2025
LexisNexis®
Corporate Affiliations™

Content Operations:
Director-News & Business Content Operations & Metadata: Tammy Bair
Manager-Corporate Affiliations & Entity Management: Elizabeth A. Powers
Lead Content Analysts: Eric Eelman, Kevin Gaven

Production:
Senior Production Specialist: Joseph C. Stewart

Reed Elsevier Philippines-Corporate Affiliations Iloilo Team:
Operations Manager: Timothy J. Vilches
Operations Supervisor: Kristel Faye B. De la Cruz
Product Lead: Raquel G. Gajardo

2025
LexisNexis® Corporate Affiliations™
International Public & Private Companies

Volume VII
G-O

QUESTIONS ABOUT THIS PUBLICATION?

For CONTENT questions concerning this publication, please call:

Content Operations Department at 800-340-3244
FAX 908-790-5405

For CUSTOMER SERVICE ASSISTANCE concerning shipments, billing or other matters, please call:
Customer Service at 800-340-3244, press 3

For SALES ASSISTANCE, please call:
The Sales Department at 800-340-3244, press 2

No part of this publication may be reproduced or transmitted in any form or by any means sorted in any information storage and retrieval system without prior written permission of LexisNexis, Content Operations, 9443 Springboro Pike, Miamisburg, OH 45342.

Library of Congress Catalog Card Number: 67-22770

International Public & Private Companies Volume 7, ISBN: 979-8-3417-0465-7

Corporate Affiliations 8-Volume Library, ISBN: 979-8-3417-0458-9

©2025 LexisNexis Group.

All Rights Reserved

LexisNexis, the knowledge burst logo and Corporate Affiliations are trademarks of Reed Elsevier Properties Inc., used under license.

The LexisNexis Group has used its best efforts in collecting and preparing material for inclusion in Corporate Affiliations: International Public & Private Companies™ but does not assume, and hereby disclaims, any liability to any person for any loss or damage caused by errors or omissions in Corporate Affiliations: International Public & Private Companies whether such errors or omissions result from negligence, accident or any other cause.

Corporate Affiliations

Content Operations
9443 Springboro Pike
Miamisburg, OH 45342

www.lexisnexis.com

ISBN 979-8-3417-0465-7

9 798341 704657

CONTENTS

Preface vii
How To Use *Corporate Affiliations*™ ix
Abbreviations xv
Country Abbreviations xvi
Company Designations xvii
Stock Market Abbreviations xviii
Exchange Rates xx
New Listings xxiii
Mergers and Acquisitions xxxi
International Public and Private Companies 2861

CONTENTS

Preface	vii
How To Use Corporate Affiliations™	ix
Abbreviations	xv
Country Abbreviations	xvi
Company Designations	xvii
Stock Market Abbreviations	xviii
Exchange Rates	xx
New Listings	xxiii
Mergers and Acquisitions	xxxi
International Public and Private Companies	2361

PREFACE

CORPORATE AFFILIATIONS

Corporate Affiliations is a logically organized business reference tool that covers major public and private businesses in the United States and throughout the world. The set consists of eight volumes:

Volume I	Master Index I
Volume II	Master Index II
Volume III	U.S. Public Companies
Volume IV	U.S. Private Companies I
Volume V	U.S. Private Companies II
Volume VI	International Public & Private Companies I
Volume VII	International Public & Private Companies II
Volume VIII	International Public & Private Companies III

The principle of organization for the set is geographical (by parent company) and hierarchical (by company reportage). Subsidiaries of a parent company, no matter where they are located, will be found in the same volume as the ultimate parent.

Please note that guidelines on the organization of the entire set for this edition can be found in the *Master Index* Volume I.

Entry criteria for the set are flexible. Generally speaking, non-U.S. based companies must demonstrate revenue in excess of $10 million. U.S. based companies must demonstrate revenues in excess of $10 million, substantial assets, a work force in excess of 300 employees, or be traded on a major stock exchange.

THE *INTERNATIONAL PUBLIC AND PRIVATE COMPANIES* VOLUME

Corporate Affiliations: International Public and Private Companies contains listings for companies with non-U.S. located headquarters or holding companies. Subsidiaries for these parent companies are included, whether or not they are located in the United States. Also included are outside service firms attached to the parent companies. These are firms that perform specialized services such as accounting, legal, pension management, etc.

Content and Coverage in Corporate Affiliations-International Public and Private Companies

Listing statistics for this edition of International are as follows:

Ultimate parent companies	58,644
U.S. located sub companies	99,843
Non-U.S. located sub companies	144,707
Total entry units listed	**303,194**
Outside service firms:	58,637

Companies are arranged alphabetically by the name of the parent company. Subsidiary companies follow the parent in order of reporting hierarchy. The bold number in parentheses shows the level of corporate reportage. Each listing can contain an extensive number of informational items. Please refer to the helpful 'How to Use' section for a guide to referencing methods and comprehensive listing samples.

The *International Public and Private Companies* volume also contains several useful features in the frontmatter including 'New Listings' for this edition, 'Mergers and Acquisitions' and the 'Currency Exchange' table.

COMPILATION

Corporate Affiliations is compiled and updated from information supplied by the companies themselves, business publications, internet research and annual reports.

RELATED SERVICES

For information on the corporateaffiliations.com web site, please call (800) 340-3244.

Mailing lists compiled from information contained in *Corporate Affiliations* may be ordered from:
R. Michael Patterson, Inside Sales Representative
DM2 Decision Maker
2000 Clearwater Drive, Oak Brook, IL
Tel: (630) 288-8348
E-mail: robert.patterson@dm2decisionmaker.com

Electronic database tapes of the directory in raw data format are available for licensing. For electronic database tapes or alliance opportunities, please contact:
LexisNexis, Corporate Affiliations
9443 Springboro Pike, Miamisburg, OH 45342
Tel: (800) 285-3947
E-mail: information@lexisnexis.com

Companies who wish to add or correct their listings can send information to:
LexisNexis, Corporate Affiliations Content Operations
9443 Springboro Pike
Miamisburg, OH 45342
Tel: (937) 865-6800

In addition to keeping the information in our directories as up to date as possible, we are constantly trying to improve their design, and add useful new features. Any comments or suggestions in this regard can be directed to the Managers of Operations at the above address.

HOW TO USE INTERNATIONAL PUBLIC AND PRIVATE COMPANIES

Corporate Affiliations, International Public and Private Companies, contains a vast amount of useful information about firms whose ultimate parent companies are located outside the United States. Included in *International Public and Private Companies* are the parent companies and their subsidiaries, no matter where they are located.

This user guide is divided into three parts.

> **Part A**, 'How to Locate a Company' gives referencing instructions and samples of indexes. It demonstrates many useful methods for getting the information you need from this volume and from the *Corporate Affiliations* set at large.
>
> **Part B**, 'Sample Entries' shows the various data elements and listing style of companies in *Corporate Affiliations*.
>
> **Part C**, 'Understanding Levels of Reportage' demonstrates how company reportage structures are simply and clearly presented throughout *Corporate Affiliations*.

PART A: HOW TO LOCATE A COMPANY

1. **If you know the name of the company, but do not know its nationality or ownership status:**

    Look in the 'Master Index of Company Names' in volume I. This index will direct you to the correct volume of the set (i.e. Public, Private or International) and the correct page listing therein.

    > **KOMAG, INCORPORATED**; *U.S. Public*, pg. 1023
    > KOMAG MATERIAL TECHNOLOGY INC.—See
    >   Komag, Incorporated; *U.S. Public*, pg. 1023
    > KOMAGANE ELECTRONICS, INC.—See Kenwood
    >   Corporation; *Int'l*, pg. 638

2. **If you know the company is a non-U.S. held parent company:**

    You can turn directly to the company listings in volumes VI, VII and VIII, all of which are alphabetized by the name of the parent company.

3. **If you cannot find the company's name in the master index:**

   It may mean that the company has been acquired or changed its name. To confirm this, try looking in the 'Mergers and Acquisitions' section at the front of this volume.

   <u>Sample of Mergers Section</u>

   Distillers Corporation S.A.–acquired & absorbed by Rothmans UK Holdings Limited
   Durr Beteiligungs-AG—name changed to Durr AG
   Elosua S.A.—ceased operations (no longer in business)
   Grand Metropolitan Plc–merged with Guinness Plc to form Diageo Plc

4. **To locate companies in a given line of business:**

   Use the 'N.A.I.C.S. (North American Industrial Classification System) Master Index' in volume II. This index interfiles data from all six volumes of *Corporate Affiliations*, arranging companies by particular products and services according to their primary N.A.I.C.S. code. The index is preceded by two helpful compendia: one sorts the codes alphabetically by the name of the product or service, the other numerically by the code itself.

   <u>Sample of Alpha Compendium of N.A.I.C.S. Codes</u>

Description	N.A.I.C.S.
Administration of Conservation Programs	924120
Administration of Education Programs	923110

   <u>Sample of Numeric Compendium of N.A.I.C.S. Codes</u>

Code	Description
111150	Corn Farming
111160	Rice Farming
111191	Oilseed and Grain Combination Farming

Both parent and sub companies are covered in this index; parent companies are printed in bold type, sub companies in regular typeface, followed by the name of its ultimate parent. A sample of the N.A.I.C.S. Master Index is shown here:

337211 — WOOD OFFICE FURNITURE MANUFACTURING

ABCO—Jami, Inc.; *Int'l*, pg. 586
ANDERSON HICKEY, INC.—Haworth, Inc.; *U.S. Public*, pg. 516
BELVEDERE COMPANY—Smith Investment Company; *Int'l*, pg. 1019
BRAYTON INTERNATIONAL INC.—Steelcase Inc.; *U.S. Public*, pg. 1048
BRODART COMPANY; *U.S. Private*, pg. 172
COMMUNITY—Jasper Seating Co., Inc.; *U.S. Private*, pg. 589
CRAMER INC.; *U.S. Public*, pg. 288
EAC CORPORATION; *Int'l*, pg. 357

PART B: BASIC COMPONENTS OF AN INTERNATIONAL COMPANY LISTING

Following is an example of a typical parent company listing with tags to some of its basic components.

SULLIVAN GRAPHICS LTD. —————— **Company Name**
52 Upper Fitzwilliam Road ——————— **Company Address**
Dublin 12, Ireland
Tel.: (353) 568 332 ————————— **Telecommunications Data**
Web Site: www.sulgrap.com
Year Founded: 1967
SULLI—(LSE) ————————————— **Ticker Symbol & Stock Exchange**
Rev.: $9,325,224,000 ————————— **Financial Information**
Assets: $2,700,000,000
Liabilities: $2,038,000,000
Net Worth: $662,000,000
Emp.: 10,950 ——————————————— **No. of Employees, Including Sub-entries**
Fiscal Year End: 12/31/24
Designs, Manufactures & Markets
Electronic Design Automation (EDA)
Software & Systems for the PC &
Systems Design Markets
N.A.I.C.S.: 334119 ————————————— **North American Industry Classification System Code**
Andrew Sullivan *(Pres)*

Following each parent company listing are the entries for each of that company's divisions, subsidiaries, affiliates, joint ventures, units, etc. Though companies vary widely in their usage of these terms, some of the more common company designations can be defined as follows:

Affiliate	A chartered business owned by the company at less than 50%.
Division	An internal unit of a company, not incorporated.
Joint Venture	A business in which two or more companies share responsibility and ownership.
Subsidiary	A chartered business owned by the company at 50% or more.

PART C: UNDERSTANDING LEVELS OF REPORTAGE

Each sub-unit of the company will have a number in parentheses to the right of the company name. This number represents the level of reportage for that particular company. Any company with a level (1) reports directly to the parent company. Level (2) companies report to the level (1) company immediately above them. Level (3) companies report to the level (2) company immediately above them, etc.

Subsidiaries:

Ericsson Systems, Inc. ─────── **(1)** ─────── Reports to the Parent Company (Sullivan Graphics, Ltd. from previous example)
2 Wellington Road Killarney
County Kerry, Ireland
Tel.: (353) 718 348
Sales Range: $25-49.9 Million
Computer Peripheral Equipment Mfr
N.A.I.C.S.: 334119 ─────── North American Industry Classification System Code
Thomas J. McSweeney (*Pres*)

Subsidiaries:

Kerrigan Co., Inc. ─────── **(2)** ─────── Reports Direct to Level 1 Company Above (Ericsson Systems, Inc.)
8 Swords Road
Dublin 17, Ireland ─────── **(100%)** ─────── Percentage of Ownership
Tel.: (353) 611 457
KC—(ISE)
Emp.: 850
Computer Printer Mfr
N.A.I.C.S.: 334119

U.S. Branch:

Kerrigan Co., Inc. ─────── **(3)** ─────── Reports Direct to Level 2 Company Above (Kerrigan Co., Inc.)
21 Reading Ave
Memphis, TN 38101
Tel.: (901) 324-8746 (100%)
Computer Printer Mfr
N.A.I.C.S.: 334119
Susan Havens (*CEO*)

Wellsley Technologies, Inc. ─────── (2) ─────── **Reports Direct to Level 1 Company**
Crown Hill Clonskeagh   **Above (Ericsson Systems, Inc.)**
Dublin 4, Ireland
Tel.: (353) 278 743   (90%)
Computer Peripheral Equipment Mfr
N.A.I.C.S.: 334119

Tennant & McDaniel, Inc. ─────── (1) ─────── **Reports Back to Parent Company (Sullivan**
Greenhills Road Tallagh   **Graphics, Ltd.)**
Dublin 24, Ireland
Tel.: (353) 268 324   (100%)
Emp: 1,200
Computer Peripheral Equipment Mfr
N.A.I.C.S.: 334119

Non-U.S. Subsidiary:

Padova Systems, Inc. ─────── (1) ─────── **Subsidiary Not in Ireland, and Not in the**
Via Laurentina, 449   **U.S. Reports to the Parent Company**
20097 Milan, Italy   **(Sullivan Graphics, Ltd.)**
Tel.: (39) 6 305291
Computer Printer Mfr
N.A.I.C.S.: 334119
Anthony Macaluso *(Pres)*

xiv

ABBREVIATIONS

Acct	Account	Matl	Material
Acctg	Accounting	Matls	Materials
Accts	Accounts	Mdse	Merchandise
Acq	Acquisition(s)	Mdsg	Merchandising
Admin	Administration	Mfg	Manufacturing
Admin	Administrative	Mfr	Manufacturer
Adv	Advertising	Mgmt	Management
Assoc	Associate	Mgr	Manager
Asst	Assistant	Mktg	Marketing
Brdcst	Broadcast	Mng	Managing
Bus	Business	Natl	National
CEO	Chief Executive Officer	Ops	Operations
CFO	Chief Financial Officer	Org	Organization
Chm	Chairman of the Board	Pkg	Packaging
CIO	Chief Information Officer	Plng	Planning
CMO	Chief Marketing Officer	Pres	President
Comm	Communication(s)	Prof	Professional
Comml	Commercial	Promo	Promotion
COO	Chief Operating Officer	Promos	Promotions
Coord	Coordinator	Pub	Public
Corp	Corporate/Corporation	Pub Rel	Public Relations
CTO	Chief Technology Officer	Publ	Publishing
Dept	Department	Publr	Publisher
Dev	Development	Pur	Purchasing
Dir	Director	R&D	Research & Development
Distr	Distribution	Reg	Regional
Div	Division	Rep	Representative
DP	Data Processing	Res	Research
Engr	Engineer	Sec	Secretary
Engrg	Engineering	Sls	Sales
Environ	Environmental	Sr	Senior
Exec	Executive	Supvr	Supervisor
Fin	Finance/Financial	Svc	Service
Gen	General	Svcs	Services
Govt	Government	Sys	Systems
Grp	Group	Tech	Technology
HR	Human Resources	Tech	Technical
Indus	Industry/Industrial	Telecom	Telecommunication(s)
Info	Information	Treas	Treasurer
Intl	International	Trng	Training
IR	Investor Relations	Vice Chm	Vice Chairman
IT	Information Technology	VP	Vice President
Jr	Junior		

COUNTRY ABBREVIATIONS

AF	Afghanistan	DK	Denmark	KG	Kyrgyzstan	KN	Saint Kitts & Nevis
AI	Albania	DJ	Djibouti	La	Laos	LC	Saint Lucia
DG	Algeria	DM	Dominica	LV	Latvia	VC	Saint Vincent & Grenadines
AD	Andorra	DO	Dominican Republic	LB	Lebanon		
AO	Angola	EC	Ecuador	LS	Lesotho	WS	Samoa
AI	Anguilla	EG	Egypt	LR	Liberia	SA	Saudi Arabia
AG	Antigua & Barbuda	SV	El Salvador	LY	Libya	SN	Senegal
Ar	Argentina	GQ	Equatorial Guinea	LI	Liechtenstein	YU	Serbia & Montenegro
AM	Armenia	ER	Eritrea	LT	Lithuania		
AW	Aruba	EE	Estonia	LU	Luxembourg	Sc	Seychelles
AU	Australia	ET	Ethiopia	Mo	Macau	SL	Sierra Leone
AT	Austria	FO	Faroe Islands	MK	Macedonia	SG	Singapore
Az	Azerbaijan	FJ	Fiji	MG	Madagascar	Sk	Slovakia
BS	Bahamas	FI	Finland	MW	Malawi	SI	Slovenia
BH	Bahrain	FR	France	MY	Malaysia	SB	Solomon Islands
BD	Bangladesh	GF	French Guiana	MV	Maldives	SO	Somalia
BB	Barbados	PF	French Polynesia	ML	Mali	ZA	South Africa
BY	Belarus	Ga	Gabon	Mt	Malta	ES	Spain
BE	Belgium	GM	Gambia	MQ	Martinique	LK	Sri Lanka
BZ	Belize	GE	Georgia	MR	Mauritania	Sd	Sudan
BJ	Benin	De	Germany	MU	Mauritius	SR	Suriname
BM	Bermuda	GH	Ghana	MX	Mexico	SZ	Swaziland
BT	Bhutan	GI	Gibraltar	Md	Moldova	SE	Sweden
BO	Bolivia	GR	Greece	MC	Monaco	CH	Switzerland
BA	Bosnia & Herzegovina	GL	Greenland	Mn	Mongolia	SY	Syria
BW	Botswana	GD	Grenada	Ms	Montserrat	TW	Taiwan
BR	Brazil	GP	Guadeloupe	Ma	Morocco	TJ	Tajikistan
BN	Brunei Darussalam	GT	Guatemala	MZ	Mozambique	TZ	Tanzania
BG	Bulgaria	Gu	Guiana	MM	Myanmar	TH	Thailand
BF	Burkina Faso	GN	Guinea	NA	Namibia	TG	Togo
BI	Burundi	GW	Guinea-Bissau	NP	Nepal	TO	Tonga
KH	Cambodia	GY	Guyana	NL	Netherlands	TT	Trinidad & Tobago
CM	Cameroon	HT	Haiti	AN	Netherlands Antilles	Tn	Tunisia
Ca	Canada	HN	Honduras	Nc	New Caledonia	TR	Turkey
CV	Cape Verde	HK	Hong Kong	NZ	New Zealand	TM	Turkmenistan
Ky	Cayman Islands	HU	Hungary	NI	Nicaragua	TC	Turks & Caicos Islands
CF	Central African Republic	IS	Iceland	Ne	Niger		
		In	India	NG	Nigeria	TV	Tuvalu
TD	Chad	Id	Indonesia	NO	Norway	UG	Uganda
CL	Chile	IR	Iran	OM	Oman	UA	Ukraine
CN	China	IQ	Iraq	PK	Pakistan	AE	United Arab Emirates
Co	Colombia	IE	Ireland	Pa	Panama		
KM	Comoros	Il	Israel	PG	Papua New Guinea	UK	United Kingdom
CD	Congo, Democratic Republic of	IT	Italy	PY	Paraguay	UY	Uruguay
		JM	Jamaica	PE	Peru	UZ	Uzbekistan
CG	Congo, Republic of	JP	Japan	PH	Philippines	VU	Vanuatu
CK	Cook Islands	JO	Jordan	PL	Poland	VE	Venezuela
CR	Costa Rica	KZ	Kazakhstan	PT	Portugal	VN	Vietnam
CI	Cote d'Ivoire	KE	Kenya	QA	Qatar	VG	Virgin Islands (British)
HR	Croatia	KI	Kiribati	RE	Reunion		
CU	Cuba	KN	Korea (North)	RO	Romania	YE	Yemen
CY	Cyprus	Ks	Korea (South)	RU	Russia	ZM	Zambia
CZ	Czech Republic	KW	Kuwait	RW	Rwanda	ZW	Zimbabwe

COMPANY DESIGNATIONS

The following designations indicate the forms of business enterprise in various countries; these forms usually represent the organizations for large enterprises.

AB	Aktiebolag	Finland, Sweden
AG	Aktiengesellschaft	Austria, Germany, Switzerland, Liechtenstein
A/S	Aksjeselskap	Norway
	Aktieselskab	Denmark
B.V.	Besloten Vennootschap	Holland
C.V.	Commanditaire Vennootschap	Holland
Cie.	Compagnie	France, Luxembourg
Co.	Company	United States, France, South Africa, Luxembourg
Ets.	Etablissement(s)	France, Luxembourg
GmbH	Gesellschaft mit beschrankter Haftung	Austria, Germany, Switzerland
I/S	Interessantelskab	Denmark, Norway
KG	Kommanditgesellschaft	Austria, Germany, Switzerland
KK	Kabushiki Kaisha	Japan
K/S	Kommanditselskab	Denmark
Lda.	Limitada	Portugal
Ltd.	Limited	United Kingdom, United States, South Africa
Ltda.	Limitada	Brazil, Portugal
Ltee.	Limitee	Canada
Mij.	Maatschappij	Holland
N.V.	Naamloze Vennootschap	Belgium, Holland
OHG	Offene Handelsgesellschaft	Austria
Oy	Osakeyhtiot	Finland
PLC	Public Limited Company	United Kingdom
P.T.	Perusahaan Terbatas	Indonesia
Pte.	Private	Singapore
Pty.	Proprietary	Australia, South Africa
Pvt.	Private	India, Rhodesia
S.A.	Societe Anonyme	Belgium, France, Luxembourg, Switzerland
Sociedad	Anonima	Spain, Latin America
S.A.C.I.	Sociedad Anonima Comercial e Industrial	Latin America
S.A. de C.V.	Sociedad Anonima de Capital Variable	Mexico
S.A.E.	Sociedad Anonima Espanola	Spain
S.A.I.C.	Sociedad Anonima Industrial y Comercial	Latin America
S.A.R.L.	Sociedad Anonima de Responsabilidade Limitada	Brazil
	Sociedade a Responsabilitie Limitee	France, Luxembourg
S.A.S.	Societa in Accomandita Semplice	Italy
S.C.	Societe en Commandite	France
S.p.A.	Societa per Azioni	Italy
S.P.R.L.	Societe de Personnes a Responsabilitie Limitee	Belgium
S.R.L.	Societa a Responsabilita Limitata	Italy
Sdn. Bhd.	Sendirian Berhad	Malaysia
Ste.	Societe	France, Switzerland
Ste. Cve.	Societe Cooperative	Belgium
V.o.F.	Vennootschap onder firma	Holland

STOCK MARKET ABBREVIATIONS

ABU	Abu Dhabi Securities Exchange
AIM	AIM Market of the London Stock Exchange
AMM	Amman Stock Exchange
ARM	Armenian NASDAQ OMX Armenia
ASX	Australian Stock Exchange
ATH	Athens Stock Exchange
BAH	Bahrain Bourse
BAK	Baku Stock Exchange
BAN	Bangalore Stock Exchange
BANJ	Banja Luka Stock Exchange
BAR	Barcelona Stock Exchange
BARB	Barbados Stock Exchange
BEL	Belgrade Stock Exchange
BER	Borse Berlin-Bremen Stock Exchange
BERM	Bermuda Stock Exchange
BERN	Bern Stock Exchange
BESA	Bond Exchange of South Africa
BEY	Beirut Stock Exchange
BHU	Royal Securities Exchange of Bhutan
BIL	Bilbao Stock Exchange
BOA	BOAG Borsen (Merger of Hannover & Hamburg Exchanges)
BOL	Bolsa de Valores de Bolivia
BOM	Bombay (Mumbai) Stock Exchange
BOT	Botswana Stock Exchange
BRA	Bratislava Stock Exchange
BRAZ	Brazil Stock Exchange (BM&F Bovespa)
BRVM	Bourse Regionale des Valeurs Mobilieres
BUC	Bucharest Stock Exchange
BUD	Budapest Stock Exchange
BUE	Buenos Aires Stock Exchange (Mercado de Valores Buenos Aires)
BUL	Bulgarian Stock Exchange
BVMAC	Securities Exchange of Central Africa
BVT	Bourse de Tunis
BX	Boston NASDAQ OMX BXSM
CAR	Caracas Stock Exchange
CAS	Casablanca Stock Exchange
CAT	Singapore Catalist
CAY	Cayman Islands Stock Exchange
CHA	Channel Islands Stock Exchange
CHI	Chicago Stock Exchange
CHIN	ChiNext (Chinese Exchange for Small & High-Tech Enterprises)
CHT	Chittagong Stock Exchange
CNSX	Canadian National Stock Exchange
COL	Colombo Stock Exchange
COLO	Colombia Bolsa de Valores
COR	Cordoba Stock Exchange
CSE	Copenhagen Stock Exchange
CYP	Cyprus Stock Exchange
DAR	Dar es Salaam Stock Exchange
DES	Delhi Stock Exchange
DEU	Deutsche Borse (Frankfurt Stock Exchange)
DFM	Dubai Financial Market
DHA	Dhaka Stock Exchange
DUS	Dusseldorf Stock Exchange
ECA	Eastern Caribbean Securities Exchange
EGX	Egyptian Exchange
EMI	Securities & Commodities Authority (d/b/a Emirates Securities Market)
EUR	Euronext
FKA	Fukuoka Stock Exchange
GEOR	Georgian Stock Exchange
GHA	Ghana Stock Exchange
GUA	Guayaquil Stock Exchange
HEL	Helsinki Stock Exchange
HKG	Hong Kong Stock Exchange
HNX	Hanoi Stock Exchange
HOSE	Ho Chi Minh Stock Exchange (Vietnam)
HYD	Hyderabad Stock Exchange
ICE	Iceland Stock Exchange
INDO	Indonesia Stock Exchange
IRAQ	Iraq Stock Exchange
ISDX	ICAP Securities & Derivatives Exchange Limited (formerly PLUS)
ISE	Irish Stock Exchange
ISL	Islamabad Stock Exchange
IST	Istanbul Stock Exchange
ISX	Inter-Connected Stock Exchange of India
ITA	Italian Stock Exchange
JAI	Jaipur Stock Exchange
JAM	Jamaica Stock Exchange
JAS	OSE JASDAQ
JSE	Johannesburg Stock Exchange
KAR	Karachi Stock Exchange
KAZ	Kazakhstan Stock Exchange
KHAR	Khartoum Stock Exchange
KLS	Bursa Malaysia (Formerly Kuala Lumpur Stock Exchange)
KOL	Kolkata Stock Exchange
KRS	Korea Exchange
KUW	Kuwait Stock Exchange
LAH	Lahore Stock Exchange
LIM	Lima Bolsa de Valores
LJU	Ljubljana Stock Exchange
LSE	London Stock Exchange
LUS	Lusaka Stock Exchange
LUX	Luxembourg Stock Exchange
MAC	Macedonian Stock Exchange
MAD	Madrid Stock Exchange
MAL	Malta Stock Exchange
MALA	Malawi Stock Exchange
MAU	Stock Exchange of Mauritius
MDS	Madras Stock Exchange
MEX	Bolsa Mexicana de Valores

Stock Market Abbreviations

MIC	MICEX Moscow Interbank Currency Exchange
MOLD	Moldova Stock Exchange
MON	Montreal Stock Exchange
MONG	Mongolian Stock Exchange
MUN	Munich Stock Exchange
MUS	Muscat Stock Exchange
NAI	Nairobi Stock Exchange
NAM	Namibian Stock Exchange
NASDAQ	National Association of Securities Dealers, Inc.
NASDAQDBAI	NASDAQ Dubai
NEP	Nepal Stock Exchange Ltd
NGO	Nagoya Stock Exchange
NIGE	Nigerian Stock Exchange
NSE	National Stock Exchange of India
NSXA	National Stock Exchange of Australia
NYSA	New York Stock Exchange Arca Options Trading System
NYSE	New York Stock Exchange
NYSE AMERICAN	NYSE American
NZE	New Zealand Exchange Limited
OMX	Stockholm/Nordic Stock Exchange
OSE	Osaka Stock Exchange
OSL	Oslo Stock Exchange
OTC	Over-the-Counter Pink Sheets
OTCB	Over-the-Counter Bulletin Board
OTCI	Over-the-Counter Exchange of India
PAL	Palestine Securities Exchange
PAN	Bolsa de Valores de Panama
PET	Saint Petersburg Stock Exchange
PHI	Philippine Stock Exchange
PHLX	Philadelphia - NASDAQ OMX PHLX
POM	Port Moresby Stock Exchange Limited (Papua New Guinea)
PRA	Prague Stock Exchange
PUN	Pune Stock Exchange (India)
QE	Qatar Stock Exchange
RIO	Rio de Janeiro, Bolsa de Valores
RSE	Riga Stock Exchange
RUS	Russian Trading System
SAP	Sapporo Stock Exchange
SARE	Sarejevo Stock Exchange
SAU	Saudi Stock Exchange
SES	Singapore Stock Exchange
SGO	Santiago Stock Exchange
SHG	Shanghai Stock Exchange
SPSE	South Pacific Stock Exchange
SSE	Shenzhen Stock Exchange
SSX	Swaziland Stock Exchange
STU	Stuttgart Stock Exchange (Baden)
SWX	Swiss Stock Exchange
TAE	Tel-Aviv Stock Exchange
TAI	Taiwan Stock Exchange
TAL	Tallinn Stock Exchange
TFE	Tokyo Financial Exchange (Futures)
THA	Stock Exchange of Thailand
THE	Tehran Stock Exchange
TKS	Tokyo Stock Exchange
TOSH	Tashkent Republican Stock Exchange
TRI	Trinidad & Tobago Stock Exchange
TSX	Toronto Stock Exchange
TSXV	Toronto Stock Venture Exchange
UGAN	Uganda Securities Exchange
UKR	Ukranian Stock Exchange
VAL	Bolsa de Valencia
VIE	Wiener Borse (Vienna Stock Exchange)
VLA	Vladivostok Stock Exchange
VSE	Vilnius Stock Exchange
WAR	Warsaw Stock Exchange
ZAG	Zagreb Stock Exchange
ZIM	Zimbabwe Stock Exchange

EXCHANGE RATES

Country	Currency	Rate
Afghanistan	Afghani	0.01927
Albania	Lek	0.00948
Algeria	Dinar	0.01273
Andorra	Euro	1.34617
Angola	Kwanza	0.01041
Antigua & Barbuda	Dollar	0.36807
Argentina	Peso	0.20132
Armenia	Dram	0.00248
Aruba	Guilder	0.55562
Australia	Dollar	1.04210
Austria	Euro	1.34617
Azerbaijan	Manat	1.27307
Bahamas	Dollar	0.99257
Bahrain	Dinar	2.59161
Bangladesh	Taka	0.01238
Barbados	Dollar	0.49196
Belarus	Ruble	0.00012
Belgium	Euro	1.34617
Belize	Dollar	0.49317
Benin	Franc	0.00205
Bermuda	Dollar	1
Bhutan	Ngultrum	0.01858
Bolivia	Boliviano	0.01400
Bosnia & Herzegovina	Marka	0.68820
Botswana	Pula	0.12310
Brazil	Real	0.49189
Brunei Darussalam	Dollar	0.80244
Bulgaria	Lev	0.68350
Burkina Faso	Franc	0.00205
Burundi	Franc	0.00065
Cambodia	Riel	0.00025
Cameroon	CFA Franc BEAC	0.00205
Canada	Dollar	0.99402
Cape Verde	Escudo	0.01194
Caribbean Netherlands	Dollar	1
Cayman Islands	Dollar	1.19325
Central African Republic	Franc	0.00205
Chad	Franc	0.00205
Chile	Peso	0.00212
China	Yuan Renminbi	0.15885
China (Hong Kong)	Dollar	0.12895
China (Macau)	Pataca	0.12319
Colombia	Peso	0.00056
Comoros	Franc	0.00273
Congo, Democratic Republic of	Franc	0.00105
Congo, Republic of	Franc	0.00205
Cook Islands	Dollar	0.83700
Costa Rica	Colon	0.00195
Cote d'Ivoire	Franc	0.00205
Croatia	Kuna	0.17771
Cuba	Peso	0.04320
Curacao	Guilder	0.54945
Cyprus	Euro	1.34617
Czech Republic	Koruna	0.05257
Denmark	Krone	0.18036
Djibouti	Franc	0.00553
Dominica	Dollar	0.36807
Dominican Republic	Peso	0.02446
East Timor	Dollar	1
Ecuador	Dollar	1
Egypt	Pound	0.14854
El Salvador	Dollar	1
Equatorial Guinea	Franc	0.00205
Eritrea	Nakfa	0.06623
Estonia	Euro	1.34617
Ethiopia	Birr	0.05412
Falkland Islands	Pound	1.58003
Faroe Islands	Krone	0.18036
Fiji	Dollar	0.56329
Finland	Euro	1.34617
France	Euro	1.34617
French Guiana	Euro	1.34617
Gabon	Franc	0.00205
Gambia	Dalasi	0.02892
Georgia	Lari	0.60234
Germany	Euro	1.34617
Ghana	Cedi	0.52035
Gibraltar	Pound	1.58033
Greece	Euro	1.34617
Greenland	Krone	0.18036
Grenada	Dollar	0.36807
Guadeloupe	Euro	1.34617
Guatemala	Quetzal	0.12538
Guernsey	Pound	1.57929
Guinea	Franc	0.00014
Guinea-Bissau	Franc	0.00205
Guyana	Dollar	0.00500
Haiti	Gourde	0.02337
Honduras	Lempira	0.04939
Hungary	Forint	0.00452
Iceland	Krona	0.00782
India	Rupee	0.01854
Indonesia	Rupiah	0.00010
Iran	Rial	0.00008
Iraq	Dinar	0.00084
Ireland	Euro	1.34617
Isle of Man	Pound	1.57929
Israel	New Shekel	0.26868
Italy	Euro	1.34617
Jamaica	Dollar	0.01061
Japan	Yen	0.01100
Jersey	Pound	1.57929
Jordan	Dinar	1.40489
Kazakhstan	Tenge	0.00655
Kenya	Shilling	0.01123
Kiribati	Dollar	0.91406
Korea (North)	North Korean Won	0.00741
Korea (South)	South Korean Won	0.00093
Kuwait	Dinar	3.54359
Kyrgyzstan	Som	0.02096
Laos	Kip	0.00012
Latvia	Lat	1.89941
Lebanon	Pound	0.00065
Lesotho	Loti	0.10957
Liberia	Dollar	0.01342
Libya	Dinar	0.78401
Liechtenstein	Swiss Franc	1.07932
Lithuania	Litas	0.38428
Luxembourg	Euro	1.34617

Exchange Rates

Country	Currency	Rate	Country	Currency	Rate
Macedonia	Denar	0.02108	Sakha	Ruble	0.03307
Madagascar	Ariary	0.00045	Samoa	Tala	0.42369
Malawi	Kwacha	0.00284	Saudi Arabia	Riyal	0.26630
Malaysia	Ringgit	0.32792	Senegal	Franc	0.00205
Maldives	Rufiyaa	0.06398	Serbia	Dinar	0.01199
Mali	Franc	0.00205	Seychelles	Rupee	0.07289
Malta	Euro	1.34617	Sierra Leone	Leone	0.00023
Marshall Islands	Dollar	1	Singapore	Dollar	0.80968
Martinique	Euro	1.34617	Slovakia	Euro	1.34617
Mauritania	Ouguiya	0.00327	Slovenia	Euro	1.34617
Mauritius	Rupee	0.03148	Solomon Islands	Dollar	0.13510
Mexico	Peso	0.07868	Somalia	Shilling	0.00062
Micronesia	Dollar	1	South Africa	Rand	0.11170
Moldolva	Leu	0.08084	Spain	Euro	1.34617
Monaco	Euro	1.34617	Sri Lanka	Rupee	0.00785
Mongolia	Tughrik	0.00072	Sudan	Pound	0.22511
Montenegro	Euro	1.34617	Sudan (South)	Pound	0.33070
Morocco	Dirham	0.11707	Suriname	Dollar	0.30303
Mozambique	Metical	0.03247	Swaziland	Lilangeni	0.10985
Myanmar	Kyat	0.00115	Sweden	Krona	0.15480
Namibia	Dollar	0.10957	Switzerland	Franc	1.07932
Nepal	Rupee	0.01150	Syria	Pound	0.01391
Netherlands	Euro	1.34617	Taiwan	New Dollar	0.03387
New Caledonia	Franc	0.01129	Tajikistan	Somoni	0.21000
New Zealand	Dollar	0.83700	Tanzania	Shilling	0.00061
Nicaragua	Cordoba	0.04078	Thailand	Baht	0.03313
Niger	Franc	0.00205	Togo	Franc	0.00205
Nigeria	Naira	0.00629	Tonga	Pa'anga	0.57887
Norway	Kroner	0.18099	Trinidad & Tobago	Dollar	0.15415
Oman	Rial	2.58772	Tunisia	Dinar	0.64350
Pakistan	Rupee	0.01013	Turkey	New Lira	0.56513
Panama	Balboa	0.97898	Turkmenistan	Manat	0.35088
Papua New Guinea	Kina	0.47154	Turks & Caico Islands	Dollar	1
Paraguay	Guarani	0.00023	Tuvalu	Dollar	1.04210
Peru	New Sol	0.38347	Uganda	Shilling	0.00037
Philippines	Peso	0.02449	Ukraine	Hryvnia	0.12179
Poland	Zloty	0.31713	United Arab Emirates	Dirham	0.27218
Portugal	Euro	1.34617	United Kingdom	Pound	1.57929
Qatar	Riyal	0.26710	Uruguay	Peso	0.05088
Reunion	Euro	1.34617	Uzbekistan	Som	0.00050
Romania	New Leu	0.30768	Vanuatu	Vatu	0.01105
Russia	Ruble	0.03307	Venezuela	Bolivar	0.23257
Rwanda	Franc	0.00159	Vietnam	Dong	0.00005
Saint Kitts & Nevis	Dollar	0.36807	Virgin Islands (British)	Dollar	1
Saint Lucia	Dollar	0.36807	Wallis & Futuna	Franc	0.01129
Saint Maarten	Guilder	0.54945	Yemen	Rial	0.00463
Saint Vincent & Grenadines	Dollar	0.36807	Zambia	Kwacha	0.00019

Exchange Rates

Country	Currency	Rate	Country	Currency	Rate
Macedonia	Denar	0.0210B	Samoa	Sakua	0.02307
Madagascar	Ariary	0.0045	Samoa	Tala	0.4256B
Malawi	Kwacha	0.0028A	Saudi Arabia	Riyal	0.2663O
Malaysia	Ringgit	0.3278Z	Senegal	Franc	0.0020S
Maldives	Rufiyaa	0.0659B	Serbia	Dinar	0.0119S
Mali	Franc	0.0020S	Seychelles	Rupee	0.0725S
Malta	Euro	1.3467	Sierra Leone	Leone	0.0002S
Marshall Islands	Dollar	1	Singapore	Dollar	0.8095
Martinique	Euro	1.3467	Slovakia	Euro	1.3467
Mauritania	Ouguiya	0.0032Z	Slovenia	Euro	1.3467
Mauritius	Rupee	0.0311B	Solomon Islands	Dollar	0.135T0
Mexico	Peso	0.0765B	Somalia	Shilling	0.0062
Micronesia	Dollar	1	South Africa	Rand	0.1117O
Moldova	Leu	0.0806A	Spain	Euro	1.3467
Monaco	Euro	1.3467	Sri Lanka	Rupee	0.0018S
Mongolia	Tughrik	0.0007Z	Sudan	Pound	0.2217
Montenegro	Euro	1.3467	Sudan (South)	Pound	0.3307O
Morocco	Dirham	0.1170Z	Suriname	Dollar	0.3080S
Mozambique	Metical	0.0324Z	Swaziland	Lilangeni	0.1085S
Myanmar	Kyat	0.0015	Sweden	Krona	0.1548O
Namibia	Dollar	0.1085Z	Switzerland	Franc	1.0793Z
Nepal	Rupee	0.0116O	Syria	Pound	0.0123Z
Netherlands	Euro	1.3467	Taiwan	New Dollar	0.0338Z
New Caledonia	Franc	0.0112S	Tajikistan	Somoni	0.2100O
New Zealand	Dollar	0.8320O	Tanzania	Shilling	0.0006
Nicaragua	Cordoba	0.0402B	Thailand	Baht	0.0331S
Niger	Franc	0.0020S	Togo	Franc	0.0020S
Nigeria	Naira	0.0062Z	Tonga	Pa'anga	0.5753Z
Norway	Kroner	0.1609S	Trinidad & Tobago	Dollar	0.154T5
Oman	Rial	2.5972	Tunisia	Dinar	0.6530O
Pakistan	Rupee	0.0101O	Turkey	New Lira	0.5651S
Panama	Balboa	0.9758B	Turkmenistan	Manat	0.3508B
Papua New Guinea	Kina	0.4779A	Turks & Caicos Islands	Dollar	1
Paraguay	Guarani	0.0002S	Tuvalu	Dollar	1.0470O
Peru	New Sol	0.3634Z	Uganda	Shilling	0.0003Z
Philippines	Peso	0.0224O	Ukraine	Hryvnia	0.1217S
Poland	Zloty	0.3171Z	United Arab Emirates	Dirham	0.2721S
Portugal	Euro	1.3467	United Kingdom	Pound	1.5792S
Qatar	Riyal	0.2710	Uruguay	Peso	0.0509Z
Reunion	Euro	1.3467	Uzbekistan	Som	0.0005
Romania	New Leu	0.3078Z	Vanuatu	Vatu	0.0110S
Russia	Ruble	0.0330O	Venezuela	Bolivar	0.2325Z
Rwanda	Franc	0.0016S	Vietnam	Dong	0.0000B
Saint Kitts & Nevis	Dollar	0.3680Z	Virgin Islands (British)	Dollar	1
Saint Lucia	Dollar	0.3680Z	Wallis & Futuna	Franc	0.0112S
Saint Maarten	Guilder	0.5454S	Yemen	Rial	0.0046S
Saint Vincent & Grenadines	Dollar	0.3680Z	Zambia	Kwacha	0.0001S

NEW LISTINGS 2025
Appearing for the first time in this publication

2

2KS CLOUD SERVICES GMBH; DARMSTADT, GERMANY

3

3AC CO., LTD.; SEOUL, KOREA (SOUTH)

A

A AGENCIA BRASILEIRA DE PROMOCAO DE EXPORTACOES E INVESTIMENTOS; BRASILIA, BRAZIL

ABOVE FOOD INGREDIENTS INC.; REGINA, CANADA

ACCENT MICROCELL LTD.; AHMEDABAD, INDIA

ACCESS TECHNOLOGY GROUP LIMITED; LOUGHBOROUGH, UNITED KINGDOM

ACTIONSPORTGAMES A/S; ESPERGAERDE, DENMARK

ACUREN CORPORATION; TORTOLA, VIRGIN ISLANDS (BRITISH)

ACWA POWER COMPANY; RIYADH, SAUDI ARABIA

ADENIA PARTNERS LTD; BEAU PLAN, MAURITIUS

AECC SHANGHAI COMMERCIAL AIRCRAFT ENGINE MANUFACTURING CO.; SHANGHAI, CHINA

AEOON TECHNOLOGIES GMBH; KRAMSACH, AUSTRIA

AFRICA RISK CONSULTING LTD.; LONDON, UNITED KINGDOM

AGNORA LTD; COLLINGWOOD, CANADA

AI CO., LTD.; TOKYO, JAPAN

AICHI FINANCIAL GROUP CO., LTD.; NAGOYA, JAPAN

AIP FOUNDATION; HANOI, VIETNAM

AKANKSHA POWER & INFRASTRUCTURE LIMITED; NASHIK, INDIA

ALGOMA STEEL GROUP INC.; SAULT SAINTE MARIE, CANADA

ALICORN LIMITED; LONDON, UNITED KINGDOM

ALLIANZ GLOBAL INVESTORS LUXEMBOURG S.A.; SENNINGERBERG, LUXEMBOURG

ALLIED CRITICAL METALS CORP.; VANCOUVER, CANADA

ALLU GROUP OY; PENNALA, FINLAND

ALMAVIVA S.P.A.; ROME, ITALY

ALPHA TECHNOLOGY GROUP LIMITED; KOWLOON, CHINA (HONG KONG)

AMAZONE H. DREYER GMBH & CO. KG; HASBERGEN, GERMANY

AMBIENTA SGR S.P.A; MILAN, ITALY

AMF-BRUNS GMBH & CO. KG; APEN, GERMANY

AMIA ENERGY GMBH; HAMBURG, GERMANY

AMMANN SWITZERLAND LTD; LANGENTHAL, SWITZERLAND

AMPYR GLOBAL ENERGY HOLDINGS PTE. LTD; SINGAPORE, SINGAPORE

ANCHOR LAS AB; ESKILSTUNA, SWEDEN

ANDALUSI BEVERAGES S.L.; SEVILLE, SPAIN

ANDERCO INVESTMENT PTE LTD; SINGAPORE, SINGAPORE

ANGLO-EASTERN UNIVAN GROUP; KOWLOON, CHINA (HONG KONG)

ANYWIRE CORPORATION; NAGAOKAKYO, JAPAN

APE ANGEWANDTE PHYSIK & ELEKTRONIK GMBH; BERLIN, GERMANY

APIARY CAPITAL LLP; LONDON, UNITED KINGDOM

ARA GROUP LIMITED; CROWS NEST, AUSTRALIA

ARAD-OPHIR LTD.; RAMAT HASHARON, ISRAEL

ARG MBH & CO. KG; OBERHAUSEN, GERMANY

ARRHYTHMIA NETWORK TECHNOLOGY SL; MADRID, SPAIN

ARVIND & COMPANY SHIPPING AGENCIES LIMITED; JAMNAGAR, INDIA

ASAS CAPITAL LTD; , UNITED ARAB EMIRATES

ASKO HOLDING A.S.; GAZIANTEP, TURKIYE

ASMPT GMBH & CO. KG; MUNICH, GERMANY

ATMOKY GMBH; GRAZ, AUSTRIA

ATS-TANNER BANDING SYSTEMS AG; ZUG, SWITZERLAND

ATTIVO GROUP; CHRISTCHURCH, NEW ZEALAND

AUSTRALIAN MEAT INDUSTRY SUPERANNUATION TRUST PTY LTD.; PARRAMATTA, AUSTRALIA

AUSTRALIAN OILSEEDS HOLDINGS LIMITED; COOTAMUNDRA, AUSTRALIA

AVERON PARK LIMITED; LONDON, UNITED KINGDOM

AZAD ENGINEERING LIMITED; HYDERABAD, INDIA

AZULIS CAPITAL; PARIS, FRANCE

B

B INVESTMENTS HOLDING SAE; CAIRO, EGYPT

BAC HOLDING INTERNATIONAL CORP.; BOGOTA, COLOMBIA

BANCA DI CIVIDALE S.P.A.; CIVIDALE DEL FRIULI, ITALY

BANCA POPOLARE PUGLIESE S.C.P.A.; MATINO, ITALY

BANCO MASTER S.A.; SAO PAULO, BRAZIL

BARRO GROUP PTY LTD; CARLTON, AUSTRALIA

BASILIC FLY STUDIO LIMITED; CHENNAI, INDIA

BASSETTI GROUP SAS; GRENOBLE, FRANCE

BAUER HOLZBAU GMBH; SATTELDORF, GERMANY

BAUMER HOLDING AG; FRAUENFELD, SWITZERLAND

BAUMGARTNER & LAMPERSTORFER INSTRUMENTS GMBH.; FELDKIRCHEN, GERMANY

BAYANAT AI PLC; ABU DHABI, UNITED ARAB EMIRATES

BAYLEYS CORPORATION LIMITED; AUCKLAND, NEW ZEALAND

BAYRIDGE RESOURCES CORP.; VANCOUVER, CANADA

New Listings—continued

BBTV HOLDINGS INC.; VANCOUVER, CANADA

BD-CAPITAL PARTNERS LIMITED; LONDON, UNITED KINGDOM

BEEDIE CAPITAL PARTNERS; VANCOUVER, CANADA

BEIJING ZOHETEC CO., LTD; BEIJING, CHINA

BENDA SUNKWANG IND. CO., LTD.; INCHEON, KOREA (SOUTH)

BENNER HOLDING GMBH; WIESBADEN, GERMANY

BEST CHIPS CO., LTD.; SAITAMA, JAPAN

BETAMEK BERHAD; SELANGOR, MALAYSIA

BHARAT HIGHWAYS INVIT.; GURUGRAM, INDIA

BIG TREE CLOUD HOLDINGS LIMITED; SHENZHEN, CHINA

BIRN SERBIA; BELGRADE, SERBIA

BITFUFU INC.; SINGAPORE, SINGAPORE

BLUE INNOVATION CO., LTD.; TOKYO, JAPAN

BLUE JET HEALTHCARE LIMITED; MUMBAI, INDIA

BM CARPENTERIE OIL & GAS S.R.L.; MILAN, ITALY

BODY ACTION ENTERPRISE CO., LTD.; TAICHUNG, TAIWAN

BOHEMIA FAKTORING, A.S.; PRAGUE, CZECH REPUBLIC

BOLDYN NETWORKS GLOBAL LTD.; LONDON, UNITED KINGDOM

BOMSOWA CO. LTD.; SEONGNAM, KOREA (SOUTH)

BTSR INTERNATIONAL S.P.A.; OLGIATE OLONA, ITALY

BUSI GROUP S.R.L.; PAITONE, ITALY

C

C&H COMMUNICATIONS; DUBAI, UNITED ARAB EMIRATES

CADRE AS; KRISTIANSAND, NORWAY

CALASTONE LIMITED; LONDON, UNITED KINGDOM

CALLEJA S.A. DE C.V.; SAN SALVADOR, EL SALVADOR

CANDY TOY - INDUSTRIA E COMERCIO DE ALIMENTOS E PLASTICOS LTDA; SAO PAULO, BRAZIL

CANNAWORLD VENTURES INC.; BURNABY, CANADA

CAPMONT GMBH; MUNICH, GERMANY

CAPSTONE COPPER CORP.; VANCOUVER, CANADA

CAPTIVISION INC.; NAILSWORTH, UNITED KINGDOM

CARAVELLE INTERNATIONAL GROUP; SINGAPORE, SINGAPORE

CASI PHARMACEUTICALS, INC.; BEIJING, CHINA

CASSA RURALE ED ARTIGIANA DI BINASCO CREDITO COOPERATIVO; BINASCO, ITALY

CEDAROME CANADA INC.; CANDIAC, CANADA

CELLO WORLD LIMITED; MUMBAI, INDIA

CENTRAL GROUP; BUDAPEST, HUNGARY

CENTRO CARDIOLOGICO MONZINO S.P.A.; MILAN, ITALY

CETUS CAPITAL ACQUISITION CORP.; TAIPEI, TAIWAN

CEVOTEC GMBH; UNTERHACHING, GERMANY

CHAPS HOLDING SAS; SURESNES, FRANCE

CHAROENRUT KARNTAW CO., LTD.; BANGKOK, THAILAND

CHEUNG HO ELECTRIC CO., LIMITED; , CHINA (HONG KONG)

CHILDREN'S HOSPITAL TRUST; CAPE TOWN, SOUTH AFRICA

CHINA MOBILE IOT COMPANY LIMITED; CHONGQING, CHINA

CHUGIN FINANCIAL GROUP, INC.; OKAYAMA, JAPAN

CHUNGNAM NATIONAL UNIVERSITY; DAEJEON, KOREA (SOUTH)

CIGALAH TRADING ESTABLISHMENT; JEDDAH, SAUDI ARABIA

CIRCULAR WATERS SOLUTIONS S.R.L; , ROMANIA

CISALFA SPORT S.P.A.; LOMBARDIA, ITALY

CLARO PRODUCTS GMBH; ANIF, AUSTRIA

CLIFFSIDE LTD.; TORONTO, CANADA

CLINICAL DESIGN TECHNOLOGIES LTD.; EXETER, UNITED KINGDOM

COME TO AGREEMENT LTD.; RICHMOND HILL, CANADA

COMMITTED CARGO CARE LIMITED; NEW DELHI, INDIA

COMPAX SOFTWARE DEVELOPMENT GMBH; VIENNA, AUSTRIA

COMRIT INVESTMENTS 1 LP; TEL AVIV, ISRAEL

CONCORD BIOTECH LIMITED; AHMEDABAD, INDIA

CONNECTENS B.V.; HAAKSBERGEN, NETHERLANDS

CONVERGENCE PARTNERS (PTY) LIMITED; ROSEBANK, SOUTH AFRICA

CONVERGENT FINANCE LLP; MUMBAI, INDIA

COPILOT CAPITAL LIMITED; LONDON, UNITED KINGDOM

COPLUS INC.; TAINAN CITY, TAIWAN

COPPER STANDARD RESOURCES INC.; VANCOUVER, CANADA

CORE NICKEL CORP.; SASKATOON, CANADA

CREDITCHECK PARTNERS PRIVATE LIMITED; MUMBAI, INDIA

CREDO BRANDS MARKETING LIMITED; MUMBAI, INDIA

CRINSURANCE S.A.S.; LA PLATA, ARGENTINA

CRYSTAL GLOBE LIMITED; TIANJIN, CHINA

CUBE BIO-ENERGY PVT LTD.; HYDERABAD, TELANGANA, INDIA

CURIOX BIOSYSTEMS CO., LTD.; SEOUL, KOREA (SOUTH)

CXJ GROUP CO., LIMITED; HANGZHOU, CHINA

D

DADAM INVESTMENT CORP.; GANGNAM-GU, KOREA (SOUTH)

DAI-ICHI HIGH FREQUENCY CO., LTD.; TOKYO, JAPAN

DAIWA CYCLE CO., LTD.; OSAKA, JAPAN

DDC ENTERPRISE LIMITED; SHEUNG WAN, CHINA (HONG KONG)

DENNEMEYER SA; HOWALD, LUXEMBOURG

DFP HOLDINGS LIMITED; TAIPEI, TAIWAN

DR. SULAIMAN AL HABIB MEDICAL SERVICES GROUP COMPANY; RIYADH, SAUDI ARABIA

DT CLOUD ACQUISITION CORP.; LONDON, UNITED KINGDOM

New Listings—continued

DUNA ASZFALT ZTR; BUDAPEST, HUNGARY

E

E B TRANS SA; MUNSBACH, LUXEMBOURG

E2S CO., LTD.; HWASUNG-SI, KOREA (SOUTH)

ECARX HOLDINGS, INC.; SHANGHAI, CHINA

EKWB D.O.O.; KOMENDA, SLOVENIA

ELBI S.P.A.; LIMENA, ITALY

ELONG POWER HOLDING LIMITED; GANZHOU, CHINA

EMIL FREY HOLDING AG; ZURICH, SWITZERLAND

ENDOGENE LTD.; BRIGHTON, AUSTRALIA

ENGENE HOLDINGS INC.; MONTREAL, CANADA

EPIPROCARE GMBH; BERLIN, GERMANY

ES NETWORKS CO., LTD.; TOKYO, JAPAN

ESGL HOLDINGS LIMITED; SINGAPORE, SINGAPORE

ESSIX BIOSCIENCES LIMITED; DERABASSI, INDIA

EV8 TECHNOLOGIES LIMITED; LONDON, UNITED KINGDOM

EXECUS SPA; MILAN, ITALY

EXICOM TELE-SYSTEMS LIMITED; GURUGRAM, INDIA

EXPORT TRADING GROUP PTE LTD.; MAURITIUS, MAURITIUS

F

F&C INVESTMENT TRUST PLC; LONDON, UNITED KINGDOM

F.P. BOURGAULT INDUSTRIES LTD.; , CANADA

FARFALLI; MANIAGO, ITALY

FBS GLOBAL LIMITED; SINGAPORE, SINGAPORE

FENBO HOLDINGS LIMITED; KOWLOON, CHINA (HONG KONG)

FIN MILE LOGISTICS LIMITED; LONDON, UNITED KINGDOM

FIOR FAMILIE GMBH; MEERBUSCH, GERMANY

FIXIT AG; HOLDERBANK, SWITZERLAND

FLEXICARE (GROUP) LIMITED; CYNON VALLEY, UNITED KINGDOM

FLY SRL; VENETO, ITALY

FONUA LTD.; DUBLIN, IRELAND

FORMICA CAPITAL HOLDING AB; GOTHENBURG, SWEDEN

FORTENOVA GROUP D.D.; ZAGREB, CROATIA

FREE RUNNING BUILDINGS LTD.; ROTHERHAM, UNITED KINGDOM

FREMMAN CAPITAL LIMITED; LONDON, UNITED KINGDOM

G

GALAXY PAYROLL GROUP LIMITED; SHEUNG WAN, CHINA (HONG KONG)

GALEMED CORPORATION; TAIPEI, TAIWAN

GEBRUDER WEISS GESELLSCHAFT M.B.H.; LAUTERACH, AUSTRIA

GELTEQ LIMITED; SOUTH MELBOURNE, AUSTRALIA

GENROBOTIC INNOVATIONS PRIVATE LIMITED; THIRUVANANTHAPURAM, INDIA

GEUMSAN GINSENG HERB DEVELOPMENT AGENCY; GEUMSAN, KOREA (SOUTH)

GIA LAI ELECTRICITY JOINT STOCK COMPANY; PLEIKU, VIETNAM

GIACOM (CLOUD) HOLDINGS LIMITED; LONDON, UNITED KINGDOM

GL GMBH METALL- UND WERKSTATTTECHNIK; FRICKENHAUSEN, GERMANY

GLENTRA CAPITAL P/S; COPENHAGEN, DENMARK

GLOBAL LIGHTS ACQUISITION CORP.; BEIJING, CHINA

GLOBAL METCORP LTD; MIDDLESEX, UNITED KINGDOM

GLOBAL MOFY METAVERSE LIMITED; BEIJING, CHINA

GLOBAVEND HOLDINGS LIMITED; PERTH, AUSTRALIA

GOLD VALLEY PTY. LTD.; PERTH, AUSTRALIA

GOYAL SALT LIMITED; JAIPUR, INDIA

GRAFTON CAPITAL LIMITED; LONDON, UNITED KINGDOM

GRAPHISADS LIMITED; NEW DELHI, INDIA

GROUPE GARNIER; LOUDEAC, FRANCE

GRUPO DON MARIO; MARTINEZ, ARGENTINA

GRUPO LAR INVERSIONES INMOBILIARIAS, SA; MADRID, SPAIN

GUANGDONG LIANXUN PRECISION MANUFACTURING CO.,LTD.; ZHAOQING, CHINA

GURU APP FACTORY CORP.; LONDON, UNITED KINGDOM

H

HAMILTON & COMPANY LIMITED; MUMBAI, INDIA

HANSSAK CO., LTD.; SEOUL, KOREA (SOUTH)

HAO YONG AUTOMOTIVE CONTROLS LTD.; DONGGUAN, CHINA

HAPPY FORGING LIMITED; LUDHIANA, INDIA

HELMHOLTZ-ZENTRUM HEREON; GEESTHACHT, GERMANY

HEXONIA GMBH; NETTETAL, GERMANY

HFBG HOLDING B.V.; HOOFDDORP, NETHERLANDS

HIVEST CAPITAL PARTNERS SAS; PARIS, FRANCE

HOMEEASE INDUSTRIAL CO. LTD.; CHIAYI, TAIWAN

HONASA CONSUMER LIMITED; NEW DELHI, INDIA

HRH NEXT SERVICES LIMITED; HYDERABAD, INDIA

HUABO BIOPHARM (SHANGHAI) CO., LTD.; SHANGHAI, CHINA

HYGON INFORMATION TECHNOLOGY CO. LTD.; BEIJING, CHINA

HYPEX BIO EXPLOSIVES TECHNOLOGY AB; FARSTA, SWEDEN

I

IDEATION TRAINING PTY LTD.; GOODNA, AUSTRALIA

ILSHINWELLS CO., LTD.; SEOUL, KOREA (SOUTH)

IMT CO., LTD.; SUWON, KOREA (SOUTH)

INDEX INTERNATIONAL GROUP; STOCKHOLM, SWEDEN

INDIA SHELTER FINANCE CORPORATION LIMITED; GURGAON, INDIA

New Listings—continued

INDIFRA LIMITED; ANAND, INDIA

INDTACT GMBH; WURZBURG, GERMANY

INFIFRESH FOODS PVT. LTD.; KARNATAKA, INDIA

INFORMASCOPE; ANKARA, TURKIYE

INNOVA CAPTAB LIMITED; PANCHKULA, INDIA

INOX INDIA LIMITED; VADODARA, INDIA

INSTITUT NATIONAL DE RECHERCHE POUR L'AGRICULTURE L'ALIMENTATION ET L'ENVIRONNEMENT; PARIS, FRANCE

INSTITUTE OF NUCLEAR ENERGY RESEARCH; TAOYUAN, TAIWAN

INTEGRATED CYBER SOLUTIONS INC.; VANCOUVER, CANADA

INTERCAM BANCO, S.A.; MEXICO, MEXICO

INTERNATIONAL ASSET RECONSTRUCTION COMPANY PRIVATE LIMITED; MUMBAI, INDIA

INTERNATIONAL CONSOLIDATED BUSINESS GROUP PTY LTD.; MELBOURNE, AUSTRALIA

INTERNATIONAL HOLDING COMPANY PJSC; ABU DHABI, UNITED ARAB EMIRATES

INVESTCORP INDIA ACQUISITION CORP.; GEORGETOWN, CAYMAN ISLANDS

IRM ENERGY LIMITED; AHMEDABAD, INDIA

ISLAMIC CORPORATION FOR THE DEVELOPMENT OF THE PRIVATE SECTOR; JEDDAH, SAUDI ARABIA

IVECO GROUP N.V.; TURIN, ITALY

IYOGIN HOLDINGS CO.,LTD.; MATSUYAMA, JAPAN

J

JADESTONE ENERGY PLC; SINGAPORE, SINGAPORE

JAPAN M&A SOLUTION INCORPORATED; TOKYO, JAPAN

JAPANET HOLDINGS CO., LTD.; SASEBO, JAPAN

JIANGSU GUOJING HOLDING GROUP CO., LTD.; CHANGZHOU, CHINA

JIO FINANCIAL SERVICES LTD.; MUMBAI, INDIA

JNC CORPORATION; TOKYO, JAPAN

JSC SUEK; MOSCOW, RUSSIA

JUNEE LIMITED; SINGAPORE, SINGAPORE

JVSPAC ACQUISITION CORP.; WANCHAI, CHINA (HONG KONG)

K

KAIRIKIYA CO., LTD.; KYOTO, JAPAN

KARINGAL ST LAURENCE LIMITED; BELMONT, AUSTRALIA

KARNIKA INDUSTRIES LIMITED; HOWRAH, INDIA

KAUSHALYA LOGISTICS LIMITED; NEW DELHI, INDIA

KAY CEE ENERGY & INFRA LIMITED; KOTA, INDIA

KBI GROUP; SEOUL, KOREA (SOUTH)

KC CO.,LTD.; ANSEONG, KOREA (SOUTH)

KEEMO FASHION GROUP LIMITED; SHENZHEN, CHINA

KIBO CAPITAL PARTNERS LTD.; EBENE, MAURITIUS

KIRTI INVESTMENTS LIMITED; THANE, INDIA

KNIGHTEC AB; SOLNA, SWEDEN

KO GOLD INC.; TORONTO, CANADA

KONTOR SPACE LIMITED; THANE, INDIA

KOREA OCEAN BUSINESS CORPORATION; BUSAN, KOREA (SOUTH)

KUZCO LIGHTING, INC.; SURREY, CANADA

KYOTO FINANCIAL GROUP, INC.; KYOTO, JAPAN

L

L.E.K. CONSULTING GROUP LIMITED; LONDON, UNITED KINGDOM

LABFORWARD GMBH; BERLIN, GERMANY

LEASE OPERATORS LIMITED; SOUTH OROPOUCHE, TRINIDAD

LEDDARTECH HOLDINGS INC.; QUEBEC, CANADA

LEGEND SPICES, INC.; YEREVAN, ARMENIA

LEMON SISTEMI S.P.A.; BALESTRATE, ITALY

LENDLOCK GROUP LIMITED; CHESTER, UNITED KINGDOM

LIAN EE HYDRAULICS PTE LTD.; SINGAPORE, SINGAPORE

LINKAGE GLOBAL INC.; TOKYO, JAPAN

LINKERS INDUSTRIES LIMITED; SUNGAI PETANI, MALAYSIA

LUNIT, INC.; SEOUL, KOREA (SOUTH)

M

MACLAREN MINERALS LTD.; VANCOUVER, CANADA

MAINI CORPORATE PVT LTD.; BANGALORE, INDIA

MAITONG SUNSHINE CULTURAL DEVELOPMENT CO., LIMITED; BEIJING, CHINA

MARINETRANS INDIA LIMITED; NAVI MUMBAI, INDIA

MARLEY SPOON GROUP SE; LUXEMBOURG, LUXEMBOURG

MARUKOME CO., LTD.; NAGANO, JAPAN

MAXMIND PHARMACEUTICAL S.L.; MADRID, SPAIN

MAXO TELECOMMUNICATIONS PTY. LTD.; HARRISTOWN, AUSTRALIA

ME THERAPEUTICS HOLDINGS INC.; VANCOUVER, CANADA

MEDICINES DEVELOPMENT FOR GLOBAL HEALTH LIMITED; SOUTHBANK, AUSTRALIA

MEIDOH CO., LTD; TOYOTA, JAPAN

MERCANTIL SERVICIOS FINANCIEROS INTERNACIONAL, S.A.; PANAMA CITY, PANAMA

MERFORD HOLDING B.V.; GORINCHEM, NETHERLANDS

METRO SUPPLY CHAIN GROUP INC.; MONTREAL, CANADA

METROPOLITAN POLICE SERVICE; LONDON, UNITED KINGDOM

MF INTERNATIONAL LIMITED; WANCHAI, CHINA (HONG KONG)

MIJU CO., LTD.; SEOUL, KOREA (SOUTH)

MINGTENG INTERNATIONAL CORPORATION INC.; WUXI, CHINA

MINOX INTERNATIONAL GROUP BERHAD; PUCHONG, MALAYSIA

MISH DESIGNS LIMITED; MUMBAI, INDIA

MOBILE-HEALTH NETWORK SOLUTIONS; SINGAPORE, SINGAPORE

MOBILITAS SA; BEAUCHAMP, FRANCE

MONO PHARMACARE LIMITED; AHMEDABAD, INDIA

New Listings—continued

MOTISONS JEWELLERS LIMITED; JAIPUR, INDIA

MULTIPLICA INSIDE S.L.; BARCELONA, SPAIN

MURAL ONCOLOGY PLC; DUBLIN, IRELAND

MUTHOOT MICROFIN LIMITED; ERNAKULAM, INDIA

N

NADER HOLDING GMBH & CO. KG; DUDERSTADT, GERMANY

NANOHELIX CO. LTD.; DAEJEON, KOREA (SOUTH)

NAPLOY CORP.; ABUJA, NIGERIA

NATIONAL ASSET RECONSTRUCTION COMPANY LIMITED; MUMBAI, INDIA

NATIONAL LAGHUBITTA BITTIYA SANSTHA LIMITED; KAVREPALANCHOWK, NEPAL

NATIONALE-NEDERLANDEN OTWARTY FUNDUSZ EMERYTALNY; WARSAW, POLAND

NATIONWIDE FLEET INSTALLATIONS LTD.; MANCHESTER, UNITED KINGDOM

NBH CAPITAL CO., LTD.; SEOUL, KOREA (SOUTH)

NDC AUSTRALIA PTY LTD; MCMAHONS POINT, AUSTRALIA

NEO-CONCEPT INTERNATIONAL GROUP HOLDINGS LIMITED; KOWLOON, CHINA (HONG KONG)

NEOLARA CORP.; PUNTARENAS, COSTA RICA

NET AVENUE TECHNOLOGIES LIMITED; CHENNAI, INDIA

NEW HORIZON AIRCRAFT LTD.; LINDSAY, CANADA

NEWTON EUROPE LTD; OXFORDSHIRE, UNITED KINGDOM

NIKS PROFESSIONAL LTD.; SINGAPORE, SINGAPORE

NIMONIK, INC.; MONTREAL, CANADA

NIPPON EXPRESS HOLDINGS, INC.; TOKYO, JAPAN

NIPPON INSURE CO., LTD.; FUKUOKA, JAPAN

NIVIKA FASTIGHETER AB; JONKOPING, SWEDEN

NOBUL AI CORP.; TORONTO, CANADA

NOCO-NOCO INC.; SINGAPORE, SINGAPORE

NOH & PARTNERS CO., LTD.; SEOUL, KOREA (SOUTH)

NORDIC CORPORATE BANK ASA; OSLO, NORWAY

NOVAAGRO GROUP; KHARKIV, UKRAINE

NOVONESIS A/S; BAGSVAERD, DENMARK

NURTURE LANDSCAPES HOLDINGS LIMITED; WINDLESHAM, UNITED KINGDOM

O

O2 CAPITAL PARTNERS B.V.; OOSTERBEEK, NETHERLANDS

OAK WOODS ACQUISITION CORPORATION; NEPEAN, CANADA

OCI CO., LTD.; SEOUL, KOREA (SOUTH)

OFFICINE PICCOLI S.P.A; CASTEL D'AZZANO, ITALY

ON DOOR CONCEPTS LIMITED; BHOPAL, INDIA

ONET SA; MARSEILLE, FRANCE

ONODERA GROUP CO., LTD.; TOKYO, JAPAN

ONSITE ELECTRO SERVICES PVT. LTD.; MUMBAI, INDIA

OPEN AIRWAY DENTAL SOLUTIONS LTD; TARINGA, AUSTRALIA

ORAVEL STAYS LIMITED; AHMEDABAD, INDIA

OYOCAR GROUP, INC.; SOSUA, DOMINICAN REPUBLIC

P

PARAGON FINE & SPECIALITY CHEMICAL LIMITED; AHMEDABAD, INDIA

PARTNER ONE CAPITAL, INC.; LAVAL, CANADA

PATTYN BELGIUM NV; BRUGGE, BELGIUM

PELION GREEN FUTURE GMBH; MUNICH, GERMANY

PERFECT MOMENT LTD.; LONDON, UNITED KINGDOM

PHANTOM DIGITAL EFFECTS LIMITED; MUMBAI, INDIA

PHARMACOSMOS A/S; HOLBAEK, DENMARK

PHM GROUP HOLDING OYJ; HELSINKI, FINLAND

PINEAPPLE FINANCIAL INC.; NORTH YORK, CANADA

PLAYTIKA HOLDING CORP.; HERZLIYA PITUACH, ISRAEL

PREMIUM CATERING (HOLDINGS) LIMITED; SINGAPORE, SINGAPORE

PRESSTONIC ENGINEERING LIMITED; BENGALURU, INDIA

PROAX TECHNOLOGIES LTD.; MISSISSAUGA, CANADA

PROGRESSIVE STAR FINANCE PRIVATE LIMITED; KOLKATA, INDIA

PROTOPIA GLOBAL HOLDINGS INC.; KOWLOON, CHINA (HONG KONG)

PS INTERNATIONAL GROUP LTD.; HONG KONG, CHINA (HONG KONG)

PSYENCE BIOMEDICAL LTD.; TORONTO, CANADA

PT AGRO BAHARI NUSANTARA TBK; TANGERANG, INDONESIA

PT BARITO RENEWABLES ENERGY TBK; JAKARTA, INDONESIA

PT CHARLIE HOSPITAL SEMARANG TBK; KENDAL, INDONESIA

PT ITSEC ASIA TBK; JAKARTA, INDONESIA

PT JANU PUTRA SEJAHTERA TBK.; DEPOK, INDONESIA

PT KIAN SANTANG MULIATAMA TBK.; BEKASI, INDONESIA

PT KOKA INDONESIA TBK; JAKARTA SELATAN, INDONESIA

PT LOGISTICSPLUS INTERNATIONAL TBK; JAKARTA, INDONESIA

PT LOVINA BEACH BREWERY TBK; DENPASAR, INDONESIA

PT MAKNA PRAKARSA UTAMA; BOGOR, INDONESIA

PT MASTERSYSTEM INFOTAMA TBK.; JAKARTA PUSAT, INDONESIA

PT MULTI GARAM UTAMA TBK; SOUTH JAKARTA, INDONESIA

PT NUSANTARA SEJAHTERA RAYA TBK; JAKARTA, INDONESIA

PUIG BRANDS S.A.; BARCELONA, SPAIN

PURIT CO., LTD.; GYEONGJU, KOREA (SOUTH)

Q

QILU BANK CO., LTD.; JINAN, CHINA

QOO10 PTE. LTD; SINGAPORE, SINGAPORE

New Listings—continued

QUALITAS SEMICONDUCTOR CO., LTD.; SEONGNAM, KOREA (SOUTH)

R

RAIZEN S.A.; SAO PAULO, BRAZIL

RANMARINE TECHNOLOGY B.V.; ROTTERDAM, NETHERLANDS

RBZ JEWELLERS LIMITED; AHMEDABAD, INDIA

RED CANYON RESOURCES LTD.; VANCOUVER, CANADA

REDBRICK INVESTMENTS S.A R.L.; LUXEMBOURG, LUXEMBOURG

REGENT GAS HOLDINGS LIMITED; LONDON, UNITED KINGDOM

RENTA GROUP OY; VANTAA, FINLAND

RESOURCE CENTRIX HOLDINGS INC.; TORONTO, CANADA

RF ACQUISITION CORP II; SINGAPORE, SINGAPORE

RF PLAST GMBH; GUNZENHAUSEN, GERMANY

ROTALA GROUP LIMITED; TIPTON, UNITED KINGDOM

S

S J LOGISTICS (INDIA) LIMITED; THANE, INDIA

S&J CORPORATION; TOKYO, JAPAN

S&P SISTEMAS DE VENTILACIÓN, S.L.U.; BARCELONA, SPAIN

SAFE SUPPLY STREAMING CO., LTD.; VANCOUVER, CANADA

SAL SAUDI LOGISTICS SERVICES COMPANY; JEDDAH, SAUDI ARABIA

SALTUS PARTNERS LLP; WHITELEY, UNITED KINGDOM - ENGLAND

SAMEERA AGRO & INFRA LIMITED; TELANGANA, INDIA

SASATOKU PRINTING CO., LTD.; TOYOAKE, JAPAN

SATA GMBH & CO. KG; KORNWESTHEIM, GERMANY

SAUDI LIME INDUSTRIES COMPANY; RIYADH, SAUDI ARABIA

SBE-VARVIT S.P.A.; REGGIO EMILIA, ITALY

SEIBU GIKEN CO., LTD.; KOGA, JAPAN

SEKUR PRIVATE DATA LTD.; VANCOUVER, CANADA

SERVUS CREDIT UNION, LTD.; EDMONTON, CANADA

SG PRIVATE EQUITY CO., LTD.; SEOUL, KOREA (SOUTH)

SHANGHAI RURAL COMMERCIAL BANK CO., LTD.; SHANGHAI, CHINA

SHANTHALA FMCG PRODUCTS LIMITED; KARNATAKA, INDIA

SHEFFIELD GREEN LTD.; SINGAPORE, SINGAPORE

SHENGHONG HOLDING GROUP CO., LTD.; SUZHOU, CHINA

SHREE OSFM E-MOBILITY LIMITED; NAVI MUMBAI, INDIA

SIAT SOCIETA' INTERNAZIONALE APPLICAZIONI TECNICHE SPA; TURATE, ITALY

SIGHTRON JAPAN INC.; TOKYO, JAPAN

SIGNPOST INDIA LIMITED; MUMBAI, INDIA

SIGNPOST NV; LOKEREN, BELGIUM

SIMONE S.P.A.; NAPLES, ITALY

SIMPLY SOLVENTLESS CONCENTRATES LTD.; CALGARY, CANADA

SKYLAND GROUP S.R.L.; MILAN, ITALY

SNEF SA; MARSEILLE, FRANCE

SOILTECH AS; SANDNES, NORWAY

SOMAI PHARMACEUTICALS LTD; CARREGADO, PORTUGAL

SOPHORA UNTERNEHMERKAPITAL GMBH; MUNICH, GERMANY

SOUND CAVE TECHNOLOGY, INC.; TORONTO, CANADA

SRIVARU HOLDING LIMITED; GRAND CAYMAN, CAYMAN ISLANDS

SSF HOME GROUP BERHAD; PETALING JAYA, MALAYSIA

STAR FASHION CULTURE HOLDINGS LIMITED; XIAMEN, CHINA

STEMCELL TECHNOLOGIES CANADA INC.; VANCOUVER, CANADA

STEVE MARSHALL GROUP LTD.; CAMPBELL RIVER, CANADA

STEWART INVESTMENT & FINANCIAL PRIVATE LIMITED; KOLKATA, INDIA

STICKIT TECHNOLOGIES INC.; VANCOUVER, CANADA

STIF FRANCE SAS; SAINT-GEORGES-SUR-LOIRE, FRANCE

STONEWEG SA; GENEVA, SWITZERLAND

SU GROUP HOLDINGS LIMITED; KOWLOON, CHINA (HONG KONG)

SUPREME POWER EQUIPMENT LIMITED; CHENNAI, INDIA

SURAJ ESTATE DEVELOPERS LIMITED; MUMBAI, INDIA

SWVL HOLDINGS CORP.; DUBAI, UNITED ARAB EMIRATES

SYENSQO SA; BRUSSELS, BELGIUM

SYNERGY PARTNERS CO., LTD.; SEOUL, KOREA (SOUTH)

T

TAIYO KOKO CO LTD; KOBE, JAPAN

TALDE GESTION, S.G.E.I.C., S.A; BILBAO, SPAIN

TANKERSKA PLOVIDBA D.D.; ZADAR, CROATIA

TEAM INDIA MANAGERS LTD.; MUMBAI, INDIA

TECT HOLDINGS LIMITED; TAURANGA, NEW ZEALAND

TELECEL GROUP LTD.; ROSE-HILL, MAURITIUS

TELESAT CORPORATION; OTTAWA, CANADA

TEYLOR AG; ZURICH, SWITZERLAND

THE CENTRE FOR GENOMIC REGULATION (CRG); BARCELONA, SPAIN

THE HELMHOLTZ ASSOCIATION; BONN, GERMANY

THE SALVATION ARMY INTERNATIONAL TRUST; LONDON, UNITED KINGDOM

TOHAN CORPORATION; TOKYO, JAPAN

TOP WEALTH GROUP HOLDING LIMITED; HONG KONG, CHINA (HONG KONG)

TPL CORP LIMITED; KARACHI, PAKISTAN

TRANSPORTS DESERT SA; ETRELLES, FRANCE

TRAXALL INTERNATIONAL LTD.; STAFFORDSHIRE, UNITED KINGDOM

TRIDENT TECHLABS LIMITED; NEW DELHI, INDIA

TUNGRAY TECHNOLOGIES INC.; SINGAPORE, SINGAPORE

U

UNIHEALTH CONSULTANCY LIMITED; MUMBAI, INDIA

New Listings—continued

UNITED AJOD INSURANCE LIMITED; KATHMANDU, NEPAL

V

VALENS SEMICONDUCTOR LTD.; HOD HASHARON, ISRAEL

VAMA SUNDARI INVESTMENTS (DELHI) PRIVATE LIMITED; NOIDA, INDIA

VIETNAM PROSPERITY JOINT-STOCK COMMERCIAL BANK; HANOI, VIETNAM

VISHNUSURYA PROJECTS & INFRA LIMITED; CHENNAI, INDIA

VIVAA TRADECOM LIMITED; AHMEDABAD, INDIA

VNE S.P.A.; LUCCA, ITALY

VRUNDAVAN PLANTATION LIMITED; AHMEDABAD, INDIA

W

WEBUY GLOBAL LTD.; SINGAPORE, SINGAPORE

WEINERT INDUSTRIES AG; SONNEBERG, GERMANY

WILCOMPUTE SYSTEMS GROUP, INC.; TORONTO, CANADA

WILEE VEGETABLE OILS SDN. BHD.; SHAH ALAM, MALAYSIA

WIREX LIMITED; LONDON, UNITED KINGDOM

WOMANCART LIMITED; NEW DELHI, INDIA

WOODFIELD SYSTEMS INTERNATIONAL PVT LTD.; THANE, INDIA

WOT CO., LTD.; HWASEONG, KOREA (SOUTH)

X

XENIA HOTELLERIE SOLUTION S.P.A.; MILAN, ITALY

XIAOMI CORPORATION; BEIJING, CHINA

Y

YAKKYO S.P.A.; ROME, ITALY

YUWANG GROUP; SELANGOR, MALAYSIA

YY GROUP HOLDING LIMITED; SINGAPORE, SINGAPORE

Z

ZAGGLE PREPAID OCEAN SERVICES LIMITED; MUMBAI, INDIA

ZHEJIANG HAOTAI CHEMICAL CO., LTD.; SHAOXING, CHINA

ZKH GROUP LIMITED; SHANGHAI, CHINA

New Listings—continued

UNITED AJOD INSURANCE LIMITED; KATHMANDU, NEPAL

V

VALENS SEMICONDUCTOR LTD.; HOD HASHARON, ISRAEL

VAMA SUNDARI INVESTMENTS (DELHI) PRIVATE LIMITED; NOIDA, INDIA

VIETNAM PROSPERITY JOINT-STOCK COMMERCIAL BANK; HANOI, VIETNAM

VISHNUSURYA PROJECTS & INFRA LIMITED; CHENNAI, INDIA

VIVAA TRADECOM LIMITED; AHMEDABAD, INDIA

VNE S.P.A.; LUCCA, ITALY

VRUNDAVAN PLANTATION LIMITED; AHMEDABAD, INDIA

W

WEBUY GLOBAL LTD.; SINGAPORE, SINGAPORE

WEINERT INDUSTRIES AG; SONNEBERG, GERMANY

WI.COMPUTE SYSTEMS GROUP INC.; TORONTO, CANADA

WILEE VEGETABLE OILS SDN. BHD.; SHAH ALAM, MALAYSIA

WIREX LIMITED; LONDON, UNITED KINGDOM

WOMANCART LIMITED; NEW DELHI, INDIA

WOODFIELD SYSTEMS INTERNATIONAL PVT.LTD.; THANE, INDIA

WOT CO. LTD.; HWASEONG, KOREA (SOUTH)

X

XENIA HOTELLERIE SOLUTION S.P.A.; MILAN, ITALY

XIAOMI CORPORATION; BEIJING, CHINA

Y

YAKKYO S.P.A.; ROME, ITALY

YUWANG GROUP; SELANGOR, MALAYSIA

YY GROUP HOLDING LIMITED; SINGAPORE, SINGAPORE

Z

ZAGGLE PREPAID OCEAN SERVICES LIMITED; MUMBAI, INDIA

ZHEJIANG HAOTAI CHEMICAL CO., LTD.; SHAOXING, CHINA

ZKH GROUP LIMITED; SHANGHAI, CHINA

Mergers and Acquisitions
January 2024—December 2024
(Parent Companies Only)

7
79North, Inc.—acquired by Miata Metals Corp.

9
92 Energy Limited—acquired by ATHA Energy Corp.

A
A&W Revenue Royalties Income Fund—acquired by TorQuest Partners Inc.
A2B Australia Limited—acquired by ComfortDelGro Corporation Limited
Accrol Group Holdings plc—acquired by SODIM, SGPS, SA
ACP Metal Finishing Pte Ltd—acquired by Grand Venture Technology Limited
Actis LLP—acquired by General Atlantic Service Company, L.P.
Adbri Limited—acquired by CRH plc and Barro Group Pty Ltd
Addison Lee Limited—acquired by ComfortDelGro Corporation Limited
Ador Fontech Ltd.—acquired by Ador Welding Ltd
Adventus Mining Corporation—acquired by Silvercorp Metals Inc.
AgroGeneration SA—acquired by NOVAAGRO group
Alcion Group—acquired by Insight Venture Management, LLC
Almacenes Exito SA—acquired by Calleja S.A. de C.V.
Alpha Financial Markets Consulting plc—acquired by Bridgepoint Group Plc
Alumina Limited—acquired by Alcoa Corporation
APM Human Services International Limited—acquired by Madison Dearborn Partners, LLC
Apontis Pharma AG—acquired by Advent International Corporation
Applus Services, S.A.—acquired by TDR Capital LLP and I Squared Capital Advisors (US) LLC
Aris International Limited—acquired by BRCCA Services Private Limited [et al]
AS Tallink Grupp—acquired by AS Infortar
Ascential plc—acquired by Informa plc
asknet GmbH—acquired by Signpost NV
Atlantska plovidba d.d.—acquired by Tankerska plovidba d.d
Australian Oilseeds Investments Pty Ltd.—merged with Edoc Acquisition Corp., to form Australian Oilseeds Holdings Limited
Australian Plastic Profiles Pty. Ltd.—acquired by Legrand S.A.
Automecanica SA—acquired by Rheinmetall AG
Azure Minerals Limited—acquired by Sociedad Quimica y Minera de Chile S.A. and Hancock Prospecting Pty. Ltd.

B
B&B Korea Corporation—acquired by Hitejinro Holdings Co., Ltd.
Banco Indusval S.A.—acquired by Banco Master S.A.
Base Resources Limited—acquired by Energy Fuels Inc.
BBTV Holdings Inc.—merged with 15384150 Canada Inc., to form BBTV Holdings Inc.
Belvoir Group PLC—acquired by The Property Franchise Group PLC
Benesse Holdings, Inc.—acquired by EQT AB
Besqab AB—merged with Aros Bostadsutveckling AB, to form Besqab AB
Bharat Serums & Vaccines Limited—acquired by Mankind Pharma Ltd.
Blackwolf Copper & Gold Ltd.—acquired by NexGold Mining Corp.

C
Calliditas Therapeutics AB—acquired by Asahi Kasei Corporation
Camlab, Ltd.—acquired by StoneCalibre, LLC
Cardano Risk Management Ltd—acquired by Marsh & McLennan Companies, Inc.
Ceapro Inc.—acquired by AEterna Zentaris Inc.
Chr. Hansen Holding A/S—acquired by Novozymes A/S
Chuo Build Industry Co., Ltd.—acquired by Asahi Kasei Corporation
Cliffside Capital Ltd.—acquired by Cliffside Ltd.
CloudMD Software & Services, Inc.—acquired by CPS Capital
CMLS Financial Ltd.—acquired by Nesto, Inc.
Complete Innovations Inc.—acquired by PowerFleet, Inc.
Connect First Credit Union Ltd.—acquired by Servus Credit Union, Ltd.
Contact Gold Corp.—acquired by Orla Mining Ltd.
Contract Pharmaceuticals Limited—acquired by Aterian Investment Management, L.P.
Costa Group Holdings Limited—acquired by Paine Schwartz Partners, LLC, Driscoll's, Inc and Brit-

Mergers and Acquisitions—continued

ish Columbia Investment Management Corporation

Crealogix Holding AG—acquired by Constellation Software Inc.

creditshelf Aktiengesellschaft—acquired by Teylor AG

Crew Energy Inc.—acquired by Tourmaline Oil Corp.

D

Dar-es-Salaam Textile Mills Limited—acquired by TPL Corp Limited, and name changed to TPL Life Insurance Limited

Darktrace Plc—acquired by Thoma Bravo, L.P.

Dechra Pharmaceuticals PLC—acquired by EQT AB

Decmil Group Limited—acquired by Macmahon Holdings Limited

Descente Ltd.—acquired by ITOCHU Corporation

DevvStream Holdings Inc.—merged with Focus Impact Acquisition Corp., to form DevvStream Corp.

Digital Magics S.p.A.—acquired by LVenture Group SpA

Diverger Limited—acquired by Count Limited

DX (Group) PLC—acquired by H.I.G. Capital, LLC

Dyna-Mac Holdings Ltd.—acquired by Hanwha Ocean Co., Ltd. and Hanwha Group

E

ECIT AS—acquired by TowerBrook Capital Partners, L.P.

ELAN Corporation—acquired by Sony Group Corporation

Electrameccanica Vehicles Corp.—acquired by XOS, INC.

Emerald Coast Truss, LLC—acquired by Bain Capital, LP

Envato Pty Ltd.—acquired by Shutterstock, Inc.

EQS Group AG—acquired by Thoma Bravo, L.P.

F

FANCL Corporation—acquired by Kirin Holdings Company, Limited

Fantasma Games AB—acquired by EveryMatrix Ltd.

Farfetch Limited—acquired by Coupang, Inc. and Greenoaks Capital Partners LLC

Fassi Gru S.p.A.—acquired by Investindustrial Advisors Ltd.

Fertiglobe plc—acquired by Abu Dhabi National Oil Company

Fluxx Limited—acquired by Newton Europe Ltd

FLYHT Aerospace Solutions Ltd.—acquired by Firan Technology Group Corporation

Foresight Sustainable Forestry Company Plc—acquired by Averon Park Limited

Formaplex Ltd.—acquired by Unipart Group of Companies Limited

Forward Partners Group Plc—acquired by Molten Ventures VCT plc

Fraser & Neave Limited—acquired by Thai Beverage Public Company Limited

Fraser Mackenzie Accelerator Corp.—acquired by Forward Water Technologies Corp

FueTrek Co., Ltd.—merged with AI Co., Ltd.

Fusion Pharmaceuticals Inc.—acquired by AstraZeneca PLC

G

Galimmo SA—acquired by Carmila SA

Genedata AG—acquired by Danaher Corporation

GLOSEL Co., Ltd.—acquired by Macnica Fuji Electronics Holdings. Inc.

Gold Line Resources Ltd.—acquired by Barsele Minerals Corp.

Goldsource Mines Inc.—acquired by Mako Mining Corp.

Gracell Biotechnologies Inc.—acquired by AstraZeneca PLC

Gram Car Carriers A.S.A.—acquired by Mediterranean Shipping Company, S.A.

GRC International Group plc—acquired by Bloom Equity Partners Management, LLC

Greenstone Resources Ltd.—acquired by Horizon Minerals Limited

Greenvolt - Energias Renovaveis, S.A.—acquired by KKR & Co. Inc.

Gresham Technologies plc—acquired by Symphony Technology Group, LLC

H

Hail Cement Company—acquired by Qassim Cement Co.

Heidelberg Engineering GmbH—acquired by EssilorLuxottica SA

Hong Kong Resources Holdings Company Limited—acquired by Luk Fook Holdings (International) Limited

Hopin Ltd.—acquired by Bending Spoons S.p.A.

Hotel Chocolat Group PLC—acquired by Mars, Incorporated

Huntswood CTC Limited—acquired by ResultsCX

I

IASO S.A.—acquired by Brookfield Corporation

IBEX Technologies Inc.—acquired by Novo Nordisk Fonden

IIFL Finance Ltd.—acquired by International Conveyors Limited

IJTT Co., Ltd.—acquired by SPARX Group Co., Ltd.

Mergers and Acquisitions—continued

Impellam Group plc—acquired by HFBG Holding B.V.
INDIVA Limited—acquired by SNDL Inc.
Innofactor Plc—acquired by CapMan PLC and Osprey Capital LLC
IQGeo Group plc—acquired by KKR & Co. Inc.
IWATSU ELECTRIC Co Ltd—acquired by AI Holdings Corp.

J

Japan Foods Co., Ltd.—acquired by Marubeni Corporation
Japan Publications Trading Co., Ltd—acquired by TOHAN CORPORATION
JASTEC Co., Ltd.—acquired by Nippon Telegraph & Telephone Corporation
Joyspeed Global Cargo China Limited—acquired by Hon Hai Precision Industry Co., Ltd.

K

Karora Resources Inc.—acquired by Westgold Resources Limited
Kensington Capital Partners Limited—acquired by AGF Management Limited
Kerry Express (Thailand) Public Company Limited—acquired by S.F. Holding Co., Ltd.
Keywords Studios Plc—acquired by EQT AB, Canada Pension Plan Investment Board and Temasek Holdings (Private) Limited
Kin + Carta Plc—acquired by BC Partners LLP
KMC Properties ASA—acquired by Logistea AB
KRACHT GmbH—acquired by Atlas Copco AB
Kuchai Development Berhad—acquired by Sungei Bagan Rubber Company (MALAYA) Berhad
Kyoden Co., Ltd.—acquired by The Carlyle Group Inc.

L

Labrador Uranium Inc.—acquired by ATHA Energy Corp.
LHD Group Deutschland GmbH—acquired by Lakeland Industries, Inc.
Link Administration Holdings Limited—acquired by Mitsubishi UFJ Financial Group, Inc.
Lithium Power International Limited—acquired by Corporacion Nacional del Cobre de Chile
Logistec Corporation—acquired by Blue Wolf Capital Partners LLC
Luminex Resources Corp.—acquired by Adventus Mining Corporation
LXI REIT plc—acquired by LondonMetric Property Plc

M

Mac Chain Co. Ltd.—acquired by Renold plc
Marathon Gold Corporation—acquired by Calibre Mining Corp.
Masmovil Ibercom, S.A.—acquired by Orange S.A.
Masonite International Corporation—acquired by Owens Corning
Mattioli Woods plc—acquired by Pollen Street PLC
McGrath Limited—acquired by Knight Frank LLP and Bayleys Corporation Limited
mdf commerce, inc.—acquired by KKR & Co. Inc.
MEDIASEEK, Inc.—merged with Japan Living Warranty, Inc., to form Solvyy Inc.
MediaValet Inc.—acquired by Symphony Technology Group, LLC
Merricks Capital Pty Ltd.—acquired by Regal Partners Limited
Metallica Minerals Limited—acquired by Diatreme Resources Limited
MHM Automation Limited—acquired by KKR & Co. Inc.
Millennium Services Group Limited—acquired by SoftBank Group Corp.
Mimasu Semiconductor Industry Co., Ltd.—acquired by Shin-Etsu Chemical Co. Ltd.
MiX Telematics Limited—acquired by PowerFleet, Inc.
Modern Living Investments Holdings Limited—acquired by Asia Allied Infrastructure Holdings Limited
Modular Automation Ireland Ltd.—acquired by Ares Management Corporation
MorphoSys AG—acquired by Novartis AG

N

Nagatanien Holdings Co., Ltd.—acquired by Mitsubishi Corporation
Namoi Cotton Limited—acquired by Louis Dreyfus Company B.V.
Nanjing Iron & Steel Co., Ltd.—acquired by CITIC Group Corporation
Navkar Corporation Ltd.—acquired by JSW Steel Ltd.
Net One Systems Co Ltd—acquired by Sumitomo Corporation
Network International Holdings PLC—acquired by Brookfield Corporation
NewOrigin Gold Corp.—acquired by Harfang Exploration Inc.
Nighthawk Gold Corp.—acquired by Moneta Gold Inc., and name changed to STLLR Gold Inc.
Nordic Waterproofing Holding AB—acquired by Kingspan Group PLC
Novatech Group, Inc—acquired by Garaga Inc.
NSL limited—acquired by YTL Corporation Berhad

Mergers and Acquisitions—continued

NSPM AG—acquired by Cactus Communications, Inc.
Nuvo Group Ltd.—merged with LAMF Global Ventures Corp. I, to form Holdco Nuvo Group D.G Ltd.

O

Oceanteam ASA—acquired by SoilTech AS
Olink Holding AB—acquired by Thermo Fisher Scientific Inc.
OneSoft Solutions Inc.—acquired by Blackstone Inc.
Ontsu Co., Ltd.—acquired by GENDA Inc.
Opdenergy Holding SA—acquired by Antin Infrastructure Partners SAS
Orascom Financial Holding SAE—acquired by B Investments Holding SAE
Orchard Therapeutics plc—acquired by Kirin Holdings Company, Limited
Osisko Mining Inc.—acquired by Gold Fields Limited
OUTSOURCING Inc.—acquired by Bain Capital, LP

P

Pagero Group AB—acquired by Thomson Reuters Corporation
Park Lawn Corporation—acquired by Homesteaders Life Co. Inc. and Birch Hill Equity Partners Management Inc.
PCI Holdings Inc.—acquired by Restar Holdings Corporation
Permascand Top Holding AB—acquired by Altor Equity Partners AB
Perpetual Energy Inc.—merged with Rubellite Energy Inc., to form Rubellite Energy Corp.
Plant Health Care plc—acquired by PI Industries Ltd.
Playmaker Capital Inc.—acquired by Better Collective A/S
Plusgrade Parent L.P.—acquired by General Atlantic Service Company, L.P.
PNX Metals Limited—merged with Kin Mining NL, to form Patronus Resources Limited
POLARIS UNO, Inc.—acquired by Polaris Office Corp.
Polycorp Ltd.—acquired by Arsenal Capital Management LP
Premium Turf-Care Ltd.—acquired by Iseki & Co., Ltd.
PROBIOTEC LIMITED—acquired by Pyridam Farma Tbk
Prospa Group Limited—acquired by Salter Brothers Emerging Companies Limited
PSC Insurance Group Limited—acquired by The Ardonagh Group Limited
PT Mitra Tirta Buwana Tbk—acquired by PT Makna Prakarsa Utama

Q

Q4 Inc.—acquired by Sumeru Equity Partners LLC
QANTM Intellectual Property Limited—acquired by Adamantem Capital Management Pty Limited
Quadpack Industries SA—acquired by PSB Industries SA
Quid Pro Quo Alquiler Seguro SOCIMI SA—acquired by Ktesios Real Estate SOCIMI, S.A.

R

Ras Al Khaimah Company for White Cement & Construction Materials PSC—acquired by The Aditya Birla Group
Redrow plc—acquired by Barratt Developments PLC
Reunion Gold Corporation—acquired by G Mining Ventures Corp.
Riso Kyoiku Co., Ltd.—acquired by Hulic Co., Ltd.
RIV Capital Inc—acquired by Cansortium, Inc.
ROBUR Industry Service Group GmbH—acquired by Clayton, Dubilier & Rice, LLC
Roctec Global Public Company Limited—acquired by BTS Group Holdings Public Company Limited
Rotala Plc—acquired by Rotala Group Limited [et al]
Route Mobile Ltd.—acquired by Proximus PLC

S

Samantha Thavasa Japan Limited—acquired by Konaka Co., Ltd.
Sauermann Industrie S.A.—acquired by Verder International B.V.
Schrole Group Limited—acquired by ONEX Corporation
SCS Group PLC—acquired by Poltronesofa Holding Srl
Seamless Group Inc.—merged with InFinT Acquisition Corporation, to form Currenc Group Inc.
SERIO Holdings Co., Ltd.—acquired by Senko Group Holdings Co., Ltd.
Shs Viveon AG—acquired by SIDETRADE S.A.
Silver Lake Resources Limited—acquired by Red 5 Limited
Singardo International Pte Ltd—acquired by Electrosteel Castings Ltd
SK Rent A Car Co., Ltd.—acquired by Affinity Equity Partners (HK) Ltd.
SKIYAKI, Inc.—merged with Space Shower Networks Inc., to form Space Shower Skiyaki Holdings, inc.
SMT Scharf AG—acquired by Yankuang Group Co., Limited
Snow Peak Inc.—acquired by Bain Capital, LP
SNU Precision Co., Ltd.—merged with CIS Co., Ltd.
Sonata Finance Pvt. Ltd.—acquired by Kotak Mahindra Bank Limited

Sopheon Plc—acquired by Wellspring Worldwide, LLC
SpareBank 1 Sorost-Norge—acquired by SpareBank 1 SR-Bank ASA, to form SpareBank 1 Sør-Norge ASA
Stelco Holdings, Inc.—acquired by Cleveland-Cliffs, Inc.
Stillwell Motor Group—acquired by Autosports Group Limited
Symbio Holdings Limited—acquired by Aussie Broadband Ltd.

T

Tatsuta Electric Wire & Cable Co., Ltd.—acquired by ENEOS Holdings, Inc.
TClarke PLC—acquired by Regent Gas Holdings Limited
Technology Metals Australia Limited—acquired by Australian Vanadium Limited
Ten Entertainment Group plc—acquired by Trive Capital Inc.
Think Research Corporation—acquired by Beedie Capital Partners
TIM S.A.—acquired by Wurth Verwaltungsgesellschaft mbH
TIMES GUARANTY LTD.—acquired by Team India Managers Ltd.
TLI Co., Ltd.—acquired by Wonik Corporation
Toho Kinzoku Co., Ltd.—acquired by TAIYO KOKO Co Ltd
Tokai Carbon Korea Co., Ltd.—acquired by Tokai Carbon Co., Ltd.
Tosei Corporation—acquired by Electrolux Professional AB
Totens Sparebank—acquired by Sparebank 1 Oestlandet
Tricon Residential Inc.—acquired by Blackstone Inc.
Trident Royalties Plc—acquired by Deterra Royalties Limited
Trinity Exploration & Production plc—acquired by Lease Operators Limited
Tritium DCFC Limited—acquired by Exicom Tele-Systems Limited
Troy Income & Growth Trust plc—acquired by STS Global Income & Growth Trust plc
TrueContext Corporation—acquired by Battery Ventures, L.P.
Tyman plc—acquired by Quanex Building Products Corp.

U

UK Commercial Property REIT Limited—acquired by Tritax Big Box REIT plc
Universal Copper Ltd.—acquired by Vizsla Copper Corp.
Urb-it AB—acquired by Fin Mile Logistics Limited

V

Vanstar Mining Resources Inc.—acquired by IAMGOLD Corporation
Vectron Systems AG—acquired by Shift4 Payments, Inc.
Virgin Money UK PLC—acquired by Nationwide Building Society
Visiodent S.A.—acquired by Cegedim S.A.
Vitesco Technologies Group AG—acquired by INA-Holding Schaeffler GmbH & Co. KG
Volatus Aerospace Corp.—acquired by Drone Delivery Canada Corp.

W

WalkMe Ltd.—acquired by SAP SE
Wincanton plc—acquired by GXO Logistics, Inc.
Woodfield Systems Limited—acquired by Woodfield Systems International Pvt Ltd.

Y

Yasue Corporation—acquired by Sala Corporation

Z

Zuken Elmic, Inc.—acquired by Zuken, Inc.

Mergers and Acquisitions—continued

Sopheon Plc—acquired by Wellspring Worldwide, LLC
SpareBank 1 Sørost-Norge—acquired by SpareBank 1 SR-Bank ASA, to form SpareBank 1 Sør-Norge ASA
Stelco Holdings, Inc.—acquired by Cleveland-Cliffs, Inc.
Stillwell Motor Group—acquired by Autosports Group Limited
Symbio Holdings Limited—acquired by Aussie Broadband Ltd.

T

Tatsuta Electric Wire & Cable Co., Ltd.—acquired by ENEOS Holdings, Inc.
TClarke PLC—acquired by Regent Gas Holdings Limited
Technology Metals Australia Limited—acquired by Australian Vanadium Limited
TenEntertainment Group plc—acquired by Trive Capital, Inc.
Think Research Corporation—acquired by Beedie Capital Partners
TIM S.A.—acquired by Würth Ve waltungsgesellschaft mbH
TIMES GUARANTY LTD.—acquired by Team India Managers Ltd.
TLI Co., Ltd.—acquired by Wonik Corporation
Toho Kinzoku Co., Ltd.—acquired by TAIYO KOKO Co.Ltd
Tokai Carbon Korea Co., Ltd.—acquired by Tokai Carbon Co., Ltd
Tosei Corporation—acquired by Electrolux Professional AB
Totens Sparebank—acquired by Sparebank 1 Oestlandet
Tricon Residential Inc.—acquired by Blackstone Inc.
Trident Royalties Plc—acquired by Deterra Royalties Limited
Trinity Exploration & Production plc—acquired by Lease Operators Limited
Tritium DCFC Limited—acquired by Exicom Tele-Systems Limited
Troy Income & Growth Trust plc—acquired by STS Global Income & Growth Trust plc
TrueContext Corporation—acquired by Battery Ventures, L.P.
Tyman plc—acquired by Quanex Building Products Corp

U

UK Commercial Property REIT Limited—acquired by Tritax Big Box REIT plc
Universal Copper Ltd.—acquired by Vizsla Copper Corp.
Urb-it AB—acquired by Fin Mile Logistics Limited

V

Venstar Mining Resources Inc.—acquired by IAM-GOLD Corporation
Vectron Systems AG—acquired by Shift4 Payments, Inc.
Virgin Money UK PLC—acquired by Nationwide Building Society
Visiodent S.A.—acquired by Ogedim S.A.
Vitesco Technologies Group AG—acquired by INA-Holding Schaeffler GmbH & Co. KG
Volatus Aerospace Corp.—acquired by Drone Delivery Canada Corp.

W

WalkMe Ltd.—acquired by SAP SE
Wincanton plc—acquired by GXO Logistics, Inc.
Woodfield Systems Limited—acquired by Woodfield Systems International Pvt Ltd.

Y

Yasue Corporation—acquired by Sala Corporation

Z

Zuken Elmic, Inc.—acquired by Zuken, Inc.

AND PRIVATE COMPANIES

G & M HOLDINGS LIMITED
Rm 1709 17/F Manhattan Centre 8 Kwai Cheong Road Kwai Cheong Road, Kwai Chung, Hong Kong, NT, China (Hong Kong)
Tel.: (852) 23990289   Ky
Web Site: http://www.gm-eng.com.hk
Year Founded: 1993
6038—(HKG)
Rev.: $48,805,215
Assets: $51,468,818
Liabilities: $14,543,670
Net Worth: $36,925,148
Earnings: $5,534,010
Emp.: 108
Fiscal Year-end: 12/31/22
Construction Work Services
N.A.I.C.S.: 238150
Chi Hung Lee *(Co-Founder, Chm & CEO)*

G ADVENTURES, INC.
19 Charlotte Street, Toronto, M5V 2H5, ON, Canada
Tel.: (416) 260-0999
Web Site:
  http://www.gadventures.com
Tour Services
N.A.I.C.S.: 561520
Timothy Chan *(Mgr-PR)*

G C PAN EUROPEAN CROSSING FRANCE
4 Rue Louis David, 75116, Paris, France
Tel.: (33) 144342700
Rev.: $38,600,000
Emp.: 50
N.A.I.C.S.: 517121
Christian Joly *(Dir)*

G CAPITAL BERHAD
D-5-10 Block D Pusat Komersial Southgate No 2 Jalan Dua, Off Jalan Chan Sow Lin, 55200, Kuala Lumpur, Wilayah Persekutuan, Malaysia
Tel.: (60) 392261222   MY
Web Site: https://gcapital.com.my
GCAP—(KLS)
Rev.: $5,687,826
Assets: $38,225,114
Liabilities: $14,794,542
Net Worth: $23,430,572
Earnings: ($4,327,434)
Emp.: 94
Fiscal Year-end: 12/31/22
Food Transportation Services
N.A.I.C.S.: 488490
Eric Toh Chee Seong *(Co-Sec)*

Subsidiaries:

Ingress Energy Sdn. Bhd.   (1)
Lot 2778 5th Floor Jalan Damansara, Sungai Penchala, 60000, Kuala Lumpur, Wilayah Persekutuan, Malaysia
Tel.: (60) 377255565
Web Site: https://www.ingresscorp.com.my
Automotive Parts Mfr & Distr
N.A.I.C.S.: 336390

G CAPITAL PUBLIC COMPANY LIMITED
9/9 Atsathorn Building 19th Floor South Sathorn Road, Yan Nawa Subdistrict Sathorn District, Bangkok, 10120, Thailand
Tel.: (66) 26519995
Web Site: https://www.gcapital.co.th
GCAP—(THA)
Rev.: $5,305,944
Assets: $36,369,693
Liabilities: $22,295,897
Net Worth: $14,073,796
Earnings: $432,553
Emp.: 49
Fiscal Year-end: 12/31/23
Financial Services
N.A.I.C.S.: 921130
Boonsak Chiempricha *(Chm)*

G CITY LTD.
Nissim Aloni 10, Tel Aviv, 6291924, Israel
Tel.: (972) 37778111   Il
Web Site: https://www.gazit-globe.com
GZTGF—(OTCIQ)
Rev.: $673,573,688
Assets: $10,739,881,031
Liabilities: $7,609,614,469
Net Worth: $3,130,266,562
Earnings: $364,691,250
Emp.: 235
Fiscal Year-end: 12/31/23
Real Estate Investment Trust
N.A.I.C.S.: 525990
Chaim K. Katzman *(Founder, Vice Chm & CEO)*

Subsidiaries:

First Capital REIT   (1)
85 Hanna Ave Suite 400, Toronto, M6K 3S3, ON, Canada   **(50.5%)**
Tel.: (416) 504-4114
Web Site: https://www.fcr.ca
Rev.: $519,508,213
Assets: $6,936,117,004
Liabilities: $3,918,538,930
Net Worth: $3,017,578,074
Earnings: ($101,460,944)
Emp.: 372
Fiscal Year-end: 12/31/2023
Shopping Center Real Estate Managers
N.A.I.C.S.: 531312
Bernard McDonell *(Chm)*

G City Europe Limited   (1)
11-15 Seaton Place, Saint Helier, JE4 0QH, Jersey   **(60.1%)**
Tel.: (44) 2078313113
Web Site: https://g-cityeu.com
Rev.: $147,801,640
Assets: $3,165,620,548
Liabilities: $1,657,668,897
Net Worth: $1,507,951,651
Earnings: $7,748,759
Emp.: 377
Fiscal Year-end: 12/31/2022
Real Estate Investment & Development Services
N.A.I.C.S.: 525990
Liad Barzilai *(CEO)*

G ENONE ENERGY CO., LTD.
43 Changeop-ro, Sujeong-gu, Seongnam, Gyeonggi-do, Korea (South)
Tel.: (82) 317572023
Web Site: https://www.genone.co.kr
Year Founded: 2017
270520—(KRS)
Rev.: $13,470,932
Assets: $50,728,806
Liabilities: $18,236,881
Net Worth: $32,491,924
Earnings: ($2,491,064)
Emp.: 41
Fiscal Year-end: 12/31/22
Renewable Energy Services
N.A.I.C.S.: 221210

G F D
Zi Et Portuaire, 90140, Bourogne, Territoire-de-Belfor, France
Tel.: (33) 384582200
Web Site: http://www.gfd.fr
Rev.: $38,600,000
Emp.: 175
N.A.I.C.S.: 332722
Christian Rosescou *(Dir)*

G G ENGINEERING LIMITED
Office No 203 2nd Floor Shivam Chambers Coop Soc Ltd S V Road, Goregaon West Near Sahara Apartment, Mumbai, 400 104, India
Tel.: (91) 7669318144
Web Site: https://ggelimited.com
Year Founded: 2006
540614—(BOM)
Rev.: $5,120,588
Assets: $5,016,062
Liabilities: $2,791,303
Net Worth: $2,224,758
Earnings: ($111,961)
Fiscal Year-end: 03/31/21
Power Supplies Mfr & Distr
N.A.I.C.S.: 335999
Vinod Harmukhrai Beriwal *(Mng Dir)*

G JACQUEMMOZ ET FILS
235 Rue De La Citadelle, 73500, Modane, Savoie, France
Tel.: (33) 479053601
Web Site:
  http://www.jacquemmoz.com
Rev.: $42,300,000
Emp.: 259
N.A.I.C.S.: 484121
Philippe Sbrizzi *(Mgr-Personnel)*

G MEDICAL INNOVATIONS HOLDINGS LTD.
99 Baker Street, London, W1U6QQ, United Kingdom
Tel.: (44) 442037292151   Ky
Web Site:
  http://www.gmedinnovations.com
Year Founded: 2014
GMVDF—(OTCEM)
Rev.: $4,420,000
Assets: $4,825,000
Liabilities: $9,396,000
Net Worth: ($4,571,000)
Earnings: ($13,958,000)
Emp.: 85
Fiscal Year-end: 12/31/22
Holding Company
N.A.I.C.S.: 551112
Yacov Geva *(Pres & CEO)*

Subsidiaries:

G Medical Diagnostic Services, Inc.   (1)
12708 Riata Vista Cir Ste A103, Austin, TX 78727   **(100%)**
Web Site: http://us.gmedinnovations.com
Diagnostic Testing Facility
N.A.I.C.S.: 621512
Yacov Geva *(Pres & CEO)*

Telerhythmics, LLC   (1)
60 Market Center Dr, Collierville, TN 38017
Tel.: (901) 316-0204
Web Site: http://www.telerhythmics.com
Health Care Srvices
N.A.I.C.S.: 622110

G MINING VENTURES CORP.
7900 W Tashereau Blvd Building D Suite 210, Three Bentall Center, Brossard, J4X 1C2, QC, Canada
Tel.: (450) 465-1950
Web Site:
  https://www.gminingventures.com
Year Founded: 2006
GMIN—(TSX)
Rev.: $4,048,028
Assets: $587,704,877
Liabilities: $324,666,419
Net Worth: $263,038,458
Earnings: ($7,179,927)
Emp.: 1,092
Fiscal Year-end: 12/31/23
Mineral Exploration Services
N.A.I.C.S.: 213115
Louis-Pierre Gignac *(Pres & CEO)*

Subsidiaries:

Reunion Gold Corporation   (1)
1111 St Charles Street West West Tower Suite 101, Longueuil, J4K 5G4, QC, Canada
Tel.: (450) 677-2585
Web Site: https://www.reuniongold.com
Assets: $5,166,311
Liabilities: $1,234,999
Net Worth: $3,931,312
Earnings: ($6,528,167)
Fiscal Year-end: 12/31/2020
Gold Ore Mining
N.A.I.C.S.: 212220
Joachim Bayah *(COO)*

G R INFRAPROJECTS LIMITED
Gr House Hiran Magri Sector 11, Udaipur, 313002, Rajasthan, India
Tel.: (91) 2942487370
Web Site: https://www.grinfra.com
Year Founded: 1995
GRINFRA—(NSE)
Rev.: $1,147,270,559
Assets: $1,652,846,148
Liabilities: $901,676,123
Net Worth: $751,170,026
Earnings: $174,381,248
Emp.: 16,157
Fiscal Year-end: 03/31/23
Road Construction Services
N.A.I.C.S.: 237310
Devkinandan Agarwal *(Pres-Plants & Equipment)*

Subsidiaries:

GR Phagwara Expressway Limited   (1)
GR House Hiran Magri Sector-11, Udaipur, 313002, Rajasthan, India
Tel.: (91) 294 248 7370
Web Site: https://www.grpel.com
Infrastructure Construction & Maintenance Services
N.A.I.C.S.: 237310

G REEKIE GROUP LTD
Cupar Trading Estate, Cupar, KY15 4SX, Fife, United Kingdom
Tel.: (44) 1334652445
Web Site: http://www.reekie.co.uk
Rev.: $15,734,686
Emp.: 76
Agricultural Vehicles Repair Services
N.A.I.C.S.: 811310
Sam Mercer *(Dir-Agricultural Sls)*

G RENT S.P.A.
Via Bernardo Quaranta 40, 20139, Milan, Italy
Tel.: (39) 027755300
Web Site: https://grentspa.com
Year Founded: 2019
GSR—(EUR)
Real Estate Development Services
N.A.I.C.S.: 531190
Antonio Ferrara *(VP)*

G STEEL PUBLIC COMPANY LIMITED
PASO Tower 18th Floor 88 Silom Road, Suriyawong Bangrak, Bangkok, 10500, Thailand
Tel.: (66) 26342222   TH
Web Site: https://www.gsteel.com
Year Founded: 1995
Rev.: $802,126,961
Assets: $878,079,168
Liabilities: $306,608,506
Net Worth: $571,470,663
Earnings: $48,470,170
Emp.: 662
Fiscal Year-end: 12/31/19
Steel Product Mfr & Distr
N.A.I.C.S.: 331221
Khunying Patama Leeswadtrakul *(Chief Corp Social Responsibility Officer)*

G THREE HOLDINGS CORP.
Tokyo Front Terrace 12F 2-3-14 Higashishinagawa, Shinagawa-ku, Tokyo, 140-0002, Japan
Tel.: (81) 357812522
Web Site:
  https://www.g3holdings.com

G THREE HOLDINGS CORP.

G Three Holdings Corp.—(Continued)
Year Founded: 2010
3647—(TKS)
Rev.: $1,610,980
Assets: $9,641,000
Liabilities: $3,321,480
Net Worth: $6,319,520
Earnings: ($4,615,240)
Emp.: 11
Fiscal Year-end: 08/31/24
Holding Company; IT Solutions
N.A.I.C.S.: 551111
Hirokazu Kasahara (Pres)

Subsidiaries:

Connect Technologies
Corporation (1)
Davinci Shinjuku Building 6F 4-3-17 Shinjuku, Tokyo, 160 0022, Shinjuku, Japan
Tel.: (81) 353685520
Web Site: http://www.connect-tech.co.jp
Sales Range: $10-24.9 Million
Mobile Phone Systems Developer
N.A.I.C.S.: 517112

Subsidiary (Domestic):

Honda Electron Co., Ltd. (2)
404 El Vergo Nogizaka 9-6-28 Akasaka, Minato-ku, Tokyo, 107-0052, Japan
Tel.: (81) 334794148
Mobile Phones Design & Mfr
N.A.I.C.S.: 334220

G&C PALERMO SRL
via Bara all Olivella 2 presso Palazzo
Branciforte, Palermo, Italy
Tel.: (39) 0916406000 IT
Magazine Publishing Services
N.A.I.C.S.: 513120

G&E HERBAL BIOTECHNOLOGY CO., LTD.
No 92 Keji 5th Rd, Annan Dist,
T'ainan, 709015, Taiwan
Tel.: (886) 63840890
Web Site:
https://www.geherbs.com.tw
Year Founded: 2002
4911—(TPE)
Rev.: $2,020,042
Assets: $24,474,721
Liabilities: $2,874,652
Net Worth: $21,600,069
Earnings: $230,779
Fiscal Year-end: 12/31/22
Biopharmaceutical Product Mfr
N.A.I.C.S.: 325414
Kou-Wha Kuo (Chm)

G&M PTE LTD.
8 Shenton Way 13-03 AXA Tower,
Singapore, 068811, Singapore
Tel.: (65) 6220 9266
Web Site: http://www.gnm.com.sg
Insurance Services
N.A.I.C.S.: 524298
Douglas Chia (CEO)

G&S ENGINEERING SERVICES PTY. LTD.
27 Len Shield Street, PO Box 5774,
Mackay, 4741, QLD, Australia
Tel.: (61) 749637777
Web Site: http://www.g-s.com.au
Year Founded: 1995
Engineeering Services
N.A.I.C.S.: 541330
Mick Crowe (Mng Dir)

G-7 HOLDINGS INC.
1-3 Yasakadai 2-chome, Suma-ku,
Kobe, 654-0161, Hyogo, Japan
Tel.: (81) 787977700
Web Site: https://www.g-7holdings.com
Year Founded: 1976
7508—(TKS)
Rev.: $1,275,677,120
Assets: $408,973,920
Liabilities: $210,852,390
Net Worth: $198,121,530
Earnings: $34,206,750
Fiscal Year-end: 03/31/24
Investment Management Service
N.A.I.C.S.: 523999
Mamoru Kinoshita (Founder)

Subsidiaries:

99 Ichiba Co., Ltd. (1)
2-18 Irie Uni Oguchi Building 202,
Kanagawa-ku, Yokohama, Japan
Tel.: (81) 454383699
Web Site: http://www.99-ichiba.jp
Supermarket Store Services
N.A.I.C.S.: 445110

G-7 Agri Japan Co., Ltd. (1)
3-1-6 Yasakadai, Suma-ku, Kobe, 654-0161, Hyogo, Japan
Tel.: (81) 787924831
Web Site: https://www.meguminosato.co.jp
Farmer's Market Operator
N.A.I.C.S.: 445110
Michio Kawabe (Pres)

G-7 Auto Service Co., Ltd. (1)
2-1-3 Yasakadai, Suma Ward, Kobe, 654-0161, Hyogo, Japan
Tel.: (81) 787977701
Web Site: https://g-7autoservice.co.jp
Auto Parts Sales & Automotive Services
N.A.I.C.S.: 441330
Tatsumi Kaneda (Chm)

G-7 Bike World Co., Ltd. (1)
Autobacs 2F 5-96-1 Kita Itami, Itami, 664-0831, Hyogo, Japan
Tel.: (81) 727708197
Web Site: https://www.bike7.jp
Motor Cycle Distr
N.A.I.C.S.: 441227

G-7 Development Co., Ltd. (1)
2-1-3 Yasakadai, Suma-ku, Kobe, 654-0161, Hyogo, Japan
Tel.: (81) 787977708
Web Site: https://g7retailjapan.co.jp
Resale Shop Operator
N.A.I.C.S.: 459510
Yoshimi Kashiwagi (Pres)

G-7 Meat Terabayashi Co., Ltd. (1)
TK Building 3rd Floor 7-15 Kinkocho,
Kanagawa-ku, Yokohama, 221-0056, Kanagawa, Japan
Tel.: (81) 454514129
Web Site: http://g-7meatterabayashi.co.jp
Meat Mfr & Distr
N.A.I.C.S.: 311612

G-7 Motors Co., Ltd. (1)
711-1 Junwa Igawadanicho, Nishi Ward,
Kobe, 651-2124, Hyogo, Japan
Tel.: (81) 789785819
Web Site: https://bike7.jp
Motor Vehicle Accessories Distr
N.A.I.C.S.: 423120
Keiichi Okumoto (Pres)

G-7 Super Mart Co., Ltd. (1)
4-8-1 Yasakadai, Suma Ward, Kobe, 654-0161, Hyogo, Japan
Tel.: (81) 787943700
Web Site: https://www.g-7supermart.co.jp
Supermarket Operator
N.A.I.C.S.: 445110

G-7.Crowntrading Co., Ltd. (1)
Matsunaga 2-8-14 Honchou, Kawasaki
Ward, Kawasaki, 210-0001, Kanagawa,
Japan
Tel.: (81) 442000985
Web Site: https://www.crown-trading.com
Used Car Dealer Services
N.A.I.C.S.: 441120

G7 INTERNATIONAL PTE. LTD. (1)
112 Robinson Road 05-01, Singapore,
068902, Singapore
Tel.: (65) 62979989
Holding Company
N.A.I.C.S.: 551112
Norio Kinoshita (Pres)

Subsidiary (Non-US):

G7 RETAIL MALAYSIA SDN.
BHD. (2)
Level 21 Suite 21 01 The Gardens South
Tower Mid Valley, Lingkaran Syed Putra,
Kuala Lumpur, 59200, Malaysia
Tel.: (60) 3 3344 0742
Web Site: http://www.g7retailmalaysia.my
Automotive Products Whslr
N.A.I.C.S.: 423120
Ryouta Yamamoto (Mng Dir)

G7 Japan Food Service Co., Ltd. (1)
501 Ibaraki Nakahozumi Building 1-1-59
Nakahozumi, Suma-ku, Ibaraki, 567-0034,
Hyogo, Japan
Tel.: (81) 726277707
Web Site: https://g7japanfoodservice.co.jp
Emp.: 100
Processed Food Mfr
N.A.I.C.S.: 311412
Naoyuki Haruna (Pres)

G-BITS NETWORK TECHNOLOGY (XIAMEN) CO., LTD.
Mansion No 4 Wanghai Rd Software
Park Second Phase, Xiamen,
361008, Fujian, China
Tel.: (86) 5923213580
Web Site: https://www.g-bits.com
Year Founded: 2004
603444—(SHG)
Rev.: $725,533,216
Assets: $911,255,010
Liabilities: $250,041,070
Net Worth: $661,213,940
Earnings: $205,106,780
Fiscal Year-end: 12/31/22
Online Game Development Services
N.A.I.C.S.: 541511
Lu Hongyan (Chm)

G-CLUSTER GLOBAL CORPORATION
Aoyama Tower Place 6F 8-4-14 Akasaka, Minato-ku, Tokyo, 107-0052,
Japan
Tel.: (81) 364393732 JP
Web Site: http://www.g-cluster.com
Year Founded: 2007
Sales Range: $25-49.9 Million
Emp.: 30
Holding Company; Broadband Videogame Streaming Technologies Developer & Marketer
N.A.I.C.S.: 551112
Taro Hashimoto (CEO)

Subsidiaries:

Oy Gamecluster Ltd. (1)
Piispanpilankuja 4, FI-02240, Espoo, Finland
Tel.: (358) 207435530
Web Site: http://www.g-cluster.com
Sales Range: $25-49.9 Million
Emp.: 15
Broadband Videogame Streaming Technologies Developer & Marketer
N.A.I.C.S.: 541519
Erik Piehl (Mng Dir)

G-FACTORY CO., LTD.
Nishi-Shinjuku 1-25-1 Shinjuku Center Building 33rd floor, Tokyo, 163-0634, Japan
Tel.: (81) 353256868
Web Site: https://www.g-fac.jp
3474—(TKS)
Rev.: $39,689,820
Assets: $32,309,130
Liabilities: $20,064,700
Net Worth: $12,244,430
Earnings: ($1,375,460)
Emp.: 610
Fiscal Year-end: 12/31/23
Administrative Support Services
N.A.I.C.S.: 561110

Subsidiaries:

GF Capital (Thailand) Co., Ltd. (1)
The Opus Building 7F 701 139 Soi Thonglor 10 Sukhumvit Klongton Nua, Wattana,
Bangkok, 10110, Thailand

INTERNATIONAL PUBLIC

Tel.: (66) 27138664
Web Site: http://www.gfc-thailand.com
Store Management Services
N.A.I.C.S.: 445110
Masaru Iwahara (Mng Dir)

G-MES HOLDINGS INC.
280 Woodlands Industrial Park E5
09-44 Woodlands Building, Singapore, 757322, Singapore
Tel.: (65) 6659 6808 NV
Web Site:
http://www.gmesholdings.com
Year Founded: 2016
Sales Range: $1-9.9 Million
Emp.: 16
Home & Floor Safety Product Service
Provider
N.A.I.C.S.: 238330
Samuel Saw Peng Hao (Chm, Pres, CEO, CFO, & Treas)

G-NEXT, INC.
4-7-1 Iidabashi, Chiyoda-Ku, Tokyo,
102-0072, Japan
Tel.: (81) 359625170
Web Site: https://www.gnext.co.jp
Year Founded: 2001
4179—(TKS)
Software Development Services
N.A.I.C.S.: 541511
Yusuke Yokoji (Founder, Chm & Pres)

G-RESOURCES GROUP LIMITED
Room 1801 18/F Capital Centre No
151 Gloucester Road, Wanchai,
China (Hong Kong)
Tel.: (852) 2283 8200
Web Site: http://www.g-resources.com
1051—(OTCIQ)
Sales Range: $25-49.9 Million
Financial Information Services
N.A.I.C.S.: 523940
Xiao Ma (Deputy CEO & Exec Dir)

Subsidiaries:

Enhanced Securities Limited (1)
37/F Times Tower 393 Jaffe Road, Wanchai, China (Hong Kong)
Tel.: (852) 28362188
Web Site: http://www.enhancedsec.com
Security Trading Services
N.A.I.C.S.: 523150
David Ki (Owner)

Funderstone Securities Limited (1)
Room 1802 Capital Centre No 151 Gloucester Road, Wanchai, China (Hong Kong)
Tel.: (852) 28457711
Web Site: http://www.funderstonesec.com
Financial Investment Services
N.A.I.C.S.: 523999

G-SHANK ENTERPRISE CO., LTD.
No 1 Jiuzhou Rd, Hsinwu Dist,
Taoyuan, 32741, Taiwan
Tel.: (886) 34775141
Web Site: https://www.gshank.info
Year Founded: 1973
2476—(TAI)
Rev.: $187,917,126
Assets: $321,182,728
Liabilities: $100,393,632
Net Worth: $220,789,095
Earnings: $24,918,963
Emp.: 1,508
Fiscal Year-end: 12/31/23
Switch Mfr
N.A.I.C.S.: 334419
Yu-Huang Lin (Chm & Pres)

Subsidiaries:

G-Shank Enterprise Co., Ltd. - Bang
Pa-in Factory (1)
Ban-Wa 116 Moo 1, Hi-tech Industrial Estate, Ayutthaya, 13160, Thailand

AND PRIVATE COMPANIES

Tel.: (66) 353514656
Stamped Metal Part Mfr
N.A.I.C.S.: 332439

G-Shank Enterprise Co., Ltd. - China-Shanghai Factory (1)
No 19 Ming-Ei Road Shin Chao, Xingsong, Shanghai, 201502, China
Tel.: (86) 21 5768 6851
Web Site: http://www.gs.com.tw
Sales Range: $200-249.9 Million
Emp.: 518
Stamping Parts Mfr
N.A.I.C.S.: 332119

G-Shank Enterprise Co., Ltd. - China-Shenzhen Factory (1)
Block 13 Long Shan Ind Nanling Buji, Long-Gang, Shenzhen, 518172, Guangdong, China
Tel.: (86) 75528728289
Sales Range: $50-74.9 Million
Emp.: 116
Metal Stamping Mfr
N.A.I.C.S.: 332119

G-Shank Enterprise Co., Ltd. - China-Suzhou Factory (1)
No 8 San Xing Road Yun Dong Economic Develpoment Zone, Song Ling Town, Wuji-ang, Jiang su, China
Tel.: (86) 51263407770
Web Site: http://www.gshank.info
Metal Stamping Mfr
N.A.I.C.S.: 332119

G-Shank Enterprise Co., Ltd. - Dong-guan Factory (1)
Xianshasier Village Gaobu Town, Dong-guan, 523000, Guangdong, China
Tel.: (86) 769 8130 6700
Web Site: http://www.gs.com.tw
Sales Range: $25-49.9 Million
Emp.: 37
Metal Stamping Mfr
N.A.I.C.S.: 332119

G-Shank Enterprise Co., Ltd. - Indo-nesia Factory (1)
Jl Industrikawasan Jababeka Tahap II Block RR 5C-5D, Cikarang, Bekasi, 17530, West Java, Indonesia
Tel.: (62) 2189833366
Sales Range: $25-49.9 Million
Emp.: 80
Metal Stamping Mfr
N.A.I.C.S.: 332119

G-Shank Enterprise Co., Ltd. - Malay-sia Factory (1)
Plot 94 Bayan Lepas Industrial Estate, 11900, Bayan Lepas, Penang, Malaysia
Tel.: (60) 46449136
Sales Range: $50-74.9 Million
Emp.: 217
Metal Stamping Mfr
N.A.I.C.S.: 332119

G-Shank Enterprise Co., Ltd. - Mexico Factory (1)
Gral Pedro Hinojosa 15 Cd Industrial, Mata-moros, 87499, Tamaulipas, Mexico
Tel.: (52) 86 8812 8800
Web Site: http://www.gs.com.tw
Sales Range: $25-49.9 Million
Emp.: 62
Metal Stamping Mfr
N.A.I.C.S.: 332119

G-Shank Enterprise Co., Ltd. - Qingdao Factory (1)
Yanyang Road, Mid-town Industrial Zone Cheng-yang District, Qingdao, Shandong, China
Tel.: (86) 5327962280
Stamped Metal Part Mfr
N.A.I.C.S.: 332439

G-Shank Enterprise Co., Ltd. - Shanghai Factory (1)
No 19 Ming-Ei Road Shin Chao, Xingsong County, Shanghai, China
Tel.: (86) 21576868515
Stamped Metal Part Mfr
N.A.I.C.S.: 332439

G-Shank Enterprise Co., Ltd. - Shen-zhen Factory (1)
Block13 Long Shan Ind Nanling, Buji Long-Gang, Shenzhen, China
Tel.: (86) 75528728289
Stamped Metal Part Mfr
N.A.I.C.S.: 332439

G-Shank Enterprise Co., Ltd. - Shen-zhen G-BAO Factory (1)
No 50 Shiwei, Pinggang Industrial Zone Ji-angshi District Gongming Baoan, Shen-zhen, China
Tel.: (86) 75529935566
Stamped Metal Part Mfr
N.A.I.C.S.: 332439

G-Shank Enterprise Co., Ltd. - Su-zhou Factory (1)
No 8 San Xing Road, Yun Dong Economic Develpoment Zone Song Ling Town, Wuji-ang, Jiangsu, China
Tel.: (86) 51263407770
Stamped Metal Part Mfr
N.A.I.C.S.: 332439

G-Shank Enterprise Co., Ltd. - Thai-land Factory (1)
Ban Wa Hi-tech Industrial Estate 116 Moo 1 Bang Pa-in, Ayutthaya, 13160, Thailand
Tel.: (66) 35351465
Web Site: http://www.gs.com.tw
Sales Range: $25-49.9 Million
Emp.: 57
Metal Stamping Mfr
N.A.I.C.S.: 332119

G-Shank Enterprise Co., Ltd. - Tianjin Factory (1)
No 21 The 6 th Street Teda, Tianjin, China
Tel.: (86) 2266200660
Stamped Metal Part Mfr
N.A.I.C.S.: 332439

G-Shank Enterprise Co., Ltd. - Xia-men Factory (1)
No 109 Xiaguang Road, Lndustrial Area Haicang, Xiamen, Fujian, China
Tel.: (86) 59265665357
Stamped Metal Part Mfr
N.A.I.C.S.: 332439

G-SMATT GLOBAL CO., LTD.
4~5F 556 Yeoksam-ro Gangnam-gu, Seoul, Korea (South)
Tel.: (82) 7048965001
Web Site: http://www.niceseti.com
Year Founded: 2000
114570—(KRS)
Rev.: $1,346,754
Assets: $22,380,636
Liabilities: $32,352,269
Net Worth: ($9,971,633)
Earnings: ($46,473,000)
Emp.: 32
Fiscal Year-end: 12/31/21
Metal Oxide Semiconductor Image Sensors Mfr
N.A.I.C.S.: 334413

Subsidiaries:

G-Smatt America Co., Ltd. (1)
19818 S Alameda St, Compton, CA 90221
Tel.: (213) 263-0066
Web Site: https://www.glaamamerica.com
Embedded Glass Product Mfr
N.A.I.C.S.: 327215
Casey Chang *(CEO & Chief Satisfaction Officer)*

G-Smatt Europe Media Limited (1)
King Charles House Park End St, Oxford, OX1 1JD, United Kingdom
Tel.: (44) 1865688221
Web Site: https://www.g-smatteurope.fr
Multimedia Glass Mfr
N.A.I.C.S.: 327211

G-Smatt Hong Kong Ltd. (1)
5/F Mass Resources Development Building 12 Humphreys Avenue, Tsim Sha Tsui, Kowloon, China (Hong Kong)
Tel.: (852) 28988268
Web Site: https://www.g-smatthk.com
LED Glass Product Mfr
N.A.I.C.S.: 327215
Matthew Ng *(CEO)*

G-TEC JAINX EDUCATION LTD.
9th Floor Pinnacle Corporate Park 12 A, Kolivery Village MMRDA Area Bandra Kurla Complex Bandra East, Mumbai, 400051, Maharashtra, India
Tel.: (91) 7700906675
Web Site: https://www.gtecjainxeducation.com
KEERTI—(NSE)
Rev.: $1,025,874
Assets: $750,710
Liabilities: $135,891
Net Worth: $614,819
Earnings: $156,214
Emp.: 9
Fiscal Year-end: 03/31/23
Education Services
N.A.I.C.S.: 611710
Sudhakar Sonawane *(Mng Dir)*

G-TECH INFO-TRAINING LTD.
Office No 1 Laura Building 1st Floor Near Metro Cinema Marine Lines, Mumbai, 400002, Maharashtra, India
Tel.: (91) 2232714672
Web Site: https://www.gtechinfolimited.com
Rev.: $1,885
Assets: $57,925
Liabilities: $25,923
Net Worth: $32,002
Earnings: ($11,537)
Fiscal Year-end: 03/31/20
Information Technology Services
N.A.I.C.S.: 541512
Sangramkumar Das *(Mng Dir)*

G-TECH OPTOELECTRONICS CORPORATION
No 99 Zhongxing Road, Tongluo, 36647, Miaoli County, Taiwan
Tel.: (886) 37236988
Web Site: https://www.gtoc.com.tw
3149—(TAI)
Rev.: $60,794,693
Assets: $134,122,399
Liabilities: $89,444,910
Net Worth: $44,677,489
Earnings: ($3,853,494)
Emp.: 266
Fiscal Year-end: 12/31/23
Optical Glass Coating
N.A.I.C.S.: 327212
Tony Chung *(Chm & Gen Mgr)*

G-TEK
180 Boulevard Bellerose West, Laval, H7L 6A2, QC, Canada
Tel.: (450) 628-4835
Web Site: http://www.gtek.ca
Year Founded: 1997
Pipelines, Sewer & Utility Lines Ser-vices
N.A.I.C.S.: 237110
Sylvain Bachand *(Pres)*

G-TEKT CORPORATION
Omiya JP Building 18F 1-11-20 Sakuragi-cho Omiya-ku, Saitama-shi, Saitama, 330-0854, Japan
Tel.: (81) 486463400
Web Site: https://www.g-tekt.jp
Year Founded: 2011
5970—(TKS)
Rev.: $2,276,847,727
Assets: $2,009,441,129
Liabilities: $652,368,499
Net Worth: $1,357,072,630
Earnings: $92,824,553
Emp.: 8,391
Fiscal Year-end: 03/31/24
Auto Body Frame Components Mfr
N.A.I.C.S.: 336110
Naohiro Takao *(Pres & CEO)*

Subsidiaries:

Austin Tri-Hawk Automotive, Inc. (1)
2001 W Just Industrial Pkwy, Austin, IN 47102
Tel.: (812) 794-0062
Web Site: http://www.tri-hawk.com
Automobile Parts Mfr
N.A.I.C.S.: 336390

Auto Parts Alliance (China) Ltd. (1)
No 62 Hefeng Road Yonghe Economic Zone, Guangzhou Economic & Technical Development District, Guangzhou, 511356, China
Tel.: (86) 20 82266490
Web Site: http://www.apac.com.cn
Auto Parts Mfr
N.A.I.C.S.: 336390
Kouichi Miyazaki *(Chm & Pres)*

G-KT do Brasil Ltda. (1)
km 84 5 Rod Dom Gabriel Paulino Bueno Cout, Cabreuva Pinhal, Sao Paulo, 13315-000, Brazil
Tel.: (55) 1145291100
Web Site: https://www.g-ktbrasil.com.br
Auto Parts Mfr
N.A.I.C.S.: 336390

G-TEKT (Deutschland) GmbH (1)
Walter-Gropius-Str23, 80807, Munich, Germany
Tel.: (49) 8924881070
Web Site: https://www.g-tekt.de
Auto Body Component Mfr
N.A.I.C.S.: 336390

G-TEKT (Thailand) Co., Ltd. (1)
104 Moo 1 Hi-Tech Industrial Estate Tambol Banwha, Bangpa-In, Ayutthaya, 13160, Thailand
Tel.: (66) 353506879
Auto Body Component Mfr
N.A.I.C.S.: 336390

G-TEKT Co., Ltd. - Gunma Plant (1)
470-9 Kamitajima-cho, Ota, 373-0044, Gunma, Japan
Tel.: (81) 276206551
Auto Body Component Mfr
N.A.I.C.S.: 336390

G-TEKT Co., Ltd. - Hamura Plant (1)
4-8-1 Shinmeidai, Hamura, 205-0023, To-kyo, Japan
Tel.: (81) 425521411
Auto Body Component Mfr
N.A.I.C.S.: 336390

G-TEKT Co., Ltd. - Saitama Plant (1)
2909-7 Shirakusadai, Fukaya, 369-1106, Saitama, Japan
Tel.: (81) 485782600
Auto Body Component Mfr
N.A.I.C.S.: 336390

G-TEKT Co., Ltd. - Shiga Plant (1)
41 Otsu Minamitsuchiyama, Tsuchiyama-cho, Koka, 528-0212, Shiga, Japan
Tel.: (81) 748661121
Web Site: http://www.g-tekt.jp
Auto Body Component Mfr
N.A.I.C.S.: 336390

G-TEKT Co., Ltd. - Tochigi Plant (1)
4814 Suganosawa Washijuku, Sakurai, 329-1411, Tochigi, Japan
Tel.: (81) 286864700
Auto Body Component Mfr
N.A.I.C.S.: 336390

G-TEKT Eastern Co., Ltd. (1)
58/1 Moo 4 Eastern Seaboard Industrial Estate Tambol, Pluakdaeng Amphur, Ray-ong, 21140, Thailand
Tel.: (66) 389546709
Auto Body Component Mfr
N.A.I.C.S.: 336390

G-TEKT Europe Manufacturing Ltd. (1)
Golf Club Lane Brockworth, Gloucester, GL3 4AJ, Gloucestershire, United Kingdom
Tel.: (44) 1452610022
Web Site: https://www.g-tem.co.uk
Industrial Supplies Whslr
N.A.I.C.S.: 423840

Jefferson Industries Corporation (1)
6670 State Route 29 NE, West Jefferson, OH 43162

G-TEKT CORPORATION

G-TEKT Corporation—(Continued)
Tel.: (614) 879-5300
Web Site: https://www.jic-ohio.com
Auto Body Component Mfr
N.A.I.C.S.: 336390
John Jenkins *(Asst Mgr-Pur)*

Subsidiary (Non-US):

Jefferson Elora Corporation (2)
60 First Line Road, Elora, N0B 1S0, ON, Canada
Tel.: (519) 846-2728
Auto Body Component Mfr
N.A.I.C.S.: 336390
Earl Browning *(Plant Mgr)*

Jefferson Southern Corporation (1)
1000 Marquette Rd, Rockmart, GA 30153
Tel.: (770) 684-1228
Web Site: https://www.jsc-ga.com
Auto Body Component Mfr
N.A.I.C.S.: 336390
Ray Wright *(Plant Mgr)*

Wuhan Auto Parts Alliance (China) Co., Ltd. (1)
No 12 Yintan Rd Jiangjunlu Street, Dongxihu District, Wuhan, 430023, Hubei, China
Tel.: (86) 2783941716
Auto Body Component Mfr
N.A.I.C.S.: 336390

G-VISION INTERNATIONAL (HOLDINGS) LIMITED

Unit 108 1/F East Ocean Centre 98 Granville Road Tsim Sha Tsui East, Kowloon, China (Hong Kong)
Tel.: (852) 2 893 8131
Web Site: http://www.g-vision.com.hk
Year Founded: 1984
0657—(HKG)
Rev.: $14,785,880
Assets: $6,896,561
Liabilities: $2,462,615
Net Worth: $4,433,945
Earnings: ($1,816,038)
Emp.: 90
Fiscal Year-end: 03/31/22
Restaurant Services
N.A.I.C.S.: 722511
Hop Fai Cheng *(Chm & Mng Dir)*

G. CAPPA PLC
8 Taylor Road Iddo, Lagos, Nigeria
Tel.: (234) 1 7395495
Web Site: http://www.gcappaplc.com
Building Construction Services
N.A.I.C.S.: 237990

G. G. AUTOMOTIVE GEARS LIMITED
Plot No 2A I S Gajra Industrial Area No1 A B Road, Dewas, 455001, Madhya Pradesh, India
Tel.: (91) 7272405310
Web Site: https://www.ggautomotive.com
Year Founded: 1974
531399—(BOM)
Rev.: $9,309,766
Assets: $8,559,451
Liabilities: $5,881,830
Net Worth: $2,677,621
Earnings: $232,684
Emp.: 289
Fiscal Year-end: 03/31/23
Automobile Gear Mfr
N.A.I.C.S.: 336350
Ram Shantiswaroop Gajra *(Chm & Mng Dir)*

G. K. GOH HOLDINGS LIMITED
50 Raffles Place 33-00 Singapore Land Tower, Singapore, 048623, Singapore
Tel.: (65) 63361888
Web Site: http://www.gkgoh.com

G41—(SES)
Rev.: $102,386,766
Assets: $534,613,886
Liabilities: $208,836,027
Net Worth: $325,777,860
Earnings: $1,143,780
Fiscal Year-end: 12/31/20
Stock Broking & Investment Banking Services
N.A.I.C.S.: 523150
Yew Lin Goh *(Mng Dir)*

Subsidiaries:

Allium Healthcare (Singapore) Pte Ltd (1)
71 Venus Drive, Singapore, 573859, Singapore
Tel.: (65) 87338099
Web Site: https://www.alliumhealthcare.com
Hospital & Health Care Services
N.A.I.C.S.: 622110

Boardroom Limited (1)
50 Raffles Place 32-01 Singapore Land Tower, Singapore, 048623, Singapore (91.3%)
Tel.: (65) 65365355
Web Site: http://www.boardroomlimited.com
Rev.: $67,978,784
Assets: $103,023,134
Liabilities: $37,261,042
Net Worth: $65,762,093
Earnings: $5,082,813
Emp.: 500
Fiscal Year-end: 12/31/2018
Holding Company; Accounting & Payroll Services
N.A.I.C.S.: 551112
Kim Poh Jin Teo *(CEO-Grp)*

Subsidiary (Domestic):

Boardroom Business Solutions Pte. Ltd. (2)
50 Raffles Place 32-01 Singapore Land Tower, Singapore, 048623, Singapore
Tel.: (65) 65364866
Web Site: http://www.boardroomltd.com
Sales Range: $25-49.9 Million
Emp.: 200
Accounting Services
N.A.I.C.S.: 541219
Elton Qua *(Mgr-HR)*

Subsidiary (Non-US):

Boardroom Corporate Services (HK) Limited (2)
2103B 21/F 148 Electric Road, North Point, China (Hong Kong)
Tel.: (852) 2598 5234
Web Site: http://www.boardroomlimited.com
Accounting & Payroll Services
N.A.I.C.S.: 541214

Boardroom Corporate Services (Johor) Sdn Bhd (2)
Suite 9D Level 9 Menara Ansar 65 Jalan Trus, 80000, Johor Bahru, Malaysia
Tel.: (60) 72241035
Web Site: http://www.boardroomlimited.com
Accounting & Payroll Services
N.A.I.C.S.: 541214

Boardroom Corporate Services (Penang) Sdn Bhd (2)
170-09-11 Livingston Tower, Jalan Argyll, 10050, Penang, Malaysia
Tel.: (60) 4 229 4390
Web Site: http://www.boardroomlimited.com
Emp.: 20
Accounting & Payroll Services
N.A.I.C.S.: 541214

Boardroom LSC Beijing Limited (2)
Room 1520 15/F NCI Tower No12A Jianguomenwai Ave, Chaoyang District, Beijing, 100022, China
Tel.: (86) 10 8580 9177
Web Site: http://www.boardroomlimited.com
Emp.: 8
Accounting & Payroll Services
N.A.I.C.S.: 541214
Zong Lei Chen *(Gen Mgr)*

Boardroom LSC China Limited (2)
Unit 1701 Sunyoung CenterNo 398 Jiangsu Road, Changning District, Beijing, 200050, China
Tel.: (86) 21 6375 8100
Web Site: http://www.boardroomlimited.com
Payroll & Accounting Services
N.A.I.C.S.: 541214
Rena Yi Ping Lim *(Exec Dir)*

Boardroom Pty Limited (2)
Tel.: (61) 292909600
Payroll & Accounting Services
N.A.I.C.S.: 541214
Rhett Tregunna *(CEO)*

G. PETER REBER MOBEL-LOGISTIK GMBH
Konrad-Nolte-Strasse 10, 76726, Germersheim, Germany
Tel.: (49) 727494940 De
Web Site: http://www.reber-moebel-logistik.de
Year Founded: 1976
Sales Range: $10-24.9 Million
Emp.: 125
Supply Chain & Logistic Services
N.A.I.C.S.: 541614
Wolfgang Schneider *(CEO)*

Subsidiaries:

TMI Transportgesellschaft der Mobelindustrie mbH (1)
Weinenweg 3, Ohlweiler, 55469, Simmern, Germany
Tel.: (49) 7274949460
Web Site: http://www.tmi-transporte.de
Freight & Cargo Transport Services
N.A.I.C.S.: 488510
Bernd Kramer *(CEO)*

TS Transport & Services Speditions GmbH (1)
Poststrasse 2, 04158, Leipzig, Germany
Tel.: (49) 341 4 67 990
Web Site: http://www.ts-transportundservice.de
Freight & Cargo Transportation Services
N.A.I.C.S.: 488510
Wolfgang Schneider *(CEO)*

G. R. (HOLDINGS) PLC
7 Queripel House, 1 Duke of York Sq, SW3 4LY, London, London, United Kingdom - England
Tel.: (44) 2077308799
Sales Range: Less than $1 Million
Emp.: 15
Sheepskin Footwear & Car Mate Products
N.A.I.C.S.: 316210
P. J. Scott *(Sec)*

Subsidiaries:

Grayshott Hall Limited (1)
Headley Rd, Grayshott, Hindhead, GU26 6JJ, Surrey, United Kingdom
Tel.: (44) 1428 602000
Web Site: http://www.grayshottspa.com
Health Spa Hotel Management Services
N.A.I.C.S.: 721110
Peter Wood *(Gen Mgr)*

Morlands (Glastonbury) Limited (1)
3 Creeches Ln, Walton, BA16 9RR, Somerset, United Kingdom
Tel.: (44) 1458446969
Web Site: http://www.morlandssheepskin.co.uk
Sheepskin Accessories Mfr
N.A.I.C.S.: 316990
Panayi Georgiou *(Dir-Fin)*

G. SIEMPELKAMP GMBH & CO. KG
Siempelkampstr 75, 47803, Krefeld, Germany
Tel.: (49) 2151 92 30
Web Site: http://www.siempelkamp.com
Year Founded: 1883
Sales Range: $900-999.9 Million
Emp.: 3,191
Industrial Machinery Mfr & Whslr

INTERNATIONAL PUBLIC

N.A.I.C.S.: 333998
Hans W. Fechner *(Mng Dir)*

Subsidiaries:

ATR Industrie-Elektronik GmbH (1)
Siempelkampstr 50, 47803, Krefeld, Germany
Tel.: (49) 2151926100
Web Site: http://www.atrie.de
Electronic Components Mfr
N.A.I.C.S.: 335313
Timo Amels *(Mgr)*

Buttner Energie- und Trocknungstechnik GmbH (1)
Lohweg 8, 30559, Hannover, Germany
Tel.: (49) 511589790
Web Site: http://www.buettner-energy-dryer.com
Industrial Dryer & Burner Whslr
N.A.I.C.S.: 423720

Carpenterie Metalliche di Colzate S.r.l. (1)
via L Rodigari 10, 24020, Colzate, Bergamo, Italy
Tel.: (39) 035737111
Web Site: http://www.cmc-texpan.com
Industrial Machinery & Equipment Mfr & Distr
N.A.I.C.S.: 333998
Raab Robert Michael *(Mng Dir)*

IOOO Siempelkamp BEL (1)
ul Rakovskaja 16B Pom 5N Kab 6, 220004, Minsk, Belarus
Tel.: (375) 164535357
Industrial Machinery & Equipment Distr
N.A.I.C.S.: 423830
Valery Kolesnikovich *(Mgr-Svc)*

OOO Siempelkamp (1)
ul 1-ya Tverskaya-Yamskaya dom 23 str 1, 125047, Moscow, Russia
Tel.: (7) 4956603485
Engineeering Services
N.A.I.C.S.: 541330
Konstantin Putintsev *(Mgr-Svc)*

Pallmann Maschinenfabrik GmbH & Co. KG (1)
Wolfslochstr 51, 66482, Zweibrucken, Germany
Tel.: (49) 63328020
Web Site: http://www.pallmann.de
Emp.: 400
Shredding & Processing Services
N.A.I.C.S.: 561990
Stefan Wissing *(Exec Dir)*

Sicoplan N.V (1)
Koningin Astridlaan 46, 8930, Lauwe, Belgium
Tel.: (32) 56439011
Web Site: http://www.sicoplan.be
Engineeering Services
N.A.I.C.S.: 541330

Siempelkamp (Qingdao) Machinery & Equipment Co. Ltd. (1)
No 5 Minshan Road, Huangdao, Qingdao, 266000, Shandong, China
Tel.: (86) 53280985012
Engineeering Services
N.A.I.C.S.: 541330

Siempelkamp (Wuxi) Machinery Manufacturing Co. Ltd. (1)
Unit 430 Landmark Tower 2 No 8 North-Dongsanhuan Rd, Chaoyang District, 100004, Beijing, China
Tel.: (86) 1065907512
Industrial Machinery & Equipment Mfr
N.A.I.C.S.: 333998
Yu Ming *(Mgr-Svc)*

Siempelkamp Barcelona (1)
Calle Norte Nr 70 local 12, Esplugues de Llobregat, 8950, Barcelona, Spain
Tel.: (34) 933713195
Industrial Machinery & Equipment Distr
N.A.I.C.S.: 423830

Siempelkamp Behaltertechnik GmbH (1)
Mellinghoferstr 55 / Bau 25, 45473, Mulheim an der Ruhr, Germany
Tel.: (49) 208941770
Industrial Machinery & Equipment Mfr

AND PRIVATE COMPANIES

N.A.I.C.S.: 333998

Siempelkamp CZ s. r. o. (1)
Prumyslova zona, PO Box 10, Blatnice pod Svatym Antoninkem 893, 696 71, Hodonin, Czech Republic
Tel.: (420) 518698210
Industrial Machinery & Equipment Distr
N.A.I.C.S.: 423830

Siempelkamp France Sarl (1)
2 Parc des Fontenelles, 78870, Bailly, France
Tel.: (33) 130800690
Industrial Machinery & Equipment Distr
N.A.I.C.S.: 423830
Gerd Schafer (Mgr-Svc)

Siempelkamp Giesserei GmbH (1)
Siempelkampstrasse 45, 47803, Krefeld, Germany
Tel.: (49) 21518940
Cast Iron Mfr
N.A.I.C.S.: 331511

Siempelkamp India Pvt. Ltd. (1)
7A Elgin Road, Kolkata, 700 020, India
Tel.: (91) 3322832014
Industrial Machinery & Equipment Distr
N.A.I.C.S.: 423830
Priyanath Chatterjee (Sr Project Mgr)

Siempelkamp Istanbul (1)
Kayisdagi cad 1 Elvan sok No 9 Ulker Unver Plaza K 4 D 10, Atasehir, Istanbul, Turkiye
Tel.: (90) 2164693593
Industrial Machinery & Equipment Distr
N.A.I.C.S.: 423830

Siempelkamp Krantechnik GmbH (1)
Daimlerstrasse 1, 26802, Moormerland, Germany
Tel.: (49) 495495910
Web Site: http://www.siempelkamp-krantechnik.com
Crane Mfr
N.A.I.C.S.: 333923
Heinrich Kampen (Mng Dir)

Siempelkamp L.P. (1)
200 N Cobb Pkwy Ste 302, Marietta, GA 30062
Tel.: (770) 424-4141
Web Site: http://www.siempelkamp-usa.com
Industrial Machinery & Equipment Distr
N.A.I.C.S.: 423830
Dirk Koltze (VP-Sls)

Siempelkamp Logistics & Service GmbH (1)
Sandweg 26, 55543, Bad Kreuznach, Germany
Tel.: (49) 6717961100
Web Site: http://www.sls-siempelkamp.com
Logistics Consulting Servies
N.A.I.C.S.: 541614
Stefan Wissing (Mng Dir)

Siempelkamp MSDG S.A.S. (1)
1 Avenue Saint Remy, 57600, Forbach, France
Tel.: (33) 387888788
Industrial Machinery & Equipment Distr
N.A.I.C.S.: 423830

Siempelkamp Maschinen- und Anlagenbau GmbH (1)
Hans-Urmiller-Ring 6D, 82515, Wolfratshausen, Germany
Tel.: (49) 81714020
Industrial Machinery & Equipment Mfr
N.A.I.C.S.: 333998

Siempelkamp Moscow OOO (1)
ul Dubininskaya 57 Bau 2 Buro 2 211A, 115054, Moscow, Russia
Tel.: (7) 4956603485
Industrial Machinery & Equipment Distr
N.A.I.C.S.: 423830
Konstantin Putintsev (Mgr-Svc)

Siempelkamp NIS Ingenieurgesellschaft mbH (1)
Industriestrasse 13, 63755, Alzenau, Germany
Tel.: (49) 6023913991
Web Site: http://www.siempelkamp-nis.com
Emp.: 160
Industrial Machinery & Equipment Mfr & Distr

N.A.I.C.S.: 333998
Hans W. Fechner (Mng Dir)

Siempelkamp Pruf-und Gutachter Gesellschaft mbH (1)
Am Lagerplatz 6 A, 01099, Dresden, Germany
Tel.: (49) 351824930
Web Site: http://www.siempelkamp-dresden.com
Industrial Inspection Services
N.A.I.C.S.: 541350

Siempelkamp Pte. Ltd. (1)
Unit 12-05 PJX-HM Shah Tower 16 A Persiaran Barat, 46050, Petaling Jaya, Selangor Darul Eshan, Malaysia
Tel.: (60) 379324233
Industrial Machinery & Equipment Distr
N.A.I.C.S.: 423830

Siempelkamp Pte. Ltd. (1)
1 Fifth Avenue 02-10 Guthrie House, Singapore, 268802, Singapore
Tel.: (65) 62233168
Industrial Machinery & Equipment Distr
N.A.I.C.S.: 423830
Philipp Schmitz (Mgr-Svc)

Siempelkamp Pty. Ltd. (1)
5 / 214 216 Bay St, Brighton, 3186, VIC, Australia
Tel.: (61) 390882121
Industrial Machinery & Equipment Distr
N.A.I.C.S.: 423830
Danielle Gilliland (Mgr-Svc)

Siempelkamp Tensioning Systems GmbH (1)
Huttenallee 80, 44534, Lunen, Germany
Tel.: (49) 23063732300
Web Site: http://www.siempelkamp-tensioning.com
Industrial Machinery Mfr
N.A.I.C.S.: 332410
Roland Lang (Bus Mgr)

Siempelkamp do Brasil Ltda. (1)
Rua Gabriela Mistral 101, Bairro Ahu, 80540-150, Curitiba, Parana, Brazil
Tel.: (55) 4132326806
Web Site: http://www.siempelkamp.com.br
Industrial Machinery & Equipment Distr
N.A.I.C.S.: 423830
Rodrigo Suchomel Alves (Mgr-Sls)

Strothmann (Shanghai) Co. Ltd. (1)
Rm 311 Tower 1 German Center 88 KeYuan Road, Pudong Zhangjiang Hi-Tech Park, 201203, Shanghai, China
Tel.: (86) 2128986176
Industrial Machinery Distr
N.A.I.C.S.: 423830

Strothmann Machines & Handling GmbH (1)
Altenkamp 11, 33758, Schloss Holte-Stukenbrock, Germany
Tel.: (49) 520791220
Web Site: http://www.strothmann.com
Emp.: 120
Industrial Machinery Mfr
N.A.I.C.S.: 333998
Christian Rippert (Project Mgr)

Ventapp GmbH (1)
Hooghe Weg 45, 47906, Kempen, Germany
Tel.: (49) 215220080
Web Site: http://www.ventapp.de
Industrial Machinery Mfr
N.A.I.C.S.: 333998

Wolfangel GmbH (1)
Roentgenstr 31, Heimerdingen, 71254, Ditzingen, Germany
Tel.: (49) 7152999200
Web Site: http://www.wolfangel.com
Emp.: 20
Electric Equipment Mfr
N.A.I.C.S.: 336320
Heike Wolfangel (Mng Dir)

G.A. HOLDINGS LIMITED
51 Goldhill Plaza 15-05, Singapore, 308900, Singapore
Tel.: (65) 67356863   Ky
Web Site: http://www.ga-holdings.com.hk
Year Founded: 1993

8126—(HKG)
Rev.: $280,110,743
Assets: $225,166,236
Liabilities: $127,104,017
Net Worth: $98,062,219
Earnings: $522,051
Emp.: 674
Fiscal Year-end: 12/31/23
Holding Company
N.A.I.C.S.: 551112
Choong Yew Choy (Mng Dir & Compliance Officer)

Subsidiaries:

Fuzhou Euro Motors Sales & Services Co., Ltd. (1)
Area B Haixia Automobile Culture Plaza, Qingkou, Fuzhou, 350100, Fujian, China
Tel.: (86) 59122258833
Web Site: http://www.fuzhou.ferraridealers.com
Automobile Sales & Services
N.A.I.C.S.: 441120
Rita Huang (Mgr-Mktg)

German Automobiles Limited (1)
Unit 1007 Level 10 Tower I Grand Century Place, 193 Prince Edward Road West Mongkok, Kowloon, China (Hong Kong)
Tel.: (852) 29736003
Web Site: https://www.ga-holdings.com.hk
Motor Vehicle Parts Distr
N.A.I.C.S.: 423120

G.A. KIESEL GMBH
Wannenackerstr 20, 74078, Heilbronn, Germany
Tel.: (49) 713128250
Web Site: http://www.kiesel-online.de
Year Founded: 1864
Rev.: $15,092,897
Emp.: 100
Pump Equipment Mfr
N.A.I.C.S.: 333914
Jochen Seeber (Mng Dir)

G.A. PAPER INTERNATIONAL INC.
327 Renfrew Drive Suite 102, Markham, L3R 9S8, ON, Canada
Tel.: (905) 479-7600
Web Site: https://www.gapaper.com
Year Founded: 1986
Rev.: $21,644,717
Emp.: 17
Pulp & Paper Suppliers
N.A.I.C.S.: 322110
Ibrahim Elgammal (Founder & Pres)

G.A.P VASSILOPOULOS PUBLIC LIMITED
20 Strovolos Av, PO Box 23897, 2011, Strovolos, Cyprus
Tel.: (357) 2 271 0000
Web Site: http://www.gapgroup.com
Emp.: 1,000
Cargo Handling Services
N.A.I.C.S.: 488320
George Vassilopoulos (Chm)

G.B. GROUP CORPORATION
Calle 50 Global Bank Tower The Caution, PO Box 0831-01843, Panama, Panama
Tel.: (507) 2062000
GBGR—(PAN)
Sales Range: Less than $1 Million
Holding Company
N.A.I.C.S.: 551112
Jorge Enrique Vallarino Strunz (Pres)

G.C. DUKE EQUIPMENT LTD
1184 Plains Rd E, Burlington, L7S 1W6, ON, Canada
Tel.: (905) 637-5216
Web Site: http://www.gcduke.com
Year Founded: 1955
Rev.: $20,000,000
Emp.: 90

Turf Equipment Distr
N.A.I.C.S.: 336320
Nolan Duke (Pres)

G.E.T.T. GOLD INC.
7055 Taschereau Blvd Suite 500, Brossard, J4Z 1A7, QC, Canada
Tel.: (450) 510-4442
Web Site: https://gettgold.com
Year Founded: 2000
GETT—(TSXV)
Rev.: $11,264
Assets: $2,264,359
Liabilities: $8,835,838
Net Worth: ($6,571,479)
Earnings: ($2,037,488)
Fiscal Year-end: 09/30/20
Metal Mineral Exploration Services
N.A.I.C.S.: 212290
Donald Brisebois (Pres & CEO)

G.F.C. GREEN FIELDS CAPITAL LTD.
Gad Feinstein St 13, Rehovot, 76121, Israel
Tel.: (972) 36133371   Il
GFC—(TAE)
Assets: $167,197,953
Liabilities: $123,466,499
Net Worth: $43,731,454
Earnings: $4,336,234
Fiscal Year-end: 12/31/23
Agricultural Product Mfr
N.A.I.C.S.: 325311
Alexander Rabinovitch (CEO)

G.G. DANDEKAR PROPERTIES LTD.
211/A MIDC Butibori Industrial Area Village Kinhi, Tal Hingana, Nagpur, 441122, India
Tel.: (91) 7103295109
Web Site: https://www.ggdandekar.com
505250—(BOM)
Rev.: $736,076
Assets: $6,073,568
Liabilities: $715,506
Net Worth: $5,358,062
Earnings: ($156,525)
Emp.: 9
Fiscal Year-end: 03/31/21
Mill Machine Equipment Mfr
N.A.I.C.S.: 335999
Nihal G. Kulkarni (Chm)

Subsidiaries:

G.G. Dandekar Machine Works Ltd. - Bhiwandi Plant (1)
Dandekar Wadi, Thane, Bhiwandi, 421 302, India
Tel.: (91) 2522 229870
Rice Milling Machinery Mfr
N.A.I.C.S.: 333241

G.H.M. (GROUP) LIMITED
Lodge Bank Unit 4 Crown Lane, Bolton, BL6 5HY, Lancs, United Kingdom
Tel.: (44) 1204 697 089   UK
Web Site: http://www.ghm-group.com
Sales Range: $1-9.9 Million
Heavy Construction Equipment Sales & Rental Services
N.A.I.C.S.: 532412
Geoff Makinson (Founder)

G.K. CONSULTANTS LIMITED
302 G K House 187 A Sant Nagar East of Kailash, New Delhi, 110065, India
Tel.: (91) 1126489431
Web Site: https://www.gkconsultantsltd.com
Year Founded: 1988
531758—(BOM)
Rev.: $78,943
Assets: $837,985

G.K. CONSULTANTS LIMITED

G.K. Consultants Limited—(Continued)
Liabilities: $21,348
Net Worth: $816,637
Earnings: ($19,110)
Emp.: 4
Fiscal Year-end: 03/31/23
Non Banking Financial Services
N.A.I.C.S.: 523999
Shilpa Verma *(Compliance Officer & Sec)*

G.K.P PRINTING & PACKAGING LTD.
Gala No 1 Champion Compound Opp Chachas Dhaba, Palghar, 401208, Maharashtra, India
Tel.: (91) 9920037770
Web Site: https://www.gkpl.in
Year Founded: 1994
542666—(BOM)
Rev.: $6,737,821
Assets: $4,480,775
Liabilities: $1,684,072
Net Worth: $2,796,703
Earnings: $102,991
Fiscal Year-end: 03/31/23
Corrugated Box Mfr
N.A.I.C.S.: 322211
Keval Harshad Goradia *(Chm & Mng Dir)*

G.M.BREWERIES LIMITED
Ganesh Niwas S Veer Savarkar Marg, Prabhadevi, Mumbai, 400 025, India
Tel.: (91) 2224331150
Web Site: https://www.gmbreweries.com
GMBREW—(NSE)
Rev.: $172,365,020
Assets: $78,207,361
Liabilities: $9,275,585
Net Worth: $68,931,777
Earnings: $10,932,353
Emp.: 183
Fiscal Year-end: 03/31/21
Alcoholic Beverage Mfr & Distr
N.A.I.C.S.: 312140
Jimmy William Almeida *(Chm & Mng Dir)*

G.M.I. TECHNOLOGY INC.
2nd Floor No 57 Xingzhong Road, Neihu District, Taipei, Taiwan
Tel.: (886) 226599838
Web Site: https://www.gmitec.com
Year Founded: 1995
3312—(TAI)
Rev.: $499,583,225
Assets: $220,963,431
Liabilities: $132,333,884
Net Worth: $88,629,546
Earnings: $10,229,471
Emp.: 222
Fiscal Year-end: 12/31/23
Electronics Mfr & Distr
N.A.I.C.S.: 334419

G.O.I. ENERGY LIMITED
5 Chytron Agioi Omologites, 1075, Nicosia, Cyprus
Web Site: https://goi.energy
Oil & Gas Services
N.A.I.C.S.: 213112
Michael Bobrov *(CEO)*

Subsidiaries:

ISAB S.r.l. (1)
Ex SS 114-Km 146, 96010, Priolo Gargallo, SR, Italy
Tel.: (39) 0931208111
Oil & Gas Services
N.A.I.C.S.: 213112
Francesco Cimato *(Project Mgr)*

G.P. GLOBAL POWERM LTD.
1 Korazin Street, Givatayim, 5358310, Israel
Tel.: (972) 37588830
Web Site: https://global-power.co.il
GPGB.M—(TAE)
Rev.: $188,976
Assets: $40,484,044
Liabilities: $26,853,709
Net Worth: $13,630,335
Earnings: ($4,094,212)
Fiscal Year-end: 12/31/23
Other Electric Power Generation
N.A.I.C.S.: 221118
Ehud Ben-Shach *(Chm)*

G.S. AUTO INTERNATIONAL LTD.
G S Estate G T Road, Ludhiana, 141014, Punjab, India
Tel.: (91) 1612511001
Web Site: https://www.gsgroupindia.com
513059—(BOM)
Rev.: $15,549,859
Assets: $12,003,813
Liabilities: $9,464,696
Net Worth: $2,539,116
Earnings: ($335,028)
Emp.: 906
Fiscal Year-end: 03/31/23
Automotive Suspension Mfr
N.A.I.C.S.: 336330
S. Jasbir Singh Ryait *(Chm)*

G.S. GALATARIOTIS & SONS LTD.
197 Arch Makariou III Avenue Gala Tower, 3030, Limassol, Cyprus
Tel.: (357) 2589 1000 CY
Web Site: http://www.galatariotisgroup.com
Year Founded: 1947
Holding Company
N.A.I.C.S.: 551112
George St. Galatariotis *(Chm & Exec Dir)*

Subsidiaries:

K + G Complex Public Company Limited (1)
197 Makarios III Avenue Gala Tower, 3030, Limassol, Cyprus (83%)
Tel.: (357) 25891000
Web Site: https://www.galatariotisgroup.com
Rev.: $401,810
Assets: $139,517,607
Liabilities: $194,282
Net Worth: $139,323,325
Earnings: $2,222,100
Emp.: 1
Fiscal Year-end: 12/31/2023
Real Estate Manangement Services
N.A.I.C.S.: 531390
George St. Galatariotis *(Chm)*

Affiliate (Domestic):

The Cyprus Cement Public Company Limited (2)
St Andrew Street 197, PO Box 378, Limassol, 30307, Cyprus (32%)
Tel.: (357) 25366111
Cement Mfr
N.A.I.C.S.: 327310
George St. Galatariotis *(Chm)*

Subsidiary (Domestic):

C.C.C. Tourist Enterprises Public Company Limited (3)
197 Makarios III Avenue Gala Tower, 3030, Limassol, Cyprus (67.3%)
Tel.: (357) 25891000
Assets: $23,350,763
Liabilities: $222,016
Net Worth: $23,128,747
Earnings: ($58,964)
Fiscal Year-end: 12/31/2019
Home Management Services
N.A.I.C.S.: 721110
Costas St. Galatariotis *(Chm)*

G2 ENERGY CORP.
430-744 W Hastings St, Vancouver, V6C 1A5, BC, Canada
Tel.: (778) 775-4985 BC
Web Site: https://www.g2.energy
Year Founded: 2014
GTOO—(CNSX)
Rev.: $170,791
Assets: $5,809,773
Liabilities: $4,902,384
Net Worth: $907,390
Earnings: ($2,384,548)
Fiscal Year-end: 06/30/22
Oil & Gas Extraction Services
N.A.I.C.S.: 211130
Gabriel Monteiro Queiroz *(CFO)*

G2 GOLDFIELDS INC.
Suite 1101 141 Adelaide St West, Toronto, M5H 3L5, ON, Canada
Tel.: (416) 628-5904 Ca
Web Site: https://g2goldfields.com
Year Founded: 2009
GUYGF—(OTCQX)
Rev.: $391,997
Assets: $47,347,889
Liabilities: $1,830,437
Net Worth: $45,517,452
Earnings: ($2,288,618)
Emp.: 3
Fiscal Year-end: 05/31/24
Gold Mining Services
N.A.I.C.S.: 212220
Daniel Noone *(CEO)*

G2POWER CO., LTD.
868-12 Chorok-ro Yanggam-myeon, Hwaseong, Gyeonggi-do, Korea (South)
Tel.: (82) 314271261
Web Site: https://www.g2p.co.kr
Year Founded: 2010
388050—(KRS)
Rev.: $28,668,014
Assets: $34,271,898
Liabilities: $10,688,034
Net Worth: $23,583,864
Earnings: $564,533
Emp.: 62
Fiscal Year-end: 12/31/22
Diagnostic Equipment Mfr & Distr
N.A.I.C.S.: 334510
Ken Lee *(Head)*

G3 COMMS LTD.
Trident House 46-48 Webber Street, London, SE1 8QW, United Kingdom
Tel.: (44) 2070751400
Web Site: http://www.g3comms.com
Telecommunication Servicesb
N.A.I.C.S.: 517810
James Arnold-Roberts *(Mng Dir)*

Subsidiaries:

Connect Managed Services (UK) Limited (1)
4th Floor Chancellor House, 5 Thomas More Square, London, EW1 1YW, United Kingdom
Tel.: (44) 20 7950 3200
Web Site: http://www.connectmanaged.com
Communications Integration Services
N.A.I.C.S.: 517810
Alex Tupman *(CEO)*

G3 EXPLORATION LIMITED
28th Floor Landmark Plaza No 1 Business Outer Ring Road, Central Business District, Zhengzhou, 450000, Henan, China
Tel.: (86) 371 6013 3388 Ky
Web Site: http://www.g3-ex.com
Rev.: $19,000
Assets: $980,681,000
Liabilities: $345,834,000
Net Worth: $634,847,000
Earnings: ($20,949,000)

INTERNATIONAL PUBLIC

Fiscal Year-end: 12/31/18
Holding Company; Gas Supplier
N.A.I.C.S.: 551112
Randeep Singh Grewal *(Chm & CEO)*

Subsidiaries:

Greka China Ltd (1)
29/F Landmark Plaza No 1 Business Outer Range Road CBD, Zheng Dong Area, Zhengzhou, 45000, Henan, China
Tel.: (86) 37160130088
Web Site: http://www.greendragongas.com
Coal Bed Methane Appraisal & Development
N.A.I.C.S.: 213113
Mahmood Lone *(VP)*

Greka Engineering & Technology Ltd. (1)
12/F No 5 Building Hua Meilong Plaza Jing Nan Wu Road, Economy & Technology Development District, Zhengzhou, 450016, Henan, China
Tel.: (86) 371 6789 6318
Engineeering Services
N.A.I.C.S.: 541330

G3 GLOBAL BERHAD
05-05-02 Block 5 Corporate Park Star Central, Lingkaran Cyber Point Timur Cyber 12, 63000, Cyberjaya, Selangor, Malaysia
Tel.: (60) 358858578
Web Site: https://www.g3global.com.my
Year Founded: 1992
G3—(KLS)
Rev.: $2,770,251
Assets: $10,209,676
Liabilities: $1,638,324
Net Worth: $8,571,352
Earnings: ($2,079,333)
Emp.: 14
Fiscal Year-end: 12/31/22
Apparel Mfr & Distr
N.A.I.C.S.: 315210
Li Ling Foo *(Co-Sec)*

Subsidiaries:

Atilze Digital Sdn. Bhd. (1)
B-23A-3A The Ascent Paradigm No 1 Jalan SS7/26A, Kelana Jaya, 47301, Petaling Jaya, Selangor, Malaysia
Tel.: (60) 327146118
Web Site: http://www.atilze.com
Information Technology & Services
N.A.I.C.S.: 541511
Haimi Edzwan Hashim *(Product Mgr)*

Bestinet Healthcare Sdn Bhd (1)
Level 3 Blk 5 Lingkaran Cyber Point Timur, Star Central Corporate Park, 63000, Cyberjaya, Selangor, Malaysia
Tel.: (60) 386892823
Web Site: https://bestinethealthcare.com
Healthcare Product Distr
N.A.I.C.S.: 423450

Maasdots Sdn. Bhd. (1)
Unit T2-17-1 and 3 Level 17 IOI City Tower Two Lebuh IRC, IOI Resort City, 62502, Putrajaya, Malaysia
Tel.: (60) 358703660
Web Site: http://www.maasdots.com.my
Information Technology & Services
N.A.I.C.S.: 541511
Rifat Sattar *(Mgr-Bus Dev)*

G5 ENTERTAINMENT AB
Birger Jarlsgatan 18, 114 34, Stockholm, Sweden
Tel.: (46) 84111115
Web Site: https://www.g5e.com
Year Founded: 2001
G5EN—(OMX)
Rev.: $131,137,617
Assets: $61,617,916
Liabilities: $14,812,255
Net Worth: $46,805,661
Earnings: $6,270,383
Emp.: 961

Fiscal Year-end: 12/31/22
Game Software Developer
N.A.I.C.S.: 513210
Vsevolod Chernushevich *(Art Dir)*

G7 ENTREPRISES
22 rue Henri Barbusse, 92110,
Clichy, France
Tel.: (33) 1 41 27 46 00
Web Site:
http://www.g7entreprises.com
Sales Range: $350-399.9 Million
Emp.: 2,079
Holding Company
N.A.I.C.S.: 551112
Nicolas Rousselet *(Chm & CEO)*

Subsidiaries:

ADA SA (1)
22-28 rue Henri Barbusse, 92110, Clichy,
France **(72%)**
Tel.: (33) 141274900
Web Site: http://www.ada.fr
Sales Range: $100-124.9 Million
Emp.: 115
Utility Vehicles, Cars & Minibuses Rental &
Leasing Services
N.A.I.C.S.: 532120
Nicolas Rousselet *(Chm)*

G7 TAXI SERVICE (1)
48 rue Eugene Berthoud, 93400, Saint
Ouen L'Aumone, France
Tel.: (33) 1 49 48 38 00
Web Site: http://www.g7taxis.fr
Emp.: 323
Car Rental & Reservation Services
N.A.I.C.S.: 561599
Serge Metz *(Chm & CEO)*

Gamma Solutions S.A. (1)
Impasse Passoir 17 rue de Neuilly, 92110,
Clichy, France
Tel.: (33) 1 47 57 56 30
Web Site: http://www.gammasolutions.fr
Emp.: 11
Automobile Parts Distr
N.A.I.C.S.: 423120

M.G.F. Logistique S.A. (1)
8 av Fondeyre, 31200, Toulouse, France
Tel.: (33) 5 61 47 40 00
Emp.: 550
Logistics Consulting Servies
N.A.I.C.S.: 541614
Allan Underwood *(CEO)*

Pragmatix sa (1)
78 rue du Docteur Bauer, 93400, Saint-
Ouen, France
Tel.: (33) 1 49 21 07 07
Emp.: 26
Software Development Services
N.A.I.C.S.: 541511
Bruno Rousselet *(Chm & CEO)*

Taxirama SAS (1)
3-6 Impasse Passoir, 92110, Clichy, France
Tel.: (33) 1 41 27 66 67
Web Site: http://www.taxirama.fr
Emp.: 61
Car Dealer
N.A.I.C.S.: 441110
Stephane Puis *(CEO)*

G8 EDUCATION LTD.
159 Varsity Parade, PO Box 515,
Varsity Lakes, 4227, QLD, Australia
Tel.: (61) 755815300 **AU**
Web Site:
http://www.g8education.edu.au
GEM—(ASX)
Rev.: $672,298,209
Assets: $1,296,092,909
Liabilities: $679,307,268
Net Worth: $616,785,641
Earnings: $38,182,685
Emp.: 7,731
Fiscal Year-end: 12/31/23
Child Care Centers Owner & Operator
N.A.I.C.S.: 624410
David Foster *(Chm)*

Subsidiaries:

Grasshoppers Early Learning Centre
Pty. Ltd. (1)
Unit 2/153-161 Gordon Rd, Redland Bay,
Brisbane, 4165, QLD, Australia
Tel.: (61) 738292266
Web Site:
https://www.earlylearningservices.com.au
Sales Range: $10-24.9 Million
Emp.: 22
Child Care Management Services
N.A.I.C.S.: 623990

G9PHARMA CO. LTD
90 Sikmakgol-ro, Jungwon-gu,
Seongnam, 223-22, Gyeonggi-do,
Korea (South)
Tel.: (82) 3017406800
Web Site: http://www.kolen.com
078650—(KRS)
Rev.: $521,168
Assets: $4,059,699
Liabilities: $29,137,291
Net Worth: ($25,077,592)
Earnings: ($29,620,725)
Emp.: 8
Fiscal Year-end: 12/31/22
Optical Lens Mfr
N.A.I.C.S.: 333310

GABATHER AB
Forskargatan 20J Byggn 215 N, 151
36, Sodertalje, Sweden
Tel.: (46) 462863600
Web Site: https://www.gabather.com
Year Founded: 2014
GABA—(NASDAQ)
Assets: $4,937,322
Liabilities: $265,782
Net Worth: $4,671,540
Earnings: ($1,530,388)
Emp.: 6
Fiscal Year-end: 12/31/19
Health Care Srvices
N.A.I.C.S.: 621999
Michael-Robin Witt *(CEO)*

GABAY PROPERTIES AND DEVELOPMENT LTD
Kremenetski 2, Tel Aviv, 6789902,
Israel
Tel.: (972) 37655000
Year Founded: 1973
GBPR—(TAE)
Rev.: $71,910,207
Assets: $373,988,114
Liabilities: $252,829,945
Net Worth: $121,158,169
Earnings: $7,627,020
Fiscal Year-end: 12/31/23
Other Activities Related to Real Estate
N.A.I.C.S.: 531390

GABBIT CORP.
Gymnasiumstrasse 19-21, 1180, Vienna, Austria
Tel.: (43) 720 816 770 **NV**
Year Founded: 2015
Sales Range: Less than $1 Million
Emp.: 1
Tour Agency Operator
N.A.I.C.S.: 561520
Vladimir Karelin *(Pres, Treas & Sec)*

GABELLI VALUE FOR ITALY SPA
Piazza Generale Armando Diaz 1,
20123, Milan, Italy
Tel.: (39) 0230578299
Web Site:
http://www.gabellivalueforitaly.it
Security Brokerage Services
N.A.I.C.S.: 523150
Marc J. Gabelli *(Chm & CEO)*

GABETTI PROPERTY SOLUTIONS SPA
Via Bernardo Quaranta 40, 20139,
Milan, Italy
Tel.: (39) 02775558 **IT**
Web Site:
https://www.gabettigroup.com
Year Founded: 1950
GAB—(ITA)
Sales Range: $10-24.9 Million
Emp.: 200
Holding Company; Real Estate Services
N.A.I.C.S.: 551112
Elio Gabetti *(Chm)*

Subsidiaries:

Gabetti S.p.A. (1)
Via Ugo Low 4-B, 20159, Milan,
Italy **(100%)**
Tel.: (39) 027755217
Web Site: http://www.gabetti.it
Real Estate Activities
N.A.I.C.S.: 531390

GABIA INC.
4th floor B-dong 660
Daewangpangyo-ro, Bundang-gu,
Seongnam, Gyeonggi-do, Korea
(South)
Tel.: (82) 15444370
Web Site: https://company.gabia.com
Year Founded: 1998
079940—(KRS)
Rev.: $183,431,076
Assets: $282,503,843
Liabilities: $96,408,621
Net Worth: $186,095,221
Earnings: $31,902,992
Emp.: 300
Fiscal Year-end: 12/31/22
Internet Services
N.A.I.C.S.: 518210
Hong-Guk Kim *(CEO)*

GABLER AS
Henrik Ibsens gate 100, PO Box
1818 Vika, 0123, Oslo, Norway
Tel.: (47) 24 13 07 00 **NO**
Web Site: http://www.gabler.no
Year Founded: 1988
Pension Management, Insurance &
Investment Consulting Services
N.A.I.C.S.: 524298
Aksel Bjerkvik *(CEO)*

GABRIEL HOLDING A/S
Hjulmagervej 55, PO Box 59, 9000,
Aalborg, Denmark
Tel.: (45) 96303100
Web Site: https://www.gabriel.dk
Year Founded: 1851
GABR—(OMX)
Rev.: $133,658,004
Assets: $120,691,096
Liabilities: $67,518,087
Net Worth: $53,173,009
Earnings: $7,622,602
Emp.: 1,207
Fiscal Year-end: 09/30/21
Furniture Textiles Mfr
N.A.I.C.S.: 314999
Jorgen Kjaer Jacobsen *(Chm)*

Subsidiaries:

Gabriel (Tianjin) International Trading
Co. Ltd. (1)
South Tower Soho Shangdu No 8
Dongdaqiao Road, Chaoyang, Beijing,
100020, China
Tel.: (86) 1059001751
Web Site: https://www.gabriel.dk
Furniture Distr
N.A.I.C.S.: 423210
Donna Dang *(Chief Comml Officer)*

Gabriel North America Inc. (1)
560 5th St NW Ste 210, Grand Rapids, MI
49504
Tel.: (616) 202-5770
Textile Mfr
N.A.I.C.S.: 313310

Screen Solutions Ltd. (1)
Beaufort House Greenwich Way, Peacehaven, BN10 8HS, East Sussex, United
Kingdom
Tel.: (44) 1273589922
Web Site: https://www.screensolutions.co.uk
Emp.: 570
Home Furnishing Mfr
N.A.I.C.S.: 337121

UAB FurnMaster (1)
Gelezinkelio g 3, 68127, Marijampole, Lithuania
Tel.: (370) 68360184
Emp.: 235
Textile Mfr
N.A.I.C.S.: 313310

GABRIEL INDIA LTD
29 Milestone Village Kuruli Pune
Nasik Highway, Taluk Khed, Pune,
410501, India
Tel.: (91) 2135610700
Web Site:
https://www.gabrielindia.com
505714—(BOM)
Rev.: $234,663,429
Assets: $165,169,914
Liabilities: $70,123,463
Net Worth: $95,046,452
Earnings: $8,227,265
Emp.: 2,329
Fiscal Year-end: 03/31/21
Shock Absorber Mfr
N.A.I.C.S.: 336330
Amitabh Srivastava *(COO-Aftermarket Bus Unit & Railways Bus Unit)*

GABRIEL RESOURCES LTD.
Suite 200-204 Lambert Street, Whitehorse, Y1A 1Z4, YT, Canada
Tel.: (207) 421-1111
Web Site:
https://www.gabrielresources.com
Year Founded: 1986
GRZ—(DEU)
Assets: $3,928,889
Liabilities: $15,638,535
Net Worth: ($11,709,646)
Earnings: ($18,829,672)
Fiscal Year-end: 12/31/23
Gold Development & Exploration Services
N.A.I.C.S.: 212220
Richard Brown *(CFO)*

Subsidiaries:

Rosia Montana Gold Corporation
S.A. (1)
Str Piata nr 321A, Alba County, 517615,
Alba Iulia, Romania
Tel.: (40) 258806750
Web Site: http://www.en.rmgc.ro
Silver Ore Mining Services
N.A.I.C.S.: 212220

GABRIELLE SHAW COMMUNICATIONS
533 Kings Road, London, SW10 0TZ,
United Kingdom
Tel.: (44) 207 731 8811
Web Site:
http://www.gabrielleshaw.com
Sales Range: $10-24.9 Million
Public Relations Agency
N.A.I.C.S.: 541820
Gabrielle Shaw *(Mng Dir)*

GABUNGAN AQRS BERHAD
G-58 Blok G Jalan Teknologi 3/9 Bistari De Kota, Kota Damansara PJU 5,
47810, Petaling Jaya, Selangor Darul
Ehsan, Malaysia

GABUNGAN AQRS BERHAD

Gabungan AQRS Berhad—(Continued)
Tel.: (60) 361418181
Web Site: https://www.gbg.com.my
5226—(KLS)
Rev.: $76,606,470
Assets: $111,060,650
Liabilities: $26,572,098
Net Worth: $84,488,552
Earnings: $4,567,630
Emp.: 361
Fiscal Year-end: 12/31/22
Building & Civil Engineering Construction & Property Development
N.A.I.C.S.: 237210
Chee Cheoon Ow *(Deputy CEO)*

Subsidiaries:

AQRS The Building Company Sdn. Bhd. (1)
D-39 40 Blok D Jalan Teknologi 3/9 Bistari De Kota, Kota Damansara PJU 5, 47810, Petaling Jaya, Selangor, Malaysia
Tel.: (60) 361418870
Building & Construction Services
N.A.I.C.S.: 236116
Jeff Wang *(Project Mgr)*

Gabungan Strategik Sdn. Bhd. (1)
D-33-G Blok D Jalan Teknologi 3/9 Bistari De Kota Kota Damansara PJU 5, 47810, Petaling Jaya, Selangor, Malaysia
Tel.: (60) 361418181
Building & Construction Services
N.A.I.C.S.: 236116

GABY INC.
200 209-8th Avenue SW, Calgary, T2P 1B8, AB, Canada
Tel.: (403) 771-4918
Web Site: http://www.gabyinc.com
GABY—(CNSX)
Rev.: $21,771,310
Assets: $22,419,114
Liabilities: $45,599,562
Net Worth: ($23,180,448)
Earnings: ($29,252,765)
Fiscal Year-end: 12/31/22
Pharmaceuticals Product Mfr
N.A.I.C.S.: 325412
Margot Micallef *(Founder, Chm & CEO)*

GAD EG
GAD Strasse 2 6, Munster, 48163, Germany
Tel.: (49) 251 7133 01
Web Site: http://www.fiduciagad.de
Emp.: 1,000
Data Processing & IT Services
N.A.I.C.S.: 518210
Jorg Dreinhofer *(Member-Mgmt Bd)*

GAD ENVIRONMENTAL TECHNOLOGY CO., LTD.
3rd Floor Lianhe Building No 1069 Nanhai Avenue Shekou, Nanshan District, Shenzhen, 518000, Guangdong, China
Tel.: (86) 75526695276
Web Site: https://gad.net.cn
Year Founded: 2001
300854—(CHIN)
Rev.: $101,486,736
Assets: $222,534,000
Liabilities: $83,922,696
Net Worth: $138,611,304
Earnings: $3,949,452
Fiscal Year-end: 12/31/22
Pollution Control Equipment Mfr
N.A.I.C.S.: 334519
Xiongjun Kong *(Chm)*

GADANG HOLDINGS BERHAD
Wisma Gadang No 52 Jalan Tago 2 Off Jalan Persiaran Utama Sri Damansar, 52200, Kuala Lumpur, Malaysia
Tel.: (60) 362796288 MY
Web Site: https://www.gadang.com.my
Year Founded: 1993
GADANG—(KLS)
Rev.: $104,988,995
Assets: $294,004,868
Liabilities: $127,441,058
Net Worth: $166,563,810
Earnings: ($8,718,730)
Emp.: 575
Fiscal Year-end: 05/31/23
Holding Company; Construction Services
N.A.I.C.S.: 551112
Sally Seok chung Tan *(Sec)*

Subsidiaries:

Gadang Engineering (M) Sdn Bhd. (1)
Wisma Gadang No 52 Jalan Tago 2 Off Jalan Persiaran Utama, Sri Damansara, 52200, Kuala Lumpur, Malaysia
Tel.: (60) 362756888
Emp.: 200
Building Construction Services
N.A.I.C.S.: 236117

Hillstrand Development Sdn Bhd (1)
Wisma Gadang No 52 Jalan Tago2 Off Jalan Persiaran Utama, Sri Damansara, 52200, Kuala Lumpur, Malaysia
Tel.: (60) 362796288
Real Estate Development Services
N.A.I.C.S.: 531390

Splendid Pavilion Sdn Bhd (1)
Wisma Gadang No 52 Jalan Tago 2 Off Jalan Persiaran Utama, Sri Damansara, 52200, Kuala Lumpur, Malaysia
Tel.: (60) 362752597
Property Development Services
N.A.I.C.S.: 236116

GADOON TEXTILE MILLS LIMITED
7-A Muhammad Ali Housing Society Abdul Aziz Haji Hashim Tabba Street, Karachi, 75350, Pakistan
Tel.: (92) 2135205479
Web Site: https://gadoontextile.com
Year Founded: 1988
GADT—(PSX)
Rev.: $224,141,499
Assets: $196,053,339
Liabilities: $129,929,610
Net Worth: $66,123,729
Earnings: $8,516,212
Emp.: 4,983
Fiscal Year-end: 06/30/19
Yarn Mfr
N.A.I.C.S.: 313110
Muhammad Yunus Tabba *(Chm)*

GAEASOFT
11th floor Building A 50 Jongro 1-gil, Jongro-gu, Seoul, Korea (South)
Tel.: (82) 221555100
Web Site: https://www.gaeasoft.co.kr
Year Founded: 1998
051160—(KRS)
Rev.: $348,703,094
Assets: $223,566,228
Liabilities: $83,128,531
Net Worth: $140,437,696
Earnings: ($3,364,992)
Emp.: 101
Fiscal Year-end: 12/31/22
Software Development & Supply Services
N.A.I.C.S.: 513210
Ahn Jun Hyung *(Head-Dept)*

GAENSLEN VOELTER
Friedrich Herrmann Strasse 3, 72555, Metzingen, Germany
Tel.: (49) 7123165100 De
Web Site: http://www.gaenslen-voelter.de
Year Founded: 1883
Sales Range: $25-49.9 Million
Emp.: 240
Mfr of Textiles
N.A.I.C.S.: 313210
Thomas Pohoralek *(Mng Dir)*

Subsidiaries:

Gaenslen Voelter GmbH & Co. KG (1)
Friedrich Hermann Strasse 3, Metzingen, 72555, Badin Wirttamberg, Germany (100%)
Tel.: (49) 71231650
Web Site: http://www.gaenslenvoelter.de
Sales Range: $10-24.9 Million
Emp.: 60
Mfr of Textiles
N.A.I.C.S.: 313210

GAFISA S.A.
Avenida Presidente Juscelino Kubitschek 1830 Tower 2 - 3rd floor, Sao Paulo, 04543-900, Brazil
Tel.: (55) 1130259000 BR
Web Site: https://www.gafisa.com.br
Year Founded: 1954
GFSA3—(BRAZ)
Rev.: $227,415,146
Assets: $1,056,437,916
Liabilities: $1,056,086,078
Net Worth: $351,837
Earnings: ($39,840,288)
Fiscal Year-end: 12/31/23
Home Construction Services
N.A.I.C.S.: 236115
Ian Monteiro de Andrade *(CFO, Officer-IR & VP-Mgmt & Fin)*

Subsidiaries:

Gafisa Vendas Intermediacao Imobiliaria Ltda. (1)
Av Pedroso de Morais 1553, 4 andar Pinheiros, Sao Paulo, 05420 002, Brazil (100%)
Tel.: (55) 11 3186 8270
Sales & Marketing for Residential Developments
N.A.I.C.S.: 561499

GAG IMMOBILIEN AG
Josef-Lammerting-Allee 20-22, Cologne, 50933, Germany
Tel.: (49) 22120110
Web Site: http://www.gag-koeln.de
Year Founded: 1913
Real Estate Services
N.A.I.C.S.: 531390

GAG LUDWIGSHAFEN AM RHEIN AKTIENGESELLSCHAFT
Mundenheimer Str 182, 67061, Ludwigshafen, Germany
Tel.: (49) 62156040 De
Web Site: http://www.gag-ludwigshafen.de
Sales Range: $600-649.9 Million
Emp.: 150
Real Estate Services
N.A.I.C.S.: 531210

GAGAN GASES LTD.
602 Sector 3, Pithampur Distt, Dhar, MP, India
Tel.: (91) 7313192887
Web Site: https://www.gagangases.com
524624—(BOM)
Rev.: $547,269
Assets: $496,253
Liabilities: $138,349
Net Worth: $357,904
Earnings: $223,764
Fiscal Year-end: 03/31/23
Automotive Lubricant Distr
N.A.I.C.S.: 811191
Kul Rattan Maheshwary *(Chm)*

INTERNATIONAL PUBLIC

GAGAN POLYCOT INDIA LIMITED
Unit 2. Gala No 2 Shiv Shankar Industrial Estate No1, Behind Burmashell Petrol Pump Village Valiv Waliv Vasai E, Thane, 401208, MH, India
Tel.: (91) 8108511999
Web Site: http://www.gaganpolycot.com
Year Founded: 1988
531196—(BOM)
Rev.: $412,582
Assets: $1,263,020
Liabilities: $104,376
Net Worth: $1,158,644
Earnings: ($39,376)
Fiscal Year-end: 03/31/21
Plastics Product Mfr
N.A.I.C.S.: 326199
Ketu Krishnavadan Parikh *(Chm, Mng Dir & CFO)*

GAGASAN NADI CERGAS BHD
F-1 8 Suria 33 Jalan PJU 1/42, 47301, Petaling Jaya, Selangor, Malaysia
Tel.: (60) 378873388
Web Site: https://www.nadicergas.com
Year Founded: 1995
0206—(KLS)
Rev.: $49,421,587
Assets: $208,226,243
Liabilities: $113,748,783
Net Worth: $94,477,460
Earnings: ($548,783)
Emp.: 220
Fiscal Year-end: 12/31/22
Construction Services
N.A.I.C.S.: 236220
Wan Azman Kamal *(Mng Dir)*

GAI BEACH HOTEL
Derech Hamerhatzaot, PO Box 274, Tiberias, Israel
Tel.: (972) 4 6700700
Web Site: http://www.gaibeach.com
GIBC—(TAE)
Year Founded: 1962
Sales Range: $10-24.9 Million
Emp.: 173
Home Management Services
N.A.I.C.S.: 721110
Vardit Oren *(CFO)*

GAIA CORPORATION CO., LTD.
4F Benepia Building 129 Munbal-ro, Ilsandong-gu, Paju, Gyeonggi-do, Korea (South)
Tel.: (82) 319212532
Web Site: https://www.gaiabiz.co.kr
Year Founded: 2010
296520—(KRS)
Infant Product Mfr & Distr
N.A.I.C.S.: 325620

GAIA GROW CORP.
750 West Pender Street Suite 303, Vancouver, V6C 2T7, BC, Canada
Tel.: (604) 681-0084 BC
Web Site: http://www.gaiagrow.com
Year Founded: 2011
GAIA—(CNSX)
Assets: $986,588
Liabilities: $402,134
Net Worth: $584,454
Earnings: ($4,853,764)
Fiscal Year-end: 12/31/20
Investment Services
N.A.I.C.S.: 523999
Zula Kropivnitski *(CEO & CFO)*

GAIA SCIENCE SDN BHD
No 60 Jalan Puteri 5/5, Bandar Put-

eri, 47100, Puchong, Selangor, Malaysia
Tel.: (60) 380653889 MY
Web Site:
http://www.gaiascience.com.my
Laboratory Equipment Distr
N.A.I.C.S.: 423490

GAIA SECURITIZADORA S.A.
Rua do Rocio 288 1 andar, Vila Olimpia, 04552-000, Sao Paulo, SP, Brazil
Tel.: (55) 11 3047 1010
Web Site: http://www.gaiasec.com.br
Year Founded: 2009
Real Estate Credit Securitization Services
N.A.I.C.S.: 522292
Ubirajara Cardoso Da Rocha Neto *(Dir-IR)*

GAIA-WIND LTD.
100 High Craighall Road Port Dundas, Glasgow, G4 9UD, United Kingdom
Tel.: (44) 845 871 4242
Web Site: http://www.gaia-wind.com
Year Founded: 1993
Sales Range: $10-24.9 Million
Emp.: 40
Wind Turbine Mfr
N.A.I.C.S.: 333611
Johnnie Andringa *(CEO)*

GAIAX CO., LTD.
253 Hirakawacho, Chiyoda-ku, Tokyo, 141-0031, Japan
Tel.: (81) 357590300
Web Site: https://www.gaiax.co.jp
37750—(NGO)
Rev.: $21,257,280
Assets: $25,961,760
Liabilities: $8,934,640
Net Worth: $17,027,120
Earnings: ($290,400)
Fiscal Year-end: 12/31/21
Website Development Services
N.A.I.C.S.: 541511
Yuji Ueda *(Founder, Pres & CEO)*

GAIL (INDIA) LIMITED
GAIL Bhawan 16 Bhikaji Cama Place, R K Puram, New Delhi, 110 066, India
Tel.: (91) 1126172580
Web Site: https://www.gailonline.com
Year Founded: 2007
GAIL—(NSE)
Rev.: $7,991,864,790
Assets: $11,109,047,040
Liabilities: $3,836,350,245
Net Worth: $7,272,696,795
Earnings: $838,494,930
Emp.: 4,682
Fiscal Year-end: 03/31/21
Natural Gas Distribution Services
N.A.I.C.S.: 221210
Prafulla Kumar Gupta *(Dir-HR)*

Subsidiaries:

Bengal Gas Company Limited (1)
1st Floor Block A Finance Centre CBD Action Area - II B, Newtown North 24 Parganas, Kolkata, 700161, West Bengal, India
Tel.: (91) 3323248078
Web Site: https://www.bgcl.co.in
Gas Distribution Services
N.A.I.C.S.: 221210

Brahmaputra Cracker and Polymer Ltd. (1)
1st Floor House No 6 Bhuban Road, Uzanbazar, Guwahati, 781 001, Assam, India
Tel.: (91) 3612733554
Web Site: http://www.bcplonline.co.in
Sales Range: $25-49.9 Million
Polymer & Cracker Mfr
N.A.I.C.S.: 311821
Pruthiviraj Dash *(Dir-Fin)*

GAIL Gas Limited (1)
GAIL Bhawan 16 Bhikaji Cama Place R K Puram, New Delhi, 110 066, India
Tel.: (91) 1126172580
Web Site: http://www.gailgas.com
Natural Gas Production Services
N.A.I.C.S.: 211130
A. K. Jana *(CEO)*

GAIL Global (USA) Inc. (1)
3200 SW Fwy Ste 1090 Phoenix Twr, Houston, TX 77027
Tel.: (832) 301-0750
Web Site: http://www.ggui.us
Gas Distribution Services
N.A.I.C.S.: 213112

GAIL Global Singapore Pte. Ltd. (1)
43-01A Suntec Tower One 7 Temasek Boulevard, Singapore, 038987, Singapore
Tel.: (65) 64306615
LNG Trading Services
N.A.I.C.S.: 523160
E. S. Ranganathan *(Chm)*

Konkan LNG Limited (1)
13th Floor GAIL Jubilee Tower Plot No B-35-36Sector-1, Noida, 201301, India
Tel.: (91) 1202424375
Web Site: http://konkanlng.in
LNG Terminal Services
N.A.I.C.S.: 221210
Nalini Malhotra *(Dir-GAIL Lender Nominee)*

GAILLAC AUTO
179 Avenue Gambetta, 81000, Albi, France
Tel.: (33) 563481888
Web Site: http://www.gaillacinfo.fr
Sales Range: $10-24.9 Million
Emp.: 38
New & Used Car Dealers for Renault
N.A.I.C.S.: 441110
Beatrice Albet *(Mgr-Sls-New Vehicles)*

GAIN PLUS HOLDINGS LIMITED
Unit 1323A Level 13 Landmark North 39 Lung Sum Avenue, Sheung Shui, China (Hong Kong)
Tel.: (852) 2 671 8585 Ky
Web Site: http://www.doublegain.hk
Year Founded: 2004
9900—(HKG)
Rev.: $122,692,096
Assets: $37,916,509
Liabilities: $9,781,972
Net Worth: $28,134,536
Earnings: $4,394,607
Emp.: 289
Fiscal Year-end: 03/31/21
Construction Management Services
N.A.I.C.S.: 236220
Chiu Kwan Tsang *(Exec Dir)*

GAINEY RESOURCES LTD.
704-595 Howe Street, Vancouver, V6C 2T5, BC, Canada
Tel.: (604) 817-0334
GRY.H—(TSX)
Sales Range: Less than $1 Million
Mineral Exploration Services
N.A.I.C.S.: 213115

GAJANAN SECURITIES SERVICES LIMITED
113/1B C R Avenue 7th Floor Room No 7C, Kolkata, 700073, West Bengal, India
Tel.: (91) 3322354215
Year Founded: 1994
538609—(BOM)
Sales Range: Less than $1 Million
Financial Services
N.A.I.C.S.: 523999
Riddhi Kanodia *(Officer-Compliance & Sec)*

GAJRA BEVEL GEARS LIMITED
3 - 7 A B Road Industrial Area, Dewas, 455001, MP, India
Tel.: (91) 07312433011
Web Site: https://www.gajrabevel.com
Year Founded: 1979
505711—(BOM)
Sales Range: Less than $1 Million
Motor Vehicle Parts Mfr
N.A.I.C.S.: 336310
Ranveer Singh *(Chm & Mng Dir)*

GAKKEN HOLDINGS CO., LTD.
2-11-8 Nishigotanda, Shinagawa-ku, Tokyo, 141-8510, Japan
Tel.: (81) 364311001
Web Site: https://www.gakken.co.jp
Year Founded: 1947
9470—(TKS)
Rev.: $1,163,582,440
Assets: $966,565,520
Liabilities: $576,374,460
Net Worth: $390,191,060
Earnings: $22,645,460
Fiscal Year-end: 09/30/23
Education Services
N.A.I.C.S.: 611699
Hitoshi Kobayakawa *(Exec Dir)*

Subsidiaries:

Bunri Co., Ltd. (1)
2-11-8 Nishigotanda, Shinagawa-ku, Tokyo, 141-8426, Japan
Tel.: (81) 570051950
Web Site: https://www.bunri.co.jp
Emp.: 122
Education Services
N.A.I.C.S.: 611710

GPlusMedia Inc. (1)
Gleams Akihabara 703 2-8-16 Higashi-Kanda, Chiyoda-ku, Tokyo, 101-0031, Japan
Tel.: (81) 358295900
Web Site: https://gplusmedia.com
Real Estate Services
N.A.I.C.S.: 531390

Gakken (Hong Kong) Co., Ltd. (1)
Room 1201 Fourseas Building 208-212 Nathan Road, Kowloon, China (Hong Kong)
Tel.: (852) 27394366
Web Site: http://www.gakkenhk.com.hk
Education Services
N.A.I.C.S.: 611710

Gakken Cocofump Nursery Co., Ltd. (1)
2-11-8 Nishigotanda, Shinagawa-ku, Tokyo, 141-8420, Japan
Tel.: (81) 364311861
Web Site:
http://www.nursery.cocofump.co.jp
Nursing Care Services
N.A.I.C.S.: 623110

Gakken Education Malaysia Sdn. Bhd. (1)
Unit No 15-5 Menara 1mk Kompleks 1 Mont Kiara No1 Jalan Kiara, Mont Kiara, 50480, Kuala Lumpur, Malaysia
Tel.: (60) 364193247
Web Site:
http://www.gakkenclassroom.com.my
Education Services
N.A.I.C.S.: 611710

Gakken Educational Co., Ltd. (1)
11-8 Nishigotanda 2-chome, Shinagawa-ku, Tokyo, 141-8411, Japan
Tel.: (81) 364311100
Web Site: http://www.gakken-educational.co.jp
Education Services
N.A.I.C.S.: 611710
Kazuhiko Fukuzumi *(Pres)*

Gakken Juku Holdings Co., Ltd. (1)
2-11-8 Nishi-Gotanda, Shinagawa-ku, Tokyo, 141-8415, Japan
Tel.: (81) 364311120
Web Site: https://gakken-jhd.co.jp
Education Services

N.A.I.C.S.: 611310

Gakken Medical Shujunsha Co., Ltd. (1)
11-8 Nishigotanda 2-chome, Shinagawa-ku, Tokyo, 141-8414, Japan
Tel.: (81) 364311200
Web Site: http://www.gakken-mesh.co.jp
Education Services
N.A.I.C.S.: 611710
Hiroyuki Kageyama *(Pres & Dir-Rep)*

Subsidiary (Domestic):

Gakken Medical Support Co., Ltd. (2)
2-11-8 Nishigotanda, Shinagawa-ku, Tokyo, 141-8414, Japan
Tel.: (81) 364311228
Web Site: https://www.gakken-meds.jp
Education Training Services
N.A.I.C.S.: 611310

Gakken Plus Co., Ltd. (1)
2-11-8 Nishigotanda, Shinagawa-ku, Tokyo, 141-8415, Japan
Tel.: (81) 364311131
Web Site: https://www.corp-gakken.co.jp
Education Services
N.A.I.C.S.: 611710

Gakken Products Support Co., Ltd. (1)
2-11-8 Nishigotan, Shinagawa-ku, Tokyo, 141-8418, Japan
Tel.: (81) 364311123
Web Site: https://www.gakken-ps.co.jp
Education Services
N.A.I.C.S.: 611710

Gakken Shuppan Holdings Co., Ltd. (1)
11- 8 Nishi-Gotanda, Shinagawa-ku, Tokyo, 141-8412, Japan
Tel.: (81) 364311570
Web Site: http://www.gakken-shd.co.jp
Magazine Publishing Services
N.A.I.C.S.: 513199
Hideyuki Ikari *(Dir)*

Gakken SmileHeart Co., Ltd. (1)
2-11-8 Nishigotanda, Shinagawa-ku, Tokyo, 141-8510, Japan
Tel.: (81) 364311810
Education Services
N.A.I.C.S.: 611710

Gakken Sta:ful Co., Ltd. (1)
2-11-8 Nishigotanda, Shinagawa-ku, Tokyo, 141-8419, Japan
Tel.: (81) 364311829
Web Site: https://www.info.gakkensf.co.jp
Education Services
N.A.I.C.S.: 611710
Takahiro Fukumoto *(Pres & CEO)*

Gakken Study Co., Ltd. (1)
5-32 Higashiomiya Minuma-ku, Saitama, Japan
Tel.: (81) 486305213
Web Site: http://www.gakken-studyet.com
Emp.: 534
Nursery, Prep School & Elderly Care Facilities Owner & Operator
N.A.I.C.S.: 611110
Masahiro Kametani *(Pres & CEO)*

IC Net Limited (1)
Land Axis Tower 27th Floor 11-2 Shintoshin, Chuo-ku, Saitama, 330-6027, Japan
Tel.: (81) 486002500
Education Services
N.A.I.C.S.: 611710

Medical Care Service Co., Ltd. (1)
Web Site: http://www.mcsg.co.jp
Nursing Care Services
N.A.I.C.S.: 623110

Syoei Co., Ltd. (1)
3165-11 Hirao, Nabari, 518-0713, Japan
Tel.: (81) 120375955
Web Site: https://www.syoei.ed.jp
Education Services
N.A.I.C.S.: 611310

Tokyo Global Gateway Co., Ltd. (1)
2-4-32 Aomi, Koto-ku, Tokyo, 135-0064, Japan
Tel.: (81) 120865961

GAKKEN HOLDINGS CO., LTD.

Gakken Holdings Co., Ltd.—(Continued)
Web Site: https://www.tokyo-global-gateway.com
Education Training Services
N.A.I.C.S.: 611310
Shoichiro Taniguchi (Dir-Sls & Mktg)

Zenkyoken Co., Ltd. (1)
1-15-9 Akasaka, Chuo-ku, Fukuoka, 810-0042, Japan
Tel.: (81) 927180080
Web Site:
 https://www.welcome.zenkyoken.com
Emp.: 238
Education Services
N.A.I.C.S.: 611710
Kazufumi Nakagaki (CEO)

GAKKYUSHA CO., LTD.
1-12-8 Yoyogi, Shibuya-ku, Tokyo, 151-0053, Japan
Tel.: (81) 363005311
Web Site:
 https://www.gakkyusha.com
Year Founded: 1976
9769—(TKS)
Rev.: $87,238,780
Assets: $72,108,490
Liabilities: $29,209,590
Net Worth: $42,898,900
Earnings: $12,076,470
Fiscal Year-end: 03/31/24
Education Services
N.A.I.C.S.: 611710
Shinichi Kawabata (Chm, Pres, CEO & Exec Officer)

GAKUJO CO., LTD.
Gakujo Umeda Compass 2-5-10 Umeda, Kita-ku, Osaka, 530-0001, Japan
Tel.: (81) 663466830 JP
Web Site:
 https://company.gakujo.ne.jp
Year Founded: 1977
2301—(TKS)
Rev.: $55,369,639
Assets: $117,976,123
Liabilities: $13,166,978
Net Worth: $104,809,145
Earnings: $8,977,803
Emp.: 266
Fiscal Year-end: 10/31/20
Employment Consulting Services
N.A.I.C.S.: 611710
Kiyokazu Nakai (Pres)

GALA INCORPORATED
WeWork Iceberg 6-12-18 Shibuya, Jingumae Shibuya-ku, Tokyo, 150-0001, Japan
Tel.: (81) 357780320 JP
Web Site: https://www.gala.biz
Year Founded: 1993
4777—(TKS)
Rev.: $5,817,273
Assets: $10,141,329
Liabilities: $5,897,240
Net Worth: $4,244,090
Earnings: ($1,801,855)
Emp.: 52
Fiscal Year-end: 03/31/22
Online Game Development Services
N.A.I.C.S.: 513210
Satoru Kikugawa (Chm & CEO)
Subsidiaries:

Gala Lab Corp. (1)
46 Nonhyeon-ro 85 gil Gangnam-gu, Seoul, 135-923, Korea (South)
Tel.: (82) 221885500
Web Site: http://www.galalab.kr
Online Game Development Services
N.A.I.C.S.: 513210
Hyunsu Kim (CEO)

GALA S.P.A.
Via Savoia 43/47, 00198, Rome, Italy
Tel.: (39) 06 37592701
Web Site: http://www.gala.it
Rev.: $1,702,112,011
Assets: $644,515,123
Liabilities: $596,754,414
Net Worth: $47,760,710
Earnings: ($59,468,772)
Emp.: 143
Fiscal Year-end: 12/31/15
Electric Power Generation
N.A.I.C.S.: 221115
Filippo Tortoriello (Chm & CEO)

GALA TECHNOLOGY HOLDING LIMITED
4203-4204 Qianhai Shimao Finance Centre II No 3040 Aohai Avenue, Nanshan Street Qianhai Shenzhen-Hong Kong Cooperation Zone, Shenzhen, China
Web Site:
 https://www.galasports.com
Year Founded: 2013
2458—(HKG)
Rev.: $97,730,514
Assets: $56,727,535
Liabilities: $37,941,844
Net Worth: $18,785,691
Earnings: $2,063,585
Emp.: 367
Fiscal Year-end: 12/31/22
Holding Company
N.A.I.C.S.: 551112
Kai Chi Chu (CFO)

GALACTICO CORPORATE SERVICES LIMITED
Office No 68 6th Floor Business Bay Shri Hari Kute Marg, Tidke Colony, Nashik, 422002, India
Tel.: (91) 8530604666
Web Site:
 https://www.galacticocorp.com
Year Founded: 2015
542802—(BOM)
Rev.: $2,947
Assets: $7,189
Liabilities: $3,810
Net Worth: $3,379
Earnings: $619
Emp.: 25
Fiscal Year-end: 03/31/22
Financial Advisory Services
N.A.I.C.S.: 523940
Vipul Lathi (Chm)

GALADA FINANCE LIMITED
Shanti Sadan Old No 4 New No 7 Shaffee Mohammed Road, Thousand Lights, Chennai, 600 006, India
Tel.: (91) 4428294830
Web Site:
 https://www.galadafinance.in
538881—(BOM)
Rev.: $112,734
Assets: $820,925
Liabilities: $203,895
Net Worth: $617,030
Earnings: $2,882
Emp.: 3
Fiscal Year-end: 03/31/23
Financial Support Services
N.A.I.C.S.: 523999
Ponniah Bhaskaran (Chm)

GALADA POWER & TELECOMMUNICATION LTD.
P 2 / 6 IDA Block III Uppal, Hyderabad, 500 039, Andhra Pradesh, India
Tel.: (91) 9392525064
Web Site:
 https://www.galadapower.com
Year Founded: 1972
504697—(BOM)
Rev.: $2,576
Assets: $1,090,585
Liabilities: $8,365,854
Net Worth: ($7,275,268)
Earnings: ($312,625)
Emp.: 20
Fiscal Year-end: 03/31/21
Aluminium Strips, Slugs, Circles Products Mfr
N.A.I.C.S.: 331318
S. M. Kankaria (Chm)

GALADARI HOTELS (LANKA) PLC
64 Lotus Road, 1, Colombo, 1, Sri Lanka
Tel.: (94) 112544544
Web Site:
 https://www.galadarihotel.lk
Year Founded: 1984
GHLL.N0000—(COL)
Rev.: $3,938,682
Assets: $35,069,770
Liabilities: $8,095,752
Net Worth: $26,974,018
Earnings: ($392,436)
Emp.: 481
Fiscal Year-end: 12/31/22
Hotel & Resort Operator
N.A.I.C.S.: 721110

GALAN LITHIUM LIMITED
Level 1 50 Kings Park Road, West Perth, 6005, WA, Australia
Tel.: (61) 892142150
Web Site:
 https://www.galanlithium.com.au
Year Founded: 2011
GLN—(ASX)
Rev.: $122,331
Assets: $69,050,964
Liabilities: $2,499,415
Net Worth: $66,551,548
Earnings: ($3,894,456)
Fiscal Year-end: 06/30/22
Other Nonmetallic Mineral Mining & Quarrying
N.A.I.C.S.: 212390
Mike Robbins (Sec)

GALANE GOLD LTD.
181 Bay Street Suite 1800, Toronto, M5J 2T9, ON, Canada
Tel.: (647) 987-7663 ON
Web Site:
 https://www.golcondagold.com
Year Founded: 2007
GGGOF—(OTCQB)
Rev.: $41,402,404
Assets: $48,258,393
Liabilities: $35,339,769
Net Worth: $12,918,624
Earnings: ($3,823,364)
Emp.: 207
Fiscal Year-end: 12/31/19
Gold Mining Services
N.A.I.C.S.: 212220
Nick Brodie (CEO)
Subsidiaries:

Gallery Gold Pty Ltd. (1)
Ground Floor 9 Havelock Street, West Perth, 6005, WA, Australia
Tel.: (61) 8 9321 8643
Gold Mining Services
N.A.I.C.S.: 212220

GALANTAS GOLD CORPORATION
82 Richmond Street East, Toronto, M5C 1P1, ON, Canada
Tel.: (416) 848-7744 Ca
Web Site: https://www.galantas.com
GALKF—(OTCQX)
Assets: $22,415,380
Liabilities: $11,545,179
Net Worth: $10,870,201
Earnings: ($12,287,759)
Fiscal Year-end: 12/31/22
Gold Mining Services
N.A.I.C.S.: 212220
Alan Buckley (CFO)
Subsidiaries:

Galantas Irish Gold Limited (1)
56 Botera Upper Rd Cavanacaw, Omagh, BT78 5LH, Tyrone, United Kingdom
Tel.: (44) 2882241100
Web Site: http://www.galantas.com
Sales Range: $25-49.9 Million
Emp.: 7
Jewelry Mfr & Distr
N.A.I.C.S.: 339910

Omagh Minerals Limited (1)
56 Botera Upper Road, Omagh, BT78 5LH, Tyrone, United Kingdom
Tel.: (44) 2882249637
Web Site: https://www.omagh.opendi.co.uk
Sales Range: $50-74.9 Million
Emp.: 45
Gold Ore Mining Services
N.A.I.C.S.: 212220
Roland Phelps (Exec Dir)

GALAPAGOS N.V.
Generaal De Wittelaan L11 A3, 2800, Mechelen, Belgium
Tel.: (32) 15342900 BE
Web Site: https://www.glpg.com
Year Founded: 1999
GLPG—(NASDAQ)
Rev.: $620,605,107
Assets: $5,814,919,272
Liabilities: $2,712,353,098
Net Worth: $3,102,566,174
Earnings: ($267,745,266)
Emp.: 1,338
Fiscal Year-end: 12/31/22
Biotechnology Research & Development Services
N.A.I.C.S.: 541714
Rajesh Parekh (Chm-Supervisory Bd)
Subsidiaries:

AboundBio Inc. (1)
1401 Forbes Ave Ste 306, Pittsburgh, PA 15219
Tel.: (412) 209-4544
Web Site: https://www.aboundbio.com
Pharmaceutical Research Services
N.A.I.C.S.: 541715

CellPoint B.V. (1)
De Limes 7, 2342 DH, Oegstgeest, Netherlands
Tel.: (31) 712077810
Web Site: https://www.cellpoint.bio
Clinician Cancer Treatment Services
N.A.I.C.S.: 562219

Galapagos B.V. (1)
Bio Science Park Darwinweg 24, 2333 CR, Leiden, Netherlands
Tel.: (31) 717506700
Web Site: http://www.glpg.com
Sales Range: $25-49.9 Million
Emp.: 60
Biotechnology Research & Development
N.A.I.C.S.: 541714

Galapagos Biopharma Austria GmbH (1)
Herrengasse 1-3, 1010, Vienna, Austria
Tel.: (43) 1930841125
Web Site: https://www.glpg.com
Emp.: 1,300
Pharmaceutical Research Services
N.A.I.C.S.: 541715

Galapagos Biopharma Norway AS (1)
Lilleakerveien 8, PO Box 200, 1326, Lilleaker, Norway
Tel.: (47) 24110100
Web Site: https://www.biopharmanorge.no
Pharmaceutical Research Services
N.A.I.C.S.: 541715

Galapagos SASU (1)
102 Avenue Gaston Roussel, 93230, Romainville, Seine-Saint-Denis, France
Tel.: (33) 149424646
Web Site: http://www.glpg.com
Pharmaceuticals Product Mfr

AND PRIVATE COMPANIES

GALAPROM A.D.
Kralja Aleksandra Kradordevica 47, 76230, Samac, Bosnia & Herzegovina
Tel.: (387) 54611601
Year Founded: 2001
GLPR-R-A—(BANJ)
Rev.: $20,973
Assets: $620,024
Liabilities: $234,864
Net Worth: $385,160
Earnings: ($90,181)
Emp.: 2
Fiscal Year-end: 12/31/12
Grocery Store Operator
N.A.I.C.S.: 445110
Momir Pisarevic *(Chm-Mgmt Bd)*

GALATA INVESTMENT COMPANY AD
1 Georgi Stamatov Str Asparuhovo, 9003, Varna, 9003, Bulgaria
Tel.: (359) 52370598
Web Site: https://www.gic.bg
Year Founded: 2003
Real Estate Development Services
N.A.I.C.S.: 531390
Ivelina Kuncheva Kuncheva-Shaban *(Exec Dir)*

GALATA WIND ENERJI A.S.
Burhaniye Mahallesi Kisikli Caddesi No 65, Uskudar, 34676, Istanbul, Turkiye
Tel.: (90) 2165569000
Web Site: https://www.galatawindenerji.com
Year Founded: 2006
GWIND—(IST)
Rev.: $62,958,303
Assets: $310,198,415
Liabilities: $72,024,652
Net Worth: $238,173,764
Earnings: $21,117,167
Emp.: 56
Fiscal Year-end: 12/31/23
Electric Power Distribution Services
N.A.I.C.S.: 221122
Caglar Gogus *(Chm & Deputy Chm)*

GALATASARAY SPORTIF SINAI VETICARI YATIRIMLAR AS
Ali Sami Yen Sports Complex RAMS Park Huzur Mahallesi, Seyrantepe, 34415, Istanbul, Turkiye
Tel.: (90) 2123051902
Web Site: https://sportif.galatasaray.org
Year Founded: 1997
GSRAY—(IST)
Rev.: $95,379,031
Assets: $226,727,164
Liabilities: $273,433,399
Net Worth: ($46,706,235)
Earnings: $1,058,728
Fiscal Year-end: 06/30/23
Sports Club Operator
N.A.I.C.S.: 713940
Dursun Aydin Ozbek *(Chm)*

GALAXIA MONEYTREE CO., LTD.
15 F Suseo Bldg 715 Suseo-dong, Gangnam-gu, Seoul, 06349, Korea (South)
Tel.: (82) 215660123
Web Site: https://www.galaxiamoneytree.co.kr
Year Founded: 1994
094480—(KRS)
Rev.: $86,123,701
Assets: $259,219,473
Liabilities: $170,950,280
Net Worth: $88,269,193
Earnings: $4,154,268
Emp.: 129
Fiscal Year-end: 12/31/22
Wireless Information Solutions Services
N.A.I.C.S.: 519290
Shin Dong Hoon *(CEO)*

GALAXIA SM INC.
7F Miseong Building 311 Hakdong-ro, Gangnam-gu, Seoul, 06061, Korea (South)
Tel.: (82) 27751300
Web Site: https://galaxiasme.com
Year Founded: 1975
011420—(KRS)
Rev.: $23,082,009
Assets: $44,380,930
Liabilities: $18,814,111
Net Worth: $25,566,819
Earnings: $3,538,256
Emp.: 82
Fiscal Year-end: 12/31/22
Sports Event Marketing Services
N.A.I.C.S.: 541830

GALAXIDI MARINE FARM S.A.
Anemokambi Place, 330 52, Galaxidi, Greece
Tel.: (30) 2265041840 GR
Web Site: http://www.gmf-sa.gr
Year Founded: 1987
Rev.: $59,594,487
Assets: $71,111,500
Liabilities: $49,613,457
Net Worth: $21,498,044
Earnings: $649,421
Fiscal Year-end: 12/31/17
Fish Farm & Fish Products Mfr
N.A.I.C.S.: 311710

Subsidiaries:

KIRFIS S.A. (1)
Anemokampi Place, 33052, Galaxidi, Phocis, Greece **(99.75%)**
Tel.: (30) 2265041843
Sales Range: $25-49.9 Million
Emp.: 160
Fish Farming Services
N.A.I.C.S.: 112511
Nancy Panteleimonitou *(Mng Dir)*

GALAXY AGRICO EXPORTS LIMITED
Survey No 236 Jai Kishan Ind Estate Behind Murlidhar Weigh Bridge, Veraval Shapar, 360024, Rajkot, 360024, Gujarat, India
Tel.: (91) 2827252676
Web Site: https://www.galaxyagrico.com
Year Founded: 1992
531911—(BOM)
Rev.: $738,133
Assets: $773,623
Liabilities: $218,009
Net Worth: $555,614
Earnings: ($49,374)
Emp.: 97
Fiscal Year-end: 03/31/23
Garden Tool Mfr
N.A.I.C.S.: 332216
Manoj Harsukhlal Shah *(Exec Dir)*

GALAXY BEARINGS LIMITED
Survey No 253 National Highway No 27 Shapar, Rajkot, 360 024, Gujarat, India
Tel.: (91) 2827252401
Web Site: https://www.galaxybearings.com
Year Founded: 1990
526073—(BOM)
Rev.: $14,553,336
Assets: $11,626,078
Liabilities: $2,698,567
Net Worth: $8,927,510
Earnings: $1,911,888
Emp.: 124
Fiscal Year-end: 03/31/23
Bearing Mfr & Distr
N.A.I.C.S.: 332991
Bharatkumar Keshavji Ghodasara *(Mng Dir)*

GALAXY BIOMEDICAL INVESTMENT CO., LTD.
Comprehensive Office Building, Yinhe Software Science and Technology Park, Beihai, 536000, Guangxi, China
Tel.: (86) 7793202636
000806—(SSE)
Rev.: $169,447,196
Assets: $325,819,450
Liabilities: $316,208,587
Net Worth: $9,610,863
Earnings: $8,933,675
Fiscal Year-end: 12/31/20
Investment Services
N.A.I.C.S.: 523999
Hongjun Xu *(Chm & Pres)*

GALAXY CLOUD KITCHENS LIMITED
Eyelet House M S Patel Compound Near John Baker Bus Stop, Opp Shah Industrial Estate Saki-Vihar Road Saki Naka Andheri E, Mumbai, 400072, India
Tel.: (91) 2228585521
Web Site: https://www.galaxycloudkitchens.in
Year Founded: 1999
506186—(BOM)
Rev.: $3,496,126
Assets: $2,278,979
Liabilities: $3,149,960
Net Worth: ($870,981)
Earnings: ($1,078,581)
Emp.: 105
Fiscal Year-end: 03/31/23
Food & Leisure, Entertainment Service
N.A.I.C.S.: 722513
Arvind Agrawal *(Mng Dir)*

GALAXY CONSOLIDATED FINANCE LIMITED
Shree Commercial Dr Yagnik Road, Rajkot, Ahmedabad, 360001, Gujarat, India
Tel.: (91) 281 2464325
Web Site: http://www.galconslimited.com
Year Founded: 1985
Rev.: $3,899
Assets: $182,336
Liabilities: $3,840
Net Worth: $178,495
Earnings: ($1,447)
Fiscal Year-end: 03/31/16
Financial Services
N.A.I.C.S.: 523999
Zalak Gajjar *(Compliance Officer & Sec)*

GALAXY ENTERTAINMENT GROUP LIMITED
22nd Floor Wing On Centre 111 Connaught Road, Central, China (Hong Kong)
Tel.: (852) 31501111 HK
Web Site: http://www.galaxyentertainment.com
Year Founded: 2002
0027—(HKG)
Rev.: $1,462,908,608
Assets: $10,322,569,830
Liabilities: $2,103,235,793
Net Worth: $8,219,334,038
Earnings: $439,642,568
Emp.: 17,000
Fiscal Year-end: 12/31/22

GALAXY SURFACTANTS LIMITED

Investment Management Service
N.A.I.C.S.: 523940
Che Woo Lui *(Founder & Chm)*

Subsidiaries:

K. Wah Asphalt Limited (1)
F Spectrum Tower 53 Hung To Road, Kwun Tong, Hong Kong, China (Hong Kong)
Tel.: (852) 23250115
Construction Equipment Distr
N.A.I.C.S.: 423910

K. Wah Construction Materials Limited (1)
Suite No 912 9/F Skyline Tower 39 Wang Kwong Road, Kowloon Bay, China (Hong Kong)
Tel.: (852) 21736688
Web Site: https://www.kwcml.com
Emp.: 3,000
Construction Materials Distr
N.A.I.C.S.: 423320
Che Woo Lui *(Chm-Exec Bd)*

New Galaxy Entertainment Company Limited (1)
Galaxy Macau Cotai, Macau, China (Macau)
Tel.: (853) 28880888
Resort Operator
N.A.I.C.S.: 721110

Quantum Limited (1)
Room 1205 International Industrial Building 175 Hoi Bun Road, Hong Kong, China (Hong Kong)
Tel.: (852) 28112786
Web Site: https://www.quantumlimited.com.hk
Dictating System Mfr
N.A.I.C.S.: 333310

StarWorld Hotel Company Limited (1)
Avenida da Amizade, Macau, China (Macau)
Tel.: (853) 28383838
Web Site: http://www.starworldmacau.com
Home Management Services
N.A.I.C.S.: 721110

GALAXY PAYROLL GROUP LIMITED
25th Floor Ovest 77 Wing Lok Street, Sheung Wan, China (Hong Kong)
Tel.: (852) 31052611 VG
Web Site: https://galaxy-hk.com
Year Founded: 2013
GLXG—(NASDAQ)
Rev.: $3,858,103
Assets: $3,404,932
Liabilities: $2,575,617
Net Worth: $829,315
Earnings: $705,088
Emp.: 29
Fiscal Year-end: 06/30/24
Payroll Services
N.A.I.C.S.: 541214

GALAXY SEMICONDUCTOR CO., LTD.
No 19 Changjiang North Road, Changzhou, 213022, Jiangsu, China
Tel.: (86) 51985121818
Web Site: http://www.galaxycn.com
Sales Range: $50-74.9 Million
Emp.: 2,100
Semiconductor Mfr
N.A.I.C.S.: 334413
Xiaoping Xu *(Exec Dir)*

Subsidiaries:

Changzhou Galaxy Electrical Co., Ltd (1)
No168 Hehai W Rd, Xinbei Dist, Changzhou, 213022, Jiangsu, China
Tel.: (86) 51985121518
Semiconductor Devices Mfr & Sales
N.A.I.C.S.: 334413

GALAXY SURFACTANTS LIMITED

GALAXY SURFACTANTS LIMITED

Galaxy Surfactants Limited—(Continued)
C 49/2 TTC Indus Area, Mumbai, 400 703, Pawne, India
Tel.: (91) 22 27616666
Web Site: http://www.galaxysurfactants.com
Year Founded: 1980
Emp.: 1,000
Surfactants & Specialty Chemicals Mfr
N.A.I.C.S.: 325998
Unnathan Shekhar *(CEO & Mng Dir)*

Subsidiaries:

Galaxy Surfactants Ltd-Asia Pacific (1)
4125 Level 41 United Center, 323 Silom Road, 105 00, Bangkok, Thailand
Tel.: (66) 2310420
Surfactants & Specialty Chemicals Mfr
N.A.I.C.S.: 325998

Surfactants International LLC (1)
6 Pearl Ct Unit H, Allendale, NJ 07401
Tel.: (201) 661-7156
Web Site: http://www.surfactantsintl.com
Chemical Products Mfr
N.A.I.C.S.: 325199

Tri-K Industries, Inc. (1)
2 Stewart Ct, Denville, NJ 07834
Tel.: (973) 298-8850
Web Site: http://www.tri-k.com
Sales Range: $10-24.9 Million
Emp.: 50
Cosmetic Ingredients Supply Distr
N.A.I.C.S.: 424210
Paola Torres *(Acct Mgr-Sls-Latin America)*

Subsidiary (Domestic):

Tri-K Industries - Proteins Div (2)
8 Willow St Dock 4, Salem, NH 03079
Tel.: (603) 898-0811
Cosmetic Ingredients Supplier
N.A.I.C.S.: 424210

GALAZ, YAMAZAKI, RUIZ URQUIZA, S.C.
Paseo de la Reforma 489 piso 6 Colonia Cuauhtemoc, Mexico, Mexico
Tel.: (52) 5550806000   MX
Web Site: http://www.deloitte.com.mx
Year Founded: 1983
Emp.: 31
Accounting Services
N.A.I.C.S.: 541211
Guillermo Elmer Monroy Hernandez *(Atty)*

GALE PACIFIC LIMITED
145 Woodlands Drive, PO Box 892, Braeside, 3195, VIC, Australia
Tel.: (61) 395183333
Web Site: https://www.galepacific.com
GAP—(ASX)
Rev.: $157,484,991
Assets: $161,081,487
Liabilities: $86,013,256
Net Worth: $75,068,231
Earnings: $5,836,069
Emp.: 600
Fiscal Year-end: 06/30/22
Polymer Fabric Mfr
N.A.I.C.S.: 313230
Sophie Karzis *(Sec)*

Subsidiaries:

Gale Pacific (NZ) Limited (1)
Unit 9 59 Pollard Drive Albany, Auckland, New Zealand
Tel.: (64) 800555171
Sales Range: $25-49.9 Million
Emp.: 3
Polymer Fabric Mfr
N.A.I.C.S.: 313230

Gale Pacific FZE (1)
LOB 16 6th Roundabout, PO Box 17696, Jebel Ali, Dubai, United Arab Emirates (100%)
Tel.: (971) 48817114
Web Site: http://www.galepacific.com
Sales Range: $25-49.9 Million
Emp.: 5
Polymer Fabric Mfr
N.A.I.C.S.: 313230
Ali Haidar *(Gen Mgr)*

Gale Pacific Inc. (1)
285 W Central Pkwy Ste 1704, Altamonte Springs, FL 32714 (100%)
Tel.: (407) 772-7900
Web Site: http://www.coolaroousa.com
Sales Range: $25-49.9 Million
Emp.: 15
Polymer Fabric Mfr
N.A.I.C.S.: 313210

Gale Pacific Special Textiles (Ningbo) Limited (1)
No 777 Hengshan W Road, Beilun, Ningbo, 315800, Zhejiang, China
Tel.: (86) 57456268888
Home Furnishing Mfr
N.A.I.C.S.: 333248

Windhager HandelsgesmbH (1)
Industriestrasse 2, 5303, Thalgau, Salzburg, Austria
Tel.: (43) 623561610
Web Site: https://www.windhager.eu
Emp.: 229
Homecare Products Mfr
N.A.I.C.S.: 339999
Johann Windhager *(Mng Dir)*

GALECTO, INC.
Ole Maaloes Vej 3, DK-2200, Copenhagen, DK-2200, Denmark
Tel.: (45) 70705210   DE
Web Site: https://www.galecto.com
Year Founded: 2011
GLTO—(NASDAQ)
Rev.: $722,000
Assets: $73,188,000
Liabilities: $11,435,000
Net Worth: $61,753,000
Earnings: ($61,624,000)
Emp.: 45
Fiscal Year-end: 12/31/22
Biotechnology Research & Development Services
N.A.I.C.S.: 541714
Hans T. Schambye *(Co-Founder, Pres & CEO)*

GALEMED CORPORATION
5F No 209 Sec 1 Fuxing S Road, Da'an, Taipei, 106, Taiwan
Tel.: (886) 287919348
Web Site: https://www.galemed.com
Year Founded: 1986
Emp.: 650
Medical Device Mfr & Distr
N.A.I.C.S.: 339112

GALENA MINING LIMITED
Tel.: (61) 861833200   AU
Web Site: https://www.galenamining.com.au
Year Founded: 2016
G1A—(ASX)
Rev.: $19,705,458
Assets: $244,463,340
Liabilities: $176,482,009
Net Worth: $67,981,331
Earnings: $90,845,099)
Fiscal Year-end: 06/30/23
Mineral Exploration & Development Services
N.A.I.C.S.: 213115
Alexander Molyneux *(CEO & Mng Dir)*

GALENIKA-FITOFARMACIJA A.D.
Batajnicki drum bb Zemun, 11080, Belgrade, Serbia
Tel.: (381) 113072314
Web Site: http://www.fitofarmacija.rs
FITO—(BEL)
Rev.: $42,051,718
Assets: $676,701,409
Liabilities: $28,627,249
Net Worth: $648,074,159
Earnings: $6,527,184
Emp.: 165
Fiscal Year-end: 12/31/19
Pesticides & Agricultural Chemicals Mfr
N.A.I.C.S.: 325320
Branimir Knezevic *(Dir-Production Dept)*

GALEO CONCEPT SA
14 F Route de Grillon, 84600, Valreas, France
Tel.: (33) 426487950
Web Site: https://www.galeoconcept.com
MLGAL—(EUR)
Sales Range: $1-4.9 Billion
Scented Product Mfr & Distr
N.A.I.C.S.: 339999
Remy Burckel *(Chm & CEO)*

GALERIES LAFAYETTE SA
44 Rue de Chateaudun, 75009, Paris, France
Tel.: (33) 144544454   FR
Web Site: http://www.groupegaleries.com
Year Founded: 1894
Department Store Owner & Operator
N.A.I.C.S.: 455110
Ginette Moulin *(VP)*

Subsidiaries:

Bazar de l'Hotel de Ville (1)
36 rue de la Verrerie, 75004, Paris, France (100%)
Tel.: (33) 142749000
Web Site: http://www.bhv.fr
Concept Department Store Operator; Retail Space Leasing Services
N.A.I.C.S.: 455110
Alexandre Liot *(Mng Dir)*

La Redoute SA (1)
57 rue de Blanchemaille, 59082, Roubaix, France
Tel.: (33) 366331780
Web Site: http://www.laredoute.com
French Fashion & Linens Mfr
N.A.I.C.S.: 458110
Nathalie Balla *(Co-Owner & Chm)*

Subsidiary (Non-US):

La Redoute Catalog Benelux (2)
Rue De Menin 4, BP 1, Estaimpuis, 7730, Hainaut, Belgium
Tel.: (32) 56 85 15 15
Web Site: http://www.laredoute.be
Clothing & Linen Mfr
N.A.I.C.S.: 424350

La Redoute Portugal (2)
Zona Industrial Da Barosa Rua Beco Dos Petigais Fraccao F N 45 E 65, 2400-431, Leiria, Portugal
Tel.: (351) 244 811 035
Web Site: http://www.laredoute.pt
French Fashion & Linens Mfr
N.A.I.C.S.: 458110

La Redoute Suisse SA (2)
Rue De La Gare 13, 1818, Montreux, Switzerland
Tel.: (41) 848848505
Web Site: http://www.laredoute.ch
French Fashion & Linen Mfr
N.A.I.C.S.: 424350
Laurent Garet *(Gen Mgr)*

Redcats Italy s.r.l. (2)
Via GB Pirelli 11, 20124, Milan, Italy
Tel.: (39) 0297386420
Web Site: http://www.laredoute.it
Clothing & Linen Mfr
N.A.I.C.S.: 424350

Lafayette Services LaSer (1)

INTERNATIONAL PUBLIC

66 Rue Des Archives, 75003, Paris, France (50%)
Tel.: (33) 44544700
Consumer Credit & Loyalty Card Schemes
N.A.I.C.S.: 522210

Subsidiary (Domestic):

Cofinoga S.A. (2)
66 Rue Des Archives, 75003, Paris, France
Tel.: (33) 556554750
Web Site: http://www.cofinoga.fr
Sales Range: $600-649.9 Million
Emp.: 2,500
Consumer Credit Services
N.A.I.C.S.: 522210

Subsidiary (Non-US):

LaSer Polska (2)
ul Suwak 3, 02 676, Warsaw, Poland
Tel.: (48) 22 591 45 45
Web Site: http://www.laserpolska.com
Consumer Finance Services
N.A.I.C.S.: 522210

GALFAR ENGINEERING & CONTRACTING SAOG
PO Box 533, 100, Muscat, 100, Oman
Tel.: (968) 24525000
Web Site: https://www.galfar.com
GECS—(MUS)
Rev.: $487,000,292
Assets: $582,359,059
Liabilities: $524,895,569
Net Worth: $57,463,490
Earnings: $3,251,868
Emp.: 23,000
Fiscal Year-end: 12/31/21
Engineering & Construction Services
N.A.I.C.S.: 541330
Salim Said Hamad Al Fannah Al Araimi *(Chm)*

Subsidiaries:

Galfar Engineering & Contracting WLL (1)
Post Box 72218, Abu Dhabi, United Arab Emirates
Tel.: (971) 26336111
Sales Range: $1-4.9 Billion
Emp.: 9,000
Heavy Construction Services
N.A.I.C.S.: 237110

Galfar Pembinaan Dan Perusahaan (B) Sdn Bhd (1)
No 16 2nd Floor Compleks Haji Tahir 2, Post Box 568, Jin Gadong BE Seri Complex, Bandar Seri Begawan, 1779, Brunei Darussalam
Tel.: (673) 2422620
Sales Range: $400-449.9 Million
Emp.: 1,900
Heavy Construction Services
N.A.I.C.S.: 237310

Galfar Training Institute LLC (1)
PO Box 2658, Seeb, 111, Oman
Tel.: (968) 24537049
Web Site: http://www.galfartraining.com
Training & Coaching Services
N.A.I.C.S.: 611430

GALIANO GOLD INC.
1133 Melville St Suite 1900, Vancouver, V6E 4E5, BC, Canada
Tel.: (604) 683-8193   BC
Web Site: https://www.galianogold.com
Year Founded: 1999
GAU—(NYSEAMEX)
Rev.: $39,419,000
Assets: $179,894,000
Liabilities: $6,203,000
Net Worth: $173,691,000
Earnings: $40,809,000
Emp.: 377
Fiscal Year-end: 12/31/22
Gold Mining & Exploration Services
N.A.I.C.S.: 212220
Paul N. Wright *(Chm)*

AND PRIVATE COMPANIES

Subsidiaries:

Keegan Resources (Ghana) Limited (1)
No 15 Senchi Loop, Airport Residential Area, Accra, Ghana
Tel.: (233) 243690224
Gold Mfr
N.A.I.C.S.: 339910
Ben Adoo *(Mng Dir)*

GALILEE ENERGY LIMITED
Level 6 167 Eagle Street, Brisbane, 4000, QLD, Australia
Tel.: (61) 731779970
Web Site: https://www.galilee-energy.com.au
GLL—(ASX)
Rev.: $4,736,210
Assets: $14,233,787
Liabilities: $5,637,375
Net Worth: $8,596,412
Earnings: ($15,139,512)
Fiscal Year-end: 06/30/22
Hydrocarbon Energy From Coal Seam Gas
N.A.I.C.S.: 324199
David King *(Mng Dir)*

Subsidiaries:

Cascade Coal Limited (1)
76 Russell St, Buller Dist, Westport, 7825, West Coast, New Zealand
Tel.: (64) 37894148
Coal Merchant Whslr
N.A.I.C.S.: 423520

Eastern Coal Supplies Limited (1)
22 Treneglos St, Washdyke, Timaru, 7910, Canterbury, New Zealand
Tel.: (64) 36880585
Coal Merchant Whslr
N.A.I.C.S.: 423520

Galilee Resources Limited (1)
Level 2 895 Ann St, Fortitude Valley, Brisbane, 4006, Queensland, Australia
Tel.: (61) 7 38320855
Web Site: http://www.galilee-energy.com.au
Coal & Coal Seam Gas Exploration Services
N.A.I.C.S.: 213113

Takitimu Coal Limited (1)
39 Company Rd, Nightcaps, 9630, Southland, New Zealand
Tel.: (64) 32257642
Web Site: http://www.easterncorp.co.nz
Coal Mining Services
N.A.I.C.S.: 213113

GALILEO GLOBAL EDUCATION
41 rue Saint-Sebastien, 75011, Paris, France
Web Site: https://www.ggeedu.com
Emp.: 100
Higher Education Services
N.A.I.C.S.: 923110
Marc-Francois Mignot Mahon *(CEO)*

Subsidiaries:

Akad Bildungsgesellschaft mbH (1)
Heilbronner Strasse 86, 70191, Stuttgart, Germany
Tel.: (49) 711814950
Web Site: http://www.akad.de
Education Services
N.A.I.C.S.: 611710

GALILEO MINING LTD.
945 Wellington Street, West Perth, 6005, WA, Australia
Tel.: (61) 894630063   AU
Web Site: https://www.galileomining.com.au
GAL—(ASX)
Rev.: $3,668,389
Assets: $32,230,226
Liabilities: $581,744
Net Worth: $31,648,482
Earnings: $2,252,989
Fiscal Year-end: 06/30/24
Mineral Exploration Services
N.A.I.C.S.: 213114
Brad Underwood *(Chm & Mng Dir)*

GALILEO RESOURCES PLC
1st Floor 7/8 Kendrick Mews, South Kensington, London, SW7 3HG, United Kingdom
Tel.: (44) 2075814477
Web Site: https://www.galileoresources.com
Year Founded: 2006
GLR—(AIM)
Assets: $15,699,915
Liabilities: $1,514,142
Net Worth: $14,185,773
Earnings: ($1,824,417)
Fiscal Year-end: 03/31/23
Metal Mining
N.A.I.C.S.: 212290
Colin Bird *(Chm & CEO)*

GALILEO TECH LTD.
128 Halutsei Hataasia Street, 2620120, Haifa, Israel
Tel.: (972) 36441335
Web Site: http://www.wtptech.com
Year Founded: 1974
GLTC—(TAE)
Assets: $59,677
Liabilities: $1,026,385
Net Worth: ($966,708)
Earnings: ($2,439,840)
Fiscal Year-end: 12/31/23
All Other Miscellaneous Waste Management Services
N.A.I.C.S.: 562998
Yehoshua Abramovich *(Chm)*

Subsidiaries:

Pilat Inc. (1)
460 US Hwy 22 W Ste 408, Whitehouse Station, NJ 08889
Tel.: (908) 823-9417
Web Site: http://www.pilat.com
Sales Range: $25-49.9 Million
Emp.: 12
Strategic Consulting, Advanced Technology & Data Analysis Services
N.A.I.C.S.: 541618
Mark Smith *(Pres)*

Pilat Israel (1)
9 Habarzel Street, Ramat Hachayal, Tel Aviv, Israel
Tel.: (972) 37679222
Web Site: http://www.pilat.co.il
Strategic Consulting, Advanced Technology & Data Analysis Services
N.A.I.C.S.: 541618

GALLAGHER HOLDINGS LTD.
Pendragon House, 65 London Road, Saint Albans, AL1 1LJ, Herts, United Kingdom
Sales Range: $50-74.9 Million
Emp.: 135
Holding Company
N.A.I.C.S.: 551112
Charles Gallagher *(Chm & Mng Dir)*

Subsidiaries:

Abbey plc (1)
2 Triton Square Regent's Place, London, NW1 3AN, United Kingdom (95.6%)
Tel.: (44) 1512648725
Web Site: http://www.santander.com
Rev.: $6,986,827,120
Assets: $406,045,174,080
Liabilities: $383,989,012,680
Net Worth: $22,056,161,400
Earnings: $594,681,360
Emp.: 22,139
Fiscal Year-end: 12/31/2020
Residential Housing Developer
N.A.I.C.S.: 236117
Charles H. Gallagher *(Chm)*

Subsidiary (Domestic):

Abbey Developments Limited (2)
Abbey House 2 Southgate Road, Potters Bar, Hertford, EN6 5DU, United Kingdom (100%)
Tel.: (44) 1707651266
Web Site: http://www.abbeydev.co.uk
Sales Range: $25-49.9 Million
Emp.: 50
New Single-Family Housing Construction
N.A.I.C.S.: 236115
Lorrie Sraqalli *(Mng Dir)*

Abbey Group Limited (2)
Abbey House, 2 Southgate Road, Watford, EN6 5DU, Hertfordshire, United Kingdom (100%)
Tel.: (44) 1707651266
Web Site: http://www.theabbey-group.com
Sales Range: $25-49.9 Million
Emp.: 25
New Single-Family Housing Construction
N.A.I.C.S.: 551112
Lorrie Sraqalli *(Mng Dir)*

Abbey Holdings Limited (2)
Abbey House, 2 Southgate Road, Hertford, EN65DU, United Kingdom (100%)
Tel.: (44) 1707651266
Sales Range: $10-24.9 Million
Emp.: 40
New Single-Family Housing Construction
N.A.I.C.S.: 561499
Lorrie Sraqalli *(Mng Dir)*

Abbey Investments Limited (2)
Abbey House 2 Southgate Rd, Potters Bar, EN6 5DU, Herts, United Kingdom (100%)
Tel.: (44) 1707651266
Web Site: http://abbeyplc.ie
Emp.: 27
Investment Services
N.A.I.C.S.: 523940
Lorrie Sraqalli *(Mng Dir)*

Subsidiary (Non-US):

Abbey, s.r.o. (2)
Terronska 727/7, 160 00, Prague, Czech Republic
Tel.: (420) 224 317 970
Web Site: http://www.abbey.cz
Property Management Services
N.A.I.C.S.: 531311

Kingscroft Developments Limited (2)
9 Abbey House Main St, Clonee, Ireland (100%)
Tel.: (353) 18253540
Web Site: http://www.kingscroft.ie
Sales Range: $25-49.9 Million
Emp.: 50
New Single-Family Housing Construction
N.A.I.C.S.: 236115
Nick Collins *(Mng Dir)*

Subsidiary (Domestic):

M & J Engineers Limited (2)
T/a M J Hire Centres Cashel House Cadwell Lane, Hitchin, SG4 0SQ, Herts, United Kingdom
Tel.: (44) 1462429311
Web Site: http://www.mjhire.co.uk
Sales Range: $25-49.9 Million
Emp.: 100
Equipment Rental & Leasing Mfr
N.A.I.C.S.: 532420

GALLAGHER SECURITY CORP.
750-1620 Dickson Ave, Kelowna, V1Y 9Y2, BC, Canada
Tel.: (778) 484-8028   BC
Web Site: https://gallaghersecurity.ca
Year Founded: 2005
AIGFF—(OTCQB)
Rev.: $504,771
Assets: $295,351
Liabilities: $591,894
Net Worth: ($296,543)
Earnings: ($1,702,639)
Fiscal Year-end: 06/30/24
Investment Services
N.A.I.C.S.: 523999

GALLANT VENTURE LTD.

GALLANT MICRO MACHINING CO., LTD.
No 2-1 Minsgeng Street, Tucheng, New Taipei City, 23679, Taiwan
Tel.: (886) 22682216
Year Founded: 2010
6640—(TPE)
Rev.: $148,015,383
Assets: $246,892,443
Liabilities: $145,533,315
Net Worth: $101,359,128
Earnings: $15,389,895
Fiscal Year-end: 12/31/22
Semiconductor Machinery Mfr & Distr
N.A.I.C.S.: 333242
Yu-Wen Liang *(Chm)*

GALLANT PRECISION MACHINING CO., LTD.
No 5-1 Innovation 1st Rd Science Based Industrial Park, Hsinchu, 300092, Taiwan
Tel.: (886) 35639999
Web Site: https://www.gpmcorp.com.tw
Year Founded: 1978
5443—(TPE)
Rev.: $148,015,383
Assets: $246,892,443
Liabilities: $145,533,315
Net Worth: $101,359,128
Earnings: $15,389,895
Emp.: 494
Fiscal Year-end: 12/31/22
Semiconductor Machinery Mfr
N.A.I.C.S.: 333242
Cheng-Hsin Chen *(Chm & CEO)*

Subsidiaries:

APEX-I International Co., Ltd. (1)
308 6 F 6/F No 5-1 Innovation 1 st Rd, Science-Based Industrial Park, Hsinchu, Taiwan
Tel.: (886) 36687070
Web Site: https://www.apex-i.com.tw
Light Emitting Diode Equipment Distr
N.A.I.C.S.: 423690

Gallant Micro. Machining (Suzhou) Co., Ltd. (1)
No 1-A2 Xiecun Road, Mudu Town, Suzhou, Jiangsu, China
Tel.: (86) 51266366699
Industrial Mold Mfr & Distr
N.A.I.C.S.: 333511

Gallant Precision Industries (Suzhou) Co., Ltd. (1)
1F No 56 Songshan Rd, Suzhou, Jiangsu, China
Tel.: (86) 51266616688
Optoelectronic Equipment Mfr
N.A.I.C.S.: 334413

GALLANT VENTURE LTD.
3 HarbourFront Place 16-01 HarbourFront Tower 2, Singapore, 099254, Singapore
Tel.: (65) 63893535
Web Site: https://www.gallantventure.com
Year Founded: 2003
5IG—(SES)
Rev.: $138,351,890
Assets: $1,059,977,277
Liabilities: $493,640,839
Net Worth: $566,336,438
Earnings: ($11,254,260)
Emp.: 1,933
Fiscal Year-end: 12/31/23
Property Development & Management Services
N.A.I.C.S.: 531311
Kok Kiong Choo *(CFO)*

Subsidiaries:

BRF Holidays Pte Ltd (1)
57 Circular Rd 03-01 049412, Singapore, 049412, Singapore

GALLANT VENTURE LTD.

Gallant Venture Ltd.—(Continued)

Tel.: (65) 62933191
Web Site: http://www.albatrossworld.com.sg
Sales Range: $25-49.9 Million
Emp.: 10
Holiday Package Tour Operating Agencies
N.A.I.C.S.: 561520
Dolly Francisco (Gen Mgr)

Bintan Resorts International Pte. Ltd. (1)
3 Harbourfront Place 16-01 Harbourfront Tower Two, Singapore, 099254, Singapore
Tel.: (65) 6 389 3535
Web Site: https://www.bintan-resorts.com
Sales Range: $25-49.9 Million
Emp.: 30
Marketing Consulting Services
N.A.I.C.S.: 541613

PT Batamindo Investment Cakrawala (1)
Batamindo Industrial Park Wisma Batamindo Jalan Rasamala 1, Mukakuning, Batam, 29433, Riau Islands, Indonesia
Tel.: (62) 770611222
Web Site: https://www.batamindoindustrial.com
Industrial Park Management Services
N.A.I.C.S.: 531312

Subsidiary (Domestic):

PT Batamindo Executive Village (2)
Jalan Gajah Mada 9 km 5kp Sei Ladi, Sekupang, Batam, 29432, Riau Islands, Indonesia
Tel.: (62) 77 832 4128
Web Site: https://www.gallantventure.com
Golf Operation Services
N.A.I.C.S.: 713910
James Wee (Exec Dir)

PT Bintan Inti Industrial Estate (2)
Wisma Bintan Industrial Estate Jalan Tanjung, Lobam, Bintan, 29154, Riau Islands, Indonesia
Tel.: (62) 770696833
Emp.: 5,000
Industrial Park Management Services
N.A.I.C.S.: 531312
Aditya Laksamana (Gen Mgr)

PT Bintan Resort Cakrawala (1)
Lj Raja Haji Teluk Sebong Lagoi, Bintan Utara, Bintan, 29155, Riau Islands, Indonesia
Tel.: (62) 77 069 1915
Web Site: https://www.gallantventure.com
Sales Range: $75-99.9 Million
Emp.: 400
Resort Management Services
N.A.I.C.S.: 115116

Subsidiary (Non-US):

Bintan Resort Ferries Private Limited (2)
3 Harbourfront Place 16-01 Harbourfront Tower Two, Singapore, 099254, Singapore
Tel.: (65) 6 661 0234
Web Site: https://www.brf.com.sg
Emp.: 50
Ferry Passenger Transportation Services
N.A.I.C.S.: 483212

PT Buana Megawisatama (1)
Jl Tiban Culindo Lestari 5, Batam, 29422, Riau Islands, Indonesia
Tel.: (62) 778 324 181
Real Estate Development Services
N.A.I.C.S.: 531210

PT Indomobil Multi Trada (1)
Jl Mh Thamrin Blok A1 No1, Tangerang, 15224, Banten, Indonesia
Tel.: (62) 816912029
Web Site: https://www.indomobilbintaro.com
Car Product Distr
N.A.I.C.S.: 441110

PT Indomobil Prima Niaga (1)
Jl Danau Sunter Selatan Blok O/III Kav 55-56, Jakarta, Indonesia
Tel.: (62) 216510050
Web Site: https://hino.indomobil.co.id
Car Product Distr
N.A.I.C.S.: 441110
Hana Ayu Krisnamaharani (Officer-HR)

PT Wahana Indo Trada (1)
Jl Raya Bekasi KM 18 Timur, Pulo Gadung, Jakarta, Indonesia
Tel.: (62) 81298886631
Web Site: https://www.nissan-datsunjakartatimur18.weebly.com
Car Product Distr
N.A.I.C.S.: 441110

GALLANTT ISPAT LIMITED
GALLANTT HOUSE I-7 Jangpura Extension, New Delhi, 110 014, India
Tel.: (91) 1141645392
Web Site: https://gallantt.com
Year Founded: 2005
GALLISPAT—(BOM)
Rev.: $150,176,754
Assets: $208,446,352
Liabilities: $52,820,600
Net Worth: $155,625,752
Earnings: $16,845,929
Emp.: 1,516
Fiscal Year-end: 03/31/21
Sponge Iron, Mild Steel Billets, Re-Rolled Products Mfr
N.A.I.C.S.: 331110
Chandra Prakash Agrawal (Chm & Mng Dir)

GALLEON GOLD CORP.
TD Canada Trust Tower 161 Bay Street Suite 2700, PO Box 508, Toronto, M5J 2S1, ON, Canada
Tel.: (416) 644-0066 YT
Web Site: https://www.galleongold.com
GGO—(TSXV)
Rev.: $78,687
Assets: $21,115,004
Liabilities: $2,744,952
Net Worth: $18,370,052
Earnings: ($760,207)
Emp.: 2
Fiscal Year-end: 11/30/22
Nickel Exploration & Mining Services
N.A.I.C.S.: 212230

GALLERY RESOURCES LIMITED
403 The Waterfront Stonehouse Park, Stonehouse, GL10 3UT, Gloucestershire, United Kingdom
Tel.: (44) 8454503200
Metal Ore Mining Services
N.A.I.C.S.: 212290
Bruce A. Costerd (Pres & CEO)

GALLIFORD TRY HOLDINGS PLC
Galliford Try Blake House 3 Frayswater Place, Cowley, Uxbridge, UB8 2AD, Middlesex, United Kingdom
Tel.: (44) 1895855001
Web Site: https://www.gallifordtry.co.uk
Year Founded: 2000
GFRD—(LSE)
Rev.: $2,240,647,114
Assets: $1,037,411,525
Liabilities: $882,709,806
Net Worth: $154,701,719
Earnings: $45,753,286
Emp.: 3,700
Fiscal Year-end: 06/30/24
Commercial & Residential Construction & Water, Rail & Infrastructure Projects
N.A.I.C.S.: 236220
Kevin Corbett (Member-Exec Bd, Gen Counsel & Sec)

Subsidiaries:

Community Ventures Partnerships Limited (1)
4340 Park Approach, Thorpe Park, Leeds, LS15 8GB, United Kingdom
Tel.: (44) 1134872390
Web Site: http://www.communityventuresltd.co.uk
Property Investment Management Services
N.A.I.C.S.: 523940
Dean Spencer (Comml Dir)

GT (Scotland) Construction Limited (1)
1 Croftfield Court Scottish Borders, Denholm, Hawick, TD9 8QB, United Kingdom
Tel.: (44) 7708338160
Web Site: https://www.gtconstruction.uk.com
Building Construction Services
N.A.I.C.S.: 236220

Galliford Try Building 2014 Limited (1)
2 Lochside View, PO Box 17452, Edinburgh, EH12 1LB, United Kingdom
Tel.: (44) 1312004400
Sales Range: $600-649.9 Million
Emp.: 300
General Construction & Civil Engineering Services
N.A.I.C.S.: 237990
Neil Corker (Dir-Fin-Building North & Scotland)

Galliford Try Construction Central (1)
Leicester Road, Wolvey, Hinckley, LE10 3JF, Leicestershire, United Kingdom
Tel.: (44) 1455222792
Web Site: http://www.gallifordtry.co.uk
Sales Range: $50-74.9 Million
Emp.: 300
Heavy & Civil Engineering Construction
N.A.I.C.S.: 237990

Galliford Try Construction Limited (1)
Blake House 3 Frayswater Place, Cowley, Uxbridge, UB8 2AD, Middlesex, United Kingdom
Tel.: (44) 1895855000
Web Site: http://www.gallifordtry.co.uk
Sales Range: $25-49.9 Million
Emp.: 50
Heavy & Civil Engineering Construction
N.A.I.C.S.: 237990
Stuart Gibbons (Mng Dir)

Galliford Try Construction South (1)
Cowley Business Park High St, Uxbridge, UB8 2AL, United Kingdom
Tel.: (44) 1895855000
Sales Range: $25-49.9 Million
Emp.: 100
Heavy & Civil Engineering Construction
N.A.I.C.S.: 237990
Mathew Pool (Mng Dir)

Galliford Try Employment Limited (1)
Cowley Business Park High Street, Uxbridge, UB8 2AL, United Kingdom
Tel.: (44) 1895855000
Web Site: http://www.gallifordtry.com
Sales Range: $25-49.9 Million
Emp.: 100
Heavy & Civil Engineering Construction
N.A.I.C.S.: 237990

Galliford Try Infrastructure Limited (1)
Leicester Road, Wolvey, Hinckley, LE10 3JF, Leicestershire, United Kingdom
Tel.: (44) 1455222792
Web Site: http://www.gallifordtry.co.uk
Civil Engineering Services
N.A.I.C.S.: 237990

Galliford Try Investments Limited (1)
2 Lochside View, PO Box 17452, Edinburgh, EH12 1LB, United Kingdom (100%)
Tel.: (44) 01312004400
Web Site: http://www.gallifordtry.co.uk
Sales Range: $50-74.9 Million
Emp.: 20
Real Estate Investment Trust
N.A.I.C.S.: 525990

Galliford Try Partnerships Limited (1)
Hodgson House 50 Rainsford Rd, Chelmsford, CM1 2XB, Essex, United Kingdom
Tel.: (44) 1245494849
Web Site: http://www.gallifordtry.co.uk
Sales Range: $25-49.9 Million
Emp.: 130
Construction Engineering Services

INTERNATIONAL PUBLIC

N.A.I.C.S.: 541330
Martin Sharkey (Head-Construction-North West)

Galliford Try Plant Limited (1)
Leicester Road, Wolvey, Hinckley, LE10 3JF, Leicestershire, United Kingdom
Tel.: (44) 1455222792
Web Site: http://www.gallifordtry.co.uk
Sales Range: $25-49.9 Million
Emp.: 18
Construction Engineering Services
N.A.I.C.S.: 541330

Galliford Try Services Limited (1)
Cowley Business Park High St, Cowley, Uxbridge, UB8 2AL, Middlesex, United Kingdom
Tel.: (44) 1895855000
Sales Range: $50-74.9 Million
Emp.: 200
Heavy & Civil Engineering Construction
N.A.I.C.S.: 237990
Matthew Pool (Mng Dir)

Gerald Wood Homes Limited (1)
Homeside House Silverhills Rd, Newton Abbot, TQ12 5YZ, United Kingdom
Tel.: (44) 1626356666
Sales Range: $25-49.9 Million
Emp.: 87
Residential Building Services
N.A.I.C.S.: 236118
Nigel Palmer (Mng Dir)

Kendall Cross Holdings Limited (1)
Mill House West Road Ponteland, Newcastle upon Tyne, NE20 9SG, United Kingdom
Tel.: (44) 1661 824211
Sales Range: $25-49.9 Million
Emp.: 100
Civil Engineering Construction Services
N.A.I.C.S.: 237990

Lintott Control Systems Limited (1)
Blake House 3 Frayswater Place, Cowley, Uxbridge, UB8 2AD, United Kingdom
Tel.: (44) 1603594200
Web Site: https://www.lintottcs.co.uk
Electronic Control Equipment Mfr & Distr
N.A.I.C.S.: 335314

Morrison Construction Scotland (1)
Unit 5 Kingseat Business Park Kingseat Ave, Kingseat Newmachar, Aberdeen, AB21 0AZ, United Kingdom
Tel.: (44) 1651863500
Web Site: http://www.morrisonconstruction.co.uk
Sales Range: $25-49.9 Million
Emp.: 35
Construction Engineering Services
N.A.I.C.S.: 327910
Donald McLachlan (Mng Dir-Building Highland)

Oak Dry Lining Limited (1)
Unit 2 Cowley Business Park, Cowley, Uxbridge, UB8 2AL, Middlesex, United Kingdom
Tel.: (44) 2038273790
Web Site: http://www.oakdrylining.co.uk
Dry Lining Supply & Installation Services
N.A.I.C.S.: 238390
Chris Vladar (Mng Dir)

Oak Fire Protection Limited (1)
Unit 21 Falcon Business Centre Ashton Road, Romford, RM3 8UN, United Kingdom
Tel.: (44) 1708383431
Web Site: http://www.oakfireprotection.co.uk
Fire Protection Services
N.A.I.C.S.: 922160
Bill Bishop (Dir-Ops)

Pentland Limited (1)
3 Frayswater Place, New Bailey St, Uxbridge, UB8 2AD, United Kingdom
Tel.: (44) 1618316500
Engineeering Services
N.A.I.C.S.: 541330

GALLINGER FORD LINCOLN
655 Main Street East, Milton, L9T 3J2, ON, Canada
Tel.: (905) 875-3673
Web Site: http://www.gallingerford.com

AND PRIVATE COMPANIES

Year Founded: 1967
Sales Range: $10-24.9 Million
New & Used Car Dealers
N.A.I.C.S.: 441110
David Gallinger *(Pres & Gen Mgr)*

GALLOO N.V.
Wervikstraat 320, 8930, Menen, Belgium
Tel.: (32) 56521300
Web Site: http://www.galloo.com
Year Founded: 1939
Sales Range: $25-49.9 Million
Emp.: 700
Ferrous & Non-Ferrous Metal Recycling Services
N.A.I.C.S.: 423930
Nico Rosseel *(Chief Comml Officer-Pur Ferrous Metals & Sls Steel Mills)*

Subsidiaries:

Galloo Halluin (1)
Premiere Avenue Port Fluvial BP 10006, 59250, Halluin, France
Tel.: (33) 320234940
Recycling Services
N.A.I.C.S.: 325612

Revival Expansion SA (1)
119 Avenue Du General Michel Bizot, 75012, Paris, France
Tel.: (33) 3 20 23 91 49
Web Site: http://www.revival-expansion.com
Sales Range: Less than $1 Million
Recyclable Material Distr
N.A.I.C.S.: 423930
Vincent Poux *(Member-Mgmt Bd)*

GALLOPS ENTERPRISE LIMITED
9th Floor Astron Tech Park Near Satellite Police Station, Satellite, Ahmedabad, 380015, India
Tel.: (91) 7926861459
Web Site:
https://www.gallopsenterprise.com
531902—(BOM)
Rev.: $1,146,375
Assets: $14,664,562
Liabilities: $254,003
Net Worth: $14,410,559
Earnings: $415,607
Fiscal Year-end: 03/31/21
Construction Contractor Services
N.A.I.C.S.: 236116
Balram Bharatbhai Padhiyar *(Mng Dir)*

GALMED PHARMACEUTICALS LTD.
16 Tiomkin Street, Tel Aviv, 6578317, Israel
Tel.: (972) 36938448 ||
Web Site:
https://www.galmedpharma.com
Year Founded: 2000
GLMD—(NASDAQ)
Assets: $16,629,000
Liabilities: $2,750,000
Net Worth: $13,879,000
Earnings: ($6,912,000)
Emp.: 3
Fiscal Year-end: 12/31/23
Pharmaceuticals Mfr
N.A.I.C.S.: 325412
Allen Baharaff *(Pres, CEO, Founder & Chm)*

GALORE RESOURCES INC.
432 Lyon Place, North Vancouver, V7L 1Y3, BC, Canada
Tel.: (210) 860-9212 BC
Web Site:
https://www.galoreresources.com
Year Founded: 2006
GALOF—(OTCQB)
Assets: $7,383,357
Liabilities: $5,130,746
Net Worth: $2,252,611
Earnings: ($892,642)
Fiscal Year-end: 03/31/23
Gold & Copper Exploration Services
N.A.I.C.S.: 212220
James Michael McMillan *(Pres & CEO)*

GALP ENERGIA SGPS, S.A.
Avenida da India 8, 1349-065, Lisbon, Portugal
Tel.: (351) 217242500
Web Site: https://www.galp.com
Year Founded: 1975
GALP—(OTCIQ)
Rev.: $30,421,972,804
Assets: $17,371,033,887
Liabilities: $11,848,694,151
Net Worth: $5,522,339,737
Earnings: $1,862,723,937
Emp.: 6,715
Fiscal Year-end: 12/31/22
Power, Oil & Natural Gas Services
N.A.I.C.S.: 551112
Paula Fernanda Ramos Amorim *(Chm)*

Subsidiaries:

Beiragas - Companhia de Gas das Beiras, S.A. (1)
Urbanizacao Moinho de Vento Lote 4 R/C, 3510-085, Viseu, Portugal
Tel.: (351) 232439300
Web Site: http://www.beiragas.pt
Natural Gas Distr
N.A.I.C.S.: 221210

C.L.T.- Companhia Logistica de Term. Maritimos, Lda. (1)
Rua Do Acucar Nr 86 Boa Nova, 1950-010, Lisbon, Portugal
Tel.: (351) 218625500
Web Site: http://www.companhia.com
Marine Terminal Operation Services
N.A.I.C.S.: 488310
Carlos Silva *(CEO)*

CORS - Companhia de Exploracao de Estacoes de Servico e Retalho de Servicos Automovel, Lda. (1)
Rua Tomas da Fonseca Torre C, Lisbon, 1600 209, Portugal
Tel.: (351) 217242500
Web Site: http://www.energia.com
Sales Range: $350-399.9 Million
Emp.: 2,000
Gasoline Stations Operation Services
N.A.I.C.S.: 457110

Companhia Logistica de Combustiveis, S.A. (1)
EN 366 Km 18, 2050-145, Aveiras de Cima, Portugal
Tel.: (351) 263470700
Web Site: http://www.clc.pt
Sales Range: $25-49.9 Million
Emp.: 100
Petroleum Pipelines & Storage
N.A.I.C.S.: 486910

Dianagas - Soc. Distrib. de Gas Natural de Evora, S.A. (1)
Rua Tomas da Fonseca Torre C, 1600-209, Lisbon, Portugal
Tel.: (351) 217242500
Natural Gas Distr
N.A.I.C.S.: 221210

Duriensegas - Soc. Distrib. de Gas Natural do Douro, S.A. (1)
Rua Nova no 80 1 andar, 5000-652, Lisbon, Vila Real, Portugal
Tel.: (351) 259 302 050
Web Site: http://www.galpenergia.com
Natural Gas Distr
N.A.I.C.S.: 221210

Galp Acores - Distrib. e Comercializacao de Combustiveis e Lubrificantes, S.A. (1)
Avenida Principe do Monaco 6 2 Dto Edificio Farmacor, 9500-237, Ponta Delgada, Portugal
Tel.: (351) 296205300

Web Site: http://www.energiacprea.pt
Sales Range: $25-49.9 Million
Emp.: 9
Petroleum Product Distr
N.A.I.C.S.: 424720

Galp Comercializacao Portugal, Lda. (1)
Rua Tomas da Fonseca Torre C, Lisbon, 100-209, Portugal
Tel.: (351) 217242500
Sales Range: $1-4.9 Billion
Emp.: 3,000
Petroleum Product Distr
N.A.I.C.S.: 424720

Galp Energia Espana SAU (1)
Calle Anabel Segura 16 Izoda Y 3 Planta Edif V Arroyo De La Vega, 28108, Alcobendas, Madrid, Spain (100%)
Tel.: (34) 917146700
Sales Range: $150-199.9 Million
Emp.: 350
Representation & Trading of Petroleum Products & Chemicals
N.A.I.C.S.: 424720
Joao Diogo *(Gen Mgr)*

Subsidiary (Domestic):

Galp Distribuicion Oil Espana, S.A.U. (2)
C/ Anabel Segura 16 Edificio Vega Norte 1-4 planta, Alcobendas Pol Ind, 28108, Alcobendas, Madrid, Spain
Tel.: (34) 915962100
Web Site: http://www.galpenergy.com
Sales Range: $150-199.9 Million
Emp.: 300
Petroleum Product Distr
N.A.I.C.S.: 424720

Petroleos de Valencia, S.A. (2)
Puerto de Valencia Cl Nuevo Dique Del Este S, 46024, Valencia, Spain
Tel.: (34) 963 67 03 33
Emp.: 12
Petroleum Products & Trucking Services
N.A.I.C.S.: 484230
Ignacio De La Pena *(Mng Dir)*

Galp Gambia, Limited (1)
Independence Drive, Banjul, Gambia
Tel.: (220) 4227434
Liquid & Gas Fuel Distr
N.A.I.C.S.: 457210
Michael Sock *(Mgr)*

Galp Serviexpress - Serv. de Distrib. e Comercializacao de Produtos Petroliferos, S.A. (1)
Rua Tomas Da Fonseca Edif Galp Energia Torre C, Lisbon, 1600-209, Portugal
Tel.: (351) 217242500
Web Site: http://www.galpenergia.com
Emp.: 2,000
Heating Oils Distr
N.A.I.C.S.: 457210

Galpgeste, Lda. (1)
Rua De Alecrim 38, 12490049, Lisbon, Portugal (55%)
Tel.: (351) 213102711
Sales Range: $25-49.9 Million
Emp.: 20
Management of Petrogal's Service Stations Network
N.A.I.C.S.: 424710

Gasinsular - Combustiveis do Atlantico, S.A. (1)
Rua Ribeira de Joao Gomes 53, Funchal, 9050-563, Portugal
Tel.: (351) 291201450
Web Site: http://www.gasinsular.com
Sales Range: $25-49.9 Million
Emp.: 49
Petroleum Product Distr
N.A.I.C.S.: 424720
Edalso Sousa *(Mng Dir)*

Lisboagas GDL - Sociedade Distribuidora de Gas Natural de Lisboa, S.A. (1)
Rua Tomas da Fonseca Torre C 5 Andar, 1600-209, Lisbon, Portugal
Tel.: (351) 218655300
Web Site:
http://www.galpgasnaturaldistribuicao.pt

GALP ENERGIA SGPS, S.A.

Sales Range: $250-299.9 Million
Emp.: 500
Natural Gas Distr
N.A.I.C.S.: 221210

Lusitaniagas Comercializacao, S.A. (1)
Avenida Congressos da Oposicao Democratica 52/54, 3800-365, Aveiro, Portugal
Tel.: (351) 234378600
Web Site: http://www.lusitaniagas.com
Sales Range: $75-99.9 Million
Emp.: 18
Natural Gas Distr
N.A.I.C.S.: 221210
Mariel Rodriguez *(Mng Dir)*

Petrogal - Counselho Fiscal (1)
Rua Tomas da Fonseca, 1600 209, Lisbon, Portugal
Tel.: (351) 213102500
Sales Range: $750-799.9 Million
Emp.: 1,200
N.A.I.C.S.: 213112

Petrogal Brasil, Lda. (1)
Av Governador Agamenon Magalhaes 4775, 50070-160, Recife, Pernambuco, Brazil
Tel.: (55) 8121199900
Sales Range: $50-74.9 Million
Emp.: 80
Oil & Gas Field Exploration Services
N.A.I.C.S.: 213112
Braulio E. S. Guerreiro Amado *(Treas)*

Petrogal Cabo Verde, Lda. (1)
Largo John Miller, Mindelo, Sao Vicente, Cape Verde
Tel.: (238) 2306060
Liquid & Gas Fuel Distr
N.A.I.C.S.: 424720
Abilio Madalena *(Mng Dir)*

Probigalp - Ligantes Betuminosos, S.A. (1)
Estrada de Varzea, Giao, 4600-551, Amarante, Portugal
Tel.: (351) 25 5460000
Bituminous Products Mfr
N.A.I.C.S.: 212114

Sacor Maritima, S.A. (1)
Rua Do Acar 86, 1250 167, Lisbon, Portugal (80%)
Tel.: (351) 218625500
Sales Range: $25-49.9 Million
Emp.: 50
Shipping
N.A.I.C.S.: 488510

Subsidiary (Domestic):

Gasmar - Transportes Maritimos, Lda. (2)
Rua Tomas da Fonseca, Lisbon, 1600-209, Portugal
Tel.: (351) 218625500
Web Site: http://www.galpenergia.com
Marine Transportation Services
N.A.I.C.S.: 483111

Tripul - Soc. de Gestao de Navios, Lda. (2)
Rua Tomas da Fonseca Torre C, 1600-209, Lisbon, Portugal
Tel.: (351) 218625500
Web Site: http://www.galpenergia.com
Marine Shipping Services
N.A.I.C.S.: 488510

Setgas - Sociedade de Producao e Distribuicao de Gas, S.A. (1)
Avenida Alexandre Herculano m 36 - R/C Dt, Setubal, Portugal
Tel.: (351) 212549600
Natural Gas Distribution Services
N.A.I.C.S.: 221210

Sociedade Acoreana de Armazenagem de Gas, S.A. (1)
Rua Maestro Edmundo Machado Oliveira 22, Santa Clara, 9500-732, Ponta Delgada, Portugal
Tel.: (351) 296304700
Web Site: http://www.saaga.pt
Sales Range: $10-24.9 Million
Emp.: 20
Liquified Petroleum Gas Storage Services
N.A.I.C.S.: 493190

GALP ENERGIA SGPS, S.A.

Galp Energia SGPS, S.A.—(Continued)

Sopor - Sociedade Distribuidora de Combustiveis, S.A. (1)
R Filipe Folque 26 4, Lisbon, 1050-113, Portugal
Tel.: (351) 213510810
Petroleum Product Distr
N.A.I.C.S.: 424720

Tanquisado - Terminais Maritimos, S.A. (1)
Estrada da mitrena KM 19, 2910-738, Setubal, Portugal
Tel.: (351) 265535174
Marine Terminal Operation Services
N.A.I.C.S.: 488310

Transgas Armazenagem - Soc. Portuguesa de Armazenagem de Gas Natural, S.A. (1)
Rua Tomas Da Fonseca Torre C, 1600-209, Lisbon, Portugal **(100%)**
Tel.: (351) 219 68 82 00
Web Site: http://www.galpenergia.com
Natural Gas Distr
N.A.I.C.S.: 221210

GALPRES A.D.
Ljube Nenadovica BB, Leskovac, Serbia
Tel.: (381) 16 241 063
Year Founded: 1997
Sales Range: Less than $1 Million
Wire Product Mfr
N.A.I.C.S.: 332618

GALT CHRYSLER DODGE LTD.
2440 Eagle Street, Cambridge, N3H 4R7, ON, Canada
Tel.: (519) 650-2440
Web Site:
http://www.galtchryslerdodge.ca
New & Used Car Dealers
N.A.I.C.S.: 441110
Fehim Zeneli (Sls Mgr)

GALVANIC APPLIED SCIENCES INC.
7000 Fisher Road SE, Calgary, T2H 0W3, AB, Canada
Tel.: (403) 252-8470 AB
Web Site: https://www.galvanic.com
Year Founded: 1997
Natural Gas Processing & Liquids Distribution Products
N.A.I.C.S.: 237120
Steve Aasen (Dir-Fin)

Subsidiaries:

Galvanic Applied Sciences USA Inc (1)
41 Wellman St, Lowell, MA 01851
Tel.: (978) 848-2701
Web Site: http://www.galvanic.com
Sales Range: $25-49.9 Million
Emp.: 13
Holding Company; Analytical Process, Environmental Monitoring
N.A.I.C.S.: 334516
Teri Olson (Office Mgr)

GALVANOTECHNIK BAUM GMBH
Lutherstrasse 18, Zwonitz, 08297, Germany
Tel.: (49) 377545050
Web Site: http://www.galvanotechnik-baum-gmbh.de
Year Founded: 1977
Rev.: $15,386,800
Emp.: 250
Plating & Polishing Services
N.A.I.C.S.: 332813
Bernd Schwarzer (Mgr-Factory)

GALWAY METALS INC.
82 Richmond Street East, Toronto, M5C 1P1, ON, Canada
Tel.: (416) 848-7744 NB
Web Site:
https://galwaymetalsinc.com
Year Founded: 2012
Assets: $10,744,397
Liabilities: $1,096,856
Net Worth: $9,647,541
Earnings: ($4,079,724)
Fiscal Year-end: 12/31/23
Metal Mining
N.A.I.C.S.: 212290
Robert D. B. Suttie (CFO)

GAM HOLDING AG
Hardstrasse 201, CH-8037, Zurich, Switzerland
Tel.: (41) 584263030 CH
Web Site:
https://www.gamholding.com
GAM—(SWX)
Rev.: $190,576,497
Assets: $391,241,685
Liabilities: $224,279,379
Net Worth: $166,962,306
Earnings: ($321,507,761)
Emp.: 541
Fiscal Year-end: 12/31/22
Holding Company; Asset Management Services
N.A.I.C.S.: 551112
Martin Jufer (Head-Continental-Europe)

Subsidiaries:

GAM (Deutschland) AG (1)
Taunusanlage 15, Postfach 17 01 05, 60325, Frankfurt, Germany
Tel.: (49) 695050500
Web Site: http://www.gam.com
Investment Management Service
N.A.I.C.S.: 523940
Daniel Durrer (Head-Sls)

GAM (Italia) SGR S.p.A. (1)
Via Duccio di Boninsegna 10, 20145, Milan, Italy
Tel.: (39) 0236604900
Emp.: 30
Investment Management Service
N.A.I.C.S.: 523940

GAM (Luxembourg) S.A. (1)
Grand-Rue 25, 1661, Luxembourg, Luxembourg
Tel.: (352) 26484401
Asset Management Services
N.A.I.C.S.: 523940

Branch (Non-US):

GAM (Luxembourg) S.A. - Madrid Branch (2)
Calle Velazquez 47 8a Planta, 28001, Madrid, Spain
Tel.: (34) 911400714
Web Site: http://www.gam.com
Investment Management Service
N.A.I.C.S.: 523940

GAM (Schweiz) AG (1)
Hardstrasse 201, 8037, Zurich, Switzerland
Tel.: (41) 58 426 3030
Web Site: http://www.gam.com
Emp.: 1,400
Asset Management Services
N.A.I.C.S.: 523999

Subsidiary (Non-US):

GAM Limited (2)
Wessex House 45 Reid Street, Hamilton, HM12, Bermuda
Tel.: (441) 295 5825
Web Site: http://www.gam.com
Investment Management Service
N.A.I.C.S.: 523940

GAM Dubai Ltd. (1)
Dubai International Financial Centre Office The Gate Village 10, PO Box 125115, Dubai, United Arab Emirates
Tel.: (971) 44019749
Web Site: http://www.gam.com
Investment Management Service
N.A.I.C.S.: 523940

GAM Fund Management Ltd. (1)
Dockline Mayor Street IFSC, Dublin, D01 K8N7, Leinster, Ireland
Tel.: (353) 16093927
Sales Range: $100-124.9 Million
Emp.: 120
Investment Management Service
N.A.I.C.S.: 523940
Kate Rhodes (Asst Mgr)

GAM Hong Kong Ltd. (1)
Suite 3502 35/F Lee Garden One 33 Hysan Avenue, Causeway Bay, China (Hong Kong)
Tel.: (852) 25250015
Investment Management Service
N.A.I.C.S.: 523940

GAM Investment Management (Switzerland) AG (1)
Hardstrasse 201, 8037, Zurich, Switzerland
Tel.: (41) 584263030
Asset Management Services
N.A.I.C.S.: 523940
Lars Jaeger (Head-Alternative Risk Premia)

GAM Investments (Australia) Pty Ltd (1)
Level 39 225 George Street, Sydney, 2000, NSW, Australia
Tel.: (61) 282774132
Investment Management Service
N.A.I.C.S.: 523999
Alex Zaika (Mng Dir)

GAM Investments (Singapore) Pte. Ltd. (1)
Level 11 Tower 1 Marina Bay Financial Centre 8 Marina Blvd, Singapore, 018981, Singapore
Tel.: (65) 66534203
Investment Management Service
N.A.I.C.S.: 523999
Terence Bong (Mng Dir)

GAM Japan Limited (1)
2F Kokusai Building 1-1 Marunouchi 3-chome, Chiyoda-ku, Tokyo, 100-0005, Japan
Tel.: (81) 352198800
Investment Management Service
N.A.I.C.S.: 523940
Shizu Kishimoto (Pres)

GAM London Ltd. (1)
8 Finsbury Circus, London, EC2M 7GB, United Kingdom
Tel.: (44) 2074939990
Sales Range: $200-249.9 Million
Emp.: 500
Investment Management Service
N.A.I.C.S.: 523940
Mark Willmott (Head-Institutional Bus)

GAM USA Inc. (1)
600 5th Ave Ste 200, New York, NY 10020
Tel.: (212) 407-4600
Sales Range: $50-74.9 Million
Emp.: 35
Investment Management Service
N.A.I.C.S.: 523940
Anne Lundberg (Mng Dir-Institutional Bus Dev-West Coast & Canada)

GAMA AVIATION PLC
First Floor 25 Templer Avenue, Farnborough, GU14 6FE, Hampshire, United Kingdom
Tel.: (44) 1252553050 UK
Web Site:
https://www.gamaaviation.com
Year Founded: 2010
GMAA—(AIM)
Rev.: $285,642,000
Assets: $187,802,000
Liabilities: $153,645,000
Net Worth: $34,157,000
Earnings: ($1,367,000)
Emp.: 1,127
Fiscal Year-end: 12/31/22
Private Jet Operators & Other Air Transportation Services
N.A.I.C.S.: 488190
Marwan Abdel-Khalek (CEO)

INTERNATIONAL PUBLIC

Subsidiaries:

Airops Software Limited (1)
1st Floor 25 Templer Avenue, Farnborough, GU14 6FE, Hampshire, United Kingdom
Tel.: (44) 1252984610
Web Site: https://myairops.com
Software Development Services
N.A.I.C.S.: 541511

FlyerTech Limited (1)
Unit C Kendal House Victoria Way, Burgess Hill, RH15 9NF, West Sussex, United Kingdom
Tel.: (44) 1444711560
Web Site: https://www.flyertech.com
Airworthiness Management Services
N.A.I.C.S.: 488190

Gama Aviation SA (1)
Chemin des Papillons 18 15 Depot, PO Box 329, 1215, Geneva, Switzerland
Tel.: (41) 22 761 4444
Airline Services
N.A.I.C.S.: 488190

Gama Support Services FZE (1)
PO Box 122389, Sharjah, United Arab Emirates
Tel.: (971) 545824777
Airline Services
N.A.I.C.S.: 488190

Hangar 8 Engineering Limited (1)
The Farmhouse Langford Lane Oxford Airport, Kidlington, OX5 1RA, Oxon, United Kingdom
Tel.: (44) 18658440
Emp.: 12
Aircraft Engineering & Maintenance Services
N.A.I.C.S.: 541330

Hangar 8 Management Limited (1)
25 Templer Avenue, Farnborough, GU14 6XA, Hamps, United Kingdom **(100%)**
Tel.: (44) 1252 553029
Web Site: http://www.gamaaviation.com
Emp.: 4
Aircraft Management Services
N.A.I.C.S.: 488190

GAMA EXPLORATIONS INC.
1130 West Pender St 820, Vancouver, V6E 4A4, BC, Canada
Tel.: (604) 961-5353 BC
Year Founded: 2018
BBRD—(CNSX)
Assets: $6,304,458
Liabilities: $72,086
Net Worth: $6,232,372
Earnings: ($3,203,957)
Emp.: 1
Fiscal Year-end: 04/30/24
Mineral Exploration Services
N.A.I.C.S.: 212220
Jatinder Sandhar (CFO & Sec)

GAMA PARTICIPACOES S.A.
Av Presidente Antonio Carlos N 51 10 Andar Pte, Centro, Rio de Janeiro, 20020-010, RJ, Brazil
Tel.: (55) 2138043700
Web Site:
http://www.gamaparticipacoes.com.br
Year Founded: 1998
OPGM3—(BRAZ)
Sales Range: Less than $1 Million
Software Product Mfr & Whslr
N.A.I.C.S.: 541511
Norberto Aguiar Tomaz (Dir-Investor Relations)

GAMAKABEL PLC
1 Han Asparuh Str, 4700, Smolyan, Bulgaria
Tel.: (359) 301 62230
Web Site: http://www.gamakabel.com
Year Founded: 1975
Cable & Conductor Mfr
N.A.I.C.S.: 335921
Elka Nikolova Angelova (Dir-IR)

AND PRIVATE COMPANIES

GAMBERO ROSSO S.P.A.
Via Ottavio Gasparri 13/17, 00152, Rome, Italy
Tel.: (39) 06551121
Web Site: https://www.gamberorosso.it
GAMB—(ITA)
Sales Range: Less than $1 Million
Magazine Publisher
N.A.I.C.S.: 513120
Paolo Cuccia *(Chm)*

Subsidiaries:

Cdg Napoli srl (1)
Interport of Nola - Palazzo dei Servizi, Nola, 80035, Naples, Italy
Tel.: (39) 0813119800
Magazine Publishing Services
N.A.I.C.S.: 513120

Cdg Torino e Piemonte srl (1)
Corso Stati Uniti 18/a, Turin, Italy
Tel.: (39) 0114546594
Magazine Publishing Services
N.A.I.C.S.: 513120

GAMBETTI KENOLOGIA SRL
Via Volta n 27, 20082, Binasco, MI, Italy
Tel.: (39) 0290093082   IT
Web Site: http://www.gambetti.it
Vacuum Product Repair Services
N.A.I.C.S.: 811412

GAMBIA TELECOMMUNICATIONS COMPANY LTD.
Gantel House 3 Nelson Mandela Street, PO Box 387, Banjul, Gambia
Tel.: (220) 4229999
Web Site: http://www.gamtel.gm
Year Founded: 1984
Sales Range: $25-49.9 Million
Emp.: 400
Telecommunication Servicesb
N.A.I.C.S.: 517111
Baboucarr J. Sanyang *(Mng Dir)*

GAMBLING.COM GROUP LIMITED
22 Grenville Street, Saint Helier, JE48PX, Jersey
Tel.: (44) 1534676000   JE
Web Site: https://www.gambling.com
Year Founded: 2006
GAMB—(NASDAQ)
Rev.: $108,652,000
Assets: $154,869,000
Liabilities: $35,945,000
Net Worth: $118,924,000
Earnings: $18,260,000
Emp.: 489
Fiscal Year-end: 12/31/23
Holding Company
N.A.I.C.S.: 551112
Charles Gillespie *(Co-Founder & CEO)*

GAME RETAIL LIMITED
Unity House Telford Road, Basingstoke, RG21 6YJ, United Kingdom
Tel.: (44) 125 678 4000   UK
Web Site: http://www.game.co.uk
Year Founded: 2011
Videogame Retailer
N.A.I.C.S.: 449210
Martyn Gibbs *(CEO)*

Subsidiaries:

Game Stores Group Sweden AB (1)
Optimusvagen 14, 194 34, Upplands Vasby, Sweden
Tel.: (46) 859096550
Web Site: http://www.game.se
Computer Software & Video Games Retailer
N.A.I.C.S.: 449210

GAMECARD-JOYCO HOLDINGS, INC.
6F Aise Ueno Building 5-18-10 Ueno, Taito-Ku, Tokyo, 110-0005, Japan
Tel.: (81) 368030301
Web Site: https://gjhd.jp
Year Founded: 2011
6249—(TKS)
Rev.: $239,870,290
Assets: $433,417,700
Liabilities: $73,992,340
Net Worth: $359,425,360
Earnings: $49,905,500
Fiscal Year-end: 03/31/24
Gaming Machinery Mfr
N.A.I.C.S.: 333310
Yasuhiko Ishibashi *(Chm & Pres)*

GAMEFORGE AG
Albert Nestler Strasse 8, 76131, Karlsruhe, Germany
Tel.: (49) 7213548080
Web Site: http://www.gameforge.de
Year Founded: 2003
Sales Range: $75-99.9 Million
Emp.: 400
Online Game Developer
N.A.I.C.S.: 513210
Alexander Rosner *(Founder)*

GAMEHOST INC.
104 548 Laura Ave, Red Deer, T4E 0A5, AB, Canada
Tel.: (403) 346-4545   AB
Web Site: https://www.gamehost.ca
Year Founded: 2003
GHIFF—(OTCIQ)
Rev.: $62,947,030
Assets: $135,466,036
Liabilities: $53,310,415
Net Worth: $82,155,621
Earnings: $15,900,939
Emp.: 27
Fiscal Year-end: 12/31/23
Casinos, Hotel & Multi-Tenant Commercial Complex Operator
N.A.I.C.S.: 721120
David J. Will *(Chm, Chm, Pres, Pres, CEO & CEO)*

Subsidiaries:

Deerfoot Inn & Casino Inc. (1)
1000 11500 - 35 Street SE, Calgary, T2Z 3W4, AB, Canada
Tel.: (403) 236-7529
Web Site: https://www.deerfootinn.com
Casino Hotel Operator
N.A.I.C.S.: 721120
Robin Featherstone *(Mgr-Ops)*

GAMELANCER MEDIA CORP.
120 Carlton Street Suite 405, Toronto, M5A 4K2, ON, Canada
Tel.: (416) 627-8868   ON
Web Site: https://www.gamelancer.com
Year Founded: 1999
GMNG—(TSX)
Rev.: $2,658,901
Assets: $36,974,494
Liabilities: $12,841,507
Net Worth: $24,132,987
Earnings: ($7,988,324)
Emp.: 3
Fiscal Year-end: 12/31/22
Advertising Agency Services
N.A.I.C.S.: 541840
Jon Dwyer *(CEO)*

GAMENET GROUP S.P.A.
Via Degli Aldobrandeschi 300, 00163, Rome, Italy
Tel.: (39) 06898651
Web Site: http://www.gamenetgroup.it
Year Founded: 2006
Rev.: $743,854,676
Assets: $796,231,108
Liabilities: $739,621,509
Net Worth: $56,609,598
Earnings: $9,511,758
Emp.: 754
Fiscal Year-end: 12/31/18
Online Betting & Gaming Services
N.A.I.C.S.: 713290
Guglielmo Angelozzi *(CEO)*

GAMEONE HOLDINGS LTD.
Office Unit No 07 5/F Workingberg Commercial Building, 41-47 Marble Road, North Point, China (Hong Kong)
Tel.: (852) 28669090   Ky
Web Site: https://www.gameone.com.hk
Year Founded: 1999
8282—(HKG)
Rev.: $11,640,750
Assets: $8,173,515
Liabilities: $2,489,693
Net Worth: $5,683,823
Earnings: ($1,418,820)
Emp.: 50
Fiscal Year-end: 12/31/22
Gaming Application Development Services
N.A.I.C.S.: 541511
Liu Yi *(Chm, CEO & Exec Dir)*

GAMES OPERATORS S.A.
Bukowinska 22B/501, 02-703, Warsaw, Poland
Tel.: (48) 782344221
Web Site: https://www.gameops.pl
GOP—(WAR)
Rev.: $1,204,268
Assets: $5,966,209
Liabilities: $1,530,488
Net Worth: $4,435,722
Earnings: $190,803
Fiscal Year-end: 12/31/23
Computer Game Development Services
N.A.I.C.S.: 541511
Jakub Ananicz *(Supervisory Bd of Dirs & Chm-Supervisory Bd)*

GAMES WORKSHOP GROUP PLC
Willow Road Lenton, Nottingham, NG7 2WS, United Kingdom
Tel.: (44) 1159140000
Web Site: https://investor.games-workshop.com
Year Founded: 1976
GAW—(LSE)
Rev.: $479,546,704
Assets: $382,469,724
Liabilities: $115,949,288
Net Worth: $266,520,436
Earnings: $165,641,840
Emp.: 2,383
Fiscal Year-end: 05/31/21
Games Mfr
N.A.I.C.S.: 339930
Rachel F. Tongue *(Sec & Grp Dir-Fin)*

Subsidiaries:

EURL Games Workshop (1)
10 Rue Joseph Serlin, 69001, Lyon, France
Tel.: (33) 487242806
Videogame Retailer
N.A.I.C.S.: 449210

Games Workshop Deutschland GmbH (1)
Am Wehrhahn 32, Dusseldorf, 40211, Germany
Tel.: (49) 21117544090
Web Site: http://www.games-workshop.com
Sales Range: $25-49.9 Million
Emp.: 35
Toy & Hobby Goods Whslr
N.A.I.C.S.: 423920

GAMESQUARE HOLDINGS, INC.

Games Workshop Good Hobby (Shanghai) Commercial Co., Ltd. (1)
Number 153-155 Xujiahui Roa Close by Madang Road Station exit 3 Line 9, Huangpu Area, Shanghai, 200021, China
Tel.: (86) 2133766176
Videogame Retailer
N.A.I.C.S.: 449210

Games Workshop Italia Srl (1)
Via Nemorense 41a, 00199, Rome, Italy
Tel.: (39) 068549821
Web Site: http://www.games-workshop.com
Sporting Goods Retailer
N.A.I.C.S.: 459110

Games Workshop Limited (1)
Willow Road, Lenton, Nottingham, NG7 2WS, Nottinghamshire, United Kingdom
Tel.: (44) 115 914 0000
Web Site: https://www.games-workshop.com
Sales Range: $200-249.9 Million
Emp.: 700
Game Toy & Children Vehicle Mfr
N.A.I.C.S.: 339930

Games Workshop Oz Pty Limited (1)
PO Box 576, Ingleburn, 1890, NSW, Australia
Tel.: (61) 2982961111
Web Site: http://www.games-workshop.com
Sales Range: $75-99.9 Million
Emp.: 150
Toy & Hobby Goods Whslr
N.A.I.C.S.: 423920

Games Workshop Retail Inc. (1)
6211 E Holmes Rd, Memphis, TN 38141
Tel.: (901) 541-7500
Games & Miniatures Distr & Retailer
N.A.I.C.S.: 459120

Games Workshop SL (1)
Calle Consell De Cent 336, Barcelona, Spain
Tel.: (34) 934921700
Web Site: http://www.games-workshop.es
Sales Range: $25-49.9 Million
Emp.: 25
Durable Goods Whslr
N.A.I.C.S.: 423990

Games Workshop Stockholm AB (1)
Master Samulesgatan 67, 11121, Stockholm, Sweden.
Tel.: (46) 8213840
Videogame Retailer
N.A.I.C.S.: 449210

Games Workshop-Square One (1)
100 City Centre Dr Unit 1-854, Mississauga, L5B 2C9, ON, Canada
Tel.: (905) 281-8695
Web Site: http://www.games-workshop.com
Toy & Hobby Goods Whslr
N.A.I.C.S.: 423920
Stan McKim *(Mgr)*

GAMESQUARE HOLDINGS, INC.
3000-77 King St West, TD Centre North Tower, Etobicoke, Toronto, M5K 1G8, ON, Canada
Tel.: (647) 725-7765   ON
Web Site: https://www.gamesquare.com
Year Founded: 2011
GAME—(NASDAQ)
Holding Company; Mobile Gaming Publisher, Events Management, Broadcasting & Production Services
N.A.I.C.S.: 551112
Lou Schwartz *(Pres)*

Subsidiaries:

FaZe Holdings Inc. (1)
720 N Cahuenga Blvd, Los Angeles, CA 90038
Tel.: (818) 688-6373
Rev.: $70,021,000
Assets: $67,238,000
Liabilities: $20,487,000
Net Worth: $46,751,000
Earnings: ($168,534,000)
Emp.: 108

GAMESQUARE HOLDINGS, INC.

GameSquare Holdings, Inc.—(Continued)
Fiscal Year-end: 12/31/2022
Lifestyle & Media Platform
N.A.I.C.S.: 541830
Christoph M. Pachler *(Interim CEO, CFO & COO)*

Frankly Inc. (1)
50 W 17th St 11th Fl, New York, NY 10011.
Tel.: (212) 931-1200
Web Site: https://ir.franklyinc.com
Rev.: $23,677,386
Assets: $6,837,562
Liabilities: $21,838,196
Net Worth: ($15,000,634)
Earnings: ($11,227,853)
Emp.: 83
Fiscal Year-end: 12/31/2018
Holding Company; Chat Technology Platform Incorporating Conversation & Direct Consumer Engagement to Mobile App Services
N.A.I.C.S.: 551112
Lou Schwartz *(CEO, CFO & COO)*

GameSquare Esports Inc. (1)
65 Queen Street West Suite 805, Toronto, M5H 2M5, ON, Canada
Tel.: (416) 309-2963
Web Site: http://www.gamesquare.com
Esports & Gaming Services
N.A.I.C.S.: 551112
Justin Kenna *(CEO)*

GAMEWITH, INC.
Roppongi Hills Mori Tower 20F
6-10-1 Roppongi Minato-ku, Tokyo, 106-6120, Japan
Year Founded: 2013
6552—(TKS)
Rev.: $23,115,170
Assets: $25,673,240
Liabilities: $6,372,040
Net Worth: $19,301,200
Earnings: ($2,293,670)
Emp.: 108
Fiscal Year-end: 05/31/24
Streaming Services
N.A.I.C.S.: 518210
Takuya Imaizumi *(Pres)*

GAMIDA FOR LIFE B.V.
Parnassustoren, Locatellikade 1, 1076 AZ, Amsterdam, Netherlands
Tel.: (31) 205408989
Web Site: http://www.gamidor.co.uk
Year Founded: 1978
Holding Company; Healthcare Products Research & Development
N.A.I.C.S.: 551112

Subsidiaries:

Danyel Biotech Ltd. (1)
Hamada Street 1 Science Park, PO Box 2417, Rehovot, 76124, Israel
Tel.: (972) 89366066
Web Site: http://www.danyel.co.il
Sales Range: $25-49.9 Million
Emp.: 30
Medical Product Distr
N.A.I.C.S.: 423450
Luly Gurevich *(Gen Mgr)*

Gamida Cell Ltd. (1)
5 Nahum Heftsadie Street, Givaat Shaul, Jerusalem, 91340, Israel
Tel.: (972) 26595666
Web Site: http://www.gamida-cell.com
Rev.: $1,784,000
Assets: $102,186,000
Liabilities: $105,135,000
Net Worth: ($2,949,000)
Earnings: ($62,996,000)
Emp.: 145
Fiscal Year-end: 12/31/2023
Biopharmaceutical Product Research & Development Services
N.A.I.C.S.: 541714
Tony Peled *(Founder)*

Gamida Ltd. (1)
10 Ashlagan St, 8671, 8202197, Kiryat Gat, Israel
Tel.: (972) 39277222

Web Site: http://www.gamida.co.il
Medical Equipment & Devices & Pharmaceutical Products Distr
N.A.I.C.S.: 423450
Moshe Reuveni *(Mng Dir)*

Gamida SA (1)
31 rue larks, 96605, Eaubonne, Cedex, France
Tel.: (33) 139598600
Web Site: http://www.gamida.net
Medical Equipment Mfr & Distr
N.A.I.C.S.: 339113
Richard Darmon *(CEO)*

Gamidor Diagnostics Ltd. (1)
32 Shaham Street, PO Box 7803, Petah Tiqwa, 49170, Israel
Tel.: (972) 39277277
Web Site: http://www.gamidor.com
Sales Range: $25-49.9 Million
Emp.: 35
Systems, Chemicals, Reagents & Services to Clinical & Research Laboratories
N.A.I.C.S.: 325990
Yacob Ofer *(Mng Dir)*

Gamidor Technical Services Ltd (1)
6 Hawksworth, Southmead Park, Didcot, OX11 7HR, Oxfordshire, United Kingdom
Tel.: (44) 1235514180
Web Site: http://www.gamidor.co.uk
Sales Range: $25-49.9 Million
Emp.: 16
Biomedical Services & Supplies
N.A.I.C.S.: 423450
Jack Swan *(Dir)*

Savyon Ltd. (1)
3 Habosem Street, Ashdod, 77610, Israel
Tel.: (972) 88562920
Web Site: http://www.savyondiagnostics.com
Sales Range: $25-49.9 Million
Emp.: 55
Diagnostic Kits for the Detection of Infectious Diseases Developer, Mfr & Marketer
N.A.I.C.S.: 339112
Natan Vilfand *(CEO)*

GAMING REALMS PLC
2 Valentine Place, London, SE1 8QH, United Kingdom
Tel.: (44) 8451233773 UK
Web Site: https://www.gamingrealms.com
GMR—(AIM)
Rev.: $19,914,631
Assets: $27,322,600
Liabilities: $9,524,924
Net Worth: $17,797,675
Earnings: $1,702,787
Emp.: 60
Fiscal Year-end: 12/31/21
Holding Company; Online Bingo & Other Gambling Software Developer & Publisher
N.A.I.C.S.: 551112
Michael Buckley *(Chm)*

Subsidiaries:

Blastworks Inc. (1)
113 Cherry St Ste 22893, Seattle, WA 98104
Tel.: (250) 900-7320
Web Site: https://www.blastworksinc.com
Social Publisher Operator
N.A.I.C.S.: 513130
Kevin Potvin *(CTO & Gen Mgr)*

GAMIVO S.A.
Aleja Piastow 22, 71-064, Szczecin, Poland
Tel.: (48) 728877078
Web Site: https://www.gamivo.co
Year Founded: 2017
GMV—(WAR)
Software Development Services
N.A.I.C.S.: 541511
Mateusz Smiezewski *(CEO)*

GAMLA HAREL RESIDENTIAL REAL-ESTATE LTD.
132 Menachem Begin Azrieli Towers, Tel Aviv, 6701101, Israel
Tel.: (972) 36086818
Web Site: https://www.gamla-harel.co.il
GMLA—(TAE)
Rev.: $38,527,420
Assets: $343,659,616
Liabilities: $257,684,483
Net Worth: $85,975,133
Earnings: $12,820,279
Fiscal Year-end: 12/31/23
Lessors of Other Real Estate Property
N.A.I.C.S.: 531190

GAMMA COMMUNICATIONS PLC
Kings House Kings Road West, Newbury, RG14 5BY, United Kingdom
Tel.: (44) 3330140000
Web Site: https://gammagroup.co
GAMA—(AIM)
Rev.: $611,714,214
Assets: $513,506,690
Liabilities: $135,193,133
Net Worth: $378,313,557
Earnings: $62,484,221
Emp.: 1,760
Fiscal Year-end: 12/31/22
Voice, Data & Mobile Products & Services
N.A.I.C.S.: 517112
Andrew Scott James Belshaw *(CFO)*

Subsidiaries:

ComyMedia Proyectos y Servicios SL (1)
Francisco Grandmontagne 1 Ground Floor - Office 2, San Sebastian, 20018, Guipuzcoa, Spain
Tel.: (34) 943316068
Web Site: https://www.comymedia.com
Information Technology Services
N.A.I.C.S.: 541512

Dean One B.V. (1)
Krijgsman 12-14, 1186 DM, Amstelveen, Netherlands
Tel.: (31) 88 500 5010
Web Site: http://www.deanone.nl
Telecommunication & Internet Communication Services
N.A.I.C.S.: 517810

Epsilon Telecommunications GmbH (1)
Ziegeleistrasse 2, 95145, Oberkotzau, Germany
Tel.: (49) 92869404400
Web Site: https://www.epsilon-telecom.de
Telecommunication Engineering Services
N.A.I.C.S.: 517810

Gamma Business Communications Limited (1)
The Port House Marina Keep Port Solent, Portsmouth, PO6 4TH, Hampshire, United Kingdom
Tel.: (44) 3330140333
Communication Service
N.A.I.C.S.: 517810

Gamma Communications Benelux B.V. (1)
Krijgsman 12-14, 1186, Amstelveen, Netherlands
Tel.: (31) 885005000
Web Site: https://www.gammacommunications.nl
Telecommunication Servicesb
N.A.I.C.S.: 517111

Gamma Communications Germany GmbH (1)
Ziegeleistrasse 2, 95145, Oberkotzau, Germany
Tel.: (49) 92869404100
Web Site: https://www.gammacommunications.de
Telecommunication Servicesb
N.A.I.C.S.: 517111

INTERNATIONAL PUBLIC

Gamma Communications GmbH (1)
Ziegeleistrasse 2, 95145, Oberkotzau, Germany
Tel.: (49) 92869404100
Web Site: https://www.gammacommunications.de
Telecommunication Servicesb
N.A.I.C.S.: 517810

Gamma Network Solutions Limited (1)
The Scalpel 18th Floor 52 Lime Street, London, EC3M 7AF, United Kingdom
Tel.: (44) 1372233333
Communication Service
N.A.I.C.S.: 517810

Gamma Telecom Limited (1)
Kings House Kings Road West, Newbury, RG14 5BY, Berkshire, United Kingdom
Tel.: (44) 3332403000
Communication Service
N.A.I.C.S.: 517810

NeoTel 2000 S.L.U. (1)
C/ Fiscal Luis Portero García N 3 Portal 7 Oficina 1-1A, 29010, Malaga, Spain
Tel.: (34) 952641034
Web Site: https://www.neotel2000.com
Telecommunication Servicesb
N.A.I.C.S.: 517810

Schiphol Connect B.V. (1)
Evert vd Beekstraat 63, 1118 CL, Schiphol, Netherlands
Tel.: (31) 88 747 0100
Web Site: https://www.schipholconnect.nl
Telecommunication & Internet Communication Services
N.A.I.C.S.: 517810

Telsis GmbH (1)
Rosslerstrasse 88, 64293, Darmstadt, Germany
Tel.: (49) 6151827850
Telecommunication Equipment Services
N.A.I.C.S.: 238210

VozTelecom OIGAA360, S.A. (1)
C/ Artesans 10, Cerdanyola del Valles, 8290, Spain
Tel.: (34) 902360305
Telecommunication Servicesb
N.A.I.C.S.: 517112
Xavier Casajoana Mogas *(CEO)*

GAMMA-CIVIC LTD
4th Floor 18 Bank Street, 72201, Ebene, Mauritius
Tel.: (230) 4038000
Web Site: https://www.gamma.mu
Year Founded: 1961
GCL—(MAU)
Rev.: $113,903,416
Assets: $154,421,590
Liabilities: $64,501,106
Net Worth: $89,920,485
Earnings: $5,624,267
Emp.: 1,525
Fiscal Year-end: 12/31/20
Building Construction Services
N.A.I.C.S.: 236210
Carl Ah Teck *(Co-Chm)*

Subsidiaries:

Gamma Construction Ltd (1)
44 Erin Park Drive, Erin, Toronto, N0B 1T0, ON, Canada
Tel.: (519) 833-0051
Web Site: http://www.gammaconstruction.ca
Industrial Building Construction Services
N.A.I.C.S.: 236210

Gamma-Civic Construction Ltd (1)
Royal Road Chapman Hill, Beau Bassin, Mauritius
Tel.: (230) 7292088
Construction Machinery Mfr
N.A.I.C.S.: 333120

North Point Holdings Ltd (1)
2309 Seal Cove Rd, Prince Rupert, V8J 3P4, BC, Canada
Tel.: (250) 624-3142
Investment Management Service
N.A.I.C.S.: 523940

AND PRIVATE COMPANIES

GAMMON INDIA LIMITED
Gammon House Veer Savarkar Marg,
Prabhadevi, Mumbai, 400025, India
Tel.: (91) 22 61114000
Web Site:
http://www.gammonindia.com
Sales Range: $1-4.9 Billion
Emp.: 2,982
Civil Engineering Services
N.A.I.C.S.: 237990
Anurag Choudhry (CFO)

Subsidiaries:

AJR Infra And Tolling Limited (1)
3rd Floor3/8 Hamilton House J N Heredia
Marg, Ballard Estate, Mumbai, 400038,
India (82.5%)
Tel.: (91) 2267487200
Web Site: https://www.ajrinfra.in
Rev.: $34,643,291
Assets: $514,939,698
Liabilities: $500,884,252
Net Worth: $14,055,446
Earnings: ($37,766,765)
Emp.: 2
Fiscal Year-end: 03/31/2021
Infrastructure Construction Services
N.A.I.C.S.: 237310

ATSL Holdings B.V. (1)
Orlyplein 10 Floor 24, Amsterdam, Noord-
Holland, Netherlands
Tel.: (31) 205773530
Civil Engineering Services
N.A.I.C.S.: 541330

Ansaldocaldai Boilers India Private
Limited (1)
Door No 719 Pathari Road, Chennai,
600002, India
Tel.: (91) 4445920101
Web Site: https://www.acboilers.com
Boiler Mfr
N.A.I.C.S.: 332410

Deepmala Infrastructure Private
Limited (1)
South T T Nagar Opposite Tin Shed, Bho-
pal, 462003, Madhya Pradesh, India
Tel.: (91) 7552570363
Web Site: www.cbd.shrishti.co
Emp.: 25
Civil Engineering Services
N.A.I.C.S.: 541330
Anil Bilawala (VP)

Franco Tosi Meccanica S.p.A. (1)
Piazza Monumento 12, 20025, Legnano,
Milan, Italy
Tel.: (39) 0331522111
Web Site: http://www.francotosimeccanica.it
Sales Range: $50-74.9 Million
Emp.: 200
Heat Exchanger Mfr
N.A.I.C.S.: 332410
Shiva Duggirala (Mng Dir)

GACTEL Turnkey Projects
Limited (1)
Karmayog Parsi Panchayat Road, Andheri
East, Mumbai, 400 069, Maharashtra, India
Tel.: (91) 2242545555
Web Site: http://www.gtpl.co.in
Sales Range: $50-74.9 Million
Emp.: 135
Cooling Towers Mfr & Distr
N.A.I.C.S.: 333415

Gammon Holdings B.V. (1)
Orlyplein 10 Floor 24, 1040 HD, Amster-
dam, Noord Holland, Netherlands
Tel.: (31) 205773530
Investment Management Service
N.A.I.C.S.: 523999

Gammon India Limited (T&D
Business) (1)
G 55 MIDC Butibori, Nagpur, 441 108, Ma-
harashtra, India
Tel.: (91) 7104265761
Web Site: http://www.transrailltd.com
Power Transmission Equipment Mfr & Distr
N.A.I.C.S.: 221121
D. C. Bagde (CEO)

Gammon International B.V. (1)
Orlyplein 10 Floor 24, Amsterdam, 1043 DP,
Noord Holland, Netherlands
Tel.: (31) 205773530
Investment Management Service
N.A.I.C.S.: 523999

Gammon International, FZE (1)
Hamriyah Free Zone, PO Box 49720,
Sharjah, United Arab Emirates
Tel.: (971) 43411558
Civil Engineering Services
N.A.I.C.S.: 541330

Gammon and Billimoria LLC (1)
Gold Diamond Park Building 2 2nd Fl Unit
221 Sheikh Zayed Road, PO Box 37871,
Dubai, United Arab Emirates
Tel.: (971) 4 341 1558
Web Site: http://www.gb-llc.com
Sales Range: $25-49.9 Million
Emp.: 160
Civil Engineering Services
N.A.I.C.S.: 541330
N. Mukesh (Gen Mgr)

P. Van Eerd Beheersmaatschappij
B.V (1)
Orlyplein 10 Floor 24, Amsterdam, 1043 DP,
Noord-Holland, Netherlands
Tel.: (31) 205773530
Civil Engineering Services
N.A.I.C.S.: 541330

SAE Powerlines S.r.l (1)
Viale T Edison 50, 20099, Sesto San Gio-
vanni, Milan, Italy
Tel.: (39) 0239839801
Web Site: http://www.saepowerlines.com
Emp.: 50
Construction Engineering Services
N.A.I.C.S.: 237130
D. C. Bagde (Mng Dir)

Sofinter S.P.A. (1)
Piazza F Buffoni 3, 21013, Gallarate, VA,
Italy
Tel.: (39) 0331738111
Web Site: https://www.sofinter.it
Heating Equipment Mfr
N.A.I.C.S.: 333414
Abhijit Jagdish Rajan (Pres)

GAMMON PAKISTAN LIMITED
Gammon House 400/2 Peshawar
Road, Rawalpindi, 46000, Pakistan
Tel.: (92) 515477326
Web Site:
https://www.gammonpakistan.com
Year Founded: 1947
GAMON—(PSX)
Rev.: $1,296,940
Assets: $6,378,225
Liabilities: $1,660,152
Net Worth: $4,718,074
Earnings: $260,205
Emp.: 42
Fiscal Year-end: 06/30/19
Engineeering Services
N.A.I.C.S.: 541330
Ali Kuli Khan Khattak (Pres)

GAMSUNG CORPORATION CO., LTD.
4F 162 Bangbae-ro, Seocho-gu,
Seoul, Korea (South)
Tel.: (82) 231401000
Web Site: https://www.virtualtek.co.kr
Year Founded: 1994
036620—(KRS)
Rev.: $90,046,688
Assets: $64,360,696
Liabilities: $25,323,332
Net Worth: $39,037,364
Earnings: $11,568,649
Emp.: 62
Fiscal Year-end: 12/31/22
Computer System Design Services
N.A.I.C.S.: 541512
Choi Joo Won (Exec Dir)

GAMUDA BERHAD
Menara Gamuda D-16-01 Block D PJ
Trade Centre No 8 Jalan PJU 8/8A,
Bandar Damansara Perdana, 47820,
Petaling Jaya, Selangor Darul Ehsan,
Malaysia
Tel.: (60) 374918288
Web Site:
https://www.gamuda.com.my
Year Founded: 1976
GAMUDA—(KLS)
Rev.: $1,783,783,280
Assets: $5,033,716,190
Liabilities: $2,721,216,296
Net Worth: $2,312,499,894
Earnings: $177,084,021
Emp.: 4,219
Fiscal Year-end: 07/31/23
Construction Services
N.A.I.C.S.: 237110
Yun Ling Lin (Mng Dir-Grp)

Subsidiaries:

Bandar Botanic Resort Berhad (1)
No 1 Jalan Ambang Botanic, Bandar Bo-
tanic, 41200, Klang, Selangor Darul Ehsan,
Malaysia
Tel.: (60) 333238222
Web Site:
https://www.botanicresortclub.com.my
Resort Services
N.A.I.C.S.: 721110

Discovery Wetlands Sdn. Bhd. (1)
Paya Indah Discovery Wetlands Centre Dis-
covery Park, Persiaran Cove Sentral Ban-
dar Gamuda Cove, 42700, Banting, Selan-
gor, Malaysia
Tel.: (60) 129321811
Web Site:
https://www.discoverywetlands.com.my
Environmental Services
N.A.I.C.S.: 541620

G.B. Kuari Sdn. Bhd. (1)
158 Jalan Raja Dr Nazrin Shah Jalan
Gopeng, 31350, Ipoh, Perak Darul
Ridzwan, Malaysia
Tel.: (60) 53125010
Web Site: https://www.gbkuari.com.my
Concrete Products Mfr
N.A.I.C.S.: 327390

Gammau Construction Sdn. Bhd. (1)
No 45 Jalan Anggerik Vanilla BF31/BF Kota
Kemuning Section 31, 40460, Shah Alam,
Selangor, Malaysia
Tel.: (60) 351221055
Property Investment Services
N.A.I.C.S.: 531390

Gamuda Industrial Building System
Sdn. Bhd. (1)
No 2 Persiaran Tanjung Kawasan Perusa-
haan Tanjung, 43900, Sepang, Selangor,
Malaysia
Tel.: (60) 38707333
Concrete Products Mfr
N.A.I.C.S.: 327390

Gamuda Land (HCMC) Joint Stock
Company (1)
No 02 D2 Street, Son Ky Ward Tan Phu
District, Ho Chi Minh City, Vietnam
Tel.: (84) 2862529999
Web Site: https://gamudaland.com.vn
Sewage Treatment Plant Services
N.A.I.C.S.: 221320

Gamuda Land Sdn. Bhd. (1)
Menara Gamuda PJ Trade Centre No 8
Jalan PJU 8/8A, Bandar Damansara Per-
dana, 47820, Petaling Jaya, Selangor Darul
Ehsan, Malaysia
Tel.: (60) 374913200
Web Site: https://gamudaland.com.my
Real Estate Investment Property Services
N.A.I.C.S.: 531390

Gamuda Land Vietnam Limited Liabil-
ity Company (1)
Km1 5 Phap Van Yen So Park, Hoang Mai
District, Hanoi, Vietnam
Tel.: (84) 902178088
Sewage Treatment Plant Services
N.A.I.C.S.: 221320

Gamuda Naim Engineering & Con-
struction (GNEC) Sdn. Bhd. (1)
Lot 7882 2nd Floor Queen's Court Block A
Jalan Wan Alwi, 93350, Kuching, Sarawak,
Malaysia
Tel.: (60) 83321028
Building Construction Services
N.A.I.C.S.: 236220

Gamuda Trading Sdn. Bhd. (1)
Menara Gamuda Block D PJ Trade Centre,
No 8 Jalan PJU 8/8A Bandar Damansara
Perdana, 47820, Petaling Jaya, Selangor,
Malaysia
Tel.: (60) 374918288
Concrete Products Mfr
N.A.I.C.S.: 327390

Gamuda Water Sdn. Bhd. (1)
36 Jalan SS221/21, Damansara Jaya,
47400, Petaling Jaya, Selangor, Malaysia
Tel.: (60) 377274879
Water Supply Services
N.A.I.C.S.: 221310

Harum Intisari Sdn Bhd (1)
1 Jalan Ambang Botanic, Bandar Botanic,
41200, Klang, Selangor, Malaysia
Tel.: (60) 333238322
Web Site: http://www.bandarbotanic.com.my
Sales Range: $50-74.9 Million
Emp.: 15
Residential Township Services
N.A.I.C.S.: 531390

Jade Homes Resort Berhad (1)
Persiaran Jade Hills Utama Jade Hills,
43000, Kajang, Selangor, Malaysia
Tel.: (60) 387308866
Resort Services
N.A.I.C.S.: 721110

Kesas Sdn. Bhd. (1)
Wisma Kesas No 1 Lebuh Raya Shah
Alam, 47500, Subang Jaya, Selangor, Ma-
laysia
Tel.: (60) 38 025 0808
Web Site: https://kesas.com.my
Concrete Products Mfr
N.A.I.C.S.: 327390

Masterpave Sdn. Bhd. (1)
16 Jalan Anggerik Mokara 31/48, Kota Ke-
muning Seksyen 31, 40460, Shah Alam,
Selangor, Malaysia
Tel.: (60) 351222213
Concrete Panel Mfr
N.A.I.C.S.: 327390

Megah Capital Sdn. Bhd. (1)
Minara Gamuda Level 17 Block D PJ Trade
Centre, No 8 Jalan PJU 8/8A Bandar Da-
mansara Perdana, 47820, Petaling Jaya,
Selangor, Malaysia
Tel.: (60) 374918288
Property Investment Services
N.A.I.C.S.: 531390

Megah Management Services Sdn.
Bhd. (1)
Menara Gamuda Block D PJ Trade Centre,
No 8 Jalan PJU 8/8A Bandar Damansara
Perdana, 47820, Petaling Jaya, Selangor,
Malaysia
Tel.: (60) 374918288
Property Investment Services
N.A.I.C.S.: 531390

Megah Sewa Sdn. Bhd. (1)
16 Jalan Anggerik Mokara 31/48, Kota Ke-
muning Seksyen 31, 40460, Shah Alam,
Malaysia
Tel.: (60) 351222213
Property Investment Services
N.A.I.C.S.: 531390

Valencia Development Sdn. Bhd. (1)
Mezzanine Floor Valencia Club Elitis
Gapura Senja, 47000, Sungai Buloh, Selan-
gor, Malaysia
Tel.: (60) 361560021
Property Investment Services
N.A.I.C.S.: 531390

GAN & LEE PHARMACEUTI-
CALS CO., LTD.
No 8 Nanfeng West 1st Street Huox-
ian, Tongzhou District, Beijing,
101109, China
Tel.: (86) 1056965000
Web Site: https://www.ganlee.com
Year Founded: 1998

Gan & Lee Pharmaceuticals Co., Ltd.—(Continued)

603087—(SHG)
Rev.: $240,402,778
Assets: $1,489,210,501
Liabilities: $143,386,701
Net Worth: $1,345,823,800
Earnings: ($61,708,103)
Emp.: 4,000
Fiscal Year-end: 12/31/22
Pharmaceutical Product Mfr & Distr
N.A.I.C.S.: 325412
Zhongru Gan (Chm)

GAN KHERLEN JOINT STOCK COMPANY

7th Bag Kherlen Soum, Choibalsan, Dornod, Mongolia
Tel.: (976) 1582 23050
HZB—(MONG)
Rev.: $177,496
Assets: $821,822
Liabilities: $46,364
Net Worth: $775,458
Earnings: $4,084
Fiscal Year-end: 12/31/20
Food & Accommodation Services
N.A.I.C.S.: 722511

GAN PLC

165, Fleet Street, London, EC4A 2DY, United Kingdom
Tel.: (44) 20 72926262
Web Site: http://www.gan.com
Year Founded: 1999
Internet Gaming Software Developer
N.A.I.C.S.: 513210
Dermot S. Smurfit Jr. (CEO)

GAN SHMUEL FOODS LTD.

DN Hefer, Gan Shemu'el, 38810, Israel
Tel.: (972) 46320040
Web Site: http://www.ganshmuel.com
Year Founded: 1993
GSFI—(TAE)
Rev.: $258,633,000
Assets: $217,660,000
Liabilities: $78,984,000
Net Worth: $138,676,000
Earnings: $14,836,000
Emp.: 546
Fiscal Year-end: 12/31/23
All Other Miscellaneous Food Manufacturing
N.A.I.C.S.: 311999

GANANOQUE MOTORS LTD

439 King St East, Gananoque, K7G 1G9, ON, Canada
Tel.: (613) 382-2168
Web Site: http://www.getgm.com
Year Founded: 1976
Sales Range: $25-49.9 Million
Emp.: 55
New & Used Car Dealers
N.A.I.C.S.: 441110
Jamie Hall (Dir-Ops)

GANDAKI BIKASH BANK LIMITED

New Road, Pokhara, 33709, Nepal
Tel.: (977) 61 540460
Web Site: http://www.gandakibank.com.np
Sales Range: Less than $1 Million
Banking Services
N.A.I.C.S.: 522110
Sushil Gauchan (Chm)

GANDER GOLD CORP.

400-1681 Chestnut Street, Vancouver, V6J 4M6, BC, Canada
Tel.: (604) 675-9985 BC
Web Site:
https://www.gandergold.com
Year Founded: 2021

GAND—(CNSX)
Gold Exploration Services
N.A.I.C.S.: 212220
Ian Fraser (VP)

GANDHI SPECIAL TUBES LTD.

201-204 2nd Floor Plaza 55 Hughes Road Next to Dharam Palace, Mumbai, 400 007, Maharashtra, India
Tel.: (91) 2223634179
Web Site:
https://www.gandhispecialtubes.com
513108—(BOM)
Rev.: $20,732,438
Assets: $24,260,968
Liabilities: $2,427,672
Net Worth: $21,833,295
Earnings: $5,675,547
Emp.: 385
Fiscal Year-end: 03/31/23
Automotive Tire Mfr
N.A.I.C.S.: 326211
Bhupatrai G. Gandhi (Co-Mng Dir)

GANESH BENZOPLAST LTD.

Ganesh House A1 Gurudutta CHS J B Nagar Andheri East, Mumbai, India
Tel.: (91) 9321703809
Web Site:
https://www.ganeshgroup.com
Year Founded: 1974
500153—(BOM)
Rev.: $37,109,846
Assets: $51,592,905
Liabilities: $19,276,530
Net Worth: $32,316,375
Earnings: $2,987,303
Emp.: 176
Fiscal Year-end: 03/31/21
Commodity Chemicals Mfr
N.A.I.C.S.: 325199
Rishi Ramesh Pilani (Chm & Mng Dir)

GANESH HOUSING CORPORATION LTD

100 FT Hebatpur -Thaltej Road Nr Sola Bridge OFF S G Highway, Ahmedabad, 380 054, Gujarat, India
Tel.: (91) 7961608888
Web Site:
https://www.ganeshhousing.com
Year Founded: 1965
GANESHHOUC—(NSE)
Rev.: $24,848,332
Assets: $154,410,947
Liabilities: $74,000,562
Net Worth: $80,410,385
Earnings: ($14,367,018)
Emp.: 120
Fiscal Year-end: 03/31/21
Construction Housing
N.A.I.C.S.: 236115
Priti Kapadia (Compliance Officer & Sec)

Subsidiaries:

Ganesh Infrastructure (India) Pvt Ltd (1)
FF Samudra Complex Nr Klassic Gold Hotel C G Rd, Ahmedabad, 380 006, Gujarat, India
Tel.: (91) 7926562345
Real Estate Agencies
N.A.I.C.S.: 531210

GANESHA ECOSPHERE LTD.

Raipur Rania Kalpi Road, Kanpur, 209304, Uttar Pradesh, India
Tel.: (91) 5122555505
Web Site:
https://www.ganeshaecosphere.com
Year Founded: 1987
GANECOS—(NSE)
Rev.: $103,817,218
Assets: $102,000,526
Liabilities: $31,435,663

Net Worth: $70,564,863
Earnings: $5,940,671
Emp.: 2,793
Fiscal Year-end: 03/31/21
Recycling Services
N.A.I.C.S.: 562998
Shyam Sunder Sharmma (Founder, Chm & Co-Mng Dir)

GANESHA ECOVERSE LTD.

P3-211 Second Floor Central Square 20 Manohar Lal Khurana Marg, Bara Hindu Rao, Delhi, 110006, India
Tel.: (91) 9415108158
Web Site:
https://www.ganeshaecoverse.com
Year Founded: 2003
539041—(BOM)
Rev.: $27,600
Assets: $2,711,084
Liabilities: $223,320
Net Worth: $2,487,765
Earnings: ($280,067)
Fiscal Year-end: 03/31/23
Steel Products Marketer & Distr
N.A.I.C.S.: 423510
Vijay Kumar (Mng Dir)

GANGA FORGING LIMITED

Sr No 55/1 P/6 P/1 P/1 Near Shree Stamping At Sadak Pipaliya, Ta Gondal Dist Rajkot, Rajkot, 360311, Gujarat, India
Tel.: (91) 2827252077
Web Site:
https://www.gangaforging.com
Year Founded: 1988
GANGAFORGE—(NSE)
Rev.: $4,014,900
Assets: $4,163,898
Liabilities: $2,565,161
Net Worth: $1,598,736
Earnings: $198,676
Emp.: 47
Fiscal Year-end: 03/31/23
Industrial Machinery Mfr
N.A.I.C.S.: 333248
Hiralal Tilva (Chm & Mng Dir)

GANGA PAPERS INDIA LIMITED

D-8 Sanskriti Prangan Society Baner, Pune, 411 045, India
Tel.: (91) 6386208117
Web Site:
https://www.gangapapers.in
Year Founded: 1985
531813—(BOM)
Rev.: $24,390,947
Assets: $11,281,795
Liabilities: $8,685,389
Net Worth: $2,596,406
Earnings: $564,315
Emp.: 161
Fiscal Year-end: 03/31/21
Paper Mfr
N.A.I.C.S.: 322130
Sandeep Kanoria (Mng Dir)

GANGA PHARMACEUTICALS LTD.

Gangatat Dhanvantri Marg Gopcharpada, Virar E, Mumbai, 401 305, India
Tel.: (91) 2506098333
Web Site:
https://www.ayurvedganga.com
539680—(BOM)
Rev.: $358,810
Assets: $1,045,625
Liabilities: $312,223
Net Worth: $733,402
Earnings: $2,778
Emp.: 19
Fiscal Year-end: 03/31/21

Herbal & Ayurvedic Product Mfr & Distr
N.A.I.C.S.: 325411
Bharat Brijmohan Sharma (CEO & Mng Dir)

GANGDONG INDUSTRY CO., LTD.

35 Yeongcheon-ro, Jangseong-eup Jangseong-gun, Gwangju, Jeollanam-do, Korea (South)
Tel.: (82) 613906300 KR
Year Founded: 1989
Holding Company; Cement, Ready-Mix Concrete & Related Products Mfr & Distr
N.A.I.C.S.: 551112
Dae-wan Kang (Chm)

Subsidiaries:

Gangdong Co., Ltd. (1)
10 Doosan Sinbong-gil, Bongdong-eup Wanju-gun, Jeonju, Jeollabuk-do, Korea (South)
Tel.: (82) 63 261 6827
Readymix Concrete Mfr
N.A.I.C.S.: 327320

Korea Cement Co., Ltd. (1)
35 Yeongcheon-ro, Jangseong-eup Jangseong-gun, Gwangju, 57218, Jeollanam-do, Korea (South)
Tel.: (82) 613906300
Web Site: http://www.koreacement.co.kr
Cement Mfr
N.A.I.C.S.: 327310
Gook-ro Lee (CEO)

GANGES SECURITIES LIMITED

91 R N Mukherjee RoadBirla Building 5th Floor, Kolkata, 700 001, India
Tel.: (91) 3322430497
Web Site: https://www.birlasugar.com
Year Founded: 2015
GANGESSECU—(NSE)
Rev.: $5,192,722
Assets: $54,827,648
Liabilities: $735,436
Net Worth: $54,092,213
Earnings: $1,168,623
Fiscal Year-end: 03/31/23
Investment Management Service
N.A.I.C.S.: 523150
Santosh Kumar Poddar (Mng Dir)

GANGLONG CHINA PROPERTY GROUP LIMITED

Building 11 2177 Shenkun Road, Hongqiao International Exhibition South District Minhang District, Shanghai, China Ky
Web Site: https://www.glchina.group
Year Founded: 2007
6968—(HKG)
Rev.: $2,433,985,794
Assets: $4,376,440,103
Liabilities: $2,805,191,488
Net Worth: $1,571,248,615
Earnings: $99,474,274
Emp.: 402
Fiscal Year-end: 12/31/23
Real Estate Development Services
N.A.I.C.S.: 531190
Ming Lui (CEO)

GANGOTRI IRON & STEEL COMPANY LTD.

307 Ashiana Towers Exhibition Road, Patna, 800 001, India
Tel.: (91) 6122922456
Web Site: http://www.giscotmt.com
Year Founded: 1992
Sales Range: $10-24.9 Million
Iron & Steel Products Mfr
N.A.I.C.S.: 331210
Ramautar Jhunjhunwala (Chm)

GANGOTRI TEXTILES LTD
25A Venkatachalam Co-oprative Colony R S Puram, Coimbatore, 641 002, India
Tel.: (91) 4224332100
Web Site: https://www.gangotritextiles.co.in
Year Founded: 1989
Rev.: $479,225
Assets: $2,583,091
Liabilities: $39,150,731
Net Worth: ($36,567,640)
Earnings: $206,925
Fiscal Year-end: 03/31/18
Yarn, Fabric & Garment Mfr
N.A.I.C.S.: 313110
Manoj Kumar Tibrewal *(Mng Dir)*

Subsidiaries:

Gangotri Textiles Ltd - Unit - I (1)
S F No 496/A 497 Kaduvettipalyam Post, Karumathampatti Palladam Taluk, Coimbatore, 641 659, Tamilnadu, India
Tel.: (91) 421 2362343
Cotton Yarn Mfr
N.A.I.C.S.: 313110

Gangotri Textiles Ltd - Unit - III (1)
Kumbhojgiri Road Village Alate, Tal Hatkanangale, Kolhapur, 416 109, Maharashtra, India
Tel.: (91) 230 2483477
Web Site: http://www.gangotritextiles.com
Cotton Yarn Mfr
N.A.I.C.S.: 313110

GANGWON CO., LTD.
919 18 Poseungjangan-ro Janganmyeon, Hwaseong, Gyeonggi-Do, Korea (South)
Tel.: (82) 266709000
Web Site: http://www.kwb21.com
Year Founded: 1971
114190—(KRS)
Rev.: $107,192,656
Assets: $132,077,234
Liabilities: $99,336,646
Net Worth: $32,740,588
Earnings: $4,051,778
Emp.: 78
Fiscal Year-end: 12/31/23
Power Plant Boilers & Other Equipment Mfr
N.A.I.C.S.: 332410

GANON PRODUCTS LIMITED
Office No 304 Khodal Chamber R B Mehta Marg, Ghatkopar East, Mumbai, 400 077, Maharashtra, India
Tel.: (91) 7208077789
Web Site: https://www.ganonproducts.com
Year Founded: 1985
512443—(BOM)
Rev.: $1,689,683
Assets: $2,529,716
Liabilities: $1,231,305
Net Worth: $1,298,411
Earnings: $1,774
Fiscal Year-end: 03/31/23
Investment Management Service
N.A.I.C.S.: 523940
Hari Prasad Agrawal *(Mng Dir & CFO)*

GANSO CO., LTD.
No 6088 Jiasong Middle Road, Qingpu District, Shanghai, 201703, China
Tel.: (86) 2159755678
Web Site: https://www.ganso.com.cn
Year Founded: 2002
603886—(SHG)
Rev.: $363,235,102
Assets: $441,312,932
Liabilities: $213,527,270
Net Worth: $227,785,662
Earnings: $37,398,938
Fiscal Year-end: 12/31/22
Bakery Product Mfr & Distr
N.A.I.C.S.: 311821
Zhang Xiuwan *(Chm)*

GANSU DUNHUANG SEED GROUP CO., LTD.
No 28 Suzhou Rd, Suzhou District, Jiuquan, 735000, Gansu, China
Tel.: (86) 9372669179
Web Site: https://www.dhseed.com
Year Founded: 1998
600354—(SHG)
Rev.: $141,057,184
Assets: $273,378,414
Liabilities: $170,876,109
Net Worth: $102,502,305
Earnings: $2,809,334
Emp.: 1,000
Fiscal Year-end: 12/31/22
Crop & Cotton Seed Farming Services
N.A.I.C.S.: 111998
Zhou Biao *(Chm)*

GANSU ENGINEERING CONSULTING GROUP CO., LTD.
No 284 Pingliang Road, Chengguan District, Lanzhou, Gansu, China
Tel.: (86) 9316956603
Web Site: https://www.gsgczx.cn
Year Founded: 1972
000779—(SSE)
Rev.: $353,812,212
Assets: $621,932,688
Liabilities: $250,997,292
Net Worth: $370,935,396
Earnings: $31,765,500
Fiscal Year-end: 12/31/22
Fabric Product Mfr
N.A.I.C.S.: 313310
Ma Ming *(Chm & Sec-Party)*

GANSU GANGTAI HOLDING GROUP CO., LTD.
549 Lanzhou Qilihe District Matan Street, Shanghai, 200120, Gansu, China
Tel.: (86) 2168865161
Web Site: http://www.gangtaikonggu.com.cn
600687—(SHG)
Sales Range: $1-4.9 Billion
Holding Company
N.A.I.C.S.: 551112
Zhang Wei *(CFO)*

GANSU GOLDEN SOLAR CO., LTD
Room 2-12 2nd Floor Chuangye Building No 1 Xiyuanjing 5th Road, Suzhou District, Jiuquan, 215200, Gansu, China
Tel.: (86) 51263108878
Web Site: https://www.goldensolarcorp.com
Year Founded: 1994
300093—(CHIN)
Rev.: $580,447,500
Assets: $2,910,689,000
Liabilities: $2,881,868,500
Net Worth: $28,820,500
Earnings: ($411,247,500)
Fiscal Year-end: 12/31/23
Solar Product Mfr & Distr
N.A.I.C.S.: 334413
Xuefeng Li *(Chm)*

GANSU GUOFANG INDUSTRY & TRADE GROUP CO., LTD.
No 4-6 Guangchang South Road, Chengguan District, Lanzhou, 730000, Gansu, China
Tel.: (86) 9318803618
Web Site: http://www.gfbs.com.cn
Year Founded: 1996
601086—(SHG)
Rev.: $105,877,760
Assets: $344,806,745
Liabilities: $128,058,643
Net Worth: $216,748,102
Earnings: $16,579,639
Fiscal Year-end: 12/31/22
Departmental Store Operator
N.A.I.C.S.: 455110
Zhang Huiyang *(Chm)*

GANSU HUANGTAI WINE-MARKETING INDUSTRY CO., LTD.
No 55 Xinjian Road Xiguan Street, Liangzhou District, Wuwei, 733000, Gansu, China
Tel.: (86) 9356139888
Web Site: http://www.huangtaijiuye.com
Year Founded: 1998
000995—(SSE)
Rev.: $19,153,368
Assets: $68,256,864
Liabilities: $49,330,944
Net Worth: $18,925,920
Earnings: $1,033,344
Fiscal Year-end: 12/31/22
Liquor Product Mfr
N.A.I.C.S.: 312140
Haifeng Zhao *(Chm)*

GANSU JINGYUAN COAL INDUSTRY & ELECTRICITY POWER CO., LTD.
No 1 Daqiao Road, Pingchuan District, Baiyin, 730917, Gansu, China
Tel.: (86) 9318508220
000552—(SSE)
Rev.: $1,721,492,136
Assets: $3,816,081,828
Liabilities: $1,945,355,724
Net Worth: $1,870,726,104
Earnings: $444,923,388
Fiscal Year-end: 12/31/22
Coal Extraction & Electric Power Generation Services
N.A.I.C.S.: 212115
Ximing Liang *(Chm)*

GANSU JIU STEEL GROUP HONGXING IRON & STEEL CO., LTD.
No 12 Xiongguan East Road, Jiayuguan, 735100, Gansu, China
Tel.: (86) 9376715370
Web Site: http://www.jisco.cn
Year Founded: 1999
600307—(SHG)
Rev.: $6,263,325,362
Assets: $5,669,912,744
Liabilities: $4,098,912,391
Net Worth: $1,571,000,352
Earnings: ($347,686,026)
Fiscal Year-end: 12/31/22
Iron & Steel Product Mfr & Whslr
N.A.I.C.S.: 331110
Zhang Zhengzhan *(Chm)*

GANSU JOY AGRICULTURAL TECHNOLOGY CO., LTD.
East City Industrial Development Zone, Minqin County, Wuwei, 733300, Gansu, China
Tel.: (86) 9354133138 VG
Web Site: http://www.joygs.com
Sales Range: $10-24.9 Million
Emp.: 65
Sunflower Seeds & Oil Cultivation & Sales
N.A.I.C.S.: 111998
Mingguang Wei *(Chm & CEO)*

GANSU LONGSHENRONGFA PHRMCTCL IND CO LTD
No 138 Jinke Road Dingyuan Town Dinglian Park High-tech Zone, Dingyuan Town Yuzhong County, Lanzhou, 730102, Gansu, China
Tel.: (86) 9312143336
Web Site: https://www.lsrfzy.com
300534—(CHIN)
Rev.: $152,125,042
Assets: $188,267,364
Liabilities: $88,051,096
Net Worth: $100,216,268
Earnings: $8,683,079
Fiscal Year-end: 12/31/23
Chinese Medicine Mfr & Distr
N.A.I.C.S.: 325412
Song Minping *(Chm & Sec-Party)*

GANSU MOGAO INDUSTRIAL DEVELOPMENT CO., LTD.
23rd Floor Lanzhou Fortune Center No 638 Donggang West Road, Chengguan District, Lanzhou, 730000, Gansu, China
Tel.: (86) 9318776209
Web Site: https://www.mogao.com
Year Founded: 1995
600543—(SHG)
Rev.: $15,207,426
Assets: $153,422,844
Liabilities: $24,102,594
Net Worth: $129,320,250
Earnings: ($15,635,197)
Fiscal Year-end: 12/31/22
Malt Product Mfr
N.A.I.C.S.: 312120
Du Guangzhen *(Chm)*

GANSU QILIANSHAN CEMENT GROUP CO., LTD.
1004 10F Tianxing Binhe Times Fu No 1 No 188 Beibinhe East Road, Caochangjie Subdistrict Chengguan District, Lanzhou, 100029, Gansu, China
Tel.: (86) 1057507166
Web Site: http://www.qlssn.com
Year Founded: 1996
600720—(SHG)
Rev.: $1,119,524,988
Assets: $1,644,978,292
Liabilities: $316,572,179
Net Worth: $1,328,406,113
Earnings: $106,482,786
Fiscal Year-end: 12/31/22
Cement & Cement Product Mfr & Whslr
N.A.I.C.S.: 327310
Cui Yuping *(Chm)*

GANSU RONGHUA INDUSTRY GROUP CO., LTD.
No 1 Ronghua Road Dongguan Street, Liangzhou District, Wuwei, 733000, Gansu, China
Tel.: (86) 935 615 1222
Web Site: http://www.rong-hua.net
600311—(SHG)
Rev.: $84,256,307
Assets: $122,738,063
Liabilities: $90,853,530
Net Worth: $31,884,533
Earnings: ($64,380,374)
Fiscal Year-end: 12/31/20
Gold Ore Processing
N.A.I.C.S.: 212220

GANSU SHANGFENG CEMENT CO., LTD.
Xixi Legu Creative Industry Park No 738 Wener West Road, Xihu District, Hangzhou, 310030, Zhejiang, China
Tel.: (86) 57156030516
Web Site: http://www.sfsn.cn
Year Founded: 1992
000672—(SSE)
Rev.: $1,001,749,788

GANSU SHANGFENG CEMENT CO LTD.

Gansu Shangfeng Cement Co Ltd.—(Continued)
Assets: $2,279,561,076
Liabilities: $988,095,888
Net Worth: $1,291,465,188
Earnings: $133,221,348
Fiscal Year-end: 12/31/22
Cement Product Mfr & Distr
N.A.I.C.S.: 327310
Feng Yu (Chm, Pres & Gen Mgr)

GANSU YASHENG INDUSTRIAL (GROUP) CO., LTD.
14F No 21 Yanxing Road, Chengguan District, Lanzhou, 730010, Gansu, China
Tel.: (86) 9318857057   CN
Web Site:
   http://www.yasheng.com.cn
Year Founded: 1998
600108—(SHG)
Rev.: $510,944,298
Assets: $1,226,118,325
Liabilities: $654,015,099
Net Worth: $572,103,226
Earnings: $10,860,108
Fiscal Year-end: 12/31/22
Agricultural Product Processing & Distr
N.A.I.C.S.: 311999
Qing Wang (Deputy Gen Mgr)

GANSU YATE INVESTMENT GROUP CO., LTD.
Jianxin Road Chengguan Town Hui County Longnan,, Gansu, 742399, China
Tel.: (86) 9397521682
Financial Services
N.A.I.C.S.: 523999

GANT SWEDEN
Tullvaktsvagen 9, 115 56, Stockholm, Strand, Sweden
Tel.: (46) 850676000   SE
Web Site: http://www.gant.se
Sales Range: $100-124.9 Million
Emp.: 1,000
Apparel, Footwear & Sportswear Mfr & Distr
N.A.I.C.S.: 315990
Bernard Gantmacher (Founder)

Subsidiaries:

Gant AB   (1)
Tullvaktsvagen 9, Stockholm, 11556, Sweden
Tel.: (46) 850676000
Web Site: http://www.gant.com
Sales Range: $25-49.9 Million
Emp.: 180
Apparel, Footwear & Sportswear
N.A.I.C.S.: 315990
Matthew Wood (Dir-Creative)

Gant Home AB   (1)
Stora Nygatan 20, SE-211 37, Malmo, Sweden
Tel.: (46) 40309270
Web Site: http://store.camp.com
Sales Range: $25-49.9 Million
Emp.: 5
Homefurnishings
N.A.I.C.S.: 449129

Gant Sweden   (1)
Tullvaktsvagen 9, Stockholm, 131 92, Sweden
Tel.: (46) 850676000
Sales Range: $25-49.9 Million
Emp.: 80
Apparel, Footwear & Sportswear
N.A.I.C.S.: 315990
Patrick Nelson (CEO)

Gant UK Ltd   (1)
2 Basil Street Knightsbridge, London, United Kingdom
Tel.: (44) 2072012900
Web Site: http://www.gant.co.uk

Sales Range: $25-49.9 Million
Emp.: 50
Apparel, Footwear & Sportswear
N.A.I.C.S.: 315990

Gant USA Corporation   (1)
64 Beaver St Ste 149, New York, NY 10004
Tel.: (646) 367-5416
Web Site: http://www.gant.com
Sales Range: $25-49.9 Million
Emp.: 10
Apparel Footwear & Sportswear Mfr
N.A.I.C.S.: 315990
Rocco Venneri (Dir-PR & Mktg)

GANTAN BEAUTY INDUSTRY CO. LTD
1-1-21 Shonandai, Fujisawa, 252-0804, Kanagawa, Japan
Tel.: (81) 466458771
Web Site: https://www.gantan.co.jp
Year Founded: 1965
5935—(TKS)
Emp.: 228
Metal Roof Products Mfr
N.A.I.C.S.: 332322
Motokatsu Funaki (Chm)

GANTOIS SA
25 rue des 4 Freres Mougeotte, 88105, Saint-Die-des-Vosges, France
Tel.: (33) 329552143
Web Site: http://www.gantois.com
Year Founded: 1894
Sales Range: $75-99.9 Million
Fabricated Metal Products Mfr
N.A.I.C.S.: 332999

GANTRY RAILING LIMITED
Sudmeadow Road, Hempsted, Gloucester, GL2 5HG, Gloucestershire, United Kingdom
Tel.: (44) 1452300688
Web Site: http://www.gantrail.com
Year Founded: 1965
Crane Rail Products & Crane Rail Ancillary Services; Structural Metal Mfr
N.A.I.C.S.: 332312
Malcolm Trigg (Mng Dir)

Subsidiaries:

Gantrail (Middle East) Ltd   (1)
Jebel Ali Free Zone, PO Box 61428, Dubai, United Arab Emirates
Tel.: (971) 48808079
Iron & Steel Product Mfr
N.A.I.C.S.: 331110

GANYUAN FOODS CO., LTD.
Qingquan Biological Medicine Food Industrial Park, Pingxiang Economic & Technological Development Zone, Pingxiang, 337000, Jiangxi, China
Tel.: (86) 7997175598
Web Site:
   http://www.ganyuanfood.com
Year Founded: 2006
002991—(SSE)
Rev.: $203,675,472
Assets: $281,315,268
Liabilities: $69,886,908
Net Worth: $211,428,360
Earnings: $22,225,320
Emp.: 2,000
Fiscal Year-end: 12/31/22
Food Products Mfr
N.A.I.C.S.: 311421
Binsheng Yan (Chm & Gen Mgr)

GANZHOU TENG YUAN COBALT NEW MATERIAL CO., LTD.
No 9 Xijin Avenue, Ganzhou Hightech Industrial Development Zone, Ganzhou, 341100, Jiangxi, China
Tel.: (86) 7977772092
Web Site: https://en.tycogz.com

Year Founded: 2004
301219—(SSE)
Rev.: $674,039,340
Assets: $1,332,376,344
Liabilities: $142,880,868
Net Worth: $1,189,495,476
Earnings: $38,536,992
Fiscal Year-end: 12/31/22
Metal Product Mfr & Distr
N.A.I.C.S.: 332119
Jie Luo (Chm)

GANZHOU YIHAO NEW MATERIALS CO., LTD.
No 16 Metallurgical Road, Zhanggong District, Ganzhou, 341000, Jiangxi, China
Tel.: (86) 7978334196
Web Site: https://www.yihaonm.com
Year Founded: 2003
301176—(CHIN)
Rev.: $179,822,225
Assets: $292,177,563
Liabilities: $64,594,958
Net Worth: $227,582,605
Earnings: ($4,641,676)
Fiscal Year-end: 12/31/23
Electronic Component Mfr & Distr
N.A.I.C.S.: 334419
Jianmeng Zhang (Chm)

GAON CABLE CO., LTD.
120 LS-ro 45beon-gil, Dongan-gu, Gunpo, Gyeonggi-do, Korea (South)
Tel.: (82) 3180683928
Web Site:
   https://www.gaoncable.com
Year Founded: 1947
000500—(KRS)
Rev.: $1,086,420,528
Assets: $577,038,985
Liabilities: $344,583,869
Net Worth: $232,455,116
Earnings: $8,025,803
Emp.: 453
Fiscal Year-end: 12/31/22
Communication & Energy Wire Mfr & Distr
N.A.I.C.S.: 335929
Jae-In Yoon (CEO)

Subsidiaries:

GAON Cable Co., Ltd. - Gunpo Plant   (1)
120 LS-ro 45beon-gil, Gunpo, Gyeonggi-do, Korea (South)
Tel.: (82) 31 459 6207
Power Cable Mfr
N.A.I.C.S.: 332618

GAON Cable Co., Ltd. - Jeonju Plant   (1)
77 Seogwi-ro, Deokjin-gu, Jeonju, Jeollabuk-do, Korea (South)
Tel.: (82) 63 210 5412
Power Cable Mfr
N.A.I.C.S.: 332618

MOBO Co., Ltd.   (1)
292-1 Galgot-dong, Osan, 447-310, Korea (South)   (100%)
Tel.: (82) 31 831 2900
Web Site: http://www.mobocable.com
Power Cable Mfr & Distr
N.A.I.C.S.: 332618
Tae-gyeong Kim (CEO)

GAON GROUP LTD
8 Ariel Sharon, PO Box 266, Or Yehuda, 6039730, Israel
Tel.: (972) 37954100
Web Site: https://www.gaon.com
Year Founded: 1951
GAGR—(TAE)
Rev.: $175,025,001
Assets: $276,391,486
Liabilities: $153,241,053
Net Worth: $123,150,433
Earnings: ($8,485,426)

INTERNATIONAL PUBLIC

Fiscal Year-end: 12/31/23
Natural Gas Distribution
N.A.I.C.S.: 221210
Harel Beit-Iyun On (Chm)

Subsidiaries:

The Middle East Tube Company Ltd.   (1)
PO Box 62, Neot Hovav, Ramla, 72100, Israel
Tel.: (972) 8 927 4332
Web Site: https://www.tzinorot.co.il
Steel Pole Mfr
N.A.I.C.S.: 331210
Guy Regev (Chm)

GAONA AERO MATERIAL CO., LTD.
No 19 Daliushu South Village, Haidian District, Beijing, 100081, China
Tel.: (86) 1062185286
Web Site: https://www.cisri-gaona.com.cn
Year Founded: 2004
300034—(CHIN)
Rev.: $480,029,476
Assets: $1,016,960,804
Liabilities: $492,032,347
Net Worth: $524,928,456
Earnings: $44,949,108
Fiscal Year-end: 12/31/23
Alloy Product Mfr
N.A.I.C.S.: 325998

Subsidiaries:

Qingdao NPA Industry Co., Ltd.   (1)
Room 21BC Huaren International Mansion No 2 Shandong Road, Qingdao, 266071, China
Tel.: (86) 53283863918
Web Site: https://en.npa-china.com
Casting Product Mfr
N.A.I.C.S.: 331529

GAOTU TECHEDU INC.
Tower C Beyondsoft Building 7 East Zone 10 Xibeiwang East Road, Haidian District, Beijing, 100193, China
Tel.: (86) 1082826826   Ky
Web Site: https://www.ir.gaotu.cn
Year Founded: 2014
GOTU—(NYSE)
Rev.: $382,751,367
Assets: $747,078,772
Liabilities: $272,766,811
Net Worth: $474,311,961
Earnings: $2,018,082
Emp.: 4,002
Fiscal Year-end: 12/31/22
Holding Company
N.A.I.C.S.: 551112
Larry Xiangdong Chen (Founder, Chm & CEO)

GAPUMA (UK) LIMITED
No 4 Kew Wharf 8 Kew Bridge Road, London, TW8 0FJ, United Kingdom
Tel.: (44) 2089692056
Web Site: http://www.gapuma.com
Year Founded: 1999
Commodities Trader & Warehousing Services
N.A.I.C.S.: 238990
Jose Miguel Camara (Principal)

Subsidiaries:

Gapuma China   (1)
New Century Plaza East Zhongshan Road, Nanjing, 210002, China
Tel.: (86) 2584723984
Web Site: http://www.gapuma.com
Commodities Trader & Warehousing Services
N.A.I.C.S.: 238990
Tong Tong (Country Mgr)

Gapuma Ghana Limited   (1)
Plot No 62 Sakaman Odorkor Road, PO Box OS 1385, Osu, Accra, Ghana

Tel.: (233) 26 301 2688
Web Site: http://www.gapuma.com
Commodities Trader & Warehousing Services
N.A.I.C.S.: 238990
Kishor Ubrani *(Mng Dir)*

Gapuma Indonesia (1)
Jl Stm/Persatuan No 42, Medan, North Sumatra, Indonesia
Tel.: (62) 61 785 2073
Web Site: http://www.gapuma.com
Commodities Trader & Warehousing Services
N.A.I.C.S.: 238990
Muktizar Roesli *(Gen Mgr)*

Gapuma Nigeria Limited (1)
28 Mojidi Street off Toyin Street Ikeja, Lagos, Nigeria
Tel.: (234) 1 775 6545
Web Site: http://www.gapuma.com
Commodities Trader & Warehousing Services
N.A.I.C.S.: 238990
Prakash Ramchandani *(Mng Dir)*

Gapuma Romania (1)
22A Nicolae G Caramfil Street 1st Floor Apartment 1V Sector 1, Bucharest, Romania
Tel.: (40) 21 233 1748
Web Site: http://www.gapuma.com
Commodities Trader & Warehousing Services
N.A.I.C.S.: 238990
Ginella Fantaneru *(Dir-Ops)*

Gapuma Thailand (1)
44/13 Moo 8 Putthamontol 5 Road, Bangkratuk Sampran, Bangkok, 73210, Nakorn Pathom, Thailand
Tel.: (66) 2 889 5726
Web Site: http://www.gapuma.com
Commodities Trader & Warehousing Services
N.A.I.C.S.: 238990
Dhanachrist Michael *(Mgr-SE Asia)*

Gapuma Uganda Limited (1)
Units No 18 Tirupati Business Park Plot 1072 Block 211 Kikaya Kyebando, Kampala, Uganda
Tel.: (256) 75 963419
Web Site: http://www.gapuma.com
Commodities Trader & Warehousing Services
N.A.I.C.S.: 238990
Anand Gupta *(Mgr-East Africa)*

GAPWAVES AB
Banehagsgatan 22, 414 51, Gothenburg, Sweden
Tel.: (46) 317626040
Web Site: https://www.gapwaves.com
Year Founded: 1988
GAPW.B—(OMX)
Rev.: $1,985,021
Assets: $12,048,075
Liabilities: $2,365,910
Net Worth: $9,682,165
Earnings: ($5,410,586)
Emp.: 26
Fiscal Year-end: 12/31/20
Wireless Equipment Mfr
N.A.I.C.S.: 334220

GARAGA INC.
8500 25th Avenue, Saint-Georges, G6A 1K5, QC, Canada
Tel.: (418) 227-2828
Web Site: http://www.garaga.com
Year Founded: 1983
Rev.: $63,701,667
Emp.: 200
Garage Door Mfr
N.A.I.C.S.: 332321
Michel Gendreau *(Pres)*

Subsidiaries:

Novatech Group, Inc (1)
1401 Nobel Street, Unit 100, Sainte-Julie, J3E 1Z4, QC, Canada
Tel.: (844) 986-8001
Web Site: https://www.groupenovatech.com

Emp.: 272
Door & Door frames Mfr
N.A.I.C.S.: 423220

Subsidiary (Domestic):

Novatech Patio Doors Ontario Inc. (2)
500 Zenway Blvd, Woodbridge, L4H 0S7, ON, Canada
Tel.: (905) 851-1006
Web Site: https://www.groupenovatech.com
Door & Door frames Mfr & Distr
N.A.I.C.S.: 332321

GARAGE AUBREE
Z D'activite Bois De Soeuvres 6 rue du Champ Martin, 35770, Vern-sur-Seiche, Ille-et-Vilaine, France
Tel.: (33) 299048488
Web Site: http://www.aubree.fr
Rev.: $43,500,000
Emp.: 110
N.A.I.C.S.: 441110
Daniel Querel *(Dir)*

GARAGE AUTO DE L OUEST
84 Route De Gouesnou, 29200, Brest, Finistere, France
Tel.: (33) 298026444
Rev.: $20,400,000
Emp.: 27
New & Used Car Dealers
N.A.I.C.S.: 441110
Rene Pohin *(Dir)*

GARAGE DU BOIS VERT
15 avenue des Cerisiers, 31120, Portet-sur-Garonne, France
Tel.: (33) 561760700
Sales Range: $25-49.9 Million
Emp.: 44
Automotive Repair Services
N.A.I.C.S.: 811198
Christine Renard Richert *(Personnel Dir)*

GARAGE HEINZLE
46 route de Seurre, 21200, Beaune, France
Tel.: (33) 380259043
Web Site: http://garageheinzle.com
Rev.: $23,500,000
Emp.: 46
New & Used Car Dealers
N.A.I.C.S.: 441110
Denise Martin *(Mgr-Fin)*

GARAGE LAMERAIN S.A.S
av 2 av Andre Ithuralde, 64500, Saint-Jean-de-Luz, Pyrenees Atlantiques, France
Tel.: (33) 559513130
Web Site: http://www.garage-lamerain.fr
Sales Range: $10-24.9 Million
Emp.: 67
Used Car Rental & Automotive Repair Services
N.A.I.C.S.: 811198
Franck Esteve *(Pres)*

GARAGE MARCEL VILLENEUVE INC.
1786 du Phare Ouest, Matane, G4W 3M6, QC, Canada
Tel.: (418) 562-0266
Web Site: http://www.villeneuvevolvo.net
Year Founded: 1927
Rev.: $13,347,016
Emp.: 30
New & Used Cars Dealers
N.A.I.C.S.: 441110
Pierre Brodeur *(Mgr-Sls)*

GARAGE VURPILLOT
Les Faienceries Avenue Aristide Bri-

and, 39110, Salins-les-Bains, Jura, France
Tel.: (33) 384730545
Rev.: $21,100,000
Emp.: 39
New & Used Car Dealers
N.A.I.C.S.: 441110
Erik Chopard Lallier *(Pres)*

GARANT INVEST HOLDING AD
Daskal Dimitriy 31 p k 113, Kyustendil, 2500, Bulgaria
Tel.: (359) 78550347
Web Site: http://www.garantholding.com
HGI—(BUL)
Sales Range: Less than $1 Million
Holding Company
N.A.I.C.S.: 551112

GARANT-INVEST COMMERCIAL BANK JSC
Pervy Kolobovsky Per 23, 127051, Moscow, Russia
Tel.: (7) 4956509003
Web Site: http://www.gibank.ru
Year Founded: 1993
Sales Range: Less than $1 Million
Commercial Banking Services
N.A.I.C.S.: 522110
Aleksei Iurevich Panfilov *(Pres)*

GARANTI FINANSAL KIRALAMA A.S.
Camcesme Mahallesi Tersane Caddesi No 15, Pendik, 34899, Istanbul, Turkiye
Tel.: (90) 2166254150
Web Site: http://www.garantibbvaleasing.com
Year Founded: 1990
GRFIN—(IST)
Rev.: $80,307,887
Assets: $685,819,802
Liabilities: $569,279,393
Net Worth: $116,540,409
Earnings: $43,732,854
Fiscal Year-end: 12/31/22
Financial Investment Services
N.A.I.C.S.: 523999
Unal Gokmen *(Gen Mgr)*

Subsidiaries:

Garanti BBVA Filo Yonetim Hizmetleri A.S. (1)
Camcesme Mahallesi Tersane Caddesi No 15 K 3, Pendik, 34899, Istanbul, Turkiye
Tel.: (90) 2166254500
Web Site: https://www.garantibbvafilo.com.tr
Vehicle Leasing Services
N.A.I.C.S.: 532112

GARANTI KOZA INSAAT SANAYI VE TICARET A.S.
Tekstilkent Koza Plaza A Blok Kat 34, 34235, Istanbul, Esenler, Turkiye
Tel.: (90) 2124672222
Web Site: http://www.garantikoza.com.tr
Year Founded: 1948
Sales Range: $250-299.9 Million
Emp.: 1,750
Construction Services
N.A.I.C.S.: 237990
Mehmet Sukru Ilkel *(Chm)*

Subsidiaries:

GARANTI KOZA Construction Industry and Commerce Co. Inc. (1)
Tekstilkent Koza Plaza A Blok Kat 34, 34235, Istanbul, Turkiye
Tel.: (90) 2124672222
Civil Construction Services
N.A.I.C.S.: 236116
Mehmet Sukru Ilkel *(Chm)*

GARANTI YATIRIM ORTAKLIGI AS
Maslak Mah Ataturk Oto Sanayi 55 Sokak 42 Maslak No 2 A, Blok D 270 A1207 Sariyer, 34485, Istanbul, Turkiye
Tel.: (90) 2123353095
Web Site: https://www.gyo.com.tr
Year Founded: 1996
GRNYO—(IST)
Sales Range: Less than $1 Million
Emp.: 9
Financial Investment Services
N.A.I.C.S.: 523999
Mehmet Reha Tanor *(Chm & Gen Mgr)*

GARBI FINVEST LTD
A502 A-Wing 5th Floor Shubham Centre-1 Cardinal Gracious Road, Chakala Andheri East, Mumbai, 400093, Maharashtra, India
Tel.: (91) 3340142800
Web Site: https://www.gptl.in
Year Founded: 1982
17148—(KOL)
Rev.: $810,947
Assets: $9,064,121
Liabilities: $351,921
Net Worth: $8,712,200
Earnings: $520,448
Emp.: 10
Fiscal Year-end: 03/31/23
Financial Support Services
N.A.I.C.S.: 523999
Richa Agarwalla *(Compliance Officer & Sec)*

GARBUIO S.P.A.
Via Enrico Azzi 1 Paese, 31038, Treviso, Italy
Tel.: (39) 0422431140
Web Site: http://www.garbuiodickinson.eu
Year Founded: 1988
Tobacco Processing Machinery Mfr
N.A.I.C.S.: 333111
Mansueto Favaro *(Co-CEO)*

Subsidiaries:

Dickinson Legg Inc. (1)
7863 Redpine Rd, Richmond, VA 23237
Tel.: (804) 279-0020
Web Site: http://www.garbuiodickinson.eu
Sales Range: $25-49.9 Million
Emp.: 5
Tobacco Process Equipment Mfr
N.A.I.C.S.: 312230
Sandy Lindsey *(Mgr-Ops)*

Dickinson Legg Ltd. (1)
Moorside Rd, Winchester, SO23 7SS, Hampshire, United Kingdom
Tel.: (44) 1962 842222
Web Site: http://www.garbuiodickinson.eu
Sales Range: $100-124.9 Million
Emp.: 100
Tobacco Process Equipment Mfr
N.A.I.C.S.: 312230
David G. Heath *(Mng Dir)*

GARDA CAPITAL GROUP
Level 21 12 Creek Street, Brisbane, 4000, QLD, Australia
Tel.: (61) 730025300 AU
Web Site: http://www.gardacapital.com.au
Year Founded: 2000
Rev.: $15,037,701
Assets: $226,817,418
Liabilities: $87,980,735
Net Worth: $138,836,683
Earnings: $18,857,419
Fiscal Year-end: 06/30/18
Property Fund Management Services
N.A.I.C.S.: 523940
Matthew Madsen *(Chm & Mng Dir)*

GARDA PROPERTY GROUP

Garda Capital Group—(Continued)

GARDA PROPERTY GROUP
Level 21 12 Creek St, Brisbane, 4000, QLD, Australia
Tel.: (61) 730025300   AU
Web Site:
https://www.gardaproperty.com.au
Year Founded: 2003
GDF—(ASX)
Rev.: $21,263,611
Assets: $419,243,007
Liabilities: $152,979,070
Net Worth: $266,263,937
Earnings: ($3,217,057)
Emp.: 16
Fiscal Year-end: 06/30/23
Property Management Services
N.A.I.C.S.: 531311
Lachlan Davidson *(Gen Counsel)*

GARDANNE AUTOMOBILES
92 bis Boulevard Jean Jaures, PO Box 47046, Nimes, Cedex, France
Tel.: (33) 442949596
Rev.: $22,100,000
Emp.: 50
New & Used Car Dealers
N.A.I.C.S.: 441110
Michel Isnardon *(Mng Dir, Mng Dir & Chm)*

GARDEN HOTEL SHANGHAI
58 Maoming Rd, Shanghai, 200020, China
Tel.: (86) 2164151111
Web Site:
http://www.gardenhotelshanghai.com
Sales Range: $75-99.9 Million
Emp.: 800
Hotel Facilities & Accommodations
N.A.I.C.S.: 721110
Frank Zhu *(Dir-Mktg)*

GARDEN REACH SHIPBUILDERS & ENGINEERS LTD.
61 Garden Reach Road, Kolkata, 700024, India
Tel.: (91) 3324698101
Web Site: https://www.grse.in
Year Founded: 1934
542011—(BOM)
Rev.: $331,272,777
Assets: $1,292,000,815
Liabilities: $1,122,488,496
Net Worth: $169,512,319
Earnings: $27,351,358
Emp.: 1,744
Fiscal Year-end: 03/31/23
Soil Engineering Services
N.A.I.C.S.: 541330
Arup Ratan Pal *(Gen Mgr-Technical)*

GARDINIA HOME DECOR GMBH
Neutrauchburger Strasse 20, 88316, Isny, Germany
Tel.: (49) 75629850
Web Site: http://www.gardinia.de
Sales Range: $150-199.9 Million
Emp.: 500
Window Treatment Mfr
N.A.I.C.S.: 337920
Reinhard Heidemann *(Mng Dir)*

GARDRUM HOLDINGS LIMITED
72-74 Omagh Road, Dromore, BT78 3AJ, County Tyrone, United Kingdom
Tel.: (44) 2882 898262
Holding Company
N.A.I.C.S.: 551112
Paddi Georgina Keys *(Sec)*

Subsidiaries:

Euro Auctions (UK) Ltd. (1)
72-74 Omagh Road, Dromore, BT78 3AJ, County Tyrone, United Kingdom
Tel.: (44) 2882 898262
Web Site: http://www.euroauctions.com
Auctioneers
N.A.I.C.S.: 459999
Jonnie Keys *(Gen Mgr & Mgr-Ops)*

Subsidiary (US):

Yoder & Frey Auctioneers LLC (2)
1670 Commerce Rd, Holland, OH 43528-1144
Tel.: (419) 865-3990
Web Site: http://www.yoderandfrey.com
Auctioneers
N.A.I.C.S.: 459999
V. Peter Clark *(Pres)*

GARELLI SA
724 Route de Grenoble, 6200, Nice, Alpes Maritimes, France
Tel.: (33) 493298808
Web Site: http://www.garelli-sa.com
Year Founded: 1959
Sales Range: $25-49.9 Million
Emp.: 100
Excavation & Site Preparation Contractors
N.A.I.C.S.: 238910
Joseph Garelli *(Chm & Mng Dir)*

GARG FURNACE LTD.
Kanganwal Road VPO Jugiana G T Road, Ludhiana, 141 120, India
Tel.: (91) 1614692500
Web Site: https://www.gargltd.com
530615—(BOM)
Rev.: $28,589,257
Assets: $7,047,227
Liabilities: $4,565,626
Net Worth: $2,481,602
Earnings: $712,128
Emp.: 74
Fiscal Year-end: 03/31/23
Textile Yarn Product Mfr
N.A.I.C.S.: 314999
Sanjeev Garg *(Mng Dir)*

Subsidiaries:

Garg International Private Limited (1)
S-445/2 School Block Shakarpur, Delhi, 110092, India
Tel.: (91) 1122493096
Surgical Equipment Distr
N.A.I.C.S.: 423450

GARIBALDI RESOURCES CORP.
Suite 1150 409 Granville Street, Vancouver, V6C 1T2, BC, Canada
Tel.: (604) 488-8851   AB
Web Site:
https://garibaldiresourcescorp.com
Year Founded: 1993
GGI—(OTCIQ)
Rev.: $43,902
Assets: $33,900,546
Liabilities: $2,897,384
Net Worth: $31,003,162
Earnings: ($1,448,269)
Fiscal Year-end: 01/31/22
Mineral Exploration Services
N.A.I.C.S.: 212220
Steve Regoci *(Pres & CEO)*

Subsidiaries:

Minera Pender S.A de C.V. (1)
Articulo 123 No 203 Col Ley 57, 83100, Hermosillo, 83100, Sonora, Mexico
Tel.: (52) 6622070563
Copper & Gold Mining Services
N.A.I.C.S.: 212220

GARIMA BIKAS BANK LIMITED
Lazimpat, Kathmandu, 02, Nepal
Tel.: (977) 14545424

Web Site:
https://www.garimabank.com.np
GBBL—(NEP)
Rev.: $81,003,660
Assets: $676,521,254
Liabilities: $616,799,939
Net Worth: $59,721,315
Earnings: $9,564,439
Emp.: 1,038
Fiscal Year-end: 07/16/23
Banking Services
N.A.I.C.S.: 522110
Shaym Prashad Basyal *(Chm)*

GARLON POLYFAB INDUSTRIES LTD.
14/102 A 1st Floor 2 Civil Lines Near Lal Imli, Kanpur, 208001, Uttar Pradesh, India
Tel.: (91) 512290773
Textile Products Mfr
N.A.I.C.S.: 314999

GARMENT MANTRA LIFESTYLE LTD.
No 15 Murthy s Plaza Karia Gounder Street, Khaderpet, Tirupur, 641 601, Tamil Nadu, India
Tel.: (91) 4212231896
Web Site:
https://www.garmentmantra.com
Year Founded: 2011
539216—(BOM)
Rev.: $20,649,637
Assets: $11,953,348
Liabilities: $7,753,228
Net Worth: $4,200,120
Earnings: $110,653
Emp.: 53
Fiscal Year-end: 03/31/23
Children's, Women's, Men's, Girls' & Boys' Garment Mfr & Distr
N.A.I.C.S.: 315250
Prem Dinanth Aggarwal *(Chm & Mng Dir)*

GARMEX SAIGON CORPORATION
252 Nguyen Van Luong Ward 17, Go Vap District, Ho Chi Minh City, Vietnam
Tel.: (84) 839844822
Web Site: https://www.garmex.vn
Year Founded: 1976
GMC—(HOSE)
Rev.: $341,836
Assets: $17,266,014
Liabilities: $1,100,040
Net Worth: $16,165,974
Earnings: ($2,140,134)
Emp.: 4,000
Fiscal Year-end: 12/31/23
Garments Mfr
N.A.I.C.S.: 314999

Subsidiaries:

Saigon Garment Manufacturing Trading Joint Stock Company - An Nhon Garment Factory (1)
252 Nguyen Van Luong street, Ward 17 Go Vap District, Ho Chi Minh City, Vietnam
Tel.: (84) 8 3984 4822
Emp.: 1,000
Sportswear Mfr
N.A.I.C.S.: 315250
Nguyen An *(Gen Mgr)*

GARMIN LTD.
Muhlentalstrasse 2, 8200, Schaffhausen, Switzerland   CH
Web Site: https://www.garmin.co.in
Year Founded: 1989
GRMN—(NYSE)
Rev.: $5,228,252,000
Assets: $8,603,569,000
Liabilities: $1,591,509,000
Net Worth: $7,012,060,000

INTERNATIONAL PUBLIC

Earnings: $1,289,636,000
Emp.: 19,900
Fiscal Year-end: 12/30/23
Consumer Electronics & Navigation Communications & Information Devices Mfr
N.A.I.C.S.: 334511
Min-Hwan Kao *(Co-Founder & Exec Chm)*

Subsidiaries:

AeroNavData, Inc. (1)
9735 Landmark Pkwy Ste 200, Saint Louis, MO 63127
Tel.: (618) 281-8986
Aeronautical Navigation Database Services
N.A.I.C.S.: 488190
Leah Wood *(Mgr-Mktg & Bus Dev)*

Garmin (Thailand) Ltd. (1)
1788 Singha Complex Building 31st Floor Unit 3107-3109, New Petchaburi Road Bangkapi Huai Kwang, Bangkok, 10310, Thailand
Tel.: (66) 22628999
Navigation & Communication Equipment Mfr
N.A.I.C.S.: 334511

Garmin Argentina SRL (1)
Av de Los Lagos 7010 Local 116 1670 Tigre, Belgrano, B1670, Buenos Aires, Capital Federal, Argentina
Tel.: (54) 8103454477
Detection & Aeronautical Instrument Mfr
N.A.I.C.S.: 334511

Garmin Chile Lda (1)
Mall Open Kennedy Av Presidente Kennedy 5601 Level 3 Local L3-06, Las Condes, Chile
Tel.: (56) 224556855
Web Site: https://www.garmin.com
Navigation & Communication Device Mfr
N.A.I.C.S.: 334511

Garmin China Co. Ltd. (1)
Room 201 Floor 2 North Of Zhaoweitalou No 14 Jiuxianqiao Road, Chaoyang District, Beijing, 100015, China
Tel.: (86) 1084475550
Navigation Communications & Information Devices Mfr
N.A.I.C.S.: 334511

Garmin Czech s.r.o (1)
Evropska 16/176, Vokovice, 160 00, Prague, 6, Czech Republic
Tel.: (420) 253253380
Detection & Aeronautical Instrument Mfr
N.A.I.C.S.: 334511

Garmin Hrvatska d.o.o. (1)
Karlovacka cesta 4K, 10000, Zagreb, Croatia
Tel.: (385) 12334033
Detection & Aeronautical Instrument Mfr
N.A.I.C.S.: 334511
Ana Colic *(Mgr-Mktg)*

Garmin Iberia S.A. (1)
C / Riera Montalegre 50, 8916, Badalona, Spain
Tel.: (34) 902007097
Web Site: http://www.garmin.com
Navigation Communications & Information Devices Mfr
N.A.I.C.S.: 334511

Garmin International, Inc. (1)
1200 E 151st St, Olathe, KS 66062-3426
Tel.: (913) 397-8200
Web Site: https://www.garmin.com
Sales Range: $400-449.9 Million
Emp.: 1,100
Navigation Communications & Information Devices
N.A.I.C.S.: 334511
Min-Hwan Kao *(Chm)*

Subsidiary (Domestic):

DeLorme Publishing Company, Inc. (2)
2 Delorme Dr, Yarmouth, ME 04096
Web Site: http://www.delorme.com
Software Publisher
N.A.I.C.S.: 513210

AND PRIVATE COMPANIES

GARODIA CHEMICALS LIMITED

Subsidiary (Non-US):

Dynastream Innovations Inc. (2)
100 Grande Boulevard Suite 201, Cochrane, T4C 0S4, AB, Canada
Tel.: (403) 932-9292
Web Site: http://www.dynastream.com
Sales Range: $25-49.9 Million
Emp.: 96
Wireless Device Design Services
N.A.I.C.S.: 334220

Garmin (Asia) Corporation (2)
No 68 Zhangshu 2nd Rd Xizhi Dist, Taipei, 00221, Taiwan
Tel.: (886) 2 26429199
Web Site: http://www.garmin.com.sg
Sales Range: $350-399.9 Million
Navigation Equipment Mfr
N.A.I.C.S.: 334220

Garmin (Europe) Ltd. (2)
Liberty House, Hounsdown Business Park, Southampton, SO40 9LR, United Kingdom (100%)
Tel.: (44) 2380524000
Sales Range: $25-49.9 Million
Emp.: 150
Navigation Communications & Information Devices
N.A.I.C.S.: 334511

Subsidiary (Non-US):

Garmin Austria GmbH (3)
Hauptstrasse 12, 8141, Nestelbach, Austria
Tel.: (43) 313331810
Web Site: http://www.garmin.at
Sales Range: $25-49.9 Million
Emp.: 30
Global Positioning System Distr
N.A.I.C.S.: 334511

Garmin Belux N.V./S.A (3)
Pierre Dupontstraat 165, 1140, Brussels, Belgium
Tel.: (32) 26725254
Web Site: https://www.garmin.com
Sales Range: $25-49.9 Million
Emp.: 25
Electronic Navigation Products Distr
N.A.I.C.S.: 423690

Garmin Suomi Oy (3)
Station Slope 9, Lohja, 8500, Finland
Tel.: (358) 19311001
Web Site: http://www.garmin.com
Sales Range: $50-74.9 Million
Emp.: 7
Electronic Navigation Products Distr
N.A.I.C.S.: 423690

Subsidiary (Domestic):

Garmin AT, Inc. (2)
2345 Turner Rd SE, Salem, OR 97302
Tel.: (503) 391-3411
Web Site: http://www.garmin.com
Sales Range: $25-49.9 Million
Emp.: 500
Global Positioning System Designer & Mfr
N.A.I.C.S.: 334511

Subsidiary (Non-US):

Garmin Austria Holding GmbH (2)
Hauptstrasse 12, 8302, Nestelbach, Austria
Tel.: (43) 313331810
Investment Management Service
N.A.I.C.S.: 523999

Garmin Corporation (2)
No 68 Zhangshu 2nd Road Xizhi Dist, Taipei, 221, Taiwan (100%)
Tel.: (886) 226429199
Web Site: https://www.garmin.com.tw
Sales Range: $150-199.9 Million
Emp.: 1,000
Provider of Navigation Communications & Information Devices
N.A.I.C.S.: 334511

Garmin Deutschland Beteligungs GmbH & Co, KG (2)
Parkring 35, 85748, Grafelfing, Germany
Tel.: (49) 898583640
Web Site: http://www.garmin.com
Emp.: 100
Investment Management Service
N.A.I.C.S.: 523940

Garmin Deutschland GmbH (2)
Parkring 35, 85748, Garching, Germany
Tel.: (49) 89541999700
Web Site: https://www.garmin.com
Emp.: 400
Communication Equipment Distr
N.A.I.C.S.: 423690

Garmin France SAS (2)
55 avenue des Champs Pierreux, 92012, Nanterre, France
Tel.: (33) 155178181
Web Site: https://www.garmin.com
Communication Equipment Distr
N.A.I.C.S.: 423690

Garmin India Private Ltd. (2)
JA0326 Jasola DLF Tower -A 3rd Floor Plot No 10 Jasola, New Delhi, 110 025, India
Tel.: (91) 1148005800
Web Site: https://www.garmin.com
Emp.: 4
Navigation Equipment Distr
N.A.I.C.S.: 423690

Garmin Polska Sp. z o.o. (2)
Al Jerozolimskie 181, 02-222, Warsaw, Poland
Tel.: (48) 223374100
Global Positioning System Mfr
N.A.I.C.S.: 334220

Garmin Portugal - Equipamentos de Comunicacoes e de Navegacao Ltda. (2)
Cacem Park Armazem 2 Estrada De Paco De Arcos, Cacem, 2735-294, Portugal
Tel.: (351) 21 444 7460
Web Site: http://www.garmin.com
Navigation Equipment Distr
N.A.I.C.S.: 423690

Garmin Singapore Pte. Ltd (2)
46 E Coast Rd Ste 05-06, Singapore, 428766, Singapore
Tel.: (65) 63480378
Web Site: http://www.garmin.com.sg
Global Positioning System Mfr
N.A.I.C.S.: 334220

Subsidiary (Domestic):

Garmin USA, Inc. (2)
1200 E 151st St, Olathe, KS 66062-3426
Tel.: (913) 397-8200
Navigation Equipment Mfr & Distr
N.A.I.C.S.: 334511

Garmin Italia S.p.A. (1)
Strada 8 Palazzo L, 20089, Rozzano, Italy
Tel.: (39) 0236576411
Web Site: http://www.garmin.com
Navigation Communications & Information Devices Mfr
N.A.I.C.S.: 334511

Garmin New Zealand Ltd. (1)
5 Wilkins Street, Freemans Bay, Auckland, 1011, New Zealand
Tel.: (64) 93692900
Detection & Aeronautical Instrument Mfr
N.A.I.C.S.: 334511

Garmin Nordic Denmark A/S (1)
Hejrevang 19, 3450, Allerod, Denmark
Tel.: (45) 4570716400
Web Site: https://www.garmin.com
Detection & Aeronautical Instrument Mfr
N.A.I.C.S.: 334511
Soren Buro (Mgr-Sls)

Garmin Nordic Finland Oy (1)
Asemanrinne 9, Lohja, 08500, Finland
Tel.: (358) 931583100
Web Site: https://www.garmin.com
Detection & Aeronautical Instrument Mfr
N.A.I.C.S.: 334511
Jouni Niskanen (Mgr-Sls)

Garmin Nordic Norway AS (1)
Dillingtoppen 15, Dilling, 1570, Oslo, Norway
Tel.: (47) 4769799430
Web Site: https://www.garmin.com
Detection & Aeronautical Instrument Mfr
N.A.I.C.S.: 334511
Lyby Trygve (Mgr-Site)

Garmin Nordic Sweden AB (1)
Uggledalsv 13, 427 40, Billdal, Sweden
Tel.: (46) 313631000

Web Site: https://www.garmin.com
Emp.: 46
Detection & Aeronautical Instrument Mfr
N.A.I.C.S.: 334511

Garmin Norge AS (1)
Dillingtoppen 15, Dilling, 1570, Norway
Tel.: (47) 69799430
Web Site: https://www.garmin.com
Navigation Communications & Information Devices Mfr
N.A.I.C.S.: 334511

Garmin Sweden AB (1)
Ugledalsvagen 13, 427 40, Billdal, Sweden
Tel.: (46) 313631001
Navigation System Distr
N.A.I.C.S.: 423690

Garmin Sweden Technologies AB (1)
Spikvagen 1, 451 75, Uddevalla, Sweden
Tel.: (46) 522442222
Web Site: https://www.empirbus.com
Electronic Product Distr
N.A.I.C.S.: 423690

Garmin Switzerland GmbH (1)
Muhlentalstrasse 2, 8200, Schaffhausen, Switzerland
Tel.: (41) 526301600
Sales Range: $25-49.9 Million
Emp.: 10
Navigation & Communications Devices Mfr
N.A.I.C.S.: 334511

Garmin Vietnam Ltd. (1)
Room No 2 3 4 Floor 16 Phu My Hung Building No 08, Hoang Van Thai Street Quarter 1 Tan Phu Ward District 7, Ho Chi Minh City, Vietnam
Tel.: (84) 2854143899
Web Site: http://www.garmin.com.vn
Navigation & Communication Equipment Mfr
N.A.I.C.S.: 334511

Garmin, trgovina in servis, d.o.o. (1)
Poslovna Cona A 22, 4208, Sencur, Slovenia
Tel.: (386) 42792500
Emp.: 9
Detection & Aeronautical Instrument Mfr
N.A.I.C.S.: 334511

JL Audio, Inc. (1)
10369 N Commerce Pkwy, Miramar, FL 33025
Tel.: (954) 443-1100
Web Site: http://www.jlaudio.com
Rev.: $41,700,000
Emp.: 210
Audio Equipment Mfr
N.A.I.C.S.: 423690
Manville Smith (VP-Mktg)

Navionics SRL (1)
Via Fondacci 269, ZI Montramito, 55054, Massarosa, Italy
Tel.: (39) 0584329111
Navigational Equipment Developer & Mfr
N.A.I.C.S.: 334511

Subsidiary (US):

Navionics Inc. (2)
259 Samuel Barnet Blvd Unit #2, New Bedford, MA 02745
Tel.: (508) 291-6000
Web Site: http://www.navionics.com
Navigational Equipment Developer & Mfr
N.A.I.C.S.: 334511

GARNET CONSTRUCTION LIMITED
501 / 531 Laxmi Mall Laxmi Industrial Estate Above Axis Bank, Andheri Link Road Andheri West, Mumbai, 400053, India
Tel.: (91) 2242578500
Web Site: https://www.garnetconstructions.com
Year Founded: 1992
526727—(BOM)
Rev.: $529,908
Assets: $19,292,848
Liabilities: $8,191,967
Net Worth: $11,100,881
Earnings: $34,962
Emp.: 24
Fiscal Year-end: 03/31/23
Real Estate Development Services
N.A.I.C.S.: 531390
Kishan Kumar Kedia (Chm & Mng Dir)

GARNET INTERNATIONAL LIMITED
901 Raheja Chambers Free Press Journal Marg, Nariman Point, Mumbai, 400 021, India
Tel.: (91) 2222820714
Web Site: https://www.garnetint.com
Year Founded: 1983
512493—(BOM)
Rev.: $7,113,590
Assets: $7,768,467
Liabilities: $3,438,895
Net Worth: $4,329,573
Earnings: $391,188
Emp.: 6
Fiscal Year-end: 03/31/23
Investment Management Service
N.A.I.C.S.: 523940
Suresh Gagger (Chm)

Subsidiaries:

Sukartik Clothing Private Limited (1)
Village - Seera Opp Sugar Godown Rahon Road, Ludhiana, 141 007, Punjab, India
Tel.: (91) 1616539941
Web Site: https://www.sukartik.com
Seamless Sport Wear & Intimate Wear Mfr
N.A.I.C.S.: 315250

GARO AB
Sodergatan 26, SE-335 33, Gnosjo, Sweden
Tel.: (46) 370332800
Web Site: https://www.garo.se
Year Founded: 1939
GARO—(OMX)
Rev.: $130,236,871
Assets: $108,039,001
Liabilities: $50,521,228
Net Worth: $57,517,772
Earnings: $11,286,259
Emp.: 400
Fiscal Year-end: 12/31/22
Electrical Products Mfr
N.A.I.C.S.: 334419
Stefan Jonsson (Chm)

Subsidiaries:

EV Charge Partner Sweden AB (1)
Anderstorpsvagen 63, 335 33, Gnosjo, Sweden
Tel.: (46) 104984850
Web Site: https://www.evchargepartner.se
Charging Station Services
N.A.I.C.S.: 238290

GARO AS (1)
Sankt Hallvardsvei 3, 3414, Lierstranda, Norway
Tel.: (47) 32896450
Web Site: https://garo.no
Emp.: 520
Electric Equipment Mfr
N.A.I.C.S.: 335999

GARO Polska Sp. z o.o. (1)
ul Kadmowa 4, 70-856, Szczecin, Poland
Tel.: (48) 918811770
Web Site: https://www.garo.com.pl
Electrical Installation Equipment Distr
N.A.I.C.S.: 423610

GARODIA CHEMICALS LIMITED
149/156 Garodia Shopping Centre Garodia Nagar, Ghatkopar East, Mumbai, 400077, India
Tel.: (91) 02267983683 In
Web Site: http://www.gchem.org
Year Founded: 1993
530161—(BOM)
Assets: $12,744

GARODIA CHEMICALS LIMITED

Garodia Chemicals Limited—(Continued)
Liabilities: $535,299
Net Worth: ($522,556)
Earnings: ($7,190)
Fiscal Year-end: 03/31/23
Chemical Products Mfr
N.A.I.C.S.: 325199
Mahesh Gordhandas Garodia *(Chm)*

GAROFALO HEALTH CARE SPA
Piazzale Belle Arti 6, 00196, Rome, Italy
Tel.: (39) 06684891
Web Site: https://www.garofalohealthcare.com
Year Founded: 1921
GHC—(ITA)
Rev.: $398,473,341
Assets: $878,907,164
Liabilities: $546,763,440
Net Worth: $332,143,725
Earnings: $23,041,175
Emp.: 2,767
Fiscal Year-end: 12/31/21
Healtcare Services
N.A.I.C.S.: 525120
Alessandro M. Rinaldi *(Pres)*

Subsidiaries:

Aesculapio S.r.l. (1)
Via Degli Scienziati 30, 41038, San Felice sul Panaro, Modena, Italy
Tel.: (39) 053585311
Web Site: http://www.aesculapio.it
Hospital Operator
N.A.I.C.S.: 622110

Bimar S.r.l. (1)
Via Giorgio Amendola 16/18, Sirmione, 25019, Brescia, Italy
Tel.: (39) 0309904555
Web Site: https://www.bimaritaly.it
Household Appliance Mfr & Distr
N.A.I.C.S.: 335220

C.M.S.R. Veneto Medica S.r.l. (1)
Via Vicenza no 204, 36077, Altavilla Vicentina, VI, Italy
Tel.: (39) 0444225111
Web Site: http://www.centromedico.it
Hospital Operator
N.A.I.C.S.: 622110

Casa di Cura Prof. Nobili S.p.A. (1)
via Fiera n25, Castiglione Dei Pepoli, 40035, Bologna, Italy
Tel.: (39) 053491099
Web Site: https://www.casadicuranobili.it
Hospital Operator
N.A.I.C.S.: 622110
Niccolo Francioli *(Chief Medical Officer)*

Casa di Cura Villa Berica S.p.A. (1)
Via Giuseppe Capparozzo 10, 36100, Vicenza, Italy
Tel.: (39) 0444219200
Web Site: http://www.villaberica.it
Nursing Care Services
N.A.I.C.S.: 623110

Casa di Cura Villa Garda S.p.A. (1)
Via Monte Baldo 89 Garda, 37016, Verona, Italy
Tel.: (39) 0456208611
Web Site: http://www.villagarda.it
Hospital Operator
N.A.I.C.S.: 622110

Centro Medico San Biagio S.r.l. (1)
Via del Commercio 69/4, Fossalta di Portogruaro, 30025, Venice, Italy
Tel.: (39) 0421244016
Web Site: https://www.centromedicosanbiagio.it
Hospital Operator
N.A.I.C.S.: 622110

Centro Medico Universita Castrense S.r.l. (1)
Via F Giorgio Bigotto 4, 33058, San Giorgio di Nogaro, UD, Italy
Tel.: (39) 0431620990
Web Site: https://www.cmuc.it
Hospital Operator

Clinica San Francesco S.R.L. (1)
Via Monte Ortigara 21/B, 37127, Verona, Italy
Tel.: (39) 0459009090
Web Site: https://www.clinicasanfrancesco.it
Healthcare Services
N.A.I.C.S.: 621610

Domus Nova S.p.A. (1)
Via Paolo Pavirani 44, 48121, Ravenna, Italy
Tel.: (39) 0544508311
Web Site: https://www.domusnova.it
Healthcare Services
N.A.I.C.S.: 621610

Fides Servizi S.c.a r.l. (1)
Piazza del Portello 6/2, 16124, Genoa, Italy
Tel.: (39) 0103762012
Web Site: http://www.gruppofides.it
Health Care Srvices
N.A.I.C.S.: 621330

Gruppo Veneto Diagnostica e Riabilitazione S.R.L. (1)
Via Gramsci 9, Di Cadoneghe, 35010, Padua, Italy
Tel.: (39) 0498874111
Web Site: https://www.gvdr.it
Rehabilitation Clinic Operator
N.A.I.C.S.: 622310

Hesperia Hospital Modena S.p.A. (1)
Via Arqua 80/A, 41125, Modena, Italy
Tel.: (39) 059449111
Web Site: http://www.hesperia.it
Hospital Operator
N.A.I.C.S.: 622110

L'Eremo di Miazzina S.r.l. (1)
Via per Miazzina 16, 28814, Cambiasca, VB, Italy
Tel.: (39) 0323553700
Web Site: https://www.eremodimiazzina.com
Rehabilitation Center Operator
N.A.I.C.S.: 622310

Ospedali Privati Riuniti S.r.l. (1)
Viale Ercolani 9, 40138, Bologna, Italy
Tel.: (39) 051396411
Web Site: https://www.ospedaliprivatiriuniti.it
Hospital Operator
N.A.I.C.S.: 622110

Poliambulatorio Dalla Rosa Prati S.r.l. (1)
Via Emilia Ovest 12/A, 43126, Parma, Italy
Tel.: (39) 05212981
Web Site: http://www.poliambulatoriodallarosaprati.it
Hospital Operator
N.A.I.C.S.: 622110
Falzoi Maurizio *(Dir-Medical)*

Prora S.r.l. (1)
Via Signorelli 2/4 - Loc, Sambuca Tavarnelle Val di Pesa, 50028, Florence, Italy
Tel.: (39) 0558050515
Web Site: https://www.prora.net
Machinery & Equipment Mfr
N.A.I.C.S.: 333111

Rugani Hospital S.r.l. (1)
SR 222 Chiantigiana localita Colombaio, Monteriggioni, 53035, Siena, Italy
Tel.: (39) 0577578311
Web Site: http://www.ruganihospital.it
Hospital Operator
N.A.I.C.S.: 622110

Villa Von Siebenthal S.r.l. (1)
via della Madonnina 1, Genzano di Roma, 00045, Rome, Italy
Tel.: (39) 0693391801
Web Site: https://www.villavonsiebenthal.it
Mental Health Care Services
N.A.I.C.S.: 621330

Xray One S.r.l. (1)
Via Mantegna 51, Poggio Rusco, Mantua, Italy
Tel.: (39) 0386734185
Web Site: http://www.xrayone.it
Hospital Operator
N.A.I.C.S.: 622110

GAROVAGLIO & ZORRAQUIN SA
Cespedes 3857/63, Buenos Aires, 1427, Argentina
Tel.: (54) 1145556000
Air Conditioner & Heating Equipment Mfr
N.A.I.C.S.: 333415
Ambrosio Nougues *(Chm)*

GARRETT MOTION INC.
La Piece 16, 1180, Rolle, Switzerland
Tel.: (41) 796010787
Web Site: https://www.garrettmotion.com
GTX—(NASDAQ)
Rev.: $3,603,000,000
Assets: $2,637,000,000
Liabilities: $2,753,000,000
Net Worth: ($116,000,000)
Earnings: $390,000,000
Emp.: 7,300
Fiscal Year-end: 12/31/22
Automotive Turbocharger, Oil Filter, Coolant, Spark Plug & Care Products Mfr
N.A.I.C.S.: 336390
Olivier Rabiller *(Pres & CEO)*

Subsidiaries:

Garrett Motion Japan Inc. (1)
New Pier Takeshiba South Tower 11F 1-16-1 Kaigan, Minato-ku, Tokyo, 105-0022, Japan
Tel.: (81) 367307070
Web Site: https://www.garrettmotion.com
Emp.: 150
Commercial Vehicle Mfr & Distr
N.A.I.C.S.: 332119

Honeywell Automotive Parts Services (Shanghai) Co., Ltd.
No 8 Niu Dun Road Zhang Jiang Hi-Tech Park Pudong New Area, Shanghai, 201203, China
Tel.: (86) 2138652842
Automobile Parts Mfr
N.A.I.C.S.: 336390

Honeywell Garrett S.A. (1)
Zone Inova 3000 2 Rue de Avenir, Thaon-les-Vosges, 88155, France
Tel.: (33) 3 29 81 30 00
Emp.: 700
Motor Vehicles Mfr
N.A.I.C.S.: 336320

GARRINGTON GROUP OF COMPANIES INC.
5734 Yonge Street Suite 400, North York, M2M 4E7, ON, Canada
Tel.: (800) 465-0400
Web Site: http://garringtongroupco.com
Emp.: 75
Privater Equity Firm
N.A.I.C.S.: 523999

Subsidiaries:

Liquid Capital Corp. (1)
5734 Yonge St Suite 400, North York, M2M 4E7, ON, Canada
Web Site: http://www.liquidcapitalcorp.com
Nondepository Credit Intermediation
N.A.I.C.S.: 522299
Steve Shriver *(Founder & Pres)*

GARRY MERCER TRUCKING INC.
1140 Midway Blvd, Mississauga, L5T 2C1, ON, Canada
Tel.: (905) 670-4721
Web Site: https://www.gmercer.com
Year Founded: 1982
Sales Range: $10-24.9 Million
Emp.: 65
Trucking & Logistics Services
N.A.I.C.S.: 484121
Andrew Crabbe *(Gen Mgr)*

GARUDA CAPITAL CORP.

INTERNATIONAL PUBLIC

502-1978 Vine Street, Vancouver, V6K 4S1, BC, Canada
Tel.: (604) 737-0203
Investment Management Service
N.A.I.C.S.: 525910
Robin A. Relph *(Pres & CEO)*

GARUDAFOOD PUTRA PUTRI JAYA
Jl Bintaro Raya No 10A RT 03/RW 10 Utara, Kebayoran Lama, Jakarta, 12240, Indonesia
Tel.: (62) 217290110
Web Site: https://www.garudafood.com
Year Founded: 1994
GOOD—(INDO)
Rev.: $684,699,602
Assets: $482,355,351
Liabilities: $228,491,164
Net Worth: $253,864,187
Earnings: $39,059,286
Emp.: 8,527
Fiscal Year-end: 12/31/23
Peanut Product Mfr
N.A.I.C.S.: 311911
Hardianto Atmadja *(Chm)*

GARWARE HI-TECH FILMS LIMITED
50-A Swami Nityanand Marg, Vile Parle East, Mumbai, 400 057, Maharashtra, India
Tel.: (91) 2249186000
Web Site: https://www.garwarehitechfilms.com
500655—(BOM)
Rev.: $137,137,455
Assets: $255,030,771
Liabilities: $41,605,596
Net Worth: $213,425,176
Earnings: $17,192,489
Emp.: 921
Fiscal Year-end: 03/31/21
Polyester Film Mfr
N.A.I.C.S.: 326113
S. B. Garware *(Chm & Co-Mng Dir)*

Subsidiaries:

Garware Polyester Ltd. - Chikalthana Works (1)
Polyester Film Plant L-6, Chikalthana Industrial Area Dr Abasaheb Garware Marg, Aurangabad, 431 210, India
Tel.: (91) 240 2485465
Web Site: http://www.garwarepoly.com
Polyester Film Mfr & Whslr
N.A.I.C.S.: 424610

Garware Polyester Ltd. - Nasik Works (1)
A-1 MIDC Ambad, Nasik, 400 010, India
Tel.: (91) 253 238 2781
Sales Range: $25-49.9 Million
Emp.: 50
Polyester Film Mfr & Whslr
N.A.I.C.S.: 424610
Pawar Nhor *(Mgr)*

Garware Polyester Ltd. - Waluj Works (1)
Naigaon Post Waluj, Aurangabad, 431 133, India
Tel.: (91) 240 2554427
Web Site: http://www.garwarepoly.com
Polyester Film Mfr & Whslr
N.A.I.C.S.: 424610

Global PET Films Inc. (1)
101 Lake Forest Bldg Ste 410, Gaithersburg, FL 20877
Tel.: (954) 499-7990
Web Site: http://www.globalwindowfilms.com
Sales Range: $50-74.9 Million
Emp.: 6
Plastic Film Mfr & Whslr
N.A.I.C.S.: 326113
Makarand Lele *(Acct Mgr)*

GARWARE MARINE INDUSTRIES LTD.

03rd Floor Prospect Chambers D N Road Fort, Dadar West, Mumbai, 400 001, India
Tel.: (91) 2224234000
Web Site:
https://www.garwaremarine.com
Year Founded: 1975
509563—(BOM)
Rev.: $179,192
Assets: $879,655
Liabilities: $95,309
Net Worth: $784,346
Earnings: $19,380
Emp.: 7
Fiscal Year-end: 03/31/21
Fishing Nets Mfr
N.A.I.C.S.: 114119
Pallavi P. Shedge *(Compliance Officer & Sec)*

GARWARE SYNTHETICS LIMITED
C/o Manish Textiles Industries Premises Opp Golden Chemical, Penkar Pada Post Mira, Thane, 401104, India
Tel.: (91) 2228457763
Web Site:
https://www.garwaresyn.com
514400—(BOM)
Rev.: $1,128,452
Assets: $1,857,478
Liabilities: $2,151,578
Net Worth: ($294,100)
Earnings: $79,592
Emp.: 63
Fiscal Year-end: 03/31/21
Nylon Mfr & Whslr
N.A.I.C.S.: 325220
Sunder K. Moolya *(Exec Dir)*

GARWARE TECHNICAL FIBRES LTD.
Plot No 11 Block D1 M I D C Chinchwad, Pune, 411 019, Maharashtra, India
Tel.: (91) 2027990301
Web Site:
https://www.garwarefibres.com
Year Founded: 1976
GARFIBRES—(BOM)
Rev.: $145,951,560
Assets: $180,026,820
Liabilities: $69,310,714
Net Worth: $110,716,106
Earnings: $21,621,095
Emp.: 1,185
Fiscal Year-end: 03/31/21
Synthetic Cordage & Netting Mfr
N.A.I.C.S.: 314994
Vayu Ramesh Garware *(Chm & Mng Dir)*

GAS ARABIAN SERVICES CO.
Unit no 8500, Dammam, 32241-5150, Saudi Arabia
Tel.: (966) 138351500
Web Site:
https://www.gasarabian.com
Year Founded: 1992
9528—(SAU)
Rev.: $132,259,616
Assets: $133,144,261
Liabilities: $48,577,253
Net Worth: $84,567,008
Earnings: $17,966,889
Emp.: 896
Fiscal Year-end: 12/31/22
Oil & Gas Machinery Equipment Distr
N.A.I.C.S.: 423830
Faisal K. AlDabal *(Vice Chm)*

GAS BETON CELKON A.D.
Veljka Mladenovica Bb, 78000, Banja Luka, Bosnia & Herzegovina
Tel.: (387) 51450254
GSBT-R-A—(BANJ)
Sales Range: Less than $1 Million
Emp.: 21
Concrete Products Mfr
N.A.I.C.S.: 327390
Slavisa Savicic *(Exec Dir)*

GAS CALL SERVICES LIMITED
Queenslie Court Summerlee Street, Queenslie Industrial Estate, Glasgow, G33 4DB, United Kingdom
Tel.: (44) 1417663333
Web Site: http://www.gascall.co.uk
Year Founded: 1996
Sales Range: $1-9.9 Million
Emp.: 130
Gas Service & Maintenance & Central Heating Installations
N.A.I.C.S.: 238220
Mike Donnelly *(Mng Dir)*

GAS KING OIL CO. LTD.
1604 2nd Avenue South, Lethbridge, T1J 0G2, AB, Canada
Tel.: (403) 320-2142
Web Site: http://www.gasking.com
Year Founded: 1985
Gasoline Service Stations
N.A.I.C.S.: 457120
Brent Morris *(Pres)*

GAS MALAYSIA BERHAD
No 5 Jalan Serendah 26/17 Seksyen 26 Peti Surat 7901, 40732, Shah Alam, Selangor Darul Ehsan, Malaysia
Tel.: (60) 351923000
Web Site:
https://www.gasmalaysia.com
Year Founded: 1992
GASMSIA—(KLS)
Rev.: $1,618,913,016
Assets: $666,059,471
Liabilities: $395,512,381
Net Worth: $270,547,090
Earnings: $82,442,963
Emp.: 575
Fiscal Year-end: 12/31/22
Natural Gas Distr
N.A.I.C.S.: 221210
Hasni Harun *(Chm)*

Subsidiaries:

Gas Malaysia Virtual Pipeline Sdn. Bhd. (1)
I-PARC 2 No 42 Jalan Serendah 26/39 Seksyen 26, 40400, Shah Alam, Selangor, Malaysia
Tel.: (60) 35 101 9696
Web Site:
https://www.gasmalaysiavirtualpipe.com
Natural Gas Distr
N.A.I.C.S.: 221210

GAS NEA SA
Av Cordoba 883 7mo Piso, 1054, Buenos Aires, Argentina
Tel.: (54) 810444427632
Web Site: http://www.gasnea.com.ar
Sales Range: $10-24.9 Million
Emp.: 85
Natural Gas Mfr
N.A.I.C.S.: 211130
Michel Collier *(Gen Mgr)*

GAS PLUS INC.
5910 50 Ave SE, Calgary, T2B 3C1, AB, Canada
Tel.: (403) 273-4199
Web Site: http://www.gasplusinc.com
Rev.: $14,097,770
Emp.: 95
Fuel & Service Station
N.A.I.C.S.: 457210
Sal Handel *(Pres)*

GAS PLUS S.P.A.
V le E Forlanini 17, 20134, Milan, Italy
Tel.: (39) 0270009499
Web Site: https://www.gasplus.it
Year Founded: 1960
GSP—(ITA)
Rev.: $95,777,638
Assets: $573,476,567
Liabilities: $380,306,250
Net Worth: $193,170,317
Earnings: $3,549,704
Emp.: 147
Fiscal Year-end: 12/31/21
Natural Gas Exploration & Production Services
N.A.I.C.S.: 211130
Achille Capelli *(Dir-Network Bus Unit)*

Subsidiaries:

Gas Plus International B.V. (1)
President Kennedylaan 19 Unit 1 05, 2517 JK, Hague, Netherlands
Tel.: (31) 708200361
Web Site: http://www.gasplus.nl
Natural Gas Exploration Service
N.A.I.C.S.: 211130

Gas Plus Vendite S.r.l. (1)
Viale Enrico Forlanini 17, 20134, Milan, Italy
Tel.: (39) 0525419499
Web Site: http://www.gasplusvendite.it
Natural Gas Exploration Service
N.A.I.C.S.: 211130

Rete Gas Fidenza S.r.l. (1)
Viale E Forlanini 17, 20134, Milan, Italy
Tel.: (39) 0524534484
Web Site: http://www.retegasfidenza.it
Gas Distribution Services
N.A.I.C.S.: 221210

GAS SERVICES NZ LTD.
42 Connett Road West Bell Block, New Plymouth, 4312, New Zealand
Tel.: (64) 800 347 784
Web Site: http://firstgas.co.nz
Year Founded: 2016
Gas Transmission & Distribution Services
N.A.I.C.S.: 221210
Paul Goodeve *(CEO)*

Subsidiaries:

Rockgas Ltd. (1)
42 Connett Road West, Bell Block, New Plymouth, 4312, New Zealand (100%)
Tel.: (64) 800762542
Web Site: http://www.rockgas.co.nz
Oil & Gas Operations
N.A.I.C.S.: 213112

GAS TO LIQUID JSC
Nauchny proezd 17, 117246, Moscow, Russia
Tel.: (7) 4956492905
Web Site: http://www.gtl-rus.com
Year Founded: 2000
GTLC—(MOEX)
Sales Range: Less than $1 Million
Gas & Liquid Technology Services
N.A.I.C.S.: 211130
Kadyrov Rafis Faizovich *(Co-Founder & Pres)*

GAS2GRID LIMITED
Suite 22 Level 5 58 Pitt Street, Sydney, 2000, NSW, Australia
Tel.: (61) 2292411927
Web Site: https://www.gas2grid.com
GGX—(ASX)
Rev.: $95
Assets: $1,790,224
Liabilities: $10,208,466
Net Worth: ($8,418,242)
Earnings: ($1,482,323)
Fiscal Year-end: 06/30/21
Exploration & Development Of Conventional Oil & Gas
N.A.I.C.S.: 213111
Dennis J. Morton *(Mng Dir)*

GASALARM A.D.
Dobropoljska 72a, 11000, Belgrade, Serbia
Tel.: (381) 11 2652 079
Web Site:
http://www.gasalarmbeograd.com
Year Founded: 1990
Sales Range: Less than $1 Million
Emp.: 6
Measuring Instruments Mfr
N.A.I.C.S.: 334513
Nikolic Aleksandar *(Exec Dir)*

GASCOGNE SA
68 rue de la papeterie, 40200, Saint-Paul-les-Dax, Cedex, France
Tel.: (33) 558565400
Web Site: https://www.groupe-gascogne.com
Year Founded: 1925
ALBI—(EUR)
Sales Range: $450-499.9 Million
Packaging, Wood & Paper Mfr & Distr
N.A.I.C.S.: 322220
Dominique Coutiere *(Chm & CEO)*

Subsidiaries:

Feutres Depland S.A.S. (1)
Le Moulin Brice, BP 30, Saint-Junien, 87201, Rochechouart, Cedex, France
Tel.: (33) 555430678
Industrial Wood Product Mfr
N.A.I.C.S.: 321999

Gascogne Bois Escource SAS (1)
Route de Cap de Pin, Escource, 40210, Mont-de-Marsan, France
Tel.: (33) 558044040
Web Site: http://www.gascognebois.com
Emp.: 60
Industrial Wood Product Mfr & Distr
N.A.I.C.S.: 321999
Eric Prolongeau *(Mng Dir)*

Gascogne Flexible Germany GmbH (1)
Rurstrasse 58, 52441, Linnich, Germany
Tel.: (49) 2462791100
Multilayer Composite Material Mfr
N.A.I.C.S.: 324122
Johannes Pelzer *(Head-Technical Support & Dev)*

Gascogne Italia SRL (1)
Via della Giustizia no 9, 20125, Milan, Italy
Tel.: (39) 0266 98 13 32
Paper & Cardboard Services
N.A.I.C.S.: 424130

Gascogne Packaging USA, Inc. (1)
3017 Douglas Blvd Ste 300, Roseville, CA 95661
Tel.: (916) 788-7291
Industrial Wood Product Mfr
N.A.I.C.S.: 321999

Gascogne Papier SAS (1)
68 rue de la Papeterie, BP 8, Mimizan, 40201, Mont-de-Marsan, Cedex, France
Tel.: (33) 558099000
Pulp & Paper Mfr
N.A.I.C.S.: 322110

Gascogne Sack Aigis SA (1)
247 28th October Str Evia, Vassiliko, 340 02, Chalkida, Greece
Tel.: (30) 2221052401
Web Site: http://www.aigis.gr
Emp.: 66
Paper Sack Mfr
N.A.I.C.S.: 322220
Yiannis Spanos *(Controller-Mfg Cost)*

Gascogne Sack Deutschland GmbH (1)
Sudstrasse 4-6, 37445, Walkenried, Germany
Tel.: (49) 55868010
Industrial Wood Product Mfr
N.A.I.C.S.: 321999

Gascogne Sacs Mimizan SAS (1)
70 rue de la Papeterie, BP 10057, Mimizan, 40201, Mont-de-Marsan, Cedex, France
Tel.: (33) 558092626

GASCOGNE SA

Gascogne SA—(Continued)
Industrial Wood Product Mfr
N.A.I.C.S.: 321999
Stephanie Taurines (Acct Mgr-Export)

Gascogne Sacs Saint-Herblain SAS (1)
2 rue du Chene Lasse Z I L, BP 253, 44818, Saint-Herblain, Cedex, France
Tel.: (33) 240923250
Industrial Wood Product Mfr
N.A.I.C.S.: 321999

Gascogne Spain SL (1)
Diputacio No 262 1 Fl, Catalunya 12 2nd Fl, 08007, Barcelona, Spain
Tel.: (34) 934122490
Web Site: http://www.gascognepaper.com
Sales Range: $50-74.9 Million
Emp.: 2
Paper Whslr
N.A.I.C.S.: 424120
Monica Casanovas (Mgr)

Gascogne UK Ltd (1)
The Turbine Innovation Centre Shireoaks Triangle Business Park, Coach Close Worksop, Nottingham, S81 8AP, United Kingdom
Tel.: (44) 1909512167
Sales Range: $25-49.9 Million
Emp.: 2
Wood Product Services
N.A.I.C.S.: 321999
Brian Robbins (Sls Mgr)

Gascogne USA Inc (1)
2050 Marconi Dr Ste 300, Alpharetta, GA 30005
Tel.: (770) 777-8260
Paper Related Services
N.A.I.C.S.: 424130
Ben Poncelet (Gen Mgr)

Branch (Domestic):

Gascogne USA, Inc. - Orangevale (2)
9262 Madison Ave, Orangevale, CA 95662
Tel.: (916) 987-0777
Sales Range: $25-49.9 Million
Emp.: 3
Wood Product Services
N.A.I.C.S.: 322220

Papeteries de Gascogne GmbH (1)
Salzstr 8, 48143, Munster, Germany
Tel.: (49) 251511043
Web Site: http://www.gascognepaper.com
Sales Range: $50-74.9 Million
Emp.: 3
Paper Related Services
N.A.I.C.S.: 424130

SAS Gascogne Flexible (1)
68 rue de la Papeterie, BP 8, Mimizan, 40201, Mont-de-Marsan, Cedex, France
Tel.: (33) 558099000
Web Site: http://www.gascogneflexible.com
Multilayer Composite Material Mfr
N.A.I.C.S.: 324122

Societe Gascogne Sack Tunisia (1)
Rue de l'exportation, BP 276, Zone Industrielle de Rades, 2040, Rades, Tunisia
Tel.: (216) 71448020
Industrial Wood Product Mfr
N.A.I.C.S.: 321999

GASCOYNE RESOURCES LIMITED
Level 1 41-47 Colin Street, West Perth, 6000, WA, Australia
Tel.: (61) 894813434
Web Site:
http://www.gascoyneresources.com
Year Founded: 2009
SPR—(ASX)
Rev.: $843,349
Assets: $173,756,009
Liabilities: $67,869,925
Net Worth: $105,886,084
Earnings: ($33,945,646)
Fiscal Year-end: 06/30/24
Gold Exploration & Mining Services
N.A.I.C.S.: 212220
Shane McBride (Sec)

Subsidiaries:

Firefly Resources Limited (1)
T2 64-68 Hay Street, Subiaco, 6008, WA, Australia
Tel.: (61) 893222338
Web Site:
http://www.fireflyresources.com.au
Rev.: $52,104
Assets: $910,302
Liabilities: $193,764
Net Worth: $716,538
Earnings: ($4,969,982)
Emp.: 7
Fiscal Year-end: 06/30/2020
Metals Exploration & Mine Development
N.A.I.C.S.: 213114
Steven Wood (Co-Sec)

Subsidiary (Domestic):

Marindi Metals Pty. Ltd. (2)
Level 3 35 Havelock St, West Perth, 6005, WA, Australia
Tel.: (61) 893222338
Web Site: http://www.marindi.com.au
Metal Exploration & Mining
N.A.I.C.S.: 213114
Joe Treacy (Mng Dir)

GASLOG LTD.
69 Akti Miaouli, 18537, Piraeus, Greece
Tel.: (30) 2104591000   BM
Web Site: http://www.gaslogltd.com
Year Founded: 2003
GLOG—(NYSE)
Rev.: $918,031,000
Assets: $5,272,464,000
Liabilities: $3,886,065,000
Net Worth: $1,386,399,000
Earnings: $196,303,000
Emp.: 149
Fiscal Year-end: 12/31/23
Holding Company; Liquefied Natural Gas Shipping Services
N.A.I.C.S.: 551112
Joseph Nelson (Head-Investor Relations)

Subsidiaries:

GasLog Asia Pte. Ltd. (1)
24-02B Asia Square Tower 2 Marina View, Singapore, 18961, Singapore
Tel.: (65) 68121900
Liquefied Natural Gas Shipping Services
N.A.I.C.S.: 486210

GasLog LNG Services Ltd. (1)
24-02B Asia Square Tower 2 Marina View, Singapore, 18961, Singapore
Tel.: (65) 68121900
Liquefied Natural Gas Shipping Services
N.A.I.C.S.: 486210

GasLog Partners LP (1)
69 Akti Miaouli, 18537, Piraeus, Greece
Tel.: (30) 2104591000
Web Site: http://www.gaslogmlp.com
Rev.: $397,838,000
Assets: $1,666,239,000
Liabilities: $145,823,000
Net Worth: $1,520,416,000
Earnings: $138,709,000
Emp.: 2,019
Fiscal Year-end: 12/31/2023
Holding Company; Liquefied Natural Gas Shipping Services
N.A.I.C.S.: 551112
Achilleas Tasioulas (CFO)

GASNETZ HAMBURG GMBH
Ausschlager Elbdeich 127, 20539, Hamburg, Germany
Tel.: (49) 40 53 79 93 98   De
Web Site: http://www.gasnetz-hamburg.de
Natural Gas Pipeline Transportation Services
N.A.I.C.S.: 486210
Udo Bottlander (Mng Dir)

GASOL PLC
40 New Bond Street, London, W1S 2RX, United Kingdom
Tel.: (44) 2072903300
Web Site: http://www.gasolplc.com
Sales Range: Less than $1 Million
Liquefied Natural Gas Exploration Services
N.A.I.C.S.: 211130
Ethelbert J L Cooper (Chm)

GASPOROX AB
Tellusgatan 13, 224 57, Lund, Sweden
Tel.: (46) 465405040
Web Site: https://www.gasporox.se
Year Founded: 2005
GPX—(OMX)
Rev.: $2,009,048
Assets: $4,161,398
Liabilities: $1,872,301
Net Worth: $2,289,097
Earnings: ($411,176)
Emp.: 17
Fiscal Year-end: 12/31/22
Electric Equipment Mfr
N.A.I.C.S.: 335999
Tore Gimse (Chm)

GASSCO AS
Bygnesvegen 75, 4250, Kopervik, Norway
Tel.: (47) 52812500   NO
Web Site: http://www.gassco.no
Year Founded: 2001
Sales Range: $10-24.9 Million
Emp.: 168
Natural Gas Pipeline Operator
N.A.I.C.S.: 486210
Kristin Kinn Kaste (Head-System Ops)

GASTERRA B.V.
Stationsweg 1, 9726 AC, Groningen, Netherlands
Tel.: (31) 503648648
Web Site: http://www.gasterra.com
Year Founded: 1963
Rev.: $9,890,603,520
Assets: $1,491,205,576
Liabilities: $241,889,760
Net Worth: $1,249,315,816
Earnings: $40,314,960
Emp.: 131
Fiscal Year-end: 12/31/19
Natural Gas Whslr
N.A.I.C.S.: 221210
Flip van Koten (CFO & Member-Mgmt Bd)

GASTON GRAWEY
2 Rue Du Xay, 88190, Golbey, Vosges, France
Tel.: (33) 329812600
Sales Range: $10-24.9 Million
Emp.: 68
New & Used Car Dealers
N.A.I.C.S.: 441110

GASTRONOM SA
Str Ion Baiesu bl 4-5 floor 1, 120037, Buzau, Romania
Tel.: (40) 238710196
Web Site:
https://www.gastronombuzau.ro
GAOY—(BUC)
Rev.: $639,632
Assets: $1,728,863
Liabilities: $78,557
Net Worth: $1,650,306
Earnings: $359,721
Emp.: 4
Fiscal Year-end: 12/31/23
Real Estate Property Leasing Services
N.A.I.C.S.: 531190

GASUM OY

INTERNATIONAL PUBLIC

Revontulenpuisto 2 C, PO Box 21, 02100, Espoo, Finland
Tel.: (358) 204471   FI
Web Site: http://www.gasum.com
Sales Range: $700-749.9 Million
Emp.: 350
Natural Gas
N.A.I.C.S.: 221210
Johanna Lamminen (CEO)

Subsidiaries:

Gaasienergia AS (1)
Liivalaia 13/15, 10116, Tallinn, Estonia
Tel.: (372) 6276560
Web Site: http://www.gaasienergia.ee
Sales Range: $25-49.9 Million
Emp.: 4
Oil & Gas Pipeline Construction
N.A.I.C.S.: 237120

Gasum Energiapalvelut Oy (1)
Asentajankatu 5 B, Helsinki, 880, Finland
Tel.: (358) 204471
Web Site: http://www.gasum.fi
Sales Range: $50-74.9 Million
Emp.: 100
Natural Gas Liquid Extraction
N.A.I.C.S.: 211130
Johanna Lamminen (CEO)

Kaasuporssi Oy (1)
Miestentie 1, 02151, Espoo, Finland
Tel.: (358) 204478613
Web Site: http://www.kaasuporssi.com
Sales Range: $50-74.9 Million
Emp.: 40
Natural Gas Distr
N.A.I.C.S.: 221210

Skangas AS (1)
Kontinentalvegen 31, 4056, Tananger, Norway   (100%)
Tel.: (47) 52 97 92 00
Web Site: http://www.skangas.com
Natural Gas Distr
N.A.I.C.S.: 221210
Johanna Lamminen (Chm)

GATACKO POLJE A.D.
Solunskih Dobrovoljaca 62, 89240, Gacko, Bosnia & Herzegovina
Tel.: (387) 59472311
Year Founded: 2001
GATP-R-A—(BANJ)
Rev.: $22,949
Assets: $1,486,604
Liabilities: $351,828
Net Worth: $1,134,776
Earnings: ($131,285)
Emp.: 7
Fiscal Year-end: 12/31/12
Grocery Store Operator
N.A.I.C.S.: 445110
Dejan Mastilovic (Chm-Mgmt Bd)

GATECHNOLOGIES CO., LTD.
3-2-1 Roppongi Sumitomo Real Estate Roppongi Grand Tower 40F, Minato-ku, Tokyo, 106-6290, Japan
Tel.: (81) 362309180
Web Site: https://www.ga-tech.co.jp
Year Founded: 2013
3491—(TKS)
Rev.: $1,039,727,230
Assets: $434,985,680
Liabilities: $289,045,120
Net Worth: $145,940,560
Earnings: $7,160,900
Emp.: 1,487
Fiscal Year-end: 10/31/23
Residential Property Management Services
N.A.I.C.S.: 531311
Fumio Sakurai (Chief Sls Officer, Exec Officer, VP & Dir)

Subsidiaries:

Itandi, Inc. (1)
Sumitomo Realty Development Roppongi Grand Tower 40F 3-2-1 Roppongi, Minato-ku, Tokyo, 106-6290, Japan
Tel.: (81) 36 441 3954

Web Site: https://www.itandi.co.jp
Real Estate Services
N.A.I.C.S.: 531210

Modern Standard Co., Ltd. (1)
Sumitomo Real Estate Roppongi Grand Tower 40F 3-2-1, Roppongi Minato-ku, Tokyo, 106-6290, Japan
Tel.: (81) 120803902
Web Site: http://www.m-standard.co.jp
Real Estate Services
N.A.I.C.S.: 531210

RENOSY (Thailand) Co., Ltd. (1)
19th Floor Bhiraj Tower at Emquartier 689 Sukhumvit Road, Klongton Nua Vadhana, Bangkok, 10110, Thailand
Tel.: (66) 345559811
Web Site: https://www.dlife.co.jp
Real Estate Brokerage Services
N.A.I.C.S.: 531210

RENOSY PLUS Co., Ltd. (1)
Sumitomo Real Estate Roppongi Grand Tower 40F 3-2-1, Roppongi Minato-ku, Tokyo, 106-6290, Japan
Tel.: (81) 120803902
Web Site: https://www.m-standard.co.jp
Real Estate Brokerage Services
N.A.I.C.S.: 531210

Renosy Asset Management Co., Ltd. (1)
Sumitomo Real Estate Roppongi Grand Tower 40th Floor 3-2-1, Roppongi Minato-ku, Tokyo, 106-6290, Japan
Tel.: (81) 120987364
Web Site: http://www.renosy-am.co.jp
Real Estate Services
N.A.I.C.S.: 531210

Renosy Finance Inc. (1)
Sumitomo Real Estate Roppongi Grand Tower 40F 3-2-1, Roppongi Minato-ku, Tokyo, Japan
Tel.: (81) 362776058
Web Site: http://www.finance.renosy.co.jp
Financial Investment Services
N.A.I.C.S.: 523999

Renosy X Co., Ltd. (1)
Sumitomo Real Estate Roppongi Grand Tower 42F 3-2-1, Roppongi Minato-ku, Tokyo, 106-6290, Japan
Tel.: (81) 355455362
Web Site: http://www.renosy-x.co.jp
Real Estate Services
N.A.I.C.S.: 531210

Shenjumiaosuan Co., Ltd. (1)
3-2-1 Roppongi 40F Sumitomo Real Estate Roppongi, Minato-ku Roppongi, Tokyo, 106-6290, Japan
Tel.: (81) 36 230 9180
Web Site: https://www.shenjumiaosuan.com
Real Estate Services
N.A.I.C.S.: 531210

GATEKEEPER SYSTEMS INC.
301-31127 Wheel Avenue, Abbotsford, V2T 6H1, BC, Canada
Tel.: (604) 864-6187   BC
Web Site: https://www.gatekeeper-systems.com
Year Founded: 2010
GSI—(OTCIQ)
Rev.: $13,479,529
Assets: $11,266,110
Liabilities: $2,582,934
Net Worth: $8,683,176
Earnings: $94,478
Fiscal Year-end: 08/31/21
Video Security & Safety Systems
N.A.I.C.S.: 334310
Douglas Dyment *(Exec Chm, Pres & CEO)*

Subsidiaries:

GSI Systems Inc. (1)
250 W 26th St 2nd Fl, New York, NY 10001
Tel.: (212) 924-9595
Ventilation Equipment Installation Services
N.A.I.C.S.: 238220

GATELEY (HOLDINGS) PLC
One Eleven Edmund Street, Birmingham, B3 2HJ, United Kingdom
Tel.: (44) 121 234 0000
Web Site: http://www.gateleyuk.com
Emp.: 600
Law firm
N.A.I.C.S.: 541199
Cara Zachariou *(Head-Comm)*

GATEMORE CAPITAL MANAGEMENT LLP
33 Cavendish Square, London, W1G 0PW, United Kingdom
Tel.: (44) 207 580 0300
Web Site: http://gatemore.com
Investment Management Service
N.A.I.C.S.: 523999
Liad Meidar *(Chief Investment Officer & Mng Partner)*

Subsidiaries:

The Legacy Agency, Inc. - New York (1)
1500 Broadway Ste 2501, New York, NY 10036
Tel.: (212) 334-6880
Sales Range: $1-9.9 Million
Emp.: 20
Athlete Representation & Sports Marketing Services
N.A.I.C.S.: 711410
Edward L. Greenberg *(Exec VP)*

The Legacy Agency, Inc. - Newport Beach (1)
500 Newport Ctr Dr Ste 800, Newport Beach, CA 92660
Tel.: (949) 720-8700
Web Site: http://www.legacy-agency.com
Sales Range: $10-24.9 Million
Emp.: 50
Athlete Representation & Sports Marketing Services
N.A.I.C.S.: 711410
Greg Genske *(Exec Dir)*

GATEWAY CONSTRUCTION & ENGINEERING LTD.
434 Archibald Street, Winnipeg, R2J 0X5, MB, Canada
Tel.: (204) 233-8550
Web Site: https://www.gatewayconstruction.ca
Year Founded: 1973
Rev.: $10,000,000
Emp.: 40
Engineering, Construction & Technical Services Provider
N.A.I.C.S.: 541330
Wesley Rist *(Pres)*

GATEWAY DISTRIPARKS LTD.
Sector-6 Dronagiri Taluka-Uran, Raigad District, Navi Mumbai, 400707, India
Tel.: (91) 2227246500
Web Site: http://www.gateway-distriparks.com
GDL—(NSE)
Rev.: $162,528,462
Assets: $327,551,174
Liabilities: $124,809,635
Net Worth: $202,741,539
Earnings: $12,893,094
Emp.: 247
Fiscal Year-end: 03/31/21
Trucking & Courier Services
N.A.I.C.S.: 484121
Prem Kishan Gupta *(Chm & Co-Mng Dir)*

Subsidiaries:

Gateway Rail Freight Ltd. (1)
SF-7 Second Floor D-2 Southern Park, Saket District Centre Saket, New Delhi, 110 017, India   **(99.93%)**
Tel.: (91) 1140554400
Web Site: http://gatewayrail.in
Logistic Services
N.A.I.C.S.: 488210

Sachin Bhanushali *(CEO)*

GATEWAY LIFESTYLE GROUP
A28 24 - 32 Lexington Drive, Bella Vista, 2153, NSW, Australia
Tel.: (61) 1300 361 311
Web Site: http://www.gatewaylifestyle.com.au
Residential Property Development & Management
N.A.I.C.S.: 237210

GATEWAY MINING LIMITED
Level 11 52 Phillip Street, Sydney, 2000, NSW, Australia
Tel.: (61) 63839969
Web Site: https://www.gatewaymining.com.au
GML—(ASX)
Rev.: $7,662
Assets: $19,092,017
Liabilities: $365,362
Net Worth: $18,726,656
Earnings: ($1,039,977)
Fiscal Year-end: 06/30/22
Gold & Base Metals Exploration
N.A.I.C.S.: 212220
Peter Langworthy *(Mng Dir)*

GATEWAY REAL ESTATE AG
Hardenbergstr, 10623, Berlin, Germany
Tel.: (49) 3040363470
Web Site: https://www.gateway-re.de
GTY—(STU)
Rev.: $20,708,601
Assets: $1,528,639,176
Liabilities: $1,302,412,058
Net Worth: $226,227,118
Earnings: ($183,176,188)
Emp.: 26
Fiscal Year-end: 12/31/23
Real Estate Manangement Services
N.A.I.C.S.: 531210
Tobias Meibom *(CFO & Member-Exec Bd)*

Subsidiaries:

Development Partner AG (1)
Kaistrasse 2, 40221, Dusseldorf, Germany
Tel.: (49) 2119123300
Web Site: http://www.developmentpartner.de
Residential & Commercial Property Development Services
N.A.I.C.S.: 531210

Development Partner Immobilien Consulting GmbH (1)
Agrippinawerft 10, 50678, Cologne, Germany
Tel.: (49) 2218016130
Web Site: http://www.dpic-gmbh.de
Real Estate Asset Management Services
N.A.I.C.S.: 531390

GATEWAY STRATEGIC ACQUISITION CO.
18/F 68 Yee Wo Street, Causeway Bay, China (Hong Kong)
Tel.: (852) 2583 7700   Ky
Year Founded: 2021
GCSA—(NYSE)
Investment Services
N.A.I.C.S.: 523999
Goodwin Gaw *(Co-Founder & Chm)*

GATHID LTD.
Suite 501 Level 5 203 Robina Town Centre Drive, Robina, 4226, QLD, Australia
Tel.: (61) 755932581   AU
Web Site: https://www.rightcrowd.com
Year Founded: 2004
GTH—(ASX)
Rev.: $241,899
Assets: $7,258,264
Liabilities: $5,465,215

Net Worth: $1,793,049
Earnings: ($6,115,929)
Fiscal Year-end: 06/30/23
Software Publisher
N.A.I.C.S.: 513210
Peter Hill *(CEO)*

Subsidiaries:

Offsite Vision Holdings, Inc. (1)
68 White St Ste 7-382, Red Bank, NJ 07701-1656   **(100%)**
Tel.: (908) 419-6694
Computer & Computer Peripheral Equipment & Software Merchant Whslr
N.A.I.C.S.: 423430

GATI LTD.
Western Pearl 4th Floor Survey No 13 P, Kondapur, Hyderabad, 500084, India
Tel.: (91) 4071204284
Web Site: https://www.gati.com
Year Founded: 1989
532345—(BOM)
Rev.: $209,344,764
Assets: $154,031,533
Liabilities: $71,529,285
Net Worth: $82,502,248
Earnings: ($1,308,075)
Emp.: 2
Fiscal Year-end: 03/31/23
Cargo Transportation Services
N.A.I.C.S.: 488490
G. S. Ravi Kumar *(CIO)*

Subsidiaries:

Gati Asia Pacific Pte Ltd. (1)
3 Changi N St 2 01-01, ABV Industrial Bldg, Singapore, 498827, Singapore
Tel.: (65) 65874284
Web Site: http://www.gati.com
Sales Range: $25-49.9 Million
Emp.: 3
Cargo Management Services
N.A.I.C.S.: 488320
Mahindra Agarwal *(Mng Dir)*

Gati Hong Kong Ltd. (1)
Unit 1377 KITEC 1 Trademart Dr, Kowloon Bay, Hong Kong, China (Hong Kong)
Tel.: (852) 28505111
Web Site: http://www.gati.com
Sales Range: $25-49.9 Million
Emp.: 6
Logistic Services
N.A.I.C.S.: 541614
Manoj Chakur *(Gen Mgr)*

Zen Cargo Movers Pvt. Ltd. (1)
605/608 Sahar Bonanza A Wing Sr M V Rd JB Nagar, Marol Andheri E, 400 059, Mumbai, Maharashtra, India
Tel.: (91) 2266750089
Sales Range: $25-49.9 Million
Emp.: 8
Cargo Services
N.A.I.C.S.: 488320

GATRON INDUSTRIES LIMITED
10th Floor G & T Tower 18 Beaumont Road Civil Lines -10, Karachi, 75530, Pakistan
Tel.: (92) 2135659500
Web Site: https://www.gatronova.com
GATI—(LAH)
Rev.: $102,822,454
Assets: $109,075,085
Liabilities: $61,378,342
Net Worth: $47,696,743
Earnings: $18,636,899
Fiscal Year-end: 06/30/21
Polyester Yarn Mfr
N.A.I.C.S.: 313110

GATSTEEL INDUSTRIES INC.
361 Attwell Drive, Etobicoke, M9W 5C2, ON, Canada
Tel.: (416) 675-2370
Web Site: http://www.gatsteel.com

GATSTEEL INDUSTRIES INC.

Gatsteel Industries Inc.—(Continued)
Year Founded: 1983
Rev.: $18,345,384
Emp.: 48
Steel Sheets Supplier
N.A.I.C.S.: 423510
Tony Kafato *(Pres)*

GATTACA PLC
1450 Parkway Solent Business Park, Fareham, PO15 7AF, Hampshire, United Kingdom
Tel.: (44) 1489898989
Web Site:
https://www.gattacaplc.com
GATC—(AIM)
Rev.: $478,304,106
Assets: $101,057,684
Liabilities: $62,785,408
Net Worth: $38,272,276
Earnings: $2,173,150
Fiscal Year-end: 07/31/23
Temporary & Permanent Staffing Services
N.A.I.C.S.: 561311
Patrick Shanley *(Chm)*

Subsidiaries:

Barclay Meade Ltd. (1)
1450 Parkway Solent Business Park, Whiteley, Fareham, PO15 7AF, Hampshire, United Kingdom
Tel.: (44) 148 989 8989
Web Site: https://www.barclaymeade.com
Employment Agency Services
N.A.I.C.S.: 561311

Gattaca Projects Limited (1)
4th Floor Queens House 2 Holly Road, Twickenham, TW1 4EG, Middlesex, United Kingdom
Tel.: (44) 2070100450
Web Site: http://www.provanis.com
Sales Range: $10-24.9 Million
Emp.: 20
IT Recruitment Services
N.A.I.C.S.: 561311

Gattaca Solutions Limited (1)
1450 Pkwy Solent Bus Pk, Whiteley, Fareham, PO15 7AF, Hampshire, United Kingdom
Tel.: (44) 1489882677
Web Site:
http://www.matchtechgroupplc.com
Sales Range: $25-49.9 Million
Emp.: 25
Recruitment Process Outsourcing Solutions
N.A.I.C.S.: 561311

Matchtech Group UK Ltd (1)
1450 Parkway Solent Business Park, Whiteley, Fareham, PO15 7AF, Hampshire, United Kingdom
Tel.: (44) 148 989 8989
Web Site: https://www.matchtech.com
Emp.: 300
Temporary & Permanent Staffing Services
N.A.I.C.S.: 561311

Networkers International LLC (1)
6400 International Pkwy Ste 1510, Plano, TX 75093
Tel.: (972) 473-1100
Employment Agency Services
N.A.I.C.S.: 561311

Networkers International Limited (1)
Hanover Place 8 Ravensbourne Road, Bromley, BR1 1HP, Kent, United Kingdom
Tel.: (44) 2083159000
Web Site: http://www.networkersplc.com
Holding Company; Employment Agency
N.A.I.C.S.: 551112

Subsidiary (Non-US):

NWI de Mexico S. de R.L. de C.V (2)
Paseo de la Reforma 296 Piso 15 A, Colonia Juarez, Mexico, 06600, Distrito Federal, Mexico
Tel.: (52) 55 3000 8250
Web Site: http://www.gattaca.com
Human Resource Consulting Services

N.A.I.C.S.: 541612

Networkers International (China) Co. Ltd (2)
1503B Building A Phoenix Place Shu Guang Xi Li, Chaoyang District, Beijing, 100028, China
Tel.: (86) 1064686168
Web Site: http://www.networksplc.com
Telecommunications Staff Recruitment Services
N.A.I.C.S.: 561311

Networkers International (Malaysia) Sdn Bhd (2)
Suite B 09 12 Block B Plaza Mont Kiara 2 Jalan Kiara, 50480, Kuala Lumpur, Malaysia
Tel.: (60) 327318100
Telecommunication Staff Recruiting Services
N.A.I.C.S.: 561311

Subsidiary (US):

Networkers Telecommunications Inc (2)
6400 International Pkwy Ste 1510, Plano, TX 75093
Tel.: (972) 473-1100
Web Site:
http://www.networkerstechnology.com
Telecommunication Software Development Services
N.A.I.C.S.: 541511

Subsidiary (Non-US):

Networkers Telecommunications Pty Ltd (2)
201 Heritage House Dreyer Street, Claremont, Cape Town, 7735, South Africa
Tel.: (27) 21 670 0600
Telecommunications Staffing Services
N.A.I.C.S.: 561311
Andrew Matthis *(Mng Dir)*

GAUDFRIN
Batiment 45 Rue De La Liberte, 78100, Saint Germain-en-Laye, Yvelines, France
Tel.: (33) 130618000
Web Site: http://www.gaudfrin.com
Rev.: $23,000,000
Emp.: 13
Engineering Services
N.A.I.C.S.: 541330
Guy Gaudfrin *(Pres)*

GAUMONT S.A.
30 avenue Charles de Gaulle, 92200, Neuilly-sur-Seine, France
Tel.: (33) 146432000
Web Site: https://www.gaumont.fr
GAM—(EUR)
Rev.: $190,140,192
Assets: $441,099,459
Liabilities: $227,071,421
Net Worth: $214,028,038
Earnings: ($3,759,797)
Emp.: 7,838
Fiscal Year-end: 12/31/23
Motion Picture Producer & Distr
N.A.I.C.S.: 512110
Sidonie Dumas *(CEO)*

GAUSELMANN AG
Merkur Allee 1215, 32339, Espelkamp, Germany
Tel.: (49) 577249 0
Web Site: http://www.gauselmann.de
Year Founded: 1964
Sales Range: $1-4.9 Billion
Emp.: 7,975
Developer & Mfr of Coin-Operated Amusement Games & Electronic Casino Games; Operator of Video Arcades
N.A.I.C.S.: 713290
Paul Gauselmann *(Co-Chm-Mgmt Bd)*

Subsidiaries:

ADP Gauselmann GmbH (1)
Merkur-Allee 1-15, 32339, Espelkamp, Germany
Tel.: (49) 5772490
Web Site: http://www.system.adp-gauselmann.com
Electronic Vending Machine Mfr
N.A.I.C.S.: 333310

BEIT GmbH (1)
Merkur-Allee 1-15, 32339, Espelkamp, Germany
Tel.: (49) 5772490
Web Site: http://www.beit.de
Software Services
N.A.I.C.S.: 541511
Christof Meier *(Mng Dir)*

BEIT Systemhaus GmbH (1)
Mercury Allee 1-15, 32339, Espelkamp, Germany
Tel.: (49) 577249555
Web Site: http://www.beit.de
Emp.: 100
Information Technology Consulting Services
N.A.I.C.S.: 541512
Ulrich Beerhorst *(Mng Dir)*

Blueprint Gaming Ltd. (1)
Fortune House Northgate Terrace Northern Road, Newark, NG24 2EU, United Kingdom
Tel.: (44) 1636343355
Web Site: http://www.blueprintgaming.com
Online Game Development Services
N.A.I.C.S.: 541511

Euro Payment Group GmbH (1)
Europa-Allee 52, 60327, Frankfurt am Main, Germany
Tel.: (49) 6967728900
Web Site:
http://www.europaymentgroup.com
Electronic Online Payment Services
N.A.I.C.S.: 522320
Christian Diegelmann *(Founder & Co-CEO)*

Gauselmann Grosshandel GmbH (1)
Helene Wessel Bogen 21, 80939, Munich, Germany
Tel.: (49) 89 3 16 95 40
Coin Operated Machine Distr
N.A.I.C.S.: 423990

GeWeTe Geldwechsel- und Sicherheitstechnik GmbH (1)
Zum Lindenbusch 5, Industriegebiet Obergartzem Mechemich, 53894, Euskirchen, Germany
Tel.: (49) 225630000
Web Site: http://www.gewete.com
Emp.: 115
Electronic Vending Machine Mfr
N.A.I.C.S.: 333310
Aristidis Tsikouras *(Mng Dir)*

Gebruder Gauselmann GmbH (1)
Oelder Str 38, 59302, Oelde, Germany
Tel.: (49) 25 22 83 44 8 0
Web Site: http://www.gg-oelde.de
Coin Operated Machine Distr
N.A.I.C.S.: 423990

HESS Cash Systems GmbH & Co. KG (1)
Robert Bosch Strasse 30, 71106, Magstadt, Germany
Tel.: (49) 7159 4009
Web Site: http://en.hess.de
Emp.: 160
Cash Handling System Mfr
N.A.I.C.S.: 333993
Ulrich Bauer *(CEO)*

Subsidiary (Non-US):

HESS Austria GmbH (2)
Harterstrasse 29, 8101, Gratkorn, Austria
Tel.: (43) 3124 23844
Coin Operated Machine Mfr & Distr
N.A.I.C.S.: 339999

HESS Schweiz AG (2)
Zentweg 9, 3006, Bern, Switzerland
Tel.: (41) 31 930 10 20
Web Site: http://www.hess-schweiz.ch
Emp.: 12
Coin Operated Machine Mfr & Distr
N.A.I.C.S.: 339999

INTERNATIONAL PUBLIC

Rudolf Steinbichler *(Mgr)*

MEGA Spielgerate Entwicklungs- und Vertriebsgesellschaft mbh & Co. KG (1)
Im Dachstuck 15, 65549, Limburg, Germany
Tel.: (49) 64 31 95 74 0
Web Site: http://www.mega-spiel.de
Coin Operator Machine Mfr
N.A.I.C.S.: 339999

MERKUR Casino Limited (1)
Merkur-Allee 1-15, 32339, Espelkamp, Germany
Tel.: (49) 5772490
Web Site: http://www.merkur-casino.de
Casino & Gaming Services
N.A.I.C.S.: 721120

Merkur Dosniha S.L. (1)
Calle de la Maquinaria 6-Poligono Son Valenti, 07011, Palma de Mallorca, Spain
Tel.: (34) 971606062
Web Site: http://www.merkurdosniha.com
Vending Machine Retailer
N.A.I.C.S.: 445132

Merkur Freizeit Leasing GmbH (1)
Merkur Allee 1-15, 32339, Espelkamp, Germany
Tel.: (49) 57724379
Web Site: http://www.mfl.de
Electronic Vending Machine Mfr
N.A.I.C.S.: 333310

Merkur Immobilien- und Beteiligungs GmbH (1)
Merkur-Allee 1-15, 32339, Espelkamp, Germany
Tel.: (49) 577249656
Web Site: http://www.merkur-immobilien.de
Real Estate Services
N.A.I.C.S.: 531390

Merkur Interactive Services GmbH (1)
Charlottenstrasse 13, 10969, Berlin, Germany
Tel.: (49) 30201644010
Web Site: http://www.merkur-services.com
Gambling Services
N.A.I.C.S.: 713290
H. Wolfgang *(Project Mgr)*

Merkur Spielbanken Sachsen-Anhalt GmbH & Co. KG (1)
Nordpark 5, 06237, Leuna, Germany
Tel.: (49) 346386610
Web Site: http://www.merkur-spielbanken.de
Casino & Gaming Services
N.A.I.C.S.: 721120

Merkur Sportwetten GmbH (1)
Tongesgasse 4, 60311, Frankfurt am Main, Germany
Tel.: (49) 6950500260
Web Site: http://www.xtip-onlineshop.de
Casino & Gaming Services
N.A.I.C.S.: 721120
Patrick Schmidt *(Head-Mktg, Retail & Sponsoring)*

Royal Casino DGB GmbH (1)
Im Obrock 37, 32278, Kirchlengern, Germany
Tel.: (49) 52237909089
Web Site: http://www.royalcasinodgs.de
Casino & Gaming Services
N.A.I.C.S.: 721120

Schneider Automaten GmbH & Co. KG (1)
Rhondorfer Str 9, 50939, Cologne, Germany
Tel.: (49) 22193 77 50 16
Web Site: http://www.schneider-automaten-home.de
Coin Operated Machine Distr
N.A.I.C.S.: 423990

Totolotek S.A. (1)
St 18 b Dance 18 b, 02 829, Warsaw, Poland
Tel.: (48) 223210300
Web Site: http://totolotek.pl
Gambling Services
N.A.I.C.S.: 713290

Walberer Automaten GmbH & Co. KG (1)

Ruttenscheider Street 295, Essen, Essen, Germany
Tel.: (49) 201 450 16
Web Site: http://www.walberer.de
Amusement Machine Distr
N.A.I.C.S.: 423440

edict egaming GmbH (1)
Schillerstrasse 44, 22767, Hamburg, Germany
Tel.: (49) 4080803990
Web Site: http://www.edict.de
Online Gambling Services
N.A.I.C.S.: 541511
Dominic-Daniel Lienard *(Mng Dir)*

msp MUnzspielpartner GmbH & Co. KG (1)
Severinstr 20, 45127, Essen, Germany
Tel.: (49) 201245400
Web Site: http://www.muenzspielpartner.de
Casino & Gaming Services
N.A.I.C.S.: 721120

GAUSH MEDITECH LTD.
Room 1808 Building A Zhonghui Plaza No 11 Dongzhimen South Street, Dongcheng, Beijing, China
Tel.: (86) 1059786328   Ky
Web Site: https://www.gaush.com
Year Founded: 1998
2407—(HKG)
Rev.: $192,092,400
Assets: $416,438,569
Liabilities: $188,663,560
Net Worth: $227,775,009
Earnings: ($54,039,006)
Emp.: 790
Fiscal Year-end: 12/31/22
Ophthalmic Medical Device Distr
N.A.I.C.S.: 423450
Jianjun Zhang *(Pres)*

Subsidiaries:

Roland Consult Stasche & Finger GmbH (1)
Heidelberger Str 7, 14772, Brandenburg, Germany
Tel.: (49) 33818902986
Web Site: https://www.roland-consult.com
Ophthalmological Diagnostic Device Mfr & Distr
N.A.I.C.S.: 334510

Teleon Surgical Vertriebs GmbH (1)
Am Borsigturm 58, 13507, Berlin, Germany
Tel.: (49) 304309550
Ophthalmic Device Distr
N.A.I.C.S.: 423460

GAUSSIN SA
11 rue du 47 d'Artillerie, 70400, Héricourt, France
Tel.: (33) 384461345
Web Site: http://www.gaussin.com
ALGAU—(EUR)
Sales Range: $1-9.9 Million
Emp.: 30
Port Trailers & Self-Propelled Barges Mfr
N.A.I.C.S.: 333924
Christophe Gaussin *(Chm & Mng Dir)*

GAUTAM EXIM LIMITED
Plot No 29 Pavitra Opp Sargam Society Chharwada Road 2nd Floor, Vapi, 396 195, Gujarat, India
Tel.: (91) 2602430106
Web Site: https://www.gautamexim.com
Year Founded: 1997
540613—(BOM)
Rev.: $33,754,091
Assets: $3,804,232
Liabilities: $2,247,455
Net Worth: $1,556,777
Earnings: $44,518
Emp.: 10
Fiscal Year-end: 03/31/23
Recyclable Material Distr
N.A.I.C.S.: 423930

Balasubramanian Raman *(Chm, Mng Dir & CFO)*

GAUTAM GEMS LIMITED
3rd Floor Office-301 Sumukh Super Compound Vasta Devadi Road, Surat, 395 004, Gujarat, India
Tel.: (91) 2612538046   In
Web Site: https://www.gautamgems.com
Year Founded: 2002
540936—(BOM)
Rev.: $10,987,637
Assets: $5,881,540
Liabilities: $2,940,980
Net Worth: $2,940,560
Earnings: $42,458
Emp.: 36
Fiscal Year-end: 03/31/23
Jewellery Product Mfr & Distr
N.A.I.C.S.: 339910
Gautam Pravinchandra Sheth *(Founder & Mng Dir)*

GAW CAPITAL ADVISORS LIMITED
18/F No 68 Yee Wo Street, Causeway Bay, China (Hong Kong)
Tel.: (852) 2583 7700   HK
Web Site: http://www.gawcapital.com
Emp.: 80
Real Estate Investment Fund Management Services
N.A.I.C.S.: 523940
Goodwin Gaw *(Co-Founder, Chm & Mng Principal)*

Subsidiaries:

GCP Hospitality Management Ltd. (1)
22/F Lyndhurst Tower 1 Lyndhurst Terrace, Central, China (Hong Kong)
Tel.: (852) 2583 7700
Web Site: http://www.gcphospitality.com
Hotel & Hospitality Asset Development & Management Services
N.A.I.C.S.: 531312
Christophe Vielle *(CEO & Mng Dir)*

Gaw Capital Advisors (Shanghai) Co., Ltd. (1)
Suite 2303 Ciro's Plaza 388 Nan Jing West Road, Shanghai, 200003, China
Tel.: (86) 21 6386 7766
Web Site: http://www.gawcapital.com
Real Estate Investment Management Services
N.A.I.C.S.: 523940

Gaw Capital Partners (USA), LLC (1)
818 W 7th St Ste 410, Los Angeles, CA 90017
Tel.: (213) 213-8500
Web Site: http://www.gawcapital.com
Real Estate Investment Management Services
N.A.I.C.S.: 523940
Timothy Walsh *(Pres & COO)*

GAY LEA FOODS CO-OPERATIVE LTD.
5200 Orbitor Dr, Mississauga, L4W 5B4, ON, Canada
Tel.: (905) 283-5300
Web Site: https://www.gaylea.com
Year Founded: 1958
Emp.: 1,300
Dairy Co-Operative; Dairy Products Mfr
N.A.I.C.S.: 112120
Michael Barrett *(Pres & CEO)*

Subsidiaries:

Salerno Dairy Products Limited (1)
20 Morley Street, Hamilton, L8H 3R7, ON, Canada
Tel.: (905) 544-6281
Web Site: http://www.salernodairy.com

Sales Range: $50-74.9 Million
Emp.: 185
Cheese Mfr
N.A.I.C.S.: 311513
Angelo Fidanza *(CEO)*

GAYATRI BIOORGANICS LTD.
C-1 1st Floor 6-3-1090 TSR Towers Raj Bhavan Road, Somajiguda, Hyderabad, 500 082, Andhra Pradesh, India
Tel.: (91) 4066100111
Web Site: http://www.gayatribioorganics.com
524564—(BOM)
Assets: $354,026
Liabilities: $4,855,633
Net Worth: ($4,501,606)
Earnings: ($67,895)
Emp.: 278
Fiscal Year-end: 03/31/21
Organic Chemical Product Mfr
N.A.I.C.S.: 325199
Tikkavarapu Sandeep Kumar Reddy *(Chm)*

GAYATRI HIGHWAYS LTD.
5 Floor A Block TSR Towers 6-3-1090 Raj Bhavan Road, Somajiguda, Hyderabad, 500 082, Telangana, India
Tel.: (91) 4040024262
Web Site: http://www.gayatrihighways.com
Year Founded: 2006
541546—(BOM)
Rev.: $2,552,185
Assets: $292,244,662
Liabilities: $449,752,353
Net Worth: ($157,507,691)
Earnings: ($14,143,289)
Fiscal Year-end: 03/31/23
Highway Rehabilitation Services
N.A.I.C.S.: 237310
K. G. Naidu *(CEO)*

GAYATRI PROJECTS LTD
B-1 T S R Towers 6-3-1090 Raj Bhavan Road Somajiguda, Hyderabad, 500082, Andhra Pradesh, India
Tel.: (91) 4023310330
Web Site: https://www.gayatri.co.in
GAYAPROJ—(NSE)
Rev.: $533,426,603
Assets: $787,572,458
Liabilities: $657,450,516
Net Worth: $130,121,942
Earnings: $5,883,464
Emp.: 2,578
Fiscal Year-end: 03/31/21
Civil Construction Services
N.A.I.C.S.: 541330
Sreedhar Babu P. *(CFO)*

GAYATRI SUGARS LIMITED
B2 2nd Floor TSR Towers Rajbhavan Road Somajiguda, Hyderabad, 500082, Telangana, India
Tel.: (91) 4023414823   In
Web Site: https://www.gayatrisugars.com
Year Founded: 1995
532183—(BOM)
Rev.: $46,623,536
Assets: $23,629,878
Liabilities: $38,520,053
Net Worth: ($14,890,174)
Earnings: $4,115,089
Emp.: 651
Fiscal Year-end: 03/31/23
Sugar Mfr & Distr
N.A.I.C.S.: 311313
T. Indira Subbarami Reddy *(Chm)*

GAZ GROUP MANAGEMENT COMPANY LLC

88 Lenin Avenue, 603004, Nizhniy Novgorod, Russia
Tel.: (7) 8312990990
Web Site: http://www.gazgroup.ru
Sales Range: $1-4.9 Billion
Emp.: 115,000
Mfr of Light Commercial Vehicles, Trucks, Buses, Cars, Diesel Engines, Power-Train Components & Road Construction Equipment
N.A.I.C.S.: 336110

GAZ-SERVIS AO
Varshavskoe shosse bldg 95 bldg 1 floor 4 room XXXII room 64, Warsaw Highway 95, Moscow, 117556, Russia
Tel.: (7) 4952801018   RU
Web Site: https://www.gaz-services.ru
GAZS—(MOEX)
Sales Range: Less than $1 Million
Financial Management Services
N.A.I.C.S.: 523999

GAZ-TEK PAO
Tel.: (7) 4952800297   RU
Web Site: http://www.gaz-tek.ru
GAZT—(MOEX)
Sales Range: Less than $1 Million
Financial Investment Services
N.A.I.C.S.: 523999

GAZELLE ASSET MANAGEMENT PTE LTD.
101 Thomson Road No. 28-04, United Square, Singapore, Singapore
Tel.: (65) 6353 0820
Financial And Investment Managers
N.A.I.C.S.: 525990

GAZKON AO
Varshavskoe shosse house 95 building 1 floor 4 room XXXII room 64 A, Warsaw Highway, Moscow, 117556, Russia
Tel.: (7) 4952801057   RU
Web Site: https://www.gazcon.ru
Year Founded: 2004
GAZC—(MOEX)
Sales Range: Less than $1 Million
Financial Management Services
N.A.I.C.S.: 523999
Kochetkov German Gennadevich *(Mgr)*

GAZOMAT SARL
11 Rue de l Industrie, 67400, Illkirch-Graffenstaden, France
Tel.: (33) 185650437
Web Site: http://www.gazomat.com
Sales Range: $10-24.9 Million
Electronic Detection Equipment Mfr
N.A.I.C.S.: 334511
Vincent Ghircoias *(Gen Mgr)*

GAZPROM GAZORASP ROSTOV AO
Sholokhov Ave 14 bldg 1, Rostov-na-Donu, 344019, Russia
Tel.: (7) 8632036161
Web Site: https://www.rostovoblgaz.ru
RTGZ—(MOEX)
Sales Range: Less than $1 Million
Natural Gas Distribution Services
N.A.I.C.S.: 213112
Sergey Vladimirovich Tabachuk *(Chm)*

GAZPROMBANK JSC
16 Building 1 Nametkina St, 117420, Moscow, Russia
Tel.: (7) 4959137474   RU
Web Site: http://www.gazprombank.ru

GAZPROMBANK JSC

Gazprombank JSC—(Continued)
Year Founded: 1990
Rev.: $6,096,849,660
Assets: $106,170,853,740
Liabilities: $94,522,219,380
Net Worth: $11,648,634,360
Earnings: $719,156,050
Fiscal Year-end: 12/31/19
Banking Services
N.A.I.C.S.: 522110
Alexey B. Miller *(Chm)*

Subsidiaries:

Bank GPB International S.A. (1)
15 rue Bender, 1229, Luxembourg, Luxembourg
Tel.: (352) 2629751
Web Site: http://www.gazprombank.lu
Commercial Banking Services
N.A.I.C.S.: 522110
Dmitry N. Derkatch *(Chm)*

Belgazprombank OJSC (1)
60/2 Pritytskogo Str, 220121, Minsk, Belarus **(49.66%)**
Tel.: (375) 17 229 1629
Web Site: http://www.belgazprombank.by
Commercial Banking Services
N.A.I.C.S.: 522110
Viktor D. Babariko *(Chm-Mgmt Bd)*

CUB OJSC (1)
7 Gagarina St, Chelyabinsk Region, Magnitogorsk, 455044, Russia
Tel.: (7) 83519248910
Commercial Banking Services
N.A.I.C.S.: 522110
Vyacheslav V. Berdnikov *(Chm)*

Centrex Europe Energy & Gas AG (1)
Wiedner Hauptstrasse 17, 1040, Vienna, Austria
Tel.: (43) 150536440
Web Site: http://www.centrex.com
Natural Oil & Gas Distr
N.A.I.C.S.: 424720

Credit Ural Bank JSC (1)
Gagarina Street House 17, 455044, Magnitogorsk, Chelyabinsk, Russia
Tel.: (7) 3519248910
Web Site: http://www.crediturral.ru
Commercial Banking Services
N.A.I.C.S.: 522110
Alexander Lazutkin *(Sr VP)*

Cryogenmash PJSC (1)
67 Lenin Avenue, Balashikha, Russia
Tel.: (7) 4955059333
Web Site: http://www.cryogenmash.ru
Industrial Gas & Equipment Mfr
N.A.I.C.S.: 325120
Vladimir Klinkov *(Dir-Logistics & Procurement)*

GPB Africa (Pty) Ltd (1)
94 8th Avenue, Edenvale, Gauteng, South Africa
Tel.: (27) 114522097
Web Site: http://www.gpbatteries.co.za
Battery Distr
N.A.I.C.S.: 441330
Vladimir Tevalinskiy *(CEO)*

GPB Financial Services Limited (1)
Interlink Hermes Plaza 1st Floor 46 Ayios Athanasios Av, CY-4102, Limassol, Cyprus
Tel.: (357) 25055100
Web Site: http://www.gpbfs.com.cy
Banking Investment Services
N.A.I.C.S.: 523150

GPB International S.A (1)
8 10 rue Mathias Hardt, 1717, Luxembourg, Luxembourg
Tel.: (352) 262975
Commercial Banking Services
N.A.I.C.S.: 522110
Dmitry N. Derkach *(Chm)*

GPB-Factoring LLC (1)
Prospekt 15A, Leninsky, Moscow, Russia
Tel.: (7) 4957899525
Web Site: http://www.gpb-factoring.ru
Financial Services
N.A.I.C.S.: 523999

Gazprom-Media Holding JSC (1)
Rochdelskaya Street 20, 123376, Moscow, Russia
Tel.: (7) 4957896800
Web Site: http://www.gazprom-media.com
Media Entertainment Services
N.A.I.C.S.: 541840
Alexey Miller *(Chm)*

Gazprombank (Switzerland) Ltd. (1)
Zollikerstrasse 183, 8008, Zurich, Switzerland
Tel.: (41) 443868686
Commercial Banking Services
N.A.I.C.S.: 522110

Gazprombank - Asset Management CJSC (1)
ul Koroviy Val d 7, Moscow, 119049, Russia
Tel.: (7) 4959804058
Web Site: http://www.gpb-am.ru
Commercial Banking Services
N.A.I.C.S.: 522110
Boris Popov *(Head-Product Mgmt)*

Gazprombank Leasing JSC (1)
BC Port Plaza No 4602 d 6 p 16, Moscow, 115432, Russia
Tel.: (7) 495 719 13 96
Web Site: http://www.gpbl.ru
Investment Leasing; Construction & Special Equipment Leasing Services
N.A.I.C.S.: 522220
Maxim Agadzhanov *(Gen Dir)*

Subsidiary (Domestic):

Carcade OOO (2)
Prospect Mira 81, 236000, Kaliningrad, 236000, Russia **(68%)**
Tel.: (7) 4012931625
Web Site: http://www.carcade.com
Emp.: 5
Financial Lending Services
N.A.I.C.S.: 523999

Gazprombank-Invest LLC (1)
Savvinskaya Naberejnaya 23 str 1, 119435, Moscow, Russia
Tel.: (7) 4959806560
Web Site: http://www.gpbi.ru
Real Estate Investment Services
N.A.I.C.S.: 531390

JSB GPB-Mortgage OJSC (1)
14 Kolomensky Proezd, Moscow, 115446, Russia
Tel.: (7) 84952234040
Commercial Banking Services
N.A.I.C.S.: 522110
Eduard A. Arakelov *(Chm)*

OMZ-Special Steels LLC (1)
Izhorskiy Zavod, Kolpino, Saint Petersburg, 196650, Russia
Tel.: (7) 8123228867
Web Site: http://www.omz-specialsteel.com
Metallurgical Billet Mfr
N.A.I.C.S.: 331110

United Heavy Machinery Plants OJSC (1)
Sadovnicheskaya st 9A, Inner-city municipal district Zamoskvorechye, Moscow, 115035, Russia **(98.94%)**
Tel.: (7) 4956621040
Web Site: https://omz.tech
Sales Range: $1-4.9 Billion
Emp.: 16,988
Heavy Equipment & Machinery Mfr
N.A.I.C.S.: 333120
Yury I. Utochkin *(Member-Mgmt Bd, Deputy Dir Gen & Dir-Technical)*

Subsidiary (Domestic):

OJSC Izhorskiye Zavody (2)
1 Pr Lenina, Kolpino, Saint Petersburg, 196651, Russia **(69.9%)**
Tel.: (7) 8123228000
Industrial Component Mfr
N.A.I.C.S.: 332410

OMZ Foundry Manufacture LLC (2)
1 Pr Lenina, Kolpino, Saint Petersburg, 196650, Russia
Tel.: (7) 812 322 8127
Web Site: http://www.omz-foundry.ru
Emp.: 150
Steel Foundry Operator

N.A.I.C.S.: 331513
Igor Martushev *(Gen Mgr)*

OMZ-Spetsstal OOO (2)
Izhorskiy Zavod, Kolpino, Saint Petersburg, Russia
Tel.: (7) 812 322 8007
Web Site: http://www.omz-specialsteel.com
Specialty Steel/Forged Products Mfr
N.A.I.C.S.: 332111

Subsidiary (Non-US):

SKODA JS a.s. (2)
Orlik 266, 31606, Plzen, Czech Republic
Tel.: (420) 378041111
Web Site: http://www.skoda-js.cz
Fabricated Metal Products Mfr
N.A.I.C.S.: 332999

GAZTRANSPORT ET TECHNIGAZ SA

1 Route de Versailles, 78470, Saint Remy-les-Chevreuse, France
Tel.: (33) 130234789
Web Site: https://www.gtt.fr
Year Founded: 1994
GTT—(EUR)
Rev.: $473,599,735
Assets: $680,416,161
Liabilities: $309,138,978
Net Worth: $371,277,183
Earnings: $222,289,436
Emp.: 623
Fiscal Year-end: 12/31/23
Engineeering Services
N.A.I.C.S.: 541330
Philippe Berterottiere *(Chm & CEO)*

Subsidiaries:

GTT Training Ltd. (1)
Gulls Cry Oakhill Road, Seaview, Isle of Wight, PO34 5AP, United Kingdom
Tel.: (44) 7909101682
Web Site: https://www.gtt-training.co.uk
Training & Technical Services
N.A.I.C.S.: 611710

GB GLOBAL LIMITED

205 to 214 Peninsula Centre Dr S S Rao Road Off Dr Ambedkar Road, Parel, Mumbai, 400 012, India
Tel.: (91) 22 43539191
Web Site: http://www.mandhana.com
Rev.: $51,886,609
Assets: $106,201,792
Liabilities: $222,846,897
Net Worth: $(116,645,104)
Earnings: $(124,339,291)
Emp.: 3,393
Fiscal Year-end: 03/31/18
Textile & Garment Mfr
N.A.I.C.S.: 314999
Vijay Thakordas Thakkar *(Mng Dir & Exec Dir)*

Subsidiaries:

Heads UP Ventures Limited (1)
008 Peninsula Center Dr S S Rao Road Parel, Mumbai, 400012, India
Tel.: (91) 2224117743
Web Site: https://huvl.in
Rev.: $181,128
Assets: $2,577,316
Liabilities: $400,360
Net Worth: $2,176,956
Earnings: $1,157,628)
Emp.: 22
Fiscal Year-end: 03/31/2023
Apparel Mfr & Distr
N.A.I.C.S.: 315250
Jagdish Pamwani *(VP-Sls)*

Mandhana Industries Limited - Mandhana Dyeing Division (1)
E-25 MIDC Tarapur Industrial Area, Thane, 401506, Maharashtra, India
Tel.: (91) 2525272426
Web Site: http://www.mandhana.com
Fabrics Dyeing Services
N.A.I.C.S.: 313210

INTERNATIONAL PUBLIC

Mandhana Industries Limited - Mandhana Dyeing Unit-II (1)
Plot No C-2 M I D C Tarapur Industrial Area, Boisar, Thane, 401506, Maharashtra, India
Tel.: (91) 2525272228
Sales Range: $350-399.9 Million
Emp.: 2,000
Fabrics Dyeing Services
N.A.I.C.S.: 313310
Pankaj Gohel *(VP)*

Mandhana Industries Ltd (Export Division) Unit I (1)
26/A II Phase Peenya Industrial Area, Bengaluru, 560058, Karnataka, India
Tel.: (91) 8028395332
Sales Range: $550-599.9 Million
Emp.: 1,500
Fabrics Export Services
N.A.I.C.S.: 424310

Mandhana Weaving House (Shirting Division) (1)
Plot No C-2 MIDC Tarapur Industrial Area, Thane, 401506, Maharashtra, India
Tel.: (91) 2525 274989
Web Site: http://www.mandhana.com
Sales Range: $100-124.9 Million
Emp.: 500
Fabric Weaving Services
N.A.I.C.S.: 313210

GB GROUP PLC

The Foundation Herons Way, Chester Business Park, Chester, CH4 9GB, United Kingdom
Tel.: (44) 1244657333 UK
Web Site: https://www.gbgplc.com
GBG—(AIM)
Rev.: $346,226,258
Assets: $1,186,068,016
Liabilities: $324,079,997
Net Worth: $861,988,019
Earnings: $(148,760,189)
Emp.: 1,250
Fiscal Year-end: 03/31/23
Identity Management Company
N.A.I.C.S.: 541611
David Rasche *(Chm)*

Subsidiaries:

Acuant, Inc. (1)
6080 Ctr Dr Ste 850, Los Angeles, CA 90045
Tel.: (213) 867-2625
Web Site: http://www.acuant.com
Electronics Stores
N.A.I.C.S.: 449210
Yossi Zekkri *(Pres & CEO)*

GBG (Australia) Pty. Ltd. (1)
Level 7 330 Collins Street, Melbourne, 3000, VIC, Australia
Tel.: (61) 385951500
Information Technology Services
N.A.I.C.S.: 541511

GBG (Malaysia) Sdn Bhd (1)
Level 7 Menara Millenium Jalan Damanlela Pusat Bandar, Damansara Heights, 50490, Kuala Lumpur, Wilayah Persekutuan, Malaysia
Tel.: (60) 327123200
Information Technology Services
N.A.I.C.S.: 541511

IDology Inc. (1)
2018 Powers Ferry Rd SE Ste 720, Atlanta, GA 30339
Tel.: (678) 324-3800
Web Site: http://www.idology.com
Data Processing, Hosting & Related Services
N.A.I.C.S.: 518210

Loqate Limited (1)
The Foundation Herons Way Chester Business Park, Chester, CH4 9GB, United Kingdom
Tel.: (44) 8001986460
Web Site: https://www.loqate.com
Information Technology Services
N.A.I.C.S.: 541511

GB GROUP S.A.

Rte Nationale 1 Chancelleres, PO Box 2493, Port-au-Prince, Haiti
Tel.: (509) 28140000
Web Site: http://www.gbgroup.com
Sales Range: $400-449.9 Million
Emp.: 2,000
Holding & Trading Company
N.A.I.C.S.: 551112
Gilbert Bigio *(Chm)*

GB PARTNERSHIPS LIMITED
15th Floor Cobalt Square 83-85 Hagley Road, Birmingham, B16 8QG, United Kingdom
Tel.: (44) 1214565662 UK
Web Site:
  http://www.gbpartnerships.co.uk
Year Founded: 2001
Local Improvement Finance Trusts; Property Development & Consulting
N.A.I.C.S.: 531390
Elaine Siew *(Mng Dir)*

GB RICAMBI S.P.A.
Via Di Mezzo 67/A, 41015, Nonantola, Modena, Italy
Tel.: (39) 059583111 IT
Web Site: http://www.gbricambi.it
Year Founded: 1962
Sales Range: $150-199.9 Million
Emp.: 200
Heavy Machinery Parts Mfr
N.A.I.C.S.: 336390
Filippo Borghi *(Pres)*

Subsidiaries:

American Crane & Tractor Parts Incorporated (1)
2200 State Line Rd, Kansas City, KS 66103
Tel.: (913) 371-8585
Web Site: http://www.actparts.com
Sales Range: $25-49.9 Million
Emp.: 50
Mfr of After-Market Parts for Heavy Machinery
N.A.I.C.S.: 336390
Dave Sellinger *(Mgr-Domestic Sls)*

CGR Cornelio Ghinassi Ricambi SPA (1)
Via Faentina 175, 48124, Ravenna, Italy
Tel.: (39) 0544 469 611
Web Site: http://www.ghinassi.com
Machinery Spare Parts Distr
N.A.I.C.S.: 423830
Sabrazio Sapirito *(CEO)*

Cervetti Ricambi SPA (1)
Via di Mezzo 67/a, Localita Casette, 41015, Nonantola, Modena, Italy
Tel.: (39) 059 583199
Web Site: http://www.cervetti.com
Machinery Spare Parts Distr
N.A.I.C.S.: 423830

GBB POWER LTD.
Momtaz Plaza 4th floor House 7 Road 4 Dhanmondi R/A, Dhaka, 1205, Bangladesh
Tel.: (880) 258613322
Web Site: https://www.gbb.com.bd
Year Founded: 2006
GBBPOWER—(DHA)
Rev.: $8,093,320
Assets: $22,970,518
Liabilities: $3,341,534
Net Worth: $19,628,984
Earnings: $1,021,229
Emp.: 113
Fiscal Year-end: 06/30/23
Electric Power Distribution Services
N.A.I.C.S.: 221122
Mohammed Taifur Hossain *(CEO & Mng Dir)*

GBB TK GMBH
Laubanger 10, 96052, Bamberg, Germany
Tel.: (49) 9516090345

Web Site: http://www.gramss.de
Rev.: $17,242,500
Emp.: 375
Food Products Mfr
N.A.I.C.S.: 311412
Gerhard Gramss *(Mng Dir)*

GBC SCIENTIFIC EQUIPMENT PTY LTD.
2-4 Lakewood Boulevard, PO Box 1135, Braeside, 3195, VIC, Australia
Tel.: (61) 3 9588 6666
Web Site: http://www.gbcsci.com
Year Founded: 1978
Emp.: 60
Scientific Equipment Mfr
N.A.I.C.S.: 334516
Ron Grey *(Mng Dir)*

Subsidiaries:

GBC Scientific Equipment USA, LLC (1)
151A N State St, Hampshire, IL 60140-9438
Tel.: (847) 683-9870
Web Site: http://www.gbcscientific.com
Sales Range: $50-74.9 Million
Emp.: 3
Scientific Equipment Mfr
N.A.I.C.S.: 423490

GBC Scientific Equipment de Mexico S.A. de C.V. (1)
Dunas 46 Colonia Acueducto de Guadalupe, 07279, Mexico, Mexico
Tel.: (52) 5553898707
Web Site: http://www.gbcsci.com.mx
Scientific Equipment Distr
N.A.I.C.S.: 423450

GBI HOLDINGS PTY., LTD.
78 Mallard Way, Cannington, 6107, WA, Australia
Tel.: (61) 894780400
Web Site: http://www.gbi.com.au
Year Founded: 1970
Sales Range: $50-74.9 Million
Emp.: 100
Holding Company
N.A.I.C.S.: 551112
Mark Gibson *(Mng Dir)*

Subsidiaries:

GBI Sales Pty., Ltd. (1)
27-33 Cleaver Ter, Belmont, 6104, WA, Australia
Tel.: (61) 894780466
Sales Range: $25-49.9 Million
Emp.: 50
Electronics & White Goods Distr
N.A.I.C.S.: 423690

Gibson Benness Industries Pty., Ltd. (1)
27-33 Cleaver Terrace, Belmont, 6104, WA, Australia
Tel.: (61) 89478044
Laminates, MDF & Particle Board Distr
N.A.I.C.S.: 423320

GBL INDUSTRIES LIMITED
801 8th Floor SAFAL PRELUDE B/h Pinnacle Business Park Corporate Road, Prahladnagar, Ahmedabad, 380 015, India
Tel.: (91) 8160162721
Web Site:
  http://www.gujaratbitumen.com
Year Founded: 1985
539009—(BOM)
Assets: $852,103
Liabilities: $112,261
Net Worth: $739,841
Earnings: ($18,656)
Fiscal Year-end: 03/31/20
Textile Products Distr
N.A.I.C.S.: 424310
Shailesh Harivadan Prajapati *(Mng Dir)*

GBLT CORP.
An Gut Nazareth 18A, 52353, Duren, 52353, Germany
Tel.: (49) 2421208560
Web Site: https://www.gbltcorp.com
GBLTF—(OTCEM)
Rev.: $42,340,744
Assets: $8,444,901
Liabilities: $8,991,757
Net Worth: ($546,856)
Earnings: $178,200
Fiscal Year-end: 12/31/22
Motor Vehicle Electrical & Electronic Equipment Manufacturing
N.A.I.C.S.: 336320
Joachim Thilo Sent *(CEO)*

GBM GOLD LIMITED
66 Ham Street Kangaroo Flat, Bendigo, 3555, VIC, Australia
Tel.: (61) 3 5445 2300
Web Site:
  http://www.gbmgold.com.au
Rev.: $543,020
Assets: $8,722,275
Liabilities: $8,307,419
Net Worth: $414,856
Earnings: ($798,753)
Emp.: 20
Fiscal Year-end: 06/30/18
Gold Exploration Services
N.A.I.C.S.: 212220
John Francis Harrison *(CEO)*

Subsidiaries:

Industrial Sands & Gravels Pty. Ltd. (1)
Ste 2 Wood St, Bendigo, 3554, VIC, Australia
Tel.: (61) 354452300
Web Site: http://www.gbgm.com.au
Sales Range: $50-74.9 Million
Industrial Sand & Gravel Mining Services
N.A.I.C.S.: 212322

GBM RESOURCES LTD
Tel.: (61) 493239674
Web Site: https://www.gbmr.com.au
GBZ—(ASX)
Rev.: $217,024
Assets: $40,822,471
Liabilities: $14,518,448
Net Worth: $26,304,023
Earnings: ($2,138,302)
Emp.: 16
Fiscal Year-end: 06/30/24
Gold & Copper Exploration
N.A.I.C.S.: 213114
Peter Thompson *(Exec Dir)*

GBST HOLDINGS LIMITED
Level 4 410 Ann Street, Brisbane, 4000, QLD, Australia
Tel.: (61) 7 3331 5555
Web Site: http://www.gbst.com
Rev.: $68,884,486
Assets: $79,222,076
Liabilities: $25,592,267
Net Worth: $53,629,809
Earnings: $4,877,282
Emp.: 530
Fiscal Year-end: 06/30/18
Provision Of Client Accounting & Securities Transaction
N.A.I.C.S.: 541219
Denis Orrock *(Head-Asia Pacific)*

Subsidiaries:

Emu Design (Qld) Pty. Ltd. (1)
Level 4 / 410 Ann St, Brisbane, 4000, QLD, Australia
Tel.: (61) 733315511
Web Site: http://www.emudesign.com.au
Sales Range: $25-49.9 Million
Emp.: 20
Web Designing & Development Services
N.A.I.C.S.: 541430
Denis Orrock *(CEO)*

GBST Holdings Limited - GBST Financial Services Division (1)
Level 4 410 Anne Street, Brisbane, 4000, QLD, Australia
Tel.: (61) 292536555
Web Site: http://www.gbst.com
Sales Range: $50-74.9 Million
Emp.: 50
Financial Advisory Services
N.A.I.C.S.: 523940
Denis Orrock *(Head-Asia Pacific)*

GBST Holdings Limited - GBST Wealth Management Division (1)
Level 24 259 George Street, Sydney, 2000, NSW, Australia
Tel.: (61) 290050900
Web Site: http://www.gbst.com
Sales Range: $50-74.9 Million
Emp.: 100
Wealth Management Services
N.A.I.C.S.: 531311

GC AESTHETICS PLC
Suite 601 Q House Furze Road, Sandyford, Dublin, 18, Ireland
Tel.: (353) 1293 3836 IE
Web Site:
  http://www.gcaesthetics.com
Sales Range: $50-74.9 Million
Emp.: 401
Holding Company; Breast Implant & Other Female Aesthetics Products Mfr
N.A.I.C.S.: 551112
Carlos Reis Pinto *(CEO-Interim & COO)*

GC BIOPHARMA CORP.
107 Ihyeon-ro 30beon-gil, Giheung-gu, Yongin, Gyeonggi-do, Korea (South)
Tel.: (82) 312609300
Web Site:
  https://www.globalgreencross.com
Year Founded: 1967
006280—(KRS)
Rev.: $1,312,576,871
Assets: $1,937,086,941
Liabilities: $735,472,580
Net Worth: $1,201,614,361
Earnings: $53,241,140
Emp.: 2,302
Fiscal Year-end: 12/31/22
Pharmaceutical Product Mfr & Whslr
N.A.I.C.S.: 325412
Hyun Namkoong *(Head)*

Subsidiaries:

GC Biopharma USA, Inc. (1)
2200 Fletcher Ave Ste 712, Fort Lee, NJ 07024
Emp.: 5,000
Pharmaceutical Product Mfr & Distr
N.A.I.C.S.: 325412

GC Health Care Corporation (1)
8F Pan-Pacific Buliding 12 Digital-ro 31-gil, Guro-gu, Seoul, 152-848, Korea (South)
Tel.: (82) 2 2040 9100
Pharmaceuticals Product Mfr
N.A.I.C.S.: 325412
John C. Lee *(CEO)*

GC JBP Corporation (1)
26 Mugeuk-ro 65beon-gil Geumwang-eup, Eumseong, 27632, Chungcheongbuk-do, Korea (South)
Tel.: (82) 43 879 2900
Web Site: http://www.greencrossbt.com
Pharmaceuticals Product Mfr
N.A.I.C.S.: 325412
Youngho Yoo *(CEO)*

GC Labtech, Inc. (1)
485 Spencer Ln, San Antonio, TX 78201
Tel.: (210) 405-4258
Web Site: https://www.gclabtech.com
Health Care Srvices
N.A.I.C.S.: 621610
Sung Park *(CEO)*

GCAM, Inc. (1)

GC BIOPHARMA CORP.

GC Biopharma Corp.—(Continued)
371 W Highland Ave, San Bernardino, CA 92405
Tel.: (909) 883-9501
Web Site: http://www.gcamplasma.com
Health Care Srvices
N.A.I.C.S.: 621999

Green Cross Corporation - Hwasun Plant (1)
40 Sandan-gil Hwasun-eup, Hwasun, Jeollanam-do, Korea (South)
Tel.: (82) 61 379 2100
Web Site: http://www.greencross.co.kr
Emp.: 300
Pharmaceuticals Product Mfr
N.A.I.C.S.: 325412

Green Cross Corporation - Ochang Plant (1)
586 Gwahaksaneop 2-ro Ochang-eup, Cheongwon-gun, Chongju, 363886, Chungcheongbuk-do, Korea (South)
Tel.: (82) 43 210 1300
Pharmaceuticals Product Mfr
N.A.I.C.S.: 325412

Green Cross Health Science (1)
813 Sun Tech city 1 474 Dunchon-daero, Jungwon-gu, Seongnam, 462-725, Gyeonggi-do, Korea (South)
Tel.: (82) 31 698 4300
Web Site: http://www.greencrosshs.com
Pharmaceuticals Product Mfr
N.A.I.C.S.: 325412

Green Cross Medical Science Corporation (1)
107 Ihyeon-ro 30beon-gil, Giheung-gu, Yongin, 16924, Gyeonggi-do, Korea (South)
Tel.: (82) 802979000
Web Site: https://www.greencrossms.com
Rev.: $86,754,694
Assets: $73,993,005
Liabilities: $46,649,042
Net Worth: $27,343,962
Earnings: ($2,346,020)
Emp.: 132
Fiscal Year-end: 12/31/2022
In-Vitro Diagnostic Substances & Medical Products Mfr
N.A.I.C.S.: 325413
Sagong Younghee (Pres)

Green Cross i-MED (1)
4F Opulence Buliding 254 Seocho-daero, Seocho-gu, Seoul, 137-601, Korea (South)
Tel.: (82) 1644 0808
Health Care Srvices
N.A.I.C.S.: 621999

UBcare Co., Ltd. (1)
29th 30th 31st floor Yeouidodong Park One Tower 2, Yeongdeungpo-gu, Seoul, 152-769, Korea (South) (52.65%)
Tel.: (82) 221055000
Web Site: https://www.ubcare.co.kr
Rev.: $102,274,258
Assets: $124,162,882
Liabilities: $29,433,086
Net Worth: $94,729,796
Earnings: $3,150,215
Emp.: 304
Fiscal Year-end: 12/31/2022
Medical Software Development Services
N.A.I.C.S.: 541511
Sang-Kyoung Lee (Pres & CEO)

GC CONSTRUCTION HOLDINGS LTD.
Unit 909 9th Floor Tower 1 Cheung Sha Wan Plaza, 833 Cheung Sha Wan Road, Kowloon, China (Hong Kong)
Tel.: (852) 26188784 Ky
Web Site: https://www.chankiu.hk
Year Founded: 2005
1489—(HKG)
Holding Company
N.A.I.C.S.: 551112

GC CORPORATION
76 1 Hasunuma Cho Itabashi Ku, Tokyo, 174 8585, Japan
Tel.: (81) 339651221
Web Site: http://www.gcdental.co.jp
Year Founded: 1921
Sales Range: $25-49.9 Million
Emp.: 1,657
Mfr of Dental Supplies & Equipment
N.A.I.C.S.: 339114
Makoto Nakao (Pres & CEO)

Subsidiaries:

DENTAL DIAMOND CO. (1)
Nishikimachidentaru Bldg, Chiyoda, Tokyo, 101-0054, Japan
Tel.: (81) 332192571
Web Site: http://www.dental-diamond.co.jp
Dental Equipment Distr
N.A.I.C.S.: 423450

GC ADVANCED TECHNOLOGIES INC. (1)
4300 W 123rd St, Alsip, IL 60803
Tel.: (708) 897-4024
Dental Equipment Distr
N.A.I.C.S.: 423450

GC ASIA DENTAL PTE. LTD. (1)
11 Tampines Concourse 03-05, Singapore, 528729, Singapore
Tel.: (65) 6546 7588
Web Site: http://www.gcasiadental.com
Emp.: 20
Dental Equipment Distr
N.A.I.C.S.: 423450
Sally Ong (Mgr-Fin)

GC AUSTRALASIA DENTAL PTY. LTD. (1)
PO Box 504, Matraville, Sydney, 2036, NSW, Australia
Tel.: (61) 2 9316 4499
Dental Equipment Distr
N.A.I.C.S.: 423450
Angela Murray (Mgr-Ops)

GC AUSTRIA GmbH (1)
Tallak 124, 8103, Graz, Austria
Tel.: (43) 3124 54020
Web Site: http://www.austria.gceurope.com
Emp.: 10
Dental Equipment Distr
N.A.I.C.S.: 423450
Mario Puschitz (Mgr-Sls)

GC America, Inc. (1)
3737 W 127th St, Alsip, IL 60803
Tel.: (708) 597-0900
Web Site: http://www.gcamerica.com
Sales Range: $25-49.9 Million
Emp.: 130
Dental Materials & Supplies Mfr
N.A.I.C.S.: 339114
Bob McCague (Controller)

GC DENTAL (SUZHOU) CO., LTD. (1)
127 Qing Qiu Street Suzhou Industrial Park, Suzhou, 215021, China
Tel.: (86) 512 6283 3083
Web Site: http://www.gcchina.com.cn
Dental Equipment Distr
N.A.I.C.S.: 423450
Qin Guo Wen (Mgr-R&D)

GC EUROPE N.V. (1)
Researchpark Haasrode-Leuven 1240, Interleuvenlaan 33, 3001, Leuven, Belgium
Tel.: (32) 16 74 10 00
Web Site: http://www.gceurope.com
Emp.: 130
Dental Equipment Distr
N.A.I.C.S.: 423450
Michele M. Puttini (Pres)

GC FRANCE S.A.S. (1)
8 rue Benjamin Franklin, 943894370, Sucy-en-Brie, France
Tel.: (33) 1 49 80 37 91
Web Site: http://europe.gc.dental
Dental Equipment Distr
N.A.I.C.S.: 423450
Jean-Francois Procquez (Gen Mgr)

GC GERMANY GmbH (1)
Seifgrundstrasse 2, 61348, Bad Homburg, Germany
Tel.: (49) 6172 99 596 0
Dental Equipment Distr
N.A.I.C.S.: 423450

GC ITALIA S.r.l. (1)
Via Calabria 1, 20098, Milan, San Giuliano, Italy
Tel.: (39) 02 98282068
Web Site: http://www.gcitalia.it
Dental Equipment Distr
N.A.I.C.S.: 423450
Franco Bartoli (CEO)

GC KOREA CO., LTD. (1)
50 Chungjeongno, Seodaemun-Gu, Seoul, 03740, Korea (South)
Tel.: (82) 2 313 2272
Web Site: http://www.gckorea.co.kr
Emp.: 26
Dental Equipment Distr
N.A.I.C.S.: 423450
Taku Kitano (CEO)

GC NORDIC AB (1)
Varuvagen 9, 125 30, Alvsjo, Sweden
Tel.: (46) 8 410 344 90
Web Site: http://nordic.gceurope.com
Dental Equipment Distr
N.A.I.C.S.: 423450
Johan Andersson (Mng Dir)

GC TAIWAN DENTAL CORP. (1)
16F No 176 Jian Yi Rd, Chung Ho, Taipei, Taiwan
Tel.: (886) 2 8227 1505
Web Site: http://www.gctaiwan.com.tw
Dental Equipment Distr
N.A.I.C.S.: 423450

GC TECH. EUROPE N.V. (1)
Researchpark Haasrode-Leuven 1511, Interleuvenlaan 13, 3001, Leuven, Belgium
Tel.: (32) 16 74 26 00
Web Site: http://www.gctech-europe.com
Dental Equipment Distr
N.A.I.C.S.: 423450

GC UNITED KINGDOM LTD. (1)
12-15 Coopers Court, Newport Pagnell, MK16 8JS, Buckinghamshire, United Kingdom
Tel.: (44) 1908 218 999
Web Site: http://www.uk.gceurope.com
Dental Equipment Distr
N.A.I.C.S.: 423450
Chris Brown (Mng Dir)

JAPAN DENTAL SUPPLY CO., LTD. (1)
4-3-9 Nihonbashi, Naniwa-ku, Osaka, 556-0005, Japan
Tel.: (81) 6 6643 0085
Web Site: http://www.dentalsupply.co.jp
Dental Equipment Distr
N.A.I.C.S.: 423450
Ohnary Hitoshi (Gen Mgr)

Showa Yakuhin Kako Co., Ltd. (1)
4F Sanei Bldg Annex 17-11-2 chome Kyobashi, Chuo-ku, Tokyo, 104-0031, Japan (100%)
Tel.: (81) 335679571
Web Site: http://www.showayakuhinkako.co.jp
Emp.: 125
Dental & Pharmaceutical Products Mfr
N.A.I.C.S.: 339114
Seiji Yoshida (Pres & CEO)

GC RIEBER AS
Solheimsgaten 15, 5058, Bergen, Norway
Tel.: (47) 55606700
Web Site: https://www.gcrieber.com
Emp.: 100
Holding Company
N.A.I.C.S.: 551112
Jan Roger Bjerkestrand (CEO)

Subsidiaries:

GC Rieber Shipping ASA (1)
Solheimsgaten 15, 5058, Bergen, Norway (76.8%)
Tel.: (47) 55606800
Web Site: http://www.gcrieber-shipping.no
Rev.: $84,837
Assets: $79,576,109
Liabilities: $12,403,366
Net Worth: $67,172,743
Earnings: $11,408,222
Emp.: 10
Fiscal Year-end: 12/31/2023
Offshore Shipping Services

INTERNATIONAL PUBLIC

N.A.I.C.S.: 483113
Paul-Christian Rieber (Chm)

GCB BANK LIMITED
GCB Bank Building Thorpe Road High Street, PO Box 134, Accra, Ghana
Tel.: (233) 302668656
Web Site: https://www.gcbbank.com.gh
Year Founded: 1953
GCB—(GHA)
Rev.: $316,667,370
Assets: $2,272,440,212
Liabilities: $2,014,691,587
Net Worth: $257,748,624
Earnings: $84,495,567
Fiscal Year-end: 12/31/23
Banking Services
N.A.I.C.S.: 522110
Jude Kofi Arthur (Chm)

GCC GLOBAL CAPITAL CORPORATION
1177 W Hastings Street Suite 2033, Vancouver, V6E 2K3, BC, Canada
Tel.: (778) 389-9960 Ca
Year Founded: 2012
GCCC—(TSXV)
Investment Services
N.A.I.C.S.: 523999
Huijun Wang (CEO)

GCC SAS
226 Avenue du Marechal Foch, PO Box 2036, 78132, Les Mureaux, Cedex, France
Tel.: (33) 1 34 92 40 00
Web Site: http://www.gcc.fr
Sales Range: $450-499.9 Million
Emp.: 1,400
Construction Services
N.A.I.C.S.: 237990
Claude Gaillard (Chm)

Subsidiaries:

Holbat SAS (1)
Rue Du 14 Juillet, 62223, Saint-Laurent-Blangy, Pas-de-Calais, France
Tel.: (33) 321214400
Web Site: http://www.holbat.fr
Sales Range: $25-49.9 Million
Emp.: 166
Construction Services
N.A.I.C.S.: 236220

GCC, S.A.B. DE C.V.
Vicente Suarez Avenue Name of God, 31105, Chihuahua, Mexico
Tel.: (52) 6144423100 MX
Web Site: https://www.gcc.com
Year Founded: 1941
GCC—(MEX)
Rev.: $1,038,804,000
Assets: $2,222,591,000
Liabilities: $911,609,000
Net Worth: $1,310,982,000
Earnings: $151,854,000
Emp.: 2,923
Fiscal Year-end: 12/31/21
Cement, Concrete Materials & Aggregates Mfr & Marketer
N.A.I.C.S.: 327310
Federico Terrazas Becerra (Chm)

Subsidiaries:

Alliance Transportation, Inc. (1)
5725 Dietrich, San Antonio, TX 78219
Tel.: (210) 661-0900
Web Site: http://www.alliancetransport.com
Truckload Carrier Services
N.A.I.C.S.: 484121

GCC Alliance Concrete Inc. (1)
PO Box 108, Orange City, IA 51041
Tel.: (712) 737-2887
Web Site: http://www.gccusa.com

Sales Range: $10-24.9 Million
Emp.: 250
Ready Mixed Concrete
N.A.I.C.S.: 327320
Manuel Reyes (Pres)

Madata IT, S.A. de C.V. (1)
Kronos Building Av Periferico de la Juventud 15500, Fracc Comercial Puerta Norte Stage 1, 31125, Chihuahua, Mexico
Tel.: (52) 6143111313
Web Site: http://madata.com
Corporate Services
N.A.I.C.S.: 561499

Mid-Continent Concrete Co. (1)
431 W 23rd St, Tulsa, OK 74107-3005
Tel.: (918) 582-8111
Web Site: http://www.gccusa.com
Sales Range: $125-149.9 Million
Emp.: 400
Ready Mixed Concrete
N.A.I.C.S.: 327320
Kevin Jackson (Gen Mgr)

Sunset Properties, LLC (1)
468 Sand Dune Dr, Gulf Shores, AL 36542
Tel.: (251) 543-1370
Web Site: http://www.sunsetproperties.com
Commercial Real Estate Management Services
N.A.I.C.S.: 531312
Becky Smith (Office Mgr)

GCCL CONSTRUCTION & REALITIES LTD.
A/115 Siddhi Vinayak Towers B/h DCP Office Off S G Highway, Makarba, Ahmedabad, 380051, India
Tel.: (91) 7929703131
Web Site:
  https://www.gcclconstruction.com
Year Founded: 1994
Real Estate Manangement Services
N.A.I.C.S.: 531390
Himanshu Kamdar (Chm)

GCCP RESOURCES LIMITED
D21-1 Menara Mitraland No 13A Jalan PJU 5 Kota Damansara, 47810, Petaling Jaya, Selangor, Malaysia
Tel.: (60) 376100823
Web Site:
  https://www.gccpresources.com
41T—(CAT)
Rev.: $163,395
Assets: $13,851,016
Liabilities: $2,927,128
Net Worth: $10,923,888
Earnings: $1,009,992
Fiscal Year-end: 12/31/23
Calcium Carbonate Quarrying & Processing
N.A.I.C.S.: 212319
Alex Loo (CEO)

GCH TECHNOLOGY CO., LTD.
6501 CTF Finance Centre No 6 Zhujiang Road East, Tianhe, Guangzhou, 510623, Guangdong, China
Tel.: (86) 2022028453
Web Site: https://www.gchchem.com
Year Founded: 2002
688625—(SHG)
Rev.: $97,564,494
Assets: $335,525,617
Liabilities: $187,118,858
Net Worth: $148,406,759
Earnings: $27,405,701
Fiscal Year-end: 12/31/22
Chemical Product Mfr & Distr
N.A.I.C.S.: 325520
Wenlin Zhao (Chm, Gen Mgr & Engr)

Subsidiaries:

GCH Polymer Material (Hongkong)
Co. Limited (1)
11/F Capital Centre 151 Gloucester Road, Wanchai, China (Hong Kong)
Tel.: (852) 25832493

Synthetic Hydrotalcite Mfr & Distr
N.A.I.C.S.: 325220

Shanghai Chenghe International Co. Ltd. (1)
Room 1605 Building A Far East International Plaza 319 Xianxia Road, Changning District, Shanghai, 200051, China
Tel.: (86) 2168868973
Synthetic Hydrotalcite Mfr & Distr
N.A.I.C.S.: 325220

Tianjin Xindafeng Import and Export Trade Co. Ltd. (1)
Guangda Business Center 511 No 50 Xinghua Street, Ji Zhou District, Tianjin, China
Tel.: (86) 2282868581
Electronic Equipment Mfr & Distr
N.A.I.C.S.: 335314

GCL ENERGY TECHNOLOGY CO., LTD.
Room 202 No 18-1 Haigang Road, Jiangyin, 215000, Jiangsu, China
Tel.: (86) 51268536900
Web Site: http://www.seeker-cn.com
Year Founded: 1998
002015—(SSE)
Rev.: $1,499,872,140
Assets: $4,203,115,488
Liabilities: $2,492,460,828
Net Worth: $1,710,654,660
Earnings: $95,448,132
Fiscal Year-end: 12/31/22
Timber Product Mfr
N.A.I.C.S.: 335921
Yufeng Zhu (Chm)

GCM CAPITAL ADVISORS LTD
805 8th Floor Raheja Centre 214 Free Press Journal Marg, Nariman Point, Mumbai, 400 021, India
Tel.: (91) 222830564
Web Site: https://www.gcmcap.com
Year Founded: 2013
538319—(BOM)
Rev.: $577,725
Assets: $5,046,404
Liabilities: $348,935
Net Worth: $4,697,469
Earnings: $11,912
Emp.: 12
Fiscal Year-end: 03/31/21
Financial Advisory & Consulting Services
N.A.I.C.S.: 541611
Dipti Jain (Exec Officer & Sec)

GCM COMMODITY & DERIVATIVES LTD.
806 8th floor Rajeha Centre 214 Free Press Journal Marg Nariman Point, Mumbai, 400021, Maharashtra, India
Tel.: (91) 2235138191
Web Site:
  https://www.gcmcommo.co.in
Year Founded: 2005
535917—(BOM)
Rev.: $32,360
Assets: $3,649,386
Liabilities: $1,852,719
Net Worth: $1,796,667
Earnings: $84,407
Emp.: 6
Fiscal Year-end: 03/31/23
Commodity & Equity Trading
N.A.I.C.S.: 523160
Samir Baid (Exec Dir)

GCM RESOURCES PLC
3 Bunhill Row, London, EC1Y 8YZ, United Kingdom
Tel.: (44) 2072901630
Web Site: https://www.gcmplc.com
GCM—(AIM)
Assets: $54,610,639
Liabilities: $8,143,724
Net Worth: $46,466,914
Earnings: ($1,639,176)

Emp.: 17
Fiscal Year-end: 06/30/23
Coal & Uranium Exploration Company
N.A.I.C.S.: 213113
M. Anwarul Islam (Gen Mgr-Environment & Community)

GCP ASSET BACKED INCOME FUND LTD.
12 Castle Street, Saint Helier, JE2 3RT, Jersey
Tel.: (44) 1534847000
Web Site:
  http://www.graviscapital.com
Year Founded: 2015
GABI—(LSE)
Rev.: $33,494,590
Assets: $506,824,954
Liabilities: $1,739,020
Net Worth: $505,085,935
Earnings: $23,251,432
Emp.: 38
Fiscal Year-end: 12/31/23
Investment Services
N.A.I.C.S.: 525910
Alex Ohlsson (Chm)

GCP INFRASTRUCTURE INVESTMENTS LIMITED
IFC 5, Saint Helier, JE1 1ST, Jersey
Tel.: (44) 2034058500   JE
Web Site:
  https://www.graviscapital.com
Year Founded: 2010
GCP—(LSE)
Rev.: $51,243,377
Assets: $1,299,359,848
Liabilities: $78,596,351
Net Worth: $1,220,763,497
Earnings: $26,082,919
Fiscal Year-end: 09/30/24
Investment Management Service
N.A.I.C.S.: 523940
Ian Reeves (Chm)

GCS CAPITAL (HK) CO., LTD.
Suite 2305 23 F Nine Queen's Road, Central, China (Hong Kong)
Tel.: (852) 2553 1422
Web Site: http://www.gcscap.com
Asset Management Services
N.A.I.C.S.: 523999
Lei Chen (Mng Partner)

GCS HOLDINGS, INC.
190 Elgin Avenue, Georgetown, KY1-9005, Cayman Islands
Tel.: (345) 3105307274
Web Site: http://www.gcsincorp.com
Rev.: $2,342,893,200
Assets: $4,082,740,800
Liabilities: $467,398,800
Net Worth: $3,615,342,000
Earnings: $381,117,600
Fiscal Year-end: 12/31/18
Semiconductor Product Mfr
N.A.I.C.S.: 334413
Brian Ann (CEO)

Subsidiaries:

Global Communication Semiconductors, Inc. (1)
23155 Kashiwa Ct, Torrance, CA 90505
Tel.: (310) 530-7274
Web Site: http://www.gcsincorp.com
Semiconductor & Related Device Mfr
N.A.I.C.S.: 334413
Wing Yau (VP-Foundry Svcs)

Subsidiary (Domestic):

D-Tech Optoelectronics Inc. (2)
18062 Rowland St, City of Industry, CA 91748-1203
Tel.: (626) 269-1102
Web Site: http://www.dtechopto.com

Blank Magnetic & Optical Recording Media Mfr
N.A.I.C.S.: 334610
Xiucheng Wu (CEO)

GCV SERVICES LIMITED
Baba House 1st Floor M V Road Near Cine Magic Cinema, Andheri E, Mumbai, 400063, India
Tel.: (91) 22 2684 3666
Web Site:
  http://www.gcvservices.com
Sales Range: Less than $1 Million
Hotel Management & HousKeeping Services
N.A.I.C.S.: 721110
Sameer Relia (Mng Dir)

GD CULTURE GROUP LIMITED
No 119 South Zhaojuesi Road 2nd Floor Room 1, Chenghua District, Chengdu, 610047, Sichuan, China
Tel.: (86) 2884112941   NV
Web Site: http://www.ccnctech.com
Year Founded: 2015
GDC—(NASDAQ)
Rev.: $153,304
Assets: $3,800,908
Liabilities: $333,784
Net Worth: $3,467,124
Earnings: ($30,821,955)
Emp.: 20
Fiscal Year-end: 12/31/22
Investment Holding Company
N.A.I.C.S.: 551112
Wei Xu (Chm, Pres & CEO)

GD EXPRESS SDN BHD.
No 19 Jalan Tandang, 46050, Petaling Jaya, Selangor Darul Ehsan, Malaysia
Tel.: (60) 364195003   MY
Web Site:
  https://www.gdexpress.com
Year Founded: 1997
Rev.: $61,678,036
Assets: $117,696,031
Liabilities: $12,774,231
Net Worth: $104,921,800
Earnings: $9,067,759
Fiscal Year-end: 06/30/17
Logistics Consulting Servies
N.A.I.C.S.: 541614
Teong Teck Lean (CEO-Grp & Mng Dir)

GD-TIKVES AD
ul Siska br 5, Kavadarci, North Macedonia
Tel.: (389) 43415916
Web Site: http://www.gd-tikves.com
Year Founded: 1999
TIKV—(MAC)
Rev.: $7,322,062
Assets: $13,721,881
Liabilities: $3,856,955
Net Worth: $9,864,927
Earnings: $126,857
Fiscal Year-end: 12/31/23
Grape Farming Services
N.A.I.C.S.: 111332

GDB HOLDINGS BERHAD
A-02-01 F-02-01 and F-02-02 Sekitar 26 Enterprise Persiaran Hulu, Seksyen 26, 40400, Shah Alam, Selangor, Malaysia
Tel.: (60) 351038162
Web Site: https://www.gdbhb.com.my
0198—(KLS)
Rev.: $107,948,181
Assets: $78,021,606
Liabilities: $43,964,638
Net Worth: $34,056,968
Earnings: $3,436,873
Emp.: 115
Fiscal Year-end: 12/31/22

GDB HOLDINGS BERHAD

GDB Holdings Berhad—(Continued)
Building Construction Services
N.A.I.C.S.: 236210
Cheah Ham Cheia *(Mng Dir)*

Subsidiaries:

GDB Geotechnics Sdn. Bhd. (1)
A-02-01 F-02-01 & F-02-02 Sekitar 26 Enterprise, Persiaran Hulu Selangor Seksyen 26, 40400, Shah Alam, Selangor, Malaysia
Tel.: (60) 35 103 8162
Web Site: https://www.gdbgsb.com.my
Engineeering Services
N.A.I.C.S.: 541330

GDD POLET
Igmanska bb, 71320, Vogosca, Bosnia & Herzegovina
Tel.: (387) 33476801
Web Site: http://www.polet.ba
GDPSRK2—(SARE)
Rev.: $88,548
Assets: $2,520,883
Liabilities: $2,520,883
Earnings: $75,729
Emp.: 1
Fiscal Year-end: 12/31/21
Graphic Design Services
N.A.I.C.S.: 541430

GDEV INC.
55 Griva Digeni, 3101, Limassol, Cyprus
Tel.: (357) 25580040
Web Site: https://gdev.inc
Year Founded: 2010
GDEV—(NASDAQ)
Rev.: $464,549,000
Assets: $320,554,000
Liabilities: $420,366,000
Net Worth: ($99,812,000)
Earnings: $46,115,000
Emp.: 726
Fiscal Year-end: 12/31/23
Software Development Services
N.A.I.C.S.: 541511
Alexander Karavaev *(CFO)*

GDH LIMITED
29th Floor Guangdong Investment Tower 148 Connaught Road, Central, China (Hong Kong)
Tel.: (852) 28529288 HK
Web Site: http://www.gdh.com.hk
Year Founded: 1999
Sales Range: $1-4.9 Billion
Emp.: 12,000
Investment Holding Company
N.A.I.C.S.: 551112
Xiaofeng Huang *(Chm)*

Subsidiaries:

GDH Guangnan (Holdings) Limited (1)
Room 290508 29th Floor Shui On Centre 6 8 Harbor Road, Wan Chai, Hong Kong, China (Hong Kong) **(59.3%)**
Tel.: (852) 28283938
Web Site: https://www.gdguangnan.com
Rev.: $1,059,748,380
Assets: $622,710,765
Liabilities: $267,761,858
Net Worth: $354,908,908
Earnings: $19,512,090
Emp.: 1,436
Fiscal Year-end: 12/31/2022
Investment Holding Company
N.A.I.C.S.: 551112
Jinzhou He *(Gen Mgr)*

Subsidiary (Non-US):

Zhongshan Zhongyue Tinplate Industrial Co. Ltd (2)
Zhongshan No 2 Export Processing District, Zhongshan, China
Tel.: (86) 7608286348
Sales Range: $350-399.9 Million
Emp.: 2,000
Iron & Steel Mills
N.A.I.C.S.: 331110

Zhongyue Posco (Qinhuangdao) Tinplate Industrial Co., Limited (2)
Economic & Technological Development Zone, Qinhuangdao, Hebei, China
Tel.: (86) 335 5351998
Web Site: http://www.zyposco.com
Fabricated Metal Products Mfr
N.A.I.C.S.: 332999

GDH Guangnan (Holdings) Limited (1)
Units 2905-08 29th Floor Shui On Centre 6-8 Harbour Road, Wanchai, China (Hong Kong)
Tel.: (852) 28283938
Web Site: https://www.gdguangnan.com
Tinplate Mfr & Distr
N.A.I.C.S.: 331110
Chen Benguang *(Chm)*

GDH Real Estates (China) Co. Limited (1)
23F Xinchuangju Mansion 123 Tiyu West Road, Tianhe Dist, Guangzhou, 510620, China
Tel.: (86) 20 3824 8018
Real Estate Development Services
N.A.I.C.S.: 531390

Guangdong Investment Limited (1)
28/F 29/F Guangdong Investment Tower 148 Connaught Road, Central, China (Hong Kong)
Tel.: (852) 28604368
Web Site: https://www.gdi.com.hk
Rev.: $2,964,489,118
Assets: $17,063,225,427
Liabilities: $9,585,709,740
Net Worth: $7,477,515,688
Earnings: $705,994,223
Emp.: 10,587
Fiscal Year-end: 12/31/2022
Investment Services
N.A.I.C.S.: 523999
Johnson Tsang *(CFO)*

Subsidiary (Domestic):

Guangdong (International) Hotel Management Holdings Limited (2)
2/F GuangDong Hotel 18 Prat Avenue Road, TsimShaTsui, Kowloon, China (Hong Kong)
Tel.: (852) 28370788
Web Site: http://www.gdhhotels.com
Hotel Operator
N.A.I.C.S.: 721110
Yang Yuhui *(CFO)*

Guangdong Land Holdings Limited (1)
18/F Guangdong Investment Tower 148 Connaught Road, Central, China (Hong Kong)
Tel.: (852) 21656262
Web Site: http://www.gdland.com.hk
Rev.: $175,655,603
Assets: $6,237,328,943
Liabilities: $5,138,550,263
Net Worth: $1,098,778,680
Earnings: $51,634,185
Emp.: 579
Fiscal Year-end: 12/31/2022
Holding Company; Property Development & Investment
N.A.I.C.S.: 551112
Mingchang Wu *(Exec Dir)*

Namyue Holdings Limited (1)
29th Floor Guangdong Investment Tower 148 Connaught Road, Central, China (Hong Kong)
Tel.: (852) 23081013
Web Site: https://www.namyueholdings.com
Rev.: $10,971,375
Assets: $22,185,893
Liabilities: $6,884,235
Net Worth: $15,301,658
Earnings: ($5,600,948)
Emp.: 327
Fiscal Year-end: 12/31/2022
Fur & Leather Apparel Mfr
N.A.I.C.S.: 315250
Hu Kuang *(Bd of Dirs & Chm)*

SuperTime Development Company Limited (1)
No 18 Fong Yang Yi Lu, Beilun, Ningbo, 315800, Zhejiang, China
Tel.: (86) 574 8685 6886
Web Site: http://www.supertime-malting.com
Holding Company; Brewing & Malting
N.A.I.C.S.: 312120

GDI INTEGRATED FACILITY SERVICES INC.
695 90th Avenue, La Salle, H8R 3A4, QC, Canada
Tel.: (514) 368-1504 AB
Web Site: https://www.gdi.com
Year Founded: 1926
GDIFF—(OTCIQ)
Rev.: $1,249,433,365
Assets: $848,506,260
Liabilities: $542,612,876
Net Worth: $305,893,384
Earnings: $33,923,572
Emp.: 30,000
Fiscal Year-end: 12/31/21
Facility Services
N.A.I.C.S.: 561210
Stephane Lavigne *(CFO & Sr VP)*

Subsidiaries:

Ainsworth, Inc. (1)
131 Bermondsey Rd, Toronto, M4A 1X4, ON, Canada
Tel.: (416) 751-4420
Web Site: http://www.ainsworth.com
Technical Trade Services & Solutions Provider
N.A.I.C.S.: 541990
Gerry Mcgrath *(CHM of the Board)*

Division (Domestic):

GDI Technical Services (2)
695 90 Avenue Lasalle, Montreal, H8R 3A4, QC, Canada
Tel.: (514) 368-1504
Janitorial & Building Maintenance Services
N.A.I.C.S.: 561720
Patrice Bergeron *(Bus Mgr-Dev)*

GDI Integrated Facility Services USA Inc.
24300 Southfield Rd Ste 300, Southfield, MI 48075
Tel.: (248) 483-3170
Web Site: http://gdi.com
Commercial Cleaning Services
N.A.I.C.S.: 561720

Subsidiary (Domestic):

IH Services, Inc. (2)
127 Tanner Rd, Greenville, SC 29607
Tel.: (864) 297-3748
Web Site: http://www.ihservices.com
Sales Range: $200-249.9 Million
Emp.: 8,000
Janitorial & Maintenance Services
N.A.I.C.S.: 561720
Dick Hendley *(Chm)*

Paramount Building Solutions, LLC (1)
10235 S 51st St Ste 185, Phoenix, AZ 85044
Tel.: (480) 348-1177
Web Site: http://www.paramountbldgsol.com
Facility Support Services
N.A.I.C.S.: 561210
Jeff Southard *(Pres & CEO)*

GDI PROPERTY GROUP
Level 23 56 Pitt Street, Sydney, 2000, NSW, Australia
Tel.: (61) 292234222
Web Site: https://www.gdi.com.au
GDI—(ASX)
Rev.: $46,618,590
Assets: $764,666,129
Liabilities: $275,092,146
Net Worth: $489,573,983
Earnings: ($3,728,632)
Fiscal Year-end: 06/30/24
Real Estate Investment Services
N.A.I.C.S.: 523999
Steven Gillard *(Mng Dir)*

INTERNATIONAL PUBLIC

GDL LEASING & FINANCE LIMITED
B-3/91 Ashok Vihar PH- II, New Delhi, 110 052, India
Tel.: (91) 1127435354
Web Site: https://www.gdf-finance.com
Year Founded: 1994
530855—(BOM)
Rev.: $40,766
Assets: $385,758
Liabilities: $2,796
Net Worth: $382,961
Earnings: $1,065
Emp.: 4
Fiscal Year-end: 03/31/23
Financial Services
N.A.I.C.S.: 523999
Deepak Gangwani Kumar *(Chm)*

GDP VENDOME
30 Avenue De L Opera, 75002, Paris, France
Tel.: (33) 153300202
Web Site: http://www.gdp-vendome.fr
Sales Range: $10-24.9 Million
Emp.: 20
Holding Companies
N.A.I.C.S.: 551112
Jean-Francois Gobertier *(Mng Partner)*

GDS AUTOMOBILES
Z I Les Rochettes Rue Des Rochettes, 91150, Etampes, France
Tel.: (33) 164945259
Rev.: $24,700,000
Emp.: 51
New & Used Car Dealers
N.A.I.C.S.: 441110
Alain Loubatie *(Dir-Fin)*

GDS GLOBAL LIMITED
86 International Road, Singapore, 629176, Singapore
Tel.: (65) 62666668
Web Site: https://www.gdsglobal.com.sg
5VP—(CAT)
Rev.: $9,042,608
Assets: $14,191,923
Liabilities: $6,911,449
Net Worth: $7,280,474
Earnings: ($1,569,470)
Emp.: 79
Fiscal Year-end: 09/30/23
Door & Shutter Mfr
N.A.I.C.S.: 332321
Michael Wong *(Chm & CEO)*

Subsidiaries:

Grimm Industries Pte. Ltd. (1)
6 Harper Road 03-07 Leong Huat Building, Singapore, 369674, Singapore
Tel.: (65) 64416995
Web Site: https://www.grimmhardware.com
Metal Hardware Mfr & Distr
N.A.I.C.S.: 332510

GDS HOLDINGS LIMITED
F4/F5 Building C Sunland International No 999 Zhouhai Road, Pudong, Shanghai, 200137, China
Tel.: (86) 2120330303
Web Site: http://investors.gds-services.com
Year Founded: 2013
GDS—(NASDAQ)
Rev.: $1,428,779,926
Assets: $11,462,245,892
Liabilities: $7,756,914,900
Net Worth: $3,705,330,993
Earnings: ($194,406,637)
Emp.: 2,185
Fiscal Year-end: 12/31/22
Holding Company
N.A.I.C.S.: 551112

AND PRIVATE COMPANIES

William Wei Huang *(CEO, Founder & Chm)*

GE POWER INDIA LIMITED
Axis House Plot No 1-14 Towers 5 & 6 Jaypee Wish Town Sector 128, Noida, 201301, Uttar Pradesh, India
Tel.: (91) 1205011011
Web Site: https://www.ge.com
Year Founded: 1892
GEPIL—(NSE)
Rev.: $225,889,335
Assets: $343,365,506
Liabilities: $315,487,081
Net Worth: $27,878,425
Earnings: ($52,824,171)
Emp.: 1,398
Fiscal Year-end: 03/31/23
Construction Engineering Services
N.A.I.C.S.: 237990
Sanjeev Agarwal *(Exec Dir)*

GE-SHEN CORPORATION BERHAD
13-05 Menara MBMR Jalan Syed Putra Utara, 58000, Kuala Lumpur, Malaysia
Tel.: (60) 327850975   MY
Web Site:
   https://www.gscorp.com.my
Year Founded: 1995
GESHEN—(KLS)
Rev.: $53,673,651
Assets: $58,255,450
Liabilities: $31,034,286
Net Worth: $27,221,164
Earnings: $2,030,476
Emp.: 1,282
Fiscal Year-end: 12/31/22
Injection Molding Mfr
N.A.I.C.S.: 333248
Choong Kong Chan *(Mng Dir)*

Subsidiaries:

Ge-Shen Plastic (M) Sdn. Bhd. (1)
No 11 Jalan Riang 23 Taman Gembira, 81100, Johor Bahru, Johor, Malaysia
Tel.: (60) 73355196
Web Site: https://ge-shen.com
Sales Range: $125-149.9 Million
Emp.: 440
Plastic Molding Mfr
N.A.I.C.S.: 326199

Kibaru Manufacturing Sdn Bhd (1)
A83 Jalan 1 B 3 Kawasan MIEL Sungai Petani Phase I, 08000, Sungai Petani, Kedah Darul Aman, Malaysia (60%)
Tel.: (60) 44421222
Web Site: http://www.kibaru.com.my
Sales Range: $50-74.9 Million
Emp.: 175
Rubber Component Mfr
N.A.I.C.S.: 326299

Polyplas Sdn. Bhd. (1)
No 2056 Mukim 14 Lorong IKS Bukit Minyak 5 Taman IKS Bukit Minyak, S P T Pulau Pinang, 14100, Bukit Mertajam, Penang, Malaysia
Tel.: (60) 45070188
Web Site: https://www.polyplassb.com
Moulding Plastic Product Mfr
N.A.I.C.S.: 326199
Rexy Martin *(Mgr-Program)*

GE-TE MEDIA AB
Persgatan 10, 753 20, Uppsala, Sweden
Tel.: (46) 18 17 21 00   SE
Advertising & Other Related Management Consulting Services
N.A.I.C.S.: 541618
Lars Roland Tipner *(CEO)*

Subsidiaries:

Lokaltidningen Mitt i Stockholm AB (1)
Liljeholmsvagen 18, 100 74, Stockholm, Sweden
Tel.: (46) 8 550 550 00
Web Site: http://www.mitti.se
Newspapers & Magazines Publisher
N.A.I.C.S.: 513110
Lisen Nordenswan *(Mgr-Mktg)*

GEA GROUP AKTIENGESELLSCHAFT
Peter Muller Str 12, 40468, Dusseldorf, Germany
Tel.: (49) 21191361081   De
Web Site: https://www.gea.com
Year Founded: 1881
G1A—(DEU)
Rev.: $5,692,958,725
Assets: $6,984,885,425
Liabilities: $4,624,884,906
Net Worth: $2,360,000,520
Earnings: $118,924,338
Emp.: 18,232
Fiscal Year-end: 12/31/20
Engineering Services & Specialty Chemicals Mfr
N.A.I.C.S.: 541330
Kurt-Jurgen Low *(Deputy Chm-Supervisory Bd)*

Subsidiaries:

AeroFreeze, Inc. (1)
18394 Redmond Way, Redmond, WA 98052-5012
Tel.: (425) 869-8889
Web Site: http://www.aerofreeze.com
Frozen Food Cold Storage Services
N.A.I.C.S.: 493120

Arbeitsgemeinschaft Zellenkuhleranlage KKW Isar GEA Energietechnik GmbH-Alpine Bau Deutschland AG (1)
Furholzener Strasse 12-14, 85386, Eching, Germany
Tel.: (49) 89 32711 0
Food Processing Machinery Mfr
N.A.I.C.S.: 333241

BOS Homogenisers B.V. (1)
Oscar Romerolaan 18, 1216 TK, Hilversum, Netherlands
Tel.: (31) 353037190
Web Site: https://bos-homogenisers.com
Automotive Parts Services
N.A.I.C.S.: 423120

Bliss Refrigeration Ltd. (1)
20 Davis Way, Fareham, PO14 1AR, Hampshire, United Kingdom
Tel.: (44) 1329 822 200
Refrigerator Equipment Mfr
N.A.I.C.S.: 333415

Bock Australia Pty. Ltd. (1)
Unit 32 75 Corish Circle, Banksmeadow, 2019, NSW, Australia
Tel.: (61) 296667052
Web Site: http://www.bock.de
Terry Compressor Mfr
N.A.I.C.S.: 333912

Breconchery Ltd. (1)
Old Wolverton Road, Milton Keynes, MK12 5PY, Buckinghamshire, United Kingdom
Tel.: (44) 153 163 2476
Web Site: https://www.breconcherry.com
Emp.: 1
Tank Cleaning Equipment Mfr
N.A.I.C.S.: 333310
Olivier Vallet *(Gen Mgr)*

Brouwers Equipment B.V. (1)
Vestaweg 5, 8938 AV, Leeuwarden, Netherlands
Tel.: (31) 58 2911129
Web Site:
   http://www.brouwersequipment.com
Sales Range: $75-99.9 Million
Emp.: 12
Farm & Garden Machinery Whslr
N.A.I.C.S.: 423820

Bruckenbau Plauen GmbH (1)
Lurgiallee 5, 60439, Frankfurt am Main, Germany
Tel.: (49) 6997121216
Construction Engineering Services
N.A.I.C.S.: 541330

CFS Asia Ltd. (1)
589/108 Flr 19th Central City Tower Bangna-trad Rd Km 3, Bangna, 10260, Bangkok, Thailand
Tel.: (66) 2 745 6981
Sales Range: $25-49.9 Million
Emp.: 16
Food Processing Equipment Distr
N.A.I.C.S.: 423830

CFS Chile Comercializadora Limitada (1)
Nueva Los Leones 0252, Santiago, Providencia, Chile
Tel.: (56) 2 2327722
Food Processing Equipment Distr
N.A.I.C.S.: 423830

CFS Commercial (Beijing) Limited (1)
A1-4 XinYing Industrial Zone No 10 2nd Street KeChuang Eastern Area, 100023, Beijing, China
Tel.: (86) 106 725 4710
Sales Range: $25-49.9 Million
Emp.: 3
Food Product Machinery Mfr
N.A.I.C.S.: 333241

CFS Italy S.p.A. (1)
Via Delle Marine 5, 24064, Grumello del Monte, Italy
Tel.: (39) 035832929
Food Processing Machinery Mfr
N.A.I.C.S.: 333241

CFS Korea Ltd. (1)
4th Floor Monhyun Building 556 gangnam gaetero gangnam ku, Seocho-gu, Seoul, 135529, Korea (South)
Tel.: (82) 25213831
Web Site: http://www.gea-foodsolutions.com
Emp.: 5
Food Processing Machinery Mfr
N.A.I.C.S.: 333241
Bruno Roux *(Office Mgr)*

CFS Nordic A/S (1)
Industrivej 6, 4200, Slagelse, Denmark
Tel.: (45) 58 55 55 00
Web Site: http://www.CFS.com
Emp.: 6
Food Processing Machinery Mfr
N.A.I.C.S.: 333241

CFS Switzerland AG (1)
Industrieweg 32, 4852, Rothrist, Switzerland
Tel.: (41) 62 7853030
Web Site: http://www.gea.com
Sales Range: $25-49.9 Million
Emp.: 15
Food Processing Equipment Mfr
N.A.I.C.S.: 333241
Hostettler Hans *(Mgr-Sls)*

Convenience Food Systems S.A. de C.V. (1)
Avenida Vallarta 4951 Fracc Prados Vallarta, Zapopan, 45020, Jalisco, Mexico
Tel.: (52) 3336293808
Food Processing Equipment Mfr
N.A.I.C.S.: 333241

Dawmec Limited (1)
Unit 1 Salterns Lane, Fareham, PO16 0SU, Hampshire, United Kingdom
Tel.: (44) 1329 828833
Sales Range: $50-74.9 Million
Emp.: 5
Air Conditioning & Refrigeration Equipment Whslr
N.A.I.C.S.: 423740

Diessel Aktiengesellschaft (1)
Gewerbestrasse 8, Cham, 6330, Zug, Switzerland
Tel.: (41) 417418855
Food Processing Equipment Mfr
N.A.I.C.S.: 333241

Farmers Industries Limited (1)
72 Portside Drive, Mount Maunganui, 3116, New Zealand
Tel.: (64) 75752162
Web Site: https://www.fil.co.nz
Emp.: 20
Animal Health Supplies Distr
N.A.I.C.S.: 424910
Ian Palmer *(CEO)*

GEA (Thailand) Co., Ltd. (1)
Kian Gwan Building III 7th Floor No 152 Wireless Road Kwang Lumpini, Khet Pathumwan, Bangkok, 10330, Thailand
Tel.: (66) 20118150
Chemical Product & Preparation Mfr
N.A.I.C.S.: 325998

GEA AWP GmbH (1)
Armaturenstr 2, 17291, Prenzlau, Germany
Tel.: (49) 398485590
Web Site: https://www.awpvalves.com
Sales Range: $25-49.9 Million
Emp.: 110
Refrigeration Valve Mfr
N.A.I.C.S.: 333415
Tobias Lange *(VP-)*

GEA Aerofreeze Systems, Inc. (1)
150-2551 Viking Way, Richmond, V6V 1N4, BC, Canada
Tel.: (604) 278-4118
Web Site: http://www.aerofreeze.com
Air Conditioning Equipment Mfr
N.A.I.C.S.: 333415
Robert Laflamme *(Pres & Mng Dir)*

GEA Andina S.A.S. (1)
Calle 93 No 12 - 14 Of 501, Bogota, DC, Colombia
Tel.: (57) 3102154886
Chemical Product & Preparation Mfr
N.A.I.C.S.: 325998

GEA Arabia Ltd. (1)
Salah Al Deen Al- Aubi Street, PO Box 260291, Albayt Building No 03 1st Floor Office No 4, 11342, Riyadh, Saudi Arabia
Tel.: (966) 48875650
Chemical Product & Preparation Mfr
N.A.I.C.S.: 325998

GEA Aseptomag AG (1)
Industrie Neuhof 28, 3422, Kirchberg, Bern, Switzerland
Tel.: (41) 344262929
Sales Range: $25-49.9 Million
Emp.: 45
Industrial Valve Mfr
N.A.I.C.S.: 332911

GEA Austria GmbH (1)
Gewerbestrasse 5, 5325, Plainfeld, Austria
Tel.: (43) 62292679
Chemical Product & Preparation Mfr
N.A.I.C.S.: 325998

GEA Avapac Ltd. (1)
24 Evolution Drive, PO Box 10266, Horotiu, Hamilton, 3288, New Zealand
Tel.: (64) 78493414
Sales Range: $25-49.9 Million
Emp.: 69
Food Processing Machinery Mfr
N.A.I.C.S.: 333241

GEA Baltics UAB (1)
Naugarduko 98, 03160, Vilnius, Lithuania
Tel.: (370) 52311900
Chemical Product & Preparation Mfr
N.A.I.C.S.: 325998

GEA Barr Rosin Ltd. (1)
48 Bell Street, Maidenhead, SL6 1BR, Berkshire, United Kingdom
Tel.: (44) 1628 641 700
Web Site: http://www.barr-rosin.com
Emp.: 30
Airstream Drying System Whslr
N.A.I.C.S.: 423830

Subsidiary (Non-US):

GEA Barr Rosin, Inc. (2)
92 Prevost St, Boisbriand, J7G 2S2, QC, Canada
Tel.: (450) 437-5252
Web Site: http://www.barr-rosin.com
Industrial Drying System Whslr
N.A.I.C.S.: 423830

GEA Bischoff GmbH (1)
Ruhrallee 311, 45136, Essen, Germany
Tel.: (49) 20189480
Web Site: https://www.lurgi-bischoff.de
Sales Range: $25-49.9 Million
Emp.: 100
Gas Cleaning Plant Design & Construction Services
N.A.I.C.S.: 333248
Alfred Knieper *(Chm)*

GEA GROUP AKTIENGESELLSCHAFT

GEA Group Aktiengesellschaft—(Continued)

Subsidiary (Non-US):

GEA Bischoff Oy (2)
Arabiankatu 12, 00560, Helsinki, Finland
Tel.: (358) 10 322 11 01
Web Site: http://www.geabischoff.com
Sales Range: $50-74.9 Million
Emp.: 3
Gas Cleaning Process Services
N.A.I.C.S.: 213112
Timo Seppala (Gen Mgr)

Subsidiary (US):

GEA Bischoff, Inc. (2)
9165 Rumsey Rd, Columbia, MD 21045-1929
Tel.: (901) 761-8850
Web Site: http://www.geabischoff.com
Sales Range: $25-49.9 Million
Emp.: 9
Gas Cleaning Plant Design & Construction Services
N.A.I.C.S.: 333248

GEA Brewery Systems GmbH (1)
Heinrich-Huppmann-Str 1, 97318, Kitzingen, Germany
Tel.: (49) 93213030
Emp.: 500
Beverage Making Machinery Mfr
N.A.I.C.S.: 333241

GEA CALDEMON, S.A. (1)
Poligono Industrial Trascueto Parcela B1 Y D1, Camargo, 39600, Cantabria, Spain
Tel.: (34) 942261525
Web Site: http://www.caldemon.com
Emp.: 30
Heat Exchanger Mfr
N.A.I.C.S.: 332410
Oscar Cubero (Gen Mgr)

GEA CFS Bakel B.V. (1)
Beekakker 11, 5761 EN, Bakel, Netherlands
Tel.: (31) 492349349
Web Site: http://www.gea.com
Emp.: 350
Food Processing Machinery Mfr
N.A.I.C.S.: 333241

GEA CFS Finance B.V. (1)
Beekakker 11, 5761 EN, Bakel, Netherlands
Tel.: (31) 492349349
Web Site: http://www.gea.com
Emp.: 400
Financial Management Services
N.A.I.C.S.: 523999

GEA CFS Group B.V. (1)
Beekakker 11, 5761 EN, Bakel, Netherlands
Tel.: (31) 492349349
Food Processing Equipment Mfr
N.A.I.C.S.: 333241

GEA CFS Holding B.V. (1)
Beekakker 11, 5761 EN, Bakel, Netherlands
Tel.: (31) 49 234 9349
Web Site: http://www.gea.com
Investment Management Service
N.A.I.C.S.: 523999

GEA CFS Holding GmbH (1)
Im Rutter 1, 35216, Biedenkopf, Germany
Tel.: (49) 6461 8010
Web Site: http://www.gea.com
Investment Management Service
N.A.I.C.S.: 523999
Bernd Klinkert (Gen Mgr)

Subsidiary (Domestic):

GEA Food Solutions GmbH (2)
Im Ruttert 1, 35216, Biedenkopf, Germany
Tel.: (49) 6461 801 0
Web Site: http://www.gea-foodsolutions.com
Food Processing Machinery Mfr
N.A.I.C.S.: 333241

Subsidiary (Domestic):

GEA CFS Buhl GmbH (3)
Ignaz-Kiechle-Str 40, 87437, Kempten, Germany
Tel.: (49) 831 51284 0
Web Site: http://www.gea.com
Emp.: 15
Food Processing Machinery Mfr
N.A.I.C.S.: 333241

Bob Smallwood (Mgr)

GEA CFS Real Estate GmbH (3)
Im Ruttert, 35216, Biedenkopf, Hessen, Germany
Tel.: (49) 6461 989824
Real Estate Manangement Services
N.A.I.C.S.: 531390

ZiAG Plant Engineering GmbH (3)
Lurgiallee 5, 60439, Frankfurt, Germany
Tel.: (49) 69 69712 120
Web Site: http://www.gea.com
Food Processing Equipment Mfr
N.A.I.C.S.: 333241

GEA CFS International B.V. (1)
Beekakker 11, 5761 EN, Bakel, Netherlands
Tel.: (31) 492349349
Sales Range: $100-124.9 Million
Emp.: 35
Food Processing Equipment Mfr
N.A.I.C.S.: 333241

GEA CFS Uden B.V. (1)
Beekakker 11, 5761 EN, Bakel, Netherlands
Tel.: (31) 492349349
Web Site: http://www.gea.com
Food Processing Equipment Mfr
N.A.I.C.S.: 333241

GEA CFS Weert B.V. (1)
De Fuus 8, 6006 RV, Weert, Netherlands
Tel.: (31) 495 457 777
Web Site: http://www.gea.com
Emp.: 150
Food Processing Equipment Mfr
N.A.I.C.S.: 333241

GEA Canada Inc. (1)
92 Prevost Street, Boisbriand, J7G 2S2, QC, Canada
Tel.: (450) 437-5252
Web Site: http://www.gea.com
Emp.: 45
Powder & Drying Technology Services
N.A.I.C.S.: 332117

Subsidiary (Domestic):

Centrifuges Unlimited Inc. (2)
3504 - 64 Avenue SE, Calgary, T2C 1P4, AB, Canada
Tel.: (403) 236-2883
Web Site: https://www.centrifuges.net
Sales Range: $25-49.9 Million
Emp.: 3
Separation Equipment Distr
N.A.I.C.S.: 423830

GEA Convenience Food Technologies B.V. (1)
Beekakker 11, 5761 EN, Bakel, Netherlands
Tel.: (31) 492 349 349
Web Site: http://www.gea.com
Emp.: 40
Food Processing & Packaging Machinery Mfr
N.A.I.C.S.: 333241

GEA Czech Republic s.r.o. (1)
Nagano Park U Nakladoveho nadrazi 3153/8, 130 00, Prague, 3, Czech Republic
Tel.: (420) 224223048
Chemical Product & Preparation Mfr
N.A.I.C.S.: 325998

GEA Diessel GmbH (1)
Steven 1, 31135, Hildesheim, Germany
Tel.: (49) 51217420
Web Site: https://www.diessel.com
Sales Range: $50-74.9 Million
Emp.: 20
Pharmaceutical & Biotechnological Equipment Mfr
N.A.I.C.S.: 334516

GEA EEC Bulgaria EOOD (1)
40 Tsarigradsko Shose Blvd, 1750, Sofia, Bulgaria
Tel.: (359) 29880081
Chemical Product & Preparation Mfr
N.A.I.C.S.: 325998

GEA EEC Serbia d.o.o. (1)
Konstantina Jovanovica 10, Zemun, 11080, Belgrade, Serbia
Tel.: (381) 14053618
Chemical Product & Preparation Mfr
N.A.I.C.S.: 325998

GEA EGI Energiagazdalkodasi Zrt. (1)
4-20 Irinyi J Str Science Park Building B, 1117, Budapest, Hungary
Tel.: (36) 1 225 6100
Web Site: http://www.brand-trend.com
Sales Range: $50-74.9 Million
Emp.: 25
Air Conditioning Equipment Mfr
N.A.I.C.S.: 333415
Jozsef Budik (Dir-Bus Dev)

GEA Engenharia de Processos e Sistema Industriais do Brasil Ltda (1)
Avenida Mercedes Benz 679 Predio 4 D2 - 1o Andar - Piso 2, 13054-750, Campinas, Sao Paulo, Brazil
Tel.: (55) 19 3725 3100
Web Site: http://www.gea-process.com.br
Food Product Machinery Whslr
N.A.I.C.S.: 423830

GEA Engenharia de Processos e Sistemas Industriais Ltda. (1)
Avenida Mercedes Benz 679 Redio 4 D2 1o Andar Piso 2, 13054-750, Campinas, Sao Paulo, Brazil
Tel.: (55) 193725 3100
Web Site: http://www.gea-process.com.br
Process Engineering Services
N.A.I.C.S.: 541330

GEA Equipamentos e Solucoes Ltda. (1)
Tel.: (55) 1935172000
Chemical Product & Preparation Mfr
N.A.I.C.S.: 325998

GEA Farm Technologies Canada Inc. (1)
4591 Blvd St Joseph, Drummondville, J2A 0C6, QC, Canada
Tel.: (819) 477-7444
Chemical Product & Preparation Mfr
N.A.I.C.S.: 325998

GEA Farm Technologies GmbH (1)
Siemensstr 25-27, 59199, Bonen, Germany
Tel.: (49) 23839370
Web Site: https://www.gea-farmtechnologies.com
Sales Range: $400-449.9 Million
Emp.: 2,000
Farm Machinery & Equipment Mfr
N.A.I.C.S.: 333111

Subsidiary (Non-US):

GEA (Shanghai) Farm Technologies Company Ltd. (2)
99 Hexiang Road, Minhang District, Shanghai, 201109, China
Tel.: (86) 2124082288
Web Site: https://www.gea-farmtechnologies.com
Livestock Farming Services
N.A.I.C.S.: 112990

GEA Farm Technologies (Ireland) Ltd. (2)
Unit A1 FotoPoint Enterprise Park Cobh Cross, Carrigtwohill, Cork, Ireland
Tel.: (353) 21 488 1300
Emp.: 5
Farm Machinery & Equipment Mfr
N.A.I.C.S.: 333111
Oliver Moore (Gen Mgr)

GEA Farm Technologies (UK) Limited (2)
Stoneleigh Park, Kenilworth, CV8 2LG, Warwickshire, United Kingdom
Tel.: (44) 2476692333
Sales Range: $350-399.9 Million
Emp.: 150
Farm Machinery & Equipment Mfr
N.A.I.C.S.: 333111
Dirk Hejnal (CEO)

GEA Farm Technologies Acier SAS (2)
18 Avenue De L'Europe, Chateau-Thierry, 02400, Aisne, France
Tel.: (33) 3 23 84 81 60
Agricultural Machinery Mfr
N.A.I.C.S.: 333111

GEA Farm Technologies Argentina S.R.L. (2)
Jorge Stephenson 2792, Tortuguitas, B1667, Buenos Aires, Argentina
Tel.: (54) 3327449955
Sales Range: $25-49.9 Million
Emp.: 3
Farm Technology Products Mfr
N.A.I.C.S.: 333111

GEA Farm Technologies Australia Pty. Ltd. (2)
14 Mace Way, PO Box 398, Melbourne Airport, Melbourne, 3045, VIC, Australia
Tel.: (61) 388779999
Sales Range: $25-49.9 Million
Emp.: 24
Food Processing Machinery Mfr
N.A.I.C.S.: 333241

GEA Farm Technologies Austria GmbH (2)
Gewerbestrasse 5, 5325, Plainfeld, Salzburg, Austria
Tel.: (43) 62292679
Web Site: http://www.westfalia.com
Emp.: 40
Farm Machinery & Equipment Mfr
N.A.I.C.S.: 333111
Peking Ludger (Office Mgr)

GEA Farm Technologies Belgium N.V./S.A. (2)
Hagelberg 1, 2250, Olen, Belgium
Tel.: (32) 14282890
Sales Range: $25-49.9 Million
Emp.: 3
Farm Machinery & Equipment Mfr
N.A.I.C.S.: 333111
Roelof Westerbeek (Gen Mgr)

GEA Farm Technologies Bulgaria EOOD (2)
Fr Olya Vachkova 99 G S Rakovski Str, 1000, Sofia, Bulgaria
Tel.: (359) 2 988 0081
Web Site: http://www.gea-farm-technologies.net
Emp.: 7
Farm Machinery & Equipment Mfr
N.A.I.C.S.: 333111
Ivan Filev (Gen Mgr)

GEA Farm Technologies CZ, spol. s.r.o. (2)
Kvitkovicka 1533, 763 61, Napajedla, Czech Republic
Tel.: (420) 572 586 115
Web Site: http://www.gea-farmtechnologies.com
Farm Machinery & Equipment Mfr
N.A.I.C.S.: 333111

GEA Farm Technologies France SAS (2)
18 Avenue De L'Europe, BP 153, 02405, Chateau-Thierry, France
Tel.: (33) 323848160
Web Site: https://www.gea-farmtechnologies.com
Livestock Farming Services
N.A.I.C.S.: 112990

GEA Farm Technologies Iberica S.L. (2)
Avda Sant Julia 147, 8403, Granollers, Spain
Tel.: (34) 938617120
Sales Range: $25-49.9 Million
Emp.: 2
Farm Machinery & Equipment Mfr
N.A.I.C.S.: 333111
Francesc Lloreta (Gen Mgr)

GEA Farm Technologies Mullerup A/S (2)
Vestergade 11B, 5540, Ullerslev, Denmark
Tel.: (45) 63351422
Web Site: https://www.mullerup.com
Sales Range: $25-49.9 Million
Emp.: 40
Farm Machinery & Equipment Mfr
N.A.I.C.S.: 333111

GEA Farm Technologies Nederland B.V. (2)
Hidalgoweg 8, 8938 BA, Leeuwarden, Netherlands
Tel.: (31) 58 2911129
Web Site: http://www.gea-farmtechnologies.com

AND PRIVATE COMPANIES
GEA GROUP AKTIENGESELLSCHAFT

Agricultural Machinery Mfr
N.A.I.C.S.: 333111

GEA Farm Technologies New Zealand Limited (2)
Tel.: (64) 78431780
Web Site: https://www.milfos.com
Sales Range: $350-399.9 Million
Emp.: 150
Farm Machinery & Equipment Mfr
N.A.I.C.S.: 333111

GEA Farm Technologies Romania S.R.L. (2)
Str Regimentul 5 Vanatori Nr 38 Jud Alba,
Alba Iulia, 510158, Romania
Tel.: (40) 258 832256
Web Site: http://www.gea-farmtechnologies.com
Emp.: 8
Farm Machinery & Equipment Mfr
N.A.I.C.S.: 333111
Sorin Anderco (Gen Mgr)

GEA Farm Technologies Serbia d.o.o. (2)
22 Lazara Mamuzica, Zemun, Belgrade, 11080, Serbia
Tel.: (381) 111900958
Livestock Farming Services
N.A.I.C.S.: 112990

GEA Farm Technologies Slovakia Spol. S.r.o. (2)
Bencurova 3731/7, 82104, Bratislava, Ruzinov, Slovakia
Tel.: (421) 2 436 342 91
Farm Machinery & Equipment Mfr
N.A.I.O.S.: 333111

GEA Farm Technologies Sp. Z o.o. (2)
Ul Olowiana 10, 85-461, Bydgoszcz, Poland
Tel.: (48) 523480440
Web Site: https://www.gea-farmtechnologies.com
Farm Machinery & Equipment Mfr
N.A.I.C.S.: 333111

GEA Farm Technologies Suisse AG (2)
Worblentalstrasse 28, 3063, Ittlgen, Bern, Switzerland
Tel.: (41) 31 924 31 31
Web Site: http://www.westfalia.com
Farm Machinery & Equipment Mfr
N.A.I.C.S.: 333111

GEA Farm Technologies Tarim Ekip. Mak. Kim. Tek. Dan. San. Tic. Ltd. Sti. (2)
Ankara Asfalti 25 Km Ansizca Koyu, 35170, Kemalpasa, Izmir, Turkiye
Tel.: (90) 232 8770225
Sales Range: $25-49.9 Million
Emp.: 91
Milking Equipment Mfr
N.A.I.C.S.: 333111
Serdar Gez (Country Mgr)

GEA Farm Technologies do Brasil Ltda. (2)
Avenida Emilio Marconato 1000 B15 Ala A Chacara Primavera, 13820 000, Jaguariuna, Sao Paulo, Brazil
Tel.: (55) 19 38 37 95 00
Web Site: http://www.gea-farmtechnologies.com
Sales Range: $25-49.9 Million
Emp.: 80
Agricultural Machinery Mfr
N.A.I.C.S.: 333111
Daniel Prestello (Pres)

GEA Farm Technologies do Brasil, Industria e Comercio de Equipamentos Agricolas e Pecuarios Ltda. (2)
Avenida Emilio Marconato 1000 B15 Ala A Chacara Primavera, Jaguariuna, 13820 000, Sao Paulo, Brazil
Tel.: (55) 19 3837 9500
Web Site: http://www.westfalia.com
Farm Machinery & Equipment Mfr
N.A.I.C.S.: 333111

OOO GEA Farm Technologies Rus (2)
Otradnaya str 2B bld 9 floor 10 room 1, Moscow, 127273, Russia
Tel.: (7) 4957872020
Sales Range: $25-49.9 Million
Emp.: 90
Farm Machinery & Equipment Mfr
N.A.I.C.S.: 333111

GEA Farm Technologies Inc. (1)
1880 Country Farm Dr, Naperville, IL 60563
Tel.: (630) 369-8100
Web Site: http://www.gea-farmtechnologies.com
Sales Range: $50-74.9 Million
Emp.: 130
Milking & Cooling Equipment Mfr
N.A.I.C.S.: 333111

GEA Filtration Inc. (1)
1600 O'Keefe Rd, Hudson, WI 54016
Tel.: (715) 386-9371
Web Site: http://www.gea.com
Sales Range: $25-49.9 Million
Emp.: 50
Filtration Process Engineering Services
N.A.I.C.S.: 541330
Swami Sundaram (VP)

GEA Finance B.V. (1)
Waalhaven O Z 77 Haven 2203 A, Rotterdam, 3087 BM, South Holland, Netherlands
Tel.: (31) 104288333
Financial Management Services
N.A.I.C.S.: 523999
Gerda Diependaal (Gen Mgr)

GEA Finland Oy (1)
Hiomotie 19, 00380, Helsinki, Finland
Tel.: (358) 207558960
Chemical Product & Preparation Mfr
N.A.I.C.S.: 325998

GEA Food Solutions Chile Comercializadora Ltda. (1)
Eliodoro Yanez N 2596, Providencia, Chile
Tel.: (56) 229638230
Web Site: https://www.foodsolution.cl
Online Food Services
N.A.I.C.S.: 722330

GEA Food Solutions Comercializadora LTDA (1)
Guardia Vieja 255 Oficina 1008 Providencia, Providenciales, Santiago, 7510186, Chile
Tel.: (56) 2 946 1430
Web Site: http://www.gea-foodsolutions.com
Sales Range: $25-49.9 Million
Emp.: 5
Food Processing Machinery Mfr
N.A.I.C.S.: 333241
Jose Diaz (Gen Mgr)

GEA Food Solutions Denmark A/S (1)
Elmedalsvej 12, 4200, Slagelse, Denmark
Tel.: (45) 58555200
Web Site: https://www.gea-foodsolutions.com
Emp.: 6
Food Processing Equipment Mfr
N.A.I.C.S.: 333241

GEA Food Solutions France S.A.S. (1)
25 rue de la Claie ZI Angers, 49070, Beaucouze, France
Tel.: (33) 241227050
Web Site: https://www.gea-foodsolutions.com
Sales Range: $25-49.9 Million
Emp.: 4
Food Processing Machinery Mfr
N.A.I.C.S.: 333241
Ronnie Bo Nielsen (CEO)

GEA Food Solutions North America, Inc. (1)
16005 Gateway Dr Ste 100, Frisco, TX 75033
Tel.: (214) 618-1100
Emp.: 150
Food Processing & Packaging Equipment Mfr
N.A.I.C.S.: 333248

GEA Food Solutions Ukraine LLC (1)
25/49 Pochainynska Str Office 78, 04071, Kiev, Ukraine
Tel.: (380) 44 545 6020
Web Site: http://www.gea-foodsolutions.com

Sales Range: $25-49.9 Million
Emp.: 8
Food Processing Machinery Mfr
N.A.I.C.S.: 333241

GEA Food Solutions Weert B.V. (1)
De Fuus 8, 6006 RV, Weert, Netherlands
Tel.: (31) 495457777
Food Processing Equipment Mfr
N.A.I.C.S.: 333241

GEA Geneglace S.A.S. (1)
9 Rue des Orfevres, 44840, Les Sorinieres, France
Tel.: (33) 25 119 1051
Web Site: https://www.geneglace.com
Sales Range: $25-49.9 Million
Emp.: 41
Refrigerator Equipment Mfr
N.A.I.C.S.: 333415
Serge Vidal (Gen Mgr)

GEA Grenco Africa (PTY) Ltd (1)
Mikocheni Industrial Area Plot No 131, PO Box 32476, Dar es Salaam, Tanzania
Tel.: (255) 222 771176
Refrigeration Equipment Distr
N.A.I.C.S.: 423740
Peet van der Westhuizen (Gen Mgr)

GEA Grenco Ireland Ltd. (1)
Unit 8 Corlurgan Business Park, Corlurgan, Cavan, Ireland
Tel.: (353) 49 436 1588
Web Site: http://www.grenco.ie
Sales Range: $25-49.9 Million
Emp.: 8
Refrigeration Equipment Maintenance Services
N.A.I.C.S.: 811310
Patrick Gilcreest (Reg Mgr)

GEA Grenco Ltd. (1)
Unit 9 Conqueror Court Velum Drive, Sittingbourne, ME10 5BH, Kent, United Kingdom
Tel.: (44) 1795514630
Refrigeration System Mfr
N.A.I.C.S.: 333415

GEA Group Holding France SAS (1)
4 rue J P Timbaud-B P 80, Montigny le Bretonneux, 78185, Maignelay-Montigny, France
Tel.: (33) 130146110
Chemical Product & Preparation Mfr
N.A.I.C.S.: 325998

GEA Group Holding GmbH (1)
Peter-Muller-Str 12, 40468, Dusseldorf, Germany
Tel.: (49) 21191360
Investment Management Service
N.A.I.C.S.: 523999

GEA Group Holdings (UK) Limited (1)
Leaceoft House Leacroft Road, Birchwood, Warrington, WA3 6JF, Cheshire, United Kingdom
Tel.: (44) 1925 812 650
Web Site: http://www.gea.com
Sales Range: $50-74.9 Million
Emp.: 8
Investment Management Service
N.A.I.C.S.: 523999
Ilija Aprcovic (Mng Dir)

GEA Houle, Inc. (1)
4591 Blvd Saint-Joseph, CP 370, Drummondville, J2A 0C6, QC, Canada
Tel.: (819) 477-7444
Web Site: http://www.gea-farmtechnologies.com
Sales Range: $100-124.9 Million
Emp.: 300
Manure Handling Equipment Mfr
N.A.I.C.S.: 332216
Madeleine Couture (CEO)

GEA Hovex B.V. (1)
Orionweg 2, Veendam, 9641 MN, Netherlands
Tel.: (31) 598 616 268
Web Site: http://www.hovex.com
Emp.: 25
Rotary Vacuum Drum Filter Mfr
N.A.I.C.S.: 333413
Peter J. Boschma (Mng Dir & Editor)

GEA ISISAN TESISAT INSAAT TAAHHUT TICARET VE SANAYI A.S. (1)
Barbaros Bulvari Bulvar Apt No 70/8 34349, Balmumcu Besiktas, 80700, Istanbul, Turkiye
Tel.: (90) 212 275 71 70
Web Site: http://www.gea-isisan.com
Sales Range: $25-49.9 Million
Emp.: 40
Air Handling Equipment Mfr
N.A.I.C.S.: 333415
Carola Wolters (Head-PR & Mktg)

GEA IT Services GmbH (1)
Werner-Habig-Str 1, Oelde, 59302, Germany
Tel.: (49) 2522772754
Information Technology Consulting Services
N.A.I.C.S.: 541512

GEA Industrial Heat Exchanger Systems (China) Ltd. (1)
No 8 Yangtian Road Jiujiang Economic Development Area, Wuhu, Anhui, China
Tel.: (86) 553 5951222 0
Heat Exchanger Mfr
N.A.I.C.S.: 332410

GEA Ireland Limited (1)
Ash House Lime Tree Avenue, Naas, W918E3C, Ireland
Tel.: (353) 45981200
Web Site: http://www.gea.com
Emp.: 80
Heat Exchanger Mfr
N.A.I.C.S.: 332410
Tim Knowles (Mng Dir)

GEA Klimatyzacja Spolka z o.o. (1)
Ul Fabryczna 10, 53-609, Wroclaw, Poland
Tel.: (48) 713565866
Web Site: http://www.gea-klimatyzacja.pl
Sales Range: $25-49.9 Million
Emp.: 2
Air Handling Unit Mfr
N.A.I.C.S.: 333415
Malgorzata Durska (Mng Dir)

GEA Korea Ltd. (1)
Tel.: (82) 25140291
Chemical Product & Preparation Mfr
N.A.I.C.S.: 325998

GEA Lyophil (Beijing) Co. Ltd. (1)
Rm 1001 C Tower Grand Pacific Building 8A Guanghua Rd, Chaoyang District, Beijing, 100026, China
Tel.: (86) 10 8739 4872
Web Site: http://www.gea.com
Pharmaceutical Freeze Drying Equipment Installation & Maintenance Services
N.A.I.C.S.: 238220

GEA Lyophil GmbH (1)
Kalscheurener Strasse 92, Cologne, 50354, Hurth, Germany
Tel.: (49) 223369990
Emp.: 220
Pharmaceutical Freeze Dryer Mfr
N.A.I.C.S.: 333415

GEA Mechanical Equipment Canada, Inc. (1)
4145 North Service Road 2nd floor, Burlington, L7L 6A3, ON, Canada
Tel.: (289) 288-5500
Web Site: http://www.gea.com
Sales Range: $25-49.9 Million
Emp.: 6
Food Separator & Decanter Mfr
N.A.I.C.S.: 333241

GEA Mechanical Equipment GmbH (1)
Werner-Habig-Str 1, 59302, Oelde, Germany
Tel.: (49) 2522770
Web Site: https://www.gea-mechanical-equipment.com
Valves & Pump Mfr
N.A.I.C.S.: 332919

Subsidiary (Non-US):

GEA Tuchenhagen GmbH (2)
(100%)
Tel.: (49) 4155490
Web Site: https://www.tuchenhagen.com
Sales Range: $50-74.9 Million
Emp.: 350
Brewery Machines Mfr

GEA GROUP AKTIENGESELLSCHAFT — INTERNATIONAL PUBLIC

GEA Group Aktiengesellschaft—(Continued)
N.A.I.C.S.: 332911

Subsidiary (Non-US):

GEA Tuchenhagen Canada, Inc. (3)
20 King St W Unit B, Stoney Creek, L8G 1G8, ON, Canada
Tel.: (905) 930-8738
Web Site: http://www.tuchenhagen.us
Industrial Valve Mfr & Distr
N.A.I.C.S.: 423840
Dominic Beaulieu (Mng Dir)

GEA Tuchenhagen France SARL (3)
29 Route de la Wantzenau, 67800, Hoenheim, France
Tel.: (33) 3 88 19 70 90
Web Site: http://www.tuchenhagen.fr
Sales Range: $25-49.9 Million
Emp.: 8
Beverage Separator Mfr
N.A.I.C.S.: 333241
Gourud Phillippe (Gen Mgr)

GEA Tuchenhagen Polska sp. z o.o. (3)
Ul Bowid 9R, 75-209, Koszalin, Poland
Tel.: (48) 943461133
Industrial Valve & Pump Mfr
N.A.I.C.S.: 332911

Subsidiary (US):

GEA Tuchenhagen US, LLC (3)
90 Evergreen Dr, Portland, ME 04103-1064 (100%)
Tel.: (207) 797-9500
Web Site: http://www.tuchenhagen.us
Sales Range: $50-74.9 Million
Emp.: 17
Mfr of Sanitary Process Valves & Equipments, Brewery & Beverage Process & Food Industry Equipments
N.A.I.C.S.: 423830

Subsidiary (Domestic):

GEA Westfalia Separator Group GmbH (2)
Werner-Habig-Str 1, 59302, Oelde, Germany
Tel.: (49) 2522770
Web Site: https://www.westfalia-separator.com
Holding Company; Industrial Separation Equipment Mfr & Distr
N.A.I.C.S.: 551112
Markus Hullmann (Chm-Mgmt Bd)

Subsidiary (Non-US):

GEA Middle East FZE (3)
Jebel Ali Free Zone gate 4 LB 15 office 601, PO Box 262952, 262952, Dubai, United Arab Emirates
Tel.: (971) 48875650
Web Site: https://www.gea-middle-east.com
Sales Range: $25-49.9 Million
Emp.: 2
Beverage Separator & Decanter Distr
N.A.I.C.S.: 423830

GEA Westfalia Separating Equipment (Tianjin) Co., Ltd. (3)
4th Floor Middle of C12 Building Venture Headquarter Base, Wuqing Development Area, Tianjin, 301700, China
Tel.: (86) 22 8217 6610
Separator & Decanter Mfr
N.A.I.C.S.: 333241

GEA Westfalia Separator (China) Ltd. (3)
Unit 805 - 806 8 F Fook Yip Building No 53 - 57 Kwai Fung Crescent, Kwai Chung, New Territories, China (Hong Kong)
Tel.: (852) 2866 0009
Web Site: http://www.china.westfalia-separator.com
Beverage Separator & Decanter Machinery Mfr
N.A.I.C.S.: 333241
Thomas Schmitz (Mng Dir)

GEA Westfalia Separator (Malaysia) Sdn Bhd (3)
No 25 Jalan SS 25/41 Mayang Industrial Park, 47301, Petaling Jaya, Malaysia

Tel.: (60) 358858700
Web Site: https://www.gea.com
Sales Range: $25-49.9 Million
Emp.: 25
Beverage Separator & Decanter Mfr
N.A.I.C.S.: 333241
Thong Siah Meng (Country Mgr)

GEA Westfalia Separator (S.E.A.) PTE. LTD. (3)
202 Kallang Bahru 06-01 06-02, Singapore, 339339, Singapore
Tel.: (65) 63388113
Web Site: https://www.gea.com
Beverage Separator & Decanter Machinery Distr
N.A.I.C.S.: 423830

GEA Westfalia Separator (Thailand) Ltd. (3)
93/20 Ladphrao Soi 87 Ladphrao Road Kwang Wangthonglang, Bangkapi, Bangkok, 10310, Thailand
Tel.: (66) 2 9323 140
Beverage Separator & Decanter Mfr
N.A.I.C.S.: 333241

GEA Westfalia Separator (Tianjin) Co., Ltd. (3)
28-A Building Innovation Incubator Park No 4668 Xinbei Road Tanggu, Tianjin, China
Tel.: (86) 22 6635 1002
Beverage Separator Machinery Mfr
N.A.I.C.S.: 333241

GEA Westfalia Separator Argentina S.A. (3)
Sarmiento 3540, Buenos Aires, C1196AAP, Argentina
Tel.: (54) 1148644700
Web Site: https://argentina.westfalia-separator.com
Emp.: 35
Beverages Separator Equipment Mfr
N.A.I.C.S.: 333241
Mycual Gasares (Mng Dir)

GEA Westfalia Separator Austria GmbH (3)
Brunnerstrasse 77-79, 1230, Vienna, Austria
Tel.: (43) 1 865 45 39 0
Web Site: http://www.westfalia-separator.at
Beverage Separator Machinery Mfr
N.A.I.C.S.: 333241
Thomas Czutta (Mng Dir)

GEA Westfalia Separator Belgium N.V. (3)
Korte Braamstraat 37, 2900, Schoten, Belgium
Tel.: (32) 36800211
Web Site: https://www.belgium.westfalia-separator.com
Sales Range: $25-49.9 Million
Emp.: 28
Beverage Separator Machinery Mfr
N.A.I.C.S.: 333241
Martine Duchesne (Editor)

GEA Westfalia Separator CIS Ltd. (3)
Ulitsa Semenovskiy Val 6 Building 1, Moscow, 105094, Russia
Tel.: (7) 495 7872 005
Web Site: http://russia.westfalia-separator.com
Emp.: 5
Beverage Separator & Decanter Mfr
N.A.I.C.S.: 333241
Nikolai Kuznetsov (Mng Dir)

GEA Westfalia Separator CZ s.r.o. (3)
Vresova 2299/5, 251 01, Ricany, Czech Republic
Tel.: (420) 2 7173 7862
Web Site: http://www.westfalia-separator.cz
Emp.: 5
Separator & Decanter Mfr
N.A.I.C.S.: 333241
Grn Breaslaer (Mng Dir)

GEA Westfalia Separator Canada, Inc. (3)
835 Harrington Ct, Burlington, L7N 3P3, ON, Canada
Tel.: (289) 288-5500
Web Site: http://www.wsus.com

Beverage Separator Machinery Mfr
N.A.I.C.S.: 333241

GEA Westfalia Separator Chile S.A. (3)
Parinacota 341, Quilicura, 8730621, Santiago, Chile
Tel.: (56) 27191600
Web Site: https://www.chile.westfalia-separator.com
Beverages Separator Machine Mfr
N.A.I.C.S.: 333241

GEA Westfalia Separator DK A/S (3)
Norskovvej 1b, 8660, Skanderborg, Denmark
Tel.: (45) 87941000
Web Site: https://www.gea-westfalia.dk
Emp.: 140
Beverage Separator & Decanter Equipment Whslr
N.A.I.C.S.: 423830

Subsidiary (Domestic):

GEA Westfalia Separator Deutschland GmbH (3)
Werner-Habig-Strasse 1, 59302, Oelde, Germany
Tel.: (49) 2522 77 0
Web Site: http://wsd.westfalia-separator.com
Mechanical Separation Equipment Mfr
N.A.I.C.S.: 333248

Subsidiary (Non-US):

GEA Westfalia Separator France SAS (3)
18 Avenue De l'Europe, 02400, Chateau-Thierry, France
Tel.: (33) 323848120
Emp.: 80
Beverage Separator & Decanter Machinery Mfr
N.A.I.C.S.: 333241

GEA Westfalia Separator Hellas S.A. (3)
Parodos Leontariou, Pallini, 15351, Athens, Greece
Tel.: (30) 2106034384
Web Site: http://www.westfalia-separator.gr
Emp.: 5
Milk Separator Machinery Mfr
N.A.I.C.S.: 333241
Stavros Fritzalas (Gen Mgr)

GEA Westfalia Separator Hungaria Kft. (3)
Malomko U 7, 2040, Budaors, Hungary
Tel.: (36) 17010121
Web Site: http://www.gea.com
Emp.: 4
Beverage Separation Machinery Mfr & Distr
N.A.I.C.S.: 333241
Laso Gramer (Mgr)

GEA Westfalia Separator Iberica, S.A. (3)
Avda San Julian 147, 8403, Granollers, Spain
Tel.: (34) 938617100
Sales Range: $25-49.9 Million
Emp.: 5
Industrial Machinery & Equipment Distr
N.A.I.C.S.: 423830
Goan Gilar (Gen Mgr)

GEA Westfalia Separator Iceland ehf (3)
Dalvegi 16d - 201 Kopavogi, Kopavogur, Iceland
Tel.: (354) 564 2888
Soft Drink Separator & Decanter Mfr
N.A.I.C.S.: 333241

GEA Westfalia Separator Ireland Ltd. (3)
Ballincollig, Cork, Ireland
Tel.: (353) 214850222
Web Site: https://ireland.westfalia-separator.com
Sales Range: $25-49.9 Million
Emp.: 2
Beverage Separator & Decanter Mfr
N.A.I.C.S.: 333241
Declan Mcnulty (Mng Dir)

GEA Westfalia Separator Italia S.r.l. (3)
Via Fedolfi 29, 43038, Sala Baganza, Parma, Italy
Tel.: (39) 0521 334911
Web Site: http://www.gea.com
Emp.: 30
Beverage Separator Machinery Mfr
N.A.I.C.S.: 333241

GEA Westfalia Separator Japan K.K. (3)
Shiba 2-17-11, Minato-ku, Tokyo, 105-0014, Japan
Tel.: (81) 3 5443 3762
Web Site: http://www.westfalia.co.jp
Beverage Separator & Decanter Machinery Mfr
N.A.I.C.S.: 333241

GEA Westfalia Separator Korea Ltd. (3)
9th Fl Nonhyun Bldg 50-1 Nonhyun-Dong, Seoul, 135-010, Korea (South)
Tel.: (82) 2 514 0291
Web Site: http://www.westfalia.co.kr
Beverage Separator & Decanter Machinery Mfr
N.A.I.C.S.: 333241
Erich Volkel (Gen Mgr)

GEA Westfalia Separator Mexicana S.A. de C.V. (3)
Calle 9 Este Esq Andador Central, Civac Cuernavaca, CP 62550, Jiutepec, Mexico
Tel.: (52) 7773201088
Web Site: https://www.gea.com
Beverages Separator Machine Mfr
N.A.I.C.S.: 333241

GEA Westfalia Separator NZ Ltd. (3)
356 Church Street 120 Penrose, Auckland, 1061, New Zealand
Tel.: (64) 9 526 3860
Emp.: 14
Beverage Separator & Decanter Machinery Mfr
N.A.I.C.S.: 333241
Christo Van Zyl (Mng Dir)

GEA Westfalia Separator Nederland B.V. (3)
Hoogveld 16, 5431 NW, Cuijk, Netherlands
Tel.: (31) 485319300
Web Site: https://netherlands.westfalia-separator.com
Sales Range: $50-74.9 Million
Emp.: 60
Beverage Separator & Decanter Machinery Whslr
N.A.I.C.S.: 423830

GEA Westfalia Separator Norway AS (3)
Gjerdrums vei 8, 0484, Oslo, Norway
Tel.: (47) 22021600
Web Site: http://www.gea-westfalia.no
Sales Range: $25-49.9 Million
Emp.: 22
Beverage Separator & Decant Machinery Mfr
N.A.I.C.S.: 333241
Dag Moxnes (Gen Mgr)

GEA Westfalia Separator Philippines Inc. (3)
Panorama Compound Veterans Centre Ground Floor 20 Phase 3, Taguig, 1000, Metro Manila, Philippines
Tel.: (63) 2 838 0722
Beverage Separator & Decanter Machinery Mfr
N.A.I.C.S.: 333241

GEA Westfalia Separator Polska Sp. z o.o. (3)
Lopuszanska 95, 02-457, Warsaw, Poland
Tel.: (48) 224567485
Web Site: https://www.gea.com
Sales Range: $25-49.9 Million
Emp.: 20
Separator & Decanter Machinery Mfr
N.A.I.C.S.: 333248

GEA Westfalia Separator Romania SRL (3)
Splaiul Unirii Nr 74 Etaj 1 Sector 4, Bucharest, 40037, Romania
Tel.: (40) 21 330 44 30
Emp.: 6
Beverage Separator & Decanter Mfr

AND PRIVATE COMPANIES — GEA GROUP AKTIENGESELLSCHAFT

N.A.I.C.S.: 333241

GEA Westfalia Separator Sanayi ve Ticaret Ltd. Sti. (3)
Kemalpasa O S B Mah Kuyucak Yolu Sok No 287/1, Kemalpasa, 35730, Izmir, Turkiye
Tel.: (90) 2328772110
Web Site: https://www.gea.com
Emp.: 75
Beverage Separator & Decanter Mfr
N.A.I.C.S.: 333241
Serdar Gez *(Gen Mgr)*

GEA Westfalia Separator South Africa (Pty) Ltd. (3)
Building No 286 16th Road, Midrand, 1685, South Africa
Tel.: (27) 11 805 6910
Web Site: http://www.southafrica.westfalia-separator.com
Sales Range: $25-49.9 Million
Emp.: 27
Separator Machinery Mfr
N.A.I.C.S.: 333248
Richard Plazier *(Gen Mgr)*

GEA Westfalia Separator Sweden AB (3)
Krokslatts Fabriker 45, 43137, Molndal, Sweden
Tel.: (46) 317271790
Web Site: http://www.gea.com
Emp.: 5
Beverage Separator & Decanter Machinery Mfr
N.A.I.C.S.: 333241
Trygve Orderud *(Mgr-Sls)*

GEA Westfalia Separator do Brasil Industria de Centrifugas Ltda. (3)
Av Mercedes-Benz 679 Edif 4D2 1 Andar, Distrito Industrial, 13054-750, Campinas, Sao Paulo, Brazil
Tel.: (55) 19 3725 3100
Web Site: http://brasil.westfalia-separator.com
Beverages Separator Equipment Mfr
N.A.I.C.S.: 333241

PT GEA Westfalia Separator Indonesia (3)
3rd Floor Wisma Presisi Jl Taman Aries A1 No 1 Meruya Utara Kembangan, Jakarta, 11620, Indonesia
Tel.: (62) 21 5890 2100
Beverage Separator & Decanter Mfr
N.A.I.C.S.: 333241

GEA Mechanical Equipment Italia S.p.A. (1)
Via Angelo Maria da Erba Edoari 29/A, 43123, Parma, Italy
Tel.: (39) 0521965411
Chemical Product & Preparation Mfr
N.A.I.C.S.: 325998

GEA Mechanical Equipment UK Limited (1)
Westfalia House Old Wolverton Road, Milton Keynes, MK12 5PY, United Kingdom
Tel.: (44) 1908 576500
Web Site: http://www.gea.com
Emp.: 5
Mechanical Equipment Mfr
N.A.I.C.S.: 333248

GEA Mechanical Equipment US, Inc. (1)
100 Fairway Ct, Northvale, NJ 07647
Tel.: (201) 767-3900
Emp.: 100
Food Product Machinery Whslr
N.A.I.C.S.: 423830

GEA Messo GmbH (1)
Friedrich-Ebert-Strasse 134, 47229, Duisburg, Germany
Tel.: (49) 20659030
Sales Range: $25-49.9 Million
Emp.: 35
Evaporation & Crystallization Waste Water Treatment Processing Services
N.A.I.C.S.: 325998

GEA Messo PT (1)
De Beverspijken 7B, PO Box 253, 5221 EE, 's-Hertogenbosch, Netherlands
Tel.: (31) 73 639 0390
Web Site: http://www.gea-messo-pt.com
Emp.: 23
Crystallisation Engineering Services
N.A.I.C.S.: 541330
Karine O'connor *(Gen Mgr)*

GEA Mts Flowtec AG (1)
Industrie Neuhof 28, 3422, Kirchberg, Switzerland
Tel.: (41) 344262989
Web Site: http://mts-flowtec.ch
Construction Services
N.A.I.C.S.: 236220

GEA Nederland B.V. (1)
De Beaverspijken 7C, 5221 EE, 's-Hertogenbosch, Netherlands
Tel.: (31) 736203111
Food Products Mfr
N.A.I.C.S.: 311999

GEA Niro PT B.V. (1)
Tel.: (31) 736390390
Industrial Engineering Services
N.A.I.C.S.: 541330

GEA Niro Soavi Brazil (1)
R Maria C Franco Andrade 858, Campinas, 13092 190, Sao Paulo, Brazil
Tel.: (55) 19 3251 7062
Web Site: http://www.nirosoavi.com
Emp.: 8
High Pressure Industrial Pump Mfr
N.A.I.C.S.: 333914
Markus Faschang *(Office Mgr)*

GEA Niro Soavi S.p.A. (1)
Via A M Da Erba Edoari 29, 43123, Parma, Italy
Tel.: (39) 0521 965411
Web Site: http://www.geagroup.com
Emp.: 150
Butter Making Machinery Mfr
N.A.I.C.S.: 333241
Letizia Ricco *(Gen Mgr-IT)*

GEA Niro Soavi U.K. (1)
The E-Centre Darwin Drive, Ollerton, Nottinghamshire, United Kingdom
Tel.: (44) 1623 867147
Mechanical Equipment Mfr
N.A.I.C.S.: 333310

GEA Norway AS (1)
Gjerdrums vei 8, 0484, Oslo, Norway
Tel.: (47) 22021600
Chemical Product & Preparation Mfr
N.A.I.C.S.: 325998

GEA Nu-Con Ltd (1)
8 Fisher Crescent, Mt Wellington, 1060, Auckland, New Zealand
Tel.: (64) 9 276 2388
Web Site: http://www.nucon.com
Sales Range: $25-49.9 Million
Emp.: 5
Material Handling Equipment Mfr
N.A.I.C.S.: 333248
Neil Simmon *(Gen Mgr)*

GEA Nu-Con Manufacturing Limited (1)
20 Fairfax Avenue, Penrose, 1061, Auckland, New Zealand
Tel.: (64) 9 579 2044
Sales Range: $25-49.9 Million
Emp.: 5
Conveying Equipment Mfr
N.A.I.C.S.: 333922

GEA Nu-Con Pty. Ltd. (1)
458 The Boulevarde, Kirrawee, 2232, NSW, Australia
Tel.: (61) 95452600
Sales Range: $25-49.9 Million
Emp.: 3
Industrial Machinery Mfr
N.A.I.C.S.: 333248

GEA PROCESS MUHENDISLIK MAKINE INSAAT TAAHUT ITHALAT IHRACAT DANISMANLIK SANAYI VE TICARET LTD. STI. (1)
Ankara Asfalti 25 Km Ansizca Koyu, Izmir, 35710, Turkiye
Tel.: (90) 2328772283
Construction Machinery Distr
N.A.I.C.S.: 423810

GEA PT France SAS (1)
4 Rue Jean Pierre Timbaud, 78180, Montigny-le-Bretonneux, Yvelines, France
Tel.: (33) 130146110
Industrial Machinery Mfr & Whslr
N.A.I.C.S.: 333248

GEA Peruana SAC (1)
Av Tomas Ramsey 930-Of 1204 Magdalena del Mar Lima 15, Lima, Peru
Tel.: (51) 13995101
Chemical Product & Preparation Mfr
N.A.I.C.S.: 325998

GEA Pharma Systems (India) Private Limited (1)
Block No 8 Phase B Village Dumad Savli Road, Vadodara, 391740, Gujarat, India
Tel.: (91) 265 3074 272
Web Site: http://www.gea-pharma.in
Sales Range: $50-74.9 Million
Emp.: 15
Pharmaceutical Processing Equipment Mfr
N.A.I.C.S.: 333248

GEA Pharma Systems AG (1)
Hauptstrasse 145, PO Box 112, 4416, Bubendorf, Switzerland
Tel.: (41) 61 936 3636
Emp.: 80
Pharmaceutical Freeze Drying Equipment Mfr
N.A.I.C.S.: 333415
Klaus Moeller *(Mng Dir)*

GEA Pharma Systems Limited (1)
Eastleigh School Lane Chandlers Ford, PO Box 15, Eastleigh, SO53 4DG, Hampshire, United Kingdom
Tel.: (44) 2380267131
Pharmaceuticals Product Mfr
N.A.I.C.S.: 325412

GEA Pilipinas Inc. (1)
Tel.: (63) 28696969
Chemical Product & Preparation Mfr
N.A.I.C.S.: 325998

GEA Polacel Cooling Towers, LLC (1)
14151 Interdrive W, Houston, TX 77032-3326
Tel.: (281) 227-7900
Web Site: http://www.gea.com
Emp.: 100
Cooling Tower Whslr
N.A.I.C.S.: 423730
Shannon Knierim *(Office Mgr)*

GEA Process Engineering (India) Limited (1)
Block No 8 Po Dumad Savli Road, Vadodara, 391740, India
Tel.: (91) 2656141700
Web Site: https://www.geap-india.com
Sales Range: $50-74.9 Million
Emp.: 400
Food Processing Machinery Mfr
N.A.I.C.S.: 333241
Anders Wilhjelm *(Chm)*

GEA Process Engineering (Pty) Ltd. (1)
48 Reedbuck Crescent Corporate Park, Midrand, 1685, South Africa
Tel.: (27) 11 805 6910
Web Site: http://www.gea-pe.co.za
Sales Range: $25-49.9 Million
Emp.: 21
Food Product Machinery Whslr
N.A.I.C.S.: 423830
Bodo Fabry *(Gen Mgr)*

GEA Process Engineering (S.E.A.) Pte. Ltd. (1)
99 Bukit Timah Road 03-08 Alfa Centre, Singapore, 229835, Singapore
Tel.: (65) 6 3388113
Web Site: http://www.geaseasia.com
Sales Range: $25-49.9 Million
Emp.: 74
Food Processing Machinery Mfr
N.A.I.C.S.: 333241
Budi Santosa *(Mgr-Indonesia)*

GEA Process Engineering A/S (1)
Gladsaxevej 305, 2860, Skanderborg, Denmark
Tel.: (45) 39545454
Chemical Product & Preparation Mfr
N.A.I.C.S.: 325998

GEA Process Engineering CEE Kft. (1)
Att Gyorgy Gabor Malomko U 7 A, 2040, Budaors, Hungary
Tel.: (36) 23 427 907
Emp.: 3
Industrial Machinery Mfr & Whslr
N.A.I.C.S.: 333248
Lars Priess *(Gen Mgr)*

GEA Process Engineering Chile S.A. (1)
Estoril 200 Tower B Office 723 ZC, Les Condes, 7591047, Santiago, Chile
Tel.: (56) 2 948 8290
Emp.: 7
Industrial Machinery Mfr
N.A.I.C.S.: 333248

GEA Process Engineering China Limited (1)
99 Hexiang Road, Minhang District, Shanghai, 201109, China
Tel.: (86) 2124082288
Web Site: https://www.geape.com.cn
Thermal Engineering Services
N.A.I.C.S.: 541330

GEA Process Engineering Inc. (1)
9165 Rumsey Rd, Columbia, MD 21045
Tel.: (410) 997-8700
Web Site: http://www.niroinc.com
Sales Range: $125-149.9 Million
Emp.: 150
Food Processing Equipment Mfr & Whslr
N.A.I.C.S.: 333241
Steven Kaplan *(Pres)*

Division (Domestic):

GEA Process Engineering Inc. - Food & Dairy Division (2)
1600 O'Keefe Rd, Hudson, WI 54016
Tel.: (715) 386-9371
Web Site: http://www.gea.com
Food Product Machinery Mfr
N.A.I.C.S.: 333241
Steve Kaplan *(Pres)*

GEA Process Engineering Ireland Ltd (1)
Ash House Lime Tree Avenue Millennium Park, Naas, County Kildare, Ireland
Tel.: (353) 45 981 200
Sales Range: $25-49.9 Million
Emp.: 80
Engineeering Services
N.A.I.C.S.: 541330
Joe O'Keeffe *(Head-Svcs)*

GEA Process Engineering Japan Ltd. (1)
1-7-8 Ebisuminami Ebisu South Wan 3f, Shibuya-Ku, Tokyo, 150-0022, Japan
Tel.: (81) 357738161
Powder Handling Equipment Whslr
N.A.I.C.S.: 423830
Toshinori Aihara *(Mng Dir)*

GEA Process Engineering Ltd. (1)
Leacroft House Leacroft Road, Birchwood, Warrington, WA3 6JF, Cheshire, United Kingdom
Tel.: (44) 1925812650
Web Site: https://www.geaprocess.co.uk
Sales Range: $50-74.9 Million
Emp.: 6
Food Processing Machinery Whslr
N.A.I.C.S.: 423830

GEA Process Engineering Ltd. (1)
356 Church Street, PO Box 12-479, Penrose, 1061, Auckland, New Zealand
Tel.: (64) 9 526 3344
Web Site: http://www.geap.co.nz
Sales Range: $25-49.9 Million
Emp.: 34
Heating & Cooling Equipment Mfr & Whslr
N.A.I.C.S.: 333415
David Bower *(Mng Dir)*

GEA Process Engineering N.V. (1)
Generaal De Wittelaan 9/2, 2800, Mechelen, Belgium
Tel.: (32) 15285110
Web Site: https://www.geap.be
Sales Range: $1-4.9 Billion
Emp.: 16
Beverage Processing Equipment Mfr
N.A.I.C.S.: 333241
Anders Wilhjelm *(Pres)*

GEA GROUP AKTIENGESELLSCHAFT

INTERNATIONAL PUBLIC

GEA Group Aktiengesellschaft—(Continued)

GEA Process Engineering Nederland B.V. (1)
Munsterstraat 5, 7418 EV, Deventer, Netherlands
Tel.: (31) 570663367
Sales Range: $25-49.9 Million
Emp.: 100
Food Processing Equipment Mfr
N.A.I.C.S.: 333241

GEA Process Engineering OOO (1)
Semjonovskiy Val Str 6 Bld 1, 105094, Moscow, Russia
Tel.: (7) 495 787 20 20
Beverage Processing Machinery Distr
N.A.I.C.S.: 423830

GEA Process Engineering Oy (1)
Koivuhaankuja 2, 1510, Vantaa, Finland
Tel.: (358) 20 755 8960
Web Site: http://www.gea-pe.fi
Industrial Dryer Whslr
N.A.I.C.S.: 423830

GEA Process Engineering Pty. Ltd. (1)
49 Railway Road, PO Box 42, Blackburn, 3130, VIC, Australia
Tel.: (61) 398754000
Web Site: http://www.gea.com
Sales Range: $25-49.9 Million
Emp.: 4
Industrial Engineering Services
N.A.I.C.S.: 541330

GEA Process Engineering S.A. (1)
Carlos Calvo 615 2 Piso, C1102AAM, Buenos Aires, Argentina
Tel.: (54) 1143626116
Web Site: https://www.gea-pe.com.ar
Food Product Equipment Installation Services
N.A.I.C.S.: 238220

GEA Process Engineering S.A. (1)
C Cantabria 2 Edificio Amura Plta 4, 28108, Alcobendas, Madrid, Spain
Tel.: (34) 916618267
Web Site: https://www.geape.es
Food Product Machinery Mfr
N.A.I.C.S.: 333241

GEA Process Engineering S.A. de C.V. (1)
Av Lomas Verdes 791 Piso 4 Jardines de Satelite, Naucalpan, 53129, Mexico
Tel.: (52) 5526251600
Web Site: https://www.gea-niro.com.mx
Industrial Equipment Mfr
N.A.I.C.S.: 333248
Luis Martin (Office Mgr)

GEA Process Engineering S.A.S. (1)
4 rue JP Timbaud, PO Box 80, 78185, Montigny-le-Bretonneux, France
Tel.: (33) 130146110
Web Site: https://www.geape.fr
Refrigerator Equipment Mfr
N.A.I.C.S.: 333415

GEA Process Engineering S.A.S. (1)
Calle 90 No 19A - 49 Of 303, Cundinamarca, Bogota, Colombia
Tel.: (57) 1 756 2262
Web Site: http://www.gea.com
Sales Range: $25-49.9 Million
Emp.: 4
Industrial Engineering Services
N.A.I.C.S.: 541330

GEA Process Engineering S.p.A. (1)
Centro Direzionale Milano 2 Palazzo Canova, 20090, Segrate, Milan, Italy
Tel.: (39) 0221010611
Web Site: https://www.gea-pe.it
Sales Range: $25-49.9 Million
Emp.: 4
Food Processing Machinery Distr
N.A.I.C.S.: 333241
Mario Nino Negri (Mng Dir)

GEA Process Engineering Sp. z o.o. (1)
Lopuszanska 95, 02-457, Warsaw, Poland
Tel.: (48) 224567484
Chemical Product & Preparation Mfr
N.A.I.C.S.: 325998

GEA Process Engineering Taiwan Ltd. (1)
Suite 1004 Floor 10 No 205 Section 1 Tun Hua South Road 106, Taipei, 10690, Taiwan
Tel.: (886) 287739180
Emp.: 12
Food Processing Machinery Mfr
N.A.I.C.S.: 333241
Jason Wu (Mgr)

GEA Process Engineering Z o.o. (1)
Al Jerozolimskie 146 D, 02-305, Warsaw, Poland
Tel.: (48) 226081400
Web Site: http://www.geape.pl
Emp.: 35
Air Conditioning Equipment Mfr & Whslr
N.A.I.C.S.: 333415
Edward Kolek (Gen Mgr)

GEA Process Engineering s.r.o. (1)
Mlynska 68, 602 00, Brno, Czech Republic
Tel.: (420) 543 532 338
Web Site: http://www.geap.cz
Industrial Engineering Services
N.A.I.C.S.: 541330

GEA Process Technologies Ireland Limited (1)
Ash House Lime Tree Avenue Millennium Park, Naas, Kildare, Ireland
Tel.: (353) 45981200
Sales Range: $25-49.9 Million
Emp.: 80
Beverage Processing Machinery Mfr & Distr
N.A.I.C.S.: 333241

GEA Process Technology Netherlands B.V. (1)
Hoogveld 16, 5431 NW, Cuijk, Netherlands
Tel.: (31) 485319300
Web Site: http://www.gea.com
Sales Range: $25-49.9 Million
Emp.: 7
Beverage Separator Mfr
N.A.I.C.S.: 333241
Kees Winkel (Mng Dir)

GEA Procomac S.p.A. (1)
Via Fedolfi 29, 43038, Sala Baganza, Parma, Italy
Tel.: (39) 0521839411
Web Site: https://www.procomac.it
Sales Range: $100-124.9 Million
Emp.: 428
Filling Line Machinery Mfr
N.A.I.C.S.: 333993

Unit (Domestic):

GEA Procomac S.p.A. - Packaging Unit (2)
Via A Moro 1/A, 43044, Collecchio, Parma, Italy
Tel.: (39) 0521 333711
Web Site: http://www.procomacpackaging.com
Packaging Machinery Mfr
N.A.I.C.S.: 333993

GEA Real Estate GmbH (1)
Lurgiallee 5, D 60439, Frankfurt am Main, Germany (99%)
Tel.: (49) 699712120
Web Site: http://www.mgvv.de
Sales Range: $50-74.9 Million
Emp.: 20
Real Estate Developers
N.A.I.C.S.: 531390

GEA Refrigeration Malaysia Sdn. Bhd. (1)
No 25 Jalan SS 25/41 Mayang Industrial Park, 47400, Petaling Jaya, Malaysia
Tel.: (60) 378040807
Chemical Product & Preparation Mfr
N.A.I.C.S.: 325998

GEA Refrigeration Technologies GmbH (1)
Industrial Street 6, Monzingen, 55569, Germany
Tel.: (49) 675193030
Web Site: https://www.gearefrigeration.com
Sales Range: $25-49.9 Million
Emp.: 100
Refrigeration & Air Conditioning Equipment Mfr
N.A.I.C.S.: 333415
Christ Marvin (Mng Dir)

Subsidiary (Non-US):

GEA Grasso (Thailand) Co. Ltd. (2)
29/90 Moo 2 Arun Sunthri Project 345 Road Lampho Bangbuathong, Nonthaburi, 11110, Thailand
Tel.: (66) 2525 8500
Sales Range: $25-49.9 Million
Emp.: 20
Refrigerator Equipment Mfr
N.A.I.C.S.: 333415

GEA Grasso Philippines, Inc. (2)
4A Panorama Compound Veterans Center, 1630, Taguig, Metro Manila, Philippines
Tel.: (63) 28 373 211
Web Site: http://www.grasso.com.ph
Refrigerator Equipment Mfr
N.A.I.C.S.: 333415
Rob den Hartog (Mng Dir)

GEA Grasso Spolka z o.o. (2)
ul Hryniewickiego 10 Bud 24, 81-340, Gdynia, Poland
Tel.: (48) 58 627 63 90
Web Site: http://www.grasso.pl
Refrigeration Equipment Whslr
N.A.I.C.S.: 423740

GEA Grasso TOV (2)
Vulytsya Pavlivska Budynok 29, Kimnata 3-3a, Kiev, 01135, Ukraine
Tel.: (380) 44 351 1472
Web Site: http://www.grasso.ua
Industrial Refrigeration Equipment Mfr
N.A.I.C.S.: 333415

GEA Grasso UAB (2)
Smolensko 10, 03201, Vilnius, Lithuania
Tel.: (370) 52311900
Web Site: http://www.grasso.lt
Sales Range: $25-49.9 Million
Emp.: 41
Refrigeration Equipment Mfr & Distr
N.A.I.C.S.: 333415
Gintautas Miskinis (Mng Dir)

GEA Grasso s.r.o. (2)
Unakladoveho Nadrzd, 111 21, Prague, Czech Republic
Tel.: (420) 224223048
Web Site: http://www.grasso.cz
Sales Range: $25-49.9 Million
Emp.: 24
Refrigeration Equipment Whslr
N.A.I.C.S.: 423740
Vaclav Ruzek (Mng Dir)

GEA Refrigeration (Thailand) Co. Ltd. (2)
29/90 Moo 2 Arun Sunthri Project 345 Road Lampho, Bangbuathong, Nonthaburi, 11110, Thailand
Tel.: (66) 2525 8500
Sales Range: $25-49.9 Million
Emp.: 20
Air Conditioning Equipment Mfr
N.A.I.C.S.: 333415
Rob den Hartog (Mng Dir)

GEA Refrigeration Africa (Pty) Ltd. (2)
19 Chain Avenue, PO Box 36815, Montague Gardens, Cape Town, 7442, South Africa
Tel.: (27) 21 555 9000
Web Site: http://www.grenco.co.za
Sales Range: $125-149.9 Million
Emp.: 30
Refrigeration Equipment Mfr & Distr
N.A.I.C.S.: 333415
Andre Schoonraad (Mng Dir)

GEA Refrigeration Canada Inc. (2)
150-2551 Viking Way, Richmond, V6V 1N4 BC, Canada
Tel.: (604) 278-4118
Refrigeration Equipment Repair & Maintanance Services
N.A.I.C.S.: 811310

GEA Refrigeration Components (Australia) Pty. Ltd. (2)
52 Frankston Gardens Drive, Carrum Downs, Melbourne, 3201, VIC, Australia
Tel.: (61) 3 9770 8832
Sales Range: $50-74.9 Million
Emp.: 6
Refrigeration Equipment Whslr
N.A.I.C.S.: 423740
Anthony Kimpton (Mng Dir)

GEA Refrigeration Components (Nordic) A/S (2)
Birkedammen 10 A, 6000, Kolding, Denmark
Tel.: (45) 7552 6015
Web Site: http://www.gearefrigerationcomponents.dk
Emp.: 4
Refrigeration Equipment Whslr
N.A.I.C.S.: 423740
Klaus Gram (Mgr-Sls)

GEA Refrigeration Components (UK) Ltd. (2)
5 Stoneyhill Industrial Estate, Whitchurch, Ross-on-Wye, HR9 6BX, Herefordshire, United Kingdom
Tel.: (44) 1600891010
Web Site: https://www.gea.com
Refrigeration Equipment Whslr
N.A.I.C.S.: 423740

Subsidiary (Domestic):

GEA Refrigeration Germany GmbH (2)
Holzhauser Str 165, 13509, Berlin, Germany
Tel.: (49) 3043592847
Emp.: 30
Refrigeration Equipment Mfr
N.A.I.C.S.: 333415

Subsidiary (Non-US):

GEA Refrigeration Iberica S.A. (2)
C/ San Rafael 3, 28108, Alcobendas, Spain
Tel.: (34) 916 61 5036
Web Site: http://www.geagrenco.es
Refrigeration Compressor Mfr
N.A.I.C.S.: 333415

GEA Refrigeration Netherlands N.V. (2)
De Beverspijken 7c, 5221 EE, 's-Hertogenbosch, Netherlands
Tel.: (31) 736203111
Refrigeration System Installation Services
N.A.I.C.S.: 238220

Division (Domestic):

Royal GEA Grasso Holding NV-Refrigeration Division (3)
Parallelweg 27, 5223 AL, 's-Hertogenbosch, Netherlands
Tel.: (31) 736203988
Sales Range: $800-899.9 Million
Emp.: 3,000
Industrial Refrigeration Equipment Mfr
N.A.I.C.S.: 333415

Subsidiary (US):

GEA Refrigeration North America Inc. (2)
3475 Board Rd, York, PA 17406
Tel.: (717) 767-6411
Emp.: 300
Engineering Products & Food Services
N.A.I.C.S.: 541330
Brian Grigg (Mgr-Control Sys Engrg)

Subsidiary (Non-US):

GEA Refrigeration Philippines, Inc. (2)
8th Floor Alabang Corporate Center Km 25 West Service Road, Alabang, Muntinlupa, 1770, Philippines
Tel.: (63) 2 869 6969
Sales Range: $25-49.9 Million
Emp.: 4
Refrigerator Equipment Mfr
N.A.I.C.S.: 333415

GEA Refrigeration Romania S.R.L. (2)
Str Buna Ziua nr 34-36 etaj 3, 400495, Cluj-Napoca, Romania
Tel.: (40) 264453206
Refrigerator Equipment Mfr
N.A.I.C.S.: 333415

GEA Refrigeration Technologies (2)
Avenida Joao Elustondo Filho 575 Bairro de Santo Agostinho, Porto Alegre, 91140-310, Rio Grande do Sul, Brazil
Tel.: (55) 51 3778 9650
Web Site: http://www.gearefrigeration.com

AND PRIVATE COMPANIES — GEA GROUP AKTIENGESELLSCHAFT

Sales Range: $25-49.9 Million
Emp.: 10
Refrigeration Compressor Mfr
N.A.I.C.S.: 333415
Paulo Mariotto (Mng Dir)

GEA Refrigeration Technologies India Pvt Ltd. (2)
Lohia Jain Business Centre 5th Floor
Friends Park Senapati Bapat Road, Pune, 411 016, India
Tel.: (91) 20 4147 8100
Sales Range: $25-49.9 Million
Emp.: 2
Air Conditioning Equipment Mfr
N.A.I.C.S.: 333415
K. N. A. Chandrasekar (Pres)

GEA Refrigeration Technologies Ireland (2)
Unit 8 Corlurgan Business Park, Corlurgan, Cavan, Ireland
Tel.: (353) 4943 61588
Sales Range: $25-49.9 Million
Emp.: 15
Refrigerator Equipment Mfr
N.A.I.C.S.: 333415
Patrick Gilcreest (Gen Mgr)

GEA Refrigeration Technology (Suzhou) Co., Ltd. (2)
No 8 Dong Chang Lu Suzhou Industrial Park, Suzhou, 215024, Jiangsu, China
Tel.: (86) 512 8777 0788
Refrigeration Equipment Mfr & Distr
N.A.I.C.S.: 333415

GEA Refrigeration Technology Co., Ltd. (2)
Room 14AB CITIC Building Tower A No 19 Jianguomenwai Dajie, Beijing, 100004, China
Tel.: (86) 10 8530 6498
Sales Range: $50-74.9 Million
Emp.: 20
Air Conditioning & Refrigeration Equipment Mfr
N.A.I.C.S.: 333415
Fred Chan (CEO)

GEA Refrigeration UK Ltd. (2)
Unit 9 Conqueror Court Watermark Velum Drive, Sittingbourne, ME10 5BH, Kent, United Kingdom
Tel.: (44) 1795514630
Web Site: https://www.gearefrigeration.co.uk
Refrigeration Compressor Mfr
N.A.I.C.S.: 333415

GEA Refrigeration Vietnam Co. Ltd. (2)
3rd Floor 3G Pho Quang Street Ward 2, Tan Binh District, Ho Chi Minh City, Vietnam
Tel.: (84) 8 38462778
Sales Range: $25-49.9 Million
Emp.: 8
Air Conditioning Equipment Mfr
N.A.I.C.S.: 333415
Rob den Hartog (Mng Dir)

Grasso Componentes Iberia Lda. (2)
Av Saboia 914-D 2765-277 Monte Estoril, 2750-028, Cascais, Portugal
Tel.: (351) 21 487 9300
Web Site: http://www.gearefrigeration.com.pt
Emp.: 3
Refrigeration Equipment Mfr & Distr
N.A.I.C.S.: 333415
Armenia Ferrao (Mng Dir)

Grasso Refrigeration Systems Shanghai Co., Ltd. (2)
399 Jin Yuan Si Road Jiangqiao, Jiading, Shanghai, China
Tel.: (86) 21 3955 7688
Refrigeration & Air Conditioning Equipment Mfr
N.A.I.C.S.: 333415

OOO GEA Refrigeration RUS (2)
Otradnaya str 2B bld 9 floor 10 room 1, Moscow, 127273, Russia
Tel.: (7) 4957872020
Web Site: https://www.gea.com
Sales Range: $25-49.9 Million
Emp.: 100
Refrigerator Equipment Mfr

N.A.I.C.S.: 333415

PT. GEA Grasso Indonesia (2)
Ruko Mutiara Taman Palem Blok C8 / No 1, Cengkareng, Jakarta, 11730, Indonesia
Tel.: (62) 21 5435 6510
Web Site: http://www.grasso-indonesia.com
Refrigeration Equipment Whslr
N.A.I.C.S.: 423740

GEA Segment Management Holding GmbH (1)
Peter-Muller-Str 12, Nordrhein-Westfalen, 40468, Dusseldorf, Germany
Tel.: (49) 211 91360
Web Site: http://www.gea.com
Investment Management Service
N.A.I.C.S.: 523999

GEA Sistemas de Resfriamento Ltda. (1)
Alameda Venus n 573, Distrito Industrial, Indaiatuba, 13347-659, Sao Paulo, Brazil
Tel.: (55) 19 3936 7930
Web Site: http://www.geasr.geagroup.com
Sales Range: $25-49.9 Million
Emp.: 53
Air Conditioning Equipment Mfr
N.A.I.C.S.: 333415

GEA Suisse AG (1)
Industrie Neuhof 28, 3422, Kirchberg, Switzerland
Tel.: (41) 315114747
Chemical Product & Preparation Mfr
N.A.I.C.S.: 325998

GEA Sweden AB (1)
Krokslatts Fabriker 45, 431 37, Molndal, Sweden
Tel.: (46) 317271790
Chemical Product & Preparation Mfr
N.A.I.C.S.: 325998

GEA TDS GmbH (1)
Voss Str 11/13, 31157, Sarstedt, Germany
Tel.: (49) 50669900
Web Site: https://www.gea-tds.com
Food Product Machinery Mfr
N.A.I.C.S.: 333241

GEA Univalve E.U.R.L (1)
29 Route De La Wantzenau, 67800, Hoenheim, France
Tel.: (33) 3 88 19 70 90
Industrial Equipment Mfr & Whslr
N.A.I.C.S.: 333248

GEA WS Southeast, Inc. (1)
6551 Broadway Ave, Jacksonville, FL 32254
Tel.: (904) 786-0030
Farm Machinery Mfr & Whslr
N.A.I.C.S.: 333111

GEA West Africa Ltd. (1)
1 Motorways Avenue Alausa, Ikeja, Lagos, Nigeria
Tel.: (234) 9090662211
Chemical Product & Preparation Mfr
N.A.I.C.S.: 325998
Cherno Njie (Mgr-On Site)

GEA Westfalia Separator Australia Pty. Ltd. (1)
14 Mace Way Melbourne Airport, Melbourne, 3045, Australia
Tel.: (61) 394631999
Web Site: https://www.gea.com
Beverage Separator Machinery Mfr
N.A.I.C.S.: 333241

GEA Westfalia Separator Hellas A.E. (1)
Parodos Leontariou, Pallini, 15351, Athens, Greece
Tel.: (30) 2106034384
Chemical Product & Preparation Mfr
N.A.I.C.S.: 325998

GEA Wiegand (Schweiz) GmbH (1)
Schopfgasschen 8, 4125, Riehen, Switzerland
Tel.: (41) 6164113 75
Web Site: http://www.gea.com
Industrial Pump Mfr
N.A.I.C.S.: 333914
Gunther Dietrich Hoepfinger (Gen Mgr)

GEA Wiegand GmbH (1)
Am Hardtwald 1, 76275, Ettlingen, Germany

Tel.: (49) 72437050
Web Site: https://www.gea-wiegand.de
Sales Range: $50-74.9 Million
Emp.: 200
Industrial Pump Mfr
N.A.I.C.S.: 333914

Gea Niro Soavi North America Inc (1)
10 Commerce Park N Unit 7, Bedford, NH 03110
Tel.: (603) 606-4060
Web Site: http://www.nirosoavi.com
Sales Range: $25-49.9 Million
Emp.: 10
Homogenizer Sales & Repair Services
N.A.I.C.S.: 334516
Robert Cupka (Pres)

Golfetto Sangati S.r.l. (1)
Via Monte Grappa 8, Galliera Veneta, 35015, Padua, Italy
Tel.: (39) 0499423111
Food Industry Machinery Mfr
N.A.I.C.S.: 333241

KET Marine Asia Pte. Ltd. (1)
18 Boon Lay Way 04-112 Tradehub 21, Singapore, Singapore
Tel.: (65) 67931319
Automotive Parts Services
N.A.I.C.S.: 423120
Johnny Yap (Mgr)

KET Marine International B.V. (1)
Koperslagerij 23, 4762 AR, Zevenbergen, Netherlands
Tel.: (31) 168328550
Web Site: https://www.ketmarine.nl
Automotive Parts Services
N.A.I.C.S.: 423120

Kupferbergbau Stadtberge zu Niedermarsberg GmbH (1)
Lurgiallee 5, 60439, Frankfurt am Main, Germany
Tel.: (49) 699578800
Copper Mining Services
N.A.I.C.S.: 212230

Kupferexplorationsgesellschaft mbH (1)
Dorstener Str 484, 44809, Bochum, Nordrhein-Westfalen, Germany
Tel.: (49) 71316441079
Copper Mining Services
N.A.I.C.S.: 212230

LL Plant Engineering AG (1)
Daniel Goldbach Str 19, Ratingen, 40880, Nordrhein-Westfalen, Germany
Tel.: (49) 21021660
Electric Power Generation Services
N.A.I.C.S.: 221118

MG Rohstoffhandel GmbH (1)
Lurgiallee 5, 60439, Frankfurt am Main, Germany (100%)
Tel.: (49) 6913826110
Web Site: http://www.mgrohstoffhandel.com
Sales Range: $25-49.9 Million
Emp.: 7
Purchase & Sale, Agency & Consultancy Services; Trading of Non-Ferrous Concentrates
N.A.I.C.S.: 331529

MVG Metallverkaufsgesellschaft mbH & Co. KG (1)
Hanauer Landstrasse 421, 60314, Frankfurt am Main, Germany (100%)
Tel.: (49) 699421300
Web Site: http://www.mvg-frankfurt.de
Sales Range: $25-49.9 Million
Emp.: 35
Sls.of lait Metal.
N.A.I.C.S.: 332999

Nu-Con Systems Sdn. Bhd. (1)
30 Jalan Pengacara U1/48 Temasya Industrial Park Glenmarie, Shah Alam, Selangor, Malaysia
Tel.: (60) 355698588
Electrical Engineering Services
N.A.I.C.S.: 541330

PT Westfalia Indonesia (1)
Wisma Presisi 3rd Floor Jl Taman Aries A1/1, Jakarta, 11620, Indonesia
Tel.: (62) 21 58902100

Sales Range: $25-49.9 Million
Emp.: 21
Beverage Separator & Decanter Machinery Mfr
N.A.I.C.S.: 333241
Peter Eddy (Gen Mgr)

Paul Pollrich GmbH (1)
Eisenhuettenstrasse 26, 57074, Siegen, Germany
Tel.: (49) 271661230
Web Site: http://www.pollrich.com
Automotive Parts & Accessory Services
N.A.I.C.S.: 423120

Pavan S.p.A. (1)
Via Monte Grappa 8, Galliera Veneta, 35015, Padua, Italy
Tel.: (39) 0499423111
Food Industry Machinery Mfr
N.A.I.C.S.: 333241
Sandro Rasera (Dir-Technical)

Pavan U.S.A., Inc. (1)
3325A Connelly Rd, Emigsville, PA 17318-0505
Tel.: (717) 767-4889
Automotive Parts Services
N.A.I.C.S.: 423120

Procomac Engenharia Ltda. (1)
Av Faria Lima Brig 2355 Jd Paulistano, Sao Paulo, 01452-000, Brazil
Tel.: (55) 11 3031 4353
Web Site: http://www.procomac.com.br
Industrial Machinery Mfr
N.A.I.C.S.: 333248

SC GEA KLIMATECHNIK SRL (1)
B-dul Mihai Viteazul 30, 300222, Timisoara, Romania
Tel.: (40) 356 423 703
Web Site: http://www.gea-klimatechnik.ro
Emp.: 8
Air Conditioning Equipment Distr
N.A.I.C.S.: 423730
Carola Wolters (Head-PR & Mktg)

Sachtleben Bergbau Verwaltungsgesellschaft mit beschrankter Haftung (1)
Meistergasse 14, 77756, Hausach, Germany
Tel.: (49) 783 196 8590
Web Site: https://www.sachtleben-bergbau.de
Barytes Mining Services
N.A.I.C.S.: 212390
Lutz Guenther (Mgr)

Shanghai Zimmer International Trading Co. Ltd. i.L. (1)
Rm 1901-1910 Changfang International Plaza No 555 Lou Shan Guan, Shanghai, 200051, China
Tel.: (86) 2122115199
Industrial Machinery Mfr
N.A.I.C.S.: 333248

Tecno-Leche S.A. (1)
Manuel Rodriguez 1190, Osorno, Chile
Tel.: (56) 64234651
Web Site: http://www.tpi.cl
Dairy Products Mfr
N.A.I.C.S.: 311514

Tullp B.V. (1)
Bliek 17, 4941 SG, Raamsdonksveer, Netherlands
Tel.: (31) 16 257 1484
Web Site: https://www.tullp.com
Filtration Equipment Product Mfr
N.A.I.C.S.: 333413
Robert Sagat (Mgr-Sls)

VDM-Hilfe GmbH (1)
Monzastrasse 4, 63225, Langen, Germany
Tel.: (49) 6103 8048335
Pension Fund Management Services
N.A.I.C.S.: 525110
Manfred Sauer (Gen Mgr)

WestfaliaSurge GmbH (1)
Siemensstrasse 25-27, Bonen, 59199, Germany (100%)
Tel.: (49) 23839370
Web Site: http://www.westfalia.com
Sales Range: $400-449.9 Million
Emp.: 600
Dairy Equipment Mfr

GEA GROUP AKTIENGESELLSCHAFT

GEA Group Aktiengesellschaft—(Continued)
N.A.I.C.S.: 333241
Friedhelm Voswinkel *(Mng Dir)*

Subsidiary (Non-US):

GEA WestfaliaSurge Acier SAS (2)
18 Av De L Europe, 2400, Chateau-Thierry, France
Tel.: (33) 3 23 84 81 60
Farm Machinery & Equipment Whslr
N.A.I.C.S.: 423820

GEA WestfaliaSurge Canada Company (2)
8-60 Bristol Rd E Unit 519, Mississauga, L4Z 3K8, ON, Canada
Tel.: (877) 973-2479
Farm Machinery & Equipment Mfr
N.A.I.C.S.: 333111
Mario Jean *(Gen Mgr)*

GEA WestfaliaSurge Chile S.A. (2)
Eleodoro Vasquez 130, Brorup, Osorno, Los Lagos, Chile
Tel.: (56) 64 200 220
Web Site: http://www.westfalia.com
Farm Machinery Mfr
N.A.I.C.S.: 333111

GEA WestfaliaSurge France SAS (2)
18 Avenue De l'Europe, 2405, Chateau-Thierry, France
Tel.: (33) 323 848 160
Farm Machinery & Equipment Mfr
N.A.I.C.S.: 333111

GEA WestfaliaSurge Mexicana S.A. de C.V. i.L (2)
Mexico-toluca 5420 El Yaqui, 2501, Mexico, Mexico
Tel.: (52) 777 3201 088
Web Site: http://www.gea.com
Emp.: 58
Separator & Decanter Mfr
N.A.I.C.S.: 333241

GEA WestfaliaSurge Nederland B.V. (2)
Planetenveld 45, 3893 GE, Zeewolde, Netherlands
Tel.: (31) 36 547 1040
Farm Machinery Mfr
N.A.I.C.S.: 333111

GEA WestfaliaSurge Nordic A/S (2)
Stenbro Alle 13, 6650, Vejen, Denmark
Tel.: (45) 74 84 10 32
Tobacco Processing Machinery Mfr
N.A.I.C.S.: 333248

GEA WestfaliaSurge UK Ltd. (2)
Stoneleigh Park, Kenilworth, CV8 2LG, Warwickshire, United Kingdom
Tel.: (44) 2476692333
Web Site: http://www.gea.com
Emp.: 20
Farm Machinery & Equipment Whslr
N.A.I.C.S.: 423820

GEA WestfaliaSurge Ukraine GmbH (2)
09100 Kievskaja Oblast Proletarska 17, 09100, Bila Tserkva, Ukraine
Tel.: (380) 44 6 35 23 33
Livestock Farming Services
N.A.I.C.S.: 112990

mg Altersversorgung GmbH (1)
Dorstener Str 484, Bochum, 44809, Nordrhein-Westfalen, Germany
Tel.: (49) 2349800
Pension Fund Management Services
N.A.I.C.S.: 525110

mg capital gmbh (1)
Dorstener Str 484, Bochum, 44809, Nordrhein-Westfalen, Germany
Tel.: (49) 2349800
Investment Management Service
N.A.I.C.S.: 523940

mg venture capital ag (1)
Dorstener Str 484, Bochum, 44809, Germany
Tel.: (49) 2349800
Financial Management Services
N.A.I.C.S.: 523999

mgvv Projektentwicklung Daimlerstrasse GmbH & Co. KG (1)
Lurgiallee 5, Frankfurt am Main, 60439, Hessen, Germany
Tel.: (49) 699712120
Engineeering Services
N.A.I.C.S.: 541330

Subsidiary (Domestic):

mgvv Projektentwicklung Daimlerstrasse Verwaltungs GmbH (2)
Lurgiallee 5, Frankfurt am Main, 60439, Hessen, Germany
Tel.: (49) 699712120
Engineeering Services
N.A.I.C.S.: 541330

GEAR ENERGY LTD.
Suite 800 205 5th Avenue SW Bow Valley Square II, Calgary, T2P 2V7, AB, Canada
Tel.: (403) 538-8435 AB
Web Site:
https://www.gearenergy.com
Year Founded: 2007
0GY—(DEU)
Rev.: $96,868,582
Assets: $250,295,486
Liabilities: $75,411,096
Net Worth: $174,884,391
Earnings: $6,342,617
Emp.: 30
Fiscal Year-end: 12/31/23
Oil & Gas Exploration & Production
N.A.I.C.S.: 211120
Ingram B. Gillmore *(Pres & CEO)*

GEAR-O-RAMA SUPPLY LTD.
9300 Golf Course Road, PO Box 90, Dawson Creek, V1G 4E9, BC, Canada
Tel.: (250) 782-8126
Web Site: https://www.gearorama.ca
Rev.: $11,476,733
Emp.: 25
New & Used Truck Dealers
N.A.I.C.S.: 423120
Andy Schurmann *(Gen Mgr)*

GEAR4MUSIC (HOLDINGS) PLC
Kettlestring Lane Clifton Moor, York, YO30 4XF, United Kingdom
Tel.: (44) 330 365 4444
Web Site:
http://www.gear4music.com
Sales Range: $10-24.9 Million
Emp.: 70
Musical Instrument & Equipment Online Retailer
N.A.I.C.S.: 551112
Andrew Paul Wass *(Editor-News)*

GEBERIT AG
Schachenstrasse 77, CH-8645, Jona, Switzerland
Tel.: (41) 552216300 CH
Web Site: https://www.geberit.com
Year Founded: 1874
GEBN—(SWX)
Rev.: $3,418,957,871
Assets: $3,942,572,062
Liabilities: $2,479,046,563
Net Worth: $1,463,525,499
Earnings: $684,035,477
Emp.: 10,947
Fiscal Year-end: 12/31/23
Building Materials Mfr
N.A.I.C.S.: 332999
Roland Iff *(CFO, Member-Exec Bd & Head-Fin)*

Subsidiaries:

Ceravid GmbH (1)
Schnieringshof 12, 45329, Essen, Germany
Tel.: (49) 201439470
Web Site: https://www.ceravid.de
N.A.I.C.S.: 327110

Ursula Behr *(Mng Dir)*

Duffin Manufacturing Company (1)
316 Warden Ave, Elyria, OH 44036
Tel.: (440) 323-4681
Web Site: http://www.duffinmfg.com
Iron & Steel Pipe & Tube Mfr
N.A.I.C.S.: 331210

Geberit A/S (1)
Laegardvej 26, 8520, Lystrup, Denmark (100%)
Tel.: (45) 8 674 1086
Web Site: https://www.geberit.dk
Sales Range: $25-49.9 Million
Emp.: 30
Sanitary Paper Product Mfr
N.A.I.C.S.: 322291
Lars Risacer *(Mng Dir)*

Geberit AB (1)
Folkets Husgatan 1, Box 140, Bromolla, 295 22, Malmo, Sweden (100%)
Tel.: (46) 4 564 8000
Web Site: https://www.geberit.se
Sales Range: $25-49.9 Million
Emp.: 25
Plumbing & Heating Equipment Whslr
N.A.I.C.S.: 423720

Geberit AS (1)
Luhrtoppen 2, Lorenskog, 1470, Norway
Tel.: (47) 6 797 8200
Web Site: https://www.geberit.no
Pipe Fitting Installation Services
N.A.I.C.S.: 238220

Geberit Apparate AG (1)
Schachenstrasse 77, Jona, 8645, See-Gaster, Switzerland
Tel.: (41) 552216111
Emp.: 900
Sanitary Products Mfr
N.A.I.C.S.: 332999

Geberit B.V. (1)
Fultonbaan 15, 3439 NE, Nieuwegein, Netherlands (100%)
Tel.: (31) 30 605 7700
Web Site: https://www.geberit.nl
Sales Range: $25-49.9 Million
Emp.: 50
Plumbing & Heating Equipment Whslr
N.A.I.C.S.: 423720
Menno Portengan *(Mng Dir)*

Geberit Beteiligungsverwaltung GmbH (1)
Gebertstrasse 1, Pottenbrunn, 3140, Saint Polten, Austria (100%)
Tel.: (43) 27424010
Web Site: http://www.geberit.at
Sales Range: $150-199.9 Million
Emp.: 350
Holding Company
N.A.I.C.S.: 551112
Albert M. Baehny *(CEO)*

Geberit Ceramica S.p.A. (1)
Via Valcellina C33 ZI Nord, Spilimbergo, 33097, Pordenone, Italy
Tel.: (39) 042786796
Construction Services
N.A.I.C.S.: 236220

Geberit Holding AG (1)
Schachenstrasse 77, PO Box 1575, 8645, Jona, Switzerland (100%)
Tel.: (41) 552216111
Web Site: http://www.geberit.ch
Sales Range: $250-299.9 Million
Emp.: 800
Holding Company
N.A.I.C.S.: 551112

Geberit Huter GmbH (1)
Statz 80, Matrei am Brenner, 6143, Tirol, Austria (100%)
Tel.: (43) 52737400
Web Site: https://www.huter.at
Sales Range: $50-74.9 Million
Emp.: 101
Enameled Iron & Metal Sanitary Ware Mfr
N.A.I.C.S.: 332999
Josef Rapp *(Mng Dir)*

Geberit India Manufacturing Pvt. Ltd. (1)
D-109 D-110 Chakan Industrial Area Phase II-MIDC, Pune, 410 502, India

INTERNATIONAL PUBLIC

Tel.: (91) 2135610005
N.A.I.C.S.: 322291

Geberit International AG (1)
Schachenstrasse 77, PO Box 1576, 8645, Jona, Switzerland (100%)
Tel.: (41) 55 221 6664
Web Site: https://www.geberit.ch
Sales Range: $150-199.9 Million
Emp.: 800
Management Consulting Services
N.A.I.C.S.: 541618

Geberit International B.V. (1)
Fultonbaan 15, 3439 NE, Nieuwegein, Netherlands (100%)
Tel.: (31) 306057700
Web Site: http://www.geberit.nl
Sales Range: $25-49.9 Million
Emp.: 50
Holding Company
N.A.I.C.S.: 551112

Geberit International Sales AG (1)
Neue Jonastrasse 59, Rapperswil, 8640, Jona, Switzerland (100%)
Tel.: (41) 552216200
Emp.: 900
Financial Investment Activities
N.A.I.C.S.: 523999
Ronald Van Triest *(Mng Dir)*

Geberit Israel Ltd. (1)
North Barkat 4 Industrial Park, Caesarea, 3079897, Israel
Tel.: (972) 46907207
Bathroom Product Mfr & Whslr
N.A.I.C.S.: 325620

Geberit Kft (1)
Allz u 2, 1117, Budapest, Hungary (100%)
Tel.: (36) 12044187
Web Site: https://www.geberit.hu
Engineeering Services
N.A.I.C.S.: 541330
Thomas Ruboczky *(Mng Dir)*

Geberit Lichtenstein GmbH (1)
Kastanienstrasse 7, 09350, Lichtenstein, Germany (100%)
Tel.: (49) 37204590
Web Site: http://www.geberit.com
Enameled Iron & Metal Sanitary Ware Mfr
N.A.I.C.S.: 332999

Geberit Logistik GmbH (1)
Theuerbachstrasse 1, 88630, Pfullendorf, Germany
Tel.: (49) 75 52 934 01
Logistics Consulting Servies
N.A.I.C.S.: 541614

Geberit Mapress GmbH (1)
Kronprinzstr 40, 40764, Langenfeld, Germany (100%)
Tel.: (49) 21732850
Web Site: http://www.geberit.com
Sales Range: $100-124.9 Million
Emp.: 500
Iron & Steel Pipe & Tube Mfr
N.A.I.C.S.: 331210

Geberit Marketing e Distribuzione SA (1)
Schachenstrasse 77, PO Box 1580, 8645, Jona, Switzerland (100%)
Tel.: (41) 552216111
Web Site: https://www.geberit.ch
Sales Range: $250-299.9 Million
Emp.: 900
Plumbing & Heating Equipment Whslr
N.A.I.C.S.: 423720

Geberit N.V. (1)
Ossegemstraat 24, 1860, Meise, Belgium (100%)
Tel.: (32) 22520111
Web Site: https://www.geberit.be
Sales Range: $25-49.9 Million
Emp.: 40
Plumbing & Heating Equipment Whslr
N.A.I.C.S.: 423720
Thierry Geers *(Mng Dir)*

Geberit Nigeria Ltd. (1)
293 Akin Olugbade Street, Victoria Island, Lagos, Nigeria
Tel.: (234) 16304304
Construction Services
N.A.I.C.S.: 236220

AND PRIVATE COMPANIES

Geberit OY (1)
Lumijalki 2, 01740, Vantaa,
Finland (100%)
Tel.: (358) 1 066 2300
Web Site: https://www.geberit.fi
Sales Range: $25-49.9 Million
Emp.: 17
Plumbing & Heating Equipment Whslr
N.A.I.C.S.: 423720
Kim Lovkviest *(CEO)*

Geberit Ozorkow Sp. z o.o. (1)
Ul Adamowek 25, 95-035, Ozorkow, Poland
Tel.: (48) 426131500
N.A.I.C.S.: 322291

Geberit Plumbing Technology Co. Ltd. (1)
1515 Huiping Road Nanxiang, Shanghai, 201802, China
Tel.: (86) 21 6185 3188
Sales Range: $125-149.9 Million
Emp.: 400
Sanitary Ware Products Mfr
N.A.I.C.S.: 326191

Geberit Plumbing Technology India Pvt. Ltd. (1)
At The LaLit Ashok Kumara Krupa High Grounds, Bengaluru, 560 001, India
Tel.: (91) 806 828 1101
Web Site: https://www.geberit.in
Sales Range: $25-49.9 Million
Emp.: 35
Sanitary Ware Products Distr
N.A.I.C.S.: 423730
Abubaker Koya *(Mng Dir)*

Geberit Production Oy (1)
Wartsilankatu 1, 10600, Tammisaari, Finland
Tel.: (358) 10662300
N.A.I.C.S.: 322291

Geberit Produkcja Sp. z o.o. (1)
Ul Torunska 154, 62-600, Kolo, Poland
Tel.: (48) 632618400
N.A.I.C.S.: 322291

Geberit Produktions AG (1)
Schachenstrasse 77, PO Box 1581, 8645, Jona, Switzerland (100%)
Tel.: (41) 552216111
Web Site: http://www.geberit.ch
Sales Range: $250-299.9 Million
Emp.: 800
Plumbing & Heating Equipment Whslr
N.A.I.C.S.: 423720
Christian Buhl *(CEO)*

Geberit Produktions GmbH (1)
Theuerbachstrasse 1, 88630, Pfullendorf, Germany (100%)
Tel.: (49) 755293401
Web Site: http://www.geberit.de
Sales Range: $450-499.9 Million
Emp.: 1,500
Plumbing Fixture & Earthenware Bathroom Accessories Mfr
N.A.I.C.S.: 327110
Karl Spachmann *(Mng Dir)*

Geberit Produktions GmbH & Co. KG (1)
Gebertstrasse 1, Pottenbrunn, 3140, Saint Polten, Austria (100%)
Tel.: (43) 27424010
Web Site: http://www.geberit.at
Sales Range: $100-124.9 Million
Emp.: 400
Enameled Iron & Metal Sanitary Ware Mfr
N.A.I.C.S.: 332999
Albert M. Baehny *(CEO)*

Geberit Produzione S.p.a. (1)
Viale Del Lavoro 4, Villadose, 45010, Rovigo, Italy (100%)
Tel.: (39) 0425908908
Web Site: http://www.geberit.it
Sales Range: $25-49.9 Million
Emp.: 100
Fabricated Pipe & Pipe Fitting Mfr
N.A.I.C.S.: 332996

Geberit Pty Ltd. (1)
Unit 8a 6-8 Byfield Street, Northryte, Macquarie Park, 2113, NSW, Australia (100%)
Tel.: (61) 29 889 7866
Web Site: https://www.geberit.com.au

Sales Range: $50-74.9 Million
Emp.: 10
Plumbing & Heating Equipment Whslr
N.A.I.C.S.: 423720
Anthony Ruston *(Mng Dir)*

Geberit RLS Beteiligungs GmbH (1)
Kronprinzstr 40, 40746, Langenfeld, Germany (100%)
Tel.: (49) 21732850
Web Site: http://www.geberit.de
Sales Range: $200-249.9 Million
Emp.: 550
Iron & Steel Pipe & Tube Mfr
N.A.I.C.S.: 331210
Ulrich Wagner *(Mng Dir)*

Geberit RUS LLC (1)
Olympiyskiy Prospect 16 Building 5, Moscow, Russia
Tel.: (7) 4957838330
Web Site: http://www.geberit.ru
Construction Services
N.A.I.C.S.: 236220

Geberit S.A.U. (1)
Plaza Europa 2-4 6 Planta, 08902, L'Hospitalet de Llobregat, Spain
Tel.: (34) 902170635
Construction Services
N.A.I.C.S.: 236220

Geberit Sales Ltd. (1)
Geberit House Academy Drive, Warwick, CV34 6QZ, United Kingdom (100%)
Tel.: (44) 1926516800
Web Site: http://www.geberit.co.uk
Sales Range: $25-49.9 Million
Emp.: 35
Fabricated Pipe & Pipe Fitting Mfr
N.A.I.C.S.: 332996
Mark Larden *(Mng Dir)*

Geberit Sanitarna Tehnika d.o.o. (1)
Smolnik 17, 2342, Ruse, Slovenia (100%)
Tel.: (386) 26690200
Web Site: http://www.geberit.si
Sales Range: $50-74.9 Million
Emp.: 240
Plastics Product Mfr
N.A.I.C.S.: 326199

Geberit Service Oy (1)
Wartsilankatu 1, 10600, Tammisaari, Finland
Tel.: (358) 10662300
N.A.I.C.S.: 322291

Geberit Service Sp. z o.o. (1)
Street Wolczanska 178, 90-530, Lodz, Poland
Tel.: (48) 422930400
N.A.I.C.S.: 541213

Geberit Shanghai Investment Administration Co., Ltd. (1)
No 1515 Huiping Road Nanxiang High Tech, Development Zone, Shanghai, 201802, China (100%)
Tel.: (86) 2161853188
Web Site: http://www.geberit.com.cn
Emp.: 500
Plumbing & Heating Equipment Whslr
N.A.I.C.S.: 423720

Geberit Shanghai Trading Co. Ltd. (1)
No 1515 Hui ping Road, Nanxiang, Shanghai, 201802, China
Tel.: (86) 216 185 3188
Web Site: https://www.geberit.com.cn
Sanitary Products Distr
N.A.I.C.S.: 423720

Geberit Slovensko s.r.o. (1)
Karadzicova 10 -1 poschodie, 821 08, Bratislava, Slovakia (100%)
Tel.: (421) 24 920 3071
Web Site: https://www.geberit.sk
Sales Range: $25-49.9 Million
Emp.: 15
Construction Materials Whslr
N.A.I.C.S.: 423390

Geberit South East Asia Pte. Ltd. (1)
8 Kallang Ave Aperia Tower 1 17-09, Singapore, 339509, Singapore (100%)
Tel.: (65) 6 250 4011
Web Site: https://www.geberit.com.sg
Sales Range: $25-49.9 Million
Emp.: 14
Plumbing & Heating Equipment Whslr

N.A.I.C.S.: 423720

Geberit Southern Africa (Pty.) Ltd. (1)
Meadowview Business Estate, Linbro park, Johannesburg, 2090, South Africa
Tel.: (27) 11 444 5070
Web Site: https://www.geberit.co.za
Sales Range: $25-49.9 Million
Emp.: 28
Sanitary Products Distr
N.A.I.C.S.: 423720

Geberit Sp.z.o.o. (1)
ul Postepu 1, Postepu 1, 02-676, Warsaw, Poland (100%)
Tel.: (48) 22 376 0102
Web Site: https://www.geberit.pl
Sales Range: $25-49.9 Million
Emp.: 50
Plumbing & Heating Equipment Whslr
N.A.I.C.S.: 423720
Andrzej Dobrut *(Mng Dir)*

Geberit Spol. S.r.o. (1)
Moravanska 85, 61900, Brno, Czech Republic (100%)
Tel.: (420) 547212335
Web Site: http://www.geberit.cz
Plumbing Fixture & Earthenware Bathroom Accessories Mfr
N.A.I.C.S.: 327110

Geberit Technik AG (1)
Schachenstrasse 77, PO Box 1577, 8645, Jona, Switzerland (100%)
Tel.: (41) 552216759
Web Site: http://www.geberit.ch
Sales Range: $250-299.9 Million
Emp.: 1,200
Plumbing & Heating Equipment Whslr
N.A.I.C.S.: 423720

Geberit Tecnologia Sanitaria S.A. (1)
Rua Cupertino de Miranda n 12 - 2 A, 1600-485, Lisbon, Portugal
Tel.: (351) 217815100
Web Site: http://www.geberit.pt
Building Materials Distr
N.A.I.C.S.: 423390

Geberit Tesisat Sistemleri Ticaret Ltd. (1)
Kosuyolu Cad No 33, Istanbul, C4718, Turkiye
Tel.: (90) 216 340 82 73
Plumbing & Piping System Installation Services
N.A.I.C.S.: 238220

Geberit Trading LLC (1)
Ave Stepana Bandera 9 Building 6 Entrance 5A Office 6-301, 04073, Kiev, Ukraine
Tel.: (380) 444929741
Web Site: http://www.geberit.ua
Plumbing Services
N.A.I.C.S.: 238220

Geberit Vertriebs AG (1)
Schachenstrasse 77, PO Box 1579, 8645, Jona, Switzerland (100%)
Tel.: (41) 55 221 6111
Web Site: http://www.geberit.ch
Sales Range: $250-299.9 Million
Emp.: 900
Plumbing & Heating Equipment Whslr
N.A.I.C.S.: 423720

Geberit Vertriebs GmbH (1)
Theuerbachstrasse 1, 88630, Pfullendorf, Germany (100%)
Tel.: (49) 75 529 3401
Web Site: https://www.geberit.de
Sales Range: $1-4.9 Billion
Emp.: 1,930
Plumbing Fixture & Earthenware Bathroom Accessories Mfr
N.A.I.C.S.: 327110
Karl Spachmann *(Member-Exec Bd)*

Geberit Vertriebs GmbH & Co. KG (1)
Gebertstrasse 1, Pottenbrunn, 3140, Saint Polten, Austria
Tel.: (43) 2 742 4010
Web Site: https://www.geberit.at
Enameled Iron & Metal Sanitary Ware Mfr
N.A.I.C.S.: 332999

Geberit Verwaltungs AG (1)

GEBR. HEINEMANN SE & CO. KG

Schachenstrasse 77, PO Box 1578, 8645, Jona, Switzerland (100%)
Tel.: (41) 552216947
Web Site: http://www.geberit.ch
Sales Range: $150-199.9 Million
Emp.: 900
Management Consulting Services
N.A.I.C.S.: 541618

Geberit Verwaltungs GmbH (1)
Theuerbachstrasse 1, Pfullendorf, 88630, Germany (100%)
Tel.: (49) 755293401
Web Site: http://www.geberit.com
Sales Range: $450-499.9 Million
Emp.: 1,500
Plumbing Fixture & Earthenware Bathroom Accessories Mfr
N.A.I.C.S.: 327110
Karl Spachmann *(Mng Dir)*

Geberit Weilheim GmbH (1)
Am Weidenbach 3, 82362, Weilheim, Germany (100%)
Tel.: (49) 8816850
Web Site: http://www.geberit.de
Enameled Iron & Metal Sanitary Ware Mfr
N.A.I.C.S.: 332999

Geberit prodaja d.o.o. (1)
Bezena 55 a, 2342, Ruse, Slovenia
Tel.: (386) 2 601 8200
Web Site: https://www.geberit.si
Emp.: 7
Sanitary Products Distr
N.A.I.C.S.: 423720

Geberit proizvodnja d.o.o. (1)
Bezena 55 a, 2342, Ruse, Slovenia
Tel.: (386) 26018306
N.A.I.C.S.: 322291

Sanitec Corporation (1)
Kaupintie 2, Helsinki, 00440, Finland (99%)
Tel.: (358) 10662500
Web Site: http://www.sanitec.com
Sales Range: $900-999.9 Million
Emp.: 6,516
Bathroom Ceramics Mfr
N.A.I.C.S.: 327110
Peter Nilsson *(Pres & CEO)*

The Chicago Faucet Company (1)
2100 S Clearwater Dr, Des Plaines, IL 60018-5999
Tel.: (847) 803-5000
Web Site: https://www.chicagofaucets.com
Sales Range: $25-49.9 Million
Emp.: 60
Mfr of Faucets & Brass Plumbing Fittings for Residential & Commercial Use
N.A.I.C.S.: 332913

GEBR. GRUNEWALD GMBH & CO. KG

Antoniusstrasse 15, 57399, Olpe, Germany
Tel.: (49) 27234080
Web Site: http://www.gruenewald-papier.de
Year Founded: 1874
Rev.: $43,959,659
Emp.: 106
Packaging Paper Products Mfr
N.A.I.C.S.: 322220
Christopher Grunewald *(Mng Dir)*

GEBR. HEINEMANN SE & CO. KG

Koreastrasse 3, 20457, Hamburg, Germany
Tel.: (49) 40 30 10 20   De
Web Site: http://www.gebr-heinemann.de
Sales Range: $1-4.9 Billion
Emp.: 6,000
Retailer & Distributor for International Travel Retail Market
N.A.I.C.S.: 459999
Claus Heinemann *(Co-Owner)*

Subsidiaries:

Heinemann Asia Pacific Pte. Ltd. (1)
10 Kallang Avenue Aperia Tower 2 12-

2905

GEBR. HEINEMANN SE & CO. KG

Gebr. Heinemann SE & Co. KG—(Continued)
14/18, Singapore, 339510, Singapore
Tel.: (65) 66717529
Web Site: http://www.heinemann.com.sg
Travel Retailer
N.A.I.C.S.: 561510
Marvin Von Plato (CEO)

GEBR. KEMPER GMBH & CO. KG

Harkortstrasse 5, 57462, Olpe, Germany
Tel.: (49) 27618910 De
Web Site: http://www.kemper-olpe.de
Year Founded: 1864
Sales Range: $150-199.9 Million
Emp.: 610
Valves & Fittings Mfr
N.A.I.C.S.: 332911
Rupprecht Kemper (Mng Dir)

Subsidiaries:

Dendrit Haustechnik-Software GmbH (1)
Fehrbelliner Platz 1, 48249, Dulmen, Germany
Tel.: (49) 25949610
Web Site: http://www.dendrit.de
Nonferrous Metal Products Mfr
N.A.I.C.S.: 332112

Gebr. Kemper UK & Ireland Ltd. (1)
2 Ripple court Brockeridge Business Park, Twyning, Tewkesbury, GL20 6FG, Gloucestershire, United Kingdom
Tel.: (44) 1684854930
Web Site: http://www.kemper-uk.com
Nonferrous Metal Product Distr
N.A.I.C.S.: 423510
Robert Moodey (Mgr-Natl Sls)

KEMPER Trading Shanghai Co. Ltd. (1)
5th floor China Merchants Tower 161 LuJiaZui E Road, Pudong, 200120, Shanghai, China
Tel.: (86) 215875353118
Semi-Finished Metal Product Distr
N.A.I.C.S.: 423510

Kemper AIP Metals LLC (1)
LLC 518 County Rd 513 Ste B, Califon, NJ 07830
Tel.: (732) 800-1247
Nonferrous Metal Product Distr
N.A.I.C.S.: 423510

Kemper Asia Pacific Trading LLP (1)
4 Battery Road 25-01 Bank of China Building, 49908, Singapore, Singapore
Tel.: (65) 96311748
Nonferrous Metal Product Distr
N.A.I.C.S.: 423510

Profiltech Stufenbandprofile GmbH (1)
Industriestrasse 3, 75210, Keltern, Germany
Tel.: (49) 708292380
Web Site: http://www.profiltech.de
Nonferrous Metal Products Mfr
N.A.I.C.S.: 332112

GEBR. KNAUF KG

Am Bahnhof 7, 97346, Iphofen, Germany
Tel.: (49) 9323310
Web Site: http://www.knauf.com
Building Materials Mfr
N.A.I.C.S.: 444180
Annette Brehm (Sr Controller)

Subsidiaries:

Knauf Gips KG (1)
Am Bahnhof 7, Iphofen, 97346, Germany
Tel.: (49) 9323310
Web Site: http://www.knauf.com
Sales Range: $1-4.9 Billion
Emp.: 1,200
Holding Company; Building Materials & Products Mfr & Distr
N.A.I.C.S.: 551112
Manfred Grundke (Mng Partner)

Subsidiary (Non-US):

B. en N. Knauf en C-Isolava G.C.V. (2)
Ooigemstraat 12, 8710, Wielsbeke, Belgium
Tel.: (32) 56 674401
Web Site: http://www.isolava.be
Emp.: 150
Building Materials Whslr
N.A.I.C.S.: 423390
Patrick Renard (Gen Mgr)

ICS Knauf Gips SRL (2)
Stefan cel Mare Str 178, 3100, Balti, Moldova
Tel.: (373) 231 22439
Building Materials Whslr
N.A.I.C.S.: 423390

IOO Knauf Marketing (2)
Ul Nemiga 40 Of 46, 220004, Minsk, Belarus
Tel.: (375) 17 200 56 18
Web Site: http://www.knauf.by
Building Materials Whslr
N.A.I.C.S.: 423390

KNAUF CO. LTD. (2)
4F No 11 Ln 202 Jingxing Rd, Wenshan Dist, 11669, Taipei, Taiwan
Tel.: (886) 2 86635068
Building Materials Whslr
N.A.I.C.S.: 423390

Subsidiary (Domestic):

KNAUF riessler GmbH & Co. KG (2)
Susswiesenstrasse 10, 74549, Wolpertshausen, Germany
Tel.: (49) 7904 94 46 81 0
Web Site: http://www.knauf-riessler.de
Gypsum Product Mfr
N.A.I.C.S.: 327420

Subsidiary (Non-US):

Knauf A.S. (2)
Universiteler Mah 1598 Cad Nr 16, 6800, Ankara, Turkiye
Tel.: (90) 312 29701 00
Web Site: http://www.knauf.com.tr
Building Materials Whslr
N.A.I.C.S.: 423390

Knauf A/S (2)
Klovermarksvej 6, 9500, Hobro, Denmark
Tel.: (45) 9657 3000
Web Site: http://www.knauf.dk
Emp.: 200
Gypsum Product Distr
N.A.I.C.S.: 423390
Mortion Subbarao (Gen Mgr)

Knauf AG (2)
Kagenstrasse 17, Reinach, 4153, Switzerland (100%)
Tel.: (41) 617161010
Web Site: http://www.knauf.ch
Rev.: $27,604,000
Emp.: 80
Provider of Construction Materials
N.A.I.C.S.: 444180
Rolland Babst (Gen Mgr)

Subsidiary (Domestic):

Knauf AMF GmbH & Co. KG (2)
Elsenthal 15, Grafenau, 94481, Germany
Tel.: (49) 85524220
Web Site: http://www.amfgrafenau.de
Sales Range: $50-74.9 Million
Emp.: 250
Ceiling Tiles Mfr
N.A.I.C.S.: 326199
Karl Wenig (Gen Mgr)

Subsidiary (Non-US):

Knauf AMF Ceilings Ltd. (2)
1 Swan Road South West Industrial Estate, Peterlee, Durham, SR8 2HS, United Kingdom
Tel.: (44) 191 5188600
Web Site: http://www.amfceilings.co.uk
Emp.: 20
Building Materials Whslr
N.A.I.C.S.: 423390
Peter Symons (Dir-Comml)

Knauf AMF EOOD (3)
Universitetska Str 2, 1164, Sofia, Bulgaria

Tel.: (359) 2 988 71 75
Web Site: http://www.knaufamf.bg
Building Materials Whslr
N.A.I.C.S.: 423390

Knauf AMF Forros do Brasil Ltda. (3)
Rua Princesa Isabel 94 sala 84, 04601-000, Brasilla, Sao Paulo, Brazil
Tel.: (55) 11 3539 3930
Web Site: http://www.knaufamf.com.br
Building Materials Whslr
N.A.I.C.S.: 423390

Knauf AMF France SARL (3)
Z I Mitry Compans 1 rue Bequerel, BP 222, 77292, Mitry-Mory, Cedex, France
Tel.: (33) 1 64676080
Web Site: http://www.amf-france.fr
Building Materials Distr
N.A.I.C.S.: 423390

Knauf AMF Hellas EPE (3)
Thessalonikis 151 street, 11852, Athens, Greece
Tel.: (30) 210 3615645
Building Materials Whslr
N.A.I.C.S.: 423390
Aggelos Sinodinos (Mgr-Sls)

Knauf AMF Interiors Hellas Ltd. (3)
Agrotemaxio 592, PO box 1362, Nea Magnisia, 57022, Thessaloniki, Greece
Tel.: (30) 2310 722197
Web Site:
http://southeast.knaufamfinteriors.com
Ceiling Mfr
N.A.I.C.S.: 335210
Sofia Tsenekidou (Mgr-Customer Svc)

Knauf AMF Italia Controsoffitti S.r.l. (3)
Via Morimondo 26, 20143, Milan, Italy
Tel.: (39) 02 87033430
Web Site: http://www.knaufamf.it
Building Materials Whslr
N.A.I.C.S.: 423390

Knauf AMF Kft. (3)
Budafoki ut 111, 1117, Budapest, Hungary
Tel.: (36) 1 204 53 50
Web Site: http://www.knaufamf.hu
Building Materials Whslr
N.A.I.C.S.: 423390

Knauf AMF Plafonds bvba (3)
Antwerpsesteenweg 124, 2630, Aartselaar, Belgium
Tel.: (32) 3 8878548
Building Materials Whslr
N.A.I.C.S.: 423390
Marc Peeters (Dir-Comml)

Knauf AMF Plafondsystemen B.V. (3)
Mesonweg 8-12, 3542 AL, Utrecht, Netherlands
Tel.: (31) 30 2415445
Building Materials Whslr
N.A.I.C.S.: 423390

Knauf AMF Sistemas de Techos S.L. (3)
Gran Via 43 2 E, 28013, Madrid, Spain
Tel.: (34) 91 541 34 20
Building Materials Whslr
N.A.I.C.S.: 423390

Knauf AMF d.o.o. (3)
Turnovse 44, 1360, Vrhnika, Slovenia
Tel.: (386) 1 7557 480
Building Materials Whslr
N.A.I.C.S.: 423390

Knauf AMF s.r.o. (3)
Chlumcanskeho 5/497, 180 21, Prague, Czech Republic
Tel.: (420) 266 790 130 1
Web Site: http://www.amf-cz.cz
Building Materials Whslr
N.A.I.C.S.: 423390

Subsidiary (Non-US):

Knauf Africa Trade (2)
Zone industrielle El M Ghira I - lot n 9, 2082, Fouchana, Tunisia
Tel.: (216) 33 389 721365
Building Materials Distr
N.A.I.C.S.: 423390

INTERNATIONAL PUBLIC

Knauf Alcopor Italia S.p.A. (2)
Strada Settimo 399/11, 10156, Turin, Italy
Tel.: (39) 05069211
Web Site: http://www.knauf.it
Sales Range: $25-49.9 Million
Emp.: 67
Mfr of Insulation Products
N.A.I.C.S.: 327993

Subsidiary (Domestic):

Knauf Aquapanel GmbH (2)
PO Box 10 30 64, 44030, Dortmund, Germany
Tel.: (49) 2 31 99 80 01
Web Site: http://www.knauf-aquapanel.com
Building Material Mfr & Whslr
N.A.I.C.S.: 326199

Subsidiary (Non-US):

Knauf Batiment SAS (2)
Zone d Activites - Rue Principale, 68600, Wolfgantzen, France
Tel.: (33) 3 89721 00
Web Site: http://www.knauf.com
Building Materials Whslr
N.A.I.C.S.: 423390

Knauf Bauprodukte Polska Sp. z o. o. (2)
ul Gipsowa 5, 97-427, Rogowiec, Poland
Tel.: (48) 22 36 95 600
Web Site: http://www.knauf.com
Building Materials Whslr
N.A.I.C.S.: 423390

Knauf Belchatow Sp. z o. o. (2)
ul Gipsowa 3, 97-427, Rogowiec, Poland
Tel.: (48) 22 3695 501
Web Site: http://www.knauf.pl
Emp.: 100
Building Materials Whslr
N.A.I.C.S.: 423390
Jacek Piwowarski (Plant Mgr)

Knauf Bratislava s.r.o. (2)
Apollo Business Center blok A1 Prievozska 2/A, 821 09, Bratislava, Slovakia
Tel.: (421) 2 58240811
Web Site: http://www.knauf.sk
Building Materials Whslr
N.A.I.C.S.: 423390
Juraj Slezak (Head-Technical Dept)

Knauf Bulgaria EOOD (2)
Str Angelov vrah 27, 1618, Sofia, Bulgaria
Tel.: (359) 2 9178910
Web Site: http://www.knauf.bg
Building Materials Whslr
N.A.I.C.S.: 423390
Zhoro Iliev (Plant Mgr)

Knauf Cyprus Limited (2)
Adjacent to the Ex-Cement Factory of Moni Pirgos, PO Box 52573, 4065, Limassol, Cyprus
Tel.: (357) 25 343371
Web Site: http://www.knauf.com.cy
Building Materials Whslr
N.A.I.C.S.: 423390

Knauf Danogips A/S (2)
Klovermarksvej 6, 9500, Hobro, Denmark
Tel.: (45) 96573000
Building Materials Whslr
N.A.I.C.S.: 423390
Helle Dam Andersen (Mgr-Laboratory)

Knauf Est SAS (2)
Zone Industrielle, 68190, Ungersheim, France
Tel.: (33) 3 89266900
Building Materials Whslr
N.A.I.C.S.: 423390

Knauf Fibre SAS (2)
14 route de la Palante, 70200, La Cote, France
Tel.: (33) 3 84890240
Building Materials Whslr
N.A.I.C.S.: 423390

Knauf Ges.m.b.H. (2)
Strobachgasse 6, 1050, Vienna, Austria
Tel.: (43) 50 567 567
Web Site: http://www.knauf.at
Building Materials Mfr
N.A.I.C.S.: 327120

Knauf Gips s.r.l. (2)

AND PRIVATE COMPANIES   GEBR. KNAUF KG

Piata Presei Libere 3-5 Sector 1 Cladirea City, Gate-Turnul de Sud Etaj 4, 013702, Bucharest, Romania
Tel.: (40) 21 650 00 40
Web Site: http://www.knauf.ro
Emp.: 30
Gypsum Product Mfr
N.A.I.C.S.: 327420

Knauf Gypsopiia ABEE (2)
Euripidou 10, Kallithea, 17674, Athens, Greece
Tel.: (30) 210 9310567
Emp.: 50
Building Materials Whslr
N.A.I.C.S.: 423390

Knauf Gypsum Thailand Limited (2)
598 Q House Ploenjit Building 9th 18th -19th Floor, Room No 9 CD 18BC 19B Ploenjit Road Lumpini Pathumwan, Bangkok, 10330, Thailand
Tel.: (66) 2 6896077
Web Site: http://www.knauf.co.th
Building Materials Distr
N.A.I.C.S.: 423390
Sanguansak Sarangkasiri *(Mgr-Technical)*

Knauf Ile-de-France SAS (2)
Route de Bray Marrolles-sur-Seine, 77876, Montereau, France
Tel.: (33) 1 64705200
Building Materials Whslr
N.A.I.C.S.: 423390

Knauf Industries Est (2)
ZAC Grenoble Air Parc, 38590, Saint Etienne, France
Tel.: (33) 4 76934700
Web Site: http://www.knauf-industries.com
Emp.: 38
Polystyrene Product Mfr
N.A.I.C.S.: 326140
Elkhanlichi Mokaneg *(Mng Dir)*

Knauf Industries Nord (2)
30 Rue Jean Moulin, 62028, Dainville, France
Tel.: (33) 3 21519393
Building Materials Whslr
N.A.I.C.S.: 423390

Knauf Industries Ouest (2)
ZI de Pradervelinvras, 56160, Guemene-sur-Scorff, France
Tel.: (33) 2 399710
Building Materials Distr
N.A.I.C.S.: 423390

Knauf Industries Sp. z o. o. (2)
ul Styropianowa 1, 96-320, Mszczonow, Poland
Tel.: (48) 46 8570 617
Building Materials Whslr
N.A.I.C.S.: 423390

Subsidiary (Domestic):

Knauf Insulation Holding GmbH (2)
Am Bahnhof 7, D-97346, Iphofen, Germany
Tel.: (49) 93 23 31 2240
Holding Company
N.A.I.C.S.: 551112

Unit (US):

Knauf Insulation - Shelbyville (3)
1 Knauf Dr, Shelbyville, IN 46176
Tel.: (317) 398-4434
Web Site: http://www.knaufinsulation.us
Insulation Mfr
N.A.I.C.S.: 327993
Mark Andrews *(CEO-Ops-North America)*

Subsidiary (Non-US):

Knauf Insulation A/S (3)
Bymidten 80, 3500, Vaerlose, Denmark
Tel.: (45) 72 44 12 00
Web Site: http://www.knaufinsulation.dk
Building Materials Whslr
N.A.I.C.S.: 423390
Soren Bendix *(Mgr-Bus Dev)*

Knauf Insulation AB (3)
Gardatorget 1, 412 50, Gothenburg, Sweden
Tel.: (46) 20 313 535
Web Site: http://www.knaufinsulation.se
Building Materials Whslr
N.A.I.C.S.: 423390

Fredrik Alvarsson *(Mgr-Bus Dev)*

Knauf Insulation AE (3)
322 Syggrou Av & Megistis 2, 176 73, Kallithea, Greece
Tel.: (30) 211 7107007
Web Site: http://www.knaufinsulation.gr
Building Materials Whslr
N.A.I.C.S.: 423390

Knauf Insulation Artix SAS (3)
Route de Mourenx, 64170, Artix, France
Tel.: (33) 559 717954
Building Materials Whslr
N.A.I.C.S.: 423390

Knauf Insulation B.V. (3)
Florijnstraat 2, Postbus 375, 4900 AJ, Oosterhout, Netherlands
Tel.: (31) 162 421245
Web Site: http://www.knaufinsulation.nl
Emp.: 60
Building Materials Whslr
N.A.I.C.S.: 423390
Jeroen Ferweyj *(Gen Mgr)*

Knauf Insulation Co. Ltd (3)
No 389 Guangxing Road Dagang Economic Development Area, 300270, Tianjin, China
Tel.: (86) 22 63252309
Building Materials Whslr
N.A.I.C.S.: 423390

Knauf Insulation EOOD (3)
Mladost 4 Business Park Sofia Str Building 8 ent B fl 6, 1766, Sofia, Bulgaria
Tel.: (359) 4899053
Web Site: http://www.knaufinsulation.bg
Building Materials Whslr
N.A.I.C.S.: 423390

Knauf Insulation GmbH (3)
Industriestrasse 18, 9586, Furnitz, Austria
Tel.: (43) 4257 3370 0
Web Site: http://www.knaufinsulation.at
Emp.: 50
Insulation Mfr
N.A.I.C.S.: 327993
Udo Klamminger *(Mng Dir)*

Subsidiary (Domestic):

Knauf Insulation GmbH (3)
Heraklithstrasse 8, Simbach, 84539, Germany
Tel.: (49) 8571400
Web Site: http://www.knaufinsulation.de
Insulation Mfr
N.A.I.C.S.: 327993
Gred Pfizenmayer *(Mgr)*

Subsidiary (Non-US):

Knauf Insulation Holding AG (3)
Obermattweg 9, Hergiswil, 6052, Switzerland
Tel.: (41) 41 632 91 64
Web Site: http://www.knaufinsulation.com
Holding Company
N.A.I.C.S.: 551112
Tony Robson *(CEO)*

Knauf Insulation Kft. (3)
Gyar U 2 Pf 115, 2058, Budaors, Hungary
Tel.: (36) 23889844
Web Site: http://www.knaufinsulation.hu
Building Materials Whslr
N.A.I.C.S.: 423390

Knauf Insulation LLC (3)
Lunacharskogo Street 4 9th floor, 2002, Kiev, Ukraine
Tel.: (380) 44 391 1727
Web Site: http://www.knaufinsulation.ua
Building Materials Whslr
N.A.I.C.S.: 423390

Knauf Insulation Lannemezan SAS (3)
501 voie Napoleon III, 65300, Lannemezan, France
Tel.: (33) 5 62500530
Building Materials Whslr
N.A.I.C.S.: 423390

Knauf Insulation Ltd (3)
Stafford Road, PO Box 10, Saint Helens, WA10 3NS, Merseyside, United Kingdom
Tel.: (44) 1744 766600
Web Site: http://www.knaufinsulation.co.uk
Mineral Wool Mfr

N.A.I.C.S.: 327993
Brendan Pettit *(Reg Mgr-Sls & Specification)*

Subsidiary (Domestic):

Knauf Insulation Operation GmbH (3)
Heraklithstrasse 8, 84359, Simbach am Inn, Germany
Tel.: (49) 8571 400
Building Materials Mfr
N.A.I.C.S.: 327120

Subsidiary (Non-US):

Knauf Insulation PTY Ltd (3)
Unit 2 44 Borthwick Avenue, Murarrie, Brisbane, 4172, QLD, Australia
Tel.: (61) 7 3393 7300
Web Site: http://www.knaufinsulation.com.au
Building Materials Whslr
N.A.I.C.S.: 423390
Stuart Dunbar *(Gen Mgr)*

Knauf Insulation S.L. (3)
C/La Selva 2 Edificio Geminis Parque empresarial Mas Blau, El Prat de Llobregat, 08820, Barcelona, Spain
Tel.: (34) 93 379 65 08
Web Site: http://www.knaufinsulation.es
Building Materials Whslr
N.A.I.C.S.: 423390

Knauf Insulation SAS (3)
42 Boulevard Gambetta, BP 19, 10001, Troyes, France
Tel.: (33) 325 7139 40
Web Site: http://www.knaufinsulation.fr
Building Materials Whslr
N.A.I.C.S.: 423390

Knauf Insulation SPRL (3)
Rue de Maestricht 95, 4600, Vise, Belgium
Tel.: (32) 43 790231
Web Site: http://www.knaufinsulation.be
Building Materials Whslr
N.A.I.C.S.: 423390
Eric Skwirzynski *(Controller-Project Cost)*

Knauf Insulation Sp. z o. o. (3)
ul 17 Stycznia 56, Warsaw, 02-146, Poland
Tel.: (48) 22 369 59 00
Web Site: http://www.knaufinsulation.pl
Building Materials Whslr
N.A.I.C.S.: 423390
Krzysztof Sobkowiak *(Mgr-Woodwool)*

Knauf Insulation SpA (3)
Via Emilio Gallo 20 - Zona Ind le Chind, Chivasso, 10034, Turin, Italy
Tel.: (39) 011 9119611
Web Site: http://www.knaufinsulation.it
Building Materials Whslr
N.A.I.C.S.: 423390
Maria Peresa Fabola *(Gen Mgr)*

Knauf Insulation d.o.o. (3)
Varazdinska 140, HR 42220, Novi Marof, Croatia
Tel.: (385) 42401300
Web Site: http://www.knaufinsulation.hr
Insulation Mfr
N.A.I.C.S.: 327993

Knauf Insulation d.o.o. (3)
Batajnicki drum 16 b, Zemun, 11080, Belgrade, Serbia
Tel.: (381) 11 3310 800
Web Site: http://www.knaufinsulation.rs
Building Materials Distr
N.A.I.C.S.: 423390

Knauf Insulation ooo (3)
Kamchatskaya 198, 625034, Tyumen, Russia
Tel.: (7) 3452550388
Web Site: http://www.knaufinsulation.ru
Building Materials Whslr
N.A.I.C.S.: 423390

Knauf Insulation spol. s r.o. (3)
Bucharova 2641/14, 158 00, Prague, Czech Republic
Tel.: (420) 234 714 011
Web Site: http://www.knaufinsulation.cz
Emp.: 100
Building Materials Whslr
N.A.I.C.S.: 423390

Knauf Insulation, d.o.o. (3)

Trata 32, 4220, Skofja Loka, Slovenia
Tel.: (386) 45114104
Web Site: http://www.knaufinsulation.com
Insulation Mfr
N.A.I.C.S.: 327993
Sasa Bavec *(Mng Mgr)*

Knauf Insulation, s.r.o. (3)
Zeleznicny rad 24, 968 14, Nova Bana, Slovakia
Tel.: (421) 456833116
Web Site: http://www.knaufinsulation.sk
Insulation Mfr
N.A.I.C.S.: 327993
Alexander Ecsi *(Mng Dir)*

Subsidiary (Domestic):

Knauf Integral KG (2)
Am Bahnhof 16, 74589, Satteldorf, Germany
Tel.: (49) 7951 497 0
Web Site: http://www.knauf-integral.de
Gypsum Product Mfr
N.A.I.C.S.: 327420

Subsidiary (Non-US):

Knauf Isba SAS (2)
Zone Industrielle Sud, 89000f, Auxerre, France
Tel.: (33) 3 86 469753
Web Site: http://www.knauf-batiment.fr
Building Materials Whslr
N.A.I.C.S.: 423390

Knauf Jaworzno III Sp. z o. o. (2)
ul Promienna 51, 43-603, Jaworzno, Poland
Tel.: (48) 22 3696 901
Building Materials Whslr
N.A.I.C.S.: 423390

Knauf Jordan (2)
Wasfi AL-Tal-Str 111 AL-Bakri Commercial Center, PO Box 143649, 11844, Amman, Jordan
Tel.: (962) 6 5521721
Emp.: 2
Building Materials Whslr
N.A.I.C.S.: 423390
Juma Abushawish *(Engr-Technical & Sls)*

Knauf KFT. (2)
Incline Way 5th, 1124, Budapest, Hungary
Tel.: (36) 1 248 2430
Web Site: http://www.knauf.hu
Building Materials Whslr
N.A.I.C.S.: 423390

Knauf LLC (2)
PO Box 112871, Dubai, United Arab Emirates
Tel.: (971) 4 337 7170
Web Site: http://www.knauf.ae
Building Material Mfr & Distr
N.A.I.C.S.: 327120
Rajesh Maheshwari *(Reg Mgr)*

Knauf Lebanon S.A.R.L. (2)
Sodeco SquareBlock C12 TH Floor RL-Achrafieh, Beirut, Lebanon
Tel.: (961) 1 612209
Building Materials Whslr
N.A.I.C.S.: 423390
Habib Haddad *(Gen Mgr)*

Knauf Lisboa GmbH (2)
Rua Poeta Bocage 14 D-1 C, 1600-581, Lisbon, Portugal
Tel.: (351) 21 7112750
Building Materials Whslr
N.A.I.C.S.: 423390

Knauf Ljubljana d.o.o. (2)
Dunajska cesta 115, 1000, Ljubljana, Slovenia
Tel.: (386) 1 5682 279
Web Site: http://www.knauf.si
Building Materials Whslr
N.A.I.C.S.: 423390

Knauf Ltd. (2)
6A Road 23 3rd floor Maadi, Cairo, Egypt
Tel.: (20) 23 59 55 44
Building Materials Whslr
N.A.I.C.S.: 423390

Knauf Marokko (2)
30 rue Abou Faris al Marini Ap nr 3, 10000, Rabat, Morocco
Tel.: (212) 7 736029

GEBR. KNAUF KG

Gebr. Knauf KG—(Continued)
Building Materials Whslr
N.A.I.C.S.: 423390

Knauf New Building Material (Wuhu) Co. Ltd (2)
No 2 Gangwan Road Economic development Zone, Wuhu, 241009, Anhui, China
Tel.: (86) 553 584 2053
Web Site: http://www.knauf.com.cn
Building Materials Whslr
N.A.I.C.S.: 423390
Andy Zhou (Supvr-Lab)

Knauf New Building Material Product Co., Ltd. (2)
No 2 Xinsha Development Zone, 523147, Dongguan, Guangdong, China
Tel.: (86) 769 88222708
Web Site: http://www.kanuf.com.cn
Emp.: 120
Building Materials Whslr
N.A.I.C.S.: 423390
Toby Ning (Gen Mgr)

Knauf OY (2)
Lars Sonckin kaari 14, PL 18, 02601, Espoo, Finland
Tel.: (358) 9 476400
Web Site: http://www.knauf.fi
Building Materials Whslr
N.A.I.C.S.: 423390
Kai Nurmi (Mng Dir)

Knauf Ouest SAS (2)
ZAC de Lestun-Cournon, BP 9, 56204, La Gacilly, France
Tel.: (33) 2 99 71 43 77
Building Materials Whslr
N.A.I.C.S.: 423390
Gilles Touron (Pres)

Subsidiary (Domestic):

Knauf PFT GmbH & Co. KG (2)
Einersheimer Strasse 53, 97346, Iphofen, Germany
Tel.: (49) 9323 31 760
Web Site: http://www.pft.eu
Building Materials Whslr
N.A.I.C.S.: 423390
Benedikt Schneider (Head-Product Mgmt & Mktg)

Subsidiary (Non-US):

Knauf Plasterboard (Jiangsu) Co., Ltd. (2)
No 18 Xiexin Road Port Development Zone, Taicang, 215433, Jiangsu, China
Tel.: (86) 512 531 86 000
Building Materials Whslr
N.A.I.C.S.: 423390

Knauf Plasterboard Pty Ltd (2)
91-99 Ajax Road, Altona, 3018, VIC, Australia
Tel.: (61) 300 724 505
Web Site: http://www.knaufplasterboard.com.au
Plasterboard Mfr & Distr
N.A.I.C.S.: 327420
Gavin Burton (Mng Dir)

Knauf Plasterboard Tianjin Co. Ltd. (2)
North Yinhe Bridge East Jingjin Road, 300400, Tianjin, China
Tel.: (86) 22 26972777
Building Materials Whslr
N.A.I.C.S.: 423390
Fugang Huang (Bus Mgr)

Knauf Platres SARL (2)
BP n 02, Boufatis, 31000, Oran, Algeria
Tel.: (213) 41 521763
Building Materials Whslr
N.A.I.C.S.: 423390

Knauf Platres et Cie. S.C.S. (2)
Zone Industrielle du Sauvoy, 77165, Saint-Soupplets, France
Tel.: (33) 1 64363700
Building Materials Whslr
N.A.I.C.S.: 423390

Knauf Porto GmbH (2)
Rua Poeta Bocage 14 D-1 C, 1600-581, Lisbon, Portugal
Tel.: (351) 217112750
Web Site: http://www.knauf.pt
Building Materials Whslr
N.A.I.C.S.: 423390

Knauf Radika AD (2)
ul 8 Septemvri bb, 1250, Debar, North Macedonia
Tel.: (389) 46 839 200
Web Site: http://www.knauf.com.mk
Building Materials Whslr
N.A.I.C.S.: 423390

Knauf SIA (2)
Daugavas iela 4, Sauriesi, Stopini, 2118, Latvia
Tel.: (371) 67 032999
Web Site: http://www.knauf.lv
Building Materials Whslr
N.A.I.C.S.: 423390

Knauf Sh.p.k. (2)
Rr Sadik Zeneli R B 3/3 Nr 2, Dardani, 10000, Pristina, Kosovo, Serbia
Tel.: (381) 38 543 926
Web Site: http://www.knauf-ks.com
Gypsum Product Mfr
N.A.I.C.S.: 327420
Driton Ibrahimi (Mgr-Sls)

Knauf Singapore Pte Ltd. (2)
80 Marine Parade Rd 14-06 Parkway Parade, Singapore, 449269, Singapore
Tel.: (65) 63459233
Web Site: http://www.knauf.com.sg
Gypsum Product Distr
N.A.I.C.S.: 423390
Jonathan Choo (Mgr-Mktg)

Knauf Sp. z o. o. (2)
ul Swiatowa 25, 02-229, Warsaw, Poland
Tel.: (48) 22 3695 100
Web Site: http://www.knauf.pl
Building Materials Whslr
N.A.I.C.S.: 423390

Knauf Sud-Est SAS (2)
583 avenue Georges Vacher Zone Industrielle, 13790, Rousset, Cedex, France
Tel.: (33) 4 42 291111
Building Materials Whslr
N.A.I.C.S.: 423390

Knauf Sud-Ouest SAS (2)
Zone Industrielle en Jacca 37 Chemin de la Salvetat, 31770, Colomiers, France
Tel.: (33) 5 61 159415
Building Materials Distr
N.A.I.C.S.: 423390

Knauf Syria (2)
Assalam Street 17 - Mazzeh East, PO Box 31, Damascus, Syria
Tel.: (963) 11 6115862
Building Materials Whslr
N.A.I.C.S.: 423390

Knauf Tallinn UU (2)
Masina 20, 10144, Tallinn, Estonia
Tel.: (372) 6518 690
Web Site: http://www.knauf.ee
Gypsum Product Distr
N.A.I.C.S.: 423390

Knauf Tirana Shpk (2)
Rr Jeronim De Rada Nd 1 H 25 Ap 4, 1017, Tirana, Albania
Tel.: (355) 42 248 714
Web Site: http://www.knauf.al
Building Materials Whslr
N.A.I.C.S.: 423390
Aurel Shulla (Mgr-Sls)

Knauf Trading (Shanghai) Co. Ltd. (2)
Rm 1901 Block A No 1600 Zhongshan W Rd, Xuhui district, 200235, Shanghai, China
Tel.: (86) 2164848900
Web Site: http://www.knauf.com
Building Materials Whslr
N.A.I.C.S.: 423390

Subsidiary (Domestic):

Knauf Trans GmbH (2)
Postfach 10, 97346, Iphofen, Germany
Tel.: (49) 9323 31 0
Building Materials Mfr
N.A.I.C.S.: 327120

Subsidiary (Non-US):

Knauf UAB (2)
Svitrigailos g 11B, 03228, Vilnius, Lithuania
Tel.: (370) 5 213 2222
Web Site: http://www.knauf.lt
Emp.: 16
Building Materials Whslr
N.A.I.C.S.: 423390
Darius Meskuotis (Gen Mgr)

Knauf d.o.o. (2)
Ul Grada Vukovara 21, 10000, Zagreb, Croatia
Tel.: (385) 1 3035 400
Web Site: http://www.knauf.hr
Building Materials Whslr
N.A.I.C.S.: 423390
Boris Simonic (Head-Technical & Dev Dept)

Knauf de Chile Ltda. (2)
AV Del Valle Sur 650 Edificio Mistral Piso 2 Ciudad Empresarial, Huechuraba, Santiago, Chile
Tel.: (56) 2 584 9400
Web Site: http://www.knauf.cl
Building Materials Whslr
N.A.I.C.S.: 423390

Knauf di Lothar Knauf s.a.s. (2)
Via Livornese 20, 56040, Castellina Marittima, Pisa, Italy
Tel.: (39) 050 69211
Web Site: http://www.knauf.it
Building Materials Whslr
N.A.I.C.S.: 423390
Iris Steinhausen (Asst Gen Mgr)

Knauf do Brasil Ltda. (2)
Praca Floriano 19 sala 3101 - Centro, 20031-050, Rio de Janeiro, Brazil
Tel.: (55) 21 2195 1161
Web Site: http://www.knauf.com.br
Building Materials Whslr
N.A.I.C.S.: 423390
Siegfried Bretzke (Mgr-Fin)

Lasselsberger-Knauf Kft. (2)
Hazgyari ut 9, PO Box 1723, 8210, Veszprem, Hungary
Tel.: (36) 6 88 590 500
Web Site: http://www.lb-knauf.hu
Building Materials Whslr
N.A.I.C.S.: 423390
Gabor Varsanyi (Mgr-Pur & Logistics)

N et B Knauf Et Cie S.C.S. (2)
Rue du Parc Industriel 1, 4480, Engis, Belgium
Tel.: (32) 4 2738311
Web Site: http://www.knauf.be
Gypsum Product Distr
N.A.I.C.S.: 423390

OOO Knauf Armenia (2)
ul Paronyana 8 of 3, 0015, Yerevan, Armenia
Tel.: (374) 10 501 420
Web Site: http://www.knauf.am
Building Materials Whslr
N.A.I.C.S.: 423390

OOO Knauf Gips (2)
Perm region Russian field, Kungur, 617472, Perm, Russia
Tel.: (7) 342271 62 100
Web Site: http://www.knauf.ru
Building Materials Whslr
N.A.I.C.S.: 423390

OOO Knauf Gips Tbilisi (2)
ul Kisiki 17, 0182, Tbilisi, Georgia
Tel.: (995) 224 25 02
Web Site: http://www.knauf.ge
Building Materials Whslr
N.A.I.C.S.: 423390

PT Knauf Gypsum Indonesia (2)
Cilandak Commercial Estate Garden Centre 5th Floor Suite 16 B, JL Raya Cilandak KKO, Jakarta, 12560, Indonesia
Tel.: (62) 21 789 1661
Web Site: http://www.knauf.co.id
Gypsum Product Mfr & Distr
N.A.I.C.S.: 327420
Duro Curlija (Country Mgr)

TOO Knauf Gips Kaptschagaj (2)
Saretschnyj, 040800, Kapchagay, Almaty, Kazakhstan
Tel.: (7) 727 29549 01
Web Site: http://www.knauf.kz
Gypsum Product Mfr & Distr
N.A.I.C.S.: 327420

INTERNATIONAL PUBLIC

Subsidiary (US):

USG Corp. (2)
550 W Adams St, Chicago, IL 60661-3676 **(100%)**
Tel.: (312) 436-4000
Web Site: http://www.usg.com
Rev.: $3,336,000,000
Assets: $3,842,000,000
Liabilities: $1,923,000,000
Net Worth: $1,919,000,000
Earnings: $196,000,000
Emp.: 7,300
Fiscal Year-end: 12/31/2018
Holding Company; Building Materials Mfr & Distr
N.A.I.C.S.: 327420
Dominic A. Dannessa (Chief Customer & Innovation Officer & Exec VP)

Subsidiary (Domestic):

Ceilings Plus, Inc. (3)
6711 E Washington Bl, Los Angeles, CA 90040
Tel.: (323) 724-8166
Web Site: http://www.ceilingsplus.com
Sales Range: $25-49.9 Million
Emp.: 150
Specialty Ceiling Products Mfr
N.A.I.C.S.: 321211
Nancy Mercolino (Founder & Pres)

Otsego Paper, Inc. (3)
320 N Farmer St, Otsego, MI 49078
Tel.: (269) 384-6300
Web Site: http://www.usg.com
Building Insulation Contractor
N.A.I.C.S.: 238310

USG Interiors, Inc. (3)
550 W Adams St S Franklin St, Chicago, IL 60661 **(100%)**
Tel.: (312) 606-4000
Web Site: http://www.usg.com
Commmercial & Residential Ceiling Products
N.A.I.C.S.: 332323

USG International, Ltd. (3)
3001 NW 125th St, Miami, FL 33167
Tel.: (305) 688-8744
Emp.: 20
Lumber & Plywood Product Distr
N.A.I.C.S.: 423310
Jesus Villegas (Principal)

Subsidiary (Non-US):

USG Netherlands Global Holdings B.V. (3)
Jollemanhof 148, 1019 GW, Amsterdam, Netherlands
Tel.: (31) 205792117
Holding Company
N.A.I.C.S.: 551112

USG Boral Building Products Pty Limited (1)
Level 3 40 Mount Street, Sydney, NSW 2060, Australia **(50%)**
Tel.: (61) 2 9220 6300
Web Site: http://www.usgboral.com
Plasterboard & Construction Materials Mfr
N.A.I.C.S.: 423320
Frederic de Rougemont (CEO)

Subsidiary (Domestic):

Lympike Pty Ltd (2)
71 Milperra Rd, Revesby, 2212, NSW, Australia
Tel.: (61) 297923022
Sales Range: $25-49.9 Million
Emp.: 20
Construction Materials Distr
N.A.I.C.S.: 423320
Mark Nuner (Gen Mgr)

GEBR. LENNARTZ GMBH & CO.KG

Hohenhagener Str 46, D - 42855, Remscheid, Germany
Tel.: (49) 219199600
Web Site: http://www.lennartz.de
Year Founded: 1896
Rev.: $21,954,846
Emp.: 102

AND PRIVATE COMPANIES

Cutting Equipments Mfr
N.A.I.C.S.: 332216
Frank Mich *(Mgr-Production)*

GEBR. MARKLIN & CIE. GMBH
Stuttgarter Strasse 55-57, 73033, Goppingen, Germany
Tel.: (49) 7161 608 0   De
Web Site: http://www.maerklin.de
Model Train Mfr
N.A.I.C.S.: 339930
Wolfrad Bachle *(Member-Mgmt Bd-Technical Engrg & Production)*

Subsidiaries:

Marklin, Inc.   (1)
16988 W Victor Rd, New Berlin, WI 53151
Tel.: (262) 522-7080
Web Site: http://www.marklin.com
Toy Distr
N.A.I.C.S.: 423920

Marklin-Vertriebs AG   (1)
Ausserfeldstrasse 9, 5036, Oberentfelden, Switzerland
Tel.: (41) 627383300
Web Site: http://www.maerklin.ch
Toy Distr
N.A.I.C.S.: 423920

GEBR. WILLACH GMBH
Stein 2, 53809, Ruppichteroth, Germany
Tel.: (49) 22959208434
Web Site: http://www.willach.com
Year Founded: 1889
Sales Range: $25-49.9 Million
Emp.: 110
Pharmaceutical Dispenser & Glass Container Mfr
N.A.I.C.S.: 327213
Sonja Fruh *(Mng Dir)*

GEBRUDER DURRBECK KUNSTSTOFFE GMBH
Bahnhofstrasse 42, Halfing, 83128, Germany
Tel.: (49) 805590690
Web Site: http://www.duerrbeck.com
Year Founded: 1956
Sales Range: $25-49.9 Million
Emp.: 138
Packaging Film Mfr
N.A.I.C.S.: 322220
Ludwig Durrbeck *(Mng Dir)*

GEBRUDER EBERHARD GMBH & CO. KG
Lerchenstrasse 36, 74226, Northeim, Germany
Tel.: (49) 71331000
Web Site: http://www.eberhard.de
Year Founded: 1933
Rev.: $200,499,790
Emp.: 400
Electrical Circuit Breakers Mfr
N.A.I.C.S.: 335999
Peter Baumgart *(Mgr-Sls)*

GEBRUDER WEISS GESELL-SCHAFT M.B.H.
Bundesstrasse 110, 6923, Lauterach, Austria
Tel.: (43) 55746960   AT
Web Site: https://www.gw-world.com
Year Founded: 1823
Transportation & Logistics Services
N.A.I.C.S.: 484121
Wolfram Senger-Weiss *(CEO)*

Subsidiaries:

Gebruder Weiss, Inc.   (1)
1020 N Wood Dale Rd, Wood Dale, IL 60191
Tel.: (847) 795-4300
Web Site: https://www.gw-world.com
Freight Forwarding Services
N.A.I.C.S.: 484110

Mark McCullough *(CEO-North America)*

Subsidiary (Domestic):

Cargo-Link International, Inc.   (2)
881 S 3760 W, Salt Lake City, UT 84104
Tel.: (801) 975-9336
Web Site: http://www.cargolink.com
Rev.: $3,129,000
Emp.: 21
Freight Transportation Arrangement Services
N.A.I.C.S.: 488510
Larry Stewart *(Mgr-Sls & Mktg)*

GECI INTERNATIONAL SA
37-39 Rue Boissiere, 75116, Paris, France
Tel.: (33) 146120000   FR
Web Site: https://www.geci.net
Year Founded: 1980
GECP—(EUR)
Sales Range: $25-49.9 Million
Transportation Engineering Services
N.A.I.C.S.: 541330
Serge Bitboul *(Chm & CEO)*

Subsidiaries:

GECI Engineering Services Srl   (1)
Boulevard Regiei 6D et 2 sector 6, Bucharest, 060204, Romania
Tel.: (40) 318052907
Web Site: http://www.geci.ro
Sales Range: $25-49.9 Million
Emp.: 70
Engineeering Services
N.A.I.C.S.: 541330

Geci GmbH   (1)
Hanna Kunath Str 4, Europa Centre Haus E, 28199, Bremen, Germany
Tel.: (49) 4212777515
Business Services
N.A.I.C.S.: 561499

Geci Ingenieria S.L.   (1)
Avenida de la Albufera 321, Planta 5-oficina 9, 28031, Madrid, Spain
Tel.: (34) 913316064
Architectural Services
N.A.I.C.S.: 541310

Geci Ltd   (1)
34 Eden St, Surrey House, Kingston upon Thames, KT1 1ER, United Kingdom
Tel.: (44) 2084813766
Management Consulting Services
N.A.I.C.S.: 541618

Geci Portugal   (1)
Avenida Eng Duarte Pacheco Torre das Amoreiras Torre 1 Piso 4 Salas 9-, 1070-101, Lisbon, Portugal
Tel.: (351) 213807410
Web Site: http://www.geci.com
Sales Range: $25-49.9 Million
Emp.: 6
Business Services
N.A.I.C.S.: 561499

Geci South Africa Pty Ltd   (1)
1st FL Bedford Centre cnr Smith & Bradford Rds, Bedford Gardens, Johannesburg, South Africa
Tel.: (27) 11 6155110
Web Site: http://www.geci.net
Aircraft Engine & Engine Parts Mfr
N.A.I.C.S.: 336412

Sky Aircraft   (1)
Base aerienne de Chambley, 54890, Onville, France
Tel.: (33) 382211800
Sales Range: $50-74.9 Million
Emp.: 200
Aircraft Mfr
N.A.I.C.S.: 336411

GECINA NOM
16 Rue de Capucines, 75084, Paris, 75084, France
Tel.: (33) 140405050
Web Site: https://www.gecina.fr
Real Estate Manangement Services
N.A.I.C.S.: 531390
Armelle Miclo *(Mgr-Comm)*

GECINA S.A.
16 rue des Capucines, 75084, Paris, Cedex 02, France
Tel.: (33) 140405050   FR
Web Site: http://www.gecina.fr
Year Founded: 1959
GFC—(EUR)
Rev.: $1,859,420,023
Assets: $22,906,517,927
Liabilities: $8,654,541,247
Net Worth: $14,251,976,680
Earnings: $1,698,704,435
Emp.: 504
Fiscal Year-end: 12/31/19
Real Estate Investment Trust
N.A.I.C.S.: 525990
Valerie Britay *(Deputy CEO-Office Div)*

Subsidiaries:

Eurosic S.A.   (1)
Strada Fabricii 46C Sector 6, 060825, Bucharest, Romania   (85.4%)
Tel.: (40) 21 316 96 10
Web Site: http://www.eurosic.ro
Real Estate Investment Trust
N.A.I.C.S.: 531390

Subsidiary (Non-US):

Fonciere de Paris SIIC   (2)
37 boulevard Montmorency, 75007, Paris, France   (100%)
Tel.: (33) 153707777
Web Site: http://www.fonciere-de-paris.fr
Sales Range: $200-249.9 Million
Emp.: 39
Real Estate Leasing & Development & Real Estate Property Rental
N.A.I.C.S.: 531390
Sophie Beuvaden *(Chm-Supervisory Bd)*

Locare SNC   (1)
16 rue des Capucines, 75002, Paris, France
Tel.: (33) 140406400
Web Site: http://www.locare.fr
Real Estate Services
N.A.I.C.S.: 531390

GECOS S.P.A.
San Marco 5278, 30124, Spinea, VE, Italy
Tel.: (39) 041 5495111   IT
Year Founded: 1958
Holding Company
N.A.I.C.S.: 551112
Arturo Bastianello *(Chm & CEO)*

Subsidiaries:

Gruppo PAM S.p.A.   (1)
San Marco 5278, 30124, Spinea, VE, Italy
Tel.: (39) 0415495111
Web Site: http://www.gruppopam.it
Sales Range: $1-4.9 Billion
Emp.: 10,000
Holding Company; Supermarkets, Hyprmarkets, Discount Stores & Restaurants Owner, Operator & Franchisor
N.A.I.C.S.: 551112
Arturo Bastianello *(Chm & CEO)*

Subsidiary (Domestic):

PAM Panorama S.p.A.   (2)
Via San Marco 5278, Spinea, VE, Italy
Tel.: (39) 042 5555
Web Site: http://www.e-pam.it
Sales Range: $1-4.9 Billion
Emp.: 7,300
Supermarket Operator
N.A.I.C.S.: 445110
Arturo Bastianello *(Chm & CEO)*

iN's Mercato S.p.A.   (2)
Via Veneto 9, 30030, Pianiga, VE, Italy
Tel.: (39) 041 5136111
Web Site: http://www.insmercato.it
Sales Range: $800-899.9 Million
Emp.: 1,600
Discount Department Store Operator
N.A.I.C.S.: 455110

GEDEON RICHTER PLC.

GEDEON RICHTER PLC.

Gyomroi ut 19-21, 1103, Budapest, Hungary
Tel.: (36) 14314000   HU
Web Site: http://www.richter.hu
Year Founded: 1901
RICHTER—(BUD)
Rev.: $2,199,810,917
Assets: $3,672,829,661
Liabilities: $767,118,821
Net Worth: $2,905,710,841
Earnings: $430,930,067
Emp.: 12,167
Fiscal Year-end: 12/31/22
Pharmaceutical Research Development & Mfr
N.A.I.C.S.: 325412
Erik Bogsch *(Chm & Member-Exec Bd)*

Subsidiaries:

CJSC Gedeon Richter - Rus   (1)
Lesnaya str 40 Shuvoe, Egoryevsk, 140342, Moscow, Russia
Tel.: (7) 4957888630
Web Site: http://www.rg-rus.ru
Sales Range: $50-74.9 Million
Emp.: 226
Pharmaceuticals Mfr
N.A.I.C.S.: 325412
Zsolt Helmeczy *(CEO & Mng Dir)*

Chemitechnik Pharma Kft   (1)
Gyomroi ut 19-21, H-1103, Budapest, Hungary
Tel.: (36) 12624058
Web Site: https://www.chph.hu
Sales Range: $25-49.9 Million
Emp.: 29
Construction Engineering Services
N.A.I.C.S.: 541330

Gedeon Richter (Schweiz) AG   (1)
Gewerbestr 5, 6330, Cham, Switzerland
Tel.: (41) 417472191
Web Site: http://www.gedeonrichter.ch
Pharmaceutical Marketing Services
N.A.I.C.S.: 541613

Gedeon Richter - Retea Farmaceutica S.R.L   (1)
N Milesku-Spetaru Str 36, MD-2075, Chisinau, Moldova
Tel.: (373) 22743308
Web Site: http://www.richter.hu
Pharmaceutical Products Mfr & Distr
N.A.I.C.S.: 325412
Boris Balmus *(Mng Dir)*

Gedeon Richter Australia Pty. Ltd.   (1)
Units 33-34 / 23 Narabang Way, Belrose, 2085, NSW, Australia
Tel.: (61) 289141904
Pharmaceutical Products Distr
N.A.I.C.S.: 424210

Gedeon Richter Austria GmbH   (1)
Hainburger Strasse 20/ Top 17, 1030, Vienna, Austria
Tel.: (43) 18904338
Web Site: https://www.gedeonrichter.com
Sales Range: $50-74.9 Million
Emp.: 10
Pharmaceutical Products Distr
N.A.I.C.S.: 424210

Gedeon Richter Bolivia SRL   (1)
Edificio Torre Duo Centro Empresarial Barrio Equipetrol, Norte Sobre el 4to Anillo Entre las Calles Victor Pinto y Jaime Roman, Santa Cruz, Bolivia
Tel.: (591) 33110373
Pharmaceutical Products Distr
N.A.I.C.S.: 424210

Gedeon Richter Bulgaria Ltd.   (1)
Blvd Acad Ivan Geshov No 2E Business Center Serdika, 1379, Sofia, Bulgaria
Tel.: (359) 28129063
Web Site: https://www.gedeonrichter.com
Pharmaceutical Product Mfr & Distr
N.A.I.C.S.: 325412

Gedeon Richter Chile SpA   (1)
Padre Mariano 82 Oficina 203, Providencia, Santiago, Chile
Tel.: (56) 229462177

GEDEON RICHTER PLC.

Gedeon Richter Plc.—(Continued)
Web Site: https://www.grchile.cl
Pharmaceutical Products Distr
N.A.I.C.S.: 424210

Gedeon Richter Colombia S.A.S. (1)
Cra 7 156-10 North Point Torre Krystal of,
3005, Bogota, Colombia
Tel.: (57) 6014824860
Web Site: https://gedeonrichter.co
Pharmaceuticals Mfr
N.A.I.C.S.: 325412

Gedeon Richter Croatia d.o.o. (1)
Radnicka Cesta 80, 10000, Zagreb, Croatia
Tel.: (385) 15625713
Web Site: https://gedeonrichter.hr
Pharmaceutical Products Distr
N.A.I.C.S.: 424210

Gedeon Richter France S.A.R.L (1)
103 Boulevard Haussmann, 75008, Paris,
France
Tel.: (33) 147420320
Web Site: https://www.gedeonrichter.fr
Pharmaceutical Products Mfr & Whslr
N.A.I.C.S.: 325412
Emmanuel Eumont (Pres)

Gedeon Richter Iberica S.A (1)
Pedro i Pons 9-11 7a, 08034, Barcelona,
Spain
Tel.: (34) 932034300
Web Site: https://www.gedeonrichter.es
Sales Range: $25-49.9 Million
Emp.: 4
Pharmaceuticals Product Mfr
N.A.I.C.S.: 325412

Gedeon Richter Italia S.R.L (1)
via Giacomo Watt 37, 20143, Milan, Italy
Tel.: (39) 0249539950
Web Site: https://www.gedeonrichter.it
Pharmaceuticals Product Mfr
N.A.I.C.S.: 325412

Gedeon Richter Marketing CR s.r.o. (1)
Na Strzi 2097/63 Trianon building, 14000,
Prague, 4, Czech Republic
Tel.: (420) 261141200
Web Site: https://www.richtergedeon.cz
Pharmaceuticals Mfr
N.A.I.C.S.: 325412
Corina Croitoru (Mng Dir)

Gedeon Richter Marketing Polska Sp. z o.o. (1)
ul Krolowej Marysienki 70, Warsaw, 2954,
Poland
Tel.: (48) 226426739
Web Site: http://www.gedeonrichter.pl
Sales Range: $50-74.9 Million
Emp.: 70
Pharmaceutical Products Distr
N.A.I.C.S.: 424210
Elzbieta Piotrkowicz (Mgr-Mktg)

Gedeon Richter Peru S.A.C. (1)
Av. Jorge Chavez 184 Office 703, Miraflores, Lima, Peru
Tel.: (51) 14150960
Web Site: https://www.grperu.pe
Pharmaceutical Products Distr
N.A.I.C.S.: 424210

Gedeon Richter Pharma GmbH (1)
Mergenthaleralle 15-21, D-65760, Eschborn, Germany
Tel.: (49) 61967666122
Web Site: https://www.gedeonrichter.com
Sales Range: $25-49.9 Million
Emp.: 5
Pharmaceuticals
N.A.I.C.S.: 325412
Tamas Neubauer (Mng Dir)

Gedeon Richter Pharma O.O.O. (1)
4th Dobryninsky per 8, 119049, Moscow,
Russia
Tel.: (7) 4959871880
Web Site: http://www.gedeonrichter.com
Pharmaceutical Product Mfr & Distr
N.A.I.C.S.: 325412

Gedeon Richter Polska Sp. z o.o (1)
ul Ks J Poniatowskiego 5, 05-825, Grodzisk
Mazowiecki, Poland
Tel.: (48) 2275550818
Web Site: https://www.gedeonrichter.pl

Pharmaceuticals Product Mfr
N.A.I.C.S.: 325412
Tomasz Nemeth (Chm & Dir Gen)

Gedeon Richter Romania S.A (1)
99-105 Cuza Voda St, Tirgu Mures,
540306, Romania
Tel.: (40) 265264067
Web Site: http://www.gedeon-richter.ro
Sales Range: $25-49.9 Million
Emp.: 30
Pharmaceuticals Product Mfr
N.A.I.C.S.: 325412
Kozma Judit (Member-Exec Bd)

Gedeon Richter Slovakia s.r.o. (1)
Karadzicova 10, 821 08, Bratislava, Slovakia
Tel.: (421) 250205801
Web Site: https://www.richter.sk
Pharmaceutical Products Distr
N.A.I.C.S.: 424210

Gedeon Richter Slovenija, d.o.o. (1)
Naslov Verovskova 55, 1000, Ljubljana,
Slovenia
Tel.: (386) 2056870
Web Site: http://www.richter.si
Pharmaceuticals Mfr
N.A.I.C.S.: 325412

Gedeon Richter UA V.A.T (1)
17 J Turgenev St, Kiev, 1054, Ukraine
Tel.: (380) 44 492 99 19
Web Site: http://www.richter.com.ua
Sales Range: $50-74.9 Million
Emp.: 200
Pharmaceuticals Product Mfr
N.A.I.C.S.: 325412

Gedeon Richter UK Ltd (1)
127 Shirland Rd, London, W9 2EP, United Kingdom
Tel.: (44) 2076048806
Web Site: https://www.gedeonrichter.com
Sales Range: $25-49.9 Million
Emp.: 4
Pharmaceuticals Product Mfr
N.A.I.C.S.: 325412

Gedeon Richter USA, Inc (1)
W Wing 3rd Fl 1200 W Ridgewood Ave,
Ridgewood, NJ 07450
Tel.: (201) 445-8300
Pharmaceuticals
N.A.I.C.S.: 325412

Gedeon Richter Ukrfarm O.O.O (1)
17/B Ul Turgenyevska, Kiev, 01054,
Ukraine
Tel.: (380) 444820956
Pharmaceutical Retailer
N.A.I.C.S.: 456110

Gedeonrichter Ecuador S.A. (1)
Av 12 de Octubre N24-68 y Av La Coruna
Edificio Mirage Piso 4, Quito, Ecuador
Tel.: (593) 26004410
Web Site: https://gedeonrichter.com.ec
Pharmaceutical Products Distr
N.A.I.C.S.: 424210
Erik Bogsch (Chm)

Gyogyszeripari Ellenorzo es Fejleszto Laboratorium (1)
Mexikoi Unit 9, 1149, Budapest, Hungary
Tel.: (36) 12732920
Web Site: http://www.gyel.hu
Laboratory Testing Services
N.A.I.C.S.: 621511

Humanco Kft (1)
Gyomroi Unit 19-21, Budapest, 1103, Hungary
Tel.: (36) 14314523
Social & Welfare Services
N.A.I.C.S.: 813410

Medimpex France S.A.RL. (1)
1/3 rue Caumartin, 75009, Paris, France
Tel.: (33) 147420320
Sales Range: $25-49.9 Million
Emp.: 3
Pharmaceuticals
N.A.I.C.S.: 325412

Medimpex Jamaica Ltd (1)
21 Balmoral Avenue, Kingston, 10, Jamaica
Tel.: (876) 9295780
Web Site: https://medimpexjamaica.com
Pharmaceutical Products Distr

N.A.I.C.S.: 325412

Medimpex UK Ltd. (1)
127 Shirland Road, Maida Vale, London,
W9 2EP, United Kingdom
Tel.: (44) 2072662669
Web Site: https://www.medimpexuk.com
Sales Range: $25-49.9 Million
Emp.: 5
Pharmaceuticals
N.A.I.C.S.: 325412

Medimpex West Indies Ltd (1)
28 Shannon Drive, Kingston Export Freezone, Kingston, 15, Jamaica
Tel.: (876) 6486545
Pharmaceutical Products Distr
N.A.I.C.S.: 424210
Endre Pokomandi (Chm)

Mediplus (Economic Zone) N.V. (1)
Economic Free Zone Hato Unit D1-Suite 5,
PO Box 8305, Willemstad, Curacao
Tel.: (599) 98339133
Pharmaceutical Products Distr
N.A.I.C.S.: 424210

PregLem SA (1)
Chemin Des Aulx 12, 1228, Plan-les-
Ouates, Geneva, Switzerland
Tel.: (41) 228840340
Web Site: https://www.preglem.com
Sales Range: $250-299.9 Million
Emp.: 700
Biopharmaceutical Products Mfr & Research Services
N.A.I.C.S.: 325412
Sven Zimmermann (CFO)

Reflex Kft (1)
Szava u 13-15, 1107, Budapest, Hungary
Tel.: (36) 14317210
Web Site: https://www.reflexkft.hu
Sales Range: $50-74.9 Million
Emp.: 140
Transportation & Carriage Services
N.A.I.C.S.: 488999
Kata Borsos (Head-Intl Transport)

Richter Szolgalato Kft (1)
Gyomroi Unit 19-21, Budapest, 1103, Hungary
Tel.: (36) 14314112
Catering Services
N.A.I.C.S.: 722320

Richter-Helm BioLogic Management GmbH (1)
Dengelsberg, 24796, Bovenau, Germany
Tel.: (49) 43311230101
Web Site: http://www.richter.hu
Pharmaceuticals Product Mfr
N.A.I.C.S.: 325412
Alexander Caliebe (Dir-Mfg)

Richter-Helm Biologics GmbH & Co KG (1)
Dengelsberg, Bovenau, 24796, Germany
Tel.: (49) 43311230101
Web Site: http://www.richter-helm-biologics.eu
Sales Range: $25-49.9 Million
Emp.: 50
Pharmaceuticals Product Mfr
N.A.I.C.S.: 325412
Kai Pohlmeyer (Mng Dir)

Richter-Themis Medicare (India) Private Ltd. (51%)
Plot 69/A/2 GIDC Industrial Estate, Wapi,
396 195, Gujarat, India
Tel.: (91) 2606532701
Sales Range: $50-74.9 Million
Emp.: 120
Pharmaceuticals Mfr
N.A.I.C.S.: 325412
Rajneesh Anand (CEO)

GEDIA S.A.

7 rue des Fontaines, F-28109, Dreux,
Cedex, France
Tel.: (33) 237650020   FR
Web Site: http://www.gedia-dreux.com
Sales Range: $25-49.9 Million
Electricity & Natural Gas Distr
N.A.I.C.S.: 221122
Philippe Rive (Dir Gen)

INTERNATIONAL PUBLIC

GEDIK YATIRIM HOLDING AS

Altaycesme Mah Camli Sok Pasco
Plaza No 21 Kat 12, Maltepe, 34876,
Istanbul, Turkiye
Tel.: (90) 2163777790
Web Site: https://inveo.com.tr
Year Founded: 1998
Holding Company
N.A.I.C.S.: 551112
Erhan Topac (Chm)

GEDIK YATIRIM MENKUL DEGERLER A.S.

Altaycesme Mahallesi camli Sokak
No 21 Kat 10-11-12, Maltepe, 34843,
Istanbul, Turkiye
Tel.: (90) 2164530053
Web Site: https://gedik.com
Year Founded: 1991
GEDIK—(IST)
Rev.: $2,478,323,839
Assets: $290,089,891
Liabilities: $253,494,024
Net Worth: $36,595,868
Earnings: $10,800,507
Fiscal Year-end: 12/31/22
Securities Brokerage Services
N.A.I.C.S.: 523150
Erhan Topac (Chm)

Subsidiaries:

Marbas Menkul Degerler A.S. (1)
Nisbetiye Mah Aytar Cad Metro Business
Center No 10 Ic Kapi No 1, Besiktas Levent, Istanbul, Turkiye
Tel.: (90) 2122863000
Web Site: http://www.marbasmenkul.com.tr
Financial Services
N.A.I.C.S.: 523999

GEDIZ AMBALAJ SANAYI VE TICARET A.S.

Kutahya Yolu 3 km P K 7, Gediz,
43600, Kutahya, Turkiye
Tel.: (90) 2744127788
Web Site:
https://www.gedizambalaj.com
Year Founded: 1982
GEDZA—(IST)
Rev.: $9,523,602
Assets: $9,626,829
Liabilities: $1,939,349
Net Worth: $7,687,480
Earnings: $2,447,277
Fiscal Year-end: 12/31/22
Polypropylene Product Mfr
N.A.I.C.S.: 326113
Ibrahim Basol (Chm)

GEDY S.P.A.

Via Dell Industria 6, Origgio, 21040,
Varese, Italy
Tel.: (39) 02969501   IT
Web Site: http://www.gedy.com
Year Founded: 1953
Sales Range: $25-49.9 Million
Emp.: 100
Bathroom Accessory Mfr
N.A.I.C.S.: 326199

Subsidiaries:

Gedy Iberica, S.A. (1)
Bernat Metge 110, Barcelona, 8205, Sabadell, Spain (100%)
Tel.: (34) 937122377
Web Site: http://www.gedyiberica.es
Sales Range: $50-74.9 Million
Emp.: 10
Sales & Distribution of Bathroom Accessories to Spain & Portugal
N.A.I.C.S.: 423220
Philipo Vluka (Pres-Italy)

GEECEE VENTURES LIMITED

209-210 Arcadia Building 2nd Floor
NCPA Marg 195 Nariman Point,
Mumbai, 400 021, India
Tel.: (91) 2240198600

AND PRIVATE COMPANIES

Web Site:
https://www.geeceeventures.com
532764—(BOM)
Rev.: $6,132,454
Assets: $73,925,957
Liabilities: $7,526,214
Net Worth: $66,399,743
Earnings: $1,389,829
Emp.: 46
Fiscal Year-end: 03/31/21
Chemical Products Producer
N.A.I.C.S.: 325320
Gaurav Shyamsukha *(Exec Dir)*

Subsidiaries:

GeeCee Ventures Ltd. - Chemical
Plant 2 (1)
7201 7211 12 GIDC Indust Estate Ankleshwar, Bharuch, 393002, Gujarat, India
Tel.: (91) 2646227175
Web Site: http://www.gcventures.com
Sales Range: $25-49.9 Million
Emp.: 25
Chemical Products Mfr
N.A.I.C.S.: 325998

GEECHS, INC.

Shibuya Scramble Square 39F
2-24-12 Shibuya, Shibuya-Ku, Tokyo,
150-6139, Japan
Tel.: (81) 366906928
Web Site: https://www.geechs.com
Year Founded: 2007
7060—(TKS)
Rev.: $156,914,790
Assets: $47,420,140
Liabilities: $27,127,440
Net Worth: $20,292,700
Earnings: ($9,736,530)
Emp.: 270
Fiscal Year-end: 03/31/24
Management Consulting Services
N.A.I.C.S.: 541618
Naruhito Sonehara *(Chm, Pres & CEO)*

GEEFCEE FINANCE LIMITED

Baroda Road Sonepat, Gohana, 131 301, Haryana, India
Tel.: (91) 11 2576 3401
Year Founded: 1990
Rev.: $12,198
Assets: $10,026,632
Liabilities: $6,987
Net Worth: $10,019,645
Earnings: $272
Fiscal Year-end: 03/31/18
Financial Support Services
N.A.I.C.S.: 523999
Giri Raj Goyal *(Chm & Mng Dir)*

GEEKAY WIRES LTD.

11-70/5 2nd Floor G P Complex
Shivalayam Road, Fathenagar,
Hyderabad, 500 018, India
Tel.: (91) 4023778090
Web Site:
https://www.geekaywires.com
GEEKAYWIRE—(NSE)
Rev.: $24,005,490
Assets: $19,272,990
Liabilities: $13,130,429
Net Worth: $6,142,561
Earnings: $860,384
Emp.: 352
Fiscal Year-end: 03/31/21
Engineering & Construction Services
N.A.I.C.S.: 541330
Ghanshyam Dass *(Chm & Mng Dir)*

GEESINK GROUP B.V.

Betonweg 8, NL-8305 BG, Emmeloord, Netherlands
Tel.: (31) 527638200 NI
Web Site:
http://www.geesinknorba.com

Holding Company; Refuse Collection & Transport Machinery Mfr
N.A.I.C.S.: 551112
Ron Wenneker *(Sls Mgr)*

Subsidiaries:

Geesink B.V. (1)
Betonweg 8, 8305 AG, Emmeloord, Netherlands
Tel.: (31) 527 638 713
Web Site: http://www.geesinknorba.com
Refuse Collection & Transport Machinery Mfr
N.A.I.C.S.: 336120
Arthur Hoffman *(Branch Mgr)*

Geesink Norba Ltd. (1)
Llantrisant Business Park, Llantrisant, Pontyclun, CF72 8XZ, United Kingdom **(100%)**
Tel.: (44) 1443222301
Refuse Collection & Transport Machinery Mfr
N.A.I.C.S.: 562111
Mick Hill *(Bus Dir)*

Geesinknorba AB (1)
Torsasgatan 38, 392 39, Kalmar, Sweden
Tel.: (46) 480427400
Web Site: http://www.norbatrucks.com
Industrial Truck Mfr
N.A.I.C.S.: 333924
Thomas Thuresson *(Gen mgr)*

Subsidiary (Non-US):

Norba A/S (2)
Silovej 40, 2690, Karlslunde,
Denmark **(100%)**
Tel.: (45) 56141449
Web Site: http://www.norba.com
Sales Range: $25-49.9 Million
Emp.: 10
Industrial Truck Mfr
N.A.I.C.S.: 333924

GEETANJALI CREDIT & CAPITAL LTD.

Shop No 26 Shree Sai Sindagi Sona Bazar Complex, Saraffa Katta Sheelavantar Oni, Hubli-Dharwad, 580020, Karnataka, India
Tel.: (91) 7931207638
Web Site:
http://www.geetanjalicredit.com
Rev.: $9,558
Assets: $543,048
Liabilities: $53,751
Net Worth: $489,297
Earnings: $3,204
Fiscal Year-end: 03/31/18
Financial Support Services
N.A.I.C.S.: 523999
Bharat Bhushan Goyal *(Exec Dir)*

GEEYA TECHNOLOGY CO., LTD.

No 50 Shuhan Road West, Chengdu, 610091, China
Tel.: (86) 2868232103
Web Site: http://www.geeya.cn
Year Founded: 1999
Sales Range: $75-99.9 Million
Emp.: 272
Digital Television Equipment Mfr & Distr
N.A.I.C.S.: 334220
Xiong Jianxin *(Chm, Pres & Sec-Interim)*

GEFEN BIOMED INVESTMENTS LTD.

Abba Hillel Junction Yakhin Park, Ashkelon, 78172, Israel
Tel.: (972) 86751122
Web Site:
http://www.gefenbiomed.com
Year Founded: 1969
GEFEN-M—(TAE)
Sales Range: Less than $1 Million
Emp.: 10
Financial Investment Services

N.A.I.C.S.: 523999
Limor Kohen *(CEO)*

GEFEN INTERNATIONAL A.I LTD.

Level 5 126-130 Phillip Street, Sydney, 2000, NSW, Australia
Tel.: (61) 280721400 AU
Web Site:
https://www.gefentechnologies.com
Year Founded: 2014
GFN—(ASX)
Rev.: $12,268
Assets: $23,600
Liabilities: $13,415
Net Worth: $10,185
Earnings: ($10,633)
Fiscal Year-end: 12/31/22
Software Development Services
N.A.I.C.S.: 541511

Subsidiaries:

Coyote Technologies Inc. (1)
58 Central Ave, Ayer, MA 01432
Tel.: (978) 456-8789
Web Site: http://www.coyotetech.com
Information Technology Consulting Services
N.A.I.C.S.: 541512

Gefen Technologies A.I. Ltd. (1)
Kalisher 30, Tel Aviv, 6525724, Israel
Tel.: (972) 507421831
Web Site: https://gefentechnologies.com
Information Technologies Services
N.A.I.C.S.: 541512

Roeto Ltd. (1)
10 Ben Avigdor Street, Tel Aviv, Israel
Tel.: (972) 747188057
Web Site: https://roeto.co.il
Technical Consulting Services
N.A.I.C.S.: 541330

GEFEN LANDA ACQUISITION CORP.

85 Medinat Hayehudim St Building G Floor 14, Herzliya, 4676670, Israel
Tel.: (972) 9 950 8690 Ky
Year Founded: 2021
GFLDU—(NASDAQ)
Emp.: 4
Investment Services
N.A.I.C.S.: 523999
Benzion Landa *(Co-Chm & Co-CEO)*

GEFFEN RESIDENCE & RENEWAL LTD

The Cranes Street 8A No, PO Box 4672559, Rehovot, 76704, Israel
Tel.: (972) 89475666
CNMD—(TAE)
Rev.: $16,268
Assets: $2,889,214
Liabilities: $1,696,492
Net Worth: $1,192,723
Earnings: ($5,444,932)
Fiscal Year-end: 12/31/22
Biotechnology Research & Development Services
N.A.I.C.S.: 541714
Kfir Gindi *(CEO)*

GEFINOR S.A.

5 rue Guillaume Kroll, 1882, Luxembourg, Luxembourg LU
Web Site: http://www.gefinor.com
Year Founded: 1960
Rev.: $624,000
Assets: $109,605,000
Liabilities: $24,689,000
Net Worth: $84,916,000
Earnings: ($15,348,000)
Fiscal Year-end: 12/31/18
Investment Holding Company; Merchant Banking Services
N.A.I.C.S.: 551112
Mohamed Ousseimi *(Chm & CEO)*

Subsidiaries:

ADC Dolls Inc. (1)
112 W 34th S, New York, NY 10120
Tel.: (800) 229-5192
Web Site:
http://www.madamealexander.com
Doll Distr
N.A.I.C.S.: 423920

Gefinor Finance S.A. (1)
Gefinor Bldg 30 Quai Gustave Ador, Geneva, 1207, Switzerland **(100%)**
Tel.: (41) 227189300
Web Site: http://www.gefinor.com
Sales Range: $25-49.9 Million
Emp.: 20
Financial Services
N.A.I.C.S.: 561499
Altre Barnath *(Mgr)*

Gefinor Finance S.A. (1)
Gefinor Ctr block A 3rd fl, PO Box 3869, Rue Clemenceau, Beirut, Lebanon **(100%)**
Tel.: (961) 1739789
Web Site: http://www.gefinor.com.lb
Sales Range: $50-74.9 Million
Emp.: 20
Financial Services
N.A.I.C.S.: 525990

Gefinor U.S.A., Inc. (1)
Seagram Bldg 375 Park Ave Ste 2401, New York, NY 10152 **(100%)**
Tel.: (212) 308-1111
Web Site: http://www.gefinorusa.com
Sales Range: $50-74.9 Million
Emp.: 6
Holding Company
N.A.I.C.S.: 525990

GEFION GROUP A/S

Ostergade 1 1 sal, 1100, Copenhagen, K, Denmark
Tel.: (45) 70 23 20 20
Web Site:
http://www.gefiongroup.com
Year Founded: 2013
Real Estate Development Services
N.A.I.C.S.: 531390
Peter Lindegaard *(Chm)*

Subsidiaries:

Victoria Properties A/S (1)
Bredgade 23A, 1260, Copenhagen, K, Denmark **(69.1%)**
Tel.: (45) 88510142
Web Site: http://www.victoriaproperties.dk
Rev: $196,382
Assets: $3,038,676
Liabilities: $1,424,145
Net Worth: $1,614,531
Earnings: ($190,386)
Fiscal Year-end: 12/31/2019
Property Management Services
N.A.I.C.S.: 531311
Rasmus Bundgaard *(Mng Dir)*

GEFIT S.P.A.

Via De Negri 9, 15121, Alessandria, Italy
Tel.: (39) 0131204411 IT
Web Site: http://www.gefit.com
Year Founded: 1967
Sales Range: $25-49.9 Million
Emp.: 300
Assembly & Handling Equipment Mfr
N.A.I.C.S.: 333248
Fulvio Fusco *(VP)*

Subsidiaries:

GEFIT Livernois Engineering, LLC (1)
12163 Globe St, Livonia, MI 48185
Tel.: (734) 464-7000
Web Site: http://www.livernois.com
Sales Range: $10-24.9 Million
Emp.: 35
Mfr of Heat Exchanger, Radiator & Condenser Manufacturing Equipment
N.A.I.C.S.: 333248
Wayne Elward *(Gen Mgr)*

GEFIT S.p.A. - GEFIT Moulds & Assembly Division (1)

GEFIT S.P.A.

GEFIT S.p.A.—(Continued)
Strada per Felizzano, Fubine, 15043, Alessandria, Italy
Tel.: (39) 0131 792817
Web Site: http://www.gefit.com
Assembly Machine Mfr
N.A.I.C.S.: 333519

Gefit Dalian Industrial Technology Co., Ltd. (1)
No 12 Fuquanbei Road Economic Development Area, 116600, Dalian, China
Tel.: (86) 411 87340892
Assembly Machine Mfr
N.A.I.C.S.: 333519
Christina Lee *(Mgr-Fin)*

Geftech Kft. (1)
Alugyari Ut 1, 2800, Tatabanya, Hungary
Tel.: (36) 34 510 580
Web Site: http://www.geftech.hu
Assembly Machine Mfr
N.A.I.C.S.: 333519

GEFRAN S.P.A.
Via Sebina 74, 25050, Iseo, BS, Italy
Tel.: (39) 03098881 **IT**
Web Site: https://www.gefran.com
GE—(ITA)
Rev.: $149,259,300
Assets: $182,342,422
Liabilities: $78,643,338
Net Worth: $103,699,084
Earnings: $13,089,745
Emp.: 651
Fiscal Year-end: 12/31/23
Industrial Automation, Sensory & Motion Control Equipment Mfr & Distr
N.A.I.C.S.: 333612
Maria Chiara Franceschetti *(Chm)*

Subsidiaries:

Elettropiemme S.r.l. (1)
Via Linz 137, 38121, Trento, Italy
Tel.: (39) 0461991935
Web Site: https://www.elettropiemme.it
Electrical Panel Installation Services
N.A.I.C.S.: 238210

Gefran Asia Pte. Ltd. (1)
31 Ubi Road 1 02-07 Aztech Building, 03-19 Loyang Industrial Estate, Singapore, 408694, Singapore **(100%)**
Tel.: (65) 68418300
Web Site: http://www.gefran.com.sg
Sales Range: $50-74.9 Million
Emp.: 12
Holding Company; Regional Manging Office
N.A.I.C.S.: 551112

Subsidiary (Non-US):

Gefran SIEI Drives Technology (Shanghai) Co.,Ltd (2)
No 1285 Beihe Road, Jiading District, Shanghai, China
Tel.: (86) 2169169898
Electric Equipment Mfr
N.A.I.C.S.: 334419

Gefran Siei Electric (Shanghai) Pte Ltd (2)
Block B Gr Flr No 155 Fu Te Xi Yi Road, Wai Gao Qiao Trade Zone, 200131, Shanghai, China **(100%)**
Tel.: (86) 2158661555
Other Motor Vehicle Electrical & Electronic Equipment Mfr
N.A.I.C.S.: 336320

Siei Drives Technology Co., Ltd. (2)
No 1285 Beihe Road, Jiading District, Shanghai, 201807, China **(100%)**
Tel.: (86) 2169169898
Web Site: http://www.sieiasia.com.cn
Sales Range: $25-49.9 Million
Emp.: 5
Other Motor Vehicle Electrical & Electronic Equipment Mfr
N.A.I.C.S.: 336320
Andy Zhu *(Mgr-Product)*

Gefran Benelux N.V. (1)
ENA 23 Zone 3 nr 3910 Lammerdries-zuid 14A, 2250, Olen, Belgium **(100%)**
Tel.: (32) 14248181
Web Site: http://www.gefran.be
Sales Range: $25-49.9 Million
Emp.: 14
Electrical Apparatus & Equipment Wiring Supplies & Construction Material Whslr
N.A.I.C.S.: 423610

Gefran Brasil Eletroeletronica Ltda. (1)
Avenida Dr Altino Arantes 377, Vila Clementino, Sao Paulo, 04042-032, Brazil **(75.5%)**
Tel.: (55) 1132150130
Web Site: https://www.gefran.com
Sales Range: $10-24.9 Million
Emp.: 50
Other Business Service Centers
N.A.I.C.S.: 561439

Gefran Brasil Elettroel. Ltda. (1)
Avenida Dr Altino Arantes 377 Vila Clementino, Sao Paulo, 04042-032, Brazil
Tel.: (55) 113 215 0130
Industrial Automation Mfr
N.A.I.C.S.: 333998

Gefran Deutschland GmbH (1)
Philipp-Reis-Str 9a, 63500, Seligenstadt, Germany **(100%)**
Tel.: (49) 61828090
Web Site: https://www.gefran.com
Sales Range: $25-49.9 Million
Emp.: 16
Other Electronic Component Mfr
N.A.I.C.S.: 334419
Torsten Fuchs *(Mng Dir)*

Gefran Drives & Motion S.r.l. (1)
Via Carducci 24, 21040, Gerenzano, Varese, Italy
Tel.: (39) 0296 7601
Automation Equipment Mfr
N.A.I.C.S.: 333998

Gefran France S.A. (1)
Parc TechnolandBatiment K-ZI Champ Dolin3 Allee des Abruzzes, BP 8237, Saint-Priest, 69800, Lyon, France **(100%)**
Tel.: (33) 478770300
Web Site: https://www.gefran.com
Sales Range: $25-49.9 Million
Emp.: 15
Instrument Mfr for Measuring & Testing Electricity & Electrical Signals
N.A.I.C.S.: 334515

Gefran India Ltd. (1)
Plot No BG-71/2/A Ground Floor Telco Road MIDC General Block, Bhosari, Pune, 411026, Maharashtra, India
Tel.: (91) 2066146500
Web Site: http://www.gefran.in
Emp.: 30
Electric Equipment Mfr
N.A.I.C.S.: 334419

Gefran Siei Drives Tech. Co., Ltd. (1)
No 1285 Beihe Road, Jiading District, Shanghai, 201807, China
Tel.: (86) 216 916 9898
Industrial Automation Mfr
N.A.I.C.S.: 333998

Gefran Suisse SA (1)
Rue Fritz Courvoisier 40, 2302, La Chaux-de-Fonds, Switzerland **(100%)**
Tel.: (41) 329684955
Web Site: http://www.gefran.com
Sales Range: $50-74.9 Million
Emp.: 5
Other Electronic Parts & Equipment Whslr
N.A.I.C.S.: 423690

Gefran UK Ltd. (1)
Unit 37 Clarendon Court Winwick Quay, Warrington, WA2 8QP, United Kingdom **(100%)**
Tel.: (44) 8452604555
Web Site: https://www.gefran.com
Sales Range: $200-249.9 Million
Emp.: 7
Instrument Mfr for Measuring & Testing Electricity & Electrical Signals
N.A.I.C.S.: 334515

Gefran, Inc. (1)
400 Willow St, North Andover, MA 01845 **(100%)**
Tel.: (781) 729-5249
Sales Range: $10-24.9 Million
Emp.: 50
Industrial Automation & Sensory Equipment Mfr & Distr
N.A.I.C.S.: 334513

Sensormate AG (1)
Steigweg 8, Aadorf, 8355, Munchwilen, Switzerland
Tel.: (41) 525232500
Industrial Automation Mfr
N.A.I.C.S.: 333998

GEHRLICHER SOLAR AG
Austrasse 101 B, 96465, Neustadt, Germany
Tel.: (49) 95688966090
Web Site: http://www.gehrlicher.com
Sales Range: $25-49.9 Million
Emp.: 200
Solar Energy System Design & Installation Services
N.A.I.C.S.: 237130
Stefan Parhofer *(Chief Strategy & Sls Officer)*

Subsidiaries:

Gehrlicher Solar Espana S.L. (1)
C/ Velazquez 22 5 izda, 28001, Madrid, Spain
Tel.: (34) 91 449 12 47
Solar Power Plant Construction Services
N.A.I.C.S.: 237130

Gehrlicher Solar France SAS (1)
97 avenue du General Leclerc, 75014, Paris, France
Tel.: (33) 6 30 24 87 84
Solar Power Plant Construction Services
N.A.I.C.S.: 237130

Gehrlicher-Ikhwezi (Pty) Ltd (1)
1 de Wet Road West Bank, East London, 5201, South Africa
Tel.: (27) 43 7018 000
Solar Power Plant Construction Services
N.A.I.C.S.: 237130

GEI INDUSTRIAL SYSTEMS LTD.
26-A Industrial Area Govindpura, Bhopal, 462 023, Madhya Pradesh, India
Tel.: (91) 7552586691
Web Site: http://www.geiind.com
Year Founded: 1970
Sales Range: $75-99.9 Million
Emp.: 691
Air Cooled Heat Exchanger & Steam Condenser Mfr
N.A.I.C.S.: 333415
C. E. Fernandes *(Chm & Mng Dir)*

GEI-IMMO AG
Sennweidstrasse 43, 6312, Steinhausen, Switzerland
Year Founded: 2006
Real Estate
N.A.I.C.S.: 531390
Veronika Kraler *(Mng Dir)*

Subsidiaries:

SKS Stakusit Bautechnik GmbH (1)
Eisenbahnstrasse 2B, D-47198, Duisburg, Homberg, Germany
Tel.: (49) 206620040
Web Site: http://www.sks-stakusit.de
Sales Range: $50-74.9 Million
Emp.: 300
Roller Shutters, Awnings & Other Outdoor Window Treatment Products Mfr
N.A.I.C.S.: 326199
Christian Schaller *(Mng Dir)*

GEIGER COUNTER LIMITED
Ordnance House 31 Pier Road, Saint Helier, Jersey **JE**
Year Founded: 2006
GCL—(LSE)
Rev.: $32,020,369
Assets: $124,827,499
Liabilities: $14,071,292
Net Worth: $110,756,207
Earnings: $29,357,098
Fiscal Year-end: 09/30/23
Investment Management Service
N.A.I.C.S.: 523999
Ian Reeves CBE *(Chm)*

GEISMAR S.A.
113 Bis Ave Charles De Gaulle, 92200, Neuilly, France
Tel.: (33) 1 41 43 4040
Web Site: http://www.geismar-mtm.com
Year Founded: 1924
Sales Range: $25-49.9 Million
Emp.: 170
Mfr & Distr of Railway Maintenance Equipment
N.A.I.C.S.: 336510
Daniel Geismar *(Owner)*

Subsidiaries:

Beijing Geismar Railways Equipment Trading Co., Ltd. (1)
26 Chaowai St, Chaoyang District, Beijing, 100020, China
Tel.: (86) 10 8565 6818
Railway Maintenance Equipment Distr
N.A.I.C.S.: 423860

GEISMAR DO BRASIL MATERIAL FERROVIARIO LTDA (1)
Estrada do Tindiba 1661 lote 1, Taquara, Rio de Janeiro, 22740-361, Brazil
Tel.: (55) 21 3382 9850
Web Site: http://www.geismardobrasil.com.br
Railway Maintenance Equipment Distr
N.A.I.C.S.: 423860

Geismar (UK) Ltd (1)
Salthouse Road, Brackmills, Northampton, NN4 7EX, United Kingdom
Tel.: (44) 1604 769191
Railway Maintenance Equipment Distr
N.A.I.C.S.: 423860
Brian Stronach *(Mng Dir)*

Geismar S.A. - COLMAR Factory (1)
5 rue d Altkirch, 68006, Colmar, cedex, France
Tel.: (33) 3 89 80 22 11
Railway Maintenance Equipment Mfr
N.A.I.C.S.: 336510

Geismar SEA Pte Ltd (1)
183A Thomson Road, Singapore, 307628, Singapore
Tel.: (65) 62562061
Web Site: http://www.geismar.com
Railway Maintenance Equipment Distr
N.A.I.C.S.: 423860

Modern Track Machinery (1)
1415 Davis Rd, Elgin, IL 60123-1321
Tel.: (847) 697-7510
Web Site: http://www.geismar-mtm.com
Sales Range: $25-49.9 Million
Emp.: 30
Railroad Track Construction & Maintenance Equipment
N.A.I.C.S.: 423860
Mike Olson *(Controller)*

Modern Track Machinery, Ltd. (1)
5926 Shawson Drive, Mississauga, L4W 3W5, ON, Canada
Tel.: (905) 564-1211
Railway Maintenance Equipment Mfr
N.A.I.C.S.: 336510

GEK TERNA SOCIETE ANONYME HOLDINGS REAL ESTATE CONSTRUCTIONS
85 Mesogeion Ave, 115 26, Athens, 115 26, Greece
Tel.: (30) 2106968000 **GR**
Web Site: https://www.gekterna.com
GEKTERNA—(ATH)
Rev.: $4,250,246,061
Assets: $6,451,015,541
Liabilities: $5,165,997,194

Net Worth: $1,285,018,347
Earnings: $191,396,503
Emp.: 3,631
Fiscal Year-end: 12/31/22
Holding Company
N.A.I.C.S.: 551112
Georgios Peristeris *(Chm & CEO)*

Subsidiaries:

GEK Services S.A. (1)
Leof Kifisias Iatridou 124, 11526, Athens, Greece
Tel.: (30) 2106968830
Web Site: https://www.gekservices.gr
Sales Range: $25-49.9 Million
Emp.: 10
Facility Management Services
N.A.I.C.S.: 561210
Stathopoulos Charalampos *(Gen Mgr)*

Highlight S.r.l. (1)
Neguostore No 12, Bucharest, Romania
Tel.: (40) 213120331
Emp.: 7
Heavy Engineering Construction Services
N.A.I.C.S.: 541330
Vavllats Constinos *(Mng Dir)*

ICON EOOD (1)
Vitosha Distr Bl No B Fl 7 110, Sofia, Bulgaria
Tel.: (359) 28549435
Real Estate Manangement Services
N.A.I.C.S.: 531390

ILIOHORA S.A. (1)
Mesogeion 85, 11526, Athens, Greece
Tel.: (30) 2106968000
Web Site: https://www.terna.gr
Sales Range: $75-99.9 Million
Emp.: 270
Heavy Engineering Construction Services
N.A.I.C.S.: 541330
Peris Teris *(Mgr)*

IOLKOS S.A. (1)
B Industrial Area, Velestino, Greece
Tel.: (30) 2425022121
Contract Management & Construction Services
N.A.I.C.S.: 236220

Icon Borovec Eood (1)
Shiroka Polyana 216, Borovets, 2010, Samokov, Bulgaria
Tel.: (359) 75099100
Web Site: https://www.borovetseuphoria.com
Hotel & Resort Operator
N.A.I.C.S.: 721110

MONASTIRIOU TECHNICAL DEVELOPMENT S.A. (1)
85 N Kazantzaki 3C, Menemeni, 54628, Thessaloniki, Greece
Tel.: (30) 2310 244596
Web Site: http://www.monastiriou.gr
Real Estate Development Services
N.A.I.C.S.: 531390

NEA ODOS SA (1)
19 Neas Erythreas av, Nea Erythrea, 146 71, Athens, Greece
Tel.: (30) 2103447300
Web Site: https://www.neaodos.gr
Highway Construction Services
N.A.I.C.S.: 237310

TERNA (1)
Tel.: (30) 2106968000
Web Site: https://www.terna.gr
Rev.: $1,071,558,839
Assets: $1,482,805,739
Liabilities: $1,300,999,340
Net Worth: $181,806,399
Earnings: $32,586,583
Fiscal Year-end: 12/31/2017
Industrial & Infrastructure Construction & Engineering Services
N.A.I.C.S.: 236210
Georgios Peristeris *(Chm)*

Subsidiary (Non-US):

TERNA Bahrain Holding W.L.L. (2)
Zinj Area Vila 418 Road 3207 Block 332, Manama, Bahrain
Tel.: (973) 17721048
Heavy Engineering Construction Services

N.A.I.C.S.: 541330
George Stratigos *(Mgr)*

Terna Energy SA (1)
85 Mesogeion, 115 26, Athens, Greece
Tel.: (30) 2106968000
Web Site: https://www.terna-energy.com
Renewable Energy Services
N.A.I.C.S.: 221118
Georgios Peristeris *(Chm)*

Terna Mag SA (1)
124 Kifisias Ave and 2 Iatridou Str, 11526, Athens, Greece
Tel.: (30) 2106968000
Magnesia Product Mfr
N.A.I.C.S.: 327992

GEKE S.A
43 Kifisias Avenue, 11523, Athens, Greece
Tel.: (30) 2106989000
PRESD—(ATH)
Sales Range: Less than $1 Million
Emp.: 143
Hotel Consulting Services
N.A.I.C.S.: 541618
Emmanouill Manousos Manousakis *(Chm & Mng Dir)*

GEL S.P.A.
Via Enzo Ferrari 1, 60022, Castelfidardo, Italy
Tel.: (39) 0717827
Web Site: https://www.iubenda.com
Year Founded: 1979
Water Treatment Equipment Mfr & Distr
N.A.I.C.S.: 333310
Aroldo Berto *(Pres & CEO)*

GELECEK VARLIK YONETIMI A.S.
Merkez Mahallesi Cendere Caddesi No 22 Kagithane, Kagithane, 34406, Istanbul, Turkiye
Tel.: (90) 2123812300
Web Site:
 http://www.gelecekvarlik.com.tr
GLCVY—(IST)
Financial Investment Services
N.A.I.C.S.: 523999
Murat Ozyegin *(Chm)*

GELION PLC
PO Box 575, PO Box 575, Alexandria, 2015, NSW, Australia
Tel.: (61) 2077492640
Web Site: https://www.gelion.com
Year Founded: 2015
GELN—(AIM)
Rev.: $2,592,780
Assets: $17,278,465
Liabilities: $1,368,341
Net Worth: $15,910,124
Earnings: ($9,349,912)
Emp.: 43
Fiscal Year-end: 06/30/23
Battery Product Mfr
N.A.I.C.S.: 335910

GELITA AG
Uferstrabe 7, Eberbach, 69412, Germany
Tel.: (49) 62718401
Web Site: http://www.gelita.com
Year Founded: 1875
Rev.: $503,500,000
Emp.: 2,600
Protein Products Mfr
N.A.I.C.S.: 325199
Eberhard Dick *(Mgr-Food Applications)*

Subsidiaries:

ATRO Provita GmbH (1)
Gammelsbacher Stra 2, 69412, Eberbach, Germany
Tel.: (49) 627171091

Chemical Products Distr
N.A.I.C.S.: 424690

GELITA (Shanghai) Enterprise Management Co., Ltd (1)
Suite 4007 Bund Center No 222 Yan An Road, Putuo District, 200002, Shanghai, China
Tel.: (86) 2163353099
Chemical Products Distr
N.A.I.C.S.: 424690

GELITA Australia Pty. Ltd. (1)
50 Flood Road Josephville via Beaudesert, Beaudesert, 4285, QLD, Australia
Tel.: (61) 7 55 41 35 44
Emp.: 80
Chemical Products Distr
N.A.I.C.S.: 424690
Rubens Maia *(Mgr-Bus Process)*

GELITA Cangnan Gelatine Co. Ltd. (1)
Subian Industrial Area, Longgang, Wenzhou, Cangnan, China
Tel.: (86) 57764359776
Chemical Products Distr
N.A.I.C.S.: 424690

GELITA Do Brasil Ltda. (1)
Av Tiradentes s/nr, Mococa, Sao Paulo, Brazil
Tel.: (55) 1121638039
Chemical Products Distr
N.A.I.C.S.: 424690

GELITA France SARL (1)
5 Rue des Allumettes Les Bureaux de l'Arche, Aix-en-Provence, France
Tel.: (33) 442632840
Chemical Products Distr
N.A.I.C.S.: 424690

GELITA Health GmbH (1)
Uferstrasse 7, 69412, Eberbach, Germany
Tel.: (49) 6271841600
Web Site: http://www.gelitahealth.com
Gelatin & Collagen Peptide Product Mfr
N.A.I.C.S.: 325411
Beate Kloppel *(Mng Dir)*

GELITA Mexico S. de R.L. de C.V. (1)
Emiliano Zapata S/N Mex C P, Lerma, Mexico
Tel.: (52) 7282850101
Chemical Products Distr
N.A.I.C.S.: 424690

GELITA NZ. Ltd. (1)
30 Barton Street, Christchurch, New Zealand
Tel.: (64) 33843093
Chemical Products Distr
N.A.I.C.S.: 424690
Gary Monk *(Plant Mgr)*

GELITA Nederland B.V. (1)
Handelsweg 24, Ter-Apel, Netherlands
Tel.: (31) 599345700
Chemical Products Distr
N.A.I.C.S.: 424690

GELITA Shanghai Consulting Co. Ltd. (1)
Room 712-713 Silver Centre 1388 North Shanxi Road, Putuo, 200060, Shanghai, China
Tel.: (86) 2161498073
Chemical Products Distr
N.A.I.C.S.: 424690

GELITA South Africa Pty. Ltd. (1)
25 Verster Street West, Krugersdorp, South Africa
Tel.: (27) 116625300
Chemical Products Distr
N.A.I.C.S.: 424690

GELITA Sweden AB (1)
Stidsvigsvagen 91, Box 502, Klippan, Sweden
Tel.: (46) 43526500
Chemical Products Distr
N.A.I.C.S.: 424690
Anders Troback *(Mgr-IT)*

GELITA UK Ltd. (1)
3 Macclesfield Road, Holmes Chapel, CW4 7NF, Cheshire, United Kingdom
Tel.: (44) 1477536900

Chemical Products Distr
N.A.I.C.S.: 424690
Mark Bethell *(Gen Mgr)*

GELITA USA Inc. (1)
2445 Port Neal Industrial Rd, Sergeant Bluff, IA 51054
Tel.: (712) 943-5516
Chemical Products Distr
N.A.I.C.S.: 424690
Lara Niemann *(Dir-Mktg-Americas)*

Gelita (Liaoyuan) Gelatine Co. Ltd. (1)
Youyi Industrial Park Liaoyuan City Economic Development Zone, Liaoyuan, Jilin, China
Tel.: (86) 41182740880
Chemical Products Distr
N.A.I.C.S.: 424690

Gelita AG - Supply Plant (1)
Alpenstr 44, 87700, Memmingen, Germany
Tel.: (49) 833185590
Chemical Products Distr
N.A.I.C.S.: 424690

GELSENWASSER AG
Willy-Brandt-Allee 26, 45891, Gelsenkirchen, Germany
Tel.: (49) 2097080   De
Web Site:
 https://www.gelsenwasser.de
Year Founded: 1887
WWG—(DEU)
Rev.: $4,470,342,339
Assets: $4,364,260,432
Liabilities: $3,304,986,780
Net Worth: $1,059,273,652
Earnings: $146,593,936
Emp.: 1,715
Fiscal Year-end: 12/31/23
Water Supply & Waste Water Treatment Services
N.A.I.C.S.: 221310
Henning R. Deters *(Chm-Mgmt Bd)*

Subsidiaries:

GELSENWASSER Energienetze GmbH (1)
Willy Brandt Allee 26, 45891, Gelsenkirchen, Germany
Tel.: (49) 2097089
Web Site: http://www.gw-energienetze.de
Emp.: 200
Natural Gas Distribution
N.A.I.C.S.: 221210

Subsidiary (Domestic):

AWS GmbH (2)
Willy Brandt Allee 26, 45891, Gelsenkirchen, Germany
Tel.: (49) 2097081970
Web Site: http://www.abwassersysteme.de
Rev.: $6,114,720
Emp.: 30
Waste Water Disposal Services
N.A.I.C.S.: 221320

Abwassergesellschaft Gelsenkirchen mbH (2)
Willy-Brandt-Allee 26, 45891, Gelsenkirchen, Germany
Tel.: (49) 2091696311
Web Site: http://www.gelsenkanal.de
Emp.: 70
Water Distr & Wastewater Discharge Services
N.A.I.C.S.: 221310
Emanuel Grun *(Mng Dir)*

Westfalische Wasser und Umweltanalytik GmbH (2)
Willy-Brandt-Allee 26, 45891, Gelsenkirchen, Germany
Tel.: (49) 209708371
Web Site: https://www.wwu-labor.de
Emp.: 49
Water Purification Services
N.A.I.C.S.: 333310

GELSENWASSER Projektgesellschaft mbH (1)
Willy Brandt Allee 26, 45891, Gelsenkirchen, Germany

GELSENWASSER AG

Gelsenwasser AG—(Continued)
Tel.: (49) 209708284
Waste Water Treatment
N.A.I.C.S.: 221310

Niederrheinische Gas- und Wasserwerke GmbH (1)
Duisburger Strasse 161-167, 47166, Duisburg, Germany
Tel.: (49) 2035400
Web Site: http://www.ngw.de
Rev.: $140,001,610
Natural Gas & Water Distribution
N.A.I.C.S.: 221210

Subsidiary (Domestic):

Gasversorgung Hunxe GmbH (2)
c/o Wasserwerk Bucholtwelmen, Waldheideweg, 46569, Hunxe, Germany
Tel.: (49) 2035400
Rev.: $3,566,920
Gas Supply service
N.A.I.C.S.: 221210

Vereinigte Gas- und Wasserversorgung GmbH (1)
Ringstrasse 144, 33378, Rheda-Wiedenbruck, Germany
Tel.: (49) 52429230
Web Site: http://www.vgw-gmbh.de
Rev.: $15,032,020
Emp.: 25
Water Distribution Services
N.A.I.C.S.: 221310

Subsidiary (Domestic):

Westfalica (2)
Stein St 9, 32547, Bad Oeynhausen, Germany
Tel.: (49) 57312440
Web Site: http://www.westfalica.de
Sales Range: $100-124.9 Million
Natural Gas Supply Services
N.A.I.C.S.: 221210
Frank Diederich (Gen Mgr)

GELTEQ LIMITED
Level 4 100 Albert Road, South Melbourne, 3025, VIC, Australia
Tel.: (61) 390873990 AU
Web Site: https://www.gelteq.com
Year Founded: 2017
GELS—(NASDAQ)
Rev.: $98,080
Assets: $13,860,831
Liabilities: $3,769,746
Net Worth: $10,091,085
Earnings: ($2,367,936)
Emp.: 7
Fiscal Year-end: 06/30/24
Pharmaceutical Product Mfr & Distr
N.A.I.C.S.: 325412

GEM CO., LTD.
20 F Building A Rongchao Binhai Mansion Haixiu Road, New Centre District Baoan, Shenzhen, 518101, China
Tel.: (86) 75533386666
Web Site: https://www.gem.com.cn
Year Founded: 2001
002340—(SSE)
Rev.: $4,126,604,508
Assets: $6,195,797,244
Liabilities: $3,265,438,644
Net Worth: $2,930,358,600
Earnings: $181,942,956
Emp.: 10,000
Fiscal Year-end: 12/31/22
Super Fine Cobalt Powder, Nickel Powder & Nickel Alloy Products
N.A.I.C.S.: 331492
Kaihua Xu (Founder, Chm & Gen Mgr)

Subsidiaries:

Fu'an Qingmei Energy Materials Co., Ltd. (1)
Banyu Village, Wanwu Town Fu'an, Ningde, Fujian, China
Tel.: (86) 5936351899

Recyclable Material Distr
N.A.I.C.S.: 423930

GEM (Chenzhou) Solid Waste Treatment Co., Ltd. (1)
Bolin Industrial Park, Tianliping Bolin Town Yongxing County, Chenzhou, Hunan, China
Tel.: (86) 7355663518
Recyclable Material Distr
N.A.I.C.S.: 423930

GEM (Jiangsu) Cobalt Industry Co., Ltd. (1)
No 8 North Binjiang Road, Taixing, Jiangsu, China
Tel.: (86) 52387671121
Emp.: 440
Cobalt Product Mfr
N.A.I.C.S.: 331410

GEM (Tianjin) Urban Minerals Recycling Industry Development Co., Ltd. (1)
No 9 No 10 Road, Ziya Circular Economy Industrial Park Jinghai County, Tianjin, China
Tel.: (86) 2259589600
Recyclable Material Distr
N.A.I.C.S.: 423930

GEM (Wuhan) New Energy Vehicle Service Co., Ltd. (1)
No 9 Bipu Village Cangbu Street, Xinzhou District, Wuhan, Hubei, China
Tel.: (86) 2789650888
Recyclable Material Distr
N.A.I.C.S.: 423930

GEM (Wuhan) Urban Minerals Recycling Industry Park Development Co., Ltd. (1)
No 9 Bipu Village Cangbu Street, Xinzhou District, Wuhan, Hubei, China
Tel.: (86) 2786989999
Emp.: 260
Recyclable Material Distr
N.A.I.C.S.: 423930

GEM (Wuxi) Energy Materials Co., Ltd. (1)
No 235 Zhenfa Road, Shuofang Town, Wuxi, Jiangsu, China
Tel.: (86) 51085131666
Emp.: 300
Battery Mfr
N.A.I.C.S.: 335910

GEM ECOPRO New Energy Materials Co., Ltd. (1)
GEM Circular Economy Industrial Park, Ebu Town Shenzhen-Shantou Special Cooperation Zone, Shenzhen, Guangdong, China
Tel.: (86) 75533386666
Recyclable Material Distr
N.A.I.C.S.: 423930

GEM Supply Chain Management (Shanghai) Co., Ltd. (1)
Block C 28th Floor Wumao Building No 2550 Zhongshan North Road, Putuo District, Shanghai, China
Tel.: (86) 2162578033
Recyclable Material Distr
N.A.I.C.S.: 423930

Henan Mutong Environmental Industry Co., Ltd. (1)
No 9 Hualiang Road Lankao County Industrial Concentration Area, Kaifeng, Henan, China
Tel.: (86) 37123300666
Emp.: 200
Recyclable Material Distr
N.A.I.C.S.: 423930

Hubei Erzhong Renewable Resources Market Development Co., Ltd. (1)
Pailou Industrial Park, Dongbao District, Jingmen, Hubei, China
Tel.: (86) 7242293318
Recyclable Material Distr
N.A.I.C.S.: 423930

Hunan GEM Yinghong Resource Recycling Co., Ltd. (1)
Xianghong Industrial Park Economic Development Zone, Xinhua County, Loudi, Hunan, China

Tel.: (86) 7383366190
Emp.: 60
Recyclable Material Distr
N.A.I.C.S.: 423930

Inner Mongolia Xinchuang Resource Recycling Co., Ltd. (1)
East of Jingwu Road and South of Weiyi Road, Sanyangliang Industrial Park Dalate Banner, Ordos, Inner Mongolia, China
Tel.: (86) 4773940101
Emp.: 200
Recyclable Material Distr
N.A.I.C.S.: 423930

Jiangxi GEM Resource Recycling Co., Ltd. (1)
Resource Recycling Industrial Base, Fengcheng, Jiangxi, China
Tel.: (86) 7956833888
Recyclable Material Distr
N.A.I.C.S.: 423930

Jiangxi GEM Scrapped Car Recycling Co., Ltd. (1)
Fengyuan Avenue Fengcheng Industrial Park, Fengcheng, Jiangxi, China
Tel.: (86) 7958356666
Recyclable Material Distr
N.A.I.C.S.: 423930

Jingmen Dewei GEM Tungsten Resource Recycling Co., Ltd. (1)
High-tech Industrial Development Zone, Jingmen, Hubei, China
Tel.: (86) 7248658608
Recyclable Material Distr
N.A.I.C.S.: 423930

Jingmen GEM Co., Ltd. (1)
High-tech Industrial Development Zone, Jingmen, Hubei, China
Tel.: (86) 7242499168
Recyclable Material Distr
N.A.I.C.S.: 423930

Jingmen GEM New Material Co., Ltd (1)
Tel.: (86) 7242499168
Chemical Preparations Mfr
N.A.I.C.S.: 325998

Jingmen Lvyuan Environmental Protection Industry Development Co., Ltd. (1)
Quanta Mountain Group 3 Baimiao Street Office, Huazhu Village Duodao District, Jingmen, Hubei, China
Tel.: (86) 7248600709
Recyclable Material Distr
N.A.I.C.S.: 423930

Shajing GEM High-Tech Co., Ltd (1)
50 Sha Yi West Industry Park, Sha Jing Town Bao An District, Shenzhen, 518104, Guangdong, China
Tel.: (86) 75529865333
Web Site: http://www.gemhi-tech.com
Wooden Boards Mfr
N.A.I.C.S.: 113110

Shanxi Hongyang Haiou WEEE Recovery & Treatment Co., Ltd. (1)
No 5 Northeast Road Changbei Bridge, Changzhi, Shanxi, China
Tel.: (86) 3555050988
Emp.: 230
Recyclable Material Distr
N.A.I.C.S.: 423930

Tianjin branch of Wuhan GEM Urban Mineral Equipment Co., Ltd. (1)
Gate 3 Building 25 No 1 No 2 Chuangxin 6th Road Xiqing High-tech Zone, Huading New District, Tianjin, China
Tel.: (86) 2283696978
Recyclable Material Distr
N.A.I.C.S.: 423930

Wuhan City Circle (Xiantao) Urban Mineral Resources Market Co., Ltd. (1)
318 National Road North, Yukou Town, Xiantao, Hubei, China
Tel.: (86) 7282511133
Recyclable Material Distr
N.A.I.C.S.: 423930

Wuhan GEM Resources Recycling Co., Ltd (1)

INTERNATIONAL PUBLIC

East Lake New Technology Development Zone, Wuhan, Hubei, China
Tel.: (86) 2787899611
Web Site: http://www.gemchina.com
Sales Range: $25-49.9 Million
Emp.: 100
E-Waste & Used Batteries Recycling Services
N.A.I.C.S.: 562998
Min Wang (Deputy Gen Mgr)

Wuhan Hannengtong New Energy Vehicle Service Co., Ltd. (1)
15/F Building A3 Optics Valley Financial Harbor, No 77 Optics Valley Avenue East Lake High-tech Development Zone, Wuhan, Hubei, China
Tel.: (86) 2787686666
Recyclable Material Distr
N.A.I.C.S.: 423930

Wuhan Sanyong GEM Auto Parts Remanufacturing Co., Ltd. (1)
No 9 Bipu Village Cangbu Street, Xinzhou District, Wuhan, Hubei, China
Tel.: (86) 2786989999
Recyclable Material Distr
N.A.I.C.S.: 423930

Yangzhou Ningda Precious Metal Co., Ltd. (1)
Road 1 Industrial Concentration Zone, Yiling Town Jiangdu District, Yangzhou, China
Tel.: (86) 5148668011
Recyclable Material Distr
N.A.I.C.S.: 423930

Yuyao Xingyou Metal Materials Co., Ltd. (1)
No 20 Cao'e Road, Binhai New Town Economic Development Zone, Yuyao, Zhejiang, China
Tel.: (86) 57458228518
Recyclable Material Distr
N.A.I.C.S.: 423930

Zhejiang Dewei Cemented Carbide Manufacturing Co., Ltd. (1)
128 Jingshi Road, Yueqing Economic Development Zone, Wenzhou, 325612, Zhejiang, China
Tel.: (86) 57762298577
Web Site: https://www.cn-dewei.com
Cemented Carbide Mfr
N.A.I.C.S.: 325180
Vincent Yu (Sls Mgr)

GEM DIAMONDS LIMITED
2 Eaton Gate, London, SW1W 9BJ, United Kingdom
Tel.: (44) 2030430280
Web Site: https://www.gemdiamonds.com
GEMD—(LSE)
Rev.: $188,940,000
Assets: $366,240,000
Liabilities: $133,190,000
Net Worth: $233,050,000
Earnings: $20,160,000
Fiscal Year-end: 12/31/22
Diamond Producer
N.A.I.C.S.: 212390
Clifford Thomas Elphick (CEO)

Subsidiaries:

Gem Diamond Technical Services (Proprietary) Limited (1)
Illovo Corner 24 Fricker Rd Illovo Boulevard, Johannesburg, 2196, Gauteng, South Africa
Tel.: (27) 11 560 9600
Web Site: https://www.gemdiamonds.com
Sales Range: $50-74.9 Million
Emp.: 35
Diamond Mining Services
N.A.I.C.S.: 212290

Gem Diamonds Marketing Services BVBA (1)
Kneller Building Hoveniersstraat 50-52, PO Box 70, 2018, Antwerp, Belgium
Tel.: (32) 3 203 4080
Web Site: https://www.gemdiamonds.com
Sales Range: $50-74.9 Million
Emp.: 2
Diamond Distr

N.A.I.C.S.: 423940
Brandon De Bruyn *(Gen Mgr)*

Gope Exploration Company (Proprietary) Limited (1)
165 Pilane Road Main Mall, Gaborone, Botswana
Tel.: (267) 318 2796
Web Site: http://www.gemdiamonds.com
Diamond Exploration Services
N.A.I.C.S.: 213114

GEM S.R.L.
Via dei Campi 2, Viareggio, 55049, Italy
Tel.: (39) 0584 389784
Web Site: http://www.gemitaly.it
Year Founded: 1994
Medical Device Mfr & Distr
N.A.I.C.S.: 339112
Lodovico Branchetti *(CEO)*

Subsidiaries:

Marsilio Editori S.p.A. (1)
Marittima - Fabbricato 205, 30135, Venice, Italy (94.71%)
Tel.: (39) 041 2406511
Web Site: http://www.marsilioeditori.it
Books Publishing Services
N.A.I.C.S.: 513130

GEM SPINNERS INDIA LIMITED
14 Mangalam Village Madhuranthagam Taluk, Kanchipuram, 603 107, India
Tel.: (91) 4428115190
Web Site: https://www.gemspin.com
Year Founded: 1990
521133—(BOM)
Assets: $855,856
Liabilities: $976,136
Net Worth: $(120,280)
Earnings: ($83,850)
Fiscal Year-end: 03/31/23
Cotton Yarn Mfr
N.A.I.C.S.: 313110
R. Veeramani *(Mng Dir)*

GEM TERMINAL IND. CO., LTD.
No 138 Lane 513 Datong Road, Luzhu District, Kaohsiung, 82145, Taiwan
Tel.: (886) 76963037
Web Site: https://www.gem.com.tw
Year Founded: 1977
2460—(TAI)
Rev.: $84,714,376
Assets: $174,776,016
Liabilities: $105,907,612
Net Worth: $68,868,404
Earnings: ($5,671,801)
Emp.: 136
Fiscal Year-end: 12/31/23
Housing & Electronic Connector Mfr
N.A.I.C.S.: 334417
Chung-Hung Su *(Co-Chm)*

Subsidiaries:

Dongguan Gem Electronics & Metal Co., Ltd. (1)
Chang-Qing 2 Road Lu-Dong Hu-Men, Dongguan, 523935, Guang Dong, China
Tel.: (86) 76985565684
Web Site: https://www.gem.net.cn
Emp.: 700
Hardware Mfr
N.A.I.C.S.: 332510

Genius Terminal Co., Ltd. (1)
Unit 12 7f Block B Hi-Tech Ind Ctr 5-21 Pak Tin Par St, Tsuen Wan, China (Hong Kong)
Tel.: (852) 24028132
International Trading Services
N.A.I.C.S.: 522299

Subsidiary (Domestic):

Genius Terminal (HK) Ltd. (2)
Unit 12 7f Block B Hi-Tech Ind Ctr 5-21 Pak Tin Par St, Tsuen Wan, NT, China (Hong Kong)
Tel.: (852) 24028132
International Trading Services
N.A.I.C.S.: 522299

Suzhou Gem Opto-Electronics Terminal Co., Ltd. (1)
Chun-Wang Rd Dongqiao Town Panyang Industrial Park Xiang Chen District, Suzhou, Jiangsu, China
Tel.: (86) 51265378728
Hardware Mfr
N.A.I.C.S.: 332510

Vietnam Gem Electronic & Metal Co., Ltd. (1)
Lot D6 Road D1 and N2 Nam Tan Uyen Industrial Park Khanh Binh Commune, Tan Uyen, Binh Duong, Vietnam
Tel.: (84) 2743639155
Hardware Mfr
N.A.I.C.S.: 332510

GEM-YEAR INDUSTRIAL CO., LTD.
No 8 Jinyi Avenue Economic Development Zone, Jiashan County, Jiaxing, 314100, Zhejiang, China
Tel.: (86) 57384185001
Web Site: https://www.gem-year.com
Year Founded: 1995
601002—(SHG)
Rev.: $381,500,693
Assets: $739,138,805
Liabilities: $138,100,683
Net Worth: $601,038,121
Earnings: $16,126,920
Fiscal Year-end: 12/31/22
Fastening Product Mfr & Whslr
N.A.I.C.S.: 332722
Yong Long Cai *(Chm)*

Subsidiaries:

Guangzhou Gem-Year Auto-parts Co., Ltd. (1)
No 58 Xinye Road Yonghe Eco Area, Guangzhou, 511356, China
Tel.: (86) 2032222501
Fastener Product Mfr
N.A.I.C.S.: 332722

GEMAC ENGINEERING MACHINERY CO., LTD.
No 1 Xinming Road High-tech Zone, Xiangyang, 441003, Hubei, China
Tel.: (86) 7103468255
Year Founded: 2001
301048—(CHIN)
Rev.: $457,725,060
Assets: $652,275,936
Liabilities: $335,841,012
Net Worth: $316,434,924
Earnings: $42,430,284
Fiscal Year-end: 12/31/22
Railway Construction Services
N.A.I.C.S.: 237990
Wei Zhang *(Chm)*

GEMADEPT CORPORATION
21st Floor 6 Le Thanh Ton St Ben Nghe Ward, District 1, Ho Chi Minh City, Vietnam
Tel.: (84) 838236236
Web Site: https://www.gemadept.com.vn
Year Founded: 1990
GMD—(HOSE)
Rev.: $158,448,043
Assets: $558,096,237
Liabilities: $157,122,426
Net Worth: $400,973,811
Earnings: $104,398,091
Emp.: 491
Fiscal Year-end: 12/31/23
Logistic Services
N.A.I.C.S.: 488510
Do Van Nhan *(Chm-Mgmt Bd)*

Subsidiaries:

Binh Duong Port Corporation (1)
Lot 712 Lot Map 8 BT B Group 5 Quyet Thang Quarter, Binh Thang Ward, Di An, Binh Duong, Vietnam
Tel.: (84) 2837325674
Port Operation Services
N.A.I.C.S.: 488310

Gemadept (Malaysia) Sdn. Bhd. (1)
Suite 6 07 Level 6 Menara Trend Intan Milennium Square No 68, Jalan Batai Laut 4 Taman Intan, 41300, Klang, Selangor, Malaysia
Tel.: (60) 333413372
Port Operation Services
N.A.I.C.S.: 488310
Maria Omar *(Sr Mgr-Documentation)*

Gemadept Dung Quat International Port J.S.C. (1)
Binh Thuan commune, Binh Soon, Quang Ngai, Vietnam
Tel.: (84) 2553618660
Web Site: https://dqp.gemadept.com.vn
Port Operation Services
N.A.I.C.S.: 488310

Nam Dinh Vu Port Joint Stock Company (1)
Lot CA1 Nam Dinh Vu Industrial Park, Dong Hai 2 Ward Hai An Dist, Haiphong, Vietnam
Tel.: (84) 2253266468
Web Site: https://ndv.gemadept.com.vn
Port Operation Services
N.A.I.C.S.: 488310

Nam Hai Dinh Vu Port J.S.C. (1)
Km6 Dinh Vu St, Dong Hai 2 Ward Hai An Dist, Haiphong, Vietnam
Tel.: (84) 2253200069
Port Operation Services
N.A.I.C.S.: 488310

Nam Hai ICD Joint Stock Company (1)
Lot CN3, Industrial Park MP Dinh Vu Dong Hai 2 Ward Hai An Dist, Haiphong, Vietnam
Tel.: (84) 2258830955
Web Site: https://nhi.gemadept.com.vn
Port Operation Services
N.A.I.C.S.: 488310

Phuoc Long Port Co., Ltd. (1)
Km7 Ha Noi highway, Phuoc Long A Ward Thu Duc city, Ho Chi Minh City, Vietnam
Tel.: (84) 2837313204
Web Site: https://pip.gemadept.com.vn
Port Operation Services
N.A.I.C.S.: 488310

GEMBALLA HOLDING SE
Vogtacker 10, 73272, Neidlingen, Germany
Tel.: (49) 70237444486
Web Site: http://www.gemballa-holding.de
Year Founded: 2010
Sports Cars Parts Mfr
N.A.I.C.S.: 336999

Subsidiaries:

Gemballa GmbH (1)
Hertichstr 59, 71229, Leonberg, Germany
Tel.: (49) 71 52 97 99 00
Web Site: http://www.gemballa.com
Car Tuning Services
N.A.I.C.S.: 811198
Steffen Korbach *(CEO & Mng Dir)*

GEMCO CONSTRUCTION LTD.
19635 Telegraph Trail, Langley, V1M 3E6, BC, Canada
Tel.: (604) 888-4950
Web Site: https://www.gemco-construction.com
Year Founded: 1986
Rev.: $18,206,578
Emp.: 60
Road Construction Services
N.A.I.C.S.: 237310
Doug Bloomfield *(Pres & CFO)*

GEMCO ENGINEERS B.V.
Science Park Eindhoven 5053, 5692 EB, Son, Netherlands
Tel.: (31) 40 2643 607
Web Site: http://www.gemco.nl
Year Founded: 1978
Engineeering Services
N.A.I.C.S.: 541330
Daan van Heereveld *(Mgr-Ops)*

Subsidiaries:

KNIGHT WENDLING GmbH (1)
Arnheimer Str 118, 40489, Dusseldorf, Germany
Tel.: (49) 211770060
Engineeering Services
N.A.I.C.S.: 541330

GEMDALE CORPORATION
32/F Gemdale Center No 2007 Shennan Boulevard Gangxia Community, Futian Sub-district Futian District, Shenzhen, 518026, China
Tel.: (86) 75582039999 CN
Web Site: https://www.gemdale.com
Year Founded: 1988
600383—(SHG)
Rev.: $12,866,906,734
Assets: $61,533,669,484
Liabilities: $47,126,136,614
Net Worth: $14,407,532,870
Earnings: $1,593,045,406
Emp.: 19,445
Fiscal Year-end: 12/31/20
Real Estate Manangement Services
N.A.I.C.S.: 531390
Ke Ling *(Chm)*

Subsidiaries:

Gemdale Dongguan Company (1)
6/F Building C Shenghe Plaza Shenghe Road, Nancheng District, Dongguan, 523071, China
Tel.: (86) 769 88991111
Property Development Services
N.A.I.C.S.: 531390

Gemdale Properties and Investment Corporation Limited (1)
19/F Central Tower 28 Queen s Road Central, Central, China (Hong Kong) (39.78%)
Tel.: (852) 28262826
Web Site: http://www.gemdalepi.com
Rev.: $1,446,469,877
Assets: $12,072,533,382
Liabilities: $8,285,404,140
Net Worth: $3,787,129,242
Earnings: $330,429,715
Emp.: 3,300
Fiscal Year-end: 12/31/2022
Holding Company; Real Estate Investment & Property Development Services
N.A.I.C.S.: 551112
Chuanjun Wei *(CFO)*

Gemdale Shaoxing Company (1)
Attached Building of Building 1 Gemdale Zizai Tiandi, Intersection of Qunxian Road and Shuangting Road Keqiao District, Shaoxing, 312030, China
Tel.: (86) 5758 568 8510
Web Site: http://www.gemdale.com
Real Estate Development Services
N.A.I.C.S.: 531390

Gemdale USA Corporation (1)
680 E Colorado Blvd Ste 300, Pasadena, CA 91101
Tel.: (626) 381-9709
Web Site: https://gemdaleusa.com
Real Estate Investment Services
N.A.I.C.S.: 531390
Justin Saechee *(Mgr-Dev)*

GEMEENTE SINT-PIETERS-LEEUW
Pastorijstraat 21, 1600, Sint-Pieters-Leeuw, Belgium
Tel.: (32) 23712211
Web Site: http://www.sint-pieters-leeuw.be
Real Estate Investment Services
N.A.I.C.S.: 531210

Gemeente Sint-Pieters-Leeuw—(Continued)
Walter Vastiau *(Mng Dir)*

GEMFIELDS GROUP LIMITED
23 25 Le Pollet, Saint Peter Port, GY1 1WQ, Guernsey
Tel.: (44) 1481740520 GY
Web Site: http://www.pallinghurst.com
Year Founded: 2007
GME—(AIM)
Rev.: $341,106,000
Assets: $774,125,000
Liabilities: $193,028,000
Net Worth: $581,097,000
Earnings: $74,268,000
Emp.: 1,334
Fiscal Year-end: 12/31/22
Investment Management Service
N.A.I.C.S.: 523999
Arne H. Frandsen *(Founder)*

Subsidiaries:

Faberge (UK) Limited (1)
70 Pall Mall, St James's, London, SW1Y 5ES, United Kingdom
Tel.: (44) 2075183399
Colored Gemstone Distr
N.A.I.C.S.: 423940

Gemfields Limited (1)
1 Cathedral Piazza, London, SW1E 5BP, United Kingdom
Tel.: (44) 2075183400
Web Site: https://www.gemfields.com
Gemstone Mining, Processing & Sales
N.A.I.C.S.: 212311

Pallinghurst Advisors (Pty) Limited (1)
PO Box 12160, Die Boord, Stellenbosch, 7613, Western Cape, South Africa
Tel.: (27) 21 886 7294
Financial Advisory Services
N.A.I.C.S.: 523940

Pallinghurst Advisors LLP (1)
54 Jermyn Street, London, SW1Y 6LX, United Kingdom
Tel.: (44) 20 7518 3399
Web Site: http://www.pallinghurst.com
Emp.: 10
Investment Management Service
N.A.I.C.S.: 523999

GEMILANG INTERNATIONAL LIMITED
PTD 42326 Jalan Seelong Mukim Senai, Senai, 81400, Johor, Malaysia
Tel.: (60) 75996666 Ky
Web Site: http://www.gml.com.my
Year Founded: 2016
6163—(HKG)
Rev.: $14,265,000
Assets: $34,152,000
Liabilities: $20,403,000
Net Worth: $13,749,000
Earnings: ($2,787,000)
Emp.: 270
Fiscal Year-end: 10/31/23
Bus Body Mfr
N.A.I.C.S.: 336211
Sun Wah Wah Phang *(Co-Founder & Chm)*

GEMINA LABORATORIES LTD.
3600 Gilmore Way Suite 302, Burnaby, V5G 4R8, BC, Canada
Tel.: (604) 760-1997 BC
Web Site: https://www.geminalabs.com
Year Founded: 2017
GLAB—(CNSX)
Assets: $1,099,666
Liabilities: $2,296,671
Net Worth: ($1,197,005)
Earnings: ($3,939,280)
Emp.: 6
Fiscal Year-end: 01/31/24

Biotechnology Research & Development Services
N.A.I.C.S.: 541714
Brian Firth *(CEO)*

GEMINI AUTO INC.
3840 Upper James Street, Hamilton, L0R 1W0, ON, Canada
Tel.: (888) 232-0843
Web Site: http://www.geminiauto.ca
Year Founded: 1967
New & Used Car Dealers
N.A.I.C.S.: 441110
Cam Briggs *(Gen Mgr)*

GEMINI COMMUNICATION LTD.
1 Dr Ranga Road, Alwarpet, Chennai, 600 018, India
Tel.: (91) 44 2466 0570
Web Site: http://www.gcl.in
Rev.: $981,190
Assets: $6,376,224
Liabilities: $64,619,283
Net Worth: ($58,243,059)
Earnings: ($321,506)
Emp.: 1,900
Fiscal Year-end: 03/31/17
Networking & Security Services
N.A.I.C.S.: 541690
B. Sreekrishna *(Mng Dir)*

Subsidiaries:

Gemini Traze RFID Pvt. Ltd. (1)
1 Dr Ranga Rd, Alwarpet, Chennai, 600 018, Tamilnadu, India
Tel.: (91) 4424660570
Web Site: http://www.traze.in
Radio Frequency Equipment Mfr
N.A.I.C.S.: 334220

PointRed Telecom Pvt. Ltd. (1)
18 11B Roopena Agrahara Begur Hobli, Hosur Main Road Madiwala, Bengaluru, 560068, Karnataka, India
Tel.: (91) 8025724853
Web Site: http://www.pointredtech.com
Wireless Broadband Equipment Mfr
N.A.I.C.S.: 517112

Veeras Infotek Pvt Ltd. (1)
5C Kences Towers 1 Ramakrishna St, T Nagar, Chennai, 600017, Tamil Nadu, India
Tel.: (91) 4442210000
Web Site: http://www.veeras.com
Sales Range: $25-49.9 Million
Emp.: 150
Software Development Services
N.A.I.C.S.: 513210
Sudarsan Ranganathan *(CEO)*

GEMINI CORPORATION
Suite180 839 - 5th Avenue SW, Calgary, T2P 3C8, AB, Canada
Tel.: (403) 255-2006 AB
Year Founded: 1982
Sales Range: $75-99.9 Million
Engineering, Fabrication & Construction Services
N.A.I.C.S.: 541330

Subsidiaries:

Gemini Engineered Solutions LP (1)
101-117 Pembina Rd, Sherwood Park, T8H 0J4, AB, Canada
Tel.: (780) 428-2814
Sales Range: $25-49.9 Million
Emp.: 10
Construction Engineering Services
N.A.I.C.S.: 541330

Gemini Engineering Limited (1)
400-839 5 Avenue SW, Calgary, T2P 3C8, AB, Canada
Tel.: (403) 255-2006
Web Site: http://www.geminieng.ab.ca
Sales Range: $25-49.9 Million
Emp.: 100
Engineeering Services
N.A.I.C.S.: 541330
Lucy Hungle *(Mgr)*

Gemini Field Solutions LP (1)
180-839 5 Ave SW, Calgary, T2P 3C8, AB, Canada
Tel.: (403) 258-1971
Construction Engineering Services
N.A.I.C.S.: 541330

Kinetic Process Systems Ltd (1)
839 5th Ave SW Ste 400, Calgary, T2P 3C8, AB, Canada
Tel.: (403) 258-1971
Web Site: http://www.kinproj.ca
Sales Range: $25-49.9 Million
Emp.: 50
Civil Engineering
N.A.I.C.S.: 237990

Kinetic Projects Inc (1)
400 - 839 5th Ave SW, Calgary, T2P 3C8, AB, Canada
Tel.: (403) 258-1971
Web Site: http://www.gemini.com
Emp.: 70
Engineeering Services
N.A.I.C.S.: 541330
Ed Nieckar *(Mgr-Sls)*

GEMINI ENGI-FAB LIMITED
501 Palmspring Ctr Link Rd, Malad West, Mumbai, 400064, Maharashtra, India
Tel.: (91) 2228808822
Web Site: http://www.geminief.com
Year Founded: 1998
Sales Range: $1-9.9 Million
Emp.: 35
Metal Fabrication & Engineering Services
N.A.I.C.S.: 332999
Dalpatram J. Panchal *(Founder & Chm)*

GEMINI SEA FOOD PLC
House No 44 Road No 16 New 27 Old Dhanmondi, Dhaka, 1209, Bangladesh
Tel.: (880) 241020596
Web Site: https://www.geminiseafood.com
Year Founded: 1982
GEMINISEA—(DHA)
Rev.: $7,083,119
Assets: $8,032,527
Liabilities: $6,638,532
Net Worth: $1,393,995
Earnings: $861,427
Emp.: 76
Fiscal Year-end: 06/30/23
Seafood Whslr
N.A.I.C.S.: 424460
Ameenah Ahmed *(Chm)*

GEMOSCAN CANADA, INC.
601 Magnetic Drive Units 39-40, Toronto, M3J 3J2, ON, Canada
Tel.: (416) 650-1200 ON
Year Founded: 2003
GES—(TSXV)
Sales Range: $1-9.9 Million
Food Sensitivity & Dietary Management Solutions
N.A.I.C.S.: 621511
Brian Kalish *(Pres & CEO)*

GEMPORIA PARTNERSHIP LIMITED
Unit 2D Eagle Road Moons Moat, Redditch, B98 9HF, Worcs, United Kingdom
Tel.: (44) 3334000011
Web Site: http://www.gemporia.com
Year Founded: 2006
Jewelry Product Whslr
N.A.I.C.S.: 423940

GEMSTONE INVESTMENTS LIMITED
Office No A/301 Shubham Centre A Building CHS, Cardinal Gracious

Road Andheri East, Mumbai, 400093, India
Tel.: (91) 2265102060
Web Site: https://gemstoneltd.com
Year Founded: 1994
531137—(BOM)
Rev.: $278,566
Assets: $3,387,294
Liabilities: $163,943
Net Worth: $3,223,351
Earnings: $53,257
Emp.: 7
Fiscal Year-end: 03/31/21
Investment Banking Services
N.A.I.C.S.: 523150
Dhara Chandravadanbhai Brahmbhatt *(Mng Dir)*

GEMVAX & KAEL CO., LTD.
58 Techno 11-ro, Yuseong-gu, Daejeon, Korea (South)
Tel.: (82) 25446221
Web Site: https://www.gemvax.com
Year Founded: 1998
082270—(KRS)
Rev.: $58,141,757
Assets: $115,926,459
Liabilities: $12,879,165
Net Worth: $103,047,294
Earnings: ($15,036,076)
Emp.: 172
Fiscal Year-end: 12/31/22
Semiconductor Machinery Mfr
N.A.I.C.S.: 333242

Subsidiaries:

Samsung Pharm Healthcare Co., Ltd. (1)
177 Yeoksam ro Gangnam gu, Gangnam-gu, Seoul, 6247, Korea (South)
Tel.: (82) 234084603
Web Site: http://www.ssphc.com
Pharmaceuticals Product Mfr
N.A.I.C.S.: 325412
Minjun kwon *(CEO)*

GEMY PONTIVY
40 Rue Colbert, 56300, Pontivy, France
Tel.: (33) 230211373
Web Site: http://www.gemy-pontivy.fr
Rev.: $24,500,000
Emp.: 900
New & Used Car Dealers
N.A.I.C.S.: 441110
Pascal Gerard *(Pres)*

GEN-S POWER GROUP CO., LTD.
Room 306 R & D Building No 1 China Southeast Big Data Industrial Park, No 2 Hujiang Road Wenwusha Town Changle District, Fuzhou, 201103, Fujian, China
Tel.: (86) 3055403192
Web Site: http://www.yinxingdf.com
Year Founded: 1996
600753—(SHG)
Rev.: $259,395,908
Assets: $56,158,835
Liabilities: $11,105,780
Net Worth: $45,053,054
Earnings: $1,997,457
Fiscal Year-end: 12/31/22
Construction Materials Distr
N.A.I.C.S.: 423320
Zhao Chenchen *(Chm)*

GENBYTE TECHNOLOGY, INC.
Floor 1-6 Building 4 Huahong Xintong Industrial Park, Intersection of Genyu Road & Nanming Rd Yutang St Guangming District, Shenzhen, 518132, Guangdong, China
Tel.: (86) 75586267202
Web Site: https://www.genbytech.com

AND PRIVATE COMPANIES

Year Founded: 1999
003028—(SSE)
Rev.: $146,312,244
Assets: $252,725,616
Liabilities: $56,269,512
Net Worth: $196,456,104
Earnings: $23,953,644
Fiscal Year-end: 12/31/22
Home Appliance Mfr
N.A.I.C.S.: 334512
Zhijie Chen *(Founder & Chm)*

GENCAN CAPITAL, INC.
106 Avenue Road, Toronto, M5R 2H3, ON, Canada
Tel.: (416) 920-0500
GCA.X—(CNSX)
Assets: $78,957
Liabilities: $29,115
Net Worth: $49,842
Earnings: ($57,308)
Fiscal Year-end: 09/30/23
Solar Energy Equipment Installation Services
N.A.I.C.S.: 221114
Mark I. Litwin *(Pres & CEO)*

GENCELL LTD.
7 Hatnufa St, Petah Tikva, 4951025, Israel
Tel.: (972) 37261616
Web Site:
https://www.gencellenergy.com
Year Founded: 2011
GNCL—(TAE)
Rev.: $4,864,000
Assets: $55,454,000
Liabilities: $13,132,000
Net Worth: $42,322,000
Earnings: ($28,302,000)
Emp.: 150
Fiscal Year-end: 06/30/23
Fuel Cell Energy Product Mfr
N.A.I.C.S.: 334413
Rami Reshef *(CEO)*

GENCURIX, INC.
15F G-HIGHCITY 243 Digital-ro, Guro-gu, Seoul, 08394, Korea (South)
Tel.: (82) 226217038
Web Site: https://www.gencurix.com
Year Founded: 2011
229000—(KRS)
Rev.: $1,963,127
Assets: $28,562,056
Liabilities: $24,210,707
Net Worth: $4,351,350
Earnings: ($18,865,870)
Emp.: 77
Fiscal Year-end: 12/31/22
Medical Instrument Mfr
N.A.I.C.S.: 339112
Park Han Earl *(Fin Mgr)*

GENDAI AGENCY INC.
29 Fl Tokyo Opera City Bldg 3-20-2 Nishi-Shinjuku, Shinjuku-ku, Tokyo, 163-1429, Japan
Tel.: (81) 353089888
Web Site: https://www.gendai-a.co.jp
Year Founded: 1995
2411—(TKS)
Rev.: $49,039,590
Assets: $35,879,080
Liabilities: $8,877,230
Net Worth: $27,001,850
Earnings: $826,250
Emp.: 143
Fiscal Year-end: 03/31/24
Advertising Services
N.A.I.C.S.: 541810
Masataka Yamamoto *(CEO)*

Subsidiaries:

Julia Japan Co. ,Ltd. (1)
Tokyo Opera City Building 29F 3-20-2,
Nishi-Shinjuku Shinjuku-ku, Tokyo, 163-1429, Japan
Tel.: (81) 353585888
Web Site: http://www.juliajapan.co.jp
Video & Web Content Production Services
N.A.I.C.S.: 512110

Land Sapport Inc. (1)
Tokyo Opera City Building 29F 3-20-2,
Nishi-Shinjuku Shinjuku-ku, Tokyo, 163-1429, Japan
Tel.: (81) 353047888
Web Site: http://www.landsupport.co.jp
Real Estate Services
N.A.I.C.S.: 531390

U & U Inc. (1)
Sakuragaoka Hirai Building 3F 4-14,
Sakuragaoka-cho Shibuya-ku, Tokyo, 150-0031, Japan
Tel.: (81) 364169377
Web Site: http://www.uandu.co.jp
Advertising Services
N.A.I.C.S.: 541890

Zealnet Inc. (1)
6-1-8 Nishikawaguchi, Kawaguchi, 332-0021, Saitama, Japan
Tel.: (81) 484466855
Web Site: https://www.zealnet.jp
Advertising Services
N.A.I.C.S.: 541890

GENDIS INC.
1370 Sony Place, Winnipeg, R3T 1N5, MB, Canada
Tel.: (204) 474-5200   MB
Web Site: https://www.gendis.ca
Year Founded: 1962
Sales Range: $1-9.9 Million
Emp.: 4
Holding Company
N.A.I.C.S.: 551112
James E. Cohen *(Pres & CEO)*

Subsidiaries:

Gendis Realty, Inc. (1)
1370 Sony Place, Winnipeg, R3T 1N5, MB, Canada   **(100%)**
Tel.: (204) 474-5200
Web Site: http://www.gendis.ca
Sales Range: $50-74.9 Million
Emp.: 8
Real Estate Management & Development
N.A.I.C.S.: 531210
James Cohen *(CEO)*

GENDRON FORD
1275 Boul Langlois, Valleyfield, J6S 1C1, QC, Canada
Tel.: (450) 371-0711
Web Site:
http://prestigeford.connection.com
Rev.: $24,083,751
Emp.: 370
New & Used Car Dealers
N.A.I.C.S.: 441110
Richard Aitken *(Co-Owner)*

GENE BIO TECH CO., LTD.
166 Sinwonsa-ro, Gyeryong-myeon, Gongju, Chungcheongnam-do, Korea (South)
Tel.: (82) 418539961
Web Site:
http://www.genebiotech.co.kr
Year Founded: 2003
086060—(KRS)
Rev.: $63,475,774
Assets: $49,119,395
Liabilities: $14,047,519
Net Worth: $35,071,876
Earnings: $1,168,375
Emp.: 52
Fiscal Year-end: 12/31/22
Animal Feed & Drug Mfr
N.A.I.C.S.: 311119
Wontak Cho *(COO)*

GENEDRIVE PLC
4 Lombard Street, London, EC3V 9HD, United Kingdom
Tel.: (44) 2079338780
Web Site:
https://www.genedriveplc.com
GDR—(AIM)
Rev.: $74,508
Assets: $5,600,518
Liabilities: $3,067,246
Net Worth: $2,533,272
Earnings: ($6,395,270)
Emp.: 40
Fiscal Year-end: 06/30/23
Biotechnology Stem Cell Researcher & Developer
N.A.I.C.S.: 541714
David Budd *(CEO)*

Subsidiaries:

Epistem Limited (1)
48 Grafton St, Manchester, M13 9XX, Lancashire, United Kingdom
Tel.: (44) 1616067258
Web Site: http://www.epistem.co.uk
Sales Range: $25-49.9 Million
Emp.: 55
Biotechnology Research & Development Services
N.A.I.C.S.: 541714
Chris Potten *(Co-Founder)*

GENEFERM BIOTECHNOLOGY CO., LTD.
No 3 Dali 2nd Rd, Southern Taiwan Science Park Shanhua Dist, Taipei, 741014, Taiwan
Tel.: (886) 65109001
Web Site: https://www.geneferm.com
Year Founded: 1999
1796—(TPE)
Rev.: $19,821,874
Assets: $37,195,760
Liabilities: $11,220,367
Net Worth: $25,975,393
Earnings: $2,921,990
Fiscal Year-end: 12/31/22
Biotechnology Research & Development Services
N.A.I.C.S.: 541714
Wei-Min Jin *(Founder)*

GENEL ENERGY PLC
12 Castle Street, Saint Helier, JE2 3RT, Jersey
Tel.: (44) 1534630080
Web Site:
http://www.genelenergy.com
GEGYY—(OTCIQ)
Rev.: $432,700,000
Assets: $943,500,000
Liabilities: $415,700,000
Net Worth: $527,800,000
Earnings: ($7,300,000)
Fiscal Year-end: 12/31/22
Oil & Gas Exploration
N.A.I.C.S.: 211120
Andrew Benbow *(Head-Comm)*

Subsidiaries:

Genel Energy Yonetim Hizmetleri
Anonim Sirketi (1)
Via Tower Bestepeler Mahallesi Nergiz Sokak No 7/52, Sogutozu, Ankara, Turkiye
Tel.: (90) 312 218 84 00
Web Site: www.genelenergy.com
Oil & Gas Exploration Services
N.A.I.C.S.: 213112

GENEMATRIX INC.
8F B Korea Bio Park 700 Daewangpangyo-ro, Bundang-gu, Seongnam, 463-400, Gyeonggi, Korea (South)
Tel.: (82) 316282101
Web Site: https://www.genematrix.net
Year Founded: 2000
109820—(KRS)
Rev.: $8,601,505
Assets: $24,469,073
Liabilities: $5,918,643

GENERAL BANK OF GREECE S.A.

Net Worth: $18,550,430
Earnings: ($6,221,392)
Emp.: 60
Fiscal Year-end: 12/31/22
Diagnostic Equipment Mfr
N.A.I.C.S.: 334510
Soo-Ok Kim *(CEO)*

GENENTA SCIENCE S.P.A.
Via Olgettina 58, 20132, Milan, Italy
Tel.: (39) 0226434681   IT
Year Founded: 2014
GNTA—(NASDAQ)
Rev.: $333,750
Assets: $24,117,359
Liabilities: $2,066,575
Net Worth: $22,050,785
Earnings: ($12,567,942)
Emp.: 14
Fiscal Year-end: 12/31/23
Biotechnology Research & Development Services
N.A.I.C.S.: 541714
Pierluigi Paracchi *(CEO, Co-Founder & Vice Chm)*

GENER8 MEDIA CORP.
138 E 7th Ave, Vancouver, V5T 1M6, BC, Canada
Tel.: (604) 669-8885   BC
Web Site: http://www.gener8.com
Year Founded: 2011
Emp.: 100
Audio & Video Products & Software Applications
N.A.I.C.S.: 334310
Rory Armes *(CEO)*

GENERA AGRI CORP LIMITED
Flat No 302 3rd Floor Metropole Apartment, Plot No 5&6 Silicon Valley Madhapur, Hyderabad, 500081, India
Tel.: (91) 4042615533   In
Web Site: http://www.genera.in
Year Founded: 1992
541999—(BOM)
Rev.: $868,601
Assets: $3,582,066
Liabilities: $1,950,204
Net Worth: $1,631,862
Earnings: $8,378
Emp.: 6
Fiscal Year-end: 03/31/21
Agricultural Services
N.A.I.C.S.: 115112
Rajesh Naidu Munirathnam *(Mng Dir)*

GENERA BIOSYSTEMS LIMITED
Small Technologies Cluster Caribbean Business Park 1 Dalmore Drive, Scoresby, 3179, VIC, Australia
Tel.: (61) 397631287
Web Site:
http://www.generabiosystems.com
Year Founded: 2001
Rev.: $693,917
Assets: $2,900,992
Liabilities: $7,827,347
Net Worth: ($4,926,355)
Earnings: ($3,497,529)
Fiscal Year-end: 06/30/18
DNA Analysis Technologies for Molecular Diagnostic Testing Products
N.A.I.C.S.: 339112
Richard Hannebery *(CEO)*

GENERAL BANK OF GREECE S.A.
109-111 Mesogeion Ave, 10911, Athens, Greece
Tel.: (30) 210 6975000   GR
Web Site: http://www.geniki.gr
Year Founded: 1937
TGEN—(ATH)
Sales Range: $250-299.9 Million

2917

GENERAL BANK OF GREECE S.A.

General Bank of Greece S.A.—(Continued)
Emp.: 1,521
All Other Banking Services
N.A.I.C.S.: 522110
Nikolaos V. Karamouzis (CEO)

GENERAL BIOLOGICALS CORPORATION
Science Based Park No. 6, Innovation First Road, Hsinchu, 30076, Taiwan
Tel.: (886) 35779221
Web Site: http://www.gbc.com.tw
Year Founded: 1984
Pharmaceutical & Diagnostic Products Mfr
N.A.I.C.S.: 325412
TC Lin (Chm & CEO)

Subsidiaries:

Pacgen Life Science Corporation (1)
Suite 1500-701 West Georgia St, Vancouver, V7Y 1C6, BC, Canada (23%)
Tel.: (604) 436-4388
Web Site: http://www.pacgenlife.com
Rev.: $337,432
Assets: $474,385
Liabilities: $189,097
Net Worth: $285,287
Earnings: ($301,995)
Fiscal Year-end: 03/31/2019
Pharmaceuticals Product Mfr
N.A.I.C.S.: 325412
Andrea Chan (CFO-Interim & Dir-Fin & Admin)

GENERAL CERAMICS LTD.
Fourth Industry Road, Sharjah, United Arab Emirates
Tel.: (971) 65582455
Web Site: http://www.generalceramics.ae
Year Founded: 1978
Sales Range: $25-49.9 Million
Emp.: 150
Ceramic Products & Sanitary Ware Mfr
N.A.I.C.S.: 327110
Mahmoud Khairallah (Mng Dir)

GENERAL COMMERCIAL & INDUSTRIAL SA
18th km Athens-Korinth National Road, Corinth, 19 300, Aspropyrgos, Greece
Tel.: (30) 2105514600
Web Site: https://www.geb.gr
Year Founded: 1974
GEBKA—(ATH)
Rev.: $54,114,186
Assets: $41,983,219
Liabilities: $9,304,042
Net Worth: $32,679,177
Earnings: $3,804,959
Emp.: 87
Fiscal Year-end: 12/31/23
Industrial & Hydraulic Equipment Whslr
N.A.I.C.S.: 423830
Kremydas K. Georgios (VP)

Subsidiaries:

General Commercial Northern Greece S.A. (1)
A 13 - O T 33B - C Phase T Th 1354, 57 022, Sindos, Thessaloniki, Greece
Tel.: (30) 2310 707059
Web Site: http://ww.geve.gr
Industrial Equipment & Pipe Distr
N.A.I.C.S.: 423830

GENERAL COMPANY FOR CERAMIC & PORCELAIN PRODUCTS
Sharekat El Petrol St, Al-Qalyubia, Egypt
Tel.: (20) 222503988
Web Site: http://www.sheeni-egypt.com
Year Founded: 1995
Ceramic Products Mfr
N.A.I.C.S.: 327110
Abdul Samea El Sayid Badr (Chm & Mng Dir)

GENERAL DE ALQUILER DE MAQUINARIA, S.A.
Pol Ind Espiritu Santo Calle Dinamarca 19 - 2, 33010, Oviedo, Spain
Tel.: (34) 985732273
Web Site: https://gamrentals.com
GAM—(MAD)
Rev.: $301,475,955
Assets: $576,668,098
Liabilities: $465,004,294
Net Worth: $111,663,804
Earnings: $9,708,029
Emp.: 1,809
Fiscal Year-end: 12/31/23
Industrial Equipment Rental Services
N.A.I.C.S.: 532490
Pedro Luis Fernandez Perez (Chm & CEO)

GENERAL ELEVATOR CO., LTD.
Qidu Development Zone, Wujiang, Suzhou, 215200, Jiangsu, China
Tel.: (86) 51263816851
Web Site: https://www.sge-elevator.com
Year Founded: 2003
300931—(SSE)
Rev.: $59,933,952
Assets: $150,240,636
Liabilities: $52,825,500
Net Worth: $97,415,136
Earnings: ($11,202,516)
Emp.: 500
Fiscal Year-end: 12/31/22
Escalator Mfr & Distr
N.A.I.C.S.: 333921
Zhiming Xu (Chm & Gen Mgr)

GENERAL ENGINEERING PUBLIC COMPANY LIMITED
44/2 Moo 2 Tivanont Road Bangkadi, Muang Pathumthani, Pathumthani, 12000, Thailand
Tel.: (66) 25011055
Web Site: https://www.gel.co.th
Year Founded: 1962
GEL—(THA)
Rev.: $120,885,950
Assets: $307,634,361
Liabilities: $185,077,595
Net Worth: $122,556,766
Earnings: ($12,065,873)
Emp.: 536
Fiscal Year-end: 12/31/23
Civil Engineering Services
N.A.I.C.S.: 237990
Borwornsak Uwanno (Chm)

Subsidiaries:

General Engineering Mauritius Limited (1)
10th Floor Standard Chartered Tower 19 Cybercity, Ebene, Mauritius
Tel.: (230) 4046000
Investment Services
N.A.I.C.S.: 523999

General Nippon Concrete Industries Limited (1)
99/9 Moo 4, Chaingraknoi Samkok, Pathumthani, 12160, Thailand
Tel.: (66) 5 518 5677
Web Site: https://www.genci.co.th
Concrete Pile Mfr
N.A.I.C.S.: 327390

Seven Wire Co., Ltd. (1)
99/9 Moo 1 Banlang-Natakwan rd, Banlang Muang, Rayong, 21000, Thailand
Tel.: (66) 3 862 2299
Web Site: https://www.7wire.co.th
Electronic Wire & Strand Mfr & Distr
N.A.I.C.S.: 332618

GENERAL ENVIRONMENTAL CONSERVATION PUBLIC COMPANY LIMITED
447 Bondstreet Road Bangpood Parkkred, Nonthaburi, 11120, Thailand
Tel.: (66) 25020900
Web Site: http://www.genco.co.th
Year Founded: 1994
GENCO—(THA)
Rev.: $8,373,717
Assets: $40,878,683
Liabilities: $5,256,598
Net Worth: $35,622,085
Earnings: ($2,581,154)
Emp.: 100
Fiscal Year-end: 12/31/23
Waste Management Services
N.A.I.C.S.: 562998
Kobchai Sungsitthisawad (Chm)

Subsidiaries:

General Environmental Conservation Public Company Limited - Map Ta-Phut Waste Treatment Facility (1)
5 Muangmai Map Ta Phut Line 6 Road, Muang Rayong, Rayong, 21150, Thailand
Tel.: (66) 38 607680
Industrial Waste Disposal Services
N.A.I.C.S.: 562211

General Environmental Conservation Public Company Limited - Samaedum Waste Treatment Facility (1)
68/39 Moo 3 Samaedum Road Samaedum, Bangkhuntien, Bangkok, 10150, Thailand
Tel.: (66) 2452 8310
Industrial Waste Disposal Services
N.A.I.C.S.: 562211

GENERAL HEALTHCARE GROUP LTD
1st Floor 30 Cannon Street, London, EC4M 6XH, England, United Kingdom
Tel.: (44) 20 7009 4500   UK
Year Founded: 2000
Healthcare Services
N.A.I.C.S.: 622110

GENERAL HOTEL MANAGEMENT LTD.
32 Gilstead Road, Singapore, 309075, Singapore
Tel.: (65) 6223 3755
Web Site: http://www.ghmhotels.com
Year Founded: 1992
Sales Range: $10-24.9 Million
Emp.: 16
Hotel Management
N.A.I.C.S.: 721110
Hans R. Jenni (Founder)

GENERAL INSURANCE COMPANY (SUDAN) LIMITED
Al Mak Nemer Road, Khartoum, Sudan
Tel.: (249) 83 780618
Year Founded: 1961
GICS—(KHAR)
Sales Range: Less than $1 Million
Insurance Services
N.A.I.C.S.: 524298
Hasan Ibrahim Malek (Chm)

GENERAL INSURANCE CORPORATION OF INDIA
Suraksha 170 Jamshedji Tata Road Churchgate, Mumbai, 400 020, India
Tel.: (91) 2222867000   In
Web Site: http://www.gicofindia.com
Year Founded: 1972

INTERNATIONAL PUBLIC

540755—(BOM)
Rev.: $1,014,826,785
Assets: $8,089,456,016
Liabilities: $3,761,658,270
Net Worth: $4,327,797,746
Earnings: $788,580,433
Emp.: 443
Fiscal Year-end: 03/31/23
Risk Managemeng Srvices
N.A.I.C.S.: 524126
Madhulika Bhaskar (Gen Mgr)

Subsidiaries:

GIC Re South Africa Ltd. (1)
Riviera Rd Office Park First Floor - Block C, 6-9 Riviera Road, Houghton, Johannesburg, 2193, South Africa
Tel.: (27) 118770760
Web Site: http://www.gicresa.co.za
Motor Insurance Services
N.A.I.C.S.: 524210

GENERAL INTERFACE SOLUTION (GIS) HOLDING LTD.
8F No 12 Kezhong Road, Zhunan Township, Miao-li, 35053, Taiwan
Tel.: (886) 37777939
Web Site: https://www.gis-touch.com
6456—(TAI)
Rev.: $3,922,751,493
Assets: $2,847,496,076
Liabilities: $1,791,313,479
Net Worth: $1,056,182,597
Earnings: $105,234,781
Emp.: 9,547
Fiscal Year-end: 12/31/22
Touch Screen Mfr
N.A.I.C.S.: 334419
Hsien-Ying Chou (Chm & Pres)

Subsidiaries:

Interface Optoelectroncis (Shenzhen) Co., Ltd. (1)
No 2 2nd Donghuan Road, Longhua, Shenzhen, Guangdong, China
Tel.: (86) 7552 770 6888
Flat Panel Display Mfr & Distr
N.A.I.C.S.: 334419
Chien-Wei Lee (Supvr)

Interface Optoelectroncis (Wuxi) Co., Ltd. (1)
No 75 Xinmei Road, Xinwu District, Wuxi, Jiangsu, China
Tel.: (86) 5108 116 3888
Flat Panel Display Mfr & Distr
N.A.I.C.S.: 334419
Wen-Hua Yang (Supvr)

Interface Optoelectronics (ShenZhen) Co., Ltd. (1)
No 2 2nd Donghuan Road, Longhua, Shenzhen, 518109, Guangdong, China
Tel.: (86) 75527706888
Touch Screen Equipment Mfr & Distr
N.A.I.C.S.: 334419

Interface Optoelectronics (Wuxi) Co., Ltd. (1)
No 75 Xinmei Road, Xinwu District, Wuxi, Jiangsu, China
Tel.: (86) 51081163888
Touch Screen Equipment Mfr & Distr
N.A.I.C.S.: 334419

Interface Technology (ChengDu) Co., Ltd. (1)
No 689 Hezuo Road Gaoxin West Zone, Chengdu, Sichuan, China
Tel.: (86) 2868828888
Flat Panel Display Mfr & Distr
N.A.I.C.S.: 334118

Radiant Elite Investments Limited (1)
Vistra Corporate Services Centre Ground Floor NPF Building Beach Road, Apia, Samoa (Western)
Tel.: (685) 37777939
Touch & Display Mfr
N.A.I.C.S.: 334419

Reco Biotek Co., Ltd. (1)
2F No 159 Youying St, Miaoli County,

AND PRIVATE COMPANIES

Toufen, Taiwan
Tel.: (886) 3 777 7939
Fingerprint Recognition Product Mfr & Distr
N.A.I.C.S.: 334419

Reco Technology (BVI) Limited (1)
Vistra Corporate Services Centre Wickhams
Cay II, Road Town, Tortola, Virgin Islands
(British)
Tel.: (284) 88637777939
Fingerprint Recognition Distr
N.A.I.C.S.: 423440

**Reco Technology (Chengdu) Co.,
Ltd.** (1)
4F Building N9 No 689 Hezuo Road,
Gaoxin West Zone, Chengdu, Sichuan,
China
Tel.: (86) 286 882 8888
Flat Panel Display Mfr & Distr
N.A.I.C.S.: 334419

**Reco Technology Hong Kong
Limited** (1)
Suite 1222 12/F Leighton Ctr 77 Leighton
Rd, Causeway Bay, China (Hong Kong)
Tel.: (852) 37777939
Fingerprint Recognition Product Distr
N.A.I.C.S.: 449210

GENERAL INVESTMENT CO., LTD.
188 Zahran Street, PO Box 312, Amman, 11118, Jordan
Tel.: (962) 62003344
Web Site: https://giojo.net
Year Founded: 1955
GENI—(AMM)
Rev.: $12,757,498
Assets: $35,798,932
Liabilities: $5,158,385
Net Worth: $30,640,547
Earnings: $1,775,861
Emp.: 130
Fiscal Year-end: 12/31/20
Alcoholic Beverage Mfr & Distr
N.A.I.C.S.: 312120

GENERAL MATERIALS BIO-CHEMISTRY FERTILIZER JOINT STOCK COMPANY
Group 5 Pham Van Coi commune,
Cu Chi Dist, Ho Chi Minh City, Vietnam
Tel.: (84) 8 7990170
Year Founded: 2007
Sales Range: $25-49.9 Million
Emp.: 290
Fertilizer Mfr & Whslr
N.A.I.C.S.: 325311
Huynh Nghia (Chm)

GENERAL MILLS DE VENEZUELA, C.A.
Av La Paragua CC La Piramide
Planta Alta Oficina 18, Prados del
Este, Caracas, 1080, Venezuela
Tel.: (58) 2129073511
Web Site:
http://www.generalmills.com.ve
Food Products Mfr
N.A.I.C.S.: 311999

GENERAL MINING
Daheiat Al-Rabeiah, PO Box 922075,
Amman, 11192, Jordan
Tel.: (962) 65537163
Web Site: http://www.minco-jo.com
Year Founded: 1973
GENM—(AMM)
Sales Range: Less than $1 Million
Emp.: 7
Industrial Rock Minerals Mining
N.A.I.C.S.: 212390

GENERAL NICE DEVELOPMENT LIMITED
7th Floor Lippo Leighton Tower, 103
Leighton Road, Causeway Bay,
China (Hong Kong)
Tel.: (852) 2808 2878 HK
Web Site:
http://www.generalnicegroup.com
Holding Company
N.A.I.C.S.: 551112
Cai Suixin (Chm & Exec Dir)

Subsidiaries:

Palabora Mining Co. Ltd. (1)
1 Copper Road, Phalaborwa, 1389, South
Africa (14.9%)
Tel.: (27) 15 780 2911
Web Site: http://www.palabora.com
Sales Range: $1-4.9 Billion
Emp.: 1,800
Copper Mining
N.A.I.C.S.: 212230
Jinghua Han (Chm & CEO)

Subsidiary (Non-US):

Palabora Asia Pte Limited (2)
101 Thomson Rd, 21 04 United Sq, Singapore, 307591, Singapore
Tel.: (65) 62514744
Web Site: http://www.palabora.com
Sales Range: $25-49.9 Million
Emp.: 9
Metal Whslr
N.A.I.C.S.: 423510

Palabora Europe Limited (2)
3000 Cathedral Hil, Guildford, GU2 7YB,
Surrey, United Kingdom
Tel.: (44) 1483 246636
Web Site: http://www.palabora.com
Sales Range: $25-49.9 Million
Emp.: 5
Metal Whslr
N.A.I.C.S.: 423510
Richard Knight (Bus Mgr)

Subsidiary (US):

Palabora US (2)
1000 Cobb Pl Ste 100, Kennesaw, GA
30144
Tel.: (770) 590-7970
Web Site: http://www.palabora.us
Sales Range: $25-49.9 Million
Emp.: 5
Ore Mining
N.A.I.C.S.: 423520
Sandra Delarm (Gen Mgr)

GENERAL OCEANS AS
4th Floor, 78 Duke Street Mayfair,
London, W1K 6JQ, United Kingdom
Tel.: (44) 0792004764
Web Site:
https://www.generaloceans.com
Year Founded: 2021
Emp.: 300
Sensors & Underwater Robotic Vehicles Mfg.
N.A.I.C.S.: 334511
Atle Lohrmann (Pres)

Subsidiaries:

Klein Marine Systems, Inc. (1)
11 Klein Dr, Salem, NH 03079
Tel.: (603) 893-6131
Web Site:
http://www.kleinmarinesystems.com
Sonar Equipment Mfr & Whslr
N.A.I.C.S.: 334511

GENERAL OYSTER, INC.
7F JRE Kayabacho 2-chome Building
2-13-13 Nihonbashi Kayabacho,
Chuo-ku, Tokyo, 103-0025, Japan
Tel.: (81) 366676606
Web Site: https://www.oysterbar.co.jp
Year Founded: 2000
3224—(TKS)
Rev.: $25,051,900
Assets: $14,773,350
Liabilities: $8,764,860
Net Worth: $6,008,490
Earnings: ($627,950)
Emp.: 90
Fiscal Year-end: 03/31/24
Seafood Sales
N.A.I.C.S.: 424460
Hidenori Yoshida (Founder & Pres)

GENERAL PACKER CO., LTD.
65 Shinmei Ubukuji, Kitanagoya, 481-8601, Aichi, Japan
Tel.: (81) 568233111
Web Site: https://www.general-packer.co.jp
Year Founded: 1966
6267—(TKS)
Rev.: $61,285,660
Assets: $74,024,220
Liabilities: $31,255,500
Net Worth: $42,768,720
Earnings: $4,484,620
Emp.: 208
Fiscal Year-end: 07/31/24
Machinery Products Mfr
N.A.I.C.S.: 333998
Koutarou Ozeki (VP)

Subsidiaries:

**General Packer America
Corporation** (1)
2701 Larsen Rd, Green Bay, WI 54313
Tel.: (920) 843-6244
Web Site: https://generalpackeramerica.com
Packaging Machinery Mfr & Distr
N.A.I.C.S.: 333993

General Packer China Co., Ltd. (1)
No 7 Sicheng Road, Zhitang Town Changshu, Suzhou, 215531, China
Tel.: (86) 51283861201
Web Site: https://www.general-packer.cn
Packaging Machinery Mfr
N.A.I.C.S.: 333993

Osa Machinery Co., Ltd. (1)
1-2-19 Kamiyama, Midori-ku, Yokohama, 226-0012, Kanagawa, Japan
Tel.: (81) 45 931 7231
Web Site: https://www.osa3.co.jp
Confectionary Production Machinery Mfr
N.A.I.C.S.: 333241
Kanshige Suzuki (Pres)

GENERAL PLASTIC INDUSTRIAL CO., LTD.
50 Tzu-Chiang Rd, Wu-Chi Dist, Taichung, 43547, Taiwan
Tel.: (886) 426393103 TW
Web Site: https://www.gpi.com.tw
Year Founded: 1978
6128—(TAI)
Rev.: $173,796,619
Assets: $268,868,037
Liabilities: $133,104,380
Net Worth: $135,763,656
Earnings: $14,167,631
Fiscal Year-end: 12/31/23
Toner Cartridges Mfr
N.A.I.C.S.: 325992
Jerry Wang (Pres)

Subsidiaries:

Katun Corporation (1)
10951 Bush Lk Rd, Minneapolis, MN
55438-2391
Tel.: (952) 941-9505
Web Site: http://www.katun.com
Copier, Printer & Fax Machine Ink, Replacement Part & Accessory Whslr
N.A.I.C.S.: 423420
William McIntyre (Chief Admin Officer & Gen Counsel)

Subsidiary (Non-US):

Katun Argentina S.R.L. (2)
Esmeralda 950 piso 7 oficina 116, Buenos
Aires, CP 1007, Argentina
Tel.: (54) 11 5365 7733
Web Site: http://www.katun.com
Copier, Printer & Fax Machine Ink, Replacement Part & Accessory Whslr
N.A.I.C.S.: 423420

Katun Benelux B.V. (2)
Edisonweg 44, 4207 HG, Gorinchem, Netherlands
Tel.: (31) 183 696945
Web Site: http://www.katun.com
Copier, Printer & Fax Machine Ink, Replacement Part & Accessory Whslr
N.A.I.C.S.: 423420

Katun Brasil Comercio De Suprimentos Pecas E Equipamentos Ltda. (2)
Ed Business Space Tower Av Ermano Marchetti 1435 4 Andar, Agua Branca, Sao
Paulo, 05038-001, Brazil
Tel.: (55) 1136473270
Web Site: http://www.katun.com
Copier, Printer & Fax Machine Ink, Replacement Part & Accessory Whslr
N.A.I.C.S.: 423420

Katun France S.A.R.L. (2)
14 A Rue Jules Saulnier Parc Le Colombier,
93207, Saint Denis, Cedex, France
Tel.: (33) 149715454
Web Site: http://www.katun.com
Copier, Printer & Fax Machine Ink, Replacement Part & Accessory Whslr
N.A.I.C.S.: 423420

Katun Germany GmbH (2)
Forumstrasse 24 Forum III, 41468, Neuss,
Germany
Tel.: (49) 213134460
Web Site: http://www.katun.com
Copier, Printer & Fax Machine Ink, Replacement Part & Accessory Whslr
N.A.I.C.S.: 423420
Thomas Wolf (Sls Dir-Central Asia & Middle East)

Katun Italy s.r.l. (2)
Franchini Via Riccardo Lombardi 19/18,
20153, Milan, Italy
Tel.: (39) 024149971
Web Site: http://www.katun.com
Copier, Printer & Fax Machine Ink, Replacement Part & Accessory Whslr
N.A.I.C.S.: 423420

Katun Portugal S.A. (2)
Rua Sargento Ajudante Manuel Antonio No
7 A-B, Reboleira, 2720-356, Amadora, Portugal
Tel.: (351) 214998960
Web Site: http://www.katun.com
Copier, Printer & Fax Machine Ink, Replacement Part & Accessory Whslr
N.A.I.C.S.: 423420

Katun Spain S.A. (2)
Calle Tropico 6 Local 2 Edificio Atisa, Torrejon de Ardoz, 28850, Madrid, Torrejon De
Ardo, Spain
Tel.: (34) 916764551
Web Site: http://www.katun.com
Copier, Printer & Fax Machine Ink, Replacement Part & Accessory Whslr
N.A.I.C.S.: 423420

Katun U.K. Ltd. (2)
4A Vulcan House Calleva Park, Aldermaston, Basingstoke, RG7 8PD, Hants, United
Kingdom
Web Site: http://www.katun.com
Copier, Printer & Fax Machine Ink, Replacement Part & Accessory Whslr
N.A.I.C.S.: 423420

**PNA Holdings Mexico S.A. de
C.V.** (2)
Circuito Aguascalientes No 137, Parque
Industrial del Valle de Aguacalientes, San
Francisco de los Romo, Aguascalientes,
20300, Mexico
Tel.: (52) 4499227100
Web Site: http://www.katun.com
Copier, Printer & Fax Machine Ink, Replacement Part & Accessory Whslr
N.A.I.C.S.: 423420

GENERAL SHOPPING E OUTLETS DO BRASIL S.A.
Av Angelica 2466 22nd Floor Conj
221 Cerqueira Cesar, 01228-200,
Sao Paulo, Brazil
Tel.: (55) 1131595100
Web Site:
http://www.generalshopping.com.br

GENERAL SHOPPING E OUTLETS DO BRASIL S.A.

General Shopping e Outlets do Brasil S.A.—(Continued)
GSHP3—(BRAZ)
Rev.: $30,733,872
Assets: $298,493,768
Liabilities: $460,386,878
Net Worth: ($161,893,110)
Earnings: ($17,304,218)
Emp.: 184
Fiscal Year-end: 12/31/22
Shopping Facilities Developer & Operator
N.A.I.C.S.: 236220
Alessandro Poli Veronezi *(Chm)*

GENERAL STEEL HOLDINGS, INC.
Room 803 Tower1 Building B Wangjing, Chaoyang District, Beijing, 100102, China
Tel.: (86) 1064709625   NV
Web Site: http://www.gshi-steel.com
Year Founded: 2002
GSIH—(OTCEM)
Sales Range: Less than $1 Million
Emp.: 5
Iron & Steel Production Services
N.A.I.C.S.: 331110
Baoning Shi *(Chm & CEO)*

Subsidiaries:

Maoming Hengda Steel Co., Ltd. (1)
Tianlun Mansion 45 Tianhe Road, Maoming, 510060, Guangdong, China   (99%)
Tel.: (86) 20 3830 2222
High-Speed Wire & Rebar Products Mfr
N.A.I.C.S.: 331222

Shaanxi Longmen Iron and Steel Co., Ltd. (1)
Longmen County, Hancheng, Shaanxi, China   (60%)
Tel.: (86) 9135182222
Web Site: http://www.gshi-steel.com
Sales Range: $1-4.9 Billion
Iron & Steel Production Services
N.A.I.C.S.: 331110

GENERAL TRANSPORT SA
Bd Preciziei Nr 38 S6, Bucharest, Romania
Tel.: (40) 21 312 55 92
Sales Range: Less than $1 Million
Food Transportation Services
N.A.I.C.S.: 485999

GENERAL, MECHANICAL & CIVIL CONTRACTORS LTD.
3000-84th Ave, Edmonton, T6P 1K3, AB, Canada
Tel.: (780) 466-7867   AB
Web Site: https://www.gmc.ab.ca
Year Founded: 1993
Heavy & Civil Engineering Construction
N.A.I.C.S.: 237120
Allen Cabalo *(Gen Mgr)*

GENERALCOM SA
39-41 Etaj 3 BIROURILE 2-6, Bucharest, Romania
Tel.: (40) 21 312 93 70
Sales Range: $1-9.9 Million
Emp.: 9
Real Estate Prorperty Leasing Services
N.A.I.C.S.: 531190

GENERALFINANCE S.P.A.
Via Giorgio Stephenson N 43a, 20157, Milan, Italy
Tel.: (39) 0287158048
Web Site: https://www.generalfinance.it
Year Founded: 1982
GF—(ITA)
Rev.: $36,852,785
Assets: $448,637,865
Liabilities: $409,375,771
Net Worth: $39,262,094
Earnings: $11,611,000
Emp.: 55
Fiscal Year-end: 12/31/21
Investment Management Service
N.A.I.C.S.: 523999
Massimo Gianolli *(CEO)*

GENERALPLUS TECHNOLOGY INC.
No 19 Industry East Road IV Hsinchu Science Park, Hsin-chu, 30077, Taiwan
Tel.: (886) 36662118
Web Site: https://www.generalplus.com
Year Founded: 2004
4952—(TAI)
Rev.: $70,866,638
Assets: $91,363,449
Liabilities: $22,226,396
Net Worth: $69,137,052
Earnings: $5,493,476
Emp.: 293
Fiscal Year-end: 12/31/22
Integrated Circuits Mfr
N.A.I.C.S.: 334412
S. R. Wang *(Vice Chm & Co-Pres)*

Subsidiaries:

Generalplus Technology (H.K.) Co., Limited, (1)
Room 1307 Telford House 16 Wang Hoi Road Kowloon Bay, Kowloon, China (Hong Kong)
Tel.: (852) 2750 5788
Web Site: http://www.generalplus.com
Emp.: 10
Electronic Components Mfr
N.A.I.C.S.: 334419

Generalplus Technology (Shenzhen) Inc. (1)
Tel.: (86) 75526984688
Web Site: http://www.generalplus.com
Marketing Research Service
N.A.I.C.S.: 541910

GENERATION CAPITAL LTD.
12 Abba Eban Avenue Herzeliya, Tel Aviv, 4672530, Israel
Tel.: (972) 722758900   II
Web Site: https://generationcapital.co.il
GNRS—(TAE)
Rev.: $430,381
Assets: $499,963,905
Liabilities: $85,842,012
Net Worth: $414,121,893
Earnings: $79,513,614
Fiscal Year-end: 12/31/20
Support Activities for Oil & Gas Operations
N.A.I.C.S.: 213112
William Geoffrey Beattie *(Executives)*

GENERATION DEVELOPMENT GROUP
Level 17 447 Collins Street, Melbourne, 3000, VIC, Australia
Tel.: (61) 386012040   AU
Web Site: https://gendevelopmentgroup.com
Year Founded: 1991
GDG—(ASX)
Rev.: $217,919,337
Assets: $2,440,297,132
Liabilities: $2,299,149,296
Net Worth: $141,147,836
Earnings: ($133,232,505)
Fiscal Year-end: 06/30/24
Financial Investment Services
N.A.I.C.S.: 523999
Terence Wong *(CFO)*

Subsidiaries:

Ascalon Capital Managers Limited (1)

167 Phillip Street, Sydney, 2000, NSW, Australia
Tel.: (61) 280241156
Financial Fund Management Services
N.A.I.C.S.: 523940

GENERATION INVESTMENT MANAGEMENT LLP
20 Air Street, London, W1B 5AN, United Kingdom
Tel.: (44) 2075344700   UK
Web Site: http://www.generationim.com
Year Founded: 2004
Investment Management Service
N.A.I.C.S.: 523940
David Blood *(Co-Founder & Sr Partner)*

Subsidiaries:

FNZ Holdings Ltd (1)
1 Tanfield, Edinburgh, EH3 5DA, United Kingdom
Tel.: (44) 303 333 3330
Sales Range: $150-199.9 Million
Emp.: 220
Investment Management Service
N.A.I.C.S.: 523940

Subsidiary (Non-US):

Brand Addition GmbH (2)
Heydastrasse 13-15, 58093, Hagen, Germany
Tel.: (49) 233195970
Web Site: http://www.brandaddition.de
Sales Range: $10-24.9 Million
Emp.: 50
Marketing of Promotional Goods
N.A.I.C.S.: 459110
Adelfo Marino *(Mng Dir)*

Subsidiary (Domestic):

FNZ (UK) Ltd (2)
Suite 1 3rd Floor 11-12 St James's Square, London, SW1Y 4LB, United Kingdom
Tel.: (44) 131 473 1786
Web Site: http://www.fnz.com
Financial Related Software Services
N.A.I.C.S.: 541511
Adrian Durham *(CEO)*

Subsidiary (Non-US):

European Bank for Financial Services GmbH (3)
Bahnhofstrasse 20, Aschheim, 80218, Germany
Tel.: (49) 89 4 54 60890
Web Site: http://www.ebase.com
Financial Investment Services
N.A.I.C.S.: 523940
Rudolf Geyer *(Mng Dir)*

Fondsdepot Bank GmbH (3)
Windmuhlenweg 12, 95030, Hof, Germany
Tel.: (49) 928172580
Web Site: http://www.fondsdepotbank.de
Investment Account Administration Services
N.A.I.C.S.: 561499
Sabine Dittmann-Stenger *(COO)*

GENERATION NEXT FASHIONS LIMITED
Building No 348 Road No 05 DOHS Baridhara, Dhaka, 1206, Bangladesh
Tel.: (880) 28414302   BD
Web Site: https://www.gnf-bd.com
Year Founded: 2006
GENNEXT—(DHA)
Rev.: $54,378,016
Assets: $90,562,739
Liabilities: $17,039,688
Net Worth: $73,523,050
Earnings: $310,708
Emp.: 5,021
Fiscal Year-end: 06/30/23
Knit Fabric Mfr
N.A.I.C.S.: 313240
Tauhidul Islam Chaudhury *(Chm)*

GENERATION PASS CO., LTD.

INTERNATIONAL PUBLIC

Head Office 5F Nishi-Shinjuku Park West Building 6-12-1 Nishi-Shinjuku, Shinjuku-ku, Tokyo, 160-0023, Japan
Tel.: (81) 333433544
Web Site: https://www.genepa.com
Year Founded: 2002
3195—(TKS)
Rev.: $107,420,590
Assets: $31,316,530
Liabilities: $17,774,630
Net Worth: $13,541,900
Earnings: ($163,070)
Emp.: 127
Fiscal Year-end: 10/31/23
Ecommerce Services
N.A.I.C.S.: 513210
Hiroaki Okamoto *(Board of Directors & Pres)*

GENERATIVE AI SOLUTIONS CORP.
101-334 East Kent Avenue South, Vancouver, V5X 4N6, BC, Canada
Tel.: (406) 879-7632
Web Site: https://www.genai-solutions.com
Year Founded: 2018
AICOF—(OTCQB)
Software Development Services
N.A.I.C.S.: 541511
Paul Ciullo *(CFO)*

GENEREACH BIOTECHNOLOGY CORP.
No 19 Keyuan 2nd Rd, Xitun Dist, Taichung, 407, Taiwan
Tel.: (886) 424639869
Web Site: https://www.genereach.com
Year Founded: 2004
4171—(TPE)
Rev.: $23,496,576
Assets: $50,711,347
Liabilities: $16,234,437
Net Worth: $34,476,910
Earnings: $6,800,081
Fiscal Year-end: 12/31/22
Biotechnological Research & Development Services
N.A.I.C.S.: 541714
Cheng-Chung Liu *(Chm)*

GENERIC ENGINEERING CONSTRUCTION AND PROJECTS LIMITED
2nd Floor Fitwell House Opp 24 7 Hub Town LBS Road Vikhroli, Mumbai, 400 079, India
Tel.: (91) 67720671
Web Site: https://www.gecpl.com
Year Founded: 1994
GENCON—(NSE)
Rev.: $32,841,221
Assets: $46,230,670
Liabilities: $16,033,499
Net Worth: $30,197,170
Earnings: $1,835,765
Emp.: 26
Fiscal Year-end: 03/31/23
Financial Management Consulting Services
N.A.I.C.S.: 541611
Manish Ravilal Patel *(Mng Dir)*

GENERIC GOLD CORP.
217 Queen Street West Suite 401, Toronto, M5V 0R2, ON, Canada
Tel.: (647) 299-1153   Ca
Web Site: https://www.genericgold.ca
Year Founded: 2017
GGCPF—(OTCIQ)
Assets: $1,462,037
Liabilities: $179,630
Net Worth: $1,282,407
Earnings: ($1,199,163)
Fiscal Year-end: 12/31/22

AND PRIVATE COMPANIES / GENESIS RESEARCH & DEVELOPMENT CORPORATION LIMITED

Gold Exploration Services
N.A.I.C.S.: 212220
Richard Patricio *(Pres & CEO)*

GENERIX GROUP FRANCE SA
6 rue du Moulin de Lezennes, 59654, Villeneuve d'Ascq, France
Tel.: (33) 320414800
Web Site: http://www.generixgroup.com
GENX—(EUR)
Sales Range: $75-99.9 Million
Emp.: 600
Software Designer & Marketer
N.A.I.C.S.: 513210
Jean-Charles Deconninck *(CEO)*

GENERTEC UNIVERSAL MEDICAL GROUP COMPANY LIMITED
20th to 28th Floor No 90 Side Road of West Third of West Third, Ring Middle Road Xicheng District, Beijing, 100037, China
Tel.: (86) 1068998465   HK
Web Site: http://www.universalmsm.com
Year Founded: 1984
2666—(HKG)
Rev.: $1,672,464,456
Assets: $10,792,656,248
Liabilities: $8,026,353,223
Net Worth: $2,766,303,025
Earnings: $293,088,791
Emp.: 20,077
Fiscal Year-end: 12/31/22
Health Care Srvices
N.A.I.C.S.: 621610
Yichen Zhang *(Chm)*

GENERTECH PAKISTAN LIMITED
Office-1 First Floor K-1 Commercial Zone K-Block Model Town, Lahore, Pakistan
Tel.: (92) 42 5916650
Eletric Power Generation Services
N.A.I.C.S.: 221111

GENES TECH GROUP HOLDINGS COMPANY LIMITED
No 80 Baotai 3rd RD, Zhubei, 30244, Hsinchu, Taiwan
Tel.: (886) 36566228   Ky
Web Site: https://www.genestech.com
Year Founded: 2009
8257—(HKG)
Rev.: $43,586,348
Assets: $68,768,858
Liabilities: $42,423,590
Net Worth: $26,345,269
Earnings: $2,964,060
Emp.: 271
Fiscal Year-end: 12/31/23
Electronic Equipment Distr
N.A.I.C.S.: 423690
Ming-Hsiang Yang *(Chm)*

GENESEAS AQUACULTURA LTDA.
Av Dr CArdoso de Melo 1955, Itaim Bibi, CEP 04548-005, Sao Paulo, SP, Brazil
Tel.: (55) 1131232100
Web Site: http://geneseas.com.br
Year Founded: 2001
Aquaculture Farm & Product Mfr
N.A.I.C.S.: 112519
Roberto Haag *(CEO)*
Subsidiaries:
Tropical Aquaculture Products, Inc.   (1)
PO Box 6311, Rutland, VT 05702
Tel.: (802) 747-6311

Web Site: http://www.eattilapia.com
Sales Range: $1-9.9 Million
Emp.: 20
Tilapia Supplier
N.A.I.C.S.: 424460
Matthew Price *(Gen Mgr-Sls)*

GENESEM INC.
24 Songdogwahak-ro 84beon-gil, Yeonsu-gu, Incheon, Korea (South)
Tel.: (82) 328108400
Web Site: https://www.genesem.com
Year Founded: 2000
217190—(KRS)
Rev.: $45,715,454
Assets: $60,727,530
Liabilities: $29,894,606
Net Worth: $30,832,925
Earnings: $9,349,606
Emp.: 140
Fiscal Year-end: 12/31/22
Semiconductor & Related Device Mfr
N.A.I.C.S.: 334413
David Han *(Pres & CEO)*

GENESIS ACQUISITION CORP.
301-1665 Ellis Street, Kelowna, V1Y 2B3, BC, Canada
Tel.: (250) 317-0996
Year Founded: 2019
REBL.P—(TSXV)
Rev.: $3,405
Assets: $117,771
Liabilities: $6,100
Net Worth: $111,672
Earnings: ($35,439)
Fiscal Year-end: 05/31/24
Business Consulting Services
N.A.I.C.S.: 522299
Charles Blair Wilson *(Pres, CEO & CFO)*

GENESIS CAPITAL S.R.O.
Na Safrance 22, 101 00, Prague, Czech Republic
Tel.: (420) 271 740 207
Web Site: http://www.genesis.cz
Year Founded: 1999
Sales Range: $10-24.9 Million
Emp.: 8
Private Investment Firm
N.A.I.C.S.: 523999
Jan Tauber *(Mng Partner)*
Subsidiaries:
GTH catering a.s.   (1)
VyskoCilova 1481/4, 140 00, Prague, Czech Republic
Tel.: (420) 241004900
Web Site: http://www.gth.cz
Catering Services
N.A.I.C.S.: 722320
Daria Choderova *(Mng Dir)*

GENESIS ENERGY LIMITED
Level 6 155 Fanshawe Street, Wynyard Quarter, Auckland, 1010, New Zealand
Tel.: (64) 78387863
Web Site: https://www.genesisenergy.co.nz
GNE—(ASX)
Rev.: $1,419,976,077
Assets: $3,044,258,373
Liabilities: $1,605,263,158
Net Worth: $1,438,995,215
Earnings: $117,045,455
Emp.: 1,268
Fiscal Year-end: 06/30/23
Electric Power & Natural Gas Generation & Distribution
N.A.I.C.S.: 221118
Tracey Hickman *(Chief Customer Officer)*

GENESIS FINANCIAL HOLDINGS LIMITED

29 Samora Machel Avenue, Harare, Zimbabwe
Tel.: (263) 4703792
Web Site: http://www.genesisbank.co.zw
Sales Range: $25-49.9 Million
Emp.: 70
Financial Holding Company
N.A.I.C.S.: 551112
Subsidiaries:
Genesis Investment Bank Limited   (1)
29 Samora Machel Avenue, Harare, Zimbabwe
Tel.: (263) 4703792
Web Site: http://www.genesisbank.co.zw
Sales Range: $10-24.9 Million
Emp.: 104
Investment Banking Services
N.A.I.C.S.: 523150

GENESIS GROWTH TECH ACQUISITION CORP.
6 General-Guisan-Strasse, 6303, Zug, Switzerland
Tel.: (41) 786079901   Ky
Web Site: https://genesisgrowthtechspac.com
Year Founded: 2021
GGAA—(NASDAQ)
Rev.: $3,634,473
Assets: $264,369,467
Liabilities: $282,284,381
Net Worth: ($17,914,914)
Earnings: $337,873
Fiscal Year-end: 12/31/22
Investment Services
N.A.I.C.S.: 523999
Simon Baker *(COO, Co-Chm & Head)*

GENESIS IBRC INDIA LIMITED
D No 40 16 2 FS 2 Sri Purna Sai complex SDMSM College Road, Vijayawada, 520010, Labbipet, India
Tel.: (91) 7995573355   In
Web Site: https://www.genesisibrc.com
Year Founded: 1992
514336—(BOM)
Sales Range: Less than $1 Million
Pro-Biotic Products Mfr
N.A.I.C.S.: 926140
K. Ratnakara Rao *(Chm)*

GENESIS INVEST AG
Stockerstrasse 38, 8002, Zurich, Switzerland
Tel.: (41) 442082535
Web Site: http://www.genesis-invest.com
Emp.: 15
Environmental Products & Services
N.A.I.C.S.: 325414
Wolfgang Goese *(Chm & CEO)*

GENESIS LAND DEVELOPMENT CORP.
6240 333 - 96 Ave NE, Calgary, T3K 0S3, AB, Canada
Tel.: (403) 265-8079   AB
Web Site: https://www.genesisland.com
Year Founded: 1997
GDC—(TSX)
Rev.: $85,863,835
Assets: $254,185,458
Liabilities: $69,615,879
Net Worth: $184,569,579
Earnings: $8,589,434
Emp.: 71
Fiscal Year-end: 12/31/21
Planned Communities Land Developer
N.A.I.C.S.: 237210
Stephen J. Griggs *(Chm)*

Subsidiaries:
Generations Group of Companies Inc.   (1)
7315 8 St Ne Calgary, Calgary, T2E 8A2, AB, Canada
Tel.: (403) 769-1300
Property Management Services
N.A.I.C.S.: 531311

Genesis Builders Group Inc   (1)
7315 8 St NE, Calgary, T2A 8A2, AB, Canada
Tel.: (403) 265-9237
Web Site: http://www.genesisbuilders.com
Sales Range: $25-49.9 Million
Industrial Building Construction Services
N.A.I.C.S.: 236210

GENESIS MINERALS LIMITED
Level 7 40 The Esplanade, Perth, 6000, WA, Australia
Tel.: (61) 863239050
Web Site: https://www.genesisminerals.com.au
GMD—(ASX)
Rev.: $292,863,914
Assets: $807,310,360
Liabilities: $145,330,528
Net Worth: $661,979,832
Earnings: $55,307,826
Emp.: 331
Fiscal Year-end: 06/30/24
Mineral Exploration Services
N.A.I.C.S.: 213115
Michael Fowler *(CEO & Mng Dir)*
Subsidiaries:
Dacian Gold Limited   (1)
Alluvion Level 19 58 Mounts Bay Road, Perth, 6000, WA, Australia   (80.08%)
Tel.: (61) 863239000
Web Site: http://www.daciangold.com.au
Rev.: $171,369,886
Assets: $139,214,424
Liabilities: $54,933,524
Net Worth: $84,280,900
Earnings: ($152,037,380)
Emp.: 136
Fiscal Year-end: 06/30/2022
Gold Mining
N.A.I.C.S.: 212220
Kevin Hart *(Sec)*

Subsidiary (Domestic):
Redcliffe Project Pty Ltd   (2)
Level 19 58 Mounts Bay Road, Perth, 6000, WA, Australia
Tel.: (61) 0863239000
Rev.: $2,626
Assets: $6,628,276
Liabilities: $257,901
Net Worth: $6,370,375
Earnings: ($770,121)
Fiscal Year-end: 06/30/2019
Uranium & Other Metal Ore Exploration & Mining
N.A.I.C.S.: 213114

GENESIS PHOTONICS INC.
No 5 Dali 3rd Rd Taiwan Science Park, T'ainan, 741, Taiwan
Tel.: (886) 6 505 3500
Web Site: http://www.gpiled.com
3383—(TAI)
Rev.: $19,616,891
Assets: $105,854,755
Liabilities: $98,719,697
Net Worth: $7,135,057
Earnings: ($10,133,537)
Emp.: 965
Fiscal Year-end: 12/31/20
Light Emitting Diode Chip Mfr
N.A.I.C.S.: 334413

GENESIS RESEARCH & DEVELOPMENT CORPORATION LIMITED
Shortland Street, PO Box 50, Auckland, 1140, New Zealand
Tel.: (64) 93735600   NZ

GENESIS RESEARCH & DEVELOPMENT CORPORATION LIMITED

Genesis Research & Development Corporation Limited—(Continued)
Web Site: http://www.genesis.co.nz
Year Founded: 1994
Sales Range: Less than $1 Million
Genomics & Immunology Researcher & Developer
N.A.I.C.S.: 541715

GENESIS RESOURCES LTD.
Level 8 555 Bourke Street, Melbourne, 3000, VIC, Australia
Tel.: (61) 398529159
Web Site:
 https://www.genesisresources.com
Year Founded: 2005
GES—(ASX)
Rev.: $58
Assets: $16,721,444
Liabilities: $10,097,430
Net Worth: $6,624,014
Earnings: ($1,578,808)
Emp.: 17
Fiscal Year-end: 06/30/22
Manganese, Gold & Copper Exploration Services
N.A.I.C.S.: 212290
Eddie Lung Yiu Pang (Mng Dir & Chm)

GENESYS INDUSTRIES INC.
30 Forzani Way NW, Calgary, T3Z 1L5, AB, Canada
Tel.: (941) 722-3600
Web Site:
 http://www.genesysindustries.com
Year Founded: 2014
FORZ—(OTCEM)
Rev.: $114,596
Assets: $91,404
Liabilities: $4,699,434
Net Worth: ($4,608,030)
Earnings: ($4,755,706)
Emp.: 2
Fiscal Year-end: 06/30/23
Industrial Machinery Mfr & Distr
N.A.I.C.S.: 333248
Johnny Forzani (Pres, CEO, CFO, Treas & Sec)

GENESYS INTERNATIONAL CORPORATION LTD
73-A SDF III Seepz Andheri E, Mumbai, 400096, India
Tel.: (91) 2244884488
Web Site: https://www.igenesys.com
GENESYS—(NSE)
Rev.: $11,092,700
Assets: $41,508,681
Liabilities: $6,710,586
Net Worth: $34,798,095
Earnings: ($7,069,089)
Emp.: 1,278
Fiscal Year-end: 03/31/21
Information Technology
N.A.I.C.S.: 541512
Sajid Malik (Chm & Mng Dir)

GENESYSTEM CO., LTD.
200-9 Techno 2-Ro, Yuseong-Gu, Daejeon, 34028, Korea (South)
Tel.: (82) 428638551
Web Site:
 https://www.genesystem.co.kr
Year Founded: 2010
363250—(KRS)
Emp.: 70
Medical Device Mfr & Distr
N.A.I.C.S.: 339112
Yujin Seo (CEO)

GENETEC CORPORATION
25F Shinjuku Island Tower 6-5-1 Nishi-Shinjuku, Shinjuku-Ku, Tokyo, 163-1325, Japan
Tel.: (81) 362585601
Web Site: https://www.genetec.co.jp
Year Founded: 1985
4492—(TKS)
Rev.: $47,241,670
Assets: $29,877,200
Liabilities: $15,242,660
Net Worth: $14,634,540
Earnings: $2,736,540
Emp.: 430
Fiscal Year-end: 03/31/24
Software Development Services
N.A.I.C.S.: 541511
Kenji Ueno (Pres)

GENETEC INC.
2280 Alfred-Nobel Blvd Suite 400, Montreal, H4S 2A4, QC, Canada
Tel.: (514) 332-4000
Web Site: http://www.genetec.com
Year Founded: 1997
Sales Range: $25-49.9 Million
Emp.: 400
Internet Security Products & Services
N.A.I.C.S.: 541511

Subsidiaries:
Genetec Asia Pacific Pte Ltd (1)
06-06 Odeon Towers 331 North Bridge Road, Singapore, 188720, Singapore
Tel.: (65) 633 47585
Security Software Development Services
N.A.I.C.S.: 541511
Daniel Lee (Mng Dir)

GENETEC TECHNOLOGY BERHAD
Lot 7 Jalan P10/11 Seksyen 10 Kawasan Perusahaan Bangi, 43650, Bandar Baru Bangi, Selangor Darul Ehsan, Malaysia
Tel.: (60) 389266388 MY
Web Site: https://www.genetec.net
GENETEC—(KLS)
Rev.: $62,347,398
Assets: $105,935,929
Liabilities: $19,947,032
Net Worth: $85,988,897
Earnings: $14,367,686
Emp.: 345
Fiscal Year-end: 03/31/23
Industrial Automation Equipments Mfr
N.A.I.C.S.: 333248
Kem Weng Chin (Mng Dir)

Subsidiaries:
CLT Engineering Sdn. Bhd. (1)
Lot 11734 Persiaran Subang Indah, Taman Perindustrian Subang, 47610, Subang Jaya, Selangor, Malaysia
Tel.: (60) 356211112
Web Site: https://www.clt.com.my
Industrial Automation Products Mfr
N.A.I.C.S.: 335314

GENETETHER THERAPEUTICS INC.
301-1665 Ellis Street, Kelowna, V1Y 2B3, BC, Canada
Tel.: (514) 796-2640 BC
Web Site: https://genetether.com
Year Founded: 2018
GTTX—(CNSX)
Assets: $370,448
Liabilities: $213,223
Net Worth: $157,225
Earnings: ($1,637,610)
Fiscal Year-end: 12/31/21
Biotechnology Research & Development Services
N.A.I.C.S.: 541714
Roland Boivin (CEO)

GENETIC ANALYSIS AS
Ulvenveien 80B, 0581, Oslo, Norway
Tel.: (47) 48321610 NO
Web Site: https://www.genetic-analysis.com
Year Founded: 2008
8V8—(DEU)
Rev.: $2,139,625
Assets: $4,940,860
Liabilities: $1,985,235
Net Worth: $2,955,625
Earnings: ($2,200,066)
Emp.: 22
Fiscal Year-end: 12/31/23
Biotechnology Research & Development Services
N.A.I.C.S.: 541714
Eilert Aamodt (CFO)

GENETIC SIGNATURES LIMITED
7 Eliza Street, Newtown, 2042, NSW, Australia
Tel.: (61) 298707580
Web Site:
 https://www.geneticsignatures.com
Year Founded: 2001
GSS—(ASX)
Rev.: $27,139,216
Assets: $45,706,298
Liabilities: $3,717,554
Net Worth: $41,988,744
Earnings: $2,346,840
Fiscal Year-end: 06/30/22
Pathogen Detection Kit Mfr
N.A.I.C.S.: 334510
John R. Melki (CEO)

GENETIC TECHNOLOGIES LIMITED
60-66 Hanover Street, Fitzroy, 3065, VIC, Australia
Tel.: (61) 384127000
Web Site: https://genetype.com
GENE—(NASDAQ)
Rev.: $5,118,045
Assets: $4,130,957
Liabilities: $2,908,725
Net Worth: $1,222,232
Earnings: ($8,024,318)
Emp.: 58
Fiscal Year-end: 06/30/24
Research & Development in the Physical, Engineering & Life Sciences (except Nanotechnology & Biotechnology)
N.A.I.C.S.: 541715
Richard Allman (Chief Scientific Officer)

Subsidiaries:
GeneType Corporation Inc. (1)
1300 Baxter St Ste 157, Charlotte, NC 28204
Tel.: (704) 926-5700
Web Site: https://genetype.com
Biotechnology Research & Development Services
N.A.I.C.S.: 541714

Genetic Technologies Corporation Pty. Ltd. (1)
60 Hanover St, Fitzroy, 3065, VIC, Australia
Tel.: (61) 3 8412 7000
Web Site: http://www.gtglabs.com
Health Care Srvices
N.A.I.C.S.: 621999

GENETICS GENERATION ADVANCEMENT CORP.
6F No 28 Ln 36 Xinhu 1st Rd, Neihu District, Taipei, 11494, Taiwan
Tel.: (886) 227951777
Web Site: https://www.gga.asia
Year Founded: 2008
4160—(TPE)
Rev.: $17,128,131
Assets: $14,247,037
Liabilities: $3,383,110
Net Worth: $10,863,928
Earnings: $811,369
Fiscal Year-end: 12/31/22
Medical Diagnostic Services

N.A.I.C.S.: 621512
Han-Tung Chang (Chm)

Subsidiaries:
Genetics Generation Asia Sdn. Bhd. (1)
Unit 32-01 Level 32 The Vertical Corporate Tower B No 8, Jalan Kerinchi Bangsar South, 59200, Kuala Lumpur, Malaysia
Tel.: (60) 327863747
Web Site: https://www.ggasia.com.my
Cell Therapy & Genetic Testing Services
N.A.I.C.S.: 541714

GENETRON HOLDINGS LIMITED
No 8 Life Science Parkway 1-2/F Building 11 Zone 1, Changping District, Beijing, 102206, China
Tel.: (86) 1050907500 Ky
Year Founded: 2018
GTH—(NASDAQ)
Rev.: $81,500,060
Assets: $232,514,407
Liabilities: $47,122,341
Net Worth: $185,392,067
Earnings: ($77,003,040)
Emp.: 1,154
Fiscal Year-end: 12/31/21
Holding Company
N.A.I.C.S.: 551112
Sizhen Wang (Co-Founder & CEO)

GENEURO SA
3 Chemin du Pre-Fleuri Plan-les-Ouates, 1228, Geneva, Switzerland
Tel.: (41) 225524800
Web Site: https://geneuro.ch
Year Founded: 2006
GNRO—(EUR)
Rev.: $83,784
Assets: $7,022,740
Liabilities: $22,231,924
Net Worth: ($15,209,184)
Earnings: ($16,289,877)
Emp.: 19
Fiscal Year-end: 12/31/23
Pharmaceutical Product Mfr & Distr
N.A.I.C.S.: 325412
Jesus Martin-Garcia (Chm & CEO)

GENEVA FINANCE LIMITED
Tel.: (64) 800800132
Web Site:
 https://www.genevafinance.co.nz
GFL—(NZX)
Rev.: $9,960,526
Assets: $104,344,498
Liabilities: $81,141,746
Net Worth: $23,202,751
Earnings: $2,078,947
Emp.: 62
Fiscal Year-end: 03/31/23
Financial Services
N.A.I.C.S.: 522291
David Gerard O'Connell (Mng Dir)

Subsidiaries:
Geneva Capital Limited (1)
6B Pacific Rise Mount Wellington, Auckland, 1060, New Zealand
Tel.: (64) 2 146 2818
Web Site: https://genevacapital.co.nz
Financial Services
N.A.I.C.S.: 522110
Alvin Kumar (Mgr-Business Development)

Stellar Collections Limited (1)
6a Pacific Rise, Mount Wellington, Auckland, 1060, New Zealand
Tel.: (64) 95732945
Web Site: http://www.stellarcollections.co.nz
Credit Management Solutions
N.A.I.C.S.: 561450

GENEW TECHNOLOGIES CO., LTD.
F5/6 RichInfo Innovation Center 3176 South Keyuan Road, South Hitech

Park NanShan, Shenzhen, China
Tel.: (86) 75586099888
Web Site: https://www.genew.com
Year Founded: 2005
688418—(SHG)
Rev.: $74,758,704
Assets: $227,794,184
Liabilities: $91,001,566
Net Worth: $136,792,619
Earnings: ($30,232,950)
Emp.: 1,500
Fiscal Year-end: 12/31/22
Telecommunications Equipment Mfr
N.A.I.C.S.: 334290
Minhua Wu *(Chm & Gen Mgr)*

GENEX POWER LIMITED
Level 12 35 Clarence Street, Sydney, 2000, NSW, Australia
Tel.: (61) 290488850
Web Site:
   https://www.genexpower.com.au
GNX—(ASX)
Rev.: $20,834,882
Assets: $472,883,995
Liabilities: $319,404,631
Net Worth: $153,479,364
Earnings: ($3,113,359)
Fiscal Year-end: 06/30/22
Other Electric Power Generation
N.A.I.C.S.: 221118
Michael Addison *(Founder)*

GENEXINE INC.
Bio Park B Building 4th Floor 700 Daewangpangyo-ro, Bundang-gu, Seongnam, 13488, Gyeonggi-do, Korea (South)
Tel.: (82) 316283200
Web Site: https://www.genexine.com
Year Founded: 1999
095700—(KRS)
Rev.: $12,378,638
Assets: $298,195,109
Liabilities: $82,738,702
Net Worth: $215,456,407
Earnings: ($43,162,612)
Emp.: 121
Fiscal Year-end: 12/31/22
Therapeutic Vaccines & Antibody Fusion Protein Medications Mfr
N.A.I.C.S.: 325411
Young Chul Sung *(Founder & Chm)*

Subsidiaries:

Colmmune, Inc.   (1)
4233 Technology Dr, Durham, NC 27704
Tel.: (919) 287-6300
Web Site: https://www.coimmune.com
Biopharmaceutical Researcher, Developer & Mfr
N.A.I.C.S.: 325412
Lori R. Harrelson *(CFO)*

Subsidiary (Domestic):

Formula Pharmaceuticals, Inc.   (2)
1055 Westlakes Dr 3rd Fl, Berwyn, PA 19312
Tel.: (610) 727-4172
Web Site: http://www.formulapharma.com
Chemicals Mfr
N.A.I.C.S.: 325412
Eric L. Steager *(Treas & Sr VP-Fin)*

Genexine Inc. - New York Branch   (1)
295 Madison Ave Ste 1201, New York, NY 10017
Tel.: (646) 647-1242
Pharmaceutical Preparation Mfr
N.A.I.C.S.: 325411

GENEXTRA S.P.A.
Via Privata Giovannino De Grassi 11, 20123, Milan, Italy
Tel.: (39) 0236515110
Web Site: http://www.genextra.it
Year Founded: 2004
Sales Range: $10-24.9 Million
Emp.: 30
Pharmaceuticals Mfr
N.A.I.C.S.: 325412
Paolo Fundaro *(CFO)*

Subsidiaries:

DAC s.r.l.   (1)
214 Via Della Magliana, 00146, Rome, Italy
Tel.: (39) 065506520
Web Site: http://www.dacresearch.it
Biotechnology Research & Development Services
N.A.I.C.S.: 541714
David Galliano *(Mgr-Ops)*

Tethis Labs Inc.   (1)
104 W 40th St Ste 400, New York, NY 10018
Tel.: (855) 894-5352
Web Site: http://www.tethis-lab.com
Biotechnology Research & Development Services
N.A.I.C.S.: 541714
Erik Sandvick *(CEO)*

Tethis S.p.A.   (1)
Via Russoli 3, 20143, Milan, Italy
Tel.: (39) 02 3656 8349
Web Site: http://www.tethis-lab.com
Biotechnology Research & Development Services
N.A.I.C.S.: 541714
Lorenzo Tallarigo *(Chm)*

GENFIT S.A.
Parc Eurasante 885 Avenue Eugene Avinee, 59120, Loos, France
Tel.: (33) 320164000   FR
Web Site: https://www.genfit.com
Year Founded: 1999
GNFT—(NASDAQ)
Rev.: $32,629,424
Assets: $264,734,850
Liabilities: $148,631,779
Net Worth: $116,103,071
Earnings: ($29,132,625)
Emp.: 148
Fiscal Year-end: 12/31/22
Pharmaceuticals Product Mfr
N.A.I.C.S.: 325412
Xavier Guille des Buttes *(Vice Chm)*

Subsidiaries:

GENFIT Corporation   (1)
45 Propect St Ste 214, Cambridge, MA 02139
Tel.: (617) 444-8416
Pharmaceutical Products Distr
N.A.I.C.S.: 424210

GENFLOW BIOSCIENCES PLC
6 Heddon Street, London, W1B 4BT, United Kingdom   UK
Web Site:
   https://www.genflowbio.com
Year Founded: 2021
GENFF—(OTCQB)
Rev.: $615,114
Assets: $3,304,041
Liabilities: $316,824
Net Worth: $2,987,217
Earnings: ($1,685,591)
Emp.: 5
Fiscal Year-end: 12/31/22
Biotechnology Research & Development Services
N.A.I.C.S.: 541714
Eric Leire *(CEO)*

Subsidiaries:

Genflow Biosciences S.R.L.   (1)
Biopark Gosselies Rue Clement Ader 10B, 6041, Charleroi, Belgium
Tel.: (32) 477495881
Pharmaceuticals Mfr
N.A.I.C.S.: 325412

GENFOOT INC.
1940 55th Ave, Lachine, H8T 3H3, QC, Canada
Tel.: (514) 341-3950   QC
Web Site: http://www.kamik.com
Year Founded: 1898
Emp.: 400
Mfr & Importer of Men's, Women's & Children's Footwear Including Rubber Boots, Winter Boots & Canvas Footwear
N.A.I.C.S.: 316210

Subsidiaries:

Genfoot, Inc.   (1)
1940 55th Ave, Lachine, H8T 3H3, QC, Canada   (100%)
Tel.: (514) 341-3950
Web Site: http://www.kamik.com
Sales Range: $25-49.9 Million
Mfr of Rain Boots & Liners
N.A.I.C.S.: 316210
Stephen Cook *(VP-Domestic Sls)*

GENIA PHOTONICS INC.
500 Cartier Boulevard West Suite 131, Laval, H7V 5B7, QC, Canada
Tel.: (450) 680-3401
Web Site:
   http://www.geniaphotonics.com
Sales Range: $1-9.9 Million
High-Speed Picosecond Fiber-Based Lasers & Spectroscopic Measurement Systems Mfr
N.A.I.C.S.: 334516
Francois Gonthier *(Co-Founder & CEO)*

GENIANS INC
12th Floor Building A Highfield Knowledge Industry Center, 66 Beolmal-ro Dongan-gu, Anyang, 14057, Gyeonggi-do, Korea (South)
Tel.: (82) 3180849770
Web Site: https://www.genians.co.kr
Year Founded: 2005
263860—(KRS)
Rev.: $29,493,127
Assets: $45,784,219
Liabilities: $9,044,024
Net Worth: $36,740,196
Earnings: $5,481,201
Emp.: 161
Fiscal Year-end: 12/31/22
Software Development Services
N.A.I.C.S.: 541511

GENIC CO., LTD.
3rd floor Solbrain Building 34 Pangyo-ro 255beon-gil, Bundang-gu, Seongnam, Gyeonggi-do, Korea (South)
Tel.: (82) 317255600
Web Site: https://www.genic21.com
Year Founded: 2001
123330—(KRS)
Rev.: $24,121,252
Assets: $23,283,285
Liabilities: $11,055,101
Net Worth: $12,228,184
Earnings: ($2,561,801)
Emp.: 183
Fiscal Year-end: 12/31/22
Skin & Beauty Products Mfr
N.A.I.C.S.: 325620
Heo Nam *(CEO)*

Subsidiaries:

Genic Co., Ltd. - Nonsan 1st plant   (1)
5 4-gil Saneopdangi-ro Seongdong-myeon, Nonsan, Chungnam, Korea (South)
Tel.: (82) 41 733 8237
Cosmetics Mfr
N.A.I.C.S.: 325620

Genic Co., Ltd. - Nonsan 2nd plant   (1)
5 5-gil Saneopdangi-ro Seongdong-myeon, Nonsan, Chungnam, Korea (South)
Tel.: (82) 417338269
Web Site: http://www.genic21.com
Cosmetics Mfr
N.A.I.C.S.: 325620

GENIEE, INC.
6-8-1 Nishi Shinjuku, Sumitomo Realty and Development Shinjuku Oak Tower 6th Floor, Tokyo, 163-6006, Japan
Tel.: (81) 359098181   JP
Web Site: https://www.geniee.co.jp
Year Founded: 2010
6562—(TKS)
Rev.: $52,959,320
Assets: $126,892,170
Liabilities: $78,705,270
Net Worth: $48,186,900
Earnings: $6,814,910
Emp.: 617
Fiscal Year-end: 03/31/24
Advertising Services
N.A.I.C.S.: 541810
Tomoaki Kudo *(Founder, Pres & CEO)*

Subsidiaries:

Business Search Technologies Corporation   (1)
Sumitomo Fudosan Shinjuku Oak Tower 6F 6-8-1 Nishi-Shinjuku, Shinjuku-ku, Tokyo, 163-6006, Japan
Tel.: (81) 359098186
Web Site: https://www.bsearchtech.com
Software Development Services
N.A.I.C.S.: 513210

PT. Adstars Media Pariwara   (1)
World Trade Center II Building 9th floor Jl Jend Sudirman Kav 29 - 31, RT 8/RW 3 Kuningan Karet Kuningan Setiabudi, Jakarta, 12920, Indonesia
Tel.: (62) 2129522628
Web Site: https://www.adstarsmedia.co.id
Advertising Agency Services
N.A.I.C.S.: 541810

GENII CAPITAL SA
C1 1 rue Peternelchen, 2370, Howald, Luxembourg
Tel.: (352) 2639651
Web Site: http://www.genii-capital.com
Privater Equity Firm
N.A.I.C.S.: 523999
Eric Lux *(CEO)*

Subsidiaries:

Genii Capital SA   (1)
3 rue du Marche, 1204, Geneva, Switzerland
Tel.: (41) 22 544 14 00
Investment Management Service
N.A.I.C.S.: 523940

Genii Capital UK Ltd.   (1)
22 Arlington street - 2nd floor, London, SW1A 1RD, United Kingdom
Tel.: (44) 20 3544 6230
Investment Management Service
N.A.I.C.S.: 523940

GENIMOUS TECHNOLOGY CO., LTD.
Room 401-8 56-3 Fenghuang South Road, Xinya Subdistrict Huadu District, Guangzhou, 510806, Guangdong, China
Tel.: (86) 2028616560
Web Site: http://www.hnstar.com
Year Founded: 1996
000676—(SSE)
Rev.: $383,084,208
Assets: $602,626,284
Liabilities: $105,992,172
Net Worth: $496,634,112
Earnings: ($56,832,516)
Fiscal Year-end: 12/31/22
Electronic Products Mfr
N.A.I.C.S.: 334419
Lu Hongda *(Chm)*

GENINCODE PLC

GENINCODE PLC

GENinCode Plc—(Continued)
Oxford Science Park John Eccles House Robert Robinson Avenue, Oxford, OX4 4GP, United Kingdom
Tel.: (44) 1865676125 UK
Web Site:
https://www.genincode.com
Year Founded: 2018
GENI—(AIM)
Rev.: $1,805,100
Assets: $14,891,442
Liabilities: $4,919,212
Net Worth: $9,972,229
Earnings: ($7,017,167)
Emp.: 34
Fiscal Year-end: 12/31/22
Biotechnology Research & Development Services
N.A.I.C.S.: 541714

Subsidiaries:

Genincode U.S. Inc. (1)
5 Mason Ste 200, Irvine, CA 92618
Tel.: (949) 930-0462
Medical & Scientific Research Services
N.A.I.C.S.: 541715

GENIUS INC.
4-5th Fl 70 Jeongeui-Ro Kdu Tower, Mujeong-Dong Songpa-Gu, Seoul, Korea (South)
Tel.: (82) 269496570
Web Site: https://www.kr-genius.com
Year Founded: 2018
389030—(KRS)
Pharmaceutical Preparation Mfr
N.A.I.C.S.: 325412
William Ku (CFO)

GENIUS ELECTRONIC OPTICAL CO., LTD.
No 1 Keya East Road Daya District Taichung Central Taiwan Science Park, Daya District, Taichung, 428, Taiwan
Tel.: (886) 425667115
Web Site: https://www.gseo.com
3406—(TAI)
Rev.: $708,809,974
Assets: $1,368,524,589
Liabilities: $678,637,013
Net Worth: $689,887,577
Earnings: $100,884,754
Emp.: 12,078
Fiscal Year-end: 12/31/23
Optical Lens Mfr
N.A.I.C.S.: 326199
Jones Chen (Chm)

Subsidiaries:

GeniuS Electronic Optical (Shenzhen) Co., Ltd.
Room 1309 Jinmin Building Zizhu 6th Road, Futian, Shenzhen, Guangdong, China
Tel.: (86) 75582828755
Web Site: http://www.gseo.com
Flashlight Mfr
N.A.I.C.S.: 325998

GeniuS Electronic Optical (Xiamen) Co., Ltd. (1)
No 8 Chuangxin Road, Torch Hi-Tech Industrial Development Zone, Xiamen, 361 006, Fujian, China
Tel.: (86) 592 6026011
Web Site: http://www.gseo.com
Emp.: 10,000
Optical Lenses & Light Emitting Diodes Mfr
N.A.I.C.S.: 334213

GENIUS GROUP LIMITED
8 Amoy Street 01-01, Singapore, 049950, Singapore
Tel.: (65) 68173123 SG
Web Site: https://www.geniusu.com
Year Founded: 2015
GNS—(NYSEAMEX)
Rev.: $23,062,754
Assets: $43,213,773
Liabilities: $23,498,780
Net Worth: $19,714,993
Earnings: ($5,711,222)
Emp.: 300
Fiscal Year-end: 12/31/23
Educational Support Services
N.A.I.C.S.: 611710
Roger James Hamilton (Founder, Chm & CEO)

Subsidiaries:

LZG INTERNATIONAL, INC. (1)
135 W 41st St Ste 5-104, New York, NY 10036
Tel.: (917) 310-3978
Rev.: $216,166
Assets: $21,495,942
Liabilities: $3,149,738
Net Worth: $18,346,204
Earnings: ($919,793)
Fiscal Year-end: 05/31/2022
Investment Services
N.A.I.C.S.: 523999
Peter Benjamin Ritz (Pres, CEO & Sec)

GENIUS METALS, INC
20568 de la Gare Av, Saint-Sauveur-des-Monts, J0R 1R0, QC, Canada
Tel.: (579) 476-7000
Web Site:
https://www.geniusmetals.com
GNSMF—(OTCIQ)
Assets: $4,614,326
Liabilities: $351,942
Net Worth: $4,262,385
Earnings: ($715,333)
Fiscal Year-end: 07/31/24
Mineral Exploration Services
N.A.I.C.S.: 213115
Robert Boisjoli (CFO)

GENIUS SYSTEMS LTD.
7 Hasivim Street, PO Box 7796, Petah Tiqwa, 49170, Israel
Tel.: (972) 39222204 IL
Web Site: http://www.genius.co.il
Sales Range: $1-9.9 Million
Emp.: 10
Predictive Analytics & Data Mining Software Distr
N.A.I.C.S.: 423430
Jacky Lipskier (Gen Mgr)

GENIX PHARMACEUTICALS CORPORATION
Suite 300 1055 West Hastings St, Vancouver, V6E 2E9, BC, Canada
Tel.: (604) 609-6198
Web Site: https://genixpharm.com
Year Founded: 1996
GENPF—(OTCQB)
Rev.: $9,323
Assets: $168,740
Liabilities: $1,027,584
Net Worth: ($858,844)
Earnings: ($3,319,186)
Fiscal Year-end: 10/31/23
Natural Health Products Mfr
N.A.I.C.S.: 325412
Sina Pirooz (CEO)

GENKI GLOBAL DINING CONCEPTS CORPORATION
2 320 Kamioozo cho, Utsunomiya, 320 0013, Tochigi, Japan
Tel.: (81) 286325711 JP
Web Site:
https://www.genkisushi.co.jp
Year Founded: 1979
9828—(TKS)
Rev.: $408,749,180
Assets: $216,636,140
Liabilities: $127,163,180
Net Worth: $89,472,960
Earnings: $21,561,820
Emp.: 595
Fiscal Year-end: 03/31/24
Restaurant Operators
N.A.I.C.S.: 722513
Takashi Hohshito (CEO)

Subsidiaries:

Genki Sushi Hong Kong Limited (1)
18th Floor Maxim's Center 17 Cheung Shun Street, Cheung Sha Wan, Kowloon, China (Hong Kong)
Tel.: (852) 21011161
Web Site: https://order.genkisushi.com.hk
Restaurant Operators
N.A.I.C.S.: 722511

Genki Sushi USA Inc. (1)
677 Ala Moana Blvd Ste 602, Honolulu, HI 96813
Tel.: (808) 523-3315
Web Site: https://www.genkisushiusa.com
Restaurant Operators
N.A.I.C.S.: 722511
Takashi Hoshito (Pres)

GENKO ITALIA SRL
Via Grecia 28, 71100, Foggia, Italy
Tel.: (39) 0881331444 IT
Web Site: http://www.genkoitalia.it
Medical Instrument Mfr
N.A.I.C.S.: 339112

Subsidiaries:

S.C. GENKO MED GROUP S.A. (1)
Calea Unirii 22, 720018, Suceava, Romania
Tel.: (40) 330 401525
Web Site: http://www.genkomedgroup.com
Medical Device Mfr
N.A.I.C.S.: 339112
Vincenzo Nuzziello (Pres)

GENKY DRUGSTORES CO., LTD.
38-33 Shimokumeda Maruokacho, Sakai, 910-0332, Fukui, Japan
Tel.: (81) 776675240
Web Site: https://www.genky.co.jp
Year Founded: 1988
9267—(TKS)
Rev.: $1,149,829,200
Assets: $708,700,580
Liabilities: $418,344,760
Net Worth: $290,355,820
Earnings: $39,335,280
Fiscal Year-end: 06/30/24
Pharmaceutical Product Mfr & Distr
N.A.I.C.S.: 325412
Kenichi Fujinaga (Pres & CEO)

GENKY STORES, INC.
38-33 Shimokumeda Maruoka, Sakai, 910-0332, Fukui, Japan
Tel.: (81) 77 667 5240
Web Site: http://www.genky.co.jp
Year Founded: 1988
2772—(JAS)
Sales Range: $700-749.9 Million
Drug Store Owner & Operator
N.A.I.C.S.: 456110
Kenichi Fujinaga (Pres)

GENMAB A/S
Carl Jacobsens Vej 30, 2500, Valby, Denmark
Tel.: (45) 70202728 DK
Web Site: https://www.genmab.com
Year Founded: 1998
GMAB—(NASDAQ)
Rev.: $2,364,019,000
Assets: $5,063,971,500
Liabilities: $527,936,500
Net Worth: $4,536,035,000
Earnings: $624,512,000
Emp.: 2,204
Fiscal Year-end: 12/31/23
Biotechnology Research & Development Services
N.A.I.C.S.: 541714

INTERNATIONAL PUBLIC

Jan van de Winkel (Founder, Pres & CEO)

Subsidiaries:

Genmab B.V. (1)
(100%)
Tel.: (31) 302123123
Web Site: http://www.genmab.com
Sales Range: $10-24.9 Million
Emp.: 100
N.A.I.C.S.: 326199

Genmab Holding B.V. (1)
Uppsalalaan 15, 3584 CT, Utrecht, Netherlands
Tel.: (31) 30 212 3123
Biotechnology Research Services
N.A.I.C.S.: 541714

Genmab US, Inc. (1)
777 Scudders Mill Rd, Plainsboro, NJ 08536
Tel.: (609) 430-2481
Pharmaceuticals Product Mfr
N.A.I.C.S.: 325412

Genmab, Inc. (1)
457 N Harrison St, Princeton, NJ 08540
Tel.: (609) 430-2481
Web Site: http://www.genmab.com
Sales Range: $25-49.9 Million
Emp.: 29
Bio Technology Services
N.A.I.C.S.: 541720

GENMINI LIMITED
London House Suite 3 Level 8 216 St Georges Terrace, Perth, 6000, WA, Australia
Tel.: (61) 892005812 AU
Web Site:
https://www.genmingroup.com
Year Founded: 2010
GEN—(ASX)
Rev.: $6,000
Assets: $52,480,000
Liabilities: $14,665,000
Net Worth: $37,815,000
Earnings: ($8,016,000)
Fiscal Year-end: 12/31/22
Iron Ore Mining Services
N.A.I.C.S.: 212210
Giuseppe Ariti (CEO)

GENMONT BIOTECH INCORPORATION
No 8 Nanke 7th Rd, Shanhua Dist, T'ainan, 741, Taiwan
Tel.: (886) 65052151
Web Site:
https://www.genmont.com.tw
Year Founded: 2000
3164—(TAI)
Rev.: $10,399,784
Assets: $54,062,623
Liabilities: $6,673,174
Net Worth: $47,389,448
Earnings: $733,543
Fiscal Year-end: 12/31/23
Biotech Research & Development Services
N.A.I.C.S.: 541714
Chen Ken-Te (Chm)

GENNARO AURICCHIO S.P.A.
Via Dante 27, 26100, Cremona, Italy
Tel.: (39) 0372 403311 IT
Web Site: http://www.auricchio.it
Year Founded: 1877
Sales Range: $150-199.9 Million
Emp.: 450
Cheese Mfr & Distr
N.A.I.C.S.: 311513

Subsidiaries:

The Ambriola Company, Inc. (1)
7 Patton Dr, West Caldwell, NJ 07006
Tel.: (973) 228-2648
Web Site: http://www.ambriola.com

AND PRIVATE COMPANIES — GENOTECH CORPORATION

Sales Range: $1-9.9 Million
Emp.: 13
Cheese Importer & Whslr
N.A.I.C.S.: 424430
Phil Marfuggi *(CEO)*

GENNBIO INC.
B1F Building A 700 Daewangpangyo-ro, Bundang-gu, Seongnam, Gyeonggi-do, Korea (South)
Tel.: (82) 7041485252
Web Site: https://gennbio.com
072520—(KRS)
Rev.: $6,956,852
Assets: $101,624,035
Liabilities: $55,599,807
Net Worth: $46,024,228
Earnings: ($28,051,489)
Emp.: 74
Fiscal Year-end: 12/31/22
Liquid Crystal Display Window & Decoration Plate Mfr
N.A.I.C.S.: 334419
Young Jin Lee *(CEO)*

Subsidiaries:

Taeyang Electronics Co., Ltd. - Waegwan Factory (1)
987-1 Gumsan-Lee, Chilok-Gun, Waegwan, Gyeongsangbuk-do, Korea (South)
Tel.: (82) 54 971 4400
Electronic Components Mfr
N.A.I.C.S.: 334419

GENNBIO, INC.
5F KT Tower Teheran-ro 422, Gangnam-gu, Seoul, Korea (South)
Tel.: (82) 25571088
Web Site: http://www.gennbio.co.kr
Year Founded: 1989
72520—(KRS)
Rev.: $10,898,030
Assets: $90,348,703
Liabilities: $46,065,435
Net Worth: $44,283,269
Earnings: ($19,603,716)
Emp.: 106
Fiscal Year-end: 12/31/20
Pharmaceuticals Distr
N.A.I.C.S.: 424210

GENNEX LABORATORIES LTD.
Akash Ganga 3rd Floor Plot No 144, Srinagar Colony, Hyderabad, 500 073, Telangana, India
Tel.: (91) 4067334400
Web Site: https://www.gennexlab.com
Year Founded: 1995
531739—(BOM)
Rev.: $8,339,601
Assets: $15,864,316
Liabilities: $5,491,409
Net Worth: $10,372,907
Earnings: $589,986
Emp.: 118
Fiscal Year-end: 03/31/23
Pharmaceuticals
N.A.I.C.S.: 621511
Laxmipat P. Baid *(CFO)*

GENOFOCUS, INC.
65 Techno 1-ro, Yusung-gu, Daejeon, 34014, Korea (South)
Tel.: (82) 428624483
Web Site: https://www.genofocus.com
Year Founded: 2000
187420—(KRS)
Rev.: $21,323,947
Assets: $102,712,203
Liabilities: $81,946,081
Net Worth: $20,766,122
Earnings: ($10,257,201)
Emp.: 65
Fiscal Year-end: 12/31/22
Biochemical Mfr
N.A.I.C.S.: 325998
Jong-Soo Choi *(VP)*

GENOHCO, INC.
1815 Jenoco Building Dangjeong-dong, Dongan-Gu, Anyang, 14055, Gyeonggi-do, Korea (South)
Tel.: (82) 314286000
Web Site: https://www.genohco.com
Year Founded: 2004
361390—(KRS)
Rev.: $38,890,601
Assets: $48,588,800
Liabilities: $22,653,100
Net Worth: $25,935,700
Earnings: $2,082,891
Emp.: 135
Fiscal Year-end: 12/31/22
Communication Equipment Mfr & Distr
N.A.I.C.S.: 334290
Taesam Yoo *(CEO)*

GENOLUTION INC.
63 Magokjungang 8-Ro 3-Gil, Gangseo-Gu, Seoul, Korea (South)
Tel.: (82) 24498670
Web Site: http://www.genolution.co.kr
Year Founded: 2006
225220—(KRS)
Rev.: $29,210,864
Assets: $87,786,015
Liabilities: $15,152,035
Net Worth: $72,633,980
Earnings: $11,199,637
Emp.: 106
Fiscal Year-end: 12/31/22
Biotechnology Research & Development Services
N.A.I.C.S.: 541714
Gi-Ok Kim *(CEO)*

GENOLUX CO., LTD
Rm 506 Bldg A 11 Beobwon-ro 11gil Songpa-gu, Seoul, 05836, Korea (South)
Tel.: (82) 24498670
Web Site: http://Www.genolution.cafe24.com
Year Founded: 2006
Medical Research & Development Services
N.A.I.C.S.: 541380

GENOME & COMPANY
7F GWANGGYO FLAX DESIAN 50 Changnyong-daero 256beon-gil, Yeongtong-gu, Suwon, 16229, Gyeonggi-do, Korea (South)
Tel.: (82) 316280150
Web Site: https://genomecom.co.kr
Year Founded: 2015
314130—(KRS)
Biopharmaceutical Company
N.A.I.C.S.: 325412
Jisoo Pae *(Co-Founder & Co-CEO)*

Subsidiaries:

List Biological Laboratories, Inc. (1)
540 Division St, Campbell, CA 95008-6906 (60%)
Tel.: (408) 866-6363
Web Site: http://www.listlabs.com
Chemicals Mfr
N.A.I.C.S.: 325414
Debra Booth *(VP)*

GENOMIC VALLEY BIOTECH LIMITED
4 Km Milestone Beri Chhara Road, Village - Kherka Musalman Tandaher Tehsil, Bahadurgarh, 124 507, Haryana, India
Tel.: (91) 9811341542
Web Site: https://www.genomicvalley.com
539206—(BOM)
Rev.: $331,523
Assets: $529,991
Liabilities: $107,129
Net Worth: $422,862
Earnings: $77,724
Emp.: 3
Fiscal Year-end: 03/31/23
Biotechnology Research & Development Services
N.A.I.C.S.: 541714
Yogesh Agrawal *(Chm & Mng Dir)*

GENOMIC VISION SA
Batiment E 80-84 rue des Meuniers, 92220, Bagneux, France
Tel.: (33) 1 49 08 07 40
Web Site: http://www.genomicvision.com
Year Founded: 2004
GV—(EUR)
Sales Range: $1-9.9 Million
Emp.: 40
DNA Analysis & Genetic Testing
N.A.I.C.S.: 621511
Aaron Bensimon *(Founder, Chm-Exec Bd, Pres & CEO)*

GENOMICS BIOSCI & TECH CO., LTD.
14F No 100 Sec 1 Xintai 5th Rd, Xizhi Dist, New Taipei City, 221, Taiwan
Tel.: (886) 226961658
Web Site: https://www.genomics.com.tw
Year Founded: 2001
4195—(TAI)
Emp.: 202
Scientific Research & Consulting Services
N.A.I.C.S.: 541690
Cho-Yuan Yu *(Chm)*

GENOMICTREE, INC.
44-6 Techno 10-ro Yuseong, Daejeon, 34027, Korea (South)
Tel.: (82) 428614551
Web Site: https://www.genomictree.com
Year Founded: 2000
228760—(KRS)
Rev.: $22,906,972
Assets: $124,951,916
Liabilities: $42,455,668
Net Worth: $82,496,248
Earnings: ($5,085,838)
Emp.: 84
Fiscal Year-end: 12/31/22
Molecular Diagnostics Services
N.A.I.C.S.: 621511
Sung Whan An *(CEO)*

GENOMMA LAB INTERNATIONAL SAB DE CV
Av Antonio Dovali Jaime #70 Torre C Piso 2 Despacho A Col, Santa Fe Del Alvaro Obregon Ciudad de, Mexico, CP 01210, Mexico
Tel.: (52) 5550810000
Web Site: http://www.genommalab.com
LAB—(MEX)
Rev.: $970,228,045
Assets: $1,217,495,212
Liabilities: $664,652,483
Net Worth: $552,842,728
Earnings: $60,722,312
Emp.: 1,633
Fiscal Year-end: 12/31/23
Cosmetics & Pharmaceutical Products Mfr
N.A.I.C.S.: 325620
Rodrigo Alonso Herrera Aspra *(Founder & Chm)*

GENOMTEC SA
Wroclaw Business Park 3 Bierutowska Street 57-59, 51-317, Wroclaw, Poland
Tel.: (48) 793440931
Web Site: https://www.genomtec.com
Year Founded: 2016
GMT—(WAR)
Rev.: $254
Assets: $4,057,927
Liabilities: $1,948,679
Net Worth: $2,109,248
Earnings: ($2,289,888)
Fiscal Year-end: 12/31/23
Biotechnology Research & Development Services
N.A.I.C.S.: 541714
Miron Tokarski *(Co-Founder & CEO)*

GENOR BIOPHARMA CO., LTD.
1690 Zhangheng Road Building 3, Pudong New, Shanghai, 201203, China
Tel.: (86) 2161690700 CN
Web Site: http://www.genorbio.com
Year Founded: 2007
6998—(HKG)
Pharmaceutical Product Mfr & Distr
N.A.I.C.S.: 325412
Feng Guo *(CEO)*

GENORAY CO., LTD.
3-15 Dunchon-daero 80beon-gil, Jungwon-gu, Seongnam, Gyeonggi-do, Korea (South)
Tel.: (82) 3151785500
Web Site: https://www.genoray.com
Year Founded: 2001
122310—(KRS)
Rev.: $63,357,350
Assets: $81,453,963
Liabilities: $13,985,984
Net Worth: $67,467,979
Earnings: $10,661,530
Emp.: 250
Fiscal Year-end: 12/31/22
Electrical Equipment Device Mfr
N.A.I.C.S.: 334517
Byung Wook Park *(CEO)*

Subsidiaries:

Genoray America Inc. (1)
147 E Bristol Ln, Orange, CA 92865
Web Site: https://www.genorayamerica.com
Medical Equipment Mfr
N.A.I.C.S.: 339112
Byung Wook Park *(CEO)*

Genoray EU GmbH (1)
Jerusalemer Str 14 10117, 13353, Berlin, Germany
Tel.: (49) 3050969498
Medical Equipment Mfr
N.A.I.C.S.: 339112

Genoray Japan, K.K. (1)
2nd Floor Misumi Coach Office Building 1-4-7 Shin-Yokohama, Kohoku-ku, Yokohama, 222-0033, Kanagawa, Japan
Tel.: (81) 456204971
Web Site: https://www.genorayjapan.co.jp
Medical Equipment Mfr
N.A.I.C.S.: 339112

GENOTECH CORPORATION
26-69 Gajeongbuk-ro Yuseong-gu, Daejeon, 305-343, Korea (South)
Tel.: (82) 428628404
Web Site: http://www.genotech.co.kr
Year Founded: 1997
Medicinal Antibiotic Product Mfr & Distr
N.A.I.C.S.: 325411

Subsidiaries:

GenoTech Corporation - GMP Plant (1)
100 Bio Valley 2 ro, Jecheon, 390-250,

GENOTECH CORPORATION

GenoTech Corporation—(Continued)
Chungcheongbuk-do, Korea (South)
Tel.: (82) 436528404
Pharmaceuticals Product Mfr
N.A.I.C.S.: 325412

GENOVA INC.
34F Shibuya Hikarie 2-21-1 Shibuya,
Shibuya Shibuya-ku, Tokyo, Japan
Tel.: (81) 120811009
Web Site: https://www.genova.co.jp
Year Founded: 2005
9341—(TKS)
Rev.: $57,394,630
Assets: $54,195,390
Liabilities: $14,290,820
Net Worth: $39,904,570
Earnings: $11,408,860
Emp.: 404
Fiscal Year-end: 03/31/24
Biotechnology Research & Development Services
N.A.I.C.S.: 541714

GENOVA PROPERTY GROUP AB
Smalandsgatan 12, SE-111 46,
Stockholm, Sweden
Tel.: (46) 812444360
Web Site: https://www.genova.se
Year Founded: 2006
GPG—(OMX)
Rev.: $49,933,489
Assets: $1,147,844,839
Liabilities: $720,650,438
Net Worth: $427,194,400
Earnings: ($41,296,882)
Emp.: 48
Fiscal Year-end: 12/31/23
Real Estate Manangement Services
N.A.I.C.S.: 531311
Edvard Scheele *(CFO)*

Subsidiaries:

Jarngrinden Projektutveckling AB (1)
Lilla Brogatan 6 Plan 6, PO Box 926, Pallashuset, 501 10, Boras, Sweden
Tel.: (46) 337225700
Web Site: https://www.jarngrinden.se
Property Management Services
N.A.I.C.S.: 531312

GENOVATE BIOTECHNOLOGY CO., LTD.
No1 First Industrial Rd, Hsin Chu
County, Hukou, 303036, Taiwan
Tel.: (886) 35982221
Web Site: https://www.genovate-bio.com
Year Founded: 1993
4130—(TPE)
Rev.: $13,718,507
Assets: $48,914,361
Liabilities: $4,802,583
Net Worth: $44,111,778
Earnings: ($385,298)
Fiscal Year-end: 12/31/22
Pharmaceuticals Product Mfr
N.A.I.C.S.: 325412
Chia-Chen Chu *(Pres)*

GENOVIS AB
Genovis AB Karl Johans vag 104
Kavlinge, Box 790, SE-200 07, Lund,
Sweden
Tel.: (46) 46101230
Web Site: https://investor.genovis.com
Year Founded: 1999
GENO—(OMX)
Rev.: $9,589,751
Assets: $14,098,025
Liabilities: $2,329,183
Net Worth: $11,768,841
Earnings: $1,048,139
Emp.: 37
Fiscal Year-end: 12/31/22
Biotechnology & Biopharmaceuticals
N.A.I.C.S.: 541714
Fredrik Olsson *(CEO)*

Subsidiaries:

Genovis Inc. (1)
245 1st St Ste 1800, Cambridge, MA 02142
Tel.: (617) 444-8421
Web Site: https://www.genovis.com
Biotechnology Research Services
N.A.I.C.S.: 541714

GENOWAY S.A.
Technopark 2 31 Rue Saint Jean-de-Dieu, 69007, Lyon, France
Tel.: (33) 437654100   FR
Web Site: http://www.genoway.com
Year Founded: 1999
ALGEN—(EUR)
Sales Range: $10-24.9 Million
Genetically Modified Mouse & Rat Models Research
N.A.I.C.S.: 325414
Alexandre Fraichard *(Founder & Gen Mgr)*

GENPACT LIMITED
Victoria Place 5th Floor 31 Victoria
Street, Hamilton, HM 10, Bermuda
Tel.: (441) 2948000   BM
Web Site: http://www.genpact.com
Year Founded: 1997
G—(NYSE)
Rev.: $4,476,888,000
Assets: $4,805,713,000
Liabilities: $2,557,321,000
Net Worth: $2,248,392,000
Earnings: $631,255,000
Emp.: 129,100
Fiscal Year-end: 12/31/23
Holding Company; Business Process Management & Services
N.A.I.C.S.: 551112
Sanjay Srivastava *(Chief Digital Officer)*

Subsidiaries:

Akritiv Technologies, Inc. (1)
969G Edgewater Blvd Ste 820, Foster City, CA 94404
Tel.: (415) 669-4250
Software Development Services
N.A.I.C.S.: 513210
Gary Lynam *(VP-Ops)*

Atyati Technologies Private Limited (1)
301 Diamond District Tower C, Old Airport Road Kodihali, Bengaluru, 560008, India
Tel.: (91) 8042921999
Web Site: https://www.atyati.com
Software Development Services
N.A.I.C.S.: 513210
Prakash Prabhu *(CEO)*

Barkawi Management Consultants GmbH & Co. KG (1)
Baierbrunner Str 35, 81379, Munich, Germany
Tel.: (49) 897498260
Web Site: http://www.barkawi.com
Emp.: 250
IT Infrastructure Services
N.A.I.C.S.: 518210
Wolfgang Schurholz *(Mng Partner)*

Barkawi Management Consultants, LLC (1)
100 Galleria Pkwy Ste 1500, Atlanta, GA 30339
Tel.: (678) 213-2940
Management Consultancy Services
N.A.I.C.S.: 541618
Andreas Baader *(Mng Partner)*

BrightClaim, Inc. (1)
8010 Roswell Rd, Atlanta, GA 30350
Tel.: (678) 325-5010
Web Site: http://www.brightclaim.com
Insurance Agencies & Brokerages
N.A.I.C.S.: 524210

Commonwealth Informatics, Inc. (1)
307 Waverley Oaks Rd Ste 201, Waltham, MA 02452
Tel.: (781) 209-5015
Web Site: http://www.commoninf.com
Medical Research & Development Services
N.A.I.C.S.: 541714
Geoffrey Gordon *(Co-Founder & Pres)*

Endeavour Software Technologies Inc. (1)
8140 N Mopac Expy Ste 220 Westpark 1, Austin, TX 78759
Tel.: (512) 464-1218
Software Development Services
N.A.I.C.S.: 541511

Endeavour Software Technologies Private Limited (1)
No 882 and 883 8th Main Road JP Nagar 3rd Phase, Bengaluru, 560078, India
Tel.: (91) 8042885500
Web Site: http://www.techendeavour.com
Software Development Services
N.A.I.C.S.: 541511

Enquero, Inc. (1)
1551 McCarthy Blvd Ste 207, Milpitas, CA 95035
Tel.: (408) 215-4814
Web Site: https://www.enquero.com
Data Engineering & Analytic Services
N.A.I.C.S.: 541990
Arvinder Singh *(CEO)*

Genpact (Dalian) Co. Ltd. (1)
No 30 East Road Software Park, Dalian Software Park, Dalian, 116023, Liaoning, China
Tel.: (86) 41183666998
Business Process Outsourcing Services
N.A.I.C.S.: 561499

Genpact (Dalian) Information & Technology Service Co., Ltd. (1)
No 30 East Road Software Park, Dalian, China
Tel.: (86) 41183666998
Human Resource Consulting Services
N.A.I.C.S.: 541612

Genpact (Foshan) Information & Technology Service Co., Ltd. (1)
The 6th Floor No 8 Building A Zone No 17 Shenhai Road, Guicheng Subdistrict Nanhai District, Foshan, Guangdong, China
Tel.: (86) 75786061111
Human Resource Consulting Services
N.A.I.C.S.: 541612

Genpact (Qingdao) Information & Technology Service Co., Ltd. (1)
25/F Changjiang Center 517 Changjiang Middle Road, Qingdao Economic and Technological Development Zone, Qingdao, China
Tel.: (86) 53267798820
Human Resource Consulting Services
N.A.I.C.S.: 541612

Genpact (Suzhou) Information & Technology Service Co., Ltd. (1)
No 1 Jin Jie Road Huaqiao Economic Development Zone, Kunshan, Jiangsu, China
Tel.: (86) 51236621533
Human Resource Consulting Services
N.A.I.C.S.: 541612

Genpact Australia Pty Ltd (1)
Suite 3 01 Level 3 55 Clarence Street, Sydney, 2000, NSW, Australia
Tel.: (61) 282977700
Business Management Consulting Services
N.A.I.C.S.: 541611
Nitin Bhat *(Sr VP)*

Genpact Canada Services Company (1)
100 King St W Suite 56033, Toronto, M5X 1A9, ON, Canada
Tel.: (647) 255-3112
Professional Firm Services
N.A.I.C.S.: 541990

Genpact Consulting KK (1)
9F Marunouchi Kitaguchi Building 1-6-5, Marunouchi Chiyoda-ku, Tokyo, 100-0005, Japan
Tel.: (81) 366887306
Web Site: http://www.consulting.genpact.co.jp

INTERNATIONAL PUBLIC

Emp.: 50
Business Management Consulting Services
N.A.I.C.S.: 541611

Genpact Enterprise Risk Consulting LLP (1)
Delhi IT Park DMRC Building Shastri Park, New Delhi, 110053, India
Tel.: (91) 1149325000
Business Management Consulting Services
N.A.I.C.S.: 541611
Jayant Dhawan *(Sr Mgr)*

Genpact India (1)
DLF City - Phase V Sector 53, DLF City Phase 5, Gurgaon, 122002, Haryana, India
Tel.: (91) 1244022000
Web Site: http://www.genpact.com
Business Process Management & Services
N.A.I.C.S.: 561499

Subsidiary (Domestic):

Axis Risk Consulting Services Pvt. Ltd. (2)
3rd Floor The Ruby 29 Senapati Bapat Marg Dadar West, Mumbai, 400028, India
Tel.: (91) 2261551000
Software Development Services
N.A.I.C.S.: 513210
Himanshu Sardana *(Sr Mgr)*

Genpact Israel Ltd. (1)
Hamahshev St 1 Entrance C 3rd Floor Poleg IZ, Netanya, 4250711, Israel
Tel.: (972) 98853633
Professional Firm Services
N.A.I.C.S.: 541990

Genpact Kenya Limited (1)
Tusker House Thika Road, Nairobi, Kenya
Tel.: (254) 208641008
Management Services
N.A.I.C.S.: 541611

Genpact LLC (1)
521 5th Ave 14th Fl, New York, NY 10175
Tel.: (212) 896-6600
Web Site: https://www.genpact.com
Sales Range: $25-49.9 Million
Emp.: 17
Business Process Management & Services
N.A.I.C.S.: 561499

Subsidiary (Domestic):

Genpact International, Inc. (2)
42 Old Ridgebury Rd Ste 1, Danbury, CT 06810-5119
Tel.: (203) 730-5100
Emp.: 6,600
Software Development Services
N.A.I.C.S.: 513210

Genpact Services LLC (2)
1155 Avenues of Americas 4th Fl, New York, NY 10036
Tel.: (646) 624-5917
Web Site: http://www.genpact.com
Business Process Outsourcing Services
N.A.I.C.S.: 561499

Rightpoint Consulting LLC (2)
29 N Uppr Wacker Dr 4th Fl, Chicago, IL 60606
Tel.: (312) 920-8383
Web Site: http://www.rightpoint.com
Software Products Whslr
N.A.I.C.S.: 541519
Brad Schneider *(Co-Founder & Advisor)*

Subsidiary (Domestic):

Rightpoint Company (3)
50 Milk St 19th Fl, Boston, MA 02110
Tel.: (617) 383-9007
Web Site: http://www.raizlabs.com
Mobile & Web Application Designer & Developer
N.A.I.C.S.: 513210

Genpact Latvia SIA (1)
Gustava Zemgala gatve 76, Riga, 1039, Latvia
Tel.: (371) 40372064437
Administrative Management Consulting Services
N.A.I.C.S.: 541611
Andra Elena Dediu *(Mgr-Recruitment Project)*

AND PRIVATE COMPANIES

Genpact NL B.V (1)
Mercuriusweg 5, 1531 AD, Wormer, Netherlands
Tel.: (31) 756518518
Software Development Services
N.A.I.C.S.: 513210
Barend van Doorn (VP)

Genpact Netherlands B.V. (1)
Mercuriusweg 5, 1531 AD, Wormer, Netherlands
Tel.: (31) 756518518
Web Site: http://www.genpact.com
Emp.: 300
Business Process Outsourcing Services
N.A.I.C.S.: 561499

Subsidiary (Domestic):

Genpact Resourcing Services B.V. (2)
Mathenesserlaan 231, Rotterdam, 3021 HB, Netherlands
Tel.: (31) 104776456
Business Process Outsourcing Services
N.A.I.C.S.: 561499

Genpact Outsourcing Services Costa Rica, S.R.L. (1)
Lagunilla Ultra Park II Building 4, Heredia, Costa Rica
Tel.: (506) 25621634
Professional Firm Services
N.A.I.C.S.: 541990

Genpact PL Sp. Z O.O. (1)
Opolska 112 Street O3 Business Campus, 31-323, Krakow, Poland
Tel.: (48) 124436000
Web Site: http://www.genpact.com
Software Development Services
N.A.I.C.S.: 513210

Genpact Regulatory Affairs UK Limited (1)
4th Floor 66 Buckingham Gate, London, SW1E 6AU, United Kingdom
Tel.: (44) 2072275200
Software Development Services
N.A.I.C.S.: 513210
Casper Synnott (VP)

Genpact Romania Srl (1)
5-7 Dimitrie Pompeiu Blvd Building A sector 2, HERMES Business Park, 020335, Bucharest, Romania
Tel.: (40) 212538451
Web Site: http://www.genpact.com
Software Development Services
N.A.I.C.S.: 513210

Genpact Services Czech s.r.o. (1)
Slavickova 1a, 638 00, Brno, Czech Republic
Tel.: (420) 545193222
Management Services
N.A.I.C.S.: 541611
Barend van Doorn (VP)

Genpact Services Hungary Kft (1)
Building A Budapest Vaci ut 117-119 Vaci Greens, Budapest, 1138, Hungary
Tel.: (36) 13308915
Web Site: http://www.genpact.com
Software Development Services
N.A.I.C.S.: 513210

Subsidiary (Domestic):

Genpact Hungary Process Szolgaltato Kft. (2)
Duna Plz Vaci ut 178 4.e, 1138, Budapest, Hungary
Tel.: (36) 13308900
Sales Range: $75-99.9 Million
Emp.: 300
Software Development Services
N.A.I.C.S.: 513210

Genpact Singapore Pte. Ltd. (1)
30/F Singapore Land Tower 50 Raffles Place, Singapore, 048623, Singapore
Tel.: (65) 66323455
Software Development Services
N.A.I.C.S.: 513210
Sitesh Kaushik (VP-Sls & Bus Dev)

Genpact South Africa (Proprietary) Limited (1)
Limited Building 2 Woodmead Country Club Estate 21 Woodlands Drive, Woodmead Gauteng, Johannesburg, 2191, South Africa
Tel.: (27) 119712000
Business Process Outsourcing Services
N.A.I.C.S.: 561499

Genpact WB LLC (1)
335 New Commerce Blvd, Wilkes Barre, PA 18703
Tel.: (570) 825-6191
Software Development Services
N.A.I.C.S.: 513210

Headstrong Corporation (1)
11921 Freedom Dr Ste 550, Reston, VA 20190
Tel.: (703) 272-6761
Web Site: http://www.headstrong.com
Sales Range: $400-449.9 Million
Emp.: 2,300
Software Development Services
N.A.I.C.S.: 513210

Subsidiary (Domestic):

Headstrong Business Services, Inc. (2)
11911 Freedom Dr 900, Reston, VA 20190
Tel.: (703) 995-2107
Web Site: http://www.genpact.com
Software Development Services
N.A.I.C.S.: 513210

Subsidiary (Non-US):

Headstrong Philippines, Inc. (2)
15th To 17th Floors Export Bank Pla, Senator Gil Puyat Avenue Corner Chi, Makati, 1200, Philippines
Tel.: (63) 28861888
Software Development Services
N.A.I.C.S.: 513210

Subsidiary (Domestic):

iX Partners Ltd. (2)
54 Stiles Rd Ste 207, Salem, NH 03079
Tel.: (603) 890-1212
Sales Range: $1-9.9 Million
Emp.: 26
Software Publisher
N.A.I.C.S.: 513210

Jawood Business Process Solutions, LLC (1)
32270 Telegraph Rd Ste 200, Bingham Farms, MI 48025
Tel.: (248) 833-8000
Healthcare Support Services
N.A.I.C.S.: 561499

LeaseDimensions, Inc. (1)
1410 SW Morrison St, Portland, OR 97205
Tel.: (503) 222-9828
Computer System Design Services
N.A.I.C.S.: 541512

Leasedimensions, Inc. (1)
1410 SW Morrison St 7th Fl, Portland, OR 97205
Tel.: (503) 222-9828
Web Site: http://www.leasedimensions.com
Leasing & Loan Service Provider
N.A.I.C.S.: 522320

PNMSoft Ltd. (1)
HaMahshev St 1 Entrance C 3rd Floor, Netanya, 4250711, Israel
Tel.: (972) 98853633
Software Development Services
N.A.I.C.S.: 541511

PNMSoft Portugal SOC Unipessoal, Lda. (1)
Av Infante D Henrique 26 Santa Maria da Feira, Lisbon, 1149-096, Portugal
Tel.: (351) 211212038
Software Development Services
N.A.I.C.S.: 541511

PNMSoft UK Limited (1)
38 Clarendon Road, Watford, WD17 1JJ, Hertfordshire, United Kingdom
Tel.: (44) 1923813420
Software Development Services
N.A.I.C.S.: 541511

PNMSoft USA Inc.Inc... (1)
1155 Ave of the Americas 4th Fl, New York, NY 10036
Tel.: (212) 896-6600
Software Development Services
N.A.I.C.S.: 541511

Pharmalink Consulting Inc. (1)
245 Pk Ave 39th Fl, New York, NY 10167
Tel.: (800) 434-5808
Web Site: http://www.pharmalinkconsulting.com
General Management Consulting Services
N.A.I.C.S.: 541611

Pharmalink Consulting Ltd. (1)
Vandervell House Vanwall Business Park, Maidenhead, SL6 4UB, Berkshire, United Kingdom
Tel.: (44) 1628 860300
Web Site: http://www.pharmalinkconsulting.com
Emp.: 75
Regulatory Affairs Consulting Services
N.A.I.C.S.: 541611

Pharmalink Consulting Operations Ltd. (1)
Vandervell House Vanwall Business Park, Maidenhead, SL6 4UB, Berkshire, United Kingdom
Tel.: (44) 1628860300
Web Site: http://www.pharmalinkconsulting.com
Healthcare Support Services
N.A.I.C.S.: 561499

Pharmalink Consulting Operations Pvt. Ltd. (1)
C-715 to 717 215 Atrium Andheri-Kurla Road, Near Courtyard Marriott Hotel Andheri, Mumbai, 400059, India
Tel.: (91) 2261437777
Healthcare Support Services
N.A.I.C.S.: 561499
Suprabha A. Naralkar (Asst VP-Regulatory Affairs)

Pharmalink Consulting Pte. Ltd. (1)
50 Raffles Place 04, Singapore, 48616, Singapore
Tel.: (65) 68297203
Healthcare Support Services
N.A.I.C.S.: 561499

RAGE Frameworks India Pvt. Ltd.. (1)
The Cerebrum IT Park B-1 Suite 1B Kalyani Nagar, Pune, 411014, India
Tel.: (91) 2041413000
Financial Investment Advice Services
N.A.I.C.S.: 523940
Aashish Mehta (Head-Ops)

RAGE Frameworks, Inc. (1)
3 Allied Dr Ste 230, Dedham, MA 02026
Tel.: (781) 493-6900
Web Site: http://www.genpact.com
Financial Investment Advice Services
N.A.I.C.S.: 523940

Rightpoint India Digital Private Limited (1)
Raghukul Tower 5th Floor, Jaipur, 302021, Rajasthan, India
Tel.: (91) 1414919262
Information Technology Services
N.A.I.C.S.: 541519

SomethingDigital.Com LLC (1)
58 W 40th St 7th Fl, New York, NY 10018
Tel.: (646) 561-6600
Web Site: http://www.somethingdigital.com
Information Technology Services
N.A.I.C.S.: 541511
Greg Steinberg (Pres)

TandemSeven, Inc. (1)
4 Court St, Plymouth, MA 02360
Tel.: (508) 746-6116
Web Site: http://www.tandemseven.com
Business Management & Outsourcing Services
N.A.I.C.S.: 561311

Triumph On-Demand, Inc. (1)
100 Tri County Pkwy 200, Cincinnati, OH 45246
Tel.: (513) 438-4036
Engineeering Services
N.A.I.C.S.: 541330

GENPHARMASEC LIMITED

Office No 104 and 105 Akurli Road, Gundecha Industrial Premises Co-Operative Society Ltd Kandivali East, Mumbai, 400101, India
Tel.: (91) 8655550242
Web Site: https://www.genpharmasec.com
531592—(BOM)
Rev.: $2,953,222
Assets: $3,797,370
Liabilities: $977,054
Net Worth: $2,820,316
Earnings: $171,642
Emp.: 2
Fiscal Year-end: 03/31/21
Chemical Products Mfr
N.A.I.C.S.: 325998
Dollar Azad Chheda (CFO)

GENROBOTIC INNOVATIONS PRIVATE LIMITED

Building Technopark Campus, Thiruvananthapuram, 695581, Kerala, India
Tel.: (91) 9961616166
Year Founded: 2017
Software Development Services
N.A.I.C.S.: 541511

GENSCRIPT BIOTECH CORPORATION

28 Yongxi Road, Jiangning Science Park, Nanjing, Jiangsu, China
Tel.: (86) 2558897288   Ky
Web Site: https://www.genscript.com
Year Founded: 2002
1548—(HKG)
Rev.: $511,062,000
Assets: $2,232,770,000
Liabilities: $1,139,815,000
Net Worth: $1,092,955,000
Earnings: ($500,954,000)
Emp.: 5,255
Fiscal Year-end: 12/31/21
Life Science Research Services
N.A.I.C.S.: 541715
Frank Zhang (Co-Founder, Chm & CEO)

Subsidiaries:

GenScript USA Incorporated (1)
860 Centennial Ave, Piscataway, NJ 08854   (100%)
Tel.: (732) 885-9188
Life Science Research Services
N.A.I.C.S.: 541714

Subsidiary (Domestic):

Customarray, Inc. (2)
18916 N Creek Pkwy Ste 115, Bothell, WA 98011-8017
Tel.: (732) 885-9188
Web Site: http://www.customarrayinc.com
Analytical Laboratory Instrument Mfr
N.A.I.C.S.: 334516

Genscript Japan Inc. (1)
ism Kanda 4F 48 Kandahigashimatsushitacho, Chiyoda-ku, Tokyo, 101-0042, Japan
Tel.: (81) 368116572
Life Science Research & Development Services
N.A.I.C.S.: 541715

GENSIGHT BIOLOGICS S.A.

74 Rue du Faubourg Saint-Antoine, 75012, Paris, France
Tel.: (33) 176217220   FR
Web Site: https://www.gensight-biologics.com
Year Founded: 2012
SIGHT—(EUR)
Rev.: $1,398,609
Assets: $10,080,583
Liabilities: $43,971,741
Net Worth: ($33,891,158)
Earnings: ($28,943,592)
Emp.: 16

GENSIGHT BIOLOGICS S.A.

GenSight Biologics S.A.—(Continued)
Fiscal Year-end: 12/31/23
Biotechnology Research & Development Services
N.A.I.C.S.: 541714
Bernard Gilly *(Co-Founder)*

GENSOL ENGINEERING LTD.
Block A 15th Floor Westgate Business Bay, Makarba, Ahmedabad, 380051, Gujarat, India
Tel.: (91) 7961690000
Web Site: https://www.gensol.in
Year Founded: 2007
GENSOL—(NSE)
Rev.: $22,167,600
Assets: $28,340,130
Liabilities: $21,994,245
Net Worth: $6,345,885
Earnings: $1,513,785
Emp.: 450
Fiscal Year-end: 03/31/22
Engineeering Services
N.A.I.C.S.: 541330
Anmol Singh Jaggi *(Mng Dir)*

GENSOURCE POTASH CORPORATION
Suite 1100 - 201 1st Ave S, Saskatoon, S7K 1J5, SK, Canada
Tel.: (306) 974-6414
Web Site: https://www.gensourcepotash.ca
UGN—(DEU)
Rev.: $930
Assets: $18,430,718
Liabilities: $7,014,256
Net Worth: $11,416,462
Earnings: ($1,840,779)
Fiscal Year-end: 12/31/22
Mineral Exploration Services
N.A.I.C.S.: 212390
Mike Ferguson *(Pres & CEO)*

GENTAS AS
Tasdelen Street No 27, 6160, Ankara, Turkiye
Tel.: (90) 3123530206
Web Site: https://www.en.gentas.com.tr
GENTS—(IST)
Rev.: $48,469,380
Assets: $39,559,881
Liabilities: $17,896,632
Net Worth: $21,663,249
Earnings: $7,178,263
Fiscal Year-end: 12/31/22
Paper Material Product Mfr
N.A.I.C.S.: 322299
Orhan Kahraman *(CEO)*

Subsidiaries:

5K Yuzey Teknolojileri A.S. (1)
Yildirim Beyazit Cd No 9, Balikhisar Akyurt, 06750, Ankara, Turkiye
Tel.: (90) 3128475585
Web Site: https://www.5k.com.tr
Furniture Product Mfr & Distr
N.A.I.C.S.: 337126

GENMAR Yapi Urunleri A.S. (1)
Tasdelen Caddesi No 27 Siteler, 06160, Ankara, Turkiye
Tel.: (90) 3123483434
Web Site: https://en.genmaryapi.com
Furniture Mfr & Distr
N.A.I.C.S.: 337126

GENTAS KIMYA Sanayi ve Ticaret Pazarlama A.S. (1)
Istanbul Tuzla Kimya Sanayicileri Organize Sanayi Bolgesi, Melek Aras Bulvari Analitik Cd No 82 Tuzla, Istanbul, Turkiye
Tel.: (90) 21659317252627
Web Site: https://www.gentaskimya.com
Formaldehyde Resin Mfr
N.A.I.C.S.: 325211

GENTEC
2625 Dalton Avenue, Quebec, G1P 3S9, QC, Canada
Tel.: (418) 651-8000
Web Site: http://www.gentec-intl.com
Year Founded: 1959
Sales Range: $10-24.9 Million
Emp.: 100
Industrial Equipment Mfr
N.A.I.C.S.: 335314
Joel Seigel *(Pres & CEO)*

GENTEK BUILDING PRODUCTS LTD.
1001 Corporate Dr, Burlington, L7L 5V5, ON, Canada
Tel.: (905) 319-5633
Web Site: https://www.gentek.ca
Rev.: $68,451,600
Emp.: 600
Vinyl, Aluminum & Steel Exterior Building Products Mfr
N.A.I.C.S.: 238190
Carole Matthewson *(Mgr-HR)*

GENTERA, S.A.B. DE C.V.
Insurgentes Sur 1458 Col Actipan, Alcaldia Benito Juarez, 03230, Mexico, Mexico
Tel.: (52) 5552767250   MX
Web Site: https://www.gentera.com.mx
Year Founded: 1990
GENTERA—(MEX)
Rev.: $1,915,449,135
Assets: $5,103,641,719
Liabilities: $3,460,582,425
Net Worth: $1,643,059,294
Earnings: $297,666,770
Emp.: 24,861
Fiscal Year-end: 12/31/23
Bank Holding Company
N.A.I.C.S.: 551111

Subsidiaries:

Banco Compartamos, S.A., Institucion de Banca Multiple (1)
Av Insurgentes Sur 553 piso 1 de oficinas, Col Escandon, CP 11800, Mexico, DF, Mexico
Tel.: (52) 5552766398
Web Site: http://www.compartamos.com
Rev.: $1,399,776,219
Assets: $2,891,763,146
Liabilities: $2,131,039,537
Net Worth: $760,723,608
Earnings: $191,079,441
Emp.: 15,050
Fiscal Year-end: 12/31/2023
General Banking & Financial Services
N.A.I.C.S.: 522110
Carlos Antonio Danel Cendoya *(Pres)*

GENTIAN DIAGNOSTICS AS
Bjornasveien 5, 1596, Moss, Norway
Tel.: (47) 99339905
Web Site: http://www.gentian.com
Year Founded: 2001
GENT—(OSL)
Rev.: $10,338,260
Assets: $17,346,204
Liabilities: $3,105,487
Net Worth: $14,240,717
Earnings: ($2,181,600)
Emp.: 55
Fiscal Year-end: 12/31/22
Diagnostic Products Mfr
N.A.I.C.S.: 325413
Tomas Settevik *(Chm)*

Subsidiaries:

Gentian USA Inc. (1)
215 N Eola Dr, Orlando, FL 32801
Pharmaceuticals Mfr
N.A.I.C.S.: 325412

Getica AB (1)
Medicinaregatan 9C, 413 90, Gothenburg, Sweden
Tel.: (46) 728588187
Web Site: https://www.geticadiagnostics.com
Biotechnology Research & Development Services
N.A.I.C.S.: 541714

PreTect AS (1)
Ustadhagan 8, 3490, Klokkarstua, Norway
Tel.: (47) 32798800
Web Site: http://www.pretect.no
Pharmaceuticals Mfr
N.A.I.C.S.: 325412
Bente Falang *(CEO)*

GENTILI MOSCONI S.P.A.
Via Tevere 7/9 Casnate con Bernate, 22070, Como, Italy
Tel.: (39) 031451436
Web Site: https://www.gentilimosconi.it
GM—(ITA)
Rev.: $55,777,680
Assets: $56,061,375
Liabilities: $14,284,137
Net Worth: $41,777,238
Earnings: $5,778,784
Emp.: 157
Fiscal Year-end: 12/31/23
Textile Products Mfr
N.A.I.C.S.: 313310
Francesco Gentili *(Chm)*

GENTING BERHAD
14th Floor Wisma Genting, Jalan Sultan Ismail, 50250, Kuala Lumpur, Malaysia
Tel.: (60) 321782288   MY
Web Site: https://www.genting.com
Year Founded: 1965
GENTING—(KLS)
Rev.: $4,737,291,005
Assets: $21,695,153,439
Liabilities: $10,501,523,810
Net Worth: $11,193,629,630
Earnings: $9,417,989
Emp.: 52,000
Fiscal Year-end: 12/31/22
Holding Company
N.A.I.C.S.: 551112
Kok Thay Lim *(Chm & CEO)*

Subsidiaries:

ACGT Sdn Bhd (1)
Tel.: (60) 323332288
Sales Range: $25-49.9 Million
Emp.: 180
Genomics Research & Development Services
N.A.I.C.S.: 541715
Derrik Khoo Sin Huat *(CEO)*

Ascend Solutions Sdn Bhd (1)
19th Fl Wisma Genting Jalan Sultan Ismail, 50250, Kuala Lumpur, Malaysia
Tel.: (60) 323336930
Web Site: https://www.ascendsolutions.com.my
Sales Range: $75-99.9 Million
Emp.: 420
Software Development Services
N.A.I.C.S.: 541511

DNA Electronics Ltd. (1)
Ugli Campus Block C, 56 Wood Lane, London, W12 7SB, United Kingdom (63.8%)
Tel.: (44) 20 7036 2100
Web Site: http://www.dnae.com
Emp.: 80
DNA Analysis Equipment Mfr
N.A.I.C.S.: 339112

Subsidiary (US):

nanoMR, Inc. (2)
5741 Midway Park Blvd Ste 110, Albuquerque, NM 87109
Tel.: (505) 924-6301
Web Site: http://www.nanomr.com
Medical Diagnostic Devices Mfr
N.A.I.C.S.: 339112

DNA Electronics, Inc. (1)

INTERNATIONAL PUBLIC

1891 Rutherford Rd Ste 100, Carlsbad, CA 92008
Tel.: (760) 444-9410
Clinical Diagnostic Mfr
N.A.I.C.S.: 325412
Christofer Toumazou *(Chm)*

DNA Electronics, Inc. (1)
1891 Rutherford Rd Ste 100, Carlsbad, CA 92008
Tel.: (760) 444-9410
Web Site: https://www.dnae.com
Clinical Diagnostic Mfr
N.A.I.C.S.: 325412
Christofer Toumazou *(Chm)*

GT Diagnostics (UK) Limited (1)
395 King Street, Aberdeen, AB24 5RP, United Kingdom
Tel.: (44) 1224440990
Web Site: https://www.gtdiag.com
Pharmaceuticals Product Mfr
N.A.I.C.S.: 325412

Genting (Labuan) Limited (1)
Lot 3 2nd Fl Lazenda Phase 3 Shophouse Jalan Abdullah, 87000, Labuan, Malaysia
Tel.: (60) 87427018
Investment Management Service
N.A.I.C.S.: 523999

Genting Bio-Oil Sdn Bhd (1)
22nd Floor Wisma Genting 28 Jalan Sultan Ismail, 50250, Kuala Lumpur, Malaysia
Tel.: (60) 323332211
Oil & Gas Exploration Services
N.A.I.C.S.: 213112

Genting International (Singapore) Pte Ltd (1)
9 Penang Road 11-18 Park Mall, Singapore, 238459, Singapore
Tel.: (65) 68239888
Investment Management Service
N.A.I.C.S.: 523999

Genting International Japan Co. Ltd (1)
1-6-12 Nishishimbashi Aios Toranomon 1005, Minato-Ku, Tokyo, 105-0003, Japan
Tel.: (81) 335004088
Home Management Services
N.A.I.C.S.: 721110

Genting International Sdn Bhd (1)
16th Floor Wisma Genting 28 Jalan Sultan Ismail, Kuala Lumpur, 50250, Malaysia
Tel.: (60) 321782288
Investment Management Service
N.A.I.C.S.: 523999

Genting Malaysia Berhad (1)
14th Floor Wisma Genting Jalan Sultan Ismail, 50250, Kuala Lumpur, Malaysia
Tel.: (60) 321782233
Web Site: https://www.gentingmalaysia.com
Rev.: $1,820,740,741
Assets: $6,059,470,899
Liabilities: $3,534,814,815
Net Worth: $2,524,656,085
Earnings: ($141,248,677)
Emp.: 15,278
Fiscal Year-end: 12/31/2022
Hotel & Casino Operator
N.A.I.C.S.: 721110
Kok Thay Lim *(Deputy Chm & CEO)*

Genting Management and Consultancy Services Sdn Bhd (1)
24th Floor Wisma Genting, Jalan Sultan Ismail, 50250, Kuala Lumpur, Malaysia
Tel.: (60) 321782288
Web Site: http://www.genting.com
Management Consulting Services
N.A.I.C.S.: 541618

Genting Oil & Gas Limited (1)
22th Floor Wisma Genting, Jalan Sultan Ismail, 50250, Kuala Lumpur, Malaysia
Tel.: (60) 321782288
Oil & Gas Operations
N.A.I.C.S.: 213112

Genting Oil & Gas Sdn Bhd (1)
22nd Floor Wisma Genting Jalan Sultan Ismail, 50250, Kuala Lumpur, Malaysia
Tel.: (60) 321782211
Investment Holding Company Services
N.A.I.C.S.: 551112

Genting Plantations Berhad (1)

AND PRIVATE COMPANIES

14th Floor Wisma Genting Jalan Sultan Ismail, 50250, Kuala Lumpur, Malaysia
Tel.: (60) 321782288
Web Site:
https://www.gentingplantations.com
Rev.: $675,086,138
Assets: $1,860,701,376
Liabilities: $737,067,513
Net Worth: $1,123,633,862
Earnings: $102,292,275
Emp.: 2,070
Fiscal Year-end: 12/31/2022
Property Development Services
N.A.I.C.S.: 531311
Kok Thay Lim *(Deputy Chm)*

Genting Property Sdn. Bhd. (1)
3rd Floor Wisma Genting, Jalan Sultan Ismail, 50250, Kuala Lumpur, Malaysia
Tel.: (60) 323332255
Land Subdivision
N.A.I.C.S.: 237210

Genting Sanyen Paperboard Sdn Bhd (1)
Lot 7090 Mukim Tanjung 12 Bukit Canggang, Daerah Kuala Langat Banting, Kuala Langat, Malaysia
Tel.: (60) 331826800
Paperboard Mills
N.A.I.C.S.: 322130

Genting Sanyen Power Sdn Bhd (1)
Lot 7090 Mukim Tanjung 12 Bukit Canggang, Daerah Kuala Langat Banting, Kuala Langat, Malaysia
Tel.: (60) 331826800
Web Site: http://www.gentingsanyen.com
Sales Range: $500-549.9 Million
Emp.: 1,000
Electric Power Generation
N.A.I.C.S.: 221118
T. S. Ong *(CEO)*

Genting Singapore Limited (1)
10 Sentosa Gateway, Singapore, 98270, Singapore
Tel.: (65) 65778888
Web Site:
https://www.gentingsingapore.com
Rev.: $1,831,120,199
Assets: $6,927,792,922
Liabilities: $723,031,886
Net Worth: $6,204,761,036
Earnings: $463,214,421
Emp.: 4,113
Fiscal Year-end: 12/31/2023
Developer & Operator of Hotels, Resorts & Casinos
N.A.I.C.S.: 721120
Kok Thay Lim *(Chm)*

Co-Headquarters (Domestic):

Genting Singapore PLC (2)
10 Sentosa Gateway Resorts World Sentosa, Singapore, 098270, Singapore
Tel.: (65) 65778888
Web Site: http://www.gentingsingapore.com
Investment Services
N.A.I.C.S.: 523999
Hee Teck Tan *(Pres & COO)*

PT Genting Plantations Nusantara (1)
DBS Tower 15th Floor Ciputra World 1 Jl Prof Dr Satrio Kav 3-5, Jakarta, 12940, Indonesia
Tel.: (62) 2129887600
Bio Technology Services
N.A.I.C.S.: 541714

Resorts World Las Vegas LLC (1)
3000 S Las Vegas Blvd, Las Vegas, NV 89109
Tel.: (702) 676-7000
Web Site: https://www.rwlasvegas.com
Hotel Services
N.A.I.C.S.: 721110

Resorts World at Sentosa Pte. Ltd. (1)
8 Sentosa Gateway, Singapore, 098269, Singapore
Tel.: (65) 65778888
Web Site: http://www.rwsentosa.com
Leisure Resort Operation & Management Services
N.A.I.C.S.: 721110

Star Eagle Holdings Limited (1)
C/o Offshore Incorporations Limited Offshore Incorporations Centre, Road Town, Virgin Islands (British)
Tel.: (284) 494 8184
Investment Management Service
N.A.I.C.S.: 523999

GENTING HONG KONG LIMITED
Suite 1501 Ocean Centre 5 Canton Road, Tsimshatsui, Kowloon, China (Hong Kong)
Tel.: (852) 23782000 BM
Web Site: http://www.gentinghk.com
Year Founded: 1993
0678—(OTCIQ)
Rev.: $366,822,000
Assets: $6,720,633,000
Liabilities: $3,978,226,000
Net Worth: $2,742,407,000
Earnings: ($1,715,630,000)
Emp.: 7,000
Fiscal Year-end: 12/31/20
Holding Company; Cruise Lines & Casino Resorts Owner & Operator
N.A.I.C.S.: 551112
Walter Littlejohn III *(Sr VP-Crystal River Cruises & Mng Dir-Crystal River Cruises)*

Subsidiaries:

Crystal Cruises, LLC (1)
11755 Wilshire Blvd Ste 900, Los Angeles, CA 90025
Tel.: (310) 785-9300
Web Site: http://www.crystalcruises.com
Emp.: 200
Cruise Operator
N.A.I.C.S.: 483112
Nitsa Lewis *(VP-Mktg)*

MV Werften Rostock GmbH (1)
Werftallee 10, Warnemunde, 18119, Rostock, Germany
Tel.: (49) 3815100
Ship Building Services
N.A.I.C.S.: 336611

MV Werften Stralsund GmbH (1)
An der Werft 5, 18439, Stralsund, Germany
Tel.: (49) 3831660
Ship Building Services
N.A.I.C.S.: 336611

Star Cruises (HK) Limited (1)
Ste 1501 Ocean Ctr 5 Canton Rd, Tsimshatsui, Kowloon, China (Hong Kong)
Tel.: (852) 23782000
Web Site: http://www.starcruises.com
Sales Range: $25-49.9 Million
Cruise Line; Joint Venture of Star Cruises PLC (60%) & Carnival Corporation (40%)
N.A.I.C.S.: 483114
Terry Chu *(Asst Gen Mgr)*

Subsidiary (Non-US):

Lloyd Werft Bremerhaven GmbH (2)
Bruckenstrasse 25, Bremerhaven, 27568, Germany
Tel.: (49) 4714780
Web Site: http://www.lloydwerft.com
Ship Building & Repairing Services
N.A.I.C.S.: 336611
Thorsten Beiler *(Dir-Technical)*

Travellers International Hotel Group, Inc. (1)
10/F Newport Entertainment & Commercial Centre Newport Boulevard, Newport City, Pasay, 1309, Metro Manila, Philippines (58.42%)
Tel.: (63) 2 908 8000
Web Site: http://www.travellers.com.ph
Rev.: $422,660,333
Assets: $1,728,409,033
Liabilities: $843,735,869
Net Worth: $884,673,164
Earnings: $4,833,959
Emp.: 4,785
Fiscal Year-end: 12/31/2017
Holding Company; Hotel & Casino Operator
N.A.I.C.S.: 551112

Walter L. Mactal *(Pres, CEO, Mng Dir, CFO, Chief Admin Officer & Chief Legal Officer)*

GENTLEMENS EQUITY S.A.
Avenida da Liberdade N110 1st, 1269-046, Lisbon, Portugal
Tel.: (351) 213404620
Web Site:
https://www.gentlemensequity.com
MLGEQ—(EUR)
Rev.: $202,660
Assets: $2,249,835
Liabilities: $517,392
Net Worth: $1,732,442
Earnings: ($2,937,953)
Fiscal Year-end: 12/31/20
Holding Company
N.A.I.C.S.: 551112
Nikola Trajanov *(Chm & CEO)*

GENTOO GROUP LTD.
Emperor House 2 Emperor Way Doxford International Business Park, Sunderland, SR3 3XR, United Kingdom
Tel.: (44) 191 525 5000
Web Site:
http://www.gentoogroup.com
Sales Range: $300-349.9 Million
Emp.: 1,700
Residential Housing Development & Management Services
N.A.I.C.S.: 236115
Nigel Wilson *(CEO)*

GENTOR RESOURCES, INC.
1. First Canadian Place 100 King St W Ste 7070, PO Box 419, Toronto, M5X 1E3, ON, Canada
Tel.: (416) 361-2510 FL
Web Site:
https://www.gentorresources.com
Year Founded: 2005
GNTOF—(OTCIQ)
Rev.: $8
Assets: $25,085
Liabilities: $1,092,950
Net Worth: ($1,067,865)
Earnings: ($257,913)
Emp.: 3
Fiscal Year-end: 12/31/22
Gold, Molybdenum & Tungsten Mining & Exploration Services
N.A.I.C.S.: 212220
Arnold T. Kondrat *(Founder, Pres & CEO)*

GENTOR, S.A. DE C.V.
Padre Mier Ote 578, Monterrey, 64000, NL, Mexico
Tel.: (52) 8 183 446500
Develops & Operates Co-Generation & Renewable Energy Facilities
N.A.I.C.S.: 335312
Rodolfo Flores Dominguez *(CEO)*

Subsidiaries:

American Gentor Corporation (1)
8415 Datapoint Dr Ste 75, San Antonio, TX 78229
Tel.: (210) 697-8155
Rev.: $18,000,000
Emp.: 1
Motors & Generators
N.A.I.C.S.: 335312
Isaac Ayala *(Pres)*

Subsidiary (Domestic):

AGC Manufacturing Services Inc (2)
20701 E 81st St, Broken Arrow, OK 74014
Tel.: (918) 251-0490
Web Site: http://www.agcmfg.com
Power Generators
N.A.I.C.S.: 335312

GENTRACK GROUP LIMITED
17 Hargreaves Street St Marys Bay, Auckland, 1011, New Zealand
Tel.: (64) 99666090 NZ
Web Site: https://www.gentrack.com
Year Founded: 1989
GTK—(ASX)
Rev.: $101,605,263
Assets: $149,266,148
Liabilities: $40,763,756
Net Worth: $108,502,392
Earnings: $6,008,373
Emp.: 748
Fiscal Year-end: 09/30/23
Computer System Design Services
N.A.I.C.S.: 541512
Kenton Judson *(Dir-Ops-UK & Europe)*

Subsidiaries:

Blip Systems A/S (1)
Haekken 2, 9310, Vodskov, Denmark
Tel.: (45) 98258200
Web Site: http://www.blipsystems.com
Analytical Application Software Development Services
N.A.I.C.S.: 541511
Peter Knudsen *(CEO & Sls Mgr-EMEA)*

CA Plus Limited (1)
SkyParks Business Centre Malta International Airport, Luqa, LQA 4000, Malta
Tel.: (356) 21319977
Web Site: http://concessionaireanalyzer.com
Software Development Services
N.A.I.C.S.: 541511

Gentrack UK Limited (1)
203 Eversholt Street, London, NW1 1BU, United Kingdom
Tel.: (44) 2039061000
Web Site: https://www.gentrack.com
Software Development Services
N.A.I.C.S.: 541511

Subsidiary (Domestic):

Evolve Analytics Limited (2)
Imperial Place 2 Maxwell Road, Borehamwood, WD6 1JN, Herts, United Kingdom
Tel.: (44) 2082362050
Web Site: http://www.evolve-analytics.com
Imbalance Analysis & Recovery Services for Utility Industry
N.A.I.C.S.: 541618
Alan Duggan *(Mng Dir)*

GENTRACK LIMITED
17 Hargreaves Street St Marys Bay, Auckland, 1011, New Zealand
Tel.: (64) 9 966 6090 NZ
Web Site: http://www.gentrack.com
Emp.: 550
Fiscal Year-end: 09/30/18
Software Development Services
N.A.I.C.S.: 513210
John Clifford *(Chm)*

Subsidiaries:

Gentrack Ltd. (1)
203 Eversholt Street, Mabledon Place, London, NW1 1BU, United Kingdom
Tel.: (44) 2039061000
Web Site: http://www.gentrack.com
Utility Billing, Customer Management & Meter Data Management Solutions
N.A.I.C.S.: 513210

Gentrack Pty. Ltd. (1)
Level 9 390 St Kilda Rd, Melbourne, 3004, VIC, Australia
Tel.: (61) 398679100
Web Site: http://www.gentrack.com
Sales Range: $25-49.9 Million
Emp.: 40
Utility Billing Customer Management & Meter Data Management Solution Services
N.A.I.C.S.: 513210

GENTRACO FEED JSC
72 Nguyen Thai Hoc Street, Thot Not Ward, Thot Not District, Can Tho, Vietnam
Tel.: (84) 7103611366

GENTRACO FEED JSC

Gentraco Feed JSC—(Continued)
Web Site:
http://www.gentracofeed.com.vn
Sales Range: $50-74.9 Million
Emp.: 100
Animal Feed Mfr & Sales
N.A.I.C.S.: 311119
Kien T. Nguyen *(Chm-Mgmt Bd)*

GENUI GMBH

Neuer Wall 80, 20354, Hamburg, Germany
Tel.: (49) 40 320 8669 0   De
Web Site: http://www.genui.de
Private Investment Firm
N.A.I.C.S.: 523999
Patrick Gehlen *(Mng Dir)*

Subsidiaries:

Berge & Meer Touristik GmbH   (1)
Andreestrasse 27, 56578, Rengsdorf, Germany
Tel.: (49) 2634 962 6099
Web Site: http://www.berge-meer.de
Tour Operating Services
N.A.I.C.S.: 561520
Thomas Klein *(Chm & Mng Dir)*

Magnolia International Ltd.   (1)
St Johanns-Vorstadt 38, Basel, 4056, Switzerland
Tel.: (41) 61 228 90 00
Web Site: http://www.magnolia-cms.com
Sales Range: $10-24.9 Million
Content Management Software
N.A.I.C.S.: 513210
Pascal Mangold *(Co-Founder & CEO)*

Subsidiary (US):

Magnolia Americas, Inc.   (2)
168 SE 1st St Ste 1007, Miami, FL 33131
Tel.: (305) 673-3033
Content Management Software
N.A.I.C.S.: 513210

Subsidiary (Non-US):

Magnolia Espana Software and Computer Applications S.L.   (2)
Paseo de la Castellana 177 3B, 28046, Madrid, Spain
Tel.: (34) 601259014
Content Management Software
N.A.I.C.S.: 513210

Magnolia Software & Services CZ s.r.o.   (2)
Chobot 1578, 76701, Kromeriz, Czech Republic
Tel.: (420) 571 118 715
Content Management Software
N.A.I.C.S.: 513210
Jan Haderka *(Gen Mgr)*

GENUINE SOLUTIONS LIMITED

Solutions House Unit 1 HQ3 223 Hook Rise South, Surbiton, KT6 7LD, Surrey, United Kingdom
Tel.: (44) 20 3177 0000
Web Site:
http://www.genuinesolutions.co.uk
Year Founded: 2004
Sales Range: $125-149.9 Million
Emp.: 59
Mobile Accessory Whslr
N.A.I.C.S.: 423690
Paul Crossman *(CEO)*

GENUIT GROUP PLC

Polypipe 2024 Polypipe Broomhouse Lane, Doncaster, DN12 1ES, United Kingdom
Tel.: (44) 1709770000   UK
Web Site: https://www.polypipe.com
Year Founded: 2007
GEN—(LSE)
Rev: $749,439,900
Assets: $1,238,466,900
Liabilities: $483,124,950
Net Worth: $755,341,950
Earnings: $43,964,250
Fiscal Year-end: 12/31/22
Offices of Other Holding Companies
N.A.I.C.S.: 551112
Martin Payne *(CEO)*

Subsidiaries:

Polypipe Limited   (1)
Broomhouse Ln, Edlington, Doncaster, DN12 1ES, S Yorkshire, United Kingdom
Tel.: (44) 1709 770 000
Web Site: http://www.polypipe.com
Sales Range: $400-449.9 Million
Emp.: 2,000
Plastic Pipe & Pipe Fittings Mfr
N.A.I.C.S.: 326122
David Jaina *(Mng Dir)*

Subsidiary (Non-US):

Polypipe Gulf FZ LLC   (2)
Level 14 & 15 Commercial Bank Plaza Tower, PO Box 27111, Doha, 27111, Qatar
Tel.: (974) 44528394
Web Site: http://www.polypipegulf.com
Sales Range: $25-49.9 Million
Emp.: 3
Plastic Tank Mfr
N.A.I.C.S.: 326122
Adam Smith *(Gen Mgr)*

Polypipe Gulf FZ LLC   (2)
Dubai Media City Loft Office No 03 Entrance A 4th Floor Office no 404, PO Box 502320, Dubai, United Arab Emirates
Tel.: (971) 4 454 8328
Web Site: http://www.polypipe.com
Emp.: 15
Plastic Tank Mfr
N.A.I.C.S.: 326122
Robin Appleby *(Gen Mgr)*

Polypipe Italia s.r.l.   (2)
Pianmercato 5C-5D, Monleone di Cicagna, 16044, Genoa, Italy
Tel.: (39) 0185 92 399
Web Site: http://www.polypipeitalia.com
Sales Range: $25-49.9 Million
Emp.: 40
Plastic Tank Mfr
N.A.I.C.S.: 326122

Division (Domestic):

Polypipe Limited - Polypipe Building Products Division   (2)
Broomhouse Lane, Edlington, Doncaster, DN12 1ES, United Kingdom
Tel.: (44) 1709 770000
Plastic Piping Systems Mfr
N.A.I.C.S.: 326191
Gary Foord *(Reg Mgr-Sls)*

Polypipe Limited - Polypipe Civils Division   (2)
Charnwood Business Park North Road, Loughborough, LE11 1LE, United Kingdom
Tel.: (44) 1509 615100
Sales Range: $25-49.9 Million
Emp.: 100
Plastic Tank Mfr
N.A.I.C.S.: 326122

Polypipe Limited - Polypipe TDI Division   (2)
Broomhouse Lane, Edlington, Doncaster, DN12 1ES, South Yorkshire, United Kingdom
Tel.: (44) 1709770000
Plastic Tank Mfr
N.A.I.C.S.: 326122

Polypipe Limited - Polypipe Terrain Division   (2)
New Hythe Business Park College Road, Aylesford, ME20 7PJ, Kent, United Kingdom
Tel.: (44) 1622 795200
Web Site: http://www.polypipe.com
Sales Range: $50-74.9 Million
Emp.: 200
Plumbing Supplies Mfr
N.A.I.C.S.: 332913

Polypipe Limited - Polypipe Ventilation Division   (2)
Sandall Stones Road Kirk Sandall Industrial Estate, Doncaster, DN3 1QR, United Kingdom
Tel.: (44) 8443 715523
Web Site: http://www.polypipe.com
Sales Range: $25-49.9 Million
Emp.: 50
Ventilation System Mfr
N.A.I.C.S.: 335210
Neil Tilsley *(Mng Dir)*

Subsidiary (Domestic):

Robimatic Ltd.   (2)
Sandall Stones Road Kirk Sandall Insudtrial Estate, Doncaster, DN3 1QR, South Yorkshire, United Kingdom
Tel.: (44) 1302 790790
Plastic Product Merchandising Services
N.A.I.C.S.: 561990

GENUS PLC

Matrix House Basing View, Basingstoke, RG21 4DZ, Hampshire, United Kingdom
Tel.: (44) 1256347100
Web Site: https://www.genusplc.com
GNS—(LSE)
Rev: $845,298,280
Assets: $1,300,429,725
Liabilities: $612,992,921
Net Worth: $687,436,804
Earnings: $3,033,367
Emp.: 3,500
Fiscal Year-end: 06/30/24
Developer & Breeder of Genetically Improved Cattle, Pigs & Shrimp & Distr of Bovine Semen
N.A.I.C.S.: 115210
Bill Christianson *(COO-PIC)*

Subsidiaries:

ABS Argentina S.A.   (1)
Aaron Castellanos 1169, 3080, Santa Fe, Argentina
Tel.: (54) 3496428990
Web Site: https://www.absglobal.com
Dairy Product Mfr & Distr
N.A.I.C.S.: 311514

ABS Chile Limitada   (1)
Av Del Parque 4161-Office 601, Huechuraba, Chile
Tel.: (56) 27575500
Dairy Product Mfr & Distr
N.A.I.C.S.: 311514

ABS Global (Canada) Inc.   (1)
1525 Floradale Rd, Elmira, N3B 2Z1, ON, Canada
Dairy Product Mfr & Distr
N.A.I.C.S.: 311514
B. J. Mayfield *(Sls Mgr-Ontario & Atlantic Canada)*

ABS Italia S.r.l.   (1)
Via Bastida 6 Loc, Cavatigozzi, 26100, Cremona, Italy
Tel.: (39) 0372532011
Dairy Product Mfr & Distr
N.A.I.C.S.: 311514

ABS Pecplan Ltda.   (1)
Rod BR-050 Km 196, Caixa Postal 4046, Delta, 38020-300, MG, Brazil
Tel.: (55) 34 3319 5400
Web Site: http://www.abspecplan.com.br
Sales Range: $50-74.9 Million
Emp.: 80
Dairy Products Distr
N.A.I.C.S.: 424430

Bovec SAS   (1)
69 Chemin des Molieres - PA du Charpenay, 69210, Lentilly, France
Tel.: (33) 472522460
Web Site: https://www.bovec.fr
Livestock Farming Services
N.A.I.C.S.: 112990

Genus ABS Colombia SAS   (1)
Carrera 70 no 105-51, Bogota, Colombia
Tel.: (57) 3213707537
Dairy Product Mfr & Distr
N.A.I.C.S.: 311514

Genus Australia Pty Ltd   (1)
Langiballa Gerogery Rd, Table Top, Albury,

2642, NSW, Australia
Tel.: (61) 2 6049 9200
Web Site: http://www.absaust.com
Sales Range: $25-49.9 Million
Emp.: 20
Livestock Services
N.A.I.C.S.: 115210

Genus Breeding India Private Limited   (1)
5th Floor C wing Eternia Premises Co-op Soc Near Da Unit no 505 506, Dagdi Bunglow Wakdewadi, Pune, 411005, Maharashtra, India
Tel.: (91) 8002109210
Web Site: https://www.genusabsindia.com
Bovine Genetic & Reproduction Services
N.A.I.C.S.: 115210
Abhishek Kumar *(Head-Sls & Mktg)*

Genus Breeding Ltd   (1)
Alpha Building London Road, Nantwich, CW5 7JW, Cheshire, United Kingdom
Tel.: (44) 1270616681
Web Site: https://www.absglobal.com
Sales Range: $25-49.9 Million
Emp.: 100
Developer of Nutrition, Foot & Udder Care Products for Cattle
N.A.I.C.S.: 115210

Subsidiary (US):

ABS Global   (2)
1525 River Rd, De Forest, WI 53532-0459
Tel.: (608) 846-3721
Web Site: http://www.absglobal.com
Sales Range: $75-99.9 Million
Developer of Artificial Insemination Products for Cattle & Distr of Genetically Enhanced Bovine Semen
N.A.I.C.S.: 115210
Doug Frank *(Product Mgr-Beef)*

Subsidiary (Non-US):

ABS Mexico S.A. de C.V.   (3)
Kansas 2028 Quintas Campestre, Chihuahua, 31213, Mexico
Tel.: (52) 6144108847
Livestock Breeding Services
N.A.I.C.S.: 112990

Genus Ukraine LLC   (1)
Podlesnaya st 1, 03164, Kiev, Ukraine
Tel.: (380) 444226075
Web Site: http://www.absukraine.com
Cattle Breeding Services
N.A.I.C.S.: 115210

LLC Genus ABS Rus   (1)
Zheleznodorozhnaya Street Building 51 Letter Zh Room 2, 300062, Tula, Russia
Tel.: (7) 4872717170
Web Site: http://www.absglobal.com
Dairy Product Mfr & Distr
N.A.I.C.S.: 311514

PIC Genetics LLC   (1)
b-r Narodny 79A 9th floor, 308000, Belgorod, Russia
Tel.: (7) 4722200258
Web Site: http://ru.pic.com
Pig Farming Services
N.A.I.C.S.: 112210

PIC UK   (1)
2 Kingston Business Park, Kingston Bagpuize, OX13 5FE, Oxfordshire, United Kingdom
Tel.: (44) 1865822200
Web Site: http://www.pic.com
Sales Range: $200-249.9 Million
Emp.: 1,166
Supplier of Genetically Improved Swine Breeding Stock
N.A.I.C.S.: 112210
Stephanie Furniss *(Dir-Comml)*

Affiliate (Non-US):

Agroceres PIC   (2)
Rua 1 JN 1411 - Jardim Novo, Rio Claro, 13502-741, SP, Brazil
Tel.: (55) 1935268580
Web Site: https://agrocerespic.com.br
Sales Range: $75-99.9 Million
Emp.: 400
Supplier of Genetically Improved Swine Breeding Stock
N.A.I.C.S.: 112210

AND PRIVATE COMPANIES

Atahuampa PIC S.A. (2)
Calle Alfa 199, Callao, 18, Peru
Tel.: (51) 14 562 4004
Web Site: http://www.picperu.com
Sales Range: $10-24.9 Million
Emp.: 33
Supplier of Genetically Improved Swine Breeding Stock
N.A.I.C.S.: 112210
Julio Favre (Pres)

Subsidiary (Non-US):

Ceska PIC s.r.o. (2)
Marikova 2215/5a, 621 00, Brno, Czech Republic
Tel.: (420) 777602848
Web Site: https://www.ceskapic.cz
Sales Range: $25-49.9 Million
Emp.: 14
Supplier of Genetically Improved Swine Breeding Stock
N.A.I.C.S.: 112210
Pavel Mezera (Gen Mgr)

Affiliate (Non-US):

Iwatani Camborough Co. Ltd. (2)
Nihonbashi SOYIC Building 3F 3-11 Nihonbashi Koamicho, Chuo-Ku, Tokyo, 103-0016, Japan
Tel.: (81) 336685360
Web Site: http://www.camb.co.jp
Sales Range: $25-49.9 Million
Emp.: 100
Supplier of Genetically Improved Swine Breeding Stock
N.A.I.C.S.: 112210

Subsidiary (Non-US):

Kanhym Estates PIC South Africa (2)
PO Box 89, Middelburg, 1050, South Africa
Tel.: (27) 132497800
Web Site: http://www.kanhym.com
Sales Range: $10-24.9 Million
Emp.: 19
Pig Breeding, Genetic Technology, Health & Services
N.A.I.C.S.: 112210

Affiliate (Non-US):

PIC Andina S.A. (2)
Av de Parque 4161 Oficina 601, Huechuraba, 8580675, Chile
Tel.: (56) 227575500
Web Site: http://latam.pic.com
Sales Range: $25-49.9 Million
Emp.: 80
Pig Breeding Services
N.A.I.C.S.: 115210
Martin Parez (Comml Dir)

PIC Argentina (2)
Esmeralda 950 Torre Bellini CABA, 1425, Buenos Aires, Capital Federal, Argentina
Tel.: (54) 1153657445
Web Site: http://agrocerespic.com.ar
Sales Range: $10-24.9 Million
Emp.: 37
Supplier of Genetically Improved Swine Breeding Stock & Distr of Swine Semen
N.A.I.C.S.: 112210

PIC Australia (2)
Junee St, Box 39, Grong Grong, 2652, NSW, Australia
Tel.: (61) 269562105
Web Site: http://www.picaustralia.com.au
Sales Range: $10-24.9 Million
Emp.: 40
Supplier of Genetically Improved Swine Breeding Stock
N.A.I.C.S.: 112210
Clark Forbes (Mgr-Southern)

Subsidiary (Non-US):

PIC Benelux BV (2)
Saffierborch 18, 5241, Rosmalen, Netherlands
Tel.: (31) 735222080
Web Site: http://www.pic.com
Sales Range: $25-49.9 Million
Emp.: 6
Supplier of Genetically Improved Swine Breeding Stock
N.A.I.C.S.: 112210

Affiliate (Non-US):

PIC Colombia S.A. (2)
Carrera 48 N 26 Sur - 181 Local 101 Centro Integral Las Vegas, Envigado, Antioquia, Colombia
Tel.: (57) 4037435
Web Site: https://www.pic.co
Sales Range: $25-49.9 Million
Emp.: 170
Pig Breeding Services
N.A.I.C.S.: 112210

Subsidiary (Non-US):

PIC Denmark A/S (2)
Strandvej 16, 9000, Aalborg, SV, Denmark
Tel.: (45) 96340777
Web Site: http://www.pic.dk
Sales Range: $25-49.9 Million
Emp.: 5
Supplier of Genetically Improved Swine Breeding Stock
N.A.I.C.S.: 112210

PIC Deutschland GmbH (2)
Jathostrasse 11 A, 30163, Hannover, Germany
Tel.: (49) 511870850
Web Site: https://www.picdeutschland.de
Sales Range: $10-24.9 Million
Emp.: 50
Supplier of Genetically Improved Swine Breeding Stock
N.A.I.C.S.: 112210
Stewart Crichton (Mng Dir)

PIC Espana (2)
C/Pau Vila 22 2 piso, 08174, Sant Cugat del Valles, Barcelona, Spain
Tel.: (34) 935890360
Web Site: http://es.pic.com
Sales Range: $25-49.9 Million
Emp.: 200
Supplier of Genetically Improved Swine Breeding Stock
N.A.I.C.S.: 112210
Isaac Huerta (Mgr-Tech)

PIC France (2)
69 Chemin des Molieres - Parc d'activites du Charpenay, 69210, Lentilly, France
Tel.: (33) 296765050
Web Site: https://fr.pic.com
Sales Range: $25-49.9 Million
Emp.: 30
Supplier of Genetically Improved Swine Breeding Stock
N.A.I.C.S.: 112210

PIC Ireland GTC (2)
South Cregg, Knockannanig, Fermoy, Co Cork, Ireland
Tel.: (353) 2533091
Web Site: http://www.pic.com
Emp.: 5
Supplier of Genetically Improved Swine Breeding Stock
N.A.I.C.S.: 112210
Eduard Aldeweireldt (Gen Mgr)

PIC Italia S.p.a. (2)
Strada dei Loggi 22, Ponte San Giovanni, 06135, Perugia, Ponte San Giovanni, Italy
Tel.: (39) 0755990056
Web Site: https://it.pic.com
Sales Range: $25-49.9 Million
Emp.: 15
Supplier of Genetically Improved Swine Breeding Stock
N.A.I.C.S.: 112210

Affiliate (Non-US):

PIC Korea Inc. (2)
3F 237 Uam-ro Gayang-dong 436-9, Dong-gu, Daejeon, 300 805, Korea (South)
Tel.: (82) 426362947
Web Site: http://www.pickorea.co.kr
Sales Range: $25-49.9 Million
Emp.: 9
Pig Breeding Services
N.A.I.C.S.: 112210

Subsidiary (Non-US):

PIC Mexico (2)
W de la Barquera 7 Col, Villas Del Sur, 76040, Queretaro, Qro, Mexico
Tel.: (52) 4422129876
Web Site: http://latam.pic.com
Sales Range: $10-24.9 Million
Emp.: 34
Supplier of Genetically Improved Swine Breeding Stock
N.A.I.C.S.: 112210

Affiliate (Non-US):

PIC New Zealand (2)
5 Ross Street, PO Box 43019, Darfield, Dunedin, 7541, New Zealand
Tel.: (64) 33179035
Web Site: https://www.picnz.co.nz
Sales Range: $10-24.9 Million
Emp.: 39
Pig Breeding Services
N.A.I.C.S.: 112210

Subsidiary (Non-US):

PIC Philippines Inc. (2)
Unit 2102 21st Floor Jollibee Plaza F Ortigas Jr Road, Ortigas Center, Pasig, 1605, Manila, Philippines
Tel.: (63) 79142594
Web Site: http://ph.pic.com
Sales Range: $25-49.9 Million
Emp.: 95
Supplier of Genetically Improved Swine Breeding Stock
N.A.I.C.S.: 112210
Aurea Ortega (Officer-HR)

PIC Polska Sp. z.o.o. (2)
Wazow 8A, 01 986, Warsaw, Poland
Tel.: (48) 228647316
Web Site: http://www.genus.com
Sales Range: $25-49.9 Million
Emp.: 23
Supplier of Genetically Improved Swine Breeding Stock
N.A.I.C.S.: 112210

PIC Portugal (2)
Av General Norton de Matos n 59 A 1 A/B, 1495-148 Miraflores, Alges, Portugal
Tel.: (351) 219240987
Web Site: http://www.pic.com
Sales Range: $25-49.9 Million
Emp.: 9
Supplier of Genetically Improved Swine Breeding Stock
N.A.I.C.S.: 112210
Ean Bond (Gen Mgr)

PIC Siam Co., Ltd. (2)
91/1 Chaiyo Building 5A Floor Room 5A2 Rama 9 Rd, Huaykwang, Bangkok, 10310, Thailand
Tel.: (66) 26439961
Web Site: http://th.pic.com
Sales Range: $25-49.9 Million
Emp.: 10
Supplier of Genetically Improved Swine Breeding Stock
N.A.I.C.S.: 112210

PIC USA, Inc. (1)
100 Bluegrass Commons Blvd Ste 2200, Hendersonville, TN 37075
Tel.: (615) 265-2700
Web Site: https://www.pic.com
Sales Range: $25-49.9 Million
Emp.: 100
Supplier of Genetically Improved Swine Breeding Stock & Distr of Swine Semen
N.A.I.C.S.: 112210

Subsidiary (Non-US):

PIC Canada Ltd. (2)
99 Scurfield Blvd, Winnipeg, R3Y 1Y1, MB, Canada
Tel.: (204) 927-7120
Web Site: http://cae.pic.com
Sales Range: $25-49.9 Million
Emp.: 75
Supplier of Genetically Improved Swine Breeding Stock & Distr of Swine Semen
N.A.I.C.S.: 112210

Pig Improvement Company Deutschland GmbH (1)
Lorbeerrosenweg 10, 30916, Isernhagen, Germany
Tel.: (49) 511870850
Web Site: https://www.picdeutschland.de
Livestock Breeding Services
N.A.I.C.S.: 115210

GEO ENERGY RESOURCES LIMITED

Pig Improvement Company UK Limited (1)
Alpha Building London Road Stapeley, Nantwich, CW5 7JW, Cheshire, United Kingdom
Tel.: (44) 1270616710
Web Site: http://www.pic.com
Livestock Farming Services
N.A.I.C.S.: 115210
Steve Furniss (Dir-Comml)

Promar International Limited (1)
Alpha Building London Road, Stapeley, Nantwich, CW5 7JW, Cheshire, United Kingdom
Tel.: (44) 1270 616800
Web Site: http://www.promar-international.com
Emp.: 25
Agri Food Consulting Services
N.A.I.C.S.: 541690
Sandra Callwood (Head-Res)

St Jacobs Animal Breeding Corp. (1)
1525 River Rd, De Forest, WI 53525
Tel.: (608) 279-2016
Web Site: https://www.stjacobsabc.com
Cattle Breeding Services
N.A.I.C.S.: 115210
Brian Behnke (Bus Mgr)

Zitery S.A. (1)
Gral Maximo Tajes 7189, Montevideo, Uruguay
Tel.: (598) 26062036
Dairy Product Mfr & Distr
N.A.I.C.S.: 311514

GENUS POWER INFRASTRUCTURES LTD.

SPL-3 RIICO Industrial Area Sitapura Tonk Road, Jaipur, 302 022, India
Tel.: (91) 1417102400
Web Site: https://www.genuspower.com
Year Founded: 1994
530343—(BOM)
Rev.: $98,568,239
Assets: $199,268,797
Liabilities: $81,745,986
Net Worth: $117,522,810
Earnings: $3,473,928
Emp.: 832
Fiscal Year-end: 03/31/23
Electrical Meter Installation Services
N.A.I.C.S.: 238210
Ishwar Chand Agarwal (Chm)

GENUSPLUS GROUP LTD.

Level 1 63 Abernethy Road, Belmont, 6104, WA, Australia
Tel.: (61) 893906999 AU
Web Site: https://www.genus.com.au
Year Founded: 2017
GNP—(ASX)
Rev.: $292,018,873
Assets: $148,281,001
Liabilities: $79,834,674
Net Worth: $68,446,328
Earnings: $8,740,643
Emp.: 813
Fiscal Year-end: 06/30/23
Construction Services
N.A.I.C.S.: 237120
David Riches (Founder, CEO & Mng Dir)

GEO ENERGY RESOURCES LIMITED

7 Temasek Boulevard Suntec Tower One 3902, Singapore, 018982, Singapore
Tel.: (65) 67020888
Web Site: https://www.geocoal.com
RE4—(SES)
Rev.: $488,974,701
Assets: $937,367,723
Liabilities: $437,763,300
Net Worth: $499,604,423
Earnings: $62,743,199
Emp.: 342

GEO ENERGY RESOURCES LIMITED

Geo Energy Resources Limited—(Continued)
Fiscal Year-end: 12/31/23
Coal Mining & Distribution
N.A.I.C.S.: 212115
Charles Antonny Melati *(Co-Founder & Chm)*

Subsidiaries:

PT. Geo Energy Coalindo (1)
The Suites Tower 17th Floor Jl Boulevard Pantai Indah Kapuk, No 1 Kav Ofs, Jakarta, 14470, Indonesia
Tel.: (62) 2122511055
Coal Mining Services
N.A.I.C.S.: 213113

GEO HOLDINGS CORPORATION

OMC Bldg 8-8 Fujimi-cho, Naka-ku, Nagoya, 460-0014, Aichi, Japan
Tel.: (81) 523505700   JP
Web Site: https://www.geonet.co.jp
Year Founded: 1989
2681—(TKS)
Rev.: $2,867,735,280
Assets: $1,527,736,250
Liabilities: $950,359,360
Net Worth: $577,376,890
Earnings: $72,062,220
Emp.: 5,912
Fiscal Year-end: 03/31/24
Game Software, DVDs, CDs & Books Sales & Rental Services; Movie Theaters, Gaming Facilities & Bowling Alleys Owner & Operator
N.A.I.C.S.: 532282
Yasushi Yoshikawa *(Sr Mng Operating Officer & Exec Dir)*

Subsidiaries:

Chelsea International Co., Ltd. (1)
8th floor Imai Mitsubishi Building 3-53-11 Minami-Otsuka, Toshima-ku, Tokyo, 170-0005, Japan
Tel.: (81) 359049100
Web Site: https://www.chelsea.co.jp
Bag & Fashion Accessory Whslr
N.A.I.C.S.: 424130

EISYS, Inc. (1)
12th floor Sumitomo Fudosan Akihabara Ekimae Building, 300 Kanda Neribei-cho Chiyoda-ku, Tokyo, 101-0022, Japan
Tel.: (81) 358294613
Web Site: https://www.eisys.co.jp
Sales Range: $25-49.9 Million
Emp.: 40
Information Processing Services
N.A.I.C.S.: 519290

Entertainment Network Frontier Inc. (1)
Urano Bldg 1-50 Kanda Jinbocho, Chiyoda-ku, Tokyo, 171-0021, Japan
Tel.: (81) 359799938
Web Site: http://www.enet-f.com
Sales Range: $50-74.9 Million
Emp.: 17
Entertainment Software & Movie Videos Distr
N.A.I.C.S.: 423430

Family Book co., Ltd. (1)
319-3 Kiyoharacho, Ota, 373-0012, Gunma, Japan
Tel.: (81) 276379878
Book Whslr
N.A.I.C.S.: 424920

GEO Networks Corporation (1)
3-53-11 Imai Mitsubishi Building 7th Floor Minamiotsuka, Toshima-ku, Tokyo, 171-0005, Japan
Tel.: (81) 359797851
Web Site: http://www.geo-networks.co.jp
Movie Distr, Rental & Advertising Services
N.A.I.C.S.: 532282
Toshiki Hayashi *(CEO)*

GEO System Solutions Vietnam Co., Ltd. (1)
Lot 11 Floor 12A Vincom Center Building 70-72 Le Thanh Ton, Ben Nghe Ward District 1, Ho Chi Minh City, Vietnam
Tel.: (84) 2838220239
Web Site: https://geo-ssv.vn
Management Consulting Services
N.A.I.C.S.: 541611

GEO WEB SERVICE Co., Ltd (1)
2-1-25 Dojima, Kita-ku, Osaka, 530-0003, Japan
Tel.: (81) 662243136
Software Development Services
N.A.I.C.S.: 541511

GEO payment service corporation (1)
Erupisu Bldg 6-15-8 Honkomagome, Bunkyo, Tokyo, 113-0021, Japan
Tel.: (81) 570001293
Web Site: http://www.lueca.jp
Reloadable Prepaid Card Services
N.A.I.C.S.: 522210

Geo Business Support Co., Ltd. (1)
3 Parkside Hirota Part II 3F 5-11 Nyoishin-cho, Kasugai, 486-0918, Aichi, Japan
Tel.: (81) 526786334
Web Site: http://www.cococolorfull.com
Emp.: 38
Store Management Services
N.A.I.C.S.: 541611

Okura Holdings Corporation (1)
3F O-KURA Building 1-9-33 Hakata Station Minami, Hakata-ku, Fukuoka, 812-0016, Japan
Tel.: (81) 120096905
Web Site: https://www.wb-ookura.com
Watch Distr
N.A.I.C.S.: 423940

SBIGEO Marketing Co., Ltd. (1)
1-6-1 Roppongi, Minato-ku, Tokyo, 106-6019, Japan
Tel.: (81) 362290126
Financial Support Services
N.A.I.C.S.: 522299

T&G Corp. (1)
2-4-1 Sakashita Tohan Itabashi Center 4F, Itabashi-ku, Tokyo, 174-0043, Japan
Tel.: (81) 367748590
Web Site: http://www.tandg.jp
Books & Multimedia Retailer
N.A.I.C.S.: 459210

World Mobile Corporation (1)
4-7-19 Nihonbashi, Naniwa-ku, Osaka, 556-0005, Japan
Tel.: (81) 666490022
Web Site: https://www.worldmobile.jp
Mobile Device Whslr
N.A.I.C.S.: 423690

GEO-JADE PETROLEUM CORPORATION

3rd Floor Block A Pengrun Building 26 Yuyun Road, Chaoyang District, Beijing, 100016, China
Tel.: (86) 1051081800
Web Site: https://www.geojade.com
Year Founded: 1984
600759—(SHG)
Rev.: $398,205,063
Assets: $1,828,089,572
Liabilities: $1,265,222,111
Net Worth: $562,867,461
Earnings: ($103,697,474)
Fiscal Year-end: 12/31/22
Petroleum & Natural Gas Exploration & Production Services
N.A.I.C.S.: 211120
Huanlong Chen *(Chm & Pres)*

Subsidiaries:

Bankers Petroleum Ltd. (1)
Suite 800 777 - 8th Avenue SW, Calgary, T2P 3R5, AB, Canada
Tel.: (1) 403 513-2699
Web Site: http://www.bankerspetroleum.com
Sales Range: $250-299.9 Million
Emp.: 500
Petroleum & Natural Gas Exploration & Production Services
N.A.I.C.S.: 211120
Suneel Gupta *(COO & Exec VP)*

KoZhaN JSC (1)
31 Pirogov Str 6th floor, Almaty, 050040, Kazakhstan (100%)
Tel.: (7) 727 259 89 03
Petrochemical Mfr
N.A.I.C.S.: 325110
Darkhan Mendekulov *(CEO & Gen Dir)*

GEOBRA BRANDSTATTER GMBH & CO. KG

Brandstatter Str 2 10, 90513, Zirndorf, Germany
Tel.: (49) 91196660
Web Site: http://www.playmobil.de
Year Founded: 1974
Toy Mfr
N.A.I.C.S.: 339930
Horst Brandstatter *(Owner & Mng Dir)*

Subsidiaries:

PLAYMOBIL Austria GmbH (1)
Magazinstr 4, 5027, Salzburg, Austria
Tel.: (43) 662 88921 0
Web Site: http://www.playmobil.at
Toy Distr
N.A.I.C.S.: 423920

PLAYMOBIL Canada Inc. (1)
2421 Bristol Circle Suite 107, Oakville, L6H 5S9, ON, Canada
Tel.: (905) 696-7529
Web Site: https://www.playmobil.ca
Sales Range: $50-74.9 Million
Emp.: 10
Toy Distr
N.A.I.C.S.: 423920

PLAYMOBIL FRANCE SARL (1)
ZAC du Bois Chaland 12 rue des Pyrenees, 91029, Evry, France
Tel.: (33) 1 69 11 27 30
Web Site: http://www.playmobil.fr
Toy Distr
N.A.I.C.S.: 423920

PLAYMOBIL Hellas S.A. (1)
9 Matsa St, 14564, Kifissia, Greece
Tel.: (30) 2108000018
Web Site: http://www.playmobil.gr
Emp.: 40
Toy Distr
N.A.I.C.S.: 423920
George Pagonis *(Gen Mgr)*

PLAYMOBIL Iberica S.A.U. (1)
Ctra Alcoy Yecla km 26 2, 03430, Alicante, Spain
Tel.: (34) 966 557 820
Web Site: http://www.playmobil.es
Toy Distr
N.A.I.C.S.: 423920
Patrick Hell *(Mgr-HR & Production)*

PLAYMOBIL Merchandising Mexicana, S.A. de C.V. (1)
Av Insurgentes Sur 1863 Piso 7 Col Guadalupe Inn, Alvaro Obregon, 01020, Mexico, Mexico
Tel.: (52) 55 5661 8309
Web Site: http://www.playmobil.mx
Toy Distr
N.A.I.C.S.: 423920

PLAYMOBIL Swiss GmbH (1)
Vorstadt 32, Postfach 4755, 6304, Zug, Switzerland
Tel.: (41) 848 77 37 33
Web Site: http://www.playmobil.ch
Toy Distr
N.A.I.C.S.: 423920

PLAYMOBIL UK Ltd. (1)
6 Argent Ct Sylvan Way, Southfields Bus Pk, Basildon, SS15 6TH, Essex, United Kingdom
Tel.: (44) 1268548111
Web Site: http://www.playmobil.de
Sales Range: $25-49.9 Million
Emp.: 24
Toy Distr
N.A.I.C.S.: 423920
Uffe Kloster *(Dir-Comml)*

PLAYMOBIL USA Inc. (1)
26 Commerce Dr, Cranbury, NJ 08512
Tel.: (609) 395-5566
Web Site: http://www.playmobil.us

INTERNATIONAL PUBLIC

Sales Range: $25-49.9 Million
Emp.: 30
Toy Retailer, Distr & Catalog Sales
N.A.I.C.S.: 459120
Nathan Selvanathan *(Controller)*

Division (Domestic):

PLAYMOBIL FunPark Orlando (2)
Florida Mall Space 1226 8001 S Orange Blossom Trl, Orlando, FL 32809
Tel.: (407) 812-6336
Web Site: http://www.playmobil.com.br
Toy Retailer
N.A.I.C.S.: 459120

Playmobil Malta Ltd (1)
HF80 Industrial Estate, Hal Far, BBG 3000, Malta
Tel.: (356) 2224 2445
Web Site: http://www.playmobilmalta.com
Toy Mfr
N.A.I.C.S.: 339930
Kenneth Micallef *(Mgr-Injection Ops)*

GEOCENTER TOURISTIK MEDIENSERVICE GMBH

Kurze Strasse 40, 70794, Filderstadt, Germany
Tel.: (49) 711 78 19 46 10
Web Site: http://www.geocenter.de
Sales Range: $10-24.9 Million
Emp.: 30
Map & Travel Literature Publisher
N.A.I.C.S.: 513199
Klaus Hohne *(Mng Dir)*

GEOCODE CO., LTD.

4-1-6 Shinjuku, Shinjuku-Ku, Tokyo, 106-0022, Japan
Tel.: (81) 362748081
Web Site: https://www.geo-code.co.jp
Year Founded: 2005
7357—(TKS)
Digital Marketing Services
N.A.I.C.S.: 541870
Daisuke Haraguchi *(Founder & Pres)*

GEOCOMPLEX AS

Grosslingova 45, 811 09, Bratislava, Slovakia
Tel.: (421) 245243994
Web Site: https://www.geocomplex.sk
Year Founded: 1992
1GEC01AE—(BRA)
Sales Range: Less than $1 Million
Hydrology Power Services
N.A.I.C.S.: 221111

GEOCONCEPT SA

52 avenue Aristide Briand, 92220, Bagneux, France
Tel.: (33) 1 7274 7678   FR
Web Site:
http://www.geoconcept.com
Year Founded: 1990
Emp.: 100
Cartographic Optimization Technologies Designer & Software Publisher
N.A.I.C.S.: 513210
Eric Lanzi *(CEO)*

Subsidiaries:

GEOCONCEPT JAPAN KK (1)
Nishi-Shinjuku Mitsui Building 6-24-1 Nishi-Shinjuku, Shinjuku-Ku, Tokyo, 160-0023, Japan
Tel.: (81) 3 5323 6500
Geographic Information Services
N.A.I.C.S.: 541360

GeoConcept International Software (Suisse) SA (1)
Rue de la Gabelle 34 Case Postale, Case Postale 1627, CH 1227, Carouge, Switzerland
Tel.: (41) 22 343 35 09
Geographic Information Services
N.A.I.C.S.: 541360

Geoconcept China Ltd (1)

AND PRIVATE COMPANIES

Room 2012 20/F Catic Building 212 Jiangning Road near Beijing West Rd, Jing'An District, Shanghai, 200041, China
Tel.: (86) 21 2230 6600
Geographic Information Services
N.A.I.C.S.: 541360

Geoconcept India Private Limited (1)
2nd Floor Khivraj complex -1 480 Anna Salai Nandanam, Chennai, 600035, India
Tel.: (91) 44 43156075
Web Site: http://www.geoconcept.in
Geographic Information Services
N.A.I.C.S.: 541360
Jaladanki Sukumar *(Head-Tech)*

Opti-Time -GEOCONCEPT Group (1)
52 Avenue Aristide Briand, 92220, Bagneux, France **(95%)**
Tel.: (33) 1 72 74 76 78
Web Site: http://www.opti-time.com
Sales Range: $1-9.9 Million
Emp.: 37
Software Publisher
N.A.I.C.S.: 513210
Marie Denel *(Mgr-Corp Comm)*

GEODESIC LIMITED
B-3 Lunic Industries Cross Road B MIDC Andheri East, Mumbai, 400093, India
Tel.: (91) 2228311849
Web Site: http://www.geodesic.com
Sales Range: $150-199.9 Million
Emp.: 700
Software Consultancy Services
N.A.I.C.S.: 541519
Pankaj Kumar *(Co-Founder & Chm)*

GEODIGITAL INTERNATIONAL INC.
McMaster Innovation Park 175 Longwood Rd S Ste 400A, Hamilton, L8P 0A1, ON, Canada
Tel.: (905) 667-7204
Web Site: http://www.geodigital.com
Sales Range: $10-24.9 Million
Emp.: 250
Digital Field Data Acquisition & Asset Mapping Technologies Developer & Services
N.A.I.C.S.: 334511
Alastair Jenkins *(Pres & CEO)*

Subsidiaries:

GeoDigital Solutions, Inc. (1)
720 Main St Ste 201, Mendota Heights, MN 55118 **(100%)**
Tel.: (651) 251-3005
Web Site: http://www.powelinc.com
Infrastructure Software & Analytics Services
N.A.I.C.S.: 513210
Scott Rogers *(Pres)*

Geodigital International Corp. (1)
137 W Central Ave, Lompoc, CA 93436
Tel.: (805) 740-0077
Web Site: http://www.geodigital.com
Digital Field Data Acquisition & Asset Mapping Technical Services
N.A.I.C.S.: 541990

GEODRILL LIMITED
20 Kofi Annan Street Airport Residential Area, PO Box KIA 16184, Airport, Accra, GA-153-1438, Ghana
Tel.: (233) 302768879 IM
Web Site: https://www.geodrill-gh.com
Year Founded: 1998
GEODF—(OTCQX)
Rev.: $130,544,622
Assets: $148,609,445
Liabilities: $38,646,006
Net Worth: $109,963,439
Earnings: $3,764,153
Emp.: 1,635
Fiscal Year-end: 12/31/23
Mining Machinery & Equipment Manufacturing
N.A.I.C.S.: 333131
David Harper *(Pres & CEO)*

Subsidiaries:

Geodrill Cote d'Ivoire SARL (1)
Bouake Quartier Ahougnansou, BP 359, 04, Bouake, Cote d'Ivoire
Tel.: (225) 88751895
Mining Services
N.A.I.C.S.: 212290

Geodrill Limited (1)
Plot number 1407/1408 Senama Road Industrial Area, Chingola, Zambia
Tel.: (260) 977825479
Exploration Drilling Services
N.A.I.C.S.: 532412
Raymond Nienaber *(Mgr-Bus Dev)*

Geodrill Zambia Limited (1)
1407 Senama Road Industrial Area, Chingola, Zambia
Tel.: (260) 95 518 1570
Mining Services
N.A.I.C.S.: 212290

Recon Drilling S.A.C. (1)
Calle Los Eucaliptos Mz D Lote 15 Urb Los Huertos de Santa Genoveva, Lurin, Lima, Peru
Tel.: (51) 174857737
Web Site: https://recondrilling.com
Diamond Mining Services
N.A.I.C.S.: 212390

GEOFON A.D.
Aleksandra Rajkovica BB, Teslic, 74270, Bosnia & Herzegovina
Tel.: (387) 53 431 452
Web Site: http://www.geofon.biz
Year Founded: 1989
GEOF—(BANJ)
Sales Range: Less than $1 Million
Emp.: 10
Electronic Components Mfr
N.A.I.C.S.: 334290
Dusan Stojicic *(Chm-Mgmt Bd)*

GEOGRACE RESOURCES PHILIPPINES, INC.
7th Floor Peaksun Bldg 1505 Princeton Street Brgy, Wack-Wack Greenhills East, Mandaluyong, 1552, Philippines
Tel.: (63) 288562011
Web Site: http://www.geograce.com
Year Founded: 1970
GEO—(PHI)
Rev.: $19,862
Assets: $361,015
Liabilities: $167,750
Net Worth: $193,265
Earnings: ($27,268)
Emp.: 2
Fiscal Year-end: 12/31/21
Mineral Exploration Services
N.A.I.C.S.: 212390
Amor Roselle S. Herrera *(Asst Sec)*

GEOJIT FINANCIAL SERVICES LIMITED
34/659-P Civil Line Road, Padivattom, Kochi, 682024, India
Tel.: (91) 4842901000
Web Site: https://www.geojit.com
Year Founded: 1994
532285—(BOM)
Rev.: $58,260,152
Assets: $159,367,436
Liabilities: $69,460,537
Net Worth: $89,906,899
Earnings: $17,268,888
Emp.: 1,973
Fiscal Year-end: 03/31/21
Retail Financial Services
N.A.I.C.S.: 523999
C. J. George *(Founder & Mng Dir)*

Subsidiaries:

Geojit Credits Private Limited (1)
34/659-P 2nd Floor Civil Line Road, Padivattom, Kochi, 682024, Kerala, India
Tel.: (91) 9995800541
Web Site: https://www.geojitcredits.com
Financial Services
N.A.I.C.S.: 523999
C. J. George *(Mng Dir)*

Geojit Financial Distribution Private Limited (1)
4th Floor Finance Towers Kaloor, Kochi, 682017, Kerala, India
Tel.: (91) 48 42405501
Financial Support Services
N.A.I.C.S.: 522320

Geojit Technologies Private Limited (1)
9th Floor 34/659-P Civil Line Rd, Padivattom Ernakulam, Kochi, 682024, Kerala, India
Tel.: (91) 4842901901
Web Site: https://geojit.tech
Sales Range: $25-49.9 Million
Emp.: 100
Information Technology Consulting Services
N.A.I.C.S.: 541512
R. Bupathy *(Chm)*

Qurum Business Group Geojit Securities LLC (1)
Building No 184 Opposite Avenues Mall Al Ghubrah, PO Box 205, Next to Bank Beirut and Muscat University, 103, Muscat, Oman
Tel.: (968) 22522875
Web Site: https://www.qbggeojit.com
Financial Services
N.A.I.C.S.: 523999
Abdul Aziz Ahamed Sultan Al Hosni *(Chm)*

GEOJUNXION NV
9th Floor Rivium Quadrant 75, 2909 LC, Capelle aan den IJssel, Netherlands
Tel.: (31) 108851200
Web Site: http://www.geojunxion.com
Year Founded: 1984
GOJXN—(EUR)
Sales Range: $1-9.9 Million
Emp.: 57
Mapping Software Development Services
N.A.I.C.S.: 541511
Kees Molenaar *(Chm-Supervisory Bd)*

Subsidiaries:

GeoJunxion B.V. (1)
Rivium Quadrant 75, 2909 LC, Capelle aan den IJssel, Netherlands
Tel.: (31) 108851200
Web Site: https://www.geojunxion.com
Geophysical Mapping Services
N.A.I.C.S.: 541360

GEOLGICA RESOURCE CORP.
Suite 1735-555 Burrard Street, Vancouver, V7X 1M9, BC, Canada
Tel.: (604) 762-5355 BC
Web Site: https://www.geologicaresource.com
Year Founded: 2016
862—(STU)
Assets: $226,521
Liabilities: $295,894
Net Worth: ($69,373)
Earnings: ($353,556)
Fiscal Year-end: 12/31/23
Mineral Mining Services
N.A.I.C.S.: 213115

GEOLOCATION TECHNOLOGY, INC.
4F Arthur First Building 18-22 Ichibancho, Mishima, 411-0036, Shizuoka, Japan
Tel.: (81) 559915544
Web Site: https://www.geolocation.co.jp
Year Founded: 2000
4018—(TKS)
Internet Publishing Services
N.A.I.C.S.: 513199
Keisuke Yamamoto *(Founder, Pres & CEO)*

GEOMASINA A.D.
Batajnicki put br 3, 11080, Zemun, Serbia
Tel.: (381) 11 26 17 342
Web Site: http://www.geomasina.co.rs
Year Founded: 1949
Sales Range: Less than $1 Million
Emp.: 2
Mining Equipment Mfr
N.A.I.C.S.: 333131

GEOMATEC (WUXI) CO., LTD.
No B18-C Lot Wuxi National Hi-Tech Industrial Development Zone, Wuxi, Jiangsu, China
Tel.: (86) 51088157145 CN
Year Founded: 2002
Optical Component Mfr
N.A.I.C.S.: 333310

GEOMATEC CO., LTD.
Yokohama Landmark Tower 9th Floor 2-2-1 Minato Mirai, Nishi-ku, Yokohama, 220-8109, Japan
Tel.: (81) 452225720
Web Site: https://www.geomatec.com
Year Founded: 1953
6907—(TKS)
Rev.: $60,587,120
Assets: $182,477,680
Liabilities: $81,825,040
Net Worth: $100,652,640
Earnings: ($774,400)
Emp.: 495
Fiscal Year-end: 03/31/22
Flat Panel Displays Mfr
N.A.I.C.S.: 334419
Kentaro Matsuzaki *(Pres & CEO)*

Subsidiaries:

GEOMATEC Co., Ltd. - Ako Factory (1)
1325-80 Inariyama Kizu, Ako, 678-0165, Hyogo, Japan
Tel.: (81) 791481417
Optical Component Mfr
N.A.I.C.S.: 333310

GEOMATEC Co., Ltd. - Kannari Factory (1)
51 Kinsei Kannari, Kurihara, 989-5164, Miyagi, Japan
Tel.: (81) 228423001
Optical Component Mfr
N.A.I.C.S.: 333310

GEOMEGA RESOURCES INC.
75 Boulevard de Mortagne, Boucherville, J4B 6Y4, QC, Canada
Tel.: (450) 641-5119 Ca
Web Site: https://ressourcesgeomega.ca
Year Founded: 2008
GMA—(OTCIQ)
Rev.: $4,682
Assets: $4,500,017
Liabilities: $806,870
Net Worth: $3,693,147
Earnings: ($1,137,250)
Fiscal Year-end: 05/31/21
Metal Mining Services
N.A.I.C.S.: 212290
Alain P. Cayer *(VP-Exploration)*

GEOPACIFIC RESOURCES LIMITED
Level 1 278 Stirling Highway, Claremont, 6010, WA, Australia
Tel.: (61) 861431820 AU
Web Site: https://www.geopacific.com.au
Year Founded: 2006
Rev.: $65,568

GEOPACIFIC RESOURCES LIMITED

Geopacific Resources Limited—(Continued)
Assets: $56,313,968
Liabilities: $7,022,097
Net Worth: $49,291,871
Earnings: ($5,131,924)
Emp.: 5,000
Fiscal Year-end: 12/31/19
Gold & Copper Ore Exploration & Mining
N.A.I.C.S.: 213114
Ron S. Heeks (Mng Dir)

Subsidiaries:

Kula Gold Limited (1)
Suite 2 20 Howard Street, Perth, 6000, WA, Australia **(85.01%)**
Tel.: (61) 861440592
Web Site: https://www.kulagold.com.au
Rev: $298,522
Assets: $2,465,737
Liabilities: $187,126
Net Worth: $2,278,610
Earnings: ($1,079,997)
Emp.: 2
Fiscal Year-end: 12/31/2022
Gold Mining Services
N.A.I.C.S.: 212220
Mark Stowell (Chm)

GEOPARK LIMITED

Calle 94 N 11-30 8 floor, Bogota, Colombia
Tel.: (57) 17432337
Web Site: https://www.geo-park.com
Year Founded: 2002
GPRK—(NYSE)
Rev: $1,049,579,000
Assets: $973,975,000
Liabilities: $858,390,000
Net Worth: $115,585,000
Earnings: $224,435,000
Emp.: 482
Fiscal Year-end: 12/31/22
Oil & Gas Exploration Services
N.A.I.C.S.: 211120
Gerald Eugene O'Shaughnessy (Co-Founder)

Subsidiaries:

Amerisur Resources PLC (1)
Lakeside, St Mellons, Cardiff, CF3 0FB, United Kingdom
Tel.: (44) 3303338270
Web Site: http://www.amerisurresources.com
Sales Range: $100-124.9 Million
Gold Mining Services
N.A.I.C.S.: 212220
Brian James (Sec)

GeoPark Argentina Limited-Bermuda (1)
Ing Enrique Butty 275 8 piso, C1001AFA, Buenos Aires, Argentina
Tel.: (54) 1143129400
Oil & Gas Exploration Services
N.A.I.C.S.: 213112

GeoPark Chile Limited-Bermuda (1)
Lautaro Navarro 1021, Punta Arenas, Chile
Tel.: (56) 612745100
Oil & Gas Exploration Services
N.A.I.C.S.: 333132

GEOPROMINING LTD.

PO Box 3321 Drake Chambers, Road Town, Tortola, Virgin Islands (British)
Tel.: (284) 4944541
Holding Company
N.A.I.C.S.: 551112
Maureen Lettsom (Corp Mgr)

GEORG FISCHER AG

Amsler-Laffon-Strasse 9, 8201, Schaffhausen, Switzerland
Tel.: (41) 526311111 **CH**
Web Site: https://www.georgfischer.com
Year Founded: 1802
Rev: $415,936,536
Assets: $4,607,259,350
Liabilities: $2,656,524,851
Net Worth: $1,950,734,499
Earnings: $239,888,282
Emp.: 144
Fiscal Year-end: 12/31/23
Plastic Products, Steel & Custom Castings Mfr
N.A.I.C.S.: 326199
Yves Serra (Pres)

Subsidiaries:

Agie Charmilles China (Shanghai) Ltd (1)
1F Part B Development Building, Shanghai, 200131, China
Tel.: (86) 21 586 85 000
Industrial Machinery Mfr & Distr
N.A.I.C.S.: 333248

Agie Charmilles Holding Limited (1)
Rue du Pre de la Fontaine 8, Myrin, Geneva, 1217, Switzerland
Tel.: (41) 22 783 31 11
Web Site: http://www.georgfischer.com
Sales Range: $800-899.9 Million
Emp.: 300
Electric Dishcharge & High-Speed Machine Tools Developer, Mfr & Sales
N.A.I.C.S.: 333248

Subsidiary (Non-US):

Agie Charmilles BV (2)
Spikweien 21, NL 5943 AC, Lomm, Pays Bas, Netherlands **(100%)**
Tel.: (31) 774738200
Web Site: http://www.gfac.com
Sales Range: $25-49.9 Million
Emp.: 15
Sales of Plastics Products
N.A.I.C.S.: 326199

Agie Charmilles China (Shenzhen) Ltd (2)
Room 1703 Chang Ping Commercial Building, Shenzhen, 518038, China
Tel.: (86) 755 8348 04 43
Web Site: http://www.gfac.com
Sales Range: $25-49.9 Million
Emp.: 76
Industrial Machinery Distr
N.A.I.C.S.: 423830

Agie Charmilles China (Tianjin) Ltd (2)
Unit B-201 Guo Men Building No 1 Zuo Jia Zhuang, Chaoyang District, Beijing, 100028, China
Tel.: (86) 10 6460 6822
Web Site: http://www.gfac.com
Industrial Machinery Distr
N.A.I.C.S.: 423830

Agie Charmilles GmbH (2)
Steinbeisstrasse 22-24, 73614, Schorndorf, Germany **(100%)**
Tel.: (49) 71819260
Web Site: http://www.gfac.com
Sales Range: $50-74.9 Million
Emp.: 180
Sales of Machine Tools
N.A.I.C.S.: 423830

Agie Charmilles Japan Ltd. (2)
TVP Building 3 9 13, Moriya Cho Kanagawa Ku, Yokohama, 221 0022, Japan **(100%)**
Tel.: (81) 454501521
Web Site: http://www.gfac.com
Sales Range: $25-49.9 Million
Emp.: 40
Sales of Electrical Discharge Systems
N.A.I.C.S.: 425120

Agie Charmilles Korea Co Ltd (2)
902 Ace Techno-Tower III 197-48 Gurodong, Guro-gu, Seoul, 152-050, Korea (South)
Tel.: (82) 2 2109 65 80
Web Site: http://www.gfms.com
Sales Range: $25-49.9 Million
Emp.: 35
Industrial Machinery Mfr & Distr
N.A.I.C.S.: 333248

Subsidiary (US):

Agie Charmilles LLC (2)
560 Bond St, Lincolnshire, IL 60069
Tel.: (847) 955-7172
Industrial Machinery Mfr & Distr
N.A.I.C.S.: 333248
Darlene Regilio (Mgr-HR)

Subsidiary (Non-US):

Agie Charmilles Ltd. (2)
Unit 12 Chelmsley Wood Industrial Estate Waterloo Ave, Birmingham, B37 6QQ, United Kingdom **(100%)**
Tel.: (44) 1217888686
Web Site: http://www.agie.co.uk
Sales Range: $25-49.9 Million
Emp.: 10
Sales Machine Tools
N.A.I.C.S.: 423830

Agie Charmilles Ltd. (2)
North View, Coventry, CV2 2SJ, United Kingdom **(100%)**
Tel.: (44) 2476538666
Web Site: http://www.gfms.com
Sales Range: $10-24.9 Million
Emp.: 40
Distr of Machine Tools
N.A.I.C.S.: 423710

Agie Charmilles Ltda (2)
Av das Nacoes Unidas 21 689, Sao Paulo, 04795-100, Brazil
Tel.: (55) 11 56 94 83 22
Web Site: http://www.gfac.com
Industrial Machinery Mfr & Distr
N.A.I.C.S.: 333248

Agie Charmilles Machine Tool Co., Ltd. (2)
No 127th Hanjiang Road, Xinbei District, Changzhou, 213125, Jiangsu, China
Tel.: (86) 519 8960 8300
Web Site: http://www.gfac.com
Machine Tools Mfr
N.A.I.C.S.: 333517

Subsidiary (Domestic):

Agie Charmilles Management SA (2)
Rue du Pre-de-la-Fontaine 8, Meyrin, 1217, Geneva, Switzerland
Tel.: (41) 22 783 31 11
Web Site: http://www.agiecharmilles.ch
Industrial Machinery Mfr & Distr
N.A.I.C.S.: 333248

Agie Charmilles New Technologies SA (2)
Rue du Pre-de-la-Fontaine 8, Meyrin, Geneva, 1217, Switzerland
Tel.: (41) 22 783 31 11
Industrial Machinery Mfr & Distr
N.A.I.C.S.: 333248

Subsidiary (Non-US):

Agie Charmilles S.A.R.L. (2)
12 Ave du Mai 1, 91127, Palaiseau, Cedex, France
Tel.: (33) 169316900
Web Site: http://www.gfac.com
Sales Range: $25-49.9 Million
Emp.: 50
Mfr of Plastic Products
N.A.I.C.S.: 326199

Subsidiary (Domestic):

Agie Charmilles SA (2)
Via dei Pioppi 2, 6616, Lausanne, Switzerland
Tel.: (41) 918069111
Sales Range: $125-149.9 Million
Industrial Machinery Distr
N.A.I.C.S.: 423830
Stephan Maerz (Dir-Mktg)

Agie Charmilles Sales Ltd. (2)
Via Dei Pioppi 2, CH 6616, Lausanne, Switzerland
Tel.: (41) 918069030
Web Site: http://www.gfac.com
Emp.: 450
Electrical Discharge Machines
N.A.I.C.S.: 333517

Agie Charmilles Services SA (2)
Rue du Pre-de-la-Fontaine 8, Meyrin, 1217, Geneva, Switzerland
Tel.: (41) 22 783 31 11
Industrial Machinery Distr

INTERNATIONAL PUBLIC

N.A.I.C.S.: 423830

Subsidiary (Non-US):

Agie Charmilles South East Asia Pte Ltd (2)
04 01 Olivine Bldg 130 Joo Seng Rd, Singapore, 368357, Singapore **(100%)**
Tel.: (65) 62810341
Web Site: http://www.gfac.com
Sales Range: $25-49.9 Million
Emp.: 56
Sale & Servicing of Electric Discharge Machines & Machine Tools
N.A.I.C.S.: 333517

Agie Charmilles s.r.o. (2)
Dornych 54/47, 617 00, Brno, Czech Republic
Tel.: (420) 511 120 200
Web Site: http://www.gfac.com
Sales Range: $25-49.9 Million
Emp.: 17
Industrial Machinery Mfr
N.A.I.C.S.: 333248

Subsidiary (US):

Agie Ltd (2)
9009 G Perimeter Woods Dr, Charlotte, NC 28216
Tel.: (704) 927-8900
Web Site: http://www.gfac.com
Sales Range: $25-49.9 Million
Emp.: 20
Plastics Product Manufacturing
N.A.I.C.S.: 326199

Subsidiary (Non-US):

Agie S.p.A. (2)
Via Per Cantalupo 5, IT-21040, Origgio, Italy **(100%)**
Tel.: (39) 029630921
Mfr of Tooling Machines
N.A.I.C.S.: 333517

Beijing AGIE Charmilles Industrial Electronics Ltd. (2)
Mapo Shunyi County, Beijing, 101300, China
Tel.: (86) 1069404616
Web Site: http://www.gfac.com
Sales Range: $100-124.9 Million
Emp.: 300
Mfr of Plastic Products
N.A.I.C.S.: 326199

Subsidiary (US):

Charmilles Mikron (2)
560 Bond St, Lincolnshire, IL 60069-4224 **(100%)**
Tel.: (847) 913-5300
Web Site: http://www.charmillesus.com
Sales Range: $25-49.9 Million
Emp.: 100
Mfr of Electro Discharge Machines (EDM) & Machine Tools
N.A.I.C.S.: 423830
Gisbert Ledvon (Mgr-Bus Dev)

Subsidiary (Domestic):

Charmilles Technologies SA (2)
8 10 Rue Du Pre De La Fontaine, PO Box 373, 1217, Meyrin, Switzerland **(70%)**
Tel.: (41) 227833111
Web Site: http://www.gfac.com
Sales Range: $75-99.9 Million
Wire Cutting & Diesinking Electrical Discharge (EDM) Systems
N.A.I.C.S.: 333517

Subsidiary (US):

GF AgieCharmilles (2)
560 Bond St, Lincolnshire, IL 60069 **(100%)**
Tel.: (847) 913-5300
Web Site: http://www.gfms.com
Sales Range: $25-49.9 Million
Emp.: 20
Mfr of Machine Tools
N.A.I.C.S.: 423830
Gisbert Ledvon (Mgr-Bus Dev)

Subsidiary (Non-US):

GF Machining Solutions Ltd. (2)
1F No 94 Hsing Te Road, San Chung, Tai-

AND PRIVATE COMPANIES — GEORG FISCHER AG

pei, 24158, Hsien, Taiwan
Tel.: (886) 2 8511 1158
Web Site: http://www.gfms.com
Emp.: 34
Machines, Automation Solutions & Services
N.A.I.C.S.: 333517
Karl Kleppek *(Dir-Bus Dev)*

GF Machining Solutions Sp. z o.o. (2)
Aleja Krakowska 81 Sekocin Nowy, Raszyn, Warsaw, 05-090, Poland
Tel.: (48) 22 326 50 50
Web Site: http://www.gfms.com
Sales Range: $25-49.9 Million
Emp.: 30
Machines, Automation Solutions & Services to the Tool & Mold Making Industries & Manufacturers of Precision Components
N.A.I.C.S.: 333248
Mariusz Wardzinski *(Mgr)*

L'Usinage Electrique Sarl (2)
17 Rue Leon Blum, F 91120, Palaiseau, France **(100%)**
Tel.: (33) 169316905
Sales Range: $25-49.9 Million
Emp.: 12
Import of Electric Discharge Machines
N.A.I.C.S.: 333517

System 3R International AB (2)
Sorterargatan 1, Vallingby, 16250, Sweden **(100%)**
Tel.: (46) 86202000
Web Site: http://www.system3r.se
Sales Range: $25-49.9 Million
Develops, Designs, Produces & Markets Methods, Handling Equipment & Tooling Systems for the Engineering Industry
N.A.I.C.S.: 332216
Roger Janze *(CFO)*

Subsidiary (Non-US):

Hassas Baglama Ekipmanlari Tic Ltd. Sti (3)
Abdi Ipekci 150-249, Bayramppasa, 34030, Istanbul, Türkiye **(100%)**
Tel.: (90) 2126138062
Web Site: http://www.system3r.com
Sales Range: Less than $1 Million
Emp.: 2
Develops, Designs, Produces & Markets Methods, Handling Equipment & Tooling Systems for the Engineering Industry
N.A.I.C.S.: 332216

Mecatool AG (3)
Wiler strasse 98, 9230, Flawil, Switzerland **(100%)**
Tel.: (41) 713941350
Web Site: http://www.system3r.com
Sales Range: $1-9.9 Million
Emp.: 10
Mfr & Sales of Tooling Machines
N.A.I.C.S.: 332216

System 3R (UK) Ltd. (3)
Paradise Way Walsgrave Triangle, Coventry, CV2 2ST, W Midlands, United Kingdom
Tel.: (44) 2476538653
Web Site: http://www.system3r.com
Sales Range: $25-49.9 Million
Emp.: 2
Develops, Designs, Produces & Markets Methods, Handling Equipment & Tooling Systems for the Engineering Industry
N.A.I.C.S.: 332216

System 3R AG (3)
Wiler Strasse 98, 9230, Flawil, Switzerland **(100%)**
Tel.: (41) 713941363
Web Site: http://www.system3r.com
Sales Range: $1-9.9 Million
Emp.: 28
Develops, Designs, Produces & Markets Methods, Handling Equipment & Tooling Systems for the Engineering Industry
N.A.I.C.S.: 332216

System 3R Czech s.r.o. (3)
Tiskarska 10 257, 08 28, Prague, 10, Malesice, Czech Republic **(100%)**
Tel.: (420) 234054224
Web Site: http://www.system3r.com
Sales Range: $25-49.9 Million
Emp.: 2

Develops, Designs, Produces & Markets Methods, Handling Equipment & Tooling Systems for the Engineering Industry
N.A.I.C.S.: 332216

System 3R Far East Pte Ltd. (3)
6 Harper Rd Leong Huat Bldg 05 01, Singapore, 369674, Singapore **(100%)**
Tel.: (65) 62894811
Web Site: http://www.system3r.com
Sales Range: $25-49.9 Million
Emp.: 8
Develops, Designs, Produces & Markets Methods, Handling Equipment & Tooling Systems for the Engineering Industry
N.A.I.C.S.: 332216

System 3R France S.A.S. (3)
56 Blvd de Courcerin Les Espaces Mulitiservices no 15, F 77183, Croissy-Beaubourg, France **(100%)**
Tel.: (33) 160959080
Web Site: http://www.system3r.com
Sales Range: $1-9.9 Million
Emp.: 10
Develops, Designs, Produces & Markets Methods, Handling Equipment & Tooling Systems for the Engineering Industry
N.A.I.C.S.: 332216

System 3R Italia SRL (3)
Via Giotto 2 4, 20040, Cambiago, MI, Italy **(100%)**
Tel.: (39) 0295345095
Web Site: http://www.system3r.com
Sales Range: $50-74.9 Million
Emp.: 8
Sales of Tooling Machines
N.A.I.C.S.: 423830

System 3R Japan Co., Ltd. (3)
9-11 Nishidai 4 chome Itabashi-ku, Tokyo, 175 0045, Japan **(100%)**
Tel.: (81) 3 6906 7077
Web Site: http://www.system3r.com
Sales Range: $25-49.9 Million
Emp.: 21
Develops, Designs, Produces & Markets Methods, Handling Equipment & Tooling Systems for the Engineering Industry
N.A.I.C.S.: 332216

System 3R Shanghai Co Ltd (3)
Room 3D Software Building 55-56 No 461 Hongcao Road, Xuhui District, Shanghai, 200233, China
Tel.: (86) 21 6432 7927
Web Site: http://www.system3r.com
Machine Tool Distr
N.A.I.C.S.: 423830

Subsidiary (US):

System 3R USA Inc. (3)
915 Busse Rd, Elk Grove Village, IL 60007
Tel.: (847) 439-4888
Web Site: http://www.system3r.com
Sales Range: $50-74.9 Million
Emp.: 10
Develops, Designs, Produces & Markets Methods, Handling Equipment & Tooling Systems for the Engineering Industry
N.A.I.C.S.: 423830

Arabian Plastic Manufacturing Company (1)
PO Box 6193, Riyadh, 11442, Saudi Arabia **(26%)**
Tel.: (966) 14480250
Web Site: http://www.aplaco.com.sa
Sales Range: $50-74.9 Million
Emp.: 190
Mfr of Plastic Piping Systems
N.A.I.C.S.: 326122

DISA Industries Inc. (1)
80 Kendall Point Dr, Oswego, IL 60543 **(100%)**
Tel.: (630) 820-3000
Web Site: http://www.disagroup.com
Sales Range: $400-449.9 Million
Emp.: 22
Plastics Product Mfr
N.A.I.C.S.: 326199

Eisen-Bibliothek Stiftung der Georg Fischer AG
Klostergut Paradies, Schlatt, 8252, Switzerland
Tel.: (41) 52 631 27 43

Web Site: http://www.eisenbibliothek.ch
Emp.: 3
Library Management Services
N.A.I.C.S.: 519210

Georg Fischer (Great Britain) Ltd.
Paradise Way, Coventry, CV2 2ST, United Kingdom **(100%)**
Tel.: (44) 24 76 535535
Web Site: http://www.georgfischer.co.uk
Sales Range: $25-49.9 Million
Emp.: 90
Sales of Piping Systems
N.A.I.C.S.: 326122

Georg Fischer A.S. (1)
Rudsletta 97, 1351, Rud, Norway **(100%)**
Tel.: (47) 67182900
Web Site: http://www.georgfischer.no
Sales Range: $1-9.9 Million
Emp.: 8
Sales of Piping Systems
N.A.I.C.S.: 326122

Georg Fischer A/S (1)
Malervej 4, Taastrup, 2630, Denmark **(100%)**
Tel.: (45) 70221975
Web Site: http://www.georgfischer.dk
Sales Range: $25-49.9 Million
Emp.: 12
Sales of Piping Systems
N.A.I.C.S.: 423830

Georg Fischer AB (1)
Gognundaghean 34, PO Box 113, S 125 23, Stockholm, Sweden **(100%)**
Tel.: (46) 850677500
Web Site: http://www.georgfischer.com
Sales Range: $25-49.9 Million
Emp.: 35
Sales of Piping Systems
N.A.I.C.S.: 326122

Georg Fischer Automobilguss GmbH (1)
Julius Buhrer Strasse 12, Singen, D78224, Germany **(100%)**
Tel.: (49) 77318860
Web Site: http://www.georgfischer.com
Sales Range: $400-449.9 Million
Emp.: 1,300
Automotive Castings Mfr
N.A.I.C.S.: 331523

Georg Fischer Automobilguss GmbH (1)
Wiener Strasse 41-43, Postfach 23, 3130, Herzogenburg, Austria
Tel.: (43) 27 82 800 24 67
Web Site: http://www.gfau.com
Sales Range: $400-449.9 Million
Emp.: 1,200
Cast Iron Mfr
N.A.I.C.S.: 331511

Georg Fischer Automotive (Kunshan) Co., Ltd. (1)
No 300 Tian E Lu, 215300, Kunshan, China
Tel.: (86) 512 5715 7888
Web Site: http://www.gfau.com
Sales Range: $125-149.9 Million
Emp.: 260
Automotive Casting Mfr
N.A.I.C.S.: 336390

Georg Fischer Automotive (Suzhou) Co Ltd (1)
Changyang Street Suzhou Industrial Park, Suzhou, 6283, Jiangsu, China
Tel.: (86) 512 6283 6333
Web Site: http://www.gfau.com
Sales Range: $50-74.9 Million
Emp.: 240
Die Casting Mfr
N.A.I.C.S.: 331511
Weijun Zhao *(Gen Mgr)*

Georg Fischer Automotive AG (1)
Amsler-Laffon-Strasse 9, 8201, Schaffhausen, Switzerland
Tel.: (41) 52 631 11 11
Web Site: http://www.gfau.com
Steel Casting Mfr
N.A.I.C.S.: 331513
Yves Serra *(CEO)*

Georg Fischer Automotive Products Inc. (1)

2655 S Woodward Ave Ste 300, Bloomfield Hills, MI 48304-1670
Tel.: (248) 465-9500
N.A.I.C.S.: 326199

Georg Fischer Co Ltd (1)
2F No 88 XingDe Rd San Chong Dist, San-Chong Dist, Taipei, 24158, Taiwan
Tel.: (886) 2 8512 2822
Web Site: http://www.georgfischer.tw
Emp.: 6
Piping Supplies Distr
N.A.I.C.S.: 423830

Georg Fischer DEKA GmbH (1)
Kreuzstrasse 22, Mornshausen, 35232, Dautphetal, Germany
Tel.: (49) 64689150
Web Site: http://www.piping.georgfischer.com
Emp.: 110
Plastic Piping System Mfr & Distr
N.A.I.C.S.: 326122

Georg Fischer Eisenguss GmbH (1)
Wiener Strasse 41-43, Herzogenburg, 3130, Austria
Tel.: (43) 2782 800 0
Web Site: http://www.gfau.com
Sales Range: $50-74.9 Million
Emp.: 210
Cast Iron Mfr
N.A.I.C.S.: 331511

Georg Fischer Engineering AG (1)
Amsler-Laffon-Strasse 9, 8200, Schaffhausen, Switzerland
Tel.: (41) 52 631 11 11
Web Site: http://www.goergfischer.com
Industrial Machinery Mfr & Distr
N.A.I.C.S.: 333248

Georg Fischer Fahrzeugtechnik AG (1)
Ebnatstrasse 101, 8200, Schaffhausen, Switzerland **(100%)**
Tel.: (41) 526311111
Web Site: http://www.georgfischer.com
Sales Range: $400-449.9 Million
Emp.: 1,500
Mfr of Automotive Products
N.A.I.C.S.: 336340

Georg Fischer Finanz AG (1)
Amsler-Laffon-Strasse 9, Postfach 8201, Schaffhausen, Switzerland
Tel.: (41) 52 631 11 11
Web Site: http://www.georgfischer.com
Financial Management Services
N.A.I.C.S.: 523999

Georg Fischer Fittings Gmbh (1)
Mariazellerstrasse 75, Traisen, 3160, Austria **(51%)**
Tel.: (43) 2762 90300 0
Web Site: http://www.fittings.at
Sales Range: $200-249.9 Million
Emp.: 630
Mfr of Malleable Iron Fittings
N.A.I.C.S.: 332996

Georg Fischer Fluorpolymer Products GmbH (1)
Industriestr 1, Ettenheim, 77955, Baden-Wurttemberg, Germany
Tel.: (49) 78224457652
Plastic Tank Mfr
N.A.I.C.S.: 326122

Georg Fischer Geschaftsfuhrungs-GmbH (1)
Julius-Buhrer-Strasse 12, 78224, Singen, Germany
Tel.: (49) 77318860
Industrial Machinery Mfr & Distr
N.A.I.C.S.: 333248

Georg Fischer Giessereitechnologie GmbH (1)
Julius-Buhrer-Strasse 12, Singen, 78224, Germany
Tel.: (49) 7731 8860
Engineeering Services
N.A.I.C.S.: 541330

Georg Fischer GmbH (1)
Georg Fischer Str 2, PO Box 341156, Leipzig, 04249, Germany **(100%)**
Tel.: (49) 34148230
Web Site: http://www.automotive.georgfisher.com

GEORG FISCHER AG INTERNATIONAL PUBLIC

Georg Fischer AG—(Continued)
Sales Range: $50-74.9 Million
Emp.: 300
Mfr & Foundry of Automotive Castings
N.A.I.C.S.: 325998

Georg Fischer GmbH & Co KG (1)
Flurstr 15 17, Mettmann, 40822,
Germany **(100%)**
Tel.: (49) 21049840
Web Site:
http://www.automotive.georgfischer.com
Sales Range: $250-299.9 Million
Emp.: 1,000
Mfr of Automotive Products
N.A.I.C.S.: 326199

Georg Fischer GmbH & Co KG (1)
Essling 41, Altenmarkt bei Sankt Gallen,
8934, Austria
Tel.: (43) 3632 335 0
Web Site: http://www.gfau.com
Sales Range: $200-249.9 Million
Emp.: 650
Aluminum & Magnesium Pressure Die Cast
Component Mfr
N.A.I.C.S.: 331523

Georg Fischer Gmbh (1)
Daimlerstrasse 6, Albershausen, 73095,
Germany **(100%)**
Tel.: (49) 71613020
Web Site: http://www.rls.georgfischer.de
Sales Range: $75-99.9 Million
Emp.: 120
Sales of Piping Systems
N.A.I.C.S.: 326122
Udo Jirmann *(Mng Dir)*

Georg Fischer Holding (N.V.) (1)
Lange Veenteweg 19, 8161 PA, Epe,
Netherlands **(100%)**
Tel.: (31) 578678222
Web Site: http://www.georgfischer.nl
Sales Range: $10-24.9 Million
Emp.: 50
Holding Company
N.A.I.C.S.: 551112

Georg Fischer Holding Srl (1)
Via Enrico Fermi 12, 35030, Selvazzano
Dentro, Italy
Tel.: (39) 0498971411
Investment Management Service
N.A.I.C.S.: 523940

Georg Fischer Immobilien AG (1)
Amsler Laffon Strasse 9, 8201, Schaff-
hausen, Switzerland **(100%)**
Tel.: (41) 526311111
Web Site: http://www.georgfischer.com
Sales Range: $450-499.9 Million
Emp.: 1,500
Mfr of Plastic Products
N.A.I.C.S.: 326199

Georg Fischer JRG AG (1)
Hauptstrasse 130, 4450, Sissach, Switzer-
land
Tel.: (41) 61 975 22 22
Web Site: http://www.jrg.ch
Emp.: 400
Metal Valve Mfr & Distr
N.A.I.C.S.: 332999
Jurg Roth *(Mgr-Production)*

Georg Fischer Kokillenguss GmbH (1)
Wiener Strasse 41-43, 3130, Herzogen-
burg, Austria
Tel.: (43) 2782 800 0
Sales Range: $200-249.9 Million
Emp.: 650
Aluminum Casting Mfr
N.A.I.C.S.: 331523
Markus Rosenthal *(Mng Dir)*

Georg Fischer Korea Co. Ltd (1)
Unit 2501 U-Tower 120 Heungdeokjungang-
Ro, Yongin, 446982, Gyeonggi-do, Korea
(South)
Tel.: (82) 31 8017 1450
Web Site: http://www.georgfischer.kr
Sales Range: $25-49.9 Million
Emp.: 10
Plastic Piping Systems Mfr
N.A.I.C.S.: 326122

Georg Fischer Kunststoffarmaturen AG (1)
Losliweg 26, Bern, 7212, Seewis-Pardisla,
Switzerland **(100%)**
Tel.: (41) 813075500
Web Site: http://www.gfps.com
Sales Range: $10-24.9 Million
Emp.: 200
Mfr of Piping Systems
N.A.I.C.S.: 326122

Georg Fischer LLC (1)
9271 Jeronimo, Irvine, CA 92618 **(100%)**
Tel.: (714) 731-8800
Web Site: http://www.gfpiping.com
Sales Range: $25-49.9 Million
Emp.: 100
Industrial Plastic Piping Systems
N.A.I.C.S.: 326122
Chris Blumer *(Pres-America Div)*

Subsidiary (Domestic):

Georg Fischer Signet LLC (2)
3401 Aero Jet Ave, El Monte, CA
91734-1770 **(100%)**
Tel.: (626) 571-2770
Web Site: http://www.gfps.com
Sales Range: $25-49.9 Million
Emp.: 100
Flow & Analytical Sensors, Instrumentation
& Ultrasonics
N.A.I.C.S.: 334513
Charlotte Hill *(Pres)*

George Fischer Sloane, Inc. (2)
7777 Sloane Dr, Little Rock, AR 72206-
3872
Tel.: (501) 490-7777
Web Site:
http://www.sloane.georgefischer.com
Sales Range: $50-74.9 Million
Emp.: 200
Industrial Thermoplastic Pipe, Valves &
Fittings
N.A.I.C.S.: 326122

Georg Fischer Liegenschaften AG (1)
Amslerlaffonstrasse 9, Schaffhausen, 8201,
Switzerland
Tel.: (41) 526 31 11 11
Web Site: http://www.georgfischer.com
Real Estate Development Services
N.A.I.C.S.: 531390

Georg Fischer Ltd (1)
13 Jupiter Grove, PO Box 40399, Upper
Hutt, 5140, New Zealand
Tel.: (64) 4 527 9813
Web Site: http://www.georgfischer.co.nz
Plumbing Equipment Mfr & Distr
N.A.I.C.S.: 332913
Jennifer Leigh Hauschildt *(Chief HR Officer-Global)*

Georg Fischer Ltd. (1)
13 8 Nanbanaka 1 chome, Naniwa ku,
Osaka, 556 0011, Japan
Tel.: (81) 666352691
Web Site: http://www.georgfischer.jp
Sales Range: $25-49.9 Million
Emp.: 40
Mfr of Piping Systems
N.A.I.C.S.: 326122

Georg Fischer N.V. (1)
Lange Veenteweg 19, PO Box 35, Epe,
8161, Netherlands **(100%)**
Tel.: (31) 578678222
Web Site: http://www.georgfischer.nl
Sales Range: $10-24.9 Million
Emp.: 30
Sales of Piping Systems
N.A.I.C.S.: 237110

Georg Fischer NV-SA (1)
Vaartdijk 109 11 Digue Du Camal, Brussels,
1070, Brabant, Belgium **(99%)**
Tel.: (32) 25564020
Web Site: http://www.georgfischer.be
Sales Range: Less than $1 Million
Emp.: 19
Sales of Piping Systems
N.A.I.C.S.: 326122

Georg Fischer Omicron Srl (1)
Via Enrico Fermi 12, Selvazzano Dentro,
35030, Padua, Italy
Tel.: (39) 049 8971411
Web Site: http://www.georgfischer-Omicron.com
Sales Range: $25-49.9 Million
Emp.: 40
Piping Equipment Mfr & Distr
N.A.I.C.S.: 326122

Georg Fischer Pfci Srl (1)
24 Via Degli Imprenditori, 37067, Valeggio
sul Mincio, Verona, Italy
Tel.: (39) 0456 372 911
Web Site:
http://www.piping.georgfischer.com
Sales Range: $25-49.9 Million
Emp.: 80
Piping System Mfr
N.A.I.C.S.: 326122

Georg Fischer Piping Systems Ltd. (1)
Amsler Laffon Str 9, CH 8200, Schaff-
hausen, Switzerland **(100%)**
Tel.: (41) 526311111
Web Site: http://www.georgfischer.com
Sales Range: $450-499.9 Million
Emp.: 1,250
Sales of Piping Systems
N.A.I.C.S.: 326122

Subsidiary (US):

Georg Fischer Central Plastics Co. (2)
39605 Independence Rd, Shawnee, OK
74804
Tel.: (405) 273-6302
Web Site: http://www.centralplastics.com
Sales Range: $75-99.9 Million
Emp.: 435
Special Dies, Tools, Jigs & Fixtures Mfr
N.A.I.C.S.: 331511

Subsidiary (Non-US):

Georg Fischer Central Plastics Sudamerica SRL (3)
Agustin Alvarez 1502, Florida, B1602EBC,
Buenos Aires, Argentina
Tel.: (54) 1145120290
Web Site: http://www.gf.com
Emp.: 18
Plastic Piping Systems Mfr
N.A.I.C.S.: 326122

Subsidiary (Domestic):

Independent Pipe Products Inc. (3)
4949 Joseph Hardin Dr, Dallas, TX 75236
Tel.: (972) 641-2080
Web Site: http://www.indpipe.net
Sales Range: $50-74.9 Million
Emp.: 100
Plumbing Product Distr
N.A.I.C.S.: 423720
Lane Hayes *(Project Coord)*

Subsidiary (US):

Georg Fischer Harvel LLC (2)
300 Kuebler Rd, Easton, PA 18040
Tel.: (610) 252-7355
Web Site: http://www.harvel.com
Sales Range: $50-74.9 Million
Emp.: 150
PVC Pipe Mfr
N.A.I.C.S.: 326122

Plant (Domestic):

Georg Fischer Harvel LLC - Bakersfield Plant (3)
7001 Schirra Ct, Bakersfield, CA 93313
Tel.: (661) 396-0653
Web Site: http://www.harvel.com
Sales Range: $25-49.9 Million
Emp.: 40
PVC Pipe Mfr
N.A.I.C.S.: 326122
Scott Happel *(Plant Mgr)*

Subsidiary (Non-US):

Georg Fischer Piping Systems (Trading) Ltd (2)
A2&J2 No 23 warehouse No 150 Ri Jing
Road Waigaoqiao Free Trade Zone, Shanghai, 201319, China
Tel.: (86) 21 5868 0278
Pipe Fitting Distr
N.A.I.C.S.: 423720
Vivian Zhang *(Mgr-Warehouse)*

Georg Fischer Piping Systems Ltd (2)
Unit 2501 2502 U-Tower 120
HeungdeokJungang-ro Giheung-gu Yongin-
si, Yongin, 16950, Korea (South)
Tel.: (82) 31 8017 1450
Web Site:
http://www.piping.georgfischer.com
Emp.: 14
Plastic Piping System Distr
N.A.I.C.S.: 423720

Georg Fischer Piping Systems Ltd (2)
6200 Vipond Drive, Mississauga, L5T 2B2,
ON, Canada
Tel.: (905) 670-8005
Web Site: http://www.gfpiping.ca
Sales Range: $25-49.9 Million
Emp.: 10
Plastic Pipe & Valve Distr
N.A.I.C.S.: 423720

Georg Fischer Piping Systems Ltd (2)
No 218 Kang Qiao Dong Road, Pudong,
Shanghai, 201319, China
Tel.: (86) 21 3899 3899
Web Site:
http://www.cn.piping.georgfischer.com
Sales Range: $25-49.9 Million
Emp.: 100
Plastic Pipe & Fitting Mfr
N.A.I.C.S.: 332913

Georg Fischer Piping Systems PVT Ltd (2)
Plot No 9-B 1st Floor Kopri Village Valley
Restaurant Powai, Mumbai, 400 076, India
Tel.: (91) 22 4007 2000
Web Site: http://www.georgfischer.in
Sales Range: $25-49.9 Million
Emp.: 25
Plumbing Product Distr
N.A.I.C.S.: 423720

Georg Fischer Pte. Ltd. (1)
11Tatines St 92, Trivec Building Unit 04-01,
Singapore, 528872, Singapore **(100%)**
Tel.: (65) 67470611
Web Site: http://www.georgfischer.com.sg
Sales Range: $25-49.9 Million
Emp.: 35
Forwarding & Shipping Services
N.A.I.C.S.: 488510

Georg Fischer Pty. Ltd. (1)
186 190 Kings Grove Rd, Kings Grove,
Sydney, 2208, VIC, Australia **(100%)**
Tel.: (61) 395638899
Web Site: http://www.georgefischer.com.au
Sales Range: $25-49.9 Million
Emp.: 5
Sales of Piping Systems
N.A.I.C.S.: 326122

Georg Fischer Pty. Ltd. (1)
PO Box 1011, Riverwood, 2210, NSW,
Australia **(100%)**
Tel.: (61) 295543977
Web Site: http://www.georgefischer.com.au
Sales Range: $25-49.9 Million
Emp.: 30
Mfr & Sales of Piping Systems
N.A.I.C.S.: 326122

Georg Fischer Risk Management AG (1)
Amsler Laffon Strasse 9, 8201, Schaff-
hausen, Switzerland **(100%)**
Tel.: (41) 526312226
Web Site: http://www.georgfischer.com
Sales Range: $150-199.9 Million
Emp.: 800
Provider of Risk Management Services
N.A.I.C.S.: 561499

Georg Fischer Rohrleitungssysteme (Elvetia) S.A. (1)
Str Giuseppe Verdi 9A Sector 2, Bucharest,
20257, Romania
Tel.: (40) 311 040 492
Web Site: http://www.georgfischer.com
Emp.: 6
Plumbing Equipment Mfr & Distr
N.A.I.C.S.: 332913

Georg Fischer Rohrleitungssysteme (Schweiz) AG (1)
Ebnatstrasse 101, 8201, Schaffhausen,
Switzerland

AND PRIVATE COMPANIES — GEORG FISCHER AG

Tel.: (41) 52 631 30 26
Web Site: http://www.gspf.ch
Emp.: 30
Plumbing Product Distr
N.A.I.C.S.: 423720

Georg Fischer Rohrleitungssysteme AG (1)
Ebnatstrasse 101, Schaffhausen, 8201, Switzerland
Tel.: (41) 52 631 30 26
Plumbing Equipment Mfr & Distr
N.A.I.C.S.: 332913

Georg Fischer Rohrleitungssystems GmbH (1)
Sandgasse 16, AT 3130, Herzogenburg, Austria **(100%)**
Tel.: (43) 2782856430
Web Site: http://www.georgfischer.at
Sales Range: $25-49.9 Million
Emp.: 20
Sales of Piping Systems
N.A.I.C.S.: 326122

Georg Fischer S.p.A. (1)
Sondrio 1, Cernusco, 20063, Milan, Italy **(99%)**
Tel.: (39) 02 92186 1
Web Site: http://www.georgfischer.it
Sales Range: $25-49.9 Million
Emp.: 40
Sales Agent for Piping Systems
N.A.I.C.S.: 237110

Georg Fischer S.p.A. (1)
Via Sondrio 1, Cernusco sul Naviglio, 20063, MI, Italy **(100%)**
Tel.: (39) 02921861
Web Site: http://www.georgfischer.com
Sales Range: $25-49.9 Million
Emp.: 40
Piping Systems Sales
N.A.I.C.S.: 326122

Georg Fischer SA de CV (1)
Av Isidoro Sepulveda 744 Parque Industrial Multipark, Apodaca, 66600, Nuevo Leon, Mexico
Tel.: (52) 81 1340 8586
Web Site: http://www.georgfischer.mx
Emp.: 15
Plastic & Metal Piping System Distr
N.A.I.C.S.: 423510
Gustavo Rojo *(Mgr-Sls-Automation)*

Georg Fischer SAS (1)
Batiment le Rabelais Paris Nord 2 22 avenue des Nations, Roissy-en-France, 95932, France
Tel.: (33) 1 41 84 68 84
Web Site: http://www.georgfischer.fr
Sales Range: $25-49.9 Million
Emp.: 30
Plastic Piping Systems Mfr
N.A.I.C.S.: 326112

Georg Fischer Sales Ltd. (1)
Paradise Way, Coventry, CV22ST, United Kingdom **(100%)**
Tel.: (44) 2476535535
Web Site: http://www.georgfischer.co.uk
Sales Range: $25-49.9 Million
Emp.: 30
Sales of Piping Systems
N.A.I.C.S.: 326122
Richard Trevaskis *(Mng Dir)*

Georg Fischer Sistemas de Tubulacoes Ltda (1)
Av das Nacoes Unidas 21 689, Sao Paulo, 04795-100, Brazil
Tel.: (55) 11 5525 13 11
Web Site: http://www.georgfischer.com.br
Plumbing Product Distr
N.A.I.C.S.: 423720

Georg Fischer Sp. z.o.o. (1)
Al Krakowska 81, Sekocin Nowy, 02-180, Poland
Tel.: (48) 22 31 31 050
Web Site: http://www.georgfischer.pl
Emp.: 10
Pipe Fitting Mfr
N.A.I.C.S.: 332919
Dariusz Baran *(Mgr-Market Segment-IS)*

Georg Fischer TPA Srl (1)
Via Seminella 50/M, 16012, Busalla, Genoa, Italy

Tel.: (39) 010 962 4711
Web Site: http://www.tp-piping.com
Sales Range: $25-49.9 Million
Emp.: 100
Valve & Fitting Mfr
N.A.I.C.S.: 332912

Georg Fischer Trenton Ltd. (1)
Brabhat Bhavan 2nd Fl LBS Marg, Mumbai, 400 083, Vikhroli West, India **(51%)**
Tel.: (91) 2240072000
Web Site: http://www.georgfischer.in
Sales Range: $25-49.9 Million
Emp.: 20
Piping System Mfr
N.A.I.C.S.: 326122

Georg Fischer Verwaltungs GmbH (1)
Flurstrasse 15-17, Mettmann, 40822, Germany
Tel.: (49) 2104 9840
Emp.: 1,100
Business Management Consulting Services
N.A.I.C.S.: 541618

Georg Fischer WAGA N.V. (1)
Lange Veentweg 19, PO Box 290, Epe, 8161PA, Netherlands **(100%)**
Tel.: (31) 578678378
Web Site: http://www.waga.nl
Sales Range: $25-49.9 Million
Emp.: 30
Mfr of Couplings
N.A.I.C.S.: 332919

Georg Fischer, S.A. (1)
Castalena St 184 7th Fl, ES 28046, Madrid, Spain **(100%)**
Tel.: (34) 917819890
Web Site: http://www.georgfischer.es
Sales Range: $25-49.9 Million
Emp.: 18
Sales of Piping Systems
N.A.I.C.S.: 326122

George Fischer (M) SDN BHD (1)
No 14 Jalan Anggerik Mokara 31/50 Kota Kemuning, Shah Alam, 40460, Selangor Darul Ehsan, Malaysia
Tel.: (60) 3 5122 5585
Web Site: http://www.piping.georgfischer.com
Sales Range: $25-49.9 Million
Emp.: 42
Mining Equipment Distr
N.A.I.C.S.: 423830
Justin Wong *(Mgr-Market Segment)*

George Fischer IPS Pty Ltd (1)
100 Belmore Road North, Riverwood, 2210, NSW, Australia
Tel.: (61) 2 9554 3977
Web Site: http://www.georgfischer.com.au
Emp.: 30
Plumbing Equipment Distr
N.A.I.C.S.: 423720

George Fischer Sales Ltd (1)
Paradise Way, Coventry, CV2 2ST, United Kingdom
Tel.: (44) 2476535535
Web Site: http://www.georgfischer.co.uk
Sales Range: $50-74.9 Million
Emp.: 100
Plumbing Product Distr
N.A.I.C.S.: 423720
Richard Trevaskis *(Mng Dir)*

Jarfalla Hardverkstad AB (1)
Elektronikhojden 8, 175 26, Jarfalla, Sweden
Tel.: (46) 8 580 125 50
Web Site: http://www.jhv.se
Sales Range: $25-49.9 Million
Emp.: 9
Heat Treatment Services
N.A.I.C.S.: 332811

Lincoln Casting Ltd. (1)
Sta Rd, N Hykeham, LN69AS, Lincoln, United Kingdom **(100%)**
Tel.: (44) 522681515
Sales Range: $25-49.9 Million
Emp.: 500
Mfr of Automotive Products
N.A.I.C.S.: 326199

Rhenum Metall Ltd. (1)
Ebnat St 111, Schaffhausen, A201, Switzerland **(100%)**

Tel.: (41) 526311111
Sales Range: $50-74.9 Million
Emp.: 10
N.A.I.C.S.: 326199

System 3R Europe GmbH (1)
Wasserweg 19, 64521, Gross-Gerau, Germany
Tel.: (49) 6152 80 02 0
Industrial Machinery Distr
N.A.I.C.S.: 423830

Uponor Oyj (1)
Ayritie 20, FI-01511, Vantaa, Finland **(93.15%)**
Tel.: (358) 20129211
Web Site: http://www.uponor.com
Rev.: $1,496,006,907
Assets: $1,046,622,059
Liabilities: $469,566,156
Net Worth: $577,055,903
Earnings: $105,223,397
Emp.: 4,055
Fiscal Year-end: 12/31/2022
Pipes Mfr
N.A.I.C.S.: 332919
Sebastian Bondestam *(Pres-Infra)*

Subsidiary (Domestic):

Jita Oy (2)
Lakarintie 10, 34800, Virrat, Finland
Tel.: (358) 34756100
Web Site: https://www.jita.fi
Sales Range: $25-49.9 Million
Emp.: 40
Wastewater Treatment Equipments Mfr
N.A.I.C.S.: 333310
Kari Kohtala *(CEO & Mng Dir)*

Nereus Oy (2)
Sorvarintie 1, PL 36, 23501, Uusikaupunki, Finland
Tel.: (358) 28425200
Web Site: http://www.nereus.fi
Radiant Floor Heating Equipment Sales & Installation Services
N.A.I.C.S.: 423730

Subsidiary (Non-US):

SIA Uponor Latvia (2)
Ganibu dambis 7A, Riga, 1010, Latvia
Tel.: (371) 67821321
Web Site: http://www.uponor.lv
Sales Range: $50-74.9 Million
Emp.: 10
Plumbing Supplies & Indoor Climate Systems Distr
N.A.I.C.S.: 423720

The Underfloor Heating Company Limited (2)
Unit 1 Skelmanthorpe Technology Park Station Road, Skelmanthorpe, Huddersfield, HD8 9GA, West Yorkshire, United Kingdom
Tel.: (44) 1484 860 811
Web Site: http://www.velta-uk.com
Sales Range: $25-49.9 Million
Emp.: 30
Heating & Cooling Systems Design & Installation Services
N.A.I.C.S.: 238220

Uponor A/S (2)
Kornmarksvej 21, 2605, Brondby, Denmark
Tel.: (45) 43263400
Web Site: http://www.uponor.dk
Plumbing & Indoor Climate Systems Distr
N.A.I.C.S.: 423720

Uponor AB (2)
Sintervagen 14, 721 30, Vasteras, Sweden
Tel.: (46) 22338000
Web Site: http://www.uponor.se
Sales Range: $150-199.9 Million
Emp.: 500
Plumbing & Indoor Climate Systems Distr
N.A.I.C.S.: 423720

Subsidiary (Non-US):

Uponor Vertriebs GmbH (3)
Strasse 7 Obj 58D2 Wr, 2353, Wiener Neudorf, Austria
Tel.: (43) 2236230030
Web Site: http://www.uponor.at
Plumbing Supplies & Indoor Climate Systems Distr
N.A.I.C.S.: 423720

Subsidiary (Non-US):

Uponor AS (2)
Stottumveien 7, 1540, Vestby, Norway
Tel.: (47) 64 956 600
Web Site: http://www.uponor.no
Sales Range: $25-49.9 Million
Emp.: 40
Construction Engineering Services
N.A.I.C.S.: 541330

Uponor Beteiligungs GmbH (2)
Industriestr 56, Hassfurt, 97437, Bayern, Germany
Tel.: (49) 95216900
Sales Range: $350-399.9 Million
Emp.: 450
Investment Management Service
N.A.I.C.S.: 523999
Richard Kraus *(Mng Dir)*

Subsidiary (Domestic):

Uponor (Deutschland) GmbH (3)
Industriestr 56, 97437, Hassfurt, Bayern, Germany
Tel.: (49) 95216900
Plumbing Supplies Whslr
N.A.I.C.S.: 423720

Subsidiary (Domestic):

Uponor GmbH (4)
Industriestrasse 56, 97437, Hassfurt, Germany
Tel.: (49) 95216900
Web Site: http://www.uponor.de
Emp.: 300
Plumbing & Indoor Climate Systems Distr
N.A.I.C.S.: 423720
Richard Kraus *(Mng Dir)*

Subsidiary (Non-US):

Uponor S.A.R.L. (5)
60 Ave Des Arrivaux, 38070, Saint-Quentin-Fallavier, Isere, France
Tel.: (33) 4 74 95 70 70
Web Site: http://www.uponor.fr
Sales Range: $25-49.9 Million
Emp.: 50
Plumbing Supplies & Indoor Climate Systems Distr
N.A.I.C.S.: 423720

Subsidiary (Non-US):

Uponor Hispania, S.A. (3)
Antigua Carretera de Extremadura km 20 700, 28935, Mostoles, Madrid, Spain
Tel.: (34) 916853600
Web Site: http://www.uponor.es
Sales Range: $75-99.9 Million
Emp.: 200
Plumbing & Indoor Climate Systems Distr
N.A.I.C.S.: 423720

Subsidiary (Domestic):

Uponor Business Solutions Oy (2)
Robert Huberntie 3 B, PL 37, 01511, Vantaa, Finland
Tel.: (358) 20129211
Business Management Consulting Services
N.A.I.C.S.: 561499

Subsidiary (Non-US):

Uponor Eesti OU (2)
Osmussaare 8 A3, 13811, Tallinn, Harju, Estonia
Tel.: (372) 6052070
Web Site: http://www.uponor.ee
Plumbing Supplies & Indoor Climate Systems Distr
N.A.I.C.S.: 423720

Uponor Epuletgepeszeti Korlatolt Felelossegu Tarsasag (2)
Uponor Epuletgepeszeti Kft Lorantffy Zsuzsanna u 15/b, 1043, Budapest, Hungary
Tel.: (36) 302291978
Web Site: https://www.uponor.com
Pipeline System Mfr & Distr
N.A.I.C.S.: 332996

Subsidiary (Domestic):

Uponor Infra Oy (2)
Kouvolantie 365, PL 21, 15561, Nastola, Finland **(100%)**

GEORG FISCHER AG

Georg Fischer AG—(Continued)
Tel.: (358) 20129211
Radiant Heating & Cooling Infrastructure Services
N.A.I.C.S.: 238220

Subsidiary (Non-US):

Uponor Innovation AB (2)
Industrivagen 11, Fristad, 51332, Sweden
Tel.: (46) 33172750
Web Site: http://www.uponor.se
Industrial Research & Development Services
N.A.I.C.S.: 541715

Uponor Kft (2)
Loranttfy Zsuzsanna Utca 15/b, Budapest, 1043, Hungary
Tel.: (36) 12033611
Web Site: http://www.uponor.hu
Sales Range: $25-49.9 Million
Emp.: 11
Plumbing Services
N.A.I.C.S.: 238220

Uponor Limited (2)
Snapethorpe House Rugby Road, Lutterworth, LE17 4HN, Leicestershire, United Kingdom
Tel.: (44) 1455 551307
Web Site: http://www.uponor.co.uk
Plumbing & Heating Systems Distr
N.A.I.C.S.: 423720

Subsidiary (US):

Uponor North America (2)
5925 148th St W, Apple Valley, MN 55124
Tel.: (952) 997-7900
Sales Range: $50-74.9 Million
Emp.: 212
Mfr of Radiant Floor Heating Systems, Plumbing Systems & Fire Protection Systems
N.A.I.C.S.: 333414
Jennifer Leigh Hauschildt *(CIO & VP-HR)*

Division (Domestic):

Uponor USA (3)
5925 148th St W, Apple Valley, MN 55124-8197
Tel.: (952) 891-2000
Web Site: http://www.uponor-usa.com
Sales Range: $100-124.9 Million
Mfr of Radiant Floor Heating Systems, Plumbing Systems & Fire Protection Systems
N.A.I.C.S.: 333414
Rusty Callier *(Dir-Sustainability & Corp Responsibility)*

Subsidiary (Domestic):

Stadler-Viega (4)
301 N Main Street, Wichita, KS 67202
Tel.: (316) 425-7400
Web Site: http://www.viega.com
Sales Range: $25-49.9 Million
Emp.: 26
Radiant Wall & Floor Heating Systems
N.A.I.C.S.: 423720

Subsidiary (Non-US):

Uponor Portugal - Sistemas para Fluidos Lda. (2)
Rua Central do Olival 1100, Olival, 4415-726, Vila Nova de Gaia, Portugal
Tel.: (351) 227860200
Web Site: http://www.uponor.pt
Sales Range: $50-74.9 Million
Emp.: 21
Plumbing & Indoor Climate Systems Distr
N.A.I.C.S.: 423720
Angal Lopez *(Gen Mgr)*

Uponor Sp. z o.o. (2)
Ul Kolejowa 5/7, 01-217, Warsaw, Poland
Tel.: (48) 227310100
Web Site: http://www.uponor.pl
Plumbing Supplies & Indoor Climate Systems Distr
N.A.I.C.S.: 423720

Subsidiary (Domestic):

Uponor Suomi Oy (2)
Kouvolantie 365, PO Box 21, 15561, Nastola, Finland
Tel.: (358) 20129211
Web Site: http://www.uponor.fi
Plumbing Supplies & Indoor Climate Systems Distr
N.A.I.C.S.: 423720
Ville Ruohio *(Mgr-Sls Unit & CEO)*

Subsidiary (Non-US):

Uponor Texnikes Lyseis gia Ktiria AE (2)
Dormition of the Virgin Mary 40, Agios Stefanos, 14565, Athens, Greece
Tel.: (30) 2109400343
Web Site: http://www.uponor.gr
Sales Range: $50-74.9 Million
Emp.: 3
Heating Systems Distr
N.A.I.C.S.: 423720

Uponor s.r.o. (2)
Zeleny Pruh 95/97, 140 00, Prague, Czech Republic
Tel.: (420) 233313844
Web Site: http://www.uponor.cz
Sales Range: $50-74.9 Million
Emp.: 10
Plumbing & Indoor Climate Systems Distr
N.A.I.C.S.: 423720

WIIK Public Company Limited (2)
90 CW Tower A 35th Floor Ratchadapisek Rd, Huaykwang, Bangkok, 10310, Thailand
Tel.: (66) 26128600
Web Site: http://www.wiik.co.th
Rev.: $39,057,561
Assets: $78,547,900
Liabilities: $16,100,689
Net Worth: $62,447,211
Earnings: $1,442,369
Emp.: 310
Fiscal Year-end: 12/31/2023
Plastic Tank Mfr
N.A.I.C.S.: 326122
Wiboon Sangwithayanon *(CEO)*

ZAO Uponor Rus (2)
5A Detskaya St, 199026, Saint Petersburg, Russia
Tel.: (7) 8123275688
Sales Range: $50-74.9 Million
Emp.: 6
Construction Materials Whslr
N.A.I.C.S.: 423610

GEORG FISCHER DRUCKGUSS GMBH & CO KG
Wiener Strasse 41-43, 3130, Herzogenburg, Austria
Tel.: (43) 2782 800 0
Web Site: http://www.gfau.com
Year Founded: 1862
Sales Range: $200-249.9 Million
Emp.: 680
Aluminum Pressure Die & Mold Casting Services
N.A.I.C.S.: 331523
Markus Rosenthal *(Mng Dir)*

GEORG H. LUH FARBEN- UND CHEMIKALIEN GROSSHANDELSGES GMBH
Schone Aussicht 39, 65393, Walluf, Germany
Tel.: (49) 61237980   De
Web Site: http://www.luh.de
Raw Materials Distr
N.A.I.C.S.: 488999
Klaus Rathberger *(Mng Dir)*

GEORG SCHARDT KG
Am Riegel 15, 96268, Kronach, Germany
Tel.: (49) 926699070
Web Site: http://www.schardt.com
Year Founded: 1936
Rev.: $14,353,506
Emp.: 78
Children Furniture Mfr
N.A.I.C.S.: 339930
Rainer Schardt *(Mng Dir)*

GEORGE FORREST INTERNATIONAL S.A.
Ave Pasteur 9, 1300, Wavre, Belgium
Tel.: (32) 10239680
Web Site:
  http://www.forrestgroup.com
Sales Range: $1-4.9 Billion
Emp.: 5,000
Holding Company
N.A.I.C.S.: 551112
George A. Forrest *(Pres)*

Subsidiaries:

ENTREPRISE GENERALE MALTA FORREST S.A. (1)
Avenue Kigoma 22, BP 1531, Lubumbashi, Katanga, Congo, Democratic Republic of
Tel.: (243) 99 604 01 00
Metal Ore Mining Services
N.A.I.C.S.: 212290
Hans Mestdagh *(Mgr-Technical)*

Subsidiary (Non-US):

EGMF Kenya (2)
PO Box 1322 - 00217, Limuru, Kenya
Tel.: (254) 20 354 7741
Web Site: http://www.egmfkenya.co.ke
Wind Power Generation Services
N.A.I.C.S.: 221115

Grands Elevages de Katongola (1)
Avenue de la Revolution 272, Lubumbashi, Congo, Democratic Republic of
Tel.: (243) 9 941 11800
Cattle Ranching Services
N.A.I.C.S.: 112111

NEW BARON LEVEQUE INTERNATIONAL AFRIQUE (1)
Avenue Kibati 20 Quartier Industriel, BP 1531, Lubumbashi, Congo, Democratic Republic of
Tel.: (243) 23 43 535
Building Renovation Services
N.A.I.C.S.: 236118

New Lachaussee s.a. (1)
Rue de Milmort 670, Herstal, 4041, Milmort, Belgium
Tel.: (32) 4 248 88 11
Web Site: http://www.lachaussee.com
Emp.: 90
Industrial Machinery Mfr
N.A.I.C.S.: 333998
Daniel Arend *(Dir-Comml)*

GEORGE KENT (MALAYSIA) BERHAD
1115 Blok A Jalan Puchong, Taman Meranti Jaya, 47120, Puchong, Selangor, Malaysia
Tel.: (60) 380648000
Web Site: https://www.georgekent.net
GKENT—(KLS)
Rev.: $52,283,598
Assets: $170,864,550
Liabilities: $59,284,868
Net Worth: $111,579,683
Earnings: $151,323
Emp.: 225
Fiscal Year-end: 03/31/23
Water Supply Services
N.A.I.C.S.: 221310
Yong Fah Teh *(Co-Sec)*

Subsidiaries:

GK Equities Sdn. Bhd. (1)
Lot 1115 Batu 15 Jalan Dengkil, 47100, Puchong, Selangor, Malaysia
Tel.: (60) 380615455
Industrial Control Instrument Distr
N.A.I.C.S.: 423610

GEORGE WESTON LIMITED
22 St Clair Avenue East, Toronto, M4T 2S7, ON, Canada
Tel.: (416) 922-2500   ON
Web Site: https://www.weston.ca
Year Founded: 1882
WN—(TSX)
Rev.: $42,794,627,400

INTERNATIONAL PUBLIC

Assets: $37,608,111,000
Liabilities: $27,111,477,960
Net Worth: $10,496,633,040
Earnings: $753,335,540
Emp.: 220,000
Fiscal Year-end: 12/31/20
Food Processing & Distr Services; Fresh & Frozen Bakeries, Dairy & Supermarket Operations
N.A.I.C.S.: 311812
Gordon A. M. Currie *(Chief Legal Officer & Exec VP)*

Subsidiaries:

Choice Properties Real Estate Investment Trust (1)
700-22 St Clair Avenue East, Toronto, M4T 2S5, ON, Canada (65.4%)
Tel.: (416) 628-7771
Web Site: https://www.choicereit.ca
Rev.: $1,010,956,872
Assets: $12,651,503,875
Liabilities: $10,062,007,659
Net Worth: $2,589,496,215
Earnings: $17,998,698
Emp.: 298
Fiscal Year-end: 12/31/2021
Real Estate Investment Trust
N.A.I.C.S.: 525990
Rael L. Diamond *(Pres & CEO)*

Loblaw Companies Limited (1)
22 St Clair Avenue East, Toronto, M4T 2S5, ON, Canada (47%)
Tel.: (416) 922-8500
Web Site: https://www.loblaw.ca
Rev.: $41,593,827,600
Assets: $28,642,399,920
Liabilities: $19,460,779,560
Net Worth: $9,181,620,360
Earnings: $1,545,785,280
Emp.: 215,000
Fiscal Year-end: 01/01/2022
Food Distr & Grocery Chain
N.A.I.C.S.: 445110
Barry K. Columb *(Member-Exec Bd)*

Subsidiary (Domestic):

Atlantic Wholesalers Ltd. (2)
3711 Joseph, Halifax, B3l4HH, NS, Canada
Tel.: (902) 468-8866
Web Site: http://www.superstorejobsns.ca
Sales Range: $25-49.9 Million
Emp.: 70
Food Distribution
N.A.I.C.S.: 445110
Darlene Durant *(Dir-HR)*

Loblaw Brands Limited (2)
1 President's Choice Cir, Brampton, L6Y 5S5, ON, Canada (100%)
Tel.: (905) 459-2500
Web Site: http://www.loblaw.ca
Sales Range: $350-399.9 Million
Emp.: 2,500
Food Distribution
N.A.I.C.S.: 445110

Loblaw Properties Limited (2)
1 President's Choice Circle, Brampton, L6Y 5S5, ON, Canada (100%)
Tel.: (905) 459-2500
Web Site: http://www.loblaw.ca
Sales Range: $250-299.9 Million
Emp.: 1,000
Property Management
N.A.I.C.S.: 531120

Loblaw Properties West, Inc. (2)
3225 12th St NE, Calgary, T2E 7S9, AB, Canada (100%)
Tel.: (403) 291-7700
Web Site: http://www.loblaw.ca
Sales Range: $25-49.9 Million
Emp.: 200
Food Distr
N.A.I.C.S.: 445110

President's Choice Bank (2)
25 York Str 7 Fl, Toronto, M5J 2V5, ON, Canada (100%)
Tel.: (416) 204-2600
Web Site: http://www.pcfinancial.ca
Sales Range: $75-99.9 Million
Emp.: 170
Provider of Financial Services
N.A.I.C.S.: 523940

AND PRIVATE COMPANIES

Provigo Inc. (2)
400 Ave Sainte Croix, Saint Laurent, H4N
3L4, QC, Canada (100%)
Tel.: (514) 383-8800
Web Site: http://www.provigo.ca
Sales Range: $75-99.9 Million
Emp.: 500
Operator of Grocery Stores
N.A.I.C.S.: 457110

Subsidiary (Domestic):

Provigo Distribution (3)
400 Saint Croix Ave, Saint Laurent, H4N
3L4, QC, Canada (100%)
Tel.: (514) 383-3000
Web Site: http://www.provigo.ca
Provider of Food Distribution Services
N.A.I.C.S.: 445110

Subsidiary (Domestic):

QHR Corporation (2)
1620 Dickson Avenue Suite 300, Kelowna,
V1Y 9Y2, BC, Canada
Tel.: (250) 448-7095
Web Site: https://www.qhrtechnologies.com
Software Publisher
N.A.I.C.S.: 513210
Michael Checkley (Pres)

Subsidiary (Domestic):

Cloudwerx Data Solutions Inc. (3)
2 1440 28th Street NE, Calgary, T2A 7W6,
AB, Canada
Web Site: https://cloudwerx.com
Data Storage Solution Services
N.A.I.C.S.: 518210

Optimed Software Corporation (3)
1632 Dickson Ave Ste 300, Kelowna, V1Y
9Y2, BC, Canada
Tel.: (866) 729-8889
Web Site: http://www.qhrtechnologies.com
Software Mfr
N.A.I.C.S.: 513210

Subsidiary (Domestic):

Shoppers Drug Mart Corporation (2)
243 Consumers Road, Toronto, M2J 4W8,
ON, Canada
Tel.: (416) 493-1220
Web Site:
    http://corporate.shoppersdrugmart.ca
Sales Range: $5-14.9 Billion
Emp.: 1,400
Licensed & Company-Owned Drug Store
Operator
N.A.I.C.S.: 456110
Jeff Yeats (Dir-Loss Prevention)

Subsidiary (Domestic):

Lifemark Health Corporation (3)
20 Eglinton Avenue West Suite 600, Toronto, M4R 1K8, ON, Canada
Tel.: (855) 485-1344
Web Site: http://www.lifemark.ca
Emp.: 1,500
Health Rehabilitation Services
N.A.I.C.S.: 621610

Division (Domestic):

MediSystem Pharmacy (3)
75 Lesmill Rd, Toronto, M3B 2T8, ON,
Canada
Tel.: (416) 441-2293
Web Site:
    http://www.medisystempharmacy.com
Sales Range: $25-49.9 Million
Emp.: 250
Retirement & Long Term Care Facility Pharmacy Services
N.A.I.C.S.: 456110
Helen Huh (Pres)

Subsidiary (Domestic):

T & T Supermarket, Inc. (2)
6311 Fraserwood Pl, Richmond, V6W 1J8,
BC, Canada
Tel.: (604) 276-9889
Web Site: http://www.tnt-supermarket.com
Sales Range: $800-899.9 Million
Emp.: 3,500
Asian Goods Supermarket
N.A.I.C.S.: 445110

Zehrmart Inc. (2)
100 Holiday Inn Dr, Cambridge, N3C 3K1,
ON, Canada (100%)
Tel.: (519) 658-5131
Web Site: http://www.zehr.ca
Sales Range: $25-49.9 Million
Emp.: 150
Food Distribution
N.A.I.C.S.: 445110

Weston Bakeries Limited (1)
1425 The Queensway, Toronto, M8Z 1T3,
ON, Canada (100%)
Tel.: (416) 252-7323
Web Site: http://www.westonfoodscanada.ca
Sales Range: $1-4.9 Billion
Emp.: 22,500
Breads, Rolls, Cakes & Other Bakery Products Mfr
N.A.I.C.S.: 311812

Subsidiary (US):

George Weston Consumer Services (2)
100 N Riverview Dr, Wayne, NJ 07470
Tel.: (973) 872-6167
Web Site: http://www.weston.ca
Sales Range: $25-49.9 Million
Emp.: 140
Production of Breads, Cakes & Related
Products
N.A.I.C.S.: 311812
Maria Liang (Pres-Weston Bakeries)

Interbake Foods LLC (2)
3951 Westerre Pkwy Ste 200, Richmond,
VA 23233 (100%)
Tel.: (804) 755-7107
Web Site: http://www.interbake.com
Sales Range: $350-399.9 Million
Emp.: 55
Food Processing
N.A.I.C.S.: 311821
Tiffany Reeve (Dir-Fin)

Division (Domestic):

Norse Dairy Systems LLC (3)
1740 Joyce Ave, Columbus, OH 43219-1026
Tel.: (614) 294-4931
Web Site: http://www.norse.com
Sales Range: $50-74.9 Million
Mfr of Ice Cream Novelty Machines
N.A.I.C.S.: 333241
Sue Paap (Dir-Mktg)

Subsidiary (US):

Maplehurst Bakeries, Inc. (2)
50 Maplehurst Dr, Brownsburg, IN 46112
Tel.: (317) 858-9000
Web Site:
    http://www.maplehurstbakeries.com
Sales Range: $100-124.9 Million
Emp.: 500
Frozen Bakery Products for In-Store & Food
Service Bakeries Mfr
N.A.I.C.S.: 311812

Subsidiary (Domestic):

Creative Occasions Inc. (3)
1605 County Hospital Rd, Nashville, TN
37218
Tel.: (615) 742-1270
Emp.: 105
Decorated Cakes Mfr
N.A.I.C.S.: 311520
Kevin Chachere (Dir-Pur)

Subsidiary (Domestic):

Ready Bake Foods Inc. (2)
2095 Meadow Vale Boulevard, Mississauga,
L5N 5N1, ON, Canada (100%)
Tel.: (905) 567-0660
Supplier of Frozen Dough & Fully Baked
Products
N.A.I.C.S.: 311824

Subsidiary (US):

Rubschlager Baking Corporation (2)
3220 W Grand Ave, Chicago, IL 60651
Tel.: (773) 826-1245
Web Site:
    http://www.rubschlagerbaking.com

Sales Range: $1-9.9 Million
Emp.: 55
Commercial Bakeries
N.A.I.C.S.: 311812

Weston Foods (Canada) Inc. (1)
1425 The Queensway, Etobicoke, M8Z 1T3,
ON, Canada
Web Site: http://www.westonfoods.ca
Bakery Product Mfr & Retailer
N.A.I.C.S.: 311812
Luc Mongeau (Pres)

GEORGE WILSON INDUSTRIES LIMITED
Unit 2a Barlow Road, Longford Industrial Estate, Coventry, CV6 6BP,
United Kingdom
Tel.: (44) 2476709050
Web Site: https://www.gwi-ltd.co.uk
Year Founded: 1903
Gas Meter Mfr
N.A.I.C.S.: 334513

GEORGIA CAPITAL PLC
1 Erekle Tatishvili Str, 0108, Tbilisi,
Georgia
Tel.: (995) 322000000   UK
Web Site:
    https://www.georgiacapital.ge
Year Founded: 2017
CGEO—(LSE)
Rev.: $102,566,218
Assets: $669,686,270
Liabilities: $689,170
Net Worth: $668,997,101
Earnings: $99,893,002
Emp.: 20,314
Fiscal Year-end: 12/31/20
Investment Management Service
N.A.I.C.S.: 523940
Irakli Gilauri (Chm & CEO)

Subsidiaries:

British International School of Tbilisi LLC (1)
Leo Kvachadze 17 Lisi Lake Area, 186, Tbilisi, Georgia
Tel.: (995) 322801919
Web Site: https://bist.ge
Internet Service Provider
N.A.I.C.S.: 561730

Buckswood International School - Tbilisi, LLC (1)
156 Rustaveli Street, Tskneti, Tbilisi, Georgia
Tel.: (995) 577992993
Web Site: https://buckswood.ge
Internet Service Provider
N.A.I.C.S.: 561730

Caucasus Medical Center, LLC (1)
23 P Kavtaradze str, Tbilisi, Georgia
Tel.: (995) 599325553
Web Site: https://www.cmchospital.ge
Healtcare Services
N.A.I.C.S.: 621610

Georgia Healthcare Group PLC (1)
84 Brook Street, London, W1K 5EH, United
Kingdom (100%)
Tel.: (44) 2031784052
Web Site: http://www.ghg.com.ge
Healtcare Services
N.A.I.C.S.: 621511
Nick Gamkrelidze (CEO)

Georgian Water and Power, LLC (1)
Medea Mzia Jugeli st N10, 0179, Tbilisi,
Georgia
Tel.: (995) 2931111
Web Site: https://www.gwp.ge
Emp.: 3,000
Water Supply Services
N.A.I.C.S.: 221310

GEORGIAN AIRWAYS LTD.
Rutsaveli Ave 12, Tbilisi, Georgia
Tel.: (995) 32999180
Web Site: http://www.georgian-
    airways.com
Year Founded: 1994

Sales Range: $75-99.9 Million
Emp.: 350
Oil Transportation Services
N.A.I.C.S.: 481111
Tamaz Gaiashvili (Chm & Pres)

GEORGIAN CHEVROLET BUICK GMC
65 Barrie View Dr, Barrie, L4N 8V4,
ON, Canada
Tel.: (705) 733-2222
Web Site:
    http://www.georgianchevrolet.com
Year Founded: 1980
Rev.: $53,281,356
Emp.: 106
New & Used Car Dealers
N.A.I.C.S.: 441110
Daniel J. Revell (CFO & VP)

GEORGIAN INTERNATIONAL LIMITED
85 Bayfield Street Suite 500, Barrie,
L4M 3A7, ON, Canada
Tel.: (705) 730-5900
Web Site:
    http://www.georgianinternational.com
Year Founded: 1981
Rev.: $159,930,480
Emp.: 390
Real Estate Investment Services
N.A.I.C.S.: 523940
Daniel G. DeVos (Co-Founder &
Chm)

Subsidiaries:

Air Georgian Ltd (1)
2450 Derry Road East Shell Aerocentre,
Mississauga, L5S 1B2, ON, Canada
Tel.: (905) 676-1221
Web Site: http://www.airgeorgian.ca
Passenger Transportation Services
N.A.I.C.S.: 481111
Daniel J. Revell (Chm)

MINI Georgian (1)
220 Essa Road, Barrie, L4N 6N2, ON,
Canada
Tel.: (705) 797-4200
Web Site: https://www.minigeorgian.ca
Automobile Parts Mfr
N.A.I.C.S.: 336110
Craig Batte (Mgr-Svc)

GEORGIAN PARTNERS GROWTH LP
2 St Clair Ave West Suite 1400, Toronto, M4V 1L5, ON, Canada
Tel.: (416) 868-9696
Web Site:
    http://georgianpartners.com
Year Founded: 2008
Growth Equity Firm
N.A.I.C.S.: 551112
Jason Brenier (VP-Strategy)

GEORGIAN STOCK EXCHANGE
74a Chavchavadze Ave, 380062, Tbilisi, Georgia
Tel.: (995) 32220718
Web Site: http://www.gse.ge
Year Founded: 1999
Stock Exchange Services
N.A.I.C.S.: 523210
George Loladze (Chm)

GEORGIOU GROUP PTY. LTD.
68 Hasler Road, Osborne Park, 6017,
WA, Australia
Tel.: (61) 892002500
Web Site:
    http://www.georgiou.com.au
Year Founded: 1977
Emp.: 636
Building Construction Services
N.A.I.C.S.: 236220

GEORGIOU GROUP PTY. LTD.

Georgiou Group Pty. Ltd.—(Continued)

Gary Georgiou *(Gen Mgr-Eastern Region)*

GEORGSMARIENHUTTE HOLDING GMBH
Neue Huttenstrasse 1, 49124, Georgsmarienhutte, Germany
Tel.: (49) 5401390   De
Web Site: http://www.gmh-gruppe.de
Year Founded: 1993
Emp.: 6,000
Holding Company Steel Cast Iron & Aluminum Mfr
N.A.I.C.S.: 551112
Hero Brahms *(Vice Chm-Supervisory Bd)*

Subsidiaries:

BALO-MOTORTEX GmbH (1)
Bodelschwinger Str 84, D-44577, Castrop-Rauxel, Germany
Tel.: (49) 2305 9666 0
Web Site: http://www.balo.de
Sales Range: $25-49.9 Million
Emp.: 50
Iron & Steel Automotive Castings
N.A.I.C.S.: 332111

Bahntechnik Brand-Erbisdorf GmbH (1)
Berthelsdorfer Strasse 8, D-09618, Brand-Erbisdorf, Germany
Tel.: (49) 3732216302
Web Site: http://www.bt-be.de
Sales Range: $25-49.9 Million
Emp.: 82
Metal Products Mfr
N.A.I.C.S.: 332999
Joerg Villmann *(Mng Dir-Tech & Production)*

BeTraCo Stahl Vertriebs GmbH (1)
Otto-Hahn-Strasse 33, 40591, Dusseldorf, Germany
Tel.: (49) 2117793500
Web Site: http://www.betraco.de
Automotive Part Mfr & Distr
N.A.I.C.S.: 336390
Elizaveta Malczyk *(Exec Dir)*

Berufsbildungsgesellschaft Georgsmarienhutte mbH (1)
Malberger Strasse 2 - 8, 49124, Georgsmarienhutte, Germany
Tel.: (49) 5401 39 49 00
Web Site: http://www.bgg-gmh.de
Industrial Training Services
N.A.I.C.S.: 611430

Bishop Steering Technology Pty Ltd (1)
Unit 6 / 148 James Ruse Drive, Canberra, 2142, NSW, Australia
Tel.: (61) 2 8836 2500
Web Site: http://www.bishopsteering.com.au
Automobile Spare Parts Mfr
N.A.I.C.S.: 336330
Bernd Failenschmid *(Mng Dir)*

Dieckerhoff Guss GmbH (1)
Oststrasse 25-27, 58285, Gevelsberg, Germany
Tel.: (49) 233296840
Web Site: http://www.dieckerhoff-guss.de
Sales Range: $25-49.9 Million
Emp.: 200
Iron & Steel Automotive Castings
N.A.I.C.S.: 332111

EICKHOFF Industrie-Anlagenbau udn Montagen GmbH (1)
Timmerhelstrasse 35-39, 45478, Mulheim an der Ruhr, Germany
Tel.: (49) 20899900
Web Site: http://www.eickhoff-gmbh.de
Sales Range: $50-74.9 Million
Emp.: 150
Plant Engineering Services
N.A.I.C.S.: 237990
Egbert Reinersmann *(Mng Dir)*

Energietechnik Essen GmbH (1)
Westendstrasse 15, 45143, Essen, Germany
Tel.: (49) 201177860
Web Site: http://www.energietechnik-essen.de
Open-Die Iron & Steel Forging
N.A.I.C.S.: 332111
Volkswirt Martin Kausler *(Mng Dir)*

Engineering Steel Belgium SPRL (1)
Rue de l'Environnement 8, 4100, Seraing, Belgium
Tel.: (32) 4 338 85 50
Web Site: http://www.esb.be
Rolled Steel Mfr & Distr
N.A.I.C.S.: 331221
Didier Troisfontaines *(Gen Mgr)*

Friedrich Wilhelms - Huette GmbH (1)
Friedrich-Ebert Strasse 125, 45473, Mulheim an der Ruhr, Germany
Tel.: (49) 2084518
Web Site: http://www.fwh.de
Sales Range: $75-99.9 Million
Emp.: 557
Iron & Steel Castings & Mechanical Engineering
N.A.I.C.S.: 332111

GMH Akademie GmbH (1)
Malberger Strasse 2-8, Georgsmarienhutte, 49124, Osnabruck, Germany
Tel.: (49) 5401394900
Construction Materials Mfr
N.A.I.C.S.: 327999

GMH Blankstahl GmbH (1)
Neue Huttenstrasse 1, 49124, Georgsmarienhutte, Germany
Tel.: (49) 5401390
Web Site: http://www.gmh-blankstahl.de
Sales Range: $450-499.9 Million
Emp.: 1,300
Blast Furnaces Mfr
N.A.I.C.S.: 333994
Marco Altenhoefer *(Head-Sls)*

GMH East Europe GmbH (1)
Office Katowice Korfantego 2/Room No 935, 40-004, Katowice, Poland
Tel.: (48) 327810440
Construction Materials Mfr
N.A.I.C.S.: 327999

GMH France S.a.r.l. (1)
2 Rue Augustin Fresnel, 88230, Metz, France
Tel.: (33) 387187202
Construction Materials Mfr
N.A.I.C.S.: 327999

GMH Group do Brasil (1)
Rodavia Vito Ardito s/n - Km 1, Cacapava, 12282-535, Sao Paulo, Brazil
Tel.: (55) 12 3221 2498
Steel Product Distr
N.A.I.C.S.: 423510

GMH India Pvt. Ltd. (1)
Suite No 307 Sky Station, Viman Nagar, Pune, 411014, India
Tel.: (91) 2065 111 099
Steel Product Distr
N.A.I.C.S.: 423510

GMH International S.r.l. (1)
Via XX Settembre n 30, 16121, Genoa, Italy
Tel.: (39) 0335227562
Construction Materials Mfr
N.A.I.C.S.: 327999
Stefano Gobbi *(Mng Dir)*

GMH International S.r.l. (1)
37 Novena Terrace, Singapore, 307921, Singapore
Tel.: (65) 96702150
Construction Materials Mfr
N.A.I.C.S.: 327999

GMH Ringvertriebs GmbH (1)
Halskestrasse 27, 47877, Willich, Germany
Tel.: (49) 215488588 0
Web Site: http://www.gmh-rvg.de
Emp.: 25
Steel Product Distr
N.A.I.C.S.: 423510
Dominik Butter *(Dir-Sls)*

GMH Systems GmbH (1)
Neue Huttenstrasse 2, 49124, Georgsmarienhutte, Germany
Tel.: (49) 5401 33919 0
Web Site: http://www.gmh-systems.de

Information Technology Consulting Services
N.A.I.C.S.: 541511

GMH UK Ltd. (1)
Stephenson Road, Staveley, Chesterfield, S43 3JN, United Kingdom
Tel.: (44) 1246472829
Construction Materials Mfr
N.A.I.C.S.: 327999
Melanie Clark *(Sls Mgr)*

GSG Georgsmarienhuette Service Gesellschaft mbH (1)
Neue Huettenstrasse 1, 49124, Georgsmarienhutte, Germany
Tel.: (49) 5401390
Web Site: http://www.gmh-holding.com
Emp.: 10,000
Metals Mfr
N.A.I.C.S.: 332999
Harald Schoolartru *(Mng Dir-HR)*

Georgsmarienhutte GmbH (1)
Neue Huttenstrasse 1, 49124, Georgsmarienhutte, Germany
Tel.: (49) 5401390
Web Site: http://www.gmh.de
Sales Range: $600-649.9 Million
Emp.: 1,249
Steel Products Mfr
N.A.I.C.S.: 331513
Juergen Grossmann *(Founder)*

Subsidiary (Domestic):

GMH Recycling Saar GmbH (2)
Saarstrasse, 66359, Bous, Germany
Tel.: (49) 6834920213
Web Site: https://metall.alba.info
Waste Disposal Management Services
N.A.I.C.S.: 562998

GmH Pruftechnik GmbH (1)
Thomas-Mann-Strasse 63, 90471, Nuremberg, Germany
Tel.: (49) 911 48080 0
Web Site: http://www.gmh-prueftechnik.de
Measuring & Test Equipment Mfr
N.A.I.C.S.: 334519

Groditz Celik Endustri Malz. San.ve Tic. A.S. (1)
Cumhuriyet Mah Ismet Inonu Cad No 47, Cayirova, Kocaeli, Turkiye
Tel.: (90) 2626581390
Construction Materials Mfr
N.A.I.C.S.: 327999

Groditzer Vertriebsgesellschaft mbH (1)
Halskestrasse 23-25, 47877, Willich, Germany
Tel.: (49) 21549415 0
Steel Product Distr
N.A.I.C.S.: 423510
Markus Hundshagen *(Mgr-Offshore Div)*

Groeditzer Kurbelwelle Wildau GmbH (1)
Schmiedestrasse, 15745, Wildau, Germany
Tel.: (49) 3375586201
Web Site: http://www.kurbelwellewildau.com
Sales Range: $50-74.9 Million
Emp.: 120
Metal Machining
N.A.I.C.S.: 332710

Groeditzer Werkzeugstahl Burg GmbH (1)
Troxel 1b, D-39288, Burg, Germany
Tel.: (49) 392172260
Web Site: http://www.werkzeugstahl-burg.de
Sales Range: $25-49.9 Million
Emp.: 24
Open-Die Iron & Steel Forging
N.A.I.C.S.: 332111
Andreas Scharf *(Mng Dir)*

Harz Guss Zorge GmbH (1)
Walkenrieder Strasse 32, Sudharz, 37449, Zorge, Germany (100%)
Tel.: (49) 55868020
Web Site: http://www.harzguss.de
Sales Range: $100-124.9 Million
Emp.: 500
Cast Part Mfr
N.A.I.C.S.: 331523
Andreas Beck *(Mng Dir)*

Heinrich Geissler GmbH (1)

INTERNATIONAL PUBLIC

Bebbelsdorf 105, Witten, 58454, Germany
Tel.: (49) 2302910220
Web Site: http://www.geissler-gmbh.de
Sales Range: $25-49.9 Million
Emp.: 100
Blast Furnace Mfr
N.A.I.C.S.: 333994

IAG Industrie-Anlagen-Bau Georgsmarienhuette GmbH (1)
Mallberger Strasse 2-8, 49124, Georgsmarienhutte, Germany
Tel.: (49) 54013310
Web Site: http://www.iag-gmbh.de
Plant Engineering Services
N.A.I.C.S.: 237990

Subsidiary (Domestic):

WeserWind GmbH Offshore Construction Georgsmarienhutte (2)
Am Lunedeich 158, 27572, Bremerhaven, Germany
Tel.: (49) 4719026280
Web Site: http://www.weserwind.de
Sales Range: $50-74.9 Million
Emp.: 110
Plant Engineering Services
N.A.I.C.S.: 237990
Dirk Kassen *(Mng Dir-Technical)*

Subsidiary (Non-US):

WeserWind UK Ltd. (3)
16 Sheepbridge Business Park 655 Sheffield Road, Chesterfield, Derbyshire, United Kingdom
Tel.: (44) 1246 453 794
Steel Product Distr
N.A.I.C.S.: 423510

IAG MAGNUM GmbH (1)
Bessemerstrasse 1, 49084, Osnabruck, Germany
Tel.: (49) 5413220
Web Site: http://www.iag-magnum.de
Sales Range: $50-74.9 Million
Emp.: 160
Ball Bearing Mfr
N.A.I.C.S.: 332991
Andre Buitenhuis *(Controller)*

J. Adolf Baeuerle GmbH & Co. KG (1)
Klotzbachstrasse 2, 73560, Bobingen, Germany
Tel.: (49) 717391870
Web Site: http://www.baeuerle-gmbh.de
Steel Producer
N.A.I.C.S.: 331110
Josef Strecker *(Mng Dir)*

Kranbau Koethen GmbH (1)
Am Hollander Weg 5-7, 06366, Kothen, Germany
Tel.: (49) 34967000
Web Site: http://www.kranbau-koethen.de
Sales Range: $50-74.9 Million
Emp.: 200
Hoists, Cranes & Monorails Mfr
N.A.I.C.S.: 333923
Horst Bugner *(Head-Sls-Steelworks)*

MVO USA Inc. (1)
8802 Bash St Ste A, Indianapolis, IN 46256
Tel.: (317) 585-5785
Web Site: http://www.mvousa.com
Emp.: 17
Automobile Spare Parts Mfr
N.A.I.C.S.: 336330
Tammy Borden *(Pres & CEO)*

Mannstaedt-Werke GmbH & Co. KG (1)
Mendener Strasse 51, 53840, Troisdorf, Germany
Tel.: (49) 2241840
Web Site: http://www.mannstaedt.de
Sales Range: $100-124.9 Million
Emp.: 500
Steel Mfrs
N.A.I.C.S.: 331513

Metallverarbeitung Ostalb GmbH (1)
Nikolaus-Otto-Strasse 1, 73529, Schwabisch Gmund, Germany
Tel.: (49) 7171 10424 0
Web Site: http://www.mvo-g.de
Automobile Spare Parts Mfr
N.A.I.C.S.: 336330

AND PRIVATE COMPANIES

Murat Arslan *(Mgr-Technical Sls)*

Pleissner Guss GmbH (1)
Duderstaedter Strasse 17, Herzberg, 37412, Germany
Tel.: (49) 552183220
Web Site: http://www.pleissner-guss.de
Sales Range: $125-149.9 Million
Emp.: 300
Iron & Steel Blast Furnaces Mfr
N.A.I.C.S.: 333994
Ulf Achenbach *(Mng Dir)*

RRO Rohstoff Recycling Osnabrueck GmbH (1)
Rheinstrasse 90-122, 49090, Osnabruck, Germany
Tel.: (49) 541961240
Web Site: http://www.rro-gmbh.de
Sales Range: $25-49.9 Million
Emp.: 97
Raw Materials Recycling Services
N.A.I.C.S.: 562998
Knut Schemme *(CEO)*

Subsidiary (Domestic):

Adolf Ellermann GmbH (2)
Rheinstrasse 103-105, 49090, Osnabruck, Germany
Tel.: (49) 541961160
Web Site: http://www.rro-gmbh.de
Sales Range: $10-24.9 Million
Emp.: 20
Raw Materials Recycling Services
N.A.I.C.S.: 562998

Radsatzfabrik Ilsenburg GmbH (1)
Schmiedestrasse 15/16, 38871, Ilsenburg, Germany
Tel.: (49) 39452930
Web Site: http://www.rafil-gmbh.de
Sales Range: $50-74.9 Million
Emp.: 200
Metal Products Mfr
N.A.I.C.S.: 332999
Joerg Villmann *(Head-Engrg)*

Rohstoff Recycling Dortmund GmbH (1)
Luetge Heidestrasse 115, 44147, Dortmund, Germany
Tel.: (49) 2318808410
Web Site: http://www.rrd-gmbh.de
Sales Range: $10-24.9 Million
Emp.: 70
Raw Materials Recycling Services
N.A.I.C.S.: 562998
Gustav Schreiber *(Mng Dir)*

SMB Schwermechanik GmbH (1)
Schmiedestrasse, 15745, Wildau, Germany
Tel.: (49) 3375586201
Construction Materials Mfr
N.A.I.C.S.: 327999
Sven Alisch *(Sls Mgr)*

Schmiedag GmbH (1)
Gruntaler Strasse 11, 58089, Hagen, Germany
Tel.: (49) 2331 128 385
Web Site: http://www.schmiedag.de
Iron & Steel Forging Services
N.A.I.C.S.: 332111
Detlef Muller *(Head-Pur Dept)*

Schmiedewerke Groeditz GmbH (1)
Riesaer Strasse 1, 01609, Groditz, Germany
Tel.: (49) 35263620
Web Site: http://www.stahl-groeditz.de
Sales Range: $200-249.9 Million
Emp.: 600
Open-Die Iron & Steel Forging
N.A.I.C.S.: 332111
Michael Schiller *(CEO)*

Stahl Judenburg GmbH (1)
Gussstahlwerkstrasse 21, 8750, Judenburg, Austria
Tel.: (43) 35727010
Web Site: http://www.stahl-judenburg.com
Sales Range: $125-149.9 Million
Emp.: 350
Steel Producer
N.A.I.C.S.: 331110
Ewald Thaller *(CEO-Comml)*

Subsidiary (Domestic):

Veredelungstechnik Krieglach GmbH (2)
Eisenhammerstrasse 7, Krieglach, 8670, Austria
Tel.: (43) 38554010352
Web Site: http://www.veredelungstechnik.com
Emp.: 30
Steel Producer
N.A.I.C.S.: 331110
Guenther Jauk *(Mng Dir)*

Stahlguss Groditz GmbH (1)
Riesaer Strasse 1, 01609, Groditz, Germany
Tel.: (49) 35263 62 943
Web Site: http://www.stahlguss-groeditz.de
Iron & Steel Forging Services
N.A.I.C.S.: 332111

Stahlwerk Bous GmbH (1)
Saarstrasse, 66359, Bous, Germany
Tel.: (49) 6834811
Web Site: http://www.stahlwerk-bous.de
Sales Range: $125-149.9 Million
Emp.: 380
Preliminary Pipe Materials & Ingots Producer
N.A.I.C.S.: 332919
Franz Josef Schu *(Mng Dir)*

Umformtechnik Baeuerle GmbH (1)
Klotzbachstrasse 2, 73560, Bobingen, Germany
Tel.: (49) 7173185630
Sales Range: $25-49.9 Million
Emp.: 40
Steel Producer
N.A.I.C.S.: 331110

WISTA Stahlhandel Witten GmbH (1)
Bebbelsdorf 104, Witten, 58454, Germany
Tel.: (49) 2302910800
Web Site: http://www.wista-gmbh.de
Sales Range: $25-49.9 Million
Emp.: 14
Blast Furnace Mfr
N.A.I.C.S.: 333994
Lars Kracke *(Mng Dir)*

Walzwerk Burg GmbH (1)
Troxel 1b, D-39288, Burg, Germany
Tel.: (49) 3921720
Web Site: http://www.walzwerk-burg.de
Open-Die Iron & Steel Forging
N.A.I.C.S.: 332111

Wildauer Schmiedewerke GmbH & Co. KG (1)
Schmiedestrasse, 15745, Wildau, Germany
Tel.: (49) 3375 586 601
Web Site: http://www.wildauer-schmiedewerke.de
Iron & Steel Forging Services
N.A.I.C.S.: 332111

Windhoff Bahn- und Anlagentechnik GmbH (1)
Hovestrasse 10, 48431, Rheine, Germany
Tel.: (49) 5971580
Web Site: http://www.windhoff.de
Sales Range: $50-74.9 Million
Emp.: 250
Hoists, Cranes & Monorail Systems Mfr
N.A.I.C.S.: 333923
George Sennmann *(Mng Dir)*

GEOSONDA KONSOLIDACIJA A.D.
Kraljice Marije 25, 11120, Belgrade, Serbia
Tel.: (381) 11 32 22 157
Web Site: http://www.geosonda.org
Year Founded: 2007
GSKO—(BEL)
Sales Range: $1-9.9 Million
Emp.: 112
Construction Engineering Services
N.A.I.C.S.: 237990
Sretkovic Ivana *(Sec)*

GEOSONDA-FUNDIRANJE A.D.
Vodovodska 158, 11147, Belgrade, Serbia
Tel.: (381) 113225059
Web Site: http://www.geosonda-fundiranje.rs
Year Founded: 1948
GSFD—(BEL)
Sales Range: Less than $1 Million
Construction Management Services
N.A.I.C.S.: 236220
Milan Barackov *(Mng Dir)*

GEOSTRATA RESOURCES INC.
9727 Horton Road SW, Calgary, T2V 2X5, AB, Canada
Tel.: (403) 319-0922
Web Site: http://www.geostrata.ca
Year Founded: 2000
Rev.: $28,915,929
Emp.: 70
Geophysical Seismic Services
N.A.I.C.S.: 541360
Mitch Peters *(Pres)*

GEOTAB, INC.
1081 South Service Road West, Oakville, L6L 6K3, ON, Canada
Tel.: (416) 434-4309
Web Site: http://www.geotab.com
Year Founded: 1996
Emp.: 70
Global Positioning System Mfr & Distr
N.A.I.C.S.: 334220
Clive Cawse *(Co-COO)*

Subsidiaries:

BSM Technologies Inc. (1)
75 International Blvd Suite 100, Toronto, M9W 6L9, ON, Canada
Tel.: (866) 768-4771
Web Site: http://bsmtechnologies.com
Rev.: $47,584,304
Assets: $11,857,242
Liabilities: $66,370,286
Net Worth: ($54,513,043)
Earnings: $15,454,643
Fiscal Year-end: 09/30/2018
After-Market, Wireless, High Security Vehicle Surveillance Products & Monitoring Services
N.A.I.C.S.: 517112

Subsidiary (US):

Mobi Corp. (2)
708 Congress Ave, Austin, TX 78701
Tel.: (512) 617-5300
Web Site: http://www.mobicorp.com
Sales Range: $1-9.9 Million
Software Publisher
N.A.I.C.S.: 513210
Greg Gray *(VP-Sls)*

Subsidiary (Non-US):

SecTrack N.V. (2)
Bredastraat 123, 2060, Antwerp, Belgium
Tel.: (32) 32291717
Sales Range: $25-49.9 Million
Emp.: 30
Satellite Communication Services
N.A.I.C.S.: 334220

GEOTECH HOLDINGS LTD.
Unit 1920 19/F Cheung Kong Center 2 Queens Road, Central, China (Hong Kong)
Tel.: (852) 34695188   Ky
Web Site: http://www.geotech.hk
Year Founded: 1994
1707—(HKG)
Rev.: $35,892,780
Assets: $28,873,778
Liabilities: $4,175,880
Net Worth: $24,697,898
Earnings: ($4,040,858)
Emp.: 62
Fiscal Year-end: 12/31/22
Civil Engineering Services
N.A.I.C.S.: 541330
Kin Wing Sino Yau *(CEO)*

GEOTECH LTD.

GEOTECH SEISMIC SERVICES PJSC

245 Industrial Parkway North, Aurora, L4G 4C4, ON, Canada
Tel.: (905) 841-5004
Web Site: http://www.geotech.ca
Year Founded: 1981
Emp.: 200
Airborne Geological Surveys
N.A.I.C.S.: 541360
Ed Morrison *(Pres)*

Subsidiaries:

Aeroquest International Limited (1)
245 Industrial Parkway North, Aurora, L4G 4Z4, ON, Canada
Tel.: (905) 672-9129
Web Site: http://www.aeroquest.ca
Sales Range: $50-74.9 Million
Emp.: 15
Commercial Airborne Geophysical Surveys For Use in Mineral, Oil & Gas Exploration
N.A.I.C.S.: 541360
Richard William Morrison *(Chm)*

Subsidiary (Non-US):

Aeroquest Airborne (2)
116 Fauntleroy Ave, Perth Airport, Redcliffe, 6105, WA, Australia
Tel.: (61) 8 9479 4232
Web Site: http://www.aeroquestairborne.com
Sales Range: $25-49.9 Million
Airborne Geophysical Technologies
N.A.I.C.S.: 541360

Subsidiary (Domestic):

Aeroquest Limited (2)
245 Industrial Parkway N, Aurora, L4G 4C4, ON, Canada
Tel.: (905) 672-9129
Web Site: http://www.aeroquestsurveys.com
Sales Range: $10-24.9 Million
Geophysical Surveying Services
N.A.I.C.S.: 541360

Subsidiary (US):

Geophex Ltd. (2)
605 Mercury St, Raleigh, NC 27603
Tel.: (919) 839-8515
Web Site: http://www.geophex.com
Sales Range: $25-49.9 Million
Emp.: 10
Geophysical Instruments Mfr
N.A.I.C.S.: 334519
Bob Lawson *(Supvr-Production)*

Subsidiary (Domestic):

Optimal Geomatics Inc. (2)
625 W Kent Ave Ste 100, Vancouver, VP6 6T7, BC, Canada
Tel.: (604) 654-1850
Web Site: http://www.optimalgeo.com
Sales Range: $10-24.9 Million
Geomatic Services & Software Mfr
N.A.I.C.S.: 541360

Aeroquest Mapcon Ltd. (1)
1214 Austin Avenue, Coquitlam, V3K 3P5, BC, Canada
Tel.: (778) 383-3733
Web Site: https://www.aeroquestmapcon.com
Geophysical Surveying Services
N.A.I.C.S.: 541360

Geotech Aviation Ltd. (1)
Sudbury Airport 3020 Skyline Drive, Garson, P3L 1V4, ON, Canada
Tel.: (705) 699-0252
Geophysical Surveying Services
N.A.I.C.S.: 541360

GEOTECH SEISMIC SERVICES PJSC
Ul Respubliki 173, 625023, Tyumen, 625023, Russia
Tel.: (7) 3452532500
Web Site: https://www.gseis.ru
Year Founded: 2009
Oil & Gas Exploration Services
N.A.I.C.S.: 213112
Vladimir Tolkachev *(CEO)*

GEOVIS TECHNOLOGY CO., LTD.

Geotech Seismic Services PJSC—(Continued)

GEOVIS TECHNOLOGY CO., LTD.
1F 5F 7F No 1A-4 Industry Park No 2 Airport East Road, Linkong Economic Core District Shunyi District, Beijing, 101399, China
Tel.: (86) 1050986900
Web Site: https://www.geovis.com.cn
Year Founded: 2006
688568—(SHG)
Rev.: $221,374,029
Assets: $652,225,350
Liabilities: $181,087,176
Net Worth: $471,138,174
Earnings: $34,081,651
Fiscal Year-end: 12/31/22
Software Development Services
N.A.I.C.S.: 541511
Kun Fu *(Chm)*

GEOVISION INC.
9F No 246 Sec 1 Neihu Rd, Neihu District, Taipei, 114, Taiwan
Tel.: (886) 287978377
Web Site:
https://www.geovision.com.tw
3356—(TAI)
Rev.: $41,338,630
Assets: $81,031,097
Liabilities: $14,199,254
Net Worth: $66,831,843
Earnings: $9,573,138
Emp.: 361
Fiscal Year-end: 12/31/23
Video Recorders Mfr
N.A.I.C.S.: 334515
James Lee *(CFO)*
Subsidiaries:

Europe Vision Systems s.r.o. (1)
Drtinova 8, 150 00, Prague, Czech Republic
Tel.: (420) 222224309
Web Site: http://www.geovision.co.rs
Sales Range: $25-49.9 Million
Emp.: 13
Video Surveillance System Installation Services
N.A.I.C.S.: 238210

GeoVision Japan Inc. (1)
Tomiokabashi Bldg 5F 2-6-11 Fukagawa, Koto-ku, Tokyo, 135-0033, Japan
Tel.: (81) 356399355
Web Site: http://www.geovision.co.jp
Emp.: 10
Surveillance Systems Distr
N.A.I.C.S.: 423410

GeoVision Technology (Shanghai) Co., Ltd. (1)
Rm 607 Building 4 No 123 Juli Road Pudong Zhangjiang Hi-tech Park, Shanghai, 200041, China
Tel.: (86) 2162173366
Web Site: http://www.geovision.com.cn
Sales Range: $50-74.9 Million
Emp.: 10
Surveillance Systems Distr
N.A.I.C.S.: 423410

GeoVision Vietnam Systems Co., Ltd. (1)
Lau 8 456 Phan Xich Long Phuong 2 Quan, Phu Nhuan, Ho Chi Minh City, Vietnam
Tel.: (84) 2835357800
Camera Mfr & Distr
N.A.I.C.S.: 333310

USA Vision Systems Inc. (1)
9301 Irvine Blvd, Irvine, CA 92618
Tel.: (949) 421-5910
Sales Range: $25-49.9 Million
Emp.: 25
Surveillance Systems Distr
N.A.I.C.S.: 423410

GEPE HOLDING AG
Baarerstrasse 43, PO Box 7313, 6302, Zug, Switzerland
Tel.: (41) 417117588
Web Site: http://www.gepegroup.com
Year Founded: 1955
Sales Range: $100-124.9 Million
Emp.: 340
Holding Company
N.A.I.C.S.: 551112
Sven Pettersson *(Owner & Chm)*
Subsidiaries:

Gepe-Biwex AB (1)
Hantverksgatan, Box 71, 533 21, Gotene, Sweden
Tel.: (46) 511 676 00
Web Site: http://www.gepe-biwex.se
Plastic Product Distr
N.A.I.C.S.: 424610

Gepe-Geimuplast GmbH (1)
Partenkirchner Str 50, 82490, Farchant, Germany
Tel.: (49) 8821 6850
Web Site: http://www.gepe.com
Emp.: 40
Injection Molded Plastic Product Mfr & Distr
N.A.I.C.S.: 326199

HP Marketing Corp. (1)
16 Chapin Rd, Pine Brook, NJ 07058-9718
Tel.: (973) 808-9010
Web Site: http://www.hpmarketingcorp.com
Sales Range: $50-74.9 Million
Emp.: 8
Photography Equipment Importer & Distr
N.A.I.C.S.: 423410
Roger Bartzke *(Pres)*

GEPIC ENERGY DEVELOPMENT CO., LTD.
24F Gansu Investment Group Building No 69 Beibinhe East Road, Chengguan District, Lanzhou, 730046, Gansu, China
Tel.: (86) 9318378559
Web Site: http://www.gepiced.com
Year Founded: 1997
000791—(SSE)
Rev.: $287,317,368
Assets: $3,066,761,412
Liabilities: $1,750,351,356
Net Worth: $1,316,410,056
Earnings: $42,381,144
Fiscal Year-end: 12/31/22
Hydroelectric Power Generation Services
N.A.I.C.S.: 221111
Peiwen Pu *(Chm)*

GERAER BATTERIE-DIENST GMBH
Leibnizstrasse 86, 07548, Gera, Germany
Tel.: (49) 365833280
Web Site: https://www.gbd-gera.de
Appliances, Electrical & Electronics Mfr
N.A.I.C.S.: 334419

GERAMA
Route departmentale 23 le Champ du chataignier, 72210, Le Mans, Voivres, France
Tel.: (33) 222 06 6000
Web Site: http://www.gerama.fr
Sales Range: $25-49.9 Million
Emp.: 52
Cooperative Offering Plumbing, Heating & Electrical Contractor Projects
N.A.I.C.S.: 236220

GERARD PERRIER INDUSTRIE S.A.
Airparc 160 Rue de Norvege, 69125, Lyon, France
Tel.: (33) 472478058
Web Site: https://www.gerard-perrier.com
PERR—(EUR)
Sales Range: $200-249.9 Million
Emp.: 2,000
Electrical & Electronic Equipment Mfr
N.A.I.C.S.: 335999
Subsidiaries:

ARDATEM (1)
75 chemin d En Cros, BP 101, 07700, Bourg-Saint-Andeol, France
Tel.: (33) 475547800
Web Site: https://www.ardatem.fr
Electrical & Electronic Equipment Mfr
N.A.I.C.S.: 334419

Bontronic GmbH (1)
Tertzstrasse 14, 53844, Troisdorf, Germany
Tel.: (49) 2289658600
Web Site: http://www.bontronic.de
Electric Equipment Mfr
N.A.I.C.S.: 334419
Francois Rousseau *(Head-Engrg & Sls)*

GERAL AUTOMATION SA (1)
ZI La Pelissiere, BP 49, 01302, Belley, France
Tel.: (33) 4 79 81 49 01
Web Site: http://www.geral.com
Electrical & Electronic Equipment Mfr
N.A.I.C.S.: 334419

Geral Constructions Electriques Et Travaux Industriels Sas (1)
ZI La Pelissiere - Route de Lyon, 01302, Belley, Cedex, France
Tel.: (33) 479814901
Web Site: http://www.geral.com
Electric Equipment Mfr
N.A.I.C.S.: 334419
Christian Grange *(Mgr-Bus Unit)*

SEIREL AUTOMATION EN (1)
137 route d'Heyrieux, BP 123, 69803, Saint Priest, Cedex, France
Tel.: (33) 4 78 21 08 16
Web Site: http://www.seirel.com
Electric Equipment Mfr
N.A.I.C.S.: 335999

SERA (1)
ZAC du Crouloup, 69380, Chasselay, France
Tel.: (33) 4 78 47 36 22
Web Site: http://www.sera-gpi.com
Electrical & Electronic Equipment Mfr
N.A.I.C.S.: 335999

SOTEB (1)
Le Parc de la grive 18 rue de Lombardie, 69150, Decines-Charpieu, France
Tel.: (33) 4 72 47 80 40
Web Site: http://www.soteb.fr
Electrical & Electronic Equipment Mfr
N.A.I.C.S.: 335999

Technisonic Sas (1)
45 route de Verdun, Terville, 57180, Thionville, France
Tel.: (33) 382869213
Web Site: http://www.technisonic.fr
Electrical Equipment Installation Services
N.A.I.C.S.: 238210

GERATHERM MEDICAL AG
Fahrenheitstrasse 1, 99331, Geschwenda, Germany
Tel.: (49) 36205980
Web Site:
https://www.geratherm.com
GME—(MUN)
Rev.: $23,137,115
Assets: $39,430,236
Liabilities: $14,780,819
Net Worth: $24,649,417
Earnings: $1,225,296
Emp.: 189
Fiscal Year-end: 12/31/23
Medical Technology Company
N.A.I.C.S.: 339112
Rudolf Brocker *(Chm-Supervisory Bd)*
Subsidiaries:

Apoplex Medical Technologies GmbH (1)
Zweibrucker Str 185, 66954, Pirmasens, Germany
Tel.: (49) 63316989980
Web Site: http://www.apoplexmedical.com
Emp.: 20

INTERNATIONAL PUBLIC

Medical Product Device Mfr
N.A.I.C.S.: 339112
Albert Hirtz *(Mng Dir)*

Capillary Solutions GmbH (1)
Fahrenheitstrasse 1, Geratal, 99331, Geschwenda, Germany
Tel.: (49) 36205980
Web Site: http://www.capillary-solutions.com
Glass Tube Mfr
N.A.I.C.S.: 327215

Geratherm Respiratory GmbH (1)
Kasernenstrasse 4, 97688, Bad Kissingen, Germany
Tel.: (49) 97178570430
Web Site: http://www.geratherm-respiratory.com
Medical Product Device Mfr
N.A.I.C.S.: 339112
Florian Dassel *(Mng Dir)*

LMT Medical Systems GmbH (1)
Maria-Goeppert-Strasse 5, 23562, Lubeck, Germany
Tel.: (49) 451580980
Web Site: http://www.lmt-medicalsystems.com
Medical Product Device Mfr
N.A.I.C.S.: 339112

GERDAU SA (CHILE)
La Union 3007 Renca, 7464522, Santiago, Chile
Tel.: (56) 26418683   CL
Web Site: http://www.gerdauaza.cl
Sales Range: $150-199.9 Million
Mfr of Steel
N.A.I.C.S.: 331110

GERHARD HAAS KG
Heinrich-Fahr-Strasse 17-19, 78333, Stockach, Germany
Tel.: (49) 777193610
Web Site: http://www.rival-haas.de
Year Founded: 1952
Rev.: $17,208,146
Emp.: 150
Household Products Mfr
N.A.I.C.S.: 335220
Dieter Haas *(Co-CEO)*

GERMAIN ARMATURES
140 Route de Saint-Etienne du Bois, Bourg-en-Bresse, 01370, Treffort-Cuisiat, France
Tel.: (33) 474513133
Web Site: http://www.germain.fr
Year Founded: 1966
Sales Range: $10-24.9 Million
Emp.: 100
Miscellaneous Fabricated Wire Products
N.A.I.C.S.: 332618
Francois Germain *(Pres)*

GERMAN ASSET MANAGERS AG
Bettinastrasse 30, 60325, Frankfurt, Germany
Tel.: (49) 6997461134
Web Site:
https://www.germanasset.com
GMRA—(DEU)
Asset Management Services
N.A.I.C.S.: 523999
Carsten Straush *(Pres)*

GERMAN AUTO IMPORT NETWORK - VANCOUVER ISLAND
2546 Government Street, Victoria, V8T 4P7, BC, Canada
Tel.: (778) 406-1380
Web Site: https://www.gain-vi.ca
Year Founded: 2008
Emp.: 50
Car Dealership Operator
N.A.I.C.S.: 441110

AND PRIVATE COMPANIES

Subsidiaries:

Three Point Motors (1)
2546 Government Street, Victoria, V8T 5H8, BC, Canada
Tel.: (250) 385-6737
Web Site: http://www.threepointmotors.com
Rev.: $15,938,106
Emp.: 34
New & Used Car Dealers
N.A.I.C.S.: 441110

Volkswagen Victoria (1)
3329 Douglas Street, Victoria, V8Z 3L2, BC, Canada
Tel.: (250) 475-2415
Web Site: http://www.vwvictoria.com
Rev.: $16,084,816
Emp.: 35
New & Used Car Dealers
N.A.I.C.S.: 441110
Kyle Dripps (Gen Mgr)

GERMAN HIGH STREET PROPERTIES A/S

Mosehojvej 17, 2920, Charlottenlund, 2920, Denmark
Tel.: (45) 81100800
Web Site:
 https://www.germanhighstreet.com
GERHSP.B—(OMX)
Rev.: $7,308,028
Assets: $138,361,236
Liabilities: $64,568,577
Net Worth: $73,792,659
Earnings: ($8,008,125)
Emp.: 2
Fiscal Year-end: 12/31/20
Real Estate Support Services
N.A.I.C.S.: 531210
Michael Hansen (CEO)

GERMAN STARTUPS GROUP GMBH & CO. KGAA

Senckenberganlage 21, 60325, Frankfurt, Germany
Tel.: (49) 348690520
Web Site: https://www.german-startups.com
Year Founded: 2012
GSJ—(DEU)
Rev.: $5,287,537
Assets: $22,850,109
Liabilities: $4,172,629
Net Worth: $18,677,480
Earnings: ($89,976,444)
Emp.: 11
Fiscal Year-end: 12/31/23
Investment Management Service
N.A.I.C.S.: 523940
Gerhard A. Koning (Chm-Supervisory Bd)

GERMAN VALUES PROPERTY GROUP AG

Trondlinring 9, D-04105, Leipzig, Germany
Tel.: (49) 34135572750
Web Site: https://german-values.de
Year Founded: 1996
TVD6—(DEU)
Rev.: $3,410,317
Assets: $61,536,801
Liabilities: $59,896,395
Net Worth: $1,640,406
Earnings: ($6,637,168)
Emp.: 5
Fiscal Year-end: 12/31/22
Travel Arrangement & Reservation Services
N.A.I.C.S.: 561599

GERMICOPA S.A.

1 Allee Loeiz Herrieu, PO Box 33033, 29334, Quimper, Cedex, France
Tel.: (33) 298100100
Web Site: http://www.germicopa.com
Year Founded: 1989
Potato Breeding Services
N.A.I.C.S.: 111211
Joseph Lallouet (Dir-Production & Logistics)

GEROLYMATOS GROUP OF COMPANIES

13 Askliplou St, 145 68, Athens, Greece
Tel.: (30) 2108161107
Web Site: http://www.gerolymatos.gr
Sales Range: $200-249.9 Million
Emp.: 750
Healthcare & Beauty Products Distr
N.A.I.C.S.: 456191
George Joakimidis (COO & VP)

Subsidiaries:

Foltene Labs S.p.A. (1)
Pzza XX Settembre 2, Villa Guardia, 22079, Como, Italy
Tel.: (39) 031385555
Web Site: http://www.foltene.eu
Sales Range: $10-24.9 Million
Emp.: 14
Medical Laboratories
N.A.I.C.S.: 621511

Gerolpharm S.A. (1)
13 Asklipiou, Krioneri, 14568, Athens, Greece
Tel.: (30) 2108194556
Sales Range: $100-124.9 Million
Medical Laboratories
N.A.I.C.S.: 621511

Gerolymatos Inc (1)
1160 5th Ave Ofc 106, New York, NY 10029-6932 (100%)
Tel.: (212) 426-4864
Web Site: http://www.gerolymatos.com
Sales Range: $25-49.9 Million
Emp.: 10
Pharmaceutical Preparation Mfr
N.A.I.C.S.: 325412

Medexis S.A (1)
4 Asklipiou 13, 14556, Athens, Greece
Tel.: (30) 2108161107
Sales Range: $10-24.9 Million
Emp.: 100
Medical Laboratories
N.A.I.C.S.: 621511

GEROM SA

Aleea Industriilor 1-3, 120230, Buzau, Romania
Tel.: (40) 238436565
Web Site: http://www.gerom-buzau.ro
Year Founded: 1967
Sales Range: $1-9.9 Million
Emp.: 192
Glass Products Mfr
N.A.I.C.S.: 327212

GEROQUIP INC.

4795 Louis B Mayer, Laval, H7P 6G5, QC, Canada
Tel.: (450) 978-0200
Web Site: http://www.geroquip.com
Year Founded: 1984
Sales Range: $10-24.9 Million
Emp.: 26
Construction Equipment Distr
N.A.I.C.S.: 423390
Carole Mathieu (Controller)

GEROVA FINANCIAL GROUP, LTD.

Cumberland House 5th Floor 1 Victoria Street, Hamilton, HM 11, Bermuda
Tel.: (441) 2697777 Ky
Web Site: http://phx.corporate-ir.net
Year Founded: 2007
GVFG—(OTCEM)
Reinsurance Services
N.A.I.C.S.: 524130

GERPANG HEALTHCARE GROUP

27/F Block F Jinan Pharma Valley, Jinan, Shandong, China
Tel.: (86) 53158708846
Web Site:
 http://www.gerpanghealthcare.com
Biomedical Research & Development
N.A.I.C.S.: 541714
Fengyou Lu (Pres)

GERRESHEIMER AG

Klaus-Bungert-Strasse 4, 40468, Dusseldorf, Germany
Tel.: (49) 211618100 De
Web Site:
 https://www.gerresheimer.com
Year Founded: 1864
GXI—(DEU)
Rev.: $2,197,246,937
Assets: $3,785,339,442
Liabilities: $2,160,030,909
Net Worth: $1,625,308,533
Earnings: $132,558,781
Emp.: 11,660
Fiscal Year-end: 11/30/23
Container Glass & Tubing Glass Packaging Mfr
N.A.I.C.S.: 327213
Axel Herberg (Chm-Supervisory Bd)

Subsidiaries:

Gerresheimer Boleslawiec S.A. (1)
ul Boleslawa Chrobrego 15, 59-700, Boleslawiec, Poland
Tel.: (48) 757350400
Web Site: https://www.gerresheimer.com
Plastic Packaging Products Mfr
N.A.I.C.S.: 326199

Gerresheimer Bunde GmbH (1)
Erich-Martens-Strasse 26-32, Herford District, 32257, Bunde, Germany
Tel.: (49) 52231640
Web Site: https://www.gerresheimer.com
Sales Range: $200-249.9 Million
Emp.: 700
Medical Instrument Mfr
N.A.I.C.S.: 339112
Bernd Janas (Mgr-Sls)

Gerresheimer Chalon S.A. (1)
7 rue George Eastman, BP 35, 71109, Chalon-sur-Saone, 71100, France
Tel.: (33) 385424960
Web Site: https://www.gerresheimer.com
Sales Range: $50-74.9 Million
Emp.: 150
Laboratory Glassware Mfr
N.A.I.C.S.: 327215
Eric Mouton (Plant Mgr)

Gerresheimer Denmark A/S (1)
Walgerholm 2, Vaerlose, 3500, Denmark
Tel.: (45) 44777888
Sales Range: $25-49.9 Million
Emp.: 100
Laboratory Plastic Products Mfr
N.A.I.C.S.: 326199
Gustav Levander (Mng Dir)

Gerresheimer Essen GmbH (1)
Ruhrau 50, 45279, Essen, Germany
Tel.: (49) 20156020
Emp.: 450
Pharmaceutical Equipment Mfr
N.A.I.C.S.: 334510

Gerresheimer Glas GmbH (1)
Klaus Bungert Strasse 4, 40468, Dusseldorf, Germany
Tel.: (49) 211618100
Sales Range: $25-49.9 Million
Emp.: 80
Pharmaceutical & Cosmetic Bottles Mfr
N.A.I.C.S.: 327213
Gens Kurten (Dir-Corp Comm & Mktg)

Gerresheimer Glass Inc. (1)
537 Crystal Ave, Vineland, NJ 08360-3287 (100%)
Tel.: (856) 692-3600
Web Site: https://www.gerresheimer.com
Tubular & Moulded Glass Products Mfr
N.A.I.C.S.: 327215

Plant (Domestic):

Gerresheimer Glass Inc. - Chicago Heights Plant (2)
1131 Arnold St, Chicago Heights, IL 60411
Tel.: (708) 757-5555
Web Site: https://www.gerresheimer.com
Pharmaceutical Bottles Mfr
N.A.I.C.S.: 327212

Gerresheimer Glass Inc. - Forest Grove Plant (2)
91 W Forest Grove Rd, Vineland, NJ 08360
Tel.: (856) 507-5500
Web Site: https://www.gerresheimer.com
Sales Range: $50-74.9 Million
Emp.: 200
Pharmaceuticals Product Mfr
N.A.I.C.S.: 325412

Gerresheimer Glass Inc. - Millville Plant (2)
1300 Wheaton Ave, Millville, NJ 08332
Tel.: (856) 974-7400
Web Site: http://www.gerresheimer.com
Sales Range: $100-124.9 Million
Emp.: 256
Pharmaceutical & Cosmetic Bottles Mfr
N.A.I.C.S.: 327212

Gerresheimer Glass Inc. - Morganton Plant (2)
114 Wamsutta Mill Rd, Morganton, NC 28655
Tel.: (828) 433-5000
Web Site: https://www.gerresheimer.com
Vials Mfr
N.A.I.C.S.: 327212

Gerresheimer Holdings GmbH (1)
Benrather Strasse 18-20, 40213, Dusseldorf, Nordrhein-Westfalen, Germany
Tel.: (49) 211618100
Pharmaceutical Equipment Mfr
N.A.I.C.S.: 334510

Gerresheimer Horsovsky Tyn spol. s r.o. (1)
Zahradni 282, 346 01, Horsovsky Tyn, Plzen, Czech Republic
Tel.: (420) 373726111
Web Site: https://www.gerresheimer.com
Injection Molded Plastic Products Mfr
N.A.I.C.S.: 326121

Gerresheimer Item GmbH (1)
Am Mittelhafen 10, 48155, Munster, Germany
Tel.: (49) 2514909440
Medicinal Product Mfr
N.A.I.C.S.: 339112

Gerresheimer Lohr GmbH (1)
Rodenbacher Strasse 38, 97816, Lohr am Main, Germany
Tel.: (49) 93525040
Web Site: https://www.gerresheimer.com
Sales Range: $125-149.9 Million
Emp.: 350
Pharmaceutical & Cosmetic Bottles Mfr
N.A.I.C.S.: 327213
Andreas Kohl (Mng Dir)

Gerresheimer Medical Plastic Systems Dongguan Co. Ltd. (1)
Building 5-6 Zone No 4 Zhong HanQiao Industrial Park, Wangniudun Town, Dongguan, 523200, Guangdong, China
Tel.: (86) 76988517100
Web Site: https://www.gerresheimer.com
Sales Range: $25-49.9 Million
Emp.: 90
Laboratory Plastic Products Mfr
N.A.I.C.S.: 339113

Gerresheimer Momignies S.A. (1)
Rue Mandenne 19/20, 6590, Momignies, Hainaut, Belgium
Tel.: (32) 60510211
Web Site: https://www.gerresheimer.com
Emp.: 700
Pharmaceutical & Cosmetic Bottles Mfr
N.A.I.C.S.: 327213

Gerresheimer Moulded Glass GmbH. (1)
Tettaugrundstrasse 1, 96355, Tettau, Germany
Tel.: (49) 9269910
Web Site: https://www.gerresheimer.com
Sales Range: $125-149.9 Million
Emp.: 500
Pharmaceutical & Cosmetic Bottles Mfr
N.A.I.C.S.: 327213

GERRESHEIMER AG

Gerresheimer AG—(Continued)

Gerresheimer Peachtree City (USA), L.P. (1)
650 Hwy 74 S, Peachtree City, GA 30269
Tel.: (770) 631-4939
Web Site: https://www.gerresheimer.com
Pharmaceutical & Cosmetic Bottles Mfr
N.A.I.C.S.: 326160

Subsidiary (Domestic):

Gerresheimer Peachtree City, Inc. (2)
650 Hwy 74 S, Peachtree City, GA 30269
Tel.: (770) 631-4939
Medical Plastic Products Mfr
N.A.I.C.S.: 326199

Gerresheimer Pharmaceutical Packaging Mumbai Private Ltd. (1)
906 Windfall Sahar Plaza Complex Mathurdas Vasanji Road, J B Nagar Andheri East, Mumbai, 400 059, India
Tel.: (91) 2241632323
Web Site: https://www.gerresheimer.com
Packaging Glass Product Mfr
N.A.I.C.S.: 327213

Gerresheimer Plastic Packaging (Changzhou) Co., Ltd. (1)
Block 3 No 355 LongJin Road Changzhou Economic Development Zone, Changzhou, 213000, Jiangsu, China
Tel.: (86) 13901828508
Web Site: https://www.gerresheimer.com
Plastic Mfr
N.A.I.C.S.: 325211

Gerresheimer Plastic Packaging S.A.S. (1)
11 rue La Fayette, BP 34011, 25071, Besancon, France
Tel.: (33) 381211760
Web Site: https://www.gerresheimer.com
Sales Range: $50-74.9 Million
Emp.: 3
Plastic Packaging Materials Retailer
N.A.I.C.S.: 424610

Gerresheimer Plasticos Sao Paulo Ltda. (1)
Estr Velha de Cotia 1453 - Jardim Passargada I, Cotia, 06712-430, Sao Paulo, Brazil
Tel.: (55) 1121331212
Web Site: https://www.gerresheimer.com
Pharmaceutical & Cosmetic Bottles Mfr
N.A.I.C.S.: 326160

Gerresheimer Queretaro S.A. (1)
Av Coahuila No 9, Zona Industrial Benito Juarez, 76120, Queretaro, Mexico
Tel.: (52) 4424411102
Web Site: https://www.gerresheimer.com
Sales Range: $200-249.9 Million
Emp.: 600
Pharmaceuticals Product Mfr
N.A.I.C.S.: 325412

Gerresheimer Regensburg GmbH (1)
Kumpfmuehler Strasse 2, 93047, Regensburg, Germany
Tel.: (49) 9412982800
Web Site: https://www.gerresheimer.com
Sales Range: $450-499.9 Million
Emp.: 1,600
Perfume & Cosmetic Bottles Mfr
N.A.I.C.S.: 327213

Gerresheimer Regensburg GmbH - Pfreimd Plant (1)
Hirtenstrasse 50, Schwandorf, 92536, Pfreimd, Bavaria, Germany
Tel.: (49) 9606 87 300
Web Site: http://www.gerresheimer.com
Medical Plastic Systems Mfr
N.A.I.C.S.: 326199

Gerresheimer Shuangfeng Pharmaceutical Glass (Danyang) Co. Ltd. (1)
No 35 East Road, Fangxian, Danyang, 212321, Jiangsu, China
Tel.: (86) 51186462216
Web Site: https://www.gerresheimer.com
Vials & Test Tubes Mfr
N.A.I.C.S.: 327212

Plant (Domestic):

Gerresheimer Shuangfeng Pharmaceutical Glass (Danyang) Co. Ltd. - New Plant (2)
No 1 Bei Yiwei Road Development Zone, Danyang, 212314, Jiangsu, China
Tel.: (86) 51186997010
Web Site: http://www.gerresheimer.com
Laboratory Glassware Mfr
N.A.I.C.S.: 327212

Gerresheimer Shuangfeng Pharmaceutical Packaging (Zhenjiang) Co. Ltd. (1)
Weiyi Road Dingmao Development Zone, Zhenjiang, 212009, Jiangsu, China
Tel.: (86) 51188898000
Electromedical Equipment Mfr
N.A.I.C.S.: 334510

Gerresheimer Singapore Pte. Ltd. (1)
1 Harbourfront Place, Singapore, 098633, Singapore
Tel.: (65) 67223781
Plastic Mfr
N.A.I.C.S.: 325211

Gerresheimer Sistemas Plasticos Medicinais Sao Paulo Ltda. (1)
Rua Vitorio Emmanuel Soliani No 190 Distrito Industrial, Domingos Giomi, Indaiatuba, 13347-380, Sao Paulo, Brazil
Tel.: (55) 1939369700
Web Site: https://www.gerresheimer.com
Emp.: 70
Insulin Pen Mfr
N.A.I.C.S.: 339112

Gerresheimer Tettau GmbH (1)
Tettaugrundstrasse 1, 96355, Tettau, Germany
Tel.: (49) 9269910
Web Site: https://www.gerresheimer.com
Emp.: 500
Perfume & Cosmetic Bottles Mfr
N.A.I.C.S.: 327213
Bernd Hoerauf (Gen Mgr)

Gerresheimer Vaerloese A/S (1)
Walgerholm 2-8, 3500, Vaerlose, Denmark
Tel.: (45) 44777888
Web Site: https://www.gerresheimer.com
Laboratory Glassware Mfr
N.A.I.C.S.: 327215

Gerresheimer Werkzeug- und Automatisierungstechnik GmbH (1)
Oskar Von Miller Strasse 4, 92442, Wackersdorf, Germany
Tel.: (49) 94316397000
Emp.: 60
Injection Molding Machine Mfr
N.A.I.C.S.: 333248

Gerresheimer Werkzeugbau Wackersdorf GmbH (1)
Oskar-von-Miller-Strasse 6, 92442, Wackersdorf, Germany
Tel.: (49) 94316397000
Web Site: https://www.gerresheimer.com
Injection Mold Product Mfr
N.A.I.C.S.: 333511

Gerresheimer Wertheim GmbH (1)
Dertinger Weg 1, 97877, Wertheim, Germany
Tel.: (49) 934292810
Web Site: https://www.gerresheimer.com
Sales Range: $50-74.9 Million
Emp.: 150
Pharmaceutical Bottles Mfr
N.A.I.C.S.: 327213

Gerresheimer Wilden Asia Medical and Technical Plastic Systems Co. Ltd. (1)
Zhonghanqiao Industrial Park, Wangniudun Town, Dongguan, 523200, Guangdong, China
Tel.: (86) 76988517100
Web Site: http://www.gerresheimer.com
Sales Range: $25-49.9 Million
Emp.: 190
Medical Plastic Containers Mfr
N.A.I.C.S.: 326199

Gerresheimer Wilden Czech spol. s r.o. (1)
Zahradni 242, Horsovsky Tyn, Plzen, Czech Republic
Tel.: (420) 373 726 111
Pharmaceutical & Cosmetic Bottles Mfr
N.A.I.C.S.: 327213
Stilar Jindrich (Co-Mng Dir)

Gerresheimer Zaragoza S.A. (1)
Pl Valdemuel Camino del Sabinar, 50290, Epila, Zaragoza, Spain
Tel.: (34) 976817408
Sales Range: $25-49.9 Million
Emp.: 100
Pharmaceutical & Cosmetic Bottles Mfr
N.A.I.C.S.: 327213
Ariel Martin Antolinetti (Gen Mgr)

Gerresheimer respimetrix GmbH (1)
Klaus-Bungert-Strasse 4, 40468, Dusseldorf, Germany
Tel.: (49) 2116181409
Pharmaceutical Packaging Services
N.A.I.C.S.: 561910

Kimble Bomex (Beijing) Glass Co. Ltd. (1)
No A4 Dougezhuang West Road, Chaoyang District, Beijing, 100121, China
Tel.: (86) 1052077939
Web Site: http://www.gerresheimer.com
Laboratory Glassware Mfr
N.A.I.C.S.: 327212

Neutral Glass & Allied Industries Private Ltd. (1)
Block No - 19 23 812 813 Railway station, Village-Kunvarda Sub Distt Mangro Kosamba, Surat, 394120, Gujarat, India
Tel.: (91) 2229262323
Web Site: https://www.gerresheimer.com
Plastic & Glass Product Mfr
N.A.I.C.S.: 327215

Scherf-Prazision Europa GmbH (1)
Herpfer Strasse 31, 98617, Meiningen, Thuringia, Germany
Tel.: (49) 369381360
Emp.: 60
Laboratory Glassware Mfr
N.A.I.C.S.: 327212
Klaus Walber (CEO)

Sensile Medical AG (1)
Solothurnerstrasse 235, 4600, Olten, Switzerland
Tel.: (41) 622097100
Web Site: https://www.gerresheimer.com
Emp.: 100
Medical Micro Pump Mfr
N.A.I.C.S.: 339112
Paul Senn (Chief Comml Officer)

GERRY WEBER INTERNATIONAL AG

Neulehenstrasse 8, 33790, Halle, Germany
Tel.: (49) 52011850   De
Web Site:
   https://group.gerryweber.com
Year Founded: 1973
GWI2—(DEU)
Rev.: $358,043,014
Assets: $531,845,115
Liabilities: $462,899,091
Net Worth: $68,946,024
Earnings: ($80,391,993)
Emp.: 2,497
Fiscal Year-end: 12/31/20
Fashion Apparels Mfr
N.A.I.C.S.: 424350
Gerhard Weber (Founder)

Subsidiaries:

Energieversorgungsbetrieb Gerry Weber GmbH (1)
Neulehenstr 8, Halle, 33790, Nordrhein-Westfalen, Germany
Tel.: (49) 52011850
Power Supply Services
N.A.I.C.S.: 221122

GERRY WEBER FAR EAST LIMITED (1)
Rm 1603 Nina Tower 2, Tsuen Wan, New Territories, China (Hong Kong)
Tel.: (852) 23053033

INTERNATIONAL PUBLIC

Clothing Stores Operation Services
N.A.I.C.S.: 458110

Gerry Weber Belgien GmbH (1)
Eynatterner Strasse 31, Raeren, 4730, Liege, Belgium
Tel.: (32) 87301143
Clothing Stores Operation Services
N.A.I.C.S.: 458110

Gerry Weber Canada Ltd. (1)
79 Wingold Avenue Unit 2, Toronto, M6B 1P8, ON, Canada
Tel.: (416) 595-0707
Women Fashion Accessory Mfr & Retailer
N.A.I.C.S.: 315990
Joe Caporrella (Country Mgr)

Gerry Weber Denmark ApS (1)
Bella Center/Ciff Gerry Weber B0-201 Center Boulevard 5, 2300, Copenhagen, Denmark
Tel.: (45) 88180300
Women Fashion Accessory Mfr & Retailer
N.A.I.C.S.: 315990

Gerry Weber Fashion Iberica S.L. (1)
Avenida Gabriel Roca 54, Palma de Mallorca, 07015, Baleares, Spain
Tel.: (34) 971700045
Apparels Mfr & Retailer
N.A.I.C.S.: 315250

Gerry Weber France s.a.r.l. (1)
101 rue Reaumur, 75002, Paris, France
Tel.: (33) 142724512
Women Fashion Accessory Mfr & Retailer
N.A.I.C.S.: 315990

Gerry Weber GmbH (1)
Gusswerk Halle 5 B 3/EG Sollheimerstr 16, 5020, Salzburg, Austria
Tel.: (43) 662265726
Women Fashion Accessory Mfr & Retailer
N.A.I.C.S.: 315990

Gerry Weber Iberica S.L.U (1)
Nunez de Balboa 80 Planta Baja derecha, 28006, Madrid, Spain
Tel.: (34) 913206185
Women Fashion Accessory Mfr & Retailer
N.A.I.C.S.: 315990

Gerry Weber Life-Style Fashion GmbH (1)
Neulehenstr 8, Halle, 33790, Nordrhein-Westfalen, Germany
Tel.: (49) 52011850
Web Site: http://www.gerryweber.de
Sales Range: $150-199.9 Million
Emp.: 800
Garments Mfr
N.A.I.C.S.: 315210

Gerry Weber Management & Event oHG (1)
Neulehenstrasse 8, Halle, 33790, Nordrhein-Westfalen, Germany
Tel.: (49) 52018955
Web Site: http://www.gerryweber-stadion.de
Emp.: 20
Sports Event Management Services
N.A.I.C.S.: 711310
Ralsweber Weber (Mgr)

Gerry Weber Norge AS (1)
Prinsens Gate 32, 7011, Trondheim, Norway
Tel.: (47) 41309080
Web Site: http://gerryweber.no
Women's Clothing Retailer
N.A.I.C.S.: 458110
Johannes Ehling (Mng Dir)

Gerry Weber Outlet BVBA (1)
Herbesthalerstr 281, 4700, Eupen, Belgium
Tel.: (32) 87788874
Women Fashion Accessory Mfr & Retailer
N.A.I.C.S.: 315990

Gerry Weber Retail GmbH (1)
Neulehenstrasse 8, 33790, Halle, Germany
Tel.: (49) 52011809404
Web Site: http://www.gerryweber.com
Clothing Mfr & Retailer
N.A.I.C.S.: 458110

Gerry Weber Sportpark Hotel GmbH & Co. KG (1)
RogerFederer-Allee 6, Halle, 33790,

Nordrhein-Westfalen, Germany
Tel.: (49) 52018990
Web Site: http://www.gerryweber-world.de
Emp.: 100
Home Management Services
N.A.I.C.S.: 721110

Gerry Weber Support S.R.L. (1)
Strada Crucii 8, Santana, 547565, Romania
Tel.: (40) 265265123
Web Site: http://www.gerryweber.com
Sales Range: $100-124.9 Million
Emp.: 300
Clothing Mfr
N.A.I.C.S.: 315210
Gerhard Schmidt *(Mgr-Production)*

Gerry Weber UK Ltd. (1)
4th Floor 40-44 Newmann Street, London, W1T 7QD, United Kingdom
Tel.: (44) 2074368383
Women Fashion Accessory Mfr & Retailer
N.A.I.C.S.: 315990

Gerry Weber Wholesale Fashion GmbH (1)
Thurgauerstrasse 109, Glattpark, 8152, Opfikon, Switzerland
Tel.: (41) 448802294
Women Fashion Accessory Mfr & Retailer
N.A.I.C.S.: 315990

Golfplatz Eggeberg GmbH & Co. Anlagen KG (1)
Gruner Weg 25a, 33790, Halle, Germany
Tel.: (49) 52016279
Web Site: http://www.gctw.de
Sales Range: $50-74.9 Million
Emp.: 1,000
Golf Club Management Services
N.A.I.C.S.: 713910

Life-Style Fashion GmbH (1)
Neulehenstr 8, Westphalia, 33790, Halle, Germany
Tel.: (49) 5201185109
Women Fashion Accessory Mfr & Retailer
N.A.I.C.S.: 315990
Michael Dotterweich *(Dir-Wholesale)*

OOO Gerry Weber RUS (1)
Shabolovka 31G, Moscow, 115162, Russia
Tel.: (7) 9060330564
Women Fashion Accessory Mfr & Retailer
N.A.I.C.S.: 315990

R & U Weber GmbH & Co. KG (1)
Neulehenstr 3, 33790, Halle, Nordrhein-Westfalen, Germany
Tel.: (49) 52011850
Business Management Services
N.A.I.C.S.: 561499

SAMOON-Collection Fashion-Concept Gerry Weber GmbH (1)
Neulehenstr 8, Halle, 33790, Nordrhein-Westfalen, Germany
Tel.: (49) 52011850
Web Site: http://www.gerryweber.de
Emp.: 1,200
Fashion Apparels Whslr
N.A.I.C.S.: 458110
Ralf Weber *(CEO)*

TAIFUN-Collection Gerry Weber Fashion GmbH (1)
Neulehenstr 8, Halle, 33790, Nordrhein-Westfalen, Germany
Tel.: (49) 52011850
Web Site: http://www.gerryweber.de
Sales Range: $150-199.9 Million
Emp.: 850
Branded Sports Apparel Mfr
N.A.I.C.S.: 315250
Gerhard Weber *(Mng Dir)*

TB Frashion Gerry Weber GmbH (1)
Neulehenstrasse 8, 33790, Halle, Germany
Tel.: (49) 3047907770
Web Site: http://www.tbfashiongerryweber.de
Women's Clothing Retailer
N.A.I.C.S.: 458110

GERRY'S TRUCK CENTRE LTD.
4049 Eastgate Cres, London, N6L 1B7, ON, Canada
Tel.: (519) 652-2100

Web Site:
https://www.gerrystrucks.com
Rev.: $21,562,348
Emp.: 45
Truck Repair & Services
N.A.I.C.S.: 423120
Doug Wardle *(Mgr-Sls)*

GERS DISTRIBUTION
Route De Limoges, 86400, Niort, France
Tel.: (33) 562088140
Sales Range: $10-24.9 Million
Emp.: 47
Groceries & Related Products
N.A.I.C.S.: 424490
Jean-Jacques Farbos *(Pres)*

GERSAN ELEKTRIK TICARET VE SANAYI AS
Istanbul Anadolu Yakasi Organize Sanayi Bolgesi Gazi Bulvari No 39, PK 57 Tuzla, 34953, Istanbul, Turkiye
Tel.: (90) 2165930050
Web Site: https://www.gersan.com.tr
Year Founded: 1980
GEREL—(IST)
Rev.: $49,432,922
Assets: $37,370,940
Liabilities: $22,172,540
Net Worth: $15,198,400
Earnings: ($3,869,594)
Fiscal Year-end: 12/31/23
Electrical Equipment Mfr & Whslr
N.A.I.C.S.: 335311
Erkan Izgi *(Chm)*

GES LTD.
24 London Road West, Amersham, HP7 0EZ, Buckinghamshire, United Kingdom
Tel.: (44) 1494787250
Web Site: http://www.ges.co.uk
Sales Range: $25-49.9 Million
Emp.: 10
Radio Industry Software Services
N.A.I.C.S.: 513210
Jon Bareford *(Chm & CEO)*

GESCO AG
Johannisberg 7, 42103, Wuppertal, Germany
Tel.: (49) 202248200
Web Site: https://www.gesco.de
GSC1—(MUN)
Rev.: $628,141,075
Assets: $517,675,240
Liabilities: $211,180,042
Net Worth: $306,495,198
Earnings: $24,440,888
Emp.: 1,899
Fiscal Year-end: 12/31/23
Industry Machinery Mfr
N.A.I.C.S.: 333310
Klaus Moellerfriedrich *(Chm-Supervisory Bd)*

Subsidiaries:

Alro GmbH (1)
Goethestr 3, 29392, Wesendorf, Germany
Tel.: (49) 171 746 7585
Web Site: https://www.alro-gmbh.com
Window & Door Mfr
N.A.I.C.S.: 321911

Amtrion GmbH (1)
Sand stips 1, 32457, Porta Westfalica, Germany
Tel.: (49) 573176070
Web Site: https://www.amtrion.de
Emp.: 100
Medical Technology Equipment Mfr
N.A.I.C.S.: 339112

AstroPlast Kunststofftechnik GmbH & Co. KG (1)
Steinwiese 7, Enste, 59872, Meschede, Germany
Tel.: (49) 29 195 2950

Web Site: https://www.astroplast.de
Injection Molded Plastic Products Mfr
N.A.I.C.S.: 326199

C.F.K. CNC-Fertigungstechnik Kriftel GmbH (1)
Gutenbergstrasse 8, 65830, Kriftel, Germany
Tel.: (49) 61 929 9450
Web Site: https://www.cfk-online.de
Industrial Precision Machinery Distr
N.A.I.C.S.: 423830
Christoph Over *(CEO)*

Doerrenberg Special Steels Taiwan Ltd. (1)
No335 Xinzhong St yongkong st, Yongkang Dist, T'ainan, 71066, Taiwan
Tel.: (886) 6 2536060
Steel Casting Services
N.A.I.C.S.: 331512

Domer GmbH & Co. KG Stanz- und Umformtechnologie (1)
At Karlshutte 5, 57368, Lennestadt, Germany
Tel.: (49) 27 239 1400
Web Site: https://www.doemer-ring.de
Industrial Supplies Whslr
N.A.I.C.S.: 423840
Michael Dammer *(Mng Dir)*

Dorrenberg Edelstahl GmbH (1)
Hammerweg 1, 51766, Engelskirchen, Germany
Tel.: (49) 226 3790
Web Site: https://www.doerrenberg.de
Emp.: 500
Steel Rod Mfr & Distr
N.A.I.C.S.: 331221
Gerd Bohner *(Mng Dir)*

Subsidiary (Domestic):

Hubl GmbH (2)
Reutwiesenstrasse 44-50, 71665, Vaihingen, Germany
Tel.: (49) 70 428 2450
Web Site: https://www.hubl-gmbh.de
Emp.: 140
Precision Turned Product Mfr
N.A.I.C.S.: 332721
Rainer Kiefer *(Exec Dir)*

Protomaster Riedel & Co. GmbH (2)
Gewerbering 1, 08112, Wilkau-Hasslau, Germany
Tel.: (49) 375679140
Web Site: http://www.protomaster.com
Automotive Structural Parts Mfr
N.A.I.C.S.: 336211

VWH Vorrichtungs- und Werkzeugbau Herschbach GmbH (2)
Bahnhofstrasse 104, 56414, Herschbach, Germany
Tel.: (49) 6435 309 0
Web Site: http://www.vwh.de
Emp.: 100
Sensor & Mould Mfr
N.A.I.C.S.: 333511

Dorrenberg Special Steels Pte. Ltd. (1)
25 International Business Park 05-01 German Centre, Singapore, 609916, Singapore
Tel.: (65) 6 562 9021
Web Site: https://www.doerrenberg.com.sg
Steel Tool Product Mfr
N.A.I.C.S.: 333515
Gerd Bohner *(Mng Dir)*

Dorrenberg Tratamientos Termicos SL (1)
Poligono Sargaiz B10-B11, Uharte Arakil, 31840, Navarra, Spain
Tel.: (34) 94 856 7105
Web Site: https://www.dorrenberg.es
Heat Treating Services
N.A.I.C.S.: 332811

Frank Lemkex Tow (1)
street Lozovetska 30, Ternopil, Ukraine
Tel.: (380) 35 252 1967
Web Site: https://www.frank-lemex.com.ua
Cutting Tool Mfr
N.A.I.C.S.: 333515

Frank Walz- und Schmiedetechnik GmbH (1)

Frankstr 1 Reddighauser Hammer, 35116, Hatzfeld, Germany
Tel.: (49) 64 529 3310
Web Site: https://www.frank-original.com
Emp.: 300
Agricultural Machinery Mfr & Distr
N.A.I.C.S.: 333111
Frank Grote *(Mng Dir)*

Frank-Hungaria Kft. (1)
Kovacs-Hagyo Gyula ut 7, 3600, Ozd, Hungary
Tel.: (36) 48572158
Steel Products Mfr
N.A.I.C.S.: 331513

Franz Funke Zerspanungstechnik GmbH & Co. KG (1)
Am Gelben Berg 3, Westenfeld, 59846, Sundern, Germany
Tel.: (49) 2 933 8400
Web Site: https://www.franzfunke.de
Precision Turned Product Mfr
N.A.I.C.S.: 332721

Georg Kesel GmbH & Co. KG (1)
Maybachstrasse 6, 87437, Kempten, Germany
Tel.: (49) 83 125 2880
Web Site: https://www.kesel.com
Milling Machine & Clamping System Mfr
N.A.I.C.S.: 333515
Martin K. Klug *(Pres & CEO)*

Haseke GmbH & Co. KG (1)
Sandtrift 1, 32457, Porta Westfalica, Germany
Tel.: (49) 57 317 6070
Web Site: https://www.haseke.com
Electrical System Installation Services
N.A.I.C.S.: 238210
Uwe Kunitschke *(Mng Dir)*

INEX-solutions GmbH (1)
Gewerbestrasse 32, 75015, Bretten, Germany
Tel.: (49) 7042824515
Web Site: https://www.inex-solutions.de
Stainless Steel Filtration Mfr
N.A.I.C.S.: 332999

Jiashan Doerrenberg Mould & Die Trading Co. (1)
4th Floor No 6 Jinji Road Huimin Street, Jiashan, 314100, Zhejiang, China
Tel.: (86) 57384801899
Steel Products Mfr
N.A.I.C.S.: 331513

MAE Machines (Beijing) Co., Ltd. (1)
Room 15E Building D Oriental Kenzo Plaza No 48 Dongzhimenwai Street, Dongcheng District, Beijing, 100027, China
Tel.: (86) 1087513901
Machine Tools Mfr
N.A.I.C.S.: 333517

MAE Maschinen- und Apparatebau Gotzen GmbH (1)
Steinhof 65, 40699, Erkrath, Germany
Tel.: (49) 21189093333
Web Site: https://www.mae-group.com
Automotive Tool Mfr
N.A.I.C.S.: 336390

MAE.ch GmbH (1)
Obere Breitlen 16, Unterstammheim, Zurich, Switzerland
Tel.: (41) 527402150
Business Support Services
N.A.I.C.S.: 561990

Maschinen und Apparatebau Gotzen GmbH (1)
Tel.: (49) 21 189 0930
Web Site: https://www.mae-group.com
Hydraulic Presses Mfr
N.A.I.C.S.: 423830
Rudiger Schury *(Mng Dir & Member-Exec Bd)*

Subsidiary (US):

MAE-Eitel Inc. (2)
97 Pinedale Industrial Rd, Orwigsburg, PA 17961
Tel.: (570) 366-0585
Web Site: https://www.mae-america.com
Straightening Presses Mfr

GESCO AG

Gesco AG—(Continued)
N.A.I.C.S.: 333998
Scott Donaldson (VP-Sls)

Modell Technik GmbH & Co. Formenbau KG (1)
Franz-Mehring-Strasse 11, 99610, Sommerda, Germany
Tel.: (49) 363468610
Web Site: http://www.modelltechnik.com
Emp.: 115
Industrial Mold Mfr
N.A.I.C.S.: 333511

OOO Frank RUS (1)
st Razdolnaya 103A, 302038, Orel, Russia
Web Site: https://frank-original.ru
Agriculture Machinery Part Mfr
N.A.I.C.S.: 333111

Paul Beier GmbH Werkzeug- und Maschinenbau & Co. KG (1)
Naumburger Strasse 36 Rothenditmold, 34127, Kassel, Germany
Tel.: (49) 56 180 7020
Web Site: https://www.beier-kassel.de
Machinery Component & Tool Mfr
N.A.I.C.S.: 333517
Rainer Bierlich (Mng Dir)

Pickhardt & Gerlach GmbH & Co. KG (1)
An der Kormke 19-21, 58802, Balve, Germany
Tel.: (49) 23 759 1830
Web Site: https://www.pickhardt-gerlach.de
Plastic Tank Mfr
N.A.I.C.S.: 326199
Christian Propper (COO & Production Mgr)

SETTER GmbH & Co. Papierverarbeitung (1)
Reeser Strasse 87, 46446, Emmerich am Rhein, Germany
Tel.: (49) 282 291 4580
Web Site: https://www.setter-germany.com
Emp.: 50
Paper Sack Mfr
N.A.I.C.S.: 322299
Steffen Grasse (Mng Dir)

Subsidiary (US):

Setterstix Corp. (2)
261 S Main St, Cattaraugus, NY 14719
Tel.: (716) 257-3451
Web Site: https://www.setterstix.com
Sales Range: $10-24.9 Million
Emp.: 40
Mfr of Rolled Paper Sticks for Candy, Health & Beauty Aids
N.A.I.C.S.: 322299

SVT Apac Pte. Ltd. (1)
1 Corporation Drive REVV No 08-15, Singapore, 619775, Singapore
Tel.: (65) 82610012
Web Site: https://www.svt-apac.com
Oil & Gas Loading Equipment Mfr
N.A.I.C.S.: 333132

Setter GmbH & Co. (1)
Reeser Strasse 87, D-46446, Emmerich am Rhein, Germany
Tel.: (49) 2822914580
Web Site: https://www.setter-germany.com
Emp.: 50
Paper Stick Mfr & Distr
N.A.I.C.S.: 332999

Sommer & Strassburger Edelstahlanlagenbau GmbH & Co. KG (1)
Gewerbestrasse 32, Golshausen, 75015, Bretten, Germany
Tel.: (49) 72 529 3950
Web Site: https://www.sus-bretten.de
Steel Products Mfr
N.A.I.C.S.: 331110
Gerhard Hilpp (Mng Dir)

Werkzeugbau Laichingen GmbH (1)
Geislinger Strasse 32, 89150, Laichingen, Germany
Tel.: (49) 733 3810
Web Site: https://werkzeugbau-laichingen.de
Cutting Tool Mfr
N.A.I.C.S.: 333515
Thomas Hansmann (Mng Dir)

Werkzeugbau Leipzig GmbH (1)
Zschochersche Strasse 79c, 04229, Leipzig, Germany
Tel.: (49) 34 148 5260
Web Site: https://www.werkzeugbau-laichingen.de
Emp.: 170
Machine Tools Mfr
N.A.I.C.S.: 333517

GESTETNER OF CEYLON PLC
Tel.: (94) 112323826
Web Site: https://www.gestetner.lk
Year Founded: 1953
GEST—(COL)
Rev.: $4,684,196
Assets: $2,093,851
Liabilities: $771,162
Net Worth: $1,322,689
Earnings: $280,088
Emp.: 200
Fiscal Year-end: 03/31/23
Office Supply Product Mfr
N.A.I.C.S.: 339940
S. J. M. Anzsar (Chm)

GESTION AUDEM, INC.
5 Place Ville-Marie Bureau 915, H3B 3P2, Montreal, QC, Canada
Tel.: (514) 874-2600
Year Founded: 1980
Holding Company
N.A.I.C.S.: 551112

Subsidiaries:

Cogeco Inc. (1)
1 Place Ville-Marie Office 3301, Montreal, H3B 3N2, QC, Canada
Tel.: (514) 764-4600
Web Site: https://corpo.cogeco.com
Rev.: $2,342,937,987
Assets: $7,406,646,597
Liabilities: $4,848,971,967
Net Worth: $2,557,674,630
Earnings: $358,092,581
Emp.: 5,200
Fiscal Year-end: 08/31/2022
Holding Company; Telecommunications
N.A.I.C.S.: 551112
Louis Audet (Chm)

Subsidiary (Domestic):

Cogeco Communications Inc. (2)
1 Place Ville Marie Office 3301, Montreal, H3B 3N2, QC, Canada (100%)
Tel.: (514) 764-4600
Web Site: https://www.corpo.cogeco.com
Rev.: $2,269,123,611
Assets: $7,258,392,021
Liabilities: $4,763,598,622
Net Worth: $2,494,793,399
Earnings: $354,964,244
Emp.: 4,700
Fiscal Year-end: 08/31/2022
Telecommunication Servicesb
N.A.I.C.S.: 516210
Louis Audet (Chm)

Subsidiary (US):

Atlantic Broadband Group LLC (3)
2 Batterymarch Park Ste 205, Quincy, MA 02169
Tel.: (617) 786-8800
Web Site: http://www.atlanticbb.com
High Speed Broadband Services
N.A.I.C.S.: 517810
Heather McCallion (VP-Product & Programming)

Subsidiary (Domestic):

MetroCast Communications (4)
1059 E 10th St, Hazleton, PA 18201
Cable, Internet & Phone Services
N.A.I.C.S.: 516210

Division (Domestic):

Cogeco Cable Ontario (3)
950 Syscon Rd, PO Box 5076, Burlington, L7R 4S6, ON, Canada (100%)
Tel.: (905) 333-5343
Web Site: http://www.cogeco.ca

Sales Range: $150-199.9 Million
Emp.: 700
Cable Communication Services
N.A.I.C.S.: 517810

Cogeco Cable Quebec (3)
1630 6th Street Office 200, Trois Rivieres, G8Y 5B8, QC, Canada
Tel.: (819) 372-9292
Web Site: http://www.cogeco.ca
Sales Range: $25-49.9 Million
Emp.: 32
Provider of Cable Television Services
N.A.I.C.S.: 516210

Subsidiary (Domestic):

Cogeco Media Inc. (2)
800 De la Gauchetiere Street West Office 1100, Montreal, H5A 1M1, QC, Canada
Tel.: (514) 787-7799
Web Site: https://www.cogecomedia.com
Telecommunication Servicesb
N.A.I.C.S.: 517111
Michel Lorrain (Pres)

GESTION CLAUDE ROBERT INC.
500 Rte 112, Rougemont, J0L 1M0, QC, Canada
Tel.: (450) 469-3153
Web Site: http://www.robert.ca
Sales Range: $50-74.9 Million
Emp.: 150
Holding Company
N.A.I.C.S.: 551112
Claude Robert (Pres)

Subsidiaries:

Groupe Robert Inc. (1)
500 Route 112, Rougemont, J0L 1M0, QC, Canada
Tel.: (450) 469-3153
Web Site: http://www.robert.ca
Logistics Services; Owned 37.5% by Gestion Claude Robert Inc., 37.5% by Placements Robert Bernard Ltee. & 25% by Fonds de Solidrite des Travailleurs du Quebec
N.A.I.C.S.: 541614

Subsidiary (Domestic):

Rollex Transportation Inc (2)
910 boul Lionel-Boulet, Varennes, J3X 1P7, QC, Canada
Tel.: (450) 652-4482
Web Site: http://www.rollex.ca
Waste Transportation Services
N.A.I.C.S.: 562211

GESTION MARTIN POITRAS INC
33-5th street L'Islet, Quebec, G0R 2C0, QC, Canada
Tel.: (418) 247-5025
Web Site: http://www.anisco.com
Sales Range: $10-24.9 Million
Emp.: 100
Holding Company
N.A.I.C.S.: 551112
Rejean Poitras (Pres & CEO)

Subsidiaries:

Amisco Industries Ltd. (1)
33 5th Street L'Islet, Quebec, G0R 2C0, QC, Canada
Tel.: (418) 247-5025
Web Site: https://www.amisco.com
Sales Range: $25-49.9 Million
Emp.: 150
Painted Tubular & Sheet Steel Residential Furniture Designer & Mfr
N.A.I.C.S.: 337126
Rejean Poitras (Pres & CEO)

GESUNDHEITSWELT CHIEMGAU AG
Strobinger Strase 18a, Bad Endorf, 83093, Rosenheim, Germany
Tel.: (49) 80532000
Web Site:
https://www.gesundheitswelt.de

INTERNATIONAL PUBLIC

Health Care Srvices
N.A.I.C.S.: 621610
Mario Gerber (Head-Pur)

GET HOLDINGS LIMITED
Room 1204-05 Centre Point 181-185 Gloucester Road, Hong Kong, China (Hong Kong)
Tel.: (852) 21108100
Web Site: https://www.geth.com.hk
Year Founded: 1999
8100—(HKG)
Rev.: $13,518,570
Assets: $38,445,968
Liabilities: $7,098,180
Net Worth: $31,347,788
Earnings: ($176,970)
Emp.: 22
Fiscal Year-end: 12/31/22
Holding Company
N.A.I.C.S.: 551112
Jing Shong Wong (Chm, & Officer-Compliance & Exec Dir)

Subsidiaries:

e-Perfect IT Limited (1)
318 Town Health Technology Centre 10-12 Yuen Shun Circuit, Siu Lek Yuen, Sha Tin, China (Hong Kong)
Tel.: (852) 36698888
Business Outsourcing Services
N.A.I.C.S.: 541513

Subsidiary (Domestic):

Wafer Systems (Hong Kong) Limited (2)
Units 02-03 18F AIA Financial Centre, No 712 Prince Edward Road East San Po Kong, Kowloon, China (Hong Kong)
Tel.: (852) 39008800
Wireless Telecommunication Services
N.A.I.C.S.: 517112

GET NICE HOLDINGS LIMITED
G/F-3/F Cosco Tower Grand Millennium Plaza183 Queens Road, Central, China (Hong Kong)
Tel.: (852) 2 970 8000 Ky
Web Site: http://www.getnice.com.hk
Year Founded: 1989
0064—(HKG)
Rev.: $56,889,854
Assets: $1,015,209,448
Liabilities: $119,475,206
Net Worth: $895,734,242
Earnings: $12,326,877
Emp.: 96
Fiscal Year-end: 03/31/22
Financial Services
N.A.I.C.S.: 523910
Hon Man Hung (Founder, Chm & CEO)

Subsidiaries:

Get Nice Financial Group Limited (1)
10/F Cosco Tower Grand Millennium Plaza 183 Queens Road, Central, China (Hong Kong)
Tel.: (852) 2 970 8000
Web Site: http://www.getnicefg.com.hk
Rev.: $49,677,163
Assets: $616,181,829
Liabilities: $97,547,316
Net Worth: $518,634,513
Earnings: $27,499,697
Emp.: 73
Fiscal Year-end: 03/31/2021
Investment Management Service
N.A.I.C.S.: 523940
Frankie Kin Wai Shum (Mng Dir)

GET PRICE PTY. LTD.
Level 22 175 Liverpool Street, Sydney, 2000, NSW, Australia
Tel.: (61) 2 8114 6333 AU
Web Site: http://www.getprice.com.au
Online Shopping Services
N.A.I.C.S.: 449210

AND PRIVATE COMPANIES

Chris Hitchen *(CEO)*

GETABEC PUBLIC COMPANY LIMITED
335/7 Srinakarin Road, Nongbon Prawet, Bangkok, 10250, Thailand
Tel.: (66) 023660400
Web Site:
https://www.getabecboiler.com
Year Founded: 1983
GTB—(THA)
Rev.: $32,525,401
Assets: $33,059,322
Liabilities: $9,743,404
Net Worth: $23,315,918
Earnings: $1,762,027
Emp.: 400
Fiscal Year-end: 12/31/23
Boiler & Pressure Vessel Manufacturing
N.A.I.C.S.: 332410

GETALONG ENTERPRISE LIMITED
Office No 307 308 Yogeshwar 135 139 Kazi Sayed Street, Masjid Bunder West, Mumbai, 400003, India
Tel.: (91) 8591343631
Web Site:
https://www.getalongenterprise.com
Year Founded: 2020
543372—(BOM)
Textile Products Mfr
N.A.I.C.S.: 313310
Sweety Rahul Jain *(Mng Dir & CFO)*

GETBACK SPOLKA AKCYJNA
Rtm Witolda Pileckiego 63 street, 02-781, Warsaw, Poland
Tel.: (48) 717710100
Web Site: http://www.getbacksa.pl
Year Founded: 2012
GBK—(WAR)
Collection Agency Services
N.A.I.C.S.: 561440
Tomasz Strama *(Vice Chm)*

GETBUSY PLC
Suite 8 The Works 20 West Street Unity Campus, Pampisford, Cambridge, CB22 3FT, United Kingdom
Tel.: (44) 1223666880 UK
Web Site: https://www.getbusy.com
Year Founded: 2017
GETB—(AIM)
Rev.: $24,353,699
Assets: $12,865,438
Liabilities: $16,624,590
Net Worth: ($3,759,152)
Earnings: $35,345
Emp.: 138
Fiscal Year-end: 12/31/22
Software Development Services
N.A.I.C.S.: 541511
Daniel Rabie *(CEO)*

GETCHELL GOLD CORP.
Suite 488 - 625 Howe Street, Vancouver, V6C 2T6, BC, Canada
Tel.: (647) 249-4798 ON
Web Site: https://getchellgold.com
Year Founded: 2000
GGLDF—(OTCQB)
Assets: $437,474
Liabilities: $98,565
Net Worth: $338,909
Earnings: ($5,229,284)
Fiscal Year-end: 03/31/23
Gold & Copper Mining
N.A.I.C.S.: 212290
William Wagener *(Chm & CEO)*

GETEC ENERGIE HOLDING GMBH
Albert-Vater-Strasse 50, 39108, Magdeburg, Germany
Tel.: (49) 391 2568 100 De
Web Site: http://www.getec.de
Sales Range: $800-899.9 Million
Emp.: 1,165
Holding Company Energy & Utility Services Contractor
N.A.I.C.S.: 551112
Karl Gerhold *(Mng Dir)*

Subsidiaries:

Emmtec Services B.V. (1)
Eerste Bokslootweg 17, 7821 AT, Emmen, Netherlands
Tel.: (31) 591692555
Web Site: http://www.emmtecservices.com
Energy & Utilities Services Contractor
N.A.I.C.S.: 238990

GETEC Heat & Power AG (1)
Albert-Vater-Strasse 50, 39108, Magdeburg, Germany
Tel.: (49) 391 2568 100
Sales Range: $250-299.9 Million
Energy & Utilities Services Contractor
N.A.I.C.S.: 238990
Volker Schulz *(Chm-Mgmt Bd & CEO)*

GETECH GROUP PLC
Nicholson House Elmete Hall Elmete Lane, Leeds, LS8 2LJ, United Kingdom
Tel.: (44) 1133222200 UK
Web Site: https://www.getech.com
Year Founded: 1994
GTC—(AIM)
Rev.: $6,399,899
Assets: $15,699,318
Liabilities: $3,858,874
Net Worth: $11,840,444
Earnings: ($3,569,806)
Emp.: 60
Fiscal Year-end: 12/31/22
Petroleum & Mineral Consultancy
N.A.I.C.S.: 213112
Jonathan Copus *(CEO)*

Subsidiaries:

ERCL Limited (1)
Tel.: (44) 1133222200
Web Site: https://www.ercl.com
Oil & Gas Consultancy Services
N.A.I.C.S.: 213112

Geophysical Exploration Technology Inc. (1)
3000 Wilcrest Dr Ste 155, Houston, TX 77042-3498
Tel.: (713) 979-9900
Web Site: http://www.getech.com
Sales Range: $25-49.9 Million
Emp.: 2
Geophysical Services
N.A.I.C.S.: 541360
Jennifer Sayyaf *(Office Mgr)*

GETEIN BIOTECH, INC.
No 9 Bofu Road, Luhe District, Nanjing, 211505, Jiangsu, China
Tel.: (86) 2568568594
Web Site: https://www.getein.com
Year Founded: 2002
603387—(SHG)
Rev.: $255,789,242
Assets: $516,312,281
Liabilities: $142,202,806
Net Worth: $374,109,475
Earnings: $70,046,964
Emp.: 1,700
Fiscal Year-end: 12/31/22
Vitro Diagnostic Device Mfr
N.A.I.C.S.: 325413
Enben Su *(Chm, Pres & Gen Mgr)*

GETIN HOLDING S.A.
ul Gwiazdzista 66, 53-413, Wroclaw, Poland
Tel.: (48) 717977777
Web Site: https://getin.pl
Year Founded: 1996
GTN—(WAR)
Rev.: $426,523
Assets: $392,416,546
Liabilities: $213,860,853
Net Worth: $178,555,693
Earnings: ($35,519,769)
Emp.: 5,000
Fiscal Year-end: 12/31/21
Investment Banking & Securities Intermediation
N.A.I.C.S.: 523150
Leszek Czarnecki *(Chm-Supervisory Bd)*

Subsidiaries:

Carcade Service sp. z o.o. (1)
St Plastunskaya d 82-A BC Apricot 6th Floor Office 602, Sochi, 354000, Russia
Tel.: (7) 8007003030
Car Lending Services
N.A.I.C.S.: 532112

Idea Bank S.A. (1)
Ul Galitskaya 7, Ivano-Frankivs'k, 76000, Ukraine
Tel.: (380) 342558702
Web Site: http://www.pbank.if.ua
Commercial Banking Services
N.A.I.C.S.: 522110

Idea Bank S.A. (1)
11 Byaduli Z st, Minsk, 220034, Belarus
Tel.: (375) 172299645
Web Site: http://www.ideabank.by
Online Banking Services
N.A.I.C.S.: 522110

Idea Bank SA (1)
ul Przyokopowa 33, 01-208, Warsaw, Poland (55.04%)
Tel.: (48) 22 101 10 10
Web Site: http://www.ideabank.pl
Investment Banking
N.A.I.C.S.: 523150
Marek Grzegorzewicz *(Member-Mgmt Bd)*

Idea Fleet S.A. (1)
ul Strzegomska 42b, 53-611, Wroclaw, Poland
Tel.: (48) 713344249
Web Site: http://www.idea-fleet.pl
Passenger Car Rental Services
N.A.I.C.S.: 532111
Agnieszka Wieczorek *(Acct Mgr)*

Idea Money S.A. (1)
ul Przyokopowa 33, 01-208, Warsaw, Poland
Tel.: (48) 222762618
Online Factoring Services
N.A.I.C.S.: 522299
Michal Pluta *(CFO)*

Subsidiary (Domestic):

Tax Care S.A. (2)
Domaniewska 45, 02-672, Warsaw, Poland
Tel.: (48) 222620000
Web Site: http://www.taxcare.pl
Accounting Services
N.A.I.C.S.: 541219

M.W. Trade S.A. (1)
Ul Powstancow Slaskich 125/200, 53-317, Wroclaw, Poland (51.27%)
Tel.: (48) 717902050
Web Site: https://www.mwtrade.pl
Rev.: $180,640
Assets: $7,436,738
Liabilities: $539,380
Net Worth: $6,897,358
Earnings: ($649,136)
Emp.: 230
Fiscal Year-end: 12/31/2023
Financial Services
N.A.I.C.S.: 523999
Dariusz Strojewski *(Member-Mgmt Bd)*

GETIN NOBLE BANK S.A.
ul Przyokopowa 33, 01-208, Warsaw, Poland
Tel.: (48) 225415158 PL
Web Site: http://www.gnb.pl
GNB—(WAR)
Rev.: $451,773,075
Assets: $13,461,785,291
Liabilities: $12,921,412,169
Net Worth: $540,373,122
Earnings: ($150,816,868)
Emp.: 3,849
Fiscal Year-end: 12/31/20
Investment Banking Services
N.A.I.C.S.: 523150
Leszek Czarnecki *(Chm-Supervisory Bd)*

Subsidiaries:

Noble Securities S.A. (1)
Rondo Ignacego Daszynskiego 2C Building The Warsaw HUB 8th Floor, 00-843, Warsaw, Poland
Tel.: (48) 222441303
Web Site: http://www.noblesecurities.pl
Investment Brokerage Services
N.A.I.C.S.: 523150

GETINGE AB
Lindholmspiren 7, PO Box 8861, 417 56, Gothenburg, Sweden
Tel.: (46) 103350000 SE
Web Site: https://www.getinge.com
Year Founded: 1904
GETI.B—(OMX)
Rev.: $3,302,141,920
Assets: $5,439,274,400
Liabilities: $2,365,788,320
Net Worth: $3,073,486,080
Earnings: $366,240,000
Emp.: 10,729
Fiscal Year-end: 12/31/21
Holding Company; Healthcare & Life Sciences Equipment & Systems Mfr & Whslr
N.A.I.C.S.: 551112
Carl Bennet *(Chm)*

Subsidiaries:

Applikon Biotechnology B.V. (1)
Heertjeslaan 2, NL-2629 JG, Delft, Netherlands
Tel.: (31) 102083555
Medical Device Mfr & Distr
N.A.I.C.S.: 325412

Arjo AB (1)
Michelsensgatan, Scheelevagen 19F, SE-223 70, Malmo, Sweden
Tel.: (46) 41364500
Sales Range: $25-49.9 Million
Emp.: 70
Medical Device Developer & Distr
N.A.I.C.S.: 423450

Subsidiary (Non-US):

Arjo Austria GmbH (2)
Fohrebweg 5, 6065, Thaur, Austria (100%)
Tel.: (43) 5223493350
Sales Range: $25-49.9 Million
Emp.: 20
Hygiene Systems & Patient Handling Systems Mfr
N.A.I.C.S.: 339113

Arjo Equipements Hospitaliers S.A. (2)
2 Ave Gasteri, PO Box 133, 59346, Roncq, Cedex, France (100%)
Tel.: (33) 320281313
Web Site: http://www.arjo.fr
Sales Range: $10-24.9 Million
Emp.: 22
Hygiene Systems & Patient Handling Equipment
N.A.I.C.S.: 339113
Gerrae Srob *(Gen Mgr)*

Arjo Far East Ltd. (2)
Unit 3A 4th Fl Hoi Luen Industrial Center, 55 Hoi Yuen Rd, Kwun Tong, China (Hong Kong) (100%)
Tel.: (852) 25089553
Sales Range: $25-49.9 Million
Emp.: 7
Hygiene Systems & Patient Handling Equipment Mfr
N.A.I.C.S.: 339113

Subsidiary (Domestic):

Arjo Hospital Equipment AB (2)
Verkstadsvagan 5, PO Box 61, SE 241 21,

GETINGE AB

Getinge AB—(Continued)
Eslov, Sweden **(100%)**
Tel.: (46) 41364500
Web Site: http://www.arjo.com
Sales Range: $25-49.9 Million
Mfr & Sales of Hygiene Systems & Patient Handling Equipment
N.A.I.C.S.: 339113

Subsidiary (Non-US):

Arjo Hospital Equipment Pty Ltd. (2)
1/205 Queensport Road North, Murarrie, Brisbane, 4172, QLD, Australia **(100%)**
Tel.: (61) 7 3107 8100
Web Site: http://www.arjohuntleigh.com.au
Sales Range: $25-49.9 Million
Emp.: 40
Mfr of Hygiene Systems & Patient Handling Equipment
N.A.I.C.S.: 339113

Arjo Hospital Equipment s.r.o. (2)
Hlink 118, Brno, 60300, Czech Republic **(100%)**
Tel.: (420) 549254252
Web Site: http://www.arjohuntleigh.com
Sales Range: $25-49.9 Million
Emp.: 9
Hygiene Systems & Patient Handling Equipment Mfr
N.A.I.C.S.: 339113
Dusan Chytry *(Mgr-Fin)*

Arjo Italia S.p.A. (2)
Via Poggio Verde 34, IT 00148, Rome, Italy **(100%)**
Tel.: (39) 066566356
Web Site: http://www.arjo.com
Sales Range: $25-49.9 Million
Emp.: 60
Hygiene Systems & Patient Handling Equipment Mfr
N.A.I.C.S.: 339113

Arjo Spain S.A. (2)
San Rafael 6, 28108, Alcobendas, Spain **(100%)**
Tel.: (34) 914900636
Web Site: http://www.arjo.com
Sales Range: $25-49.9 Million
Emp.: 16
Hygiene Systems & Patient Handling Equipment Mfr
N.A.I.C.S.: 339113

ArjoHuntleigh Canada Inc. (2)
350 - 90 Matheson Blvd, West Mississauga, L5R 3R3, ON, Canada **(100%)**
Tel.: (905) 238-7880
Web Site: https://www.arjo.com
Sales Range: $25-49.9 Million
Emp.: 50
N.A.I.C.S.: 339114
Anne Segiun *(Pres)*

ArjoHuntleigh GmbH (2)
Peter-Sander-Strasse 10, Mainz-Kastel, 55252, Germany
Tel.: (49) 61341860
Web Site: http://www.arjohuntleigh.com
Sales Range: $25-49.9 Million
Medical Device Sales & Distr
N.A.I.C.S.: 339112

ArjoHuntleigh Healthcare Polska Sp. z o.o. (2)
ul Ks Wawrzyniaka 2 w Komorniakch, Komorniki, Poznan, 62-052, Poland
Tel.: (48) 616621550
Web Site: http://www.arjohuntleigh.com
Sales Range: $50-74.9 Million
Emp.: 3
Medical Device Sales & Distr
N.A.I.C.S.: 532283

ArjoHuntleigh Iberica S.L. (2)
Poligono Can Salvatella c/ Cabanyes 1-7, Barbera del Valles, 08210, Barcelona, Spain
Tel.: (34) 90 092 1850
Web Site: http://www.arjohuntleigh.com
Sales Range: $25-49.9 Million
Emp.: 50
Medical Device Sales & Distr
N.A.I.C.S.: 532283

ArjoHuntleigh Nederland B.V. (2)
Biezenwei 21, 4004 MB, Tiel, Netherlands **(100%)**
Tel.: (31) 344640800
Web Site: https://www.arjo.com
Sales Range: $25-49.9 Million
Hygiene Systems & Patient Handling Equipment Mfr
N.A.I.C.S.: 339113

ArjoHuntleigh Pty Ltd. (2)
78 Forsyth Street, O'Connor, 6163, WA, Australia
Tel.: (61) 8 9337 4111
Web Site: http://www.huntleigh-healthcare.com
Sales Range: $50-74.9 Million
Emp.: 150
Medical Device Sales & Distr
N.A.I.C.S.: 423450
Graeme Gurney *(Reg Mgr-Sls-Asia Pacific)*

ArjoHuntleigh South Africa (Pty) Ltd (2)
2 Willem Cruywagen Ave, Klerksoord, 0200, Pretoria, South Africa
Tel.: (27) 125424680
Web Site: http://www.arjohuntleigh.com
Sales Range: $50-74.9 Million
Medical Device Sales & Distr
N.A.I.C.S.: 423450

ArjoHuntleigh UK (2)
Regus Gloucester Docks North Warehouse, Gloucester, GL1 2EP, United Kingdom **(100%)**
Tel.: (44) 345 611 4114
Web Site: http://www.arjohuntleigh.co.uk
Sales Range: $100-124.9 Million
Hygiene Systems & Patient Handling Equipment Mfr
N.A.I.C.S.: 339113
Paul Lyon *(Reg Pres-Intl Emerging Markets)*

HNE Medical SA (2)
451 Chemin De Champivost, BP 20, 69579, Limonest, France
Tel.: (33) 478666266
Sales Range: $50-74.9 Million
Medical Devices Sales & Distr
N.A.I.C.S.: 339112

Huntleigh Healthcare A/S (2)
Vassingeroed Vej 52, Lynge, 3504, Denmark
Tel.: (45) 49138486
Web Site: http://www.arjohuntleigh.com
Sales Range: $25-49.9 Million
Emp.: 40
Medical Device Sales & Distr
N.A.I.C.S.: 423450
Jorgen Mann *(Mng Dir)*

Subsidiary (US):

Huntleigh Healthcare LLC (2)
40 Christopher Way, Eatontown, NJ 07724-3327
Tel.: (732) 578-9898
Sales Range: $75-99.9 Million
Medical Device Mfr & Distr
N.A.I.C.S.: 423450

Subsidiary (Non-US):

Huntleigh Healthcare Pte Ltd (2)
20 Bendemeer Road Singapore Unit 0603, 04-08 Leong Huat Bldg, Singapore, 339914, Singapore
Tel.: (65) 62933387
Web Site: http://wwwarjohuntleigh.com
Sales Range: $50-74.9 Million
Emp.: 20
Medical Device Sales & Distr
N.A.I.C.S.: 532283
Paul Lyon *(Mng Dir-Asia Pacific)*

Subsidiary (US):

ReNu Medical Inc. (2)
830 80th St SW Ste 100, Everett, WA 98203
Tel.: (425) 353-1110
Web Site: https://renumedical.com
Medical/Hospital Equipment
N.A.I.C.S.: 423450

ArjoHuntleigh Ltd (1)
41 Vestey Drive, Mount Wellington, Auckland, 1060, New Zealand
Tel.: (64) 9 573 5344

Sales Range: $25-49.9 Million
Emp.: 20
Medical & Surgical Equipment Whslr
N.A.I.C.S.: 423450
Anthony Blyth *(Pres)*

Subsidiary (Non-US):

Arjo LTD Med. AB (2)
Box 69, 310 44, Getinge, Halland, Sweden
Tel.: (46) 35 155500
Medical & Surgical Equipment Whslr
N.A.I.C.S.: 423450

Arjo Ltd (2)
St Catherine Street, Gloucester, GL1 2SL, United Kingdom
Tel.: (44) 8702 430430
Medical & Surgical Equipment Whslr
N.A.I.C.S.: 423450

ArjoHuntleigh (Hong Kong) Ltd (2)
Room 411-414 4/F Manhattan Centre 8 Kwai Cheong Road, Kwai Chung, China (Hong Kong)
Tel.: (852) 2 960 7668
Web Site: https://www.arjo.com
Medical & Surgical Equipment Whslr
N.A.I.C.S.: 327910
Kandy Lo *(Pres)*

ArjoHuntleigh (Shanghai) Medical Trading Co. Ltd (2)
7/F Metro Plaza 555 Lou Shan Guan Road, Shanghai, 200051, China
Tel.: (86) 21 62280202
Web Site: http://www.arjohuntleigh.com
Sales Range: $25-49.9 Million
Medical & Surgical Equipment Whslr
N.A.I.C.S.: 423450

ArjoHuntleigh - UK (2)
ArjoHuntleigh House Houghton Hall Business Park, Houghton Regis, LU5 5XF, Bedfordshire, United Kingdom
Tel.: (44) 1582 41 3104
Medical & Surgical Equipment Whslr
N.A.I.C.S.: 423450
Paul Lyon *(Reg Pres-Emerging Markets-Intl)*

ArjoHuntleigh A/S (2)
Vassingerodvej 52, 3540, Lynge, Denmark
Tel.: (45) 4913 8486
Sales Range: $25-49.9 Million
Medical & Surgical Equipment Whslr
N.A.I.C.S.: 423450

ArjoHuntleigh AB (2)
Neptunigatan 1, Malmo, 211 20, Sweden
Tel.: (46) 413 645 00
Medical & Surgical Equipment Distr
N.A.I.C.S.: 423450

ArjoHuntleigh AG (2)
Florenzstrasse 1D, Basel, 4023, Switzerland
Tel.: (41) 61 337 97 77
Web Site: http://www.arjohuntleigh.com
Medical & Surgical Equipment Whslr
N.A.I.C.S.: 423450
Matthias Brumm *(Pres)*

ArjoHuntleigh Healthcare India Pvt. Ltd. (2)
Plot No 8 Shah Industrial Estate Off Veera Desai Road, Andheri West, Mumbai, 400053, India
Tel.: (91) 22 6694 6697
Medical & Surgical Equipment Distr
N.A.I.C.S.: 423450
Chander Tahiliani *(Pres)*

ArjoHuntleigh Hospital Equipment AB (2)
Verkstadsvagen 5, 241 21, Eslov, Sweden
Tel.: (46) 413 645 00
Web Site: http://www.arjohuntleigh.com
Medical Equipment Whslr
N.A.I.C.S.: 423450

ArjoHuntleigh International Ltd (2)
310-312 Dallow Road, Luton, LU1 1TD, Bedfordshire, United Kingdom
Tel.: (44) 1582 745800
Web Site: http://www.arjohuntleigh.com
Sales Range: $50-74.9 Million
Medical & Surgical Equipment Whslr
N.A.I.C.S.: 423450

ArjoHuntleigh Magog Inc. (2)

INTERNATIONAL PUBLIC

2001 Tanguay, Magog, J1X 5Y5, QC, Canada
Tel.: (819) 868-0441
Web Site: http://www.arjohuntleigh.com
Sales Range: $50-74.9 Million
Emp.: 110
Medical & Surgical Equipment Whslr
N.A.I.C.S.: 423450
Julien Bouchard *(Gen Dir)*

ArjoHuntleigh Middle East (2)
Ahmed Bin Office MO5 Juma Al Maktoum Building SH Zayed Road, PO Box 102869, Dubai, 214742, United Arab Emirates
Tel.: (971) 4 447 0942
Web Site: http://www.arjohuntleigh.com
Sales Range: $25-49.9 Million
Emp.: 11
Medical & Surgical Equipment Whslr
N.A.I.C.S.: 423450
Iyadall Junaidi *(Pres)*

ArjoHuntleigh NV/SA (2)
Evenbroekveld 16, 9420, Erpe-Mere, Belgium
Tel.: (32) 53 60 73 80
Web Site: http://www.arjohuntleigh.be
Medical & Surgical Equipment Distr
N.A.I.C.S.: 423450
Frank Robeers *(Pres)*

ArjoHuntleigh Norway A/S (2)
Ryenstubben 2, 0679, Oslo, Norway
Tel.: (47) 22 08 00 50
Web Site: http://www.arjohuntleigh.com
Medical & Surgical Equipment Whslr
N.A.I.C.S.: 423450

ArjoHuntleigh Polska Sp. z.o.o. (2)
ul Ks Wawrzyniaka 2, Komorniki, 62-052, Poznan, Poland
Tel.: (48) 616621552
Web Site: https://www.arjo.com
Sales Range: $125-149.9 Million
Medical & Surgical Equipment Whslr
N.A.I.C.S.: 423450
Roman Sobstyl *(Dir-HR)*

ArjoHuntleigh SAS (2)
2 Avenue Alcide de Gasperi CS 70133, BP 133, Roncq, 59436, France
Tel.: (33) 320 281 313
Web Site: http://www.arjohuntleigh.com
Medical & Surgical Equipment Whslr
N.A.I.C.S.: 423450
Frank Robeers *(Pres)*

ArjoHuntleigh Singapore Pte Ltd (2)
20 Bendemeer Road 06-03 Cyberhub Building, Singapore, 339914, Singapore
Tel.: (65) 6293 3387
Web Site: http://www.arjohuntleigh.com
Sales Range: $25-49.9 Million
Medical & Surgical Equipment Whslr
N.A.I.C.S.: 423450
Creig Roddy *(Mng Dir)*

ArjoHuntleigh Spa (2)
Via Tor Vergata 432, 00133, Rome, Italy
Tel.: (39) 06 87426214
Web Site: http://www.arjohuntleigh.com
Medical & Surgical Equipment Distr
N.A.I.C.S.: 423450

ArjoHuntleigh UK and Ireland (2)
ArjoHuntleigh House Houghton Hall Business Park, Houghton Regis, LU5 5XF, Bedfordshire, United Kingdom
Tel.: (44) 1582 745 700
Web Site: http://www.arjohuntleigh.com
Medical & Surgical Equipment Whslr
N.A.I.C.S.: 423450
Paul Lyon *(Reg Pres-Intl Emerging Markets)*

ArjoHuntleigh s.r.o. (2)
Hl inky 11, Brno, 603 00, Czech Republic
Tel.: (420) 5 49 25 42 52
Web Site: http://www.arjohuntleigh.com
Sales Range: $25-49.9 Million
Emp.: 11
Medical & Surgical Equipment Distr
N.A.I.C.S.: 423450
Mireille Mazard *(Gen Mgr)*

Subsidiary (US):

Arjohuntleigh Inc (2)
2349 W Lk St Ste 250, Addison, IL 60101
Tel.: (630) 785-4490
Web Site: http://www.arjohuntleigh.com

AND PRIVATE COMPANIES — GETINGE AB

Medical & Surgical Equipment Whslr
N.A.I.C.S.: 423450
Rick Lytle *(Pres-North America)*

Subsidiary (Non-US):

Arjohuntleigh International AB (2)
Hanf Michelse Nsgatan No 10, 241 38, Malmo, Sweden
Tel.: (46) 41364500
Medical Equipment Whslr
N.A.I.C.S.: 423450
Harald Stock *(Gen Mgr)*

Huntleigh (SST) Ltd (2)
Houghton Hall Business Park, Houghton Regis, LU5 5XF, Bedfordshire, United Kingdom
Tel.: (44) 1582 413 104
Web Site: http://www.arjohuntleigh.com
Emp.: 200
Investment Management Service
N.A.I.C.S.: 523999
Avril Forde *(Mng Dir)*

Huntleigh Diagnostics Ltd (2)
35 Portmanmoor Road, Cardiff, CF24 5HN, United Kingdom
Tel.: (44) 29 2048 5885
Web Site: http://www.huntleigh-diagnostics.co.uk
Emp.: 140
Medical Equipment Distr
N.A.I.C.S.: 423450
Jan Mouncher *(Mgr-HR)*

Huntleigh Holdings BV. (2)
Biezenwei 21, 4004 MB, Tiel, Netherlands
Tel.: (31) 344 64 08 00
Investment Management Service
N.A.I.C.S.: 523999

Huntleigh International Holdings Ltd. (2)
Houghton Regis, Dunstable, LU55XF, Bedfordshire, United Kingdom
Tel.: (44) 1582 413104
Web Site: http://www.arjohuntleigh.com
Emp.: 200
Investment Management Service
N.A.I.C.S.: 523999
Nicole Mc Glennon *(Mng Dir)*

Huntleigh Nesbit Evans Healthcare GmbH (2)
Industriering Ost 66, Kempen, 47906, Germany
Tel.: (49) 2152 5511 10
Web Site: http://www.nesbitevans.de
Sales Range: $25-49.9 Million
Emp.: 10
Medical & Surgical Equipment Distr
N.A.I.C.S.: 423450
Juergen Gatzemeier *(Mgr-Natl Sls)*

Huntleigh Renray Ltd. (2)
Road Five Winsford Industrial Estate, Winsford, Cheshire, United Kingdom
Tel.: (44) 1606 593 456
Household Furniture Mfr
N.A.I.C.S.: 337122
Graham Silman *(Mng Dir)*

Huntleigh Technology (Engineering) Ltd (2)
Arjohuntleigh House Houghton Hall Business Park Houghton Regis, Dunstable, LU5 5XF, Bedfordshire, United Kingdom
Tel.: (44) 1582 413 104
Bed & Mattress Mfr
N.A.I.C.S.: 337910

Huntleigh Technology Ltd (2)
ArjoHuntleigh House Houghton Hall Business Park Houghton, Bedford, LU5 5XF, United Kingdom
Tel.: (44) 15 8241 3104
Medical & Surgical Equipment Mfr & Whslr
N.A.I.C.S.: 339112

Atrium Australia-Pacific Rim Pty. Ltd (1)
Level 6 579 Harris Street, Ultimo, 2007, NSW, Australia
Tel.: (61) 2 8272 3100
Medical & Surgical Equipment Whslr
N.A.I.C.S.: 423450

Atrium Europe BV (1)
Oscar Romerolaan 3, 3641, Hilversum, Netherlands
Tel.: (31) 297230420
Web Site: http://www.maquet.com
Medical & Surgical Equipment Whslr
N.A.I.C.S.: 423450
Rob Stoopman *(Gen Mgr)*

Atrium Medical India Pvt Ltd (1)
Old No 54 New No 11 NRD Tower 3rd Floor First Avenue J N Road, Ashok Nagar, Chennai, 600 083, India
Tel.: (91) 44 24719390
Web Site: http://www.atriummed.com
Medical & Surgical Equipment Whslr
N.A.I.C.S.: 423450

Biocleanse Ltd. (1)
Unit 1 3 Western Campus Starling Way, Strathclyde Business Park, Bellshill, Ml4 3PU, United Kingdom
Tel.: (44) 1698749941
Web Site: https://biocleansers.co.uk
Cleaning Service
N.A.I.C.S.: 561740

Dalian Medical Equipment Holding BV (1)
Biezenwei 21, 4004 MB, Tiel, Netherlands
Tel.: (31) 344640800
Investment Management Service
N.A.I.C.S.: 523999

Dentisan Ltd. (1)
Bateman Street, Derby, DE23 8JL, United Kingdom
Tel.: (44) 1332268526
Web Site: https://dentisan.co.uk
Dental Product Distr
N.A.I.C.S.: 423450

Fluoptics Imaging Inc. (1)
185 Alewife Brook Pkwy Ste 210, Cambridge, MA 02138
Tel.: (561) 843-0220
Web Site: https://fluoptics.us
Medical Equipment Mfr & Distr
N.A.I.C.S.: 334510

Fluoptics S.A.S. (1)
44 rue des Berges, 38000, Grenoble, France
Tel.: (33) 485870671
Web Site: https://fluoptics.com
Medical Equipment Mfr & Distr
N.A.I.C.S.: 334510

Getinge (Shanghai) Trading Co. Ltd. (1)
No 3 Lane 128 Lin Hong Road, Shanghai, 200335, China
Tel.: (86) 2161973999
Web Site: http://www.getinge.com
Medical & Surgical Equipment Whslr
N.A.I.C.S.: 423450

Getinge (Suzhou) Co. Ltd. (1)
No 158 Fang Zhou Road Suzhou Industrial Park, Suzhou, 215024, Jiangsu, China
Tel.: (86) 512 6283 8966
Sales Range: $50-74.9 Million
Emp.: 100
Medical & Surgical Equipment Whslr
N.A.I.C.S.: 423450

Getinge Arjo A/S (1)
Enebak VN 117 D, Oslo, 680, Norway (100%)
Tel.: (47) 23051180
Sales Range: $25-49.9 Million
Emp.: 17
Provider of Medical Equipment
N.A.I.C.S.: 339112

Getinge Arjo Holding Netherlands B.V. (1)
De Blomboogerd 8, 4003BX, Tiel, Netherlands
Tel.: (31) 344640800
Sales Range: $75-99.9 Million
Emp.: 160
Medical & Surgical Equipment Whslr
N.A.I.C.S.: 423450

Getinge Australia Pty Ltd. (1)
Unit1 205 Queens Port Road, Bulimba, Murarrie, 4172, QL, Australia (100%)
Tel.: (61) 733993311
Sales Range: $25-49.9 Million
Emp.: 90
Provider of Sterilization Equipment
N.A.I.C.S.: 339114
Richard Hili *(Head-Fin)*

Getinge B.V. (1)
Fruiteniersstraat 27, 3334 KA, Zwijndrecht, Netherlands
Tel.: (31) 78 610 24 33
Web Site: http://www.getinge.com
Medical Equipment Whslr
N.A.I.C.S.: 423450

Getinge Canada Ltd. (1)
90 Matheson Blvd W Suite 300, Mississauga, L5R 3R3, ON, Canada (100%)
Tel.: (905) 752-3300
Web Site: http://www.getingeusa.com
Sales Range: $25-49.9 Million
Emp.: 45
Hospital Equipment Distr
N.A.I.C.S.: 423450

Getinge Cetrea A/S (1)
Brendstrupgardsvej 21F, Aarhus, Denmark
Tel.: (45) 38400570
Web Site: https://www.cetrea.com
Pharmaceuticals Mfr
N.A.I.C.S.: 325412

Getinge Colombia SAS (1)
Edificio Astoria Carrera 16 No 95 - 70 Oficina 701, Bogota, Colombia
Tel.: (57) 17438124
Pharmaceuticals Mfr
N.A.I.C.S.: 325412

Getinge Czech Republic, s.r.o. (1)
Na Strzi 1702/65, 140 00, Prague, Czech Republic
Tel.: (420) 225092302
Web Site: http://www.getinge.com
Sales Range: $25-49.9 Million
Emp.: 15
Medical & Surgical Equipment Whslr
N.A.I.C.S.: 423450

Getinge D.S.E. NV (1)
Evenbroekveld 16, 9420, Erpe-Mere, Belgium (100%)
Tel.: (32) 33542865
Sales Range: $1-9.9 Million
Emp.: 20
Sterilization Equipment Mfr
N.A.I.C.S.: 339113
Bettina Quaedvlieg *(Mng Dir)*

Getinge Danmark A/S (1)
Industriparken 44B 1st floor, 2750, Ballerup, DK, Denmark
Tel.: (45) 45932727
Web Site: https://www2.getinge.com
Sales Range: $25-49.9 Million
Emp.: 30
Provider of Medical Equipment
N.A.I.C.S.: 339113
Oldem Eddisson *(Mng Dir)*

Getinge Deutschland GmbH (1)
Kehler Strasse 31, 76437, Rastatt, Germany
Tel.: (49) 72229320
Web Site: https://www2.getinge.com
Pharmaceuticals Mfr
N.A.I.C.S.: 325412

Getinge Disinfection AB (1)
Ljungadalsgatan 11, PO Box 1505, 351 15, Vaxjo, Sweden (100%)
Tel.: (46) 103359800
Web Site: http://www.getinge.com
Sales Range: $50-74.9 Million
Emp.: 220
Mfr of Sterilization Equipment
N.A.I.C.S.: 339114
Marcus Johansson *(Mng Dir)*

Getinge Financial Services GmbH (1)
kehler Str 31, 76437, Rastatt, Germany
Tel.: (49) 72229320
Pharmaceutical Product Mfr & Distr
N.A.I.C.S.: 325412

Getinge Finland Oy (1)
(100%)
Tel.: (358) 96824120
Web Site: http://www.getinge.com
Sales Range: $1-9.9 Million
Emp.: 30
Medical Equipment & Supplies
N.A.I.C.S.: 339113
Raisa Vaahtersalo *(Gen Mgr)*

Getinge France SAS (1)
7 Ave Du Canada, BP 49, 91942, Courtaboeuf, Cedex, France (100%)
Tel.: (33) 164868900
Web Site: http://www.getinge.com
Sales Range: $25-49.9 Million
Emp.: 100
Mfr of Sterilization Equipment
N.A.I.C.S.: 339114

Subsidiary (Domestic):

Lancer S.N.C. (2)
30 Blvd De L Industrie, FR 31170, Tournefeuille, France (100%)
Tel.: (33) 561151111
Web Site: http://www.lancer.fr
Provider of High-Performance Washing Systems for Laboratory & Medical Use
N.A.I.C.S.: 339113

Subsidiary (Non-US):

Lancer Holland B.V. (3)
Elekoepparhaeda 11 B, Postbus 33, NL 6651 PA, Wamel, Netherlands (100%)
Tel.: (31) 487518088
Web Site: http://www.lancer.nl
Sales Range: $25-49.9 Million
Emp.: 6
Mfr of High-Performance Washing Systems for Medical & Laboratory Use
N.A.I.C.S.: 339113

Subsidiary (US):

Lancer USA Inc. (3)
1150 Emma Oaks Ste 140, Lake Mary, FL 32746 (100%)
Tel.: (407) 327-8488
Web Site: http://www.lancer.com
Sales Range: $25-49.9 Million
Emp.: 30
Glassware Washers Sales
N.A.I.C.S.: 325412

Getinge Group Hong Kong Ltd. (1)
26/F Port 33 33 Tseuk Luk Street, San Po Kong, Kowloon, China (Hong Kong)
Tel.: (852) 22076111
Pharmaceuticals Mfr
N.A.I.C.S.: 325412

Getinge Group Logistics Americas, LLC (1)
45 Barbour Pond Dr, Wayne, NJ 07470
Tel.: (973) 709-7000
Pharmaceutical Product Mfr & Distr
N.A.I.C.S.: 325412

Getinge Group Middle East FZ-LLC (1)
19th Floor HQ Complex - North Tower Dubai Science Park, Dubai, United Arab Emirates
Tel.: (971) 44470963
Pharmaceuticals Mfr
N.A.I.C.S.: 325412

Getinge Group Portugal Unipessoal Lda. (1)
Rua Poeta Bocage 2 - 2 G, Telheiras, Lisbon, Portugal
Tel.: (351) 214189815
Pharmaceuticals Mfr
N.A.I.C.S.: 325412

Getinge Group South East Europe d.o.o (1)
Spanskih Boraca 3, Belgrade, Serbia
Tel.: (381) 117856370
Pharmaceuticals Mfr
N.A.I.C.S.: 325412

Getinge Group Spain SL (1)
C/Marie Curie 5 Edificio Alfa Planta 6 oficina 6 1-6 2, Rivas Vacia, 28521, Madrid, Spain
Tel.: (34) 916781652
Pharmaceuticals Mfr
N.A.I.C.S.: 325412

Getinge Group Taiwan Co., Ltd. (1)
Rm 8 6F No 288 Sec 6 Civic Blvd, Xinyi Dist, Taipei, 110, Taiwan
Tel.: (886) 287582738
Pharmaceuticals Mfr
N.A.I.C.S.: 325412

Getinge Healthcare SAS (1)

GETINGE AB / INTERNATIONAL PUBLIC

Getinge AB—(Continued)
7 avenue du Canada, 91978, Les Ulis, France
Tel.: (33) 1 64 86 89 00
Web Site: http://www.getinge.com
Sales Range: $25-49.9 Million
Emp.: 50
Medical & Surgical Equipment Whslr
N.A.I.C.S.: 423450
Francois Pointurier (Pres)

Getinge Hong Kong Company Ltd. (1)
51 Kwai Cheong Road, Hong Kong, China (Hong Kong)
Tel.: (852) 2207 6328
Web Site: http://www.getinge.com
Medical & Surgical Equipment Whslr
N.A.I.C.S.: 423450

Getinge IC Production Poland Sp. z o.o. (1)
Ul Szkolna 30, 62-064, Plewiska, Poland
Tel.: (48) 616309901
Pharmaceuticals Mfr
N.A.I.C.S.: 325412

Getinge IT Solutions GmbH (1)
Sudportal 5, 22848, Norderstedt, Germany
Tel.: (49) 40514350
Pharmaceuticals Mfr
N.A.I.C.S.: 325412

Getinge IT Solutions Ltd. (1)
14-15 Burford Way Boldon Business Park, Tyne and Wear, Sunderland, NE35 9PZ, United Kingdom
Tel.: (44) 1915196200
Pharmaceuticals Mfr
N.A.I.C.S.: 325412

Getinge IT-Solution Aps (1)
Amaliegade 4, Copenhagen, 1256, Denmark
Tel.: (45) 33 33 88 55
Web Site: http://www.tdoc.com
Emp.: 40
Medical & Surgical Equipment Whslr
N.A.I.C.S.: 423450
Michael Lunau (Pres)

Getinge Iberica S.L. (1)
Parque Empresarial Rivas Futura C/Marie Curie 5, Edificio Alfa Planta 6 oficina 6 1-6 2, 28521, Rivas-Vaciamadrid, Spain (100%)
Tel.: (34) 91 678 2626
Web Site: http://www.skarhamn.getinge.com
Sales Range: $25-49.9 Million
Emp.: 11
Hospital Equipments Mfr
N.A.I.C.S.: 339113

Getinge India Pvt Ltd. (1)
203-204 Fulcrum B wing Sahar Road Andheri East, Mumbai, 400099, India
Tel.: (91) 2262332100
Sales Range: $25-49.9 Million
Emp.: 32
Medical & Surgical Equipment Whslr
N.A.I.C.S.: 423450
Anant Agarwal (Pres)

Getinge Infection Control AB (1)
Ekebergsvagen 26, Getinge, 305 75, Sweden
Tel.: (46) 10 335 0000
Web Site: http://www.getingegroup.com
Sales Range: $250-299.9 Million
Emp.: 500
Medical & Surgical Equipment Distr
N.A.I.C.S.: 423450
Anders Grahm (Pres)

Getinge International AB (1)
Ekebergsvagen 26, PO Box 69, Getinge, 305 05, Sweden
Tel.: (46) 10 335 0000
Web Site: http://www.getingegroup.com
Emp.: 500
Medical & Surgical Equipment Distr
N.A.I.C.S.: 423450
Hansson John (Pres)

Getinge International Asia Ltd. (1)
29/F Tower 1 Kowloon Commerce Centre 51 Kwai Cheong Road, 290916, Kwai Chung, China (Hong Kong)
Tel.: (852) 2393 9511
Web Site: http://www.getinge.com
Emp.: 20
Medical & Surgical Equipment Distr
N.A.I.C.S.: 423450

Getinge Ireland Ltd. (1)
B6 Calmount Park, Ballymount, Dublin, Ireland
Tel.: (353) 14260032
Pharmaceuticals Mfr
N.A.I.C.S.: 325412

Getinge Italia S.r.l. (1)
Via Gozzano 14, 20092, Cinisello Balsamo, MI, Italy
Tel.: (39) 026111351
Health Care Srvices
N.A.I.C.S.: 622110

Getinge Japan KK (1)
Toshin Takanawa Bldg 9F 3113 Takanawa, Minato-ku, Tokyo, 108-0074, Japan
Tel.: (81) 3 5791 7560
Web Site: http://www.getinge.co.jp
Medical & Surgical Equipment Whslr
N.A.I.C.S.: 423450

Getinge Korea Co. Ltd. (1)
13F KeumKang Building 304 Bongeunsa-ro, Gangnam-gu, Seoul, 135916, Korea (South)
Tel.: (82) 2 567 1240
Web Site: http://www.getinge.com
Sales Range: $50-74.9 Million
Emp.: 2
Medical & Surgical Equipment Whslr
N.A.I.C.S.: 423450

Getinge La Calhene France SA (1)
1 rue du Comte de Donegal, 41100, Vendome, France
Tel.: (33) 25 473 4747
Web Site: https://www.lacalhene.com
Emp.: 150
Medical & Surgical Equipment Whslr
N.A.I.C.S.: 423450
Girard Thierry (Gen Mgr)

Getinge Lancer SAS (1)
30 Boulevard de lIndustrie - ZI de Pahin, 31170, Tourneteuille, France
Tel.: (33) 5 61 15 11 11
Web Site: http://www.lancer.fr
Sales Range: $25-49.9 Million
Emp.: 160
Cleaning Service Provider
N.A.I.C.S.: 561740
Boris Leonard (Pres)

Getinge Letting AB (1)
Ekebergsvagen 26, Box 69, 310 44, Getinge, Sweden
Tel.: (46) 35155500
Web Site: http://www.getinge.com
Sales Range: $200-249.9 Million
Emp.: 500
Investment Management Service
N.A.I.C.S.: 523999
Alex Myers (CEO)

Getinge Life Science Americas (1)
1150 Emma Oaks Tr Ste 140, Lake Mary, FL 32746
Tel.: (800) 475-9040
Web Site: http://www.getinge.com
Medical & Surgical Equipment Whslr
N.A.I.C.S.: 423450

Getinge Life Sciences SAS (1)
30 Boulevard de l'Industrie Zi Pahin, 31170, Tourneteuille, France
Tel.: (33) 5 61 15 34 90
Web Site: http://www.getinge.com
Medical & Surgical Equipment Whslr
N.A.I.C.S.: 423450

Getinge Linac Technologies SA (1)
16 Rue Nicolas Appert, 91400, Orsay, France
Tel.: (33) 1 69 35 24 00
Sales Range: $25-49.9 Million
Emp.: 10
Electromedical Apparatus Mfr
N.A.I.C.S.: 334510

Getinge Medical India Pvt Ltd. (1)
203 and 204 B Wing Fulcrum Sahar Road, Andheri E, Mumbai, 400 099, India
Tel.: (91) 2262332100
Pharmaceuticals Mfr
N.A.I.C.S.: 325412

Getinge Medical Korea Co., Ltd. (1)
13F KeumKang Building 304 Bongeunsa-ro, Gangnam-gu, Seoul, Korea (South)
Tel.: (82) 25671240
Pharmaceuticals Mfr
N.A.I.C.S.: 325412

Getinge Medikal Sistemler San ve Tic A.S
Mah Kayisdagi Cad Allianz Plaza No 1 Inner Door 96, Kucukbakkalkoy Atasehir, Istanbul, Turkiye
Tel.: (90) 2164446678
Pharmaceuticals Mfr
N.A.I.C.S.: 325412

Getinge Middle East & Africa (1)
G005 Nucleotide Complex Dubai Biotechnology & Research Park, PO Box 214742, Dubai, 214742, United Arab Emirates
Tel.: (971) 4 447 0941
Sales Range: $25-49.9 Million
Emp.: 50
Medical & Surgical Equipment Whslr
N.A.I.C.S.: 423450

Getinge Norge AS (1)
Enebakkveien 150, 0680, Oslo, Norway
Tel.: (47) 23035200
Web Site: http://www.getinge.com
Sales Range: $25-49.9 Million
Emp.: 20
Medical Equipment Whslr
N.A.I.C.S.: 423450

Getinge Odelga GmbH (1)
Perfektastrasse 87, 1230, Vienna, Austria
Tel.: (43) 1 8958080
Web Site: http://www.getinge.com
Sales Range: $50-74.9 Million
Emp.: 10
Medical & Surgical Equipment Distr
N.A.I.C.S.: 423450
Georg Fiedler (Pres)

Getinge Osterreich GmbH (1)
Lembockgasse 49 Haus 2 Stiege D, 1230, Vienna, Austria
Tel.: (43) 186514870
Pharmaceuticals Mfr
N.A.I.C.S.: 325412

Getinge Poland Sp. z.o.o. (1)
Ul Zwirki i Wigury 18, 02-092, Warsaw, Poland
Tel.: (48) 22 882 0644
Web Site: https://www2.getinge.com
Sales Range: $25-49.9 Million
Emp.: 24
Provider of Sterilization Equipment
N.A.I.C.S.: 339114

Getinge Polska Sp. z o.o. (1)
Ul Zwirki i Wigury 18, 02-092, Warsaw, Poland
Tel.: (48) 228820644
Pharmaceuticals Mfr
N.A.I.C.S.: 325412

Getinge Production France SAS (1)
ZI de Courtaboeuf 7 Avenue du Canada, BP 49, 91942, Les Ulis, France
Tel.: (33) 1 64 86 89 00
Web Site: http://www.getinge.com
Sales Range: $25-49.9 Million
Emp.: 100
Medical & Surgical Equipment Whslr
N.A.I.C.S.: 423450
Leroy Stephane (Mgr)

Getinge S.p.A. (1)
Via Gozzano 14, 20092, Cinisello Balsamo, Italy
Tel.: (39) 02 611 1351
Web Site: https://www.getinge.com
Medical & Surgical Equipment Whslr
N.A.I.C.S.: 423450

Getinge Shared Services Sp. z o.o. (1)
Klimeckiego 1, 30-705, Krakow, Poland
Tel.: (48) 123854222
Pharmaceutical Product Mfr & Distr
N.A.I.C.S.: 325412

Getinge Singapore Pte. Ltd. (1)
20 Bendemeer Road 06-01 / 02 BS Bendemeer Center, Singapore, 339914, Singapore
Tel.: (65) 6 296 1992

Web Site: https://www.getinge.com
Sales Range: $25-49.9 Million
Emp.: 18
Medical & Surgical Equipment Whslr
N.A.I.C.S.: 423450
Jacob Petersen (Pres)

Getinge Skarhamn AB (1)
Industrivagen 5, Skarhamn, 47131, Sweden (100%)
Tel.: (46) 304600200
Web Site: http://www.skarhamn.getinge.com
Sales Range: $25-49.9 Million
Emp.: 37
Mfr of Sterilizers
N.A.I.C.S.: 339112
Gert Linder (CEO & Mng Dir)

Getinge Slovakia s.r.o. (1)
Pribinova 25, Bratislava, Slovakia
Tel.: (421) 233554150
Pharmaceuticals Mfr
N.A.I.C.S.: 325412

Getinge Sourcing LLC (1)
1777 E Henrietta Rd, Rochester, NY 14623
Tel.: (585) 475-1400
Surgical & Medical Instrument Mfr
N.A.I.C.S.: 339112
David Pritchard (Pres)

Getinge South Africa (Pty) Ltd. (1)
PO Box 48492, Hercules, Pretoria, ZA-0030, Kirkney, South Africa (100%)
Tel.: (27) 123721370
Web Site: http://www.skarhamn.getinge.com
Sales Range: $25-49.9 Million
Emp.: 19
Hospital Equipments Mfr
N.A.I.C.S.: 339113

Getinge South East Asia Pte. Ltd. (1)
20 Bendemeer Road 06-01/02 BS Bendemeer Centre, Singapore, 339914, Singapore
Tel.: (65) 62961992
Pharmaceuticals Mfr
N.A.I.C.S.: 325412

Getinge Stericool Medikal Aletler San. Ve Tic. A.S (1)
Bestepe Mahallesi Nergiz Sokak No 7/2 Lc Kapi No 71, Yenimhalle, Ankara, Turkiye
Tel.: (90) 3123873940
Pharmaceutical Product Mfr & Distr
N.A.I.C.S.: 325412

Getinge Sterilization AB (1)
Ekebergsvagen 26, PO Box 69, 30575, Getinge, Sweden (100%)
Tel.: (46) 103350000
Web Site: http://www.getingegroup.com
Sales Range: $100-124.9 Million
Emp.: 500
Sterilization Equipment Mfr
N.A.I.C.S.: 339113

Getinge Sverige AB (1)
Ekebergsvagen 26, PO Box 69, 305 75, Getinge, Sweden (100%)
Tel.: (46) 103350000
Web Site: https://www.getinge.com
Sales Range: $100-124.9 Million
Emp.: 500
Sterilization Equipment Mfr
N.A.I.C.S.: 339113

Getinge Treasury AB (1)
Ekebergsvagen 26, 305 75, Getinge, Halland, Sweden
Tel.: (46) 103350000
Sales Range: $150-199.9 Million
Emp.: 500
Pharmaceutical Products Distr
N.A.I.C.S.: 424210

Getinge Treasury Ireland DAC (1)
3 Harbourmaster Place IFSC, Dublin, IE-D01K8F1, Ireland
Tel.: (353) 863805182
Medical Device Mfr & Distr
N.A.I.C.S.: 325412

Getinge UK Ltd. (1)
Orchard Way Calladine Park, Sutton in Ashfield, NG17 1JU, Notts, United Kingdom (100%)
Tel.: (44) 16 2351 0033
Web Site: http://www.getinge.com

AND PRIVATE COMPANIES

Sales Range: $25-49.9 Million
Emp.: 120
Sterilization & Infectious Control Equipment Mfr
N.A.I.C.S.: 621511

Getinge USA Sales, LLC (1)
1 Geoffrey Way, Wayne, NJ 07470
Pharmaceuticals Product Mfr
N.A.I.C.S.: 325412

Getinge USA, Inc. (1)
1777 E Henrietta Rd, Rochester, NY 14623 **(100%)**
Tel.: (585) 475-1400
Web Site: http://www.getingeusa.com
Sales Range: $200-249.9 Million
Emp.: 900
Sterility Assurance Systems Examining & Operating Equipment & Related Accessories & Consumables Mfr
N.A.I.C.S.: 339113
Andrew Cserey *(Pres & CEO)*

Subsidiary (Domestic):

Atrium Medical Corporation (2)
5 Wentworth Dr, Hudson, NH 03051
Tel.: (603) 880-1433
Web Site: http://www.gettinge.com
Sales Range: $200-249.9 Million
Emp.: 700
Medical Device Mfr
N.A.I.C.S.: 339112
Gary Sufat *(CFO & Exec VP-Fin)*

Branch (Domestic):

Getinge USA, Inc. - Florida (2)
8200 NW 27th St Ste 107, Doral, FL 33122-1902
Tel.: (305) 447-9144
Sales Range: $25-49.9 Million
Emp.: 4
N.A.I.C.S.: 339114

Getinge Vertrieb und Service GmbH (1)
Kehler Strasse 31, 76437, Rastatt, Germany
Tel.: (49) 7222 932 306
Web Site: http://www.getinge.com
Sales Range: $50-74.9 Million
Emp.: 65
Medical & Surgical Equipment Whslr
N.A.I.C.S.: 423450
Christian Klein *(Gen Mgr)*

Getinge Vietnam Company Ltd. (1)
Floor 6 Yoco Bldg 41, Nguyen Thi Minh Khai Ben Nghe Ward District 1, Ho Chi Minh City, Vietnam
Tel.: (84) 2838243391
Pharmaceuticals Product Mfr
N.A.I.C.S.: 325412

Getinge do Brasil Equipamentos Medicos Ltda. (1)
Av Manuel Bandeira 291 - Bloco B - 2 Andar Conjuntos 33 E 34, Vila Leopoldina, Sao Paulo, 05317-020, Brazil
Tel.: (55) 1126087400
Pharmaceuticals Mfr
N.A.I.C.S.: 325412

Getinge-La Calhene USA Inc (1)
1325 Frandsen Ave S, Rush City, MN 55069
Tel.: (320) 358-4713
Web Site: http://www.getinge-lacalhene.com
Emp.: 14
Medical & Surgical Equipment Whslr
N.A.I.C.S.: 423450
Brian Hudoba *(CEO)*

Getinge-Maquet Germany Holding GmbH (1)
Kehler Str 31, Rastatt, 76437, Baden-Wurttemberg, Germany
Tel.: (49) 7222 9320
Web Site: http://www.maquet.com
Sales Range: $700-749.9 Million
Emp.: 1,200
Investment Management Service
N.A.I.C.S.: 523999
Heinz Jaqui *(Mng Dir)*

HNE Huntleigh Nesbit Evans Health care GmbH. (1)
Im Hulsenfeld 19, Hilden, 40721, Germany

Tel.: (49) 2103971 10
Medical & Surgical Equipment Whslr
N.A.I.C.S.: 423450

Healthmark Industries Co. Inc. (1)
22522 E 9 Mile Rd, Saint Clair Shores, MI 48080
Tel.: (586) 774-7600
Web Site: http://www.hmark.com
Sales Range: $1-9.9 Million
Emp.: 22
Medical, Dental & Hospital Equipment & Supplies Merchant Whslr
N.A.I.C.S.: 423450
Mark Basile *(Pres)*

Intervascular Sarl. (1)
Z I Athelia I, La Ciotat, 13705, France
Tel.: (33) 4 42 08 46 46
Web Site: http://www.maquet.com
Emp.: 200
Surgical Appliance Mfr
N.A.I.C.S.: 339113
Herze Lazarz *(Mgr)*

Lancer Inc. (1)
135 S Lancer Rd, Star, NC 27356
Tel.: (910) 428-2181
Web Site: https://www.lancerfurniture.com
Furniture Mfr
N.A.I.C.S.: 337121

Lancer Sales USA Inc (1)
1150 Emma Oaks Trl Ste 140, Lake Mary, FL 32746-7120
Tel.: (407) 327-8488
Web Site: http://www.lancer.com
Emp.: 20
Glassware Washer Distr
N.A.I.C.S.: 423490

Lancer Uk Ltd. (1)
1 Pembroke Avenue Waterbeach, Cambridge, CB25 9QP, United Kingdom
Tel.: (44) 1223 861665
Web Site: http://www.getinge.com
Emp.: 100
Glassware Washer Distr
N.A.I.C.S.: 423490
Nick Satchell *(Pres)*

MAQUET GmbH & Co. KG (1)
Kehler Strasse 31, 76437, Rastatt, Germany **(100%)**
Tel.: (49) 72229320
Web Site: http://www.maquet.com
Sales Range: $1-4.9 Billion
Emp.: 5,000
Surgical & Medical Equipment Developers
N.A.I.C.S.: 339112

Subsidiary (Non-US):

MAQUET & ALM Belgique N.V. (2)
Assesteenweg 117 Bldg 3, 1740, Ternat, Belgium
Tel.: (32) 24678585
Web Site: http://www.maquet.com
Sales Range: $25-49.9 Million
Emp.: 33
Medical Equipment
N.A.I.C.S.: 339112
Patrick Blyau *(Gen Mgr)*

MAQUET (Shanghai) Medical Equipment Co., Ltd. (2)
20F Building 1 188 Ruby Road, Changning District, Shanghai, 201103, China
Tel.: (86) 2161973999
Medical & Surgical Equipment Whslr
N.A.I.C.S.: 423450

Subsidiary (Domestic):

MAQUET Cardiovascular GmbH (2)
Kehlerstrasse 31, 64625, Rastatt, Germany
Tel.: (49) 625117050
Web Site: http://www.ca.maquet.com
Sales Range: $10-24.9 Million
Emp.: 3
Minimally Invasive Surgical Procedures
N.A.I.C.S.: 339112

Subsidiary (Non-US):

MAQUET Critical Care AB (2)
Rontgenvagen 2, Box 6108, 171 54, Solna, Sweden
Tel.: (46) 103357300
Surgical & Medical Instrument Mfr
N.A.I.C.S.: 339112

Johan Hagstrom *(CFO)*

MAQUET Italia S.p.A. (2)
Via Gozzano 14, Cinisello Balsamo, 200 92, Milan, Italy
Tel.: (39) 026111351
Web Site: http://www.ca.maquet.com
Sales Range: $10-24.9 Million
Emp.: 100
Polyester, Collagen-Coated Knitted & Woven Vascular Grafts, Patches & Graft Stents Supplier
N.A.I.C.S.: 339112

MAQUET SA (2)
Parc de Limere Avenue de la Pomme de Pin Ardon, Orleans, 45074, France
Tel.: (33) 238258888
Sales Range: $10-24.9 Million
Emp.: 250
Polyester, Collagen-Coated Knitted & Woven Vascular Grafts, Patches & Graft Stents Supplier
N.A.I.C.S.: 339113
Tiffin Leroy *(Gen Mgr)*

Subsidiary (US):

MAQUET, Inc. (2)
45 Barbour Pond Dr, Wayne, NJ 07470
Tel.: (973) 709-7654
Web Site: http://www.maquet.com
Emp.: 50
Surgical & Medical Instruments Mfr & Sales
N.A.I.C.S.: 334510
Joseph Knight *(VP-Surgical Workplaces Sls)*

Subsidiary (Domestic):

MAQUET Cardiovascular LLC (3)
45 Barbour Pond Dr, Wayne, NJ 07470
Tel.: (973) 709-7000
Web Site: http://www.maquet.com
Sales Range: $75-99.9 Million
Vascular Graft Mfr
N.A.I.C.S.: 339113

Subsidiary (Non-US):

Artema Medical AB (4)
Rissneleden 136, Sundbyberg, 174 57, Sweden
Tel.: (46) 855554100
Web Site: http://www.artema.se
Sales Range: $10-24.9 Million
Emp.: 40
Medical Breathing Gas Analyzers Mfr
N.A.I.C.S.: 334516

Subsidiary (Domestic):

Datascope Investment Corp. (4)
1300 Macarthur Blvd, Mahwah, NJ 07430-2052
Tel.: (201) 391-8100
Sales Range: $10-24.9 Million
Emp.: 8
Investment Operations
N.A.I.C.S.: 523999

Genisphere Inc. (4)
2801 Sterling Dr, Hatfield, PA 19440
Tel.: (215) 996-3002
Web Site: http://www.genisphere.com
Emp.: 15
DNA Test Kit Mfr
N.A.I.C.S.: 541380
Jim Kadushin *(Dir-Ops)*

Subsidiary (Domestic):

MAQUET Medical Systems USA LLC (3)
1300 Macarthur Blvd, Mahwah, NJ 07430
Tel.: (201) 995-8700
Medical Equipment Mfr
N.A.I.C.S.: 334510

Maquet Cardiovascular US Sales, LLC (3)
45 Barbour Pond Dr, Wayne, NJ 07470
Tel.: (973) 709-7000
Surgical & Medical Instrument Whslr
N.A.I.C.S.: 423450

Subsidiary (Non-US):

Maquet (Suzhou) Co. Ltd. (2)
No 158 Fangzhou Road Suzhou Industrial Park, Suzhou, 215024, China

GETINGE AB

Tel.: (86) 51262839880
Web Site: http://www.maquet.com
Sales Range: $25-49.9 Million
Emp.: 130
Surgical & Medical Instrument Mfr
N.A.I.C.S.: 339112
Florian Mond *(Pres)*

Maquet Australia Pty Ltd (2)
9/35 Paringa Road, Murarrie, Brisbane, 4172, QLD, Australia
Tel.: (61) 7 3339 3900
Web Site: http://www.maquet.com
Sales Range: $25-49.9 Million
Emp.: 25
Surgical & Medical Instrument Mfr
N.A.I.C.S.: 339112

Maquet Belgium NV (2)
Evenbroekveld 16, Erpe-Mere, 9420, Belgium
Tel.: (32) 24 67 85 85
Web Site: http://www.maquet.com
Sales Range: $25-49.9 Million
Emp.: 30
Surgical & Medical Instrument Mfr
N.A.I.C.S.: 339112
Rob Geraedts *(Mng Dir)*

Subsidiary (Domestic):

Maquet Bistro GmbH. (2)
Kehler Str 31, Rastatt, 76437, Baden-Wurttemberg, Germany
Tel.: (49) 7222 9320
Medical & Surgical Equipment Whslr
N.A.I.C.S.: 423450
Uwi Horn *(Mgr-Global Mktg Comm)*

Maquet Cardiopulmonary AG (2)
Kehler Strasse 31, Rastatt, 76437, Germany
Tel.: (49) 7222 932 0
Web Site: http://www.maquet.com
Emp.: 1,000
Surgical & Medical Instrument Mfr
N.A.I.C.S.: 339112
Axel Ruoff *(Office Mgr)*

Subsidiary (Non-US):

Maquet Cardiopulmonary Medikal Teknik SanTic Ltd. Sti (2)
Antalya Serbest Bolge, R Ada 1 Cd No 8 Adres No 2419050956 Yeni Liman, TR-Konyaalti, Antalya, Turkiye
Tel.: (90) 2422499000
Pharmaceutical Product Mfr & Distr
N.A.I.C.S.: 325412

Maquet Cardiopulmonary do Brasil. Ind. e Com S.A (2)
Rua Nazzareno Doninni 67-Jd Monte Kemel, 05634-140, Sao Paulo, Brazil
Tel.: (55) 11 3744 7768
Surgical & Medical Instrument Mfr
N.A.I.C.S.: 339112

Maquet Denmark A/S (2)
Industriparken 44B 1 sal, 2750, Ballerup, Denmark
Tel.: (45) 4694 4216
Web Site: http://ca.maquet.com
Sales Range: $25-49.9 Million
Emp.: 10
Surgical & Medical Instrument Mfr
N.A.I.C.S.: 339112

Subsidiary (Domestic):

Maquet Financial Services GmbH. (2)
Kehler Strasse 31, DE-76437, Rastatt, Germany
Tel.: (49) 7222 932 0
Web Site: http://www.getingegroup.com
Sales Range: $600-649.9 Million
Emp.: 1,500
Investment Management Service
N.A.I.C.S.: 523999
Heinz Jacqui *(Exec VP-Medical Sys Bus Area-Getinge AB)*

Subsidiary (Non-US):

Maquet Finland Oy (2)
Vuoritontuntie 22, 02200, Espoo, Finland
Tel.: (358) 8093824120
Web Site: http://www.ca.maquet.com

GETINGE AB

Getinge AB—(Continued)
Sales Range: $25-49.9 Million
Emp.: 13
Surgical & Medical Instrument Mfr
N.A.I.C.S.: 339112

Maquet Hong Kong Ltd. (2)
Unit 1510-17 Kowloon Commerce Centre Tower 2 15 Fl 51 Kwai Cheong Road, Kwai Chung, China (Hong Kong)
Tel.: (852) 2207 6111
Web Site: http://www.maquet.com
Sales Range: $25-49.9 Million
Emp.: 20
Surgical & Medical Instrument Mfr
N.A.I.C.S.: 339112
C. M. Leung (Gen Mgr)

Subsidiary (Domestic):

Maquet Hospital Solutions GmbH. (2)
Kehlerstrasse 31, 76437, Rastatt, Germany
Tel.: (49) 7222 932 376
Web Site: http://www.maquet-hospital-solutions.com
Surgical & Medical Instrument Mfr
N.A.I.C.S.: 339112

Subsidiary (Non-US):

Maquet Ireland Ltd (2)
B6 Calmount Park Ballymount, Dublin, Ireland
Tel.: (353) 1 426 0032
Emp.: 5
Surgical & Medical Instrument Mfr
N.A.I.C.S.: 339112
Avril Forde (VP)

Maquet Japan KK (2)
Sphere Tower Tennoz 23F 2-2-8 Higashi-shinagawa, Shinagawa-ku, Tokyo, Japan
Tel.: (81) 3 5463 8310
Sales Range: $25-49.9 Million
Emp.: 60
Surgical & Medical Instrument Mfr
N.A.I.C.S.: 339112

Maquet LLC (2)
Kievskoe shosse 22d km bld 6/1 XXV room 1e, Moscow, 108811, Russia
Tel.: (7) 4955140055
Web Site: http://www.maquet.ru
Emp.: 50
Surgical & Medical Instrument Mfr
N.A.I.C.S.: 339112

Maquet Ltd (2)
14-15 Burford Way Boldon Business Park, Sunderland, NE35 9PZ, Tyne & Wear, United Kingdom
Tel.: (44) 1915196200
Web Site: http://www.maquet.co.uk
Sales Range: $25-49.9 Million
Emp.: 30
Surgical & Medical Instrument Mfr
N.A.I.C.S.: 339112
Ezril Forda (CEO)

Maquet Medical India Pvt Ltd (2)
8 Shah Industrial Estate Off Veera Desai Road, Andheri, Mumbai, 400 053, India
Tel.: (91) 224 260 8000
Web Site: http://www.maquet.com
Emp.: 70
Surgical & Medical Instrument Mfr
N.A.I.C.S.: 339112
Bhavesh Bhatt (Gen Mgr)

Maquet Medical Korea Co. Ltd. (2)
13F KeumKang Building 304 Bongeunsa-ro, Gangnam-gu, Seoul, 135916, Korea (South)
Tel.: (82) 2 558 2271
Web Site: http://ca.maquet.com
Surgical & Medical Instrument Mfr
N.A.I.C.S.: 339112

Maquet Medizintechnik Vertrieb und Service GmbH-o.s (2)
Na Strzi 65/1702, 140 00, Prague, 4, Czech Republic
Tel.: (420) 26 114 2520
Web Site: http://ca.maquet.com
Sales Range: $25-49.9 Million
Emp.: 15
Surgical & Medical Instruments Mfrs
N.A.I.C.S.: 339112

Maquet Mexicana, S.de R.L.de CV (2)
World Trade Center Calle de Montecito No 38 piso 10 Oficina 17, Colonia Napoles, Mexico, 03810, Mexico
Tel.: (52) 55 9000 8970
Sales Range: $25-49.9 Million
Emp.: 25
Surgical & Medical Instrument Mfr
N.A.I.C.S.: 339112

Maquet Middle East FZ-LLC (2)
G005 Nucleotide Complex Dubai Biotechnology & Research Park, PO Box 214742, Dubai, United Arab Emirates
Tel.: (971) 4 447 0963
Web Site: http://www.ca.maquet.com
Emp.: 80
Surgical & Medical Instrument Mfr
N.A.I.C.S.: 339112
Khizar Iqbal (Mgr-HR)

Maquet Netherlands B.V. (2)
Oscar Romerolaan 3, 1216 TJ, Hilversum, Netherlands
Tel.: (31) 356255320
Web Site: http://www.maquetnetherlands.nl
Sales Range: $25-49.9 Million
Emp.: 50
Surgical & Medical Instrument Distr
N.A.I.C.S.: 339112
Frans de Kok (Engr-Svc-Cardiovascular Div)

Maquet Poland Sp.z.o.o (2)
ul Lirowa 27, 02-387, Warsaw, Poland
Tel.: (48) 22 882 06 44
Surgical & Medical Instrument Mfr
N.A.I.C.S.: 339112

Maquet Portugal Lda (2)
Rua Poeta Bocage 2 - 2G, Telheiras, Lisbon, 1600-233, Portugal
Tel.: (351) 214 189 815
Web Site: http://www.ca.maquet.com
Sales Range: $25-49.9 Million
Emp.: 22
Surgical & Medical Instrument Mfr
N.A.I.C.S.: 339112
Rui Viegas (Mng Dir)

Maquet South East Asia Ltd. (2)
20 Bendemeer Road 06-01/02 Cyberhub Bldg, Singapore, 339914, Singapore
Tel.: (65) 6 296 1992
Web Site: http://www.ca.maquet.com
Surgical & Medical Instrument Mfr
N.A.I.C.S.: 339112

Maquet Southern Africa (Pty) Ltd. (2)
Harrowdene Office Park Building 7 Western Services Road, Woodmead, Sandton, 2148, South Africa
Tel.: (27) 116563306
Pharmaceutical Product Mfr & Distr
N.A.I.C.S.: 325412

Maquet Spain S.L.U. (2)
Parque Empresarial Rivas Futura C/Marie Curie 5 Edificio Alfa Planta 6, Oficina 6 1-6 2, 28521, Rivas-Vaciamadrid, Spain
Tel.: (34) 91 678 1652
Web Site: http://ca.maquet.com
Surgical & Medical Instrument Mfr
N.A.I.C.S.: 339112

Subsidiary (Domestic):

Maquet Vertrieb und Service. Deutschland GmbH (2)
Kehler Strasse 31, 76437, Rastatt, Germany
Tel.: (49) 1803 212 133
Surgical & Medical Instrument Mfr
N.A.I.C.S.: 339112

Subsidiary (Non-US):

Maquet do Brasil Equipamentos. Medicos Ltda. (2)
Rua Tenente Alberto Spicciati 200, Barra Funda, Sao Paulo, 01140-130, Brazil
Tel.: (55) 11 2608 7400
Web Site: http://www.maquet.com.br
Surgical & Medical Instrument Mfr
N.A.I.C.S.: 339112

Maquet-Dynamed Inc (2)
235 Shields Court, Markham, L3R 8V2, ON, Canada
Tel.: (905) 752-3300
Web Site: http://www.maquet-dynamed.com
Emp.: 50
Medical & Surgical Equipment Whslr
N.A.I.C.S.: 423450
Peter Bennett (Pres & CEO)

MediKomp GmbH (1)
Kehler Strasse 31, 76437, Rastatt, Germany
Web Site: http://www.medikomp.de
Rev.: $72,676,450
Emp.: 300
Steel Products Mfr
N.A.I.C.S.: 331221

Medical Ultrasonics Ltd (1)
Arjohuntleigh House Houghton Hall Bussiness Park, Dunstable, LU5 5XF, Bedfordshire, United Kingdom
Tel.: (44) 1582 413 104
Medical & Surgical Equipment Whslr
N.A.I.C.S.: 423450

Meditechnik GmbH (1)
Ernst Vezort St 4 Wetzlar, Wetzlar, 35578, Germany (100%)
Tel.: (49) 644197810
Web Site: http://www.meditechnik.de
Sales Range: $25-49.9 Million
Emp.: 15
Hospital Equipments Mfr
N.A.I.C.S.: 339113

Meditechnik Holding GmbH (1)
Ernst-Befort-Str 4, 35578, Wetzlar, Hessen, Germany
Tel.: (49) 6441 97810
Investment Management Service
N.A.I.C.S.: 523999

PULSION Medical Systems SE (1)
Hans-Riedl-Str 17, 85622, Feldkirchen, Germany
Tel.: (49) 894599140
Sales Range: $25-49.9 Million
Emp.: 131
Medical Equipment Mfr, Developer & Researcher
N.A.I.C.S.: 339112

Subsidiary (Non-US):

PULSION Benelux N.V. (2)
Maaltecenter Blok G, Derbystraat 341, Gent, 9051, Belgium
Tel.: (32) 92429910
Web Site: http://www.pulsion.com
Sales Range: $25-49.9 Million
Emp.: 5
Life Science Research & Development Services
N.A.I.C.S.: 541715
Pieter Vergaert (Gen Mgr)

PULSION Medical Systems Iberica S.L. (2)
C/Valle del Roncal 12, Las Rozas, 28230, Madrid, Spain
Tel.: (34) 916266108
Web Site: http://www.pulsion.com
Sales Range: $25-49.9 Million
Emp.: 8
Medical Equipments Mfr & Supplier
N.A.I.C.S.: 334510
Ricardo De La Pena (Gen Mgr)

PULSION Medical UK Ltd. (2)
Unit C4 Heathrow Corporate Park Green Ln, Hounslow, TW4 6ER, Middlesex, United Kingdom
Tel.: (44) 2088147974
Web Site: http://www.pulsion.com
Sales Range: $25-49.9 Million
Emp.: 7
Medical Equipment Mfr & Distr
N.A.I.C.S.: 334510

PULSION Switzerland GmbH (2)
Wilerstrasse 75, 9201, Gossau, Switzerland
Tel.: (41) 415003792
Sales Range: $25-49.9 Million
Emp.: 2
Life Science Research & Development Services
N.A.I.C.S.: 541715
Oliver Lupoli (Mng Dir)

Pulsion France S.A.R.L. (2)
Immeuble Le Delta Hall 4 Bat B, 3 5 Rue du Pont des Halles, 94150, Rungis, France
Tel.: (33) 141730904
Sales Range: $25-49.9 Million
Emp.: 10
Life Science Research & Development Services
N.A.I.C.S.: 541715
Alenka Klarica (Mgr)

Peristel S.A. (1)
33 Bis Route De Chartres, FR 91855, Gometz La Ville, France (100%)
Tel.: (33) 164868970
Provider of Medical Equipment
N.A.I.C.S.: 334510

Polystan A/S (1)
Firskovvej 23, PB 209, 2800, Kongens Lyngby, Denmark
Tel.: (45) 26 27 99 30
Medical & Surgical Equipment Whslr
N.A.I.C.S.: 423450

Quadralene Ltd. (1)
Bateman St, Derby, DE23 8JL, United Kingdom
Tel.: (44) 1332292500
Web Site: https://quadralene.com
Pharmaceuticals Mfr
N.A.I.C.S.: 325412

Steritec Products Mfg. Co., Inc. (1)
74 Inverness Dr E, Englewood, CO 80112
Tel.: (303) 660-4201
Medical Device Mfr & Distr
N.A.I.C.S.: 325412

Talis Clinical LLC (1)
650 Mondial Pkwy, Streetsboro, OH 44241
Tel.: (234) 284-2400
Pharmaceuticals Product Mfr
N.A.I.C.S.: 325412

Ultra Clean Systems Inc. (1)
110 Douglas Rd E, Oldsmar, FL 34677
Tel.: (813) 403-5329
Web Site: http://www.ultracleansystems.com
Surgical & Medical Instrument Mfr
N.A.I.C.S.: 339112
O'Brien Cale (CEO & Founder)

GETLINK SE

3 rue La Boetie, 75008, Paris, France
Tel.: (33) 8443353535 FR
Year Founded: 1994
GET—(EUR)
Rev.: $951,090,100
Assets: $10,011,682,702
Liabilities: $8,391,352,875
Net Worth: $1,620,329,827
Earnings: ($281,483,130)
Emp.: 21
Fiscal Year-end: 12/31/21
Transportation Infrastructure Management Services
N.A.I.C.S.: 488210
Pascal Sainson (Chm-Europorte SAS & COO-Europorte SAS)

Subsidiaries:

Channel Tunnel Rail Link (1)
2 Oshulston Street, London, NW1 1HT, United Kingdom (100%)
Tel.: (44) 2076815000
Web Site: http://www.lcrhq.co.uk
Sales Range: $25-49.9 Million
Emp.: 50
Train Operator
N.A.I.C.S.: 237310
Lorraine Baldry (Chm)

Europorte (1)
15 rue des Sablons, 75116, Paris, France
Tel.: (33) 1 71 75 12 74
Web Site: http://www.europorte.com
Rail Freight Services
N.A.I.C.S.: 482111

Subsidiary (Domestic):

Europorte Proximit SAS (2)
Azur Plus 1, 13161, Chateauneuf-les-Martigues, France
Tel.: (33) 4 42 13 13 52
Web Site: http://www.europorte.com
Emp.: 1

AND PRIVATE COMPANIES

Rail Transportation Services
N.A.I.C.S.: 488210
Pascal Sainson *(Pres)*

Socorail SAS (2)
RN 568 Batiment Azur Plus 1, BP 14, 13161, Chateauneuf-les-Martigues, France
Tel.: (33) 442131352
Railway Transportation Services
N.A.I.C.S.: 488210
Pascal Sainson *(Pres)*

Europorte France SAS (1)
11 Parvis de Rotterdam Tour LillEurope, Euralille, 59 777, Lille, France
Tel.: (33) 328365370
Sales Range: $50-74.9 Million
Emp.: 162
Rail Freight Transportation Services
N.A.I.C.S.: 488510
Pascal Sainson *(Gen Mgr)*

Eurotunnel Developments Limited (1)
Ashford Road, Folkestone, CT18 8XX, Kent, United Kingdom **(100%)**
Tel.: (44) 1303 282549
Web Site: http://www.eurotunnel.co.uk
Sales Range: $25-49.9 Million
Emp.: 40
Development of Property
N.A.I.C.S.: 237210

Eurotunnel Developments S.A. (1)
BP 69, F-62904, Coquelles, Cedex, France **(100%)**
Tel.: (33) 810 63 03 04
Web Site: http://www.eurotunnel.com
Sales Range: $25-49.9 Million
Emp.: 12
Tunnel Construction
N.A.I.C.S.: 237310

Eurotunnel Services GIE (1)
BP 69, 62904, Coquelles, France **(100%)**
Tel.: (33) 321006000
Web Site: http://nv.eurotunnel.com
Sales Range: $300-349.9 Million
Emp.: 1,500
Employment Services for Eurotunnel S.A. Companies
N.A.I.C.S.: 561330

Eurotunnel Services Limited (1)
Ashford Road, Folkestone, CT18 8XX, Kent, United Kingdom **(100%)**
Tel.: (44) 1303 282549
Web Site: http://www.eurotunnel.com
Sales Range: $150-199.9 Million
Emp.: 1,000
Employment Service for Group Companies
N.A.I.C.S.: 561311

EurotunnelPlus Limited (1)
UK Terminal Ashford Road, Folkestone, CT18 8XX, United Kingdom
Tel.: (44) 1303272222
Web Site: http://www.eurotunnelplus.co.uk
Channel Tunnel Operating Services
N.A.I.C.S.: 488490

GETMAPPING PLC
Fleet 27 Rye Close, Fleet, GU51 2UH, Hampshire, United Kingdom
Tel.: (44) 1252845444 UK
Web Site:
  http://www.getmapping.com
Year Founded: 1999
Rev.: $7,528,584
Assets: $6,433,398
Liabilities: $2,739,932
Net Worth: $3,693,466
Earnings: ($716,134)
Emp.: 78
Fiscal Year-end: 12/31/19
Online Aerial Mapping Services
N.A.I.C.S.: 541360
Dave Horner *(CEO)*

GETRIEBEBAU NORD GMBH & CO. KG
Getriebebau-Nord-Strasse 1, 22941, Bargteheide, Germany
Tel.: (49) 45322890 De
Web Site: http://www.nord.com
Year Founded: 1965
Sales Range: $10-24.9 Million
Emp.: 400
Electric Motor, Gear & Frequency Inverter Mfr
N.A.I.C.S.: 335999
G. A. Kuchenmeister *(Mng Dir)*

Subsidiaries:

Getriebebau NORD AG (1)
Bachigenstrasse 18, 9212, Arnegg, Switzerland
Tel.: (41) 71 38899 11
Motor Distr
N.A.I.C.S.: 423610

Getriebebau NORD GmbH (1)
Deggendorfstrasse 8, 4030, Linz, Austria
Tel.: (43) 732 31 89 20
Motor Distr
N.A.I.C.S.: 423610
Thomas Wurm *(Area Mgr-Sls)*

NORD (China) Power Transmission Co., Ltd. (1)
No 510 Changyang Street Suzhou Ind Park, 215026, Suzhou, China
Tel.: (86) 512 85180277
Motor Mfr
N.A.I.C.S.: 333996
Liping Weng *(Mgr-Export)*

NORD Aandrijvingen Belgie NV (1)
Boutersem Dreef 24, 2240, Zandhoven, Belgium
Tel.: (32) 3 4845921
Web Site: http://www.nord.be
Seal Distr
N.A.I.C.S.: 423840

NORD Aandrijvingen Nederland B.V. (1)
Voltstraat 12, PO Box 136, 2181 HA, Hillegom, Netherlands
Tel.: (31) 252 529544
Seal Distr
N.A.I.C.S.: 423840
Arno Klasen *(Product Mgr)*

NORD DRIVE SYSTEMS SA DE CV (1)
Carr Estatal 431 Km 5 75 6 Parque Industrial PYME, Huimilpan, 76971, Queretaro, Mexico
Tel.: (52) 442 240 5371
Electric Motor, Gear & Frequency Inverter Mfr
N.A.I.C.S.: 335999

NORD Drivesystems Brasil Ltda. (1)
Rua Dr Moacyr Antonio de Moraes 127, Guarulhos, 07140-285, Sao Paulo, Brazil
Tel.: (55) 11 2402 8855
Motor Distr
N.A.I.C.S.: 423610
Claudio Falcao *(Mng Dir)*

NORD Drivesystems Co., Ltd. (1)
15 Mayu-ro 32Beon-gil, Siheung, 429-450, GyeongGi-do, Korea (South)
Tel.: (82) 31 381 4474
Motor Distr
N.A.I.C.S.: 423610

NORD Drivesystems Guc Aktarma Sistemleri San. ve Tic. Ltd. Sti. (1)
Istanbul Anadolu Yakasi OSB 1 sok no 6, Tuzla, 34959, Istanbul, Turkiye
Tel.: (90) 216 5933237
Motor Distr
N.A.I.C.S.: 423610
H. Tolga Kanli *(Mng Dir)*

NORD Drivesystems PTP, Lda. (1)
Zona industrial de Oia Rua da Etar Lote 8 Apt 79, Oliveira do Bairro, 3770-059, Aveiro, Portugal
Tel.: (351) 234 727 090
Motor Distr
N.A.I.C.S.: 423610
Filipe Lopes *(Engr-Sls & Application)*

NORD Drivesystems Pty Ltd (1)
18 Stoney Way, Derrimut, 3030, VIC, Australia
Tel.: (61) 3 9394 0500
Web Site: http://www.nord.com
Motor Distr
N.A.I.C.S.: 423610

NORD Drivesystems Pvt. Ltd. (1)
282/2 & 283/2 Village Mann Tal Mulshi, Adj Hinjawadi MIDC-II, Pune, 411057, Maharashtra, India
Tel.: (91) 20 39801200
Web Site: http://www.norddrivesystems.co.in
Motor Distr
N.A.I.C.S.: 423610
Amit Deokule *(Deputy Gen Mgr-Sls)*

NORD Drivsystem AB (1)
Ryttargatan 277, 194 02, Upplands Vasby, Sweden
Tel.: (46) 8 594 114 00
Motor Distr
N.A.I.C.S.: 423610
Tony Isaksson *(Mng Dir)*

NORD GEAR NORGE A/S (1)
Hestehagen 5, 1442, Drobak, Norway
Tel.: (47) 64 90 55 80
Motor Distr
N.A.I.C.S.: 423610

NORD Gear Corporation (1)
800 Nord Dr, Waunakee, WI 53597
Tel.: (608) 849-7300
Web Site: http://www.nord.com
Electric Motor, Gear & Frequency Inverter Mfr
N.A.I.C.S.: 333612
Eric Luedtke *(Mgr-Customer Svc)*

NORD Gear Limited (1)
41 West Drive, Brampton, L6T 4A1, ON, Canada
Tel.: (905) 796-3606
Speed Reducer & Electric Motor Mfr
N.A.I.C.S.: 333612

NORD Gear Ltd. (1)
11 Barton Lane, Abingdon Science Park, Abingdon, OX14 3NB, Oxon, United Kingdom
Tel.: (44) 1235534404
Web Site: http://www.nord-uk.com
Emp.: 25
Electric Motor, Gear & Frequency Inverter Mfr
N.A.I.C.S.: 333612
Andrew Stephenson *(Mng Dir)*

NORD Gear Oy (1)
Golfkentantie 6, 33960, Pirkkala, Finland
Tel.: (358) 3 254 1800
Web Site: http://www.nordgear.com
Emp.: 7
Motor Distr
N.A.I.C.S.: 423610
Sampo Laine *(Area Mgr)*

NORD Gear Pte Ltd (1)
33 Kian Teck Dr, Jurong, 628850, Singapore, Singapore
Tel.: (65) 6265 9118
Motor Mfr
N.A.I.C.S.: 335312

NORD Hajtastechnika Kft. (1)
Pomazi ut 11, 1037, Budapest, Hungary
Tel.: (36) 1 437 0127
Web Site: http://www.nord.com
Motor Distr
N.A.I.C.S.: 423610

NORD Motorreductores S.A. (1)
C/ Montsia 31-37 Poligon Industrial Can Carner, Castellar del Valles, 08211, Barcelona, Spain
Tel.: (34) 93 723 5322
Motor Distr
N.A.I.C.S.: 423610
Jose Villegas *(Gen Mgr)*

NORD Napedy sp. z o.o. (1)
Krakowska 58, 32-020, Wieliczka, Poland
Tel.: (48) 122889900
Motor Distr
N.A.I.C.S.: 423610
Jaroslaw Nowak *(Mgr-Support Electronics)*

NORD Pogoni d.o.o (1)
Obrtnicka Ulica 9, 48260, Krizevci, Croatia
Tel.: (385) 48 711 900
Motor Distr
N.A.I.C.S.: 423610

NORD Pohony, s.r.o. (1)
Stromova 13, 83101, Bratislava, Slovakia
Tel.: (421) 55 729 9600
Motor Distr
N.A.I.C.S.: 423610

NORD-Motoriduttori s.r.l. (1)
Via Newton 22, San Giovanni Persiceto, 40017, Bologna, Italy
Tel.: (39) 051 6870 711
Emp.: 170
Motor Distr
N.A.I.C.S.: 423610
Sergio Felicissimo *(Mgr-Indus Sector)*

NORD-Pohaneci technika, s. r. o. (1)
Becovska 1398/11 Uhrineves, 104 00, Prague, Czech Republic
Tel.: (420) 541 229 741
Motor Distr
N.A.I.C.S.: 423610

Nord Gear Danmark A/S (1)
Kliplev Erhvervspark 28, 6200, Aabenraa, Denmark
Tel.: (45) 73 68 78 00
Motor Distr
N.A.I.C.S.: 423610

Nord Reducteurs Sarl (1)
17 Ave Georges Clemenceau, 93421, Villepinte, Cedex, France
Tel.: (33) 1 49 63 01 89
Motor Distr
N.A.I.C.S.: 423610

OOO NORD Privody (1)
Ul Vozduhoplavatelnaja 19, 196084, Saint Petersburg, Russia
Tel.: (7) 8124491268
Web Site: http://www.nord.com
Motor Distr
N.A.I.C.S.: 423610

S.C.Nord Drivesystems S.R.L. (1)
Str Iorga Nicolae 55, 550361, Sibiu, Romania
Tel.: (40) 269 232880
Motor Distr
N.A.I.C.S.: 423610

GETRONICS BELGIUM NV/SA
De Kleetlaan 12B 1831 Diegem, Brussels, 1831, Belgium
Tel.: (32) 22299111
Web Site: http://www.getronics.com
Year Founded: 1887
Sales Range: $75-99.9 Million
Emp.: 500
Information Technology & Communications Infrastructure Services
N.A.I.C.S.: 561499
Danniel Minschaert *(CEO)*

GETTER GROUP LTD.
7th Shimshon St Kiryat-Arie, Petah Tiqwa, Israel
Tel.: (972) 35766702
Web Site: http://www.getter.co.il
Year Founded: 1955
Sales Range: $150-199.9 Million
Emp.: 517
Wholesale Trade Agency Services
N.A.I.C.S.: 425120
Slav Mendelbaum *(Chm)*

GETTOP ACOUSTIC CO., LTD.
No 68 Fengshan Road, Fangzi District, Weifang, Shandong, China
Tel.: (86) 865362283666
Web Site:
  https://www.gettopacoustic.com
Year Founded: 2001
002655-‐‐(SSE)
Rev.: $135,223,452
Assets: $168,216,048
Liabilities: $68,386,032
Net Worth: $99,830,016
Earnings: $8,718,840
Emp.: 1,900
Fiscal Year-end: 12/31/22
Electro-Acoustic Components & Assemblies
N.A.I.C.S.: 334310
Xie Guanhong *(Chm)*

GETTY COPPER INC.

Getty Copper Inc.—(Continued)
1000 Austin Avenue, Coquitlam, V3K 3P1, BC, Canada
Tel.: (604) 931-3231 BC
Web Site: https://www.gettycopper.com
Year Founded: 1985
GTC—(TSXV)
Rev.: $1,323
Assets: $5,283,703
Liabilities: $2,787,009
Net Worth: $2,496,694
Earnings: ($339,783)
Fiscal Year-end: 12/31/23
Copper Mining Services
N.A.I.C.S.: 212230
John B. Lepinski (CEO, Mng Dir & COO)

GETZNER TEXTIL AG
Bleichestrasse 1, 6700, Bludenz, Austria
Tel.: (43) 55526010
Web Site: http://www.getzner.at
Year Founded: 1818
Rev.: $108,700,000
Emp.: 740
Fabrics Mfr
N.A.I.C.S.: 315990
Wolfgang Kunze (Dir-Mktg & Sls-Africa Damask)

Subsidiaries:

Getzner Textil Handel GmbH (1)
Zellgasse 43, 6890, Lustenau, Austria
Tel.: (43) 5577846410
Fabric Product Distr
N.A.I.C.S.: 424310

Getzner Textil Weberei GmbH (1)
Lange Strasse 73, 7551, Gera, Thuringen, Germany
Tel.: (49) 365733340
Fabric Product Distr
N.A.I.C.S.: 424310

Klingler Textil AG (1)
Werkstrasse 10, 9444, Diepoldsau, Switzerland
Tel.: (41) 713888939
Web Site: http://www.klingler-textil.com
Fabric Product Mfr
N.A.I.C.S.: 315990

Meyer Mayor AG (1)
Toggenburgerstrasse 13, 9652, Nesslau, Switzerland
Tel.: (41) 719956010
Web Site: http://www.meyer-mayor.ch
Fabric Product Mfr
N.A.I.C.S.: 315990

TFE Textil GmbH (1)
Klarenbrunnstrasse 59, 6700, Bludenz, Austria
Tel.: (43) 555267411
Web Site: http://www.tfe.at
Fabric Product Mfr
N.A.I.C.S.: 315990

WR Weberei Russikon AG (1)
Madetswilerstrasse 29, 8332, Pfaffikon, Switzerland
Tel.: (41) 449566161
Web Site: http://www.weberei-russikon.ch
Fabric Product Mfr
N.A.I.C.S.: 315990

GEUMHWA PSC CO., LTD.
15-4 Teheran-ro 25-gil, Gangnam-gu, Seoul, Korea (South)
Tel.: (82) 221866220
Web Site: https://www.geumhwa.co.kr
Year Founded: 1981
036190—(KRS)
Rev.: $190,482,835
Assets: $306,808,495
Liabilities: $78,501,861
Net Worth: $228,306,634
Earnings: $21,305,957
Emp.: 1,121

Fiscal Year-end: 12/31/22
Industrial Plant Construction Services
N.A.I.C.S.: 237130
Kyung-Tae Kim (CEO)

GEUMSAN GINSENG HERB DEVELOPMENT AGENCY
Insamgwangjang-ro 25 Shin Dae-ri 678-7-8, Geumsan, 32724, Chungcheongnam, Korea (South)
Tel.: (82) 417501600
Web Site: https://gghda.kr
Year Founded: 2021
Herbal Product Distr
N.A.I.C.S.: 424210

GEUMVIT CORP.
14 Saneop-ro 104beon-gil, Ojeong-gu, Bucheon, 14402, Gyeonggi-do, Korea (South)
Tel.: (82) 326703345
Web Site: http://www.gvcorp.co.kr
Year Founded: 1989
045890—(KRS)
Rev.: $50,440,219
Assets: $88,450,325
Liabilities: $61,765,152
Net Worth: $26,685,173
Earnings: ($31,668,526)
Emp.: 161
Fiscal Year-end: 12/31/19
Electric Lamp Mfr
N.A.I.C.S.: 335139

Subsidiaries:

Dongbu Lightec (YANTAI) Co., Ltd. (1)
No 8 Rongyao Street Jichang Road, Zhifuqu, Yantai, Shandong, China
Tel.: (86) 535 6020375
Electric Lamp Distr
N.A.I.C.S.: 423610

Dongbu Lightec Europe Ltd. (1)
Ober der ROth 4, 65824, Schwalbach am Taunus, Germany
Tel.: (49) 6196 65212 21
Electric Lamp Distr
N.A.I.C.S.: 423610

Dongbu Lightec JAPAN Co., Ltd (1)
2F Arcadia Building 1-12-3 Kanda Sudacho, Chiyoda-ku, Tokyo, 101-0041, Japan
Tel.: (81) 3 5577 5760
Web Site: http://www.dongbulightec.com
Emp.: 6
Electric Lamp Distr
N.A.I.C.S.: 423610
Kim Minsoo (CEO)

Dongbu Lightec USA Inc (1)
205 Robin Rd Ste 203, Paramus, NJ 07652
Tel.: (201) 265-6600
Web Site: http://www.dongbulightecusa.com
Emp.: 2
Electric Lamp Distr
N.A.I.C.S.: 423610
T. J. Kim (Pres)

GV (Geumvit Corp.) (Yantai) Co., Ltd. (1)
No 29 Haite Road, Zhifuqu, Yantai, Shandong, China
Tel.: (86) 707 733 3248
Light Emitting Diode Mfr
N.A.I.C.S.: 334413

GV (Geumvit Corp.) Japan Co., Ltd. (1)
2F Arcadia Building 1-12-3 Kanda Sudacho, Chiyoda-ku, Tokyo, 101-0041, Japan
Tel.: (81) 707 733 3230
Light Emitting Diode Mfr
N.A.I.C.S.: 334413

GEVELOT S.A.
6 Bd Bineau, 92532, Levallois-Perret, Cedex, France
Tel.: (33) 141490303
Web Site: https://gevelot-sa.fr
Year Founded: 1820
ALGEV—(EUR)
Rev.: $150,831,049

Assets: $328,950,421
Liabilities: $102,155,821
Net Worth: $226,794,601
Earnings: $8,896,373
Emp.: 5
Fiscal Year-end: 12/31/22
Industrial Interests & Related Activities Management Services
N.A.I.C.S.: 561499
Philippe Barbelane (Acting Mng Dir)

Subsidiaries:

Cougar Machine Ltd. (1)
3712 56 Ave NW, Edmonton, T6B 3R8, AB, Canada
Tel.: (780) 490-1661
Web Site: https://www.cougarmachine.com
Engineering Services
N.A.I.C.S.: 541330
Leo Wentland (Ops Mgr)

Cougar Wellhead Services inc. (1)
3716 56 Ave NW, Edmonton, T6B 3R8, AB, Canada
Tel.: (780) 432-2000
Web Site: https://www.cougarwellheadservices.com
Engineering Services
N.A.I.C.S.: 541330

Gevelot Extrusion (1)
6 Blvd Bineau, 92532, Levallois-Perret, France (99.99%)
Tel.: (33) 141490333
Web Site: http://www.gevelot.com
Sales Range: $50-74.9 Million
Emp.: 5
Steel Parts Cold & Semi-Hot Extrusion Services; Machining & Thermal Treatment Services
N.A.I.C.S.: 332111
Patrick Lhuillery (CEO)

Subsidiary (Non-US):

Dold Kaltfliesspressteile GmbH (2)
Langenbacher Strasse 17-19, D-78147, Voehrenbach, Germany (100%)
Tel.: (49) 77275090
Web Site: http://www.doldgmbh.de
Sales Range: $125-149.9 Million
Steel Parts Cold & Semi-Hot Extrusion Services; Machining & Thermal Treatment Services
N.A.I.C.S.: 332111
Patrick Lhuillery (Chm)

Gurtner (1)
40 rue de la Liberation, BP 129, Pontarlier, 25302, France (100%)
Tel.: (33) 381467022
Web Site: http://www.gurtner.fr
Sales Range: $25-49.9 Million
Emp.: 90
Engine Equipment & Gas Equipment Fluid Flow Solutions
N.A.I.C.S.: 333996
Bruno Tracco (Chm)

PCM Europe S.A.S. (1)
6 Boulevard Bineau, 92300, Levallois-Perret, France
Tel.: (33) 803433972
Pump Equipment Mfr
N.A.I.C.S.: 333996

PCM Manufacturing France S.A.S. (1)
6 Boulevard Bineau, 92300, Levallois-Perret, France
Tel.: (33) 803933399
Pump Equipment Mfr
N.A.I.C.S.: 333996

PCM Pompes (1)
6 Boulevard Bineau, BP 35, 92173, Levallois-Perret, France (99.99%)
Tel.: (33) 141081515
Web Site: http://www.pcm.eu
Emp.: 50
Volumetric Pump Designer, Mfr & Sales
N.A.I.C.S.: 333996
Mario Martignoni (CEO)

Subsidiary (Non-US):

PCM Pumps Ltd. (2)
Pilot Road Phoenix Parkway, Corby, NN17

INTERNATIONAL PUBLIC

5YF, Northants, United Kingdom (99.99%)
Tel.: (44) 01536740200
Web Site: http://www.pcm.eu
Sales Range: $25-49.9 Million
Emp.: 25
Volumetric Pump Designer, Mfr, Sales & Services
N.A.I.C.S.: 333914
Andy Ballinger (Mng Dir)

Subsidiary (US):

PCM USA Inc. (2)
11940 Brittmoore Park Dr, Houston, TX 77041
Tel.: (713) 896-4888
Web Site: http://www.pcm-pump.com
Industrial Pump Distr
N.A.I.C.S.: 423830
Chinedu Obeleagu (Mgr-Production)

PCM S.A. (1)
6 Blvd Bineau, Levallois-Perret, 92300, France
Tel.: (33) 141081515
Web Site: http://www.pcm.com
Sales Range: $50-74.9 Million
Emp.: 200
Pumps Mfr
N.A.I.C.S.: 333996
Mario Martignoni (Gen Mgr)

Subsidiary (Non-US):

PCM Deutschland GmbH (2)
Wiesbadener Landstrasse 18, 65203, Wiesbaden, Germany
Tel.: (49) 611609770
Emp.: 9
Pumps Mfr
N.A.I.C.S.: 333996

Subsidiary (US):

PCM Flow Technology Inc (2)
11940 Brittmoore Park Dr, Houston, TX 77041
Tel.: (713) 896-4888
Industrial Investment Management Services
N.A.I.C.S.: 523999

Subsidiary (Non-US):

PCM Group Italia Srl (2)
via Rutilia, 20135, Milan, Italy
Tel.: (39) 0289655647
Web Site: http://www.pcm-pompe.it
Pumps Mfr
N.A.I.C.S.: 333996

PCM Group UK Ltd (2)
Pilot Road Phoenix Parkway, Corby, NN17 5YF, Northamptonshire, United Kingdom
Tel.: (44) 1536740200
Web Site: http://www.pcm.eu
Sales Range: $25-49.9 Million
Emp.: 27
Volumetric Pumps Mfr
N.A.I.C.S.: 333914
Dave Burrows (Mgr-Sls)

PCM Trading (Shanghai) Co. Ltd (2)
Unit 10 A 01 & 10 G 03 Shanghaimart 2299 Yanan Road West, 200336, Shanghai, China
Tel.: (86) 2162362521
Web Site: http://www.pcm.eu
Pumps Mfr
N.A.I.C.S.: 333914

PCM Technologies S.A.S. (1)
6 Boulevard Bineau, 92300, Levallois-Perret, France
Tel.: (33) 802419960
Pump Equipment Mfr
N.A.I.C.S.: 333996

Sydex Srl (1)
Via Baden Powell 24, 36045, Lonigo, Italy
Tel.: (39) 0444432588
Web Site: http://www.sydexpump.com
Pump Equipment Mfr
N.A.I.C.S.: 333996
Franco Gechele (CEO)

Subsidiary (Non-US):

Sydex Flow Ltda. (2)
Square Vale da Romeira 12, 2840-449, Seixal, Portugal
Tel.: (351) 212270359

AND PRIVATE COMPANIES

Web Site: http://www.sydexflow.com
Pump Equipment Mfr
N.A.I.C.S.: 333996

Sydex Singapore Ltd. (2)
158 Kallang Way 02-16 Performance Building, Singapore, 349245, Singapore
Tel.: (65) 67442823
Web Site: http://www.sydexpump.com.sg
Pump Equipment Mfr
N.A.I.C.S.: 333996
Darius Yap (Sls Mgr)

Subsidiary (US):

Sydex USA LLC (2)
9302 Deer Run Rd, Waxhaw, NC 28173
Tel.: (704) 843-5048
Pump Equipment Mfr
N.A.I.C.S.: 333996
Michael Morris (Pres)

GEWISS S.P.A.
Via A Volta 1, 24069, Cenate Sotto, Bergamo, Italy
Tel.: (39) 035946111   IT
Web Site: http://www.gewiss.com
Year Founded: 1970
Sales Range: $450-499.9 Million
Emp.: 1,600
Electronic Products Mfr
N.A.I.C.S.: 335999
Luca Bosatelli (CEO & VP)

Subsidiaries:

GEWISS CHILE LTDA (1)
Avenida Isidora Goyenechea 3365 - Office 1203, Las Condes, Santiago, Chile
Tel.: (56) 223645800
Electronic Goods Distr
N.A.I.C.S.: 423690
Jonathan Andres Yanez (Product Mgr)

GEWISS Elektrik Tesisat Malzemeleri Ticaret Ltd. (1)
Nida Kule Is Merkezi Degirmen Sok No 18, kozyatagi, 34742, Istanbul, Turkiye
Tel.: (90) 2165697100
Electronic Goods Distr
N.A.I.C.S.: 423690

GEWISS FRANCE SA (1)
Rue du Rio Salado 1 Z A de Courtaboeuf, BP 113, 91944, Les Ulis, Cedex, France
Tel.: (33) 164868080
Electronic Goods Distr
N.A.I.C.S.: 423690

GEWISS GULF FZE (1)
Building 6W Entrance A 3rd Floor Office 301 Dubai Airport Free Zone, PO Box 54818, Dubai, United Arab Emirates
Tel.: (971) 42936000
Electronic Goods Distr
N.A.I.C.S.: 423690
Paolo Manca (Gen Mgr)

GEWISS IBERICA SA (1)
Calle Belgica 4 C T, Coslada, 28821, Madrid, Spain
Tel.: (34) 916707100
Electronic Goods Distr
N.A.I.C.S.: 423690
Sergio Molina (Mgr-Natl IT)

GEWISS ROMANIA srl (1)
Aurel Vlaicu Office Building Sos Pipera Nr 4 Etaj 4, 014255, Bucharest, Romania
Tel.: (40) 314370650
Electronic Goods Distr
N.A.I.C.S.: 423690
Anca Ivanov (Product Mgr)

GEWISS Trading (Shanghai) Co., Ltd. (1)
Rm 1704 Tower B Sunyoung Center No 28 Xuanhua Road, Changning District, Shanghai, 200050, China
Tel.: (86) 2162523535
Electronic Goods Distr
N.A.I.C.S.: 423690

Gewiss Deutschland GmbH (1)
Industriestrasse 2, D 35799, Merenberg, Germany   (100%)
Tel.: (49) 64715010
Web Site: http://www.gewiss.com

Sales Range: $25-49.9 Million
Emp.: 20
N.A.I.C.S.: 444180
Bosa Telli (Gen Mgr)

Gewiss Portugal Lda (1)
Rua das Condominhas 738, 4150-221, Porto, Portugal
Tel.: (351) 226155480
Electronic Goods Distr
N.A.I.C.S.: 423690
Goncalo Pacheco (Dir-Indus)

Gewiss S.p.A. (1)
Via Emilia Pavese 53, I 29015, Castel San Giovanni, Italy   (100%)
Tel.: (39) 035946111
Sales Range: $200-249.9 Million
Emp.: 1,000
Mfr of Rigid & Flexible Conduits & Plastic Accessories for Electrical Systems
N.A.I.C.S.: 335932
Domenico Bosatelly (Pres)

Gewiss UK Ltd. (1)
2020 Bldg Cambourne Bus Park, Cambourne, Cambridge, CB23 6DW, United Kingdom   (100%)
Tel.: (44) 1249444734
Web Site: http://www.gewiss.co.uk
Sales Range: $25-49.9 Million
Emp.: 14
Equipment & Accessories Marketer for Electrical Systems with Applications in the Civil, Services & Industrial Sectors
N.A.I.C.S.: 423610
Paul Black (Mng Dir)

MR&D Institute S.r.l. (1)
Viale dell'Unione Europea, 21013, Gallarate, VA, Italy   (40%)
Tel.: (39) 0331791940
Web Site: http://www.mrd-institute.com
Sales Range: $25-49.9 Million
Emp.: 50
Mechanical & Electrical Products
N.A.I.C.S.: 335999

Meltec S.A. (1)
Calle 20 No 69B-73, Bogota, Colombia   (20%)
Tel.: (57) 14111899
Web Site: http://www.meltec.com.co
Sales Range: $25-49.9 Million
Emp.: 60
N.A.I.C.S.: 444180

OOO GEWISS Russia (1)
8 Ul Ivana Franco Kutuzoff Tower 5th floor, 121108, Moscow, Russia
Tel.: (7) 495660
Electronic Goods Distr
N.A.I.C.S.: 423690
Marco Sabbatini (Gen Mgr)

GEXEED CO., LTD.
5F HF Aobadai Bldg Aobadai Meguro-ku, Tokyo, 153-0042, Japan
Tel.: (81) 354563051
Web Site: http://www.gexeed.co.jp
Year Founded: 1964
3719—(TKS)
Sales Range: $10-24.9 Million
Emp.: 120
Business Consulting Services
N.A.I.C.S.: 541618
Ryo Arai (Pres)

GEYSER BRANDS, INC.
116-1776 Broadway st, Port Coquitlam, V3C 2M8, BC, Canada
Tel.: (778) 903-5472
Web Site:
https://www.geyserbrands.com
GYSR—(TSXV)
Rev.: $4,806
Assets: $3,742,347
Liabilities: $801,412
Net Worth: $2,940,934
Earnings: ($16,515,112)
Fiscal Year-end: 03/31/19
Pharmaceuticals Product Mfr
N.A.I.C.S.: 325412
Wei Zhong (Interim CEO)

GF SECURITIES CO., LTD.
GF Securities Tower 26 Machang Rd, Tianhe District, Guangzhou, 510627, Guangdong, China
Tel.: (86) 2066338888   CN
Web Site: https://en.gf.com.cn
Year Founded: 1996
000776—(SSE)
Rev.: $3,226,009,581
Assets: $94,453,599,801
Liabilities: $74,975,904,021
Net Worth: $19,477,695,780
Earnings: $966,133,072
Emp.: 14,802
Fiscal Year-end: 12/31/23
Financial Investment Services
N.A.I.C.S.: 523999
Sun Xiaoyan (CFO & Deputy Gen Mgr)

Subsidiaries:

GF Asset Management (Hong Kong) Limited (1)
29th & 30th Floor Li Po Chun Chambers 189 Des Voeux Road Central, Hong Kong, China (Hong Kong)
Tel.: (852) 37191111
N.A.I.C.S.: 523999

GF Canada Holdings Company Limited (1)
Suite 2270-1055 West Georgia Street, Vancouver, V6E 3P3, BC, Canada
Tel.: (778) 297-5888
N.A.I.C.S.: 523999

GF Capital (Hong Kong) Limited (1)
29th & 30th Floor Li Po Chun Chambers 189 Des Voeux Road Central, Hong Kong, China (Hong Kong)
Tel.: (852) 37191111
N.A.I.C.S.: 523999

GF Commodities Co., Ltd. (1)
Room A-805 188 Yesheng Road Lin-Gang Special Area, Pilot Free Trade Zone, Shanghai, China
Tel.: (86) 2088838016
N.A.I.C.S.: 523999

GF Financial Markets (U.K.) Ltd. (1)
1 Finsbury Square, London, EC2A 1AE, United Kingdom
Tel.: (44) 2073301688
Web Site: https://www.gffm.com
Security & Commodity Exchange Services
Edward Shi (Mng Dir)

GF Fund Management Co., Ltd. (1)
31-33/F South Tower Poly International Plaza No 1 East Pazhou Road, Haizhu District, Guangzhou, 510308, China   (60.63%)
Tel.: (86) 2083936999
Web Site: https://www.gffunds.com.cn
Security Brokerage Services
N.A.I.C.S.: 523150

GF Futures Co., Ltd. (1)
29-30/F Li Po Chun Chambers 189 Des Voeux Road Central, Central, China (Hong Kong)
Tel.: (852) 37191150
Web Site: http://www.gfqh.com.cn
Security Brokerage Services
N.A.I.C.S.: 523150

GF Futures Co., Ltd. (1)
38th Floor 41st Floor 42nd Floor 43rd Floor Metropolitan Plaza 183-187, Tianhe North Road Tianhe District, Guangzhou, China
Tel.: (86) 2088800000
Web Site: http://www.gfqh.com.cn
Brokerage Services
N.A.I.C.S.: 523150

GF Global Capital Limited (1)
29th & 30th Floor Li Po Chun Chambers 189 Des Voeux Road Central, Hong Kong, China (Hong Kong)
Tel.: (852) 37191111
N.A.I.C.S.: 523999

GF Holdings (Hong Kong) Corporation Limited (1)
29-30/F Li Po Chun Chambers 189 Des Voeux Road, Central, China (Hong Kong)

Tel.: (852) 37191111
Investment Management Service
N.A.I.C.S.: 523940

GF International Investment Management Limited (1)
Suites 3503-3505 35/F Two International Finance Centre 8, Finance Street, Central, China (Hong Kong)
Tel.: (852) 36952800
Web Site: http://www.gffunds.com.hk
Investment Management Service
N.A.I.C.S.: 523940

GF Investment Management (Hong Kong) Company Limited (1)
29th & 30th Floor Li Po Chun Chambers 189 Des Voeux Road Central, Hong Kong, China (Hong Kong)
Tel.: (852) 37191111
N.A.I.C.S.: 523999

GF Investments (Hong Kong) Company Limited (1)
29th & 30th Floor Li Po Chun Chambers 189 Des Voeux Road Central, Hong Kong, China (Hong Kong)
Tel.: (852) 37191111
N.A.I.C.S.: 523999

GF Lighthouse Capital Management Company Limited (1)
Ritter House Wickhams Cay II, PO Box 3170, Road Town, VG1110, Tortola, Virgin Islands (British)
Tel.: (284) 37191111
N.A.I.C.S.: 523999

GF Securities (Canada) Co., Ltd. (1)
130-5911 No 3 Rd, Richmond, V6X 0K9, BC, Canada
Tel.: (778) 297-5888
Web Site: http://www.gfsecurities.ca
Investment Banking & Security Services
N.A.I.C.S.: 523150
David Hui Qing Wen (Chm)

GF Securities (Hong Kong) Brokerage Limited (1)
27/F GF Tower 81 Lockhart Road, Wan Chai, Hong Kong, China (Hong Kong)
Tel.: (852) 37191111
N.A.I.C.S.: 523999

GF Wealth Management (Hong Kong) Limited (1)
27/F GF Tower 81 Lockhart Road, Wan Chai, Hong Kong, China (Hong Kong)
Tel.: (852) 37602160
N.A.I.C.S.: 523999

GF Xinde Investment Management Co., Ltd. (1)
Race Course Road 26 GF Securities Building 26th Floor, Tianhe District, Guangzhou, China
Tel.: (86) 2066336059
Web Site: http://www.gfinvestment.cn
Investment Management Service
N.A.I.C.S.: 523940
Zeng Hao (Chm)

Ruiyuan Capital Asset Management Co., Ltd. (1)
Office 2607 3018 Huandao East Road, Hengqin New District, Zhuhai, China
Tel.: (86) 2089188990
N.A.I.C.S.: 523999

GFA CO., LTD.
Win Aoyama BIZ 2-2-15 Minami-aoyama, Minato-Ku, Tokyo, 107-0062, Japan
Tel.: (81) 364329140
Web Site: https://www.gfa.co.jp
Year Founded: 2002
8783—(TKS)
Rev.: $27,590,140
Assets: $29,824,320
Liabilities: $28,608,080
Net Worth: $1,216,240
Earnings: ($16,253,990)
Fiscal Year-end: 03/31/24
Financial Services
N.A.I.C.S.: 523999
Tomoki Katada (Board of Directors & Pres)

GFBIOCHEMICALS ITALY SPA

GFA Co., Ltd.—(Continued)

GFBIOCHEMICALS ITALY SPA
Via Durini 24, 20122, Milan, Italy
Tel.: (39) 0344 2379251
Web Site:
http://www.gfbiochemicals.com
Year Founded: 2008
Emp.: 50
Biobased Chemicals Mfr
N.A.I.C.S.: 325199
Maxim Katinov *(CEO)*

Subsidiaries:

Segetis (1)
684 Mendelssohn Ave N, Golden Valley, MN 55427
Tel.: (763) 795-7200
Web Site: http://www.segetis.bio
Biobased Chemicals Mfr
N.A.I.C.S.: 325199
Shauna Paul *(Dir-Corp Dev)*

GFC, LTD.
13 F 88 Sec 2 NanKing East Road
Section 2, Taipei, Taiwan
Tel.: (886) 225511166
Web Site: https://www.gfc.com.tw
Year Founded: 1974
4506—(TPE)
Rev.: $148,188,319
Assets: $282,186,724
Liabilities: $127,584,185
Net Worth: $154,602,539
Earnings: $26,508,176
Emp.: 1,325
Fiscal Year-end: 12/31/22
Elevator Distr
N.A.I.C.S.: 423830
Po-Lung Tang *(Chm)*

GFE-MIR HOLDINGS AG
Gartenstrasse 2, 6304, Zug, Switzerland
Tel.: (41) 417112570 CH
Web Site: http://gfe-mir.com
Sales Range: $250-299.9 Million
Emp.: 80
Holding Company; Metal Service Centers
N.A.I.C.S.: 551112
Frank Mitschke *(Gen Mgr)*

Subsidiaries:

GfE-MIR GmbH (1)
Berliner Allee 51-53, 40212, Dusseldorf, Germany
Tel.: (49) 211866080
Web Site: http://www.gfe-mir.com
Sales Range: $50-74.9 Million
Emp.: 11
Specialty Alloy Marketer & Distr
N.A.I.C.S.: 425120

Subsidiary (Non-US):

GfE-MIR Poland Sp (2)
ul Wielopole 18 B, 31-072, Krakow, Poland
Tel.: (48) 12 427 22 29
Metal Product Distr
N.A.I.C.S.: 331110
Wojciech Siekierko *(Pres)*

GfE-MIR (Shanghai) Ltd (1)
Room 1008 Times Square Building No 93 Huai Hai Zhong Road, Shanghai, China
Tel.: (86) 21 63910288 0
Metal Product Distr
N.A.I.C.S.: 331110
Jill Sang *(Gen Mgr)*

GfE-MIR Alloys and Minerals SA (PTY) Ltd (1)
2 Atomic Street, Vulcania, Johannesburg, 1554, South Africa
Tel.: (27) 11 740 1034
Metal Product Distr
N.A.I.C.S.: 331110
Nadia James *(Mgr-Fin)*

GfE-MIR Berlin (1)
Friedrichstr 95, PO Box 153, Berlin, Germany
Tel.: (49) 30 2060 9175
Metal Product Distr
N.A.I.C.S.: 331110

GFG ALLIANCE LIMITED
7 Hertford Street, Mayfair, London, W1J 7RH, United Kingdom
Tel.: (44) 203 205 8550 UK
Web Site: http://www.gfgalliance.com
Holding Company; Infrastructure, Mining, Energy Generation & Engineering Services
N.A.I.C.S.: 551112
Sanjeev Gupta *(Chm & CEO)*

Subsidiaries:

Adhunik Metaliks Limited (1)
Lansdowne Towers 2/1A Sarat Bose Road, Kolkata, 700020, West Bengal, India
Tel.: (91) 33 30517100
Web Site: http://www.adhunikgroup.com
Sales Range: $1-4.9 Billion
Emp.: 1,798
Metals Industry
N.A.I.C.S.: 331110
Nirmal Kumar Agarwal *(Mng Dir)*

Subsidiary (Domestic):

Adhunik Power & Natural Resources Ltd. (2)
2 Inner Cir Rd Shanti Hari Tower, Bistupur, Jamshedpur, 832001, Jharkhand, India
Tel.: (91) 6572224678
Web Site: http://www.adhunikgroup.com.in
Sales Range: $250-299.9 Million
Emp.: 500
Power Generation Services
N.A.I.C.S.: 221112
Naresh Goel *(Gen Mgr)*

Australian Tube Mills Pty. Limited (1)
Building 7 Industrial Drive, Mayfield, 2304, NSW, Australia
Tel.: (61) 800 281 424
Web Site: http://www.austubemills.com
Structural Steel Pipe & Tube Mfr
N.A.I.C.S.: 331210

InfraBuild Steel (Manufacturing) Pty Limited (1)
88 Phillip St, Sydney, 2000, NSW, Australia
Tel.: (61) 393602360
Web Site: http://www.infrabuild.com
Steel Mfrs
N.A.I.C.S.: 331513

Liberty House Limited (1)
7 Hertford Street, London, W1J 7RH, United Kingdom
Tel.: (44) 203 205 8550
Web Site: http://www.libertyhousegroup.com
Steel & Other Commodities Wholesale Trading & Supply Chain Services; Steel Products Mfr
N.A.I.C.S.: 425120
Sanjeev Gupta *(Founder & Chm)*

Subsidiary (Non-US):

ArcelorMittal Dudelange S.A. (2)
Zone Industrielle Wolser, BP 92, L 3401, Dudelange, Luxembourg
Tel.: (352) 5186861
Web Site: http://www.galvalange.lu
Strip Coating of Steel
N.A.I.C.S.: 332812

ArcelorMittal Galati S.A. (2)
Str Smardan nr 1, 6200, Bucharest, Romania
Tel.: (40) 236407633
Iron & Steel Mills
N.A.I.C.S.: 331110

ArcelorMittal Liege SA (2)
Quai du Halage 10, 4400, Flemalle, Belgium
Tel.: (32) 42361111
Rolled Steel Products Mfr
N.A.I.C.S.: 331221

ArcelorMittal Ostrava a.s. (2)
Vratimovska 689, Ostrava, 707 02, Kuncice, Czech Republic **(82.55%)**
Tel.: (420) 597331111
Web Site: http://www.mittal-steel.pl
Iron & Steel Mills

N.A.I.C.S.: 331110
Augustine Kochuparampil *(Chm-Supervisory Bd)*

ArcelorMittal Piombino S.p.A. (2)
Via Portovecchio 34, 57025, Piombino, Livorno, Italy
Tel.: (39) 0565 65111
Web Site: http://www.magona.it
Rolled Steel Products Mfr
N.A.I.C.S.: 331221
Giovanni Carpino *(COO & CTO)*

ArcelorMittal Skopje (CRM) AD (2)
Str 16 Makedonska Brigada No 18, MK 1000, Skopje, North Macedonia
Tel.: (389) 2 3247 300
Rolled Steel Products Mfr
N.A.I.C.S.: 331221

Subsidiary (US):

Johnstown Wire Technologies, Inc. (2)
124 Laurel Ave, Johnstown, PA 15906-2246 **(100%)**
Tel.: (814) 532-5600
Web Site: http://www.johnstownwire.com
Sales Range: $25-49.9 Million
Emp.: 250
Steel Wire Products Mfr
N.A.I.C.S.: 331222
Howard Phillips *(Mgr-Tech Sls)*

Liberty Steel Georgetown, Inc. (2)
420 S Hazard St, Georgetown, SC 29440
Tel.: (843) 485-4724
Web Site: http://www.libertyhousegroup.com
Emp.: 50
Carbon Wire Rod Mfr & Distr
N.A.I.C.S.: 331222

SIMEC Group Limited (1)
7 Hertford Street, London, W1J 7RH, United Kingdom
Tel.: (44) 203 205 8550
Web Site: http://www.simec.com
Infrastructure, Mining, Energy Generation & Engineering Services
N.A.I.C.S.: 541330
Jay Hambro *(CEO-Energy & Mining)*

Subsidiary (Non-US):

Tahmoor Coal Pty. Limited (2)
Remembrance Drive, PO Box 100, Tahmoor, 2573, NSW, Australia
Tel.: (61) 2 4640 0100
Web Site: http://www.simec.com
Coal Mining
N.A.I.C.S.: 212115

Tasmanian Electro Metallurgical Company Pty. Ltd. (1)
Temco Road, Bell Bay, 7253, TAS, Australia **(60%)**
Tel.: (61) 363820200
Web Site: http://www.south32.net
Sales Range: $200-249.9 Million
Emp.: 270
Manganese Mining
N.A.I.C.S.: 212290
Greg Hannan *(Pres-Asset)*

GFG RESOURCES INC.
202-640 Broadway Ave, Saskatoon, S7N 1A9, SK, Canada
Tel.: (306) 931-0930 BC
Web Site:
https://www.gfgresources.com
Year Founded: 2012
2GQ—(DEU)
Rev.: $705,271
Assets: $25,701,836
Liabilities: $1,060,220
Net Worth: $24,641,616
Earnings: $(911,157)
Fiscal Year-end: 06/30/24
Metal Mining & Exploration Services
N.A.I.C.S.: 212290
Brian Skanderbeg *(Pres & CEO)*

GFH FINANCIAL GROUP B.S.C.
Harbor House 2nd Floor, PO Box 10006, Manama, Bahrain

INTERNATIONAL PUBLIC

Tel.: (973) 17538538
Web Site: https://www.gfh.com
Year Founded: 1999
GFH—(ABU)
Rev.: $369,527,000
Assets: $11,121,479,000
Liabilities: $10,047,117,000
Net Worth: $1,074,362,000
Earnings: $105,227,000
Emp.: 821
Fiscal Year-end: 12/31/23
Investment Banking Services
N.A.I.C.S.: 523150
Hisham Ahmed Al-Rayes *(CEO)*

Subsidiaries:

Britus International School for Special Education W.L.L. (1)
Building 2312 Road 5755 Block 457, Bu Quwah, Bahrain
Tel.: (973) 16568120
Web Site: https://britus-se.edu.bh
Educational Institution Services
N.A.I.C.S.: 611710

Capital Real Estate Projects B.S.C. (1)
15th Floor Al Zamil Tower, PO Box 11183, Manama, Bahrain
Tel.: (973) 17507888
Web Site: https://caprealco.com
Real Estate Investment Services
N.A.I.C.S.: 531210

GBCORP Tower Real Estate W.L.L. (1)
GFH Tower Bahrain Financial Harbour, Floor 5 Building 1411 Road 4626 Block 346 Area Sea-front, Manama, Bahrain
Tel.: (973) 17200200
Web Site: https://www.gbcorponline.com
Property Development Services
N.A.I.C.S.: 531390

GFH Partners Ltd (1)
Unit 401 Level 4 Precinct Building 3, PO Box 506544, Gate District Dubai International Financial Centre, Dubai, United Arab Emirates **(100%)**
Tel.: (971) 43651500
Web Site: https://gfhpartners.com
Asset Management & Investment Banking Services
N.A.I.C.S.: 523940
Ahmed Khalifa Al Khalifa *(Chm)*

Gbcorp BSC (1)
GBCORP Tower Bahrain Financial Harbour Floor 5 Building 1411 Road, PO Box 1486, Block 346 Area Sea-fron, Manama, Bahrain
Tel.: (973) 17200200
Web Site: https://www.gbcorponline.com
Investment Banking Services
N.A.I.C.S.: 523999
Hisham Alrayes *(Chm)*

Gulf Holding Company KSCC (1)
Shayma Tower 10th Floor Murgad Block 3 Omar Ibin Alkhattab Street, Kuwait, Kuwait
Tel.: (965) 2 227 1777
Web Site: https://www.gfholding.com
Real Estate Services
N.A.I.C.S.: 531390
Esam Al Rifai *(Chm)*

Khaleeji Bank B.S.C. (1)
GFH Tower Bahrain Financial Harbour District, PO Box 60002, 2nd-4th-6th-7th Floors Building 1411 Road 4626 Block 346, Manama, Bahrain **(69.05%)**
Tel.: (973) 17505050
Web Site: https://khaleeji.bank
Rev.: $77,417,045
Assets: $3,781,581,390
Liabilities: $1,758,019,681
Net Worth: $2,023,561,709
Earnings: $37,152,861
Emp.: 195
Fiscal Year-end: 12/31/2022
Commercial Banking Services
N.A.I.C.S.: 522110
Husam Ghanem Saif *(Asst Gen Mgr-Treasury Investments)*

Roebuck Asset Management LLP (1)
60 St James's Street, London, SW1A 1LE, United Kingdom

AND PRIVATE COMPANIES

Tel.: (44) 203 829 9657
Web Site: https://www.roebuckam.com
Real Estate Services
N.A.I.C.S.: 531390
Hugh Macdonald-Brown *(Mng Partner)*

The Lost Paradise of Dilmun Water Park BSC (1)
Near Bahrain International Circut Formula One Zallaq Building 1663, Road 6227 Block 1062, Manama, Bahrain
Tel.: (973) 17845100
Web Site: http://www.lpodwaterpark.com
Water Amusement Park
N.A.I.C.S.: 713110

GFI SOFTWARE S.A.
7a Rue Robert Stuemper, L-2557, Luxembourg, Luxembourg
Tel.: (352) 27860231   LU
Web Site: http://www.gfi.com
Year Founded: 1992
Network Security, Content Security & Messaging Software
N.A.I.C.S.: 513210
Dan Beer *(Sr VP & Gen Mgr)*

Subsidiaries:

Exinda Inc. (1)
8 Faneuil Hall Marketplace 3rd Floor, Boston, MA 02109
Tel.: (877) 439-4632
Innovative WAN Optimization & Network Control Solutions
N.A.I.C.S.: 517112

GFI Asia Pacific Pty Ltd (1)
83 King William Road, Unley, 5061, Australia
Tel.: (61) 3 8273 3000
Web Site: http://www.gfiap.com
Network Security, Content Security & Messaging Software
N.A.I.C.S.: 513210

GFI Software USA, Inc. (1)
4309 Emperor Blvd, Durham, NC 27703
Tel.: (919) 379-3397
Web Site: http://www.gfi.com
Network Security, Content Security & Messaging Software Sales
N.A.I.C.S.: 423430
Walter Scott *(CEO)*

Subsidiary (Domestic):

Engine Yard, Inc. (2)
401 Congress Ave Ste 2650, Austin, TX 78701
Tel.: (415) 624-8380
Web Site: http://www.engineyard.com
Software Publisher
N.A.I.C.S.: 513210
Andy Tryba *(CEO)*

GFINITY PLC
16 Great Queen Street, London, WC2B 5AH, United Kingdom
Tel.: (44) 2080176172   UK
Web Site: https://www.gfinityplc.com
GFIN—(LSE)
Rev.: $7,730,023
Assets: $7,818,241
Liabilities: $3,033,881
Net Worth: $4,784,360
Earnings: ($5,221,241)
Emp.: 38
Fiscal Year-end: 06/30/21
Internet Gaming Services
N.A.I.C.S.: 541511
Neville Upton *(Founder & Chm)*

GFM SERVICES BERHAD
A-3A-1 Melawati Corporate Centre Jalan Bandar Melawati, Taman Melawati, 53100, Kuala Lumpur, Malaysia
Tel.: (60) 341010555   MY
Web Site: https://www.gfmservices.com.my
GFM—(KLS)
Rev.: $29,798,624
Assets: $112,228,996
Liabilities: $77,761,887
Net Worth: $34,467,109
Earnings: $3,870,001
Emp.: 458
Fiscal Year-end: 12/31/22
Investment Holding Services
N.A.I.C.S.: 551112
Ruslan Nordin *(Vice Chm)*

GFOOT CO., LTD.
1-23-5 Shinkawa, Chuo-ku, Tokyo, 104-0033, Japan
Tel.: (81) 355668850
Web Site: http://www.g-foot.co.jp
Year Founded: 1971
2686—(TKS)
Rev.: $458,021,090
Assets: $231,438,870
Liabilities: $265,166,000
Net Worth: ($33,727,130)
Earnings: ($12,535,120)
Emp.: 888
Fiscal Year-end: 02/29/24
Shoe Retailer & Wholesaler
N.A.I.C.S.: 424340
Yasufumi Horie *(Pres)*

GFPT PUBLIC COMPANY LIMITED
312 Rama II Road, Chom Thong District, Bangkok, 10150, Thailand
Tel.: (66) 24738000
Web Site: https://www.gfpt.co.th
Year Founded: 1981
GFPT—(THA)
Rev.: $553,555,334
Assets: $739,518,669
Liabilities: $221,709,071
Net Worth: $517,809,598
Earnings: $40,370,388
Emp.: 3,361
Fiscal Year-end: 12/31/23
Frozen Food Mfr & Distr
N.A.I.C.S.: 424420
Prasit Sirimongkolkasem *(Chm)*

Subsidiaries:

GFPT Public Company Limited - GFPT Plant (1)
209 Moo 1 Teparak Road KM 20 5, Bangsaothong, Samut Prakan, 10540, Thailand
Tel.: (66) 2 315 9400
Broiler Chicken Production Services
N.A.I.C.S.: 112320

GFT TECHNOLOGIES SE
Schelmenwasenstr 34, 70567, Stuttgart, Germany
Tel.: (49) 711620420   De
Web Site: https://www.gft.com
GFT—(DEU)
Rev.: $885,016,600
Assets: $620,949,414
Liabilities: $354,845,156
Net Worth: $266,104,258
Earnings: $53,388,383
Emp.: 9,134
Fiscal Year-end: 12/31/23
IT Solutions
N.A.I.C.S.: 541512
Jochen Ruetz *(Mng Dir, CFO & Member-Exec Bd)*

Subsidiaries:

GFT Canada Inc. (1)
70 University Avenue Suite 1460, Toronto, M5J 2M4, ON, Canada
Tel.: (647) 954-9907
IT & Software Development Services
N.A.I.C.S.: 541512

GFT Costa Rica S.A. (1)
Edificio 1B Ultrapark La Aurora, Heredia, Costa Rica
Tel.: (506) 22930207
IT & Software Development Services
N.A.I.C.S.: 541512

GFT Financial Limited (1)
6th floor 7 Bishopsgate, London, EC2N 3AR, United Kingdom
Tel.: (44) 2033729200
IT & Software Development Services
N.A.I.C.S.: 541512

GFT IT Consulting, S.L.U. (1)
Avinguda Alcalde Barnils 71, 08174, Sant Cugat del Valles, Spain
Tel.: (34) 935639000
Sales Range: $200-249.9 Million
Emp.: 800
Bank Software Maintenance & Development Services
N.A.I.C.S.: 541511
Carlos Eres *(Mng Dir)*

GFT Iberia Solutions S.A. (1)
C Caleruega 81 5 A, 28033, Madrid, Spain
Tel.: (34) 917814880
Sales Range: $25-49.9 Million
Emp.: 80
Information Technology Solutions
N.A.I.C.S.: 541511

Subsidiary (Non-US):

GFT Brasil Consultoria Informatica Ltda. (2)
Alameda Rio Negro n 500 - 13 Andar - Torre A, Alphaville, Barueri, 06454-000, SP, Brazil
Tel.: (55) 1121763253
Sales Range: $25-49.9 Million
Emp.: 10
Information Technology Solutions
N.A.I.C.S.: 541511
Marco Santos *(Mgr)*

Subsidiary (US):

GFT USA Inc. (2)
261 Madison Ave 19th Fl, New York, NY 10016
Tel.: (929) 484-1240
Information Technology Solutions
N.A.I.C.S.: 541511

GFT Italia S.r.l. (1)
Via Sile 18, 20139, Milan, Italy
Tel.: (39) 02581581
IT & Software Development Services
N.A.I.C.S.: 541512

GFT Mexico S.A. de C.V. (1)
Calle Gobernador Agustin Vicente Eguia 46 6, Colonia San Miguel Chapultepec, 11850, Mexico, Mexico
Tel.: (52) 5528816400
IT & Software Development Services
N.A.I.C.S.: 541512

GFT Poland Sp. z o.o (1)
ul Kilinskiego 66, 90-118, Lodz, Poland
Tel.: (48) 426630860
IT & Software Development Services
N.A.I.C.S.: 541512
Pawel Cebula *(Mgr-Delivery)*

GFT Switzerland AG (1)
Baumackerstrasse 24, 8050, Zurich, Switzerland
Tel.: (41) 448781600
IT & Software Development Services
N.A.I.C.S.: 541512
Arno Jordan *(Mgr-Project)*

GFT Technologies (Schweiz) AG. (1)
Baumackerstrasse 24, 8050, Zurich, Switzerland
Tel.: (41) 44 878 1600
Web Site: https://www.gft.com
Sales Range: $25-49.9 Million
Emp.: 50
Information Technology Solutions
N.A.I.C.S.: 541511
Soavo Curte *(Gen Mgr)*

GFT Technologies Canada Inc. (1)
990 Avenue de Bourgogne Suite 510, Quebec, G1W 0E8, QC, Canada
Tel.: (418) 780-0801
IT & Software Development Services
N.A.I.C.S.: 541512

GFT UK Limited (1)
Cheapside House 138 Cheapside, London, EC2V 6BJ, United Kingdom
Tel.: (44) 2077767676
Web Site: http://www.gft.com
Sales Range: $25-49.9 Million
Emp.: 30
Information Technology Solutions
N.A.I.C.S.: 541511
Andrew Rossiter *(Head-Tech Svcs)*

GFT inboxx GmbH. (1)
Mittelweg 177, 20148, Hamburg, Germany
Tel.: (49) 40355500
Web Site: http://www.gftinboxx.com
Documents & Data Archiving Services
N.A.I.C.S.: 519210
Joachim Moser *(Mng Dir)*

Med-Use S.r.l. (1)
Via Sile 18, 20139, Milan, Italy
Tel.: (39) 02581581
IT & Software Development Services
N.A.I.C.S.: 541512

SW34 Gastro GmbH (1)
Schelmenwasenstr 34, 70567, Stuttgart, Germany
Tel.: (49) 71162042252
Web Site: https://sw34.restaurant
Restaurant Services
N.A.I.C.S.: 722511

GGI GENEVA GROUP INTERNATIONAL AG
Schaffhauserstrasse 550, PO Box 286, 8052, Zurich, Switzerland
Tel.: (41) 44 256 18 18
Web Site: http://www.ggi.com
Accounting, Law & Consulting Firms
N.A.I.C.S.: 541110
Claudio G. Cocca *(Founder & Chm)*

GGI SOLUTIONS
1455 32nd Avenue, Lachine, H8T 3J1, QC, Canada
Tel.: (514) 631-6662
Web Site: https://e2ip.com
Year Founded: 1990
Electronic Products Mfr
N.A.I.C.S.: 334419
Eric Saint-Jacques *(CEO)*

Subsidiaries:

The Bergquist Company - Bigfork Facility (1)
61959 State Hwy 38, Bigfork, MN 56628-4436
Tel.: (218) 743-1200
Membrane Switch & Touch Screen Product Mfr
N.A.I.C.S.: 334419

GGK ZURICH WERBEAGENTUR AG
Seefeldstrasse 229, CH-8034, Zurich, Switzerland
Tel.: (41) 44 388 69 69   CH
Web Site: http://www.ggk.ch
Year Founded: 1979
Advetising Agency
N.A.I.C.S.: 541810
Hermann Strittmatter *(Chm)*

Subsidiaries:

Aichner Clodi GGK (1)
Petersbrunnstrasse 19 1-2, 5020, Salzburg, Austria
Tel.: (43) 662624640
Emp.: 26
Advetising Agency
N.A.I.C.S.: 541810

GGL RESOURCES CORP.
Suite 510 1100 Melville Street, Vancouver, V6E 4A6, BC, Canada
Tel.: (604) 688-0546
Web Site: https://www.gglresourcescorp.com
Year Founded: 1981
GGLXF—(OTCIQ)
Rev.: $8,862
Assets: $4,231,565
Liabilities: $502,420
Net Worth: $3,729,145
Earnings: ($1,530,234)
Fiscal Year-end: 11/30/22
Mineral Exploration Services
N.A.I.C.S.: 213114

GGL Resources Corp.—(Continued)
David Kelsch (Pres & COO)

GGP SWEDEN AB
Vastra Vagen 31, PO Box 1006, 573 28, Tranas, Sweden
Tel.: (46) 14067700
Web Site: http://www.steiga.se
Sales Range: $1-9.9 Million
Emp.: 2,000
Lawnmower, Chipper, Shredder & Snowblower Mfr
N.A.I.C.S.: 333112
Pir-Olos Ryd (Mgr)

GGUMBI CO,. LTD.
A-713 Gwanggyo SK View Lake 25 Beopjo-ro, Yeongtong-gu, Suwon, Gyeonggi-do, Korea (South)
Tel.: (82) 7078093253
Web Site:
https://www.en.ggumbi.com
Year Founded: 2014
407400—(KRS)
Clothing Products Distr
N.A.I.C.S.: 424350

GGX GOLD CORP.
888 Dunsmuir Street Suite 888, Vancouver, V6C 3K4, BC, Canada
Tel.: (604) 488-3900   BC
Web Site: https://www.ggxgold.com
Year Founded: 2007
GGXXF—(OTCIQ)
Assets: $95,013
Liabilities: $886,389
Net Worth: ($791,376)
Earnings: ($1,378,045)
Fiscal Year-end: 06/30/19
Gold Exploration Services
N.A.I.C.S.: 212220
Barry Brown (CEO)

GH RESEARCH PLC
Joshua Dawson House Dawson Street, Dublin, D02 RY95, Ireland
Tel.: (353) 14378443   IE
Web Site: https://www.ghres.com
Year Founded: 2021
GHRS—(NASDAQ)
Rev.: $8,978,000
Assets: $226,300,000
Liabilities: $7,332,000
Net Worth: $218,968,000
Earnings: ($35,587,000)
Emp.: 49
Fiscal Year-end: 12/31/23
Biotechnology Research & Development Services
N.A.I.C.S.: 541714
Theis Terwey (Co-Founder & CEO)

GHABBOUR AUTO S.A.E.
Cairo-Alexandria Desert Road Km 28 Industrial Zone Abou Rawash, PO Box 60 Smart Village, Giza, Egypt
Tel.: (20) 235391047
Web Site:
http://www.ghabbourauto.com
AUTO—(EGX)
Rev.: $916,189,818
Assets: $1,377,823,436
Liabilities: $691,855,816
Net Worth: $685,967,620
Earnings: $58,611,083
Emp.: 17,852
Fiscal Year-end: 12/31/23
Motor Vehicle Mfr, Importer & Distr
N.A.I.C.S.: 336110
Raouf Ghabbour (Chm & CEO)

Subsidiaries:

Egyptian Vehicles Manufacturing Co. S.A.E. (1)
Km 3 Cairo-Alexandria Agricultural Road Meet Nama, Cairo, Egypt

Tel.: (20) 242141224
Luxury Cars Mfr
N.A.I.C.S.: 336999

GB Polo Bus Manufacturing Company (1)
Economic & Industrial Zone, North West Suez Gulf, Suez, Egypt
Tel.: (20) 2 4215 0790
Bus Mfr; Joint Venture of Marcopolo S.A. & Ghabbour Auto S.A.E.
N.A.I.C.S.: 336110

Ghabbour Continental Trading Co, S.A.E. (1)
Ghabbour Auto Building Alexandria Desert Road Abu Rawash, PO Box 120, Industrial Zone km 28, Giza, Egypt
Tel.: (20) 235391201
Automobile Dealers
N.A.I.C.S.: 441110

Haram Transportation Co. S.A.E. (1)
Km 28 Industrial Zone Cairo Alexandria Desert Road, Abo Rawash, Giza, Egypt
Tel.: (20) 239100438
Passenger & Cargo Transportation Services
N.A.I.C.S.: 484110

International Trade Agencies and Marketing Co. S.A.E. (1)
28 Km Cairo Alex Desert Road Next to Emirates Gas Station, PO Box 120, Cairo, Egypt
Tel.: (20) 235390760
New Car Dealers
N.A.I.C.S.: 441110

GHADIR INVESTMENT COMPANY
No 58 Sarve Street Upper Than Mirdamad Ave Valie asr Ave, PO Box 15815-1874, 19696, Tehran, Iran
Tel.: (98) 2188787163
Web Site: http://www.ghadir-invest.com
Year Founded: 1991
GDIR1—(THE)
Sales Range: Less than $1 Million
Holding Companies
N.A.I.C.S.: 551112
Seyed Majid Ebne-Reza (Chm)

GHANA COCOA BOARD
PO Box 933, Accra, Ghana
Tel.: (233) 302661752
Web Site: http://www.cocobod.gh
Cocoa Promotion & Administrative Services
N.A.I.C.S.: 926140
Jospeh Boahen Aidoo (Acting CEO)

Subsidiaries:

Cocoa Marketing Company (Ghana) Limited (1)
Room 302 Cocoa House, PO Box 1017, Accra, Ghana
Tel.: (233) 23321668281
Web Site: http://www.cocoamarketing.com
Cocoa Product Distr
N.A.I.C.S.: 424590
Joseph Darko Mperey (Deputy Mgr-Transport)

Ghana Cocoa Board - Cocoa Health and Extension Division (1)
PO Box 3197, Accra, Ghana
Tel.: (233) 302666946
Cocoa Product Distr
N.A.I.C.S.: 424590

Ghana Cocoa Marketing Company (UK) Ltd (1)
5 Granard Business Centre Bunns Lane Mill Hill, London, NW7 2DQ, United Kingdom
Tel.: (44) 2089064877
Cocoa Product Distr
N.A.I.C.S.: 424590
Edem Amegashie-Duvon (Head-UK & Europe & Mgr-Resident)

PBC Limited (1)
106 Olusegun Obasanjo Highway Dzorwulu, Accra, Ghana
Tel.: (233) 302745754

Web Site: https://www.pbcgh.com
Sales Range: $150-199.9 Million
Cocoa Purchasing, Inspecting & Storage Services
N.A.I.C.S.: 926140
Vivian Boadi Apenteng (Deputy CEO-Fin & Admin)

GHANA STOCK EXCHANGE
5th Floor Cedi House Liberia Road, PO Box 1849, Accra, Ghana
Tel.: (233) 21669908
Web Site: http://www.gse.com.gh
Stock Exchange Services
N.A.I.C.S.: 523210

GHANI AUTOMOBILE INDUSTRIES LIMITED
274B N Block Model Town Etx, Lahore, Pakistan
Tel.: (92) 4235168873
Web Site:
http://www.ghaniautomobiles.com
GAIL—(LAH)
Rev.: $1,069,765
Assets: $2,089,651
Liabilities: $1,675,042
Net Worth: $414,609
Earnings: ($170,507)
Emp.: 42
Fiscal Year-end: 06/30/19
Automobile Mfr
N.A.I.C.S.: 336991
Aftab Ahmad Khan (CEO)

GHANI GLASS LIMITED
Ghani Complex 40-L Model Town Extension, Lahore, Pakistan
Tel.: (92) 42111949949
Web Site:
https://www.ghaniglass.com
GHGL—(KAR)
Rev.: $123,841,555
Assets: $163,812,685
Liabilities: $51,975,499
Net Worth: $111,837,186
Earnings: $22,570,472
Emp.: 2,394
Fiscal Year-end: 06/30/19
Flat Glass Mfr
N.A.I.C.S.: 327120
Aftab Ahmad Khan (Deputy CEO)

Subsidiaries:

Ghani Glass Limited - Hattar Plant (1)
22 km Haripur Taxila Road, Haripur, Khyber Pakhtunkhwa, Pakistan
Tel.: (92) 995639236
Web Site: http://www.ghaniglass.com
Sales Range: $200-249.9 Million
Emp.: 800
Glass Mfr
N.A.I.C.S.: 327211
Amnullah Khan (Plant Mgr)

Ghani Glass Limited - Sheikhupura (Float Glass Plant) (1)
30-km Lahore-Sheikhupura Road, Sheikhupura, Punjab, Pakistan
Tel.: (92) 563406796
Web Site: http://www.ghanigroup.com.pk
Flat Glass Mfr
N.A.I.C.S.: 327211

RAK Ghani Glass LLC (1)
Villa 89 Al-Hamra Village Jazeera Al Hamra Near Al Hamra Mall, Ras al Khaimah, United Arab Emirates
Tel.: (971) 72434973
Web Site: https://rakghaniglassllc.com
Glass Container Mfr
N.A.I.C.S.: 327213

GHANI GLOBAL HOLDINGS LIMITED
10-N Model Town Ext, Lahore, 54000, Pakistan
Tel.: (92) 42351614245

Web Site:
https://www.ghaniglobal.com
Year Founded: 2007
GGL—(PSX)
Rev.: $26,973,830
Assets: $62,615,144
Liabilities: $20,266,640
Net Worth: $42,348,505
Earnings: $2,252,005
Emp.: 640
Fiscal Year-end: 06/30/23
Medical Gas Mfr
N.A.I.C.S.: 325120
Atique Ahmad Khan (CEO)

Subsidiaries:

Ghani Global Glass Limited (1)
10-N Model Town Ext, Lahore, 54000, Pakistan
Tel.: (92) 42351614245
Web Site: https://www.ghaniglobalglass.com
Glass Equipment Mfr
N.A.I.C.S.: 327215
Atique Ahmad Khan (Chm)

GHANI VALUE GLASS LIMITED
40-L Model Town, Lahore, Pakistan
Tel.: (92) 111949949   PK
Web Site:
https://www.ghanivalueglass.com
Year Founded: 1967
GVGL—(PSX)
Rev.: $13,767,085
Assets: $15,375,631
Liabilities: $6,573,133
Net Worth: $8,802,498
Earnings: $1,853,897
Emp.: 504
Fiscal Year-end: 06/30/23
Glass Products Mfr
N.A.I.C.S.: 327215
Imtiaz Ahmad Khan (Chm)

GHARDA CHEMICALS LIMITED
Gharda House 48 Hill Road, Bandra West, Mumbai, 400 050, India
Tel.: (91) 2266265600   In
Web Site: http://www.gharda.com
Year Founded: 1964
Sales Range: $75-99.9 Million
Emp.: 1,500
Agrochemicals, Intermediates, Veterinary Drugs & Polymers Mfr & Sales
N.A.I.C.S.: 325320
Keki H. Gharda (Chm & Mng Dir)

Subsidiaries:

Gharda Chemicals Limited - Dombivili Plant (1)
B-27 Phase 1 MIDC Dombivili, Thane, 421 201, Maharashtra, India
Tel.: (91) 251 2803380
Insecticides Mfr
N.A.I.C.S.: 325320

Gharda Chemicals Limited - Lote Plant (1)
D-1/2 MIDC Lote Parshuram Taluka Khed, Ratnagiri, 415 709, Maharashtra, India
Tel.: (91) 2356 272252
Insecticides Mfr
N.A.I.C.S.: 325320

Gharda Chemicals Limited - Panoli Plant (1)
Plot No 3525 GIDC Estate, Panoli, Bharuch, 394 116, Gujarat, India
Tel.: (91) 2646 272513
Insecticides Mfr
N.A.I.C.S.: 325320

Gujarat Insecticides Limited (1)
Plot No 805/806 GIDC Estate, PO Box No 90, Ankleshwar, 393 002, Bharuch, Gujarat, India (100%)
Tel.: (91) 2646222271
Web Site: http://www.gilgharda.com
Emp.: 440
Pesticide & Agricultural Chemical Mfr

AND PRIVATE COMPANIES

N.A.I.C.S.: 325320
K. H. Gharda (Chm & Mng Dir)

GHARIBWAL CEMENT LIMITED
Pace Tower 1st Floor 27 H-Block College Road Gulberg-II, Lahore, Pakistan
Tel.: (92) 4236060600
Web Site:
https://www.gharibwalcement.com
GWLC—(KAR)
Rev.: $81,535,491
Assets: $167,024,003
Liabilities: $77,407,221
Net Worth: $89,616,782
Earnings: $5,287,438
Emp.: 427
Fiscal Year-end: 06/30/19
Cement Mfr
N.A.I.C.S.: 325520
Abdur Rafique Khan (Exec Dir)

Subsidiaries:

Gharibwal Cement Ltd. - Factory (1)
Ismailwal, Chakwal, Punjab, Pakistan
Tel.: (92) 5444351678
Cement Mfr
N.A.I.C.S.: 327310

GHAZI FABRICS INTERNATIONAL LIMITED
8-C Block E-III Gulberg III, Lahore, 54660, Pakistan
Tel.: (92) 4235764026
Web Site:
https://www.ghazifabrics.com
GFIL—(KAR)
Rev.: $38,906,887
Assets: $22,565,552
Liabilities: $14,016,901
Net Worth: $8,548,651
Earnings: $(369,370)
Emp.: 1,813
Fiscal Year-end: 06/30/19
Yarn & Fabric Mfr
N.A.I.C.S.: 313110
Muhammad Kamran Arshad (Dir-Technical & Comml)

GHAZVIN SUGAR COMPANY
1st South Unit No 121 Hamsiyan Street Between Kargar, And Jamalzadeh Street Keshavarz Boulevard, Tehran, Iran
Tel.: (98) 21 66435306
Year Founded: 1964
Sugar Mfr
N.A.I.C.S.: 311314

GHCL LIMITED
GHCL House B-38 Institutional Area Sector-1, Noida, 203 301, India
Tel.: (91) 1204939900
Web Site: https://www.ghcl.co.in
Year Founded: 1983
500171—(BOM)
Rev.: $399,551,880
Assets: $542,977,890
Liabilities: $203,877,765
Net Worth: $339,100,125
Earnings: $44,515,380
Emp.: 5,006
Fiscal Year-end: 03/31/21
Textile Product & Soda Ash Mfr
N.A.I.C.S.: 314120
R. S. Jalan (Mng Dir)

Subsidiaries:

Best Manufacturing Group LLC (1)
10 Exchange Pl Unit 22, Jersey City, NJ 07302-3917
Tel.: (201) 356-3800
Web Site: http://www.bestmfg.com
Sales Range: $400-449.9 Million
Emp.: 1,020
Mfr of Men's & Women's Washable Apparel; Wholesale Textiles

N.A.I.C.S.: 315250
Division (Domestic):

Best Textiles Acquisition, LLC (2)
424 W Taylor St Ste 11, Griffin, GA 30223
Tel.: (770) 227-5561
Web Site: http://www.besttextiles.com
Sales Range: $25-49.9 Million
Emp.: 20
Apparel
N.A.I.C.S.: 313310
Sandy Harris (Office Mgr)

Grace Home Fashions LLC (1)
34 W 33rd St Ste 1015, New York, NY 10001
Tel.: (212) 273-0760
Web Site:
https://www.gracehomefashions.com
Home Furnishing Product Mfr & Distr
N.A.I.C.S.: 337121

GHD GROUP PTY LTD.
Level 15 133 Castlereagh St, Sydney, 2000, NSW, Australia
Tel.: (61) 2 9239 7100   AU
Web Site: http://www.ghd.com
Year Founded: 1928
Sales Range: $1-4.9 Billion
Emp.: 8,500
Holding Company; Engineering, Architecture & Environmental Consulting Services
N.A.I.C.S.: 551112
Rob Knott (Chm)

Subsidiaries:

GHD Limited (1)
GHD Centre Level 3 27 Napier Street, Freemans Bay, Auckland, 1036, New Zealand
Tel.: (64) 9 370 8000
Emp.: 120
Engineeering Services
N.A.I.C.S.: 541330
Ian Fraser (Mgr)

GHD S.A. (1)
Avda Apoquindo No 4775 Piso 6 Oficina 601 Torre Apoquindo, Las Condes, Santiago, Chile
Tel.: (56) 24335400
Emp.: 90
Engineeering Services
N.A.I.C.S.: 541330
Ignacio Gaueca (Mgr-Bus Dev)

eSolutions Group (1)
455 Phillip Street, Waterloo, N2L 3X2, ON, Canada
Tel.: (519) 884-3352
Web Site: http://www.esolutionsgroup.ca
Emp.: 55
Marketing, Communications & Creative Services
N.A.I.C.S.: 541613
Karen Mayfield (Pres)

GHISALBA S.P.A.
Via Tevere 15, Cascine Vica, 10098, Rivoli, Turin, Italy
Tel.: (39) 01195991
Web Site: http://www.ghisalba.com
Year Founded: 1947
Sales Range: $10-24.9 Million
Emp.: 90
Electrical Equipment & Supply Mfr
N.A.I.C.S.: 335999
Gian Luigi Quario (Pres)

GHM MESSTECHNIK GMBH
Tenter Weg 2-8, 42897, Remscheid, Germany
Tel.: (49) 219196720   De
Web Site: http://www.ghm-group.de
Year Founded: 2009
Sales Range: $25-49.9 Million
Emp.: 330
Industrial Measurement & Control Product Designer, Mfr & Whslr
N.A.I.C.S.: 335314
Johannes Overhues (Mng Dir)

Subsidiaries:

Delta OHM S.r.l. (1)
Via G Marconi 5, 35030, Caselle di Selvazzano, PD, Italy
Tel.: (39) 049 8977150
Web Site: http://www.deltaohm.com
Environmental Measuring Equipment Mfr
N.A.I.C.S.: 334519
Michaela Zavan (Dir-Site)

GHM Messtechnik GmbH - Standort Greisinger (1)
Hans-Sachs-Strasse 26, 93128, Regenstauf, Germany
Tel.: (49) 9402 9383 0
Web Site: http://www.greisinger.de
Industrial Indicators, Regulators & Measuring Devices Mfr
N.A.I.C.S.: 334513
Roland Bauml (Member-Exec Bd & Mgr-Site-Greisinger)

GHM Messtechnik GmbH - Standort Honsberg (1)
Tente Weg 2, 42897, Remscheid, Germany
Tel.: (49) 2191 9252 0
Web Site: http://www.ghm-group.de
Industrial Measuring & Monitoring Equipment Mfr
N.A.I.C.S.: 334513
Hans Muller (Dir-Site)

GHM Messtechnik GmbH - Standort Imtron (1)
Carl-Benz-Strasse 11, 88696, Owingen, Germany
Tel.: (49) 7551 9290 0
Web Site: http://www.ghm-group.de
Stationary, Mobile & Automobile Measuring Equipment Mfr
N.A.I.C.S.: 334519
Markus Kleemann (Dir-Site)

GHM Messtechnik GmbH - Standort Martens (1)
Kiebitzhorn 18, 22885, Barsbuttel, Germany
Tel.: (49) 40 67073 0
Web Site: http://www.ghm-group.de
Industrial Measuring, Controlling & Regulating Equipment Mfr
N.A.I.C.S.: 334513
Michael Wulf (Dir-Site)

Val.co Srl (1)
Via Rovereto 9/11, Nerviano, 20014, Milan, Italy
Tel.: (39) 0331 53 5920
Web Site: http://www.valco.it
Industrial Flow Control & Temperature Instrumentation Designer, Mfr & Whslr
N.A.I.C.S.: 334513
Alessandro Perego (Gen Mgr)

GHN AGRISPAN HOLDING COMPANY
402 M 16 Xinfeng 3rd Road, Xiamen, China
Tel.: (86) 136 66001113   NV
Web Site:
http://www.ghnagrispan.com
Year Founded: 2009
Sales Range: $25-49.9 Million
Emp.: 255
Holding Company; Catering Services; Fruits, Vegetables & Dry Food Supplies Distr & Sales to Restaurants
N.A.I.C.S.: 551112
Yizhen Xu (Pres & CEO)

GHO CAPITAL PARTNERS LLP
44 Davies Street, London, W1K 5JA, United Kingdom
Tel.: (44) 2037007440   UK
Web Site: http://www.ghocapital.com
Year Founded: 2014
Emp.: 14
Healthcare Investment Company
N.A.I.C.S.: 523999
Mike Turner (Partner)

Subsidiaries:

DNA Diagnostics Center, Inc. (1)
1 DDC Way, Fairfield, OH 45014

Tel.: (513) 881-7800
Web Site: http://www.dnacenter.com
DNA Testing Laboratories
N.A.I.C.S.: 541380
Michael Baird (Chief Science Officer)

Envision Pharma Inc. (1)
75 Kings Highway Cutoff, Fairfield, CT 06824
Tel.: (203) 480-0080
Web Site:
http://www.envisionpharmagroup.com
Emp.: 1,000
Scientific Communications & Technology Services
N.A.I.C.S.: 541990
Loubna Bouarfa (Chm)

Subsidiary (Non-US):

Envision Pharma Limited (2)
Ground Floor 26-28 Hammersmith Grove, London, W6 7HA, United Kingdom
Tel.: (44) 208 834 3930
Web Site:
http://www.envisionpharmagroup.com
Scientific Communications & Technology Services
N.A.I.C.S.: 541990

Sanner GmbH (1)
Schillerstrasse 76 Bensheim, 64625, Hessen, Germany
Tel.: (49) 62519380
Web Site: https://www.sanner-group.com
Emp.: 600
Packaging & Containers Mfg.
N.A.I.C.S.: 333993

Sterling Pharma Solutions Ltd. (1)
Sterling Place Dudley, Cramlington, NE23 7QG, Northd, United Kingdom
Tel.: (44) 1912500471
Web Site:
https://www.sterlingpharmasolutions.com
Pharmaceutical Manufacturing
N.A.I.C.S.: 325412

Subsidiary (Non-US):

Novartis Ringaskiddy Limited (2)
Raheens East Co Cork, Ringaskiddy, P43 FR63, Ireland
Tel.: (353) 214862000
Pharmaceuticals Product Mfr
N.A.I.C.S.: 325412

Velocity Clinical Research, Inc (1)
807 E Main St Ste 06-100, Durham, NC 27701
Tel.: (919) 937-2458
Web Site: https://velocityclinical.com
Clinical & Pharmaceutical Research
N.A.I.C.S.: 541714
Paul G. Evans (Pres & CEO)

Subsidiary (Domestic):

Medpharmics, LLC (2)
3800 Houma Blvd Ste 335, Metairie, LA 70006
Tel.: (504) 782-8896
Web Site: http://www.medpharmics.com
Health Practitioners
N.A.I.C.S.: 621399
Andrea Jeanfreau (CEO)

Meridian Clinical Research, LLC (2)
3319 N 107th St, Omaha, NE 68134
Tel.: (402) 933-6500
Web Site: http://www.mcrmed.com
Sales Range: $1-9.9 Million
Emp.: 200
Scientific Research & Development Services
N.A.I.C.S.: 541714
Nicole Osborn (CEO)

Subsidiary (Domestic):

North Cliff Consultants, Inc. (3)
3747 Warsaw Ave, Cincinnati, OH 45205
Tel.: (513) 251-4930
Web Site: http://www.northclifftesting.com
Educational Support Services
N.A.I.C.S.: 611710
Paul McOsker (Pres)

GHOST STUDIO LTD.
RoomA-B 31/F Montery Plaza 15

GHOST STUDIO LTD.

Ghost Studio Ltd.—(Continued)
ChongYip Street, Gangnam-gu, Kwun Tong, China (Hong Kong)
Tel.: (852) 260043329
Web Site: https://www.me2zen.com
Year Founded: 2016
950190—(KRS)
Rev.: $75,943,773
Assets: $97,421,705
Liabilities: $6,856,084
Net Worth: $90,565,621
Earnings: $20,019,348
Emp.: 173
Fiscal Year-end: 12/31/22
Software Development Services
N.A.I.C.S.: 541511

GHOST-BIKES GMBH
An der Tongrube 3, 95652, Waldsassen, Germany
Tel.: (49) 963292550
Web Site: http://www.ghost-bikes.com
Rev.: $19,054,341
Emp.: 92
Bike Whslr
N.A.I.C.S.: 441227
Klaus Mohwald (Co-CEO)

GHP GROUP
17 Ostogenka, 119034, Moscow, Russia
Tel.: (7) 4954115300
Web Site: http://www.ghpgroup.com
Year Founded: 2000
Sales Range: $75-99.9 Million
Emp.: 110
Private Equity, Wealth Management & Real Estate Investment Services
N.A.I.C.S.: 523999
Denis Sukhanov (Deputy Chm & Partner)

Subsidiaries:

GHP Asset Management Limited (1)
Regency Court Glategny Esplanade, Saint Peter Port, GY1 1WW, Guernsey
Tel.: (44) 148 173 0945
Asset Management Services
N.A.I.C.S.: 531390

GHP Group - Real Estate Division (1)
4 Romanov Pereulok, Moscow, 125009, Russia
Tel.: (7) 495 411 5300
Emp.: 75
Real Estate Investment & Asset Management Services
N.A.I.C.S.: 531390
Oleg Myshkin (Mng Partner)

GHP NOETIC SCIENCE-PSYCHEDELIC PHARMA, INC.
18 Lumley Avenue, Toronto, M4G 2X5, ON, Canada
Tel.: (647) 949-2663
PSYF.P—(TSXV)
Sales Range: Less than $1 Million
Business Consulting Services
N.A.I.C.S.: 522299
Michael Franks (CEO)

GHT CO., LTD.
No 16 Nanyun 1st Road Science City, Huangpu District, Guangzhou, 510663, Guangdong, China
Tel.: (86) 2035812888
Web Site: https://www.ghtchina.com
Year Founded: 1986
300711—(CHIN)
Rev.: $63,509,026
Assets: $142,290,346
Liabilities: $42,938,714
Net Worth: $99,351,632
Earnings: $8,621,513
Fiscal Year-end: 12/31/23
Telecommunication Services

N.A.I.C.S.: 517410
Sun Yequan (Chm & Gen Mgr)

GHUSHINE FINTRRADE OCEAN LIMITED
Meznine Floor M-12 Nilkamal Apt Mahatmawadi Salabatpura, Surat, 395003, Gujarat, India
Tel.: (91) 9377647822
Web Site: https://ghushineindia.com
Year Founded: 1995
Rev.: $2,571,190
Assets: $805,856
Liabilities: $7,938
Net Worth: $797,918
Earnings: $6,243
Fiscal Year-end: 03/31/17
Textile Products Distr
N.A.I.C.S.: 424310
Alok Bhopalsingh Jain (CEO & Mng Dir)

GHW INTERNATIONAL
Unit 15C 15/F 235 Wing Lok Street Trade Centre, Sheung Wan, China (Hong Kong)
Tel.: (852) 35908200   Ky
Web Site: http://www.goldenhighway.com
Year Founded: 1995
9933—(HKG)
Rev.: $474,370,463
Assets: $235,680,073
Liabilities: $151,072,225
Net Worth: $84,607,848
Earnings: $38,557,631
Emp.: 1,028
Fiscal Year-end: 12/31/22
Chemical Product Mfr & Distr
N.A.I.C.S.: 325199
Yanbin Yin (Founder, Chm & CEO)

Subsidiaries:

GHW (Vietnam) Chemicals Limited Company (1)
DC Tower No 111D Ly Chinh Thang Street, Ward 7 District 3, Ho Chi Minh City, Vietnam
Tel.: (84) 2835268260
Chemical Products Distr
N.A.I.C.S.: 424690

GHW Eurochemicals s.r.o. (1)
Spitalska 53, 811 01, Bratislava, Slovakia
Tel.: (421) 233418556
Web Site: https://www.ghw-eu.com
Chemical Products Distr
N.A.I.C.S.: 424690

GHW USA LLC (1)
5819 Highway 6 Ste 120, Missouri City, TX 77459
Tel.: (832) 850-7611
Web Site: https://www.ghwus.com
Chemical Products Distr
N.A.I.C.S.: 424690

Golden Highway Mexico, S. de R.L. de C.V. (1)
Av de las Americas No 1166A 2o Piso Int 8 Colonia Country Club, 44610, Guadalajara, Jalisco, Mexico
Tel.: (52) 3315294249
Chemical Products Distr
N.A.I.C.S.: 424690

Guangzhou GHW Trading Co., Ltd. (1)
Room 611 No 4 Huating Road, Tianhe District, Guangzhou, Guangdong, China
Tel.: (86) 2038878773
Chemical Products Distr
N.A.I.C.S.: 424690

Havay Industry Inc. (1)
14888 23 Ave, Surrey, V4A 9X2, BC, Canada
Tel.: (514) 802-3446
Chemical Products Distr
N.A.I.C.S.: 424690

Star International Saint-Petersburg LLC (1)

Koli Tomchaka str 28 lit A off 311, 196006, Saint Petersburg, Russia
Tel.: (7) 8122426613
Web Site: https://starpu.ru
Chemical Product Mfr & Distr
N.A.I.C.S.: 325180

Taian Havay Group Co., Ltd. (1)
Dawenkou Industrial Park, Da'an, Shandong, China
Tel.: (86) 5385052177
Web Site: http://en.havay.com.cn
Chemical Product Mfr & Distr
N.A.I.C.S.: 325180

Ukrhimformacia Limited Company (1)
Knyazhyi Zaton St 9, 2095, Kiev, Ukraine
Tel.: (380) 445775202
Chemical Products Distr
N.A.I.C.S.: 424690

GHY CULTURE & MEDIA HOLDING CO., LIMITED
988 Toa Payoh North 07-08, Singapore, 319002, Singapore
Tel.: (65) 63526778   Ky
Web Site: https://www.ghyculturemedia.com
Year Founded: 2018
XJB—(SES)
Rev.: $55,785,049
Assets: $131,939,711
Liabilities: $38,246,611
Net Worth: $93,693,100
Earnings: ($7,430,887)
Emp.: 158
Fiscal Year-end: 12/31/23
Holding Company
N.A.I.C.S.: 551112
Guo Jingyu (Chm & CEO)

Subsidiaries:

Ghy Culture & Media (Malaysia) Sdn. Bhd. (1)
Suite 13 01A 13th Floor Wisma Chuang 34 Jalan Sultan Ismail, 50250, Kuala Lumpur, Malaysia
Tel.: (60) 321106678
Film Production Services
N.A.I.C.S.: 512110

GI ENGINEERING SOLUTIONS LIMITED
Unit 1308 Aggarwal Corporate Heights Netaji Subhash Palace, Andheri E, New Delhi, 110034, India
Tel.: (91) 1144789583
Web Site: https://www.giesl.in
Year Founded: 2006
533048—(BOM)
Rev.: $27,603
Assets: $626,042
Liabilities: $32,007
Net Worth: $594,035
Earnings: ($344,245)
Emp.: 1
Fiscal Year-end: 03/31/21
Engineeering Services
N.A.I.C.S.: 541330
Sajid Malik (Chm & Mng Dir)

Subsidiaries:

Genesys Enterprises Inc. (1)
777 Westchester Ave Ste 101, White Plains, NY 10604
Tel.: (914) 694-9040
Information Technology Consulting Services
N.A.I.C.S.: 541512

GI INNOVATION INC.
1116 Building A Terra Tower 167 Songpa-daero, Songpa-gu, Seoul, 005855, Korea (South)
Tel.: (82) 24042003
Web Site: https://www.gi-innovation.com
Year Founded: 2017
358570—(KRS)
Rev.: $1,839,564

INTERNATIONAL PUBLIC

Assets: $97,827,880
Liabilities: $9,833,366
Net Worth: $87,994,514
Earnings: ($73,446,415)
Emp.: 88
Fiscal Year-end: 12/31/22
Biotechnology Research & Development Services
N.A.I.C.S.: 541714
Myoung Ho Jang (Founder)

GI TECH CO LTD.
42 Asanbaelli-Ro 387Beon-Gil, Dunpo-Myeon, Asan, Chungcheongnam-do, Korea (South)
Tel.: (82) 415431316
Web Site: https://www.gitech.com
Year Founded: 1990
382480—(KRS)
Mold Mfr
N.A.I.C.S.: 333511
In-Young Lee (Pres & Co-CEO)

GI TECHNOLOGY GROUP CO., LTD.
Dongzhimen South Street A Central No 11 Room 1101, Beijing Dongcheng District, Beijing, 100007, China
Tel.: (86) 1067806016
Web Site: http://www.gi-tech.cn
Year Founded: 1996
300309—(CHIN)
Rev.: $29,397,935
Assets: $855,722,281
Liabilities: $838,116,920
Net Worth: $17,605,361
Earnings: ($88,008,420)
Fiscal Year-end: 12/31/20
Oil Exploration & Development Services; Oil Well Logging Instrument Mfr
N.A.I.C.S.: 333131

Subsidiaries:

Xinjiang jichuang Asset Management Co., Ltd. (1)
No 366 South Station Road, Huangpu District, Shanghai, 200011, China
Tel.: (86) 2163288366
Petroleum Refining Services
N.A.I.C.S.: 324110

GI VENTURES
72 New Cavendish Street, London, W1G 8AU, United Kingdom
Tel.: (44) 2031371108
Year Founded: 2010
Investment Services
N.A.I.C.S.: 523999
Dennis Hoffmann (Chm & CEO)

Subsidiaries:

INFURN (USA) LLC (1)
19C Trolley Sq, Wilmington, DE 19806
Tel.: (888) 231-4253
Web Site: http://www.infurn.com
Data Processing Services
N.A.I.C.S.: 518210

GIA LAI ELECTRICITY JOINT STOCK COMPANY
114 Truong Chinh Street, Phu Dong Ward,, Pleiku, Gia Lai, Vietnam
Tel.: (84) 2693823604
Web Site: https://geccom.vn
Year Founded: 1989
Emp.: 546
Renewable Energy
N.A.I.C.S.: 221118

GIA TZOONG ENTERPRISE CO., LTD.
No 39-4 Xingbang Rd, Taoyuan, 330, Taiwan
Tel.: (886) 33625499

AND PRIVATE COMPANIES

Web Site: https://www.gia-tzoong.com.tw
Year Founded: 1988
5355—(TPE)
Rev.: $15,348,248
Assets: $45,740,425
Liabilities: $7,143,482
Net Worth: $38,596,942
Earnings: ($2,136,885)
Emp.: 369
Fiscal Year-end: 12/31/22
Circuit Board Mfr
N.A.I.C.S.: 334418
Jerry Tseng (CEO)

GIACOM (CLOUD) HOLDINGS LIMITED
Milton Gate, 60 Chiswell Street,, London, EC1Y 4AG, United Kingdom
Tel.: (44) 3304333888
Web Site: https://giacom.com
Year Founded: 2016
Holding Company
N.A.I.C.S.: 551111

Subsidiaries:

Giacom (Cloud) Limited (1)
Milton Gate 60 Chiswell Street, London, EC1Y 4AG, United Kingdom
Tel.: (44) 3304333888
Web Site: https://www.giacom.com
Software Development Services
N.A.I.C.S.: 513210
Terry O'Brien (CEO)

Subsidiary (Domestic):

IntY Ltd. (2)
170 Aztec West, Bristol, BS32 4TN, United Kingdom
Tel.: (44) 1454640500
Software Development Services
N.A.I.C.S.: 513210
Spencer Wilkinson (CTO)

GIAI JACQUIS SAS
Quartier De Romezieres Route D Orange, 84600, Valence, France
Tel.: (33) 490351460
Rev.: $21,000,000
Emp.: 40
New & Used Car Dealers
N.A.I.C.S.: 441110
Philippe Giai (Pres)

GIAN LIFE CARE LIMITED
7/216 6 Swaroop Nagar, Kanpur, 208002, Uttar Pradesh, India
Tel.: (91) 8808051576
Web Site: https://gianlifecare.org
542918—(BOM)
Health Care Srvices
N.A.I.C.S.: 621610
Arun Kumar Gupta (Chm & Mng Dir)

GIANT BIOGENE HOLDING CO., LTD.
No 1855 Shanglinyuan Seventh Road, High-tech Zone, Xi'an, Shaanxi, China
Tel.: (86) 2981156502   Ky
Web Site: https://www.xajuzi.com
Year Founded: 2000
2367—(HKG)
Rev.: $362,256,618
Assets: $480,807,452
Liabilities: $46,145,626
Net Worth: $434,661,826
Earnings: $153,452,991
Emp.: 933
Fiscal Year-end: 12/31/22
Holding Company
N.A.I.C.S.: 551112
Daidi Fan (Chief Scientific Officer)

GIANT MANUFACTURING CO., LTD.
No 999 Sec 1 Dongda Rd, Xitun Dist, Taichung, 40763, Taiwan
Tel.: (886) 24609099
Web Site: https://www.giant-bicycles.com
Year Founded: 1972
9921—(TAI)
Rev.: $2,516,548,713
Assets: $2,767,367,599
Liabilities: $1,579,451,329
Net Worth: $1,187,916,270
Earnings: $116,628,793
Emp.: 13,695
Fiscal Year-end: 12/31/23
Bicycles & Related Products Mfr
N.A.I.C.S.: 336991

Subsidiaries:

AIPS Technology Co., Ltd. (1)
No 901 Sec 2 Zhongshan Rd, Dajia Dist, Taichung, 437101, Taiwan
Tel.: (886) 424609099
Web Site: https://www.aips.com.tw
Sporting Goods Mfr & Distr
N.A.I.C.S.: 339920

Bike Group S.A. (1)
Av Libertador 3994 La Lucila, 1938, Buenos Aires, Argentina (100%)
Tel.: (54) 1145121640
Web Site: http://www.bikegroup.com
Sales Range: $25-49.9 Million
Emp.: 10
Sporting Goods Retailer
N.A.I.C.S.: 459110

D. Mag (Kunshan) New Material Technology Co., Ltd. (1)
No 118 Pengxi South Road, Kunshan, Jiangsu, China
Tel.: (86) 51257639000
Alloys Product Mfr & Distr
N.A.I.C.S.: 331314

GIANT Belgium N.V. (1)
Burchtstraat 190, 9150, Kruibeke, Belgium
Tel.: (32) 3 722 99 99
Bicycle & Gear Mfr
N.A.I.C.S.: 336991

GIANT France S.A.R.L. (1)
780 rue J R Guillibert G de la Lauziere, 13290, Aix-en-Provence, France
Tel.: (33) 809549590
Web Site: http://www.giant-bicycles.com
Emp.: 20
Bicycle & Gear Mfr
N.A.I.C.S.: 336991

GIANT Sales Company Ltd. (1)
No 117 Section 2 Henan Road, Xitun District, Taichung, 407, Taiwan
Tel.: (886) 423112357
Bicycle & Gear Mfr
N.A.I.C.S.: 336991

Giant (China) Co. Ltd. (1)
No 1 Shunfan Rd, Economic Technology Developmen, Kunshan, China
Tel.: (86) 51257709888
Web Site: http://www.giant-bicycles.com
Motorcycle Bicycle & Parts Mfr
N.A.I.C.S.: 336991

Giant Benelux B.V. (1)
Pascallaan 66, 8218 NJ, Lelystad, Netherlands
Tel.: (31) 850138261
Bicycle Mfr & Distr
N.A.I.C.S.: 336991

Giant Bicycle Canada, Inc. (1)
100-2255 Dollarton Highway, North Vancouver, V7H 3B1, BC, Canada
Tel.: (604) 987-3600
Bicycle & Gear Mfr
N.A.I.C.S.: 336991

Giant Bicycle Co. Ltd. (1)
89 Seongsuil-ro, Seongdong-gu, 100-829, Seoul, Korea (South)
Tel.: (82) 2 463 7171
Web Site: http://www.giant-korea.com
Sales Range: $25-49.9 Million
Emp.: 10
Motorcycle Bicycle & Parts Mfr
N.A.I.C.S.: 336991

Giant Bicycle Co. Pty. Ltd. (1)
Unit 7 3-5 Gilda Court, Mulgrave, 3170, VIC, Australia (100%)
Tel.: (61) 385414800
Sales Range: $25-49.9 Million
Emp.: 13
Sporting & Recreational Goods & Supplies Whslr
N.A.I.C.S.: 423910
Darren Rtherford (Gen Mgr)

Giant Bicycle De Mexico S de R.L. de C.V. (1)
Blvd Adolfo Ruiz Cortines 5183 Piso 1 Col Isidro Fabela, Tlalpan, 14030, Mexico, Mexico
Tel.: (52) 5576927100
Web Site: https://www.giant-bicycles.com
Bicycle Mfr & Distr
N.A.I.C.S.: 336991

Giant Bicycle Inc. (1)
3587 Old Conejo Rd, Newbury Park, CA 91320
Tel.: (805) 267-4600
Emp.: 60
Bicycle & Gear Mfr
N.A.I.C.S.: 336991
Sean Burkey (Acct Exec-Ohio & Northern Kentucky)

Giant Bike Co., Ltd. (1)
89 Seongsuil-ro, Seongdong-gu, Seoul, Korea (South)
Tel.: (82) 2 463 7171
Bicycle Mfr & Distr
N.A.I.C.S.: 336991

Giant Bikes Iberica S.A. (1)
Portuetxe 23 B Bajo 2, 20018, San Sebastian, Spain
Tel.: (34) 943314758
Web Site: http://www.giant.es
Sales Range: $25-49.9 Million
Emp.: 14
Sporting & Recreational Goods & Supplies Whslr
N.A.I.C.S.: 423910

Giant Colombia Disandina S.A. (1)
Cll 80 south 47D-65 Bod 108, Sabaneta, Antioquia, Colombia
Tel.: (57) 4 444 2404
Web Site: https//www.disandina.com
Sports Product Distr
N.A.I.C.S.: 459110

Giant Deutschland GmbH (1)
Mettmanner Str 25, 40699, Erkrath, Germany (100%)
Tel.: (49) 8001972001
Web Site: http://www.giant-bicycles.com
Sales Range: $25-49.9 Million
Emp.: 25
Sporting & Recreational Goods & Supplies Merchant Whslr
N.A.I.C.S.: 423910
Oliver Hensche (Mng Dir)

Giant Electric Vehicle (Kunshan) Co., Ltd. (1)
No 1 Yue-he South Road Economic & Technical Develop, Kunshan, Jiangsu, China
Tel.: (86) 51257725888
Electric Bike Mfr & Distr
N.A.I.C.S.: 336320

Giant Europe B.V. (1)
Pascallaan 66, 8218 NJ, Lelystad, Netherlands (100%)
Tel.: (31) 320296296
Web Site: http://www.giant-bicycles.com
Sales Range: $75-99.9 Million
Emp.: 200
Sporting & Recreational Goods & Supplies Whslr
N.A.I.C.S.: 423910

Giant Europe Manufacturing B.V. (1)
Pascallaan 66, 8218 NJ, Lelystad, Netherlands (100%)
Tel.: (31) 320296296
Sales Range: $50-74.9 Million
Emp.: 180
Motorcycle Bicycle & Parts Mfr
N.A.I.C.S.: 336991
Jeffrey Chin (Gen Mgr-Production)

Giant Holland B.V. (1)
Pascallaan 66, 8218 NJ, Lelystad, Netherlands (100%)
Tel.: (31) 320296296
Web Site: http://www.giant-bicycles.com
Sales Range: $75-99.9 Million
Emp.: 200
Sporting & Recreational Goods & Supplies Whslr
N.A.I.C.S.: 423910

Giant Italia S.r.l. (1)
Via Gallarate 49 Gazzada Schianno, 21045, Gazzada, Italy
Tel.: (39) 0332462295
Web Site: http://www.giant-bicycles.com
Sales Range: $50-74.9 Million
Emp.: 8
Sporting & Recreational Goods & Supplies Merchant Whslr
N.A.I.C.S.: 423910

Giant Korea Co., Ltd. (1)
89 Seongsuil-ro Seongsu-dong 1-ga, Seongdong-gu, Seoul, 04790, Korea (South)
Tel.: (82) 24637171
Bike Product Distr
N.A.I.C.S.: 423120

Giant Light Metal Technology (Malaysia) Sdn. Bhd. (1)
8-1 Jalan Prima Setapak 3 Off Jalan Genting Kelang Setapak, 53300, Kuala Lumpur, Malaysia
Tel.: (60) 376658685
Web Site: https://www.glmwheels.com
Aluminum Wheel Hub Product Distr
N.A.I.C.S.: 423510

Giant Manufacturing Hungary Ltd. (1)
Jedlik Anyos utca 1, 3200, Gyongyos, Hungary
Tel.: (36) 37557500
Bike Product Mfr & Distr
N.A.I.C.S.: 336991

Giant Mexico S. de R.L. de C.V. (1)
Av Division del Norte 208 4 Del Valle, Mexico, 03100, Mexico
Tel.: (52) 55 6267 7937
Bicycle & Gear Mfr
N.A.I.C.S.: 336991

Giant Polska Sp. z o.o. ul. (1)
Ul Osmanska 12 building C1, 02-823, Warsaw, Poland
Tel.: (48) 22 395 6590
Bicycle Mfr & Distr
N.A.I.C.S.: 336991

Giant Polska Sp. z o.o. (1)
ul Osmanska 12 budynek C1, 02-823, Warsaw, Poland (80%)
Tel.: (48) 223956590
Web Site: https://www.giant-bicycles.com
Sales Range: $25-49.9 Million
Emp.: 12
Sporting & Recreational Goods & Supplies Whslr
N.A.I.C.S.: 423910

Giant UK Ltd. (1)
Charnwood Edge Syston Road, Leicester, LE7 4UZ, United Kingdom
Sales Range: $25-49.9 Million
Emp.: 25
Sporting & Athletic Goods Mfr
N.A.I.C.S.: 339920

Giant Vietnam Manufacturing Company Limited (1)
No 19 VSIP II-A Road No 32 Vietnam-Singapore II-A Industrial Park, Tan Binh Commune, Tan Uyen, Binh Duong, Vietnam
Tel.: (84) 2743803991
Bike Product Mfr & Distr
N.A.I.C.S.: 336991

YouBike Co., Ltd. (1)
No 798 Beian Rd, Zhongshan Dist, Taipei, Taiwan
Tel.: (886) 289788822
Web Site: https://en.youbike.com.tw
Bicycle Rental Services
N.A.I.C.S.: 532284

GIANT NETWORK GROUP CO., LTD.
5th Floor Building 1 Wanda Plaza No

GIANT NETWORK GROUP CO., LTD.

Giant Network Group Co., Ltd.—(Continued)

8 Jiangnan Avenue, Nan'an District, Chongqing, 201613, China
Tel.: (86) 2133979919
Web Site: https://www.ga-me.com
Year Founded: 2006
002558—(SSE)
Rev.: $286,094,484
Assets: $1,854,553,428
Liabilities: $183,577,212
Net Worth: $1,670,976,216
Earnings: $119,473,380
Emp.: 1,643
Fiscal Year-end: 12/31/22
Cruise & Tour Operator
N.A.I.C.S.: 487210
Liu Wei *(Pres)*

Subsidiaries:

Giant Interactive Group Inc. (1)
11/F No 3 Building 700 Yishan Road, Shanghai, 200233, China
Tel.: (86) 21 3397 9999
Web Site: http://www.ga-me.com
Sales Range: $300-349.9 Million
Emp.: 1,529
Online Game Developer & Operator
N.A.I.C.S.: 713990
Yuzhu Shi *(Chm)*

GIANTCODE CORPORATION PLC

4th Floor 36 Spital Square, London, E1 6DY, United Kingdom
Tel.: (44) 203 397 1606
Web Site:
http://www.giantcodecorp.com
Biotechnology Researcher, Developer & Mfr
N.A.I.C.S.: 541714
Andre Rafnsson *(Chm)*

GIANTSTEP INC.

2F 8 Hakdong-Ro 37-Gil, Gangnam-Gu, Seoul, 06053, Korea (South)
Tel.: (82) 25490005
Web Site: https://www.giantstep.co.kr
Year Founded: 2008
289220—(KRS)
Rev.: $31,155,425
Assets: $112,203,467
Liabilities: $17,889,932
Net Worth: $94,313,536
Earnings: ($9,722,705)
Emp.: 339
Fiscal Year-end: 12/31/22
Digital Media Production Services
N.A.I.C.S.: 512110
Min-Hee Ahn *(CFO)*

GIAT INDUSTRIES S.A.

13 route de la Miniere, 78034, Versailles, Cedex, France
Tel.: (33) 1 3097 3737   FR
Web Site: http://www.nexter-group.fr
Year Founded: 2006
Sales Range: $1-4.9 Billion
Emp.: 2,700
Holding Company; Military Equipment, Weapon Systems & Munitions Mfr
N.A.I.C.S.: 551112
Michel Bonnefis *(CEO-Equipment Subsidiaries)*

Subsidiaries:

Euro-Shelter SA (1)
72 rue Claude Bernard CS 64338, 35043, Rennes, France
Tel.: (33) 2 99 01 73 73
Military Equipment Mfr
N.A.I.C.S.: 336992

NBC-Sys SAS (1)
8 Rue Bonnevialle, BP 10226, 42408, Saint-Chamond, France
Tel.: (33) 4 77 29 96 00
Military Equipment Mfr
N.A.I.C.S.: 336992

Nexter Electronics S.A. (1)
6 rue Claude-Marie Perroud, F-31100, Toulouse, France
Tel.: (33) 534466800
Web Site: http://www.nexter-group.fr
Sales Range: $25-49.9 Million
Emp.: 114
Embedded Electronic Systems Mfr
N.A.I.C.S.: 334418
Michel Bonnefis *(CEO)*

Nexter Mechanics S.A. (1)
20 rue du 9 juin 1944, BP 210, F-19012, Tulle, Cedex, France
Tel.: (33) 555206000
Web Site: http://www.nexter-group.fr
Sales Range: $25-49.9 Million
Emp.: 162
Mechanical & Hydraulic Equipment Mfr
N.A.I.C.S.: 333613
Michel Bonnefis *(CEO)*

Nexter Munitions S.A. (1)
Route de Villeneuve, La Chapelle-Saint-Ursin, 18570, France
Tel.: (33) 248687171
Web Site: http://www.nexter-group.fr
Sales Range: $200-249.9 Million
Emp.: 524
Ammunition Mfr
N.A.I.C.S.: 332993
Jean-Patrick Baillet *(CEO)*

Nexter Robotics (1)
14 route de la Miniere, 78034, Versailles, Cedex, France
Tel.: (33) 1 39 49 33 22
Military Equipment Mfr
N.A.I.C.S.: 336992

Nexter Systems S.A. (1)
34 boulevard de Valmy, BP 504, 42328, Roanne, Cedex, France
Tel.: (33) 477447900
Sales Range: $900-999.9 Million
Emp.: 900
Military Tank & Weapon Systems Mfr
N.A.I.C.S.: 332994
Jean-Patrick Baillet *(Mng Dir)*

Subsidiary (Non-US):

Mecar S.A. (2)
50 Rue Grinfaux, 7181, Petit-Roeulx-lez-Nivelles, Belgium (100%)
Tel.: (32) 6787 6411
Web Site: http://www.mecar.be
Sales Range: $125-149.9 Million
Emp.: 450
Ammunition & Weapon System Mfr
N.A.I.C.S.: 332994
Simon Haye *(Mng Dir)*

Simmel Difesa S.p.A. (2)
Via Consolare Latina I Traversa 200, 00034, Colleferro, Italy
Tel.: (39) 06 9730 4624
Sales Range: $50-74.9 Million
Emp.: 250
Small Arms Ammunition Mfr
N.A.I.C.S.: 332992
Massimiliano Cocorocchio *(Mgr-Pur)*

Nexter Training (1)
11 Allee Des Marronniers, Versailles, 78000, Yvelines, France
Tel.: (33) 1 39 49 30 00
Educational Support Services
N.A.I.C.S.: 611710

Optsys SAS (1)
7 rue Salvador Dali, BP 505, 42 007, Saint Etienne, France
Tel.: (33) 4 77 91 32 00
Emp.: 31
Military Equipment Mfr
N.A.I.C.S.: 336992

SNPE SA (1)
13 route de la miniere, 78034, Versailles, Cedex, France
Tel.: (33) 1 39 20 56 56
Web Site: http://www.snpe.com
Sales Range: $300-349.9 Million
Emp.: 2,000
Propellants & High Explosives Mfr
N.A.I.C.S.: 325920
Philippe Burtin *(Chm & CEO)*

Subsidiary (Domestic):

EURENCO (2)
30 avenue Carnot, 91300, Massy, France
Tel.: (33) 1 80 00 21 90
Web Site: http://www.eurenco.com
Sales Range: $100-124.9 Million
Emp.: 800
Propellants, High Explosives & Other Energetic Materials; Owned 60.2% by SNPE Materiaux Energetiques, 19.9% by SAAB AB & 19.9% by Patria Plc
N.A.I.C.S.: 325998

Subsidiary (Non-US):

EURENCO Bofors AB (3)
Bjorkborns Industriomr, 691 86, Karlskoga, Sweden (100%)
Tel.: (46) 58683050
Web Site: http://www.eurenco.com
Sales Range: $150-199.9 Million
Emp.: 410
Production & Sale of Propellants, Explosives & Formulations
N.A.I.C.S.: 325998
Thomas Resare *(Gen Mgr)*

Subsidiary (US):

EURENCO Bofors, Inc. (3)
20130 Lakeview Plaza Ctr Ste 400, Ashburn, VA 20147
Tel.: (703) 765-0625
Web Site: http://www.eurenco.com
Sales Range: Less than $1 Million
Emp.: 2
Remediation Services
N.A.I.C.S.: 562910

GIB CAPITAL GROUP, INC.

B-26F Oriental Kenzo, Dongcheng District, Beijing, 100027, China
Tel.: (86) 1064168816   NV
Year Founded: 1999
GIBX—(OTCIQ)
Assets: $2,063
Liabilities: $79,415
Net Worth: ($77,352)
Earnings: ($79,918)
Fiscal Year-end: 06/30/21
Digital Publishing
N.A.I.C.S.: 513199

GIBB RIVER DIAMONDS LIMITED

Ground Floor 16 Ord Street, West Perth, 6005, WA, Australia
Tel.: (61) 894229500   AU
Web Site:
https://www.gibbriverdiamonds.com
GIB—(ASX)
Rev.: $1,694,715
Assets: $7,193,243
Liabilities: $299,078
Net Worth: $6,894,165
Earnings: ($18,353)
Fiscal Year-end: 06/30/22
Phosphate Exploration & Mining Services
N.A.I.C.S.: 212390
James Mcarthur Richards *(Exec Chm)*

GIBCA LIMITED

GIBCA Building Al Wahda Street, Sharjah, United Arab Emirates
Tel.: (971) 65333333
Web Site: http://www.gibca.com
Year Founded: 1975
Sales Range: $350-399.9 Million
Emp.: 2,000
Holding Company
N.A.I.C.S.: 551112
Faisal Bin Sultan Al Qassimi *(Chm)*

Subsidiaries:

AIL Industries Co., Ltd. (1)
Industrial Area 13, PO Box 6011, Sharjah, United Arab Emirates
Tel.: (971) 6534777
Web Site: http://www.ailind.com

INTERNATIONAL PUBLIC

Emp.: 70
Aluminum, Brass & Bronze Architectural Products Mfr
N.A.I.C.S.: 332999
Sheikh Sultan *(Mng Dir)*

Aluminium & Light Industries Co. Ltd. (1)
Industrial Area 13, PO Box 6011, Sharjah, United Arab Emirates
Tel.: (971) 6 55 82 444
Web Site: http://www.alicoalum.net
Architectural Design Services
N.A.I.C.S.: 541310

Arabian Profile Company Limited (1)
Industrial Area 5 Maliha Road Opp Abu Dhabi Commercial Bank, Sharjah, United Arab Emirates
Tel.: (971) 65432624
Web Site: http://www.apl.ae
Sales Range: $100-124.9 Million
Emp.: 800
Construction Materials Mfr
N.A.I.C.S.: 333120
Harald Halvorsen *(Mng Dir)*

Continental Trading Co. LLC (1)
Industrial Area 18 Maliya Road, PO Box 3180, Sharjah, 3180, United Arab Emirates
Tel.: (971) 6 5983555
Web Site: http://www.ctcuae.com
Cleaning Machinery Mfr
N.A.I.C.S.: 333248
Julia Blance *(Office Mgr)*

EMA Lubricants Co. Ltd. (1)
PO Box 22316, Sharjah, United Arab Emirates
Tel.: (971) 65062600
Web Site: https://www.mobiluae.com
Sales Range: $75-99.9 Million
Lubricant Marketer & Distr
N.A.I.C.S.: 213112
Samy El Ansary *(Gen Mgr)*

GIBCA Crushing & Quarry Operations Co. Ltd. (1)
PO Box 289, Sharjah, United Arab Emirates
Tel.: (971) 6 561 77 75
Web Site: http://www.gibcacrusher.com
Building Materials Distr
N.A.I.C.S.: 423320

GIBCA Furniture Industries Co. Ltd. (1)
PO Box 20923, Ajman, United Arab Emirates
Tel.: (971) 6 7436888
Web Site: http://www.gfiuae.com
Furniture Mfr
N.A.I.C.S.: 337127

GIBCA Petroleum Services LLC (1)
PO Box 2570, Abu Dhabi, United Arab Emirates
Tel.: (971) 2 6260222
Web Site: http://www.gibca.com
Oil & Gas Exploration Services
N.A.I.C.S.: 213112

Grand Stores (1)
Khaleejia Street, PO Box 425, Abu Dhabi, United Arab Emirates
Tel.: (971) 26312100
Web Site: http://www.grandstores.com
Sales Range: $125-149.9 Million
Emp.: 300
Departmental Store Operator
N.A.I.C.S.: 455110
Mohammed Abu Issa *(Mng Dir)*

Gulf Air Conditioning Manufacturing Industries L.L.C (1)
Plot No 36D14 ICAD-1 Industrial City, PO Box 28131, Mussaffah, Abu Dhabi, United Arab Emirates
Tel.: (971) 25506777
Web Site: http://www.gami.ae
Emp.: 185
Air Conditioning Equipment Mfr
N.A.I.C.S.: 333415
Ammar Abdulatif *(Mgr-Quality Assurance)*

Gulf Glass Industries LLC (1)
PO Box 6022, Sharjah, United Arab Emirates
Tel.: (971) 6 5385500
Web Site: http://www.gulfglass.com
Construction Materials Distr

AND PRIVATE COMPANIES

N.A.I.C.S.: 423390
Ali ElSheikh (Mgr-Technical Sls)

TEKAB CO. LTD. (1)
Industrial Area No 13, PO Box 40474,
Sharjah, 0474, United Arab Emirates
Tel.: (971) 6 503 4900
Web Site: http://www.tekab.com
Emp.: 100
Cable Mfr
N.A.I.C.S.: 335921
Dina Tahan (Mgr-Admin & HR)

The Glasshouse L.L.C (1)
PO Box 6335, Sharjah, United Arab Emirates
Tel.: (971) 6 5432929
Web Site: http://www.glasshouseco.com
Decorative Glass Mfr
N.A.I.C.S.: 327212

GIBMEDIA S.A.R.L.
The Phenix 118 route d'Espagne,
31100, Toulouse, France
Tel.: (33) 177510600   FR
Web Site: http://www.gibmedia.fr
Year Founded: 2005
Payment Solutions
N.A.I.C.S.: 522320
Loic Jauson (Gen Mgr)

Subsidiaries:

HiPay SAS (1)
94 rue de villiers, Levallois-Perret, 92300,
Paris, France
Tel.: (33) 171255555
Web Site: http://www.hipay.com
Mobile Payment & Credit Card Processing
Services
N.A.I.C.S.: 522320
Nabil Naimy (COO)

GIBRALT CAPITAL CORPORATION
1075 West Georgia Street Suite
2600, Vancouver, V6E 3C9, BC,
Canada
Tel.: (604) 687-3707
Web Site: http://www.gibralt.com
Privater Equity Firm
N.A.I.C.S.: 523999
Ryan Chan (CFO)

GIBSON ENERGY INC.
Tel.: (403) 206-4000   AB
Web Site:
  https://www.gibsonenergy.com
GEI—(TSX)
Rev.: $3,862,950,270
Assets: $2,399,377,925
Liabilities: $1,867,701,323
Net Worth: $531,676,602
Earnings: $94,897,605
Emp.: 2,520
Fiscal Year-end: 12/31/20
Oil & Gas Exploration Services
N.A.I.C.S.: 211120
James M. Estey (Chm)

Subsidiaries:

Gibson Energy Marketing, LLC (1)
3819 Towne Crossing Blvd, Mesquite, TX
75150-2799
Tel.: (469) 941-7197
Petroleum Product Distr
N.A.I.C.S.: 424720

Gibson Energy ULC (1)
Suite 1700 440 2nd Avenue SW, Calgary,
T6P 1P4, AB, Canada
Tel.: (403) 206-4000
Holding Company
N.A.I.C.S.: 551112

Link Petroleum Inc. (1)
1440 Port of Tacoma Rd, Tacoma, WA
98421-3704
Tel.: (866) 584-0979
Propane Distr
N.A.I.C.S.: 424710

Moose Jaw Refinery Partnership (1)
641 Manitoba Street East, Box 2000,
Moose Jaw, S6H 6E3, SK, Canada
Tel.: (306) 691-7800
Web Site: http://www.moosejawrefinery.com
Emp.: 80
Petroleum Refining & Distribution Services
N.A.I.C.S.: 324110

OMNI Energy Services Corp. (1)
4500 NE Evangeline Thruway, Carencro,
LA 70520
Tel.: (337) 896-6664
Web Site: http://www.gibsonenergy.com
Sales Range: $100-124.9 Million
Emp.: 1,200
Fiscal Year-end: 12/31/2014
Oil Field Services
N.A.I.C.S.: 213112
Gregory B. Milton (VP & Chief Acctg Officer)

Subsidiary (Domestic):

A&A Tank Truck, Inc. (2)
3230 Bart Conner Dr, Norman, OK 73072
Tel.: (405) 364-2601
Web Site: http://www.aatank.com
Emp.: 4
Oil Field Services
N.A.I.C.S.: 213112

BEG Liquid Mud Services Corp. (2)
2502 E Austin St, Giddings, TX 78942
Tel.: (979) 542-7000
Oil Field Services
N.A.I.C.S.: 213112
Dan S. Keen (Gen Mgr)

Industrial Lift Truck & Equipment Co., Inc. (2)
700 Beau Pre Rd, Lafayette, LA 70508
Tel.: (337) 234-6313
Industrial Lifting Equipment Rental Services
N.A.I.C.S.: 532412
Eddie Boudreaux (Reg Mgr)

Keeton Services, Inc. (2)
3322 Longmire Dr, College Station, TX
77845
Tel.: (979) 693-7687
Web Site: http://www.gibsons.com
Emp.: 35
Oil Field Services
N.A.I.C.S.: 213112
Ralph Griswold (Mgr)

Preheat, Inc. (2)
4500 NE Evangeline Trwy, Carencro, LA
70520
Tel.: (337) 896-3906
Web Site: http://www.omnienergy.com
Sales Range: $50-74.9 Million
Emp.: 64
Oilfield, Commercial & Industrial Cleaning
Equipment & Services
N.A.I.C.S.: 213112

Rig Tools, Inc. (2)
Hwy 89 1920, Youngsville, LA 70592
Tel.: (337) 837-2496
Web Site: http://www.omnienergy.com
Sales Range: $10-24.9 Million
Emp.: 12
Construction & Mining Equipment Leasing &
Rental
N.A.I.C.S.: 532412

Trussco, Inc. (2)
4500 NE Evangeline Trwy, Carencro, LA
70520-5253
Tel.: (337) 325-1719
Web Site: http://www.trussco.com
Sales Range: $50-74.9 Million
Emp.: 55
Industrial Cleaning Services
N.A.I.C.S.: 213112

WISCO, Inc. (2)
4903 2 Ave W, Williston, ND 58801
Tel.: (701) 572-2135
Web Site: http://www.gibsonenergy.com
Sales Range: $50-74.9 Million
Emp.: 200
Construction, Mining & Forestry Machinery
& Equipment Rental & Leasing
N.A.I.C.S.: 532412

GIBUI HOLDING LTD.
Jabotinsky Street 7, Ramat Gan,
52520, Israel
Tel.: (972) 35107460   IL
GIBUI—(TAE)
Rev.: $10,847,887
Assets: $114,859,952
Liabilities: $91,249,908
Net Worth: $23,610,044
Earnings: $2,560,709
Fiscal Year-end: 12/31/22
Holding Company
N.A.I.C.S.: 551112
Yehonatan Cohen (Chm)

GIBUNCO GROUP LIMITED
Europort Building 7, PO Box 51, Gibraltar, Gibraltar
Tel.: (350) 20070454
Web Site: http://www.gibunco.com
Year Founded: 1965
Sales Range: $10-24.9 Million
Emp.: 40
Underwater Ship Maintenance & Marine Services
N.A.I.C.S.: 336611
John Bassadone (Chm)

Subsidiaries:

Gibunco Mechanical Ltd (1)
No 4 Jetty North Mole, PO Box 51, Gibraltar, Gibraltar
Tel.: (350) 200 42994
Mechanical Engineering Services
N.A.I.C.S.: 541330

Gibunco Ship Agency SL (1)
Calle 030 2Z, 51001, Ceuta, Spain
Tel.: (34) 956 52 21 88
Marine Shipping Services
N.A.I.C.S.: 488510

Peninsula Petroleum (Brokers) Ltd (1)
68 Pall Mall, London, SW1Y 5ES, United Kingdom
Tel.: (44) 20 7766 3999
Petroleum Product Distr
N.A.I.C.S.: 424720
James Davy (CFO)

Peninsula Petroleum (Monaco) S.a.r.l (1)
57 Rue Grimaldi, Monte Carlo, 98000, Monaco
Tel.: (377) 99 99 54 00
Web Site:
  http://www.peninsulapetroleum.com
Emp.: 5
Petroleum Product Distr
N.A.I.C.S.: 424720

Peninsula Petroleum AS (1)
Jarlsoveien 50, 3124, Tonsberg, Norway
Tel.: (47) 333 40 100
Petroleum Product Distr
N.A.I.C.S.: 424720
Bjorn Isaksen (Gen Mgr)

Peninsula Petroleum DMCC (1)
Unit 701 JBC 1 Jumeirah Lake Towers, PO
Box 111425, Dubai, United Arab Emirates
Tel.: (971) 4 445 8435
Petroleum Lubricant Distr
N.A.I.C.S.: 424720

Peninsula Petroleum EPE (1)
A Papandreou 90, Glyfada, 16674, Greece
Tel.: (30) 210 4287800
Petroleum Product Distr
N.A.I.C.S.: 424720

Peninsula Petroleum Far East Pte Ltd (1)
8 Temasek Boulevard 39-03 Suntec Tower
Three, 038988, Singapore, Singapore
Tel.: (65) 6238 6621
Petroleum Product Distr
N.A.I.C.S.: 424720
Martin Fynbo (Mgr-Mktg)

Peninsula Petroleum Inc. (1)
Ste 5201 Williams Tower 2800 Post Oak
Blvd, Houston, TX 77056
Tel.: (713) 850-7728
Web Site:
  http://www.peninsulapetroleum.com
Emp.: 8
Petroleum Lubricant Distr

N.A.I.C.S.: 424720
Alonso Young (Mgr-Sls)

Peninsula Petroleum Panama Inc. (1)
PH Office One Calle 64 y calle 50 Floor 12
Suite 1202, Panama, Panama
Tel.: (507) 380 0430
Web Site:
  http://www.peninsulapetroleum.com
Emp.: 5
Petroleum Lubricant Distr
N.A.I.C.S.: 424720
Sara Garcia (Mgr-Ops)

Peninsula Petroleum SA (1)
Rue du Conseil General 14, Geneva, 1205,
Switzerland
Tel.: (41) 22 322 9600
Petroleum Product Distr
N.A.I.C.S.: 424720
Alberto Fernandez de la Reguera (Mgr-Trading)

Peninsula Petroleum SL (1)
Muell De Embarcaciones Auxillares Modula
5 A, 11201, Cadiz, Spain
Tel.: (34) 956 668 965
Petroleum Product Distr
N.A.I.C.S.: 424720

Peninsula Petroleum South America SA (1)
Imperium Building 25 de Mayo 713 Office
612, 11000, Montevideo, Uruguay
Tel.: (598) 2903 3450
Petroleum Product Distr
N.A.I.C.S.: 424720

Scamp Marine SL (1)
Muelle Embarcadero Aux Mod 5 Recinto
Portuario, 11201, Algeciras, Spain
Tel.: (34) 956 633 918
Underwater Engineering Services
N.A.I.C.S.: 541330

GIBUS SPA
Via L Einaudi 35, Saccolongo, 35030,
Padua, Italy
Tel.: (39) 0498015392
Web Site: https://www.gibus.com
GBUS—(ITA)
Sales Range: $50-74.9 Million
Textile Products Mfr
N.A.I.C.S.: 314120
Gianfranco Bellin (Chm & CEO)

GIC HOUSING FINANCE LIMITED
National Insurance Building 6th floor
14 Jamshedji Tata Road, Churchgate,
Mumbai, 400020, Maharashtra, India
Tel.: (91) 2243041900
Web Site: https://www.gichfindia.com
Year Founded: 1989
GICHSGFIN—(NSE)
Rev.: $169,305,045
Assets: $1,725,474,660
Liabilities: $1,540,132,230
Net Worth: $185,342,430
Earnings: $14,410,305
Emp.: 319
Fiscal Year-end: 03/31/21
Financial Services
N.A.I.C.S.: 523999
S. Shridharan (CFO, Compliance Officer, Sec & Sr VP)

GIC PTE. LTD.
168 Robinson Road, 37-01 Capital
Tower, Singapore, 068912, Singapore
Tel.: (65) 68898888   SG
Web Site: http://www.gic.com.sg
Year Founded: 1981
Holding Company; Investment Management, Private Equity & Real Estate Investment Services
N.A.I.C.S.: 551112
Kee Chong Lim (Pres-Americas & Deputy Chief Investment Officer)

GIC PTE. LTD.

GIC Pte. Ltd.—(Continued)

Subsidiaries:

Allfunds Bank, S.A. (1)
Calle de los Padres Dominicos 7, 28109, Madrid, Spain
Tel.: (34) 912746400
Web Site: http://www.allfundsbank.com
Mutal Fund Distr
N.A.I.C.S.: 523150
Juan Alcaraz (CEO)

Cerved Group S.p.A (1)
Via dell Unione Europea No 6A 6B, San Donato, 20142, Milan, Italy
Tel.: (39) 0277541
Web Site: http://cerved.com
Rev.: $606,530,705
Assets: $1,853,969,324
Liabilities: $1,224,362,446
Net Worth: $629,606,878
Earnings: $36,150,788
Emp.: 2,600
Fiscal Year-end: 12/31/2020
Holding Company; Credit Information & Other Financial Services
N.A.I.C.S.: 551112

Subsidiary (Domestic):

Cerved Group SpA (2)
Via dell Unione Europea 6/A-6/B, San Donato Milanese, 20097, Milan, Italy
Tel.: (39) 02 77541
Web Site: http://www.cerved.com
Credit Management Services
N.A.I.C.S.: 561450
Gianandrea De Bernardis (Chm)

Subsidiary (Domestic):

Cerved Credit Management Group Srl (3)
Via San Vigilio n 1, 20142, Milan, Italy (80%)
Tel.: (39) 06 93370200
Credit Management Services
N.A.I.C.S.: 561450
Andrea Mignanelli (Founder & CEO)

Subsidiary (Domestic):

Cerved Credit Management Spa (4)
Via San Vigilio n 1, 20142, Milan, Italy (100%)
Tel.: (39) 06 93370200
Credit Management Services
N.A.I.C.S.: 561450
Andrea Mignanelli (Founder & CEO)

Subsidiary (Domestic):

Cerved Rating Agency S.p.A (3)
Via San Vigilio n 1, 20142, Milan, Italy (100%)
Tel.: (39) 02 77541
Web Site: http://ratingagency.cerved.com
Credit Rating Assessment Services
N.A.I.C.S.: 561450
Mauro Alfonso (Mng Dir)

ExamWorks Group, Inc. (1)
3280 Peachtree Rd NE Ste 2625, Atlanta, GA 30305
Tel.: (404) 952-2400
Web Site: http://www.examworks.com
Holding Company; Independent Medical Examinations, Peer & Bill Reviews & Related Services
N.A.I.C.S.: 551112
James K. Price (Co-Founder)

Subsidiary (Non-US):

Capital Vocational Specialists (2)
2781 Lancaster Road Suite 304, Ottawa, K1B 1A7, ON, Canada
Tel.: (613) 736-9117
Web Site: http://www.cvs.ca
Medical & Rehabilitation Services
N.A.I.C.S.: 624310
Stuart Jolliffe (Gen Mgr)

Subsidiary (Domestic):

ExamWorks Clinical Solutions, LLC (2)
2397 Huntcrest Way Ste 200, Lawrenceville, GA 30043
Tel.: (866) 270-2516
Web Site: http://www.examworks-cs.com
Medical Claim Case Management & Cost Containment Services
N.A.I.C.S.: 561499
Kevin Mahoney (COO)

Examworks Group, Inc. (2)
4141 Southwest Fwy Ste 500, Houston, TX 77027
Tel.: (800) 761-1177
Web Site: http://www.examworks.com
Diagnostic Imaging Services
N.A.I.C.S.: 621512

Examworks Group, Inc. (2)
4 Becker Farm Rd 1st Fl, Roseland, NJ 07068-1739
Tel.: (800) 761-1177
Web Site: http://www.examworks.com
Medical Examination Services
N.A.I.C.S.: 541990

MES Solutions (2)
150 Presidential Way Ste 110, Woburn, MA 01801
Tel.: (781) 933-1782
Web Site: http://www.messolutions.com
Medical Examination Services
N.A.I.C.S.: 621999
Donna Walthall (Mgr-Peer Review)

MLS Group of Companies, LLC (2)
20750 Civic Ctr Dr Ste 600, Southfield, MI 48034-1097
Tel.: (888) 657-4634
Web Site: http://www.mls-ime.com
Medical Examination Services
N.A.I.C.S.: 621999
Amanda Horvath (Dir-Provider Rels)

Subsidiary (Non-US):

Matrix Health Management Corp. (2)
5025 Orbitor Drive Building #5 Suite #400, Mississauga, L4W 4Y5, ON, Canada
Tel.: (905) 624-2900
Web Site: http://matrixhealth.ca
Medical Examination Services
N.A.I.C.S.: 541990
Rafael Chow (Dir-Medical)

MedHealth Pty Limited (2)
Level 10 451 Little Bourke Street, Melbourne, 3000, VIC, Australia
Tel.: (61) 386889388
Web Site: http://www.medhealthgroup.com.au
Emp.: 1,000
Data Management Services
N.A.I.C.S.: 561410
Tim Morphy (CEO & Dir)

Subsidiary (Domestic):

Medicolegal Services, LLC (2)
20300 W 12 Mile Rd Ste 201, Southfield, MI 48076
Tel.: (248) 352-6747
Web Site: http://www.medicolegal-mi.com
Emp.: 12
Medical Examination Services
N.A.I.C.S.: 621999

Prizm LLC (2)
10 E Stow Rd Ste 100, Marlton, NJ 08053
Tel.: (856) 596-5600
Web Site: http://www.prizmllc.com
Medical & Insurance Claim Management Software & Services
N.A.I.C.S.: 513210
Linda Diekmann (Pres & CEO)

Subsidiary (Non-US):

SOMA Medical Assessments Corp. (2)
8800 Dufferin Street Suite 105, Vaughan, L4K 0C5, ON, Canada
Tel.: (905) 881-8855
Web Site: http://www.somamedical.com
Medical Examination Services
N.A.I.C.S.: 541990
Mark Wigle (Pres)

UK Independent Medical Services Limited (2)
Brenner House Rainton Bridge Business Park, Houghton le Spring, DH4 5RA, United Kingdom
Tel.: (44) 3334141988
Web Site: http://www.ukindmed.com
Medical Examination Services

N.A.I.C.S.: 541990
Paul Healey (Chm)

direct IME Corp. (2)
3760 14th Avenue Suite 201, Markham, L3R 3T7, ON, Canada
Tel.: (416) 609-3211
Web Site: http://www.directime.ca
Health Care Srvices
N.A.I.C.S.: 621999

GIC Asset Management Pte. Ltd. (1)
168 Robinson Road 37-01 Capital Tower, Singapore, 068912, Singapore
Tel.: (65) 6889 8888
Web Site: http://www.gic.com.sg
Public Market Asset Management Services
N.A.I.C.S.: 523940
Jeffrey Jeansubhakij (Pres)

GIC Real Estate Pte. Ltd. (1)
168 Robinson Road 37-01 Capital Tower, Singapore, 068912, Singapore
Tel.: (65) 6889 8888
Web Site: http://www.gic.com.sg
Real Estate Investment & Development
N.A.I.C.S.: 531390

GIC Real Estate, Inc. (1)
280 Park Ave 9th Fl, New York, NY 10017
Tel.: (212) 856-2500
Web Site: https://www.gic.com.sg
Financial Services
N.A.I.C.S.: 523999
Michael Michael Jordan Jordan (Sr VP)

Joint Venture (Domestic):

INDUS Realty Trust, Inc. (2)
641 Lexington Ave, New York, NY 10022
Tel.: (212) 218-7910
Web Site: https://www.indusrt.com
Rev.: $49,195,000
Assets: $596,807,000
Liabilities: $199,538,000
Net Worth: $397,269,000
Earnings: $6,110,000
Emp.: 32
Fiscal Year-end: 12/31/2022
Real Estate Investment Trust
N.A.I.C.S.: 525990
Michael S. Gamzon (CEO)

Division (Domestic):

Griffin Land (3)
204 W Newberry Rd, Bloomfield, CT 06002-1308 (100%)
Tel.: (860) 286-7660
Web Site: http://www.griffinland.com
Sales Range: $1-9.9 Million
Emp.: 20
Real Estate Services
N.A.I.C.S.: 531390
Frederick Michael Danziger (Chm & CEO)

Joint Venture (Domestic):

STORE Capital Corporation (2)
8377 E Hartford Dr Ste 100, Scottsdale, AZ 85255
Tel.: (480) 256-1100
Web Site: http://www.storecapital.com
Rev.: $782,664,000
Assets: $9,773,082,000
Liabilities: $4,628,953,000
Net Worth: $5,144,129,000
Earnings: $268,348,000
Emp.: 117
Fiscal Year-end: 12/31/2021
Real Estate Investment Services
N.A.I.C.S.: 525990
Mary B. Fedewa (Pres & CEO)

Subsidiary (Domestic):

STORE Master Funding I, LLC (3)
8501 E Princess Dr 190, Scottsdale, AZ 85255
Tel.: (480) 256-1100
Mortgage Banking Services
N.A.I.C.S.: 522292

GIC Special Investments Pte. Ltd. (1)
168 Robinson Road #37-01 Capital Tower, Singapore, 068912, Singapore
Tel.: (65) 6889 8888
Web Site: http://www.gic.com.sg
Privater Equity Firm
N.A.I.C.S.: 523999

INTERNATIONAL PUBLIC

Yong Cheen Choo (Chief Investment Officer-Private Equity)

Joint Venture (Non-US):

Associated British Ports Holdings Ltd. (2)
25 Bedford Street, London, WC2E 9ES, United Kingdom (33.33%)
Tel.: (44) 2074301177
Web Site: https://www.abports.co.uk
Holding Company; Marine Ports Operator & Cargo Handling Activities
N.A.I.C.S.: 551112
Harm van Weezel (CIO)

Unit (Domestic):

ABP Ayr (3)
Port Office North Harbour Street, Ayr, KA8 8AH, United Kingdom
Tel.: (44) 1292281687
Sales Range: $100-124.9 Million
Emp.: 30
Marine Cargo Handling
N.A.I.C.S.: 488320

ABP Barrow (3)
Port Office Ramsey Way, Barrow-in-Furness, LA14 2GR, Cumbria, United Kingdom
Tel.: (44) 1229822911
Sales Range: $25-49.9 Million
Emp.: 30
Marine Cargo Handling Distr
N.A.I.C.S.: 488320
Paul Jervis (Mgr-Port)

ABP Cardiff (3)
QA House Cargo Road, Cardiff, CF10 4LY, United Kingdom
Tel.: (44) 8706096699
Sales Range: $25-49.9 Million
Emp.: 100
Marine Cargo Handling
N.A.I.C.S.: 488320
Matthew Kennerley (Dir-Ports-South Wales)

ABP Fleetwood (3)
Dock Office, Fleetwood, FY7 6PP, Lancs, United Kingdom
Tel.: (44) 1253872323
Sales Range: $100-124.9 Million
Emp.: 15
Marine Cargo Handling
N.A.I.C.S.: 488320
Nick Ridehalgh (Dir-Short-Sea Ports)

ABP Garston (3)
Port Office Garston, Liverpool, L19 2JW, United Kingdom
Tel.: (44) 1514275971
Sales Range: $25-49.9 Million
Emp.: 20
Marine Cargo Handling
N.A.I.C.S.: 488320
Paul Jervis (Mgr-Port)

ABP Goole (3)
Port Office East Parade, Goole, DN14 5RB, East Yorkshire, United Kingdom
Tel.: (44) 1482327171
Web Site: http://www.abport.co.uk
Sales Range: $50-74.9 Million
Emp.: 250
Marine Cargo Handling
N.A.I.C.S.: 488320
Phil Coombes (Mgr-Comml)

ABP Hull (3)
Port House Northern Gateway, PO Box 1, Hull, HU9 5PQ, Yorkshire, United Kingdom
Tel.: (44) 1482327171
Sales Range: $25-49.9 Million
Emp.: 125
Port & Harbor Operations
N.A.I.C.S.: 488310

ABP Ipswich (3)
Old Custom House Key Street, Ipswich, IP4 1BY, United Kingdom
Tel.: (44) 1473231010
Sales Range: $25-49.9 Million
Emp.: 23
Marine Cargo Handling
N.A.I.C.S.: 488320
Alastair MacFarlane (Mgr-Port)

ABP Plymouth (3)
Port Office Millbay Docks, Plymouth, PL1 3EF, Devon, United Kingdom

AND PRIVATE COMPANIES — GIC PTE. LTD.

Tel.: (44) 1752662191
Sales Range: $25-49.9 Million
Emp.: 22
Passenger Ferry & Marine Cargo Handling Services
N.A.I.C.S.: 488320

Joint Venture (Non-US):

Kelda Group Limited (2)
Tel.: (44) 1274600111
Web Site: https://www.keldagroup.com
Emp.: 3,500
Holding Company; Water, Sewage, Environmental & Land Management Services
N.A.I.C.S.: 551112

Nets A/S (2)
Klausdalsbrovej 601, DK-2750, Ballerup, Denmark
Tel.: (45) 44684468
Web Site: http://www.nets.eu
Rev.: $1,264,993,856
Assets: $4,521,658,722
Liabilities: $2,816,559,886
Net Worth: $1,705,098,836
Earnings: $36,059,492
Emp.: 2,460
Fiscal Year-end: 12/31/2019
Holding Company; Payment Solutions, Information Services & Digital Security Solutions
N.A.I.C.S.: 551112
Soren Winge (Head-Media)

Subsidiary (Domestic):

Nets Denmark A/S (3)
Lautrupbjerg 10, DK-2750, Ballerup, Denmark
Tel.: (45) 4468 4468
Web Site: http://www.nets.eu
Payment, Card & Information Services
N.A.I.C.S.: 522320
Nevena Duric (Officer-Press)

Subsidiary (Non-US):

Nets Norway AS (3)
Haavard Martinsensvei 54, 0978, Oslo, Norway
Tel.: (47) 22898989
Web Site: http://www.nets.eu
Payment Solutions
N.A.I.C.S.: 522320
Stein-Arne Tjore (Mgr-Press)

Nets Sweden AB (3)
Lumaparksvagen 11, 120 31, Stockholm, Sweden
Tel.: (46) 8609 9400
Web Site: http://www.nets.eu
Electronic Payment Systems
N.A.I.C.S.: 522320
Soren Winge (Mgr-Press)

Joint Venture (Non-US):

Total Infrastructures Gaz France SA (2)
40 avenue de l'Europe, CS 20522, 64010, Pau, Cedex, France **(31.5%)**
Tel.: (33) 559133400
Web Site: https://www.terega.fr
Sales Range: $400-449.9 Million
Emp.: 500
Natural Gas Transportation & Storage Services
N.A.I.C.S.: 486210
Bernard Clement (Chm)

Genesee & Wyoming Inc. (1)
20 West Ave, Darien, CT 06820
Tel.: (203) 202-8900
Web Site: http://www.gwrr.com
Rev.: $2,348,550,000
Assets: $7,868,461,000
Liabilities: $4,238,409,000
Net Worth: $3,630,052,000
Earnings: $244,418,000
Emp.: 8,000
Fiscal Year-end: 12/31/2018
Short Line & Regional Freight Railroad Services
N.A.I.C.S.: 482111
Jack Hellmann (CEO)

Subsidiary (Domestic):

Arizona & California Railroad Company (2)
1301 S California Ave, Parker, AZ 85344
Tel.: (928) 669-6662
Sales Range: $10-24.9 Million
Emp.: 29
Short Line Railroad
N.A.I.C.S.: 482111

Arizona Eastern Railway Company (2)
5903 S Calle de Loma, Claypool, AZ 85532
Tel.: (928) 473-2447
Rev.: $4,200,000
Emp.: 45
Railroad Services
N.A.I.C.S.: 482111

Arkansas Louisiana & Mississippi Railroad Co. (2)
140 Plywood Mill Rd, Crossett, AR 71635
Tel.: (870) 364-9000
Sales Range: $1-9.9 Million
Emp.: 19
Short Line Railroads Services
N.A.I.C.S.: 482112

Arkansas Midland Railroad (2)
314 Reynolds Rd Bldg 41, Malvern, AR 72104
Tel.: (501) 844-4444
Web Site: https://www.gwrr.com
Railroad Services
N.A.I.C.S.: 482111
Gene Cox (Gen Mgr)

Subsidiary (Non-US):

Atlantic and Western Railway LP (2)
Tel.: (919) 776-7521
Web Site: http://www.gwrr.com
Sales Range: $1-9.9 Million
Emp.: 3
Railroad Line-Haul Services
N.A.I.C.S.: 488210

Subsidiary (Domestic):

Atlas Railroad Construction Co., Inc. (2)
1370 Washington Pike Ste 202, Bridgeville, PA 15017
Tel.: (412) 677-2020
Web Site: http://gwrr.com
Emp.: 50
Short Line Railroads Services
N.A.I.C.S.: 482112

Bauxite & Northern Railway Company (2)
6232 Cynamide Rd, Bauxite, AR 72011
Tel.: (501) 557-2600
Web Site: https://www.gwrr.com
Short Line Railroads Services
N.A.I.C.S.: 482112

Buffalo & Pittsburgh Railroad, Inc. (2)
400 Meridian Center Ste 300, Rochester, NY 14618
Tel.: (585) 328-8601
Web Site: http://www.gwrr.com
Sales Range: $1-9.9 Million
Emp.: 100
Freight Transportation Arrangement
N.A.I.C.S.: 561110

Division (Domestic):

Allegheny & Eastern Railroad, LLC (3)
1210 4th Ave, Warren, PA 16365
Tel.: (814) 726-3551
Short Line Railroads Services
N.A.I.C.S.: 482112

Branch (Domestic):

Buffalo & Pittsburgh Railroad, Inc. (3)
201 N Penn St, Punxsutawney, PA 15765
Tel.: (814) 938-5500
Web Site: http://www.gwrr.com
Sales Range: $1-9.9 Million
Emp.: 10
Line-Haul Operating Railroads
N.A.I.C.S.: 482111

Joint Venture (Domestic):

CG Railway, LLC (2)
601 Poydras St Ste 1625, New Orleans, LA 70130 **(40%)**
Tel.: (251) 266-5239
Web Site: http://www.cgrailway.com
Short Line Railroad
N.A.I.C.S.: 482112

Subsidiary (Domestic):

California Northern Railroad Company (2)
1801 Hanover Dr Ste D, Davis, CA 95616
Tel.: (530) 753-7826
Web Site: http://www.gwrr.com
Sales Range: $10-24.9 Million
Emp.: 40
Short Line Railroads Services
N.A.I.C.S.: 482112

Subsidiary (Non-US):

Cape Breton & Central Nova Scotia Railway Limited (2)
121 King Street, PO Box 2240, Stellarton, B0K 1S0, NS, Canada
Web Site: http://www.gwrr.com
Sales Range: $25-49.9 Million
Emp.: 125
Short Line Railroad
N.A.I.C.S.: 482112

Subsidiary (Domestic):

Carolina Piedmont Railroad (2)
268 E Main St, Laurens, SC 29360
Web Site: https://www.gwrr.com
Sales Range: $1-9.9 Million
Emp.: 9
Short Line Railroad
N.A.I.C.S.: 482111
Yurgen Harter (Mgr-Ops)

Cascade & Columbia River Railroad Company (2)
901 Omak Ave, Omak, WA 98841
Tel.: (509) 826-3752
Web Site: http://www.gwrr.com
Sales Range: $1-9.9 Million
Emp.: 8
Short Line Railroad
N.A.I.C.S.: 482111

Central Oregon & Pacific Railroad, Inc. (2)
333 SE Mosher, Roseburg, OR 97470
Tel.: (802) 527-3499
Sales Range: $25-49.9 Million
Emp.: 75
Short Line Railroads Services
N.A.I.C.S.: 482112

Central Railroad Company of Indianapolis (2)
1990 E Washington St, East Peoria, IL 61611
Tel.: (309) 698-2600
Web Site: http://www.gwrr.com
Short Line Railroads Services
N.A.I.C.S.: 482112

Chattahoochee Industrial Railroad (2)
160 CIRR Ln, Cedar Springs, GA 39832
Tel.: (229) 793-4546
Containerboard Mill Railroad Services
N.A.I.C.S.: 482111

Chattooga & Chickamauga Railway Co. (2)
413 W Villanow St, La Fayette, GA 30728
Tel.: (706) 638-9552
Web Site: https://www.gwrr.com
Freight Railroad Services
N.A.I.C.S.: 482111
Donnie Owens (Mgr)

Columbus & Chattahoochee Railroad, Inc. (2)
621 9th Ave, Columbus, GA 31901
Tel.: (229) 698-2000
Web Site: https://www.gwrr.com
Emp.: 21
Short Line Railroads Services
N.A.I.C.S.: 482112

Conecuh Valley Railway, L.L.C. (2)
812 N Main St, Enterprise, AL 36330
Tel.: (904) 596-1086
Web Site: https://www.gwrr.com

Short Line Railroads Services
N.A.I.C.S.: 482112
Bill Jasper (Pres)

Connecticut Southern Railroad, Inc. (2)
440 Windsor St, Hartford, CT 06142
Web Site: https://www.gwrr.com
Sales Range: $1-9.9 Million
Emp.: 14
Short Line Railroads Services
N.A.I.C.S.: 482112

Dallas, Garland & Northeastern Railroad, Inc. (2)
403 International Pkwy Ste 500, Richardson, TX 75081
Tel.: (972) 808-9800
Web Site: http://www.gwrr.com
Sales Range: $1-9.9 Million
Emp.: 95
Short Line Railroads Services
N.A.I.C.S.: 482112

Subsidiary (Domestic):

Texas Northeastern Railroad (3)
403 International Pkwy Ste 500, Richardson, TX 75081-2899
Tel.: (972) 808-9800
Web Site: http://www.gwrr.com
Short Line Railroad
N.A.I.C.S.: 482112

Subsidiary (Domestic):

East Tennessee Railway, L.P. (2)
132 Legion St, Johnson City, TN 37601
Tel.: (802) 527-3499
Web Site: https://www.gwrr.com
Sales Range: $1-9.9 Million
Emp.: 3
Short Line Railroads Services
N.A.I.C.S.: 482112

Eastern Alabama Railway, LLC (2)
2413 Hill Rd, Sylacauga, AL 35151
Tel.: (251) 513-1100
Web Site: https://www.gwrr.com
Emp.: 10
Short Line Railroads Services
N.A.I.C.S.: 482112

Subsidiary (Non-US):

Ferrocarriles Chiapas-Mayab, S.A. de C.V. (2)
480 Colonial Centro Entre 44 Y 46, Merida, CP 97000, Yucatain, Mexico
Tel.: (52) 9999302500
Web Site: http://www.rosasandxocolate.com
Sales Range: $100-124.9 Million
Emp.: 300
Freight Transportation Arrangement
N.A.I.C.S.: 488510

Subsidiary (Domestic):

First Coast Railroad Inc. (2)
404 Gum St, Fernandina Beach, FL 32034
Tel.: (904) 261-0888
Web Site: https://www.gwrr.com
Short Line Railroads Services
N.A.I.C.S.: 482112

Fordyce and Princeton R.R. Co. (2)
105 W 2nd Ave, Crossett, AR 71635-2803
Tel.: (870) 364-9000
Railroad Transportation Services
N.A.I.C.S.: 482111

Subsidiary (Non-US):

Freightliner Group Limited (2)
6th Floor The Lewis Building 35 Bull Street, Birmingham, B4 6EQ, United Kingdom
Tel.: (44) 2072003974
Web Site: http://www.freightliner.co.uk
Emp.: 80
Holding Company; Intermodal Rail Freight Transportation Services
N.A.I.C.S.: 551112
Tim Shakerley (Mng Dir-UK Rail)

Subsidiary (Non-US):

ERS Railways B.V. (3)
Albert Plesmanweg 61 B, 3088 GB, Rotterdam, Netherlands
Tel.: (31) 104285220
Web Site: http://www.ersrail.com

GIC PTE. LTD.

GIC Pte. Ltd.—(Continued)
Line Haul Railroad Services
N.A.I.C.S.: 482111

Freightliner Australia Pty Ltd (3)
Suite 1 Building 1 Pymble Corporate Centre
20 Bridge Street, Pymble, 2073, Australia
Tel.: (61) 294496222
Web Site:
  http://www.freightlineraustralia.com.au
Emp.: 8
Bulk Freight Rail Transportation Services
N.A.I.C.S.: 482112

Freightliner DE GmbH (3)
Strasse am Flugplatz 6A, 12487, Berlin, Germany
Tel.: (49) 30632234711
Web Site: https://de.freightliner.eu
Bulk Freight Rail Transportation
N.A.I.C.S.: 482112

Subsidiary (Domestic):

Freightliner Heavy Haul Limited (3)
3rd Floor The Podium 1 Eversholt Street,
London, NW1 2FL, United Kingdom
Tel.: (44) 7739823448
Web Site: http://www.freightliner.co.uk
Short Line Railroads Services
N.A.I.C.S.: 482112

Freightliner Limited (3)
Third Floor 90 Whitfield Street, Fitzrovia,
London, W1T 4EZ, United Kingdom
Tel.: (44) 3330168556
Web Site: http://www.freightliner.co.uk
Emp.: 70
Intermodal Rail Freight Transportation Services
N.A.I.C.S.: 482111
Gary Long (CEO)

Subsidiary (Non-US):

Freightliner PL Sp. z o. o. (2)
Ul Polna 11, 00-633, Warsaw, Poland
Tel.: (48) 226486655
Rail Freight Services
N.A.I.C.S.: 488210
Wojciech Jurkiewicz (COO)

Freightliner Scotland Ltd (2)
100 Gartsherrie Road, Coatbridge, ML5 2DR, United Kingdom
Tel.: (44) 1236503700
Shunting Terminal Services
N.A.I.C.S.: 488210

GWI Acquisitions Pty Ltd (2)
33 Richmond Road 5035, Adelaide, 5035, SA, Australia
Tel.: (61) 883435455
Regional Rail Services
N.A.I.C.S.: 482111

GWI Holding BV (2)
Industrial Road 17, 6662 NG, Elst, Netherlands
Tel.: (31) 481451034
Short Line Railroads Services
N.A.I.C.S.: 482112

Genesee & Wyoming Australia Pty Ltd (2)
Level 3 33 Richmond Road, Keswick, 5035, SA, Australia
Tel.: (61) 883435455
Web Site: http://www.gwrr.com
Sales Range: $300-349.9 Million
Emp.: 484
Short Line Railroads Services
N.A.I.C.S.: 482112
Michael Morris (CFO)

Genesee & Wyoming Canada Inc. (2)
9001 boul de lAcadie Bureau 600, Montreal, H4N 3H5, QC, Canada
Tel.: (514) 948-6999
Web Site: http://www.gwrr.com
Emp.: 40
Short Line Railroads Services
N.A.I.C.S.: 482112

Subsidiary (Domestic):

Huron Central Railway Inc. (3)
30 Oakland Avenue, Sault Sainte Marie,
P6A 2T3, ON, Canada
Tel.: (705) 254-4511
Rail Freight Transportation Services
N.A.I.C.S.: 482111

Quebec Gatineau Railway (3)
9001 Bureau 600, Montreal, H4N 3H5, QC, Canada
Tel.: (514) 948-6999
Web Site: http://www.gwrr.com
Rail Transportation
N.A.I.C.S.: 482112

St. Lawrence & Atlantic Railroad (Quebec) Inc. (3)
9001 boul de l Acadie Bureau 600, Montreal, H4N 3H5, QC, Canada
Tel.: (514) 948-6999
Web Site: http://www.gwrr.com
Short Line Railroad
N.A.I.C.S.: 482112

Western Labrador Rail Services Inc. (3)
Suite 210-1 210 Humber Avenue, Labrador City, A2V 2W8, NL, Canada
Tel.: (709) 944-6564
Web Site: http://www.gwrr.com
Short Line Railroads Services
N.A.I.C.S.: 482112

Subsidiary (Domestic):

Genesee & Wyoming Railroad Company (2)
200 Meridian Ctr Ste 300, Rochester, NY 14618-3972
Tel.: (585) 328-8601
Sales Range: $200-249.9 Million
Emp.: 2,600
Line-Haul Operating Railroads
N.A.I.C.S.: 482111

Genesee & Wyoming Railroad Services, Inc. (2)
200 Meridian Ctr Blvd Ste 300, Rochester, NY 14618
Tel.: (585) 328-8601
Emp.: 130
Short Line Railroads Services
N.A.I.C.S.: 482112

Georgia Central Railway, L.P. (2)
186 Winge Rd, Lyons, GA 30436
Tel.: (912) 526-6165
Web Site: https://www.gwrr.com
Short Line Railroads Services
N.A.I.C.S.: 482112

Subsidiary (Non-US):

Goderich-Exeter Railway Company Limited (2)
101 Shakespeare Street Unit 2, Stratford, N5A 3W5, ON, Canada
Tel.: (519) 271-4441
Web Site: http://www.gwrr.com
Short Line Railroads Services
N.A.I.C.S.: 482112

Subsidiary (Domestic):

Golden Isles Terminal Railroad, Inc. (2)
179 Penniman Cir, Brunswick, GA 31523
Tel.: (802) 527-3499
Web Site: https://www.gwrr.com
Short Line Railroads Services
N.A.I.C.S.: 482112

Heart of Georgia Railroad, Inc. (2)
908 Elm Ave, Americus, GA 31709
Tel.: (229) 924-7662
Web Site: http://www.gwrr.com
Emp.: 11
Regional Rail Services
N.A.I.C.S.: 482111

Huron & Eastern Railway Company, Inc. (2)
101 Enterprise Dr, Vassar, MI 48768-9505
Tel.: (989) 823-0090
Web Site: http://www.gwrr.com
Sales Range: $1-9.9 Million
Emp.: 22
Short Line Railroads Services
N.A.I.C.S.: 482112

Illinois & Midland Railroad, Inc. (2)
1500 N Grand Ave E, Springfield, IL 62702
Tel.: (217) 788-8601
Web Site: https://www.gwrr.com
Sales Range: $25-49.9 Million
Emp.: 80
Line-Haul Operating Railroads
N.A.I.C.S.: 482111

Indiana Southern Railroad, LLC (2)
202 W Illinois St, Petersburg, IN 47567
Tel.: (812) 354-8080
Sales Range: $10-24.9 Million
Emp.: 29
Short Line Railroads Services
N.A.I.C.S.: 482112

KWT Railway, Inc. (2)
908 Depot St, Paris, TN 38242
Web Site: http://www.gwrr.com
Rail Transportation Services
N.A.I.C.S.: 488210

Kiamichi Railroad Company L.L.C. (2)
800 Martin Luther King Blvd, Hugo, OK 74743
Tel.: (508) 916-7600
Emp.: 16
Short Line Railroads Services
N.A.I.C.S.: 482112

Kyle Railroad Company (2)
38 Railroad Ave, Phillipsburg, KS 67661
Tel.: (785) 628-7700
Sales Range: $25-49.9 Million
Emp.: 85
Short Line Railroads Services
N.A.I.C.S.: 482112

Louisiana & Delta Railroad, Inc. (2)
402 W Washington St, New Iberia, LA 70560
Tel.: (337) 364-9625
Sales Range: $10-24.9 Million
Emp.: 40
Short Line Railroads Services
N.A.I.C.S.: 482112

M & B Railroad L.L.C. (2)
119 22nd Ave, Meridian, MS 39301
Tel.: (601) 693-4351
Sales Range: $1-9.9 Million
Emp.: 10
Provider of Railroad Line-Haul Services
N.A.I.C.S.: 482111

Marquette Rail, LLC (2)
239 N Jebavy Dr, Ludington, MI 49431
Tel.: (231) 845-9000
Web Site: http://www.gwrr.com
Emp.: 30
Short Line Railroads Services
N.A.I.C.S.: 482112

Maryland Midland Railway, Inc. (2)
40 N Main St, Union Bridge, MD 21791
Tel.: (410) 775-7718
Short Line Railroads Services
N.A.I.C.S.: 482112

Michigan Shore Railroad (2)
101 Enterprise Dr, Vassar, MI 48768
Tel.: (989) 797-5100
Web Site: http://www.gwrr.com
Sales Range: $25-49.9 Million
Emp.: 70
Short Line Railroad
N.A.I.C.S.: 482112

Mid-Michigan Railroad, Inc. (2)
101 Enterprise Dr, Vassar, MI 48768-9505
Tel.: (989) 797-5124
Web Site: http://www.gwrr.com
Sales Range: $1-9.9 Million
Emp.: 18
Short Line Railroad
N.A.I.C.S.: 482111

Missouri & Northern Arkansas Railroad Company, Inc. (2)
514 N Orner, Carthage, MO 64836
Tel.: (417) 358-8800
Sales Range: $1-9.9 Million
Emp.: 130
Short Line Railroads Services
N.A.I.C.S.: 482112

New England Central Railroad, Inc. (2)
2 Federal St Ste 201, Saint Albans, VT 05478
Tel.: (802) 527-3411
Web Site: http://www.gwrr.com

INTERNATIONAL PUBLIC

Sales Range: $100-124.9 Million
Emp.: 250
Short Line Railroads Services
N.A.I.C.S.: 482112
Robert Richardson (Asst Gen Mgr)

North Carolina & Virginia Railroad Company, LLC (2)
214 Railroad St N, Ahoskie, NC 27910
Tel.: (904) 223-1110
Sales Range: $1-9.9 Million
Emp.: 8
Short Line Railroads Services
N.A.I.C.S.: 482112

Division (Domestic):

Chesapeake & Albemarle Railroad (3)
214 Railroad St N, Ahoskie, NC 27910
Tel.: (252) 332-2778
Sales Range: $1-9.9 Million
Emp.: 4
Short Line Railroad
N.A.I.C.S.: 482112

Virginia Southern Railroad (3)
Keysville Depot Railroad Ave PO Box 12,
Keysville, VA 23947
Tel.: (919) 332-2778
Short Line Railroad
N.A.I.C.S.: 482112
Carl Hollowell (Gen Mgr)

Subsidiary (Domestic):

Ohio Central Railroad, Inc. (2)
47849 Papermill Rd, Coshocton, OH 43812
Tel.: (740) 622-8092
Web Site: https://www.gwrr.com
Short Line Railroad
N.A.I.C.S.: 482112

Ohio Southern Railroad, Inc. (2)
47849 Papermill Rd, Coshocton, OH 43812
Tel.: (740) 622-8092
Short Line Railroad
N.A.I.C.S.: 482112

Subsidiary (Non-US):

Ottawa Valley Railway (2)
445 Oak Street East, North Bay, P1B 1A3, ON, Canada
Tel.: (802) 527-3490
Web Site: https://www.gwrr.com
Emp.: 35
Short Line Railroad
N.A.I.C.S.: 482112

Subsidiary (Domestic):

Otter Tail Valley Railroad Company, Inc. (2)
200 N Mill St, Fergus Falls, MN 56537
Tel.: (218) 736-6073
Web Site: https://www.gwrr.com
Sales Range: $1-9.9 Million
Emp.: 8
Short Line Railroads Services
N.A.I.C.S.: 482112

Subsidiary (Non-US):

Pentalver Cannock Limited (2)
Pentalver Way, Cannock, WS11 8XY, United Kingdom
Tel.: (44) 3331508300
Container Operator
N.A.I.C.S.: 488490

Pentalver Transport Limited (2)
Western Docks Dock Gate 10, Southampton, SO15 1AW, United Kingdom
Tel.: (44) 3330168556
Web Site: https://www.pentalver.com
Emp.: 600
Freight Container Transport, Storage & Logistics Services
N.A.I.C.S.: 488320

Subsidiary (Domestic):

Portland & Western Railroad Inc (2)
1200 Howard Dr SE, Albany, OR 97321
Tel.: (802) 527-3499
Web Site: https://www.gwrr.com
Sales Range: $75-99.9 Million
Emp.: 200
Switching & Terminal Services
N.A.I.C.S.: 482111

AND PRIVATE COMPANIES

GIC PTE. LTD.

Roberta Kane (VP-HR)

Providence & Worcester Railroad Company (2)
381 Southbridge St, Worcester, MA 01608
Tel.: (802) 527-3499
Web Site: https://www.gwrr.com
Short Line Railroads Services
N.A.I.C.S.: 482112
James Rivers (Asst Gen Mgr)

Puget Sound & Pacific Railroad (2)
501 N 2nd St, Elma, WA 98541
Tel.: (360) 807-4325
Web Site: http://www.gwrr.com
Sales Range: $10-24.9 Million
Emp.: 46
Short Line Railroads Services
N.A.I.C.S.: 482112

Rail Link, Inc. (2)
13901 Sutton Park Dr S Ste 125, Jacksonville, FL 32224
Tel.: (904) 223-1110
Web Site: http://www.gwrr.com
Sales Range: $1-9.9 Million
Emp.: 15
Short Line Railroads Services
N.A.I.C.S.: 482112

Subsidiary (Domestic):

The Bayline Railroad LLC (3)
2037 Industrial Dr, Panama City, FL 32045
Tel.: (850) 785-4609
Emp.: 35
Railroad Services
N.A.I.C.S.: 482111

Subsidiary (Domestic):

RailAmerica Transportation Corp. (2)
7411 Fullerton St Ste 300, Jacksonville, FL 32256
Tel.: (904) 538-6100
Short Line Railroads Services
N.A.I.C.S.: 482112

RailAmerica, Inc. (2)
13901 Sutton Park Dr S, Jacksonville, FL 32224
Tel.: (904) 538-6100
Sales Range: $800-899.9 Million
Emp.: 1,808
Short Line Railroads Services
N.A.I.C.S.: 482112
Christopher Liucci (Pres)

Subsidiary (Non-US):

Railcare Inc. (2)
500 Sherman Ave N Unit 80, Hamilton, L8L 8J6, ON, Canada
Tel.: (905) 527-8238
Short Line Railroads Services
N.A.I.C.S.: 482112

Subsidiary (Domestic):

Railroad Distribution Services, Inc. (2)
425 E Southlake Blvd, Southlake, TX 76092
Tel.: (501) 844-4484
Railroad Distribution Services
N.A.I.C.S.: 482111
Gene Cox (Gen Mgr)

Rapid City, Pierre & Eastern Railroad, Inc. (2)
246 Founders Park Dr Ste 202, Rapid City, SD 57701
Tel.: (605) 877-3699
Web Site: https://www.gwrr.com
Line-Haul Railroad Related Services
N.A.I.C.S.: 482111

Rockdale, Sandow & Southern Railroad Company (2)
PO Box 387, Rockdale, TX 76567
Tel.: (512) 446-3478
Short Line Railroads Services
N.A.I.C.S.: 482112

Salt Lake City Southern Railroad Company, Inc. (2)
4692 N 300 W, Provo, UT 84604
Tel.: (801) 221-7460
Short Line Railroads Services
N.A.I.C.S.: 482112

San Diego & Imperial Valley Railroad Company, Inc. (2)
1501 National Ave Ste 200, San Diego, CA 92113
Tel.: (928) 669-6662
Sales Range: $1-9.9 Million
Emp.: 15
Short Line Railroads Services
N.A.I.C.S.: 482112

San Joaquin Valley Railroad Co. (2)
221 N F St, Exeter, CA 93221
Tel.: (559) 592-1857
Sales Range: $25-49.9 Million
Emp.: 200
Short Line Railroads Services
N.A.I.C.S.: 482112
Dave Siegel (Dir-Sls & Mktg)

Savannah Port Terminal Railroad, Inc. (2)
2 Main St, Garden City, GA 31408
Tel.: (802) 527-3499
Web Site: https://www.gwrr.com
Short Line Railroads Services
N.A.I.C.S.: 482112

South Carolina Central Railroad Company, LLC (2)
621 Field Pond Rd, Darlington, SC 29540
Tel.: (843) 398-9850
Web Site: https://www.gwrr.com
Sales Range: $1-9.9 Million
Emp.: 28
Short Line Railroads Services
N.A.I.C.S.: 482112

Subsidiary (Non-US):

Southern Ontario Railway (2)
3258 Highway 6, PO Box 601, Jarvis, N0A 1J0, ON, Canada
Tel.: (905) 777-1234
Web Site: http://www.gwrr.com
Sales Range: $10-24.9 Million
Emp.: 35
Short Line Railroad
N.A.I.C.S.: 482112

Subsidiary (Domestic):

St. Lawrence & Atlantic Railroad Company (2)
225 First Flight Dr Ste 201, Auburn, ME 04210
Web Site: https://www.gwrr.com
Sales Range: $10-24.9 Million
Emp.: 75
Short Line Railroads Services
N.A.I.C.S.: 482112
Laurie Therrien (Mgr-Sls & Mktg)

Tazewell & Peoria Railroad, Inc. (2)
301 Wesley Rd, Creve Coeur, IL 61610
Tel.: (309) 694-8619
Web Site: https://www.gwrr.com
Short Line Railroads Services
N.A.I.C.S.: 482112

The Aliquippa & Ohio River Railroad Co. (2)
208 Islands Ave, McKees Rocks, PA 15136
Tel.: (740) 622-8092
Short Line Railroad
N.A.I.C.S.: 482112

The Central Railroad Company of Indiana (2)
2856 Cypress Way, Cincinnati, OH 45212
Tel.: (513) 860-1000
Web Site: https://www.gwrr.com
Short Line Railroad
N.A.I.C.S.: 482111

The Indiana & Ohio Railway Company (2)
2856 Cypress Way, Cincinnati, OH 45212
Tel.: (513) 860-1000
Sales Range: $10-24.9 Million
Emp.: 156
Line-Haul Operating Railroad
N.A.I.C.S.: 482111

The Pittsburgh & Ohio Central Railroad Company (2)
208 Islands Ave, McKees Rocks, PA 15136
Tel.: (412) 331-6200
Web Site: https://www.gwrr.com
Short Line Railroads Services
N.A.I.C.S.: 482112

The Prescott and Northwestern Railroad Company (2)
314 Reynolds Rd Bldg 41, Malvern, AR 72104
Web Site: https://www.gwrr.com
Rail Transportation Services
N.A.I.C.S.: 488210

Toledo, Peoria & Western Railway Corp. (2)
1990 E Washington St, East Peoria, IL 61611-2961
Tel.: (309) 698-2600
Web Site: https://www.gwrr.com
Sales Range: $10-24.9 Million
Emp.: 35
Short Line Railroad
N.A.I.C.S.: 482112

Tomahawk Railway Limited Partnership (2)
17 S Marinette St, Tomahawk, WI 54487
Tel.: (715) 453-2303
Sales Range: $1-9.9 Million
Emp.: 12
Provider of Railroad Line-Haul Services
N.A.I.C.S.: 482112
Katie Kaiser (Mgr-Warehouse)

Ventura County Railroad Company (2)
351 Warehouse Ave, Oxnard, CA 93030
Tel.: (559) 592-4247
Web Site: http://www.gwrr.com
Sales Range: $1-9.9 Million
Emp.: 25
Short Line Railroads Services
N.A.I.C.S.: 482112

Wellsboro & Corning Railroad, LLC (2)
900 Airport Rd Ste 6, West Chester, PA 19380
Tel.: (610) 458-0600
Web Site: http://www.gwrr.com
Short Line Railroads Services
N.A.I.C.S.: 482112

Wilmington Terminal Railroad, Limited Partnership (2)
2128 Burnett Blvd, Wilmington, NC 28401
Tel.: (910) 343-0461
Web Site: https://www.gwrr.com
Sales Range: $25-49.9 Million
Emp.: 6
Short Line Railroads Services
N.A.I.C.S.: 482112

Wiregrass Central Railway, L.L.C. (2)
812 N Main St, Enterprise, AL 36330
Tel.: (334) 347-6070
Web Site: https://www.gwrr.com
Line-Haul Railroad Related Services
N.A.I.C.S.: 482111

York Railway Company (2)
2790 W Market St, York, PA 17404
Tel.: (904) 710-0235
Web Site: https://www.gwrr.com
Sales Range: $1-9.9 Million
Emp.: 32
Rail Freight Transportation & Distribution Services
N.A.I.C.S.: 482111

Subsidiary (Non-US):

SLR Leasing Corp. (3)
605 Rue Principale Nord, PO Box 788, Richmond, J0B, BC, Canada
Tel.: (819) 826-1561
Web Site: http://www.gwrr.com
Rev.: $407,000
Emp.: 10
Locomotive Leasing Company
N.A.I.C.S.: 532411

St. Lawrence & Atlantic Railroad (Quebec) Inc. (3)
605 Rue Principale Nord C, Richmond, J0B 2H0, QC, Canada
Tel.: (819) 826-5460
Short Line Railroads Services
N.A.I.C.S.: 482112

Subsidiary (Domestic):

York Rail Logistics, Inc. (3)
2790 W Market St, York, PA 17404
Tel.: (717) 792-1425
Sales Range: $1-9.9 Million
Emp.: 4
Short Line Railroads Services
N.A.I.C.S.: 482112
Jarrod Hutcheson (Gen Mgr)

Subsidiary (Domestic):

Youngstown & Austintown Railroad, Inc. (2)
123 Division St Ext, Youngstown, OH 44510
Tel.: (740) 622-8092
Web Site: https://www.gwrr.com
Short Line Railroads Services
N.A.I.C.S.: 482112
Brian McClain (Gen Mgr)

Miller Insurance Services LLP (1)
70 Mark Lane, London, EC3R 7NQ, United Kingdom
Tel.: (44) 2074882345
Web Site: https://www.miller-insurance.com
Insurance Agency Services
N.A.I.C.S.: 524210
Greg Collins (CEO)

Division (Domestic):

Special Contingency Risks Limited (2)
70 Mark Ln 30 Fenchurch Avenue, London, EC3M 5AD, United Kingdom
Tel.: (44) 2070889100
Web Site: https://www.scr-ltd.co.uk
Insurance Brokerage Services
N.A.I.C.S.: 524210

Nouryon Chemicals Holding B.V. (1)
Tel.: (31) 889841000
Web Site: https://www.nouryon.com
Emp.: 78,000
Holding Company; Chemicals Mfr & Whslr
N.A.I.C.S.: 551112
Charlie Shaver (Chm & CEO)

Subsidiary (Domestic):

Nobian Chemicals B.V. (2)
Van Asch van Wijckstraat, 53 3811 LP, Amersfoort, Netherlands (100%)
Tel.: (31) 850006000
Web Site: https://www.nobian.com
Specialty Chemicals Mfr
N.A.I.C.S.: 325998

Joint Venture (Domestic):

Delamine B.V. (3)
Stationsplein 121 Argonaut, 3818 LE, Amersfoort, Netherlands
Tel.: (31) 334224600
Web Site: http://www.delamine.com
Ethylene Amines Mfr
N.A.I.C.S.: 325199

Subsidiary (Domestic):

Nobian Industrial Chemicals B.V. (3)
Van Asch v. Wijckstraat, 53 3811 LP, Amersfoort, Netherlands
Tel.: (31) 850006000
Web Site: https://www.nobian.com
Industrial Chemicals Mfr
N.A.I.C.S.: 325998
Michael Koenig (CEO)

Subsidiary (Domestic):

Nouryon Chemicals International B.V. (2)
Haaksbergerweg 88, De Oliphant Building Floor 14 and 15, 1101 BZ, Amsterdam, Netherlands
Tel.: (31) 889841000
Holding Company
N.A.I.C.S.: 551112

Subsidiary (Non-US):

Akzo Nobel Chemical Ltd. (3)
1 City Ctr Dr Ste 318, Mississauga, L5B 1M2, ON, Canada (100%)
Tel.: (905) 273-5959
Web Site: http://www.akzonnobel.com
Industrial Inorganic Chemicals
N.A.I.C.S.: 325998

Subsidiary (US):

Akzo Nobel Chemicals LLC (3)

GIC PTE. LTD.

GIC Pte. Ltd.—(Continued)
525 W Van Buren St, Chicago, IL 60607
Tel.: (312) 544-7000
Mfr Specialty Chemicals & Industrial Products
N.A.I.C.S.: 325199

Subsidiary (Domestic):

Akzo Nobel Surface Chemistry LLC (4)
525 W Van Buren St, Chicago, IL 60607
Tel.: (312) 544-7159
Surface Active Agent Mfr
N.A.I.C.S.: 325613

Subsidiary (Non-US):

Akzo Nobel Chemicals Pty Ltd (3)
8 Kellaway Pl, Wetherill Park, 2164, NSW, Australia
Tel.: (61) 2 9616 6900
Sales Range: $25-49.9 Million
Emp.: 3
Chemical Products Mfr
N.A.I.C.S.: 325199
Brian Patten (Country Mgr)

Akzo Nobel Chemicals S.A. (3)
Autovia de Castelldefels Km 4 65, El Prat de Llobregat, 8820, Barcelona, Spain
Tel.: (34) 93 4784411
Chemical Products Mfr
N.A.I.C.S.: 325998

Akzo Nobel Chemicals Sa de CV (3)
Av Morelos 49 Col Tecamachalco, 56500, Los Reyes, La Paz, Mexico (100%)
Tel.: (52) 5558580700
Organic Peroxides & Other Specialty Chemicals
N.A.I.C.S.: 325199

Akzo Nobel Functional Chemicals AB (3)
Horneborgvagen 11, 89126, Ornskoldsvik, Sweden
Tel.: (46) 303 850 00
Emp.: 110
Cellulose Derivative Mfr
N.A.I.C.S.: 325998

Akzo Nobel Functional Chemicals Verwaltungs-GmbH (3)
Liebigstrasse 7, 07973, Greiz, Germany
Tel.: (49) 3661780
Chemical Products Mfr
N.A.I.C.S.: 325998

Akzo Nobel Industrial Chemicals AB (3)
Marieholmsgatan 70, Gothenburg, 41502, Sweden
Tel.: (46) 31 733 1880
Sales Range: $50-74.9 Million
Emp.: 6
Industrial Chemical Mfr & Distr
N.A.I.C.S.: 325998

Akzo Nobel Pulp and Performance Chemicals AB (3)
Farjvagen 1, SE 445 34, Bohus, Sweden (100%)
Tel.: (46) 31587000
Miscellaneous Chemical Product Mfr
N.A.I.C.S.: 325998

Akzo Nobel Pulp and Performance Chemicals Norway AS (3)
Svaddeveien 119, 3660, Rjukan, Norway
Tel.: (47) 35080880
Web Site: http://www.nouryon.com
Specialty Chemicals Mfr
N.A.I.C.S.: 325998

Akzo Nobel Salt A/S (3)
Hadsundvej 17, 9550, Mariager, Denmark (50%)
Tel.: (45) 96687888
Specialty Chemicals Mfr
N.A.I.C.S.: 212390

Akzo Nobel UK Limited (3)
The Akzonobel Building, Wexham Road, Slough, SL2 5DS, United Kingdom
Tel.: (44) 1928511521
Research & Development Technologies
N.A.I.C.S.: 325998

AkzoNobel (3)
Sutton Fields Industrial Estate, Rotterdam Rd, Hull, HU7 OXX, United Kingdom
Tel.: (44) 1482825101
Coatings Marketing, Production & Research
N.A.I.C.S.: 325910

Carbosulf Chemische Werke GmbH (3)
Geestemunderstasse 26, Cologne, 50735, Germany (67%)
Tel.: (49) 22174960
Web Site: https://www.nouryon.com
Specialty Chemicals Mfr
N.A.I.C.S.: 325998

Celanese Switzerland AG (3)
Industriestrasse 17A, Sempach Station, 6203, Lucerne, Switzerland
Tel.: (41) 414696969
Web Site: http://www.elotex.com
Building Material Additives Mfr & Distr
N.A.I.C.S.: 541715
Nicolas Ruiz (Key Acct Mgr)

Subsidiary (Domestic):

Claviag AG (4)
Neumattstrasse 196, Moosleerau, 5054, Aargau, Switzerland
Tel.: (41) 627388888
Web Site: http://www.elotex.ch
Synthetic Polymers Mfr
N.A.I.C.S.: 325998

Subsidiary (Non-US):

Eka Chemicals (Australia) Pty Ltd (3)
15 Conquest Way, Hallam, VIC, Australia
Tel.: (61) 397023422
Chemical Product Mfr & Distr
N.A.I.C.S.: 325998

Eka Chemicals (Guangzhou) Co. Ltd. (3)
61 Hong Jing Rd East Section, Guangzhou Economic & Technolog, Guangzhou, 510760, China
Tel.: (86) 2083969688
Chemical Product Mfr & Distr
N.A.I.C.S.: 325998

Eka Chemicals Canada, Inc. (3)
1900 Rue St Patrice E, Magog, J1X4X6, QC, Canada (100%)
Tel.: (819) 843-8772
Web Site: https://www.nouryon.com
Bleaching Chemical Preparations
N.A.I.C.S.: 325998

Eka Chemicals do Brasil S.A. (3)
Rod Dom Gabriel Paulino Bueno Couto Km 65 2, PO Box 151, 13200-970, Jundiai, Sao Paulo, Brazil
Tel.: (55) 1145894800
Chemical Products Mfr
N.A.I.C.S.: 325998

Joint Venture (Non-US):

Lion Akzo Co., Ltd. (3)
3 17 3-chome Obata, Yokkaichi, 510-0875, Mie, Japan
Tel.: (81) 593468218
Web Site: http://www.lion.co.jp
Nitriles, Amines, Quarternary Ammonium Salts, Amine Oxides, Monoamides & Alkoxylated Amines Mfr; Joint Venture of Lion Corporation (50%) & Akzo Nobel N.V. (50%)
N.A.I.C.S.: 325998

Subsidiary (Non-US):

Nouryon Chemicals Argentina SAU (3)
Ruta 11 Km 25, S2200MEC, San Lorenzo, Santa Fe, Argentina
Tel.: (54) 3476422005
Sulfuric Acid Mfr
N.A.I.C.S.: 325180

Nouryon Chemicals Argentina SAU (3)
Ruta 11 Km 25, S2200FQB, San Lorenzo, Argentina
Tel.: (54) 3476422005
Web Site: https://www.nouryon.com
Sulfuric Acid, Sulphur Derivatives, Polyethylene & Phthalic Anhydride Mfr
N.A.I.C.S.: 325180

Nouryon Chemicals Argentina SAU (3)
Avenida Paseo Colon 221 5 Piso, Buenos Aires, C1063ACC, Argentina
Tel.: (54) 1143432011
Web Site: https://www.nouryon.com
Mfr of Wine Chemicals, Tartaric Acid, Vinic Alcohol & Grape Seed Oil
N.A.I.C.S.: 325199
Mario Mariuzzi (Pres)

Nouryon Chemicals GmbH (3)
Am Coloneum 2,, 50829, Köln, Germany (100%)
Tel.: (49) 22174960
Production of Thiocyanites, Amonium Sulfide, Sodium, Hydrosulfide
N.A.I.C.S.: 325998

Nouryon Chemicals GmbH (3)
Amtsgericht Hauptniederlassung, Düren, HRB 63, Germany
Tel.: (49) 2822976900
Polymer Chemicals Marketing, Sales & Mfr
N.A.I.C.S.: 325998

Nouryon Chemicals Limited (3)
Suite 1, 7th Floor 50 Broadway, London, SW1H 0BL, United Kingdom
Tel.: (44) 1932247891
Production of Specialty Chemicals
N.A.I.C.S.: 325998

Nouryon Chemicals MCA (Taixing) Co. Ltd (3)
Bin Jiang Bei Road 2-8 Jiangsu Province, Taixing, 225404, Greater, China
Tel.: (86) 52387676001
Web Site: https://www.nouryon.com
Polymer Chemical Product Mfr
N.A.I.C.S.: 325998

Nouryon Functional Chemicals AB (3)
Stenunge Allé 3 Stenungsund, Västra Gotaland, 44430, Sweden (100%)
Tel.: (46) 0317242197
Marketing & Sales of Salt & Basic Chemicals
N.A.I.C.S.: 424690

Nouryon Functional Chemicals GmbH (3)
Liebigstrasse 7, Greiz, 7973, Germany
Tel.: (49) 3661780
Web Site: https://www.nouryon.com
Chemical Products Mfr
N.A.I.C.S.: 325998

Nouryon Pulp and Performance Chemicals (Taiwan) Co. Ltd (3)
6th Fl No 51 Sec 2 Gongyi Road, Nantun District, Taichung, 408, Taiwan
Tel.: (886) 423270520
Web Site: https://www.nouryon.com
Chemical Product Mfr & Distr
N.A.I.C.S.: 325998
Steve Wang (Gen Mgr)

Joint Venture (Non-US):

Perla Greek Salt Ltd. (3)
22 Fleming Street, 182 33, Agios Ioannis Rentis, Greece
Tel.: (30) 2104832466
Salt Producer
N.A.I.C.S.: 325998

Subsidiary (Domestic):

Nouryon Functional Chemicals B.V. (2)
Haaksbergweg 88, De Oliphant Building Floor 14 and 15, 1101 BZ, Amsterdam, Netherlands
Tel.: (31) 889841000
Web Site: https://www.nouryon.com
Chemical Intermediates & Performance Chemicals Mfr
N.A.I.C.S.: 325998

Nouryon Pulp and Paper Chemicals B.V. (2)
Haaksbergweg 88, De Oliphant Building Floor 14 and 15, 1101 BZ, Amsterdam, Netherlands
Tel.: (31) 889841000
Web Site: https://www.nouryon.com

INTERNATIONAL PUBLIC

Chemical Products Mfr
N.A.I.C.S.: 325998

Summit Industrial Income REIT (1)
75 Summerlea Road Unit B, Brampton, L6T 4V2, ON, Canada
Tel.: (905) 791-1181
Web Site: https://www.summitiireit.com
Sales Range: $50-74.9 Million
Real Estate Investment Services
N.A.I.C.S.: 523999
Paul Dykeman (CEO)

GICIEL
26 Avenue Des Champs Pierreux, 92000, Nanterre, Hauts De Seine, France
Tel.: (33) 155693300
Rev.: $30,400,000
Emp.: 14
N.A.I.C.S.: 423430
Fred Boukobza (Chm)

GIEAG IMMOBILIEN AG
Oettingenstrasse 35, 80538, Munich, Germany
Tel.: (49) 892905160
Web Site: https://www.gieag.de
Year Founded: 1999
Sales Range: $1-9.9 Million
Emp.: 6
Commercial Real Estate Developer; Residential Real Estate Investor
N.A.I.C.S.: 236220
Phillipp Pferschy (Member-Exec Bd)

GIEBELER GMBH
Dietzholzstrasse 21, 35713, Eschenburg, Germany
Tel.: (49) 27747060
Web Site: http://www.giebeler.eu
Year Founded: 1956
Sales Range: $10-24.9 Million
Emp.: 200
Moulded Parts Mfr
N.A.I.C.S.: 333517
Markus Noll (Dir-Technical)

GIELDA PAPIEROW WARTOSCIOWYCH W WARSZAWIE S.A.
Ul Ksiazeca 4, 00-498, Warsaw, Poland
Tel.: (48) 226283232
Web Site: https://www.gpw.pl
Year Founded: 1991
GPW—(WAR)
Rev.: $97,790,534
Assets: $297,004,472
Liabilities: $45,578,305
Net Worth: $251,426,167
Earnings: $36,420,640
Emp.: 439
Fiscal Year-end: 12/31/22
Stock Exchange Services
N.A.I.C.S.: 523210
Marek Dietl (Chm-Mgmt Bd)

Subsidiaries:

BondSpot S.A. (1)
ul Ksiazeca 4, 00-498, Warsaw, Poland
Tel.: (48) 225377400
Web Site: https://www.bondspot.pl
Capital Marketing Services
N.A.I.C.S.: 541613

GPW Benchmark S.A. (1)
ul Ksiazeca 4, 00-498, Warsaw, Poland
Tel.: (48) 226283232
Web Site: https://gpwbenchmark.pl
Capital Market Services
N.A.I.C.S.: 523999

InfoEngine S.A. (1)
4 Ksiazeca Street, 00-498, Warsaw, Poland
Tel.: (48) 607314176
Web Site: https://infoengine.pl
Trade Operator Services
N.A.I.C.S.: 238990
Dariusz Katulski (Co-Pres)

AND PRIVATE COMPANIES

Towarowa Gielda Energii SA (1)
4 Ksiazeca Street, 00-498, Warsaw, Poland (80.3%)
Tel.: (48) 223419912
Web Site: https://www.tge.pl
Energy Markets Exchange
N.A.I.C.S.: 523210
Piotr Zawistowski *(Chm-Mgmt Bd)*

GIELDA PRAW MA-JATKOWYCH VINDEXUS S.A.
ul Serocka 3 lok B 2, 04-333, Warsaw, Poland
Tel.: (48) 227402650
Web Site: https://www.gpm-vindexus.pl
Year Founded: 1995
VIN—(WAR)
Rev.: $8,628,303
Assets: $86,142,022
Liabilities: $25,890,752
Net Worth: $60,251,270
Earnings: $6,725,102
Fiscal Year-end: 12/31/23
Debt Recovery Services
N.A.I.C.S.: 541219
Jan Piotr Kuchno *(Chm-Mgmt Bd)*

GIES HOLDING GMBH
Beim Zeugamt 8, 21509, Glinde, Germany
Tel.: (49) 407100070 De
Web Site: http://www.gies-kerzen.de
Year Founded: 1899
Sales Range: $25-49.9 Million
Emp.: 200
Candles & Decorative Object Mfr
N.A.I.C.S.: 339999
Jorgen Dreyer *(Mng Dir)*

Subsidiaries:

Asp-Holmblad A/S (1)
Hammervej 7, 2605, Horsholm, Denmark
Tel.: (45) 43229696
Web Site: http://www.asp-holmblad.dk
Sales Range: $10-24.9 Million
Emp.: 6
Mfr of Candles & Decorative Objects
N.A.I.C.S.: 339999
Metti Paulson *(Mng Dir)*

Gies Kerzen GmbH (1)
Beim Zeugamt 8, Glinde, 21509, Germany
Tel.: (49) 407100070
Web Site: http://www.gies-kerzen.de
Sales Range: $25-49.9 Million
Mfr of Candles & Decorative Objects
N.A.I.C.S.: 339999
Jorgen Dreyer *(Mng Dir)*

Gies Natura Handelsgesellschaft mbH (1)
Beim Zeugamt 8, 21509, Glinde, Germany
Tel.: (49) 407100070
Web Site: http://www.gies-kerzen.de
Sales Range: $25-49.9 Million
Mfr of Candles & Decorative Objects
N.A.I.C.S.: 339999

Liljeholmens Stearinfabriks AB (1)
Grondalsgatan 31-33, 572 35, Oskarshamn, Sweden
Tel.: (46) 49187800
Web Site: http://www.liljeholmens.se
Sales Range: $25-49.9 Million
Emp.: 100
Candles & Decorative Object Mfr
N.A.I.C.S.: 339999

GIESECKE & DEVRIENT GMBH
Prinzregentenstrasse 159, D-81677, Munich, Germany
Tel.: (49) 8941190 De
Web Site: http://www.gi-de.com
Year Founded: 1852
Rev.: $2,740,297,420
Assets: $3,086,782,104
Liabilities: $2,519,908,972
Net Worth: $566,873,132
Earnings: $90,036,744
Emp.: 11,510
Fiscal Year-end: 12/31/19
Credit Cards, Security Cards, Bank Notes & Money Sorting Machines Mfr
N.A.I.C.S.: 323111
Peter Zattler *(CFO & Member-Mgmt Bd)*

Subsidiaries:

BA International (1)
975 Gladstone Ave, Ottawa, K1Y 4W5, ON, Canada (100%)
Tel.: (613) 728-5854
Web Site: http://www.babanknote.com
Sales Range: $75-99.9 Million
Emp.: 170
National & International Supplier of Security Printing
N.A.I.C.S.: 323111

CI Tech Components AG (1)
Oberburgstr 10, 3400, Burgdorf, Switzerland
Tel.: (41) 344208833
Web Site: http://www.citech.com
Sensor Mfr
N.A.I.C.S.: 334514
Christoph Woenckhaus *(Mng Dir)*

Currency Tech Ltd. (1)
Unit 7 Torc MK Chippenham Drive, Milton Keynes, MK10 0BZ, United Kingdom
Tel.: (44) 8456016431
Web Site: http://www.currencytech.co.uk
Currency Handling Machine Whslr
N.A.I.C.S.: 423420
Ramas Lal *(Mgr-Bus Dev)*

G&D America do Sul Industria e Comercio de Smart Cards Sociedade Anonima (1)
Estrada de Santa Isabel 7235, Perobal Itaquaquecetuba, 08586-260, Sao Paulo, Brazil
Tel.: (55) 1146466601
Currency Handling Machine Whslr
N.A.I.C.S.: 423420
Adriana Barbieri *(Mgr-Customer Svc)*

G&D LOMO, ZAO (1)
Torfjanaja doroga 8, 197374, Saint Petersburg, Russia
Tel.: (7) 8123241851
Currency Handling Machine Whslr
N.A.I.C.S.: 423420
Gromakova Natalia *(Acct Mgr-Mobile Network Operators)*

Giesecke & Devrient (China) Information Technologies Co., Ltd. (1)
19/F Block C Central International Trade Center 6A Jianguomenwai, Chaoyang, Beijing, 100022, China
Tel.: (86) 1085073497
Currency Handling Machine Whslr
N.A.I.C.S.: 423420
Yong Zhang *(CFO)*

Giesecke & Devrient (Southern Africa) (Pty) Ltd. (1)
Block E - Crownwood Office Park 100 Northern Parkway Road, Private Bag X20, Ormonde Southdale, Johannesburg, 2135, South Africa
Tel.: (27) 113094900
Currency Handling Machine Whslr
N.A.I.C.S.: 423420
Sean Sannasy *(Head-Sls-Mobile Network Operators)*

Giesecke & Devrient 3S AB (1)
Rio de Janeiro Av Rio Branco 1 - 12 andar - sala 3 - Centro Infinity, 20090-003, Rio de Janeiro, Brazil
Tel.: (55) 2125888062
Currency Handling Machine Whslr
N.A.I.C.S.: 423420

Giesecke & Devrient 3S GmbH (1)
Willy-Brandt-Platz 2, 81829, Munich, Germany
Tel.: (49) 894521330
Currency Handling Machine Whslr
N.A.I.C.S.: 423420
Peter Dostert *(Mgr-Svc Design)*

Giesecke & Devrient 3S Oy (1)
Itamerenkatu 1, 180, Helsinki, Finland
Tel.: (358) 503142116

Currency Handling Machine Whslr
N.A.I.C.S.: 423420
Esa Heikkinen *(Sr Engr-Software)*

Giesecke & Devrient Africa Ltd. (1)
36 Oyinkan Abayomi Drive, PO Box 73842, Ikoyi, Lagos, Victoria Island, Nigeria
Tel.: (234) 12692619
Currency Handling Machine Whslr
N.A.I.C.S.: 423420
Akinsola Akinmurele *(Engr-Field)*

Giesecke & Devrient America, Inc. (1)
45925 Horseshoe Dr, Dulles, VA 20166-6588 (100%)
Tel.: (703) 480-2000
Web Site: http://www.gdai.com
Sales Range: $150-199.9 Million
Emp.: 300
Mfr of Credit Cards & Bank Note Processing Machines
N.A.I.C.S.: 323120

Division (Domestic):

Giesecke & Devrient America-Print Inspection Division (2)
14 Craig Rd, Acton, MA 01720-5405
Tel.: (978) 206-2600
Web Site: http://www.gdai.com
Sales Range: $10-24.9 Million
Emp.: 15
Credit Cards, Security Cards, Bank Notes & Money Sorting Machines Mfr
N.A.I.C.S.: 561499

Giesecke & Devrient Asia Pacific (Korea) (1)
1502 Coryo Daeyungak Tower 97 Toegyero, Junggu, Seoul, 100-706, Korea (South)
Tel.: (82) 27567652
Currency Handling Machine Whslr
N.A.I.C.S.: 423420

Giesecke & Devrient Asia Pacific Banking Systems (Shanghai) Co. Ltd. (1)
Room 2401 24/F Tower A 391 Guiping Road Caohejing Hi-tech Park, Xuhui District, Shanghai, China
Tel.: (86) 2134181000
Currency Handling Machine Whslr
N.A.I.C.S.: 423420

Giesecke & Devrient Asia Pacific Ltd (1)
2901 Hysan Place 500 Hennessy Road, Causeway Bay, China (Hong Kong)
Tel.: (852) 37667300
Currency Handling Machine Whslr
N.A.I.C.S.: 423420
Matthias Roehrich *(VP & Head-Sls & Mktg)*

Giesecke & Devrient Asia Pte. Ltd. (1)
123 Genting Lane 04-01 Yenom Industrial Building, Singapore, 349574, Singapore
Tel.: (65) 68436363
Currency Handling Machine Whslr
N.A.I.C.S.: 423420
Bernard Goh *(Acct Mgr)*

Giesecke & Devrient Australasia Pty. Ltd. (1)
94 Rushdale Street, Knoxfield, Melbourne, 3180, VIC, Australia
Tel.: (61) 397651200
Currency Handling Machine Whslr
N.A.I.C.S.: 423420
Uli Klink *(Mng Dir)*

Giesecke & Devrient Brasil Ltda. (1)
Praca General Gentil Falcao 108 16 andar Brooklin Novo, 04571-150, Sao Paulo, Brazil
Tel.: (55) 1151056100
Emp.: 211
Currency Handling Machine Whslr
N.A.I.C.S.: 423420
Flamarion Pirtouscheg *(Mng Dir)*

Giesecke & Devrient Egypt Services LLC (1)
81 Abdel Hamid Badawi St 4th Floor, Heliopolis, Cairo, Egypt
Tel.: (20) 26201391
Currency Handling Machine Whslr
N.A.I.C.S.: 423420

GIESECKE & DEVRIENT GMBH

Giesecke & Devrient FZE (1)
Building No 6W B Block 7th Floor Dubai Airport Free Zone, PO Box 54325, Dubai, United Arab Emirates
Tel.: (971) 46017111
Currency Handling Machine Whslr
N.A.I.C.S.: 423420
Alfred Ptacek *(Dir-Fin)*

Giesecke & Devrient France S.A.S. (1)
77 rue la Boetie, 75008, Paris, France
Tel.: (33) 147030426
Currency Handling Machine Whslr
N.A.I.C.S.: 423420
Timothee Mangenot *(Dir-Sls-Banking,OEM & Transit)*

Giesecke & Devrient GB Ltd. (1)
Globe House Unit 1 Westlinks Alperton Lane, Wembley, HA0 1ER, Middlesex, United Kingdom
Tel.: (44) 2087998100
Currency Handling Machine Whslr
N.A.I.C.S.: 423420
David Cooke *(Dir-HR)*

Giesecke & Devrient India Private Limited (1)
Development Center India 9/1A Padale Prime, Erandwane, Pune, 411 004, Maharashtra, India
Tel.: (91) 2047114000
Currency Handling Machine Whslr
N.A.I.C.S.: 423420
Sheetal Upare *(Sr Engr-Software)*

Giesecke & Devrient Istanbul Ticaret ve Servis Ltd. Sirketi (1)
Morbasan Sokak Koza Is Merkezi B blok 2 kat Barbaros Bulvari, Besiktas, 34349, Istanbul, Turkiye
Tel.: (90) 2123472827
Currency Handling Machine Whslr
N.A.I.C.S.: 423420

Giesecke & Devrient Italia, S.R.L. (1)
Via Tommaso da Cazzaniga 4, 20121, Milan, Italy
Tel.: (39) 0288896121
Currency Handling Machine Whslr
N.A.I.C.S.: 423420
Giuseppe Balconi *(Acct Mgr-Sls-Banks & Transit-Mobile Security)*

Giesecke & Devrient Kabushiki Kaisha (1)
1-24-14 Nishi-Shimbashi, Minato-ku, Tokyo, 105-0003, Japan
Tel.: (81) 335045910
Currency Handling Machine Whslr
N.A.I.C.S.: 423420

Giesecke & Devrient Malaysia SDN BHD (1)
Lot 6 Off Jalan Delima 1/1 Batu Tiga, 40150, Shah Alam, Selangor, Malaysia
Tel.: (60) 56292929
Currency Handling Machine Whslr
N.A.I.C.S.: 423420
Badiah Hanim Abu Bakar *(Mgr-Talent Dev)*

Giesecke & Devrient Matsoukis, Security Printing, S.A. (1)
69 Dimocratias Ave, Ilion, 13122, Athens, Greece
Tel.: (30) 2102386221
Currency Handling Machine Whslr
N.A.I.C.S.: 423420
Michalis Kokkoris *(Production Mgr)*

Giesecke & Devrient Slovakia, s.r.o. (1)
Dolne Hony 11, 949 01, Nitra, Slovakia
Tel.: (421) 376419241
Currency Handling Machine Whslr
N.A.I.C.S.: 423420
Matej Siles *(Head-Security)*

Giesecke & Devrient Systems Canada, Inc. (1)
316 Markland Street, Markham, L6C 0C1, ON, Canada
Tel.: (905) 475-1333
Industrial Machinery & Equipment Whslr
N.A.I.C.S.: 423830
Susan Bishop *(VP-HR)*

Giesecke y Devrient Currency Technology de Mexico, S.A. de C.V. (1)

GIESECKE & DEVRIENT GMBH

Giesecke & Devrient GmbH—(Continued)
Santa Rosa 11 Colonia La Joya Ixtacala,
54160, Mexico, Mexico
Tel.: (52) 5550399900
Software Development Services
N.A.I.C.S.: 334610

Giesecke y Devrient de Mexico S.A. de C.V. (1)
Av Santa Rosa No 11 Col La Joya Ixtacala,
54160, Tlalnepantla, Mexico
Tel.: (52) 5550399900
Currency Handling Machine Whslr
N.A.I.C.S.: 423420
Paul Rivera *(Project Mgr)*

Giesecke+Devrient advance52 GmbH (1)
Balanstrasse 69b, 81541, Munich, Germany
Tel.: (49) 8921540750
Web Site: http://www.advance52.com
Business Development Services
N.A.I.C.S.: 541613
Markus Rachals *(Mng Dir)*

GyD Iberica S.A. (1)
Carrer del Numero 114 n 27 Poligon Pratenc, El Prat de Llobregat, 8820, Barcelona, Spain
Tel.: (34) 932027200
Currency Handling Machine Whslr
N.A.I.C.S.: 423420
Daniel Sojo Diez *(Mgr-Logical Security)*

GyD Latinoamericana S.A. (1)
La Pampa 1534 6, C1428DZF, Buenos Aires, Argentina
Tel.: (54) 1157878700
Currency Handling Machine Whslr
N.A.I.C.S.: 423420

Huangshi G&D Wanda Security Card Co. Ltd. (1)
Hangzhou West Road Tuanchengshan Development Zone, Huangshi, Hubei, China
Tel.: (86) 7146359988
Currency Handling Machine Whslr
N.A.I.C.S.: 423420
Wei Xiao *(Gen Mgr)*

MC Holding GmbH & Co. KG (1)
Sprungleitenweg 1, 82327, Tutzing, Germany
Tel.: (49) 8941190
Currency Handling Machine Whslr
N.A.I.C.S.: 423420

Original1 GmbH (1)
Mainzer Landstrasse 205, 60326, Frankfurt, Germany
Tel.: (49) 6917536620
Web Site: http://www.original1.net
Sales Range: $25-49.9 Million
Emp.: 12
Supply Chain Integrity & Security Services; Joint Venture of SAP AG, Nokia Corporation & Giesecke & Devrient GmbH
N.A.I.C.S.: 513210

PT Giesecke & Devrient Indonesia (1)
Intiland Tower 9th Floor Jl Jend Sudirman Kav 32, Jakarta, 10220, Indonesia
Tel.: (62) 2157851057
Currency Handling Machine Whslr
N.A.I.C.S.: 423420
Anto Giyantoro *(Dir-Sls)*

Papierfabrik Louisenthal GmbH (1)
Louisenthal 1, PO Box 11 85, 83701, Gmund am Tegernsee, Germany
Tel.: (49) 802276001
Currency Handling Machine Whslr
N.A.I.C.S.: 423420

Procoin GmbH (1)
Amperestr 7 11, 63225, Langen, Germany
Tel.: (49) 6103509970
Web Site: http://www.procoin.de
Counting Machine Mfr
N.A.I.C.S.: 333310
Sven Geis *(Mng Dir)*

Secustack GmbH (1)
Zeitenstromung - Bldg 30 Konigsbrucker Str 96, 01099, Dresden, Germany
Tel.: (49) 35147936735
Web Site: http://www.secustack.com
Software Development Services
N.A.I.C.S.: 334610

Kai Martius *(Mng Dir)*

Transtrack International B.V. (1)
Science Park 400, 1098 XH, Amsterdam, Netherlands
Tel.: (31) 208884722
Web Site: http://www.transtrackinternational.com
Software Development Services
N.A.I.C.S.: 334610
Maarten De Bakker *(Mng Dir)*

Veridos America Inc. (1)
Oranienstr 91, 10969, Berlin, Germany
Tel.: (49) 30258998439
Web Site: http://www.veridos.com
Software Development Services
N.A.I.C.S.: 334610
Andreas Raschmeier *(CEO & Mng Dir)*

Veridos GmbH (1)
Oranienstrasse 91, 10969, Berlin,
Germany (60%)
Tel.: (49) 30 25899840
Web Site: http://www.veridos.com
Identity Products & Services
N.A.I.C.S.: 323111
Marc-Julian Siewert *(CEO)*

Subsidiary (US):

E-Seek, Inc. (2)
9471 Ridgehaven Ct Ste E, San Diego, CA 92123
Tel.: (858) 495-1900
Web Site: http://www.e-seek.com
Computer Peripheral Equipment Mfr
N.A.I.C.S.: 334118

Veridos Matsoukis S.A. (1)
69 Dimokratias Av, Ilion, 131 22, Athens, Greece
Tel.: (30) 2102386221
Web Site: http://www.veridosmatsoukis.com
Printing Services
N.A.I.C.S.: 323111
Efthimios Matsoukis *(Mng Dir)*

secunet Security Networks AG (1)
Kronprinzenstrasse 58, 45128, Essen,
Germany (51%)
Tel.: (49) 20154540
Web Site: https://www.secunet.com
Rev.: $434,571,542
Assets: $362,775,837
Liabilities: $210,717,744
Net Worth: $152,058,092
Earnings: $32,177,810
Emp.: 1,043
Fiscal Year-end: 12/31/2023
Information Technology Security Services
N.A.I.C.S.: 541512
Thomas Pleines *(CFO & Member-Exec Bd)*

GIFI SA

ZI La Boulbene, BP 79, 47301,
Villeneuve-sur-Lot, France
Tel.: (33) 553405454
Web Site: http://www.gifi.fr
Sales Range: $700-749.9 Million
Emp.: 271
Discount Store Operator
N.A.I.C.S.: 455110
Philippe Ginestet *(Founder, Chm & CEO)*

GIFORE AGRICULTURAL SCIENCE & TECHNOLOGY SERVICE CO., LTD.

No 219 Gangtong North 2nd Road
North Park, Pidu District Chengdu
Modern Industrial Port, Chengdu,
611743, Sichuan, China
Tel.: (86) 2887868752
Web Site: http://www.gifore.com
Year Founded: 1994
300022—(CHIN)
Rev.: $373,203,315
Assets: $259,108,730
Liabilities: $133,515,786
Net Worth: $125,592,945
Earnings: $2,366,872
Fiscal Year-end: 12/31/23
Agricultural Machinery Distr
N.A.I.C.S.: 423820

Xinming Wang *(Chm & Gen Mgr)*

GIFT HOLDINGS INC.

6-27-19 Haramachida, Machida, Tokyo, 194-0013, Japan
Tel.: (81) 428607182
Web Site: https://www.gift-group.co.jp
Year Founded: 2008
9279—(TKS)
Rev.: $162,942,380
Assets: $88,816,430
Liabilities: $40,802,950
Net Worth: $48,013,480
Earnings: $11,322,730
Emp.: 600
Fiscal Year-end: 10/31/23
Food Products Distr
N.A.I.C.S.: 424490

Subsidiaries:

Gift USA Inc. (1)
35088 Lido Blvd Unit D, Newark, CA 94560
Tel.: (408) 364-6239
Web Site: https://www.giftusa.org
Education Services
N.A.I.C.S.: 611710
Nelson Roy *(Sls Mgr)*

GIFT INFINITE PUBLIC COMPANY LIMITED

27 RS Group Bldg 9 FL Tower A
Prasert-Manukitch Rd, Sena Nikhom
Chatuchak, Bangkok, 10900, Thailand
Tel.: (66) 20378989
Web Site: https://www.giftinfinite.co.th
Year Founded: 1999
GIFT—(THA)
Rev.: $23,510,533
Assets: $64,524,914
Liabilities: $20,157,329
Net Worth: $44,367,586
Earnings: $3,680,816
Emp.: 17
Fiscal Year-end: 12/31/23
Chemical Distr
N.A.I.C.S.: 424690
Jesadavat Priebjrivat *(Chm)*

Subsidiaries:

Lavish Laboratory Company Limited (1)
27 RS Group Tower A 9thfloor Prasert
Manukit Road, Sena Nikhom Sub-district
Chatuchak District, Bangkok, 10900, Thailand
Tel.: (66) 868426529
Web Site: http://www.lavishlab.com
Soap & Cosmetic Product Mfr
N.A.I.C.S.: 325620

GIFT SAS

64 bis rue La Boetie, 75008, Paris,
France
Tel.: (33) 1 42 127701
Web Site: http://www.groupegift.com
Holding Company
N.A.I.C.S.: 551112
Albert Benamran *(Pres)*

Subsidiaries:

Sup Sante S.A.R.L. (1)
46 rue de la Tour, 75116, Paris,
France (100%)
Tel.: (33) 156912345
Web Site: http://www.supsante.com
Vocational Education Services
N.A.I.C.S.: 923110
Isabelle Meierhans *(Coord-Medicine, Paramedical & Social)*

GIFT UNIVERSE GROUP LIMITED

The Atrium Business Centre Curtis
Road, Dorking, Surrey, United Kingdom
Tel.: (44) 3445670710   UK
Web Site: https://giftuniverse.com

INTERNATIONAL PUBLIC

Emp.: 100
Gift, Novelty & Souvenir Stores
N.A.I.C.S.: 459420
Paul Kraftman *(Chm & CEO)*

Subsidiaries:

Prezzybox.com Ltd (1)
Hollybank Farm House, No Mans Heath Lane, Austrey, CV9 3EW, Warwickshire, United Kingdom
Tel.: (44) 1827 839 916
Web Site: http://www.prezzybox.com
Emp.: 20
Online Gifts Retailer
N.A.I.C.S.: 449210
Zak Edwards *(Founder)*

GIFTCRAFT LTD.

8550 Airport Road, Brampton, L6T
5A3, ON, Canada
Tel.: (905) 790-2000
Web Site: http://www.giftcraft.com
Rev.: $22,125,537
Emp.: 150
Decor & Giftware Products Supplier
N.A.I.C.S.: 459420
Tom Kydd *(Treas)*

Subsidiaries:

Giftcraft Inc. (1)
300 International Dr Ste 100, Williamsville, NY 14221
Tel.: (877) 387-4888
Toy & Hobby Goods Distr
N.A.I.C.S.: 423920
Trevor Cohen *(CEO)*

GIFTEE, INC.

12th Floor Higashi-gotanda Square
2-10-2 Higashigotanda, Shinagawa-ku, Tokyo, 141-0022, Japan
Tel.: (81) 363039318
Web Site: https://www.giftee.co.jp
Year Founded: 2010
4449—(TKS)
Rev.: $51,232,340
Assets: $157,142,760
Liabilities: $98,260,310
Net Worth: $58,882,450
Earnings: $914,610
Emp.: 367
Fiscal Year-end: 12/31/23
E Commerce Site Operator
N.A.I.C.S.: 423690
Mutsumi Ota *(CEO)*

Subsidiaries:

Giftee Mekong Company Ltd. (1)
Floor 11 58 Vo Van Tan, Vo Thi Sau Ward District 3, Ho Chi Minh City, Vietnam
Tel.: (84) 286 291 3077
Web Site: http://biz.giftee.com.vn
Gift Product Distr
N.A.I.C.S.: 459420

P.T. Giftee International Indonesia (1)
Plaza Indonesia 5th Level Unit E021 AB Jl MH Thamrin Kav 28-30, Jakarta Pusat, 10350, Indonesia
Tel.: (62) 85174474496
Web Site: https://biz.giftee.id
Software Development Services
N.A.I.C.S.: 541511

paintory Inc. (1)
60-2 Motoumachi, Tsuyama, 708-0061, Okayama, Japan
Tel.: (81) 12093185
Web Site: https://paintory.co.jp
Apparel Mfr & Distr
N.A.I.C.S.: 315210

GIFU LANDSCAPE ARCHITECT CO., LTD.

4-79-1 Akanabehishino, Gifu, 500-8268, Japan
Tel.: (81) 582724120
Web Site: https://www.gifu-zohen.co.jp
Year Founded: 1927

AND PRIVATE COMPANIES ... GIGAMEDIA LIMITED

14380—(NGO)
Rev.: $33,049,224
Assets: $31,020,813
Liabilities: $7,723,819
Net Worth: $23,296,994
Earnings: $1,968,946
Fiscal Year-end: 09/30/23
Landscaping Services
N.A.I.C.S.: 561730
Tatsuhiro Oguri *(Chm & Dir)*

GIG WORKS INC.
7-22-27 Nishi-Shinjuku KN Building 4F, Shinjuku-ku, Tokyo, 160-0023, Japan
Tel.: (81) 368328109
Web Site: https://www.gig.co.jp
Year Founded: 1977
2375—(TKS)
Rev.: $187,402,880
Assets: $65,178,370
Liabilities: $43,234,820
Net Worth: $21,943,550
Earnings: ($5,090,620)
Emp.: 933
Fiscal Year-end: 10/31/23
Business Support Services
N.A.I.C.S.: 541613

GIGA METALS CORPORATION
Suite 203 700 West Pender Street, Vancouver, V6C 1G8, BC, Canada
Tel.: (604) 681-2300   BC
Web Site:
  https://www.gigametals.com
Year Founded: 1983
HNCKF—(OTCQX)
Assets: $8,009,238
Liabilities: $518,724
Net Worth: $7,490,513
Earnings: ($1,581,612)
Emp.: 2
Fiscal Year-end: 12/31/20
Nickel Mining Services
N.A.I.C.S.: 212230
Leslie Young *(Sec)*

GIGA PRIZE CO., LTD.
3-6 Maruyamacho, Shibuya-Ku, Tokyo, 150-0044, Japan
Tel.: (81) 354598400
Web Site: https://www.gigaprize.co.jp
3830—(NGO)
Rev.: $153,699,040
Assets: $108,338,560
Liabilities: $68,592,480
Net Worth: $39,746,080
Earnings: $13,484,240
Fiscal Year-end: 03/31/21
Security System Services
N.A.I.C.S.: 561621
Yasutaka Yanase *(Pres)*

GIGA SOLAR MATERIALS CORP.
1F No 3 Gongye 1st Rd, Hukou Township, Hsinchu, 30351, Taiwan
Tel.: (886) 35981886
Web Site:
  https://www.gigasolar.com.tw
Year Founded: 2006
3691—(TPE)
Rev.: $176,807,835
Assets: $381,822,843
Liabilities: $115,070,162
Net Worth: $266,752,681
Earnings: ($17,885,470)
Fiscal Year-end: 12/31/22
Semiconductor Devices Mfr
N.A.I.C.S.: 334413
Jimmy Chen *(Chm)*

Subsidiaries:

Suzhou Giga Solar Materials Corp.   (1)
3rd Floor Building 3 No 38 Beiguandu Road Yuexi Street, Wuzhong District, Suzhou, Jiangsu, China
Tel.: (86) 51282259500
PV Conductive Paste Mfr
N.A.I.C.S.: 325520

GIGA-BYTE TECHNOLOGY CO., LTD.
No 6 Baoqiang Rd, Xindian Dist, New Taipei City, 231, Taiwan
Tel.: (886) 289124000
Web Site: https://www.gigabyte.com
2376—(TAI)
Rev.: $4,472,788,640
Assets: $2,686,497,822
Liabilities: $1,445,968,061
Net Worth: $1,240,529,761
Earnings: $156,351,902
Emp.: 2,040
Fiscal Year-end: 12/31/23
Notebook Computers Mfr
N.A.I.C.S.: 334111
Mou-Ming Ma *(Sr VP)*

Subsidiaries:

Cloudmatrix Co., Ltd.   (1)
B2 No 205 Section 3 Beixin Road, Xindian, New Taipei City, Taiwan
Tel.: (886) 289124000
Web Site: https://www.cloudmatrix.com.tw
Information Technology Services
N.A.I.C.S.: 541511

G.B.T. Inc,.   (1)
17358 Railroad St, City of Industry, CA 91748
Tel.: (626) 854-9338
Sales Range: $25-49.9 Million
Emp.: 90
Computer Peripheral Equipment Mfr
N.A.I.C.S.: 334118
Eric Lu *(Pres)*

G.B.T. Technology Trading GmbH   (1)
Am Stadtrand 63, 22047, Hamburg, Germany
Tel.: (49) 402533040
Computer Peripherals Mfr & Sales
N.A.I.C.S.: 334111

Giga-Byte Communication Inc.   (1)
B2F No 207 Sec 3 Beixin Road Xindian, Taipei, 231, Taiwan
Tel.: (886) 289132220
Web Site: http://www.gigabytecm.com
Sales Range: $50-74.9 Million
Emp.: 220
Communication Equipment Mfr
N.A.I.C.S.: 334290

Giga-Byte Technology B.V.   (1)
Verdunplein 8, 5627, Eindhoven, Netherlands
Tel.: (31) 402902088
Web Site: https://www.gigabyte.com
Sales Range: $25-49.9 Million
Emp.: 35
Computer Peripheral Equipment Distr
N.A.I.C.S.: 423430

Giga-Byte Technology Co., Ltd. - GIGABYTE Nanping Factory   (1)
No 215 Nanping Road 324, Pingzhen, Taoyuan, 324, Taiwan
Tel.: (886) 422623476
Communication Equipment Mfr
N.A.I.C.S.: 334290

Gigabyte Technology Pty. Ltd.   (1)
Unit 1 19-23 Clarinda Rd, Oakleigh, 3167, VIC, Australia
Tel.: (61) 385616288
Web Site: http://www.gigabyte.com.au
Electronic Computer Mfr
N.A.I.C.S.: 334111

Green Share Co., Ltd.   (1)
B1-A No 205 Sec 3 Beixin Rd, Xindian Dist, New Taipei City, 231-43, Taiwan
Tel.: (886) 289131312
Web Site: http://www.gigaipc.com
Computer Hardware Mfr
N.A.I.C.S.: 332510

Ningbo Giga-Byte Technology Co., Ltd.   (1)
Ningbo Free Trade Zone West Building 1 Block 0212 1, Ningbo, Zhejiang, China
Tel.: (86) 574 8681 4452
Web Site: http://www.gigabyte.cn
Computer Peripheral Equipment Mfr & Sales
N.A.I.C.S.: 334118

Senyun Precision Optical Co., Ltd.   (1)
No 18 Gongye 1st Rd, Pingzhen Dist, Taoyuan, 324, Taiwan
Tel.: (886) 34690630
Web Site: https://www.senyun.com.tw
Electronic Equipment Mfr & Distr
N.A.I.C.S.: 335314

GIGACLEAR PLC
Windrush Court Blacklands Way, Abingdon, OX14 1SY, Oxfordshire, United Kingdom
Tel.: (44) 1865 591100
Web Site: http://www.gigaclear.com
Year Founded: 2010
Fiber-To-The-Premises (FTTP) Networks
N.A.I.C.S.: 335921
Joe Frost *(Dir-Sls & Mktg)*

GIGACLOUD TECHNOLOGY, INC.
Unit A 12/F Shun Ho Tower 24-30 Ice House Street, Central, China (Hong Kong)
Tel.: (852) 23698219   Ky
Web Site:
  https://www.gigacloudtech.com
Year Founded: 2006
GCT—(NASDAQ)
Rev.: $490,071,000
Assets: $418,600,000
Liabilities: $223,435,000
Net Worth: $195,165,000
Earnings: $23,031,000
Emp.: 764
Fiscal Year-end: 12/31/22
Online Shopping Services
N.A.I.C.S.: 459999
Larry Lei Wu *(Founder, Chm & CEO)*

GIGADEVICE SEMICONDUCTOR (BEIJING) INC
Building No8 IC Park No9 Fenghao East Road, Haidian, Beijing, 100083, China
Tel.: (86) 1082881666   CN
Web Site:
  https://www.gigadevice.com
Year Founded: 2005
603986—(SHG)
Rev.: $1,141,450,933
Assets: $2,336,967,238
Liabilities: $204,918,475
Net Worth: $2,132,048,763
Earnings: $288,180,589
Fiscal Year-end: 12/31/22
Memory Chip Mfr & Distr
N.A.I.C.S.: 334413
Zhu Yiming *(Chm)*

Subsidiaries:

Gigadevice Semiconductor (Beijing) Inc - Santa Clara Branch   (1)
2975 Bowers Ave Ste 323, Santa Clara, CA 95051
Tel.: (408) 596-3166
Non Volatile Memory Device Distr
N.A.I.C.S.: 423690

Gigadevice Semiconductor (Hefei) Inc.   (1)
Fanhua Avenue 266 Economic and Technological Development Area, Hefei, Anhui, China
Tel.: (86) 55168999734
Non Volatile Memory Device Mfr
N.A.I.C.S.: 334413

Gigadevice Semiconductor Europe Ltd   (1)
Innovation House Molly Millars Close, Wokingham, RG41 2RX, Berkshire, United Kingdom
Tel.: (44) 7585707735
Non Volatile Memory Device Distr
N.A.I.C.S.: 423690

GIGALANE CO., LTD.
61 Dongtansandan 10-gil, Hwaseong, 445-170, Gyeonggi, Korea (South)
Tel.: (82) 312337325
Web Site: https://www.gigalane.com
Year Founded: 2001
049080—(KRS)
Rev.: $41,975,183
Assets: $70,363,011
Liabilities: $23,616,773
Net Worth: $46,746,239
Earnings: ($6,380,056)
Emp.: 177
Fiscal Year-end: 12/31/22
RF Products Mfr
N.A.I.C.S.: 334220

Subsidiaries:

Faithtek Limited   (1)
Rm D Suite C1 6/F 14 Hing Yip Street, Wing Hing Industrial Building Kwun Tong, Kowloon, China (Hong Kong)
Tel.: (852) 51267072058
Semiconductor Equipment Mfr & Distr
N.A.I.C.S.: 333242

QuantumTek Innovatives Corporation   (1)
5F No 158 Rd Sec 1 Wenxing Rd, Zhubei, 302, Taiwan
Tel.: (886) 36673889
Semiconductor Equipment Mfr & Distr
N.A.I.C.S.: 333242

TACTRON Elektronik GmbH & Co. KG   (1)
Akilindastr 10a, 82166, Grafelfing, Germany
Tel.: (49) 898955690
Web Site: https://www.tactron.de
Semiconductor Equipment Mfr & Distr
N.A.I.C.S.: 333242

Woken Technology Inc.   (1)
7F-4 No 146 Wenxing Road, Guishan District, Taoyuan, Taiwan
Tel.: (886) 33979900
Web Site: https://www.woken.com.tw
Semiconductor Equipment Mfr & Distr
N.A.I.C.S.: 333242

GIGAMEDIA LIMITED
8th Floor No 22 Lane 407 Section 2 Tiding Boulevard, Taipei, 114, Taiwan
Tel.: (886) 226568000   SG
Web Site:
  https://www.gigamedia.com
Year Founded: 1999
GIGM—(NASDAQ)
Rev.: $5,585,000
Assets: $52,136,000
Liabilities: $3,530,000
Net Worth: $48,606,000
Earnings: ($2,752,000)
Emp.: 101
Fiscal Year-end: 12/31/22
Internet Access & Content Services & Entertainment Software Developer
N.A.I.C.S.: 513210
James Cheng Ming Huang *(Chm, CEO & CFO)*

Subsidiaries:

FunTown Hong Kong Limited   (1)
Suite 1403-1405 Sunbeam Plaza, 1155 Canton Road, Kowloon, China (Hong Kong)
Tel.: (852) 22509311
Web Site: https://www.funtown.com.hk
Sales Range: $25-49.9 Million
Emp.: 46
Online Games
N.A.I.C.S.: 541511

Hoshin Gigamedia Center Inc.   (1)
4F 57 Dongxing Road, Taipei, 110, Taiwan   (100%)
Tel.: (886) 287707966
Cable-Base Internet Access Services

GIGAMEDIA LIMITED

GigaMedia Limited—(Continued)
N.A.I.C.S.: 517810

GIGANTE SALMON AS
Sjogata 21, 8006, Bodo, Norway
Tel.: (47) 98844724
Web Site:
https://www.gigantesalmon.no
Year Founded: 2001
GIGA—(OSL)
Rev.: $514,502
Assets: $60,747,552
Liabilities: $16,269,906
Net Worth: $44,477,646
Earnings: $67,246
Emp.: 12
Fiscal Year-end: 12/31/23
Agriculture Product Distr
N.A.I.C.S.: 424910
Rune Johansen (CFO)

GIGAS HOSTING S.A
Av de Fuencarral 44 Gigas Building, Alcobendas, 28108, Madrid, Spain
Tel.: (34) 900247000
Web Site: https://www.gigas.com
Year Founded: 2011
GIGA—(MAD)
Sales Range: Less than $1 Million
Web Hosting Services
N.A.I.C.S.: 518210
Moises Israel (Chm)

GIGASET AG
Frankenstr 2, 46395, Bocholt, Germany
Tel.: (49) 2871912912
Web Site: https://www.gigaset.com
Year Founded: 1880
GGS—(DUS)
Rev.: $260,433,844
Assets: $206,624,218
Liabilities: $180,031,297
Net Worth: $26,592,920
Earnings: ($6,011,224)
Emp.: 833
Fiscal Year-end: 12/31/22
Telecommunication Servicesb
N.A.I.C.S.: 517810
Helvin Hau Yan Wong (Chm-Supervisory Bd)

Subsidiaries:

Gigaset Communications GmbH (1)
Frankenstr 2, 46395, Bocholt, Germany (80%)
Tel.: (49) 287 191 2912
Web Site: https://www.gigaset.com
Cordless Telephone Mfr
N.A.I.C.S.: 334210

Gigaset Iletisim Cihazlari A.S. (1)
Barbaros Mah Mor Sumbul Sk No 1, Meridian I Blok 2 M4 Atasehir, Istanbul, Türkiye
Tel.: (90) 2162880600
Communication Service
N.A.I.C.S.: 517810

van Netten GmbH (1)
Hesslingweg 30, 44309, Dortmund, Germany (90%)
Tel.: (49) 2 31 25 05 0
Web Site: http://www.van-netten.de
Sales Range: $50-74.9 Million
Emp.: 115
Candy Mfr
N.A.I.C.S.: 311340

GIGASTONE CORPORATION
4F No 166 Xinhu 2nd Rd, Neihu Dist, Taipei, 114, Taiwan
Tel.: (886) 226582588
Web Site: https://www.gigastone.com
Year Founded: 2010
5262—(TAI)
Semiconductor Mfr
N.A.I.C.S.: 334413
Wang Li-Ming (Chm)

GIGASTORAGE CORP.
No 3 Kung Yen 1st Rd Hsinchu Industrial Park, Hsin-chu, 30351, Taiwan
Tel.: (886) 35985510
Web Site:
https://www.gigastorage.com.tw
Year Founded: 1997
2406—(TAI)
Rev.: $128,849,434
Assets: $487,538,554
Liabilities: $194,900,055
Net Worth: $292,638,499
Earnings: ($40,363,352)
Fiscal Year-end: 12/31/23
Compact Disc Record Mfr
N.A.I.C.S.: 334413
Jimmy Chen (Chm)

Subsidiaries:

Wafering Technology Corporation (1)
27 Zhonghe Street Lane 62 Hsinchu, 302, Zhubei, Taiwan
Tel.: (886) 35518989
Multi-crystalline Wafer Mfr
N.A.I.C.S.: 334413

GIGAVIS CO., LTD.
53-86 Jinwisandanro Jinwi-Myeon, Pyeongtaek, Gyeonggi-Do, Korea (South)
Tel.: (82) 316152199
Web Site: https://www.gigavis.com
Year Founded: 2004
420770—(KRS)
Semiconductor Machinery Mfr
N.A.I.C.S.: 333242
HaeCheol Kang (CEO)

GIGLIO GROUP S.P.A.
Via Visconti di Modrone 11, 20122, Milan, Italy
Tel.: (39) 0289693240
Web Site: https://www.giglio.org
Year Founded: 2003
GG—(ITA)
Rev.: $39,659,657
Assets: $37,271,840
Liabilities: $41,904,401
Net Worth: ($4,632,560)
Earnings: ($2,269,673)
Emp.: 60
Fiscal Year-end: 12/31/22
Digital Marketing Services
N.A.I.C.S.: 423620
Alessandro Giglio (Chm)

Subsidiaries:

Ibox S.r.l. (1)
Via Talete 52, Eboli, 84025, Salerno, Italy
Tel.: (39) 0828601327
Web Site: http://www.iboxsrl.it
Prefabricated Metal Product Mfr
N.A.I.C.S.: 332311

GIGLIO.COM S.P.A.
Via Giovanni Ferro Luzzi 3, 90143, Palermo, Italy
Tel.: (39) 0916257729
Web Site: https://www.giglio.com
Year Founded: 1996
GCOM—(EUR)
Emp.: 80
Apparel Product Retailer
N.A.I.C.S.: 424350
Giuseppe Giglio (Chm)

GIIB HOLDINGS BERHAD
Lot PT1654 & PT1657 Nilai Industrial Estate, Negeri Sembilan, 71800, Nilai, Selangor, Malaysia
Tel.: (60) 67994833
Web Site: https://www.giibworld.com
GIIB—(KLS)
Rev.: $8,503,687
Assets: $22,092,696
Liabilities: $11,751,105
Net Worth: $10,341,590
Earnings: ($4,983,874)
Emp.: 160
Fiscal Year-end: 06/30/23
Rubber Mfr
N.A.I.C.S.: 339113
Boon Wee Tai (CEO)

Subsidiaries:

GIIB Healthcare Products Sdn. Bhd. (1)
Lot PT1654 & PT1657 Nilai Industrial Estate, 71800, Nilai, Negeri Sembilan, Malaysia
Tel.: (60) 122091566
Web Site: https://healthcare.giibworld.com
Rubber Products Mfr
N.A.I.C.S.: 326291

Goodway Europe (Sweden) AB (1)
Magasinsvagen 7, PO Box 197, 435 24, Molnlycke, Vastra Gotaland, Sweden
Tel.: (46) 31917575
Sales Range: $25-49.9 Million
Emp.: 3
Tiles Mfr
N.A.I.C.S.: 326211
Paolo Borjianni (Mgr)

Goodway Rubber Industries Sdn. Bhd. (1)
Lot PT1654 PT1657 Nilai Industrial Estate, 71800, Nilai, Negeri Sembilan, Malaysia
Tel.: (60) 67994833
Sales Range: $75-99.9 Million
Emp.: 250
Tire & Rubber Products Mfr
N.A.I.C.S.: 326211
Tai Boon Wee (Mng Dir)

Nantong Shibake Rubber Product Co. Ltd. (1)
Mudanjiang Road Rudong Economic Development Zone New District, Nantong, 226400, Jiangsu, China
Tel.: (86) 513 8416 6890
Web Site: http://www.goodwayrubber.com
Sales Range: $25-49.9 Million
Emp.: 50
Rubber Products Mfr
N.A.I.C.S.: 326299

GIK OKO D.D.
Dzemala Bijedica 185, Sarajevo, 71000, Bosnia & Herzegovina
Tel.: (387) 3 345 5333
Web Site: http://www.gikoko.ba
GIKORK5—(SARE)
Rev.: $1,092,421
Assets: $15,424,952
Liabilities: $7,701,686
Net Worth: $7,723,266
Earnings: ($535,579)
Emp.: 18
Fiscal Year-end: 12/31/20
Graphic Design & Publishing Services
N.A.I.C.S.: 541430

GIKEN HOLDINGS CO., LTD.
3-7-2 Asagaya-minami Suginami-ku, Tokyo, 166-0004, Japan
Tel.: (81) 362769393
Web Site: http://www.giken-hd.co.jp
Year Founded: 2018
1443—(TKS)
Rev.: $34,167,090
Assets: $113,877,080
Liabilities: $40,744,040
Net Worth: $73,133,040
Earnings: $2,934,840
Emp.: 162
Fiscal Year-end: 03/31/24
Civil Engineering Services
N.A.I.C.S.: 541330
Sasaki Veggie (Pres & CEO)

GIKEN KOGYO CO., LTD.
3-7-2 Asagaya-minami, Suginami-ku, Tokyo, 166-0004, Japan
Tel.: (81) 3 3398 8500

INTERNATIONAL PUBLIC

Web Site: http://www.gikenko.co.jp
Year Founded: 1958
Rev.: $20,181,283
Assets: $104,504,138
Liabilities: $43,228,701
Net Worth: $61,275,437
Earnings: $436,612
Emp.: 177
Fiscal Year-end: 03/31/18
Civil Engineering Services
N.A.I.C.S.: 541330

GIKEN LTD.
3948-1 Nunoshida, Kochi, 781-5195, Japan
Tel.: (81) 888462933
Web Site: https://www.giken.com
Year Founded: 1967
6289—(TKS)
Rev.: $183,371,820
Assets: $299,362,380
Liabilities: $47,788,260
Net Worth: $251,574,120
Earnings: $15,158,140
Emp.: 691
Fiscal Year-end: 08/31/24
Construction Equipment Mfr & Whslr
N.A.I.C.S.: 333120
Akio Kitamura (Pres)

Subsidiaries:

CITEC INC. (1)
1-3-28 Ariake, Koto-ku, Tokyo, 135-0063, Japan
Tel.: (81) 355000911
Web Site: http://www.citec-inc.co.jp
Measuring & Surveying Services
N.A.I.C.S.: 541370
Toshio Ikeda (Pres)

GIKEN Ltd. - Tokyo Factory (1)
75-1 Minato, Urayasu-shi, Chiba, 279-0024, Japan
Tel.: (81) 473189111
Industrial Machinery Mfr
N.A.I.C.S.: 333998

Giken America Corporation (1)
5850 T G Lee Blvd Ste 535, Orlando, FL 32822
Tel.: (407) 380-3232
Building Contracting Services
N.A.I.C.S.: 236116
Atsushi Ohira (Pres)

Giken Europe B.V. (1)
Damsluisweg 13, 1332 EA, Almere, Netherlands
Tel.: (31) 367370481
Industrial Machinery Distr
N.A.I.C.S.: 423830

Giken Seisakusho Asia Pte., Ltd. (1)
138 Robinson Road 16-02, Oxley Tower, Singapore, 068906, Singapore
Tel.: (65) 68630330
Industrial Machinery Distr
N.A.I.C.S.: 423830

Giken Seko Co., Ltd. (1)
75-1 Minato, Urayasu, 279-0024, Chiba, Japan
Tel.: (81) 47 318 9111
Web Site: https://www.gikenseko.co.jp
Emp.: 130
Building Contracting Services
N.A.I.C.S.: 236116
Atsushi Ohira (Pres)

Plant (Domestic):

Giken Seko Co., Ltd. - Kansai Factory (2)
401 Yashiro, Ichishimacho, Tanba, 669-4342, Hyogo, Japan
Tel.: (81) 795852764
Industrial Machinery Mfr
N.A.I.C.S.: 333998

GIKEN SAKATA (SINGAPORE) LIMITED
Blk 4012 Ang Mo Kio Ave 10 05-01 Techplace 1, Singapore, 569628, Singapore

AND PRIVATE COMPANIES

Tel.: (65) 6354 6661   SG
Web Site: http://www.giken.com.sg
Year Founded: 1979
Sales Range: $50-74.9 Million
Precision Turned Product Mfr
N.A.I.C.S.: 332721
Kin Bond Yeung *(Chm)*

GIL INVESTMENTS LTD.
5 The Courtyard Timothys Bridge Road, Stratford-upon-Avon, CV37 9NP, Warcs, United Kingdom
Tel.: (44) 1789415566   UK
Web Site: http://www.gilinvest.com
Year Founded: 1991
Privater Equity Firm
N.A.I.C.S.: 523999
Les Litwinowicz *(CEO)*

Subsidiaries:

Erlson Precision Components Limited (1)
4 Priorswood Place, East Pimbo, Skelmersdale, WN8 9QB, Lancs, United Kingdom   (100%)
Tel.: (44) 1695 720 149
Web Site: http://www.erslon.com
Sales Range: $50-74.9 Million
Emp.: 152
Automotive Engineered Components & Assemblies Mfr & Whslr
N.A.I.C.S.: 336390
Brendan Johnson *(Mng Dir)*

Monks & Crane Industrial Group Limited (1)
Unit 2 Atlantic Way Black Country New Road, Wednesbury, WS10 7WW, W Midlands, United Kingdom
Tel.: (44) 121 506 4000
Web Site: http://www.monks-crane.com
Hardware Whslr
N.A.I.C.S.: 423710

Trueform Engineering Limited (1)
Unit 12 Pasadena Trading Estate Pasadena Close, Hayes, UB3 3NQ, Mddx, United Kingdom
Tel.: (44) 20 8561 4959
Web Site: http://www.trueform.co.uk
Sales Range: $25-49.9 Million
Public Transport Infrastructure Designer, Mfr & Installer
N.A.I.C.S.: 237990
Robert Ian Macnaughton *(Fin Dir)*

GILADA FINANCE & INVESTMENTS LTD.
105 RR TAKT 37 Bhoopsandra Main Road, Sanjay Nagar, Bengaluru, 560 094, India
Tel.: (91) 8040620000
Web Site: http://www.gfil.co.in
538788—(BOM)
Rev.: $697,187
Assets: $3,245,311
Liabilities: $812,404
Net Worth: $2,432,908
Earnings: $181,812
Fiscal Year-end: 03/31/23
Financial Investment Services
N.A.I.C.S.: 523999
Rajgopal Gilada *(Mng Dir)*

GILAT SATELLITE NETWORKS LTD.
Gilat House 21 Yegia Kapayim Street Kiryat Arye, Petah Tiqwa, 4913020, Israel
Tel.: (972) 39252000   Il
Web Site: https://www.gilat.com
GILT—(NASDAQ)
Rev.: $239,840,000
Assets: $385,411,000
Liabilities: $141,286,000
Net Worth: $244,125,000
Earnings: ($5,928,000)
Emp.: 987
Fiscal Year-end: 12/31/22

Telecommunications Solutions Based on VSAT Satellite Network Technology
N.A.I.C.S.: 334220
Adi Sfadia *(CEO)*

Subsidiaries:

DataPath, Inc. (1)
2205 Northmont Pkwy Ste 100, Duluth, GA 30096-5892
Tel.: (678) 597-0300
Web Site: http://www.datapath.com
Satellite Earth Terminals & Communications Networks Integrator
N.A.I.C.S.: 517410
Brad Majeres *(COO)*

Gilat Colombia S.A. E.S.P (1)
Calle 93B N 11a - 44 Office 201, Bogota, Colombia
Tel.: (57) 3187014787
Satellite Telecommunication Services
N.A.I.C.S.: 517410

Gilat Satellite Network MDC (1)
Str Vlaicu Pircalab 63 Skytower floor 9 Office B C, MD-2012, Chisinau, Moldova
Tel.: (373) 22846451
Sales Range: $25-49.9 Million
Emp.: 50
Satellite Telecommunication Services
N.A.I.C.S.: 517410

Gilat Satellite Networks (Holland) B.V. (1)
Joop Geesinkweg 999, Amsterdam, 1096 AZ, Noord-Holland, Netherlands
Tel.: (31) 205616444
Sales Range: $50-74.9 Million
Emp.: 3
Real Estate Development Services
N.A.I.C.S.: 531390

Gilat Satellite Networks (Mexico) S.A. de C.V. (1)
Laguna de Terminos 221 Int A 801 Col Granada, Delg Miguel Hidalgo, 11520, Mexico, Mexico
Tel.: (52) 5511001600
Satellite Telecommunication Services
N.A.I.C.S.: 517410

Gilat Satellite Networks (Thailand) Ltd. (1)
88 Paso Tower 20th Floor Unit B Silom Road, Suriyawongse Bangrak, Bangkok, 10500, Thailand
Tel.: (66) 26341780
Sales Range: $25-49.9 Million
Emp.: 10
Satellite Network
N.A.I.C.S.: 517410

Gilat Satellite Networks B.V. (1)
27 Suschevskaya Street, 127055, Moscow, Russia
Tel.: (7) 4959810965
Web Site: http://www.gilat.com
Emp.: 10
Satellite Telecommunication Services
N.A.I.C.S.: 517410
Denis Stafeyev *(CEO-Eurasia)*

Gilat Satellite Networks India Private Ltd. (1)
H-151 Sector - 63, Noida, 201 301, India
Tel.: (91) 1204858800
Sales Range: $25-49.9 Million
Emp.: 13
Satellite Telecommunication Services
N.A.I.C.S.: 517410

Gilat Satellite Networks Ltd. (1)
Level 7 436 St Kilda Road, Melbourne, 3004, VIC, Australia
Tel.: (61) 383060000
Satellite Telecommunication Services
N.A.I.C.S.: 517410

Gilat do Brazil Ltda. (1)
Av Americas 3434 BL 2 SA 307 Barra da Tijuca, Rio de Janeiro, 22640-102, Brazil
Tel.: (55) 2121426606
Satellite Telecommunication Services
N.A.I.C.S.: 517410

Gilat to Home Peru S.A (1)
Calle Amador Merino Reyna 339, San Isidro, Lima, Peru

Tel.: (51) 12224000
Satellite Telecommunication Services
N.A.I.C.S.: 517410

Raysat Antenna Systems LLC (1)
8460-D Tyco Rd, Vienna, VA 22182
Tel.: (703) 462-5010
Web Site: http://www.raysat.com
Rev.: $2,500,000
Emp.: 7
Communication Equipment Mfr & Distr
N.A.I.C.S.: 334220

Wavestream Corp. (1)
545 W Ter Dr, San Dimas, CA 91773
Tel.: (909) 599-9080
Web Site: https://www.wavestream.com
Sales Range: $50-74.9 Million
Emp.: 43
Solid State Amplifier Mfr
N.A.I.C.S.: 334220

GILAT TELECOM LTD.
21 Yegia Kapayim St, PO Box 7144, Petach Tikva, 4913020, Israel
Tel.: (972) 39255027
Web Site: https://www.gilat.net
GLTL—(TAE)
Rev.: $55,154,000
Assets: $46,288,000
Liabilities: $34,850,000
Net Worth: $11,438,000
Earnings: $715,000
Fiscal Year-end: 09/30/23
All Other Telecommunications
N.A.I.C.S.: 517410
Asaf Rosenheck *(CEO)*

GILBERT STEEL LIMITED
1650 Britannia Rd E, Mississauga, L4W 1J2, ON, Canada
Tel.: (905) 670-5771
Web Site: https://www.gilbertsteel.com
Rev.: $69,648,832
Emp.: 200
Steel Supplier
N.A.I.C.S.: 238120
Gary Gilbert *(Pres)*

GILDAN ACTIVEWEAR INC.
600 de Maisonneuve Boulevard West, Montreal, H3A 3J2, QC, Canada
Tel.: (514) 735-2023   Ca
Web Site: http://www.gildan.com
GIL—(NYSE)
Rev.: $2,922,570,000
Assets: $3,136,682,000
Liabilities: $1,217,277,000
Net Worth: $1,919,405,000
Earnings: $607,183,000
Emp.: 48,000
Fiscal Year-end: 02/01/22
Imprintable Apparel & Activewear Mfr
N.A.I.C.S.: 313240
Glenn J. Chamandy *(Founder, Pres & CEO)*

Subsidiaries:

A & G, Inc. (1)
1501 E Cerritos Ave, Anaheim, CA 92805   (100%)
Tel.: (714) 765-0400
Web Site: http://www.alstyle.com
Emp.: 100
Activewear Apparel Mfr & Distr
N.A.I.C.S.: 458110

Gildan Activewear (Eden) Inc. (1)
602 E Meadow Rd, Eden, NC 27289
Tel.: (336) 623-9555
Web Site: http://www.gildan.com
Mens & Boys Clothing & Furnishings Whslr
N.A.I.C.S.: 424350

Subsidiary (Domestic):

Anvil Holdings, Inc. (2)
521 Fifth Ave 9th Fl, New York, NY 10175
Tel.: (212) 476-0300
Web Site: http://www.anvilknitwear.com

GILDE BRAUEREI AG

Sales Range: $150-199.9 Million
Emp.: 4,200
Activewear Designer, Mfr & Marketer
N.A.I.C.S.: 339920

Subsidiary (Domestic):

Anvil Knitwear, Inc. (3)
228 E 45th St 4 Fl, New York, NY 10017-3303
Tel.: (212) 476-0300
Web Site: http://www.anvilknitwear.com
Sales Range: $25-49.9 Million
Emp.: 35
Designer, Marketer & Mfr of Womens, Mens & Childrens Clothing
N.A.I.C.S.: 424350

Spectratex Inc. (3)
9200 W Marlboro Rd, Farmville, NC 27828-8505
Tel.: (252) 753-7163
Sales Range: $25-49.9 Million
Emp.: 55
Apparels Mfr
N.A.I.C.S.: 458110
Mike Sutherland *(Plant Mgr)*

Subsidiary (Domestic):

Gildan Activewear Distribution Inc. (2)
750 Fieldcrest Rd, Eden, NC 27288
Tel.: (336) 627-8619
Rev.: $1,812,000
Emp.: 12
Mens & Boys Clothing Whslr
N.A.I.C.S.: 424350

Gildan Activewear (UK) Limited (1)
50 Victoria Embankment Fleet Street, London, EC4Y 0LS, United Kingdom
Tel.: (44) 2089595511
Knit Apparel Mfr
N.A.I.C.S.: 315120

Gildan Activewear Dominican Republic Textile Company Inc. (1)
Zona Franca Bella Vista, Santo Domingo, Dominican Republic
Tel.: (809) 7283000
Emp.: 5,000
Mens & Boys Cut & Sew Shirt Work Shirt Mfr
N.A.I.C.S.: 315250

Gildan Activewear SRL (1)
Bldg A Newton Industrial Park Newton, Christ Church, BB17047, Barbados
Tel.: (246) 4217751
Sales Range: $25-49.9 Million
Emp.: 130
Manufactures & Sells T-shirts, Placket-Collar Sport Shirts & Fleece
N.A.I.C.S.: 315210
Garry Bell *(VP-Mktg)*

Gildan Honduras (1)
155 Km Puerto Cortes Hwy, Zip Miguel 6, Rio Nance, Choloma, 050600, Honduras
Tel.: (504) 6696500
Activewear Mfr
N.A.I.C.S.: 315250

Gildan USA Inc. (1)
1980 Clements Ferry Rd, Charleston, SC 29492-7723
Tel.: (843) 606-3600
Knit Apparel Mfr
N.A.I.C.S.: 315120

Peds Legwear Inc. (1)
9451 Neuville Ave, Hildebran, NC 28637
Tel.: (828) 397-5566
Web Site: http://www.peds.com
Foot Apparel & Legwear Mfr & Distr
N.A.I.C.S.: 315990

GILDE BRAUEREI AG
Hildesheimer Strasse 132, 30173, Hannover, Germany
Tel.: (49) 51198080   De
Web Site: http://www.gilde-brauerei.com
Year Founded: 1546
Sales Range: $1-9.9 Million
Emp.: 70
Beer Brewer & Whslr
N.A.I.C.S.: 312120

GILDE BRAUEREI AG

Gilde Brauerei AG—(Continued)

Mike Gartner *(Mng Dir)*

GILDE BUY OUT PARTNERS B.V.
Herculesplein 104, 3584 AA, Utrecht, Netherlands
Tel.: (31) 88 220 2600 NI
Web Site: http://www.gilde.com
Year Founded: 1982
Privater Equity Firm
N.A.I.C.S.: 523999
Nikolai R. D. Pronk *(Mng Dir & Head-Benelux)*

Subsidiaries:

COMCAVE AG (1)
Hauert 1, 44227, Dortmund, Germany
Tel.: (49) 231 725260
Web Site: http://www.comcave-group.de
Information Technology Consulting Services
N.A.I.C.S.: 541512
Maximilian Jaber *(Founder & CEO)*

Caseking GmbH (1)
Gaussstr 1, 10589, Berlin, Germany
Tel.: (49) 30 5268473 01
Web Site: http://www.caseking.de
Computer Peripheral Equipment Distr
N.A.I.C.S.: 423430
Kay Kostadinov *(CFO)*

Gamma Holding N.V. (1)
Panovenweg 12, PO Box 80, 5700 AB, Helmond, Netherlands
Tel.: (31) 492566600
Web Site: http://www.gammaholding.com
Sales Range: $800-899.9 Million
Emp.: 4,500
Holding Company; Textile Products Developer, Mfr & Whslr
N.A.I.C.S.: 551112

Subsidiary (US):

Clear Edge Filtration, Inc. (2)
2021 S Lewis Ave Ste 570, Tulsa, OK 74104
Tel.: (918) 728-8111
Web Site: http://www.clear-edge.com
Sales Range: $25-49.9 Million
Filtration Products Mfr
N.A.I.C.S.: 314999
Rick Von Drehle *(CEO)*

Subsidiary (Non-US):

Clear Edge Filtration (Australia) Pty. Ltd. (3)
6 Garden Boulevard, Dingley Village, Dingley, 3172, VIC, Australia
Tel.: (61) 385516400
Web Site: http://www.clear-edge.com
Sales Range: $10-24.9 Million
Emp.: 60
Filtration Products Mfr
N.A.I.C.S.: 314999
Kenneth Shue *(Mng Dir-Asia Pacific)*

Clear Edge Filtration (NZ) Ltd. (3)
126 Lansford Cres, Avondale, Auckland, New Zealand
Tel.: (64) 98282182
Web Site: http://www.clearedge.com
Sales Range: $10-24.9 Million
Emp.: 15
Filtration Products Mfr
N.A.I.C.S.: 314999
Tim Girdimeleer *(Gen Mgr)*

Clear Edge Filtration CFE GmbH (3)
Erzwenge 44, Salzgitter, 382229, Germany
Tel.: (49) 534181510
Web Site: http://www.clear-edge.com
Sales Range: $1-9.9 Million
Filtration Products Mfr
N.A.I.C.S.: 314999

Clear Edge Filtration GmbH (3)
Kevelaerer Strasse 78, 47608, Geldern, Walbeck, Germany
Tel.: (49) 28311220
Web Site: http://www.clear-edge.com
Sales Range: $25-49.9 Million
Emp.: 180
Filtration Products Mfr
N.A.I.C.S.: 314999

Peter Bonnes-Varkyser *(Controller)*

Clear Edge Filtration Polska Sp. z o.o. (3)
Ul Koscielna 15, Konstantynow Lodzki, 95050, Poland
Tel.: (48) 42 211 12 65
Filtration Products Mfr
N.A.I.C.S.: 314999
Collin Waudby *(Gen Mgr)*

Clear Edge Filtration South Africa Pty. Ltd. (3)
44 Jasper Rd Robertsham, PO Box 38262, Booysens, 2016, South Africa
Tel.: (27) 116805300
Web Site: http://www.clearedge.com
Sales Range: $1-9.9 Million
Filtration Products Mfr
N.A.I.C.S.: 314999
elsabath Kuman *(Gen Mgr)*

Clear Edge Filtration Sweden AB (3)
Brevensvgen, SE 640 10, Hogsjo, Sweden
Tel.: (46) 15147500
Web Site: http://www.clear-edge.com
Sales Range: $25-49.9 Million
Filtration Products Mfr
N.A.I.C.S.: 339999

Clear Edge Filtration UK Ltd. (3)
Knowsley Road Industrial Estate, Haslingden, BB4 4EJ, Lancs, United Kingdom
Tel.: (44) 1706 239 500
Filtration Products Mfr
N.A.I.C.S.: 314999

Subsidiary (Domestic):

Clear Edge Filtration, Inc.-Skaneateles Falls (3)
4563 Jordan Rd, Skaneateles Falls, NY 13153-0238
Tel.: (315) 685-3466
Sales Range: $10-24.9 Million
Filtration Product Mfr & Sales
N.A.I.C.S.: 314999

Industrial Fabrics Corp. (3)
7160 Northland Cir, Minneapolis, MN 55428
Tel.: (763) 535-3220
Web Site: http://www.ifcfabrics.com
Industrial Fabric Mfr
N.A.I.C.S.: 314999
Michael Burks *(Supvr-Weaving)*

Subsidiary (Non-US):

Deutsche Gamma GmbH (2)
Girmesgath 5, D47803, Krefeld, Germany
Tel.: (49) 2151890222
Sales Range: $250-299.9 Million
Emp.: 3,300
Holding Company
N.A.I.C.S.: 551112

Subsidiary (Domestic):

Verseidag AG (3)
Girmesgath 5, D 47803, Krefeld, Germany
Tel.: (49) 2151890
Web Site: http://www.verseidag.de
Sales Range: $300-349.9 Million
Screen & Filter Technology, Coating & Composites for Sailcloth Mfr
N.A.I.C.S.: 333998

Subsidiary (Domestic):

Verseidag-Indutex GmbH (4)
Industrie Strasse 56, 47803, Krefeld, Germany
Tel.: (49) 21518760
Web Site: http://www.verseidag.de
Sales Range: $50-74.9 Million
Coated Fabric Mfr
N.A.I.C.S.: 313320
Markus Simon *(Mng Dir)*

Subsidiary (Non-US):

Gamma Grundstucksverwaltungsgesellschaft mbH (2)
Girmesgath 5, 47803, Krefeld, Germany
Tel.: (49) 2151890222
Web Site: http://www.verseigag.de
Sales Range: $25-49.9 Million
Emp.: 16
Mfr of Textiles
N.A.I.C.S.: 313230

Subsidiary (Domestic):

Gamma Holding Nederland N.V. (2)
Panovenweg 12, PO Box 80, 5708 HR, Helmond, Netherlands
Tel.: (31) 492 56 66 00
Web Site: http://www.gammaholding.nl
Sales Range: $900-999.9 Million
Conveyor Belts, Flat Belts, Modular Belts, Endless Woven Belts, Engineered Belts & Timing Belts Mfr
N.A.I.C.S.: 326220

Gilde Buy Out Partners AG (1)
Muhlebachstrasse 8, 8008, Zurich, Switzerland
Tel.: (41) 432682030
Web Site: http://www.gilde.com
Investment Management Service
N.A.I.C.S.: 523940

Gilde Buy Out Partners BVBA (1)
Regentschapsstraat 58 Rue de la Regence 58, 1000, Brussels, Belgium
Tel.: (32) 2503 0627
Investment Management Service
N.A.I.C.S.: 523940

Koninklijke Ten Cate, B.V. (1)
Stationsstraat 11, 7607 GX, Almelo, Netherlands
Tel.: (31) 546544911
Web Site: http://www.tencate.com
Emp.: 3,796
Holding Company; Technical Textiles & Technical Components Mfr & Whslr
N.A.I.C.S.: 551112
Don M. Olsen *(CEO-Protective Fabrics)*

Subsidiary (Domestic):

GreenFields Holding BV (2)
G van der Muelenweg 2, 7443 RE, Nijverdal, Netherlands
Tel.: (31) 548633333
Web Site: http://www.greenfields.eu
Holding Company; Artificial Turf Installation Services
N.A.I.C.S.: 551112

Subsidiary (Domestic):

GreenFields BV (3)
G van der Muelenweg 2, 7443 RE, Nijverdal, Netherlands
Tel.: (31) 548633333
Web Site: http://www.greenfields.eu
Artificial Turf Installation Services
N.A.I.C.S.: 339999

Subsidiary (Non-US):

GreenFields Sports & Leisure Pty Ltd. (4)
20 Chesterfield Road, Pietermaritzburg, 3201, South Africa
Tel.: (27) 338977500
Sport Goods Distr
N.A.I.C.S.: 532284

GreenFields Swiss AG (4)
Talstrasse 26, CH-8200, Schaffhausen, Switzerland
Tel.: (41) 526320101
Web Site: http://www.greenfields.eu
Artificial Turf Installation Services
N.A.I.C.S.: 339999

Subsidiary (US):

Polyloom Corporation of America (2)
1131 Broadway St, Dayton, TN 37321-1802
Tel.: (423) 775-0792
Web Site: http://www.tencategrass.com
Artificial Turf Fibers & Backing Mfr
N.A.I.C.S.: 325220

Subsidiary (Non-US):

SOLMAX (2)
Av Puente Cultural 10, San Sebastian de los Reyes, 28702, Madrid, Spain
Tel.: (34) 607499962
Web Site: http://www.tencategeo.eu
Geosynthetics & Industrial Fabrics Mfr
N.A.I.C.S.: 313220

Solmax (2)
Bd Mircea Voda 43 Bucuresti-Sector 3, Bucharest, Romania
Tel.: (40) 740955194

INTERNATIONAL PUBLIC

Web Site: http://www.tencategeo.eu
Geosynthetics & Industrial Fabrics Mfr
N.A.I.C.S.: 313220

Ten Cate Advanced Armour UK Limited (2)
Regus 2430/2440 The Quadrant Aztec West, Bristol, BS32 4AQ, United Kingdom
Tel.: (44) 1454877600
Web Site: http://www.tencateadvancedarmor.com
Customized Lightweight Ballistic Protection Solutions Mfr
N.A.I.C.S.: 336992

Subsidiary (Domestic):

Ten Cate Advanced Textiles BV (2)
G van der Muelenweg 2, PO Box 186, 7440 AD, Nijverdal, Netherlands
Tel.: (31) 548 633922
Web Site: http://eu.tencatefabrics.com
Holding Company
N.A.I.C.S.: 551112

Subsidiary (US):

Southern Mills, Inc. (3)
6501 Mall Blvd, Union City, GA 30291
Tel.: (770) 969-1000
Web Site: http://us.tencatefabrics.com
Industrial Textiles & Protective Fabrics Mfr
N.A.I.C.S.: 313210
Jean Harris *(VP-HR)*

Subsidiary (Non-US):

Ten Cate Danmark a/s (3)
Damsbovej 10, 5492, Vissenbjerg, Denmark
Tel.: (45) 65481600
Web Site: http://www.tencateadvancedarmour.com
Protective Fabrics Mfr
N.A.I.C.S.: 313220

Subsidiary (Domestic):

Ten Cate Advanced Armour Danmark a/s (3)
Damsbovej 10, 5492, Vissenbjerg, Denmark
Tel.: (45) 65481600
Web Site: http://www.tencateadvancedarmour.com
Customized Lightweight Ballistic Protection Solutions Mfr
N.A.I.C.S.: 336992
Helle Specht *(Mng Dir)*

Subsidiary (Non-US):

Ten Cate Geosynthetics (UK) Limited (2)
39 High Street, Wednesfield, Wolverhampton, WV11 1ST, W Midlands, United Kingdom
Tel.: (44) 1952588066
Web Site: http://www.tencategeo.eu
Geosynthetics & Industrial Fabrics Mfr
N.A.I.C.S.: 313220

Subsidiary (Domestic):

Ten Cate Thiobac bv (2)
Hoge Dijkje 2, 7442 AE, Nijverdal, Netherlands
Tel.: (31) 548633944
Web Site: http://www.tencate.com
Synthetic Turf Components Mfr
N.A.I.C.S.: 325220

Subsidiary (Non-US):

TenCate Advanced Armour SASU (2)
50 Route de Louvier, 38270, Primarette, France
Tel.: (33) 474795050
Web Site: http://www.tencateadvancedarmor.com
Customized Lightweight Ballistic Protection Solutions Mfr
N.A.I.C.S.: 336992

TenCate France SASU (2)
9 Rue Marcel Paul, BP 40080, F-95873, Bezons, Cedex, France
Tel.: (33) 134235363
Web Site: http://www.tencategeo.eu
Geosynthetics & Industrial Fabrics Mfr
N.A.I.C.S.: 325998

AND PRIVATE COMPANIES

TenCate Geosynthetics (Thailand) Ltd (2)
555 Rasa Tower 26th Floor Phaholyothin Road Soi 19, Chatuchak, Bangkok, 10900, Thailand
Tel.: (66) 26926680
Web Site: http://www.tencategeo.asia
Geosynthetics & Industrial Fabrics Mfr
N.A.I.C.S.: 313220

TenCate Geosynthetics Asia Sdn. Bhd. (2)
14 Jalan Sementa 27/91 Seksyen 27, Shah Alam, 40400, Selangor Darul Ehsan, Malaysia
Tel.: (60) 351928568
Web Site: http://www.tencategeo.asia
Geosynthetics & Industrial Fabrics Mfr
N.A.I.C.S.: 314999

TenCate Geosynthetics Austria GES.M.B.H (2)
Schachermayerstrasse 18, A-4021, Linz, Austria
Tel.: (43) 73269830
Web Site: https://www.tencategeo.eu
Geosynthetics & Industrial Fabrics Mfr
N.A.I.C.S.: 314999

TenCate Geosynthetics France S.A.S. (2)
9 rue Marcel Paul, BP 40080, F-95873, Bezons, Cedex, France
Tel.: (33) 134235363
Web Site: https://www.tencategeo.eu
Geosynthetics Products Mfr
N.A.I.C.S.: 325998

TenCate Geosynthetics Malaysia Sdn Bhd (2)
14 Jalan Sementa 27/91 Seksyen 27, Shah Alam, 40400, Selangor, Malaysia
Tel.: (60) 351928568
Web Site: http://www.tencategeo.asia
Geosynthetics & Industrial Fabrics Mfr
N.A.I.C.S.: 313220

Subsidiary (Domestic):

TenCate Geosynthetics Netherlands B.V. (2)
Europalaan 206, 7559 SC, Hengelo, Netherlands
Tel.: (31) 546544811
Web Site: http://www.tencategeo.eu
Geosynthetics & Industrial Fabrics Mfr
N.A.I.C.S.: 313220

Subsidiary (Non-US):

TenCate Industrial Zhuhai Co. Ltd. (2)
South of Nangang West Road Gaolan Port Economic Zone, Zhuhai, 519050, Guangdong, China
Tel.: (86) 7568861616
Web Site: http://www.tencategeo.asia
Geosynthetics & Industrial Fabrics Mfr
N.A.I.C.S.: 313220
Neil Nong (Mgr-Production)

Subsidiary (Domestic):

TenCate Protective Fabrics Holding BV (2)
G van der Muelenweg 2, PO Box 186, 7440 AD, Nijverdal, Netherlands
Tel.: (31) 548 633922
Web Site: http://eu.tencatefabrics.com
Protective Workwear Mfr
N.A.I.C.S.: 339999

Subsidiary (US):

TenCate Protective Fabrics USA Inc. (2)
6501 Mall Blvd, Union City, GA 30291
Tel.: (770) 969-1000
Web Site: http://us.tencatefabrics.com
Protective Workwear Mfr
N.A.I.C.S.: 339999
Daniel Hauert (VP-Sls & Bus Dev-Americas)

Subsidiary (Non-US):

TigerTurf (UK) Limited (2)
229 Ikon Droitwich Road, Hartlebury, DY10 4EU, Worcs, United Kingdom
Tel.: (44) 1299 253 966
Web Site: http://www.tigerturf.com
Synthetic Turf Mfr
N.A.I.C.S.: 339999
Paul Langford (Mng Dir-EMEA)

TigerTurf Australia Pty Ltd (2)
2/12 Latitude Boulevard, Thomastown, Melbourne, 3074, VIC, Australia
Tel.: (61) 3 9464 5052
Web Site: http://tigerturf.com
Synthetic Turf Mfr
N.A.I.C.S.: 325130

TigerTurf NZ Limited (2)
384 Neilson Street, Onehunga, Auckland, 1061, New Zealand
Tel.: (64) 96344134
Web Site: http://www.tigerturf.co.nz
Synthetic Grass & Turf Mfr
N.A.I.C.S.: 339999
Peter Leeves (Gen Mgr)

Subsidiary (Domestic):

Xtra Grass (2)
G van der Muelenweg 2, 7443 RE, Nijverdal, Netherlands
Tel.: (31) 548633333
Web Site: http://www.xtragrass-hybrid-turf.com
Artificial Turf Installation Services
N.A.I.C.S.: 238990

Losberger GmbH (1)
Gottlieb-Daimler-Ring 14, D-74906, Bad Rappenau, Germany
Tel.: (49) 7066 9800
Web Site: http://www.losbergergroup.com
Temporary & Semi-Permanent Tents & Stand-Alone Structures Mfr & Distr
N.A.I.C.S.: 332311
Berndt Zoepffel (CEO)

Subsidiary (Non-US):

Losberger France SAS (2)
CD 58 1 rue Bruch Zone Industrielle, BP 58, Brumath, 67170, France (100%)
Tel.: (33) 388593400
Web Site: http://www.losberger.fr
Temporary & Semi-Permanent Tent, Building & Pool Cover Mfr
N.A.I.C.S.: 332311

Subsidiary (Domestic):

Losberger Rapid Deployment Systems SAS (3)
58 A rue du Dessous des Berges, 75013, Paris, France
Tel.: (33) 1 46 72 42 69
Web Site: http://www.losberger-rds.com
Military & Civil Service Tent & Semi-Permanent Structure Mfr
N.A.I.C.S.: 332311
Berndt Zoepffel (Pres)

Subsidiary (Domestic):

Losberger Modular Systems GmbH (2)
Ruhrorter Strasse 2-6, Mannheim, 68219, Germany
Tel.: (49) 621 8444 4
Web Site: http://www.losberger.com
Commercial Modular Construction Services
N.A.I.C.S.: 321991
Patrick Korsch (Mng Dir)

Subsidiary (Non-US):

Losberger Shanghai Co., Ltd. (2)
258 Jinglian Rd. Minhang District Blk 5 Xunhao Industrial Park, 201108, Shanghai, China
Tel.: (86) 21 6161 1005
Web Site: http://www.losbergerchina.com
Tent Rental Services
N.A.I.C.S.: 532289

Subsidiary (US):

Losberger U.S., LLC (2)
285 Bucheimer Rd Ste A285 Bucheimer RD Ste A, Frederick, MD 21701
Tel.: (301) 682-8000
Web Site: http://www.losberger.com
Semi-Permanent Clear Span Tent & Flooring Products Distr
N.A.I.C.S.: 423990
Pat Moughan (Gen Mgr)

Subsidiary (Non-US):

Losberger UK Ltd. (2)
139 High Street, Collingham, Newark, NG23 7NH, United Kingdom
Tel.: (44) 1636 893 776
Web Site: http://www.losberger.co.uk
Tent & Hall Rental Services
N.A.I.C.S.: 711310
Nick Edwards (Mng Dir)

Swets Information Services B.V. (1)
Dellaerweg 9b, 2316 WZ, Leiden, Netherlands
Tel.: (31) 884679387
Web Site: http://www.swetsinformationservices.com
Sales Range: $1-4.9 Billion
Subscription-Based Information Services
N.A.I.C.S.: 519290
Elisabeth van Dijk (Chief Legal Officer)

Subsidiary (US):

Swets Information Services, Inc. (2)
160 E 9th Ave, Runnemede, NJ 08078
Tel.: (856) 312-2690
Web Site: http://www.swets.com
Sales Range: $25-49.9 Million
Subscription-Based Information Services
N.A.I.C.S.: 519290
Christine Stamison (Sr Mgr-Customer Rels)

Veco B.V. (1)
Karel van Gelreweg 22, 6961 LB, Eerbeek, Netherlands
Tel.: (31) 313 672 911
Web Site: http://www.vecoprecision.com
Commercial Graphics & Printing Metal Precision Products Mfr
N.A.I.C.S.: 332721

pack2pack Halsteren B.V. (1)
Steenbergseweg 42, 4661 RH, Halsteren, Netherlands
Tel.: (31) 164650650
Web Site: http://www.pack2pack.com
Sales Range: $25-49.9 Million
Industrial Tinplate Product Mfr
N.A.I.C.S.: 332439
Chris Paelinck (CEO)

GILDE EQUITY MANAGEMENT (GEM) BENELUX PARTNERS B.V.

Langoed Heemstede Poortgebouw Zuid Heemsteedseweg 22, 3992 LS, Houten, Netherlands
Tel.: (31) 307605910 NI
Web Site: http://gembenelux.com
Year Founded: 1996
Privater Equity Firm
N.A.I.C.S.: 523999
Bas Glas (Partner)

Subsidiaries:

Bruynzeel Storage Systems B.V. (1)
Industrieterrein 7, 5981 NK, Panningen, Netherlands
Tel.: (31) 773069000
Web Site: http://www.bruynzeel-storage.com
Storage Systems
N.A.I.C.S.: 337215
Alexander Collot d'Escury (CEO)

Subsidiary (US):

Delta Designs Ltd. (2)
1535 NW 25th St, Topeka, KS 66618
Tel.: (785) 234-2244
Web Site: http://www.deltadesignsltd.com
Rev: $2,333,333
Emp.: 40
Metal Household Furniture Mfr
N.A.I.C.S.: 337126
Bruce Danielson (Mgr)

DPA Group N.V. (1)
Gatwickstraat 11, PO Box 9396, 1043 GL, Amsterdam, Netherlands
Tel.: (31) 205151555
Web Site: http://www.dpagroep.nl
Professional Management, Recruitment & Outsourcing Services
N.A.I.C.S.: 541990
Ron Icke (Chm-Supervisory Bd)

ISFI - International Spice & Food Import SA (1)
Avenue de l Industrie 20, 1420, Brussels, Belgium
Tel.: (32) 2 384 60 77
Web Site: http://www.isfi-spices.com
Food Products Distr
N.A.I.C.S.: 424420
Anne-Marie Stevens (Co-Founder)

Wasco Holding BV (1)
Tel.: (31) 880995000
Web Site: https://www.wasco.nl
Sales Range: $150-199.9 Million
Emp.: 350
Plumbing & Heating Equipment & Supplies (Hydronics) Merchant Wholesalers
N.A.I.C.S.: 423720

GILDE HEALTHCARE PARTNERS B.V.

Newtonlaan 91, 3508 AB, Utrecht, Netherlands
Tel.: (31) 30 219 2565 NI
Web Site: http://www.gildehealthcare.com
Health Care Private Equity Investment Firm
N.A.I.C.S.: 523999
C. David Nicholson (Operating Partner)

Subsidiaries:

Gilde Healthcare Partners US (1)
222 3rd St Ste 1321, Cambridge, MA 02142
Tel.: (617) 395-9080
Web Site: http://www.gildehealthcare.com
Health Care Private Equity Investment Firm
N.A.I.C.S.: 523999
Geoff Pardo (Partner)

GILDE INVESTMENT MANAGEMENT B.V.

Newtonlaan 91, NL-3584 BP, Utrecht, Netherlands
Tel.: (31) 302192535 NI
Web Site: http://gilde.nl
Year Founded: 1982
Private Equity Investment Management Services
N.A.I.C.S.: 523940

GILEVE

2 Rue Louis Miquel, 22400, Lamballe, France
Tel.: (33) 296311796
Sales Range: $25-49.9 Million
Emp.: 50
Miscellaneous General Merchandise Stores,
N.A.I.C.S.: 444180
Evelyne Castel (Gen Mgr)

GILKYO E&C CO., LTD.

306 Ganghwa-ro, Nam-gu, Pohang, Gyeongsangbuk-do, Korea (South)
Tel.: (82) 542841235 KR
Bridge Construction Services
N.A.I.C.S.: 237310

GILLANDERS ARBUTHNOT & CO., LTD.

C-4 Gillander House Netaji Subhas Road, Kolkata, 700 001, West Bengal, India
Tel.: (91) 3322302331
Web Site:
https://www.gillandersarbuthnot.com
532716—(BOM)
Rev: $57,852,522
Assets: $81,507,044
Liabilities: $44,673,365
Net Worth: $36,833,679
Earnings: $2,230,410
Emp.: 7,078
Fiscal Year-end: 03/31/22
Textile Products Mfr
N.A.I.C.S.: 314999

GILLANDERS ARBUTHNOT & CO., LTD.

Gillanders Arbuthnot & Co., Ltd.—(Continued)

Mahesh Sodhani (Mng Dir)

Subsidiaries:

Naming'omba Tea Estates
Limited (1)
PO Box 2, Thyolo, Blantyre, Malawi
Tel.: (265) 473300
Web Site: https://www.namingomba.com
Tea Mfr
N.A.I.C.S.: 311920

GILLANDERS CONSTRUCTION INC.

7 Dohme Avenue, Toronto, M4B 1Y7, ON, Canada
Tel.: (416) 750-7313
Web Site: http://www.gillanders.com
Year Founded: 1956
Rev.: $19,570,754
Emp.: 21
Building Construction Services
N.A.I.C.S.: 236220
Berto Ramos (Pres)

GILLFOR DISTRIBUTION INC.

244 Ellwood Dr West, Bolton, L7E 4W4, ON, Canada
Tel.: (905) 857-4061
Web Site: https://www.gillfor.com
Year Founded: 2012
Wholesale Building Materials Dist.
N.A.I.C.S.: 423390

GILLIS QUARRIES LTD.

2895 Wenzel Street, Winnipeg, R2E 1H4, MB, Canada
Tel.: (204) 222-2242
Web Site: https://www.tyndallstone.com
Year Founded: 1910
Rev.: $10,626,605
Emp.: 50
Quarry Supplier
N.A.I.C.S.: 212311
Keith Gillis (Gen Mgr)

GIMBERT SURGELES SARL

3 rue Perrin, 32500, Fleurance, France
Tel.: (33) 562066551
Web Site: http://www.gimbertocean.com
Sales Range: $25-49.9 Million
Emp.: 100
Frozen Food Mfr & Distr
N.A.I.C.S.: 424420
Bernard Gimbert (Pres)

GIMSAN GEDIZ IPLIK VE MENSUCAT SANAYII AS

Antalya Organize Sanayi Bolgesi 1 Kisim Ataturk Bulvari No 19, Dosemealti, Antalya, Turkiye
Tel.: (90) 242 2581010
Cotton Yarn Mfr
N.A.I.C.S.: 313110

GIMV NV

Karel Oomsstraat 37, 2018, Antwerp, Belgium
Tel.: (32) 32902100
Web Site: https://www.gimv.com
Year Founded: 1980
GIMB—(EUR)
Rev.: $395,813,851
Assets: $2,260,691,175
Liabilities: $510,737,811
Net Worth: $1,749,953,364
Earnings: $223,295,260
Emp.: 90
Fiscal Year-end: 03/31/22
Private Equity & Venture Capital Investment Firm
N.A.I.C.S.: 523999
Kristof Vande Capelle (CFO)

Subsidiaries:

Acertys Healthcare nv (1)
Oeyvaersbosch 12, 2630, Aartselaar, Belgium (51.38%)
Tel.: (32) 3 870 1111
Web Site: https://www.acertys.com
Medical Equipment Distr
N.A.I.C.S.: 423450

AgroBiothers Laboratoire SAS (1)
ZI Les Platieres, BP-5, 71290, Cuisery, France
Tel.: (33) 385322840
Web Site: http://agrobiothers.com
Emp.: 250
Pet Food Mfr
N.A.I.C.S.: 311111

DataContact Sp. z o.o. (1)
ul Jagiellonska 74, 03-301, Warsaw, Poland (80.01%)
Tel.: (48) 22 763 60 00
Web Site: http://www.datacontact.pl
Telemarketing Services
N.A.I.C.S.: 561422
Tomasz Kalbarczyk (Mgr-IT)

Europlasma NV (1)
De Bruwaan 15, 9700, Oudenaarde, Belgium
Tel.: (32) 5 530 3205
Web Site: https://www.europlasma.net
Plasma-Based Coating Products & Application Technologies Designer, Mfr & Whslr
N.A.I.C.S.: 325510
Filip Legein (Dir-Next Generation Tech)

Gimv Germany Holding GmbH (1)
Promenadeplatz 12, 80333, Munich, Germany
Tel.: (49) 89442327500
Financial Investment Services
N.A.I.C.S.: 523940

Laser 2000 GmbH (1)
Argelsrieder Feld 14, 82234, Wessling, Germany
Tel.: (49) 8 153 4050
Web Site: https://www.laser2000.de
Laser Material Mfr
N.A.I.C.S.: 334413

Smart Battery Solutions GmbH (1)
Lindigstrasse 8a, 63801, Kleinostheim, Germany
Tel.: (49) 6027 990 8130
Web Site: https://smart-battery-solutions.de
Battery Mfr
N.A.I.C.S.: 335910
Jens Pohl (Mng Dir)

Societe Comtoise De Specialites Fromageres (1)
ZA de l'Aupretin, 71500, Louhans, France
Tel.: (33) 385757150
Web Site: http://www.comtoisefromagere.fr
Cheese; Natural & Processed
N.A.I.C.S.: 311513

VCST N.V. (1)
Rellestraat 5030, 3800, Sint-Truiden, Belgium (79.83%)
Tel.: (32) 1167 0211
Web Site: http://www.vcst.be
Emp.: 500
Holding Company; Motor Vehicle Components Mfr
N.A.I.C.S.: 551112

Subsidiary (Domestic):

Surface Treatment Company N.V. (2)
Industriezone Schurhovenveld 4077, 3800, Saint Truiden, Belgium
Tel.: (32) 1167 2901
Sales Range: $25-49.9 Million
Emp.: 133
Industrial Heat & Surface Treating Services
N.A.I.C.S.: 332811
Rudy Herman (Mgr)

Subsidiary (Non-US):

VCST Automotive Components (Changzhou) Co, Ltd. (2)
8 Fushan Road, Wujin Economic Zone, Changzhou, 213149, China
Tel.: (86) 5198 169 0996

Web Site: https://www.vcst.com
Automobile Parts Mfr
N.A.I.C.S.: 336390
Frank Yuan (Plant Mgr)

VCST Automotive Production Alba SRL (2)
No 9 Calea Ciugudului Street, Alba, Alba Iulia, 517240, Romania
Tel.: (40) 37 213 3700
Web Site: https://www.vcst.com
Automobile Parts Mfr
N.A.I.C.S.: 336390

Subsidiary (Domestic):

VCST Industrial Products bvba (2)
Industriezone Schurhovenveld 3025, 3800, Saint Truiden, Belgium
Tel.: (32) 1167 0211
Sales Range: $200-249.9 Million
Motor Vehicle Engine & Transmission Components Mfr
N.A.I.C.S.: 336310
Eric Willekens (CEO)

Subsidiary (Non-US):

VCST Reichenbach GmbH (2)
Am Fernblick 15, 08499, Mylau, Germany
Tel.: (49) 3 765 7950
Web Site: https://www.vcst.com
Automotive Parts Mfr & Distr
N.A.I.C.S.: 336390

VCST de Mexico S. de R.L. de C.V. (2)
Boulevard Aeropuerto No 3202 Loc A San Juan de Otates, 37670, Leon, Guanajuato, Mexico
Tel.: (52) 477 152 6100
Web Site: https://www.vcst.com
Automobile Parts Mfr
N.A.I.C.S.: 336390
Gerardo Alvarez (Plant Mgr)

Subsidiary (US):

VCST, Inc. (2)
13854 Lakeside Cir Ste 201, Sterling Heights, MI 48313
Tel.: (586) 685-1747
Web Site: https://www.vcst.be
Motor Vehicle Components Distr
N.A.I.C.S.: 423120

GIN-COR INDUSTRIES INC.

5151 Hwy 17 West, PO Box 220, Mattawa, P0H 1V0, ON, Canada
Tel.: (705) 744-5543
Web Site: https://www.gincor.com
Year Founded: 1978
Sales Range: $10-24.9 Million
Emp.: 50
Service Vehicles Whslr
N.A.I.C.S.: 423110

GINAR TECHNOLOGY CO., LTD.

No 250 Changfa Rd, Nangang Vil Dayuan Dist, Taoyuan, 33759, Taiwan
Tel.: (886) 33868820
Web Site: https://www.ginar.com.tw
Year Founded: 1982
6151—(TPE)
Rev.: $53,202,858
Assets: $51,902,386
Liabilities: $19,232,499
Net Worth: $32,669,887
Earnings: $3,230,873
Emp.: 57
Fiscal Year-end: 12/31/22
Plastic & Composite Material Mfr
N.A.I.C.S.: 325211
Chung Chun-Chung (Chm & Pres)

Subsidiaries:

Jiangsu Ginar Plastic Technology Co., Ltd. (1)
No 685 Huaihe Road, Huaiyin District, Huai'an, Jiangsu, China
Tel.: (86) 51780860591
Plastics Product Mfr
N.A.I.C.S.: 326199

INTERNATIONAL PUBLIC

GINEGAR PLASTIC PRODUCTS LTD.

Kibbutz, Ginegar, 3658000, Israel
Tel.: (972) 46544222
Web Site: https://www.ginegar.com
GNGR—(TAE)
Rev.: $164,924,987
Assets: $181,083,572
Liabilities: $120,014,641
Net Worth: $61,068,931
Earnings: ($84,542)
Fiscal Year-end: 12/31/23
Plastics Packaging Film & Sheet (including Laminated) Manufacturing
N.A.I.C.S.: 326112

Subsidiaries:

Agriplast Tech India Private Limited (1)
Survey No 426/3B-1B Opp Nallur Government High School, Nallur Village Hosur Panchayat Union & Taluk Krishnagiri Dist, Hosur, 635 103, Tamil Nadu, India
Tel.: (91) 8141446666
Web Site: https://www.agriplast.co.in
Agricultural Services
N.A.I.C.S.: 115116

Flextech S.R.L. (1)
Via Boves 19, 12089, Villanova Canavese, CN, Italy
Tel.: (39) 0174699108
Web Site: https://www.flextechsrl.com
Technical Film Product Mfr
N.A.I.C.S.: 326113

Ginegar Iberica S.L. (1)
Calle Pintores 19, Pol Ind Primores La Mojonera, 4745, Almeria, Spain
Tel.: (34) 174699108
Plastic Product Mfr & Distr
N.A.I.C.S.: 326199

Ginegar Industria De Plasticos Ltda. (1)
Av Ana Maria 600, Leme, Sao Paulo, CCEP 13610-430, SP, Brazil
Tel.: (55) 1935549800
Agriculture Equipment Mfr & Distr
N.A.I.C.S.: 333111

Ginegar Plastic Inc. (1)
3042 Industrial Pkwy, Santa Maria, CA 93455
Tel.: (805) 925-9000
Plastic Product Mfr & Distr
N.A.I.C.S.: 326199

Ginegar Specialty Plastic Private Limited (1)
Tal-Vasai Nallasopara west, Mumbai, 401203, Maharashtra, India
Tel.: (91) 7246544282
Plastic Product Mfr & Distr
N.A.I.C.S.: 326199

GINGER BEEF CORPORATION

5521 3rd Street SE, Calgary, T2H 1K1, AB, Canada
Tel.: (403) 272-8088
Web Site: http://www.gingerbeef.com
Year Founded: 1992
GB—(TSXV)
Rev.: $7,388,156
Assets: $4,846,754
Liabilities: $1,720,560
Net Worth: $3,126,194
Earnings: $149,961
Fiscal Year-end: 12/31/21
Frozen & Ready-To-Serve Deli Chinese Food Products Mfr; Take Out & Delivery Restaurant Franchisor
N.A.I.C.S.: 311412
Stanley Leung (Owner)

Subsidiaries:

Ginger Beef Choice Ltd. (1)
5521 3rd Street Southeast, Calgary, T2H 1K1, AB, Canada
Tel.: (403) 272-8088
Web Site: https://www.gingerbeefchoice.com
Chinese Food Mfr, Distr & Marketer
N.A.I.C.S.: 311412

Ginger Beef Express Ltd. (1)
5521 3rd Street SE, Calgary, T2H 1K1, AB, Canada
Tel.: (403) 272-8088
Web Site: http://www.gingerbeef.ca
Chinese Restaurant, Take Out & Delivery Franchisor
N.A.I.C.S.: 722511

GINI SILK MILLS LIMITED
413 Tantia Jogani Industrial Estate Opposite Kasturba Hospital, J R Boricha Marg Lower Parel East, Mumbai, 400011, Maharashtra, India
Tel.: (91) 2240750601 In
Web Site: https://www.ginitex.com
Year Founded: 1963
531744—(BOM)
Rev.: $5,740,699
Assets: $7,321,671
Liabilities: $2,224,099
Net Worth: $5,097,572
Earnings: $183,526
Emp.: 119
Fiscal Year-end: 03/31/23
Cotton Fabric Mfr
N.A.I.C.S.: 313220
Deepak Harlalka (Chm & Mng Dir)

GINKO INTERNATIONAL CO., LTD.
No 8 Keya 2nd Rd, Daya Dist, Taichung, Taiwan
Tel.: (886) 425658333
Web Site: http://www.ginkointernational.com.tw
Year Founded: 2007
8406—(TPE)
Contact Lens Mfr
N.A.I.C.S.: 339115
Subsidiaries:

Jiangsu Horien Contact Lens Co., Ltd. (1)
9F Bldg 2 No 1177 Husong Highway, Jiuting Town Songjiang District, Shanghai, China
Tel.: (86) 2157076165
Web Site: https://en.horien.net
Emp.: 740
Optical Product Mfr & Distr
N.A.I.C.S.: 339115

GINLONG TECHNOLOGIES CO., LTD.
No 188 Jinkai Road Binhai Industrial Park, Xiangshan County, Ningbo, 315712, Zhejiang, China
Tel.: (86) 57465802608
Web Site: https://www.ginlong.com
Year Founded: 2005
300763—(CHIN)
Rev.: $859,302,891
Assets: $3,041,276,413
Liabilities: $1,948,829,587
Net Worth: $1,092,446,826
Earnings: $109,772,490
Fiscal Year-end: 12/31/23
Solar Inverter Mfr
N.A.I.C.S.: 335999
Yiming Wang (Founder & Pres-Solis)

GINNI FILAMENTS LIMITED
D-196 Sector-63, Noida, 201307, India
Tel.: (91) 1204058400
Web Site: https://www.ginnifilaments.com
GINNIFILA—(NSE)
Rev.: $106,607,947
Assets: $79,641,280
Liabilities: $47,063,330
Net Worth: $32,577,950
Earnings: $5,636,849
Emp.: 2,311
Fiscal Year-end: 03/31/21

Yarn Mfr
N.A.I.C.S.: 339999
Shishir Jaipuria (Chm & Mng Dir)

GINSMS INC.
Suite 3000 700 9th Avenue SW, Calgary, T2P 3V4, AB, Canada
Tel.: (651) 644-1029 Ca
Web Site: https://www.ginsms.com
Year Founded: 2009
GOK—(TSXV)
Rev.: $2,407,691
Assets: $795,270
Liabilities: $2,662,752
Net Worth: ($1,867,482)
Earnings: ($97,905)
Fiscal Year-end: 12/31/23
Inter-Operator Short Messaging Services
N.A.I.C.S.: 517112
Koon Fai Lam (CFO-Grp)
Subsidiaries:

GIN International Ltd. (1)
Suite 2103 21/F Infinitus Plaza 199 Des Voeux Road, Central, China (Hong Kong)
Tel.: (852) 31963939
Mobile Software Development Services
N.A.I.C.S.: 541511

Inphosoft Malaysia Sdn Bhd (1)
B-3-2 Level 3 Tower B North Point Offices Mid Valley City No 1, Medan Syed Putra Utara, 59200, Kuala Lumpur, Malaysia
Tel.: (60) 322022880
Mobile Software Development Services
N.A.I.C.S.: 541511

Inphosoft Singapore Pte Ltd (1)
10 Eunos Road 8 13-08 Singapore Post Centre, Singapore, 408600, Singapore
Tel.: (65) 68370366
Mobile Software Development Services
N.A.I.C.S.: 541511

PT Inphosoft Indonesia (1)
Wisma Staco Lantai 5 Jalan Casablanca Kav 18, Menteng Dalam Tebet, Jakarta Selatan, 12870, Indonesia
Tel.: (62) 218317151
Mobile Software Development Services
N.A.I.C.S.: 541511

GINTECH ENERGY CORPORATION
No 21 Kebei 1st Rd Hsinchu Science Park Jhunan Township, Miaoli County, 350, Taipei, Taiwan
Tel.: (886) 37 586 198
Web Site: http://www.gintechenergy.com
Rev.: $484,197,219
Assets: $576,048,764
Liabilities: $212,142,724
Net Worth: $363,906,041
Earnings: ($50,225,923)
Emp.: 1,632
Fiscal Year-end: 12/31/17
Solar Cell Mfr
N.A.I.C.S.: 334413
Stone Liu (VP-Production Div)

GINWA ENTERPRISE (GROUP) INC.
No 202 Keji 4th Road High-tech Zone, Xi'an, 710065, Shaanxi, China
Tel.: (86) 2982200221
Web Site: https://www.ginwa.com.cn
Year Founded: 1996
600080—(SHG)
Rev.: $81,344,180
Assets: $277,208,371
Liabilities: $40,807,709
Net Worth: $236,400,662
Earnings: $4,697,714
Fiscal Year-end: 12/31/22
Pharmaceutical Product Mfr & Distr
N.A.I.C.S.: 325412
Xing Yajiang (Chm)

GINZA INDUSTRIES LTD.
A 501-502 5th Floor Lotus Corporate Park Jay Coach Lane, off Western Express Highway, 400063, Mumbai, India
Tel.: (91) 93 22976587
Web Site: http://www.ginzalimited.com
Year Founded: 1986
Sales Range: $1-9.9 Million
Emp.: 4,000
Mfr & Designer of Warp Knit Fabrics & Elastic Tapes, Also Home Furnishings, Curtains, Jacquard Fabrics & Embroidery Threads
N.A.I.C.S.: 313240

GINZA RENOIR CO., LTD.
Ginza Renoir Building 4-60-3 Chuo, Nakano-Ku, Tokyo, 164-0011, Japan
Tel.: (81) 353420881
Web Site: https://www.ginza-renoir.co.jp
Year Founded: 1979
9853—(TKS)
Rev.: $44,111,760
Assets: $66,453,200
Liabilities: $31,653,600
Net Worth: $34,799,600
Earnings: $3,358,960
Fiscal Year-end: 03/31/22
Hotel Operator
N.A.I.C.S.: 721110

GINZA YAMAGATAYA CO., LTD.
Sekimachikita chome 3 20, Nerima-ku, Tokyo, 177-0051, Japan
Tel.: (81) 366808711
Web Site: http://www.ginyama.co.jp
Year Founded: 1946
8215—(TKS)
Rev.: $34,102,640
Assets: $42,495,200
Liabilities: $21,005,600
Net Worth: $21,489,600
Earnings: $425,920
Fiscal Year-end: 03/31/22
Apparel Product Whslr
N.A.I.C.S.: 424350
Hiroaki Oguchi (Pres & CEO)

GINZA YOSHINOYA CO., LTD.
2-5 Kuramae 1-Chome, Taito-Ku, Tokyo, 111-0051, Japan
Tel.: (81) 338659222 JP
Web Site: http://www.ginza-yoshinoya.co.jp
Year Founded: 1907
Sales Range: $75-99.9 Million
Emp.: 250
Shoes Retailer & Designer
N.A.I.C.S.: 458210
Takeo Nohara (Import Buyer)

GIOCHI PREZIOSI S.P.A.
Via del Primule 5, Cogliate, 20815, MB, Italy
Tel.: (39) 02964751
Web Site: http://www.giochipreziosi.it
Year Founded: 1978
Toy Distr, Mfr & Whslr
N.A.I.C.S.: 423920
Enrico Peziosi (Pres)
Subsidiaries:

Fabricas Agrupadas de Munecas de Onil, S.A. (1)
C/ Chile 4 Edificio 1 Planta 2 Las, Madrid, 28290, Spain
Tel.: (34) 914401120
Web Site: http://www.famosa.es
Toy Mfr & Whslr
N.A.I.C.S.: 339930
Cristina Garcia (Mgr-Export)

GIORDANO INTERNATIONAL LIMITED
5/F Tin On Industrial Building 777-779, Cheung Sha Wan Road, Kowloon, China (Hong Kong)
Tel.: (852) 27464668 HK
Web Site: http://www.giordano.com.hk
Year Founded: 1981
0709—(HKG)
Rev.: $484,372,500
Assets: $511,020,000
Liabilities: $189,465,000
Net Worth: $321,555,000
Earnings: $41,947,500
Emp.: 5,749
Fiscal Year-end: 12/31/22
Casual Apparel & Accessories Distr
N.A.I.C.S.: 458110
Peter Kwok Kuen Lau (Chm & CEO)
Subsidiaries:

Aberdeen Fund Management Limited (1)
WTC H-Tower 20th Floor Zuidplein 166, 1077 XV, Amsterdam, Netherlands
Tel.: (31) 206870500
Web Site: https://www.abrdn.com
Sales Range: $50-74.9 Million
Emp.: 22
Investment Advice
N.A.I.C.S.: 523940

Bluestar Exchange Limited (1)
5th Floor Tin On Industrial Building, 777-779 Cheung Sha Wan Road, Kowloon, China (Hong Kong) (100%)
Tel.: (852) 27464668
Web Site: https://www.hk.e-giordano.com
Women's Clothing Store
N.A.I.C.S.: 458110

East Jean Limited (1)
5/F Tin on Industrial Building 777-779 Cheung Sha Wan Road, Cheung Sha Wan, China (Hong Kong)
Tel.: (852) 27465168
Web Site: http://www.giordano.com.hk
Casual Apparels Distr
N.A.I.C.S.: 424350

Giordano (Australia) Pty. Limited (1)
L 1 486 Station Street, Box Hill, 3128, Australia (79%)
Tel.: (61) 398961100
Web Site: http://www.giordano.com.au
Sales Range: $50-74.9 Million
Emp.: 200
Women's Clothing Store
N.A.I.C.S.: 458110

Giordano (M) Sdn. Bhd. (1)
lot 5001-5004 5th floor block a kompleks sentral, no 33 jalan segambut atas, 51200, Kuala Lumpur, Malaysia (100%)
Tel.: (60) 12 703 5113
Web Site: https://www.giordano.com
Men & Women Cloth Mfr & Distr
N.A.I.C.S.: 315250

Giordano (Thai) Co., Ltd. (1)
475 siripinyo tower 12th floor unit no 1205 sri ayutthaya road, thanon phayathai ratchathewi, Bangkok, 10400, Thailand
Tel.: (66) 26425455
Web Site: https://www.giordano.com
Men & Women Cloth Mfr & Distr
N.A.I.C.S.: 315250

Giordano Fashions (India) Private Limited (1)
B-24 Mugappair Industrial Estate Mugappair West, Chennai, 600 037, Tamil Nadu, India
Tel.: (91) 4443508880
Web Site: http://www.giordano.in
Sales Range: $25-49.9 Million
Emp.: 20
Apparels & Accessories Retailers
N.A.I.C.S.: 458110

Giordano Limited (1)
5th Floor Tin On Industrial Building 777-779 Cheung Sha Wan Road, Kowloon, China (Hong Kong) (100%)
Tel.: (852) 2 746 4668
Web Site: https://corp.giordano.hk

GIORDANO INTERNATIONAL LIMITED

Giordano International Limited—(Continued)
Mens & Boys Clothing & Furnishings Whslr
N.A.I.C.S.: 424350

Giordano Middle East FZE (1)
Sheikh Suhail Building Next to Time Square Mall, Sheikh Zayed Road, Dubai, United Arab Emirates
Tel.: (971) 44097000
Web Site: https://www.giordano-me.com
Men & Women Cloth Mfr & Distr
N.A.I.C.S.: 315250
Ishwar Chugani *(Mng Dir)*

Giordano Originals (Singapore) Private ltd (1)
11 Ubi Rd 1 04-02 Meiban Industrial Building, Singapore Warehouse, Singapore, 408723, Singapore **(100%)**
Tel.: (65) 6 513 7200
Web Site: https://www.giordano.com.sg
Sales Range: $150-199.9 Million
Emp.: 400
Mens & Boys Clothing & Furnishings Whslr
N.A.I.C.S.: 424350

Gloss Mind Apparel (Hong Kong) Limited (1)
3/F Block B Tin On Industrial Bldg, 777-779 Cheung Sha Wan Road, Kowloon, China (Hong Kong) **(51%)**
Tel.: (852) 27854113
Web Site:
https://www.greatmindapparel.com
Mens & Boys Clothing & Furnishings Whslr
N.A.I.C.S.: 424350

PT. Giordano Indonesia (1)
Rukan Plaza Pasifik B3 No 54-56, Raya Boulevard Barat Kelapa Gading, Jakarta, 14250, Indonesia
Tel.: (62) 2145847338
Cloth Retailer
N.A.I.C.S.: 458110

Shenzhen Tiger Garment Ltd (1)
Floor 3 Block 13 Luogang Industrial Zone, Buji Baoan, Shenzhen, 518112, China
Tel.: (86) 75582239694
Apparels & Accessories Retailers
N.A.I.C.S.: 458110

Tiger Enterprises Ltd (1)
10 Merrion Street, Leeds, United Kingdom **(100%)**
Tel.: (44) 1132430832
Sales Range: $25-49.9 Million
Emp.: 4
Travel Agencies
N.A.I.C.S.: 561510

Walton International Group Inc. (1)
25th Floor 500 - 4th Avenue SW, Calgary, T2P 2V6, AB, Canada
Tel.: (403) 265-4255
Web Site:
http://www.waltoninternational.com
Sales Range: $75-99.9 Million
Emp.: 205
Holding Company
N.A.I.C.S.: 551112

GIORGIO ARMANI S.P.A.
Via Borgonuovo 11, 20121, Milan, Italy
Tel.: (39) 02723181
Web Site: http://www.armani.com
Year Founded: 1975
Emp.: 5,000
Clothing Mfr
N.A.I.C.S.: 315990
Giorgio Armani *(Founder, Chm & CEO)*
Subsidiaries:

Antinea S.r.l. (1)
Via Borgonovo 11, 20121, Milan, Italy **(100%)**
Tel.: (39) 02723181
Mens & Boys Clothing & Furnishings Whslr
N.A.I.C.S.: 424350

Borgo 21 S.p.A. (1)
Via Catoni 149, Mattarello, 38100, Trento, Italy **(60%)**
Tel.: (39) 0461949111
Web Site: http://www.borgo21.it

Mens & Boys Cut & Sew Suit Coat & Overcoat Mfr
N.A.I.C.S.: 315250

Borgo 21 SA (1)
Via Penate 4, Casella postale 1020, 6850, Mendrisio, Switzerland **(60%)**
Tel.: (41) 916400080
Web Site: http://www.borgo21.ch
Dry Goods Whslr
N.A.I.C.S.: 424310

Factory Store S.p.A. (1)
Via Provinciale Per Bregnano 13, Vertemate Con Minoprio, Como, 22070, Italy **(100%)**
Tel.: (39) 031887373
Web Site: http://www.giorgioarmani.com
Sales Range: $25-49.9 Million
Emp.: 25
Family Clothing Stores
N.A.I.C.S.: 458110
Tuller Cevestra *(Gen Mgr)*

Giorgio Armani Corporation (1)
450 W 15th St, New York, NY 10011-5604
Tel.: (212) 366-9720
Web Site: http://www.giorgioarmani.com
Sales Range: $75-99.9 Million
Emp.: 200
Clothing Designer & Mfr
N.A.I.C.S.: 315990
Garine Zerounian *(VP-IR)*

Giorgio Armani Distribuzione Srl (1)
Via Borgonuovo 11, Milan, 20121, Italy **(99.5%)**
Tel.: (39) 02723181
Web Site: http://www.giorgioarmani.it
Mens & Boys Clothing & Furnishings Whslr
N.A.I.C.S.: 424350

Giorgio Armani France Sarl (1)
34 Rue Lauriston, Paris, 75116, France **(100%)**
Tel.: (33) 155732250
Web Site: http://www.armani.com
Sales Range: $25-49.9 Million
Emp.: 50
Family Clothing Stores
N.A.I.C.S.: 458110

Giorgio Armani Retail Srl (1)
Via Borgonuovo 11, 20021, Milan, Italy **(100%)**
Tel.: (39) 02723181
Web Site: http://www.armani.com
Sales Range: $150-199.9 Million
Emp.: 500
Mens & Boys Clothing & Furnishings Whslr
N.A.I.C.S.: 424350

Nobu Armani Srl (1)
Via Pizzone No 1, 20121, Milan, Italy **(100%)**
Tel.: (39) 0272318645
Web Site: http://www.armani.com
Sales Range: $50-74.9 Million
Emp.: 55
Shopping Centers
N.A.I.C.S.: 459999

Simint S.p.A. (1)
Via P Giardini 1324, Frazione Baggiovara, I-41100, Modena, Italy **(100%)**
Tel.: (39) 059584509
Sales Range: $150-199.9 Million
Emp.: 400
Mens & Boys Clothing & Furnishings Whslr
N.A.I.C.S.: 424350

Trimil SA (1)
Via Penate 4, 6850, Mendrisio, Switzerland **(51%)**
Tel.: (41) 916403800
Web Site: http://www.giorgioarmani.ch
Sales Range: $25-49.9 Million
Emp.: 14
Textile & Fabric Finishing Mills
N.A.I.C.S.: 313110

GIORGIO VISCONTI S.P.A.
Via Camurati 47, Valenza, 15048, Al, Italy
Tel.: (39) 0131955988
Web Site: http://www.giorgiovisconti.it
Year Founded: 1993
Sales Range: $10-24.9 Million
Emp.: 22

Medium & High End Jewelry Designer, Mfr & Marketer
N.A.I.C.S.: 339910
Giorgio Giovanni Visconti *(Pres)*

GIOVANNI AGNELLI B.V.
Gustav Mahlerplein 25, 1082 MS, Amsterdam, Netherlands
Tel.: (31) 202402222
Holding Company
N.A.I.C.S.: 551112
Subsidiaries:

EXOR N.V. (1)
Gustav Mahlerplein 25, 1082 MS, Amsterdam, Netherlands **(52.99%)**
Tel.: (31) 202402222
Web Site: https://www.exor.com
Rev: $160,985,474,300
Assets: $193,300,154,460
Liabilities: $145,641,152,580
Net Worth: $47,659,001,880
Earnings: $9,983,551,900
Emp.: 343,415
Fiscal Year-end: 12/31/2019
Investment Holding Company
N.A.I.C.S.: 551112
Guido De Boer *(CEO, Exec Mng Dir, Exec Mng Dir, CFO, COO & Exec VP)*
Joint Venture (Non-US):

Eng Teknologi Holdings Bhd. (2)
Plot 69-70 Pesara Kampung Jawa Bayan Lepas Industrial Zone, 11900, Bayan Lepas, Penang, Malaysia
Tel.: (60) 46166122
Web Site: http://www.engtek.com
Sales Range: $150-199.9 Million
Emp.: 2,400
Engineering Solutions & Services
N.A.I.C.S.: 541330
Sook Fun Thum *(Sec)*
Subsidiary (Non-US):

Altum Precision Co., Ltd. (3)
146 Moo 1 Hi-Tech Industrial Estate Asia-Nakornsawan Road T.Banlane, A.Bangpa-in, Ayutthaya, 13160, Thailand **(100%)**
Tel.: (66) 35729100
Web Site: http://www.engtek.com
Automotive Mechanical Components Mfr
N.A.I.C.S.: 336310
Subsidiary (Domestic):

Altum Precision Sdn. Bhd. (3)
Plo 185 Jalan Siber 9 Kawasan Perindustrian Senai IV, 81400, Senai, Johor, Malaysia
Tel.: (60) 75989928
Web Site: http://www.altumjb.com.my
Automated Die Castings Mfr
N.A.I.C.S.: 331523

Eng Teknologi Sdn. Bhd. (3)
Plot 69-70 Pesara Kampung Jawa Bayan Lepas Industrial Zone, 11900, Bayan Lepas, Penang, Malaysia **(100%)**
Tel.: (60) 46166122
Web Site: http://www.engtek.com
Precision Components Mfr & Distr
N.A.I.C.S.: 332721
YS Teh *(Mng Dir)*
Subsidiary (Non-US):

Engtek (Thailand) Co., Ltd. (3)
2/6 Moo 5 Rojana Industrial Park Rojana Road, Ayutthaya, 13210, Thailand
Tel.: (66) 35719579
Electronic Components Mfr
N.A.I.C.S.: 334416

Engtek International Limited (3)
16/F Flat 1612 Cheung Fung Industrial Building, 23-39 Pak Tin Par Street, Tsuen Wan, China (Hong Kong)
Tel.: (852) 24024618
Precision Machined Components Mfr
N.A.I.C.S.: 339999

Engtek Precision Philippines, Inc. (3)
L10 Phase II-A Special Export Processing Zone II, Carmelray Industrial Park I, Calamba, 4027, Laguna, Philippines

Tel.: (63) 495491748
Precision Engineering Components Mfr
N.A.I.C.S.: 335999
Subsidiary (Domestic):

Selekta Inovatif (M) Sdn. Bhd. (3)
800 Jalan Perindustrian Bukit Minyak, Kawasan Perindustrian, Bukit Mertajam, 14000, Penang, Malaysia
Tel.: (60) 45023688
Sales Range: $25-49.9 Million
Emp.: 50
Magnet Plates Mfr
N.A.I.C.S.: 332999
Subsidiary (Non-US):

GEDI Gruppo Editoriale S.p.A. (2)
Via Cristoforo Colombo 90, 00147, Rome, Italy **(100%)**
Tel.: (39) 0684781
Web Site: http://www.gedispa.it
Magazine & Newspaper Publisher; Radio, Television & Internet Broadcasting Services
N.A.I.C.S.: 513110
Pierangelo Calegari *(Dir-Central-Production, Info Sys & Gen Svcs)*
Subsidiary (Domestic):

A.Manzoni And C. Spa (3)
Via Nervesa 21, 20139, Milan, Italy **(100%)**
Tel.: (39) 02574941
Web Site:
http://www.manzoniadvertising.com
Sales Range: $25-49.9 Million
Emp.: 200
Advertising Material Distribution Services
N.A.I.C.S.: 541870
Sabio Vaccarono *(Mng Dir)*

Editoriale FVG Spa (3)
Viale Palmanova 290, 33100, Udine, Italy **(92.21%)**
Tel.: (39) 0432527217
Web Site: http://www.messaggeroveneto.it
Sales Range: $50-74.9 Million
Emp.: 80
Newspaper Publishers
N.A.I.C.S.: 513110
Omar Monestier *(Mng Dir)*

Editoriale La Nuova Sardegna Spa (3)
Preba niepda 31, 07100, Sassari, Italy **(100%)**
Tel.: (39) 079222400
Web Site: http://www.lanuovasardegna.it
Sales Range: $25-49.9 Million
Emp.: 100
Newspaper Publishers
N.A.I.C.S.: 513110

Editoriale Metropoli Spa (3)
Via Tortona 33, 20144, Milan, Italy **(100%)**
Tel.: (39) 02489691
Periodical Publishers
N.A.I.C.S.: 513120

Ksolutions Spa (3)
Via Lenin 132 A 26, San giuliano Terme, 56017, Florence, Italy **(100%)**
Tel.: (39) 050898111
Office Equipment Whslr
N.A.I.C.S.: 423420

Selpi Spa (3)
Via Francesco Ferruccio 8, 20145, Milan, Italy **(70%)**
Tel.: (39) 0234811
Sales Range: $25-49.9 Million
Emp.: 5
Newspaper Publishers
N.A.I.C.S.: 513110
Subsidiary (Non-US):

Juventus Football Club S.p.A (2)
Via Druento 175, 10151, Turin, Italy **(60%)**
Tel.: (39) 0116563538
Web Site: https://www.juventus.com
Rev: $547,866,677
Assets: $900,036,591
Liabilities: $854,602,191
Net Worth: $45,434,400
Earnings: ($133,491,880)
Emp.: 1,049
Fiscal Year-end: 06/30/2023

AND PRIVATE COMPANIES

Professional Soccer Club
N.A.I.C.S.: 711211
Andrea Agnelli *(Chm)*

GIPS D.D.
Bukinje bb, 75000, Tuzla, Bosnia & Herzegovina
Tel.: (387) 35366100
Web Site: http://www.gipstk.com
GIPSRK2—(SARE)
Rev.: $3,254,564
Assets: $4,309,420
Liabilities: $1,194,488
Net Worth: $3,114,932
Earnings: ($62,650)
Emp.: 138
Fiscal Year-end: 12/31/20
Food Transportation Services
N.A.I.C.S.: 488490

GIRARDIN BLUE BIRD COMPANY
4000 Girardin Street, Drummondville, J2E 0A1, QC, Canada
Tel.: (819) 477-3222
Web Site: http://www.girardinbluebird.com
School Bus Distr
N.A.I.C.S.: 485113
Dave Girardin *(Pres)*

Subsidiaries:

School Lines, Inc. (1)
75 Ciro Rd, North Branford, CT 06471-1521
Tel.: (203) 488-1382
Web Site: http://www.schoollinesinc.com
Sales Range: $1-9.9 Million
Emp.: 8
Automobile & Other Motor Vehicle Merchant Whslr
N.A.I.C.S.: 423110
David Lintern *(Pres)*

GIRDHARILAL SUGAR & ALLIED INDUSTRIES LIMITED
45/47 A Industrial Area No 1 Agra-Bombay Road, Dewas, 455001, MP, India
Tel.: (91) 7272258502
Web Site: http://www.gsail.org
Year Founded: 1989
Sales Range: $1-9.9 Million
Agricultural Commodities Trading Services
N.A.I.C.S.: 523160
Rajesh Agrawal *(Mng Dir)*

GIRIRAJ CIVIL DEVELOPERS LTD.
006 A Wing Ground Floor Western Edge-2 Behind Metro Mall Off, Western Express Highway Borivali East, Mumbai, 400066, India
Tel.: (91) 2228906356
Web Site: https://giriraj.co
Year Founded: 2005
Civil Engineering Services
N.A.I.C.S.: 541330
Mahesh Shah *(Chm & Mng Dir)*

GIRMATIC AG
Badstrasse 14, 8590, Romanshorn, Switzerland
Tel.: (41) 71 466 1515 CH
Web Site: http://www.girmatic.ch
Year Founded: 2006
Sales Range: $10-24.9 Million
Emp.: 45
Hydraulic, Pneumatic & Electronic Control Equipment Mfr & Distr
N.A.I.C.S.: 332912
Christoph Girsberger *(Chm)*

Subsidiaries:

Vektor AG (1)
Gewerbestrasse 8, 8606, Nanikon, Switzerland

Tel.: (41) 449082222
Web Site: http://www.vektor.ch
Hydraulic, Pneumatic & Process Control Equipment Mfr & Distr
N.A.I.C.S.: 333996

GIRMES INTERNATIONAL GMBH
Maysweg 10, Toenisvorst, 47918, Viersen, Germany
Tel.: (49) 2151935040
Web Site: http://www.redaellivelluti.it
Year Founded: 1989
Sales Range: $150-199.9 Million
Emp.: 1,000
Apparel & Upholstery Woven Fabrics Mfr
N.A.I.C.S.: 313310
Simone Pini *(Mng Dir)*

GIRO INC.
75 Port-Royal St E Ste 500, Montreal, H3L 3T1, QC, Canada
Tel.: (514) 383-0404
Web Site: http://www.giro.ca
Year Founded: 1979
Rev.: $10,000,000
Emp.: 250
Software Development & Services
N.A.I.C.S.: 513210
Pierre Trudeau *(VP-Bus Dev)*

GISBORNE HOLDINGS LTD.
7476 Hedley Ave, Burnaby, V5E 2P9, BC, Canada
Tel.: (604) 520-7300
Web Site: http://www.gisborne.com
Year Founded: 1953
Rev.: $30,042,801
Emp.: 1,000
Industrial Construction & Fire Protection & Safety Services
N.A.I.C.S.: 236210
Rae Clarkson *(Pres)*

GISH INTERNATIONAL CO., LTD.
14F No 260 Section 2 Xinbei Blvd, Sanchong District, New Taipei City, Taiwan
Tel.: (886) 229953666
Web Site: https://www.gish-int.com
Year Founded: 1989
8067—(TPE)
Rev.: $4,581,027
Assets: $10,988,181
Liabilities: $6,303,255
Net Worth: $4,684,926
Earnings: ($591,439)
Fiscal Year-end: 12/31/22
Optical Storage Product Distr
N.A.I.C.S.: 423430
Gary Chen *(Founder & Pres)*

GISMONDI 1754 S.P.A.
via Galata 34r, 16121, Genoa, Italy
Tel.: (39) 0108691098
Web Site: https://gismondi1754.com
Year Founded: 2004
Jewelry Product Mfr
N.A.I.C.S.: 339910
Massimo Gismondi *(Chm)*

Subsidiaries:

Stelle S.r.l. (1)
Via Ponza 7, 80026, Casoria, Italy
Tel.: (39) 0815845009
Web Site: http://www.lestellesrl.it
Gift Product Distr
N.A.I.C.S.: 459420

GITA RENEWABLE ENERGY LIMITED
Survey No 180 & 181 OPG Nagar Periya Obulapuram Village, Nagarajakandigai Madharapakkam Road, Gummidipoondi, 601 201, India

Tel.: (91) 44427991450 In
Web Site: https://www.gitarenewable.com
539013—(BOM)
Rev.: $445,877
Assets: $5,878,805
Liabilities: $3,701,798
Net Worth: $2,177,007
Earnings: $324,940
Emp.: 2
Fiscal Year-end: 03/31/22
Electric Power Transmission Services
N.A.I.C.S.: 221122
Natarajan R. *(Chm & Mng Dir)*

GITEC CONSULT GMBH
Carlswerkstr 13d, 51063, Cologne, Germany
Tel.: (49) 22129203600
Web Site: http://www.gitec-consult.eu
Year Founded: 1977
Sales Range: $10-24.9 Million
Emp.: 100
Engineeering Services
N.A.I.C.S.: 541330
Thomas Harbauer *(Mng Dir)*

GITENNES EXPLORATION INC.
Suite 410 325 Howe Street, Vancouver, V6C 1Z7, BC, Canada
Tel.: (604) 682-7970
Web Site: https://www.gitennes.com
Year Founded: 1993
GILXF—(OTCIQ)
Assets: $200,569
Liabilities: $362,131
Net Worth: ($161,562)
Earnings: ($322,040)
Fiscal Year-end: 12/31/23
Mineral Exploration Services
N.A.I.C.S.: 213114
Kenneth D. Booth *(CEO)*

GITI TIRE PTE. LTD.
150 Beach Road No 22-01/08 Gateway West, The Oxley, Singapore, 189720, Singapore
Tel.: (65) 62495399 SG
Web Site: http://www.corp.giti.com
Year Founded: 1993
Sales Range: $1-4.9 Billion
Holding Company; Tire Mfr & Whslr
N.A.I.C.S.: 551112
Enk Ee Tan *(Chm)*

Subsidiaries:

Giti Tire (China) Investment Co., Ltd. (1)
280-2 Linhong Road, Changning District, Shanghai, 200335, China
Tel.: (86) 21 2207 3333
Holding Company
N.A.I.C.S.: 551112

Affiliate (Domestic):

Giti Tire Corporation (2)
280-2 Linhong Road, Changning District, Shanghai, 200335, China (44.4%)
Tel.: (86) 2122073131
Web Site: http://www.gititirecorp.com
Rev.: $492,383,699
Assets: $483,088,208
Liabilities: $227,466,449
Net Worth: $255,621,759
Earnings: $4,832,947
Emp.: 30,000
Fiscal Year-end: 12/31/2022
Tire Mfr & Whslr
N.A.I.C.S.: 326211

Giti Tire (USA) Ltd. (1)
10404 6th St, Rancho Cucamonga, CA 91730-5831
Web Site: http://www.gitiusa.com
Tire Mfr & Distr
N.A.I.C.S.: 423130
Armand Allaire *(Exec VP-Comml Sls)*

GIVAUDAN S.A.

PT Gajah Tunggal Tbk (1)
Wisma Hayam Wuruk 10th Floor Jl Hayam Wuruk 8, Jakarta, 10120, Indonesia (49.7%)
Tel.: (62) 2150985916
Web Site: http://www.gt-tires.com
Rev.: $1,153,857,062
Assets: $1,277,876,006
Liabilities: $792,310,646
Net Worth: $485,565,360
Earnings: ($12,806,438)
Emp.: 17,428
Fiscal Year-end: 12/31/2022
Tire Mfr & Whslr
N.A.I.C.S.: 326211
Budhi Santoso Tanasaleh *(Vice Chm)*

Plant (Domestic):

PT Gajah Tunggal Tbk - Plant 1 (2)
Komplek Industri Gajah Tunggal Jl Gajah Tunggal Desa Pasir Jaya, Kecamatan Jati Uwung, Tangerang, Indonesia
Tel.: (62) 21 5901312
Tire Cord & Synthetic Rubber Mfr
N.A.I.C.S.: 314994

PT Gajah Tunggal Tbk - Plant 2 (2)
Desa Mangunrejo Bojonegara, Serang, Banten, Indonesia
Tel.: (62) 254 5750931
Tire Cord & Synthetic Rubber Mfr.
N.A.I.C.S.: 314994

Subsidiary (Domestic):

PT. Prima Sentra Megah (2)
Wisma Hayam Wuruk 12th Floor Jl Hayam Wuruk No 8, Jakarta, 10120, Indonesia
Tel.: (62) 21 231 5228
Tire Cord & Synthetic Rubber Distr
N.A.I.C.S.: 424690

GIURGIU NAV SA
Zona Port Corp Administrativ Biroul Nr 2, Teleorman, Zimnicea, Romania
Tel.: (40) 246 212490
Sales Range: $10-24.9 Million
Emp.: 249
Inland Freight Water Transportation Services
N.A.I.C.S.: 483211
Mariana Stoicescu *(Pres)*

GIVAUDAN S.A.
Chemin de la Parfumerie 5, 1214, Vernier, Switzerland
Tel.: (41) 227809111 CH
Web Site: https://www.givaudan.com
Year Founded: 1895
GVDNY—(OTCIQ)
Rev.: $7,569,429,480
Assets: $12,932,807,400
Liabilities: $8,469,743,130
Net Worth: $4,463,064,270
Earnings: $929,757,870
Emp.: 16,800
Fiscal Year-end: 12/31/21
Fragrance & Flavor Compounds Mfr
N.A.I.C.S.: 325620
Calvin Grieder *(Chm)*

Subsidiaries:

Albert Vieille S.A.S. (1)
629 Route de Grasse, BP 217, 06227, Vallauris, Cedex, France
Tel.: (33) 493641672
Web Site: https://www.albertvieille.com
Essential Oil Mfr & Distr
N.A.I.C.S.: 325199

Alderys SAS (1)
Batiment Meleze 86 rue de Paris, 91400, Orsay, France
Tel.: (33) 184000002
Web Site: https://www.alderys.fr
Biotechnology Research & Development Services
N.A.I.C.S.: 541714

DDW Colours Sdn. Bhd. (1)
PLO 221 Jalan Bakau 6 Tg Langsat Industrial Complex, Johor Bahru, 81700, Pasir Gudang, Johor, Malaysia
Tel.: (60) 72575757

GIVAUDAN S.A.

Givaudan S.A.—(Continued)
Food Mfr & Distr
N.A.I.C.S.: 311991

Expressions Parfumees S.A.S. (1)
136 Chemin de Saint Marc, 06130, Grasse, France
Tel.: (33) 493090530
Web Site: https://www.epparfums.com
Perfume Fragrance Mfr
N.A.I.C.S.: 325620

Fragrance Oils (International) Limited (1)
Eton Hill Road, Manchester, M26 2FR, United Kingdom
Tel.: (44) 1617249311
Web Site: https://www.fragrance-oils.com
Emp.: 250
Perfumery Essences Mfr & Distr
N.A.I.C.S.: 325199

Fragrance Oils Limited (1)
Eton Hill Road, Manchester, M26 2FR, United Kingdom
Tel.: (44) 1617249311
Web Site: https://www.fragrance-oils.com
Fragrance Product Mfr
N.A.I.C.S.: 325620

Givaudan (India) Pvt. Ltd. (1)
Plot No 26 2nd Cross Jigani Industrial Area, Anekal Taluk Jigani, Bengaluru, 560105, Karnataka, India
Tel.: (91) 8027826301
Toilet Preparation Mfr
N.A.I.C.S.: 325620

Givaudan (Thailand) Ltd. (1)
719 KPN Tower 16th 25th Floor Rama 9 Road, Bangkapi Huaykwang, Bangkok, 10310, Thailand
Tel.: (66) 27604900
Fragrance Mfr
N.A.I.C.S.: 325620

Givaudan Argentina S.A. (1)
Tel.: (54) 113327456800
Web Site: https://www.givaudan.com.ar
Sales Range: $25-49.9 Million
Emp.: 60
Fragrances Creation, Application & Retail Services
N.A.I.C.S.: 325199

Givaudan Argentina SA (1)
San Lorenzo 4759 Esquina Ave Mitre, Munro, 1605, Buenos Aires, Argentina **(100%)**
Tel.: (54) 1147629000
Web Site: http://www.givaudan.com
Sales Range: $50-74.9 Million
Emp.: 270
Mfr & Sales
N.A.I.C.S.: 325412

Givaudan Argentina Servicios SA (1)
Prilidiano Pueyrredon 3001 Martinez, B1640ILC, Buenos Aires, Argentina
Tel.: (54) 1145185600
Toilet Preparation Mfr
N.A.I.C.S.: 325620

Givaudan Aroma ve Esans Sanayi ve Ticaret Ltd. Sti. (1)
Akat Mah Ebulula Mardin Cad Maya Meridien is Merkezi, No 16 ic Kapi No 29 Besiktas, 34335, Istanbul, Turkiye
Tel.: (90) 2123506800
Sales Range: $25-49.9 Million
Emp.: 10
Fragrances, Flavors & Food Ingredients Mfr
N.A.I.C.S.: 311999

Givaudan Australia Pty Ltd. (1)
12 Britton St, Smithfield, 2164, NSW, Australia
Tel.: (61) 298273996
Web Site: http://www.givaudan.com
Sales Range: $25-49.9 Million
Emp.: 200
Food Flavorings Mfr
N.A.I.C.S.: 311999

Givaudan Australia Pty. Ltd. (1)
14 Woodruff St, Melbourne, 3207, VIC, Australia
Tel.: (61) 392512120
Sales Range: $25-49.9 Million
Emp.: 1
Food Flavorings Mfr
N.A.I.C.S.: 311999

Givaudan Austria GmbH (1)
Twin Tower Vienna Wienerbergstrasse 11, 1109, Vienna, Austria
Tel.: (43) 15452240
Emp.: 25
Cosmetic Flavor Distr
N.A.I.C.S.: 424210

Givaudan Business Solutions Kft (1)
Bence utca 1 Vaci Greens B, 1138, Budapest, Hungary
Tel.: (36) 18846000
Toilet Preparation Mfr
N.A.I.C.S.: 325620

Givaudan CR, S.R.O. (1)
Klimentska 10, 110 00, Prague, Czech Republic
Tel.: (420) 2 9657 8677
Web Site: http://www.givaudan.com
Emp.: 2
Cosmetic Flavoring Distr
N.A.I.C.S.: 424210

Givaudan Canada, Inc. (1)
2855 Argentia Road Unit 1, Mississauga, L5N 8G6, ON, Canada **(100%)**
Tel.: (905) 821-5075
Sales Range: $25-49.9 Million
Emp.: 25
Mfr of Flavorings & Fragrance Chemicals
N.A.I.C.S.: 311930

Givaudan Chile Ltda (1)
Avda Del Valle 869 Oficina 202-203 Ciudad Empresarial, Region Metropolitana, Huechuraba, Chile
Tel.: (56) 24280500
Sales Range: $50-74.9 Million
Emp.: 1
Cosmetic Fragrance & Flavor Products Distr
N.A.I.C.S.: 424210

Givaudan Colombia SA (1)
Carrera 98 No 25 G 40, 151196, Bogota, Colombia
Tel.: (57) 14252929
Emp.: 8
Cosmetic Fragrance & Flavoring Products Distr
N.A.I.C.S.: 424210

Givaudan Colombia SAS (1)
Carrera 98 No 25 G 40, 151196, Bogota, Colombia
Tel.: (57) 14252929
Toilet Preparation Mfr
N.A.I.C.S.: 325620

Givaudan Deutschland GmbH (1)
Lehmweg 17, 20251, Hamburg, Germany **(100%)**
Tel.: (49) 405328950
Web Site: http://www.givaudan.com
Sales Range: $25-49.9 Million
Emp.: 20
Sales & Marketing of Fragrances & Specialties
N.A.I.C.S.: 424210

Givaudan Deutschland GmbH (1)
Gieselherstrasse 11, 44319, Dortmund, Germany **(100%)**
Tel.: (49) 23121860
Web Site: http://www.givaudan.com
Sales Range: $150-199.9 Million
Emp.: 200
Flavor Creations, Sales & Production
N.A.I.C.S.: 311930

Givaudan Do Brasil Ltda (1)
Avenida Engenheiro Billings 2185, PO Box 66041, Jaguare, Sao Paulo, 0532-1010, SP, Brazil **(100%)**
Tel.: (55) 1137608000
Web Site: https://www.givaudan.com.br
Sales Range: $1-9.9 Million
Emp.: 213
Mfr of Flavorings & Perfumes
N.A.I.C.S.: 325620

Givaudan Egypt Fragrance LLC (1)
46 El Thawra St 3rd Floor Apt 304, Heliopolis, Egypt
Tel.: (20) 224195727
Toilet Preparation Mfr
N.A.I.C.S.: 325620

Givaudan Egypt SAE (1)
Piece 37 Industrial Zone 3 6th of October City, PO Box 95, Cairo, Egypt
Tel.: (20) 238281400
Cosmetic Fragrance & Flavor Products Mfr
N.A.I.C.S.: 325620

Givaudan Erftstadt GmbH & Co. KG (1)
Bonner Ring 43, Erftstadt, 50374, Germany
Tel.: (49) 223579010
Sales Range: $25-49.9 Million
Emp.: 40
Food & Fragrance Mfr
N.A.I.C.S.: 311999

Givaudan Flavors (Nantong) Ltd. (1)
No 7 Jianghai Road Nantong Economic and Technological Development Area, Nantong, Jiangsu, China
Tel.: (86) 51389181588
Toilet Preparation Mfr
N.A.I.C.S.: 325620

Givaudan Flavours & Fragrances Malaysia Sdn. Bhd. (1)
121 Jalan Usaha 10 Kawasan Perindustrian, Ayer Keroh, 75450, Malacca, Malaysia
Tel.: (60) 63183800
Toilet Preparation Mfr
N.A.I.C.S.: 325620

Givaudan Fragrances (Guangzhou) Co. Ltd. (1)
66 Hongjing Road, Guangzhou, 510760, Guangdong, China
Tel.: (86) 2062985000
Fragrance Mfr & Distr
N.A.I.C.S.: 325620

Givaudan Fragrances (Shanghai) Ltd. (1)
298 Li Shi Zhen Road Zhangjiang Hi-Tech Park Pudong New Area, Shanghai, 201203, China
Tel.: (86) 2128931288
Toilet Preparation Mfr
N.A.I.C.S.: 325620

Givaudan France Aromes SAS (1)
19-23 Rue de la Voie des Bans, BP 24, 95102, Argenteuil, France
Tel.: (33) 139981515
Cosmetic Product Distr
N.A.I.C.S.: 424210

Givaudan France Fragrances SAS (1)
55 Voie Des Bans, PO Box 24, 95102, Argenteuil, France **(100%)**
Tel.: (33) 139981515
Web Site: http://www.givaudan.com
Sales Range: $250-299.9 Million
Emp.: 600
N.A.I.C.S.: 325620

Givaudan France Naturals S.A.S. (1)
Les Chapelles Sud, 01190, Reyssouze, France
Tel.: (33) 385239383
Fragrance Mfr
N.A.I.C.S.: 325620

Givaudan Guatemala, S.A. (1)
Boulevar Los Proceres 18 Calle 24-69 Zona 10 Empresarial Zona Pradera, Guatemala, Guatemala
Tel.: (502) 22617094
Toilet Preparation Mfr
N.A.I.C.S.: 325620

Givaudan Holdings UK Ltd (1)
Kennington Road, Ashford, TN24 0LT, United Kingdom
Tel.: (44) 1233644444
Investment Management Service
N.A.I.C.S.: 523999

Subsidiary (Domestic):

Givaudan UK Limited (2)
Kennington Road, Ashford, TN24 0LT, Kent, United Kingdom
Tel.: (44) 1233 644 444
Web Site: http://www.givaudan.com
Sales Range: $100-124.9 Million
Emp.: 300
Cosmetic Ingredients & Dental Flavors Mfr
N.A.I.C.S.: 325620

INTERNATIONAL PUBLIC

Branch (Domestic):

Givaudan UK Limited - Staines (3)
Magna House 76-80 Church Street, Staines-upon-Thames, TW18 4XR, Mddx, United Kingdom
Tel.: (44) 1784417700
Web Site: http://www.givaudan.com
Sales Range: $25-49.9 Million
Emp.: 20
Fragrances Whslr
N.A.I.C.S.: 424990

Plant (Domestic):

Givaudan UK Limited - Wirral (3)
Bromborough Port Dock Road S, Wirral, CH62 4SU, Merseyside, United Kingdom
Tel.: (44) 151 645 2060
Flavors Creation, Application & Retail Services
N.A.I.C.S.: 311999

Subsidiary (Domestic):

Givaudan UK Ltd (3)
Chippenham Drive Kingston, Milton Keynes, MK10 0AE, United Kingdom
Tel.: (44) 1908242424
Flavours & Fragrances Mfr & Sales
N.A.I.C.S.: 311930

Givaudan Hong Kong Ltd. (1)
7/F K11 Atelier Victoria Dockside 18 Salisbury Road, Tsim Tsa Tsui, China (Hong Kong) **(100%)**
Tel.: (852) 28908031
Sales Range: $25-49.9 Million
Emp.: 4
Flavors & Fragrances Mfr & Whslr
N.A.I.C.S.: 325620

Givaudan Hungary Kft (1)
Tel.: (36) 704290063
Sales Range: $25-49.9 Million
Emp.: 17
Flavoring Additives Mfr
N.A.I.C.S.: 311930

Givaudan Iberica SA (1)
Placa d Europa 2-4 3a, Hospitalet de Llobregat, 08902, Barcelona, Spain
Tel.: (34) 933741730
Sales Range: $50-74.9 Million
Emp.: 7
Fragrances, Flavors & Food Ingredients
N.A.I.C.S.: 424490

Givaudan International SA (1)
Chemin De La Parfumerie 5, 1214, Vernier, Switzerland
Tel.: (41) 227809111
Emp.: 900
Cosmetic Fragrance Mfr
N.A.I.C.S.: 325620

Givaudan Italia S.p.A (1)
Via XI Febbraio 99, Vimodrone, 20055, Milan, Italy **(100%)**
Tel.: (39) 02250811
Sales Range: $25-49.9 Million
Emp.: 30
Flavors & Fragrances Mfr & Sales
N.A.I.C.S.: 325620
Maria Giovanna Labbate *(Mng Dir)*

Givaudan Japan K.K. (1)
3-6-6 Tokiwa New Building, Shinagawa-ku Osaki, Tokyo, 141-0032, Japan
Tel.: (81) 357456110
Sales Range: $75-99.9 Million
Emp.: 200
Fragrance Mfr
N.A.I.C.S.: 325620

Plant (Domestic):

Givaudan Japan K.K. - Yokohama (2)
3014-1 Shinohara-cho, Kohoku-ku, Yokohama, 222-0026, Kanagawa, Japan
Tel.: (81) 454233161
Sales Range: $25-49.9 Million
Emp.: 100
Fragrances, Flavors & Food Ingredients Mfr
N.A.I.C.S.: 311999

Givaudan Korea Ltd. (1)
12/F Dongwon F B Bldg 60 Mabang-ro, Seocho-gu, Seoul, 06775, Korea (South) **(100%)**

AND PRIVATE COMPANIES　　　　　　　　　　　　　　　　　　　　　GIVAUDAN S.A.

Tel.: (82) 221495800
Sales Range: $25-49.9 Million
Emp.: 25
Flavor Applications & Sales
N.A.I.C.S. 325620

Givaudan Malaysia Sdn. Bhd (1)
A-901 Menara 1Kelana Brem TowerJalan SS 7/15, Jalan Staduim, 47301, Petaling Jaya, Selangor, Malaysia
Tel.: (60) 378064095
Web Site: http://www.givaudan.com
Sales Range: $25-49.9 Million
Emp.: 11
Cosmetic Fragrance & Flavour Mfr
N.A.I.C.S. 325620

Givaudan Middle East & Africa FZE (1)
Office No LB180502 Jafza View 18, PO Box 33170, Jebel Ali, Dubai, United Arab Emirates
Tel.: (971) 44342363
Toilet Preparation Mfr
N.A.I.C.S. 325620

Givaudan NZ Ltd. (1)
2 Birmingham Road, East Tamaki, Auckland, 1702, New Zealand
Tel.: (64) 92745393
Web Site: https://www.givaudan.com
Sales Range: $25-49.9 Million
Emp.: 3
Fragrances, Flavors & Food Ingredients Mfr
N.A.I.C.S. 311999

Givaudan Nederland BV (1)
Huizerstraatweg 28, 1411 GP, Naarden, Netherlands
Tel.: (31) 356999111
Emp.: 500
Flavor & Fragrance Ingredients Mfr
N.A.I.C.S. 311999

Subsidiary (Domestic):

Givaudan Nederland Finance BV (2)
Nijverheidsweg 60, 3771 ME, Barneveld, Netherlands
Tel.: (31) 342410411
Sales Range: $25-49.9 Million
Emp.: 5
Cosmetics Products Mfr
N.A.I.C.S. 325620
Attie Sarelse (Gen Mgr)

Givaudan Treasury International B.V. (2)
Huizerstraatweg 28, 1411 GP, Naarden, Netherlands
Tel.: (31) 356999111
Web Site: http://www.givaudan.com
Sales Range: $100-124.9 Million
Emp.: 500
Cosmetic Fragrance & Flavour Mfr
N.A.I.C.S. 325620

Givaudan North Europe AB (1)
Rabyholmf Alle 4, Lund, 223 55, Sweden
Tel.: (46) 46235800
Sales Range: $25-49.9 Million
Emp.: 13
Flavors & Food Ingredients
N.A.I.C.S. 311999

Givaudan Peru SAC (1)
Tel.: (51) 12227733
Sales Range: $25-49.9 Million
Emp.: 11
Cosmetic Fragrance Distr
N.A.I.C.S. 424210

Givaudan Polska Sp. Z o.o. (1)
Pulawska 182 IO 1 Building, 02 670, Warsaw, Poland
Tel.: (48) 228408315
Web Site: https://www.givaudan.com
Sales Range: $50-74.9 Million
Emp.: 8
Flavoring Syrup Distr
N.A.I.C.S. 424490

Givaudan Rus LLC (1)
Tel.: (7) 4957778686
Web Site: https://www.givauvan.com
Sales Range: $25-49.9 Million
Fragrances, Flavors & Food Ingredients Mfr
N.A.I.C.S. 311999

Givaudan Scandinavia A/S (1)
Gongehusvej 280, 2970, Horsholm, Denmark
Tel.: (45) 45 894569
Cosmetic Flavoring Products Distr
N.A.I.C.S. 424210

Givaudan Singapore Pte Ltd. (1)
1 Woodlands Ave 8, Singapore, 738972, Singapore (100%)
Tel.: (65) 67519100
Sales Range: $75-99.9 Million
Emp.: 250
N.A.I.C.S. 325620

Branch (Non-US):

Givaudan Singapore Pte Ltd. Philippines (2)
37 F Robinsons Equitable Tower, Ortigas Center, ADB Ave Poveda St, Pasig, 1605, Philippines
Tel.: (63) 26872903
Sales Range: $25-49.9 Million
Emp.: 24
Fragrance Compounds & Ingredients Mfr
N.A.I.C.S. 325620

Givaudan Suisse SA (1)
5 Chemin De La Perfumerie, 1214, Vernier, Switzerland (100%)
Tel.: (41) 227809111
Sales Range: $200-249.9 Million
Emp.: 800
Producer & Seller of Fragrances
N.A.I.C.S. 325620

Givaudan United States, Inc. (1)
1199 Edison Dr, Cincinnati, OH 45216
Tel.: (513) 948-8000
Web Site: https://www.givaudan.com
Cosmetic Fragrance & Flavor Products Mfr & Distr
N.A.I.C.S. 325620

Subsidiary (Domestic):

Givaudan Flavors and Fragrances, Inc. (2)
1199 Edison Dr 1-2, Cincinnati, OH 45216-2265
Tel.: (513) 948-8000
Cosmetic Fragrance & Flavour Products Mfr
N.A.I.C.S. 325620

Subsidiary (Domestic):

Givaudan Flavors Corporation (3)
1199 Edison Dr Ste 1011-2, Cincinnati, OH 45216 (100%)
Tel.: (513) 948-8000
Flavor Creation, Application & Retail Services
N.A.I.C.S. 325199

Unit (Domestic):

Givaudan Flavors Corporation - Elgin (4)
580 Tollgate Rd Ste A, Elgin, IL 60123
Tel.: (847) 608-6200
Web Site: http://www.givaudan.com
Sales Range: $25-49.9 Million
Emp.: 180
Flavors & Food Ingredients Mfr
N.A.I.C.S. 311999

Givaudan Flavors Corporation - Itasca (4)
880 W Thorndale Ave, Itasca, IL 60143-1341
Tel.: (630) 773-8484
Sales Range: $10-24.9 Million
Emp.: 50
Flavours & Food Ingredients Mfr
N.A.I.C.S. 311930

Subsidiary (Domestic):

Givaudan Fragrances Corporation (3)
300 Waterloo Valley Rd, Mount Olive, NJ 07828
Tel.: (973) 448-6500
Fragrances & Dental Flavors Mfr
N.A.I.C.S. 325620

Givaudan Venezuela SA (1)
Calle Veracruz con Calle Cali Torre ABA Piso 8 Oficina 8A, 1060, Las Mercedes, Caracas, Venezuela
Tel.: (58) 2129920978

Web Site: https://www.givaudan.com
Emp.: 10
Cosmetic Fragrance & Flavoring Products Mfr
N.A.I.C.S. 325620

Givaudan de Mexico S.A. de C.V. (1)
Camino a Quintanares km 1 5 Pedro Escobedo, 76700, Mexico, Queretaro, Mexico (100%)
Tel.: (52) 4422112500
Sales Range: $25-49.9 Million
Emp.: 30
Mfr & Sales of Fragrance & Flavor
N.A.I.C.S. 325620

Plant (Domestic):

Givaudan de Mexico SA de CV (2)
Camino a Quintanares km 1 5, Pedro Escobedo, 76700, Queretaro, Mexico
Tel.: (52) 4422112500
Web Site: http://www.questintl.com
Sales Range: $25-49.9 Million
Emp.: 100
Fragrance Materials & Flavors Mfr
N.A.I.C.S. 325620

Major International Ltd. (1)
Higham Business Park Bury Close Higham Ferrers, Rushden, NN10 8HQ, United Kingdom
Tel.: (44) 1933356012
Toilet Preparation Mfr
N.A.I.C.S. 325620

Naturex Australia Pty Ltd (1)
9 Garling Road Kings Park, Sydney, 2148, NSW, Australia
Tel.: (61) 296795855
Toilet Preparation Mfr
N.A.I.C.S. 325620

Naturex GmbH (1)
Im Zollhafen 24 Kranhaus Sud, 50678, Cologne, Germany
Tel.: (49) 2212722890
Toilet Preparation Mfr,
N.A.I.C.S. 325620

Naturex Holdings Singapore Pte. Ltd. (1)
20 Changi Business Park Central 2 05-04A, Singapore, 486031, Singapore
Tel.: (65) 65365168
Toilet Preparation Mfr
N.A.I.C.S. 325620

Naturex India Private Limited (1)
Roth Khurd Kolad Road, Raigad, Roha, 402116, Maharashtra, India
Tel.: (91) 2226598700
Toilet Preparation Mfr
N.A.I.C.S. 325620

Naturex K.K. (1)
NBC MITA Building 7F 5-29-18 Shiba, Minato-ku, Tokyo, 108-0014, Japan
Tel.: (81) 368096723
Toilet Preparation Mfr
N.A.I.C.S. 325620

Naturex Ltd. (1)
Park Road Overseal, Swadlincote, DE12 6JX, Derbyshire, United Kingdom
Tel.: (44) 1283224221
Toilet Preparation Mfr
N.A.I.C.S. 325620

Naturex S.A. (1)
250 rue Pierre Bayle, BP 81218, 84911, Avignon, Cedex 9, France (40.5%)
Tel.: (33) 490239689
Web Site: http://www.naturex.com
Rev.: $485,013,514
Assets: $788,551,238
Liabilities: $337,317,376
Net Worth: $451,233,862
Earnings: $14,134,748
Fiscal Year-end: 12/31/2017
Natural Ingredients for Food, Pharmaceutical & Cosmetic Products Mfr
N.A.I.C.S. 311930
Serge Sabrier (Chief Procurement Officer)

Subsidiary (US):

Gaia Herbs Inc. (2)
101 Gaia Herbs Dr, Brevard, NC 28712
Tel.: (828) 883-5918

Web Site: http://www.gaiaherbs.com
Sales Range: $25-49.9 Million
Emp.: 120
Food Mfr
N.A.I.C.S. 311999
Ric Scalzo (Founder)

Naturex Inc. (2)
375 Huyler St, South Hackensack, NJ 07626
Tel.: (201) 440-5000
Web Site: http://www.naturex.com
Sales Range: $25-49.9 Million
Emp.: 150
Solid, Liquid & Powdered Botanical Extracts Mfr
N.A.I.C.S. 325411
Jacques Dikansky (Pres & CEO)

Subsidiary (Non-US):

Naturex S.P.A (2)
Via Galileo Ferrario 44, 21042, Caronno Pertusella, VA, Italy
Tel.: (39) 0296651201
Web Site: https://www.naturex.com
Food & Beverage Products Mfr
N.A.I.C.S. 311412

Naturex UK Ltd. (2)
Park Road Overseal, Swadlincote, DE12 6JX, Derbys, United Kingdom
Tel.: (44) 1865512030
Sales Range: $25-49.9 Million
Emp.: 90
Food Mfr
N.A.I.C.S. 311999

Subsidiary (US):

Vegetable Juices Inc. (2)
7400 S Narragansett Ave, Bedford Park, IL 60638
Tel.: (708) 924-9500
Web Site: https://www.vegetablejuices.com
Sales Range: $25-49.9 Million
Emp.: 75
Vegetable Ingredients Production & Distr
N.A.I.C.S. 311421

PT. Givaudan Indonesia (1)
Capital Place 9th Floor, Jl Jend Gatot Subroto Kav 18, Jakarta, 12710, Indonesia
Tel.: (62) 2129955700
Sales Range: $25-49.9 Million
Emp.: 50
Fragrances Application & Retail Services
N.A.I.C.S. 325620

Plant (Domestic):

PT. Givaudan Indonesia - Depok (2)
Jalan Raya Jakarta-Bogor Km 35, Cimanggis, Depok, 16951, West Java, Indonesia
Tel.: (62) 2177815000
Web Site: http://www.givaudan.com
Sales Range: $25-49.9 Million
Emp.: 200
Fragrances, Flavors & Food Ingredients Mfr
N.A.I.C.S. 311999

Shanghai Givaudan Ltd (1)
298 Li Shi Zhen Road, PuDong, Shanghai, 201203, China
Tel.: (86) 2128931288
Web Site: http://www.givaudan.com
Sales Range: $25-49.9 Million
Emp.: 100
Fragrances, Flavors & Food Ingredients Mfr
N.A.I.C.S. 311999

Subsidiary (Domestic):

Givaudan Flavors (Shanghai) Ltd. (2)
No 668 Jing Ye Road, Jin Qiao Export Area Pudong New Area, Shanghai, 201201, China
Tel.: (86) 2128937668
Sales Range: $25-49.9 Million
Emp.: 250
Mfr of Fragrances, Flavors & Food Ingredients
N.A.I.C.S. 311999

Givaudan Specialty Products (Shanghai) Ltd (2)
222 Jiang Tian East Road, Songjiang Develoment Zone, Shanghai, 201600, China
Tel.: (86) 2157746899

GIVAUDAN S.A.

Givaudan S.A.—(Continued)
Sales Range: $25-49.9 Million
Emp.: 50
Cosmetic Fragrance & Flavoring Products Mfr
N.A.I.C.S.: 325620

Soliance S.A. (1)
Route de Bazancourt, 51110, Pomacle, France
Tel.: (33) 3 26 88 84 10
Web Site: http://www.soliance.com
Sales Range: $10-24.9 Million
Emp.: 57
Cosmetic Ingredient Mfr
N.A.I.C.S.: 325411

The Williamson Group, Inc. (1)
5 Janet Ct, Miller Place, NY 11764
Tel.: (631) 821-0678
Web Site: https://williamsongroup.net
Food Mfr & Distr
N.A.I.C.S.: 311991

Ungerer & Company (1)
4Ungerer Way, Lincoln Park, NJ 07035-1439
Tel.: (973) 628-0600
Web Site:
https://www.ungererandcompany.com
Sales Range: $75-99.9 Million
Emp.: 125
Essential Oil Aromatic Chemical Fragrance Base Perfume Specialtie Imitation & Genuine Fruit Flavor Developer & Marketer Mfr
N.A.I.C.S.: 311930
John Olsen (VP-Sls)

Subsidiary (Non-US):

Ungerer Australia (2)
52 Cook Street, Kurnell, 2231, NSW, Australia (100%)
Tel.: (61) 296689896
Web Site: http://www.ungereraus.com
Essential Oils, Aromatic Chemicals, Fragrance Bases, Perfume Specialties, Imitation & Genuine Fruit Flavors
N.A.I.C.S.: 325998

Ungerer Fragrance & Flavour (Shanghai) Co. Ltd. (2)
1-2 Building No 508 Lane 2655 Fengzhe Road, Fengxian, Shanghai, China
Tel.: (86) 21 61765959
Flavour & Aroma Chemical Whslr
N.A.I.C.S.: 424690

Ungerer Limited (2)
Sealand Rd, Sealand Industrial Estate, Chester, CH1 4LP, United Kingdom (100%)
Tel.: (44) 1244371711
Web Site:
https://www.ungererandcompany.com
Sales Range: $10-24.9 Million
Emp.: 80
Mfr & Sales of Essential Oils, Aromatic Chemicals, Fragrance Bases, Perfume Specialties, Imitation & Genuine Fruit Flavors
N.A.I.C.S.: 325998

Ungerer de Colombia Ltda (2)
Calle 22D 127-84 Bdg 8, Bogota, Colombia
Tel.: (57) 14134020
Fragrance Mfr
N.A.I.C.S.: 325199

Ungerer de Mexico S.A. de C.V. (2)
Calle 5 KM-1, Industrial Alce Blanco, 53520, Naucalpan, Mexico (100%)
Tel.: (52) 5553571717
Essential Oils, Aromatic Chemicals, Fragrance Bases, Perfume Specialties, Imitation & Genuine Fruit Flavors Mfr
N.A.I.C.S.: 325998

Ungerer Industries, Inc (1)
4 Ungerer Way, Lincoln Park, NJ 07035
Tel.: (973) 628-0600
Web Site:
https://www.ungererandcompany.com
Fragrance Product Mfr
N.A.I.C.S.: 325620

Vika B.V. (1)
Nizolaan 4, 6718 ZC, Ede, Netherlands
Tel.: (31) 318619042
Toilet Preparation Mfr
N.A.I.C.S.: 325620

GIVEMEPOWER CORP.
204 16 Midlake Blvd SE, Calgary, T2X 2X7, AB, Canada
Tel.: (403) 287-6001
Web Site:
https://www.givemepower.com
Year Founded: 2001
GMPW—(OTCIQ)
Rev.: $490,000
Assets: $44,592
Liabilities: $241,379
Net Worth: ($196,787)
Earnings: ($111,426)
Fiscal Year-end: 12/31/22
Software Development Services
N.A.I.C.S.: 541511
Frank I. Igwealor (Pres, CEO & CFO)

GIVING.COM LIMITED
First Floor 30 Eastbourne Terrace, London, W2 6LA, United Kingdom
Tel.: (44) 8450212110
Web Site: http://www.justgiving.com
Year Founded: 2001
Sales Range: $10-24.9 Million
Emp.: 57
Online Fundraising Platform Operator
N.A.I.C.S.: 513210
Zarine Kharas (Co-Founder & CEO)

GIVOT OLAM OIL EXPLORATION LIMITED PARTNERSHIP (1993)
fire Hartom 11, PO Box 45422, Jerusalem, 9777511, Israel
Tel.: (972) 3946040
Web Site: https://www.givot.co.il
Year Founded: 1990
GIVOT—(TAE)
Rev.: $115,000
Assets: $6,323,000
Liabilities: $25,353,000
Net Worth: ($19,030,000)
Earnings: ($20,679,000)
Fiscal Year-end: 12/31/22
Oil & Gas Exploration Services
N.A.I.C.S.: 211120
Shmuel Laurence Becker (Co-Founder & Chm)

GIX MARTECH INNOVATION
14 Shenkar Street 2Nd Floor, Herzliya, 46733, Israel
Tel.: (972) 97741505
Web Site: https://www.gix-internet.com
Year Founded: 2013
GIX—(TAE)
Rev.: $79,988,942
Assets: $28,120,966
Liabilities: $24,600,399
Net Worth: $3,520,567
Earnings: ($3,758,012)
Emp.: 35
Fiscal Year-end: 06/30/23
Other Computer Related Services
N.A.I.C.S.: 541519
Yoram Bauman (Chm)

GIYANI METALS CORP.
Suite 1700 666 Burrard Street, Vancouver, V6C 2X8, BC, Canada
Tel.: (416) 453-8818   BC
Web Site:
https://www.giyanimetals.com
Year Founded: 2007
EMM—(TSXV)
Assets: $17,815,244
Liabilities: $1,725,550
Net Worth: $16,089,694
Earnings: ($3,637,114)
Emp.: 26
Fiscal Year-end: 12/31/23
Gold Ore Exploration Services
N.A.I.C.S.: 213114
Jonathan Henry (Exec Chm)

Subsidiaries:

Canoe Mining Ventures Corp. (1)
4th Floor 217 Queen St W, Toronto, M5V 0R2, ON, Canada (57.7%)
Tel.: (289) 837-0066
Web Site: https://www.canoemining.ca
Assets: $249,335
Liabilities: $425,290
Net Worth: ($175,955)
Earnings: ($198,131)
Fiscal Year-end: 12/31/2020
Metal Ore Exploration Services
N.A.I.C.S.: 213114

Subsidiary (Domestic):

Coldstream Mineral Ventures Corp. (2)
1055 West Georgia Street Suite 1500 Royal Centre, PO Box 11117, Vancouver, V6E 4N7, BC, Canada
Tel.: (905) 844-7612
Gold Ore Exploration Services
N.A.I.C.S.: 213114
R. Charles Allen (Pres)

GIZA GENERAL CONTRACTING & REAL ESTATE INVESTMENT
46 El-Falaki ST Bab El-Louk, Cairo, Egypt
Tel.: (20) 223990561
Web Site: https://www.al-giza.com
Year Founded: 1988
GGCC.CA—(EGX)
Sales Range: Less than $1 Million
Real Estate Investment Services
N.A.I.C.S.: 531390
Mohamed Ezzat El Maayergy (Chm, Chm, Mng Dir & Mng Dir)

GIZEH VERPACKUNGEN GMBH & CO. KG
Breiter Weg 40, 51702, Bergneustadt, Germany
Tel.: (49) 2261 401 0   De
Web Site: http://www.gizeh.com
Year Founded: 1920
Emp.: 580
Plastic Packaging Container Mfr
N.A.I.C.S.: 326160
Birgit Klein-Neumann (Editor)

Subsidiaries:

GIZEH Dispoform Sp. z o.o. (1)
ul 23 Pazdziernika 61, 62-080, Tarnowo Podgorne, Poland
Tel.: (48) 618167900
Supermarket Operator
N.A.I.C.S.: 445110
Lukasz Wanago (Acct Mgr)

GIZEH Emballages Angers SAS (1)
Rue de L'Ebeaupin Z I Angers, 49070, Beaucouze, France
Tel.: (33) 241368070
Supermarket Operator
N.A.I.C.S.: 445110

GIZEH Packaging NA Inc. (1)
Tel.: (519) 720-0035
Supermarket Operator
N.A.I.C.S.: 445110
Brandon Bower (Mgr-Pur & Admin)

GJ STEEL PUBLIC COMPANY LIMITED
88 PASO Tower 24th Floor Silom Road Suriyawong, Bangrak, Bangkok, 10500, Thailand
Tel.: (66) 22678222   TH
Web Site: https://www.gjsteel.co.th
Year Founded: 1994
GJS—(THA)
Rev.: $367,727,804
Assets: $375,198,716
Liabilities: $19,120,789
Net Worth: $356,077,927
Earnings: ($14,353,216)
Emp.: 689
Fiscal Year-end: 12/31/23

INTERNATIONAL PUBLIC

Steel & Steel Products Mfr
N.A.I.C.S.: 331110
Khunying Patama Leeswadtrakul (Chief Corp Social Responsibility Officer)

Subsidiaries:

Thai Nippon Steel Engineering & Construction Corporation Co., Ltd. (1)
5th Floor Ample Tower 909 Debaratna Road, Bangna, Bangkok, 10260, Thailand
Tel.: (66) 27552800
Web Site: https://www.thainippon.co.th
Construction Services
N.A.I.C.S.: 236220

GJENSIDIGE FORSIKRING ASA
Schweigaardsgate 21, 0191, Oslo, Norway
Tel.: (47) 91503100   NO
Web Site: https://www.gjensidige.no
GJNSY—(OTCIQ)
Rev.: $3,383,022,354
Assets: $13,696,840,938
Liabilities: $11,458,248,661
Net Worth: $2,238,592,278
Earnings: $381,525,956
Emp.: 4,001
Fiscal Year-end: 12/31/23
Financial Investment Services
N.A.I.C.S.: 523999
Oystein Thoresen (Dir-Comm)

Subsidiaries:

AAS Gjensidige Baltic (1)
Gustava Zemgala 74A, Riga, LV-1039, Latvia
Tel.: (371) 67112222
Web Site: http://www.gjensidige.lv
Sales Range: $50-74.9 Million
Emp.: 100
Insurance Services
N.A.I.C.S.: 524298

Subsidiary (Non-US):

Gjensidige Baltic (2)
J Basanaviciaus g 95E, Kedainiai, 03111, Lithuania
Tel.: (370) 52721626
Web Site: http://www.gjensidige.lt
Insurance Services
N.A.I.C.S.: 524298

Dansk Tandforsikring A/S (1)
Jaegersborg Alle 14, 2920, Charlottenlund, Denmark
Tel.: (45) 70204647
Web Site: https://dansktandforsikring.dk
Insurance Services
N.A.I.C.S.: 524210

Molholm Forsikring A/S (1)
Lille Tornbjerg Vej 30, 5220, Odense, Denmark
Tel.: (45) 65202120
Web Site: http://www.molholmforsikring.dk
Insurance Agency Services
N.A.I.C.S.: 524210

GK RESOURCES LTD.
1055 West Georgia Street Suite 1500, Vancouver, V6E4N7, BC, Canada
Tel.: (647) 407-2515
NIKL.H—(TSXV)
Rev.: $4,174
Assets: $7,597
Liabilities: $348,605
Net Worth: ($341,008)
Earnings: ($96,516)
Fiscal Year-end: 09/30/23
Nickel Mining Services
N.A.I.C.S.: 212230
Ian Mcdonald (Pres & CEO)

GK TNS ENERGO PAO
Nastasyinsky Lane 4/1, Moscow, 127006, Russia
Tel.: (7) 4952872484

AND PRIVATE COMPANIES — GKN PLC

Web Site: http://www.tns-e.ru
Year Founded: 2003
TNSE—(MOEX)
Sales Range: Less than $1 Million
Electric Power Generation Services
N.A.I.C.S.: 221118
Oksana Borisova *(Deputy Gen Dir-Legal Affairs)*

Subsidiaries:

TNS Energo Karelia JSC (1)
Br -Internationalists d 17A, Petrozavodsk, 185016, Russia
Tel.: (7) 8142792500
Web Site: http://www.karelia.tns-e.ru
Electricity Power Distribution Services
N.A.I.C.S.: 221122

TNS Energo NN PJSC (1)
Beketova d 3V, Nizhniy Novgorod, 603950, Russia
Tel.: (7) 8312430799
Web Site: http://www.nn.tns-e.ru
Electricity Power Distribution Services
N.A.I.C.S.: 221122

TNS Energo Penza LLC (1)
Gagarina 11-b, Penza, 440039, Russia
Tel.: (7) 8412987848
Web Site: http://www.penza.tns-e.ru
Electricity Power Distribution Services
N.A.I.C.S.: 221122

TNS Energo Tula JSC (1)
Kaminskym d 31a, Tula, 300041, Russia
Tel.: (7) 4872950977
Web Site: http://www.tula.tns-e.ru
Electricity Power Distribution Services
N.A.I.C.S.: 221122

TNS Energo Velikiy Novgorod LLC (1)
Pskov d 13, Velikiy Novgorod, 173015, Russia
Tel.: (7) 8162502516
Web Site: http://www.novgorod.tns-e.ru
Electricity Power Distribution Services
N.A.I.C.S.: 221122

GKB OPHTHALMICS LTD.
16-A Tivim Industrial Estate Mapusa, Goa, 403 526, India
Tel.: (91) 8322257335
Web Site: http://www.gkb.net
Year Founded: 1981
Ophthalmic Lens Mfr
N.A.I.C.S.: 333310
K. G. Gupta *(Chm & Mng Dir)*

GKD - GEBR. KUFFERATH AG
Metallweberstrasse 46, 52353, Duren, Germany
Tel.: (49) 24218030
Web Site: http://www.gkd.de
Sales Range: $75-99.9 Million
Emp.: 600
Filter Units Mfr
N.A.I.C.S.: 333248
Stephan Kufferath-Kassner *(Co-CEO)*

Subsidiaries:

GKD (BEIJING) IND. TECHNOLOGIES CO., LTD. (1)
Middle Road No 11 Jinma Industrial Zone, Shunyi District, 101318, Beijing, China
Tel.: (86) 1051659618
Web Site: http://www.gkd-china.com
Stainless Steel Products Distr
N.A.I.C.S.: 423390
Jing Chen *(Mng Dir)*

GKD (UK) Ltd. (1)
Genesis 4 Church Lane, Heslington, York, YO10 5DQ, North Yorkshire, United Kingdom
Tel.: (44) 1904420500
Web Site: http://www.gkd.uk.com
Stainless Steel Products Mfr
N.A.I.C.S.: 331110

GKD BUISMET (PTY) LTD. (1)
Aureus Ext 3 Cnr Fiat and Chrysler Streets, 1759, Randfontein, South Africa
Tel.: (27) 114124770
Web Site: http://www.gkd.co.za
Stainless Steel Products Distr
N.A.I.C.S.: 423390

GKD INDIA LTD. (1)
52 Industrial Area Jhotwara, 302012, Jaipur, Rajasthan, India
Tel.: (91) 1417105100
Web Site: http://www.gkd-india.com
Stainless Steel Products Distr
N.A.I.C.S.: 423390
Sanjeev Pathak *(Supvr-Production)*

GKD LatAm S.A. (1)
La Estera 418, Lampa, Santiago, Chile
Tel.: (56) 224891040
Web Site: http://www.gkd-latam.com
Stainless Steel Products Distr
N.A.I.C.S.: 423390

GKD-USA, INC. (1)
825 Chesapeake Dr, Cambridge, MD 21613
Tel.: (410) 221-0542
Web Site: http://www.gkdusa.com
Other Fabricated Wire Product Mfr
N.A.I.C.S.: 332618
Steven Culver *(Dir-Bus Dev)*

GKE CORPORATION LIMITED
39 Benoi Road 06-01, Singapore, 627725, Singapore
Tel.: (65) 62617770   SG
Web Site: https://gke.listedcompany.com
595—(SES)
Rev.: $81,922,934
Assets: $137,196,739
Liabilities: $67,296,035
Net Worth: $69,900,704
Earnings: $3,188,588
Emp.: 881
Fiscal Year-end: 05/31/24
Energy, Biotech & Logistics Services
N.A.I.C.S.: 541614
Cheow Hui Neo *(CEO)*

Subsidiaries:

Fair Chem Industries Pte Ltd. (1)
3 Tuas Avenue 11, Singapore, 639069, Singapore
Tel.: (65) 68653386
Web Site: https://fairchem.com.sg
Chemical Mfr & Distr
N.A.I.C.S.: 325998

GKE Express Logistics Pte Ltd (1)
30 Pioneer Rd, Singapore, 628502, Singapore
Tel.: (65) 62617770
Logistics Management Services
N.A.I.C.S.: 541614

GKE Freight Pte Ltd (1)
No 1 Jalan Besut, Singapore, 619554, Singapore
Tel.: (65) 62617770
Air & Sea Freight Transportation Services
N.A.I.C.S.: 481112

GKE Metal Logistics Pte. Ltd. (1)
30 Pioneer Road, Singapore, 628805, Singapore (100%)
Tel.: (65) 62617770
Emp.: 200
Metal Warehousing & Logistics Services
N.A.I.C.S.: 493110
Neo Cheow Hui *(Gen Mgr)*

Subsidiary (Non-US):

GKE (Shanghai) Metal Logistics Co., Ltd. (2)
Room 1611 Huai Hai China Building No 885 Ren Min Road, Shanghai, 200080, China
Tel.: (86) 216 326 8369
Web Site: http://www.gkeml.com
Sales Range: $10-24.9 Million
Emp.: 15
General Warehousing Services
N.A.I.C.S.: 493110
Jason Li *(Gen Mgr)*

GKE Private Limited (1)
39 Benoi Road 06-01, Singapore, 627725, Singapore
Tel.: (65) 62617770
Web Site: https://www.gke.com.sg
Logistic Services
N.A.I.C.S.: 541614

GKE Services Pte. Ltd. (1)
30 Pioneer Road 06-01, Singapore, 628502, Singapore
Tel.: (65) 62252250
Web Site: https://www.gkeservices.com
Logistic Services
N.A.I.C.S.: 541614

GKE Warehousing & Logistics Pte Ltd (1)
39 Benoi Rd 06-01, Singapore, 627725, Singapore
Tel.: (65) 62617770
Sales Range: $25-49.9 Million
Emp.: 60
Logistics & Warehousing Services
N.A.I.C.S.: 493110
Marina Neo Hwee Lee *(Mng Dir)*

TNS Ocean Lines (S) Pte. Ltd. (1)
138 Cecil Street 12-02/03 Cecil Court, Singapore, 069538, Singapore
Tel.: (65) 6 225 2250
Web Site: https://www.tnsocean.com
Transportation Services
N.A.I.C.S.: 484110
George Ng *(Asst Mgr-HR & Admin)*

GKG PRECISION MACHINE CO., LTD.
No 2 Shalang Road Dongcheng Science and Technology Industrial Park, Dongcheng, Dongguan, 523000, Guangdong, China
Tel.: (86) 76938823222
Web Site: https://www.gkg.cn
Year Founded: 2005
301338—(CHIN)
Rev.: $109,419,336
Assets: $261,597,492
Liabilities: $64,244,232
Net Worth: $197,353,260
Earnings: $17,844,840
Fiscal Year-end: 12/31/22
Precision Product Mfr & Distr
N.A.I.C.S.: 332721
Guoliang Qiu *(Chm)*

Subsidiaries:

GKG Asia Pte. Ltd. (1)
52 Ubi Avenue 3 02-38 Frontier, Singapore, 408867, Singapore
Tel.: (65) 65478065
Printing Machine Mfr & Distr
N.A.I.C.S.: 333413

GKM HOLDINGS JOINT STOCK COMPANY
Chau Son Industrial Park, Le Hong Phong Ward, Phu Ly, Ha Nam, Vietnam
Tel.: (84) 3516257888
GKM—(HNX)
Rev.: $31,180,700
Assets: $63,424,300
Liabilities: $30,337,400
Net Worth: $33,086,900
Earnings: $1,806,100
Fiscal Year-end: 12/31/22
Building Materials Mfr
N.A.I.C.S.: 327120
Dang Viet Le *(Chm-Mgmt Bd)*

GKN PLC
Ipsley House Ipsley Church Lane, PO Box 55, Redditch, B98 0TL, Worcs, United Kingdom
Tel.: (44) 1527517715   UK
Year Founded: 1759
Rev.: $13,047,339,520
Assets: $11,955,901,440
Liabilities: $8,475,171,840
Net Worth: $3,480,729,600
Earnings: $686,702,080
Emp.: 51,117
Fiscal Year-end: 12/31/17
Automotive, Off-Road Vehicle & Aerospace Components & Systems Designer & Mfr
N.A.I.C.S.: 336390

Subsidiaries:

Fokker Technologies Holding B.V. (1)
Industrieweg 4, NL-3351LB, Papendrecht, Netherlands
Tel.: (31) 78 6419 911
Web Site: http://www.fokker.com
Emp.: 4,900
Holding Company; Aerospace Technologies Developer, Mfr & Whslr
N.A.I.C.S.: 551112
Hans Buthker *(Chm-Mgmt Bd & CEO)*

Subsidiary (Domestic):

Fokker Aircraft Services B.V. (2)
Aviolandalaan 31, 4631 RP, Hoogerheide, Netherlands
Tel.: (31) 164 618 000
Web Site: http://www.fokker.com
Aircraft Maintenance & Repair Services
N.A.I.C.S.: 811310
Erik Geertsema *(VP-Bus Dev & Supply Chain Mgmt)*

Fokker Elmo B.V. (2)
Aviolandalaan 33, 4631 RP, Hoogerheide, Netherlands
Tel.: (31) 164617000
Web Site: http://www.fokker.com
Aircraft Electrical Systems Design & Mfr
N.A.I.C.S.: 238210
Michiel Barendse *(Mng Dir & VP)*

GKN Fokker Aerospace (2)
Anthony Fokkerweg 4, 3351NL, Papendrecht, Netherlands
Tel.: (31) 786419911
Web Site: https://www.gknaerospace.com
Aircraft Components Mfr
N.A.I.C.S.: 336413

Plant (Domestic):

Fokker Aerostructures B.V. - Hoogeveen (3)
Edisonstraat 1, PO Box 59, 7900 AB, Hoogeveen, Netherlands
Tel.: (31) 528285000
Web Site: http://www.fokker.com
Aircraft Components Mfr
N.A.I.C.S.: 336413
Rob Goossens *(Mng Dir-Special Products & VP)*

GKN (United Kingdom) Plc (1)
Ipsley House Ipsley Church Lane, Redditch, B98 0AJ, Worcestershire, United Kingdom
Tel.: (44) 1527 517715
Web Site: http://www.gkn.com.uk
Emp.: 200
Investment Management Service
N.A.I.C.S.: 523999
Nigel M. Stein *(CEO)*

GKN Aerospace - Monitor, Inc. (1)
1000 New Horizons Blvd, Amityville, NY 11701-1138   (100%)
Tel.: (631) 957-2300
Web Site: http://www.monair.com
Sales Range: $125-149.9 Million
Emp.: 400
Titanium & Aluminum Airframe Components & Assemblies Mfr
N.A.I.C.S.: 336413
Kevin Carolan *(Dir-Engrg)*

GKN Aerospace Aerostructures North America (1)
142 JS McDonnell Blvd, Hazelwood, MO 63042   (100%)
Tel.: (314) 264-3000
Web Site: http://www.gkn.com
Aircraft Parts Designer & Mfr
N.A.I.C.S.: 336413

GKN Aerospace Alabama (1)
3951 Alabama Hwy 229 S, Tallassee, AL 36078
Tel.: (334) 283-9200
Sales Range: $250-299.9 Million
Emp.: 950
Complex Metal Alloy Structures & Special Products Including Canopy Systems, Aircraft Transparencies & De-icing System Designer & Mfr

GKN PLC

GKN plc—(Continued)
N.A.I.C.S.: 336413
Jeff Barger (Gen Mgr)

GKN Aerospace Bandy Machining Inc (1)
3420 N San Fernando Blvd, Burbank, CA 91504
Tel.: (818) 846-9020
Web Site: http://www.stellex.com
Aircraft Part Mfr
N.A.I.C.S.: 336413

GKN Aerospace Chem-tronics, Inc. (1)
1150 W Bradley Ave, El Cajon, CA 92020-1504
Tel.: (619) 448-2320
Mfr of Aerospace Components & Provider of Aircraft Repair Services
N.A.I.C.S.: 336412

GKN Aerospace Cincinnati Inc (1)
11230 Deerfield Rd, Cincinnati, OH 45242
Tel.: (513) 489-9800
Web Site: http://www.cincinnati.gknaerospace.com
Emp.: 225
Electro Chemical Machining Products Mfr & Distr
N.A.I.C.S.: 335999
Floyd McConnell (Plant Mgr)

GKN Aerospace Deutschland GmbH (1)
Brunhamstr 21, 81249, Munich, Germany
Tel.: (49) 89 8715 0
Web Site: http://www.gkn-aerospace.com
Aircraft Equipment Whslr
N.A.I.C.S.: 423860

GKN Aerospace Engine Products (1)
11230 Deerfield Rd, Cincinnati, OH 45242-2024
Tel.: (513) 489-9800
Web Site: http://www.gknaerospace.com
Sales Range: $125-149.9 Million
Emp.: 300
Aerospace Technology
N.A.I.C.S.: 336412

GKN Aerospace Muncie Inc (1)
3901 S Delaware Dr, Muncie, IN 47302
Tel.: (765) 747-7147
Aerospace Metal Forging Mfr
N.A.I.C.S.: 333517

GKN Aerospace New England Inc (1)
280 Adams St, Manchester, CT 06040-1900
Tel.: (860) 643-2473
Compressor Blades & Turbine Component Mfr
N.A.I.C.S.: 336413

GKN Aerospace North America Inc (1)
142 J S McDonnell Blvd, Hazelwood, MO 63042
Tel.: (314) 264-3000
Aircraft Part Mfr
N.A.I.C.S.: 336413
Kevin Cummings (CEO)

GKN Aerospace Services Ltd (1)
Ferry Road, East Cowes, PO32 6RA, Isle of Wight, United Kingdom (100%)
Tel.: (44) 1983294101
Web Site: http://www.gknaerospace.com
Sales Range: $200-249.9 Million
Emp.: 650
Mfr & Designer of Aerospace Products
N.A.I.C.S.: 336413

GKN Aerospace Transparency Systems Inc (1)
12122 Western Ave, Garden Grove, CA 92841-2915
Tel.: (714) 893-7531
Aircraft Part Mfr
N.A.I.C.S.: 336413
Clayton Fox (Office Mgr)

GKN America Corp (1)
550 Warrenville Rd 400, Lisle, IL 60532-4308
Tel.: (630) 719-7204
Automobile Parts Mfr

GKN Armstrong Wheels Inc. (1)
5453 6th Ave, Armstrong, IA 50514-7573 (100%)
Tel.: (712) 864-3202
Web Site: http://www.gkn.com
Sales Range: $50-74.9 Million
Emp.: 180
Mfr of Wheels & Hubs for Agricultural, Heavy Industrial & Off-Highway Vehicles.
N.A.I.C.S.: 336390

GKN AutoStructures Ltd. (1)
Hadley Castle Works, PO Box 20, Telford, TF1 6AA, Shropshire, United Kingdom (100%)
Tel.: (44) 1952244321
Sales Range: $400-449.9 Million
Emp.: 500
Mfr of Chassis Components for Motor Vehicles
N.A.I.C.S.: 336340

GKN Ayra Servicio SA (1)
Pol Ind Can Salvatella, Avenida Arrahona 54 56, E 08210, Barbera del Valles, Barcelona, Spain (100%)
Tel.: (34) 937184015
Web Site: http://www.gknservice.com
Sales Range: $25-49.9 Million
Emp.: 20
Mfr & Sale of Automotive Transmission Components
N.A.I.C.S.: 336350

GKN Cedu Limited (1)
Raynesway Park Drive Raynesway, Derby, DE1 7BH, United Kingdom
Tel.: (44) 1332758694
Sales Range: $25-49.9 Million
Emp.: 3
Storage Facility Services
N.A.I.C.S.: 493190

GKN Danyang Industries Company Ltd (1)
Qilin Road 888 Industrial Park Development Zone, Danyang, 212910, Jiangsu, China
Tel.: (86) 511 8688 5178
Powder Metallurgy Component Mfr
N.A.I.C.S.: 332117

GKN Driveline (Thailand) Ltd (1)
Eastern Seaboard Industrial Estate 64/9 Moo 4 Tambon Pluakdaeng, Amphur Pluakdaeng, Rayong, 21140, Thailand
Tel.: (66) 38 954 965
Emp.: 600
Automotive Driveline Component Distr
N.A.I.C.S.: 423120

GKN Driveline Arnage (1)
Rte D Angers, 72230, Arnage, Le Mans, France (98.5%)
Tel.: (33) 243412121
Sales Range: $200-249.9 Million
Emp.: 560
Mfr of Constant Velocity Joints & Driveshafts
N.A.I.C.S.: 336350

GKN Driveline Bowling Green Inc (1)
2223 Woodbridge Blvd, Bowling Green, OH 43402
Tel.: (419) 354-3955
Automotive Driveline Component Mfr
N.A.I.C.S.: 336390

GKN Driveline Bruneck AG (1)
Rienzfeldstrasse 8, 39031, Bruneck, BZ, Italy
Tel.: (39) 0474 580 111
Sales Range: $250-299.9 Million
Emp.: 800
Automotive Driveline Component Whslr
N.A.I.C.S.: 423120

GKN Driveline Celaya Sa de CV (1)
2a Fraccion De Crespo Apartado Postal No 44-A, 38110, Celaya, Guanajuato, Mexico
Tel.: (52) 461 618 5397
Automotive Driveline Component Mfr
N.A.I.C.S.: 336390

GKN Driveline Deutschland GmbH (1)
Carl Legien Strasse 10, Offenbach, 63073, Germany

Tel.: (49) 6989040
Emp.: 2,000
Automotive Driveline Component Mfr
N.A.I.C.S.: 336390

GKN Driveline Firenze SpA (1)
Via Fratelli Cervi 1, I 50013, Campi Bisenzio, Florence, Italy (100%)
Tel.: (39) 05589431
Sales Range: $100-124.9 Million
Emp.: 500
Mfr of Constant Velocity Joints
N.A.I.C.S.: 336350

GKN Driveline International GmbH (1)
Hauptstr 130, Lohmar, 53797, Germany
Tel.: (49) 22461001
Automotive Driveline Component Mfr
N.A.I.C.S.: 336390

GKN Driveline JTEKT Manufacturing Ltd (1)
Eastern Seaboard Industrial Estate 64/9 Moo 4 Tambon Pluakdaeng, Amphur Pluakdaeng, Rayong, 21140, Thailand
Tel.: (66) 38 954 965
Emp.: 800
Automotive Part Whslr
N.A.I.C.S.: 423120

GKN Driveline Japan Ltd (1)
2388 Ohmiya-cho, Tochigi, 328-8502, Japan
Tel.: (81) 282 27 1111
Automotive Part Whslr
N.A.I.C.S.: 423120
Adam Touhig (Pres)

GKN Driveline Kiel (1)
Rendsburger Landstrasse 191, 197, Kiel, 24113, Germany (100%)
Tel.: (49) 43164830
Mfr of Interconnecting Shafts
N.A.I.C.S.: 333613
Kay Stade (Mng Dir)

GKN Driveline Koping AB (1)
Volvogatan 6, Box 961, 731 30, Koping, Sweden
Tel.: (46) 221 762 000
Web Site: http://www.gkn.com
Sales Range: $150-199.9 Million
Emp.: 640
Develops, Manufactures & Sells Wheel Drive Systems & Chassis Components
N.A.I.C.S.: 336390

Branch (Non-US):

GKN Driveline Koping AB (2)
Scarletallee 2, 50735, Cologne, Germany
Tel.: (49) 221 977 611 11
Web Site: http://www.getrag.de
Sales Range: $25-49.9 Million
Emp.: 15
Vehicle Parts Mfr
N.A.I.C.S.: 336390

GKN Driveline Korea Ltd (1)
Foreign Investors Industrial Park 735 Baeksuk-dong, Cheonan, 330-220, Chongnam, Korea (South)
Tel.: (82) 41 620 6600
Sales Range: $50-74.9 Million
Emp.: 10
Automotive Part Whslr
N.A.I.C.S.: 423120
Joo Bong Jung (Gen Mgr)

GKN Driveline Legazpi (1)
Urola 10, Legazpi, 20230, Guipuzcoa, Spain (100%)
Tel.: (34) 943737000
Sales Range: $50-74.9 Million
Emp.: 145
Mfr of Warm & Cold Formed Precision Parts
N.A.I.C.S.: 332721

GKN Driveline Lohmar (1)
Haupt Strasse 130, Lohmar, 53797, Germany (100%)
Tel.: (49) 22461001
Sales Range: $250-299.9 Million
Emp.: 1,000
Holding Company & Management Company
N.A.I.C.S.: 551112

GKN Driveline Ltd. (1)
Unit 5 Kingsbury Business Park Kingsbury Rd, Sutton Coldfield, B76 9DL, West

INTERNATIONAL PUBLIC

Midlands, United Kingdom (100%)
Tel.: (44) 213131661
Sales Range: $25-49.9 Million
Emp.: 75
Distribution of Driveline Components for the Automotive & Agricultural Industries
N.A.I.C.S.: 336330
Ramon Kuczera (Sr VP-Engrg)

Plant (Domestic):

GKN Driveline Birmingham - Erdington Plant (2)
Chester Road, Erdington, B24 0RB, United Kingdom (100%)
Tel.: (44) 1213777000
Sales Range: $100-124.9 Million
Emp.: 500
Mfr of Constant Velocity & Universal Joints & Propeller Shafts
N.A.I.C.S.: 336350

GKN Driveline Newton LLC (1)
1848 GKN Way, Newton, NC 28658
Tel.: (828) 428-3711
Sales Range: $200-249.9 Million
Emp.: 1,600
Vehicle Parts Mfr
N.A.I.C.S.: 336390
Jan Stenner (Gen Mgr)

GKN Driveline North America Inc. (1)
3300 University Dr, Auburn Hills, MI 48326-2362 (100%)
Tel.: (248) 377-1200
Sales Range: $50-74.9 Million
Emp.: 200
Mfr & Marketing of Constant Velocity Products & Viscous Couplings
N.A.I.C.S.: 336350
Igor Skornik (VP-Niche Customer, Motorsport & Aftermarket)

Plant (Domestic):

GKN Automotive, Inc - Alamance Facility (2)
1067 Trollingwood Hawfields Rd, Mebane, NC 27302-9740
Tel.: (248) 377-1200
Mfr of Auto Parts
N.A.I.C.S.: 236115

GKN Driveline Offenbach (1)
Carl Legien Strasse 10, Offenbach, 63073, Germany (98.5%)
Tel.: (49) 6989040
Sales Range: $400-449.9 Million
Emp.: 4,000
Mfr of Constant Velocity Joints
N.A.I.C.S.: 336350

GKN Driveline SA (1)
100 Avenue Vanderbilt, 78955, Carrieres-sous-Poissy, France
Tel.: (33) 139797070
Automotive Driveline Component Mfr
N.A.I.C.S.: 336390
Eric Martineau (Mng Dir)

GKN Driveline Service Ltd (1)
Higher Woodcroft, Leek, ST13 5QF, Staffordshire, United Kingdom
Tel.: (44) 153 838 4278
Web Site: http://www.gknservice.com
Sales Range: $25-49.9 Million
Emp.: 50
Automotive Driveline Component Maintenance Services
N.A.I.C.S.: 811121

GKN Driveline Service Scandinavia AB (1)
Alfred Nobels Alle 110, Tullinge, 146 48, Stockholm, Sweden
Tel.: (46) 86039700
Sales Range: $25-49.9 Million
Emp.: 30
Automobile Parts Mfr
N.A.I.C.S.: 336390
Kristina Berntsson Ljungs (Gen Mgr)

GKN Driveline Singapore Pte Ltd (1)
163 Penang Rd 07 01 02, Winsland House II, Singapore, 238463, Singapore (100%)
Tel.: (65) 67306100
Sales Range: $1-9.9 Million
Emp.: 30
Mfr of Automotive Parts

AND PRIVATE COMPANIES — GKN PLC

N.A.I.C.S.: 336340

GKN Driveline Slovenija d.o.o. (1)
Rudniska Cesta 20, 3214, Zrece, Slovenia
Tel.: (386) 3757 4410
Automotive Driveline Component Mfr
N.A.I.C.S.: 336390

GKN Driveline Torque Technology (Shanghai) Co Ltd (1)
Building 48 No 128 Dieqiao Road Jushuo Plant Kangqiao Industrial Zone, Shanghai, 201319, China
Tel.: (86) 21 6818 7111
Automotive Component Whslr
N.A.I.C.S.: 423140

GKN Driveline Trier (1)
Hafenstrasse 41, Trier, 54293, Germany **(100%)**
Tel.: (49) 65196610
Sales Range: $200-249.9 Million
Emp.: 600
Mfr of Forgings & Pressings for Axle Components
N.A.I.C.S.: 332111

GKN Driveline Uruguay SA (1)
Punta De Rieles 2902 Barrio Punta De Rieles, 12100, Montevideo, Uruguay
Tel.: (598) 2 514 20 51
Web Site: http://www.gkndriveline.com
Automotive Part Whslr
N.A.I.C.S.: 423120

GKN Driveline Vigo (1)
Avenida De Citroen, 36210, Vigo, Spain **(100%)**
Tel.: (34) 986268500
Sales Range: $200-249.9 Million
Emp.: 1,000
Mfr of Constant Velocity Joints
N.A.I.C.S.: 336350

GKN Driveline Villagran Sa de CV (1)
Carretera Panamericana Km 11 Col El Pintor, Villagran, Guanajuato, Mexico
Tel.: (52) 411 160 3150
Automotive Component Whslr
N.A.I.C.S.: 423120

GKN Driveline Walsall Ltd (1)
Middlemore Lane West, Aldridge, Walsall, WS9 8DT, United Kingdom **(100%)**
Tel.: (44) 1922453371
Sales Range: $100-124.9 Million
Emp.: 350
Universal Joints, Propeller & Axle Shafts Mfr
N.A.I.C.S.: 333613

GKN Driveline Zumaia (1)
Sagarbidea 2, 20750, Zumaya, Gepuzkoa, Spain **(100%)**
Tel.: (34) 943899000
Web Site: http://www.gknayra.com
Sales Range: $100-124.9 Million
Emp.: 280
Mfr of Constant Velocity Joints
N.A.I.C.S.: 336350

GKN Driveline polska Sp. z o.o. (1)
Poludniowa 18, 56-400, Olesnica, Poland
Tel.: (48) 71 399 8000
Automotive Driveline Component Mfr
N.A.I.C.S.: 336390

GKN Eskisehir Automotive Products Manufacture and Sales A.S. (1)
Organize Sanayi Bolgesi 20 Cadde No 17, 26110, Eskisehir, Turkiye
Tel.: (90) 222 236 25 05
Automotive Driveline Component Mfr
N.A.I.C.S.: 336390

GKN Florange SARL (1)
Zone Industrielle Sainte Agathe, Rue Carnot, 57190, Florange, France **(100%)**
Tel.: (33) 382593575
Mfr & Assembly of Constant Velocity Joints
N.A.I.C.S.: 336350

GKN Freight Services Ltd., Edgware (1)
Equity House 128-136 High St, Edgware, HA8 7EL, Middlesex, United Kingdom **(100%)**
Tel.: (44) 2082383503
Web Site: http://www.gknfreightservices.com

Sales Range: $25-49.9 Million
Emp.: 45
Freight Forwarding & Management Services
N.A.I.C.S.: 488510

GKN Gelenkwellenwerk Kaiserslautern GmbH (1)
Opelkreisel 1 9, 67663, Kaiserslautern, Germany **(100%)**
Tel.: (49) 63135090
Sales Range: $100-124.9 Million
Emp.: 471
Mfr of Constant Velocity Joints
N.A.I.C.S.: 336350

GKN Geplasmetal SA (1)
Pol Malpica C/ J N 1, 50057, Zaragoza, Spain
Tel.: (34) 902 465 254
Web Site: http://www.geplasmetal.com
Automotive Wheel Mfr
N.A.I.C.S.: 331110

GKN Glenco SA (1)
170 rue Leonard De Vinci, 78955, Poissy, France **(98%)**
Tel.: (33) 130068400
Web Site: http://www.gknservice.com
Sales Range: $50-74.9 Million
Emp.: 60
Automotive Components Sales Company
N.A.I.C.S.: 423120

GKN Holdings Plc (1)
Ipsley House Ipsley Church Lane, Redditch, B98 0TL, United Kingdom
Tel.: (44) 1527 517715
Web Site: http://www.gkn.com
Sales Range: $100-124.9 Million
Emp.: 250
Investment Management Service
N.A.I.C.S.: 523999

GKN Industries Ltd (1)
Ipsley House, Redditch, B98 0AJ, Worcestershire, United Kingdom
Tel.: (44) 1527517715
Automotive Components Mfr
N.A.I.C.S.: 336390

GKN Land Systems Ltd (1)
Ipsley House Ipsley Church Lane, Redditch, B98 0TL, Worcestershire, United Kingdom
Tel.: (44) 1527 517715
Web Site: http://www.gknlandsystems.com
Sales Range: $1-4.9 Billion
Emp.: 600
Automotive Component Mfr & Whslr
N.A.I.C.S.: 336390

GKN North America Services Inc. (1)
3300 University Dr, Auburn Hills, MI 48326-2362 **(100%)**
Tel.: (248) 377-1200
Web Site: http://www.gkplc.com
Sales Range: $25-49.9 Million
Emp.: 12
Administrative & Financial Services
N.A.I.C.S.: 336390

GKN Offhighway Systems Ltd. (1)
Hadley Castle Works, PO Box 85, Telford, TF1 6TE, Shropshire, United Kingdom **(100%)**
Tel.: (44) 1952244321
Sales Range: $200-249.9 Million
Emp.: 300
Mfr & Supply of Agritechnical Components & Parts
N.A.I.C.S.: 336999
Neil Geldard-Williams *(Gen Mgr)*

GKN Ribemont SARL (1)
7 Rue De La Briqueterie, F 02240, Ribemont, France **(98.4%)**
Tel.: (33) 323637429
Sales Range: $25-49.9 Million
Emp.: 92
Mfr of Driveshafts
N.A.I.C.S.: 333613

GKN Rockford, Inc. (1)
1200 Windsor Rd, Loves Park, IL 61111
Tel.: (815) 633-7460
Sales Range: $50-74.9 Million
Emp.: 250
Motor Vehicle Transmissions, Drive Assemblies & Parts Mfr
N.A.I.C.S.: 336390

GKN Sankey Ltd. (1)
, Hadley Castle Works, Telford, TF1 6PF, Salop, United Kingdom **(100%)**
Tel.: (44) 01952244321
Sales Range: $200-249.9 Million
Emp.: 1,000
Mfr of Agricultural Wheel Rims, Tractor Cabs, Car Parts & Telphone Kiosks
N.A.I.C.S.: 333924

GKN Service Austria GmbH (1)
Slamastrasse 32, 1232, Vienna, Austria **(98.5%)**
Tel.: (43) 16163880
Web Site: http://www.gkn.co.at
Sales Range: $25-49.9 Million
Emp.: 45
Automotive Components Sales Company
N.A.I.C.S.: 423120

GKN Service Benelux BV (1)
Haarlemmerstraatweg 155, Halfweg, 1165 MK, North Holland, Netherlands
Tel.: (31) 204070207
Sales Range: $25-49.9 Million
Emp.: 40
Automotive Part Whslr
N.A.I.C.S.: 423120

GKN Service International GmbH (1)
Nussbaumweg 19-21, Rosrath, 51492, Germany **(100%)**
Tel.: (49) 22058060
Web Site: http://www.gknservice.com
Sales Range: $100-124.9 Million
Emp.: 300
Automotive Components Sales Company
N.A.I.C.S.: 336330

GKN Sheepbridge Stokes Ltd. (1)
Sheepbridge Lane, Chesterfield, S41 9QD, United Kingdom **(100%)**
Tel.: (44) 1246260026
Web Site: http://www.gkn.com
Sales Range: $200-249.9 Million
Emp.: 650
Cylinder Linings & Centrifugal Castings Mfr
N.A.I.C.S.: 336340

GKN Sinter Metals Cape Town (Pty) Ltd (1)
Sacks Circle, Bellville South, 7530, Bellville, South Africa
Tel.: (27) 21 9506200
Web Site: http://www.gknsintermetals.com
Sales Range: $50-74.9 Million
Emp.: 110
Stainless Steel Filter Mfr
N.A.I.C.S.: 331210

GKN Sinter Metals Components GmbH (1)
Pennefeldsweg 5-11, Bonn, 53177, Germany
Tel.: (49) 22893350
Metal Component Mfr
N.A.I.C.S.: 332999

GKN Sinter Metals Engineering GmbH (1)
Krebsoge 10, Radevormwald, 42477, Germany
Tel.: (49) 21916930
Web Site: http://www.gkn.com
Engineeering Services
N.A.I.C.S.: 541330

GKN Sinter Metals Filters GmbH (1)
Dahlienstrasse 43, 42477, Radevormwald, Germany
Tel.: (49) 21 95 6 09 0
Web Site: http://www.gkn-filters.de
Sales Range: $25-49.9 Million
Emp.: 150
Metal Filter Mfr
N.A.I.C.S.: 332999

GKN Sinter Metals GmbH Bad Bruckenau (1)
Industriestr 1, Bad Bruckenau, Germany
Tel.: (49) 9741810
Industrial Machinery Whslr
N.A.I.C.S.: 423830

GKN Sinter Metals GmbH Radevormwald Germany (1)
Krebsoge 10, Radevormwald, 42477, Germany
Tel.: (49) 21916930
Metal Products Mfr

N.A.I.C.S.: 332999

GKN Sinter Metals Holdings Ltd (1)
Ipsley House Ipsley Church La, Redditch, B98 0AJ, Worcestershire, United Kingdom
Tel.: (44) 1527 517715
Web Site: http://www.gkn.com
Emp.: 250
Investment Management Service
N.A.I.C.S.: 523999

GKN Sinter Metals Ltd. (1)
PO Box 9211, Nottingham, NG10 9BD, United Kingdom **(100%)**
Tel.: (44) 1543403000
Web Site: http://www.gkn.com
Mfr of Heat-Treated Metal Components
N.A.I.C.S.: 332811

Subsidiary (US):

GKN Sinter Metals (2)
112 Harding St, Worcester, MA 01604-5020
Tel.: (508) 792-6400
Sales Range: $100-124.9 Million
Emp.: 350
Powder Metallurgy Mfr, Structurals & Bearings Including Secondary Machining
N.A.I.C.S.: 332117

Division (US):

GKN Sinter Metals Inc. (2)
3300 University Dr, Auburn Hills, MI 48326-2362 **(100%)**
Tel.: (248) 371-0800
Web Site: http://www.gknsintermetals.com
Sales Range: $25-49.9 Million
Emp.: 60
Mfr of Powder Metal Parts for the Automotive & Industrial Marketplace
N.A.I.C.S.: 336390

GKN Sinter Metals Ltda (1)
Da Emancipacao 4 500, Hortolandia, 13186-542, Sao Paulo, Brazil
Tel.: (55) 1921189400
Web Site: http://www.gknsintermetals.com
Sales Range: $150-199.9 Million
Emp.: 300
Metal Powder Precision Component Distr
N.A.I.C.S.: 423510

GKN Sinter Metals Private Ltd (1)
C - 18 Midc Area, Ahmednagar, 414111, Maharashtra, India
Tel.: (91) 2412777981
Metal Products Mfr
N.A.I.C.S.: 332999

GKN Sinter Metals SpA (1)
Via Delle Fabbriche 5, Brunico, 39031, Italy
Tel.: (39) 0474570211
Steel Products Mfr
N.A.I.C.S.: 331110

GKN Sinter Metals St Thomas Ltd (1)
7 Michigan Blvd, Saint Thomas, N5P 1H1, ON, Canada
Tel.: (519) 631-4880
Sales Range: $50-74.9 Million
Emp.: 150
Powder Metal Component Mfr
N.A.I.C.S.: 333517

GKN Thompson Chassis Ltd (1)
Chester Rd, PO Box 4128, Erdington, Birmingham, B24 0AW, United Kingdom **(100%)**
Tel.: (44) 213777000
Mfr of Automotive Chassis
N.A.I.C.S.: 551112

GKN Viscodrive GmbH (1)
Hauptstrasse 130, 53797, Lohmar, Germany **(100%)**
Tel.: (49) 22461001
Sales Range: $75-99.9 Million
Emp.: 240
Mfr & Sales of Automotive Transmission Components
N.A.I.C.S.: 336340

GKN Walterscheid Getriebe GmbH (1)
Alte Bautzener Strasse 1-3, 02689, Sohland, Germany
Tel.: (49) 35936 3660
Emp.: 250
Agricultural Machinery Whslr

GKN PLC

GKN plc—(Continued)
N.A.I.C.S.: 423820
Robert Berge (Plant Mgr)

GKN Waltersscheid AS (1)
Verpetveien 34, N 1540, Vestby, Norway (98.5%)
Tel.: (47) 64981100
Web Site: http://www.gkn.no
Sales Range: $25-49.9 Million
Emp.: 20
Automotive Components Sales Company
N.A.I.C.S.: 423120

GKN Westland Aerospace Inc (1)
3951 Al Hwy 229 S, Tallassee, AL 36078-4733
Tel.: (334) 283-9200
Web Site: http://www.gknaerospace.com
Aircraft Part Mfr
N.A.I.C.S.: 336413

GKN Wheels (Liuzhou) Company Ltd (1)
7 Liu Tai Rd, Liuzhou, 545007, Guangxi, China
Tel.: (86) 772 3915 378
Automotive Wheel Mfr
N.A.I.C.S.: 326211
Phil Bailey (Gen Mgr)

GKN Wheels Nagbol A/S (1)
Nagbolvej 31, 6640, Lundersksov, Denmark
Tel.: (45) 79845100
Web Site: http://www.gkn.com
Sales Range: $100-124.9 Million
Emp.: 300
Automobile Parts Mfr
N.A.I.C.S.: 336390

GKN Wheels, Ltd. (1)
PO Box 85, Telford, TF1 6TG, United Kingdom (100%)
Tel.: (44) 952244321
Web Site: http://www.gkmlandsystems.com
Sales Range: $100-124.9 Million
Emp.: 300
Mfr of Agricultural Vehicle & Off-Highway Wheels
N.A.I.C.S.: 336340

GKN do Brasil Ltda. (1)
Joaquim Silveira 557 Jardim Lindoia, 04532 082, Porto Alegre, Brazil (100%)
Tel.: (55) 5133499500
Web Site: http://www.gkn.com
Sales Range: $50-74.9 Million
Emp.: 1,600
Holding Company
N.A.I.C.S.: 551112

Glaenzer-Seurre NV/SA (1)
Avenue Paul Gilsonlaan 441, B-1620, Drogenbos, Belgium
Tel.: (32) 23711811
Automotive Components Sales Company
N.A.I.C.S.: 423120

Hoeganaes Corp. (1)
1001 Taylors Ln, Cinnaminson, NJ 08077-2017 (100%)
Tel.: (856) 829-2220
Web Site: http://www.hoeganaes.com
Sales Range: $25-49.9 Million
Emp.: 80
Supplier of Ferrous Powdered Metals
N.A.I.C.S.: 331221

Hoeganaes Corporation Europe GmbH (1)
Peterstr 69, Huckeswagen, 42499, Germany
Tel.: (49) 219285360
Metal Products Mfr
N.A.I.C.S.: 332999

Spicer Gelenkwellenbau GmbH & Co. KG (1)
Westendhof 5 9, D 45143, Essen, Germany (100%)
Tel.: (49) 20181240
Web Site: http://www.gwb-essen.de
Sales Range: $200-249.9 Million
Emp.: 600
Mfr of Universal Joints & Propeller Shafts
N.A.I.C.S.: 333613

Taiway Industry Co., Ltd. (1)
No 14 Kwang Fu Rd, Hukou, 303, Hsianchu, Taiwan

Tel.: (886) 35983601
Web Site: http://www.roc-spicer.com.tw
Automotive Front-wheel Drive Shaft, Hub Bearings & Other Precision Mechanical Parts & Components Mfr
N.A.I.C.S.: 336390

Unidrive Pty. Ltd. (1)
45 49 McNaughton Rd, Clayton, 3168, VIC, Australia
Tel.: (61) 395424100
Sales Range: $100-124.9 Million
Emp.: 120
Automotive Transmission Product Mfr; Owned 60% by GKN plc & 40% by NTN Corporation
N.A.I.C.S.: 336350

Volvo Aero Corporation (1)
PO Box 46181, SE-461 81, Trollhattan, Sweden (100%)
Tel.: (46) 52094000
Web Site: http://www.gknaerospace.com
Sales Range: $400-449.9 Million
Emp.: 2,300
Development, Design, Production & Sale of Jet Engines & Engine Components for Military & Commercial Aircraft & Space Projects; Hydraulic Machinery, Transmission Systems & Heaters
N.A.I.C.S.: 336412

Subsidiary (Domestic):

Applied Composites AB (2)
13 Bopksatin, Linkoping, 580 13, Sweden (100%)
Tel.: (46) 13209700
Web Site: http://www.acab.se
Sales Range: $10-24.9 Million
Emp.: 120
Industrial & Military Advanced Composite Components Mfr
N.A.I.C.S.: 326130

Subsidiary (Non-US):

Volve Car Norway A.S. (2)
PO Box 601, 1411, Kolbotn, Norway (100%)
Tel.: (47) 66 81 8604
Web Site: http://www.volvo.com
Sales Range: $100-124.9 Million
Emp.: 450
Automobile Mfr
N.A.I.C.S.: 336110
Oystein Herland (Pres)

Subsidiary (Domestic):

Volvo Aero Engine Services AB (2)
Kzarnbackszagen 13, PO Box 218, 168 74, Bromma, Sweden (100%)
Tel.: (46) 87992100
Web Site: http://www.volvoaero.com
Sales Range: $100-124.9 Million
Emp.: 500
N.A.I.C.S.: 336412

Volvo Aero Engine Services Arboga AB (2)
Tundasvagen 60, 732 82, Arboga, Sweden
Tel.: (46) 58985000
Aircraft Engine & Parts Manufacturing
N.A.I.C.S.: 336412

Subsidiary (Non-US):

Volvo Aero Turbines (UK) Ltd. (2)
PO Box 422, Coventry, CV3 4YX, United Kingdom
Tel.: (44) 24 76 382951
N.A.I.C.S.: 336412

GKW LIMITED
1st Floor 97 Andul Road, Howrah, 711 103, West Bengal, India
Tel.: (91) 3326685247
Web Site: https://www.gkwltd.com
GKWLIMITED—(NSE)
Rev.: $2,480,703
Assets: $336,080,667
Liabilities: $71,488,916
Net Worth: $264,591,751
Earnings: $1,051,963
Emp.: 15
Fiscal Year-end: 03/31/23
Engineeering Services

N.A.I.C.S.: 541330
J. D. Curravala (Mng Dir)

Subsidiaries:

GKW (Overseas Trading) Limited (1)
Wakefield House Ballard Estate Fort, Mumbai, 400 001, Maharastra, India
Tel.: (91) 22 22650171
Metal Product Distr
N.A.I.C.S.: 423510

GKW Limited - Powmex Steels Division (1)
Turla, PB No 9, Titilagarh, 767 033, India
Tel.: (91) 6655 220503
Emp.: 50
Steel Products Mfr
N.A.I.C.S.: 331110
Jean-Marie Sevar (Deputy Gen Mgr)

GL GMBH METALL- UND WERKSTATTTECHNIK
Nurtinger Strasse 23 25, D-72636, Frickenhausen, Germany
Tel.: (49) 7022943220
Web Site: https://www.gl-gmbh.de
Precision Metal Part Mfr
N.A.I.C.S.: 332721

GL PHARM TECH CORP
210 Building B Seongnam Global Convergence Center 46 Dalraenaero, Sujeong-gu, Seongnam, Korea (South)
Tel.: (82) 316025220
Year Founded: 2014
204840—(KRS)
Rev.: $12,830,762
Assets: $31,335,262
Liabilities: $18,993,856
Net Worth: $12,341,405
Earnings: ($606,058)
Emp.: 28
Fiscal Year-end: 12/31/22
Financial Investment Management Services
N.A.I.C.S.: 523940

GL SCIENCES INC.
Shinjuku Square Tower 30F 6-22-1 Nishi Shinjuku, Shinjuku-ku, Tokyo, 163-1130, Japan
Tel.: (81) 353236633
Web Site: https://www.glsciences.com
Year Founded: 1968
7705—(TKS)
Rev.: $320,591,920
Assets: $415,998,000
Liabilities: $110,797,280
Net Worth: $305,200,720
Earnings: $27,055,600
Emp.: 436
Fiscal Year-end: 03/31/22
Analysis Equipment Mfr & Whslr
N.A.I.C.S.: 334516
Shoichi Ryo (Mng Dir)

Subsidiaries:

Flom Inc. (1)
5-32-10 Shinmachi, Ome, 198-0024, Tokyo, Japan
Tel.: (81) 42 830 7454
Web Site: https://www.flom.co.jp
Analytical Device Mfr
N.A.I.C.S.: 334516

GL Sciences (Shanghai) Limited (1)
Room 2003 Block B Far East International Plaza No 317 Xianxia Road, Changning District, Shanghai, China
Tel.: (86) 216 278 2272
Web Site: https://www.glsciences.com.cn
Emp.: 430
Medical Equipment Distr
N.A.I.C.S.: 423450

GL Sciences B.V. (1)
Dillenburgstraat 7C, 5652 AM, Eindhoven, Netherlands
Tel.: (31) 40 254 9531

INTERNATIONAL PUBLIC

Web Site: https://www.glsciences.eu
Analytical Laboratory Instrument Mfr
N.A.I.C.S.: 334516

Techno Quartz Inc. (1)
1322 Honmachi, Nakano-ku, Tokyo, 164-0012, Japan
Tel.: (81) 353548171
Web Site: https://www.techno-q.com
Rev.: $153,137,600
Assets: $177,240,800
Liabilities: $43,860,080
Net Worth: $133,380,720
Earnings: $21,296,000
Fiscal Year-end: 03/31/2022
Quartz Component Mfr & Distr
N.A.I.C.S.: 334419

GL TECH CO., LTD.
No 10 Changchun Road, High-tech industrial Development Zone, Zhengzhou, 450001, Henan, China
Tel.: (86) 37167858887
Web Site: https://www.gltech.cn
300480—(CHIN)
Rev.: $93,078,596
Assets: $293,879,440
Liabilities: $88,097,407
Net Worth: $205,782,033
Earnings: $9,752,116
Fiscal Year-end: 12/31/23
Coal Mine Safety Monitoring Equipment Mfr
N.A.I.C.S.: 333131

Subsidiaries:

Loadpoint Bearings Limited (1)
Unit B 6 Nimrod Way, Stirling Business Park East Dorset Trade Park, Wimborne, BH21 7SH, United Kingdom
Tel.: (44) 1202894447
Web Site: https://www.loadpoint-bearings.co.uk
Machine Tool Mfr & Distr
N.A.I.C.S.: 333517

Loadpoint Limited (1)
Chelworth Industrial Estate Cricklade, Swindon, SN6 6HE, Wilts, United Kingdom
Tel.: (44) 1793751160
Web Site: http://www.loadpoint.co.uk
Hand Tool Mfr
N.A.I.C.S.: 332216

GL&V PULP & PAPER
3100 Rue Westinghouse, Trois Rivieres, G9A 5E1, QC, Canada
Tel.: (819) 371-8282
Web Site: http://www.glvpulppaper.com
Emp.: 100
Pulp & Paper Production Equipment Designer, Mfr & Marketer
N.A.I.C.S.: 333243

Subsidiaries:

GL&V India Pvt. Ltd. (1)
GL&V House Plot No 2C No 162/4A-5A Off DP Road, Aundh, Pune, 411007, India
Tel.: (91) 2025800000
Emp.: 4
Pulp & Paper Equipment Mfr
N.A.I.C.S.: 423830

GL&V Sweden AB - Stockholm (1)
Liljeholmsstranden 3, Stockholm, 11743, Sweden
Tel.: (46) 852244400
Pulp & Paper Equipment Mfr
N.A.I.C.S.: 423830

Unit (Non-US):

GL&V Russia (2)
9 Lva Toistogo Street, Saint Petersburg, 197022, Russia
Tel.: (/) 8126358850
Emp.: 5
Pulp & Paper Equipment Mfr
N.A.I.C.S.: 322130
Svetlana G. Vinogradova (Reg Mgr)

GL&V Sweden AB - Tampere (2)
Yliopistonkatu 60 A, Tampere, 3310, Finland
Tel.: (358) 102878700

AND PRIVATE COMPANIES

Pulp & Paper Equipment Mfr
N.A.I.C.S.: 423830
Janne Hautala (Bus Mgr)

GL&V USA Inc. - Lenox (1)
175 Crystal St, Lenox, MA 01240
Tel.: (413) 637-2424
Pulp & Paper Production Equipment Mfr
N.A.I.C.S.: 333243
Kevin Kuliga (Gen Mgr)

Unit (Domestic):

GL&V USA Inc. - Hudson Falls (2)
27 Allen St, Hudson Falls, NY 12839-1901
Tel.: (518) 747-2444
Sales Range: $25-49.9 Million
Pulp & Paper Production Equipment Mfr
N.A.I.C.S.: 333243
Becky Monahan (Gen Mgr)

GL&V USA Inc. - Nashua (2)
1 Cellu Dr Ste 200, Nashua, NH 03063-1008
Tel.: (603) 882-2711
Pulp & Paper Production Equipment Mfr
N.A.I.C.S.: 333243

GLACIER LAKE RESOURCES, INC.
Suite 1588 - 609 Grandville Street, Vancouver, V7Y 1G5, BC, Canada
Tel.: (604) 688-2922 BC
Web Site: http://www.glacierlake.ca
Year Founded: 2008
KDM—(DEU)
Assets: $319,699
Liabilities: $88,003
Net Worth: $231,696
Earnings: ($537,157)
Fiscal Year-end: 03/31/23
Metal Mining Services
N.A.I.C.S.: 212290
Satvir Dhillon (CEO)

GLACIER MEDIA INC.
2188 Yukon Street, Vancouver, V5Y 3P1, BC, Canada
Tel.: (604) 872-8565 Ca
Web Site:
  https://www.glaciermedia.ca
Year Founded: 2000
GVC—(TSX)
Rev.: $141,408,700
Assets: $207,490,235
Liabilities: $55,766,865
Net Worth: $151,723,370
Earnings: $28,558,757
Emp.: 160
Fiscal Year-end: 12/31/19
Newspaper, Trade Publications, Directories, Electronic & Online Publisher
N.A.I.C.S.: 513110
Sam Grippo (Chm)

Subsidiaries:

Alaska Highway News (1)
9916-98th Street, Fort Saint John, V1J 3T8, BC, Canada
Tel.: (250) 785-5631
Web Site:
  https://www.alaskahighwaynews.ca
Sales Range: $25-49.9 Million
Emp.: 15
Newspapers
N.A.I.C.S.: 513110

Alberta Newspaper Group Inc. (1)
3257 Dunmore Rd SE, Medicine Hat, T1B 3R2, AB, Canada (59%)
Tel.: (403) 527-1101
Web Site:
  https://www.medicinehatnews.com
Sales Range: $50-74.9 Million
Emp.: 100
Holding Company; Newspaper Publisher
N.A.I.C.S.: 551112

Unit (Domestic):

Medicine Hat News (2)
3257 Dunmore Road S E, Medicine Hat, T1B 3R2, AB, Canada

Tel.: (403) 527-1101
Web Site: https://medicinehatnews.com
Sales Range: $10-24.9 Million
Emp.: 100
Newspaper Publishing
N.A.I.C.S.: 513110
Tom Peterson (Dir-Mfg)

Nanaimo Daily News (1)
777 Poplar Street, Nanaimo, V9S 2H7, BC, Canada
Tel.: (250) 753-3707
Web Site: http://www.nanaimobulletin.com
Sales Range: $25-49.9 Million
Emp.: 60
Newspaper Publishers
N.A.I.C.S.: 513110
Cale Cowan (Mng Editor)

North Shore News (1)
Unit 116-980 West First St, North Vancouver, V7P 3N4, BC, Canada
Tel.: (604) 986-1337
Web Site: http://www.nsnews.com
Sales Range: $25-49.9 Million
Emp.: 65
Newspaper Publishers
N.A.I.C.S.: 513110
Vicki Magnison (Dir-Sls & Mktg)

Northern Miner (1)
225 Duncan Mill Road Suite 320, Toronto, M3B 3K9, ON, Canada
Tel.: (416) 510-6789
Web Site: https://www.northernminer.com
Sales Range: $25-49.9 Million
Emp.: 5
Distr Newspapers
N.A.I.C.S.: 513110
John Cumming (Editor-in-Chief)

The Kamloops Daily News (1)
393 Seymour St, Kamloops, V2C 6P6, BC, Canada
Tel.: (250) 372-2331
Web Site: http://www.kamloopsnews.ca
Sales Range: $25-49.9 Million
Emp.: 80
Newspaper Publishing
N.A.I.C.S.: 513110

The Northerner (1)
9916 98 Street, Fort Saint John, V1J 3T8, BC, Canada
Tel.: (250) 785-2890
Web Site: http://www.thenortherner.ca
Sales Range: $25-49.9 Million
Emp.: 5
Newspapers
N.A.I.C.S.: 513110

The Prince George Citizen (1)
505 4th Avenue, Prince George, V2L 3H2, BC, Canada
Tel.: (250) 562-2441
Web Site:
  https://www.princegeorgecitizen.com
Sales Range: $25-49.9 Million
Emp.: 100
Newspaper Publishing
N.A.I.C.S.: 513110
Neil Godbout (Editor-in-Chief)

Times Colonist (1)
201-655 Tyee Road, Victoria, V9A 6X5, BC, Canada
Tel.: (250) 380-5211
Web Site: https://www.timescolonist.com
Newspaper Publishers
N.A.I.C.S.: 513110
Catherine McConnell (Dir-Fin)

GLADEDALE HOLDINGS PLC
Regency House Crossgates Road, Dunfermline, KY11 7EG, Fife, United Kingdom
Tel.: (44) 1383745555
Web Site: http://www.gladedale.com
Sales Range: $250-299.9 Million
Emp.: 1,500
Residential Building Services
N.A.I.C.S.: 236117
Neil Fitzsimmons (CEO)

Subsidiaries:

Ben Bailey Ltd. (1)
Elizabeth House Cliff Street, Mexborough, S64 9HQ, S Yorkshire, United Kingdom

Tel.: (44) 1709586261
Web Site: http://www.ben-baileyhomes.com
Sales Range: $150-199.9 Million
Emp.: 334
Real Estate Services
N.A.I.C.S.: 531390

GLADIATOR RESOURCES LIMITED
Suite 1 Level 11 1 Castlereagh St, Sydney, 2200, NSW, Australia
Tel.: (61) 283979888 AU
Web Site:
  https://gladiatorresources.net
GLA—(ASX)
Rev.: $20,625
Assets: $3,384,623
Liabilities: $83,582
Net Worth: $3,301,040
Earnings: ($1,587,945)
Emp.: 3
Fiscal Year-end: 06/30/24
Minerals Exploration
N.A.I.C.S.: 213115
Ian Hastings (Bd of Dirs & Chm)

GLADSTONE PACIFIC NICKEL LIMITED
Level 2 380 Queen St, Brisbane, 4000, QLD, Australia
Tel.: (61) 732317100
Web Site:
  http://www.gladstonepacific.com.au
Sales Range: $1-9.9 Million
Nickel Mining Services
N.A.I.C.S.: 212230
Blair Brewster (CEO)

GLADSTONE PLC
Hithercroft Road, Wallingford, OX10 9BT, Oxfordshire, United Kingdom
Tel.: (44) 1491201010 UK
Web Site:
  http://www.gladstonesoftware.co.uk
Sales Range: $10-24.9 Million
Emp.: 122
Electronic Member Relationship Management Services
N.A.I.C.S.: 541519
Said Ziai (Chm)

Subsidiaries:

Gladstone MRM Limited (1)
Gladstone House Hithercroft Road, Wallingford, OX10 9BT, Oxon, United Kingdom
Tel.: (44) 1491201010
Web Site: http://www.gladstonemrm.com
Emp.: 100
Electronic Member Relationship Management Services
N.A.I.C.S.: 541519

Division (Non-US):

Gladstone MRM Australia Pty Ltd (2)
Suite 904 Level 9 275 Alfred Street North, Sydney, 2060, NSW, Australia
Tel.: (61) 289203028
Web Site: http://www.gladstoneplc.com
Electronic Member Relationship Management Services
N.A.I.C.S.: 541519

GLADSTONE PORTS CORPORATION LIMITED
40 Goondoon Street, PO Box 259, Gladstone, 4680, QLD, Australia
Tel.: (61) 7 4976 1333 AU
Web Site: http://www.gpcl.com.au
Year Founded: 1914
Rev.: $334,779,836
Assets: $1,745,568,548
Liabilities: $965,582,240
Net Worth: $779,986,308
Earnings: $43,041,987
Emp.: 719
Fiscal Year-end: 06/30/19
Cost Management Services

GLANBIA CO-OPERATIVE SOCIETY LIMITED

N.A.I.C.S.: 488310
Peter Corones (Chm)

GLAMOUR TEXTILE MILLS LIMITED
11 km Manga Raiwind Road, Raiwind, Lahore, Pakistan
Tel.: (92) 42 35392794 PK
Web Site:
  http://www.glamourtextiles.com
Year Founded: 1991
Sales Range: $10-24.9 Million
Emp.: 651
Cotton Yarn Mfr
N.A.I.C.S.: 313110
Azher Elahi (CEO)

GLANBIA CO-OPERATIVE SOCIETY LIMITED
Glanbia House, Kilkenny, Ireland
Tel.: (353) 567772200
Web Site: http://www.glanbia.ie
Sales Range: $900-999.9 Million
Emp.: 4,000
Holding Company
N.A.I.C.S.: 551112
Michael O'Neill (CEO-Glanbia Milk)

Subsidiaries:

Glanbia Plc (1)
Glanbia House Ring Road, Kilkenny, Ireland
Tel.: (353) 567772200
Web Site: https://www.glanbia.com
Rev.: $5,154,800,456
Assets: $4,455,563,424
Liabilities: $2,318,057,352
Net Worth: $2,137,506,072
Earnings: $205,607,376
Emp.: 8,071
Fiscal Year-end: 01/01/2022
Dairy Products & Food Ingredients Mfr
N.A.I.C.S.: 311511
Brian Phelan (CEO-Glanbia Nutritionals)

Subsidiary (US):

Aseptic Solutions USA Ventures, LLC (2)
484 Alcoa Cir, Corona, CA 92880
Tel.: (951) 736-9230
Web Site: http://www.asepticusa.com
Beverages Mfr
N.A.I.C.S.: 312120
Robert Danko (General Counsel & VP)

Bio-Engineered Supplements & Nutrition, Inc. (2)
5901 Broken Sound Pkwy, Boca Raton, FL 33487
Tel.: (561) 994-8335
Web Site: http://www.bsnonline.net
Sales Range: $50-74.9 Million
Emp.: 130
Nutritional Supplements Mfr
N.A.I.C.S.: 325412

Flavor Producers, LLC (2)
28350 W Witherspoon Pkwy, Valencia, CA 91355
Tel.: (661) 257-3400
Web Site: https://www.flavorproducers.com
Mobile Food Services
N.A.I.C.S.: 722330
Janet Guzman (VP-Sls & Mktg)

Plant (Domestic):

Glanbia - Ballyragget Factory (2)
Ballyragget Factory, Ballyragget Co, Kilkenny, Ireland
Tel.: (353) 568836000
Web Site: http://www.glanbia.com
Sales Range: $75-99.9 Million
Emp.: 300
Milk Product Mfr
N.A.I.C.S.: 311514
Owen Maher (Controller-Fin)

Division (Domestic):

Glanbia Agribusiness (2)
Glanbia House, Kilkenny, R95 E866, Ireland (100%)
Tel.: (353) 567772288
Web Site: http://www.glanbia.com

2987

GLANBIA CO-OPERATIVE SOCIETY LIMITED

Glanbia Co-Operative Society Limited—(Continued)
Sales Range: $125-149.9 Million
Emp.: 400
Feed Milling; Fertilizer, Feed & Grain Marketer; Fertilizer Producer; Veterinary Whlsr; Malting & Port Services
N.A.I.C.S.: 321918
Collin Eustace (CEO)

Joint Venture (Domestic):

Co-Operative Animal Health Limited (3)
Indust Est, R93 W0D8, Tullow, Carlow, Ireland
Tel.: (353) 599151251
Web Site: http://www.cahl.ie
Sales Range: $25-49.9 Million
Emp.: 100
Animal Health Products Whlsr; Owned 50% by Glanbia plc & 50% by Dairygold Co-op Society Limited
N.A.I.C.S.: 311119
Donald O'Sullivan (Mng Dir)

Subsidiary (Non-US):

Glanbia Cheese (2)
Brunel Court Rudheath Way, Northwich, CW9 7LP, Cheshire, United Kingdom (100%)
Tel.: (44) 1606 810900
Web Site: http://www.galnbia.com
Emp.: 150
Cheese Processing & Administrative Offices
N.A.I.C.S.: 561110

Division (Domestic):

Glanbia Consumer Foods Limited (2)
3008 Lake Dr Citywest Bus Campus, Dublin, 24, Ireland (100%)
Tel.: (353) 14881000
Web Site: http://www.glanbia.ie
Sales Range: $25-49.9 Million
Emp.: 60
Dairy & Beverage Products Mfr & Distr
N.A.I.C.S.: 112120
Michael Spillane (Mgr-HR)

Subsidiary (Domestic):

Glanbia Consumer Foods Ltd. - Ireland (3)
3008 Lake Drive City West, Citywest Business Count, Dublin, 24, Ireland
Tel.: (353) 14881000
Web Site: http://www.glanbia.ie
Sales Range: $25-49.9 Million
Food Products Mfr
N.A.I.C.S.: 311423
Colin Gordon (Mng Dir)

Division (Domestic):

Glanbia Food Ingredients (2)
Valley Rocket, Kilkenny, Ireland (100%)
Tel.: (353) 567772200
Web Site: http://www.glanbia.com
Sales Range: $250-299.9 Million
Emp.: 1,150
Milk, Cheese, Whey Protein Ingredients, Formulated Milk Powders (Including Infantformulas), Casein, Skim Milk Powder & Lactose Processor
N.A.I.C.S.: 112120
Jim Bergin (CEO-Ingredients)

Subsidiary (US):

Glanbia Foods Inc. (3)
1373 Fillmore St, Twin Falls, ID 83301 (100%)
Tel.: (208) 733-7555
Web Site: http://www.glanbiausa.com
Sales Range: $100-124.9 Million
Emp.: 500
Cheese & Whey Products Mfr
N.A.I.C.S.: 311513

Subsidiary (Domestic):

Glanbia Ingredients Ireland (3)
Ballyragget, Kilkenny, Ireland (100%)
Tel.: (353) 568836000
Web Site: http://www.glanbia.ie
Sales Range: $75-99.9 Million
Emp.: 400

Milk, Cheese & Whey Protein Ingredients Processer & Marketer
N.A.I.C.S.: 112120
Jim Bergin (CEO-Food Ingredients-Ireland)

Subsidiary (Non-US):

Glanbia Foods B.V. (2)
Krijtenbogtstraat 2 A, Moergestel, 5066 BJ, Netherlands
Tel.: (31) 135133757
Holding Company
N.A.I.C.S.: 551112

Subsidiary (US):

Glanbia Ingredients, Inc (2)
523 6th St, Monroe, WI 53566
Tel.: (608) 329-2800
Dairy Products Distr
N.A.I.C.S.: 424490

Subsidiary (Domestic):

Glanbia Investments (Ireland) Limited (2)
Glanbia House, Kilkenny, Ireland
Tel.: (353) 567772200
Sales Range: $25-49.9 Million
Emp.: 70
Investment Holding
N.A.I.C.S.: 551112
Siobhan Talboc (Gen Mgr)

Glanbia Nutritionals (Europe) Limited (2)
Main St, Dungarvan, Ireland
Tel.: (353) 5844444
Dairy Products Mfr
N.A.I.C.S.: 311514

Glanbia Nutritionals (Ireland) Limited (2)
Glanbia Innovation Centre Carlow Rd, Kilkenny, Ireland
Tel.: (353) 56 77 96000
Dairy Products Mfr
N.A.I.C.S.: 311514

Subsidiary (US):

Glanbia Nutritionals (NA), Inc. (2)
5500 Nobel Dr Ste 250, Fitchburg, WI 53711
Tel.: (608) 316-8500
Dairy Products Distr
N.A.I.C.S.: 424490

Subsidiary (Domestic):

Watson LLC (3)
301 Heffernan Dr, West Haven, CT 06516
Tel.: (203) 932-3000
Web Site: http://www.watson-inc.com
Food Ingredients & Related Products Mfr
N.A.I.C.S.: 311999
James Watson (Pres)

Subsidiary (Non-US):

Glanbia Nutritionals (Suzhou) Company Limited (2)
128 Fangzhong Street Suzhou Industrial Park, 215025, Suzhou, China
Tel.: (86) 512 8718 6700
Web Site: http://www.glanbia.com
Dairy Products Distr
N.A.I.C.S.: 424490
Joachin Sieber (Dir-Ops)

Glanbia Nutritionals (UK) Limited (2)
Unit 3 Romaldkirk Rd Riverside Park, Middlesbrough, TS2 1XA, United Kingdom
Tel.: (44) 1642 248866
Dairy Products Distr
N.A.I.C.S.: 424490

Glanbia Nutritionals Deutschland GmbH (2)
Gewerbestrasse 3, 78359, Berlin, Germany
Tel.: (49) 7774 9397 0
Dairy Products Distr
N.A.I.C.S.: 424490

Glanbia Nutritionals Singapore Pte Limited (2)
700 Beach Road, Singapore, Singapore
Tel.: (65) 6222 0118
Dairy Products Distr
N.A.I.C.S.: 424490
Gwend Chan (Office Mgr)

Subsidiary (US):

Slim-Fast Foods Company (2)
800 Sylvan Ave, Englewood Cliffs, NJ 07632
Tel.: (201) 567-8000
Web Site: http://www.slimfast.com
Sales Range: $25-49.9 Million
Weight Loss Products Mfr & Retailer
N.A.I.C.S.: 311999
Darren Hopkins (VP-Mktg)

Affiliate (Domestic):

South Eastern Cattle Breeding Society Limited (2)
, Dovea Thurles, Tipperary, Ireland (57%)
Tel.: (353) 50421755
Web Site: http://www.dovea.ie
Sales Range: $10-24.9 Million
Emp.: 40
Cattle Breeding
N.A.I.C.S.: 112990
Ger Ryan (Mng Dir)

GLANCE FINANCE LIMITED
7 Kitab Mahal 192 Dr Dn Road Fort, Mumbai, 400 001, India
Tel.: (91) 2240100193
Web Site: https://www.glancefinance.com
Year Founded: 1994
531199.—(BOM)
Rev.: $556,151
Assets: $3,366,620
Liabilities: $610,011
Net Worth: $2,756,609
Earnings: $173,068
Emp.: 5
Fiscal Year-end: 03/31/21
Financial Advisory Services
N.A.I.C.S.: 523940
Narendra Karnavat (Chm)

GLANTUS LTD.
Estuary House Block P7 Eastpoint Business Park, Clontraf, Dublin, D03 Y6A2, Ireland
Tel.: (353) 8895300
Web Site: http://www.glantus.com
Data Aanalytics Solutions Services
N.A.I.C.S.: 519290
Maurice Healy (Founder & CEO)

GLARNER KANTONALBANK
Hauptstrasse 21, 8750, Glarus, Switzerland
Tel.: (41) 844773773
Web Site: https://www.glkb.ch
Year Founded: 1884
GLKBN—(SWX)
Sales Range: Less than $1 Million
Banking Services
N.A.I.C.S.: 522110
Sven Wiederkehr (Chm-Mgmt Bd & CEO)

GLARUN TECHNOLOGY CO., LTD.
Building No 1 Glarun Building No 359 Jiangdong Middle Road, Jianye District, Nanjing, 210019, Jiangsu, China
Tel.: (86) 2552787053
Web Site: http://www.glaruntech.com
Year Founded: 1994
600562.—(SHG)
Rev.: $452,776,845
Assets: $1,149,495,656
Liabilities: $430,195,091
Net Worth: $719,300,565
Earnings: $77,115,332
Fiscal Year-end: 12/31/22
Communication Equipment Mfr & Distr
N.A.I.C.S.: 334220
Mingchun Hu (Chm)

GLAS PODRINJA A.D.
Kneza Lazara 1, Sabac, Serbia

Tel.: (381) 15 353 276
Web Site: http://www.glaspodrinja.rs
Year Founded: 1993
GLPD—(BEL)
Sales Range: Less than $1 Million
Emp.: 17
Newspaper Publishing Services
N.A.I.C.S.: 513110
Dragan Mirkovic (CEO)

GLAS SRPSKI-TRGOVINA A.D.
Brace Pisteljic 1, 78000, Banja Luka, Bosnia & Herzegovina
Tel.: (387) 51342900
Web Site: https://www.glasrpske.com
Year Founded: 2003
GLST-R-A—(BANJ)
Sales Range: Less than $1 Million
Food Product Retailer
N.A.I.C.S.: 445298
Marigold Kopanja (Pres)

GLAS TROSCH HOLDING AG
Industriestrasse 29, 4922, Butzberg, Switzerland
Tel.: (41) 629585251 CH
Web Site: http://www.glastroesch.ch
Year Founded: 1981
Emp.: 6,000
Provider of Glass Fabrication Services
N.A.I.C.S.: 238150

Subsidiaries:

Europtec GmbH (1)
Alte Heerstrasse 14, Goslar, 38644, Germany (100%)
Tel.: (49) 53213590
Web Site: http://www.europtec.com
Sales Range: $50-74.9 Million
Emp.: 200
Mfr of Glass Products
N.A.I.C.S.: 333310
Dieter Wagner (Gen Mgr-Goslar)

Glas Trosch AG Hy-Tech-Glass (1)
Industrie Strasse 12, Butzberg, 4922, Switzerland (100%)
Tel.: (41) 629585400
Web Site: http://www.luxar.com
Sales Range: $25-49.9 Million
Emp.: 35
Mfr of Glass Coatings
N.A.I.C.S.: 325510

GLASBAU HAHN GMBH
Hanauer Landstrasse 211, 60314, Frankfurt am Main, Germany
Tel.: (49) 69944170
Web Site: http://www.glasbau-hahn.com
Year Founded: 1829
Sales Range: $25-49.9 Million
Emp.: 85
Glass Contracting Services
N.A.I.C.S.: 238150
Isabel Hahn (Mgr-Sls-Area)

Subsidiaries:

GLASBAU HAHN America LLC (1)
15 Little Brook Ln, Newburgh, NY 12550
Tel.: (845) 566-3331
Glass Distr
N.A.I.C.S.: 423390

GLASBAU Japan Co. Ltd. (1)
Muratec Bldg 6F Higashi-Kujo-Muromachi 64-4, Minami-ku, Kyoto, 601-8001, Japan
Tel.: (81) 757486050
Web Site: http://www.glasbau-hahn.jp
Glass Distr
N.A.I.C.S.: 423390

GLASER ISB CAD PROGRAMMSYSTEME GMBH
Am Waldwinkel 21, 30974, Wennigsen, Germany
Tel.: (49) 510558920 De
Web Site: http://www.isbcad.de

Year Founded: 1978
Emp.: 20
Software Development Services
N.A.I.C.S.: 541511
Matthias Glaser *(Mng Partner)*

GLASGOW PRESTWICK AIRPORT LIMITED
Aviation House, Prestwick, KA9 2PL, United Kingdom
Tel.: (44) 871 223 0700
Web Site:
http://www.glasgowprestwick.com
Year Founded: 1934
Sales Range: $125-149.9 Million
Emp.: 350
Airport Operator
N.A.I.C.S.: 488119
Andrew Miller *(Chm)*

GLASMEYER & CO. KG
Friesenweg 4 Haus 20, 22763, Hamburg, Germany
Tel.: (49) 4089726910
Web Site: http://www.glasco.de
Year Founded: 1961
Sales Range: $10-24.9 Million
Emp.: 50
Supermarket Retailer
N.A.I.C.S.: 445110
Olaf Glasmeyer *(Partner-Personally Liable)*

GLASS ONE TECHNOLOGY CORPORATION
3rd Floor Palace Building 1-1-1 Marunouchi, Chiyoda-ku, Tokyo, 100-0005, Japan
Tel.: (81) 3 6256 0991
Web Site: http://www.glass-one.jp
Year Founded: 2013
Emp.: 30
Touch Panel Mfr
N.A.I.C.S.: 334419
Takahiko Furuhashi *(Pres)*

Subsidiaries:

Glass One Technology Taiwan Corporation (1)
9th Floor No 552 Sec 5 Zhongxiao East Road, Xinyi District, Taipei, 110, Taiwan
Tel.: (886) 2 2269 7347
Touch Panel Mfr
N.A.I.C.S.: 334419

Yutaka Electric Manufacturing Company Ltd. (1)
7-25-5 Nishi-Gotanda, Shinagawa-ku, Tokyo, 141-0031, Japan
Tel.: (81) 3 5436 2771
Web Site: http://www.yutakadenki.jp
Sales Range: $50-74.9 Million
Emp.: 178
Electronic Components Mfr
N.A.I.C.S.: 334419
Fumiaki Inuzuka *(Pres)*

GLASSBOX LTD.
25 Bazel Street, Petah Tikva, 4951038, Israel
Tel.: (972) 747022321
Web Site: https://www.glassbox.com
Year Founded: 2010
GLBX—(TAE)
Rev.: $48,623,000
Assets: $57,961,000
Liabilities: $34,927,000
Net Worth: $23,034,000
Earnings: $16,583,000
Emp.: 241
Fiscal Year-end: 12/31/23
Computer Programming Services
N.A.I.C.S.: 541511
Hanan Blumstein *(Gen Mgr)*

Subsidiaries:

Glassbox US Inc. (1)
42 Broadway Ste 12-530, New York, NY 10004
Tel.: (646) 397-5283
Software Development Services
N.A.I.C.S.: 541511

Sessioncam Ltd. (1)
St Vedast House, Norwich, NR1 1BT, United Kingdom
Tel.: (44) 1603618382
Web Site: http://www.glassbox.com
Digital Analytic Services
N.A.I.C.S.: 541511

GLASSFORD MOTORS LIMITED
30 Samnah Cres, Ingersoll, N5C3J7, ON, Canada
Tel.: (519) 485-0940
Web Site:
http://www.glassfordmotors.com
Year Founded: 1966
Rev.: $13,650,357
Emp.: 30
New & Used Car Dealers
N.A.I.C.S.: 441110
J. M. Glassford *(Pres)*

GLASSWELLS LTD
Newmarket Road, Bury Saint Edmunds, IP33 3TU, Suffolk, United Kingdom
Tel.: (44) 1284752804
Web Site:
http://www.glasswells.co.uk
Year Founded: 1946
Sales Range: $25-49.9 Million
Emp.: 258
Furniture Whslr
N.A.I.C.S.: 423210
Kevin Robertson *(Dir-Sls)*

GLASTON OYJ ABP
Lonnrotinkatu 11, FI 00120, Helsinki, Finland
Tel.: (358) 10500500 FI
Web Site: https://www.glaston.net
GLA1V—(HEL)
Rev.: $230,433,844
Assets: $210,330,240
Liabilities: $136,472,048
Net Worth: $73,858,191
Earnings: $3,335,852
Emp.: 783
Fiscal Year-end: 12/31/22
Safety Glass Machinery Designer, Mfr & Marketer
N.A.I.C.S.: 333310
Teuvo Salminen *(Chm)*

Subsidiaries:

Bystronic Maschinen AG (1)
Industriestrasse 5, 4922, Butzberg, Switzerland (100%)
Tel.: (41) 629587777
Web Site: http://www.bystronic-glass.com
Sales Range: $25-49.9 Million
Emp.: 220
Machine Tool (Metal Cutting Types) Mfr
N.A.I.C.S.: 333517
Richard Jacob *(CEO)*

Glaston America Inc (1)
6000 Commerce Pkwy Ste D, Mount Laurel, NJ 08054
Tel.: (336) 299-8300
Web Site: http://www.glaston.net
Sales Range: $25-49.9 Million
Emp.: 45
Glass Products Mfr
N.A.I.C.S.: 327215

Glaston Emerging Technologies Oy (1)
Vehmaistenkatu 5, PO Box 25, 33731, Tampere, Finland
Tel.: (358) 1 050 0500
Industrial Machinery Mfr
N.A.I.C.S.: 333248

Glaston Estonia Ou (1)
Endla 4, 10142, Tallinn, Estonia
Tel.: (372) 6263110
Sales Range: $25-49.9 Million
Emp.: 10
Commercial & Service Industry Machinery Mfr
N.A.I.C.S.: 333310

Glaston Finland Oy (1)
Vehmaistenkatu 5, PO Box 25, 33731, Tampere, Finland (100%)
Tel.: (358) 10500500
Web Site: http://www.glaston.net
Sales Range: $100-124.9 Million
Emp.: 300
Commercial & Service Industry Machinery Mfr
N.A.I.C.S.: 333310

Glaston France S.A.S.U. (1)
62 Avenue des Freres Montgolfier, 69740, Genas, France
Tel.: (33) 478902667
Web Site: http://www.glaston.net
Sales Range: $25-49.9 Million
Emp.: 20
Commercial & Service Industry Machinery Mfr
N.A.I.C.S.: 333310

Glaston Germany GmbH (1)
Hermannstr 15, 90439, Nuremberg, Germany (100%)
Tel.: (49) 911615005
Web Site: http://www.glaston.net
Sales Range: $25-49.9 Million
Emp.: 8
Commercial & Service Industry Machinery Mfr
N.A.I.C.S.: 333310

Glaston Management (Shanghai) Co. Ltd (1)
Central Towers 1502-1504 Tower B 567 Lan Gao Road Putuo, Pudong, 200120, Shanghai, China
Tel.: (86) 2158409778
Sales Range: $25-49.9 Million
Emp.: 15
Glass Products Mfr
N.A.I.C.S.: 327215

Glaston Mexico, S.A. de C.V. (1)
Calle 30 Num 2646 Zona Industrial, Guadalajara, Jalisco, Mexico
Tel.: (52) 33 3145 00 47
Web Site: http://www.glaston.net
Sales Range: $25-49.9 Million
Emp.: 10
Glass Processing Machinery Mfr
N.A.I.C.S.: 333248
Matteo Gherseni *(Gen Mgr)*

Glaston Middle East (1)
18G Gold Tower Jumeirah Lakes Towers, PO Box 625784, Dubai, United Arab Emirates
Tel.: (971) 43698033
Web Site: http://www.glaston.net
Sales Range: $25-49.9 Million
Emp.: 6
Commercial & Service Industry Machinery Mfr
N.A.I.C.S.: 333310

Glaston North America (USA), Inc (1)
6000 Commerce Pkwy Ste D, Mount Laurel, NJ 08054
Tel.: (336) 299-8300
Web Site: http://www.glaston.net
Sales Range: $25-49.9 Million
Emp.: 50
Commercial & Service Industry Machinery Mfr
N.A.I.C.S.: 333310

Glaston SPAIN S.L. (1)
Avenue Meridiana, 350 12 C, 08027, Barcelona, Spain
Tel.: (34) 93 274 49 90
Glass Processing Machinery Mfr
N.A.I.C.S.: 333248

Glaston Services Ltd. Oy (1)
Vehmaistenkatu 5, PO Box 25, 33731, Tampere, Finland (100%)
Tel.: (358) 10500500
Sales Range: $100-124.9 Million
Emp.: 300
Commercial & Service Industry Machinery Mfr
N.A.I.C.S.: 333310
Arto Metsanen *(Mng Dir)*

Glaston Shanghai Co., Ltd. (1)
Central Towers 1502-1504 Tower B 567 Lan Gao Road, Putuo, Shanghai, 200333, China
Tel.: (86) 21 5840 9778
Web Site: http://www.glaston.net
Glass Products Mfr
N.A.I.C.S.: 327215

Glaston Singapore Pte. Ltd. (1)
2 Leng Kee Road, 03-05 Thye Hong Centre, Singapore, 159086, Singapore
Tel.: (65) 62990842
Sales Range: $25-49.9 Million
Emp.: 12
Commercial & Service Industry Machinery Mfr
N.A.I.C.S.: 333310

Glaston South America Ltda. (1)
Travessa Claudio Armando n 171 complex 24, Assuncao Sao Bernardo do Campo, Sao Paulo, 09861-730, Brazil
Tel.: (55) 1140616511
Web Site: http://www.glaston.net
Commercial & Service Industry Machinery Mfr
N.A.I.C.S.: 333310

Glaston Switzerland AG (1)
Industriestrasse 5, 4922, Butzberg, Switzerland
Tel.: (41) 629587777
Information Technology Services
N.A.I.C.S.: 541511

Glaston Swizerland AG (1)
Industriestrasse 5, 4922, Butzberg, Switzerland
Tel.: (41) 62 958 7777
Industrial Machinery Mfr
N.A.I.C.S.: 333248

Glaston Tianjin Co. Ltd. (1)
11 Huifeng Road, Wuqing Development Area, Tianjin, 301700, China
Tel.: (86) 2282191100
Glass Products Mfr
N.A.I.C.S.: 327215

Glaston UK Ltd. (1)
7 Swanwick Court, Alfreton, DE55 7AS, Derbyshire, United Kingdom
Tel.: (44) 1952677971
Web Site: http://glaston.net
Sales Range: $25-49.9 Million
Emp.: 12
Commercial & Service Industry Machinery Mfr
N.A.I.C.S.: 333310

LLC Glaston (1)
Suschevskiy Val str 3/5 Floor 8 Of I, 127018, Moscow, Russia
Tel.: (7) 495 6457172
Sales Range: $25-49.9 Million
Emp.: 15
Glass Processing Machinery Distr
N.A.I.C.S.: 423830

Z. Bavelloni South America Ltda (1)
Avenida Dona Ruyce Ferraz Alvim 3036 Jardim Ruyce, Diadema, 09961-540, Brazil
Tel.: (55) 11 4061 6511
Web Site: http://www.glaston.net
Glass Products Mfr
N.A.I.C.S.: 327215

GLASWEGIAN ENTERPRISES LTD
1200 Lougheed Hwy, Coquitlam, V3K 6S4, BC, Canada
Tel.: (604) 522-4000
Year Founded: 1980
Rev.: $12,986,470
Emp.: 50
Electronic Stores & Services
N.A.I.C.S.: 449210
Jim Orr *(Owner)*

GLAUSER INTERNATIONAL MM
24 rue Barbes, 92120, Montrouge, France
Tel.: (33) 1 40 847939

GLAUSER INTERNATIONAL MM

Glauser International MM—(Continued)

Web Site: http://www.glauser.fr
Rev.: $23,600,000
Emp.: 100
Craftsmen & Subcontractor Projects
N.A.I.C.S.: 238140
Marc Meunier *(CEO)*

GLEAM FABMAT LIMITED
Plot No 5504/15 Basti Harphool singh Sadar Thana Road, New Delhi, 110006, India
Tel.: (91) 1123539696
Web Site: http://www.gfl.org.in
Year Founded: 2018
Textile Products Distr
N.A.I.C.S.: 424310
Amit Gupta *(Mng Dir)*

GLEN EAGLE RESOURCES INC.
2075 Victoria Street Suite 201, Saint-Lambert, J4S 1H1, QC, Canada
Tel.: (514) 808-9807
Web Site:
  https://gleneagleresources.ca
GERFF—(OTCEM)
Rev.: $655,013
Assets: $3,482,087
Liabilities: $2,815,133
Net Worth: $666,954
Earnings: ($612,176)
Fiscal Year-end: 12/31/22
Mining Exploration Services
N.A.I.C.S.: 213114
Jean Labrecque *(Pres & CEO)*

GLENCOE RESOURCES LTD.
801 6th Ave SW Suite 1100, Calgary, T2P 3W2, AB, Canada
Tel.: (403) 233-8560
Sales Range: $75-99.9 Million
Drilling & Oil & Gas Extraction Services
N.A.I.C.S.: 211120
Glenn Brant *(Founder)*

GLENCORE PLC
Baarermattstrasse 3, CH 6340, Baar, Switzerland
Tel.: (41) 417092000   JE
Web Site: https://www.glencore.com
Year Founded: 2011
GLEN—(LSE)
Rev.: $217,829,000,000
Assets: $123,869,000,000
Liabilities: $85,632,000,000
Net Worth: $38,237,000,000
Earnings: $3,210,000,000
Emp.: 83,426
Fiscal Year-end: 12/31/23
Holding Company; Commodity & Raw Material Supply, Trading & Logistics Services
N.A.I.C.S.: 551112
Steven Kalmin *(CFO)*

Subsidiaries:

Astron Energy   (1)
5 Century Blvd Century 30, Cape Town, 7441, South Africa   **(75%)**
Tel.: (27) 214037911
Gasoline, Motor Oils, Lubricants & Other Petroleum Products Mfr & Distr
N.A.I.C.S.: 324110

Canadian Electrolytic Zinc Limited   (1)
860 Boul Gerard-Cadieux, Salaberry-de-Valleyfield, J6T 6L4, QC, Canada
Tel.: (450) 373-9144
Web Site: https://www.cezinc.com
Mining Services
N.A.I.C.S.: 212311

Chemoil Energy Limited   (1)
4 E Sheridan Ave Ste 400, Oklahoma City, OK 73104
Tel.: (405) 605-5436
Web Site: https://www.chemoil.com
Marine Fuel Generate Services
N.A.I.C.S.: 221112

El Pachon S.A.   (1)
Av Ignacio de la Roza 125 East 4th floor, 5400, San Juan, Argentina
Tel.: (54) 2644309300
Web Site: https://www.elpachon.com.ar
Mining Services
N.A.I.C.S.: 212311

Glencore Australia Holdings Pty Ltd   (1)
Level 44 Gateway 1 Macquarie Place, Sydney, 2000, NSW, Australia
Tel.: (61) 282476300
Web Site: https://www.glencore.com.au
Zinc Alloy Mfr
N.A.I.C.S.: 331491

Glencore International AG   (1)
Baarermattstrasse 3, CH-6340, Baar, Switzerland
Tel.: (41) 417092000
Web Site: https://www.glencore.com
Emp.: 800
Oil & Gas Exploration Services
N.A.I.C.S.: 551112

Subsidiary (Non-US):

AR ZINC S.A.   (2)
Maitu 812 1st Floor Office F, Buenos Aires, C1006ACL, Argentina
Tel.: (54) 11 4320 4100
Web Site: http://www.aguilar-arzinc.com
Zinc & Lead Mining Services & Distr
N.A.I.C.S.: 212230

African Fine Carbon (Pty) Limited   (2)
22 Goedehoop Farm, Witbank, 1055, Mpumalanga, South Africa
Tel.: (27) 132825799
Charcoal Mfr
N.A.I.C.S.: 325998

Asturiana de Zinc S.A.   (2)
Plaza Pablo Ruiz Picasso 1 2 planta Torre Picasso, 28020, Madrid, Spain   **(100%)**
Tel.: (34) 91 334 4200
Web Site: https://www.azsa.es
Sales Range: $50-74.9 Million
Emp.: 25
Zinc Smelting & Refining
N.A.I.C.S.: 331410

Britannia Refined Metals Limited   (2)
Botany Road Northfleet, Gravesend, DA11 9BG, Kent, United Kingdom
Tel.: (44) 01474538200
Web Site: http://www.xstrata.com
Sales Range: $125-149.9 Million
Emp.: 345
Metal Refining Services
N.A.I.C.S.: 423510

Char Technology (Pty) Limited   (2)
50 Van Eck Road, Witbank, 1035, Mpumalanga, South Africa
Tel.: (27) 136968000
Charcoal Mfr
N.A.I.C.S.: 325998

Affiliate (US):

Chemlube International, Inc.   (2)
500 Mamaroneck Ave, Harrison, NY 10528   **(50%)**
Tel.: (914) 381-5800
Web Site: https://www.chemlube.com
Chemicals & Lubricants Whslr
N.A.I.C.S.: 424690
Robert Nobel *(Pres)*

Subsidiary (Non-US):

Chemoil Energy Pte Limited   (2)
1 Temasek Avenue 34-01 Millenia Tower, Singapore, 039192, Singapore **(100%)**
Tel.: (65) 6880 8200
Web Site: http://www.chemoil.com
Sales Range: $10-24.9 Million
Marine Fuel Mfr
N.A.I.C.S.: 324110
Mark Jonathan Catton *(Chm)*

Compania Minera Antapaccay S.A.   (2)
Tel.: (51) 84301150
Copper Mining
N.A.I.C.S.: 212230

Cook Resources Mining Pty Ltd   (2)
Arduard Rd, Blackwater, 4717, QLD, Australia
Tel.: (61) 7 4986 1600
Coal Mining Services
N.A.I.C.S.: 213113

Correcta Industria e Comercio Ltdo.   (2)
Av Miguel Frias e Vasconcelos 852, Jaguare, Sao Paulo, 05345-000, Brazil
Tel.: (55) 113 718 6400
Web Site: https://www.correcta.ind.br
Wheat Flour Milling Services
N.A.I.C.S.: 311211

Enex Oakbridge Pty Ltd   (2)
Level 38 1 Macquarie Place, Sydney, 2000, NSW, Australia
Tel.: (61) 2 9253 6700
Web Site: http://www.glencore.com
Coal Mining Services
N.A.I.C.S.: 213113

Falconbridge Dominicana S.A.   (2)
Loma Peguera, PO Box 025522, Bonao, Monsenor Nouel, Dominican Republic   **(85.3%)**
Tel.: (809) 6826041
Web Site: https://www.falcondo.do
Sales Range: $700-749.9 Million
Emp.: 200
Nickel Mining
N.A.I.C.S.: 212230
David Soares *(Pres)*

Subsidiary (Domestic):

Glencore (Schweiz) AG   (2)
Baremattstrasse 3, 6341, Baar, Switzerland
Tel.: (41) 417092000
Web Site: http://www.glencore.com
Holding Company
N.A.I.C.S.: 551112

Subsidiary (Non-US):

Glencore Canada Corporation   (2)
100 King Street West Suite 6900, Toronto, M5X 1E3, ON, Canada
Tel.: (416) 775-1500
Web Site: https://www.glencore.ca
Metal Recycling Whslr
N.A.I.C.S.: 423930

Subsidiary (Domestic):

Glencore Canada Financial Corp.   (3)
100 King St W Suite 6900, Toronto, M5X 1E3, ON, Canada
Tel.: (416) 775-1500
Financial Services
N.A.I.C.S.: 523999

Subsidiary (US):

Glencore Recycling Inc.   (3)
1695 Monterey Hwy, San Jose, CA 95112
Tel.: (408) 998-4930
Web Site: http://www.glencorerecycling.com
Metal Recycling Services
N.A.I.C.S.: 562920

Plant (Domestic):

Glencore Recycling LLC   (3)
80 Commercial Way, East Providence, RI 02914
Tel.: (401) 438-9220
Web Site: http://www.glencorerecycling.com
Metal Recycling Services
N.A.I.C.S.: 562920

Subsidiary (Non-US):

Glencore Coal Pty. Ltd.   (2)
Level 38 Gateway 1 Macquarie Place, Sydney, 2000, NSW, Australia   **(100%)**
Tel.: (61) 2 9253 6700
Web Site: http://www.glencorecoal.com.au
Coal Mining
N.A.I.C.S.: 212115

Subsidiary (Domestic):

Glencore Coal Queensland Pty. Limited   (3)

INTERNATIONAL PUBLIC

Level 9 Riverside Centre 123 Eagle Street, Brisbane, 4000, QLD, Australia
Tel.: (61) 7 3115 5300
Coal Mining
N.A.I.C.S.: 212115
Reinhold Schmidt *(Gen Mgr)*

Subsidiary (Non-US):

Mangoola Coal Operations Pty. Limited   (3)
Tel.: (61) 265495500
Web Site:
  http://www.xstratamangoola.com.au
Coal Mining
N.A.I.C.S.: 212115

Oakbridge Pty Limited   (3)
Tel.: (61) 249256400
Emp.: 150
Coal Mining Services
N.A.I.C.S.: 213113

Subsidiary (Domestic):

Ravensworth Operations Pty Limited   (3)
Level 44 1 Macquarie Place, Ravensworth, Sydney, 2000, NSW, Australia
Tel.: (61) 265700700
Sales Range: $75-99.9 Million
Emp.: 700
Coal Mining Services
N.A.I.C.S.: 213113

United Collieries Pty Limited   (3)
134 Jerry s Plains Road, Warkworth, 2330, NSW, Australia
Tel.: (61) 2 65 789 500
Web Site: http://www.unitedcollieries.com.au
Sales Range: $50-74.9 Million
Emp.: 10
Coal Mining Services
N.A.I.C.S.: 213113
Mike Carrucan *(Dir-Bus Dev & Project)*

Subsidiary (Non-US):

Glencore Grain Pty. Ltd.   (2)
Level 8 484 St Kilda Road, Melbourne, 3004, VIC, Australia
Tel.: (61) 3 9864 2000
Web Site: http://www.glencoregrain.com.au
Emp.: 60
Grain Wholesale Trade Agency
N.A.I.C.S.: 425120
Jason Rees *(Dir-Fin-Australia & New Zealand)*

Subsidiary (Non-US):

Glencore Grain B.V.   (3)
Blaak 31, 3011 GA, Rotterdam, Netherlands
Tel.: (31) 104 12 96 35
Grain Wholesale Trade Agency
N.A.I.C.S.: 425120
David Mattiske *(Reg Dir-Europe)*

Viterra Inc.   (2)
2625 Victoria Avenue, Regina, S4T 7T9, SK, Canada
Tel.: (306) 569-4411
Web Site: https://www.viterra.ca
Sales Range: $5-14.9 Billion
Emp.: 5,108
Holding Company; Grain & Agricultural Products Processor, Marketer & Distr
N.A.I.C.S.: 551112
Kyle Jeworski *(Pres & CEO-North America)*

Subsidiary (Non-US):

Viterra Ltd.   (4)
Level 1 186 Greenhill Rd, Parkside, 5063, SA, Australia
Tel.: (61) 882117199
Sales Range: $1-4.9 Billion
Emp.: 1,100
Grain Storage, Handling, Distribution, Marketing & Malting Services
N.A.I.C.S.: 311213

Subsidiary (Non-US):

Glencore Group Funding Limited   (2)
Unit 09 Level 2 Gate Village Building 1, PO Box 49321, Dubai International Financial Centre, Dubai, United Arab Emirates
Tel.: (971) 44231741
Financial Management Services
N.A.I.C.S.: 523999

AND PRIVATE COMPANIES

Unit (Non-US):

Glencore Nickel - Sudbury (2)
6 Lindsley Street, Sudbury, P0M 1S0, ON, Canada
Tel.: (705) 693-2761
Nickel Mining & Smelting
N.A.I.C.S.: 212230

Subsidiary (Non-US):

Glencore Nikkelverk AS (2)
Vesterveien 31, 4606, Kristiansand, Norway
Tel.: (47) 38101010
Web Site: https://www.nikkelverk.no
Sales Range: $125-149.9 Million
Emp.: 517
Nickel Refining, Smelting & Sales
N.A.I.C.S.: 331410

Glencore Queensland Limited (2)
Tel.: (61) 731155300
Sales Range: $1-4.9 Billion
Emp.: 5,875
Holding Company; Copper Mining
N.A.I.C.S.: 551112

Subsidiary (Non-US):

Xstrata Copper Chile S.A. (3)
Mariano Sanchez Fontecilla 310 Piso 4, Las Condes, Santiago, Chile
Tel.: (56) 2 478 2200
Emp.: 830
Copper Mining
N.A.I.C.S.: 212230

Joint Venture (Domestic):

Compania Minera Dona Ines de Collahuasi SCM (4)
Andres Bello 2687 Piso 11, Las Condes, Santiago, Chile (44%)
Tel.: (56) 223626500
Web Site: https://www.collahuasi.cl
Sales Range: $300-349.9 Million
Copper Mining
N.A.I.C.S.: 212230
Fernando Hernandez *(VP-HR)*

Subsidiary (Non-US):

Glencore Services UK Limited (2)
50 Berkeley Street, London, W1J 8HD, United Kingdom
Tel.: (44) 2074 123 296
Emp.: 20
Business Support Services
N.A.I.C.S.: 561499

Glencore Technology Pty. Ltd. (2)
Level 10 160 Ann St, Brisbane, 4000, QLD, Australia
Tel.: (61) 73 833 8500
Web Site:
   https://www.glencoretechnology.com
Sales Range: $25-49.9 Million
Emp.: 80
Engineeering Services
N.A.I.C.S.: 541330

Kazzinc Ltd. (2)
1 Promyshlennaya Str Building 2, East Kazakhstan Region, 070002, Ust'-Kamenogorsk, Kazakhstan
Tel.: (7) 7232291001
Web Site: https://www.kazzinc.com
Zinc, Copper & Lead Mining Services
N.A.I.C.S.: 212220
Zhanat Zhanbotin *(CEO)*

Subsidiary (Domestic):

Altyntau Kokshetau JSC
Building 1 Konysbay Village Industrial Area, Zerendy District, Kokshetau, 021216, Akmola, Kazakhstan
Tel.: (7) 716 259 5528
Rev.: $806,094,000
Assets: $820,656,000
Liabilities: $98,454,000
Net Worth: $722,202,000
Earnings: ($433,028,000)
Fiscal Year-end: 12/31/2020
Gold Ore Mining Services
N.A.I.C.S.: 212220
Igor Kogay *(Gen Dir)*

Subsidiary (Non-US):

McArthur River Mining Pty. Ltd. (2)
Level 44 1 Macquarie Place, Sydney, 2000, NSW, Australia
Tel.: (61) 889758179
Web Site:
   http://www.mcarthurrivermine.com.au
Emp.: 1,250
Zinc Mining
N.A.I.C.S.: 212230

Minara Resources Limited (2)
Level 3 30 The Esplanade, Perth, 6000, WA, Australia
Tel.: (61) 89 212 8400
Web Site: https://www.minara.com.au
Sales Range: $450-499.9 Million
Emp.: 737
Producer of Nickel & Cobalt
N.A.I.C.S.: 212230

Subsidiary (Domestic):

Minara Resources Holdings Pty Ltd (3)
Level 4 30 The Esplanade, Perth, 6000, WA, Australia (100%)
Tel.: (61) 892128400
Web Site: http://www.minara.com.au
Sales Range: $250-299.9 Million
Emp.: 700
Holding Company
N.A.I.C.S.: 551112

Murrin Murrin Investments Pty Ltd (3)
Level 4 30 The Esplanade, 6000, Perth, WA, Australia
Tel.: (61) 892128400
Sales Range: $350-399.9 Million
Emp.: 700
Uranium-Radium-Vanadium Ore Mining
N.A.I.C.S.: 212290
Peter Johnston *(Mng Dir)*

Subsidiary (Non-US):

Murrin Murrin Operations Pty Ltd (3)
(100%)
Tel.: (61) 892128400
Web Site: http://www.minara.com.au
Sales Range: $150-199.9 Million
Emp.: 700
Nonferrous Rolling & Drawing
N.A.I.C.S.: 331491

Affiliate (Non-US):

Minera Alumbrera Limited (2)
AV Belgrano 485 1st floor of 3, C1092AAE, Buenos Aires, Argentina (50%)
Tel.: (54) 114 853 8300
Web Site: https://www.alumbrera.com.ar
Sales Range: $50-74.9 Million
Emp.: 10
Copper Mining Services
N.A.I.C.S.: 212230

Subsidiary (Non-US):

Mount Isa Mines Limited (2)
Level 44 1 Macquarie Place, Private Mail Bag 6, Sydney, 2000, NSW, Australia
Tel.: (61) 747442011
Web Site:
   http://www.mountisamines.com.au
Emp.: 4,450
Copper & Zinc Mining Services
N.A.I.C.S.: 212230

Subsidiary (US):

NorFalco Inc. (2)
6000 Lombardo Ctr The Genesis Bldg Ste 650, Seven Hills, OH 44131
Tel.: (216) 642-7342
Web Site: http://www.myh2so4.norfalco.com
Sales Range: $25-49.9 Million
Emp.: 29
Sulphuric Acid Marketing Services
N.A.I.C.S.: 424690

Subsidiary (Non-US):

NorFalco Sales Inc. (3)
6755 Mississauga Road Suite 304, Mississauga, L5N 7Y2, ON, Canada
Tel.: (905) 542-6901
Web Site: http://www.xstratazinc.ca
Sales Range: $25-49.9 Million
Emp.: 19
Sulphuric Acid Sales
N.A.I.C.S.: 424690

Affiliate (Non-US):

Noranda Inc. (2)
1400 Norman St, Lachine, H8S 1A8, QC, Canada (25%)
Tel.: (514) 637-3591
Sales Range: $100-124.9 Million
Emp.: 400
Non-Ferrous Metals Smelting
N.A.I.C.S.: 331410

Subsidiary (Non-US):

Nordenhamer Zinkhutte GmbH (2)
Johannastrasse 1, 26954, Nordenham, Germany
Tel.: (49) 47313682
Web Site: https://www.nordenhamer-zinkhuette.de
Emp.: 400
Zinc Smelting & Refining
N.A.I.C.S.: 331410
Thomas Huser *(Mng Dir)*

Prodeco Group (2)
Tel.: (57) 6053855599
Web Site: https://www.grupoprodeco.com.co
Coal Mining Services
N.A.I.C.S.: 213113

Zaklady Tluszozowe w Bodaczowie Sp.z.o.o. (2)
Ul Cypriana Kamila Norwida 2, 80-280, Gdansk, Poland
Tel.: (48) 84 682 20 90
Web Site: http://www.ztb.pl
Food Products Mfr
N.A.I.C.S.: 311919

Kamoto Copper Company SA (1)
Usines de Luilu, Commune de Dilala, Kolwezi, Lualaba, Congo, Democratic Republic of
Tel.: (243) 991001909
Web Site:
   https://www.kamotocoppercompany.com
Copper Mining Services
N.A.I.C.S.: 212230

Katanga Mining Limited (1)
Obmoos 4, 6301, Zug, Switzerland (100%)
Tel.: (41) 417667110
Web Site: https://www.katangamining.com
Rev.: $1,265,094,000
Assets: $6,110,794,000
Liabilities: $7,347,398,000
Net Worth: ($1,236,604,000)
Earnings: ($806,211,000)
Emp.: 4,457
Fiscal Year-end: 12/31/2018
Copper & Cobalt Mining Services
N.A.I.C.S.: 212230

Mt Owen Pty Limited (1)
Upper Hunter Valley, PO Box 320, Singleton, 2330, NSW, Australia
Tel.: (61) 265702600
Emp.: 800
Metal Products Mfr
N.A.I.C.S.: 331420

Oaky Creek Coal Joint Venture (2)
Oaky Creek Mine Access Road, Lilyvale, Sydney, 4723, QLD, Australia
Tel.: (61) 749847200
Emp.: 838
Coal Mining Services
N.A.I.C.S.: 213113

Pasar Group (1)
Leyte Industrial Development Estate, Isabel, 6539, Leyte, Philippines
Tel.: (63) 535251000
Web Site: https://www.pasar.com.ph
Precious Metal Mfr
N.A.I.C.S.: 331492

Philippine Associated Smelting & Refining Corporation (1)
11th Floor Zuellig Building Paseo de Roxas corner Makati Avenue, Makati, 1227, Metro Manila, Philippines
Tel.: (63) 28 845 6000
Web Site: https://www.pasar.com.ph
Nonferrous Metal Extraction Services
N.A.I.C.S.: 213114
Javier Herrero *(Chm)*

PolyMet Mining Corp. (1)
444 Cedar St Ste 2060, Saint Paul, MN 55101 (82.18%)

GLENMARK PHARMACEUTICALS LIMITED

Tel.: (651) 389-4100
Web Site: https://www.polymetmining.com
Rev.: $43,000
Assets: $492,853,000
Liabilities: $164,679,000
Net Worth: $328,174,000
Earnings: ($34,092,000)
Emp.: 21
Fiscal Year-end: 12/31/2022
Metal Mining & Exploration Services
N.A.I.C.S.: 213114
Patrick Keenan *(CFO & Exec VP)*

Subsidiary (Domestic):

PolyMet Mining, Inc. (2)
444 Cedar St Ste 2060, Saint Paul, MN 55101
Tel.: (651) 389-4100
Web Site: http://www.polymetmining.com
Emp.: 15
Metal Mining & Exploration Services
N.A.I.C.S.: 213114

GLENDOWER CAPITAL LLP

1 St Jamess Market, London, SW1Y 4AH, United Kingdom
Tel.: (44) 21039477000
Web Site:
   http://glendowercapital.com
Investment Services
N.A.I.C.S.: 523999
Carlo Pirzio-Biroli *(Mng Partner & CEO)*

GLENMARK PHARMACEUTICALS LIMITED

Glenmark House B D Sawant Marg Chakala Off Western Express Highway, Andheri E, Mumbai, 400099, India
Tel.: (91) 2240189999
Web Site:
   https://www.glenmarkpharma.com
GLENMARK—(NSE)
Rev.: $1,500,700,793
Assets: $2,129,888,261
Liabilities: $1,165,614,996
Net Worth: $964,273,265
Earnings: $132,417,012
Emp.: 10,964
Fiscal Year-end: 03/31/21
Pharmaceutical Preparation Mfr
N.A.I.C.S.: 325412
Glenn Saldanha *(Chm & Mng Dir)*

Subsidiaries:

Glenmark Arzneimittel Gmbh (1)
Industriestrasse 31, 82194, Grobenzell, Germany
Tel.: (49) 80045366275
Web Site: https://www.glenmark.de
Pharmaceuticals Product Mfr
N.A.I.C.S.: 325412

Glenmark Farmaceutica Ltda. (1)
Rua Gomes de Carvalho 1195, Vila Olimpia, Sao Paulo, 04547-000, SP, Brazil
Tel.: (55) 1155042700
Web Site:
   https://www.glenmarkpharma.com.br
Pharmaceutical Product Mfr & Distr
N.A.I.C.S.: 325412

Glenmark Generics Limited (1)
Glenmark House HDO-Corp Bldg Wing-A B D S Marg Chakala off Western, Express Highway Andheri (East), Mumbai, 400099, India
Tel.: (91) 2240189999
Web Site: http://www.glenmark-generics.com
Sales Range: $200-249.9 Million
Pharmaceuticals Mfr
N.A.I.C.S.: 325412

Subsidiary (US):

Glenmark Generics Inc. (2)
750 Corporate Dr, Mahwah, NJ 07430
Tel.: (201) 684-8000
Web Site: http://us.glenmark-generics.com
Pharmaceutical Product Mfr & Distr
N.A.I.C.S.: 325412

GLENMARK PHARMACEUTICALS LIMITED

Glenmark Pharmaceuticals Limited—(Continued)

Vijay Nasare *(Sr Dir-Intellectual Property)*

Glenmark Generics S.A. (1)
Calle 9 Ing Meyer Oks N 593 Pilar, Buenos Aires, B1629MAX, Argentina
Tel.: (54) 2304529555
Pharmaceutical Product Mfr & Distr
N.A.I.C.S.: 325412
Adrian Schwarz *(Mgr-Supply Chain)*

Glenmark Holding S.A. (1)
Chemin De La Combeta 5 La Chaux-De-Fonds, Neuchatel, 2300, Switzerland
Tel.: (41) 327293550
Holding Company
N.A.I.C.S.: 551112
Kurt Stoeckli *(Pres & Gen Mgr)*

Glenmark Pharmaceuticals B.V. (1)
Gooimeer 1, 1411 DC, Naarden, Netherlands
Tel.: (31) 8003355533
Web Site: https://glenmarkpharma.nl
Pharmaceutical Ingredient Mfr & Distr
N.A.I.C.S.: 325412

Glenmark Pharmaceuticals Colombia Ltda. (1)
AV 82 10 62 P 5, Bogota, Colombia
Tel.: (57) 16341500
Pharmaceutical Products Distr
N.A.I.C.S.: 424210

Glenmark Pharmaceuticals Ecuador S.A. (1)
Centro Corporativo Ekopark Torre 2 Piso 7, Ofc 703 Ave Simon Bolivar y Calle Nayon, Quito, Ecuador
Tel.: (593) 23826020
Web Site: https://www.glenmarkpharma.com.ec
Pharmaceuticals Mfr
N.A.I.C.S.: 325412

Glenmark Pharmaceuticals Europe Ltd. (1)
Building 2 Croxley Park, Watford, WD18 8YA, United Kingdom
Tel.: (44) 1923202950
Web Site: https://glenmarkpharma.co.uk
Pharmaceutical Ingredient Mfr & Distr
N.A.I.C.S.: 325412

Glenmark Pharmaceuticals Inc. (1)
750 Corporate Dr, Mahwah, NJ 07430
Tel.: (201) 684-8000
Web Site: https://glenmarkpharma-us.com
Pharmaceutical Ingredient Mfr & Distr
N.A.I.C.S.: 325412

Glenmark Pharmaceuticals Malaysia Sdn. Bhd. (1)
D- 31-02 Menara Suezcap 1 No 2 Jalan Kerinchi, 59200, Kuala Lumpur, Malaysia
Tel.: (60) 321666318
Pharmaceutical Ingredient Mfr & Distr
N.A.I.C.S.: 325412

Glenmark Pharmaceuticals Nordic AB (1)
Propellergatan 2, 211 15, Malmo, Sweden
Tel.: (46) 40354810
Web Site: https://glenmarkpharma.se
Pharmaceutical Ingredient Mfr & Distr
N.A.I.C.S.: 325412

Glenmark Pharmaceuticals S.A. (1)
Chemin de la Combeta 5, La Chaux-de-Fonds, 2300, Switzerland
Tel.: (41) 32 729 35 50
Pharmaceutical Research & Development Services
N.A.I.C.S.: 541715
Kurt Stoeckli *(Pres, Chief Scientific Officer)*

Glenmark Pharmaceuticals S.R.L. (1)
Baneasa Bussines Technology Park Bucuresti-Ploiesti Road 42-44, Building B2 1st floor District 1, Bucharest, Romania
Tel.: (40) 21 206 2474
Web Site: http://www.glenmarkpharma.ro
Emp.: 16
Pharmaceutical Products Distr
N.A.I.C.S.: 424210
Razvar Constantinescu *(Mgr-Comm)*

Glenmark Pharmaceuticals S.R.O. (1)
City Tower 3 podlazi Hvezdova 1716/2b, 140 78, Prague, Czech Republic
Tel.: (420) 227629511
Web Site: https://www.glenmarkpharma.cz
Pharmaceutical Products Distr
N.A.I.C.S.: 424210
Martina Kratka *(Head-Quality)*

Glenmark Pharmaceuticals SK SRO (1)
Tomasikova 64, 831 04, Bratislava, Slovakia
Tel.: (421) 220255041
Web Site: https://www.glenmarkpharma.sk
Pharmaceutical Products Distr
N.A.I.C.S.: 424210

Glenmark Pharmaceuticals South Africa (Pty) Ltd. (1)
Block A First Floor 34 Monte Carlo Cres Kyalami Park, Midrand, 1686, South Africa
Tel.: (27) 115643900
Web Site: https://www.glenmarkpharma.co.za
Emp.: 35
Pharmaceuticals Product Mfr
N.A.I.C.S.: 325412

Glenmark Pharmaceuticals Sp Z.o.o. (1)
ul Osmanska 14, 02-823, Warsaw, Poland
Tel.: (48) 223512500
Web Site: https://www.glenmark-pharma.pl
Pharmaceutical Products Distr
N.A.I.C.S.: 424210
Cherylann Maria Pinto *(Member-Mgmt Bd)*

Glenmark Philippines Inc. (1)
Unit 901-902 9th Floor 11th Corporate Center, 11th Avenue Corner Triangle Drive Bonifacio Global City, Taguig, 1634, Philippines
Tel.: (63) 288023235
Pharmaceutical Ingredient Mfr & Distr
N.A.I.C.S.: 325412

Glenmark Ukraine LLC (1)
Str Illinska 8 Entrance 12, 04070, Kiev, Ukraine
Tel.: (380) 445313484
Web Site: https://glenmarkpharma.ua
Pharmaceutical Ingredient Mfr & Distr
N.A.I.C.S.: 325412

Ichnos Sciences Inc. (1)
1 World Trade Ctr 76th Fl Ste D, New York, NY 10007
Tel.: (201) 786-3216
Web Site: https://www.ichnossciences.com
Scientific Research Services
N.A.I.C.S.: 541720

Sintesy Pharma S.R.L. (1)
Via Giordano Colombo 8, Cernusco sul Naviglio, 20063, Milan, Italy
Tel.: (39) 0292502558
Web Site: https://sintesy.it
Laboratory Monitoring Services
N.A.I.C.S.: 621511

Viso Farmaceutica S.L.U. (1)
Calle de la Retama 7 - 7th Floor, 28045, Madrid, Spain
Tel.: (34) 915030613
Web Site: https://visofarmaceutica.com
Emp.: 16
Pharmaceuticals Mfr
N.A.I.C.S.: 325412

GLENMOORE CAPITAL REIT
Shipka St No 10 Floor 5, 9000, Varna, Bulgaria
Tel.: (359) 883452002
Web Site: https://www.gmr-reit.com
GLMC—(BUL)
Sales Range: Less than $1 Million
Financial & Insurance Services
N.A.I.C.S.: 524210
Valentina Dimitrova *(Chm)*

GLENNON SMALL COMPANIES LIMITED
Level 17 25 Bligh Street, Sydney, 2000, NSW, Australia
Tel.: (61) 280271000 AU
Web Site:
 http://www.glennonsmallcos.com.au
GC1—(ASX)
Rev.: $6,130
Assets: $33,789,745
Liabilities: $4,492,172
Net Worth: $29,297,573
Earnings: ($7,135,527)
Fiscal Year-end: 06/30/22
Investment Management Service
N.A.I.C.S.: 525910
Michael Glennon *(Chm & Chief Investment Officer)*

GLENORA LUMBER & BUILDING SUPPLIES LTD.
14505-116 Avenue, Edmonton, T5M 3E8, AB, Canada
Tel.: (780) 453-5691
Web Site:
 https://www.glenoralumber.ca
Year Founded: 1960
Rev.: $13,041,743
Emp.: 25
Building Materials Whslr
N.A.I.C.S.: 423310
Kim Galbraith *(Office Mgr)*

GLENTRA CAPITAL P/S
Havnegade 23, 2, Copenhagen, 1058, Denmark
Tel.: (45) 20217130
Web Site: https://www.glentra.com
Year Founded: 2022
Investment Management
N.A.I.C.S.: 523999

GLENVEAGH PROPERTIES PLC
15 Merrion Square, Dublin, Ireland
Tel.: (353) 19037100
Web Site: https://www.glenveagh.ie
Year Founded: 2003
GVR—(ISE)
Rev.: $671,087,317
Assets: $1,032,500,276
Liabilities: $283,901,093
Net Worth: $748,599,183
Earnings: $52,001,325
Emp.: 502
Fiscal Year-end: 12/31/23
Apartment Rental Services
N.A.I.C.S.: 531110
John Mulcahy *(Co-Founder & Chm)*

GLENWOOD PRIVATE EQUITY CO., LTD.
Two IFC 20th Fl 10 Gukjegeumyung-ro, Yeongdeungpo-gu, Seoul, Korea (South)
Tel.: (82) 2 598 9800
Web Site:
 http://www.glenwoodpe.com
Privater Equity Firm
N.A.I.C.S.: 523999
Sang Ho lee *(Co-Founder, CEO & Mng Partner)*

GLG CORP LTD.
Tel.: (61) 62113600 AU
Web Site: https://www.ghimli.com
GLE—(ASX)
Rev.: $116,555,000
Assets: $100,387,000
Liabilities: $48,762,000
Net Worth: $51,625,000
Earnings: ($3,685,000)
Emp.: 9,000
Fiscal Year-end: 06/30/24
Apparel Mfr & Retailer
N.A.I.C.S.: 315990

GLG LIFE TECH CORPORATION
Suite 280 13071 Vanier Place, Richmond, V6V 2J1, BC, Canada
Tel.: (604) 285-2602 BC
Web Site: https://www.glglifetech.com

INTERNATIONAL PUBLIC

GLG.H—(TSXV)
Rev.: $7,793,304
Assets: $7,601,422
Liabilities: $135,914,762
Net Worth: ($128,313,340)
Earnings: ($4,235,712)
Emp.: 12
Fiscal Year-end: 12/31/23
Sports Nutrition, Research, Preventative Health Software, Manufacturing, Retail Chain Stores & Medical Clinics
N.A.I.C.S.: 456191
Luke Yong Zhang *(Chm & CEO)*

Subsidiaries:

Qingdao Runde Biotechnology Company Limited (1)
Lingshanwei Town, Jiaonan, Qingdao, 266427, Shangdong, China
Tel.: (86) 53283181169
Web Site: http://www.glg-runde.com
Agro & Stevia Products Mfr
N.A.I.C.S.: 115112

GLINTT - GLOBAL INTELLIGENT TECHNOLOGIES, S.A.
Beloura Office Park Edificio 10 Quinta da Beloura, 2710-693, Sintra, Portugal
Tel.: (351) 219100200
Web Site:
 https://www.glinttglobal.com
GLINT—(EUR)
Sales Range: $75-99.9 Million
Investment Management Service
N.A.I.C.S.: 523940
Nuno Vasco Lopes *(CEO)*

Subsidiaries:

Consoft, S.A.U. (1)
Partida Madrigueres Nord 12 esc 1 pl 1 puerta 13, Apartado de Correos nro 310, 03700, Denia, Spain
Tel.: (34) 966 42 60 30
Web Site: http://www.consoft.es
Information Technology Consulting Services
N.A.I.C.S.: 541511

Glintt Angola, Lda. (1)
Rua Cordeiro da Mata N 14, Maianga, Luanda, Angola
Tel.: (244) 222 354 590
Investment Management Service
N.A.I.C.S.: 523940

Glintt Brasil, Ltda. (1)
Alameda dos Maracatins 780 14 Andar - Conjunto 1403, Moema, 04089-001, Sao Paulo, Brazil
Tel.: (55) 11 981 782 649
Investment Management Service
N.A.I.C.S.: 523940

Glintt Espana, S.L. (1)
Av Alfonso XIII N 21, 28002, Madrid, Spain
Tel.: (34) 914 158 506
Investment Management Service
N.A.I.C.S.: 523940

Glintt Polska, Sp. Z o.o. (1)
Al Niepodleglosci 69 7th Floor, 02-626, Warsaw, Poland
Tel.: (48) 22 322 7667
Investment Management Service
N.A.I.C.S.: 523940

Pulso Informatica, S.L.U. (1)
Colon 86 1, 46004, Valencia, Spain
Tel.: (34) 96 352 91 92
Web Site: http://www.pulsoinformatica.es
Information Technology Consulting Services
N.A.I.C.S.: 541511

GLITTEK GRANITES LTD.
Plot No 42 KIADB Industrial Area Hoskote, Bengaluru, 562114, Karnataka, India
Tel.: (91) 8027971896
Web Site: https://www.glittek.com
513528—(BOM)
Rev.: $1,991,138
Assets: $4,677,254
Liabilities: $2,766,696

AND PRIVATE COMPANIES — GLOBAL CAPITAL MARKETS LIMITED

Net Worth: $1,910,558
Earnings: ($422,659)
Emp.: 54
Fiscal Year-end: 03/31/21
Granite Mfr
N.A.I.C.S.: 327991
Kamal Kumar Agarwal (Co-Mng Dir)

GLOBAL ACCESS (PTY) LTD.
Broadcast House 169-171 Fox Street, Johannesburg, 2001, South Africa
Tel.: (27) 11 350 6111 ZA
Web Site: http://www.globalaccess.co.za
Year Founded: 1995
Digital Content & Media Broadcasting Software & Services
N.A.I.C.S.: 513210
Ivano Stipcevich (Head-Digital Signage)

GLOBAL ADVANCED METALS PTY. LTD.
Level 3 Centerpoint Tower 123 B Collins St, West Perth, 6005, WA, Australia
Tel.: (61) 8 6217 2500 AU
Web Site: http://www.globaladvanced.com
Year Founded: 2009
Tantalum Mining & Processing
N.A.I.C.S.: 212290
Bryan Ellis (Vice Chm)

Subsidiaries:

Global Advanced Metals K. K., (1)
Shinkokusai Building 9F 3-4-1, Marunouchi Chiyoda, Tokyo, 100-0005, Japan
Tel.: (81) 3 3548 7200
Metal Ore Mining Services
N.A.I.C.S.: 212290

Global Advanced Metals USA Inc. (1)
County Line Rd, Boyertown, PA 19512
Tel.: (610) 367-1500
Web Site: http://www.globaladvancedmetals.com
Emp.: 500
Tantalum Powder & Wire Product Mfr
N.A.I.C.S.: 331410
Steve Krause (Pres)

Plant (Domestic):

Global Advanced Metals USA, Inc. - Global Advanced Metals (2)
County Line Rd, Boyertown, PA 19512
Tel.: (610) 367-1500
Metal Ore Mining Services
N.A.I.C.S.: 212290

GLOBAL AEROSPACE UNDERWRITING MANAGERS LIMITED
Fitzwilliam House 10 St Mary Axe, London, EC3A 8EQ, United Kingdom
Tel.: (44) 20 7369 2244 UK
Web Site: http://www.global-aero.com
Year Founded: 2001
Management & Clerical Services
N.A.I.C.S.: 927110
Michael Bannon (Chief Underwriting Officer-Europe)

Subsidiaries:

Global Aerospace, Inc. (1)
1 Sylvan Way Ste 2, Parsippany, NJ 07054-3879
Tel.: (973) 490-8500
Web Site: http://www.global-aero.com
Sales Range: $10-24.9 Million
Emp.: 271
Management & Clerical Services
N.A.I.C.S.: 927110
Jeffrey Bruno (Pres & Chief Underwriting Officer)

GLOBAL ASSET MANAGEMENT LIMITED
Building 2 Clearwater Office Park, Cnr Christiaan de Wet and Millennium Boulevard Strubensvalley, Roodepoort, 1724, South Africa
Tel.: (27) 11 662 3800 ZA
Web Site: http://www.global-ltd.co.za
Year Founded: 2002
GAM—(JSE)
Sales Range: $10-24.9 Million
Asset Management Services
N.A.I.C.S.: 523940
Niels Penzhorn (Mng Dir)

GLOBAL ATOMIC CORPORATION
8 King Street East Suite 1700, Toronto, M5C 1B5, ON, Canada
Tel.: (416) 203-8336
Web Site: https://globalatomiccorp.com
SYI—(TSXV)
Sales Range: Less than $1 Million
Waste Recovery Services
N.A.I.C.S.: 562920
Stephen G. Roman (Chm, Pres & CEO)

GLOBAL BANK CORPORATION
Torre Global Bank Tower Street 50, Panama, 0831-01843, Panama
Tel.: (507) 2062000
Web Site: http://www.globalbank.com.pa
Year Founded: 1994
GBAN—(PAN)
Rev.: $503,666,534
Assets: $8,520,282,632
Liabilities: $7,788,906,847
Net Worth: $731,375,785
Earnings: $47,832,787
Fiscal Year-end: 06/30/24
Commercial Banking Services
N.A.I.C.S.: 522110
Domingo Diaz A. (Co-Pres)

GLOBAL BATTERY METALS LTD.
1100-1199 West Hastings Street, Vancouver, V6E 3T5, BC, Canada
Tel.: (604) 649-2350 AB
Web Site: https://www.gbml.ca
Year Founded: 2005
REZ—(DEU)
Assets: $5,144,924
Liabilities: $260,824
Net Worth: $4,884,099
Earnings: ($1,280,530)
Emp.: 1
Fiscal Year-end: 04/30/23
Gold & Copper Mining Services
N.A.I.C.S.: 212220
Michael Murphy (Pres & CEO)

GLOBAL BIO-CHEM TECHNOLOGY GROUP COMPANY LIMITED
Suites 2202-4 22nd Floor Tower 6 the Gateway 9 Canton Road, Tsim Sha Tsui, Kowloon, China (Hong Kong)
Tel.: (852) 28388155
Web Site: http://www.globalbiochem.com
0809—(HKG)
Rev.: $47,465,445
Assets: $745,860,593
Liabilities: $1,738,710,233
Net Worth: ($992,849,640)
Earnings: ($193,744,538)
Emp.: 3,500
Fiscal Year-end: 12/31/22
Refined Corn Products Mfr & Sales
N.A.I.C.S.: 311340
Guicheng Wang (COO)

Subsidiaries:

Bio-chem Technology (HK) Limited (1)
Suite 1002 10/F Tower A Cheung Kei Center, 18 Hung Luen Road Hung Hom, Kowloon, China (Hong Kong)
Tel.: (852) 28388155
Web Site: https://www.globalbiochem.com
Sales Range: $25-49.9 Million
Emp.: 20
Biochemical Products Sales
N.A.I.C.S.: 424690

Changchun GBT Bio-Chemical Co., Ltd. (1)
Xi Huancheng Rd 886, Changchun, 130062, Jilin, China
Tel.: (86) 43186783050
Biopropylene Glycol Chemical Products Mfr & Sales
N.A.I.C.S.: 325199

GLOBAL BIOENERGIES SA
5 rue Henri Desbrueres, 91000, Evry, 91000, France
Tel.: (33) 164982050
Web Site: https://www.global-bioenergies.com
Year Founded: 2008
ALGBE—(EUR)
Sales Range: Less than $1 Million
Emp.: 69
Biological Hydrocarbon Producer
N.A.I.C.S.: 213112
Marc Delcourt (Co-Founder & CEO)

GLOBAL BLUE GROUP HOLDING AG
Zurichstrasse 38, 8306, Bruttisellen, 8306, Switzerland
Tel.: (41) 223637740 CH
Web Site: https://www.globalblue.com
Year Founded: 2019
GB—(NYSE)
Rev.: $455,753,621
Assets: $1,177,036,070
Liabilities: $1,101,141,706
Net Worth: $75,894,364
Earnings: $22,583,548
Emp.: 1,939
Fiscal Year-end: 03/31/24
Holding Company
N.A.I.C.S.: 551112
Thomas W. Farley (Chm)

GLOBAL BRANDS GROUP HOLDING LTD
9th Floor LiFung Tower 888 Cheung Sha Wan Road, Kowloon, China (Hong Kong)
Tel.: (852) 2300 2787
Web Site: http://www.globalbrandsgroup.com
Rev.: $1,512,822,000
Assets: $3,277,232,000
Liabilities: $2,404,620,000
Net Worth: $872,612,000
Earnings: ($388,183,000)
Emp.: 2,431
Fiscal Year-end: 03/31/19
Apparel, Footwear & Fashion Accessories Mfr & Sales
N.A.I.C.S.: 315990
Bruce Philip Rockowitz (Vice Chm)

Subsidiaries:

GBG Socks, LLC (1)
350 6th Ave 9th Fl, New York, NY 10118
Tel.: (212) 239-1485
Web Site: www.planetsox.com
Socks, Legwear & Related Accessories Mfr & Distr
N.A.I.C.S.: 315120
Elie Levy (Founder & Pres)

Sean John Clothing, Inc. (1)
1710 Broadway, New York, NY 10019
Tel.: (212) 500-2200
Web Site: http://www.seanjohn
Men's Apparel Designer, Producer & Distr
N.A.I.C.S.: 315250

GLOBAL BRANDS MANUFACTURE LTD.
4F No 48-3 Minquan Rd, Xindian Dist, Taipei, 231, Taiwan
Tel.: (886) 229108800
Web Site: https://www.gbm.com.tw
6191—(TAI)
Rev.: $748,200,534
Assets: $1,218,097,505
Liabilities: $543,833,558
Net Worth: $674,263,947
Earnings: $103,488,469
Emp.: 5,534
Fiscal Year-end: 12/31/23
Circuit Board Mfr
N.A.I.C.S.: 334412
Yu-Heng Chiao (Chm)

Subsidiaries:

ELNA Printed Circuits Co., Ltd. (1)
Tamachi 30, Nagahama, 529-0142, Shiga, Japan
Tel.: (81) 749733021
Emp.: 320
Printed Wiring Board Mfr & Distr
N.A.I.C.S.: 334412

Global Brands Manufacture (Dongguan) Ltd. (1)
Yuyuan Industrial Park, Huangjiang Town, Dongguan, 512200, Guangdong, China
Tel.: (86) 76983633303
Web Site: http://www.gbm.com.tw
Printed Circuit Board Mfr
N.A.I.C.S.: 334412

Global Brands Manufacture Ltd - China Guangdong Huangjian PCBA Plant (1)
Yue Yuen Industrial Estate, Huangjiang Town, Dongguan, 523758, Guangdong, China
Tel.: (86) 769 8363 2679
Printed Circuit Board Mfr
N.A.I.C.S.: 334412

Kunshan Yuan Mao Electronics Technology Co., Ltd. (1)
Kunshan Economy and Technical Development Zone No 8 Jinshajiang Road, Kunshan, Jiangsu, China
Tel.: (86) 51257721888
Sales Range: $800-899.9 Million
Emp.: 2,700
Electronic Components Mfr
N.A.I.C.S.: 334416

San Tai Distribution Co., Ltd. (1)
8F Allied Cargo Centre 150-160 Texaco Road, Tsuen Wan, New Territories, China (Hong Kong)
Tel.: (852) 2408 0282
Web Site: http://www.santai.hk
Emp.: 30
Logistics & Distribution Services
N.A.I.C.S.: 541614
Eric Cheng (Gen Mgr)

GLOBAL CAPITAL MARKETS LIMITED
Sir RNM House 5th Floor 3B Lal Bazar Street, Kolkata, 700 001, India
Tel.: (91) 3322481053
Web Site: https://www.globecapital.com
Year Founded: 1989
530263—(BOM)
Rev.: $629,249
Assets: $7,043,333
Liabilities: $81,356
Net Worth: $6,961,978
Earnings: $65,276
Emp.: 9
Fiscal Year-end: 03/31/21
Financial Investment Services
N.A.I.C.S.: 523999
Inder Chand Baid (Chm)

GLOBAL CAPITAL MARKETS LIMITED

Global Capital Markets Limited—(Continued)

Subsidiaries:

GCM Securities Limited (1)
9 Sir R N M House 3B Lal Bazar 5th Floor Block-2, Kolkata, 700 001, India
Tel.: (91) 3322481053
Web Site: https://www.gcmsecuritiesltd.com
Rev.: $370,336
Assets: $2,457,534
Liabilities: $852,159
Net Worth: $1,605,374
Earnings: $245,608
Emp.: 9
Fiscal Year-end: 03/31/2021
Securities Dealing
N.A.I.C.S.: 523150
Inder Chand Baid *(Chm)*

GLOBAL CARRIERS BHD

11th Floor Tower Block E Plaza Pekeliling Jalan Tun Razak, 50400, Kuala Lumpur, Malaysia
Tel.: (60) 34042 3113
Web Site:
http://www.globalcarriers.com.my
Sales Range: $1-9.9 Million
Shipping Management Services
N.A.I.C.S.: 483111
Nor Azrina Azlan *(Chm)*

Subsidiaries:

Global TS Sdn. Bhd. (1)
10th Floor Global Tower Plaza Pekeliling, Jalan Tun Razak, 50400, Kuala Lumpur, Wilayah Persekutuan, Malaysia
Tel.: (60) 341453333
Web Site: http://www.globalcarriers.com
Sales Range: $25-49.9 Million
Emp.: 80
Shipping Management Services
N.A.I.C.S.: 483111

GLOBAL CHAMPIONS SPLIT CORP.

Suite 210 Brookfield Place 181 Bay Street, Toronto, M5J 2T3, ON, Canada
Tel.: (647) 503-6516 **ON**
Web Site:
http://www.globalchampions.com
Year Founded: 2012
Sales Range: $1-9.9 Million
Investment Services
N.A.I.C.S.: 523999
Frank N. C. Lochan *(Chm)*

GLOBAL CITY HOLDINGS N.V.

Weena 210-212, 3012 NJ, Rotterdam, Netherlands
Tel.: (31) 102013602 **NI**
Web Site:
http://www.globalcityholdings.com
Year Founded: 1931
Sales Range: $700-749.9 Million
Emp.: 23
Holding Company
N.A.I.C.S.: 551112

GLOBAL COMMUNICATION EXPERTS GMBH

Hanauer Landstrasse 184, Frankfurt, 60314, Germany
Tel.: (49) 69 17 53 71 00
Web Site: http://www.gce-agency.com
Sales Range: $1-9.9 Million
Emp.: 20
Public Relations & Marketing Consulting
N.A.I.C.S.: 541820
Dorothea Hohn *(Mng Dir)*

GLOBAL COMMUNICATION PLANNING CO., LTD.

1-28-8 Ojidai, Sakura, Chiba, 285-0837, Japan
Tel.: (81) 434643348
Web Site: https://www.gck.co.jp
Year Founded: 1995
4073—(TKS)
Telecommunication Services b
N.A.I.C.S.: 517810

GLOBAL COMPLIANCE APPLICATIONS CORP.

830 1100 Melville Street, Vancouver, V6E 4A6, BC, Canada
Tel.: (514) 561-9091 **BC**
Web Site:
https://globalcompliance.app
Year Founded: 2014
FUAPF—(OTCIQ)
Rev.: $6,216
Assets: $136,719
Liabilities: $1,710,457
Net Worth: ($1,573,738)
Earnings: ($1,618,663)
Fiscal Year-end: 06/30/23
Mobile Applications
N.A.I.C.S.: 513210
Brad Moore *(CEO)*

GLOBAL CONNECTIONS PUBLIC COMPANY LIMITED

13/1 Village No 2 Kingkaew Road, Bangplee, Samut Prakan, 10540, Thailand
Tel.: (66) 27637999
Web Site: https://www.gc.co.th
Year Founded: 1994
GC—(THA)
Rev.: $149,208,989
Assets: $53,764,711
Liabilities: $36,062,264
Net Worth: $17,702,447
Earnings: $5,438,078
Emp.: 114
Fiscal Year-end: 12/31/23
Plastic Resin Product Distr
N.A.I.C.S.: 424610
Virah Mavichak *(Chm)*

GLOBAL CORD BLOOD CORPORATION

48th Floor Bank of China Tower 1 Garden Road, Central, China (Hong Kong)
Tel.: (852) 36058180 **Ky**
Web Site:
http://www.globalcordbloodcorp.com
Year Founded: 2008
CO—(NYSE)
Rev.: $177,668,291
Assets: $1,211,328,666
Liabilities: $538,974,088
Net Worth: $672,354,578
Earnings: $77,868,523
Emp.: 1,215
Fiscal Year-end: 03/31/21
Cord Blood Storage Services
N.A.I.C.S.: 621511
Tina Ting Zheng *(Chm & CEO)*

Subsidiaries:

Life Corporation Services (S) Pte. Ltd. (1)
988 Toa Payoh North 07-05, Singapore, 319002, Singapore
Tel.: (65) 6266 4320
Web Site: http://www.lifecorplimited.com
Funeral Support Services
N.A.I.C.S.: 812210

Subsidiary (Domestic):

SFS Care Pte Ltd (2)
Block 4 Toa Payoh Industrial Park 01-1341, Singapore, 319055, Singapore
Tel.: (65) 68414666
Web Site: http://www.sfs.com.sg
Funeral Services
N.A.I.C.S.: 812210

GLOBAL COSMETICS, INC.

Pavilion 96 Kensington High Street Kensington, London, W8 4SG, United Kingdom
Tel.: (44) 207 667 8883 **NV**
Year Founded: 2015
Emp.: 3
Cosmetic Product Distr
N.A.I.C.S.: 424210
Keith McCulloch *(Chm)*

GLOBAL DAILY FANTASY SPORTS, INC.

Suite 1305 1090 West Georgia Street, Vancouver, V6E 3V7, BC, Canada
Tel.: (604) 685-9316
Web Site:
http://www.lariatenergy.com
Year Founded: 1985
Oil & Gas Exploration Services
N.A.I.C.S.: 213112

GLOBAL DIGITAL CREATIONS HOLDINGS LIMITED

Unit 2112 21/F K Wah Centre 191 Java Road North Point, Hong Kong, China (Hong Kong)
Tel.: (852) 25236851 **BM**
Web Site: http://www.gdc-world.com
Year Founded: 2002
8271—(HKG)
Rev.: $9,217,613
Assets: $80,626,283
Liabilities: $39,248,198
Net Worth: $41,378,085
Earnings: ($1,272,323)
Emp.: 165
Fiscal Year-end: 12/31/22
Holding Company
N.A.I.C.S.: 551112
Zheng Chen *(Deputy Chm)*

Subsidiaries:

Beijing GDC Media Technologies Co., (1)
Rm 609-618 Office Building 20 Xinde Street, Xicheng District, Beijing, 100088, China
Tel.: (86) 1062057040
Motion Picture Production Services
N.A.I.C.S.: 512110

Guangdong GDC Cultural Park Limited (1)
Block No 11 Starlight Walk No 354 Xin Gang Zhong Road, Haizhu District, Guangzhou, China
Tel.: (86) 2084068888
Web Site: http://www.starlight-walk.com
Commercial Investment Services
N.A.I.C.S.: 523940

Institute of Digital Media Technology (Shanghai) Limited (1)
Block A4 No 121 North Zhongshan Road Hongkou District, Shanghai, China
Tel.: (86) 75586088005
Web Site: https://www.idmt.cn
Computer Graphic Training Services
N.A.I.C.S.: 611519

Institute of Digital Media Technology (Shenzhen) Limited (1)
7th Floor GDC Building 9 Gaoxin Central Avenue 3rd, Nanshan District, Shenzhen, China
Tel.: (86) 75586088018
Web Site: http://sz.gdc-world.com
Motion Picture Production Services
N.A.I.C.S.: 512110

Shenzhen Global Digital Creations Technology Limited (1)
6th Floor GDC Building 9 Gaoxin Central Avenue 3rd, Nanshan District, Shenzhen, China
Tel.: (86) 75586088018
Film Animation & Graphic Production Services
N.A.I.C.S.: 512191

GLOBAL DINING, INC.

8F Column Minami-Aoyama 7-1-5

INTERNATIONAL PUBLIC

Minami-Aoyama, Minato-ku, Tokyo, 107-0062, Japan
Tel.: (81) 334070561
Web Site: https://www.global-dining.com
Year Founded: 1973
7625—(TKS)
Rev.: $78,628,100
Assets: $60,690,400
Liabilities: $28,161,480
Net Worth: $32,528,920
Earnings: $6,005,230
Emp.: 188
Fiscal Year-end: 12/31/23
Restaurant Operators
N.A.I.C.S.: 722511
Kozo Hasegawa *(Pres & CEO)*

Subsidiaries:

Global Dining, Inc. - Myogadani Factory (1)
1F Domi Koishikawa 5-6-9 Koishikawa, Bunkyo-ku, Tokyo, Japan
Tel.: (81) 3 3943 9882
Web Site: http://www.decadence.jp
Chocolate Whslr
N.A.I.C.S.: 424450

Global-Dining, Inc. (1)
1212 3rd St Promenade, Santa Monica, CA 90401
Tel.: (310) 576-9922
Web Site: http://www.globaldiningca.com
Emp.: 50
Restaurant Services
N.A.I.C.S.: 722511
Toru Toyokawa *(CFO)*

GLOBAL DISPLAY CO., LTD.

174 Daesin-ro 146 Beon-gil Heungdeok-gu, Cheongju, Chungcheongbuk-do, Korea (South)
Tel.: (82) 70 74353721
Web Site: http://www.g-display.com
Rev.: $11,936,107
Assets: $95,878,631
Liabilities: $30,477,815
Net Worth: $65,400,816
Earnings: ($23,513,656)
Emp.: 119
Fiscal Year-end: 12/31/17
Glass Slimming Services
N.A.I.C.S.: 238150

GLOBAL DISPOMEDIKA, PT

Jalan Penjernihan 1 no 38 Bendungan Hilir, Tanah Abang, Jakarta, 10210, Indonesia
Tel.: (62) 215722593
Web Site:
http://www.globaldispomedika.com
Year Founded: 1961
Sales Range: $50-74.9 Million
Emp.: 130
Pharmaceuticals Mfr
N.A.I.C.S.: 325412
Fotuho Larosa *(Mng Dir)*

GLOBAL DIVERSIFIED INVESTMENT GRADE INCOME TRUST II

National Bank Financial Wealth Management 1155 Metcalfe 5th Floor, Montreal, H3B 4S9, QC, Canada
Tel.: (514) 879-2222 **ON**
Web Site: http://www.nbfwm.ca
Year Founded: 2005
GII—(TSX)
Sales Range: $1-9.9 Million
Closed-End Investment Fund
N.A.I.C.S.: 525990
Robert Y. Girard *(Sec)*

GLOBAL DIVIDEND GROWERS INCOME FUND

812 Memorial Dr NW, Calgary, T2N 3C8, AB, Canada
Tel.: (403) 269-2100 **AB**

Web Site: http://www.middlefield.com
Year Founded: 2013
GDG.UN—(TSX)
Rev.: $9,048,084
Assets: $53,743,475
Liabilities: $7,326,908
Net Worth: $46,416,567
Earnings: $8,057,554
Fiscal Year-end: 12/31/19
Investment Services
N.A.I.C.S.: 523999

GLOBAL DOMINION ACCESS SA
Ibanez de Bilbao 28-8th Floor, Bilbao, 48009, Spain
Tel.: (34) 944793787
Web Site: http://www.dominion-global.com
Emp.: 3,634
Software & Logistic Services
N.A.I.C.S.: 513210
Anton Pradera *(Chm)*

Subsidiaries:

ICC Commonwealth Corporation (1)
795 Wurlitzer Dr N, Tonawanda, NY 14120
Tel.: (716) 634-3967
Web Site: https://www.icc-commonwealth.com
Chimney Construction & Maintenance Services
N.A.I.C.S.: 238140

Subsidiary (Domestic):

Commonwealth Dynamics, Inc. (2)
95 Court St, Portsmouth, NH 03801
Tel.: (603) 433-6060
Web Site: http://www.comdynam.com
Sales Range: $1-9.9 Million
Emp.: 15
Structural Steel & Precast Concrete Contractors
N.A.I.C.S.: 238120
Lisa Onyon *(Controller)*

GLOBAL DRAGON LIMITED
456 Alexandra Road 02-09 Fragrance Empire Bldg, Singapore, 119962, Singapore
Tel.: (65) 69161028   SG
Year Founded: 1981
586—(CAT)
Rev.: $26,907,886
Assets: $200,464,919
Liabilities: $139,971,438
Net Worth: $60,493,481
Earnings: $2,061,068
Fiscal Year-end: 06/30/21
Holding Company; Real Estate Investment & Development Services
N.A.I.C.S.: 551112
Jeffrey Yew Ting Kwan *(CFO & Dir-Corp Svcs)*

GLOBAL ECONOMIC ADVANTAGE PVT LTD
Spaze I-Tech Park Sohna Road 411 Tower-A Sec-49, Gurgaon, 122018, India
Tel.: (91) 124 4521999
Web Site: http://www.thegea.com
Information Technology & Engineering Services
N.A.I.C.S.: 541330
Mohit Singh *(Sr Mgr-Mktg)*

GLOBAL ECOPOWER SA
Arteparc du Bachasson Batiment A Rue de la Carriere de Bachasson, FR-13590, Meyreuil, Cedex, France
Tel.: (33) 442245016
Web Site: http://www.global-ecopower.com
ALGEP—(EUR)
Sales Range: $1-9.9 Million
Emp.: 10
Renewable Energy

N.A.I.C.S.: 221118
Philippe Perret *(Deputy CEO)*

Subsidiaries:

GEP Energies SA (1)
Village entreprise St Henri II Rue Anne Gacon Bat 10-11, 13016, Marseille, France
Tel.: (33) 442245016
Web Site: http://www.gepenergies.com
Renewable Energy Services
N.A.I.C.S.: 221118
Jean-Marie Santander *(Pres)*

GLOBAL EDUCATION COMMUNITIES CORP
Unit 1200 777 West Broadway, Vancouver, V5Z 4J7, BC, Canada
Tel.: (604) 871-9909   BC
Web Site: http://www.cibt.net
Year Founded: 1986
MBA—(OTCIQ)
Rev.: $47,616,601
Assets: $406,033,829
Liabilities: $246,774,920
Net Worth: $159,258,909
Earnings: $4,049,864
Emp.: 341
Fiscal Year-end: 08/31/21
Education, Training, Graphic Design & Advertising Services
N.A.I.C.S.: 923110
Toby Chu *(Chm, Pres & CEO)*

Subsidiaries:

GEC Smart Furniture Ltd. (1)
Vancouver BC Showroom 108 1311 Howe Street, Vancouver, V6Z 2P3, BC, Canada
Tel.: (604) 396-0728
Web Site: https://www.spave.ca
Home Furniture Distr
N.A.I.C.S.: 423220

Global Education Alliance Inc. (1)
15F 543 Granville Street, Vancouver, V6C 1X8, BC, Canada
Tel.: (604) 512-8877
Web Site: https://geaeducation.ca
Educational Consultancy Services
N.A.I.C.S.: 611710

Global Education City Holdings Inc. (1)
103-1311 Howe Street, Vancouver, V6Z 2P3, BC, Canada
Tel.: (604) 669-6686
Web Site: https://gecliving.com
Student Residence Operator
N.A.I.C.S.: 721199

Irix Design Group Inc. (1)
777 W Broadway 1200, Vancouver, V5Z 4J7, BC, Canada
Tel.: (604) 876-1812
Web Site: https://www.irix-design.com
Marketing Services
N.A.I.C.S.: 541613

Sprott Shaw College Corp. (1)
501 - 333 Terminal Avenue, Vancouver, V6A 4C1, BC, Canada
Tel.: (604) 337-1280
Web Site: http://www.sprottshaw.com
Education Services
N.A.I.C.S.: 611310

GLOBAL EDUCATION LIMITED
4 Floor Usha Complex 345 Kingsway, Nagpur, 440001, Maharashtra, India
Tel.: (91) 7126630882
Web Site: https://www.globaledu.net.in
Year Founded: 2015
GLOBAL—(NSE)
Rev.: $7,699,167
Assets: $8,851,376
Liabilities: $1,017,697
Net Worth: $7,833,679
Earnings: $2,708,075
Emp.: 41
Fiscal Year-end: 03/31/23
Educational Support Services
N.A.I.C.S.: 611710

Preeti Pacheriwala *(Sec & Compliance Officer)*

Subsidiaries:

Global BIFS Academy Pvt. Ltd. (1)
5th floor Riaan House lic square Kingsway Rd opp KP ground Mohan Nagar, Nagpur, 440001, Maharashtra, India
Tel.: (91) 7722093249
Web Site: https://bifsacademy.com
Financial Services
N.A.I.C.S.: 522320

YOCO Stays Pvt. Ltd. (1)
4th floor Usha Complex Kingsway, Nagpur, 440001, Maharashtra, India
Tel.: (91) 7126630882
Web Site: https://yocostays.com
Hotel Services
N.A.I.C.S.: 721110

GLOBAL ENERGY (HOLDINGS) LTD.
13 Henderson Road, Inverness, IV1 1SN, United Kingdom
Tel.: (44) 1463 725460
Web Site: http://www.gegroup.com
Oil & Gas Operations Support Services
N.A.I.C.S.: 213112
Roy MacGregor *(Chm)*

Subsidiaries:

Caledonian Petroleum Services Ltd. (1)
Howe Moss Place Kirkhill Industrial Estate, Aberdeen, AB21 0ES, United Kingdom
Tel.: (44) 1224725345
Web Site: http://www.cpsaberdeen.co.uk
Sales Range: $25-49.9 Million
Emp.: 165
Engineeering Services
N.A.I.C.S.: 541330
Bob Steel *(Mng Dir)*

Caledonian Towage Ltd (1)
37 ShoreRoad, Invergordon, IV18 0EH, United Kingdom
Tel.: (44) 1349 852611
Engineeering Services
N.A.I.C.S.: 541330

Global Energy Services Limited (1)
Nigg Energy Park, London, IV19 1QU, Nigg Ross-shire, United Kingdom
Tel.: (44) 1862 852390
Web Site: http://www.globalenergyservices.co.uk
Engineeering Services
N.A.I.C.S.: 541330
Alex Mackay *(Mgr-Ops)*

Global Port Services Limited (1)
13 Henderson Road, Inverness, IV1 1SN, United Kingdom
Tel.: (44) 1349 852444
Web Site: http://www.globalportservices.co.uk
Engineeering Services
N.A.I.C.S.: 541330

Global SCS Ltd (1)
In-spec House Wellheads Drive, Aberdeen, AB21 7GQ, United Kingdom
Tel.: (44) 1224 356 500
Web Site: http://www.global-scs.com
Engineeering Services
N.A.I.C.S.: 541330

Global TCC (1)
Centre Kirkhill Place, Kirkhill Industrial Estate, Aberdeen, AB21 0GU, United Kingdom
Tel.: (44) 1224 255470
Web Site: http://www.globaltcc.com
Engineeering Services
N.A.I.C.S.: 541330
Lisa Murphy *(Mng Dir)*

Isleburn Ltd. (1)
8 Airfield Road Evanton Industrial Estate, Evanton, IV16 9XJ, United Kingdom
Tel.: (44) 1349832000
Web Site: http://www.isleburn.com
Sales Range: $150-199.9 Million
Emp.: 500
Engineeering Services
N.A.I.C.S.: 541330

Neil MacArthur *(COO)*

Labtech Services Ltd. (1)
Blackness Road Altens Industrial Estate, Aberdeen, AB12 3LH, United Kingdom
Tel.: (44) 1224337777
Web Site: http://www.labtechservicesltd.com
Sales Range: $50-74.9 Million
Emp.: 120
Modular Structure Mfr
N.A.I.C.S.: 332311
Paul Duncan *(Mng Dir)*

Maris Subsea Ltd (1)
In-Spec House, Wellheads Drive dyce, Aberdeen, AB21 7GQ, United Kingdom
Tel.: (44) 1224356500
Web Site: http://www.marissubsea.com
Engineeering Services
N.A.I.C.S.: 541330

REEL Group Inc (1)
16420 Park 10th Pl Ste 455, Houston, TX 77084
Tel.: (832) 358-2663
Web Site: http://www.reelgroup.com
Engineeering Services
N.A.I.C.S.: 541330
Alan Thomson *(Mng Dir)*

Rigfit Offshore Ltd (1)
5B International Avenue, ABZ Business Park Dyce, Aberdeen, AB21 0BH, United Kingdom
Tel.: (44) 1224 799640
Web Site: http://www.rigfitoffshore.com
Emp.: 10
Engineeering Services
N.A.I.C.S.: 541330
Graham Cowperthwaite *(Sr VP)*

Ross-shire Engineering Ltd (1)
Muir of Ord Industrial Estate, Muir of Ord, IV6 7UA, Ross-Shire, United Kingdom
Tel.: (44) 1463 870049
Web Site: http://www.ross-eng.com
Engineeering Services
N.A.I.C.S.: 541330
Allan Dallas *(Mng Dir)*

Vertech Group Pty Ltd (1)
19 Walters Drive, Osborne Park, 6017, WA, Australia
Tel.: (61) 8 9243 1203
Web Site: http://www.vertech.com.au
Engineeering Services
N.A.I.C.S.: 541330
Tom Brenan *(Mng Dir)*

Vertech UK (1)
Unit H1-Enterprise Energy Park, Claymore Avenue Bridge of Don, Aberdeen, AB23 8GW, United Kingdom
Tel.: (44) 1224 608608
Web Site: http://www.vertechuk.com
Engineeering Services
N.A.I.C.S.: 541330
Alan Melia *(Mgr-Offshore Diving)*

GLOBAL ENERGY METALS CORPORATION
Suite 1501-128 West Pender Street, Vancouver, V6B 1R8, BC, Canada
Tel.: (604) 688-4219
Web Site: https://www.globalenergymetals.com
GBLEF—(OTCQB)
Rev.: $59,572
Assets: $6,701,419
Liabilities: $338,636
Net Worth: $6,362,783
Earnings: ($842,179)
Fiscal Year-end: 06/30/21
Mining Services
N.A.I.C.S.: 213114
Luis Hadic *(CFO)*

GLOBAL ENVIRONMENTAL ENERGY CORP.
PO Box CB-13277, Cable Beach, Nassau, Bahamas
Tel.: (242) 3230086   BS
Web Site: http://www.geecf.ru
GEECF—(OTCEM)
Sales Range: $25-49.9 Million
Emp.: 3

GLOBAL ENVIRONMENTAL ENERGY CORP.

Global Environmental Energy Corp.—(Continued)
Oil & Gas Exploration Services
N.A.I.C.S.: 211120

GLOBAL ENVIRONMENTAL MANAGEMENT SERVICES, LLC
Red Sea Plaza Al-Andalus Street 3rd Floor, PO Box 5425, Jeddah, 21514, Saudi Arabia
Tel.: (966) 26145733
Web Site: http://www.gems-ksa.com
Waste Water Management Services
N.A.I.C.S.: 221320
Khaled Alrashed *(CEO)*

GLOBAL EQUITY PARTNERS BETEILIGUNGS-MANAGEMENT AG
Mariahilfer Strasse 1/Getreidemarkt 17, Vienna, 1060, Austria
Tel.: (43) 15818390   AT
Web Site: http://www.gep.at
Privater Equity Firm
N.A.I.C.S.: 523999
Michael Tojner *(Founder & CEO)*

Subsidiaries:

ASTA Holdings GmbH   (1)
Bezirk Wiener Neustadt, Oed, 2755, Austria
Tel.: (43) 2632700
Web Site: http://www.asta.at
Sales Range: $200-249.9 Million
Holding Company
N.A.I.C.S.: 551112

Subsidiary (Non-US):

ASTA Conductors Co., Ltd.   (2)
No 62 Taishan Road, Baoying, 225800, Jiangsu, China
Tel.: (86) 514 88248700
Web Site: http://www.asta-china.com
Sales Range: $25-49.9 Million
Insulated Wires Mfr
N.A.I.C.S.: 335929

Subsidiary (Domestic):

ASTA Elektrodraht GmbH & Co KG
Bezirk Wiener Neustadt, 2755, Oed, Austria
Tel.: (43) 2632700
Web Site: http://www.asta.at
Silo Mfr
N.A.I.C.S.: 335929
Christian Grosspointner *(Mng Dir)*

Subsidiary (Non-US):

ASTA India Private Limited   (2)
Plot No 725/726 GIDC Manjusar, Savli, Vadodara, 391 775, Gujarat, India
Tel.: (91) 2667665000
Web Site: http://www.asta.in
Copper Wires Mfr
N.A.I.C.S.: 332618

Buy-Out Central Europe II Beteiligungs-Invest AG   (1)
Mariahilfer Strasse 1, Getreidemarkt 17, 1060, Vienna, Austria
Tel.: (43) 1 585 1400
Web Site: http://www.buy-out.at
Sales Range: $50-74.9 Million
Closed-End Investment Fund
N.A.I.C.S.: 525990
Kurt Stiassny *(Chm-Mgmt Bd)*

Hahl Filaments GmbH   (1)
Rottenacker Strasse 2-18, 89597, Munderkingen, Germany
Tel.: (49) 7393530
Web Site: http://www.hahl-pedex.com
Plastics Product Mfr
N.A.I.C.S.: 325211
Michael Holzmann *(Mng Dir)*

Subsidiary (US):

Hahl Inc.   (2)
126 Glassmaster Rd, Lexington, SC 29072-3710
Tel.: (803) 359-0706
Sales Range: $10-24.9 Million
Plastic Mfr
N.A.I.C.S.: 325211
Luther Hicklin *(Mgr-Production)*

Montana Tech Components AG   (1)
Haupstrasse 35, CH 5737, Menziken, Switzerland
Tel.: (41) 627652500
Web Site: http://www.montanatechcomponents.com
Sales Range: $500-549.9 Million
Aerospace & Industrial Components Mfr; Metallurgical Identification Systems; Battery Mfr
N.A.I.C.S.: 336413
Valerie Ferencic *(Head-IR & PR)*

Subsidiary (Domestic):

Aluflexpack AG   (2)
Alte Aarauerstrasse 11, 5734, Reinach, Switzerland   (53.6%)
Tel.: (41) 627652520
Web Site: https://www.aluflexpack.com
Rev.: $390,018,347
Assets: $483,530,110
Liabilities: $275,895,748
Net Worth: $207,634,362
Earnings: $4,785,236
Emp.: 1,537
Fiscal Year-end: 12/31/2022
Packaging Product Mfr & Distr
N.A.I.C.S.: 326112
Martin Ohneberg *(Chm)*

Subsidiary (Non-US):

EK Mittelstandsfinanzierungs AG   (2)
Mariahilfer Strasse 1/Getreidemarkt 17, A-1060, Vienna, Austria
Tel.: (43) 1 581 83 90
Web Site: http://www.ekfin.at
Financial Management Services
N.A.I.C.S.: 523999

Subsidiary (US):

Universal Alloy Corporation   (2)
180 Lamar Haley Pkwy, Canton, GA 30114
Tel.: (770) 479-7230
Web Site: http://www.universalalloy.com
Aluminum Rolling, Drawing & Extruding Services
N.A.I.C.S.: 331318
Michael Colt *(Sr VP-Ops)*

Subsidiary (Non-US):

VARTA AG   (2)
VARTA-Platz 1, 73479, Ellwangen, Germany   (60.48%)
Tel.: (49) 79619210
Web Site: https://www.varta-ag.com
Rev.: $792,718,208
Assets: $1,236,301,280
Liabilities: $1,001,055,776
Net Worth: $235,245,504
Earnings: $(196,892,608)
Emp.: 4,560
Fiscal Year-end: 12/30/2022
Holding Company
N.A.I.C.S.: 551112
Michael Tojner *(Chm-Supervisory Bd)*

Subsidiary (Domestic):

VARTA Consumer Batteries GmbH & Co. KGaA   (3)
Alfred-Krupp Strasse 9, 73479, Ellwangen, Germany
Tel.: (49) 7961830
Web Site: http://www.varta-consumer.com
Battery & Flashlight mfr
N.A.I.C.S.: 335910

Subsidiary (Non-US):

VARTA B.V.   (4)
Rutherfordweg 103, NL 3542 AW, Utrecht, Netherlands
Tel.: (31) 302480480
Web Site: http://www.varta.nl
Emp.: 30
Portable Batteries
N.A.I.C.S.: 335910

VARTA Baterie spol. s.r.o.   (4)
Kosovska Cesta 24, 97131, Prievidza, Slovakia
Tel.: (421) 465422165

Battery Mfr & Distr
N.A.I.C.S.: 335910

VARTA Batterie GES. m.b.H.   (4)
Europaring A04 501, Brunn am Mountain, A - 2345, Vienna, Austria
Tel.: (43) 86339175
Web Site: http://www.varta-consumer.at
Sales Range: $10-24.9 Million
Emp.: 18
Automotive & Industrial Batteries
N.A.I.C.S.: 335910

VARTA Hungaria Kereskedelmi es Szolgaltato Kft.   (4)
Ady Road 42-44, Budapest, 1191, Hungary
Tel.: (36) 13479000
Web Site: http://www.varta-consumer.hu
Automotive, Portable & Industrial Batteries
N.A.I.C.S.: 335910

VARTA Ltd.   (4)
Unit 1 Cropmead Ind Est, Crewkerne, Somerset, TA18 7HQ, United Kingdom
Tel.: (44) 146073366
Accumulator & Battery Mfr
N.A.I.C.S.: 335910

VARTA S.A.   (4)
157 Rue Jean-Pierre Timbaud, Courbevoie, 92403, France
Tel.: (33) 146916600
Web Site: http://www.varta.fr
Emp.: 120
Automotive Batteries
N.A.I.C.S.: 335910

Varta Pilleri Ticaret Limited Sirketi   (4)
Istoc 25 Ada Sonu Kuzey Plaza Kat 1 D 4, Mahmutbey, Istanbul, Türkiye (100%)
Tel.: (90) 212 659 50 60
Web Site: http://www.tr.varta-consumer.com
Battery Mfr
N.A.I.C.S.: 335910

Subsidiary (Domestic):

VARTA Microbattery GmbH   (3)
Daimlerstr 1, 73479, Ellwangen, Germany
Tel.: (49) 79619210
Web Site: http://www.varta-microbattery.com
Sales Range: $150-199.9 Million
Designer & Mfr of Rechargeable & Primary Battery Systems
N.A.I.C.S.: 335910
Herbert Schein *(CEO & Mng Dir)*

Subsidiary (Non-US):

VARTA Microbattery Pte. Ltd.   (4)
300 Tampines Ave 5, 05 01 Tampines Jct, Singapore, 529653, Singapore
Tel.: (65) 62605801
Web Site: http://www.varta-microbattery.com
Sales Range: $25-49.9 Million
Designer & Mfr of Rechargeable & Primary Battery Systems
N.A.I.C.S.: 335910

Subsidiary (US):

VARTA Microbattery, Inc.   (4)
555 Vheovore Fremd Ave, Rye, NY 10580
Tel.: (914) 592-2500
Web Site: http://www.varta-microbattery.com
Sales Range: $25-49.9 Million
Emp.: 20
Designer & Mfr of Rechargeable & Primary Battery Systems
N.A.I.C.S.: 335910
Jerry Nathanson *(VP-Sls & Mktg)*

Subsidiary (Domestic):

VARTA Storage GmbH   (3)
Nurnberger Strasse 65, 86720, Nordlingen, Germany
Tel.: (49) 9081 240 8660
Web Site: http://www.varta-storage.com
Storage Battery Mfr & Whslr
N.A.I.C.S.: 335910
Herbert Schein *(CEO & Mng Dir)*

Pedex GmbH   (1)
Hauptstrasse Nord 67, 69483, Munich, Germany   (100%)
Tel.: (49) 6207 946
Web Site: http://www.hahl-pedex.com

INTERNATIONAL PUBLIC

Sales Range: $25-49.9 Million
Brush Filaments Mfr
N.A.I.C.S.: 326199

GLOBAL FERRONICKEL HOLDINGS, INC.
Unit 34D Rufino Pacific Tower, Makati, 1226, Metro Manila, Philippines
Tel.: (63) 4032410   PH
Web Site: https://www.gfni.com.ph
Year Founded: 1994
FNI—(PHI)
Rev.: $158,625,294
Assets: $314,430,637
Liabilities: $92,703,619
Net Worth: $221,727,018
Earnings: $32,737,022
Fiscal Year-end: 12/31/23
Nickel Ore Producer
N.A.I.C.S.: 212230
Joseph C. Sy *(Chm & CEO)*

GLOBAL FINANCE SA
7 Fragoklissias str, Athens, 15125, Greece
Tel.: (30) 210 812 4500
Web Site: http://www.globalfinance.gr
Year Founded: 1991
Investment Services
N.A.I.C.S.: 523999
ngelos Plakopitas *(Mng Partner)*

GLOBAL FINANCIAL INVESTMENTS HOLDING SAOG
Global Financial Investment Building MBD Area Second Floor, Ruwi, Oman
Tel.: (968) 24822706   OM
Web Site: https://www.gfioman.com
Year Founded: 1997
GFIC—(MUS)
Rev.: $34,452,175
Assets: $184,592,021
Liabilities: $83,395,963
Net Worth: $101,196,058
Earnings: $(768,832)
Emp.: 6
Fiscal Year-end: 12/31/19
Holding Company
N.A.I.C.S.: 551112
Hussam Hisham Omar Bostami *(CEO-Acting)*

Subsidiaries:

Al Madina Logistics Service S.A.O.C   (1)
PO Box 1466, 133, Muscat, Oman
Tel.: (968) 26895600
Web Site: http://www.almadinalogistics.com
Logistic Services
N.A.I.C.S.: 488510
Hassan Ehsan *(Chm)*

Sohar Gases Company L.L.C   (1)
PC 327, PO Box 6, Industrial Estate, Sohar, Oman
Tel.: (968) 26750468
Web Site: http://www.sohargas.com
Gas Production Services
N.A.I.C.S.: 211130
Jalal H. Al-Qaisy *(Gen Mgr)*

Sohar University LLC   (1)
PO Box 44, 311, Sohar, Oman
Tel.: (968) 26850100
Web Site: https://www.su.edu.om
Education Services
N.A.I.C.S.: 611710
Jamal Said Al Ojaili *(Chm)*

GLOBAL FOOD CREATORS CO., LTD.
978-1 Dendai, Kasamatsu-cho, Hashima, 501-6193, Gifu, Japan
Tel.: (81) 583878181
Web Site: https://gfc-jp.com
Year Founded: 1972

AND PRIVATE COMPANIES

7559—(TKS)
Rev.: $144,823,217
Assets: $133,069,008
Liabilities: $21,176,076
Net Worth: $111,892,932
Earnings: $3,957,713
Emp.: 237
Fiscal Year-end: 03/31/24
Foodstuff Whslr
N.A.I.C.S.: 311999
Koichi Nishimura (Pres)

Subsidiaries:

BLOCK47 Eats LLP (1)
3-54 Chiyoda, Fukujucho, Hashima, 501-6256, Japan
Tel.: (81) 583722773
Web Site: https://block47.jp
Hotel & Resort Services
N.A.I.C.S.: 721110

GLOBAL FORTUNE INVESTMENT LIMITED
Level 25 88 Phillip Street, Sydney, 2000, NSW, Australia
Tel.: (61) 02 8211 0671
Web Site: http://www.gfinvest.com.au
Mining Investment
N.A.I.C.S.: 523999
Eric Yuan Lin (Vice Chm, CEO & Mng Dir)

GLOBAL GREEN CHEMICALS PUBLIC COMPANY LIMITED
555/1 Energy Complex Building A 4th Floor Vibhavadi-Rangsit Road, Chatuchak Chatuchak, Bangkok, 10900, Thailand
Tel.: (66) 25587300
Web Site: http://www.ggcplc.com
Year Founded: 2005
Oleochemical Products Mfr
N.A.I.C.S.: 325998
Supattanapong Punmeechaow (Chm)

GLOBAL GREEN SOLUTIONS INC.
4326 Dunbar Street, PO Box 45100, Vancouver, V6S 2M8, BC, Canada
Tel.: (604) 408-0153   NV
Web Site:
http://www.globalgreensolutions.com
Year Founded: 2003
Waste Biomass Combustion Converting into Steam & Electricity; Biomass Algae Production
N.A.I.C.S.: 562219
Elden Schorn (Chm)

GLOBAL HEALTH CLINICS LTD.
400-837 West Hastings Street, Vancouver, V6C 3N6, BC, Canada
Tel.: (604) 283-1722   BC
Web Site: https://globalhealthltd.ca
Year Founded: 2013
MJRX—(CNSX)
Rev.: $76,729
Assets: $180,163
Liabilities: $1,810,006
Net Worth: ($1,629,843)
Earnings: ($1,212,395)
Fiscal Year-end: 07/31/23
Nickel & Copper Exploration & Mining
N.A.I.C.S.: 213114
Jatinder Dhaliwal (CEO)

GLOBAL HEALTH LIMITED
Level 2 696 Bourke Street, Melbourne, 3000, VIC, Australia
Tel.: (61) 396750600
Web Site: https://www.global-health.com
GLH—(ASX)
Rev.: $5,787,382
Assets: $2,054,406
Liabilities: $3,990,793
Net Worth: ($1,936,387)
Earnings: ($876,142)
Emp.: 40
Fiscal Year-end: 06/30/24
Health Care Srvices
N.A.I.C.S.: 621491
Mathew Cherian (CEO & Mng Dir)

Subsidiaries:

Working Systems Solutions Pty. Ltd. (1)
Level 2 607 Bourke St, Melbourne, 3000, VIC, Australia
Tel.: (61) 396750600
Web Site: http://www.global-health.com
Sales Range: $100-124.9 Million
Healtcare Services
N.A.I.C.S.: 621999

GLOBAL HELIUM CORP.
Suite 800 555 4th Avenue SW, Calgary, T2P 3E7, AB, Canada
Tel.: (403) 650-5766   AB
Web Site:
https://www.globalhelium.com
Year Founded: 2019
HECOF—(OTCIQ)
Assets: $5,385,019
Liabilities: $117,071
Net Worth: $5,267,948
Earnings: $3,509,930
Emp.: 4
Fiscal Year-end: 12/31/22
Mineral Mining Services
N.A.I.C.S.: 213115
Duncan MacKenzie (VP)

GLOBAL HEMP GROUP INC.
106 - 1169 Mt Seymour Road, North Vancouver, V7H 2Y4, BC, Canada
Tel.: (778) 726-2900   BC
Web Site:
https://www.globalhempgroup.com
Year Founded: 2009
GHG—(CNSX)
Assets: $32,290
Liabilities: $4,398,659
Net Worth: ($4,366,369)
Earnings: ($1,948,603)
Fiscal Year-end: 09/30/23
Cannabis & Hemp Investment Holding Company
N.A.I.C.S.: 551112
Curt Huber (Chm, Pres & CEO)

GLOBAL HUNTER CORPORATION
502-535 Thurlow Street, Vancouver, V6E 3L2, BC, Canada
Tel.: (604) 681-4653   BC
Web Site: http://www.globalhunter.ca
Year Founded: 1988
Sales Range: Less than $1 Million
Copper, Molybdenum & Other Base Metals Mining, Exploration & Development Services
N.A.I.C.S.: 212230
James Mackie (CFO)

GLOBAL IME BANK LIMITED
Kamaladi, PO Box 19327, Kathmandu, Nepal
Tel.: (977) 5328671
Web Site:
https://www.globalimebank.com
Year Founded: 2012
GBIME—(NEP)
Rev.: $370,909,938
Assets: $4,005,137,899
Liabilities: $3,548,672,484
Net Worth: $456,465,416
Earnings: $52,018,383
Emp.: 3,677
Fiscal Year-end: 07/16/23
Commercial Banking Services
N.A.I.C.S.: 522110

Chandra Prasad Dhakal (Chm)

Subsidiaries:

Global IME Capital Ltd. (1)
Laxman Babu Bhawan Naxal, Kathmandu, Nepal
Web Site: http://www.globalimecapital.com
Banking Services
N.A.I.C.S.: 522110
Kalyan Bandhu Aryal (Chm)

Global IME Laghubitta Bittiya Sanstha Ltd. (1)
26 Bijayapur Kaski, Pokhara, Nepal
Tel.: (977) 61411438
Web Site: https://www.gilb.com.np
Rev.: $9,069,402
Assets: $64,925,635
Liabilities: $56,792,935
Net Worth: $8,132,699
Earnings: $731,574
Fiscal Year-end: 07/16/2023
Commercial Banking Services
N.A.I.C.S.: 522110
Hari Krishna Joshi (CEO & Sec)

Janata Capital Ltd. (1)
Thapathali, Kathmandu, Nepal
Tel.: (977) 14265272
Web Site: http://www.janatacapital.com.np
Banking Services
N.A.I.C.S.: 522110
Sujit Kumar Shakya (Chm)

Lord Buddha Finance Limited (1)
Phasikeba New Road, PO Box 20100, Kathmandu, Nepal
Tel.: (977) 1 4212770
Web Site:
http://www.lordbuddhafinance.com.np
Financial Services
N.A.I.C.S.: 523999
Bharat Kumar Shrestha (Chm)

GLOBAL INFORMATION, INC.
7F Ursis Bldg 1-2-3 Manpukuji, Asao-Ku, Kawasaki, 215-0004, Japan
Tel.: (81) 449520102
Web Site:
https://www.giiresearch.com
Year Founded: 1983
4171—(TKS)
Rev.: $20,681,530
Assets: $20,724,070
Liabilities: $4,487,970
Net Worth: $16,236,100
Earnings: $2,708,380
Fiscal Year-end: 12/31/23
Information Technology Services
N.A.I.C.S.: 541512
Sosuke Higuchi (Pres & CEO)

Subsidiaries:

Giv-Tech, Inc. (1)
7F Arsis Building 1-2-3 Manpukjin, Asao-ku, Kawasaki, 215-0004, Kanagawa, Japan
Tel.: (81) 44 952 0807
Web Site: https://www.giv-tech.co.jp
Communication Equipment Mfr
N.A.I.C.S.: 334290

GLOBAL INFOTECH CO., LTD.
Floor E Block A Guozun Yingdi Center Building 2 No 28 Xiaoyun Road, Chaoyang District, Beijing, 100027, China
Tel.: (86) 1057321188
Web Site: https://www.git.com.cn
Year Founded: 1998
300465—(CHIN)
Rev.: $202,258,836
Assets: $193,580,712
Liabilities: $104,781,924
Net Worth: $88,798,788
Earnings: ($10,531,404)
Emp.: 2,040
Fiscal Year-end: 12/31/22
Financial Information Software
N.A.I.C.S.: 513210
Yu Wei (Chm)

GLOBAL INTERNATIONAL CREDIT GROUP LIMITED

Subsidiaries:

Chengdu Global Infotech Information Technology Co., Ltd. (1)
Room 1610 AVIC City Plaza No 88 Middle Section of Fucheng Avenue, High-tech Zone, Chengdu, 610000, Sichuan, China
Tel.: (86) 2885442886
Information Technology Services
N.A.I.C.S.: 541511

Jiangsu Yingda Information Technology Co., Ltd. (1)
Room 1601 Building 2 Juhuiyuan Xuzhuang High-tech Zone No 108, Xuanwu Avenue, Nanjing, 210042, Jiangsu, China
Tel.: (86) 2585790057
Information Technology Services
N.A.I.C.S.: 541511

Shanghai Xizhen Information Technology Co., Ltd. (1)
F607 NO 2075 Kongjiang Road, Yangpu District, Shanghai, China
Tel.: (86) 213 532 8973
Web Site: https://www.shxzxx.com
Software Services
N.A.I.C.S.: 541511

GLOBAL INFRATECH & FINANCE LIMITED
Office No 16 Ground Floor Rukmani Pushottam 21 J P Road, Andheri West, Mumbai, 400058, Maharashtra, India
Tel.: (91) 2265544550
Web Site:
http://www.globalinfrafin.com
Rev.: $1,054,657
Assets: $5,914,356
Liabilities: $515,036
Net Worth: $5,399,320
Earnings: ($244,261)
Emp.: 9
Fiscal Year-end: 03/31/18
Financial Investment Services
N.A.I.C.S.: 523999

GLOBAL INSURANCE LIMITED
Al-Razi Complex 12th floor 166-167 Shaheed Syed Nazrul Islam Sarani, Purana Paltan, Dhaka, 1000, Bangladesh
Tel.: (880) 29567186
Web Site:
https://www.globalinsurancebd.com
Year Founded: 2000
GLOBALINS—(CHT)
Rev.: $1,333,076
Assets: $12,554,494
Liabilities: $4,037,242
Net Worth: $8,517,251
Earnings: $865,389
Emp.: 810
Fiscal Year-end: 12/31/22
Insurance Services
N.A.I.C.S.: 524298
Mohammad Abdul Muqtadir (Chm)

GLOBAL INTERNATIONAL CREDIT GROUP LIMITED
Room 2301 23F 19 World-Wide House, Des Voeux Road, Central, China (Hong Kong)
Tel.: (852) 21110998
Web Site: http://www.gic.com.hk
1669—(HKG)
Rev.: $11,541,810
Assets: $120,352,478
Liabilities: $7,486,928
Net Worth: $112,865,550
Earnings: $6,497,273
Emp.: 18
Fiscal Year-end: 12/31/22
Mortgage Lending
N.A.I.C.S.: 522310
Yao Wang (Co-Founder, Chm & CEO)

GLOBAL INVACOM GROUP LIMITED

Global Invacom Group Limited—(Continued)

GLOBAL INVACOM GROUP LIMITED
7 Temasek Boulevard Level 32 Suntec Tower One, Singapore, 38987, Singapore
Tel.: (65) 66786777
Web Site:
https://www.globalinvacom.com
B73—(SES)
Rev.: $72,769,000
Assets: $56,250,000
Liabilities: $22,667,000
Net Worth: $33,583,000
Earnings: ($15,532,000)
Emp.: 260
Fiscal Year-end: 12/31/22
Satellite Communication Equipment Mfr
N.A.I.C.S.: 334290
Anthony Brian Taylor *(Chm)*

Subsidiaries:

GI Provision Limited (1)
6 Richmond Road, Essex, Chelmsford, CM2 6UA, United Kingdom
Tel.: (44) 1621745646
Satellite Equipment Mfr & Distr
N.A.I.C.S.: 334220

Global Invacom Limited (1)
Freeman House John Roberts Business Park, Kent, Canterbury, CT5 3BJ, United Kingdom
Tel.: (44) 2030533520
Satellite Equipment Mfr & Distr
N.A.I.C.S.: 334220

Global Invacom Manufacturing (UK) Limited (1)
Metcalf Drive Altham Industrial Estate, Lancashire, Accrington, BB5 5TU, United Kingdom
Tel.: (44) 1282770000
Satellite Equipment Mfr & Distr
N.A.I.C.S.: 334220

Global Invacom Manufacturing Pte Ltd (1)
8 Temasek Boulevard 18-02A Suntec Tower Three, Singapore, 038988, Singapore
Tel.: (65) 6431 0788
Satellite Equipment Mfr & Distr
N.A.I.C.S.: 334220

Subsidiary (Non-US):

Global Invacom Manufacturing (Shanghai) Co., Ltd. (2)
139 Fu Te Nan Road Waigaoqiao Free Trade Zone, Pudong, Shanghai, 200131, China
Tel.: (86) 2150480188
Satellite Equipment Mfr & Distr
N.A.I.C.S.: 334290

Global Invacom Sdn. Bhd. (1)
No 7 Lot 2608 Jalan Subang 6, Taman Perindustrian Subang, 47600, Subang Jaya, Selangor, Malaysia
Tel.: (60) 380814994
Communication Equipment Mfr
N.A.I.C.S.: 334290

Global Invacom Waveguide (1)
King Charles Business Park Old Newton Road, Newton Abbot Devon, Heathfield, TQ12 6UT, United Kingdom
Tel.: (44) 1626835255
Web Site: http://www.giwaveguide.com
Satellite Equipment Mfr & Distr
N.A.I.C.S.: 334220

Raven Antenna Systems, Inc. (1)
1315 Outlet Center Dr, Smithfield, NC 27577
Tel.: (919) 934-9711
Web Site: http://www.globalskyware.com
Wireless Communication Equipment Mfr & Whslr
N.A.I.C.S.: 334220
Bob Lockhart *(Gen Mgr)*

GLOBAL INVESTMENT SERVICES SA
23 rue Balzac, 75008, Paris, France
Tel.: (33) 144433300
Web Site: http://www.globalinse.com
Financial Support Services
N.A.I.C.S.: 523940
Gilles Boyer *(Chm & CEO)*

GLOBAL INVESTMENTS CAPITAL CORP.
1900 520-3rd Avenue SW, Calgary, T2P 0R3, AB, Canada
Tel.: (403) 669-4848
GLIN.P—(TSXV)
Assets: $222,315
Liabilities: $7,473
Net Worth: $214,842
Earnings: ($21,352)
Fiscal Year-end: 08/31/22
Business Consulting Services
N.A.I.C.S.: 522299
Thane R. Ritchie *(CEO)*

GLOBAL INVESTMENTS LIMITED
4 Shenton Way 02-01 SGX Centre 2, Singapore, 68807, Singapore
Tel.: (65) 65357511   SG
Web Site:
https://www.globalinvestmentltd.com
Year Founded: 2006
B73—(SES)
Rev.: $10,810,422
Assets: $196,927,213
Liabilities: $1,183,822
Net Worth: $195,743,392
Earnings: $6,518,216
Fiscal Year-end: 12/31/23
Investment Management Service
N.A.I.C.S.: 523940

GLOBAL JUHAN CORPORATION
2-4-1 Nishi-shinjuku 18th Floor-NS Building, Shinjuku-ku, Tokyo, 163-0818, Japan
Tel.: (81) 359083601
Web Site: http://www.global-j.co.jp
Year Founded: 1998
Real Estate Services
N.A.I.C.S.: 531390
Akihisa Okuda *(Dir)*

GLOBAL KEY INVESTMENT LIMITED
Suite 1601 1166 Alberni Street, Vancouver, V6E 3Z3, BC, Canada
Tel.: (604) 638-2234   BC
Web Site: http://www.globalkey.ca
Year Founded: 2007
Sales Range: Less than $1 Million
Wine Products Distr
N.A.I.C.S.: 424820
Vincent Fong *(Pres, CEO & Sec)*

GLOBAL KIDS COMPANY CORP.
2-14-36 Fujimi Chiyoda-Ku, Tokyo, 102-0071, Japan
Tel.: (81) 332397088
Web Site: http://www.gkids.jp
6189—(TKS)
Rev.: $178,214,240
Assets: $118,225,750
Liabilities: $60,768,390
Net Worth: $57,457,360
Earnings: ($389,950)
Fiscal Year-end: 09/30/23
Nursery School Management Services
N.A.I.C.S.: 624410
Yuichi Nakasho *(CEO)*

GLOBAL LAND MASTERS CORPORATION LIMITED
Village Daghota P O Barog Solan, Solan, 173211, Himachal Pradesh, India
Tel.: (91) 172 6543009
Web Site:
http://www.globallandmasters.com
Assets: $2,060,580
Liabilities: $2,783,233
Net Worth: ($722,653)
Earnings: ($24,943)
Fiscal Year-end: 03/31/18
Real Estate Development Services
N.A.I.C.S.: 531390
Surender Singh Deswal *(Mng Dir)*

GLOBAL LEADERS CORP.
Unit 305 3/F New East Ocean Centre No 9 Science Museum Road, Tsim Sha Tsui, Kowloon, China (Hong Kong)
Tel.: (852) 35823146   NV
Web Site:
http://www.globalleaders.com.hk
Year Founded: 2020
Assets: $2,838
Liabilities: $66,297
Net Worth: ($63,459)
Earnings: ($109,321)
Fiscal Year-end: 10/31/22
Management Consulting Services
N.A.I.C.S.: 541611
Peter Hoi Hing Yip *(Chm, Pres, CEO, CFO, Treas & Sec)*

GLOBAL LEISURE PARTNERS LLP
8th Floor 20 Balderton Street Mayfair, London, W1K 6TL, United Kingdom
Tel.: (44) 20 7016 8050   UK
Web Site:
http://www.globalleisurepartner.com
Year Founded: 2004
Emp.: 650
Investment Advisory & Private Equity Investment Services
N.A.I.C.S.: 523940
Mark W. B. Harms *(CEO, Founder & Chm)*

Subsidiaries:

Global Leisure Partners LLC (1)
525 Okeechobee Blvd Ste 1650, Palm Beach, FL 33401
Tel.: (561) 228-5381
Investment Advisory & Private Equity Investment Services
N.A.I.C.S.: 523940
Bader Alam *(VP)*

Affiliate (Domestic):

Bespoke Capital Partners, LLC (2)
525 Okeechobee Blvd Ste 1650, Palm Beach, FL 33401   (50%)
Tel.: (561) 228-5381
Web Site: http://www.bespokecp.com
Privater Equity Firm
N.A.I.C.S.: 523999
Mark W. B. Harms *(Founder & Co-Mng Partner)*

Joint Venture (Domestic):

Nomacorc, LLC (3)
400 Vintage Park Dr, Zebulon, NC 27597   (50%)
Tel.: (919) 460-2200
Web Site: http://www.nomacorc.com
Extruded Synthetic Wine Closures Mfr & Whslr
N.A.I.C.S.: 339999
Malcolm Thompson *(VP-Strategy & Innovation)*

GLOBAL LI-ION GRAPHITE CORP.
Suite 908 - 510 Burrard Street, Vancouver, V6C 3A8, BC, Canada
Tel.: (604) 608-6314

INTERNATIONAL PUBLIC

Web Site: https://www.globalliiongraphite.com
Year Founded: 2014
LION—(CNSX)
Rev.: $1,582
Assets: $3,295,574
Liabilities: $304,086
Net Worth: $2,991,489
Earnings: ($892,599)
Fiscal Year-end: 08/31/21
Graphite Mfr
N.A.I.C.S.: 335991
John Roozendaal *(Pres & CEO)*

GLOBAL LIGHTING TECHNOLOGIES INC.
1149 Sec 3 Min-Chuan Rd, Chung-Li, Zhongli, Taiwan
Tel.: (886) 34262828
Web Site: http://www.glthome.com
Year Founded: 2000
Sales Range: $100-124.9 Million
LED Lighting Mfr
N.A.I.C.S.: 334419
Mang-Shiang Lee *(Chm)*

Subsidiaries:

Global Lighting Technologies, Inc. (1)
55 Andrews Cir, Brecksville, OH 44141
Tel.: (440) 922-4584
Web Site: http://www.glthome.com
Sales Range: $25-49.9 Million
Emp.: 24
Lighting Equipment
N.A.I.C.S.: 335139

GLOBAL LIGHTS ACQUISITION CORP.
Room 902 Unit 1 8th Floor Building 5 No 201 Tangli Road, Chaoyang District, Beijing, 100123, China
Tel.: (86) 1059480786   Ky
Year Founded: 2021
GLAC—(NASDAQ)
Rev.: $449,957
Assets: $70,104,912
Liabilities: $72,435,390
Net Worth: ($2,330,478)
Earnings: $79,994
Fiscal Year-end: 12/31/23
Investment Management Service
N.A.I.C.S.: 523999

GLOBAL LINK MANAGEMENT, INC.
Mark City West 21F 1-12-1 Dogenzaka, Shibuya-Ku, Tokyo, 150-0043, Japan
Tel.: (81) 364156525
Web Site: https://www.global-link-m.com
Year Founded: 2005
3486—(TKS)
Rev.: $292,519,220
Assets: $227,213,230
Liabilities: $163,835,720
Net Worth: $63,377,510
Earnings: $20,405,020
Fiscal Year-end: 12/31/23
Real Estate Management Services
N.A.I.C.S.: 531390
Daejoong Kim *(CEO)*

Subsidiaries:

Global Link Partners Inc. (1)
Mark City West 14F 1-12-1 Dogenzaka, Shibuya-Ku, Tokyo, Japan
Tel.: (81) 364156523
Rental Management Services
N.A.I.C.S.: 531120
Yasumasa Tominaga *(CEO)*

GLOBAL LITHIUM RESOURCES LIMITED
Level 1 16 Ventnor Ave, West Perth, 6005, WA, Australia

AND PRIVATE COMPANIES

Tel.: (61) 861037488   AU
Web Site:
https://www.globallithium.com.au
Year Founded: 2018
GL1—(ASX)
Rev.: $33,112
Assets: $47,396,641
Liabilities: $2,920,530
Net Worth: $44,476,110
Earnings: ($3,257,998)
Fiscal Year-end: 06/30/22
Exploration & Mining Services
N.A.I.C.S.: 213115
Kevin Hart *(CFO)*

GLOBAL LOCK SAFETY (INTERNATIONAL) GROUP CO., LTD.
19/F Shenzhen Cadre Group Center Mansion, No 168 Tongsha Road Nanshan, Shenzhen, 518055, China
Tel.: (86) 755 83660755
Web Site: http://www.globallock.com
Sales Range: $10-24.9 Million
Emp.: 1,135
Security Related Products Mfr
N.A.I.C.S.: 561621
Jiafa Wang *(CTO)*

GLOBAL LOGISTIC PROPERTIES LIMITED
501 Orchard Road 08-01 Wheelock Place, Singapore, 238880, Singapore
Tel.: (65) 66436388   SG
Web Site: http://www.glprop.com
Year Founded: 2007
Sales Range: $800-899.9 Million
Emp.: 1,126
Holding Company; Logistics Facilities Investment, Development & Property Management Services
N.A.I.C.S.: 551112
Ming Z. Mei *(Co-Founder & CEO)*

Subsidiaries:

GLP Investment Management (China) Co., Ltd.   (1)
Room 2708 Azia Center 1233 Lujiazui Ring Road, Pudong, Shanghai, China **(66.21%)**
Tel.: (86) 21 6105 3999
Web Site: http://www.glprop.com
Logistics Facilities Investment, Development & Property Management Services
N.A.I.C.S.: 531312
Higashi Michihiro *(Chief Investment Officer)*

GLP Investment Management Pte. Ltd.   (1)
501 Orchard Road 08-01 Wheelock Place, Singapore, 238880, Singapore **(100%)**
Tel.: (65) 6643 6388
Web Site: http://www.glprop.com
Logistics Facilities Investment, Development & Property Management Services
N.A.I.C.S.: 531312
Ming Z. Mei *(CEO)*

Subsidiary (Non-US):

GLP Brasil Empreendimentos e Participacoes Ltda.   (2)
510 Pres Juscelino Kubitschek Avenida 6th Floor, Sao Paulo, 04543-000, SP, Brazil **(100%)**
Tel.: (55) 11 3500 3700
Web Site: http://www.glprop.com
Logistics Facilities Investment, Development & Property Management Services
N.A.I.C.S.: 531312
Mauro Dias *(Pres)*

Subsidiary (US):

GLP US Management LLC   (2)
2 N Riverside Plz Ste 2350, Chicago, IL 60606 **(100%)**
Tel.: (312) 940-5300
Web Site: http://www.glp-us.com
Logistics Facilities Investment, Development & Property Management Services
N.A.I.C.S.: 531312
Charles E. Sullivan *(Pres & COO)*

Global Logistics Properties Inc.   (1)
4F Shiodome City Center 1-5-2 Higashi-Shimbashi, Minato-ku, Tokyo, Japan **(100%)**
Tel.: (81) 3 6858 2250
Web Site: http://www.glprop.com
Logistics Facilities Investment, Development & Property Management Services
N.A.I.C.S.: 531312
Yoshiyuki Chosa *(Pres)*

Subsidiary (Domestic):

GLP Japan Advisors Inc.   (2)
4F Shiodome City Center 1-5-2 Higashi-Shimbashi, Minato-ku, Tokyo, 105-7104, Japan **(100%)**
Tel.: (81) 3 6858 2250
Web Site: http://www.glpja.com
Logistics Facilities Investment Advisory & Portfolio Management Services
N.A.I.C.S.: 523940
Masato Miki *(Pres & CEO)*

GLOBAL LONGLIFE HOSPITAL & RESEARCH LIMITED
Nr Bodakbev Garden Pakwan Cross Road, Nr sindhubhavan Road Off S G Highway Bodakdev, Ahmedabad, 380054, Gujarat, India
Tel.: (91) 7575001766
Web Site:
https://www.globalhospital.co.in
Year Founded: 2012
543520—(BOM)
Rev.: $2,846,400
Assets: $9,104,766
Liabilities: $1,396,631
Net Worth: $7,708,135
Earnings: $219,112
Emp.: 103
Fiscal Year-end: 03/31/23
Health Care Srvices
N.A.I.C.S.: 621610

GLOBAL MARKET GROUP LIMITED
No 28 & No 33 Yunshan North Street No 1128 Baiyun South Ave, Baiyun District, Guangzhou, 510420, China
Tel.: (86) 208 600 2299   Ky
Web Site:
http://www.globalmarket.com
Business-To-Business E-Commerce Services
N.A.I.C.S.: 425120

GLOBAL MASTERMIND HOLDINGS LTD.
Unit 1201 12/F West Tower Shun Tak Centre 168-200 Connaught Road, Central, China (Hong Kong)
Tel.: (852) 31522700   Ky
8063—(HKG)
Rev.: $1,708,755
Assets: $39,626,363
Liabilities: $16,784,100
Net Worth: $22,842,263
Earnings: ($20,759,040)
Emp.: 27
Fiscal Year-end: 12/31/22
Holding Company
N.A.I.C.S.: 551112
Elton Kwok Wai Cheung *(Chm)*

GLOBAL MASTERS FUND LIMITED
Level 12 Corporate Centre One 2 Corporate Court, Bundall, 4217, QLD, Australia
Tel.: (61) 56444400
Web Site:
https://www.globalmastersfund.com
GFL—(ASX)
Rev.: $451,981
Assets: $29,454,480
Liabilities: $9,496,951
Net Worth: $19,957,529
Earnings: ($930,355)

Fiscal Year-end: 06/30/22
Other Financial Vehicles
N.A.I.C.S.: 525990
Emmanuel Pohl *(Mng Dir)*

Subsidiaries:

EC Pohl & Co Pty. Ltd.   (1)
Level 12 Corporate Centre One 2 Corporate Court, Bundall, 4217, QLD, Australia
Tel.: (61) 756444400
Web Site: https://ecpohl.com
Portfolio Management Services
N.A.I.C.S.: 525910

GLOBAL METCORP LTD
Grove House, 55 Lowlands Road, Harrow On The Hill,, Middlesex, HA1 3AW, United Kingdom
Tel.: (44) 2084234449
Web Site:
https://www.globalmetcorp.com
Emp.: 100
Metal Product Whslr
N.A.I.C.S.: 423510

Subsidiaries:

Global Ardour Recycling Limited   (1)
Longridge Rd,, Preston, PR2 5BX, United Kingdom
Tel.: (44) 1772654321
Web Site: https://globalardour.co.uk
Waste Management Services
N.A.I.C.S.: 562998

GLOBAL MIXED-MODE TECHNOLOGY INC.
No 2 Industry E RD III Hsinchu Science Park, Hsin-chu, 300, Taiwan
Tel.: (886) 35788833
Web Site: https://www.gmt.com.tw
8081—(TAI)
Rev.: $258,702,695
Assets: $343,360,627
Liabilities: $68,452,530
Net Worth: $274,908,096
Earnings: $48,593,772
Emp.: 346
Fiscal Year-end: 12/31/23
Integrated Circuits Mfr
N.A.I.C.S.: 334413
Jiin-Cuan Wu *(Vice Chm & Pres)*

GLOBAL MOFY METAVERSE LIMITED
No 102 No A12 Xidian Memory Cultural & Creative Town 1st Floor, Gaobeidian Township Chaoyang District, Beijing, 100000, China
Tel.: (86) 1060525125   Ky
Web Site: https://www.globalmofy.cn
Year Founded: 2021
GMM—(NASDAQ)
Emp.: 28
Information Technology Services
N.A.I.C.S.: 541512
Haogang Yang *(CEO)*

GLOBAL MUTUAL PROPERTIES LIMITED
3rd Floor 43-45 Dorset Street, London, W1U 7NA, United Kingdom
Tel.: (44) 20 3355 9470
Web Site:
http://www.globalmutual.com
Year Founded: 2009
Property Investment & Management Platform
N.A.I.C.S.: 531311
Jonathan Feldman *(Exec Partner)*

Subsidiaries:

The Georgian Hotel   (1)
1415 Ocean Ave, Santa Monica, CA 90401
Tel.: (310) 395-9945
Web Site: http://www.georgianhotel.com
Hotels (except Casino Hotels) & Motels
N.A.I.C.S.: 721110
Everardo Choza *(Chief Engr)*

GLOBAL ORIENTAL BERHAD

GLOBAL NEW MATERIAL INTERNATIONAL HOLDINGS LIMITED
No 380 Feilu Road, Luzhai Town Luzhai County Guangxi Zhuang Autonomous Region, Liuzhou, China
Tel.: (86) 7726825678   Ky
Web Site: https://www.chesir.net
Year Founded: 2011
6616—(HKG)
Rev.: $147,327,066
Assets: $713,790,707
Liabilities: $148,169,168
Net Worth: $565,621,539
Earnings: $29,531,042
Emp.: 765
Fiscal Year-end: 12/31/23
Holding Company
N.A.I.C.S.: 551112
Ertian Su *(CEO)*

GLOBAL OFFSHORE SERVICES LTD.
3rd Floor Prospect Chambers D N Road Fort, Dadar West, Mumbai, 400001, India
Tel.: (91) 2235481800
Web Site:
https://www.globaloffshore.in
GLOBOFFS—(NSE)
Rev.: $18,972,193
Assets: $141,320,743
Liabilities: $219,970,896
Net Worth: ($78,650,153)
Earnings: ($99,754,360)
Emp.: 25
Fiscal Year-end: 03/31/19
Oil & Gas Exploration Services
N.A.I.C.S.: 213112
Aditya A. Garware *(Chm)*

Subsidiaries:

Global Offshore Services B.V.   (1)
Beurplein 37 Office No 1352, 3011 AA, Rotterdam, Netherlands
Tel.: (31) 102051401
Web Site: http://www.globaloffshore.nl
Vessel Requirement Services
N.A.I.C.S.: 488390

GLOBAL ONE REAL ESTATE INVESTMENT CORPORATION
13F East Tower Otemachi First Square 1-5-1 Otemachi, Chiyoda-ku, Tokyo, Japan
Tel.: (81) 332621494
Web Site: https://www.go-reit.co.jp
Year Founded: 2003
8958—(TKS)
Sales Range: $25-49.9 Million
Real Estate Investment Services
N.A.I.C.S.: 523999
Akio Uchida *(Exec Dir)*

GLOBAL OPPORTUNITIES TRUST PLC
28 Walker Street, Edinburgh, EH3 7HR, United Kingdom
Tel.: (44) 1313780500   UK
Web Site:
https://globalopportunitiestrust.com
Year Founded: 2003
GOT—(LSE)
Rev.: $4,636,614
Assets: $162,091,402
Liabilities: $393,739
Net Worth: $161,697,663
Earnings: ($3,895,299)
Fiscal Year-end: 12/31/20
Investment Management Service
N.A.I.C.S.: 525990
Sandy Nairn *(Portfolio Mgr)*

GLOBAL ORIENTAL BERHAD
G1-08 Galleria 2 Persiaran Equine

2999

GLOBAL ORIENTAL BERHAD

Global Oriental Berhad—(Continued)
Perdana Taman Equine, 43300, Seri Kembangan, Selangor Darul Ehsan, Malaysia
Tel.: (60) 389417878
Web Site: http://www.gob.com.my
GOB—(KLS)
Rev.: $83,096,720
Assets: $197,378,836
Liabilities: $142,620,317
Net Worth: $54,758,519
Earnings: $1,650,370
Emp.: 155
Fiscal Year-end: 03/31/23
Property Development Services
N.A.I.C.S.: 531311
Pei Fung Chin *(Sec)*

Subsidiaries:

Syarikat Tenaga Sahabat Sdn. Bhd. (1)
No 1 Jalan Putra Permai 1A Taman Equine, 43300, Seri Kembangan, Selangor, Malaysia
Tel.: (60) 389457878
Sales Range: $75-99.9 Million
Emp.: 110
Property Development Services
N.A.I.C.S.: 531311

Taman Equine (M) Sdn. Bhd. (1)
1 Jalan Putra Permai 1A Taman Equine, 43300, Seri Kembangan, Selangor, Malaysia
Tel.: (60) 389417878
Web Site: http://www.gob.com.my
Sales Range: $50-74.9 Million
Emp.: 100
Property Development Services
N.A.I.C.S.: 531311
Ranjeet Singh *(COO)*

Subsidiary (Domestic):

Duta Security Sdn. Bhd. (2)
No 2 Jalan Academy Purdana Taman Equine, Seri Kembangan, 43300, Selangor, Malaysia
Tel.: (60) 389417878
Sales Range: $10-24.9 Million
Emp.: 50
Security Consulting Services
N.A.I.C.S.: 541690

Tujuan Ehsan Sdn. Bhd. (2)
1 Jalan Putra Permai 1a Tmn Equine, Seri Kembangan, 43300, Selangor, Malaysia
Tel.: (60) 389417878
Web Site: http://www.gob.com.my
Sales Range: $50-74.9 Million
Emp.: 80
Property Development Services
N.A.I.C.S.: 531390
Ranjeet Singh *(COO)*

GLOBAL PALM RESOURCES HOLDINGS LIMITED

105 Cecil Street 24-01 The Octagon, Singapore, 069534, Singapore
Tel.: (65) 62200170
Web Site: http://www.gprholdings.com
BLW—(SES)
Rev.: $211,318,540,043
Assets: $664,235,121,893
Liabilities: $101,575,681,835
Net Worth: $562,659,440,058
Earnings: ($5,597,531,038)
Emp.: 824
Fiscal Year-end: 12/31/20
Crude Palm Oil
N.A.I.C.S.: 311224
Hong Kiat Tan *(Chm & CEO)*

GLOBAL PERSONALS LTD.

Minton Place Victoria Street, Windsor, SL4 1EG, United Kingdom
Tel.: (44) 1753 271280
Web Site: http://www.globalpersonals.co.uk
Year Founded: 2003
Sales Range: $25-49.9 Million
Emp.: 150
Internet Publishing Services
N.A.I.C.S.: 516210
Matthew Pitt *(Dir-Ops)*

GLOBAL PETROLEUM LIMITED

Level 4 91 William Street, Melbourne, 3000, VIC, Australia
Tel.: (61) 386115333 AU
Web Site: https://www.globalpetroleum.com.au
GBP—(LSE)
Rev.: $46,048
Assets: $2,364,843
Liabilities: $324,175
Net Worth: $2,040,668
Earnings: ($1,041,261)
Fiscal Year-end: 06/30/24
Oil & Gas Exploration
N.A.I.C.S.: 211120
Peter Hill *(CEO & Mng Dir)*

GLOBAL PHARMATECH, INC.

89 Ravine Edge Drive, Richmond Hill, L4E 4J6, ON, Canada
Tel.: (905) 787-8225
Year Founded: 2001
Pharmaceuticals Product Mfr
N.A.I.C.S.: 325412
Lianqin Qu *(Pres & CEO)*

GLOBAL PHILATELIC NETWORK

Wilhelmstrasse 48, 65138, Wiesbaden, Germany
Tel.: (49) 611 393 81
Web Site: http://www.heinrich-koehler.de
Holding Company; Rare Stamp Auction Services
N.A.I.C.S.: 551112

Subsidiaries:

Corinphila Auktionen AG (1)
Wiesenstrasse 8, 8032, Zurich, Switzerland
Tel.: (41) 44 389 9191
Web Site: http://www.corinphila.ch
Rare Stamp Auction Services
N.A.I.C.S.: 561990
Karl Louis *(Mng Dir)*

Corinphila Veilingen BV (1)
Heemraadschapslaan 100, 1181 VC, Amstelveen, Netherlands
Tel.: (31) 20 624 9740
Web Site: http://www.corinphila.nl
Emp.: 8
Rare Stamp Auction Services
N.A.I.C.S.: 561990
Nathan Bouscher *(Mng Dir)*

H.R. Harmer, Global Philatelic Network, Inc. (1)
2680 Walnut Ave Ste AB, Tustin, CA 92780
Tel.: (714) 389-9178
Web Site: http://www.hrharner.com
Rare Stamp Auction Services
N.A.I.C.S.: 561990
Jo Mills *(CFO & Dir-Auction)*

Heinrich Kohler Auctionshaus GmbH & Co. KG (1)
Wilhelmstrasse 48, 65183, Wiesbaden, Germany
Tel.: (49) 611 393 81
Web Site: http://www.heinrich-koehler.de
Rare Stamp Auction Services
N.A.I.C.S.: 561990
Dieter Michelson *(Mng Dir)*

John Bull Stamp Auctions, Ltd. (1)
7/F Kwong Fat Hong Building 1 Rumsey Street, Sheung Wan, China (Hong Kong)
Tel.: (852) 2890 5767
Web Site: http://www.jbull.hk
Rare Stamp Auction Services
N.A.I.C.S.: 561990
Philip Cheng *(Gen Mgr)*

GLOBAL PIELAGO, SOCIMI, S.A.

13th floor Paseo de la Castellana 93, 28046, Madrid, Spain
Web Site: https://www.niding.es
Year Founded: 2020
MLNDG—(EUR)
Rev.: $11,931,799
Assets: $387,600,617
Liabilities: $167,894,889
Net Worth: $219,705,728
Earnings: $31,959,395
Fiscal Year-end: 12/31/23
Real Estate Investment Services
N.A.I.C.S.: 531190
Maria Lorena Salamanca Cuevas *(Sec)*

GLOBAL PMX CO., LTD.

16th Floor No 102 Section 1 Xintai 5th Road, Xizhi District, New Taipei City, 221, Taiwan
Tel.: (886) 226962060
Web Site: https://www.global.com.tw
Year Founded: 1987
4551—(TAI)
Rev.: $232,899,170
Assets: $417,378,970
Liabilities: $158,032,533
Net Worth: $259,346,437
Earnings: $16,859,282
Fiscal Year-end: 12/31/23
Motor Vehicle Parts Mfr
N.A.I.C.S.: 336390
Maggie Lin *(Gen Mgr)*

GLOBAL PREMIUM HOTELS LIMITED

456 Alexandra Road, 25-01 Fragrance Empire Building, Singapore, 119962, Singapore
Tel.: (65) 6348 7888 SG
Web Site: http://www.gphl.com.sg
Year Founded: 1995
Rev.: $40,887,402
Assets: $873,530,242
Liabilities: $362,062,788
Net Worth: $511,467,455
Earnings: $8,375,432
Fiscal Year-end: 12/31/16
Hotel Operator
N.A.I.C.S.: 721110

GLOBAL RADIO GROUP LIMITED

30 Leicester Square, London, WC2H 7LA, United Kingdom
Tel.: (44) 2077666000
Web Site: http://www.thisisglobal.com
Sales Range: $50-74.9 Million
Emp.: 150
Radio Station Operator
N.A.I.C.S.: 516210
Ashley Tabor *(Grp CEO)*

Subsidiaries:

Classic FM (1)
30 Leicester Square, London, WC2H 7LA, United Kingdom
Tel.: (44) 2073439000
Web Site: http://www.classicfm.co.uk
Sales Range: $100-124.9 Million
Emp.: 500
Radio Stations
N.A.I.C.S.: 516110
Darren Henley *(Mng Dir)*

Essex FM (1)
Radio House 31 Glebe Rd, Chelmsford, CM1 1QG, Essex, United Kingdom
Tel.: (44) 1245525252
Web Site: http://www.essexfm.co.uk
Radio Stations
N.A.I.C.S.: 516110
James Haart *(Gen Mgr)*

Heart 102.4 (1)
St Georges Plain, 47-49 Colegate, Norwich, NR3 1DB, United Kingdom
Tel.: (44) 1603630621
Web Site: http://www.heart.co.uk

INTERNATIONAL PUBLIC

Sales Range: $25-49.9 Million
Emp.: 30
Radio Stations
N.A.I.C.S.: 516110
Roz Walker *(Head-Sls)*

Heart 103 (1)
Mold Road, Parc Menai, Wrexham, LL57 4BN, Wales, United Kingdom
Tel.: (44) 1248673400
Web Site: http://www.heart.co.uk
Sales Range: $25-49.9 Million
Emp.: 100
Radio Stations
N.A.I.C.S.: 516110

Heart FM (1)
Hawthorn House Exeter Business Park, Exeter, EX1 3QS, United Kingdom
Tel.: (44) 3332002000
Web Site: http://www.heart.co.uk
Sales Range: $25-49.9 Million
Emp.: 35
Radio Stations
N.A.I.C.S.: 516110
Sara Bond *(Mng Dir)*

Heart Home Counties (1)
Midsummer Boulevard 328 428 Chiltum Rd, Milton, MK9 2EA, United Kingdom
Tel.: (44) 1582676200
Web Site: http://www.heart.co.uk
Sales Range: $25-49.9 Million
Emp.: 20
Radio Stations
N.A.I.C.S.: 516110
Ian Stuart *(Mng Dir)*

Heart Thames Valley (1)
The Chase, Calcot, Reading, RG31 7RB, Berks, United Kingdom
Tel.: (44) 118 945 4400
Web Site: http://www.heart.co.uk
Sales Range: $25-49.9 Million
Emp.: 100
Radio Stations
N.A.I.C.S.: 516110
Becky East *(Mng Dir)*

Heart Wales (1)
The Red Dragon Centre, Cardiff, CF10 4DJ, United Kingdom
Tel.: (44) 2920315100
Web Site: http://www.heart.co.uk
Sales Range: $25-49.9 Million
Emp.: 50
Radio Stations
N.A.I.C.S.: 516110
Nicola Davies *(Mng Dir)*

GLOBAL REAL ESTATE GROUP

3 Shortlands, London, W6 8DA, United Kingdom
Tel.: (44) 203 609 8710
Web Site: http://www.globalrealestategroup.com
Real Estate Investment, Development & Sales
N.A.I.C.S.: 531210
Rishi Passi *(CEO)*

GLOBAL SAE-A CO., LTD

Sae-A Building 429 Yeongdong-daero, Gangnam-gu, Seoul, Korea (South)
Tel.: (82) 6252 7000 KR
Web Site: https://www.globalsae-a.com
Emp.: 100
Holding Company
N.A.I.C.S.: 551112

GLOBAL SERVICE CENTER PUBLIC COMPANY LIMITED

2991/14-15 Wisut Thani Building Ladproa Road, Khlongjan Sub-District Bangkapi District, Bangkok, 10240, Thailand
Tel.: (66) 27653999
Web Site: http://www.gsc-servicecenter.com
Year Founded: 2004

AND PRIVATE COMPANIES

GSC—(THA)
Rev.: $4,539,935
Assets: $3,874,650
Liabilities: $690,682
Net Worth: $3,183,968
Earnings: ($3,435,895)
Fiscal Year-end: 12/31/23
Telecommunication Servicesb
N.A.I.C.S.: 517112
Chun-Ting Wu *(Chm)*

GLOBAL SHIP LEASE, INC.
25 Wilton Road, London, SW1V 1LW, United Kingdom
Tel.: (44) 2039980063   MH
Web Site:
   http://www.globalshiplease.com
GSL—(NYSE)
Rev.: $674,795,000
Assets: $2,171,780,000
Liabilities: $987,392,000
Net Worth: $1,184,388,000
Earnings: $294,964,000
Emp.: 7
Fiscal Year-end: 12/31/23
Containership Owner & Operator
N.A.I.C.S.: 483111
Ian J. Webber *(CEO)*

Subsidiaries:

Global Ship Lease Services
Limited   (1)
25 Wilton Road, Stag Place, London, SW1V 1LW, United Kingdom
Tel.: (44) 2039980063
Shipping Services
N.A.I.C.S.: 532411

Poseidon Containers Holdings
LLC   (1)
Trust Company Complex Ajeltake Road, Ajeltake Island, Majuro, Marshall Islands   (100%)
Tel.: (44) 2039980060
Deep Sea Freight Transportation
N.A.I.C.S.: 483111

GLOBAL SM TECH LIMITED
928 223 Baengma-ro, Llsandong-gu, Goyang, Gyeonggi-do, Korea (South)
Tel.: (82) 319329970
Web Site:
   https://www.globalsmtech.com
Year Founded: 2008
900070—(KRS)
Rev.: $495,430
Assets: $644,096
Liabilities: $163,114
Net Worth: $480,982
Earnings: $33,117
Emp.: 747
Fiscal Year-end: 12/31/22
Fastener Mfr & Sales
N.A.I.C.S.: 339993
Yun Bak Na *(CEO)*

GLOBAL SMART CAPITAL CORP.
Room 1905 Nam Wo Hong Building 148 Wing Lok Street, Sheung Wan, China (Hong Kong)
Tel.: (852) 27833959532   NV
Year Founded: 2014
TDXP—(OTCBB)
Software Developer & Publisher
N.A.I.C.S.: 513210
Johannes Petrus Roux *(Pres & Treas)*

GLOBAL STANDARD TECHNOLOGY CO., LTD.
15-13 Dongtansandan6-gil, Dongtan-myeon, Hwaseong, Gyeonggi-do, Korea (South)
Tel.: (82) 313712200
Web Site: https://www.gst-in.com
Year Founded: 2001
083450—(KRS)
Rev.: $239,954,268
Assets: $193,154,731
Liabilities: $38,720,605
Net Worth: $154,434,125
Earnings: $36,510,728
Emp.: 719
Fiscal Year-end: 12/31/22
Semiconductor Machinery Mfr
N.A.I.C.S.: 333242

Subsidiaries:

GST America Inc.   (1)
1006 E Yager Ln Ste C-102, Austin, TX 78753
Tel.: (512) 289-6246
Scrubber Product Mfr
N.A.I.C.S.: 333242

GST Taiwan Ltd.   (1)
5F-1 No 6 Taiyuan 1st Street, Hsinchu County, Zhubei, 302, Taiwan
Tel.: (886) 932353364
Scrubber Product Mfr
N.A.I.C.S.: 333242

GLOBAL STEEL HOLDINGS LTD.
Office # 501 5th Floor LOB # 16 6th Roundabout, Jebel Ali Free Zone, Dubai, United Arab Emirates
Tel.: (971) 4 881 8384
Steel Producer
N.A.I.C.S.: 332111
Pramod Kumar Mittal *(Chm)*

GLOBAL STRATEGIC GROUP LIMITED
Unit A 11/F Neich Tower 128 Gloucester Road, Wanchai, China (Hong Kong)
Tel.: (852) 21059600   Ky
Web Site:
   http://www.globalstrategicgroup.com
8007—(HKG)
Rev.: $9,220,264
Assets: $31,631,442
Liabilities: $22,263,367
Net Worth: $9,368,075
Earnings: ($2,936,488)
Emp.: 50
Fiscal Year-end: 09/30/21
Information Technology Consulting Services
N.A.I.C.S.: 541512
Chi Kin Nip *(Controller-Fin)*

Subsidiaries:

Logo Plus Limited   (1)
786 Nathan Road Prosperity Commercial Building 11/F Prince Edward, 999077, Hong Kong, China (Hong Kong)
Tel.: (852) 23601900
Ecommerce Services
N.A.I.C.S.: 541890

GLOBAL STYLE CO., LTD.
MG Meguro Ekimae Building Room 915 21519 KamiOsaki, Shinagawa, Tokyo, 141-0021, Japan
Tel.: (81) 364554725
Web Site: https://www.glstyle.co.jp
Year Founded: 2016
7126—(TKS)
Rev.: $133,496,880
Assets: $317,349,120
Liabilities: $191,557,520
Net Worth: $125,791,600
Earnings: ($12,622,720)
Fiscal Year-end: 03/31/22
Apparel Retailer
N.A.I.C.S.: 424350

GLOBAL SURFACES LIMITED
Plot No PA-010-006 Engineering & Related Industries SEZ, Mahindra World City Jaipur Ltd Tehsil-Sanganer, Jaipur, 302037, Rajasthan, India
Tel.: (91) 1417190000   In
Web Site:
   https://www.globalsurfaces.in
Year Founded: 1991
GSLSU—(NSE)
Rev.: $21,682,393
Assets: $55,399,436
Liabilities: $24,066,663
Net Worth: $31,332,774
Earnings: $2,905,581
Emp.: 305
Fiscal Year-end: 03/31/23
Engineeering Services
N.A.I.C.S.: 541330
Rajesh Gattani *(CFO)*

Subsidiaries:

Global Surfaces FZE   (1)
S50902 Jebel Ali Freezone, PO Box 261236, Dubai, United Arab Emirates
Tel.: (971) 44939672
Mining Services
N.A.I.C.S.: 212210

GLOBAL SWEETENERS HOLDINGS LIMITED
Suites 2202-4 22nd Floor Tower 6 the Gateway 9 Canton Road, Tsim Sha Tsui, Kowloon, China (Hong Kong)
Tel.: (852) 28660186
Web Site: http://www.global-sweeteners.com
3889—(HKG)
Rev.: $45,844,793
Assets: $87,606,143
Liabilities: $174,429,435
Net Worth: ($86,823,293)
Earnings: ($27,092,603)
Emp.: 890
Fiscal Year-end: 12/31/22
Sweetener Products Producer
N.A.I.C.S.: 325199
Tieguang Wang *(Exec Dir)*

Subsidiaries:

Changchun Dihao Foodstuff Development Co., Ltd.   (1)
No 1326 Xihuan Road, Changchun, 130062, China
Tel.: (86) 43187875123
Corn Product Mfr & Distr
N.A.I.C.S.: 311999

Global Sweeteners Trade Development (Dalian) Co., Ltd.   (1)
No 499 Binhai West Road, Shahekou District, Dalian, 116021, China
Tel.: (86) 41183715091
Corn Product Distr
N.A.I.C.S.: 424510

Jinzhou Yuancheng Bio-chem Technology Co., Ltd.   (1)
No 9 Section 1 Xinghai Road, Jinzhou Economic and Technical Development Zone, Jinzhou, 121007, China
Tel.: (86) 4163588789
Corn Product Mfr & Distr
N.A.I.C.S.: 311999

Shanghai Hao Cheng Food Development Co., Ltd.   (1)
No 2017 Jiangchuan Road, Minhang District, Shanghai, 201111, China
Tel.: (86) 2134098878
Corn Product Mfr & Distr
N.A.I.C.S.: 311999

GLOBAL TAX FREE CO., LTD.
9Fl Sinil Bldg 131 Toegye-ro, Jung-gu, Seoul, Korea (South)
Tel.: (82) 025180837
Web Site: https://www.global-taxfree.com
Year Founded: 2014
204620—(KRS)
Rev.: $37,858,898
Assets: $111,490,731
Liabilities: $30,490,400

GLOBAL TOKEN LIMITED

Net Worth: $81,000,331
Earnings: ($8,585,694)
Emp.: 97
Fiscal Year-end: 12/31/22
Financial Investment Management Services
N.A.I.C.S.: 523940
Kang Jin Won *(CEO)*

GLOBAL TEK FABRICATION CO., LTD.
Building C 15F No 94 Sec 1 Xintai 5TH Rd, Xizhi Dist, Xinbei City, 221, Taiwan
Tel.: (886) 226963988
Web Site:
   https://www.globaltek.com.tw
Year Founded: 2008
4566—(TAI)
Rev.: $137,625,751
Assets: $272,255,655
Liabilities: $143,722,418
Net Worth: $128,533,237
Earnings: $8,576,245
Emp.: 550
Fiscal Year-end: 12/31/23
Automobile Parts Mfr
N.A.I.C.S.: 336110
Donald Huang *(Pres & CEO)*

GLOBAL TESTING CORPORATION LIMITED
No 75 Guangfu Road, Hu-Kou Hsin-Chu Industrial Park, Hsin-chu, 303, Taiwan
Tel.: (886) 35987168   SG
Web Site: https://www.gttw.com.tw
Year Founded: 1998
AYN—(SES)
Rev.: $40,586,000
Assets: $56,174,000
Liabilities: $10,989,000
Net Worth: $45,185,000
Earnings: $3,402,000
Emp.: 500
Fiscal Year-end: 12/31/23
Investment Management Service
N.A.I.C.S.: 523940
Tie-Min Pierre Chen *(Co-Chm & Sr Exec Dir)*

GLOBAL TOKEN LIMITED
3008-10 30th Floor Tower 6 The Gateway Harbour City 9 Canton Road, Tsim Sha Tsui, Kowloon, China (Hong Kong)
Tel.: (852) 2912 9288   BM
Web Site: http://www.8192.com.hk
Rev.: $23,089,800
Assets: $28,764,088
Liabilities: $2,503,490
Net Worth: $26,260,598
Earnings: ($19,743,045)
Emp.: 192
Fiscal Year-end: 12/31/18
Engineering Consultancy Services
N.A.I.C.S.: 541330
An Zhong Wang *(Exec Dir)*

Subsidiaries:

Blue Sky Environmental Technology (Shenzhen) Limited   (1)
Room 1206B Phase 2 North Zone Jingji Binhe Times Square, South of Binhe Avenue Fu Tian Street Fu Tian District, Shenzhen, China
Tel.: (86) 75582912860
Computer Products Distr
N.A.I.C.S.: 423430

Hing Lee Securities Limited   (1)
9 Canton Rd tsim Sha Tsui, Kowloon, China (Hong Kong)
Tel.: (852) 25212171
Security Trading Services
N.A.I.C.S.: 523150

United Property Finance Limited   (1)
Suite 2035 2nd Floor United Centre 95

GLOBAL TOKEN LIMITED

Global Token Limited—(Continued)
Queensway, Hong Kong, China (Hong Kong)
Tel.: (852) 21562186
Web Site: http://unitedpropertyfinance.com
Consumer Lending Services
N.A.I.C.S.: 522291

GLOBAL TOP E-COMMERCE CO., LTD.
No 632 Jianshe South Road, Yingze District, Taiyuan, 030027, Shanxi, China
Tel.: (86) 3515270116
Web Site: http://www.kjtbao.com
Year Founded: 2003
002640—(SSE)
Rev.: $1,018,530,396
Assets: $560,075,256
Liabilities: $356,530,356
Net Worth: $203,544,900
Earnings: $2,504,736
Fiscal Year-end: 12/31/22
Online Apparel Store Operator
N.A.I.C.S.: 459999
Li Yong *(Chm)*

GLOBAL TRADE CENTRE S.A.
Komitetu Obrony Robotnikow 45A, Nothus Building, 02-146, Warsaw, Poland
Tel.: (48) 221660700
Web Site: http://www.gtc.com.pl
Year Founded: 1994
G91—(DEU)
Rev.: $151,451,595
Assets: $2,932,553,262
Liabilities: $1,689,369,688
Net Worth: $1,243,183,575
Earnings: $13,688,045
Emp.: 219
Fiscal Year-end: 12/31/23
Real Estate Services
N.A.I.C.S.: 531390
Malgorzata Czaplicka *(Dir-IR)*

GLOBAL UAV TECHNOLOGIES LTD.
459-409 Granville St, Vancouver, V6C 1T2, BC, Canada   BC
Web Site: http://www.globaluavtech.com
Year Founded: 1987
YAB—(DEU)
Assets: $24,047
Liabilities: $1,015,517
Net Worth: ($991,469)
Earnings: ($121,707)
Fiscal Year-end: 10/31/23
Mineral Exploration Services
N.A.I.C.S.: 213114
James Rogers *(Pres)*

Subsidiaries:

Minera Alta Vista S.A. de C.V. (1)
Blvd las Quintas No 64 Col Santa Fe, Hermosillo, 83249, Sonora, Mexico
Tel.: (52) 662 210 4737
Emp.: 2
Mineral Exploration Services
N.A.I.C.S.: 212290

GLOBAL UIN INTELLIGENCE HOLDINGS LIMITED
Unit A 12/F China Overseas Building 139 Hennessy Road, Wanchai, China (Hong Kong)   Ky
Year Founded: 2013
8496—(HKG)
Rev.: $8,283,105
Assets: $2,004,742
Liabilities: $5,442,156
Net Worth: ($3,437,413)
Earnings: ($3,886,013)
Emp.: 76
Fiscal Year-end: 06/30/23
Holding Company

N.A.I.C.S.: 551112
Chun Kit Yu *(Sec)*

GLOBAL UNICHIP CORP.
No 10 Li-Hsin 6th Road Hsinchu Science Park, Hsinchu, 300096, Taiwan
Tel.: (886) 35646600
Web Site: https://www.guc-asic.com
Year Founded: 1998
3443—(TAI)
Rev.: $858,128,553
Assets: $689,163,518
Liabilities: $372,555,432
Net Worth: $316,608,085
Earnings: $114,714,506
Emp.: 861
Fiscal Year-end: 12/31/23
Integrated Circuits Mfr
N.A.I.C.S.: 334413
Daniel Chien *(CFO & Sr VP)*

Subsidiaries:

Global Unichip (Nanjing) Ltd. (1)
Room 140 1 Block C Fuying Building No 99 Tuanjie Road Pukou District, Nanjing, China
Tel.: (86) 18217787539
Soc Integration Services
N.A.I.C.S.: 541512

Global Unichip (Shanghai) Company, Limited (1)
Room 2305 No 1350 North Sichuan Road, Hongkou District, Shanghai, 200080, China
Tel.: (86) 2133665868
Soc Integration Services
N.A.I.C.S.: 541512

Global Unichip Corp. (1)
3F AnnJay Tower 208 Teheran-ro, Gangnam-gu, Seoul, 06220, Korea (South)
Tel.: (82) 25533842
Soc Integration Services
N.A.I.C.S.: 541512

Global Unichip Corp. (1)
2851 Junction Ave Ste 101, San Jose, CA 95134
Tel.: (408) 382-8900
Soc Integration Services
N.A.I.C.S.: 541512

Global Unichip Corp. Europe B.V. (1)
World Trade Center Tower H - 6th Floor Zuidplein 58, 1077, Amsterdam, Netherlands
Tel.: (31) 203052901
Soc Integration Services
N.A.I.C.S.: 541512

Global Unichip Japan Co., Ltd. (1)
Yokohama Landmark Tower 16F 2-2-1 Minatomirai, Yokohama, 220-8116, Japan
Tel.: (81) 452228256
Soc Integration Services
N.A.I.C.S.: 541512

GLOBAL VALUE FUND LIMITED
Level 7 330 Collins Street, Melbourne, 3000, VIC, Australia
Tel.: (61) 386899997
Web Site: https://www.globalvaluefund.com.au
GVF—(ASX)
Rev.: $26,595,167
Assets: $157,666,505
Liabilities: $16,287,991
Net Worth: $141,378,514
Earnings: $13,377,335
Fiscal Year-end: 06/30/24
Investment & Portfolio Management Services
N.A.I.C.S.: 523150
Jonathan Trollip *(Chm)*

GLOBAL VECTRA HELICORP LTD.
A-54 Kailash Colony, New Delhi, 110 048, India
Tel.: (91) 1146433300

Web Site: https://www.globalhelicorp.com
Year Founded: 1998
GLOBALVECT—(NSE)
Rev.: $44,478,238
Assets: $96,178,077
Liabilities: $89,640,410
Net Worth: $6,537,668
Earnings: ($3,996,270)
Emp.: 400
Fiscal Year-end: 03/31/21
Helicopter Charter Services
N.A.I.C.S.: 481212
Raakesh D. Soni *(Officer-Compliance & Sec)*

GLOBAL VIEW COMPANY LIMITED
35F No 287 Sec 2 Wenhua Rd, Banqiao Dist, New Taipei City, 220, Taiwan
Tel.: (886) 22578866
Web Site: http://www.gv.com.tw
3040—(TAI)
Rev.: $5,188,037
Assets: $53,248,175
Liabilities: $3,807,449
Net Worth: $49,440,725
Earnings: $2,099,742
Fiscal Year-end: 12/31/23
Electronic Products Mfr
N.A.I.C.S.: 334419
Wei-Jen shu *(Gen Mgr)*

GLOBAL WATER ASSET CORPORATION
1170 Place du Frere Andre 2 e etage, Montreal, H3B 3C6, QC, Canada
Tel.: (514) 518-0164
Waste Management Services
N.A.I.C.S.: 221310
Michel Pelletier *(Pres & CEO)*

GLOBAL WELLNESS STRATEGIES INC.
1100 - 1111 Melville St, Vancouver, V6E 3V6, BC, Canada
Tel.: (604) 484-0355   BC
Web Site: http://redfundcapital.com
Year Founded: 1998
GWSFF—(OTCQB)
Rev.: $79,692
Assets: $3,128
Liabilities: $207,034
Net Worth: ($203,905)
Earnings: ($1,075,626)
Fiscal Year-end: 09/30/20
Funding Solutions
N.A.I.C.S.: 525190
Meris Kott *(CEO)*

GLOBAL YATIRIM HOLDING A.S.
Buyukdere St No 193 Sisli, Beyoglu, Istanbul, Turkiye
Tel.: (90) 2122446000
Web Site: https://www.globalyatirim.com.tr
Year Founded: 2004
GLYHO—(IST)
Rev.: $246,631,664
Assets: $732,089,961
Liabilities: $586,425,489
Net Worth: $145,664,473
Earnings: $48,979,872
Emp.: 1,510
Fiscal Year-end: 12/31/22
Financial & Investment Services
N.A.I.C.S.: 523999
Mehmet Kutman *(Chm)*

Subsidiaries:

Crotone Cruise Port S.R.L. (1)
Molo Giunti - porto, 88900, Crotone, Crotone, Italy
Tel.: (39) 070660323

INTERNATIONAL PUBLIC

Web Site: https://www.crotonecruiseport.com
Shipping Services
N.A.I.C.S.: 811310

Ege Liman isletmeleri A.S (1)
Quay Street No 57 F 4 Karakoy, Istanbul, 34425, Turkiye
Tel.: (90) 2122446000
Web Site: http://www.egeports.com
Sales Range: $25-49.9 Million
Emp.: 15
Cost Management Services
N.A.I.C.S.: 488310

GES Enerji A.S (1)
Karakoy Rihtim Cad No 51, 34425, Istanbul, Turkiye
Tel.: (90) 2122446000
Sales Range: $25-49.9 Million
Emp.: 100
General Management Services
N.A.I.C.S.: 541611

Global Liman Isletmeleri A.S (1)
Rihtim Caddesi No 51 Karakoy, 34425, Istanbul, Turkiye
Tel.: (90) 2122446000
Web Site: http://www.globalyatirim.com.tr
Sales Range: $50-74.9 Million
Emp.: 200
Cost Management Services
N.A.I.C.S.: 488310

Global Menkul Degerler A.S (1)
Yesilce Mahallesi Eski Buyukdere Caddesi No 65 Kat 1, 34418, Istanbul, Turkiye
Tel.: (90) 2122445566
Web Site: http://www.global.com.tr
Sales Range: $100-124.9 Million
Emp.: 200
General Insurance Services
N.A.I.C.S.: 524210
Gokhan Ozer *(Vice Chm)*

Global Portfoy Yonetimi A.S (1)
Rihtim Caddesi No 51 Kat 2 Kemankes Mahallesi, 34425, Istanbul, Turkiye
Tel.: (90) 212 244 62 00
Web Site: http://www.portfoy.com
Asset Management Services
N.A.I.C.S.: 541618

Global Ports Holding Plc (1)
3rd Floor 35 Albemarle Street, London, W1S 4JD, United Kingdom (58.96%)
Tel.: (44) 2039112315
Web Site: https://www.globalportsholding.com
Rev.: $213,596,000
Assets: $900,600,000
Liabilities: $865,303,000
Net Worth: $35,297,000
Earnings: ($10,549,000)
Emp.: 562
Fiscal Year-end: 03/31/2023
Marine Cargo Handling Services
N.A.I.C.S.: 488320
Stephen Xuereb *(COO)*

Subsidiary (Non-US):

AD Port of Adria-Bar (2)
Street barskih logorasa 2, 85 000, Bar, Montenegro
Tel.: (382) 30301100
Web Site: http://www.portofadria.me
Port Operation Services
N.A.I.C.S.: 488310
Sedat Kara *(CEO)*

Cagliari Cruise Port Srl (2)
Molo Rinascita - Porto, 09123, Cagliari, CA, Italy
Tel.: (39) 070660323
Web Site: http://www.cagliaricruiseport.com
Port Operation Services
N.A.I.C.S.: 488310
Antonio Di Monte *(Gen Mgr)*

Catania Cruise Terminal Srl (2)
Terminal Crociere Sporgente Centrale, 95121, Catania, Italy
Tel.: (39) 0957465114
Web Site: http://www.cataniacruiseport.com
Port Operation Services
N.A.I.C.S.: 488310

Creuers del Port de Barcelona, S.A. (2)
World Trade Center - Terminal Sud Moll de

AND PRIVATE COMPANIES

Barcelona s/n, 08039, Barcelona, Spain
Tel.: (34) 934127914
Web Site: http://www.bcncruiseport.com
Port Operation Services
N.A.I.C.S.: 488310

Ravenna Terminali Passegeri Srl (2)
Porto Corsini, 48123, Ravenna, Italy
Tel.: (39) 0337560065
Web Site: http://www.ravennacruiseport.com
Port Operation Services
N.A.I.C.S.: 488310
Antonio Di Monte *(Gen Mgr)*

Valletta Cruise Port PLC (2)
Vault 1 Upper Floor Pinto Wharf Valletta Waterfront, Floriana, FRN 1913, Malta
Tel.: (356) 25673000
Web Site: http://www.vallettacruiseport.com
Port Operation Services
N.A.I.C.S.: 488310
John Portelli *(CEO)*

Zadar International Port Operations d.o.o. (2)
Gazenicka Cesta 28C, 23000, Zadar, Croatia
Tel.: (385) 23643390
Port Operation Services
N.A.I.C.S.: 488310

Global Securities (USA), Inc. (1)
9 Koritsas st, New York, NY 54639
Tel.: (211) 800-6563
Web Site: http://www.global.com.gr
Sales Range: $50-74.9 Million
Emp.: 80
Investment Services
N.A.I.C.S.: 523999

Global Sigorta Aracilik Hizmetleri A.S (1)
Ilpa Tesisleri No 126 Corlu, 59860, Corlu, Tekirdag, Turkiye (100%)
Tel.: (90) 2826734555
General Insurance Services
N.A.I.C.S.: 524210

Nassau Cruise Port Ltd. (1)
384 Bay Street The Kelly Building, Nassau, Bahamas
Tel.: (242) 603 1870
Web Site: https://www.nassaucruiseport.com
Port Operation Services
N.A.I.C.S.: 488310

Naturelgaz Sanayi ve Ticaret A.S. (1)
Esentepe Mah Ali Kaya Sok Polat Plaza B Blok No 1/1 IC Kapi No 86, Sisli, 34394, Istanbul, Turkiye
Tel.: (90) 2126137080
Web Site: https://www.naturelgaz.com
Rev.: $127,273,905
Assets: $62,280,027
Liabilities: $18,034,854
Net Worth: $44,245,173
Earnings: $25,985,780
Emp.: 245
Fiscal Year-end: 12/31/2023
Natural Gas Distribution Services
N.A.I.C.S.: 221210
Mehmet Kutman *(Chm)*

Sem Yayincilik A.S (1)
Buyukdere Cad Akabe Is Merk No 1/A, Istanbul, Turkiye
Tel.: (90) 2123473230
General Management Services
N.A.I.C.S.: 541611

Taranto Cruise Port S.R.L. (1)
Terminal Crociere Molo, S Cataldo, 74123, Taranto, Italy
Tel.: (39) 070660323
Web Site: https://www.tarantocruiseport.com
Cruise Ship Logistics Services
N.A.I.C.S.: 561910

Torba insaat ve Turistik A.S (1)
Rihtim Cad No 57 Karakoy, Istanbul, Turkiye
Tel.: (90) 2122446000
Residential Building Construction Services
N.A.I.C.S.: 236118

GLOBAL-E ONLINE LTD.
9 HaPsagot Street, Petah Tikva, 4951041, Israel
Tel.: (972) 732605078
Web Site: https://www.global-e.com
Year Founded: 2013
GLBE—(NASDAQ)
Rev.: $569,946,000
Assets: $1,202,360,000
Liabilities: $300,381,000
Net Worth: $901,979,000
Earnings: ($133,805,000)
Emp.: 923
Fiscal Year-end: 12/31/23
Online Shopping Services
N.A.I.C.S.: 423690
Amir Schlachet *(Co-Founder, Chm & CEO)*

Subsidiaries:

Borderfree, Inc. (1)
292 Madison Ave 5th Fl, New York, NY 10017
Tel.: (212) 299-3500
Web Site: http://shop.borderfree.com
Sales Range: $125-149.9 Million
International Ecommerce Services
N.A.I.C.S.: 518210

GLOBAL-TECH ADVANCED INNOVATIONS INC.
12 F Kin Teck Industrial Building 26 Wong Chuk Hang Road, Aberdeen, China (Hong Kong)
Tel.: (852) 2814 0601   HK
Web Site: http://www.global-webpage.com
Year Founded: 1991
Investment Holding Company; Electronic Components Mfr & Whslr
N.A.I.C.S.: 551112

Subsidiaries:

Global Optics Limited (1)
12/F Kin Teck Industrial Building 26 Wong Chuk Hang Road, Aberdeen, China (Hong Kong)
Tel.: (852) 28140601
Sales Range: $25-49.9 Million
Emp.: 100
Electronic & Optical Components Whslr
N.A.I.C.S.: 423690
John C. K. Sham *(CEO)*

Guangdong Lite Array Company Limited (1)
Yinxing Industrial Zone Qingxi, Dongguan, 523660, China (100%)
Tel.: (86) 75582703481
Web Site: http://www.globaloptics.cn
Electronic Component Mfr & Distr
N.A.I.C.S.: 334419

Kwong Lee Shun Trading Co., Ltd. (1)
12/F Kin Teck Industrial Building 26 Wong Chuk Hang Road, Aberdeen, China (Hong Kong)
Tel.: (852) 28140601
Web Site: http://www.kwong.com
Electric Products Wholesale Trade Broker
N.A.I.C.S.: 425120
John C. K. Sham *(CEO)*

GLOBALBLOCK DIGITAL ASSET TRADING LIMITED
The Canadian Venture Building 82 Richmond Street East 1st Floor, Toronto, M5C 1P1, ON, Canada
Tel.: (604) 513-0007
Web Site: http://www.helixapps.ca
Year Founded: 1997
BLVDF—(OTCEM)
Rev.: $530
Assets: $497,833
Liabilities: $56,445
Net Worth: $441,388
Earnings: $267,550
Fiscal Year-end: 12/31/23
Mineral Exploration Services
N.A.I.C.S.: 213114

Subsidiaries:

Belvedere Mining Oy (1)
Hitura Mine, Kummuntie 8, 85560, Ainastalo, Finland (100%)
Tel.: (358) 8 44991
Web Site: http://www.belmining.com
Nickel Mining
N.A.I.C.S.: 212230

GLOBALDATA PLC
John Carpenter House 7 Carmelite Street, London, EC4Y 0BS, United Kingdom
Tel.: (44) 2079366400   UK
Web Site: http://www.globaldata.com
Year Founded: 1999
DATA—(AIM)
Rev.: $306,993,184
Assets: $645,796,516
Liabilities: $584,827,064
Net Worth: $60,969,452
Earnings: $38,500,379
Emp.: 3,652
Fiscal Year-end: 12/31/22
Holding Company; Online Direct Marketing, Market Research & Website Hosting Services
N.A.I.C.S.: 551112
Michael Thomas Danson *(CEO)*

Subsidiaries:

AffiliateFuture Inc. (1)
Saint James Bldg 1133 Broadway Ste 1227, New York, NY 10010 (100%)
Tel.: (212) 242-8011
Web Site: http://www.affiliatefuture.com
Sales Range: $25-49.9 Million
Emp.: 5
Web Performance Advertising Services
N.A.I.C.S.: 541890

AffiliateFuture UK (1)
12-13 Essex St Standard House, London, WC2R 3AA, United Kingdom
Tel.: (44) 2071495954
Web Site: http://www.affiliatefuture.co.uk
Sales Range: $100-124.9 Million
Emp.: 300
Web Performance Advertising Services
N.A.I.C.S.: 541890

Canadean Limited (1)
Northern Cross Basing View, Basingstoke, RG21 4HL, Hants, United Kingdom
Tel.: (44) 1256394200
Web Site: https://www.canadean.com
Sales Range: $25-49.9 Million
Emp.: 5
Beverages Mfr
N.A.I.C.S.: 312111
Javier Artiach *(Dir-Canadean Peninsula Iberica & Latin America)*

Current Analysis, Inc. (1)
21335 Signal Hill Plz Ste 200, Sterling, VA 20164
Tel.: (703) 404-9200
Web Site: http://www.currentanalysis.com
Sales Range: $10-24.9 Million
Emp.: 160
Analytical Business Information & Competitive Response Solutions
N.A.I.C.S.: 561499
Jeremiah Caron *(Sr VP-Analysis)*

GD Research Centre Private Limited (1)
3rd Floor Jyothi Pinnacle Building Survey No 11, Kondapur Village Serilingampally Mandal Ranga Reddy District, Hyderabad, 500081, Telangana, India
Tel.: (91) 406 742 6700
Web Site: https://www.gdresearchcenter.com
Data Analytic Services
N.A.I.C.S.: 518210

GlobalData Australia Pty Limited (1)
Bourke Place Level 16 600 Bourke Street, Melbourne, 3000, VIC, Australia
Tel.: (61) 39 948 4089
Web Site: https://www.globaldata.net.au
Data Analytic Services
N.A.I.C.S.: 518210
Tony Bulzomi *(CEO)*

GlobalData Trading (Shanghai) Co., Limited (1)
Unit 01 15th Floor Office Building 1788 Nanjing West Road, International Center Jing'an, Shanghai, 200040, China
Tel.: (86) 2126018581
Consulting Services
N.A.I.C.S.: 541618

Infinata, Inc. (1)
41 Farnsworth St, Boston, MA 02205
Tel.: (781) 762-9450
Web Site: http://www.infinata.com
Data Management & Information Services Software
N.A.I.C.S.: 513210
Jason Krantz *(Founder)*

LMC International Limited (1)
4th Floor Clarendon House 52 Cornmarket Street, Oxford, OX1 3HJ, United Kingdom
Tel.: (44) 1865791737
Web Site: https://www.lmc.co.uk
Economic Consulting Services
N.A.I.C.S.: 541690

LMC Tyre & Rubber Limited (1)
4th Floor Clarendon House 52 Cornmarket Street, Oxford, OX1 3HJ, United Kingdom
Tel.: (44) 1865797602
Web Site: https://www.lmc-tyre.com
Synthetic Rubber Mfr & Distr
N.A.I.C.S.: 325212

MEED Media FZ LLC (1)
GBS building 6th Floor Al Falak Street Dubai Media City, PO Box 25960, Dubai, United Arab Emirates
Tel.: (971) 4 818 0263
Web Site: https://www.meed.com
Data Analytic Services
N.A.I.C.S.: 518210
Marianne Makdisi *(Head-Production)*

Media Business Insight Limited (1)
Standard House 12-13 Essex Street, London, WC2R 3AA, United Kingdom
Tel.: (44) 2081020900
Web Site: https://www.mb-insight.com
Film & Advertising Services
N.A.I.C.S.: 541840

Progressive Digital Media Limited (1)
John Carpenter House John Carpenter Street, London, EC4Y 0AN, United Kingdom
Tel.: (44) 2079366400
Web Site: https://www.progressivedigitalmedia.com
Sales Range: $125-149.9 Million
Emp.: 400
Online Marketing Services
N.A.I.C.S.: 541810

Sportcal Global Communications Limited (1)
John Carpenter House 7 Carmelite Stree, London, EC4Y 0BS, United Kingdom
Tel.: (44) 2089448786
Web Site: http://www.sportcal.com
Market Intelligence Services
N.A.I.C.S.: 541910

Tapps B.V. (1)
Oosteinde 7, NL-1017 WT, Amsterdam, Netherlands (100%)
Tel.: (31) 205244020
Web Site: http://www.tapps.nl
Sales Range: $50-74.9 Million
Emp.: 15
E-mail Direct Marketing Services
N.A.I.C.S.: 425120

Verdict Media Limited (1)
John Carpenter House 7 Carmelite Street, London, EC4Y 0BS, United Kingdom
Tel.: (44) 207 936 6400
Web Site: https://www.verdict.co.uk
Data Analytic Services
N.A.I.C.S.: 518210

World Market Intelligence Limited (1)
40-42 Hatton Garden, London, EC1N 3EB, United Kingdom
Tel.: (44) 207 936 6400
Web Site: https://www.wmipublishing.com
Data Analytic Services
N.A.I.C.S.: 518210

iD Factor Limited (1)

GLOBALDATA PLC

GlobalData Plc—(Continued)
John Carpenter House John Carpenter Street, London, EC4Y 0BS, United Kingdom **(100%)**
Tel.: (44) 2079366550
Web Site: http://www.theidfactor.com
Emp.: 500
Online Market Research Services
N.A.I.C.S.: 541910
Chris Herbert *(Head-Res)*

GLOBALE RUECKVERSICHERUNGS-AG
Im Mediapark 4b, Cologne, 50670, Germany
Tel.: (49) 22128890
Web Site: http://www.globalre.com
Sales Range: $50-74.9 Million
Emp.: 100
Reinsurance Services
N.A.I.C.S.: 524130
Volker Weisbrodt *(Chm)*

Subsidiaries:

GLOBAL General & Reinsurance Company Ltd. **(1)**
4 Eastcheap, London, EC3M 1AE, United Kingdom
Tel.: (44) 2071733300
Web Site: http://www.globalre.uk.com
Sales Range: $50-74.9 Million
Emp.: 11
Reinsurance Services
N.A.I.C.S.: 524130

GLOBAL International Reinsurance Company Ltd. **(1)**
Suite 3 Pasea Financial Centre corner Dayrells Rd, Harts Gap, Saint Michael, BB 14030, Barbados
Tel.: (246) 2281411
Web Site: http://www.globalre.com
Sales Range: $50-74.9 Million
Emp.: 1
Reinsurance Services
N.A.I.C.S.: 524130

GLOBAL Life Reinsurance Company of Australia Pty. Ltd. **(1)**
Gerling House, 44 Pitt Street, Sydney, 2000, NSW, Australia
Tel.: (61) 292518055
Web Site: http://www.globalre.com
Sales Range: $50-74.9 Million
Emp.: 20
Life & Reinsurance Services
N.A.I.C.S.: 524130

GLOBAL Reinsurance Company **(1)**
480 University Ave Suite 1400, Toronto, M5G 1V6, ON, Canada
Tel.: (416) 598-4688
Web Site: http://www.globalre.com
Sales Range: $50-74.9 Million
Emp.: 80
Reinsurance Services
N.A.I.C.S.: 524130

GLOBAL Reinsurance Company **(1)**
Level 29 Wisma Goldhill 67 Jalan Raja Chulan, 50200, Kuala Lumpur, Malaysia
Tel.: (60) 3 20318090
Reinsurance Services
N.A.I.C.S.: 524130

GLOBALE Rueckversicherungs-AG **(1)**
31 Rue Jean Giraudoux, 75016, 75116, Paris, France
Tel.: (33) 140672100
Web Site: http://www.globalre.com
Sales Range: $50-74.9 Million
Emp.: 7
Reinsurance Services
N.A.I.C.S.: 524130

GLOBALE Rueckversicherungs-AG **(1)**
Via Andrea Appiani 12, 20121, Milan, Italy
Tel.: (39) 02636141
Web Site: http://www.globalre.com
Sales Range: $1-9.9 Million
Reinsurance Services
N.A.I.C.S.: 524130

GLOBALINK, LTD.
385 Boundary Road, Vancouver, V5K 4S1, BC, Canada
Tel.: (604) 828-8822 **NV**
Year Founded: 2006
GOBK—(OTCBB)
Sales Range: Less than $1 Million
Online Hotel Booking Services
N.A.I.C.S.: 561599
Robin Young *(Sec)*

GLOBALIVE COMMUNICATIONS INC.
48 Yonge Street Suite 1200, Toronto, M5E 1G6, ON, Canada
Tel.: (416) 204-7559 **Ca**
Web Site: http://www.globalive.com
Year Founded: 1998
Sales Range: $25-49.9 Million
Emp.: 1,200
Telecommunication Servicesb
N.A.I.C.S.: 517112
Anthony Lacavera *(Founder & Chm)*

GLOBALIVE TECHNOLOGY, INC.
48 Yonge St, Toronto, M5E 1G6, ON, Canada
Tel.: (416) 204-7559
Web Site: https://www.globalive.com
LVVEF—(OTCIQ)
Rev.: $202,322
Assets: $18,523,056
Liabilities: $116,934
Net Worth: $18,406,122
Earnings: ($11,156,379)
Fiscal Year-end: 12/31/19
Telecommunication Servicesb
N.A.I.C.S.: 517112
Anthony Lacavera *(Founder, Chm & CEO)*

GLOBALM-GROUP PLC
145-147 St John Street, London, EC1V 4PW, United Kingdom
Tel.: (44) 2071930107
Web Site: http://www.klareswasser.biz
Investment Services
N.A.I.C.S.: 523999
Bryan Cook *(Chm)*

GLOBALPORT 900 INC.
Unit 2701 One Corporate Centre, Meralco Avenue corner Julia Vargas Avenue Ortigas Center, Pasig, Philippines
Tel.: (63) 286378851
Web Site: https://www.globalport900.com
Year Founded: 1933
PORT—(PHI)
Assets: $4,629,059
Liabilities: $1,589,435
Net Worth: $3,039,624
Earnings: ($278,658)
Fiscal Year-end: 12/31/19
Insurance Related Services
N.A.I.C.S.: 531390
Sheila Marie B. Romero *(Chm & CEO)*

GLOBALSAT WORLDCOM CORP.
16F No 186 Jian 1st Rd, Zhonghe Dist, New Taipei City, Taiwan
Tel.: (886) 282263799
Web Site: https://www.globalsat.com.tw
Year Founded: 2000
3499—(TPE)
Rev.: $10,239,971
Assets: $34,323,516
Liabilities: $16,409,874
Net Worth: $17,913,642
Earnings: ($127,505)
Fiscal Year-end: 12/31/22
Hardware Equipment Mfr
N.A.I.C.S.: 334290
Cheng Hsien-Lung *(Pres)*

GLOBALSPACE TECHNOLOGIES LIMITED
Office No 605 A-1 B-Wing Rupa Solitaire, Millennium Business Park Mahape, Navi Mumbai, 400 710, Maharashtra, India
Tel.: (91) 2246006568 **In**
Web Site: https://www.globalspace.in
540654—(BOM)
Rev.: $3,709,426
Assets: $7,313,676
Liabilities: $2,428,939
Net Worth: $4,884,737
Earnings: $774,887
Emp.: 65
Fiscal Year-end: 03/31/21
Software Development Services
N.A.I.C.S.: 513210
Krishna Murari Singh *(Founder, Chm & Mng Dir)*

Subsidiaries:

Makebot Robotic Solutions Private Limited **(1)**
No 606 A-1 B-Wing Rupa Solitaire Building Millennium Business Park, Mahape, Navi Mumbai, 400710, India
Tel.: (91) 8879421010
Web Site: https://www.makebot.in
Education Management Services
N.A.I.C.S.: 611710
Amit Verma *(Co-Founder)*

GLOBALSTAR EMEA LTD.
Stephenson House 75 Hampstead Road, London, NW1 2PL, United Kingdom
Tel.: (44) 2077538811
Web Site: http://www.globalstartravel.com
Year Founded: 2001
Sales Range: $500-549.9 Million
Emp.: 16,253
Travel Services
N.A.I.C.S.: 561510
Jason Harris *(Exec Dir-Supplier Rels & Hotel Program)*

GLOBALTEC FORMATION BERHAD
Unit 23A-12 Menara Q Sentral No 2A Jalan Stesen Sentral 2, Kuala Lumpur Sentral, 50470, Kuala Lumpur, Malaysia
Tel.: (60) 322760195 **MY**
Web Site: https://www.globaltec.com.my
Year Founded: 2011
GLOTEC—(KLS)
Rev.: $44,664,550
Assets: $89,749,630
Liabilities: $20,509,418
Net Worth: $69,240,212
Earnings: $1,988,995
Emp.: 846
Fiscal Year-end: 06/30/23
Holding Company
N.A.I.C.S.: 551112
Tian Chuan Goh *(Founder & Chm)*

Subsidiaries:

AIC Corporation Berhad **(1)**
Wisma AIC Lot 3 Persiaran Kemajuan, Seksyen 16, Shah Alam, 40200, Selangor Darul Ehsan, Malaysia
Tel.: (60) 355431413
Web Site: http://www.aic.com.my
Sales Range: $50-74.9 Million
Semiconductor Devices Mfr
N.A.I.C.S.: 334413
Heng Mun Chen *(CFO)*

INTERNATIONAL PUBLIC

Subsidiary (Domestic):

Prodelcon Sdn. Bhd. **(2)**
78 Lintang Bayan Lepas 7 Phase IV Kawasan Perindustrian, 11900, Bayan Lepas, Pulau Pinang, Malaysia
Tel.: (60) 46438913
Web Site: https://www.psb.com.my
Emp.: 300
Mfr of Precision Toolings, Die-Sets, Semiconductor Molds & High Precision Jigs & Fixtures for Semiconductor Industry
N.A.I.C.S.: 333514

AutoV Corporation Berhad **(1)**
Wisma AIC Lot 3 Persiaran Kemajuan Seksyen 16, 40200, Shah Alam, Selangor Darul Ehsan, Malaysia
Tel.: (60) 355415518
Web Site: https://www.autov.com.my
Sales Range: $25-49.9 Million
Emp.: 250
Automotive Components Mfr & Supplier
N.A.I.C.S.: 336390
Bernard Kong *(Chm)*

Subsidiary (Domestic):

Autoventure Mando Sdn. Bhd. **(2)**
PT 19237 Lorong Hj Abdul Manan 2 Jalan Hj Abdul Manan, Bt 5 1/2 off Jalan Meru, 41050, Kelang, Selangor, Malaysia
Tel.: (60) 3 3392 7634
Automotive Steering Equipment Mfr
N.A.I.C.S.: 336330

Proreka (M) Sdn. Bhd. **(2)**
No 17 Jalan Industri PBP 3 Taman Industri Pusat Bandar Puchong, 47100, Puchong, Selangor Darul Ehsan, Malaysia
Tel.: (60) 358822661
Web Site: https://www.proreka.com
Automotive Component Mfr & Distr
N.A.I.C.S.: 336330
Yong Nam Yun *(CEO)*

AutoV Corporation Sdn. Bhd. **(1)**
Wisma AIC Lot 3 Persiaran Kemajuan Seksyen 16, 40200, Shah Alam, Selangor Darul Ehsan, Malaysia
Tel.: (60) 355415518
Web Site: https://www.autov.com.my
Automotive Component Mfr & Distr
N.A.I.C.S.: 314110

Autoventure Corporation Sdn. Bhd. **(1)**
Wisma AIC Lot 3 Persiaran Kemajuan Seksyen 16, 40200, Shah Alam, Selangor Darul Ehsan, Malaysia
Tel.: (60) 355415518
Web Site: https://www.autov.com.my
Automotive Components Mfr
N.A.I.C.S.: 336390

GLOBALTRANS INVESTMENT PLC
Omirou 20 Agios Nikolaos, CY-3095, Limassol, CY-3095, Cyprus
Tel.: (357) 25212382 **CY**
Web Site: https://www.globaltrans.com
Year Founded: 2004
GLTR—(MOEX)
Rev.: $1,170,739,324
Assets: $1,457,285,199
Liabilities: $341,252,197
Net Worth: $1,116,033,001
Earnings: $431,618,158
Emp.: 1,802
Fiscal Year-end: 12/31/23
Freight Rail Transportation Services
N.A.I.C.S.: 488210
Alexander Eliseev *(Co-Founder)*

Subsidiaries:

AS Spacecom **(1)**
Moisa 4, Tallinn, EE-13522, Estonia
Tel.: (372) 678 8240
Web Site: http://www.spacecom.ee
Railway Tank Car Services
N.A.I.C.S.: 532411

BaltTransServis, OOO **(1)**
Lakhtinsky pr 85 building 3 structure 1 Business Center Business Box, Saint Peters-

AND PRIVATE COMPANIES

burg, 197229, Russia
Tel.: (7) 8123265010
Web Site: https://www.bts.ru
Railway Transportation Services
N.A.I.C.S.: 482111

GLOBALVIA INVERSIONES, S.A.U.

Torre De Cristal Paseo Dela Castellana, 259 C Plantas 21-22, 28046, Madrid, Spain
Tel.: (34) 914565850
Web Site: https://www.globalvia.com
Sales Range: $500-549.9 Million
Transport Infrastructure Management & Services
N.A.I.C.S.: 488999
Javier Perez Fortea *(CEO)*

Subsidiaries:

The Go-Ahead Group plc (1)
3rd Floor 41-51 Grey Street, Newcastle upon Tyne, NE1 6EE, United Kingdom
Tel.: (44) 1912323123
Web Site: http://www.go-ahead.com
Rev.: $5,292,935,648
Assets: $3,082,703,260
Liabilities: $2,718,019,668
Net Worth: $364,683,592
Earnings: ($16,428,412)
Emp.: 30,000
Fiscal Year-end: 06/27/2020
Holding Company; Commuter Bus, Rail & Parking Services
N.A.I.C.S.: 551112
Martin Harris *(Mng Dir-Brighton & Hove Buses)*

Subsidiary (Domestic):

Brighton & Hove Bus & Coach Company Limited (2)
43 Conway Street, Hove, BN3 3LT, East Sussex, United Kingdom (100%)
Tel.: (44) 127 388 6200
Web Site: https://www.buses.co.uk
Sales Range: $550-599.9 Million
Emp.: 1,050
Urban Bus Transportation Services
N.A.I.C.S.: 485113

City of Oxford Motor Services Limited (2)
Cowley House Watlington Road, Cowley, Oxford, OX4 6GA, United Kingdom
Tel.: (44) 186 578 5400
Web Site: https://www.oxfordbus.co.uk
Sales Range: $125-149.9 Million
Emp.: 600
Bus Transportation Services
N.A.I.C.S.: 485210

East Yorkshire Motor Services Limited (2)
3rd Floor 41-51 Grey Street, Newcastle upon Tyne, NE1 6EE, United Kingdom
Tel.: (44) 148 259 2929
Web Site:
   https://www.eastyorkshirebuses.co.uk
Travel Management Services
N.A.I.C.S.: 561510

Go North East Limited (2)
3rd Floor 41-51 Grey Street, Newcastle upon Tyne, NE1 6EE, United Kingdom (99%)
Tel.: (44) 1914205050
Web Site: http://www.simplygo.com
Sales Range: $550-599.9 Million
Emp.: 2,050
Urban Bus Transportation Services
N.A.I.C.S.: 485113

Go North West Limited (2)
Boyle Street, Manchester, M8 8UT, United Kingdom
Tel.: (44) 330 123 4121
Web Site: https://www.gonorthwest.co.uk
Truck Transportation Services
N.A.I.C.S.: 484121

Go South Coast Limited (2)
2-8 Parkstone Road, Poole, BH15 2PR, Dorset, United Kingdom
Tel.: (44) 120 233 6420
Web Site: https://gosouthcoast.co.uk
Emp.: 1,700

Holding Company; Urban Bus Transportation Services
N.A.I.C.S.: 551112

Subsidiary (Domestic):

Solent Blue Line Ltd. (3)
3rd Floor 41-51 Grey Street, Newcastle, NE1 6EE, United Kingdom
Tel.: (44) 1202338421
Web Site: http://www.bluestarbus.co.uk
Urban Bus Transportation Services
N.A.I.C.S.: 485113

Southern Vectis Omnibus Company Ltd. (3)
Nelson Road, Newport, PO30 1RD, Isle of Wight, United Kingdom
Tel.: (44) 1983827000
Web Site: http://www.islandbuses.info
Sales Range: $50-74.9 Million
Emp.: 250
Local Bus Transportation Services
N.A.I.C.S.: 485113

Wilts and Dorset Bus Company Ltd. (3)
Third Floor 41-51 Grey Street, Newcastle, NE1 6EE, United Kingdom
Tel.: (44) 1202338420
Web Site: http://www.morebus.co.uk
Urban Bus Transportation Services
N.A.I.C.S.: 485113

Subsidiary (Domestic):

Go-Ahead Leasing Limited (2)
3rd Floor 41-51 Grey Street, Newcastle upon Tyne, NE1 6EE, United Kingdom
Tel.: (44) 19 1232 3123
Web Site: http://www.go-ahead.com
Sales Range: $50-74.9 Million
Emp.: 40
Financial Lending Services
N.A.I.C.S.: 522220

Go-Ahead London (2)
No 18 Merton High Street, London, SW19 1DN, United Kingdom (100%)
Tel.: (44) 2085456100
Web Site: http://www.goaheadlondon.com
Holding Company; Urban Bus Transportation Services
N.A.I.C.S.: 551112

Unit (Domestic):

London Central (3)
18 Merton High St, London, SW19 1DN, United Kingdom (100%)
Tel.: (44) 2085456100
Web Site: http://www.londoncentral.com
Sales Range: $50-74.9 Million
Emp.: 150
Urban Bus Transportation Services
N.A.I.C.S.: 485113

London General (3)
18 Merton High Street, London, SW19 1DN, United Kingdom (100%)
Tel.: (44) 2086461747
Web Site: http://www.londongeneral.co.uk
Sales Range: $50-74.9 Million
Emp.: 150
Urban Bus Transportation Services
N.A.I.C.S.: 485113

Subsidiary (Non-US):

Go-Ahead Transport Services (Dublin) Limited (2)
Ballymount Road Lower, Dublin, D12 X201, Ireland
Tel.: (353) 81 880 4071
Web Site: https://www.goaheadireland.ie
Travel Management Services
N.A.I.C.S.: 561510
Andy Edwards *(Mng Dir)*

Subsidiary (Domestic):

Govia Limited (2)
6th Floor 1 Warwick Row, London, SW1E 5ER, United Kingdom (65%)
Tel.: (44) 2078213939
Web Site: http://www.govia.info
Sales Range: $50-74.9 Million
Emp.: 15
Holding Company; Commuter Rail Services & Train Station Operator
N.A.I.C.S.: 551112

Subsidiary (Domestic):

London & South Eastern Railway Limited (3)
Friars Bridge Court 41-45 Blackfriars Road, PO Box 63428, London, SE1 8PG, United Kingdom
Tel.: (44) 3453227021
Web Site:
   http://www.southeasternrailway.co.uk
Commuter Rail Services
N.A.I.C.S.: 485112

London Midland (3)
102 New Street, PO Box 4323, Birmingham, B2 4JB, W Midlands, United Kingdom (100%)
Tel.: (44) 1216541278
Web Site: http://www.londonmidland.com
Commuter Rail Services
N.A.I.C.S.: 485112

Southern Railway Limited (3)
Go Ahead House 26-28 Addiscombe Road, Croydon, CR9 5GA, Surrey, United Kingdom (100%)
Tel.: (44) 2089298600
Web Site: http://www.southernrailway.com
Commuter Railway Transportation Services
N.A.I.C.S.: 485112
Charles Horton *(CEO)*

Subsidiary (Domestic):

Konectbus Limited (2)
Norwich Bus Station Surrey Street, Norwich, NR1 3NX, United Kingdom
Tel.: (44) 3300539358
Web Site: http://www.konectbus.co.uk
Bus Operating Services
N.A.I.C.S.: 485210

London General Transport Services Limited (2)
No 18 Merton High Street, London, SW19 1DN, United Kingdom
Tel.: (44) 208 545 6100
Web Site: https://www.goaheadlondon.com
Transportation Services
N.A.I.C.S.: 484122

London and Birmingham Railway Limited (2)
102 New St, PO Box 4323, Birmingham, B24HQ, United Kingdom
Tel.: (44) 1216541318
Web Site: http://www.londonmidland.com
Rail Transportation Services
N.A.I.C.S.: 488210

Metrobus Limited (2)
Wheatstone Close, Crawley, RH10 9UA, West Sussex, United Kingdom
Tel.: (44) 1293449191
Web Site: http://www.metrobus.co.uk
Sales Range: $550-599.9 Million
Emp.: 1,400
Urban Bus Transportation Services
N.A.I.C.S.: 485113

Plymouth CityBus Limited (2)
1 Milehouse Road Milehouse, Plymouth, PL3 4AA, Devon, United Kingdom (100%)
Tel.: (44) 1752662271
Web Site: http://www.plymouthcitybus.co.uk
Sales Range: $150-199.9 Million
Emp.: 500
Urban Bus Transportation Services
N.A.I.C.S.: 485113
Richards Stevens *(Mng Dir)*

Thames Travel (Wallingford) Limited (2)
Thames Travel Collett Southmead Park, Didcot, OX11 7ET, United Kingdom
Tel.: (44) 1865785400
Web Site: http://www.thames-travel.co.uk
Sales Range: $25-49.9 Million
Emp.: 110
Passenger Bus Transportation Services
N.A.I.C.S.: 485210

The Oxford Bus Company Ltd (2)
Cowley House Watlington Road, Oxford, OX4 6GA, Cowley, United Kingdom (100%)
Tel.: (44) 865785400
Web Site: http://www.oxfordbus.co.uk
Sales Range: $250-299.9 Million
Emp.: 550
Urban Bus Transportation Services

GLOBAVEND HOLDINGS LIMITED

N.A.I.C.S.: 485113

GLOBALWAY, INC.

19th floor Sumitomo Real Estate Harajuku Building 2-34-17 Jingumae, Tokyo, 150-0001, Japan
Tel.: (81) 354417193
Web Site:
   https://www.globalway.co.jp
Year Founded: 2004
3936—(TKS)
Rev.: $16,234,160
Assets: $12,876,280
Liabilities: $3,086,870
Net Worth: $9,789,410
Earnings: ($1,315,390)
Emp.: 139
Fiscal Year-end: 03/31/24
Web Media Services
N.A.I.C.S.: 518210
Masato Kakamu *(Pres & Dir-Social & Web Media Bus)*

GLOBALWORTH REAL ESTATE INVESTMENTS LIMITED

Globalworth Tower 201 Barbu Vacarescu St, 2nd District, 020276, Bucharest, Romania
Tel.: (40) 372800000   GY
Web Site:
   https://www.globalworth.com
Year Founded: 2013
GWI—(AIM)
Rev.: $274,277,046
Assets: $4,458,588,579
Liabilities: $2,302,580,300
Net Worth: $2,156,008,279
Earnings: ($57,475,491)
Fiscal Year-end: 12/31/20
Investment Management Service
N.A.I.C.S.: 523940
Ioannis Papalekas *(Founder)*

Subsidiaries:

Globalworth Poland (1)
Spektrum Tower Twarda 18 St 7th floor, 00-105, Warsaw, Poland
Tel.: (48) 222780600
Web Site: http://www.en.globalworth.pl
Real Estate Manangement Services
N.A.I.C.S.: 531390
Dimitris Raptis *(CEO)*

GLOBANT S.A.

37A Avenue J F Kennedy, L-1855, Luxembourg, Luxembourg
Tel.: (352) 20301596   LU
Web Site: http://www.globant.com
Year Founded: 2003
GLOB—(NYSE)
Rev.: $2,095,939,000
Assets: $2,735,355,000
Liabilities: $948,739,000
Net Worth: $1,786,616,000
Earnings: $158,508,000
Emp.: 29,150
Fiscal Year-end: 12/31/23
Software Solutions
N.A.I.C.S.: 513210
Martin Migoya *(Co-Founder, Chm & CEO)*

Subsidiaries:

Exusia Inc. (1)
140 Broadway 46th Fl, New York, NY 10005
Tel.: (222) 222-2222
Web Site: http://www.exusia.com
General Management Consulting Services
N.A.I.C.S.: 541611
Trevor Noon *(CTO & Partner)*

GLOBAVEND HOLDINGS LIMITED

Office 1401 Level 14 197 St Georges Tce, Perth, 6000, WA, Australia
Tel.: (61) 861413263   Ky

GLOBAVEND HOLDINGS LIMITED

Globavend Holdings Limited—(Continued)
Web Site:
https://www.globavend.com
Year Founded: 2016
GVH—(NASDAQ)
Rev.: $18,586,528
Assets: $4,474,778
Liabilities: $3,972,602
Net Worth: $502,176
Earnings: $1,077,392
Emp.: 7
Fiscal Year-end: 09/30/23
Offices of Other Holding Companies
N.A.I.C.S.: 551112

GLOBE CAPITAL LIMITED
10th Floor Exchange Tower 5 Happiness Street Business Bay, Dubai, 346, United Arab Emirates
Tel.: (971) 755 8270 9909
Year Founded: 1990
Rev.: $8,080
Assets: $342,226
Liabilities: $223,084
Net Worth: $119,142
Earnings: ($270,888)
Fiscal Year-end: 12/31/18
Financial Advisory Services
N.A.I.C.S.: 523940
David Barnett *(Chm)*

GLOBE COMMERCIALS LIMITED
04 Prathmesh Leela CHS Ltd new MHB Colony Gorai Rd, Near Sai Lee Hospital, Mumbai, 400 091, India
Tel.: (91) 2228684836
Web Site:
https://www.globecommercials.com
Year Founded: 1985
540266—(BOM)
Rev.: $19,916
Assets: $1,044,797
Liabilities: $217,384
Net Worth: $827,413
Earnings: ($1,722)
Fiscal Year-end: 03/31/21
Commodity Trading Services
N.A.I.C.S.: 523160
Prasad Meghshyam Bagwe *(Mng Dir)*

GLOBE EXPLORATION (Y.C.D.) LIMITED PARTNERSHIP
Beit HaPraklit 5 Zadal St, Rishon le Zion, 7526657, Israel
Tel.: (972) 36141856
Web Site: http://www.goe.co.il
Year Founded: 2009
GLEX.M—(TAE)
Rev.: $300,000
Assets: $4,730,000
Liabilities: $2,092,000
Net Worth: $2,638,000
Earnings: ($2,375,000)
Fiscal Year-end: 12/31/22
Oil & Gas Exploration Services
N.A.I.C.S.: 213112
Arie Carasso-Lev *(Co-Founder & Chm)*

GLOBE INDUSTRIES CORPORATION
7F No 61 Sec 3 Nanjing E Rd, Zhongshan Dis, Taipei, 104507, Taiwan
Tel.: (886) 225066666
Web Site: https://www.globetape.com
Year Founded: 1951
1324—(TAI)
Rev.: $30,132,116
Assets: $39,623,564
Liabilities: $7,866,575
Net Worth: $31,756,989
Earnings: $1,290,330
Emp.: 133
Fiscal Year-end: 12/31/23
Insulating Tape Mfr
N.A.I.C.S.: 321999

Subsidiaries:

Globe Adhesive Technology (Zhuhai) Co., Ltd. (1)
No 9599 Zhuhai Avenue, NanShui Town Gaolan Port Economic Zone, Zhuhai, Guangdong, China
Tel.: (86) 7563985398
Wood Products Mfr
N.A.I.C.S.: 321999

GLOBE INTERNATIONAL CARRIERS LTD.
301-306 Prakashdeep Complex Near Mayank Trade Centre Station Road, Jaipur, 302 006, Rajasthan, India
Tel.: (91) 1414083700
Web Site: https://www.gicl.co
Year Founded: 1965
GICL—(NSE)
Rev.: $13,651,136
Assets: $7,175,085
Liabilities: $3,787,651
Net Worth: $3,387,435
Earnings: $317,259
Emp.: 62
Fiscal Year-end: 03/31/23
Logistic Services
N.A.I.C.S.: 541614
Subhash Agrawal *(Chm & Mng Dir)*

Subsidiaries:

GRC Logistics LLP (1)
Shop No 7 Buildin No 2 Prem Nagar Borivali West, Mumbai, 400092, Maharashtra, India
Tel.: (91) 7039703942
Web Site: https://www.grclogistics.com
Passenger Transportation Services
N.A.I.C.S.: 532411

GLOBE INTERNATIONAL LIMITED
1 Fennell Street, Port Melbourne, 3207, VIC, Australia
Tel.: (61) 385349999
Web Site:
https://www.globecorporate.com
Year Founded: 1984
GLB—(ASX)
Rev.: $210,290,806
Assets: $115,870,914
Liabilities: $57,589,905
Net Worth: $58,281,009
Earnings: $14,282,548
Fiscal Year-end: 06/30/22
Footwear & Apparel Mfr
N.A.I.C.S.: 316210
Peter Hill *(Co-Founder & Co-Pres)*

GLOBE METALS & MINING LIMITED
Tel.: (61) 861187240
Web Site: https://www.globemm.com
GBE—(ASX)
Assets: $22,045,436
Liabilities: $183,628
Net Worth: $21,861,808
Earnings: ($2,292,351)
Emp.: 4
Fiscal Year-end: 06/30/24
Uranium & Specialty Metal Mining
N.A.I.C.S.: 213114
Alistair Stephens *(Deputy Chm, CEO & Mng Dir)*

GLOBE TELECOM, INC.
The Globe Tower 32nd St Cor 7th Ave Bonifacio Global City, Taguig, 1634, Philippines
Tel.: (63) 277972000
Web Site: https://www.globe.com.ph
Year Founded: 1991
GTMEF—(OTCIQ)
Rev.: $3,252,946,706
Assets: $11,043,209,880
Liabilities: $8,155,663,857
Net Worth: $2,887,546,023
Earnings: $443,766,539
Emp.: 7,542
Fiscal Year-end: 12/31/23
Wireless Telecommunication Services
N.A.I.C.S.: 517112
Fernando Zobel de Ayala *(Vice Chm)*

Subsidiaries:

Entertainment Gateway Group Corp (1)
3/F Bloomingdale Building 205 Salcedo St, Legaspi Village, Makati, Philippines
Tel.: (63) 28928101
Web Site: http://www.egg.ph
Mobile Internet Services
N.A.I.C.S.: 517810

Innove Communications Inc (1)
Globe Telecom Plaza Pioneer Corner Madison Streets, Mandaluyong, 1552, Philippines
Tel.: (63) 27302000
Web Site: http://www.innove.com.ph
Wireline Data Processing Services
N.A.I.C.S.: 518210

Kickstart Ventures, Inc. (1)
55 Paseo de Roxas Metro Manila, Urdaneta Village, Makati, 1225, Philippines
Tel.: (63) 276258723
Web Site: https://www.kickstart.ph
Investment Firm Services
N.A.I.C.S.: 523999
Ernest L. Cu *(CEO)*

Liberty Telecoms Holdings, Inc. (1)
Technology Centre Building, 2298 Chino Roces Avenue Extension, Makati, 1231, Philippines
Tel.: (63) 28130377
Web Site:
http://www.libertytelecomsholdingsinc.net
Sales Range: $1-9.9 Million
Emp.: 47
Holding Company; Telecommunications Tower Construction & Maintenance Services
N.A.I.C.S.: 551112

NCSI (Philippines) Inc. (1)
9/F Corporate Center 139 Valero Street, Salcedo Village, Makati, 1227, Philippines
Tel.: (63) 27931400
Web Site: http://www.ayalasystems.com
Sales Range: $1-9.9 Million
Emp.: 100
Systems Integration & Information Technology Services
N.A.I.C.S.: 541512
Leila Verceles *(Pres & Mng Dir)*

Subsidiary (Domestic):

GlobalBridge Resources Corporation (2)
15F Corporate Center 139 Valero St, Salcedo Village, Makati, 1227, Philippines
Tel.: (63) 2 793 1447
Web Site:
http://www.globalbridgeresources.com
Corporate Human Resource Support Services
N.A.I.C.S.: 541612

GLOBE TEXTILE MILLS (OE) LIMITED
Suite 105 1st Floor Ibrahim Trade Tower Shahrah-e-Faisal, Karachi, Pakistan
Tel.: (92) 4327534
Textile Products Mfr
N.A.I.C.S.: 314999

GLOBE TEXTILES (INDIA) LTD.
Plot no 38-41 Apparel Park GIDC Khokhra, Ahmedabad, 380008, Gujarat, India
Tel.: (91) 7926441880
Web Site:
https://www.globetextiles.net
Year Founded: 1995
GLOBE—(NSE)
Rev.: $48,178,383
Assets: $28,674,132
Liabilities: $22,150,531
Net Worth: $6,523,602
Earnings: $540,171
Emp.: 399
Fiscal Year-end: 03/31/23
Timber Product Mfr
N.A.I.C.S.: 335921
Bhavik Parikh *(Mng Dir)*

GLOBE TRADE CENTRE S.A.
45A Komitetu Obrony Robotnikow Nothus building, 02-146, Warsaw, Poland
Tel.: (48) 221660700
Web Site: https://www.gtcgroup.com
GBCEY—(OTCEM)
Rev.: $151,451,595
Assets: $2,932,553,262
Liabilities: $1,689,369,688
Net Worth: $1,243,183,575
Earnings: $13,688,045
Emp.: 219
Fiscal Year-end: 12/31/23
Real Estate Investment Services
N.A.I.C.S.: 523999
Ariel Alejandro Ferstman *(CFO & Member-Mgmt Bd)*

Subsidiaries:

GTC Bulgaria (1)
5 Lachezar Stanchev Str 7th floor Sopharma Business Towers building B, 1756, Sofia, Bulgaria
Tel.: (359) 2 962 75 34
Web Site: https://www.gtc.bg
Real Estate Development Services
N.A.I.C.S.: 531390
Danny Bercovich *(Country Mgr)*

GTC Croatia (1)
Avenija Dubrovnik 16, 10000, Zagreb, Croatia
Tel.: (385) 1 66 59 400
Web Site: https://www.gtc.pl
Emp.: 5
Real Estate Development Services
N.A.I.C.S.: 531390
Arn Willems *(Country Mgr)*

GTC Czech Republic (1)
Jankocova 1569/2c, 170 00, Prague, Czech Republic
Tel.: (420) 234 379 200
Real Estate Development Services
N.A.I.C.S.: 531390
Tamir Winterstein *(Country Mgr)*

GTC Hungary (1)
Vaci Ut 81, 1139, Budapest, Hungary
Tel.: (36) 1 412 3680
Web Site: http://www.gtc.hu
Emp.: 15
Real Estate Development Services
N.A.I.C.S.: 531390
Yovav Carmi *(CFO)*

GTC Real Estate Investments Bulgaria B.V. (1)
Claude Debussylaan 30vi Olyb 13e, Amsterdam, 1082 MD, Netherlands
Tel.: (31) 203050010
Real Estate Manangement Services
N.A.I.C.S.: 531390

GTC Real Estate Investments Serbia B.V. (1)
Claude Debussylaan 30, Vinoly Building 13th Floor, 1082MD, Amsterdam, Netherlands
Tel.: (31) 203050010
Web Site: http://www.kardan.nl
Sales Range: $100-124.9 Million
Emp.: 200
Real Estate Investment Trust
N.A.I.C.S.: 525990
Alain Ickovics *(Mng Dir)*

GTC Real Estate Investments Ukraine B.V. (1)
Claude Debussylaan 30, Vinoly Building 13th Floor, 1082 MD, Amsterdam, Netherlands

Tel.: (31) 203050010
Web Site: http://www.kardan.nl
Sales Range: $50-74.9 Million
Emp.: 100
Real Estate Investment Trust
N.A.I.C.S.: 525990
Alain Ickovics (Mng Dir)

GTC Real Estate Management, s.r.o. (1)
Jarosova 1, 811 07, Bratislava, Slovakia
Tel.: (421) 254410153
Web Site: http://www.gtc-ba.sk
Real Estate Development Services
N.A.I.C.S.: 531390
Robert Snow (Country Mgr)

GTC Romania (1)
Str Jean Texier nr 3 sector 1, Bucharest, 011901, Romania
Tel.: (40) 21 231 65 52
Web Site: http://www.gtcromania.ro
Emp.: 30
Real Estate Development Services
N.A.I.C.S.: 531390
Ziv Gigi (CEO)

GTC Serbia (1)
Zoran Djindjic Boulevard 64a, 11070, Belgrade, Serbia
Tel.: (381) 11 313 07 51
Web Site: http://www.gtcserbia.com
Real Estate Development Services
N.A.I.C.S.: 531390
Alain Ickovics (Pres)

GLOBE UNION INDUSTRIAL CORP.
No 22 Chien-Kuo Rd, Tanzi Dist, Taichung, Taiwan
Tel.: (886) 425349676
Web Site: https://en.globeunion.com
Year Founded: 1979
9934—(TAI)
Rev.: $598,905,403
Assets: $506,399,569
Liabilities: $313,465,504
Net Worth: $192,934,065
Earnings: $19,788,122
Emp.: 2,059
Fiscal Year-end: 12/31/23
Plumbing Products Mfr
N.A.I.C.S.: 332913
Eric Chen (CFO)

Subsidiaries:

PJH Group Ltd. (1)
PJH House Lomax Way, Bolton, BL5 1FQ, Lancashire, United Kingdom
Tel.: (44) 800 877 8899
Web Site: https://www.pjh.uk
Kitchen & Bathroom Product Mfr
N.A.I.C.S.: 337126

GLOBEE INC.
2nd Watanabe Building 4th floor
1-7-3 Higashi-Azabu, Minato-ku, Tokyo, 106-0044, Japan
Tel.: (81) 362309016
Web Site: https://www.globee.io
Year Founded: 2014
5575—(TKS)
Emp.: 48
Educational Support Services
N.A.I.C.S.: 611710
Kenzaburo Ikushima (Pres)

GLOBERIDE, INC.
3-14-16 Maesawa, Higashi Kurume, Tokyo, 203-8511, Japan
Tel.: (81) 424752111
Web Site: http://www.globeride.jp
Year Founded: 1945
7990—(TKS)
Rev.: $832,912,880
Assets: $718,619,370
Liabilities: $358,453,690
Net Worth: $360,165,680
Earnings: $36,897,020
Emp.: 6,765
Fiscal Year-end: 03/31/24

Sporting Goods Including Fishing & Golf Equipment Mfr
N.A.I.C.S.: 339920
Kazunari Suzuki (Pres & CEO)

Subsidiaries:

Daiwa (H.K) Co., Ltd (1)
Rm 415 4th Fl Fu Hang Indl Bldg, Hung Hom, Kowloon, China (Hong Kong)
Tel.: (852) 27663189
Web Site: http://www.globeride.co.jp
Sales Range: $50-74.9 Million
Emp.: 5
Spectator Sports
N.A.I.C.S.: 711219

Daiwa Cormoran Sportartikel-Vertriebs GmbH (1)
Industriestr 28, Postfach 1163, 82179, Grobenzell, Germany
Tel.: (49) 814250050
Web Site: http://www.daiwa-cormoran.info
Sales Range: $50-74.9 Million
Emp.: 60
Fishing Tackle & Sports Equipment Mfr
N.A.I.C.S.: 711219
Stan Miyasaka (Mng Dir)

Daiwa Corporation (1)
11137 Warland Dr, Cypress, CA 90630-5034
Tel.: (562) 375-6800
Web Site: http://www.daiwa.com
Sales Range: $25-49.9 Million
Emp.: 50
Fishing Rods & Reels Distr
N.A.I.C.S.: 423910

Daiwa France S.A.S. (1)
25 Boulevard industriel, BP 30208, 76304, Sotteville-les-Rouen, France
Tel.: (33) 232919650
Web Site: http://www.daiwa.fr
Fishing Tackle & Sports Equipment Mfr
N.A.I.C.S.: 339920
Guillaume Fourrier (Dir-Publication, Mktg & Comm)

Daiwa Sports Ltd. (1)
Netherton Industrial Estate, Wishaw, ML2 0EY, Strathclyde, United Kingdom
Tel.: (44) 1698355723
Web Site: https://www.daiwasports.co.uk
Sales Range: $50-74.9 Million
Emp.: 100
Spectator Sports
N.A.I.C.S.: 711219

Desco, Inc. (1)
1383-1 Higashi Naganuma, Inagi-shi, Tokyo, 206-0802, Japan
Tel.: (81) 423798080
Sales Range: $50-74.9 Million
Emp.: 4
Insurance Agencies & Brokerages
N.A.I.C.S.: 524210

Fishing World, Inc. (1)
3 15 1 Arae Sawara Ku, Fukuoka, 814-0021, Japan
Tel.: (81) 928451701
Web Site: http://www.fishingworld.co.jp
Spectator Sports
N.A.I.C.S.: 711219

Nasu Daiwa, Inc. (1)
1464 11 Sabui, Otawara, Tochigi, 3240246, Japan
Tel.: (81) 287543111
Sales Range: $50-74.9 Million
Emp.: 69
Spectator Sports
N.A.I.C.S.: 711219

World Sports, Inc. (1)
2129 Kashiwacho, Tachikawa, Tokyo, Japan
Tel.: (81) 425356851
Web Site: http://www.fisherman.co.jp
Sales Range: $75-99.9 Million
Emp.: 150
Spectator Sports
N.A.I.C.S.: 711219

GLOBETRONICS TECHNOLOGY BHD.
Plot 2 Phase 4 Free Industrial Zone, 11900, Penang, Bayan Lepas, Malaysia

Tel.: (60) 46444906
Web Site: https://www.globetronics.com.my
Year Founded: 1991
GTRONIC—(KLS)
Rev.: $28,694,602
Assets: $73,148,237
Liabilities: $6,075,316
Net Worth: $67,072,922
Earnings: $5,749,891
Emp.: 2,500
Fiscal Year-end: 12/31/23
Electroplating Mfr
N.A.I.C.S.: 333248
Peng Loon Lee (Co-Sec)

Subsidiaries:

Globetronics (KL) Sdn. Bhd. (1)
Lot 1 Jalan SS 8/4 Sungai Way FTZ, 47300, Petaling Jaya, Selangor Darul Ehsan, Malaysia
Tel.: (60) 37 874 5145
Web Site: http://www.globe.com.my
Sales Range: $150-199.9 Million
Emp.: 1,000
Electronics Testing & Designing Services
N.A.I.C.S.: 561990
Eng Choon Ong (Mgr-HR)

Globetronics Manufacturing Sdn. Bhd. (1)
Plot 2 Phase 4 Free Industrial Zone, 11900, Bayan Lepas, Penang, Malaysia
Tel.: (60) 46444906
Optoelectronic Product Mfr
N.A.I.C.S.: 334413

Globetronics Medical Technology Sdn Bhd (1)
Plot 2 Phase 4, Free Industrial Zone, 11900, Bayan Lepas, Penang, Malaysia
Tel.: (60) 46444906
Web Site: http://www.globetronics.com.my
Fiscal Year-end: 12/31/2017
Electronic Business Management & Information Technology Solutions
N.A.I.C.S.: 561499

Globetronics Sdn. Bhd. (1)
Plot 2 Phase 4 Free Industrial Zone, 11900, Bayan Lepas, Penang, Malaysia
Tel.: (60) 46444906
Sales Range: $150-199.9 Million
Emp.: 700
Electronics Testing & Designing Services
N.A.I.C.S.: 561990

ISO Technology Sdn. Bhd. (1)
Plot 290 291 and 292 Phase 3 Free Industrial Zone, 11900, Bayan Lepas, Penang, Malaysia
Tel.: (60) 4 646 2069
Web Site: http://www.globetronics.com
Electronics Testing & Designing Services
N.A.I.C.S.: 561990
Heng Huck Lee (CEO)

GLOBEX MINING ENTERPRISES INC.
86-14th Street, Rouyn-Noranda, J9X 2J1, QC, Canada
Tel.: (819) 797-5242 Ca
Web Site: https://www.globexmining.com
Year Founded: 1949
GMX—(TSX)
Rev.: $1,477,766
Assets: $23,088,501
Liabilities: $155,008
Net Worth: $22,933,493
Earnings: ($3,053,838)
Fiscal Year-end: 12/31/22
Mineral Exploration Services
N.A.I.C.S.: 213115
Jack Stoch (Pres & CEO)

GLOBIS CORPORATION
Sumitomo Fudosan Kojimachi Bldg
5-1 Niban-cho, Chiyoda-ku, Tokyo, 102-0084, Japan
Tel.: (81) 352753900
Web Site: http://www.globis.co.jp
Year Founded: 1992

Sales Range: $25-49.9 Million
Emp.: 300
Professional Management Education School & Venture Capital Firm
N.A.I.C.S.: 611310
Yoshito Hori (Pres)

Subsidiaries:

GLOBIS Asia Pacific Pte. Ltd. (1)
80 Raffles Place UOB Plaza 1 35-17, Singapore, 048624, Singapore
Tel.: (65) 6248 4585
Web Site: http://www.globis.sg
Human Resource Consulting Services
N.A.I.C.S.: 541612
Toru Takahashi (Pres & Mng Dir)

GLOBIS China Co., Ltd. (1)
Room 1805 18/F Silver Court Office Tower 218 South Xizang Road, Huangpu District, Shanghai, China
Tel.: (86) 21 6075 2295
Web Site: http://www.globis.cn
N.A.I.C.S.: 541612
Reika Cho (Pres)

Globis Capital Partners & Co. (1)
9F Sumitomo Fudosan Kojimachi Building 5-1 Niban-cho, Chiyoda-ku, Tokyo, 102-0084, Japan
Tel.: (81) 352753939
Web Site: http://www.globiscapital.co.jp
Sales Range: $50-74.9 Million
Emp.: 15
Venture Capital Firm
N.A.I.C.S.: 523999
Yoshito Hori (CEO & Partner)

GLOBLEX HOLDING MANAGEMENT PUBLIC COMPANY LIMITED
87/2 CRC Tower All Seasons Place
12th Floor Wireless Road, Lumpini Pathumwan, Bangkok, 10330, Thailand
Tel.: (66) 26725995
Web Site: https://www.globlexholding.co.th
Year Founded: 2003
GBX—(THA)
Rev.: $13,721,176
Assets: $76,559,652
Liabilities: $33,418,140
Net Worth: $43,141,511
Earnings: $1,891,589
Emp.: 301
Fiscal Year-end: 12/31/23
Gold Trading Services
N.A.I.C.S.: 238990
Oran Koohapremkit (Chm)

Subsidiaries:

Globlex Securites Co., Ltd. (1)
87/2 CRC All Seasons Place Floor 8 12 Wireless Road, Lumpini Subdistrict Pathumwan District, Bangkok, 10330, Thailand
Tel.: (66) 26725999
Web Site: http://www.globlex.co.th
Security Management Services
N.A.I.C.S.: 561621
Narisara Chaiwathana (Mng Dir)

GLOBO FOODS LTD.
482 Mu 1 Soi Pookmitr Rod Rang Kao Rd Samrongtai Phrapradaeng, Samut Prakan, 10130, Thailand
Tel.: (66) 23840036
Web Site: http://www.globofoods.com
Sales Range: $75-99.9 Million
Emp.: 500
Food Ingredients Mfr & Distr
N.A.I.C.S.: 311423
Akom Palanuwech (Mng Dir)

GLOBOFORCE GROUP PLC
21 Beckett Way Park West Business Park, Dublin, 12, Ireland
Tel.: (353) 1 625 8800
Web Site: http://www.globoforce.com
Year Founded: 1999

GLOBOFORCE GROUP PLC

Globoforce Group PLC—(Continued)
Sales Range: $150-199.9 Million
Cloud-Based Social Recognition Software Services
N.A.I.C.S.: 513210
Eric Mosley *(Founder & CEO)*

GLOBOKAS PERU SA
Av Caminos del Inca 777, Santiago de Surco, Lima, Peru
Tel.: (51) 12118300
Web Site: http://www.globokas.net
GLOBOKC1—(LIM)
Sales Range: Less than $1 Million
Financial Banking Services
N.A.I.C.S.: 522110
Juan Jose Marthans *(Exec VP)*

GLOBON CO., LTD.
331 Dosan-daero Gangnam-gu, Seoul, 06019, Korea (South)
Tel.: (82) 269340800
Web Site: http://www.globon.co.kr
Year Founded: 1986
019660—(KRS)
Rev.: $14,173,646
Assets: $21,384,216
Liabilities: $9,940,079
Net Worth: $11,444,137
Earnings: ($4,912,407)
Emp.: 31
Fiscal Year-end: 12/31/22
Investment Consulting Services
N.A.I.C.S.: 523999
Han Sang Young *(CEO)*

GLOBOS OSIGURANJE A.D.
Knez Mihailova 11-15, Belgrade, Serbia
Tel.: (381) 112620015
Web Site: http://www.globos.co.rs
Year Founded: 1994
GLOS—(BEL)
Sales Range: $1-9.9 Million
Emp.: 49
Insurance Agency Services
N.A.I.C.S.: 524210
Milovan Durovic *(CEO)*

GLOBRANDS GROUP LTD.
Haskalah Boulevard 9, Tel Aviv, 6789009, Israel
Tel.: (972) 39483535
Web Site: https://www.globrands.co.il
Year Founded: 2000
GLRS—(TAE)
Rev.: $180,259,476
Assets: $133,813,513
Liabilities: $120,861,938
Net Worth: $12,951,575
Earnings: $14,471,558
Fiscal Year-end: 09/30/23
Marketing Consulting Services
N.A.I.C.S.: 541613
Gadi Netzer *(CEO)*

GLOBUS KONFEKCIJA D.D.
Ul Visnjica Polje bb, 71250, Kiseljak, Bosnia & Herzegovina
Tel.: (387) 30877400
GLOBR—(SARE)
Rev.: $986,504
Assets: $1,973,249
Liabilities: $1,074,674
Net Worth: $898,575
Earnings: $13,997
Emp.: 105
Fiscal Year-end: 12/31/20
Clothing Apparel Mfr
N.A.I.C.S.: 314999

GLOBUS MARITIME LIMITED
128 Vouliagmenis Ave 3rd Floor, 166 74, Glyfada, Athens, Greece
Tel.: (30) 2109608300

Web Site:
https://www.globusmaritime.gr
GLBS—(NASDAQ)
Rev.: $61,755,000
Assets: $225,458,000
Liabilities: $54,760,000
Net Worth: $170,698,000
Earnings: $24,280,000
Emp.: 22
Fiscal Year-end: 12/31/22
Shipping Services
N.A.I.C.S.: 488510
Georgios Feidakis *(Founder & Chm)*

GLOBUS POWER GENERATION LIMITED
Shyam House Plot No 3 Amrapali Circle Vaishali Nagar, Jaipur, 302021, Rajasthan, India
Tel.: (91) 1414025631
Web Site: https://www.gpgl.in
Year Founded: 1985
526025—(BOM)
Rev.: $516
Assets: $1,443,115
Liabilities: $1,576,081
Net Worth: ($132,966)
Earnings: ($1,492,620)
Emp.: 5
Fiscal Year-end: 03/31/23
Power Generation Services
N.A.I.C.S.: 221118
Abhay Khanna *(Exec Dir)*

GLOBUS SPIRITS LTD
F0 Ground Floor The Mira Corporate Suites Plot No12, Ishwar Nagar Mathura Road, New Delhi, 110065, India
Tel.: (91) 1166424600
Web Site:
https://www.globusspirits.com
533104—(BOM)
Rev.: $229,141,199
Assets: $135,410,266
Liabilities: $55,639,188
Net Worth: $79,771,078
Earnings: $19,221,903
Emp.: 568
Fiscal Year-end: 03/31/21
Liquor Mfr, Marketer & Sales
N.A.I.C.S.: 312140
Ajay Kumar Swarup *(Co-Mng Dir)*

Subsidiaries:

Unibev Limited (1)
102 1st Floor Sunny Vale 35/1 Meanee Avenue Road, Opposite HDFC Bank Near Ulsoor Lake, Bengaluru, 560042, India
Tel.: (91) 8042197000
Web Site: http://www.unibev.in
Alcoholic Beverages Mfr
N.A.I.C.S.: 312140

GLODON CO., LTD.
E-13 10 Xibeiwang East Road, Haidian Dist, Beijing, 100193, China
Tel.: (86) 1056403000
Web Site: https://www.glodon.com
Year Founded: 1998
002410—(SSE)
Rev.: $925,353,936
Assets: $1,620,986,796
Liabilities: $666,110,952
Net Worth: $954,875,844
Earnings: $135,728,892
Emp.: 8,000
Fiscal Year-end: 12/31/22
Software Publisher
N.A.I.C.S.: 513210
Robert Yuan *(Chm & Pres)*

Subsidiaries:

MagiCAD Group Oy (1)
Aurakatu 8, 20100, Turku, Finland
Tel.: (358) 283876000
Web Site: https://www.magicad.com
Software Development Services
N.A.I.C.S.: 541511

GLOMAC BERHAD
Level 15 Menara Glomac Glomac Damansara Jalan Damansara, 60000, Kuala Lumpur, Malaysia
Tel.: (60) 377239000
Web Site:
https://www.glomac.com.my
Year Founded: 1988
GLOMAC—(KLS)
Rev.: $72,173,462
Assets: $431,031,135
Liabilities: $167,654,102
Net Worth: $263,377,033
Earnings: $6,909,328
Emp.: 182
Fiscal Year-end: 04/30/23
Construction Services
N.A.I.C.S.: 236115
Richard Loong Tuck Fong *(Vice Chm)*

Subsidiaries:

FDA Sdn. Bhd. (1)
12th Floor Wisma Glomac 3 Komplek Kelana Centre Point, Jalan SS7/19 Kelana Jaya, 47301, Petaling Jaya, Selangor, Malaysia
Tel.: (60) 378036160
Sales Range: $75-99.9 Million
Emp.: 241
Property Development Services
N.A.I.C.S.: 531390

Glomac Alliance Sdn. Bhd. (1)
Ground Fl Wisma Glomac 3 Kompleks Kelana Ctr Point Jalan SS7/19, 47301, Petaling Jaya, Selangor, Malaysia
Tel.: (60) 378046160
Web Site: http://www.glomac.com
Sales Range: $75-99.9 Million
Emp.: 220
Property Development Services
N.A.I.C.S.: 531311

Glomac Bina Sdn. Bhd. (1)
No 336 Level 3 Block A Kompleks Kelana Centre Point, Jalan SS 7/19 Kelana Jaya, 47301, Petaling Jaya, Selangor, Malaysia
Tel.: (60) 378806160
Sales Range: $25-49.9 Million
Emp.: 30
Building Construction Services
N.A.I.C.S.: 236220
Mohd Yasin *(Mng Dir)*

Glomac City Sdn. Bhd. (1)
Ground Floor Wisma Glomac 3 Kompleks Kelana Centre Point Jalan SS7/19, Kelana Jaya, 47301, Petaling Jaya, Selangor, Malaysia
Tel.: (60) 378019000
Sales Range: $75-99.9 Million
Emp.: 220
Property Development & Investment Services
N.A.I.C.S.: 531311

Glomac Rawang Sdn. Bhd. (1)
Ground Floor Wisma Glomac 3 Kompleks Kelana Centre Point, Jalan SS7/19 Kelana Jaya, 47301, Petaling Jaya, Selangor, Malaysia
Tel.: (60) 360936160
Sales Range: $50-74.9 Million
Emp.: 20
Property Development Services
N.A.I.C.S.: 531311
Gary Goh *(Asst Gen Mgr)*

Glomac Sutera Sdn. Bhd. (1)
No 1 Jalan SS 2/6A Sri Saujana, Kota Tinggi, 81900, Johor, Malaysia
Tel.: (60) 78821033
Web Site: http://www.glomac.com.my
Sales Range: $50-74.9 Million
Emp.: 6
Property Development & Investment Services
N.A.I.C.S.: 531390

Prima Sixteen Sdn. Bhd. (1)
Basement Blok A Prima 16 1 Jln 16/18 Seksyen 16 122, 46350, Petaling Jaya, Selangor, Malaysia
Tel.: (60) 379549441
Property Management Services
N.A.I.C.S.: 531311

INTERNATIONAL PUBLIC

Prominent Excel Sdn. Bhd. (1)
Basement 1 Block A Kelana Centre Point Jalan SS 7/19, Kelana Jaya, 47301, Petaling Jaya, Selangor, Malaysia
Tel.: (60) 378043522
Web Site: https://www.excelparking.com
Parking Services
N.A.I.C.S.: 812930

Regency Land Sdn. Bhd. (1)
A-G-1 Jalan Seroja 1/6 Sg Buloh Country Resort, 47000, Sungai Buloh, Selangor, Malaysia
Tel.: (60) 360385888
Web Site: http://www.glomac.com.my
Sales Range: $25-49.9 Million
Emp.: 50
Property Development Services
N.A.I.C.S.: 531311
Soontan Yap *(Gen Mgr)*

GLOME HOLDING, INC.
Ark Mori Building 22F 1-12-32 Akasaka, Minato-ku, Tokyo, 107-6022, Japan
Tel.: (81) 355458101
Web Site: https://www.glome-holdings.com
Year Founded: 1987
8938—(TKS)
Rev.: $8,183,180
Assets: $55,272,820
Liabilities: $3,926,340
Net Worth: $51,346,480
Earnings: ($1,308,780)
Fiscal Year-end: 03/31/24
Holding Company
N.A.I.C.S.: 551112
Hitoshi Miyashita *(Pres & CEO)*

Subsidiaries:

GLOME Management, Inc. (1)
31F Ark Mori Building 1-12-32 Akasaka, Minato-ku, Tokyo, 107-6031, Japan
Tel.: (81) 368567320
Web Site: https://www.glome-management.com
Consulting Services
N.A.I.C.S.: 541611
Kazuhisa Hashimoto *(Pres & CEO)*

GLORIA MATERIAL TECHNOLOGY CORP.
No 10 Gong 2nd Rd, Liuying Dist, Tainan City, 736, Taiwan
Tel.: (886) 66520031
Web Site: https://www.gmtc.com.tw
Year Founded: 1993
5009—(TPE)
Rev.: $386,621,549
Assets: $789,763,155
Liabilities: $441,694,494
Net Worth: $348,068,661
Earnings: $65,597,818
Emp.: 736
Fiscal Year-end: 12/31/22
Metal Products Mfr
N.A.I.C.S.: 331110
Jiongfen Wang *(Chm)*

GLORIOUS PROPERTY HOLDINGS LTD.
Room 2202 22/F China Evergrande Centre 38 Gloucester Road, Wanchai, China (Hong Kong)
Tel.: (852) 31014888
Web Site: https://www.gloriousphl.com.cn
0845—(HKG)
Rev.: $896,458,914
Assets: $6,808,571,780
Liabilities: $6,790,716,410
Net Worth: $17,855,370
Earnings: ($41,764,226)
Emp.: 509
Fiscal Year-end: 12/31/22
Residential Real Estate Developer
N.A.I.C.S.: 236117
Xiang Yang Ding *(Chm & CEO)*

GLORIOUS SUN ENTERPRISES LIMITED
36F One Kowloon 1 Wang Yuen Street, Kowloon, China (Hong Kong)
Tel.: (852) 22633000 BM
Web Site: https://www.glorisun.com
GLV—(DEU)
Rev.: $135,555,485
Assets: $398,421,537
Liabilities: $87,915,958
Net Worth: $310,505,578
Earnings: $5,814,153
Emp.: 490
Fiscal Year-end: 12/31/22
Casual Wear Apparel Mfr & Whslr
N.A.I.C.S.: 315250
Charles Chun Kam Yeung (Founder & Chm)

Subsidiaries:

Jeanswest Corporation Pty. Ltd. (1)
Level 1 14-16 Yarra Street, South Yarra, 3141, VIC, Australia
Tel.: (61) 385928934
Web Site: http://www.jeanswest.com.au
Emp.: 1,300
Apparel Retailer
N.A.I.C.S.: 458110

Jeanswest International (H.K.) Limited (1)
1/F Glorious Sun Group Building 97 How Ming Street, Kwun Tong, Kowloon, 100176, China (Hong Kong)
Tel.: (852) 22633600
Apparel Retailer
N.A.I.C.S.: 458110

Pacific Potential Trading Company Limited (1)
37/F One Kowloon 1 Wang Yuen Street, Kowloon, China (Hong Kong)
Tel.: (852) 2263 3923
Web Site: http://www.ppthk.com
Emp.: 24
Apparel Retailer
N.A.I.C.S.: 458110

GLORY FILMS LIMITED
Vintage Pearl 2nd floor A Wing, 29th Road Bandra West, Mumbai, 400 050, India
Tel.: (91) 2226514810
Web Site: http://www.gloryfilms.in
Year Founded: 1997
Sales Range: $10-24.9 Million
Polyethylene Film Mfr
N.A.I.C.S.: 326112
Yogesh P. Kela (Chm & Mng Dir)

GLORY FLAME HOLDINGS LIMITED
Suite 3513 Tower 6 Harbour City The Gateway 9 Canton Rd TST Kln, Hong Kong, China (Hong Kong)
Tel.: (852) 31089959 Ky
Web Site: http://www.gf-holdings.com
Year Founded: 2014
8059—(HKG)
Rev.: $15,112,958
Assets: $17,470,305
Liabilities: $17,575,493
Net Worth: ($105,188)
Earnings: ($339,023)
Emp.: 98
Fiscal Year-end: 12/31/22
Concrete Demolition Services
N.A.I.C.S.: 238910
Wai Kee Cheung (Sec)

Subsidiaries:

Drillcut Limited (1)
Unit C 6/F Cheong Shing Industrial Bldg No 17 Walnut Street, Tai Kok Tsui, Kowloon, China (Hong Kong)
Tel.: (852) 23990282
Concrete Demolition Services
N.A.I.C.S.: 238910

GLORY HEALTH INDUSTRY LIMITED
RM2802 28/F Harbour Centre 25 Harbour Road, Wanchai, China (Hong Kong)
Tel.: (852) 28733180 Ky
Web Site: http://www.glorypty.com
2329—(HKG)
Rev.: $548,215,949
Assets: $8,057,052,385
Liabilities: $6,038,253,702
Net Worth: $2,018,798,683
Earnings: ($139,739,137)
Emp.: 492
Fiscal Year-end: 12/31/22
Holding Company
N.A.I.C.S.: 551112
Zhangsun Zhang (Founder, Chm & Pres)

GLORY LTD.
1-3-1 Shimoteno, Himeji, 670-8567, Hyogo, Japan
Tel.: (81) 792973131 JP
Web Site: http://www.glory-global.com
Year Founded: 1918
3O5—(DEU)
Rev.: $1,834,494,690
Assets: $2,733,727,410
Liabilities: $1,328,522,130
Net Worth: $1,405,205,280
Earnings: ($68,387,460)
Emp.: 11,000
Fiscal Year-end: 03/31/23
Coin & Money Handling Machines; Terminals for Data Processing & Money Handling; Vending Machines
N.A.I.C.S.: 445132
Hirokazu Onoe (Chm & Pres)

Subsidiaries:

GLORY Currency Automation India Pvt. Ltd. (1)
105-106 Rectangle 1 Commercial Complex D-4 Saket, New Delhi, 110 017, India
Tel.: (91) 114 601 0920
Web Site: http://www.glory-global.com
Sales Range: $25-49.9 Million
Emp.: 4
Currency Counting Machine Mfr
N.A.I.C.S.: 333310

GLORY France (1)
Parc d'Affaires du Vivier 5 rue de la Plaine, Saint-Nom-la-Breteche, 78860, France
Tel.: (33) 1 30565184
Web Site: http://www.glory-global.com
Sales Range: $25-49.9 Million
Emp.: 22
Money Handling Machinery Mfr
N.A.I.C.S.: 333310

GLORY Friendly Co., Ltd. (1)
1-3-1 Shimoteno, Himeji, 670-0063, Hyogo, Japan
Tel.: (81) 792946273
Vending Machine Mfr
N.A.I.C.S.: 333310

GLORY IPO China Ltd. (1)
No 509 5/F Office Building B2 Zone-4F Xingda Logistics Building, No 3 Lanhua Road Futian Free Trade Zone, Shenzhen, 518038, China
Tel.: (86) 7558 254 0787
Web Site: http://www.gloryusa.com
Emp.: 44
Coin Operated Vending Machine Mfr
N.A.I.C.S.: 333310
Tsuyoshi Yamashita (Mgr)

GLORY Ltd. - Saitama Factory (1)
2-4-1 Furukawa, Kazo, 347-0004, Saitama, Japan
Tel.: (81) 480684661
Emp.: 20
Currency Counting Machine Mfr
N.A.I.C.S.: 333310

GLORY NASCA Ltd. (1)
Tokyo Sky Tree East Tower 16F 1-1-2 Oshiage, Sumida-ku, Tokyo, 131-0045, Japan
Tel.: (81) 36 284 1900
Web Site: https://www.glory-nasca.co.jp
Emp.: 287
Welding Machine Distr
N.A.I.C.S.: 423830

GLORY System Create Ltd. (1)
1-3-1 Shimoteno, Himeji, 670-0063, Hyogo, Japan
Tel.: (81) 792973170
Sales Range: $25-49.9 Million
Emp.: 10
Vending Machine Mfr
N.A.I.C.S.: 333310

Glory (Philippines) Inc. (1)
Lot 1 and 3 Block 19 Phase 3, Cavite Economic Zone Rosario, 4106, Cavite, Philippines
Tel.: (63) 464370501
Sales Range: $100-124.9 Million
Emp.: 400
Industrial Machinery Mfr
N.A.I.C.S.: 333248
James Anda (Mgr-HR)

Glory Austria GmbH (1)
Campus 21 Europaring F15 101, 2345, Brunn am Gebirge, Austria
Tel.: (43) 22363122190
Web Site: http://www.glory-austria.at
Sales Range: $25-49.9 Million
Emp.: 6
Automatic Vending Machine Mfr
N.A.I.C.S.: 333310

Glory Az System Co., Ltd. (1)
5-5-17 Kamikoshien, Nishinomiya, 663-8114, Hyogo, Japan
Tel.: (81) 79 826 3100
Web Site: https://www.gazs.co.jp
Electronic Computer Mfr
N.A.I.C.S.: 334111

Glory Denshi Kogyo (Suzhou) Ltd. (1)
No 1458 Xiang Jiang Road, Suzhou New District, Suzhou, 215129, Jiangsu, China
Tel.: (86) 51266 653 8830
Web Site: http://www.glory-global.com
Accounting Services
N.A.I.C.S.: 541219

Glory Engineering Ltd. (1)
1-21-11 Minami Rokugo, Ota-ku, Tokyo, 144-0045, Japan
Tel.: (81) 33 733 3721
Web Site: http://www.glory-global.com
Accounting Services
N.A.I.C.S.: 541219

Glory F&C Co., Ltd. (1)
166 Higashi Nihon-bashi Chuo-ku, Tokyo, 103-0004, Japan
Tel.: (81) 338654581
Sales Range: $25-49.9 Million
Emp.: 20
Industrial Machinery Mfr
N.A.I.C.S.: 333248

Glory Global Solutions (Australia) Pty. Ltd. (1)
Suite 1 2-4 Giffnock Avenue, Macquarie Park, 2113, NSW, Australia
Tel.: (61) 288992200
Information Technology Services
N.A.I.C.S.: 541511

Glory Global Solutions (Belgium) N. V./S. A. (1)
Doornveld 20, 1731, Zellik, Belgium
Tel.: (32) 27499630
Information Technology Services
N.A.I.C.S.: 541511

Glory Global Solutions (Colombia) S.A. (1)
Calle 71 12-67 Cundinamarca, Bogota, Colombia
Tel.: (57) 12170604
Information Technology Services
N.A.I.C.S.: 541511

Glory Global Solutions (Hong Kong) Ltd. (1)
26/F Aitken Vanson Centre No 61 Hoi Yuen Road, Kwun Tong, Kowloon, China (Hong Kong)
Tel.: (852) 2 628 1800
Web Site: http://www.glory-global.com
Sales Range: $25-49.9 Million
Emp.: 47
Commercial Equipment Whslr
N.A.I.C.S.: 423440

Glory Global Solutions (International) Ltd. (1)
Infinity View 1 Hazelwood Lime Tree Way, Chineham, Basingstoke, RG24 8WZ, Hants, United Kingdom
Tel.: (44) 1256 368000
Cash Handling Equipment Mfr
N.A.I.C.S.: 333310

Subsidiary (Non-US):

Acrelec Group SAS (2)
3 Rue Louis de Broglie, 77400, Saint-Thibault-des-Vignes, France (80%)
Tel.: (33) 172 032 410
Web Site: http://www.acrelec.com
Emp.: 800
Kiosk Mfr
N.A.I.C.S.: 333310
Jacques Mangeot (Co-CEO)

Subsidiary (Non-US):

Acrelec ApS (3)
Rugvaenget 21, 2630, Taastrup, Denmark
Tel.: (45) 88807730
Software Development Services
N.A.I.C.S.: 541511

Acrelec Finland Oy (3)
Tarmontie 6 E, 15860, Hollola, Finland
Tel.: (358) 447737737
Web Site: http://www.acrelec.fi
Software Development Services
N.A.I.C.S.: 541511
Markku Nopanen (Mng Dir)

Acrelec GmbH (3)
Lise-Meitner-Strasse 1, Unterschleissheim, 85716, Munich, Germany
Tel.: (49) 89414142340
Software Development Services
N.A.I.C.S.: 541511

Acrelec Group BVBA (3)
Lammerdries-Oost 32, 2250, Olen, Belgium
Tel.: (32) 14258191
Software Development Services
N.A.I.C.S.: 541511

Subsidiary (US):

Acrelec Inc. (3)
Oak Brook Pointe 700 Commerce Dr Ste 500, Oak Brook, IL 60523
Tel.: (630) 288-2727
Software Development Services
N.A.I.C.S.: 541511

Subsidiary (Non-US):

Acrelec Informatica Group Sl. (3)
Avda Camino de lo Cortao n 28 Nave 6, 28703, Madrid, Spain
Tel.: (34) 916591810
Software Development Services
N.A.I.C.S.: 541511

Acrelec Sweden AB (3)
Djupdalsvagen 7, 192 51, Sollentuna, Sweden
Tel.: (46) 84669888
Software Development Services
N.A.I.C.S.: 541511
Toni Leinonen (Mgr-Ops)

Acrelec Uk Limited (3)
Innovation House 39 Mark Road, Hemel Hempstead, HP2 7DN, United Kingdom
Tel.: (44) 8456436453
Software Development Services
N.A.I.C.S.: 541511

Subsidiary (US):

Hyperactive Technologies, Inc. (3)
5490 Campbells Run Rd, Pittsburgh, PA 15205
Tel.: (412) 322-3060
Web Site: http://www.gohyper.com
Rev.: $2,000,000
Emp.: 20
Custom Computer Programming Services
N.A.I.C.S.: 541511
Frank Guarnaccio (Treas, Sec & VP-Fin)

GLORY LTD.

GLORY Ltd.—(Continued)

Ordermatic Electronics, Inc. (3)
PO Box 25463, Oklahoma City, OK 73125
Web Site: http://www.ordermatic.com
Building Equipment Contractors
N.A.I.C.S.: 238290
Robert Powell (Pres & CEO)

Subsidiary (Domestic):

Glory Global Solutions Ltd. (2)
Infinity View 1 Hazelwood Lime Tree Way, Chineham Industrial Estate, Basingstoke, RG24 8WZ, Hants, United Kingdom
Tel.: (44) 1256 368000
Web Site: http://www.gloryglobalsolutions.com
Sales Range: $500-549.9 Million
Emp.: 2,300
Cash Handling Equipment Mfr
N.A.I.C.S.: 333310

Branch (Domestic):

Glory Global Solutions (3)
Unit 7/8 Wolfe Close, Parkgate Industrial Estate, Knutsford, WA16 8XJ, Cheshire, United Kingdom
Tel.: (44) 1565 654662
Sales Range: $25-49.9 Million
Emp.: 60
Cash Handling Equipment Mfr
N.A.I.C.S.: 333310
Gregor Dobbie (Mng Dir)

Subsidiary (Non-US):

Glory Global Solutions (Brasil) Maquinas e Equipamentos Ltda. (3)
Rua Constantino de Souza 330, Campo Belo, Sao Paulo, 04605-000, Brazil
Tel.: (55) 11 5090 1200
Sales Range: $25-49.9 Million
Emp.: 40
Cash Handling Equipment Mfr
N.A.I.C.S.: 333310
Edson Matunaga (Mgr)

Glory Global Solutions (Canada) Inc. (3)
1105 Chomedey Highway A-13, Laval, H7W 5J8, QC, Canada
Tel.: (450) 686-8800
Sales Range: $25-49.9 Million
Emp.: 5
Cash Handling Equipment Mfr
N.A.I.C.S.: 333310
Nathali Gravel (Controller)

Glory Global Solutions (France) S.A.S. (3)
15 Rue des Veilles Vignes, PO Box 87, Croissy-Beaubourg, 77314, Marne-la-Vallee, Cedex 2, France
Tel.: (33) 164616283
Sales Range: $50-74.9 Million
Emp.: 230
Cash Handling Equipment Mfr
N.A.I.C.S.: 333310
Vincent Nakache (Mng Dir)

Glory Global Solutions (Germany) GmbH (3)
Thomas-Edison-Platz 1, 63263, Neu-Isenburg, Germany
Tel.: (49) 6102 8334 0
Sales Range: $25-49.9 Million
Emp.: 80
Cash Handling Equipment Mfr
N.A.I.C.S.: 333310
Oliver Kapahnke (Mng Dir)

Glory Global Solutions (Netherlands) BV (3)
Sportlaan 14, 4131 NN, Vianen, Netherlands
Tel.: (31) 347327446
Sales Range: $25-49.9 Million
Emp.: 50
Cash Handling Equipment Mfr
N.A.I.C.S.: 333310
Vincent Nakache (Pres)

Glory Global Solutions (Spain) S.A. (3)
Puerto de Pajares 17 Poligono Industrial Prado Overa, Leganes, 28919, Madrid, Spain
Tel.: (34) 913297100

Sales Range: $50-74.9 Million
Emp.: 120
Cash Handling Equipment Mfr
N.A.I.C.S.: 333310
Carlos Santa Mariea (Dir-Tech Svs)

Subsidiary (US):

Glory Global Solutions Inc. (3)
2441 Warrenville Rd Ste 100, Lisle, IL 60532-3664
Tel.: (630) 577-1000
Sales Range: $75-99.9 Million
Emp.: 30
Cash Handling Equipment Mfr
N.A.I.C.S.: 333310
Chris Regan (Pres)

Glory Global Solutions (Ireland) Ltd. (1)
Block 13 Unit H Blanchardstown Corporate Park 1, Blanchardstown, Dublin, D15 KW27, Ireland
Tel.: (353) 15713990
Information Technology Services
N.A.I.C.S.: 541511

Glory Global Solutions (Malaysia) Sdn. Bhd. (1)
S-2-61 & S-3-62 The Scott Garden Kompleks Rimbun Scott 289, Jalan Kelang Lama, 58000, Kuala Lumpur, Malaysia
Tel.: (60) 379819199
Information Technology Services
N.A.I.C.S.: 541511

Glory Global Solutions (New Zealand) Ltd. (1)
Building 5 Ground Floor Central Park 666 Great South Rd, Penrose, Auckland, New Zealand
Tel.: (64) 95250582
Information Technology Services
N.A.I.C.S.: 541511

Glory Global Solutions (Portugal) S. A. (1)
Rua Manuel Martinho Lote 1 a 11, Zona Industrial Cruz do Barro, 2564-910, Torres Vedras, Portugal
Tel.: (351) 261320800
Information Technology Services
N.A.I.C.S.: 541511

Glory Global Solutions (Shanghai) Co., Ltd. (1)
Unit AD 2nd Floor Building A BenQ Plaza 207 Songhong Road, Changning District, Shanghai, 200335, China
Tel.: (86) 2160315100
Information Technology Services
N.A.I.C.S.: 541511

Glory Global Solutions (Singapore) Pte. Ltd. (1)
438A Alexandra Road 08-01/02 Alexandra Technopark, Singapore, 119967, Singapore
Tel.: (65) 68372813
Information Technology Services
N.A.I.C.S.: 541511

Glory Global Solutions (South Asia) Pvt. Ltd. (1)
401-403 Vaibhav Chambers Bandra Kurla Complex Bandra East, Mumbai, 400051, India
Tel.: (91) 2266926660
Information Technology Services
N.A.I.C.S.: 541511

Glory Global Solutions (Switzerland) A. G. (1)
Meriedweg 8, 3172, Niederwangen, Switzerland
Tel.: (41) 319804141
Information Technology Services
N.A.I.C.S.: 541511

Glory Global Solutions Asia Pacific (1)
78 Shenton Way #27-02/03, Singapore, 79120, Singapore
Tel.: (65) 6837 2813
Web Site: http://www.gloryglobalsolutions.com
Sales Range: $25-49.9 Million
Emp.: 45
Cash Management Systems
N.A.I.C.S.: 525990

Yutaka Shoji (Mng Dir)

Glory Global Solutions GmbH (1)
Thomas-Edison-Platz 1, 63263, Neu-Isenburg, Germany
Tel.: (49) 61 028 3340
Web Site: https://www.glory-global.com
Sales Range: $25-49.9 Million
Emp.: 30
Industrial Machinery & Equipment Whslr
N.A.I.C.S.: 423830
Oliva Kaphnka (Gen Mgr)

Glory Global Solutions Mexico, S.A. De C.V. (1)
Rio Mississipi no 58, Colonia Cuauhtemoc Alcaldia Cuauhtemoc, 06500, Mexico, Mexico
Tel.: (52) 5552194444
Information Technology Services
N.A.I.C.S.: 541511

Glory Global Solutions Nakit Otomasyon Teknolojileri Ltd. Sti. (1)
Bayar Cad Gulbahar Sokak No 17 PS Plaza K 7 D 71-7273, Kozyatagi Kadikoy, 34742, Istanbul, Turkiye
Tel.: (90) 2164106290
Information Technology Services
N.A.I.C.S.: 541511

Glory Global Solutions Rus, LLC (1)
68-70 Butyrsky Val Str bld 1 room 85, 127055, Moscow, Russia
Tel.: (7) 4957992403
Information Technology Services
N.A.I.C.S.: 541511

Glory IST Co., Ltd. (1)
2-11-45 Shinonome, Koto-ku, Tokyo, 135-0062, Japan
Tel.: (81) 335277297
Information Technology Services
N.A.I.C.S.: 541511

Glory International Trading (Shanghai) Co., Ltd. (1)
B401-405 Far East International Plaza, No 317 Xianxia Road, 200051, Shanghai, China
Tel.: (86) 2162351008
Web Site: http://www.glory-global.com
Industrial Machinery Mfr
N.A.I.C.S.: 333248

Glory Ipo Asia Ltd. (1)
Units 01&03 27/F Aitken Vanson Centre No 61 Hoi Yuen Road, Kwun Tong, Kowloon, China (Hong Kong)
Tel.: (852) 35684413
Information Technology Services
N.A.I.C.S.: 541511

Glory Kiki Co., Ltd. (1)
67 Kokubunji Mikuninocho Himeji, 671-0234, Hyogo, Japan
Tel.: (81) 792520721
Web Site: http://www.glory-kiki.co.jp
Automatic Vending Machine Mfr
N.A.I.C.S.: 333310

Glory Mechatronics Ltd. (1)
1-3-1 Shimoteno Himeji, Hyogo, 670-0063, Japan
Tel.: (81) 79 294 6074
Web Site: http://www.glory-global.com
Industrial Machinery & Equipment Whslr
N.A.I.C.S.: 423830

Glory Products Ltd. (1)
860-3 Saiji, Fukusaki-cho Kanzaki-gun, Hyogo, 679-2284, Japan
Tel.: (81) 79 022 6900
Web Site: https://www.glory.co.jp
Financial Services
N.A.I.C.S.: 541219

Glory Service Co., Ltd. (1)
Ujiden Building 5F 4-8-17 Nishitenma, Kita-ku, Osaka, 530-0047, Japan
Tel.: (81) 66 363 4784
Web Site: https://www.glory-service.co.jp
Emp.: 118
Equipment Rental & Leasing
N.A.I.C.S.: 532420

Glory Techno 24 Co., Ltd. (1)
1-6-10 Kitahama, Chuo-ku, Osaka, 541-0041, Japan
Tel.: (81) 66 202 0731
Web Site: http://www.glory-global.com

INTERNATIONAL PUBLIC

Industrial Machinery & Equipment Sales
N.A.I.C.S.: 423830

Glory USA, Inc. (1)
10 York Ave, West Caldwell, NJ 07006-6411
Tel.: (973) 228-4500
Web Site: http://www.gloryusa.com
Sales Range: $25-49.9 Million
Emp.: 40
Mfr of Coin Wrapping & Counting Machines
N.A.I.C.S.: 423850
Priscilla Neubauer (Asst Mgr-HR)

Hokkaido Glory Co., Ltd. (1)
17-1-45 Kita 13 West, Chuo-ku, Sapporo, 060-0013, Hokkaido, Japan
Tel.: (81) 11 707 4545
Web Site: https://www.hokkaido-glory.co.jp
Office Equipment Whslr
N.A.I.C.S.: 423420

Japan Settlement Information Center Ltd. (1)
3-8-27 Toranomon, Minato-ku, Tokyo, 105-0001, Japan
Tel.: (81) 364309371
Information Technology Services
N.A.I.C.S.: 541511

Maruesu Gt Co., Ltd. (1)
2-1-2 Niwaji-honmachi, Neyagawa, 572-0076, Osaka, Japan
Tel.: (81) 728392630
Automatic Vending Machine Mfr
N.A.I.C.S.: 333310

PT. Glory Global Solutions Indonesia (1)
Equity Tower 45th Floor-Unit B Jl Jend Sudirman Kav 52-53 SCBD, Jakarta, 12190, Indonesia
Tel.: (62) 215153591
Information Technology Services
N.A.I.C.S.: 541511

Reis Service GmbH (1)
Grabener Strasse 19, 76646, Bruchsal, Germany
Tel.: (49) 72517890
Web Site: http://www.reis-service.de
Sales Range: $50-74.9 Million
Emp.: 100
Industrial Machinery & Equipment Whslr
N.A.I.C.S.: 423830

Revolution Retail Systems, LLC (1)
1400 Valwood Pkwy Ste 100, Carrollton, TX 75006
Tel.: (469) 317-2910
Web Site: https://www.revolutionretailsystems.com
Financial Services
N.A.I.C.S.: 522320

Sitrade Italia S.p.A. (1)
Via Cassanese 94/96, 20090, Segrate, Milan, Italy (75.5%)
Tel.: (39) 022 694 6001
Web Site: https://www.sitradeitalia.com
Sales Range: $75-99.9 Million
Emp.: 130
Currency Handling Machine Distr
N.A.I.C.S.: 423420

Standardwerk Eugen Reis GmbH (1)
Grabener Strasse 19, 76646, Bruchsal, Germany
Tel.: (49) 72517890
Web Site: http://www.reis.de
Sales Range: $50-74.9 Million
Emp.: 100
Industrial Machinery & Equipment Whslr
N.A.I.C.S.: 423830
Jurgen Riffel (Mgr)

viafintech GmbH (1)
Wallstrasse 14a, 10179, Berlin, Germany (51.93%)
Tel.: (49) 30346461607
Web Site: http://www.viafintech.com
Information Technology Services
N.A.I.C.S.: 541511
Sebastian Seifert (Mng Dir)

GLORY SUN FINANCIAL GROUP LIMITED

18/F Wing On Centre 111 Connaught Road, Central, China (Hong Kong)

AND PRIVATE COMPANIES   **GM LEATHER S.P.A.**

Tel.: (852) 28136828
Web Site: http://www.hk1282.com
1282—(HKG)
Rev.: $103,452,098
Assets: $1,012,415,663
Liabilities: $360,709,103
Net Worth: ($651,706,560)
Earnings: ($68,512,380)
Emp.: 292
Fiscal Year-end: 12/31/22
Investment Holding Company
N.A.I.C.S.: 551112

Subsidiaries:

Glory Sun Land Group Limited (1)
Unit 2602 26/F Tower 1 Lippo Centre, No 89 Queensway Admiralty, Hong Kong, China (Hong Kong) (66.42%)
Tel.: (852) 25988788
Web Site: http://www.hk0299.com
Rev.: $206,227,043
Assets: $2,127,278,468
Liabilities: $1,720,227,833
Net Worth: $407,050,635
Earnings: ($116,186,160)
Emp.: 361
Fiscal Year-end: 12/31/2022
Outsourcing Software Developer
N.A.I.C.S.: 513210
Xiaodong Zhang (Vice Chm)

Subsidiary (Non-US):

SinoCom Japan Corporation (2)
5F Across Shinkawa Building Annex 1-16-14 Shinkawa, Chuo-ku, Tokyo, 104-0033, Japan
Tel.: (81) 3 3553 0361
Web Site: http://www.sinocom.jp
Sales Range: $25-49.9 Million
Emp.: 165
Outsourcing Software Developer
N.A.I.C.S.: 334610

GLORY VIEW TECHNOLOGY CO., LTD.
Hongjing Technology Building No 111 Yingri Road, Huangpu District, Guangzhou, 510663, China
Tel.: (86) 2032211688
Web Site: https://www.gloryview.com
Year Founded: 1997
301396—(CHIN)
Rev.: $104,777,712
Assets: $257,429,016
Liabilities: $78,904,800
Net Worth: $178,524,216
Earnings: $8,856,432
Fiscal Year-end: 12/31/22
Software Development Services
N.A.I.C.S.: 541511
Hua Ouyang (Chm)

GLOSTER LIMITED
21 Strand Road, Kolkata, 700 001, West Bengal, India
Tel.: (91) 3322309601
Web Site:
   https://www.glosterjute.com
Year Founded: 1992
542351—(BOM)
Rev.: $105,224,970
Assets: $169,220,756
Liabilities: $23,085,917
Net Worth: $146,134,839
Earnings: $8,911,307
Emp.: 3,902
Fiscal Year-end: 03/31/22
Jute & Jute Products Mfr
N.A.I.C.S.: 339999
Hemant Bangur (Chm)

Subsidiaries:

Fort Gloster Industries Limited (1)
21 Strand Road, Kolkata, 700 001, West Bengal, India
Tel.: (91) 3322309601
Web Site: https://www.fortgloster.in
Wires & Cables Mfr & Distr
N.A.I.C.S.: 332618

GLOTECH INDUSTRIAL CORP.
No 718 Sec 2 Yanghu Rd, Taoyuan County Yangmei, Taoyuan, 32669, Taiwan
Tel.: (886) 34726448
Web Site: https://www.glotechgf.com
Year Founded: 1997
5475—(TPE)
Rev.: $20,933,496
Assets: $68,440,453
Liabilities: $33,542,413
Net Worth: $34,898,040
Earnings: ($11,324,422)
Fiscal Year-end: 12/31/22
Electronic Component Mfr & Distr
N.A.I.C.S.: 334419
William Liu (Chm)

Subsidiaries:

Glotech Electronics (Suzhou) Corp. (1)
No 136 Hua-Shan Rd, Suzhou, 215011, China
Tel.: (86) 5126 661 9489
Glass Fibber Fabric Mfr
N.A.I.C.S.: 325220

Glotech Technical Materials Corp. (1)
No 102 Sec 4 Zhongxing Rd, Zhudong Township, Hsinchu, 31061, Taiwan
Tel.: (886) 3 582 6226
Glass Fibber Fabric Mfr
N.A.I.C.S.: 325220

GLP J-REIT
16F Yaesu Central Tower Tokyo Midtown Yaesu 2-2-1 Yaesu, Chuo-ku, Tokyo, Japan
Tel.: (81) 368978810
Web Site: https://www.glpjreit.com
Year Founded: 2011
3281—(TKS)
Sales Range: $75-99.9 Million
Investment Management Service
N.A.I.C.S.: 523940
Yoji Tatsumi (Exec Dir)

GLSG GERSTHOFER LOGISTIK- UND SPEDITIONSGESELLSCHAFT MBH
Otto Hahn Strasse 8a, 86368, Gersthofen, Germany
Tel.: (49) 821249620
Web Site: http://www.glsg-logistik.de
Rev.: $11,035,200
Emp.: 14
Logistic Services
N.A.I.C.S.: 488510
Valesca Mayer (Gen Mgr)

GLUCOSAN COMPANY
No 41 Sepand St Nejatullahi St, 15988 17611, Tehran, Iran
Tel.: (98) 2188890750
Web Site: https://www.glucosan.ir
Year Founded: 1970
GCOZ—(THE)
Sales Range: Less than $1 Million
Emp.: 130
Starch Mfr
N.A.I.C.S.: 311221
Mohammad Mimaran Mimaran Kashani (CEO)

GLUCOTRACK, INC.
19 Ha'Yahalomim Street, PO Box 12163, Ashdod, 7760049, Israel
Tel.: (972) 86757878   DE
Web Site: http://www.integrity-app.com
Year Founded: 2010
GCTK—(NASDAQ)
Assets: $2,438,000
Liabilities: $1,208,000
Net Worth: $1,230,000
Earnings: ($4,435,000)
Emp.: 3

Fiscal Year-end: 12/31/22
System Integration & Software Engineering Services
N.A.I.C.S.: 541330
Paul V. Goode (CEO)

GLUNZ & JENSEN HOLDING A/S
Selandia Park 1, DK-4100, Ringsted, Denmark
Tel.: (45) 57688181   DK
Web Site: https://www.glunz-jensen.com
Year Founded: 1973
GJ—(CSE)
Rev.: $22,605,676
Assets: $35,039,904
Liabilities: $22,845,028
Net Worth: $12,194,876
Earnings: $141,135
Emp.: 119
Fiscal Year-end: 03/31/21
Prepress Machinery Mfr & Distr
N.A.I.C.S.: 333248
Thomas Haase (Product Mgr-iCtP Sls)

Subsidiaries:

Glunz & Jensen Ltd. (1)
Wyatt Way, Thetford, Norfolk, IP24 1HB, United Kingdom
Tel.: (44) 1842 762300
Mfr of Industrial Equipment
N.A.I.C.S.: 333248

Glunz & Jensen s.r.o. (1)
Kosicka 50, 080 01, Presov, Slovakia
Tel.: (421) 517563811
Sales Range: $25-49.9 Million
Emp.: 100
Prepress Machinery Mfr & Distr
N.A.I.C.S.: 333248

Glunz & Jensen, Inc. (1)
2185 Hwy 292, Inman, SC 29349
Tel.: (864) 568-4638
Sales Range: $25-49.9 Million
Emp.: 35
Mfr of Industrial Equipment
N.A.I.C.S.: 333310

Imacon, Inc. (1)
15207 Northeast 95th St, Redmond, WA 98052-2562
Tel.: (425) 861-6434
Sales Range: $50-74.9 Million
Emp.: 10
Mfr of Industrial Equipment
N.A.I.C.S.: 423430

Selandia Park A/S (1)
Selandia Park 1, 4100, Ringsted, Denmark
Tel.: (45) 57688181
Industrial Machinery Mfr
N.A.I.C.S.: 333248

GLYCONEX, INC.
8F No 97 Sec 1 Xintai 5th Rd, Xizhi Dist, New Taipei City, 221, Taiwan
Tel.: (886) 226974168
Web Site:
   https://www.glyconex.com.tw
Year Founded: 2001
4168—(TPE)
Rev.: $940,656
Assets: $53,683,144
Liabilities: $8,483,788
Net Worth: $45,199,356
Earnings: $6,873,089
Emp.: 48
Fiscal Year-end: 12/31/22
Research & Development Services
N.A.I.C.S.: 541720
Tong-Hsuan Chang (Chm)

GLYCOREX TRANSPLANTATION AB
Scheelevagen 27, 223 63, Lund, Sweden
Tel.: (46) 462865230
Web Site: https://glycorex.com

Year Founded: 2001
O33—(DEU)
Medical Equipment Mfr & Distr
N.A.I.C.S.: 334510
Johan Nilsson (CEO)

GLYN GMBH & CO. KG
Am Wortgarten 8, 65510, Idstein, Germany
Tel.: (49) 6126590222
Web Site: http://www.glyn.com
Year Founded: 1980
Rev.: $96,105,346
Emp.: 160
Semiconductor Product Mfr
N.A.I.C.S.: 334413
Glyn Jones (Co-Mng Dir)

Subsidiaries:

GLYN Hungary Kft. (1)
Infopark Setany 1/ I, 1117, Budapest, Hungary
Tel.: (36) 12049571
Semiconductor Component Distr
N.A.I.C.S.: 423690

GLYN Ltd. (1)
Unit 3B/64 Talavera Road Macquarrie Park 2113 North Ryde, Sydney, NSW, Australia
Tel.: (61) 288500320
Web Site: http://www.glyn.com.au
Semiconductor Component Distr
N.A.I.C.S.: 423690

GLYN Ltd. (1)
Unit 5/18 Airborne Road Albany, North Shore City, 632, Auckland, New Zealand
Tel.: (64) 94419050
Web Site: http://www.glyn.co.nz
Semiconductor Component Distr
N.A.I.C.S.: 423690
Mike Benson (Mng Dir)

GLYN Poland (1)
ul Krupnicza 13, 50-075, Wroclaw, Poland
Tel.: (48) 717828758
Web Site: http://www.glyn.pl
Semiconductor Component Distr
N.A.I.C.S.: 423690

GLYN Schweden (1)
Tammsvag 13, 81576, Soderfors, Sweden
Tel.: (46) 29330084
Semiconductor Component Distr
N.A.I.C.S.: 423690

GLYN Switzerland (1)
Bachweg 3, Esslingen, 8133, Zurich, Switzerland
Tel.: (41) 449445500
Web Site: http://www.glyn.com
Semiconductor Components Mfr
N.A.I.C.S.: 334413

GM CAPITAL CORP
02 Prue Avenue, Toronto, M6B 1R5, ON, Canada
Tel.: (416) 792-4708
Emp.: 100
Investment Services
N.A.I.C.S.: 523999

Subsidiaries:

Terra Firma Capital Corporation (1)
22 St Clair Avenue East Suite 200, Toronto, M4T 2S3, ON, Canada (100%)
Tel.: (416) 792-4700
Web Site: http://www.tfcc.ca
Rev.: $16,241,159
Assets: $139,305,967
Liabilities: $95,726,747
Net Worth: $43,579,220
Earnings: $3,340,552
Emp.: 11
Fiscal Year-end: 12/31/2021
Real Estate Services
N.A.I.C.S.: 531390
Y. Dov Meyer (Chm)

GM LEATHER S.P.A.
Via Olimpica 11, 36071, Arzignano, VI, Italy
Tel.: (39) 0444477269

3011

GM LEATHER S.P.A.

GM Leather S.p.A.—(Continued)
Web Site:
https://www.gmleatherspa.com
Year Founded: 1976
GML—(ITA)
Leather Product Mfr
N.A.I.C.S.: 316110
Marco Malagutti (CEO)

GM POLYPLAST LIMITED

A/66 New Empire Industrial Estate Kondivita Road, Near J B Nagar Andheri East, Mumbai, 400059, Maharashtra, India
Tel.: (91) 52362432
Web Site:
https://www.gmpolyplast.com
Year Founded: 2003
543239—(BOM)
Rev.: $9,872,622
Assets: $4,419,987
Liabilities: $1,381,452
Net Worth: $3,038,535
Earnings: $589,929
Emp.: 75
Fiscal Year-end: 03/31/23
Granule Mfr
N.A.I.C.S.: 326199
Dinesh Balbirsingh Sharma (Mng Dir)

GMA HOLDINGS, INC.

GMA Network Center GMA Complex EDSA Diliman, Fort Bonifacio, Quezon City, 1634, Philippines
Tel.: (63) 29827777 PH
Web Site:
http://www.gmanetwork.com
Year Founded: 2006
GMAP—(PHI)
Rev.: $47,431
Assets: $885,520
Liabilities: $861,297
Net Worth: $24,223
Earnings: $21,587
Fiscal Year-end: 12/31/23
Investment Services
N.A.I.C.S.: 523940
Roberto O. Parel (Sec)

Subsidiaries:

Alta Productions Group, Inc. (1)
10F Sagittarius Bldg HV Dela Costa St, Salcedo Village, Makati, 2000, Philippines
Tel.: (63) 253102902
Web Site: https://altaproductions.com
Emp.: 27
Television Commercials & Progam Production Services
N.A.I.C.S.: 512110
Edmond Alcaraz (Pres)

GMA New Media, Inc. (1)
12/F GMA Network Center EDSA Corner Timog Avenue, Diliman, Quezon City, 1103, Philippines
Tel.: (63) 89827777
Web Site: https://www.gmanmi.ph
Emp.: 100
Interactive Mobile Application Development Services
N.A.I.C.S.: 541511
Dennis Augusto L. Caharian (Pres & COO)

GMA Worldwide (Philippines), Inc. (1)
10th Floor GMA Network Center EDSA Corner Timog Avenue, Diliman, Quezon City, Philippines
Tel.: (63) 29285073
Web Site: http://www.gmanetwork.com
Films & Television Programs Distr
N.A.I.C.S.: 512120

Scenarios, Inc. (1)
GMA Network Studios GMA Network Drive, Diliman, Quezon City, Philippines
Tel.: (63) 29285507
Stage Set Contracting Services
N.A.I.C.S.: 238990

GMA NETWORK, INC.

GMA Network Center GMA Complex EDSA Corner Timog Avenue, GMA Network Drive cor Samar Street Diliman, Quezon City, 1103, Philippines
Tel.: (63) 89827777 PH
Web Site:
https://www.gmanetwork.com
Year Founded: 1950
GMA7—(PHI)
Rev.: $383,694,437
Assets: $440,012,240
Liabilities: $164,821,006
Net Worth: $275,191,234
Earnings: $97,089,168
Emp.: 2,862
Fiscal Year-end: 12/31/22
Television & Radio Broadcasting Services; Motion Picture Production & Distribution Services; Music Production & Publishing Services
N.A.I.C.S.: 516120
Felipe L. Gozon (Chm & CEO)

Subsidiaries:

Digify, Inc. (1)
GMA Network Center EDSA cor Timog Avenue Diliman, Quezon City, Philippines
Tel.: (63) 9284553
Television Broadcasting Services
N.A.I.C.S.: 516120

GMB CORP.

150-3 Handa Kwanishichou, Shikigun, Nara, Japan
Tel.: (81) 745 44 1911
Web Site: http://www.gmb.jp
Year Founded: 1943
Sales Range: $150-199.9 Million
Emp.: 339
Motor Vehicle Parts Mfr
N.A.I.C.S.: 336390
Nobuo Matsuoka (Chm)

Subsidiaries:

GMB Korea Corp. (1)
618 Ungnam-ro, Seongsan-gu, Changwon, Gyeongsangnam-do, Korea (South)
Tel.: (82) 552632131
Web Site: https://www.gmb.co.kr
Rev.: $468,258,186
Assets: $422,478,635
Liabilities: $217,052,240
Net Worth: $205,426,395
Earnings: $9,272,914
Emp.: 692
Fiscal Year-end: 12/31/2022
Automotive Parts & Equipment Mfr
N.A.I.C.S.: 336390
Sei-Young Chung (CEO)

GMB North America, Inc. (1)
100 Herrod Blvd, Dayton, NJ 08810
Tel.: (609) 655-2422
Web Site: http://www.gmb.net
Automobile Component Distr
N.A.I.C.S.: 441330
Sarah Porter (Mgr-Mktg)

Qingdao GMB Automotive Co., Ltd (1)
Qingdao Northern Industrial Park Longquan-Township Jimo, Qingdao, Shandong, China
Tel.: (86) 53285587945
Emp.: 230
Automotive Component Mfr & Distr
N.A.I.C.S.: 334515
Joong Koo Kim (Pres)

Qingdao GMB Machinery Product Co., Ltd. (1)
Industrial Area 2 Wang Cheng-Township Laixi, Qingdao, Shandong, China
Tel.: (86) 53288413112
Emp.: 890
Automotive Components Mfr
N.A.I.C.S.: 334515
Chan Sub Kim (Pres)

THAI GMB INDUSTRY Co., Ltd (1)
304 Industrial Park Approx 150km from Bangkok 239 Moo, 7 Tumbol Tha Toom Amphur Sri-Mahaphote, Bangkok, 25140, Prachinburi, Thailand
Tel.: (66) 374141168
Web Site: http://www.gmb.co.th
Emp.: 429
Automotive Components Mfr
N.A.I.C.S.: 334515
Takeshi Sasaki (Pres)

YAO Office & Plant (1)
4-36-3 Kusunechou, Yao, Osaka, Japan
Tel.: (81) 729971521
Automotive Components Mfr
N.A.I.C.S.: 334515
Yuichi Sakaguchi (Pres)

GMCI CORP.

Level 1 Tower 1Avenue 3 The Horizon, Bangsar South City, Kuala Lumpur, 59200, Malaysia
Tel.: (60) 3 2242 2259 NV
Web Site: http://www.gmcicorp.com
Year Founded: 2006
Metal Mining Services
N.A.I.C.S.: 212290
Kevin Chea Lin Liu (Chief Sls Officer)

GME GROUP HOLDINGS LIMITED

Room 1001-2 10/F 148 Electric Road, Hong Kong, China (Hong Kong)
Tel.: (852) 31060333 Ky
Web Site: https://www.gmehk.com
Year Founded: 1994
8188—(HKG)
Rev.: $56,167,320
Assets: $20,010,615
Liabilities: $11,137,125
Net Worth: $8,873,490
Earnings: $739,755
Emp.: 542
Fiscal Year-end: 12/31/22
Underground Construction Services
N.A.I.C.S.: 237990
Boris Chun Ngok Chuang (Chm & Compliance Officer)

GME INNOTAINMENT, INC.

Room 1902 19/F Kodak House 2, 321 Java Road North Point, Hong Kong, China (Hong Kong)
Tel.: (852) 35431208 FL
Web Site:
www.gmeinnotainment.com
GMEV—(OTCEM)
Rev.: $1,000
Assets: $272,000
Liabilities: $3,746,000
Net Worth: ($3,474,000)
Earnings: ($1,315,000)
Emp.: 2
Fiscal Year-end: 12/31/22
Water Purification Services
N.A.I.C.S.: 221310
Yves R. Michel (CEO & CFO)

GMM GRAMMY PUBLIC COMPANY LIMITED

50 GMM Grammy PLACE Sukhumvit 21 Rd, Khlongtoeinuea Wattana, Bangkok, 10110, Thailand
Tel.: (66) 26699000
Web Site:
https://www.gmmgrammy.com
Year Founded: 1983
GRAMMY—(THA)
Rev.: $174,808,769,864
Assets: $182,867,063,223
Liabilities: $138,401,147,898
Net Worth: $44,465,915,325
Earnings: ($3,693,240,008)
Emp.: 1,013
Fiscal Year-end: 12/31/23
Entertainment Industry Business Services
N.A.I.C.S.: 561499
Phawit Chitrakorn (CEO-GMM Music)

INTERNATIONAL PUBLIC

Subsidiaries:

Clean Karaoke Co., Ltd. (1)
50 Sukhumvit Rd Khlong Toei Nua, Vadhana, Bangkok, 10110; Thailand
Tel.: (66) 23815519
Web Site: http://www.cleankaraoke.com
Music Publishers
N.A.I.C.S.: 512230

Exact Co. Ltd. (1)
Toey-nua Wattana, 10110, Bangkok, Thailand (100%)
Tel.: (66) 26699260
Web Site: http://www.exact.co.th
Sales Range: $50-74.9 Million
Emp.: 200
Musical Instrument Mfr
N.A.I.C.S.: 339992
Somsii Pieuttitan (Mgr-HR)

GDH 559 Company Limited (1)
92/11 Soi Sukhumvit 31 Sawasdee, Khlong Tan Nuea Subdistrict Watthana District, Bangkok, 10110, Thailand
Tel.: (66) 26623404
Web Site: https://www.gdh559.com
Emp.: 59
Film Studio Services
N.A.I.C.S.: 512110

GMM Fitness Club Co., Ltd. (1)
AA Floor GMM Grammy Place Bldg 1-50 Sukhumvit 21 Asoke Klongtoey, Watthana, Bangkok, 10110, Thailand
Tel.: (66) 2 669 9399
Fitness Club Management Services
N.A.I.C.S.: 713940

GMM Media Plc (1)
50 36-38/F GMM Grammy Place Sukhumvit 21, Klongtoey Nua Wattana, Bangkok, 10110, Thailand
Tel.: (66) 26699333
Radio Broadcasting Services
N.A.I.C.S.: 516210

Subsidiary (Domestic):

3-RD Co., Ltd. (2)
38 Chalantip Bld 6 Floor Convent Rd, Silom, Bangkok, 10500, Thailand
Tel.: (66) 20121401
Web Site: http://www.3-rd.co.th
Database Marketing Services
N.A.I.C.S.: 561990

A Gen Event Agency Co., Ltd. (2)
1755/4 Soi Ladprao 94 Punjamit Plubpla, Wangthonglang, Bangkok, 10310, Thailand
Tel.: (66) 2559 3854
Sales Range: $25-49.9 Million
Emp.: 17
Music Publishing Services
N.A.I.C.S.: 512230

GMM Tai Hub Co., Ltd. (2)
92/11 Sukhumvit 31 Sukhumvit Road, Klongton-Nua Wattana, Bangkok, 10110, Thailand
Tel.: (66) 2 662 3404
Web Site: http://www.gth.co.th
Video Publishing Services
N.A.I.C.S.: 512199
Visute Poolvoralaks (CEO)

Image Publishing Co. Ltd. (2)
217-7 Khlongtoey Soi 63, Klongton Wattana, 10110, Bangkok, Thailand (100%)
Tel.: (66) 238125016
Web Site: http://image.gmember.com
Sales Range: $25-49.9 Million
Emp.: 100
Book Publishers
N.A.I.C.S.: 512230

In Publishing Co., Ltd. (2)
26th fl 50 Gmm Grammy Asoke rd Klongtoei-nua, Wattana, Bangkok, 10110, Thailand
Tel.: (66) 81 555 2195
Media Publishing & Broadcasting Services
N.A.I.C.S.: 516210

The Post Publishing Company Ltd. (2)
136 Sunthorn Kosa Road, Kwang Klong Toey Khet Klong To, Bangkok, 10110, Thailand
Tel.: (66) 22403700
Web Site: http://www.bangkokpost.co.th

AND PRIVATE COMPANIES

Sales Range: $400-449.9 Million
Emp.: 1,200
Newspaper Publishers
N.A.I.C.S.: 513110

GMM Music Publishing International Co., Ltd (1)
50 Sukhumvit Rd Khlong Toei Nua, Vadhana, Bangkok, 10110, Thailand
Tel.: (66) 26699000
Music Publishing Services
N.A.I.C.S.: 512230

Media Vision (1994) Co. Ltd. (1)
999 999/9 Moo 2 Ngamwongwan Rd, Bangkhen Muang, Nonthaburi, 11000, Thailand
Tel.: (66) 2 951 0101
Web Site: https://www.mediavision1994.com
Sound Recording Industries
N.A.I.C.S.: 512290

Mifah Co. Ltd. (1)
59-1 Sukumvit 39 Sukumvit Road, Klongton Wattana, 10110, Bangkok, Thailand **(100%)**
Tel.: (66) 22594545
Web Site: http://www.mifagmm.com
Sales Range: $50-74.9 Million
Emp.: 10
Music School
N.A.I.C.S.: 711130

Phenomena Motion Pictures Co. Ltd (1)
14 & 16Soi Suwanmanee, Samsennok Huay Kwang, Bangkok, 10310, Thailand **(100%)**
Tel.: (66) 26904555
Web Site: http://www.pheno.com
Sales Range: $50-74.9 Million
Emp.: 160
Teleproduction & Postproduction Services
N.A.I.C.S.: 512191
Yodethtt Sudesawad *(Mng Dir)*

GMO GLOBALSIGN HOLDINGS K.K.
10F Cerulean Tower 26-1 Sakuragaoka-cho, Shibuya-ku, Tokyo, 150-8512, Japan
Tel.: (81) 364156100
Web Site: https://www.gmogshd.com
3788—(TKS)
Rev.: $124,067,910
Assets: $111,263,370
Liabilities: $49,828,520
Net Worth: $61,434,850
Earnings: $5,239,510
Emp.: 999
Fiscal Year-end: 12/31/23
Information Technology Services
N.A.I.C.S.: 541512
Kanno Michiari *(Mng Dir)*

Subsidiaries:

GMO DIGITAL Lab K.K. (1)
Shikishima Building 5F Kita 2-jo Nishi 3-chome, Chuo-ku, Sapporo, 060-0002, Hokkaido, Japan
Tel.: (81) 112190037
Web Site: https://www.digitallab.jp
Emp.: 83
Web Consulting Services
N.A.I.C.S.: 541511
Yuichi Yamada *(Pres)*

GMO GlobalSign Certificate Services Private Limited (1)
Tel.: (91) 1141106000
Security Application Development Services
N.A.I.C.S.: 541511
Ichiro Chujo *(CEO)*

GMO GlobalSign FZ-LLC (1)
207 Second Floor Building No 14, PO Box 345890, Dubai Internet City, Dubai, United Arab Emirates
Tel.: (971) 523861073
Computer System Design Services
N.A.I.C.S.: 541512
Aditya Anand *(CEO)*

GMO GlobalSign K.K. (1)
Computer System Design Services
N.A.I.C.S.: 541512

GMO GlobalSign Ltd. (1)
Springfield House Sandling Road, Maidstone, ME14 2LP, Kent, United Kingdom
Tel.: (44) 1622766766
Web Site: https://www.globalsign.com
Security Application Development Services
N.A.I.C.S.: 541511
Ichiro Chujo *(Chm, Pres & CEO)*

GMO GlobalSign Pte. Ltd. (1)
1 Wallich Street 25-01A, Singapore, 078881, Singapore
Tel.: (65) 31580349
Web Site: https://www.globalsign.com
Security Application Development Services
N.A.I.C.S.: 541511

GMO GlobalSign Russia LLC (1)
Savvinskaya naberezhnaya 15 Floor 6 Room 1, 119435, Moscow, Russia
Tel.: (7) 4996782210
Web Site: http://www.globalsign.com
Security Application Development Services
N.A.I.C.S.: 541511
Semiletopulo Juri Leonidovich *(CEO)*

GMO GlobalSign, Inc. (1)
2 International Dr Ste 150, Portsmouth, NH 03801
Tel.: (603) 570-7060
Web Site: https://www.globalsign.com
Computer System Design Services
N.A.I.C.S.: 541512
Ichiro Chujo *(Chm & CEO)*

GMO GlobalSign, inc. (1)
23rd Fl Zuellig Building Paseo de Roxas Ave, Corner Makati Ave, Makati, 1225, Philippines
Tel.: (63) 288474774
Web Site: https://www.globalsign.com
Security Application Development Services
N.A.I.C.S.: 541511
Ichiro Chujo *(Chm, Pres & CEO)*

GlobalSign China Co., Ltd (1)
Rm 706 Fortune Times Tower No 1438 North Shaanxi Road, Putuo Dist, Shanghai, 200060, China
Tel.: (86) 2160952260
Web Site: https://www.cn.globalsign.com
Security Application Development Services
N.A.I.C.S.: 541511
Ichiro Chujo *(CEO)*

GlobalSign NV (1)
Diestsevest 14, 3000, Leuven, Belgium
Tel.: (32) 16891900
Web Site: https://www.globalsign.be
Security Application Development Services
N.A.I.C.S.: 541511

Toriton, Inc (1)
2-1-3 Kobukuroya Hills Kamakura 1F, Kamakura, 247-0055, Kanagawa, Japan
Tel.: (81) 467555822
Security Application Development Services
N.A.I.C.S.: 541511
Tatsuya Ishimori *(Pres)*

GMO INTERNET GROUP, INC.
Cerulean Tower 4-14F 26-1 Sakuragaokacho, Shibuya-ku, Tokyo, 150-8512, Japan
Tel.: (81) 354562555
Web Site: https://www.gmo.jp
9449—(TKS)
Rev.: $1,833,778,870
Assets: $12,461,639,240
Liabilities: $11,236,210,730
Net Worth: $1,225,428,510
Earnings: $100,614,190
Emp.: 6,413
Fiscal Year-end: 12/31/23
Internet & Website Services
N.A.I.C.S.: 517810
Masatoshi Kumagai *(Founder & CEO-Grp)*

Subsidiaries:

FX Prime by GMO Corporation (1)
Shibuya Infoss Tower 20-1 Sakuragaoka-cho, Shibuya-ku, Tokyo, 150-0031, Japan
Tel.: (81) 354897130
Web Site: http://www.fxprime.com

Sales Range: $25-49.9 Million
Emp.: 60
Securities & Commodity Broker
N.A.I.C.S.: 523150

GMO AD Marketing Inc. (1)
Tel.: (81) 354570909
All Other Telecommunication Services
N.A.I.C.S.: 517810

GMO AD Partners Inc. (1)
1-2-3 Dogenzaka, Shibuya-ku, Tokyo, 150-0043, Japan **(50.2%)**
Tel.: (81) 357287900
Web Site: https://www.gmo-ap.jp
Rev.: $105,669,360
Assets: $76,905,230
Liabilities: $39,739,450
Net Worth: $37,165,780
Earnings: $283,600
Emp.: 221
Fiscal Year-end: 12/31/2023
Internet Related Advertising Services
N.A.I.C.S.: 541890

Subsidiary (Domestic):

JWord, Inc. (2)
26-1 Sakuragaokacho Cerulean Tower, Shibuya-ku, Tokyo, 150-8512, Japan **(72.4%)**
Tel.: (81) 354286900
Web Site: http://www.jword.jp
Sales Range: $10-24.9 Million
Develops & Markets Keyword Search Software
N.A.I.C.S.: 513210

GMO Beauty Inc. (1)
Cerulean Tower 26-1, Sakuragaoka-cho Shibuya-ku, Tokyo, 150-8512, Japan
Tel.: (81) 337709090
Web Site: https://beauty.gmo
Beauty Salon Operator
N.A.I.C.S.: 812112

GMO Brand Security Inc. (1)
Cerulean Tower 26-1, Sakuragaoka-cho Shibuya-ku, Tokyo, 150-8512, Japan
Tel.: (81) 357841069
Web Site: https://www.brandsecurity.gmo
Crypto Asset Trading Services
N.A.I.C.S.: 518210

GMO Brights Consulting Inc. (1)
4103 Teheran-ro 425, Gangnam-gu, Seoul, 135-877, Korea (South)
Tel.: (82) 357841069
All Other Telecommunication Services
N.A.I.C.S.: 517810

GMO CARS K.K. (1)
Cerulean Tower 26-1 Sakuragaokacho, Shibuya-ku, Tokyo, 150-8512, Japan
Tel.: (81) 364157355
All Other Telecommunication Services
N.A.I.C.S.: 517810

GMO CLICK Securities, Inc. (1)
Shibuya Fukuras 1-2-3, Dogenzaka Shibuya-ku, Tokyo, 150-0043, Japan **(100%)**
Tel.: (81) 36 221 0190
Web Site: https://www.gmo.jp
Online Securities Brokerage Services
N.A.I.C.S.: 523150

GMO Card System, Inc. (1)
1-14-6 Dogenzaka, Shibuya-ku, Tokyo, 150-0043, Japan
Tel.: (81) 368050039
Web Site: https://gmo-cas.com
Employee Recruitment Services
N.A.I.C.S.: 561311

GMO Commerce, Inc. (1)
Tel.: (81) 337707030
All Other Telecommunication Services
N.A.I.C.S.: 517810

GMO Connect Inc. (1)
7F Cerulean Tower 26-1, Sakuragaoka-cho Shibuya-ku, Tokyo, 150-8512, Japan
Tel.: (81) 365554390
Web Site: https://gmo-connect.jp
Software Development Services
N.A.I.C.S.: 541511

GMO Creators Network, Inc. (1)
Cerulean Tower 26-1 Sakuragaoka-cho, Shibuya-ku, Tokyo, 150-8512, Japan

GMO INTERNET GROUP, INC.

Tel.: (81) 35 458 8056
Web Site: https://www.gmo-cn.jp
Emp.: 15
Website Designing & Hosting Services
N.A.I.C.S.: 518210

GMO Data, Inc. (1)
Humax Shibuya Bldg 7F 1-14-6, Dogenzaka Shibuya-ku, Tokyo, 150-0043, Japan
Tel.: (81) 364163881
Payment Processing Services
N.A.I.C.S.: 522320

GMO DigiRock, Inc. (1)
23rd floor Grand Front Osaka Tower B 3-1 Ofuka-cho, Kita-ku, Osaka, 530-0011, Japan
Tel.: (81) 662416585
Web Site: https://www.digirock.co.jp
Emp.: 23
Internet Services
N.A.I.C.S.: 517410

GMO Dream Wave Inc. (1)
1-5-3 Hiroshima Miyazaki City, Miyazaki, 880-8539, Japan
Tel.: (81) 985615730
Web Site: http://www.recruit.gmo.jp
Internet Advertising Services
N.A.I.C.S.: 541810

GMO E-Lab Marketing Research (Shanghai) Co, Ltd. (1)
Tel.: (86) 2133301227
All Other Telecommunication Services
N.A.I.C.S.: 517810

GMO Engine Inc. (1)
Cerulean Tower 26-1, Sakuragaoka-cho Shibuya-ku, Tokyo, 150-8512, Japan
Tel.: (81) 334440147
Web Site: https://www.engine-f.co.jp
Television Commercials Services
N.A.I.C.S.: 512110

GMO Financial Gate, Inc. (1)
1-14-6 Humax Shibuya Building, Dogenzaka Shibuya, Tokyo, 150-0043, Japan
Tel.: (81) 364163881
Web Site: https://gmo-fg.com
Payment Processing Services
N.A.I.C.S.: 522320

GMO Financial Holdings, Inc. (1)
Shibuya Fukuras 1-2-3, Dogenzaka Shibuya-Ku, Tokyo, 150-0043, Japan
Tel.: (81) 362210183
Web Site: https://www.gmofh.com
Rev.: $364,652,880
Assets: $7,979,780,820
Liabilities: $7,650,521,220
Net Worth: $329,259,600
Earnings: $54,231,410
Emp.: 479
Fiscal Year-end: 12/31/2023
Holding Company
N.A.I.C.S.: 551112
Hiroyasu Kito *(Pres)*

GMO Gamepot Inc. (1)
26-1 Sakuragaokacho, Shibuya-ku, Tokyo, 150-8512, Japan **(100%)**
Tel.: (81) 357915288
Web Site: http://www.gamepot.co.jp
Sales Range: $25-49.9 Million
Mobile Applications Retailer & Online Gaming Services
N.A.I.C.S.: 334610
Shuhei Ueda *(CEO)*

GMO GlobalSign China Co., Ltd. (1)
Room 706 Fortune Times Building No 1438 Shaanxi North Road, Putuo District, Shanghai, China
Tel.: (86) 2160952260
Web Site: https://www.globalsign.cn
Emp.: 500
Information Security Services
N.A.I.C.S.: 561621

GMO GlobalSign Philippines Corp. (1)
23rd Floor Zuellig Building 8767 Paseo de Roxas Corner Makati Ave, Makati, 1227, Philippines
Tel.: (63) 28474774
All Other Telecommunication Services
N.A.I.C.S.: 517810

GMO INSIGHT Inc. (1)
Tel.: (81) 354286900

GMO INTERNET GROUP, INC.

GMO Internet Group, Inc.—(Continued)

Web Site: http://www.gmo-insight.jp
All Other Telecommunication Services
N.A.I.C.S.: 517810

GMO Japan Market Intelligence K.K. (1)
26-1 Sakuragaoka-cho Cerulean Tower,
Shibuya-Ku, Tokyo, 150-8512, Japan
Tel.: (81) 357841100
Web Site: http://www.gmo-jmi.jp
Sales Range: $25-49.9 Million
Emp.: 100
Market Research Consulting Services
N.A.I.C.S.: 541910
Tatsuhiro Gomi *(Dir-Res Dept)*

GMO Kumapon Inc. (1)
Cerulean Tower 26-1 Sakuragaokacho,
Shibuya-ku, Tokyo, 150-8512, Japan
Tel.: (81) 337707566
All Other Telecommunication Services
N.A.I.C.S.: 517810

GMO MAKESHOP Co. Ltd. (1)
Cerulean Tower 11th floor of reception 26-1
Sakuragaoka-cho, Shibuya-ku, Tokyo, 150-0031, Japan
Tel.: (81) 35 728 6227
Web Site: https://www.makeshop.jp
Online Shopping Services
N.A.I.C.S.: 425120

GMO Media, Inc. (1)
12th floor Cerulean Tower 26-1
Sakuragaoka-cho, Shibuya-ku, Tokyo, 150-8512, Japan
Tel.: (81) 354562626
Web Site: https://www.gmo.media
Emp.: 150
Internet Media Services
N.A.I.C.S.: 541840
Mori Teruyuki *(Pres & CEO)*

GMO Medical Reservations Technology Co., Ltd. (1)
7F Humax Shibuya Building 1-14-6 Dogenzaka, Shibuya-ku, Tokyo, 150-0043, Japan
Tel.: (81) 364130612
Web Site: https://www.dentry.jp
Medical Equipment Mfr
N.A.I.C.S.: 339112

GMO Mobile, Inc. (1)
No 1 Sakuragaoka-cho, Shibuya-ku, Tokyo, 150-8512, Japan
Tel.: (81) 368617700
Web Site: http://www.gmo-mobile.jp
Sales Range: $25-49.9 Million
Emp.: 11
Mobile Internet Software Development Services
N.A.I.C.S.: 541511

GMO NIKKO Inc. (1)
Shibuya Fukurasu 1-2-3 Dogenzaka,
Shibuya-ku, Tokyo, 150-0043, Japan
Tel.: (81) 12 025 0047
Web Site: https://www.koukoku.jp
Sales Range: $25-49.9 Million
Emp.: 239
Internet Advertising Services
N.A.I.C.S.: 541810
Kentaro Watanabe *(VP)*

GMO NetShop Support, Inc. (1)
Head Office Building No 6 No 9 Sato, Numazu, 410-0048, Shinzyuku, Japan
Tel.: (81) 559231812
Web Site: http://www.toku10.jp
Online Software Support Services
N.A.I.C.S.: 541519

GMO Oshiete AI, Inc. (1)
Cerulean Tower 26-1, Sakuragaokacho
Shibuya-ku, Tokyo, 150-8512, Japan
Tel.: (81) 354562555
Portal Site Operation Services
N.A.I.C.S.: 518210

GMO Payment Gateway Inc. (1)
1-14-6 Dogenzaka, Shibuya-ku, Tokyo, 150-0043, Japan
Tel.: (81) 334642740
Web Site: https://www.gmo-pg.com
Rev.: $447,513,710
Assets: $2,072,733,140
Liabilities: $1,400,572,780
Net Worth: $672,160,360
Earnings: $95,537,750

Emp.: 825
Fiscal Year-end: 09/30/2023
Credit Card Payment Processing Services
N.A.I.C.S.: 522320
Masatoshi Kumagai *(Chm)*

GMO Pepabo, Inc. (1)
Cerulean Tower 26-1 Sakuragaokacho,
Shibuya ku, Tokyo, 150-8512, Japan **(57%)**
Tel.: (81) 354562622
Web Site: https://pepabo.com
Rev.: $77,302,270
Assets: $77,096,660
Liabilities: $64,256,670
Net Worth: $12,839,990
Earnings: ($4,452,520)
Emp.: 359
Fiscal Year-end: 12/31/2023
Customized Software & Communications Solutions
N.A.I.C.S.: 513210
Masatoshi Kumagai *(Chm)*

GMO ReTech, Inc. (1)
Cerulean Tower 26-1, Sakuragaoka-cho
Shibuya-ku, Tokyo, 150-8512, Japan
Tel.: (81) 364165500
Web Site: https://gmoretech.com
Real Estate Services
N.A.I.C.S.: 531390

GMO Registry, Inc. (1)
Cerulean Tower 26-1 Sakuragaoka-cho,
Shibuya-ku, Tokyo, 150-8512, Japan
Tel.: (81) 35 456 1601
Web Site: https://www.gmoregistry.com
Sales Range: $25-49.9 Million
Emp.: 7
Domain Extensions Register Services
N.A.I.C.S.: 541511
Masatoshi Kumagai *(Chm)*

GMO Research & AI, Inc. (1)
26-1 Sakuragaoka-cho Cerulean Tower,
Shibuya-Ku, Tokyo, 150-8512,
Japan **(78.18%)**
Tel.: (81) 354563244
Web Site: https://gmo-research.ai
Rev.: $36,279,530
Assets: $21,220,370
Liabilities: $6,707,140
Net Worth: $14,513,230
Earnings: $2,176,630
Emp.: 187
Fiscal Year-end: 12/31/2023
Internet Research Services
N.A.I.C.S.: 541910

GMO Research Pte. Ltd. (1)
1 Wallich Street Guoco Tower 25-01A, Singapore, 078881, Singapore
Tel.: (65) 84359426
All Other Telecommunication Services
N.A.I.C.S.: 517810

GMO Research Pvt. Ltd. (1)
221 1st Floor Okhla Industrial Estate Okhla Phase 1, New Delhi, 110020, India
Tel.: (91) 1141049336
All Other Telecommunication Services
N.A.I.C.S.: 517810

GMO Research Sdn. Bhd. (1)
Level 32 R38 Menara Allianz Sentral 203
Jalan Tun Sambanthan Sentral, Kuala Lumpur, 50470, Malaysia
Tel.: (60) 327212013
All Other Telecommunication Services
N.A.I.C.S.: 517810

GMO Runsystem Inc. (1)
Cerulean Tower 7F 26-1 Sakuragaoka-cho,
Shibuya-ku, Tokyo, 150-8512, Japan
Tel.: (81) 359620056
Software Development Services
N.A.I.C.S.: 541511

GMO Solution Partner, Inc. (1)
Cerulean Tower 6F 26-1 Sakuragaoka-cho,
Shibuya-ku, Tokyo, 150-8512, Japan
Tel.: (81) 35 428 6621
Web Site: https://www.gmo-sol.jp
Emp.: 190
Search Engine Optimization Services
N.A.I.C.S.: 531210

GMO System Consulting, Inc. (1)
Shibuya Sakuragaoka Square 2F 31-15
Sakuragaoka-cho, Shibuya-ku, Tokyo, 150-0031, Japan

Tel.: (81) 3 5459 4940
Web Site: http://www.gmo-systemconsulting.com
E Commerce Solutions
N.A.I.C.S.: 425120

GMO TECH, Inc. (1)
Cerulean Tower 26-1 Sakuragaoka-cho,
Shibuya, Tokyo, 150-8512, Japan **(56.27%)**
Tel.: (81) 354896370
Web Site: https://gmo.tech
Rev.: $44,355,040
Assets: $19,540,040
Liabilities: $13,825,500
Net Worth: $5,714,540
Earnings: $2,871,450
Emp.: 213
Fiscal Year-end: 12/31/2023
Internet Advertising Services
N.A.I.C.S.: 541890

GMO UniteX Inc. (1)
Shibuya Fukuras 1-2-3, Dogenzaka
Shibuya-ku, Tokyo, 150-0043, Japan
Tel.: (81) 368613003
Web Site: https://www.gmo-ux.com
Social Media Marketing Services
N.A.I.C.S.: 541870

GMO Venture Partners, Inc. (1)
Cerulean Tower 26-1 Sakuragaokacho,
Shibuya ku, Tokyo, 150-8512, Japan
Tel.: (81) 35 458 8663
Web Site: https://www.gmo-vp.com
Investment Management Service
N.A.I.C.S.: 523940
Masatoshi Kumagai *(Chm)*

GMO Z com Research Sdn. Bhd. (1)
Level 32 R38 Menara Allianz Sentral 203
Jalan Tun Sambanthan, 50470 KL, Kuala Lumpur, Malaysia
Tel.: (60) 327212013
Cloud Panel Services
N.A.I.C.S.: 518210

GMO-Z com NetDesign Holdings Co., Ltd. (1)
No 1 Fortune Town Building 22nd Floor
Ratchadaphisek Road, Din Daeng Subdistrict, Bangkok, 10400, Thailand
Tel.: (66) 26421100
All Other Telecommunication Services
N.A.I.C.S.: 517810

GMO-Z.com ACE Co., Ltd. (1)
Tel.: (95) 12305236
All Other Telecommunication Services
N.A.I.C.S.: 517810

GMO-Z.com Brand Security Vietnam Co., Ltd. (1)
801 8th Floor Ha Do Airport Building 2
Hong Ha, Ward 2 Tan Binh, Ho Chi Minh City, Vietnam
Tel.: (84) 915620975
Web Site: https://vn.brandsecurity.gmo
System Development Services
N.A.I.C.S.: 518210

GMO-Z.com Brights Vietnam Co., Ltd. (1)
11th Floor TNR Tower 180-192 Nguyen Cong Tru, Nguyen Thai Binh Ward District 1, Ho Chi Minh City, Vietnam
Tel.: (84) 915620975
Web Site: http://www.brights.vn
All Other Telecommunication Services
N.A.I.C.S.: 517810

GMO-Z.com RUNSYSTEM JSC (1)
6th and 12th Floor Ocean Park Building No 1 Dao Duy Anh Str, Phuong Mai Ward
Dong Da Dist, Hanoi, Vietnam
Tel.: (84) 2437724304
All Other Telecommunication Services
N.A.I.C.S.: 517810

GMO-Z.com Research Pte. Ltd. (1)
Wallich Street Guoco Tower 25-01A, Singapore, 078881, Singapore
Tel.: (65) 96160488
Cloud Panel Services
N.A.I.C.S.: 518210

GMO-Z.com Research Pvt. Ltd. (1)
First floor Plot No 23 Okhla Industrial Estate Phase-III, New Delhi, 110020, India

INTERNATIONAL PUBLIC

Tel.: (91) 1141060725
Cloud Panel Services
N.A.I.C.S.: 518210

GMO-Z.com USA Inc. (1)
4685 MacArthur Ct Ste 150, Newport Beach, CA 92660
Tel.: (949) 296-6260
Web Site: http://www.us.gmocloud.com
Internet Hosting Services
N.A.I.C.S.: 518210
Ryo Tamura *(Pres & CEO)*

GMO-Z.com Vietnam Lab Center Co., Ltd. (1)
6th Floor - Ocean Park Building-01 Dao Duy Anh, Dong Da District, Hanoi, Vietnam
Tel.: (84) 2437724304
Web Site: http://www.vietnamlab.vn
All Other Telecommunication Services
N.A.I.C.S.: 517810

Global Card System, Inc. (1)
1-14-6 Dogenzaka, Shibuya-ku, Tokyo, 150-0043, Japan
Tel.: (81) 68050039
Web Site: http://www.globalcard.co.jp
Payment Processing Services
N.A.I.C.S.: 522320

GlobalSign K.K. (1)
Shibuya Sakuragaoka-cho 26-1 Shibuya Cerulean Tower 10F, Shibuya-ku, Tokyo, 150-8512, Japan
Tel.: (81) 364153277
Sales Range: $25-49.9 Million
Emp.: 50
Website Certification Services
N.A.I.C.S.: 518210
Nakazyou Itirou *(Pres & CEO)*

INTERNET Number Corporation (1)
Cerulean Tower 26-1 Sakuragaoka-cho,
Shibuya-ku, Tokyo, 150-8512, Japan
Tel.: (81) 3 6415 8150
Web Site: http://www.888.jp
Internet Support Services
N.A.I.C.S.: 518210

Macro Blob Sdn. Bhd. (1)
Level 21 The Gardens South Tower Mid Valley City Lingkaran Syed Putra, 592000, Kuala Lumpur, Malaysia
Tel.: (60) 321648100
All Other Telecommunication Services
N.A.I.C.S.: 517810

Macro Kiosk (Myanmar) Co. Ltd. (1)
Suite 45 14-00 Junction City Tower No 3/A Bogyoke Aung San Road, Pabedan Township, 11143, Yangon, Myanmar
Tel.: (95) 19253336
All Other Telecommunication Services
N.A.I.C.S.: 517810

Macro Kiosk (Taiwan) Technology Limited (1)
Suite 2 4th Floor No 925 Sec 4 Taiwan Boulevard, Xitun District, Taichung, 407, Taiwan
Tel.: (886) 423585100
All Other Telecommunication Services
N.A.I.C.S.: 517810

Wineyasan, Inc. (1)
3-18-16 Minami-Aoyama, Minato-ku, Tokyo, 107-0062, Japan
Tel.: (81) 354105555
Web Site: https://www.wineyasan.shop
Beverage & Food Distr
N.A.I.C.S.: 424490

GMP PROPERTY SOCIMI SA

Luchana 23, 28010, Madrid, Spain
Tel.: (34) 914442800
Web Site: https://www.grupogmp.com
Year Founded: 1979
YGMP—(MAD)
Rev.: $123,019,097
Assets: $2,724,214,594
Liabilities: $1,060,477,978
Net Worth: $1,663,736,616
Earnings: ($85,291,975)
Emp.: 171
Fiscal Year-end: 12/31/23
Asset Management Services
N.A.I.C.S.: 523940

AND PRIVATE COMPANIES

Francisco Luis Montoro Aleman *(Chm & CEO)*

GMR AIRPORTS INFRASTRUCTURE LIMITED
Unit No 12 18th Floor DLF Cyber City Building No 5, Tower A Phase -III, Gurgaon, 122002, Haryana, India
Tel.: (91) 1246637750
Web Site: https://gmrinfra.com
Year Founded: 1996
532754—(BOM)
Rev.: $873,927,223
Assets: $5,288,823,212
Liabilities: $5,172,661,111
Net Worth: $116,162,101
Earnings: ($100,704,994)
Emp.: 137
Fiscal Year-end: 03/31/23
Airport Infrastructure Services
N.A.I.C.S.: 236220
Grandhi Kiran Kumar *(CEO & Mng Dir)*

Subsidiaries:

GMR Aero Technic Limited (1)
Plot No 1 GMR Aerospace Park Rajiv Gandhi International Airport GMR, Shamshabad, Hyderabad, 500 108, Telangana, India
Tel.: (91) 4067251123
Web Site: https://www.gmraerotech.in
Airframe Repair & Maintenance Services
N.A.I.C.S.: 488190
G. B. S. Raju *(Chm)*

GMR Aviation Private Limited (1)
Room No 10 Ground Floor Terminal 1D, Indira Gandhi International Airport South West Delhi, New Delhi, 110 037, India
Tel.: (91) 1147197473
Web Site: http://www.gmraviation.com
Aircraft Charter Services
N.A.I.C.S.: 481219
Ashutosh Kapil *(CFO)*

Raxa Security Services Limited (1)
25/1 Skip House Museum Road, Shanthala Nagar Ashok Nagar, Bengaluru, 560025, Karnataka, India
Tel.: (91) 8040432424
Web Site: https://www.raxatechnosecuritysolutions.in
Security Guard Services
N.A.I.C.S.: 561612

GMT COMMUNICATIONS PARTNERS LLP
Sackville House 40 Piccadilly, London, W1J 0DR, United Kingdom
Tel.: (44) 2072929333
Web Site: http://www.gmtpartners.com
Year Founded: 1993
Sales Range: $25-49.9 Million
Emp.: 23
Privater Equity Firm
N.A.I.C.S.: 523999
Timothy S. Green *(Mng Partner)*

Subsidiaries:

Primesight Ltd. (1)
3 Waterhouse Square, 138-142 Holborn, London, EC1N 2NY, United Kingdom
Tel.: (44) 2078821200
Web Site: http://www.primesight.co.uk
Sales Range: $1-9.9 Million
Outdoor Advertising Company
N.A.I.C.S.: 541850
Naren Patel *(CEO)*

GMUL INVESTMENT COMPANY, LTD.
Medinat HaYehudim 85, Herzliyya, Israel
Tel.: (972) 7 32787000
Venture Capital Firm
N.A.I.C.S.: 523999

GMV MINERALS INC.
Suite 280-1090 West Georgia Street, Vancouver, V6E 3V7, BC, Canada
Tel.: (604) 899-0106
Web Site: https://www.gmvminerals.com
Year Founded: 2006
GMVMF—(OTCQB)
Rev.: $61,142
Assets: $5,458,510
Liabilities: $56,728
Net Worth: $5,401,782
Earnings: ($1,009,481)
Fiscal Year-end: 06/30/21
Gold Exploration Services
N.A.I.C.S.: 212220
Michele Pillon *(CFO)*

GN STORE NORD A/S
Lautrupbjerg 7, 2750, Ballerup, Denmark
Tel.: (45) 45750000   DK
Web Site: https://www.gn.com
Year Founded: 1869
GNNDY—(OTCIQ)
Rev.: $2,683,053,224
Assets: $4,537,202,920
Liabilities: $3,117,642,695
Net Worth: $1,419,560,224
Earnings: $39,386,984
Emp.: 7,165
Fiscal Year-end: 12/31/23
High-Tech Hearing Instruments & Equipment & Hands-Free Communications Equipment Mfr
N.A.I.C.S.: 334290
Rene Svendsen-Tune *(CEO)*

Subsidiaries:

GN Audio (China) Ltd. (1)
3B A Building No17 Xiang Xing Yi Road, Modern Logistics Zone Bonded Area, Xiamen, 361006, Fujian, China
Tel.: (86) 5922634900
Hearing Aid Product Distr
N.A.I.C.S.: 423450

GN Audio (Shanghai) Co., Ltd. (1)
Suite 308-309 Block B The MIXC 1799 Wuzhong Road, Shanghai, 201103, China
Tel.: (86) 2161952188
Hearing Aid Product Distr
N.A.I.C.S.: 423450

GN Audio Australia Pty. Ltd. (1)
2 Elizabeth Plaza Level 11, North Sydney, 2060, NSW, Australia
Tel.: (61) 1800636086
Web Site: https://www.jabra.com
Hearing Aid Product Distr
N.A.I.C.S.: 423450

GN Audio France SA (1)
Parc Omega - Batiment 2 3 Boulevard Jean Moulin, 78990, Elancourt, 78990, France
Tel.: (33) 130583031
Web Site: https://www.jabra.com
Hearing Aid Product Distr
N.A.I.C.S.: 423450

GN Audio Hong Kong Limited (1)
Unit 1003-6 & 6B Exchange Tower 33 Wang Chiu Road, Kowloon Bay, China (Hong Kong)
Tel.: (852) 35509900
Web Site: https://www.jabra.com
Hearing Aid Product Distr
N.A.I.C.S.: 423450

GN Audio Italy s.r.l. (1)
Centro Direzionale Torri Bianche 6, Palazzo Tiglio - Via Torri Bianche 6, 20871, Vimercate, Italy
Tel.: (39) 0258328253
Web Site: https://www.jabra.com
Hearing Aid Product Distr
N.A.I.C.S.: 423450

GN Audio Logistic (Xiamen) Ltd. (1)
3B A Building No 17 Xiangxing Yi Road, Modern Logistics Zone Bonded Area, Xiamen, 361006, China
Tel.: (86) 1065832310
Hearing Aid Product Distr
N.A.I.C.S.: 423450

GN Audio Singapore Pte. Ltd. (1)
3 Fraser Street 08-25 Duo Tower, Singapore, 189352, Singapore
Tel.: (65) 63903600
Web Site: https://www.jabra.com
Hearing Aid Product Distr
N.A.I.C.S.: 423450

GN Audio Spain, S.A. (1)
Paseo de la Castellana 93, 28046, Madrid, 28046, Spain
Tel.: (34) 258328253
Web Site: https://www.jabra.com
Hearing Aid Product Distr
N.A.I.C.S.: 423450

GN Audio Sweden AB (1)
Vretenvagen 2, 171 54, Solna, 171 54, Sweden
Tel.: (46) 86930900
Web Site: https://www.jabra.com
Hearing Aid Product Distr
N.A.I.C.S.: 423450

GN Audio UK Ltd. (1)
The Curve Axis Business Park, Hurricane Way, Langley, SL3 8AG, Berkshire, United Kingdom
Tel.: (44) 1784220140
Web Site: https://www.jabra.com
Hearing Aid Product Distr
N.A.I.C.S.: 423450

GN Audio USA, Inc. (1)
900 Chelmsford St Tower II 8th Fl, Lowell, MA 01851
Tel.: (978) 322-4700
Web Site: https://www.jabra.com
Audio Solutions Mfr
N.A.I.C.S.: 334310

Subsidiary (Domestic):

Altia Systems Inc. (2)
20400 Stevens Creek Blvd Ste 750, Cupertino, CA 95014
Tel.: (800) 852-3970
Web Site: http://www.altiasystems.com
Camera & Video Solutions Services
N.A.I.C.S.: 512199

GN Ejendomme A/S (1)
Lautrupbjerg 7, Ballerup, 2750, Denmark
Tel.: (45) 45750000
Hearing Instruments Mfr & Distr
N.A.I.C.S.: 334510

GN Hearing A/S (1)
Tel.: (45) 45751444
Hearing Aid Mfr
N.A.I.C.S.: 334510

Subsidiary (Non-US):

GN Hearing (Malaysia) Sdn. Bhd. (2)
No 5 Jalan i-Park 1/1 Kawasan Perindustrian i-Park, Bandar Indahpura Kulaijaya, 81000, Johor, Malaysia
Tel.: (60) 76618000
Hearing Aid Product Mfr & Distr
N.A.I.C.S.: 334510

GN Hearing Australia Pty. Ltd. (2)
Gate C 19 - 25 Khartoum Road, Macquarie Technology Park Macquarie, Macquarie Park, 2113, NSW, Australia
Tel.: (61) 297439707
Hearing Aid Product Distr
N.A.I.C.S.: 423450

GN Hearing Austria GmbH (2)
Modecenterstrasse 22 TOP D48-D52, A-1030, Vienna, Austria
Tel.: (43) 152454000
Hearing Aid Product Distr
N.A.I.C.S.: 423450

GN Hearing Care S.A. (2)
Puerto de la Morcuera 14-16, Leganes, 28919, Madrid, 28919, Spain
Tel.: (34) 914282220
Hearing Aid Product Mfr & Distr
N.A.I.C.S.: 334510

GN Hearing Czech Republic spol. s r.o. (2)
Prokopovych 827/3, Jinonice, 158 00, Prague, 5, Czech Republic
Tel.: (420) 224941641
Hearing Aid Product Distr

N.A.I.C.S.: 423450

GN Hearing Finland Oy/Ab (2)
Pojoinen Rautatiekatu 15, 00100, Helsinki, 00100, Finland
Tel.: (358) 947779700
Hearing Aid Product Distr
N.A.I.C.S.: 423450

GN Hearing India Private Limited (2)
4th Floor Office No 401-408 Plot No 74 Sector No 15, CBD Belapur, Navi Mumbai, 400 614, India
Tel.: (91) 2227524700
Hearing Aid Product Mfr & Distr
N.A.I.C.S.: 334510

GN Hearing Japan K.K. (2)
MM Park Bldg 8F 3-6-3 Minatomirai, Nishiku, Yokohama, 220-0012, Kanagawa, Japan
Tel.: (81) 452771133
Hearing Aid Product Mfr & Distr
N.A.I.C.S.: 334510

GN Hearing Korea Co., Ltd. (2)
7F Deokmyung B/D 625 Teheran-ro, Gangnam-gu, Seoul, 06173, Korea (South)
Tel.: (82) 25419222
Hearing Aid Product Mfr & Distr
N.A.I.C.S.: 334510

GN Hearing New Zealand Limited (2)
4 Fred Thomas Drive North Entrance, Takapuna, 622, New Zealand
Tel.: (64) 4853296
Hearing Aid Product Mfr & Distr
N.A.I.C.S.: 334510

GN Hearing Norway AS (2)
Brynsveien 13, 0667, Oslo, 0667, Norway
Tel.: (47) 22477530
Hearing Aid Product Mfr & Distr
N.A.I.C.S.: 334510

GN Hearing Pte. Ltd. (2)
2 Kallang Avenue Ct Hub 07-19, Singapore, 339407, Singapore
Tel.: (65) 63209388
Hearing Aid Product Mfr & Distr
N.A.I.C.S.: 334510

GN Hearing SAS (2)
Batiment Quebec 19 Rue d'Arcueil Zone SILIC, 94150, Rungis, France
Tel.: (33) 175377000
Hearing Aid Product Mfr & Distr
N.A.I.C.S.: 334510

GN Hearing Sverige AB (2)
Ringvagen 40, 118 67, Stockholm, 118 67, Sweden
Tel.: (46) 31800150
Hearing Aid Product Mfr & Distr
N.A.I.C.S.: 334510

GN Hearing Switzerland AG (2)
Seestrasse 353, CH-8038, Zurich, Switzerland
Tel.: (41) 447229111
Hearing Aid Product Mfr & Distr
N.A.I.C.S.: 334510

GN Hearing Benelux B.V. (1)
Florijnweg 25, NL-6883JN, Velp, Netherlands
Tel.: (31) 263195000
Web Site: http://www.gnresound.nl
Sales Range: $25-49.9 Million
Emp.: 45
Hearing Instruments Mfr
N.A.I.C.S.: 334510
Eric Knipfer *(Mng Dir)*

GN Hearing Care Canada Ltd (1)
2 East Beaver Creek Road Building 3, Richmond Hill, L4B 2N3, ON, Canada
Tel.: (416) 736-4444
Web Site: https://www.resound.com
Sales Range: $25-49.9 Million
Emp.: 40
Hearing Instruments Mfr
N.A.I.C.S.: 334510
Frank Skubski *(Gen Mgr)*

GN Hearing Care Corporation (1)
8001 E Bloomington Fwy, Bloomington, MN 55420
Tel.: (952) 769-8000
Web Site: https://www.resound.com

GN STORE NORD A/S

GN Store Nord A/S—(Continued)
Sales Range: $100-124.9 Million
Emp.: 300
Hearing Aid Mfr
N.A.I.C.S.: 334510
Todd Murray *(Pres)*

Subsidiary (Domestic):

American Hearing Systems Inc (2)
8001 E Bloomington Fwy, Bloomington, MN 55420
Tel.: (763) 404-1122
Hearing Aid Mfr
N.A.I.C.S.: 334290

GN Hearing GmbH (1)
An Der Kleimannbrucke 75, 48157, Munster, Germany
Tel.: (49) 25120396000
Web Site: https://www.resound.com
Sales Range: $25-49.9 Million
Emp.: 60
Hearing Instruments Mfr
N.A.I.C.S.: 334510
Jakob Gudbrand *(CEO)*

GN Hearing Srl (1)
Via Nino Bixio 1, 35036, Montegrotto Terme, PD, Italy
Tel.: (39) 049 891 1511
Web Site: http://www.resound.com
Sales Range: $50-74.9 Million
Emp.: 54
Hearing Aid Distr
N.A.I.C.S.: 423440

GN Netcom A/S (1)
Lautrupbjerg 7, 2750, Ballerup, Denmark (100%)
Tel.: (45) 45758888
Web Site: https://www.jabra.com
Sales Range: $75-99.9 Million
Emp.: 180
Development, Production & Marketing of Lightweight Headsets for Telephony
N.A.I.C.S.: 334290

Subsidiary (Non-US):

GN Netcom (Iberica) S.A. (2)
Avda De Espana 97 13, 28230, Las Rozas, Madrid, Spain
Tel.: (34) 916398064
Web Site: http://www.jabra.com
Hearing Instruments Mfr
N.A.I.C.S.: 334510

GN Netcom (Italia) S.r.l (2)
Via Fernanda Wittgens 3, 20123, Milan, Italy
Tel.: (39) 0258328253
Headset Whslr
N.A.I.C.S.: 423440

GN Netcom (UK) Ltd. (2)
Tamesis The Glanty, Egham, TW20 9AW, Surrey, United Kingdom
Tel.: (44) 1784220140
Web Site: http://www.jabra.com
Sales Range: $25-49.9 Million
Emp.: 20
Communication Equipment Distr
N.A.I.C.S.: 423440

GN Netcom AB (2)
Vretenvagen 2, 171 54, Solna, Sweden
Tel.: (46) 8 693 09 00
Sales Range: $25-49.9 Million
Emp.: 17
Communication Equipment Distr
N.A.I.C.S.: 423440
Carin Brink *(Gen Mgr)*

GN Netcom Benelux B.V. (2)
Boschstraat 34 A, 4811 GH, Breda, Netherlands
Tel.: (31) 76 515 04 28
Web Site: http://www.jabra.com
Headset Whslr
N.A.I.C.S.: 423440

GN Netcom GmbH (2)
Traberhofstrasse 12, 83026, Rosenheim, Germany
Tel.: (49) 803126510
Web Site: http://www.jabra.com
Headset Whslr
N.A.I.C.S.: 423440

Subsidiary (US):

GN Netcom Inc. (2)
77 Northeastern Blvd, Nashua, NH 03062-3128 (100%)
Tel.: (603) 598-1100
Web Site: http://www.jabra.com
Sales Range: $25-49.9 Million
Telephone Headsets
N.A.I.C.S.: 334210

Subsidiary (Non-US):

Jabra (2)
Zone De Pissaloup 16 Avenue Jean D Alembert, Trappes, 78190, France
Tel.: (33) 130583031
Web Site: http://www.jabra.com
Sales Range: $25-49.9 Million
Emp.: 25
Communications Equipment
N.A.I.C.S.: 517111
Barb Huelskamp *(VP-Channel Sls)*

GN ReSound A/S (1)
Lautrupekbjerg No 7, Ballerup, 2750, Denmark (100%)
Tel.: (45) 45751111
Web Site: http://www.gnresound.com
Sales Range: $100-124.9 Million
Emp.: 500
Development, Production & Marketing of Hearing Aids & Audiological Equipment
N.A.I.C.S.: 339112

Subsidiary (US):

Audigy Group LLC (2)
1201 SE Tech Center Dr Ste 110, Vancouver, WA 98683
Web Site: https://www.audigy.com
Hearing Care Management Services
N.A.I.C.S.: 621340
Mason Walker *(Pres)*

Subsidiary (Non-US):

GN ReSound AB (2)
Gullbergs Strandgata 6, Box 11034, 404 21, Gothenburg, Sweden
Tel.: (46) 31800150
Web Site: http://www.gnresound.se
Hearing Instruments Mfr
N.A.I.C.S.: 334510

GN ReSound AG (2)
Schutzenstrasse 1, 8800, Thalwil, Switzerland
Tel.: (41) 44 722 91 11
Web Site: http://www.resound.ch
Sales Range: $25-49.9 Million
Emp.: 14
Diagnostic Audiological Instruments Mfr
N.A.I.C.S.: 334510

GN ReSound China Ltd. (2)
Room 203 Cnfc Mansion 31 Minfeng Lane Xidan, Beijing, 100032, China
Tel.: (86) 5925607188
Web Site: http://www.gnresound.com.cn
Hearing Instruments Mfr
N.A.I.C.S.: 334510

Subsidiary (US):

GN ReSound Corporation (2)
8001 Bloomington Fwy, Bloomington, MN 55420 (100%)
Tel.: (952) 769-8000
Web Site: http://www.gnresound.com
Mfr of Hearing Devices
N.A.I.C.S.: 334510

Subsidiary (Domestic):

Beltone Electronics LLC (3)
2601 Patriot Blvd, Glenview, IL 60026 (100%)
Tel.: (773) 583-3600
Web Site: https://www.beltone.com
Sales Range: $100-124.9 Million
Emp.: 500
Hearing Aid Mfr
N.A.I.C.S.: 334510

Subsidiary (Non-US):

Bel Tone India Limited (4)
Office No 807-808-809 8th floor Vindhya Co-Op Hsg Society Ltd, Plot No 1 Sector 11 CBD Belapur, Navi Mumbai, 400614, Maharashtra, India
Tel.: (91) 224 126 9999
Web Site: https://hearing-aids.beltone.in
Hearing Aid Mfr
N.A.I.C.S.: 334290

Beltone Electronics of Canada Ltd. (4)
2 East Beaver Creek Road Building 3, Richmond Hill, L4B 2N3, ON, Canada (100%)
Tel.: (416) 736-4444
Web Site: http://www.beltone.com
Sales Range: $25-49.9 Million
Emp.: 40
Surgical Appliances & Supplies
N.A.I.C.S.: 339113

Beltone Europe Holdings ApS (4)
Markaervej 2 A, Taastrup, Denmark
Tel.: (45) 7211 1111
Hearing Aid Mfr
N.A.I.C.S.: 334510

Subsidiary (Non-US):

GN ReSound Hearing Care Equ. (Shanghai) (2)
4 F Building G Red Town No 570 Huaihai West Road, Changning District, Shanghai, 200052, China
Tel.: (86) 2122113333
Web Site: http://www.gnresound.com.cn
Sales Range: $25-49.9 Million
Emp.: 70
Hearing Instruments Mfr
N.A.I.C.S.: 334510

GN ReSound India Private Limited (2)
4th Floor Office No 401-408 Plot No 74 Sector No 15 CBD-Belapur, Navi Mumbai, 400 614, Maharashtra, India
Tel.: (91) 222 752 4700
Web Site: http://www.gnresound-group.com
Hearing Aid Mfr
N.A.I.C.S.: 334510

GN ReSound Italia SRL (2)
Via Nino Bixio 1/b, 35036, Montegrotto Terme, Padova, Italy
Tel.: (39) 0498911511
Web Site: http://www.resounditalia.com
Hearing Aid Mfr
N.A.I.C.S.: 339112

GN ReSound Ltd. (2)
Building A Kirtlington Business Centre, Oxford, OX5 3JA, United Kingdom
Tel.: (44) 1869352800
Web Site: http://www.gnresound.co.uk
Hearing Aid Mfr
N.A.I.C.S.: 334290

GN ReSound Norge AS (2)
Brynsveien 13, 0667, Oslo, Norway
Tel.: (47) 22477530
Web Site: http://www.resoundpro.com
Hearing Instruments Mfr
N.A.I.C.S.: 334510

GN ReSound Pty. Ltd. (2)
Unit R1 391 Park Rd, Regents Park, Sydney, 2143, NSW, Australia
Tel.: (61) 297439707
Web Site: http://www.gnresound.com.au
Sales Range: $25-49.9 Million
Emp.: 50
Hearing Aid Mfr
N.A.I.C.S.: 334290

GN ReSound S.A.S (2)
Immeuble Le Newton C 7 Mail B Thimonnier, 77437, Lognes, Seine-et-Marne, France
Tel.: (33) 1 60 53 06 60
Web Site: http://www.resound.fr
Sales Range: $25-49.9 Million
Emp.: 45
Hearing Aid Mfr
N.A.I.C.S.: 334510

GN ReSound Singapore Pte. Ltd. (2)
9 Penang Road 07-11-12 Park Mall, Singapore, 238459, Singapore
Tel.: (65) 6333 8333
Web Site: http://www.gnresound.com.sg
Hearing Aid Mfr
N.A.I.C.S.: 334510
Winston Oh *(Gen Mgr)*

INTERNATIONAL PUBLIC

GN ReSound do Brazil Ltda. (2)
Rua Do Paraiso 139-8 Andar, Paraiso, 04103-000, Brazil
Tel.: (55) 11 3016 8376
Web Site: http://www.resound.com.br
Sales Range: $25-49.9 Million
Emp.: 50
Hearing Aid Mfr
N.A.I.C.S.: 334510

Sluchadlova Akustika spol S.R.O. (1)
Prokopovych 3, 15800, Prague, Czech Republic
Tel.: (420) 224941641
Web Site: http://www.interton.cz
Sales Range: $25-49.9 Million
Emp.: 10
Hearing Instruments Mfr
N.A.I.C.S.: 334510

VXi Corporation (1)
271 Locust St, Dover, NH 03820
Tel.: (603) 742-2888
Web Site: http://bluebeliever.vxicorp.com
Communication Equipment Mfr
N.A.I.C.S.: 334220
Mike Ferguson *(Pres & CEO)*

GNA AXLES LIMITED

Gna House 1-C Chhoti Baradari - II Garha Road, Jalandhar, 144001, Punjab, India
Tel.: (91) 1814630477
Web Site: https://gnaaxles.in
Year Founded: 1993
GNA—(NSE)
Rev.: $121,629,908
Assets: $130,977,988
Liabilities: $60,329,983
Net Worth: $70,648,005
Earnings: $9,640,040
Emp.: 1,344
Fiscal Year-end: 03/31/21
Rear Axle Shaft Mfr
N.A.I.C.S.: 336350
Rachhpall Singh *(Chm)*

GNBS ECO CO.,LTD

401-14 Mosan-ro Daedeok-myeon, Anseong, Gyeonggi-do, Korea (South)
Tel.: (82) 316586276
Web Site: https://www.gnbseng.com
Year Founded: 2005
382800—(KRS)
Rev.: $50,309,135
Assets: $68,192,540
Liabilities: $12,696,951
Net Worth: $55,495,589
Earnings: $11,330,478
Emp.: 106
Fiscal Year-end: 12/31/22
Industry Machinery Mfr
N.A.I.C.S.: 333310
Jin-Wook Bae *(Mgr)*

GNC ENERGY CO., LTD.

49 Magokjungang 2-ro, Gangseo-gu, Seoul, Korea (South)
Tel.: (82) 221647200
Web Site: https://gncenergyeng.com
Year Founded: 1989
119850—(KRS)
Rev.: $113,935,084
Assets: $130,976,650
Liabilities: $41,207,885
Net Worth: $89,768,766
Earnings: $19,937,022
Emp.: 113
Fiscal Year-end: 12/31/22
Electricity Generation Equipment Mfr
N.A.I.C.S.: 335312
Byung-Chul Ahn *(CEO)*

GNCO CO., LTD.

Dongnamro-4gil 41, Seoul, Songppa-gu, Korea (South)
Tel.: (82) 221858510
Web Site: http://www.gnco.co.kr

AND PRIVATE COMPANIES / GOA CARBON LTD.

065060—(KRS)
Rev.: $109,892,758
Assets: $174,081,546
Liabilities: $79,008,627
Net Worth: $95,072,918
Earnings: ($4,691,744)
Emp.: 127
Fiscal Year-end: 12/31/22
Casual Apparel Mfr
N.A.I.C.S.: 315250

GNI GROUP LTD.
3rd Floor Nihonbashi-Honcho YS Bldg 2-2-2 Nihonbashi Honcho, Chuo-ku, Tokyo, 103-0023, Japan
Tel.: (81) 362143600
Web Site:
https://www.gnipharma.com
Year Founded: 2001
2160—(TKS)
Rev.: $184,410,900
Assets: $442,373,460
Liabilities: $186,764,780
Net Worth: $255,608,680
Earnings: $57,386,460
Emp.: 960
Fiscal Year-end: 12/31/23
Pharmaceutical Mfr, Researcher & Developer
N.A.I.C.S.: 325412
Toru Saito (Exec Officer)

Subsidiaries:

Beijing Continent Pharmaceutical Co., Ltd. (1)
Room 320507-320509 Building 5 Wangjing SOHO Tower Yard 1, Futong East Street Chaoyang District, Beijing, China
Tel.: (86) 1088877935
Web Site: https://www.bjcontinent.com
Pharmaceuticals Product Mfr
N.A.I.C.S.: 325412

Berkeley Advanced Biomaterials, Inc. (1)
2800 7th St, Berkeley, CA 94710 (100%)
Tel.: (510) 883-0500
Web Site: https://www.ostetic.com
Surgical & Medical Instrument Mfr
N.A.I.C.S.: 339112

Gyre Therapeutics, Inc. (1)
12770 High Bluff Dr Ste 150, San Diego, CA 92130
Tel.: (858) 567-7770
Web Site: https://www.gyretx.com
Rev.: $794,000
Assets: $28,444,000
Liabilities: $50,133,000
Net Worth: ($21,689,000)
Earnings: ($8,242,000)
Emp.: 7
Fiscal Year-end: 12/31/2022
Holding Company; Biopharmaceutical Developer & Marketer
N.A.I.C.S.: 551112
Seline Miller (Interim Chief Fin & Principal Acctg Officer & Sr VP-Fin)

Subsidiary (Domestic):

Catalyst Bio, Inc. (2)
611 Gateway Blvd Ste 120, South San Francisco, CA 94080
Tel.: (650) 266-8679
Web Site:
https://www.catalystbiosciences.com
Biopharmaceutical Developer & Marketer
N.A.I.C.S.: 325412

Shanghai Genomics Technology, Ltd. (1)
Bldg 6 230 ChuanHong Road ChuanSha PuDong New Area, Shanghai, 201202, China
Tel.: (86) 68788728804
Pharmaceuticals Product Mfr
N.A.I.C.S.: 325412

Shanghai Genomics, Inc., (1)
Bldg 6 230 ChuanHong Road, ChuanSha PuDong New Area, Shanghai, 201202, China
Tel.: (86) 215 080 2786

Web Site:
http://www.shanghaigenomics.com
Sales Range: $25-49.9 Million
Emp.: 50
Therapeutic Product Mfr
N.A.I.C.S.: 334510
Ying Luo (Gen Mgr)

GNOMESTAR CRAFT INC.
8788 River Road, Delta, V4G 1B5, BC, Canada
Tel.: (604) 428-7050   BC
Web Site: http://www.vodis.ca
Year Founded: 2011
VP—(CNSX)
Assets: $543,612
Liabilities: $1,267,560
Net Worth: ($723,948)
Earnings: ($3,083,995)
Fiscal Year-end: 03/31/19
Cannabis Mfr
N.A.I.C.S.: 325411
Mark Lotz (CEO-Interim & CFO)

GNUTTI CARLO S.P.A.
Via Artigiani 2, 25030, Maclodio, BS, Italy
Tel.: (39) 030 97890   IT
Web Site: http://www.gnutticarlo.com
Year Founded: 1920
Emp.: 364
Engine Component Mfr
N.A.I.C.S.: 333618
Paolo Groff (CEO)

Subsidiaries:

Gnutti Carlo (Wuxi) Engine Components Co., Ltd. (1)
No 169 7 Chunjiang Rd W near Chunsun Rd M, Xishan, 214101, Wuxi, China
Tel.: (86) 51088263998
Emp.: 49
Automotive Accessory Mfr
N.A.I.C.S.: 336370

Gnutti Carlo Germany GmbH (1)
Hans-Bellinghausen-Str 21, 56070, Koblenz, Germany
Tel.: (49) 26198899778
Automotive Accessory Distr
N.A.I.C.S.: 441330

Gnutti Carlo INDIA Ltd (1)
Mukundarayapuram Village, Ranipet, 632 405, Vellore, India
Tel.: (91) 4172243200
Emp.: 107
Automotive Accessory Mfr
N.A.I.C.S.: 336370

Gnutti Carlo SWEDEN AB Kungsor Facility (1)
Kungsgatan 6, Kungsor, 736 25, Sweden
Tel.: (46) 472268000
Emp.: 232
Automotive Accessory Mfr
N.A.I.C.S.: 336370

Gnutti Carlo Sweden AB (1)
Agardsvagen 16, Box 110, SE 342 22, Alvesta, Sweden
Tel.: (46) 472 268000
Web Site: http://www.gnutticarlo.com
Emp.: 250
Developer & Mfr of Complex Precision Components & Subsystems for Engines & Power Transmission
N.A.I.C.S.: 333618
Jorgen Oldenstedt (Gen Mgr)

Gnutti Carlo UK Ltd (1)
33 West Street, Alford, LN13 9DQ, Lincolnshire, United Kingdom
Tel.: (44) 1507463427
Emp.: 40
Automotive Accessory Mfr
N.A.I.C.S.: 336370

Gnutti Carlo USA, Inc. (1)
140 Ludlow Ave, Northvale, NJ 07647
Tel.: (201) 768-8200
Sales Range: $25-49.9 Million
Emp.: 160
Mfr of Rocker Arms Shafts & Castings for Engine Parts

N.A.I.C.S.: 333618
Jonathan Arici (Mgr-Bus Improvement)

Division (Domestic):

Shelco Foundry (2)
1310 W Francis St, Jacksonville, AL 36265
Tel.: (256) 436-2200
Web Site: http://www.shelcofoundry.com
Emp.: 80
Metal Castings Foundry
N.A.I.C.S.: 331511
Burt Wilchar (Plant Mgr)

Gnutti Ltd. (1)
404 Canada Ave, PO Box 541, Huron Park, N0M 1Y0, ON, Canada
Tel.: (519) 228-6685
Web Site: http://www.gnutti.ca
Emp.: 140
Engine Component Mfr
N.A.I.C.S.: 333618

Ljunghall s.r.o. (1)
Vrchovska 1813, Caslav, 28601, Czech Republic
Tel.: (420) 327300030
Emp.: 314
Automotive Accessory Mfr
N.A.I.C.S.: 336370

Metallfabriken Ljunghall AB (1)
Norra Storgatan 41, PO Box 148, 598 71, Vimmerby, Sweden
Tel.: (46) 49216600
Emp.: 470
Automotive Accessory Mfr
N.A.I.C.S.: 336370
Henning Solli (Mgr-HR & Comm)

GO AUTO
Suite 200 10220-184 St, Edmonton, T5S 0B9, AB, Canada
Tel.: (780) 777-7777
Web Site: http://www.goauto.ca
Year Founded: 1996
Car Dealership Operator
N.A.I.C.S.: 441110
Latha Thomas-Back (Sr VP)

Subsidiaries:

Columbia Chrysler Dodge Jeep Ltd. (1)
5840 Minoru Boulevard, Richmond, V6X 2A9, BC, Canada
Tel.: (604) 273-8018
Web Site: http://www.columbiachrysler.com
Sales Range: $25-49.9 Million
Emp.: 78
New & Used Car Dealer
N.A.I.C.S.: 441110
Justin Gebara (Gen Mgr)

GO ELEMENT CO., LTD.
3 Gil 30 Geumseok-Dong, Anseong, 17539, Gyeonggi-do, Korea (South)
Tel.: (82) 316119123
Web Site:
https://www.goelement.co.kr
Year Founded: 2005
311320—(KRS)
Rev.: $21,963,915
Assets: $40,735,800
Liabilities: $3,248,204
Net Worth: $37,487,596
Earnings: $5,126,355
Emp.: 93
Fiscal Year-end: 12/31/22
Electronic Components Mfr
N.A.I.C.S.: 334419
Mu-Yeon Oh (Sr Mng Dir)

GO FASHION INDIA LIMITED
No 4 5th Floor Sathak Center Nungambakkam High Road, Chennai, 600034, India
Tel.: (91) 4442111777
Web Site: https://www.gocolors.com
Year Founded: 2010
GOCOLORS—(NSE)
Rev.: $57,617,592
Assets: $102,540,711
Liabilities: $42,698,087

Net Worth: $59,842,624
Earnings: $4,859,509
Emp.: 3,164
Fiscal Year-end: 03/31/22
Bottom Wear Retailer
N.A.I.C.S.: 458110
Sridhar Srinivasan (Chm)

GO GASTSTATTENBETRIEBS GMBH
Europaplatz 1a, 4020, Linz, Austria
Tel.: (43) 732659622771   AT
Web Site: http://www.go-gastro.at
Year Founded: 2002
Sales Range: $25-49.9 Million
Cafeteria Operator & Corporate Catering Services
N.A.I.C.S.: 722514
Markus Millidorfer (Mng Dir-HR Mgmt, Mktg & Sls Pur)

GO INTERNET S.P.A.
Piazza Bernini snc, Gubbio, 6024, Perugia, Umbria, Italy
Tel.: (39) 0757829100
Web Site: https://www.gointernet.it
GO—(ITA)
Sales Range: Less than $1 Million
Broadband Communications
N.A.I.C.S.: 517112
Giuseppe Colaiacovo (Chm)

GO LIFE INTERNATIONAL LTD.
6th Floor Ken Lee Building, Cnr Edith Cavell & Brown Sequrd Street, Port Louis, Mauritius
Tel.: (230) 4681166
Web Site: https://www.golife.co.za
XII—(JSE)
Rev.: $56,114
Assets: $303
Liabilities: $329,558
Net Worth: ($329,255)
Earnings: ($62,842)
Fiscal Year-end: 02/28/22
Pharmaceuticals Product Mfr
N.A.I.C.S.: 325412
Mxolisi Motau (Exec Dir)

GO METALS CORP.
1111 Melville Street 11th Floor, Vancouver, V6E 3V6, BC, Canada
Tel.: (604) 725-1857
Web Site: https://www.gometals.ca
47GA—(DEU)
Rev.: $27,654
Assets: $1,985,460
Liabilities: $805,748
Net Worth: $1,179,712
Earnings: ($2,105,741)
Fiscal Year-end: 07/31/23
Metal Mining Services
N.A.I.C.S.: 213114
Scott Sheldon (CEO)

GOA CARBON LTD.
Dempo House Campal, Panaji, 403 001, Goa, India
Tel.: (91) 8322441300
Web Site:
https://www.goacarbon.com
509567—(NSE)
Rev.: $104,923,196
Assets: $58,280,163
Liabilities: $42,638,355
Net Worth: $15,641,808
Earnings: $5,156,874
Emp.: 179
Fiscal Year-end: 03/31/22
Calcined Petroleum Coke Mfr & Sales
N.A.I.C.S.: 324199
Shrinivas Vasudeva Dempo (Chm)

GOA CARBON LTD.

Goa Carbon Ltd.—(Continued)

Subsidiaries:

Dempo Shipbuilding & Engineering Pvt. Ltd. (1)
Dempo House, Campal, Panaji, 403001, Goa, India
Tel.: (91) 8322441300
Web Site:
https://www.dempshipbuilding.com
Shipbuilding Repair & Maintenance Services
N.A.I.C.S.: 811310

Dempo Sports Club Pvt. Ltd. (1)
Dempo Sports Club Academy Complex, Carambolim Ella, Goa, 403110, India
Tel.: (91) 9403708677
Web Site:
https://www.demposportsclub.com
Sports Club Services
N.A.I.C.S.: 711211

Devashri Nirman LLP (1)
710 7th Floor Dempo Tower EDC Plaza Patto, Panaji, 403001, Goa, India
Tel.: (91) 7066486671
Web Site: https://www.devashrigroup.com
Real Estate Development Services
N.A.I.C.S.: 531390

Modest Infrastructure Pvt. Ltd. (1)
11 Rex Chambers Gr Floor Walchand Hirachand MargBallard Estate, Mumbai, 400 001, India
Tel.: (91) 2222703571
Web Site: https://www.modship.com
Shipbuilding Repair & Maintenance Services
N.A.I.C.S.: 811310

GOALS SOCCER CENTRES PLC

Orbital House Peel Park, East Kilbride, G74 5PR, United Kingdom
Tel.: (44) 1355 234 800 **UK**
Web Site: http://www.goalsplc.co.uk
Sales Range: $25-49.9 Million
Holding Company; Sports Centers Owner & Operator
N.A.I.C.S.: 551112

GOAT INDUSTRIES LTD.

885 W Georgia St 2200, Vancouver, V6C 3E8, BC, Canada **BC**
Web Site:
https://www.goatindustries.co
Year Founded: 2020
BGTTF—(OTCQB)
Assets: $1,662,106
Liabilities: $319,053
Net Worth: $1,343,053
Earnings: ($10,456,662)
Fiscal Year-end: 12/31/22
Software Development Services
N.A.I.C.S.: 541511
David Jackson (Sr VP)

GOBARTO SA

Wspolna 70, 00-687, Warsaw, Poland
Tel.: (48) 223199300
Web Site: https://www.gobarto.pl
GOB—(WAR)
Rev.: $868,936,990
Assets: $309,370,426
Liabilities: $170,053,353
Net Worth: $139,317,073
Earnings: $24,571,138
Emp.: 1,600
Fiscal Year-end: 12/31/23
Veal Product Mfr
N.A.I.C.S.: 311612
Roman Miler (Vice Chm-Mgmt Bd)

GOBI ACQUISITION CORP.

33/F Three Pacific Place 1 Queens Road East, Hong Kong, China (Hong Kong)
Tel.: (852) 2918 0088 **Ky**
Year Founded: 2021
GOBI—(NASDAQ)
Investment Services
N.A.I.C.S.: 523999
Jack Li (CEO & CFO)

GOBI JOINT STOCK COMPANY

Chinggis Ave Industrial Stree, PO Box 36/434, Khan-Uul District, Ulaanbaatar, 17062, Mongolia
Tel.: (976) 70139977
Web Site: https://www.gobi.mn
Year Founded: 1981
GOV—(MONG)
Rev.: $74,350,840
Assets: $90,676,005
Liabilities: $90,724,415
Net Worth: ($48,410)
Earnings: ($1,968,325)
Emp.: 1,765
Fiscal Year-end: 12/31/23
Textile Products Mfr
N.A.I.C.S.: 314999
D. Gerelmaa (Chm)

GOBLIN INDIA LTD.

Camex House 1St Floor Stadium-Commerce Road, Navrangpura, Ahmedabad, 380009, India
Tel.: (91) 7926465080
Web Site:
https://www.goblinindia.com
Year Founded: 2001
542850—(BOM)
Rev.: $2,809,506
Assets: $8,008,527
Liabilities: $4,691,691
Net Worth: $3,316,837
Earnings: ($217,894)
Emp.: 20
Fiscal Year-end: 03/31/22
Bags Distr
N.A.I.C.S.: 424490
Manojkumar Choukhany (Mng Dir)

Subsidiaries:

Goblin France SARL (1)
61 Rue de la Haie Coq, 93300, Aubervilliers, France
Tel.: (33) 144022001
Luggage Distr
N.A.I.C.S.: 423990

GOC (PAK) LIMITED

Small Industries Estate, Sialkot, Pakistan
Tel.: (92) 3563051
Web Site: https://www.gocpak.com
GOC—(KAR)
Rev.: $1,964,699
Assets: $2,465,294
Liabilities: $280,161
Net Worth: $2,185,133
Earnings: $460,662
Emp.: 139
Fiscal Year-end: 06/30/19
Sports Goods Mfr
N.A.I.C.S.: 339920
Khawar Anwar Khawaja (CEO)

GOC CO., LTD.

10 Cheomdan venture-ro 60 beon-gil Buk-gu, Gwangju, Korea (South)
Tel.: (82) 629736118
Web Site: http://www.goc2001.com
Year Founded: 2001
Indoor Optical Cable Mfr
N.A.I.C.S.: 332618
Inchul Park (CEO)

GOCARDLESS LTD.

338-346 Goswell Road, London, EC1V 7LQ, United Kingdom
Tel.: (44) 20 7183 8674 **UK**
Web Site: http://www.gocardless.com
Year Founded: 2011
Direct Debit Collection & Processing Services
N.A.I.C.S.: 522320

GOCONNECT LIMITED

Level 1 951 Nepean Hwy, Bentleigh, 3204, VIC, Australia
Tel.: (61) 388337242 **AU**
Web Site:
http://www.goconnect.com.au
Year Founded: 1999
Sales Range: Less than $1 Million
Emp.: 10
Online Media Communication Services
N.A.I.C.S.: 518210
Richard Li (Chm)

GOD A.D.

Dunis bb, Dunis, Serbia
Tel.: (381) 37 494 167
Year Founded: 2003
Sales Range: Less than $1 Million
Emp.: 9
Wood Products Whslr
N.A.I.C.S.: 423310

GODACO SEAFOOD JOINT STOCK COMPANY

Lot 45 My Tho Industrial Park, Ho Chi Minh City, Tien Giang, Vietnam
Tel.: (84) 73 3 953227 **VN**
Web Site: http://www.godaco-seafood.com.vn
Year Founded: 1998
Emp.: 6,500
Frozen Seafood Products Mfr & Whslr
N.A.I.C.S.: 311710
Cong Binh Nguyen (Mgr-Import & Export)

GODAVARI DRUGS LIMITED

1st Floor Mayfair Sardar Patel Road, Secunderabad, 500 003, Telangana, India
Tel.: (91) 4027842602
Web Site:
https://www.godavaridrugs.com
530317—(BOM)
Rev.: $19,217,085
Assets: $14,559,439
Liabilities: $10,552,821
Net Worth: $4,006,618
Earnings: $453,906
Emp.: 104
Fiscal Year-end: 03/31/23
Pharmaceutical Product Mfr & Whslr
N.A.I.C.S.: 325412
Ghanshyam Jaju (Chm)

GODAWARI POWER & ISPAT LTD.

First Floor Hira Arcade 1st Floor Near New Bus Stand, Pandri, Raipur, 492 001, Chattisgarh, India
Tel.: (91) 7714082735
Web Site:
https://www.godawaripowerispat.com
GPIL—(NSE)
Rev.: $556,367,967
Assets: $474,140,148
Liabilities: $186,396,224
Net Worth: $287,743,925
Earnings: $89,340,997
Emp.: 2,656
Fiscal Year-end: 03/31/21
Steel Plant & Power Generation
N.A.I.C.S.: 562213
Dinesh Kumar Agrawal (Exec Dir)

Subsidiaries:

Godawari Energy Limited (1)
G-9 Hira Arcade 1st Floor Near Bus Stand, Pandri, Raipur, 492 004, Chhattisgarh, India
Tel.: (91) 7714082752
Wind Electric Power Generation Services
N.A.I.C.S.: 221115

Hira Energy Limited (1)
Ground Floor Hira Arcade Near new bus stand, Pandri, Raipur, Chattisgarh, India
Tel.: (91) 7714082789
Wind Electric Power Generation Services
N.A.I.C.S.: 221115

GODDARD ENTERPRISES LIMITED

Top Floor The Goddard Building, Haggatt Hall, Saint Michael, BB11059, Barbados
Tel.: (246) 4305700 **BB**
Web Site:
http://www.goddardenterprisesltd.com
Year Founded: 1921
GEL—(BARB)
Rev.: $544,131,000
Assets: $272,005,000
Liabilities: $144,140,500
Net Worth: $127,864,500
Earnings: $44,925,500
Emp.: 6,900
Fiscal Year-end: 09/30/23
Holding Company; Catering, Manufacturing, Finance, International Trade & Consumer Services
N.A.I.C.S.: 551112
Ian A. Alleyne (Gen Mgr-Automotive, Building Supplies & Svcs)

Subsidiaries:

Airport Restaurants (1996) Limited (1)
Grantley Adams Intl Airport, Christ Church, BB17089, Barbados
Tel.: (246) 4280989
Sales Range: $10-24.9 Million
Emp.: 2
Restaurant Management Services
N.A.I.C.S.: 722511

Caribbean Label Crafts Ltd. (1)
Wildey Industrial Estate, Wildey, 14006, Saint Michael, Barbados
Tel.: (246) 4367877
Web Site: https://label-crafts.com
Sales Range: $50-74.9 Million
Emp.: 100
Commercial Label Designer & Mfr
N.A.I.C.S.: 322220

Corea & Co. (1988) Limited (1)
Shipping Freight Transportation Services
N.A.I.C.S.: 488510

Coreas Hazells Inc. (1)
Tel.: (784) 4561201
Web Site:
https://www.goddardenterprisesltd.com
Building Materials Whslr
N.A.I.C.S.: 444180
Joel Providence (Mng Dir)

Courtesy Garage Ltd. (1)
Wildey Main Road, Saint Michael, Barbados (99%)
Tel.: (246) 4314100
Web Site: https://www.courtesygarage.com
Holding Company; New & Used Car Dealerships & Automotive Repair Service Centers Operator
N.A.I.C.S.: 551112
Nicholas Mackie (Sr Gen Mgr)

Division (Domestic):

Courtesy Garage Limited - Tropical Battery Division (2)
Wildey, 1246, Saint Michael, Barbados
Tel.: (246) 4314100
Automobile Batteries Mfr
N.A.I.C.S.: 335910
Nicholas Mackie (Sr Gen Mgr)

Subsidiary (Non-US):

Fidelity Motors Ltd. (2)
5-18 Hanover Street, Kingston, 876, Jamaica
Tel.: (876) 8769485409
Web Site: http://www.nissanjamaica.com
Sales Range: $25-49.9 Million
Emp.: 52
New & Used Car Dealer

AND PRIVATE COMPANIES

GODFREYS GROUP LIMITED

N.A.I.C.S.: 441110
Leslie Nembhard *(Mgr-Sls & Mktg)*

GCG Ground Services (Barbados) Limited (1)
Grantley Adams Itnernational Airport, Christ Church, Barbados
Tel.: (246) 4280973
Airport Maintenance Services
N.A.I.C.S.: 488119
Chris Wilson *(Mgr-Customer Service)*

GCG Ground Services, LLC (1)
Cyril E King Airport, Saint Thomas, VI 00802
Tel.: (340) 776-4646
Airport Maintenance Services
N.A.I.C.S.: 488119
Jahmal Dyer *(Gen Mgr)*

GCG Group (1)
2525 Embassy Dr Ste 13, Cooper City, FL 33026
Tel.: (954) 438-9855
Web Site: http://www.gcggroup.com
Emp.: 3,000
Airline Catering Management Services
N.A.I.C.S.: 722320
Francisco Mayorga *(Mgr-Catering Ops-Latin America)*

GL Food Market Ltd. (1)
Baywalk Shopping Mall, Rodney Bay, Saint Lucia
Tel.: (758) 455 3663
Web Site: http://www.glfoodmarket.com
Food Market Management Services
N.A.I.C.S.: 445110

Goddard Catering Group (Antigua) Limited (1)
V C Bird International Airport Pavilion Drive, PO Box W520, Osbourn, Antigua, Antigua & Barbuda
Tel.: (268) 4623121
Web Site: https://www.gcg-catering.com
Sales Range: $10-24.9 Million
Emp.: 46
Airline Catering Management Services
N.A.I.C.S.: 722320

Goddard Catering Group (Guatemala) S.A. (1)
7 Avenida 11-97 Zona 13, Guatemala, Guatemala
Tel.: (502) 23050485
Web Site: https://www.gcggroup.com
Sales Range: $25-49.9 Million
Emp.: 200
Airline Catering Management Services
N.A.I.C.S.: 722320
Ever Santis *(Gen Mgr)*

Goddard Catering Group Bogota Ltda. (1)
Aeropuerto Internacional, Bogota, Colombia
Airline Catering Services
N.A.I.C.S.: 722310
Rigoberto Comenares *(Mgr)*

Goddard Catering Group Caracas S.A. (1)
Aeropuerto Internacional Simon Bolivar Maiquetia Area Norte, Maiquetia, Venezuela
Tel.: (58) 2123552091
Sales Range: $25-49.9 Million
Emp.: 148
Airline Catering Management Services
N.A.I.C.S.: 722320
Rolf Romer *(Gen Mgr)*

Goddard Catering Group Curacao, N.V (1)
Hato International Airport, Willemstad, Curacao
Tel.: (599) 98681061
Web Site: http://www.goddardenterprisesltd.com
Sales Range: $10-24.9 Million
Emp.: 34
Catering Management Services
N.A.I.C.S.: 722320
Francisco Mayorga *(Gen Mgr)*

Goddard Catering Group El Salvador, S.A. de C.V (1)
Aerpuerto Internacional, San Salvador, El Salvador
Tel.: (503) 23124900
Web Site: https://www.gcg-catering.com

Sales Range: $25-49.9 Million
Emp.: 210
Catering Management Services
N.A.I.C.S.: 722320

Goddard Catering Group Guayaquil S.A. (1)
Aeropuerto Jose Joaquin De Olmedo, Guayaquil, Ecuador
Tel.: (593) 42924705
Web Site: https://www.gcggroup.com
Sales Range: $10-24.9 Million
Emp.: 110
Airline Catering Services
N.A.I.C.S.: 722320

Goddard Catering Group Inc. (1)
2525 Embassy Dr S Ste 13, Cooper City, FL 33026
Tel.: (954) 438-9855
Web Site: http://www.goddard-catering.com
Sales Range: $750-799.9 Million
Emp.: 2,100
Holding Company; Airline & Event Catering Services
N.A.I.C.S.: 551112
J. G. Stewart Massiah *(Pres)*

Subsidiary (Non-US):

Caribbean Dispatch Services Ltd. (2)
Beanfield Vieux-Fort, Castries, Saint Lucia
Tel.: (758) 7584596500
Airline Operation Services
N.A.I.C.S.: 488119
Aaron Grant *(Gen Mgr)*

Goddard Catering Group (Jamaica) Ltd. (2)
Norman Manley International Airport, Kingston, Jamaica (51%)
Tel.: (876) 9248131
Sales Range: $25-49.9 Million
Emp.: 100
Airline Catering Services
N.A.I.C.S.: 722320

Goddard Catering Group Uruguay S.A. (1)
Mirlo N 71 Ex oficial 3, Canelones, Uruguay
Tel.: (598) 26011415
Web Site: https://www.gcggroup.com
Sales Range: $25-49.9 Million
Emp.: 350
Airline Catering Management Services
N.A.I.C.S.: 722320
Bernardo Villar *(Gen Mgr)*

Goddards Shipping & Tours Limited (1)
Goddards Complex Fontabelle, Saint Michael, BB11149, Barbados
Tel.: (246) 426 9918
Web Site: http://www.goddardsshippingltd.com
Sales Range: $25-49.9 Million
Emp.: 3
Shipping & Tour Operating Services
N.A.I.C.S.: 488510

Hipac Limited (1)
Goddards Complex Fontabelle, Saint Michael, BB11000, Barbados
Tel.: (246) 4275621
Web Site: https://hipacfoods.com
Sales Range: $50-74.9 Million
Emp.: 185
Meat & Seafood Mfr
N.A.I.C.S.: 311710
Tony Gill *(Mgr-Engrg)*

Hutchinson (Antigua) Limited (1)
PO Box 1048, Saint John's, Antigua & Barbuda
Tel.: (268) 481 1550
Web Site: http://www.goddardenterprisesltd.com
Emp.: 30
Grocery Product Whslr
N.A.I.C.S.: 424490

Jamaica Dispatch Services Limited (1)
Sangster International Airport, Montego Bay, 1876, Saint James, Jamaica
Tel.: (876) 9524570
Web Site: https://www.gcggroup.com
Airport Ground Handling Services
N.A.I.C.S.: 488119

Jonas Browne and Hubbard (Grenada) Limited (1)
Scott Street, PO Box 25, Saint George's, Grenada
Tel.: (473) 4402087
Web Site: https://www.hubbards.gd
Emp.: 367
Frozen Food Whslr & Supermarket Services
N.A.I.C.S.: 424420

Label Crafts Jamaica Ltd. (1)
Ferry Warehouse Phase 2 Tom Cringle Drive, Kingston, 19, Jamaica
Tel.: (876) 8769068837
Packaging & Labeling Services
N.A.I.C.S.: 561910
Catherine Gregory *(Gen Mgr)*

McBride (Caribbean) Limited (1)
Lowlands, Christ Church, BB17046, Barbados
Tel.: (246) 4287766
Web Site: https://mcbridegroup.info
Sales Range: $25-49.9 Million
Emp.: 26
Aerosol Products Mfr
N.A.I.C.S.: 325998

Peter & Company Limited (1)
Cul De Sac, Culdees, Castries, Saint Lucia
Tel.: (758) 4577000
Web Site: http://peterandcompanydistribution.com
Sales Range: $50-74.9 Million
Emp.: 20
Building Material Retailer
N.A.I.C.S.: 444180

Precision Packaging Inc. (1)
Lower Estate Sugar Factory, Saint Michael, BB19188, Barbados
Tel.: (246) 4293943
Web Site: http://www.goddardenterprisesltd.com
Emp.: 54
Packaging Products Mfr
N.A.I.C.S.: 322220
Winston Thompson *(Gen Mgr)*

Purity Bakeries (1)
Purity Bakeries Lower Collymore Rock, Saint Michael, BB11142, Barbados
Tel.: (246) 4264705
Web Site: http://www.goddardenterprisesltd.com
Sales Range: $25-49.9 Million
Emp.: 20
Bakery Management Services
N.A.I.C.S.: 311812
Andrea Greenidge *(Controller-Fin)*

Sea Freight Agencies & Stevedoring Limited (1)
Goddards Complex Fontabelle, Saint Michael, Barbados
Tel.: (246) 4299688
Web Site: https://www.seafreightagencies.com
Stevedoring Services
N.A.I.C.S.: 488320

Sunbilt Ltd. (1)
PO Box 60, Castries, Saint Lucia (100%)
Tel.: (758) 4580001
Web Site: http://www.goddardenterprisesltd.com
Sales Range: $1-9.9 Million
Hardware & Building Supplies Wholesale Trade Agency
N.A.I.C.S.: 425120

Tropical Laundries (1)
Laundry Road Country Road, Saint Michael, Barbados
Tel.: (246) 437 6832
Emp.: 70
Laundry Services
N.A.I.C.S.: 812332
Audley Grimes *(Gen Mgr)*

GODEX INTERNATIONAL CO., LTD.
13F No 168 Jian-Kang Road, Zhonghe Dist, New Taipei City, 235, Taiwan
Tel.: (886) 222258580
Web Site: https://www.godexintl.com
Year Founded: 1993

4987—(TPE)
Rev.: $40,243,504
Assets: $45,342,369
Liabilities: $11,267,673
Net Worth: $34,074,696
Earnings: $5,927,712
Fiscal Year-end: 12/31/22
Barcode Printer Mfr
N.A.I.C.S.: 333248
Feng-I Tai *(Chm & Pres)*

Subsidiaries:

Godex Europe GmbH (1)
Industriestrasse 19, 42477, Radevormwald, Germany
Tel.: (49) 2195595990
Electronic Parts Mfr
N.A.I.C.S.: 334419

Godex International America, LLC (1)
3963 Camino Ranchero, Camarillo, CA 93012
Tel.: (805) 987-5100
Electronic Components Mfr
N.A.I.C.S.: 334419

GODFREY PHILLIPS INDIA LTD.
Omaxe Square Plot No 14, Jasola District Centre, New Delhi, 110 025, India
Tel.: (91) 1126832155
Web Site: https://www.godfreyphillips.co.in
Year Founded: 1936
500163—(BOM)
Rev.: $530,889,527
Assets: $595,675,307
Liabilities: $169,651,688
Net Worth: $426,023,620
Earnings: $82,784,833
Emp.: 969
Fiscal Year-end: 03/31/23
Cigarette & Tobacco Products Mfr
N.A.I.C.S.: 312230
K. K. Modi *(Pres & Mng Dir)*

Subsidiaries:

Chase Investments Limited (1)
14 Omaxe Square Centre, Jasola District, New Delhi, 110025, India
Tel.: (91) 1126832155
Cigarette Mfr
N.A.I.C.S.: 312230

Godfrey Phillips MiddleEast DMCC (1)
Unit No AU-11-02 AU Tower Gold Plot No 13 Jumeirah Lakes Towers, Dubai, United Arab Emirates
Tel.: (971) 43688216
Cigarette Mfr
N.A.I.C.S.: 312230

International Tobacco Company Limited (1)
Ground Floor Frontside Macropolo Building Next to Kala Chowky, Post Office Dr Baba Saheb Ambedkar Road, Mumbai, 400012, India
Tel.: (91) 2261952300
Cigarette Mfr
N.A.I.C.S.: 312230

GODFREYS GROUP LIMITED
26 34 Aylesbury Drive, Altona, VIC, Australia
Tel.: (61) 800815270 AU
Web Site: http://www.godfreys.com.au
Year Founded: 1931
Sales Range: $125-149.9 Million
Household Vacuum Cleaner Distr
N.A.I.C.S.: 423620

Subsidiaries:

Electrical Home-Aids Pty Ltd (1)
Building 2 L 1 Brandon Business Par, Glen Waverley, 3150, Australia
Tel.: (61) 385422100

GODFREYS GROUP LIMITED

Godfreys Group Limited—(Continued)
Vacuum Cleaner Distr
N.A.I.C.S.: 423620

The Service Company Limited (1)
10 Donnor Place Mt Wellington, Auckland,
New Zealand
Tel.: (64) 95740377
Web Site: http://www.theservice.co.nz
Cleaning Product Distr
N.A.I.C.S.: 424210
Ian Jemmett *(Founder & CEO)*

GODHA CABCON & INSULATION LTD.

36-D Sector-B Sanwer Road, Industrial Area, Indore, MP, India
Tel.: (91) 7314029509
Web Site:
    https://www.godhacabcon.com
GODHA—(NSE)
Rev.: $521,276
Assets: $3,187,495
Liabilities: $336,790
Net Worth: $2,850,704
Earnings: ($168,227)
Emp.: 8
Fiscal Year-end: 03/31/23
Steel Products Mfr
N.A.I.C.S.: 331221
Dipesh Godha *(CEO)*

GODIN GUITARS

19420 Clark-Graham Ave, Baie-d'Urfe, H9X 3R8, QC, Canada
Tel.: (514) 457-7977
Web Site: http://www.lasido.com
Sales Range: $50-74.9 Million
Emp.: 450
Guitar Mfr
N.A.I.C.S.: 339992
Robert Godin *(Pres & CEO)*

GODO STEEL, LTD.

Toyobo Building 8F 2-8 Dojimahama 2-chome, Kita-ku, Osaka, 530-0004, Japan
Tel.: (81) 663437660
Web Site: https://www.godo-steel.co.jp
Year Founded: 1937
5410—(TKS)
Rev.: $1,473,038,500
Assets: $1,790,073,930
Liabilities: $939,955,220
Net Worth: $850,118,710
Earnings: $100,425,730
Emp.: 744
Fiscal Year-end: 03/31/24
Steel Product Mfr & Whslr
N.A.I.C.S.: 331110
Hiroyuki Uchida *(Pres)*

Subsidiaries:

ASAHI Industries Co., Ltd. (1)
5-13-8 Imadera Oume-shi, Tokyo, 198-0021, Japan (86.96%)
Tel.: (81) 428316841
Web Site: http://www.asahiindustry.co.jp
Rev.: $318,596,640
Assets: $270,245,040
Liabilities: $200,341,680
Net Worth: $69,903,360
Earnings: ($3,214,560)
Emp.: 465
Fiscal Year-end: 03/31/2018
Structural Steel Production & Sale
N.A.I.C.S.: 238120
Masahiro Sugimoto *(Pres & CEO)*

Plant (Domestic):

ASAHI Industries Co., Ltd. - Chiba Plant (2)
13 Sakuradai 1-chome, Asahi, 289-050, Chiba, Japan
Tel.: (81) 479 68 1600
Web Site: http://www.asahi-kg.co.jp
Fertilizer Mfr
N.A.I.C.S.: 325314

ASAHI Industries Co., Ltd. - Kansai Plant (2)
6776 Minakuchi Minakuchi-cho, Koka, 528-0005, Shiga, Japan
Tel.: (81) 748 62 8171
Web Site: http://www.asahi-kg.co.jp
Fertilizer Mfr
N.A.I.C.S.: 325314

Subsidiary (Domestic):

ASAHI Industries Co., Ltd. - Saitama Plant (2)
222 Wataruse Kamikawa-machi, Kodama-gun, Saitama, 367-0394, Japan
Tel.: (81) 274522713
Steel Recycling Services
N.A.I.C.S.: 562920

Jobu Co,. Ltd. (2)
3085-1 Kanazawa Minano-machi, Chichibu-gun, Saitama, 369-1601, Japan
Tel.: (81) 494621321
Web Site: https://www.jobu-sg.co.jp
Emp.: 53
Crushed Stone & Sand Whslr
N.A.I.C.S.: 423320

Plant (Domestic):

Jobu Co,. Ltd. - Material Recycling Plant (3)
162-2 Ofuchi Minano-machi, Chichibu-gun, Saitama, 369-1623, Japan
Tel.: (81) 494 62 0522
Web Site: http://www.asahi-kg.co.jp
Steel Recycling Services
N.A.I.C.S.: 562920

Funabashi Kiko Co., Ltd. (1)
2-1 Minami-kaijin 2-chome, Funabashi, 273-0023, Chiba, Japan
Tel.: (81) 474332251
General Freight Trucking Services
N.A.I.C.S.: 484110
Souji Taguchi *(Pres)*

Godo Ceramics Ltd. (1)
936 Inbe, Bizen, 705-0001, Okayama, Japan
Tel.: (81) 869643347
Ceramic Material Mfr & Distr
N.A.I.C.S.: 327120

Godo Steel, Ltd. - Funabashi Works (1)
2-1 Minamikaijin 2-chome, Funabashi, Chiba, 273-0023, Japan
Tel.: (81) 474312095
Steel Products Mfr
N.A.I.C.S.: 331110

Godo Steel, Ltd. - Himeji Works (1)
2946 Nakajima, Shikama-ku, Himeji, 672-8655, Hyogo, Japan
Tel.: (81) 79 234 9311
Steel Products Mfr
N.A.I.C.S.: 331110

Godo Steel, Ltd. - Osaka Works (1)
1-2 Nishijima 1-chome, Nishiyodogawa-ku, Osaka, 555-0042, Japan
Tel.: (81) 6 6472 1532
Steel Products Mfr
N.A.I.C.S.: 331110

Gotetsu Osaka Buturyu Co., Ltd. (1)
1-2 Nishijima 1-chome, Nishiyodogawa-ku, Osaka, 555-0042, Japan
Tel.: (81) 664728298
General Freight Trucking Services
N.A.I.C.S.: 484110
Takashi Morimitsu *(Pres)*

Gotetsu Sangyo Co., Ltd. (1)
5F Furukawa Osaka Building-West Wing 2-1-9 Dojimahama, Kita-ku, Osaka, 530-0004, Japan
Tel.: (81) 6 6344 0728
Web Site: http://www.go-sun.co.jp
Steel Product Mfr & Distr
N.A.I.C.S.: 331110

Kanto D-Bar Steel Corporation (1)
10th Floor Marunouchi Central Bldg 9-1 Marunouchi 1-chome, Chiyoda-ku, Tokyo, 100-0005, Japan
Tel.: (81) 362670030
Steel Material Distr
N.A.I.C.S.: 423510

Teruo Yamazaki *(Pres)*
Mitsuboshi Metal Industry Co., Ltd. (1)
736 Koseki, Tsubame, 959-1286, Niigata, Japan
Tel.: (81) 256 61 1000
Web Site: http://www.mitsuboshi-scon.co.jp
Steel Bar Mfr & Distr
N.A.I.C.S.: 331221

Nihon Senko Co., Ltd. (1)
2946 Nakajima, Shikama-ku, Himeji, 672-8035, Hyogo, Japan
Tel.: (81) 792357043
Waste Disposal Services
N.A.I.C.S.: 562211
Osamu Kuniwake *(Pres)*

Tokai Steel Corporation (1)
1-banchi Oaza Anse, Wakamatsu-ku, Kita-kyushu, 808-0022, Fukuoka, Japan
Tel.: (81) 937521611
Fabricated Structural Metal Mfr
N.A.I.C.S.: 332312
Tetsuya Yano *(Pres)*

Wire Techno, Ltd. (1)
3-3-8 Imazukita, Tsurumi-ku, Osaka, 538-0041, Japan
Tel.: (81) 669611751
Web Site: http://www.wire-techno.co.jp
Wire Mfr & Distr
N.A.I.C.S.: 331110

GODOLPHIN RESOURCES LIMITED

Unit 13 11-19 William Street, PO Box 9497, Orange, 2800, NSW, Australia
Tel.: (61) 263188144
Web Site:
    https://www.godolphinresources.com
Year Founded: 1996
GRL—(ASX)
Assets: $5,793,996
Liabilities: $365,315
Net Worth: $5,428,681
Earnings: $2,176,301
Fiscal Year-end: 06/30/23
Exploration & Mining Services
N.A.I.C.S.: 213115
Jeneta Owens *(Mng Dir)*

GODREJ & BOYCE MFG. CO. LTD.

Unit No 5C 5th Floor Godrej One Pirojshanagar, Vikhroli, Mumbai, 400 079, India
Tel.: (91) 2261698500
Web Site:
    http://www.godrejproperties.com
Year Founded: 1897
Sales Range: $900-999.9 Million
Emp.: 10,700
N.A.I.C.S.: 551112
Jamshyd N. Godrej *(Chm)*

Subsidiaries:

Argencos SA (1)
Francia 3765, San Martin, Argentina
Tel.: (54) 11 4753 6060
Haircare Product Mfr
N.A.I.C.S.: 333310

Busbar Systems (India) Limited (1)
Plot 4N KIADB Industrial Area, Dabaspet, Bengaluru, 562 111, Karnataka, India
Tel.: (91) 8027735254
Web Site: http://www.busbarducts.com
Busbar System Mfr
N.A.I.C.S.: 335313
Jayasimhan Leon *(Sr Gen Mgr-Bus Ops)*

Cosmetica Nacional S.A. (1)
Vargas Fontecilla, Quinta Normal, Chile
Tel.: (56) 2 2438 7900
Cosmetic Product Distr
N.A.I.C.S.: 424210
Geraldine Cabrera Geisser *(Product Mgr)*

Frika Weave (PTY) LTD (1)
30 Auckland St Paarden Eiland, 7405, Cape Town, South Africa
Tel.: (27) 21 511 6767

INTERNATIONAL PUBLIC

Beauty Care Services
N.A.I.C.S.: 812112
Babalwa Lupondwana *(Brand Mgr)*

Godrej (Malaysia) Sdn. Bhd. (1)
1 Jalan asas Larkin Industrial Estate, 80350, Johor Bahru, Malaysia
Tel.: (60) 7 2761941
Web Site: http://www.godrejmalaysia.com
Office Furniture Mfr
N.A.I.C.S.: 337214

Godrej (Singapore) Pte. Ltd. (1)
11 Lok Yang Way, Singapore, 628632, Singapore
Tel.: (65) 62656677
Web Site: http://www.godrejsingapore.com
Office Furniture Mfr
N.A.I.C.S.: 337214

Godrej (Vietnam) Co. Ltd. (1)
10 Tu Do Avenue Vietnam Singapore Industrial Park, Thuan An, Binh Duong, Vietnam
Tel.: (84) 650 743400
Web Site: http://www.godrejvietnam.com
Office Furniture Mfr
N.A.I.C.S.: 337214
Sathyamoorthy A. *(Gen Mgr-Plant)*

Godrej Americas Inc. USA. (1)
9801 Westheimer Rd Ste 302, Houston, TX 77042-3955
Tel.: (713) 351-6491
Industrial Equipment Distr
N.A.I.C.S.: 423830
Apoorv Shrivastava *(Head-Bus Dev & Mgr-Ops)*

Godrej Efacec Automation & Robotics Ltd. (1)
Plant 19-A Pirojshanagar, Vikhroli, Mumbai, 400 079, India (49%)
Tel.: (91) 2267965347
Web Site: http://www.godrejefacec.com
Automated Storage & Retrieval Systems Developer & Mfr
N.A.I.C.S.: 333248

Godrej Global Mid East FZE (1)
B2/23 SAIF Zone, PO Box 7966, Sharjah, United Arab Emirates
Tel.: (971) 6 5572323
Web Site: http://www.godrejmideast.com
Consumer Product Mfr
N.A.I.C.S.: 325620

Godrej Industries Ltd. (1)
Godrej One Pirojshanagar Eastern Express Highway, Vikhroli, Mumbai, 400079, India (59%)
Tel.: (91) 2225188010
Web Site: https://www.godrejindustries.com
Rev.: $262,022,670
Assets: $921,818,625
Liabilities: $713,478,675
Net Worth: $208,339,950
Earnings: ($14,679,210)
Emp.: 1,070
Fiscal Year-end: 03/31/2021
Oleochemicals, Edible Oils & Bakery Fats Mfr & Marketer;
N.A.I.C.S.: 311225
Nadir B. Godrej *(Mng Dir)*

Subsidiary (Domestic):

Godrej Agrovet Ltd. (2)
Pirojshanagar Eastern Express Highway, Vikhroli, Mumbai, 400079, India
Tel.: (91) 2225188010
Web Site: http://www.godrejagrovet.com
Sales Range: $150-199.9 Million
Emp.: 1,000
Animal Feed & Agricultural Product Distr
N.A.I.C.S.: 311119
Mark Kahn *(Exec VP-Strategy & Bus Dev)*

Subsidiary (Domestic):

Godrej Tyson Foods Ltd. (3)
Godrej One 3rd floor Pirojshanagar Eastern Express Highway, Vikhroli, Navi Mumbai, 400 079, Mumbai, India (100%)
Tel.: (91) 2225188010
Sales Range: $250-299.9 Million
Poultry Processing Services
N.A.I.C.S.: 311615
Prashant Vatkar *(CEO)*

Subsidiary (Domestic):

Godrej Consumer Products Limited (2)

Godrej One 4th floor Pirojshanagar Eastern Express Highway, Vikhroli East, Mumbai, 400079, India **(100%)**
Tel.: (91) 2225188030
Web Site: https://www.godrejcp.com
Rev.: $1,687,987,665
Assets: $2,202,299,190
Liabilities: $624,914,745
Net Worth: $1,577,384,445
Earnings: $243,432,735
Emp.: 2,601
Fiscal Year-end: 03/31/2022
Personal Care & Household Product Mfr
N.A.I.C.S.: 325611
Nisaba Godrej *(Chm & Mng Dir)*

Subsidiary (Domestic):

Godrej Household Products Limited **(3)**
Pirojshanagar, Eastern Express Highway, Vikhroli East, Mumbai, 400 079, India **(100%)**
Tel.: (91) 2267976700
Sales Range: $25-49.9 Million
Emp.: 750
Mfr & Marketer of Household Insecticides, Shoe Care Products, Male Hair Care Products & Air Care Products
N.A.I.C.S.: 325998

Subsidiary (Domestic):

Godrej Properties Limited **(2)**
Godrej One 5th floor Pirojshanagar Eastern Express Highway, Vikhroli East, Mumbai, 400 079, India **(80.26%)**
Tel.: (91) 2261698500
Web Site: https://www.godrejproperties.com
Rev.: $181,966,785
Assets: $2,217,805,590
Liabilities: $1,082,195,205
Net Worth: $1,135,610,385
Earnings: ($25,857,195)
Emp.: 504
Fiscal Year-end: 03/31/2021
Commercial & Residential Property Developer
N.A.I.C.S.: 236220
Pirojsha Godrej *(Chm)*

Godrej Infotech Ltd.
1 Sidco Industrial Estate, Ambattur, Chennai, 600 098, India **(52%)**
Tel.: (91) 4466544444
Web Site: http://www.godrejinfotech.com
Sales Range: $1-9.9 Million
Emp.: 211
Computer Programming Services & Software Development
N.A.I.C.S.: 541511
Ajay Pimparkar *(CEO)*

Godrej Nigeria Ltd. **(1)**
Plot 2A Ayodele Diyan Street, LKeija, Lagos, Nigeria
Tel.: (234) 8058299222
Consumer Products Distr
N.A.I.C.S.: 424210
Vijayanarayanan Thampi *(Mgr-Factory)*

Mercury Manufacturing Co. Ltd. **(1)**
D-3 Phase 2 MEPZ - Special Economic Zone, Chennai, 600 045, India
Tel.: (91) 4422628002
Web Site: http://www.mercuryfurniture.com
Office Furniture Mfr
N.A.I.C.S.: 337214

PT Intrasari Raya **(1)**
Jl Gatot Subroto - Kawasan Industri Candi Blok 18 C-D-E, Jakarta, Indonesia
Tel.: (62) 24 762 7461
Consumer Products Distr
N.A.I.C.S.: 424210
Herry R. Munadji *(Branch Mgr)*

Style Industries Limited **(1)**
PO Box 30682, 100, Nairobi, Kenya
Tel.: (254) 20 2470675
Web Site: http://www.darlingkenya.biz
Beauty Care Services
N.A.I.C.S.: 812112
Mahmoud Saffideen *(CEO)*

Veromatic International BV **(1)**
Donker Duyvisweg 56, 3316 BM, Dordrecht, Netherlands
Tel.: (31) 78 654 09 55
Web Site: http://www.veromatic.eu

Coffee Machine Mfr
N.A.I.C.S.: 333310
Marco DeWildt *(Mng Dir)*

GODSINLOSEN NORDIC AB
Handelsvagen 34, 245 34, Staffanstorp, Sweden
Tel.: (46) 462718800
Web Site: https://www.giabnordic.se
Year Founded: 2012
GIAB—(OMX)
Rev.: $13,701,432
Assets: $4,625,052
Liabilities: $4,702,484
Net Worth: ($77,432)
Earnings: ($1,622,094)
Emp.: 55
Fiscal Year-end: 12/31/23
Telecommunication Servicesb
N.A.I.C.S.: 517810
Christian Jansson *(CEO)*

GOEASY LTD.
33 City Centre Dr 5th floor, Mississauga, L5B 2N5, ON, Canada
Tel.: (905) 272-2788   Ca
Web Site: https://www.goeasy.com
Year Founded: 1990
1ES—(DEU)
Rev.: $943,952,103
Assets: $3,144,445,785
Liabilities: $2,348,491,161
Net Worth: $795,954,624
Earnings: $187,192,738
Emp.: 2,404
Fiscal Year-end: 12/31/23
Mechandise Leasing & Retail Services
N.A.I.C.S.: 532210
Jason Mullins *(Pres & CEO)*

Subsidiaries:

RTO Asset Management Inc. **(1)**
2500 Hurontario St Unit 7 8, Mississauga, L5B 1N4, ON, Canada
Tel.: (905) 897-5511
Web Site: https://www.easyhome.ca
Sales Range: $50-74.9 Million
Emp.: 100
Furniture Leasing Services
N.A.I.C.S.: 532289

RTO Distribution Inc **(1)**
10239 178 Street Northwest, Edmonton, T5S 1M3, AB, Canada
Tel.: (780) 444-2575
Sales Range: $550-599.9 Million
Emp.: 1,126
Electrical Appliance Television & Radio Set Whslr
N.A.I.C.S.: 423620

easyfinancial Services Inc. **(1)**
930 18th St, Brandon, R7A 5C1, MB, Canada
Tel.: (204) 725-2855
Web Site: http://www.easyfinancialservices.ca
Consumer Lending Services
N.A.I.C.S.: 522291

easyhome U.S. Ltd. **(1)**
33 City Centre Drive Suite 510, Mississauga, L5B 2N5, ON, Canada
Tel.: (905) 272-2788
Web Site: http://easyhome.ca
Sales Range: $200-249.9 Million
Emp.: 320
Household Merchandise Leasing Services
N.A.I.C.S.: 522220

GOEL FOOD PRODUCTS LIMITED
76/1/2 Golaghata Road, Kolkata, 700048, West Bengal, India
Tel.: (91) 8961333312
Web Site: https://www.bika.co.in
Year Founded: 1996
543538—(BOM)
Rev.: $2,315,381
Assets: $6,112,129
Liabilities: $4,769,679

Net Worth: $1,342,450
Earnings: $315,602
Fiscal Year-end: 03/31/22
Food Products Mfr
N.A.I.C.S.: 311412

GOENKA BUSINESS & FINANCE LTD.
18 Rabindra Sarani Poddar Court Gate No 4 2nd Floor Room No 17, Kolkata, 700001, India
Tel.: (91) 9051466844
Web Site: https://www.goenkabusiness.in
Year Founded: 1987
538787—(BOM)
Rev.: $29,834,183
Assets: $14,805,527
Liabilities: $11,313,219
Net Worth: $3,492,309
Earnings: $17,337
Emp.: 6
Fiscal Year-end: 03/31/23
Commercial Banking Services
N.A.I.C.S.: 522110
Bhavikkumar Shankarlal Prajapati *(CFO)*

GOENKA DIAMOND AND JEWELS LIMITED
401 Panchratana M S B Ka Rasta, Johari Bazar, Jaipur, 302 003, Rajasthan, India
Tel.: (91) 1412574175
Web Site: https://www.goenkadiamonds.com
533189—(BOM)
Rev.: $583,060
Assets: $108,005,666
Liabilities: $75,069,404
Net Worth: $32,936,262
Earnings: $374,556
Emp.: 11
Fiscal Year-end: 03/31/22
Diamonds & Jewelry Mfr
N.A.I.C.S.: 339910
Nand Lal Goenka *(Founder & Chm)*

GOERTEK INC.
No 268 Dongfang Road High-Tech Industry Development District, Weifang, 261031, Shandong, China
Tel.: (86) 5363051234
Web Site: http://www.goertek.com
Year Founded: 2001
002241—(SSE)
Rev.: $13,648,358,205
Assets: $10,210,513,043
Liabilities: $5,845,265,438
Net Worth: $4,365,247,605
Earnings: 150,653,065
Emp.: 81,370
Fiscal Year-end: 12/31/23
Semiconductor Mfr
N.A.I.C.S.: 334413
Jiang Bin *(Founder & Chm)*

Subsidiaries:

GoerTek Electronics,Inc. **(1)**
1230 Midas way Ste 210, Sunnyvale, CA 94085
Tel.: (408) 844-9980
Web Site: http://www.goertek.com
Sales Range: $25-49.9 Million
Emp.: 10
Management Consulting Services
N.A.I.C.S.: 541611

GoerTek Korea Technology Inc. **(1)**
Rm 1117 SJ Technovill, 60-19 Gasan-dong Geumcheon-gu, 153769, Seoul, Korea (South)
Tel.: (82) 233973071
Electronic Parts Manufacturing
N.A.I.C.S.: 334419

Goertek Robotics Co., Ltd. **(1)**
eTong World Huaxin Park No 1777 Hualong Road, Qingpu District, Shanghai, China

Tel.: (86) 2160329213
Aerial Composite Material Mfr
N.A.I.C.S.: 336411

Goertek ShinNei Technology Co., Ltd. **(1)**
Web Site: http://www.goertek-st.com
FA Automation Equipment Mfr & Distr
N.A.I.C.S.: 333998

Goertek Technology Japan Co., Ltd. **(1)**
14th Floor Akihabaradai Bldg 1-18-13 Sotokanda, Chiyoda-ku, Tokyo, 101-0021, Japan
Tel.: (81) 362629858
Web Site: http://www.goertek.jp
Electronic Component Mfr & Distr
N.A.I.C.S.: 334419
Zhang Tao *(Pres)*

Qingdao GoerTek Technology Co., Ltd. **(1)**
No 401-No 4364F No 3 Building No 18 Fortune Center QinLing Road, Laoshan District, Qingdao, 266061, China
Tel.: (86) 53288973000
Sales Range: $150-199.9 Million
Emp.: 300
Electronic Product Whslr
N.A.I.C.S.: 423690

Weifang GoerTek Electronics Co., Ltd. **(1)**
Dongfang North Rd New & High-Tech Indus Dev Zone, 261031, Weifang, Shandong, China
Tel.: (86) 5368525777
Web Site: http://www.goertek.com
Electronic Product Whslr
N.A.I.C.S.: 423690

GOFINTECH INNOVATION LIMITED
Units No 4102-06 41/F Cosco Tower 183 Queens Road Central, Hong Kong, China (Hong Kong)
Tel.: (852) 31051863
Web Site: http://www.290.com.hk
0290—(HKG)
Rev.: $7,543,653
Assets: $77,982,598
Liabilities: $46,013,744
Net Worth: $31,968,854
Earnings: ($10,229,275)
Emp.: 69
Fiscal Year-end: 03/31/22
Security Management Services
N.A.I.C.S.: 523999
Qing Sun *(Exec Dir)*

Subsidiaries:

China Fortune Group Strategic Investment Company Limited **(1)**
Fl 32 Fortune Plz Jintian Rd, Futian Dist, Shenzhen, China
Tel.: (86) 75533335566
Web Site: http://www.cfortgroup.com
Investment Management Service
N.A.I.C.S.: 523999

Excalibur Futures Limited **(1)**
Rm 2512 Cosco Tower 83 Queens Rd, Central, China (Hong Kong)
Tel.: (852) 28449862
Web Site: http://www.excalibur.hk
Sales Range: $50-74.9 Million
Emp.: 30
Securities Trading Services
N.A.I.C.S.: 523150
Allan Poon *(Mng Dir)*

Excalibur Securities Limited **(1)**
2512 Cosco Tower 183 Queen's Road, Central, China (Hong Kong)
Tel.: (852) 25260388
Web Site: http://www.excalibur.hk
Sales Range: $50-74.9 Million.
Emp.: 20
Securities Trading Services
N.A.I.C.S.: 523150
Allan Poon *(Pres)*

Fortune (HK) Securities Limited **(1)**
4102-06 41/F COSCO Tower 183 Queen's Road, Central, China (Hong Kong)
Tel.: (852) 31051829

GoFintech Innovation Limited—(Continued)

Web Site: http://fortune3369.com.hk
Emp.: 35
Securities Trading Services
N.A.I.C.S.: 523150

Fortune Wealth Management Limited (1)
Unit 1609 16 F 113 Argyle St, Mongkok, Kowloon, China (Hong Kong)
Portfolio Management & General Insurance Services
N.A.I.C.S.: 523940

GOFORE PLC
Kalevantie 2, 33100, Tampere, Finland
Tel.: (358) 104397777
Web Site: https://www.gofore.com
Year Founded: 2002
GOFORE—(HEL)
Rev.: $161,796,892
Assets: $160,184,546
Liabilities: $74,107,490
Net Worth: $86,077,056
Earnings: $13,191,237
Emp.: 1,297
Fiscal Year-end: 12/31/22
Information Technology Services
N.A.I.C.S.: 541511
Timur Karki (Chm)

Subsidiaries:

Rebase Consulting Oy (1)
Lonnrotinkatu 5, 120, Helsinki, Finland
Tel.: (358) 405182663
Web Site: https://rebase.fi
Software Development Services
N.A.I.C.S.: 541511

eMundo Gmbh (1)
Hofmannstrasse 25-27, 81379, Munich, Germany
Tel.: (49) 8966598450
Web Site: https://www.e-mundo.de
Information Technology Services
N.A.I.C.S.: 541511

GOGAS GOCH GMBH & CO. KG
Zum Ihnedieck 18, D-44265, Dortmund, Germany
Tel.: (49) 231465050
Web Site: http://www.gogas.com
Year Founded: 1946
Rev.: $15,518,250
Emp.: 80
Heat Treatment Services
N.A.I.C.S.: 332811
Heinz Goch (Founder)

GOGIA CAPITAL SERVICES LIMITED
The Capital court 6th Floor OLOF Palme Marg Munirka, New Delhi, 110 067, India
Tel.: (91) 1149418888
Web Site: https://www.gogiacap.com
Year Founded: 1994
531600—(BOM)
Rev.: $561,533
Assets: $8,415,429
Liabilities: $2,678,846
Net Worth: $5,736,583
Earnings: $82,543
Emp.: 50
Fiscal Year-end: 03/31/23
Commodities Brokerage Services
N.A.I.C.S.: 523160
Satish Gogia (Chm & Mng Dir)

GOGLIO S.P.A.
Via Solari 10, 20144, Milan, Italy
Tel.: (39) 0332940111 IT
Web Site: http://www.goglio.it
Year Founded: 1850
Consumer Product Packaging Mfr
N.A.I.C.S.: 326111
Giorgio Bottini (Manager)

GOGOLD RESOURCES INC.
Suite 1301 2000 Barrington St, Halifax, B3J 3K1, NS, Canada
Tel.: (902) 482-1998 Ca
Web Site: https://www.gogoldresources.com
Year Founded: 2008
GLGDF—(OTCQX)
Rev.: $26,972,000
Assets: $84,742,000
Liabilities: $11,931,000
Net Worth: $72,811,000
Earnings: $8,114,000
Emp.: 4
Fiscal Year-end: 09/30/19
Gold Ore Exploration Services
N.A.I.C.S.: 213114
Dana Hatfield (CFO)

GOGOLOOK CO., LTD.
6 F No 319 Sec 2 Dunhua S Rd, Da'an Dist, Taipei, 106033, Taiwan
Tel.: (886) 223658099
Web Site: https://www.gogolook.com
Year Founded: 2012
6902—(TAI)
Rev.: $25,200,660
Assets: $22,237,940
Liabilities: $7,440,367
Net Worth: $14,797,573
Earnings: $166,912
Emp.: 197
Fiscal Year-end: 12/31/23
Software Development Services
N.A.I.C.S.: 541511
Ian Huang (CFO)

GOGORO INC.
Building C 11F No 225 Sec 2 Chang an E Rd, SongShan District, Taipei, 105404, Taiwan
Tel.: (886) 32730900 Ky
Web Site: https://www.gogoro.com
Year Founded: 2011
GGR—(NASDAQ)
Rev.: $382,826,000
Assets: $873,423,000
Liabilities: $574,449,000
Net Worth: $298,974,000
Earnings: ($98,908,000)
Emp.: 2,048
Fiscal Year-end: 12/31/22
Battery Mfr
N.A.I.C.S.: 335910
Alan Pan (Chief Revenue Officer)

GOGOX HOLDINGS LIMITED
Room 212 Building C Kaide Building Complex No 7 Rongyuan Road, Huayuan Industrial Park Binhai Hi-tech Zone, Tianjin, China
Web Site: https://www.gogoxholdings.com
Year Founded: 2013
2246—(HKG)
Rev.: $104,233,773
Assets: $120,040,153
Liabilities: $53,625,249
Net Worth: $66,414,904
Earnings: ($152,386,464)
Emp.: 818
Fiscal Year-end: 12/31/23
Holding Company
N.A.I.C.S.: 551112
Wing Sze Yu (Sec)

Subsidiaries:

GoGo Energy Limited (1)
PO Box No 62475, Kwun Tong, China (Hong Kong)
Tel.: (852) 21307630
Web Site: https://gogoxenergy.hk
Fuel Card Arrangement Services
N.A.I.C.S.: 522210

GoGo Energy Singapore Pte. Ltd. (1)
601 MacPherson Road 08-10 Grantral Complex MacPherson, Singapore, 368242, Singapore
Tel.: (65) 62452800
Web Site: https://gogoxenergy.sg
Fuel Card Arrangement Services
N.A.I.C.S.: 522210

GOHIGH NETWORKS CO., LTD.
Building 1 North District No 9 Dongran North Street, Haidian District, Beijing, 100191, China
Tel.: (86) 1062301907
Web Site: https://www.gohigh.com.cn
Year Founded: 1994
000851—(SSE)
Rev.: $962,818,272
Assets: $1,458,983,448
Liabilities: $755,512,056
Net Worth: $703,471,392
Earnings: $3,136,536
Fiscal Year-end: 12/31/22
Communication Equipment Mfr
N.A.I.C.S.: 334290
Fu Jinglin (Chm)

GOIL PLC
House No D 659/4 Kojo Thompson Road & Adjabeng Roads, PO Box GP 3183, Accra, Ghana
Tel.: (233) 302688215
Web Site: https://www.goil.com.gh
Year Founded: 1960
GOIL—(GHA)
Rev.: $945,262,400
Assets: $357,214,981
Liabilities: $255,034,891
Net Worth: $102,180,090
Earnings: $15,336,092
Emp.: 280
Fiscal Year-end: 12/31/20
Petroleum Products Marketer & Distr
N.A.I.C.S.: 424720
Alex Josiah Adzew (COO)

Subsidiaries:

Goenergy Company Limited (1)
12B 5th Circular Road, Cantonments, 38081, Accra, Ghana
Tel.: (233) 303960972
Web Site: https://www.goenergy.com.gh
Kerosene Mfr
N.A.I.C.S.: 324110
Kwabena Adjei (Mgr-Fin & Acctg)

GOINGPUBLIC MEDIA AG
Hofmannstrasse 7a, 81379, Munich, Germany
Tel.: (49) 8920003390
Web Site: https://www.goingpublic.de
G6P—(DEU)
Rev.: $1,802,288
Assets: $1,305,849
Liabilities: $161,882
Net Worth: $1,143,967
Earnings: $21,584
Emp.: 15
Fiscal Year-end: 12/31/23
Magazine Publisher & Distr
N.A.I.C.S.: 513120

GOK REGLER- UND ARMATUREN- GESELLSCHAFT MBH & CO. KG
Obernbreiter Strasse 2 16, Marktbreit, 97340, Kitzingen, Germany
Tel.: (49) 93324040
Web Site: http://www.gok-online.de
Year Founded: 1968
Rev.: $68,712,280
Emp.: 260
Measurement & Control Technology Services
N.A.I.C.S.: 334513
Karl-Heinz Kleine (Co-Founder)

GOKAK TEXTILES LTD.
1 2nd Floor 12th Cross Ideal Homes Near Jayanna Circle, Rajarajeshwari Nagar, Bengaluru, 560098, India
Tel.: (91) 829744077
Web Site: https://www.gokakmills.com
Year Founded: 1885
GLOBE.RE—(NSE)
Rev.: $10,539,116
Assets: $12,331,899
Liabilities: $19,087,717
Net Worth: ($6,755,818)
Earnings: $750,519
Emp.: 926
Fiscal Year-end: 03/31/23
Yarn Mill
N.A.I.C.S.: 313110

GOKALDAS EXPORTS LTD
No 25 Second Cross Third Main Industrial Suburb Yeshwantpur, Bengaluru, 560 022, Karnataka, India
Tel.: (91) 8068951000
Web Site: https://www.gokaldasexports.com
532630—(BOM)
Rev.: $269,435,801
Assets: $160,903,459
Liabilities: $54,644,698
Net Worth: $106,258,761
Earnings: $20,738,133
Emp.: 4,294
Fiscal Year-end: 03/31/23
Ready Made Garment Industry
N.A.I.C.S.: 315250
Poorana Seenivasan (Pres)

GOKE MICROELECTRONICS CO., LTD.
No 9 Dongshi Road South Section Quantang Subdistrict, Economic and Technological Development Zone, Changsha, 410131, Hunan, China
Tel.: (86) 73188218880
Web Site: https://www.goke.com
Year Founded: 2008
300672—(CHIN)
Rev.: $595,973,379
Assets: $1,033,877,156
Liabilities: $455,831,207
Net Worth: $578,045,949
Earnings: $13,531,727
Fiscal Year-end: 12/31/23
Electronic Components Mfr
N.A.I.C.S.: 334413

GOKUL REFOILS AND SOLVENT LIMITED
State Highway No 41 Near Sujanpur Patia, Siddhapur, 384151, Gujarat, India
Tel.: (91) 2767223475
Web Site: https://www.gokulgroup.com
GOKULEQ—(NSE)
Rev.: $377,305,126
Assets: $101,180,709
Liabilities: $61,833,116
Net Worth: $39,347,593
Earnings: $2,894,083
Emp.: 12
Fiscal Year-end: 03/31/23
Vegetable Oils Refining, Seed Procurement, Processing, Solvent Extraction & Marketing Services
N.A.I.C.S.: 311225
Balvantsinh C. Rajput (Chm & Mng Dir)

Subsidiaries:

Gokul Agri International Ltd. (1)
3rd Floor Gokul House 43 Shreemali Cooperative Housing Society Ltd, Opposite Shikhar Building Navrangpura, Ahmedabad, 380009, Gujarat, India
Tel.: (91) 7961905500
Web Site: https://www.gokulagri.com

Gokul Agro Resources Ltd. (1)
Crown 3 Inspire Bus Park Shantigram Nr Vaishnodevi Circle S G Highway, Opp Visamo Society B/H Atishay Belleview Motera, Ahmedabad, 380 005, Gujarat, India
Tel.: (91) 9099908537
Web Site: https://www.gokulagro.com
Rev.: $1,146,838,179
Assets: $212,058,510
Liabilities: $164,915,628
Net Worth: $47,142,882
Earnings: $6,099,939
Emp.: 549
Fiscal Year-end: 03/31/2021
Edible & Non-Edible Oil Mfr & Distr
N.A.I.C.S.: 311224
Kanubhai J. Thakkar *(Chm & Co-Mng Dir)*

Gokul Refoils and Solvent Limited - Gandhidham Unit
89 Meghpur-Borichi Nr Sharma Resort Galpadar Rd, Kutch, Anjar, 370110, Gujarat, India
Tel.: (91) 2836247075
Web Site: http://www.gokulgroup.com
Sales Range: $25-49.9 Million
Emp.: 40
Vegetable Oil Mfr
N.A.I.C.S.: 311225

Maurigo Pte.Ltd. (1)
371 Beach Road 15-11 Keypoint, 199597, Singapore, Singapore
Tel.: (65) 63464406
Sales Range: $25-49.9 Million
Emp.: 1
Palm Oil Mfr
N.A.I.C.S.: 311225

GOKUL SOLUTIONS LIMITED
6 Lyons Range Mezzanine Floor Room No 38, Kolkata, 700 001, West Bengal, India
Tel.: (91) 3340081393   In
Web Site:
   http://www.gokulsolutions.com
Rev.: $128,136
Assets: $1,659,891
Liabilities: $25,174
Net Worth: $1,634,717
Earnings: $2,222
Fiscal Year-end: 03/31/18
Textile Product Trading Services
N.A.I.C.S.: 523160
Bikash Adhikari *(CFO)*

GOKURAKUYU HOLDINGS CO., LTD.
6F Kojimachi Tsuruya Hachiman Building 2-4 Kojimachi, Chiyoda-Ku, Tokyo, 102-0083, Japan
Tel.: (81) 352750580   JP
Web Site: https://www.gokurakuyu-holdings.co.jp
Year Founded: 1980
2340—(TKS)
Rev.: $93,082,020
Assets: $74,990,450
Liabilities: $55,180,280
Net Worth: $19,810,170
Earnings: $4,607,170
Emp.: 172
Fiscal Year-end: 03/31/24
Holding Company
N.A.I.C.S.: 551112
Takahisa Shinkawa *(Co-Pres)*

GOL LINHAS AEREAS INTELIGENTES S.A.
Praca Comandante Linnneu Gomes S/N Portaria 3, Jardim Aeroporto, Sao Paulo, 04626-900, Brazil
Tel.: (55) 1121284700   BR
Web Site: https://www.voegol.com.br
Year Founded: 2001
GOLL4—(BRAZ)
Rev.: $3,743,947,353
Assets: $3,335,565,660
Liabilities: $7,955,590,388
Net Worth: ($4,620,024,728)
Earnings: ($243,744,940)
Emp.: 13,837
Fiscal Year-end: 12/31/23
Passenger Air Transportation Services
N.A.I.C.S.: 481111
Paulo Sergio Kakinoff *(VP-Ops)*

Subsidiaries:

GOL Transportes Aereos (1)
Rua Tamoios 246 Jardim Aeroporto, 04630 000, Sao Paulo, Brazil
Tel.: (55) 1150334200
Passenger Air Transport Services
N.A.I.C.S.: 481111

Smiles Fidelidade SA (53%)
Alameda Rio Negro 585 2nd Andar Bioco B, Barueri, 06454-000, Sao Paulo, Brazil
Tel.: (55) 33231569
Web Site: http://www.smiles.com.br
Sales Range: Less than $1 Million
Loyalty Program Services
N.A.I.C.S.: 561990
Andre Fehlauer *(CEO)*

GOLAN PLASTIC PRODUCTS LTD.
Kibbutz, Sha'ar HaGolan, 15145, Israel
Tel.: (972) 779021000
Web Site: https://www.pexgol.com
Year Founded: 1964
GRIN—(TAE)
Rev.: $118,867,245
Assets: $138,565,546
Liabilities: $54,050,559
Net Worth: $84,514,987
Earnings: $10,898,190
Fiscal Year-end: 12/31/23
Plastics Pipe & Pipe Fitting Manufacturing
N.A.I.C.S.: 326122
Shlomo Shaked *(VP-Fin)*

Subsidiaries:

ArgPex S.A. (1)
Auxiliary Route 40 Lot 2 Las Heras Industrial Park, Las Heras, 5543, Mendoza, Argentina
Tel.: (54) 92615773636
Web Site: https://www.argpex.com
Steel Pipe Mfr & Distr
N.A.I.C.S.: 331210

Crosspipe Systems S.A. (1)
Av Hector Gomez Cobo N 910 Sector La Negra, Antofagasta, Chile
Tel.: (56) 552688048
Web Site: https://www.crosspipe.cl
Pipes Mfr
N.A.I.C.S.: 332996

Golan Pipe Systems ApS (1)
Lollandsvej 16, 5500, Middelfart, Denmark
Tel.: (45) 64417732
Web Site: https://golan.dk
Plumbing & Heating Products Mfr & Distr
N.A.I.C.S.: 332919

Pelegol Ltd. (1)
Kibbutz Shaar HaGolan, Sha'ar HaGolan, 1514500, Israel
Tel.: (972) 543976631
Web Site: https://www.pelegol.com
Electron Beam Treatment Services
N.A.I.C.S.: 221118

GOLAR LNG LIMITED
2nd Floor S E Pearman Building 9 Par-la-Ville Road, Hamilton, HM 11, Bermuda
Tel.: (441) 2954705
Web Site: https://www.golarlng.com
Year Founded: 1946
GLNG—(NASDAQ)
Rev.: $267,740,000
Assets: $4,279,560,000
Liabilities: $1,379,386,000
Net Worth: $2,900,174,000
Earnings: $787,773,000
Emp.: 490
Fiscal Year-end: 12/31/22
Holding Company; Shipping Services
N.A.I.C.S.: 551112
Oistein Dahl *(COO-Golar Management-Norway)*

Subsidiaries:

Golar Cameroon SASU (1)
162 rue 2 371 Avenue de Gaulle Bonapriso, PO Box 3922, Douala, Cameroon
Tel.: (237) 656242588
Liquefied Natural Regasification Services
N.A.I.C.S.: 488999

Golar Management (UK) Limited (1)
6th Floor The Zig Zag 70 Victoria Street, 17 Crosswall, London, SW1E 6SQ, United Kingdom
Tel.: (44) 2070637900
Transportation of Liquid Natural Gas
N.A.I.C.S.: 483111

Golar Management Ltd. (1)
6th Floor The Zig Zag 70 Victoria Street, London, SW1E 6SQ, United Kingdom
Tel.: (44) 2070637900
Marine Environmental Services
N.A.I.C.S.: 211130

Golar Management Oslo (1)
Fridtjof Nansens Plass 4, PO Box 2008, 0160, Oslo, Norway
Tel.: (47) 23114120
Emp.: 35
Liquid Natural Gas Transport Services
N.A.I.C.S.: 488320

Golar Viking Management d.o.o. (1)
Zrinsko-Frankopanska 64, 21000, Split, Croatia
Tel.: (385) 21682182
Liquefied Natural Regasification Services
N.A.I.C.S.: 488999

GOLCAP RESOURCES CORP.
595 Burrard St Suite 3043, Vancouver, V7X 1J1, BC, Canada
Tel.: (778) 819-3793   BC
Web Site:
   https://www.golcapresources.com
Year Founded: 2019
GCRCF—(OTCIQ)
Rev.: $798
Assets: $187,650
Liabilities: $201,775
Net Worth: ($14,125)
Earnings: ($724,154)
Fiscal Year-end: 09/30/22
Mineral Exploration Services
N.A.I.C.S.: 213115
Alan Tam *(CFO)*

GOLD 50 LIMITED
Suite 16 01 Level 16 213 Miller Street, North Sydney, 2060, NSW, Australia
Tel.: (61) 283551819   AU
Web Site: https://www.g50corp.com
Year Founded: 2020
G50—(ASX)
Rev.: $17,597
Assets: $6,638,527
Liabilities: $470,329
Net Worth: $6,168,198
Earnings: ($1,577,337)
Fiscal Year-end: 06/30/23
Gold Exploration Services
N.A.I.C.S.: 212220
Mark Wallace *(Mng Dir)*

GOLD BASIN RESOURCES CORPORATION
1170-1040 West Georgia Street, Vancouver, V6E 4H1, BC, Canada
Tel.: (778) 650-5457
Web Site:
   http://www.goldbasincorp.com
GXX—(CNSX)
Assets: $12,318,194
Liabilities: $323,886
Net Worth: $11,994,308
Earnings: ($2,461,485)
Fiscal Year-end: 12/31/20
Mineral Exploration Services
N.A.I.C.S.: 213115
Michael Povey *(Pres & CEO)*

GOLD BOND GROUP LTD.
Ashdod Northern Industrial Zone Kedma Street Safety, PO Box 2727, Ashdod, 7712602, Israel
Tel.: (972) 88547000   Il
Web Site: https://goldbond.co.il
Year Founded: 1963
GOLD—(TAE)
Rev.: $51,033,567
Assets: $299,202,095
Liabilities: $60,674,125
Net Worth: $238,527,970
Earnings: $7,710,181
Emp.: 109
Fiscal Year-end: 12/31/23
Offices of Other Holding Companies
N.A.I.C.S.: 551112
Arye Kerman *(CEO)*

GOLD BULL RESOURCES CORP.
Suite 717-1030 West Georgia Street, Vancouver, V6E 2Y3, BC, Canada
Tel.: (604) 628-5623
Web Site: http://www.goldbull.ca
GBRCF—(OTCQB)
Assets: $12,519,936
Liabilities: $102,269
Net Worth: $12,417,667
Earnings: ($3,591,217)
Fiscal Year-end: 06/30/21
Mineral Exploration Services
N.A.I.C.S.: 213115
Cherie Leeden *(CEO)*

GOLD BULL RESOURCES CORP.
Suite 717-1030 West Georgia Street, Vancouver, V6E 2Y3, BC, Canada
Tel.: (778) 401-8545
Web Site: https://goldbull.ca
Year Founded: 1995
GBRC—(OTCIQ)
Assets: $12,519,936
Liabilities: $102,269
Net Worth: $12,417,667
Earnings: ($3,591,217)
Fiscal Year-end: 06/30/21
Mineral Exploration Services
N.A.I.C.S.: 213114
Cherie Leeden *(CEO)*

GOLD BY GOLD S.A.
111 avenue Victor Hugo, 75784, Paris, Cedex 16, France
Tel.: (33) 153651230
Web Site: https://www.goldbygold-groupe.com
ALGLD—(EUR)
Sales Range: $1-9.9 Million
Gold & Silver Buying & Recycling
N.A.I.C.S.: 423940
Patrick Schein *(Chm & CEO)*

GOLD CAP RESOURCES INC.
First Canadian Place Suite 5600 100 King Street West, Toronto, M5X 1C9, ON, Canada
Tel.: (888) 803-2770
Web Site:
   http://www.goldcapresources.com
Sales Range: Less than $1 Million
Gold & Copper Mining
N.A.I.C.S.: 212220

GOLD CIRCUIT ELECTRONICS

GOLD CIRCUIT ELECTRONICS

Gold Circuit Electronics—(Continued)
No 113 Shiyuan Rd, Chungli Dist,
Taoyuan, 320, Taiwan
Tel.: (886) 34612541
Web Site: https://www.gce.com.tw
Year Founded: 1981
2368—(TAI)
Rev.: $982,502,661
Assets: $1,082,482,807
Liabilities: $532,068,327
Net Worth: $550,414,479
Earnings: $115,392,651
Emp.: 4,683
Fiscal Year-end: 12/31/23
Printed Circuit Board Mfr
N.A.I.C.S.: 334412
Chen-Tse Yang *(Board of Directors, Chm & Gen Mgr)*

Subsidiaries:

Gold Circuit Electronics - Changshu Plant (1)
Jiulong Road ChangHun Ind Park Southeast, Changshu, 215500, Jiangsu, China
Tel.: (86) 51252355235
Web Site: http://www.gce.com.tw
Sales Range: $400-449.9 Million
Printed Circuit Board Mfr
N.A.I.C.S.: 334412

Gold Circuit Electronics - Chung Li Plant (1)
No 113 Xi-Yuan Road Chung Li Industrial Zone, Chung-li, 32057, Tao Yuan, Taiwan
Tel.: (886) 34612541
Sales Range: $400-449.9 Million
Printed Circuit Board Mfr
N.A.I.C.S.: 334412
Steve Yang *(Chm)*

GOLD COIN HOLDINGS SDN BHD

Suite 9-6 9th Floor Wisma UOA Damansara II 6 Changkat Semantan, Damansara Heights, Kuala Lumpur, 50490, Malaysia
Tel.: (60) 320921999
Web Site: http://www.goldcoin-group.com
Sales Range: $350-399.9 Million
Emp.: 2,400
Holding Company
N.A.I.C.S.: 551112
Gerald Emslie *(Co-CFO)*

Subsidiaries:

Gold Coin Biotechnologies Sdn. Bhd. (1)
No 19 Jalan Perigi Nanas 7/2 KS II Kawasan Perindustrian Pulau Indah, 42920, Pulau Indah, Selangor, Malaysia
Tel.: (60) 3 3102 3071
Web Site: http://www.goldcoinaqua.com
Animal Food Product Mfr
N.A.I.C.S.: 311119

Gold Coin Feed Mills (Lanka) Limited (1)
205 Vystwyk Road, Colombo, Sri Lanka
Tel.: (94) 11 2527298
Animal Food Product Mfr
N.A.I.C.S.: 311119

Gold Coin Feedmill (Dong Nai) Co Ltd (1)
Lot D12-1 1 Long Binh Techno Park Loteco, Route 15/A Long Binh Ward, Bien Hoa, Dongnai, Vietnam
Tel.: (84) 613 993586
Animal Food Product Mfr
N.A.I.C.S.: 311119

Gold Coin Feedmill (Dongguan) Co. Ltd. (1)
Wenwuchong Road Xinsha Industrial Zone, Machong, Dongguan, 523130, Guandong, China
Tel.: (86) 769 82396288
Animal Food Product Mfr
N.A.I.C.S.: 311119

Gold Coin Feedmill (Kunming) Co. Ltd. (1)
Junction of Qiaogang Kunrui Road, Taiping Town Anning, Kunming, 650301, Yunnan, China
Tel.: (86) 871 68633061
Animal Food Product Mfr
N.A.I.C.S.: 311119

Gold Coin Feedmill (Sabah) Sdn. Bhd. (1)
Pulau Enoe Ranca Ranca Industrial Complex, PO Box 382, 87000, Labuan, Malaysia
Tel.: (60) 87426535
Animal Food Product Mfr
N.A.I.C.S.: 311119

Gold Coin Specialities (Thailand) Co. Ltd. (1)
15/3 M 3 T Watkhanun Singhanakorn, Songkhla, 90330, Thailand
Tel.: (66) 74 483600 5
Animal Food Product Mfr
N.A.I.C.S.: 311119

Myanmar Gold Coin International Co., Ltd. (1)
91 C3 U Aung Kane Street Than Lwin Road, Shwe Taung Gyar Ward (1) Bahan Township, Yangon, Myanmar
Tel.: (95) 1 523026
Animal Feed Product Distr
N.A.I.C.S.: 424910

PT Gold Coin Indonesia (1)
Jl Pulau Bali No 2 Kawasan Industri Medan II Medan - Belawan Km 10 5, Medan, 20242, Sumatera Utara, Indonesia
Tel.: (62) 61 6855127
Animal Feed Product Distr
N.A.I.C.S.: 424910

PT Gold Coin Specialities (1)
Jl Raya Bekasi Km 28 Desa Medan Satria, Bekasi, 17132, Jawa Barat, Indonesia
Tel.: (62) 21 8853668
Animal Food Product Mfr
N.A.I.C.S.: 311119

GOLD CREST CO., LTD.

12th floor Otemachi Nomura Building 2-1-1 Otemachi, Chiyoda-ku, Tokyo, 100-0004, Japan
Tel.: (81) 335167111
Web Site: https://www.goldcrest.co.jp
Year Founded: 1992
8871—(TKS)
Rev.: $164,225,450
Assets: $1,347,170,880
Liabilities: $478,530,950
Net Worth: $868,639,930
Earnings: $24,807,330
Fiscal Year-end: 03/31/24
Real Estate Development Services
N.A.I.C.S.: 531390
Hidetoshi Yasukawa *(Founder, Chm & Pres)*

GOLD DRAGON ENTERPRISES INC.

12F World Trade Centre 25 Tongxing Street, Zhongshan District, Dalian, 116001, China
Tel.: (86) 13079888886   NV
Year Founded: 2008
Gold Mining Services
N.A.I.C.S.: 212220
Yuan Kun Deng *(Pres, CEO, CFO, Chief Acctg Officer, Treas & Sec)*

GOLD FIELDS LIMITED

150 Helen Road, Sandown, Sandton, 2196, South Africa
Tel.: (27) 115629700   ZA
Web Site: https://www.goldfields.com
Year Founded: 1887
GFI—(NYSE)
Rev.: $4,500,700,000
Assets: $8,226,300,000
Liabilities: $3,606,500,000
Net Worth: $4,619,800,000
Earnings: $703,300,000
Emp.: 6,297
Fiscal Year-end: 12/31/23
Gold Exploration & Mining Services
N.A.I.C.S.: 212220
Paul A. Schmidt *(CFO)*

Subsidiaries:

GFL Mining Services Limited (1)
24 St Andrews Rd, Parktown, 2193, Sandton, South Africa   (100%)
Tel.: (27) 116442400
Web Site: http://www.goldfields.co.za
Gold Ore Mining
N.A.I.C.S.: 212220

Subsidiary (Non-US):

Gold Fields Orogen Holding (BVI) Limited (2)
9 Columbus Centre Pelican Drive, Road Town, Virgin Islands (British)
Tel.: (284) 4944567
Investment Management Service
N.A.I.C.S.: 523999

Gold Fields Australia Pty Ltd (1)
Level 5/ 50 Colin St, West Perth, 6005, WA, Australia
Tel.: (61) 8 9211 9200
Web Site: http://www.goldfields.co.za
Sales Range: $50-74.9 Million
Emp.: 60
Gold Mining Services
N.A.I.C.S.: 212220

Subsidiary (Domestic):

Agnew Gold Mining Company (Pty) Limited (2)
L 5 50 Colin St, 6005, Perth, Australia   (100%)
Tel.: (61) 892119200
Web Site: http://www.goldfields.co.za
Sales Range: $100-124.9 Million
Emp.: 140
Gold Ore Mining
N.A.I.C.S.: 212220

St. Ives Gold Mining Company Pty Limited (2)
Durkin Rd, Kambalda, 6442, WA, Australia
Tel.: (61) 890881111
Web Site: http://www.goldfields.com.au
Gold Mining Services
N.A.I.C.S.: 212220

Gold Fields Ghana Limited (1)
PO Box 30740, Accra, Ghana   (71.1%)
Tel.: (233) 21228633
Web Site: http://www.goldfields.co.za
Gold Ore Mining
N.A.I.C.S.: 212220

Gold Fields Group Services Limited (1)
150 Helen Rd, Sandown, Johannesburg, 2196, Gauteng, South Africa
Tel.: (27) 115629700
Web Site: http://www.goldfields.com
Emp.: 70
Gold Mining Services
N.A.I.C.S.: 212220

Gold Fields Netherlands Services B.V. (1)
Crown Business Center Key-Point Schipholweg 103 Third Floor, Units D7-D10, 2316 XC, Leiden, Netherlands
Tel.: (31) 715247560
Emp.: 1
Gold Mining Services
N.A.I.C.S.: 212220
Femmie Vermaak *(Office Mgr)*

Minera Gold Fields Peru SA (1)
Av El Derby 55 Int 301 Santiago de Surco, Lima, Peru
Tel.: (51) 1 7070900
Web Site: http://www.goldfields.com.pe
Gold Mining Services
N.A.I.C.S.: 212220

Osisko Mining Inc. (1)
155 University Avenue Suite 1440, Toronto, M5H 3B7, ON, Canada
Tel.: (416) 363-8653
Web Site: https://www.osiskomining.com
Rev.: $131,653,662
Assets: $922,841,969
Liabilities: $171,153,234

INTERNATIONAL PUBLIC

Net Worth: $751,688,735
Earnings: ($168,681,726)
Fiscal Year-end: 12/31/2023
Gold & Other Precious Metals Exploration & Mining
N.A.I.C.S.: 213114
Peter J. Hawley *(Founder)*

St James Corporate Services Limited (1)
107 Cheapside Second Floor, London, EC2V 6DN, United Kingdom
Tel.: (44) 2077968644
Web Site: http://www.corpserv.co.uk
Sales Range: $25-49.9 Million
Emp.: 3
Management & Administrative Services
N.A.I.C.S.: 541611

GOLD HORN INTERNATIONAL ENTERPRISES GROUP LIMITED

Tower 6 The Gateway Suite 3603 36/F, Harbour Tsimshatsui, Kowloon, China (Hong Kong)
Tel.: (852) 587 5851776   HK
Year Founded: 2014
Financial Investment Services
N.A.I.C.S.: 523999
Jason Krueger *(CEO, CFO & Sec)*

GOLD HORSE INTERNATIONAL, INC.

31 TongDao South Road, Huiming District, Hohhot, 010030, Inner Mongolia, China
Tel.: (86) 471 339 7038   FL
Web Site: http://www.goldhorseinternational.com
Year Founded: 2000
Sales Range: $75-99.9 Million
Emp.: 136
Real Estate Services
N.A.I.C.S.: 531390
Lian Kuan Yang *(Chm, Pres & CEO)*

GOLD HYDROGEN LIMITED

GPO Box 801, Brisbane, 4001, QLD, Australia
Tel.: (61) 735218038   AU
Web Site: https://www.goldhydrogen.com.au
Year Founded: 2021
GHY—(ASX)
Rev.: $121,583
Assets: $15,413,118
Liabilities: $332,973
Net Worth: $15,080,145
Earnings: ($3,381,224)
Fiscal Year-end: 06/30/23
Gold Exploration Services
N.A.I.C.S.: 212220
Luke Titus *(COO)*

GOLD LINE INTERNATIONAL FINVEST LIMITED

203 MB 156 2nd Floor, Opp Madhuban Park, New Delhi, 110092, India
Tel.: (91) 1165670016
Web Site: http://www.goldlineinternationalltd.com
Year Founded: 1992
538180—(BOM)
Rev.: $158,499
Assets: $7,458,475
Liabilities: $1,061,824
Net Worth: $6,396,651
Earnings: $21,306
Emp.: 1
Fiscal Year-end: 03/31/22
Investment Advisory Services
N.A.I.C.S.: 523940
Parmod Panda *(Exec Dir)*

GOLD LION RESOURCES, INC.

AND PRIVATE COMPANIES

305 1770 Burrard Street, Vancouver, V6J 3G7, BC, Canada
Tel.: (604) 789-6128
Web Site:
http://www.goldlionresources.com
2BC—(DEU)
Rev.: $3,645
Assets: $1,896,230
Liabilities: $128,131
Net Worth: $1,768,098
Earnings: ($4,476,201)
Fiscal Year-end: 06/30/22
Mineral Exploration Services
N.A.I.C.S.: 213115
Oliver Friesen *(CEO & Sec)*

GOLD MOUNTAIN LIMITED
Tel.: (61) 731849133
Web Site:
https://www.goldmountainltd.com.au
GMN—(ASX)
Rev.: $39,958
Assets: $10,587,090
Liabilities: $122,564
Net Worth: $10,464,527
Earnings: ($2,639,874)
Fiscal Year-end: 06/30/24
Gold & Other Metal Mining
N.A.I.C.S.: 212220
Sin Pyng Teng *(Mng Dir)*

GOLD MOUNTAIN MINING CORP.
Suite 1000 1285 West Pender Street, Vancouver, V6E 4B1, BC, Canada
Tel.: (604) 309-6340
Web Site: https://www.gold-mountain.ca
GMTN—(TSX)
Rev.: $580
Assets: $25,553,836
Liabilities: $7,573,275
Net Worth: $17,980,561
Earnings: ($9,712,235)
Fiscal Year-end: 01/31/22
Business Consulting Services
N.A.I.C.S.: 522299
Kevin Smith *(CEO)*

GOLD PEAK TECHNOLOGY GROUP LIMITED
9/F Building 12W 12 Science Park West Avenue, Hong Kong Science Park, Kwai Chung, New Territories, China (Hong Kong)
Tel.: (852) 24271133
Web Site: http://www.goldpeak.com
0040—(HKG)
Year Founded: 1964
Rev.: $864,962,709
Assets: $1,130,401,357
Liabilities: $809,993,497
Net Worth: $320,407,860
Earnings: $26,835,063
Emp.: 7,510
Fiscal Year-end: 03/31/21
Micro Batteries, Electrical Accessories & Electronics Mfr
N.A.I.C.S.: 551112
Victor Chung Wing Lo *(Chm & CEO)*

Subsidiaries:

GP Batteries (China) Ltd. (1)
Gu Tang Au Industrial District, Huizhou, 516008, Guangdong, China **(100%)**
Tel.: (86) 7522264882
Web Site: http://www.gpbatteries.com
Sales Range: $200-249.9 Million
Primary & Rechargable Batteries & Powerbanks Mfr
N.A.I.C.S.: 335910

GP Batteries (Malaysia) Sdn. Bhd (1)
5 Jalan Tampoi Tujuh, Kawasan Perindustrian Tampoi, 81200, Johor Bahru, Malaysia **(100%)**
Tel.: (60) 73300033

Web Site: http://www.gpbatteries.com
Sales Range: $200-249.9 Million
N.A.I.C.S.: 335910

GP Batteries International Limited (1)
83 Clemenceau Avenue 14-01 UE Square, Singapore, 239920, Singapore **(85.8%)**
Tel.: (65) 65599800
Web Site:
https://international.gpbatteries.com
Sales Range: $500-549.9 Million
Mfr, Development & Distribution of Batteries & Battery Related Products
N.A.I.C.S.: 335910
Victor Chung Wing Lo *(Chm & CEO)*

GP Battery Marketing (HK) Ltd. (1)
8/F Building 12W 12 Science Park West Avenue Hong Kong Science Park, Hong Kong, New Territories, China (Hong Kong) **(100%)**
Tel.: (852) 24200281
Web Site: https://hk.gpbatteries.com
Sales Range: $1-9.9 Million
Primary & Rechargable Batteries & Powerbanks Mfr
N.A.I.C.S.: 335910
Richard Ku *(Mng Dir)*

GP Battery Marketing (Malaysia) Sdn. Bhd. (1)
A-05-3A Level 5 Capital 1 No 2 PJU 1A/7A Oasis Square, Oasis Damansara, 47301, Petaling Jaya, Selangor Darul Ehsan, Malaysia
Tel.: (60) 378323496
Web Site: http://www.gpbatteries.com
Sales Range: $25-49.9 Million
Batteries Whslr
N.A.I.C.S.: 423690

GP Battery Marketing (Taiwan) Ltd. (1)
Rm 1200 International Trade Bldg 205 Sec 1, Tun Hua S Rd, Taipei, 10647, Taiwan **(100%)**
Tel.: (886) 227414919
Web Site: http://www.gpbatteries.com.hk
Sales Range: $1-9.9 Million
Emp.: 30
N.A.I.C.S.: 335910

GP Electronics (Huizhou) Co., Ltd. (1)
No 76 Hui Feng Si Road, Zhong Kai Hi-Tech Ind Dev Zone, Huizhou, 516006, Guangdong, China
Tel.: (86) 7522633888
Battery Mfr
N.A.I.C.S.: 335910

GP Electronics Limited (1)
9 F Building 12W 12 Science Park West Avenue Phase 3, HK Science Park, Tai Po, China (Hong Kong) **(100%)**
Tel.: (852) 24243521
Web Site: http://www.gpe-hkg.com
Sales Range: $25-49.9 Million
Emp.: 100
Mfrs. Car Stereos & Audio Equipment
N.A.I.C.S.: 334310
Brian Li *(Mng Dir)*

GP Industries Limited (1)
83 Clemenceau Avenue 1401 UE Square, Singapore, 138543, Singapore
Tel.: (65) 63950850
Web Site: https://gp.industries
Rev.: $821,141,904
Assets: $916,592,811
Liabilities: $603,248,610
Net Worth: $313,344,201
Earnings: ($34,852,908)
Emp.: 5,400
Fiscal Year-end: 03/31/2024
Batteries Mfr & Distr
N.A.I.C.S.: 335910
Brian Yiu Cheung Li *(Exec VP)*

Subsidiary (Non-US):

Dongguan Chao Ba Batteries Co., Ltd. (2)
No 3 Hong Ye 11 Road North Hong Ye Industrial Area 138, Tangxia, Dongguan, 523710, Guangdong, China
Tel.: (86) 76987910215
Emp.: 1,500
Battery Mfr

GOLD PEAK TECHNOLOGY GROUP LIMITED

N.A.I.C.S.: 335910

Subsidiary (Domestic):

Famingo Pte Ltd. (2)
3 Fusionopolis Link 06-11 Nexus One-North, Singapore, 138543, Singapore
Tel.: (65) 63950850
Electronic Equipment Distr
N.A.I.C.S.: 423690

Subsidiary (Non-US):

GP Acoustics (HK) Limited (2)
9/F Building 12W 12 Science Park West Avenue Hong Kong Science Park, Hong Kong, New Territories, China (Hong Kong)
Tel.: (852) 24222308
Web Site: http://www.gp-industries.com
Sales Range: $25-49.9 Million
Audio Equipment Whslr
N.A.I.C.S.: 423620

GP Acoustics (Middle East) DWC-LLC (2)
385 Building-E Business Park Dubai World Central, Dubai, United Arab Emirates
Tel.: (971) 48879694
Acoustic & Electronic Product Distr
N.A.I.C.S.: 423690
Rajeev Abraham *(Gen Mgr)*

GP Acoustics (Taiwan) Limited (2)
5/F No 415 Sec 4 Xinyi Road, Xinyi District, Taipei, 11051, Taiwan
Tel.: (886) 227230868
Acoustic & Electronic Product Distr
N.A.I.C.S.: 423690

GP Acoustics (UK) Limited (2)
Eccleston Road, Tovil, Maidstone, ME15 6QP, Kent, United Kingdom
Tel.: (44) 1622 672 261
Web Site: http://www.gp-industries.com
Sales Range: $25-49.9 Million
Electronic Components Mfr
N.A.I.C.S.: 334419

GP Acoustics GmbH (2)
Nordhofstrasse 2, 45127, Essen, Germany
Tel.: (49) 201170390
Acoustic & Electronic Product Distr
N.A.I.C.S.: 423690
Klaus Spiegel *(Head-Svc & Sls Admin)*

GP Acoustics International Limited (2)
9/F Building 12W Hong Kong Science Park, Kowloon, New Territories, China (Hong Kong)
Tel.: (852) 24222308
Acoustic & Electronic Product Distr
N.A.I.C.S.: 423690
Simon Davies *(Dir-Product Plng & Design)*

Subsidiary (US):

GP Batteries (Americas) Inc. (2)
9485 Sunset Dr Ste A-225, Miami, FL 33173
Tel.: (305) 471-7717
Battery Distr
N.A.I.C.S.: 423610

Subsidiary (Non-US):

GP Batteries (Shenzhen) Co., Ltd. (2)
6/F A-1 Building Lanzhu Road Shenzhen Export Processing Zone, Haixiang Industrial Park Longgang, Shenzhen, 518118, Guangdong, China
Tel.: (86) 75589595885
Electronic Battery Mfr
N.A.I.C.S.: 335910

GP Batteries (U.K.) Limited (2)
Monument View Chelston Business Park, Wellington, Somerset, TA21 9ND, United Kingdom
Tel.: (44) 1823660044
Battery Distr
N.A.I.C.S.: 423610
Adam Stent *(Sls Mgr)*

GP Batteries (Vietnam) Limited Liability Company (2)
N3 Road C Area Hoamac Industrial, Hoamac Town Duytien Dist, Hung Yen, Hanam, Vietnam
Tel.: (84) 2263553324

Electronic Battery Mfr
N.A.I.C.S.: 335910

GP Battery (Poland) Sp. z.o.o (2)
Ul Lopuszanska 36, 02-220, Warsaw, Poland
Tel.: (48) 225009500
Electronic Battery Mfr
N.A.I.C.S.: 335910
Grzegorz Kucharski *(Sls Dir)*

GP Battery Marketing (Korea) Limited (2)
5/F WhaDeok Building 319-11, Yangjae-Dong Seocho-Gu, Seoul, Korea (South)
Tel.: (82) 25497188
Battery Distr
N.A.I.C.S.: 423610

Subsidiary (Domestic):

GP Battery Marketing (Singapore) Pte. Ltd. (2)
83 Clemenceau Avenue 14-01 UE Square, Singapore, 239920, Singapore
Tel.: (65) 65599800
Battery Distr
N.A.I.C.S.: 423610
Ken Hoon *(Sls Mgr)*

Subsidiary (Non-US):

GP Electronics (Hong Kong) Limited (2)
9/F Building 12W 12 Science Park West Avenue Hong Kong Science Park, Pak Shek Kok, Tai Po, New Territories, China (Hong Kong)
Tel.: (852) 24243521
Audio Product Distr
N.A.I.C.S.: 423690
Vincent Ng *(Asst Dir-Tech)*

GP Electronics (SZ) Limited (2)
16/F C Building Oriental Xintiandi Plaza 1003 Shen Nan Avenue, Futian District, Shenzhen, 518033, Guangdong, China
Tel.: (86) 75582463828
Electronic Products Mfr
N.A.I.C.S.: 334419

Huizhou GP Wiring Technology Ltd. (2)
106 Jin Long Rd, Xiao Jin Kou Town, Huizhou, 516023, China
Tel.: (86) 7522821866
Automotive Wire Harness & Transformer Mfr
N.A.I.C.S.: 336320
Daniel Leung *(Deputy Gen Mgr)*

KEF Japan, Inc. (2)
1st floor TFT Building East 3-6-11 Ariake, Koto-ku, Tokyo, 135-0063, Japan
Tel.: (81) 423882030
Acoustic & Electronic Product Distr
N.A.I.C.S.: 423690

Maxson Industries Limited (2)
6/F Gold Peak Bldg 30-34 Kwai Wing Rd, Kwai Chung, New Territories, China (Hong Kong)
Tel.: (852) 24243521
Electronic Equipment Whslr
N.A.I.C.S.: 423690

Ningbo GP Energy Co., Ltd. (2)
No 128 Xingguang Road, High-tech Zone, Ningbo, China
Tel.: (86) 57487913954
Web Site: http://www.nbgpe.com
Battery Mfr
N.A.I.C.S.: 335910

GPI International Limited (1)
7/F Building 16W 16 Science Park West Avenue Hong Kong Science Park, Hong Kong, New Territories, China (Hong Kong) **(100%)**
Tel.: (852) 24843333
Web Site: http://www.gpbatteries.com.hk
Sales Range: $25-49.9 Million
Emp.: 200
Management of Major Marketing & Trading
N.A.I.C.S.: 561110

Gold Peak Industries (Taiwan) Ltd. (1)
211 Chung Cheng Rd Section 2 Hukow, Hsin-chu, 303, Taiwan **(100%)**

GOLD PEAK TECHNOLOGY GROUP LIMITED

Gold Peak Technology Group Limited—(Continued)
Tel.: (886) 35992711
Web Site: http://www.gpbatteries.com
Sales Range: $100-124.9 Million
Emp.: 300
Mfr of Carbon Zinc Layer-Built Batteries
N.A.I.C.S.: 335910

Shanghai Bi Ba Batteries Co. Ltd. (1)
1279 Huadong Road, Pu Dong, Shanghai, 201209, China (100%)
Tel.: (86) 2158543051
Sales Range: $200-249.9 Million
Emp.: 1,000
N.A.I.C.S.: 335910

Shanghai JinJiang Battery Co. Ltd. (1)
30309 Jinqiao Rd 88, Shanghai, China
Tel.: (86) 2158992435
Sales Range: $50-74.9 Million
Emp.: 220
N.A.I.C.S.: 335910

Shenzhen Sylva Electrochemical Ltd. (1)
No 144 Zhongxin Rd Luohu District, Shenzhen, 58001, China (100%)
Tel.: (86) 75582172089
Web Site: http://www.permasteelisa.com
N.A.I.C.S.: 335910

Sylva Industries Limited (1)
Gold Peak Bldg 2 F, 30 Kwai Wing Rd, Kwai Chung, NT, China (Hong Kong) (100%)
Tel.: (852) 24843111
Web Site: http://www.goldpeak.com
Sales Range: $100-124.9 Million
Emp.: 300
Mfr of Micro Batteries
N.A.I.C.S.: 335910
Victor Lo *(Vice Chm)*

T.G. Battery Co. (China) Ltd. (1)
Gu Tang Au Industrial District, Huizhou, 516008, Guangdong, China
Tel.: (86) 7522380038
Web Site: http://www.gpbatteries.com
Primary & Rechargable Batteries & Powerbanks Mfr
N.A.I.C.S.: 335910

GOLD PORT CORPORATION
1681 Chestnut St Suite 400, Vancouver, V6J 4M6, BC, Canada
Tel.: (954) 684-8040   BC
Web Site:
https://www.goldportcorporation.com
Year Founded: 2016
GPOTF—(OTCQB)
Rev.: $44,357
Assets: $3,329,220
Liabilities: $178,093
Net Worth: $3,151,127
Earnings: ($1,333,196)
Fiscal Year-end: 12/31/22
Gold Exploration Services
N.A.I.C.S.: 212220
Adrian F. C. Hobkirk *(Pres & CEO)*

GOLD RAIN ENTERPRISES CORP.
No 101 Lane 411 PU-NEI Street Yen-ho-li, Chang-Hua, Taiwan
Tel.: (886) 47115298
Web Site: http://www.alona.com.tw
Year Founded: 1977
4503—(TPE)
Rev.: $5,482,381
Assets: $23,742,863
Liabilities: $5,235,907
Net Worth: $18,506,957
Earnings: ($1,169,465)
Fiscal Year-end: 12/31/22
Vending Machine Mfr
N.A.I.C.S.: 333310
Mike Cho *(Chm)*

GOLD RIDGE EXPLORATION CORP.
Suite 730 1015 - 4th Street SW, Calgary, T2R 1J4, AB, Canada
Tel.: (403) 237-0018
Year Founded: 2011
Mineral Exploration Services
N.A.I.C.S.: 212290

GOLD ROAD RESOURCES LIMITED
Level 2 26 Colin Street, West Perth, 6005, WA, Australia
Tel.: (61) 892001600
Web Site:
http://www.goldroad.com.au
GOR—(ASX)
Rev.: $255,649,409
Assets: $687,516,511
Liabilities: $132,190,141
Net Worth: $555,326,370
Earnings: $42,524,117
Emp.: 70
Fiscal Year-end: 12/31/22
Gold Exploration Services
N.A.I.C.S.: 212220
Tim Netscher *(Bd of Dirs & Chm)*

Subsidiaries:

DGO Gold Limited (1)
Suite 2 Level 9 63 Exhibition St, Melbourne, 3000, VIC, Australia
Tel.: (61) 3 9133 6251
Web Site: http://www.dgogold.com.au
Rev.: $43,385
Assets: $76,110,945
Liabilities: $1,102,210
Net Worth: $75,008,735
Earnings: ($5,339,884)
Emp.: 5
Fiscal Year-end: 06/30/2021
Gold Exploration Services
N.A.I.C.S.: 212220
Eduard Eshuys *(Chm)*

GOLD ROYALTY CORP.
1000 Catheral Place 925 West Georgia Street, Vancouver, V6C 3L2, BC, Canada
Tel.: (604) 396-3066
Web Site:
https://www.goldroyalty.com
GROY—(NYSEAMEX)
Rev.: $3,048,000
Assets: $690,994,000
Liabilities: $170,044,000
Net Worth: $520,950,000
Earnings: ($26,756,000)
Emp.: 12
Fiscal Year-end: 12/31/23
Financial Investment Services
N.A.I.C.S.: 523999
David Garofalo *(Chm, Pres & CEO)*

Subsidiaries:

Abitibi Royalties Inc. (1)
2864 chemin Sullivan, Val d'Or, J9P 0B9, QC, Canada
Tel.: (604) 824-2808
Web Site: http://www.abitibiroyalties.com
Sales Range: $1-9.9 Million
Metal Mining Services
N.A.I.C.S.: 212290
Daniel Poisson *(Sec)*

Ely Gold Royalties Inc. (1)
2833-595 Burrard St, Box 49195, Vancouver, V7X 1K8, BC, Canada
Tel.: (604) 488-1104
Web Site: http://www.elygoldinc.com
Rev.: $1,593,865
Assets: $8,802,119
Liabilities: $3,261,640
Net Worth: $5,540,478
Earnings: ($1,184,445)
Fiscal Year-end: 12/31/2019
Gold Exploration Services
N.A.I.C.S.: 212220
Trey Wasser *(Exec VP-Corp Dev)*

Subsidiary (Domestic):

DHI Minerals Ltd. (2)
789 Pender St W, Vancouver, V6C 1H2, BC, Canada
Tel.: (604) 488-1104
Sales Range: $50-74.9 Million
Emp.: 5
Property Development Services
N.A.I.C.S.: 531312

GOLD RUSH CARIBOO CORP.
393 University Avenue Suite 1810, Toronto, M5G1E6, ON, Canada
Tel.: (416) 985-7810   ON
Web Site:
http://www.goldrushcariboo.com
Year Founded: 1997
Assets: $55,278
Liabilities: $1,431,822
Net Worth: ($1,376,544)
Earnings: ($3,956,372)
Fiscal Year-end: 06/30/19
Mineral Exploration Services
N.A.I.C.S.: 213114
David Robinson *(CFO)*

GOLD SPRINGS RESOURCE CORP.
1100 1199 West Hastings Street, Vancouver, V6E 3T5, BC, Canada
Tel.: (604) 639-4527   Ca
Web Site:
https://www.goldspringresource.com
Year Founded: 2006
GRC—(OTCIQ)
Rev.: $78,384
Assets: $23,716,428
Liabilities: $756,911
Net Worth: $22,959,517
Earnings: ($1,350,960)
Emp.: 2
Fiscal Year-end: 12/31/20
Silver Mining
N.A.I.C.S.: 212220
Tina M. Woodside-Shaw *(Chm)*

Subsidiaries:

Compania Minera Malku Khota S.A. (1)
Av 20 octubre No 2685 Piso 2 Oficina 2A Edificio Csapek Sopocachi, La Paz, Bolivia
Tel.: (591) 22113901
Silver Ore Mining Services
N.A.I.C.S.: 212220

TriMetals Mining Inc. - Chile Office (1)
Padre Mariano 10 Suite 408, Santiago, Chile
Tel.: (56) 2 236 2930
Web Site: http://www.trimetalsmining.com
Silver, Gold & Copper Ore Mining Services
N.A.I.C.S.: 212220

GOLD TERRA RESOURCE CORP.
Suite 410 - 325 Howe Street, Vancouver, V6C 1Z7, BC, Canada
Tel.: (604) 689-1749
Web Site:
https://www.goldterracorp.com
Year Founded: 2007
YGT—(OTCIQ)
Rev.: $16,692
Assets: $32,383,519
Liabilities: $457,613
Net Worth: $31,925,906
Earnings: ($1,455,117)
Fiscal Year-end: 01/31/21
Mineral Exploration Services
N.A.I.C.S.: 213114
Joseph William Campbell *(COO)*

GOLD TREE RESOURCES LTD.
Suite 810-789 West Pender Street, Vancouver, V6C 1H2, BC, Canada
Tel.: (604) 687-2038   BC
Web Site:
https://www.goldtreeresources.com
Year Founded: 2019

INTERNATIONAL PUBLIC

LIVE—(CNSX)
Assets: $1,204,443
Liabilities: $39,920
Net Worth: $1,164,523
Earnings: ($95,107)
Fiscal Year-end: 10/31/23
Mineral Exploration Services
N.A.I.C.S.: 212220
Adrian Smith *(Pres & CEO)*

GOLD VALLEY PTY. LTD.
10 Kings Park Road West, Perth, 6005, WA, Australia
Tel.: (61) 892002267   AU
Web Site: https://goldvalley.com.au
Mining Services
N.A.I.C.S.: 212210
Yuzheng Xie *(Chm)*

GOLD&S CO., LTD.
712719 721 7F 166 Yeongsin-ro, Yeongdeungpo-gu, Seoul, Korea (South)
Tel.: (82) 25654874
Web Site: http://www.a1n.co.kr
Year Founded: 1994
035290—(KRS)
Rev.: $7,277,954
Assets: $14,358,945
Liabilities: $3,197,958
Net Worth: $11,160,987
Earnings: ($2,796,784)
Emp.: 88
Fiscal Year-end: 12/31/22
Educational Training Program Services
N.A.I.C.S.: 611710
Shin Seoung Ho *(CEO)*

GOLD-ZACK AG
Gold-Zack-Str 6, Mettmann, 40822, Germany
Tel.: (49) 21041490
GOZ2—(DEU)
Sales Range: Less than $1 Million
Financial Investment Services
N.A.I.C.S.: 523940
Pascal Decker *(Chm)*

GOLD79 MINES LTD.
Suite 551 - 409 Granville St, PO Box 279, Vancouver, V6C 1T2, BC, Canada
Tel.: (416) 294-6713
Web Site: https://gold79mines.com
AUU—(TSXV)
Assets: $5,073,047
Liabilities: $195,826
Net Worth: $4,877,221
Earnings: ($420,385)
Fiscal Year-end: 12/31/23
Metal Exploration Services
N.A.I.C.S.: 213114
Gary R. Thompson *(CEO)*

GOLDBANK MINING CORPORATION
702 - 889 West Pender Street, Vancouver, V6C 3B2, BC, Canada
Tel.: (604) 683-3288
Web Site:
https://www.goldbankmining.com
GLB—(TSXV)
Rev.: $206,721
Assets: $4,666,681
Liabilities: $7,836,736
Net Worth: ($3,170,054)
Earnings: ($969,608)
Fiscal Year-end: 12/31/20
Mining Exploration Services
N.A.I.C.S.: 213114
James Boyce *(Pres & CEO)*

GOLDBELL CORPORATION
47 Scotts Road 12-01/02 Goldbell

Towers, Singapore, 228233, Singapore
Tel.: (65) 68610007
Web Site:
http://www.goldbellcorp.com
Year Founded: 1980
Vehicle Leasing Services
N.A.I.C.S.: 532490
William Chua *(Chm)*

Subsidiaries:

Aviation Equipment Leasing (Australia) Pty Ltd (1)
PO Box 618, Ryde, 1680, NSW, Australia
Tel.: (61) 4403430105
Aircraft Equipment Leasing Services
N.A.I.C.S.: 532411

Aviation Equipment Leasing Pte Ltd (1)
Blk 3 35 Abingdon Road, Singapore, 499941, Singapore
Tel.: (65) 65928857
Web Site: http://www.avel.com.sg
Aircraft Equipment Leasing Services
N.A.I.C.S.: 532411
Teo Lye Seng *(Gen Mgr)*

BlueSG Pte. Ltd. (1)
16 Science Park Drive 04-01 DNV GL Technology Centre, Singapore, 118227, Singapore
Tel.: (65) 31637800
Web Site: http://www.bluesg.com.sg
Electric Vehicle Charging Services
N.A.I.C.S.: 457120
Franck Vitte *(Mng Dir)*

Goldbell Car Rental Pte Ltd (1)
10 Raeburn Park 03-10, Singapore, 088702, Singapore
Tel.: (65) 68386300
Web Site: http://www.gbcr.com.sg
Vehicle Rental Services
N.A.I.C.S.: 532111

Goldbell Equipment (Vietnam) Co., Ltd (1)
7th Floor South Building 60 Truong Son Str W 2, Tan Binh, Ho Chi Minh City, Vietnam
Tel.: (84) 835471817
Web Site: http://www.goldbell.com.vn
Industrial Equipment Rental Services
N.A.I.C.S.: 532490

Goldbell Equipment Sdn Bhd (1)
Lot 2-36 & Lot 2-38 Jalan SU 7, Seksyen 26 Persiaran Tengku Ampuan, 40400, Shah Alam, Selangor, Malaysia
Tel.: (60) 351922881
Web Site: http://www.goldbell.my
Forklift Truck Distr
N.A.I.C.S.: 423830

Goldbell Leasing (Dalian) Co., Ltd (1)
New Economic Development Zone Jin Ma Lu No 120, Fu Jia International Building Unit 27-22, Dalian, 116600, China
Tel.: (86) 41187579463801
Industrial Equipment Rental Services
N.A.I.C.S.: 532490

Goldbell Leasing (Shanghai) Co., Ltd (1)
Room 403 No 801 Qu Xi Road, Huangpu, Shanghai, 200023, China
Tel.: (86) 2154332160
Industrial Equipment Rental Services
N.A.I.C.S.: 532490

Goldbell Leasing Pte Ltd (1)
14 Benoi Road, Singapore, 629887, Singapore
Tel.: (65) 64942888
Web Site: http://www.gbl.com.sg
Industrial Equipment Rental Services
N.A.I.C.S.: 532490

STVE Pte Ltd (1)
48 Changi South Street 1, Singapore, 486130, Singapore
Tel.: (65) 65928800
Web Site: http://www.stve.com.sg
Vehicle Rental Services
N.A.I.C.S.: 532111

GOLDBELT EMPIRES LIMITED

183 Queens Road East Level 54 Hopewell Centre, Hong Kong, China (Hong Kong)
Tel.: (852) 7730692637
GBE—(TSXV)
Assets: $1,040,639
Liabilities: $1,298,743
Net Worth: ($258,104)
Earnings: ($416,777)
Mineral Exploration Services
N.A.I.C.S.: 213115
James Varanese *(Chm)*

GOLDBLOCK CAPITAL, INC.

1510-789 West Pender Street, Vancouver, V6C 1H2, BC, Canada
Tel.: (604) 980-2445
GBLK—(CNSX)
Rev.: $4,122
Assets: $452,809
Liabilities: $24,851
Net Worth: $427,957
Earnings: ($86,340)
Fiscal Year-end: 05/31/20
Mineral Exploration Services
N.A.I.C.S.: 213115
Jim Mustard *(CEO)*

GOLDBOND GROUP

Unit 3901 39/F Tower One Lippo Centre 89 Queensway, Hong Kong, China (Hong Kong)
Tel.: (852) 21115666
Web Site:
http://www.goldbondgroup.com
Rev.: $33,657,248
Assets: $90,402,049
Liabilities: $25,008,467
Net Worth: $65,393,582
Earnings: ($39,359,595)
Emp.: 32
Fiscal Year-end: 03/31/18
Financial Services
N.A.I.C.S.: 551112
Charles Yu Lung Wong *(Chm)*

GOLDCARD SMART GROUP CO., LTD.

No 158 Jinqiao Street, Hangzhou, China
Tel.: (86) 57156633333
Web Site: https://www.jinka.cn
300349—(CHIN)
Rev.: $384,571,004
Assets: $848,930,004
Liabilities: $296,175,204
Net Worth: $552,754,800
Earnings: $37,973,988
Emp.: 2,000
Fiscal Year-end: 12/31/22
Integrated Circuit Gas Meters & Measuring Control Management Systems Mfr
N.A.I.C.S.: 334514
Li Lingling *(Sec)*

Subsidiaries:

Eslink Cloud Computing Co., Ltd. (1)
Room 406 Building 4 Haichuang Technology Center No 1288, Wenyi West Road Yuhang District, Hangzhou, China
Tel.: (86) 4006665727
Emp.: 200
Information Technology Development Services
N.A.I.C.S.: 541519

Goldard Water Technology Co., Ltd. (1)
No 158 Jinqiao Street, Qiantang Area, Hangzhou, China
Tel.: (86) 57156633333
Smart Utility Solution Services
N.A.I.C.S.: 561990

Tancy Instrument Group Co., Ltd. (1)
198 Hualian Road, Cangnan County Industrial Park, Wenzhou, Zhejiang, China
Tel.: (86) 57768858028
Web Site: https://www.tancy.com
Flow Meter & Gas Application Mfr
N.A.I.C.S.: 334514

Zhejiang Tancy Ultrasonic Technology Co., Ltd. (1)
No 3468 Tonfu Road Xizhen, Cangnan County, Wenzhou, Zhejiang, China
Tel.: (86) 57768883322
Flow Meter & Gas Application Mfr
N.A.I.C.S.: 334514

GOLDCLIFF RESOURCE CORPORATION

Suite 400 - 789 W Pender Street, Vancouver, V6C 1H2, BC, Canada
Tel.: (250) 764-8879   BC
Web Site: https://www.goldcliff.com
Year Founded: 1986
GCFFF—(OTCIQ)
Rev.: $4,487
Assets: $667,947
Liabilities: $186,290
Net Worth: $481,657
Earnings: ($968,360)
Emp.: 5
Fiscal Year-end: 10/31/22
Gold Mining & Exploration Services
N.A.I.C.S.: 212220
Graham H. Scott *(Sec)*

GOLDCOIN HEALTH FOODS LIMITED

66/392 Pragatinagar Naranpura, Ahmedabad, 380 013, India
Tel.: (91) 9426768644
Web Site:
https://www.goldcoinhealthfoods.in
Year Founded: 1989
538542—(BOM)
Rev.: $7,354
Assets: $252,618
Liabilities: $71,880
Net Worth: $180,739
Earnings: ($124,445)
Fiscal Year-end: 03/31/23
Dairy Product Mfr & Distr
N.A.I.C.S.: 311512
Devang P. Shah *(Mng Dir)*

GOLDCREST CORPORATION LIMITED

3rd Floor Devidas Mansion Mereweather Road Behind Taj Hotel, Colaba, Mumbai, 400 039, India
Tel.: (91) 22 2283 7489   In
Web Site:
http://www.goldcrestgroup.com
Year Founded: 1983
505576—(BOM)
Rev.: $2,704,931
Assets: $9,118,397
Liabilities: $1,320,222
Net Worth: $7,798,175
Earnings: $1,297,375
Emp.: 11
Fiscal Year-end: 03/31/21
Real Estate Development Services
N.A.I.C.S.: 531390
Anupa Tanna Shah *(CEO & Mng Dir)*

GOLDCUP ELECTRIC APPARATUS CO., LTD.

No 580 Dongfanghong Middle Road, Hi-tech Industrial Development Zone, Changsha, 410205, Hunan, China
Tel.: (86) 4009002533
Web Site:
https://www.goldcupelectric.com
Year Founded: 1999
002533—(SSE)
Rev.: $1,853,664,696
Assets: $1,073,025,252
Liabilities: $515,162,700
Net Worth: $557,862,552
Earnings: $52,033,644
Emp.: 4,000
Fiscal Year-end: 12/31/22
Electric Wires & Cables Mfr & Distr
N.A.I.C.S.: 335931
Wu Xueyu *(Chm)*

Subsidiaries:

Chengdu Sandian Cables Co., Ltd. (1)
No 39 Jintai Road, Chengdu, Sichuan, China
Tel.: (86) 2885044988
Cable Mfr
N.A.I.C.S.: 335921

Gold Cup Electric Hengyang Cables Co., Ltd. (1)
Baishazhou Industrial Park, Yanfeng district, Hengyang, Hunan, China
Tel.: (86) 7348496993
Cable Mfr
N.A.I.C.S.: 335921

GOLDEN AGE EXPLORATION LTD.

501-815 Hornby Street, Vancouver, V6Z 2E6, BC, Canada
Tel.: (604) 969-4070
Web Site:
https://www.goldenexploration.com
Year Founded: 2021
GDN—(CNSX)
Mineral Exploration Services
N.A.I.C.S.: 212390
Aziz-Ur Rehman *(CFO)*

GOLDEN AGRI-RESOURCES LTD.

108 Pasir Panjang Road 06-00 Golden Agri Plaza, Singapore, 118535, Singapore
Tel.: (65) 65900800
Web Site:
https://www.goldenagri.com.sg
Year Founded: 1996
E5H—(OTCIQ)
Rev.: $11,438,798,000
Assets: $9,902,072,000
Liabilities: $4,647,723,000
Net Worth: $5,254,349,000
Earnings: $846,540,000
Emp.: 99,800
Fiscal Year-end: 12/31/22
Holding Company; Crude Palm Oil Producer & Distr
N.A.I.C.S.: 551112
Muktar Widjaja *(Pres)*

Subsidiaries:

GAR Pakistan (Pvt.) Limited (1)
9th Floor Al-Tijarah Centre Shahra-e-Faisal, Karachi, Pakistan
Tel.: (92) 2134169360
Palm Oil Mfr & Distr
N.A.I.C.S.: 311225

Gemini Edibles & Fats India Private Limited (1)
Freedom House Opp SBI Executive Enclave 8-2-334/70 71 Road No 5, Banjara Hills, Hyderabad, 500 034, Telangana, India
Tel.: (91) 4067357857
Web Site: https://www.gefindia.com
Edible Oil Mfr
N.A.I.C.S.: 311225

Golden Agri International (M) Trading Sdn. Bhd. (1)
D-05-05 Level 5 Block D Sky Park One City Jalan USJ 25/1, 47650, Subang Jaya, Selangor, Malaysia
Tel.: (60) 351150205
Palm Oil Mfr & Distr
N.A.I.C.S.: 311225

Golden Agri Resources (India) Private Limited (1)
5th Floor Unit-A Plot No 58 Sector 44, Gurgaon, 122 001, Haryana, India
Tel.: (91) 1244896611
Palm Oil Mfr & Distr

GOLDEN AGRI-RESOURCES LTD.

Golden Agri-Resources Ltd.—(Continued)
N.A.I.C.S.: 311225

Golden Agri-Resources Colombia S.A.S. (1)
Carrera 1 22-58 Piso 4, 470001, Santa Marta, Colombia
Tel.: (57) 3172180237
Palm Oil Mfr & Distr
N.A.I.C.S.: 311225

Golden Agri-Resources Iberia, S.L. (1)
Paseo General Martinez Campos 46-2 A, 28010, Madrid, Spain
Tel.: (34) 910607316
Crude Palm Oil Mfr
N.A.I.C.S.: 311224

Ningbo Shining Gold Cereal Oil Port Co., Ltd
No 1 Huanghe N Rd Beilun, 315800, Ningbo, China
Tel.: (86) 57427688818
Emp.: 102
Palm Oil Refining Services
N.A.I.C.S.: 311225
Shijie Wang *(Gen Mgr)*

PT Dami Mas Sejahtera (1)
Sinarmasland Plaza Tower 2 Lt 28-32 Jl MH Thamrin Kav 22, Jakarta, 10350, Indonesia
Tel.: (62) 2150338899
Web Site: https://www.damimas.com
Crude Palm Oil Mfr
N.A.I.C.S.: 311224
Ivana Syahril *(Officer-Sls)*

PT Djuandasawit Lestari (1)
Jl Garuda Dempo 42 Rt 001 03 Lubuk Linggau Ilir, Lubuk Linggau Barat, Lubuklinggau, 31611, South Sumatra, Indonesia
Tel.: (62) 733320992
Palm Oil Mfr
N.A.I.C.S.: 311224

PT Kreasi Mas Indah (1)
Jl Rawa Terate II No 8, Kawasan Industri Pulo Gadung, Jakarta, 13930, Indonesia
Tel.: (62) 214601672
Web Site: https://kreasimas.wordpress.com
Soft Drinks Mfr
N.A.I.C.S.: 312111

PT Kresna Duta Agroindo (1)
Jl Sukarno Hatta 183 RT 001 01, Paal Merah Jambi Selatan, Jambi, 36139, Indonesia
Tel.: (62) 741571855
Palm Oil Suppliers
N.A.I.C.S.: 311225

PT Purimas Sasmita (1)
Plz BII Tower II 30th Fl, Jl M H Thamrin Kav 22, Jakarta, 10350, Indonesia
Tel.: (62) 213181388
Palm Oil Mfr
N.A.I.C.S.: 311225

PT Sinar Kencana Inti Perkasa (1)
Sinar Mas Land Plaza Tower II 30th Floor Jl M H Thamrin No 51, Gondangdia Menteng, Jakarta, 10350, Indonesia
Tel.: (62) 213188899
Palm Oil Cultivation Services
N.A.I.C.S.: 111120

PT Sinar Mas Agro Resources & Technology, Tbk (1)
Sinar Mas Land Plaza Menara 2 Lt 28-30 Jl M H Thamrin No 51, Jakarta, 10350, Indonesia
Tel.: (62) 2150338899
Web Site: https://www.smart-tbk.com
Rev.: $4,320,493,852
Assets: $2,579,180,613
Liabilities: $1,340,653,830
Net Worth: $1,238,526,783
Earnings: $59,606,478
Emp.: 24,246
Fiscal Year-end: 12/31/2023
Palm Oil Mfr
N.A.I.C.S.: 311224
Jo Daud Dharsono *(Chm)*

PT Sinarmas Distribusi Nusantara (1)
BSD Green Office Park 9 GOP 9 1st Floor Wing B Jl BSD Grand Boulevard, BSD City, Tangerang, 15345, Indonesia
Tel.: (62) 2150560021
Logistic Services
N.A.I.C.S.: 541614

PT Soci Mas (1)
Jl Pulau Irian Kawasan Industri Medan No 2 Saentis, Percut, Northern Sumatra, Indonesia
Tel.: (62) 616851582
Web Site: https://www.soci.co.id
Sales Range: $125-149.9 Million
Fatty Acids Glycerine Mfr
N.A.I.C.S.: 325199

PT Sumber Indahperkasa (1)
Jl MH Thamrin Kav 22 51 Plz BII Lt 30, Gondangdia Menteng, Jakarta, Indonesia
Tel.: (62) 213181388
Palm Oil Mfr
N.A.I.C.S.: 311224
Daud Dharsono *(Pres)*

PT Tapian Nadenggan (1)
Jl Wolter Monginsidi 14 16 Polonia, Medan Polonia, Medan, 20157, North Sumatra, Indonesia
Tel.: (62) 614556566
Investment Holding Services
N.A.I.C.S.: 541618

PT Tarunacipta Kencana (1)
Graha Cempaka Mas E26 Jl LetJend Soeprapto, Jakarta Pusat, 10640, Indonesia
Tel.: (62) 214267068
Web Site: http://www.tck.co.id
Ship Chartering Services
N.A.I.C.S.: 483111

Parsec Innovation Labs LLC (1)
7101 Northland Cir N, Minneapolis, MN 55428
Tel.: (612) 286-1500
Web Site: https://parseclabs.com
Software Technology Services
N.A.I.C.S.: 541513

Shining Gold Foodstuffs (Ningbo) Co., Ltd (1)
No 1 Huanghe N Rd Beilun, Beilun, Ningbo, 305800, China
Tel.: (86) 57486888188
Web Site: https://www.gar-china.com
Palm Oil Refining Services
N.A.I.C.S.: 311225

Shining Gold Oilseed Crushing (Ningbo) Co., Ltd (1)
No 1 N Rd Beilun District, Ningbo, 315800, China **(100%)**
Tel.: (86) 57486888188
Oilseed Crushing & Refinery Operations
N.A.I.C.S.: 311224

GOLDEN ARROW RESOURCES CORPORATION

Suite 411 837 West Hastings Street, Vancouver, V6C 3N6, BC, Canada
Tel.: (604) 687-1828 **BC**
Web Site: https://www.goldenresources.com
Year Founded: 2004
GARWF—(OTCQB)
Rev.: $5,891
Assets: $19,559,057
Liabilities: $352,712
Net Worth: $19,206,345
Earnings: ($4,540,632)
Fiscal Year-end: 12/31/20
Metal Exploration Services
N.A.I.C.S.: 213114
Joseph Grosso *(Chm, Pres & CEO)*

Subsidiaries:

Golden Arrow Resources Corporation - Exploration Services (1)
Sobremonte 579, Mendoza, CP 5500, Argentina
Tel.: (54) 261 425 9567
Web Site: https://www.goldenarrowresources.com
Emp.: 15
Gold Mining Services
N.A.I.C.S.: 212220
Brian McEwen *(VP-Exploration & Dev)*

GOLDEN BALES CORPORATION

Km 14 After Panacan Sub-station, Panacan, Davao, 8000, Philippines
Tel.: (63) 822349429
Web Site: http://www.goldenbales.com.ph
Year Founded: 2002
Paper Recycling Materials Buyer/Seller & Corrugated Cardboard Boxes Mfr
N.A.I.C.S.: 322211
Edna Ko *(Controller)*

GOLDEN BIOTECHNOLOGY CORP.

15F No 27-6 Sec 2 Zhongzheng E Rd, Tamsui Dist, New Taipei City, 251, Taiwan
Tel.: (886) 228086006
Web Site: https://www.goldenbiotech.com
Year Founded: 2002
4132—(TAI)
Biotechnology Research & Development Services
N.A.I.C.S.: 541714
Sheng-Yung Liu *(Chm)*

GOLDEN BRIDGE ELECTECH INC.

3F No 6 Lane 270 Section 3 Beishen Road, ShenKeng Dist, New Taipei City, Taiwan
Tel.: (886) 226627300
Web Site: https://www.gbe.com.tw
6133—(TAI)
Rev.: $32,942,966
Assets: $63,891,753
Liabilities: $27,544,098
Net Worth: $36,347,656
Earnings: $362,438
Emp.: 1,500
Fiscal Year-end: 12/31/23
Electrical Wires Mfr
N.A.I.C.S.: 238210

GOLDEN BRIDGE VIETNAM SECURITIES JOINT STOCK COMPANY

4 Lieu Giai Street, Ba Dinh District, Hanoi, Vietnam
Tel.: (84) 4 3793 0880
Emp.: 60
Investment Banking & Securities Dealing
N.A.I.C.S.: 523150
Jong Woong Bak *(Chm)*

GOLDEN CARPETS LIMITED

8-2-596/5/B/1 Road No 10 Banjara Hills, Hyderabad, 500 034, Telangana, India
Tel.: (91) 4066771111
Web Site: https://www.goldencarpets.com
531928—(BOM)
Rev.: $84,088
Assets: $640,209
Liabilities: $640,561
Net Worth: ($352)
Earnings: ($23,464)
Emp.: 8
Fiscal Year-end: 03/31/23
Woven Carpet Mfr
N.A.I.C.S.: 314110
Krishna Naik *(Chm & Mng Dir)*

GOLDEN CENTURY INTERNATIONAL HOLDINGS GROUP LIMITED

45/F Tower 1 Times Square, Causeway Bay, China (Hong Kong)
Tel.: (852) 28020006 **HK**
Web Site: http://www.gci.com.hk
0091—(HKG)
Rev.: $5,705,243
Assets: $15,858,833

INTERNATIONAL PUBLIC

Liabilities: $31,969,223
Net Worth: ($16,110,390)
Earnings: ($19,911,293)
Emp.: 40
Fiscal Year-end: 12/31/22
Semiconductor Product Mfr
N.A.I.C.S.: 334413
Jibiao Pan *(Chm & CEO)*

Subsidiaries:

International Standard Resources Securities Limited (1)
Room 1506 15/F Office Plus No 93-103 Wing Lok Street, Sheung Wan, China (Hong Kong)
Tel.: (852) 26132188
Web Site: http://www.isrsecurities.com
Security Trading Platform Services
N.A.I.C.S.: 523210

Strong Way International Limited (1)
Unit 602 6/F Sun Cheong Industrial Building 1 Cheung Shun Streert, Lai Chi Kok, Kowloon, China (Hong Kong)
Tel.: (852) 2642 6588
Web Site: http://www.strongway.com.hk
Emp.: 60
Computer Peripheral Distr
N.A.I.C.S.: 423430

GOLDEN COAST COMPANY

140 - 26th of July Street Zamalek, Cairo, Egypt
Tel.: (20) 227360147
Web Site: http://www.goldencoast-eg.com
Year Founded: 2004
GOCO.CA—(EGX)
Sales Range: Less than $1 Million
Hotel Operator
N.A.I.C.S.: 721110

GOLDEN COAST ENERGY CORP.

Suite 620 - 650 West Georgia Street, Vancouver, V6B 4N9, BC, Canada
Tel.: (604) 687-7551 **BC**
Web Site: http://www.sunridge-energy.com
Year Founded: 2006
Sales Range: Less than $1 Million
Oil & Gas Exploration Services
N.A.I.C.S.: 211120
David Gurvey *(CFO)*

GOLDEN CONCORD HOLDINGS LIMITED

Unit 1703-1706 Level 17 Intl Commerce Centre 1 Austin Road West, Kowloon, China (Hong Kong)
Tel.: (852) 2526 8368 **HK**
Web Site: http://www.gcl-power.com
Year Founded: 1999
Emp.: 30,000
Holding Company; Green Energy Technologies & Services
N.A.I.C.S.: 551112
Gongshan Zhu *(Chm)*

Subsidiaries:

GCL New Energy Holdings Limited (1)
Unit 1707A Level 17 International Commerce Centre 1 Austin Road West, Kowloon, China (Hong Kong)
Tel.: (852) 26069200
Web Site: http://www.gclnewenergy.com
Rev.: $130,439,603
Assets: $1,707,763,262
Liabilities: $868,447,570
Net Worth: $839,315,693
Earnings: ($180,888,692)
Emp.: 792
Fiscal Year-end: 12/31/2022
Holding Company
N.A.I.C.S.: 551112
Xiaoyan Hu *(Exec Dir)*

GCL System Integration Technology Co., Ltd (1)

No 28 Xinqing Road, Suzhou Industrial Park, Suzhou, Jiangsu, China
Tel.: (86) 51269832999
Web Site: https://en.gclsi.com
Rev.: $1,172,846,844
Assets: $1,429,451,712
Liabilities: $1,112,755,644
Net Worth: $316,696,068
Earnings: $8,328,528
Fiscal Year-end: 12/31/2022
Solar Cell Components Mfr & Distr
N.A.I.C.S.: 334413
Zhu Yufeng *(Chm)*

GCL Technology Holdings Limited (1)
GCL Energy Center No 28 Xinqing Road, Suzhou Industrial Park, Suzhou, China (Hong Kong)
Tel.: (852) 25268368
Web Site: http://www.gcltech.com
Rev.: $4,974,867,772
Assets: $11,847,096,256
Liabilities: $5,539,648,455
Net Worth: $6,307,447,801
Earnings: $2,143,325,072
Emp.: 11,527
Fiscal Year-end: 12/31/2022
Power & Steam Generation Facility Operator
N.A.I.C.S.: 221112
Gongshan Zhu *(Founder)*

GOLDEN CREST EDUCATION & SERVICES LIMITED
62A Dr Meghnad Shah Sarani Room No 2 2nd Floor Southern Avenue, Kolkata, 700 029, West Bengal, India
Tel.: (91) 8232009012   In
Web Site: https://www.goldencrest.in
Year Founded: 1982
540062—(BOM)
Rev.: $40,028
Assets: $1,436,725
Liabilities: $6,627
Net Worth: $1,430,098
Earnings: $3,759
Fiscal Year-end: 03/31/21
Educational Support Services
N.A.I.C.S.: 611710
Yogesh Lama *(Exec Dir)*

GOLDEN CROSS RESOURCES LIMITED
Suite 301 66 Berry Street, North Sydney, 2060, NSW, Australia
Tel.: (61) 299221266   AU
Web Site: https://www.goldencross.com.au
GCR—(ASX)
Rev.: $3,339
Assets: $8,776,042
Liabilities: $5,604,968
Net Worth: $3,171,074
Earnings: ($793,937)
Emp.: 4
Fiscal Year-end: 06/30/24
Minerals Exploration
N.A.I.C.S.: 213115
Jordan G. Li *(Exec Chm & Chm)*

Subsidiaries:

Golden Cross Operations Pty. Ltd. (1)
22 Edgeworth David Ave, Hornsby, 2077, NSW, Australia
Tel.: (61) 2 9472 3500
Web Site: http://www.goldencross.com.au
Sales Range: $50-74.9 Million
Metal Exploration Services
N.A.I.C.S.: 213114
Kim Stanton-Cook *(Mng Dir)*

GOLDEN DEEPS LIMITED
Level 1 8 Parliament Place, West Perth, 6005, WA, Australia
Tel.: (61) 894817833
Web Site: http://goldendeeps.com
GED—(ASX)
Rev.: $138,566
Assets: $7,718,589
Liabilities: $206,271
Net Worth: $7,512,318
Earnings: ($656,199)
Emp.: 10
Fiscal Year-end: 06/30/24
Minerals Exploration
N.A.I.C.S.: 213115
Scott Matthewson *(Board of Directors & Exec Gen Mgr-Ops)*

GOLDEN EAGLE RETAIL GROUP LIMITED
Unit1206 12/F Tower 2 Lippo Centre 89 Queensway, Hong Kong, China (Hong Kong)
Tel.: (852) 31163918
Web Site: http://www.geretail.com
3308—(OTCIQ)
Rev.: $856,178,540
Assets: $3,689,772,211
Liabilities: $2,496,057,332
Net Worth: $1,193,714,878
Earnings: $238,072,406
Emp.: 2,810
Fiscal Year-end: 12/31/20
Department Store Owner & Operator
N.A.I.C.S.: 455110
Roger Hung Wang *(Chm & CEO)*

GOLDEN ENERGY AND RESOURCES LIMITED
20 Cecil Street 05-05 PLUS, Singapore, 49705, Singapore
Tel.: (65) 68387500   SG
Web Site: https://gear.com.sg
Year Founded: 1995
AUE—(SES)
Rev.: $5,616,803,000
Assets: $4,896,708,000
Liabilities: $2,915,938,000
Net Worth: $1,980,770,000
Earnings: $1,280,847,000
Fiscal Year-end: 12/31/22
Construction Services
N.A.I.C.S.: 236220
Fuganto Widjaja *(CEO-Grp)*

GOLDEN ENERGY OFFSHORE SERVICES AS
St Olavs Plass 1, 6002, Alesund, Norway
Tel.: (47) 70102660
Web Site: https://www.geoff.no
Year Founded: 2013
GEOS—(EUR)
Rev.: $8,307,039
Assets: $54,917,072
Liabilities: $45,914,350
Net Worth: $9,002,722
Earnings: ($7,370,006)
Fiscal Year-end: 12/31/21
Offshore Services
N.A.I.C.S.: 211130
Sten Gustavsen *(Chm)*

GOLDEN FAITH GROUP HOLDINGS LIMITED
15/F Honest Building 9-11 Leighton Road, Causeway Bay, Hong Kong, China (Hong Kong)
Tel.: (852) 3905 4567   Ky
Web Site: http://www.goldenfaith.hk
Year Founded: 1987
2863—(HKG)
Rev.: $32,872,230
Assets: $41,389,295
Liabilities: $4,284,587
Net Worth: $37,104,708
Earnings: $2,224,647
Emp.: 287
Fiscal Year-end: 09/30/21
Electrical Contracting Services
N.A.I.C.S.: 238210
On Wah Yung *(Chm & Mng Dir)*

GOLDEN FOREST, S.A.
Villa Rosario, Panama, Panama
Tel.: (507) 221 2749
Year Founded: 1994
GOLD—(PAN)
Sales Range: Less than $1 Million
Forestry Services
N.A.I.C.S.: 115310
Arthuro Donaldo Melo *(Pres)*

GOLDEN FRONTIER BERHAD
5th Floor No 11 Lorong Kinta, 10400, Penang, Malaysia
Tel.: (60) 42262226   MY
Web Site: http://www.goldenfrontier.com.my
Year Founded: 1972
Sales Range: $25-49.9 Million
Emp.: 300
Carton Mfr
N.A.I.C.S.: 322299
Kelvin Seang Chiat Khor *(Exec Dir)*

Subsidiaries:

Golden Frontier Packaging Sdn. Bhd. (1)
Lot 616 & 617 Mukim 12 Ladang Valdor, Seberang Prai Selatan, Sungai Bakap, 14200, Penang, Malaysia
Tel.: (60) 45824011
Web Site: http://www.goldenfrontier.com.my
Sales Range: $125-149.9 Million
Corrugated Fibreboard Cartons Mfr
N.A.I.C.S.: 326199
Khor Leong *(Gen Mgr)*

GOLDEN GOLIATH RESOURCES LTD.
Suite 618 - 688 West Hastings Street, Vancouver, V6B 1P1, BC, Canada
Tel.: (604) 682-2950
Web Site: https://www.goldengoliath.com
GGZA—(DEU)
Rev.: $9,149
Assets: $3,106,440
Liabilities: $265,475
Net Worth: $2,840,965
Earnings: ($412,246)
Fiscal Year-end: 08/31/23
Gold & Silver Exploration Services
N.A.I.C.S.: 212220
J. Paul Sorbara *(Pres & CEO)*

Subsidiaries:

Minera Delta S.A. de C.V. (1)
C Juan Felipe Orozco 516 Col San Felipe, 31240, Chihuahua, Chih, Mexico
Tel.: (52) 6144146226
Metal Mining Exploration Service
N.A.I.C.S.: 213114

GOLDEN GRASS, INC.
31 Ibn Khuzaimah St, PO Box 21570, Riyadh, 11485, Saudi Arabia
Tel.: (966) 14783024
Web Site: http://www.goldengrass.com
Year Founded: 1982
Sales Range: $50-74.9 Million
Emp.: 300
N.A.I.C.S.: 111992
Turki Faisal Rasheed *(Chm & Pres)*

GOLDEN GUINEA BREWERIES PLC
Aba Road Afara Layout, Umuahia, Abia, Nigeria
Tel.: (234) 222616
Year Founded: 1962
GOLDBREW—(NIGE)
Rev.: $10,011
Assets: $12,212,780
Liabilities: $5,273,308
Net Worth: $6,939,472
Earnings: ($754,240)
Fiscal Year-end: 03/31/19
Distilled Alcoholic Beverage Merchant Whslr
N.A.I.C.S.: 424820
J. C. Onyearugbulem *(Chm)*

GOLDEN HARP RESOURCES INC.
777 Hornby Street Suite 2080, Vancouver, V6Z 1S4, BC, Canada
Tel.: (604) 683-7361   BC
Year Founded: 2006
GHR—(TSXV)
Assets: $10,493
Liabilities: $329,961
Net Worth: ($319,468)
Earnings: ($97,884)
Fiscal Year-end: 06/30/24
Gold & Metal Mining & Exploration Services
N.A.I.C.S.: 212220
Anthony Shaun Maskerine *(CEO)*

GOLDEN HARVEST ENTERTAINMENT (HOLDINGS) LTD.
16 F The Peninsula Office Tower 18 Middle Rd, Tsim Tsa Tsui, China (Hong Kong)
Tel.: (852) 23528222
Web Site: http://www.goldenharvest.com
Year Founded: 1972
Sales Range: $25-49.9 Million
Emp.: 100
Film Production & Distribution & Print Processing Services
N.A.I.C.S.: 512120

GOLDEN HEAVEN GROUP HOLDINGS LTD.
No 8 Banhouhaichuan Rd, Xiqin Town Yanping District, Nanping, 353001, Fujian, China
Tel.: (86) 5998508022   Ky
Web Site: https://ir.jsyoule.com
Year Founded: 2020
GDHG—(NASDAQ)
Rev.: $38,517,742
Assets: $71,762,697
Liabilities: $31,964,010
Net Worth: $39,798,687
Earnings: $13,580,375
Emp.: 612
Fiscal Year-end: 09/30/21
Holding Company
N.A.I.C.S.: 551112
Jinguang Gong *(CFO)*

GOLDEN HOUSE LTD.
Moshe Dayan 66, Tel Aviv, 67320, Israel
Tel.: (972) 1800300801
Web Site: https://www.goldenhouse.co.il
Year Founded: 1982
GOHO—(TAE)
Rev.: $16,890,178
Assets: $174,043,650
Liabilities: $77,179,720
Net Worth: $96,863,930
Earnings: $4,461,113
Emp.: 148
Fiscal Year-end: 12/31/23
Women Healthcare Services
N.A.I.C.S.: 621610

GOLDEN LADY S.P.A.
Via Giacomo Leopardi 3 5, I 46043, Castiglione della Stiviere, MN, Italy
Tel.: (39) 0376941211
Web Site: http://www.goldenlady.com
Year Founded: 1967
Sales Range: $350-399.9 Million
Emp.: 3,000
Women's Hosiery Mfr
N.A.I.C.S.: 315120

GOLDEN LADY S.P.A.

Golden Lady S.p.A.—(Continued)

Subsidiaries:

Kayser-Roth Corporation (1)
102 Corporate Ctr Blvd, Greensboro, NC 27408 **(100%)**
Tel.: (336) 852-2030
Web Site: http://www.kayser-roth.com
Sales Range: $350-399.9 Million
Emp.: 1,600
Legwear & Apparel Mfr & Distr
N.A.I.C.S.: 315120
Kevin Toomey *(Pres & CEO)*

Division (Domestic):

Kayser-Roth Corporation (2)
330 5th Ave 14th Fl, New York, NY 10001-3101
Tel.: (212) 613-4500
Web Site: http://www.kayser-roth.com
Sales Range: $25-49.9 Million
Emp.: 30
Legwear & Apparel Mfr & Distr
N.A.I.C.S.: 424350
Liz Gardea *(Dir-Intimates Dev)*

GOLDEN LAKE EXPLORATION, INC.
1240789 W Pender St, Vancouver, V6C 1H2, BC, Canada
Tel.: (604) 683-3995
Web Site: https://www.goldenlakex.com
GOLXF—(OTCQB)
Rev.: $34,127
Assets: $7,443,933
Liabilities: $49,413
Net Worth: $7,394,520
Earnings: ($940,168)
Emp.: 3
Fiscal Year-end: 11/30/23
Mineral Exploration Services
N.A.I.C.S.: 213115
Michael B. England *(Pres & CEO)*

GOLDEN LAND BERHAD
A-09-03 Empire Tower Empire Subang Jalan SS16/1, 47500, Subang Jaya, Selangor, Malaysia
Tel.: (60) 356118844 **MY**
Web Site: https://www.glbhd.com
Year Founded: 1994
GLBHD—(KLS)
Rev.: $17,578,870
Assets: $135,333,652
Liabilities: $56,925,725
Net Worth: $78,407,927
Earnings: ($3,042,725)
Emp.: 1,489
Fiscal Year-end: 06/30/23
Oil Palm Plantation Services
N.A.I.C.S.: 111191
Yap Phing Cern *(CEO)*

GOLDEN LEAF HOLDINGS LTD.
82 Richmond Street East, Toronto, M5C 1P1, ON, Canada
Tel.: (416) 848-7744 **ON**
Web Site: http://www.goldenleafholdings.com
Year Founded: 2011
CHALF—(OTCEM)
Rev.: $21,909,156
Assets: $28,018,011
Liabilities: $22,545,813
Net Worth: $5,472,198
Earnings: ($10,028,810)
Fiscal Year-end: 12/31/20
Holding Company
N.A.I.C.S.: 551112
John Varghese *(Chm)*

Subsidiaries:

GL Management, Inc. (1)
226 E Howe Rd, Kent, OH 44240
Tel.: (330) 678-9962
Cannabis Oil Mfr
N.A.I.C.S.: 111191

GOLDEN LEGAND LEASING & FINANCE LTD.
202 Shri Ramkrishna Chambers Plot No 67B TPS-IV Linking Road, Khar, Mumbai, 400052, India
Tel.: (91) 2226000457
Web Site: https://www.gllfl.com
Equipment Rental Services
N.A.I.C.S.: 532490
Divya Singh *(Mng Dir)*

GOLDEN LIME PUBLIC COMPANY LIMITED
No 89 Cosmo Office Park 6th Floor Unit H Popular Road Banmai, Pakkret, Nonthaburi, 11120, Thailand
Web Site: http://www.goldenlime.co.th
SUTHA—(THA)
Rev.: $42,152,443
Assets: $64,621,364
Liabilities: $35,096,934
Net Worth: $29,524,430
Earnings: $1,346,261
Emp.: 488
Fiscal Year-end: 12/31/23
Lime Products Mfr & Distr
N.A.I.C.S.: 327410
Sripop Sarasas *(Chm)*

Subsidiaries:

Thai Marble Corp., Ltd. (1)
565/1 Soi Ramkhamhaeng 39 Thepleela Ramkhamhaeng Rd Plubpla, Wangthonglang, Bangkok, 10310, Thailand
Tel.: (66) 23197972
Web Site: https://thaimarble.co.th
Calcium Carbonate Power Distr
N.A.I.C.S.: 424490

GOLDEN LONG TENG DEVELOPMENT CO., LTD.
No 33 Mingcheng 4th Road, Gushan District, Kaohsiung, 80457, Taiwan
Tel.: (886) 75557880
3188—(TPE)
Rev.: $33,191,883
Assets: $211,841,197
Liabilities: $138,483,601
Net Worth: $73,357,596
Earnings: $2,730,075
Fiscal Year-end: 12/31/22
Real Estate Manangement Services
N.A.I.C.S.: 531311
Huang Ching-Chia *(CEO)*

GOLDEN MEDITECH HOLDINGS LIMITED
No 11 Wan Yuan Street Beijing Economic Technological Development Area, Beijing, 100176, China
Tel.: (86) 1067877171 **Ky**
Web Site: http://www.goldenmeditech.com
Year Founded: 2000
0801—(HKG)
Sales Range: $25-49.9 Million
Emp.: 926
Medical Device Mfr
N.A.I.C.S.: 339112
Yuen Kam *(Chm, CEO & Officer-Compliance)*

Subsidiaries:

Golden Meditech (BVI) Company Limited (1)
Ste A 48 F Bank Of China Tower, 1 Garden Rd, Central, China (Hong Kong)
Tel.: (852) 28683369
Web Site: http://www.goldenmeditech.com
Sales Range: $25-49.9 Million
Emp.: 20
Investment Holding Services
N.A.I.C.S.: 551112
Samuel Kong *(Dir)*

Golden Meditech Herbal Treatment (BVI) Company Limited (1)
48 F Bank Of China Tower 1 Garden Rd, Central, China (Hong Kong)
Tel.: (852) 85228683369
Web Site: http://www.tangherb.com.hk
Investment Holding Services
N.A.I.C.S.: 551112

GOLDEN METROPOLIS INTERNATIONAL LIMITED
278 Suxi Road Binhu District, Wuxi, 214123, Jiangsu, China
Tel.: (86) 510 85407636 **VG**
Year Founded: 2017
Sales Range: $75-99.9 Million
Emp.: 232
Building Construction & Design Services
N.A.I.C.S.: 236210
Zuoliang Zha *(Chm)*

GOLDEN MILE RESOURCES LTD.
Level 5 126 Phillip St, Sydney, 2000, NSW, Australia
Tel.: (61) 386784091
Web Site: https://www.goldenresources.com
G88—(ASX)
Rev.: $11,485
Assets: $4,272,466
Liabilities: $109,909
Net Worth: $4,162,557
Earnings: ($1,035,202)
Fiscal Year-end: 06/30/24
Mineral Exploration Services
N.A.I.C.S.: 213114
Lachlan Reynolds *(Mng Dir)*

GOLDEN MOOR INC.
38 Industrial Road, Casselman, K0A 1M0, ON, Canada
Tel.: (613) 764-6667 **ON**
Web Site: http://www.goldenmoor.com
Year Founded: 1987
Sales Range: Less than $1 Million
Emp.: 7
Mud-Based Beauty Supplies Mfr
N.A.I.C.S.: 325620
Francine Turpin *(Dir-Sls-Global)*

GOLDEN MV HOLDINGS INC.
2F Golden Haven Bldg C5 Extension Villar SIPAG Complex, Brgy Pulanglupa Uno, Las Pinas, 1742, Philippines
Tel.: (63) 288732922 **PH**
Web Site: https://www.goldenhaven.com.ph
Year Founded: 1982
HVN—(PHI)
Rev.: $88,309,154
Assets: $498,889,043
Liabilities: $273,055,597
Net Worth: $225,833,446
Earnings: $23,003,088
Emp.: 728
Fiscal Year-end: 12/31/22
Cemetery Management Services
N.A.I.C.S.: 812220
Maribeth C. Tolentino *(Pres)*

GOLDEN OCEAN GROUP LTD.
Par-la-Ville Place 14 Par-la-Ville Road, Hamilton, HM 08, Bermuda
Tel.: (441) 2956935 **BM**
Web Site: https://www.goldenocean.bm
Year Founded: 1996
GOGL—(NASDAQ)
Rev.: $1,113,456,000
Assets: $3,257,291,000
Liabilities: $1,340,258,000
Net Worth: $1,917,033,000
Earnings: $461,847,000

Emp.: 38
Fiscal Year-end: 12/31/22
Holding Company; Freight Shipping Services
N.A.I.C.S.: 551112
Tord Brath *(Head-Ops-Global)*

Subsidiaries:

Golden Ocean Management AS (1)
Bryggegata 3, 125, Oslo, Norway
Tel.: (47) 2201 7340
Emp.: 20
Freight Shipping Management Services
N.A.I.C.S.: 488510
Per Heiberg *(CFO)*

Golden Ocean Management Asia Pte. Ltd. (1)
Tel.: (65) 62261926
Freight Shipping Management Services
N.A.I.C.S.: 488510

Golden Ocean Shipping Co Pte. Ltd. (1)
1 Wallich Street 14-02 Guoco Tower, Singapore, 078881, Singapore
Tel.: (65) 6 226 1926
Logistic Services
N.A.I.C.S.: 541614

GOLDEN PHAROS BERHAD
66-2 Taman Seri Intan Jalan Sultan Omar, 20300, Kuala Terengganu, Terengganu, Malaysia
Tel.: (60) 96301330 **MY**
Web Site: https://goldenpharos.com.my
Year Founded: 1986
GPHAROS—(KLS)
Rev.: $19,423,161
Assets: $29,312,582
Liabilities: $9,700,697
Net Worth: $19,611,885
Earnings: $5,065,520
Emp.: 295
Fiscal Year-end: 12/31/23
Timber Doors; Tempered Safety & Sheet Glass
N.A.I.C.S.: 337212
Syukri Ali *(Head-Fin)*

Subsidiaries:

Golden Pharos Doors Sdn Bhd (1)
Lot 6471 Batu 6, Jalan Kapar, 42100, Kelang, Selangor, Malaysia
Tel.: (60) 332912911
Web Site: http://www.gpdoors.com
Sales Range: $50-74.9 Million
Emp.: 160
Engineered & Solid Wood Doors Mfr
N.A.I.C.S.: 321911

Golden Pharos Europe Ltd (1)
Holden Ing Way, Birstall, Batley, WF17 9AD, West Yorkshire, United Kingdom
Tel.: (44) 1924350500
Web Site: http://www.xljoinery.co.uk
Sales Range: $50-74.9 Million
Emp.: 60
External & Internal Door Distr
N.A.I.C.S.: 423310

Golden Pharos Glass Sdn Bhd (1)
7 Jalan Perak, Kawasan Perusahaan, 42500, Teluk Panglima Garang, Selangor, Malaysia
Tel.: (60) 331226115
Web Site: http://www.gpglass.com
Sales Range: $25-49.9 Million
Emp.: 25
Mfr of Tempered Safety Glass
N.A.I.C.S.: 327211

Permint Timber Corporation Sdn Bhd (1)
Kawasan Perindustrian, Bandar Al-Muktafi Billah Shah, 23400, Dungun, Terengganu, Malaysia **(100%)**
Tel.: (60) 9 822 1215
Web Site: http://www.goldenpharos.com
Production of High Quality Wood Panel Products
N.A.I.C.S.: 321211

AND PRIVATE COMPANIES **GOLDEN SOLAR NEW ENERGY TECHNOLOGY HOLDINGS LIMITED**

Subsidiary (Domestic):

Kumpulan Pengurusan Kayu Kayan Terengganu Sdn Bhd (2)
Jalan Kalsium Bandar Bukit Besi, 23200, Dungun, Terengganu, Malaysia
Tel.: (60) 9 833 7245
Web Site: https://www.kpkkt.com.my
Management of Forest Harvesting & Forest Rehabilitative Activities
N.A.I.C.S.: 113210

Permint Plywood Sdn Bhd (2)
Kawasan Perindustrian, Bandar Almuktafi Billah Shah, 23400, Dungun, Terengganu, Malaysia
Tel.: (60) 122718361
Web Site:
http://www.permintplywoodsdnbhd.com
Production of High Quality Wood Panel Products
N.A.I.C.S.: 321211

Pesaka Terengganu Berhad (2)
Kilang Papan Pesaka, Bandar Bukit Besi, 23200, Dungun, Terengganu, Malaysia
Tel.: (60) 9 833 7232
Web Site: https://www.pesaka.com.my
Emp.: 287
Saw Milling, Timber Treatment & Kiln Drying of Wood
N.A.I.C.S.: 333243

Pesama Timber Corporation Sdn Bhd (2)
Kawasan Perindustrian Jakar, 23000, Kemaman, Terengganu, Malaysia
Tel.: (60) 98591122
Web Site: http://www.pesama.com
Sales Range: $50-74.9 Million
Emp.: 150
Saw Milling, Timber Treatment & Kiln Drying of Wood
N.A.I.C.S.: 333243

GOLDEN PONDER HOLDINGS LIMITED
Office F and G Floor 23 Maxgrand Plaza No 3 Tai Yau Street, San Po Kong, Kowloon, China (Hong Kong)
Tel.: (852) 2 778 7547   Ky
Web Site:
http://www.headfame.com.hk
1783—(HKG)
Rev.: $27,170,927
Assets: $30,201,054
Liabilities: $8,537,960
Net Worth: $21,663,094
Earnings: ($1,588,260)
Emp.: 66
Fiscal Year-end: 03/31/21
Commercial Building Construction Services
N.A.I.C.S.: 236220
Kam Tong Chan *(Chm)*

Subsidiaries:

Head Fame Company Limited (1)
Offfice F and G Floor 23 Maxgrand Plaza No 3 Tai Yau Street, San Po Kong, Kowloon, China (Hong Kong)
Tel.: (852) 27787547
Building Construction Services
N.A.I.C.S.: 236220
K. T. Chan *(Co-Founder, Chm & Exec Dir)*

GOLDEN POWER GROUP HOLDINGS LTD.
Flat C 20/F Block 1 Tai Ping Industrial Centre 57 Ting Kok Road, Tai Po, New Territories, China (Hong Kong)
Tel.: (852) 31252288   Ky
Web Site:
http://www.goldenpower.com
Year Founded: 2012
3919—(HKG)
Rev.: $42,106,493
Assets: $80,024,228
Liabilities: $43,384,935
Net Worth: $36,639,293
Earnings: ($2,906,235)

Emp.: 475
Fiscal Year-end: 12/31/22
Battery Mfr & Distr
N.A.I.C.S.: 335910
King Tien Chu *(Chm)*

GOLDEN PURSUIT RESOURCES LTD.
652 Millbank, Vancouver, V5Z 4B7, BC, Canada
Tel.: (604) 730-6982
Web Site: https://www.goldpursuit.ca
Year Founded: 2007
GDP—(TSXV)
Assets: $154,063
Liabilities: $347,134
Net Worth: ($193,071)
Earnings: ($595,814)
Fiscal Year-end: 09/30/23
Mineral Exploration Services
N.A.I.C.S.: 213114
Brian A. McClay *(Pres & CEO)*

GOLDEN PYRAMIDS PLAZA
2 Al Raed Ali Rashid St Star Capital 2 Bldg, Nasr City, Cairo, Egypt
Tel.: (20) 224800500
Web Site:
https://goldenpyramidsplaza.com.eg
Year Founded: 1991
GPPL.CA—(EGX)
Sales Range: Less than $1 Million
Hotel Operator
N.A.I.C.S.: 721110
Abdul Rahman Ali Abdul Rahman Al Turki *(Chm & Mng Dir)*

GOLDEN RESOURCES DEVELOPMENT INTERNATIONAL LIMITED
Golden Resources Foods Centre 2-12 Cheung Tat Road, Tsing Yi, New Territories, China (Hong Kong)
Tel.: (852) 24490998   BM
Web Site: http://www.grdil.com
0677—(HKG)
Rev.: $228,840,572
Assets: $233,907,552
Liabilities: $81,207,872
Net Worth: $152,699,680
Earnings: $1,561,174
Emp.: 3,792
Fiscal Year-end: 03/31/22
Rice Whslr & Distr
N.A.I.C.S.: 424490
Siu Hung Tsang *(Exec Dir)*

Subsidiaries:

Aland Limited (1)
Room 1808 Shanghai bank building NO 168 Middle Yincheng Rd, Pudong New Area, Shanghai, 200050, China
Tel.: (86) 4000909888
Web Site: http://www.aland.cn
Nutritional Product Mfr
N.A.I.C.S.: 325411

GR Vietnam International Limited (1)
25 Ton Dan St Ward 13 Dist 4, Ho Chi Minh City, Vietnam
Tel.: (84) 839408345
Operator of Convenience Stores
N.A.I.C.S.: 445131

Golden Resources Development Limited (1)
Sterling Ctr 3rd Fl Rm 3 11 Cheung Yue St, Lai Chi Kok, Kowloon, China (Hong Kong)
Tel.: (852) 24280000
Rice Processing Services
N.A.I.C.S.: 311212

Golden Resources Rice Trading Limited (1)
11 F Golden Resources Ctr 2-12 Cheung Tat Rd, Tsing Yi, New Territories, China (Hong Kong)
Tel.: (852) 24328188
Web Site: http://www.trtil.com.hk

Sales Range: $50-74.9 Million
Emp.: 150
Wine Whslr
N.A.I.C.S.: 424490
Tsang Siu Hung *(Controller-Fin)*

GOLDEN RIDGE RESOURCES LTD.
Suite 335-1632 Dickson Ave, Kelowna, V1Y 7T2, BC, Canada
Tel.: (250) 717-3151   Ca
Web Site:
https://www.goldenresources.com
44GG—(DEU)
Rev.: $18,915
Assets: $6,733,367
Liabilities: $181,695
Net Worth: $6,551,672
Earnings: ($1,330,481)
Fiscal Year-end: 06/30/22
Precious Metal Exploration & Mining Services
N.A.I.C.S.: 213114
Michael Blady *(Pres & CEO)*

GOLDEN RIM RESOURCES LTD
Level 23 Collins Square Tower Five 727 Collins Street, Melbourne, 3008, VIC, Australia
Tel.: (61) 386770829
Web Site:
http://www.goldenrim.com.au
ALM1—(BER)
Rev.: $5,940
Assets: $18,836,269
Liabilities: $1,119,448
Net Worth: $17,716,821
Earnings: ($982,693)
Emp.: 31
Fiscal Year-end: 06/30/24
Minerals Exploration
N.A.I.C.S.: 213115
Craig Mackay *(Mng Dir)*

GOLDEN RIVER RESOURCES CORPORATION
Level 8 580 St Kilda Road, Melbourne, 3004, VIC, Australia
Tel.: (61) 3 8532 2860
Web Site:
http://www.goldenriverresource.com
Mining Exploration Services
N.A.I.C.S.: 212220
Joseph Isaac Gutnick *(Chm, Pres & CEO)*

GOLDEN ROCK GLOBAL PLC
14/F Golden Centre 188 Des Voeux Road Central, Hong Kong, China (Hong Kong)
Tel.: (852) 28052000   JE
Web Site: https://www.grglondon.com
Year Founded: 2016
GCG—(LSE)
Assets: $287,091
Liabilities: $205,065
Net Worth: $82,026
Earnings: $287,091)
Fiscal Year-end: 12/31/20
Investment Management Service
N.A.I.C.S.: 523940
Wei Chen *(Exec Dir)*

GOLDEN SAINT RESOURCES LIMITED
Level 3 Gledden Building 731 Hay Street, Perth, 6000, WA, Australia
Tel.: (61) 8 6145 4400   VG
Web Site:
http://www.goldensaintresource.com
Gold & Diamond Mining
N.A.I.C.S.: 212220
Tone Goh *(Chm)*

Subsidiaries:

Golden Saint Australia Limited (1)
UnitLevel 3 Gledden Building, Hay Street, Perth, 6000, WA, Australia
Tel.: (61) 8 6467 7778
Web Site:
http://www.goldensaintaustralia.com
Gold Mining Services
N.A.I.C.S.: 212220

GOLDEN SECRET VENTURES LTD.
3123 - 595 Burrard Street, Vancouver, V7X 1J1, BC, Canada
Tel.: (604) 609-6125   BC
Year Founded: 1969
Rev.: $32,286
Assets: $1,993,832
Liabilities: $13,650
Net Worth: $1,980,182
Earnings: ($86,408)
Fiscal Year-end: 12/31/17
Metal Mining Services
N.A.I.C.S.: 212290

GOLDEN SHARE RESOURCES CORPORATION
7-145 Riviera Drive, Markham, L3R 5J6, ON, Canada
Tel.: (905) 968-1199   Ca
Web Site:
https://www.goldenshare.ca
GSH—(TSXV)
Rev.: $130,257
Assets: $327,183
Liabilities: $368,462
Net Worth: ($41,278)
Earnings: ($139,335)
Fiscal Year-end: 12/31/23
Mineral Exploration Services
N.A.I.C.S.: 213114
Demin Huang *(Pres & CFO)*

GOLDEN SHIELD HOLDINGS (INDUSTRIAL) LTD.
Wenyi Road Jingyang County, Xianyang, 710080, Shaanxi, China
Tel.: (86) 29 36218118
Web Site:
http://www.goldenshield.com.cn
Sales Range: $100-124.9 Million
Emp.: 2,626
Holding Company; Yarn Mfr
N.A.I.C.S.: 313210
Binghui Chen *(Chm)*

GOLDEN SKY MINERALS CORP.
650 W Georgia St 2110, Vancouver, V6B 4N9, BC, Canada
Tel.: (604) 568-8807
Web Site:
https://www.goldenskyminerals.com
AUEN—(TSXV)
Rev.: $19,872
Assets: $10,842,034
Liabilities: $198,427
Net Worth: $10,643,607
Earnings: ($367,185)
Fiscal Year-end: 12/31/20
Mineral Exploration Services
N.A.I.C.S.: 213115
John Newell *(Pres & CEO)*

GOLDEN SOLAR NEW ENERGY TECHNOLOGY HOLDINGS LIMITED
Huoju Industrial Zone Jiangnan Town, Licheng District, Quanzhou, 362300, Fujian, China
Tel.: (86) 59536616680
Web Site:
http://www.baofengmodern.com
1121—(HKG)
Rev.: $38,508,491
Assets: $128,513,876

GOLDEN SOLAR NEW ENERGY TECHNOLOGY HOLDINGS LIMITED

Golden Solar New Energy Technology Holdings Limited—(Continued)
Liabilities: $37,983,956
Net Worth: $90,529,920
Earnings: ($23,452,416)
Emp.: 930
Fiscal Year-end: 12/31/22
Slippers & Other Footwear Mfr
N.A.I.C.S.: 316210
Jingdong Zheng *(Exec Dir)*
Subsidiaries:

BAOF International Limited (1)
Room 504 5/F 93-103 Wing Lok Street, Sheung Wan, China (Hong Kong)
Tel.: (852) 31608750
Slipper Distr
N.A.I.C.S.: 424340

GOLDEN SON LIMITED
Road No 90 House No 10/B 1st Floor Gulshan-2, Dhaka, 1212, Bangladesh
Tel.: (880) 31617934
Web Site:
https://www.goldensonbd.com
GOLDENSON—(DHA)
Rev.: $6,790,480
Assets: $70,339,523
Liabilities: $40,591,055
Net Worth: $29,748,468
Earnings: ($1,181,343)
Emp.: 550
Fiscal Year-end: 06/30/23
Home Appliances, Household Products & Toys Mfr & Exporter
N.A.I.C.S.: 335220
Belal Ahmed *(Mng Dir)*

GOLDEN SPIKE RESOURCES CORP.
830 1100 Melville, Vancouver, V6E 4A6, BC, Canada
Tel.: (604) 786-7774   BC
Web Site:
https://www.goldenresources.com
Year Founded: 2020
GSPRF—(OTCQB)
Assets: $3,547,942
Liabilities: $118,683
Net Worth: $3,429,258
Earnings: ($695,259)
Fiscal Year-end: 08/31/22
Mineral Exploration Services
N.A.I.C.S.: 213115
Joseph Meagher *(CFO)*

GOLDEN STAR RESOURCES LTD.
333 Bay Street Suite 2400, Toronto, M5H 2T6, ON, Canada
Tel.: (416) 583-3800   Ca
Web Site: http://www.gsr.com
GSS—(NYSEAMEX)
Rev.: $272,481,000
Assets: $343,861,000
Liabilities: $318,087,000
Net Worth: $25,774,000
Earnings: ($18,281,000)
Emp.: 1,626
Fiscal Year-end: 12/31/20
Gold Mining Services
N.A.I.C.S.: 212220
Timothy C. Baker *(Chm)*

GOLDEN STATE MINING LIMITED
Suite 15 19-21 Outram Street, West Perth, 6005, WA, Australia
Tel.: (61) 863232384   AU
Web Site:
https://www.goldenstatemining.com
Year Founded: 2017
GSM—(ASX)
Rev.: $66,440
Assets: $1,293,434
Liabilities: $286,030

Net Worth: $1,007,405
Earnings: ($1,803,994)
Fiscal Year-end: 06/30/24
Mineral Exploration Services
N.A.I.C.S.: 213114
Michael Moore *(Mng Dir)*

GOLDEN SUN HEALTH TECHNOLOGY GROUP LIMITED
Room 503-504 Building C2 No 1599 Xinjinqiao Road, Pudong New District, Shanghai, China
Tel.: (86) 2165248395   Ky
Web Site: https://www.jtyjyjt.com
Year Founded: 2018
GSUN—(NASDAQ)
Rev.: $6,155,593
Assets: $19,448,093
Liabilities: $15,071,828
Net Worth: $4,376,265
Earnings: ($5,786,311)
Emp.: 316
Fiscal Year-end: 09/30/23
Educational Support Services
N.A.I.C.S.: 611710
Xueyuan Weng *(Chm & CEO)*

GOLDEN TAG RESOURCES LTD.
Bay Adelaide Centre - East Tower 22 Adelaide St West Suite 2020, Toronto, M5H 4E3, ON, Canada
Tel.: (416) 504-2024
Web Site: http://www.goldentag.ca
Year Founded: 1980
SVR—(DEU)
Rev.: $140,654
Assets: $25,269,705
Liabilities: $10,981,042
Net Worth: $14,288,664
Earnings: ($7,086,864)
Fiscal Year-end: 03/31/24
Mineral Exploration Services
N.A.I.C.S.: 213114
Greg McKenzie *(Pres & CEO)*
Subsidiaries:

Golden Tag Mexico SA de Cv (1)
Jamie-Nunio 1669-7 Chapultepec Country, 44620, Guadalajara, Jalisco, Mexico
Tel.: (52) 3338140530
Mineral Resource Exploration Services
N.A.I.C.S.: 213114

GOLDEN TEXTILES & CLOTHES WOOL
38 Abbas Al-Akkad St, Nasr City, Cairo, Egypt
Tel.: (20) 2 15 410696
Web Site:
http://www.goldentex.com.eg
Year Founded: 1982
GTWL.CA—(EGX)
Sales Range: Less than $1 Million
Textile Products Mfr
N.A.I.C.S.: 314999

GOLDEN THROAT HOLDINGS GROUP CO. LTD.
No 28 Yuejin Road, Guangxi, Liuzhou, China
Tel.: (86) 7722825718   Ky
Web Site:
http://www.goldenthroat.com
Year Founded: 1956
6896—(HKG)
Rev.: $139,278,766
Assets: $322,820,316
Liabilities: $106,729,132
Net Worth: $216,091,184
Earnings: $39,483,007
Emp.: 853
Fiscal Year-end: 12/31/22
Holding Company
N.A.I.C.S.: 551112
Yong Zeng *(Vice Chm & Gen Mgr)*

GOLDEN TOBACCO LIMITED
At Darjipura Post Amaliyara, Vadodara, 390022, Gujarat, India
Tel.: (91) 2652540116
Web Site:
https://www.goldentobacco.in
Year Founded: 1930
500151—(BOM)
Rev.: $6,263,494
Assets: $20,284,828
Liabilities: $48,121,765
Net Worth: ($27,836,936)
Earnings: $1,041,440
Emp.: 123
Fiscal Year-end: 03/31/21
Tobacco Product Mfr & Sales
N.A.I.C.S.: 424940
Sunil Kumar Dhandhania *(Compliance Officer & Sec)*

GOLDEN VALLEY MINES LTD.
2864 chemin Sullivan, Val d'Or, J9P 0B9, QC, Canada
Tel.: (819) 824-2808   Ca
Web Site:
http://www.goldenvalleymines.com
Year Founded: 2002
GZZ—(OTCIQ)
Rev.: $11,369,234
Assets: $44,676,730
Liabilities: $9,876,820
Net Worth: $34,799,910
Earnings: $7,269,652
Emp.: 12
Fiscal Year-end: 12/31/19
Metal & Non-Metal Mineral Exploration & Mining Services
N.A.I.C.S.: 212290
Glenn J. Mullan *(Chm, Pres & CEO)*

GOLDEN VENTURES ACQUISITION CORP.
1 Kim Seng Promenade Room 10-01 East Tower, Singapore, 237994, Singapore
Tel.: (65) 67373023   Ky
Year Founded: 2021
GVACU—(NYSE)
Investment Services
N.A.I.C.S.: 523999
Mulyadi Tjandra *(Chm & CFO)*

GOLDEN VENTURES LEASEHOLD REAL ESTATE INVESTMENT TRUST
57 Park Venture Eco-duplex 22 Wireless Road, Bangkok, 10330, Thailand
Tel.: (66) 26437100
Web Site: http://www.gvreit.com
GVREIT—(THA)
Rev.: $31,919,809
Assets: $333,060,529
Liabilities: $87,329,153
Net Worth: $245,731,375
Earnings: ($4,227,374)
Fiscal Year-end: 09/30/23
Real Estate Investment Trust Services
N.A.I.C.S.: 531190

GOLDEN WEB LTD.
Ex-GIHOC Industrial Estate Chirapatre, PO Box AH 8520, Ahensan, Kumasi, Ghana
Tel.: (233) 51 30923
Year Founded: 1982
Vegetable Oil Mfr
N.A.I.C.S.: 311224
Thomas Wabi Bello *(Mng Dir)*

GOLDEN WHEEL TIANDI HOLDINGS COMPANY LIMITED
Unit A 18th Floor Convoy Lee and Man Commercial Center, 169 Electric

INTERNATIONAL PUBLIC

Road Fortress Hill, Hong Kong, China (Hong Kong)
Tel.: (852) 25663090   Ky
Web Site: http://www.gwtd.com.hk
1232—(HKG)
Rev.: $373,456,418
Assets: $1,728,399,535
Liabilities: $1,457,925,534
Net Worth: $270,474,001
Earnings: ($139,741,945)
Emp.: 563
Fiscal Year-end: 12/31/22
Holding Company
N.A.I.C.S.: 551112
Yam Yin Wong *(Chm)*

GOLDEN WILL FASHIONS LIMITED
2/F Tungtex Building 203 Wai Yip Street Kwun Tong, Kowloon, China (Hong Kong)
Tel.: (852) 23890318
Year Founded: 1991
Ladies Apparel Mfr
N.A.I.C.S.: 315250
Edmond Louk *(Gen Mgr)*

GOLDEN WINDOWS LIMITED
888 Guelph St, Kitchener, N2H 5Z6, ON, Canada
Tel.: (519) 579-3810
Web Site:
http://www.goldenwindows.com
Year Founded: 1961
Rev.: $23,183,585
Emp.: 140
Windows & Doors Mfr
N.A.I.C.S.: 321911
Joe Gatta *(Mgr-Sls-NorthEast Reg)*

GOLDENBRIDGE ACQUISITION LIMITED
15/F Aubin House 171-172 Gloucester Road, Wanchai, China (Hong Kong)
Tel.: (852) 18602172929   VG
Year Founded: 2019
GBRG—(NASDAQ)
Rev.: $3,200
Assets: $58,387,730
Liabilities: $2,839,981
Net Worth: $55,547,749
Earnings: ($821,842)
Fiscal Year-end: 06/30/21
Investment Services
N.A.I.C.S.: 523999
Yongsheng Liu *(Chm, CEO & CFO)*

GOLDENBRIDGE NO.2 SPECIAL PURPOSE ACQUISITION CO., LTD
50 Chungjeong-ro, Seodaemun-gu, Seoul, Korea (South)
Tel.: (82) 237793128
Year Founded: 2014
Assets: $903,041
Liabilities: $513,890
Net Worth: $389,151
Earnings: ($10,736)
Financial Investment Management Services
N.A.I.C.S.: 523940

GOLDENBRIDGE NO.4 SPECIAL PURPOSE ACQUISITION CO., LTD.
50 Chungjung-ro, Seodaemun-gu, Seoul, Korea (South)
Tel.: (82) 237793129
Year Founded: 2015
227950—(KRS)
Rev.: $16,910,356
Assets: $86,278,431
Liabilities: $9,469,519
Net Worth: $76,808,913
Earnings: $778,173

AND PRIVATE COMPANIES

Emp.: 65
Fiscal Year-end: 12/31/22
Investment Holding Company
N.A.I.C.S.: 551112

GOLDENEYE RESOURCES CORP.
409 Granville Street Suite 1000, Vancouver, V6C 1T2, BC, Canada
Tel.: (604) 602-0001 BC
Web Site:
  https://www.goldeneyeresources.ca
Year Founded: 2011
GOE—(TSXV)
Assets: $532,060
Liabilities: $84,906
Net Worth: $447,154
Earnings: ($338,332)
Fiscal Year-end: 04/30/21
Investment Services
N.A.I.C.S.: 523999
Geoff Balderson (CFO)

GOLDENHOME LIVING CO., LTD.
No 190 Jihe Road Tongan Industrial Park, Xiamen, Fujian, China
Tel.: (86) 5925580361
Web Site:
  https://www.goldenhome.cc
Year Founded: 1999
603180—(SHG)
Rev.: $498,889,877
Assets: $682,862,595
Liabilities: $317,505,516
Net Worth: $365,357,079
Earnings: $38,895,223
Emp.: 2,000
Fiscal Year-end: 12/31/22
Kitchen Cabinet Mfr & Distr
N.A.I.C.S.: 337126
Wen Jianhuai (Chm)

GOLDENPORT HOLDINGS INC.
41 Athinas Ave Vouliagmeni, 166 71, Athens, Greece
Tel.: (30) 2108910500 MH
Web Site: http://www.goldenport.biz
Sales Range: $25-49.9 Million
Emp.: 525
Marine Transportation Services
N.A.I.C.S.: 483111
Robert Crawley (Chm)

GOLDENWAY, INC.
28/F Tower 2 The Gateway Harbour City, Tsim Sha Tsui, Kowloon, China (Hong Kong)
Tel.: (852) 3719 9399 NV
Year Founded: 2007
Sales Range: $50-74.9 Million
Emp.: 135
Metal Trading & Foreign Exchange Brokerage Services
N.A.I.C.S.: 425120

GOLDEX RESOURCES CORPORATION
Suite 2300 - 1177 W Hastings St, Vancouver, V6E 2K3, BC, Canada
Tel.: (604) 669-4300
Web Site: https://goldex.ca
GDXRF—(OTCIQ)
Assets: $1,116,624
Liabilities: $2,083,981
Net Worth: ($967,357)
Earnings: ($214,184)
Fiscal Year-end: 12/31/20
Gold Mining Services
N.A.I.C.S.: 212220
Larry D. Kornze (VP-Exploration)

GOLDFIELD PROPERTIES LIMITED
Mansfield Lodge Slough Road, Iver Heath, SL0 0EB, United Kingdom
Tel.: (44) 1895274400 UK
Web Site:
  http://www.goldfieldproperties.co.uk
Property & Financial Management Services
N.A.I.C.S.: 531311
Mark Donnellan (Founder)

GOLDFINE MANUFACTURERS PUBLIC COMPANY LIMITED
291 Moo 4 Export Processing Zone 3 Lat Krabang Industrial Estate, Chalongkrung Road Kwang Lamplathew Ket Latkrabang, Bangkok, 10520, Thailand
Tel.: (66) 2326 0180
Web Site:
  http://www.goldfinemfg.com
Year Founded: 1989
Sales Range: $25-49.9 Million
Gold, Silver & Platinum Jewelry Sets Mfr & Exporter
N.A.I.C.S.: 339910
Anchatach Taechamatavorn (Chm)

GOLDFLARE EXPLORATION INC.
255 Boul Cure-Labelle Suite 204, Laval, H7L 2Z9, QC, Canada
Tel.: (450) 622-4066 Ca
Web Site:
  http://www.explorationtyphon.com
TYP—(TSXV)
Rev.: $17,418
Assets: $1,967,443
Liabilities: $55,435
Net Worth: $1,912,008
Earnings: ($7,606,893)
Emp.: 2
Fiscal Year-end: 02/28/19
Mineral Exploration Services
N.A.I.C.S.: 212220
David McDonald (Pres & CEO)

Subsidiaries:

Terranueva Corporation (1)
803 Boulevard de l'Ange-Gardien, L'Assomption, J5W 1T3, QC, Canada
Tel.: (450) 591-1011
Web Site: http://www.terranueva.ca
Sales Range: Less than $1 Million
Pharmaceutical Preparation Mfr
N.A.I.C.S.: 325412
Jean-Luc Landry (Chm & CEO)

GOLDGROUP MINING INC.
Suite 1201 1166 Alberni Street, Vancouver, V6E 3Z3, BC, Canada
Tel.: (604) 682-1943
Web Site:
  https://www.goldgroupmining.com
GGA—(TSXV)
Rev.: $9,793,000
Assets: $9,419,000
Liabilities: $15,788,000
Net Worth: ($6,369,000)
Earnings: ($6,746,000)
Emp.: 148
Fiscal Year-end: 12/31/23
Gold & Silver Mineral Deposit & Sales
N.A.I.C.S.: 332813
Anthony Balic (CFO)

GOLDHAVEN RESOURCES CORP.
1570 200 Burrard Street, Vancouver, V6C 3L6, BC, Canada
Tel.: (604) 638-5938
Web Site:
  https://www.goldresources.com
GOH—(OTCIQ)
Assets: $8,597,051
Liabilities: $205,127
Net Worth: $8,391,924

Earnings: ($3,550,915)
Fiscal Year-end: 07/31/21
Mineral Exploration Services
N.A.I.C.S.: 213115
Justin Canivet (CEO)

GOLDHILLS HOLDING LTD.
400 837 West Hastings Street, Vancouver, V6C 3N6, BC, Canada
Tel.: (604) 630-7296 ON
Web Site: https://www.goldhills.co
Year Founded: 1996
GHL—(DEU)
Assets: $29,330
Liabilities: $345,288
Net Worth: ($315,958)
Earnings: ($347,297)
Fiscal Year-end: 07/31/23
Oil & Gas Exploration Services
N.A.I.C.S.: 211120
Ronnie Doman (CFO)

GOLDIAM INTERNATIONAL LIMITED
Gems and Jewellery Complex Seepz, Andheri East, Mumbai, 400 096, India
Tel.: (91) 2228291893
Web Site: https://www.goldiam.com
526729—(BOM)
Rev.: $75,660,735
Assets: $96,210,305
Liabilities: $15,386,621
Net Worth: $80,823,684
Earnings: $11,628,230
Emp.: 35
Fiscal Year-end: 03/31/23
Jewelry Mfr
N.A.I.C.S.: 339910
Rashesh Manhar Bhansali (Chm)

Subsidiaries:

Diagold Designs Limited (1)
CC - 2070A C Tower Bharat Diamond Bourse, BKC Bandra East, Mumbai, 400 051, India
Tel.: (91) 2223644960
Web Site: https://www.diagolddesigns.net
Sales Range: $25-49.9 Million
Emp.: 50
Jewelry Mfr
N.A.I.C.S.: 339910
Niket Shah (Mgr-Bus Dev)

Goldiam Jewellery Limited (1)
Gems & Jewellery Complex II, Mumbai, 400 096, India
Tel.: (91) 2228292235
Jewelry & Precious Metal Mfr
N.A.I.C.S.: 339910

Goldiam USA, Inc. (1)
579 5TH Ave Ste Ste 1415, New York, NY 10017
Tel.: (212) 838-5252
Emp.: 5
Jewelry Mfr
N.A.I.C.S.: 339910

GOLDIN FINANCIAL HOLDINGS LIMITED
25/F Goldin Financial Global Centre 17 Kai Cheung Road, Kowloon, China (Hong Kong)
Tel.: (852) 2 882 9171 BM
Web Site:
  http://www.goldinfinancial.com
0530—(HKG)
Sales Range: $100-124.9 Million
Emp.: 323
Investment Services
N.A.I.C.S.: 523940
Xiaojian Huang (Exec Dir)

Subsidiaries:

Goldin Factoring Limited (1)
23/F Two International Finance Centre, 8 Financial Street, Central, China (Hong Kong)
Tel.: (852) 2100 0819
Financial Services

GOLDLION HOLDINGS LIMITED

N.A.I.C.S.: 523999

GOLDIN PROPERTIES HOLDINGS LIMITED
22/F Two International Finance Centre 8 Finance Street, Central, China (Hong Kong)
Tel.: (852) 2882 9171 HK
Web Site: http://www.goldinppt.com
Sales Range: $50-74.9 Million
Emp.: 999
Property Development Services
N.A.I.C.S.: 531390
Sutong Pan (Founder, Chm & CEO)

GOLDKART JEWELS LIMITED
7 Ground Floor Millenium Plaza Judges Bunglow Road, Ahmedabad, 380054, Gujarat, India
Tel.: (91) 7926750014
Web Site:
  http://www.sonahisona.com
Year Founded: 2001
SONAHISONA—(NSE)
Rev.: $7,001,905
Assets: $4,460,262
Liabilities: $1,714,837
Net Worth: $2,745,425
Earnings: $181,034
Emp.: 6
Fiscal Year-end: 03/31/23
Jewelry Retailer
N.A.I.C.S.: 458310
Vijay Chinubhai Shah (Mng Dir)

GOLDLINK INSURANCE PLC.
Goldlink Plaza 6 Emmanuel Street, PO Box 5987, Maryland Marina, 101233, Lagos, Nigeria
Tel.: (234) 70046535465
Web Site:
  https://goldlinkinsuranceplc.com
Year Founded: 1992
GOLDINSURE—(NIGE)
Sales Range: $1-9.9 Million
Insurance Management Services
N.A.I.C.S.: 524298
Oyindamola Unuigbe (Chm)

GOLDLION HOLDINGS LIMITED
7/F Goldlion Holdings Centre 13-15 Yuen Shun Circuit Siu Lek Yuen, New Territories, Sha Tin, China (Hong Kong)
Tel.: (852) 26860666
Web Site: https://www.goldlion.com
0533—(HKG)
Rev.: $180,502,898
Assets: $700,075,343
Liabilities: $133,034,010
Net Worth: $567,041,333
Earnings: $19,693,905
Emp.: 1,672
Fiscal Year-end: 12/31/22
Men's Apparel & Accessories Sales
N.A.I.C.S.: 315210
Lei Kuan Wong (Founder)

Subsidiaries:

Goldlion Distribution (M) Sdn. Bhd. (1)
50 G 2 Kelana Mall Jalan SS 6 14, 47301, Petaling Jaya, Selangor, Malaysia
Tel.: (60) 378807680
Web Site: http://www.goldlion.com
Emp.: 10
Garment Distr
N.A.I.C.S.: 424350
Barbara Chan (Gen Mgr)

Goldlion Enterprise (Singapore) Pte Limited (1)
161 Kampong Ampat 02-03 GOLDLION Building, Singapore, 368329, Singapore
Tel.: (65) 62842828
Garment Distr
N.A.I.C.S.: 424350

Goldlok Holdings (Guangdong) Co., Ltd.—(Continued)

GOLDLOK HOLDINGS (GUANGDONG) CO., LTD.
Room 711-717 7 F Tower A New Madarin Plaza 14 Science Museum Road, Tsimshatsui East, Kowloon, China (Hong Kong)
Tel.: (852) 23121577
Web Site: https://www.goldlok.com
Year Founded: 1989
002348—(SSE)
Rev.: $44,600,868
Assets: $112,780,512
Liabilities: $32,016,816
Net Worth: $80,763,696
Earnings: ($11,741,652)
Emp.: 780
Fiscal Year-end: 12/31/22
Electronic & Other Toys Mfr & Distr
N.A.I.C.S.: 339930
Xuen Yang (Chm)

GOLDMINING INC.
1188 W Georgia Street Suite 1830, Vancouver, V6E 4A2, BC, Canada
Tel.: (604) 630-1000   BC
Web Site:
  https://www.goldmining.com
Year Founded: 2009
GLDG—(NYSEAMEX)
Rev.: $627,389
Assets: $115,252,530
Liabilities: $9,573,543
Net Worth: $105,678,987
Earnings: ($10,326,096)
Emp.: 28
Fiscal Year-end: 11/30/22
Gold Ore Exploration & Mining Services
N.A.I.C.S.: 213114
Amir Adnani (Founder & Chm)

Subsidiaries:

U.S. GoldMining Inc.   (1)
301 Calista Ct Ofc 203 Ste 200, Anchorage, AK 99518
Tel.: (604) 388-9788
Web Site: https://www.usgoldmining.us
Exploration & Mining Services
N.A.I.C.S.: 213114

GOLDON RESOURCES LTD.
179 - 2945 Jacklin Road Suite 416, Victoria, V9B 6J9, BC, Canada
Tel.: (250) 474-7999
Web Site:
  https://www.goldonresources.com
6NR2—(DEU)
Rev.: $67
Assets: $236,226
Liabilities: $25,952
Net Worth: $210,274
Earnings: ($747,371)
Fiscal Year-end: 06/30/24
Gold Mining Services
N.A.I.C.S.: 212220
Michael Romanik (Pres & CEO)

GOLDPAC GROUP LIMITED
Room 1301 13th Floor Bank of East Asia Harbour View Centre, No 56 Gloucester Road, Wanchai, China (Hong Kong)
Tel.: (852) 28386202   HK
Web Site: https://www.goldpac.com
Year Founded: 1995
3315—(HKG)
Rev.: $214,847,240
Assets: $395,065,523
Liabilities: $104,358,478
Net Worth: $290,707,045
Earnings: $22,601,452
Emp.: 1,583
Fiscal Year-end: 12/31/22
Computer Peripherals Mfr
N.A.I.C.S.: 334118

Run Ting Lu (Chm)

GOLDPLAT PLC
Salisbury House London Wall, London, EC2M 5PS, United Kingdom
Tel.: (44) 1932918070
Web Site: https://www.goldplat.com
G7N—(DEU)
Rev.: $58,683,374
Assets: $51,010,898
Liabilities: $26,839,409
Net Worth: $24,171,489
Earnings: $5,380,644
Emp.: 427
Fiscal Year-end: 06/30/22
Gold Ore & Silver Ore Mining
N.A.I.C.S.: 212220
Stephen Ronaldson (Sec)

Subsidiaries:

Goldplat Recovery (Pty) Ltd.   (1)
Daveyton Rd, PO Box 40, Benoni, 1500, Gauteng, South Africa
Tel.: (27) 117496300
Sales Range: $100-124.9 Million
Emp.: 200
Gold & Platinum Mining Services
N.A.I.C.S.: 212220

GOLDQUEST MINING CORP.
133 Richmond Street West Suite 501, Toronto, M5H 2L3, ON, Canada
Tel.: (416) 583-5606   Ca
Web Site:
  http://www.goldquestcorp.com
Year Founded: 1989
GQC—(OTCIQ)
Rev.: $220,313
Assets: $13,110,727
Liabilities: $357,799
Net Worth: $12,752,928
Earnings: ($1,495,505)
Fiscal Year-end: 12/31/19
Gold Exploration Services
N.A.I.C.S.: 212220
William J. Fisher (Chm)

GOLDREA RESOURCES CORP.
543 Granville Street 5th Floor, Vancouver, V6C 1X8, BC, Canada
Tel.: (604) 559-7230   BC
Web Site: http://www.goldrea.com
Year Founded: 1981
GOR—(OTCIQ)
Assets: $29,107
Liabilities: $182,795
Net Worth: ($153,688)
Earnings: ($199,060)
Fiscal Year-end: 07/31/23
Mineral Exploration Services
N.A.I.C.S.: 213114
James Elbert (Pres & CEO)

GOLDROOSTER AG
Markgrafenstrasse 33, 10117, Berlin, Germany
Tel.: (49) 3069529234
Web Site: http://www.goldrooster.de
Sales Range: Less than $1 Million
Emp.: 700
Athletic Apparel, Footwear & Accessories Mfr & Retailer
N.A.I.C.S.: 315990
Wenwen Li (Chm-Mgmt Bd & CEO)

GOLDSANDS DEVELOPMENT COMPANY
Calle Juan Fanning 219, Miraflores, Lima, Peru
Tel.: (51) 1 446 6807   DE
Year Founded: 2000
Sales Range: Less than $1 Million
Mineral, Oil & Gas Mining & Exploration Services
N.A.I.C.S.: 212390
Michael Stocker (Pres & CEO)

GOLDSEEK RESOURCES, INC.
1231 Huron Street, London, N5Y 4L1, ON, Canada
Tel.: (226) 271-5170
Web Site:
  https://www.goldseekresources.com
AMQ—(CNSX)
Rev.: $268,763
Assets: $19,870,024
Liabilities: $3,372,551
Net Worth: $16,497,473
Earnings: ($1,763,725)
Fiscal Year-end: 06/30/24
Mineral Exploration Services
N.A.I.C.S.: 213115
Jon Deluce (Pres & CEO)

GOLDSHORE RESOURCES INC.
1030 West Georgia St Suite 918, Vancouver, V6E 2Y3, BC, Canada
Tel.: (604) 410-2277   BC
Web Site:
  http://www.sierradevelopments.com
8X00—(DEU)
Assets: $65,348,941
Liabilities: $10,276,401
Net Worth: $55,072,539
Earnings: ($5,237,705)
Fiscal Year-end: 03/31/23
Gold & Silver Mining Services
N.A.I.C.S.: 212220
Hani Zabaneh (CEO)

GOLDSTAR MINERALS INC.
850 av des Jesuites app 2B, Quebec, G1S 3N1, QC, Canada
Tel.: (581) 983-6815   BC
Web Site:
  https://greenmininginnovation.ca
Year Founded: 2010
GMI—(TSXV)
Rev.: $15,102
Assets: $1,602,522
Liabilities: $386,590
Net Worth: $1,215,932
Earnings: ($422,598)
Fiscal Year-end: 12/31/23
Gold Mining Services
N.A.I.C.S.: 212220
David Crevier (Chm & CEO)

GOLDSTONE INVESTMENT GROUP LIMITED
Room 901 Sing Ho finance Building 166-168 Gloucester Road, Wanchai, China (Hong Kong)
Tel.: (852) 39010901   Ky
Web Site:
  http://www.eaglerideinvestment.com
901—(HKG)
Rev.: $37,246
Assets: $13,254,359
Liabilities: $24,777,059
Net Worth: ($11,522,700)
Earnings: ($4,444,484)
Emp.: 3
Fiscal Year-end: 12/31/22
Investment Management Service
N.A.I.C.S.: 523940
Clement Yiu Pun Chan (Exec Dir)

GOLDSTONE RESOURCES LTD.
2 nd Floor International House 41 The Parade, Saint Helier, JE2 3QQ, Jersey
Tel.: (44) 215519009   DE
Web Site:
  https://www.goldstoneresource.com
GRL—(AIM)
Rev.: $8,900,000
Assets: $21,070,000
Liabilities: $8,290,000

Net Worth: $12,780,000
Earnings: ($670,000)
Fiscal Year-end: 12/31/22
Gold Exploration & Mining Services
N.A.I.C.S.: 212220
Emma Priestley (CEO)

GOLDSTREAM INVESTMENT LIMITED
Suite 08 70/F Two International Finance Centre No 8 Finance Street, Central, China (Hong Kong)
Tel.: (852) 39619700
Web Site: http://www.iel.hk
1328—(HKG)
Rev.: $4,497,180
Assets: $98,060,888
Liabilities: $5,077,433
Net Worth: $92,983,455
Earnings: ($4,258,118)
Emp.: 30
Fiscal Year-end: 12/31/22
Customer Relationship Management Services
N.A.I.C.S.: 561469
Fergus Tsan Fai Lam (CFO & COO)

Subsidiaries:

China Elite Information Co., Ltd.   (1)
Room 3813 15 Hong Kong Plaza 188 Connaught Road West, Hong Kong, China (Hong Kong)
Tel.: (852) 2126086500
Liabilities: $895,449
Net Worth: ($859,449)
Earnings: ($36,308)
Fiscal Year-end: 11/30/2020
Data Processing Computer Services
N.A.I.C.S.: 518210
Kin Shing Li (Pres, CEO & CFO)

Global Link Communications Holdings Limited   (1)
Room 3815 Hong Kong Plaza 188 Connaught Road West, Hong Kong, China (Hong Kong)
Tel.: (852) 2 542 2838
Web Site: http://www.glink.hk
Rev.: $23,257,158
Assets: $23,105,735
Liabilities: $10,923,058
Net Worth: $12,182,677
Earnings: ($2,733,344)
Emp.: 133
Fiscal Year-end: 03/31/2022
Holding Company
N.A.I.C.S.: 551112
Yuanguang Ma (Founder & CEO)

Goldstream Capital Management Limited   (1)
Room 08 70th Floor Phase 2 International Finance Center, 8 Finance Street, Central, China (Hong Kong)
Tel.: (852) 39619700
Web Site:
  https://www.goldstreaminvestment.com
Investment Management Service
N.A.I.C.S.: 525910

GOLDSTREAM MINERALS INC.
366 Bay Street Suite 200, Toronto, M5H 4B2, ON, Canada
Tel.: (775) 335-5050
Web Site:
  http://www.goldstreamminerals.com
Assets: $3,957
Liabilities: $175,390
Net Worth: ($171,433)
Earnings: ($176,855)
Fiscal Year-end: 12/31/17
Metal Ore Mining Services
N.A.I.C.S.: 212290
Brady Cobb (CEO)

GOLDSTRIKE RESOURCES LTD.
650 W Georgia St 2110, Vancouver, V6B 4N9, BC, Canada

AND PRIVATE COMPANIES

Tel.: (604) 681-1820 BC
Web Site:
https://www.trailresources.com
Year Founded: 1989
GSR—(DEU)
Sales Range: Less than $1 Million
Emp.: 5
Gold Exploration Services
N.A.I.C.S.: 213114
Lucy Zhang (CFO)

GOLDSUN BUILDING MATERIALS CO., LTD.
7F No 8 Xinhu 1st Road, Neihu District, Taipei, 114, Taiwan
Tel.: (886) 87928088
Web Site: https://www.gdc.com.tw
2504—(TAI)
Rev.: $688,090,853
Assets: $1,326,045,242
Liabilities: $488,283,935
Net Worth: $837,761,308
Earnings: $118,417,079
Emp.: 949
Fiscal Year-end: 12/31/23
Readymix Concrete Mfr
N.A.I.C.S.: 327320
Ming-Shen Lin (Vice Chm)

GOLDWAY EDUCATION GROUP LIMITED
Shop 203 Kin Sang Commercial Centre Kin Sang Estate, Tuen Mun, New Territories, China (Hong Kong)
Tel.: (852) 2 462 2198 Ky
Web Site:
http://www.goldwayedugp.com
8160—(HKG)
Rev.: $4,696,678
Assets: $4,794,445
Liabilities: $1,160,304
Net Worth: $3,634,140
Earnings: ($898,733)
Emp.: 72
Fiscal Year-end: 03/31/22
Tutoring Services
N.A.I.C.S.: 611691
Lick Keung Cheung (Chm, CEO & Compliance Officer)

GOLDWIN, INC.
Seihou Building 3-5-6 Kita-Aoyama, Minato-ku, Tokyo, 107-8570, Japan
Tel.: (81) 367779378 JP
Web Site: https://www.goldwin.co.jp
Year Founded: 1951
8111—(TKS)
Rev.: $838,855,270
Assets: $931,857,970
Liabilities: $269,734,270
Net Worth: $662,123,700
Earnings: $160,497,410
Emp.: 2,997
Fiscal Year-end: 03/31/24
Sportswear & Sporting Equipment Mfr & Marketer; Sales Training; Logistics Services; Golf Courses & Ski Resort Operations; Non-Life Insurance; Tourism & Real Estate Services
N.A.I.C.S.: 315990
Massaki Kondo (Auditor)

Subsidiaries:

Beijing Goldwin Co., Ltd. (1)
Area B Tianzhu airport industrial zone, Shunyi District, Beijing, China
Tel.: (86) 1080497777
Web Site: http://www.goldwin.co.jp
Sportswear Mfr
N.A.I.C.S.: 339920

Black & White Sportswear Co., Ltd. (1)
Kyohan-Kudan Bld 1-5-10 Iidabash, Chiyoda-ku, Tokyo, 102-0072, Japan
Tel.: (81) 362656570
Travel Agency Services
N.A.I.C.S.: 561510

Canterbury of New Zealand Japan Inc. (1)
Yubinbango 4 87 Building Iwato cho 3F, Shinjuku-ku, Tokyo, 162-0832, Japan
Tel.: (81) 352275699
Sports Equipment Mfr & Distr
N.A.I.C.S.: 339920

ESG Inc. (1)
2-20-6 Shoto, Shibuya-ku, Tokyo, 150-8517, Japan
Tel.: (81) 334817135
Travel Agency Services
N.A.I.C.S.: 561510

Goldwin America, Inc. (1)
444 Jackson St, San Francisco, CA 94111
Tel.: (628) 221-2342
Web Site: https://www.goldwin-global.com
Travel Agency Services
N.A.I.C.S.: 561510

Goldwin China,Ltd. (1)
402-4 Shi Mao Tower B Jianguo Lu Jia 92, Chaoyang, Beijing, China
Tel.: (86) 1080497777
Sporting Goods Mfr & Distr
N.A.I.C.S.: 339920

Goldwin Development Inc. (1)
1 Koboji, Oyabe, 932-0127, Toyama, Japan
Tel.: (81) 766613000
Travel Agency Services
N.A.I.C.S.: 561510

Goldwin Enterprise Inc. (1)
230 Kiyosawa, Oyabe, 932-0112, Toyama, Japan
Tel.: (81) 766614817
Travel Agency Services
N.A.I.C.S.: 561510

Goldwin Europe AG (1)
Taefernstrasse 14A, 5405, Baden, Switzerland
Tel.: (41) 564830505
Travel Agency Services
N.A.I.C.S.: 561510

Goldwin Italia Srl (1)
Via Gaudenzio Fantoli 7, 20138, Milan, Italy
Tel.: (39) 0255401010
Web Site: http://www.goldwin-europe.com
Sales Range: $25-49.9 Million
Emp.: 4
Sportswear Mfr
N.A.I.C.S.: 339920
Katia Arturo (Gen Mgr)

Goldwin Korea Corporation (1)
70 11 Hawolgok Dong, Sung Buk gu, Seoul, Korea (South)
Tel.: (82) 29401114
Sportswear Mfr

Goldwin Logitem Inc. (1)
135-1 Asaji Jodoji, Oyabe, 932-0122, Toyama, Japan
Tel.: (81) 766614867
Travel Agency Services
N.A.I.C.S.: 561510

Goldwin Sai Gon Vietnam Co., Ltd. (1)
7th Floor 86 Xuan Thuy Street, Thao Dien Ward Thu Duc City, Ho Chi Minh City, Vietnam
Tel.: (84) 2836208962
Sporting Goods Mfr & Distr
N.A.I.C.S.: 339920

Goldwin Technical Center Inc. (1)
230 Kiyosawa, Oyabe, 932-0112, Toyama, Japan
Tel.: (81) 766614800
Travel Agency Services
N.A.I.C.S.: 561510

Goldwin Trading Inc. (1)
2-20-6 Shoto, Shibuya-ku, Tokyo, 150-8517, Japan
Tel.: (81) 334817291
Travel Agency Services
N.A.I.C.S.: 561510

Nanamica inc. (1)
12-8 Uguisudanicho, Shibuya-ku, Tokyo, 150-0032, Japan
Tel.: (81) 357288715
Web Site: https://www.nanamica.com

Clothing Mfr & Whslr
N.A.I.C.S.: 339999

PPH.Fordex Sp.z.o.o. (1)
Ul Winogrady 149, Poznan, 61626, Poland
Tel.: (48) 618526990
Web Site: http://www.fordex.pl
Sporting Goods Distr
N.A.I.C.S.: 459110

Shanghai Goldwin Co., Ltd. (1)
Shanghai Universal Mansion Room 1703 17F 172YuYuan Road, Jingan, Shanghai, China
Tel.: (86) 2162883989
Web Site: http://www.goldwin.co.jp
Sportswear Mfr
N.A.I.C.S.: 339920

Sprint spol s.r.o. (1)
Becovska 1083/3, Uhrineves, 104 00, Prague, Czech Republic
Tel.: (420) 267090616
Emp.: 25
Sporting Goods Distr
N.A.I.C.S.: 459110

Torau Sport AG (1)
Industriestrasse 15, Buron, 6233, Brittnau, Aargau, Switzerland
Tel.: (41) 627375560
Web Site: http://www.torau.ch
Sales Range: $25-49.9 Million
Emp.: 16
Sporting Goods Distr
N.A.I.C.S.: 423910

Woolrich Japan Inc. (1)
6F Sophia Building 6-10-11, Jingumae Shibuya-ku, Tokyo, 150-0001, Japan
Tel.: (81) 120566120
Web Site: http://www.woolrich.jp
Clothing Mfr & Whslr
N.A.I.C.S.: 339999

Youngone Outdoor Corporation (1)
293 Gwangmyeong-Ro, Jungwon-Ku, Seongnam, Gyeonggi-Do, Korea (South)
Tel.: (82) 29401114
Travel Agency Services
N.A.I.C.S.: 561510

GOLECHHA GLOBAL FINANCE LTD.
522 Tobacco House No 1 Old Court House Corner, Kolkata, 700001, West Bengal, India
Tel.: (91) 3322131698
Web Site:
https://www.golechhaglobal.com
531360—(BOM)
Rev.: $129,994
Assets: $1,259,302
Liabilities: $19,200
Net Worth: $1,240,102
Earnings: $41,664
Emp.: 7
Fiscal Year-end: 03/31/21
Financial Investment Services
N.A.I.C.S.: 523999
Gyan Swaroop Garg (Mng Dir)

GOLETZ GMBH
Am Funkenhof 2, 58566, Kierspe, Germany
Tel.: (49) 2359 91 4050
Web Site: http://www.goletz-gmbh.de
Plastic Components & Molding Products Mfr
N.A.I.C.S.: 326199
Rolf Danzebrink (Mng Dir)

GOLF DIGEST ONLINE INC.
Higashi-Gotanda Square 8F 2-10-2 Higashi-Gotanda, Shinagawa-ku, Tokyo, Japan
Tel.: (81) 56562865
Web Site:
https://company.golfdigest.co.jp
Year Founded: 2000
3319—(TKS)
Rev.: $375,188,620
Assets: $331,103,000
Liabilities: $318,823,120

GOLFZON CO., LTD.

Net Worth: $12,279,880
Earnings: $1,120,220
Emp.: 1,119
Fiscal Year-end: 12/31/23
Golf Related Services
N.A.I.C.S.: 423910
Nobuya Ishizaka (Pres & CEO)

Subsidiaries:

GDO Sports, Inc. (1)
4660 La Jolla Village Dr Ste 100, San Diego, CA 92122
Tel.: (858) 646-3046
Web Site: http://www.gdosports.com
Golf Sports Products & Consulting Services
N.A.I.C.S.: 713940
Nobuya Ishizaka (CEO)

Subsidiary (Domestic):

GOLFTEC Intellectual Property, LLC (2)
67 Inverness Dr E Ste A, Englewood, CO 80112 (51.9%)
Tel.: (303) 779-9900
Web Site: http://www.golftec.com
Sporting Club Operating Services
N.A.I.C.S.: 713910
Joe Assell (Co-Founder & CEO)

GOLF DO CO., LTD.
2-3-1 Kamiochiai, Chuo-Ku, Saitama, 338-0001, Japan
Tel.: (81) 488513111
Web Site: https://www.golfdo.co.jp
Year Founded: 2000
3032—(NGO)
Rev.: $55,476,080
Assets: $32,544,160
Liabilities: $24,906,640
Net Worth: $7,637,520
Earnings: $2,197,360
Fiscal Year-end: 03/31/22
Golf Club Operator
N.A.I.C.S.: 713910
Isao Sakuma (Pres)

GOLF HOUSE DIREKTVERSAND GMBH
Schnackenburgallee 149, 22525, Hamburg, Germany
Tel.: (49) 404313610 De
Web Site: http://www.golfhouse.de
Year Founded: 1976
Golf Products & Services
N.A.I.C.S.: 459110
Frank Ewers (Mng Dir)

GOLFWALKER PTE LTD
Block 65 Ubi Road 1 Oxley Bizhub 03-50/51, Singapore, 408729, Singapore
Tel.: (65) 67027493 SG
Web Site:
http://www.golfwalker.com.sg
Golf Simulator & Golf Training Services
N.A.I.C.S.: 713910

GOLFZON CO., LTD.
Golfzon Tower 735 Yeongdong-daero, Gangnam-gu, Seoul, Korea (South)
Tel.: (82) 15774333
Web Site: http://www.golfzon.com
Year Founded: 2015
215000—(KRS)
Rev.: $473,633,228
Assets: $452,167,895
Liabilities: $165,951,704
Net Worth: $286,216,191
Earnings: $87,230,224
Emp.: 484
Fiscal Year-end: 12/31/22
Golf Simulation Machinery Mfr
N.A.I.C.S.: 333310
Deok-Hyung Choi (Co-CEO)

GOLFZON NEWDIN HOLDINGS CO., LTD.

GOLFZON Co., Ltd.—(Continued)

GOLFZON NEWDIN HOLDINGS CO., LTD.
Golfzon Tower Seoul 735 Yeongdong-Daero, Gangnam-Gu, Seoul, 06072, Korea (South)
Tel.: (82) 7086406202
Web Site: http://golfzon.com
Year Founded: 2000
121440—(KRS)
Rev.: $374,874,843
Assets: $773,768,234
Liabilities: $248,150,687
Net Worth: $525,617,546
Earnings: $67,503,924
Emp.: 36
Fiscal Year-end: 12/31/22
Golf Gaming Software Publisher
N.A.I.C.S.: 513210
Yonggu Kim (CFO)

GOLGOHAR MINING & INDUSTRIAL CO.
No 231-8th Floor-Opposite Of Laleh Hotel Dr Fatemi Ave, Tehran, Iran
Tel.: (98) 21 88977261
Web Site: http://www.geg.ir
Year Founded: 1992
Emp.: 640
Iron Ore Mining Services
N.A.I.C.S.: 212210

GOLIATH INTERNATIONAL HOLDING BV
Vijzelpad 80, 8051 KR, Hattem, Netherlands
Tel.: (31) 900 5003030
Web Site: http://www.goliathgames.nl
Holding Company
N.A.I.C.S.: 551112
Jochanan Golad (CEO)

Subsidiaries:

Goliath Games, LLC (1)
5068 W Plano Pkwy, Plano, TX 75093-4439
Web Site: http://www.goliathgames.us
Hobby, Toy & Game Stores
N.A.I.C.S.: 459120
David Norman (Mgr)

Subsidiary (Domestic):

Endless Games Inc. (2)
620 Newark Ave, Jersey City, NJ 07306-2311
Tel.: (201) 386-9465
Web Site: http://www.endlessgames.com
Toy & Hobby Goods & Supplies Merchant Whslr
N.A.I.C.S.: 423920
Michael Gasser (Owner)

GOLIATH RESOURCES LIMITED
82 Richmond Street East, Toronto, M5C 1P1, ON, Canada
Tel.: (416) 488-2887 ON
Web Site:
https://www.goliathresourcesltd.com
Year Founded: 2006
GOTRF—(NASDAQ)
Assets: $11,088,200
Liabilities: $479,358
Net Worth: $10,608,842
Earnings: ($10,086,002)
Fiscal Year-end: 06/30/22
Mineral Mining Services
N.A.I.C.S.: 213115
Roger Rosmus (Founder & CEO)

GOLIK HOLDINGS LIMITED
Suite 6505 Central Plaza 18 Harbour Road, Wanchai, China (Hong Kong)
Tel.: (852) 28270938
Web Site: https://golik.com
1118—(HKG)
Rev.: $544,573,028
Assets: $386,995,523
Liabilities: $224,033,183
Net Worth: $162,962,340
Earnings: $11,543,595
Emp.: 1,477
Fiscal Year-end: 12/31/22
Steel & Metal Products Mfr
N.A.I.C.S.: 212290
Sammy Wai Yu Ho (Vice Chm, Sec & Fin Dir)

Subsidiaries:

Dah Bang Printing Ink Manufactory Limited (1)
Rm B 12 F Edwick Industrial Centre 4-30 Lei Muk Road, Kwai Chung, New Territories, China (Hong Kong)
Tel.: (852) 25259261
Web Site: http://www.dahbang.com
Printing Materials & Spare Parts Sales
N.A.I.C.S.: 423830

Dongguan Steel Wealth Metal Co., Ltd. (1)
Golden Phoenix Ind Area, Feng Gang Town, Dongguan, 523689, Guangdong, China
Tel.: (86) 76987752768
Steel & Metal Product Distr
N.A.I.C.S.: 423510

Dongguan Widehold Metal Company Limited (1)
Golden Phoenix Ind Area, Feng Gang Town, Dongguan, 523689, Guangdong, China
Tel.: (86) 76987512068
Steel & Metal Product Distr
N.A.I.C.S.: 423510

Fulwealth Metal Factory Limited (1)
12 Dai Fat Street, Tai Po Industrial Estate, Tai Po, New Territories, China (Hong Kong)
Tel.: (852) 26957332
Web Site: http://www.fulwealth.com
Sales Range: $25-49.9 Million
Emp.: 13
Rolled Steel Products Mfr
N.A.I.C.S.: 331513

Golik Concrete (HK) Limited (1)
89 Tong Yan San Tsuen Road, Yuen Long, New Territories, China (Hong Kong)
Tel.: (852) 26341818
Steel & Metal Product Mfr & Distr
N.A.I.C.S.: 331110

Golik Concrete Limited (1)
89 Tong Yan San Tsuen Road, Yuen Long, New Territories, China (Hong Kong)
Tel.: (852) 26341818
Sales Range: $25-49.9 Million
Emp.: 50
Concrete Batch Plants Operating Services
N.A.I.C.S.: 327320
Pang Chung Tang (Chm)

Golik Godown Limited (1)
Suite 6505 Central Plaza 18 Harbour Road, Wanchai, New Territories, China (Hong Kong)
Tel.: (852) 24723565
Warehousing Services
N.A.I.C.S.: 493110
Tak Chung Pang (Mng Dir)

Golik Metal Industrial Company Limited (1)
Suite 6505 Central Plaza 18 Harbour Road, Wanchai, China (Hong Kong)
Tel.: (852) 28270938
Sales Range: $25-49.9 Million
Emp.: 12
Metal Products Mfr
N.A.I.C.S.: 331529

Golik Metal Manufacturing Co. Limited (1)
3 Dai Shing Street Tai, Po Industrial Estate, Tai Po, New Territories, China (Hong Kong)
Tel.: (852) 26743580
Emp.: 30
Steel Pole Mfr
N.A.I.C.S.: 331222

Golik Steel (HK) Limited (1)
Suite 6505 Central Plaza 18 Harbour Road, Wanchai, China (Hong Kong)
Tel.: (852) 25200012
Steel & Metal Product Mfr & Distr
N.A.I.C.S.: 331110

Golik Steel Company Limited (1)
Suite 6505 Central Plaza 18 Harbour Road, Wanchai, China (Hong Kong)
Tel.: (852) 2 520 0012
Web Site: http://www.golik.com.hk
Sales Range: $50-74.9 Million
Emp.: 10
Steel Bars & Metal Products Whslr
N.A.I.C.S.: 423510

Golik Wire Rope Hong Kong Limited (1)
Suite 6505 Central Plaza 18 Harbour Road, Wanchai, New Territories, China (Hong Kong)
Tel.: (852) 26734808
Steel & Metal Product Mfr & Distr
N.A.I.C.S.: 331110

Heshan Golik Metal Manufacturing Co., Limited (1)
No 2102 Renmindong Road, Shaping Town, Heshan, 529700, Guangdong, China
Tel.: (86) 7508829301
Steel & Metal Product Distr
N.A.I.C.S.: 423510

Heshan Hang Kei Steel Wire Manufacturing Co., Limited (1)
No 2102 Renmindong Road, Shaping Town, Heshan, 529700, Guangdong, China
Tel.: (86) 7508821069
Steel & Metal Product Distr
N.A.I.C.S.: 423510

Jiangmen Golik Metal Manufacturing Co., Ltd. (1)
24 Gao Sha Zhong Lu, Jiangmen, 529030, Guangdong, China
Tel.: (86) 7503167288
Steel & Metal Product Distr
N.A.I.C.S.: 423510

Shenzhen Dyna Precast Concrete Products Co., Limited (1)
No 39 Shajing Section Guangshen Road, Shangliao Community Shajing Sub-District Baoan District, Shenzhen, 518125, China
Tel.: (86) 75527297810
Steel & Metal Product Distr
N.A.I.C.S.: 423510

The Spacers & Bar Chairs Manufacturer Company Limited (1)
D D 77 Lot No 1566A Ping Che Road, Fanling, New Territories, China (Hong Kong)
Tel.: (852) 26745326
Steel & Metal Product Mfr & Distr
N.A.I.C.S.: 423510

Tianjin Goldsun Wire Rope Ltd. (1)
No 1 No 1 Road North Area of Jinghai Economic Development Zone, Hexi Dist, Tianjin, 301616, China
Tel.: (86) 2259528696
Web Site: https://www.goldsunchn.com
Elevator Wire Ropes Mfr
N.A.I.C.S.: 333923

GOLKONDA ALUMINIUM EXTRUSIONS LTD.
A-2/78-B Keshav Puram, New Delhi, 110035, India
Tel.: (91) 1140110240
Web Site: https://www.gael.co.in
513309—(BOM)
Rev.: $198,664
Assets: $941,535
Liabilities: $9,667
Net Worth: $931,867
Earnings: $70,625
Fiscal Year-end: 03/31/22
Metal Products Extrusion & Mfr
N.A.I.C.S.: 331318
Hera Siddiqui (Compliance Officer & Sec)

GOLKONDA ENGINEERING ENTERPRISES LIMITED
1-7-241/11/D S D Road, Secunderabad, 500 003, India
Tel.: (91) 40 40176211

INTERNATIONAL PUBLIC

Web Site:
http://www.golkondaengineering.com
Year Founded: 1985
Sales Range: $10-24.9 Million
Emp.: 55
Cable Mfr
N.A.I.C.S.: 335929
Ravi Surana (Exec Dir)

GOLKUNDA DIAMONDS & JEWELLERY LIMITED
G-30 Gems and Jewellery Complex III-Seepz Andheri East, Mumbai, 400 096, India
Tel.: (91) 2228290155
Web Site: https://www.golkunda.com
Year Founded: 1990
523676—(BOM)
Rev.: $32,557,527
Assets: $13,267,173
Liabilities: $8,209,035
Net Worth: $5,058,138
Earnings: $1,006,187
Emp.: 22
Fiscal Year-end: 03/31/22
Jewelry Mfr
N.A.I.C.S.: 339910
Kanti Kumar Dadha (Chm & Mng Dir)

GOLLEY SLATER GROUP LIMITED
Wharton Place Wharton Street, Cardiff, CF10 1GS, United Kingdom
Tel.: (44) 29 2038 8621 UK
Web Site: http://www.golleyslater.com
Year Founded: 1957
Advetising Agency
N.A.I.C.S.: 541810
David Longden (CEO)

Subsidiaries:

Golley Slater Central (1)
205 Fort Dunlop Fort Parkway, Edgbaston, Birmingham, B24 9FD, United Kingdom
Tel.: (44) 121 384 9700
Web Site:
http://www.golleyslatercentral.co.uk
Sales Range: $25-49.9 Million
Emp.: 80
Advertising Agency
N.A.I.C.S.: 541810
Anna Shackleton (Dir-PR)

Golley Slater London (1)
Hogarth House 136 High Holborn, London, WC1V 6PX, United Kingdom
Tel.: (44) 2039840340
Web Site:
http://www.golleyslaterlondon.co.uk
Rev.: $129,000,000
Emp.: 20
Advertising Agency Services
N.A.I.C.S.: 541810
Mike Leeson (Mng Partner)

Golley Slater Retail (1)
Richmond House 5-8 Richmond Terrace Otley Road, Guiseley, Leeds, LS20 8BP, United Kingdom
Tel.: (44) 1943 484 848
Web Site: http://www.golleyretail.co.uk
Emp.: 80
Advertising Agency Services
N.A.I.C.S.: 541810
Jason Horsman (Mng Dir)

GOLO, INC.
3500 Blvd Maisonneuve West, Montreal, H3Z 3C1, QC, Canada
Web Site: http://www.corpo.golo.io
Information Technology Services
N.A.I.C.S.: 513210

GOLOG HOLDING S.A.
34 Ilot du Chateau 2 rue Hannelanst, 9544, Wiltz, Luxembourg
Tel.: (352) 95978683
Web Site: http://www.golog.net
Sales Range: $1-9.9 Million
Online Marketing Services
N.A.I.C.S.: 541613

AND PRIVATE COMPANIES

Francois-Luc Collignon *(Pres)*

GOLSTA SDN. BHD.
No 11 Jalan TTC 30 Taman Teknologi Cheng, 75260, Melaka, Malaysia
Tel.: (60) 63352153   MY
Web Site: http://www.golsta.com.my
Year Founded: 1976
Emp.: 80
Industrial Machinery Mfr
N.A.I.C.S.: 333248
Boon Hiong Chua *(Co-Owner)*

Subsidiaries:

Foundry Engineering Corporation Sdn. Bhd. (1)
No 11 Jalan Ttc 30 Taman Teknologi Cheng, Batu Berendam, Melaka, 75350, Malaysia   **(100%)**
Tel.: (60) 6 335 2153
Food Processing & Other Manufacturing Machinery Engineering, Fabrication & Plant Construction Services
N.A.I.C.S.: 333241

GOLTAS CIMENTO A.S.
Visnezade Mah Prof Alaeddin Yavasca Sok Marmara Apt No 4/2, Besiktas, 34357, Istanbul, Turkiye
Tel.: (90) 2123270080   TR
Web Site: https://www.goltas.com.tr
Year Founded: 1969
GOLTS—(IST)
Rev.: $87,705,039
Assets: $90,997,369
Liabilities: $51,656,979
Net Worth: $39,340,390
Earnings: $18,192,207
Emp.: 650
Fiscal Year-end: 12/31/22
Cement Mfr
N.A.I.C.S.: 327310

Subsidiaries:

Elmasu A.S. (1)
Marmara Apt No 4 D 2, 34357, Istanbul, Turkiye
Tel.: (90) 2123270080
Web Site: https://www.elmasu.com.tr
Fruit Vegetable Distr
N.A.I.C.S.: 424480

Elmatas A.S. (1)
Prof Dr Alaeddin Yavasca Sk Marmara Apt No 4 D 2, Besiktas, 34357, Istanbul, Turkiye
Tel.: (90) 2123270080
Web Site: https://www.elmasu.com.tr
Fruit & Vegetable Juicer Mfr
N.A.I.C.S.: 311421

GOMAJI CORP LTD.
2F-6 No 262 Section 2 Beixin Road, Xindian District, New Taipei City, Taiwan
Tel.: (886) 227118177
Web Site: https://www.gomaji.com
Year Founded: 2010
8472—(TPE)
Rev.: $10,366,382
Assets: $37,886,784
Liabilities: $24,899,947
Net Worth: $12,986,837
Earnings: ($2,667,261)
Fiscal Year-end: 12/31/22
Online Marketing Services
N.A.I.C.S.: 541810
Alex Wu *(Chm)*

GOMAX ELECTRONICS, INC.
14F-1 No 251 Fusing 1st St, Hsinchu County, Zhubei, 302, Taiwan
Tel.: (886) 36681958
Web Site: https://www.gomax-electronics.com.tw
Year Founded: 2006
6512—(TPE)
Rev.: $10,442,172
Assets: $14,639,746
Liabilities: $1,548,260
Net Worth: $13,091,486
Earnings: $703,436
Fiscal Year-end: 12/31/22
Electronic Design & Testing Services
N.A.I.C.S.: 541420
Yu-Chin Chang *(Chm & Pres)*

GOME FINANCE TECHNOLOGY CO., LTD.
Suite 2912 29/F Two International Finance Centre 8 Finance Street, Central, China (Hong Kong)
Tel.: (852) 21211387   BM
Web Site: http://www.gomejr.com
0628—(HKG)
Rev.: $11,262,748
Assets: $285,848,503
Liabilities: $56,671,618
Net Worth: $229,176,886
Earnings: ($791,575)
Emp.: 22
Fiscal Year-end: 12/31/22
Holding Company; Financial Services
N.A.I.C.S.: 551112
Wei Chen *(Exec Dir)*

GOME RETAIL HOLDINGS LIMITED
Suite 2915 29th Floor Two International Finance Centre, 8 Finance Street, Central, China (Hong Kong)
Tel.: (852) 21229133
Web Site: https://www.gome.com.hk
Year Founded: 1987
0493—(HKG)
Rev.: $6,526,326,082
Assets: $11,361,569,404
Liabilities: $8,892,651,971
Net Worth: $2,468,917,433
Earnings: ($670,120,074)
Emp.: 32,278
Fiscal Year-end: 12/31/21
Electrical Appliance & Electronics Retailer
N.A.I.C.S.: 449210
Da Zhong Zhang *(Chm)*

Subsidiaries:

Gansu Gome Logistics Company Limited (1)
12 F Zhongguang Mansion, No 87 Zha, Lanzhou, China
Tel.: (86) 9314818787
Logistic Services
N.A.I.C.S.: 541614

Wuhan Gome Electrical Appliance Company Limited (1)
Special No 1 Baofeng Rd, Wuhan, China
Tel.: (86) 2783331500
Electric Appliances Mfr
N.A.I.C.S.: 423620

GOME TELECOM EQUIPMENT CO., LTD.
No 12 Baotuquan North Road, Lixia District, Jinan, 250011, Shandong, China
Tel.: (86) 53186096772
600898—(SHG)
Rev.: $16,539,176
Assets: $57,656,622
Liabilities: $42,568,620
Net Worth: $15,088,002
Earnings: ($10,925,226)
Fiscal Year-end: 12/31/22
Household Electrical Appliances Distr
N.A.I.C.S.: 423620
Wu Qian *(Sec)*

GOMEEKI PTY LTD.
9 Middlemiss St Lavender Bay, Sydney, 2060, NSW, Australia
Tel.: (61) 282630000
Web Site: http://www.gomeeki.com
Sales Range: $10-24.9 Million
Emp.: 20
Digital Media Services
N.A.I.C.S.: 541890
Maurie Dobbin *(Founder)*

Subsidiaries:

2ergo Australia Pty. Ltd. (1)
Ste 203 13-15 Wentworth Ave, Surry Hills, Sydney, 2010, NSW, Australia
Tel.: (61) 292115286
Cellular Phone Marketing Services
N.A.I.C.S.: 517112

GOMSPACE GROUP AB
Ulls Vag 29A, 756 51, Uppsala, Sweden
Tel.: (46) 71741741
Web Site: http://www.gomspace.com
Software Publisher
N.A.I.C.S.: 513210
Niels Buus *(CEO)*

Subsidiaries:

Swedish Space Corporation (1)
Solna Strandvag 86, PO Box 4207, Solna, 171 54, Sweden
Tel.: (46) 86276200
Web Site: http://www.sscspace.com
Sales Range: $125-149.9 Million
Emp.: 150
Satellite Management Aerospace Engineering Science & Technology Services
N.A.I.C.S.: 517410
Stefan Gardefjord *(Pres & CEO)*

Subsidiary (Domestic):

ECAPS AB (2)
Solna Streesvag, PO Box 4207, 17104, Solna, 17104, Sweden   **(100%)**
Tel.: (46) 86276200
Web Site: http://www.ecaps.se
Sales Range: $25-49.9 Million
Emp.: 100
Satellite Telecommunications
N.A.I.C.S.: 517410
Stesam Garde Fjord *(Mng Dir)*

Subsidiary (Non-US):

LSE Space Engineering & Operations AG (2)
Munchener Strasse 20, PO Box 1144, Wessling, 82234, Munich, Germany   **(100%)**
Tel.: (49) 70057377223
Web Site: http://www.lsespace.com
Satellite Telecommunications
N.A.I.C.S.: 517410

LSE Space GmbH (2)
Argelsrieder Feld 22, 82234, Wessling, Germany
Tel.: (49) 8153 88 10 99 26
Web Site: http://www.lsespace.com
Space Management & Consulting Services
N.A.I.C.S.: 541618
Daniel Gestal *(Co-Mng Dir)*

Subsidiary (Non-US):

Aurora Technology B.V. (3)
Crown Business Centre Heereweg 345, 2161 CA, Lisse, Netherlands
Tel.: (31) 252 532239
Web Site: http://www.aurora.nl
Engineering & Scientific Services
N.A.I.C.S.: 541330
Alex Jeanes *(Mng Dir)*

LSE Space Middle East JLT (3)
Fortune Tower Office 1606 Jumeirah Lakes Towers, PO Box 115738, Dubai, United Arab Emirates
Tel.: (971) 55 55 04 379
Engineeering Services
N.A.I.C.S.: 541330

Subsidiary (Domestic):

NanoSpace AB (2)
Uppsala Science Park Dag Hammarskjolds vag 36B, 751 83, Uppsala, Sweden
Tel.: (46) 8 627 62 00.
Spacecraft Machinery Mfr
N.A.I.C.S.: 336413

GOOCH & HOUSEGO PLC

Subsidiary (Non-US):

SSC Chile S.A. (2)
Autopista Los Libertadores Km 28, Peldehue, Santiago, Chile
Tel.: (56) 2 698 1702
Satellite Station Operator
N.A.I.C.S.: 516110

SSC Space Australia Pty Ltd. (2)
PO Box 1218, West Perth, 6872, WA, Australia
Tel.: (61) 8 9929 1000
Satellite Communication Services
N.A.I.C.S.: 517410
Steve Montgomery *(Mng Dir)*

GONGIN PRECISION INDUSTRIAL CO., LTD.
No 168 Bade 2nd Road, Renwu Dist, Kaohsiung, 81453, Taiwan
Tel.: (886) 73597177
Web Site: https://www.gongin.com.tw
Year Founded: 1978
3178—(TPE)
Rev.: $47,466,779
Assets: $87,857,956
Liabilities: $49,866,648
Net Worth: $37,991,308
Earnings: $7,160,585
Fiscal Year-end: 12/31/22
Industrial Mold Mfr
N.A.I.C.S.: 333511
Yu-Hsin Su *(Chm & Pres)*

GOO CHEMICAL CO., LTD.
58 Ijiri Iseda-cho, Uji, 611-0043, Kyoto, Japan
Tel.: (81) 774 46 7777
Web Site: http://www.goo-chem.co.jp
Year Founded: 1953
4962—(TKS)
Rev.: $65,217,040
Assets: $148,645,700
Liabilities: $20,192,340
Net Worth: $128,453,360
Earnings: $2,897,720
Emp.: 228
Fiscal Year-end: 03/31/20
Chemical Product Mfr & Distr
N.A.I.C.S.: 325998
Haruki Fujimura *(Pres)*

Subsidiaries:

GOO Chemical Co., Ltd. - Fukui Factory (1)
Technoport Fukui 151 Aza Hamawari 49 Yonozu Mikuni-Cho, Sakai, 913-0036, Fukui, Japan
Tel.: (81) 776816077
Resin Mfr
N.A.I.C.S.: 325211

GOO Chemical Co., Ltd. - Shiga Factory (1)
Hino Industrial Park No 2 Kamiyama 1-108 Kitawaki Hino-cho Gamou-gun, Shiga, 529-1663, Japan
Tel.: (81) 748538070
Resin Mfr
N.A.I.C.S.: 325211

GOOCH & HOUSEGO PLC
Innovation Centre University Way, Cranfield, MK43 0BT, Bedfordshire, United Kingdom
Tel.: (44) 1460256440
Web Site: https://www.gandh.com
Year Founded: 1948
GHH—(AIM)
Rev.: $168,457,751
Assets: $218,192,393
Liabilities: $63,037,582
Net Worth: $155,154,811
Earnings: $4,621,679
Emp.: 908
Fiscal Year-end: 09/30/21
Optical Component Mfr
N.A.I.C.S.: 333310
Mark Webster *(CEO)*

GOOCH & HOUSEGO PLC

Gooch & Housego PLC—(Continued)

Subsidiaries:

Alfalight, Inc. (1)
1832 Wright St, Madison, WI
53704 **(100%)**
Tel.: (608) 240-4885
Web Site: http://www.alfalight.com
Sales Range: $1-9.9 Million
Emp.: 40
Designs & Manufactures Laser & Electro-Optical Systems for Defense & Security Applications
N.A.I.C.S.: 334419
Aaron Marshall *(VP-Fin & Ops)*

Artemis Optical Limited (1)
1 Western Wood Way Langage Science Park, Plympton, Plymouth, PL7 5BG, Devon, United Kingdom
Tel.: (44) 1752341943
Web Site: http://www.artemis-optical.co.uk
Sales Range: $25-49.9 Million
Emp.: 35
Optical Thin Film Coatings Mfr
N.A.I.C.S.: 333310
Ian Moyes *(Chm)*

Gooch & Housego (California) LLC (1)
5390 Kazuko Ct, Moorpark, CA 93021-1790
Tel.: (805) 529-3324
Precision Optical Components Mfr
N.A.I.C.S.: 333310

Gooch & Housego (Deutschland) GmbH (1)
Berliner Allee 55, 22850, Norderstedt, Germany
Tel.: (49) 4035734343
Web Site:
http://www.goochandhousego.com
Emp.: 600
Electronic Equipment Developer, Mfr & Distr
N.A.I.C.S.: 334419

Gooch & Housego (Ohio) LLC (1)
676 Alpha Dr, Highland Heights, OH 44143-2123
Tel.: (216) 486-6100
Sales Range: $25-49.9 Million
Emp.: 60
Optical Goods Retailer
N.A.I.C.S.: 456130

Gooch & Housego (Palo Alto) LLC (1)
44247 Nobel Dr, Fremont, CA 94538
Tel.: (650) 300-5744
Optical Component Mfr & Distr
N.A.I.C.S.: 333310

Gooch & Housego (Torquay) Limited (1)
Broomhill Way, Torquay, TQ2 7QL, United Kingdom
Tel.: (44) 1803611700
Web Site:
http://www.goochandhousego.com
Sales Range: $25-49.9 Million
Emp.: 100
Fiber Optic Products Mfr
N.A.I.C.S.: 334417

Gooch & Housego (UK) Limited (1)
Dowlish Ford, Ilminster, TA19 0PF, Somerset, United Kingdom
Tel.: (44) 1460256440
Sales Range: $50-74.9 Million
Emp.: 160
Precision Optical Components Mfr
N.A.I.C.S.: 333310
Andy Rowswell *(Gen Mgr)*

Gooch & Housego Japan KK (1)
Level 4 Nikko Shoken Building 3-2-3, Sakae Naka-ku, Nagoya, 460-0008, Japan
Tel.: (81) 9056152610
Optical Component Mfr & Distr
N.A.I.C.S.: 333310

Gould Technology LLC (1)
1121 Benfield Blvd Stes J-P, Millersville, MD 21108-2640
Tel.: (410) 987-5600
Web Site: http://www.gouldfo.com
Fiber Optic Cable Mfr
N.A.I.C.S.: 335921

StingRay Optics, LLC (1)
Tel.: (603) 358-5577
Web Site: http://www.stingrayoptics.com
Optical Design, Product Development & Prototyping of Optical Systems
N.A.I.C.S.: 333310
Christopher C. Alexay *(Founder)*

GOOD COM ASSET CO., LTD.
17F Sumitomo Real Estate NishiShinjuku Building 7201 NishiShinjuku, Shinjuku-ku, Tokyo, 160-0023, Japan
Tel.: (81) 353380170 JP
Web Site:
https://www.goodcomasset.co.jp
Year Founded: 2005
3475—(TKS)
Rev.: $157,327,100
Assets: $379,286,640
Liabilities: $296,985,920
Net Worth: $82,300,720
Earnings: $7,302,700
Emp.: 172
Fiscal Year-end: 10/31/23
Residential Real Estate Management Services
N.A.I.C.S.: 531210
Yoshikazu Nagashima *(Pres & CEO)*

Subsidiaries:

Good Com Co., Ltd. (1)
Sumitomo Fudosan Nishi-Shinjuku Bld 17F, 7-20-1 Nishishinjuku, Shinjuku-ku, Tokyo, 160-0023, Japan
Tel.: (81) 353380170
Building Management Services
N.A.I.C.S.: 236115
Nagashima Yoshikazu *(CEO)*

Room Bank Insure., Ltd. (1)
Fujikyu West Bld No1 1-18-2 Nishiikebukuro, Toshima-ku, Tokyo, Japan
Tel.: (81) 35 468 3315
Web Site: https://roombankinsure.com
Real Estate Guarantor Services
N.A.I.C.S.: 531110
Hironobu Sugiyama *(Pres & CEO)*

Shanghai Good Com Business Consulting Co., Ltd. (1)
2517 Room Nanjing West Road, Shanghai, China
Tel.: (86) 2161575127
Marketing Consulting Services
N.A.I.C.S.: 541613
Nagashima Yoshikazu *(CEO)*

Taiwan Good Com Co., Ltd. (1)
Renfu International Business Center 6F No 53 Sec 2, Nanjing E Rd Zhongshan Dist, Taipei, Taiwan
Tel.: (886) 277306221
Real Estate Brokerage Services
N.A.I.C.S.: 531210
Nagashima Yoshikazu *(CEO)*

GOOD DRINKS AUSTRALIA LTD.
14 Absolon Street, Palmyra, Perth, 6157, WA, Australia
Tel.: (61) 893140000
Web Site:
http://www.gageroads.com.au
GDA—(ASX)
Rev.: $75,365,918
Assets: $88,327,323
Liabilities: $47,104,033
Net Worth: $41,223,290
Earnings: ($1,868,990)
Emp.: 240
Fiscal Year-end: 06/30/24
Brewing, Packaging, Marketing & Selling of Craft Brewed Beer
N.A.I.C.S.: 312120
John Hoedemaker *(Founder & Mng Dir)*

GOOD ENERGY GROUP PLC
Monkton Park Offices Monkton Park, Chippenham, SN15 1GH, Wiltshire, United Kingdom
Tel.: (44) 8002540000
Web Site:
https://www.goodenergy.co.uk
Year Founded: 2000
GOOD—(AIM)
Rev.: $313,913,153
Assets: $146,859,379
Liabilities: $97,647,059
Net Worth: $49,212,320
Earnings: $10,900,025
Emp.: 292
Fiscal Year-end: 12/31/22
Renewable Energy Developer & Distr
N.A.I.C.S.: 324199
Juliet Davenport *(Founder & CEO)*

Subsidiaries:

Next Green Car Ltd. (1)
Unit 52 Runway East 1 Victoria St, Redcliffe, Bristol, BS1 6AA, United Kingdom
Tel.: (44) 7810095877
Web Site: https://www.nextgreencar.com
New Car Dealers
N.A.I.C.S.: 441110

GOOD FELLOW HEALTHCARE HOLDINGS LIMITED
Unit 3309 33 rd Floor West Tower Shun Tak Centre, 168-200 Connaught Road, Central, China (Hong Kong)
Tel.: (852) 2 722 4388 Ky
Web Site: http://www.huaxia-healthcare.com
8143—(HKG)
Rev.: $6,995,617
Assets: $7,796,583
Liabilities: $4,395,767
Net Worth: $3,400,816
Earnings: ($1,143,408)
Emp.: 137
Fiscal Year-end: 03/31/22
Holding Company; Hospital Investment & Management Services
N.A.I.C.S.: 551112
Chi Lung Ng *(Chm & Compliance Officer)*

Subsidiaries:

Grandy Environmental (H.K.) Limited (1)
10 F Luk Kwok Centre 72 Gloucester Road, Wanchai, China (Hong Kong)
Tel.: (852) 27224388
General Medical Services
N.A.I.C.S.: 622110

GOOD FINANCE SECURITIES CO LTD
4th Floor No 174 No 176 Sec 2 Minsheng East Road, Taipei, Taiwan
Tel.: (886) 225084888
Year Founded: 1988
6021—(TPE)
Rev.: $27,181,596
Assets: $374,899,759
Liabilities: $232,325,579
Net Worth: $142,574,180
Earnings: $1,641,403
Fiscal Year-end: 12/31/22
Securities Brokerage Services
N.A.I.C.S.: 523150
Huang Ku Han *(Chm)*

GOOD FRIEND INTERNATIONAL HOLDINGS INC.
Room 2003 20/F Kai Tak Commercial Building 317-319 Des Voeux Road, Central, China (Hong Kong)
Tel.: (852) 35868080
Web Site: http://www.goodfriend.hk
2398—(HKG)
Rev.: $130,320,455
Assets: $303,955,848
Liabilities: $202,572,503
Net Worth: $101,383,345
Earnings: $1,739,953

INTERNATIONAL PUBLIC

Emp.: 1,080
Fiscal Year-end: 12/31/19
Numerical Control Machine Tools Design & Production
N.A.I.C.S.: 332999
Tai On Lo *(Sec)*

GOOD LIFE COMPANY, INC.
3F 2-17-8 Hakataekimae, Hakata-Ku, Fukuoka, 812-0011, Japan
Tel.: (81) 924714123
Web Site: https://www.goodlife-c.jp
Year Founded: 2008
2970—(TKS)
Rev.: $81,074,150
Assets: $66,369,490
Liabilities: $43,256,090
Net Worth: $23,113,400
Earnings: $4,934,640
Emp.: 165
Fiscal Year-end: 12/31/23
Real Estate Investment Services
N.A.I.C.S.: 531190
Hayato Takamura *(Chm & Pres)*

GOOD NATURED PRODUCTS INC.
814-470 Granville St, Vancouver, V6C 1V5, BC, Canada
Tel.: (604) 998-4058 AB
Web Site:
https://goodnaturedproducts.com
Year Founded: 2006
2VL—(DEU)
Rev.: $57,829,042
Assets: $72,521,332
Liabilities: $65,924,639
Net Worth: $6,596,693
Earnings: ($11,689,949)
Emp.: 185
Fiscal Year-end: 12/31/23
Plastic Material & Resin Mfr
N.A.I.C.S.: 325211
Paul Antoniadis *(CEO)*

Subsidiaries:

Ex-Tech Plastics, Inc. (1)
N 11413 Burlington Rd, Richmond, IL 60071
Tel.: (847) 829-8100
Web Site: http://www.extechplastics.com
Plastic Film & Sheet Mfr
N.A.I.C.S.: 326113
Emily E. Pichon *(Chm)*

Formtex Plastics Corp. (1)
6817 Wynnwood Ln, Houston, TX 77008
Tel.: (713) 864-7300
Web Site: http://www.formtex.com
Sales Range: $1-9.9 Million
Emp.: 32
Plastics Product Mfr
N.A.I.C.S.: 326199
Frank Yerich *(Founder & CEO)*

GOOD PEOPLE CO., LTD
165-5 Donggyo-Dong, Mapp-Gu, Seoul, Korea (South)
Tel.: (82) 23206600
Web Site:
http://www.goodpeople.co.kr
Year Founded: 1991
033340—(KRS)
Rev.: $61,720,571
Assets: $56,705,497
Liabilities: $15,619,005
Net Worth: $41,086,491
Earnings: ($4,780,733)
Emp.: 155
Fiscal Year-end: 12/31/22
Innerwear Mfr
N.A.I.C.S.: 315250

GOOD RESOURCES HOLDINGS LIMITED
Unit 3310-11 33rd Floor West Tower, Shun Tak Centre 168-200 Connaught Road, Central, China (Hong Kong)
Tel.: (852) 2587 8368 BM

AND PRIVATE COMPANIES

Sales Range: $1-9.9 Million
Emp.: 10
Holding Company
N.A.I.C.S.: 551112
Chuan Jin Chen *(Chm)*

GOOD SPIRITS HOSPITALITY LIMITED
GSH—(NZX)
Rev.: $17,057,164
Assets: $19,228,199
Liabilities: $30,952,498
Net Worth: ($11,724,300)
Earnings: ($8,538,089)
Emp.: 9
Fiscal Year-end: 06/30/23
Investment Management Service
N.A.I.C.S.: 523940
Geoff Tuttle *(CEO)*

GOOD STEEL PARTNERS CO., LTD.
ES Buliding 239-4 Gasan-dong, Geumcheon-gu, Seoul, 153-801, Korea (South)
Tel.: (82) 28509900   KR
Web Site: http://www.goodsteel.net
Year Founded: 2006
Stainless Steel Whslr
N.A.I.C.S.: 423510
Jong Wook Kim *(CEO)*

GOOD WAY TECHNOLOGY CO., LTD.
3F No 135 Ln 235 Baociao Rd, Sindian Dist, New Taipei City, 231, Taiwan
Tel.: (886) 289191200
Web Site:
   https://www.goodway.com.tw
Year Founded: 1983
3272—(TPE)
Rev.: $212,614,201
Assets: $200,817,497
Liabilities: $137,599,881
Net Worth: $63,217,616
Earnings: $7,041,303
Emp.: 1,200
Fiscal Year-end: 12/31/22
Computer Peripheral Equipment Mfr
N.A.I.C.S.: 334118

GOOD WILL INSTRUMENT CO., LTD.
No 7-1 Jhongsing Road, Tucheng Dist, New Taipei City, 236, Taiwan
Tel.: (886) 222680389
Web Site: https://www.gwinstek.com
Year Founded: 1975
2423—(TAI)
Rev.: $98,915,298
Assets: $124,129,921
Liabilities: $34,471,695
Net Worth: $89,658,226
Earnings: $14,005,395
Emp.: 138
Fiscal Year-end: 12/31/23
Electronics Instrument Mfr
N.A.I.C.S.: 334419

Subsidiaries:

Good Will Instrument (Sea) Sdn. Bhd.   (1)
No 1-3-18 Elit Avenue Jalan Mayang Pasir 3, 11950, Bayan Baru, Penang, Malaysia
Tel.: (60) 46111122
Electrical Measurement Instrument Mfr & Distr
N.A.I.C.S.: 334515

Good Will Instrument Euro B.V.   (1)
De Run 5427A, 5504DG, Veldhoven, Netherlands
Tel.: (31) 402557790
Electrical Measurement Instrument Mfr & Distr
N.A.I.C.S.: 334515

Good Will Instrument Korea Co., Ltd.   (1)
Room 503 Building 1 Ace High Tech City 55-20 Mullae-dong 3-ga, Yeongdeungpo-gu, Seoul, 07299, Korea (South)
Tel.: (82) 234392205
Web Site: https://www.gwinstek.co.kr
Electrical Measurement Instrument Mfr & Distr
N.A.I.C.S.: 334515

Gw Instek India LLP   (1)
823 Tower-C Noida One B8 Sector-62, Noida, 201309, Uttar Pradesh, India
Tel.: (91) 1203101942
Electrical Measurement Instrument Mfr & Distr
N.A.I.C.S.: 334515

Instek America Corp.   (1)
5198 Brooks St, Montclair, CA 91763
Tel.: (909) 399-3535
Electrical Measurement Instrument Mfr & Distr
N.A.I.C.S.: 334515

Instek Electronic (Shanghai) Co., Ltd.   (1)
8F of No 2 Building No 889 Yishan Road, Shanghai, China
Tel.: (86) 2164853399
Electrical Measurement Instrument Mfr & Distr
N.A.I.C.S.: 334515

Texio Technology Corporation   (1)
Towa-fudosan Shin Yokohama Bld 7F 2-18-13 Shin, Kohoku-ku, Yokohama, 222-0033, Kanagawa, Japan
Tel.: (81) 456202303
Web Site: https://www.texio.co.jp
Electrical Measurement Instrument Mfr & Distr
N.A.I.C.S.: 334515

GOOD YEAR LASTIKLERI TAS
Sumer Sokak MOB Binasi No 4 Kat 10-11, Maslak Mahallesi, 34485, Sariyer, Turkiye
Tel.: (90) 2123295000
Web Site: https://www.goodyear.eu
GOODY—(IST)
Sales Range: Less than $1 Million
Rubber Product Mfr & Distr
N.A.I.C.S.: 326299
Dominikus Golsong *(Chm)*

GOOD2GO CORP.
1 King Street West Suite 1505, Toronto, M5C 1T4, ON, Canada
Tel.: (416) 364-4039   Ca
Year Founded: 2018
GFOE.P—(TSXV)
Rev.: $2,502
Assets: $123,880
Liabilities: $11,672
Net Worth: $112,208
Earnings: ($41,053)
Fiscal Year-end: 06/30/24
Business Consulting Services
N.A.I.C.S.: 522299

GOODBABY INTERNATIONAL HOLDINGS LIMITED
No 20 Luxi Rd Lujia Town, Kunshan, 215331, Jiangsu, China
Tel.: (86) 51257871888
Web Site:
   http://www.gbinternational.com.hk
Year Founded: 1994
1086—(HKG)
Rev.: $1,057,249,380
Assets: $1,493,623,613
Liabilities: $785,022,855
Net Worth: $708,600,758
Earnings: $5,116,320
Emp.: 7,357
Fiscal Year-end: 12/31/22
Stroller Mfr
N.A.I.C.S.: 339930
Zhenghuan Song *(Chm & Co-CEO)*

Subsidiaries:

Cybex GmbH   (1)
Riedinger Str 18, 95448, Bayreuth, Germany
Tel.: (49) 921785110
Baby Carrier Kit Furniture & Stroller Mfr
N.A.I.C.S.: 339930
Pawel Palmowski *(Mgr-Country)*

Cybex Retail GmbH   (1)
Riedingerstr 18, 95448, Bayreuth, Germany
Tel.: (49) 921785119621
Web Site: https://www.cybex-online.com
Car Seat & Accessory Mfr & Retailer
N.A.I.C.S.: 336360

Evenflo Company, Inc.   (1)
1801 Commerce Dr, Piqua, OH 45346
Tel.: (937) 415-3300
Web Site: https://www.evenflo.com
Sales Range: $50-74.9 Million
Emp.: 2,300
Baby Equipment & Supplies Mfr
N.A.I.C.S.: 337126
Jon Chamberlain *(CEO)*

Holding (Non-US):

Evenflo Canada   (2)
6345 Dixie Road Suite 1, Mississauga, L5T 2E6, ON, Canada
Tel.: (905) 670-2213
Web Site: http://www.evenflo.com
Baby Equipment & Accessories Sales
N.A.I.C.S.: 423210

Evenflo Mexico S.A. de C.V.   (2)
Avenida Central N 62 Int A Col Tepalcates, Alcaldia Iztapalapa, 08400, Mexico, Mexico
Tel.: (52) 5552827310
Web Site:
   https://www.evenflofeeding.com.mx
Baby Equipment & Accessories Sales
N.A.I.C.S.: 423210

GB GmbH   (1)
Riedingerstr 18, 95448, Bayreuth, Germany
Tel.: (49) 921785110
Web Site: https://gb-online.com
Baby Car Seat & Stroller Retailer
N.A.I.C.S.: 424350

Goodbaby (Hong Kong) Limited   (1)
Room 2001 20th Floor Two Chinachem Exchange Square 338 Kings Road, North Point, Hong Kong, China (Hong Kong)
Tel.: (852) 28060338
Child Care Products Mfr & Distr
N.A.I.C.S.: 339930

Goodbaby China Commercial Co., Ltd   (1)
660rm A5 Corporation Garden NO 2 Xugongqiao Road, Huaqiao Town, Kunshan, 215332, Jiangsu, China
Tel.: (86) 2136626114
Web Site: http://www.babybowcn.com
Juvenile Products Mfr & Distr
N.A.I.C.S.: 339930

Goodbaby Japan Co., Ltd.   (1)
No 10 No 5 1 Chome Soto-Kanda, Chiyoda-ku, Tokyo, Japan
Tel.: (81) 3 3255 5092
Child Care Products Mfr & Distr
N.A.I.C.S.: 339930

Turn Key Design B.V   (1)
Herenstraat 12, 3512 KC, Utrecht, Netherlands
Tel.: (31) 30 2400 888
Web Site: http://www.turnkeydesign.nl
Child Care Products Mfr & Distr
N.A.I.C.S.: 339930

GOODBULK LTD.
7 Rue du Gabian Gildo Pastor Center, Monaco, 98000, Monaco
Tel.: (377) 97 98 59 87   BM
Web Site: http://www.goodbulk.com
Year Founded: 2016
Rev.: $182,181,000
Assets: $677,001,000
Liabilities: $259,612,000
Net Worth: $417,389,000
Earnings: $37,776,000
Fiscal Year-end: 12/31/18

GOODERSON LEISURE CORPORATION

Bulk Cargo Distr
N.A.I.C.S.: 484230
John Michael Radziwill *(Chm & CEO)*

GOODBYE KANSAS GROUP AB
Hammarbyterrassen 3, SE-12030, Stockholm, Sweden
Tel.: (46) 855699000
Web Site:
   https://goodbyekansasgroup.com
Year Founded: 2015
GBK—(OMX)
Rev.: $28,947,896
Assets: $25,701,106
Liabilities: $26,838,162
Net Worth: ($1,137,055)
Earnings: ($11,839,707)
Emp.: 218
Fiscal Year-end: 12/31/22
Software Development Services
N.A.I.C.S.: 541511
Maria A. Grimaldi *(CEO)*

GOODDAYS HOLDINGS, INC.
1-23-19 Kitashinagawa, Shinagawa-ku, Tokyo, 140-0001, Japan
Tel.: (81) 357819070
Web Site: https://www.gooddays.jp
4437—(TKS)
Rev.: $49,237,890
Assets: $33,373,890
Liabilities: $15,434,350
Net Worth: $17,939,540
Earnings: $1,983,000
Fiscal Year-end: 03/31/24
Real Estate Brokerage Services
N.A.I.C.S.: 531210
Hiroshi Ogura *(Pres)*

GOODERSON LEISURE CORPORATION
85 O R Tambo Parade South Beach, Durban, 4056, Natal, South Africa
Tel.: (27) 313374222   ZA
Web Site:
   http://www.goodersonleisure.co.za
Year Founded: 1957
Sales Range: $125-149.9 Million
Emp.: 650
Hotel Restaurant & Leisure Resort Owner & Operator
N.A.I.C.S.: 722511
Alan William Gooderson *(Chm & CEO)*

Subsidiaries:

Bushlands Game Lodge   (1)
Lot H99 Bushlands Road, Hluhluwe, 3960, KwaZulu-Natal, South Africa
Tel.: (27) 355620144
Web Site:
   http://www.goodersonleisure.co.za
Sales Range: $10-24.9 Million
Emp.: 40
Hotel & Game Lodge Operator
N.A.I.C.S.: 721110
Courtney Goddard *(Gen Mgr)*

Drakensberg Gardens Golf & Spa Resort   (1)
Drakensberg Gardens Road, Southern Drakensberg, Underberg, 3257, KwaZulu-Natal, South Africa
Tel.: (27) 337011106
Web Site:
   http://www.goodersonleisure.co.za
Sales Range: $25-49.9 Million
Emp.: 20
Hotel, Golf & Spa Resort Operator
N.A.I.C.S.: 721110
Peter Muil *(Gen Mgr)*

DumaZulu Lodge & Traditional Village   (1)
Lot H29 Bushlands Road, Hluhluwe, 3960, KwaZulu-Natal, South Africa
Tel.: (27) 355622260
Web Site:
   http://www.goodersonleisure.co.za

GOODERSON LEISURE CORPORATION

Gooderson Leisure Corporation—(Continued)
Emp.: 1,000
Hotel Operator
N.A.I.C.S.: 721110
Gavin Castleman (CEO)

Mtunzini Forest Lodge (1)
Las 167 Valley Drive, PO Box 132,
Mtunzini, 3867, KwaZulu-Natal, South Africa
Tel.: (27) 313685642
Web Site:
http://www.goodersonleisure.com
Forest Vacation Camp & Lodge Operator
N.A.I.C.S.: 721110

The Beach Hotel (1)
107 OR Tambo Parade, Durban, 4000,
KwaZulu-Natal, South Africa
Tel.: (27) 313375511
Web Site:
http://www.goodersonleisure.co.za
Sales Range: $10-24.9 Million
Emp.: 69
Hotel Operator
N.A.I.C.S.: 721110
Petra Boshoff (Gen Mgr)

Tropicana Hotel - Golden Mile (1)
85 OR Tambo Parade, South Beach, Durban, 4001, Kwazulu Natal, South Africa
Tel.: (27) 313681511
Web Site:
http://www.goodersonleisure.co.za
Sales Range: $50-74.9 Million
Emp.: 500
Hotel Operator
N.A.I.C.S.: 721110
A. Visser (Gen Mgr)

GOODFELLOW INC.

225 rue Goodfellow, Delson, J5B
1V5, QC, Canada
Tel.: (450) 635-6511 Ca
Web Site:
https://www.goodfellowinc.com
Year Founded: 1972
O3Z—(DEU)
Rev.: $493,763,402
Assets: $193,158,231
Liabilities: $47,044,755
Net Worth: $146,113,476
Earnings: $25,564,128
Emp.: 677
Fiscal Year-end: 11/30/22
Lumber & Wood Products Mfr, Distr & Broker
N.A.I.C.S.: 321999
Patrick Goodfellow (Pres & CEO)

Subsidiaries:

Goodfellow Inc. - Manchester
Branch (1)
368 Pepsi Rd, Manchester, NH 03109
Tel.: (603) 623-9811
Wood Product Distr
N.A.I.C.S.: 423310

Goodfellow Inc. - Oliver Lumber
Division (1)
9184 Twiss Road, PO Box 460, Campbellville, L0P 1B0, ON, Canada
Tel.: (416) 233-1227
Web Site: http://www.oliverlumber.com
Lumber Product Distr
N.A.I.C.S.: 423310

Goodfellow UK Ltd (1)
Elm Point Wrexham Industrial Estate, PO
Box 36, Wrexham, LL13 9UE, United Kingdom
Tel.: (44) 1691718872
Web Site: https://www.goodfellowuk.com
Wood Flooring Distr
N.A.I.C.S.: 423310

Quality Hardwoods Ltd. (1)
196 Latour Cres, PO Box 40, Powassan,
P0H 1Z0, ON, Canada
Tel.: (705) 724-2424
Web Site:
http://www.qualityhardwoodsltd.com
Lumber Product Mfr & Distr
N.A.I.C.S.: 321113

GOODFOOD MARKET CORP.

4600 Hickmore Street, Saint Laurent,
H4T 1K2, QC, Canada
Tel.: (416) 972-6294 ON
Web Site:
https://www.makegoodfood.ca
Year Founded: 2015
76O—(DEU)
Rev.: $125,744,268
Assets: $43,124,768
Liabilities: $60,612,500
Net Worth: ($17,487,732)
Earnings: ($12,281,398)
Emp.: 780
Fiscal Year-end: 09/02/23
Investment Services
N.A.I.C.S.: 523999
Roslane Aouameur (Sr Dir-FP&A & IR)

GOODLAND GROUP LIMITED

3 Kim Chuan Lane 07-01 Goodland
Group Building, Singapore, 537069,
Singapore
Tel.: (65) 62890003
Web Site:
https://www.goodlandgroup.com.sg
Year Founded: 2004
5PC—(SES)
Rev.: $15,778,380
Assets: $275,970,708
Liabilities: $101,935,194
Net Worth: $174,035,514
Earnings: $1,024,777
Emp.: 42
Fiscal Year-end: 09/30/23
Property Developer & Sales
N.A.I.C.S.: 236117
Ben Chee Beng Tan (Chm)

Subsidiaries:

GPM Builders Pte. Ltd. (1)
3 Kim Chuan Lane, 07-01 Goodland Group
Building, Singapore, 537069, Singapore
Tel.: (65) 62935505
Building Contracting Services
N.A.I.C.S.: 236220

Goodland Capital Pte. Ltd. (1)
18 Roberts Ln No 02-01 02 Goodland Bldg,
Singapore, 218297, Singapore
Tel.: (65) 62890003
Web Site: http://www.goodlandgroup.com.sg
Property Management Services
N.A.I.C.S.: 531312

Goodland Development Pte. Ltd. (1)
18 Roberts Ln No 02-01 02 Goodland Bldg,
Singapore, 218297, Singapore
Tel.: (65) 62890003
Web Site: http://www.goodlandgroup.com.sg
Property Development Services
N.A.I.C.S.: 531312
Alvin Tan (Co-Founder)

Goodland Group Construction Pte.
Ltd. (1)
3 Kim Chuan Lane 07-01 Goodland Group
Building, Singapore, 537069, Singapore
Tel.: (65) 62890003
Web Site:
https://www.goodlandgroup.com.sg
Emp.: 100
Property Development Services
N.A.I.C.S.: 531312

Goodland Homes Pte. Ltd. (1)
3 Kim Chuan Lane 07-01 Goodland Group
Building, Singapore, 537069, Singapore
Tel.: (65) 62890003
Web Site: http://www.goodlandgroup.com.sg
Property Management Services
N.A.I.C.S.: 531312

Goodland Investments Pte. Ltd. (1)
3 Hillside Terrace, Singapore, 218297, Singapore
Tel.: (65) 62890003
Property Development Services
N.A.I.C.S.: 531312
Melanie Tan (Exec Dir)

T City (Ipoh) Sdn. Bhd. (1)
No 180 182 Jalan Sultan Azlan Shah Selatan, 30250, Ipoh, Perak, Malaysia

Tel.: (60) 52413560
Web Site: https://www.tcity.com.my
Commercial Township Development Services
N.A.I.C.S.: 531120

GOODLUCK INDIA LIMITED

Good Luck House II F 166-167,
Nehru Nagar 2 Ambedkar Road,
Ghaziabad, 201001, Uttar Pradesh,
India
Tel.: (91) 1204196600
Web Site:
https://www.goodluckindia.com
Year Founded: 1986
530655—(BOM)
Rev.: $421,348,418
Assets: $200,788,647
Liabilities: $116,157,105
Net Worth: $84,631,542
Earnings: $11,984,823
Emp.: 3,500
Fiscal Year-end: 03/31/23
Galvanised Tubes & Pipes Mfr
N.A.I.C.S.: 331110
Abhishek Agrawal (Officer-Compliance & Sec)

GOODLUCK INDUSTRIES LTD.

S-49/A SITE Mauripur Road, Karachi,
Pakistan
Tel.: (92) 2132354361
Web Site:
https://www.goodluckind.com
Year Founded: 1967
GIL—(PSX)
Rev.: $6,368,885
Assets: $4,031,105
Liabilities: $416,037
Net Worth: $3,615,068
Earnings: $15,567
Emp.: 42
Fiscal Year-end: 06/30/23
Flour Mill Operator
N.A.I.C.S.: 311211
Ashfaq Hasham (CEO)

GOODMAN LIMITED

The Hayesbery 1-11 Hayes Rd,
Rosebery, 2018, NSW, Australia
Tel.: (61) 292307400 AU
Web Site: https://www.goodman.com
GMG—(ASX)
Rev.: $767,946,795
Assets: $3,457,847,037
Liabilities: $1,626,067,679
Net Worth: $1,831,779,357
Earnings: $130,534,003
Emp.: 971
Fiscal Year-end: 06/30/23
Real Estate Manangement Services
N.A.I.C.S.: 551112
Gregory Leith Goodman (CEO-Grp)

Subsidiaries:

GELF Management (Lux) Sarl (1)
5 Rue de Strasbourg, 2561, Luxembourg,
Luxembourg
Tel.: (352) 26363220
Web Site: https://www.gep.eu
Financial Management Services
N.A.I.C.S.: 523999

Goodman Asia Limited (1)
Suite 901 Three Pacific Place 1 Queen's
Road East, Hong Kong, 999077, China
(Hong Kong)
Tel.: (852) 22493100
Property Management Services
N.A.I.C.S.: 531390
Nancy Wu (Dir-HR)

Goodman Belgium NV (1)
Medialaan 50, 1800, Vilvoorde, Belgium
Tel.: (32) 22634000
Web Site: https://be.goodman.com
Property Development Services
N.A.I.C.S.: 531390
Lien Standaert (Country Mgr)

Goodman France Sarl (1)

INTERNATIONAL PUBLIC

24 rue de Prony, 75017, Paris, France
Tel.: (33) 155350850
Web Site: https://fr.goodman.com
Property Development Services
N.A.I.C.S.: 531390
Philippe Arfi (Country Dir)

Goodman Germany GmbH (1)
Airgate-Airport City Peter-Muller-Strasse 10,
40468, Dusseldorf, Germany
Tel.: (49) 21149980
Web Site: https://de.goodman.com
Property Development Services
N.A.I.C.S.: 531390
Christof Prange (Head-Bus Dev)

Goodman Italy S.R.L. (1)
Via Manin 3, 20121, Milan, Italy
Tel.: (39) 0236009111
Web Site: https://it.goodman.com
Property Development Services
N.A.I.C.S.: 531390
Audrey Foresto (Mktg Mgr)

Goodman Japan Funds Limited (1)
GranTokyo North Tower 36F 1-9-1,
Marunouchi Chiyoda Ward, Tokyo, 100-6736, Japan
Tel.: (81) 369103310
Property Development Services
N.A.I.C.S.: 531390
Minoru Hirohata (Pres & CEO)

Goodman Japan Limited (1)
GranTokyo North Tower 36F 1-9-1,
Marunouchi Chiyoda-ku, Tokyo, 100-6736,
Japan
Tel.: (81) 369103300
Web Site: https://jp.goodman.com
Emp.: 60
Property Development Services
N.A.I.C.S.: 531390
Angus Brooks (CEO)

Goodman Logistics Developments
(UK) Ltd (1)
Nelson House Central Boulevard Blythe
Valley Park, Solihull, B90 8BG, United Kingdom
Tel.: (44) 121 506 8100
Web Site:
http://www.uklogistics.goodman.com
Logistics Consulting Servies
N.A.I.C.S.: 541614
Charles Crossland (Mng Dir)

Goodman Management Consulting
(Beijing) Co., Ltd. (1)
Room 2304 One Indigo 20 Jiuxianqiao
Road, Chaoyang District, Beijing, 100016,
China
Tel.: (86) 1085730700
Property Development Services
N.A.I.C.S.: 531390

Goodman Management Consulting
(Shanghai) Co., Ltd. (1)
10/F Tower 2 Jing An Kerry Centre 1539
Nanjing Road West, Jing An District,
Shanghai, 200040, China
Tel.: (86) 2161332000
Property Development Services
N.A.I.C.S.: 531390

Goodman Management Holdings
(Lux) Sarl (1)
5 Rue De Strasbourg, Grand Duchy, 2561,
Luxembourg, Luxembourg
Tel.: (352) 26363220
N.A.I.C.S.: 561110

Goodman Netherlands BV (1)
Zuidplein 164 Tower H Level 20, 1077 XV,
Amsterdam, Netherlands
Tel.: (31) 207093930
Web Site: https://nl.goodman.com
Property Development Services
N.A.I.C.S.: 531390
Lien Standaert (Country Mgr)

Goodman Operator (UK) Limited (1)
Cornwall House Blythe Valley Park, Solihull,
B90 8AF, United Kingdom
Tel.: (44) 1215068100
Web Site: https://uk.goodman.com
Property Development Services
N.A.I.C.S.: 531390
Charles Crossland (Mng Dir-Logistics)

Goodman Property Services (NZ)
Limited (1)

AND PRIVATE COMPANIES | GOODWIN PLC

Level 2 KPMG Centre 18 Viaduct Harbour Avenue, Auckland, 1010, New Zealand
Tel.: (64) 93756060
N.A.I.C.S.: 561110

Goodman Real Estate (Spain) S.L. (1)
Paseo de la Castellana 93 12th Floor East, Edificio Cadagua, 28046, Madrid, Spain
Tel.: (34) 914141550
Web Site: https://es.goodman.com
Real Estate Brokerage Services
N.A.I.C.S.: 531210

Goodman UK Ltd. (1)
Cornwall House, Blythe Valley Park, Solihull, B90 8AF, United Kingdom
Tel.: (44) 1215068100
Web Site: https://www.goodman.com
Sales Range: $150-199.9 Million
Emp.: 40
Industrial & Commercial Real Estate Developer & Property Management Services
N.A.I.C.S.: 237210

Moorabbin Airport Corporation Pty Ltd (1)
66 Bundora Parade Airport, Moorabbin, 3194, VIC, Australia
Tel.: (61) 385878000
Web Site: https://www.moorabbinairport.com.au
Airport Services
N.A.I.C.S.: 488190

GOODMAN PLUS TRUST
Level 17 60 Castlereagh Street, Sydney, 2000, NSW, Australia
Tel.: (61) 2 9230 7400 AU
Web Site: http://www.goodman.com
Investment Management Service
N.A.I.C.S.: 523940
Gregory Goodman *(Grp CEO)*

GOODPATCH, INC.
3-3 Uguisudanicho 2F VORT Shibuya South, Shibuya-Ku, Tokyo, 150-0032, Japan
Tel.: (81) 364169238
Web Site: https://goodpatch.com
Year Founded: 2011
7351—(TKS)
Rev.: $24,519,240
Assets: $29,084,720
Liabilities: $5,000,880
Net Worth: $24,083,840
Earnings: $68,420
Emp.: 265
Fiscal Year-end: 08/31/24
Application Development Services
N.A.I.C.S.: 541511
Naofumi Tsuchiya *(Founder & Pres)*

GOODSPEED CO., LTD.
8F Takaoka KANAME Building 2-28-23 Izumi, Higashi-ku, Nagoya, 461-0001, Japan
Tel.: (81) 529334092
Web Site: https://www.goodspeed-group.co.jp
Year Founded: 2002
7676—(TKS)
Automobile Parts Distr
N.A.I.C.S.: 423120
Hisanori Kato *(Founder, Chm & Pres)*

GOODTECH ASA
Innspurten 15, PO Box 6578, Etterstad, 0607, Oslo, Norway
Tel.: (47) 81568600
Web Site: https://www.goodtech.no
GOD—(OSL)
Sales Range: $50-74.9 Million
Emp.: 300
Environmental Engineering Services
N.A.I.C.S.: 541330
Synnove Granli *(CFO)*

Subsidiaries:

Goodtech Environment AB (1)
Gamla Godbyvagen 2, 22100, Mariehamn, Aland, Finland
Tel.: (358) 1823100
Sales Range: $25-49.9 Million
Emp.: 39
Agricultural Equipments Distr
N.A.I.C.S.: 811310

Goodtech Environment Sorumsand AS (1)
Noractor Industriomrade, 1920, Sorumsand, Akershus, Norway
Tel.: (47) 63866460
Web Site: http://www.goodtech.no
Sales Range: $25-49.9 Million
Emp.: 20
Wastewater Treatment Plants Distr
N.A.I.C.S.: 423830

Goodtech Germany GmbH (1)
Industriering Ost 66, 47906, Kempen, Nordrhein-Westfalen, Germany
Tel.: (49) 21521489403
Web Site: http://www.good-tech.de
Emp.: 5
Labeling Machinery Mfr
N.A.I.C.S.: 323120
Christopher Bahrs *(Mng Dir)*

Goodtech Packaging Systems AS (1)
Tormod Gjestlands Veg 16, 3908, Porsgrunn, Telemark, Norway
Tel.: (47) 35924850
Web Site: http://www.goodtech.no
Sales Range: $25-49.9 Million
Emp.: 8
Industrial Packaging Equipment Mfr
N.A.I.C.S.: 333993

Goodtech Process AB (1)
Nobelvagen 2, Boks 975, 801 33, Gavle, Gastrikland, Sweden
Tel.: (46) 36345150
Web Site: http://www.goodtech.no
Industrial Automation Services
N.A.I.C.S.: 238210

Goodtech Projects & Services AB (1)
Mariehemsvagen 6, Box 3152, Umea, 906 54, Vasterbotten, Sweden
Tel.: (46) 90154600
Web Site: http://www.goodtech.se
Electrical & Environmental Engineering Services
N.A.I.C.S.: 541330

Goodtech Recovery Technology AS (1)
Per Krohgs vei 4, 1065, Oslo, Norway
Tel.: (47) 23177100
Web Site: http://www.goodtech.no
Sales Range: $25-49.9 Million
Emp.: 4
Wastewater Treatment Equipments Mfr
N.A.I.C.S.: 333310

Goodtech Solutions AB (1)
Gjuterigatan 38C, 652 21, Karlstad, Sweden
Tel.: (46) 54240300
Web Site: http://www.goodtech.no
Material Handling Equipment Mfr
N.A.I.C.S.: 333310

Goodtech Solutions AS (1)
Mosseveien 39 B, 1610, Fredrikstad, Norway
Tel.: (47) 69394500
Web Site: http://www.goodtech.no
Industrial Automation Services
N.A.I.C.S.: 541330

Goodtech Solutions Industriautomation AB (1)
Grasdalsgatan 15, 653 43, Karlstad, Sweden
Tel.: (46) 54180201
Web Site: http://www.goodtech.no
Sales Range: $25-49.9 Million
Emp.: 60
Industrial Automation Services
N.A.I.C.S.: 238210

Goodtech Solutions Karlstad AB (1)
Grasdalsgatan 15, 653 43, Karlstad, Sweden
Tel.: (46) 54240300
Web Site: http://www.goodtech.se
Sales Range: $25-49.9 Million
Emp.: 60
Mechanical & Electrical Engineering Services
N.A.I.C.S.: 541330

Goodtech Solutions Saffle AB (1)
Tingvallastrand 12, 661 40, Saffle, Varmland, Sweden
Tel.: (46) 53312425
Sales Range: $25-49.9 Million
Emp.: 30
Industrial Automation Services
N.A.I.C.S.: 238210
Bernt Paulson *(Mng Dir)*

GOODWAY MACHINE CORP.
No 38 Keyuan Rd, Situn District, Taichung, 407, Taiwan
Tel.: (886) 424636000
Web Site: https://www.goodwaycnc.com
Year Founded: 1975
1583—(TAI)
Rev.: $173,929,422
Assets: $433,218,402
Liabilities: $198,920,199
Net Worth: $234,298,202
Earnings: $26,695,672
Fiscal Year-end: 12/31/23
Turning Machinery Mfr & Distr
N.A.I.C.S.: 333517

Subsidiaries:

Goodway (Suzhou) Machine Corp. (1)
No 589 Chengyang Rd Xiang Cheng Economic Development District, Suzhou, 215138, Jiangsu, China
Tel.: (86) 51265763699
Web Site: http://www.goodwaycnc.com
Machine Tools Mfr
N.A.I.C.S.: 333517

Yama Seiki USA Inc. (1)
5788 Schaefer Ave, Chino, CA 91710
Tel.: (909) 628-5568
Web Site: http://www.yamaseiki.com
Sales Range: $25-49.9 Million
Emp.: 15
Industrial Precision Machinery Distr
N.A.I.C.S.: 332216

GOODWILL FINANCE LIMITED
Hattisar Kamalpokhari, PO Box 8867, Kathmandu, Nepal
Tel.: (977) 14444039
Web Site: https://goodwillfinance.com.np
Year Founded: 1995
GFCL—(NEP)
Rev.: $12,363,268
Assets: $110,894,471
Liabilities: $98,828,719
Net Worth: $12,065,751
Earnings: ($691,893)
Emp.: 96
Fiscal Year-end: 07/16/23
Financial Services
N.A.I.C.S.: 523999
Bishwa Prakash Saakha *(Chm)*

GOODWIN PLC
Ivy House Foundry, Hanley, Stoke-on-Trent, ST1 3NR, United Kingdom
Tel.: (44) 1782220000
Web Site: https://www.goodwin.co.uk
Year Founded: 1883
GDWN—(LSE)
Rev.: $178,174,953
Assets: $274,817,463
Liabilities: $114,568,487
Net Worth: $160,248,976
Earnings: $17,658,506
Emp.: 1,129
Fiscal Year-end: 04/30/21
Holding Company
N.A.I.C.S.: 551112
Matthew S. Goodwin *(Mng Dir-Mechanical Engrg Div)*

Subsidiaries:

Dupre Minerals Limited (1)
Spencroft Road, Newcastle-under-Lyme, ST5 9JE, Staffordshire, United Kingdom
Tel.: (44) 1782383000
Web Site: http://www.dupreminerals.com
Sales Range: $25-49.9 Million
Emp.: 40
Jewelry, Industrial Metal & Dental Casting Powders Mfr
N.A.I.C.S.: 332111
Richard Goodwin *(Mng Dir)*

Subsidiary (Domestic):

Hoben International Ltd. (2)
Brassington Works Maystones Lane, Matlock, DE4 4HF, Derbyshire, United Kingdom
Tel.: (44) 1629540201
Web Site: http://www.hobeninternational.com
Sales Range: $25-49.9 Million
Ceramic, Glass & Refractory Products
N.A.I.C.S.: 212323
David Andrew Hazlewood *(Gen Mgr & Dir)*

Easat Antennas Ltd. (1)
Goodwin House Leek Road, Hanley, Stoke-on-Trent, ST1 3NR, United Kingdom
Tel.: (44) 1782208028
Web Site: http://www.easat.co.uk
Sales Range: $25-49.9 Million
Emp.: 14
Radar Sensor Systems, Antennas & Turning Units
N.A.I.C.S.: 561621
James Long *(Mng Dir)*

Easat Radar Systems Limited (1)
Newstead Industrial Estate Alderflat Dr, Stoke-on-Trent, ST4 8HU, United Kingdom
Tel.: (44) 178 220 8028
Web Site: https://www.easat.com
Radar System & Equipment Mfr
N.A.I.C.S.: 334511

Goodwin (Shanxi) Pump Co., Ltd. (1)
1105 Building 1 Wangucheng Moma No 16 Changfeng West Street, Taiyuan, 030021, Shanxi, China
Tel.: (86) 351 408 1128
Web Site: http://www.goodwinshanxi.com
Industrial Pump Mfr
N.A.I.C.S.: 333914
Sam Yang *(Engr-Sls)*

Goodwin Industria e Comercio de Valvulas de Retencao e Bombas Submersas Ltda. (1)
Rua das Margaridas 70 Terra Preta, Mairipora, 07600-000, SP, Brazil
Tel.: (55) 1144861429
Web Site: http://www.goodwinlatina.com
Submersible Pump Mfr
N.A.I.C.S.: 333914
Rafel Armengou *(Gen Mgr)*

Goodwin International Ltd. (1)
Plantation Road, Trentham, Stoke-on-Trent, ST4 8HU, United Kingdom
Tel.: (44) 1782654000
Web Site: http://www.goodwininternational.co.uk
Water Check Valves & Submersible Slurry Pumps Mfr
N.A.I.C.S.: 333914

Goodwin Korea Ltd. (1)
13-1 Jungbong-daero 396beon-gil, Seo-gu, Incheon, 22771, Korea (South)
Tel.: (82) 325796313
Web Site: http://www.goodwin.co.kr
Sales Range: $25-49.9 Million
Emp.: 4
Plate Check Valve Mfr
N.A.I.C.S.: 332911

Goodwin Refractory Services Holdings Limited (1)
Spencroft Road, Newcastle-under-Lyme, ST5 9JE, Staffordshire, United Kingdom
Tel.: (44) 178 266 3600
Web Site: https://www.grscastingpowders.com
Molding Material Mfr
N.A.I.C.S.: 333511

Goodwin Refractory Services Limited (1)

GOODWIN PLC

Goodwin PLC—(Continued)

Spencroft Road, Newcastle-under-Lyme, ST5 9JE, Staffordshire, United Kingdom
Tel.: (44) 1782663600
Web Site: http://www.grscastingpowders.com
Sales Range: $25-49.9 Million
Emp.: 30
Mechanical Engineering Services
N.A.I.C.S.: 541330

Subsidiary (Non-US):

Gold Star Brazil Limited (2)
Rua das Margaridas 70-Terra Preta, Mairipora, 07600-970, Sao Paulo, Brazil
Tel.: (55) 11 4486 1292
Web Site: http://www.goldstarbr.com.br
Sales Range: $25-49.9 Million
Emp.: 20
Investment Casting Powders Mfr
N.A.I.C.S.: 331523

Gold Star Powders Private Limited (2)
112/2 Chinna Amman Koil Street Kalavakkam, Old Mahabalipuram Road, Thiruporur, Kanchipuram, 603 110, Tamil Nadu, India
Tel.: (91) 4447439955
Web Site: http://www.goldstarpowders.in
Jewelry, Industrial Metal & Dental Casting Powders Mfr
N.A.I.C.S.: 212323

Subsidiary (Domestic):

Gold Star Powders UK (2)
Spencroft Road, Newcastle-under-Lyme, ST5 9JE, Staffordshire, United Kingdom
Tel.: (44) 1782663600
Web Site: http://www.goldstarpowders.com
Emp.: 40
Investment Casting Powder Mfr
N.A.I.C.S.: 339999

Affiliate (Non-US):

Siam Casting Powders Ltd. (3)
99/9 Moo 5 KhlongYong Bhudhamontol, Nakhon Pathom, 73170, Thailand
Tel.: (66) 34 246 037
Web Site: http://www.siamcasting.com
Sales Range: $50-74.9 Million
Powder Processor for Metal Casting
N.A.I.C.S.: 212323
Boonchana Anuruk *(Gen Mgr)*

Goodwin Steel Castings Ltd. (1)
Ivy House Foundry Ivy House Road, Hanley, Stoke-on-Trent, ST1 3NR, Staffordshire, United Kingdom
Tel.: (44) 1782220000
Web Site: http://www.goodwinsteelcastings.com
Sales Range: $100-124.9 Million
Emp.: 165
Steel Casting Mfr
N.A.I.C.S.: 332111

Internet Central Ltd. (1)
Innovation Centre Keele Science Park, Keele, ST5 5NB, Staffordshire, United Kingdom
Tel.: (44) 1782667700
Web Site: http://ic.uk
Sales Range: $25-49.9 Million
Emp.: 15
Internet Services
N.A.I.C.S.: 517810

Metal Proving Services Limited (1)
Ivy House Road, Hanley, Stoke-on-Trent, ST1 3NR, United Kingdom
Tel.: (44) 178 278 9713
Web Site: https://www.metalprovingservices.com
Technical Testing Services
N.A.I.C.S.: 541380
Tom Ayre *(Head-Quality)*

NRPL Aero Oy (1)
Koivupuistontie 34, 01510, Vantaa, Finland
Tel.: (358) 46 870 2233
Web Site: https://nrpl.aero
Air Traffic Control Equipment Mfr & Distr
N.A.I.C.S.: 334511

Noreva GmbH (1)
Hocksteiner Weg 56, 41189, Monchengladbach, Germany
Tel.: (49) 216 612 6860
Web Site: https://www.noreva.de
Industrial Machinery Mfr
N.A.I.C.S.: 333248

SRS (Qingdao) Casting Materials Company Limited (1)
Northern Industrial Park, XiFu Town ChengYang District, Qingdao, Shandong, China
Web Site: https://www.srs-china.com
Casting Material Mfr
N.A.I.C.S.: 333511

Sandersfire International Limited (1)
Brassington Works Manystones Lane, Matlock, DE4 4HF, Derbyshire, United Kingdom
Tel.: (44) 1629540201
Web Site: http://www.sanders-fire.co.uk
Fire Prevention Products Mfr
N.A.I.C.S.: 332994

Ultratec Jewelry Supplies (Guangzhou) Ltd. (1)
Minli Industrial Zone Lan He Town, Pan Yu District, Guangzhou, 511480, China
Tel.: (86) 2039970330
Investment Casting Powder Mfr
N.A.I.C.S.: 339999
Kevin Xie *(Gen Mgr)*

GOODY SCIENCE & TECHNOLOGY CO., LTD.
No 18 Wuchu Avenue, Economic Development Zone, Ezhou, 436099, Hubei, China
Tel.: (86) 7113350050
Web Site: https://www.goody.com.cn
Year Founded: 1979
002694—(SSE)
Rev.: $148,221,684
Assets: $256,457,448
Liabilities: $251,522,388
Net Worth: $4,935,060
Earnings: ($18,702,684)
Emp.: 2,130
Fiscal Year-end: 12/31/22
Plastic Piping Mfr
N.A.I.C.S.: 326122
Su Xiaozhong *(Chm)*

GOOROO VENTURES LIMITED
169 Fullarton Road, Dulwich, 5065, SA, Australia
Tel.: (61) 8 8133 5000   AU
Web Site: http://www.goorooventures.com
Year Founded: 2016
Human Resource Consulting Services
N.A.I.C.S.: 541612
Narendra Kotti *(CEO)*

GOPA CONSULTANTS
Hindenburgring 18, 61348, Bad Homburg, Germany
Tel.: (49) 61729300
Web Site: http://www.gopa.de
Year Founded: 1965
Rev.: $49,651,302
Emp.: 185
Consulting Services
N.A.I.C.S.: 541611
Martin Guldner *(Mng Dir)*

GOPAL IRON & STEELS CO. (GUJARAT) LIMITED
Plot No 1401/2 GIDC Kerala Industrial Estate N H No 8-A, Ta Bavla, Ahmedabad, 382 220, Gujarat, India
Tel.: (91) 2714268268   In
Web Site: https://www.gopaliron.com
Year Founded: 1994
531913—(BOM)
Rev.: $152,881
Assets: $330,867
Liabilities: $228,128
Net Worth: $102,740
Earnings: $15,934
Emp.: 3
Fiscal Year-end: 03/31/23
Steel Bar Mfr
N.A.I.C.S.: 331110
Bhaveshbhai Patel *(CFO)*

GOPENG BERHAD
A-17-15 Level 17 Menara UOA Bangsar No 5 Jalan Bangsar Utama 1, 59000, Kuala Lumpur, Malaysia
Tel.: (60) 322877577   MY
Web Site: https://www.gopeng.com.my
GOPENG—(KLS)
Rev.: $2,725,216
Assets: $63,197,929
Liabilities: $6,498,630
Net Worth: $56,699,299
Earnings: ($773,949)
Fiscal Year-end: 12/31/22
Oil Palm Cultivation Services
N.A.I.C.S.: 111120
Mohd Salleh Hashim *(Chm)*

GORAN CAPITAL INC.
2 Eva Rd Ste 200, Etobicoke, M9C 2A8, ON, Canada
Tel.: (416) 622-0660
Emp.: 800
Nonstandard Auto Insurance Services
N.A.I.C.S.: 524128
Douglas H. Symons *(Pres, CEO & Sec)*

Subsidiaries:

Symons International Group, Inc. (1)
4720 Kingsway Dr, Indianapolis, IN 46205
Tel.: (317) 613-4171
Sales Range: $50-74.9 Million
Emp.: 12
Insurance Services
N.A.I.C.S.: 524126

Subsidiary (Domestic):

Pafco General Insurance Company (2)
4720 Kingsway Dr, Indianapolis, IN 46205-1555
Tel.: (317) 259-6300
Provider of Insurance Services
N.A.I.C.S.: 524126

GORANI INDUSTRIES LIMITED
Plot No 32-33 Sector F Sanwer Road Industrial Area, Indore, 452 015, Madhya Pradesh, India
Tel.: (91) 7312723202
Web Site: https://www.goraniindustries.com
Year Founded: 1996
531608—(BOM)
Rev.: $3,940,496
Assets: $2,840,087
Liabilities: $1,520,078
Net Worth: $1,320,010
Earnings: $227,013
Emp.: 189
Fiscal Year-end: 03/31/22
Kitchen Appliance Mfr & Distr
N.A.I.C.S.: 332215
Sanjay Gorani *(Mng Dir)*

GORAZDE PUTEVI D.D. GORAZDE
Ul 22 Maj bb, 73000, Gorazde, Bosnia & Herzegovina
Tel.: (387) 3 822 1147
GZPTR—(SARE)
Rev.: $2,301,477
Assets: $2,870,004
Liabilities: $452,976
Net Worth: $2,417,028
Earnings: $240,433
Emp.: 34
Fiscal Year-end: 12/31/21
Road & Airport Runway Construction Services
N.A.I.C.S.: 237310

INTERNATIONAL PUBLIC

GORD SCOTT NISSAN
7130 50th Ave, Red Deer, T4P 6A5, AB, Canada
Tel.: (403) 347-2258
Web Site: http://www.gordscott.ca
Year Founded: 1985
Rev.: $11,476,733
Emp.: 25
New & Used Car Dealers
N.A.I.C.S.: 441110

GORDON AUTO BODY PARTS CO., LTD.
No 48 Nieh Hsi Road, Luchu Dist, Taoyuan, 338, Taiwan
Tel.: (886) 33244011
Web Site: https://www.gordon.com.tw
Year Founded: 1986
1524—(TAI)
Rev.: $88,215,864
Assets: $174,371,359
Liabilities: $86,142,055
Net Worth: $88,229,304
Earnings: $11,496,778
Emp.: 220
Fiscal Year-end: 12/31/23
Bumpers, Doors & Radiators Mfr
N.A.I.C.S.: 423120
Mao Yuan Li *(Chm)*

Subsidiaries:

Gordon Auto Body Parts Co., Ltd. - Plant 2 (1)
No 32 Da Keng St, Keng Kou Vil Luchu Dist, Taoyuan, 338, Taiwan
Tel.: (886) 33248369
Web Site: http://www.gordon.com.tw
Sales Range: $100-124.9 Million
Emp.: 400
Automobile Body Parts Mfr
N.A.I.C.S.: 441330

GORDON BROTHERS INDUSTRIES PTY. LIMITED
21 Michael Street, Brunswick, 3056, VIC, Australia
Tel.: (61) 393896666   AU
Web Site: http://www.gordonrefrig.com.au
Year Founded: 1917
Sales Range: $25-49.9 Million
Emp.: 150
Air Conditioning & Refrigeration Contractor
N.A.I.C.S.: 238220
John Mott *(Mng Dir & CFO)*

Subsidiaries:

Gordon Brothers Industries Pty. Limited - BENDIGO FACTORY (1)
15 Prospect Road, Bendigo, 3539, VIC, Australia
Tel.: (61) 3 5441 4404
Industrial Refrigeration Equipment Mfr
N.A.I.C.S.: 333415

GORDON CREEK ENERGY INC.
734 7th Avenue SW Suite 1207, Calgary, T2P 3P8, AB, Canada
Tel.: (403) 453-1608   Ca
Web Site: http://www.gordoncreekenergy.com
Year Founded: 1983
Oil & Gas Exploration Services
N.A.I.C.S.: 211120
Rupert Evans *(Pres & CEO)*

GORDON ELECTRIC
533 Queens Ave, London, N6B 1Y3, ON, Canada
Tel.: (519) 672-1273
Web Site: http://www.gordon-electric.com
Year Founded: 1975
Sales Range: $10-24.9 Million
Electrical Contractor

AND PRIVATE COMPANIES

N.A.I.C.S.: 238210
Al Gordon (Pres)

GORE MUTUAL INSURANCE COMPANY
252 Dundas St N, Cambridge, N1R 5T3, ON, Canada
Tel.: (519) 623-1910
Web Site: http://www.goremutual.ca
Year Founded: 1839
Sales Range: $50-74.9 Million
Emp.: 200
Property & Casualty Insurance Carrier
N.A.I.C.S.: 524126
Paul Jackson (Chief Mktg & Distr Officer)

GORE STREET ENERGY STORAGE FUND PLC
First Floor 16-17 Little Portland St, London, W1W 8BP, United Kingdom
Tel.: (44) 2038260290
Web Site: https://www.gsenergystorage.com
GSF—(LSE)
Assets: $496,761,232
Liabilities: $3,120,656
Net Worth: $493,640,576
Earnings: ($7,421,392)
Fiscal Year-end: 03/31/22
Investment Services
N.A.I.C.S.: 525910
Paula Travesso (Mgr-Investments)

GORENJSKI TISK STORITVE D.O.O.
Ulica Mirka Vadnova 6, 4000, Kranj, Slovenia
Tel.: (386) 42016300
Web Site: http://www.go-tisk.si
Sales Range: $10-24.9 Million
Emp.: 120
Commercial Printing Services
N.A.I.C.S.: 323111
Andrej Krope (Dir-Comml)

GORILLA TECHNOLOGY GROUP INC.
Grand Pavilion Hibiscus Way 802 West Bay Road, Grand Cayman, E9 KY1-1205, Cayman Islands
Tel.: (886) 886226277
Web Site: https://www.gorilla-technology.com
GRRR—(NASDAQ)
Rev.: $64,694,991
Assets: $115,437,748
Liabilities: $61,286,015
Net Worth: $54,151,733
Earnings: $13,495,614
Emp.: 142
Fiscal Year-end: 12/31/23
VIdeo Intelligence & IoT Technology Services
N.A.I.C.S.: 518210
Jay Chandan (Chm & CEO)

Subsidiaries:

Global SPAC Partners Co. (1)
2093 Philadelphia Pike Ste 1968, Claymont, DE 19703
Tel.: (424) 299-7798
Rev.: $9,697,638
Assets: $169,608,149
Liabilities: $181,886,329
Net Worth: ($12,278,180)
Earnings: $8,502,767
Emp.: 3
Fiscal Year-end: 12/31/2021
Investment Services
N.A.I.C.S.: 523999

GORISKE OPEKARNE D.D.
Merljaki 7, 5292, Rence, Slovenia
Tel.: (386) 53985200
Web Site: http://www.go-opekarne.si
Sales Range: $10-24.9 Million
Emp.: 80
Clay Roof Tiles, Concrete Bricks & Other Building Materials Mfr
N.A.I.C.S.: 327120
Jozef Stibilj (Chm)

GORJI BISCUIT COMPANY
555 Building Iranshahr St Karimkhan Blvd, Tehran, Iran
Tel.: (98) 2188491823
Web Site: http://www.gorjico.com
Year Founded: 1960
GORJ1—(THE)
Sales Range: Less than $1 Million
Emp.: 459
Biscuit Mfr
N.A.I.C.S.: 311821

GOSA FOM A.D.
Industrijska 70, 11420, Smederevska Palanka, Serbia
Tel.: (381) 264150777
Web Site: https://www.gosafom.com
Year Founded: 1923
GFOM—(BEL)
Rev.: $36,592,715
Assets: $44,853,933
Liabilities: $30,095,677
Net Worth: $14,758,255
Earnings: $129,310
Fiscal Year-end: 12/31/22
Lifting & Handling Equipment Mfr
N.A.I.C.S.: 333998
Srdan Dimitrijevic (Gen Mgr)

GOSA MONTAZA A.D.
28 oktobra br 65, 11320, Velika Plana, Serbia
Tel.: (381) 26 317 126
Web Site: http://www.gosamontaza.com
Year Founded: 1923
GMON—(BEL)
Sales Range: $10-24.9 Million
Metal Structure & Parts Mfr
N.A.I.C.S.: 332312
Branko Sljivar (Gen Mgr)

GOSFORD QUARRIES PTY. LTD.
301 Mona Vale Road, Terrey Hills, Sydney, 2084, NSW, Australia
Tel.: (61) 285858282   AU
Web Site: http://www.gosfordquarries.com.au
Year Founded: 1922
Sales Range: $10-24.9 Million
Sandstone Quarrying & Product Distr
N.A.I.C.S.: 423320
Charlie Sarkis (Mng Dir)

GOSPELL DIGITAL TECHNOLOGY CO., LTD.
Gosbell Industrial Park Guanshandong Street, Suxian District, Chenzhou, 423031, Hunan, China
Tel.: (86) 7352666666
Web Site: https://www.gospell.com
Year Founded: 2001
002848—(SSE)
Rev.: $53,253,720
Assets: $83,199,636
Liabilities: $51,949,404
Net Worth: $31,250,232
Earnings: ($758,160)
Fiscal Year-end: 12/31/22
Digital Hardware Mfr & Distr
N.A.I.C.S.: 335932
Sun Huashan (Chm)

Subsidiaries:

Chenzhou Xipoint Technology Co., Ltd. (1)
Blk F10-12 F518 Idea Land Baoyuan Road Baoan Central Area, Shenzhen, 518102, Guangdong, China
Tel.: (86) 75527750518
Web Site: http://www.xipoint.com
Digital Television Receiver Mfr & Distr
N.A.I.C.S.: 334220

GOSSAN RESOURCES LIMITED
Suite 404 - 171 Donald Street, Winnipeg, R3C 1M4, MB, Canada
Tel.: (204) 943-1990
Web Site: https://www.gossan.ca
Year Founded: 1980
GSR—(DEU)
Assets: $241,876
Liabilities: $182,257
Net Worth: $59,618
Earnings: ($884,791)
Fiscal Year-end: 03/31/23
Mineral Exploration Services
N.A.I.C.S.: 213114
Douglas Reeson (Pres & CEO)

GOSSELIN EXPRESS
1537 boulevard Caouette Ouest CP 248, Thetford Mines, QC, Canada
Tel.: (418) 335-7551
Web Site: http://www.gosselinexpress.com
Year Founded: 1927
Rev.: $20,800,000
Emp.: 150
Freight Trucking & General Transportation Services
N.A.I.C.S.: 484110
Emile Gosselin (Founder)

GOSTA TORSSELL HOLDING AB
Kraftvagen 5, 182 53, Danderyd, Sweden
Tel.: (46) 87090060
Holding Company
N.A.I.C.S.: 551112
Gosta Torssell (Mng Dir)

Subsidiaries:

Diskomat AB (1)
Arsta Skolgrand 12A, Stockholm, 117 43, Sweden (100%)
Tel.: (46) 87940640
Web Site: http://www.diskomat.se
Sales Range: $50-74.9 Million
Emp.: 15
Industrial Equipment Distr
N.A.I.C.S.: 425120
Gosta Torssell (Mng Dir)

GOSTATS
428 Woolwich Street, Waterloo, N2K 2L4, ON, Canada
Tel.: (519) 496-7873
Web Site: http://www.gostats.com
Sales Range: $1-9.9 Million
Website Tracking & Reporting Services
N.A.I.C.S.: 513210
Richard Chmura (Founder)

GOSUN HOLDING CO., LTD.
Room 2002 20F Block A IFC Building Jia No 8 Jianguomenwai Street, Chaoyang District, Beijing, 100022, China
Tel.: (86) 1082602198
Web Site: https://gosun.com
000971—(SSE)
Rev.: $72,352,332
Assets: $186,522,804
Liabilities: $152,071,452
Net Worth: $34,451,352
Earnings: ($75,307,752)
Emp.: 298
Fiscal Year-end: 12/31/22
Holding Company; Textile Products
N.A.I.C.S.: 551112
Dai Zhang (Chm & Gen Mgr)

GOSUNCN TECHNOLOGY

GOTION HIGH-TECH CO., LTD.

GROUP CO., LTD.
No 2819 Kaichuang Avenue Science City, Huangpu District, Guangzhou, 510530, Guangdong, China
Tel.: (86) 2032068888
Web Site: https://www.gosuncn.com
Year Founded: 1997
300098—(CHIN)
Rev.: $253,367,473
Assets: $735,888,671
Liabilities: $304,607,914
Net Worth: $431,280,756
Earnings: ($14,542,819)
Fiscal Year-end: 12/31/23
Software Development Services
N.A.I.C.S.: 541511
Shuangguang Liu (Chm)

GOTA MEDIA AB
S Langgatan 33, Kalmar, Sweden
Tel.: (46) 48 059100   SE
Web Site: http://www.gotamedia.se
Newspaper Publishers
N.A.I.C.S.: 513110
Boine Gepertz (Pres & CEO)

GOTAVERKEN ARENDAL AB
PO Box 8728, S 402 74, Gothenburg, Sweden
Tel.: (46) 31658600
Offshore Activities
N.A.I.C.S.: 336611

GOTENEHUS GROUP AB
Kraftgatan 1 Box 17, Gotene, 533 21, Sweden
Tel.: (46) 511345300
Web Site: http://www.gotenehus.com
GHUS.B—(OMX)
Rev.: $131,408,133
Assets: $96,022,024
Liabilities: $59,825,304
Net Worth: $36,196,720
Earnings: $2,760,229
Emp.: 251
Fiscal Year-end: 12/31/20
Building Construction Services
N.A.I.C.S.: 236220

GOTESCO LAND INC.
12/F Ever-Gotesco Corporate Center, 1958 C M Recto Avenue, Manila, 1001, Philippines
Tel.: (63) 736 2639
Year Founded: 1935
Real Estate Services
N.A.I.C.S.: 531390
Jose C. Go (Chm, Pres & CEO)

GOTHI PLASCON INDIA LIMITED
17/5B 1A Vazhudavur Road Opp Agriculture Research Center, Kurumbapet, Pondicherry, 605009, India
Tel.: (91) 4132271151   In
Web Site: https://www.gothiplascon.com
Year Founded: 1987
531111—(BOM)
Rev.: $510,158
Assets: $1,808,466
Liabilities: $359,154
Net Worth: $1,449,312
Earnings: $198,336
Emp.: 29
Fiscal Year-end: 03/31/23
Real Estate Manangement Services
N.A.I.C.S.: 531312
Saniay Gothi (Chm & Mng Dir)

GOTION HIGH-TECH CO., LTD.
No 566 Huayuan Avenue, Baohe District, Hefei, 230051, Anhui, China
Tel.: (86) 55162100213
Web Site: https://en.gotion.com.cn
Year Founded: 2006

3043

GOTION HIGH-TECH CO., LTD.

Gotion High-tech Co., Ltd.—(Continued)
002074—(SSE)
Rev.: $3,236,458,680
Assets: $10,196,882,748
Liabilities: $6,757,395,840
Net Worth: $3,439,486,908
Earnings: $43,745,832
Fiscal Year-end: 12/31/22
Electric Equipment Mfr
N.A.I.C.S.: 335311
Zhen Li *(Chm & Gen Mgr)*

Subsidiaries:

Feidong Gotion New Material Co., Ltd. (1)
No 1 Yongquan Road, Qiaotouji Town Feidong County, Hefei, Anhui, China
Tel.: (86) 55166686612
Lithium Battery Mfr & Distr
N.A.I.C.S.: 335910

GOTSE DELCHEV TABAC AD
Ul Tsaritsa Yoanna 12, Gotse Delchev, 2900, Blagoevgrad, Bulgaria
Tel.: (359) 75160521
Web Site: http://gdtabac.com
GDBT—(BUL)
Sales Range: Less than $1 Million
Real Estate Rental & Leasing Services
N.A.I.C.S.: 531110
Elena Kirova *(Dir-IR)*

GOTTFERT WERKSTOFF-PRUFMASCHINEN GMBH
Siemensstrasse 2, PO Box 1261, 74722, Buchen, Germany
Tel.: (49) 62814080
Web Site: http://www.goettfert.com
Year Founded: 1962
Testing Equipment Mfr
N.A.I.C.S.: 334515
Axel Gottfert *(Mng Dir)*

Subsidiaries:

GOETTFERT (China) Limited (1)
2-1211 Xiaoyun Tower No 15 Xiaguangli, Chaoyang District, Beijing, China
Tel.: (86) 1084832051
Testing Equipment Distr
N.A.I.C.S.: 423830

GOETTFERT - Dataphysics Instruments India Pvt. Ltd. (1)
P 84A C I T Road Scheme IVM, Kolkata, India
Tel.: (91) 3323630025
Web Site: http://www.gdinstruments.co.in
Testing Equipment Distr
N.A.I.C.S.: 423830

GOETTFERT Inc. (1)
488 Lakeshore Pkwy, Rock Hill, SC 29730
Tel.: (803) 324-3883
Testing Equipment Distr
N.A.I.C.S.: 423830

GOTTLIEB TESCH BAUUNTERNEHMEN GMBH
Ruhlsdorfer Strasse 103, 14532, Stahnsdorf, Germany
Tel.: (49) 332963520   De
Web Site: http://www.gottliebtesch.de
Year Founded: 1876
Foundation Engineering & Piping Construction Contracting Services
N.A.I.C.S.: 238190
Andreas Amoulong *(Mng Dir)*

GOUGEON FOURNITURES S.A.S.
Route De Courtonne, Glos, 14100, Bernay, France
Tel.: (33) 2 31 62 71 40
Web Site: http://www.gougeonsa.com
Rev.: $23,100,000
Emp.: 69
Groceries & Related Products
N.A.I.C.S.: 424490

Olivier Villey *(Dir-Comml)*

GOUR MEDICAL AG
21 Baarermattstrasse, 6304, Zug, Switzerland
Tel.: (41) 435080072   CH
Web Site: http://www.gour-medical.com
Year Founded: 2014
MLGML—(EUR)
Sales Range: Less than $1 Million
Veterinary Care Product Mfr & Distr
N.A.I.C.S.: 325412
Serge Goldner *(Chm & CEO)*

GOURMET KINEYA CO., LTD.
3-4-7 Kitakagaya, Suminoe-ku, Osaka, 559-8561, Japan
Tel.: (81) 666831222
Web Site: https://www.gourmet-kineya-hd.co.jp
Year Founded: 1967
9850—(TKS)
Rev.: $225,263,280
Assets: $388,874,640
Liabilities: $300,970,560
Net Worth: $87,904,080
Earnings: $4,965,840
Fiscal Year-end: 03/31/22
Restaurant Operators
N.A.I.C.S.: 722511
Atsushi Mukumoto *(Chm, Pres & CEO)*

Subsidiaries:

AAS Catering Co., Ltd. (1)
Minami-1 Senshu-kuko, Sennan, 549-0021, Osaka, Japan
Tel.: (81) 724553500
Web Site: https://www.aascatering.co.jp
Emp.: 250
Aircraft Food Services
N.A.I.C.S.: 722310
Harunobu Higuchi *(Pres & CEO)*

ASAHI Wellness Foods Co., Ltd. (1)
7-11 Nishiki Nakamachi, Kaizuka, 597-0093, Osaka, Japan
Tel.: (81) 724579210
Web Site: https://www.asahi-wf.jp
Emp.: 422
Frozen Food Mfr
N.A.I.C.S.: 311412

Mizuma Railway Co., Ltd. (1)
1488-8 Chikaki, Kaizuka, 597-0001, Osaka, Japan
Tel.: (81) 724224567
Web Site: https://www.suitetsu.com
Emp.: 61
Automotive Distr
N.A.I.C.S.: 423110

GOURMET MASTER CO. LTD.
No 35 23rd, Nantun District, Taichung, Taiwan
Tel.: (886) 435039090
Web Site: https://www.85cafe.com
Year Founded: 2003
2723—(TAI)
Rev.: $667,893,693
Assets: $635,581,879
Liabilities: $277,158,301
Net Worth: $358,423,578
Earnings: $24,308,871
Fiscal Year-end: 12/31/23
Coffee & Bakery Products Store Owner & Operator
N.A.I.C.S.: 445298
Cheng-Hsueh Wu *(Chm & CEO)*

GOURMET OCEAN PRODUCTS INC.
8420 Fraser Street, Vancouver, V5X 0A4, BC, Canada
Tel.: (778) 328-8898   BC
Web Site: http://gourmetoceanproducts.com
Year Founded: 2008
GOP.H—(TSX)

Assets: $6,233
Liabilities: $367,392
Net Worth: ($361,159)
Earnings: ($72,236)
Fiscal Year-end: 09/30/22
Seafood Production & Distribution
N.A.I.C.S.: 311710
Peter Hughes *(Pres & CEO)*

GOVERNANCE FOR OWNERS LLP
26 Throgmorton Street, London, EC2N 2AN, United Kingdom
Tel.: (44) 2076144750   UK
Web Site: http://www.governanceowners.com
Year Founded: 2004
Equity Investment Firm
N.A.I.C.S.: 523999
Peter Butler *(Co-Founder, Partner & CEO)*

Subsidiaries:

Governance for Owners Japan KK (1)
3-7-1 Kasumigaseki, Chiyoda-ku, Tokyo, 100-0013, Japan
Tel.: (81) 3 5532 3080
Financial Investment Services
N.A.I.C.S.: 523999

Governance for Owners USA, Inc. (1)
1120 Ave of the Americas 4th Fl, New York, NY 10036
Tel.: (212) 626-6621
Web Site: http://www.governanceforowners.com
Equity Investment Firm
N.A.I.C.S.: 523999
Peter C. Clapman *(Chm)*

GOVIEX URANIUM INC.
999 Canada Place Suite 606, Vancouver, V6C 3E1, BC, Canada
Tel.: (604) 681-5529   BC
Web Site: https://www.goviex.com
Year Founded: 2011
GVXXF—(OTCQX)
Rev.: $19,000
Assets: $72,448,000
Liabilities: $5,137,000
Net Worth: $67,311,000
Earnings: ($6,448,000)
Fiscal Year-end: 12/31/20
Uranium Mining
N.A.I.C.S.: 212290
Govind Friedland *(Chm)*

GOVIND POY OXYGEN LTD.
Fabrica de Gas Carbonico N H-17 Nuvem Salcette, Goa, 403 604, India
Tel.: (91) 8322791703
Web Site: http://www.govindpoy.com
Year Founded: 1972
Industrial Gas Mfr
N.A.I.C.S.: 325120
Sanjay A. Poy Raiturcar *(Chm & Mng Dir)*

GOVIND RUBBER LTD.
A 69 FIEE Complex Okhla Industrial Area Phase 2, Sitaram Mill Compound 72-N M Joshi Marg Lower Parel, New Delhi, 110020, India
Tel.: (91) 9289935899
Web Site: https://www.grltires.com
Year Founded: 1964
509148—(BOM)
Sales Range: $10-24.9 Million
Rubber Products Mfr
N.A.I.C.S.: 326299
Vinod Poddar *(Chm)*

Subsidiaries:

GRL B.V. (1)
Milaanstraat 16, 1175 RJ, Lijnden, Netherlands

Tel.: (31) 204493264
Tire & Tube Distr
N.A.I.C.S.: 423130

GOWAII VACATION HOLDING S.L.
Calle de Los Robles S/N Edificio Portofino Park Local 4A, Puerto de la Cruz, 38400, Tenerife, Spain
Tel.: (34) 9223706003
Web Site: http://www.gowaii.com
Year Founded: 2011
Travel Arrangement Services
N.A.I.C.S.: 561599
Javier Diaz *(Founder)*

Subsidiaries:

Nautalia Viajes, S.L. (1)
c/Mahonia No 2 5th Floor, Madrid, Spain
Tel.: (34) 902 811 811
Web Site: http://www.nautaliaviajes.com
Travel Arrangement Services
N.A.I.C.S.: 561599

GOWEST GOLD LTD.
80 Richmond Street West Suite 1400, Toronto, M5H 2A4, ON, Canada
Tel.: (416) 363-1210   Ca
Web Site: https://www.gowestgold.com
Year Founded: 1982
1GWA—(DEU)
Emp.: 100
Fiscal Year-end: 12/31/24
Metal Exploration Services
N.A.I.C.S.: 213114
C. Fraser Elliott *(Chm)*

GOWING BROTHERS LIMITED
The Gowings Building 303 / 35-61 Harbour Drive, Coffs Harbour, 2450, NSW, Australia
Tel.: (61) 292646321   AU
Web Site: https://www.gowings.com
Year Founded: 1868
GOW—(ASX)
Rev.: $44,795,673
Assets: $215,012,018
Liabilities: $85,301,148
Net Worth: $129,710,870
Earnings: ($26,042)
Fiscal Year-end: 07/31/24
Long Term Investments & Retail & Property Operations
N.A.I.C.S.: 525990
John E. Gowing *(Mng Dir)*

Subsidiaries:

Coffs Central Pty. Ltd. (1)
Harbour Drive, Coffs Harbour, 2450, NSW, Australia
Tel.: (61) 256228900
Web Site: https://www.coffscentralshopping.com.au
General Merchandise Retailer
N.A.I.C.S.: 445110

Kempsey Central Pty. Ltd. (1)
2-14 Belgrave St, Kempsey, 2440, NSW, Australia
Tel.: (61) 255251000
Web Site: https://www.kempseycentralshopping.com
General Merchandise Retailer
N.A.I.C.S.: 445110

SHI Holdings Pty Limited (1)
5-7 By The Sea Rd, Mona Vale, 2103, Australia
Tel.: (61) 299974744
Investment Management Service
N.A.I.C.S.: 523940
Michael Heath *(Gen Mgr)*

Subsidiary (Non-US):

Surf Hardware International Europe SARL (2)
ZA des II pins 4 Rue des resiniers, Capbreton, 40130, Biarritz, France
Tel.: (33) 55 870 0040

AND PRIVATE COMPANIES

Web Site: https://www.surffcs.eu
Sporting Goods Store Operator
N.A.I.C.S.: 459110

Surf Hardware International USA Inc. (1)
1255 Keystone Way Ste 106, Vista, CA 92081
Tel.: (858) 300-2640
Web Site: http://surfhardware.com
Emp.: 20
Sporting Goods Store Operator
N.A.I.C.S.: 423210
Rory Kelly *(Dir-Ops)*

GOWLING WLG INTERNATIONAL LIMITED
4 More London, Riverside, London, SE1 2AU, United Kingdom
Tel.: (44) 370 903 1000   UK
Web Site: http://www.gowlingwlg.com
Emp.: 1,400
Legal Services Organization
N.A.I.C.S.: 813910
Andrew Witts *(Chm)*

Subsidiaries:

Gowling WLG (Canada) LLP (1)
1 First Canadian Place 100 King Street West Suite 1600, Toronto, M5X 1G5, ON, Canada
Tel.: (416) 862-7525
Web Site: http://www.gowlings.com
Law firm
N.A.I.C.S.: 541110

Gowling WLG (UK) LLP (1)
4 More London Riverside, London, SE1 2AU, United Kingdom
Tel.: (44) 870 903 1000
Web Site: http://www.wragge-law.com
Law firm
N.A.I.C.S.: 541110
Quentin Poole *(Sr Partner)*

GOWRA LEASING & FINANCE LIMITED
501 5th Floor Gowra Grand Behind Gowra Plaza 1-8-384 and 385 S P Road, Begumpet, Secunderabad, 500 003, Telangana, India
Tel.: (91) 4027843086
Web Site: https://www.gowraleasing.com
Year Founded: 1993
530709—(BOM)
Rev.: $266,639
Assets: $1,846,352
Liabilities: $31,113
Net Worth: $1,815,239
Earnings: $123,602
Emp.: 7
Fiscal Year-end: 03/31/23
Financial Lending Services
N.A.I.C.S.: 522220
Dwarakadas Suresh *(Chm)*

GOXUS INC.
11th Floor Guanghe Building No 5 Building Lv Di Qi Hang international, Fangshan District, Beijing, China
Tel.: (86) 1052878052   Ky
Web Site: http://www.goxus.com.cn
Year Founded: 2018
Rev.: $47,175,847
Assets: $24,085,327
Liabilities: $7,827,332
Net Worth: $16,257,995
Earnings: $7,050,224
Emp.: 128
Fiscal Year-end: 03/31/19
Holding Company
N.A.I.C.S.: 551112
Xingpeng Zhao *(Co-Founder, Chm & CEO)*

GOYAL ALUMINIUMS LIMITED
2814/6 Ground Floor Chuna Mandi Paharganj, New Delhi, 110055, India
Tel.: (91) 1149536409

Web Site: https://www.goyalaluminiums.com
541152—(BOM)
Rev.: $7,528,872
Assets: $3,560,326
Liabilities: $1,609,886
Net Worth: $1,950,440
Earnings: $19,375
Emp.: 2
Fiscal Year-end: 03/31/21
Metal Products Mfr
N.A.I.C.S.: 331110
Sandeep Goyal *(CFO)*

GOYAL ASSOCIATES LTD
401 Phoenix Complex Waghodia Road, Vadodara, 390019, Gujarat, India
Tel.: (91) 8712640674
Web Site: https://www.goyalassociatesltd.com
Year Founded: 1994
530663—(BOM)
Rev.: $408,453
Assets: $599,556
Liabilities: $286,518
Net Worth: $313,039
Earnings: $69,564
Fiscal Year-end: 03/31/23
Financial Management Services
N.A.I.C.S.: 523999
Durga Prasad Kattamuri *(Mng Dir)*

GOYAL SALT LIMITED
Plot No 229-230 Guru Jambeshwar Nagar Lane No-07 Gandhi Path, Vaishali Nagar, Jaipur, 302021, Rajasthan, India
Tel.: (91) 7568018883
Web Site: https://www.goyalsaltltd.com
Year Founded: 2010
GOYALSALT—(NSE)
Rev.: $14,266,064
Assets: $3,638,339
Liabilities: $1,674,414
Net Worth: $1,963,925
Earnings: $428,745
Fiscal Year-end: 03/31/23
Salt Mfr & Distr
N.A.I.C.S.: 311942

GOYO FOODS INDUSTRY CO., LTD.
819-2 Taku, Itoshima, 819-1134, Fukuoka, Japan
Tel.: (81) 92 3329610
Web Site: http://www.goyofoods.co.jp
Year Founded: 1975
2230—(TKS)
Sales Range: $10-24.9 Million
Baked Product Mfr & Distr
N.A.I.C.S.: 311813
Keisuke Masuda *(Pres)*

GOYO INTEX CO., LTD.
5-411 Koki, Komaki, 485-0058, Aichi, Japan
Tel.: (81) 568 761050
Web Site: http://www.goyointex.co.jp
Year Founded: 1979
Rev.: $13,870,860
Assets: $11,868,600
Liabilities: $5,635,320
Net Worth: $6,233,280
Earnings: ($3,787,080)
Emp.: 48
Fiscal Year-end: 03/31/19
Interior Decoration Product Whslr
N.A.I.C.S.: 423520
Motohiro Yoshikawa *(Chm & Pres)*

GOZDE GIRISIM SERMAYESI YATIRIM ORTAKLIGI A.S.
Kisikli Neighborhood Cesme Dead End Street, Yildiz Holding Apt No 6/1 Uskudar, Istanbul, Turkiye
Tel.: (90) 2165242500
Web Site: https://www.gozdegirisim.com.tr
Year Founded: 2010
GOZDE—(IST)
Rev.: $3,068,779
Assets: $860,264,440
Liabilities: $104,465,385
Net Worth: $755,799,055
Earnings: ($298,220,522)
Fiscal Year-end: 12/31/23
Financial Investment Services
N.A.I.C.S.: 523999
Murat Ulker *(Bd of Dirs & Chm)*

GOZDE GIYIM SAN. VE TIC. A.S.
Abdi Ipekci Cad No 183, Bayrampasa, 43150, Istanbul, Turkiye
Tel.: (90) 2125457322   TR
Real Estate Development Services
N.A.I.C.S.: 531390

GP 7. JUL A.D.
Ruda Hrubika 5, Backi Petrovac, Serbia
Tel.: (381) 21 822 882
Year Founded: 1976
GPSJ—(BEL)
Sales Range: Less than $1 Million
Emp.: 1
Heavy Construction Engineering Services
N.A.I.C.S.: 237990
Udovicic Sandra *(Exec Dir)*

GP BULLHOUND LLP
52 Jermyn Street, London, SW1Y 6LX, United Kingdom
Tel.: (44) 207 101 7560
Web Site: http://www.gpbullhound.com
Year Founded: 1999
Private Investment Firm
N.A.I.C.S.: 523999
Hugh Campbell *(Mng Partner)*

GP CAPITAL CO., LTD.
Room 4901 49/F One Lujiazui No 68 Yin Cheng Rd, Shanghai, 200120, China
Tel.: (86) 21 2032 9333
Web Site: http://www.gpcapital.com.cn
Year Founded: 2009
Emp.: 60
Privater Equity Firm
N.A.I.C.S.: 523999
Yaliang Shao *(Chm)*

GP GUNTER PAPENBURG AG
Anderterstrasse 99c, 30559, Hannover, Germany
Tel.: (49) 5112288990
Web Site: http://www.gp.ag
Year Founded: 1963
Construction Services
N.A.I.C.S.: 236220

GP INVESTMENTS, LTD.
16 Burnaby Street, Hamilton, HM1, Bermuda
Tel.: (441) 2790604   BM
Web Site: https://www.gp-investments.com
GPINA—(LUX)
Rev.: $32,120,000
Assets: $511,763,000
Liabilities: $123,271,000
Net Worth: $388,492,000
Earnings: ($13,656,000)
Fiscal Year-end: 12/31/23
Private Equity & Real Estate Investment Firm
N.A.I.C.S.: 523999

GP INVESTMENTS, LTD.

Antonio Carlos Augusto Bonchristiano *(CEO)*

Subsidiaries:

BR Properties S.A. (1)
BR-050 - Fazenda Velha, Cajamar, Sao Paulo, 07750-000, Brazil
Web Site: https://www.bgrasset.com.br
Real Estate Development Services
N.A.I.C.S.: 531110
Antonio Carlos Augusto Bonchristiano *(Chm)*

GP Investimentos Ltda. (1)
Avenida Brigadeiro Faria Lima 3900 7th Floor, Sao Paulo, 04538-132, SP, Brazil
Tel.: (55) 11 3556 5505
Web Site: http://www.gp-investments.com
Private Equity Investment & Asset Management Services
N.A.I.C.S.: 523999
Laerte Gama *(Mgr-HR)*

GP North America, LLC (1)
300 Park Ave S-219, New York, NY 10022
Tel.: (212) 430-4340
Web Site: http://www.gp-investments.com
Private Equity Investment & Asset Management Services
N.A.I.C.S.: 523999

Spice Private Equity Ltd. (1)
Industriestrasse 13c, CH-6302, Zug, Switzerland   (58.48%)
Tel.: (41) 41 710 7060
Web Site: http://www.spice-private-equity.com
Rev.: $39,015,000
Assets: $157,015,000
Liabilities: $1,132,000
Net Worth: $155,883,000
Earnings: $35,666,000
Emp.: 220
Fiscal Year-end: 12/31/2021
Private Equity Investment Services
N.A.I.C.S.: 523999
Fersen Lamas Lambranho *(Vice Chm)*

Subsidiary (Non-US):

Argo Seguras Brasil, SA (2)
Avenida Nacoes Unidas 12399 Floor 14, Sao Paulo, 04578-000, Brazil
Tel.: (55) 11 3056 5530
Sales Range: $50-74.9 Million
Emp.: 80
Insurance Providing Services
N.A.I.C.S.: 524298
Ana Carolina Mello *(COO & Chief Underwriting Officer)*

Subsidiary (US):

FoodFirst Global Restaurants, Inc. (2)
420 S Orange Ave CNL Tower II Ste 900, Orlando, FL 32801
Tel.: (407) 735-7082
Web Site: http://www.foodfirst.com
Holding Company; Restaurant Owner & Operator
N.A.I.C.S.: 551112
Brad Blum *(Chm & CEO)*

Subsidiary (Domestic):

Brio Freehold, LLC (3)
3710 US Route 9, Freehold, NJ 07728
Tel.: (732) 683-1045
Web Site: http://www.brioitalian.com
Restaurant Operators
N.A.I.C.S.: 722511

Brio Marlton, LLC (3)
500 Route 73 S, Marlton, NJ 08053
Tel.: (856) 983-0277
Web Site: http://www.brioitalian.com
Restaurant Operating Services
N.A.I.C.S.: 722511

Brio Tuscan Grille of Cherokee, LLC (3)
777 Casino Dr, Cherokee, NC 28719
Tel.: (828) 497-8233
Web Site: http://www.brioitalian.com
Restaurant Operating Services
N.A.I.C.S.: 722511

Brio Tuscan Grille of Maryland, Inc. (3)

GP INVESTMENTS, LTD.

GP Investments, Ltd.—(Continued)

305 Sail Place, Annapolis, MD 21401
Tel.: (410) 571-5660
Web Site: http://www.brioitalian.com
Restaurant Operating Services
N.A.I.C.S.: 722511

GP KRAJINA A.D.
Trg Srpskih junaka br 4, 78 000,
Banja Luka, Republika Srpska, Bosnia & Herzegovina
Tel.: (387) 51215611
Web Site: https://www.gpkrajina.com
Year Founded: 1945
KRJN—(BANJ)
Sales Range: $1-9.9 Million
Emp.: 160
Construction Services
N.A.I.C.S.: 236210

GP PETROLEUMS LTD.
804 Ackruti Star 8th Floor MIDC Central Road Opposite Ackruti, Centre Point Andheri East, Mumbai, 400093, India
Tel.: (91) 2261482500
Web Site:
  https://www.gppetroleums.co.in
Year Founded: 1991
532543—(BOM)
Rev.: $94,891,194
Assets: $41,401,103
Liabilities: $8,288,472
Net Worth: $33,112,631
Earnings: $3,020,107
Emp.: 274
Fiscal Year-end: 03/31/23
Automotive Lubricating Oil Mfr
N.A.I.C.S.: 324191
Prashant Achar *(CEO)*

GP PLANUM AD
22 Oktobra 15, Zemun, 11080, Belgrade, 11080, Serbia
Tel.: (381) 112108618
Web Site: https://www.planum.rs
Year Founded: 1948
PLNM—(BEL)
Rev.: $2,869,024
Assets: $17,143,146
Liabilities: $3,590,067
Net Worth: $13,553,079
Earnings: $1,263
Emp.: 104
Fiscal Year-end: 12/31/22
Construction Services
N.A.I.C.S.: 237990
Ratomir Todorovic *(Gen Mgr)*

Subsidiaries:

Planum Cyprus Limited **(1)**
22 Kassou Street Block Lambda Flat 34,
Nicosia, 1086, Cyprus
Tel.: (357) 22675331
Emp.: 180
Construction & Civil Project Management Services
N.A.I.C.S.: 236220

GP PLANUM AD BEOGRAD
Bulevar Ivana Crnojevica 54/I, 81000,
Podgorica, Montenegro
Tel.: (382) 69057181
Construction & Civil Project Management Services
N.A.I.C.S.: 236220

GP PUT D.D. SARAJEVO
Trampina 12/3, 71000, Sarajevo,
Bosnia & Herzegovina
Tel.: (387) 33 277 140
Web Site: http://www.gpput.ba
Year Founded: 1952
GPUTR—(SARE)
Road & Motorway Construction Services
N.A.I.C.S.: 237310

Terzic Adnan *(Member-Mgmt Bd)*

GP ZGP D.D. SARAJEVO
Dolina 11, 71000, Sarajevo, Bosnia & Herzegovina
Tel.: (387) 3 325 0900
Web Site: http://www.zgp.ba
Year Founded: 1947
ZGPSR—(SARE)
Rev.: $7,552,701
Assets: $24,296,055
Liabilities: $12,211,769
Net Worth: $12,084,287
Earnings: $33,231
Emp.: 110
Fiscal Year-end: 12/31/20
Bridges & Tunnels Construction Services
N.A.I.C.S.: 237310

GPC PARTICIPACOES SA
Rua do Passeio 70 13 Andar centro,
Rio de Janeiro, CEP 22 290-160, RJ,
Brazil
Tel.: (55) 21 2212 4700
Web Site: http://www.gpc.com.br
Holding Company
N.A.I.C.S.: 551112

GPD DRINA D.D.
Sinica 14, 73 000, Gorazde, Bosnia & Herzegovina
Tel.: (387) 38221145
GPDDRK3—(SARE)
Rev.: $2,406,035
Assets: $2,912,587
Liabilities: $1,250,746
Net Worth: $1,661,841
Earnings: $19,203
Emp.: 38
Fiscal Year-end: 12/31/20
Construction Materials Mfr
N.A.I.C.S.: 327120

GPH ISPAT LIMITED
Crown Chamber 325 Asadgonj, Chittagong, 4000, Bangladesh
Tel.: (880) 2333361460   BD
Web Site:
  https://www.gphispat.com.bd
Year Founded: 2006
GPHISPAT—(DHA)
Rev.: $538,278,378
Assets: $787,956,947
Liabilities: $564,824,630
Net Worth: $223,132,317
Earnings: $2,441,039
Emp.: 2,286
Fiscal Year-end: 06/30/23
Steel Products Mfr
N.A.I.C.S.: 331110
Md. Alamgir Kabir *(Chm)*

GPI S.P.A.
Via Ragazzi del 99 13, 38123,
Trento, Italy
Tel.: (39) 0461381515   IT
Web Site: https://www.gpi.it
Year Founded: 1988
GPIM—(AIM)
Rev.: $390,382,614
Assets: $773,070,670
Liabilities: $503,244,093
Net Worth: $269,826,577
Earnings: $10,753,306
Emp.: 6,877
Fiscal Year-end: 12/31/22
Holding Company; Health Care Industry Management & Administration Consulting Services
N.A.I.C.S.: 551112
Fausto Manzana *(Chm & CEO)*

Subsidiaries:

Accura S.r.l. **(1)**
Via Palmanova 67, 20132, Milan, Italy
Tel.: (39) 024 772 0300

Web Site: https://www.accura.it
Healtcare Services
N.A.I.C.S.: 622110

Argentea Srl **(1)**
Ragazzi del 99 nr 38123, Trento, Italy
Tel.: (39) 0461381666
Online Payment Business
N.A.I.C.S.: 425120
Marco Torresani *(CEO)*

Subsidiary (Domestic):

UNI IT SRL **(2)**
Via G Galilei 1, 38122, Trento, Italy
Tel.: (39) 0461 1575696
Web Site: http://www.uniit.it
Software Development Services
N.A.I.C.S.: 541511

Bim Italia S.r.l. **(1)**
Via Ragazzi del 99 13, 38123, Trento, Italy
Tel.: (39) 0243981701
Web Site: https://www.bim.it
Information Technology Services
N.A.I.C.S.: 541511

Consorzio Stabile Cento Orizzonti
Scarl **(1)**
Via del Credito 5, 31033, Castelfranco
Veneto, TV, Italy
Tel.: (39) 0423723432
Web Site: https://www.centorizzonti.it
Call Center Services
N.A.I.C.S.: 561422

Esakon Italia S.R.L. **(1)**
Via Per Marco 12/E, Rovereto, 38068,
Trento, Italy
Tel.: (39) 0464490340
Web Site: https://www.esakon.it
Software Development Services
N.A.I.C.S.: 541511

GPI USA Inc. **(1)**
2200 Post Oak Blvd Ste 1000, Houston, TX 77056
Web Site: https://www.gpigroup.com
Cloud Based Software Services
N.A.I.C.S.: 541511

Gpi Chile SpA **(1)**
Huerfanos 886, 1112, Santiago, Chile
Tel.: (56) 23 203 3247
Web Site: https://www.gpi-inversiones.cl
Cleaning & Digitization Services
N.A.I.C.S.: 561720

Guyot-Walser Informatique
S.a.r.l. **(1)**
2 Rue Des Chapelains, 51100, Reims,
France
Tel.: (33) 32 602 0269
Web Site: https://www.gw-informatique.fr
Software Development Services
N.A.I.C.S.: 541511

Healtech S.R.L. **(1)**
Via E De Amicis 23, Carini, 90044,
Palermo, Italy
Tel.: (39) 0918669618
Web Site: https://www.healtechsrl.com
Radiological Equipment Services
N.A.I.C.S.: 621512

Hemasoft America Corp. **(1)**
1400 La Concha Ln, Houston, TX 77054
Software Development Services
N.A.I.C.S.: 541511

Insiel Mercato S.p.A. **(1)**
Localita Padriciano 99 Area Science Park,
34149, Trieste, Italy **(55%)**
Tel.: (39) 0409227111
Web Site: http://www.insielmercato.it
Medical & Management Software Development Services
N.A.I.C.S.: 541511
Francesca Verbacci *(Product Mgr)*

Oslo Italia S.r.l. **(1)**
Via Dei Crollalanza 5, 20143, Milan, Italy
Tel.: (39) 02833016
Web Site: https://www.oslo.it
Management Control Services
N.A.I.C.S.: 541611

PCS Professional Clinical Software
GmbH **(1)**
Industriering 11, 9020, Klagenfurt, Austria
Tel.: (43) 4633003

INTERNATIONAL PUBLIC

Web Site: http://www.pcs.at
Medical Software Development Services
N.A.I.C.S.: 541511
Alfred Amann *(Mgr-Ops)*

Riedl G.m.b.H. **(1)**
Roonstrasse 5a, 44629, Herne, Germany
Tel.: (49) 23 235 0446
Web Site: https://riedl-gmbh.com
Construction Machinery Mfr
N.A.I.C.S.: 333120

Tesi S.p.A. **(1)**
Via Piave 20/11, Vermezzo Con Zelo,
20071, Milan, Italy
Tel.: (39) 029440501
Web Site: https://www.tesigroup.com
Oil & Gas Equipment Mfr
N.A.I.C.S.: 333132

Tesi de Mexico S.A. de C.V. **(1)**
Bosques de los Ciruelos No 168 Int 8 Col
Bosques de las Lomas Del, Miguel Hidalgo,
11700, Mexico, Mexico
Tel.: (52) 5555966616
Information Technology Services
N.A.I.C.S.: 541519

Umana Medical Technologies
Ltd. **(1)**
Umana Building Triq San Tumas, Luqa,
LQA 9033, Malta
Tel.: (356) 27639710
Web Site: https://www.umanamedical.com
Medical Device Mfr
N.A.I.C.S.: 339112

Xidera S.r.l. **(1)**
Lodi courses 111, 20139, Milan, Italy
Tel.: (39) 0236551459
Web Site: https://www.xidera.com
Information Technology Services
N.A.I.C.S.: 541511

GPM METALS INC.
1101 - 141 Adelaide St W, Toronto,
M5H 3L5, ON, Canada
Tel.: (416) 628-5904
Web Site: https://gpmmetals.com
Year Founded: 1994
GPMTF—(OTCIQ)
Rev.: $10,920
Assets: $209,243
Liabilities: $59,274
Net Worth: $149,970
Earnings: ($519,808)
Fiscal Year-end: 12/31/23
Metal Mining
N.A.I.C.S.: 212290
Daniel Noone *(Chm & CEO-Interim)*

GPRO TITANIUM INDUSTRY CO., LTD.
No 480 Jigu Road, Jilin Economic
and Technological Development
Zone, Jilin, 210047, China
Tel.: (86) 2583799778
000545—(SSE)
Rev.: $352,404,000
Assets: $433,013,256
Liabilities: $169,492,284
Net Worth: $263,520,972
Earnings: ($20,484,360)
Emp.: 2,000
Fiscal Year-end: 12/31/22
Titanium Producer
N.A.I.C.S.: 325180
Anzheng Peng *(Gen Mgr)*

GPS ALLIANCE HOLDINGS LIMITED
106 International Road, Singapore,
629175, Singapore
Tel.: (65) 6253 1110
Web Site:
  http://www.gpsalliance.com.au
Year Founded: 2010
Rev.: $790,796
Assets: $2,254,548
Liabilities: $986,457
Net Worth: $1,268,091
Earnings: ($1,077,618)

Fiscal Year-end: 12/31/19
Holding Company
N.A.I.C.S.: 551112
Lim Pang Hern *(Chm)*

Subsidiaries:

Ecobuild Products Pte Ltd (1)
8 Sg Kadut St 6, Singapore, 728856, Singapore
Tel.: (65) 6269 1380
Building Materials Distr
N.A.I.C.S.: 444180
Tan Thiam Hee *(Chm)*

GPS Alliance Holdings Pte. Ltd. (1)
3 Bishan Place #02-03, CPF Bishan Building, Singapore, 579838, Singapore
Tel.: (65) 6866 0707
Web Site: http://www.gps.com.sg
Emp.: 40
Investment Holding Company
N.A.I.C.S.: 551112
Dennis Yong *(CEO)*

Subsidiary (Domestic):

Global Property Strategic Alliance Pte. Ltd. (2)
3 Bishan Place #06-03, CPF Bishan Building, Singapore, 579838, Singapore (100%)
Tel.: (65) 6866 0707
Web Site: http://www.gps.com.sg
Real Estate Development, Brokerage & Leasing Services
N.A.I.C.S.: 531210
Dennis Yong *(Co-Founder)*

GPT GROUP
Level 51 25 Martin Place, Sydney, 2000, NSW, Australia
Tel.: (61) 282393555 AU
Web Site: https://www.gpt.com.au
GPT—(ASX)
Rev.: $614,808,256
Assets: $11,089,026,632
Liabilities: $3,755,602,479
Net Worth: $7,333,424,153
Earnings: ($163,476,602)
Emp.: 3,000
Fiscal Year-end: 12/31/23
Real Estate Investment Trust
N.A.I.C.S.: 525990
Mark Fookes *(COO)*

Subsidiaries:

Brampton Island Pty Limited (1)
Brampton Island Resort, 4740, Mackay, QLD, Australia (100%)
Tel.: (61) 749514499
Web Site: http://www.voyages.com.au
Sales Range: $10-24.9 Million
Emp.: 100
Hotels & Motels
N.A.I.C.S.: 721110

GPT Nominees Pty Limited (1)
Mlc Ctr L 50 19-29 Martin Pl, Sydney, 2000, NSW, Australia (100%)
Tel.: (61) 282393555
Web Site: http://www.gptgroup.com
Sales Range: $75-99.9 Million
Emp.: 400
Religious Organizations
N.A.I.C.S.: 813110

GPT Pty Ltd (1)
Level 51 19 Martin Place, Sydney, 2000, NSW, Australia (100%)
Tel.: (61) 282393555
Real Estate Agency
N.A.I.C.S.: 531210

Silky Oaks Pty Limited (1)
Finlayvale Road, Mosman, 4873, QLD, Australia (100%)
Tel.: (61) 740981666
Web Site: http://www.silkyoakslodge.com.au
Sales Range: $10-24.9 Million
Emp.: 60
Hotels & Motels
N.A.I.C.S.: 721110
Paul Vinmin *(Mng Dir)*

Voyages Hotel & Resorts Ltd. (1)
Level 51 25 Martin Place, Sydney, 2000, NSW, Australia (100%)
Tel.: (61) 282393555
Web Site: https://www.gpt.com.au
Sales Range: $25-49.9 Million
Emp.: 150
Hotels & Motels
N.A.I.C.S.: 721110

Voyages Hotels & Resorts Pty Limited (1)
179 Elizabeth St, Sydney, 2000, NSW, Australia (100%)
Tel.: (61) 282968000
Web Site: http://www.voyages.com.au
Sales Range: $10-24.9 Million
Emp.: 60
Hotels & Motels
N.A.I.C.S.: 721110

GPT INFRAPROJECTS LIMITED
GPT Centre JC - 25 Sector - III Salt Lake, Kolkata, 700 106, India
Tel.: (91) 3340507000 In
Web Site: https://www.gptinfra.in
Year Founded: 1980
GPTINFRA—(NSE)
Rev.: $92,595,580
Assets: $98,231,119
Liabilities: $63,074,289
Net Worth: $35,156,831
Earnings: $3,131,296
Emp.: 886
Fiscal Year-end: 03/31/22
Construction Engineering Services
N.A.I.C.S.: 541330
Atul Tantia *(CFO & CFO)*

Subsidiaries:

GPT Concrete Products South Africa (Pty.) Limited (1)
Danskraal Station Yard Transnet Freight Rail Fairclough Road, PO Box No 1879, 3370, Ladysmith, KwaZulu-Natal, South Africa
Tel.: (27) 366374144
Web Site: https://www.gptgroup.com
Emp.: 200
Construction Engineering Services
N.A.I.C.S.: 541330
Rahul Sharma *(Gen Mgr)*

GR CABLES LIMITED
36 Santosh Nagar, Mehdipatnam, Hyderabad, 500028, Andhra Pradesh, India
Tel.: (91) 40 23521246
Rev.: $72
Assets: $527,912
Liabilities: $2,157,520
Net Worth: ($1,629,608)
Earnings: ($6,700,634)
Fiscal Year-end: 03/31/18
Cable Mfr
N.A.I.C.S.: 332618
G. R. Reddy *(Chm & Mng Dir)*

GR ENGINEERING SERVICES LIMITED
71 Daly Street, ASCOT, Perth, 6104, WA, Australia
Tel.: (61) 862726000
Web Site: https://www.gres.com.au
Year Founded: 2006
GNG—(ASX)
Rev.: $283,162,518
Assets: $151,412,077
Liabilities: $107,123,534
Net Worth: $44,288,543
Earnings: $20,819,900
Emp.: 200
Fiscal Year-end: 06/30/24
Engineering & Construction Services
N.A.I.C.S.: 237990
Geoff M. Jones *(Mng Dir)*

Subsidiaries:

Upstream Production Solutions Pty. Ltd. (1)
Level 7 276 Flinders Street, Melbourne, 3000, VIC, Australia
Tel.: (61) 400015369
Web Site: https://www.upstreamps.com
Emp.: 350
Oil & Gas Engineering Services
N.A.I.C.S.: 213112
Cameron Wills *(CEO)*

GR PROPERTIES LIMITED
Room 3505 35th Floor Tower 1 Lippo Centre 89 Queensway Admiralty, Hong Kong, China (Hong Kong)
Tel.: (852) 36282530 HK
Web Site: https://www.grproperties.com.hk
0108—(HKG)
Rev.: $44,915,190
Assets: $795,607,395
Liabilities: $381,407,198
Net Worth: $414,200,198
Earnings: ($40,816,065)
Emp.: 189
Fiscal Year-end: 12/31/22
Holding Company
N.A.I.C.S.: 551112
Shuhua Liu *(CEO)*

GR SILVER MINING LTD.
409 Granville Street 15th Floor Vancouver BC V6C 1T2, Vancouver, V6C 1T2, BC, Canada
Tel.: (647) 293-8457
Web Site: https://www.grsilvermining.com
GRSLF—(OTCQB)
Rev.: $13,693
Assets: $8,483,053
Liabilities: $920,554
Net Worth: $7,562,499
Earnings: ($6,839,999)
Fiscal Year-end: 12/31/20
Gold Mining Services
N.A.I.C.S.: 212220
Blaine Bailey *(CFO)*

GR. SARANTIS S.A.
26 Amaroussiou - Halandriou Street, 151 25, Maroussi, Athens, Greece
Tel.: (30) 2106173000 GR
Web Site: https://www.sarantisgroup.com
SRTSF—(OTCIQ)
Rev.: $517,571,785
Assets: $594,185,570
Liabilities: $214,579,408
Net Worth: $379,606,163
Earnings: $41,878,903
Emp.: 2,324
Fiscal Year-end: 12/31/23
Distr of Cosmetics, Household Products, Car Accessories, Pharmaceutical Products & Pet Care Products
N.A.I.C.S.: 325620
Gregory Sarantis *(Chm)*

Subsidiaries:

Astrid TM A.S. (1)
Zerotinova 1133/32, 130 00, Prague, Czech Republic
Tel.: (420) 222801700
Web Site: https://www.astrid.cz
Homecare Product Distr
N.A.I.C.S.: 456199

Ergopack LLC (1)
Str Sobornosti 36, Boyarka, 08150, Kiev, Ukraine
Tel.: (380) 459846882
Web Site: https://www.ergopack.sarantisgroup.com
Emp.: 2,700
Homecare Product Mfr & Distr
N.A.I.C.S.: 325612

Hoztorg LLC (1)
10D build 1 Botanicheskaya str 1st Floor room 29, 127276, Moscow, Russia
Tel.: (7) 4957637100
Web Site: http://www.russia.sarantisgroup.com
Homecare Product Distr
N.A.I.C.S.: 456199

Polipak Sp. z o.o. (1)
ul Fabryczna 7, 63-000, Sroda Wielkopolska, Poland
Tel.: (48) 512334433
Web Site: https://www.polipak.com.pl
Emp.: 300
Food Packaging Products Mfr
N.A.I.C.S.: 322220

S.C. Elmi Prodfarm S.R.L. (1)
Bucuresti-Ploiesti 172-176 Sector 1, Bucharest, Romania
Tel.: (40) 213170317
Web Site: http://www.elmiplant.com
Cosmetic Products Mfr & Distr
N.A.I.C.S.: 325620

SARANTICS CZECH REPUBLIC sro (1)
Zerotinova 1133/32, 130 00, Prague, Czech Republic
Tel.: (420) 222801700
Web Site: http://www.sarantis.cz
Cosmetic Product Distr
N.A.I.C.S.: 424210

SARANTIS BULGARIA LTD (1)
1 Business Park Sofia Str, 1766, Sofia, Bulgaria
Tel.: (359) 29690966
Web Site: https://bulgaria.sarantisgroup.com
Sales Range: $50-74.9 Million
Emp.: 85
Consumer Products Distr
N.A.I.C.S.: 424130

SARANTIS SERBIA LTD (1)
Zelengorska 1g, Novi Beograd, Belgrade, 11070, Serbia
Tel.: (381) 112090000
Web Site: http://www.serbia.sarantis.rs
Emp.: 40
Cosmetics Distr
N.A.I.C.S.: 424210

Sarantis Banja Luka D.O.O. (1)
Dunavska 1c, 78000, Banja Luka, Bosnia & Herzegovina
Tel.: (387) 51379300
Web Site: https://www.bosniaherzegovina.group.com
Emp.: 2,300
Homecare Product Distr
N.A.I.C.S.: 456199

Sarantis Belgrade D.O.O. (1)
Zelengorska 1G, 11070, Novi Beograd, Serbia
Tel.: (381) 112090000
Web Site: https://serbia.sarantisgroup.com
Emp.: 2,300
Personal Care Product Mfr & Distr
N.A.I.C.S.: 325620

Sarantis Hungary Kft. (1)
Vasut utca 11, 2040, Budaors, Hungary (100%)
Tel.: (36) 23430627
Web Site: https://hungary.sarantisgroup.com
Emp.: 2,300
Non-Durable Goods Whslr
N.A.I.C.S.: 424990

Sarantis Polska S.A. (1)
ul Pulawska 42C, 05500, Piaseczno, Poland (100%)
Tel.: (48) 22 715 9800
Web Site: https://poland.sarantisgroup.com
Laminated Aluminum Foil Mfr
N.A.I.C.S.: 322220

Sarantis Romania S.A. (1)
Sos Bucuresti-Ploiesti nr 172-176 Cladirea B Etaj 2 Spatiul B2, Sector 1, 015016, Bucharest, 015016, Romania
Tel.: (40) 213170317
Web Site: https://www.romania.sarantisgroup.com
Emp.: 2,700
Homecare Product Distr
N.A.I.C.S.: 456199

Sarantis d.o.o. (1)
Zelengorska 1G, 11070, Novi Beograd, Serbia (100%)
Tel.: (381) 11 209 0000
Web Site: http://www.serbia.sarantis.rs
Household Appliance Stores

GR. SARANTIS S.A.

Gr. Sarantis S.A.—(Continued)
N.A.I.C.S.: 449210

Sarantis-Skopje D.O.O. (1)
Bul 8th Septemvri 40/2, 1000, Skopje, North Macedonia (100%)
Tel.: (389) 22700551
Web Site:
https://northmacedonia.sarantisgroup.com
Sales Range: $25-49.9 Million
Emp.: 26
Household Appliance Stores
N.A.I.C.S.: 449210
Zoren Sdogenovski (Mng Dir)

GRAAL S.A.
St Zachodnia 22, 84-200, Wejherowo, Poland
Tel.: (48) 58 677 58 20
Web Site: http://www.graal.pl
GRL—(WAR)
Fish Hatchery Operator
N.A.I.C.S.: 112511
Boguslaw Kowalski (Chm)

GRAB HOLDINGS LIMITED
3 Media Close, Singapore, 138498, Singapore
Tel.: (65) 96841256 Ky
Web Site: https://grab.com
Year Founded: 2021
GRAB—(NASDAQ)
Rev.: $2,359,000,000
Assets: $8,792,000,000
Liabilities: $2,324,000,000
Net Worth: $6,468,000,000
Earnings: ($485,000,000)
Emp.: 10,604
Fiscal Year-end: 12/31/23
Holding Company
N.A.I.C.S.: 551112
Anthony Tan (Co-Founder, Chm & CEO)

GRABARZ & PARTNER WERBEAGENTUR GMBH
Alter Wall 55, 20457, Hamburg, Germany
Tel.: (49) 40 37 641 0 De
Web Site:
http://www.grabarzundpartner.de
Year Founded: 1993
Emp.: 200
Full Service
N.A.I.C.S.: 541810
Andreas Grabarz (Mng Dir)

GRABTAXI PTE. LTD.
Block 22 Sin Ming Lane 07-71, Midview City, 573969, Singapore, Singapore
Tel.: (65) 6570 3925
Web Site: http://www.grabtaxi.com
Emp.: 500
Online Limousine & Taxi Reservation Services
N.A.I.C.S.: 513210
Anthony Tan (Co-Founder & Grp CEO)

GRACE BREEDING LTD.
Prof Hillel VeHanan Oppenheimer 7, PO Box 1304, Rehovot, 7611201, Israel
Tel.: (972) 765304680 Il
Web Site:
https://www.gracebreeding.com
Year Founded: 2015
GRAC—(TAE)
Rev.: $127,918
Assets: $696,505
Liabilities: $558,917
Net Worth: $137,588
Earnings: ($2,369,112)
Emp.: 12
Fiscal Year-end: 12/31/23

Research & Development in Biotechnology (except Nanobiotechnology)
N.A.I.C.S.: 541714

GRACE FABRIC TECHNOLOGY CO., LTD.
No 123 Xiuyan Road, Kangqiao Industrial Zone Pudong, Shanghai, 201315, China
Tel.: (86) 2138299688
Web Site:
https://www.gracefabric.com
Year Founded: 1998
603256—(SHG)
Rev.: $85,938,391
Assets: $365,722,583
Liabilities: $154,111,253
Net Worth: $211,611,329
Earnings: $7,353,001
Fiscal Year-end: 12/31/22
Glass Fabric Product Mfr & Distr
N.A.I.C.S.: 327215
Jiaming Mao (Chm & Gen Mgr)

GRACE LIFE-TECH HOLDINGS LIMITED
Unit 2413A 24/F Lippo Centre Tower One 89 Queensway, Hong Kong, China (Hong Kong)
Tel.: (852) 53492737 Ky
Web Site: http://www.caa-resources.com
2112—(HKG)
Rev.: $32,347,000
Assets: $133,558,000
Liabilities: $213,878,000
Net Worth: ($80,320,000)
Earnings: ($55,740,000)
Emp.: 31
Fiscal Year-end: 12/31/22
Iron Ore Mining Services
N.A.I.C.S.: 212210
Yang Li (Chm & CEO)

GRACE TECHNOLOGY, INC.
Toranomon 33 Mori Building 7th Floor 3-8-21 Toranomon Minato-ku, Tokyo, 105-0001, Japan
Tel.: (81) 357773838
Web Site: http://www.g-race.com
6541—(TKS)
Rev.: $26,048,880
Assets: $61,622,880
Liabilities: $30,608,160
Net Worth: $31,014,720
Earnings: $10,415,680
Fiscal Year-end: 03/31/21
Electronic Document Processing Services
N.A.I.C.S.: 561410
Yukiharu Matsumura (Chm & CEO)

GRACE WINE HOLDINGS LTD.
Unit 705 7/F Westlands Centre No 20 Westlands Road, Quarry Bay, China (Hong Kong)
Tel.: (852) 23053308 Ky
Web Site:
http://www.gracewine.com.hk
Year Founded: 1997
8146—(HKG)
Rev.: $8,721,508
Assets: $46,449,234
Liabilities: $10,468,786
Net Worth: $35,980,448
Earnings: ($83,959)
Emp.: 176
Fiscal Year-end: 12/31/22
Wine Product Mfr & Distr
N.A.I.C.S.: 312130
Judy Chan (Chm & CEO)

GRACEKENNEDY LIMITED
42-56 Harbour Street, Kingston, Jamaica
Tel.: (876) 9223440

Web Site:
https://www.gracekennedy.com
Year Founded: 1922
GK—(JAM)
Rev.: $1,005,581,543
Assets: $353,322,131
Liabilities: $156,940,555
Net Worth: $196,381,577
Earnings: $54,359,413
Emp.: 2,003
Fiscal Year-end: 12/31/23
Distribution, Financial, Remittance & Food Processing Services
N.A.I.C.S.: 425120
Donald G. Wehby (Grp CEO)

Subsidiaries:

Allied Insurance Brokers Ltd. (1)
26 Belmont Road, 8769268, Kingston, Jamaica
Tel.: (876) 9266784
Web Site: https://youraib.com
Sales Range: $50-74.9 Million
Emp.: 80
Insurance Agencies & Brokerages
N.A.I.C.S.: 524210
Richard McElhaney (Asst VP-Safety & Risk Mgmt-Pittsburgh)

Chadha Oriental Foods Limited (1)
Grace House Bessemer Road, Welwyn Garden City, AL7 1HW, Herts, United Kingdom
Tel.: (44) 1707 325888
Web Site: http://www.gracefoods.co.uk
Emp.: 150
Food Products Mfr
N.A.I.C.S.: 311999
Faizal Fulat (Dir-Buying)

Consumer Brands Limited (1)
73 Harbour Street, Kingston, Jamaica
Tel.: (876) 922 3440
Web Site: https://consumerbrandsja.com
Consumer Products Distr
N.A.I.C.S.: 424490

Enco Products Limited (1)
Grace House Centrapark Bessemer Road, Welwyn Garden City, AL7 1HW, United Kingdom
Tel.: (44) 1707302332
Web Site:
http://www.caribbeanfoodcentre.com
Emp.: 11
Food Products & Soft Drink Whslr
N.A.I.C.S.: 424490
Andy Coult (Gen Mgr)

First Global Bank Ltd (1)
28-48 Barbados Avenue, LOJ Centre - Ground Floor, Kingston, Jamaica
Tel.: (876) 929 3383 6
Web Site: http://www.firstglobal-bank.com
Commericial Banking
N.A.I.C.S.: 522110
Mariame Robinson (Pres & CEO)

First Global Financial Services Ltd. (1)
2 St Lucia Avenue, Kingston, Jamaica
Tel.: (876) 9261275
Web Site: http://www.fgfs.com
Sales Range: $100-124.9 Million
Emp.: 110
Financial Vehicles
N.A.I.C.S.: 525990
Jason Chambers (Pres)

First Global Holdings Limited (1)
401 E Thomas St, Wilkes Barre, PA 18705-3816
Tel.: (570) 825-9022
Investment Management Service
N.A.I.C.S.: 523999

First Global Insurance Brokers Limited
Caribbean Place, PO Box 117, Leeward Highway, Providenciales, Turks & Caicos Islands
Tel.: (649) 946 4823
Web Site: http://www.gracekennedy.com
Insurance Brokerage Services
N.A.I.C.S.: 524210
Paul Mitchell (Mng Dir)

First Global Trinidad & Tobago Limited (1)

INTERNATIONAL PUBLIC

96 96A Fredrick Street Excellent Uptown Mall, Port of Spain, Trinidad & Tobago
Tel.: (868) 623 4957
Investment Management Service
N.A.I.C.S.: 523999
Jason Clarke (CEO)

Funnybones Foodservice Limited (1)
Grace House Bessemer Road, Welwyn Garden City, AL7 1HW, Herts, United Kingdom
Tel.: (44) 1707 321234
Web Site: http://www.funnybones.co.uk
Emp.: 11
Bakery Food Products Distr
N.A.I.C.S.: 424420
Phil Arthurs (Gen Mgr)

GK Insurance Brokers Limited (1)
Leeward Highway, Providenciales, Turks & Caicos Islands
Tel.: (649) 9464823
Insurance Services
N.A.I.C.S.: 524210

Grace Food Processors (Canning) Ltd. (1)
2-6 Twickenham Close, Kingston, 11, Jamaica
Tel.: (876) 9236060
Fruit & Vegetable Canning
N.A.I.C.S.: 311421
Dave Mitchell (Gen Mgr)

Grace Food Processors Ltd. (1)
Paradise Street Sav-la-Mar, Westmoreland, Kingston, Jamaica
Tel.: (876) 9552757
Sales Range: $25-49.9 Million
Emp.: 150
Miscellaneous Food Mfr
N.A.I.C.S.: 311999
Carl Barnett (Gen Mgr)

Grace Foods & Services Company (1)
73 Harbour Street, Kingston, Jamaica
Tel.: (876) 92234409
Miscellaneous Food Mfr
N.A.I.C.S.: 311999

Grace Foods International Ltd. (1)
39 Second St Newport West, Kingston, Jamaica
Tel.: (876) 9235120
Web Site: http://www.gracefoods.com
Sales Range: $25-49.9 Million
Emp.: 40
Grocery Product Whslr
N.A.I.C.S.: 424490

Grace Foods UK Limited (1)
Centrapark Bessemer Road, Welwyn Garden City, AL7 1HT, Hertfordshire, United Kingdom
Tel.: (44) 1707322332
Web Site:
https://www.gracefoodsukgroup.com
Food Distr
N.A.I.C.S.: 424490

Grace Kennedy Currency Trading Services Limited (1)
42-56 Harbour Street, Kingston, Jamaica
Tel.: (876) 9291331
Financial Investment
N.A.I.C.S.: 523999

Grace Kennedy Payment Services Limited (1)
2-6 Trafford Place, Kingston, 5, Jamaica
Tel.: (876) 9208724
Web Site: http://www.billexpressonline.com
Financial Investment
N.A.I.C.S.: 523999
Michelle Allen (CEO)

Grace, Kennedy (U.S.A.) Inc. (1)
169 Nebula Rd, Piscataway, NJ 08854
Tel.: (732) 572-7337
Food Products Mfr
N.A.I.C.S.: 311999

Grace, Kennedy Remittance Services (Guyana) Limited (1)
19 C Water Street, Georgetown, 592, Guyana
Tel.: (592) 227 5141
Web Site: http://www.psc.org
Money Transfer Services

N.A.I.C.S.: 541219
Stephen Fraser *(Exec Dir)*

GraceKennedy (Belize) Ltd. (1)
2 1-2 Miles Northern Hwy, PO Box 557, Belize, Belize
Tel.: (501) 22305723
Web Site:
http://www.gracekennedybelize.com
Sales Range: $50-74.9 Million
Emp.: 61
Grocery Product Whslr
N.A.I.C.S.: 424490
Marcello Blake *(Gen Mgr)*

GraceKennedy (Ontario) Inc. (1)
70 W Wilmot, Richmond Hill, L4B 1H8, ON, Canada
Tel.: (905) 886-1002
Web Site: http://www.gracefoods.ca
Sales Range: $25-49.9 Million
Emp.: 45
Miscellaneous Food Mfr
N.A.I.C.S.: 311999
Lucky Lankage *(Pres)*

GraceKennedy (Trinidad And Tobago) Limited (1)
Excellent Uptown Mall Third Floor, 96-96A Frederick Street, Port of Spain, Trinidad & Tobago
Tel.: (868) 6236000
Web Site: http://www.gracekennedy.com
Emp.: 50
Insurance Funds
N.A.I.C.S.: 525190
Donald Edward *(Country Mgr)*

GraceKennedy (USA) Inc. (1)
3350 SW 148th Ave Ste 110, Miramar, FL 33027
Tel.: (954) 874-1731
Sales Range: $25-49.9 Million
Emp.: 10
Miscellaneous Food Mfr
N.A.I.C.S.: 311999
Gregory Solomon *(Pres)*

Subsidiary (Domestic):

Grace Foods (USA) Inc. (2)
3350 SW 148th Ave Ste 110, Miramar, FL 33027
Tel.: (954) 874-1731
Web Site: http://www.gracefoods.com
Food Products Distr
N.A.I.C.S.: 311999

Subsidiary (Domestic):

Gonzalez & Tapanes Foods Inc. (3)
230 Moonachie Ave, Moonachie, NJ 07074
Tel.: (201) 329-6260
Web Site: http://www.lafe.com
Rev.: $39,600,000
Emp.: 25
Groceries, General Line
N.A.I.C.S.: 424410

GraceKennedy Money Services (Anguilla) Limited (1)
Lake's World, PO Box 76, The Valley, Anguilla
Tel.: (264) 4970324
Sales Range: $50-74.9 Million
Emp.: 4
Insurance Brokerage Services
N.A.I.C.S.: 524210
Susan Lake Marlin *(Gen Mgr)*

GraceKennedy Money Services (UK) Limited (1)
Centrapark, Welwyn Garden City, AL7 1HT, Herts, United Kingdom
Tel.: (44) 1707 322332
Money Transferring Services
N.A.I.C.S.: 522320

GraceKennedy Money Services Caribbean SRL (1)
Bishops Court Hill Erin Court, Saint Michael, Barbados
Tel.: (246) 4367000
Money Transfer & Bill Payment Services
N.A.I.C.S.: 541219

GraceKennedy Remittance Services (Guyana) Limited (1)
19C Water Street, George Town, Demerara, Guyana
Tel.: (592) 2275147
Sales Range: $50-74.9 Million
Emp.: 40
Insurance Agencies & Brokerages
N.A.I.C.S.: 524210

GraceKennedy Remittance Services (Trinidad And Tobago) Ltd. (1)
53 Alfredo Street, Woodbrook, Port of Spain, Trinidad & Tobago
Tel.: (868) 628 628
Financial Investment
N.A.I.C.S.: 523999
Lisa Mahabir *(Mgr-Mktg)*

GraceKennedy Remittance Services Limited (1)
42-56 Harbour Street, Kingston, 5, Jamaica
Tel.: (876) 9291331
Management Consulting Services
N.A.I.C.S.: 541618
Sandra Forbes *(Mgr-Mktg)*

GraceKennedy Trade Finance Limited (1)
2nd Floor 73 Harbour Street, Kingston, Jamaica
Tel.: (876) 9323335
Financial Activities
N.A.I.C.S.: 921130

Hardware & Lumber Limited (1)
697 Spanish Town Road, Kingston, 11, Jamaica
Tel.: (876) 765 9656
Web Site:
http://www.hardwareandlumberja.com
Hardware Whslr
N.A.I.C.S.: 423710

Hi-Lo Food Stores (JA) Ltd. (1)
13 Old Hope Road, Kingston, Jamaica
Tel.: (876) 9266123
Sales Range: $25-49.9 Million
Emp.: 42
Gasoline Stations
N.A.I.C.S.: 457120

Horizon Shipping Limited (1)
Icerenkoy Mah Eski Uskudar Cad Partas Center - Floor 15, Atasehir, Istanbul, 34752, Turkiye
Tel.: (90) 216 577 70 00
Web Site: http://www.horizonships.com
Marine Fleet Management Services
N.A.I.C.S.: 488330

Inversiones PCS Chile S.A. (1)
Gertrudis Echenique 30 Piso 13, Las Condes, Santiago, Chile
Tel.: (56) 23673000
Coal Mining Services
N.A.I.C.S.: 213113
Jose Manual Vergara *(Gen Mgr)*

Jamaica International Insurance Company Limited (1)
19-21 Knutsford Boulevard, Kingston, Jamaica
Tel.: (876) 92632049
Web Site: http://www.jiiconline.com
Insurance Related Activities
N.A.I.C.S.: 524298
Grace Burnett *(Mng Dir)*

Key Insurance Company Limited (1)
6C Half Way Tree Rd, Kingston, Jamaica
Tel.: (876) 926 6278
Web Site: https://keyinsurancejm.com
Insurance Services
N.A.I.C.S.: 524210
Donald Wehby *(Chm)*

National Processors Ltd. (1)
Temple Hall, Kingston, Jamaica
Tel.: (876) 9425224
Sales Range: $10-24.9 Million
Emp.: 77
Drinking Places
N.A.I.C.S.: 722410

ONE1 Financial Limited (1)
13A Pembroke Street, Port of Spain, Trinidad & Tobago
Tel.: (868) 6240335
Financial Vehicles
N.A.I.C.S.: 525990

Signia Financial Group Inc (1)
1st Floor Carlisle House, Bridgetown, Barbados
Tel.: (246) 4297344
Web Site:
http://www.signiafinancialgroup.com
Sales Range: $10-24.9 Million
Emp.: 30
Business Support Services
N.A.I.C.S.: 561499
Paul Ashby *(CEO)*

World Brands Services Ltd. (1)
258 Spanish Town Road, Kingston, 11, Jamaica
Tel.: (876) 923 6447
Web Site:
http://www.worldbrandsservices.com
Beverage Whslr
N.A.I.C.S.: 424810

GRADAC FAVRO A.D.
Derdaski put bb, 19320, Kladovo, Serbia
Tel.: (381) 19 803 661
Web Site: http://www.ac-favro.ls.rs
Year Founded: 1977
Sales Range: Less than $1 Million
Fastener, Screw & Machine Product Mfr
N.A.I.C.S.: 332722

GRADEVINAR A.D.
Radomira Markovica 46 b, Belgrade, Serbia
Tel.: (381) 11 2402 670
Year Founded: 2001
Sales Range: Less than $1 Million
Building Construction Services
N.A.I.C.S.: 236620
Jovica Boskovic *(Exec Dir)*

GRADEVINAR A.D.
Mosa Pijade 29, 26214, Debeljaca, Serbia
Tel.: (381) 13 664 255
Web Site:
http://www.gradjevinarad.com
Year Founded: 2005
Sales Range: $50-74.9 Million
Emp.: 28
Construction Product Mfr
N.A.I.C.S.: 327120
Janos Alfeldi *(Exec Dir)*

GRADEZEN INSTITUT MAKEDONIJA
Dresdenska 52, Skopje, North Macedonia
Tel.: (389) 23066816
Web Site: https://gim.mk
Civil Engineering Services
N.A.I.C.S.: 237990
Miho Janevski *(Pres & Member-Mgmt Bd)*

Subsidiaries:

Fabrika Karpos AD (1)
Ul Aco Sopov br 76, Skopje, North Macedonia
Tel.: (389) 22032082
Rev.: $17,949,978
Assets: $25,639,565
Liabilities: $18,690,727
Net Worth: $6,948,838
Earnings: $596,377
Fiscal Year-end: 12/31/2019
Concrete Products Mfr
N.A.I.C.S.: 327390

GRADIANT CORPORATION
Samseongdong Bldg 10th Floor 512 Samseong-ro, Gangnam-Gu, Seoul, 06168, Korea (South)
Tel.: (82) 262035157
Web Site:
http://www.globalinterpark.com
Year Founded: 1997
035010—(KRS)
Rev.: $2,749,576,723
Assets: $1,357,130,085
Liabilities: $680,450,503
Net Worth: $676,679,582
Earnings: $259,908,806
Fiscal Year-end: 12/31/22
Holding Company; Shopping Mall & Theater Operator; Tourism Services; E-Commerce Services
N.A.I.C.S.: 551112
Kang Donghwa *(CFO)*

Subsidiaries:

Gradiant Corporation (1)
Bldg 10th Floor 512 Samseong-ro, Gangnam-gu, Seoul, 06168, Korea (South)
Tel.: (82) 0234843993
Web Site: https://www.interpark.com
Rev.: $2,915,671,437
Assets: $1,474,631,271
Liabilities: $913,639,491
Net Worth: $560,991,780
Earnings: ($23,743,208)
Emp.: 620
Fiscal Year-end: 12/31/2020
Electronic Shopping Services
N.A.I.C.S.: 449210

GRADINA A.D.
George Clemenceau 19, Belgrade, Serbia
Tel.: (381) 114130400
Web Site: http://www.gradinaad.rs
Year Founded: 1946
GRDN—(BEL)
Rev.: $388,306
Assets: $3,547,054
Liabilities: $727,513
Net Worth: $2,819,540
Earnings: ($98,774)
Fiscal Year-end: 12/31/23
Real Estate Manangement Services
N.A.I.C.S.: 531390
Dragan Vlajkovic *(Dir)*

GRADIP A.D. PRNJAVOR
Svetog Save 28, 78430, Prnjavor, Bosnia & Herzegovina
Tel.: (387) 51660910
Web Site: http://www.gradip.com
Year Founded: 1948
GRDP—(BANJ)
Sales Range: $1-9.9 Million
Emp.: 141
Construction Services
N.A.I.C.S.: 236210
Branimir Bijelic *(Chm-Mgmt Bd)*

GRADISKA TRZNICA A.D.
Kozarskih Ustanika 36/1, 78400, Gradiska, Bosnia & Herzegovina
Tel.: (387) 51 815 218
Sales Range: Less than $1 Million
Emp.: 11
Real Estate Prorperty Leasing Services
N.A.I.C.S.: 531190

GRADITELJ A.D.
Vodovodska 69, Zeleznik, 11147, Belgrade, Serbia
Tel.: (381) 117440650
Web Site:
https://www.graditeljbeograd.com
Year Founded: 1959
GRDB—(BEL)
Rev.: $958,273
Assets: $3,980,495
Liabilities: $1,003,496
Net Worth: $2,976,999
Earnings: $1,721
Fiscal Year-end: 12/31/23
Building Construction Services
N.A.I.C.S.: 236220
Anakijev Bojko *(Gen Mgr)*

GRADITELJSKO DIONICKO DRUSTVO VIADUKT
Fallerovo setaliste 22, 10000, Zagreb, Croatia
Tel.: (385) 1 3032 800
Web Site: http://www.viadukt.hr

Graditeljsko dionicko drustvo VIADUKT—(Continued)
Year Founded: 1947
Rev.: $114,902,298
Assets: $143,460,012
Liabilities: $91,444,686
Net Worth: $52,015,326
Earnings: $328,578
Emp.: 1,724
Fiscal Year-end: 12/31/16
Construction Engineering Services
N.A.I.C.S.: 237990

GRADNJA A.D.
Karadordeva 2, Zemun, Belgrade, Serbia
Tel.: (381) 11 2106 548
Year Founded: 1993
Sales Range: Less than $1 Million
Emp.: 9
Building Construction Services
N.A.I.C.S.: 236220

GRADNJA GP A.D.
Ulica Boraca srpskih 12, 70260, Mrkonjic Grad, Bosnia & Herzegovina
Tel.: (387) 50211271
Year Founded: 2003
GRAD-R-A—(BANJ)
Assets: $996,263
Liabilities: $718,102
Net Worth: $278,161
Earnings: ($44,112)
Emp.: 7
Fiscal Year-end: 12/31/12
Building Construction Services
N.A.I.C.S.: 236116
Mirko Milanovic *(Chm-Mgmt Bd)*

GRADSKA CISTOCA A.D.
Svetog Save 84, 75420, Bratunac, Bosnia & Herzegovina
Tel.: (387) 56410208
GCBR—(BANJ)
Sales Range: Less than $1 Million
Emp.: 22
Sanitation & Remediation Services
N.A.I.C.S.: 562910
Mirjana Mladenovic *(Pres-Supervisory Bd)*

GRADSKI TRGOVSKI CENTAR AD
Kej 13 November, 1000, Skopje, North Macedonia
Tel.: (389) 70236527
Web Site: https://gtcskopje.com.mk
Year Founded: 1996
GTC—(MAC)
Rev.: $3,841,723
Assets: $15,003,453
Liabilities: $692,294
Net Worth: $14,311,159
Earnings: ($620,343)
Fiscal Year-end: 12/31/19
Real Estate Property Renting Services
N.A.I.C.S.: 531190

GRADUS AD-STARA ZAGORA
110B Simeonovsko shose Blvd floor 4 office 22, Sofia, Bulgaria
Tel.: (359) 24214065
Web Site: https://www.gradus.bg
Year Founded: 1992
GR6—(BUL)
Rev.: $79,623,110
Assets: $180,051,871
Liabilities: $21,918,111
Net Worth: $158,133,760
Earnings: ($6,881,691)
Emp.: 1,175
Fiscal Year-end: 12/31/23
Meat Product Distr
N.A.I.C.S.: 424470
Luka Angelov *(Chm)*

GRAFF DIAMONDS INTERNATIONAL LTD.
6 7 New Bond St, London, W1S 3SJ, United Kingdom
Tel.: (44) 2075848571
Web Site:
http://www.graffdiamonds.com
Sales Range: $750-799.9 Million
Emp.: 300
Jewelry Mfr & Whslr
N.A.I.C.S.: 339910
Laurence Graff *(Chm & Mng Dir)*

Subsidiaries:

Graff Diamonds (New York) Inc. (1)
46 E 61st St, New York, NY 10065
Tel.: (212) 355-9292
Web Site: http://www.graffdiamonds.com
Sales Range: $25-49.9 Million
Emp.: 25
Jewelry Stores
N.A.I.C.S.: 458310
Laurence Graff *(Chm)*

Graff Diamonds Hong Kong Limited (1)
Rooms 1107-8 II/F St George's Building 2 Ice House Street, Central, China (Hong Kong)
Tel.: (852) 31251500
Jewellery Distr
N.A.I.C.S.: 423940
Vincent Guy Raffin *(Dir-Sls)*

GRAFOID, INC.
945 Princess Street, Kingston, K7L 0E9, ON, Canada
Tel.: (613) 238-7417
Web Site: http://www.grafoid.com
Year Founded: 2011
Graphite Mfr
N.A.I.C.S.: 335991
Jeffrey York *(Chm)*

Subsidiaries:

ALCERECO Inc. (1)
Grafoid Global Technology Centre 945 Princess Street, Kingston, K7L 3N6, ON, Canada
Tel.: (613) 900-4600
Web Site: http://www.alcereco.com
Alloy Mfr
N.A.I.C.S.: 331314
Mark Gallerneault *(Dir-Tech)*

Ames Corporation (1)
19 Ames Blvd, Hamburg, NJ 07419-1514
Tel.: (973) 827-9101
Web Site: http://www.theamescorp.com
Elastomeric Component Mfr
N.A.I.C.S.: 325220
Ben Bordoloi *(Mgr-Matls Dev)*

MuAnalysis Inc. (1)
2301 St Laurent Blvd Suite 500, Ottawa, K1G 4J7, ON, Canada
Tel.: (613) 721-4664
Web Site: https://www.muanalysis.com
Analytical Equipment Mfr
N.A.I.C.S.: 334516
Martine Simard-Normandin *(Founder)*

GRAFOPROJEKT A.D.
Albanske spomenice 17, Belgrade, Serbia
Tel.: (381) 11 2763 792
Year Founded: 1963
Sales Range: Less than $1 Million
Emp.: 5
Information Technology Consulting Services
N.A.I.C.S.: 541511

GRAFOPROMET A.D.
3 Decembar bb, Cacak, Serbia
Tel.: (381) 32 5373 709
Year Founded: 1998
Sales Range: Less than $1 Million
Paperboard Product Mfr
N.A.I.C.S.: 322130

GRAFF DIAMONDS INTERNA- GRAFT POLYMER (UK) PLC
Eccleston Yards 25 Eccleston Place, London, SW1W 9NF, United Kingdom
Tel.: (44) 7795430246 UK
Web Site: https://graftpolymer.co.uk
Year Founded: 2017
GPL—(LSE)
Chemical Products Mfr
N.A.I.C.S.: 325998
Yifat Steuer *(CFO)*

GRAFTON CAPITAL LIMITED
2 Portman Stree, London, W1H 6DU, United Kingdom
Tel.: (44) 2031291700
Web Site:
https://www.graftoncapital.com
Emp.: 100
Investment Services
N.A.I.C.S.: 523999

Subsidiaries:

Third Financial Software Limited (1)
17 Neal's Yard, London, WC2H 9DP, United Kingdom
Tel.: (44) 20 7349 0034
Web Site: http://www.thirdfin.com
Emp.: 50
Wealth & Investment Management Software Publisher
N.A.I.C.S.: 513210
Ian Partington *(CEO)*

GRAFTON FRASER, INC.
44 Apex Rd, Toronto, M6A 2V2, ON, Canada
Tel.: (416) 780-9922 ON
Web Site:
http://www.graftonfraser.com
Year Founded: 1853
Sales Range: $200-249.9 Million
Emp.: 1,500
Clothing Retailer; Menswear
N.A.I.C.S.: 315210
Brian E. Reel *(CFO, Treas, Sec & Controller)*

GRAFTON GROUP PLC
The Hive Carmanhall Road, Sandyford Business Park, Dublin, D18 Y2X6, Ireland
Tel.: (353) 12160600 IE
Web Site: https://www.graftonplc.com
Year Founded: 1902
GROUF—(OTCIQ)
Rev.: $2,905,177,985
Assets: $3,770,301,691
Liabilities: $1,566,844,231
Net Worth: $2,203,457,460
Earnings: $263,340,066
Emp.: 8,826
Fiscal Year-end: 12/31/22
Building & Plumbing Merchant Services
N.A.I.C.S.: 423720
Charles Rinn *(Sec & Controller-Grp Fin)*

Subsidiaries:

Absolute Bathrooms Limited (1)
Thomas P Fox & Co Leixlip Centre, Naas, Co Kildare, Ireland
Tel.: (353) 12765689
Web Site: http://www.tavies.ie
Sales Range: $50-74.9 Million
Emp.: 80
Bathroom Fixtures Whslr
N.A.I.C.S.: 423220

Barretts of Ballinasloe Limited (1)
Society Street, Ballinasloe, Galway, Ireland
Tel.: (353) 909642212
Sales Range: $25-49.9 Million
Emp.: 24
Building Materials Distr
N.A.I.C.S.: 444180
Gerry Barrett *(Gen Mgr)*

Bluebell Sawmills Limited (1)
82 Kingsmead Road, High Wycombe, HP11 1YH, Bucks, United Kingdom
Tel.: (44) 1874690271
Timber Product Mfr
N.A.I.C.S.: 321113

Buildbase Limited (1)
Gemini One 5520 Oxford Bus Pk, Oxford, OX4 2LL, United Kingdom
Tel.: (44) 1865871700
Web Site: http://www.buildbase.com
Sales Range: $75-99.9 Million
Emp.: 200
Construction Materials Sales & Distr
N.A.I.C.S.: 423390

CPI Limited (1)
Laraghcon, Lucan, Dublin, Ireland
Tel.: (353) 16302500
Web Site: http://www.cpi.ie
Dry Mortars Mfr & Distr
N.A.I.C.S.: 327120

CPI Mortars Limited (1)
Willow House Strathclyde Business Park, Bellshill, ML4 3PB, United Kingdom
Tel.: (44) 8458509090
Web Site: https://www.cpieuromix.com
Dry Mortars Mfr & Distr
N.A.I.C.S.: 327120

Cork Builders Providers Limited (1)
West Link Togher Industrial Estate, Togher, Cork, T12 A324, Ireland
Tel.: (353) 214961700
Web Site: https://corkbp.ie
Building Materials Distr
N.A.I.C.S.: 444180

Drainage Systems Dublin Limited (1)
150 Harmonstown Road, Raheny, Dublin, 5, Ireland
Tel.: (353) 18511800
Web Site: https://www.drainagesystems.ie
Sales Range: $25-49.9 Million
Drainage & Pressure Pipe Systems Distr
N.A.I.C.S.: 423320

F&T Buckley (Holdings) Limited (1)
Robinhood Road, Clondalkin, Dublin, 22, Ireland
Tel.: (353) 14507770
Sales Range: $25-49.9 Million
Emp.: 40
Building Materials Distr
N.A.I.C.S.: 444180
Shea Nugent *(Gen Mgr)*

F&T Buckley Limited (1)
Naas Road, Dublin, 22, Ireland
Tel.: (353) 14034000
Building Materials Whslr
N.A.I.C.S.: 444180
Patrick Atkinson *(CEO)*

GKL Ventilatie Techniek B.V. (1)
Touwbaan 1h, 2352 CZ, Leiderdorp, Netherlands
Tel.: (31) 887651550
Web Site: https://gkl.nl
Ventilation Product Mfr & Distr
N.A.I.C.S.: 333413

Garvey Builders Providers Limited (1)
Lanesboro Road, Roscommon, Ireland
Tel.: (353) 906627722
Sales Range: $25-49.9 Million
Emp.: 13
Building Materials Distr
N.A.I.C.S.: 444180
Marion Cunningham *(Mgr)*

Grafton Merchanting GB Limited (1)
Llangefni Industrial Estate, Cowley, Llangefni, LL77 7JA, United Kingdom
Tel.: (44) 345 685 4467
Web Site:
https://www.graftonmerchantinggb.co.uk
Rev.: $1,631,140,000
Emp.: 4,500
Builders & Plumbers Merchants Indus Services
N.A.I.C.S.: 236115

Division (Domestic):

Grafton Merchanting GB Limited - Buildbase Support Centre Division (2)
Gemini One 5520 Oxford Business Park

AND PRIVATE COMPANIES

South, Cowley, Oxford, OX4 2LL, United Kingdom
Tel.: (44) 1865871700
Web Site: http://www.buildbase.co.uk
Emp.: 300
Building Materials Distr
N.A.I.C.S.: 444180
John Anderson (Mgr-Aberdeen Branch)

Grafton Merchanting GB Limited - Civils & Lintels Division
Gemini One 5520 Oxford Business Park, Cowley, Oxford, OX4 2LL, United Kingdom
Tel.: (44) 1865 871700
Web Site: http://www.buildbasecivils.co.uk
Emp.: 20
Building Materials Distr
N.A.I.C.S.: 444180

Subsidiary (Domestic):

Hendricks Lovell Ltd. (2)
Appin House Stewart Quay Printing House Lane, Hayes, UB3 1AP, Middlesex, United Kingdom
Tel.: (44) 2085731000
Web Site: http://www.hendricks-lovell.co.uk
Emp.: 40
Building Materials Distr
N.A.I.C.S.: 444180
Martin Lovell (Mng Dir)

Division (Domestic):

Jackson Building Centres Ltd. - Classic Hardware (2)
Unit 10 Fell Road, Sheffield, S9 2AL, United Kingdom
Tel.: (44) 1904420490
Sales Range: $25-49.9 Million
Emp.: 5
Hardware Retailer
N.A.I.C.S.: 423710
David Thomson (Brand Mgr)

Subsidiary (Domestic):

L & G Forest Products Ltd. (2)
Unit 3 Aerodrome Estate, Detling, Maidstone, ME14 3HU, Kent, United Kingdom
Tel.: (44) 1622738246
Web Site: http://www.lgforestproducts.com
Emp.: 35
Lumber Product Whslr
N.A.I.C.S.: 423990
Jeffry William Foot (Mng Dir)

Plumbing & Drainage Merchants Ltd. (2)
302 Drumoyne Road, Drumoyne, Glasgow, G51 4DX, United Kingdom
Tel.: (44) 1418928900
Web Site: http://www.pdmltd.co.uk
Drainage & Pressure Pipe Systems Distr
N.A.I.C.S.: 423320

Plumbline Supplies Ltd. (2)
72 Rogart Street, Glasgow, G40 2AA, Lanarkshire, United Kingdom
Tel.: (44) 1415510701
Plumbing Materials Retailer
N.A.I.C.S.: 444180

Secon Solar Ltd. (2)
Unit F Colima Avenue Sunderland Enterprise Park, Enterprise Park East, Sunderland, SR5 3XB, United Kingdom
Tel.: (44) 1915166554
Web Site: https://www.seconrenewables.com
Sales Range: $25-49.9 Million
Solar Equipment Distr
N.A.I.C.S.: 423720
Ann Pinder (Office Mgr)

Grafton Merchanting ROI Limited (1)
Ashfield Naas Road, Dublin, 22, Ireland
Tel.: (353) 14034000
Building Materials Distr
N.A.I.C.S.: 444180

Isero B.V. (1)
Dirk Verheulweg 3, 2742 JR, Waddinxveen, Netherlands
Tel.: (31) 850666888
Web Site: https://www.isero.nl
Hardware Merchant Whslr
N.A.I.C.S.: 423710

Isojoen Konehalli Oy (1)
Keskustie 26, 61850, Kauhajoki, Finland

Tel.: (358) 201323232
Web Site: https://www.ikh.fi
Construction Equipment Distr
N.A.I.C.S.: 423810

J.E. Telford Limited (1)
Clonminam business park, Athy, Portlaoise, Laois, Ireland
Tel.: (353) 598631462
Web Site: http://www.telford.ie
Building Materials Distr
N.A.I.C.S.: 444180

MFP Plastics Limited (1)
Laraghcon Lucan, Dublin, Ireland
Tel.: (353) 16302500
Plastic Material Distr
N.A.I.C.S.: 424610
Peadar Kearins (Gen Mgr)

MFP Sales Ltd. (1)
Dargan Road, Belfast, BT3 9JU, United Kingdom
Tel.: (44) 2890774790
Web Site: https://mfp.ie
Building Materials Distr
N.A.I.C.S.: 444180

MacNaughton Blair Limited (1)
10 Falcon Road, Belfast, BT12 6RD, United Kingdom
Tel.: (44) 2890385363
Web Site: https://www.macblair.com
Sales Range: $800-899.9 Million
Emp.: 60
Builders Materials Supplier
N.A.I.C.S.: 236117

Subsidiary (Domestic):

Lowdens (2)
42 Duncrue Crescent, Belfast, BT3 9BW, United Kingdom
Tel.: (44) 890370357
Web Site: http://www.macblair.com
Sales Range: $25-49.9 Million
Emp.: 20
Cement Mfr
N.A.I.C.S.: 327310

Market Hardware Limited (1)
Quin Road Business Park Quinn Road, Ennis, Munster, Ireland
Tel.: (353) 656828232
Web Site: http://www.graftonplc.com
Sales Range: $25-49.9 Million
Emp.: 16
Hardware Whslr
N.A.I.C.S.: 423710

Panelling Centre Limited (1)
Furry Park Industrial Estate Swords Road, Santry, Dublin, D09 FW60, Ireland
Tel.: (353) 18841111
Web Site: https://www.panellingcentre.ie
Sales Range: $25-49.9 Million
Kitchen & Bedroom Fixtures Retailer
N.A.I.C.S.: 449110

Sam Hire Limited (1)
Robinhood Road Off Long Mile Road, Clondalkin, Dublin, D22 V5T3, Ireland
Tel.: (353) 4089500
Web Site: http://www.samhire.ie
Household Tools & Equipment Rental Services
N.A.I.C.S.: 532490

Selco Trade Centres Limited (1)
2 Queens Drive Kings Norton Business Centre, Kings Norton, B30 3HH, W Midlands, United Kingdom
Tel.: (44) 1214157270
Web Site: http://www.selcobw.com
Sales Range: $400-449.9 Million
Emp.: 1,500
Building Materials Distr
N.A.I.C.S.: 444180
Chris Roach (Mgr-Bradford Branch)

Telfords (Portlaoise) Limited (1)
Clonminam Business Park, Co Laois, Portlaoise, Ireland
Tel.: (353) 578672700
Web Site: http://www.telfords.ie
Sales Range: $25-49.9 Million
Hardware & Building Materials Distr
N.A.I.C.S.: 423710

Toolbox.co.uk (1)
Units 2-4 Millennium Court, Enterprise Way,

Evesham, WR11 1GS, Worcs, United Kingdom
Tel.: (44) 1386 768498
Web Site: http://www.toolbox.co.uk
Online Tool Retailer
N.A.I.C.S.: 444140

Tullamore Hardware Limited (1)
Rahan Road, Tullamore, Ireland
Tel.: (353) 579341411
Sales Range: $25-49.9 Million
Emp.: 15
Hardware Whslr
N.A.I.C.S.: 423710
Jimmy Feery (Gen Mgr)

Universal Providers Limited (1)
Kells Road, Kilkenny, Ireland
Tel.: (353) 567762658
Sales Range: $25-49.9 Million
Emp.: 11
Building Materials Distr
N.A.I.C.S.: 444180
Vincent Maher (Branch Mgr)

Woodie's DIY (1)
Arena Whitestown Way Tallaght Bypass, Dublin, 24, Ireland
Tel.: (353) 1 459 6944
Web Site: http://www.woodiesdiy.com
Sales Range: $200-249.9 Million
Hardware & Building Materials Retailer
N.A.I.C.S.: 444140

Woodie's DIY Limited (1)
Turners Cross Kinsale Road, Cork, Ireland
Tel.: (353) 214967072
Web Site: http://www.woodiesdiy.com
Hardware & Building Materials Distr
N.A.I.C.S.: 423710

GRAHAM BROS. CONSTRUCTION LIMITED
290 Clarence Street, Brampton, L6W 1T4, ON, Canada
Tel.: (905) 453-1200
Web Site: http://www.grahambros.com
Year Founded: 1959
Rev.: $15,476,201
Emp.: 100
Highway & Bridge Construction Services
N.A.I.C.S.: 237310
Alfredo Maggio (Pres)

GRAHAM GROUP LTD.
10840 27th St SE, Calgary, T2Z 3R6, AB, Canada
Tel.: (403) 570-5000
Web Site: http://www.graham.ca
Year Founded: 1926
Sales Range: $1-4.9 Billion
Emp.: 1,600
Construction Services
N.A.I.C.S.: 236220
Patrick Schmidtz (VP-Labour)

Subsidiaries:

Gracom Masonry (1)
16903 129th Avenue, Edmonton, T5V 1L2, AB, Canada
Tel.: (780) 496-7728
Web Site: http://www.brixton.com
Sales Range: $25-49.9 Million
Emp.: 28
Masonry Contractors
N.A.I.C.S.: 238140
M. Labas (Pres)

Graham Construction & Management, Inc. (1)
331 N Fancher Rd, Spokane, WA 99212
Tel.: (509) 534-1030
Web Site: http://www.grahamus.com
Sales Range: $25-49.9 Million
Emp.: 35
Construction Services
N.A.I.C.S.: 236220

Division (Domestic):

Graham Construction - Omaha (2)
4403 S 139 St, Omaha, NE 68127
Tel.: (402) 891-9651

Web Site: http://www.grahamus.com
Sales Range: $25-49.9 Million
Construction Services
N.A.I.C.S.: 236220
Greg Ritke (District Mgr)

Graham Construction Services, Inc. (1)
2995 Lone Oak Cir Ste 1, Eagan, MN 55121
Tel.: (651) 687-0648
Web Site: http://www.grahamus.com
Construction Services
N.A.I.C.S.: 236220
Scott Fowler (District Mgr)

Graham Contracting Ltd. (1)
9709 3rd Ave NE Ste 300, Seattle, WA 98115
Tel.: (206) 729-8844
Web Site: http://www.graham.ca
Sales Range: $50-74.9 Million
Emp.: 40
Construction Services
N.A.I.C.S.: 236220

Graham Group Ltd. - Delta (1)
7216 Brown Street, Delta, V4G 1G8, BC, Canada
Tel.: (604) 940-4500
Sales Range: $50-74.9 Million
Emp.: 40
Construction Services
N.A.I.C.S.: 236220
Lee Holland (VP)

Graham Group Ltd. - Edmonton (1)
8404 McIntyre Road, Edmonton, T6E 6V3, AB, Canada
Tel.: (780) 430-9600
Web Site: http://www.grahamgroup.ca
Sales Range: $50-74.9 Million
Emp.: 200
Construction Services
N.A.I.C.S.: 236220
M. Senger (Sr VP-Indus)

Graham Group Ltd. - Kelowna (1)
7216 Brown Street, Delta, V4G 1G8, BC, Canada
Tel.: (250) 765-6662
Web Site: http://www.graham.ca
Sales Range: $25-49.9 Million
Emp.: 100
Construction Services
N.A.I.C.S.: 236220

Graham Group Ltd. - Mississauga (1)
2105 Matheson Blvd East Suite 400, Mississauga, L4W 0G2, ON, Canada
Tel.: (905) 694-4000
Web Site: http://www.graham.com
Sales Range: $25-49.9 Million
Emp.: 30
Construction Services
N.A.I.C.S.: 236220

Graham Group Ltd. - Regina (1)
1903E Turvey Road, Regina, S0G 3Z0, SK, Canada
Tel.: (306) 721-1444
Sales Range: $25-49.9 Million
Emp.: 35
Construction Services
N.A.I.C.S.: 236220
Colin Anderson (VP-Comml East)

Graham Group Ltd. - Saskatoon (1)
875 57th St E, Saskatoon, S7K 5Z2, SK, Canada
Tel.: (306) 934-6644
Sales Range: $25-49.9 Million
Emp.: 100
Construction Services
N.A.I.C.S.: 236220
June Verhelst (Sr VP)

GRAINCORP LIMITED
Level 20 Tower 2 International Towers 200 Barangaroo Avenue, Sydney, 2000, NSW, Australia
Tel.: (61) 293259100   AU
Web Site:
https://www.graincorp.com.au
Year Founded: 1916
GNC—(ASX)
Rev.: $4,609,708,518

GRAINCORP LIMITED

GrainCorp Limited—(Continued)
Assets: $2,007,547,341
Liabilities: $969,046,398
Net Worth: $1,038,500,943
Earnings: $42,709,362
Fiscal Year-end: 09/30/24
Grain & Field Bean Merchant Wholesalers
N.A.I.C.S.: 424510
Alistair Bell *(CFO)*

Subsidiaries:

Auscol Pty Ltd **(1)**
79 Dohertys Rd, Laverton, 3026, VIC, Australia
Tel.: (61) 1800629476
Web Site: http://www.auscol.com.au
Cooking Oil Recycling Services
N.A.I.C.S.: 311225

GrainCorp Liquid Feeds Pty Ltd **(1)**
Locked Bag 191, Tingalpa, 4173, QLD, Australia **(100%)**
Tel.: (61) 1800333010
Emp.: 7
Liquid Animal Feed Products Mfr & Distr
N.A.I.C.S.: 311119
Brad Monk *(Sls Mgr-Feedlot & Pasture)*

GrainCorp Malt **(1)**
1620 Dodge St Ste 1700, Omaha, NE 68102
Tel.: (402) 346-6416
Web Site: http://www.graincorpmalt.com
Malt Producer
N.A.I.C.S.: 551112

Subsidiary (Non-US):

Bairds Malt Ltd. **(2)**
Station Maltings Station Road, Witham, CM8 2DU, Essex, United Kingdom
Tel.: (44) 1376513566
Malt Producers
N.A.I.C.S.: 311213

Subsidiary (Domestic):

Saxon Agriculture, Ltd. **(3)**
Acorn House Turbine Way, Swaffham, Norfolk, PE37 7XN, United Kingdom
Tel.: (44) 1760725516
Sales Range: $25-49.9 Million
Emp.: 35
Malting Barley Producers
N.A.I.C.S.: 111199

Scotgrain Agriculture Ltd. **(3)**
Elliot Industrial Estate, Arbroath, DD11 2NB, Angus, United Kingdom
Tel.: (44) 1241870431
Web Site: https://scotgrain.co.uk
Barley, Wheat, Oats & Oilseeds Purchase & Marketing
N.A.I.C.S.: 311213

Subsidiary (Non-US):

Barrett Burston Malting Co. Pty. Ltd. **(2)**
15 Gough Street, Richmond, 3121, VIC, Australia
Tel.: (61) 39 425 2300
Web Site: https://bbmalt.com.au
Sales Range: $10-24.9 Million
Emp.: 50
Malt Mfr
N.A.I.C.S.: 311213
Noel Johnson *(CEO)*

Subsidiary (Domestic):

Barrett Burston Malting Co. WA Pty. Limited **(3)**
47 McDowell St, Welshpool, 6106, WA, Australia **(100%)**
Tel.: (61) 893564600
Sales Range: $10-24.9 Million
Emp.: 22
Malt Mfr
N.A.I.C.S.: 311213
Jennifer Cutajar *(Mgr-Fin)*

Subsidiary (Non-US):

Canada Malting Co Limited **(2)**
579 Maureen Street, PO Box 10490, Thunder Bay, P7B 6T2, ON, Canada
Tel.: (807) 344-6460
Web Site: https://www.canadamalting.com
Sales Range: $10-24.9 Million
Emp.: 40
Malted Barley Mfr
N.A.I.C.S.: 311213
Armand Parisien *(Pres)*

Subsidiary (Domestic):

Coastal Containers Ltd. **(3)**
2525 Commissioner St, V5K 5E5, Vancouver, BC, Canada
Tel.: (604) 255-9390
Bulk Malt Export Container Loading & Shipping Facility
N.A.I.C.S.: 488510

Subsidiary (Domestic):

Great Western Malting Co. **(2)**
1705 NW Harborside Dr, Vancouver, WA 98660
Tel.: (360) 693-3661
Malt Mfr & Supplier
N.A.I.C.S.: 311213
Robert Seggewiss *(Mgr)*

GrainCorp Operations Limited **(1)**
Level 26 175 Liverpool Street, Sydney, 2000, NSW, Australia
Tel.: (61) 293259100
Farm Product Warehousing Services
N.A.I.C.S.: 493130

Vicgrain Pty Limited **(1)**
Level 26 175 Liverpool St, Sydney, 2000, NSW, Australia
Tel.: (61) 293259100
Malt Mfr
N.A.I.C.S.: 311213

GRAINES VOLTZ SA

23 rue Denis Papin, 68000, Colmar, France
Tel.: (33) 389201819
Web Site: https://www.graines-voltz.com
Year Founded: 1985
GRVO—(EUR)
Rev.: $141,792,301
Assets: $124,901,003
Liabilities: $76,118,088
Net Worth: $48,782,914
Earnings: $10,754,594
Emp.: 294
Fiscal Year-end: 09/30/21
Seed Distr
N.A.I.C.S.: 424910
Serge Voltz *(Pres & Dir Gen)*

GRAINGER & WORRALL LIMITED

Stanmore Industrial Estate, Bridgnorth, WV15 5HP, Shropshire, United Kingdom
Tel.: (44) 1746768250
Web Site: http://www.gwcast.com
Year Founded: 1946
Sales Range: $25-49.9 Million
Emp.: 650
Iron Casting Mfr
N.A.I.C.S.: 331511
Geoff Tillson *(Mgr-Quality Systems)*

Subsidiaries:

GRAINGER & WORRALL MACHINING LTD **(1)**
Unit 13 Stafford Park 13, Telford, TF3 3AZ, Shropshire, United Kingdom
Tel.: (44) 1952293793
Industrial Machinery Mfr
N.A.I.C.S.: 333998

GRAINGER PLC

Citygate St James Boulevard, Newcastle upon Tyne, NE1 4JE, United Kingdom
Tel.: (44) 1912611819 UK
Web Site: https://www.graingerplc.co.uk
Year Founded: 1912
GRI—(LSE)
Rev.: $337,936,508
Assets: $4,442,731,384
Liabilities: $2,081,656,304
Net Worth: $2,361,075,080
Earnings: $148,670,340
Emp.: 322
Fiscal Year-end: 09/30/21
Residential Property Investment Services
N.A.I.C.S.: 531390
Adam McGhin *(Sec)*

Subsidiaries:

BPT Limited **(1)**
Citygate, Saint James Boulevard, Newcastle upon Tyne, NE1 4JE, United Kingdom
Tel.: (44) 1912611819
Web Site: http://www.graingerplc.co.uk
Sales Range: $75-99.9 Million
Emp.: 80
Residential Property Management Services
N.A.I.C.S.: 531390

Bridgewater Equity Release Limited **(1)**
Citygate Saint James Blvd, Newcastle upon Tyne, NE1 4JE, United Kingdom
Tel.: (44) 1912611819
Web Site: http://www.bridgewaterequityrelease.co.uk
Sales Range: $75-99.9 Million
Emp.: 120
Real Estate Property Lessors
N.A.I.C.S.: 531190
Steve Groves *(Chm)*

Bridgewater Tenancies Limited **(1)**
3rd Floor Scross House W Gate Road, Newcastle upon Tyne, NE1 4JE, United Kingdom
Tel.: (44) 1912424820
Property Development Services
N.A.I.C.S.: 531390
Andrew Cunningham *(Gen Mgr)*

Bromley Property Investments Limited **(1)**
Citygate St James Blvd, Newcastle upon Tyne, NE1 4JE, United Kingdom
Tel.: (44) 1912611819
Web Site: http://www.grainger.plc.co.uk
Sales Range: $75-99.9 Million
Emp.: 120
Real Estate Property Lessors
N.A.I.C.S.: 531190
Helen Gordon *(CEO)*

City North Group plc **(1)**
Citygate St James Blvd, Newcastle upon Tyne, NE1 4JE, United Kingdom
Tel.: (44) 1912611819
Web Site: http://www.graingerplc.co.uk
Sales Range: $10-24.9 Million
Emp.: 80
Residential Property Development & Management Services
N.A.I.C.S.: 531390

Grainger Limited **(1)**
5 Chapman Way, Tunbridge Wells, TN2 3EP, Kent, United Kingdom
Tel.: (44) 8701128103
Web Site: http://www.barrygraingerinsurance.co.uk
Sales Range: $50-74.9 Million
Emp.: 85
Insurance Related Activities
N.A.I.C.S.: 524298

Grainger Luxembourg Germany Holdings Sarl **(1)**
9 Parc D Activite Syrdall, 5365, Munsbach, Luxembourg
Tel.: (352) 26351262
Web Site: http://www.grainger.lu
Holding Company
N.A.I.C.S.: 551112

Grainger Residential Management Limited **(1)**
Citygate, Saint James Boulevard, Newcastle upon Tyne, NE1 4JE, United Kingdom
Tel.: (44) 1912611819
Web Site: http://www.graingerplc.co.uk

INTERNATIONAL PUBLIC

Emp.: 80
Real Estate Management Services
N.A.I.C.S.: 531390

Grainger Stuttgart Portfolio 1 Sarl & Co KG **(1)**
Emanuel-Leutze-Strasse 17, 40547, Dusseldorf, Germany
Tel.: (49) 21159750
Web Site: http://www.grainger.de
Sales Range: $25-49.9 Million
Emp.: 50
Real Estate Property Lessors
N.A.I.C.S.: 531190

Northumberland & Durham Property Trust Limited **(1)**
Citygate, Saint James Boulevard, Newcastle upon Tyne, NE1 4JE, United Kingdom
Tel.: (44) 1912611819
Web Site: http://www.graingerplc.co.uk
Sales Range: $75-99.9 Million
Emp.: 125
Real Estate Property Lessors
N.A.I.C.S.: 531190

PHA Limited **(1)**
PHA UK Resource Centre Unit 1 Newton Chambers Road, Newton Business Centre Thorncliffe Park Chapeltown, Sheffield, S35 2PH, United Kingdom
Tel.: (44) 170 976 1450
Web Site: https://www.phauk.org
Health Organization Services
N.A.I.C.S.: 813212
Iain Armstrong *(Chm)*

Sovereign Reversions Limited **(1)**
31 Goldington Rd, Bedford, MK40 3LH, United Kingdom
Tel.: (44) 84511122
Web Site: http://www.sovereign-reversions.co.uk
Sales Range: $125-149.9 Million
Emp.: 26
Mortgage Services
N.A.I.C.S.: 522310

Subsidiary (Domestic):

The Home & Capital Trust Group Limited **(2)**
31 Goldington Rd, Bedford, MK40 3LH, United Kingdom
Tel.: (44) 1234340511
Web Site: http://www.homecapital.co.uk
Sales Range: $50-74.9 Million
Emp.: 5
Financial Services
N.A.I.C.S.: 522320

Subsidiary (Domestic):

Home & Capital Advisers Limited **(3)**
31 Goldington Rd, Bedford, United Kingdom
Tel.: (44) 1234340511
Web Site: http://www.homecapital.co.uk
Sales Range: $50-74.9 Million
Financial Services
N.A.I.C.S.: 522320

Home & Capital Trust Limited **(3)**
31 Goldington Rd, Bedford, MK40 3LH, United Kingdom
Tel.: (44) 1234340511
Web Site: http://www.homecapital.co.uk
Investment Management Service
N.A.I.C.S.: 541618

Home & Capital Trustee Company Limited **(3)**
31 Goldington Rd, Bedford, MK40 3LH, United Kingdom
Tel.: (44) 1234340511
Web Site: http://www.homecapital.co.uk
Sales Range: $50-74.9 Million
Financial Services
N.A.I.C.S.: 522320

Subsidiary (Domestic):

The Welfare Dwellings Trust Limited **(2)**
31 Goldington Rd, Bedford, MK40 3LH, United Kingdom
Tel.: (44) 1234340511
Sales Range: $50-74.9 Million
Emp.: 20
Financial Services

N.A.I.C.S.: 522320

GRAMMER AG
Postfach 1454, PO Box 1454,
D-92204, Amberg, Germany
Tel.: (49) 9621660
Web Site: https://www.grammer.com
GMM—(MUN)
Rev.: $2,544,298,924
Assets: $1,693,800,205
Liabilities: $1,402,444,758
Net Worth: $291,355,448
Earnings: $1,986,966
Emp.: 14,241
Fiscal Year-end: 12/31/23
Motor Vehicle Passenger Seats &
Seating Systems Mfr
N.A.I.C.S.: 336360
Horst Ott *(Deputy Chm-Supervisory Bd)*

Subsidiaries:

GRA-MAG Truck Interior Systems LLC (1)
470 E High St, London, OH 43140
Tel.: (740) 490-1000
Web Site: https://gramag.com
Truck Seat Mfr & Distr
N.A.I.C.S.: 336360

GRAMMER Automotive Espanola S.A. (1)
Avda Hostal Nou 26 30 Ind Sant Pere Molanta E, PO Box 08799, Olerdola, Spain
Tel.: (34) 938182008
Web Site: http://www.grammer.com
Sales Range: $50-74.9 Million
Emp.: 150
Automobile Seats Mfr
N.A.I.C.S.: 336360

GRAMMER Automotive Puebla S.A. de C.V. (1)
Blvd Tetla lote 1 Mzna 2 No 107, CD Industrial Xicohtencatl Tetla, Tlaxcala, CP 90434, Mexico
Tel.: (52) 2414127288
Automobile Seats Mfr
N.A.I.C.S.: 336360

GRAMMER Automotive Slovenija D.O.O. (1)
Web Site: http://www.grammer.com
Sales Range: $100-124.9 Million
Emp.: 270
Automobile Seats Mfr
N.A.I.C.S.: 336360

GRAMMER Industries, LLC (1)
1975 Technology Dr Bldg J Ste A, Troy, MI 48083
Tel.: (248) 530-1201
Automobile Equipment Mfr
N.A.I.C.S.: 336110

GRAMMER Interior (Shanghai) Co. Ltd.. (1)
Web Site: http://www.grammer.com
Sales Range: $50-74.9 Million
Emp.: 150
Automobile Seats Mfr
N.A.I.C.S.: 336360

GRAMMER Interior (Tianjin) Co. Ltd. (1)
Building 2 172 Huanghai Road, Tianjin, 300457, China
Tel.: (86) 2266299955
Emp.: 140
Automobile Seats Mfr
N.A.I.C.S.: 336360

GRAMMER Interior Components GmbH (1)
Industriestrasse 9, 74736, Hardheim, Germany
Tel.: (49) 6283570
Web Site: http://www.grammer.com
Plastic Components for Automotive Ventilation Systems & Climate Controls Mfr & Marketer
N.A.I.C.S.: 336390
Peter Busing *(Mng Dir)*

GRAMMER Mexicana S.A. de C.V. (1)
Av de la Luz No 24 3 y 4 Acceso III Parque Induatrial Benito Juarez, 76120, Queretaro, Mexico
Tel.: (52) 4422384497
Sales Range: $25-49.9 Million
Emp.: 100
Motor Vehicle Parts & Accessories Mfr
N.A.I.C.S.: 336360

GRAMMER Seating Systems Ltd. (1)
Willenhall Lane Industrial Estate, Bloxwich, Walsall, WS3 2XN, W Midlands, United Kingdom
Tel.: (44) 1922407035
Sales Range: $25-49.9 Million
Emp.: 7
Vehicle Seats Mfr
N.A.I.C.S.: 336360
Simon Range *(Mgr-After Market Sls)*

GRAMMER Wackersdorf GmbH (1)
Oskar-von-Miller-Str 7, 92442, Wackersdorf, Germany
Tel.: (49) 9431 737 0
Web Site: http://www.grammer.com
Automobile Seats Mfr
N.A.I.C.S.: 336360

Grammer AD (1)
Tzar Osvoboditel Str 2, Trudovetz, 2610, Sofia, Bulgaria
Tel.: (359) 72368601
Automotive Seat Mfr
N.A.I.C.S.: 336360
Metin Deniz *(Plant Mgr)*

Grammer Argentina S.A. (1)
Alte Brown 2146 1650, San Martin, Buenos Aires, Argentina
Tel.: (54) 1147161610
Automotive Seat Mfr
N.A.I.C.S.: 336360

Grammer Automotive CZ s.r.o. (1)
U Obecniho Lesa 2988, 47001, Ceska Lipa, Czech Republic
Automotive Seat Mfr
N.A.I.C.S.: 336360
Jakub Vondruska *(Mgr-HR & EHS)*

Grammer Automotive Metall GmbH (1)
Schafhof II Jubatus Allee 3, 92263, Ebermannsdorf, Germany
Tel.: (49) 943894490
Automotive Seat Mfr
N.A.I.C.S.: 336360
Markus Schlaffer *(Engr-Industrial)*

Grammer CZ s.r.o. (1)
Okruzni 2042, 34701, Tachov, Czech Republic
Tel.: (420) 374799011
Automotive Seat Mfr
N.A.I.C.S.: 336360
Zdenek Skacel *(Mgr-Quality)*

Grammer Electronics N.V. (1)
Bell Telephonelaan 2D, 2440, Geel, Belgium
Tel.: (32) 14564600
Automotive Seat Mfr
N.A.I.C.S.: 336360

Grammer France Sarl (1)
1 Rue des Vergers, 69760, Limonest, France
Tel.: (33) 478668200
Automotive Seat Mfr
N.A.I.C.S.: 336360
Cecile Basset Giry *(Acct Mgr)*

Grammer Inc. (1)
231 Laney Rd Tupelo Lee Industrial Park, Shannon, MS 38868
Tel.: (662) 556-1660
Web Site: http://usa.grammer.com
Automotive Seat Mfr
N.A.I.C.S.: 336360
Eduardo Aschenbach *(Plant Mgr)*

Grammer Interior (Beijing) Co. Ltd. (1)
2nd Floor Building 3 No 28 Jinghai 2nd Road, Jintian Hengye Industrial Park, Beijing, 100023, China
Automotive Seat Mfr
N.A.I.C.S.: 336360
Dennis Liu *(Mgr-Maintenance)*

Grammer Interior (Changchun) Co., Ltd. (1)
No 3088 East Shengtai Street, Jingyue State High Technology Development Zone, Changchun, 130119, Jilin, China
Tel.: (86) 431846678752939
Automotive Seat Mfr
N.A.I.C.S.: 336360
Enhui Max Zhang *(Project Mgr)*

Grammer Japan Ltd. (1)
8-4-30-202 Tsuruma, Machida, 194-0004, Tokyo, Japan
Tel.: (81) 427883021
Automotive Seat Mfr
N.A.I.C.S.: 336360

Grammer Koltuk Sistemleri Sanayi ve Ticaret A.S. (1)
Mustafa Karaer Cad No 38, 16369, Bursa, Turkiye
Tel.: (90) 2242193012
Automotive Seat Mfr
N.A.I.C.S.: 336360
Barbaros Ersozlu *(Sr Mgr-Sls & Project)*

Grammer Seating (Jiangsu) Co., Ltd. (1)
No 25 Zhenyang Road, Qingyang, Jiangyin, 214401, Jiangsu, China
Tel.: (86) 51066287887
Automotive Seat Mfr
N.A.I.C.S.: 336360
Tang Ji *(Mgr-Controlling)*

Grammer Seating (Shaanxi) Co., Ltd. (1)
No 4 High-Tech Zone, Fuping, Weinan, 711700, Shaanxi, China
Tel.: (86) 9138220168
Automotive Seat Mfr
N.A.I.C.S.: 336360
Thomas Stolte *(Gen Mgr-Grammer Truck-China)*

Grammer System d.o.o. (1)
22 decembra 1Tihomira Djordjevica bb, 18220, Aleksinac, Serbia
Tel.: (381) 18809100
Automotive Seat Mfr
N.A.I.C.S.: 336360
Jelena Vuckovic *(Mgr-Controlling)*

Grammer Technical Components GmbH (1)
Koferinger Str 9-13, Kummersbruck, 92245, Amberg, Germany
Tel.: (49) 9621660
Automotive Seat Mfr
N.A.I.C.S.: 336360

Grammer do Brasil Ltda. (1)
Av Industrial Walter Kloth 888Jd Cherry trees, Atibaia, Sao Paulo, 12951-200, Brazil
Web Site: http://www.brasil.grammer.com
Automotive Seat Mfr
N.A.I.C.S.: 336360
Marcelo Capodeferro *(Acct Mgr)*

Toledo Molding & Die Inc. (1)
1429 Coining Dr, Toledo, OH 43612
Tel.: (419) 470-3950
Web Site: http://www.tmdinc.com
Sales Range: $125-149.9 Million
Injection Molded Finished Plastics Products
N.A.I.C.S.: 326199
Joni Schmidt *(Co-Owner)*

Subsidiary (Domestic):

TMDWEK North, LLC (2)
1085 Jefferson-Eagleville Rd, Jefferson, OH 44047
Tel.: (440) 576-6940
Web Site: http://www.tmdwek.com
Sales Range: $25-49.9 Million
Plastic & Rubber Molded Products Mfr
N.A.I.C.S.: 326121
Shawn Houser *(Mgr)*

Toledo Molding & Die, LLC (1)
1429 Coining Dr, Toledo, OH 43612
Tel.: (419) 470-3950
Web Site: https://www.tmdinc.com
Automotive Interior Components Distr
N.A.I.C.S.: 423610

Toledo Molding CZ s.r.o. (1)
Okruzni 2042, 347 01, Tachov, Czech Republic

Tel.: (420) 374799011
Seat Cushion Mfr & Distr
N.A.I.C.S.: 336360

GRAMPET SA
114 Calea Victoriei, Bucharest, 010092, Romania
Tel.: (40) 21 317 30 90
Web Site: http://grampet.ro
Railway Freight Trasnportation Services
N.A.I.C.S.: 488510
Gruia Stoica *(Co-Founder & Pres)*

GRAN COLOMBIA GOLD CORP.
401 Bay Street Suite 2400, PO Box 15, Toronto, M5H 2Y4, ON, Canada
Tel.: (416) 360-4653   BC
Web Site:
https://www.grancolombiagold.com
ARMN—(NYSE)
Rev.: $447,674,000
Assets: $1,352,871,000
Liabilities: $728,216,000
Net Worth: $624,655,000
Earnings: $11,419,000
Emp.: 3,485
Fiscal Year-end: 12/31/23
Gold & Silver Mining Services
N.A.I.C.S.: 212220
Serafino Iacono *(Chm)*

Subsidiaries:

Gold X Mining Corp. (1)
3123-595 Burrard Street, Vancouver, V7X 1J1, BC, Canada
Tel.: (604) 609-6138
Web Site: http://goldxmining.com
Mineral Exploration Services
N.A.I.C.S.: 213114

GRAN TIERRA ENERGY INC.
900 520 - 3 Ave SW, Calgary, T2P 0R3, AB, Canada
Tel.: (403) 265-3221   NV
Web Site: https://www.grantierra.com
Year Founded: 2005
GTE—(NYSEAMEX)
Rev.: $636,957,000
Assets: $1,326,289,000
Liabilities: $929,895,000
Net Worth: $396,394,000
Earnings: ($6,287,000)
Emp.: 351
Fiscal Year-end: 12/31/23
Oil & Gas Exploration Services
N.A.I.C.S.: 211120
Ryan Paul Ellson *(CFO & Exec VP)*

Subsidiaries:

Gran Tierra Energy Colombia, Ltd. (1)
AR Building Calle 113 No 7 - 80 17th Floor, Bogota, Colombia
Petroleum & Natural Gas Exploration & Production
N.A.I.C.S.: 211120

Gran Tierra Exchangeco Inc. (1)
Suite 200 150 - 13 Avenue SW, Calgary, T2R 0V2, AB, Canada
Tel.: (403) 265-3221
Web Site: http://www.grantierra.com
Crude Petroleum & Natural Gas Extraction Services
N.A.I.C.S.: 211120

Petroleos Del Norte S.A. (1)
Tel.: (34) 946357000
Crude Petroleum Extraction Services
N.A.I.C.S.: 211120

GRANADA GOLD MINE INC.
3028 Quadra Court, Coquitlam, V3B 5X6, BC, Canada
Tel.: (819) 797-4144   BC
Web Site:
https://www.granadagoldmine.com
Year Founded: 1985

GRANADA GOLD MINE INC.

Granada Gold Mine Inc.—(Continued)
GBBFF—(OTCIQ)
Rev.: $220
Assets: $550,017
Liabilities: $5,288,858
Net Worth: ($4,738,841)
Earnings: ($3,492,768)
Fiscal Year-end: 06/30/19
Mineral Exploration Services
N.A.I.C.S.: 213114
Frank J. Basa *(Chm, Pres & Co-CEO)*

GRANADILLA COUNTRY CLUB S.A.
Camino A Granadilla S/N, PO Box 593, Vina del Mar, Chile
Tel.: (56) 689249
Web Site: http://www.granadilla.cl
GRANADILLA—(SGO)
Sales Range: Less than $1 Million
Golf Club Operator
N.A.I.C.S.: 713910
Juan Fernando Tapia Santibanez *(CEO)*

GRANARIA HOLDINGS B.V.
Lange Voorhout 16, 2514 EE, Hague, Netherlands
Tel.: (31) 703121100
Web Site: http://www.granaria.com
Year Founded: 1912
Sales Range: $1-4.9 Billion
Emp.: 2
Investment Holding Company
N.A.I.C.S.: 551112
Joel P. Wyler *(Chm)*

GRANAT SA
Cap Aurora, Constanta, Mangalia, Romania
Tel.: (40) 31 825 28 37
Sales Range: Less than $1 Million
Emp.: 1
Accommodation Services
N.A.I.C.S.: 721110

GRAND BANKS YACHTS LIMITED
274 Upper Bukit Timah Road 03-16, Singapore, 588213, Singapore
Tel.: (65) 65452929   SG
Web Site:
    http://www.grandbanks.com
Year Founded: 1976
G50—(SES)
Rev.: $84,602,445
Assets: $95,947,388
Liabilities: $44,726,195
Net Worth: $51,221,193
Earnings: $7,490,182
Emp.: 880
Fiscal Year-end: 06/30/23
Yacht Mfr
N.A.I.C.S.: 336612
Mark Jonathon Richards *(CEO)*

Subsidiaries:

GB Yachts Pte. Ltd.   (1)
274 Upper Bukit Timah Road 03-16, Singapore, 588213, Singapore
Tel.: (65) 65452929
Web Site: http://www.yachtworld.com
Ship Building & Ship Repair Mfr
N.A.I.C.S.: 336611

Grand Banks Yachts Australia Pty Ltd   (1)
1 Queens Parade, Hope Island, Newport, 2106, NSW, Australia
Tel.: (61) 299795601
Motor Yachts Sales & Maintenance Services
N.A.I.C.S.: 336611

Grand Banks Yachts Sdn. Bhd.   (1)
Lot 488 Jalan Suasa, Pasir Gudang, 81700, Johor, Malaysia   (100%)
Tel.: (60) 72517488
Web Site: http://www.grandbank.com
Sales Range: $100-124.9 Million
Mfr & Retailer of Yachts
N.A.I.C.S.: 336612
Lee Choon Hong *(Mgr-Bus Dev)*

Grand Banks Yachts, Ltd.   (1)
450 SW Salerno Rd, Stuart, FL 34997
Tel.: (954) 530-4379
Web Site: https://www.grandbanks.com
Sales Range: $25-49.9 Million
Emp.: 20
Boat Building
N.A.I.C.S.: 336612

Palm Beach Motor Yacht Co. Pty. Ltd.   (1)
1 Queens Parade, Newport, 2106, NSW, Australia
Tel.: (61) 299795601
Web Site:
    https://www.palmbeachmotoryachts.com
Ship Building & Ship Repair Mfr
N.A.I.C.S.: 336611

GRAND BRILLIANCE GROUP HOLDINGS LTD.
Units 2901 03 05 06 29 F The Octagon 6 Sha Tsui Road, Tsuen Wan, New Territories, China (Hong Kong)
Tel.: (852) 24250926   Ky
Web Site:
    https://www.grandbrilliance.com
Year Founded: 1997
8372—(HKG)
Rev.: $9,779,378
Assets: $14,694,120
Liabilities: $2,113,568
Net Worth: $12,580,553
Earnings: $964,155
Emp.: 41
Fiscal Year-end: 03/31/23
Medical Device Whslr
N.A.I.C.S.: 424210
Bikie Bik Kwan Wong *(Chm, CEO & Compliance Officer)*

GRAND CAPITAL FOR FINANCIAL INVESTMENTS
8 Agriculture Ministry St Alahrar Corner, El Dokki, Giza, Egypt
Tel.: (20) 34795882
Web Site: https://grandcapital.com.eg
Year Founded: 2007
Financial Investment Services
N.A.I.C.S.: 523999

GRAND CENTRAL ENTERPRISES BHD.
No 1 & 1A 2nd Floor Room 2 Jalan Ipoh Kecil, 50350, Kuala Lumpur, Malaysia
Tel.: (60) 376226988
Web Site: https://www.ghihotels.com
Year Founded: 1968
GCE—(KLS)
Rev.: $4,814,139
Assets: $45,158,666
Liabilities: $2,921,447
Net Worth: $42,237,219
Earnings: ($727,177)
Emp.: 274
Fiscal Year-end: 12/31/22
Home Management Services
N.A.I.C.S.: 561110
Hwa Imm Tan *(Exec Dir)*

Subsidiaries:

Grand Central (K.L.) Sdn. Bhd.   (1)
Jalan Belia/Jalan Raja Laut, 50350, Kuala Lumpur, Malaysia
Tel.: (60) 3 2693 9333
Web Site: http://www.ghihotels.com.my
Home Management Services
N.A.I.C.S.: 721110

Grand Central Enterprises (Sarawak) Sdn. Bhd.   (1)
538 Jalan Lee Kai Teng Bentong, Bentung, 95700, Sarawak, Malaysia
Tel.: (60) 83472790
Web Site: http://www.centralenterprise.com
Sales Range: $25-49.9 Million
Emp.: 20
Food Processing Machinery Maintenance Services
N.A.I.C.S.: 811310
Wong Kee Chong *(Mgr)*

Grand Central Trans-Services Sdn. Bhd.   (1)
Lot 604 Jalan Belia Jalan Raja Laut, 50350, Kuala Lumpur, Federal Territory, Malaysia
Tel.: (60) 326939333
Sales Range: $50-74.9 Million
Emp.: 120
Airline Limousine & Online Reservation Services
N.A.I.C.S.: 485999
Clement Lee *(Mgr-Hotel)*

Grand Island Hotel (Langkawi) Sdn. Bhd.   (1)
No 398 Jln Padang Matsirat Batu 1, Kampung Kelibang, 07000, Kuah, Kedah, Malaysia
Tel.: (60) 49660333
Web Site: http://www.ghihotels.com.my
Sales Range: $10-24.9 Million
Emp.: 54
Home Management Services
N.A.I.C.S.: 721110

GRAND CITY PROPERTIES SA
37 Boulevard Joseph II, L-1840, Luxembourg, Luxembourg
Tel.: (352) 28778786   LU
Web Site:
    https://www.grandcityproperties.com
Year Founded: 2011
GYC—(DEU)
Assets: $12,052,218,240
Liabilities: $8,213,366,812
Net Worth: $3,838,851,428
Earnings: ($604,379,864)
Emp.: 847
Fiscal Year-end: 12/31/23
Trust Management Services
N.A.I.C.S.: 541618
Rafael Zamir *(CEO, CFO & Member-Mgmt Bd)*

GRAND CONSTRUCTION LTD.
4539 210A Street, Langley, V3A 8Z3, BC, Canada
Tel.: (604) 530-1931
Web Site:
    http://www.grandconstruction.net
Rev.: $11,476,733
Emp.: 40
Building Construction Services
N.A.I.C.S.: 236220
Eric Guran *(Pres)*

GRAND DEPARTMENT STORE CO., LTD.
678-14 Deungchon 3-dong, Kangseogu, Seoul, 157-033, Korea (South)
Tel.: (82) 236650101
Web Site: http://www.granddept.co.kr
019010—(KRS)
Rev.: $45,197,519
Assets: $475,671,828
Liabilities: $206,038,894
Net Worth: $269,632,934
Earnings: ($13,446,489)
Emp.: 185
Fiscal Year-end: 12/31/22
Departmental Store Operator
N.A.I.C.S.: 455110
Man Jin Kim *(Chm & CEO)*

GRAND FIELD GROUP HOLDINGS LIMITED
Unit 1004B 10/F Tower 5 China Hong Kong City 33 Canton Road, Tsim Sha Tsui, Kowloon, China (Hong Kong)
Tel.: (852) 23801330   BM
Web Site: http://www.gfghl.com

INTERNATIONAL PUBLIC

0115—(HKG)
Rev.: $17,758,838
Assets: $359,710,523
Liabilities: $199,168,133
Net Worth: $160,542,390
Earnings: ($75,698,535)
Emp.: 132
Fiscal Year-end: 12/31/22
Holding Company
N.A.I.C.S.: 551112
Xuemian Ma *(Chm)*

GRAND FORTUNE HIGH GRADE LIMITED
Room 1805 Times New World Center 2193 Guangyuan East, Tianhe District, Guangzhou, Guangdong, China
Tel.: (86) 208 764 9676   Ky
Web Site: http://www.gf-hg.com
GFHG—(LSE)
Rev.: $29,099
Assets: $3,758,542
Liabilities: $39,281
Net Worth: $3,719,261
Earnings: ($679,916)
Fiscal Year-end: 04/30/19
Professional Training Services
N.A.I.C.S.: 611519
Yan Wing Cheung *(CFO)*

GRAND FOUNDRY LIMITED
302 Cabin No1 Sanjay Appa Chambers Plot No 82, Behind Charat Singh Colony, Mumbai, 400093, Maharashtra, India
Tel.: (91) 9711989548
Web Site: https://www.gfsteel.co.in
Year Founded: 1973
GFSTEELS—(NSE)
Rev.: $145,571
Assets: $246,651
Liabilities: $661,888
Net Worth: ($415,237)
Earnings: ($24,038)
Emp.: 28
Fiscal Year-end: 03/31/21
Steel Products Mfr
N.A.I.C.S.: 331110
Minal Jangla *(CEO)*

GRAND GULF ENERGY LIMITED
Suite 4 246-250 Railway Parade, West Leederville, 6007, WA, Australia
Tel.: (61) 861024826
Web Site:
    https://www.grandgulfenergy.com
GRGUF—(OTCIQ)
Rev.: $364,412
Assets: $16,034,577
Liabilities: $607,106
Net Worth: $15,427,471
Earnings: ($1,212,561)
Emp.: 2
Fiscal Year-end: 06/30/24
Oil & Gas Exploration
N.A.I.C.S.: 213112
Mark Freeman *(Exec Dir)*

Subsidiaries:

Alto Energy Limited   (1)
Ste 8 7 The Esplanade, Mount Pleasant, 6153, WA, Australia
Tel.: (61) 8 93243011
Oil & Gas Field Exploration Services
N.A.I.C.S.: 213112

Subsidiary (US):

Grand Gulf Energy Inc.   (2)
9525 Katy Fwy Ste 142, Houston, TX 77024-1433
Tel.: (713) 337-6001
Web Site: http://www.grandgulfenergy.com
Sales Range: $50-74.9 Million
Oil & Gas Field Exploration Services
N.A.I.C.S.: 213112

AND PRIVATE COMPANIES

GRAND HALL ENTERPRISE COMPANY LTD.
9th Fl No 298 Rueiguang Rd, Neihu, Taipei, 114, Taiwan
Tel.: (886) 226591119
Web Site: https://www.grandhall.com
Year Founded: 1976
8941—(TPE)
Rev.: $94,795,477
Assets: $71,038,455
Liabilities: $38,972,234
Net Worth: $32,066,221
Earnings: $6,228,425
Emp.: 700
Fiscal Year-end: 12/31/23
Grills & Related Appliances Mfr
N.A.I.C.S.: 335220
William Home (Pres & CEO)

Subsidiaries:

Barbeques Galore, Inc. (1)
2173 Salk Ave Ste 200, Carlsbad, CA 92008
Tel.: (949) 597-2400
Web Site: http://www.bbqgalore.com
Barbecue Grill & Accessories Mfr & Retailer
N.A.I.C.S.: 335220

Grand Hall Europe B.V (1)
Zwollestraat 15, 7575 EP, Oldenzaal, Netherlands
Tel.: (31) 541 531669
Web Site: http://www.grandhall.eu
Gas Grill Cooking Appliances Supplies Distr
N.A.I.C.S.: 423720
Remco Holtslag (Gen Mgr)

GRAND HARBOUR MARINA P.L.C.
The Capitanerie, Vittoriosa Wharf, Il-Birgu, 1721, Vittoriosa, Malta
Tel.: (356) 21800700
Web Site: https://www.ghm.com.mt
Marina Operations & Management Services
N.A.I.C.S.: 713930

GRAND HOLIDAY VILLA KHARTOUM CO. LTD.
Nile Avenue, PO Box 316, Khartoum, 00249, Sudan
Tel.: (249) 183774039 Sd
Web Site: http://www.holidayvillakhartoum.com
Emp.: 300
Hotel & Resort Operator
N.A.I.C.S.: 721110
Hossam Sublime (Mng Dir)

GRAND HOTEL BUCHAREST SA
sector 1 Bvd Nicolae Balcescu nr 4, 10051, Bucharest, Romania
Tel.: (40) 213102020
Web Site: https://www.grandbucharest.com
RCHI—(BUC)
Rev.: $6,758,568
Assets: $27,137,957
Liabilities: $1,812,648
Net Worth: $25,325,309
Earnings: $902,251
Emp.: 62
Fiscal Year-end: 12/31/23
Accommodation Services
N.A.I.C.S.: 721110
Grigore Dan Adamescu (Owner)

GRAND HOTEL INTER-CONTINENTAL PARIS SNC
2 Rue Scribe, 75009, Paris, France
Tel.: (33) 1 40073232 FR
Web Site: http://www.ihg.com
Year Founded: 1862
Home Management Services
N.A.I.C.S.: 721110
Christophe Laure (Gen Mgr)

GRAND HOTEL UNION D.D.
Miklosiceva ulica 1, 1000, Ljubljana, Slovenia
Tel.: (386) 13081270
Web Site: http://www.union-hotels.eu
Emp.: 200
Hotel Owner & Operator
N.A.I.C.S.: 721110

Subsidiaries:

Grand Hotel Union Business d.d. (1)
Miklosiceva 1, 1000, Ljubljana, Slovenia
Tel.: (386) 13081270
Home Management Services
N.A.I.C.S.: 561110

Union Hotels d.d. (1)
Miklosiceva Cesta 1, Ljubljana, SI-1000, Slovenia
Tel.: (386) 13081270
Web Site: http://www.gh-union.si
Emp.: 220
Hotel Services
N.A.I.C.S.: 721110
Tomislav Tah (Gen Mgr)

GRAND INDUSTRIAL HOLDING CO., LTD.
No 6 Beijiao Road Xingpu District, Lianyungang, 222006, Jiangsu, China
Tel.: (86) 5185153595
Year Founded: 1994
000626—(SSE)
Rev.: $11,513,909,160
Assets: $1,094,106,312
Liabilities: $633,973,392
Net Worth: $460,132,920
Earnings: $16,088,436
Emp.: 1,154
Fiscal Year-end: 12/31/22
Commodity Trading & Logistics Services
N.A.I.C.S.: 425120
Zhaoping Qin (Chm)

Subsidiaries:

Lianyungang Ajinomoto Ruyi Foods Co., Ltd. (1)
Dingzi Road East, Xinpu, Lianyungang, 222002, Jiangsu, China
Tel.: (86) 51885150741
Frozen Food Mfr & Distr
N.A.I.C.S.: 424420

Lianyungang Fushi Food Co., Ltd. (1)
East Dingzi Rd, Xinpu, Lianyungang, 222004, Jiangsu, China
Tel.: (86) 518 5153535
Sales Range: $75-99.9 Million
Emp.: 120
Vegetable & Fruit Mfr
N.A.I.C.S.: 424480

Lianyungang Life Ruyi Foods Co., Ltd (1)
No 6 Beijiao Rd, Xinpu, Lianyungang, 222002, Jiangsu, China
Tel.: (86) 518 5153538
Sales Range: $75-99.9 Million
Emp.: 188
Fish, Fruits & Vegetables Mfr & Franchiser
N.A.I.C.S.: 424480

GRAND INVESTMENT INTERNATIONAL LIMITED
Unit 3 5th Floor Greenfield Tower Concordia Plaza, No 1 Science Museum Road Kowloon, Hong Kong, China (Hong Kong)
Tel.: (852) 2388 9871 BM
Web Site: http://www.grandinv.com
Rev.: $1,919
Assets: $3,553,683
Liabilities: $1,026,671
Net Worth: $2,527,013
Earnings: ($1,335,542)
Emp.: 4
Fiscal Year-end: 03/31/18
Holding Company; Investment Management Services
N.A.I.C.S.: 551112
Leung So Sze (Sec)

GRAND KOREA LEISURE CO.LTD
GKL 610 Samseong-ro, Gangnam-gu, Seoul, Korea (South)
Tel.: (82) 264216100
Web Site: http://www.grandkorea.com
114090—(KRS)
Rev.: $201,038,793
Assets: $467,496,599
Liabilities: $174,153,301
Net Worth: $293,343,298
Earnings: ($17,444,930)
Emp.: 1,754
Fiscal Year-end: 12/31/22
Casino Operator
N.A.I.C.S.: 721120

GRAND MING GROUP HOLDINGS LIMITED
22/F Railway Plaza No 39 Chatham Road South Tsim Sha Tsui, Kowloon, China (Hong Kong)
Tel.: (852) 27560828
Web Site: https://www.grandming.com.hk
Year Founded: 1995
1271—(HKG)
Rev.: $105,488,486
Assets: $1,376,697,695
Liabilities: $1,102,544,385
Net Worth: $274,153,310
Earnings: $2,263,212
Emp.: 181
Fiscal Year-end: 03/31/22
Building Construction
N.A.I.C.S.: 236220
Hung Ming Chan (Co-Founder & Chm)

GRAND MOTORS PRESTIGE PTY LTD.
265 Ferry Road, Southport, 4215, QLD, Australia
Tel.: (61) 755836555
Web Site: http://www.grandmotors.com.au
Year Founded: 1950
Sales Range: $25-49.9 Million
Emp.: 140
Car Dealership
N.A.I.C.S.: 441110
Gregory Beresford Scott (Principal)

GRAND OCEAN RESOURCES COMPANY LIMITED
Suite 1602 Sino Plaza 255-257 Gloucester Road, Hong Kong, China (Hong Kong)
Tel.: (852) 28319905 Ky
Web Site: http://www.grandocean65.com
0065—(HKG)
Rev.: $24,375,450
Assets: $38,932,125
Liabilities: $14,272,350
Net Worth: $24,659,775
Earnings: $3,327,750
Emp.: 451
Fiscal Year-end: 12/31/22
Coal Production & Sales
N.A.I.C.S.: 324199
Ying Kit Ng (Exec Dir)

GRAND OCEAN RETAIL GROUP LIMITED
14F No 237 Sec 2 Fuxing S Rd, Daan Dist, Taipei, 106, Taiwan
Tel.: (886) 227078833
Web Site: http://www.grandocean.com.cn
5907—(TAI)
Rev.: $124,926,677

GRAND PACIFIC PETROCHEMICAL CORPORATION

Assets: $792,583,181
Liabilities: $626,691,595
Net Worth: $165,891,586
Earnings: ($68,151,245)
Fiscal Year-end: 12/31/23
Department Stores
N.A.I.C.S.: 455110

Subsidiaries:

Grand Ocean Classic Commercial Group Co., Ltd. (1)
3-5 Unit 27 Floor Tianan Centre No 338 Nanjing Western Road, Huangpu District, Shanghai, 200003, China
Tel.: (86) 2160127800151
Web Site: https://www.grandocean.com.cn
Departmental Store Operator
N.A.I.C.S.: 455110

Grand Ocean Department Store Group Co., Ltd (1)
122 Zhongshan Nanlu, Nanjing, China
Tel.: (86) 25 8473 8888
Departmental Store Operator
N.A.I.C.S.: 455110

GRAND PACIFIC PETROCHEMICAL CORPORATION
No 4 Xinggong Rd, Dashe District, Kaohsiung, 81567, Taiwan
Tel.: (886) 73513911
Web Site: https://www.gppc.com.tw
Year Founded: 1973
1312—(TAI)
Rev.: $514,051,748
Assets: $2,026,502,000
Liabilities: $832,362,243
Net Worth: $1,194,139,757
Earnings: ($47,643,021)
Emp.: 1,208
Fiscal Year-end: 12/31/23
Synthetic Resin Mfr
N.A.I.C.S.: 424690
Pin Cheng Yang (Bd of Dirs & Chm)

Subsidiaries:

BC Chemical Co., Ltd. (1)
66 Chang Hsin Road, Lu-Chu Hsiang, Kaohsiung, Taiwan
Tel.: (886) 76967135
High Impact Polystyrene Products Mfr
N.A.I.C.S.: 326140

GPPC Chemical Co., Ltd. (1)
No 66 Changsing Rd, Lujhu Dist, Kaohsiung, 82150, Taiwan
Tel.: (886) 28 770 4567
Web Site: https://www.gppc.com.tw
Sales Range: $125-149.9 Million
Emp.: 400
High Impact Polystyrene Products Mfr
N.A.I.C.S.: 326140

KK Enterprise (Kunshan) Co., Ltd. (1)
No 568 Old Town Road, Bacheng Town, Kunshan, Jiangsu, China
Tel.: (86) 51257659669
Adhesive Tape Mfr
N.A.I.C.S.: 325520

KK Enterprise (Malaysia) Sdn. Bhd. (1)
2576 Lorong Perusahaan 10, Prai Ind Est, 13600, Prai, Penang, Malaysia
Tel.: (60) 43979128
Web Site: https://kkma.com.my
Adhesive Tape Mfr
N.A.I.C.S.: 325520

QuanZhou Grand Pacific Chemical Co., Ltd. (1)
Quangang Petrochemical Park, Quangang District, Quanzhou, Fujian, China
Tel.: (86) 59587995678
Web Site: https://www.qzgppc.com
Petrochemical Products Mfr
N.A.I.C.S.: 325110
Zhang Congming (Gen Mgr)

Videoland, Inc. (1)
3F No 480 Ruiguang Road, Neihu District, Taipei, 11492, Taiwan
Tel.: (886) 287977122

GRAND PACIFIC PETROCHEMICAL CORPORATION

Grand Pacific Petrochemical Corporation—(Continued)
Web Site: https://www.videoland.com.tw
Television Program Production Services
N.A.I.C.S.: 512110

GRAND PARADE INVESTMENTS LIMITED
33 Heerengracht, Foreshore, Cape Town, 8001, South Africa
Tel.: (27) 214121400
Web Site:
http://www.grandparade.co.za
GPL—(JSE)
Rev.: $71,610
Assets: $61,267,335
Liabilities: $4,455,687
Net Worth: $56,811,648
Earnings: ($803,293)
Emp.: 16
Fiscal Year-end: 06/30/23
Investments in Gaming, Leisure & Tourism Industries
N.A.I.C.S.: 523999
Mohsin Tajbhai (CEO)

Subsidiaries:

GPI Management Services (Proprietary) Limited (1)
Po Box 3003, Parramatta, 2124, NSW, Australia
Tel.: (61) 298916044
Web Site: http://www.lcipartners.com
Sales Range: $10-24.9 Million
Emp.: 30
Third Party Business Management Services
N.A.I.C.S.: 561110
Anna Sorcella (Office Mgr)

Grand Foods (Pty) Ltd. (1)
82 Barry Rd, Campbellfield, 3061, VIC, Australia
Tel.: (61) 93579244
Web Site: https://www.grandfoods.com.au
Food Product Mfr & Distr
N.A.I.C.S.: 311999

GRAND PEACE GROUP HOLDINGS LIMITED
Room 1005 10/F CC Wu Building 302-8 Hennessy Road, Wanchai, China (Hong Kong)
Tel.: (852) 2838 8108 BM
Web Site:
http://www.grandpeace.com.hk
Rev.: $11,640,476
Assets: $70,603,632
Liabilities: $29,850,219
Net Worth: $40,753,413
Earnings: ($9,737,895)
Emp.: 62
Fiscal Year-end: 12/31/18
Holding Company; Funeral Products & Services
N.A.I.C.S.: 551112
Kai Ming Hung (Sec)

Subsidiaries:

Able Profit (Hong Kong) Limited (1)
6 Cheong Hang Rd Hung Hom, Kowloon, China (Hong Kong)
Tel.: (852) 28172817
Funeral Equipment Distr
N.A.I.C.S.: 423850

Kowloon Funeral Parlour Company Limited (1)
1A Maple Street Tai Kok Tsui, Kowloon West, Kowloon, China (Hong Kong)
Tel.: (852) 69962992
Web Site: http://kowloonfuneral.com.hk
Funeral Services
N.A.I.C.S.: 812210

GRAND PEAK CAPITAL CORP.
Suite 210 9648 128 Street, Surrey, V4K 3N3, BC, Canada
Tel.: (604) 357-4725 BC
Web Site:
http://www.grandpeakcapital.com

GPK—(OTCIQ)
Rev.: $268,878
Assets: $2,111,369
Liabilities: $191,605
Net Worth: $1,919,764
Earnings: ($1,138,583)
Fiscal Year-end: 09/30/23
Financial Services
N.A.I.C.S.: 523999
Tajinder Johal (CEO & CFO)

GRAND PHARMACEUTICAL GROUP LIMITED
Units 3302 33/F The Center 99 Queens Road, Central, China (Hong Kong)
Tel.: (852) 28663718 BM
Web Site:
http://www.chinagrandpharm.com
0512—(HKG)
Rev.: $1,219,191,338
Assets: $2,852,310,278
Liabilities: $1,040,706,128
Net Worth: $1,811,604,150
Earnings: $267,527,003
Emp.: 10,172
Fiscal Year-end: 12/31/22
Holding Company
N.A.I.C.S.: 551112
Chengwei Liu (Chm)

Subsidiaries:

Grand Pharma (China) Co., Ltd. (1)
23rd Floor City Plaza No 160 Qiaokou Road, Qiaokou District, Wuhan, 430032, China
Tel.: (86) 4009909097
Web Site: https://www.grandpharma.cn
Pharmaceutical Product Mfr & Distr
N.A.I.C.S.: 325412
Xiaofeng Shi (Chm & Pres)

Subsidiary (Non-US):

Cardionovum GmbH (2)
Am Bonner Bogen 2, 53227, Bonn, Germany
Tel.: (49) 2289090590
Web Site: https://cardionovum.de
Medical Device Mfr & Distr
N.A.I.C.S.: 339112
Andrew Traver (CTO)

Subsidiary (Domestic):

Hubei Grand Fuchi Pharmaceutical & Chemical Company Limited (1)
No 12 Wangfen Road, Fuchi Town Yangxin County, Huangshi, 435229, Hubei, China
Tel.: (86) 278 384 8187
Web Site: https://en.fuchigroup.com
Agrochemical Product Mfr & Distr
N.A.I.C.S.: 325320

Tianjin JingMing New Technological Development Co., Ltd. (2)
K2-8-401 Haitai Green Industrial Base No 6 Haitai Fazhan Sixth Road, Huayuan Industry Development Area, Tianjin, 300384, China
Tel.: (86) 222 378 2229
Web Site: https://www.tjjm-eye.com
Pharmaceutical Product Mfr & Distr
N.A.I.C.S.: 325412

Tianjin Tanabe Seiyaku Co., Ltd. (2)
No 16 MIP Third Road Micro-Electronics Industrial Park Jingang Highway, Xiqing District, Tianjin, China (100%)
Tel.: (86) 2223960505
Pharmaceuticals Product Mfr & Distr
N.A.I.C.S.: 325412

Wuhan Grand Hoyo Company Limited (2)
Rm 601 Block B Dingye Bldg Int Ent Center No T1 Guanshan 2nd Road, East Lake High-tech Development Zone, Wuhan, 430074, China (62.4%)
Tel.: (86) 278 745 2702
Web Site: https://www.grandhoyo.com
Amino Acid Mfr & Distr
N.A.I.C.S.: 325199

Wuhan Kernel Bio-Technology Co., Ltd. (2)
Guannan Industry Zone, off East Lake High-Tech Development Zone on the 17th, Wuhan, 430074, China
Tel.: (86) 2787514122
Web Site: https://en.biokn.com
Emp.: 400
Biopesticide Product Mfr & Distr
N.A.I.C.S.: 325320

Wuhan Wuyao Pharmaceutical Co., Ltd. (2)
No 5 Gutian Road, Wuhan, 430035, Hubei Province, China
Tel.: (86) 278 382 2224
Web Site: https://en.wyzy.cn
Pharmaceutical Product Mfr & Distr
N.A.I.C.S.: 325412

Xian Beilin Pharmaceutical Company Limited (2)
23rd Floor Building 18 Landis City No 101 Xingqing South Road, Beilin District, Xi'an, 710048, Shaanxi Province, China
Tel.: (86) 298 322 2143
Web Site: https://www.beilinchina.cn
Emp.: 1,000
Pharmaceutical Product Mfr & Distr
N.A.I.C.S.: 325412

Jiangsu Grand Xianle Pharmaceutical Co., Ltd. (1)
Coastal Chemical Zone, Binhai County, Shanghai, Jiangsu, China
Tel.: (86) 51584383317
Web Site: http://www.xypharm.com
Pharmaceutical & Chemical Product Mfr
N.A.I.C.S.: 325998

Zhejiang Xianju Xianle Pharmaceutical Company Limited (1)
No 5 Chuancheng South Road, Xianju, 317300, Zhejiang, China
Tel.: (86) 5768 778 9188
Web Site: https://www.xianle.com
Steroid Product Mfr & Distr
N.A.I.C.S.: 325411

GRAND PLASTIC TECHNOLOGY CORP.
No 89 Sec 6 Zhonghua Rd, Xiangshan Dist, Hsinchu, Taiwan
Tel.: (886) 35183030
Web Site: https://www.gptc.com.tw
Year Founded: 1993
3131—(TPE)
Rev.: $116,417,347
Assets: $216,181,690
Liabilities: $109,707,032
Net Worth: $106,474,658
Earnings: $22,683,770
Fiscal Year-end: 12/31/22
Electric Equipment Mfr
N.A.I.C.S.: 335999
Hung-Tai Chang (Chm)

GRAND PLAZA HOTEL CORPORATION
10th Floor The Heritage Hotel Manila, Roxas Boulevard corner EDSA Extension, Pasay, 1300, Philippines
Tel.: (63) 28548838
Web Site:
https://www.grandplazahotel.com
Year Founded: 1989
GPH—(PHI)
Rev.: $8,455,204
Assets: $27,039,181
Liabilities: $9,994,871
Net Worth: $17,044,310
Earnings: $557,252
Emp.: 287
Fiscal Year-end: 12/31/23
Hotel Operator
N.A.I.C.S.: 721110
Aloysius Lee (Chm, Pres & CEO)

GRAND POWER LOGISTICS GROUP LIMITED
Room 611 6/F Tower 1 Harbour Centre 1 Hok Cheung Street, Hung Hom, Kowloon, China (Hong Kong)
Tel.: (852) 35824128 Ky
Web Site:
https://www.grandpowerexpress.com
Year Founded: 2018
8489—(HKG)
Rev.: $86,982,435
Assets: $30,503,383
Liabilities: $12,895,936
Net Worth: $17,607,447
Earnings: ($3,558,558)
Emp.: 41
Fiscal Year-end: 12/31/22
Logistic Services
N.A.I.C.S.: 541614
Chun Fung Li (Sec)

Subsidiaries:

Grand Power Express International (China) Limited (1)
3/Floor No 328 Hai Tian 1 Road Pudong International Airport, Shanghai, 201202, China
Tel.: (86) 2168838110
Air & Ocean Freight Forwarding Services
N.A.I.C.S.: 532411

Grand Power Express International (Shenzhen) Limited (1)
Rm 1718 Changping Business Building No 99 Honghua Rd, Futian Free Trade Zone, Shenzhen, 518026, China
Tel.: (86) 75523604096
Air & Ocean Freight Forwarding Services
N.A.I.C.S.: 532120

Grand Power Express International Limited (1)
13/F Yoo Hoo Tower 38-42 Kwai Fung Crescent, Kwai Chung, China (Hong Kong)
Tel.: (852) 35824128
Air & Ocean Freight Forwarding Services
N.A.I.C.S.: 532411

GRAND PRIX INTERNATIONAL PUBLIC COMPANY LIMITED
4/299 Moo 5 Soi Ladplakhao 66 Ladplakhao Rd, Anusawaree Bangkhen, Bangkok, 10220, Thailand
Tel.: (66) 25221731 TH
Web Site: https://www.grandprix.co.th
Year Founded: 1970
GPI—(THA)
Rev.: $18,323,199
Assets: $25,546,242
Liabilities: $4,046,316
Net Worth: $21,499,926
Earnings: $2,307,633
Emp.: 181
Fiscal Year-end: 12/31/23
Media & Advertising Agency Services
N.A.I.C.S.: 541840
Anothai Eamlumnow (COO-Bus Dev)

GRAND REAL ESTATE PROJECTS CO. K.S.C.C.
No 1 Floor 4 Mabanee Building, Ali Al Salem Street Block 11, Al Qibla, Kuwait, Kuwait
Tel.: (965) 22495599
Web Site: http://www.grandq8.com
Year Founded: 1989
Sales Range: Less than $1 Million
Real Estate Services
N.A.I.C.S.: 531390
Abdul Aziz Bader Al-Jenai (Vice Chm & CEO)

GRAND RIVER FOODS
190 Vondrau Dr, Cambridge, N3E 1B8, ON, Canada
Tel.: (519) 653-3577
Web Site:
http://www.grandriverfoods.com
Year Founded: 1978
Rev.: $100,000,000
Emp.: 200
Processed Chicken Supplier

N.A.I.C.S.: 112320
Dean Cebulski (Pres)

GRAND T G GOLD HOLDINGS LIMITED
Room A-B 8th Floor Centre Mark II
305-311 Queens Road Central,
Sheung Wan, China (Hong Kong) Ky
Tel.: (852) 2 598 8566
Web Site: http://www.grandtg.com
8299—(HKG)
Rev.: $16,565,417
Assets: $119,206,154
Liabilities: $84,149,905
Net Worth: $35,056,248
Earnings: $1,011,719
Emp.: 60
Fiscal Year-end: 03/31/22
Holding Company
N.A.I.C.S.: 551112
Li Dahong (Chm)

GRAND TALENTS GROUP HOLDINGS LIMITED
Office 15 9/F Mega Cube 8 Wang
Kwong Road, Kowloon, China (Hong Kong) Ky
Web Site:
https://www.grandtalentsgroup.com
Year Founded: 2010
8516—(HKG)
Rev.: $3,761,167
Assets: $5,582,578
Liabilities: $2,499,649
Net Worth: $3,082,930
Earnings: ($3,483,967)
Emp.: 10
Fiscal Year-end: 03/31/23
Holding Company
N.A.I.C.S.: 551112
Chu Shing Ip (CEO)

GRAND VALLEY FORTIFIERS LIMITED
486 Main Street East, PO Box 726,
Cambridge, N1T 2C9, ON, Canada
Tel.: (519) 621-4400
Web Site:
http://www.grandvalley.com
Year Founded: 1960
Rev.: $48,477,587
Emp.: 90
Animal Feed Mfr
N.A.I.C.S.: 311119
Ian Ross (Pres & CEO)

GRAND VENTURE TECHNOLOGY LIMITED
2 Changi North Street 1, Singapore,
498828, Singapore
Tel.: (65) 65423000 SG
Web Site: https://www.gvt.com.sg
Year Founded: 2012
JLB—(SES)
Rev.: $84,296,751
Assets: $154,039,233
Liabilities: $64,202,833
Net Worth: $89,836,401
Earnings: $4,199,046
Emp.: 1,380
Fiscal Year-end: 12/31/23
Semiconductor Components Mfr
N.A.I.C.S.: 334413

Subsidiaries:

ACP Metal Finishing Pte Ltd (1)
6 Joo Koon Circle, Singapore, 629037, Singapore
Tel.: (65) 6 863 8318
Web Site: https://www.acpanode.com.sg
Emp.: 190
Metals Service Center
N.A.I.C.S.: 423510
Chan Seng Koh (Mgr-Mktg)

Formach Asia Sdn. Bhd. (1)
15 & 17 Jalan Mahir 4 Taman Perindustrian Cemerlang, 81800, Ulu Tiram, Johar, Malaysia
Tel.: (60) 78612321
Web Site: https://www.formachasia.com
Sheet Metal Products Mfr
N.A.I.C.S.: 332322

Grand Venture Technology (Suzhou) Co., Ltd. (1)
No 38 Jujin Road, Taiping Xiangcheng area, Suzhou, 215026, Jiangsu, China
Tel.: (86) 51265438891
Semiconductor Product Mfr
N.A.I.C.S.: 334413

Grand Venture Technology Sdn. Bhd. (1)
1144 Lorong Perindustrian Bukit Minyak 22 Penang Science Park, Taman Perindustrian Bukit Minyak, 14100, Simpang Empat, Pulau Pinang, Malaysia
Tel.: (60) 45040828
Semiconductor Product Mfr
N.A.I.C.S.: 334413

GRAND VISION MEDIA HOLDINGS PLC
Flat D 5 F World Tech Centre 95
How Ming Street Kwun Tong Kowloon, Kennedy Town, Hong Kong,
China (Hong Kong)
Tel.: (852) 35902602 UK
Web Site: https://www.gvmh.co.uk
Year Founded: 2014
GVMH—(LSE)
Rev.: $763,476
Assets: $329,217
Liabilities: $5,528,796
Net Worth: ($5,199,579)
Earnings: ($732,732)
Emp.: 35
Fiscal Year-end: 12/31/22
Media Advertising Services
N.A.I.C.S.: 541840
Alex Lee (COO)

Subsidiaries:

Ying Interactive Marketing Services Ltd. (1)
Room 705 7/F Liven House 61-63 King Yip Street, Kwun Tong, Kowloon, 999077, China (Hong Kong)
Tel.: (852) 37137800
Web Site: https://www.yinginteractive.com
Digital Marketing Services
N.A.I.C.S.: 541613
Zero Tang (Sls Mgr-Social Media)

GRAND-TEK TECHNOLOGY CO., LTD.
8F No 2 Lane 233 Pao-Chaio Rd,
Hsin-Tien, Taipei, Taiwan
Tel.: (886) 229177353
Web Site: https://www.grand-tek.com
Year Founded: 1995
3684—(TPE)
Rev.: $18,567,540
Assets: $31,108,490
Liabilities: $13,159,442
Net Worth: $17,949,049
Earnings: $1,734,749
Fiscal Year-end: 12/31/20
Fiber Optic Electrical Equipment Mfr
N.A.I.C.S.: 335921
Chia-Jung Chen (Chm)

GRANDALL SOLUTIONS INC.
2680 Matheson Blvd East Suite 102,
Mississauga, L4W 0A5, ON, Canada
Tel.: (905) 267-8505
Web Site:
http://www.grandallsolutions.com
Residential & Commercial Building Construction Services
N.A.I.C.S.: 236220
Johnny Grandinetti (Pres)

GRANDBLUE ENVIRONMENT CO., LTD.
Hanlan Plaza No 23 Ronghe Road Guicheng Street, Nanhai District, Foshan, 528200, Guangdong, China
Tel.: (86) 75786280996
Web Site: https://www.grandblue.cn
Year Founded: 1992
600323—(SHG)
Rev.: $1,807,658,873
Assets: $4,673,603,385
Liabilities: $3,045,058,520
Net Worth: $1,628,544,865
Earnings: $160,946,726
Fiscal Year-end: 12/31/22
Gas Distribution Services
N.A.I.C.S.: 221210
Tang Yuyun (Sec)

GRANDBRIDGE LIMITED
14 View Street, Perth, 6006, WA,
Australia
Tel.: (61) 893288400
Web Site:
http://www.grandbridge.com.au
Rev.: $649,044
Assets: $1,782,434
Liabilities: $951,126
Net Worth: $831,308
Earnings: ($3,144,888)
Fiscal Year-end: 06/30/17
Investment & Development Services
N.A.I.C.S.: 523940
David Breeze (Exec Dir)

GRANDE ASSET HOTELS & PROPERTY PUBLIC COMPANY LIMITED
Room 3203-4 Exchange Tower 32th
388 Sukhumvit Road, Klongtoey,
Bangkok, 10110, Thailand
Tel.: (66) 22049900
Web Site:
https://www.grandeasset.com
Year Founded: 1988
GRAND—(THA)
Rev.: $76,523,295
Assets: $533,225,265
Liabilities: $440,377,979
Net Worth: $92,847,287
Earnings: ($22,050,226)
Emp.: 1,026
Fiscal Year-end: 12/31/23
Asset Management & Property Development Services
N.A.I.C.S.: 531312
Suradej Narula (Exec Dir)

Subsidiaries:

Royal Orchid Hotel (Thailand) Public Company Limited (1)
2 Captain Bush Lane New Road, Bang Bak, Bangkok, 10500, Thailand (98.48%)
Tel.: (66) 22660123
Web Site:
http://www.royalorchidsheraton.com
Rev.: $23,632,248
Assets: $243,903,030
Liabilities: $166,061,225
Net Worth: $77,841,805
Earnings: ($1,393,599)
Emp.: 370
Fiscal Year-end: 12/31/2023
Holding Company; Luxury Hotel Property Manager
N.A.I.C.S.: 551112
Wichai Thongtang (Chm)

The Sails Pattaya (1)
3203-3204 32nd Fl Exchange Tower 399 Sukhumvit Rd, Klongtoey Wattana, Bangkok, 10110, Thailand
Tel.: (66) 22049900
Sales Range: $50-74.9 Million
Emp.: 60
Property Developers & Asset Management Services
N.A.I.C.S.: 531390

The Trendy Condominium (1)
Soi 13 Sukhumvit Rd, Bangkok, 10110, Thailand
Tel.: (66) 22532888
Web Site:
http://www.thetrendycondominium.com
Property Developers & Asset Management Services
N.A.I.C.S.: 531390

GRANDE CHEESE COMPANY LIMITED
468 Jevlan Dr, Woodbridge, L4L 8L4,
ON, Canada
Tel.: (905) 856-6880
Sales Range: $10-24.9 Million
Emp.: 185
Cheese & Dairy Products Mfr
N.A.I.C.S.: 311513
Albert Contardi (Pres)

GRANDE PORTAGE RESOURCES LTD.
Suite 10501090 West Georgia Street,
Vancouver, V6E 3V7, BC, Canada
Tel.: (604) 899-0106
Web Site:
https://www.grandeportage.com
GPB—(DEU)
Rev.: $12,215
Assets: $15,766,432
Liabilities: $835,532
Net Worth: $14,930,900
Earnings: ($828,022)
Emp.: 1
Fiscal Year-end: 10/31/23
Mineral Exploration Services
N.A.I.C.S.: 213114
Ian McCulloch Klassen (Pres)

GRANDES INC.
2-1-10 Miyakomachi, Oita, 870-0034,
Japan
Tel.: (81) 975486700
Web Site: https://www.grandes.jp
3261—(FKA)
Rev.: $17,123,920
Assets: $43,472,880
Liabilities: $25,613,280
Net Worth: $17,859,600
Earnings: $813,120
Fiscal Year-end: 12/31/20
Residential Properties Construction & Sales
N.A.I.C.S.: 236116
Hiroshi Kamei (Pres)

Subsidiaries:

Morizou Co., Ltd. (1)
1-14-8 Shimomae Park Sky Mansion 2nd Floor, Toda, 335-0016, Saitama, Japan
Tel.: (81) 48 420 9743
Web Site: https://www.mori-zou.com
Building Construction & Maintenance Services
N.A.I.C.S.: 236220

GRANDEUR PRODUCTS LIMITED
1st Floor Sravana Complex Kamalapuri Colony Lane, Next to L V
Prasad Hospital Road No 2 Banjara
Hills, Hyderabad, 500034, Telangana,
India
Tel.: (91) 4048526655 In
Web Site:
http://www.grandeurproducts.com
Year Founded: 1983
539235—(BOM)
Rev.: $7,968,123
Assets: $22,133,149
Liabilities: $14,378,864
Net Worth: $7,754,285
Earnings: ($856,214)
Emp.: 2
Fiscal Year-end: 03/31/21
Food Product Mfr & Distr
N.A.I.C.S.: 311920
Vijay Kumar Deekonda (Chm & CFO)

GRANDEUR PRODUCTS LIMITED

Grandeur Products Limited—(Continued)

Subsidiaries:

Tierra Agrotech Private Limited (1)
1-62-192 3rd Floor Dwaraka Avenue Kavuri Hills, Madhapur, Hyderabad, 500033, India
Tel.: (91) 4048506656
Web Site: http://www.tierraagrotech.com
Seed Research & Development Services
N.A.I.C.S.: 541714

Tierra Seed Science Private Limited (1)
Plot No 198 Khajaguda Golconda Post, Hyderabad, 500008, India
Tel.: (91) 4069905888
Web Site: http://www.tierraseedscience.com
Seed Breeding Services
N.A.I.C.S.: 111191
Suresh Atluri (Co-Founder & Mng Dir)

GRANDHOPE BIOTECH CO., LTD.
No 12 Yuyan Road, Huangpu District, Guangzhou, 510530, Guangdong, China
Tel.: (86) 2032052806
Web Site:
https://www.grandhopebio.com
Year Founded: 1999
300238—(CHIN)
Rev.: $52,971,516
Assets: $94,097,484
Liabilities: $33,601,932
Net Worth: $60,495,552
Earnings: ($43,220,736)
Emp.: 500
Fiscal Year-end: 12/31/22
Medical Device Mfr
N.A.I.C.S.: 339112
Zhang Yongming (Chm & Gen Mgr)

Subsidiaries:

Grandhope Biotech (Shanghai) Co. Ltd (1)
Building 15 439 Chunxiao Road Zhangjiang High-tech Park, Shanghai, 201203, China
Tel.: (86) 21 31260898
Regenerative Medical Devices Mfr
N.A.I.C.S.: 339112
Wenjie Zhao (Gen Mgr)

GRANDI NAVI VELOCI S.P.A.
Via Fieschi 17, 16121, Genoa, Italy
Tel.: (39) 0102094591
Web Site: http://www.gnv.it
Year Founded: 1992
Sales Range: $50-74.9 Million
Emp.: 200
Ship Transportation Services
N.A.I.C.S.: 483112
Ariodante Valeri (Gen Mgr)

GRANDLAND HOLDINGS GROUP CO., LTD.
2098 Shennan East Road, Luohu District, Shenzhen, 518000, China
Tel.: (86) 755 36800555
Private Investment Firm
N.A.I.C.S.: 523999

GRANDMA TRADING & AGENCIES LIMITED
Office no 117 First Floor Hubtown Solaris NS Phadke Marg Andheri E, Mumbai, 400069, Maharashtra, India
Tel.: (91) 4040148192
Web Site:
https://www.grandmatrading.co.in
Year Founded: 1981
Rev.: $20,321
Assets: $2,877,915
Liabilities: $741,496
Net Worth: $2,136,419
Earnings: $5,259
Fiscal Year-end: 03/31/18
Textile Product Whslr
N.A.I.C.S.: 424310

GRANDSHORES TECHNOLOGY GROUP LIMITED
Unit 1503 15/F Greenfield Tower Concordia Plaza 1 Science Museum, Tsim Sha Tsui, Kowloon, China (Hong Kong)
Tel.: (852) 34683589 Ky
Web Site:
http://www.grandshorestech.com
Year Founded: 2016
1647—(HKG)
Rev.: $7,365,421
Assets: $8,738,041
Liabilities: $1,345,500
Net Worth: $7,392,541
Earnings: ($827,282)
Emp.: 333
Fiscal Year-end: 03/31/23
Building Construction Services
N.A.I.C.S.: 236220
Yao Yongjie (Chm & Exec Dir)

Subsidiaries:

DRC Engineering Pte. Ltd. (1)
105 Sims Avenue Unit 06-05 Chancerlodge Complex, Singapore, 387429, Singapore
Tel.: (65) 68582988
Building Contracting Services
N.A.I.C.S.: 236220

GRANDTECH C.G.SYSTEM, INC.
3/F 33 Lane 76 Jui-Kuang Road, Neihu District, Taipei, Taiwan
Tel.: (886) 287923001
Web Site: https://www.grandtech.com
Year Founded: 1991
6123—(TPE)
Rev.: $165,300,910
Assets: $100,318,169
Liabilities: $44,820,530
Net Worth: $55,497,639
Earnings: $12,175,593
Emp.: 306
Fiscal Year-end: 12/31/21
Computer Graphic Software Distr
N.A.I.C.S.: 423430
Hsu Cheng-Chiang (Chm & Pres)

GRANDVILLE EQUITIES CORP.
Suite 400 909 17 Ave SW, Calgary, T2T 0A4, AB, Canada
Tel.: (587) 390-3128
Web Site: https://www.gecworks.com
Year Founded: 2000
Privater Equity Firm
N.A.I.C.S.: 523999

Subsidiaries:

Practicar Systems Inc. (1)
3000 421 7th Avenue SW, Calgary, T2P 4K9, AB, Canada
Tel.: (403) 259-6666
Web Site: http://www.practicar.ca
Used Car Rentals & Dealer
N.A.I.C.S.: 532111

GRANDY HOUSE CORPORATION
4-3-18 Odori, Utsunomiya, 320-0811, Tochigi, Japan
Tel.: (81) 286507755
Web Site: https://www.grandy.co.jp
Year Founded: 1991
8999—(TKS)
Rev.: $340,553,810
Assets: $492,233,480
Liabilities: $326,633,150
Net Worth: $165,600,330
Earnings: $2,749,760
Emp.: 889
Fiscal Year-end: 03/31/24
Real Estate Development Services
N.A.I.C.S.: 531210
Hiroaki Hayashi (Chm)

Subsidiaries:

Chiba Grandy House Co., Ltd. (1)
1-14-5 Minamikashiwa, Kashiwa, 277-0855, Chiba Prefecture, Japan
Tel.: (81) 471428844
Web Site: https://www.grandy.co.jp
Emp.: 58
Construction Contracting Services
N.A.I.C.S.: 236220

Grandy Reform Co., Ltd. (1)
1-4-22 Odori MSC 2nd Building 2nd Floor, Utsunomiya, 320-0811, Tochigi, Japan
Tel.: (81) 286507770
Web Site: http://www.grandy-reform.jp
Construction Contracting Services
N.A.I.C.S.: 236220

Gunma Grandy House Co., Ltd. (1)
302-5 Egicho, Takasaki, 370-0046, Gunma Prefecture, Japan
Tel.: (81) 273863311
Web Site: https://www.grandy.co.jp
Emp.: 69
Construction Contracting Services
N.A.I.C.S.: 236220

Ibaraki Grandy House Co., Ltd. (1)
3-56 Keyakidai, Mito, 310-0842, Ibaraki, Japan
Tel.: (81) 293046622
Web Site: https://www.grandy.co.jp
Emp.: 117
Construction Contracting Services
N.A.I.C.S.: 236220

Plaza House Inc. (1)
3-1-12 Kubota, Okinawa, 904-0023, Japan
Tel.: (81) 989324480
Web Site: https://www.plazahouse.co.jp
Emp.: 120
General Goods Retailer
N.A.I.C.S.: 455219
Yoshino Taira (Pres)

GRANEXPORT AD
Luka Dunav 5, 26000, Pancevo, Serbia
Tel.: (381) 13 2190 090
Web Site:
http://www.granexport.co.rs
Year Founded: 1952
Maize Flour Mill Product Production & Trading
N.A.I.C.S.: 311211
Ivan Colovic (Mgr-Sls Dept)

GRANGE RESOURCES LIMITED
34A Alexander Street, PO Box 659, Burnie, 7320, TAS, Australia
Tel.: (61) 364300222 AU
Web Site:
https://www.grangeresources.com
GRR—(ASX)
Rev.: $396,924,918
Assets: $733,171,004
Liabilities: $129,576,487
Net Worth: $603,594,518
Earnings: $114,650,286
Emp.: 642
Fiscal Year-end: 12/31/22
Iron Ore Mining & Pellet Production
N.A.I.C.S.: 212210
Ben Maynard (Gen Mgr-Ops)

Subsidiaries:

Barrack Mines Pty. Ltd. (1)
Level 11 200 St George Terrace, Perth, 6000, WA, Australia
Tel.: (61) 893211118
Sales Range: $50-74.9 Million
Emp.: 12
Mining Services
N.A.I.C.S.: 213114

Subsidiary (Domestic):

BML Holdings Pty. Ltd. (2)
L 11 200 St Georges Ter, Perth, 6000, WA, Australia
Tel.: (61) 893211118

INTERNATIONAL PUBLIC

Sales Range: $50-74.9 Million
Mineral Exploration Services
N.A.I.C.S.: 212390

Grange Capital Pty Ltd (1)
Suite 33 574 Plummer Street, Port Melbourne, 3207, VIC, Australia
Tel.: (61) 43 885 3330
Web Site: https://grangecapital.com.au
Investment Management Service
N.A.I.C.S.: 523940
Carlos Sala (Co-Founder)

Grange ROC Property Pty Ltd (1)
Level 6 60 City Road, PO Box 94, Southbank, 3006, VIC, Australia
Tel.: (61) 36 430 0223
Web Site: https://grangerocproperty.com.au
Real Estate Services
N.A.I.C.S.: 531390

Grange Resources (Tasmania) Pty. Ltd. (1)
34a Alexander Street, Burnie, 7320, TAS, Australia
Tel.: (61) 36 430 0222
Web Site:
http://www.grangeresources.com.au
Sales Range: $200-249.9 Million
Emp.: 400
Iron Ore Mining Services
N.A.I.C.S.: 212210

GRANGES AB
Linnegatan 18, 114 47, Stockholm, Sweden
Tel.: (46) 84595900 SE
Web Site: https://www.granges.com
GRNG—(OMX)
Rev.: $2,235,392,259
Assets: $1,656,640,289
Liabilities: $782,158,967
Net Worth: $874,481,322
Earnings: $100,264,064
Emp.: 2,800
Fiscal Year-end: 12/31/23
Heat Exchanger Mfr
N.A.I.C.S.: 332410
Johan Menckel (CEO)

Subsidiaries:

Granges Americas Inc. (1)
501 Corporate Centre Dr Ste 280, Franklin, TN 37067-4615
Tel.: (615) 778-2000
Aluminum Roll-Formed Products Mfr
N.A.I.C.S.: 331318
Patrick Lawlor (Pres)

Plant (Domestic):

Granges Americas Inc. - Newport Plant (2)
3814 Hwy 67 N, Newport, AR 72112
Tel.: (870) 523-2771
Emp.: 130
Aluminum Rolling Mill
N.A.I.C.S.: 331318

Granges Finspang AB (1)
Slottsvagen 1-3, 612 81, Finspang, Sweden
Tel.: (46) 12283800
Rolled Aluminium Materials Mfr
N.A.I.C.S.: 331221

Granges Konin S.A. (1)
Ul Hutnicza 1, 62-510, Konin, Poland
Tel.: (48) 632474900
Rolled Aluminium Materials Mfr
N.A.I.C.S.: 331221

GRANICAR A.D.
Marsala Tita br 26, Konak, 23253, Serbia
Tel.: (381) 23 3856 025
Web Site:
http://www.granicarkonak.co.rs
Year Founded: 1949
Sales Range: $10-24.9 Million
Farming Services
N.A.I.C.S.: 111140
Dusan Brkanlic (Exec Dir)

GRANINVESTIMENTOS SA

AND PRIVATE COMPANIES

Av Brig Faria Lima 2277 15 andar, Conjunto 1503 Jd Paulistano, CEP 01452-000, Sao Paulo, Brazil
Tel.: (55) 11 2739 0500 BR
Web Site: http://www.granbio.com.br
Year Founded: 2010
Holding Company
N.A.I.C.S.: 551112

Subsidiaries:

GranBio Investimentos SA (1)
Avenida Brigadeiro Faria Lima 2277 15 andar Conjunto 1503, Jd Paulistano, CEP 01452-000, Sao Paulo, Brazil **(85%)**
Tel.: (55) 11 2739 0500
Web Site: http://www.granbio.com.br
Biomass Electric Power Generation
N.A.I.C.S.: 221117
Bernardo Gradin *(Pres)*

Subsidiary (US):

American Process, Inc. (2)
56 17th St NE, Atlanta, GA 30309 **(100%)**
Tel.: (404) 872-8807
Web Site: http://americanprocess.com
Rev.: $2,300,000
Emp.: 35
Other Scientific & Technical Consulting Services
N.A.I.C.S.: 541690
Steve Rutherford *(COO)*

GRANIT AD
Dimitrie Cupovski 8, 1000, Skopje, 1000, North Macedonia
Tel.: (389) 23218700
Web Site: https://www.granit.com.mk
Year Founded: 1952
GRNT—(MAC)
Rev.: $92,121,402
Assets: $147,126,002
Liabilities: $32,653,328
Net Worth: $114,472,674
Earnings: $2,286,039
Fiscal Year-end: 12/31/23
Building Construction Services
N.A.I.C.S.: 236116
Straso Milkovski *(Co-Pres & Member-Mgmt Bd)*

GRANIT CONSTRUCTION STOCK CO.
Dimitrie Cupovski 8, 1000, Skopje, North Macedonia
Tel.: (389) 23218700
Web Site: https://www.granit.com.mk
Year Founded: 1952
Rev.: $104,836,711
Assets: $155,570,489
Liabilities: $58,523,414
Net Worth: $97,047,075
Earnings: $2,681,959
Fiscal Year-end: 12/31/17
Construction Services
N.A.I.C.S.: 237310
Ivana Milkovska Simeva *(Chm-Supervisory Bd)*

GRANIT D.D. JABLANICA
Zeljeznicka br 15, Jablanica, 88420, Bosnia & Herzegovina
Tel.: (387) 61 198 848
Web Site: http://www.granit-jablanica.ba
GMONRK2—(SARE)
Rev.: $20,613
Assets: $1,675,427
Liabilities: $681,926
Net Worth: $993,501
Earnings: $9,618
Fiscal Year-end: 12/31/19
Stone Exploitation Services
N.A.I.C.S.: 212311
Amel Mandzuka *(Member-Mgmt Bd)*

GRANIT PESACAR A.D.
Ravnogorska bb, Ljig, Serbia
Tel.: (381) 14 3445 205

Web Site: http://www.granit.rs
Year Founded: 1952
GRPE—(BEL)
Sales Range: $400-449.9 Million
Emp.: 207
Limestone & Gypsum Product Mfr
N.A.I.C.S.: 327420
Zoran Radivojevic *(Exec Dir)*

GRANITE REAL ESTATE INVESTMENT TRUST
77 King St W Ste 4010, PO Box 159, Toronto-Dominion Centre, Toronto, M5K 1H1, ON, Canada
Tel.: (647) 925-7500 ON
Web Site: https://www.granitereit.com
Year Founded: 2012
GRP.U—(NYSE)
Rev.: $356,390,340
Assets: $7,259,835,327
Liabilities: $2,972,669,476
Net Worth: $4,287,165,851
Earnings: $121,896,434
Emp.: 69
Fiscal Year-end: 12/31/22
Real Estate Investment Trust
N.A.I.C.S.: 525990
Lorne Kumer *(Exec VP & Head-Real Estate-Global)*

Subsidiaries:

Granite REIT Inc. (1)
77 King Street West Suite 4010, PO Box 159, Toronto-Dominion Centre, Toronto, M5K 1H1, ON, Canada
Tel.: (647) 925-7500
Web Site: http://www.granitereit.com
Rev.: $356,390,339
Assets: $7,259,835,326
Liabilities: $2,972,669,475
Net Worth: $4,287,165,850
Earnings: $121,896,433
Emp.: 68
Fiscal Year-end: 12/31/2022
Commercial & Industrial Real Estate Acquisition, Development, Management & Leasing Services
N.A.I.C.S.: 531390
Lorne Kumer *(Exec VP & Head-Real Estate-Global)*

Subsidiary (Non-US):

Granite Austria GmbH (2)
Schubertring 14, 1010, Vienna, Austria **(100%)**
Tel.: (43) 19078800
Emp.: 15
Commercial & Industrial Real Estate Acquisition, Development, Management & Leasing Services
N.A.I.C.S.: 531390

GRANITIFIANDRE S.P.A
Via Radici Nord 112, 42014, Castellarano, RE, Italy
Tel.: (39) 0536819611
Web Site: http://www.granitifiandre.com
Sales Range: $200-249.9 Million
Vitrified Stoneware Materials Producer
N.A.I.C.S.: 327110
Mauro Tabellini *(Mgr-Fin)*

GRANITUL SA
Soseaua Vergului numarul 18 Sector 3, Bucharest, Romania
Tel.: (40) 212553030
Web Site: https://www.granitul.ro
RANT—(BUC)
Rev.: $69,062
Assets: $1,646,339
Liabilities: $31,653
Net Worth: $1,614,686
Earnings: ($88,041)
Emp.: 6
Fiscal Year-end: 12/31/23
Concrete Products Mfr
N.A.I.C.S.: 327390

Ioan Purge *(Pres & Gen Mgr)*

GRANO RETAIL INVESTMENTS INC.
89 Tycos, Toronto, M6B 1W3, ON, Canada
Tel.: (416) 642-7432
Web Site: http://www.granoretail.com
Year Founded: 2007
Private Investment Firm
N.A.I.C.S.: 523999
Stephen Granovsky *(Pres & Partner)*

Subsidiaries:

Samuelsohn Limited (1)
6930 avenue du Parc, Montreal, H3N 1W9, QC, Canada
Tel.: (514) 273-7741
Web Site: http://www.samuelsohn.com
Sales Range: $50-74.9 Million
Emp.: 375
Mens Tailored Clothing Mfr
N.A.I.C.S.: 315250
Lesser Samuelsohn *(Founder)*

Subsidiary (US):

Hickey Freeman Tailored Clothing, Inc. (2)
1155 N Clinton Ave, Rochester, NY 14621
Tel.: (585) 467-7240
Web Site: http://www.hickeyfreeman.com
Men's Tailored Apparel Mfr
N.A.I.C.S.: 315250
Chris Linares *(Sr VP-Retail)*

GRANOLIO D.D
Budmanijeva 5, 10000, Zagreb, Croatia
Tel.: (385) 16320200
Web Site: https://www.granolio.hr
Year Founded: 1996
GRNL—(ZAG)
Rev.: $100,130,257
Assets: $72,768,518
Liabilities: $46,988,630
Net Worth: $25,779,887
Earnings: $2,695,662
Emp.: 430
Fiscal Year-end: 12/31/23
Fruit & Vegetable Canning
N.A.I.C.S.: 311421
Hrvoje Filipovic *(Pres)*

GRANT EMBLEMS LIMITED
427 Horner Ave, Toronto, M8W4W3, ON, Canada
Tel.: (416) 255-3421
Year Founded: 1921
Sales Range: $10-24.9 Million
Emp.: 100
Provider of Pleating & Stitching Services
N.A.I.C.S.: 314999
Sally Grant *(Pres)*

Subsidiaries:

Voyager Emblems, Inc. (1)
PO Box 487, Lockport, NY 14095-0487
Tel.: (716) 439-0305
Web Site: http://www.voyager-emblems.com
Mfr of Swiss Embroidered Emblems & Caps; Apparel Distribution & Digitizing Services
N.A.I.C.S.: 313310

GRANT SAMUEL GROUP
Level 19 Governor Macquarie Tower 1 Farrer Place, Sydney, 2000, NSW, Australia
Tel.: (61) 293244211
Web Site: http://www.grantsamuel.com.au
Year Founded: 1988
Management Consulting Services
N.A.I.C.S.: 541611
Ross Grant *(Chm)*

GRANT THORNTON INTERNATIONAL LIMITED
20 Fenchurch Street Level 25, Euston, London, EC3M 3BY, United Kingdom
Tel.: (44) 2073919500 UK
Web Site: http://www.grantthornton.global
Sales Range: $1-4.9 Billion
Emp.: 30,000
Accounting, Auditing, Tax & Management Consulting Services
N.A.I.C.S.: 813920
Jonathan Geldart *(Exec Dir-Markets Dev)*

Subsidiaries:

Goodtech GmbH (1)
Industriering Ost 66, 47906, Kempen, Germany
Tel.: (49) 21521489403
Web Site: https://www.good-tech.de
Industrial Consumable & Spare Parts Mfr & Distr
N.A.I.C.S.: 333998

GRANT THORNTON LLP - CANADA
12th Floor 50 Bay Street, Toronto, M5J 2Z8, ON, Canada
Tel.: (416) 366-4240 Ca
Web Site: http://www.grantthornton.ca
Sales Range: $450-499.9 Million
Emp.: 2,242
Accounting, Auditing, Tax & Management Consulting Services
N.A.I.C.S.: 541211
Kevin Ladner *(CEO & Exec Partner)*

GRANT THORNTON SOUTH AFRICA (PTY) LTD.
137 Daisy Street Corner, Grayston Drive, Sandton, 2196, South Africa
Tel.: (27) 113224500
Web Site: http://www.gt.co.za
Year Founded: 1920
Sales Range: $50-74.9 Million
Emp.: 900
Accounting, Auditing, Tax & Management Consulting Services
N.A.I.C.S.: 541211
Deepak Nagar *(Mng Partner-Durban)*

Subsidiaries:

First Light Administration Services (Pty) Ltd. (1)
Suite 5 4th Floor Waterford House Waterford Road, PO Box X28, Benmore, 2010, Western Cape, South Africa
Tel.: (27) 21 713 8500
Web Site: http://www.firstlightadmin.co.za
Financial Services
N.A.I.C.S.: 523999
Bruce Knight *(CEO)*

GRANT THORNTON UK LLP
Grant Thornton House Melton Street, Euston Square, London, NW1 2EP, United Kingdom
Tel.: (44) 20 7383 5100 UK
Web Site: http://www.grantthornton.co.uk
Sales Range: $700-749.9 Million
Emp.: 4,500
Accounting, Auditing, Tax & Management Consulting Services
N.A.I.C.S.: 541211
Scott C. Barnes *(Partner-London)*

GRANULES INDIA LTD
2nd Floor 3rd Block My Home Hub Madhapur, Hyderabad, 500081, Telangana, India
Tel.: (91) 4069043500
Web Site: https://www.granulesindia.com
Year Founded: 1991

GRANULES INDIA LTD

Granules India Ltd—(Continued)
532482—(BOM)
Rev.: $540,841,203
Assets: $661,965,742
Liabilities: $275,223,016
Net Worth: $386,742,726
Earnings: $48,596,669
Emp.: 3,838
Fiscal Year-end: 03/31/24
producer of active pharmaceutical ingredients
N.A.I.C.S.: 325199
Krishna Prasad Chigurupati *(Mng Dir & Chm)*

Subsidiaries:

Granules USA Inc (1)
111 Howard Blvd Ste 101, Mount Arlington, NJ 07856
Tel.: (973) 770-3181
Emp.: 5
Drug & Pharmaceutical Supplies
N.A.I.C.S.: 456110
Vijay Ramanavarapu *(Pres)*

GRANVILLE GMBH

Raboisen 38, 20095, Hamburg, Germany
Tel.: (49) 4037480210 De
Web Site: http://www.granville-pe.de
Year Founded: 1999
Privater Equity Firm
N.A.I.C.S.: 523999
Mathias Schirmer *(Mng Dir)*

GRANVILLE TOYOTA

8265 Fraser St, Vancouver, V5X 3X9, BC, Canada
Tel.: (604) 263-2711
Web Site: http://www.granvilletoyota.com
New & Used Car Dealers
N.A.I.C.S.: 441110
Doug Shorman *(Gen Mgr)*

GRAPE KING BIO LTD.

No 402 Sec 2 Jinling Rd, Pingzhen Dist, Taoyuan, 324, Taiwan
Tel.: (886) 34572121
Web Site: https://www.grapeking.com.tw
Year Founded: 1969
1707—(TAI)
Rev.: $347,802,858
Assets: $507,271,017
Liabilities: $126,946,789
Net Worth: $380,324,228
Earnings: $70,032,078
Emp.: 850
Fiscal Year-end: 12/31/23
Medical Products Mfr
N.A.I.C.S.: 325411
Andrew Sheng-Lin Tseng *(Chm, CEO & Gen Mgr)*

Subsidiaries:

Pro-partner Inc. (1)
3F No 18 Jinzhuang Road, Neihu Dist, Taipei, Taiwan
Tel.: (886) 227922103
Web Site: http://www.pro-partner.com.tw
Health Food Distr
N.A.I.C.S.: 456191

Shanghai Grape King Enterprise Co., Ltd. (1)
No 518 Chexin Highway, Chedun Songjiang, Shanghai, 201611, China
Tel.: (86) 2157609598
Web Site: https://www.grapeking.com.cn
Health Food Mfr & Distr
N.A.I.C.S.: 325412

GRAPHANO ENERGY LTD.

219-120 Carlton Street, Toronto, M5A 4K2, ON, Canada
Tel.: (647) 462-6039 BC
Web Site: https://graphano.com

Year Founded: 2020
GEL—(TSXV)
Assets: $2,708,507
Liabilities: $144,547
Net Worth: $2,563,960
Earnings: ($1,700,717)
Fiscal Year-end: 07/31/22
Mining Machinery & Equipment Mfr
N.A.I.C.S.: 333131
Luisa Moreno *(CEO)*

GRAPHENE MANUFACTURING GROUP LTD.

5/848 Boundary Road, Richlands, 4077, QLD, Australia
Tel.: (61) 730636638 AU
Web Site: https://www.graphenemg.com
Year Founded: 2016
GMG—(TSXV)
Rev.: $36,335
Assets: $11,132,850
Liabilities: $4,389,974
Net Worth: $6,742,876
Earnings: ($7,857,830)
Fiscal Year-end: 06/30/22
Graphene Material Mfr
N.A.I.C.S.: 335991
Craig Nicol *(CEO & Mng Dir)*

GRAPHENE NANOCHEM PLC

Suite 9 2 Level 9 WORK Clearwater Changkat Semantan, Off Jalan Semanta Damansara Heights, 50490, Kuala Lumpur, Malaysia
Tel.: (60) 3 2092 3080
Web Site: http://www.graphenenanochem.com
Sales Range: $50-74.9 Million
Emp.: 157
Chemicals Mfr
N.A.I.C.S.: 325998
Jespal Singh Deol Balbir Singh *(CEO)*

Subsidiaries:

Zurex Corporation Sdn. Bhd. (1)
A-15-4 Northpoint Ofc Medan Syed Putra Utara No 1 Jalan Syed Putra, Mid Valley City, 59200, Kuala Lumpur, Malaysia
Tel.: (60) 322870080
Web Site: http://www.biofuturesplc.com
Sales Range: $25-49.9 Million
Emp.: 6
Biodiesel Mfr
N.A.I.C.S.: 324110

GRAPHEX GROUP LIMITED

11/F COFCO Tower 262 Gloucester Road, Causeway Bay, China (Hong Kong)
Tel.: (852) 25599438
Web Site: http://www.ea-dg.com
6128—(HKG)
Rev.: $43,508,228
Assets: $114,071,190
Liabilities: $66,916,335
Net Worth: $47,154,855
Earnings: ($8,880,375)
Emp.: 408
Fiscal Year-end: 12/31/22
Landscape Architectural Services
N.A.I.C.S.: 541320
Patrick Hing Tat Lau *(Chm)*

Subsidiaries:

Thai Gallery SRL (1)
Piazza Alvar Aalto Via Amerigo Vespucci 12, 20124, Milan, Italy
Tel.: (39) 0289280745
Web Site: http://www.thaigallery.it
Interior Art Services
N.A.I.C.S.: 541410

GRAPHEX GROUP LIMITED

11/F COFCO Tower 262 Gloucester Road, Causeway Bay, Causeway Bay, China (Hong Kong)
Tel.: (852) 25599438 Ky
Web Site: https://graphexgroup.com
Year Founded: 1981
GRFX—(NYSEAMEX)
Rev.: $50,154
Assets: $141,408
Liabilities: $120,758
Net Worth: $20,649
Earnings: ($12,424)
Emp.: 102
Fiscal Year-end: 12/31/20
Holding Company
N.A.I.C.S.: 551112
John DeMaio *(Pres)*

GRAPHISADS LIMITED

4/24 A AB House Asaf Ali Road Near Delhi Gate, New Delhi, 110002, India
Tel.: (91) 1145379999
Web Site: https://www.graphisads.com
Year Founded: 1987
GRAPHISAD—(NSE)
Rev.: $8,173,367
Assets: $10,920,327
Liabilities: $6,721,304
Net Worth: $4,199,023
Earnings: $556,509
Emp.: 94
Fiscal Year-end: 03/31/23
Digital Marketing Services
N.A.I.C.S.: 541910

GRAPHISOFT PARK SE

Zahony utca 7, 1031, Budapest, Hungary
Tel.: (36) 18153400
Web Site: https://www.graphisoftpark.com
Year Founded: 1996
GSPARK—(BUD)
Rev.: $16,768,832
Assets: $268,888,409
Liabilities: $107,417,440
Net Worth: $161,470,969
Earnings: $9,481,977
Emp.: 24
Fiscal Year-end: 12/31/22
Real Estate Management Services
N.A.I.C.S.: 531311
Janos Kocsany *(CEO)*

Subsidiaries:

Graphisoft Park Kft (1)
Tel.: (36) 18153400
Web Site: https://www.graphisoftpark.hu
Real Estate Development Services
N.A.I.C.S.: 531390

GRAPHITE CAPITAL MANAGEMENT LLP

Berkeley Square House Berkeley Square, London, W1J 6BQ, United Kingdom
Tel.: (44) 20 7825 5300 UK
Web Site: http://www.graphitecapital.com
Year Founded: 1981
Rev.: $2,492,160,000
Emp.: 55
Private Equity & Investment Management Firm
N.A.I.C.S.: 523999
Rod Richards *(Chm & Mng Partner)*

Subsidiaries:

Beck & Pollitzer Engineering Ltd (1)
Burnham Road, Dartford, DA1 5BD, Kent, United Kingdom
Tel.: (44) 1322 223 494
Web Site: http://www.beck-pollitzer.com
Industrial Machinery Transportation Services
N.A.I.C.S.: 541614
Andrew Hodgson *(CEO)*

INTERNATIONAL PUBLIC

Subsidiary (Non-US):

Beck & Pollitzer Czech s.r.o. (2)
Ovcarecka 1452, 280 02, Kolin, Czech Republic
Tel.: (420) 321 800 047
Web Site: http://www.beck-pollitzer.cz
Industrial Machinery Transportation Services
N.A.I.C.S.: 541614

Beck & Pollitzer Deutschland GmbH (2)
Hangebank 13, 45307, Essen, Germany
Tel.: (49) 201 598048 0
Web Site: http://www.beck-pollitzer.de
Industrial Machinery Transportation Services
N.A.I.C.S.: 541614

Beck & Pollitzer France SAS (2)
25 rue du Champ des Oiseaux, BP 70222, ZI du Moulin Blanc, 59230, Saint-Amand-les-Eaux, France
Tel.: (33) 3 27 29 56 20
Web Site: http://www.beck-pollitzer.fr
Industrial Machinery Transportation Services
N.A.I.C.S.: 541614
Fabrice Dezitter *(Dir-Ops)*

Beck & Pollitzer Hungary Kft. (2)
Vahot u 6, 1119, Budapest, Hungary
Tel.: (36) 1 205 3461
Web Site: http://www.beck-pollitzer.hu
Industrial Machinery Transportation Services
N.A.I.C.S.: 541614

Beck & Pollitzer India Pvt. Ltd. (2)
Office No 103 Sohrab Hall 21 Sassoon Road, Pune, 411001, India
Tel.: (91) 20 260 570 26
Industrial Machinery Transportation Services
N.A.I.C.S.: 541614
Pravin Devanpalli *(Sr Project Engr)*

Beck & Pollitzer Italia S.r.l. (2)
Corso Italia 8, 20122, Milan, Italy
Tel.: (39) 0366 1548005
Web Site: http://www.beck-pollitzer.it
Industrial Machinery Transportation Services
N.A.I.C.S.: 541614

Beck & Pollitzer Polska Sp.z.o.o (2)
ul Lelewela 23, 41-219, Sosnowiec, Poland
Tel.: (48) 32 290 5800
Web Site: http://www.beck-pollitzer.pl
Industrial Machinery Transportation Services
N.A.I.C.S.: 541614

Beck & Pollitzer Romania SRL (2)
BD Iuliu Maniu NR 246 Corp C37 Et 3 Camera 327, Bucharest, 061126, Romania
Tel.: (40) 31 425 2255
Web Site: http://www.beck-pollitzer.ro
Industrial Machinery Transportation Services
N.A.I.C.S.: 541614
Andreea Retevoescu *(Mgr-Admin)*

Beck & Pollitzer Ticaret Ltd. Sti. (2)
Kosekoy San Slt L Blok No 199, Kocaeli, Turkiye
Tel.: (90) 262 373 6495
Web Site: http://www.beck-pollitzer.com
Industrial Machinery Transportation Services
N.A.I.C.S.: 541614

City & County Healthcare Group Limited (1)
3rd Floor Caparo House 101-103 Baker Street, London, W1U 6LN, Mddx, United Kingdom
Tel.: (44) 2071860518
Web Site: http://www.candchealthcare.co.uk
Holding Company Home Health Care Services
N.A.I.C.S.: 551112
Craig Rushton *(Head-M&A)*

Subsidiary (Domestic):

Quality Care Services Limited (2)
2nd Floor Olympic House 3 Olympic Way, Wembley, HA9 0NP, Mddx, United Kingdom

Tel.: (44) 20 8795 6500
Web Site:
http://www.qualitycareserviceslimited.co.uk
Women Healthcare Services
N.A.I.C.S.: 621610
James Thorburn-Muirhead *(CEO)*

The Groucho Club Ltd. (1)
45 Dean Street, London, W1D 4QB, United Kingdom
Tel.: (44) 20 7439 4685
Web Site: http://www.thegrouchoclub.com
Pub Operator
N.A.I.C.S.: 721310
Matthew Hobbs *(Mng Dir)*

GRAPHITE DESIGN INC.
2474-1 Ota, Chichibu, 368-0065, Saitama, Japan
Tel.: (81) 494622800
Web Site: https://www.gd-inc.co.jp
Year Founded: 1989
78470—(TKS)
Sales Range: Less than $1 Million
Emp.: 120
Golf Shaft Mfr
N.A.I.C.S.: 339920
Takuro Yamada *(Pres)*

GRAPHITE INDIA LTD
31 Chowringhee Road, Kolkata, 700016, India
Tel.: (91) 3340029600
Web Site:
https://www.graphiteindia.com
509488—(BOM)
Rev.: $453,226,410
Assets: $859,812,135
Liabilities: $184,537,080
Net Worth: $675,275,055
Earnings: $68,865,615
Emp.: 1,719
Fiscal Year-end: 03/31/22
Graphite Electrode Mfr
N.A.I.C.S.: 335991
B. Shiva *(Compliance Officer, Sec & Sr VP-Legal)*

Subsidiaries:

Graphite India Ltd - Glass Reinforced Plastic (GRP) Pipes and Tanks Division (1)
Gut No 523 524 Vlg Gonde Tal Igatpuri, Nasik, 422403, Maharashtra, India
Tel.: (91) 2553225038
Sales Range: $50-74.9 Million
Emp.: 150
Graphite Electrode Mfr
N.A.I.C.S.: 335991
Sanjay W. Barnerkar *(Exec VP-Fin)*

Graphite India Ltd - Impervious Graphite Equipment Division (1)
C-7 MIDC, Ambad, Nasik, 422 010, Maharashtra, India
Tel.: (91) 2532302100
Web Site: http://www.graphiteindia.com
Graphite Electrode Mfr
N.A.I.C.S.: 335991

Graphite International B.V. (1)
Burgemeester de Manlaan 2, Breda, 4837 BN, Netherlands
Tel.: (31) 765609900
Sales Range: $50-74.9 Million
Emp.: 1
Inorganic Chemicals Whslr
N.A.I.C.S.: 424690
Desiree Poot *(Acct Mgr)*

Subsidiary (Non-US):

Bavaria Carbon Holdings GmbH (2)
Gruthal 1 6 Pegnitz, Swabia Lindau Dist, 90552, Rothenberg, Germany
Tel.: (49) 91157080
Web Site: http://www.graphitecova.com
Investment Management Service
N.A.I.C.S.: 522320

Bavaria Carbon Specialties GmbH (2)
Grunthal 1 to 6, Swabia Lindau, 90552, Rothenbach, Germany

Tel.: (49) 91157080
Web Site: http://www.graphitecova.com
Sales Range: $125-149.9 Million
Emp.: 300
Inorganic Chemicals Whslr
N.A.I.C.S.: 424690

Bavaria Electrodes GmbH (2)
Grnthal 1 6 Pegnitz, Swabia Lindau, 90552, Rothenbach, Germany
Tel.: (49) 91157080
Web Site: http://www.graphitecova.com
Sales Range: $25-49.9 Million
Emp.: 150
Electric Equipment Mfr
N.A.I.C.S.: 334513

Graphite COVA GmbH (2)
Grunthal 1-6, Swabia Lindau, D-90552, Rothenbach, Germany
Tel.: (49) 91157080
Web Site: https://www.graphitecova.com
Sales Range: $75-99.9 Million
Graphite Electrode Mfr
N.A.I.C.S.: 335991
Rounak Poddar *(Mng Dir)*

GRAPHITE ONE INC.
600 - 777 Hornby Street, Vancouver, V6Z 1S4, BC, Canada
Tel.: (604) 681-8780
Web Site:
https://www.graphiteresources.com
Year Founded: 2006
GPHOF—(OTCQX)
Assets: $20,906,385
Liabilities: $7,143,100
Net Worth: $13,763,285
Earnings: ($2,127,753)
Fiscal Year-end: 12/31/20
Graphite Mining
N.A.I.C.S.: 212290
David R. Hembree *(Gen Mgr-Ops)*

GRAPHJET TECHNOLOGY
Unit No L4-E-8 Enterprise 4 Technology Park Malaysia Bukit Jalil, 57000, Kuala Lumpur, Malaysia
Tel.: (60) 018272779
Year Founded: 2019
GTI—(NASDAQ)
Rev.: $858,423
Assets: $13,985,692
Liabilities: $6,721,721
Net Worth: ($6,695,162)
Earnings: ($46,367)
Fiscal Year-end: 12/31/23
Investment Services
N.A.I.C.S.: 523999
Tham Choi Kuen *(CFO)*

GRASDORF GMBH
Ziegeleistrasse 29, D-31188, Holle, Germany
Tel.: (49) 50629020
Web Site: http://www.grasdorf-rad.eu
Rev.: $102,682,536
Emp.: 137
Special Wheels Mfr
N.A.I.C.S.: 333924

GRASSROOTS INC.
5-4-35 Minami-Aoyama Tatsumura Aoyama Mansion 1009, Minato-ku, Tokyo, 107-0062, Japan
Tel.: (81) 357745561
Web Site: http://www.grassroots.co.jp
Emp.: 5
Website Design & Hosting Services
N.A.I.C.S.: 541430
Mayumi Ono *(CEO)*

GRATEX INDUSTRIES LIMITED
Gratex House A73 TTC Industrial Area MIDC Kopar Khairne, Mumbai, 400 016, India
Tel.: (91) 2262992121
Web Site: https://www.gratex.in
526751—(BOM)
Rev.: $510,750

Assets: $494,401
Liabilities: $85,531
Net Worth: $408,870
Earnings: $22,522
Emp.: 21
Fiscal Year-end: 03/31/23
Wallpaper Whslr
N.A.I.C.S.: 424950
Baldevkrishan Sharma *(Chm & Mng Dir)*

GRATEX INTERNATIONAL, A.S.
GBC IV Galvaniho 17/C, Bratislava, 821 04, Slovakia
Tel.: (421) 253411441
Web Site: http://www.gratex.com
Year Founded: 1991
Sales Range: $10-24.9 Million
Emp.: 200
Software Design Services
N.A.I.C.S.: 541512
Jozef Kozar *(Chm & CEO)*

Subsidiaries:

Gratex International AUST Pty Ltd. (1)
Heritage Business Park Level 1 Unit 1 5-9 Ricketty St, Mascot, 2020, NSW, Australia
Tel.: (61) 2 8335 1100
Web Site: http://www.gratex.com.au
Emp.: 10
Information Technology Consulting Services
N.A.I.C.S.: 541512
Milan Neklapil *(Mng Dir)*

GRATOMIC INC.
22 Adelaide Street West Suite 3600 Bay Adelaide Centre-East Tower, Toronto, M5H 4E3, ON, Canada
Tel.: (416) 561-4095
Web Site: https://www.gratomic.ca
Year Founded: 2007
CB82—(DEU)
Assets: $19,701,099
Liabilities: $2,627,934
Net Worth: $17,073,165
Earnings: ($6,026,206)
Fiscal Year-end: 12/31/22
Graphite Exploration Services
N.A.I.C.S.: 212290
Arno Brand *(Pres & CEO)*

GRATTERPALM, LTD.
Bridge Rd, Kirkstall, Leeds, LS5 3BW, United Kingdom
Tel.: (44) 113 275 9326
Emp.: 110
Advertising, Retail, T.V.
N.A.I.C.S.: 541810
Gordon Bethell *(Mng Partner)*

GRAUBUENDNER KANTONALBANK
Grabenstrasse 8, 7001, Chur, Switzerland
Tel.: (41) 812569601
Web Site: https://www.gkb.ch
GRKP—(SWX)
Sales Range: Less than $1 Million
Commercial Banking Services
N.A.I.C.S.: 522110
Daniel Fust *(Chm-Mgmt Bd, CEO & Head-Bus Unit Corp Center)*

GRAUER & WEIL INDIA LIMITED
Growel Corporate Akurli Road, Kandivli E, Mumbai, 400 101, Maharashtra, India
Tel.: (91) 2266993000
Web Site: http://www.growel.com
GRAUWEIL—(NSE)
Rev.: $136,614,660
Assets: $130,257,855
Liabilities: $37,545,690
Net Worth: $92,712,165

Earnings: $15,419,040
Emp.: 900
Fiscal Year-end: 03/31/23
Specialty Chemicals Mfr
N.A.I.C.S.: 325320
Nirajkumar U. More *(Mng Dir)*

Subsidiaries:

Digikore Studios Ltd. (1)
Kundan Bhavan Kundan Nagar Opp Alfa Laval Mumbai - Pune Road, Dapodi, Pune, 411 012, Maharashtra, India
Tel.: (91) 9130034656
Web Site: https://www.digikore.com
Sales Range: $25-49.9 Million
Animation Film Production Services
N.A.I.C.S.: 512199
Abhishek More *(Founder, Pres & CEO)*

Grauer & Weil India Ltd - Dadra Plant (1)
Plot No 10 Surv No 215 1, Dadra, 396191, India
Tel.: (91) 2602669985
Web Site: http://www.growel.com
Sales Range: $25-49.9 Million
Emp.: 70
Chemicals Mfr
N.A.I.C.S.: 325199
Rakesh Singh *(VP)*

Grauer & Weil India Ltd - Vapi Plant (1)
Plot No 407 2nd OG I D C, Vapi, Valsad, 396195, Gujarat, India
Tel.: (91) 2602401389
Web Site: http://www.growel.com
Sales Range: $50-74.9 Million
Emp.: 200
Chemicals Mfr
N.A.I.C.S.: 325199
Vinod Paleria *(Gen Mgr)*

Growel Softech Ltd. (1)
Growel House Dapodi Opp Alfa Laval Old Mumbai-Pune Road, Pune, 411 012, Maharashtra, India
Tel.: (91) 2030213000
Web Site: http://growelsoftech.com
Sales Range: $10-24.9 Million
Emp.: 56
Software Training Solutions
N.A.I.C.S.: 611420

GRAUPNER / SJ GMBH
Henriettenstr 96, 73230, Kirchheim, Germany
Tel.: (49) 70217220
Web Site: http://www.graupner.de
Year Founded: 1930
Aircraft Model Building Products Distr
N.A.I.C.S.: 423920
Hannes Runknagel *(Mng Dir)*

GRAVIS ENERGY CORP.
Suite 950 - 1130 West Pender Street, Vancouver, V6E 4A4, BC, Canada
Tel.: (778) 331-3816
Web Site:
http://www.gravisenergy.com
Year Founded: 2007
GVE—(CNSX)
Sales Range: Less than $1 Million
Oil & Gas Exploration Services
N.A.I.C.S.: 211120
Nizar Bharmal *(CFO)*

GRAVISS HOSPITALITY LIMITED
Strand Cinema 1st Floor Arthur Bunder Road CS No 506 Colaba, Mumbai, 400005, Maharashtra, India
Tel.: (91) 2262513131
Web Site:
https://www.gravisshospitality.com
Year Founded: 1959
509546—(BOM)
Rev.: $8,048,846
Assets: $25,245,980
Liabilities: $3,660,632
Net Worth: $21,585,349
Earnings: $713,363

GRAVISS HOSPITALITY LIMITED

GRAVISS HOSPITALITY LIMITED—(Continued)
Emp.: 101
Fiscal Year-end: 03/31/23
Home Management Services
N.A.I.C.S.: 721110
Farangilal B. Goyal *(CFO)*

Subsidiaries:

Graviss Hotels & Resorts Limited (1)
Strand Cinema Bldg 1st Floor C S No 506
Arthur Bunder Road Colaba, Worli, Mumbai,
400 005, India
Tel.: (91) 2240501111
Banquet Services
N.A.I.C.S.: 722320

GRAVITA INDIA LIMITED
Gravita Tower A-27-B Shanti Path,
Tilak Nagar, Jaipur, 302004, Rajasthan, India
Tel.: (91) 1414057800
Web Site:
https://www.gravitaindia.com
533282—(BOM)
Rev.: $394,987,320
Assets: $164,509,800
Liabilities: $82,377,750
Net Worth: $82,132,050
Earnings: $27,858,285
Emp.: 1,000
Fiscal Year-end: 03/31/23
Lead Product Mfr
N.A.I.C.S.: 332999
Rajat Agarwal *(Mng Dir)*

Subsidiaries:

FLORET TRADELINK PRIVATE
LIMITED (1)
House No 340 Lane 4 Vashistha Marg,
Raja Park, Jaipur, 302004, Rajasthan, India
Tel.: (91) 1414057852
Web Site: http://www.gravitaindia.com
Emp.: 100
Lead Smelting & Refining Services
N.A.I.C.S.: 331410

GRAVITA EXIM LTD (1)
No 102 Rajputana Tower A-27B Shanti
Path, Tilak Nagar, Jaipur, 302004, Rajasthan, India
Tel.: (91) 1414057800
Web Site: http://www.gravitaexim.com
Sales Range: $50-74.9 Million
Emp.: 200
Lead Recycling & Smelting Services
N.A.I.C.S.: 331410

Subsidiary (Domestic):

Penta Exim. Pvt. Ltd (2)
A 27 B Shanti Path 501 Gravita Tower,
Jaipur, 302004, Rajasthan, India
Tel.: (91) 1412622697
Web Site: http://www.gravitaexim.com
Sales Range: $25-49.9 Million
Emp.: 35
Lead Smelting & Recycling Services
N.A.I.C.S.: 331410

GRAVITA GEORGIA LIMITED (1)
King Mirian Street 68a, 0159, Tbilisi, Georgia
Tel.: (995) 322357272
Web Site: https://gravita.ge
Lead Product Mfr
N.A.I.C.S.: 334419

Gravita Ghana Ltd (1)
Ind/A/43/1B Heavy Industrial Area, Tema,
00233, Ghana
Tel.: (233) 249652222
Web Site: http://www.gravitaghana.com
Sales Range: $25-49.9 Million
Emp.: 80
Lead Product Mfr
N.A.I.C.S.: 332999

Gravita Honduras SA (1)
Cortes, San Pedro Sula, Honduras
Tel.: (504) 5045515777
Web Site: http://www.gravitahonduras.com
Lead Smelting & Refining Services
N.A.I.C.S.: 331410
George Gatlin *(Pres)*

Gravita Mozambique LDA (1)
Samora Machel Estrada Maputo - Witbank
No 672-EN4, Bairro Matola Gare
Tchumene-2, 1114, Matola, Maputo, Mozambique
Tel.: (258) 84 398 6299
Web Site:
https://www.gravitamozambique.com
Lead Product Mfr
N.A.I.C.S.: 332999

Gravita Tanzania Limited (1)
Plot No 7 Block No A, PO Box 20105,
Visiga Zegereni Kibaha Industrial Area, Dar
es Salaam, Pwani, Tanzania
Tel.: (255) 67 708 7970
Web Site: https://www.gravitatanzania.com
Aluminum Alloy Mfr
N.A.I.C.S.: 331314

Gravita USA Inc. (1)
3100 University Blvd S Ste 240, Jacksonville, FL 32256
Tel.: (832) 382-5462
Web Site: https://www.gravitausa.com
Lead Product Mfr
N.A.I.C.S.: 332999

Navam Lanka Ltd. (1)
Plot No 27 A MEPZ Mirigama Export Processing Zone, Dist - Gampha, Mirigama,
11200, Western Province, Sri Lanka
Tel.: (94) 332275394
Web Site: http://www.navamlanka.com
Emp.: 70
Lead Ingots & Polypropylene Chips Mfr
N.A.I.C.S.: 339999

GRAVITON CAPITAL S.A.
ul Kielbasnicza 28, 50-109, Wroclaw,
Poland
Tel.: (48) 71 79 11 555
Web Site: http://www.wdmsa.pl
Financial Services
N.A.I.C.S.: 525990

Subsidiaries:

Nexity Global SA (1)
Ul Bronowicka 130, 30-121, Krakow, Poland
Tel.: (48) 185428428
Web Site: https://www.nexity.io
Rev.: $19,309
Assets: $156,504
Liabilities: $204,014
Net Worth: ($47,510)
Earnings: ($69,360)
Fiscal Year-end: 12/31/2023
Private Equity Fund Investment Services
N.A.I.C.S.: 523999
Lukasz Kaleta *(CEO)*

WDM Autoryzowany Doradca sp.
z.o.o (1)
Plac Powstancow Slaskich 1 lok 201, 53-329, Wroclaw, Poland
Tel.: (48) 71 79 11 555
Web Site: http://www.wdmad.pl
Investment Advisory Services
N.A.I.C.S.: 523940

GRAVITY (INDIA) LIMITED
106 Hallmark Vasant Oscar LBS
Marg, Mulund West, Mumbai,
400080, India
Tel.: (91) 2225926000
Web Site: http://www.gravityindia.net
532015—(BOM)
Rev.: $1,231,689
Assets: $1,995,708
Liabilities: $768,995
Net Worth: $1,226,713
Earnings: ($119,309)
Emp.: 30
Fiscal Year-end: 03/31/23
Fabric Product Mfr
N.A.I.C.S.: 313240
Varun Thakkar *(Chm & Mng Dir)*

GRAVITY CO., LTD.
15F 396 World Cup buk-ro Mapo-gu,
Seoul, 03925, Korea (South)
Tel.: (82) 221327000 KR
Web Site: http://www.gravity.co.kr
Year Founded: 2000

GRVY—(NASDAQ)
Rev.: $426,528,560
Assets: $408,566,480
Liabilities: $104,800,880
Net Worth: $303,765,600
Earnings: $76,413,360
Emp.: 894
Fiscal Year-end: 12/31/22
Online Game Developer & Distr
N.A.I.C.S.: 339930
Kazuki Morishita *(Exec Dir)*

Subsidiaries:

Gravity Communications Co.,
Ltd. (1)
4F No 335 Ruiguang Rd, Neihu Dist, Taipei,
11492, Taiwan
Tel.: (886) 226580626
Online Game Development Services
N.A.I.C.S.: 541512

Gravity Game Arise Co., Ltd. (1)
3-14-4-2F Hatchobori, Chuo-ku, Tokyo, 104-0032, Japan
Tel.: (81) 362632656
Web Site: https://www.gravityga.jp
Emp.: 42
Game Development & Online Game Operating Services
N.A.I.C.S.: 713120

Gravity Game Hub (GGH) Pte.,
Ltd. (1)
100 Cecil Street 10-01 The Globe, Singapore, 069532, Singapore
Tel.: (65) 69808062
Web Site: https://www.gnjoy.asia
Mobile Game Developing Services
N.A.I.C.S.: 541512

Gravity Game Tech Co., Ltd. (1)
159 Serm-Mit Tower Sukhumvit 21 Road,
North Klongtoey Sub-District Wattana District, Bangkok, 10110, Thailand
Tel.: (66) 21267966
Computer Peripheral Equipment Repair &
Maintenance Services
N.A.I.C.S.: 541519

Gravity Game Vision Limited (1)
Rm1501-08 Millennium City 5 418 Kwun
Tong Road, Kwun Tong, Kowloon, China
(Hong Kong)
Tel.: (852) 37508656
Online Game Development Services
N.A.I.C.S.: 541512

Gravity Interactive LLC (1)
7001 Village Dr Ste 150, Buena Park, CA
90621
Tel.: (714) 736-3487
Online Game Development Services
N.A.I.C.S.: 541512

Gravity Neocyon Inc. (1)
12Fl Nuritkum Square R & D Tower 396
Worldcupbuk-ro 1605 Sangam-dong, Mapo-gu, Seoul, 03925, Korea (South)
Tel.: (82) 15889897
Web Site: https://www.gravityneocyon.com
Mobile Technology Development Services
N.A.I.C.S.: 541511

Neo Cyon Inc. (1)
Web Site: http://www.neocyon.com
Online Game Developer
N.A.I.C.S.: 339930

GRAVITY MEDIA GROUP LIMITED
32-34 Greenhill Crescent Watford
Business Park, Watford, WD18 8JU,
Hertfordshire, United Kingdom
Tel.: (44) 1923288348
Web Site:
http://www.gravitymedia.com
Year Founded: 2000
Sales Range: $75-99.9 Million
Emp.: 109
Electric Device Mfr
N.A.I.C.S.: 334419
John Newton *(CEO)*

Subsidiaries:

Gearhouse Actis SAS (1)

INTERNATIONAL PUBLIC

21 Avenue Francisco Ferrer, 93310, Le Pre-Saint-Gervais, France
Tel.: (33) 149159142
Web Site: http://www.gearhouseactis.com
Broadcasting Equipment Rental Services
N.A.I.C.S.: 532490
Mathieu Rocton *(Mng Dir)*

Gearhouse Broadcast LLC (1)
Building No 5 Zone 14 Ahamed Bin Mohamed Bin Thani, PO Box 22497, Fereej
Abdul Aziz, Doha, Qatar
Tel.: (974) 44583422
Web Site:
http://www.gearhousebroadcast.com
Television Broadcasting Services
N.A.I.C.S.: 516120
Eamonn Dowdall *(Mng Dir & Dir-Bus Dev)*

Gearhouse Broadcast Pty
Limited (1)
Unit 1 154 O'Riordan Street, Mascot, 2020,
NSW, Australia
Tel.: (61) 293133100
Web Site:
http://www.gearhousebroadcast.com
Television Broadcasting Services
N.A.I.C.S.: 516120
John Newton *(CEO)*

GRAYCLIFF EXPLORATION LIMITED
2702 401 Bay Street, Toronto, M5H
2Y4, ON, Canada
Tel.: (416) 862-7003
Web Site:
https://www.graycliffexploration.com
GRYCF—(OTCQB)
Rev.: $3,650
Assets: $1,702,913
Liabilities: $49,633
Net Worth: $1,653,280
Earnings: ($3,765,479)
Fiscal Year-end: 12/31/21
Mineral Exploration Services
N.A.I.C.S.: 213115
James Macintosh *(Pres)*

GRAYMONT LIMITED
200-10991 Shellbridge Way, Richmond, V6X 3C6, BC, Canada
Tel.: (604) 207-4292
Web Site: https://www.graymont.com
Year Founded: 1948
Sales Range: $350-399.9 Million
Emp.: 1,500
Lime & Limestone Product Mfr &
Distr
N.A.I.C.S.: 327410

Subsidiaries:

Graymont Dolime (OH) Inc. (1)
21880 State Route 163, Genoa, OH 43430
Tel.: (419) 855-8336
Web Site: http://www.graymont-oh.com
Sales Range: $25-49.9 Million
Emp.: 71
Quicklime & Hydrated Lime Producer
N.A.I.C.S.: 327410

Graymont Inc. (1)
1220 Alexander Ave, Tacoma, WA 98421
Tel.: (253) 572-7600
Web Site: http://www.graymont.com
Sales Range: $25-49.9 Million
Precipitated Calcium Carbonate Producer
N.A.I.C.S.: 327410

Graymont Limited - Lamont County
Facility (1)
-, PO Box 968, Lamont, T0B 2R0, AB,
Canada
Tel.: (403) 609-7307
Lime Mfr
N.A.I.C.S.: 327410

Graymont Limited - Rivergate
Facility (1)
13939 N Rivergate Blvd, Portland, OR
97203
Tel.: (801) 263-5833
Lime Mfr & Distr
N.A.I.C.S.: 327410

AND PRIVATE COMPANIES

Graymont Limited - Saint-Marc-des-Carrieres Facility (1)
100 rue Gauthier, Saint-Marc-des-Carrieres,
G0A 4B0, QC, Canada
Tel.: (418) 268-3584
Construction Materials Distr
N.A.I.C.S.: 423320

Graymont Limited Bedford Plant (1)
1015 Chemin de la Carriere, Bedford, J0J 1A0, QC, Canada
Tel.: (450) 248-3307
Lime Mfr & Distr
N.A.I.C.S.: 327410

Graymont Limited Cricket Mountain Plant (1)
PO Box 669, Delta, UT 84624
Tel.: (435) 864-3823
Lime Mfr & Transportation Services
N.A.I.C.S.: 327410

Graymont Limited Eden Plant (1)
N4520 County Rd V, Eden, WI 53019
Tel.: (920) 477-5032
Lime Mfr & Shipping Services
N.A.I.C.S.: 327410

Graymont Limited Exshaw Plant (1)
-, PO Box 130, Exshaw, T0L 2C0, AB, Canada
Tel.: (403) 673-3595
Lime Mfr & Distr
N.A.I.C.S.: 327410

Graymont Limited Faulkner Plant (1)
-, PO Box 1, Faulkner, R0C 0Y0, MB, Canada
Tel.: (204) 449-2078
Lime Mfr
N.A.I.C.S.: 327410

Graymont Limited Green Bay Plant (1)
137 James St, Green Bay, WI 54303
Tel.: (920) 437-4054
Lime Mfr & Warehousing Services
N.A.I.C.S.: 327410

Graymont Limited Havelock Plant (1)
4634 Route 880, Havelock, E4Z 5K8, NB, Canada
Tel.: (506) 534-2311
Lime Mfr & Distr
N.A.I.C.S.: 327410

Graymont Limited Indian Creek Plant (1)
PO Box 550, Townsend, MT 59644
Tel.: (406) 266-5221
Lime Mfr & Warehousing Services
N.A.I.C.S.: 327410

Graymont Limited Joliette Plant (1)
1300 rue Notre-Dame, CP 380, Joliette, J6E 3Z9, QC, Canada
Tel.: (450) 759-8195
Lime Mfr
N.A.I.C.S.: 327410

Graymont Limited Makareao Plant (1)
-, PO Box 118, Palmerston, 9443, Otago, New Zealand
Tel.: (64) 34650854
Limestone Mfr & Distr
N.A.I.C.S.: 327410

Graymont Limited Marbleton Plant (1)
303 Principale O, Marbleton, J0B 1G0, QC, Canada
Tel.: (819) 887-6381
Lime Mfr & Warehousing Services
N.A.I.C.S.: 327410

Graymont Limited Pavilion Plant (1)
-, PO Box 187, Cache Creek, V0K 1H0, BC, Canada
Tel.: (250) 457-6291
Lime Mfr & Distr
N.A.I.C.S.: 327410

Graymont Limited Pilot Peak Plant (1)
PO Box 2520, West Wendover, NV 89883
Tel.: (775) 483-5463
Lime Mfr & Distr
N.A.I.C.S.: 327410

Graymont Limited Pleasant Gap Plant (1)
965 E Coll Ave, Pleasant Gap, PA 16823
Tel.: (814) 357-4500
Warehousing & Transportation Services
N.A.I.C.S.: 493110

Graymont Limited Port Inland Plant (1)
181 W County Rd 432, Gulliver, MI 49840
Tel.: (906) 283-2900
Lime Mfr & Warehousing Services
N.A.I.C.S.: 327410

Graymont Limited Schuyler Falls Plant (1)
1024 Military Tpke, Plattsburgh, NY 12901
Tel.: (518) 563-0700
Lime Mfr
N.A.I.C.S.: 327410

Graymont Limited Summit Plant (1)
2018 - 9th Street, PO Box 40, Coleman, T0K 0M0, AB, Canada
Tel.: (403) 563-3374
Lime Mfr & Warehousing Services
N.A.I.C.S.: 327410

Graymont Limited Superior Plant (1)
800 Hill Ave, Superior, WI 54880
Tel.: (715) 392-5146
Lime Mfr & Distr
N.A.I.C.S.: 327410

Graymont Limited Te Kuiti Plant (1)
Beros Road, Te Kuiti, 3983, New Zealand
Tel.: (64) 92224338
Lime Mfr
N.A.I.C.S.: 327410

Graymont Western Lime Inc. (1)
206 N 6th Ave, West Bend, WI 53095
Tel.: (262) 334-3005
Sales Range: $10-24.9 Million
Emp.: 100
Lime Mfr
N.A.I.C.S.: 327410

Plant (Domestic):

Graymont Western Lime Inc. - Green Bay (2)
137 James St, Green Bay, WI 54303
Tel.: (920) 437-4054
Sales Range: Less than $1 Million
Emp.: 30
Lime Mfr
N.A.I.C.S.: 327410

McDonald's Lime - Otorohanga Plant (1)
498 Old Te Kuiti Rd RD 6, Otorohanga, 3976, New Zealand
Tel.: (64) 7 850 3540
Web Site: http://www.onlime.co.nz
Quality Burnt & Hydrated Lime Products Mfr
N.A.I.C.S.: 212312
Ian Cook *(Mgr-Sls & Mktg)*

GRAYS LEASING LIMITED
701-A 7th Floor City Towers 6-K Main Boulevard Gulberg II, Lahore, Pakistan
Tel.: (92) 4235770381
Web Site:
https://www.graysleasing.com
Year Founded: 1995
GRYL—(LAH)
Rev.: $107,183
Assets: $2,100,105
Liabilities: $1,615,693
Net Worth: $484,412
Earnings: ($13,344)
Emp.: 9
Fiscal Year-end: 06/30/19
Corporate Leasing & Financial Services
N.A.I.C.S.: 541611
Muhammad Tahir Butt *(CEO)*

GRAZIELLA GREEN POWER S.P.A
Via ERossi 9, 52100, Arezzo, Italy
Tel.: (39) 057532641
Web Site: http://www.graziellagreen.it
Electric Power Distr
N.A.I.C.S.: 221114
Gianni Gori *(Pres)*

Subsidiaries:

Magma Energy Italia S.R.L. (1)
Via Ernesto Rossi 9, 52100, Arezzo,
Italy (55%)
Tel.: (39) 05 753 2641
Web Site: https://www.magmaenergyitalia.it
Geothermal Electric Power Generation Services
N.A.I.C.S.: 221116

GRAZZIOTIN S.A.
Rua Valentin Grazziotin 77 Sao Cristovao, Passo Fundo, 99060-030, RS, Brazil
Tel.: (55) 8006447444 BR
Web Site:
https://www.grazziotin.com.br
Year Founded: 1879
CGRA4—(BRAZ)
Rev.: $139,480,474
Assets: $262,672,436
Liabilities: $80,449,047
Net Worth: $182,223,390
Earnings: $19,711,901
Fiscal Year-end: 12/31/23
Consumer Goods Distr
N.A.I.C.S.: 423620
Renata Grazziotin *(Chm, Co-Pres, CEO & Dir-IR)*

GRCS INC.
5F Palace Building 1-1-1 Marunouchi, Chiyoda-ku, Tokyo, 100-0005, Japan
Tel.: (81) 362729191
Web Site: https://www.grcs.co.jp
Year Founded: 2005
9250—(TKS)
Rev.: $18,387,843
Assets: $9,474,727
Liabilities: $8,034,357
Net Worth: $1,440,370
Earnings: ($1,850,017)
Emp.: 202
Fiscal Year-end: 11/30/23
Software Development Services
N.A.I.C.S.: 541511

Subsidiaries:

Valurate Co., Ltd. (1)
5F Palace Building 1-1-1 Marunouchi, Chiyoda-ku, Tokyo, 100-0005, Japan
Tel.: (81) 363271859
Web Site: https://valurate.co.jp
Emp.: 20
Visualization Services
N.A.I.C.S.: 541430

GREAT ATLANTIC RESOURCES CORP.
888 Dunsmuir Street Suite 888, Vancouver, V6C 3K4, BC, Canada
Tel.: (604) 488-3900 BC
Web Site:
https://www.greatatlantic.com
Year Founded: 1997
PH02—(DEU)
Assets: $319,044
Liabilities: $1,826,875
Net Worth: ($1,507,831)
Earnings: ($2,031,714)
Fiscal Year-end: 02/29/24
Oil & Gas Exploration Services
N.A.I.C.S.: 211120
Christopher Ross Anderson *(Pres & CEO)*

GREAT BOULDER RESOURCES LIMITED
Level 1 51 Colin Street, West Perth, 6005, WA, Australia
Tel.: (61) 893216037
Web Site:
https://www.greatboulder.com.au

GREAT CHINA HOLDINGS (HONG KONG) LIMITED

GBR—(ASX)
Rev.: $35,886
Assets: $14,966,620
Liabilities: $641,179
Net Worth: $14,325,441
Earnings: ($10,309,099)
Fiscal Year-end: 06/30/24
Gold Exploration Services
N.A.I.C.S.: 212220
Melanie Ross *(Sec)*

GREAT CANADIAN GAMING CORPORATION
39 Wynford Drive, North York, M3C 3K5, ON, Canada
Tel.: (604) 303-1000 BC
Web Site: https://greatcanadian.com
Year Founded: 1982
GC—(TSX)
Rev.: $1,037,359,344
Assets: $2,182,387,956
Liabilities: $1,676,411,268
Net Worth: $505,976,688
Earnings: $227,276,280
Emp.: 9,700
Fiscal Year-end: 12/31/19
Gaming & Casino Operations
N.A.I.C.S.: 721120
Peter Graham Meredith *(Chm)*

Subsidiaries:

Casino Nova Scotia (1)
1983 Upper Water St, Halifax, B3J 3Y5, NS, Canada
Tel.: (902) 425-7777
Web Site: https://casinonovascotia.com
Sales Range: $150-199.9 Million
Emp.: 800
Casino
N.A.I.C.S.: 721120

Flamboro Downs Limited (1)
PO Box 8220, Dundas, L9H6Y6, ON,
Canada (100%)
Tel.: (905) 627-3561
Racetracks
N.A.I.C.S.: 711212

Georgian Downs Limited (1)
7485 - 5th Side Road, Innisfil, L9S 3S1,
ON, Canada (100%)
Tel.: (705) 726-9400
Web Site: http://www.georgiandowns.com
Sales Range: $75-99.9 Million
Emp.: 150
Racetracks
N.A.I.C.S.: 711212

Great Canadian Casinos Inc. (1)
1708 Island Hwy, Victoria, V9B1H8, BC,
Canada (100%)
Tel.: (250) 391-0311
Web Site:
http://www.greatcanadiancasinos.com
Sales Range: $50-74.9 Million
Emp.: 200
Hotels & Motels
N.A.I.C.S.: 721110

Orangeville Raceway Limited (1)
17755 60 Ave, Surrey, V3S 1V3, BC, Canada
Tel.: (604) 576-9141
Web Site: http://www.elementscasino.com
Racetrack & Casino Operations Services
N.A.I.C.S.: 713990
Michael Kim *(Gen Mgr)*

TBC Teletheatre B.C. Ltd. (1)
17667 65 A Ave Ste 220, V3S 1Z8, Surrey,
BC, Canada (50%)
Tel.: (604) 574-6900
Web Site:
http://www.thebettingcompany.com
Sales Range: $50-74.9 Million
Emp.: 8
Racetracks
N.A.I.C.S.: 711212

GREAT CHINA HOLDINGS (HONG KONG) LIMITED
Suite 6403A-4 Central Plaza 18 Harbour Road, Wanchai, China (Hong Kong)

GREAT CHINA HOLDINGS (HONG KONG) LIMITED

Great China Holdings (Hong Kong) Limited—(Continued)
Tel.: (852) 22922500
Web Site:
  http://www.greatchinaproperties.com
0021—(HKG)
Rev.: $1,599,615
Assets: $281,540,145
Liabilities: $167,380,980
Net Worth: $114,159,165
Earnings: $6,760,178
Emp.: 55
Fiscal Year-end: 12/31/22
Investment Management Service
N.A.I.C.S.: 531390
Shih Tsai Huang *(Chm)*

GREAT CHINA METAL IND. CO., LTD.
No 293 805sung Chiang Rd, Tai Shang Dist, Taipei, Taiwan
Tel.: (886) 225030340
Web Site:
  http://www.greatchina.com.tw
Year Founded: 1990
9905—(TAI)
Rev.: $274,856,852
Assets: $351,498,989
Liabilities: $96,058,075
Net Worth: $255,440,914
Earnings: $14,335,491
Emp.: 814
Fiscal Year-end: 12/31/23
Aluminium Cans Mfr
N.A.I.C.S.: 332431
Carol Cheng *(Mgr-Exports Sls)*

Subsidiaries:

GCM Packaging (Vietnam) Co., Ltd. (1)
29 Dai Lo Doc Lap Vietnam Singapore Industrial Park, Thuan An, Binh Duong, Vietnam
Tel.: (84) 6503767494
Metal Tank Mfr
N.A.I.C.S.: 332420

Great China Metal Ind. Co., Ltd. - Fugang Plant (1)
No 155 Fulian Rd Yangmei, Taoyuan, Taiwan
Tel.: (886) 34721517
Packaging Container Mfr
N.A.I.C.S.: 332439

Great China Metal Ind. Co., Ltd. - Toufen Plant (1)
No 631 Jianfeng Rd, Toufen, Miaoli, Taiwan
Tel.: (886) 37624813
Packaging Container Mfr
N.A.I.C.S.: 332439

Huatong United (Nantong) Plastic Industry Co., Ltd. (1)
No 895 Xiushan Economic and Technological Development Zone, Haimen, 226100, Jiangsu, China
Tel.: (86) 51382225694
Web Site: https://www.htplastic.com.cn
Packaging Film Mfr
N.A.I.C.S.: 326112

Jinan United Can Co., Ltd. (1)
Mingshui Economic and Technological Development Zone, Zhangqiu City, Jinan, Shandong, China
Tel.: (86) 53181290398
Metal Tank Mfr
N.A.I.C.S.: 332420

Shanghai United Can Co., Ltd. (1)
No 89 Chexin Highway, Chedun Town Songjiang District, Shanghai, 201611, China
Tel.: (86) 2157602801
Web Site: https://www.suc.cn
Metal Tank Mfr
N.A.I.C.S.: 332420

GREAT CHINASOFT TECHNOLOGY CO., LTD.
21F Block B World Trade Center No 1588 Su Zhan Road, Mudu, Suzhou, 215101, China
Tel.: (86) 51266167989   CN
Web Site: https://www.gcstgroup.com
002453—(SSE)
Rev.: $378,707,940
Assets: $436,385,664
Liabilities: $202,329,036
Net Worth: $234,056,628
Earnings: ($25,950,132)
Emp.: 2,000
Fiscal Year-end: 12/31/22
Chemicals Mfr
N.A.I.C.S.: 325998
Minyi Zhang *(Exec VP)*

GREAT EAGLE HOLDINGS LIMITED
33/F Great Eagle Centre 23 Harbour Road, Wanchai, China (Hong Kong)
Tel.: (852) 28273668   BM
Web Site:
  http://www.greateagle.com.hk
Year Founded: 1989
0041—(OTCIQ)
Rev.: $1,135,485,322
Assets: $14,426,947,103
Liabilities: $5,330,006,390
Net Worth: $9,096,940,713
Earnings: ($52,502,205)
Emp.: 5,639
Fiscal Year-end: 12/31/22
Property Development & Investment Holding Company
N.A.I.C.S.: 551112
Ka Shui Lo *(Chm & Mng Dir)*

Subsidiaries:

Champion Global Services Limited (1)
Suite 3002-3 Great Eagle Centre 23 Harbour Road, Wanchai, China (Hong Kong)
Tel.: (852) 28284488
Web Site:
  https://www.championglobalservices.com
Procurement Services
N.A.I.C.S.: 541990
Jim Wilkinson *(Pres)*

Cordis Hong Kong Limited (1)
555 Shanghai St, Mongkok, Kowloon, China (Hong Kong)
Tel.: (852) 35523388
Web Site: http://www.cordishotels.com
Home Management Services
N.A.I.C.S.: 721110

Eagle Asset Management (CP) Limited (1)
Room 3008 30F Great Eagle Centre 23 Harbour Road, Wanchai, China (Hong Kong)
Tel.: (852) 28791288
Web Site: https://www.championreit.com
Sales Range: $50-74.9 Million
Emp.: 12
Asset Management Services
N.A.I.C.S.: 523999

Eaton Residences Management Limited (1)
4H Village Road, Happy Valley, Hong Kong, China (Hong Kong)
Tel.: (852) 31827000
Web Site:
  https://www.eatonresidences.com.hk
Residential Property
N.A.I.C.S.: 623990

Great Eagle Hotels (Auckland) Limited (1)
83 Symonds Street, Auckland, 1010, New Zealand
Tel.: (64) 93795132
Web Site: https://www.langhamhotels.com
Sales Range: $50-74.9 Million
Emp.: 350
Home Management Services
N.A.I.C.S.: 721110

Great Eagle Hotels (Canada) Limited (1)
33 Gerrard St W, Toronto, M5G 1Z4, ON, Canada
Tel.: (416) 595-1975
Home Management Services
N.A.I.C.S.: 721110
Josef Ebner *(VP)*

Great Eagle Hotels (New Zealand) Limited (1)
83 Symonds Street, Auckland, 1140, New Zealand
Tel.: (64) 93795132
Web Site: https://www.langhamhotels.com
Sales Range: $25-49.9 Million
Emp.: 200
Home Management Services
N.A.I.C.S.: 721110

Great Eagle Hotels (UK) Limited (1)
C/o Offshore Incorporations Limited Offshore Incorporations Centre, Road Town, Tortola, Virgin Islands (British)
Tel.: (284) 4948184
Home Management Services
N.A.I.C.S.: 561110

Grow On Development Limited (1)
33/F Great Eagle Centre 23 Harbour Road, Wanchai, China (Hong Kong)
Tel.: (852) 28273668
Web Site: https://www.greateagle.com.hk
Home Management Services
N.A.I.C.S.: 721110

Harvest Star International Limited (1)
8 Peking Road, Tsim Sha Tsui, Kowloon, China (Hong Kong)
Tel.: (852) 23751133
Home Management Services
N.A.I.C.S.: 721110
Shaun Campbell *(Mng Dir)*

Keysen Engineering Company Limited (1)
33rd Floor Great Eagle Centre 23rd Habour Road, Wanchai, China (Hong Kong)
Tel.: (852) 28273668
Web Site: https://www.greateagle.com.hk
Sales Range: $25-49.9 Million
Emp.: 50
Advertising Agencies
N.A.I.C.S.: 541810

Keysen Property Management Services Limited (1)
32/F Great Eagle Centre 23 Harbour Road, Wanchai, China (Hong Kong)
Tel.: (852) 28792118
Property Management Services
N.A.I.C.S.: 531311

Langham Hospitality Group Limited (1)
27/F Great Eagle Centre 23 Harbour Road, Wanchai, China (Hong Kong)
Tel.: (852) 21862388
Web Site:
  https://www.langhamhospitalitygroup.com
Hotel Services
N.A.I.C.S.: 721110
Lo Ka Shui *(Chm)*

Langham Hotels International Limited (1)
L59 Office Tower Langham Place Hotel 8 Argyle Street, Mongkok, Kowloon, China (Hong Kong)
Tel.: (852) 35523984
Web Site:
  http://www.langhamhospitality.com
Home Management Services
N.A.I.C.S.: 721110
Ka Shui Lo *(Chm)*

Pacific Eagle Holdings Corporation (1)
201 California St Ste 500, San Francisco, CA 94111
Tel.: (415) 780-7300
Web Site:
  https://www.pacificeagleholdings.com
Real Estate Investment & Development Services
N.A.I.C.S.: 531390
Lo Ka Shui *(Chm)*

Pacific Ygnacio Corporation (1)
500 Ygnacio Vly Rd Ste 340, Walnut Creek, CA 94596

INTERNATIONAL PUBLIC

Tel.: (925) 939-3275
Emp.: 6
Property Management Services
N.A.I.C.S.: 531312
Robin Jarreau *(Office Mgr)*

Selex Engineering Services Limited (1)
32/F Great Eagle Centre 23 Harbour Road, Wanchai, China (Hong Kong)
Tel.: (852) 25099168
Property Management Services
N.A.I.C.S.: 531311

The Great Eagle Properties Management Company, Limited (1)
33 F Great Eagle Centre 23 Harbour Road, Wanchai, China (Hong Kong)
Tel.: (852) 28273668
Web Site: http://www.greateagle.com.hk
Emp.: 500
Property Management Services
N.A.I.C.S.: 531311
Henry Tat Kai Leung *(Gen Mgr)*

The Langham Melbourne (1)
1 Southgate Avenue, Southbank, 3006, VIC, Australia
Tel.: (61) 386968888   (100%)
Web Site:
  http://melbourne.langhamhotels.com.au
Sales Range: $75-99.9 Million
Emp.: 500
Hotel Operations
N.A.I.C.S.: 721110
Ben Sington *(Mng Dir)*

Toptech (Shanghai) Building Material Ltd. (1)
Room 810 333 Huai Hai Road, Shanghai, 200021, China   (100%)
Tel.: (86) 2163268877
Web Site: http://www.toptech.com.hk
Sales Range: $25-49.9 Million
Emp.: 5
Building Material Dealers
N.A.I.C.S.: 444180

Toptech Co. Limited (1)
Suite 3002-3 Great Eagle Centre 23 Harbour Road, Wanchai, China (Hong Kong)
Tel.: (852) 28284488
Web Site: https://www.toptech.com.hk
Sales Range: $25-49.9 Million
Emp.: 50
Building Materials Distr
N.A.I.C.S.: 444110

GREAT EASTERN ENERGY CORPORATION LTD.
Signature Towers - A 14th Floor South City NH-8, Gurgaon, 122 001, Haryana, India
Tel.: (91) 1244559900
Web Site: http://www.geecl.com
GEEC—(AIM)
Rev.: $27,163,254
Assets: $145,024,663
Liabilities: $56,061,539
Net Worth: $88,963,124
Earnings: $1,392,858
Emp.: 100
Fiscal Year-end: 03/31/22
Coal-Bed Methane Exploration, Production & Distribution Services
N.A.I.C.S.: 212115
Yogendra Kumar Modi *(Founder & Chm)*

GREAT GROUP HOLDINGS LIMITED
Linjiang Industrial Zone Nanhuan Road, Licheng District, Quanzhou, Fujian, China
Tel.: (86) 59528050990   SG
Web Site: http://www.asia-great.com
Sales Range: $50-74.9 Million
Emp.: 1,927
Undergarment Mfr & Distr
N.A.I.C.S.: 315250
Wenwei Weng *(Exec Dir)*

GREAT HARVEST MAETA

AND PRIVATE COMPANIES

HOLDINGS LIMITED
12/Floor The Suns Group Centre 200 Gloucester Road, Wanchai, China (Hong Kong)
Tel.: (852) 28366801   KY
Web Site:
https://www.greatharvestmg.com
Year Founded: 2010
3683—(HKG)
Rev.: $18,233,000
Assets: $132,992,000
Liabilities: $102,255,000
Net Worth: $30,737,000
Earnings: ($17,109,000)
Emp.: 103
Fiscal Year-end: 03/31/23
Marine Transportation Services
N.A.I.C.S.: 483111
Kim Po Yan *(Co-Founder & Chm)*

GREAT LAKES GRAPHITE INC.   ON
Year Founded: 2004
GLKIF—(OTCIQ)
Sales Range: Less than $1 Million
Mineral Exploration Services
N.A.I.C.S.: 213114
Robert D. B. Suttie *(CFO)*

GREAT LITTLE BOX COMPANY LTD.
11300 Twigg Place Mitchell Island, Richmond, V6V 3C1, BC, Canada
Tel.: (604) 301-3700
Web Site: http://www.glbc.com
Year Founded: 1982
Rev.: $27,822,384
Emp.: 225
Custom & Stock Corrugated Boxes Mfr
N.A.I.C.S.: 322211
Brad Tindall *(Pres)*

GREAT NIGERIA INSURANCE PLC
8 Omo Osagie Street Off Awolowo Road, PO Box 2314, S/W Ikoyi, Lagos, Lagos, Nigeria
Tel.: (234) 1 3429161
Web Site:
http://www.greatnigeriaplc.com
Year Founded: 1960
Insurance & Financial Management Services
N.A.I.C.S.: 524298
Cecilia Olapeju Osipitan *(CEO & Mng Dir)*

GREAT NORTHERN MINERALS LIMITED
Level 1 33 Colin Street, West Perth, 6005, WA, Australia
Tel.: (61) 862140148   AU
Web Site:
https://www.greatnorthern.com.au
Year Founded: 1899
GNM—(ASX)
Rev.: $45,345
Assets: $2,503,007
Liabilities: $1,556,227
Net Worth: $946,780
Earnings: ($975,216)
Fiscal Year-end: 06/30/24
Natural Gas Extraction Services
N.A.I.C.S.: 211130
Cameron McLean *(CEO, CEO, Mng Dir & Mng Dir)*

Subsidiaries:

Greenpower Group Pty. Ltd. (1)
Locked Bag 5022, Parramatta, 2124, NSW, Australia
Tel.: (61) 299955468
Web Site: https://www.greenpower.gov.au
Electricity Distribution Services
N.A.I.C.S.: 221122

GREAT PANTHER MINING LIMITED
1330 - 200 Granville Street, Vancouver, V6C 1S4, BC, Canada
Tel.: (604) 608-1766   BC
Web Site:
https://www.greatpanther.com
Year Founded: 1965
GPL.GPR—(NYSEAMEX)
Rev.: $185,678,000
Assets: $264,043,000
Liabilities: $176,052,000
Net Worth: $87,991,000
Earnings: ($42,241,000)
Emp.: 1,094
Fiscal Year-end: 12/31/21
Silver & Other Precious Metal Ore Exploration & Mining
N.A.I.C.S.: 212220
Rob Henderson *(Pres & CEO)*

Subsidiaries:

Beadell Resources Limited (1)
Level 2 16 Ord Street, West Perth, 6005, WA, Australia
Tel.: (61) 894290800
Web Site:
http://www.beadellresources.com.au
Rev.: $164,735,683
Assets: $230,090,793
Liabilities: $103,287,705
Net Worth: $126,803,088
Earnings: $78,961,393
Emp.: 10
Fiscal Year-end: 12/31/2017
Gold Exploration
N.A.I.C.S.: 212220
Gregory Barrett *(CFO & Sec)*

GREAT PLAINS FORD SALES
206 Sims Avenue West, Weyburn, S4H 2H6, SK, Canada
Tel.: (306) 842-2645
Web Site:
http://www.greatplainsford.com
Year Founded: 1978
Sales Range: $10-24.9 Million
New & Used Car Dealers
N.A.I.C.S.: 441110
Keith Schlosser *(Mgr-Fin Svcs)*

GREAT PORTLAND ESTATES PLC
33 Cavendish Square, London, W1G 0PW, United Kingdom
Tel.: (44) 2076473000   UK
Web Site: https://www.gpe.co.uk
Year Founded: 1959
GPOR—(LSE)
Rev.: $120,158,220
Assets: $3,475,627,428
Liabilities: $798,746,676
Net Worth: $2,676,880,752
Earnings: ($274,123,668)
Emp.: 120
Fiscal Year-end: 03/31/21
Commercial Building Investor & Operator
N.A.I.C.S.: 236220
Toby Courtauld *(CEO)*

Subsidiaries:

Collin Estates Limited (1)
18 Margaret St, Newry, BT34 1DF, United Kingdom
Tel.: (44) 2830266602
Web Site: http://www.collinscollins.biz
Sales Range: $50-74.9 Million
Emp.: 8
Property Management Services
N.A.I.C.S.: 531312

G.P.E. (88/104 Bishopsgate) Limited (1)
33 Cavendish Sq, London, W1G 0PW, United Kingdom
Tel.: (44) 2076473000
Web Site: http://www.gpe.co.uk

Sales Range: $50-74.9 Million
Emp.: 80
Property Management Services
N.A.I.C.S.: 531311
Toby Courtauld *(Mng Dir)*

Knighton Estates Limited (1)
33 Cavendish Sq, London, W1G 0PW, United Kingdom
Tel.: (44) 2076473000
Web Site: http://www.gpe.com
Sales Range: $50-74.9 Million
Emp.: 85
Property Management Services
N.A.I.C.S.: 531312
Tony Courtald *(Mng Dir)*

Portman Square Properties Limited (1)
40 Portman Square, London, W1H 6LT, United Kingdom
Tel.: (44) 207 563 1400
Web Site: https://portmanestate.co.uk
Leasing Real Estate Services
N.A.I.C.S.: 531110
Oliver Fenn-Smith *(CEO)*

GREAT QUEST GOLD LTD.
10th Floor 595 Howe Street, Vancouver, V6C 2T5, BC, Canada
Tel.: (416) 849-9203
Web Site:
https://www.greatquest.com
GQMLF—(OTCIQ)
Rev.: $50
Assets: $4,206,214
Liabilities: $1,136,037
Net Worth: $3,070,177
Earnings: ($608,889)
Fiscal Year-end: 12/31/19
Phosphate Fertilizer Mining
N.A.I.C.S.: 212390
John A. Clarke *(Chm)*

GREAT RICH TECHNOLOGIES LTD
Room 01 21st Floor Prosper Commercial Building 9 Yin Chong Street, Kowloon, China (Hong Kong)
Emp.: 615
Optical Film Mfr & Distr
N.A.I.C.S.: 325992
Zhou Yongnan *(Chm & CEO)*

GREAT SOUTHERN COPPER PLC
Salisbury House London Wall, London, EC2M 5PS, United Kingdom
Tel.: (44) 2076389271   UK
Web Site: https://www.gscplc.com
Year Founded: 2020
GSCU—(LSE)
Assets: $4,795,506
Liabilities: $257,511
Net Worth: $4,537,995
Earnings: ($2,220,399)
Emp.: 6
Fiscal Year-end: 03/31/24
Support Activities for Nonmetallic Minerals (except Fuels) Mining
N.A.I.C.S.: 213115
Charles Bond *(Chm)*

GREAT SOUTHERN MINING LIMITED
Suite 4 213 Balcatta Road, Balcatta, 6021, WA, Australia
Tel.: (61) 892404111
Web Site: https://www.gsml.com.au
Year Founded: 2011
GSN—(ASX)
Rev.: $8,776
Assets: $9,161,535
Liabilities: $313,229
Net Worth: $8,848,306
Earnings: ($1,329,935)
Fiscal Year-end: 06/30/24
Base Metals & Gold Mining Services
N.A.I.C.S.: 212290

GREAT WALL MOTOR COMPANY LIMITED

John Terpu *(Exec Chm, Chm & Chm)*

GREAT TREE PHARMACY CO., LTD.
18F No 186 Fuxing Rd, Taoyuan Dist, Taoyuan, 330, Taiwan
Tel.: (886) 34333123
Web Site:
https://www.greattree.com.tw
Year Founded: 2001
6469—(TPE)
Rev.: $455,387,081
Assets: $316,370,228
Liabilities: $234,303,630
Net Worth: $82,066,598
Earnings: $21,902,354
Emp.: 2,147
Fiscal Year-end: 12/31/22
Pharmaceutical Product Mfr & Distr
N.A.I.C.S.: 325411
Ming-Lung Cheng *(Chm)*

GREAT WALL BUILDERS LTD.
Via Kennedy 16/a Cap, 40069, Bologna, Italy   TX
Web Site:
http://www.staarttechnologies.com
Year Founded: 2007
Fuel Efficiency & Emission Device Mfr
N.A.I.C.S.: 811198
Fabio Gobbo *(VP)*

GREAT WALL INTERNATIONAL ACG CO., LTD.
No 16 Ziwei East Road Hi-tech Zone, Chengdu, 310012, Sichuan, China
Tel.: (86) 57128806888
Web Site: http://www.000835.com
000835—(SSE)
Rev.: $363,108
Assets: $18,804,995
Liabilities: $177,311,465
Net Worth: ($158,506,470)
Earnings: ($69,496,056)
Emp.: 658
Fiscal Year-end: 12/31/21
Petroleum Product Mfr
N.A.I.C.S.: 324199
Tongsu Yuan *(Pres)*

GREAT WALL MOTOR COMPANY LIMITED
No 2266 South of Chaoyang Road, Baoding, 071000, Hebei, China
Tel.: (86) 3122196670
Web Site: https://www.gwm-global.com
GWLLF—(OTCIQ)
Rev.: $23,982,620,287
Assets: $27,867,507,833
Liabilities: $18,381,909,701
Net Worth: $9,485,598,132
Earnings: $972,365,519
Emp.: 82,439
Fiscal Year-end: 12/31/23
Automobile Parts Mfr
N.A.I.C.S.: 336110
Zhi Juan Yang *(Exec Dir)*

Subsidiaries:

American Haval Motor Technology, LLC (1)
3401 Del Amo Blvd, Torrance, CA 90503-1636
Tel.: (424) 488-4731
Emp.: 12
Automobile Parts & Motor Vehicle Whslr
N.A.I.C.S.: 423110
David Dean *(Mgr-IT)*

Baoding Great Machinery Company Limited (1)
NO 126 Yunshan Road, Baoding, 71051, Hebei, China
Tel.: (86) 312 333 6869
Web Site:
https://www.greatmachinery.com.cn

GREAT WALL MOTOR COMPANY LIMITED

Great Wall Motor Company Limited—(Continued)

Motor Vehicle Parts Mfr
N.A.I.C.S.: 336330

Baoding Nobo Rubber Production Co., Ltd. (1)
No 299 Chaoyang North Street, Baoding, China
Tel.: (86) 3128655865
Web Site: https://www.noborubber.net
Automotive Rubber Product Distr
N.A.I.C.S.: 423840

Baoding Nuobo Rubber Production Company Limited (1)
Great Wall Automobile Spare Parts Center 2288 South Street of Chaoyang, Baoding, China
Tel.: (86) 3128655865
Web Site: http://www.nuobo.net
Rubber Products Mfr
N.A.I.C.S.: 326299

Feige Intelligent Technology Co., Ltd. (1)
2 Floor Building No 51 Bantian No 3, Industrial Area Longgang District, Shenzhen, China
Tel.: (86) 75582338710
Web Site: https://www.smartfeigete.com
Biometric Product Mfr
N.A.I.C.S.: 334118
Cindy Hu *(Sls Mgr)*

Great Wall India Research & Development Private Limited (1)
Unit 4 7th Floor Navigator Building International Tech Park Bangalore, Whitefield Road, Bengaluru, 560066, Karnataka, India
Tel.: (91) 8068706900
Web Site: https://www.gwmidc.in
N.A.I.C.S.: 336211

Great Wall Japan Motor Co., Ltd. (1)
Shin-Yokohama Marubun Building 3-16-8 Shin-Yokohama, Kohoku-ku, Yokohama, 222-0033, Japan
Tel.: (81) 456249337
Web Site: https://www.gwm-japan.com
N.A.I.C.S.: 541720
Wang YuanLi *(CEO)*

Haval Motors Australia Pty. Ltd. (1)
745 Springvale Rd, Mulgrave, 3170, VIC, Australia
Tel.: (61) 800335132
Web Site: https://www.gwmanz.com
Automobile Mfr
N.A.I.C.S.: 336110

Haval Motors South Africa Proprietary Limited (1)
42 Saturn Crescent Linbro Business Park Extension 27, Sandton, 2146, Gauteng, South Africa
Tel.: (27) 108802366
Web Site: http://www.haval.co.za
Automobile Mfr
N.A.I.C.S.: 336110

Nobo Automotive Systems Germany GmbH (1)
Comotorstrasse 12, 66802, Uberherrn, Germany
Tel.: (49) 68364700
Web Site: https://nobo-eu.com
Automobile Equipment Mfr
N.A.I.C.S.: 336110

GREAT WALL MOVIE AND TELEVISION CO., LTD.

Great Wall Television Securities Department Wener West Road, Xixi Cultural & Creative Park, Hangzhou, 310013, China
Tel.: (86) 57185128967
2071—(SSE)
Rev.: $70,229,187
Assets: $194,867,856
Liabilities: $274,347,027
Net Worth: ($79,479,171)
Earnings: ($135,195,156)
Fiscal Year-end: 12/31/19
Television & Radio Broadcasting Services
N.A.I.C.S.: 516120

Ruijun Zhao *(Chm)*

GREAT WALL TERROIR HOLDINGS LIMITED

Suite 1402 14/F Henley Building No 5 Queen's Road Central, Central, China (Hong Kong)
Tel.: (852) 25223800   BM
Web Site: http://www.gwbrhk.com
0524—(HKG)
Rev.: $11,543,468
Assets: $11,169,893
Liabilities: $3,154,350
Net Worth: $8,015,543
Earnings: ($2,571,803)
Emp.: 25
Fiscal Year-end: 12/31/22
Information Technology Services
N.A.I.C.S.: 541512
Zhao Rui Yong *(Chm)*

Subsidiaries:

Relevant Marketing (HK) Limited (1)
Unit 11A Capella HTR 47 Hung To Road Kwun Tong, Kowloon, China (Hong Kong)
Tel.: (852) 8209 0880
Web Site: http://www.rmigroupasia.com
Insurance Services
N.A.I.C.S.: 524128
Kathy Wong *(Officer-IT)*

ZONE Limited (1)
Unit C 8/F Capella HTR 47 Hung To Road Kwun Tong, Kowloon, China (Hong Kong)
Tel.: (852) 58049663
Web Site: http://www.zonetel.com
Telecommunication Servicesb
N.A.I.C.S.: 517810

ZONE Telecom Pte Ltd (1)
1 Lorong 2 Toa Payoh 05-08, Singapore, 319637, Singapore
Tel.: (65) 6221 1511
Web Site: http://www.zonetel.com.sg
Telecommunication Servicesb
N.A.I.C.S.: 517810
Peter Ong *(Mng Dir)*

Subsidiary (Domestic):

Cybersite Services Pte Limited (2)
140 Paya Lebar Road 08-02 AZ, Paya Lebar, 409015, Singapore
Tel.: (65) 67272277
Web Site: http://www.cybersite.com.sg
Cloud Hosting Services
N.A.I.C.S.: 518210

GREAT WESTERN CORPORATION PTY. LTD.

Level 10 500 Queen Street, Brisbane, 4000, QLD, Australia
Tel.: (61) 730072600
Web Site:
http://www.greatwesterncorp.com.au
Sales Range: $125-149.9 Million
Emp.: 160
Holding Company Services
N.A.I.C.S.: 551112
Chris Thornton *(Mng Dir-Mfg)*

Subsidiaries:

Agpoint Australia (1)
Borrow Street, Freeling, 5372, SA, Australia
Tel.: (61) 8 8525 3500
Web Site: http://www.agpoint.com.au
Emp.: 30
Agricultural Machinery Distr
N.A.I.C.S.: 423820
Martin Schmid *(Mgr-Sls)*

Excel Agriculture (1)
74 - 92 Buckland Street, PO Box 665, Toowoomba, 4350, QLD, Australia
Tel.: (61) 7 4636 9100
Web Site: http://www.excelagr.com.au
Agriculture Machinery Mfr & Distr
N.A.I.C.S.: 333111
Brian Moran *(Mgr-Sls)*

Great Western Tillage (1)
94 Buckland Street, Toowoomba, 4350, QLD, Australia

Tel.: (61) 7 4636 9150
Web Site: http://www.gwtillage.com.au
Agricultural Machinery Distr
N.A.I.C.S.: 423820
Chris Thornton *(Mng Dir)*

Westco Truck Sales Pty Ltd. (1)
Taylor St, Wilsonton, Toowoomba, 4350, QLD, Australia
Tel.: (61) 7 4631 4000
Web Site:
http://www.westcotrucksales.com.au
New & Used Truck Dealer
N.A.I.C.S.: 441110

GREAT WESTERN EXPLORATION LIMITED

Level 2 160 St Georges Terrace, Perth, 6005, WA, Australia
Tel.: (61) 863112852
Web Site:
https://www.greatexploration.com.au
GTE—(ASX)
Rev.: $14,776
Assets: $9,203,766
Liabilities: $658,827
Net Worth: $8,544,939
Earnings: ($3,742,676)
Fiscal Year-end: 06/30/24
Gold & Nickel Exploration
N.A.I.C.S.: 213114
Jordan Ashton Luckett *(Mng Dir)*

GREAT WESTERN MINERALS GROUP LTD.

2121 Airport Drive Unit 201B, Saskatoon, S7L 6W5, SK, Canada
Tel.: (306) 659-4500   BC
Web Site: https://www.gwmg.ca
Year Founded: 1983
GWG—(TSXV)
Sales Range: $10-24.9 Million
Emp.: 83
Rare Metals Mining Services
N.A.I.C.S.: 212290
Vernon J. Kiss *(Sr VP-Bus & Corp Dev)*

Subsidiaries:

Great Western Technologies Inc. (1)
1826 Northwood Dr, Troy, MI 48084   (100%)
Tel.: (248) 293-3200
Web Site: http://www.greatwesterntech.com
Specialty Metal Manufacturing Facilities Owner & Operator
N.A.I.C.S.: 423510

Less Common Metals Limited (1)
Valley Road Business Park, Birkenhead, CH41 7EL, United Kingdom
Tel.: (44) 1516529747
Web Site: http://www.gwmg.ca
Rare Earth Alloys Mfr & Whslr
N.A.I.C.S.: 212290

GREAT WESTERN MINING CORPORATION PLC

1 Stokes Place St Stephen's Green, Dublin, DO2 DE03, Ireland
Tel.: (353) 16798727
Web Site:
https://www.greatwesternmining.com
8GW—(EUR)
Rev.: $4,760
Assets: $10,159,336
Liabilities: $679,499
Net Worth: $9,479,837
Earnings: ($1,022,600)
Emp.: 10
Fiscal Year-end: 12/31/23
Gold, Silver & Uranium Exploration & Mining Services
N.A.I.C.S.: 212220
Robert O'Connell *(Dir-US Ops)*

GREAT WORKS AB

Drottninggatan 89, 113 60, Stockholm, Sweden

Tel.: (46) 852 807 770
Web Site: http://www.greatworks.se
Year Founded: 1998
Sales Range: $10-24.9 Million
Emp.: 45
Advertising Services
N.A.I.C.S.: 541810
Asa Drake *(CFO)*

GREAT WORLD COMPANY HOLDINGS LIMITED

Room 1202 12th Floor Great Eagle Centre 23 Harbour Road, Wanchai, China (Hong Kong)
Tel.: (852) 2 910 0868   Ky
Web Site: http://www.gwchl.com
8003—(HKG)
Rev.: $41,742,313
Assets: $42,996,515
Liabilities: $33,187,844
Net Worth: $9,808,671
Earnings: ($6,372,773)
Emp.: 85
Fiscal Year-end: 03/31/22
Holding Company
N.A.I.C.S.: 551112
Yanqiang Zhang *(Compliance Officer)*

GREAT-SUN FOODS CO.,LTD.

No 13 Of Yujin Middle Rd, Longhu District, Shantou, 515041, Guangdong, China
Tel.: (86) 75488802291
Web Site:
https://www.greatsunfoods.com
Year Founded: 1992
603336—(SHG)
Rev.: $159,047,324
Assets: $249,781,049
Liabilities: $88,658,346
Net Worth: $161,122,703
Earnings: $6,656,069
Fiscal Year-end: 12/31/22
Vegetable Warehousing Services
N.A.I.C.S.: 493130
Junhui Huang *(Chm & Gen Mgr)*

Subsidiaries:

Fujian Honghui Fruit & Vegetable Co. Ltd. (1)
North Area Zhaoan Industry Zone, Zhangzhou, Fujian, China
Tel.: (86) 5963301878
Vegetable & Fruit Distr
N.A.I.C.S.: 424480

Guangzhou Jiajiamai Oils And Fats Co., Ltd. (1)
No 1 Yongda Rd, Huadong Town Huadu District, Guangzhou, Guangdong, China
Tel.: (86) 2086777008
Food Product Mfr & Distr
N.A.I.C.S.: 333241

Guangzhou Zhengtong Logistics Co. Ltd. (1)
Yongxing Road, Huadong Town Huadu District, Guangzhou, China
Tel.: (86) 2086777009
Vegetable & Fruit Distr
N.A.I.C.S.: 424480

Shanghai Honghui Food Co., Ltd. (1)
No 4598 Yanqian Road Qinggang Industry Zone Qingcun Town, Fenxian District, Shanghai, China
Tel.: (86) 2157567559
Vegetable & Fruit Distr
N.A.I.C.S.: 424480

Yantai Honghui Food Co., Ltd. (1)
Haihe Street Laiyang Economy Development Area, Shandong, China
Tel.: (86) 5353368393
Vegetable & Fruit Distr
N.A.I.C.S.: 424480

GREATCELL SOLAR LTD.

3 Dominion Place, Queanbeyan, 2620, NSW, Australia

Tel.: (61) 262991592
Web Site:
   http://www.greatcellsolar.com
Year Founded: 2004
GSL—(ASX)
Sales Range: $700-749.9 Million
Dye Solar Cell (DSC) Technology
N.A.I.C.S.: 334413
Andrew King *(Pres-Greatcell Solar Europe)*

Subsidiaries:

Dyesol Industries Pty. Ltd.   (1)
3 Dominion Place, Queanbeyan, 2620, NSW, Australia
Tel.: (61) 262991592
Web Site: http://www.dyesol.com
Emp.: 30
Solar Cell Mfr
N.A.I.C.S.: 334413
Richard Caldwell *(Mng Dir)*

Subsidiary (Domestic):

Dyesol Australia Pty. Ltd.   (2)
3 Dominion Pl, Queanbeyan, 2620, NSW, Australia
Tel.: (61) 262991592
Web Site: http://www.dyesol.com
Sales Range: $25-49.9 Million
Emp.: 30
Solar Cell Mfr
N.A.I.C.S.: 334413
Richard Caldwell *(Mng Dir)*

Subsidiary (Non-US):

Dyesol UK Ltd.   (2)
OpTIC Technium Ford William Morgan, St Asaph Bus Park, Saint Asaph, LL17 0JD, Denbighshire, United Kingdom
Tel.: (44) 1745535175
Web Site: http://www.dyesol.com
Sales Range: $25-49.9 Million
Emp.: 10
Solar Cell Mfr
N.A.I.C.S.: 334413

GREATECH TECHNOLOGY BERHAD

Plot 287 A Lengkok Kampung Jawa Satu, Bayan Lepas Fiz Phase 3, 11900, Pulau Penang, Malaysia
Tel.: (60) 46463260   MY
Web Site: https://www.greatech-group.com
Year Founded: 1997
GREATEC—(KLS)
Rev.: $115,600,949
Assets: $200,391,780
Liabilities: $76,208,705
Net Worth: $124,183,075
Earnings: $27,912,794
Emp.: 1,247
Fiscal Year-end: 12/31/22
Information Technology Services
N.A.I.C.S.: 541512
Thum Soon Fun *(Co-Sec)*

Subsidiaries:

Greatech Integration (M) Sdn. Bhd.   (1)
Plot 287 A Lengkok Kampung Jawa Satu, Bayan Lepas Fiz Phase 3, 11900, Penang, Malaysia
Tel.: (60) 46463260
Automation Product Mfr
N.A.I.C.S.: 334512

GREATEK ELECTRONICS INC.

No 136 Gongyi Rd, Zhunan, 350, Miaoli, Taiwan
Tel.: (886) 37638568
Web Site:
   https://www.greatek.com.tw
Year Founded: 1983
2441—(TAI)
Rev.: $443,771,068
Assets: $801,617,289
Liabilities: $97,447,624
Net Worth: $704,169,665

Earnings: $65,293,761
Emp.: 4,119
Fiscal Year-end: 12/31/23
Electronic Chip Probing & Mfr
N.A.I.C.S.: 334419
D. K. Tsai *(Bd of Dirs & Chm)*

Subsidiaries:

Greatek Electronics Inc. - Toufen Plant   (1)
No 9 ZhuongMin, Toufen, 35154, Miaoli, Taiwan
Tel.: (886) 37638568
Electrical Chip Distr
N.A.I.C.S.: 336320

GREATER BAY AREA DYNAMIC GROWTH HOLDINGS LIMITED

Room 3401 34th Floor Hopewell Centre 183 Queens Road East, Wanchai, China (Hong Kong)
Tel.: (852) 21219988   BM
Web Site:
   http://www.gbadynamic.com
1189—(HKG)
Rev.: $6,788,228
Assets: $245,484,930
Liabilities: $8,474,033
Net Worth: $237,010,898
Earnings: ($3,242,580)
Emp.: 334
Fiscal Year-end: 12/31/22
Home Management Services
N.A.I.C.S.: 721110
Chung Sun Tam *(Chm)*

Subsidiaries:

Rosedale Hotel Group Limited   (1)
26/F 250 Hennessy 250 Hennessy Road, Wanchai, China (Hong Kong)
Tel.: (852) 2 831 8228
Web Site: https://www.rosedalehotels.com
Hotel Services
N.A.I.C.S.: 721110
Louis Cheng *(Gen Mgr-Hotels)*

Rosedale Hotel Kowloon Limited   (1)
86 Tai Kok Tsui Rd, Kowloon, China (Hong Kong)
Tel.: (852) 3919 8888
Sales Range: $10-24.9 Million
Emp.: 80
Home Management Services
N.A.I.C.S.: 721110
Louis Cheng *(Gen Mgr)*

Rosedale Hotel Shenyang Company Limited   (1)
99 North Station Road, Shenhe District, Shenyang, 110013, Liaoning, China
Tel.: (86) 2422532828
Hotel Services
N.A.I.C.S.: 721110

Rosedale Park Limited   (1)
8 Shelter St, Causeway Bay, China (Hong Kong)
Tel.: (852) 21278888
Web Site: http://www.rosedale.com.hk
Sales Range: $25-49.9 Million
Emp.: 20
Home Management Services
N.A.I.C.S.: 721110

GREATER CHINA FINANCIAL HOLDINGS LTD.

Suites 3001-11 Tower Two Times Square 1 Matheson Street, Causeway Bay, China (Hong Kong)
Tel.: (852) 31517919   BM
0431—(HKG)
Rev.: $25,748,753
Assets: $124,344,120
Liabilities: $128,871,773
Net Worth: ($4,527,653)
Earnings: ($50,735,438)
Emp.: 122
Fiscal Year-end: 12/31/22
Holding Company
N.A.I.C.S.: 551112

Kequan Liu *(Chm)*

GREATER THAN AB

Karlavagen 60, 11449, Stockholm, Sweden
Tel.: (46) 855593200   SE
Web Site: https://www.greaterthan.eu
Year Founded: 2014
GREAT—(OMX)
Rev.: $2,806,401
Assets: $5,078,722
Liabilities: $1,640,955
Net Worth: $3,437,767
Earnings: ($3,198,523)
Emp.: 40
Fiscal Year-end: 12/31/23
Automotive Insurance Price Risk Artificial Intelligence Solutions Developer & Services
N.A.I.C.S.: 518210
Markus Waldenstrom *(CFO)*

GREATIME INTERNATIONAL HOLDINGS LIMITED

4408 44/F 183 Queen's Road East, Hopewell Centre Wan Chai, Hong Kong, China (Hong Kong)
Tel.: (852) 28181982
Web Site:
   http://www.greatimeintl.com
0844—(HKG)
Rev.: $65,853,778
Assets: $71,056,019
Liabilities: $33,369,289
Net Worth: $37,686,730
Earnings: ($21,902)
Emp.: 2,076
Fiscal Year-end: 12/31/22
Innerwear Mfr
N.A.I.C.S.: 315250
Shao Hua Wang *(Gen Mgr-Zhucheng Eternal Knitting Company Limited)*

Subsidiaries:

Zhucheng Eternal Knitting Co., Limited   (1)
No 102 Renmin Dong Road, Zhucheng, Shandong, China
Tel.: (86) 5366089808
Web Site: http://www.eternal-garment.com
Emp.: 1,000
Apparel Mfr & Distr
N.A.I.C.S.: 315250
Li Zhou *(Deputy Gen Mgr)*

GREATLAND GOLD PLC

Salisbury House, London Wall, London, EC2M 5PS, United Kingdom
Tel.: (44) 2037094900   UK
Web Site:
   https://www.greatlandgold.com
GGP—(AIM)
Assets: $113,700,444
Liabilities: $61,931,100
Net Worth: $51,769,344
Earnings: ($18,794,193)
Emp.: 17
Fiscal Year-end: 06/30/24
Explorer -Natural Resources
N.A.I.C.S.: 213115
Stephen F. Ronaldson *(Sec)*

GREATOO INTELLIGENT EQUIPMENT INC.

middle section of No 5 Road Jiedong Economic Development Zone, east side of Renmin Avenue Jiedong District, Jieyang, 515500, Guangdong, China
Tel.: (86) 6633271838
Web Site: http://www.greatoo.com
Year Founded: 2001
002031—(SSE)
Rev.: $138,969,324
Assets: $616,037,292
Liabilities: $269,753,328
Net Worth: $346,283,964

Earnings: $5,307,120
Fiscal Year-end: 12/31/22
Automobile Tire Equipment Mfr
N.A.I.C.S.: 326211
Wu Chaozhong *(Chm)*

Subsidiaries:

Greatoo (Guangzhou) Robot & Intelligent Manufacturing Co., Ltd.   (1)
First floor B2 of Technology Enterprise Accelerator, No 11 of Kaiyuan Avenue Huangpu District, Guangzhou, 510700, China
Tel.: (86) 2032066366
Industrial Equipment Mfr
N.A.I.C.S.: 333248

Greatoo (India) Private Co., Ltd.   (1)
No 59/2 First Cross Street Chengalpattu Bazaar, 8th Avenue Mahindra World City, Chengalpattu, 603002, India
Tel.: (91) 4437471900
Industrial Equipment Distr
N.A.I.C.S.: 423830

GREATSTAR GROUP CO., LTD.

No 35 Jiuhuan Road, Jiubao Town, Hangzhou, 310019, Zhejiang, China
Tel.: (86) 571 8160 1388
Web Site:
   http://www.en.greatstargroup.com
Year Founded: 1993
Holding Company
N.A.I.C.S.: 551112
Champin Chou *(Chm & CEO)*

Subsidiaries:

Hangcha Group Co., Ltd.   (1)
666 Xiangfu Road, Hangzhou, 311305, Zhejiang, China
Tel.: (86) 57188926735
Web Site: https://www.hcforklift.com
Rev.: $2,023,503,263
Assets: $1,641,778,211
Liabilities: $685,608,483
Net Worth: $956,169,728
Earnings: $138,680,507
Emp.: 1,011
Fiscal Year-end: 12/31/2022
Forklift Mfr & Distr
N.A.I.C.S.: 333924

Subsidiary (US):

HC Forklift America Corporation   (2)
10405-A Granite St, Charlotte, NC 28273
Tel.: (980) 888-8335
Web Site: http://www.hcforkliftamerica.com
Forklift Truck Distr
N.A.I.C.S.: 423830
Dana Hopkins *(Dir-Dealer Dev)*

Hangzhou Great Star Industrial Co., Ltd.   (1)
35 Jiuhuan Road, Shangcheng District, Hangzhou, 310000, Zhejiang, China
Tel.: (86) 57181601388
Web Site: https://en.greatstartools.com
Rev.: $1,770,470,676
Assets: $2,608,568,820
Liabilities: $695,684,808
Net Worth: $1,912,884,012
Earnings: $199,306,224
Emp.: 13,000
Fiscal Year-end: 12/31/2022
Hand Tool Mfr & Whslr
N.A.I.C.S.: 332216
Qiu Jianping *(Chm)*

Subsidiary (Non-US):

Joh. Friedrich Behrens AG   (2)
Bogenstrasse 4345, 22926, Ahrensburg, Germany
Tel.: (49) 4102780
Web Site: https://www.behrens.ag
Sales Range: Less than $1 Million
Machine Tool Mfr & Distr
N.A.I.C.S.: 333517
Tobias Fischer-Zernin *(Member-Mgmt Bd)*

Subsidiary (US):

Shop-Vac Corporation   (2)

GREATSTAR GROUP CO., LTD.

GreatStar Group Co., Ltd.—(Continued)

2323 Reach Rd, Williamsport, PA 17701-5579
Tel.: (570) 326-0502
Web Site: http://www.shopvac.com
Rev.: $48,000,000
Emp.: 275
Mfr of Wet/Dry Utility Vacuum Cleaners & Portable Vacuum Cleaners
N.A.I.C.S.: 333310
Jonathan Miller *(Pres)*

Lista Holding AG **(1)**
Fabrikstrasse 1, 8586, Erlen, Switzerland
Tel.: (41) 716492111
Web Site: http://www.lista.com
Holding Company
N.A.I.C.S.: 551112

Subsidiary (Domestic):

Lista AG **(2)**
Fabrikstrasse 1, Erlen, 8586, Switzerland **(100%)**
Tel.: (41) 71 649 21 11
Web Site: http://www.lista.com
Storage Equipment for Industrial & Office Use
N.A.I.C.S.: 337127

Subsidiary (Non-US):

Lista Austria GmbH **(2)**
Prager Strasse 245, A-1210, Vienna, Austria **(100%)**
Tel.: (43) 1 291 20
Web Site: http://www.lista.com
Workspace Equipment & Drawer Systems Sls
N.A.I.C.S.: 423830

Lista GmbH **(2)**
Bruckenstrasse 1, 51702, Bergneustadt, Germany
Tel.: (49) 2261 40 30
Web Site: http://www.lista.com
Drawer Systems & Workspace Equipment Mfr & Whslr
N.A.I.C.S.: 332999

Lista Italia s.r.l. **(2)**
Viale Lombardia 9, Colzate, 24020, Bergamo, Italy **(100%)**
Tel.: (39) 02 935 70 196
Web Site: http://www.lista.com
Drawer Systems & Workspace Equipment Sls
N.A.I.C.S.: 423830

Lista Sistemas de Almacenaje, S.A. **(2)**
Edificio CIM Valles planta 9, E 08130, Santa Perpetua de Mogoda, Spain **(100%)**
Tel.: (34) 938 575 927
Web Site: http://www.lista.com
Workspace Equipment & Drawer Systems Sls
N.A.I.C.S.: 423830

Lista UK Ltd. **(2)**
14 Warren Yard Warren Farm Office Village, Wolverton Mill, Milton Keynes, MK12 5NW, United Kingdom **(100%)**
Tel.: (44) 1 908 222 333
Web Site: http://www.lista.com
Workspace Equipment & Drawer Systems Sls
N.A.I.C.S.: 423830

GREATTOWN HOLDINGS LTD.

Area A 5F Block 1 No 1116 Hongsong East Road, Minhang District, Shanghai, 201103, China
Tel.: (86) 2162470088
Web Site: http://www.greattown.cn
Year Founded: 1996
600094—(SHG)
Rev.: $1,033,540,504
Assets: $4,861,861,884
Liabilities: $3,077,312,289
Net Worth: $1,784,549,595
Earnings: $24,002,545
Fiscal Year-end: 12/31/22
Holding Company
N.A.I.C.S.: 551112
Peidi Yu *(Chm)*

GREATVIEW ASEPTIC PACKAGING COMPANY LIMITED

A4-2F No 14 Jiuxianqiao Road, Chaoyang District, Beijing, 100015, China
Tel.: (86) 1064356368
Web Site: http://www.greatviewpack.com
0468—(HKG)
Rev.: $552,756,344
Assets: $600,863,281
Liabilities: $233,025,952
Net Worth: $367,837,330
Earnings: $25,608,539
Emp.: 1,780
Fiscal Year-end: 12/31/22
Soft Drinks Mfr
N.A.I.C.S.: 312111
Jeff Hua Bi *(CEO)*

Subsidiaries:

Greatview Aseptic Packaging Europe GmbH **(1)**
Bankstrasse 4, 8400, Winterthur, Switzerland
Tel.: (41) 52 268 1888
Web Site: http://greatviewpack.com
Sales Range: $50-74.9 Million
Emp.: 10
Aseptic Package Material Mfr & Distr
N.A.I.C.S.: 322220

Greatview Aseptic Packaging Manufacturing GmbH **(1)**
Orionstrasse 8, Kabelsketal, 06184, Halle, Germany
Tel.: (49) 3452 799 8500
Web Site: http://www.greatviewpack.com
Emp.: 160
Aseptic Package Material Mfr
N.A.I.C.S.: 322220

Greatview Beijing Trading Co., Ltd. **(1)**
A4-2F No 14 Jiuxianqiao Road, Chaoyang District, Beijing, 100015, China
Tel.: (86) 1064356368
Grocery & Food Related Product Distr
N.A.I.C.S.: 424490

GREATWALLE INC.

18/F So Tao Centre 11-15 Kwai Sau Road, Kwai Chung, NT, China (Hong Kong)
Tel.: (852) 2 922 9000
Web Site: http://www.kingforce.com.hk
8315—(HKG)
Rev.: $7,344,895
Assets: $13,043,360
Liabilities: $9,053,364
Net Worth: $3,989,996
Earnings: ($5,074,331)
Emp.: 1,347
Fiscal Year-end: 03/31/22
Holding Company
N.A.I.C.S.: 551112

Subsidiaries:

King Force Security Limited **(1)**
18/F So Tao Centre 11-15 Kwai Sau Road, Kwai Chung, China (Hong Kong)
Tel.: (852) 29229000
Security Guard Services
N.A.I.C.S.: 561612

GREAVES COTTON LTD

No 1A 5th Floor Tower 3 Equinox Business Park, LBS Marg Kurla W, Mumbai, 400070, India
Tel.: (91) 2241711700
Web Site: https://www.greavescotton.com
GREAVESCOT—(NSE)
Rev.: $205,941,645
Assets: $176,145,060
Liabilities: $69,332,445
Net Worth: $106,812,615
Earnings: ($2,563,470)
Emp.: 1,101
Fiscal Year-end: 03/31/21

Engineering & Industrial Products Mfr
N.A.I.C.S.: 541330
Sanjay Behl *(CEO & Exec Dir)*

Subsidiaries:

Greaves Technologies Inc. **(1)**
2675 Bellingham Rd, Troy, MI 48083
Tel.: (248) 571-5168
Web Site: https://greavestechnologies.com
Engineering Research & Development Services
N.A.I.C.S.: 541715

Greaves Technologies Limited **(1)**
9 Sambandam Gardens First Floor Taramani Link Rd, Velachery, Chennai, 600042, India
Tel.: (91) 7401009191
Web Site: https://greavestechnologies.com
Information Technology Services
N.A.I.C.S.: 541512

GRECIAN MAGNESITE S.A

45 Michalacopoulou str, 115 28, Athens, Greece
Tel.: (30) 210 7240446
Web Site: http://www.grecianmagnesite.com
Year Founded: 1959
Sales Range: $75-99.9 Million
Emp.: 340
Magnesite Ore Mining & Production & Distr of Magnesia Products
N.A.I.C.S.: 212290
P. Vetoulas *(Mgr-Mktg & Sls)*

Subsidiaries:

Akdeniz Mineral Kaynaklari A.S **(1)**
Cumhuriyet Caddesi Selbasi Sokak No 14, Harbiye, 34373, Istanbul, Turkiye
Tel.: (90) 212 343 41 08
Web Site: http://www.akdenizmineral.com.tr
Magnesite Ore Mining Services
N.A.I.C.S.: 212290
Orhan Dogancay *(Plant Mgr)*

Magnesitas Navarras S.A. **(1)**
Avda Roncesvalles s/n, 31630, Navarra, Spain
Tel.: (34) 948 421 617
Web Site: http://www.magnesitasnavarras.es
Magnesite Ore Mining Services
N.A.I.C.S.: 212323
Javier Creixell Catalan *(Dir Gen)*

Subsidiary (Non-US):

MAGNA REFRACTARIOS MEXICO SA de CV **(2)**
C Sta Maria Piso 10 Bld Diaz Ordaz No 130, Rincon de Sta Maria, Monterrey, 64 650, Nuevo Leon, Mexico
Tel.: (52) 81 8338 1421
Magnesite Ore Mining Services
N.A.I.C.S.: 212323
Paulino Faz *(Project Mgr)*

MAGNA REFRACTORIES INC. **(2)**
8 3eme rang O, Saint Simon, J0H 1Y4, QC, Canada
Tel.: (514) 777-6113
Magnesite Ore Mining Services
N.A.I.C.S.: 212323

Van Mannekus & Co. B.V. **(1)**
Nieuwe Waterwegstraat 45, NL 3115 HE, Schiedam, Netherlands **(50%)**
Tel.: (31) 10 40 91 500
Web Site: http://www.mannekus.com
Sales Range: $25-49.9 Million
Emp.: 35
Magnesium Oxide Processor & Trader
N.A.I.C.S.: 325998
Timothee Le Moulec *(Dir-Sls)*

Subsidiary (Domestic):

Van Mannekus Universal V.O.F. **(2)**
Oudlandsedijk 8, Oudenbosch, NL 4731 TB, Netherlands
Tel.: (31) 165312740
Web Site: http://www.mannekus.com
Sales Range: $25-49.9 Million
Emp.: 8
Magnesium Oxide Processor & Distr

N.A.I.C.S.: 325998
Alexander Dietz *(Mgr-Fin)*

GREE ELECTRIC APPLIANCES, INC. OF ZHUHAI

West Jinji Rd, Qianshan, Zhuhai, 519070, Guangdong, China
Tel.: (86) 7568614883
Web Site: https://global.gree.com
Year Founded: 1991
000651—(SSE)
Rev.: $26,697,154,068
Assets: $49,845,476,304
Liabilities: $35,542,078,884
Net Worth: $14,303,397,420
Earnings: $3,440,729,448
Emp.: 90,000
Fiscal Year-end: 12/31/22
Air Conditioner & Appliance Mfr
N.A.I.C.S.: 335220
Mingzhu Dong *(Chm & Pres)*

Subsidiaries:

Gree Air Conditioner (Vietnam) Co., Ltd. **(1)**
Tel.: (84) 2862876538
Web Site: http://www.gree.com.vn
Air Conditioner Mfr
N.A.I.C.S.: 333415

Gree Aircons LLP **(1)**
Tel.: (91) 9385351292
Air Conditioner Mfr
N.A.I.C.S.: 333415

Gree Electric (Thailand) Co., Ltd. **(1)**
1988 Phatthanakan Road, Suan Luang Subdistrict Suan Luang District, Bangkok, 10250, Thailand
Tel.: (66) 272296615
Web Site: https://www.greethailand.com
Home Appliance Whslr
N.A.I.C.S.: 423620

Gree Electric Appliances do Brasil Ltda **(1)**
Air Conditioner Mfr
N.A.I.C.S.: 333415

Gree GmbH **(1)**
Industriestrasse 12, St Margarethen, 8321, Raaba, Austria
Tel.: (43) 311540457
Web Site: http://www.greeaustria.at
Air Conditioner Mfr
N.A.I.C.S.: 333415

Gree Inc. **(1)**
114 5th Floor No 217 Section 1 Tiding Avenue, Neihu District, Taipei, Taiwan
Tel.: (886) 227962511
Web Site: http://www.gree.com.tw
Air Conditioner Mfr
N.A.I.C.S.: 333415

Gree Malaysia Sdn. Bhd. **(1)**
No 1 Lorong Pedada 16, 96000, Sibu, Sarawak, Malaysia
Tel.: (60) 84353588
Air Conditioner Mfr.
N.A.I.C.S.: 333415

Gree Products France SAS **(1)**
14 rue de l Aqueduc, 75010, Paris, France
Tel.: (33) 187651656
Web Site: http://www.greeproducts.fr
Air Conditioner Mfr
N.A.I.C.S.: 333415

Gree Products, S.L. **(1)**
Tel.: (34) 932687586
Web Site: http://www.greeproducts.es
Air Conditioner Mfr & Distr
N.A.I.C.S.: 333415

GreeIndia Air conditioners & Appliances Ltd. **(1)**
B- 803 Advant Navis Business IT Park Noida Greater Noida Expressway, Sector 142 Gautam Budh Nagar, Noida, 201305, Uttar Pradesh, India
Web Site: http://www.greeind.com
Air Conditioner Mfr
N.A.I.C.S.: 333415

Greemak Group DOO **(1)**
Tel.: (389) 23079020

Web Site: http://www.gree.com.mk
Air Conditioner Mfr
N.A.I.C.S.: 333415

Imex Group Co. Ltd. (1)
Tbilisi highway 25, Yerevan, 52, Armenia
Tel.: (374) 1 155 5525
Web Site: https://idealsystem.am
Construction Materials Distr
N.A.I.C.S.: 423220

Zhuhai Kaibang Motor Manufacture Co., Ltd. (1)
No 6 West Longshan 2rd Road, Doumen Town Doumen District, Zhuhai, China
Tel.: (86) 7565790630
Web Site: https://www.gree-kb.com
Motor Parts Mfr & Distr
N.A.I.C.S.: 336320

GREE GROUP CO., LTD.
Beiling Industrial Zone, Zhuhai, 519020, Guangdong, China
Tel.: (86) 7568131888
Web Site: http://www.gree.cn
Holding Company
N.A.I.C.S.: 551112

Subsidiaries:

Gree Household Electric Appliances Co., Ltd. (1)
No 2 Jinwan Road, Zhongshan, Zhongshan, Guangdong, China
Tel.: (86) 760 6686593
Household Electrical Appliance Mfr
N.A.I.C.S.: 335220

GREE INC.
Roppongi Hills Gate Tower 6-11-1, Roppongi, Minato-ku, Tokyo, Japan
Tel.: (81) 335603823
Web Site: https://corp.gree.net
Year Founded: 2004
3632—(TKS)
Rev.: $381,341,980
Assets: $801,061,360
Liabilities: $206,864,760
Net Worth: $594,196,600
Earnings: $28,798,600
Emp.: 1,597
Fiscal Year-end: 06/30/24
Social Networking Services
N.A.I.C.S.: 541519
Yoshikazu Tanaka *(Co-Founder, Chm & CEO)*

Subsidiaries:

Atlantis Co., Ltd. (1)
Roppongi Hills Mori Tower 12F 6-10-1 Roppongi, Minato-ku, Tokyo, 106-6112, Japan
Tel.: (81) 3 5770 9547
Web Site: http://www.atlantiss.jp
Online Marketing Services
N.A.I.C.S.: 541613

ExPlay, Inc. (1)
1-6-35 Central, Aoba-ku, Sendai, 980-0021, Miyagi, Japan
Tel.: (81) 22 713 6857
Web Site: https://explay.co.jp
Emp.: 180
Customer Experience Academy Services
N.A.I.C.S.: 611430

Glossom, Inc. (1)
6-18-1 Nishi-Shinjuku Tower 13th Floor, Sumitomo Realty and Development Shinjuku Central Park Shinjuku-ku, Tokyo, 160-0023, Japan
Tel.: (81) 35 770 9547
Web Site: https://glossom.co.jp
Emp.: 140
Marketing Services
N.A.I.C.S.: 541613

aumo, Inc. (1)
6-18-1 Nishi-Shinjuku Tower 13F, Sumitomo Realty and Development Shinjuku Central Park Shinjuku-ku, Tokyo, 160-0023, Japan
Tel.: (81) 35 770 9659
Web Site: https://aumo.co.jp
Software Development Services
N.A.I.C.S.: 541511

GREE REAL ESTATE CO., LTD.
No 213 Shihua West Road Jida, Zhuhai, 519020, China
Tel.: (86) 7568860606
Web Site: https://www.greedc.com
Year Founded: 1999
600185—(SHG)
Rev.: $568,146,220
Assets: $4,248,325,397
Liabilities: $3,359,085,781
Net Worth: $889,239,616
Earnings: ($288,848,809)
Fiscal Year-end: 12/31/22
Real Estate Development Services
N.A.I.C.S.: 531390
Chen Hui *(Chm)*

GREEK NATIONAL TOURIST ORGANIZATION
7 An Tsoha street, Ampelokipoi, 11521, Athens, Greece
Tel.: (30) 2108707000
Web Site: http://www.visitgreece.gr
Year Founded: 1950
Tourism Promotion & Services
N.A.I.C.S.: 813910
Elizabeth Chatzinikolaou *(Pres)*

Subsidiaries:

Greek National Tourist Organization (1)
305E47th St, New York, NY 10017
Tel.: (212) 421-5777
Web Site: http://www.gnto.gr
Sales Range: Less than $1 Million
Emp.: 10
Travel Information & Services
N.A.I.C.S.: 561591
Fay Georgousis *(Dir-PR & Mktg)*

GREEK ORGANISATION OF FOOTBALL PROGNOSTICS S.A.
Athinon Av 112, 10442, Athens, 10442, Greece
Tel.: (30) 2105798930   GR
Web Site: https://www.opap.gr
Year Founded: 1958
Rev.: $1,769,460,287
Assets: $2,001,544,428
Liabilities: $1,132,794,747
Net Worth: $868,749,681
Earnings: $166,193,831
Emp.: 1,493
Fiscal Year-end: 12/31/18
Lottery & Sports Betting Games Operator & Manager
N.A.I.C.S.: 713290
Spyros Fokas *(Vice Chm)*

Subsidiaries:

Opap Services S.A. (1)
62 Kifisou St Peristeri, Athens, 12132, Greece
Tel.: (30) 2103711100
Lottery Operations Management Services
N.A.I.C.S.: 713290

Tora Wallet Single Member S.A. (1)
Athens Avenue 112, 104 42, Athens, Greece
Tel.: (30) 2106475600
Web Site: https://www.tora.gr
Financial Transaction Services
N.A.I.C.S.: 522320

GREELEY CONTAINMENT AND REWORK INC.
200 Baseline Road East, Bowmanville, L1C 1A2, ON, Canada
Tel.: (905) 623-5678
Web Site: https://www.greeley.ca
Year Founded: 1990
Rev.: $10,032,000
Emp.: 150
Business Services
N.A.I.C.S.: 561499

GREEN & SMART HOLDINGS PLC
73-M Jalan Medan Setia 1 Bukit Damansara, 50490, Kuala Lumpur, Malaysia
Tel.: (60) 20950024   JE
Web Site: http://www.greennsmart.com.my
Year Founded: 2015
Rev.: $462,991
Assets: $24,003,599
Liabilities: $11,678,981
Net Worth: $12,324,618
Earnings: ($3,288,105)
Fiscal Year-end: 12/31/18
Waste Water Treatment Services
N.A.I.C.S.: 221320
Saravanan Rasaratnam *(CEO)*

GREEN 2 BLUE ENERGY CORP.
192 - 198 East Fanger Street, Vancouver, V6C 2V6, BC, Canada
Tel.: (778) 775-4985
Web Site: https://www.g2benergy.com
Year Founded: 2014
GTOO—(CNSX)
Rev.: $1,067,835
Assets: $5,741,964
Liabilities: $5,281,438
Net Worth: $460,527
Earnings: ($1,915,490)
Fiscal Year-end: 06/30/23
Wood Pellet Mfr & Distr
N.A.I.C.S.: 321114

GREEN AGREVOLUTION PVT LTD.
MIG-33, Lohiyanagar, Kankarbagh, Patna,, Bihar, 800020, India
Tel.: (91) 8001036110
Web Site: https://agrevolution.in
IT Services
N.A.I.C.S.: 513210
Shashank Kumar *(Co-Founder & CEO)*

Subsidiaries:

Freshtrop Fruits Ltd. (1)
A-603 Shapath IV Opp Karnavati Club S G Road, Ahmedabad, 380015, Gujarat, India
Tel.: (91) 7940307050
Web Site: https://www.freshtrop.com
Rev.: $13,104,411
Assets: $19,418,273
Liabilities: $2,400,122
Net Worth: $17,018,150
Earnings: $7,188,077
Emp.: 150
Fiscal Year-end: 03/31/2024
Fresh Fruit Distr
N.A.I.C.S.: 424480
Ashok V. Motiani *(Founder, Chm & Mng Dir)*

Plant (Domestic):

Freshtrop Fruits Ltd. - Plant - II (2)
Survey No 1366 Savlej-Wayfale Road Post Siddhewadi, Sangli, Tasgaon, 416 311, Maharashtra, India
Tel.: (91) 2346 254871
Packaged Fruits Whslr
N.A.I.C.S.: 424480

GREEN AQUA COMPANY SGPS, S.A.
Rua Eng Clement Dumoulin Business Park - Edificio P 1st Piso, 2625-106, Povoa de Santa Iria, Portugal
Tel.: (351) 211395398   PT
Web Site: https://greenaqua.pt
Holding Company; Aquatic & Marine Biotechnology Products Mfr
N.A.I.C.S.: 551112

Subsidiaries:

GREEN AQUA Povoa, S.A. (1)
Rua Eng Clement Dumoulin Business Park - Edificio P 1st Piso, 2625-106, Povoa de Santa Iria, Portugal
Tel.: (351) 211395398
Web Site: https://greenaqua.pt
Industrial Microalgae Mfr
N.A.I.C.S.: 325414

Joint Venture (Domestic):

Solvay Portugal - Produtos Quimicos S.A. (2)
Rua Eng Clement Dumoulin, 2625-106, Povoa de Santa Iria, Portugal
Tel.: (351) 219534000
Web Site: http://www.solvay.com
Alkalis, Salt, Chlorine Products, Sodium Chlorate, Aquaculture Mfr
N.A.I.C.S.: 325180

GREEN ARROW RESOURCES INC.
666 Burrard Street Suite 600, Vancouver, V6C 3P6, BC, Canada
Tel.: (604) 689-9600   AB
Web Site: http://www.greenarrowresources.com
Year Founded: 2007
GAR.H—(TSXV)
Assets: $2,502
Liabilities: $621,364
Net Worth: ($618,861)
Earnings: ($77,469)
Fiscal Year-end: 12/31/23
Mineral Exploration Services
N.A.I.C.S.: 212290
Alan MacDonald *(CEO)*

GREEN BATTERY MINERALS INC.
900-885 West Georgia Street, Vancouver, V6C 3H1, BC, Canada
Tel.: (604) 343-7740   BC
Web Site: https://greenbatteryminerals.com
Year Founded: 1979
GEM—(OTCIQ)
Assets: $4,215,124
Liabilities: $60,890
Net Worth: $4,154,234
Earnings: ($1,913,301)
Fiscal Year-end: 02/28/22
Mineral Exploration Services
N.A.I.C.S.: 213114
Thomas Yingling *(Pres & CEO)*

GREEN BUILD TECHNOLOGY LTD.
No 7 HongJun Street, Nangang District, Harbin, 150090, Heilongjiang, China
Tel.: (86) 45151176667   SG
Web Site: https://gbtlimited.com
Year Founded: 2004
Y06—(SES)
Rev.: $10,657,594
Assets: $150,826,052
Liabilities: $141,466,454
Net Worth: $9,359,599
Earnings: $398,040
Emp.: 600
Fiscal Year-end: 12/31/20
Flexible Packaging Products Mfr
N.A.I.C.S.: 326112
Xueying Wu *(CEO)*

GREEN CHEMICAL CO., LTD.
103 Dokgot2-ro Daesan-eup, Seosan, 31900, Chungcheongnam-do, Korea (South)
Tel.: (82) 231588823
Year Founded: 2003
083420—(KRS)
Rev.: $249,219,282
Assets: $150,826,972
Liabilities: $56,886,974
Net Worth: $93,939,998
Earnings: $2,201,552
Emp.: 174

Green Chemical Co., Ltd.—(Continued)
Fiscal Year-end: 12/31/22
Chemicals Mfr
N.A.I.C.S.: 325613
Kyu-Mo Yang (Chm)

GREEN CHINA HOLDINGS LIMITED
Suites 1106-08 11th Floor The Chinese Bank Building, 61-65 Des Voeux Road, Central, China (Hong Kong)
Tel.: (852) 25989838   Ky
0904—(HKG)
Rev.: $75,376,715
Assets: $149,703,176
Liabilities: $178,980,535
Net Worth: ($29,277,359)
Earnings: ($89,727,896)
Emp.: 284
Fiscal Year-end: 04/30/21
Fertilizer Distr & Retailer
N.A.I.C.S.: 424690
Sun Shao Feng (CEO)

GREEN COAST ENTERPRISES LLC
Nad al Hamar Road, PO Box 552, Nad Al Hamar, Dubai, United Arab Emirates
Tel.: (971) 4 2570222
Web Site: http://www.greencoast.ae
Sales Range: $25-49.9 Million
Emp.: 50
Holding Company Mfr
N.A.I.C.S.: 551112
Abdul Ghaffar Hussain (Chm)

Subsidiaries:

Corys Building Materials (1)
PO Box 2345, Dubai, United Arab Emirates
Tel.: (971) 42894670
Web Site:
  http://www.buildingmaterials.corys.ae
Construction & Building Material Distr
N.A.I.C.S.: 423810
Jeremy Rowson (CEO)

GREEN CRITICAL MINERALS LIMITED
349 Hay Street, Subiaco, 6008, WA, Australia
Tel.: (61) 893880051   AU
Web Site: https://gcminerals.com.au
GCM—(ASX)
Rev.: $16,233
Assets: $8,202,161
Liabilities: $339,225
Net Worth: $7,862,937
Earnings: ($877,760)
Fiscal Year-end: 06/30/24
Mineral Exploration Services
N.A.I.C.S.: 213114
Leon Eugene Pretorius (Chm, CEO & Exec Dir)

GREEN CROSS CELL CORP.
6F SJ Texhnovile 60-19 Gasan-dong, Geumcheon-gu, Seoul, 153-769, Korea (South)
Tel.: (82) 221010635
Web Site:
  http://www.greencrosscell.com
Year Founded: 1992
031390—(KRS)
Rev.: $32,596,836
Assets: $132,200,917
Liabilities: $59,018,375
Net Worth: $73,182,543
Earnings: $9,509,504
Emp.: 250
Fiscal Year-end: 12/31/19
Pharmaceutical Product Mfr & Whslr
N.A.I.C.S.: 325412
Duck-Joo Lee (Pres & CEO)

GREEN CROSS HEALTH LIMITED
Millennium Centre Ground Floor Building B 602 Gt South Road, Ellerslie, Auckland, 1051, New Zealand
Tel.: (64) 95719080   NZ
Web Site:
  https://www.greencrosshealth.co.nz
Year Founded: 1981
GXH—(NZX)
Rev.: $295,223,684
Assets: $239,836,722
Liabilities: $119,020,335
Net Worth: $120,816,388
Earnings: $12,138,158
Emp.: 11
Fiscal Year-end: 03/31/23
Healtcare Services
N.A.I.C.S.: 621610
Kim Ellis (Chm)

Subsidiaries:

Access Community Health Limited (1)
L4 NZRB Building 106-110 Jackson St, Petone, New Zealand
Tel.: (64) 44734886
Web Site: http://www.access.org.nz
Women Healthcare Services
N.A.I.C.S.: 621610

Drury Surgery Limited (1)
175 Great South Road, Drury, New Zealand
Tel.: (64) 2943005
Web Site: http://www.drurysurgery.co.nz
Women Healthcare Services
N.A.I.C.S.: 621610

Shirley Pharmacy Limited (1)
175 Shirley Road, Croydon, CR0 8SS, United Kingdom
Tel.: (44) 2086564627
Web Site: http://www.shirleypharmacy.co.uk
Pharmacy Services
N.A.I.C.S.: 456110

Silverstream Health Centre Limited (1)
Shop 1 Silverstream Village Shops cnr Kiln Street & Whiteman Road, 5019, Upper Hutt, New Zealand
Tel.: (64) 45277376
Health Care Srvices
N.A.I.C.S.: 621610

The Doctors (Hastings) Limited (1)
110 Russell Street South, Hastings, 4122, New Zealand
Tel.: (64) 68768445
Web Site: http://thedoctors.co.nz
Women Healthcare Services
N.A.I.C.S.: 621610

The Doctors (Huapai) Limited (1)
321-323 Main Road SH16 Huapai Kumeu, Auckland, 0891, New Zealand
Tel.: (64) 94129133
Web Site: https://thedoctors.co.nz
Women Healthcare Services
N.A.I.C.S.: 621610

The Doctors (New Lynn) Limited (1)
19 Delta Avenue, New Lynn, Auckland, 0600, New Zealand
Tel.: (64) 98277810
Web Site: https://thedoctors.co.nz
Women Healthcare Services
N.A.I.C.S.: 621610

The Doctors (Whangaparaoa) Limited (1)
6/651 Whangaparaoa Road, Stanmore Bay, Auckland, 0932, New Zealand
Tel.: (64) 94243001
Web Site: https://thedoctors.co.nz
Women Healthcare Services
N.A.I.C.S.: 621610

Waihi Medical Centre Limited (1)
1 Mueller Street, Waihi, 3610, New Zealand
Tel.: (64) 78638195
Medical Devices
N.A.I.C.S.: 622110

GREEN CROSS HOLDINGS CORP.
107 Ihyeon-ro 30-beongil, Giheung-gu, Yongin, Gyeonggi, Korea (South)
Tel.: (82) 312609300
Web Site: http://www.greencross.com
Year Founded: 1967
005250—(KRS)
Rev.: $1,595,022,498
Assets: $2,755,110,584
Liabilities: $1,246,388,204
Net Worth: $1,508,722,379
Earnings: $45,174,274
Emp.: 163
Fiscal Year-end: 12/31/22
Holding Company
N.A.I.C.S.: 551112
Il Sup Huh (Chm & CEO)

GREEN CROSS WELLBEING CORP.
33F 108 Yeoui-daero, Yeongdeungpo-gu, Seoul, Korea (South)
Tel.: (82) 15775560
Web Site:
  https://www.greencrosswb.com
Year Founded: 2004
234690—(KRS)
Rev.: $84,162,232
Assets: $115,236,512
Liabilities: $41,478,512
Net Worth: $73,758,000
Earnings: $6,136,805
Emp.: 296
Fiscal Year-end: 12/31/22
Biotechnology Research & Development Services
N.A.I.C.S.: 541714
Jin-Dong Jung (CFO)

Subsidiaries:

Able Analytics Co., Ltd. (1)
107 Ihyeon-ro 30beon-gil Bojeong-dong Mokam Building, Giheung-gu, Yongin, Gyeonggi-do, Korea (South)
Tel.: (82) 31 270 1374
Web Site: https://www.able-analytics.com
Business Consulting Services
N.A.I.C.S.: 541690

Curevo Inc. (1)
Tel.: (206) 492-5722
Research & Development Services
N.A.I.C.S.: 541714
George Simeon (CEO)

GC Cell Corp. (1)
Tel.: (82) 317366700
Research & Development Services
N.A.I.C.S.: 541714

GC Genome Corporation (1)
107 Ihyeon-ro 30beon-gil, Giheung-gu, Yongin, 16924, Gyeonggi-do, Korea (South)
Tel.: (82) 312809939
Research & Development Services
N.A.I.C.S.: 541714

GC Invacfarm Inc. (1)
40 Sandan-gil, Hwasun-eup, Hwasun, Jeollanam-do, Korea (South)
Tel.: (82) 61 379 2114
Research & Development Services
N.A.I.C.S.: 541714

GC Mogam, Inc. (1)
2200 Fletcher Ave, Fort Lee, NJ 07024
Web Site: https://www.gcmogam.com
Pharmaceuticals Product Mfr
N.A.I.C.S.: 325412
Woo Jin Lee (CEO)

Gc do Brasil Consultoria de Negocios Ltda. (1)
Av Roque Petroni Junior 1 089 Conjuntos 214 e 216 Jardim das Acacias, Sao Paulo, 04707-000, Brazil
Tel.: (55) 112 597 5963
Research & Development Services
N.A.I.C.S.: 541714

Green Cross Medical Science Corp. (1)
107 Ihyeon-ro 30beon-gil Bojeong-dong, Giheung-gu, Yongin, 446770, Gyeonggi-do, Korea (South)
Web Site: https://www.greencrossms.com
Research & Development Services
N.A.I.C.S.: 541714

Green Cross Medis corp. (1)
16 Jeongja 1-gil Seonggeo-eup, Seobuk-gu, Cheonan, Chungcheongnam-do, Korea (South)
Tel.: (82) 415510600
Research & Development Services
N.A.I.C.S.: 541714

GREEN DELTA INSURANCE COMPANY LIMITED
Green Delta AIMS Tower 6th Floor 51 52, Mohakhali, Dhaka, 1212, Bangladesh
Tel.: (880) 222261170
Web Site: https://www.green-delta.com
Year Founded: 1985
GREENDELT—(DHA)
Rev.: $21,095,725
Assets: $156,672,664
Liabilities: $76,107,925
Net Worth: $80,564,739
Earnings: $15,648,238
Emp.: 492
Fiscal Year-end: 12/31/21
Insurance Services
N.A.I.C.S.: 524298
Abdul Hafiz Chowdhury (Chm)

Subsidiaries:

GD Assist Ltd. (1)
51-52 Bir Uttam AK Khandakar Road, Dhaka, 1212, Bangladesh
Tel.: (880) 1617666888
Web Site: https://www.gdassist.com
Medical Tourism Services
N.A.I.C.S.: 561599
Nasir A. Choudhury (Chm)

Green Delta Capital Ltd. (1)
Green Delta AIMS Tower 3rd floor 51-52 Mohakhali C/A, Dhaka, 1212, Bangladesh
Tel.: (880) 29851902
Web Site:
  https://www.greendeltacapital.com
Investment Management Service
N.A.I.C.S.: 523940

GREEN DIAMOND EQUIPMENT LTD.
325 Baig Boulevard, Moncton, E1E 1E1, NB, Canada
Tel.: (833) 443-3373
Web Site: https://www.green-diamond.ca
Year Founded: 2007
Commercial & Service Industry Machinery Mfg.
N.A.I.C.S.: 333310

GREEN EARTH INSTITUTE CO., LTD.
6F Q Plaza Shinjuku 3-chome 3-5-6 Shinjuku, Shinjuku-ku, Tokyo, 160-0022, Japan
Tel.: (81) 338189211
Web Site: https://www.gei.co.jp
Year Founded: 2011
9212—(TKS)
Renewable Energy Services
N.A.I.C.S.: 221210

GREEN ECONOMY DEVELOPMENT LIMITED
Room 2001-2010 118 Connaught Road West Sai Ying Pun 20/F, Hong Kong, China (Hong Kong)
Tel.: (852) 28111602   Ky
Web Site: http://www.visionfame.com
1315—(HKG)
Rev.: $675,452,266
Assets: $110,773,957
Liabilities: $91,161,903
Net Worth: $19,612,054

Earnings: $658,701
Emp.: 440
Fiscal Year-end: 03/31/21
Building Construction Services
N.A.I.C.S.: 327910

Subsidiaries:

Wan Chung Construction (Singapore) Pte. Limited (1)
212 Hougang Street 21 04-325, Singapore, 530212, Singapore
Tel.: (65) 6283 4325
Web Site: http://www.wanchung.com.sg
Building Construction Services
N.A.I.C.S.: 236220
Eng Son Yam *(Mng Dir)*

Subsidiary (Domestic):

Vision Foundation Pte. Ltd. (2)
212 Hougang Street 21 03-343, Singapore, 530212, Singapore
Tel.: (65) 62855590
Building Construction Services
N.A.I.C.S.: 236220

GREEN ENERGY 4 SEASONS
Rue Porte Basse 3, 6900, Marche-en-Famenne, Belgium
Tel.: (32) 84222909
Web Site: http://www.greenenergy4seasons.be
Sales Range: $25-49.9 Million
Energy Saving Products Importer, Distr & Installer
N.A.I.C.S.: 238290

GREEN ENERGY GROUP LIMITED
4C Derrick Industrial Building 49 Wong Chuk Hang Road, Hong Kong, China (Hong Kong)
Tel.: (852) 25491223   BM
Web Site: http://www.capitalfp.com.hk
0979—(HKG)
Rev.: $56,913,715
Assets: $9,234,452
Liabilities: $3,672,834
Net Worth: $5,561,618
Earnings: ($4,211,197)
Emp.: 55
Fiscal Year-end: 06/30/22
Holding Company
N.A.I.C.S.: 551112
Jerry Wai Leung Yip *(Chm)*

GREEN ENERGY SOLUTION INDUSTRIES, INC.
11228 West Hastings Street Suite 602, Vancouver, V6E 46S, BC, Canada
Tel.: (615) 426-2565
Electric Power Distribution Services
N.A.I.C.S.: 221122

GREEN FUTURE FOOD HYDROCOLLOID MARINE SCIENCE COMPANY LIMITED
Flat A 16th Floor 169 Electric Road, North Point, Hong Kong, China (Hong Kong)
Tel.: (852) 35430708   Ky
Web Site: https://greenfood.wisdomir.com
Year Founded: 2001
1084—(HKG)
Rev.: $209,586,795
Assets: $241,355,970
Liabilities: $119,720,588
Net Worth: $121,635,383
Earnings: $29,697,683
Emp.: 1,234
Fiscal Year-end: 12/31/22
Seaweed Product Mfr
N.A.I.C.S.: 311710
Kam Chung Chan *(Chm & CEO)*

Subsidiaries:

PT Hongxin Algae International (1)
7WWF WW2 Krojan Barat, Klatakan Kec Kendit Situbondo Regency, East Java, 68352, Indonesia
Tel.: (62) 3383890300
Web Site: https://hongxin.co.id
Food Products Mfr
N.A.I.C.S.: 311999

GREEN GIANT INC.
6 Xinghan Road 19th Floor, Hanzhong, 723000, Shaanxi, China
Tel.: (86) 9162622612   FL
Web Site: http://www.chinahgs.com
Year Founded: 2001
GGE—(NASDAQ)
Rev.: $993,954
Assets: $205,092,468
Liabilities: $189,398,511
Net Worth: $15,693,957
Earnings: ($110,121,478)
Emp.: 95
Fiscal Year-end: 09/30/23
Holding Company; Real Estate Development & Construction
N.A.I.C.S.: 551112
Xiaojun Zhu *(Chm, Pres & CEO)*

GREEN GRASS ECOLOGICAL TECHNOLOGY DEVELOPMENT CO., LTD.
9th Floor Lvdi Zhihai Tower A3 North Kerqin Road Nandian Street, Xincheng District, Huhehaote, 010000, China
Tel.: (86) 4715287999   Ky
Year Founded: 2019
Rev.: $24,131,248
Assets: $26,389,967
Liabilities: $1,267,397
Net Worth: $25,122,570
Earnings: $5,751,192
Emp.: 30
Fiscal Year-end: 06/30/19
Holding Company
N.A.I.C.S.: 551112
Jian Sun *(Chm & CEO)*

GREEN GROWTH BRANDS, INC.
5300 Commerce Court West 199 Bay Street, Toronto, M5L 1B9, ON, Canada
Tel.: (647) 495-8798
GGB—(CNSX)
Rev.: $15,729,803
Assets: $149,785,547
Liabilities: $107,248,031
Net Worth: $42,537,516
Earnings: ($64,331,809)
Fiscal Year-end: 06/30/19
Cannabis Product Mfr & Distr
N.A.I.C.S.: 325412
Ed Kistner *(Chief Admin Officer)*

GREEN HOLDING S.P.A.
Via Cassanese 45, Segrate, 20090, Milan, Italy
Tel.: (39) 02893801
Web Site: http://www.greenh.com
Sales Range: $100-124.9 Million
Emp.: 400
Holding Company
N.A.I.C.S.: 551112
Giuseppe Grossi *(Chm)*

Subsidiaries:

Blue Holding S.p.A. (1)
Via Cassanese 45, 20090, Segrate, MI, Italy
Tel.: (39) 02893801
Holding Company
N.A.I.C.S.: 551112

Ind.eco S.r.l. (1)
Via Monfalcone 23/A, 4010, Rome, Italy

Tel.: (39) 0773 45781
Landfill Management Services
N.A.I.C.S.: 562212

Rea Dalmine S.p.A. (1)
Via Dossi snc, 24044, Dalmine, Bergamo, Italy
Tel.: (39) 0354157411
Web Site: https://readalmine.greenthesisgroup.com
Emp.: 40
Environmental Consulting Services
N.A.I.C.S.: 541620
Sperandio Marco *(Mgr)*

GREEN HYDROGEN SYSTEMS A/S
Nordager 21, 6000, Kolding, Denmark
Tel.: (45) 75503500
Web Site: https://www.greenhydrogen.com
Year Founded: 2007
GREENH—(CSE)
Rev.: $6,074,142
Assets: $342,351,001
Liabilities: $214,755,393
Net Worth: $127,595,607
Earnings: ($58,774,435)
Emp.: 295
Fiscal Year-end: 12/31/23
Hydrogen Product Mfr
N.A.I.C.S.: 325120
Peter Friis *(Interim CEO)*

GREEN IMPACT PARTNERS INC.
666 Burrard St 2500, Vancouver, V6C 2X8, BC, Canada
Tel.: (604) 230-6736   BC
Web Site: https://www.greenipi.com
Year Founded: 2011
GIPIF—(OTCIQ)
Rev.: $121,695,990
Assets: $142,348,410
Liabilities: $54,097,259
Net Worth: $88,251,152
Earnings: $976,365
Fiscal Year-end: 12/31/23
Metal Mining
N.A.I.C.S.: 212290
Nikolaus Kiefer *(Chief Investment Officer)*

GREEN INTERNATIONAL HOLDINGS LIMITED
Suite 2102 21/F West Tower Shun Tak Centre 200 Connaught Road, Central, China (Hong Kong)
Tel.: (852) 21690813   Ky
Web Site: http://www.green-international.com
Year Founded: 2006
2700—(HKG)
Rev.: $6,022,590
Assets: $21,501,218
Liabilities: $14,548,005
Net Worth: $6,953,213
Earnings: ($1,761,285)
Emp.: 180
Fiscal Year-end: 12/31/22
Holding Company
N.A.I.C.S.: 551112
Hanhong Chen *(Exec Dir)*

Subsidiaries:

Green Securities Limited (1)
Unit 201 2/F So Hong Commercial Building 41-47 Jervois Street, Sheung Wan, China (Hong Kong)
Tel.: (852) 21290099
Web Site: http://www.greentrade.hk
Security Dealing Services
N.A.I.C.S.: 523150

GREEN LEADER HOLDINGS GROUP LIMITED
Units 2001-2 20th Floor Li Po Chun Chambers, 189 Des Voeux Road, Central, China (Hong Kong)
Tel.: (852) 28896289   BM
Web Site: http://www.greenleader.hk
0061—(HKG)
Rev.: $293,989,373
Assets: $1,143,602,963
Liabilities: $1,202,978,438
Net Worth: ($59,375,475)
Earnings: $44,330,985
Emp.: 1,122
Fiscal Year-end: 12/31/22
Mineral Resources Exploration, Development & Mining
N.A.I.C.S.: 212220
Michael Nam Tse *(CEO)*

Subsidiaries:

Beijing Advanced Digital Technology Co., Ltd. (1)
4th Floor Building 3 No 1 Chedagou, Haidian District, Beijing, 100089, China
Tel.: (86) 1068700009
Web Site: https://www.adtec.com.cn
Rev.: $385,592,411
Assets: $366,174,351
Liabilities: $134,729,476
Net Worth: $231,444,875
Earnings: $22,240,764
Fiscal Year-end: 12/31/2023
Financial Software Solution Services
N.A.I.C.S.: 541511
Li Kai *(Chm)*

Golden Pogada LLC (1)
Suite 402 403 405 Rokmon Building 24 Constitution Street, Bayangol, Ulaanbaatar, 925, Mongolia
Tel.: (976) 7011 9966
Web Site: http://www.goldenpogada.com
Emp.: 5
Coal Exploration Services
N.A.I.C.S.: 213113
Bayarmagnai M. *(Gen Mgr)*

Sequent China/Hong Kong Limited (1)
9 F Wincome Ctr 39 Des Voeux Rd C, Hong Kong, China (Hong Kong)
Tel.: (852) 28 89 6289
Computer Network System Integration Services
N.A.I.C.S.: 541512

GREEN LIFE SCIENCE CO., LTD
84 Yeosusandan 2-ro, Yeosu, Jeollanam-Do, Korea (South)
Tel.: (82) 616814600
Web Site: https://www.korgl.com
Year Founded: 1978
114450—(KRS)
Rev.: $27,999,264
Assets: $47,885,139
Liabilities: $7,511,045
Net Worth: $40,374,093
Earnings: ($2,704,110)
Emp.: 61
Fiscal Year-end: 12/31/22
Pharmaceuticals Product Mfr
N.A.I.C.S.: 325412

GREEN MINERALS AS
Nedre Slottsgate 8, 157, Oslo, Norway
Tel.: (47) 91554644
Web Site: https://www.greenminerals.no
Year Founded: 2020
GEM—(OSL)
Rev.: $554
Assets: $1,170,423
Liabilities: $112,137
Net Worth: $1,058,286
Earnings: ($1,012,932)
Emp.: 3
Fiscal Year-end: 12/31/23
Mineral Mining Services
N.A.I.C.S.: 213115
Stale Rodahl *(Chm)*

GREEN OCEAN CORPORATION BERHAD

Green Ocean Corporation Berhad—(Continued)

GREEN OCEAN CORPORATION BERHAD
Lot 742 4th Mile Jalan Kapar, 42100, Klang, Selangor Darul Ehsan, Malaysia
Tel.: (60) 332912224   MY
Web Site:
https://www.greenoceancorp.com
Year Founded: 2003
GOCEAN—(KLS)
Rev.: $2,319,788
Assets: $28,217,778
Liabilities: $4,152,169
Net Worth: $24,065,608
Earnings: ($833,439)
Fiscal Year-end: 09/30/23
Investment Holding Services
N.A.I.C.S.: 551112
Yuet Chyn Wong *(Sec)*

GREEN OLEO SPA
Via Bergamo 66, 26100, Cremona, Italy
Tel.: (39) 03724871
Web Site: https://www.greenoleo.com
Year Founded: 2012
GRN—(ITA)
Emp.: 70
Chemical Products Mfr
N.A.I.C.S.: 325998

GREEN PACKET BERHAD
B23A3 The Ascent Paradigm No 1 Jalan SS726A Kelana Jaya, 47301, Petaling Jaya, Selangor Darul Ehsan, Malaysia
Tel.: (60) 327146288   MY
Web Site:
https://www.greenpacket.com
GPACKET—(KLS)
Rev.: $165,924,233
Assets: $54,301,376
Liabilities: $41,295,661
Net Worth: $13,005,714
Earnings: ($13,257,566)
Emp.: 186
Fiscal Year-end: 03/31/23
Wireless Telecommunication Services
N.A.I.C.S.: 517111
Kay Yen Tan *(Exec Dir)*

Subsidiaries:

Green Packet (Australia) Pty. Ltd. (1)
36 Shinfield Avenue St Ives, French's Forest, 2075, NSW, Australia
Tel.: (61) 282138676
Sales Range: $50-74.9 Million
Emp.: 1
Modems & Routers Distr
N.A.I.C.S.: 423690

Green Packet (Shanghai) Ltd. (1)
Suite 21213 498 Guoshoujing Rd Pudong New Area, Shanghai, 201203, China
Tel.: (86) 2151028028
Sales Range: $25-49.9 Million
Emp.: 44
Wireless & Telecommunications Products Mfr
N.A.I.C.S.: 334220

Green Packet Networks (Taiwan) Pte. Ltd. (1)
6F No 21 Lane 583 Rueiguang Road, Neihu District, 11492, Taipei, Taiwan
Tel.: (886) 226271355
Sales Range: $25-49.9 Million
Emp.: 30
Wireless Networking Services
N.A.I.C.S.: 517112
James Wang *(Mgr)*

Green Packet Networks W.L.L. (1)
Suite 502 Building No 2417 Road 2831, Al-Seef 428, Manama, 428, Bahrain
Tel.: (973) 17560500
Web Site: http://www.greenpacket.com

Sales Range: $50-74.9 Million
Emp.: 3
Networking Components Distr
N.A.I.C.S.: 423430
Mat Ismail *(Exec Dir)*

Green Packet, Inc. (1)
21060 Homestead Rd Ste 220, Cupertino, CA 95014
Tel.: (408) 774-9333
Web Site: http://www.greenpacket.com
Mobile Internet Software Development Services
N.A.I.C.S.: 541511
Puan Chan Cheong *(Founder, Grp CEO & Grp Mng Dir)*

Inova Venture Pte. Ltd. (1)
60 Kaki Bukit Pl #03-06, 415979, Singapore, Singapore
Tel.: (65) 63241377
Web Site: http://www.inovaventure.com
Sales Range: $25-49.9 Million
Emp.: 10
Technical Consulting Services
N.A.I.C.S.: 541690

Kiple Sdn. Bhd. (1)
B-23A-3 The Ascent Paradigm No 1 Jalan SS7/26A, Kelana Jaya, 47301, Petaling Jaya, Selangor, Malaysia
Tel.: (60) 386053357
Web Site: https://kiplelive.com
Residential Property Management Services
N.A.I.C.S.: 531311

Kiplepay Sdn. Bhd. (1)
B-23A-3 The Ascent Paradigm No 1 Jalan SS7/26A Ss 3, Kelana Jaya, 47301, Petaling Jaya, Selangor, Malaysia
Tel.: (60) 327146288
Web Site: https://kiple.com
E-Wallet Services
N.A.I.C.S.: 522320

NGT Networks Pte. Ltd. (1)
60 Paya Lebar Road 09-18 Paya Lebar Square, Singapore, 409051, Singapore
Tel.: (65) 67710881
Web Site: http://www.ngtnetworks.com
Voice Communication Carrier Services
N.A.I.C.S.: 517112
Alvin Tan Ley Chong *(CEO)*

Next Global Technology Sdn. Bhd. (1)
Level 8 Packet Hub 159 Jalan Templer, 46050, Petaling Jaya, Selangor Darul Ehsan, Malaysia
Tel.: (60) 3 7450 8809
Web Site: http://www.greenpacket.com
Wireless & Telecommunication Services
N.A.I.C.S.: 517112

Next Telecommunications Sdn. Bhd. (1)
Green Hub Lot 159 Jalan Templer Petaling Jaya, 46050, Petaling Jaya, Selangor, Malaysia
Tel.: (60) 376808333
Web Site: http://www.greenpacket.com
Sales Range: $25-49.9 Million
Emp.: 20
Telecommunication Servicesb
N.A.I.C.S.: 517810

Packet One Sdn. Bhd. (1)
159 Jln Templer, 46050, Petaling Jaya, Selangor, Malaysia
Tel.: (60) 389966022
Sales Range: $200-249.9 Million
Emp.: 700
Communication Networking Services
N.A.I.C.S.: 517810

Subsidiary (Domestic):

Packet One Networks (Malaysia) Sdn. Bhd. (2)
Packet Hub Level G 159 Jalan Templer, 46050, Petaling Jaya, Selangor, Malaysia
Tel.: (60) 374508888
Web Site: http://www.p1.com.my
Telecommunication & Internet Services
N.A.I.C.S.: 517810
Chia Yi Teng *(CTO)*

GREEN PANDA CAPITAL CORP.
3000-77 King Street West TD Centre North Tower, PO Box 95, Toronto, M5K 1G8, ON, Canada
Tel.: (416) 365-3701
GPCC.P—(TSXV)
Assets: $39,073
Liabilities: $12,682
Net Worth: $26,391
Earnings: ($30,064)
Fiscal Year-end: 07/31/23
Business Consulting Services
N.A.I.C.S.: 522299
Richard Zhou *(Pres & CEO)*

GREEN PLUS CO., LTD.
50-42 Eungbong-ro, Yesan, Chungcheongnam-do, Korea (South)
Tel.: (82) 413326421
Web Site:
https://www.greenplus.co.kr
186230—(KRS)
Rev.: $63,666,446
Assets: $81,282,391
Liabilities: $34,709,680
Net Worth: $46,572,711
Earnings: ($2,068,066)
Emp.: 123
Fiscal Year-end: 12/31/22
Nonferrous Metal Mfr & Distr
N.A.I.C.S.: 331410
Park Young-Hwan *(CEO)*

GREEN POWER GENERATION JSC
Tchaikovsky 95, 050000, Almaty, Kazakhstan
Tel.: (7) 7122315555
EXPA—(KAZ)
Assets: $184,408
Liabilities: $1,071
Net Worth: $183,337
Earnings: ($2,006)
Fiscal Year-end: 12/31/21
Hydrocarbon Mfr
N.A.I.C.S.: 325110
Mukhambetov Nariman *(CEO & Dir)*

GREEN PRAIRIE INTERNATIONAL INC.
RR 8 Site 30 Comp 11, Lethbridge, T1J 4P4, AB, Canada
Tel.: (403) 327-9941
Web Site:
http://www.greenprairie.com
Year Founded: 1988
Forage Products Whslr
N.A.I.C.S.: 424910

GREEN RESOURCES PUBLIC COMPANY LIMITED
405 Bondstreet Road, Bang Phut, Pak Kret, 11120, Thailand
Tel.: (66) 25045234
Web Site:
https://www.greenresources.co.th
Year Founded: 1992
GREEN—(THA)
Rev.: $3,721,684
Assets: $30,501,814
Liabilities: $8,106,318
Net Worth: $22,395,496
Earnings: ($896,777)
Fiscal Year-end: 12/31/23
Real Estate Development Services
N.A.I.C.S.: 531390
Chaisith Viriyamettakul *(Co-Chm, Member-Exec Bd & Exec Dir)*

GREEN RIVER GOLD CORP.
115 6220 Fulton Road, Edmonton, T6A 3T4, AB, Canada
Tel.: (780) 993-2193   Ca
Web Site: https://greenrivergold.com
Year Founded: 2006
CCR—(OTCIQ)
Mineral Mining Services

N.A.I.C.S.: 212390
Shawn Stockdale *(CFO & Sec)*

GREEN RIVER HOLDING CO., LTD.
222 Moo 4, T Thachang A Bangklum, Songkhla, 90110, Thailand
Tel.: (66) 74328955
Web Site:
https://www.greenriverholding.com
8444—(TPE)
Rev.: $152,214,684
Assets: $271,819,441
Liabilities: $223,806,231
Net Worth: $48,013,210
Earnings: ($20,429,052)
Emp.: 1,106
Fiscal Year-end: 12/31/23
Wood Products Mfr
N.A.I.C.S.: 321999
Hsieh Jung-Hui *(Chm)*

GREEN SEAL HOLDING LIMITED
5F-B 89 Songren Road, Xinyi District, Taipei, 110, Taiwan
Tel.: (886) 287890603
Rev.: $126,049,702
Assets: $363,453,479
Liabilities: $30,089,462
Net Worth: $333,364,017
Earnings: ($14,510,381)
Emp.: 600
Fiscal Year-end: 12/31/18
Biaxially Oriented Polyamide (BOPA) Films Mfr
N.A.I.C.S.: 326112
Chit Fu Wong *(Chm)*

Subsidiaries:

Xiamen Changsu Industrial Corporation Limited (1)
No 268 Wengjiao Road, Xinyang Industrial Zone Haicang, Xiamen, Fujian, China
Tel.: (86) 5926800888
Web Site: http://www.chang-su.com.cn
Film Material Mfr & Distr
N.A.I.C.S.: 326112

GREEN SHIELD CANADA
8677 Anchor Dr, PO Box 1606, Windsor, N9A 6W1, ON, Canada
Tel.: (519) 739-1133
Web Site: http://www.greenshield.ca
Year Founded: 1957
Sales Range: $1-4.9 Billion
Emp.: 500
Health Care Benefit Carrier
N.A.I.C.S.: 524114
Sherry Peister *(Chm)*

GREEN SHIFT COMMODITIES LTD.
303 - 217 Queen St West, Toronto, M5V 0R2, ON, Canada
Tel.: (416) 868-1491   ON
Web Site:
https://www.greencommodities.com
Year Founded: 2005
GCOM—(TSXV)
Rev.: $99,804
Assets: $3,967,471
Liabilities: $2,550,677
Net Worth: $1,416,795
Earnings: ($1,991,830)
Fiscal Year-end: 12/31/23
Mineral Exploration Services
N.A.I.C.S.: 212290
Keith Michael Barron *(Founder)*

GREEN STANDARD VANADIUM RESOURCES CORP.
1066 West Hastings Street Suite 2300, Vancouver, V6E 3X2, BC, Canada
Tel.: (778) 688-7346

AND PRIVATE COMPANIES

Metal Mining
N.A.I.C.S.: 212290
Yudian Zhao (CEO)

GREEN TEC CORPORATION
ORE Nishiki 2-choume Bldg 5F
2-4-15 Nishiki, Naka-ku, Nagoya,
460-0003, Aichi, Japan
Tel.: (81) 52 221 0230 JP
Web Site: http://www.green-t.co.jp
Year Founded: 1996
Quality Control, Outsourcing & Consulting Services
N.A.I.C.S.: 561499
Muneyuki Nakajima (Chm)

GREEN TECHNOLOGY METALS LIMITED
Level 1 338 Barker Road, Subiaco,
6008, WA, Australia
Tel.: (61) 865576825 AU
Web Site:
 https://www.greentm.com.au
Year Founded: 2021
GT1—(ASX)
Rev.: $472,304
Assets: $66,818,157
Liabilities: $4,295,375
Net Worth: $62,522,782
Earnings: ($5,669,918)
Emp.: 99
Fiscal Year-end: 06/30/23
Metal Exploration Services
N.A.I.C.S.: 213114
Joel Ives (Sec)

GREEN TOWER PROPERTIES, INC.
MMG Tower Floor 01 Marbella Urbanization, Panama, Panama
Tel.: (507) 208 7017
GRET—(PAN)
Sales Range: Less than $1 Million
Real Estate Prorperty Leasing Services
N.A.I.C.S.: 531190
Diana Morgan Boyd (Pres)

GREEN TOWN PROJECTS PLC
6 Vasil Levski Blv 3/F, 1000, Sofia, Bulgaria
Tel.: (359) 878566019
Web Site:
 https://www.greentown.world
Year Founded: 2018
GT2—(BUL)
Sales Range: Less than $1 Million
Real Estate Manangement Services
N.A.I.C.S.: 531210

GREEN VENTURES LIMITED
Triveni Complex Putalisadak
Kathmandu-28, Kathmandu, 45400, Nepal
Tel.: (977) 15342317
Web Site:
 https://www.greenventurenepal.com
Year Founded: 2004
GVL—(NEP)
Rev.: $11,707,424
Assets: $87,166,926
Liabilities: $61,826,757
Net Worth: $25,340,169
Earnings: $2,385,511
Fiscal Year-end: 07/16/23
Hydroelectric Power Generation Services
N.A.I.C.S.: 221111
Ashok Kumar (Gen Mgr)

GREEN VISION BIOTECHNOLOGY CORP.
Rooms 1804-06 18/F Wing On House
71 Des Voeux Road Central, Hong Kong, China (Hong Kong)
Tel.: (852) 9 492 9967
Web Site: http://www.gvbt.com
Year Founded: 2012
GVBT—(OTCIQ)
Rev.: $145,099
Assets: $2,922,168
Liabilities: $10,838,657
Net Worth: ($7,916,489)
Earnings: ($499,777)
Emp.: 9
Fiscal Year-end: 12/31/21
Fertilizer Product Mfr
N.A.I.C.S.: 325311
William Ching Wan Lam (CEO)

GREEN WORLD HOTELS
3F No 69 Sec 2 Nanjing E Rd,
Zhongshan Dist, Taipei, 104, Taiwan
Tel.: (886) 225620018
Web Site:
 http://www.greenworldhotels.com
Year Founded: 2004
8077—(TPE)
Rev.: $31,994,047
Assets: $99,940,151
Liabilities: $89,652,307
Net Worth: $10,287,844
Earnings: $1,622,944
Fiscal Year-end: 12/31/23
Hotel & Restaurant Operator
N.A.I.C.S.: 721110
Pang-Ming Wu (CFO)

GREEN'S GENERAL FOODS PTY. LIMITED
29 Glendenning Road, Glendenning, 2761, NSW, Australia
Tel.: (61) 298309999 AU
Web Site: http://www.greens.com.au
Year Founded: 1978
Sales Range: $25-49.9 Million
Emp.: 200
Snack Foods, Breakfast Cereals, Baking Mix Products & Sauces Mfr & Distr
N.A.I.C.S.: 311999
Shane Noble (Chm)

Subsidiaries:

Lowan Whole Foods Pty. Limited (1)
29 Glendenning Road, Glendenning, 2761, NSW, Australia
Tel.: (61) 298309999
Web Site: http://www.lowan.com.au
Sales Range: $25-49.9 Million
Breakfast Cereal Mfr
N.A.I.C.S.: 311230
Matthew Russell (Grp Gen Mgr)

GREENALIA SA
Plaza de Maria Pita N 10 1, 15001,
La Coruna, Spain
Tel.: (34) 900 81 50 81
Web Site: http://www.greenalia.es
Year Founded: 1996
GRN—(MAD)
Sales Range: Less than $1 Million
Electric Power Distribution Services
N.A.I.C.S.: 221118
Manuel Garcia (CEO)

GREENBANK CAPITAL INC.
100 King Street West Suite 5700,
Toronto, M5X 1C7, ON, Canada
Tel.: (214) 202-4353 BC
Web Site:
 https://www.greenbankcapital.com
Year Founded: 2013
GBC—(DEU)
Rev.: $9,779
Assets: $5,173,348
Liabilities: $2,393,503
Net Worth: $2,779,845
Earnings: ($2,529,716)
Fiscal Year-end: 07/31/21
Investment Services
N.A.I.C.S.: 523999

Danny Wettreich (CEO)
Subsidiaries:

Codikoat Ltd. (1)
The Epicentre Enterprise Way Haverhill Research Park, Withersfield, Haverhill, CB9 7LR, Suffolk, United Kingdom
Tel.: (44) 1440782071
Web Site: https://codikoat.com
Biotechnology Research Services
N.A.I.C.S.: 541714

Kabaddi Games Inc. (1)
100 King Street West Suite 5700, Toronto, M5X 1C7, ON, Canada
Tel.: (647) 531-8703
Web Site:
 https://www.kabaddigamesinc.com
Gaming Software Development Services
N.A.I.C.S.: 513210
Sarbjit Singh (CEO & Founder)

GREENBANK VENTURES INC.
535 Howe Street Suite 600, Vancouver, V6C 2Z4, BC, Canada
Tel.: (604) 209-9800
Web Site: http://www.leisgroup.com
GBNK—(TSXV)
Rev.: $61,654
Assets: $205,686
Liabilities: $958,403
Net Worth: ($752,717)
Earnings: ($96,264)
Fiscal Year-end: 12/31/23
Real Estate Development Services
N.A.I.C.S.: 531390
Andreas Schleich (CEO)

GREENBRIAR CAPITAL CORP.
632 Foster Avenue, Coquitlam, V3J 2L7, BC, Canada
Tel.: (949) 903-5906 BC
Web Site: https://greenbriarliving.com
Year Founded: 2009
GEBRF—(OTCIQ)
Rev.: $26,509
Assets: $11,775,763
Liabilities: $4,360,417
Net Worth: $7,415,346
Earnings: ($2,161,544)
Fiscal Year-end: 12/31/22
Investment Services
N.A.I.C.S.: 523999
Jeffrey J. Ciachurski (CEO)

GREENBROOK TMS, INC.
890 Yonge Street 7th Floor, Toronto, M4W 3P4, ON, Canada
Tel.: (416) 322-9700
Web Site:
 http://www.greenbrooktms.com
GBNHF—(OTCQB)
Rev.: $69,104,446
Assets: $100,446,357
Liabilities: $131,042,782
Net Worth: ($30,596,425)
Earnings: ($62,424,739)
Emp.: 629
Fiscal Year-end: 12/31/22
Health Care Srvices
N.A.I.C.S.: 621999
Elias Vamvakas (Chm)

GREENCASTLE RESOURCES LTD.
200 - 82 Richmond St, Toronto, M5H 3L5, ON, Canada
Tel.: (437) 677-5075 ON
Web Site: https://greencastle.ltd
Year Founded: 2004
VGN—(TSXV)
Sales Range: Less than $1 Million
Gold Exploration Services
N.A.I.C.S.: 212220
Anthony Roodenburg (CEO)

Subsidiaries:

Deveron Corp. (1)
141 Adelaide St W, Toronto, M5H 3L5, ON, Canada (65.8%)
Tel.: (816) 266-5329
Web Site: https://deveron.com
Rev.: $21,304,780
Assets: $85,981,173
Liabilities: $53,569,183
Net Worth: $32,411,990
Earnings: ($6,315,538)
Fiscal Year-end: 12/31/2022
Gold Mining
N.A.I.C.S.: 212220

Subsidiary (US):

Frontier Labs, Inc. (2)
3031 Hwy 122, Clear Lake, IA 50428-8506
Tel.: (641) 357-7645
Web Site: http://www.frontierlabs.net
Testing Laboratories
N.A.I.C.S.: 541380
Jim Finstad (CEO & Mgr-Ops)

GREENCITY ACQUISITION CORPORATION
505 Eshan Road Floor 6, Pudong
New District, Shanghai, 200120, China
Tel.: (86) 2120257919 Ky
Year Founded: 2018
GRCY—(NASDAQ)
Rev.: $15,212
Assets: $41,214,577
Liabilities: $36,214,573
Net Worth: $5,000,004
Earnings: ($238,425)
Emp.: 4
Fiscal Year-end: 12/31/20
Investment Services
N.A.I.C.S.: 523999
Jinlong Liu (Chm & CEO)

GREENCOAT RENEWABLES PLC
Riverside One Sir John Rogersons Quay 2, Dublin, D02 X576, Ireland
Tel.: (353) 176550883 IE
Web Site: https://www.greencoat-renewables.com
Year Founded: 2009
GRP—(ISE)
Rev.: $186,086,769
Assets: $2,305,958,342
Liabilities: $921,912,368
Net Worth: $1,384,045,975
Earnings: $147,390,460
Fiscal Year-end: 12/31/22
Investment Management Service
N.A.I.C.S.: 523940
Bertrand Gautier (Mgr-Investment)

GREENCOAT UK WIND PLC
5th Floor 20 Fenchurch Street, London, EC3M 3BY, United Kingdom
Tel.: (44) 2078329400
Web Site: https://www.greencoat-ukwind.com
Year Founded: 2009
UKW—(LSE)
Rev.: $1,234,769,085
Assets: $6,000,313,110
Liabilities: $1,335,007,575
Net Worth: $4,665,305,535
Earnings: $1,148,924,370
Fiscal Year-end: 12/31/22
Asset Management Services
N.A.I.C.S.: 523940
Lucinda Riches (Chm)

GREENCORE GROUP PLC
No 2 Northwood Avenue Northwood Business Park, Santry, Dublin, D09 X5N9, Ireland
Tel.: (353) 16051000 IE
Web Site: https://www.greencore.com
Year Founded: 1990
GNC—(LSE)
Rev.: $2,376,432,660
Assets: $1,611,483,860

GREENCORE GROUP PLC

Greencore Group plc—(Continued)
Liabilities: $1,040,504,220
Net Worth: $570,979,640
Earnings: $44,580,620
Emp.: 13,600
Fiscal Year-end: 09/29/23
Food Mfr
N.A.I.C.S.: 311423
Emma Hynes (CFO)

Subsidiaries:

Freshtime UK Limited (1)
Marsh Lane, Riverside Ind Est, Boston,
PE21 7PJ, Lincolnshire, United Kingdom
Tel.: (44) 1205312010
Web Site: http://www.freshtime.co.uk
Emp.: 350
Food Product Retailer
N.A.I.C.S.: 445298

Grassland Fertilizers Limited (1)
Ballymount House Pkwy Bus Ctr, Ballymount Cross, Dublin, 24, Ireland (100%)
Tel.: (353) 14609129
Web Site: http://www.grassland.ie
Sales Range: $25-49.9 Million
Emp.: 60
Fertilizer Mfr
N.A.I.C.S.: 325311

Greencore Developments Limited (1)
2 Northwood Avenue Northwood Business Park, Santry, Dublin, D09 X5N9, Ireland
Tel.: (353) 1 605 1000
Web Site: http://www.greencore.com
Sales Range: $25-49.9 Million
Emp.: 3
Convenience Foods Mfr
N.A.I.C.S.: 311999

Greencore Finance Limited (1)
2 Northwood Avenue Northwood Business Park Santry, Dublin, 9, Ireland (100%)
Tel.: (353) 16051000
Web Site: http://www.greencore.com
Sales Range: $50-74.9 Million
Emp.: 20
Nondepository Credit Intermediation
N.A.I.C.S.: 522299

Greencore Food to Go Limited (1)
Manton 110 Unit 8A, Manton Wood Enterprise Park, Worksop, S80 2RS, United Kingdom
Tel.: (44) 1909512600
Food Products Mfr
N.A.I.C.S.: 311999

Greencore UK Holdings plc (1)
Greencore Manton Wood Retford Road, Manton Wood Enterprise Park, Worksop, S80 2RS, Derbyshire, United Kingdom
Tel.: (44) 1909545900
Investment Management Service
N.A.I.C.S.: 523999

Subsidiary (Domestic):

Breadwinner Foods Limited (2)
8 Willen Field Rd, London, NW10 7AQ, United Kingdom
Tel.: (44) 2089566000
Web Site: http://www.greencoresandwich.co.uk
Food Products Mfr
N.A.I.C.S.: 311999

Greencore Frozen Foods Ltd (2)
Midland Road Hunslet, Leeds, LS10 2RJ, United Kingdom
Tel.: (44) 1132 976000
Emp.: 20
Frozen Food Product Distr
N.A.I.C.S.: 424420

Greencore Grocery Limited (2)
Greencore Manton Wood Retford Road, Manton Wood Enterprise Park, Worksop, S80 2RS, North Yorkshire, United Kingdom (100%)
Tel.: (44) 1757269000
Sales Range: $150-199.9 Million
Emp.: 500
Mayonnaise Dressing & Other Prepared Sauce Mfr
N.A.I.C.S.: 311941

Plant (Domestic):

Greencore Group plc - Greencore Food to Go Manton Wood Facility (2)
Retford Road Manton Wood Enterprise Park, Worksop, S80 2RS, Nottinghamshire, United Kingdom
Tel.: (44) 190 951 2600
Web Site: http://www.greencore.com
Sales Range: $300-349.9 Million
Emp.: 2,000
Sandwich Mfr
N.A.I.C.S.: 311941

Greencore Northampton (2)
Moulton Park Industrial Estate 15-17 Deer Park Road, Northampton, NN3 6RX, Northamptonshire, United Kingdom (100%)
Tel.: (44) 1604790666
Prepared Sandwiches Mfr
N.A.I.C.S.: 311991

Subsidiary (Domestic):

Greencore Prepared Meals (2)
Greencore Manton Wood Retford Road, Manton Wood Enterprise Park, Worksop, S80 2RS, County Durham, United Kingdom (100%)
Tel.: (44) 1207502999
Web Site: http://www.internationalcuisine.co.uk
Sales Range: $75-99.9 Million
Emp.: 500
Prepares Chilled Ready Meals, Chilled Pasta Sauces, Soups & Quiches for UK Retailers
N.A.I.C.S.: 311412

Plant (Domestic):

Greencore Prepared Meals-Kiveton (2)
Mansfield Road, Kiveton, Sheffield, S26 5PF, United Kingdom (100%)
Tel.: (44) 1909770861
Web Site: https://www.greencore.com
Packaged Food Services
N.A.I.C.S.: 311999

Subsidiary (Domestic):

Greencore Sandwiches Ltd. (2)
8 Willen Field Road, London, NW10 7AQ, United Kingdom (100%)
Tel.: (44) 2089566000
Sales Range: $75-99.9 Million
Emp.: 300
Food Preparations
N.A.I.C.S.: 311999

Greencore Sauces and Soups, Ltd. (2)
Unit 4 Bristol Distribution Park Hawkley Drive Woodlands Road, Bradley Stoke, Bristol, BS32 0BF, United Kingdom (100%)
Tel.: (44) 145 445 6700
Web Site: https://www.greencore.com
Sales Range: $25-49.9 Million
Emp.: 250
Food Preparations
N.A.I.C.S.: 311999

Hazlewood Convenience Food Group Limited (2)
Mansfield Road Kiveton, Sheffield, S26 5PF, United Kingdom (100%)
Tel.: (44) 1909770861
Mayonnaise Dressing & Other Prepared Sauce Mfr
N.A.I.C.S.: 311941

Hazlewood Convenience Group 1 Limited (2)
Greencore Manton Wood Retford Road, Manton Wood Enterprise Park, Worksop, S80 2RS, South Yorkshire, United Kingdom
Tel.: (44) 1909770861
Food Products Mfr
N.A.I.C.S.: 311999

Hazlewood Grocery Limited (2)
Greencore Manton Wood Retford Road, Manton Wood Enterprise Park, Worksop, S80 2RS, North Yorkshire, United Kingdom
Tel.: (44) 1757269000
Web Site: https://www.greencore.com

Food Products Mfr
N.A.I.C.S.: 311999

The Sandwich Factory Holdings Limited (2)
Midland Way Barlborough Links Business Park, Barlborough, Chesterfield, S43 4XA, United Kingdom
Tel.: (44) 1827719100
Sales Range: $100-124.9 Million
Emp.: 500
Food Products Mfr
N.A.I.C.S.: 311991
Phil Reader (Controller-Fin)

Premier Molasses Company Limited (1)
Harbour Road Foynes Co, Deepwater Berth Ringaskiddy, Limerick, Ireland (50%)
Tel.: (353) 6965311
Web Site: https://premiermolasses.ie
Sales Range: $25-49.9 Million
Emp.: 10
Cane Sugar Refining
N.A.I.C.S.: 311314

GREENCREST FINANCIAL SERVICES LIMITED
8 Ganesh Chandra Avenue Saha Court 1st Floor, Kolkata, 700013, India
Tel.: (91) 3322361366
Web Site:
https://www.greencrestfin.com
531737—(BOM)
Rev.: $519,611
Assets: $7,039,506
Liabilities: $96,501
Net Worth: $6,943,005
Earnings: $65,488
Emp.: 8
Fiscal Year-end: 03/31/21
Securities Brokerage Services
N.A.I.C.S.: 523150
Sushil Parakh (Chm, CEO & Mng Dir)

GREENERGY HOLDINGS INC.
54 National Road Dampol 2A Pulilan, Bulacan, 3005, Philippines
Tel.: (63) 29975184   PH
Web Site: https://www.ghi.com.ph
Year Founded: 1992
GREEN—(PHI)
Rev.: $629,875
Assets: $45,747,346
Liabilities: $5,848,336
Net Worth: $39,899,010
Earnings: ($326,384)
Fiscal Year-end: 12/31/21
Holding Company
N.A.I.C.S.: 551112
Antonio L. Tiu (Chm, Pres & CEO)

Subsidiaries:

MUSIC Semiconductors Philippines, Inc (1)
Units 3-D E F 3rd Fl Mafre Insular Corporate Ctr 1220 Acacia Ave, Madrigal Bus Park, Muntinlupa, 1770, Philippines
Tel.: (63) 5567425
Web Site: http://music-ic.com
Semiconductor Devices Mfr
N.A.I.C.S.: 334413

GREENFIELD SPECIALTY ALCOHOLS INC.
20 Toronto St Ste 1400, Toronto, M5C 2B8, ON, Canada
Tel.: (416) 304-1700
Web Site: http://www.gfsa.com
Sales Range: $150-199.9 Million
Emp.: 300
Mfr of Ethanol Fuels & Industrial Alcohols
N.A.I.C.S.: 325998
Jeff Stone (VP-Fin & Administration)

Subsidiaries:

PHARMCO-AAPER (1)

INTERNATIONAL PUBLIC

1101 Isaac Shelby Dr, Shelbyville, KY 40065
Tel.: (502) 232-7600
Web Site: http://www.pharmcoaaper.com
Sales Range: $25-49.9 Million
Pure & Denatured Ethanol Product Mfr & Distr
N.A.I.C.S.: 325193
Paul DiMarco (Pres & Gen Mgr)

GREENFIRE RESOURCES LTD.
Suite 1900 205 - 5th Avenue SW, Calgary, T2P 2V7, AB, Canada
Tel.: (587) 315-5656   AB
Web Site:
https://www.greenfireres.com
Year Founded: 2021
GFR—(NYSE)
Petroleum & Natural Gas Exploration
N.A.I.C.S.: 211120

Subsidiaries:

Greenfire Resources Inc. (1)
Suite 1900 205 – 5th Avenue SW, Calgary, T2P 2V7, AB, Canada
Tel.: (587) 315-5650
Web Site: https://www.greenfireres.com
Petroleum & Natural Gas Exploration
N.A.I.C.S.: 211120

Greenfire Resources Operating Corporation (1)
Ste 1900 - 205 5th Avenue SW, Calgary, T2P 2V7, AB, Canada
Tel.: (587) 315-5650
Web Site: https://www.greenfireres.com
Petroleum & Natural Gas Exploration, Development & Extraction
N.A.I.C.S.: 211120
Brad Birch (VP-Fin)

GREENFIRST FOREST PRODUCTS INC.
401 The West Mall Suite 1000, Toronto, M9C 5J5, ON, Canada
Tel.: (416) 775-2800   BC
Web Site: https://greenfirst.ca
Year Founded: 1979
ICLTF—(OTCIQ)
Investment Services
N.A.I.C.S.: 523999
Paul Rivett (Chm)

GREENHAWK RESOURCES INC.
5 Hazelton Avenue, Suite 300, Toronto, M5R 2E1, ON, Canada
Tel.: (647) 715-3707   AB
Web Site: http://www.cryptologic.com
Year Founded: 2014
2V70—(DEU)
Assets: $2,713,046
Liabilities: $105,908
Net Worth: $2,607,138
Earnings: ($824,092)
Fiscal Year-end: 12/31/23
Risk Management & Payment Processing Services
N.A.I.C.S.: 522320
Greg McKenzie (CEO)

GREENHEART GROUP LIMITED
32A 32/F Fortis Tower 77-79 Gloucester Road, Wanchai, China (Hong Kong)
Tel.: (852) 28772989   BM
Web Site:
https://www.greenheartgroup.com
Year Founded: 1988
0094—(HKG)
Rev.: $20,948,888
Assets: $123,422,168
Liabilities: $69,768,638
Net Worth: $53,653,530
Earnings: ($12,462,615)
Emp.: 152
Fiscal Year-end: 12/31/22

AND PRIVATE COMPANIES

Forestry Services
N.A.I.C.S.: 115310
Daphne Nga Ying Tse *(CFO & Sec)*
Subsidiaries:

Epro N.V. (1)
F Derbystraat 37-39, Paramaribo, Suriname
Tel.: (597) 422441
Web Site: http://epronv.com
Household Appliances Mfr
N.A.I.C.S.: 335220

Forest Management Services (NZ)
Limited (1)
87A Weraroa Road, Waverley, 4510, New Zealand
Tel.: (64) 63466118
Forest Management Services
N.A.I.C.S.: 115310
Steve Bell *(Co-CEO & Mgr-Forest)*

Greenheart (Suriname) N.V. (1)
Duisburglaan No 31, Paramaribo, Suriname
Tel.: (597) 463327
Timber & Lumber Product Whslr
N.A.I.C.S.: 423310

Northland Forest Managers (1995)
Limited (1)
13 Cobham Road, PO Box 54, Kerikeri, 0245, New Zealand
Tel.: (64) 94077115
Forest Harvesting & Management Services
N.A.I.C.S.: 115310
Neil Geerkens *(Gen Mgr)*

GREENHOUS GROUP LTD.
Collina House Holsworth Park Oxon Business Park, Shrewsbury, SY3 5HJ, United Kingdom
Tel.: (44) 1743 281800
Web Site:
http://www.greenhous.co.uk
Year Founded: 1912
Sales Range: $1-4.9 Billion
Emp.: 608
New & Used Car Dealer
N.A.I.C.S.: 441110
Steve Bayfield *(Gen Mgr)*

GREENHY2 LIMITED
Reid House 303/75 King Street, Sydney, 2000, NSW, Australia
Tel.: (61) 1300321094
Web Site:
https://www.greenhy2.com.au
Year Founded: 2011
H2G—(ASX)
Rev.: $146,119
Assets: $2,303,633
Liabilities: $257,161
Net Worth: $2,046,472
Earnings: ($1,192,215)
Fiscal Year-end: 12/31/23
Resource Services for Mining, Energy & Petrochemical Sectors
N.A.I.C.S.: 561499
Paul Dalgleish *(Chm, CEO & Mng Dir)*

GREENKO DUTCH B.V.
1131/A Sai Square Building Road No 36, Jubilee Hills, Hyderabad, 500033, India
Tel.: (91) 40 4030 1000   NL
Web Site:
http://www.greenkogroup.com
Year Founded: 2014
Holding Company; Clean Energy Electric Power Generation Services
N.A.I.C.S.: 551112
Mahesh Kolli *(Owner)*
Subsidiaries:

Greenko Energies Pvt. Ltd. (1)
1366 Road No 45 Jubilee Hills, Hyderabad, 500033, India
Tel.: (91) 40 4030 1000
Web Site: http://www.greenkogroup.com
Clean Energy Electric Power Generation Project Management Services

N.A.I.C.S.: 561110
Anil Kumar Chalamalasetty *(Co-Founder, CEO & Mng Dir)*

GREENLAM INDUSTRIES LIMITED
2nd Floor West Wing Worldmark 1 Aerocity, IGI Airport Hospitality District, New Delhi, 110 037, India
Tel.: (91) 114 279 1399
Web Site:
http://www.greenlamindustries.com
538979—(NSE)
Rev.: $164,775,948
Assets: $160,803,484
Liabilities: $82,460,851
Net Worth: $78,342,633
Earnings: $10,068,185
Emp.: 1,900
Fiscal Year-end: 03/31/21
Interior Renovation Services
N.A.I.C.S.: 236220
Shiv Prakash Mittal *(Chm)*
Subsidiaries:

Greenlam Decolan SA (1)
Corso San Gottardo 32, 6830, Chiasso, Switzerland
Tel.: (41) 916821862
Web Site: https://greenlam-decolan.ch
Laminating Product Mfr
N.A.I.C.S.: 326112

Greenlam RUS LLC (1)
1st Floor Room 3 1 Kazachiy Avenue Building 7, Moscow, 119017, Russia
Tel.: (7) 9203312810
Laminate & Decorative Veneer Mfr
N.A.I.C.S.: 337110

HG Industries Limited (1)
Panchalam Village Melpettai Post, Tindivanam, 604 307, Tamil Nadu, India   (100%)
Tel.: (91) 4147290021
Web Site: http://www.hgl.co.in
Rev.: $87,849
Assets: $259,406
Liabilities: $23,482
Net Worth: $235,925
Earnings: ($1,194)
Emp.: 3
Fiscal Year-end: 03/31/2021
Granite Mfr
N.A.I.C.S.: 327991
Ramesh Kumar Haritwal *(CEO & Mng Dir)*

PT Greenlam Indo Pacific (1)
Jl Pulo Kambing II No 26 RW 11, Kw Industri Pulogadung Jatinegara Kec Cakung, Jakarta Timur, 13930, DKI Jakarta, Indonesia
Tel.: (62) 2121057814
Emp.: 5,000
Laminate Mfr
N.A.I.C.S.: 326130

GREENLAND HOLDING A/S
Qullilerfik 2 4 sal, PO Box 1434, 3900, Nuuk, Greenland
Tel.: (299) 34 2880
Web Site: http://www.holding.gl
Year Founded: 1986
Holding Company; Investment Management Services
N.A.I.C.S.: 551112
Karsten High *(CEO)*

GREENLAND HOLDINGS CORPORATION LIMITED
No 700 Dapu Road, Huangpu District, Shanghai, 200023, China
Tel.: (86) 2153188666
Web Site: https://www.ldjt.com.cn
600606—(SHG)
Rev.: $61,201,584,007
Assets: $191,691,076,740
Liabilities: $168,627,585,251
Net Worth: $23,063,491,489
Earnings: $141,815,850
Emp.: 743
Fiscal Year-end: 12/31/22
Real Estate Investment Services

N.A.I.C.S.: 531390
Subsidiaries:

Greenland Holding Group Co., Ltd. (1)
No 700 Dapu Road, Huangpu District, Shanghai, 200023, China
Tel.: (86) 215 318 8666
Web Site: http://www.greenlandsc.com
Sales Range: Less than $1 Million
Holding Company; Real Estate Development & Construction Services
N.A.I.C.S.: 551112
Yuliang Zhang *(Chm & Pres)*

Subsidiary (Domestic):

China Rundong Auto Group Limited (2)
9F Shenzhou Wisdom Plaza No 567 West Tianshan Road, Changning District, Shanghai, China
Tel.: (86) 218 010 2288
Web Site: http://www.rundongauto.cn
Rev.: $1,092,703,157
Assets: $700,490,241
Liabilities: $1,237,666,462
Net Worth: ($537,176,221)
Earnings: ($836,430,948)
Emp.: 5,351
Fiscal Year-end: 12/31/2019
Car Dealership Owner & Operator
N.A.I.C.S.: 441110
Peng Yang *(Chm & CEO)*

Greenland Hong Kong Holdings Limited (2)
No 193 Xiehe Road, Chang Ning District, Shanghai, China   (60%)
Tel.: (86) 2161353777
Web Site: http://www.greenlandhk.com
Rev.: $3,736,650,107
Assets: $21,010,932,587
Liabilities: $17,751,913,452
Net Worth: $3,259,019,135
Earnings: $109,574,478
Emp.: 3,014
Fiscal Year-end: 12/31/2022
Holding Company; Real Estate Development & Construction Services
N.A.I.C.S.: 551112
David Wang *(Founder)*

GREENLAND RESORT COMPANY LIMITED
1616 Shimoide, Arao, 864-8691, Kumamoto, Japan
Tel.: (81) 968662111
Web Site:
https://www.greenland.co.jp
Year Founded: 1980
9656—(TKS)
Rev.: $45,418,540
Assets: $133,575,600
Liabilities: $64,058,150
Net Worth: $69,517,450
Earnings: $3,282,670
Emp.: 68
Fiscal Year-end: 12/31/23
Amusement Park Services
N.A.I.C.S.: 713110
Takanori Matsuno *(Pres)*

GREENLAND RESOURCES INC.
25 York Street Unit 1810, Toronto, M5J 2V5, ON, Canada   ON
Web Site:
https://www.greenlandresources.ca
Year Founded: 2008
GRLRF—(OTCIQ)
Rev.: $26,496
Assets: $2,761,055
Liabilities: $119,497
Net Worth: $2,641,558
Earnings: ($2,799,455)
Fiscal Year-end: 03/31/23
Mineral Mining Services
N.A.I.C.S.: 213115
Ruben Shiffman *(Pres)*

GREENLAND TECHNOLOGIES

GREENLIT VENTURES, INC.
HOLDING CORPORATION
11-F Building No 12 Sunking Plaza Gaojiao Road, Hangzhou, 311122, Zhejiang, China
Tel.: (86) 1053607082   VG
Year Founded: 2017
GTEC—(NASDAQ)
Rev.: $90,830,674
Assets: $155,115,341
Liabilities: $70,197,578
Net Worth: $84,917,763
Earnings: $3,559,565
Emp.: 330
Fiscal Year-end: 12/31/22
Investment Services
N.A.I.C.S.: 523999
Peter Zuguang Wang *(Chm)*

GREENLANE RENEWABLES, INC.
110-3605 Gilmore Way, Burnaby, V5G 4X5, BC, Canada
Tel.: (604) 259-0343
Web Site:
http://www.greenlanerenewables.com
Year Founded: 1986
Natural Gas Renewable Services
N.A.I.C.S.: 221210
Alex Chassels *(COO)*

GREENLIGHT
Level 14 The Broadgate Tower Primrose St, London, EC2A 2EW, United Kingdom
Tel.: (44) 2072537000
Web Site:
http://www.greenlightsearch.com
Year Founded: 2001
Sales Range: $10-24.9 Million
Emp.: 100
N.A.I.C.S.: 541890
Warren Cowan *(CEO)*

GREENLIGHT CAPITAL RE, LTD.
65 Market Street Suite 1207 Jasmine Court, PO Box 31110, Camana Bay, KY1-1205, Grand Cayman, Cayman Islands
Tel.: (345) 2913440   Ky
Web Site:
https://www.greenlightre.com
Year Founded: 2004
GLRE—(NASDAQ)
Rev.: $526,683,000
Assets: $1,580,381,000
Liabilities: $1,077,261,000
Net Worth: $503,120,000
Earnings: $25,342,000
Emp.: 48
Fiscal Year-end: 12/31/22
Property & Casualty Reinsurance Services
N.A.I.C.S.: 524130
Patrick O'Brien *(CEO-Ireland)*
Subsidiaries:

Greenlight Reinsurance Ireland, Limited (1)
50 City Quay, Dublin, D02 F588, Ireland
Tel.: (353) 1 687 0534
Insurance Services
N.A.I.C.S.: 524210
Finbar Griffin *(Chief Underwriting Officer)*

Greenlight Reinsurance, Ltd. (1)
65 Market St Ste 1207 Jasmine Ct Camana Bay, PO Box 31110, Georgetown, KY1 1205, Grand Cayman, Cayman Islands
Web Site: http://www.greenlightre.ky
Sales Range: $50-74.9 Million
Emp.: 16
Insurance Services
N.A.I.C.S.: 524130
Simon Burton *(CEO)*

GREENLIT VENTURES, INC.
717 Fulin Hotel 1805 Heping Rd, Lu-

GREENLIT VENTURES, INC.

Greenlit Ventures, Inc.—(Continued)
ohu, Shenzhen, 518000, China
Tel.: (86) 7788882886 DE
Year Founded: 2016
MSYN—(OTCIQ)
Liabilities: $90,514
Net Worth: ($90,514)
Earnings: ($55,452)
Emp.: 1
Fiscal Year-end: 12/31/22
Holding Company
N.A.I.C.S.: 551112
Yong Nan Fu *(CEO, CFO & Sec)*

GREENPLY INDUSTRIES LIMITED

Madgul Lounge 5th and 6th Floor 23 Chetla Central Road, Kolkata, 700027, India
Tel.: (91) 3330515000
Web Site: https://www.greenply.com
GREENPLY—(NSE)
Rev.: $223,125,028
Assets: $201,550,267
Liabilities: $124,358,528
Net Worth: $77,191,739
Earnings: $10,962,388
Emp.: 1,183
Fiscal Year-end: 03/31/23
Plywood Mfr
N.A.I.C.S.: 321211
Rajesh Mittal *(Chm & Co-Mng Dir)*

Subsidiaries:

Greenlam America, Inc. (1)
8750 NW 36th St Ste 635, Doral, FL 33178
Tel.: (305) 640-0388
Web Site: https://www.greenlamusa.com
Architectural Laminated Product Mfr
N.A.I.C.S.: 337212

Greenlam Asia Pacific Pte. Ltd. (1)
11 Sungei Kadut Crescent, Singapore, 728683, Singapore
Tel.: (65) 63659138
Web Site: https://www.greenlam.sg
Sales Range: $25-49.9 Million
Emp.: 35
Laminated Sheet Mfr
N.A.I.C.S.: 326130

Subsidiary (Non-US):

Greenlam Asia Pacific (Thailand) Co Ltd. (2)
898/34 SV City Office Tower 2 20th Floor Rama 3 Road, Bangpongpang Yannawa, Bangkok, 10120, Thailand
Tel.: (66) 22942569
Web Site: https://www.greenlamthailand.com
Sales Range: $25-49.9 Million
Emp.: 40
Laminated Product Mfr
N.A.I.C.S.: 326130

GREENPOWER MOTOR COMPANY INC.

Suite 240-209 Carrall Street, Vancouver, V6B 2J2, BC, Canada
Tel.: (604) 563-4144
Web Site: https://greenpowermotor.com
GP—(NASDAQ)
Rev.: $39,271,839
Assets: $45,203,284
Liabilities: $33,636,465
Net Worth: $11,566,819
Earnings: ($18,342,796)
Emp.: 116
Fiscal Year-end: 03/31/24
Electric Powered Vehicles
N.A.I.C.S.: 336211
Fraser Atkinson *(Founder, Chm & CEO)*

Subsidiaries:

GreenPower Motor Company, Inc. (1)
8885 Haven Ave Ste 200, Rancho Cucamonga, CA 91730
Tel.: (909) 346-1090
Electric Bus Mfr & Distr
N.A.I.C.S.: 336110

GREENPRO CAPITAL CORP.

B-23A-02 G-Vestor Tower Pavilion Embassy 200 Jalan Ampang, 50450, Kuala Lumpur, Malaysia
Tel.: (60) 384081788 NV
Web Site: https://www.greenprocapital.com
Year Founded: 2013
GRNQ—(NASDAQ)
Rev.: $3,673,997
Assets: $15,639,206
Liabilities: $3,060,988
Net Worth: $12,578,218
Earnings: ($6,350,872)
Emp.: 48
Fiscal Year-end: 12/31/22
Corporate Advisory Services; Public Listing, Asset Protection & Trust Services, Financial Review & Money Lending & Project Financing
N.A.I.C.S.: 541611
Chong Kuang Lee *(Founder, Pres & CEO)*

Subsidiaries:

Yabez (Hong Kong) Company Limited (1)
Tel.: (852) 27336100
Web Site: http://www.yabez.hk
Financial Services
N.A.I.C.S.: 523999

GREENRISE GLOBAL BRANDS INC.

224 West 5th Avenue, Vancouver, V5Y 1J4, BC, Canada
Tel.: (604) 689-7533 BC
Web Site: https://www.greenriseglobal.com
Year Founded: 2019
XCX—(CNSX)
Rev.: $153,254
Assets: $487,717
Liabilities: $3,374,253
Net Worth: ($2,886,536)
Earnings: ($330,387)
Fiscal Year-end: 12/31/23
Biotechnology Research & Development Services
N.A.I.C.S.: 541714

GREENROC STRATEGIC MATERIALS PLC

6th Floor 60 Gracechurch Street, London, EC3V 0HR, United Kingdom
Tel.: (44) 2039500724 UK
Web Site: https://greenrocplc.com
Year Founded: 2021
GROC—(AIM)
Assets: $13,970,939
Liabilities: $1,798,979
Net Worth: $12,171,960
Earnings: ($1,669,996)
Emp.: 6
Fiscal Year-end: 11/30/22
Other Nonmetallic Mineral Mining & Quarrying
N.A.I.C.S.: 212390

GREENS CO., LTD.

5-3 Hamadacho, Yokkaichi, 510-0067, Mie, Japan
Tel.: (81) 593515593
Web Site: https://www.kk-greens.jp
Year Founded: 1957
6547—(TKS)
Rev.: $254,827,180
Assets: $165,539,080
Liabilities: $116,873,800
Net Worth: $48,665,280
Earnings: $30,403,360

Emp.: 824
Fiscal Year-end: 06/30/24
Home Management Services
N.A.I.C.S.: 721110
Yuya Muraki *(Pres & CEO)*

GREENSILL CAPITAL (UK) LIMITED

One Southampton Street Covent Garden, London, WC2R 0LR, United Kingdom
Tel.: (44) 2034362000
Web Site: http://www.greensill.com
Year Founded: 2011
Financial Services
N.A.I.C.S.: 561499
James Doran *(Mktg Dir)*

GREENSMART CORP.

Unit C11 8th Floor Wing Hing Industrial Bldg, Kwun Tong, Hong Kong, China (Hong Kong)
Tel.: (852) 25193933 DE
GREN—(OTCIQ)
Sales Range: Less than $1 Million
Biotechnology Research & Development Services
N.A.I.C.S.: 541714
Lawrence Hon *(Pres & CEO)*

GREENSPACE BRANDS INC.

2087 Dundas Street East Suite 106, Mississauga, L4X 2V7, ON, Canada
Tel.: (416) 934-5034 ON
Web Site: https://www.greenspacebrands.ca
Year Founded: 2003
JTR—(TSXV)
Rev.: $14,574,450
Assets: $9,991,285
Liabilities: $16,483,104
Net Worth: ($6,491,819)
Earnings: ($8,168,081)
Fiscal Year-end: 03/31/22
Investment Services
N.A.I.C.S.: 523999
Jan Faryaszewski *(CFO)*

Subsidiaries:

Galaxy Nutritional Foods, Inc. (1)
66 Whitecap Dr Ste 2, North Kingstown, RI 02852-7445
Tel.: (401) 667-5000
Web Site: http://www.galaxyfoods.com
Vegetable Dairy Alternatives Mfr
N.A.I.C.S.: 311514

GREENTEC INTERNATIONAL INC.

95 Struck Court, Cambridge, N1R 8L2, ON, Canada
Tel.: (519) 624-3300
Web Site: https://www.greentec.com
Year Founded: 1995
Sales Range: $10-24.9 Million
Emp.: 65
Reverse Logistic & Recycling Services
N.A.I.C.S.: 562920
Betty Pereira *(COO-Greentec)*

GREENTECH ENVIRONMENTAL CO., LTD.

16th Floor of Motorola Building Tower A No 1 Wangjing East Road, Chaoyang, Beijing, 100102, China
Tel.: (86) 1064399965
Web Site: https://www.greentech.com.cn
Year Founded: 2004
688466—(SHG)
Rev.: $94,193,082
Assets: $259,664,001
Liabilities: $104,724,528
Net Worth: $154,939,473
Earnings: $10,780,712

INTERNATIONAL PUBLIC

Fiscal Year-end: 12/31/22
Waste Management Services
N.A.I.C.S.: 562998
Huichun Zhang *(Chm & Gen Mgr)*

GREENTECH METALS LIMITED

Tel.: (61) 894864036 AU
Web Site: https://www.greentechmetals.com
Year Founded: 2021
GRE—(ASX)
Rev.: $161
Assets: $4,816,345
Liabilities: $302,647
Net Worth: $4,513,698
Earnings: ($950,121)
Fiscal Year-end: 06/30/22
Metal Exploration Services
N.A.I.C.S.: 213114

GREENTECH TECHNOLOGY INTERNATIONAL LIMITED

Suite No 1B on 9/F Tower 1 China Hong Kong City, 33 Canton Road Tsim Sha Tsui, Kowloon, China (Hong Kong)
Tel.: (852) 23012309 Ky
Web Site: http://www.green-technology.com.hk
Year Founded: 2008
0195—(HKG)
Rev.: $118,750,950
Assets: $177,850,388
Liabilities: $52,769,955
Net Worth: $125,080,433
Earnings: $33,516,563
Emp.: 341
Fiscal Year-end: 12/31/22
Holding Company; Tin & Other Non-Ferrous Metal Mining
N.A.I.C.S.: 551112

Subsidiaries:

YT Parksong Australia Holding Pty Limited (1)
L 41 55 Collins St, Melbourne, 3000, VIC, Australia
Tel.: (61) 396541988
Tin Ore Mining Services
N.A.I.C.S.: 212290

GREENTOWN CHINA HOLDINGS LIMITED

Room 1406-1408 14/F New World Tower 1 16-18 Queens Road, Central, China (Hong Kong)
Tel.: (852) 25233138
Web Site: http://www.greentownchina.com
3900—(HKG)
Rev.: $17,852,291,168
Assets: $75,124,809,677
Liabilities: $59,482,435,990
Net Worth: $15,642,373,687
Earnings: $1,248,852,946
Emp.: 9,387
Fiscal Year-end: 12/31/22
Property Development & Managing Services
N.A.I.C.S.: 531312
Qingan Li *(Exec Dir)*

Subsidiaries:

Greentown Management Holdings Company Limited (1)
Room 1004 10/F New World Tower 1 16-18 Queens Road, Central, China (Hong Kong)
Tel.: (852) 38509099
Web Site: http://www.greentownmanagement.com
Rev.: $372,901,277
Assets: $865,049,188
Liabilities: $321,276,056
Net Worth: $543,773,131
Earnings: $103,245,246
Emp.: 1,529
Fiscal Year-end: 12/31/2022

AND PRIVATE COMPANIES

Holding Company
N.A.I.C.S.: 551112
Jun Li *(CEO)*

Greentown Real Estate Group Co., Ltd. (1)
Room 1205 Jiahua International Business Center No15 Hangda Road, Hangzhou, 310007, China
Tel.: (86) 57185086977
Real Estate Development Services
N.A.I.C.S.: 531210
Ping Du *(Exec Gen Mgr)*

GREENTOWN SERVICE GROUP CO. LTD.
Building B Xixi International Business Center, No 767 Wenyi West Road, Hangzhou, Zhejiang, China
Tel.: (86) 95059777   Ky
Web Site: http://www.lvchengfuwu.com
2869—(HKG)
Rev.: $2,085,830,557
Assets: $2,366,258,357
Liabilities: $1,260,447,880
Net Worth: $1,105,810,477
Earnings: $88,651,789
Emp.: 44,495
Fiscal Year-end: 12/31/22
Residential Property Management Services
N.A.I.C.S.: 531311
Hairong Li *(Chm)*

GREENTREE GAS & OIL LTD.
207-209 Consortium Court, London, N6E 2S8, ON, Canada
Tel.: (519) 681-9355   ON
Sales Range: $1-9.9 Million
Emp.: 5
Oil & Gas Exploration & Development Services
N.A.I.C.S.: 541360
Duncan Hamilton *(Pres)*

GREENTREE HOSPITALITY GROUP LTD.
2451 Hongqiao Road, Changning District, Shanghai, 200335, China
Tel.: (86) 2136174886   Ky
Web Site: http://www.998.com
Year Founded: 2017
GHG—(NYSE)
Rev.: $143,527,324
Assets: $780,770,277
Liabilities: $552,657,751
Net Worth: $228,112,526
Earnings: ($58,559,460)
Emp.: 2,063
Fiscal Year-end: 12/31/22
Franchised Hotel Operator
N.A.I.C.S.: 721110
Alex S. Xu *(CEO & Chm)*

GREENVALE ENERGY LTD
Tel.: (61) 862150372
Web Site: https://www.greenvalemining.com
GVLMF—(OTCIQ)
Rev.: $278,114
Assets: $7,673,143
Liabilities: $2,146,514
Net Worth: $5,526,628
Earnings: $1,992,265
Fiscal Year-end: 06/30/24
Oil Shale Mining
N.A.I.C.S.: 211120
Neil Biddle *(Exec Dir)*

GREENWAY MINING GROUP LIMITED
Room 102 Unit 1 Building 1 Ruiyuan Jinjiang Community Yanchang Line, Beijing Road Panlong District, Kunming, Yunnan, China
Tel.: (86) 8716 316 3172   Ky

Web Site: http://www.greenwaymining.com
Year Founded: 2009
Rev.: $15,667,017
Assets: $336,069,635
Liabilities: $85,605,854
Net Worth: $250,463,780
Earnings: ($11,773,982)
Emp.: 204
Fiscal Year-end: 12/31/19
Non Ferrous Metal Mining Services
N.A.I.C.S.: 331529
Dejun Lei *(COO)*

GREENWICH KAHALA AVIATION LTD.
Fitzwilliam Hall Fitzwilliam Place, Dublin, 2, Ireland
Tel.: (353) 16694732   BM
Web Site: http://www.kahalaaviation.com
Year Founded: 2009
Commercial Aircraft Acquisition, Leasing & Trading
N.A.I.C.S.: 488190
Bradley Smith *(CEO)*

GREENWING RESOURCES LTD.
Level 21 Matisse Tower 110 Mary Street, PO Box 15048, Brisbane, 4000, QLD, Australia
Tel.: (61) 730633233   AU
Web Site: https://greenwingresources.com
GW1—(ASX)
Rev.: $275,099
Assets: $16,621,757
Liabilities: $5,616,169
Net Worth: $11,005,588
Earnings: ($1,231,665)
Emp.: 30
Fiscal Year-end: 06/30/24
Minerals Exploration
N.A.I.C.S.: 213115
Peter Wright *(Exec Dir)*

GREENWOODS COMMUNICATIONS LTD.
Jeynes House Highway Point Gorsey Lane, Coleshill, Birmingham, B46 1JU, United Kingdom
Tel.: (44) 8452262327
Web Site: http://www.greenwoodscomms.com
Sales Range: $75-99.9 Million
Emp.: 400
Communications
N.A.I.C.S.: 334290
John Greenwood *(CEO)*

GREENWORKS (JIANGSU) CO., LTD.
No 65-1 Xinggang Avenue, Zhonglou Economic Development Zone, Changzhou, 213000, Jiangsu, China
Tel.: (86) 51989805880
Web Site: https://www.greenworkstool.com.cn
Year Founded: 2002
301260—(SSE)
Rev.: $731,639,844
Assets: $869,740,092
Liabilities: $662,543,388
Net Worth: $207,196,704
Earnings: $37,329,552
Fiscal Year-end: 12/31/22
Garden Machinery Mfr
N.A.I.C.S.: 333112
Cui Peng *(CFO)*

GREENX METALS LIMITED
Level 9 BGC Centre 28 The Esplanade, Perth, 6000, WA, Australia
Tel.: (61) 893226322   AU
Web Site: https://greenxmetals.com

GRX—(ASX)
Rev.: $577,499
Assets: $11,489,219
Liabilities: $1,373,227
Net Worth: $10,115,992
Earnings: ($3,040,821)
Fiscal Year-end: 06/30/24
Coal Mining
N.A.I.C.S.: 212115
Benjamin Stoikovich *(CEO)*

GREENYARD N.V.
Strijbroek 10, 2860, Saint-Katelijne-Waver, Belgium
Tel.: (32) 15324200   BE
Web Site: https://www.greenyard.group
Year Founded: 1965
GREEN—(EUR)
Rev.: $5,424,186,650
Assets: $2,385,405,436
Liabilities: $1,831,324,264
Net Worth: $554,081,172
Earnings: $1,475,116
Emp.: 9,279
Fiscal Year-end: 03/31/21
Frozen Vegetables & Prepared Meal Mfr & Whslr
N.A.I.C.S.: 311411
Koen Hoffman *(Chm)*

Subsidiaries:

Bakker Barendrecht B.V. (1)
Handelsweg 20, 2988 DB, Ridderkerk, Netherlands
Tel.: (31) 180695911
Web Site: https://www.bakkerbarendrecht.nl
Fresh Food Product Mfr
N.A.I.C.S.: 311991

Greenyard Flowers Netherlands B.V. (1)
Nijverheidsweg 4, 2742 RG, Waddinxveen, Netherlands
Tel.: (31) 885294400
Fresh Food Product Mfr
N.A.I.C.S.: 311991

Greenyard Fresh Austria GmbH (1)
Grossmarkt Inzersdorf Halle A1/B1 - Laxenburger Str 365, 1230, Vienna, Austria
Tel.: (43) 16100200
Web Site: https://www.greenyardfresh.at
Fresh Food Product Mfr
N.A.I.C.S.: 311991

Greenyard Fresh Belgium N.V. (1)
Drevendaal 1, Sint-Katelijne-Waver, 2860, Antwerp, Belgium
Tel.: (32) 15324700
Fresh Food Product Mfr
N.A.I.C.S.: 311991

Greenyard Fresh Brazil Ltda. (1)
Av Antonio Carlos Magalhaes 3244, Caminho das Arvores, Salvador, 41820-000, Bahia, Brazil
Tel.: (55) 7130234379
Fresh Food Product Mfr
N.A.I.C.S.: 311991

Greenyard Fresh Chile Ltda. (1)
Former Cervera Estate - Linderos s/n, Commune of Buin, Santiago, Chile
Tel.: (56) 228210100
Web Site: https://www.greenyardfresh.cl
Fresh Food Product Mfr
N.A.I.C.S.: 311991

Greenyard Fresh Colombia SAS (1)
Carrera 18B No 116-45, 110111, Bogota, DC, Colombia
Tel.: (57) 17442110
Web Site: https://www.greenyardfresh.co
Fresh Food Product Mfr
N.A.I.C.S.: 311991

Greenyard Fresh Direct Belgium N.V. (1)
Fortsesteenweg 27, Sint-Katelijne-Waver, 2860, Antwerp, Belgium
Tel.: (32) 15324800
Fresh Food Product Mfr
N.A.I.C.S.: 311991

GREENYARD N.V.

Greenyard Fresh France S.A.S. (1)
15 boulevard du Delta, Euro Delta Zone DE1, 94658, Rungis, Cedex, France
Tel.: (33) 149782000
Web Site: https://www.greenyardfresh.fr
Fresh Food Product Mfr
N.A.I.C.S.: 311991

Greenyard Fresh Germany GmbH (1)
Universitatsallee 16, 28359, Bremen, Germany
Tel.: (49) 42130921
Web Site: https://www.greenyardfresh.de
Fresh Food Product Mfr
N.A.I.C.S.: 311991

Greenyard Fresh Holding NL B.V. (1)
Handelsweg 20, 2988 DB, Ridderkerk, Netherlands
Tel.: (31) 657410872
Web Site: http://www.greenfreshholding.com
Fresh Food Product Mfr
N.A.I.C.S.: 311991

Greenyard Fresh Italy S.r.l. (1)
Via Tione 10 ZI San Pierino, Trevenzuolo, 37060, Verona, VR, Italy
Tel.: (39) 0458379112
Web Site: https://www.greenyardfresh.it
Fresh Food Product Mfr
N.A.I.C.S.: 311991

Greenyard Fresh Peru SAC (1)
Av Manuel Olguin 501 Of 604, Santiago de Surco, Lima, Peru
Tel.: (51) 14877206
Web Site: https://www.greenyardfresh.pe
Fresh Food Product Mfr
N.A.I.C.S.: 311991

Greenyard Fresh UK Ltd. (1)
Stephenson Avenue, Spalding, PE11 3SW, Lincolnshire, United Kingdom
Tel.: (44) 1775711565
Web Site: https://www.greenyardfresh.co.uk
Fresh Food Product Mfr
N.A.I.C.S.: 311991

Greenyard Frozen Belgium N.V. (1)
Romenstraat 3, Westrozebeke, 8840, Staden, Belgium
Tel.: (32) 51788200
Fresh Food Product Mfr
N.A.I.C.S.: 311991

Greenyard Frozen Brazil Ltda. (1)
Av Magalhaes de Castro 974, Butanta, Sao Paulo, 05502-001, Brazil
Tel.: (55) 1130963535
Fresh Food Product Mfr
N.A.I.C.S.: 311991

Greenyard Frozen Comines S.A.S. (1)
Chemin des Rabis, BP 97, 59559, Comines, Cedex, France
Tel.: (33) 320630620
Fresh Food Product Mfr
N.A.I.C.S.: 311991

Greenyard Frozen France S.A.S. (1)
Za Le Barderff, CS 20227, Moreac, 56502, Pontivy, Cedex, France
Tel.: (33) 297467270
Fresh Food Product Mfr
N.A.I.C.S.: 311991

Greenyard Frozen Poland Sp. z o.o. (1)
Ul Wojska Polskiego 12, 87-600, Lipno, Poland
Tel.: (48) 543067600
Fresh Food Product Mfr
N.A.I.C.S.: 311991

Greenyard Frozen UK Ltd. (1)
Marsh Lane Riverside Industrial Estate, Boston, PE21 7RY, Lincolnshire, United Kingdom
Tel.: (44) 1205313500
Fresh Food Product Mfr
N.A.I.C.S.: 311991

Greenyard Logistics Belgium N.V. (1)
Strijbroek 10, Sint-Katelijne-Waver, 2860, Antwerp, Belgium
Tel.: (32) 15324300

GREENYARD N.V.

Greenyard N.V.—(Continued)
Fresh Food Product Mfr
N.A.I.C.S.: 311991

Greenyard Logistics Poland Sp. z o.o. (1)
Ul Wisniowa 1, Zabia Wola, 96-321, Grodzisk Mazowiecki, Poland
Tel.: (48) 46858100
Fresh Food Product Mfr
N.A.I.C.S.: 311991

Greenyard Logistics USA Inc. (1)
405 Pedricktown Rd, Swedesboro, NJ 08085
Tel.: (856) 975-4000
Web Site: https://www.greenyardusa.com
Fresh Food Product Mfr
N.A.I.C.S.: 311991

Greenyard Prepared Belgium N.V. (1)
Industrieterrein Kanaal Noord 2002, 3960, Bree, Belgium
Tel.: (32) 89473800
Fresh Food Product Mfr
N.A.I.C.S.: 311991

Greenyard Prepared Netherlands B.V. (1)
Oude Venloseweg 84, Velden, 5941 HG, Venlo, Netherlands
Tel.: (31) 774728100
Fresh Food Product Mfr
N.A.I.C.S.: 311991

Greenyard Transport Belgium N.V. (1)
Drevendaal 1, Sint-Katelijne-Waver, 2860, Antwerp, Belgium
Tel.: (32) 15324600
Fresh Food Product Mfr
N.A.I.C.S.: 311991

Mahindra Greenyard Private Ltd. (1)
Mahindra Greenyard-5th Floor 506 Ambience Court Plot No 2 Sector 19D, Vashi, Navi Mumbai, 400705, India
Tel.: (91) 2241279077
Fresh Food Product Mfr
N.A.I.C.S.: 311991

GREENYIELD BERHAD
1-19 MKH Boulevard Jalan Bukit, 43000, Kajang, Selangor Darul Ehsan, Malaysia
Tel.: (60) 387368777 MY
Web Site: https://www.greenyield.com.my
Year Founded: 1937
GREENYB—(KLS)
Rev.: $12,046,982
Assets: $55,443,629
Liabilities: $14,696,354
Net Worth: $40,747,275
Earnings: $6,841,807
Emp.: 129
Fiscal Year-end: 12/31/22
Agricultural Product Mfr & Distr
N.A.I.C.S.: 333111
Foo Keong Tham *(Mng Dir-Grp)*

Subsidiaries:

Gimflow Sdn. Bhd. (1)
No 18 Jalan Bukit Puteri 9/12 Bandar Puteri Jaya, 08000, Sungai Petani, Kedah Darul Aman, Malaysia
Tel.: (60) 44211331
Agriculture Product Distr
N.A.I.C.S.: 424910

Givnflow Company Limited (1)
No 10 Vsip Ii Street 7 Vietnam Singapore Industrial Park Ii, Binh Duong Industry-Service-Urban Complex Hoa Phu Ward, Thu Dau Mot, Binh Duong, Vietnam
Tel.: (84) 6503860335
Agricultural Product Mfr & Distr
N.A.I.C.S.: 325211

Greenyield Industries (M) Sdn. Bhd. (1)
116 Jalan Lapan Kompleks Perabot Olak Lempit Tanjung Dua Belas, 42700, Banting, Selangor Darul Ehsan, Malaysia

Tel.: (60) 331493007
Agricultural Product Mfr & Distr
N.A.I.C.S.: 325311

RCP Technologies Sdn. Bhd. (1)
No 32 Jalan Seksyen 1/21 Taman Kajang Utama, 43000, Kajang, Selangor, Malaysia
Tel.: (60) 387369254
Agriculture Product Distr
N.A.I.C.S.: 424910

GREGGS PLC
Greggs House Quorum Business Park, Newcastle upon Tyne, NE12 8BU, United Kingdom
Tel.: (44) 1912817721
Web Site: https://www.greggs.co.uk
GRG—(LSE)
Rev.: $1,669,588,284
Assets: $1,206,198,448
Liabilities: $623,465,024
Net Worth: $582,733,424
Earnings: $159,532,100
Emp.: 25,174
Fiscal Year-end: 01/01/22
Takeaway Food Shops & Bakeries
N.A.I.C.S.: 311811
Richard Hutton *(Dir-Fin)*

Subsidiaries:

Greggs (Leasing) Limited (1)
Fernwood House Clayton Road, Jesmond, Newcastle upon Tyne, NE2 1TL, United Kingdom (100%)
Tel.: (44) 191 281 7721
Sales Range: $25-49.9 Million
Emp.: 150
Leasing Services
N.A.I.C.S.: 561499

J.R Birkett and Sons Limited (1)
Hutton Hall Bakery, Benson Row, Penrith, CA117YN, United Kingdom
Tel.: (44) 176864666
Frozen Cakes Pies & Pastries Mfr
N.A.I.C.S.: 311813

GREGORIO, NUMO Y NOEL WERTHEIN S.A.
Av Congreso 1685 1st Floor, Buenos Aires, C1428BUC, Argentina
Tel.: (54) 1147899555 Ar
Web Site: http://www.werthein.com.ar
Year Founded: 1959
Sales Range: $100-124.9 Million
Emp.: 365
Agricultural Farming & Products Whslr
N.A.I.C.S.: 311423
Daniel Werthein *(Pres)*

Subsidiaries:

Experta ART S.A. (1)
Arcos 3631 1st Floor, C1429AZQ, Buenos Aires, Argentina (100%)
Tel.: (54) 800 333 6060
Web Site: http://www.experta.com.ar
Insurance Products & Services
N.A.I.C.S.: 524298

Gregorio, Numo y Noel Werthein S.A. - Fruit Division (1)
Av Congreso 1685 - 1st floor, C1428BUC, Buenos Aires, Argentina
Tel.: (54) 11 4789 9555
Fruit Farming & Whslr
N.A.I.C.S.: 111336

Nortel Inversora S.A. (1)
Alicia Moreau de Justo 50 Piso 13, C1107AAB, Buenos Aires, Argentina
Tel.: (54) 1149683631
Web Site: http://www.nortelsa.com.ar
Rev.: $3,349,688,040
Assets: $3,013,726,680
Liabilities: $1,762,163,820
Net Worth: $1,251,562,860
Earnings: $250,463,340
Emp.: 3
Fiscal Year-end: 12/31/2016
Holding Company; Owned by Telecom Italia S.p.A. & by Gregorio, Numo y Noel Werthein S.A.

N.A.I.C.S.: 551112

GREGORY DISTRIBUTION (HOLDINGS) LIMITED
North Park, North Tawton, Devon, EX20 2EB, United Kingdom
Tel.: (44) 1837883300 UK
Web Site: http://www.gdl.uk.com
Year Founded: 1919
Holding Company
N.A.I.C.S.: 551112
John Gregory *(CEO)*

Subsidiaries:

Gregory Distribution Limited (1)
North Park, North Tawton, Devon, EX20 2EB, United Kingdom
Tel.: (44) 1 837 88 33 00
Web Site: http://www.gdl.uk.com
Sales Range: $200-249.9 Million
Emp.: 1,725
Freight Forwarding, Warehousing & Logistics Services
N.A.I.C.S.: 541614
John Gregory *(CEO)*

Subsidiary (Domestic):

ARR Craib Transport Ltd. (2)
Howe Moss Dr Kirkhill Industrial Estate, Dyce, AB21 0GL, Aberdeen, United Kingdom
Tel.: (44) 1224771122
Web Site: http://www.arr-craib.co.uk
Sales Range: $50-74.9 Million
Emp.: 400
Food Transportation Services
N.A.I.C.S.: 484110
Edward S. Anderson *(CEO)*

GREIFFENBERGER AG
Eberlestrasse 28, 86157, Augsburg, Germany
Tel.: (49) 8215212261
Web Site: https://www.greiffenberger.de
Year Founded: 1986
GRF—(MUN)
Rev.: $69,565,887
Assets: $66,872,445
Liabilities: $33,005,713
Net Worth: $33,866,732
Earnings: ($2,174,624)
Emp.: 325
Fiscal Year-end: 12/31/23
Electrical Product Mfr & Distr
N.A.I.C.S.: 336320

GREINER HOLDING AG
Greinerstrasse 70, 4550, Kremsmunster, Austria
Tel.: (43) 5054160301 AT
Web Site: http://www.greiner.com
Year Founded: 1868
Sales Range: $1-9.9 Million
Emp.: 10,700
Holding Company; Plastic Packaging Products Mfr
N.A.I.C.S.: 551112
Hannes Moser *(CFO)*

Subsidiaries:

AS Greiner Packaging (1)
Tammi tee 42, Tabasalu, 76901, Estonia
Tel.: (372) 6031570
Plastic Packaging Product Distr
N.A.I.C.S.: 423840
Deniss Holodkov *(Dir-Sls)*

Eurofoam GmbH (1)
Euro Plaza 5i Wagenseilgasse 3, 1120, Vienna, Austria (100%)
Tel.: (43) 1 6022 154 0
Web Site: http://www.eurofoam.eu
Sales Range: $400-449.9 Million
Emp.: 2,317
Urethane & Foam Product Mfr
N.A.I.C.S.: 326150
Jurgen Kleinrath *(CEO)*

INTERNATIONAL PUBLIC

Subsidiary (Non-US):

Eurofoam Bohemia S.r.o. (2)
Prumyslova 5, Klasterec Nad Ohri, Klasterec nad Ohri, 431 51, Czech Republic
Tel.: (420) 474316666
Sales Range: $25-49.9 Million
Emp.: 50
Polystyrene Foam Product Mfr
N.A.I.C.S.: 326140

Eurofoam Deutschland GmbH Schaumstoffe (2)
Hagenauer Strasse 42, 65203, Wiesbaden, Germany
Tel.: (49) 61192760
Plastics Product Mfr
N.A.I.C.S.: 326199

Subsidiary (Domestic):

KFM-Schaumstoff GmbH (3)
Rosenauer Str 28, Dorfl es-Esbach, 96487, Regensburg, Germany
Tel.: (49) 956185560
Web Site: http://www.kfm-schaumstoff.de
Sales Range: $25-49.9 Million
Emp.: 90
Urethane & Foam Product Mfr
N.A.I.C.S.: 326150
Josef Schmid *(Mng Dir)*

Subsidiary (Non-US):

Eurofoam G.E.I.E. (2)
Avenue Des Pleiades 15, 1200, Brussels, Belgium
Tel.: (32) 27751811
Sales Range: $10-24.9 Million
Emp.: 47
Facilities Support Services
N.A.I.C.S.: 561210
Etienne F. Davignon *(Chm)*

Eurofoam Gdansk Sp. Z o.o. (2)
Ul Przyrodnikow 23, 80-298, Gdansk, Poland
Tel.: (48) 583411881
Web Site: http://www.eurofoam.com
Sales Range: $25-49.9 Million
Emp.: 46
Polystyrene Foam Product Mfr
N.A.I.C.S.: 326140

Eurofoam Hungary Kft (2)
Sajobabony, PF. 16, 3792, Miskolc, Hungary
Tel.: (36) 46549040
Web Site: http://www.eurofoam.hu
Emp.: 240
Urethane & Foam Product Mfr
N.A.I.C.S.: 326150
Gyorgy Felfoldi *(Mng Dir)*

Eurofoam Polska Sp. Z o.o. (2)
Ul Szczawinska 42, Zgierz, 95-100, Lodz, Poland
Tel.: (48) 427163854
Web Site: http://www.eurofoam.pl
Sales Range: $125-149.9 Million
Emp.: 500
Polystyrene Foam Product Mfr
N.A.I.C.S.: 326140
Zbigniew Pilichowski *(Gen Mgr)*

Eurofoam Poznan Sp. Z o.o. (2)
Ul Gnieznienska 4, Janikowo, 62-006, Inowroclaw, Poland
Tel.: (48) 618736700
Web Site: http://www.eurofoam.poznan.pl
Polystyrene Foam Product Mfr
N.A.I.C.S.: 326140

Eurofoam S.r.l. (2)
Str Fabricii Nr 10, Baia Mare, 430015, Romania
Tel.: (40) 262206286
Web Site: http://www.eurofoam.com
Sales Range: $25-49.9 Million
Emp.: 78
Mattress Mfr
N.A.I.C.S.: 337910

France Filieres Plastiques S.A.S. (1)
206 Chemin des artisans, BP 7, 74550, Perrignier, France
Tel.: (33) 450724791
Web Site: http://www.ffp.fr
Machine Tools Mfr
N.A.I.C.S.: 335311

AND PRIVATE COMPANIES

GREINER HOLDING AG

GREINER PACKAGING Sp. z o.o. (1)
Plantowa 16, 05-825, Grodzisk Mazowiecki, Poland
Tel.: (48) 227243232
Plastic Packaging Product Distr
N.A.I.C.S.: 423840
Bartlomiej Celmerowski (Dir-Sls)

Greiner Aerospace (Shanghai) Co., Ltd. (1)
Building 13/C2 No 260 Lian Cao Rd, Minhang District, Shanghai, 201108, China
Tel.: (86) 2164340300
Aircraft Seat Distr
N.A.I.C.S.: 423860
Yun Lu (Gen Mgr)

Greiner Assistec GmbH (1)
Buchauer Strasse 104, 8933, Sankt Gallen, Austria
Tel.: (43) 3632522
Plastic Packaging Products Mfr
N.A.I.C.S.: 326199
Markus Landl (Dir-Sls)

Greiner Assistec Leresti Romania SA (1)
Strada Erou Locotenent Dumitru Lazea 408, 117430, Arges, Leresti, Romania
Tel.: (40) 248512199
Web Site: http://www.amplast.ro
Sales Range: $75-99.9 Million
Emp.: 300
Disposable Plastic Packaging Mfr
N.A.I.C.S.: 322220

Greiner Assistec S.R.L. (1)
Str Erou Locotenent Dumitru Lazea Nr 408, Leresti, 117430, Arges, Romania
Tel.: (40) 248512199
Plastic Packaging Product Distr
N.A.I.C.S.: 423840
Mihai Daraban (Dir-Sls)

Greiner Assistec, S. A. de C. V. (1)
Avenida Huinala km 2 8 400, Parque Industrial las Americas, 66640, Monterrey, Nuevo Leon, Mexico
Tel.: (52) 818568908
Plastic Packaging Product Distr
N.A.I.C.S.: 423840

Greiner Bio-One B.V. (1)
Albert Einsteinweg 16, Postbus 280, 2408 AR, Alphen aan den Rijn, Netherlands
Tel.: (31) 1 72 42 09 00
Medical Equipment Distr
N.A.I.C.S.: 423450

Greiner Bio-One GmbH (1)
Gewerbepark 2, 4261, Rainbach im Muhlkreis, Austria
Tel.: (43) 7949 2090 0
Medical Equipment Mfr
N.A.I.C.S.: 334510

Subsidiary (Non-US):

Greiner Bio-One (Thailand) Ltd. (2)
700 / 172 Moo 1 Amata Nakorn Industrial Estate, Tambon Bankao, Phan Thong, 20160, Chonburi, Thailand
Tel.: (66) 38465633
Medical Equipment Distr
N.A.I.C.S.: 423450

Greiner Bio-One Brasil Produtos Medicos Hospitalares Ltda. (2)
Rua Affonso Pansan 1967, Vila Bertini, 13473-620, Sao Paulo, Brazil
Tel.: (55) 19 3468 9600
Medical Equipment Distr
N.A.I.C.S.: 423450

Greiner Bio-One France S.A.S. (2)
3-7 avenue du Cap Horn, BP 31, Les Ulis, 91941, Courtaboeuf, France
Tel.: (33) 69862525
Medical Equipment Distr
N.A.I.C.S.: 423450

Greiner Bio-One Hungary Kft. (2)
Fertosor 7, 9200, Mosonmagyarovar, Hungary
Tel.: (36) 96213088
Medical Equipment Distr
N.A.I.C.S.: 423450

Greiner Bio-One India Private Limited (2)
Urmin House Sindhu Bhavan Road, Bodakdev, 380059, Ahmedabad, India
Tel.: (91) 79029296911
Web Site: http://www.gboindia.com
Medical Equipment Distr
N.A.I.C.S.: 423450

Subsidiary (US):

Greiner Bio-One North America, Inc. (2)
4238 Capital Dr, Monroe, NC 28110
Tel.: (704) 261-7800
Medical Equipment Distr
N.A.I.C.S.: 423450

Subsidiary (Non-US):

Greiner Bio-One Suns Co., Ltd. (2)
No 6 Guanganmen Nei Street, Xicheng District, Beijing, China
Tel.: (86) 1083551991
Web Site: http://www.gbo-suns.com
Medical Equipment Distr
N.A.I.C.S.: 423450

Greiner Bio-One VACUETTE Schweiz GmbH (2)
St Leonhardstrasse 31, 9000, Saint Gallen, Switzerland
Tel.: (41) 712285522
Medical Equipment Distr
N.A.I.C.S.: 423450

Greiner Bio-One GmbH (1)
Maybachstrasse 2, 72636, Frickenhausen, Germany
Tel.: (49) 7022 948 0
Medical Equipment Distr
N.A.I.C.S.: 423450

Subsidiary (Non-US):

Greiner Bio-One Co. Ltd. (2)
Akasaka 2-17-44 Fukuyoshizaka Building 2F, Minato-Ku, Tokyo, 107-0052, Japan
Tel.: (81) 335058875
Web Site: http://www.greiner-bio-one.co.jp
Medical Equipment Distr
N.A.I.C.S.: 423450

Greiner Bio-One Ltd. (2)
Brunel Way Stroudwater Business Park, Stonehouse, GL10 3SX, Gloucestershire, United Kingdom
Tel.: (44) 1453825255
Medical Equipment Distr
N.A.I.C.S.: 423450

Greiner Bio-One International GmbH (1)
Bad Haller Str 32, 4550, Kremsmunster, Austria
Tel.: (43) 7583 6791 0
Web Site: http://www.gbo.com
Medical Equipment Mfr
N.A.I.C.S.: 334510
Markus Riepl (Acct Mgr-OEM Intl/Exports)

Subsidiary (Non-US):

Greiner Bio-One GmbH (2)
Maybachstrasse 2, 72636, Frickenhausen, Germany
Tel.: (49) 70229480
Medical Equipment Distr
N.A.I.C.S.: 423450

Subsidiary (Domestic):

Mediscan GmbH & Co. KG (2)
Bad Haller Strasse 34, 4550, Kremsmunster, Austria
Tel.: (43) 758351520
Web Site: http://www.mediscan.at
Medical Equipment Mfr
N.A.I.C.S.: 334510

Greiner Extrusion Group GmbH (1)
Friedrich-Schiedel-Strasse 1, 4542, Nussbach, Austria
Tel.: (43) 50541410
Web Site: https://www.greinerextrusion.com
Tooling & Dies Mfr
N.A.I.C.S.: 333514
Henning Arndt (CEO)

Greiner Extrusion US, Inc. (1)
1101 Morgan Vlg Rd, Meadville, PA 16335
Tel.: (814) 333-2060
Machine Tool Distr

N.A.I.C.S.: 423830
Scot Watkins (Mgr-Sls)

Greiner MULTIfoam Sp. z o o. (1)
ul Adamowek 37B, 95-035, Ozorkow, Poland
Tel.: (48) 427188100
Web Site: http://www.greiner-multifoam.pl
Foam Products Mfr
N.A.I.C.S.: 326150
Krzysztof Gorzechowski (Acct Mgr)

Greiner PURtec CZ spol. s.r.o. (1)
Komenskeho 895, 340 22, Nyrsko, Czech Republic
Tel.: (420) 376804124
Insulation Products Distr
N.A.I.C.S.: 423330

Greiner PURtec GmbH (1)
Erwin Greiner Strasse 5, 4690, Schwanenstadt, Austria
Tel.: (43) 767360020
Web Site: http://www.greiner-purtec.com
Insulation Product Mfr
N.A.I.C.S.: 326140

Greiner Packaging B.V. (1)
Gildenveld 12a, 3892 DG, Zeewolde, Netherlands
Tel.: (31) 65236160
Plastic Packaging Product Distr
N.A.I.C.S.: 423840
AnneMarie von Laarhoven (Dir-Sls)

Greiner Packaging Corp. (1)
225 Enterprise Way, Pittston, PA 18640
Tel.: (570) 602-3900
Plastic Packaging Product Distr
N.A.I.C.S.: 423840
Bruce Alling (Dir-Sls)

Greiner Packaging Distribution SARL (1)
3 A Allee de l economie, BP 50 027, Wiwersheim, 67370, France
Tel.: (33) 388514978
Plastic Packaging Product Distr
N.A.I.C.S.: 423840
Bruno Frech (Dir-Sls)

Greiner Packaging GmbH (1)
Im Wohr 2, 76437, Rastatt, Germany
Tel.: (49) 72225030
Plastic Packaging Product Distr
N.A.I.C.S.: 423840
Christian Scheck (Dir-Sls)

Greiner Packaging Kft. (1)
Szechenyi ut 7, 8111, Seregelyes, Hungary
Tel.: (36) 22575200
Plastic Packaging Product Distr
N.A.I.C.S.: 423840
Zsolt Peller (Dir-Sls)

Greiner Packaging S.R.L (1)
Strada Stefan cel Mare numarul 156A, 550321, Sibiu, judetul Sibiu, Romania
Tel.: (40) 269215810
Plastic Packaging Product Distr
N.A.I.C.S.: 423840
Lucian Ocos (Dir-Sls)

Greiner Packaging Vertriebs GmbH (1)
Dornberger Strasse 276, 33619, Bielefeld, Germany
Tel.: (49) 5219116300
Plastic Packaging Product Distr
N.A.I.C.S.: 423840
Susanne Gneist (Dir-Sls)

Greiner Packaging d.o.o. (1)
Industrijska Ulica 33, 2345, Ruse, Slovenia
Tel.: (386) 26300360
Plastic Packaging Product Distr
N.A.I.C.S.: 423840
Borut Pogelsek (Dir-Sls)

Greiner Perfoam GmbH (1)
Hafen Enns - Wirtschaftspark Mainstrasse 1, 4470, Enns, Austria
Tel.: (47) 7223 9010 0
Web Site: http://www.greiner-perfoam.com
Automobile Spare Parts Mfr
N.A.I.C.S.: 336390
Michael Schleiss (CEO)

Subsidiary (Non-US):

Greiner Perfoam GmbH (2)

Robert-Bosch-Strasse 13, 73117, Wangen, Germany
Tel.: (49) 71612070
Emp.: 48
Automotive Spare Parts Distr
N.A.I.C.S.: 423120

Greiner perfoam spol. s r.o. (2)
Vozicka 602, 39002, Tabor, Czech Republic
Tel.: (420) 381406700
Emp.: 420
Automotive Spare Parts Distr
N.A.I.C.S.: 423120

Greiner Real Estate Sp. z o.o. (1)
Adamowek 37b, 95-035, Ozorkow, Poland
Tel.: (48) 427188100
Real Estate Manangement Services
N.A.I.C.S.: 531311

Greiner Tool.Tec GmbH (1)
Friedrich-Schiedel-Strasse 1, 4542, Nussbach, Austria
Tel.: (43) 505 41 0
Web Site: http://www.greiner-gtt.com
Machine Tools Mfr
N.A.I.C.S.: 335311

Subsidiary (Domestic):

GPN GmbH (2)
Greinerstrasse 18, 4542, Nussbach, Austria
Tel.: (43) 50541450
Web Site: http://www.gpn.at
Machine Tools Mfr
N.A.I.C.S.: 335311

Subsidiary (Non-US):

GPN strojirna s.r.o. (2)
Husova 1056, 37401, Trhove Sviny, Czech Republic
Tel.: (420) 387844900
Industrial Machinery Mfr
N.A.I.C.S.: 333248

Greiner Extrusion Technology (Shanghai) Co., Ltd. (2)
4365 Yindu Road, Xinzhuang Industry Park, Shanghai, 201108, China
Tel.: (86) 2154425766
Web Site: http://www.greiner-shanghai.com
Machine Tools Mfr
N.A.I.C.S.: 335311

Greiner aerospace Inc. (1)
7621 Pebble Dr Bldg 22, Fort Worth, TX 76118
Tel.: (817) 686-3100
Aircraft Seat Distr
N.A.I.C.S.: 423860
Alicia Gaspar Bacon (Office Mgr)

Greiner i JP Packaging d.o.o. (1)
Druga industrijska 2, 22330, Nova Pazova, Serbia
Tel.: (381) 22323273
Plastic Packaging Product Distr
N.A.I.C.S.: 423840
Dejan Prusac (Dir-Sls)

GuKo Tech GmbH (1)
Galgenbergstrasse 9, 72622, Nurtingen, Germany
Tel.: (49) 7022501340
Web Site: http://www.gukotech.com
Rubber Products Mfr
N.A.I.C.S.: 326229
Marcus Ehrentreich (CEO)

Neveon Holding GmbH (1)
The Icon Vienna /Tower 24 / Floor 9 Wiedner Gurtel 9-13, 1100, Vienna, Austria
Tel.: (43) 5054119001
Web Site: https://www.neveon.com
Mattress Mfr
N.A.I.C.S.: 337910
Jurgen Kleinrath (CEO)

OOO Greiner Packaging (1)
Dobroseleskaya 224-B, 600032, Vladimir, Russia
Tel.: (7) 4922212720
Plastic Packaging Product Distr
N.A.I.C.S.: 423840
Yan Snegirev (Dir-Sls)

Solufip S.A.S. (1)
281 rue Pierre et Marie Curie Z I de la Noe Bachelon, 44430, Le Loroux-Botteraux, France

GREINER HOLDING AG

Greiner Holding AG—(Continued)
Tel.: (33) 240341909
Machine Tools Mfr
N.A.I.C.S.: 335311

TOV Greiner Packaging (1)
8a Antonova street, 8130, Kiev, Ukraine
Tel.: (380) 44 586 5670
Plastic Packaging Product Distr
N.A.I.C.S.: 423840
Yuriy Kutsenko *(Dir-Sls)*

greiner assistec s.r.o. (1)
Brezova 181, 76315, Slusovice, Czech Republic
Tel.: (420) 577191580
Plastic Packaging Product Distr
N.A.I.C.S.: 423840
Filip Gajdosik *(Dir-Sls)*

greiner packaging ag (1)
Rheinstrasse 38, 9444, Diepoldsau, Switzerland
Tel.: (41) 717378300
Plastic Packaging Product Distr
N.A.I.C.S.: 423840
Jens Krause *(Dir-Sls)*

greiner packaging s.r.o. (1)
Greinerova 216, 43533, Louka u Litvinova, Czech Republic
Tel.: (420) 476719212
Plastic Packaging Product Distr
N.A.I.C.S.: 423840
Tomas Francirek *(Dir-Sls)*

greiner packaging slusovice s.r.o (1)
Greinerova 54, 763 15, Slusovice, Czech Republic
Tel.: (420) 577083222
Plastic Packaging Product Distr
N.A.I.C.S.: 423840
Frantisek Pavlik *(Dir-Sls)*

GREKA DRILLING LIMITED
29th Floor Landmark Plaza No 1 Business Outer Ring Road, Central Business District, Zhengzhou, 450000, Henan, China
Tel.: (86) 371 6013 3388
Web Site: http://www.grekadrilling.com
Year Founded: 2007
Rev.: $11,585,000
Assets: $91,304,000
Liabilities: $35,127,000
Net Worth: $56,177,000
Earnings: ($2,565,000)
Emp.: 665
Fiscal Year-end: 12/31/17
Holding Company; Gas Drilling Services
N.A.I.C.S.: 551112
Randeep Singh Grewal *(Chm & CEO)*

Subsidiaries:

Greka Drilling (India) Ltd (1)
Vatika Business Centre Mezzanine Floor Konnectus Building, Bhavbhuti Marg Connaught Place, New Delhi, 110001, India
Tel.: (91) 1123660100
Drilling Services
N.A.I.C.S.: 213112
Pradeep Gupta *(CFO & Exec VP)*

GREMI INWESTYCJE S.A.
Ul Wroclawska 53, 30-011, Krakow, Poland
Tel.: (48) 12 6321 350
Web Site: http://www.gremimedia.eu
GMM—(WAR)
Sales Range: Less than $1 Million
Financial Services
N.A.I.C.S.: 523999
Artur Rawski *(Chm-Mgmt Bd)*

GREMZ, INC.
Tennoz First Tower 19F 2-2-4 Higashi-Shinagawa, Shinagawa-Ku, Tokyo, 140-0002, Japan
Tel.: (81) 357693500
Web Site: https://www.gremz.co.jp
Year Founded: 2005
3150—(TKS)
Rev.: $197,691,880
Assets: $142,855,320
Liabilities: $56,984,810
Net Worth: $85,870,510
Earnings: $23,399,400
Emp.: 273
Fiscal Year-end: 03/31/24
Oil & Gas Operations
N.A.I.C.S.: 213112
Masaomi Tanaka *(Pres & CEO)*

Subsidiaries:

GR Consulting, Inc. (1)
2-2-4 Higashi-Shinagawa, Shinagawa-ku, Tokyo, 140-0002, Japan
Tel.: (81) 357693650
Web Site: https://www.gr-consulting.co.jp
Electricity Related Equipment Mfr
N.A.I.C.S.: 335999

Gremz Power, Inc. (1)
2-2-4 Higashi-Shinagawa Tennozu First Tower 19th Floor, Shinagawa-ku, Tokyo, 140-0002, Japan
Tel.: (81) 357693659
Web Site: https://www.gremz-power.co.jp
Electricity Power Distribution Services
N.A.I.C.S.: 221122

Gremz Solar, Inc. (1)
Tennozu First Tower 2-2-4 Higashi-Shinagawa, Shinagawa-ku, Tokyo, 140-0002, Japan
Tel.: (81) 357693655
Web Site: https://www.gremz-solar.co.jp
Solar Power Generation Services
N.A.I.C.S.: 221114

GRENADA ELECTRICITY SERVICES LIMITED
Dusty Highway, PO Box 381, Saint George's, Grenada
Tel.: (473) 4402650
Web Site: http://www.grenlec.com
Sales Range: $75-99.9 Million
Emp.: 206
Electronic Services
N.A.I.C.S.: 221122
Benedict Brathwaite *(Controller-Fin)*

GRENDENE S.A.
Av Pimentel Gomes 214, 62040-125, Fortaleza, 62040-125, CE, Brazil
Tel.: (55) 8831122999
Web Site: https://www.grendene.com.br
Year Founded: 1971
GRND3—(BRAZ)
Rev.: $448,865
Assets: $898,904
Liabilities: $85,655
Net Worth: $813,250
Earnings: $77,901
Emp.: 20,000
Fiscal Year-end: 12/31/20
Footwear Mfr
N.A.I.C.S.: 316210
Alexandre Grendene Bartelle *(Chm)*

Subsidiaries:

Grendene Italy S.R.L. (1)
Via S Michele, San Pietro in Gu, 35010, Padova, PD, Italy
Tel.: (39) 04441429720
Web Site: https://www.grendene.it
Office Chair Mfr
N.A.I.C.S.: 337214

GRENERGY RENOVABLES SA
Rafael Boti 26, 28023, Madrid, Spain
Tel.: (34) 917081970
Web Site: https://grenergy.eu
Year Founded: 2007
GRE—(MAD)
Rev.: $80,954,265
Assets: $176,520,183
Liabilities: $134,976,204
Net Worth: $41,543,979
Earnings: $12,807,788
Emp.: 86
Fiscal Year-end: 12/31/19
Wind Energy Equipment Mfr
N.A.I.C.S.: 333611
Antonio Jimenez Alarcon *(CFO)*

Subsidiaries:

Grenergy Erneuerbare Energien GmbH (1)
Kopenicker Strasse 40B, 10179, Berlin, Germany
Tel.: (49) 30460606880
Web Site: https://grenergy.eu
Eletric Power Generation Services
N.A.I.C.S.: 221118

Grenergy Polska Sp. z o.o. (1)
Warsaw HUB Rondo Daszynskiego 2b, 00-843, Warsaw, Poland
Tel.: (48) 666368357
Web Site: https://grenergy.eu
Eletric Power Generation Services
N.A.I.C.S.: 221118

Grenergy Renewables Uk Limited (1)
6th Floor 25 Farringdon Street, London, EC4A 4AB, United Kingdom
Tel.: (44) 7544055612
Emp.: 380
Renewable Energy Generation Services
N.A.I.C.S.: 221118

GRENKE AG
Neuer Markt 2, 76532, Baden-Baden, Germany
Tel.: (49) 722150070 De
Web Site: https://www.grenke.de
Year Founded: 1978
GLJ—(MUN)
Rev.: $515,959,877
Assets: $7,836,969,220
Liabilities: $6,546,567,267
Net Worth: $1,290,401,953
Earnings: $101,909,278
Emp.: 2,158
Fiscal Year-end: 12/31/23
Information Technology Financial Services
N.A.I.C.S.: 523150
Wolfgang Grenke *(Founder)*

Subsidiaries:

GC Credit-Bail Quebec Inc. (1)
4605 Boulevard Lapiniere Suite 280, Brossard, J4Z 3T5, QC, Canada
Tel.: (450) 445-5270
Financial Lending Services
N.A.I.C.S.: 532420
Fabrice Carpanen *(Mng Dir)*

GC Factoring AAF Srl (1)
Via Montefeltro 4, 20156, Milan, MI, Italy
Tel.: (39) 0230059410
Financial Lending Services
N.A.I.C.S.: 532420
Luca Tenca *(Mng Dir)*

GC Factoring Limited (1)
2 London Square Cross Lanes, Guildford, GU1 1UN, Surrey, United Kingdom
Tel.: (44) 1483401740
Web Site: http://www.grenke.co.uk
Office Equipment Leasing Services
N.A.I.C.S.: 532490

GC Financial Solutions Ltd. (1)
Unit B Carrowreagh Business Park Carrowreagh Road, Belfast, BT16 1QQ, Dundonald, United Kingdom
Tel.: (44) 2890820950
Financial Lending Services
N.A.I.C.S.: 532420

GC Lease Singapore Pte. Ltd. (1)
70 Shenton Way Eon Shenton 12-01, Singapore, 079118, Singapore
Tel.: (65) 63518252
Web Site: https://www.grenke.sg
Emp.: 4
Financial Lending Services
N.A.I.C.S.: 532420
Guillaume Cuny *(Mng Dir)*

INTERNATIONAL PUBLIC

GC Leasing AZ LLC (1)
3200 E Camelback Rd Ste 253, Phoenix, AZ 85018
Tel.: (602) 515-8057
Web Site: http://www.grenke.us
Office Equipment Leasing Services
N.A.I.C.S.: 532490
Thomas Sauerteig *(Mng Dir)*

GC Leasing Melbourne Pty. Ltd. (1)
Level 5 420 St Kilda Road, Melbourne, 3004, VIC, Australia
Tel.: (61) 391324500
Financial Lending Services
N.A.I.C.S.: 532420
Julian Haub *(Mng Dir)*

GC Leasing Middle East FZCO (1)
Dubai Hills Park Heights Square Building 2 Office 102, PO Box 37 10 62, Regal Tower Office 2506-2507, Dubai, United Arab Emirates
Tel.: (971) 44405020
Web Site: https://www.grenke.ae
Emp.: 15
Financial Lending Services
N.A.I.C.S.: 532420
Michal Maciej Maczewski *(Mgr)*

GC Leasing Norway AS (1)
Radhusgt 5 B, 0151, Oslo, Norway
Tel.: (47) 22336900
Equipment Leasing Services
N.A.I.C.S.: 532490

GC Leasing Ontario Inc. (1)
5600 Explorer Drive Suite 302, Mississauga, L4W 4Y2, ON, Canada
Tel.: (905) 366-6000
Web Site: http://www.grenkeleasing.ca
Financial Lending Services
N.A.I.C.S.: 532420
Fabrice Carpanen *(Mng Dir)*

GC Leasing Sydney Pty. Ltd. (1)
Suite 3 Level 2 Building B 4 Drake Avenue, Macquarie Park, 2113, NSW, Australia
Tel.: (61) 292603600
Emp.: 18
Financial Lending Services
N.A.I.C.S.: 532420
Victor Ferreira *(Mng Dir)*

GC Leasing d.o.o. (1)
Verovskova ulica 64A, 1000, Ljubljana, Slovenia
Tel.: (386) 15826200
Web Site: http://www.grenke.si
Sales Range: $50-74.9 Million
Emp.: 4
Equipment Leasing Services
N.A.I.C.S.: 532420
Ernest Plej *(Dir)*

GC Locacao de Equipamentos Ltda. (1)
Rua Surubim no 504 set 51Cidade Moncoes neighborhood, Brooklin Novo, Sao Paulo, 04571-050, Brazil
Tel.: (55) 1143022310
Web Site: https://www.grenke.com.br
Emp.: 44
Office Equipment Leasing Services
N.A.I.C.S.: 532490

GC Rent Chile SpA (1)
Av Vitacura 2969 Piso 4 Oficina 402, Las Condes, Santiago, Chile
Tel.: (56) 232017100
Web Site: http://www.grenke.cl
Office Equipment Leasing Services
N.A.I.C.S.: 532490

GF Faktor Zrt. (1)
Business Center 91 Vaci ut 91, 1139, Budapest, Hungary
Tel.: (36) 12365080
Financial Lending Services
N.A.I.C.S.: 532420
Zsombor Baltay *(CEO)*

GL Leasing British Columbia Inc. (1)
138 East 13th Street Unit 360, North Vancouver, V7L 0E5, BC, Canada
Tel.: (778) 357-0680
Financial Lending Services
N.A.I.C.S.: 532420
Michael Wozny *(Mng Dir)*

GRENKE ALQUILER S.A (1)
Passeig de Gracia 28 1 2a, 08007, Barce-

AND PRIVATE COMPANIES

Iona, Spain
Tel.: (34) 934817610
Web Site: http://www.grenke.es
Equipment Leasing Services
N.A.I.C.S.: 532420

GRENKE LEASE Sprl (1)
Chaussee de Ruisbroeck 76, 1180, Brussels, Belgium
Tel.: (32) 23335050
Web Site: https://www.grenke.be
Emp.: 30
Equipment Leasing Services
N.A.I.C.S.: 532490

GRENKE LIMITED (1)
Q House Suite 306 Furze Road, Sandyford Business Park, Dublin, 18, Ireland
Tel.: (353) 12923400
Web Site: https://www.grenke.ie
Emp.: 63
Financial Investment Services
N.A.I.C.S.: 523999

GRENKE LOCATION SAS (1)
9-9A rue de Lisbonne, 67300, Schiltigheim, France
Tel.: (33) 390208500
Web Site: https://www.grenke.fr
Emp.: 232
Equipment Leasing Services
N.A.I.C.S.: 532420

GRENKE RENT S.A. (1)
Playa de las Americas 2 Oficina B-2, Las Rozas, 28290, Madrid, Spain
Tel.: (34) 916305673
Web Site: http://www.grenke.es
Emp.: 12
Equipment Leasing Services
N.A.I.C.S.: 532420
Marco Fruehauf *(Pres & Mng Dir)*

GRENKEFACTORING GmbH (1)
Neuer Markt 2, 76491, Baden-Baden, Germany
Tel.: (49) 72215007770
Web Site: http://www.grenkefactoring.de
Emp.: 15
Factoring Services
N.A.I.C.S.: 522299

GRENKELEASING AB (1)
Kistagangen 20B 5 tr, 164 40, Kista, Sweden
Tel.: (46) 84441670
Web Site: https://www.grenke.se
Sales Range: $50-74.9 Million
Emp.: 26
Equipment Leasing Services
N.A.I.C.S.: 532420

GRENKELEASING AG (1)
Schaffhauserstrasse 611, 8052, Zurich, Switzerland
Tel.: (41) 443656000
Web Site: https://www.grenke.ch
Emp.: 42
Equipment Leasing Services
N.A.I.C.S.: 532420

GRENKELEASING ApS (1)
Marielundvej 48 3 sal, 2730, Herlev, Denmark
Tel.: (45) 44528810
Web Site: https://www.grenke.dk
Sales Range: $50-74.9 Million
Emp.: 32
Equipment Leasing Services
N.A.I.C.S.: 532420

GRENKELEASING Magyarorszag Kft. (1)
Tel.: (36) 12357041
Sales Range: $50-74.9 Million
Emp.: 9
Financial Lending Services
N.A.I.C.S.: 523999

GRENKELEASING Sp. z o.o (1)
ul Abpa A Baraniaka 88, 61-131, Poznan, Greater Poland, Poland
Tel.: (48) 618723700
Web Site: https://www.grenke.pl
Sales Range: $25-49.9 Million
Emp.: 52
Equipment Leasing Services
N.A.I.C.S.: 532420

GRENKELEASING s.r.o. (1)
Na Hrebenech II 1718/10, 140 00, Prague, Czech Republic
Tel.: (420) 221501711
Web Site: https://www.grenke.cz
Emp.: 8
Equipment Leasing Services
N.A.I.C.S.: 532420

GWFACT - Invoice solutions, Lda. (1)
Edificio Adamastor Torre B Av D Joao II n 9 I Floor 10 C, 1990-077, Lisbon, Portugal
Tel.: (351) 211233500
Web Site: http://www.grenke.pt
Financial Lending Services
N.A.I.C.S.: 532420

Grenke Bank AG (1)
Neuer Markt 2, 76532, Baden-Baden, Germany
Tel.: (49) 722150077200
Web Site: http://www.grenkebank.de
Sales Range: $50-74.9 Million
Emp.: 40
Private Banking Services
N.A.I.C.S.: 523150
Ernst-Moritz Lipp *(Chm-Supervisory Bd)*

Grenke Business Solutions GmbH Co. KG (1)
Neuer Markt 2, 76532, Baden-Baden, Germany
Tel.: (49) 722150070
Financial Lending Services
N.A.I.C.S.: 532420

Grenke Digital GmbH (1)
Alter Schlachthof 51, 76131, Karlsruhe, Germany
Tel.: (49) 721860070
Financial Lending Services
N.A.I.C.S.: 532420
Florian Setzler *(Mng Dir)*

Grenke Finance PLC (1)
Suite 410 Q-House Furze Road, Sandyford Business Park, Dublin, D18, Ireland
Tel.: (353) 12923400
Financial Lending Services
N.A.I.C.S.: 532420
Patrick Spain *(Mng Dir)*

Grenke Hrvatska d.o.o. (1)
Av Veceslava Holjevca 40, 10000, Zagreb, Croatia
Tel.: (385) 16457260
Web Site: http://www.grenke.hr
Financial Lending Services
N.A.I.C.S.: 532420

Grenke Investitionen Verwaltungs Kommanditgesellschaft auf Aktien (1)
Landsberger Strasse 224, 12623, Berlin, Germany
Tel.: (49) 305779953
Web Site: http://www.asset-broker.de
Financial Investment Services
N.A.I.C.S.: 523999

Grenke Kiralama Ltd. Sti. (1)
Buyukdere Cad Apa Giz Plaza No 191 Kat 5/9, Levent Besiktas, 34330, Istanbul, Turkiye
Tel.: (90) 2123399310
Web Site: https://www.grenke.com.tr
Emp.: 10
Office Equipment Leasing Services
N.A.I.C.S.: 532490

Grenke Leasing Ltd. (1)
No 2 London Square, Cross Lanes, Guildford, GU1 1UN, Surrey, United Kingdom
Web Site: https://www.grenke.co.uk
Emp.: 43
Equipment Leasing Services
N.A.I.C.S.: 532490

Grenke Locazione S.r.l. (1)
Via Montefeltro 4, 20156, Milan, MI, Italy
Tel.: (39) 0230059460
Financial Lending Services
N.A.I.C.S.: 532420
Giulia Laureti *(Sls Mgr-Internal)*

Grenke Rent S.L. (1)
Playa de las Americas 2, Las Rozas, 28230, Madrid, Spain
Tel.: (34) 916305672
Web Site: https://www.grenke.es

Emp.: 89
Financial Institution Services
N.A.I.C.S.: 523999

Grenke Renting Ltd. (1)
Tel.: (356) 22588500
Web Site: http://www.grenke.com.mt
Office Equipment Leasing Services
N.A.I.C.S.: 532490

Grenke Renting S.R.L. (1)
Tel.: (40) 213001987
Industrial Equipment Rental & Leasing Services
N.A.I.C.S.: 532490
Petrica Daniel Barbu *(Sls Dir)*

Grenke Renting, S.A. (1)
Avenida D Joao II n 45- 4A, 1990-084, Lisbon, Portugal
Tel.: (351) 2189344414
Web Site: http://www.grenke.pt
Sales Range: $50-74.9 Million
Emp.: 30
Equipment Leasing Services
N.A.I.C.S.: 532420
Marco Vaz Souta *(Mng Dir)*

Grenkefactoring AG (1)
Hochbergerstrasse 60C, 4057, Basel, Switzerland
Tel.: (41) 617067900
Financial Lending Services
N.A.I.C.S.: 532420

Grenkefinance N.V. (1)
Lage Biezenweg 7-G, 4131 LV, Vianen, Netherlands
Tel.: (31) 347325010
Web Site: https://www.grenke.nl
Sales Range: $50-74.9 Million
Emp.: 45
Information Technology Equipment Leasing Services
N.A.I.C.S.: 532420

Grenkeleasing D.O.O. (1)
Verovskova ulica 64A, 1000, Ljubljana, Slovenia
Tel.: (386) 15826200
Web Site: https://www.grenke.si
Business Loan Services
N.A.I.C.S.: 522291

Grenkeleasing GmbH (1)
Handelskai 92, 1200, Vienna, Austria
Tel.: (43) 170645650
Financial Lending Services
N.A.I.C.S.: 532420

Grenkeleasing Oy (1)
Karhumaentie 3, 01530, Vantaa, Finland
Tel.: (358) 103376000
Financial Lending Services
N.A.I.C.S.: 532420
Riku Jokela *(Mng Dir)*

Grenkeleasing s.r.o. (1)
City Business Center II Karadzicova 10, 821 08, Bratislava, Slovakia
Tel.: (421) 250204704
Web Site: http://www.grenke.sk
Office Equipment Leasing Services
N.A.I.C.S.: 532490

Grenkelocation SARL (1)
2 rue Gabriel Lippmann, 5365, Munsbach, Luxembourg
Tel.: (352) 2707390
Web Site: http://www.grenke.lu
Financial Lending Services
N.A.I.C.S.: 532420
Sandrine Ducrocq *(Acct Mgr)*

SIA GC Leasing Baltic (1)
Vienibas gatve 109, Riga, 1058, Latvia
Tel.: (371) 60002050
Web Site: https://www.grenkeleasing.lv
Financial Lending Services
N.A.I.C.S.: 532420
Anton Kovalovs *(Mng Dir)*

GRENOBLOISE D'ELECTRONIQUE ET D'AUTOMATISMES

Inovallee 12 Chemin de Malacher, CS60085, CS60085, 38243, Meylan, Cedex, France

Tel.: (33) 476907272 FR
Web Site: https://www.gea.fr
Year Founded: 1971
GEA—(EUR)
Sales Range: $1-9.9 Million
Toll Collection & Automatic Ticket Machine Equipment Mfr
N.A.I.C.S.: 333310

GRENSON LIMITED

Grenson House C2 Crown Way Crown Park, Crown Park, Rushden, NN10 6BS, Northamptonshire, United Kingdom
Tel.: (44) 3031231113
Web Site: http://www.grenson.co.uk
Year Founded: 1895
Sales Range: $25-49.9 Million
Emp.: 40
Holding Company Shoe Retailer & Mfr
N.A.I.C.S.: 551112
Lesley Dover *(Mgr-Fin)*

Subsidiaries:

Grenson Shoes Limited (1)
Queen Street, Rushden, NN10 0AB, Northamptonshire, United Kingdom
Tel.: (44) 933358734
Web Site: https://www.grenson.co.uk
Sales Range: $25-49.9 Million
Men's Shoes Mfr
N.A.I.C.S.: 316210

GRENVILLE PRINTING LTD.

25 Scarsdale Road, Toronto, M3B 2R2, ON, Canada
Tel.: (416) 449-4499
Rev.: $21,036,284
Emp.: 110
Printing Services
N.A.I.C.S.: 323111
Bill Burke *(Pres)*

GRENZEBACH MASCHINENBAU GMBH

Albanusstrasse 1, 86663, Asbach-Baumenheim, Germany
Tel.: (49) 9069822000
Web Site:
   http://www.grenzebach.com
Year Founded: 1960
Sales Range: $125-149.9 Million
Emp.: 1,500
Material Handling & Glass Processing Machine Mfr
N.A.I.C.S.: 333248
Renato Luck *(CEO & Mng Dir)*

Subsidiaries:

Grenzebach - INOS Automation Software Inc. (1)
1301 Rankin Dr, Troy, MI 48083
Tel.: (248) 536-0430
Industrial Automation Services
N.A.I.C.S.: 541512
Kimberly Sessoms *(Office Mgr)*

Grenzebach Automation GmbH (1)
Wikingerstr 11, 76189, Karlsruhe, Germany
Tel.: (49) 721 95240 0
Industrial Machinery & Equipment Distr
N.A.I.C.S.: 423830

Grenzebach BSH GmbH (1)
August Gottlieb Strasse 5, D 36251, Bad Hersfeld, Germany (100%)
Tel.: (49) 813651
Web Site: http://www.grenzebach.com
Sales Range: $100-124.9 Million
Emp.: 400
Provider of Planing & Veneer Equipment
N.A.I.C.S.: 333243
Bernd Minning *(Pres & CEO)*

Grenzebach Corporation (1)
10 Herring Rd, Newnan, GA 30265
Tel.: (770) 253-4980
Industrial Machinery & Equipment Distr
N.A.I.C.S.: 423830
Todd Williamson *(Mgr-Pur)*

GRENZEBACH MASCHINENBAU GMBH

Grenzebach Maschinenbau GmbH—(Continued)

Grenzebach Machinery (India) Pvt. Ltd. (1)
Devdar 4th Floor Plot No 83 S No 98 Bhusari Colony, Pune, 411038, India
Tel.: (91) 20 25286011
Industrial Machinery & Equipment Distr
N.A.I.C.S.: 423830
Abhijeet Chatterjee *(Mgr-Sls)*

Grenzebach Machinery (Jiashan) Ltd. (1)
No 100 Chenggong Road Huimin Street, 314100, Jiashan, Zheijiang, China
Tel.: (86) 573 8473 1606
Industrial Machinery & Equipment Distr
N.A.I.C.S.: 336110
Tianfang Zhang *(Project Mgr)*

Grenzebach Machinery (Shanghai) Ltd. (1)
388 Minshen Road Songjiang Industrial Zone, Shanghai, 201612, China
Tel.: (86) 21 6126 8000
Industrial Machinery & Equipment Distr
N.A.I.C.S.: 423830

Grenzebach Machinery Taiwan Ltd. (1)
No 38 1F Keya Rd Central Taiwan Science Park, Taichung, Taiwan
Tel.: (886) 4 25667796
Industrial Machinery & Equipment Distr
N.A.I.C.S.: 423830
Ludwig Huang *(Project Mgr)*

Grenzebach Mashtech, LLC (1)
Novocheremushkinskaya St 61, 117418, Moscow, Russia
Tel.: (7) 495 626 5881
Web Site: http://www.grenzebach.com
Industrial Machinery & Equipment Distr
N.A.I.C.S.: 423830

Grenzebach do Brasil (1)
Rua Lagoa Santa 160, Sao Jose dos Campos, 12238-340, Sao Paulo, Brazil
Tel.: (55) 12 3922 9400
Industrial Machinery & Equipment Distr
N.A.I.C.S.: 423830

Inos Automationssoftware GmbH (1)
Curiestrasse 4, 70563, Stuttgart, Germany
Tel.: (49) 711 68 68 97 00
Web Site: http://www.inos-automation.de
Industrial Automation Services
N.A.I.C.S.: 541512
Oliver Feldmann *(Engr-Application)*

Subsidiary (Non-US):

inos Hellas S.A. (2)
Sarantaporou 14 & Metonos, Cholargos, 15561, Athens, Greece
Tel.: (30) 2107472370
Web Site: http://www.inoshellas.inos-automation.de
Industrial Automation Services
N.A.I.C.S.: 541512
Kostas Voliotis *(Dir-R&D)*

GRESGYING DIGITAL TECHNOLOGY CO., LTD.
Energy & Finance Trade Zone Xixian New Area, Qindu District, Xianyang, 712044, Shaanxi, China
Tel.: (86) 18192025836
Web Site: https://gresgying.global
600212—(SHG)
Rev.: $40,210,911
Assets: $77,401,565
Liabilities: $57,691,006
Net Worth: $19,710,559
Earnings: ($13,554,272)
Fiscal Year-end: 12/31/22
Eletric Power Generation Services
N.A.I.C.S.: 221118
Zhang Qian *(Sec)*

GRESHAM HOUSE ENERGY STORAGE FUND PLC
The Scalpel 18th Floor 52 Lime Street, London, EC3M 7AF, United Kingdom
Tel.: (44) 2075491688   UK

GRID—(LSE)
Rev.: $115,621,593
Assets: $689,553,548
Liabilities: $282,891
Net Worth: $689,270,657
Earnings: $108,293,369
Fiscal Year-end: 12/31/21
Management Investment Services
N.A.I.C.S.: 525910

Subsidiaries:

Gridreserve Ltd. (1)
Thorney Weir House Thorney Mill Lane, Iver, SL0 9AQ, United Kingdom
Tel.: (44) 3331234333
Web Site: https://www.gridserve.com
Car Lending Services
N.A.I.C.S.: 532112

GRESHAM HOUSE STRATEGIC PLC
Octagon Point 5 Cheapside, London, EC2V 6AA, United Kingdom
Tel.: (44) 2038376270
Web Site: http://www.ghsplc.com
GHS—(AIM)
Sales Range: Less than $1 Million
Emp.: 4
Venture Capital Funding Services
N.A.I.C.S.: 523999
David R. W. Potter *(Chm)*

Subsidiaries:

SPARK Services Ltd (1)
33 Glasshouse Street, London, W1B 5DG, United Kingdom
Tel.: (44) 20 7240 7181
Business Support Services
N.A.I.C.S.: 561499

GRESHAM PARTNERS LTD.
Level 17 167 Macquarie Street, Sydney, 2000, NSW, Australia
Tel.: (61) 292215133
Web Site: http://www.gresham.com.au
Year Founded: 1985
Sales Range: $25-49.9 Million
Emp.: 60
Privater Equity Firm
N.A.I.C.S.: 523999
Bruce McLennan *(Mng Dir-Sydney)*

GRETEX CORPORATE SERVICES LTD
Office No 13 1St Floor New Bansilal Building 9-15 Homi Modi Street, Fort Near Bse, Mumbai, 400001, India
Tel.: (91) 2240025273
Web Site: https://www.gretexcorporate.com
Year Founded: 2008
543324—(BOM)
Rev.: $443,122
Assets: $1,468,150
Liabilities: $523,280
Net Worth: $944,869
Earnings: $98,596
Emp.: 12
Fiscal Year-end: 03/31/21
Investment Banking Services
N.A.I.C.S.: 523150
Alok Harlalka *(Mng Dir & CFO)*

Subsidiaries:

Sunview Nirman Private Limited (1)
Nanda Tower 90 Phears Lane Poddar Court, Tiretti, Kolkata, 700 012, India
Tel.: (91) 3340069278
Investment Banking Services
N.A.I.C.S.: 523150

GRETEX INDUSTRIES LTD.
90 Phears Lane 5th Floor, Kolkata, 700 012, India
Tel.: (91) 3340069278

Web Site: https://www.gretexindustries.com
Year Founded: 2009
GRETEX—(NSE)
Rev.: $2,738,100
Assets: $1,209,638
Liabilities: $649,840
Net Worth: $559,798
Earnings: $80,126
Emp.: 30
Fiscal Year-end: 03/31/23
Garments Mfr
N.A.I.C.S.: 315120
Arvind Harlalka *(Chm & Mng Dir)*

GREY MATTER LTD.
The Old Maltings Prigg Meadow, Ashburton, Devon, TQ13 7DF, United Kingdom
Tel.: (44) 1364 654 100   UK
Web Site: http://www.greymatter.com
Year Founded: 1983
Software Publishing Services
N.A.I.C.S.: 513210
Charles Cooke Hurle *(Chm)*

GREYBULL CAPITAL LLP
32 Sloane Street, London, SW1X 9NR, United Kingdom
Tel.: (44) 2079654557
Web Site: http://www.greybull.co.uk
Privater Equity Firm
N.A.I.C.S.: 523999
Richard Perlhagen *(Founder & Partner)*

Subsidiaries:

Nampak Plastics Europe Ltd. (1)
Jenna Way Interchange Park, Newport Pagnell, MK16 9QJ, Bucks, United Kingdom
Tel.: (44) 1908611554
Web Site: http://www.eu.nampak.com
Sales Range: $25-49.9 Million
Emp.: 90
Plastics Product Mfr
N.A.I.C.S.: 326199
Arnold Mitterer *(Mng Dir)*

GREYHOUND AUSTRALIA PTY. LTD.
PO Box 1475, Eagle Farm, 4009, QLD, Australia
Tel.: (61) 746909950
Web Site: http://www.greyhound.com.au
Sales Range: $50-74.9 Million
Emp.: 650
Express, Tour & Charter Coach Services; Freight Transportation Services
N.A.I.C.S.: 485510
Tom Esplin *(Mng Dir)*

GREYSTONE CAPITAL PARTNERS A/S
Sundkrogsgade 19, 2100, Copenhagen, O, Denmark
Tel.: (45) 4079 5456   DK
Web Site: http://www.greystonecp.com
Privater Equity Firm
N.A.I.C.S.: 523999
Anders Bonding *(Partner)*

Subsidiaries:

NOA NOA ApS (1)
Krogenbergvej 15A Nyrupgaard, 3490, Kvistgaard, Denmark
Tel.: (45) 3699 3000
Web Site: http://www.noanoa.com
Apparel Distr
N.A.I.C.S.: 458110
Steen Kristiansen *(Co-CEO & CFO)*

GREYTER WATER SYSTEMS
2345 Stanfield Rd Ste 300, Mississauga, L4Y 3Y3, ON, Canada
Tel.: (416) 883-2411
Web Site: http://www.greyter.com

INTERNATIONAL PUBLIC

Grey Water Recycling Systems
N.A.I.C.S.: 221310
Chris Thompson *(Pres & CTO)*

GREZDIS
5 Rue Launay, 69290, Grezieu-la-Varenne, Rhone, France
Tel.: (33) 478448513
Rev.: $37,600,000
Emp.: 106
N.A.I.C.S.: 444180
Jerome Rolin *(Mgr- Fin)*

GRG INTERNATIONAL LIMITED
194 Gladstone Street, Melbourne, 3205, VIC, Australia
Tel.: (61) 3 9682 4491   AU
Web Site: http://www.grgatm.com
Year Founded: 2009
Automated Teller Machine Distr, Repair & Maintenance Services
N.A.I.C.S.: 423440
Brian Kett *(Pres & Gen Mgr)*

Subsidiaries:

GRG International Corporation (1)
300 Davis Ave Ste 200, Pass Christian, MS 39571   (100%)
Tel.: (228) 452-5000
Web Site: http://www.grgatm.com
Sales Range: $1-9.9 Million
Emp.: 5
Professional Equipment Whslr
N.A.I.C.S.: 423490
Brian Kett *(Co-Pres)*

GRIBBLES VETERINARY PATHOLOGY LIMITED
37-41 Carbine Rd, Mount Wellington, Auckland, 1642, New Zealand
Tel.: (64) 95744701   NZ
Web Site: http://www.gribblesvets.co.nz
Year Founded: 1989
Sales Range: $25-49.9 Million
Veterinary Pathology Services
N.A.I.C.S.: 541940
Karen Cooper *(Mgr-Laboratory-Auckland)*

GRID BATTERY METALS INC
3028 Quadra Court, Coquitlam, V3B 5X6, BC, Canada
Tel.: (604) 428-5690   BC
Web Site: https://gridbatterymetals.com
Year Founded: 2011
EVKRF—(OTCQB)
Rev.: $37,428
Assets: $6,083,292
Liabilities: $103,226
Net Worth: $5,980,066
Earnings: ($998,481)
Emp.: 850
Fiscal Year-end: 06/30/24
Metal Mining
N.A.I.C.S.: 212290
Rick Wilson *(Pres & CEO)*

GRID METALS CORP.
3335 Yonge Street Suite 304, Toronto, M4N 2M1, ON, Canada
Tel.: (416) 955-4773   ON
Web Site: https://www.gridmetalscorp.com
Year Founded: 1997
MSMGF—(OTCQB)
Rev.: $7,807
Assets: $25,592,744
Liabilities: $1,280,827
Net Worth: $24,311,917
Earnings: ($1,810,727)
Fiscal Year-end: 12/31/20
Mineral Exploration Services
N.A.I.C.S.: 213114
David Black *(VP-IR)*

AND PRIVATE COMPANIES

GRIDSUM HOLDING INC.
South Wing High Technology Building No 229 North 4th Ring Road, Haidian District, Beijing, 100083, China
Tel.: (86) 10 8261 9988
Web Site: http://www.gridsum.com
Year Founded: 2014
GSUM—(NASDAQ)
Rev.: $46,729,591
Assets: $85,426,693
Liabilities: $136,614,994
Net Worth: ($51,188,301)
Earnings: ($76,977,640)
Emp.: 929
Fiscal Year-end: 12/31/19
Business Management Software Development Services
N.A.I.C.S.: 541511
Guosheng Qi *(Co-Founder, Chm & CEO)*

GRIEG SEAFOOD ASA
Grieg-Gaarden C Sundts gate 17/19 Sentrum, PO Box 234, N-5004, Bergen, Norway
Tel.: (47) 55576600
Web Site: https://www.griegseafood.no
GRGSF—(OTCIQ)
Rev.: $661,736,191
Assets: $1,189,300,296
Liabilities: $590,214,022
Net Worth: $599,086,274
Earnings: $106,574,820
Emp.: 698
Fiscal Year-end: 12/31/22
Seafood Processor
N.A.I.C.S.: 311710
Atle Harald Sandtorv *(CFO)*

Subsidiaries:

Grieg Seafood Canada AS (1)
1180 Ironwood St Ste 106, Campbell River, V9W 5P7, BC, Canada
Tel.: (250) 286-0838
Web Site: http://www.griegseafood.no
Emp.: 100
Fish Farming Services
N.A.I.C.S.: 112511

Grieg Seafood Finnmark AS (1)
Markedsgata 3, PO Box 1053, 9510, Alta, Finnmark, Norway
Tel.: (47) 78449595
Web Site: https://griegseafood.com
Sales Range: $25-49.9 Million
Emp.: 220
Fish Farming Services
N.A.I.C.S.: 114111
Roy Tore *(Dir)*

Grieg Seafood Rogaland AS (1)
Rygjaboveien 4, Finnoy, 4160, Rogaland, Norway
Tel.: (47) 51714000
Web Site: http://www.griegseafood.no
Sales Range: $25-49.9 Million
Emp.: 70
Salmon Hatching & Farming Services
N.A.I.C.S.: 112511

GRIESHABER HOLDING GMBH
Am Hohenstein 113-115, Schiltach, 77761, Germany
Tel.: (49) 7836 55 0
Web Site: http://www.grieshaber-praezision.de
Sales Range: $350-399.9 Million
Emp.: 1,300
Holding Company
N.A.I.C.S.: 551112
Jurgen Grieshaber *(Mng Partner)*

Subsidiaries:

Grieshaber GmbH & Co. KG (1)
Am Hohenstein 115, Schiltach, 77761, Germany
Tel.: (49) 7836550
Web Site: http://www.grieshaber-praezision.de
Sales Range: $50-74.9 Million
Emp.: 230
Precision Metal Components Mfr
N.A.I.C.S.: 332721
Simon Heil *(Mng Dir)*

Supfina Grieshaber GmbH & Co. KG (1)
Schmelzegrun 7, 77709, Wolfach, Germany
Tel.: (49) 7834 866 0
Web Site: http://www.supfina.com
Sales Range: $50-74.9 Million
Emp.: 170
Surface Finishing & Grinding Machinery Mfr
N.A.I.C.S.: 333248
Rainer Waltersbacher *(Mng Dir)*

Subsidiary (Non-US):

Schirnhofer Werkzeugmaschinen & Werkzeuge GmbH (2)
Birkengasse 2, 2551, Enzesfeld, Austria
Tel.: (43) 2256 82346
Web Site: http://www.schirnhofer.at
Machine Tools Mfr
N.A.I.C.S.: 333517

Subsidiary (US):

Supfina Machine Co., Inc. (2)
181 Circuit Dr, North Kingstown, RI 02852
Tel.: (401) 294-6600
Web Site: http://www.supfina.com
Sales Range: $25-49.9 Million
Emp.: 40
Surface Finishing & Grinding Machinery Mfr
N.A.I.C.S.: 333248
Andrew M. Corsini *(Mng Dir)*

VEGA Grieshaber KG (1)
Am Hohenstein 113, Schiltach, 77761, Germany
Tel.: (49) 7836500
Web Site: http://www.vega.com
Sales Range: $25-49.9 Million
Emp.: 1,200
Level, Switching & Pressure Instrumentation Mfr
N.A.I.C.S.: 334513
Jurgen Grieshaber *(Chm-Mgmt Bd & Mng Dir)*

Subsidiary (Non-US):

B.V. VEGA Meet - en Regeltechniek (2)
Arnhemseweg-Zuid 213-2, 3817 CG, Amersfoort, Netherlands
Tel.: (31) 33 4502502
Web Site: http://www.vega.com
Sensor & Accessories Mfr
N.A.I.C.S.: 334511

EnergoCom - VEGA distribution LLP (2)
OPS-1 Abonentskii Yashik 30, 130001, Aktau, Kazakhstan
Tel.: (7) 7292 317 411
Web Site: http://www.energocom-vegadistribution.kz
Electrical Equipment Distr
N.A.I.C.S.: 423610

Tianjin-VEGA Co. Ltd. (2)
18F Wanke Center Building 290 Zhongshan Road, Hebei District, Tianjin, 300141, China
Tel.: (86) 22 26273296
Web Site: http://www.tjvega.com.cn
Electrical Equipment Distr
N.A.I.C.S.: 423610

Subsidiary (US):

VEGA Americas, Inc. (2)
4170 Rosslyn Dr, Cincinnati, OH 45209
Tel.: (513) 272-0131
Web Site: http://www.vega-americas.com
Sales Range: $10-24.9 Million
Process Control Instruments Mfr
N.A.I.C.S.: 334513
John Kronenberger *(Co-CEO)*

Subsidiary (Non-US):

VEGA Australia Pty Ltd (2)
398 The Boulevarde, Kirrawee, 2232, NSW, Australia
Tel.: (61) 2 95426662

Electrical Equipment Distr
N.A.I.C.S.: 423610

VEGA India Level & Pressure Measurement Pvt. Ltd. (2)
3B 3rd Floor Mutha Chambers II Senapati Bapat Road, Shivaji Nagar, Pune, 411 016, India
Tel.: (91) 20 4148 4148
Electrical Equipment Distr
N.A.I.C.S.: 423610

VEGA Instrumentos S.A. (2)
Ronda Can Fatjo no 21 B 1 lanta Parc Tecnologic del Valles, 08290, Barcelona, Spain
Tel.: (34) 90 2109938
Electrical Equipment Distr
N.A.I.C.S.: 423610

VEGA Instruments (SEA) Pte Ltd. (2)
25 International Business Park 04-52 German Centre, Singapore, 609916, Singapore
Tel.: (65) 65640531
Electrical Equipment Distr
N.A.I.C.S.: 423610

VEGA Instruments Co., Ltd. (2)
202 Le Concorde Tower 10th floor 1002 Ratchadapisek Road, Huay Kwang, Bangkok, 10310, Thailand
Tel.: (66) 2 6942400
Electrical Equipment Distr
N.A.I.C.S.: 423610

VEGA Instruments Ltd. (2)
3522 Cambridge Road RD3 Monavale, Cambridge, New Zealand
Tel.: (64) 7 8270899
Electrical Equipment Distr
N.A.I.C.S.: 423610

VEGA Instruments SA Pty Ltd (2)
PO Box 692, Wilgeheuwels, Roodepoort, 1736, Gauteng, South Africa
Tel.: (27) 11 795 3249
Electrical Equipment Distr
N.A.I.C.S.: 423610

VEGA Italia S.r.l. (2)
Via G Watt 37, 20143, Milan, Italy
Tel.: (39) 02 8914081
Electrical Equipment Distr
N.A.I.C.S.: 423610

VEGA Messtechnik AG (2)
Barzloostrasse 2, Pfaffikon, Switzerland
Tel.: (41) 44 952 40 00
Web Site: http://www.vega.ch
Electrical Sensor Mfr
N.A.I.C.S.: 334413
Freddy Vollmer *(Gen Mgr)*

VEGA Middle East LLC (2)
Al-Khaimah Building Al Ittihad Road, PO Box 112830, Dubai, United Arab Emirates
Tel.: (971) 4 2947552
Web Site: http://www.vega.com
Electrical Equipment Distr
N.A.I.C.S.: 423610

VEGA Seviye ve Basinc Olcum Cihazlari Ticaret Ltd. Sti. (2)
Barbaros Caddesi Serifali Ciftligi No 12 Yukari Dudullu, Istanbul, Turkiye
Tel.: (90) 216 6000 100
Web Site: http://www.vega.com
Electrical Equipment Distr
N.A.I.C.S.: 423610
Vushesvi Hesvi *(Mgr)*

VEGA Technique S.A.S. (2)
15 Rue du Ried, 67150, Nordhouse, France
Tel.: (33) 3 88590150
Web Site: http://www.vega.com
Electrical Equipment Distr
N.A.I.C.S.: 423610

VEGA n.v./s.a. (2)
J Tieboutstraat 67, 1731, Zellik, Belgium
Tel.: (32) 2 4660505
Web Site: http://www.vega.be
Electrical Equipment Distr
N.A.I.C.S.: 423610

VEGA-Controls Ltd. (2)
Victoria Way, Burgess Hill, RH15 9NF, Sussex, United Kingdom
Tel.: (44) 1444 870055
Web Site: http://www.vegacontrols.co.uk

Emp.: 40
Electric Equipment Mfr
N.A.I.C.S.: 334513
Ray Tregale *(Mng Dir)*

GRIFAL SPA
Via XXIV Maggio 1, Cologno al Serio, 24055, Bergamo, Italy
Tel.: (39) 0354871487
Web Site: https://www.grifal.it
GRAL—(ITA)
Rev.: $41,709,128
Assets: $67,255,376
Liabilities: $47,081,251
Net Worth: $20,174,125
Earnings: $979,376
Fiscal Year-end: 12/31/23
Cardboard Packaging Product Mfr
N.A.I.C.S.: 322121
Fabio Angelo Gritti *(Pres)*

GRIFFIN INFORMATION SYSTEMS LTD.
20 St Christopher's Way, Pride Park, Derby, DE24 8JY, United Kingdom
Tel.: (44) 1332 646 600
Web Site: http://www.griffin.com
Year Founded: 1993
Sales Range: $10-24.9 Million
Emp.: 66
Internet Services
N.A.I.C.S.: 517810
Andrew Dickinson *(Mng Dir)*

GRIFFIN MINING LIMITED
8th Floor Royal Trust House 54 Jermyn Street, London, SW1Y 6LX, United Kingdom
Tel.: (44) 2076297772
Web Site: https://www.griffinmining.com
Year Founded: 1988
GFM—(AIM)
Rev.: $94,397,000
Assets: $305,590,000
Liabilities: $60,125,000
Net Worth: $245,465,000
Earnings: $7,704,000
Emp.: 461
Fiscal Year-end: 12/31/22
Zinc, Gold & Silver Ore Mining
N.A.I.C.S.: 212220
Mladen Ninkov *(Chm-Australian)*

GRIFFITHS FORD
553 Gregg Avenue, Hinton, T7V 1N1, AB, Canada
Tel.: (780) 865-3354
Web Site: http://www.griffithsford.com
Year Founded: 1965
New & Used Car Dealers
N.A.I.C.S.: 441110
Garth Griffiths *(Pres)*

GRIFOLS, S.A.
Avinguda de la Generalitat 152-158 Sant Cugat del Valles, 8174, Sant Cugat del Valles, Barcelona, Spain
Tel.: (34) 935712200
Web Site: https://www.grifols.com
Year Founded: 1941
GRFS—(NASDAQ)
Rev.: $7,448,006,828
Assets: $26,448,891,910
Liabilities: $16,060,998,068
Net Worth: $10,387,893,843
Earnings: $255,816,599
Emp.: 26,314
Fiscal Year-end: 12/31/22
Pharmaceuticals Mfr
N.A.I.C.S.: 325412
Raimon Grifols Roura *(Vice Chm & Chief Corp Officer)*

Subsidiaries:

Aigues Minerals de Vilajuiga, S.A. (1)

GRIFOLS, S.A.

Grifols, S.A.—(Continued)
C/ Sant Sebastia 2, Vilajuiga, 17493, Girona, Spain
Tel.: (34) 972530006
Web Site: http://www.vilajuiga.com
Bottled Water Mfr
N.A.I.C.S.: 312112

Alkahest, Inc. (1)
125 Shoreway Rd Ste D, San Carlos, CA 94070
Tel.: (650) 801-0474
Web Site: http://www.alkahest.com
Biopharmaceutical Research & Development Services
N.A.I.C.S.: 541714
Karoly Nikolich (Chm & CEO)

Alpha Therapeutic Italia, S.p.A. (1)
Via Carducci 62/M 2, San Giuliano Terme, 56017, Pisa, Italy
Tel.: (39) 050879934
Pharmaceuticals Product Mfr
N.A.I.C.S.: 325412

Araclon Biotech, S.L. (1)
Via Hispanidad 21, 50009, Zaragoza, Spain
Tel.: (34) 976796562
Diagnostic Research & Development Services
N.A.I.C.S.: 541714

BioDarou PLC (1)
No 84 Shahid Ravanmehr St Fakhr Razi St, Facing the main door of Tehran University Islamic Revolution, 1314854514, Tehran, Iran
Tel.: (98) 66978549
Web Site: https://biodarou.com
Health Care Srvices
N.A.I.C.S.: 524114

Biomat, S.A. (1)
Marineta nave 5-6, Parets del Valles, 08150, Barcelona, Spain
Tel.: (34) 935710200
Web Site: http://www.grifols.com
Sales Range: $25-49.9 Million
Emp.: 100
Plasma Researcher & Developer
N.A.I.C.S.: 541715

Diagnostic Grifols, S.A. (1)
Passeig Fluvial 24, Barcelona, 08150, Spain
Tel.: (34) 93 571 04 00
Pharmaceuticals Product Mfr
N.A.I.C.S.: 325412

Grifols (H.K.), Limited (1)
Berkshire House Units 1505-07 25 Westlands Road, Quarry Bay, China (Hong Kong)
Tel.: (852) 21613100
Pharmaceutical Preparation Mfr
N.A.I.C.S.: 325412

Grifols Australia Pty Ltd. (1)
Unit 5 / 80 Fairbank Road, Clayton South, Melbourne, 3169, VIC, Australia
Tel.: (61) 395359333
Sales Range: $25-49.9 Million
Emp.: 50
Diagnostic Products Mfr
N.A.I.C.S.: 325413

Grifols Colombia, Ltda (1)
Carrera 7 No 156-68 Torre III Oficina 802 Edificio North Point, Bogota, Colombia
Tel.: (57) 17028837
Pharmaceutical Preparation Mfr
N.A.I.C.S.: 325412

Grifols Diagnostics Equipment Taiwan Limited (1)
Room 801 8F No 367 Fuxing N Rd, Songshan Dist, Taipei, 10543, Taiwan
Tel.: (886) 221752946
Pharmaceutical Preparation Mfr
N.A.I.C.S.: 325412

Grifols Engineering, S.A. (1)
C/ Palou 6, Parets del Valles, 08150, Barcelona, Spain
Tel.: (34) 935710042
Sales Range: $25-49.9 Million
Emp.: 50
Project Management Services for Manufacturing Processes & Plants; Pharmaceutical & Biotech Machinery Mfr

N.A.I.C.S.: 237990

Grifols India Healthcare Private Ltd. (1)
DLF Cyber City DLF Tower 8th Road Bldg 9B - 4th Floor, Gurgaon, 122002, Haryana, India
Tel.: (91) 1244317460
Pharmaceutical Preparation Mfr
N.A.I.C.S.: 325412

Grifols International, S.A. (1)
Avinguda de la Generalitat 152 Parc empresarial Can Sant Joan, Sant Cugat del Valles, 08174, Barcelona, Spain
Tel.: (34) 935712200
Holding Company for International Operations
N.A.I.C.S.: 551112

Subsidiary (Non-US):

Grifols Argentina, S.A. (2)
Av Mitre 3790 Partido Vicente Lopez, Munro, 1605, Buenos Aires, Argentina
Tel.: (54) 11 47625100
Web Site: http://www.grifols.com
Pharmaceuticals Mfr
N.A.I.C.S.: 325412

Grifols Asia Pacific Pte Ltd (2)
Tel.: (65) 67352606
Web Site: http://www.grifols.com
Sales Range: $25-49.9 Million
Emp.: 19
Pharmaceuticals Mfr
N.A.I.C.S.: 325412

Grifols Chile, S.A. (2)
Edificios Alto El Plomo Torre Sur Los Militares 5890, Piso 11 oficina 1101-A Comuna de Las Condes, Santiago, Chile
Tel.: (56) 223557201
Sales Range: $25-49.9 Million
Emp.: 35
Pharmaceuticals Mfr
N.A.I.C.S.: 325412

Grifols Deutschland GmbH (2)
Tel.: (49) 69660593100
Web Site: http://www.grifols.com
Sales Range: $25-49.9 Million
Emp.: 100
Immunology, Pulmonology & Hemostasis Critical Care Treatments Developer & Mfr
N.A.I.C.S.: 541715

Branch (Domestic):

Grifols Deutschland GmbH (3)
Lyoner Strase 15, PO Box 1107, Frankfurt, 63225, Germany (100%)
Tel.: (49) 610375020
Web Site: http://www.grifols.com
Sales Range: $25-49.9 Million
Emp.: 20
Mfr of Pharmaceuticals
N.A.I.C.S.: 325412

Subsidiary (Non-US):

Grifols France, S.A.R.L. (2)
Parc Technologique Sainte Victoire, Batiment 10 1er etage, 13590, Meyreuil, France
Tel.: (33) 442544400
Web Site: http://www.grifols.com
Sales Range: $25-49.9 Million
Emp.: 15
Pharmaceuticals Mfr
N.A.I.C.S.: 325412

Grifols Italia S.p.A. (2)
(100%)
Sales Range: $25-49.9 Million
Emp.: 30
Mfr of Pharmaceuticals
N.A.I.C.S.: 325412

Grifols Malaysia Sdn Bhd (2)
Web Site: http://www.grifols.com
Pharmaceuticals Mfr
N.A.I.C.S.: 325412

Grifols Mexico, S.A. de C.V. (2)
Eugenio Cuzin 909-913 Colonia Parque Industrial Belenes Norte, Zapopan, 45150, Jalisco, Mexico
Tel.: (52) 3336361922
Web Site: https://www.grifols.com
Sales Range: $25-49.9 Million
Emp.: 50
Pharmaceuticals Mfr

N.A.I.C.S.: 325412
Xavier Taxonera (Gen Dir)

Grifols Portugal Produtos Farmaceuticos e Hospitalares, Lda. (2)
Rua de S Sebastiao 2, Zona Industrial Cabra Figa, 2635-448, Rio de Mouro, Portugal
Tel.: (351) 219255200
Web Site: http://www.grifols.com
Sales Range: $25-49.9 Million
Emp.: 30
Pharmaceuticals Mfr
N.A.I.C.S.: 325412

Grifols Thailand Ltd. (2)
Web Site: http://www.grifols.com
Mfr of Plasma Derivatives
N.A.I.C.S.: 325412

Grifols U.K. Ltd. (2)
(100%)
Tel.: (44) 8452413090
Sales Range: $50-74.9 Million
Emp.: 30
Mfr of Pharmaceuticals Including Research & Development
N.A.I.C.S.: 325412

Grifols s.r.o. (2)
Rohanske nabrezi 670/17, Karlin, 186 00, Prague, 8, Czech Republic
Tel.: (420) 222231415
Sales Range: $10-24.9 Million
Emp.: 24
Pharmaceuticals Mfr
N.A.I.C.S.: 325412

Subsidiary (Domestic):

Logister, S.A. (2)
Passeig Fluvial 24, Parets del Valles, Barcelona, 08150, Spain
Tel.: (34) 935710400
Web Site: http://www.grifols.com
Emp.: 22
Hospital Software Developer & Designer
N.A.I.C.S.: 541512

Movaco, S.A. (2)
P Fluvial 24, Parets del Valles, 08150, Barcelona, Spain
Tel.: (34) 935710400
Web Site: http://www.grifols.com
Sales Range: $125-149.9 Million
Emp.: 300
Pharmaceutical Products Marketer & Distr
N.A.I.C.S.: 424210

Grifols Japan K.K. (1)
F12 Toranomon Kotohira Tower 1-2-8, Toranomon Minato-ku, Tokyo, 105-0001, Japan
Tel.: (81) 367349700
Pharmaceutical Preparation Mfr
N.A.I.C.S.: 325412

Grifols Movaco, S.A. (1)
C/ Palou 6-Poligono Industrial Levante, Parets del Valles, 08150, Barcelona, Spain
Tel.: (34) 935712403
Pharmaceutical Product Mfr & Distr
N.A.I.C.S.: 325412

Grifols Nordic AB (1)
Sveavagen 166, 113 46, Stockholm, Sweden
Tel.: (46) 84113018
Web Site: https://www.grifols.com
Emp.: 5
Diagnostics Products Distr
N.A.I.C.S.: 424210

Grifols Pharmaceutical Technology (Shanghai) Co., Ltd. (1)
Floor 11 - Tower 1 Jing An Kerry Centre 1515 Nanjing Road West, Shanghai, 200040, China
Tel.: (86) 2160201518
Pharmaceutical Preparation Mfr
N.A.I.C.S.: 325412

Grifols Polska Sp.z.o.o (1)
ul Siedmiogrodzka 9, 01-204, Warsaw, Poland
Tel.: (48) 223788561
Pharmaceutical Preparation Mfr
N.A.I.C.S.: 325412

Grifols Portugal Produtos Farmaceuticos e Hospitalares, Lda. (1)
Rua de S Sebastiao 2 Zona Industrial

Cabra Figa, 2635-448, Rio de Mouro, Portugal
Tel.: (351) 219255200
Pharmaceutical Product Mfr & Distr
N.A.I.C.S.: 325412

Grifols Viajes, S.A. (1)
Calle Jesus I Maria 6, 8022, Barcelona, Spain
Tel.: (34) 935710122
Pharmaceuticals Product Mfr
N.A.I.C.S.: 325412

Grifols Worldwide Operations Limited (1)
Grange Castle Business Park, Grange Clondalkin, Dublin, Ireland
Tel.: (353) 14647938
Pharmaceutical Preparation Mfr
N.A.I.C.S.: 325412

Grifols, Inc. (1)
2410 Grifols Way, Los Angeles, CA 90032-3514
Tel.: (323) 225-2221
Holding Company; Pharmaceuticals Mfr
N.A.I.C.S.: 551112

Subsidiary (Non-US):

Grifols Canada Ltd. (2)
5060 Spectrum Way Suite 405, Mississauga, L4W 5N5, ON, Canada
Tel.: (905) 614-5575
Web Site: http://www.grifols.com
Immunology, Pulmonology & Hemostasis Critical Care Treatments Developer & Mfr
N.A.I.C.S.: 339112

Subsidiary (Domestic):

Grifols USA, Inc. (2)
2410 Grifols Way, Los Angeles, CA 90032-3514
Tel.: (323) 225-2221
Web Site: https://www.grifols.com
Pharmaceuticals Mfr
N.A.I.C.S.: 325412

Subsidiary (Domestic):

Biomat USA, Inc. (3)
2410 Lillyvale Ave, Los Angeles, CA 90032
Tel.: (323) 225-2221
Sales Range: $50-74.9 Million
Emp.: 500
Plasma Supplier
N.A.I.C.S.: 621991
Greg Rich (Pres & CEO)

Plant (Domestic):

Biomat USA - Altamonte Springs (4)
380 Northlake Blvd Ste 1024, Altamonte Springs, FL 32701
Tel.: (407) 628-4248
Plasma Center
N.A.I.C.S.: 541715
Karen Clifford (Gen Mgr)

Biomat USA - Van Nuys (4)
17641 Vanowen St, Van Nuys, CA 91406
Tel.: (818) 344-0204
Plasma Center
N.A.I.C.S.: 541715

Subsidiary (Domestic):

Grifols Biologicals, Inc. (3)
2410 Lillyvale Ave, Los Angeles, CA 90032
Tel.: (323) 225-2221
Therapeutic Proteins from Human Plasma Researcher, Developer & Producer
N.A.I.C.S.: 541715

Unit (Domestic):

Grifols Chiron Diagnostics Corp. (3)
4560 Horton St, Emeryville, CA 94608-2916
Tel.: (510) 655-8730
Sales Range: $550-599.9 Million
Blood Testing & Molecular Diagnostics Mfr
N.A.I.C.S.: 325413

Subsidiary (Domestic):

Plasmacare, Inc. (3)
1128 Main St Ste 300, Cincinnati, OH 45202
Tel.: (800) 868-1992
Web Site: http://www.plasmacare.com
Blood Plasma Distr

AND PRIVATE COMPANIES

N.A.I.C.S.: 424210

Haema AG (1)
Landsteinerstrasse 1, 04103, Leipzig, Germany
Tel.: (49) 341478300
Web Site: http://www.haema.de
Health Care Srvices
N.A.I.C.S.: 621991
Jordi Balsells *(Deputy Chm-Supervisory Bd)*

Instituto Grifols, S.A. (1)
Can Guassch 2, Parets del Valles, 08022, Barcelona, Spain
Tel.: (34) 935710100
Therapeutic Proteins from Human Plasma Researcher & Mfr
N.A.I.C.S.: 541715

Interstate Blood Bank, Inc. (1)
5700 Pleasant View Rd, Memphis, TN 38134-5028 **(100%)**
Tel.: (901) 384-6200
Web Site:
http://www.interstatebloodbank.com
Blood Laboratories & Donation Center Operator
N.A.I.C.S.: 621991
Regina Smith *(Supvr-Quality Assurance)*

Subsidiary (Domestic):

Bio-Blood Components, Inc. (2)
2585 Barclay St Ste C, Muskegon, MI 49441
Tel.: (231) 755-0389
Blood Collection Services
N.A.I.C.S.: 621991

Interstate Biologic Services, LLC (2)
1602 N Woodbine Rd, Saint Joseph, MO 64506
Tel.: (816) 901-9770
Web Site: http://www.plasmabiological.com
Biological Consulting Services
N.A.I.C.S.: 541690

Plasma Biological Services, LLC (2)
1166 N McLean Blvd, Elgin, IL 60123
Tel.: (847) 531-8185
Biological Consulting Services
N.A.I.C.S.: 541690

Kiro Grifols S.L. (1)
Goiru Kalea 1 Edificio B Planta 1, 20500, Arrasate, Gipuzkoa, Spain
Tel.: (34) 943252349
Web Site: https://www.kirogrifols.com
Industrial Equipment Distr
N.A.I.C.S.: 423830

Laboratorios Grifols, S.A. (1)
Can Guasch 2, Barcelona, 8150, Spain
Tel.: (34) 935710100
Laboratory Testing Services
N.A.I.C.S.: 541380

Logistica Grifols S.A de C.V (1)
Eugenio Cuzin No 909 Parq Ind Belenes Norte, Zapopan, 45150, Jalisco, Mexico
Tel.: (52) 3336361922
Web Site: http://www.grifols.com
Sales Range: $25-49.9 Million
Emp.: 44
Pharmaceutical Products Logistics Services
N.A.I.C.S.: 541614

Medion Grifols Diagnostic AG (1)
Bonnstrasse 9, 3186, Dudingen, Switzerland
Tel.: (41) 264928511
Web Site: https://www.grifols.com
Laboratory Testing Services
N.A.I.C.S.: 541380

GRIGEO AB

Vilniaus st 10, Grigiskes, 27101, Vilnius, Lithuania
Tel.: (370) 52435801
Web Site: https://www.grigeo.com
Year Founded: 1923
GRG1L—(VSE)
Rev.: $215,641,004
Assets: $173,175,126
Liabilities: $45,159,322
Net Worth: $128,015,804
Earnings: $27,938,950
Emp.: 860
Fiscal Year-end: 12/31/23

Paper Products Mfr
N.A.I.C.S.: 322299
Tomas Jozonis *(CEO)*

Subsidiaries:

Grigeo Baltwood UAB (1)
Vilniaus St 10, Grigiskes, LT-27101, Vilnius, Lithuania
Tel.: (370) 52435900
Hygienic Tissue Paper Mfr & Distr
N.A.I.C.S.: 322220

Grigeo Klaipeda AB (1)
Nemuno st 2, 91199, Klaipeda, Lithuania
Tel.: (370) 46395601
Paper Products Mfr
N.A.I.C.S.: 324199

GRIMALDI GROUP SPA

Via Marchese Campodisola 13, 80133, Naples, Italy
Tel.: (39) 081496440
Web Site:
http://www.grimaldi.napoli.it
Year Founded: 1947
Sales Range: $1-4.9 Billion
Emp.: 15,500
Marine Transportation Services
N.A.I.C.S.: 483111
Emanuele Grimaldi *(Co-Owner)*

Subsidiaries:

Finnlines Oyj (1)
Komentosilta 1, FIN-00980, Helsinki, Finland **(100%)**
Tel.: (358) 1034350
Web Site: http://www.finnlines.com
Rev.: $643,672,011
Assets: $1,373,957,354
Liabilities: $573,683,001
Net Worth: $800,274,353
Earnings: $110,035,204
Emp.: 1,576
Fiscal Year-end: 12/31/2019
Marine Cargo Services
N.A.I.C.S.: 488320
Diego Pacella *(Vice Chm)*

Subsidiary (Non-US):

Finanglia Ferries Limited (2)
8 Heron Quay, E144JB, London, United Kingdom **(100%)**
Tel.: (44) 2075360255
Inland Water Passenger Transportation
N.A.I.C.S.: 483212

Finnlines Belgium N.V. (2)
Blikken Haven 1333, 9130, Verrebroek, Belgium **(100%)**
Tel.: (32) 35709530
Web Site: http://www.finnlines.com
Sales Range: $25-49.9 Million
Emp.: 30
Freight Transportation Arrangement Distr
N.A.I.C.S.: 488510
Emanuele Grimaldi *(Pres & CEO)*

Finnlines Danmark A/S (2)
Osthavnsvej 11, 8000, Arhus, Denmark **(100%)**
Tel.: (45) 86206650
Web Site: http://www.finnlines.com
Sales Range: $25-49.9 Million
Emp.: 6
Water Transportation
N.A.I.C.S.: 488390
Claus Hoegh *(Mng Dir)*

Finnlines Deutschland GmbH (2)
Einsiedelstr 43-45, Lubeck, 10222, Germany **(100%)**
Tel.: (49) 45115070
Web Site: http://www.finnlines.com
Sales Range: $25-49.9 Million
Emp.: 80
Coastal & Great Lakes Freight Transportation
N.A.I.C.S.: 483113
Ute Schillaer *(Mgr-Mktg)*

Finnlines Polska Sp.z.o.o (2)
Al Solidarnosci 1c, Gdynia, 81-336, Poland **(100%)**
Tel.: (48) 586274423
Web Site: http://www.finnlines.com

Sales Range: $25-49.9 Million
Emp.: 10
Freight Transportation Arrangement
N.A.I.C.S.: 488510
Wojciech Kepczynski *(Mng Dir)*

Finnlines UK Limited (2)
8 Heron Quay, E144JB, London, United Kingdom **(100%)**
Tel.: (44) 2075197300
Coastal & Great Lakes Freight Transportation
N.A.I.C.S.: 483113

Finnlink AB (2)
Kappelskar Termi, 76015, Graddo, Sweden **(100%)**
Tel.: (46) 176207600
Web Site: http://www.finnlink.se
Sales Range: $25-49.9 Million
Emp.: 60
Freight Transportation Arrangement
N.A.I.C.S.: 488510
Oktay Akbulat *(Mgr-Sls)*

Subsidiary (Domestic):

Finnsteve Oy (2)
Komentosilta 1, 00980, Helsinki, Finland
Tel.: (358) 1056560
Web Site: http://www.finnsteve.fi
Sales Range: $200-249.9 Million
Emp.: 800
Freight Transportation Services
N.A.I.C.S.: 488510
Domenico Ferraiuolo *(Mng Dir)*

Subsidiary (Non-US):

Finnwest N.V. (2)
Land Van Waaslaan, 9130, Beveren, Belgium **(66.7%)**
Tel.: (32) 35413760
Sales Range: $25-49.9 Million
Emp.: 25
Freight Transportation Arrangement
N.A.I.C.S.: 488510

Norsteve A/S (2)
Bygning 10 Filipstadkaia, Oslo, Norway **(100%)**
Tel.: (47) 22483010
Web Site: http://www.norsteve.no
Freight Transportation Arrangement
N.A.I.C.S.: 488510

Norsteve Drammen A/S (2)
Svend Haugs Gate 8, Drammen, Norway **(100%)**
Tel.: (47) 32813060
Web Site: http://www.norsteve.no
Sales Range: $25-49.9 Million
Emp.: 20
Freight Transportation Arrangement
N.A.I.C.S.: 488510

Subsidiary (Domestic):

Oy Intercarriers AB (2)
Porkkalankatu 20a, 00180, Helsinki, Finland **(51%)**
Tel.: (358) 103435400
Web Site: http://www.intercarriers.fi
Sales Range: $25-49.9 Million
Emp.: 20
Freight Transportation Arrangement
N.A.I.C.S.: 488510
Aiatoly Vladimiroe *(Mng Dir)*

Subsidiary (Non-US):

Rederi AB Nordo-Link (2)
Lappogatan 3B, PO Box 106, 211 24, Malmo, Sweden
Tel.: (46) 40176800
Web Site: http://www.nordoe-link.com
Sales Range: $25-49.9 Million
Emp.: 35
Water Transportation
N.A.I.C.S.: 488390
Antonio Raimo *(Mgr-Line)*

Minoan Lines Shipping S.A. (1)
17 25th August Street Crete, 712 02, Iraklion, Greece **(90.84%)**
Tel.: (30) 2810399899
Web Site: http://www.minoan.gr
Rev.: $95,180,758
Assets: $527,008,090
Liabilities: $186,443,315
Net Worth: $340,564,774

Earnings: $4,888,467
Emp.: 318
Fiscal Year-end: 12/31/2017
Passenger & Freight Shipping Services
N.A.I.C.S.: 483111
Emanuele Grimaldi *(Chm)*

Port & Terminal Multiservices Limited (1)
Tin Can Island Port Complex, PO Box 2953, Apapa, Lagos, Nigeria
Tel.: (234) 127908803
Web Site: http://www.ptml-ng.com
Marine Transportation Services
N.A.I.C.S.: 483111

GRIMALDI INDUSTRI AB

Hovslagargatan 5B 2nd Fl, SE-111 48, Stockholm, Sweden
Tel.: (46) 854504410
Web Site: http://www.grimaldi.se
Sales Range: $50-74.9 Million
Emp.: 1,400
Holding Company
N.A.I.C.S.: 551112
Salvatore Grimaldi *(Founder)*

Subsidiaries:

3nine AB (1)
Cylindervagen 12, 13127, Nacka, Sweden
Tel.: (46) 8 601 35 40
Web Site: http://www.3nine.se
Commercial Machinery Mfr
N.A.I.C.S.: 333310
Oskar Olai *(CEO)*

Subsidiary (US):

3nine USA Inc. (2)
28730 S River Rd, Catoosa, OK 74015
Tel.: (918) 266-0113
Industrial Supplies Whslr
N.A.I.C.S.: 423840
Christian Grill *(Pres)*

Bianchi Cafe & Cycles Sverige AB (1)
Norrlandsgatan 16, 111 43, Stockholm, Sweden
Tel.: (46) 8 611 21 00
Web Site: http://www.bianchi.cafe
Bicycle Mfr
N.A.I.C.S.: 336991

Cycleurope Industries SAS (1)
161 rue Gabriel Peri, 10100, Romilly-sur-Seine, France
Tel.: (33) 325 393939
Bicycles Distr
N.A.I.C.S.: 423910

Cycleurope UK Ltd (1)
21-23 Mill Street, Bedford, MK40 3EU, Bedfordshire, United Kingdom
Tel.: (44) 1234 245 929
Bicycles Distr
N.A.I.C.S.: 423910

Cycleurope USA Inc. (1)
2536A Barrington Ct, Hayward, CA 94545
Tel.: (510) 264-1001
Bicycles Distr
N.A.I.C.S.: 423910

Grimaldis Mekaniska Verkstad AB (1)
Mastareg 16, Box 905, 731 29, Koping, Sweden
Tel.: (46) 221 84400
Precision Component Mfr
N.A.I.C.S.: 332721

Learnify AB (1)
Drottninggatan 61, 111 21, Stockholm, Sweden
Tel.: (46) 8 236 700
Web Site: http://www.learnify.com
Educational Support Services
N.A.I.C.S.: 611710

Morgana Systems Ltd. (1)
Davy Avenue Knowlhill, Milton, MK5 8HJ, Bucks, United Kingdom
Tel.: (44) 1908 608888
Web Site: http://www.morgana.co.uk
Printing Machinery Mfr & Distr
N.A.I.C.S.: 333248
Quen Baum *(Mng Dir)*

GRIMALDI INDUSTRI AB

Grimaldi Industri AB—(Continued)

Plockmatic International AB (1)
Telefonvagen 30, 126 26, Hagersten, Sweden
Tel.: (46) 8 602 50 00
Web Site: http://www.plockmatic.com
Commercial Printing Services
N.A.I.C.S.: 323113
Jan Marstorp *(CEO)*

Subsidiary (Non-US):

SIA Plockmatic (2)
Sampetera 2, 1067, Riga, Latvia
Tel.: (371) 67114013
Web Site: http://www.plockmatic.se
Emp.: 85
Commercial Printing Services
N.A.I.C.S.: 323113

VenCap Industrier AB (1)
Hovslagargatan 5B 2nd Floor, Stockholm, 11148, Sweden **(100%)**
Tel.: (46) 854504410
Web Site: http://www.grimaldi.se
Sales Range: $50-74.9 Million
Emp.: 10
Holding Company
N.A.I.C.S.: 551112
Salvatore Grimaldi *(CEO & Mng Dir)*

Subsidiary (Domestic):

Cycleurope AB (2)
Hovslagargatan 5 B 2nd Floor, 111 48, Stockholm, Sweden
Tel.: (46) 854504480
Web Site: http://www.cycleurope.com
Sales Range: $25-49.9 Million
Emp.: 5
Bicycle Mfr
N.A.I.C.S.: 336991
Tony Grimaldi *(Pres & CEO)*

Subsidiary (Non-US):

Cycleurope Finland Oy (3)
Sarkatie 1 A, PL 90, 1721, Vantaa, Finland
Tel.: (358) 9 849 2055
Web Site: http://www.crescent.fi
Emp.: 9
Bicycles Distr
N.A.I.C.S.: 423910
Jussi Laurikainen *(Mng Dir)*

Subsidiary (Domestic):

Velo & Oxygen Oy (4)
Kastelholmantie 2, 00900, Helsinki, Finland
Tel.: (358) 20 127 0500
Web Site: http://www.velo-oxygen.fi
Bicycles Distr
N.A.I.C.S.: 423910

Subsidiary (Non-US):

Cycleurope Norge AS (3)
Sinsenveien 47B, 0585, Oslo, Norway
Tel.: (47) 51 60 45 00
Web Site: http://www.cycleurope.no
Bicycles Distr
N.A.I.C.S.: 423910
Lars Nordberg *(Gen Mgr)*

Subsidiary (Domestic):

Cycleurope Sverige AB (3)
Birger Svenssons Vag 28, 432 82, Varberg, Sweden
Tel.: (46) 340 860 00
Web Site: http://www.cycleurope.se
Bicycle Mfr
N.A.I.C.S.: 336991
Marten Nydahl *(Mng Dir)*

Subsidiary (Non-US):

FIV E. Bianchi S.p.A. (3)
Via delle Battaglie 5, Treviglio, 24047, Italy
Tel.: (39) 03633161
Web Site: http://www.bianchi.com
Bicycle Mfr
N.A.I.C.S.: 336991

Subsidiary (Domestic):

Alpen Srl (4)
Via delle Battaglie 5, 24047, Treviglio, Bergamo, Italy
Tel.: (39) 0444 670912

Bicycle Parts Distr
N.A.I.C.S.: 423110

Subsidiary (Non-US):

Kildemoes A/S (3)
Albanivej 7 Nr Lyndelse, 5792, Arslev, Denmark
Tel.: (45) 63 90 26 00
Web Site: http://www.kildemoes.dk
Bicycles Distr
N.A.I.C.S.: 423910

Subsidiary (Domestic):

Monark Exercise AB (3)
Kroons vag 1, Box 6, 780 50, Vansbro, Sweden
Tel.: (46) 281 59 49 40
Web Site: http://www.monarkexercise.se
Emp.: 40
Bicycle Mfr & Distr
N.A.I.C.S.: 336991
Andreas Hebdum *(Gen Mgr)*

Subsidiary (Non-US):

Cycleurope Japan Co., Ltd. (2)
Kaika Bldg 2F Sotokanda 2-7-1, Chiyoda-ku, Tokyo, 101-0021, Japan
Tel.: (81) 3 3255 2431
Web Site: http://www.cycleurope.co.jp
Bicycles Distr
N.A.I.C.S.: 423910

GRINAKER-LTA CONSTRUCTION AND DEVELOPMENT LIMITED

Aveng Park Jurgens Street Jet Park, Boksburg, 1459, Gauteng, South Africa
Tel.: (27) 119235000
Web Site: http://www.grinaker-lta.co.za
Sales Range: $25-49.9 Million
Emp.: 60
Commercial Building Construction Services
N.A.I.C.S.: 236220

GRINDEKS AS

53 Krustpils St, Riga, LV 1057, Latvia
Tel.: (371) 67083500 LV
Web Site: http://www.grindeks.lv
Year Founded: 1991
Sales Range: $75-99.9 Million
Emp.: 1,162
Pharmaceuticals Product Mfr
N.A.I.C.S.: 325412
Juris Bundulis *(Chm-Mgmt Bd)*

Subsidiaries:

HBM Pharma s.r.o. (1)
Sklabinska 30, 036 80, Martin, Slovakia
Tel.: (421) 43 42 02 111
Web Site: http://www.hbmpharma.eu
Pharmaceuticals Product Mfr
N.A.I.C.S.: 325412
Iveta Bula *(Gen Dir)*

GRINDROD LIMITED

Grindrod House 108 Margaret Mncadi Avenue Victoria Embankment, Durban, 4001, KZN, South Africa
Tel.: (27) 313041451
GND—(JSE)
Rev.: $263,889,851
Assets: $793,595,041
Liabilities: $255,633,878
Net Worth: $537,961,163
Earnings: $57,714,148
Emp.: 3,798
Fiscal Year-end: 12/31/23
Shipping Trading & Freight Logistics Services
N.A.I.C.S.: 813910
David A. Polkinghorne *(CEO-Fin Svcs)*

Subsidiaries:

Grindrod (South Africa) (Pty) Ltd - Grindrod PCA Division (1)

Unit 33 Foreign Airline Cargo Ctr OR Tambo Intl Airport, Kempton Park, 1627, South Africa
Tel.: (27) 115710800
Web Site: http://www.lonrhologistics.co.za
Sales Range: $50-74.9 Million
Emp.: 60
Freight Forwarding & Logistics Management Services
N.A.I.C.S.: 488510

Grindrod (South Africa) (Pty) Ltd - MITCHELL COTTS MARITIME DIVISION (1)
Grindrod Mews 106 Margaret Mncadi Avenue, Durban, 4001, Kwazulu-Natal, South Africa
Tel.: (27) 313027555
Web Site: http://www.mitchellcotts.co.za
Sales Range: $25-49.9 Million
Emp.: 80
Marine Shipping Services
N.A.I.C.S.: 488510

Grindrod Bank Limited (1)
1st Fl N 20 Kingsmead Blvd Kingsmead Ofc Park, PO Box 3211, Durban, 4001, Kwazulu-Natal, South Africa
Tel.: (27) 313336600
Web Site: http://www.grindrodbank.co.za
Sales Range: $50-74.9 Million
Emp.: 55
Financial Support Services
N.A.I.C.S.: 522320
David Polkinghorne *(CEO)*

Grindrod Limited - Grindrod Intermodal Division (1)
Shed 10 Off Maritzburg St, Kaserne, Johannesburg, 2001, Gauteng, South Africa
Tel.: (27) 113346065
Cargo Transportation Services
N.A.I.C.S.: 488320

Grindrod Limited - Grindrod Logistics Auto Carriers Division (1)
1 Talana St Sacks Cir Bellville South, Bellville S, Cape Town, 7530, Western Cape, South Africa
Tel.: (27) 219513260
Web Site: http://www.autocarriers.co.za
Sales Range: $25-49.9 Million
Emp.: 9
Vehicles Transportation Services
N.A.I.C.S.: 484230

Grindrod Limited - Island View Shipping Division (1)
8th Fl Grindrod House 108 Margaret Mncadi Ave, Durban, 4001, Kwazulu-Natal, South Africa
Tel.: (27) 313021800
Web Site: http://www.ivs.co.za
Sales Range: $25-49.9 Million
Emp.: 80
Bulk Shipping Operation Services
N.A.I.C.S.: 488510

Grindrod Limited - Unicorn Shipping Division (1)
Quadrant House 115 Margaret Mncadi Ave Victoria Embankment, Durban, 4001, Kwazulu-Natal, South Africa
Tel.: (27) 313027911
Web Site: http://www.unicornshipping.co.za
Sales Range: $25-49.9 Million
Emp.: 50
Shipping Services
N.A.I.C.S.: 488510
Martyn Wade *(CEO)*

Grindrod Management Services (Pty) Limited (1)
108 Margaret Mncadi Avenue, Durban, 4001, Kwazulu-Natal, South Africa
Tel.: (27) 313041451
Web Site: http://www.grindrod.co.za
Emp.: 600
Business Management Services
N.A.I.C.S.: 561110
Alen Olivier *(CEO)*

Grindrod Ships Agencies (Pty) Limited (1)
108 Margaret Mncadi Avenue, Durban, 4001, Kwazulu-Natal, South Africa
Tel.: (27) 313052751
Web Site: http://www.grindrod.co.za
Shipping Services

INTERNATIONAL PUBLIC

N.A.I.C.S.: 488510

Subsidiary (Domestic):

Grindrod Marine Services (2)
48 Hannah Rd Congella, Maydon Wharf, Durban, 4001, Kwazulu-Natal, South Africa
Tel.: (27) 312744700
Web Site: http://www.grindrodmarine.co.za
Sales Range: $25-49.9 Million
Emp.: 20
Freight Forwarding Services
N.A.I.C.S.: 488510

Division (Domestic):

Grindrod Ships Agencies (Pty) Limited - King & Sons Division (2)
11th Fl Grindrod House 108 Victoria Embankment, Durban, 4001, Kwazulu-Natal, South Africa
Tel.: (27) 313010711
Web Site: http://www.kingandsons.co.za
Sales Range: $25-49.9 Million
Emp.: 60
Shipping Services
N.A.I.C.S.: 488510

Subsidiary (Domestic):

Grindrod Travel (Pty) Limited (2)
4th Fl Grindrod Mews 106 Victoria Embankment, Durban, 4001, Kwazulu-Natal, South Africa
Tel.: (27) 313011225
Web Site: http://www.grindrodtravel.co.za
Sales Range: $10-24.9 Million
Emp.: 25
Travel & Tour Operating Agencies
N.A.I.C.S.: 561520

Grindrod Tank Terminals SA (Pty) Ltd (1)
108 Margaret Mncadi Avenue, Victoria Embankment, Durban, 4001, Kwazulu-Natal, South Africa
Tel.: (27) 3041451
Web Site: http://www.grindrod.co.za
Liquid Bulk Storage & Transit Facilities
N.A.I.C.S.: 484230

Grindrod Terminals (Pty) Ltd (1)
55 Johnstone Road, Maydon Wharf, Durban, 4001, Kwazulu-Natal, South Africa
Tel.: (27) 312056226
Web Site: http://www.oiltanking.co.za
Emp.: 35
Trucking Terminals Operation Services
N.A.I.C.S.: 488490
Linda Christie *(Mgr-Terminal)*

Division (Domestic):

Grindrod Terminals (Pty) Ltd - Bay Stevedores Division (2)
Newark Rd Richards Bay Harbour, Richards Bay, 3901, Kwazulu-Natal, South Africa
Tel.: (27) 357979141
Web Site: http://www.grindrod.co.za
Sales Range: $25-49.9 Million
Emp.: 21
Truck Terminal Loading & Separation Services
N.A.I.C.S.: 488490

Maputo Car Terminal Limitada (1)
Praca dos Trabalhadores, Porto de Maputo, Maputo, Mozambique
Tel.: (258) 21359100
Car Trucking Terminal Operation Services
N.A.I.C.S.: 488490
Pieter Venter *(Gen Mgr)*

WM TransLogistics (Pty) Ltd (1)
97 Maraisburg St, Johannesburg, 2093, Gauteng, South Africa
Tel.: (27) 114740052
Web Site: http://www.wmgroup.co.za
Petrochemicals Trucking Services
N.A.I.C.S.: 484230

GRINDROD SHIPPING HOLDINGS LTD.

1 Temasek Avenue Millenia Tower 10-02, Singapore, 089763, Singapore
Tel.: (65) 63230048 SG
Web Site:
https://www.grinshipping.com
Year Founded: 2017

AND PRIVATE COMPANIES

GRIN—(NASDAQ)
Rev.: $460,460,000
Assets: $549,231,000
Liabilities: $261,782,000
Net Worth: $287,449,000
Earnings: $103,367,000
Emp.: 607
Fiscal Year-end: 12/31/22
Holding Company
N.A.I.C.S.: 551112
Deborah Davel *(CFO)*

Subsidiaries:

Grindrod Shipping (South Africa) Pty. Ltd. (1)
Tel.: (27) 313021800
Shipping Transportation Services
N.A.I.C.S.: 488510

Grindrod Shipping Services UK Limited (1)
Shipping Transportation Services
N.A.I.C.S.: 488510

GRINM ADVANCED MATERIALS CO., LTD.
No 43 North Third Rd, Beijing, 100088, China
Tel.: (86) 1062369559
Web Site: https://www.griam.cn
Year Founded: 1999
600206—(SHG)
Rev.: $2,141,653,906
Assets: $777,907,864
Liabilities: $225,824,597
Net Worth: $552,083,267
Earnings: $37,934,676
Fiscal Year-end: 12/31/22
Semiconductor Product Mfr
N.A.I.C.S.: 334413
Hai Yang *(Chm, Sec-Party, Deputy Gen Mgr & Deputy Sec)*

Subsidiaries:

GRINM Electro-optic Materials Co., Ltd. (1)
No4 Baihe Road, Langfang Economic and Technological Development Zone, Hebei, 065001, China
Tel.: (86) 3162509038
Web Site: http://www.grieom.com
Optical Instrument & Lens Mfr
N.A.I.C.S.: 333310

GRINO ECOLOGIC, S.A.
C/Historiador Josep Lladonosa 2, 25002, Lleida, Spain
Tel.: (34) 973 279 056
Web Site: http://www.grinyo.com
Waste Management & Consulting Services
N.A.I.C.S.: 562998

GRIT REAL ESTATE INCOME GROUP LIMITED
Unity Building The Precinct M2 Junction B11 Fond du Sac Road, Grand Baie, Mauritius
Tel.: (230) 2697090
Web Site: https://grit.group
Year Founded: 2012
MUR—(MAU)
Rev.: $56,249,000
Assets: $907,687,000
Liabilities: $574,070,000
Net Worth: $333,617,000
Earnings: $20,465,000
Emp.: 157
Fiscal Year-end: 06/30/23
Real Estate Investment Services
N.A.I.C.S.: 531390
Bronwyn Anne Corbett *(CEO)*

GRITEE, INC.
2-3F Juseong Building 7 Eonju-151-gil, Gangnam-gu, Seoul, 06026, Korea (South)
Tel.: (82) 269078888
204020—(KRS)
Rev.: $109,770,265
Assets: $67,880,800
Liabilities: $15,459,852
Net Worth: $52,420,948
Earnings: $1,410,523
Emp.: 108
Fiscal Year-end: 12/31/22
Apparel & Textile Product Mfr
N.A.I.C.S.: 315990
Cho Hye-Sun *(Sr Mng Dir)*

GRITIT
6-9 The Square Stockley Park, Uxbridge, UB11 1FW, United Kingdom
Tel.: (44) 203 159 5270
Web Site: http://www.gritit.com
Year Founded: 2004
Sales Range: $10-24.9 Million
Emp.: 135
Landscaping Services
N.A.I.C.S.: 561730
Jason Petsch *(Founder)*

GRIUL SA
Str Irimicului 24 S2 Mlhai Bravu nr 223 etaj 2 camera 1 s3, Bucharest, Romania
Tel.: (40) 212426286
GRIU—(BUC)
Rev.: $88,302
Assets: $404,992
Liabilities: $103,458
Net Worth: $301,534
Earnings: ($105,840)
Emp.: 1
Fiscal Year-end: 12/31/22
Bread Mfr
N.A.I.C.S.: 311812

GRIZZLY DISCOVERIES INC.
Suite 363-9768 170 Street NW, Edmonton, T5T 5L4, AB, Canada
Tel.: (780) 712-3559
Web Site: https://www.grizzlydiscoveries.com
GZD—(OTCIQ)
Rev.: $103,836
Assets: $6,267,024
Liabilities: $284,272
Net Worth: $5,982,752
Earnings: ($284,878)
Fiscal Year-end: 07/31/21
Metal & Other Mineral Mining Services
N.A.I.C.S.: 212290
Brian R. Testo *(Pres & CEO)*

GRM OVERSEAS LIMITED
128 1st Floor Shiva Market, Pitampura, Delhi, 110034, India
Tel.: (91) 1147330330
Web Site: https://www.grmrice.com
Year Founded: 1995
531449—(BOM)
Rev.: $109,994,348
Assets: $56,634,437
Liabilities: $38,177,985
Net Worth: $18,456,452
Earnings: $6,199,584
Emp.: 79
Fiscal Year-end: 03/31/21
Food Product Mfr & Distr
N.A.I.C.S.: 111160
Atul Garg *(Chm & Mng Dir)*

GRMEC A.D.
Becejski Put BB, Backa Topola, Serbia
Tel.: (381) 24 712 666
Year Founded: 1991
Sales Range: Less than $1 Million
Emp.: 5
Material Recycling Services
N.A.I.C.S.: 562920

GROCLIN S.A.
Slowianska 4, 62-065, Grodzisk Wielkopolski, Poland
Tel.: (48) 502329536
Web Site: https://www.groclin.com
Year Founded: 1977
LES—(WAR)
Rev.: $389,482
Assets: $76,982
Liabilities: $505,589
Net Worth: ($428,608)
Earnings: ($461,636)
Fiscal Year-end: 12/31/23
Car Seats Mfr
N.A.I.C.S.: 337126
Andre Gerstner *(Chm-Mgmt Bd)*

Subsidiaries:

Groclin Karpaty Sp. z o.o. (1)
Slowianska Nadberezna 31, 88 000, Uzhgorod, Ukraine
Tel.: (380) 312424101
Automobile Parts Mfr
N.A.I.C.S.: 336390
Diana Zhovtani *(Mgr-Quality)*

Groclin Seating GmbH (1)
An den Kiesgruben 2, 73240, Wendlingen am Neckar, Germany
Tel.: (49) 7024809250
Automobile Parts Mfr
N.A.I.C.S.: 336390

Groclin Service Sp. z o.o. (1)
Slowianska 4, 62-065, Nowa Sol, Poland
Tel.: (48) 616287110
Automobile Parts Mfr
N.A.I.C.S.: 336390

GROCON GROUP HOLDINGS PTY. LTD.
Level 1 577 Little Bourke Street, Melbourne, 3000, VIC, Australia
Tel.: (61) 396318833
Web Site: http://www.grocon.com.au
Year Founded: 1954
Construction Management Services
N.A.I.C.S.: 236220
Daniel Grollo *(Chm & CEO)*

GRODNO SA
ul Kwiatowa 14, Grabina, 05-126, Michalowice, Poland
Tel.: (48) 227724515
Web Site: https://www.grodno.pl
GRN—(WAR)
Rev.: $297,975,432
Assets: $125,982,013
Liabilities: $88,368,839
Net Worth: $37,613,174
Earnings: $1,560,066
Fiscal Year-end: 03/31/24
Electrical Material Distr
N.A.I.C.S.: 423610

GROEP HEYLEN BUSINESS & BUILDING BV
Diamantstraat 10, 2200, Herentals, Belgium
Tel.: (32) 14231626
Web Site: https://www.heylengroup.com
Investment Management Service
N.A.I.C.S.: 523999
Seppe Onsea *(Dir-Growth & Acq)*

Subsidiaries:

Royal United Mint BV (1)
Zone Reme 7, 2260, Westerlo, Belgium
Tel.: (32) 808217667
Web Site: https://www.royalunitedmint.be
Holding Company
N.A.I.C.S.: 551112

Subsidiary (US):

The Osborne Coinage Company (2)
2851 Massachusetts Ave, Cincinnati, OH 45225
Tel.: (513) 681-5424
Web Site: http://www.osbornecoin.com

GROMUTUAL BERHAD

Sales Range: $10-24.9 Million
Emp.: 70
Custom-made Coins & Tokens Mfr & Distr
N.A.I.C.S.: 332999
Scott Comisar *(Mng Dir)*

GROMUTUAL BERHAD
PH1 Austin18 Jalan Austin Perdana 3 Taman Austin Perdana, 81100, Johor Bahru, Johor, Malaysia
Tel.: (60) 72121333 MY
Web Site: https://www.gromutual.com
9962—(KLS)
Rev.: $11,468,923
Assets: $102,416,887
Liabilities: $21,621,446
Net Worth: $80,795,441
Earnings: $1,928,113
Emp.: 55
Fiscal Year-end: 12/31/22
Property Development Services
N.A.I.C.S.: 531311
May Li Yong *(Co-Sec)*

Subsidiaries:

Ayer Hitam Land Sdn. Bhd. (1)
No 6A Jalan Manis 1/1 Taman Manis 1, Parit Raja, 86400, Batu Pahat, Johor, Malaysia
Tel.: (60) 74545745
Property Investment & Development Services
N.A.I.C.S.: 531390

Emerald Park Sdn. Bhd. (1)
D-G-07 Pangsapuri Emerald, Bukit Beruang, 75450, Melaka, Malaysia
Tel.: (60) 62328188
Web Site: http://www.emeraldpark.com.my
Student Accommodation Services
N.A.I.C.S.: 721310

Subsidiary (Domestic):

Hillpark Development Sdn. Bhd. (2)
SU 141-1 Jalan JTH 1 Taman Terendak Heights, Masjid Tanah, 78300, Melaka, Malaysia
Tel.: (60) 63518288
Property Investment & Development Services
N.A.I.C.S.: 531390

Gromutual Berhad - Melaka (1)
C-01-03 04 & 05 Pangsapuri Bukit Beruang, 75450, Melaka, Malaysia
Tel.: (60) 62328188
Web Site: http://www.emeraldpark.com.my
Sales Range: $50-74.9 Million
Emp.: 8
Property Development Services
N.A.I.C.S.: 531311

Idealbase Sdn. Bhd. (1)
Suite 15 3 A Level 15 Menara Pelangi No 2 Jalan Kuning, 80400, Johor Bahru, Johor, Malaysia
Tel.: (60) 73319317
Property Construction & Management Services
N.A.I.C.S.: 236210

Prairie Development Sdn. Bhd. (1)
15 3A Level 15 Menara Pelangi 2 Jalan Kuning Taman Pelangi, 80400, Johor Bahru, Johor, Malaysia
Tel.: (60) 73319317
Web Site: http://www.gromutual.com
Emp.: 20
Property Development Services
N.A.I.C.S.: 531390

Rainbow Entity Sdn. Bhd. (1)
PH1 Austin18 Jalan Austin Perdana 3 Taman Austin Perdana, 81100, Johor Bahru, Malaysia
Tel.: (60) 72121253
Property Investment & Development Services
N.A.I.C.S.: 531390

Sakae Corporation Sdn. Bhd. (1)
Lot 2066 Batu 9 3/4 Tangga Batu, Tanjung Keling, 76400, Melaka, Malaysia
Tel.: (60) 63518288
Property Investment & Development Services

GROMUTUAL BERHAD

Gromutual Berhad—(Continued)
N.A.I.C.S.: 531390

Simpang Maju Enterprises Sdn. Bhd. (1)
MP6 6-1 Jalan Lesung Batu Jaya Utama Taman Lesung Batu Jaya, Alor Gajah, 78000, Melaka, Malaysia
Tel.: (60) 65568232
Property Investment & Development Services
N.A.I.C.S.: 531390

Summer Range Sdn. Bhd. (1)
Ste 15 3A Level 15 Menara Pelangi No 2 Jalan Kuning Taman Pgi, Johor Bahru, Johar, Malaysia
Tel.: (60) 73319317
Property Development Services
N.A.I.C.S.: 531390

Wisma Development Sdn. Bhd. (1)
45 2nd Fl Jalan Maharani, 84000, Muar, Johor, Malaysia
Tel.: (60) 69527216
Property Development Services
N.A.I.C.S.: 531390

GRONEMEYER IT GMBH
Konrad-Zuse-Strasse 1, 37671, Hoxter, Germany
Tel.: (49) 52719670 De
Web Site: http://www.gronemeyer-it.de
Year Founded: 1985
Sales Range: $25-49.9 Million
Information Technology Services
N.A.I.C.S.: 541519
Jens Gronemeyer (Mng Dir)

GRONG SPAREBANK
Tel.: (47) 74312860
Web Site: https://www.grong-sparebank.no
Year Founded: 1862
GRONG-ME—(OSL)
Sales Range: Less than $1 Million
Commercial Banking Services
N.A.I.C.S.: 522110
Jon Havard Solum (CEO)

GRONLANDSBANKEN A/S
Imaneq 33, PO Box 1033, 3900, Nuuk, 3900, Greenland
Tel.: (299) 701234 GL
Web Site: https://www.banken.gl
Year Founded: 1967
GRLA—(CSE)
Rev.: $32,859,169
Assets: $1,150,260,595
Liabilities: $959,467,234
Net Worth: $190,793,361
Earnings: $14,288,753
Emp.: 140
Fiscal Year-end: 12/31/22
Banking Services
N.A.I.C.S.: 522110
Martin Kviesgaard (Mng Dir)

GROOTHANDELSGEBOUWEN N.V.
Stationsplein 45 unit A2 191, 3013 AK, Rotterdam, Netherlands
Tel.: (31) 10 240 34 34
Web Site: http://www.ghg.nl
Year Founded: 1947
Sales Range: $10-24.9 Million
Office & Retail Space Leasing Services
N.A.I.C.S.: 531120
George Voorhout (Member-Mgmt Bd)

Subsidiaries:

Ghg Facilitair B.V. (1)
PO Box 29057, 3001, Rotterdam, Netherlands
Tel.: (31) 10 2403434
Real Estate Consulting Service
N.A.I.C.S.: 531210

GROSCHOPP AG
Greefsallee 49, Viersen, 41747, Germany
Tel.: (49) 21623740
Web Site: http://www.groschopp.de
Year Founded: 1948
Sales Range: $25-49.9 Million
Emp.: 250
Mfr of FHP Motors, Gearmotors, Reducers & Controls
N.A.I.C.S.: 335312
Wolfgang Pflug (CEO)

Subsidiaries:

Berkmanns Antriebe GmbH (1)
Roermonder Bahn 25, Wegberg, 41844, Huckelhoven, Germany (51%)
Tel.: (49) 2436 2001
Sales Range: $25-49.9 Million
Emp.: 15
FHP Motors Mfr
N.A.I.C.S.: 335312

GROSNOR DISTRIBUTION INC.
4 Lowry Drive, Brampton, L7A 1C4, ON, Canada
Tel.: (416) 744-3344
Web Site: http://www.grosnor.com
Year Founded: 1989
Rev.: $23,763,326
Emp.: 28
Trading & Game Card Distr
N.A.I.C.S.: 459120
David Yeates (Co-Pres & CEO)

GROSVENOR FINANCIAL SERVICES GROUP LTD.
Level 5 Alcatel-Lucent Building 13-27 Manners Street, PO Box 11-872, Wellington, New Zealand
Tel.: (64) 4 473 0262 NZ
Web Site: http://www.gfsg.co.nz
Year Founded: 1998
Brokerage, Investment & Management Consulting Services
N.A.I.C.S.: 523999
Allan Tong Yeo Seng (CEO)

GROSVENOR RESOURCE CORPORATION
Suite 202-2168 Marine Drive, Vancouver, V7V 1K3, BC, Canada
Tel.: (604) 685-6851
Web Site: https://www.gvrresource.com
GVR—(TSXV)
Rev.: $192,283
Assets: $2,091,459
Liabilities: $16,560
Net Worth: $2,074,899
Earnings: ($213,182)
Fiscal Year-end: 08/31/23
Mineral Exploration Services
N.A.I.C.S.: 213114
Ian Rozier (CEO)

GROT A.D.
Kriva Feja bb, Vranje, Serbia
Tel.: (381) 17 421 404
Year Founded: 2002
Sales Range: $1-9.9 Million
Emp.: 197
Metal Ore Exploration Services
N.A.I.C.S.: 331491

GROTHUSEN GESMBH
Albert-Schweitzer-Gasse 5, 1140, Vienna, Austria
Tel.: (43) 19702214
Web Site: http://www.grothusen.com
Year Founded: 1953
Emp.: 32
Audio & Video Equipment Distr
N.A.I.C.S.: 423690
Maximilian Gsthwandtner (Gen Mgr)

GROTTES DE HAN-SUR-LESSE
Rue J Lamotte 2, Han-sur-Lesse, 5580, Namur, Belgium
Tel.: (32) 84377213
Web Site: http://www.grotte-de-han.be
Travel Support Services
N.A.I.C.S.: 561510
Brigitte Malou (CEO)

GROUND INVESTIGATION & PILING LIMITED
Devonshire House, Ettingshall Road, Wolverhampton, WV22JT, United Kingdom
Tel.: (44) 1902459558
Web Site: http://www.gipuk.com
Heavy & Civil Engineering Construction Services
N.A.I.C.S.: 237990
Paul Smart (Mgr-Lab Quality)

GROUNDED PEOPLE APPAREL INC.
Suite 800-1199 West Georgia Street, Vancouver, V6E 3T5, BC, Canada
Tel.: (236) 521-8784 BC
Web Site: https://www.groundedpeople.com
Year Founded: 2020
GPAIF—(OTCQB)
Rev.: $90,453
Assets: $1,602,861
Liabilities: $169,611
Net Worth: $1,433,250
Earnings: ($1,567,589)
Fiscal Year-end: 02/28/23
Footwear Product Mfr
N.A.I.C.S.: 316210
Geoff Balderson (CFO)

GROUNDHEAT ENERGY SOLAR WIND CORP.
211 Rodinea Road, Vaughan, L6A 1RA, ON, Canada
Tel.: (416) 230-4949
Web Site: http://groundheat.com
Year Founded: 1985
Renewable Energy General Contructing Services
N.A.I.C.S.: 221116

Subsidiaries:

Clean Energy Developments Corp. (1)
254 Attwell Drive, Toronto, M9W 5B2, ON, Canada
Tel.: (905) 603-4340
Web Site: http://www.cleanenergy.ca
Thermal Energy Solutions
N.A.I.C.S.: 238990

GROUNDSTAR RESOURCES LIMITED
2900 First Canadian Center 350-7th Ave SW, Calgary, T2P 3N9, AB, Canada
Tel.: (403) 265-2549
Web Site: https://www.groundstar.com
Year Founded: 1968
GSA—(TSXV)
Sales Range: Less than $1 Million
Emp.: 5
Oil & Gas Exploration Services
N.A.I.C.S.: 213112
Tyron Pfeifer (COO)

GROUP 6 METALS LIMITED
Level 26 259 George Street, Sydney, 2000, NSW, Australia
Tel.: (61) 286221402
Web Site: https://www.kingislandscheelite.com

INTERNATIONAL PUBLIC

G6M—(ASX)
Rev.: $1,204,907
Assets: $93,218,457
Liabilities: $45,839,997
Net Worth: $47,378,460
Earnings: ($14,597,585)
Fiscal Year-end: 06/30/23
Tungsten Mining Services
N.A.I.C.S.: 212290
Johann Jooste-Jacobs (Chm)

Subsidiaries:

Scheelite Management Pty Ltd (1)
31 Blackwood St, 7256, Grassy, TAS, Australia
Tel.: (61) 364611010
Mining Project Management Services
N.A.I.C.S.: 541618

GROUP DE CLOEDT SA
Gachardhouse Gachardstreet 88 B12, 1050, Brussels, Belgium
Tel.: (32) 2 647 12 34 BE
Web Site: http://www.groupdecloedt.be
Dredging Services & Concrete Mfr
N.A.I.C.S.: 327390
Emmanuel Maes (Gen Mgr)

Subsidiaries:

DC Halsvik Aggregates AS (1)
Slovagen 1, 5960, Dalsoyra, Norway
Tel.: (47) 57781440
Construction Materials Distr
N.A.I.C.S.: 423320

DC Industrial n.v. (1)
Gachardstreet 88 b 12, 1050, Brussels, Belgium
Tel.: (32) 26471234
Marine Dredging Services
N.A.I.C.S.: 488310

GRANUMIX B.V. (1)
Haven Westzijde 12, 4511 AN, Breskens, Netherlands
Tel.: (31) 117381395
Marine Transportation Services
N.A.I.C.S.: 483111
Bram Meerleveld (Dir-Sls)

NHM Bruges nv (1)
Pathoekeweg 340, 8000, Bruges, Belgium
Tel.: (32) 50450180
Marine Transportation Services
N.A.I.C.S.: 483111

NHM Nieuwpoort NV (1)
Noorderhavenoever, 8620, Nieuwpoort, Belgium
Tel.: (32) 58222940
Marine Transportation Services
N.A.I.C.S.: 483111

Top Meerhout NV (1)
Nijverheidsweg 11, 2450, Meerhout, Belgium
Tel.: (32) 89858985
Web Site: http://www.meerhout.be
Educational Support Services
N.A.I.C.S.: 611710
Tom Gielen (Mgr-Site)

GROUP ELEVEN RESOURCES CORP.
Suite 2200 885 West Georgia, Vancouver, V6C 3E8, BC, Canada
Tel.: (604) 630-8839
Web Site: https://www.groupeleven.com
GRLVF—(OTCIQ)
Rev.: $2,962
Assets: $7,766,344
Liabilities: $478,103
Net Worth: $7,288,241
Earnings: ($1,600,279)
Fiscal Year-end: 12/31/21
Mineral Exploration Services
N.A.I.C.S.: 213115
Daniel MacInnis (Chm)

GROUP FIVE LIMITED

AND PRIVATE COMPANIES

2 Eglin Road Sunninghill, Sandton, 2157, South Africa
Tel.: (27) 100601555
Web Site: http://www.groupfive.co.za
GRF—(JSE)
Rev.: $593,461,307
Assets: $518,176,835
Liabilities: $424,425,700
Net Worth: $93,751,134
Earnings: ($105,645,952)
Emp.: 7,394
Fiscal Year-end: 06/30/18
Building Construction
N.A.I.C.S.: 236116
Nonqaba C. Katamzi *(Sec)*

Subsidiaries:

Everite Building Products Pty Ltd (1)
Heidelberg Rd, PO Box 8644, Kliprivier, Johannesburg, 1871, Gauteng, South Africa
Tel.: (27) 114394400
Web Site: http://www.everite.co.za
Sales Range: $250-299.9 Million
Emp.: 700
Roofing Sheets Mfr
N.A.I.C.S.: 423330
Jurgen A.E. Stragier *(Mng Dir)*

Group Five Building (Proprietary) Limited (1)
Woodmead N Ofc Park Maxwell Dr, Johannesburg, 2128, Gauteng, South Africa
Tel.: (27) 112538400
Bridge & Tunnel Construction Services
N.A.I.C.S.: 237130

Group Five Civil Engineering (Proprietary) Limited (1)
16 Skeen Blvd, Bedfordview, 2007, Gauteng, South Africa
Tel.: (27) 114096600
Sales Range: $700-749.9 Million
Emp.: 4,000
Civil Engineering Services
N.A.I.C.S.: 541330

Group Five Construction (Proprietary) Limited (1)
371 Rivonia Blvd, Johannesburg, 2128, Gauteng, South Africa
Tel.: (27) 118060111
Web Site: http://www.groupfive.co.za
Sales Range: $100-124.9 Million
Emp.: 300
Airport Runway Construction Services
N.A.I.C.S.: 237310

Division (Domestic):

Afrimix Ready Mixed Concrete (Proprietary) Limited (2)
16 Lakeview Crescent Kleinfontein Lake Ofc Park, Benoni, 1501, Gauteng, South Africa
Tel.: (27) 117414500
Web Site: http://www.afrimix.co.za
Ready Mixed Concrete & Mortars Supplier
N.A.I.C.S.: 327320

Plant (Domestic):

Afrimix Ready Mixed Concrete (Proprietary) Limited - Benoni Plant (3)
Zimbiwe Quarry Main Reef Rd, Benoni, 1501, Gauteng, South Africa
Tel.: (27) 11 423 2389
Sales Range: $25-49.9 Million
Emp.: 100
Readymix Concrete Mfr
N.A.I.C.S.: 327320

Afrimix Ready Mixed Concrete (Proprietary) Limited - Blue Hills Plant (3)
Plot 21 Summit Rd, Bluehills, Midrand, 0156, Gauteng, South Africa
Tel.: (27) 82 898 0078
Readymix Concrete Mfr
N.A.I.C.S.: 327320

Division (Domestic):

Sky Sands (Proprietary) Limited (2)
No 9 Country Estate Dr Waterfall Business Estate Jukskei View, Johannesburg, 1662, Gauteng, South Africa
Tel.: (27) 10 060 1555

Web Site: http://www.groupfive.co.za
Plaster & Washed Sand Products Distr
N.A.I.C.S.: 423320
Eric Verner *(Mng Dir)*

Group Five Design and Project Management (Proprietary) Limited (1)
Woodmead N Ofc Park 54 Maxwell Dr Postnet Ste 500, Woodmead, Johannesburg, 2191, Gauteng, South Africa
Tel.: (27) 112538700
Web Site: http://www.g5.co.za
Commercial Building Construction Services
N.A.I.C.S.: 236220

Group Five Energy (Proprietary) Limited (1)
33 Langermann Dr, Johannesburg, 2094, Gauteng, South Africa
Tel.: (27) 11 3235500
Commercial Building Construction Services
N.A.I.C.S.: 236220

Group Five Housing (Proprietary) Limited (1)
54 Maxwell Dr Woodmead N Ofc Park, Sandton, 2128, Gauteng, South Africa
Tel.: (27) 112538700
Sales Range: $100-124.9 Million
Emp.: 300
Residential Building Construction Services
N.A.I.C.S.: 236116

Group Five Infrastructure Developments (Proprietary) Limited (1)
371 Rivonia Blvd, Rivonia, Sandton, 2128, Gauteng, South Africa
Tel.: (27) 118060111
Commercial Building Construction Services
N.A.I.C.S.: 236220

Group Five KwaZulu-Natal (Proprietary) Limited (1)
41 Island Circle Riverhorse Valley, PO Box 201219, Effingham, Durban, 4016, South Africa
Tel.: (27) 100602800
Web Site: http://www.g5.co.za
Sales Range: $25-49.9 Million
Emp.: 50
Bridge & Highway Construction Services
N.A.I.C.S.: 237310
Mike Upton *(CEO)*

Group Five Limited - Building Western Cape Business Unit (1)
Plum Park 25 Gabriel Road, Plumstead, Cape Town, 7800, Western Cape, South Africa
Tel.: (27) 21 763 6100
Web Site: http://www.groupfive.co.za
Sales Range: $25-49.9 Million
Emp.: 35
Commercial Building Construction Services
N.A.I.C.S.: 236220
Alice Round *(Office Mgr)*

Group Five Oil & Gas (Proprietary) Limited (1)
15 Cliff Crescent, Edwin Swales Business Park, Durban, 4091, KwaZulu-Natal, South Africa
Tel.: (27) 315690300
Web Site: http://www.groupfive.co.za
Sales Range: $25-49.9 Million
Emp.: 80
Oil & Gas Pipeline Construction Services
N.A.I.C.S.: 237120
Dave Morgan *(Gen Mgr)*

Group Five Plant & Equipment (Proprietary) Limited (1)
Corner Grader and Lovato Roads Spartan Ext 9, PO Box X06, Kempton Park, 1620, Gauteng, South Africa
Tel.: (27) 119223600
Web Site: http://www.g5.co.za
Sales Range: $200-249.9 Million
Emp.: 850
Plant & Equipment Rental Services
N.A.I.C.S.: 238220
Enzo Ermacora *(Dir-Plant)*

Group Five Projects (Proprietary) Limited (1)
130 Thirteenth Ave Corner Paul Smit Road, Anderbolt, Boksburg, 1459, Gauteng, South Africa
Tel.: (27) 118994600

Web Site: http://www.groupfive.co.za
Sales Range: $50-74.9 Million
Emp.: 200
Commercial Building Construction Services
N.A.I.C.S.: 236220

Group Five Property Developments (Proprietary) Limited (1)
20 Georgian Crescent, 2128, Bryanston, South Africa
Tel.: (27) 118060222
Web Site: http://www.group5.co.za
Sales Range: $75-99.9 Million
Emp.: 150
Property Development Services
N.A.I.C.S.: 531210

Group Five Western Cape (Proprietary) Limited (1)
25 Gabriel Rd Plum Park, Plumstead, Cape Town, 7800, Western Cape, South Africa
Tel.: (27) 213861940
Commercial Building Construction Services
N.A.I.C.S.: 236220

Kayema Energy Solutions (Proprietary) Limited (1)
1st Floor Building No 5 Harrowdene Office Park, Western Service Road, Woodmead, 2196, South Africa
Tel.: (27) 11 202 0340
Web Site: http://kayema.co.za
Sales Range: $25-49.9 Million
Emp.: 7
Solar & Wind Energy Systems Installation Services
N.A.I.C.S.: 238220
Dovvi Finger *(Mgr-Comml Project)*

GROUP M5
42 O'Leary Avenue, PO Box 13305 Stn A, Saint John's, A1B 4B7, NL, Canada
Tel.: (709) 753-5559
Web Site: http://www.m5.ca
Year Founded: 2011
Holding Company; Advertising, Public Relations & Media Buying Agencies
N.A.I.C.S.: 551112
Trudy Groves *(VP)*

Subsidiaries:

m5 Marketing Communications Inc. (1)
42 O'Leary Avenue, PO Box 13305 Stn A, Saint John's, A1B 4B7, NL, Canada
Tel.: (709) 753-5559
Web Site: http://www.m5.ca
Advetising Agency
N.A.I.C.S.: 541810
Gary Wadden *(Founder & CEO)*

Subsidiary (US):

m5 Marketing Communications, Inc. (2)
707 Chestnut St, Manchester, NH 03104
Tel.: (603) 627-9600
Advetising Agency
N.A.I.C.S.: 541810

GROUP PSAGOT FOR FINANCE AND INVESTMENTS LTD.
3 Sderot Rothschild, Tel Aviv, 6688106, Israel
Tel.: (972) 737968774
Web Site: https://www.psagot.co.il
GPST—(TAE)
Rev.: $71,914,755
Assets: $337,116,208
Liabilities: $280,152,649
Net Worth: $56,963,559
Earnings: ($3,448,023)
Fiscal Year-end: 12/31/22
Building Construction Services
N.A.I.C.S.: 236210
Tzachi Iron *(CEO)*

GROUP THERMOTE & VANHALST
Brabantstraat 15, 8790, Waregem, Belgium

Tel.: (32) 56 43 42 11
Web Site: http://www.tvh.com
Year Founded: 1969
Sales Range: $600-649.9 Million
Emp.: 3,000
Industrial Equipment Supplier
N.A.I.C.S.: 423830

Subsidiaries:

BEPCO DEUTSCHLAND GMBH (1)
Neuer Weg 5, Bad Sassendorf, 59505, Soest, Germany
Tel.: (49) 2927919590
Web Site: http://www.bepco-deutschland.de
Industrial Machinery & Equipment Distr
N.A.I.C.S.: 423830

BEPCO IBERICA SA (1)
C/ Xarol 7 Polig Ind Les Guixerfs, 08915, Badalona, Spain
Tel.: (34) 933810062
Machinery Repair & Maintenance Services
N.A.I.C.S.: 811310

C-Tech Industries, LLC (1)
8950 Global Way, West Chester, OH 45069
Tel.: (877) 755-7311
Web Site: http://www.ctech-ind.com
Electric Equipment Mfr
N.A.I.C.S.: 334515
Greg Greene *(Gen Mgr)*

CAM srl (1)
Via Villa S Cuore 10, Triuggio, 20844, Monza, Italy
Tel.: (39) 0362919533
Web Site: http://www.camsrl.com
Paint & Coating Mfr
N.A.I.C.S.: 325510

CC-heftrucks BVBA (1)
Kwalestraat 65a, Nieuwerkerken, 9320, Hasselt, Belgium
Tel.: (32) 53849092
Web Site: http://www.tvh.com
Forklift Truck Repair & Maintenance Services
N.A.I.C.S.: 423830

GEPBER HUNGARIA KFT (1)
Izsaki ut 6, 6000, Kecskemet, Hungary
Tel.: (36) 24222222
Web Site: http://www.gepber.hu
Forklift Truck Repair & Maintenance Services
N.A.I.C.S.: 423830
Csaba Farkas *(Founder & CEO)*

HDW BV (1)
Nikkelstr 35, 2984 AM, Ridderkerk, Netherlands
Tel.: (31) 180491010
Machinery Repair & Maintenance Services
N.A.I.C.S.: 811310

MATECO LOCATION DE NACELLES SA (1)
12 Rue John L Macadam, 1113, Luxembourg, Luxembourg
Tel.: (352) 3509991
Machinery Repair & Maintenance Services
N.A.I.C.S.: 811310
Sydney Gircourt *(Acct Mgr-Comml)*

MATECO PODESTY RUCHOME SP Z OO (1)
ul Murarska 27, 43-100, Tychy, Poland
Tel.: (48) 323232000
Web Site: http://www.mateco.pl
Forklift Truck Repair & Maintenance Services
N.A.I.C.S.: 423830

Romlift Serv s.r.l. (1)
Street Budvar 42, 535600, Odorheiu Secuiesc, Harghita County, Romania
Tel.: (40) 266216169
Web Site: http://www.romlift.ro
Equipment Rental Services
N.A.I.C.S.: 532490

STATECH SLOVAKIA s.r.o. (1)
Hronska 27, 962 31, Banska Bystrica, Slovakia
Tel.: (421) 455410763
Web Site: http://www.statech-slovakia.sk
Forklift Truck Repair & Maintenance Services
N.A.I.C.S.: 423830

GROUP THERMOTE & VANHALST

Group Thermote & Vanhalst—(Continued)

STATECH s.r.o. (1)
Pocapelska 346, 277 01, Melnik, Czech Republic
Tel.: (420) 728270270
Web Site: http://www.statech.cz
Forklift Truck Repair & Maintenance Services
N.A.I.C.S.: 423830

TVH Australasia Pty Ltd. (1)
735 Boundary Road, Richlands, 4077, QLD, Australia
Tel.: (61) 732770877
Web Site: http://www.tvh.com
Automobile Parts Distr
N.A.I.C.S.: 423120
Grant Adam (Mng Dir)

TVH Australia Pty Ltd (1)
735 Boundary Road, Richlands, Brisbane, 4077, QLD, Australia
Tel.: (61) 732770877
Automotive Parts Mfr & Distr
N.A.I.C.S.: 336390

TVH CANADA LTD (1)
1140-550 Sherling Place, Port Coquitlam, V3B 0J6, BC, Canada
Tel.: (604) 944-7040
Automobile Parts Distr
N.A.I.C.S.: 423120
Kyle Barrette (Territory Mgr)

TVH Deutschland GmbH (1)
Nurnberger Str 5, 30855, Langenhagen, Germany
Tel.: (49) 5117808810
Automotive Parts Mfr & Distr
N.A.I.C.S.: 336390

TVH France SASU (1)
BP 90097, 59393, Wattrelos, Cedex, France
Tel.: (33) 820227722
Automotive Parts Mfr & Distr
N.A.I.C.S.: 336390

TVH India Private Ltd. (1)
7th Floor Tower 1 Fountainhead Phoenix Market City, Nagar Road Survey No 207 Vimannagar, Pune, 411 014, India
Tel.: (91) 2067617400
Automotive Parts Mfr & Distr
N.A.I.C.S.: 336390

TVH Italia SRL (1)
Via Sempione 3bis, Marano, 28040, Italy
Tel.: (39) 0114545620
Automobile Parts Distr
N.A.I.C.S.: 423120
Mirko Alps (Gen Mgr)

TVH MEXICO, S DE RL DE CV (1)
Pirules 134-E Zona IV, Parque Industrial San Martin Obispo, 54763, Cuautitlan Izcalli, Mexico
Tel.: (52) 5558618550
Automobile Parts Distr
N.A.I.C.S.: 423120

TVH Malaysia Sdn. Bhd. (1)
10 Jalan Bawang Putih 24/34 - Seksyen 24, Shah Alam, 40300, Selangor, Malaysia
Tel.: (60) 355456166
Automobile Parts Distr
N.A.I.C.S.: 423120

TVH Middle East FZE (1)
Sharjah Airport International Free Zone Building Q4-141, PO Box 120030, Sharjah, United Arab Emirates
Tel.: (971) 65489774
Automotive Parts Mfr & Distr
N.A.I.C.S.: 336390

TVH New Zealand Ltd. (1)
11K Echelon Pl East Tamaki Auckland, Auckland, New Zealand
Tel.: (64) 92749695
Automobile Parts Distr
N.A.I.C.S.: 423120

TVH Nordic AB (1)
Jordbrovagen 22 Ed, 668 32, Vastra Gotaland, Sweden
Tel.: (46) 53462200
Automobile Parts Distr
N.A.I.C.S.: 423120
Hans-Olov Blom (Mng Dir)

TVH Parts Co. (1)
16355 S Lone Elm Rd, Olathe, KS 66062-3519
Tel.: (913) 829-1000
Web Site: http://www.tvh.com
Sales Range: $75-99.9 Million
Emp.: 400
Forklift Replacement Parts & Accessories Mfr
N.A.I.C.S.: 423830
Patrick J. McLaughlin (Pres)

Subsidiary (Domestic):

Superior Signals, Inc. (2)
16355 S Lone Elm Rd, Olathe, KS 66062-3519
Tel.: (913) 780-1440
Web Site: http://www.superiorsignals.com
Sales Range: $10-24.9 Million
Emp.: 14
Mfr Of Electrical Apparatus & Equipment
N.A.I.C.S.: 423610
Dirk Von Holt (VP-Sls & Mktg)

TVH Parts Mexico S. De R.L. De C.V. (1)
Logistic Park CPA Bodega 018 Champana-Lecheria Highway Km 2 5, San Martin Obispo, 54769, Cuautitlan Izcalli, Mexico
Tel.: (52) 5558618550
Automobile Parts Mfr
N.A.I.C.S.: 336390

TVH Parts South Africa (PTY) LTD (1)
90 Electron Avenue Isando Kempton Park, Isando, 1600, Gauteng, South Africa
Tel.: (27) 112812700
Automobile Parts Distr
N.A.I.C.S.: 423120

TVH Polska Sp.z o.o. (1)
Murarska 27, Tychy, 43-100, Poland
Tel.: (48) 664724484
Automobile Parts Distr
N.A.I.C.S.: 423120
Marek Adamczyk (Gen Mgr)

TVH Rus, LLC (1)
Aeroportovskaya St bld No 5, 141580, Moscow, Moskovskaya, Russia
Tel.: (7) 4957394482
Web Site: http://www.tvh.com
Automobile Parts Distr
N.A.I.C.S.: 423120

TVH Singapore PTE LTD (1)
6 Gul Street 3, Singapore, 629264, Singapore
Tel.: (65) 62761450
Automobile Parts Distr
N.A.I.C.S.: 423120
Han Fei Kang (Mng Dir)

TVH Trading (Xiamen) Co. Ltd. (1)
4 Qingxi Road, Guankou Town Jimei Qu, Xiamen, 200085, Fujian Sheng, China
Tel.: (86) 5925531732
Automotive Parts Mfr & Distr
N.A.I.C.S.: 336390

TVH Trading Co., Ltd. (1)
21 Pham Huu Chi Street Ward 12 District 5, Ho Chi Minh City, Vietnam
Tel.: (84) 839557576
Automobile Parts Distr
N.A.I.C.S.: 423120

TVH UK Ltd. (1)
Unit 17 Paragon Way, Exhall, CV7 9QS, Coventry, United Kingdom
Tel.: (44) 2476 585000
Web Site: http://www.tvh-uk.co.uk
Industrial Machinery Distr
N.A.I.C.S.: 423830

TVH Yedek Parca Ticaret A.S. (1)
Ikitelli O S B Demirciler Sanayi Sites A2 Blok No 32, Istanbul, 34306, Turkiye
Tel.: (90) 2126714884
Automobile Parts Distr
N.A.I.C.S.: 423120

Tvh Brasil Pecas Ltda. (1)
Rua Francisco Foga 840, Industrial District of Vinhedo, Vinhedo, 13288-166, SP, Brazil
Tel.: (55) 1930454250
Web Site: https://tvh.com.br
Industrial Equipment Whsr
N.A.I.C.S.: 423830

mateco GmbH (1)
Bottroper Str 16, 70376, Stuttgart, Germany
Tel.: (49) 711955560
Web Site: http://www.mateco.de
Platform Rental Services
N.A.I.C.S.: 238910
Armin Rappen (Mng Dir)

GROUP UP INDUSTRIAL CO., LTD.

188 Heping Road, Yangmei District, Taoyuan, 32647, Taiwan
Tel.: (886) 34853536
Web Site: https://www.gpline.com.tw
Year Founded: 1990
6664—(TPE)
Rev.: $73,697,058
Assets: $190,830,535
Liabilities: $115,682,519
Net Worth: $75,148,016
Earnings: $19,671,669
Emp.: 398
Fiscal Year-end: 12/31/22
Industrial Machinery Mfr
N.A.I.C.S.: 333248
An-Shun Chen (Chm & CEO)

GROUP7 AG

Eschenallee 8, 85445, Schwaig, Germany
Tel.: (49) 8122 9453 0
Web Site: http://www.group-7.de
Sales Range: $75-99.9 Million
Logistic Services
N.A.I.C.S.: 541614
Hans-Ulrich Birkhofer (Chm-Supervisory Bd)

GROUPAMA SA

8 & 10 rue d Astorg, 75008, Paris, France
Tel.: (33) 144567777
Web Site: http://www.groupama.com
Year Founded: 1900
Rev.: $17,605,215,680
Assets: $110,756,617,070
Liabilities: $100,580,317,440
Net Worth: $10,176,299,630
Earnings: $514,705,500
Emp.: 29,126
Fiscal Year-end: 12/31/18
Mutual Insurance, Banking & Financial Services
N.A.I.C.S.: 524298
Jean-Yves Dages (Chm)

Subsidiaries:

Cesvi France (1)
Z A De Chalembert Rue Evariste Galois, PO Box 23, 86130, Jaunay-Clan, Vienne, France (50%)
Tel.: (33) 549303700
Web Site: http://www.cesvifrance.fr
Sales Range: $50-74.9 Million
Emp.: 26
Insurance Services
N.A.I.C.S.: 524128
Langlade Guillaume (Gen mgr)

Cofintex 6 SA (1)
126 Perzzamont Des, 93194, Noisy-le-Grand, Paris, France (100%)
Tel.: (33) 149319600
Sales Range: $50-74.9 Million
Emp.: 18
Provider of Insurance Services
N.A.I.C.S.: 524298

Europa-Gan Biztosito (1)
Hamzsabegi Utca 37, 1114, Budapest, Hungary (90%)
Tel.: (36) 13610090
Sales Range: $50-74.9 Million
Emp.: 66
Life & Non-Life Insurance
N.A.I.C.S.: 524128

Gan Italia Vita S.p.A. (1)
45 Via Guidubaldo Del Monte, Rome, 197, Italy (98.36%)
Tel.: (39) 06809741
Web Site: http://www.gan.it

INTERNATIONAL PUBLIC

Sales Range: $50-74.9 Million
Emp.: 92
Life Insurance
N.A.I.C.S.: 524113

Gan Outre Mer IARD (1)
8 Rue D Astorg, Paris, France
Tel.: (33) 144567777
Insurance Services
N.A.I.C.S.: 524298

Subsidiary (Non-US):

Gan Pacifique (2)
9 Ave Bruat, BP 339, 98713, Papeete, French Polynesia (100%)
Tel.: (689) 503150
Web Site: http://www.groupama.es
N.A.I.C.S.: 524128

Gan Pacifique (2)
58 bis avenue de la Victoire, BP 223, 98845, Noumea, Cedex, New Caledonia (100%)
Tel.: (687) 243 070
Web Site: http://www.groupama.es
Direct Insurance
N.A.I.C.S.: 524128

Groupama Asigurari SA (1)
Str Mihai Eminescu Nr 45 Sector 1, Bucarest, 010513, Romania
Tel.: (40) 213058000
Web Site: http://www.groupama.ro
Automobile Insurance Services
N.A.I.C.S.: 524126
Jean-Yves Dages (Pres)

Groupama Asset Management (1)
58 bis rue la Boetie, 75008, Paris, France (100%)
Tel.: (33) 144567676
Web Site: http://www.groupama.am.fr
Sales Range: $650-699.9 Million
Emp.: 2,050
Provider of Asset Management Services
N.A.I.C.S.: 531390
Francis Ailhaud (CEO)

Groupama Assicurazioni SpA (1)
Viale Cesare Pavese 385, 00144, Rome, Italy
Tel.: (39) 0630181
Web Site: http://www.groupama.it
Fire Insurance Services
N.A.I.C.S.: 524210
Dominique Uzel (Mng Dir & Gen Mgr)

Groupama Assurances et Services (1)
5 7 St Rue Du Ctr, Noisy-le-Grand, 93199, France (100%)
Tel.: (33) 149313131
Web Site: http://www.groupama.com
Sales Range: $350-399.9 Million
Emp.: 1,000
Insurance
N.A.I.C.S.: 524128

Groupama Emeklilik A.S. (1)
Resitpasa Quarter Old Buyukdere Street Groupama Plaza No 2, 34398, Istanbul, Turkiye
Tel.: (90) 2123676767
Web Site: http://www.groupama.com.tr
General Insurance Services
N.A.I.C.S.: 524210
Nicolas Schwartzmann (Asst Gen Mgr)

Groupama Gan Vie (1)
5 7 Rue Du Ctr, 93199, Noisy-le-Grand, Cedex, France (100%)
Tel.: (33) 149313131
Sales Range: $50-74.9 Million
Emp.: 50
Direct Insurance
N.A.I.C.S.: 524128

Groupama Garancia Biztosito Zrt (1)
Oktober 6 u 20, Budapest, 1051, Hungary
Tel.: (36) 14673500
Web Site: http://www.groupama-garancia.hu
General Insurance Services
N.A.I.C.S.: 524210
Istvan Zsoter (Mgr-IT)

Groupama Garancia poistovna, a.s. (1)
Mileticova 21, 821 08, Bratislava, Slovakia
Tel.: (421) 850211411
Web Site: http://www.groupama.sk

AND PRIVATE COMPANIES

General Insurance Services
N.A.I.C.S.: 524210

Groupama Immobilier (1)
150 Avenue Des Champs-Elysees CS
60106, 75383, Paris, Cedex 08,
France (100%)
Tel.: (33) 155074000
Web Site: http://www.groupama-immobilier.fr
Sales Range: $75-99.9 Million
Emp.: 150
Provider of Real Estate Services
N.A.I.C.S.: 531390

Groupama Insurance (China) Ltd (1)
16 th Floor Western China Business Tower,
N 19 section 4 South Renmin Road,
610041, Chengdu, China
Tel.: (86) 2885268806
Agricultural Insurance Services
N.A.I.C.S.: 524128
Ivy Lin (Dir-HR)

Groupama PJ Societe de Protection Juridique (1)
45 Rue De La Bienfaisance, 75008, Paris,
France (95.14%)
Tel.: (33) 156886400
Sales Range: $50-74.9 Million
Emp.: 70
Insurance
N.A.I.C.S.: 524113

Groupama Phoenix Asfalistiki (1)
213-215 Syngrou Avenue, Athens, 17121,
Greece
Tel.: (30) 210 329 5111
Web Site: http://www.groupama-phoenix.com
Health & Medical Insurance Services
N.A.I.C.S.: 524114
Christos Katsios (Dir-Comml, Org & Processes)

Groupama Phoenix Asfalistiki (1)
213-215 Syngrou Avenue, Athens, 17121,
Greece
Tel.: (30) 302103295111
Web Site: http://www.groupama-phoenix.com
Health & Medical Insurance Services
N.A.I.C.S.: 524114
Christos Katsios (Dir-Comml, Org & Processes)

Groupama Seguros Portugal (1)
24 D Avenida de Berna, 1069-170, Lisbon,
Portugal (98.36%)
Tel.: (351) 217923100
Web Site: http://www.groupama.pt
Sales Range: $100-124.9 Million
Emp.: 102
Non-Life Insurance
N.A.I.C.S.: 524128

Groupama Vie Benin (1)
Villa Sise Au Lot 636 D Les Cocotiers, 04
BP 1419, Cotonou, Benin
Tel.: (229) 305456
Provider of Insurance Services
N.A.I.C.S.: 524128

Groupama Zastrahovane EAD (1)
47A Tsarigradsko shosse Blvd - Flat V Floor
3, 1124, Sofia, Bulgaria
Tel.: (359) 29158888
Web Site: http://www.groupama.bg
General Insurance Services
N.A.I.C.S.: 524210
Celine Bolard (CEO)

Groupe des Assurances de Tunisie (GAT) (1)
Lac De Come Lesberges Dulac, 80, Tunis,
Tunisia (24%)
Tel.: (216) 71285533
Web Site: http://www.best-re.com
Non-Life, Life Insurance & Reinsurance
N.A.I.C.S.: 524114

Gunes Sigorta (1)
Gunes Plaza Buyukdere Cad No 110,
Esentepe - Sisli, 34394, Istanbul,
Turkiye (35.4%)
Tel.: (90) 8502221957
Web Site: http://www.gunessigorta.com.tr
Sales Range: $100-124.9 Million
Emp.: 400
Non-Life & Life Insurance Services
N.A.I.C.S.: 524128

Luxlife (1)
PO Box 723, 2017, Luxembourg,
Luxembourg (83.6%)
Tel.: (352) 2527711
Web Site: http://www.luxlife.com
Sales Range: $50-74.9 Million
Emp.: 1
Life Insurance
N.A.I.C.S.: 524113

Mutuaide Assistance (1)
8-14 ave des Freres Lumiere, Bry-sur-Marne, 94366, Paris, France (100%)
Tel.: (33) 145166300
Web Site: http://www.mutuaide.fr
Sales Range: $50-74.9 Million
Emp.: 50
Insurance Carrier Service
N.A.I.C.S.: 524128
Olivier Remondini (Sec)

Presence Verte SA (1)
8-14 avenue des Freres Lumiere, Bry-sur-Marne, 94360, Paris, France (100%)
Tel.: (33) 145166300
Web Site: http://www.presenceverte.fr
Sales Range: $50-74.9 Million
Emp.: 70
Insurance
N.A.I.C.S.: 524128

RMA Wataniya (1)
83 Ave De Larmee Royale, Casablanca, 20
000, Morocco (67%)
Tel.: (212) 22310169
Web Site: http://www.alwataniya.com
Sales Range: $200-249.9 Million
Emp.: 452
Non-Life & Life Insurance
N.A.I.C.S.: 524113

Societe Tunisienne d'Assurances et de Reassurances (1)
Square de l Avenue de Paris 1, 1002, Tunis, Tunisia (35%)
Tel.: (216) 71256800
Web Site: http://www.star.com.tn
Sales Range: $350-399.9 Million
Emp.: 700
Insurance Services
N.A.I.C.S.: 524128
Lassaad Zarrouk (Chm)

GROUPE AB S.A.
132 ave du President Wilson, La
Plaine, 93210, Saint Denis, France
Tel.: (33) 149222001 FR
Web Site: http://www.abgroupe.fr
Year Founded: 1977
Sales Range: $150-199.9 Million
Emp.: 400
Holding Company; Pay Cable Television Station Operator
N.A.I.C.S.: 551112
Claude Berda (Chm & CEO)

Subsidiaries:

AB Broadcast (1)
132 avenue du President Wilson, BP 95, La
Plaine, 93210, Saint Denis, France
Tel.: (33) 149222278
Web Site: http://www.ab1.tv
Sales Range: $50-74.9 Million
Emp.: 150
Pay Cable Television Broadcasting
N.A.I.C.S.: 516120
Claude Berda (Mgr)

Belgium Television SA (1)
7 rue de Livourne, 1060, Brussels, Belgium
Tel.: (32) 26500920
Web Site: http://www.ab3.be
Sales Range: $25-49.9 Million
Emp.: 13
Television Broadcasting
N.A.I.C.S.: 516120

Via Production (1)
122 Ave Des Champs Elysees, 75008,
Paris, France (100%)
Tel.: (33) 153761400
Web Site: http://www.viaproduction.com
Motion Picture & Video Production
N.A.I.C.S.: 512110

GROUPE ADEO S.A.
135 Rue Sadi Carnot, 59790,
Ronchin, France
Tel.: (33) 359315300
Web Site: http://www.groupe-adeo.com
Year Founded: 1923
Sales Range: $5-14.9 Billion
Emp.: 7,000
Home Improvement Store Operator
N.A.I.C.S.: 444110
Damien Deleplanque (CEO)

Subsidiaries:

Bricolaje Bricoman S.L.U. (1)
Avenida Puerta de Sol n 2 Parque Comercial Plaza Nueva, 28919, Leganes, Spain
Tel.: (34) 914286190
Web Site: http://www.bricomart.com
Supermarket Operator
N.A.I.C.S.: 445110

Bricoman Italia S.r.L. (1)
Via Marconi 24, 20089, Rozzano, Italy
Tel.: (39) 0292890111
Web Site: http://www.bricoman.it
Supermarket Operator
N.A.I.C.S.: 445110

Bricoman Poland Sp. z o.o. (1)
ul Murmanska 25, 04-203, Warsaw, Poland
Tel.: (48) 22 516 67 00
Supermarket Operator
N.A.I.C.S.: 445110
Wioletta Darnowska (Dir-HR)

Bricoman S.A. (1)
1 rue Nicolas Appert, 59260, Lezennes,
France
Tel.: (33) 3 28 80 55 00
Web Site: http://www.bricoman.fr
Emp.: 150
Supermarket Operator
N.A.I.C.S.: 445110
Sebastian Antenna (Gen Mgr)

Dompro, S.A.S. (1)
Business Park-Paris Nord II 165 rue de la
Belle Etoile CS 89051, 95933, Roissy-en-France, Cedex, France
Tel.: (33) 1 77 80 72 00
Supermarket Operator
N.A.I.C.S.: 445110

KBANE SAS (1)
Parc de l innovation 1 Rue de Menin,
59520, Lille, France
Tel.: (33) 3 61 08 56 00
Supermarket Operator
N.A.I.C.S.: 445110

LEROY MERLIN Italy S.R.L (1)
Strada 8 Palazzo N, 20089, Rozzano, Italy
Tel.: (39) 02 399 76 1
Web Site: http://www.leroymerlin.com
Supermarket Operator
N.A.I.C.S.: 445110

LEROY MERLIN Pologne Sp. z.o.o. (1)
ul Targowa 72, 03-734, Warsaw, Poland
Tel.: (48) 22 528 58 00
Web Site: http://www.leroymerlin.pl
Supermarket Operator
N.A.I.C.S.: 445110
Iwona Sniady (Reg Sr Mgr-HR)

Leroy Merlin Bresil Ltda (1)
Rua Domingas Galleteri Blotta 315 Jd Consorcio, 04455-360, Sao Paulo, Brazil
Tel.: (55) 11 5670 8600
Web Site: http://www.leroymerlin.com.br
Supermarket Operator
N.A.I.C.S.: 445110

Leroy Merlin Bricolaj Romania SRL (1)
Sos Chitilei 284, Bucharest, Romania
Tel.: (40) 374 133 096
Web Site: http://www.leroymerlin.ro
Supermarket Operator
N.A.I.C.S.: 445110
Radu Florescu (Product Mgr)

Leroy Merlin Espana S.L.U. (1)
Avenida de la Vega 2, 28108, Alcobendas,
Madrid, Spain
Tel.: (34) 917496000
Web Site: http://www.leroymerlin.es

GROUPE B.M.R. INC.

Supermarket Operator
N.A.I.C.S.: 445110
Marc Decornet (Product Mgr)

WELDOM France S.A. (1)
ZI Breuil le Sec, 60608, Clermont, Cedex,
France
Tel.: (33) 3 44 77 80 00
Web Site: http://www.weldom.fr
Supermarket Operator
N.A.I.C.S.: 445110

ZODIO France (1)
3/5 rue Nicolas Appert, 59260, Lezennes,
France
Tel.: (33) 3 28 76 92 30
Supermarket Operator
N.A.I.C.S.: 445110

GROUPE AG3I SA
121 chemin Saint Marc, 06130,
Grasse, France
Tel.: (33) 493408606
Web Site: http://www.sagi-maintenance.fr
Industrial Machinery Maintenance
Services
N.A.I.C.S.: 811310
Christian Ghio (Chm & CEO)

GROUPE AIRWELL SA
10 Rue du Fort de Saint Cyr, 78180,
Montigny-le-Bretonneux, France
Web Site: https://www.groupe-airwell.com
Year Founded: 1947
ALAIR—(EUR)
Rev.: $70,617,615
Assets: $51,180,158
Liabilities: $39,735,457
Net Worth: $11,444,701
Earnings: $1,490,887
Emp.: 107
Fiscal Year-end: 12/31/23
Air Conditioning Equipment Distr
N.A.I.C.S.: 423730
Damien Riccio (Deputy Mng Dir)

GROUPE APICIL
38 Rue Francois Peissel, 69300,
Caluire-et-Cuire, France
Tel.: (33) 4 72 27 72 72
Web Site: http://www.mon.apicil.com
Insurance Services
N.A.I.C.S.: 524210

Subsidiaries:

Legal & General (France) SA (1)
58 Rue De La Victoire, Paris, 75440,
France
Tel.: (33) 155312400
Web Site: http://www.lgfrance.com
General Insurance Services
N.A.I.C.S.: 524298

GROUPE AXOR INC.
1950 Sherbrooke Street West Suite
400, Montreal, H1T 2F3, QC, Canada
Tel.: (514) 846-4000
Web Site: http://www.axor.com
Year Founded: 1972
Rev.: $44,713,198
Emp.: 300
Engineeering Services
N.A.I.C.S.: 541330
Simon Gourdeau (Pres)

GROUPE B.M.R. INC.
1501 Rue Ampere Bureau 200,
Boucherville, J4B 5Z5, QC, Canada
Tel.: (450) 655-2441
Web Site: https://www.bmr.ca
Year Founded: 1967
Sales Range: $300-349.9 Million
Emp.: 8,000
Lumber & Other Building Materials
Distr
N.A.I.C.S.: 423310
Alexandre Lefebvre (CEO)

GROUPE B.M.R. INC.

Groupe B.M.R. Inc.—(Continued)

Subsidiaries:

Matco Ravary Inc. (1)
355 Sir Wilfrid Laurier Blvd, Saint Basile Le Grand, Saint-Basile, J3N 1M9, QC, Canada
Tel.: (450) 461-5822
Sales Range: $75-99.9 Million
Emp.: 300
Construction & Renovation Materials Retailer
N.A.I.C.S.: 444180

GROUPE BEAUMANOIR

The Moinerie 10 Impasse Grand Garden, CS 11887, 35418, Saint-Malo, Cedex, France
Tel.: (33) 2 99 19 98 98
Web Site: http://www.groupe-beaumanoir.fr
Rev.: $1,446,947,600
Women's Clothing Retailer
N.A.I.C.S.: 458110
Roland Beaumanoir (Pres)

GROUPE BERKEM SA

20 Rue Jean Duvert, 33290, Blanquefort, France
Tel.: (33) 564310660
Web Site: https://www.groupeberkem.com
Year Founded: 1964
ALKEM—(EUR)
Rev.: $47,311
Assets: $126,473
Liabilities: $38,510
Net Worth: $87,963
Earnings: $173
Emp.: 169
Fiscal Year-end: 12/31/21
Chemical Products Mfr
N.A.I.C.S.: 335991
Olivier Fahy (CEO)

GROUPE BERMEX INC.

1273 Boulevard Saint-Laurent Ouest, Louiseville, J5V 2L4, QC, Canada
Tel.: (819) 601-8702
Web Site: http://www.groupebermex.com
Year Founded: 1983
Sales Range: $125-149.9 Million
Emp.: 794
Furniture Mfr
N.A.I.C.S.: 337126
Denis Darveau (VP-Sls)

GROUPE BERTRAND SARL

59 Rue de Tocqueville, 75017, Paris, France
Tel.: (33) 1 53 45 83 83
Web Site: http://www.groupe-bertrand.com
Year Founded: 1997
Restaurants & Hotels
N.A.I.C.S.: 722511
Olivier Bertrand (Founder)

Subsidiaries:

Burger King France SAS (1)
1 rue du Chevalier de Saint George, 75008, Paris, France
Tel.: (33) 1 53 45 83 83
Web Site: http://www.burgerking.fr
Fast-Food Restaurant, Chain
N.A.I.C.S.: 722513
Jocelyn Olive (Dir Gen)

Subsidiary (Domestic):

France Quick S.A.S. (2)
Parc des Portes de Paris, - Bat 123, 50 avenue du President Wilson, 93214, La Plaine Saint-Denis, Cedex, France
Tel.: (33) 1 4951 6464
Web Site: http://www.quick.fr
Restaurant Operators
N.A.I.C.S.: 561110
Cedric Dugardin (CEO)

Groupe Flo SA (1)
Tour Manhattan 5-6 place de l'Iris La Defense, 92095, Paris, Cedex, France (77.2%)
Tel.: (33) 141923000
Web Site: http://www.groupeflo.com
Sales Range: $250-299.9 Million
Restaurant Operators
N.A.I.C.S.: 722511
Vincent Lemaitre (Gen Dir)

GROUPE BPCE

7 promenade Germaine Sablon, 75013, Paris, France
Tel.: (33) 158404142 FR
Web Site: https://groupebpce.com
Year Founded: 2009
Rev.: $27,039,019,700
Net Worth: $86,611,092,260
Earnings: $4,184,916,820
Emp.: 105,019
Fiscal Year-end: 12/31/19
Holding Company
N.A.I.C.S.: 551112

Subsidiaries:

AEW Asia Limited (1)
Level 8 99 Elizabeth Street, Sydney, 2000, NSW, Australia
Tel.: (61) 437940714
Real Estate Investment Services
N.A.I.C.S.: 531210

AEW Asia Pte. Ltd. (1)
6 Battery Road 38-06, Singapore, 049909, Singapore
Tel.: (65) 63039000
Real Estate Investment Services
N.A.I.C.S.: 531390
Jane Cheong (Office Mgr)

AEW Central Europe Sp. Z O.O (1)
Atrium Tower Al Jana Pawla II 25 7th Floor, 00-854, Warsaw, Poland
Tel.: (48) 221634800
Asset Management Services
N.A.I.C.S.: 523940
Edyta Stelmach (Assoc Dir)

AEW Invest GmbH (1)
Steinstrasse 1-3, 40212, Dusseldorf, Germany
Tel.: (49) 21131113812
Real Estate Investment Services
N.A.I.C.S.: 531210

Alliance Entreprendre SAS (1)
5/7 rue de Monttessuy, 75007, Paris, France
Tel.: (33) 170629527
Web Site: http://www.allianceentreprendre.com
Emp.: 22
Investment Banking Services
N.A.I.C.S.: 523150
Chloe Bessieres (Head-IR)

BIC Bred (Suisse) SA (1)
Boulevard du Theatre 8, 1204, Geneva, Switzerland
Tel.: (41) 223123070
Web Site: http://www.bic-bred.com
Commercial Banking Services
N.A.I.C.S.: 522110

BPCE Car Lease SASU (1)
8 rue Vidailhan, CS 73131, 31132, Balma, Cedex, France
Tel.: (33) 562247373
Car Lending Services
N.A.I.C.S.: 532112
Didier Trupin (Chm)

BPCE Factor SA (1)
50 Avenue Pierre Mendes France, 75013, Paris, France
Tel.: (33) 158328000
Financial Services
N.A.I.C.S.: 523999
Dominique Garnier (Chm)

BPCE Infogerance & Technologies EIG (1)
110 Avenue de France, 75013, Paris, France
Tel.: (33) 187254000
Web Site: http://www.bpce-it.fr

Information Technology Services
N.A.I.C.S.: 541512
Gilles Sokoudjou (Mgr-IT)

BPCE Lease Madrid SE (1)
Calle de Serrano 90 6 Planta, 28006, Madrid, Spain
Tel.: (34) 911117979
Financial Services
N.A.I.C.S.: 523999
Miryan Garlin (Mgr-Reporting VIE)

BPCE Lease SA (1)
50 Avenue Pierre Mendes France, 75201, Paris, Cedex, France
Tel.: (33) 158328080
Web Site: http://www.lease.bpce.fr
Leasing Financial Services
N.A.I.C.S.: 522220

BTP Banque SA (1)
48 rue La Perouse, CS 51686, 75773, Paris, France
Tel.: (33) 140673500
Web Site: http://www.btp-banque.fr
Corporate Banking Services
N.A.I.C.S.: 522110

BTP Capital Conseil SAS (1)
48 rue La Perouse, 75016, Paris, France
Tel.: (33) 144117349
Corporate Banking Services
N.A.I.C.S.: 522110

Banco Primus S.A (1)
Quinta da Fonte Edificio D Joao I - 1, 2770-203, Paco d'Arcos, Portugal
Tel.: (351) 214468900
Web Site: http://www.bancoprimus.pt
Credit Financial Services
N.A.I.C.S.: 522299
Goncalo Silva (Mgr-Organization)

Banco Primus Spain S.A (1)
Avenida del Partenon 10 2 Planta Puerta 1, 28042, Madrid, Spain
Tel.: (34) 911781500
Web Site: http://www.bancoprimus.es
Credit Financial Services
N.A.I.C.S.: 522299

Banque Franco Lao Ltd. (1)
Lane Xang Avenue, PO Box 5720, Hatsady Village-Chantabouly District, Vientiane, Lao People's Democratic Republic
Tel.: (856) 21285444
Web Site: http://www.bfl-bred.com
Private Banking Services
N.A.I.C.S.: 522110
Arnaud Caulier (CEO)

Banque Populaire Aquitaine Centre Atlantique SCCV (1)
10 quai des Queyries, 33072, Bordeaux, Cedex, France
Tel.: (33) 549085050
Web Site: http://www.bpaca.banquepopulaire.fr
Private Banking Services
N.A.I.C.S.: 522110

Banque Populaire Auvergne Rhone Alpes SCM (1)
4 Boulevard Eugene Deruelle, 69003, Lyon, France
Tel.: (33) 478955555
Web Site: http://www.bpaura.banquepopulaire.fr
Private Banking Services
N.A.I.C.S.: 522110

Banque Populaire Du Sud SCCV (1)
38 bd Clemenceau, 66966, Perpignan, Cedex, France
Tel.: (33) 468382200
Web Site: http://www.sud.banquepopulaire.fr
Private Banking Services
N.A.I.C.S.: 522110

Banque Populaire Grand Ouest SCA (1)
15 Boulevard de la Boutiere, CS 26858, 35768, Saint-Gregoire, France
Tel.: (33) 272794040
Web Site: http://www.bpgo.banquepopulaire.fr
Private Banking Services
N.A.I.C.S.: 522110

Banque Tuniso Koweitienne SA (1)
1 Rue Medinat El Katif Cite Ennasr II, 2037,

INTERNATIONAL PUBLIC

Ariana, Tunisia
Tel.: (216) 71817026
Web Site: http://www.btknet.com
Commercial Banking Services
N.A.I.C.S.: 522110

Banque de Nouvelle-Caledonie SA (1)
10 avenue Marechal Foch, BP L3, 98849, Noumea, Cedex, New Caledonia
Tel.: (687) 687257400
Web Site: http://www.bnc.nc
Banking Services
N.A.I.C.S.: 522110

Batimap SA (1)
3 Avenue Henri Becquerel, BP 30262, 33698, Merignac, Cedex, France
Tel.: (33) 556340032
Web Site: http://www.batimap.fr
Real Estate Services
N.A.I.C.S.: 531390

Batiroc Bretagne Pays de Loire SA (1)
180 ter route de Vannes, CS 70145, 44700, Orvault, Cedex, France
Tel.: (33) 255587200
Web Site: http://www.batirocbpl.fr
Real Estate Services
N.A.I.C.S.: 531390

Bleu Residence Lormont SCI (1)
20 Avenue Salvador Allende, Lormont, 33310, Bordeaux, France
Tel.: (33) 556817438
Web Site: http://www.residence-senior-bordeaux.fr
Retirement Senior Living Facility Services
N.A.I.C.S.: 623312

Bred Bank Cambodia PLC (1)
No 30 Preah Norodom Boulevard Sangkat Phsar Thmey 3, Khan Daun Penh, Phnom Penh, Cambodia
Tel.: (855) 23999222
Web Site: http://www.bredcambodia.com
Commercial Banking Services
N.A.I.C.S.: 522110
Sakhina Chor (Mgr-Credit)

Bred Bank Fiji Ltd. (1)
Level 5 Tappoo City, Suva, Fiji
Tel.: (679) 132100
Web Site: http://www.bred.com.fj
Commercial Banking Services
N.A.I.C.S.: 522110

Bred I.T. Thailand Ltd. (1)
No 44 Smooth Life Tower 20th-21st Floor North Sathorn Road, Silom Bangrak, Bangkok, 10500, Thailand
Tel.: (66) 26791070
Web Site: http://www.bred-it.com
Commercial Banking Services
N.A.I.C.S.: 522110

Bred Vanuatu Ltd. (1)
Kumul Highway Downtown, Port-Vila, Vanuatu
Tel.: (678) 29111
Web Site: http://www.bred.vu
Commercial Banking Services
N.A.I.C.S.: 522110
Santos Vatoko (Head-Bus Banking)

COFACE (Singapore) Pte Ltd. (1)
16 Collyer Quay 25-00, Singapore, 049318, Singapore
Tel.: (65) 68278700
Financial Services
N.A.I.C.S.: 523999
Sandra Ciuriloviciute (Mgr-Comml)

COFACE Argentina SA (1)
Olga Cossettini 263 Floor 3 Yacht IV Dique IV Building Puerto Madero, C1107CCE, Buenos Aires, Argentina
Tel.: (54) 1152885000
Web Site: http://www.coface.com.ar
Credit Insurance Services
N.A.I.C.S.: 524113

COFACE Australia Pty Ltd. (1)
Level 11 1 Market Street, Sydney, 2000, NSW, Australia
Tel.: (61) 282358600
Web Site: http://www.coface.com.au
Credit Insurance Services
N.A.I.C.S.: 524113

COFACE Austria GmbH (1)
Marxergasse 4c, 1030, Vienna, Austria
Tel.: (43) 1515540
Web Site: http://www.coface.at
Credit Insurance Services
N.A.I.C.S.: 522299
Declan Daly *(Country Mgr)*

COFACE Belgium SA (1)
Vorstlaan 100 Boulevard du Souverain, 1170, Brussels, Belgium
Tel.: (32) 24040111
Web Site: http://www.coface.be
Credit Insurance Services
N.A.I.C.S.: 524113
Alix La-Balme *(Fin Dir)*

COFACE Bulgaria EOOD (1)
42 Petar Parchevich Str, 1000, Sofia, Bulgaria
Tel.: (359) 28213735
Web Site: http://www.coface.bg
Credit Insurance Services
N.A.I.C.S.: 524113

COFACE Canada Inc. (1)
2235 Sheppard Ave East Ste 902B, Toronto, M2J 5B5, ON, Canada
Tel.: (647) 426-4050
Web Site: https://www.coface.ca
Credit Insurance Services
N.A.I.C.S.: 524113
Oscar Villalonga *(Pres & CEO)*

COFACE Chile SA (1)
Magdalena 140 Piso 24 Oficina 2402, Las Condes, Santiago, Chile
Tel.: (56) 224285500
Web Site: https://www.coface.cl
Credit Insurance Services
N.A.I.C.S.: 524113

COFACE Czech Insurance S.R.O (1)
U S IP Pavlova 1789/5, 120 00, Prague, Czech Republic
Tel.: (420) 246085411
Web Site: http://www.coface.cz
Financial Services
N.A.I.C.S.: 523999

COFACE Debitoren GmbH (1)
Isaac-Fulda-Allee 1, 55124, Mainz, Germany
Tel.: (49) 613160040
Web Site: http://www.coface.de
Credit Insurance Services
N.A.I.C.S.: 524113

COFACE Do Brasil Seguros de Credito S.A. (1)
Pca Joao Duran Alonso 34-10th Floor, Brooklin Novo, Sao Paulo, CEP 04571-070, SP, Brazil
Tel.: (55) 1155098181
Web Site: https://www.coface.com.br
Credit Insurance Services
N.A.I.C.S.: 524113

COFACE Grece SA (1)
10 Kifissias Ave, 151 24, Maroussi, Greece
Tel.: (30) 2106178120
Web Site: http://www.coface.gr
Insurance Services
N.A.I.C.S.: 524210
Maria Papazarkada *(Gen Mgr)*

COFACE Hungary Kft (1)
Vaci ut 45 H/7, 1134, Budapest, Hungary
Tel.: (36) 12992070
Web Site: http://www.coface.hu
Insurance Services
N.A.I.C.S.: 524210
Katalin Ficsor *(Product Mgr)*

COFACE Ireland Limited (1)
Suite 5 Adelphi House Upper Georges Street, Dun Laoghaire, Dublin, Ireland
Tel.: (353) 12304669
Insurance Services
N.A.I.C.S.: 524210
Mike Culloty *(Mgr-Receivables)*

COFACE Japan Co., Ltd. (1)
Atago Green Hills Mori Tower 38/F 2-5-1 Atago, Minato-Ku, Tokyo, 105-6238, Japan
Tel.: (81) 354026100
Web Site: http://www.coface.jp
Insurance Services
N.A.I.C.S.: 524210

COFACE Nederland BV (1)
Stadionstraat 20, 4815 NG, Breda, Netherlands
Tel.: (31) 765737171
Web Site: http://www.coface.nl
Credit Insurance & Financial Services
N.A.I.C.S.: 523999
Tim Kooremans *(Mgr-Direct Sls)*

COFACE Pkz D.D (1)
Davcna ulica 1, 1000, Ljubljana, Slovenia
Tel.: (386) 12005801
Web Site: http://www.coface.si
Credit Insurance & Financial Services
N.A.I.C.S.: 523999

COFACE Poland Factoring Sp. Z O.O. (1)
Al Jerozolimskie 142 A, 02-305, Warsaw, Poland
Tel.: (48) 224650000
Web Site: https://www.coface.pl
Financial Services
N.A.I.C.S.: 523999
Pawel Tobis *(Deputy Mng Dir)*

COFACE Portugal, SA (1)
Av Jose Malhoa n 16-B - 7th Floor- Fraction B1 Edificio Europa, 1070-159, Lisbon, Portugal
Tel.: (351) 211545400
Web Site: http://www.coface.pt
Credit Insurance & Financial Services
N.A.I.C.S.: 523999

COFACE Romania Cms S.R.L (1)
Soseaua Pipera 42-Et 6, 020112, Bucharest, Romania
Tel.: (40) 212316020
Financial Services
N.A.I.C.S.: 523999

COFACE Romania Insurance Srl (1)
Soseaua Pipera 42-Et 6, 020112, Bucharest, Romania
Tel.: (40) 374670720
Financial Services
N.A.I.C.S.: 523999

COFACE Rus Insurance Company ZAO (1)
2nd Brestskaya st 8 floor 9 Business center, Moscow, 125047, Russia
Tel.: (7) 4957855710
Web Site: https://www.coface.ru
Credit Insurance & Financial Services
N.A.I.C.S.: 523999

COFACE Seguro de Credito Mexico S.A. de C.V. (1)
Insurgentes Sur 1685 Piso 15, CP 01020, Mexico, Mexico
Tel.: (52) 5550892626
Web Site: https://www.coface.com.mx
Insurance Services
N.A.I.C.S.: 524210

COFACE Servicios Espana S.L. (1)
C/ Via de los Poblados 3 Cristalia Business Park Building 6 Floor 5, 28033, Madrid, Spain
Tel.: (34) 913104224
Web Site: https://www.coface.es
Credit Insurance Services
N.A.I.C.S.: 524113

COFACE Sigorta Turquie A.S (1)
Buyukdere Cad Yapi Kredi Plaza B Blok Kat 6, Levent, 34330, Istanbul, Turkiye
Tel.: (90) 2123859900
Web Site: http://www.coface.com.tr
Insurance Services
N.A.I.C.S.: 524210

COFACE Slovakia Insurance SA (1)
Soltesovej 14, 811 08, Bratislava, Slovakia
Tel.: (421) 267201616
Web Site: http://www.coface.sk
Credit Insurance & Financial Services
N.A.I.C.S.: 523999

COFACE South Africa Pty Ltd. (1)
3021 Winnie Mandela Drive, Bryanston, Johannesburg, South Africa
Tel.: (27) 112449444
Web Site: https://www.cofaceza.com
Debt Collection Services
N.A.I.C.S.: 561440
Jacqui Jooste *(CEO & Country Mgr)*

COFACE Sverige AB (1)
Kungsgatan 30, 111 35, Stockholm, Sweden
Tel.: (46) 853481500
Web Site: http://www.coface.se
Credit Insurance & Financial Services
N.A.I.C.S.: 523999
Ajowey Omagbemi *(Sls Mgr)*

COFACE Switzerland SA (1)
Rue Belle-Fontaine 18, 1003, Lausanne, Switzerland
Tel.: (41) 213310040
Web Site: http://www.coface.ch
Insurance Services
N.A.I.C.S.: 524210
Olivier Abulker *(CFO)*

COFACE Taiwan Limited (1)
Room A5 6th Floor No 16 Section 4 Nanjing East Road, Taipei, 10553, Taiwan
Tel.: (886) 225775797
Web Site: http://www.coface.com.tw
Insurance Services
N.A.I.C.S.: 524210
Chris Huang *(Mgr-Risk Mgmt)*

Caisse D'Epargne Aquitaine Poitou-Charentes SCA (1)
1 Parvis Corto Maltese, CS 31271, 33076, Bordeaux, Cedex, France
Tel.: (33) 556001515
Web Site: http://www.caisse-epargne-aquitaine-poitou-charentes.fr
Commercial Banking Services
N.A.I.C.S.: 522110

Caisse D'Epargne Bretagne Pays de Loire SCA (1)
2 place Graslin, CS 10305, 44003, Nantes, Cedex, France
Tel.: (33) 820200420
Web Site: http://www.caissedepargnebretagne.fr
Commercial Banking Services
N.A.I.C.S.: 522110

Caisse D'Epargne Cote D'Azur S.A (1)
L'Arenas 455 Promenade des Anglais, BP 3297, 06205, Nice, Cedex, France
Tel.: (33) 969362738
Commercial Banking Services
N.A.I.C.S.: 522110

Caisse D'Epargne D'Auvergne Et Du Limousin SCA (1)
63 rue Montlosier, 63961, Clermont-Ferrand, Cedex, France
Tel.: (33) 969362738
Private Banking Services
N.A.I.C.S.: 522110

Caisse D'Epargne Grand Est Europe SCA (1)
1 Avenue du Rhin, 67100, Strasbourg, France
Tel.: (33) 969362738
Private Banking Services
N.A.I.C.S.: 522110

Caisse D'Epargne Hauts de France SAS (1)
135 Pont de Flandres, Eurallile, 59777, Lille, France
Tel.: (33) 810810100
Web Site: http://www.caisse-epargne.fr
Private Banking Services
N.A.I.C.S.: 522110

Caisse D'Epargne Languedoc-Roussillon SCA (1)
254 rue Michel Teule, BP 7330, 34184, Montpellier, Cedex, France
Tel.: (33) 467918000
Private Banking Services
N.A.I.C.S.: 522110

Caisse D'Epargne Loire Drome Ardeche SCA (1)
Espace Fauriel 17 rue P et D Ponchardier, BP 147, 42012, Saint-Etienne, Cedex, France
Tel.: (33) 477477477
Private Banking Services
N.A.I.C.S.: 522110
Catherine Amin-Garde *(Co-Chm)*

Caisse D'Epargne Loire-Centre SCA (1)
12 rue de Maison Rouge, CS 10620, 45146, Saint-Jean-de-la-Ruelle, France
Tel.: (33) 820201660
Private Banking Services
N.A.I.C.S.: 522110
Jean Arondel *(Co-Chm)*

Caisse D'Epargne Normandie SAS (1)
151 rue d'Uelzen, 76230, Bois-Guillaume, France
Tel.: (33) 969362000
Private Banking Services
N.A.I.C.S.: 522110

Caisse D'Epargne Rhone Alpes SCA (1)
116 cours Lafayette, BP 3276, 69404, Lyon, Cedex, France
Tel.: (33) 472602000
Web Site: http://www.caissedepargnerhonealpes.fr
Private Banking Services
N.A.I.C.S.: 522110

Caisse D'Epargne de Bourgogne Franche-Comte SAS (1)
1 Rond-Point de la Nation, BP 23088, 21088, Dijon, Cedex, France
Tel.: (33) 969362000
Private Banking Services
N.A.I.C.S.: 522110

Caisse D'Epargne de Midi-Pyrenees S.A (1)
10 Avenue James-Clerk Maxwell, BP 22 306, 31023, Toulouse, Cedex, France
Tel.: (33) 562121262
Private Banking Services
N.A.I.C.S.: 522110
Alain Di Crescenzo *(Co-Chm)*

Caisse Solidaire SCCV (1)
235 boulevard Paul Painleve, 59000, Lille, France
Tel.: (33) 320819970
Web Site: http://www.caisse-solidaire.fr
Credit Institution Services
N.A.I.C.S.: 522299

Capitole Finance SAS (1)
2839 La Lauragaise, 31670, Labege, France
Tel.: (33) 62241212
Web Site: http://www.capitole-finance.com
Financial Services
N.A.I.C.S.: 523999

Compagnie Europeenne de Garanties Et de Cautions SA (1)
16 rue Hoche -Tour Kupka B-TSA 39999, La Defense, 92919, Paris, Cedex, France
Tel.: (33) 158198585
Web Site: http://www.c-garanties.com
Real Estate Agency Services
N.A.I.C.S.: 531210
Aurelie Barbe *(Mgr-Team)*

Credit Foncier Immobilier SA (1)
10 Place de la Coupole, 94220, Charenton-le-Pont, France
Tel.: (33) 142600100
Web Site: http://www.creditfoncierimmobilier.fr
Real Estate Agency Services
N.A.I.C.S.: 531210

Cristal Immo SC (1)
1455 Chemin de Vosgelade, Vence, Grasse, France
Tel.: (33) 664339719
Web Site: http://www.cristal-immobilier.fr
Real Estate Services
N.A.I.C.S.: 531390

Dalenys Payment SAS (1)
110 Avenue de France, 75013, Paris, France
Tel.: (33) 184070707
Web Site: http://www.dalenys.com
Online Payment Services
N.A.I.C.S.: 522320
Ludovic Houri *(Dir-Publication)*

Dnca Finance S.P.A (1)
Via Dante 9, 20123, Milan, Italy
Tel.: (39) 020062281
Investment Management Service
N.A.I.C.S.: 523999
Enrico Trassinelli *(Mng Dir)*

GROUPE BPCE

Groupe BPCE—(Continued)

Dnca Luxembourg SA (1)
1 Place d'Armes, 1136, Luxembourg, Luxembourg
Tel.: (352) 27621307
Investment Management Service
N.A.I.C.S.: 523999
Ousseini Nadhir *(Mgr-Risk)*

Ecofi Investissement SA (1)
22 Rue Joubert, 75009, Paris, France
Tel.: (33) 144883900
Web Site: http://www.ecofi.fr
Cooperative Banking Services
N.A.I.C.S.: 522110
Pierre Valentin *(Chm)*

El Istifa SA (1)
11 Rue Hedi Nouira Immeuble BTK 9eme etage, 1001, Tunis, Tunisia
Tel.: (216) 71345044
Web Site: http://www.elistifa.com.tn
Debt Collection Services
N.A.I.C.S.: 561440

Epbf SA (1)
Chaussee de la Hulpe 181 B11, 1170, Watermael-Boitsfort, Belgium
Tel.: (32) 26630064
Web Site: http://www.epbf.be
Cost Management Services
N.A.I.C.S.: 541611

Esfin Gestion SA (1)
22 Rue Joubert, 75009, Paris, France
Tel.: (33) 140233060
Web Site: http://www.esfingestion.fr
Private Equity Services
N.A.I.C.S.: 523940
Antoine Vedrenne *(Mgr-Investments & Fund)*

Euro Capital SAS (1)
La Grande Arche de la Defense Paroi Nord, La Defense, 92044, Paris, France
Tel.: (33) 674582665
Web Site: http://www.eurocapital.biz
Financial Investment Services
N.A.I.C.S.: 523999

Federation Nationale des Banques Populaires (1)
76-78 avenue de France, 75204, Paris, Cedex 13, France
Tel.: (33) 15840 6973
Web Site: http://www.fnbp.fr
Banking Association
N.A.I.C.S.: 813910
Michel Roux *(Dir Gen)*

Affiliate (Domestic):

BPCE S.A. (2)
50 Avenue Pierre Mendes France, 75013, Paris, France **(50%)**
Tel.: (33) 158404142
Web Site: http://groupebpce.com
Rev.: $13,043,009,420
Assets: $874,955,576,880
Liabilities: $843,944,413,760
Net Worth: $31,011,163,120
Earnings: $1,488,293,940
Fiscal Year-end: 12/31/2019
Financial Holding Company
N.A.I.C.S.: 551111
Laurent Mignon *(Chm-Mgmt Bd)*

Subsidiary (Domestic):

Banque Palatine S.A. (3)
42 rue d'Anjou, F 75382, Paris, Cedex 08, France
Tel.: (33) 155279494
Web Site: http://www.palatine.fr
Rev.: $248,378,000
Banking Services
N.A.I.C.S.: 522110
Katia Gely *(Dir-Comm)*

Credit Foncier de France (3)
19 Rue des Capucines, BP 65, 75001, Paris, Cedex 1, France
Tel.: (33) 157448000
Web Site: http://www.creditfoncier.fr
Sales Range: $1-4.9 Billion
Real Estate Banking Services
N.A.I.C.S.: 522292

Subsidiary (Non-US):

Cube Infrastructure Managers SA (3)
41 avenue de la Liberte, 1931, Luxembourg, Luxembourg
Tel.: (352) 2487346800
Web Site: https://www.cubeinfrastructure.com
Investment Management Service
N.A.I.C.S.: 523999
Saket Trivedi *(Partner)*

Subsidiary (Non-US):

ENETIQA a.s. (4)
Kacirkova 982/4, Jinonice, 158 00, Prague, Czech Republic
Tel.: (420) 272113113
Web Site: http://www.mvv.cz
Sales Range: $25-49.9 Million
Emp.: 32
Energy Consulting Services
N.A.I.C.S.: 541690
Jorg Ludorf *(Chm)*

Subsidiary (Domestic):

Ceskolipske teplo a.s. (5)
Pivovarska 2073, 470 01, Ceska Lipa, Czech Republic
Tel.: (420) 48 7805926
Heat Production & Distribution Services
N.A.I.C.S.: 221330

ENERGIE Holding a.s. (5)
K Vytopne 1987, 412 01, Litomerice, Czech Republic
Tel.: (420) 416 725 951
Web Site: http://enh.mvv.cz
Heat Production & Distribution Services
N.A.I.C.S.: 221330

Subsidiary (Domestic):

Teplarna Liberec a.s. (6)
Dr Milady Horakove 641/34a, PO Box 68, Liberec IV-Perstyn, 460 01, Liberec, Czech Republic
Tel.: (420) 485386111
Web Site: http://www.tlib.mvv.cz
Sales Range: $150-199.9 Million
Electric Power Generation Services
N.A.I.C.S.: 221118

Subsidiary (Domestic):

IROMEZ s.r.o. (5)
Pod naspem 2005, 393 01, Pelhrimov, Czech Republic
Tel.: (420) 565349216
Web Site: http://iro.mvv.cz
Thermal & Electric Energy Production & Distribution Services
N.A.I.C.S.: 221330

Jablonecka teplarenska a realitni a.s. (5)
Liberecka 120, 466 01, Jablonec nad Nisou, Czech Republic
Tel.: (420) 483359833
Web Site: http://www.jtr.mvv.cz
Heat Production & Supply Services
N.A.I.C.S.: 221330

MVV enservis a.s. (5)
Pivovarska 2073, 470 01, Ceska Lipa, Czech Republic
Tel.: (420) 487 805 925
Industrial Equipment Repair & Maintenance Services
N.A.I.C.S.: 811310

OPATHERM a.s. (5)
Horni namesti 283/58, 746 01, Opava, Czech Republic
Tel.: (420) 553 777 555
Web Site: http://www.opa.mvv.cz
Heat & Hot Water Production & Distribution Services
N.A.I.C.S.: 221330

Zasobovani teplem Vsetin a.s. (5)
Jiraskova 1326, 75501, Vsetin, Czech Republic
Tel.: (420) 571815111
Web Site: http://www.ztv.mvv.cz
Sales Range: $75-99.9 Million
Heat Production & Distribution Services
N.A.I.C.S.: 221118
Michal Chmela *(Chm)*

Subsidiary (Domestic):

Mancelle d'Habitation SA (3)
11 rue du Donjon, 72055, Le Mans, Cedex 2, France
Tel.: (33) 2 43 74 45 45
Web Site: http://www.mancelle-habitation.fr
Rental & Home Ownership Services
N.A.I.C.S.: 531110

Natixis, S.A. (3)
30 avenue Pierre Mendes, 75013, Paris, France **(70.66%)**
Tel.: (33) 158323000
Web Site: http://www.natixis.com
Rev.: $8,973,521,440
Assets: $608,371,836,800
Liabilities: $584,548,893,760
Net Worth: $23,822,943,040
Earnings: $223,539,680
Emp.: 16,943
Fiscal Year-end: 12/31/2020
Bank Holding Company; Investment & Commercial Banking, Private Equity, Insurance & Asset Management Services
N.A.I.C.S.: 551111
Laurent Mignon *(Chm)*

Holding (Domestic):

Dalenys S.A. (4)
55 rue Raspail, 92300, Levallois-Perret, France
Tel.: (33) 178020201
Web Site: http://www.dalenys.com
Financial Technology Services
N.A.I.C.S.: 541511
Ludovic Houri *(CEO)*

Division (Domestic):

Natixis - Corporate & Investment Banking (4)
47 Quai D'austerlitz, 75648, Paris, Cedex 13, France
Tel.: (33) 158551515
Web Site: http://wwwnatixis.com
Sales Range: $5-14.9 Billion
Corporate & Investment Banking Services
N.A.I.C.S.: 523150
Asif Khan *(Mng Dir & Head-Structured Credit Capital Markets)*

Branch (Non-US):

Natixis - Bogota (5)
Carrera 15 n 91-30- of 601, Bogota, Colombia
Tel.: (57) 16231631
Web Site: http://www.coface.com.co
Sales Range: $25-49.9 Million
Emp.: 30
Commercial Banking Services
N.A.I.C.S.: 522110

Natixis - Buenos Aires (5)
Cerrito 1294 6th Fl, C1010AAZ, Buenos Aires, Argentina
Tel.: (54) 1148160388
Web Site: http://www.natixis.com
Sales Range: $25-49.9 Million
Emp.: 45
Commercial Banking Services
N.A.I.C.S.: 522110

Natixis - Hanoi (5)
Prime Center 53 Quang Trung, Room 16-02 16th Floor, Hanoi, Vietnam
Tel.: (84) 49433667
Web Site: http://www.natixis.com
Commercial Banking Services
N.A.I.C.S.: 522110

Natixis - Ho Chi Minh (5)
173 Vo Thi Sau, 3e arrondissement, Ho Chi Minh City, Vietnam
Tel.: (84) 89320827
Web Site: http://www.natixis.com
Commercial Banking Services
N.A.I.C.S.: 522110

Natixis - Hong Kong (5)
Level 23 Two Pacific Place, 88 Queensway, Hong Kong, China (Hong Kong)
Tel.: (852) 28280999
Web Site: http://www.natixis.com
Rev.: $128,210
Emp.: 50
Commercial Banking Services
N.A.I.C.S.: 522110
John Wade *(Head-Asia Pacific)*

Natixis - Kuala Lumpur (5)
Marketing Office Suite 16-5 Level 16th, Menara Weld 76, Jalan Raja Chulan, MY 50200, Kuala Lumpur, Malaysia
Tel.: (60) 60320263900
Web Site: http://www.natixis.com
Sales Range: $50-74.9 Million
Emp.: 7
Commercial Banking Services
N.A.I.C.S.: 522110

Natixis - Labuan (5)
Unit Level 9 Main Office Tower, Financial Park Labuan Complex, Jalan Merdeka, 87000, Labuan, Malaysia
Tel.: (60) 87582009
Web Site: http://www.natixis.com
Commercial Banking Services
N.A.I.C.S.: 522110

Natixis - London (5)
Cannon Bridge House, 25 Dowgate Hill, London, EC4R 2YA, United Kingdom
Tel.: (44) 2032169000
Web Site: http://www.natixis.com
Sales Range: $50-74.9 Million
Emp.: 200
Commercial Banking Services
N.A.I.C.S.: 522110
Christopher Lovgren *(Head-Global High-Yield Corp Distr & Trading)*

Natixis - Singapore (5)
41st Storey Singapore Land Tower 50 Raffles Place, Singapore, 48623, Singapore
Tel.: (65) 6224 1455
Web Site: http://www.natixis.com
Sales Range: $25-49.9 Million
Emp.: 100
Commercial & Corporate Banking Services
N.A.I.C.S.: 522110
Jenny Ong *(Head-Origination)*

Subsidiary (Domestic):

Natixis Finance (5)
30 Avenue Pierre Mendes, 75013, 75013, France
Tel.: (33) 158192400
Web Site: http://www.natixis.com
Sales Range: $150-199.9 Million
Emp.: 400
Commercial Banking Services to Agribusiness; Foreign Exchange; Credit & Cash Management Services
N.A.I.C.S.: 522299
Laurent Mignon *(CEO)*

Natixis Lease (5)
4 place de la Coupole, F-94676, Charenton-le-Pont, Cedex, France
Tel.: (33) 158328080
Web Site: http://www.lease.natixis.fr
Sales Range: $25-49.9 Million
Emp.: 50
Mobile & Property Lease Financing Services
N.A.I.C.S.: 522299
Didier Falsimagne *(Dir-Fin)*

Subsidiary (US):

Natixis North America Inc. (5)
1251 Avenue of the Americas, New York, NY 10020
Tel.: (212) 891-6100
Web Site: http://www.cm.natixis.com
Holding Company
N.A.I.C.S.: 551112
Philippe Becret *(CIO)*

Subsidiary (Domestic):

Natixis Bleichroeder Inc. (6)
1251 Ave of the Americas, New York, NY 10105-4300
Tel.: (212) 698-3000
Sales Range: $50-74.9 Million
Emp.: 50
Investment Banking & Securities Brokerage Services
N.A.I.C.S.: 523150

Natixis Capital Markets Inc. (6)
1251 Avenue of the Americas, New York, NY 10020
Tel.: (212) 891-6100
Web Site: http://www.cm.natixis.com
Corporate Investment Banking & Risk Management Services
N.A.I.C.S.: 523150

AND PRIVATE COMPANIES　　　　　　　　　　　　　　　　　　　　　　　　　　　　　　　GROUPE BPCE

Mitch Karig *(VP-Mktg Comm)*

Subsidiary (Domestic):

Natixis Real Estate Capital Inc. (7)
1251 Avenue of the Americas, New York, NY 10020
Tel.: (212) 891-5700
Web Site: http://www.re.natixis.com
Sales Range: $10-24.9 Million
Emp.: 25
Commercial Real Estate Financing Services
N.A.I.C.S.: 522310
Greg Murphy *(Head-Fin & Real Estate)*

Natixis Securities North America Inc. (7)
1251 Avenue of the Americas, New York, NY 10020
Tel.: (212) 891-6100
Web Site: http://www.sp.natixis.com
Securities Broker & Dealer
N.A.I.C.S.: 523150
Gregory Vial *(VP-Cross Asset Investment Solutions)*

Subsidiary (Domestic):

Peter J. Solomon Company (6)
1345 Avenue of the Americas 31st Fl, New York, NY 10105
Tel.: (212) 508-1600
Web Site: http://www.pjsc.com
Sales Range: $25-49.9 Million
Emp.: 70
Investment Services
N.A.I.C.S.: 523999
Peter J. Solomon *(Founder & Chm)*

Division (Domestic):

Natixis - Private Equity & Private Banking (4)
5-7 rue de Monttessuy, F-75007, Paris, France
Tel.: (33) 158323000
Web Site: http://www.privatebanking.natixis.com
Sales Range: $1-4.9 Billion
Emp.: 100
Private Equity & Private Banking Services
N.A.I.C.S.: 523999
Nicolas Homassel *(CEO)*

Subsidiary (Domestic):

Banque Privee Saint Dominique (5)
12-14 Rond Point des Champs Elysees, F-75382, Paris, Cedex 08, France
Tel.: (33) 156888000
Web Site: http://www.bpsd.fr
Sales Range: $100-124.9 Million
Emp.: 125
Private Banking & Wealth Management Services
N.A.I.C.S.: 523940

Natixis Private Equity (5)
5-7 rue de Monttessuy, F-75340, Paris, France
Tel.: (33) 158192000
Web Site: http://www.natixis-pe.com
Sales Range: $50-74.9 Million
Privater Equity Firm
N.A.I.C.S.: 523999
Jean Duhau de Berenx *(CEO)*

Joint Venture (Non-US):

Cape-Natixis S.G.R. S.p.A. (6)
Monte Rosa No 88, I-20149, Milan, Italy
Tel.: (39) 027636131
Web Site: http://www.cape.it
Sales Range: $125-149.9 Million
Emp.: 25
Private Equity Funds Management Services
N.A.I.C.S.: 523999

Subsidiary (Non-US):

Finatem Beteiligungsgesellschaft (6)
feldbergstrasse 35, Frankfurt am Main, 60323, Germany
Tel.: (49) 695095640
Web Site: http://www.finatem.de
Sales Range: $125-149.9 Million
Emp.: 11
Privater Equity Firm
N.A.I.C.S.: 523999
Christophe Hemmerle *(Founder, Mng Dir & Partner)*

Subsidiary (Domestic):

Initiative & Finance (6)
20 rue Quentin Bauchart, Paris, 75008, France
Tel.: (33) 156899700
Web Site: http://www.initiative-finance.com
Sales Range: $125-149.9 Million
Emp.: 16
Equity Investment Firm
N.A.I.C.S.: 523999
Thierry Giron *(Partner)*

Joint Venture (Non-US):

Krokus Private Equity Sp. z o.o. (6)
Al Jana Pawla II 25, 00-854, Warsaw, Poland
Tel.: (48) 226534700
Web Site: http://www.krokuspe.pl
Sales Range: $125-149.9 Million
Emp.: 10
Private Equity Firm
N.A.I.C.S.: 523999
Witold Radwanski *(CEO & Mng Partner)*

Subsidiary (Non-US):

MCH Private Equity Asesores, S.L. (6)
Plaza de Colon 2 Torre I Planta 15, 28046, Madrid, Spain
Tel.: (34) 914264444
Web Site: http://www.mch.es
Sales Range: $125-149.9 Million
Emp.: 20
Private Equity Firm
N.A.I.C.S.: 523999
Jaime Hernandez Soto *(Co-Founder & Mng Partner)*

Subsidiary (Domestic):

Natixis Investissement Partners (6)
5-7 rue de Monttessuy, F-75340, Paris, Cedex 07, France
Tel.: (33) 158192100
Web Site: http://www.ni-partners.com
Sales Range: $125-149.9 Million
Emp.: 15
Private Equity Firm
N.A.I.C.S.: 523999

Division (Domestic):

Natixis Private Equity International (6)
5-7 rue de Monttessuy, F-75340, Paris, Cedex 07, France
Tel.: (33) 158192350
Web Site: http://www.natixis-pe.com
Sales Range: $150-199.9 Million
Emp.: 7
Private Equity Firm
N.A.I.C.S.: 523999

Subsidiary (Domestic):

Naxicap Partners SA (6)
5-7 Rue De Monttessuy, 75340, Paris, Cedex 07, France
Tel.: (33) 158192220
Web Site: http://www.naxicap.fr
Sales Range: $100-124.9 Million
Emp.: 50
Equity Investment Firm
N.A.I.C.S.: 523999
Eric Aveillan *(CEO)*

Holding (Domestic):

E.CF SAS (7)
1 rue Rene Clair, BP 17, 91350, Grigny, France
Tel.: (33) 1 6902 5700
Web Site: http://www.ecf.fr
Emp.: 500
Holding Company; Hospitality, Cleaning & Catering Supplies Distr
N.A.I.C.S.: 551112
Thierry Drecq *(Dir-Publication)*

Subsidiary (Non-US):

Reward Supply Co. Pty. Ltd. (8)
13 Business Street, PO Box 6303, Yatala, 4207, QLD, Australia
Tel.: (61) 734415800
Web Site: http://www.rewardhospitality.com.au

Emp.: 350
Hospitality, Cleaning & Catering Supplies Distr
N.A.I.C.S.: 423850

Holding (Domestic):

Genoyer S.A. (7)
9/11 Groupe Agvnoyer 911 Roag rue de Lisbonne Zone Industrielle, BP 600 61, 13742, Vitrolles, France
Tel.: (33) 442794000
Sales Range: $500-549.9 Million
Emp.: 1,200
Oil, Gas & Chemical Industry Steel Piping Products & Services
N.A.I.C.S.: 332919

Subsidiary (Non-US):

Bon Accord Caspian (8)
13 km Salyan Highway, Shikh District, Baku, AZ1023, Azerbaijan
Tel.: (994) 124474336
Sales Range: $25-49.9 Million
Emp.: 18
Piping Equipment Warehousing & Distr
N.A.I.C.S.: 423830
Ilgar Akhundov *(Mng Dir)*

Subsidiary (US):

Genoyer Group, Inc. (8)
16360 Park 10 Pl Ste 300, Houston, TX 77084
Tel.: (281) 578-2718
Sales Range: $25-49.9 Million
Emp.: 15
Industrial Pipe Products Distr
N.A.I.C.S.: 423830
Penny Henson *(Office Mgr)*

Subsidiary (Domestic):

Phoceenne SAS (8)
9 rue de Lisbonne, CS 60061, ZI Les Estroublans, 13742, Vitrolles, France
Tel.: (33) 442 794 000
Web Site: http://www.phoceenne.com
Piping Equipment & Supplies Distr
N.A.I.C.S.: 423720

Subsidiary (Non-US):

PT Phoceenne Indonesie (8)
Permata Plaza 11th Floor, Jalan MH Thamrin #57, Jakarta, 10 350, Indonesia
Tel.: (62) 213903330
Industrial Pipe Products Distr
N.A.I.C.S.: 423830

Phoceenne Asia Pte. Ltd. (9)
30 Raffles Place Level 17 Chevron House, 11-09 San Centre, Singapore, 048622, Singapore
Tel.: (65) 64382444
Sales Range: $25-49.9 Million
Emp.: 2
Industrial Pipe Products Distr
N.A.I.C.S.: 423830
Cliff Wee *(Mgr-Sls)*

Phoceenne Chili Ltda. (9)
Napoleon 3 200 Oficina 805, Las Condes, Santiago, Chile
Tel.: (56) 22429888
Sales Range: $25-49.9 Million
Emp.: 2
Industrial Pipe Products Distr
N.A.I.C.S.: 423830

Phoceenne S.A. (9)
Plaza de Castilla 3, Planta 8aA, 28046, Madrid, Spain
Tel.: (34) 913237662
Emp.: 10
Industrial Pipe Products Distr
N.A.I.C.S.: 423830

Subsidiary (Domestic):

RTI (8)
Zone Artisanale 22 route de Creton, Les Culs Menaux, 18110, Vasselay, France
Tel.: (33) 248697420
Web Site: http://www.genoyer.com
Steel Pipe Fittings Mfr
N.A.I.C.S.: 332996

SBS (8)
La Gare, PO Box 6, 42130, Boen, France

Tel.: (33) 477968000
Web Site: http://www.sbs-forge.com
Sales Range: $25-49.9 Million
Emp.: 83
Forged Steel Flanges Mfr
N.A.I.C.S.: 332919
Bernard Giry *(Gen Dir)*

Subsidiary (Non-US):

SC Vilmar S.A. (8)
10 Platforma Industriala Street, 240050, Ramnicu Valcea, Romania
Tel.: (40) 250703800
Web Site: http://www.vilmar.ro
Sales Range: $150-199.9 Million
Emp.: 740
Metal Valves, Flanges & Pipe Fittings Mfr
N.A.I.C.S.: 332919
Khelifa Guemra *(Mng Dir)*

Special Flange Services, Ltd. (8)
Elevator Road, Trafford Park, Manchester, M17 1BR, United Kingdom
Tel.: (44) 1618764422
Metal Flanges Mfr
N.A.I.C.S.: 332919

Holding (Domestic):

Onedirect SAS (7)
58 Avenue de Rivesaltes Zone Industrielle La Mirande, PO Box 4, 66240, Saint-Esteve, Cedex, France
Tel.: (33) 4 68 92 93 22
Web Site: http://www.onedirect.fr
Emp.: 200
Online Shopping Services
N.A.I.C.S.: 449210

Shark S.A. (7)
110 Route de la Valentine, 13011, Marseilles, France
Tel.: (33) 491182323
Web Site: http://www.shark-helmets.com
Emp.: 550
Custom Motorcycle Helmet Designer & Mfr
N.A.I.C.S.: 336991
Patrick Francois *(Pres)*

Technicis SAS (7)
35 rue de paris, 92100, Boulogne-Billancourt, France
Tel.: (33) 1 46 04 66 00
Web Site: http://www.technicisgroup.com
Emp.: 820
Professional Translation Services
N.A.I.C.S.: 541930
Benjamin du Fraysseix *(CEO)*

Subsidiary (Non-US):

AAC Global Oy (8)
Porkkalankatu 20 C, FI-00180, Helsinki, Finland
Tel.: (358) 947667800
Web Site: http://www.aacglobal.com
Emp.: 300
Globalization Services
N.A.I.C.S.: 561990
Jaana Rainivaara *(Mgr & Coord-HR)*

Subsidiary (Non-US):

AAC Global AB (9)
Torshamnsgatan 39B, PO Box 13, 164 93, Kista, Sweden
Tel.: (46) 84578800
Web Site: http://www.aacglobal.com
Globalization Services
N.A.I.C.S.: 561990
Tommy Tengvall *(Mng Partner-Sweden & Denmark)*

AAC Global Denmark (9)
Fruebjergvej 3, 2100, Copenhagen, Denmark
Tel.: (45) 33 113 200
Web Site: http://www.aacglobal.com
Globalization Services
N.A.I.C.S.: 561990
Steen Nielsen *(Mng Dir)*

Subsidiary (Domestic):

Seventure Partners (6)
5-7 Rue de Monttessuy, 75340, Paris, Cedex 07, France
Tel.: (33) 158192270
Web Site: http://www.seventure.fr
Rev.: $584,044,800

GROUPE BPCE

INTERNATIONAL PUBLIC

Groupe BPCE—(Continued)
Emp.: 25
Equity Investment Firm
N.A.I.C.S.: 523999
Isabelle de Cremoux *(CEO & Mng Partner)*

Affiliate (Non-US):

The Axxon Group Servicos de Consultoria e Assessoria Ltda (6)
Ladeira de Nossa Senhora 311, Gloria, 22211-100, Rio de Janeiro, RJ, Brazil
Tel.: (55) 2132350770
Web Site: http://www.axxongroup.com.br
Rev.: $150,000,000
Emp.: 20
Privater Equity Firm
N.A.I.C.S.: 523999

Subsidiary (Domestic):

Ventech (6)
5-7 rue de Monttessuy, F-75007, Paris, Cedex 07, France
Tel.: (33) 158192150
Web Site: http://www.ventech.fr
Rev.: $474,536,400
Emp.: 16
Equity Investment Firm
N.A.I.C.S.: 523999
Mounia Chaoui *(Gen Partner)*

nempartners (6)
5-7 rue de Monttessuy, F-75340, Paris, Cedex 07, France
Tel.: (33) 158192130
Web Site: http://www.nem-partners.com
Sales Range: $125-149.9 Million
Emp.: 15
Equity Investment Firm
N.A.I.C.S.: 523999

Division (Domestic):

Natixis - Receivables Management (4)
30 Ave Tierr Menges France, F-75013, Paris, France
Tel.: (33) 158323000
Web Site: http://www.natixis.fr
Receivables Management, Credit Insurance, Factoring & Collections Services
N.A.I.C.S.: 522390

Subsidiary (Domestic):

Natixis Factor S.A. (5)
10-12 Avenue Winston Churchill, F-94676, Charenton-le-Pont, Cedex, France
Tel.: (33) 158328000
Web Site: http://www.factor.natixis.com
Sales Range: $150-199.9 Million
Emp.: 475
Factoring & Credit Insurance Services
N.A.I.C.S.: 522180
Gils Berrous *(Chm)*

Subsidiary (Non-US):

Natixis Algerie Sp.A. (4)
62 chemin Mohamed Drareni, Hydra, 16035, Algeria
Tel.: (213) 2154 9015
Web Site: http://www.natixis.com
Commercial Banking Services
N.A.I.C.S.: 522110

Subsidiary (Domestic):

Natixis Assurances S.A. (4)
115 Rue Reaumur CS 461240 Phase 5580, 75580, Paris, Cedex, France
Tel.: (33) 158199000
Web Site: http://www.assurances.natixis.fr
Sales Range: $1-4.9 Billion
Emp.: 310
Holding Company; Life, Personal Risk & Other Insurance Carrier
N.A.I.C.S.: 551112
Nathalie Broutele *(Dir Gen)*

Subsidiary (Domestic):

Vitalia Vie (5)
115 rue Reaumur CS 40230 75086, F-75606, Paris, Cedex 02, France
Tel.: (33) 158199381
Life Insurance Carrier
N.A.I.C.S.: 524113

Division (Domestic):

Natixis Global Asset Management S.A. (4)
21 Quai d'Austerlitz, 75634, Paris, Cedex 13, France
Tel.: (33) 178409000
Web Site: http://ngam.natixis.com
Sales Range: $1-4.9 Billion
Emp.: 2,800
Financial & Real Estate Asset Management Services
N.A.I.C.S.: 551112
Caren Leedom *(Exec VP-Global Comm)*

Division (Domestic):

Natixis Global Asset Management (France) (5)
21 quai d'Austerlitz, F-75634, Paris, Cedex 13, France
Tel.: (33) 178409000
Holding Company; Financial & Real Estate Asset Management Services
N.A.I.C.S.: 551112

Subsidiary (Domestic):

AEW Europe (6)
43 avenue Pierre Mendes-France, 75013, Paris, France
Tel.: (33) 178409200
Web Site: http://www.aeweurope.com
Rev.: $22,463,630,000
Emp.: 270
Real Estate Investment Management Services
N.A.I.C.S.: 525990
Jean Lavieille *(Head-Funds)*

Subsidiary (Domestic):

AEW Ciloger (7)
22 rue du Docteur, 75008, Paris, France
Tel.: (33) 1 78 40 53 00
Web Site: http://www.ciloger.fr
Investment Services
N.A.I.C.S.: 523940
Julien Duquenne *(Dir-Dev & Client Relationship)*

Subsidiary (Non-US):

AEW Global Limited (7)
33 Jermyn Street, London, SW1Y 6DN, United Kingdom
Tel.: (44) 2070164800
Emp.: 80
Real Estate Investment Management Services
N.A.I.C.S.: 525990
Marcus Davidson-Wright *(Dir-Portfolio Mgmt)*

Subsidiary (Domestic):

NAMI-AEW Europe (7)
Nami Aew Europe 8 rue des Pirogues, Paris, 75009, France
Tel.: (33) 178403300
Web Site: http://www.namiaeweurope.com
Real Estate Fund Management Services
N.A.I.C.S.: 531390

Subsidiary (Domestic):

Mirova S.A. (6)
59 avenue Pierre Mendes, 75013, Paris, France
Tel.: (33) 178408000
Web Site: https://www.mirova.com
Investment Management Service
N.A.I.C.S.: 523999
Philippe Zaouati *(CEO)*

Joint Venture (Non-US):

Oslofjord Varme AS (7)
Brynsveien 2, 1338, Sandvika, Norway (42.5%)
Tel.: (47) 67804960
Web Site: http://www.oslofjordvarme.no
Sales Range: $75-99.9 Million
Emp.: 14
District Heating & Cooling Services
N.A.I.C.S.: 221330

Subsidiary (Domestic):

Natixis Asset Management S.A. (6)
21 quai d'Austerlitz, F-75634, Paris, Cedex 13, France
Tel.: (33) 178408000
Web Site: http://www.am.natixis.com
Asset Management Services
N.A.I.C.S.: 523940
Philippe Zaouati *(Dir-Corp Dev)*

VEGA Investment Managers (6)
115 rue Montmarte, 75002, Paris, France
Tel.: (33) 1 5819 6100
Web Site: http://www.vega-im.com
Investment Management Service
N.A.I.C.S.: 523940
Isabelle Gourmelon *(Dir-Mktg)*

Subsidiary (Non-US):

Natixis Global Asset Management Canada Corp. (5)
145 King Street West Suite 1500, Toronto, M5H 1J8, ON, Canada
Tel.: (416) 775-3700
Web Site: http://www.nexgenfinancial.ca
Emp.: 50
Holding Company
N.A.I.C.S.: 551112
Abe Goenka *(CEO)*

Subsidiary (Domestic):

NGAM Canada LP (6)
36 Toronto St Ste 1070, Toronto, M5C 2C5, ON, Canada
Tel.: (416) 775-3727
Web Site: http://secure.nexgenfinancial.ca
Investment Management Service
N.A.I.C.S.: 523940
Abe Goenka *(CEO, COO & CFO)*

Subsidiary (US):

Natixis Global Asset Management, L.P. (5)
399 Boylston St 13th Fl, Boston, MA 02116-3305
Tel.: (617) 449-2100
Rev.: $884,900,000,000
Emp.: 1,400
Holding Company; Financial & Real Estate Asset Management Services
N.A.I.C.S.: 551112
Rodrigo Nunez Aguilar *(Dir-Global Key Accts-Latin America & US Offshore)*

Subsidiary (Domestic):

AEW Capital Management, L.P. (6)
World Trade Ctr E 2 Seaport Ln, Boston, MA 02210-2021
Tel.: (617) 261-9000
Web Site: http://www.aew.com
Rev.: $26,000,000,000
Emp.: 150
Real Estate Investment Management Services
N.A.I.C.S.: 525990
Steven D. Corkin *(Mng Dir-Mktg & Client Svcs)*

Capital Growth Management, L.P. (6)
1 International Pl 45th Fl, Boston, MA 02110
Tel.: (617) 737-3225
Web Site: http://www.cgmfunds.com
Sales Range: $75-99.9 Million
Emp.: 20
Mutual Funds & Advisory Accounts Management Services
N.A.I.C.S.: 525910
David C. Fietze *(Chief Compliance Officer)*

Gateway Investment Advisers, L.P. (6)
312 Walnut St Fl 35, Cincinnati, OH 45202-9834
Tel.: (513) 719-1100
Web Site: http://www.gia.com
Sales Range: $5-14.9 Billion
Emp.: 17
Investment & Portfolio Management Services
N.A.I.C.S.: 525910
Daniel Ashcraft *(Co-Portfolio Mgr-Gateway Fund)*

Loomis, Sayles & Company, L.P. (6)
1 Financial Ctr, Boston, MA 02111-2621
Tel.: (617) 482-2450
Web Site: http://www.loomissayles.com
Rev.: $229,400,000,000
Emp.: 200
Securities Investment & Fund Management Services
N.A.I.C.S.: 523150
John Gallagher *(Dir-Institutional Svcs)*

Natixis Global Associates, LLC (6)
399 Bolston St, Boston, MA 02116
Tel.: (617) 449-2600
Sales Range: $400-449.9 Million
Emp.: 500
Holding Company; Financial Investment Advisory & Distribution Services
N.A.I.C.S.: 551112

Subsidiary (Domestic):

Harris Associates, L.P. (7)
2 N La Salle St Ste 500, Chicago, IL 60602-3790
Tel.: (312) 621-0600
Web Site: http://www.harrisassoc.com
Sales Range: $50-74.9 Billion
Emp.: 190
Investment & Portfolio Management Services
N.A.I.C.S.: 523150
Diane L. Mustain *(Portfolio Mgr)*

Natixis Asset Management Advisors, L.P. (7)
399 Bolston St, Boston, MA 02116
Tel.: (617) 449-2600
Investment Advisory Services
N.A.I.C.S.: 523940

Natixis Distributors, L.P. (7)
399 Bolston St, Boston, MA 02116
Tel.: (617) 449-2600
Rev.: $10,000,000,000
Financial Distribution Services
N.A.I.C.S.: 524292

Unit (Non-US):

Natixis Global Associates International (7)
21 Quai d'Austerlitz, F-75013, Paris, Cedex 13, France
Tel.: (33) 178409600
Investment Advisory & Distribution Services
N.A.I.C.S.: 523940

Subsidiary (Domestic):

Premis Capital Partners, Inc. (6)
101 NE 3rd Ave Ste 320, Fort Lauderdale, FL 33301
Tel.: (954) 522-5150
Web Site: http://www.premiscapital.com
Emp.: 5
Investment Management Service
N.A.I.C.S.: 523150
Jessica Davis *(Chief Admin Officer & Mgr-Compliance)*

Subsidiary (Non-US):

Hansberger Growth Investors, LP (7)
5500 North Service Rd Ste 1103, Burlington, L7L 6W6, ON, Canada
Tel.: (905) 331-5770
Web Site: http://www.hansberger.com
Sales Range: $10-24.9 Million
Emp.: 11
Investment Management Service
N.A.I.C.S.: 523150
Thomas R.H. Tibbles *(CEO & Chief Investment Officer)*

Subsidiary (Domestic):

Snyder Capital Management, L.P. (6)
101 Mission St Ste 1400, San Francisco, CA 94105
Tel.: (415) 392-3900
Web Site: http://www.snydercapital.com
Sales Range: $125-149.9 Million
Emp.: 13
Small & Mid-Cap Equities Investment Management
N.A.I.C.S.: 525910
Sonja L. Commer *(Chief Compliance Officer)*

Vaughan Nelson Investment Management, L.P. (6)

AND PRIVATE COMPANIES

600 Travis St Ste 6300, Houston, TX 77002-3071
Tel.: (713) 224-2545
Web Site: http://www.vaughannelson.com
Sales Range: $125-149.9 Million
Emp.: 50
Investment Management Service
N.A.I.C.S.: 523940
Mark E. Farrell *(Dir-Institutional Mktg & Private Client Svcs)*

Subsidiary (Domestic):

Vaughan Nelson Trust Company (7)
600 Travis St Ste 6300, Houston, TX 77002
Tel.: (713) 224-2545
Web Site: http://www.vaughannelson.com
Sales Range: $10-24.9 Million
Emp.: 50
Financial Trust Services
N.A.I.C.S.: 523991

Subsidiary (Domestic):

Natixis Interepargne S.A. (4)
Avenue Ge Marthal Montzgomery, BP 4
75060, Caen, 94220, France
Tel.: (33) 158194300
Web Site: http://www.interepargne.natixis.fr
Employee Savings Plans Management Services
N.A.I.C.S.: 525990

Subsidiary (Non-US):

Natixis Luxembourg S.A. (4)
51 avenue JF Kennedy, L-1855, Luxembourg, Luxembourg
Tel.: (352) 253418315
Web Site: http://www.natixis.com
Sales Range: $50-74.9 Million
Emp.: 9
Bank Holding Company; Investment & Commercial Banking Services
N.A.I.C.S.: 551111

Subsidiary (Domestic):

Natixis Partners (4)
32 rue de Lisbonne, 75008, Paris, France
Tel.: (33) 1 7344 4400
Web Site: http://www.natixispartners.com
Investment Advisory Services
N.A.I.C.S.: 523940
Patrick Maurel *(CEO)*

SLIB S.A. (4)
22-28 rue Joubert, 75009, Paris, France
Tel.: (33) 170369700
Web Site: http://www.slib.fr
Sales Range: $25-49.9 Million
Emp.: 100
Investment Banking Software Publisher & Information Technologies Management
N.A.I.C.S.: 513210
Philippe Cognet *(CEO & Dir-Publication)*

Societe de Banque Francaise et Internationale (4)
30 Ave Pierre Mendes, F-75013, Paris, France
Tel.: (33) 158323000
Web Site: http://www.natixis.com
Sales Range: $700-749.9 Million
Emp.: 2,000
Commercial Bank
N.A.I.C.S.: 522110
Laurent Mignon *(Mng Dir)*

Thermocompact SA (4)
route de Sarves, BP 21, Zone Industrielle
Metz-Tessy, 74371, Pringy, France
Tel.: (33) 4 50 27 20 02
Web Site: http://www.thermocompact.com
Metal Heat Treating
N.A.I.C.S.: 332811

Subsidiary (US):

Diamond Materials Tech, Inc. (5)
3505 N Stone Ave, Colorado Springs, CO 80907
Tel.: (719) 570-1150
Web Site: http://www.dmt-inc.com
Sales Range: $25-49.9 Million
Emp.: 50
Diamond Wire Cutting Technology & Services
N.A.I.C.S.: 332618
Derek Taylor *(CFO)*

Affiliate (Domestic):

BRED Banque Populaire (2)
18 quai de la Rapee, 75012, Paris, France
Tel.: (33) 148986000
Web Site: http://www.bred.banquepopulaire.fr
Sales Range: $1-4.9 Billion
Emp.: 3,397
Banking Services
N.A.I.C.S.: 522110
Steve Gentili *(Chm)*

Banque Populaire Alsace Lorraine Champagne (2)
3 rue Francois de Curel, BP 40124, 57000, Metz, France
Tel.: (33) 3 54 22 10 00
Web Site: http://www.bpalc.banquepopulaire.fr
Sales Range: $250-299.9 Million
Emp.: 1,354
Banking Services
N.A.I.C.S.: 522110
Thierry Cahn *(Chm)*

Banque Populaire Atlantique (2)
1 rue Francoise Sagan, Saint Herblain, F-44919, Nantes, Cedex 9, France
Tel.: (33) 2 40 46 08 08
Web Site: http://www.atlantique.banquepopulaire.fr
Sales Range: $350-399.9 Million
Emp.: 1,808
Banking Services
N.A.I.C.S.: 522110
Stephanie Paix *(Co-CEO)*

Banque Populaire Bourgogne Franche-Comte (2)
14 Boulevard De La Tremouille, PO Box 20810, 21008, Dijon, Cedex, France
Tel.: (33) 820337500
Web Site: http://www.bpbfc.banquepopulaire.fr
Banking Services
N.A.I.C.S.: 522110
Michel Grass *(Pres)*

Banque Populaire Centre Atlantique (2)
32 boulevard Carnot, BP 10416, 87011, Limoges, Cedex 1, France
Tel.: (33) 5 33 63 99 98
Web Site: http://www.centreatlantique.banque.fr
Sales Range: $200-249.9 Million
Emp.: 1,004
Banking Services
N.A.I.C.S.: 522110

Banque Populaire Cote d'Azur (2)
457 promenade des Anglais, BP 241, F-06292, Nice, Cedex 3, France
Tel.: (33) 493215200
Sales Range: $200-249.9 Million
Emp.: 1,148
Banking Services
N.A.I.C.S.: 522110

Banque Populaire Loire et Lyonnais (2)
141 Rue Garibaldi, BP 3152, 69211, Lyon, Cedex 3, France
Tel.: (33) 478955555
Web Site: http://wwwloirelyonnais.banquepopulaire.fr
Sales Range: $250-299.9 Million
Emp.: 1,252
Banking Services
N.A.I.C.S.: 522110

Banque Populaire Lorraine Champagne (2)
3 rue Francois de Curel, BP 40124, 57021, Metz, Cedex 1, France
Tel.: (33) 890 90 90 90
Web Site: http://www.bplc.fr
Sales Range: $400-449.9 Million
Emp.: 1,655
Banking Services
N.A.I.C.S.: 522110

Banque Populaire Occitane (2)
33-43 avenue Georges Pompidou, F-31135, Balma, Cedex, France
Tel.: (33) 5 65 23 66 50
Web Site: http://www.occitane.banquepopulaire.fr

Sales Range: $550-599.9 Million
Emp.: 2,315
Banking Services
N.A.I.C.S.: 522110
Michel Dolige *(Chm)*

Banque Populaire Provencale et Corse (2)
245 Boulevard Michelet, BP 25, 13274, Marseilles, Cedex 09, France
Tel.: (33) 491302430
Web Site: http://www.provencecorse.banque.fr
Sales Range: $150-199.9 Million
Emp.: 806
Regional Banking Services
N.A.I.C.S.: 522110
Jean-Louis Tourret *(Chm)*

Banque Populaire Rives de Paris (2)
76-78 avenue de France, F-75204, Paris, Cedex 13, France
Tel.: (33) 141862440
Web Site: http://www.rivesparis.banquepopulaire.fr
Sales Range: $700-749.9 Million
Emp.: 2,852
Banking Services
N.A.I.C.S.: 522110
Marc Jardin *(Chm)*

Banque Populaire Val de France (2)
9 avenue Newton, F-78180, Montigny-le-Bretonneux, France
Tel.: (33) 1 30 14 66 00
Web Site: http://www.bpvf.banquepopulaire.fr
Sales Range: $500-549.9 Million
Emp.: 2,345
Banking Services
N.A.I.C.S.: 522110
Gonzague de Villele *(Dir Gen)*

Banque Populaire de l'Ouest (2)
1 place de la Trinite, CS 86434, F-35064, Rennes, Cedex, France
Tel.: (33) 299297979
Web Site: http://www.ouest.banquepopulaire.fr
Sales Range: $350-399.9 Million
Emp.: 1,807
Banking Services
N.A.I.C.S.: 522110
Pierre Delourmel *(Chm)*

Banque Populaire des Alpes (2)
30 avenue Charles de Gaulle, BP 17, F-74808, La Roche-sur-Foron, France
Tel.: (33) 820870870
Web Site: http://www.alpes.banquepopulaire.fr
Sales Range: $350-399.9 Million
Emp.: 1,534
Banking Services
N.A.I.C.S.: 522110
Pascal Marchetti *(CEO)*

Banque Populaire du Massif Central (2)
18 Blvd Jean Moulin, BP 53, 63002, Clermont-Ferrand, Cedex 1, France
Tel.: (33) 473234623
Web Site: http://www.massifcentral.banque.fr
Sales Range: $150-199.9 Million
Emp.: 911
Banking Services
N.A.I.C.S.: 522110
Dominique Martinie *(Chm)*

Banque Populaire du Nord (2)
847 Avenue de la Republique, F-59700, Marcq-en-Baroeul, France
Tel.: (33) 66 333000
Web Site: http://www.nord.banquepopulaire.fr
Sales Range: $200-249.9 Million
Emp.: 1,128
Banking Services
N.A.I.C.S.: 522110

Banque Populaire du Sud (2)
38 boulevard Clemenceau, F-66000, Perpignan, Cedex 09, France
Tel.: (33) 468382200
Web Site: http://www.sud.banquepopulaire.fr
Banking Services
N.A.I.C.S.: 522110
Claude Cordel *(Chm)*

GROUPE BPCE

Banque Populaire du Sud-Ouest (2)
10 Quai des Queyries, Cedex, F-33 072, Bordeaux, France
Tel.: (33) 5 57 776809
Web Site: http://www.sudouest.banquepopulaire.fr
Sales Range: $250-299.9 Million
Emp.: 1,124
Banking Services
N.A.I.C.S.: 522110

Casden Banque Populaire (2)
1bis rue Jean Wiener, 77420, Champs-sur-Marne, France
Tel.: (33) 164807000
Web Site: http://www.casden.fr
Sales Range: $250-299.9 Million
Emp.: 454
Banking Services
N.A.I.C.S.: 522110
Sylvie Garcelon *(CEO)*

Credit Cooperatif (2)
2 Boulevard de Pesaro, BP 211, F-92002, Nanterre, France
Tel.: (33) 147248500
Web Site: http://www.credit-cooperatif.coop
Sales Range: $450-499.9 Million
Emp.: 1,702
Commercial Banking Services
N.A.I.C.S.: 522110
Hugues Sibille *(COO)*

Federation Nationale des Caisses d'Epargne (1)
5 rue Masseran, 75007, Paris, France
Tel.: (33) 144385050
Web Site: http://www.federation.caisse-epargne.fr
Banking Association
N.A.I.C.S.: 813910
Florence Raineix *(Dir Gen)*

Affiliate (Domestic):

Banque BCP S.A.S. (2)
14 avenue Franklin Roosevelt, Paris, 75008, France (80.1%)
Tel.: (33) 1 44 20 51 19
Web Site: http://www.banquebcp.fr
Sales Range: $200-249.9 Million
Emp.: 500
Banking Services
N.A.I.C.S.: 522110

Caisse d'Epargne et de Prevoyance Ile-de-France (2)
19 rue du Louvre, 75001, Paris, France
Tel.: (33) 9 69 362 000
Web Site: http://www.caisse-epargne.fr
Commericial Banking
N.A.I.C.S.: 522110
Didier Patault *(Chm-Mgmt Bd)*

Caisse d'Epargne et de Prevoyance Provence-Alpes-Corse (2)
Place Estrangin Pastre, 13006, Marseille, France
Tel.: (33) 4 9157 6600
Web Site: http://www.caisse-epargne.fr
Commericial Banking
N.A.I.C.S.: 522110
Alain Lacroix *(Chm-Mgmt Bd)*

Subsidiary (Domestic):

Banque de la Reunion SA (3)
27 rue Jean Chatel, 97711, Saint Denis, Cedex 9, France (88.9%)
Tel.: (33) 2 62 40 01 33
Web Site: http://www.banquedelareunion.fr
Emp.: 449
Banking Services
N.A.I.C.S.: 522110
Bernard Fremont *(CEO)*

Affiliate (Domestic):

Caisse d'Epargne et de Prevoyance de Rhone Alpes (2)
42 boulevard Eugene Deruelle, 69003, Lyon, France
Tel.: (33) 4 7260 2040
Web Site: http://www.caisse-epargne.fr
Commericial Banking
N.A.I.C.S.: 522110
Stephanie Paix *(Chm-Mgmt Bd)*

Fidor Bank AG (1)
Sandstr 33, 80335, Munich, Germany

GROUPE BPCE — INTERNATIONAL PUBLIC

Groupe BPCE—(Continued)
Tel.: (49) 89189085233
Web Site: http://www.fidor.de
Commercial Banking Services
N.A.I.C.S.: 522110
Boris Joseph *(CEO)*

Fipromer SASU (1)
35 rue des Mathurins, 75008, Paris, France
Tel.: (33) 145611370
Web Site: http://www.fipromer.fr
Financial Investment Services
N.A.I.C.S.: 523999

Flexstone Partners LLC (1)
745 5th Ave 28th Fl, New York, NY 10151
Tel.: (212) 703-0300
Emp.: 40
Asset Management Services
N.A.I.C.S.: 523940
Nitin Gupta *(Mng Partner)*

Flexstone Partners SAS (1)
5-7 rue de Monttessuy, 75007, Paris, France
Tel.: (33) 183755601
Private Equity Services
N.A.I.C.S.: 523940
Benoit De Kerleau *(Mng Partner)*

G Immo SCI (1)
193 Rue du Faubourg Poissonniere, 75009, Paris, France
Tel.: (33) 153264260
Web Site: http://www.g-immo.fr
Real Estate Services
N.A.I.C.S.: 531390

H2O AM Asia Pte Ltd. (1)
20 Collyer Quay 10-01, Singapore, 049319, Singapore
Tel.: (65) 63810740
Asset Management Services
N.A.I.C.S.: 523940
Cedric Philippon *(Head-Ops)*

H2O Asset Management LLP (1)
10 Old Burlington Street, London, W1S 3AG, United Kingdom
Tel.: (44) 2072921600
Web Site: http://www.h2o-am.com
Emp.: 88
Investment Management Service
N.A.I.C.S.: 523999
Bruno Crastes *(CEO)*

Habitat En Region Services SAS (1)
31-35 rue de la Federation, 75015, Paris, France
Tel.: (33) 182823066
Web Site: http://www.habitat-en-region.fr
Real Estate Agency Services
N.A.I.C.S.: 531210

Informatique Banques Populaires SA (1)
23 Place de Wicklow, 78180, Montigny-le-Bretonneux, France
Tel.: (33) 130558101
Web Site: http://www.informatique.banque.fr
Information Technology Development Services
N.A.I.C.S.: 541511

Ingepar SA (1)
88 Avenue de France, 75013, Paris, France
Tel.: (33) 145611370
Web Site: http://www.ingepar.fr
Financial Investment Services
N.A.I.C.S.: 523999

Investors Mutual Limited (1)
Level 24 25 Bligh Street, Sydney, 2000, NSW, Australia
Tel.: (61) 292327500
Web Site: http://www.iml.com.au
Equity Fund Management Services
Wayne McGauley *(Head-Retail)*

It-Ce EIG (1)
182 Avenue de France, 75013, Paris, France
Tel.: (33) 820032008
Web Site: http://www.it-ce.fr
Information Technology Services
N.A.I.C.S.: 541512

Loomis Sayles Investments Asia Pte. Ltd. (1)
10 Collyer Quay 05-01/03, Ocean Financial Centre, Singapore, 049315, Singapore
Tel.: (65) 116569228688
Financial Services
N.A.I.C.S.: 523999
Paul Ong *(Mng Dir)*

Loomis Sayles Investments Ltd. (1)
Smithson Tower 25 St James's Street, London, SW1A 1HA, United Kingdom
Tel.: (44) 2031946500
Web Site: http://www.loomissaylesinvestments.co.uk
Emp.: 747
Investment Management Service
N.A.I.C.S.: 523999
Kevin Charleston *(Chm & CEO)*

MV Credit Limited (1)
45 Old Bond Street, Mayfair, London, W1S 4QT, United Kingdom
Tel.: (44) 2039618820
Web Site: http://www.mvcredit.com
Investment Management Service
N.A.I.C.S.: 523999
Francois Decoeur *(Mng Dir)*

Massena Partners S.A (1)
78 Avenue Raymond Poincare, 75116, Paris, France
Tel.: (33) 153706390
Web Site: http://www.massenapartners.com
Investment Banking Services
N.A.I.C.S.: 523150

Massena Partners SA (1)
1 Place d'Armes, 1136, Luxembourg, Luxembourg
Tel.: (352) 2626598001
Investment Banking Services
N.A.I.C.S.: 523150
Marc Jaumot *(Mng Dir)*

Midt Factoring A/S (1)
Nygade 111, PO Box 250, 7430, Ikast, Denmark
Tel.: (45) 96601100
Web Site: http://www.midtfactoring.dk
Financial Investment Services
N.A.I.C.S.: 523999
Jette Faartoft *(Acct Mgr)*

Mirova US LLC (1)
888 Boylston St, Boston, MA 02199
Tel.: (212) 632-2803
Asset Management Services
N.A.I.C.S.: 523940
Amber Baker *(Deputy CEO, COO & Chief Legal Officer)*

Natixis Australia Pty Ltd. (1)
Level 26 8 Chifley Square, Sydney, 2000, NSW, Australia
Tel.: (61) 280631700
Financial Investment Services
N.A.I.C.S.: 523940

Natixis Distribution, LP (1)
888 Boylston St, Boston, MA 02199
Tel.: (617) 449-2828
Asset Management Services
N.A.I.C.S.: 523940

Natixis Dubai Limited (1)
Dubai International Financial Center, PO Box 506694, ICD Brookfield Place Level 10 Unit 02, Dubai, United Arab Emirates
Tel.: (971) 7026777
Asset Management Services
N.A.I.C.S.: 523940

Natixis Im Mexico, S. de R.L. de C.V. (1)
Paseo de la Reforma 250 Torre A Piso 8, Colonia Cuauhtemoc, 06600, Mexico, Mexico
Tel.: (52) 5536007290
Investment Banking Services
N.A.I.C.S.: 523150

Natixis Investment Managers Australia Pty Limited (1)
Suite 24 02 Level 24 Governor Phillip Tower 1 Farrer Place, Sydney, 2000, NSW, Australia
Tel.: (61) 282242900
Web Site: http://www.im.natixis.com
Financial Investment Services
N.A.I.C.S.: 523940
Damon Hambly *(CEO)*

Natixis Investment Managers Hong Kong Limited (1)
Unit 7103B 71/F International Commerce Centre 1 Austin Road West, Kowloon, China (Hong Kong)
Tel.: (852) 39151233
Investment Banking Services
N.A.I.C.S.: 523150
Kylie Chan *(Head-Wholesale & Retail Sls)*

Natixis Investment Managers International SA (1)
43 Avenue Pierre Mendes France, CS 41432, 75648, Paris, Cedex, France
Tel.: (33) 178408000
Investment Management Service
N.A.I.C.S.: 523999

Natixis Investment Managers Korea Limited (1)
21F Seoul Finance Center 136 Sejongdaero, Jung-gu, Seoul, 100-768, Korea (South)
Tel.: (82) 237824911
Asset Management Services
N.A.I.C.S.: 523940

Natixis Investment Managers Middle East LLC (1)
Unit L10-02 Level 10 ICD Brookfield Place Dubai International, PO Box 506752, Financial Centre, Dubai, United Arab Emirates
Tel.: (971) 47026840
Asset Management Services
N.A.I.C.S.: 523940

Natixis Investment Managers S.A (1)
Via San Clemente 1, 20122, Milan, Italy
Tel.: (39) 027273051
Investment Banking Services
N.A.I.C.S.: 523150
Antonio Bottillo *(Exec Mng Dir & Head-Country)*

Natixis Investment Managers S.A,ZwEIGnierderlaasung Deutschland (1)
Im Trutz Frankfurt 55, 60322, Frankfurt am Main, Germany
Tel.: (49) 6997153236
Web Site: http://www.im.natixis.com
Asset Management Services
N.A.I.C.S.: 523940
Sebastian Romer *(Head-Central & Eastern Europe)*

Natixis Investment Managers SA (1)
2 rue Jean Monnet, 2180, Luxembourg, Luxembourg
Tel.: (352) 2704591
Investment Management Service
N.A.I.C.S.: 523999

Natixis Investment Managers Securities Investment Consulting Co., Ltd. (1)
16F-1 No 76 Section2 Tun Hwa South Road, Taipei, Taiwan
Tel.: (886) 227845777
Investment Banking Services
N.A.I.C.S.: 523150

Natixis Investment Managers Switzerland SARL (1)
Rue du Vieux-College 10, 1204, Geneva, Switzerland
Tel.: (41) 228178020
Investment Banking Services
N.A.I.C.S.: 523150

Natixis Investment Managers UK Ltd. (1)
One Carter Lane, London, EC4V 5ER, United Kingdom
Tel.: (44) 2034056000
Investment Banking Services
N.A.I.C.S.: 523150
Darren Pilbeam *(Mng Dir & Head-Wholesale & Retail Sls)*

Natixis Investment Managers Uruguay S.A. (1)
San Lucar 1491 Suite 103, Montevideo, 11500, Uruguay
Tel.: (598) 95222307
Investment Banking Services
N.A.I.C.S.: 523150

Natixis Investment Managers, LP (1)
888 Boylston St, Boston, MA 02199
Tel.: (617) 449-2100
Asset Management Services
N.A.I.C.S.: 523940
David L. Giunta *(Pres & CEO)*

Natixis Investment Managers, Nederlands S.A (1)
Stadsplateau 7, 3521 AZ, Utrecht, Netherlands
Tel.: (31) 203331703
Financial Services
N.A.I.C.S.: 523999

Natixis Investment Managers, Nordics Filial AB (1)
Kungsgatan 48 5tr, 111 35, Stockholm, Sweden
Tel.: (46) 8211082
Investment Banking Services
N.A.I.C.S.: 523150

Natixis Investment Managers, Sucursal En Espana SL (1)
Serrano n 90 6th Floor, 28006, Madrid, Spain
Tel.: (34) 911922201
Asset Management Services
N.A.I.C.S.: 523940

Natixis Japan Securities Co., Ltd. (1)
Ark Hills South Tower 8/F 1-4-5 Roppongi, Minato-ku, Tokyo, 1060032, Japan
Tel.: (81) 345192100
Investment Banking Services
N.A.I.C.S.: 523150
Laurent Depus *(Pres)*

Natixis Life SA (1)
51 Avenue JF Kennedy, 1855, Luxembourg, Luxembourg
Tel.: (352) 2288811
Web Site: http://www.life.natixis.com
Investment Management Service
N.A.I.C.S.: 523999
Philippe Schmitt *(CEO-Risk Mgmt)*

Natixis Milan S.A (1)
Via Borgogna 8, 20122, Milan, Italy
Tel.: (39) 0200667200
Investment Banking Services
N.A.I.C.S.: 523150

Natixis Payment Solutions SA (1)
30 Avenue Pierre Mendes France, 75013, Paris, France
Tel.: (33) 158323000
Web Site: http://www.payments.natixis.com
Investment Management Service
N.A.I.C.S.: 523999

Natixis Pfandbriefbank AG (1)
Im Trutz Frankfurt 55, 60322, Frankfurt am Main, Germany
Tel.: (49) 69971530
Web Site: http://www.pfandbriefbank.cib.natixis.com
Real Estate Investment Services
N.A.I.C.S.: 531210
Hansjorg Patzschke *(Chm)*

Natixis Securities Americas LLC (1)
1251 Avenue of the Americas, New York, NY 10020
Tel.: (212) 891-6100
Asset Management Services
N.A.I.C.S.: 523940

Natixis Taiwan Limited (1)
34F Cathay Landmark Building No 68 Section 5 ZhongXiao East Road, Taipei, Taiwan
Tel.: (886) 266334968
Investment Banking Services
N.A.I.C.S.: 523150

Natixis Wealth Management Luxembourg SA (1)
51 Avenue J F Kennedy, 1855, Luxembourg, Luxembourg
Tel.: (352) 4638161
Web Site: http://www.wealthmanagement.natixis.lu
Investment Management Service
N.A.I.C.S.: 523999
Olivier Smolarz *(Head-Investment Advisory)*

Natixis Wealth Management SA (1)

AND PRIVATE COMPANIES

115 rue Montmartre, CS 21818, 75080, Paris, Cedex, France
Tel.: (33) 158197000
Web Site: http://www.wealthmanagement.natixis.com
Banking Services
N.A.I.C.S.: 522110

Natixis ZwElGniederlassung Deutschland SE (1)
Im Trutz Frankfurt 55, 60322, Frankfurt am Main, Germany
Tel.: (49) 69971530
Real Estate Investment Services
N.A.I.C.S.: 531210

Nova Immo SAS (1)
40 Rue de Paris, 95500, Gonesse, France
Tel.: (33) 130112121
Web Site: http://www.nova-immobilier.fr
Real Estate Services
N.A.I.C.S.: 531390

Oney Bank SA (1)
34 Avenue de Flandre, 59170, Croix, France
Tel.: (33) 969328686
Banking Services
N.A.I.C.S.: 522110
Jean-Yves Forel *(Chm)*

Oney Insurance (PCC) Limited (1)
Il-Piazzetta Block B-Office 13 15 Tower Road, Sliema, SLM 1605, Malta
Tel.: (356) 22585110
Web Site: http://www.oneyinsurance.com
Insurance Services
N.A.I.C.S.: 524210
Mark Tanti Desjardins *(Ops Mgr)*

Oney Polska S.A. (1)
ul Ogrodowa58, 00-876, Warsaw, Poland
Tel.: (48) 801700307
Web Site: http://www.oney.com.pl
Financial Services
N.A.I.C.S.: 523999
Izabela Krawczyk *(Reg Sls Mgr)*

Ossiam SA (1)
6 Place de la Madeleine, 75008, Paris, France
Tel.: (33) 184794270
Web Site: http://www.ossiam.com
Investment Management Service
N.A.I.C.S.: 523999
Bruno Poulin *(Founder, CEO & Partner)*

Ouest Croissance SCR SAS (1)
3 Impasse Claude Nougaro-ZAC Ar Mor Plaza, 44821, Saint Herblain, France
Tel.: (33) 240586219
Web Site: http://www.ouest-croissance.com
Equity Financing Services
N.A.I.C.S.: 523940

Palatine Asset Management SA (1)
42 rue d'Anjou, 75008, Paris, France
Tel.: (33) 155279537
Web Site: http://www.palatine-am.com
Asset Management Services
N.A.I.C.S.: 523940

Payplug SAS (1)
23-25 rue Jean-Jacques Rousseau, 75001, Paris, France
Tel.: (33) 176340155
Web Site: http://www.payplug.com
Emp.: 60
Transaction Payment Services
N.A.I.C.S.: 522320
Camille Tyan *(Co-Founder)*

Poincare Capital Management Ltd. (1)
Suite 1902-04 Kinwick Centre 32 Hollywood Road, Central, China (Hong Kong)
Tel.: (852) 31638080
Web Site: http://www.poincarecapital.com
Investment Management Service
N.A.I.C.S.: 523999
Catherine Au *(COO)*

Prepar-Vie SA (1)
Tour Franklin 101 Quartier Boieldieu, 92800, Puteaux, France
Tel.: (33) 141254125
Web Site: http://www.prepar-vie.fr
Fire Insurance Services
N.A.I.C.S.: 524113

SASU BFC Croissance (1)
14 Boulevard de la, Tremouille, 21000, Dijon, France
Tel.: (33) 381659103
Web Site: http://www.bfccroissance.fr
Private Equity Services
N.A.I.C.S.: 523940

Saudi Arabia Investment Company (1)
Al Faisaliah Tower 24th FL King Fahd Road, PO Box 19078, Riyadh, 11435, Saudi Arabia
Tel.: (966) 112508000
Web Site: http://www.sanabil.com
Real Estate Investment Services
N.A.I.C.S.: 531210
Yasir Othman Al-Rumayyan *(Chm)*

Seeyond SA (1)
43 Avenue Pierre Mendes-France, CS 81436, 75648, Paris, Cedex, France
Tel.: (33) 158190980
Web Site: http://www.seeyond-am.fr
Emp.: 25
Investment Management Service
N.A.I.C.S.: 523999
Emmanuel Bourdeix *(CEO)*

Smartney Sp. Z O O (1)
ul Krakowiakow 46, 02-255, Warsaw, Poland
Tel.: (48) 225288888
Web Site: http://www.smartney.pl
Financial Services
N.A.I.C.S.: 523999
Katarzyna Jozwik *(Gen Mgr)*

Socfim SA (1)
10 Grenelle 10 boulevard de Grenelle, CS 62305, 75740, Paris, Cedex, France
Tel.: (33) 140645858
Web Site: http://www.socfim.com
Real Estate Agency Services
N.A.I.C.S.: 531210

Sofider SASU (1)
3 rue Labourdonnais, BP 867, 97477, Saint Denis, Cedex, France
Tel.: (33) 820321000
Web Site: http://www.sofider.re
Financial Services
N.A.I.C.S.: 523999

Trez Commercial Finances LP (1)
1700-745 Thurlow Street, Vancouver, V6E 0C5, BC, Canada
Tel.: (604) 689-0821
Web Site: https://www.trezcapital.com
Debt Collection Services
N.A.I.C.S.: 561440
John D. Hutchinson *(Vice Chm & Co-CEO)*

Vauban Infrastructure Partners SCA (1)
115 rue Montmartre, 75002, Paris, France
Tel.: (33) 178409025
Web Site: http://www.vauban-ip.com
Banking Services
N.A.I.C.S.: 522110
Gwenola Chambon *(Co-Founder, CEO & Partner)*

Vermilion Partners (UK) Limited (1)
42 Brook Street, London, W1K 5DB, United Kingdom
Tel.: (44) 2031784601
Web Site: http://www.vermilion-partners.com
Investment Banking Services
N.A.I.C.S.: 523150
Peter Batey *(Chm)*

Vermilion Partners Limited (1)
19/F Ruttonjee House Ruttonjee Centre 11 Duddell Street, Central, China (Hong Kong)
Tel.: (852) 93501916
Investment Banking Services
N.A.I.C.S.: 523150

Vialink SAS (1)
23-25 rue Daviel, 75013, Paris, France
Tel.: (33) 140029112
Web Site: http://www.vialink.fr
KYC Solution Providing Services
N.A.I.C.S.: 541512
Philippe Sanchis *(Mng Dir)*

GROUPE BRIAND SAS
29 Avenue des Sables, Les Herbiers, 85500, France
Tel.: (33) 251910373
Web Site: http://www.groupebriand.fr
Year Founded: 1950
Design, Construction & Building Services
N.A.I.C.S.: 236210
Gil Briand *(Owner & CEO)*

GROUPE BRUXELLES LAMBERT SA
Avenue Marnix 24, B-1000, Brussels, Belgium
Tel.: (32) 22891786   BE
Web Site: https://gbl.com
Year Founded: 1902
GBLB—(EUR)
Rev.: $6,774,809,583
Assets: $31,526,217,026
Liabilities: $12,749,641,243
Net Worth: $18,776,575,784
Earnings: $427,751,408
Emp.: 1,693
Fiscal Year-end: 12/31/23
Holding Company
N.A.I.C.S.: 551112
Ian Gallienne *(CEO)*

Subsidiaries:

Deutsche Intensivpflege Holding B.V. (1)
Kathe-Kollwitz-Ufer 77, 01309, Dresden, Germany
Tel.: (49) 35185073510
Web Site: http://www.opseo-intensivpflege.de
Outpatient Care Services
N.A.I.C.S.: 621999

Ergon Capital Management SA (1)
Route dArlon 19-21, 8009, Strassen, Luxembourg
Tel.: (352) 2060042620
Web Site: http://www.ergoncapital.com
Rev.: $1,064,423,750
Emp.: 7
Privater Equity Firm
N.A.I.C.S.: 523999
Wolfgang de Limburg Stirum *(Mng Partner)*

Holding (Non-US):

Farmabios SpA (2)
Via Pavia 1, Gropello Cairoli, 27027, Milan, PV, Italy
Tel.: (39) 03828191
Web Site: https://www.farmabios.com
Active Pharmaceutical Ingredients Mfr & Distr
N.A.I.C.S.: 325412
Mario Di Giacomo *(CEO)*

Keesing Media Group B.V. (2)
Naritaweg 235, 1043 CB, Amsterdam, Netherlands
Tel.: (31) 20 564 1234
Web Site: https://www.keesing.com
Emp.: 400
Puzzle Magazines Publishing Services
N.A.I.C.S.: 513199

PharmaZell GmbH (2)
Rosenheimer Str 43, 83064, Raubling, Germany
Tel.: (49) 8035880
Web Site: https://pharmazell-group.com
Sales Range: $50-74.9 Million
Active Pharmaceutical Ingredients Mfr & Distr
N.A.I.C.S.: 325412
Oliver Bolzern *(CEO & COO)*

SVT GmbH (2)
Eisenwerkstrasse 21-27, 58332, Schwelm, Germany
Tel.: (49) 23364430
Web Site: https://www.svt-gmbh.com
Loading Arm Mfr
N.A.I.C.S.: 333131
Michael Schauerte *(Mng Dir)*

Subsidiary (US):

Connex SVT Inc. (3)
3402 Torchlite Terrace Ct Ste D, Katy, TX 77494
Tel.: (281) 391-1244
Web Site: http://www.connexsvt.com
Loading Arm Equipment Mfr
N.A.I.C.S.: 333131
Barry Craig *(Pres)*

Imerys SA (1)
43 quai de Grenelle, 75015, Paris, France   (66.78%)
Tel.: (33) 149556300
Web Site: https://www.imerys.com
Rev.: $4,665,469,640
Assets: $8,586,748,664
Liabilities: $4,956,562,520
Net Worth: $3,630,186,144
Earnings: $36,970,024
Emp.: 16,400
Fiscal Year-end: 12/31/2020
Holding Company; Non-Ferrous Mining & Metal Activities; Chemicals; Tubing; Building Materials; Refractories & Worldwide Trading
N.A.I.C.S.: 551112
Paul Desmarais III *(Vice Chm)*

Subsidiary (Domestic):

AGS SA (2)
La Gare, Clerac, 17270, France
Tel.: (33) 5 46 04 17 11
Web Site: http://www.ags-mineraux.com
Emp.: 177
Clay Minerals Mining Services
N.A.I.C.S.: 212323

Ardoisieres d'Angers (2)
56 rue Albert Camus, BP 148, 49800, Trelaze, France
Tel.: (33) 2 41 96 70 04
Ceramic Tile Mfr
N.A.I.C.S.: 327120

Calderys France SAS (2)
Route de Troyes, BP 93, Sezanne, Cedex, France
Tel.: (33) 32 680 5444
Web Site: https://www.calderys.com
Sales Range: $650-699.9 Million
Emp.: 2,000
Heat Transfer Equipment Mfr & Distr
N.A.I.C.S.: 333415

Subsidiary (Non-US):

Calderys Austria Gmbh (3)
IZ-No Sud - Strasse 16 Objekt 69/7, Postfach 71, Wiener Neudorf, 2355, Austria
Tel.: (43) 2236 677 090 0
Web Site: http://www.calderys.at
Emp.: 30
Mineral Mining Services
N.A.I.C.S.: 213115

Calderys Belgium SA/NV (3)
Avenue Albert Einstein 13, Louvain-la-Neuve, 1348, Belgium
Tel.: (32) 10 45 44 24
Web Site: http://www.calderys.be
Sales Range: $50-74.9 Million
Emp.: 13
Mineral Mining Services
N.A.I.C.S.: 212390

Calderys Italia Srl (3)
Via Sacco E Vanzetti 63, 41042, Fiorano-Modenese, Italy
Tel.: (39) 0 536 91 29 11
Monolithic Clay Refractory Mfr
N.A.I.C.S.: 327120

Calderys Magyarorszag KFT (3)
Wesseleny U 2, 1077, Budapest, Hungary
Tel.: (36) 12 68 03 50
Emp.: 4
Metallic Mineral Exploration Services
N.A.I.C.S.: 213115
Thomas Bergmann *(Gen Mgr)*

Calderys Nordic AB (3)
Brucksgatan 37, 263 39, Hoganas, Sweden
Tel.: (46) 31540900
Emp.: 60
Mineral Mining Services
N.A.I.C.S.: 212390

Calderys South Africa Pty Ltd (3)
6 Kariba Street, PO Box 2422, Powerville, Vereeniging, 1930, South Africa
Tel.: (27) 16 440 6400
Web Site: http://www.calderys.co.za
Emp.: 200
Mineral Mining Services
N.A.I.C.S.: 212390

GROUPE BRUXELLES LAMBERT SA

Groupe Bruxelles Lambert SA—(Continued)
Subsidiary (Domestic):

Ceradel - Socor (2)
17 23 Rue Frederic Bastiat LP 1598, PO Box 1598, 87022, Limoges, France **(100%)**
Tel.: (33) 555350235
Web Site: http://www.ceradelsocor.fr
Sales Range: $25-49.9 Million
Emp.: 25
Ceramic Products
N.A.I.C.S.: 327120

Ceratera S A (2)
Ave Pierre De Couber017927n, F 36001, Chateauroux, France **(100%)**
Tel.: (33) 254085500
N.A.I.C.S.: 327910

Cesar SA (2)
ZI du Clos Bonnet 154 Boulevard Jean Moulin, 49400, Saumur, France **(100%)**
Tel.: (33) 24 150 2654
Web Site: https://cesar-group.fr
Sales Range: $25-49.9 Million
Emp.: 50
Mining of Contruction Materials
N.A.I.C.S.: 333120

Charges Minerales du Perigord (2)
Verdinas, 24340, Sainte-Croix-de-Mareuil, France
Tel.: (33) 553605555
Mineral Mining Services
N.A.I.C.S.: 212390
Pierre Dessalles *(Gen Mgr)*

Subsidiary (Non-US):

Ecca Holdings Pty Ltd (2)
259 West St, Centurion, Pretoria, 0157, South Africa
Tel.: (27) 12 6435880
Web Site: http://www.eccaholdings.com
Sales Range: $25-49.9 Million
Emp.: 30
Ceramic Clay & Mineral Distr
N.A.I.C.S.: 423520

Subsidiary (Domestic):

Edilians SASU (2)
Parc D Activites De Limonest Silic 3 1 Rue Des Vergers, PO Box 22, 69760, Limonest, France **(100%)**
Tel.: (33) 472520272
Web Site: http://www.imerystc.com
Sales Range: $25-49.9 Million
Emp.: 25
Mfr of Roof Tiles & Bricks
N.A.I.C.S.: 327120
Jonnard Pierre *(Pres)*

Subsidiary (Non-US):

Umbelino Monteiro S.A. (3)
Rua do Areeiro n 72, 3105-222, Meirinhas, Portugal
Tel.: (351) 236 949000
Web Site: http://www.umbelino.pt
Emp.: 200
Building Materials Mfr
N.A.I.C.S.: 339999

Subsidiary (Non-US):

Haznedar Refrakter Sanayii A.S. (2)
Buyukcavuslu Mah Cerkezkoy Cad, Silivri, 34594, Istanbul, Turkiye **(60%)**
Tel.: (90) 212 745 3505
Web Site: https://www.hazref.com
Emp.: 250
Construction Material Mfr & Whslr
N.A.I.C.S.: 327120

Subsidiary (Domestic):

Imerys Aluminates S.A. (2)
Immeuble Pacific 11, cours Valmy, Puteaux, 92800, France
Tel.: (33) 146379000
Web Site: http://www.kerneos.com
Calcium Aluminate Cement Mfr & Whslr
N.A.I.C.S.: 327310
Francois Conradie *(Plant Mgr)*

Subsidiary (US):

Kerneos Inc. (3)

1316 Priority Ln, Chesapeake, VA 23324
Tel.: (757) 284-3200
Web Site: http://www.kerneosinc.com
Calcium Aluminate Cements Mfr
N.A.I.C.S.: 327310
Nancy Bunt *(Sr Mgr-Refractories)*

Subsidiary (Non-US):

Kerneos Ltd. (3)
Dolphin Way, Purfleet, RM19 1NZ, Essex, United Kingdom
Tel.: (44) 1708863333
Web Site: http://www.kerneosinc.com
Calcium Aluminate Cements Mfr
N.A.I.C.S.: 327310

Kerneos Southern Africa (Pty) Ltd. (3)
21 Dartfield Road Eastgate Ext 12, PO Box 783602, Sandton, 2146, South Africa
Tel.: (27) 114443090
Web Site: http://www.kerneos.com
Calcium Aluminate Cements Mfr
N.A.I.C.S.: 327310

Kerneos do Brazil Producao E Comercio de Aluminosos Ltda (3)
Estrada de Guaxindiba 1500, CEP 24 722-030, Sao Goncalo, RJ, Brazil
Tel.: (55) 2126023700
Web Site: http://www.kerneos.com
Calcium Aluminate Cements Mfr
N.A.I.C.S.: 327310

Subsidiary (Domestic):

Imerys Ceramics France (2)
87 Rue Ampere, PO Box 40008, 36005, Chateauroux, France
Tel.: (33) 677659322
Web Site: http://www.imerys-ceramics.com
Ceramic Products Mfr
N.A.I.C.S.: 327120

Imerys Kiln Furniture France (2)
4 rue du Micy, 45380, La Chapelle-Saint-Mesmin, France **(100%)**
Tel.: (33) 2 3822 3270
Web Site: http://www.imerys.com
Kiln Furniture & Technical Ceramics Mfr
N.A.I.C.S.: 327120

Subsidiary (Non-US):

Imerys Kiln Furniture Espana, S.A. (3)
Lg As Cachadas s/n, 36780, La Guardia, Spain
Tel.: (34) 986609000
Web Site: https://www.imerys.com
Emp.: 85
Kiln Furniture & Technical Ceramics Mfr
N.A.I.C.S.: 327120

Imerys Kiln Furniture Hungary kft (3)
Erzsebeti Ut 7, 6800, Hodmezovasarhely, Hungary
Tel.: (36) 62 242 914
Emp.: 17
Ceramic Furniture Distr
N.A.I.C.S.: 423210
Thomas Hindkaer *(Mng Dir)*

Imerys Kiln Furniture Thailand Ltd. (3)
228 Vibhavadi Rangist Road, Din Daeng, Bangkok, 10400, Thailand
Tel.: (66) 2 695 0900
Web Site: http://www.ikf-solutions.com
Kiln Furniture & Technical Ceramics Mfr
N.A.I.C.S.: 327120

Subsidiary (US):

Imerys Marble Inc. (2)
16 North Rd, Wheatland, WY 82201
Tel.: (307) 322-2479
Sales Range: $25-49.9 Million
N.A.I.C.S.: 327910

Subsidiary (Non-US):

Imerys Minerali S.p.A. (2)
via Longobarda Snc, 54100, Massa, Massa-Carrara, Italy
Tel.: (39) 0585 839501
Crushed & Broken Limestone Mining Services
N.A.I.C.S.: 212313

Imerys Minerals Ab (2)
Nya Hamnvagen, Koping, 731 36, Sweden
Tel.: (46) 22136900
Web Site: http://www.imerys.com
Sales Range: $25-49.9 Million
Emp.: 100
Inorganic Basic Chemical Mfr
N.A.I.C.S.: 325180

Imerys Mineraux Belgique S.A./NV (2)
Rue du Canal 2, Lixhe, 4600, Vise, Belgium
Tel.: (32) 4 379 9811
Emp.: 120
Kaolin & Ball Clay Mining Services
N.A.I.C.S.: 212323
Patrice Coppe *(Mng Dir)*

Subsidiary (Domestic):

Imerys Mineraux France SA (2)
Chemin De Halage, Villers-sous-Saint-Leu, 60340, France
Tel.: (33) 344277001
Mineral Mining Services
N.A.I.C.S.: 212390

Imerys Refractory Minerals Glomel SAS (2)
154 rue de l'Universite, 75007, Paris, France
Tel.: (33) 1 49 55 6560
Web Site: http://www.imerys-refractoryminerals.com
Refractory Minerals Mfr
N.A.I.C.S.: 327120

Imerys Services SAS (2)
154 Rue De l'Universite, 75007, Paris, France
Tel.: (33) 1 49 55 63 00
Web Site: http://www.imerys.com
Sales Range: $75-99.9 Million
Emp.: 20
Mineral Mining Services
N.A.I.C.S.: 212390

Imerys Tableware (2)
1 Rue Jeanne d Albret, 87700, Aixe sur Vienne, France **(100%)**
Tel.: (33) 555702868
Web Site: http://www.imerys.wa.com
Sales Range: $25-49.9 Million
Emp.: 60
N.A.I.C.S.: 327910

Subsidiary (Non-US):

Imerys Tiles Minerals Italia SRL (2)
Via Vincenzo Monti 1, Reggio nell'Emilia, 42122, Italy
Tel.: (39) 0522268511
Ceramic Minerals Mining Services
N.A.I.C.S.: 212323

Subsidiary (US):

Imerys USA, Inc. (2)
100 Mansell Ct E Ste 300, Roswell, GA 30076
Tel.: (770) 594-0660
Web Site: http://www.imerys.com
Sales Range: $25-49.9 Million
Emp.: 200
Engineeering Services
N.A.I.C.S.: 541330

Subsidiary (Domestic):

Nizerolles S.A. (2)
Tour Maine Montparnasse 33, avenue du Maine, 75755, Paris, Cedex 15, France
Mineral Mining
N.A.I.C.S.: 212323

Pomel (Etablissements) (2)
Vergongheon, 43360, Avant, France
N.A.I.C.S.: 327120

Subsidiary (Non-US):

Rhino Minerals Pty Ltd (2)
259 West Ave, Centurion, 46, South Africa
Tel.: (27) 126435880
Sales Range: $25-49.9 Million
Emp.: 30
Mineral Mining Services
N.A.I.C.S.: 213115
Wendy Heathcote *(Office Mgr)*

INTERNATIONAL PUBLIC

Subsidiary (Domestic):

SEG (2)
Chaume Lauzon-Gournay, 36230, Saint Sepulchre, France
Refractory Production
N.A.I.C.S.: 212323

Subsidiary (Non-US):

Samrec Pty Ltd (2)
259 West Av, Centurion, 0157, Gauteng, South Africa
Tel.: (27) 126435880
Web Site: http://www.imerys.com
Sales Range: $25-49.9 Million
Emp.: 30
Mineral Mining Services
N.A.I.C.S.: 212390

Spica Srl (2)
Km 2 850 Via Falerina, 01033, Civita Castellana, Viterbo, Italy
Tel.: (39) 0761516100
Mineral Mining Services
N.A.I.C.S.: 212390

Treibacher Schleifmittel AG (2)
Seebach 2, PO Box 1, A9523, Landskron, Fila, Austria **(100%)**
Tel.: (43) 424241885
Web Site: http://www.treibacher-schleifm.com
Mfr & Sale of Abrasives
N.A.I.C.S.: 327910

Subsidiary (US):

Treibacher Schleifmittel North America, Inc. (3)
2000 College Ave M, Niagara Falls, NY 14305-1734
Tel.: (716) 286-1250
Web Site: http://www.treibacher-schleifm.com
Sales Range: $25-49.9 Million
Emp.: 35
Mfr of Fused Aluminum Oxides & Silicon Carbide Abrasive Grits
N.A.I.C.S.: 327910
Serge Arutunjan *(Controller)*

Subsidiary (US):

World Minerals, Inc. (2)
130 Castilian Dr, Santa Barbara, CA 93117-3028
Tel.: (805) 562-0200
Web Site: http://www.worldminerals.com
Sales Range: $25-49.9 Million
Holding Company for Mining Subsidiaries
N.A.I.C.S.: 212390

Subsidiary (Domestic):

Celite Corporation (3)
130 Castilian Dr, Santa Barbara, CA 93117
Tel.: (805) 735-7791
Web Site: http://www.worldminerals.com
Sales Range: $50-74.9 Million
Diatom Mfr
N.A.I.C.S.: 212390

Subsidiary (Non-US):

World Minerals France (3)
154 rue de l'Universite, 75007, Paris, France
Tel.: (33) 1 49 55 63 00
Mineral Mining Services
N.A.I.C.S.: 212390

World Minerals International Sales SA (3)
Rue Du Laboratoire 9, Luxembourg, 1911, Luxembourg
Tel.: (352) 27026906
Ceramic Mineral Distr
N.A.I.C.S.: 423520

World Minerals Italia Srl (3)
Via Alzaia Trento 6, 20094, Corsico, Italy
Tel.: (39) 02 451 74200
Sales Range: $50-74.9 Million
Emp.: 25
Mineral Mining Services
N.A.I.C.S.: 212390
Lamberto Tirelli *(Mgr)*

Sienna Capital International Ltd. (1)
7th Floor Berkeley Square House Berkeley

AND PRIVATE COMPANIES

Square, London, W1J 6BE, United Kingdom
Tel.: (44) 2079274060
Investment Platform Services
N.A.I.C.S.: 523999
Victoria Bond *(Office Mgr)*

Sienna Capital S.a r.l. (1)
Immeuble Serenity 19-21 route d'Arlon, 8009, Strassen, Luxembourg
Tel.: (352) 272122
Web Site: https://www.sienna-im.com
Investment Platform Services
N.A.I.C.S.: 523999
Colin Hall *(CEO)*

GROUPE CANVAR INC.
100-2700 Rufus Rockhead, Montreal, H3J 2Z7, QC, Canada
Tel.: (514) 738-4725
Web Site: http://www.canvar.ca
Year Founded: 1975
Sales Range: $10-24.9 Million
Emp.: 5
Real Estate Development Services
N.A.I.C.S.: 531390

GROUPE CASPERA SA
59 avenue de Victor Hugo, 75116, Paris, France
Tel.: (33) 174901515
Apparel Product Distr
N.A.I.C.S.: 458110
Anne Siros *(CEO)*

GROUPE CEGERCO INC.
1180 rue Bersimis, Chicoutimi, G7K 1A5, QC, Canada
Tel.: (418) 543-6159
Web Site: http://www.cegerco.com
Year Founded: 1976
Sales Range: $125-149.9 Million
Emp.: 550
Construction Services
N.A.I.C.S.: 236220
Jeannot Harvey *(Founder & Pres)*

GROUPE CENTENNIAL HOLDING SAH
Frydenbergveien 46 B, 0575, Oslo, Norway
Tel.: (47) 22 884240
Web Site: http://www.centennial.no
Holding Company
N.A.I.C.S.: 551112
Endre Rosjo *(Chm)*

Subsidiaries:

Centennial AS (1)
PO Box 1428 Vika, 0115, Oslo, Norway (100%)
Tel.: (47) 2288 4240
Web Site: http://www.centennial.no
Emp.: 8
Investment Services
N.A.I.C.S.: 523999
Endre Rosjo *(Chm)*

GROUPE CIMENT QUEBEC, INC.
145 boul Du Centenaire, Saint-Basile, G0A 3G0, QC, Canada
Tel.: (418) 329-2100
Year Founded: 1959
Sales Range: $100-124.9 Million
Emp.: 700
Cement Mfr
N.A.I.C.S.: 327310
M. Andre Morissette *(VP)*

GROUPE CIOA SA
Immeuble Le Nobel avenue de Universite, 83160, La Valette-du-Var, France
Tel.: (33) 494141240
Web Site: http://www.cioa.com MLCIO—(EUR)
Sales Range: $10-24.9 Million
Financial Support Services
N.A.I.C.S.: 523940

Leon Lucide *(Chm & CEO)*

GROUPE CRIT, S.A.
6 rue Toulouse Lautrec, 75017, Paris, France
Tel.: (33) 149185555 FR
Web Site: http://www.groupe-crit.com
Year Founded: 1962
Employment Services
N.A.I.C.S.: 561320
Claude Guedj *(Chm & CEO)*

Subsidiaries:

ATIAC (1)
15 Boulevard Roger Combe, 19100, Brive-la-Gaillarde, France
Tel.: (33) 5 55 22 84 65
Airport Maintenance Services
N.A.I.C.S.: 488119

Adaptalia Outsourcing SL (1)
C/ Jose Abascal 55 1 Derecha, 28007, Madrid, Spain
Tel.: (34) 915015500
Web Site: http://www.gropo-crat.com
Emp.: 1,000
Airport Maintenance Services
N.A.I.C.S.: 488119
Rafael Alcocer *(Mgr)*

Arkeo Inc. (1)
1845 Precinct Line Rd Ste 200, Hurst, TX 76054
Tel.: (817) 485-5885
Web Site: http://www.arkeo.com
Educational Support Services
N.A.I.C.S.: 611710
Roger Olson *(Founder & Pres)*

CRIT MAROC (1)
67 boulevard Al Massira Al Khadra, Casablanca, Morocco
Tel.: (212) 522 23 48 45
Web Site: http://www.crit-maroc.com
Human Resource Consulting Services
N.A.I.C.S.: 561311

CRIT TUNISIE (1)
5 place Pasteur - Belvedere, 1002, Tunis, Tunisia
Tel.: (216) 71 78 17 21
Web Site: http://www.crit-tunisie.net
Human Resource Consulting Services
N.A.I.C.S.: 561311

Cobalt Ground Solutions Ltd (1)
Room 2535 Terminal 4 Heathrow Airport London, Hounslow, TW6 3XQ, Mddx, United Kingdom (100%)
Tel.: (44) 20 8750 9881
Web Site: http://www.cobaltgs.com
Emp.: 800
Airport Ground Handling Services
N.A.I.C.S.: 488119
Paul Montgomery *(Mgr-Comml)*

GROUPE EUROPE HANDLING (1)
Zone Cargo 4 3 rue du Te, 93290, Tremblay, Cedex, France
Tel.: (33) 1 48 16 17 22
Web Site: http://www.groupe-europe-handling.fr
Airport Maintenance Services
N.A.I.C.S.: 488119

LES COMPAGNONS (1)
82 rue de l Hotel-de-Ville, 75004, Paris, France
Tel.: (33) 1 44 78 22 50
Web Site: http://www.compagnons-du-devoir.com
Human Resource Consulting Services
N.A.I.C.S.: 561311

Maser Engineering SA (1)
92/98 Boulevard Victor Hugo Bat A2 / 7eme Etage, 92110, Clichy, France
Tel.: (33) 1 55 46 50 97
Web Site: http://www.maser-engineering.com
Human Resource Consulting Services
N.A.I.C.S.: 561311

OTESSA (1)
Bat DeltaParc Paris Nord 2 Villepinte 93 Avenue des Nations, PO Box 51283, 95958, Roissy-en-France, Cedex, France
Tel.: (33) 1 45 91 11 68

Web Site: http://www.otessa.fr
Airport Management Services
N.A.I.C.S.: 488119

PEOPULSE (1)
16-20 avenue de l Agent Sarre, 92700, Colombes, France
Tel.: (33) 141 19 24 80
Web Site: http://www.peopulse.com
Human Resource Consulting Services
N.A.I.C.S.: 561311

PRESTINTER (1)
90 Boulevard Victor Hugo, 92110, Clichy, France
Tel.: (33) 9 62 10 03 74
Airport Maintenance Services
N.A.I.C.S.: 488119

PeopleLink Inc. (1)
3835 Cypress Dr Ste 205, Petaluma, CA 94954
Tel.: (707) 769-5152
Web Site: http://www.peoplelink.org
Educational Support Services
N.A.I.C.S.: 611710
Barbara La Rue *(Co-Founder)*

Subsidiary (Domestic):

Sustained Quality LLC (2)
431 E Colfax Ave Ste 200, South Bend, IN 46617
Tel.: (800) 287-0215
Web Site: http://www.sustained-quality.com
Quality Sort & Containment Services
N.A.I.C.S.: 541330
Jeff Weisenauer *(VP-Sls)*

Subsidiary (Domestic):

EHD Technologies, LLC (3)
1600 Westgate Cir Ste 275, Brentwood, TN 37027
Tel.: (615) 953-1907
Web Site: http://www.ehdtech.com
Emp.: 200
Talent Acquisition Staffing Solutions & Quality Assurance Services
N.A.I.C.S.: 561311
Jeff McKeehan *(Pres)*

Subsidiary (Domestic):

Teamsoft, Inc. (2)
1350 Deming Way Ste 250, Middleton, WI 53562 (100%)
Tel.: (608) 827-7772
Web Site: http://www.teamsoftinc.com
Sales Range: $25-49.9 Million
Emp.: 45
Staffing & Consulting Services
N.A.I.C.S.: 541690
Eric Larson *(Founder & Partner)*

PeopleLink Staffing Solutions Inc. (1)
431 E Colfax Ave Ste 200, South Bend, IN 46617
Tel.: (574) 232-5400
Web Site: http://www.peoplelinkstaffing.com
Sales Range: $100-124.9 Million
Emp.: 180
Staffing Services
N.A.I.C.S.: 561311
Jay Wilkinson *(CEO)*

Propartner Zeitarbeit + Handelsagentur GmbH (1)
St Georgener Strasse 9, 79111, Freiburg, Germany
Tel.: (49) 761 4598990
Web Site: http://www.propartner.net
Human Resource Consulting Services
N.A.I.C.S.: 561311

SKY HANDLING PARTNER (1)
Horizon House Unit 4 Corballis Park, Dublin, Ireland
Tel.: (353) 1 8080 300
Web Site: http://www.skyhandlingpartner.ie
Emp.: 4,200
Airport Management Services
N.A.I.C.S.: 488119

Sky Handling Partner UK Limited (1)
6th Floor Lesley Tower 42 Fountain Street, Belfast, BT1 5EF, United Kingdom
Tel.: (44) 20 7646 0700
Ground Handling Services
N.A.I.C.S.: 488119

GROUPE DESCHENES INC.

GROUPE DE SCIERIES G.D.S. INC.
207 Route 295, Degelis, G5T 1R1, QC, Canada
Tel.: (418) 853-2566
Web Site: http://www.groupgds.com
Year Founded: 1947
Sales Range: $50-74.9 Million
Emp.: 450
Lumber, Logging & Milling Mfr
N.A.I.C.S.: 321999
Sylvain Deschenes *(CEO)*

Subsidiaries:

G.D.S. Valoribois inc. (1)
80 Du Pc Industriel, Matane, G4W 3P6, QC, Canada
Tel.: (418) 566-6555
Wood Products Mfr
N.A.I.C.S.: 321211

GROUPE DESCHENES INC.
3901 Jarry Street E Office 250, Montreal, H1Z 2G1, QC, Canada
Tel.: (514) 253-3110
Web Site: http://www.groupedeschenes.com
Sales Range: $550-599.9 Million
Emp.: 2,600
Plumbing & Heating Products Wholesale Distr
N.A.I.C.S.: 423720
Martin Deschenes *(Pres & CEO)*

Subsidiaries:

Bardon Supplies Limited (1)
405 College St E, PO Box 1023, Belleville, K8N 4Z6, ON, Canada
Tel.: (613) 966-5643
Web Site: https://www.bardonsupplies.com
Sales Range: $150-199.9 Million
Emp.: 375
Plumbing, Heating, Air Conditioning & Ventilation Products Wholesale Distr
N.A.I.C.S.: 423730

Boone Plumbing & Heating Supply Inc. (1)
1282 Algoma Road, Ottawa, K1B 3W8, ON, Canada
Tel.: (613) 746-7070
Web Site: https://www.boone.ca
Sales Range: $75-99.9 Million
Emp.: 150
Plumbing, Heating, Ventilation, Air Conditioning & Mechanical Systems Wholesale Distr; Waterworks & Sewer Systems Distr
N.A.I.C.S.: 423730

Crane Canada Co. (1)
615 Dixon Rd, M9W 1H9, Toronto, ON, Canada
Tel.: (416) 244-5351
Sales Range: $150-199.9 Million
Emp.: 450
Plumbing Fittings Distr
N.A.I.C.S.: 423720
Tom Frazer *(Pres)*

Descair Inc. (1)
8335 boulevard Saint-Michel, Montreal, H1Z 3E6, QC, Canada
Tel.: (514) 744-6752
Web Site: https://www.descair.ca
Sales Range: $25-49.9 Million
Emp.: 50
Heating, Ventilation, Air Conditioning, Refrigeration, Heating Controls & Related Products Wholesale Distr
N.A.I.C.S.: 423730
Charles Abiad *(VP & Gen Mgr)*

Deschenes & Fils Ltee (1)
3901 Jarry St East Ste 100, Montreal, H1Z 2G1, QC, Canada
Tel.: (514) 374-3110
Web Site: http://www.deschenes.ca
Sales Range: $75-99.9 Million
Emp.: 200
Plumbing, Heating & Fire Protection Products Wholesale Distr
N.A.I.C.S.: 423730
Sophie Pelletier *(Sec)*

GROUPE DESCHENES INC.

Groupe Deschenes Inc.—(Continued)

Deschenes & Fils Ltee (1)
1105 Rue des Rocailles, Quebec, G2K 2K6, QC, Canada
Tel.: (418) 627-4711
Web Site: https://www.deschenes.qc.ca
Sales Range: $75-99.9 Million
Emp.: 125
Plumbing, Heating, Electrical & Industrial Supplies Wholesale Distr
N.A.I.C.S.: 423730

Deschenes & Fils Ltee (1)
2204 rue Louis-Allyson, Trois Rivieres, G8Z 4P3, QC, Canada
Tel.: (819) 693-2244
Plumbing & Heating Equipment Distr
N.A.I.C.S.: 423720

Desco Plumbing & Heating Supply Inc. (1)
65 Worcester Road, Etobicoke, M9W 5N7, ON, Canada
Tel.: (416) 213-1555
Web Site: http://www.desco.ca
Sales Range: $50-74.9 Million
Emp.: 80
Plumbing, Heating, Waterworks Systems & Air Conditioning Products Wholesale Distr
N.A.I.C.S.: 423730
Joe Senese (VP & Gen Mgr)

Flocor Inc. (1)
470 Seaman Street, Stoney Creek, L8E 2V9, ON, Canada
Tel.: (905) 664-1459
Web Site: http://www.flocor.ca
Plumbing & Heating Equipment Distr
N.A.I.C.S.: 423720
Tom Murray (VP & Gen Mgr)

Ideal Supply Company Limited (1)
1045 Wallace Ave N, Listowel, N4W 1M6, ON, Canada
Tel.: (519) 291-1060
Web Site: http://www.idealsupply.com
Electrical & Industrial Products Distr
N.A.I.C.S.: 423830

Real Huot Inc. (1)
2640 Dalton Avenue, Sainte-Foy, G1P 3S4, QC, Canada
Tel.: (418) 651-9909
Web Site: https://www.realhuot.ca
Sales Range: $75-99.9 Million
Emp.: 24
Waterworks & Sewer Systems Distr
N.A.I.C.S.: 221310

GROUPE DUBREUIL SA
Actipole 85, BP 42, 85170, Belleville-sur-Vie, France
Tel.: (33) 2 51 47 77 90   FR
Web Site: http://www.groupedubreuil.com
Year Founded: 1981
Sales Range: $1-4.9 Billion
Emp.: 3,140
Holding Company
N.A.I.C.S.: 551112
Jean-Paul Dubreuil (Chm-Supervisory Bd)

Subsidiaries:

Huray Automobiles SAS (1)
Zone Industrielle Sous Cotard Route de Rennes, 35600, Redon, France
Tel.: (33) 299723636
Sales Range: $50-74.9 Million
Emp.: 93
New Car Dealers
N.A.I.C.S.: 441110
Patrice Huray (Pres)

M3 SAS (1)
Actipole 85, 85170, Belleville-sur-Vie, France
Tel.: (33) 2 51 06 90 80
Web Site: http://www.m3france.fr
Sales Range: Less than $1 Million
Agricultural Machinery Distr
N.A.I.C.S.: 423820

GROUPE DUTAILIER INC.
299 Chaput Street, Saint-Pie, J0H 1W0, QC, Canada
Tel.: (450) 772-2403
Web Site: http://www.dutailier.com
Year Founded: 1976
Sales Range: $125-149.9 Million
Emp.: 650
Children Infant Chair & Bedroom Furniture Mfr
N.A.I.C.S.: 337122
Fernand Fontaine (Pres)

Subsidiaries:

Dutailier Ltd. (1)
3 Elstree Distribution Park, Elstree Way, Borehamwood, WD6 1RU, Middlesex, United Kingdom
Tel.: (44) 2082386950
Sales Range: $25-49.9 Million
Emp.: 20
Childrens' Furniture Distr
N.A.I.C.S.: 423210

GROUPE DYNAMITE INC.
5592 Rue Ferrier, Mont Royal, H4P 1M2, QC, Canada
Tel.: (514) 733-3962
Web Site: http://www.groupdynamite.com
Year Founded: 1975
Rev.: $210,000,000
Emp.: 2,200
Women Apparel Distr
N.A.I.C.S.: 424350
Andrew Lutfy (Pres & CEO)

GROUPE EGIS S.A.
15 Avenue du Centre, PO Box 20538, Guyancourt, 78286, Saint-Quentin-en-Yvelines, Cedex, France
Tel.: (33) 139414000
Web Site: http://www.egis.fr
Sales Range: $800-899.9 Million
Emp.: 14,850
Holding Company; Construction Services
N.A.I.C.S.: 551112
Nicolas Jachiet (Chm & CEO)

Subsidiaries:

Autostrada Eksploatacja Sa (1)
Ul Glogowska 431, 60-004, Poznan, Poland
Tel.: (48) 618383100
Web Site: http://www.aesa.pl
Automobile Parts Mfr
N.A.I.C.S.: 336390
Krzysztof Bernatowicz (Pres)

Bonaventura Services GmbH (1)
Bonaventuraplatz 1, Grossebersdorf, 2203, Zaya, Austria
Tel.: (43) 22452263722100
Construction Services
N.A.I.C.S.: 236220

Daejeon Riverside Expressway Co., Ltd. (1)
540-1 Daewha-dong, Daedeok-gu, 306-800, Daejeon, Korea (South)
Tel.: (82) 426702766
Construction Services
N.A.I.C.S.: 236220

Egis D.O.O. Beograd (1)
Trg Nikole Pasica 2, 11000, Belgrade, Serbia
Tel.: (381) 113031888
Construction Services
N.A.I.C.S.: 236220

Egis Emirates LLC (1)
Unit No RU05 Ground Level Adnec Grandstand Khaeej Al Arabi street, PO Box 31520, Abu Dhabi, United Arab Emirates
Tel.: (971) 26319933
Construction Services
N.A.I.C.S.: 236220
Ajay Vellat (Mgr-HR)

Egis Lagan Services Ltd. (1)
Depot N 1 Machinery Yard Clonkeen, Co Laois, Portlaoise, Ireland
Tel.: (353) 877778804
Construction Services
N.A.I.C.S.: 236220
Gregory McMahon (Gen Mgr)

Egis Parking Services B.V. (1)
Kabelweg 22-24, 1014 BB, Amsterdam, Netherlands
Tel.: (31) 858886378
Web Site: http://www.egisparkingservices.nl
Information Technology Development Services
N.A.I.C.S.: 541511
Arnold Klamer (Project Mgr)

Egis Rail Ksa (1)
Modern Home Building King Abdullah Road 2nd Floor Office 206, PO Box 14566, 12434, Riyadh, Saudi Arabia
Tel.: (966) 112154658
Construction Services
N.A.I.C.S.: 236220

Egis Road & Tunnel Operation Ireland Limited (1)
Tunnel Control Building Dublin Tunnel East Wall Road, Dublin, D03 NH33, Ireland
Tel.: (353) 18848442
Web Site: http://www.erto.ie
Construction Services
N.A.I.C.S.: 236220
Terry Woodley (Mgr-Duty)

Egis Road Operation M40 Ltd. (1)
Unit 15 Wildmere Road, Wildmere Industrial Estate, Banbury, OX16 3JU, Oxon, United Kingdom
Tel.: (44) 1295270920
Construction Services
N.A.I.C.S.: 236220
Adrian Smith (Gen Mgr)

Egis Road Operation Portugal S.A. (1)
Quinta de Calvilhe Se, Lamego, Viseu, Portugal
Tel.: (351) 254697045
Transportation Services
N.A.I.C.S.: 484110
Luis Simao (Gen Mgr)

Egis Romania Sa (1)
64-66 Dionisie Lupu Street 1st Floor Bucharest Sector 1, 010458, Bucharest, Romania
Tel.: (40) 213122448
Web Site: http://www.egis-romania.com
Construction Services
N.A.I.C.S.: 236220

Egis Tunel Isletmeciligi A.S. (1)
Barbaros Mahallesi Dr Eyup Aksoy Caddesi No 9, Uskudar, 34662, Istanbul, Turkiye
Tel.: (90) 2162256901
Construction Services
N.A.I.C.S.: 236220
Kivanc Guvenler (Gen Mgr)

Egismex, S. de R.L. de C.V. (1)
Avenida Baja California 245 Piso 08 Colonia Hipodromo Condesa, 06100, Mexico, Mexico
Tel.: (52) 5556066000
Construction Services
N.A.I.C.S.: 236220

Fulton Hogan Egis O&M Pty Ltd. (1)
123 Adderley Street, Auburn, 2144, NSW, Australia
Tel.: (61) 413962732
Construction Services
N.A.I.C.S.: 236220

Gebze Izmir Otoyolu Isletme A.S. (1)
Universiteler Mahallesi 1598 Caddesi Bilkent Plaza A3-Apt n 3-44, Bilkent Ankara, 06800, Cankaya, Turkiye
Tel.: (90) 3122913300
Facility Management Services
N.A.I.C.S.: 561210

Isis Belgique Sprl (1)
Place E de Neckere 5, 7700, Mouscron, Belgium
Tel.: (32) 620362006
Construction Services
N.A.I.C.S.: 236220

M6 Tolna Uzemelteto Kft (1)
Hrsz 048/119, Dunaszentgyorgy, 7135, Paks, Hungary
Tel.: (36) 74887650

INTERNATIONAL PUBLIC

Construction Services
N.A.I.C.S.: 236220

Mid-Link M7/M8 Ltd. (1)
M7 Toll Plaza, Fatharnagh Mountrath Co Laois, Portlaoise, R32 VX02, Ireland
Tel.: (353) 578694900
Web Site: http://www.midlink.ie
Tool Booth Construction Services
N.A.I.C.S.: 236220
Henry Ritchie (Gen Mgr)

North-Link M1 Ltd. (1)
M1 Toll Plaza Co Meath, Balgeen Julianstown, Drogheda, A92 P785, Ireland
Tel.: (353) 419829820
Web Site: http://www.northlink.ie
Tool Booth Construction Services
N.A.I.C.S.: 236220
Derek Lydon (Gen Mgr)

Ocacsa S.A. (1)
Domingo Diez 1003 Sexto piso Colonia del empleado, Cuernavaca, Morelos, Mexico
Tel.: (52) 5556113367
Construction Services
N.A.I.C.S.: 236220

Road Safety Operations Ireland Ltd. (1)
Clieveragh Industrial Estate, Co Kerry, Listowel, Ireland
Tel.: (353) 766887236
Construction Services
N.A.I.C.S.: 236220
Brian McGuire (Gen Mgr)

South-Link N25 Ltd. (1)
N25 Toll Plaza Gracedieu Lower, Waterford, X91 YD25, Ireland
Tel.: (353) 51319700
Web Site: http://www.southlink.ie
Tool Booth Construction Services
N.A.I.C.S.: 236220

Tunnel Network Services Pty Ltd. (1)
41 O Connell Terrace Bowen Hills, Brisbane, 4006, QLD, Australia
Tel.: (61) 733700606
Transportation Services
N.A.I.C.S.: 484110
Brett Van Breda (Mgr-I&M)

GROUPE ELYDAN
33 Route de Grenoble, Les Apprets, F-38590, Saint-Etienne, France
Tel.: (33) 4 7693 4343   FR
Web Site: http://elydan.eu
Year Founded: 1962
Polyethylene Pipe Systems Mfr
N.A.I.C.S.: 326122
Marc-Antoine Blin (Pres)

Subsidiaries:

Kulker S.A.S. (1)
117 Route d'Orleans, Sully-sur-Loire, 45600, Loiret, France
Tel.: (33) 238377140
Web Site: http://www.kulker.fr
Sales Range: $10-24.9 Million
Emp.: 25
Agricultural Irrigation Pipe Systems Distr
N.A.I.C.S.: 423820
Georges Costes (Mgr-Comml)

Polypipe France SAS (1)
359 avenue du Douard, 13400, Aubagne, France
Tel.: (33) 442 82 40 50
Web Site: http://www.polypipe.fr
Plastic Tank Mfr
N.A.I.C.S.: 326122

GROUPE ETPO SA
Challenge 92 Building, 101 avenue Francois Arago, 92000, Nanterre, France
Tel.: (33) 240442700
Web Site: https://www.infe.fr
INFE—(EUR)
Sales Range: $200-249.9 Million
Real Estate Support Services
N.A.I.C.S.: 531390

GROUPE FNAC S.A.

AND PRIVATE COMPANIES

9 rue des Bateaux-Lavoirs, 94200, Ivry-sur-Seine, France
Tel.: (33) 978970970 FR
Web Site: https://www.fnacdarty.com
Year Founded: 1957
FNAC—(EUR)
Rev.: $8,579,106,411
Assets: $7,281,351,176
Liabilities: $5,638,139,434
Net Worth: $1,643,211,742
Earnings: ($30,325,923)
Emp.: 25,175
Fiscal Year-end: 12/31/22
Consumer Electronics, Books, Stationary, CDs & DVDs Retailer
N.A.I.C.S.: 459999
Jacques Veyrat *(Chm)*

Subsidiaries:

Fnac SA (1)
Zac Du Perou Mezzanine Est, Paris, 91300, Essonne, France
Tel.: (33) 169758000
Online Retailer
N.A.I.C.S.: 449210

Subsidiary (Domestic):

CODIREP SNC (2)
2 Rue Des Italiens, Paris, 75009, France
Tel.: (33) 155215793
Online Retailer
N.A.I.C.S.: 449210

Subsidiary (Non-US):

FNAC BRESIL SARL (2)
Avenida Coronel Fernando Ferreira Leite 1540 / Lj 205, Jardim California, Ribeirao Preto, Sao Paulo, Brazil
Tel.: (55) 16 3621 5174
Online Retailer
N.A.I.C.S.: 449210

FNAC SUISSE SA (2)
Route des Moulieres 10, 1242, Satigny, Switzerland
Tel.: (41) 22 306 41 41
Online Retailer
N.A.I.C.S.: 449210

France Billet S.A. (1)
27-35 rue Victor Hugo, 94200, Ivry-sur-Seine, France
Tel.: (33) 155215940
Web Site: https://www.francebillet.com
Event Booking Ticket Services
N.A.I.C.S.: 713990

GROUPE GARNIER

ZI De Tres Le Bois, BP 272, 22602, Loudeac, Cedex, France
Tel.: (33) 296661212 FR
Web Site: https://www.groupe-garnier.com
Year Founded: 1973
Truck Transportation Services
N.A.I.C.S.: 484110

Subsidiaries:

Tratel S.a.s (1)
Les Technodes, 78931, Guerville, Cedex, France
Tel.: (33) 134777800
Web Site: http://www.tratel.fr
Cement Transportation Services
N.A.I.C.S.: 484110

Subsidiary (Domestic):

Tratel Airvault (2)
28 Rue De L Aumonerie, 79600, Airvault, France
Tel.: (33) 549647125
Logistic Services
N.A.I.C.S.: 541614

Tratel Moult (2)
ZI De La Gare, 14370, Moult, France
Tel.: (33) 2 31 38 38 38
Logistics Consulting Servies
N.A.I.C.S.: 541614

Tratel Pessac (2)
162 Avenue de Haut Leveque, 33600, Pessac, France

Tel.: (33) 5 57 26 27 81
Logistics Consulting Servies
N.A.I.C.S.: 541614

GROUPE GORGE S.A.

19 rue du Quatre-Septembre, 75002, Paris, France
Tel.: (33) 144779477
Web Site: https://www.exail-technologies.com
Year Founded: 2009
EXA—(EUR)
Rev.: $191,731,547
Assets: $896,475,887
Liabilities: $671,958,689
Net Worth: $224,517,197
Earnings: ($7,303,470)
Emp.: 1,636
Fiscal Year-end: 12/31/22
Metal Cutting Machine Tool Mfr
N.A.I.C.S.: 333517
Raphael Gorge *(Chm & CEO)*

Subsidiaries:

CLF-Satrem (1)
ZI Les Garennes 1/3 rue Chappe, Yvelines, 78130, Les Mureaux, France
Tel.: (33) 1 30 90 41 80
Web Site: http://www.clf-satrem.com
Personal & Property Protection Services
N.A.I.C.S.: 561612

ECA S.A. (1)
Z I. Toulon Est 262 rue des Freres Lumiere, 83130, La Garde, France (65.2%)
Tel.: (33) 4 94 08 90 00
Web Site: http://www.ecagroup.com
Sales Range: $100-124.9 Million
Robotic & Military Equipment Mfr
N.A.I.C.S.: 333248
Jean Louis Sambarino *(Head-Simulation Dept)*

Faure QEI S.A. (1)
27 Blvd des Alpes, Meylan, 38920, Crolles, France
Tel.: (33) 4 76 92 81 00
Web Site: http://www.faure-qei.com
Laboratory Protection Services
N.A.I.C.S.: 561612

Nucleaction (1)
15 rue des Mathurins, 75009, Paris, France
Tel.: (33) 1 44 77 94 77
Web Site: http://www.nucleaction.com
Sales Range: $25-49.9 Million
Emp.: 150
Nuclear Environment Protection Services
N.A.I.C.S.: 561612
Raphael Gorge *(CEO)*

Subsidiary (Domestic):

Baumert (2)
50 Rue Principale, 67150, Schaeffersheim, France
Tel.: (33) 388646600
Web Site: http://www.baumert.fr
Sales Range: $25-49.9 Million
Emp.: 100
Industrial & Nuclear Environment Safety Materials Distr
N.A.I.C.S.: 423450
Olivier Schaal *(Mgr-Safety Glass Panels)*

NTC Nucleaction (2)
Livraindieres Industrial Area 10 ch Notre Dame de la Ronde, 28100, Dreux, Eure-et-Loir, France
Tel.: (33) 237648844
Web Site: http://www.ntc-nucleaction.fr
Industrial & Nuclear Environment Safety Materials Distr
N.A.I.C.S.: 423840

SCM-Verboom (2)
Livraindieres Industrial Area 10 ch Notre Dame de la Ronde, 28100, Dreux, Eure-et-Loir, France
Tel.: (33) 237648844
Web Site: http://www.nucleaction.com
Industrial & Nuclear Environment Safety Materials Distr
N.A.I.C.S.: 423450

Prodways Group SA (1)
30 rue de Gramont, 75002, Paris, France

Tel.: (33) 144779477
Web Site: https://www.prodways-group.com
Holding Company; Industrial Printing Services
N.A.I.C.S.: 551112
Raphael Gorge *(Chm & CEO)*

Subsidiary (US):

Solidscape, Inc. (2)
316 Daniel Webster Hwy, Merrimack, NH 03054
Tel.: (603) 429-9700
Web Site: http://www.solid-scape.com
Modelmaking Hardware & Software Mfr
N.A.I.C.S.: 332510
Alban d'Halluin *(CEO)*

GROUPE GRIMAUD LA CORBIERE SA

3 La Corbiere, Sevremoine, Roussay, 49450, France
Tel.: (33) 241703690
Web Site: http://www.grimaud.com
Sales Range: $200-249.9 Million
Emp.: 1,400
Holding Company
N.A.I.C.S.: 551112
Frederic Grimaud *(Dir-Pub)*

Subsidiaries:

Choice Genetics SAS (1)
Route de Bovel, BP 3, 35380, Paris, France
Tel.: (33) 2 99 92 07 00
Laboratory Testing Services
N.A.I.C.S.: 621511
Jodie O'Brien *(Mgr-Mktg)*

Subsidiary (Non-US):

Choice Genetics Argentina (2)
Parana 899 1 Piso CC 17, CP 2300, Rafaela, Santa Fe, Argentina
Tel.: (54) 3492 570199
Laboratory Testing Services
N.A.I.C.S.: 621511

Choice Genetics Brasil Ltda (2)
Rua Jorge Tibirica 63 Centro, Espirito Santo do Pinhal, Rio de Janeiro, 13990-000, Brazil
Tel.: (55) 193 661 99 95
Laboratory Testing Services
N.A.I.C.S.: 621511

Choice Genetics Canada inc. (2)
435 Boulevard Sainte-Anne Bureau 201, Joliette, J6E 5A1, QC, Canada
Tel.: (450) 756-9109
Laboratory Testing Services
N.A.I.C.S.: 621511

Choice Genetics Deutschland GmbH (2)
Aufm Halskamp 12, 49681, Berlin, Germany
Tel.: (49) 4474 8907 654
Laboratory Testing Services
N.A.I.C.S.: 621511

Choice Genetics Polska Sp z o.o. (2)
Ul Spoldzielcza 2h, 64-100, Leszno, Poland
Tel.: (48) 65 529 40 71
Laboratory Testing Services
N.A.I.C.S.: 621511

Choice Genetics Vietnam (2)
Ap 5 Tan Hung, Dong Phu, Binh Phuoc, Vietnam
Tel.: (84) 9 1925 1025
Laboratory Testing Services
N.A.I.C.S.: 621511

FILAVIE S.A.S (1)
20 La Corbiere, 49450, Roussay, France
Tel.: (33) 2 41 75 46 16
Web Site: http://www.filavie.com
Vaccines Mfr
N.A.I.C.S.: 325414
Dominique Fournier *(Dir-Site Publ)*

HUBBARD SAS (1)
Mauguerand, PO Box 169, Quintin, 22800, Le Foeil, France
Tel.: (33) 2 96 79 63 70
Web Site: http://www.hubbardbreeders.com
Poultry Breeding Services
N.A.I.C.S.: 311615

GROUPE GUILLIN SA

Frederic Fagnoul *(Mgr-R&D)*

Subsidiary (US):

HUBBARD LLC (2)
195 Main St, Walpole, NH 03608
Tel.: (603) 756-3311
Poultry Breeding Services
N.A.I.C.S.: 311615
Mark Barnes *(CEO)*

Newsham Choice Genetics (1)
1415 28th St Ste 400, West Des Moines, IA 50266
Tel.: (515) 225-9420
Web Site: http://www.choicegenetics.com
Sales Range: $25-49.9 Million
Emp.: 100
Pork Production Scientific Support Services
N.A.I.C.S.: 115210
Brent Mitchell *(COO)*

GROUPE GUILBAULT LTEE

435 rue Faraday, Quebec, G1N 4G6, QC, Canada
Tel.: (418) 681-5272
Web Site: http://www.groupeguilbault.com
Year Founded: 1929
Rev.: $94,230,022
Emp.: 850
Food Transportation Services
N.A.I.C.S.: 488490

GROUPE GUILLIN SA

Zone Industrielle Avenue du Marechal de Lattre de Tassigny, 25290, Ornans, France
Tel.: (33) 381402323
Web Site: https://www.groupeguillin.fr
Year Founded: 1972
ALGIL—(EUR)
Sales Range: $750-799.9 Million
Plastic Packaging Products Mfr
N.A.I.C.S.: 322220
Francois Guillin *(Chm)*

Subsidiaries:

Alphaform (1)
291 route des Pierrelles, 26240, Beausemblant, France
Tel.: (33) 4 75 03 79 00
Emp.: 175
Food Packaging Products Mfr
N.A.I.C.S.: 322220
Hitoshi Nakano *(Gen Mgr)*

Anis Opakowania Sp. z.o.o (1)
Ul Przemyslowa 3, 56-400, Olesnica, Poland
Tel.: (48) 71 399 21 11
Food Packaging Materials Distr
N.A.I.C.S.: 423840

Dynaplast SA (1)
rue Just Meisonasse, BP 128, 89600, Saint Florentin, France
Tel.: (33) 386438100
Sales Range: $50-74.9 Million
Emp.: 20
Food Packaging Products Mfr
N.A.I.C.S.: 322220
Olivier Vautrin *(Gen Mgr)*

Guillin Deutschland GmbH (1)
Ostring 57, 66740, Saarlouis, Germany
Tel.: (49) 68314877565
Plastic Packaging Product Distr
N.A.I.C.S.: 424130
Eve Feld Renard *(Mgr-Admin)*

Guillin Emballages (1)
Zone Industrielle, BP 89, 25290, Ornans, France
Tel.: (33) 381402300
Food Packaging Products Mfr
N.A.I.C.S.: 322220

Subsidiary (Non-US):

GPI UK (2)
Unit 6 - Merlin Way - North Weald Airfield, Epping, CM16 6HR, Essex, United Kingdom
Tel.: (44) 1992 524 439
Web Site: http://www.v1.groupeguillin.fr
Food Packaging Products Mfr

GROUPE GUILLIN SA

Groupe Guillin SA—(Continued)
N.A.I.C.S.: 322220

Guillin Espana SL (2)
C/ Asturias 4 - Pol Ind Salinas, 08830, Sant Boi de Llobregat, Barcelona, Spain
Tel.: (34) 93 652 46 34
Web Site: http://www.groupeguillin.fr
Food Packaging Products Mfr & Distr
N.A.I.C.S.: 322220

Guillin Portugal (2)
Poligono Industrial Parque Tejo En 10 Km 131 2, 2625-445, Forte da Casa, Portugal
Tel.: (351) 219580714
Emp.: 3
Plastic Packaging Products Mfr
N.A.I.C.S.: 326113

Guillin Italia Spa (1)
Via Bernini 6, Usmate Velate, 20865, Monza, MB, Italy
Tel.: (39) 0396014371
Plastic Packaging Product Distr
N.A.I.C.S.: 424130

Guillin Nederland B.V. (1)
Ampereweg 6, 3752 LR, Bunschoten, Netherlands
Tel.: (31) 334656262
Fruit & Vegetable Distr
N.A.I.C.S.: 424480

Guillin Polska Niepruszewo Sp. z o.o. (1)
Jodlowa 2, 64-320, Niepruszewo, Poland
Tel.: (48) 618940570
Plastic Packaging Product Distr
N.A.I.C.S.: 424130

Guillin Portugal, Unipessoal, Lda (1)
Rua do Rio Tejo N 1, Vila Nova, 2050-540, Caldas da Rainha, Portugal
Tel.: (351) 263101750
Plastic Packaging Product Distr
N.A.I.C.S.: 424130
Jose Carlos Maia (Sls Mgr)

Guillin Romania Srl. (1)
Str Soseaua Sibiului Nr 1, Sura Mica, 055270, Sibiu, Romania
Tel.: (40) 269577116
Plastic Packaging Products Mfr
N.A.I.C.S.: 326112

KIV Verpackungen GmbH (1)
Julius Pintsch Ring 20, 15517, Furstenwalde, Germany
Tel.: (49) 336136880
Web Site: http://www.kiv-kreis.de
Plastic Packaging Products Mfr
N.A.I.C.S.: 326112
Arie Kooijman (Dir-Ops)

Nespak Imballaggi SpA (1)
Via Damano 1, 48024, Massa Lombarda, RA, Italy
Tel.: (39) 0545979511
Plastic Packaging Products Mfr
N.A.I.C.S.: 326112
Abdus Salam (Gen Mgr)

Rescaset Concept (1)
2521 Route du tram, 38690, Colombe, France
Tel.: (33) 4 76 91 21 25
Web Site: http://www.groupeguillin.fr
Food Packaging Machinery Mfr
N.A.I.C.S.: 333993

SOCAMEL UK LIMITED (1)
Wessex House - 1 Harris Road, Calne, SN11 9PT, Wiltshire, United Kingdom
Tel.: (44) 1249 811 396
Sales Range: $50-74.9 Million
Emp.: 5
Institutional Catering Equipment Distr
N.A.I.C.S.: 423440
Vicky Soffe (Gen Mgr)

Sharpak Aylesham Ltd. (1)
Aylesham Industrial Estate, Aylesham, Dover, CT3 3EF, Kent, United Kingdom
Tel.: (44) 1304840581
Bakery Products Mfr
N.A.I.C.S.: 311821
Pop Florin (Mgr-IT)

Sharpak Bridgwater Limited (1)
Colley Lane Estate, Bridgwater, TA6 5YS, Somerset, United Kingdom
Tel.: (44) 3330068000
Packaging Equipment Mfr & Distr
N.A.I.C.S.: 333241
Jon Harrod (Fin Dir)

Sharpak Yate Ltd. (1)
Highway, Bristol, BS37 7AA, Yate, United Kingdom
Tel.: (44) 3330068000
Packaging Equipment Mfr & Distr
N.A.I.C.S.: 333241
Andrew Fisher (Mng Dir)

Socamel Deutschland GmbH (1)
Wittestrasse 30 K, 13509, Berlin, Germany
Tel.: (49) 3043572524
Web Site: http://www.socamel-speisenverteilsysteme.de
Kitchen Equipment Mfr & Distr
N.A.I.C.S.: 333241

Socamel Espana SL (1)
C Cal Pi de l Olla 40 42 ZAL II, 08820, El Prat de Llobregat, Barcelona, Spain
Tel.: (34) 931772400
Kitchen Equipment Mfr & Distr
N.A.I.C.S.: 333241
Michel Albea (Mng Dir)

Socamel Technologies (1)
Chemin Allivet 38 Renage, Rives, 38148, France
Tel.: (33) 4 76 91 21 21
Web Site: http://www.socamel.com
Sales Range: $50-74.9 Million
Emp.: 150
Catering Equipment Mfr & Distr
N.A.I.C.S.: 333241
Laurent Courneil (Mgr-Sls)

Thermoflex AG (1)
Route de Denges 34, 1027, Lonay, Switzerland
Tel.: (41) 218023772
Food Packaging Distr
N.A.I.C.S.: 424130
Philippe Besson (Owner)

Thiolat Packaging SA (1)
5 Rue Roger Dion, BP 1304, 41013, Blois, Cedex, France
Tel.: (33) 254903030
Web Site: http://www.thiolat.com
Food Packaging Products Mfr
N.A.I.C.S.: 311813

Thiolat SAS (1)
5 Rue Roger Dion, BP 1304, 41000, Blois, Cedex, Loir-et-Cher, France
Tel.: (33) 254903030
Web Site: http://www.thiolat.com
Sales Range: $25-49.9 Million
Folding Paperboard Boxes
N.A.I.C.S.: 322212
Marie-Pierre Tondereau (Dir-Supply Chain)

Veripack Embalajes SL (1)
Mogoda 26 64 Pol Ind Can Salvatella Barbera del Valles, 08210, Barcelona, Spain
Tel.: (34) 937292010
Plastic Food Containers Mfr
N.A.I.C.S.: 326199

GROUPE HAMELIN S.A.

9 rue Guyon de Guercheville, Herouville Saint-Clair, 14200, Caen, France
Tel.: (33) 2 31 46 37 37   FR
Web Site: http://www.hamelinbrands.com
Year Founded: 1864
Sales Range: $500-549.9 Million
Emp.: 2,200
Office & Educational Supplies Mfr
N.A.I.C.S.: 322230
Philippe Meunier (CFO)

Subsidiaries:

Canson Inc. (1)
21 Industrial Dr, South Hadley, MA 01075
Tel.: (413) 538-9250
Web Site: http://www.canson-infinity.com
Sales Range: $25-49.9 Million
Emp.: 100
Specialty Paper Mfr
N.A.I.C.S.: 322299

HAMELIN A/S (1)
Noglegardsvej 1, 3540, Lynge, Denmark
Tel.: (45) 48 16 50 00
Web Site: http://www.hamelin.dk
Office Supplies Mfr & Distr
N.A.I.C.S.: 322230

HAMELIN Brands Ltd (1)
Kings Warren Business Park, Red Lodge, IP28 8WG, Suffolk, United Kingdom
Tel.: (44) 1638 554500
Web Site: http://www.hamelinbrands.co.uk
Emp.: 50
Office Supplies Mfr & Distr
N.A.I.C.S.: 322230
Philip Beer (Mng Dir)

HAMELIN GmbH (1)
Robert-Hamelin Strasse 1, 31028, Gronau, Germany
Tel.: (49) 5182 901 0
Web Site: http://www.hamelin-paperbrands.com
Office Supplies Mfr & Distr
N.A.I.C.S.: 322230

HAMELIN Polska sp. z o.o. (1)
ul Ryzowa 49, 02-495, Warsaw, Poland
Tel.: (48) 22 589 51 11
Web Site: http://www.hamelinbrands.pl
Office Supplies Distr
N.A.I.C.S.: 424120

HAMELIN S.A.S. (1)
8 rue Leopold Sedar-Senghor, 14460, Colombelles, France
Tel.: (33) 2 14 40 62 00
Office Supplies Distr
N.A.I.C.S.: 424120

HAMELIN S.p.A. (1)
Via Fracastoro 7, 20128, Milan, Italy
Tel.: (39) 02 25 90 59 1
Office Supplies Distr
N.A.I.C.S.: 424120

HAMELIN b.v. (1)
Celciusweg 35, 5928, Venlo, Netherlands
Tel.: (31) 77 373 1551
Office Supplies Distr
N.A.I.C.S.: 424120

HAMELIN, Lda. (1)
Rua Torre 1591, 2715-311, Lisbon, Portugal
Tel.: (351) 21 192 2372
Office Supplies Distr
N.A.I.C.S.: 424120

Hamelin S.A. (1)
CTRA C-66 km 22 8, Flaca, 17463, Gerona, Spain
Tel.: (34) 972 48 82 00
Office Supplies Distr
N.A.I.C.S.: 424120

Hamelin b.v. (1)
Rue de la Technologie 1, 1082, Brussels, Belgium
Tel.: (32) 2 464 21 31
Office Supplies Distr
N.A.I.C.S.: 424120

GROUPE HOMMELL

48 Blvd Senard, 92210, Saint-Cloud, France
Tel.: (33) 147112000
Web Site: http://www.hommell-magazines.com
Sales Range: $25-49.9 Million
Emp.: 170
Periodical Publishing
N.A.I.C.S.: 513120
Michel Hommell (Mng Dir)

GROUPE INDUSPAC EMBALLAGE INC.

1805 50e Avenue, Lachine, H8T 3C8, QC, Canada
Tel.: (514) 636-7951
Web Site: http://www.IndusPac.com
Year Founded: 1977
Sales Range: $150-199.9 Million
Emp.: 1,000
Corrugated, Plastic & Film Packaging Mfr
N.A.I.C.S.: 322220
Paul Gaulin (Pres)

INTERNATIONAL PUBLIC

Subsidiaries:

Ivex Packaging LLC (1)
8100 S 77th Ave, Bridgeview, IL 60455
Tel.: (708) 728-8000
Web Site: http://www.ivexpackaging.com
Sales Range: $250-299.9 Million
Emp.: 800
Corrugated Packaging Mfr
N.A.I.C.S.: 322211

Subsidiary (Non-US):

Ivex Packaging Corporation (2)
930J Britannia Road East, Mississauga, L4W 5M7, ON, Canada
Tel.: (416) 259-8966
Web Site: http://www.ivexpackaginglc.com
Sales Range: $25-49.9 Million
Emp.: 80
Paper & Plastic Packaging Products Mfr
N.A.I.C.S.: 322211

GROUPE INDUSTRIEL MARCEL DASSAULT S.A.

9 rond point des Champs-Elysees Marcel Dassault, 75008, Paris, France
Tel.: (33) 1 53 76 93 00
Web Site: http://www.dassault.fr
Holding Company; Aeronautics, Advanced Digital Technology & Communication
N.A.I.C.S.: 551112
Serge Dassault (Chm)

Subsidiaries:

ARTCURIAL HOLDING SA (1)
7 rond-point des Champs-Elysees, 75008, Paris, France
Tel.: (33) 1 42 99 20 20
Web Site: http://www.artcurial.com
Emp.: 150
Holding Company
N.A.I.C.S.: 551112
Nicolas Orlowski (Chm & CEO)

Chateau Dassault SA (1)
Dassault Wine Estates, 33330, Saint-Emilion, France
Tel.: (33) 5 57 55 1000
Web Site: http://www.dassaultwineestates.com
Wine Mfr
N.A.I.C.S.: 312130

Dassault Aviation (1)
9 Rond-point des Champs-Elysees-Marcel Dassault, 75008, Paris, France (50.55%)
Tel.: (33) 153769300
Web Site: https://www.dassault-aviation.com
Rev: $8,900,069,003
Assets: $19,916,971,571
Liabilities: $13,406,707,559
Net Worth: $6,510,264,012
Earnings: $743,566,670
Emp.: 12,371
Fiscal Year-end: 12/31/2021
Military & Civil Aircraft Mfr
N.A.I.C.S.: 336411
Eric Trappier (Chm & CEO)

Subsidiary (Domestic):

Corse Composites Aeronautique (2)
Zone Industrielle Du Vazzio, PO Box 902, F 20700, Ajaccio, France
Tel.: (33) 495290400
Web Site: http://www.cca.fr
Sales Range: $25-49.9 Million
Emp.: 135
Aircraft Construction
N.A.I.C.S.: 336411

Dassault Assurances Courtage (2)
78 Quai Marcel Dassault, 92214, Saint Cloud, France
Tel.: (33) 147114000
Web Site: http://www.dassault-aviation.com
Sales Range: $800-899.9 Million
Emp.: 3,000
N.A.I.C.S.: 336411

Dassault Aviation (2)
78 Quai Marcel Dassault, 92214, Saint Cloud, France
Tel.: (33) 147114000

AND PRIVATE COMPANIES

GROUPE LACTALIS SA

Web Site: http://www.dassault_aviation.com
Emp.: 8,000
Aircraft Assembly
N.A.I.C.S.: 336411
Frederic Leboeuf *(VP-Falcon Operational Support)*

Subsidiary (Non-US):

Dassault Aircraft Services India Pvt. Ltd. (3)
Dassault House A-280 Defense Colony, New Delhi, 110 024, India
Tel.: (91) 112 465 24 65
Aircraft Parts Distr
N.A.I.C.S.: 423860

Plant (Domestic):

Dassault Aviation SA - Argonay Facility (3)
2105 Avenue Marcel Dassault, BP 32, 74371, Pringy, Cedex, France
Tel.: (33) 4 50 09 10 00
Aircraft Part Mfr
N.A.I.C.S.: 336413

Subsidiary (Non-US):

Dassault Falcon Middle East (3)
Dubai Airport Free Zone Building 5W - Block A Office 315, PO Box 293884, Dubai, United Arab Emirates
Tel.: (971) 4 299 39 50
Aircraft Parts Distr
N.A.I.C.S.: 423860

Dassault International do Brasil Ltda
Setor Comercial Quadra 1 no 30 - Bloco H Edificio Morro Vermelho 16, Andar, Brasilia, 70397-900, Brazil
Tel.: (55) 61 33 21 94 37
Aircraft Parts Distr
N.A.I.C.S.: 423860

Plant (Domestic):

Dassault Aviation Poitiers (2)
24 Ave Marcel Dassault Larnay, F 86580, Biard, France
Tel.: (33) 549376200
Web Site: http://www.dassaultaviation.fr
Sales Range: $25-49.9 Million
Emp.: 130
Aircraft Assembly
N.A.I.C.S.: 336411
Eric Trappier *(CEO)*

Dassault Aviation Saint-Cloud (2)
78 Quai Marcel Dassault, F 92214, Saint-Cloud, France
Tel.: (33) 147114000
Web Site: http://www.dassaultaviation.com
Sales Range: $700-749.9 Million
Emp.: 3,000
Aircraft Assembly
N.A.I.C.S.: 336411

Subsidiary (US):

Dassault Falcon Jet Corp. (2)
200 Riser Rd, Little Ferry, NJ 07643
Tel.: (201) 440-6700
Web Site: http://www.dassaultfalconjet.com
Emp.: 400
Sales, Charters & Maintenance of Business Jets
N.A.I.C.S.: 423860
Carlos Brana *(Sr VP-Teterboro)*

Subsidiary (Domestic):

Aero Precision & Repair Overhaul Company Inc. (3)
580 S Military Trl, Deerfield Beach, FL 33442-3011
Tel.: (954) 428-9500
Web Site: http://www.aero-precision.com
Sales Range: $25-49.9 Million
Emp.: 83
Aircraft Repair & Maintenance ServicesAircraft Repair & Maintenance Services
N.A.I.C.S.: 811310

Dassault Falcon Jet Corp. (3)
Teterboro Airport PO Box 2000, South Hackensack, NJ 07606-0620
Tel.: (201) 440-6700
Web Site: http://www.falconjet.com

Sales Range: $150-199.9 Million
Emp.: 400
Mfr, Sale & Service of Business Jets
N.A.I.C.S.: 423860
John Rosanvallon *(Pres & CEO)*

Subsidiary (Non-US):

Dassault Falcon Business Services (Beijing) Co., Ltd. (4)
Suite 8-D-2 of n 1 Building n 28 Tianzhu Road Tianzhu Airport, Economic Development Zone Shunyi, Beijing, China
Tel.: (86) 10 8042 7902
Web Site: http://www.dassaultfalcon.cn
Aircraft Parts Distr
N.A.I.C.S.: 423860

Dassault Falcon Jet do Brasil Ltda. (4)
Av Das Nacoes Unidas 12 551 17 Andar-Sala 1724 Edificio WTC, Sao Paulo, 04578, Brazil
Tel.: (55) 11 3443 7043
Aircraft Parts Distr
N.A.I.C.S.: 423860
Rodrigo Pesoa *(Sr Dir-Sls-Latin America)*

Subsidiary (Domestic):

Dassault Falcon Jet-Wilmington Corp. (3)
191 N Dupont Hwy, New Castle, DE 19720
Tel.: (302) 322-7000
Web Site: http://www.dassaultfalcon.com
Executive Aircraft Rental, Maintenance & Services
N.A.I.C.S.: 481211

Subsidiary (Domestic):

Dassault Falcon Service (2)
Aeroport Du Bourget 1445 Ave De l'Europe, F 93352, Le Bourget, Cedex, France **(100%)**
Tel.: (33) 149342020
Web Site: http://www.dassaultfalcon.com
Sales Range: $150-199.9 Million
Emp.: 530
Aircraft Services, Logistics & Corporate Travel Arrangements
N.A.I.C.S.: 336411
Giovanni Luciolli *(Mgr-Sls & Mktg-FalconCare Program-Western Hemisphere)*

Subsidiary (Domestic):

Falcon Training Centre (3)
Aeroport Du Bourget, 93352, Le Bourget, Cedex, France
Tel.: (33) 141691709
Sales Range: $25-49.9 Million
Aircraft Instruction
N.A.I.C.S.: 488119

Subsidiary (US):

Dassault Procurement Services (2)
900 Huyler St, Teterboro, NJ 07608
Tel.: (201) 261-4130
Web Site: http://www.dassdev.com
Sales Range: $25-49.9 Million
Emp.: 30
Procurement Services
N.A.I.C.S.: 423860
Patrick Dutertre *(Pres)*

Subsidiary (Domestic):

Midway Aircraft Instrument Corp. (3)
1419 N Rocky River Rd, Monroe, NC 28110
Tel.: (704) 993-2100
Web Site: http://www.midwayaircraft.com
Aircraft Repair & Maintenance Services
N.A.I.C.S.: 488190
Peter Rothwell *(Gen Counsel)*

Plant (Domestic):

Division Equipements Dassault (DED) (2)
78 Quai Marcel Dassault, 92552, Saint-Cloud, France
Tel.: (33) 147113539
Web Site: http://www.dassault-aviation.com
Aircraft Assembly
N.A.I.C.S.: 336411

Etablissement d'Argonay (2)
Ave Marcel Dassault, PO Box 32, F 74371, Pringy, France

Tel.: (33) 450091000
Aircraft Assembly
N.A.I.C.S.: 336411

Etablissement d'Istres (2)
Essais En Vol, 13804, Istres, France
Tel.: (33) 442567777
Web Site: http://www.dassaultaviation.com
Sales Range: $150-199.9 Million
Emp.: 800
Aircraft Assembly
N.A.I.C.S.: 336411

Etablissement de Martignas (2)
Avenue des Martyrs-de-la-Resistance, BP 38, F-33127, Martignas-sur-Jalle, France
Tel.: (33) 556978500
Web Site: http://www.martignas.org
Aircraft Assembly
N.A.I.C.S.: 336411

Etablissement de Merignac (2)
BP 24, F 33701, Merignac, Cedex, France
Tel.: (33) 556139000
Web Site: http://www.dassaultaviation.com
Sales Range: $350-399.9 Million
Emp.: 1,030
Aircraft Assembly
N.A.I.C.S.: 336411

Affiliate (Domestic):

Eurotradia International (2)
33 Ave Des Champs Elysees, 75008, Paris, France
Tel.: (33) 140762001
Web Site: http://www.eurotradia.fr
Sales Range: $25-49.9 Million
Provider of Aviation Services
N.A.I.C.S.: 488119

SECBAT-Breguet Atlantic (2)
78 quai Marcel Dassault, 92552, Saint-Cloud, Cedex 300, France **(36%)**
Tel.: (33) 147114000
Aircraft Mfr
N.A.I.C.S.: 336411

Subsidiary (Domestic):

SEPECAT (2)
Zone aeronautique Louis Breguet, BP 12, F-78140, Velizy-Villacoublay, France
Tel.: (33) 1 47 11 40 00
Aircraft Construction
N.A.I.C.S.: 336411

Sogitec Industries (2)
4 Rue Marcel Monge Immeuble Nobel, Suresnes, 92158, France
Tel.: (33) 141185700
Web Site: http://www.sogitec.fr
Sales Range: $25-49.9 Million
Emp.: 20
Aircraft Wholesale
N.A.I.C.S.: 441227

Groupe Le Figaro (1)
14 Boulevard Haussmann, 75009, Paris, France
Tel.: (33) 170373170
Web Site: http://www.lefigaro.fr
Sales Range: $650-699.9 Million
Emp.: 2,037
Newspaper Publishers
N.A.I.C.S.: 513110
Marc Feuillee *(CEO)*

Subsidiary (Domestic):

Figaro Classifieds S.A. (2)
14 Boulevard Haussmann, Paris, 75009, France
Tel.: (33) 176630300
Web Site: http://www.figaroclassifieds.fr
Internet Classified Advertising Services
N.A.I.C.S.: 541890
Thibaut Gemignani *(CEO & Dir-Publication)*

Subsidiary (Domestic):

Microcode SARL (3)
1 Rue Jacques Offenbach, Nice, 06000, France
Tel.: (33) 493555859
Software Programming Services
N.A.I.C.S.: 541511

Subsidiary (Non-US):

Seminus GmbH (3)

Pankgrafenstrasse 23, Berlin, 13125, Germany
Tel.: (49) 30 755 65 886
Web Site: http://www.seminus.de
Sales Range: $10-24.9 Million
Emp.: 10
Professional Database Training Services
N.A.I.C.S.: 611430
Jens Quilitzki *(CEO)*

Subsidiary (Domestic):

Viadeo SA (3)
14 Boulevard Haussman, 75009, Paris, France
Tel.: (33) 157087293
Web Site: http://www.viadeo.com
Social Network Website Operations
N.A.I.C.S.: 516210

Immobiliere Dassault SA (1)
9 rond-point des Champs-Elysees, 75008, Paris, France
Tel.: (33) 153769300
Web Site: http://www.immobiliere-dassault.com
Sales Range: $125-149.9 Million
Real Estate Support Services
N.A.I.C.S.: 531390

GROUPE IRD SA
40 rue Eugene Jacquet, BP 52004, 59700, Marcq-en-Baroeul, France
Tel.: (33) 359302004
Web Site: http://www.groupeird.fr
DP—(EUR)
Sales Range: $10-24.9 Million
Financial Investment Services
N.A.I.C.S.: 523940
Marc Verly *(CEO)*

GROUPE LACASSE INC.
99 Rue Saint Pierre, Saint-Pie, J0H 1W0, QC, Canada
Tel.: (450) 772-2495   QC
Web Site: http://www.groupelacasse.com
Year Founded: 1956
Sales Range: $150-199.9 Million
Emp.: 200
Office Furniture Designer, Mfr & Whslr
N.A.I.C.S.: 337211
Kevin Glynn *(Exec VP)*

Subsidiaries:

Via, Inc. (1)
205 Vista Blvd, Sparks, NV 89434
Tel.: (775) 331-6001
Web Site: http://www.viaseating.com
Wood Office Furniture Mfr
N.A.I.C.S.: 337211
Chas Hepler *(Pres & CEO)*

GROUPE LACTALIS SA
10-20 Rue Adolphe Beck, 53089, Laval, France
Tel.: (33) 243594259   FR
Web Site: https://www.lactalis.com
Year Founded: 1933
Sales Range: $15-24.9 Billion
Emp.: 80,000
Milk, Cheese & Dairy Products Mfr
N.A.I.C.S.: 311511

Subsidiaries:

Albalact S.A. (1)
DN 1 Km 392 600 comuna GALDA DE JOS sat OIEJDEA, 517293, Alba Iulia, Romania
Tel.: (40) 258846980
Web Site: http://www.albalact.ro
Dairy Products Mfr
N.A.I.C.S.: 112120
Cristina Miclea *(Mktg Dir)*

Aspen Nutritionals (Pty) Ltd (1)
20 Spanner Road, Boksburg, 1665, Gauteng, South Africa
Tel.: (27) 105958751
Infant Nutritional Products Mfr
N.A.I.C.S.: 311230

DUKAT mljecna industrija d.d. (1)

GROUPE LACTALIS SA

Groupe Lactalis SA—(Continued)

Marijana Cavica 9, 10 000, Zagreb, Croatia
Tel.: (385) 12392222
Web Site: http://www.dukat.hr
Sales Range: $350-399.9 Million
Emp.: 2,300
Milk Producer
N.A.I.C.S.: 112120
Daniel Marie Jaouen (Chm-Supervisory Bd)

GRUPO LACTALIS IBERIA S.A. (1)
C T M Edificio de Oficinas Planta 7a Ctra
Villaverde a Vallecas, 28053, Madrid, Spain
Tel.: (34) 915079697
Dairy Products Distr
N.A.I.C.S.: 424490

Gruppo Lactalis Italia S.p.A. (1)
Via Togliatti 8, 20066, Melzo, MI, Italy
Tel.: (39) 02 433 56 111
Web Site:
  http://www.gruppolactalisitalia.com
Sales Range: $1-4.9 Billion
Emp.: 3,100
Holding Company
N.A.I.C.S.: 551112
Pamela Cardona (Mgr-Internal & External Rels)

Subsidiary (Domestic):

Egidio Galbani SpA (2)
Via Flavio Gioia 8, 20149, Milan, Italy
Tel.: (39) 02 43356 111
Web Site: http://www.galbani.it
Cheese Mfr
N.A.I.C.S.: 311513

LACTALIS DEUTSCHLAND GmbH (1)
Am Yachthafen 2, 77694, Kehl, Germany
Tel.: (49) 785194380
Web Site: http://www.lactalis.de
Dairy Products Distr
N.A.I.C.S.: 424490

LACTALIS EUROPE DU NORD S.A. (1)
Bastion Tower Place du Champ de Mars N 5 bte 20, 1050, Brussels, Belgium
Tel.: (32) 22110920
Dairy Products Distr
N.A.I.C.S.: 424490

LACTALIS HONGRIE, s.r.o. (1)
Forgach u 9/b, 1139, Budapest, Hungary
Tel.: (36) 13230909
Dairy Products Distr
N.A.I.C.S.: 424490

LACTALIS PORTUGAL, Lda (1)
Rua de Pe de Mouro 36 Linho, 2714-508, Sintra, Portugal
Tel.: (351) 214467670
Dairy Products Distr
N.A.I.C.S.: 424490

LACTALIS UNITED KINGDOM Ltd (1)
2nd Floor 3 Princess Way, Redhill, RH1 1QG, Surrey, United Kingdom
Tel.: (44) 1737783300
Web Site: http://www.lactalis.co.uk
Dairy Products Distr
N.A.I.C.S.: 424490

LACTALIS-ALBA S.R.L. (1)
str Stefan cel Mare 133, 3000, Soroca, Moldova
Tel.: (373) 69959494
Web Site: http://www.lactalis-alba.md
Dairy Products Distr
N.A.I.C.S.: 424490

LACTALIS-UKRAINE, CJSC (1)
Estonska str 120, Kiev, 03062, Ukraine
Tel.: (380) 445902868
Web Site: http://www.lactalis.com.ua
Dairy Products Distr
N.A.I.C.S.: 424430

Lactalis International Snc (1)
16 avenue Jean Jaures, 94600, Choisy-le-Roi, France
Tel.: (33) 149785600
Web Site: http://www.lactalis-international.com
Dairy Products Distr
N.A.I.C.S.: 424430
Catherine Leporini (Dir-Export Mktg)

Lactalis Luxembourg SENC (1)
BP 16, 6101, Luxembourg, Luxembourg
Tel.: (352) 787171
Dairy Products Distr
N.A.I.C.S.: 424490

Lactalis McLelland (1)
2nd Floor 3 Princess Way, Redhill, RH1 1QG, Surrey, United Kingdom
Tel.: (44) 1415522962
Web Site: http://www.mclelland.co.uk
Sales Range: $25-49.9 Million
Emp.: 30
Cheese Mfr
N.A.I.C.S.: 311513

Lactalis Polska. Sp. z o.o. (1)
Ul Olkuska 7, 02-604, Warsaw, Poland
Tel.: (48) 223760800
Web Site: http://www.lactalis.pl
Dairy Products Distr
N.A.I.C.S.: 424490

Nestle Manufacturing (Malaysia) Sdn. Bhd. (1)
Lot 3857 - 3862 Jalan Perusahaan 4, Kawasan Perindustrian Chembong Rembau, 71300, Negeri Sembilan, Malaysia
Tel.: (60) 37965 6000
Web Site: http://www.nestle.com.my
Roasted Coffee & Other Beverages Mfr
N.A.I.C.S.: 311920

Plant (Domestic):

Nestle Manufacturing (Malaysia) Sdn. Bhd. - Shah Alam Complex Factory (2)
Jalan Playar 15/1, PO Box 7010, Shah Alam, 40700, Selangor, Malaysia
Tel.: (60) 3 5522 5600
Dairy Products Mfr
N.A.I.C.S.: 311514

Nuova Castelli Spa (1)
Via Tancredi Galimberti 4, Reggio Emilia, 42100, Italy
Tel.: (39) 0522368311
Web Site: http://www.castelligroup.com
Cheese Mfr & Distr
N.A.I.C.S.: 311513

Subsidiary (Non-US):

Castelli UK Ltd (2)
Unit E Great Hollanden Business Centre Mill Lane, Underriver, Sevenoaks, TN15 0SQ, Kent, United Kingdom
Tel.: (44) 1732 835446
Web Site: http://www.castelli-uk.com
Cheese Mfr & Distr
N.A.I.C.S.: 311513

Parmalat S.p.A. (1)
Via delle Nazioni Unite 4, 43044, Collecchio, Parma, Italy (83.3%)
Tel.: (39) 0521808367
Web Site: http://www.parmalat.com
Rev.: $8,083,039,494
Assets: $6,237,137,234
Liabilities: $2,377,871,886
Net Worth: $3,859,265,348
Earnings: $124,098,296
Emp.: 26,234
Fiscal Year-end: 12/31/2017
Milk, Dairy Products & Fruit Drinks Mfr
N.A.I.C.S.: 311511
Paolo Tanghetti (Dir-HR)

Holding (US):

Lactalis American Group, Inc. (2)
2376 S Park Ave, Buffalo, NY 14220 (100%)
Tel.: (716) 823-6262
Web Site:
  http://www.lactalisamericangroup.com
Sales Range: $900-999.9 Million
Emp.: 300
Cheese Mfr
N.A.I.C.S.: 311513
John Zielinski (VP-Fin)

Subsidiary (Domestic):

Karoun Dairies, LLC (3)
13023 Arroyo St, San Fernando, CA 91340
Tel.: (818) 767-7000
Web Site: http://www.karouncheese.com

Dairy Farming, Milk Production & Dairy Products Mfr & Whslr
N.A.I.C.S.: 112120

Lactalis Deli, Inc. (3)
77 Water St Mezzanine, New York, NY 10005 (100%)
Tel.: (212) 758-6666
Sales Range: $25-49.9 Million
Emp.: 40
Cheese Mfr & Exporter
N.A.I.C.S.: 311513

Subsidiary (Non-US):

Lactalis Canada Inc. (2)
405 The West Mall 10th Floor, Toronto, M9C 5J1, ON, Canada (100%)
Tel.: (416) 626-1973
Web Site: http://www.parmalat.ca
Sales Range: $1-4.9 Billion
Emp.: 2,974
Producer & Marketer of Dairy Products
N.A.I.C.S.: 311511

Subsidiary (Domestic):

Ultima Foods Inc. (3)
2177 Blvd Fernand Lafontaine, Longueuil, J4G 2V2, QC, Canada
Tel.: (450) 651-3737
Web Site: http://www.ultimayog.ca
Sales Range: $150-199.9 Million
Dairy Products Mfr
N.A.I.C.S.: 311511
Martin Tarent (Pres & CEO)

Subsidiary (Non-US):

Parmalat Australia Ltd. (2)
Level 5 35 Boundary St, Brisbane, 4101, QLD, Australia (100%)
Tel.: (61) 738400100
Web Site: http://www.parmalat.com.au
Sales Range: $900-999.9 Million
Emp.: 1,500
Milk & Dairy Products Mfr & Distr
N.A.I.C.S.: 311511
B.R. Jardine (Mgr-Legal-Australia/Asia)

Affiliate (Domestic):

Gold Coast Milk Pty. Ltd. (3)
Corner Pine Ridge Road And Brisbane Road, PO Box 530, Labrador, Southport, 4215, QLD, Australia (40%)
Tel.: (61) 755940288
Web Site: http://www.norco.com.au
Emp.: 200
Processing & Distribution of Milk & Ice Cream
N.A.I.C.S.: 311520
Andrew Byns (Gen Mgr)

Subsidiary (Domestic):

Harvey Fresh (1994) Ltd. (3)
Lot 4 Third Street, Harvey, 6220, WA, Australia
Tel.: (61) 897290600
Web Site: http://www.harveyfresh.com.au
Sales Range: $150-199.9 Million
Emp.: 250
Beverages Mfr
N.A.I.C.S.: 311411
Kevin Sorgiovanni (Mgr)

Affiliate (Domestic):

Swan Hill Milk Distributors Pty. Ltd. (3)
93 Bannister Street, PO Box 452, Bendigo, 3550, VIC, Australia
Tel.: (61) 354450200
N.A.I.C.S.: 311511

Subsidiary (Non-US):

Parmalat South Africa (Pty) Ltd. (2)
Strand Road, 7600, Stellenbosch, South Africa (100%)
Tel.: (27) 218091400
Web Site: http://www.parmalat.co.za
Sales Range: $450-499.9 Million
Emp.: 1,788
Producer & Distr of Cheese, Yogurt & Fruit Drinks
N.A.I.C.S.: 311513
Louise Cooke (CEO)

Stonyfield Farm, Inc. (1)

INTERNATIONAL PUBLIC

10 Burton Dr, Londonderry, NH 03053
Tel.: (603) 437-4040
Web Site: http://www.stonyfield.com
Organic Yogurts & Dairy Products Mfr
N.A.I.C.S.: 311520
Rolf Carlson (VP-Sourcing & Product Dev)

GROUPE LAGASSE INC.
455 rue King Ouest Ste 610, Sherbrooke, J1H 6E9, QC, Canada
Tel.: (819) 569-3085
Web Site:
  http://www.groupelagasse.com
Holding Company
N.A.I.C.S.: 551112
Louis Lagasse (Chm & CEO)

Subsidiaries:

SR Telecom & Co. S.E.C. (1)
8150 Trans Canada Hwy, Montreal, H4S 1M5, QC, Canada
Tel.: (514) 335-1210
Web Site: http://www.srtelecom.com
Sales Range: $75-99.9 Million
Emp.: 588
Wireless Access Technology Mfr
N.A.I.C.S.: 334220

GROUPE LEBEL INC.
54 rue Amyot, Riviere-du-Loup, G5R 3E9, QC, Canada
Tel.: (418) 867-1695
Web Site: https://groupelebel.com
Paper & Forest Products Design & Mfr
N.A.I.C.S.: 333243

GROUPE LEGRIS INDUSTRIES
56 rue des Colonies, 1000, Brussels, Belgium
Tel.: (32) 22906000   FR
Web Site: http://www.legris-industries.com
Year Founded: 1986
Rev.: $244,129,480
Assets: $440,552,924
Liabilities: $363,842,514
Net Worth: $76,710,410
Earnings: ($12,766,404)
Emp.: 1,383
Fiscal Year-end: 12/31/19
Holding Company; Automation Machinery Manufacturing
N.A.I.C.S.: 551112
Pierre-Yves Legris (Chm-Supervisory Bd)

Subsidiaries:

Clextral SAS (1)
1 rue du Colonel Riez, 42700, Firminy, France
Tel.: (33) 477403131
Web Site: http://www.clextral.com
Sales Range: $50-74.9 Million
Service Industry Systems & Equipment Mfr
N.A.I.C.S.: 333310

Subsidiary (US):

Clextral Inc. (2)
14450 Carlson Cir, Tampa, FL 33626 (100%)
Tel.: (813) 854-4434
Sales Range: $25-49.9 Million
Emp.: 20
Twin Screw Extrusion Systems & Equipment Mfr
N.A.I.C.S.: 333310

Division (Domestic):

DKM (2)
1 rue du Colonel Riez, BP 10, 42700, Firminy, France
Tel.: (33) 477403143
Web Site: http://www.dkm-pumps.com
Sales Range: $25-49.9 Million
Emp.: 150
Food-Processing, Chemical, Petrochemical & Nuclear-Power Industry Dosing Pump Mfr
N.A.I.C.S.: 333914

Keller HCW GmbH (1)

AND PRIVATE COMPANIES

Carl-Keller-Strasse 2-10, 49479, Ibbenburen, Germany
Tel.: (49) 5451850
Web Site: http://www.keller.de
Sales Range: $150-199.9 Million
Emp.: 400
Building Material Industrial Plant & Manufacturing Equipment Design, Construction & Installation Services
N.A.I.C.S.: 236210
Jean-Michel Strauss *(CEO, Mng Dir & Member-Mgmt Bd)*

Subsidiary (Non-US):

Morando S.R.L. **(2)**
Strada Rilate 22, 14100, Asti, Italy
Tel.: (39) 0141417311
Web Site: http://www.morando.ws
Sales Range: $50-74.9 Million
Emp.: 100
Industrial Machinery & Equipment Whslr
N.A.I.C.S.: 423830

GROUPE LIMAGRAIN HOLDING SA

Biopole Clermont-Limagne Rue Henri Mondor, 63360, Saint-Beauzire, France
Tel.: (33) 473634000 **FR**
Web Site: http://www.limagrain.com
Year Founded: 1942
Sales Range: $1-4.9 Billion
Emp.: 6,000
Seed Production & Research Services
N.A.I.C.S.: 111422
Emmanuel Rougier *(CEO & VP-Garden Products)*

Subsidiaries:

AgriGold **(1)**
5381 Akin Rd, Saint Francisville, IL 62460-9989
Tel.: (618) 943-5776
Web Site: http://www.agrigold.com
Sales Range: $50-74.9 Million
Emp.: 135
Corn Seeds
N.A.I.C.S.: 336390

Auvergne Creations **(1)**
Rue Limagrain, PO Box 1, Chappes, 63720, France **(100%)**
Tel.: (33) 473634000
Web Site: http://www.limagrain.com
Sales Range: $700-749.9 Million
Emp.: 2,672
Agricultural Services
N.A.I.C.S.: 111998
Daniel Cheron *(Mng Dir)*

Ble Or **(1)**
2eme Avenue Zamin, 59160, Lomme, France
Tel.: (33) 320099009
Sales Range: $150-199.9 Million
Emp.: 500
Frozen Dough, Bread, Cakes & Farmhouse Bread Mfr
N.A.I.C.S.: 311812
Gilles Guerlet *(Gen Mgr)*

CNOS Vilmorin Polska Sp zoo **(1)**
Ul Kopanina 28 32, 60951, Poznan, Poland **(100%)**
Tel.: (48) 618305751
Web Site: http://www.cnos-vilmorin.pl
Sales Range: $10-24.9 Million
Emp.: 42
Marketer of Vegetable & Flower Seeds for Home Gardeners
N.A.I.C.S.: 111219

Cave Saint-Verny **(1)**
2 Route D Issoire, BP 2, Veyre-Monton, 63960, France
Tel.: (33) 473696011
Web Site: http://www.saint-verny.com
Sales Range: $25-49.9 Million
Emp.: 13
Harvesting, Processing, Packaging & Marketing in the Wine Sector
N.A.I.C.S.: 445320
Jean Paul Berthoumieu *(Gen Mgr)*

Cooperative Limagrain **(1)**
Rue Limagrain, BP 1, 63720, Chappes, France **(100%)**
Tel.: (33) 473634000
Web Site: http://www.limagrain.com
Sales Range: $75-99.9 Million
Emp.: 300
Seed & Grain Production
N.A.I.C.S.: 111199

G.E.I.E. A.I.G.L.E. **(1)**
BP 1, F 63720, Chappes, France
Tel.: (33) 473634154
Sales Range: $50-74.9 Million
Emp.: 2
Provider of Member Purchasing Services
N.A.I.C.S.: 522299

G.E.I.E. Nickerson International Research **(1)**
Ruerue Henri Mondor, BP 1, 63720, Saint-Beauzire, France **(100%)**
Tel.: (33) 473634000
Web Site: http://www.limagrain.com
Sales Range: $25-49.9 Million
Emp.: 136
Researcher in Cereals & Winter Rape Seed
N.A.I.C.S.: 541715
Daniel Cheron *(Gen Mgr)*

Gene Shears **(1)**
Building 5 Suite 1 105 Delhi Rd, North Ryde, 2113, NSW, Australia
Tel.: (61) 298788200
Sales Range: $25-49.9 Million
Emp.: 8
Scientific Research & Development
N.A.I.C.S.: 541715

Groupe Limagrain Holding **(1)**
Biopoe Clermont-Limagne Rue Henri Mondor, 63360, Saint-Beauzire, France **(100%)**
Tel.: (33) 473634000
Web Site: http://www.limagrain.com
Sales Range: $75-99.9 Million
Emp.: 200
Financial Services
N.A.I.C.S.: 551112
Jean-Yves Foucault *(Pres)*

Groupe Limagrain, Paris Office **(1)**
1 Rue Edouard Colonne, 75001, Paris, France **(100%)**
Tel.: (33) 145088408
Sales Range: $700-749.9 Million
Emp.: 3,284
Seed Research & Development
N.A.I.C.S.: 541715

Limagrain A/S **(1)**
Marsalle 111, 8700, Horsens, Denmark
Tel.: (45) 7589 2200
Web Site: http://www.limagrain.dk
Grain Seed Production Services
N.A.I.C.S.: 111199

Limagrain Argentina S.A. **(1)**
Rue Basavilbaso 1350 Etage 9 11, 1006, Buenos Aires, Argentina
Tel.: (54) 11 4515 1213
Seed Production Services
N.A.I.C.S.: 111130

Limagrain Belgium NV **(1)**
Kaaistaat 5, 8581, Avelgem, Belgium
Tel.: (32) 55 39 02 21
Seed Production Services
N.A.I.C.S.: 111130

Limagrain Bulgaria Ltd **(1)**
103 Jeyms Boucher Boulvd Fl 2 Office 6, 1407, Sofia, Bulgaria
Tel.: (359) 2 962 43 91
Seed Production Services
N.A.I.C.S.: 111130

Limagrain Central Europe Cereals, s.r.o. **(1)**
Sazecska 8, 10825, Prague, Czech Republic
Tel.: (420) 266 021 593
Web Site: http://www.odrudynickerson.cz
Seed Production Services
N.A.I.C.S.: 111130

Limagrain Central Europe S.E. **(1)**
Biopole Clermont-Limagne, 63360, Saint-Beauzire, France
Tel.: (33) 4 73 64 70 00
Web Site: http://www.limagraincentraleurope.com
Seed Production Services
N.A.I.C.S.: 111130

Limagrain Cereal Seeds LLC **(1)**
2040 SE Frontage Rd, Fort Collins, CO 80525
Tel.: (970) 498-2200
Web Site: http://www.limagraincerealseeds.com
Emp.: 12
Seed Production Services
N.A.I.C.S.: 111130
Frank Curtis *(Exec VP)*

Limagrain Cereales Ingredients **(1)**
Zone Agro Industrielle, PO Box 20, St Ignat, Ennezat, 63720, France **(100%)**
Tel.: (33) 473634444
Web Site: http://www.lci.limagrain.com
Sales Range: $50-74.9 Million
Emp.: 178
Enhancement & Processing of Agricultural Products
N.A.I.C.S.: 325320

Limagrain Ceska republika, s.r.o. **(1)**
Pardubuka 1197, 76312, Vizovice, Czech Republic
Tel.: (420) 57 74 54 054
Web Site: http://www.lgc.cz
Emp.: 12
Seed Production Services
N.A.I.C.S.: 111130
Ondrej Takac *(Country Mgr)*

Limagrain Europe **(1)**
Ferme De l Etang, 77390, Verneuil l'Etang, France **(100%)**
Tel.: (33) 164424141
Web Site: http://www.limagrain.com
Sales Range: $75-99.9 Million
Emp.: 500
Production & Marketing of Corn Seeds
N.A.I.C.S.: 111150

Joint Venture (Domestic):

Biogemma S.A.S. **(2)**
5 rue Saint-Germain l'Auxerrois, 75001, Paris, France
Tel.: (33) 155349400
Web Site: http://www.biogemma.com
Emp.: 80
Agricultural Seed Genetic Research & Development
N.A.I.C.S.: 541715

Limagrain GMBH **(1)**
Am Griewenkamp 2, Edemissen, 31234, Germany **(100%)**
Tel.: (49) 517698910
Web Site: http://www.lgseeds.de
Sales Range: $25-49.9 Million
Emp.: 82
Marketing of Field & Lawn Seeds
N.A.I.C.S.: 561730
Tanga Naunann *(Mgr-Personnel)*

Limagrain Genetics Grandes Cultures S.A. **(1)**
BP 1, 63720, Chappes, France **(100%)**
Tel.: (33) 473634000
Sales Range: $25-49.9 Million
Emp.: 45
Provider of Research in Field Crop Species-Corn, Sunflowers, Rapeseed, Forage & Lawn Seeds
N.A.I.C.S.: 541715
Daniel Cheron *(CEO)*

Limagrain Genetics International **(1)**
CS 50005 Beazire, BP 1, Gerzat, 63720, France
Tel.: (33) 473634000
Web Site: http://www.limagrain.com
Sales Range: $10-24.9 Million
Emp.: 38
Management & Organization of Limagrain Agro-Genetics
N.A.I.C.S.: 621511
Cheron Danniel *(Gen Mgr)*

Limagrain Iberica S.A. **(1)**
Ctra Pamplona-Huesca Km 12, ELORZ, 31470, Navarra, Spain
Tel.: (34) 902 39 40 50
Web Site: http://www.limagrain.es
Seed Production Services
N.A.I.C.S.: 111130

Limagrain Italia SpA **(1)**
Via frescarolo 115, Busseto, 43011, Italy
Web Site: http://www.limagrain.com
Sales Range: $75-99.9 Million
Emp.: 114
Marketing of Field Seeds
N.A.I.C.S.: 424910

Limagrain Magyarorszag Kft. **(1)**
Gyar ut 2, PF 325, 2040, Budaors, Hungary
Tel.: (36) 23 418 104
Web Site: http://www.limagrain.hu
Seed Production Services
N.A.I.C.S.: 111130

Limagrain Moldova Srl **(1)**
bd Stefan cel mare 162, 2004, Chisinau, Moldova
Tel.: (373) 322 21 00 49
Web Site: http://www.limagrain.md
Seed Production Services
N.A.I.C.S.: 111130

Limagrain Nederland BV **(1)**
Van der Haveweg 2, Postbus 1, 4411 RB, Rilland, Netherlands **(100%)**
Tel.: (31) 113557100
Web Site: http://www.lgseeds.nl
Sales Range: $25-49.9 Million
Emp.: 50
Field & Lawn Seed Services
N.A.I.C.S.: 561730
Huub Beelen *(Gen Mgr)*

Limagrain Polska Sp. z o.o. **(1)**
ul Ks P Wawrzyniaka 2, 62052, Komorniki, Poland
Tel.: (48) 616571985
Web Site: http://www.limagrain.pl
Emp.: 21
Seed Production Services
N.A.I.C.S.: 111130
Mariusz Koczara *(Mng Dir)*

Limagrain RU LLC **(1)**
Str Jankowski d 169 st Novokuznechnaya d40, 350015, Krasnodar, Russia
Tel.: (7) 861 255 59 96
Web Site: http://www.lgseeds.ru
Seed Production Services
N.A.I.C.S.: 111199

Limagrain Slovensko, s.r.o. **(1)**
M Razusa 29, 984 01, Lucenec, Slovakia
Tel.: (421) 47 451 2160
Web Site: http://www.lgseeds.sk
Emp.: 10
Seed Production Services
N.A.I.C.S.: 111130
Alien Barbarian *(Gen Mgr)*

Limagrain UK Ltd **(1)**
Rothwell, Lincoln, LN7 6DT, United Kingdom
Tel.: (44) 14 72 37 14 71
Web Site: http://www.limagrain.co.uk
Seed Production Services
N.A.I.C.S.: 111130

Limagrain Ukraine LLC **(1)**
55 Turgenivska Str 2nd floor, 04050, Kiev, Ukraine
Tel.: (380) 44 484 67 76
Web Site: http://www.limagrain.ua
Seed Production Services
N.A.I.C.S.: 111130

Maicentre **(1)**
PO Box 63200, 63720, Chappes, France **(100%)**
Tel.: (33) 473634035
Sales Range: $25-49.9 Million
Emp.: 188
Promotion, Growing & Marketing of Industrial & Consumption Quality Corn
N.A.I.C.S.: 111150

Pain Jacquet **(1)**
5 rue Pauling Techniparc, 91240, Saint-Michel-sur-Orge, France **(100%)**
Tel.: (33) 1 69 46 83 00
Web Site: http://www.jacquet.com
Sales Range: $25-49.9 Million
Production & Sales of Commercial Bakery Breads & Rolls
N.A.I.C.S.: 311812

Subsidiary (Non-US):

Jacquet Milcamps Benelux **(2)**
77 Rue de Lusambo, 1190, Brussels, Belgium

GROUPE LIMAGRAIN HOLDING SA

Groupe Limagrain Holding SA—(Continued)
Tel.: (32) 2 332 15 62
Web Site: http://www.milcamps.be
Sales Range: $25-49.9 Million
Emp.: 65
Waffles Mfr & Distr
N.A.I.C.S.: 311812
Renno Geanmarie (Gen Mgr)

Progalim (1)
Les Vionots, 63720, Chappes,
France **(100%)**
Tel.: (33) 473634200
Web Site: http://www.domaine-de-limagne.com
Sales Range: $25-49.9 Million
Emp.: 73
Production, Processing & Marketing of Products Derived From Poultry, Ducks & Other Animals
N.A.I.C.S.: 445240

Selia (1)
Rue Limagrain, 63720, Chappes,
France **(100%)**
Tel.: (33) 473634000
Web Site: http://www.limigrain.com
Sales Range: $25-49.9 Million
Emp.: 200
Animal Product Production Services
N.A.I.C.S.: 115210

Semillas Limagrain de Chile Ltda. (1)
Panamericana Sur Km 65 Casilla 20, San Francisco de Mostazal, Santiago,
Chile **(100%)**
Tel.: (56) 72491496
Sales Range: $25-49.9 Million
Emp.: 94
Provider of Seed Research & Services
N.A.I.C.S.: 541715

Senasa (1)
Cr De Jaca S A 12 Km, Elorz, 31470,
Spain **(100%)**
Tel.: (34) 902394050
Sales Range: $25-49.9 Million
Emp.: 100
Provider of Research, Production & Marketing of Seeds
N.A.I.C.S.: 541715

Valgrain (1)
Zone d'activite, 26740, Les Tourettes,
France **(100%)**
Tel.: (33) 475902300
Web Site: http://www.valgrain.com
Sales Range: $10-24.9 Million
Emp.: 30
Production of Corn Seeds
N.A.I.C.S.: 111150
Prevost Michel (Mgr)

Vilmorin & Cie SA (1)
4 Quai de La Megisserie, F-75001, Paris,
France **(95.7%)**
Tel.: (33) 473634485
Web Site: http://www.vilmorin.info
Rev.: $2,044,463,630
Assets: $3,889,704,295
Liabilities: $2,316,101,878
Net Worth: $1,573,602,417
Earnings: $102,093,676
Emp.: 7,382
Fiscal Year-end: 06/30/2023
Vegetable & Field Crop Seed Producer & Distr
N.A.I.C.S.: 111998
Daniel Jacquemond (Co-CEO)

Joint Venture (US):

AgReliant Genetics LLC (2)
1122 E 169th St, Westfield, IN 46074-9601
Tel.: (317) 896-5552
Web Site: https://www.agreliantgenetics.com
Sales Range: $10-24.9 Million
Emp.: 50
Seed Producer & Distr; Joint Venture of Groupe Limagrain (50%) & KWS SAAT AG (50%)
N.A.I.C.S.: 111998
Peter Lynch (VP-Res)

Division (Domestic):

AgReliant Genetics LLC - Lebanon (3)
4640 E State Rd 32, Lebanon, IN 46052-9299
Tel.: (765) 482-9833
Research Into Corn Soybean & Canola Seeds
N.A.I.C.S.: 424910
Craig Newman (Pres & CEO)

Subsidiary (Domestic):

LG Seeds (3)
1122 E 169th St, Westfield, IN 46074
Tel.: (317) 896-0662
Web Site: https://www.lgseeds.com
Development of Agricultural Seeds
N.A.I.C.S.: 111998
Kim Robertson (Mgr-Mktg)

Subsidiary (Domestic):

Clause S.A. (2)
46 Blvd Pierre Brossolette, BP 19, 91221,
Bretigny-sur-Orge, Cedex, France **(100%)**
Tel.: (33) 169884848
Web Site: http://www.clause-vegseeds.com
Sales Range: $25-49.9 Million
Emp.: 152
Provider of Research, Production & Marketing of Vegetable Seeds
N.A.I.C.S.: 541715

Subsidiary (Domestic):

Clause-Tezier S.A. (3)
ZI La Motte Rue Louis Suillant, 26802,
Portes-les-Valence, France **(100%)**
Tel.: (33) 475575757
Sales Range: $75-99.9 Million
Provider of Research, Production & Marketing of Vegetable & Flower Seeds
N.A.I.C.S.: 541715

Subsidiary (Non-US):

HM.Clause Italia S.p.A. (3)
Via Emilia 11, 10078, Venaria Reale, TO,
Italy
Tel.: (39) 011 453 0093
Sales Range: $25-49.9 Million
Emp.: 32
Provider of Research & Marketing of Vegetable Seeds
N.A.I.C.S.: 541715

Subsidiary (US):

Harris Moran Seed Co. (2)
555 Codoni Ave, Modesto, CA 95357-0507
Tel.: (209) 579-7333
Web Site: http://www.harrismoran.com
Sales Range: $100-124.9 Million
Emp.: 260
Vegetable Seeds Producer
N.A.I.C.S.: 111422
John Molyet (Mgr-Sls-Northeastern Reg)

Subsidiary (Non-US):

Nickerson Zwaan B.V. (2)
Shanseind 27, Made, 4921 PM,
Netherlands **(100%)**
Tel.: (31) 162690900
Web Site: http://www.nickerson-zwaan.com
Sales Range: $25-49.9 Million
Emp.: 100
Provider of Research, Production & Marketing of Vegetable Seeds
N.A.I.C.S.: 541715
Rami Dar (Gen Mgr)

Subsidiary (Non-US):

Nickerson Zwaan GmbH (3)
NPZ GmbH Am Grievenkamp 2, Edemissen, 31234, Germany **(100%)**
Tel.: (49) 5176989116
Web Site: http://www.nickerson-zwaan.com
Sales Range: $1-9.9 Million
Emp.: 20
Marketing of Vegetable Seeds
N.A.I.C.S.: 111219
Nanne Veldhuijzen van Zanten (Gen Mgr)

Nickerson Zwaan Ltd. (3)
Joseph Nickerson Research Centre, Rothwell, Market Rasen, LN7 6DT, Lincolnshire, United Kingdom **(100%)**
Tel.: (44) 1472371471
Web Site: http://www.nickersonseeds.co.uk
Sales Range: $25-49.9 Million
Emp.: 25
Marketing of Vegetable Seeds
N.A.I.C.S.: 111219
Les Daubney (Mgr-Oilseeds & Pulses Products)

Subsidiary (US):

Shamrock Seed Company Inc. (2)
3 Harris Pl, Salinas, CA 93901
Tel.: (831) 771-1500
Web Site: http://www.shamrockseed.com
Sales Range: $10-24.9 Million
Emp.: 41
Field, Garden & Flower Seeds
N.A.I.C.S.: 111422
Timothy J. Finnegan (Pres)

Subsidiary (Non-US):

Vilmorin Anadolu Tohumculuk (2)
Guzelyali Bati Sahili Ciftlik Sok No 9,
34903, Istanbul, Pendik, Turkiye
Tel.: (90) 216 392 3604
Web Site: http://www.anatoh.com
Sales Range: $25-49.9 Million
Emp.: 128
Marketing of Vegetable Seeds
N.A.I.C.S.: 111219

Vilmorin Iberica S.A. (2)
Calle Joaquin Orozco 17, 3006, Alicante,
Spain **(100%)**
Tel.: (34) 902193436
Web Site: http://www.vilmorin.com
Sales Range: $25-49.9 Million
Emp.: 25
Provider of Research & Marketing of Vegetable Seeds
N.A.I.C.S.: 541715
Fabien Duffaut (Gen Mgr)

Subsidiary (US):

Vilmorin Inc. (2)
2551 N Dragoon Ste 131, Tucson, AZ 85745
Tel.: (520) 884-0011
Web Site: http://www.vilmorin.com
Sales Range: $25-49.9 Million
Emp.: 8
Vegetable Seed Marketing
N.A.I.C.S.: 111422

Subsidiary (Non-US):

Vilmorin Italia S.R.L. (2)
Blocco 22 Via dei Notai 123, PO Box 97,
Fuño, 40050, BO, Italy **(100%)**
Tel.: (39) 051863313
Web Site: http://www.vilmorin.com
Sales Range: $25-49.9 Million
Emp.: 15
Research & Marketing of Vegetable Seeds
N.A.I.C.S.: 541715
Gianni Luca (Mgr-R&D)

Subsidiary (Domestic):

Vilmorin Jardin SA (2)
Parc Des Chesnes ZI Tharabie 5 Rue De Luzais, PO Box 37, 38291, Saint-Quentin-Fallavier, France **(99%)**
Tel.: (33) 474821010
Web Site: http://www.vilmorin-jardin.com
Sales Range: $25-49.9 Million
Emp.: 80
Vegetable, Flower & Lawn Seeds, Flower Bulbs, Pet Items & Horticultural Products for Home Gardeners
N.A.I.C.S.: 111219

Subsidiary (Non-US):

Oxadis S.L. (3)
Avenida Carlos III N 11 1 Izda, 31002, Navarra, Spain
Tel.: (34) 948203478
Sales Range: $25-49.9 Million
Emp.: 34
Marketer of Vegetable & Flower Seeds for Home Gardeners
N.A.I.C.S.: 444240

Oxadis S.r.L. (3)
Via Del Cappucini N 4 B, 26100, Cremona,
Italy **(100%)**
Tel.: (39) 0372434943
Web Site: http://www.oxadis.it

INTERNATIONAL PUBLIC

Sales Range: $25-49.9 Million
Emp.: 44
Marketer of Vegetable & Flower Seeds for Home Gardeners
N.A.I.C.S.: 444240

Subsidiary (Domestic):

Vilmorin S.A. (2)
Rue Du Manoir, 49250, La Menitre,
France **(100%)**
Tel.: (33) 241794179
Web Site: http://www.vilmorin.com
Sales Range: $25-49.9 Million
Emp.: 180
Provider of Research, Production & Marketing of Vegetable & Flower Seeds
N.A.I.C.S.: 541715
Millet Rodolthe (Sr Mgr)

GROUPE LUCIEN BARRIERE S.A.

35 Blvd des Capucines, 75002, Paris,
France
Tel.: (33) 142865400
Web Site: http://www.lucienbarriere.com
Sales Range: $1-4.9 Billion
Emp.: 6,465
Casinos, Hotels, Restaurants, Spas & Golf Courses Owner & Operator
N.A.I.C.S.: 721120
Philippe Perrot (Mng Dir & Dir-Fin)

GROUPE MARCELLE, INC.

9200 Cote de Liesse, Lachine, H8T 1A1, QC, Canada
Tel.: (514) 631-7710
Web Site: http://www.groupemarcelle.com
Emp.: 360
Skin Care & Cosmetic Products Mfr
N.A.I.C.S.: 325620
David Cape (Pres)

Subsidiaries:

Lise Watier Cosmetiques Inc. (1)
5600 Cote de Liesse, Mount-Royal, H4T 4L1, QC, Canada
Tel.: (514) 735-4959
Web Site: http://www.lisewatier.com
Emp.: 60
Cosmetic Product Mfr & Distr.
N.A.I.C.S.: 325620
Paul Fournier (Dir-Ops)

GROUPE MECALAC S.A.

Parc des Glaisins 2 av du Pre de, Challes, F-74940, Annecy-le-Vieux,
France
Tel.: (33) 450640163   FR
Web Site: http://www.mecalac.com
Year Founded: 1974
Construction Equipment Mfr
N.A.I.C.S.: 333120
Henri Marchetta (Pres)

Subsidiaries:

MECALAC Baumaschinen GmbH (1)
Am Friedrichsbrunnen 2, 24782, Büdelsdorf, Germany
Tel.: (49) 43 31 351 319
Web Site: http://www.mecalac.com
Emp.: 50
Construction Machinery Mfr
N.A.I.C.S.: 333120
Christian Streffler (Gen Mgr)

MECALAC IDF, S.A.S (1)
13 Route de Tilloy, 62217, Beaurains,
France
Tel.: (33) 3 21 59 50 36
Construction Equipment Distr
N.A.I.C.S.: 423810

GROUPE MINOTERIES SA

Tel.: (41) 266685111
Web Site: https://www.gmsa.ch
GMI—(SWX)
Sales Range: Less than $1 Million

AND PRIVATE COMPANIES

Flour & Grain Mfr
N.A.I.C.S.: 311211
Alain Raymond *(Chm-Mgmt Bd & CEO)*

GROUPE MONIN SAS
5 rue Ferdinand de Lesseps, BP 25, Bourges, 18000, France
Tel.: (33) 2 4850 6436   FR
Web Site: http://www.monin.com
Year Founded: 1912
Sales Range: $25-49.9 Million
Emp.: 690
Syrup & Flavoring Mfr
N.A.I.C.S.: 311930
Olivier Monin *(Pres)*

Subsidiaries:

MONIN SHANGHAI   (1)
3rd Floor Bldg C No 128 Yanping Rd, Shanghai, China
Tel.: (86) 21 5688 8366
Food Products Distr
N.A.I.C.S.: 424420

Monin Asia KL Sdn Bhd   (1)
Lot 911-A Jalan Industri 3/4 Taman Rawang Integrated Industri, 48 000, Rawang, Malaysia
Tel.: (60) 3 60990999
Food Products Distr
N.A.I.C.S.: 424420

Monin, Inc.   (1)
2100 Range Rd, Clearwater, FL 33765
Tel.: (727) 461-3033
Web Site: http://www.monin.com
Sales Range: $50-74.9 Million
Emp.: 60
Syrups & Flavorings Mfr
N.A.I.C.S.: 311930
Olivier Monin *(Pres)*

GROUPE MTD FINANCE
1 Rue Castex, 75004, Paris, France
Tel.: (33) 144789090
Web Site: http://www.mtd-finance.fr
Sales Range: $1-9.9 Million
Emp.: 15
Investment Services
N.A.I.C.S.: 523999

GROUPE OMERIN
Zone Industrielle, 63 600, Ambert, France
Tel.: (33) 4 7382 5000   FR
Web Site: http://www.groupe-omerin.com
Year Founded: 1959
Emp.: 1,100
Holding Company; Wire & Cable Mfr
N.A.I.C.S.: 551112
Xavier Omerin *(CEO)*

Subsidiaries:

Omerin Usa, Inc.   (1)
95 Research Pkwy, Meriden, CT 06450
Tel.: (203) 237-2297
Web Site: http://www.omerin-usa.com
Commercial Wire & Cable Mfr
N.A.I.C.S.: 332618
Maria Ryan *(Ops Mgr)*

Division (Domestic):

OMERIN USA, Inc. - QS Technologies Division   (2)
95 Research Pkwy, Meriden, CT 06450
Tel.: (203) 237-2297
Web Site: http://www.omerin-usa.com
Electrical Wire & Cable Mfr
N.A.I.C.S.: 335921
Maria Ryan *(Ops Mgr)*

Union Plastic SA   (1)
ZA Robert, BP 27, 43140, Saint Didier, France
Tel.: (33) 471611309
Web Site: http://www.union-plastic.com
Medical Equipment Mfr
N.A.I.C.S.: 339112

GROUPE ONEPOINT SAS
29 Rue Des Sablons, 75116, Paris, France
Tel.: (33) 170230300   FR
Web Site: http://www.groupeonepoint.com
Year Founded: 2002
Emp.: 1,800
Technical Consulting Services
N.A.I.C.S.: 541690
David Layani *(Founder & Pres)*

GROUPE OPEN S.A.
24-32 rue Jacques Ibert, 92300, Levallois-Perret, France
Tel.: (33) 1 71 06 31 28   FR
Web Site: http://www.groupe-open.com
Year Founded: 1989
OPN—(EUR)
Sales Range: $350-399.9 Million
Emp.: 3,700
Information & Communications Technology Application Engineering, Consulting & Infrastructure Services
N.A.I.C.S.: 541990
Guy Mamou-Mani *(Co-Chm)*

Subsidiaries:

Groupe OPEN Nederland B.V.   (1)
Bahialaan 500, 3065 WC, Rotterdam, Netherlands
Tel.: (31) 107891800
Web Site: http://www.open-groupe.nl
Sales Range: $25-49.9 Million
Emp.: 100
Information & Communications Technology Services
N.A.I.C.S.: 541990

GROUPE OUELLET CANADA INC.
180 3rd Avenue, L'Isletville, G0R 2C0, QC, Canada
Tel.: (418) 247-3947
Web Site: http://www.ouellet.com
Electric Heating Products Mfr
N.A.I.C.S.: 333414

Subsidiaries:

Ouellet Canada Inc.   (1)
180 3rd Avenue, L'Isletville, G0R 2C0, QC, Canada
Tel.: (418) 247-3947
Web Site: http://www.ouellet.com
Rev.: $37,310,976
Emp.: 235
Electric Heating Products Mfr
N.A.I.C.S.: 333414

Subsidiary (US):

Delta-Therm Corporation   (2)
398 W Liberty St, Wauconda, IL, 60084
Tel.: (847) 526-2407
Web Site: http://www.delta-therm.com
Rev.: $3,660,000
Emp.: 18
All Other Miscellaneous Electrical Equipment & Component Mfr
N.A.I.C.S.: 335999
Tom Slagis *(Pres)*

GROUPE PAROT SA
Rue de Fieuzal, 33520, Bruges, Belgium
Tel.: (32) 519800020
Web Site: https://www.groupe-parot.com
Year Founded: 1978
ALPAR—(EUR)
Sales Range: $600-649.9 Million
Vehicle Distr
N.A.I.C.S.: 423110

GROUPE PARTOUCHE S.A.
141 Bis Rue de Saussure, 75017, Paris, France
Tel.: (33) 147643345   FR
Web Site: https://www.partouche.com
Year Founded: 1973

PARP—(EUR)
Rev.: $421,854,995
Assets: $967,461,311
Liabilities: $510,638,324
Net Worth: $456,822,988
Earnings: ($18,666,792)
Emp.: 4,068
Fiscal Year-end: 10/31/20
Casino Hotel Operator
N.A.I.C.S.: 713210
Kathy Zenou *(Member-Mgmt Bd)*

Subsidiaries:

Casinos du Touquet S.A.S.   (1)
26 Rue Saint Jean, Pas de Calais, 62520, Le Touquet-Paris-Plage, France
Tel.: (33) 321051699
Gambling Facility
N.A.I.C.S.: 713290

Forges Thermal S.A.   (1)
87 Ave des Sources, 76440, Forges-les-Eaux, France   (59.5%)
Tel.: (33) 232895050
Hotel, Spa & Golf Club Operations
N.A.I.C.S.: 721110
Richard Frischer *(Dir Gen)*

Groupe Partouche International S.A.   (1)
141 BIS RUE Saussure, PO Box 17, 75017, Paris, France
Tel.: (33) 147643345
Web Site: http://www.partouche.com
Sales Range: $10-24.9 Million
Emp.: 50
Casino Hotels
N.A.I.C.S.: 721120

Jean Metz S.A.S.   (1)
Casino SAS Jean Metz, 62600, Berck, France
Tel.: (33) 321848758
Casino Hotel Operator
N.A.I.C.S.: 713210
N. Vincent *(Mgr)*

Sarl Thermes de Contrexeville   (1)
Spa Gallery, 88 140, Contrexeville, France
Tel.: (33) 329080324
Web Site: http://www.thermescontrexeville.fr
Body Care Services
N.A.I.C.S.: 713940

Societe du Casino de Saint Amand S.A.S.   (1)
Rocade Nord, Saint-Amand-les-Eaux, 59230, France
Tel.: (33) 327481900
Web Site: http://www.casinosaintamand.com
Sales Range: $50-74.9 Million
Emp.: 300
Hotels & Motels Operating Services
N.A.I.C.S.: 721110
Karen Pamart *(Mgr)*

GROUPE PETIT FORESTIER SAS
11 Route de Tremblay, 93420, Villepinte, France
Tel.: (33) 141525252
Web Site: http://www.petitforestier.com
Year Founded: 1907
Refrigerated Vehicle & Container Rental Services
N.A.I.C.S.: 532411

Subsidiaries:

Mendon Leasing Corporation   (1)
362 Kingsland Ave, Brooklyn, NY 11222-1905
Tel.: (718) 391-5300
Web Site: http://www.mendonleasing.com
Truck Rental & Leasing Services
N.A.I.C.S.: 532120
Barry Barrskell *(Pres)*

GROUPE PIZZORNO ENVIRONNEMENT S.A.
109 Rue Jean Aicard, 83300, Draguignan, France
Tel.: (33) 494505050
Web Site: https://www.pizzorno.com
GPE—(EUR)

GROUPE PORCHER INDUSTRIES

Sales Range: $250-299.9 Million
Waste Management Services; Cleaning Services & Waste Treatment
N.A.I.C.S.: 562111
Maria De Via-Carrozza *(CFO & Dir-IR)*

GROUPE PLAFOLIFT INC.
430 Cantin, Victoriaville, G6P 7E6, QC, Canada
Tel.: (819) 358-3550
Web Site: http://www.plafolift.com
Year Founded: 1973
Rev.: $11,700,000
Emp.: 60
Lifting Products Mfr
N.A.I.C.S.: 327390

GROUPE PLOMBACTION INC
575 boul Pierre Roux Est, Victoriaville, G6T 1S7, QC, Canada
Tel.: (819) 752-6064
Web Site: http://www.groupeplombaction.com
Year Founded: 1987
Rev.: $22,441,969
Emp.: 70
Construction Services
N.A.I.C.S.: 236220

GROUPE PLUS VALUES SA
Tour Rosny 112 avenue du, 93110, Rosny-sous-Bois, France
Tel.: (33) 148947461
Web Site: http://www.groupe-pv.com
Internet Site Publishing Services
N.A.I.C.S.: 513199
Josiane Herbet *(Chm & CEO)*

GROUPE PORCHER INDUSTRIES
75 RD 1085, 38300, Badinieres, France
Tel.: (33) 474431010
Web Site: http://www.porcher-ind.com
Year Founded: 1912
Sales Range: $350-399.9 Million
Emp.: 2,000
Technical Textile Mfr
N.A.I.C.S.: 313210
Andre Genton *(Pres & CEO)*

Subsidiaries:

BGF Industries Inc.   (1)
3802 Robert Porcher Way, Greensboro, NC 27410-2190
Tel.: (336) 545-0011
Web Site: http://www.bgf.com
Sales Range: $150-199.9 Million
Emp.: 800
Fibre Glass Mfr
N.A.I.C.S.: 313210
Robert Porcher *(Owner)*

Fothergill Crenette Ltd   (1)
Green Vale Mill Summit, Littleborough, OL15 9QP, United Kingdom
Tel.: (44) 170 6371137
Web Site: http://www.porcher-ind.com
Emp.: 18
Textile Products Distr
N.A.I.C.S.: 424990

Porcher Industries Asia-Pacific   (1)
Rm 703 Carpo Commercial Building No 18 Lyndhurst Terrace, Central, China (Hong Kong)   (100%)
Tel.: (852) 25277733
Web Site: http://www.porcher-ind.com
Sales Range: $25-49.9 Million
Emp.: 30
Specialist Glass & Textile Mfr
N.A.I.C.S.: 313210
J. P. Gry *(Gen Mgr)*

Porcher Industries, Russia   (1)
Ulitsa Taininskaya dom 15, Korpus 1 Kvartira 140, 129345, Moscow, Russia
Tel.: (7) 95 185 17 54
Specialty Glass & Textile Mfr

GROUPE PORCHER INDUSTRIES

Groupe Porcher Industries—(Continued)
N.A.I.C.S.: 313210

Porcher Industries, UK (1)
23 Fulmar Crescent, Kidderminster, DY10 4HL, Worcs, United Kingdom **(100%)**
Tel.: (44) 1562748830
Web Site: http://www.porcherind.com
Sales Range: $25-49.9 Million
Emp.: 2
Specialty Textile Mfr
N.A.I.C.S.: 313210

Porcher Italiana (1)
Via Magalotti 6, I 28100, Novara, Italy
Tel.: (39) 0321 362 17
Specialty Textile Mfr
N.A.I.C.S.: 313210

Porcher do Brasil Tecidos de Vidros Ltda. (1)
Avenida Caetano Ruggieri 4153 Vila Sao Jose Itu, Sao Paulo, Brazil
Tel.: (55) 114 0231966
Textile Products Distr
N.A.I.C.S.: 424990
Faruk Elias Miguel *(Mgr-Indus)*

Shanghai Porcher Industries Co., Ltd. (1)
626 Ying Gang East Rd, Qingpu, Shanghai, 201700, China **(100%)**
Tel.: (86) 2159720102
Web Site: http://www.porcherind.com
Sales Range: $100-124.9 Million
Emp.: 450
Speciality Textile & Glass Mfr
N.A.I.C.S.: 313210
Phillipe Torcher *(Pres)*

GROUPE PRIMONIAL SAS

51 rue Francois 1er, 75008, Paris, France
Tel.: (33) 144217070
Web Site: http://www.primonial.com
Year Founded: 1998
Asset Management Services
N.A.I.C.S.: 523150
Camo Andre *(Mng Dir)*

Subsidiaries:

W Finance Groupe Primonial (1)
8385 Ave Marceau, Cedex, F-75016, Paris, France
Tel.: (33) 153244646
Web Site: http://www.wfinance.primonial.com
Sales Range: $25-49.9 Million
Emp.: 40
Financial Services
N.A.I.C.S.: 523150

GROUPE R.Y. BEAUDOIN, INC.

1400 Boulevard Pierre-Roux Est, Victoriaville, G6T 2T7, QC, Canada
Tel.: (446) 41396
Web Site: http://www.gryb.ca
Year Founded: 2007
Heavy Equipment Attachments Mfr
N.A.I.C.S.: 333998
Yvon Beaudoin *(Owner)*

Subsidiaries:

Winkle Industries, Inc. (1)
2080 W Main St, Alliance, OH 44601
Tel.: (330) 823-9730
Web Site: http://www.winkleindustries.com
Electronic & Precision Equipment Repair & Maintenance
N.A.I.C.S.: 811210
Joseph T. Schatz *(CEO)*

GROUPE RENAUD-BRAY, INC.

5655 Ave Pierre de Coubertin, Montreal, H1N 1R2, QC, Canada
Tel.: (514) 272-4049
Web Site: http://www.renaud-bray.com
Emp.: 100
Online Book Stores
N.A.I.C.S.: 459210
Blaise Renaud *(Pres)*

Subsidiaries:

Groupe Archambault Inc. (1)
510 Ste Catherine Street East, Montreal, H2L 4W2, QC, Canada
Tel.: (514) 849-8589
Web Site: https://www.archambault.ca
Sales Range: $25-49.9 Million
Entertainment Products Distr
N.A.I.C.S.: 459999

GROUPE ROCHER OPERATIONS SAS

La Croix des Archers, La Gacilly, 56200, France
Tel.: (33) 1 41 08 55 00 **FR**
Web Site: http://www.groupe-rocher.com
Year Founded: 1959
Emp.: 15,000
Cosmetic Products Developer, Distr & Sales
N.A.I.C.S.: 456120
Yann-Etienne Le Gall *(Deputy CEO-HR, Comm & Organization)*

Subsidiaries:

Arbonne International, LLC (1)
21 Technology Dr, Irvine, CA 92618
Tel.: (949) 770-2610
Web Site: https://www.arbonne.com
Personal Skincare & Wellness Products Mfr
N.A.I.C.S.: 325620
Jen Orlando *(CEO)*

Petit Bateau UK Limited (1)
Floor 26 Salesforce Tower - 110 Bishopsgate, London, EC2N 4AY, United Kingdom
Tel.: (44) 2077347259
Web Site: http://www.petit-bateau.co.uk
Men & Women Cloth Retailer
N.A.I.C.S.: 458110
Erin Scott *(Mgr-Retail)*

Stanhome France SAS (1)
Chemin de Primeveres, 56200, La Gacilly, France
Tel.: (33) 800430430
Web Site: http://www.stanhome.fr
Beauty Product Retailer
N.A.I.C.S.: 456120

GROUPE SECHE SAS

Les Hetres, 20020, Change, Cedex 9, France
Tel.: (33) 243596000 **FR**
Web Site: http://www.groupe-seche.com
Holding Company; Waste Collection & Treatment Services
N.A.I.C.S.: 551112
Joel Seche *(Chm)*

Subsidiaries:

Seche Environnement SA (1)
Les Hetres, CS20020, Change, Cedex 9, France **(59.04%)**
Tel.: (33) 243596000
Web Site: https://www.groupe-seche.com
Rev.: $1,201,979,247
Assets: $1,750,424,992
Liabilities: $1,368,133,348
Net Worth: $382,291,644
Earnings: $55,178,276
Emp.: 5,855
Fiscal Year-end: 12/31/2023
Waste Collection & Treatment Services
N.A.I.C.S.: 562219

Subsidiary (Domestic):

Bearn Environnement SA (2)
20 Boulevard Des Pyrenees, 64000, Pau, Pyrenees-Atlantiques, France
Tel.: (33) 559985080
Waste Treatment Services
N.A.I.C.S.: 562211

Drimm SAS (2)
3525 Highway Lavilledieu, 82700, Montech, Tarn-et-Garonne, France
Tel.: (33) 563231300
Sales Range: $25-49.9 Million
Emp.: 100

Household Waste Collection & Recycling Services
N.A.I.C.S.: 562112

Gerep SAS (2)
ZI de Mitry-Compans 14 rue Jacquard, 77292, Mitry-Mory, Seine-et-Marne, France
Tel.: (33) 1 64 27 17 71
Sales Range: $10-24.9 Million
Emp.: 30
Organic Waste Incineration Services
N.A.I.C.S.: 562211

Subsidiary (Non-US):

Hungaropec Ltd. (2)
Hegedus Gyula Utca 12, 1136, Budapest, Hungary
Tel.: (36) 13293290
Web Site: http://www.hungaropec.hu
Industrial Wastes Treatment Services
N.A.I.C.S.: 562211

IberTredi Medioambiental S.A. (2)
Galileu 303 - 5B, 08028, Barcelona, Spain
Tel.: (34) 934394022
Web Site: http://www.ibertredi.com
Emp.: 5
Chemical Waste Disposal Services
N.A.I.C.S.: 562211

Interwaste Holdings Limited (2)
2 Brammer Street Industries East, PO Box 382, Germiston, 1400, South Africa
Tel.: (27) 11 323 7300
Web Site: http://www.interwaste.co.za
Rev.: $68,256,124
Assets: $75,140,375
Liabilities: $35,151,328
Net Worth: $39,989,047
Earnings: $3,232,940
Emp.: 2,400
Fiscal Year-end: 12/31/2016
Waste Management Services
N.A.I.C.S.: 562998
Alan Willcocks *(CEO)*

Subsidiary (Domestic):

Earth2Earth Proprietary Limited (3)
Sappi Farm Ngodwana Factory, Nelspruit, Mpumalanga, South Africa
Tel.: (27) 13 734 4852 3
Web Site: http://www.earth2earth.co.za
Organic Fertilizer Mfr & Distr
N.A.I.C.S.: 325311

Envirowaste SA Proprietary Limited (3)
PostNet Suite 138, Private Bag X1037, Germiston, 1401, South Africa
Tel.: (27) 87 803 0900
Web Site: http://www.envirowaste.co.za
Waste Management Services
N.A.I.C.S.: 562998

Inter-Waste Proprietary Limited (3)
9 Ceramic Curve Alton North, Richards Bay, 3900, South Africa
Tel.: (27) 35 751 2092
Web Site: http://www.interwaste.co.za
Waste Management Services
N.A.I.C.S.: 562998
Allen Willcocks *(CEO)*

Subsidiary (Domestic):

Opale Environnement (2)
52 rue Clement Ader, BP 136, 62103, Calais, Pas-de-Calais, France
Tel.: (33) 321347070
Sales Range: $25-49.9 Million
Emp.: 74
Waste Collection Services
N.A.I.C.S.: 562112

SCI LCDL (2)
Ld Les Hetres, 53810, Change, Mayenne, France
Tel.: (33) 2 43 59 60 60
Web Site: http://www.groupe-seche.com
Sales Range: $150-199.9 Million
Emp.: 550
Electronic Waste Recycling Services
N.A.I.C.S.: 562920

SCI Mezerolles (2)
Ld Les Hetres, 53810, Change, Mayenne, France
Tel.: (33) 2 43 59 60 00
Web Site: http://www.groupe-seche.com

INTERNATIONAL PUBLIC

Sales Range: $25-49.9 Million
Emp.: 200
Waste Hauling Services
N.A.I.C.S.: 562112
Joel Seche *(Gen Mgr)*

SVO Eco-industries (2)
La Reissiere, BP 14, 86150, Le Vigeant, Vienne, France
Tel.: (33) 549845791
Hazardous Waste Treatment Services
N.A.I.C.S.: 562211

Seche Alliance SAS (2)
Les Hetres, Change, 53810, France
Tel.: (33) 243596000
Web Site: http://www.groupseche.com
Sales Range: $75-99.9 Million
Emp.: 380
Hazardous Waste Treatment Services
N.A.I.C.S.: 562211
Joel Seche *(Pres)*

Seche Eco-industries SAS (2)
Les Hetres, 53811, Change, Mayenne, France
Tel.: (33) 2 43 5960 00
Web Site: http://www.groupe-seche.com
Waste Material Recycling Services
N.A.I.C.S.: 562920
Severine Roger *(Mgr-Comm)*

Seche Eco-services SAS (2)
Les Hetres, 53811, Change, Mayenne, France
Tel.: (33) 2 43 59 60 83
Household Waste Collection & Recycling Services
N.A.I.C.S.: 562211

Seche Transports SAS (2)
Lieu Dit Les Hetres, BP 20, 53811, Change, Mayenne, France
Tel.: (33) 243596030
Waste Hauling Services
N.A.I.C.S.: 562111

Senerval (2)
3 Route Du Rohrschollen, Strasbourg, 67100, Bas-Rhin, France
Tel.: (33) 388795000
Sales Range: $10-24.9 Million
Emp.: 35
Household Waste Incineration Services
N.A.I.C.S.: 562213

Speichim Processing S.A. (2)
Parc Industriel de la Plaine de l'Ain, Allee des Pins, Saint-Vulbas, 01150, Ain, France
Tel.: (33) 474465555
Sales Range: $25-49.9 Million
Emp.: 20
Chemical Waste Disposal Services
N.A.I.C.S.: 562211
Cecile Rosset *(Mgr-Mktg & Comm)*

Subsidiary (Non-US):

Tredi Argentina (2)
Montevideo 456 10 Piso, 1019, Buenos Aires, Argentina
Tel.: (54) 1143711218
Web Site: https://www.trediargentina.com.ar
Sales Range: $25-49.9 Million
Emp.: 11
Industrial Wastes Treatment Services
N.A.I.C.S.: 562112
Marcella Culla *(Mgr)*

Subsidiary (Domestic):

Tredi SA (2)
Parc Industriel de la Plaine de l'Ain, BP 55, Lagnieu, 01152, Saint-Vulbas, France
Tel.: (33) 4 74 4622 00
Web Site: http://www.groupe-seche.com
Hazardous Waste Treatment Services
N.A.I.C.S.: 562211
Jean-Pierre Vallee *(Mng Dir)*

Subsidiary (Non-US):

Sem Tredi S.A. DE C.V. (3)
Amores No 707 - 502 Col Del Valle, Mexico, 3100, Mexico
Tel.: (52) 5555432677
Web Site: http://www.semtredi.com
Electronic Waste Recycling Services
N.A.I.C.S.: 562920
Claire van Ruymbeke *(Gen Mgr)*

AND PRIVATE COMPANIES

Subsidiary (Domestic):

Sotrefi Etupes (3)
ZI Technoland 48 Rue des Tonneliers, 25461, Etupes, Doubs, France **(100%)**
Tel.: (33) 3 81 95 53 46
Web Site: http://www.groupe-seche.com
Hazardous Waste Treatment Services
N.A.I.C.S.: 562211

Subsidiary (Domestic):

Triadis Etampes (2)
Rue de Grenots ZA Sud Essor, 91150, Etampes, Essonne, France
Tel.: (33) 1 69 16 13 35
Sales Range: $10-24.9 Million
Emp.: 30
Hazardous Waste Treatment Services
N.A.I.C.S.: 562211
Mickael Prestadine *(Mgr-Comml)*

Triadis Services S.A.S. (2)
11 Avenue de Bellevue, 35136, Saint-Jacques-de-la-Lande, Ille-et-Vilaine, France
Tel.: (33) 2 99 35 38 35
Hazardous Waste Treatment Services
N.A.I.C.S.: 562211

Subsidiary (Non-US):

Valls Quimica S.A. (2)
Galileu 303 5B, 08028, Barcelona, Spain
Tel.: (34) 934394022
Web Site: http://www.vallsquimica.com
Organic Solvents Recycling Services
N.A.I.C.S.: 562920

GROUPE SFPI SA

20 rue de l Arc de Triomphe, 75017, Paris, France
Tel.: (33) 146220900   FR
Web Site: https://www.sfpi-group.com
Year Founded: 1983
SFPI—(EUR)
Rev.: $612,659,623
Assets: $647,464,260
Liabilities: $382,301,982
Net Worth: $265,162,277
Earnings: $21,780,380
Emp.: 3,910
Fiscal Year-end: 12/31/20
Holding Company; Construction Equipment Mfr
N.A.I.C.S.: 551112
Henri Morel *(CEO)*

Subsidiaries:

BARRIQUAND TECHNOLOGIES THERMIQUES SAS (1)
9-13 Rue Saint-Claude, F-42334, Roanne, Cedex, France
Tel.: (33) 469650207
Web Site: https://www.barriquand.com
Heat Exchanger Mfr
N.A.I.C.S.: 332410

Plant (Domestic):

BARRIQUAND TECHNOLOGIES THERMIQUES SAS - ASET Production Facility (2)
2 rue de bourgogne, 69803, Saint Priest, France
Tel.: (33) 4 78 20 16 16
Heat Exchanger Mfr
N.A.I.C.S.: 332410

Benidorm Locks S.L. (1)
Avd Marina Baixa s/n Ptda Torrent, La Nucia, 03530, Alicante, Spain
Tel.: (34) 966 897 979
Web Site: http://www.benidormlocks.com
Security Device Distr
N.A.I.C.S.: 423710

C. P. JAKOBSENS eftf. ApS. (1)
Dynamovej 12 B, 2730, Herlev, Denmark
Tel.: (45) 48 18 47 00
Web Site: http://www.cpj.dk
Security Device Distr
N.A.I.C.S.: 423710

CR Serrature Spa (1)
Via Regaldi 13, 10 154, Turin, Italy
Tel.: (39) 0112482320
Web Site: http://www.cr-serrature.com

Security Locks Mfr & Distr
N.A.I.C.S.: 339999

DOM Sicherheitstechnik GmbH & Co. KG (1)
Missindorfstrasse 19-23, 1140, Vienna, Austria
Tel.: (43) 1 7897377
Web Site: http://www.dom.at
Security Device Distr
N.A.I.C.S.: 423710

DOM Sicherheitstechnik GmbH & Co. KG (1)
Wesselinger Str 10-16, PO Box 1949, 50321, Bruhl, Germany **(100%)**
Tel.: (49) 22327040
Web Site: http://www.dom-security.com
Sales Range: $100-124.9 Million
Emp.: 500
Security Products Mfr
N.A.I.C.S.: 236118

Subsidiary (Non-US):

DOM AG Sicherheitstechnik (2)
Breitenstrasse 11, PO Box 167, CH 8852, Altendorf, Switzerland **(100%)**
Tel.: (41) 554510707
Web Site: http://www.domgroup.ch
Sales Range: $25-49.9 Million
Emp.: 15
Security Products Mfr
N.A.I.C.S.: 236118
Marco Raeber *(Mng Dir)*

DOM Polska Sp.z.o.o. (2)
ul Krotka 7/9, 42-202, Czestochowa, Silesian, Poland
Tel.: (48) 343241967
Web Site: https://www.dom-security.com
Emp.: 20
Security Locks Distr
N.A.I.C.S.: 423840
Bartlomiej Wypych *(Mng Dir)*

DOM S.A.R.L. (2)
259 Chem des Clapiers, Le Pradet, 83220, Bonneuil-Matours, Cedex, France
Tel.: (33) 498016500
Web Site: https://dom-france.fr
Sales Range: $1-9.9 Million
Emp.: 30
Security Products Mfr
N.A.I.C.S.: 236118

DOM-Nederland (2)
Tiber 32-34, 2491 DH, Hague, Netherlands
Tel.: (31) 703193006
Web Site: http://www.dom-security.com
Sales Range: $25-49.9 Million
Emp.: 40
Security Locks Distr
N.A.I.C.S.: 423840

DOM-Metalux S.A.S. (1)
47 bis rue Jeanne d'Arc, 52115, Saint Dizier, Cedex, France
Tel.: (33) 325050386
Web Site: https://www.dom-security.com
Emp.: 150
Security Device Mfr & Distr
N.A.I.C.S.: 334290

Delta Neu S.A.S. (1)
Parc d'Activites de la Houssoye Rue Andre Ampere, 59930, La Chapelle-d'Armentieres, France
Tel.: (33) 320105050
Emp.: 200
Air Conditioning Equipment Distr
N.A.I.C.S.: 423730

Subsidiary (Non-US):

DELTA NEU BENELUX N.V. (2)
Battelsesteenweg 455 D, Mechelen, Belgium
Tel.: (32) 15459410
Web Site: http://www.delta-neu.com
Emp.: 7
Air Conditioning Equipment Distr
N.A.I.C.S.: 423730

DELTA NEU MAROC S.A. (2)
282 Angle Strasbourg et la Resistance N 601, 20000, Casablanca, Morocco
Tel.: (212) 22 44 53 63
Air Conditioning Equipment Distr
N.A.I.C.S.: 423730

DELTA NEU NEDERLAND BV (2)
Postbus 4122, 5604 EC, Eindhoven, Netherlands
Tel.: (31) 40 291 14 05
Air Conditioning Equipment Distr
N.A.I.C.S.: 423730

Delta Neu Limited (2)
9 Station View, Hazel Grove, Stockport, SK7 5ER, Cheshire, United Kingdom
Tel.: (44) 1614565511
Web Site: https://www.delta-neu.co.uk
Ventilation Equipment Distr
N.A.I.C.S.: 423730
David James *(Engr-Project & Sls)*

Deny Fontaine (1)
Route de Saint Valery, BP 1, 80960, Saint-Blimont, France
Tel.: (33) 820821421
Web Site: http://www.denyfontaine.com
Emp.: 160
Security Locks Mfr & Distr
N.A.I.C.S.: 332510

Euro-Elzett Kft. (1)
3 Csepel street, 9400, Sopron, Hungary
Tel.: (36) 99514100
Web Site: http://www.euro-elzett.hu
Sales Range: $25-49.9 Million
Emp.: 140
Security Locks Mfr
N.A.I.C.S.: 332510

HOBERG Luxembourg AG (1)
2 rue d'Anvers, 1130, Luxembourg, Luxembourg
Tel.: (352) 26 18 75 75
Hardware Distr
N.A.I.C.S.: 423710

Hoberg N.V. (1)
Avenue Edison 27, B-1300, Wavre, Belgium
Tel.: (32) 10232220
Web Site: https://www.dom-security.com
Hardware Distr
N.A.I.C.S.: 423710

MMD SAS (1)
2 Sente Pierre au Roy, 60240, Tourly, France
Tel.: (33) 344030959
Electronic Equipment Distr
N.A.I.C.S.: 423690

Metalplast-Czestochowa Sp. z o.o. (1)
Ul Krotka 7/9, Czestochowa, 42202, Silesian, Poland
Tel.: (48) 343241966
Web Site: http://www.metalplast-czestochowa.pl
Sales Range: $50-74.9 Million
Emp.: 115
Security Locks Distr
N.A.I.C.S.: 423710

Metalux (1)
47Bis Rue Jeanne D Arc, 52115, Saint Dizier, Haute-Marne, France
Tel.: (33) 325050386
Web Site: http://www.metalux.fr
Sales Range: $50-74.9 Million
Emp.: 130
Locking Systems Mfr & Distr
N.A.I.C.S.: 337215

NEU Automation SAS (1)
Houssoye Business Park Rue Andre Ampere, 59930, La Chapelle-d'Armentieres, France
Tel.: (33) 320456575
Web Site: http://www.neu-automation.com
Industrial Automation Equipments Mfr
N.A.I.C.S.: 334513

NEU International Railways s.a.s. (1)
70 rue du College, BP 4039, 59704, Marcq-en-Baroeul, France
Tel.: (33) 3 20 45 64 64
Web Site: http://www.neu-railways.com
Emp.: 30
Track Maintenance Services
N.A.I.C.S.: 561720
Franck Vinchon *(Mng Dir)*

Picard Serrures (1)
20 rue Henri Barbusse, 80210, Feuquieres-en-Vimeu, France

GROUPE TERA SA

Tel.: (33) 322602740
Web Site: http://www.picard-serrures.com
Sales Range: $25-49.9 Million
Emp.: 80
Security Locks Distr
N.A.I.C.S.: 423710

RONIS S.A.S. (1)
Rue de Neuilly, 18600, Sancoins, France
Tel.: (33) 248745000
Web Site: http://www.ronis.fr
Sales Range: $25-49.9 Million
Emp.: 180
Locking Devices Mfr
N.A.I.C.S.: 332510

RONIS-DOM Ltd. (1)
Unit 1 Junction 2 Industrial Estate, Demuth Way, Oldbury, B69 4LT, Birmingham, United Kingdom
Tel.: (44) 8009884348
Web Site: http://www.ronis-dom.co.uk
Sales Range: $25-49.9 Million
Emp.: 20
Security Locks Mfr & Distr
N.A.I.C.S.: 332510

STERIFLOW SAS (1)
9 a 13 rue, Saint Claude, F42334, Roanne, France
Tel.: (33) 477442210
Web Site: https://www.steriflow.com
Emp.: 90
Autoclave Mfr
N.A.I.C.S.: 332420

Titan d.d. (1)
Kovinarska 28, 1241, Kamnik, Slovenia
Tel.: (386) 18309100
Web Site: http://www.dom-security.com
Sales Range: $25-49.9 Million
Emp.: 200
Security Locks Mfr
N.A.I.C.S.: 339999

UCEM Sistemas de Seguridad S.a. (1)
Poligono Kataide s/n Apartado 1, 20500, Mondragon, Guipuzcoa, Spain
Tel.: (34) 943 770 502
Web Site: http://www.ucem.es
Security Device Distr
N.A.I.C.S.: 423710

GROUPE SIPAREX

27 rue Marbeuf, 75008, Paris, France
Tel.: (33) 1 53 93 02 20
Web Site: http://www.siparex.com
Holding Company
N.A.I.C.S.: 551112
Nicolas Eschermann *(Mng Partner-IR & Bus Dev)*

Subsidiaries:

SI Participations S.C.A. (1)
107 Rue Servient, 69003, Lyon, France
Tel.: (33) 4 72832323
Web Site: http://www.siparticipations.com
Sales Range: Less than $1 Million
Privater Equity Firm
N.A.I.C.S.: 523999
Bertrand Rambaud *(Chm-Mgmt Bd)*

Subsidiary (Domestic):

XAnge Private Equity, S.A. (2)
27 rue Marbeuf, 75008, Paris, France
Tel.: (33) 1 53 43 05 30
Web Site: http://www.xange.fr
Rev.: $343,009,800
Privater Equity Firm
N.A.I.C.S.: 523999
François Cavalie *(Mng Dir)*

GROUPE SOLOTECH, INC.

5200 Hochelaga Str, Montreal, H1V 1G3, QC, Canada
Tel.: (514) 526-7721
Web Site: http://www.solotech.com
Emp.: 450
Audio & Video Equipment Services
N.A.I.C.S.: 532490
Martin Tremblay *(Pres)*

GROUPE TERA SA

628 Rue Charles de Gaulle, FR-

GROUPE TERA SA

Groupe Tera SA—(Continued)
38920, Crolles, France
Tel.: (33) 476921517
Web Site: https://www.groupe-tera.com
ALGTR—(EUR)
Sales Range: $1-9.9 Million
Health Care Srvices
N.A.I.C.S.: 813920
Pascal Kaluzny (Chm & CEO)

GROUPE UNIPEX SAS
Tour Franklin 100 - 101 Terrasse Boieldieu, La Defense, 92042, Paris, Cedex, France
Tel.: (33) 147328130   FR
Web Site: http://www.unipex.com
Year Founded: 2008
Sales Range: $50-74.9 Million
Emp.: 80
Holding Company; Pharmaceutical, Industrial, Cosmetic & Nutritional Chemicals Distr
N.A.I.C.S.: 551112
Patrice Barthelmes (Pres)

Subsidiaries:

Unipex Benelux NV   (1)
Office Park Val d'Or Gulleddelle 94, 1200, Brussels, Belgium
Tel.: (32) 2761 1030
Web Site: http://www.unipexsolutions.be
Cosmetic Product Distr
N.A.I.C.S.: 424210
Frederic Marquet (Mgr-Technical Sls-Homecare/Pharmaceuticals)

Unipex Solutions France S.A.S.   (1)
5 rue du Compas ZI des Bethunes, BP 29235, 95310, Saint-Ouen, France
Tel.: (33) 1 47 32 81 11
Web Site: http://www.unipex.fr
Cosmetic Product Distr
N.A.I.C.S.: 424210
Patrice Barthelmes (Pres)

GROUPE VENDOME ROME
24 rue Jacques Ibert, 92533, Levallois-Perret, France
Tel.: (33) 147592600
Real Estate Services
N.A.I.C.S.: 531390
Alex Rizkallah (Dir-Fin)

GROUPE VIAL SA
151 Avenue Alphonse Lavallee Z I de Toulon Est, 83130, La Garde, France
Tel.: (33) 494143354
Web Site: http://www.vial-habitat.com
Building Product Mfr & Distr
N.A.I.C.S.: 337110
Elisabeth Marro Vial (Chm & CEO)

GROUPEMENT FLO
Rue de Barcelone Bat 1 Zone de Bordeaux Fret, 33521, Bruges, Cedex, France
Tel.: (33) 556438484
Web Site: http://www.groupement-flo.com
Year Founded: 1993
Sales Range: $1-4.9 Billion
Emp.: 110
Holding Company; Freight Transportation & Logistic Services
N.A.I.C.S.: 551112

Subsidiaries:

Transports Gazeau SAS   (1)
ZA de Bel Air, Chaudron-en-Mauges, 49110, France
Tel.: (33) 2 4170 1798
Web Site: http://www.transports-gazeau.fr
Sales Range: $25-49.9 Million
Emp.: 150
Freight Transportation Services
N.A.I.C.S.: 484121
Richard Gazeau (CEO)

Subsidiary (Domestic):

Brelet Transport SAS   (2)
8 rue des Fabriques, ZI Beau Soleil, 44450, Saint-Julien-de-Concelles, France
Tel.: (33) 2 4036 8900
Web Site: http://www.brelet-transport.fr
Sales Range: $10-24.9 Million
Emp.: 140
Freight Transportation Services
N.A.I.C.S.: 484121
Yves Arnaud (Dir-Mktg)

GROUPIMO S.A.
Immeuble Trident 12-14 avenue Louis Domergue, 97200, Fort-de-France, Martinique
Tel.: (596) 5 96757677
Web Site: http://www.groupimo.fr
ALIMO—(EUR)
Sales Range: $1-9.9 Million
Real Estate Services
N.A.I.C.S.: 531390
Stephane Plaissy (Chm & CEO)

GROVE INTERNATIONAL PTY LIMITED
Level 14 67 Albert Avenue, Chatswood, 2067, NSW, Australia
Tel.: (61) 294142255
Web Site: http://www.groveint.com.au
Year Founded: 1958
Sales Range: $50-74.9 Million
Emp.: 40
Export, Logistics & International Trade Financial Services
N.A.I.C.S.: 425120
Rashmi Shah (CEO)

Subsidiaries:

Geoffrey Hughes (Export) Pty Limited   (1)
Level 14 67 Albert Avenue, Chatswood, Sydney, 2067, NSW, Australia
Tel.: (61) 294151666
Web Site: http://www.geoffreyhughes.com.au
Sales Range: $25-49.9 Million
Emp.: 36
Export Services
N.A.I.C.S.: 425120
Richard McGuirk (Gen Mgr-Sls)

Kerr Brothers (Exports) Pty Limited   (1)
Level 14 67 Albert Ave, Chatswood, Sydney, 3047, NSW, Australia
Tel.: (61) 294142255
Web Site: http://www.kerrbros.com.au
Sales Range: $25-49.9 Million
Emp.: 30
Export Services
N.A.I.C.S.: 561499
David Young (Gen Mgr)

Ronane International Pty Ltd   (1)
Level 14 67 Albert Avenue, PO Box 1065, Chatswood, 2067, NSW, Australia
Tel.: (61) 2 9419 2799
Web Site: http://www.ronane.com.au
Metal Products Mfr
N.A.I.C.S.: 332312

GROVEPOINT CAPITAL LLP
8 - 12 York Gate, London, NW1 4QG, United Kingdom
Tel.: (44) 20 7486 5954   UK
Web Site: http://www.grovepoint.co.uk
Year Founded: 2010
Private Equity, Corporate Lending & Investment Management Services
N.A.I.C.S.: 523999
Leon Blitz (Mng Partner)

Subsidiaries:

Bremer Kreditbank AG   (1)
Wachtstrasse 16, 28195, Bremen, Germany
Tel.: (49) 42136840
Web Site: http://www.bkb-bank.com
Commercial Banking Asset Management & Investment Banking Services

---

N.A.I.C.S.: 522110
Jutta Nikolic (Sr VP)

Subsidiary (Domestic):

Oldenburgische Landesbank AG   (2)
Stau 15/17, 26122, Oldenburg, Germany
Tel.: (49) 4412210
Web Site: https://www.olb.de
Sales Range: $400-449.9 Million
International Banking
N.A.I.C.S.: 522299

Subsidiary (Domestic):

Degussa Bank AG   (3)
Theodor Heuss Allee 74, 60486, Frankfurt am Main, Germany
Tel.: (49) 6936005555
Web Site: http://www.degussa-bank.de
Sales Range: $50-74.9 Million
Emp.: 400
Banking Services
N.A.I.C.S.: 522299

EnServe Group Limited   (1)
8-12 York Gate, Wakefield, NW1 4QG, Leeds, United Kingdom
Tel.: (44) 8451642020
Web Site: http://www.enservegroup.com
Commercial, Public & Utilities Support Services
N.A.I.C.S.: 561499
Mark Perkins (CEO)

Subsidiary (Domestic):

Meter-U Limited   (2)
159 Huddersfield Road, Oldham, OL1 3PA, United Kingdom
Tel.: (44) 8450505102
Web Site: http://www.meter-u.co.uk
Meter Reading Services
N.A.I.C.S.: 561499
Matthew Hardcastle (Mng Dir)

National Industrial Fuel Efficiency Limited   (2)
Hawson Hubilee House 32 Duncan Close Moulton Park, Industrial Estate, Northampton, NN3 6WL, England, United Kingdom
Tel.: (44) 1619694901
Web Site: http://www.nifes.co.uk
Energy Management Services
N.A.I.C.S.: 541690
Douglas McNicol (Mng Dir & Member-Mgmt Bd)

The Freedom Group of Companies Limited   (2)
Freedom House 3 Red Hall Avenue, Paragon Business Village, Wakefield, WF1 2UL, United Kingdom
Tel.: (44) 8451642400
Web Site: http://www.freedom-group.co.uk
Emp.: 1,000
Electrical Engineering Services
N.A.I.C.S.: 541330
Mark Perkins (CEO)

Payzone UK Limited   (1)
4th Floor Highbank House Exchange Street, Stockport, SK3 0ET, Cheshire, United Kingdom
Tel.: (44) 1606566600
Web Site: http://www.payzone.co.uk
Emp.: 80
Retail Payment Outlet Services
N.A.I.C.S.: 522320

GROVER ZAMPA VINEYARDS LIMITED
B12 2nd Fl Jer Mansion Waman Pundlik Warde Marg Tata Block Bandra West, Mumbai, 400 050, India
Tel.: (91) 22 6820 5441   In
Web Site: http://www.groverzampa.in
Wine & Spirits Mfr & Distr
N.A.I.C.S.: 312130
Vivek Chandramohan (CEO)

Subsidiaries:

Charosa Wineries Limited   (1)
13th fl B Wing, Hincon House 247 Park LBS Park, Mumbai, 400083, India
Tel.: (91) 22 42386000
Web Site: http://www.charosavineyards.com
Wine Mfr

INTERNATIONAL PUBLIC

N.A.I.C.S.: 312130

Four Seasons Wines Ltd.   (1)
UB Tower UB City 24 Vittal Mallya Road, Bengaluru, 560 001, India
Tel.: (91) 80 3985 6500
Web Site:
   http://www.fourseasonsvineyards.com
Wine Mfr & Distr
N.A.I.C.S.: 312130
Abhay Kewadkar (Head-Bus & Chief Winemaker)

GROVY INDIA LIMITED
122 Vinobapuri Lajpat Nagar 2, New Delhi, 110 024, India
Tel.: (91) 1146740000
Web Site:
   https://www.grovyindia.com
Year Founded: 1985
539522—(BOM)
Rev.: $2,538,733
Assets: $4,212,721
Liabilities: $2,103,207
Net Worth: $2,109,514
Earnings: $108,531
Emp.: 9
Fiscal Year-end: 03/31/23
Real Estate Support Services
N.A.I.C.S.: 561499
Prakash Chand Jalan (Chm)

GROWENS S.P.A.
Via Pola 9, 20124, Milan, Italy
Tel.: (39) 0271040485   IT
Web Site: https://www.growens.io
GROW—(ITA)
Rev.: $87,496,085
Assets: $71,332,994
Liabilities: $49,801,207
Net Worth: $21,531,788
Earnings: $452,739
Emp.: 249
Fiscal Year-end: 12/31/21
Email Marketing
N.A.I.C.S.: 541613
Nazzareno Gorni (Founder)

Subsidiaries:

Acumbamail SL   (1)
Avda Del Rey Santo 3D 3rd floor Office 4, 13001, Ciudad Real, Spain
Tel.: (34) 911988405
Web Site: http://acumbamail.com
Mail Advertising Services
N.A.I.C.S.: 541860

Agile Telecom SpA   (1)
Via delle Magliale 53, 41012, Carpi, MO, Italy
Tel.: (39) 059640824
Web Site: https://www.agiletelecom.com
Emp.: 19
Telecommunication Servicesb
N.A.I.C.S.: 517810

Mailup Inc.   (1)
450 Townsend St, San Francisco, CA 94107
Information Technology Services
N.A.I.C.S.: 541511

GROWINGTON VENTURES INDIA LIMITED
4th Floor Shiv Chamber Plot No 21, Sector 11 CBD Belapur, Navi Mumbai, 400614, Maharashtra, India
Tel.: (91) 2249736901
Web Site: https://growington.in
Year Founded: 2010
539222—(BOM)
Rev.: $2,465,458
Assets: $2,672,382
Liabilities: $601,090
Net Worth: $2,071,292
Earnings: $150,921
Emp.: 3
Fiscal Year-end: 03/31/23
Travel Agencies
N.A.I.C.S.: 561510
Lokesh Patwa (Exec Dir)

GROWN ROGUE INTERNATIONAL INC.
340 Richmond Street West, Toronto, M5V 1X2, ON, Canada
Tel.: (503) 765-8108 ON
Web Site:
https://www.grownrogue.com
Year Founded: 1978
GRUSF—(OTCIQ)
Rev.: $17,757,283
Assets: $16,370,582
Liabilities: $7,430,882
Net Worth: $8,939,700
Earnings: $419,951
Emp.: 181
Fiscal Year-end: 10/31/22
Investment Services
N.A.I.C.S.: 523999
Sarah Strickler (Co-Founder)

Subsidiaries:

Grown Rogue Unlimited, LLC (1)
655 Rossanley Dr, Medford, OR 97501 (100%)
Tel.: (541) 613-7173
Web Site: http://www.grownrogue.com
Investment Services
N.A.I.C.S.: 523999
Obie Strickler (CEO)

GROWN UP GROUP INVESTMENT HOLDINGS LIMITED
Flat D-7/F-Blk 2 Tai Ping Industrial Centre 55 Ting Kok Road, Tai Po, New Territories, China (Hong Kong)
Tel.: (852) 26660383 Ky
Web Site: http://www.grown-up-europe.com
Year Founded: 1989
1842—(HKG)
Rev.: $50,250,173
Assets: $35,174,063
Liabilities: $18,059,610
Net Worth: $17,114,453
Earnings: ($59,415)
Emp.: 399
Fiscal Year-end: 12/31/22
Holding Company
N.A.I.C.S.: 551112
Thomas Berg (Chm)

GROWNERS S.A.
Chaussee de Louvain 431 Batiment F, 1380, Lasne, Brabant wallon, Belgium
Tel.: (32) 23573300
Web Site: http://www.growners.be
Real Estate Property Developer
N.A.I.C.S.: 531390
Vincent Schobbens (CEO)

GROWTHOPS LIMITED
Level 11 31 Queen St, Melbourne, 3000, VIC, Australia
Tel.: (61) 392438145 AU
Web Site:
http://www.growthops.com.au
Year Founded: 2017
TGO—(ASX)
Rev.: $61,002,195
Assets: $39,041,349
Liabilities: $29,049,863
Net Worth: $9,991,486
Earnings: ($30,569,638)
Fiscal Year-end: 06/30/20
Software Development & Integration Services
N.A.I.C.S.: 541512
Clint Cooper (CEO & Mng Dir)

Subsidiaries:

IECL Pty. Ltd. (1)
Level 2 249 Pitt Street, Sydney, NSW, Australia
Tel.: (61) 282700600
Web Site: https://www.iecl.com
Education Coaching Services
N.A.I.C.S.: 611710

GROWTHPOINT PROPERTIES LIMITED
The Place 1 Sandton Drive, Sandton, 2196, Gauteng, South Africa
Tel.: (27) 119446000
Web Site:
http://www.growthpoint.co.za
GRT—(JSE)
Rev.: $890,265,040
Assets: $11,239,459,670
Liabilities: $5,088,798,090
Net Worth: $6,150,661,580
Earnings: $759,399,900
Emp.: 606
Fiscal Year-end: 06/30/22
Investment Services
N.A.I.C.S.: 523999
Leon Norbert Sasse (CEO-Grp)

Subsidiaries:

Growthpoint Building Managers (Pty) Limited (1)
The Place 1 Sandton Drive, Sandton, 2196, Gauteng, South Africa
Tel.: (27) 119446000
Web Site: http://www.growthpoint.co.za
Portfolio Fund Management Services
N.A.I.C.S.: 523940

Growthpoint Management Services (Pty) Limited (1)
The Place 1 Sandton Drive, Sandton, 2196, Gauteng, South Africa
Tel.: (27) 119446000
Sales Range: $50-74.9 Million
Emp.: 66
Portfolio Fund Management Services
N.A.I.C.S.: 523940
Leon Norbert Sasse (CEO)

Growthpoint Properties Australia Limited (1)
Level 18 101 Collins Street, Melbourne, 3000, VIC, Australia (63.66%)
Tel.: (61) 386812900
Web Site: https://www.growthpoint.com.au
Rev.: $221,955,127
Assets: $3,181,690,692
Liabilities: $1,437,767,088
Net Worth: $1,743,923,604
Earnings: ($199,118,589)
Fiscal Year-end: 06/30/2024
Property Investment
N.A.I.C.S.: 525990
Timothy Collyer (Mng Dir)

Paramount Property Fund Limited (1)
The Place 1 Sandton Drive, Sandton, 2196, Gauteng, South Africa
Tel.: (27) 119446000
Web Site: http://www.crosspoint.co.za
Emp.: 500
Fund Management Services
N.A.I.C.S.: 541618
Norvert Sasse (CEO)

GROZ-BECKERT KG
Parkweg 2, 72458, Albstadt, Germany
Tel.: (49) 7431 10 0 De
Web Site: http://www.groz-beckert.com
Year Founded: 1852
Sales Range: $650-699.9 Million
Emp.: 7,628
Textile Industry Tools, Industrial Needles & Other Precision Components Mfr & Whslr
N.A.I.C.S.: 333248
Thomas Lindner (Chm-Exec Bd-Corp Functions Controlling, Fin & Corp Dev)

Subsidiaries:

Groz-Beckert (Shanghai) Trading Co., Ltd. (1)
803 Tower B Dawning Center 500 Hong Bao Shi Road, 201103, Shanghai, China
Tel.: (86) 2162754465
Textile Products Distr
N.A.I.C.S.: 424310

Groz-Beckert (Yantai) Trading Co., Ltd. (1)
No 3 No 10 Songhuajiang Road Yeda, Yantai, 264006, China
Tel.: (86) 5356386827
Industrial Precision Part Mfr & Distr
N.A.I.C.S.: 332721

Groz-Beckert Asia Private Limited (1)
Coral Square 5th Floor Vijay Garden Naka Near Suraj Water Park, Ghodbunder Road, 400 607, Thane, India
Tel.: (91) 2239478000
Textile Products Distr
N.A.I.C.S.: 424310

Groz-Beckert Carding Belgium NV. (1)
Kleine Tapuitstraat 12, 8540, Deerlijk, Belgium
Tel.: (32) 56651920
Textile Products Distr
N.A.I.C.S.: 424310

Groz-Beckert Carding China Co., Ltd. (1)
Xiyu Road 1038 Xishan Econimic Development Zone, Wuxi, 214101, China
Tel.: (86) 51082952922
Industrial Precision Part Mfr & Distr
N.A.I.C.S.: 332721

Groz-Beckert Carding India Private Limited (1)
Gat No 1087/5 Nagar Road Shirur, Sanaswadi, 412208, Pune, India
Tel.: (91) 2138610400
Industrial Precision Part Mfr & Distr
N.A.I.C.S.: 332721
Rizwan Khan (Asst Mgr-Pur)

Groz-Beckert France S.A. (1)
2 rue de Gribeauval, 75007, Paris, France
Tel.: (33) 145496070
Industrial Precision Part Mfr & Distr
N.A.I.C.S.: 332721

Groz-Beckert Japan K.K. (1)
4-chome 6-16 Hiranomachi, Chuo-Ku, Osaka, 541-0046, Japan
Tel.: (81) 662229400
Textile Products Distr
N.A.I.C.S.: 424310

Groz-Beckert Korea Co., Ltd. (1)
Namsong Building A-Dong 701 272 Soweol-Ro, Yongsan, 140-775, Seoul, Korea (South)
Tel.: (82) 220110200
Textile Products Distr
N.A.I.C.S.: 424310

Groz-Beckert Sales & Services Vietnam Co., Ltd. (1)
A8 Tower Office Building 1st Floor 55 Truong Quoc Dung Street, Ward 10 Phu Nhuan, Ho Chi Minh City, Vietnam
Tel.: (84) 873055200
Textile Products Distr
N.A.I.C.S.: 424310

Groz-Beckert Singapore Pte. Ltd. (1)
159 Kampong Ampat 05-03A/04 KA Place, Singapore, 368328, Singapore
Tel.: (65) 66570300
Textile Products Distr
N.A.I.C.S.: 424310

Groz-Beckert Taiwan LTD. (1)
5F No 202 Sec 2 Yanping N Rd, Datong, Taipei, Taiwan
Tel.: (886) 225531608
Textile Products Distr
N.A.I.C.S.: 424310

Groz-Beckert Trading (Shenzhen) Co., Ltd. (1)
5/F Yantai ETDZ 10 Song Hua Jiang Road, 264006, Yantai, China
Tel.: (86) 5356386827
Textile Products Distr
N.A.I.C.S.: 424310

Groz-Beckert Turkey Tekstil Makine Parcalari Ticaret Limited Sirketi (1)
Gen Ali Riza Gurcan Caddesi Alparslan Is Merkezi No 29/1, 34169, Istanbul, Turkiye
Tel.: (90) 2129246868
Textile Products Distr
N.A.I.C.S.: 424310

Groz-Beckert USA, Inc. (1)
Lakemont Business Park 3480 Lakemont Blvd, Fort Mill, SC 29708
Tel.: (803) 548-4769
Web Site: http://www.groz-beckert.com
Textile Industry Tools, Industrial Needles & Other Precision Components Mfr & Whslr
N.A.I.C.S.: 333248
Joe Ramey (Mgr-Technical-Non-Wovens)

Groz-Beckert de Mexico S.A. de C.V. (1)
Ricardo Torres No 3 Col Lomas de Sotelo, 53390, Naucalpan, Mexico
Tel.: (52) 5555804322
Textile Products Distr
N.A.I.C.S.: 424310

PT Groz-Beckert Indonesia (1)
Jl Haji Hasan 26B BDSP 40122, PO Box 7788, 40132, Bandung, Indonesia
Tel.: (62) 222534499
Textile Products Distr
N.A.I.C.S.: 424310

Schmeing GmbH & Co. KG (1)
Ostring 26, Raesfeld, 46348, Borken, Germany
Tel.: (49) 28659090
Web Site: http://www.schmeing.com
Precision Component Mfr & Distr
N.A.I.C.S.: 332721

Sinotech Asia Ltd. (1)
C702 Beijing Lufthansa Centre 50 Liangmaqiao Road, Chaoyang, Beijing, 100125, China
Tel.: (86) 1064651545
Industrial Precision Part Mfr & Distr
N.A.I.C.S.: 332721

GRP LIMITED
510 A Wing Kohinoor City Commercial - I Kirol Road Off, L B Shastri Marg Kurla W, Mumbai, 400 070, India
Tel.: (91) 2267082600
Web Site: https://www.grpweb.com
Year Founded: 1974
GRPLTD—(NSE)
Rev.: $40,597,448
Assets: $33,815,063
Liabilities: $15,854,216
Net Worth: $17,960,847
Earnings: $227,832
Emp.: 1,134
Fiscal Year-end: 03/31/21
Rubber Products Mfr
N.A.I.C.S.: 326299
Rajendra V. Gandhi (Co-Mng Dir)

GRP LIMITED
30 Cecil Street 10-01/02, Singapore, 49712, Singapore
Tel.: (65) 62661622 SG
Web Site: https://www.grp.com.sg
Year Founded: 1977
BLU—(SES)
Rev.: $15,363,139
Assets: $32,358,319
Liabilities: $7,354,939
Net Worth: $25,003,380
Earnings: ($4,716,682)
Emp.: 1,014
Fiscal Year-end: 06/30/23
Property Rental & Leasing Services
N.A.I.C.S.: 531190
Daniel Tong how Teo (Chm)

Subsidiaries:

Luminor Financial Holdings Limited (1)
30 Cecil Street 10-01/02 Prudential Tower, Singapore, 049712, Singapore
Tel.: (65) 68659960
Web Site:
https://www.luminorfinancialholdings.com

GRP Limited—(Continued)

Holding Company; Real Estate Management & Development
N.A.I.C.S.: 551112
Peck Yen Peng *(Exec Dir)*

Region Suppliers Pte Ltd (1)
Blk 16 Kallang Place 01-02, Kallang Basin Industrial Estate, Singapore, 339156, Singapore
Tel.: (65) 6 295 2288
Web Site: http://www.regionsg.com.sg
Tool Product Mfr
N.A.I.C.S.: 333517

GRUBER GMBH & CO. KG

Muldenstrasse 17-25, 67069, Ludwigshafen, Germany
Tel.: (49) 621660020
Web Site: http://www.sped-gruber.de
Year Founded: 1954
Sales Range: $50-74.9 Million
Logistic Services
N.A.I.C.S.: 541614
Kurt Richter *(Co-Mng Dir)*

Subsidiaries:

Gruber UK Ltd. (1)
Britannia Road, Goole, DN14 6ET, East Yorkshire, United Kingdom
Tel.: (44) 1405726000
Logistics Consulting Servies
N.A.I.C.S.: 541614

GRUMA, S.A.B. DE C.V.

Calzada del Valle 407 Oriente Colonia del Valle, San Pedro, Garza Garcia, 66220, Nuevo Leon, Mexico
Tel.: (52) 8183993300 MX
Web Site: http://www.gruma.com
Year Founded: 1949
GRUMA—(MEX)
Rev.: $4,103,093,627
Assets: $3,546,129,767
Liabilities: $2,168,800,915
Net Worth: $1,377,328,853
Earnings: $256,472,427
Emp.: 20,785
Fiscal Year-end: 12/31/19
Corn Flour, Corn Tortillas & Wheat Flour Mfr
N.A.I.C.S.: 311211
Juan Antonio Gonzalez Moreno *(Chm & CEO)*

Subsidiaries:

Derivados de Maiz Alimenticio, S.A. (1)
Tel.: (506) 25431300
Web Site: https://grumacentroamerica.com
Flour Mfr
N.A.I.C.S.: 311211

Derivados de Maiz de El Salvador, S.A. (1)
Autopista A Aeropuerto, San Luis Talpa, El Salvador
Tel.: (503) 23399551
Flour Distr
N.A.I.C.S.: 311211

Gruma Corporation (1)
1159 Cottonwood Ln Ste 200, Irving, TX 75038
Tel.: (972) 232-5000
Web Site: http://www.gruma.com
Sales Range: $100-124.9 Million
Emp.: 300
Corn Flour & Tortilla Mfr
N.A.I.C.S.: 311830

Branch (Domestic):

Azteca Milling LP (2)
5601 Executive Dr, Irving, TX 75038
Tel.: (972) 232-5000
Flour Milling Operations & Distribution
N.A.I.C.S.: 311211
Don Schleppegrel *(Pres)*

Subsidiary (Non-US):

SEMOLINA MISIR IRMIGI GIDA SANAYI ve TICARET A.S. (3)
Tel.: (90) 3622664390
Web Site: https://www.semolinagruma.com
Sales Range: $25-49.9 Million
Emp.: 67
Corn Milling Services
N.A.I.C.S.: 311221

Branch (Domestic):

Gruma Corporation (2)
1565 1st Ave NW, New Brighton, MN 55112-1948
Tel.: (651) 697-5500
Web Site: http://www.missionfoods.com
Sales Range: $25-49.9 Million
Emp.: 300
Tortilla Chips, Salsas & Other Snack Food Products Mfr & Distr
N.A.I.C.S.: 311999
Michiel Butcher *(Gen Mgr)*

Gruma Netherlands B.V. (1)
Produktieweg 5, 6045 JC, Roermond, Netherlands
Tel.: (31) 475324446
Tortilla Mfr
N.A.I.C.S.: 311830

Gruma Oceania Pty. Ltd. (1)
49 Gateway Blvd, Epping, 3076, VIC, Australia
Tel.: (61) 1800641529
Web Site: https://www.missionfoods.com.au
Tortilla Mfr
N.A.I.C.S.: 311830

Grupo Industrial Maseca, S.A.B. de C.V. (1)
Calzada del Valle 407 Ote, San Pedro, 66220, Garza Garcia, NL, Mexico
Tel.: (52) 8183993300
Web Site: http://www.gimsa.com
Rev.: $6,576,230,000
Assets: $4,683,094,000
Liabilities: $2,839,816,000
Net Worth: $1,843,278,000
Earnings: $432,650,000
Fiscal Year-end: 12/31/2023
Corn Flour Production, Distribution & Sales
N.A.I.C.S.: 311211
Juan Antonio Gonzalez Moreno *(Chm)*

Subsidiary (Domestic):

Harinera de Maiz de Jalisco, S.A. de C.V. (2)
Acueducto Chapala-Guadalajara Km 39.2, Tlajomulco de Zuniga, Jalisco, Mexico
Tel.: (52) 3336010681
Grain Processing Services
N.A.I.C.S.: 111199

Harinera de Maiz de Mexicali, S.A. de C.V. (2)
Av Michoacan de Ocampo No 2000, Ejido Puebla, Mexicali, Mexico
Tel.: (52) 6865628200
Corn Processing Services
N.A.I.C.S.: 311211

Molinos Azteca, S.A. de C.V. (2)
Calle 7 Ste 1057 Zona Industrial, Guadalupe, CP 44970, Jalisco, Mexico
Tel.: (52) 3336456980
Sales Range: $10-24.9 Million
Emp.: 150
Grain Milling Services
N.A.I.C.S.: 311211
Javier Ortiz Radillo *(Gen Mgr)*

Mission Foods (Malaysia) Sdn. Bhd. (1)
Block C Lot 506 Jalan Pelabuhan Bandar Sultan Suleiman 4200, 42000, Port Klang, Selangor, Malaysia
Tel.: (60) 67986988
Web Site: https://www.missionfoods.com.my
Bakery Products Mfr
N.A.I.C.S.: 311821

Mission Foods (Shanghai) Co., Ltd. (1)
No 933 Wuxing Central Road, Nan Qiao Town Feng Xian Distri, Shanghai, 201499, China
Tel.: (86) 2137108500
Food Mfr
N.A.I.C.S.: 311412

Mission Foods UK, Ltd. (1)
Renown Avenue Coventry Business Park, Coventry, CV5 6UJ, United Kingdom
Tel.: (44) 2476701710
Web Site: https://www.missionfoodservice.co.uk
Food Mfr
N.A.I.C.S.: 311999

Molinos Nacionales, C.A. (1)
Av Universidad Cumana Estado Sucre, Caracas, Venezuela (98%)
Tel.: (58) 2934512670
Web Site: http://www.monaca.com.ve
Rev.: $177,900,000
Emp.: 1,931
Diversified Food Manufacturing & Marketing
N.A.I.C.S.: 311999

NDF Azteca Milling Europe SRL (1)
Via 1 Maggio 367, Ceggia, 30022, Venice, Italy
Tel.: (39) 0421467700
Web Site: https://www.ndfgruma.com
Tortilla Mfr
N.A.I.C.S.: 311830

Productos y Distribuidora Azteca, S.A. de C.V. (1)
Ave Revolucion 110 Col Buenos Aires, Monterrey, 64800, Nuevo Leon, Mexico
Tel.: (52) 81 8153 8600
Sales Range: $150-199.9 Million
Emp.: 300
Food Products Distr
N.A.I.C.S.: 424420

Tortimasa, S.A. (1)
Km 6 Carretera Norte De Donde Fue Siemens, Managua, Nicaragua
Tel.: (505) 22522101
Corn Flour Mfr
N.A.I.C.S.: 311211

ZAO Solntse Mexico (1)
7 Izhorskaya Ul, Moscow, 125599, Russia
Tel.: (7) 4957257728
Web Site: http://www.solntsemexico.ru
Emp.: 220
Tortilla Mfr
N.A.I.C.S.: 311830
Nataliya Marchenko *(Office Mgr)*

GRUNENTHAL GMBH

Zieglerstrasse 6, 52078, Aachen, Germany
Tel.: (49) 241 569 0 De
Web Site: http://www.grunenthal.com
Year Founded: 1946
Emp.: 5,200
Pharmaceutical Developer & Mfr
N.A.I.C.S.: 325412
Gabriel Baertschi *(Chm-Exec Bd & CEO)*

Subsidiaries:

Adhesys Medical GmbH (1)
Pauwelsstrasse 17, 52074, Aachen, Germany
Tel.: (49) 24114250320
Web Site: http://www.adhesys-medical.com
Pharmaceuticals Product Mfr
N.A.I.C.S.: 325412
Sebastian Kohler *(Mng Dir)*

Farmaceutici Formenti S.p.A. (1)
Via Di Vittorio 2, 21040, Origgio, Italy
Tel.: (39) 02969581
Pharmaceuticals Product Mfr
N.A.I.C.S.: 325412

Grunenthal B.V. (1)
De Corridor 21K, 3621 ZA, Breukelen, Netherlands
Tel.: (31) 306046370
Web Site: http://www.grunenthal.nl
Pharmaceuticals Product Mfr
N.A.I.C.S.: 325412

Grunenthal Chilena Ltda. (1)
Av Quilin 5273, Penalolen, Santiago, Chile
Tel.: (56) 225948000
Web Site: http://www.grunenthal.cl
Pharmaceuticals Product Mfr
N.A.I.C.S.: 325412
Richard Nevares *(Gen Mgr)*

Grunenthal Colombiana S.A. (1)
Calle 93 No 16-20 Apartado Aereo No 250381 Santa Fe de, Bogota, Colombia
Tel.: (57) 16185550
Pharmaceuticals Product Mfr
N.A.I.C.S.: 325412
Jose Maria Mora *(Gen Mgr)*

Grunenthal Denmark ApS (1)
Arne Jacobsens Alle 7, 2300, Copenhagen, Denmark
Tel.: (45) 88883200
Pharmaceuticals Product Mfr
N.A.I.C.S.: 325412
Magnus Rehnstrom *(CFO)*

Grunenthal Ecuatoriana C. Ltda. (1)
Av Manuel Cordova Galarza Km 6 1/2 Via a la Mitad del Mundo Apartado, PO Box 17-17-075, Pusuqui, Quito, Ecuador
Tel.: (593) 22989000
Pharmaceuticals Product Mfr
N.A.I.C.S.: 325412
Guillermo Menendez *(Gen Mgr)*

Grunenthal Ges. m. b. H. (1)
Campus 21 Liebermannstr A01/501, 2345, Brunn am Gebirge, Austria
Tel.: (43) 2236379550
Web Site: http://www.grunenthal.at
Billing Services
N.A.I.C.S.: 541219

Grunenthal Italia S.r.l. (1)
Via Carlo Bo 11, 20143, Milan, Italy
Tel.: (39) 0243051
Pharmaceuticals Product Mfr
N.A.I.C.S.: 325412
Marilena Ritrovato *(Head-Legal & Compliance)*

Grunenthal Ltd. (1)
Unit 1 Stokenchurch Business Park, Stokenchurch, HP14 3FE, United Kingdom
Tel.: (44) 8703518960
Pharmaceuticals Product Mfr
N.A.I.C.S.: 325412
Julia Pinto *(Brand Mgr)*

Grunenthal Norway AS (1)
C J Hambros Plass 2 C, 0164, Oslo, Norway
Tel.: (47) 22996054
Pharmaceuticals Product Mfr
N.A.I.C.S.: 325412

Grunenthal Peruana S.A. (1)
Calle De Las Letras 261, San Borja, Lima, Peru
Tel.: (51) 5190600
Web Site: http://www.grunenthal.com.pe
Pharmaceuticals Product Mfr
N.A.I.C.S.: 325412
Guillermo Sifuentes Mitterhofer *(Brand Mgr)*

Grunenthal Pharma AG (1)
Sandli 2, Mitlodi, 8756, Glarus, Switzerland
Tel.: (41) 556473131
Pharmaceuticals Product Mfr
N.A.I.C.S.: 325412

Grunenthal Pharma Ltd. (1)
4045 Kingswood Road Citywest Business Park Citywest Co, Dublin, Ireland
Tel.: (353) 8703518960
Pharmaceuticals Product Mfr
N.A.I.C.S.: 325412

Grunenthal Pharma SA (1)
C/ Doctor Zamenhof 36, 28027, Madrid, Spain
Tel.: (34) 3019300
Web Site: http://www.grunenthal.es
Pharmaceuticals Product Mfr
N.A.I.C.S.: 325412
Montserrat Sivilla *(Mgr-Learning & Dev)*

Grunenthal S.A. (1)
Alameda Fernao Lopes 12 8A, 1495-190, Alges, Portugal
Tel.: (351) 1214726300
Pharmaceuticals Product Mfr
N.A.I.C.S.: 325412

Grunenthal Sweden AB (1)
Gustav III s Boulevard 34 4tr, 169 73, Solna, Sweden
Tel.: (46) 86434060
Pharmaceuticals Product Mfr
N.A.I.C.S.: 325412

Grunenthal USA, Inc. (1)

AND PRIVATE COMPANIES

360 Mount Kemble Ave, Morristown, NJ 07960
Tel.: (908) 306-0024
Web Site: http://www.grunenthal.com
Rev.: $2,700,000
Emp.: 15
Pharmaceutical Developer & Mfr
N.A.I.C.S.: 325412

Grunenthal Venezolana Farmaceutica C.A. (1)
Av Francisco de Miranda Edif Centro Galipan, Tower C Floor 12 Urb El Rosal Chacao Municipality, Caracas, Venezuela
Tel.: (58) 2122745611
Pharmaceuticals Product Mfr
N.A.I.C.S.: 325412

Grunenthal de Mexico S.A. de C.V. (1)
Periferico Sur No 5991 Col Arenal Tepepan Delegation, Tlalpan, 14610, Mexico, Mexico
Tel.: (52) 5556414488
Web Site: http://www.grunenthal.com.mx
Pharmaceuticals Product Mfr
N.A.I.C.S.: 325412
Wilber Azanza (Mgr-Medical)

Laboratoires Grunenthal S.A.S. (1)
Immeuble Eureka 19 rue Ernest Renan, CS 90001, 92024, Nanterre, Cedex, France
Tel.: (33) 141494580
Web Site: http://www.grunenthal.fr
Pharmaceuticals Product Mfr
N.A.I.C.S.: 325412

Laboratorios Silesia S.A. (1)
Avenida Quilin 5273, Penalolen, Santiago, Chile
Tel.: (56) 225948200
Pharmaceuticals Product Mfr
N.A.I.C.S.: 325412

Tecnandina S.A. (1)
Av Manuel Cordova Galarza Km 6 1/2 Via e la Mitad del Mundo Pusuqui, Quito, Ecuador
Tel.: (593) 2989111
Pharmaceuticals Product Mfr
N.A.I.C.S.: 325412

Thar Pharmaceuticals, Inc. (1)
150 Gamma Dr, Pittsburgh, PA 15238
Tel.: (412) 963-6800
Pharmaceutical Preparation Mfr
N.A.I.C.S.: 325412

GRUNWALD EQUITY MANAGEMENT GMBH
Sudliche Munchner Str 10, Grunwald, 82031, Germany
Tel.: (49) 8950080860
Web Site: http://www.gruenwaldequity.de
Sales Range: $10-24.9 Million
Emp.: 2
Privater Equity Firm
N.A.I.C.S.: 523999
Raimund Konig (Mng Partner)

GRUP SIMEX S.R.L.
Str Barajului Nr 3, 540191, Targu Mures, Romania
Tel.: (40) 265320083
Web Site: http://grupsimex.ro
Emp.: 35
Furniture Mfr
N.A.I.C.S.: 337126

Subsidiaries:

Cesimex S.R.L. (1)
Plopilor Nr 1, Cehu Silvaniei, 455100, Romania
Tel.: (40) 26 067 8653
Household Furniture Mfr
N.A.I.C.S.: 337126

Nord Simex S.R.L. (1)
Str Depozitelor Nr 21, Satu-Mare, 440198, Romania
Tel.: (40) 72 245 8691
Household Furniture Mfr
N.A.I.C.S.: 337126

Simex Plus S.R.L. (1)
Str Tudor Vladimirescu Nr 48, Simleu Silvaniei, 455300, Romania
Tel.: (40) 26 067 9035
Household Furniture Mfr
N.A.I.C.S.: 337126

GRUPA AZOTY S.A.
ul E Kwiatkowskiego 8, 33-101, Tarnow, Poland
Tel.: (48) 146373737 PL
Web Site: https://www.grupaazoty.com
Year Founded: 1927
ATT—(WAR)
Rev.: $3,441,334,849
Assets: $6,172,896,326
Liabilities: $4,529,530,222
Net Worth: $1,643,366,104
Earnings: ($835,991,868)
Fiscal Year-end: 12/31/23
All Other Basic Organic Chemical Manufacturing
N.A.I.C.S.: 325199
Wojciech Piotr Wardacki (Chm-Mgmt Bd)

Subsidiaries:

Compo Expert Argentina SRL (1)
Zapiola 4248 - 5th floor dp A-B, 1429 AOD, Buenos Aires, Argentina
Tel.: (54) 1145453342
Web Site: https://www.compo-expert.com
Fertilizer Mfr
N.A.I.C.S.: 325314

Compo Expert Asia Pacific Sdn. Bhd. (1)
Suite B-05-13 Empire SOHO Empire Subang Jalan SS16/1, 47500, Subang Jaya, Selangor, Malaysia
Tel.: (60) 356120513
Web Site: https://www.compo-expert.com
Fertilizer Mfr
N.A.I.C.S.: 325311

Compo Expert Austria GmbH (1)
Hietzinger Hauptstr 119, 1130, Vienna, Austria
Tel.: (43) 87663930
Web Site: https://www.compo-expert.com
Fertilizer Mfr
N.A.I.C.S.: 325314

Compo Expert Benelux N. V. (1)
Filliersdreef 14, 9800, Deinze, Belgium
Tel.: (32) 93818383
Web Site: https://www.compo-expert.com
Fertilizer Mfr
N.A.I.C.S.: 325314

Compo Expert Brasil Fertilizantes Ltda. (1)
Rua Cristovao Nunes Pires 110 100 Andar Bairro Centro, Florianopolis, 88010120, SC, Brazil
Tel.: (55) 4837229500
Web Site: https://www.compo-expert.com
Fertilizer Mfr
N.A.I.C.S.: 325311

Compo Expert Chile Fertilizantes Ltda. (1)
Carmencita 25 Piso 9 Oficina 91, Las Condes, Santiago, Chile
Tel.: (56) 25978400
Web Site: https://www.compo-expert.com
Fertilizer Mfr
N.A.I.C.S.: 325314

Compo Expert France SAS (1)
120 Rue Jean Jaures, 92300, Levallois-Perret, France
Tel.: (33) 141054945
Web Site: https://www.compo-expert.com
Fertilizer Mfr
N.A.I.C.S.: 325314

Compo Expert GmbH (1)
Krogerweg 10, 48155, Munster, Germany
Tel.: (49) 251297981000
Web Site: https://www.compo-expert.com
Fertilizer Mfr
N.A.I.C.S.: 325311
Thomas H. Ahrens (CEO)

Compo Expert Hellas S.A. (1)
Egialias 54, 151 25, Maroussi, Athens, Greece
Tel.: (30) 2111769100
Web Site: https://www.compo-expert.com
Fertilizer Mfr
N.A.I.C.S.: 325311

Compo Expert India Private Limited (1)
Office No 108 1st Floor Tower No 2 World Trade Center, Kharadi, Pune, 411014, India
Tel.: (91) 8698255888
Web Site: https://www.compo-expert.com
Fertilizer Mfr
N.A.I.C.S.: 325314

Compo Expert Italia S.r.l. (1)
Via Marconato 8, 20811, Cesano Maderno, MB, Italy
Tel.: (39) 03621869011
Web Site: https://www.compo-expert.com
Fertilizer Mfr
N.A.I.C.S.: 325311

Compo Expert Mexico S. A. de C. V. (1)
Av Mariano Otero 1249 Int B2121, Col Rinconada Del Bosque, 44530, Guadalajara, Jalisco, Mexico
Tel.: (52) 3336121512
Web Site: https://www.compo-expert.com
Fertilizer Mfr
N.A.I.C.S.: 325314

Compo Expert Polska Sp. z o.o. (1)
Aleje Solidarnosci 46, 61-696, Poznan, Poland
Tel.: (48) 616286531
Web Site: https://www.compo-expert.com
Fertilizer Mfr
N.A.I.C.S.: 325311

Compo Expert Portugal, Unipessoal Lda. (1)
Rua Luciano Cordeiro 116- 3, 1050-140, Lisbon, Portugal
Tel.: (351) 913527314
Web Site: https://www.compo-expert.com
Fertilizer Mfr
N.A.I.C.S.: 325311

Compo Expert South Africa (Pty) Ltd. (1)
3 Leipoldt Street Bellville, Cape Town, 7530, Western Cape, South Africa
Tel.: (27) 825535431
Web Site: https://www.compo-expert.com
Fertilizer Mfr
N.A.I.C.S.: 325314

Compo Expert Spain S.L. (1)
Pl La Mezquita C/ B-3 parc 203, 12600, La Vall d'Uixo, Spain
Tel.: (34) 964652732
Fertilizer Mfr
N.A.I.C.S.: 325311

Compo Expert Techn. (Shenzhen) Co., Ltd. (1)
No 2601 26th Floor Great China International East Plaza, Jintian South Road Futian District, Shenzhen, 518048, China
Tel.: (86) 75583205389
Web Site: https://www.compo-expert.com.cn
Fertilizer Mfr
N.A.I.C.S.: 325311

Compo Expert Turkiye Tarim San.ve Tic. Ltd. (1)
Barbaros Mah Cigdem Sok Agaoglu My Office No 1 K 14 D 60, Atasehir, Istanbul, Turkiye
Tel.: (90) 2166885118
Web Site: https://www.compo-expert.com
Fertilizer Mfr
N.A.I.C.S.: 325314

Compo Expert UK Ltd. (1)
Office 5 16 New Street, Stourport-on-Severn, DY13 8UW, United Kingdom
Tel.: (44) 337721904
Fertilizer Mfr
N.A.I.C.S.: 325311

Compo Expert USA & Canada Inc. (1)
PO Box 5106, Vero Beach, FL 32961-5106
Tel.: (859) 469-0579
Web Site: https://www.compo-expert.com
Fertilizer Mfr
N.A.I.C.S.: 325311

Grupa Azoty ATT Polymers GmbH (1)
Forster Strasse 72, 03172, Guben, Germany
Tel.: (49) 356162055
Web Site: https://www.att.grupaazoty.com
Chemical Products Mfr
N.A.I.C.S.: 325199

Grupa Azoty Compounding Sp. z o.o. (1)
ul Chemiczna 118, 33-101, Tarnow, Poland
Tel.: (48) 146373310
Web Site: https://compounding.grupaazoty.com
Plastic Product Distr
N.A.I.C.S.: 424610

Grupa Azoty Jednostka Ratownictwa Chemicznego Sp. Z.o.o. (1)
St E Kwiatkowskiego 8, 33-101, Tarnow, Poland
Tel.: (48) 146330682
Web Site: https://jrch.grupaazoty.com
Biochemical Mfr
N.A.I.C.S.: 325199

Grupa Azoty Koltar Sp. z o.o. (1)
ul E Kwiatkowskiego 8, 33-101, Tarnow, Poland
Tel.: (48) 146372634
Web Site: https://koltar.grupaazoty.com
Railway Transportation Services
N.A.I.C.S.: 488210

Grupa Azoty Kopalnie i Zakiady Chemiczne Siarki Siarkopol S. A. (1)
Grzybow, 28-200, Staszow, Poland
Tel.: (48) 158648000
Web Site: https://siarkopol.grupaazoty.com
Mining Services
N.A.I.C.S.: 212321

Grupa Azoty Kopalnie i Zakiady Chemiczne Siarki "Siarkopol" S.A. (1)
Grzybow 34, 28-200, Staszow, Poland
Tel.: (48) 158648000
Web Site: https://siarkopol.grupaazoty.com
Sulphur Mining Services
N.A.I.C.S.: 212390

Grupa Azoty Polskie Konsorcjum Chemiczne Sp. z o.o. (1)
ul E Kwiatkowskiego 7, 33-101, Tarnow, Poland
Tel.: (48) 146372320
Web Site: https://www.pkch.grupaazoty.com
Chemical Products Mfr
N.A.I.C.S.: 325199
Jerzy Wolinski (Pres)

Subsidiary (Domestic):

Grupa Azoty Automatyka Sp. z o.o. (2)
ul E Kwiatkowskiego 8, 33-101, Tarnow, Poland
Tel.: (48) 146373554
Web Site: https://automatyka.grupaazoty.com
Emp.: 380
Construction Services
N.A.I.C.S.: 236220
Artur Maciejczyk (Pres)

Grupa Azoty PROREM Sp. z o.o. (2)
ul Mostowa 24 D, 47-200, Kedzierzyn-Kozle, Poland
Tel.: (48) 774812838
Web Site: https://www.prorem.grupaazoty.com
Emp.: 600
Construction Engineering Services
N.A.I.C.S.: 541330
Artur Sebesta (Pres)

Grupa Azoty Zakiady Azotowe Kedzierzyn S. A. (1)
Ul Mostowa 30 A, PO Box 163, 47-220, Kedzierzyn-Kozle, Poland
Tel.: (48) 774812000
Web Site: https://zak.grupaazoty.com
Compound Fertilizers Mfr & Distr
N.A.I.C.S.: 325311

Grupa Azoty Zakiady Azotowe Pulawy S. A. (1)
Al Tysiaclecia Panstwa Polskiego 13, 24-110, Pulawy, Poland

GRUPA AZOTY S.A.

Grupa Azoty S.A.—(Continued)
Tel.: (48) 818863431
Web Site: https://pulawy.grupaazoty.com
Chemical Products Mfr & Distr
N.A.I.C.S.: 325998

Grupa Azoty Zaklady Azotowe chorzow S. A. (1)
St Narutowicza 15, 41-503, Chorzow, Poland
Tel.: (48) 327362000
Web Site: https://chorzow.grupaazoty.com
Biochemical Mfr
N.A.I.C.S.: 325199

Grupa Azoty Zaklady Chemiczne Police S. A. (1)
Ul Kuznicka 1, 72-010, Police, Poland
Tel.: (48) 913171717
Web Site: https://zchpolice.grupaazoty.com
Compound Fertilizers Mfr & Distr
N.A.I.C.S.: 325311

Grupa Azoty Zaklady Azotowe Kedzierzyn S.A. (1)
ul Mostowa 30 A, Skr Poczt 163, 47-220, Kedzierzyn-Kozle, Poland
Tel.: (48) 774812000
Web Site: https://www.zak.grupaazoty.com
Chemical Products Mfr
N.A.I.C.S.: 325199
Adam Leszkiewicz *(Pres & Gen Dir)*

Subsidiary (Domestic):

Zaksa S.A. (2)
ul Mostowa 1A, 47-223, Kedzierzyn-Kozle, Poland
Tel.: (48) 774054142
Web Site: https://zaksa.pl
Sports Club Services
N.A.I.C.S.: 711211

Grupa Azoty Zaklady Chemiczne "Police" S.A. (1)
ul Kuznicka 1, 72-010, Police, Poland
Tel.: (48) 913171717
Web Site: https://zchpolice.grupaazoty.com
Chemical Product Mfr & Distr
N.A.I.C.S.: 325199
Krzysztof Jalosinski *(Pres & Dir General)*

Subsidiary (Non-US):

African Investment Group S.A. (2)
Route de Ngor Villa N 12 Almadies, 38000, Dakar, Senegal
Tel.: (221) 3 3869 9151
Web Site: http://www.aigsa.sn
Emp.: 50
Metal Mining Services
N.A.I.C.S.: 212290

Subsidiary (Domestic):

Grupa Azoty Police Serwis Sp. z o.o. (2)
ul Kuznicka 1, 72-010, Police, Poland
Tel.: (48) 913174214
Web Site: https://policeserwis.grupaazoty.com
Construction Services
N.A.I.C.S.: 236220

Grupa Azoty Transtech Sp. z o.o. (2)
ul Kuznicka 1, 72-010, Police, Poland
Tel.: (48) 913174335
Web Site: https://www.grupaazoty.transtech.pl
Automotive Repair & Maintenance Services
N.A.I.C.S.: 811111

Supra Agrochemia Sp. z o.o. (2)
ul Monopolowa 6, 51-501, Wroclaw, Poland
Tel.: (48) 713481031
Web Site: http://www.gasupra.pl
Fertilizer Mfr
N.A.I.C.S.: 325311

SCF Natural Sp.z.o.o. (1)
Suchodoly 120, 21-060, Fajslawice, Poland
Tel.: (48) 814679988
Web Site: https://scfnatural.pl
Natural Product Mfr
N.A.I.C.S.: 325199

Zaklady Azotowe Pulawy S.A. (1)
Al Tysiaclecia Panstwa Polskiego 13, 24-110, Pulawy, Poland **(95.98%)**
Tel.: (48) 818863431
Web Site: https://pulawy.grupaazoty.com
Rev.: $864,444,612
Assets: $1,487,935,261
Liabilities: $523,678,601
Net Worth: $964,256,660
Earnings: $58,197,475
Emp.: 4,704
Fiscal Year-end: 12/31/2020
Fertilizers & Chemicals Mfr
N.A.I.C.S.: 325311
Tomasz Hryniewicz *(Chm-Mgmt Bd)*

Subsidiary (Domestic):

Agrochem Pulawy Sp. z o.o. (2)
ul Mickiewicza 5, 77-300, Czluchow, Poland
Tel.: (48) 593070606
Web Site: https://www.agrochem.com.pl
Chemical Products Distr
N.A.I.C.S.: 424690

Grupa Azoty Zaklady Azotowe Chorzow S.A. (2)
ul Narutowicza 15, 41-503, Chorzow, Poland
Tel.: (48) 327362000
Web Site: https://chorzow.grupaazoty.com
Chemical Products Distr
N.A.I.C.S.: 424690

PROZAP Sp. z o.o. (2)
Al Tysiaclecia Panstwa Polskiego 13, 24-110, Pulawy, Poland
Tel.: (48) 814731600
Web Site: https://www.prozap.com.pl
Construction Engineering Services
N.A.I.C.S.: 541330

REMZAP Sp. z o.o. (2)
12 Ignacego Moscickiego St, 24-110, Pulawy, Poland
Tel.: (48) 815066000
Web Site: https://www.remzap.pl
Construction Engineering Services
N.A.I.C.S.: 541330
Jozef Strzalkowski *(Pres)*

STO-ZAP Sp. z o.o. (2)
Al Tysiaclecia Panstwa Polskiego 12, 24-110, Pulawy, Poland
Tel.: (48) 814731280
Web Site: https://www.stozap.pl
Chemical Products Distr
N.A.I.C.S.: 424690

GRUPA FORTIS D.O.O. BANJA LUKA
Tunjice bb, 78 000, Banja Luka, Bosnia & Herzegovina
Tel.: (387) 51366160   BA
Web Site: http://www.fortisgroup.ba
Year Founded: 2008
Holding Company; Civil Engineering & Construction Services
N.A.I.C.S.: 551112

Subsidiaries:

Prijedorputevi a.d. Prijedor (1)
27 juni br 17, 79 000, Prijedor, Bosnia & Herzegovina
Tel.: (387) 52233117
Web Site: http://www.prijedorputevi.ba
Construction & Maintenance Services
N.A.I.C.S.: 237310
Mile Janjic *(Chm-Mgmt Bd)*

Subsidiary (Domestic):

Industroprojekt a.d. (2)
Vozda Karadorda 14, 79101, Prijedor, Bosnia & Herzegovina **(56.17%)**
Tel.: (387) 52232645
Web Site: https://industroprojektpd.com
Sales Range: Less than $1 Million
Technical Consulting Services
N.A.I.C.S.: 541690

Kozaraputevi d.o.o. Banja Luka (2)
Tunjice bb, 78 000, Banja Luka, Bosnia & Herzegovina
Tel.: (387) 52233117
Web Site: http://www.kozaraputevi.ba
Road Maintenance & Protection Services
N.A.I.C.S.: 488490

Subsidiary (Domestic):

Bijeljina Put AD (3)
Baje Pivljanina bb, 76300, Bijeljina, Bosnia & Herzegovina
Tel.: (387) 55 247 879
Construction Services
N.A.I.C.S.: 236210

GRUPA GRASS SP. Z O.O.
ul Mazowiecka 6, 09 100, Plonsk, Poland
Tel.: (48) 23 662 6801   PL
Web Site: http://www.grupa-grass.pl
Emp.: 120
Holding Company; Ceramics, Shower Products & Other Household Goods Mfr & Distr
N.A.I.C.S.: 551112
Monika Nowakowska *(Gen Mgr)*

Subsidiaries:

DLH Poland Sp. z o.o. (1)
Siedziba Zarzadu ul Sosnkowskiego 1d, 02-495, Warsaw, Poland
Tel.: (48) 22 667 4414
Web Site: http://www.en.dlh.pl
Wood Whslr
N.A.I.C.S.: 423310
Dariusz Bielski *(Product Mgr)*

DLH Slovakia s.r.o. (1)
Tuhovska 1, 831 07, Bratislava, Slovakia
Tel.: (421) 910991483
Web Site: http://www.dlh-slovakia.com
Wood Products Whslr
N.A.I.C.S.: 423310
Marcel Novak *(CEO)*

GRUPA KAPITALOWA IMMOBILE S.A.
Plac Koscieleckich 3, 85-033, Bydgoszcz, Poland
Tel.: (48) 525612330
Web Site: https://www.immobile.com.pl
Year Founded: 1868
GKI—(WAR)
Rev.: $238,855,945
Assets: $244,001,524
Liabilities: $177,608,485
Net Worth: $66,393,038
Earnings: $1,278,963
Fiscal Year-end: 12/31/23
Steel Structural Mfr
N.A.I.C.S.: 238120
Slawomir Winiecki *(Vice Chm-Mgmt Bd)*

GRUPA KETY S.A.
Ul Kosciuszki 111, 32-650, Kety, Poland
Tel.: (48) 338446000
Web Site: https://www.grupakety.com
Year Founded: 1996
KETY—(WAR)
Rev.: $343,709,360
Assets: $307,675,929
Liabilities: $129,857,254
Net Worth: $177,818,674
Earnings: $53,895,447
Emp.: 5,000
Fiscal Year-end: 12/31/19
Aluminium Products Mfr
N.A.I.C.S.: 331315
Piotr Stepniak *(Chm/Deputy Chm-Supervisory Bd)*

Subsidiaries:

Aluminium Kety Emmi D.O.O. (1)
Kolodvorska 37 a, 2310, Slovenska Bistrica, Slovenia
Tel.: (386) 28050500
Web Site: http://www.emmi.si
Aluiminium Component Mfr
N.A.I.C.S.: 331524
Roman Stegne *(CEO)*

Alupol Packaging Kety Sp. z o.o. (1)
Ul Kosciuszki 111, 32-650, Kety, Poland

INTERNATIONAL PUBLIC

Tel.: (48) 338446433
Plastic Packaging Sheet Mfr
N.A.I.C.S.: 326112

Subsidiary (Domestic):

Alupol Films Sp. z o.o. (2)
Ul Gospodarcza 18, 32-600, Oswiecim, Poland
Tel.: (48) 323245741
Web Site: http://www.alupolfilms.eu
Plastic Packaging Products Mfr
N.A.I.C.S.: 322220
Tomasz Zielinski *(Reg Dir)*

Alupol Packaging S.A. (1)
ul Strefowa 4, 43-109, Tychy, Poland **(100%)**
Tel.: (48) 323245700
Web Site: http://www.alupolpackaging.eu
Sales Range: $100-124.9 Million
Emp.: 300
Flexible Packaging
N.A.I.C.S.: 326112
Rafal Lechowacz *(Pres, CEO & Member-Mgmt Bd)*

Aluprof Deutschland GmbH (1)
Steller Heide 20, Schwanewede, 28790, Bremen, Germany **(100%)**
Tel.: (49) 42189818920
Web Site: http://www.aluprof.eu
Sales Range: $25-49.9 Million
Emp.: 5
Primary Aluminum Production
N.A.I.C.S.: 331313
Rafal Altheim *(Mng Dir)*

Aluprof S.A. (1)
Ul Warszawska 153, 43-300, Bielsko-Biala, Poland
Tel.: (48) 338195300
Web Site: http://www.aluprof.eu
Emp.: 2,200
Aluminum Mfr
N.A.I.C.S.: 331313
Tomasz Grela *(Pres & CEO)*

Subsidiary (Non-US):

Aluprof Belgium N.V. (2)
Industriepark Hoogveld Zone F1 Wissenstraat 2, 9200, Dendermonde, Belgium
Tel.: (32) 52258110
Plastic Packaging Sheet Mfr
N.A.I.C.S.: 326112
Emmanuel Gregoire *(Mng Dir)*

Aluprof Hungary Kft. (2)
Bagoly U 11, Dunakeszi, 2120, Budapest, Hungary
Tel.: (36) 27542600
Plastic Packaging Sheet Mfr
N.A.I.C.S.: 326112
Lidia Gruszczynska *(Mgr-Ops)*

Aluprof Netherlands B.V. (2)
Platinawerf 20g, 6641 TL, Beuningen, Netherlands
Tel.: (31) 246759999
Plastic Packaging Sheet Mfr
N.A.I.C.S.: 326112
John Goossens *(Mgr-Sls)*

Aluprof UK Ltd. (2)
Unit A5 Altrincham Business Park Stuart Road, Altrincham, WA14 5GJ, United Kingdom
Tel.: (44) 1619414005
Web Site: http://www.aluprof.co.uk
Aluminium Mfr
N.A.I.C.S.: 331313

Subsidiary (Domestic):

Romb S.A. (2)
Kujanska 10E, 77-400, Zlotow, Poland
Tel.: (48) 672650402
Web Site: http://www.romb.pl
Building Accessory Mfr
N.A.I.C.S.: 327110

Aluprof System - Romania Srl (1)
A1 Business Park Autostrada Pitesti Km 13 5 Sat Dragomiresti-Deal, Comuna Dragomiresti-Vale Str Maria-Laura nr 13 Hala F4-5, 077096, Bucharest, Romania **(100%)**
Tel.: (40) 374004594
Web Site: http://www.aluprof.eu
Primary Aluminum Production

AND PRIVATE COMPANIES

N.A.I.C.S.: 331313

Aluprof System Czech, S.r.o. (1)
Na Rovince 879, Hrabova, 720 00, Ostrava, Czech Republic (100%)
Tel.: (420) 608128005
Web Site: http://www.aluprof.eu
Sales Range: $25-49.9 Million
Emp.: 10
Primary Aluminum Production
N.A.I.C.S.: 331313

Celtech Sp. z o.o. (1)
Ul Rubiez 46 C3/28, 61-612, Poznan, Poland (100%)
Tel.: (48) 616232932
Web Site: http://www.celtech.pl
Specialty Trade Contractors
N.A.I.C.S.: 238990

Impet Sp. Z o.o. (1)
Czermin 61, Czermin, 39-304, Mielec, Poland (100%)
Tel.: (48) 177740342
Web Site: http://www.impet.biz
Sales Range: $25-49.9 Million
Emp.: 25
Telephone Answering Services
N.A.I.C.S.: 561421

GRUPA KLEPSYDRA SA
ul Solec 5, 94-247, Lodz, Poland
Tel.: (48) 426305428
Web Site: https://www.grupaklepsydra.pl
Year Founded: 2010
MEI—(WAR)
Rev.: $4,207,063
Assets: $17,177,337
Liabilities: $3,441,057
Net Worth: $13,736,280
Earnings: $10,925
Fiscal Year-end: 12/31/23
Funeral Services
N.A.I.C.S.: 812210
Marek Cichewicz *(Chm & Pres)*

GRUPA LOTOS S.A.
135 Elblaska Street, 80-718, Gdansk, Poland
Tel.: (48) 58 326 4300   PL
Web Site: http://www.lotos.pl
Year Founded: 1971
LTS—(WAR)
Rev.: $8,930,453,796
Assets: $7,000,369,728
Liabilities: $3,011,786,349
Net Worth: $3,988,583,379
Earnings: $865,933,398
Emp.: 4,897
Fiscal Year-end: 12/31/21
Oil & Petroleum Products Mfr
N.A.I.C.S.: 211130
Beata Kozlowska-Chya *(Chm-Supervisory Bd)*

Subsidiaries:

LOTOS Asfalt Sp. z o.o. (1)
ul Elblaska 135, 80-718, Gdansk, Poland
Tel.: (48) 583087239
Web Site: http://www.lotosasfalt.pl
Emp.: 300
Asphalt Mfr & Distr
N.A.I.C.S.: 212390

LOTOS Czechowice S.A. (1)
ul Lukasiewicza 2, 43-502, Czechowice-Dziedzice, Silesian, Poland
Tel.: (48) 323237900
Web Site: http://www.lotos.pl
Fuel Distr
N.A.I.C.S.: 424720

LOTOS Infrastruktura S.A. (1)
ul 3 Maja 101, 38-200, Jaslo, Poland
Tel.: (48) 134466011
Fuel Distr
N.A.I.C.S.: 424720

LOTOS Jaslo S.A. (1)
ul 3 Maja 101, 38-200, Jaslo, Subcarpathian, Poland
Tel.: (48) 134466011
Web Site: http://www.lotosjaslo.pl

Fuel Distr
N.A.I.C.S.: 457210

LOTOS Kolej Sp. z o.o. (1)
ul Michalki 25, 80-716, Gdansk, Podkarpacie, Poland
Tel.: (48) 583087655
Sales Range: $200-249.9 Million
Emp.: 750
Railway Transportation Services
N.A.I.C.S.: 482112

LOTOS Lab Sp. z o.o. (1)
ul Elblaska 135, 80-718, Gdansk, Podkarpacie, Poland
Tel.: (48) 583088258
Web Site: http://www.lotos.pl
Sales Range: $25-49.9 Million
Emp.: 140
Laboratory Testing Services
N.A.I.C.S.: 621511

LOTOS Ochrona Sp. z o.o. (1)
ul Elblaska 135, 80-718, Gdansk, Podkarpacie, Poland
Tel.: (48) 583087233
Web Site: http://www.lotos.pl
Sales Range: $75-99.9 Million
Emp.: 160
Property Management Services
N.A.I.C.S.: 531312

LOTOS Oil S.A. (1)
Elblaska 135, 80-718, Gdansk, Poland
Tel.: (48) 583087350
Sales Range: $1-4.9 Billion
Emp.: 5,500
Lubricating Oils Mfr & Distr
N.A.I.C.S.: 324110
Cezary Kogucik *(Vice Dir-Comml & Mgr-Export)*

LOTOS Paliwa Sp. z o.o. (1)
ul Elblaska 135, 80-718, Gdansk, Poland
Tel.: (48) 583264300
Web Site: http://www.lotos.pl
Fuel & Oil Whslr
N.A.I.C.S.: 424720

LOTOS Parafiny Sp. z o.o. (1)
ul 3 Maja 101, 38-200, Jaslo, Podkarpacie, Poland
Tel.: (48) 58 326 43 00
Web Site: http://www.grupalotos.pl
Paraffin Mfr & Distr
N.A.I.C.S.: 325110

LOTOS Petrobaltic S.A. (1)
9 Stary Dwor St, 80-958, Gdansk, Poland
Tel.: (48) 583013061
Web Site: http://www.lotos.pl
Sales Range: $50-74.9 Million
Emp.: 1
Oil & Gas Exploration Services
N.A.I.C.S.: 211120

Subsidiary (Domestic):

Energobaltic Sp. z o.o. (2)
ul Starowiejska 41, 84-120, Wladyslawowo, Poland
Tel.: (48) 587740600
Web Site: http://www.energobaltic.com.pl
Sales Range: $50-74.9 Million
Oil & Gas Exploration Services
N.A.I.C.S.: 211120

Subsidiary (Non-US):

LOTOS Exploration and Production Norge AS (2)
Jaettaevaegveien 7 Blokk C, PO Box 132, 4020, Stavanger, Rogaland, Norway
Tel.: (47) 94148900
Web Site: http://www.lotosupstream.no
Sales Range: $50-74.9 Million
Petroleum Exploration Services
N.A.I.C.S.: 213112
Tor Helge Hetland *(Mgr-Bus Dev)*

LOTOS Serwis Sp. z o.o. (1)
ul Elblaska 135, 80-718, Gdansk, Podkarpacie, Poland
Tel.: (48) 583088390
Web Site: http://www.lotosserwis.pl
Sales Range: $75-99.9 Million
Emp.: 500
Electrical Equipment Maintenance Services
N.A.I.C.S.: 811310

LOTOS Straz Sp. z o.o. (1)

ul Elblaska 135, 80-718, Gdansk, Podkarpacie, Poland
Tel.: (48) 583088195
Sales Range: $25-49.9 Million
Emp.: 20
Fire Protection Services
N.A.I.C.S.: 922160

LOTOS Tank Sp. z o.o. (1)
ul Elblaska 135, 80-718, Gdansk, Podkarpacie, Poland
Tel.: (48) 583088076
Petroleum Product Whslr
N.A.I.C.S.: 424720

LOTOS Terminale S.A. (1)
ul Lukasiewicza 2, 43-502, Czechowice-Dziedzice, Poland
Tel.: (48) 323237901
Fuel Distr
N.A.I.C.S.: 424720

LOTOS Upstream Sp. z o.o. (1)
135 Elblaska St, 80-718, Gdansk, Poland
Tel.: (48) 801345678
Crude Petroleum Production Services
N.A.I.C.S.: 211130

PLASTEKOL Organizacja Odzysku S.A. (1)
ul 3 Maja 101, 38-200, Jaslo, Subcarpathian, Poland
Tel.: (48) 134466660
Web Site: http://www.plastekol.pl
Waste Treatment Services
N.A.I.C.S.: 562219

UAB LOTOS Baltija (1)
Gedimino pr 5, 01103, Vilnius, Lithuania
Tel.: (370) 852499165
Web Site: http://www.lotosbaltija.lt
Lubricating Oils Whslr
N.A.I.C.S.: 424720

GRUPA MASPEX SP. Z O.O.
ul Chopina 10 Legionow 37 St, Wadowice, 34-100, Krakow, Poland
Tel.: (48) 33 870 84 96
Web Site: https://maspex.com
Emp.: 100
Food & Beverage Mfr
N.A.I.C.S.: 311999
Krzysztof Pawinski *(CEO)*

Subsidiaries:

CEDC International sp. z o.o. (1)
Kowanowska 48, 64-600, Oborniki, Poland
Tel.: (48) 612974300
Alcoholic Beverages Mfr
N.A.I.C.S.: 312140

GRUPA NOKAUT S.A.
ul Pokorna nr 2/211, 00-199, Warsaw, 00-199, Poland
Tel.: (48) 530282726
Web Site: http://www.3r.games
Year Founded: 2012
3RG—(WAR)
Sales Range: Less than $1 Million
Software Publisher
N.A.I.C.S.: 513210
Shawomir Ropczewski *(CEO)*

GRUPA PRACUJ S.A.
Prosta 68, 00-838, Warsaw, Poland
Tel.: (48) 223737300
Web Site: https://www.grupapracuj.pl
Year Founded: 2000
GPP—(WAR)
Rev.: $184,044,207
Assets: $261,358,993
Liabilities: $169,086,890
Net Worth: $92,272,103
Earnings: $47,694,614
Emp.: 1,016
Fiscal Year-end: 12/31/23
Employee Recruitment Services
N.A.I.C.S.: 561311
Gracjan Fiedorowicz *(CFO)*

Subsidiaries:

Absence.io GmbH (1)
Ridlerstrasse 31, 80339, Munich, Germany

GRUPA ZYWIEC S.A.

Tel.: (49) 89143777477
Web Site: https://www.absence.io
Online Tool Management Services
N.A.I.C.S.: 541611

Softgarden e-recruiting GmbH (1)
Tauentzienstrasse 14, 10789, Berlin, Germany
Tel.: (49) 30884940400
Web Site: https://softgarden.com
Emp.: 140
Software Development Services
N.A.I.C.S.: 541511

eRecruitment Solutions sp. z o.o. (1)
ul Prosta 68, 00-838, Warsaw, Poland
Tel.: (48) 223737469
Web Site: https://erecruiter.pl
Emp.: 78
Data Processing & Hosting Services
N.A.I.C.S.: 518210

GRUPA SMT S.A.
Jutrzenki Street 183, 02-231, Warsaw, Poland
Tel.: (48) 586695262
Web Site: http://www.grupa-adv.pl
Sales Range: $25-49.9 Million
Emp.: 150
Holding Company; Marketing Communication, Innovative Technology & Ecommerce
N.A.I.C.S.: 551112
Szymon Pura *(VP-Mgmt Bd)*

Subsidiaries:

AdvFinance Sp. z o.o. (1)
Swietojanska 9 lok 4, 81-368, Gdynia, Poland
Tel.: (48) 586695262
Financial Management Services
N.A.I.C.S.: 523999

Codemedia SA (1)
ul Wernyhory 15, 02-727, Warsaw, Poland
Tel.: (48) 22 549 71 80
Web Site: http://www.codemedia.pl
Emp.: 35
Online Marketing Services
N.A.I.C.S.: 541613

MAT Sp. z o.o. (1)
ul Pandy 8, 02-202, Warsaw, Poland
Tel.: (48) 22 850 50 40
Web Site: http://www.matadv.pl
Sales Range: $25-49.9 Million
Emp.: 10
Advertising Agency Services
N.A.I.C.S.: 541810

SMT Software S.A. (1)
ul Marszalka Jozefa Pilsudskiego, 50-048, Wroclaw, Poland
Tel.: (48) 71 769 59 00
Web Site: http://www.smtsoftware.com
Sales Range: $25-49.9 Million
Emp.: 100
Information Technology Consulting Services
N.A.I.C.S.: 541512

GRUPA ZASTAVA VOZILA U RESTRUKTURIRANJU A.D.
Kosovska 4, Kragujevac, Serbia
Tel.: (381) 34 324 203
Year Founded: 2001
ZAST—(BEL)
Sales Range: $1-9.9 Million
Investment Management Service
N.A.I.C.S.: 523940
Dragan Srejovic *(Dir Gen)*

GRUPA ZYWIEC S.A.
ul Konstruktorska 13 Entrance E, 2-673, Warsaw, Poland
Tel.: (48) 22 5376000
Web Site: http://www.grupazywiec.pl
ZWC—(WAR)
Sales Range: $800-899.9 Million
Brewery Operator
N.A.I.C.S.: 312120
Stefan Orlowski *(Chm-Supervisory Bd)*

3117

GRUPE, S.A.B. DE C.V.

Grupa Zywiec S.A.—(Continued)

GRUPE, S.A.B. DE C.V.
Av Camaron Sabalo Sn Fraccionamiento El Cid, 82110, Mazatlan, Sinaloa, Mexico
Tel.: (52) 6699135577
Year Founded: 1980
CIDMEGA—(MEX)
Rev.: $192,788
Assets: $557,624
Liabilities: $205,574
Net Worth: $352,050
Earnings: $6,658
Emp.: 3,841
Fiscal Year-end: 12/31/23
Holding Company
N.A.I.C.S.: 551112
Carlos Berdegue Sacristan *(Chm, Pres & CEO)*

GRUPEX D.D
I Muslimanske brigade bb, 77230, Velika Kladusa, Bosnia & Herzegovina
Tel.: (387) 37 775 147
Web Site: http://www.grupex.ba
Year Founded: 1935
Rev.: $4,189,640
Assets: $15,611,266
Liabilities: $4,883,098
Net Worth: $10,728,168
Earnings: ($1,478,260)
Emp.: 55
Fiscal Year-end: 12/31/18
Mineral Mining & Exploration Services
N.A.I.C.S.: 212390

GRUPO ACERERO DEL NORTE S.A. DE C.V.
Campos Eliseos 29 10th Fl, 11580, Polanco, Mexico
Tel.: (52) 5552559900
Web Site: http://www.almasa.com.mx
Year Founded: 1991
Sales Range: $450-499.9 Million
Emp.: 18,000
Production of Steel & Urea; Extraction of Iron Ore & Baryta; Production of Nitrogenous Solutions
N.A.I.C.S.: 212210
Alonso Ancira Elizondo *(Pres)*

Subsidiaries:

Altos Hornos de Mexico, S.A. de C.V. **(1)**
Prolongacion Juarez s/n Col La Loma, Edificio GAN Modulo II, Monclova, 25770, Coahuila, Mexico **(100%)**
Tel.: (52) 8666493400
Web Site: http://www.ahmsa.com
Steel Mfrs
N.A.I.C.S.: 331110
Alonso Ancira Elizondo *(Chm)*

Subsidiary (Domestic):

Minera del Norte **(2)**
Abasolo E Independencia 508, Col Centro, C P 33700, Ciudad Camargo, Mexico **(100%)**
Tel.: (52) 8666332390
Web Site: http://www.ahmsa.com
Sales Range: $650-699.9 Million
Emp.: 1,708
Extraction of Iron Ore & Limestone
N.A.I.C.S.: 212311

Nacional De Acero **(2)**
Av Conductores 313, Col Rincon Del Oriente, 66470, San Nicolas, NL, Mexico **(100%)**
Tel.: (52) 8183696200
Web Site: http://www.nacionaldeacero.com
Sales Range: $75-99.9 Million
Emp.: 267
Steel Mills
N.A.I.C.S.: 331110

Hojalata Mexicana, S.A. de C.V. **(1)**
Road 30 KM 10 800 Fracc, Frontera, San Antonio, Coahuila, Mexico
Tel.: (52) 18666359714
Hot Rolled Plate Mfr
N.A.I.C.S.: 331221

GRUPO AEROMEXICO, S.A.B. DE C.V.
Av Paseo de la Reforma 243, Piso 25 Cuauhtemoc Colonia, Mexico, CP 06500, DF, Mexico
Tel.: (52) 5511324000 MX
Web Site:
https://www.aeromexico.com
Year Founded: 1934
AEROMEX—(MEX)
Rev.: $3,645,973,479
Assets: $5,354,406,612
Liabilities: $5,048,126,561
Net Worth: $306,280,051
Earnings: ($125,600,669)
Fiscal Year-end: 12/31/19
Holding Company; Air Transportation Services
N.A.I.C.S.: 551112
Javier Arrigunaga Gomez del Campo *(Chm)*

Subsidiaries:

Aerovias de Mexico, S.A. de C.V. **(1)**
Av Paseo de la Reforma 445, Colonia Cuauhtemoc, Mexico, CP 06500, DF, Mexico **(100%)**
Tel.: (52) 55 9132 4000
Web Site: http://www.aeromexico.com
Sales Range: $1-4.9 Billion
Scheduled Passenger & Freight Air Transportation Services
N.A.I.C.S.: 481111
Andres Conesa Labastida *(CEO)*

Subsidiary (Domestic):

Aerolitoral, S.A. de C.V. **(2)**
Carretera Miguel Aleman Km 22 8 8 Apodaca, Nuevo Leon, 66600, Mexico **(99.74%)**
Tel.: (52) 5551334000
Web Site: http://www.aerolitoral.com
Scheduled Passenger & Freight Air Transportation Services
N.A.I.C.S.: 481111

Representative Office (US):

Aerovias de Mexico, S.A. de C.V. - USA Sales Office **(2)**
110 W 34th St Ste 110, New York, NY 10001-2115
Tel.: (52) www.aeromexico.com
Web Site: http://www.aeromexico.com
Scheduled Passenger & Freight Air Transportation Services
N.A.I.C.S.: 551114

GRUPO AEROPORTUARIO DEL CENTRO NORTE, S.A.B. DE C.V.
Plaza Metropoli Patriotismo Piso 5 Av Patriotismo 201, Col San Pedro de los Pino Benito Juarez, Ciudad Juarez, Mexico
Tel.: (52) 8186254300
Web Site: https://www.oma.aero
Year Founded: 1998
OMAB—(NASDAQ)
Rev.: $599,960,787
Assets: $1,159,727,794
Liabilities: $729,687,047
Net Worth: $430,040,747
Earnings: $196,922,922
Emp.: 1,256
Fiscal Year-end: 12/31/22
Airport Terminal Operator
N.A.I.C.S.: 488119
Diego Quintana Kawage *(Chm)*

Subsidiaries:

Aeropuerto de San Luis Potosi, S.A. de C.V. **(1)**
Carretera a Matehuala km 9 5, 78380, San Luis Potosi, SLP, Mexico
Tel.: (52) 4444787000
Oil Transportation Services
N.A.I.C.S.: 488190

Aeropuerto de Zihuatanejo, S.A. de C.V. **(1)**
Carretera Nacional a Acapulco, 40880, Zihuatanejo, Guerrero, Mexico
Tel.: (52) 7555542070
Oil Transportation Services
N.A.I.C.S.: 488190

OMA-VYNMSA Aero Industrial Park, S.A. de C.V. **(1)**
Av San Jeronimo 310-Piso 12, San Jeronimo, 64640, Monterrey, NL, Mexico
Tel.: (52) 18122028599
Web Site: http://www.vynmsa.com
Industrial Building Leasing Services
N.A.I.C.S.: 532490

GRUPO AEROPORTUARIO DEL PACIFICO, S.A.B. DE C.V.
Avenida Mariano Otero No 1249-B Torre Pacifico Piso 6, Col Rinconada del Bosque, 44530, Guadalajara, Jalisco, Mexico
Tel.: (52) 3338801100
Web Site:
https://www.aeropuertosgap.com.mx
PAC—(NYSE)
Rev.: $1,376,411,502
Assets: $3,041,603,492
Liabilities: $2,044,847,670
Net Worth: $996,755,822
Earnings: $461,753,778
Emp.: 2,314
Fiscal Year-end: 12/31/22
Airport Operations
N.A.I.C.S.: 488119
Saul Villarreal Garcia *(CFO)*

Subsidiaries:

Aeropuerto de Aguascalientes, S.A. de C.V. **(1)**
Carretera Panamericana Km 22 Ejido, Buenavista de Penuelas, 20340, Aguascalientes, Mexico
Tel.: (52) 4499182806
Airport Operation Services
N.A.I.C.S.: 488119

Aeropuerto de Guadalajara, S.A. de C.V. **(1)**
Carretera Guadalajara Chapala km 17 5, 45659, Tlajomulco de Zuniga, Mexico
Tel.: (52) 3336885248
Cloud Data Migration Services
N.A.I.C.S.: 518210

Aeropuerto de Hermosillo, S.A. de C.V. **(1)**
Carretera a Bahia de Kino Km 9 5, 83220, Hermosillo, Sonora, Mexico
Tel.: (52) 6622610000
Sales Range: $25-49.9 Million
Emp.: 65
Airport Operation Services
N.A.I.C.S.: 488119

Aeropuerto de La Paz, S.A. de C.V. **(1)**
Carretera Transpeninsular km 13, 23201, La Paz, Mexico
Tel.: (52) 612 124 63 07
Web Site:
http://www.aeropuertosgap.com.mx
Airport Operation Services
N.A.I.C.S.: 488119

Aeropuerto de Los Cabos, S.A. de C.V. **(1)**
Transpeninsular Highway Km 43 5, 23420, San Jose del Cabo, Mexico
Tel.: (52) 6241465111
Oil Transportation Services
N.A.I.C.S.: 488190

Aeropuerto de Los Mochis, S.A. de C.V. **(1)**
Km 12 5 Los Mochis Road Topolobampo, Ahome, 81360, Los Mochis, Sinaloa, Mexico **(100%)**
Tel.: (52) 6688186870
Sales Range: $25-49.9 Million
Emp.: 80
Airport Operations

INTERNATIONAL PUBLIC

N.A.I.C.S.: 488119

Aeropuerto de Manzanillo, S.A. de C.V. **(1)**
Carretera Manzanillo-Barra de Navidad Km 42 Col Playa de Oro, 28219, Manzanillo, Mexico
Tel.: (52) 3143331119
Cloud Data Migration Services
N.A.I.C.S.: 518210

Aeropuerto de Mexicali, S.A. de C.V. **(1)**
Carretera Mesa de Andrade Km 23 5 S/N Col Mariano Abasolo, 21600, Mexicali, Baja California, Mexico
Tel.: (52) 6865522317
Airport Operator
N.A.I.C.S.: 488119

Aeropuerto de Morelia, S.A. de C.V. **(1)**
Km 27 Carretera Morelia-Zinapecuaro, Alvaro Obregon, 58920, Michoacan, Mexico
Tel.: (52) 4433136780
Aircraft Maintenance Services
N.A.I.C.S.: 488119

Aeropuerto de Puerto Vallarta, S.A. de C.V. **(1)**
Avenida Mariano Otero No 1249-B Torre Pacifico Floor 6, Rinconada del Bosque, 45140, Guadalajara, Jalisco, Mexico **(100%)**
Tel.: (52) 3338801100
Sales Range: $200-249.9 Million
Airport Operations
N.A.I.C.S.: 488119

Aeropuerto de San Jose del Cabo, S.A. de C.V. **(1)**
Carretera Transpeninsular Km 43 5, 23420, San Jose del Cabo, Baja California Sur, Mexico
Tel.: (52) 6241465111
Cloud Data Migration Services
N.A.I.C.S.: 518210

Aeropuerto de Tijuana, S.A. de C.V. **(1)**
Carretera Aeropuerto S/N Col Nueva Tijuana, Delegacion Meza de Otay, 22435, Tijuana, Mexico
Tel.: (52) 664 607 82 00
Web Site:
http://www.aeropuertodetijuana.com.mx
Airport Operation Services
N.A.I.C.S.: 488119

Aeropuerto del Bajio, S.A. de C.V. **(1)**
Km 5 5 Carretera Silao-Leon, Col Nuevo Mexico, 36273, Silao, Guanajuato, Mexico
Tel.: (52) 4727482120
Airport Operation Services
N.A.I.C.S.: 488119

Servicios a la Infraestructura Aeroportuaria del Pacifico, S.A. de C.V. **(1)**
Mariano Otero No 1249 B Piso 6 Rincon Del Bosque, 44530, Guadalajara, Jalisco, Mexico
Tel.: (52) 33 3880 1100
Web Site: http://www.aeroportuaria.com
Airport Operator
N.A.I.C.S.: 488119
Fernando Bosque *(Gen Mgr)*

GRUPO AEROPORTUARIO DEL SURESTE, S.A.B. DE C.V.
Bosque de Alisos No 47A 4th Floor Bosques de las Lomas, 05120, Mexico, DF, Mexico
Tel.: (52) 5552840408 MX
Web Site: https://www.asur.com.mx
Year Founded: 1998
ASR—(NYSE)
Rev.: $1,559,409,853
Assets: $4,248,090,056
Liabilities: $1,132,416,146
Net Worth: $3,115,673,910
Earnings: $644,737,115
Emp.: 1,882
Fiscal Year-end: 12/31/23
Airport Operation Services
N.A.I.C.S.: 488119

AND PRIVATE COMPANIES

Adolfo Castro Rivas *(CEO & Dir-Fin)*

Subsidiaries:

Aeropuerto de Cozumel S.A. de C.V. (1)
Av. 65 y Boulevard Aeropuerto, Edo de Quintana Roo, 77600, Chihuahua, Mexico **(99.99%)**
Tel.: (52) 9878722081
Web Site: http://www.asur.com.mx
Airport Operations
N.A.I.C.S.: 488119

Aeropuerto de Huatulco S.A. de C.V. (1)
Huatulco International Airport Carretera Pinotepa Cruz Km 237, Huatulco, Oaxaca, Mexico **(99.99%)**
Tel.: (52) 9585819004
Sales Range: $25-49.9 Million
Emp.: 40
Airport Operations
N.A.I.C.S.: 488119

Aeropuerto de Merida S.A. de C.V. (1)
Km 14.5 Carretera Merida-Uman, Edo de Yucatan, 97295, Merida, Mexico **(99.99%)**
Tel.: (52) 99 9946 1530
Airport Operations
N.A.I.C.S.: 492110

Aeropuerto de Veracruz S.A. de C.V. (1)
Veracruz International Airport Carretera Veracruz Xalapa Km 13 5, 91698, Veracruz, Mexico **(99.99%)**
Tel.: (52) 2299349008
Airport Operations
N.A.I.C.S.: 488119

Aerostar Airport Holdings, LLC (1)
Terminal D Arrivals Ave, Carolina, PR 00979 **(60%)**
Tel.: (787) 289-7240
Web Site: https://www.aerostarairports.com
Holding Company; Airport Operator
N.A.I.C.S.: 551112
Maria Fuentes *(Coord-Quality)*

GRUPO ALBION

Calle de Castello 77, 28006, Madrid, Spain
Tel.: (34) 915312388 ES
Web Site: http://www.grupoalbion.net
Sales Range: $75-99.9 Million
Emp.: 30
Public Relation & Consultation Services
N.A.I.C.S.: 541820
Padget Langford-Holt *(CEO)*

GRUPO ALIADO S.A.

Urbanizacion Obarrio Calle 50 y 56 Edifacio Banco Aliado, Postal Box 0831-02109, Aliado Building, Panama, Panama
Tel.: (507) 3021555
Web Site: http://grupoaliado.com
Rev.: $147,478,603
Assets: $2,732,751,040
Liabilities: $2,450,369,559
Net Worth: $282,381,481
Earnings: $31,775,937
Fiscal Year-end: 06/30/18
Bank Holding Company
N.A.I.C.S.: 551111
Moises S. Chreim *(Chm)*

Subsidiaries:

Banco Aliado, S.A. (1)
Urbanizacion Obarrio Calle 50 y 56, Apartado Postal 0831-02109, Panama, Panama
Tel.: (507) 302 1555
Web Site: http://www.bancoaliado.com
Sales Range: Less than $1 Million
Banking Services
N.A.I.C.S.: 522110
Moises Chreim Sasson *(Pres)*

Subsidiary (Domestic):

Aliado Factoring, S.A. (2)
Urbanizacion Obarrio Calle 50 y 56, Apartado Postal 0831-02109, Panama, Panama
Tel.: (507) 302 1555
Web Site: http://www.bancoaliado.com
Emp.: 14
Financial Services
N.A.I.C.S.: 523999

Aliado Leasing, S.A. (2)
Urbanizacion Obarrio Calle 50 y 56, Apartado Postal 0831-02109, Panama, Panama
Tel.: (507) 302 1555
Web Site: http://www.bancoaliado.com
Emp.: 16
Financial Services
N.A.I.C.S.: 523999

Financiera Finacredit, S.A. (2)
Ave Peru y Calle 37, Perejil, Panama, Panama
Tel.: (507) 209 2460
Web Site: http://www.bancoaliado.com
Emp.: 27
Financial, Pension & Credit Services
N.A.I.C.S.: 523999

GRUPO ALIMENTARIO ARGAL SA

25242 Miralcamp, Lleida, Spain
Tel.: (34) 973 71 10 10
Web Site: http://www.argal.com
Year Founded: 1914
Meat Products Mfr & Whslr
N.A.I.C.S.: 424470
David Rodriguez *(CEO)*

Subsidiaries:

Ogier SAS (1)
10 Avenue Louis Pasteur, BP 75, 84232, Chateauneuf-du-Pape, France
Tel.: (33) 4 9039 3232
Web Site: http://www.ogier.fr
Grape Vineyard & Winery
N.A.I.C.S.: 312130

GRUPO ANTOLIN-IRAUSA, S.A.

Ctra Madrid-Irun Km 244 8, E09007, Burgos, Spain
Tel.: (34) 947477700 ES
Web Site: http://www.grupoantolin.com
Year Founded: 1950
Rev.: $6,318,090,078
Assets: $4,185,333,492
Liabilities: $3,253,899,544
Net Worth: $931,433,949
Earnings: $54,044,078
Emp.: 30,646
Fiscal Year-end: 12/31/18
Automotive Interior Components Mfr
N.A.I.C.S.: 336360
Ernesto Antolin Arribas *(Chm)*

Subsidiaries:

CML Innovative Technologies, GmbH & Co. KG (1)
Kirschackerstrasse 9, 96052, Bamberg, Germany
Tel.: (49) 951 93380
Lighting Equipment Mfr
N.A.I.C.S.: 335139

CML Innovative Technologies, Ltd. (1)
69-70 Eastern Way, Bury Saint Edmunds, IP32 7AB, Suffolk, United Kingdom
Tel.: (44) 1284 762411
Lighting Equipment Mfr
N.A.I.C.S.: 335139
Alan Palfrey *(Mgr-Sls & Mktg)*

CML Innovative Technologies, s.r.o. (1)
Vilova 873, 351 24, Hranice, Czech Republic
Tel.: (420) 35 44 00 120
Lighting Equipment Mfr
N.A.I.C.S.: 335139

CML Technologies, GmbH & Co. KG (1)
Philipp-Kramer-Ring 5, 67098, Bad Durkheim, Germany

Tel.: (49) 63 22 95 67 0
Web Site: http://www.cml-it.com
Lighting Equipment Mfr
N.A.I.C.S.: 335139
Mike Hemingway *(Mng Dir)*

GRUPO ANTOLIN-LOUISIANA, Inc. (1)
4980 Flournoy Lucas Rd, Shreveport, LA 71129
Tel.: (318) 688-8933
Motor Vehicle Parts Distr
N.A.I.C.S.: 423120
Steve Head *(Mgr-Matls)*

Grupo Antolin Kentucky, Inc. (1)
208 Commerce Ct, Hopkinsville, KY 42240
Tel.: (270) 885-2703
Sales Range: $50-74.9 Million
Emp.: 500
Automotive Components Mfr
N.A.I.C.S.: 336390

Grupo Antolin Loire SAS (1)
Blvd Blaise Pascal, Roche-la-Moliere, 42230, France
Tel.: (33) 477505300
Sales Range: $50-74.9 Million
Emp.: 185
Automotive Components Mfr
N.A.I.C.S.: 336390

Grupo Antolin Matorell, S.A.U. (1)
C/ Doctor Fleming 15-17 Pol Can Estella, Sant Esteve Sesrovires, 08635, Barcelona, Spain
Tel.: (34) 93 775 86 00
Automobile Parts Mfr
N.A.I.C.S.: 336390

Grupo Antolin Michigan (1)
6300 Euclid St, Marlette, MI 48453
Tel.: (989) 635-5055
Sales Range: $25-49.9 Million
Emp.: 20
Automotive Components Mfr
N.A.I.C.S.: 335999

Grupo Antolin Silao SA de CV (1)
Av Ingenieros No 51 Parque Ind Fipasi, Silao, 36101, Guanajuato, Mexico
Tel.: (52) 4727224100
Sales Range: $10-24.9 Million
Emp.: 500
Automotive Components Mfr
N.A.I.C.S.: 336390

Grupo Antolin-Amsterdam, B.V. (1)
Prins Bernhardplein 200, 1097 JB, Amsterdam, Netherlands
Tel.: (31) 20 5214777
Holding Company
N.A.I.C.S.: 551112

Grupo Antolin-Ara SL (1)
c/ Lopez Bravo 71, Burgos, E-09001, Spain
Tel.: (34) 947478600
Web Site: http://www.grupoantolin.com
Sales Range: $50-74.9 Million
Emp.: 260
Automotive Components Mfr
N.A.I.C.S.: 336390

Grupo Antolin-Aragusa, S.A.U. (1)
Camino Casas del Monte de la Abadesa Parque Empresarial, 09001, Burgos, Spain
Tel.: (34) 947 47 95 00
Automobile Parts Mfr
N.A.I.C.S.: 336390

Grupo Antolin-Ardasa, S.A.U. (1)
C/ Lopez Bravo n 11 Pol Ind Villalonquejar, 09001, Burgos, Spain
Tel.: (34) 947 47 36 61
Motor Vehicle Parts Mfr
N.A.I.C.S.: 336390

Grupo Antolin-Autotrim, S.A.U. (1)
C/Ullals 2 Pol Ind Norte, Almussafes, 46440, Valencia, Spain
Tel.: (34) 961 78 82 00
Automotive Components Mfr
N.A.I.C.S.: 336390

Grupo Antolin-Bohemia AS (1)
U Nisy 178, Chrastava, 463 31, Czech Republic
Tel.: (420) 482428011
Sales Range: $100-124.9 Million
Emp.: 470
Automotive Components Mfr

GRUPO ANTOLIN-IRAUSA, S.A.

N.A.I.C.S.: 336390

Grupo Antolin-Bratislava, s.r.o. (1)
Commercial Court Bratislava I No Sro - 24057/B Opletalova 73, 841 07, Bratislava, Slovakia
Tel.: (421) 2 693 07 511
Automobile Parts Mfr
N.A.I.C.S.: 336390

Grupo Antolin-Dapsa, S.A.U. (1)
Alcalde Martin Cobos s/n Pol Ind Gaomal-Villiimar Apdo 2190, 09007, Burgos, Spain
Tel.: (34) 947 48 58 66
Automotive Components Mfr
N.A.I.C.S.: 336390

Grupo Antolin-Deutschland, GmbH (1)
Schanzenstr 27, 51063, Cologne, Germany
Tel.: (49) 2215792070
Automobile Parts Distr
N.A.I.C.S.: 423690
Antonio Barquier *(Project Mgr-Quality)*

Grupo Antolin-France, S.A.S. (1)
Parc Club Ariane - Batiment Le Pluton 4 Boulevard des Chenes, 78280, Guyancourt, France
Tel.: (33) 176 78 38 00
Automobile Parts Distr
N.A.I.C.S.: 423690

Subsidiary (Domestic):

CML Innovative Technologies, S.A.S. (2)
12 Rue du Barlot, BP 909, 25051, Besancon, France
Tel.: (33) 3 81 47 77 00
Lighting Equipment Mfr
N.A.I.C.S.: 335139

Grupo Antolin Cambrai S.A.S. (2)
Actipole de L'A2, BP 55, 59554, Raillencourt-Sainte-Olle, France
Tel.: (33) 327 70 79 00
Automobile Component Distr
N.A.I.C.S.: 423690

Grupo Antolin Iga SAS (2)
734 Boulevard Ferdinand de Lesseps, 62110, Henin-Beaumont, France
Tel.: (33) 321747880
Sales Range: $50-74.9 Million
Emp.: 238
Automotive Components Mfr
N.A.I.C.S.: 336390
Gecosger Francke *(Mgr-Engrg)*

Grupo Antolin Ingenierie Sieges, S.A.S. (2)
Boulevard Blaise Pascal Loire 42, 42230, Roche-la-Moliere, France
Tel.: (33) 477 50 53 00
Engineeering Services
N.A.I.C.S.: 541330

Grupo Antolin Vosges (2)
30 rue dAlsace, 88360, Rupt-sur-Moselle, France
Tel.: (33) 329234646
Sales Range: $100-124.9 Million
Emp.: 300
Automotive Components Mfr
N.A.I.C.S.: 336390

Grupo Antolin-Jarny, S.A.S. (2)
Rue Gustave Eiffel - ZI Jarny Giraumont, BP 38, 54800, Jarny, Meurthe-et-Moselle, France
Tel.: (33) 3 82 47 54 40
Automobile Parts Mfr
N.A.I.C.S.: 336390

Grupo Antolin-Italia, S.r.L (1)
Viale Primo Maggio 13, Pinerolo, 10064, Turin, Italy
Tel.: (39) 0121 78 333
Automobile Parts Mfr
N.A.I.C.S.: 336390

Grupo Antolin-Japan, Co. (1)
4th floor 5-2-6 Toranomon, Minato-ku, Tokyo, 105-0001, Japan
Tel.: (81) 3 5733 0848
Automobile Parts Mfr
N.A.I.C.S.: 336390

Grupo Antolin-Korea, L.L.C. (1)
Office no 910 H-Square S-Bldg 680

GRUPO ANTOLIN-IRAUSA, S.A.

Grupo Antolin-Irausa, S.A.—(Continued)
Sampyeong-dong, Bundang-gu, Seongnam,
463-440, Gyeonggi, Korea (South)
Tel.: (82) 31 789 3890
Automobile Parts Mfr
N.A.I.C.S.: 336390

Grupo Antolin-Logistik Deutschland
GmbH
Ford Industrial Supplier Park Ivenshofweg
41, Niehl, 50769, Cologne, Germany
Tel.: (49) 221 77899920
Vehicle Interior Component Mfr
N.A.I.C.S.: 336390

Grupo Antolin-Magnesio, S.L.U. (1)
Pol Ind Montenuevo - Avenida Madrid S/N,
Valdorros, 09320, Burgos, Spain
Tel.: (34) 947 28 36 00
Automobile Parts Mfr
N.A.I.C.S.: 336390

Grupo Antolin-Navarra, S.A.U. (1)
Poligono Arazuri-Orcoyen Calle D- Parvela
3 1, 31170, Arazuri, Navarre, Spain
Tel.: (34) 948 32 44 45
Automobile Parts Mfr
N.A.I.C.S.: 336390

Grupo Antolin-North America,
Inc. (1)
1700 Atlantic Blvd, Auburn Hills, MI 48326
Tel.: (248) 373-1749
Web Site: http://www.grupoantolin.com
Emp.: 200
Automobile Parts Mfr
N.A.I.C.S.: 336390

Subsidiary (Domestic):

Grupo Antolin-Illinois, Inc. (2)
642 Crystal Pkwy, Belvidere, IL 61008
Tel.: (815) 544-8020
Web Site: http://www.grupoantolin.com
Emp.: 150
Automobile Parts Mfr
N.A.I.C.S.: 336390
Ricardo Lopez *(Plant Mgr)*

Grupo Antolin-Michigan, Inc. (2)
25800 Sherwood Ave, Warren, MI 48091
Tel.: (248) 364-2633
Motor Vehicle Parts Mfr
N.A.I.C.S.: 336390

Grupo Antolin-Missouri, LLC (2)
1601 Southern Rd, Kansas City, MO 64120
Tel.: (816) 605-7003
Automobile Parts Mfr
N.A.I.C.S.: 336390
Mark Jorgensen *(Plant Mgr)*

Grupo Antolin-Ostrava, s.r.o. (1)
Na rovince 912, Hrabova, 720 00, Ostrava,
Czech Republic
Tel.: (420) 595 701 210
Automobile Parts Mfr
N.A.I.C.S.: 336390
Michaela Skutova *(Mgr-HR)*

Grupo Antolin-Plasbur, S.A.U. (1)
C/ Condado de Trevino n 21 Pol Industrial
Villalonquejar, 09001, Burgos, Spain
Tel.: (34) 947 47 30 80
Automobile Parts Mfr
N.A.I.C.S.: 336390

Grupo Antolin-Pune PVT, Ltd. (1)
G-9 Sipcot Industrial Park Irungattukottai Tal
Sriperumbudur Dist, Kanheepuram, Chennai, 602 105, Tamil Nadu, India
Tel.: (91) 44 4712 8101
Automobile Parts Distr
N.A.I.C.S.: 423120
Arun Soman *(Sr Mgr-HR)*

Grupo Antolin-RyA, S.A.U. (1)
C/Aluminio n 13 Pol Ind Cerro de San Cristobal Apdo 2127, 47012, Valladolid, Spain
Tel.: (34) 983 21 79 60
Automobile Parts Mfr
N.A.I.C.S.: 336390

Grupo Antolin-Saltillo, S. de R.L.de
C.V. (1)
Dr Jesus Valdes Sanchez Km 8 5 - Int A
Parque Industrial Arteaga, Arteaga, 25350,
Saltillo, Coahuila, Mexico
Tel.: (52) 844 9 86 03 00
Automobile Parts Mfr

N.A.I.C.S.: 336390
Sergio Guitron *(Engr-Quality)*

Grupo Antolin-South Africa, Ltd. (1)
Nelson Mandela Bay Logistics Park Central
Hub, Jagtvlake Industrial Area, 6012, Uitenhage, South Africa
Tel.: (27) 41 9950700
Automobile Parts Mfr
N.A.I.C.S.: 336390
Manuel Hijar *(Dir-Technical)*

Grupo Antolin-Turnov, s.r.o. (1)
Prumyslova 3000, 511 01, Turnov, Czech
Republic
Tel.: (420) 481 363 711
Automobile Parts Mfr
N.A.I.C.S.: 336390

Grupo Antolin-Valenca Componentes
Automovel Soc. Unipessoal, Lda, (1)
Zona Industrial de Gandra - Apdo 40, 4930-
310, Valenca, Portugal
Tel.: (351) 251 806050
Automobile Component Distr
N.A.I.C.S.: 423690

Grupo Antolin-Valplas, S.A.U. (1)
Poligono Industrial La Ermita del Romani C/
Casa Zuriaga n 18, Sollana, 46439, Valencia, Spain
Tel.: (34) 961 485 565
Automobile Parts Mfr
N.A.I.C.S.: 336390

Grupo Antolin-Vigo, S.L.U. (1)
Parque Tecnologico y Logistico Valladares
Parcela 11 y 12 01, Valladares, 36315,
Vigo, Pontevedra, Spain
Tel.: (34) 986 82 97 00
Automobile Parts Mfr
N.A.I.C.S.: 336390

Guangzhou Antolin Auto-Parts Co.,
Ltd. (1)
No 9 Building American Industrial Park
Hongmian Road 48, Huadu, 510800,
Guangzhou, Guangdong, China
Tel.: (86) 20 36873378
Automobile Parts Mfr
N.A.I.C.S.: 336390

Intertrim, Ltda. (1)
Av Henry Nestle 3 000, Barrio de Grama,
12280-000, Cacapava, Sao Paulo, Brazil
Tel.: (55) 12 3654 4100
Automobile Parts Mfr
N.A.I.C.S.: 336390

GRUPO ARBULU S.L.

Lanzarote 14 3rd Fl, 280703, Madrid,
Spain
Tel.: (34) 916549411
Web Site:
http://www.grupoarbulu.com
Year Founded: 1999
Sales Range: $25-49.9 Million
Emp.: 154
Marine Electronics Mfr
N.A.I.C.S.: 334511
Luis Arbulu *(Pres)*

Subsidiaries:

Aage Hempel Group (1)
Edificio de Servicios Area de el Fresno, Oficina B101-117 Los Barrios, 11370, Cadiz,
Spain
Tel.: (34) 956 573 276
Web Site: http://www.aagehempel.com
Emp.: 120
Electric Equipment Mfr
N.A.I.C.S.: 334513
Alberto Olmos *(Gen Mgr-Sls)*

Crame, S.A. (1)
Lanzarote 14, San Sebastian De Los
Reyes, 28703, Madrid, Spain
Tel.: (34) 916586508
Web Site: http://www.crame.es
Sales Range: $25-49.9 Million
Emp.: 35
Marine Electronics Mfr
N.A.I.C.S.: 334511
Akiglu Barcuin *(Gen Mgr)*

E3 Group SA (1)
Paseo Calvia 2 No 4 Piso 1 Local A, Portals Nous Baleares, 7181, Mallorca, Spain

Tel.: (34) 971 404 208
Web Site: http://www.e3s.com
Emp.: 34
Marine Equipment Mfr
N.A.I.C.S.: 334220
Adam Aquilina *(Mgr-IT)*

Subsidiary (Non-US):

e3 Systems Italy (2)
Via Santa Maria 25, 56126, Pisa, Italy
Tel.: (39) 0643 913 416
Marine Equipment Mfr
N.A.I.C.S.: 334220
Dermot Crotty *(Mgr-Sls)*

e3 Systems Malta (2)
Flat 2 Ivanhoe St Augustus Bartolo Street,
Ta' Xbiex, Malta
Tel.: (356) 9999 0003
Marine Equipment Mfr
N.A.I.C.S.: 334220
Christopher Curmi *(Branch Mgr)*

Subsidiary (US):

e3 Systems USA (2)
4312 NW 120th Ave, Coral Springs, FL
33065
Tel.: (954) 368-9980
Marine Equipment Mfr
N.A.I.C.S.: 334220
David Horacek *(VP-Direct Sales)*

Marine Instruments S.A. (1)
Rua dos Padrons n 4 Vial 3 Parque Empresarial, Porto do Molle Nigran, 36350, Pontevedra, Spain
Tel.: (34) 986 36 63 60
Web Site: http://www.marineinstruments.es
Marine Equipment Mfr
N.A.I.C.S.: 334513
Gabriel Gomez Celaya *(Gen Mgr)*

NAVTEAM A/S (1)
Norgesvej 7, Svendborg, 5700, Denmark
Tel.: (45) 63 21 80 80
Web Site: http://www.navteam.com
Marine Equipment Mfr
N.A.I.C.S.: 334513

Nautical, Luis Arbulu, S.L.U. (1)
Explanada Pantalan de Cory s/n, 35008,
Las Palmas, Spain
Tel.: (34) 928 474 020
Web Site: http://www.nautical.es
Marine Equipment Mfr
N.A.I.C.S.: 334220
Brain Nunn *(Co-CFO & Mgr-Strategic)*

SMD Marine Electronics Namibia
(Pty) Ltd (1)
198 Sam Nujoma Avenue, Walvis Bay,
9000, Namibia
Tel.: (264) 64 200 300
Web Site: http://www.smdnamibia.com
Emp.: 6
Marine Equipment Mfr
N.A.I.C.S.: 334513
Andile Dhlomo *(Gen Mgr)*

GRUPO ARGOS S.A.

Carrera 43a No 1aSur - 143 Centro
Santillana - Torre Sur, Medellin, Colombia
Tel.: (57) 43158400
Web Site:
https://www.grupoargos.com
Year Founded: 1934
GRUPOARGOS—(COLO)
Rev.: $368,278,817
Assets: $5,060,250,069
Liabilities: $677,970,167
Net Worth: $4,382,279,902
Earnings: $203,681,552
Emp.: 11,500
Fiscal Year-end: 12/31/23
Holding Company; Cement Mfr
N.A.I.C.S.: 551112
Jorge Mario Velasquez Jaramillo
(Pres & CEO)

Subsidiaries:

Argos Guatemala S.A. (1)
Avenida Reforma 10-00 Zona 9 Condominium Reforma Office 5B, Guatemala,
Guatemala

Tel.: (502) 79481626
Web Site: http://www.guatemala.argos.co
Cement Mfr & Distr
N.A.I.C.S.: 327310

Argos USA LLC (1)
3015 Windward Plz Ste 300, Alpharetta, GA
30005
Tel.: (678) 368-4300
Web Site: http://www.argos-us.com
Emp.: 3,000
Ready Mix Cement Mfr
N.A.I.C.S.: 327310
Bill Wagner *(Pres)*

Autopistas del Cafe S.A. (1)
Carrera 10 Avenida del Ferrocarril No 75-51
La Romelia, Dosquebradas, Risaralda, Colombia
Tel.: (57) 6063280062
Web Site: http://www.autopistasdelcafe.com
Highway Construction Services
N.A.I.C.S.: 237310

Autopistas del Nordeste S.A. (1)
Av Lope de Vega No 29 Edif Novo Centro
local 606, Ens Naco, Santo Domingo, Dominican Republic
Tel.: (809) 4766578
Web Site:
http://www.autopistasdelnordeste.com
Highway Construction Services
N.A.I.C.S.: 237310

Celsia S.A. (1)
Carrera 43 A No 1 A Sur 143 Edificio Centro Santillana Torre Sur, Piso 6, Medellin,
Colombia
Tel.: (57) 18000123420
Web Site: https://www.celsia.com
Electric Power Distribution Services
N.A.I.C.S.: 221122

Celsia SA Esp (1)
Cra 43 A 1 A Sur 143 Piso 5, Medellin, Colombia
Tel.: (57) 43266600
Web Site: https://www.celsia.com
Rev.: $1,607,569,073
Assets: $3,549,289,882
Liabilities: $2,125,752,357
Net Worth: $1,423,537,525
Earnings: $90,026,801
Emp.: 2,270
Fiscal Year-end: 12/31/2023
Electric Power Distribution Services
N.A.I.C.S.: 221122
Ricardo Andres Sierra Fernandez *(CEO)*

Cementos Argos S.A. (1)
Carrera 43A 1A Sur 143, Medellin, Colombia
Tel.: (57) 3198457
Web Site: https://www.argos.com.co
Rev.: $3,295,135,551
Assets: $5,055,342,110
Liabilities: $2,703,958,875
Net Worth: $2,351,383,235
Earnings: $101,844,314
Emp.: 6,784
Fiscal Year-end: 12/31/2023
Cement Mfr
N.A.I.C.S.: 327310
Jorge Mario Velasquez Jaramillo *(Chm)*

Plant (US):

Argos USA Corporation - Gainesville
Block/Ready-Mix (2)
924 S Main St, Alachua, FL 32601-2025
Tel.: (352) 376-2182
Sales Range: $25-49.9 Million
Emp.: 43
Ready Mixed Concrete, Concrete Block &
Building Materials
N.A.I.C.S.: 327320
Matt Carcaba *(Gen Mgr)*

Argos USA Corporation - Linebaugh
Ready-Mix (2)
5920 W Linebaugh Ave, Tampa, FL 33624
Tel.: (813) 962-3213
Sales Range: $100-124.9 Million
Emp.: 200
Ready Mixed Concrete, Concrete Block &
Building Materials
N.A.I.C.S.: 327320
Rick Edwards *(VP)*

Argos USA Corporation - Palmetto
Ready-Mix (2)

700 Palmetto St, Jacksonville, FL 32202-2406
Tel.: (904) 354-8286
Sales Range: $125-149.9 Million
Emp.: 254
Ready Mixed Concrete & Building Materials
N.A.I.C.S.: 327320

Subsidiary (US):

Caribbean Construction and Development Ltd. (2)
181 Harbor Dr, Key Biscayne, FL 33149-1325
Tel.: (305) 785-8257
Web Site:
https://caribbeanconstructioninc.com
Cement Mfr & Distr
N.A.I.C.S.: 325520

Subsidiary (Non-US):

Caricement Antigua Limited (2)
Crabbs Peninsular, Saint John's, Antigua & Barbuda
Tel.: (268) 463 2172
Cement Mfr & Distr
N.A.I.C.S.: 327310

Subsidiary (US):

Essroc San Juan Inc. (2)
Carr 2 Km 26 7 Bo Espinosa, Dorado, PR 00646
Tel.: (787) 721-5878
Cement Mfr
N.A.I.C.S.: 327310

Southern Star Concrete, Inc. (2)
8500 Freeport Pkwy, Irving, TX 75063-2505
Tel.: (972) 621-0999
Web Site:
http://www.southernstarconcrete.com
Sales Range: $25-49.9 Million
Emp.: 40
Ready Mix Concrete Distr
N.A.I.C.S.: 327320
Dan Hilton *(VP-Fin)*

Subsidiary (Domestic):

Southern Star Leasing, LLC (3)
1946 California Crossing Rd, Dallas, TX 75220-7006
Tel.: (972) 556-0735
Web Site:
http://www.southernstarconcrete.com
Sales Range: $25-49.9 Million
Emp.: 26
Concrete Product Distr
N.A.I.C.S.: 423810
Tommy Abbott *(VP)*

Concesion La Pintada S.A.S. (1)
Cra 29C 10C-125 office 501 Edificio Select Building, Medellin, Antioquia, Colombia
Tel.: (57) 45208340
Web Site:
http://www.concesionlapintada.com
Highway Construction Services
N.A.I.C.S.: 237310

Concesion Vial de los Llanos S.A.S. (1)
Carrera 1 N 14-24 on the Ring Road Next to the Transport Terminal, La Gracielita Neighborhood, Villavicencio, Meta, Colombia
Tel.: (57) 86655053
Web Site: http://www.cllanos.co
Highway Construction Services
N.A.I.C.S.: 237310

Odinsa (1)
Street 24A 59 - 42 Tower Argos - Floor 10, Bogota, Colombia
Tel.: (57) 6016501919
Web Site: https://www.odinsa.com
Airport Construction Services
N.A.I.C.S.: 236220

Sociedad Concesionaria Operadora Aeroportuaria Internacional S.A.- Opain S.A. (1)
CISA Building-Calle 26 No 103-09, Bogota, Colombia
Tel.: (57) 14397070
Web Site: http://www.opain.co
Airport Maintenance Services
N.A.I.C.S.: 488119

Sociedad Portuaria Golfo de Morrosquillo S.A (1)
Km 4 Via De Santiago De Tolu A Covenas, Tolu, Sucre, Colombia
Tel.: (57) 5 2823232
Web Site: http://www.siinco.inco.gov.co
Marine Cargo Handling Services
N.A.I.C.S.: 488320

GRUPO ASSA, S.A.
Avenue of Nicanor Obarrio between Calle 56 & 57, PO Box 0816 01622, Panama, Panama
Tel.: (507) 300 2772 Pa
ASSA—(PAN)
Sales Range: Less than $1 Million
General Insurance Services
N.A.I.C.S.: 524210
Stanley Alberto Motta Cunninghan *(Pres)*

Subsidiaries:

ASSA Compania de Seguros, S.A. (1)
7 Avenida 12-23 zona 9 Edificio Etisa 3er Nivel Ala Norte, Guatemala, Guatemala (100%)
Tel.: (502) 22855900
Web Site: http://www.assanet.com.gt
Insurance Services
N.A.I.C.S.: 524126
Ian Van Hoorde *(Exec VP & Gen Mgr)*

GRUPO AVAL ACCIONES Y VALORES S.A.
Carrera 13 No 26-47 23rd floor Banco de Occidente Building, Bogota, DC, Colombia
Tel.: (57) 3077127 Co
Web Site: https://www.grupoaval.com
AVAL—(NYSE)
Rev.: $7,493,180,081
Assets: $78,037,843,930
Liabilities: $69,870,727,024
Net Worth: $8,167,116,906
Earnings: $564,102,989
Emp.: 74,036
Fiscal Year-end: 12/31/23
Bank Holding Company
N.A.I.C.S.: 551111
Luis Carlos Sarmiento Angulo *(Founder & Chm)*

Subsidiaries:

Banco de Occidente S.A. (1)
Banking Services
N.A.I.C.S.: 522110
Cesar Prado Villegas *(Pres)*

Concesionaria Panamericana S.A.S. (1)
Av Calle 26 N Of 703 59-41, Bogota, Colombia
Web Site:
http://www.cpanamericana.com.co
Highway Construction Services
N.A.I.C.S.: 237310

Concesionaria Vial Andina S.A.S. (1)
Web Site: http://www.coviandina.com
Highway Construction Services
N.A.I.C.S.: 237310

Concesionaria Vial Del Pacifico S.A.S. (1)
Titiribi-Bolombolo, Titiribi, Antioquia, Colombia
Tel.: (57) 6045209300
Web Site: https://www.covipacifico.co
Highway Construction Services
N.A.I.C.S.: 237310

Concesiones CCFC S.A.S. (1)
Avenida Calle 26 N 59-51 Office 901, Bogota, Colombia
Tel.: (57) 6017424196
Web Site: http://www.ccfc.com.co
Highway Construction Services
N.A.I.C.S.: 237310

Gases del Pacifico S.A.C. (1)
Av Las Orquideas N 585 apartment 1102 - Fibra Building, San Isidro, Lima, Peru
Tel.: (51) 80100001
Natural Gas Distribution Services
N.A.I.C.S.: 221210

Promioriente S.A. E.S.P. (1)
Carrera 27 36-14 Centro Empresarial Sura Piso 8, Bucaramanga, Colombia
Tel.: (57) 76450002
Web Site: http://www.promioriente.com
Natural Gas Distribution Services
N.A.I.C.S.: 221210
M. Cesar Augusto Torres *(Gen Mgr)*

Proyectos de Infraestructura S.A. (1)
Calle 10 No 4-47 piso 10, Cali, Colombia
Tel.: (57) 6024851596
Web Site: https://www.pisa.com.co
Highway Construction Services
N.A.I.C.S.: 237310

Sociedad Portuaria El Cayao S.A. E.S.P. (1)
Natural Gas Distribution Services
N.A.I.C.S.: 221210

Surtigas S.A. E.S.P. (1)
Avenida Pedro de Heredia Cl 31 N 47-30, Cartagena, Bolivar, Colombia
Tel.: (57) 56723200
Web Site: http://www.surtigas.com.co
Natural Gas Distribution Services
N.A.I.C.S.: 221210

Transmetano E.S.P. S.A. (1)
Carrera 42 Calle 3 Sur 81 Torre 2 Interior 1512, Distrito de Negocios Milla de Oro, Medellin, Colombia
Tel.: (57) 8000914500
Web Site: https://www.transmetano.co
Natural Gas Distribution Services
N.A.I.C.S.: 221210

GRUPO BAFAR, S.A.B DE C.V.
Km 7 5 Carretera a Cuauhtemoc, Col Las Animas, 31450, Chihuahua, Mexico
Tel.: (52) 6144390100
Web Site: http://www.grupobafar.com
Year Founded: 1996
BAFAR—(MEX)
Rev.: $1,274,957,867
Assets: $1,344,490,164
Liabilities: $803,151,450
Net Worth: $541,338,714
Earnings: $103,214,340
Emp.: 11,625
Fiscal Year-end: 12/31/22
Meat Product Mfr & Whslr
N.A.I.C.S.: 311612
Oscar Eugenio Baeza Fares *(Dir Gen)*

GRUPO BAL
Moliere 222 Los Morales Seccion Palmas, Mexico, Distrito Federal, Mexico
Tel.: (52) 5552836700 MX
Web Site: http://www.bal.com.mx
Sales Range: $1-4.9 Billion
Emp.: 500
Holding Company Services
N.A.I.C.S.: 551112
Alberto Bailleres Gonzalez *(Chm)*

Subsidiaries:

Arrendadora Valmex (1)
Viena No 5 1st Floor Col Juarez, 6600, Mexico, Mexico
Tel.: (52) 5557052618
Web Site: http://www.avalmex.com.mx
Sales Range: $50-74.9 Million
Emp.: 25
Credit Services
N.A.I.C.S.: 525990
Gnp Seguros *(Owner)*

Aseguradora Porvenir GNP (1)
Av. Cerro de las Torres No. 395 Col. Campestre Churubusco, 04200, Mexico, Mexico
Tel.: (52) 55 5227 3999
Web Site: http://www.porvenirgnp.com.mx
Financial Services
N.A.I.C.S.: 525990

BAL Holdings Inc. (1)
2 Stamford Plz Fl 12 281 Tresser Blvd, Stamford, CT 06901
Tel.: (203) 359-6775
Web Site: http://www.balnet.com
Sales Range: $10-24.9 Million
Emp.: 50
Nonferrous Metal Sheets, Bars, Rods & Other Related Items
N.A.I.C.S.: 423510

Subsidiary (Domestic):

BAL Metals International Inc (2)
281 Tresser Blvd, Stamford, CT 06901
Tel.: (203) 359-6775
Web Site: http://www.balmet.com
Rev.: $1,400,000
Emp.: 25
Nonferrous Metal Sheets, Bars, Rods & Other Related Items
N.A.I.C.S.: 423510
Elliott Levy *(VP-Fin)*

Penoles Metals & Chemicals Inc (2)
281 Tresser Blvd, Stamford, CT 06901
Tel.: (203) 359-6775
Web Site: http://www.penoles.com
Rev.: $11,084,208
Emp.: 23
Metal Products Marketing Services
N.A.I.C.S.: 423510
Sergio Pucheta *(Mgr-Logistics & Traffic)*

Wideco US Inc (2)
1244 Robinhood St Ste 110, Brownsville, TX 78521
Tel.: (956) 544-2861
Web Site: http://www.wideco.com
Rev.: $11,786,997
Emp.: 13
Industrial Machinery & Equipment
N.A.I.C.S.: 423830

Credito Afianzador, S.A. (1)
Viena 5 Piso 6 Col Juarez, 06600, Mexico, Mexico
Tel.: (52) 5128 1380
Web Site:
http://www.creditoafianzador.com.mx
Credit Management Services
N.A.I.C.S.: 541990

Grupo Nacional Provincial (1)
Av Cerro de las Torres No 395 Col Campestre Churubusco, 04200, Mexico, Mexico
Tel.: (52) 5552279000
Web Site: http://www.gnp.com.mx
Insurance
N.A.I.C.S.: 524113
Alejandro Bailleres *(CEO)*

Grupo Palacio de Hierro S.A. de C.V. (1)
Durango 230 Col Roma, Delegacion Cuauhtemoc, Mexico, 06700, Mexico
Tel.: (52) 52293154
Web Site: http://www.elpalaciodehierro.com
Sales Range: $800-899.9 Million
Emp.: 9,701
Department Stores
N.A.I.C.S.: 455110

Industrias Penoles, S.A. de C.V. (1)
Calzada Legaria No 549 Torre 2 Piso 14 Col 10 de abril, Delegacion Miguel Hidalgo, 11250, Mexico, Mexico
Tel.: (52) 5552793000
Web Site: http://www.penoles.com.mx
Rev.: $5,928,965,000
Assets: $9,979,256,000
Liabilities: $4,473,468,000
Net Worth: $5,505,788,000
Earnings: $286,536,000
Emp.: 15,573
Fiscal Year-end: 12/31/2023
Silver Mining & Production Services
N.A.I.C.S.: 212220
Alejandro Bailleres *(Chm & Deputy Chm)*

Subsidiary (Domestic):

Quimica del Rey S.A. de C.V. (2)
Laguna del Rey, 27000, Coahuila, Torreon, Mexico (100%)
Tel.: (52) 8727752121
Web Site: http://www.penoles.com.mx
Sales Range: $200-249.9 Million
Emp.: 450
Sodium Sulfate, Magnesium Oxide & Magnesium Sulfate Production

GRUPO BAL

INTERNATIONAL PUBLIC

Grupo BAL—(Continued)
N.A.I.C.S.: 212390

Profuturo GNP (1)
Blvd. Adolfo Lopez Mateos No 2009, Col
Los Alpes, Mexico, 1010, Mexico
Tel.: (52) 58096555
Web Site: http://www.profuturognp.com.mx
Pension Fund Management
N.A.I.C.S.: 525110

GRUPO BIMBO, S.A.B. DE C.V.

Prolongacion Paseo de la Reforma
1000, Col Pena Blanca Santa Fe,
01210, Mexico, Mexico
Tel.: (52) 5552686600
Web Site:
https://www.grupobimbo.com
Year Founded: 1945
BIMBO—(OTCIQ)
Rev.: $15,477,916,520
Assets: $14,796,874,620
Liabilities: $10,644,825,400
Net Worth: $4,152,049,220
Earnings: $391,022,500
Emp.: 133,827
Fiscal Year-end: 12/31/19
N.A.I.C.S.: 311999
Daniel Javier Servitje Montull *(Chm)*

Subsidiaries:

Barcel S.A. De C.V. (1)
Calle 4 No 320-A Col Arenal, 02980,
Mexico, Mexico
Tel.: (52) 5553280400
Web Site: http://www.ricolino.com.mx
Sales Range: $100-124.9 Million
Emp.: 400
Confectionery Mfr
N.A.I.C.S.: 311352

Bimbo Bakeries USA Inc. (1)
255 Business Center Dr, Horsham, PA
19044
Web Site:
https://www.bimbobakeriesusa.com
Emp.: 20,000
Baked Foods Mfr & Distr
N.A.I.C.S.: 311811
Fred Penny *(Pres)*

Plant (Domestic):

Bimbo Bakeries USA Inc. - Earth
City (2)
3301 Rider Trail S, Earth City, MO 63045-1109
Tel.: (314) 291-5480
Sales Range: $25-49.9 Million
Emp.: 250
Commercial Bakery
N.A.I.C.S.: 311812
Virgil H. Rehkomper *(VP & Controller)*

Bimbo Bakeries USA Inc. - Fort
Worth (2)
7301 S Fwy PO Box 937, Fort Worth, TX
76134-4004
Tel.: (817) 293-6230
Web Site:
http://www.bimbobakeriesusa.com
Sales Range: $150-199.9 Million
Emp.: 600
Bread Cake & Related Products
N.A.I.C.S.: 311830

Bimbo Bakeries USA Inc. -
Frederick (2)
7110 English Muffin Way, Frederick, MD
21704-8314
Tel.: (301) 694-8100
Sales Range: $25-49.9 Million
Emp.: 130
Bakery Products Mfr
N.A.I.C.S.: 311812

Bimbo Bakeries USA Inc. -
Gastonia (2)
1029 Cox Rd, Gastonia, NC 28054
Tel.: (704) 865-9883
Sales Range: $25-49.9 Million
Emp.: 100
Bakery Products Mfr
N.A.I.C.S.: 311812

Bimbo Bakeries USA Inc. - Grand
Rapids (2)
210 28th St SE, Grand Rapids, MI 49548-1106
Tel.: (616) 245-9127
Sales Range: $300-349.9 Million
Emp.: 600
Bakery Services
N.A.I.C.S.: 311812
Ben Zorn *(Plant Mgr)*

Bimbo Bakeries USA Inc. -
Knoxville (2)
2110 Chapman Hwy, Knoxville, TN 37920-1904
Tel.: (865) 573-1941
Web Site: http://www.saraleebread.com
Sales Range: $800-899.9 Million
Emp.: 1,300
Wholesale Bread, Rolls & Cake
N.A.I.C.S.: 445298

Bimbo Bakeries USA Inc. - La
Crosse (2)
334 5th Ave S, La Crosse, WI 54601-4002
Tel.: (608) 782-8488
Sales Range: $50-74.9 Million
Emp.: 80
Baked Goods
N.A.I.C.S.: 311812
Scott Reynen *(Mgr-Plant)*

Bimbo Bakeries USA Inc. -
Madison (2)
3401 E Washington Ave, Madison, WI
53704-4113
Tel.: (608) 244-4747
Sales Range: $125-149.9 Million
Emp.: 250
Bakery Services
N.A.I.C.S.: 311812

Bimbo Bakeries USA Inc. -
Milwaukee (2)
7301 W Dean Rd, Milwaukee, WI 53205-2339
Tel.: (414) 263-1700
Sales Range: $75-99.9 Million
Emp.: 150
Baked Goods Producer
N.A.I.C.S.: 311812

Bimbo Bakeries USA Inc. -
Montebello (2)
480 S Vail Ave, Montebello, CA 90640-4900
Tel.: (323) 720-6000
Web Site:
http://www.bimbobakeriesusa.com
Sales Range: $75-99.9 Million
Emp.: 500
Mfr of Bread & Related Products
N.A.I.C.S.: 311812

Bimbo Bakeries USA Inc. -
Oconomowoc (2)
318 E Summit Ave, Oconomowoc, WI
53066
Tel.: (262) 567-0667
Web Site:
http://www.bimbobakeriesusa.com
Sales Range: $25-49.9 Million
Emp.: 200
Bakery Products Mfr
N.A.I.C.S.: 311812

Bimbo Bakeries USA Inc. - Saint
Paul (2)
2745 Long Lake Rd, Saint Paul, MN 55113-1131
Tel.: (906) 226-2587
Sales Range: $25-49.9 Million
Emp.: 80
Bakery Services
N.A.I.C.S.: 311812

Subsidiary (Domestic):

EarthGrains Baking Co. Inc. (2)
255 Business Center Dr, Horsham, PA
19044
Web Site: http://www.earthgrains.com
Sales Range: $10-24.9 Million
Emp.: 10
Bakery Product Sales
N.A.I.C.S.: 445291

East Balt. Inc. (2)
1801 W 31st Pl, Chicago, IL 60608
Tel.: (773) 376-4444

Web Site: http://www.eastbalt.com
Emp.: 2,100
Holding Company; Commercial Bakeries
Operator
N.A.I.C.S.: 551112
Mark Bendix *(CEO)*

Subsidiary (Non-US):

EB Bakery of Beijing Co., Ltd. (3)
#6A Hong Da Zhong Lu, Beijing Econ &
Tech Develop Ar, Beijing, 100176, China
Tel.: (86) 10 6787 7396
Web Site: http://www.eastbalt.eu
Commercial Bakery
N.A.I.C.S.: 311812
Richard Xiaoyuan An *(Gen Mgr)*

Subsidiary (Domestic):

EB Bakery of Shenyang Co.,
Ltd. (4)
30 Huahai Street, Shenyang Econ & Tech
Develop Z, Shenyang, 110141, China
Tel.: (86) 24 8581 0259
Web Site: http://www.eastbalt.eu
Commercial Bakery
N.A.I.C.S.: 311812

Subsidiary (Non-US):

EB Gida Sanayi ve Ticaret Ltd.
Sirketi (3)
Cumhuriyet Mah Erhan Sok No 15B Cay-
irova, Kocaeli, 41400, Turkiye
Tel.: (90) 262 658 8641
Web Site: http://www.eastbalt.eu
Commercial Bakery
N.A.I.C.S.: 311812

Subsidiary (Domestic):

East Balt Commissary LLC (3)
1801 W 31st Pl, Chicago, IL 60608
Tel.: (773) 376-4444
Web Site: http://www.eastbalt.eu
Commercial Bakery
N.A.I.C.S.: 311812
Mark Bendix *(CEO)*

Subsidiary (Non-US):

East Balt France S.a.r.l. (3)
Rue Condorcet Zone Industrielle des Ra-
dars, Fleury Merogis, 91700, France
Tel.: (33) 1 6925 3400
Web Site: http://www.eastbalt.eu
Commercial Bakery
N.A.I.C.S.: 311812
Christophe Blaise *(Gen Mgr)*

East Balt Italia S.R.L. (3)
Via Aldo Moro 25, Bomporto, 41030, Italy
Tel.: (39) 0598170701
Web Site: http://www.eastbalt.eu
Commercial Bakery
N.A.I.C.S.: 311812

Plant (Domestic):

Entenmann's Bakery (2)
82 Newport Ave, Rumford, RI 02916-2068
Tel.: (401) 434-1719
Web Site: http://www.entenmanns.com
Sales Range: $25-49.9 Million
Emp.: 3
Retail Bakery Products
N.A.I.C.S.: 311812
Maureen Marcotte *(Mgr)*

Entenmann's Bakery Outlet (2)
170 S Tustin St, Orange, CA 92866-2320
Tel.: (714) 997-3207
Sales Range: $25-49.9 Million
Emp.: 4
Bakery Products
N.A.I.C.S.: 424490

Entenmann's/Oroweat (2)
4260 Buckingham Dr, Colorado Springs,
CO 80907-9027 (100%)
Tel.: (719) 577-0074
Web Site: http://www.bimbobakeries.com
Sales Range: $25-49.9 Million
Emp.: 18
Crackers, Cookies & Bakery Products
N.A.I.C.S.: 424490

Entenmann's/Oroweat (2)
4320 W Magnolia Blvd, Burbank, CA
91505 (100%)

Tel.: (818) 841-2832
Sales Range: $25-49.9 Million
Emp.: 4
Breadcake & Related Products
N.A.I.C.S.: 311812

Entenmann's/Oroweat (2)
8048 Auburn Blvd, Citrus Heights, CA
95610-1406 (100%)
Tel.: (916) 722-7288
Sales Range: $25-49.9 Million
Emp.: 15
Bread Cake & Related Products
N.A.I.C.S.: 311812

Entenmann's/Oroweat (2)
1798 Bryant St, San Francisco, CA 94110-1406
Tel.: (415) 863-4773
Web Site: http://www.grupobimbo.com
Sales Range: $25-49.9 Million
Emp.: 15
Bakery Products
N.A.I.C.S.: 445291

Entenmann's/Oroweat (2)
310 E Orangethorpe Ave, Placentia, CA
92870-6507 (100%)
Tel.: (714) 572-8372
Sales Range: $25-49.9 Million
Emp.: 2
Bakery Products
N.A.I.C.S.: 311811

Subsidiary (Domestic):

LaFronteriza LLC (2)
5005 S Nagle Ave, Chicago, IL
60638-1318 (100%)
Tel.: (419) 729-4070
Sales Range: $25-49.9 Million
Emp.: 66
Mfr of Food Preparations
N.A.I.C.S.: 424450

Mrs. Baird's Bakeries, Inc. (2)
7301 S Fwy, Fort Worth, TX 76134-4004
Tel.: (817) 293-6230
Web Site: http://www.mrsbairds.com
Rev.: $415,000,000
Emp.: 900
Bread, Cakes & Sweets Mfr
N.A.I.C.S.: 311812

Plant (Domestic):

Oroweat (2)
10555A Magnolia Ave, Riverside, CA
92505-1804
Tel.: (909) 687-5060
Sales Range: $25-49.9 Million
Emp.: 3
Bakery Products
N.A.I.C.S.: 424490

Oroweat Foods (2)
264 S Spruce Ave, South San Francisco,
CA 94080
Tel.: (650) 875-3100
Sales Range: $25-49.9 Million
Emp.: 40
Wet Corn Milling
N.A.I.C.S.: 311221

Subsidiary (Domestic):

Ralcorp Frozen Bakery Products (2)
7350 Commerce Ln NE, Minneapolis, MN
55432-3113 (100%)
Tel.: (763) 574-2222
Sales Range: $100-124.9 Million
Emp.: 225
Retail Bakery & Related Products Mfr
N.A.I.C.S.: 445291

Stroehmann Bakeries, L.C. (2)
255 Business Ctr Dr Ste 200, Horsham, PA
19044 (100%)
Tel.: (215) 672-8010
Web Site: http://www.stroehmann.com
Sales Range: $25-49.9 Million
Emp.: 60
Bakery Services
N.A.I.C.S.: 311812

Plant (Domestic):

Stroehmann Bakeries (3)
3996 Paxton St, Harrisburg, PA 17111-1423

AND PRIVATE COMPANIES

Tel.: (717) 561-1790
Web Site: http://www.stroehmann.com
Sales Range: $75-99.9 Million
Bakery Services
N.A.I.C.S.: 311812

Subsidiary (Domestic):

Twin City Bagel, Inc (2)
130 Hardman Ave S, South Saint Paul, MN 55075
Tel.: (651) 554-0200
Web Site: https://nationalchoicebakery.com
Rev.: $5,000,000
Emp.: 70
Commercial Bakeries
N.A.I.C.S.: 311812
Simon Harosh (Pres)

Bimbo S.A. (1)
Corres Diagonal Litoral B-2 Joset Pla No 2 Floor 4, 08019, Barcelona, Spain (100%)
Tel.: (34) 934767900
Web Site: http://www.bimbo.com
Sales Range: $25-49.9 Million
Emp.: 150
Bakery Products Mfr
N.A.I.C.S.: 311812

Subsidiary (Domestic):

Bimbo-Martinez Comercial, S.L. (2)
C Plata 92, Valladolid, 47012, Spain
Tel.: (34) 983390763
Bakery Product Distr
N.A.I.C.S.: 311999

Blue Label Mexico S.A. de C.V (1)
Av Prolongacion Paseo de la Reforma No 1236 Piso 4 Col Santa Fe, Mexico, Mexico (100%)
Tel.: (52) 15542121415
Web Site: http://www.bluelabelmexico.com
Sales Range: $50-74.9 Million
Emp.: 60
Secured Electronic Transaction Processing Services
N.A.I.C.S.: 522320

Canada Bread Company Ltd. (1)
10 Four Seasons Place Suite 1200, Etobicoke, M9B 6H7, ON, Canada (89.8%)
Tel.: (416) 622-2040
Web Site: http://www.canadabread.ca
Sales Range: $50-74.9 Million
Emp.: 1,000
Breads & Bakery Products Mfr & Distr
N.A.I.C.S.: 311812
Richard Lan (Pres & CEO)

Subsidiary (Non-US):

New York Bakery Company Limited (2)
Swinton Meadows Industrial Estate Swinton, Rotherham, S64 8AB, South Yorkshire, United Kingdom
Tel.: (44) 1709 580 840
Sales Range: $25-49.9 Million
Emp.: 250
Bakery Products Mfr
N.A.I.C.S.: 311813
Chris Harrop (Gen Mgr)

Subsidiary (US):

Wholesome Harvest Baking LLC (2)
1011 E Touhy Ave Ste 500, Des Plaines, IL 60018
Tel.: (800) 550-6810
Web Site: http://wholesomeharvestbaking.com
Bakery Products Mfr
N.A.I.C.S.: 311813

Mundo Dulce S.A. de C.V. (1)
Juan Salvador Agraz N 50 Piso 3, Santa Fe, Mexico, DF, Mexico
Tel.: (52) 1 5552 926231
Confectionary Product Mfr
N.A.I.C.S.: 311351

GRUPO BOLIVAR S.A.
Av El Dorado No 68 B 31 piso 10, Bogota, DC, Colombia
Tel.: (57) 13410077   Co
Web Site: https://www.grupobolivar.com.co
Year Founded: 1996

GRUBOLIVAR—(COLO)
Sales Range: $1-4.9 Billion
Emp.: 16,488
Holding Company; Banking, Real Estate Investment & Development, Insurance Products & Services
N.A.I.C.S.: 551112
Javier Jose Suarez Esparragoza (VP-Fin Risk)

Subsidiaries:

Banco Davivienda S.A. (1)
Avenida Calle 26 No 68C-61, Bogota, Colombia
Tel.: (57) 6013383838
Web Site: https://www.davivienda.com
Rev.: $4,547,507,043
Assets: $35,782,740,704
Liabilities: $32,418,590,909
Net Worth: $3,364,149,795
Earnings: $27,336,500
Emp.: 17,962
Fiscal Year-end: 12/31/2023
Retail & Commercial Banking, Mortgage Lending & Credit Card Issuing Services
N.A.I.C.S.: 522110
Javier Jose Suarez Esparragoza (CEO)

Subsidiary (Non-US):

Banco Davivienda (Costa Rica) S.A. (2)
Calle 0 Avenida 1, San Jose, Costa Rica
Tel.: (506) 2287 1111
Web Site: http://www.davivienda.cr
Commercial Banking Services
N.A.I.C.S.: 522110
Francisco F. Coccaro (CEO)

Banco Davivienda Honduras, S.A. (2)
Interseccion Boulevard Suyapa & Boulevard Juan Pablo II, Apartado Postal 344, Tegucigalpa, Honduras
Tel.: (504) 2240 0909
Web Site: http://www.davivienda.com.hn
Sales Range: $600-649.9 Million
Emp.: 1,100
Commercial Banking Services
N.A.I.C.S.: 522110
Alvaro Morales Patino (Pres)

Compania de Seguros Bolivar S.A. (1)
Carrera 10 No 16-39, Bogota, DC, Colombia
Tel.: (57) 1 341 0077
Web Site: http://www.segurosbolivar.com.co
Insurance Products & Services
N.A.I.C.S.: 524298

GRUPO BOLUDA
Capitan Haya N 21, 28020, Madrid, Spain
Tel.: (34) 963060200
Web Site: http://www.boluda.com.es
Year Founded: 1920
Towing & Shipbuilding Services
N.A.I.C.S.: 336611
Vicente Boluda (Chm)

Subsidiaries:

La Luz, S.A. (1)
Avda de los Cambulloneros, Muelle Virgen del Pino, Las Palmas, 35008, Spain
Tel.: (34) 928300565
Web Site: http://www.boluda.com.es
Sales Range: $25-49.9 Million
Emp.: 43
Port Operations
N.A.I.C.S.: 488320
F. Naranjo (Head-Computer Info)

Naviera del Mercosur S.A. (1)
25 de mayo esquina con Tacuari Edificio CPM Torre 25 de mayo Piso 9, Asuncion, Paraguay
Tel.: (595) 21 451310
Web Site: http://www.nmercosur.com
Maritime Cargo Transportation Services
N.A.I.C.S.: 488320

GRUPO BRASIL PARTICIPACOES
Av Marginal Pinheiros 5 200, Edificio Philadelfia, Sao Paulo, 05-693-000, CEP, Brazil
Tel.: (55) 11 3579 8666
Web Site: http://www.grupobrasil.com
Holding Company
N.A.I.C.S.: 551112

Subsidiaries:

Vulcan Material Plastico Ltda. (1)
Estr Do Colegio 380-Colegio, Rio de Janeiro, 21235-280, Brazil
Tel.: (55) 33622074
Web Site: http://www.vulcan.com.br
Thermoplastic Material Mfr
N.A.I.C.S.: 326112

GRUPO BRITT N.V.
Mercedes Norte, PO Box 528-3000, Heredia, Costa Rica
Tel.: (506) 2277 1500
Web Site: http://www.grupobritt.com
Year Founded: 1985
Sales Range: $25-49.9 Million
Holding Company: Specialty Travel Retailer
N.A.I.C.S.: 551112
Pablo E. Vargas (CEO)

Subsidiaries:

Britt Shop (1)
Mercedes Norte, PO Box 528-3000, Heredia, Costa Rica
Tel.: (506) 2277 1631
Web Site: http://www.brittshop.com
Emp.: 700
Specialty Travel Retailer
N.A.I.C.S.: 561599
Pablo E. Vargas (CEO)

Cafe Britt (1)
900 Norte 400 Oeste, Comandancia De Heredia, Heredia, Costa Rica
Tel.: (506) 2277 1500
Web Site: http://www.cafebritt.com
Gourmet Coffees, Chocolates, Nuts & Sweets Retail
N.A.I.C.S.: 311920
Jose Vasquez (Country Mgr)

Cafe Britt Chile Ltda. (1)
Aeropuerto AMB 2 Nivel MZ5 L2 Dpto B-227, Pudahuel, Santiago, Chile
Tel.: (56) 2 678 6200
N.A.I.C.S.: 445298

Cafe Britt Peru S.A.C. (1)
Avenida Corpac 112 Urbanizacion Bocanegra, Callao, Peru
Tel.: (51) 511 215 4500
Coffee Distr
N.A.I.C.S.: 445298

Cafe Britt USA (1)
Ste SJO 27042, Miami, FL 33102-5331
Tel.: (800) 462-7488
Coffee Distr
N.A.I.C.S.: 445298

GRUPO BURSATIL MEXICANO SA DE CV CASA DE BOLSA
Av Insurgentes Sur No 1605 Piso 31 Colonia San Jose Insurgentes, 03900, Mexico, Mexico
Tel.: (52) 5554817888
Web Site: https://gbm.com
Investment Banking
N.A.I.C.S.: 523150

GRUPO CARSO, S.A.B. DE C.V.
Plaza Carso Lago Zurich 245 Frisco Building 6th Floor, Ampliacion Granada, 11529, Mexico, Mexico
Tel.: (52) 5511012956   MX
Web Site: https://www.carso.com.mx
Year Founded: 1980
GCARSO—(MEX)
Rev.: $10,963,407,474
Assets: $14,456,663,124
Liabilities: $6,312,602,454
Net Worth: $8,144,060,669

GRUPO CARSO, S.A.B. DE C.V.

Earnings: $1,234,016,040
Emp.: 42,325
Fiscal Year-end: 12/31/22
Holding Company
N.A.I.C.S.: 551112
Patrick Slim Domit (Vice Chm)

Subsidiaries:

Cablena do Brasil Ltda (1)
Av Nossa Senhora do O 382 Limao, Sao Paulo, 02722-030, Brazil
Tel.: (55) 11 3587 9590
Web Site: http://www.cablena.com.br
Emp.: 3
Coaxial Cable Mfr
N.A.I.C.S.: 335929
Clemente Lavie (Mng Dir)

Plant (Domestic):

Cablena do Brasil Ltda - TELECOM PLANT (2)
Av Americo Simoes 1400, Itupeva, 13295-000, Sao Paulo, Brazil
Tel.: (55) 1135879590
Web Site: http://www.cablena.com.br
Coaxial Cables Distr
N.A.I.C.S.: 423610

Cablena, S.A. (1)
Poligono Industrial Malpica Calle E Parcelas 43-44, 50016, Zaragoza, Spain
Tel.: (34) 976 46 5650
Web Site: http://www.cablena.es
Sales Range: $25-49.9 Million
Emp.: 65
Coaxial Cable Mfr
N.A.I.C.S.: 335929
Victor Villalobos (Gen Mgr)

Carso Infraestructura y Construccion, S.A.B. de C.V. (1)
Lago Zurich No 245 Edificio Frisco piso 2, Col Ampliacion Granada, 11529, Mexico, Mexico
Tel.: (52) 498900
Web Site: http://www.ccicsa.com.mx
Construction & Engineering Services
N.A.I.C.S.: 236220

Grupo Condumex, S. A. de C. V. (1)
Poniente 140 No 720 Col Industrial Vallejo, CP 02300, Mexico, DF, Mexico (100%)
Tel.: (52) 55 5729 3316
Web Site: http://www.condumex.com.mx
Sales Range: $5-14.9 Billion
Emp.: 30,000
Electronics & Vehicle Parts Mfr
N.A.I.C.S.: 336340

Subsidiary (US):

Condumex Inc. (2)
900 Avenue S, Grand Prairie, TX 75050
Tel.: (972) 352-2300
Web Site: https://www.condumexinc.com
Emp.: 30
Building Wire Products Distr
N.A.I.C.S.: 423610
Pedro Ruiz (Pres)

Grupo Sanborns, S.A. de C.V. (1)
Avenida Calvario No 106, Tlalpan, 14000, Mexico, Mexico (99%)
Tel.: (52) 5553259900
Web Site: http://www.sanborns.com.mx
Sales Range: $5-14.9 Billion
Emp.: 35,236
Departmental Store Operator
N.A.I.C.S.: 455110

Ostar Grupo Hotelero (1)
Calle Liverpool 133, 6600, Colonia, Mexico (100%)
Tel.: (52) 5550800600
Web Site: http://www.ostar.com.mx
Hotel Services Operator
N.A.I.C.S.: 721110

Sears Roebuck de Mexico, S. A. de C. V. (1)
Vasco De Qurga 3800, Col Santa Fe De Quajimalpa, 01210, Mexico, DF, Mexico (84.94%)
Tel.: (52) 5552579300
Web Site: http://www.sears.com.mx
Sales Range: $550-599.9 Million
Emp.: 9,000
Departmental Store Operator

GRUPO CARSO, S.A.B. DE C.V.

Grupo Carso, S.A.B. de C.V.—(Continued)
N.A.I.C.S.: 455110

US Commercial Corp. S.A. de C.V. **(1)**
Miguel de Cervantes Saavedra 255, Mexico, Mexico
Tel.: (52) 5553285800
Sales Range: $250-299.9 Million
Emp.: 600
Holding Company
N.A.I.C.S.: 551112

GRUPO CATALANA OCCIDENTE, S.A.

Avda Alcalde Barnils 63, 08174, Sant Cugat del Valles, Spain
Tel.: (34) 902344000 ES
Web Site: https://www.grupocatalana.com
Year Founded: 1864
GCO—(BAR)
Rev.: $5,146,125,621
Assets: $19,014,810,058
Liabilities: $12,953,630,477
Net Worth: $6,061,179,581
Earnings: $691,558,385
Emp.: 8,615
Fiscal Year-end: 12/31/23
Insurance Services
N.A.I.C.S.: 524298
Francisco Jose Arregui Laborda *(Sec)*

Subsidiaries:

Atradius N.V. **(1)**
David Ricardostraat 1, 1066 JS, Amsterdam, Netherlands **(35.77%)**
Tel.: (31) 205539111
Web Site: http://www.atradius.com
Rev.: $1,885,568,697
Assets: $5,404,746,312
Liabilities: $3,321,403,742
Net Worth: $2,083,342,570
Earnings: $231,794,762
Emp.: 3,545
Fiscal Year-end: 12/31/2018
Credit Management Services & Solutions
N.A.I.C.S.: 522299
Isidoro Unda *(CEO & Member-Exec Bd)*

Subsidiary (Non-US):

Atradius **(2)**
179 Ave Victor Hugo, 75116, Paris, France
Tel.: (33) 53702999
Web Site: http://www.atradius.com
Sales Range: $75-99.9 Million
Emp.: 60
Credit Management Services & Solutions
N.A.I.C.S.: 524298

Atradius **(2)**
9th floor 10 Fenchurch St, London, EC3M 3BE, United Kingdom
Tel.: (44) 2077438180
Web Site: http://www.atradius.com
Sales Range: $50-74.9 Million
Emp.: 28
Credit Management Services & Solutions
N.A.I.C.S.: 524298
Olivier David *(Gen Mgr)*

Subsidiary (Domestic):

Atradius Collections B.V. **(2)**
David Ricardostraat 1, Amsterdam, 1066JS, Netherlands
Tel.: (31) 205532000
Web Site: http://www.atradiuscollections.com
Sales Range: $125-149.9 Million
Business Debt Collection Services
N.A.I.C.S.: 561440
Raymond van der Loos *(Mng Dir)*

Subsidiary (US):

Atradius Collections, Inc. **(3)**
1200 N Arlington Hts Rd Ste 410, Itasca, IL 60143-3109
Web Site: http://www.atradiuscollections.com
Sales Range: $25-49.9 Million
Emp.: 12
Business Debt Collection Services
N.A.I.C.S.: 561440

Subsidiary (Non-US):

Atradius Credit Insurance NV **(2)**
Via bracco 6, Milan, 20159, Italy
Tel.: (39) 02632411
Web Site: http://www.atradius.com
Sales Range: $75-99.9 Million
Emp.: 100
Credit Management Services & Solutions
N.A.I.C.S.: 524298
Massimo Mamcini *(Country Mgr)*

Subsidiary (US):

Atradius Trade Credit Insurance, Inc. **(2)**
230 Schilling Cir Ste 240, Hunt Valley, MD 21031-8643
Tel.: (410) 568-3850
Web Site: http://www.atradius.us
Sales Range: $50-74.9 Million
Emp.: 93
Credit & Other Financial Insurance Services
N.A.I.C.S.: 524126
Doug Collins *(Reg Dir)*

Bilbao Hipotecaria, S.A., E.F.C. **(1)**
Calle Paseo Del Puerto 20, Getxo, Bilbao, Spain **(99.72%)**
Tel.: (34) 944898550
Insurance Agencies & Brokerages
N.A.I.C.S.: 524210

Bilbao Vida y Gestores Financieros, S.A. **(1)**
Calle Paseo Del Puerto 20, Getxo, Bilbao, Spain **(99.72%)**
Tel.: (34) 944898431
Insurance Agencies & Brokerages
N.A.I.C.S.: 524210

Bilbao, Compania Anonima de Seguros y Reaseguros **(1)**
Paseo Del Puerto No 20, Apto Correos 297, 48992, Neguri, Spain
Tel.: (34) 944898211
Web Site: http://www.segurosbilbao.com
Sales Range: $550-599.9 Million
Emp.: 200
Provider of Life & Automobile Insurance Products & Financial Services
N.A.I.C.S.: 524298
Ignacio Alvarez *(CEO)*

Subsidiary (Domestic):

Orbita, Agencia de Seguros **(2)**
Calle Fortuny 6, 2 Fl Izda, 28010, Madrid, Spain
Tel.: (34) 913431926
Sales Range: $50-74.9 Million
Emp.: 80
Provider of Insurance Services
N.A.I.C.S.: 524298

C.O. CAPITAL Agencia de Valores, S.A. **(1)**
Avda Alcalde Barnils 63, Barcelona, 08174, Spain **(100%)**
Tel.: (34) 935820518
Emp.: 5
Securities Brokerage
N.A.I.C.S.: 523150
Juan Closa *(Chm)*

Cosalud, SA de Seguros **(1)**
C/Jesus Serra Santamans 1, 8174, Sant Cugat del Valles, Barcelona, Spain
Tel.: (34) 93 484 07 80
Health Care Insurance Services
N.A.I.C.S.: 524114

Depsa, SA de Seguros y Reaseguros **(1)**
Gran Via de les Corts Catalanes 645, 08010, Barcelona, Spain
Tel.: (34) 933 014 300
General Insurance Services
N.A.I.C.S.: 524210

Grupo Catalana Occidente Servicios Tecnologicos, AIE **(1)**
Avenida Alcalde Barnils 63, Sant Cugat del Valles, 8174, Spain
Tel.: (34) 935820690
General Insurance Services
N.A.I.C.S.: 524210

Nortehispana, SA de Seguros y Reaseguros **(1)**
C/ Pau Claris 132, 08009, Barcelona, Spain
Tel.: (34) 93 302 78 15
Web Site: http://www.nortehispana.com
General Insurance Services
N.A.I.C.S.: 524210
Augusto D. Huesca *(CEO)*

Prepersa, Peritacion y Prevencion de Seguros AIE **(1)**
Carrer Jesus Serra Santamans N 1 Planta 4, 08174, Sant Cugat del Valles, Barcelona, Spain
Tel.: (34) 93 484 08 80
General Insurance Services
N.A.I.C.S.: 524210

Salerno 94 S.A. **(1)**
Avda Alcalde Barnils 63, 08174, Sant Cugat del Valles, Spain **(100%)**
Tel.: (34) 935820627
Insurance Agencies & Brokerages
N.A.I.C.S.: 524210

Seguros Bilbao Fondos S.G.I.I.C. **(1)**
Plaza Independencia 2, Madrid, 28001, Spain
Tel.: (34) 914328660
Web Site: http://www.segurosbilbao.com
Sales Range: $50-74.9 Million
Emp.: 5
Insurance Related Activities
N.A.I.C.S.: 524298

Seguros Catalana Occidente, S.A. **(1)**
Avda Alcalde Barnils 63, 08174, Sant Cugat del Valles, Barcellona, Spain **(100%)**
Tel.: (34) 935820627
Web Site: http://www.seguroscatalanaoccidente.com
Insurance Services
N.A.I.C.S.: 524210
Jose M. Serra Farre *(Pres)*

Subsidiary (Domestic):

Groupama Seguros y Reaseguros SA **(2)**
Plaza de las Cortes 8, 28014, Madrid, Spain
Tel.: (34) 915899292
Web Site: http://www.plusultra.es
Life Insurance, Reinsurance & Pension
N.A.I.C.S.: 524113

Seguros de Vida y Pensiones Antares, S.A. **(1)**
Porense 11 1st Floor, 28020, Madrid, Spain **(78.67%)**
Tel.: (34) 914179950
Web Site: http://www.antares.es
Sales Range: $50-74.9 Million
Provider of Life Insurance, Pensions & Health Insurance
N.A.I.C.S.: 524114

Tecniseguros, Sociedad de Agencia de Seguros, S.A. **(1)**
Avda Alcalde Barnils 63, 08174, Sant Cugat del Valles, Spain **(100%)**
Tel.: (34) 935820627
Web Site: http://www.grupocatalanaoccidente.com
Sales Range: $350-399.9 Million
Emp.: 800
Depository Credit Intermediation
N.A.I.C.S.: 522180

GRUPO CCRR

Rua Iaia 77 7 andar Itaim Bibi, Sao Paulo, 04542-060, Brazil
Tel.: (55) 1137069800
Web Site: http://www.colacril.com.br
Year Founded: 2011
Self Adhesive Labels Mfr
N.A.I.C.S.: 325520
Ricardo Lobo *(CEO)*

Subsidiaries:

PIMACO Autoadesivos Ltda. **(1)**
Av Brasil 22773, Guadalupe, Rio de Janeiro, 21670-000, Brazil
Tel.: (55) 21 2450 9700
Web Site: http://www.pimaco.com.br
Adhesive Label Mfr & Distr
N.A.I.C.S.: 325520

INTERNATIONAL PUBLIC

GRUPO CLARIN S.A.

Piedras 1743, C1140ABK, Buenos Aires, Argentina Ar
Tel.: (54) 11 4309 7500
Web Site: http://www.grupoclarin.com
Holding Company; Telecommunications & Broadcasting Services
N.A.I.C.S.: 551112

Subsidiaries:

Arte Grafico Editorial Argentino S.A. **(1)**
Tacuari 1846, C1139AAN, Buenos Aires, Argentina
Tel.: (54) 1143097500
Web Site: http://www.clarin.com.ar
Newspaper Publishing
N.A.I.C.S.: 513110

Subsidiary (Domestic):

Artes Graficas Rioplatense S.A. **(2)**
Corrales 1393 - CP 1437, Pompeya Capital Federal, Buenos Aires, Argentina
Tel.: (54) 1149185060
Web Site: http://www.agr.com.ar
Sales Range: $125-149.9 Million
Printing Services
N.A.I.C.S.: 323111

Joint Venture (Domestic):

Impripost Tecnologias S.A **(3)**
Av de los Constituyentes 3702 ex Ruta 9 - Km 355, Buenos Aires, B1617AGS, Argentina **(50%)**
Tel.: (54) 3327451467
Web Site: http://www.impripost.com.ar
Sales Range: $25-49.9 Million
Printing Services
N.A.I.C.S.: 323111

Subsidiary (Domestic):

Unir S.A. **(3)**
Corrales 1555, C1437GLI, Buenos Aires, Argentina
Tel.: (54) 1148799100
Web Site: http://www.correounir.com.ar
Logistics Consulting Servies
N.A.I.C.S.: 541614

Subsidiary (Domestic):

Cuspide Libros S.A. **(2)**
Ascasubi 3282, C1286AAD, Buenos Aires, Argentina
Tel.: (54) 11 4126 5858
Web Site: http://www.cuspide.com
Book Distr
N.A.I.C.S.: 459210

La Voz del Interior S.A. **(2)**
Av la voz del interior 6080, Cordoba, X5008HKJ, Argentina
Tel.: (54) 3514757000
Web Site: http://www.lavoz.com.ar
Television Broadcasting Services
N.A.I.C.S.: 516120

Affiliate (Domestic):

Papel Prensa S.A.I.C.F. y de M. **(2)**
Bartolome Mitre 739, C1036AAM, Buenos Aires, Argentina **(49%)**
Tel.: (54) 1143281516
Web Site: http://www.papelprensa.com
Paper Mfr
N.A.I.C.S.: 322120

Arte Radiotelevisivo Argentino S.A. **(1)**
Lima 1261, C1138ACA, Buenos Aires, Argentina **(99.2%)**
Tel.: (54) 1143050013
Web Site: http://www.artear.com.ar
Television Broadcasting
N.A.I.C.S.: 516120

Subsidiary (Domestic):

Bariloche TV S.A **(2)**
Av Maria Elflein 251, Rio Negro, Bariloche, Argentina
Tel.: (54) 2944420511
Television Broadcasting Services

AND PRIVATE COMPANIES

N.A.I.C.S.: 516120
Affiliate (Domestic):

Patagonik Film Group S.A. (2)
Scalabrini Ortiz 764, Buenos Aires, Argentina
Tel.: (54) 11 4777 7200
Web Site: http://www.patagonik.com.ar
Emp.: 17
Cinematographic Production Services
N.A.I.C.S.: 512131
Juan Pablo Galli (Gen Mgr)

Subsidiary (Domestic):

Pol-Ka Producciones S.A. (2)
Jorge Newbery 3449, C1427EGA, Buenos Aires, Argentina
Tel.: (54) 11 4588 9200
Web Site: http://www.pol-ka.com
Emp.: 350
Motion Picture Production Services
N.A.I.C.S.: 512110

Radio Mitre S.A. (2)
Mansilla 2668 Recoleta, C1425BPD, Buenos Aires, Argentina **(100%)**
Tel.: (54) 1149641500
Web Site: http://www.radiomitre.com.ar
Radio Broadcasting AM 790
N.A.I.C.S.: 516210

Affiliate (Domestic):

Tele Red Imagen S.A. (2)
San Juan 1132, C1147AAW, Buenos Aires, Argentina
Tel.: (54) 1143003800
Web Site: http://www.tycsports.com
Sports Event Promotion
N.A.I.C.S.: 711320

Unit (Domestic):

TyC Sports (3)
San Juan 1132, C1147 AAW, Buenos Aires, Argentina
Tel.: (54) 1143003800
Web Site: http://www.tycsports.com
Sales Range: $100-124.9 Million
Sports Television
N.A.I.C.S.: 516120
Alexander Silverman (Owner)

Subsidiary (Domestic):

Teledifusora Bahiense S.A. (2)
Blandengues 223, Bahia Blanca, B8000GIE, Buenos Aires, Argentina
Tel.: (54) 2914550000
Television Broadcasting Services
N.A.I.C.S.: 516120

Canal Rural Satelital S.A. (1)
Honduras 5940, Buenos Aires, C1414BNL, Argentina **(24.99%)**
Tel.: (54) 1147774200
Television Broadcasting Services
N.A.I.C.S.: 516120

Clarin Global S.A. (1)
Piedras 1743, Buenos Aires, 1139, Argentina **(100%)**
Tel.: (54) 1143097500
Web Site: http://www.clarin.com
Emp.: 8
Internet Services
N.A.I.C.S.: 517121
Hector Magnetto (CEO)

Compania de Medios Digitales S.A. (1)
Av Colonia 170 Parque Patricios, Buenos Aires, Argentina
Tel.: (54) 11 4943 8700
Web Site: http://www.cmd.com.ar
Media Services
N.A.I.C.S.: 512191

Subsidiary (Domestic):

Ferias y Exposiciones S.A. (2)
Tacuari 1846, C1139AAN, Buenos Aires, Argentina **(100%)**
Tel.: (54) 1143097660
Web Site: http://www.fyea.com.ar
Sales Range: $50-74.9 Million
Emp.: 5
Exhibit & Events Production
N.A.I.C.S.: 711310

Gestion Compartida S.A. (2)
Av Tille 760, 1098, Buenos Aires, Capital Federal, Argentina **(100%)**
Tel.: (54) 1143705000
Web Site: http://www.gcgestion.com.ar
Business Processing Outsourcing Services
N.A.I.C.S.: 561499
Ricardo M. Rodriguez (Gen Mgr)

Editorial La Razon S.A. (1)
La Razon, Ituzaingo 647, C1141ABC, Buenos Aires, Argentina **(75%)**
Tel.: (54) 1143096000
Web Site: http://www.larazon.com.ar
Sales Range: $25-49.9 Million
Newspaper Publishing
N.A.I.C.S.: 513110

La Capital Cable S.A. (1)
Av Colon 3773, B7600FZE, Mar del Plata, Buenos Aires, Argentina **(49%)**
Tel.: (54) 8104444522
Web Site: http://www.lcc.net.ar
Television Broadcasting Services
N.A.I.C.S.: 516120

Multicanal S.A. (1)
Avalos 2057, C1431DPM, Buenos Aires, Argentina **(100%)**
Tel.: (54) 1151694700
Cable Television
N.A.I.C.S.: 516210

Primera Red Interactiva de Medios Argentinos (PRIMA) S.A. (1)
La Rioja 301, C1214ADG, Buenos Aires, Argentina **(82%)**
Tel.: (54) 11 4370 0070
Web Site: http://www.prima.com.ar
Internet Services
N.A.I.C.S.: 517810

Teledeportes S.A. (1)
Piedras 1743, C1140ABK, Buenos Aires, Argentina **(100%)**
Tel.: (54) 1143097500
Web Site: http://www.grupoclarin.com
Sports Marketing & Production
N.A.I.C.S.: 711320

Tinta Fresca Ediciones S.A. (1)
Corrientes 534 CABA, 1043, Buenos Aires, Argentina **(100%)**
Tel.: (54) 1143097500
Web Site: http://www.tintafresca.com.ar
Publishing Services
N.A.I.C.S.: 513130

Tres Arroyos Televisora Color S.A. (1)
Falucho 650, Tres Arroyos, Buenos Aires, Argentina **(49.99%)**
Tel.: (54) 2983430987
Television Broadcasting Services
N.A.I.C.S.: 516120

GRUPO COLLADO S.A. DE C.V.

Gavilan 200 Guadalupe Del Moral, 56535, Mexico, DF, Mexico
Tel.: (52) 5517375100
Web Site:
    https://www.collado.com.mx
Year Founded: 1949
COLLADO—(MEX)
Rev.: $687,977,845
Assets: $447,014,473
Liabilities: $290,107,024
Net Worth: $156,907,449
Earnings: $11,124,559
Emp.: 3,635
Fiscal Year-end: 12/31/23
Steel Product Mfr & Distr
N.A.I.C.S.: 331110
Guillermo Voguel Hinojosa (Chm)

GRUPO COMERCIAL CHEDRAUI S.A.B. DE C.V.

Privada Antonio Chedraui Caram 248 Colonia Encinal, Xalapa, 91180, Veracruz, Mexico
Tel.: (52) 5511038000   MX
Web Site:
    https://www.grupochedraui.com.mx
Year Founded: 1920

CHDRAUI—(MEX)
Rev.: $12,940,345,943
Assets: $7,157,589,733
Liabilities: $5,193,143,549
Net Worth: $1,964,446,184
Earnings: $308,169,476
Emp.: 70,101
Fiscal Year-end: 12/31/22
Grocery & General Merchandise & Motor Vehicle Store Owner & Operator
N.A.I.C.S.: 445110
Ricardo Krasovsky Satamarina (Dir-Expansion)

Subsidiaries:

Bodega Latina Corporation (1)
14601B Lakewood Blvd, Paramount, CA 90723
Tel.: (562) 616-8800
Web Site: http://www.elsupermarkets.com
Grocery Stores
N.A.I.C.S.: 445110
Carlos Smith (Pres & CEO)

Subsidiary (Domestic):

Fiesta Mart, LLC (2)
5444 Westheimer Rd Ste 101, Houston, TX 77056
Tel.: (713) 869-5060
Web Site: http://www.fiestamart.com
Supermarket Operator
N.A.I.C.S.: 445110

Tiendas Chedraui S.A. de C.V. (1)
Privada De Antonio Chedraui S N, Jalapa, 91180, Veracruz, Mexico **(100%)**
Tel.: (52) 2288421100
Web Site: http://www.chedraui.com
Sales Range: $450-499.9 Million
Emp.: 2,000
Variety Stores
N.A.I.C.S.: 459999

GRUPO COMERCIAL GOMO, S.A. DE C.V.

Av Alvaro Obregon 302 Piso 4, Roma, 6700, Mexico, Mexico
Tel.: (52) 52121907
Electronic Product Distr
N.A.I.C.S.: 423620
Juan Manuel Jimenez Gomez (Mng Dir)

GRUPO CORVI, S.A.B. DE C.V.

Pico de Tolima 29, Jardines en la Montana, 14210, Mexico, Mexico
Tel.: (52) 5556285100
Web Site: http://www.grupocorvi.com
Sales Range: $1-4.9 Billion
Emp.: 3,959
Food & Consumer Products Distr; Candy Mfr
N.A.I.C.S.: 424490
Benjamin Villasenor Costa (Chm & CEO)

Subsidiaries:

Organizacion Sahuayo, S.A. (1)
Pico de Tolima No 29, Jardines en la Montana, Mexico, 14210, Mexico
Tel.: (52) 5556285100
Grocery & Consumer Product Distr
N.A.I.C.S.: 424490

GRUPO DE INVERSIONES SURAMERICANA S.A.

Carrera 43A Suite 5a-113, Medellin, Colombia
Tel.: (57) 6044447231   Co
Web Site: https://www.gruposura.com
Year Founded: 1997
GRUPOSURA—(COLO)
Rev.: $8,413,316,218
Assets: $22,141,931,430
Liabilities: $14,461,267,072
Net Worth: $7,680,664,358
Earnings: $481,269,715
Emp.: 64,160

Fiscal Year-end: 12/31/23
Investment & Banking Services
N.A.I.C.S.: 523999
Jaime Bermudez Merizalde (Chm)

Subsidiaries:

AFP Integra S.A,. (1)
Av Canaval y Moreyra No 522 6th Floor, San Isidro, Peru
Tel.: (51) 15135050
Web Site: http://www.integra.com.pe
Investment Management Service
N.A.I.C.S.: 523940
Jose Carlos Saavedra SolanoIndependent (Chm)

Administradora de Fondos de Cesantia S.A. (1)
18 de Marzo de 2002 Notaria Nancy de La Fuente Hernandez, Santiago, Chile
Tel.: (56) 2478 2800
Web Site: http://www.afcchile.cl
Investment Management Service
N.A.I.C.S.: 523940

Afore Sura S.A. de C.V. (1)
Ave Paseo De La Reforma No 222 P 4, Mexico, 06600, Mexico
Tel.: (52) 5553451000
Web Site: http://www.suramexico.com
Asset Management Services
N.A.I.C.S.: 523940

Consultoria en Gestion de Riesgos IPS Suramericana S.A. (1)
Carrera 63 49 A 31 Piso 1 Antioquia, Medellin, Colombia
Tel.: (57) 42602100
Risk Management Consulting Services
N.A.I.C.S.: 541618

Diagnostico y Asistencia Medica S.A. I.P.S. Dinamica (1)
Cr 58 74-131, Barranquilla, Colombia
Tel.: (57) 5 3686667
Laboratory Equipment Mfr
N.A.I.C.S.: 334516

Enlace Operativo S.A. (1)
Calle 19 43 G 169 Of 803 Antioquia, Medellin, Colombia
Tel.: (57) 44447274
Web Site: http://www.enlaceoperativo.com
Information Technology Services
N.A.I.C.S.: 541512

ING Administradora de Fondos de Pensiones y Cesantias S.A. (1)
Carrera 7 99-53 Torre 2, Bogota, Colombia
Tel.: (57) 1 7441000
General Insurance Services
N.A.I.C.S.: 524298

ING Compania de inversiones y servicios LTDA (1)
Suecia 211, Santiago, Chile
Tel.: (56) 29152000
Investment Management Service
N.A.I.C.S.: 523940

Subsidiary (Domestic):

A.F.P. CAPITAL S.A. (2)
Av Suecia 211 Piso 11, Providencia, Santiago, Chile
Tel.: (56) 222521464
Web Site: http://www.afpcapital.cl
Sales Range: Less than $1 Million
Information Technology Services
N.A.I.C.S.: 519290
Andres Ricardo Castro Gonzalez (Pres)

ING Investment Management (1)
Bosque de Alisos 45 B 5to piso Col Bosques de la Lomas, 05120, Mexico, Mexico
Tel.: (52) 5591771000
Sales Range: $100-124.9 Million
Emp.: 150
Investment Management Service
N.A.I.C.S.: 523940

Seguros SURA (Brasil) S.A. (1)
Av das Nacoes Unidas 12995 4 andar, Brooklin Novo, Sao Paulo, 04578-000, Brazil **(100%)**
Tel.: (55) 1135567000
Web Site: http://www.segurossura.com.br
Emp.: 300

3125

GRUPO DE INVERSIONES SURAMERICANA S.A.

Grupo de Inversiones Suramericana S.A.—(Continued)
Property & Casualty Insurance Products & Services
N.A.I.C.S.: 524126
Marcelo Biasoli *(Head-Corp Strategy, Innovation, Mktg & Customer)*

Seguros Sura S.A. **(1)**
Boulevard Cecilia Grierson 255, Caba, C1107CPE, Buenos Aires,
Argentina **(80.67%)**
Tel.: (54) 1143390000
Web Site: http://www.segurossura.com.ar
Property & Casualty Insurance Products & Services
N.A.I.C.S.: 524126
Santiago Favelukes *(VP-Non-Traditional Channel)*

Seguros Sura, S.A de C.V. **(1)**
Blvd Adolfo Lopez Mateos No 2448 Colonia Altavista, Delegacion Alvaro Obregon,
Mexico, CP 01060, Mexico **(81.13%)**
Tel.: (52) 57 23 7999
Web Site: http://www.segurossura.com.mx
Insurance Management Services
N.A.I.C.S.: 524298
Carlos Alberto Ospina Duque *(Gen Mgr)*

Seguros Suramericana S.A. **(1)**
Plaza Marbella Calle Aquilino, Panama, Panama
Tel.: (507) 205 0700
General Insurance Services
N.A.I.C.S.: 524298

Seguros de Riesgos Profesionales Suramericana S.A. **(1)**
Calle 49 A 63 55 Antioquia, Medellin, Colombia
Tel.: (57) 42602100
General Insurance Services
N.A.I.C.S.: 524298

Servicios de Salud IPS Suramericana S.A. **(1)**
Calle 49 63 55 Piso 1 Antioquia, Medellin, Colombia
Tel.: (57) 42602100
Health Care Srvices
N.A.I.C.S.: 621999

GRUPO DE MODA SOMA S.A.
Avenida Pasteur 154, Rio de Janeiro,
CEP 22290-240, Brazil
Tel.: (212) 5036850 BR
Web Site:
https://www.somagrupo.com.br
Emp.: 100
Apparel Accessories & Apparel Mfr
N.A.I.C.S.: 315990
Marcel Sapir *(Chm)*

Subsidiaries:

Cia. Hering **(1)**
Rua Rua Hermann Hering 1790 Bom Retiro, 89010-900, Blumenau, SC, Brazil
Tel.: (55) 4733213544
Web Site: http://www.ciahering.com.br
Rev.: $383,540,785
Assets: $448,558,759
Liabilities: $95,411,390
Net Worth: $353,147,369
Earnings: $53,155,921
Emp.: 5,353
Fiscal Year-end: 12/31/2019
Apparel Mfr & Whslr
N.A.I.C.S.: 315990

Plant (Domestic):

Cia. Hering - Avenida Brasil - Anapolis Plant **(2)**
Street Av Brasil Sul 6 700 - Loteamento Polocentro 1, 75130-390, Anapolis, Goias, Brazil
Tel.: (55) 62 3701 9102
Apparels Mfr
N.A.I.C.S.: 315990

Cia. Hering - DAIA - Anapolis Plant **(2)**
Street VPR3 s/n Quadra 2-A Modulos 23 a, 25 - Distrito Agroindustrial, 75132-015, Anapolis, Goias, Brazil
Tel.: (55) 62 3316 1777

Apparels Mfr
N.A.I.C.S.: 315990

Cia. Hering - Goianesia Plant **(2)**
Street Cinquenta e Tres n 454 - Galpao 2, Santa Teresa, 76380-000, Goianesia, Goias, Brazil
Tel.: (55) 62 3353 6796
Apparels Mfr
N.A.I.C.S.: 315990

Cia. Hering - Parauna Plant **(2)**
Street 13 de Maio s/n a quadra 18-A, Parque dos Buritis, 75980-000, Parauna, Goias, Brazil
Tel.: (55) 64 3556 2296
Apparels Mfr
N.A.I.C.S.: 315990

Cia. Hering - Santa Helena Plant **(2)**
Street Rodovia GO-164 s/n Km 32 5 - Zona Rural, 75920-000, Santa Helena de Goias, Goias, Brazil
Tel.: (55) 64 3641 1795
Apparels Mfr
N.A.I.C.S.: 315990

GRUPO DON MARIO
Monsenor Magliano 3061, B1642,
Martinez, Buenos Aires, Argentina
Tel.: (54) 152302800
Web Site:
https://www.gdmseeds.com
Emp.: 100
Soybean Farming
N.A.I.C.S.: 111110

Subsidiaries:

KWS Argentina S.A. **(1)**
San Martin Avenue 4075, 7620, Balcarce, Buenos Aires, Argentina
Tel.: (54) 2266420114
Web Site: https://www.kws.com
Sales Range: $25-49.9 Million
Emp.: 62
Seed Producer & Distr
N.A.I.C.S.: 111998

GRUPO EMES S.A.
Avda Bouchard 547 Piso 26, Buenos Aires, Argentina
Tel.: (54) 1152359500
Privater Equity Firm
N.A.I.C.S.: 523999
Marcos Marcelo Mindlin *(Chm)*

Subsidiaries:

Origenes Seguros de Retiro, S.A. **(1)**
Av. Corrientes 1166, Buenos Aires, Argentina
Tel.: (54) 1143403984
Web Site: http://www.origenes.com.ar
Retirement Insurance
N.A.I.C.S.: 524298

Pampa Energia S.A. **(1)**
Maipu 1, C1084ABA, Buenos Aires, Argentina
Tel.: (54) 1143446000
Web Site: https://ri.pampa.com
Rev.: $1,829,000,000
Assets: $4,742,000,000
Liabilities: $2,458,000,000
Net Worth: $2,284,000,000
Earnings: $457,000,000
Emp.: 2,013
Fiscal Year-end: 12/31/2022
Holding Company
N.A.I.C.S.: 221118
Marcos Marcelo Mindlin *(Chm)*

Subsidiary (Domestic):

Compania de Transporte de Energia Electrica en Alta Tension Transener S.A. **(2)**
Av Paseo Colon 728 6th Floor, Buenos Aires, 1063, Argentina
Tel.: (54) 1151679100
Web Site: http://www.transener.com.ar
Sales Range: $25-49.9 Million
Electric Power Distr
N.A.I.C.S.: 221111
Carlos A. Garcia Pereira *(CEO)*

Empresa Distribuidora y Comercializadora Norte S.A. **(2)**
Avenida Del Libertador 6363, Ciudad de Buenos Aires, C1428ARG, Buenos Aires, Argentina
Tel.: (54) 1143465000
Web Site: https://www.edenor.com
Rev.: $2,447,378,150
Assets: $5,708,757,590
Liabilities: $4,214,588,850
Net Worth: $1,494,168,740
Earnings: ($207,694,520)
Emp.: 4,658
Fiscal Year-end: 12/31/2022
Electric Power Distr
N.A.I.C.S.: 221122
Gustavo Mariani *(Vice Chm)*

Petrobras Argentina S.A. **(2)**
Maipu 1, C1084ABA, Buenos Aires, Argentina **(100%)**
Tel.: (54) 1143446000
Holding Company; Oil, Gas, Construction, Farming & Forestry
N.A.I.C.S.: 211120
Ivan de Souza Monteiro *(Member-Exec Bd)*

Affiliate (Domestic):

Compania de Inversiones de Energia S.A.
Don Bosco 3672 piso 6, C1206 ABF, Buenos Aires, Argentina
Tel.: (54) 11 4865 9060
Web Site: http://www.tgs.com.ar
Exploration, Production, Pipeline Transportation, Refining, Marketing & Distribution
N.A.I.C.S.: 213112

Subsidiary (Domestic):

Transportadora de Gas del Sur S.A. **(4)**
Cecilia Grierson 26th floor, C1107, Buenos Aires, Argentina **(55.3%)**
Tel.: (54) 1137515100
Web Site: https://www.tgs.com.ar
Rev.: $1,956,199,741
Assets: $4,899,776,555
Liabilities: $1,722,479,759
Net Worth: $3,177,296,796
Earnings: $384,258,666
Emp.: 1,095
Fiscal Year-end: 12/31/2022
Gas Services; Transmission, Gathering, Treating, Delivering
N.A.I.C.S.: 221210
Alejandro Mario Basso *(CFO & VP-Svcs)*

Subsidiary (Domestic):

Petrobras Energia Internacional S.A. **(3)**
Maipu 1 Fl 22, Buenos Aires, C1084ABA, Argentina
Tel.: (54) 11 4344 6000
Eletric Power Generation Services
N.A.I.C.S.: 221118

World Energy Business S.A. **(3)**
Ln Alem 619 3rd Floor, Buenos Aires, Argentina
Tel.: (54) 911 4960 7284
Web Site: http://www.worldenergy.net
Bio Fuel Electric Power Generation Services
N.A.I.C.S.: 221112
Gene Gebolys *(Founder, Pres & CEO)*

GRUPO EMPRESARIAL ANGELES, S.A. DE C.V.
Camino a Santa Teresa 1055-Piso 14 Col Heroes de Padierna, delegacion La Magdalena Contreras, Mexico, 10700, Mexico
Tel.: (52) 5554496200 MX
Web Site:
http://www.grupoempresarial.com
Year Founded: 1998
Emp.: 23,000
Holding Company Services
N.A.I.C.S.: 551112
Olegario Vazquez Rana *(Chm)*

Subsidiaries:

Banco Multiva, S.A. **(1)**

INTERNATIONAL PUBLIC

Cerrada de Tecamachalco No 45 Col Reforma Social, Deleg Miguel Hidalgo, 11650, Mexico, Distrito Federal, Mexico **(100%)**
Tel.: (52) 5552846200
Web Site: http://www.multiva.com.mx
Commercial & Investment Banking
N.A.I.C.S.: 522110
Javier Valdez Benitez *(Dir Gen)*

GRUPO EMPRESARIAL KALUZ S.A. DE C.V.
Av Paseo de la Reforma, Colonia Alcaldia Cuauhtemoc, Mexico, 06500, Mexico
Tel.: (52) 5552515998
Web Site: http://www.kaluz.com
Holding Company
N.A.I.C.S.: 551112
C.P. Guadalupe Maria Gonzalez Vieyra *(Dir-Fin & Admin)*

Subsidiaries:

Cementos Fortaleza, S.A. de C.V. - Tula Plant **(1)**
Casco del Rancho Bateje 2 km East of km 5 of the Atitalaquia, Apaxco road El Refugio, Atotonilco de Tula, 42980, Mexico
Tel.: (52) 1 778 735 91 00
Cement Mfr
N.A.I.C.S.: 327310

Cementos Fortaleza, S.A. de C.V. - Vito Plant **(1)**
Ave 1 de Mayo 1 Col Centro Vito, 42981, Atotonilco de Tula, Hidalgo, Mexico
Tel.: (52) 1 778 735 94 00
Cement Mfr
N.A.I.C.S.: 327310

Elementia S.A. **(1)**
Poniente 134 No 719 3er piso Industrial Vallejo, Azcapotzalco, 02300, Mexico, Mexico
Tel.: (52) 55 5728 5300
Web Site: http://www.elementia.com
Sales Range: $1-4.9 Billion
Mfr of Cement, Concrete, Polyethylene, Styrene, Copper & Aluminum
N.A.I.C.S.: 325211
Juan Francisco Sanchez Kramer *(Dir-IR)*

Subsidiary (US):

Allura **(2)**
15055 Woodham Dr, Houston, TX 77073
Tel.: (844) 425-5872
Web Site: http://www.allurausa.com
Cement Mfr
N.A.I.C.S.: 327310

Plant (Domestic):

Cementos Fortaleza, S.A. de C.V. - El Palmar Plant **(2)**
Avenida prolongacion Las Palmas No 1, Comunidad El Palmar Municipio Santiago de Anaya, 42620, Mexico, Hidalgo, Mexico
Tel.: (52) 1 772 72 75 021
Cement Mfr
N.A.I.C.S.: 327310

Subsidiary (Domestic):

Comecop **(2)**
Lotes 7 y 8 Manzana 8 Zona Industrial, Tizayuca, Mexico
Tel.: (52) 779 796 9500
Tube Mfr
N.A.I.C.S.: 331210

Subsidiary (Non-US):

Duralit **(2)**
J Miguel Lanza Street No 0205 Av Blanco Galindo km 7, Cochabamba, Bolivia
Tel.: (591) 4 426 8311
Web Site: http://www.duralit.net
Cement Mfr
N.A.I.C.S.: 327310

Eternit Atlantico S.A. **(2)**
Dir Via 40 Carrera 67 Zona Industrial Loma No 3, Barranquilla, Colombia
Tel.: (57) 5 3503800
Web Site: http://www.eternit.com.co
Tiles Mfr
N.A.I.C.S.: 326199

AND PRIVATE COMPANIES

GRUPO EMPRESARIAL KALUZ S.A. DE C.V.

Eternit Colombiana S.A. (2)
Dir Autopista Sur Km 1 via, Silvania, Bogota, Colombia
Tel.: (57) 1 7306900
Tiles Mfr
N.A.I.C.S.: 326199

Eternit Ecuatoriana (2)
Panamericana Sur Km 14 1/2 junto a Ideal Alambrec - Sur, Quito, Ecuador
Tel.: (593) 2 269 1361
Insulation Material Distr
N.A.I.C.S.: 423330

Eternit Pacifico S.A. (2)
Dir Puerto Isaacs Km 15, Yumbo, Colombia
Tel.: (57) 2 6088500
Tiles Mfr
N.A.I.C.S.: 326199

Subsidiary (Domestic):

Frigocel (2)
Calzada Union No 10 Fracc Industrial Cuamatla, Cuautitlan Izcalli, Mexico
Tel.: (52) 55 5873 2100
Web Site: http://www.frigocel.com.mx
Polyethylene Product Mfr
N.A.I.C.S.: 325211

Subsidiary (US):

Giant Cement Holding, Inc. (2)
654 Judge St, Harleyville, SC 29448 **(55%)**
Tel.: (803) 496-2200
Web Site: http://www.giantcement.com
Holding Company
N.A.I.C.S.: 551112

Subsidiary (Domestic):

Dragon Products Company, LLC (3)
107 New County Rd, Thomaston, ME 04861
Tel.: (207) 593-0100
Web Site: http://www.dragonproducts.com
Cement Mfr
N.A.I.C.S.: 327310

Subsidiary (Domestic):

Coastal Cement Corporation (4)
36 Drydock Ave Ste 1, Boston, MA 02210
Tel.: (617) 350-0183
Cement Mfr
N.A.I.C.S.: 327310

Subsidiary (Domestic):

Giant Cement Company (3)
654 Judge St, Harleyville, SC 29448
Tel.: (803) 496-2200
Web Site: http://www.giantcement.com
Sales Range: $50-74.9 Million
Emp.: 225
Cement Mfr
N.A.I.C.S.: 327310

Subsidiary (Domestic):

Giant Cement NC, Inc. (4)
10910 Texland Blvd, Charlotte, NC 28273-6216
Tel.: (704) 583-1568
Web Site: http://www.giantcement.com
Cement Mfr
N.A.I.C.S.: 327310
Keith Wentzel *(Mgr)*

Subsidiary (Domestic):

Giant Resource Recovery Company, Inc. (3)
654 Judge St, Harleyville, SC 29448
Tel.: (803) 496-2200
Web Site: http://www.grr-giant.com
Environmental & Waste Management Services
N.A.I.C.S.: 562211

Keystone Cement Company (3)
6507 Nor Bath Blvd, Bath, PA 18014
Tel.: (610) 837-1881
Web Site: http://www.keystone-cement.com
Cement Mfr
N.A.I.C.S.: 327310

Subsidiary (Domestic):

Mexalit (2)
Av de las Industrias 6920, Nombre de Dios, 31110, Chihuahua, Mexico
Tel.: (52) 8003639254
Web Site: https://www.mexalit.com
Cement Roofing Mfr
N.A.I.C.S.: 324122

Subsidiary (Non-US):

Plycem (2)
Paraiso de Cartago 5Km este de la Basilica de, Cartago, Costa Rica
Tel.: (506) 2575 4300
Cement Roof Mfr
N.A.I.C.S.: 324122

Orbia Advance Corporation, S.A.B. de C.V. (1)
Avenida Paseo de la Reforma 483 47th floor Colonia Cuauhtemoc, Cuauhtemoc Mayor s Office, 6500, Mexico, Mexico
Tel.: (52) 5553664000
Web Site: https://www.orbia.com
Rev: $6,987,000,000
Assets: $10,057,000,000
Liabilities: $6,963,000,000
Net Worth: $3,094,000,000
Earnings: $327,000,000
Emp.: 22,123
Fiscal Year-end: 12/31/2019
Building & Infrastructure Services, Data Communications, Irrigation & Chemicals Mfr
N.A.I.C.S.: 325110
Sheldon Hirt *(Gen Counsel & Sr VP)*

Subsidiary (US):

AlphaGary Corporation (2)
170 Pioneer Dr, Leominster, MA 01453-3474
Tel.: (978) 537-8071
Web Site: http://www.alphagary.com
Sales Range: $50-74.9 Million
Mfr of Plastic Pellets Used In Tubing, Gamma Radiation Film, Outdoor Furniture, Toys, Construction Cables & Tubing, Food Packaging, Floor Moldings
N.A.I.C.S.: 325991
Robert N. Gingue *(Mng Dir)*

Subsidiary (Non-US):

Alphagary Limited (2)
Beler Way, Melton Mowbray, Leicester, LE13 0DG, United Kingdom
Tel.: (44) 1664 502222
Web Site: http://www.alphagary.com
Petrochemical Mfr
N.A.I.C.S.: 325110

C.I. Mexichem Compuestos Colombia, S.A.S. (2)
Zona Industrial Mamonal km 8, Cartagena, Colombia
Tel.: (57) 5 672 3150
Web Site: http://www.mexichem.com.co
Plastic Compound Mfr
N.A.I.C.S.: 326122

Subsidiary (Domestic):

Cloro de Tehuantepec, S.A. de C.V. (2)
Rio San Javier No 10, Viveros del Rio, Tlalnepantla, Mexico **(100%)**
Tel.: (52) 5553664000
Web Site: http://www.mexichem.com
Alkalies & Chlorine Mfr
N.A.I.C.S.: 325180
Antonio Echeverria *(Pres)*

Subsidiary (US):

Dura-Line Corporation (2)
11400 Parkside Dr Ste 300, Knoxville, TN 37934
Tel.: (865) 218-3460
Web Site: http://www.duraline.com
Sales Range: $25-49.9 Million
Emp.: 200
Telecommunications Conduit Products
N.A.I.C.S.: 334220
Tibor Mikula *(Mng Dir-Europe & South Africa)*

Plant (Domestic):

Dura-Line Corp. - Sparks Plant (3)
11400 Parkside Dr Ste 300, Knoxville, TN 37934-1917
Tel.: (775) 359-9118
Web Site: http://www.duraline.com
Emp.: 20
Telecommunications Conduit Products
N.A.I.C.S.: 334220
Mike Hodge *(Gen Mgr)*

Subsidiary (Domestic):

Polypipe, LLC (3)
2406 N Interstate 35, Gainesville, TX 76240
Tel.: (940) 665-1721
Web Site: http://www.polypipeinc.com
Sales Range: $50-74.9 Million
Plastic Tank Mfr
N.A.I.C.S.: 326122

Subsidiary (US):

Dura-Line Holdings, Inc. (2)
11400 Parkside Dr, Knoxville, TN 37934
Tel.: (865) 218-3460
Web Site: http://www.duraline.com
Electrical Products Mfr
N.A.I.C.S.: 335932
Dale Wilson *(VP-Sls-US & Canada)*

Subsidiary (Domestic):

Fluorita de Mexico, S.A. de C.V. (2)
Calero 76 San Angel Inn, Alvaro Obregon, 01060, Mexico, Mexico
Tel.: (52) 55 5550 8744
Chemical Products Distr
N.A.I.C.S.: 424690

Subsidiary (US):

Mexichem America, Inc. (2)
15333 JFK Blvd Ste 210, Houston, TX 77032
Tel.: (281) 227-1300
Chemical Products Distr
N.A.I.C.S.: 424690

Subsidiary (Non-US):

Mexichem Argentina, S.A. (2)
Av Perez Galdes 8760, Pablo Podesta, B1687AIN, Buenos Aires, Argentina
Tel.: (54) 11 4848 8484
Web Site: http://www.amanco.com.ar
Chemical Products Mfr
N.A.I.C.S.: 325199

Subsidiary (Domestic):

Mexichem Cid, S.A. de C.V. (2)
Rio San Javier No 10, Fracc Viveros del Rio, 54060, Tlalnepantla, Mexico **(100%)**
Tel.: (52) 5553664000
Web Site: http://www.mexichem.com
Sales Range: $25-49.9 Million
Emp.: 250
Rolled Steel Shape Mfr
N.A.I.C.S.: 331221

Subsidiary (Non-US):

Mexichem Colombia, S.A. (2)
Autopista Sur 71 75, Bogota, Colombia **(100%)**
Tel.: (57) 17825060
Web Site: http://www.mexichem.com
Rolled Steel Shape Mfr
N.A.I.C.S.: 331221

Subsidiary (Domestic):

Mexichem Resinas Colombia S.A. (3)
Autopista Sur 71-75, Bogota, Colombia
Tel.: (57) 17825060
Sales Range: $125-149.9 Million
Polyvinyl Chloride (PVC) Resins
N.A.I.C.S.: 325211
Andres Mejia *(Gen Mgr)*

Subsidiary (Domestic):

Mexichem Compuestos, S.A. De C.V. (2)
KM 4 5 Autopista Altamira S/N Puerto Industrial, Altamira, Tamaulipas, Mexico
Tel.: (52) 833 229 0100
Chemical Products Distr
N.A.I.C.S.: 424690

Subsidiary (Non-US):

Mexichem Costa Rica, S.A. (2)
150 metros oeste del puente Franscisco J Orlich, Heredia, Costa Rica
Tel.: (506) 2209 3400

Web Site: http://www.mexichem.cr
Plastic Tank Mfr
N.A.I.C.S.: 326122

Mexichem Derivados Colombia, S.A. (2)
Km 5 via, Cajica, Zipaquira, Colombia
Tel.: (57) 1 777 2590
Web Site: http://www.mexichem.com.co
Chemical Products Distr
N.A.I.C.S.: 424690

Subsidiary (Domestic):

Mexichem Derivados, S.A. de C.V. (2)
Km 22 Carr Guadalajara El Salto, Jalisco, 45680, El Salto, Mexico **(100%)**
Tel.: (52) 3332848500
Web Site: http://www.mexichem.com
Sales Range: $25-49.9 Million
Chemical Production & Preparation Mfr
N.A.I.C.S.: 325998
Antonio Echeverria *(Pres)*

Subsidiary (Non-US):

Mexichem El Salvador, S.A. (2)
Km 3 1/2 Boulevard del Ejercito Nacional, Calle y Colonia La Chacra, San Salvador, El Salvador
Tel.: (503) 2500 9200
Web Site: http://www.mexichem.com.sv
Chemical Products Distr
N.A.I.C.S.: 424690

Mexichem Fluor Japan Ltd. (2)
NYK Tennoz Building 2-20 Higashi-Shinagawa, 2-chome Shinagawa-ku, Tokyo, 140-0002, Japan
Tel.: (81) 3 54628661
Chemical Products Distr
N.A.I.C.S.: 424690

Mexichem Fluor Taiwan Limited (2)
No 1 Gongye 7th Road Pingjhen Industrial Park, Taoyuan, 32459, Taiwan
Tel.: (886) 3 4191063
Chemical Products Distr
N.A.I.C.S.: 424690

Subsidiary (Domestic):

Mexichem Fluor, S.A. de C.V. (2)
Eje 106 S/N, Zona Industrial, CP 78395, San Luis Potosi, SLP, Mexico
Tel.: (52) 444 826 7700
Sales Range: $75-99.9 Million
Emp.: 221
Fluoride Mining & Processing
N.A.I.C.S.: 212390

Subsidiary (US):

Mexichem Fluor (3)
4990 B ICI Rd Hwy 75, Saint Gabriel, LA 70776
Tel.: (225) 642-0094
Web Site: http://www.mexichemfluor
Refrigerant Mfr
N.A.I.C.S.: 325180

Subsidiary (Non-US):

Mexichem Fluor Ltd. (3)
The Heath, Runcorn, WA7 4JE, Cheshire, United Kingdom
Tel.: (44) 1928 515525
Web Site: http://www.mexichemfluor.com
Specialty Chemicals Mfr & Supplier
N.A.I.C.S.: 325998

Subsidiary (Non-US):

Mexichem Guatemala, S.A. (2)
Calzada Atanasio Tzul 16-67, Guatemala, 01012, Guatemala
Tel.: (502) 2410 1300
Web Site: http://www.mexichem.com.gt
Chemical Products Distr
N.A.I.C.S.: 424690

Mexichem Honduras, S.A. (2)
Km 10 Crrt A Puerto Cortes 500 Mts Del Peaje, Choloma, 00504, Honduras
Tel.: (504) 25452400
Chemical Products Distr
N.A.I.C.S.: 424690

Mexichem Nicaragua, S.A. (2)
Km 3 1/2 Carretera Sur Desvio A Batahola,

GRUPO EMPRESARIAL KALUZ S.A. DE C.V.

Grupo Empresarial Kaluz S.A. de C.V.—(Continued)
Managua, Nicaragua
Tel.: (505) 2266 1551
Chemical Products Distr
N.A.I.C.S.: 424690
Francisco Silva (Gen Mgr)

Mexichem Panama, S.A. (2)
Ciudad de Panama, Via Tocumen, Panama, 40703, Panama
Tel.: (507) 305 9600
Web Site: http://www.mexichem.com.pa
Plastic Pipe Mfr & Distr
N.A.I.C.S.: 325211

Subsidiary (Domestic):

Mexichem Quimir (2)
Antiguo Camino a Lago de Gpe No 59 Col Lecheria, Tultitlan, 54900, Mexico
Tel.: (52) 55 5899 2100
Chemical Products Distr
N.A.I.C.S.: 424690

Mexichem Resinas Vinilicas, S.A. de C.V. (2)
Rio San Javier 10 Fraccionamiento Viveros del Rio, Tlalnepantla, 54060, Mexico **(100%)**
Tel.: (52) 5553664000
Web Site: http://www.mexichem.com
Production & Marketing of PVC Resins
N.A.I.C.S.: 325211

Mexichem Salinera del Sur, S.A. de C.V. (2)
Camino a Rancho Viejo No 100, Jaltipan de Morelos, Veracruz, Mexico
Tel.: (52) 922 225 0770
Chemical Products Distr
N.A.I.C.S.: 424690

Mexichem Servicios Administrativos, S.A. de C.V. (2)
Rio San Javier No 10, Fracc Viveros del Rio, 54060, Tlalnepantla, Mexico **(100%)**
Tel.: (52) 5553664000
Web Site: http://www.mexichem.com
Sales Range: $25-49.9 Million
Rolled Steel Shape Mfr
N.A.I.C.S.: 331221
Antonio del Valle Ruiz (Chm)

Subsidiary (Non-US):

Mexichem UK Ltd (2)
The Heath Business & Technical Park, Runcorn, WA7 4QX, Cheshire, United Kingdom
Tel.: (44) 1928 518880
Chemical Products Distr
N.A.I.C.S.: 424690

Pavco de Venezuela, S.A. (2)
Av Chicago cruce con calle Milan, Edif Pavco La California Sur, Caracas, Venezuela
Tel.: (58) 212 256 3667
Web Site: http://www.pavco.com.ve
Chemical Products Distr
N.A.I.C.S.: 424690

Subsidiary (US):

Sylvin Technologies, Inc. (2)
84 Denver Rd, Denver, PA 17517
Tel.: (717) 336-0547
Web Site: http://www.sylvin.com
Flexible & Semi-rigid PVC Specialty & General-purpose Compounds Mfr
N.A.I.C.S.: 326199
David Wilson (Plant Engr)

Subsidiary (Domestic):

Union Minera del Sur, S.A. de C.V. (2)
Rio San Javier No 10, Tlalnepantla, Mexico **(100%)**
Tel.: (52) 5553664066
Web Site: http://www.mexichem.com
Potash Soda & Borate Mineral Mining
N.A.I.C.S.: 212390
Miguel Ruiz (CFO)

Subsidiary (Non-US):

VESTOLIT GmbH (2)
Paul Baumann Strasse 1, Marl, 45772, Germany
Tel.: (49) 23654905
Web Site: http://www.vestolit.de
Polyvinyl Chloride Mfr
N.A.I.C.S.: 325211
Carlos Manrique Rocha (Mng Dir)

Wavin Hungary Kft. (1)
Uj gyartelep Pf 44, 2072, Zsambek, Hungary
Tel.: (36) 6 23 566 000
Web Site: http://www.hu.wavin.com
Plastic Tank Mfr
N.A.I.C.S.: 326122

GRUPO EMPRESARIAL SAN JOSE, S.A.

C/Rosalia de Castro 44, ES-36001, Pontevedra, Spain
Tel.: (34) 986866464
Web Site: https://gruposanjose.biz
GSJ—(VAL)
Rev.: $1,441,652,277
Assets: $1,226,505,504
Liabilities: $992,404,490
Net Worth: $234,101,014
Earnings: $23,108,137
Emp.: 4,415
Fiscal Year-end: 12/31/23
Holding Company; Construction, Real Estate, Energy, Infrastructure & Other Services
N.A.I.C.S.: 551112
Jacinto Rey Gonzalez (Chm)

Subsidiaries:

CONSTRUCTORA SAN JOSE PORTUGAL S.A. (1)
C Rosalia de Castro 44, 36001, Pontevedra, Spain
Tel.: (34) 986866464
Web Site: http://www.gruposanjose.com
Civil Engineering Services
N.A.I.C.S.: 541330

CONSTRUTORA UDRA LTDA. (1)
Avenida Joao II Lote 1 03 2 1 7 Piso Edificio Meridiano, Parque das Nacoes, Lisbon, 1998-017, Portugal
Tel.: (351) 213 506 430
Web Site: http://www.construtoraudra.pt
Sales Range: $25-49.9 Million
Emp.: 30
Civil Engineering Services
N.A.I.C.S.: 541330
Nuno Marques (Mgr-Fin)

Cartuja Inmobiliaria, S.A.U. (1)
Avda de la Buhaira 27 1 A, 41018, Sevilla, Spain
Tel.: (34) 954989310
Web Site: https://www.cartuja.com
Construction Services
N.A.I.C.S.: 236220

Comercial Udra, S.A.U. (1)
C/ Zurbano 76 4 Izq, 28010, Madrid, Spain
Tel.: (34) 917628200
Web Site: https://www.comercialudra.es
Sporting Goods Mfr & Distr
N.A.I.C.S.: 339920

Constructora San Jose Argentina, S.A. (1)
Edificio Torre Alem Plaza Avda Leandro N Alem 855 piso 15 1001, Buenos Aires, Argentina
Tel.: (54) 1143157878
Construction Services
N.A.I.C.S.: 236220
Jose Marquez Marroqui (Country Mgr)

Constructora San Jose Cabo Verde, S.A. (1)
Santa Maria Apartado 231, Ilha do Sal, Cape Verde
Tel.: (238) 242260001
Construction Services
N.A.I.C.S.: 236220
Nilton Ramos (Country Mgr)

Constructora Udra Limitada (1)
Av D Joao II n 30 - 7 Piso Edificio Meridiano - Parque das Nacoes, 1998-017, Lisbon, Portugal
Tel.: (351) 213506430
Construction Services
N.A.I.C.S.: 236220

Nuno Marques (Country Mgr)

EBA S.L. (1)
Avenida de Los Olmos 1 Pol Ind Gamarra Edificio Inbisa, Vitoria, 1013, Alava, Spain
Tel.: (34) 945151705
Web Site: http://www.ebasl.com
Sales Range: $25-49.9 Million
Emp.: 55
Construction Engineering Services
N.A.I.C.S.: 541330
Angel Rodriguez (Mgr)

GSJ Solutions, S.L.U. (1)
C/ Ronda de Poniente 11, Tres Cantos, 28760, Madrid, Spain
Tel.: (34) 918065400
Construction Services
N.A.I.C.S.: 236220

Grupo Empresarial San Jose, S.A. - Central Office (1)
Calle Ronda de Poniente 11, ES-28760, Tres Cantos, Madrid, Spain
Tel.: (34) 918065400
Emp.: 3,500
Corporate Headquarters
N.A.I.C.S.: 551114
Miguel Zorita Lees (CEO)

Division (Domestic):

SANJOSE Inmobiliaria (2)
Calle Ronda de Poniente 11, ES-28760, Tres Cantos, Madrid, Spain
Tel.: (34) 91 799 4990
Web Site: http://www.sanjoseinmobiliaria.com
Sales Range: $150-199.9 Million
Residential Real Estate Developer & Property Manager
N.A.I.C.S.: 237210

SANJOSE Concesiones y Servicios, S.A.U (1)
C/Ronda de Poniente 11, 28760, Tres Cantos, Spain
Tel.: (34) 918065400
Web Site: http://www.grupo-sanjose.com
Construction Management Services
N.A.I.C.S.: 236118

SanJose Contracting, L.L.C. (1)
Al Bustan Complex - Office 402 Airport Road, PO Box 113781, Abu Dhabi, United Arab Emirates
Tel.: (971) 26422728
Construction Services
N.A.I.C.S.: 236220
Miguel Angel Bravo (Country Mgr)

Sanjose Energia Y Medio Ambiente S A. (1)
C/ Ronda de Poniente 11, 28760, Tres Cantos, Madrid, Spain
Tel.: (34) 918076315
Construction Engineering Services
N.A.I.C.S.: 541330
Casinto Rej (Chm)

Sanjose Panama, S.A. (1)
Edificio Capital Plaza Piso 7 Ave Costa del Este y Ave, Roberto Motta Costa del Este, Panama, Panama
Tel.: (507) 2642338
Construction Services
N.A.I.C.S.: 236220
Lesmes Arribas (Country Mgr)

Tecnocontrol Chile Ltda. (1)
Maria Luisa Santander, Providencia, 0237, Santiago, Chile
Tel.: (56) 222049453
Web Site: https://www.tecnocontrol.cl
Measurement Equipment Distr
N.A.I.C.S.: 423830

Tecnocontrol Servicios, S.A.U. (1)
Ronda de poniente 11, Tres Cantos, 28760, Madrid, Spain
Tel.: (34) 918076334
Web Site: https://www.tecnocontrol.es
Emp.: 242
Building Maintenance Services
N.A.I.C.S.: 561790

Udra Mexico S.A. de C.V. (1)
Calle Francisco Petrarca N 223 Oficina 505, Colonia Polanco Delegacion Miguel Hidalgo, 11570, Mexico, Mexico
Tel.: (52) 5552030242

INTERNATIONAL PUBLIC

Construction Services
N.A.I.C.S.: 236220
Fernando Marin (Country Mgr)

GRUPO EMPRESAS NAVIERAS S.A.

Av Andreas Belloe2687 Floor 15, PO Box 4246, Las Condes, Santiago, Chile
Tel.: (56) 3391300
Web Site: http://www.naviera.cl
NAVIERA—(SGO)
Sales Range: Less than $1 Million
Cargo Transportation Services
N.A.I.C.S.: 488310
Felipe Irarrazaval Ovalle (CEO)

Subsidiaries:

Agencias Universales SA (1)
Av Andres Bello 2687 piso 15, Las Condes, Santiago, Chile
Tel.: (56) 224602700
Web Site: http://www.agunsa.com
Freight Transportation Services
N.A.I.C.S.: 488510
Jose Manuel Urenda (Chm)

Portuaria Cabo Froward SA (1)
Urriola 87 Piso 3, Valparaiso, Chile
Tel.: (56) 322556390
Web Site: https://www.froward.cl
Sales Range: Less than $1 Million
Transportation & Logistic Consulting Services
N.A.I.C.S.: 541614
Franco Montalbetti Moltedo (Pres)

GRUPO ENERGIA BOGOTA S.A. E.S.P.

Cra 9 Ste 73-44 Piso 6, Bogota, Colombia
Tel.: (57) 13268000
Web Site:
http://www.grupoenergiabogota.com
EEB—(COLO)
Rev.: $1,466,158,200
Assets: $8,316,388,200
Liabilities: $4,249,439,400
Net Worth: $4,066,948,800
Earnings: $586,180,500
Fiscal Year-end: 12/31/19
Electricity Generation & Distribution Services; Natural Gas Distr
N.A.I.C.S.: 221112
Martha Yaneth Veleno Quintero (VP)

Subsidiaries:

Transportadora de Energia de Centroamerica S.A. (1)
Blvd Los Proceres 24-69 Zona 10 Empresarial Zona, PraderaTorre V Level 3, Guatemala, Guatemala
Tel.: (502) 23123000
Web Site: https://www.trecsa.com.gt
Electricity Distribution Services
N.A.I.C.S.: 221122

GRUPO EROSKI

Barrio San Augustin, Elorrio, 48230, Bilbao, Spain
Tel.: (34) 944943444
Web Site: http://www.eroski.es
Year Founded: 1969
Sales Range: $5-14.9 Billion
Emp.: 29,192
Food Retailer
N.A.I.C.S.: 445110
Emilio Cebrian (Dir-Social)

Subsidiaries:

Viajes Eroski SA (1)
S/n Barrio San Agustin, Elorz, E-48230, Spain
Tel.: (34) 946211211
Web Site: http://www.viajeseroski.es
Sales Range: $200-249.9 Million
Emp.: 160
Travel Agency
N.A.I.C.S.: 561510

AND PRIVATE COMPANIES

GRUPO EZENTIS S.A.
Calle Automocion Numero 26-28 Poligono Industrial Calonge, CP 41007, Seville, Spain
Tel.: (34) 954673230 ES
Web Site: https://www.ezentis.com
Year Founded: 1959
EZE—(BIL)
Rev.: $509,760,272
Assets: $424,440,378
Liabilities: $408,410,702
Net Worth: $16,029,676
Earnings: $447,944
Fiscal Year-end: 12/31/19
Telecommunication Servicesb
N.A.I.C.S.: 517810
Fernando Gonzalez Sanchez *(CEO)*

Subsidiaries:

Ezentis Chile, S.A. (1)
Calle Las Hortensias 501, Comuna de Cerrillos, Santiago, Chile
Tel.: (56) 22 770 2810
Telecommunication Servicesb
N.A.I.C.S.: 517810
Fernando Verdeja *(COO)*

Vertice 360 S.A. (1)
C/ Alcala 516 y 518, 28027, Madrid, Spain
Tel.: (34) 917546700
Web Site: http://www.vertice360.com
Sales Range: $150-199.9 Million
Audiovisual Services
N.A.I.C.S.: 512199
Jose Miguel Fernandez Sastron *(Pres & CEO)*

GRUPO FAMSA S.A.B. DE C.V.
Pino Suarez 1202 Nte 3Rd Floor Unit A Center, 64000, Monterrey, NL, Mexico
Tel.: (52) 18183893405
Web Site: http://www.grupofamsa.com
Year Founded: 1970
GFAMSA—(MEX)
Rev.: $1,088,754,725
Assets: $3,185,586,716
Liabilities: $2,851,572,062
Net Worth: $334,014,654
Earnings: $25,976,142
Emp.: 17,589
Fiscal Year-end: 12/31/19
Specialty Retail Stores
N.A.I.C.S.: 449110
Abelardo Garcia Lozano *(CFO)*

GRUPO FERRER INTERNACIONAL, S.A.
Avenida Diagonal 549, 08029, Barcelona, Spain
Tel.: (34) 93 600 3700 ES
Web Site: http://www.ferrer.com
Year Founded: 1959
Holding Company; Pharmaceutical Mfr & Whslr
N.A.I.C.S.: 551112
Sergi Ferrer-Salat Serra Di Migni *(Chm)*

Subsidiaries:

Alexza Pharmaceuticals, Inc. (1)
2091 Stierlin Ct, Mountain View, CA 94043 **(100%)**
Tel.: (650) 944-7000
Web Site: http://www.alexza.com
Drug Research, Development & Commercialization
N.A.I.C.S.: 325412
Edwin S. Kamemoto *(Exec VP-R&D, Regulatory & Quality)*

Ferrer Espana, S.A. (1)
Avenida Diagonal 549, 08029, Barcelona, Spain
Tel.: (34) 93 600 3700
Web Site: http://www.ferrer.com
Pharmaceutical Mfr & Whslr
N.A.I.C.S.: 325412

GRUPO FERROMINERO, S.A. DE C.V.
Mariano Escobedo 510 Piso 9, Col Valle Oriente, 66269, Garza Garcia, Mexico
Tel.: (52) 5555459502
Web Site: http://www.gfm.com.mx
Holding Company
N.A.I.C.S.: 551112

Subsidiaries:

Compania Minera Autlan S.A. de C.V. (1)
Arq Pedro Ramirez Vazquez 20010, San Pedro, 66269, Garza Garcia, Mexico
Tel.: (52) 8181521500
Web Site: https://www.autlan.com.mx
Rev.: $442,900,000
Assets: $865,400,000
Liabilities: $504,500,000
Net Worth: $360,900,000
Earnings: ($12,200,000)
Emp.: 2,500
Fiscal Year-end: 12/31/2019
Manganese & Ferroalloy Production
N.A.I.C.S.: 331110

Subsidiary (Non-US):

GFM Resources Limited (2)
Suite 11001111 Melville Street, Vancouver, V6E 3V6, BC, Canada **(80%)**
Tel.: (604) 925-2839
Web Site: https://www.gfm-resources.com
Assets: $32,924
Liabilities: $929,083
Net Worth: ($896,159)
Earnings: ($153,988)
Fiscal Year-end: 12/31/2021
Mineral Mining Services
N.A.I.C.S.: 212290
Salvador Miranda *(CFO)*

GRUPO FINACCESS S.A.P.I. DE C.V.
Homero 1500 201 Colonia Los Morales Section Palmas, Delegacion Miguel Hidalgo, 11540, Mexico, Mexico
Tel.: (52) 5540 2311
Web Site: http://www.grupofinaccess.com
Year Founded: 2011
Holding Company
N.A.I.C.S.: 551112
Jose Pares Gutierrez *(CEO)*

Subsidiaries:

Finaccess Capital, S.A. de C.V. (1)
Homero 1500 Piso 2 Colonia Los Morales seccion Palmas, 11540, Mexico, Mexico
Tel.: (52) 55402311
Web Site: http://www.grupofinaccess.com
Investment Services
N.A.I.C.S.: 523999
Begona Orgambide *(Dir-IR)*

Subsidiary (Non-US):

Restaurant Brands New Zealand Limited (2)
PO Box 22-749, Otahuhu, Auckland, 1640, New Zealand **(75%)**
Tel.: (64) 95258700
Web Site: https://www.restaurantbrands.co.nz
Rev.: $664,879,432
Assets: $843,360,397
Liabilities: $677,651,029
Net Worth: $165,709,368
Earnings: $22,244,422
Emp.: 12,073
Fiscal Year-end: 12/31/2020
Restaurant Operators
N.A.I.C.S.: 722513
Grant Ellis *(CFO-Grp)*

Subsidiary (Non-US):

Restaurant Brands Australia Pty Limited (3)
450 Burwood Highway, Wantirna, 3152, VIC, Australia
Tel.: (61) 3 9800 2600

Restaurant Management Services
N.A.I.C.S.: 722511

Subsidiary (Domestic):

Restaurant Brands Limited (3)
Level 3 Building 7 666 Great South Road, Penrose, Auckland, 1051, New Zealand
Tel.: (64) 95258700
Sales Range: $10-24.9 Million
Emp.: 60
Restaurant Management Services
N.A.I.C.S.: 722511
Russel Creedy *(CEO)*

Subsidiary (US):

TD Food Group, Inc. (3)
828 Fort St Mall Ste 130, Honolulu, HI 96813
Tel.: (808) 566-3200
Holding Company; Fast Food Restaurant Franchisor & Operator
N.A.I.C.S.: 551112

Subsidiary (Domestic):

Hawaii Pizza Hut, Inc. (4)
828 Fort St Mall Ste 130, Honolulu, HI 96813 **(100%)**
Tel.: (808) 566-3200
Web Site: http://www.pizzahuthawaii.com
Pizzeria Restaurants Franchisor & Operator
N.A.I.C.S.: 722513

Taco Aloha, Inc. (4)
828 Fort St Mall Ste 130, Honolulu, HI 96813 **(100%)**
Tel.: (808) 566-3200
Web Site: http://www.tacobellhawaii.com
Fast Food Mexican Restaurants Franchisor & Operator
N.A.I.C.S.: 722511

GRUPO FINANCIERO BANORTE, S.A.B. DE C.V.
Av Revolucion 3000, Col Primavera, CP 64830, Monterrey, NL, Mexico
Tel.: (52) 8181569600 MX
Web Site: https://www.banorte.com
Year Founded: 1899
GBOOF—(OTCQX)
Rev.: $8,136,255,481
Assets: $111,777,505,345
Liabilities: $97,450,207,143
Net Worth: $14,327,298,202
Earnings: $2,116,604,061
Emp.: 32,392
Fiscal Year-end: 12/31/21
Banking Services
N.A.I.C.S.: 523999
Carlos Hank Gonzalez *(Chm)*

Subsidiaries:

Grupo Financiero Interacciones, S.A. de C.V. (1)
Paseo de la Reforma 383 Piso 13, Cuauhtemoc, 06500, Mexico, Mexico
Tel.: (52) 15553268600
Web Site: http://www.grupofinanciero.mx
Financial & Banking Services
N.A.I.C.S.: 522110
Carlos Alberto Rojo Macedo *(Mng Dir)*

GRUPO FINANCIERO GALICIA S.A.
Tte Gral Juan D Peron 430 25th Floor, C1038AAJ, Buenos Aires, Argentina
Tel.: (54) 1143437528 Ar
Web Site: https://www.gfgsa.com
Year Founded: 1999
GGAL—(NASDAQ)
Rev.: $5,543,252,545
Assets: $11,911,379,423
Liabilities: $9,559,380,333
Net Worth: $2,351,999,090
Earnings: $393,121,833
Emp.: 9,489
Fiscal Year-end: 12/31/23
Financial Services Holding Company
N.A.I.C.S.: 551111
Pablo Alberto Gutierrez *(Vice Chm)*

GRUPO GICSA, S.A.B. DE C.V.

Subsidiaries:

Banco de Galicia y Buenos Aires S.A. (1)
Teniente General Juan D Peron 407, 1038, Buenos Aires, Argentina **(99.6%)**
Tel.: (54) 1163290000
Web Site: http://www.bancogalicia.com.ar
Sales Range: $1-4.9 Billion
Emp.: 8,800
Banking Services
N.A.I.C.S.: 522320

Galicia Administradora de Fondos (1)
Tte Gral JD Peron 430-Floor 22 Office Galicia Administradora de Fondos, San Martin side, C1038AAJ, Buenos Aires, Argentina
Tel.: (54) 1163296241
Web Site: http://www.fondosfima.com.ar
Mutual Fund Services
N.A.I.C.S.: 523940

Galicia Securities S.A. (1)
Lt Gral Juan D Peron 407 Floor 2, C1038AAF, Buenos Aires, Argentina
Tel.: (54) 63293445
Web Site: https://www.galiciasecurities.com.ar
Settlement & Compensation Services
N.A.I.C.S.: 525190

IGAM LLC (1)
205 Greencastle Rd Ste B, Tyrone, GA 30290
Tel.: (678) 750-4961
Web Site: http://www.igam.com
Automation Product Mfr & Distr
N.A.I.C.S.: 336350
Greg Owens *(Co-Founder & CEO)*

GRUPO FINANCIERO INBURSA, S.A. DE C.V.
Insurgentes Sur No 3500 Inbursa Building Ground Floor, Col Pena Pobre Tlalpan, CP 14060, Mexico, DF, Mexico
Tel.: (52) 5554478000 MX
Web Site: https://www.inbursa.com.mx
Year Founded: 1985
GFINBUR—(MEX)
Assets: $40,728,334,966
Liabilities: $27,461,869,962
Net Worth: $13,266,465,004
Earnings: $1,825,658,309
Emp.: 9,215
Fiscal Year-end: 12/31/23
Financial Investment Services
N.A.I.C.S.: 551111
Marco Antonio Slim Domit *(Chm & Pres)*

Subsidiaries:

Afore Inbursa S.A. de C.V. (1)
Av Insurgentes Sur No 825 PB Col Pena Pobre, Del Alvaro Obregon, Mexico, DF 14060, Mexico
Tel.: (52) 5556873136
Pension Fund Administration
N.A.I.C.S.: 525110

Banco Inbursa S.A. (1)
Insurgente Sur 3500, Mexico, Mexico
Tel.: (52) 5553250505
Web Site: http://www.bancoinbursa.com.mx
Banking Services
N.A.I.C.S.: 522110

Inversora Bursatil S.A. de C.V. (1)
Paseo de Las Palmas 736, Mexico, Mexico
Tel.: (52) 5556254900
Security Brokers
N.A.I.C.S.: 523150

GRUPO GICSA, S.A.B. DE C.V.
Paseo de los Tamarindos No 90 Torre 1 Piso 32, Bosques de las Lomas, 5120, Mexico, Mexico
Tel.: (52) 51480400
Web Site: https://www.gicsa.com.mx
Year Founded: 1989

3129

GRUPO GICSA, S.A.B. DE C.V.

Grupo GICSA, S.A.B. de C.V.—(Continued)
GICSA—(MEX)
Rev.: $297,607,850
Assets: $4,586,672,550
Liabilities: $2,643,471,822
Net Worth: $1,943,200,728
Earnings: $123,615,377
Emp.: 832
Fiscal Year-end: 12/31/23
Real Estate Development Services
N.A.I.C.S.: 531390
Abraham Cababie Daniel *(Vice Chm & CEO)*

GRUPO GIGANTE, S.A.B. DE C.V.

Av Ejercito Nacional 769 Torre B Piso 12 Esquina Moliere, Miguel Hidalgo, 11520, Mexico, Mexico
Tel.: (52) 5552698000
Web Site:
https://www.grupogigante.com.mx
Year Founded: 1962
GPGNF—(OTCEM)
Rev.: $2,002,173,571
Assets: $3,088,553,700
Liabilities: $1,568,936,438
Net Worth: $1,519,617,261
Earnings: $121,745,650
Emp.: 11,000
Fiscal Year-end: 12/31/23
Retail Outlets & Restaurants Owner & Operator
N.A.I.C.S.: 459999
Angel Losada Moreno *(Board of Directors & Chm)*

Subsidiaries:

Office Depot de Mexico S.A. de C.V. (1)
Av Juan Salvador Agraz 101, Santa Fe Cuajimalpa, 05348, Mexico, Mexico **(100%)**
Tel.: (52) 5552927970
Web Site: http://www.officedepot.com.mx
Office Supplies Retailer
N.A.I.C.S.: 459410
Angel Alverde *(Pres)*

Subsidiary (Domestic):

RadioShack de Mexico S.A. de C.V. (2)
Avenida Jardin No 248, Mexico, 02860, Mexico **(100%)**
Tel.: (52) 5525820941
Web Site: http://www.radioshack.com.mx
Electronics Retailer
N.A.I.C.S.: 449210

GRUPO HERDEZ, S.A.B. DE C.V.

Monte Pelvoux No 215 Colonia Lomas de Chapultepec, 11000, Mexico, Mexico
Tel.: (52) 5552015655
Web Site:
https://www.grupoherdez.com.mx
HERDEZ—(MEX)
Rev.: $2,133,690,964
Assets: $2,222,896,722
Liabilities: $1,239,158,718
Net Worth: $983,738,004
Earnings: $195,969,849
Emp.: 11,595
Fiscal Year-end: 12/30/23
Food & Beverage Products Distr
N.A.I.C.S.: 424420
Enrique Hernandez-Pons Torres *(Vice Chm & Deputy Gen Mgr)*

Subsidiaries:

McCormick de Mexico, S.A. de C.V. (1)
Calzada de San Bartolo Naucalpan 360 Col Argentina Pte, Delegacion Miguel Hidalgo, 11230, Mexico, Mexico
Tel.: (52) 5550494280
Web Site: http://www.mccormick.com.mx
Sales Range: $200-249.9 Million
Emp.: 460
Specialty Food Products, Seasonings, Flavorings & Food Decorations; Owned 50% by McCormick & Company, Incorporated & 50% by Grupo Herdez, S.A. de C.V.
N.A.I.C.S.: 311930

MegaMex Foods, LLC (1)
333 S Anita Dr Ste 1000, Orange, CA 92868 **(50%)**
Web Site: http://www.megamexfoods.com
Mexican Food Products & Ingredients Mfr
N.A.I.C.S.: 311941

Subsidiary (Domestic):

Don Miguel Mexican Foods, Inc. (2)
1501 W Orangewood Ave, Orange, CA 92868
Tel.: (714) 634-8441
Web Site: http://www.donmiguel.com
Mexican Food Product Mfr
N.A.I.C.S.: 311422

GRUPO HOTELERO SANTA FE, S.A.B. DE C.V.

Juan Salvador Agraz No 65 piso 20 Col Santa Fe Cuajimalpa, Del Cuajimalpa de Morelos, 5348, Mexico, 5348, Mexico
Tel.: (52) 5552610800
Web Site: https://www.gsf-hotels.com
HOTEL—(MEX)
Rev.: $174,358,193
Assets: $685,546,074
Liabilities: $283,613,505
Net Worth: $401,932,570
Earnings: $34,933,776
Emp.: 3,200
Fiscal Year-end: 12/31/23
Hotel Operator
N.A.I.C.S.: 721110
Carlos Gerardo Ancira Elizondo *(Chm)*

GRUPO INDUSTRIAL SALTILLO S.A. DE C.V.

No 1495 Zona Centro Coahuila de Zaragoza, 25000, Saltillo, Coahuila, Mexico
Tel.: (52) 8444111000
Web Site: https://www.gis.com.mx
Year Founded: 1928
GISSA—(MEX)
Rev.: $908,184,829
Assets: $1,263,802,111
Liabilities: $599,127,166
Net Worth: $664,674,944
Earnings: $42,820,861
Emp.: 6,539
Fiscal Year-end: 12/31/19
Metal & Ceramic Products Mfr
N.A.I.C.S.: 327110
Manuel Rivera Garza *(CEO)*

Subsidiaries:

Automotive Components Europe S.A. (1)
38 Boulevard Napoleon 1er, L-2210, Luxembourg, Luxembourg **(100%)**
Tel.: (352) 26 37 711
Web Site: http://www.acegroup.lu
Automotive Parts Mfr & Distr
N.A.I.C.S.: 336390
Jose Manuel Corrales *(CEO)*

Calentadores Cinsa, S.A. de C.V. (1)
Blvd Venustiano Carranza No 4010 Col Villa Olimpica, 25230, Saltillo, Mexico **(100%)**
Tel.: (52) 8444111000
Web Site: http://www.gis.com.mx
Sales Range: $200-249.9 Million
Emp.: 550
Iron & Steel Mills
N.A.I.C.S.: 331110

Ceramica Santa Anita, S.A. de C.V. (1)
Blvd Isidro Lopez Zertuche No 1495, Zona Industrial, 25000, Saltillo, Coahuila, Mexico **(100%)**
Tel.: (52) 844 4117100
Ceramic Products Mfr
N.A.I.C.S.: 327120

Cifunsa del Bajio, S.A. de C.V. (1)
Carretera Libramiento Leon - Queretaro Km 4 6, Irapuato, Mexico **(100%)**
Tel.: (52) 4626069400
Web Site: http://www.cifunsa.com.mx
Sales Range: $25-49.9 Million
Emp.: 40
Machine Tools Mfr
N.A.I.C.S.: 333517

Cifunsa, S.A. de C.V. (1)
Blvd Isidro Lopez Zertuche No 4003, Saltillo, Mexico **(100%)**
Tel.: (52) 8444112000
Web Site: http://www.gis.com
Sales Range: $25-49.9 Million
Emp.: 55
Fabricated Metal Products Mfr
N.A.I.C.S.: 332999

Cinsa Enasa Productos para el Hogar, S.A. de C.V. (1)
Blvd Isidro Lopez Zertuche No 1495, 25000, Saltillo, Mexico **(100%)**
Tel.: (52) 8444116047
Fabricated Metal Products Mfr
N.A.I.C.S.: 332999

Comesco, S.A. de C.V. (1)
Blvd Isidro Lopez Zertuche No 1495, 25000, Saltillo, Mexico **(100%)**
Tel.: (52) 8444116047
Fabricated Metal Products Mfr
N.A.I.C.S.: 332999

Fluida, S.A. de C.V. (1)
Blvd Isidro Lopez Zertuche No 1839, 25260, Saltillo, Mexico **(100%)**
Tel.: (52) 8444392469
Web Site: http://www.fluida.com.mx
Sales Range: $25-49.9 Million
Emp.: 100
Iron & Steel Mills
N.A.I.C.S.: 331110

Industria Automotriz Cifunsa, S.A. de C.V. (1)
Blvd Isidro Lopez Zertuche No 4003, Saltillo, Mexico **(100%)**
Tel.: (52) 8444112000
Holding Company
N.A.I.C.S.: 551112

Manufacturas Cifunsa, S.A. de C.V. (1)
Blvd Isidro Lopez Zertuche No, 4003, Saltillo, Mexico **(100%)**
Tel.: (52) 8444112000
Web Site: http://www.cifunsa.com.mx
Motor Vehicle Metal Stamping
N.A.I.C.S.: 336370

Manufacturas Vitromex, S.A. de C.V. (1)
Blvd Isidro Lopez Zertuche 4103, 25230, Saltillo, Coahuila, Mexico **(100%)**
Tel.: (52) 8444115000
Web Site: http://www.vitromex.com.mx
Sales Range: $200-249.9 Million
Emp.: 775
Mfr of Ceramic Industrial Products & Wall & Floor Tile
N.A.I.C.S.: 327120

Porcelanizados Enasa, S.A. de C.V. (1)
Blvd Isidro Lopez Zertuche No 1495, 25000, Saltillo, Mexico **(100%)**
Tel.: (52) 8444116047
Fabricated Metal Products Mfr
N.A.I.C.S.: 332999

Servicios de Produccion Saltillo, S.A. de C.V. (1)
Blvd Isidro Lopez Zertuche No 1255, 25000, Saltillo, Mexico **(100%)**
Tel.: (52) 8444111048
Securities Brokerage
N.A.I.C.S.: 523150

Vitromex, S.A. de C.V. (1)
Blvd Isidro Lopez Zertuche 4103, 25230, Saltillo, Mexico **(100%)**
Tel.: (52) 8444115000
Web Site: http://www.vitromex.com.mx
Ceramic Wall & Floor Tile Mfr
N.A.I.C.S.: 327120

GRUPO INMOBILIARIO DE CAPITAL PRIVADO I (GICAP I) LTD.

A 35 Regent Street Jazmine Court Suite 101, PO Box 1777, Belize, Belize
Tel.: (501) 227 6687
Holding Company
N.A.I.C.S.: 551112

GRUPO KONECTANET S.L.

Serrano 41 2nd Floor, 28001, Madrid, Spain
Tel.: (34) 902193106   ES
Web Site:
http://www.grupokonecta.com
Year Founded: 1999
Sales Range: $350-399.9 Million
Emp.: 14,264
Holding Company; Business Process Outsourcing Services
N.A.I.C.S.: 551112
Jose Maria Pacheco Guardiola *(Pres)*

Subsidiaries:

Konecta Argentina (1)
Av Leandro N Alem 896 pisos 2 y 3 Ciudad Autonoma de, C1001AAQ, Buenos Aires, Argentina
Tel.: (54) 11 5275 3581
Emp.: 300
Business Process Outsourcing Services
N.A.I.C.S.: 561110
Barbara Celoria *(Country Mgr)*

Konecta BTO, S.L. (1)
Avenida de la Industria 49, 28108, Alcobendas, Spain
Tel.: (34) 902193106
Web Site: http://www.grupokonecta.es
Emp.: 2,000
Business Process Outsourcing Services
N.A.I.C.S.: 561499

Konecta Chile Sa (1)
Rodrigo de Araya 1045, Macul, Santiago, Chile
Tel.: (56) 2 23992042
Business Process Outsourcing Services
N.A.I.C.S.: 561110
Rodolfo Vignati Rodriguez *(Dir-Comml)*

Konecta Portugal, Lda (1)
Rua Gregorio Lopes LT 1596B, 1449-970, Lisbon, Portugal
Tel.: (351) 21 300 20 69
Business Process Outsourcing Services
N.A.I.C.S.: 561110
Alfonso Maldonado Lopez de Carrizosa *(Country Mgr)*

Konecta UK Ltd (1)
1st Floor South Station House 500 Eldergate, Milton Keynes, MK9 1BB, United Kingdom
Tel.: (44) 1908 207 210
Emp.: 381
Business Process Outsourcing Services
N.A.I.C.S.: 561110
Stuart Walland *(Mgr-Bus Dev)*

GRUPO KUO, S.A.B. DE C.V.

Paseo de los Tamarindos 400 B piso 31, Bosques de las Lomas, 05120, Mexico, DF, Mexico
Tel.: (52) 5552618000   MX
Web Site: https://www.kuo.com.mx
Year Founded: 1972
KUO—(MEX)
Rev.: $2,285,070,366
Assets: $2,591,817,681
Liabilities: $1,619,980,103
Net Worth: $971,837,578
Earnings: $43,337,442
Emp.: 24,654
Fiscal Year-end: 12/31/23

AND PRIVATE COMPANIES

Holding Company; Motor Vehicle Parts; Chemicals; Foods
N.A.I.C.S.: 551112
Cesar Ramos Valdes *(Mng Dir-Polystyrene)*

Subsidiaries:

Authentic Specialty Foods, Inc. (1)
4340 Eucalyptus Ave, Chino, CA 91710-9705
Tel.: (909) 631-2000
Sales Range: $100-124.9 Million
Emp.: 300
Mfr of Mexican Salsa, Sauces & Spices
N.A.I.C.S.: 311941

Dacomsa, S.A. de C.V. (1)
San Bartolo Naucalpan No 136 Argentina Poniente Miguel Hidalgo, Mexico, 11230, Mexico
Tel.: (52) 5557268224
Web Site: http://www.dacomsa.com
Precision Component Distr
N.A.I.C.S.: 423690

Forestaciones Operativas de Mexico, S.A. de C.V. (1)
Km 31 Car Huimanguillo a Fco Rueda, 86420, Huimanguillo, Tabasco, Mexico
Tel.: (52) 19232372963
Web Site: http://www.kuo.com.mx
Precision Component Mfr
N.A.I.C.S.: 332721

KUO Aerospace, S.A. de C.V. (1)
Autopista Mexico - Queretaro El Chamiza, Pedro Escobedo, 76700, Queretaro, Mexico
Tel.: (52) 4422380900
Aircraft Equipment Mfr
N.A.I.C.S.: 336413

KUO Concentradora, S.A. de C.V. (1)
Paseo De Los Tamarindos No 400-B Bosques De Las Lomas Cuajimalpa, Mexico, 05120, Mexico
Tel.: (52) 5552618000
Precision Component Mfr
N.A.I.C.S.: 332721

Macro-M, S.A. de C.V. (1)
Av de los Sauces N 87 Manzana 6 Parque Industrial Lerma, 52000, Lerma, Mexico
Tel.: (52) 728 282 9770
Web Site: http://www.macro-m.com
Sales Range: $25-49.9 Million
Emp.: 40
Plastic Materials Mfr
N.A.I.C.S.: 325211

Resirene, S.A. de C.V. (1)
Km 15 5 Carr Federal Puebla-Tlaxcala Sto Toribio Xicohtzinco, Tlaxcala, 90780, Mexico
Tel.: (52) 222 223 31 01
Web Site: http://www.resirene.com.mx
Sales Range: $50-74.9 Million
Emp.: 25
Styrenic Resin Mfr
N.A.I.C.S.: 325211
Cesar Ramos *(Gen Mgr)*

TF Victor, S.A. de C.V. (1)
Calle 4 No 22 Naucalpan De Juarez, Mexico, 53377, Mexico
Tel.: (52) 55 2122 8533
Web Site: http://www.tfvictor.com.mx
Gaskets Mfr
N.A.I.C.S.: 339991
Carlos Saldana *(Gen Mgr)*

Transmisiones y Equipos Mecanicos, S.A. de C.V. (1)
Avenida 5 de Febrero 2115 Fracc Industrial Benito Juarez, Queretaro, 76120, Mexico
Tel.: (52) 4 4221 17300
Automobile Gear Box Mfr
N.A.I.C.S.: 336390

GRUPO LA MODERNA, S.A.B. DE C.V.

Leandro Valle No 404-200 Col Reforma y FFCC Nacionales, 50070, Toluca, Mexico
Tel.: (52) 7222653100
Web Site: http://www.lamoderna.com.mx

Year Founded: 1920
Sales Range: $350-399.9 Million
Emp.: 4,077
Wheat & Cereal Based Food Product Mfr
N.A.I.C.S.: 311230
Luis Miguel Monroy Carrillo *(Dir Gen)*

Subsidiaries:

Comercializadora La Moderna de Toluca, S.A. de C.V. (1)
Leandro Valle 404 201 Col Reforma Y FFCC Nales, 50070, Toluca, Mexico (99%)
Tel.: (52) 7222797901
Sales Range: $50-74.9 Million
Emp.: 135
Trader & Distributor of La Moderna Products
N.A.I.C.S.: 332999

Fabrica de Galletas La Moderna, S.A. de C.V. (1)
Vialidad Naucalpan 110, Col Zona Industrial, Toluca, 50010, Mexico (99.7%)
Tel.: (52) 7222720180
Web Site: http://www.lamoderna.com.mx
Sales Range: $150-199.9 Million
Emp.: 961
Cookie Production
N.A.I.C.S.: 311821

Harinera Los Pirineos, S.A. de C.V. (1)
Carretera Panamericana Km 11 Tramo, Emiliano Zapata, Salamanca, 36770, Guanajuato, Mexico
Tel.: (52) 4646423555
Web Site: http://www.pirineos.com.mx
Wheat Mill
N.A.I.C.S.: 311211

La Moderna de Toluca, S.A. de C.V. (1)
Leandro Valle 404-200 Col Reforma y FFCC Nales, Apdo Postal 456, CP 50070, Toluca, Mexico (99%)
Tel.: (52) 722 265 3100
Web Site: http://www.lamoderna.com.mx
Sales Range: $25-49.9 Million
Emp.: 33
Pasta & Baked Goods Mfr & Distr
N.A.I.C.S.: 311812

Molinos Del Sudeste, S.A. de C.V. (1)
Carretera Campeche Hampolol Km 8 Metres 500, C P 24560, Campeche, Mexico (99%)
Tel.: (52) 98175273
Web Site: http://www.lamoderna.com.mx
Sales Range: $25-49.9 Million
Emp.: 70
Wheat Mill
N.A.I.C.S.: 311211

Papeles Corrugados, S.A. de C.V. (1)
Vialidad Toluca Tenango Km 6 San Lorenzo Coacalco, 52140, Metepec, Mexico (50%)
Tel.: (52) 17222757009
Web Site: http://www.papelescorrugados.com.mx
Sales Range: $50-74.9 Million
Emp.: 150
Card Board Mfr
N.A.I.C.S.: 321999

Peliculas Plasticas, S.A. de C.V. (1)
Lote 1 Manzana 3 1A Seccion Parque Industrial, Apartado Postal 23, 50450, Atlacomulco, Mexico (100%)
Tel.: (52) 7121222910
Web Site: http://www.peliculasplasticas.com.mx
Sales Range: $125-149.9 Million
Emp.: 300
Plastic Film Company Mfr
N.A.I.C.S.: 326199
Mario Gonzalez Hamz *(Gen Mgr)*

Productos Alimenticies La Moderna S.A. de C.V. (1)
Leandro Valle No 404-200, Col Reforma Y FFCC Nacionales, Toluca, 50070, Mexico (100%)

Tel.: (52) 7222653100
Web Site: http://www.lamoderna.com.mx
Commercialized Foods Mfr
N.A.I.C.S.: 311999
Luis M. Carrillo *(Gen Dir)*

Productos Alimenticios La Moderna, S.A. de C.V. (1)
Leandro Valle No 404-200 Col Reforma and FFCC National, PO Box 456, 50070, Toluca, Mexico (99.9%)
Tel.: (52) 7222653100
Web Site: http://www.lamoderna.com.mx
Sales Range: $150-199.9 Million
Emp.: 700
Pasta Production Mfr
N.A.I.C.S.: 311824

Tablex Miller, S.A. de C.V. (1)
Carretera Federal Los Mochis Cd Obregon Km 173 175, Navojoa, 85236, Sonora, Mexico (50%)
Tel.: (52) 6424245050
Web Site: http://www.tamisa.com.mx
Sales Range: $25-49.9 Million
Emp.: 95
Wheat Mill
N.A.I.C.S.: 311211

GRUPO LALA S.A. DE C.V.

Lazaro Cardenas No 185 y, Gomez Palacio, 35077, DGO, Mexico
Tel.: (52) 8717293123
Web Site: http://www.lala.com.mx
Sales Range: $5-14.9 Billion
Emp.: 35,000
Dairy Products Producer.
N.A.I.C.S.: 311511
Eduardo Tricio *(Chm)*

Subsidiaries:

Abastecedora de Alimentos de Mexico, S.A. de C.V. (1)
Calz Lazaro Cardenas 545, 35077, Gomez Palacio, Mexico
Tel.: (52) 871 759 1320
Dairy Products Distr
N.A.I.C.S.: 424490
Ricardo Martinez Reza *(Mgr-Admin)*

Farmland Dairies LLC (1)
520 Main Ave, Wallington, NJ 07057-1830
Tel.: (973) 777-2500
Web Site: http://www.farmlanddairies.com
Sales Range: $100-124.9 Million
Emp.: 300
Dairy Products Mfr
N.A.I.C.S.: 311511

Vigor Alimentos S.A. (1)
Rua Joaquim Carlos N 396, CEP 03019-000, Sao Paulo, Brazil
Tel.: (55) 11 2799 5507
Web Site: http://www.vigoralimentos.com.br
Dairy Product Mfr & Whslr
N.A.I.C.S.: 112120
Anderson Rezende *(Exec Mgr-IR)*

GRUPO LAMOSA S.A. DE C.V.

Ave Pedro Ramirez Vazquez No 200-1, piso 8 Valle Oriente San Pedro, 66269, Garza Garcia, NL, Mexico
Tel.: (52) 8180474200   MX
Web Site: http://www.lamosa.com
LAMOSA—(MEX)
Rev.: $1,860,231,949
Assets: $2,581,691,119
Liabilities: $1,631,611,555
Net Worth: $950,079,563
Earnings: $191,525,705
Emp.: 11,543
Fiscal Year-end: 12/31/23
Tiles & Flooring, Adhesives, Waterproofing & Sanitary Ware Mfr
N.A.I.C.S.: 333310
Sergio Narvaez Garza *(VP-Wall & Floor Tiles Div)*

Subsidiaries:

Adhesivos Perdura, S. A. de C. V. (1)
Periferico Sur 5869, Toluquilla, 45610,

Jalisco, Mexico
Tel.: (52) 13334784600
Web Site: https://www.perdura.com.mx
Adhesive Product Mfr
N.A.I.C.S.: 325520

Adhesivos de Jalisco (Leon), S.A. de C.V. (1)
Gasoducto 140, Col Plaza de Toros, Leon, 37490, Mexico
Tel.: (52) 4777071811
Sales Range: $25-49.9 Million
Emp.: 17
Mfr of Adhesives
N.A.I.C.S.: 325520
Jojeefuf Herrnandes *(Mgr)*

Adhesivos de Jalisco, S.A. de C.V. (1)
Blvd Gasoducto No 140 Col Cd Industrial, Leon, 37450, Guanajuato, Mexico
Tel.: (52) 477 707 1808
Adhesive Mfr
N.A.I.C.S.: 325520

Ceramica San Lorenzo S.A.C. (1)
Av Industrial s/n Las Praderas de Lurin, Lurin, Peru
Tel.: (51) 4170800
Web Site: https://www.sanlorenzo.com.pe
Building Materials Mfr
N.A.I.C.S.: 339999

Crest (Mexico City), S.A. de C.V. (1)
Mariano Escobedo 525 Piso 3, Rincon Del Bosque, 11580, Mexico, Mexico
Tel.: (52) 25815400
Web Site: http://www.crest.com.mx
Sales Range: $25-49.9 Million
Emp.: 26
Mfr of Adhesives
N.A.I.C.S.: 325520

Crest (Tizayuca), S.A. de C.V. (1)
Camino a Huitzila s/n, Col Huitzila, 43800, Tizayuca, Hidalgo, Mexico
Tel.: (52) 7791005500
Web Site: http://www.crest.com.mx
Sales Range: $25-49.9 Million
Emp.: 40
Mfr of Adhesives
N.A.I.C.S.: 325520

Crest Norteamerica, S. A. de C. V. (1)
Av Pedro Ramirez Vazquez 200-1, Col Del Valle Oriente, 66260, Garza Garcia, Nuevo Leon, Mexico
Tel.: (52) 8180475000
Web Site: https://www.crest.com.mx
Adhesive & Sealants Mfr
N.A.I.C.S.: 325520

Crest, S.A. de C.V. (1)
Pedro Ramirez Vazquez No 200-1 Col Valle Oriente San Pedro, 66269, Garza Garcia, Nuevo Leon, Mexico
Tel.: (52) 8180475000
Web Site: http://www.crest.com.mx
Adhesive Mfr
N.A.I.C.S.: 325520

Plant (Domestic):

Planta Crest Monterrey (2)
Carretera A Saltillo Km 339 5, 66350, Santa Catarina, Nuevo Leon, Mexico
Tel.: (52) 8182205050
Web Site: http://www.crest.com.mx
Adhesive Mfr
N.A.I.C.S.: 325520

General de Minerales, S.A. de C.V. (1)
Av Pedro Ramirez Vazquez 200 1st Tower 8th Flr, Colonia Valle Oriente, San Pedro, 66269, NL, Mexico
Tel.: (52) 8182204000
Web Site: http://www.lamosa.com
Sales Range: $1-9.9 Million
Emp.: 440
Mfr & Sale of Wall & Floor Tiles
N.A.I.C.S.: 238330

Grupo Lamosa, SA de CV (1)
Arq Pedro Ramirez Vazquez N 200-1 Floor 8 Ucalli Corporate Park, Colonia Valle Oriente, 66269, San Pedro Garza Garcia, Mexico
Tel.: (52) 8180474200

GRUPO LAMOSA S.A. DE C.V.

Grupo Lamosa S.A. de C.V.—(Continued)
Web Site: https://grupolamosa.com
Sales Range: $1-4.9 Billion
Emp.: 3,100
Provider of Real Estate Services
N.A.I.C.S.: 531210

Industrias Niasa, S.A. de C.V. (1)
Av Mariano Escobedo No 510, Miguel Hidalgo Nueva Anzures, Mexico, 11590, Mexico
Tel.: (52) 8005064272
Adhesive Mfr
N.A.I.C.S.: 325520

Italaise, S.A. de C.V. (1)
Av San Diego No 1 Felipe Del Carrillo, Queretaro, 76138, Mexico
Tel.: (52) 4422170809
Ceramic Products Mfr
N.A.I.C.S.: 327120

Lamosa Desarrollos Inmobiliarios, S.A. de C.V. (1)
Arq Pedro Ramirez Vazquez No 200 Int 1 Piso 9 Valle Oriente, Garza Garcia, 66220, Nuevo Leon, Mexico
Tel.: (52) 8182204000
Real Estate Agents & Brokerage Services
N.A.I.C.S.: 531210

Lamosa Revestimientos (Guadalajara), S.A. de C.V. (1)
Pedro Ramirez Vazquez No 200 Torre 1 Col Valle Oriente, San Pedro Garza Garcia, Mexico, 66269, NL, Mexico
Tel.: (52) 8182204000
Web Site: http://www.lamosa.com
Sales Range: $100-124.9 Million
Emp.: 350
Mfr & Sale of Wall & Floor Tiles
N.A.I.C.S.: 238330
Sedereico Goussaint (Pres)

Lamosa Revestimientos (Monterrey), S.A. de C.V. (1)
Avenida Ricardo Covarrubias 2701 Oeste, Col Ladrillera, Monterrey, 64721, N L, Mexico
Tel.: (52) 8182204000
Web Site: http://www.lamosa.com.mx
Sales Range: $100-124.9 Million
Emp.: 350
Mfr & Sale of Wall & Floor Tiles
N.A.I.C.S.: 238330

Lamosa Revestimientos (Tlaxcala), S.A de C.V. (1)
Km 6 5 Carretera San Martin, Texmelucan Ixtacuixtla, Tlaxcala, 90120, Mexico
Tel.: (52) 2484841999
Web Site: http://www.lamosa.com
Sales Range: $100-124.9 Million
Emp.: 400
Mfr & Sale of Wall & Floor Tiles
N.A.I.C.S.: 238330

Mercantil de Pisos y Banos, S.A. de C.V. (1)
San Jeronimo No 800, San Jeronimo, Monterrey, 64640, Nuevo Leon, Mexico
Tel.: (52) 8183475400
Web Site: http://www.amlyenteonteo.kueroz.com
Emp.: 1
Ceramic Products Mfr
N.A.I.C.S.: 327120

Niasa Mexico, S. A. de C. V. (1)
Gral Mariano Escobedo 501 5th floor, Alc. Miguel Hidalgo Col Nueva Anzures, 11590, Mexico, Mexico
Tel.: (52) 5553545680
Web Site: https://www.niasa.com.mx
Adhesive Product Distr
N.A.I.C.S.: 424690

Pavillion, S.A. de C.V. (1)
Carr Puebla - Santa Ana Km 20 San Luis Teolocholco, Mexico, 90850, Mexico
Tel.: (52) 2464652010
Ceramic Products Mfr
N.A.I.C.S.: 327120

Planta Monterrey, S.A. de C.V. (1)
Av Ricardo Covarrubias 2701 Ote, Col Ladrillera, Monterrey, 64830, Mexico
Tel.: (52) 8182204000
Web Site: http://www.lamosa.com

Sales Range: $200-249.9 Million
Emp.: 1,000
Mfr & Sales of Bricks
N.A.I.C.S.: 327120
Adolfo Galindo (Mgr)

Porcelanite Lamosa, S.A. de C.V. (1)
Av Pedro Ramirez Vazquez 200-1 Colonia Valle Oriente, 66260, Garza Garcia, Nuevo Leon, Mexico
Tel.: (52) 5559506185
Web Site: https://porcelanite.com.mx
Ceramic Products Mfr
N.A.I.C.S.: 327120

Porcelanite SA de CV (1)
Bosques De Ceruelos 130-9 Piso, Bosques De Las Lomas, 11700, Mexico, DF, Mexico (74.5%)
Tel.: (52) 5552469912
Web Site: http://www.porcelanite.com
Rev.: $32,000,000
Emp.: 100
Mfr of Ceramic Wall & Floor Tile
N.A.I.C.S.: 327120

Proyeso, S.A. de C.V. (1)
Priv San Carlos No 105 Del Valle, Garza Garcia, 66220, Nuevo Leon, Mexico
Tel.: (52) 8182205000
Gypsum Mining Services
N.A.I.C.S.: 212390

Revestimientos Porcelanite Lamosa, S.A. de C.V. (1)
Av Vallarta Eje Poniente No 6503, Zapopan, 45010, Jalisco, Mexico
Tel.: (52) 3331100519
Sales Range: $450-499.9 Million
Emp.: 200
Ceramic Products Mfr
N.A.I.C.S.: 327120
Hector Welsh (Mng Dir)

Roca Tiles Spain, S.L. (1)
Poligono Industrial Belcaire Calle C No 34, La Vall d'Uixo, Spain
Tel.: (34) 937395119
Web Site: https://www.rocatiles.com
Emp.: 24,000
Bathroom Construction Services
N.A.I.C.S.: 238390

Servicios Administrativos Lamosa, S.A. de C.V. (1)
Avenida Ricardo Covarrubias 2701 Oeste, Col Ladrillera, Monterrey, 64830, NL, Mexico
Tel.: (52) 8182204000
Web Site: http://www.lamosa.com
Sales Range: $150-199.9 Million
Emp.: 900
Provider of Administrative Services
N.A.I.C.S.: 561110

Servicios Comerciales Lamosa, S.A. de C.V. (1)
Pedro Ramirez Vazquez No 200 Valle Oriente, Garza Garcia, 66269, Nuevo Leon, Mexico
Tel.: (52) 8180474200
Ceramic Products Mfr
N.A.I.C.S.: 327120

Servicios de Administracion de Adhesivos, S.A. de C.V. (1)
Calle General Rosalio Hernandez 3 - Colonia Nombre De Dios, Chihuahua, Mexico
Tel.: (52) 614 4241412
Industrial Adhesives Mfr
N.A.I.C.S.: 325520

Tecnocreto, S.A. (1)
Sexta Avenida A 13 24 Zona 9, Guatemala, Guatemala
Tel.: (502) 3611865
Sales Range: $25-49.9 Million
Emp.: 25
Mfr of Adhesives
N.A.I.C.S.: 325520

GRUPO LAR INVERSIONES INMOBILIARIAS, SA
Maria de Molina 39, 10th floor, 28006, Madrid, Spain
Tel.: (34) 914360437
Web Site: https://www.grupolar.com

Year Founded: 1969
Real Estate Management
N.A.I.C.S.: 531210

GRUPO LECHE PASCUAL S.A.
Avenida Manoteras 24, Madrid, 28050, Spain
Tel.: (34) 912035500
Web Site: http://www.lechepascual.com
Year Founded: 1969
Sales Range: $500-549.9 Million
Emp.: 4,300
Mfr & Marketer of Dairy Products, Fruit Juices, Liquid Egg & Omelettes, Breakfast Cereals & Mineral Water
N.A.I.C.S.: 311514
Tomas Pascual Gomez Cuetara (CEO)

GRUPO MELO S.A.
Via Espana No 2313, Apartado Postal 0816-07582, Corregimiento de Rio Abajo, Panama, Panama
Tel.: (507) 3236900
Web Site: http://www.grupomelo.com.pa
MELO—(PAN)
Sales Range: Less than $1 Million
Poultry Product Distr
N.A.I.C.S.: 424440
Eduardo Jaspe Lescure (Treas, Treas & Sr Dir)

GRUPO MEXICANO DE DESARROLLO S.A.B. DE C.V.
Carretera Mexico Toluca 4000, Cuajimalpa, 05000, Mexico, Mexico
Tel.: (52) 5585037000
Web Site: https://www.gmd.mx
Year Founded: 1975
GMXDF—(OTCEM)
Rev.: $299,021,944
Assets: $642,175,401
Liabilities: $183,891,130
Net Worth: $458,284,271
Earnings: $46,841,861
Emp.: 1,926
Fiscal Year-end: 12/31/23
Holding Company; Provider of Construction Services
N.A.I.C.S.: 237310
Manuel Gomez Daza Rangel (Bd of Dirs & Vice Chm)

GRUPO MEXICO, S.A.B. DE C.V.
Campos Eliseos 400, Col Lomas de Chapultepec Alcaldia Miguel Hidalgo, 11000, Mexico, Mexico
Tel.: (52) 58368200 MX
Web Site: https://www.gmexico.com
Year Founded: 1936
GMEXICO—(MEX)
Rev.: $13,870,322,000
Assets: $30,168,496,000
Liabilities: $12,330,978,000
Net Worth: $17,837,518,000
Earnings: $3,492,121,000
Emp.: 30,086
Fiscal Year-end: 12/31/22
Copper, Nickel, Lead & Zinc Mining
N.A.I.C.S.: 212290
German Larrea Mota-Velasco (Chm & Pres)

Subsidiaries:

Asarco Incorporated (1)
8224 S 48th Ste 220, Phoenix, AZ 85044
Tel.: (602) 977-6500
Web Site: http://www.asarco.com
Sales Range: $50-74.9 Million
Emp.: 30
Producer of Nonferrous Metals Principally Copper, Lead, Zinc & Silver
N.A.I.C.S.: 212230

INTERNATIONAL PUBLIC

Subsidiary (Domestic):

Bridgeview Management Co. Inc. (2)
1160 State St, Perth Amboy, NJ 08861
Tel.: (732) 826-1800
Rev.: $1,400,000
Emp.: 2
Refining of Metals
N.A.I.C.S.: 531120
Vincent L. Wildman (VP)

Encycle/Texas, Inc. (2)
1150 N 7th Ave, Tucson, AZ 85705 (100%)
Tel.: (520) 798-7500
Web Site: http://www.asarco.com
Sales Range: $10-24.9 Million
Waste Recycling: Recovers & Recycles Nonferrous Metals From Hazardous & Nonhazardous Inorganic Solids & Solutions
N.A.I.C.S.: 562219

Ferrocarril Mexicano, S.A. De C.V. (1)
Bosque de Ciruelos 99, Col Bosques de las Lomas, 11700, Mexico, Mexico
Tel.: (52) 5552463700
Web Site: http://www.ferromex.com.mx
Sales Range: $750-799.9 Million
Emp.: 6,200
Rail & Railroad Services
N.A.I.C.S.: 488210
German Larrea Mota-Velasco (Chm)

Ferrosur, Sa De Cv (1)
Plz Polanco Jaime Balmes No 11, Tower C 4 Piso, DF 11510, Mexico, Mexico
Tel.: (52) 5553876500
Web Site: http://www.ferrosur.com
Rail & Railroad Transportation
N.A.I.C.S.: 488210

Florida East Coast Railway, LLC (1)
7411 Fullerton St Ste 100, Jacksonville, FL 32256-3628
Tel.: (904) 538-6100
Web Site: http://www.fecrwy.com
Operators of Retail Food Stores
N.A.I.C.S.: 482111
Francis J. Chinnici (COO & Sr VP)

Grupo Industrial Minera Mexico, S.A. de C.V. (1)
Avenida Baja California 200, Colonia Roma Sur, 06760, Mexico, Mexico (99.8%)
Tel.: (52) 5511035000
Sales Range: $750-799.9 Million
Emp.: 2,500
Exploration, Processing & Sales of Minerals
N.A.I.C.S.: 212390

Intermodal Mexico, S.A. de C.V. (1)
Bosque de los Ciruelos 180 Bosque de las Lomas, Miguel Hidalgo, 11700, Mexico, Mexico
Tel.: (52) 55 5246 3977
Web Site: http://www.intermodalmexico.com.mx
Sales Range: $125-149.9 Million
Freight Forwarding Services
N.A.I.C.S.: 488510

Recursos Millrock S de R.L. de C.V. (1)
Boulevard Garcia Morales 200, 83210, Hermosillo, Sonora, Mexico
Tel.: (52) 6622672121
Gold Ore Mining Services
N.A.I.C.S.: 212220
Kati Gibler (Gen Mgr)

Southern Copper Corporation (1)
7310 N 16th St Ste 135, Phoenix, AZ 85020 (75.1%)
Tel.: (602) 264-1375
Web Site: https://www.southerncoppercorp.com
Rev.: $9,895,800,000
Assets: $16,725,300,000
Liabilities: $9,244,100,000
Net Worth: $7,481,200,000
Earnings: $2,425,200,000
Emp.: 15,810
Fiscal Year-end: 12/31/2023
Copper Mining Services
N.A.I.C.S.: 212230
German Larrea Mota-Velasco (Chm)

Subsidiary (Non-US):

Compania Minera Los Tolmos S.A. (2)

AND PRIVATE COMPANIES

Cal Montebello Nro 170, Urb Chacarilla Of
Are, Lima, Peru
Tel.: (51) 5120440
Copper Mining & Processing Services
N.A.I.C.S.: 212230

Minera Mexico S.A. De C.V. (2)
Campos Eliseos No 400 Colonia Lomas de
Chapultepec, Delegacion Miguel Hidalgo,
11000, Mexico, Mexico
Tel.: (52) 5511035000
Sales Range: $75-99.9 Million
Emp.: 15
Copper, Zinc, Silver, Gold & Ore Mining
N.A.I.C.S.: 212290
Xavier Garcia de Quevedo *(Pres)*

Subsidiary (Domestic):

Buenavista del Cobre, S.A de
C.V. (3)
Campos Eliseos No 400, Mexico, 11000,
Mexico
Tel.: (52) 5511035000
Copper Mining & Processing Services
N.A.I.C.S.: 212230

Mexicana de Cobre, S.A. de
C.V. (3)
Avenida Baja California 200 Col Roma Sur,
Mexico, 06760, Mexico
Tel.: (52) 5550800050
Copper Mining & Processing Services
N.A.I.C.S.: 212230

Subsidiary (Non-US):

Southern Copper Corporation (2)
Av Caminos del Inca 171Urb, Chacarilla Del
Estanque Santiago De Surco, Lima, 33,
Peru
Tel.: (51) 15120440
Web Site:
    http://www.southerncoppercorp.com
Copper Mining Services
N.A.I.C.S.: 212230
Oscar Gonzalez Rocha *(Pres & CEO)*

GRUPO MINSA, S.A.B. DE C.V.
Prolongacion Toltecas 4 Los Reyes
Ixtacala, 54090, Tlalnepantla, 54090,
Mexico
Tel.: (52) 5557221900
Web Site: http://www.minsa.com
Year Founded: 1950
MINSA—(MEX)
Rev.: $431,065,320
Assets: $274,237,060
Liabilities: $137,817,770
Net Worth: $136,419,290
Earnings: ($5,406,552)
Emp.: 1,970
Fiscal Year-end: 12/31/23
Cereal Mfr
N.A.I.C.S.: 311230
Altagracia Comez Sierra *(Chm)*

GRUPO MRF CARTUJA SL
Calle Formento 12, Mairena del Alja-
rafe, 41927, Seville, Spain
Tel.: (34) 90 238 3333   ES
Web Site:
    http://www.grupomrfcartuja.com
Year Founded: 2001
Holding Company
N.A.I.C.S.: 551112
Mariano J. Gutierrez Reyes *(Pres)*

GRUPO MUNDIAL TENEDORA, S.A.
East Coast, PH GMT 5th La Rotonda
Boulevard Ave, PO Box 0830-01433,
Panama, Panama
Tel.: (507) 3062000
Web Site:
    https://www.grupomundial.com
Year Founded: 1981
GMUN—(PAN)
Sales Range: Less than $1 Million
Holding Company
N.A.I.C.S.: 551111
Fernando N. Lewis *(Treas)*

GRUPO MZ
Avenida Nacoes Unidas 12 995 20th
Floor, Brooklin, Sao Paulo, CEP
04578-911, Brazil
Tel.: (55) 11 3529 3777
Web Site: http://www.groupmz.com
Year Founded: 1999
Sales Range: $50-74.9 Million
Emp.: 250
Holding Company; Investor Relations,
Applied Technology, Corporate Gov-
ernance & Communications Consult-
ing Services
N.A.I.C.S.: 551112
Enzo Villani *(Pres-North America)*

Subsidiaries:

MZ Consult Participacoes S.A. (1)
rua Prof Manoelito de Ornellas 303 6th Fl
Chacara Santo Antonio, Sao Paulo, CEP
04719-040, Brazil
Tel.: (55) 11 3529 3777
Investor Relations, Applied Technologies,
Corporate Governance & Communications
Consulting Services
N.A.I.C.S.: 541611

Subsidiary (Domestic):

CorpBrasil Comunicacao Corporativa
Ltda. (2)
Avenida Nacoes Unidas 12 995 20th Floor,
Sao Paulo, Brazil
Tel.: (55) 11 3529 3777
Web Site: http://www.corpbas.com
Corporate Governance Consulting Services
N.A.I.C.S.: 541611

Subsidiary (Non-US):

MZ Asia-Pacific Ltd. (2)
2/F Elton Tower 8 Hysan Avenue, Cause-
way Bay, China (Hong Kong)
Tel.: (852) 28513828
Web Site: http://www.mz-ir.com
Investor Relations, Applied Technology, Cor-
porate Governance & Communications
Consulting Services
N.A.I.C.S.: 541611

Subsidiary (US):

MZ Consult NY LLC (2)
1001 Ave of the Americas 4th Fl Ste 411,
New York, NY 10018
Tel.: (212) 813-2975
Web Site: http://www.mz-ir.com
Investor Relations, Applied Technology, Cor-
porate Governance & Communications
Consulting Services
N.A.I.C.S.: 541611
Greg Falesnik *(Mng Dir-North America)*

Subsidiary (Domestic):

MZIlios LLC (3)
550 W Van Buren St Ste 1420, Chicago, IL
60607
Tel.: (312) 261-6400
Web Site: http://www.mzilios.com
Sales Range: $1-9.9 Million
Emp.: 50
Shareholder Research & Market Intelligence
Services
N.A.I.C.S.: 541618
Nick Trikolas *(Pres)*

MZ Taiwan (1)
9F 59 Tianxiang Rd, Zhongshan Dist, Tai-
pei, 10452, Taiwan
Tel.: (886) 2 2585 1928
Financial Management Services
N.A.I.C.S.: 541611

GRUPO NACION GN, S.A.
Apartado Postal 10138-1000, San
Jose, Costa Rica
Tel.: (506) 2247 4747
Web Site: http://www.nacion.com
Sales Range: $75-99.9 Million
Emp.: 1,200
Paper Products Printer & Newspaper
Publisher
N.A.I.C.S.: 323111
Manuel F. Jimenez Echeverria *(Pres)*

GRUPO NUTRESA S.A.
Cra 43A No 1A Sur-143, Medellin,
Colombia
Tel.: (57) 6043258731   Co
Web Site:
    https://www.gruponutresa.com
Year Founded: 1920
NUTRESA—(COLO)
Rev.: $2,987,655,300
Assets: $4,693,572,300
Liabilities: $2,088,113,100
Net Worth: $2,605,459,200
Earnings: $154,032,300
Emp.: 45,803
Fiscal Year-end: 12/31/19
Food Products Mfr
N.A.I.C.S.: 311821
Carlos Ignacio Gallego Palacio *(CEO)*

Subsidiaries:

Alimentos Carnicos S.A.S. (1)
Carrera 40 No 12A-13, Acopi, Yumbo, Co-
lombia
Tel.: (57) 2 431 10 25
Web Site:
    http://www.alimentoscarnicos.com.co
Bakery Products Mfr
N.A.I.C.S.: 311821

Atlantic FS S.A.S. (1)
Calle 6 No 50-169, Medellin, Colombia
Tel.: (57) 3164789598
Web Site: http://www.tienda.atlantic.la
Food Products Distr
N.A.I.C.S.: 424490

Comercial Nutresa S.A.S. (1)
Carrera 52 No 20-124, Avenida Guayabal,
Medellin, Colombia
Tel.: (57) 6044028000
Processed Food Mfr & Distr
N.A.I.C.S.: 311999

Compania Nacional de Chocolates
S.A.S. (1)
Carrera 43A No 1A Sur 143 Edificio Santil-
lana, Medellin, Colombia
Tel.: (57) 6042661500
Processed Food Mfr & Distr
N.A.I.C.S.: 311999

Compania Nacional de Chocolates de
Peru S.A. (1)
Av Maquinarias 2360, Lima, 1, Peru
Tel.: (51) 1 612 4040
Web Site: http://www.chocolates.com.pe
Emp.: 800
Chocolate & Confectionery Mfr & Distr
N.A.I.C.S.: 311351
Ruben Fernandez *(Gen Mgr)*

Cordialsa Boricua Empaque, Inc. (1)
Tadeo Rivera St Corner S Corner, San
Juan, PR 00902
Tel.: (787) 723-5366
Chocolate Mfr
N.A.I.C.S.: 311351

Cordialsa USA, Inc. (1)
6141 Randolph St, Los Angeles, CA 90040
Tel.: (713) 460-4527
Bakery Snacks Distr
N.A.I.C.S.: 424450

Corporacion Distribuidora de Alimen-
tos S.A. (1)
Av Naciones Unidas E2-30 y Nunez de
Vela Edif, Metropolitan 14th Floor Ofc 1407,
Quito, Ecuador
Tel.: (593) 1800110120
Web Site: https://cordialsa.com.ec
Food Products Distr
N.A.I.C.S.: 424420

Industria Colombiana de Cafe
S.A.S. (1)
Calle 8 Sur No 50-67, Medellin, Colombia
Tel.: (57) 6042856600
Processed Food Mfr & Distr
N.A.I.C.S.: 311999

Industria de Alimentos Zenu
S.A.S. (1)
Carrera 64C No 104-03, Medellin, Colombia
Tel.: (57) 44705222
Web Site:
    http://www.industriadealimentos.com.co

Nutritional Food Mfr
N.A.I.C.S.: 311999

Industrias Aliadas S.A.S. (1)
Avenida Calle 26 No 69D 91 Of 504 Edificio
Arrecife, Bogota, Colombia
Tel.: (57) 6012630866
Processed Food Mfr & Distr
N.A.I.C.S.: 311999

La Recetta Soluciones Gastronomi-
cas Integradas S.A.S. (1)
Carrera 16 95-70 Astoria Building, Bogota,
Colombia
Tel.: (57) 6016020203
Web Site: http://www.larecetta.com
Food Service
N.A.I.C.S.: 722310

Meals Mercadeo de Alimentos de Co-
lombia S.A.S. (1)
Avenida Carrera 70 No 98-09, Bogota, Co-
lombia
Tel.: (57) 6016439120
Processed Food Mfr & Distr
N.A.I.C.S.: 311999

Molinos Santa Marta S.A.S. (1)
Km 12 5 Alternate Port Way, Santa Marta,
Colombia
Tel.: (57) 5 438 18 30
Baked Goods Mfr
N.A.I.C.S.: 311812

Novaventa S.A.S. (1)
Carrera 52 No 20-124, Medellin, Colombia
Tel.: (57) 6043068600
Processed Food Mfr & Distr
N.A.I.C.S.: 311999

Productos Alimenticios Doria
S.A.S. (1)
Km 5 6 -Troncal de Occidente-Mosquera,
Cundinamarca, Colombia
Tel.: (57) 6018293600
Processed Food Mfr & Distr
N.A.I.C.S.: 311999

Productos Naturela S.A.S. (1)
Finca La Pradera Parcelacion El Bosque,
Meta, Cumaral, Colombia
Tel.: (57) 6086870726
Web Site: http://www.naturela.com
Processed Food Mfr & Distr
N.A.I.C.S.: 311999

Servicios Nutresa S.A.S. (1)
Carrera 52 No 2-38, Medellin, Colombia
Tel.: (57) 43655600
Web Site: http://www.serviciosnutresa.com
Business Related Services
N.A.I.C.S.: 561439

Setas Colombianas S.A. (1)
Carrera 43A No 1A Sur 29 Edificio Colmena
Oficina 302, Medellin, Colombia
Tel.: (57) 6043525088
Processed Food Mfr & Distr
N.A.I.C.S.: 311999

TMLUC Argentina S.A. (1)
Las Piedras 4599, Monte Chingolo Lanus,
B1825AQW, Buenos Aires, Argentina
Tel.: (54) 1142890891
Soft Drink Mfr & Distr
N.A.I.C.S.: 312111

Tropical Coffee Company S.A.S. (1)
Calle 18 No 4-249, Zona Industrial de
Gaira, Santa Marta, Colombia
Tel.: (57) 6054228046
Processed Food Mfr & Distr
N.A.I.C.S.: 311999

GRUPO POCHTECA S.A.B. DE C.V.
Gob Manuel Reyes Veramendi No 6,
Col San Miguel Chapultepec, 11850,
Mexico, DF, Mexico
Tel.: (52) 1 55 5278 5900
Web Site:
    http://www.grupopochteca.com.mx
Year Founded: 1988
POCHTEC—(MEX)
Sales Range: Less than $1 Million
Industrial Supply Whslr
N.A.I.C.S.: 423840
Armando Santacruz Gonzalez *(CEO)*

GRUPO POSADAS S.A.B. DE C.V.

Grupo Posadas S.A.B. de C.V.—(Continued)

GRUPO POSADAS S.A.B. DE C.V.
Prolongacion Paseo de la Reforma 1015 Torre A Piso 9, Col Santa Fe Del Alvaro Obregon, CP 01210, Mexico, CP 01210, DF, Mexico
Tel.: (52) 5553266700 MX
Web Site: https://www.posadas.com
Year Founded: 1982
POSADAS—(MEX)
Rev.: $262,695,939
Assets: $967,400,907
Liabilities: $921,690,396
Net Worth: $45,710,511
Earnings: ($106,507,049)
Emp.: 11,510
Fiscal Year-end: 12/31/20
Hotel Owner & Manager
N.A.I.C.S.: 721110
Pablo Azcarraga Andrade (Chm)

Subsidiaries:

Altiuspar Solutions S.A. de C.V. (1)
Paseo de la Reforma 155 Lomas de Chapultepec, Mexico, 11000, Mexico
Tel.: (52) 55 5201 8316
Information Technology Consulting Services
N.A.I.C.S.: 541512

Bia Acquisition Ltd (1)
1700 Pacific Ave Ste 270, Dallas, TX 75201
Tel.: (214) 891-3130
Home Management Services
N.A.I.C.S.: 721110

Hotelera Administradora de Monterrey, S.A. de C.V. (1)
Carretera Miguel Aleman 105 La Fe, San Nicolas, 66486, Nuevo Leon, Mexico
Tel.: (52) 8183197512
Hotel Business Services
N.A.I.C.S.: 721110

Inmobiliaria Hotelera Posadas, S.A. de C.V. (1)
Paseo De La Reforma 155 2o Piso, Ciudad Delicias, Mexico
Tel.: (52) 5553266700
Owner & Manager of Hotels
N.A.I.C.S.: 531210

Subsidiary (Domestic):

Gran Operadora Posadas, S.A. de C.V. (2)
Blvd Eusebio Kino No 369 Lomas Pitic, Hermosillo, 83010, Sonora, Mexico
Tel.: (52) 6622596000
Sales Range: $25-49.9 Million
Emp.: 150
Home Management Services
N.A.I.C.S.: 721110
Louis Stalli (Mgr)

Hotelera Inmobiliaria de Monclova, S.A. de C.V. (2)
Blvd Harold R Pape No 1909 Jardines de La Salle, Monclova, 25730, Coahuila, Mexico
Tel.: (52) 8666494900
Home Management Services
N.A.I.C.S.: 721110
Adriana Armengual (Gen Mgr)

Inmobiliaria Hotelera de Toluca, S.A. de C.V. (2)
Paseo Tollocan No 1132 Esq Francisco I Madero Santa Ana Tlapaltitlan, Toluca de Lerd, Toluca, 50160, Mexico
Tel.: (52) 7222761000
Web Site: http://www.piestainn.com
Emp.: 70
Home Management Services
N.A.I.C.S.: 721110

Mexicana de Aviacion S.A. de C.V. (1)
813 Xola 535 Edificio De Mexicana, PO Box 12, Colonia Del Valle, 3100, Mexico, DF, Mexico
Tel.: (52) 5554483000
Web Site: http://www.mexicana.com
Sales Range: $50-74.9 Million
Emp.: 150
International Airline

N.A.I.C.S.: 481111

Posadas USA Inc. (1)
1700 Pacific Ave Ste 270, Dallas, TX 75201-4840 (100%)
Tel.: (214) 891-3130
Web Site: http://www.posadasusa.com
Sales Range: $10-24.9 Million
Emp.: 25
N.A.I.C.S.: 721199

Posadas de Mexico, S.A. de C.V. (1)
Paseo de la Reforma No 165 2nd Floor, 11000, Ciudad Delicias, Mexico
Tel.: (52) 5553266700
Hotels & Motels
N.A.I.C.S.: 721110

Servicios Hoteleros Posadas, S.A. de C.V. (1)
Paseo de La Reforma 155 2o Piso, Ciudad Delicias, Mexico
Tel.: (52) 5553266700
Web Site: http://www.posadas.com
Sales Range: $25-49.9 Million
Emp.: 100
Management Consulting Services
N.A.I.C.S.: 541618

Subsidiary (US):

Altiuspar, Inc. (2)
501 Elm St Ste 575, Dallas, TX 75202
Tel.: (972) 351-8830
Hospitality Software Development Services
N.A.I.C.S.: 541511

Subsidiary (Domestic):

Conectum S.A. de C.V. (2)
Pirindas No 435 Mezzanine Felix Ireta, 58070, Morelia, Michoacan, Mexico
Tel.: (52) 4431131300
Web Site: http://www.conectum.com.mx
Business Consulting Services
N.A.I.C.S.: 561499

Servicios Administrativos Los Cabos, S.A. de C.V. (2)
Carretera Transpeninsular Km 10 3, Vesarrollo del Sol, San Lucas, 23110, Baja California Sur, Mexico
Tel.: (52) 6241456200
Home Management Services
N.A.I.C.S.: 721110

GRUPO PRIVAL S.A.
Santa Maria Boulevard 72 Tower 1, PO Box 0832-00396, Santa Maria Business District, Panama, Panama
Tel.: (507) 3031900
Web Site: https://www.prival.com
Year Founded: 2010
GPRI—(PAN)
Rev.: $9,995,734
Assets: $31,306,376
Liabilities: $598,576
Net Worth: $30,707,800
Earnings: $4,650,993
Fiscal Year-end: 06/30/21
Investment Banking Services
N.A.I.C.S.: 523150
Maria Gabriela Ucar Conte (VP)

GRUPO PROEZA, S.A.P.I. DE C.V.
Ave Constitucion 405 Pte, Col Centro, Monterrey, 64000, NL, Mexico
Tel.: (52) 81 83 69 70 00
Web Site: http://www.proeza.com.mx
Sales Range: $100-124.9 Million
Emp.: 300
Holding Company
N.A.I.C.S.: 551112
Enrique Zambrano (Chm)

Subsidiaries:

Metalsa, S.A. de C.V. (1)
Carr Miguel Aleman Km 16 5 No 100, Apodaca, 66600, NL, Mexico (100%)
Tel.: (52) 8183697400
Web Site: http://www.metalsa.com
Passenger Automobile Frames; Truck Frames & Stampings

N.A.I.C.S.: 336390

GRUPO PROTEXA S.A. DE C.V.
Carr Monterrey-Saltillo km 339, Santa Catarina, 66350, Nuevo Leon, Mexico
Tel.: (52) 8183992828
Web Site: http://www.protexa.com.mx
Year Founded: 1945
Holding Company Construction Drilling & Marine Work Capital Goods & Services
N.A.I.C.S.: 551112

Subsidiaries:

Protexa Industrias S.A. de C.V. (1)
Carretera Monterrey Saltillo Km 339, 66350, Santa Catarina, Nuevo Leon, Mexico (100%)
Tel.: (52) 8183992626
Web Site: http://www.protexa.com.mx
Sales Range: $125-149.9 Million
Emp.: 280
Mfr of Chemicals
N.A.I.C.S.: 325998

Protexa S.A. de C.V. (1)
Carretera Monterrey Saltillo Km 339, 66350, Santa Catarina, Nuevo Leon, Mexico (100%)
Tel.: (52) 8183992626
Web Site: http://www.protexa.com.mx
Sales Range: $100-124.9 Million
Oil & Gas Well Drilling
N.A.I.C.S.: 213111
Mariano Escobedo (Mgr-Fin)

GRUPO QUMMA, S.A. DE C.V.
Av Insurgentes Sur No 2453 Tizapan, 01090, Mexico, DF, Mexico
Tel.: (52) 50907700
Year Founded: 1984
QUMMA—(MEX)
Sales Range: Less than $1 Million
Book Publishing & Distribution Services
N.A.I.C.S.: 513130
Alberto Ramirez Luna (Dir-Fin & Admin)

GRUPO RADIO CENTRO, S.A. DE C.V.
Constituyentes 1154, Colonia Lomas Atlas, 11950, Mexico, DF, Mexico
Tel.: (52) 5557284800
Web Site: http://www.grc.com.mx
Year Founded: 1946
RCENTRO—(MEX)
Rev.: $41,444,265
Assets: $180,841,637
Liabilities: $129,548,561
Net Worth: $51,293,075
Earnings: ($15,827,894)
Emp.: 362
Fiscal Year-end: 12/31/23
Radio Broadcasting Services
N.A.I.C.S.: 516210
Gonzalo Yanez (Dir-Mktg & Ops)

GRUPO RADIO NOTICIAS S.R.L.
Vicente Gil 437, Ciudad, 5500, Mendoza, Argentina
Tel.: (54) 2614299273 Ar
Web Site: http://www.radionoticias.com
Radio Broadcasting Services
N.A.I.C.S.: 516210

GRUPO RAF, S.A. DE C.V.
Edificio RAF km 8 Carreterra a Santa Tecla Antiguo Cuscatlan, La Libertad, El Salvador
Tel.: (503) 2213 3376
Web Site: http://www.raf.com
Sales Range: $125-149.9 Million
Emp.: 650

INTERNATIONAL PUBLIC

Electronic, Photographic Equipment & Supplies Distr
N.A.I.C.S.: 334419
Dave Reeves (CEO)

GRUPO REAL TURISMO S.A. DE C.V.
Mariano Escobedo No 700, Nueva Aazures, 11590, Mexico, Mexico
Tel.: (52) 52638888
Web Site: http://www.gruporealturismo.com
Hotel & Resort Operator
N.A.I.C.S.: 721110
Eduardo Ymay Seemann (Mng Dir)

GRUPO ROMERO
Avenida Arenales 450 Jesús María, Lima, 15072, Peru
Tel.: (51) 13150800
Web Site: http://www.gruporomero.com.pe
Emp.: 100
Holding Company
N.A.I.C.S.: 551112
Dionisio Romero Paoletti (Chm & Pres)

Subsidiaries:

Alicorp S.A. (1)
Avenida Argentina 4793, Carmen de la Legua Reynoso - Callao, Lima, Peru (52,5%)
Tel.: (51) 13150800
Web Site: https://www.alicorp.com.pe
Food & Personal Hygiene Products
N.A.I.C.S.: 311999
Dionisio Romero Paoletti (Chm)

Subsidiary (Non-US):

Industrias de Aceite S.A. (2)
Carretera al Norte Km 6 5, Santa Cruz, Bolivia
Tel.: (591) 3 3443000
Web Site: http://www.fino.com.bo
Consumer Oils & Grain Products
N.A.I.C.S.: 111191
Oliver Rojas (Mgr-Sls)

The Value Brands Company de Argentina S.C.A. (2)
Uruguay 3170, Beccar, (B1643EKU), Buenos Aires, Argentina
Tel.: (54) 1148764100
Web Site: http://www.tvbco.com
Sales Range: $75-99.9 Million
Emp.: 500
Detergent, Soap & Personal Products Mfr
N.A.I.C.S.: 325611

Compania Universal Textil S.A. (1)
Av Avenida Venezuela 2505, Lima, Peru
Tel.: (51) 13375260
Sales Range: $150-199.9 Million
Emp.: 900
Textiles
N.A.I.C.S.: 313310
Javier Seminario De la Fuente (Gen Mgr)

Consorcio Naviero Peruano S.A. (1)
Av Republica de Colombia 643 7 y 8 Piso, San Isidro, 27, Lima, Peru
Tel.: (51) 14116500
Web Site: http://www.cnpsa.com
Sales Range: $50-74.9 Million
Emp.: 100
Cargo Freight
N.A.I.C.S.: 483111
Alejandro Peraza (Gen Mgr)

Corperacion General de Servicios S.A. (1)
Av Nicolas Arriola 780, Lima, 13, Peru
Tel.: (51) 12154130
Financial, Legal & IT Consulting Services
N.A.I.C.S.: 541611

Multimercados Zonales S.A. (1)
Ave Argentina 3093, Lima, Peru
Tel.: (51) 13137000
Web Site: http://www.minka.com.pe
Sales Range: $75-99.9 Million
Emp.: 150
Shopping Centers
N.A.I.C.S.: 455219

AND PRIVATE COMPANIES

Primax S.A. (1)
Avenida Nicolas Arriola 740, Lima, 13, Peru
Tel.: (51) 12033100
Web Site: http://www.primax.com.pe
Emp.: 200
Fuel Import & Export
N.A.I.C.S.: 221210
Rafael Aysanoa *(Mgr-Legal)*

Ransa Comercial S.A. (1)
Av Argentina 2833 - Av Nestor Gambeta
Km 35 Apartado, Postal N 18, Callao, Peru
Tel.: (51) 13136000
Web Site: http://www.ransa.net
Sales Range: $700-749.9 Million
Emp.: 3,000
Shipping Logistics
N.A.I.C.S.: 541614
Emilio Fantozzi *(Gen Mgr)*

Terminal Internacional del Sur S.A. (1)
Terminal Portuar Matarani 0, Arequipa, Peru
Tel.: (51) 54557044
Web Site: http://www.tisur.com.pe
Sales Range: $25-49.9 Million
Emp.: 35
Marine Terminal Operations
N.A.I.C.S.: 488310
Erick Hein Dupont *(Gen Mgr)*

Trabajos Maritimos S.A. (1)
Av Avenida Saenz Pena Ste 177, Callao, Peru **(65%)**
Tel.: (51) 4130400
Web Site: http://www.tramarsa.com.pe
Port Operations
N.A.I.C.S.: 488310

Wigo (1)
Av Camino Real 390 Of 601, Torre Central
San Isidro, Lima, Peru
Tel.: (51) 513 2968
Web Site: http://www.wigo.pe
Telecommunication Servicesb
N.A.I.C.S.: 517112

GRUPO ROTOPLAS, S.A.B. DE C.V.
Torre Virreyes Calle Pedregal 24 Piso 19, Col Molino del Rey Delegacion Miguel Hidalgo, 11040, Mexico, Mexico
Tel.: (52) 5552015000
Web Site: https://www.rotoplas.com
Year Founded: 1978
AGUA—(MEX)
Rev.: $428,744,427
Assets: $606,033,817
Liabilities: $266,119,575
Net Worth: $339,914,242
Earnings: $2,763,349
Emp.: 2,926
Fiscal Year-end: 12/31/19
Water Storage & Improvement Accessory Mfr
N.A.I.C.S.: 237110
Carlos Rojas Mota Velasco *(Founder & Chm)*

GRUPO SALINAS, S.A. DE C.V.
Periferico Sur Suite 4121 Col Fuentes del Pedregal, 14141, Mexico, DF, Mexico
Tel.: (52) 15517201313   MX
Web Site:
  http://www.gruposalinas.com
Year Founded: 2001
Sales Range: $1-4.9 Billion
Emp.: 34,260
Media, Internet, Retail, Telecommunications & Financial Investment Services
N.A.I.C.S.: 523999
Ricardo B. Salinas *(Founder & Chm)*

Subsidiaries:

Azteca America, Inc. (1)
2049 Century Park E Ste 1000, Los Angeles, CA 90067
Tel.: (310) 432-7650
Television Program Production Services
N.A.I.C.S.: 512110

Grupo Elektra S.A.B. de C.V. (1)
Av FFCC de Rio Frio N 419 CJ, Colonia Fraccionamiento Industrial del Moral, CP 09010, Mexico, DF, Mexico **(71%)**
Tel.: (52) 5517209167
Web Site: https://www.grupoelektra.com.mx
Rev.: $10,850,261,632
Assets: $26,173,876,220
Liabilities: $20,808,996,381
Net Worth: $5,364,879,839
Earnings: $353,096,954
Emp.: 71,278
Fiscal Year-end: 12/31/2023
Specialty Retail Stores & Banks
N.A.I.C.S.: 522110
Mario Gordillo Rincon *(Dir Gen)*

Subsidiary (US):

Advance America, Cash Advance Centers, Inc. (2)
135 N Church St, Spartanburg, SC 29306
Tel.: (864) 515-5600
Web Site: http://www.advanceamerica.net
Sales Range: $600-649.9 Million
Emp.: 6,465
Cash Advance Services
N.A.I.C.S.: 522291
James A. Ovenden *(CFO)*

Subsidiary (Domestic):

AAFA of Mississippi, Inc. (3)
1506 Hwy 278 E Ste E, Amory, MS 38821
Tel.: (662) 256-9254
Sales Range: $50-74.9 Million
Emp.: 2
Financial Management Services
N.A.I.C.S.: 525990
Denita Satterwhite *(Gen Mgr)*

ADVANCE AMERICA, CASH ADVANCE CENTERS OF SOUTH CAROLINA, INC. (3)
135 N Church St, Spartanburg, SC 29306
Tel.: (864) 342-5600
Financial Management Services
N.A.I.C.S.: 541611
Eric Bonnell *(Mgr-Info Security & Risk)*

ADVANCE AMERICA, CASH ADVANCE CENTERS OF TENNESSEE, INC. (3)
1019 Gallatin Pike S B1, Madison, TN 37115-4629
Tel.: (615) 612-2956
Financial Management Services
N.A.I.C.S.: 523999

ADVANCE AMERICA, CASH ADVANCE CENTERS OF VIRGINIA, INC. (3)
849 Chimney Hill Shopping Ctr, Virginia Beach, VA 23452
Tel.: (757) 631-0902
Financial Management Services
N.A.I.C.S.: 523999

MCKENZIE CHECK ADVANCE OF OHIO, LLC (3)
1515 S Byrne Rd, Toledo, OH 43614-3458
Tel.: (419) 382-5600
Financial Management Services
N.A.I.C.S.: 541611

Subsidiary (Domestic):

Banco Azteca SA (2)
Av Santa Fe 498 3Rd Floor Santa Fe, Cuajimalpa de Morelos, 05349, Mexico, Mexico
Tel.: (52) 75880250
Web Site: http://www.bancoazteca.com.mx
Rev.: $43,151,665
Assets: $1,002,352,900
Liabilities: $323,417,479
Net Worth: $678,935,421
Earnings: $31,392,414
Emp.: 11
Fiscal Year-end: 12/31/2023
Commercial Banking Services
N.A.I.C.S.: 522110
Ricardo Benjamin Salinas Pliego *(Chm)*

Blockbuster de Mexico, S.A. de C.V. (2)
Blvd Manuel Avila Camacho 1 Piso 5, Col Lomas de Chapultepec, CP 11009, Mexico, DF, Mexico **(100%)**
Tel.: (52) 5552795200

Web Site: http://www.blockbuster.com.mx
Sales Range: $400-449.9 Million
Emp.: 550
Video Tape, DVD & Video Game Rental & Retailing Services
N.A.I.C.S.: 532282
Edward J. Arguelles *(Dir Gen)*

Movil@ccess, S.A. de C.V. (1)
Insurgentes Sur 3579, Torre 1 2 Piso, Col Tlalpan La Joya, Mexico, DF, Mexico
Tel.: (52) 5585827338
Web Site: http://www.movilaccess.com
Sales Range: $1-9.9 Million
Emp.: 53
Messaging & Internet Services
N.A.I.C.S.: 517111

TV Azteca S.A.B de C.V. (1)
Periferico Sur 4121 Colonel Fuentes del Pedregal, 14140, Mexico, DF, Mexico
Tel.: (52) 5517201313
Web Site: https://www.tvazteca.com
Sales Range: $800-899.9 Million
Spanish Programming
N.A.I.C.S.: 516120
Mario San Roman Flores *(CEO)*

GRUPO SALVADOR CAETANO (SGPS) S.A.
Avenida Vasco da Gama 1410, Oliveira do Douro, Vila Nova de Gaia, 4431 956, Portugal
Tel.: (351) 227867000
Web Site:
  http://www.gruposalvadorcaetano.pt
Sales Range: $1-4.9 Billion
Emp.: 6,500
Holding Company; Automotive Retail & Distribution
N.A.I.C.S.: 551112
Salvador Fernandes Caetano *(Chm)*

GRUPO SBF S.A.
Av Dra Ruth Cardoso, 7221, Sao Paulo, 7221, Brazil
Tel.: (55) 1121103802
Web Site: https://ri.gruposbf.com.br
SBFG3—(BRAZ)
Rev.: $1,249,293,151
Assets: $1,539,916,478
Liabilities: $1,085,580,493
Net Worth: $454,335,985
Earnings: $30,176,793
Fiscal Year-end: 12/31/23
Sporting Goods Retailer
N.A.I.C.S.: 423910
Pedro De Souza Zemel *(CEO & Member-Exec Bd)*

GRUPO SECURITY S.A.
Apoquindo 3150 Piso 14, Las Condes, Santiago, Chile
Tel.: (56) 225844540
Web Site: https://www.security.cl
Year Founded: 1991
SECURITY—(SGO)
Rev.: $904,058,283
Assets: $12,082,984,735
Liabilities: $11,079,713,388
Net Worth: $1,003,271,347
Earnings: $200,536,222
Emp.: 3,534
Fiscal Year-end: 12/31/23
Asset Management Services
N.A.I.C.S.: 523940
Francisco Silva Silva *(Chm)*

Subsidiaries:

Travel Security S.A. (1)
Avenida Andres Bello N 2233 Office 0101 in the Municipality, Providencia, Santiago, Chile
Tel.: (56) 225815100
Web Site: http://www.travelsecurity.cl
Transportation Services
N.A.I.C.S.: 485999

GRUPO SIRO S.L.
Industrial Estate Venta de BaNos C /

Fast Train s / n, 34200, Palencia, Spain
Tel.: (34) 979 16 82 00
Web Site: http://www.gruposiro.com
Year Founded: 1991
Sales Range: $700-749.9 Million
Emp.: 4,000
Bakery Products Mfr
N.A.I.C.S.: 311821
Juan Manuel Gonzalez Serna *(Pres)*

GRUPO SPORTS WORLD, S.A.B. DE C.V.
Av Vasco de Quiroga No 3880 Nivel 2 Col Santa Fe Cuajimalpa, CP 05348, Mexico, CP 05348, Mexico
Tel.: (52) 5554817777   MX
Web Site:
  https://www.sportsworld.com.mx
Year Founded: 2005
SPORT—(MEX)
Rev.: $104,928,420
Assets: $202,857,194
Liabilities: $193,977,626
Net Worth: $8,879,567
Earnings: $7,388,464
Emp.: 2,019
Fiscal Year-end: 12/31/23
Fitness & Recreational Services
N.A.I.C.S.: 713940
Xavier Mangino Duenas *(Sec)*

GRUPO SUPERVIELLE S.A.
Bartolome Mitre 434, C1036AAH, Buenos Aires, Argentina
Tel.: (54) 1143403100
Web Site:
  https://www.gruposupervielle.com
Year Founded: 1887
SUPV—(NYSE)
Rev.: $2,994,779,791
Assets: $8,285,752,161
Liabilities: $7,187,757,829
Net Worth: $1,097,994,332
Earnings: ($59,794,275)
Emp.: 3,814
Fiscal Year-end: 12/31/22
Financial Support Services
N.A.I.C.S.: 522299
Julio Patricio Supervielle *(Chm)*

Subsidiaries:

Supervielle Seguros S.A. (1)
San Martin 344 Piso 15, C1004AAH, Buenos Aires, Argentina
Tel.: (54) 8103450178
Web Site:
  http://www.superviellseguros.com.ar
Insurance Claims Services
N.A.I.C.S.: 524291

GRUPO TECNOLOGICO E INDUSTRIAL GMV, S.A.
Isaac Newton 11 PTM Tres Cantos, 28760, Madrid, Spain
Tel.: (34) 91 807 2100   ES
Web Site: http://www.gmv.com
Year Founded: 1984
Sales Range: $150-199.9 Million
Emp.: 1,541
Holding Company; Technological & Industrial Products Mfr & Whslr
N.A.I.C.S.: 551112
Jesus B. Serrano Martinez *(CEO)*

Subsidiaries:

GMV Innovating Solutions, S.L. (1)
Isaac Newton 11 PTM Tres Cantos, 28760, Madrid, Spain
Tel.: (34) 918072100
Web Site: http://www.gmv.com
Technological & Industrial Products Mfr & Whslr
N.A.I.C.S.: 339999
Jesus B. Serrano Martinez *(CEO)*

Subsidiary (US):

Syncromatics Corp. (2)

GRUPO TECNOLOGICO E INDUSTRIAL GMV, S.A.

Grupo Tecnologico e Industrial GMV, S.A.—(Continued)

523 W 6th St Ste 444, Los Angeles, CA 90014 **(100%)**
Tel.: (310) 728-6997
Web Site: http://www.syncromatics.com
Sales Range: $10-24.9 Million
Cloud-Based Transportation Technologies Developer, Mfr & Whslr
N.A.I.C.S.: 334413
Alex Fay *(VP-Bus Dev)*

GRUPO TELEVISA, S.A.B.

Av Vasco de Quiroga No 2000 Colonia Santa Fe, 01210, Mexico, Mexico
Tel.: (52) 5552612000 **MX**
Web Site: https://www.televisair.com
Year Founded: 1950
TV—(NYSE)
Rev.: $3,796,722,634
Assets: $15,036,135,583
Liabilities: $7,790,725,259
Net Worth: $7,245,410,324
Earnings: $2,276,417,832
Emp.: 37,374
Fiscal Year-end: 12/31/22
Spanish Language Media & Broadcast Services
N.A.I.C.S.: 516120
Bernardo Gomez Martinez *(Co-CEO)*

Subsidiaries:

Apuestas Internacionales, S.A. de C.V. (1)
Via Atlixcayotl No 5208, San Andres Cholula, 72810, Puebla, Mexico
Tel.: (52) 5554834900
Gambling Club Operator
N.A.I.C.S.: 713290

Cable Sistema de Victoria, S.A. de C.V. (1)
Porfirio Diaz No 814, Ciudad Victoria, 87050, Mexico
Tel.: (52) 8343187000
Television Broadcasting Services
N.A.I.C.S.: 516120

Cablemas, S.A. de C.V. (1)
Sevilla No 4 Colonia Juarez, 06600, Mexico, Mexico
Tel.: (52) 55 24545800
Web Site: http://www.cablemas.com
Telecommunication Servicesb
N.A.I.C.S.: 517810

Constructora Cablemas, S.A. de C.V. (1)
Avenida San Salvador No 471 OthA N P, Othon P. Blanco, 77034, Mexico
Tel.: (52) 9838320328
Business Management Consulting Services
N.A.I.C.S.: 541611

Corporatel, S.A. de C.V. (1)
Av Vasco De Quiroga No 2000, Mexico, 01210, Mexico
Tel.: (52) 5552612000
Business Management Consulting Services
N.A.I.C.S.: 541611

Corporativo Vasco de Quiroga, S.A. de C.V. (1)
Av Vasco de Quiroga 2000 Pblo Santa Fe Alvaro Obregon, Mexico, 01210, Mexico
Tel.: (52) 5552612180
Television Broadcasting Services
N.A.I.C.S.: 516120

Distribuidora Los Andes, S.A. (1)
Cdla The Garzota Mz 2 Calle 7th Augustine Avenue and Freire, Guayaquil, Ecuador
Tel.: (593) 4 2271 651
Magazine Publishing Services
N.A.I.C.S.: 513120

ECO Producciones, S.A. de C.V. (1)
Calle 2 Sur No 106 Doctores, Cuauhtemoc, 06720, Mexico
Tel.: (52) 5557619494
Commercial Printing Services
N.A.I.C.S.: 323111

ET Publishing International, LLC (1)
6355 NW 36th St 2200, Miami, FL 33166
Tel.: (305) 871-6400

Sales Range: $25-49.9 Million
Emp.: 20
Periodical Publishers
N.A.I.C.S.: 513120
Diana Ortic *(Mgr-HR)*

Editorial Televisa S.A. de C.V. (1)
Avenida Vasco De Quiroga No 2000 Edificio E Colonia Santa Fe, Delegacion Alvaro Obregon, 1210, Mexico, Mexico
Tel.: (52) 5552612761
Web Site: http://www.esmas.com
Magazine Publisher
N.A.I.C.S.: 513120

Subsidiary (Non-US):

Editorial C&P S.A.S. (2)
Calle 74 No 6-65, Bogota, Colombia
Tel.: (57) 1 376 6060
Newspaper Publishers
N.A.I.C.S.: 513110

Subsidiary (Domestic):

Editorial GyJ Televisa, S.A. de C.V. (2)
Av Vasco De Quiroga No 2000, Mexico, 01210, Mexico
Tel.: (52) 5552612600
Commercial Printing Services
N.A.I.C.S.: 323111
Porfirio Sanchez *(Pres)*

Editorial Motorpress-Televisa, S.A. de C.V. (2)
Vasco De Quiroga No 2000, Santa Fe, Mexico, 01210, Mexico
Tel.: (52) 55 52 61 20 00
Car Magazine Publisher
N.A.I.C.S.: 513120

Subsidiary (Non-US):

Editorial Televisa Colombia Cultural, S.A. (2)
Calle 74 6-65, Bogota, Colombia
Tel.: (57) 1 376 6060
Journal Publishing Services
N.A.I.C.S.: 513120

Subsidiary (Domestic):

Editorial Televisa International, S.A. (2)
Av Vasco De Quiroga No 2000, Mexico, 01210, Mexico
Tel.: (52) 5552612600
Magazine Publishing Services
N.A.I.C.S.: 513120

Publicaciones Aquario, S. de R.L. de C.V. (2)
Avenida Vasco de Quiroga No 2000, Col Santa Fe, Mexico, 01210, Mexico
Tel.: (52) 5552245000
Magazine Publishing Services
N.A.I.C.S.: 513120

Subsidiary (Non-US):

VeneTel Servicios Publicitarios, S.A. (2)
Av Venezuela Con Calle Mohedano De El Rosal, Caracas, Venezuela
Tel.: (58) 2129357051
Digital Publishing Services
N.A.I.C.S.: 513199

Empresas Cablevision, S.A.B. de C.V. (1)
Dr Rio de la Loza 182 Colonia Doctores, PO Box 06720, Cuauhtemoc, Mexico
Tel.: (52) 5591831800
Web Site: http://www.cablevision.net.mx
Cable Television Operator
N.A.I.C.S.: 516210

Subsidiary (Domestic):

Milar, S.A. de C.V. (2)
Dr Rio De La Loza No 182 Doctorez, Cuauhtemoc, 06720, Mexico
Tel.: (52) 5591831746
Telecommunication Servicesb
N.A.I.C.S.: 517810

Espacio de Vinculacion, A.C. (1)
Av Vasco de quiroga 2000, Alvaro Obregon, Mexico, 01210, Mexico
Tel.: (52) 5552613355

Web Site: http://www.vinculacion.org
Business Management Consulting Services
N.A.I.C.S.: 541611

Grupo Distribuidoras Intermex, S.A. de C.V. (1)
Lucio Blanco No 435 San Juan Tlihuaca Azcapotzalco, Mexico, 02400, Mexico
Tel.: (52) 5552309500
Magazine Distr
N.A.I.C.S.: 424920

Subsidiary (Non-US):

Distribuidora Alfa, S.A. (2)
Avenida Hermanos Carrera Pinto 159 Of Parque, Industrial Los Libertadores, Colina, Chile
Tel.: (56) 2 5105412
Web Site: http://www.alfa.cl
Newspaper Distr
N.A.I.C.S.: 424920

Distribuidora Bolivariana, S.A. (2)
Av Republica De Panama 3635, San Isidro, Lima, Peru
Tel.: (51) 1 441 2948
Web Site: http://www.dibosa.pe
Magazine Publisher
N.A.I.C.S.: 513120

Distribuidoras Unidas, S.A. (2)
Vda Vuelta Grande Aut Medellin Km 1 Via Siberia Cota, Cundinamarca, Colombia
Tel.: (57) 18966111
Magazine Distr
N.A.I.C.S.: 424920

Subsidiary (Domestic):

Gonarmex, S.A. de C.V. (2)
Lucio Blanco No 435 San Juan Tlihuaca Azcapotzalco, Mexico, 02400, Mexico
Tel.: (52) 5552309500
Property Insurance Services
N.A.I.C.S.: 524126

Grupo Nueva Comercial TB, S.A. de C.V. (1)
Francisco I Madero No 26 Centro De La Ciudad De Mexico Area 1, 06000, Cuauhtemoc, Mexico
Tel.: (52) 55 5512 0011
Lottery Ticket & Sports Betting Services
N.A.I.C.S.: 713290

Grupo Telesistema, S.A. de C.V. (1)
Zedec Santa Fe Alvaro Obregon, 1210, Mexico, Mexico
Tel.: (52) 5552612000
Television Broadcasting Services
N.A.I.C.S.: 516120

Subsidiary (Domestic):

Corporativo TD Sports, S.A. de C.V. (2)
Av Canal de Miramontes No 2053 Los Girasoles III, Coyoacan, Mexico, 04920, Mexico
Tel.: (52) 5555991900
Sales Range: $100-124.9 Million
Emp.: 260
Sports Channel Operator
N.A.I.C.S.: 516120

Impulsora del Deportivo Necaxa, S.A. de C.V. (1)
Blvd Juan Pablo II No 1301 Cantera, Aguascalientes, 20280, Mexico
Tel.: (52) 4499761600
Sales Range: $25-49.9 Million
Emp.: 30
Sports Club Operator
N.A.I.C.S.: 711211

Letseb, S.A. de C.V. (1)
Av Vallarta No 6503-I-8 Plaza Concentro Cd Granja, Zapopan, 45010, Jalisco, Mexico
Tel.: (52) 3340001220
Television Broadcasting Services
N.A.I.C.S.: 516120

Subsidiary (Domestic):

Bestphone, S.A. de C.V. (2)
Av Vasco de Quiroga No 2000, Mexico, 01210, Mexico
Tel.: (52) 5540002848
Telecommunication Servicesb
N.A.I.C.S.: 517810

INTERNATIONAL PUBLIC

Operbes, S.A. de C.V. (2)
Montecito No 38 Condominio 9 Piso 28 Oficina 1 Napoles Benito Juarez, Mexico, 03810, Mexico
Tel.: (52) 5540002100
Television Broadcasting Services
N.A.I.C.S.: 516120

Multimedia Telecom, S.A. de C.V. (1)
Av Vasco De Quiroga No 2000, Mexico, 01210, Mexico
Tel.: (52) 5552612000
Business Management Consulting Services
N.A.I.C.S.: 541611

Publicidad Virtual, S.A. de C.V. (1)
Bosques De Reforma 1813 Floor 7, Bosques de las Lomas, 05100, Mexico, Mexico
Tel.: (52) 5550028400
Web Site: https://www.publicidadvirtual.com
Emp.: 60
Advertising Agencies
N.A.I.C.S.: 541810

Recursos Corporativos Alameda, S.C. (1)
Av Vasco De Quiroga No 2000, Mexico, 01210, Mexico
Tel.: (52) 5552612000
Business Management Consulting Services
N.A.I.C.S.: 541611

Saral Publications, Inc. (1)
6355 NW 36th St, Miami, FL 33166-7027
Tel.: (305) 871-6400
Books Publishing Services
N.A.I.C.S.: 513130

Servicios Administrativos Cablemas, S.A. de C.V. (1)
Sevilla No 4 Piso 6, Mexico, 06600, Mexico
Tel.: (52) 5541218483
Business Management Consulting Services
N.A.I.C.S.: 541611

Servicios Novasat, S, de R.L. de C.V. (1)
Insurgentes Sur No 694 Del Valle, Benito Juarez, 03100, Mexico, Mexico
Tel.: (52) 55 54484000
Television Broadcasting Services
N.A.I.C.S.: 516120

Servicios Operbes, S.A. de C.V. (1)
Piso 28 Oficina 1 Colonia Napoles, Benito Juarez, 03810, Mexico, Mexico
Tel.: (52) 81 81344242
Telecommunication Servicesb
N.A.I.C.S.: 517810

TV Santa Fe, S.A. de C.V. (1)
Av Vasco De Quiroga No 2000, Mexico, Mexico
Tel.: (52) 5552612000
Television Broadcasting Services
N.A.I.C.S.: 516120

Tarrague A.G. (1)
Dammstrasse 19, Zug, 6301, Switzerland
Tel.: (41) 723 24 20
Business Management Consulting Services
N.A.I.C.S.: 541611

Teatro de los Insurgentes, S.A. de C.V. (1)
Insurgentes Sur 1587, Col San Jose Insurgentes, 03900, Mexico, Mexico
Web Site: http://www.teatroinsurgentes.com.mx
Video Production Services
N.A.I.C.S.: 512110

Tele Tips Digital, S.A. de C.V. (1)
Av Vasco De Quiroga No 2000, Mexico, 01210, Mexico
Tel.: (52) 5552612000
Motion Picture & Video Production Services
N.A.I.C.S.: 512110

Televimex, S.A. de C.V. (1)
Cima Del Cerro S/N, Amecameca, 56900, Mexico
Tel.: (52) 5552306618
Radio Broadcasting Services
N.A.I.C.S.: 516110

Televisa Consumer Products USA, LLC (1)

AND PRIVATE COMPANIES

4550 Post Oak Place Dr, Houston, TX 77027
Tel.: (713) 255-1024
Consumer Electronics Mfr
N.A.I.C.S.: 321999

Televisa Corporacion, S.A. de C.V. (1)
Rincon Del Onix No 2320, Ciudad Juarez, 32690, Chihuahua, Mexico
Tel.: (52) 6566881056
Television Broadcasting Services
N.A.I.C.S.: 516120

Televisa Entretenimiento, S.A. de C.V. (1)
Av Vasco De Quiroga No 2000, Mexico, 01210, Mexico
Tel.: (52) 5552612000
Motion Picture & Video Production Services
N.A.I.C.S.: 512110

Televisa Internacional, LLC (1)
6355 NW 36th St 304, Miami, FL 33166
Tel.: (305) 492-1600
Motion Picture & Video Production Services
N.A.I.C.S.: 512110

Televisat, S.A. de C.V. (1)
Ave Jose Maria Morelos 50 L - A Centro, Apatzingan, 60600, Michoacan, Mexico
Tel.: (52) 45 3537 4747
Telecommunication Servicesb
N.A.I.C.S.: 517810

Televisora Peninsular, S.A. de C.V. (1)
Calle 60 No 385, Merida, 97000, Mexico
Tel.: (52) 9999301500
Music Recording Services
N.A.I.C.S.: 512290
Gabriel Moguel *(Mgr)*

Televisora de Mexicali, S.A. de C.V. (1)
Av Romulo O Farril No 938, Mexicali, 21000, Baja California, Mexico
Tel.: (52) 6865576008
Television Broadcasting Services
N.A.I.C.S.: 516120

Televisora de Occidente, S.A. de C.V. (1)
Av Alemania No 1469, Guadalajara, 44190, Jalisco, Mexico
Tel.: (52) 3333433200
Television Broadcasting Services
N.A.I.C.S.: 516120

Videocine, S.A. de C.V. (1)
Benito Juarez 7, Del Carmen Coyoacan, 04100, Mexico, Mexico
Tel.: (52) 5553393000
Web Site: https://www.videocine.com.mx
Motion Picture & Video Production Services
N.A.I.C.S.: 512110

Subsidiary (US):

Pantelion, LLC (2)
2700 Colorado Av Fl 2, Santa Monica, CA 90404-5502
Tel.: (310) 255-3000
Video & Motion Picture Production Services
N.A.I.C.S.: 512110

Videopersel, Ltd. (1)
Dammstrasse 19, 6301, Zug, Switzerland
Tel.: (41) 41 761 25 65
Sales Range: $25-49.9 Million
Emp.: 4
Television Broadcasting Services
N.A.I.C.S.: 516120

GRUPO TERMOINDUSTRIAL ECA, S.A. DE C.V.
Km 21 5 Carr Federal Mexico Puebla, Col Emiliano Zapata, CP 56400, Los Reyes, Mexico
Tel.: (52) 5558550301
Web Site: http://www.grupocea.com.mx
Year Founded: 1963
Sales Range: $1-9.9 Million
Emp.: 350
Heating Solutions; Industrial Equipment Mfr
N.A.I.C.S.: 333414

GRUPO TERRA S.A. DE C.V.
Residencial Las Cumbras 1era Avenida 3era Calle Bloque E, Apdo Postal 1119, Tegucigalpa, Honduras
Tel.: (504) 22368788 HN
Web Site: http://www.grupoterra.com
Year Founded: 2011
Holding Company; Energy, Petroleum, Infrastucture & Real Estate Products & Services
N.A.I.C.S.: 551112
Fredy Antonio Nasser Selman *(Pres & CEO)*

Subsidiaries:

Terra Energia (1)
Km 2 5 Carretera a Ticamaya a una cuadra de Pacasa, Frente a Ciudad Jardines, Comayagua, Honduras
Tel.: (504) 2634 1150
Web Site: http://www.corporaciongrupoterra.com
Geothermal, Hydroelectric & Wind Power Generation
N.A.I.C.S.: 221116
Miguel Antonio Nasser Facusse *(VP & Gen Mgr)*

UNO S.A. de C.V. (1)
Residencial Las Cumbras 1era Avenida 3era Calle Bloque E, Tegucigalpa, Honduras
Tel.: (504) 2236 8788
Web Site: http://www.uno-terra.com
Fuel & Petroleum Products Distr
N.A.I.C.S.: 424720
Fredy Antonio Nasser Facusse *(VP & Gen Mgr)*

GRUPO TMM, S.A.B.
Paseo de la Reforma No 296 P 19, Colonia Juarez, 06600, Mexico, Mexico
Tel.: (52) 5556298866
Web Site: https://www.tmm.com.mx
TMM.A—(MEX)
Rev: $71,803,388
Assets: $192,483,518
Liabilities: $76,152,080
Net Worth: $116,331,438
Earnings: $910,794
Emp.: 788
Fiscal Year-end: 12/31/23
Logistics & Transportation Services
N.A.I.C.S.: 488210
Elvira Ruiz Carreno *(Dir-Corp Audit)*

Subsidiaries:

API Ciudad de Mexico (1)
Paseo de la Reforma No 296 P19 Col Juarez, 06600, Mexico, D F, Mexico **(100%)**
Tel.: (52) 556298866
Web Site: https://www.tmm.com.mx
Sales Range: $50-74.9 Million
Emp.: 200
N.A.I.C.S.: 483111

ATL Puebla (1)
Autopista Mexico Km 116, Planta Volkswagen, Cuautlancingo, 72008, Puebla, Mexico **(51%)**
Tel.: (52) 2222105321
Web Site: http://www.tmm.com.mx
Sales Range: $125-149.9 Million
Emp.: 500
Logistics & Transport Services
N.A.I.C.S.: 488999

Administracion Portuaria Integral de Alcapulco, S.A. de C.V. (1)
Costera Miguel Aleman S N, 39300, Acapulco, Mexico **(51%)**
Tel.: (52) 7444837969
Web Site: http://www.ate.com
Sales Range: $1-9.9 Million
Emp.: 25
N.A.I.C.S.: 483111

Agencia Maritima Mexicana, S.A. de C.V. (1)
Av De La Cuspide 4755 6 Piso Col Parques Del Pedregal, CP 14010, Mexico, DF, Mexico
Tel.: (52) 5556298866
Web Site: http://www.grupotmm.com.mx
Sales Range: $50-74.9 Million
Emp.: 200
N.A.I.C.S.: 483111

Subsidiary (Domestic):

Agencia Maritima Mexicana, S.A. de C.V. (2)
Av Costera Miguel Aleman s/n Malecon Fiscal, Col. Centro, CP 39300, Acapulco, Mexico
Tel.: (52) 744 82 2960
N.A.I.C.S.: 483111

Agencia Maritima Mexicana, S.A. de C.V. (2)
Calle 55 No 2 Col Electricista, 24120, Campeche, Mexico **(100%)**
Tel.: (52) 9383842449
Web Site: http://www.tmm.com.mx
Sales Range: $25-49.9 Million
Emp.: 18
Sea Transportation-Freight
N.A.I.C.S.: 483111

Agencia Maritima Mexicana, S.A. de C.V. (2)
Av Lerdo No 431 Esq 16 Septiembre Col Centro, 96400, Coatzacoalcos, Mexico **(100%)**
Tel.: (52) 9212126939
Sales Range: $25-49.9 Million
Emp.: 4
Sea Transportation
N.A.I.C.S.: 483111

Agencia Maritima Mexicana, S.A. de C.V. (2)
Boulevard Porfirio Hernandez y Calz. Cap. Diego Martinez Corona, Entrada Recinto Portuario, Col. Punta Arena, C.P. 85430, Sonora, Mexico
Tel.: (52) 62220501
N.A.I.C.S.: 483111

Transporcian Maritima Mexicana, S.A. de C.V. (2)
Carretera Paraiso Dos Bocas 1057 N, CP Paraiso Col El Limon, 86600, Dos Bocas, Tabasco, Mexico **(100%)**
Tel.: (52) 9333332919
Web Site: http://www.tmm.com.mx
Sales Range: $50-74.9 Million
Emp.: 130
N.A.I.C.S.: 483111

Granportuaria S.A. (1)
Carrera 12 No 9704, Bogota, Colombia **(100%)**
Tel.: (57) 16019000
Web Site: http://www.granportuaria.com
Sales Range: $25-49.9 Million
Emp.: 60
N.A.I.C.S.: 483111

Grupo TMM Ciudad del Carmen (1)
Calle 55 No2 Col Electricista, 24120, Ciudad del Carmen, Campeche, Mexico
Tel.: (52) 5556298866
Sales Range: $25-49.9 Million
Emp.: 4
Specialized Maritime Services, Ports & Terminals Management & Logistics
N.A.I.C.S.: 483111

Linear Maritime Mexicana S.A. de C.V. (1)
Blvd Miguel De La Madrid No 402, A Un Costado Del Crucero Del P, Manzanillo, Mexico **(100%)**
Tel.: (52) 3143310202
Web Site: http://www.linearmaritime.com
Sales Range: $25-49.9 Million
Emp.: 30
Provider of Maritime Transport Services
N.A.I.C.S.: 483111

Maritima Mexicana, S.A. de C.V. (1)
Av De La Cuspide 4755 7 Piso, CP 14010, Mexico, Mexico
Tel.: (52) 5556298866
Web Site: http://www.grupo.com.mx
Sales Range: $50-74.9 Million
Emp.: 250
N.A.I.C.S.: 483111

GRUPO TMM, S.A.B.

Maritima Mexicana, S.A. de C.V. (1)
Calle 55 No 2 Col Electricistas, CP 24100, Campeche, Mexico
Tel.: (52) 9383810991
Web Site: http://www.tmm.com.mx
Sales Range: $25-49.9 Million
Emp.: 50
N.A.I.C.S.: 483111

Maritima Mexicana, S.A. de C.V., Morgan City (1)
5005 Railroad Ave, Morgan City, LA 70380-2352
Tel.: (985) 385-3475
Sales Range: $25-49.9 Million
Emp.: 80
N.A.I.C.S.: 483111

Naviera Del Pacifico, S.A. de C.V. (1)
Av De La Cuspide 4755 7 Piso, Col Parques Del Pedregal, CP 14010, Mexico, DF, Mexico **(80%)**
Tel.: (52) 5556298866
Web Site: http://www.grouptmm.com.mx
Sales Range: $125-149.9 Million
Emp.: 300
N.A.I.C.S.: 483111

Operadora Portuaria del Golfo, S.A. de C.V. (1)
Emparan No 200 1Er Piso, CP 91700, Veracruz, Mexico **(100%)**
Tel.: (52) 2299894700
Web Site: http://www.ssamexico.com
Marine Cargo Terminal Operator
N.A.I.C.S.: 488320

Subsidiary (Domestic):

Agemar S.A. de C.V.-Veracruz, VER. (2)
Emparan 200 3rd Fl, CP 91700, Veracruz, Mexico
Tel.: (52) 2299313242
Web Site: http://www.sfamexico.com
Sales Range: $25-49.9 Million
Emp.: 35
N.A.I.C.S.: 483111

Promar Institucion Cultural Maritima Mexicana, A.C. (1)
Av De La Cuspide 4755 2 Piso Col Parques Del Pedregal, CP 14010, Mexico, Mexico **(100%)**
Tel.: (52) 5556298866
Web Site: http://www.tmm.com.mx
Sales Range: $25-49.9 Million
Emp.: 100
N.A.I.C.S.: 483111

Servicios Administrativos API Acapulco, S.A. de C.V. (1)
Av Costera Miguel Aleman s/n Malecon Fiscal, 39300, Acapulco, Guerrero, Mexico
Tel.: (52) 7444341710
Sales Range: $25-49.9 Million
Emp.: 3
Business Management Consulting Services
N.A.I.C.S.: 541611
Brenda Fernandes *(Office Mgr)*

Servicios Dedicados de Transportacion, S.A. de C.V. (1)
Av De La Cuspide No 4755, CP 14010, Mexico, Mexico **(100%)**
Tel.: (52) 5556298866
Web Site: http://www.grouptmm.com.mx
Sales Range: $50-74.9 Million
Emp.: 200
N.A.I.C.S.: 483111

TMM Agencias Acapulco (1)
Av Costera Miguel Aleman, s/n Malecon Fiscal, Col Centro, CP 39300, Acapulco, Mexico **(100%)**
Tel.: (52) 744 483 2960
Web Site: http://www.grupotmm.com
Sea Transportation-Freight
N.A.I.C.S.: 483111

TMM Agencias Coatzacoalcos (1)
Ignacio De La Llave No 106, CP 96400, Coatzacoalcos, Mexico **(100%)**
Tel.: (52) 9212124511
Web Site: http://www.tmm.com.mx
Sales Range: $25-49.9 Million
Emp.: 4
Sea Transportation-Freight

GRUPO TMM, S.A.B.

Grupo TMM, S.A.B.—(Continued)
N.A.I.C.S.: 483111

TMM Agencias Dos Bocas (1)
Carretera a Dos Bocas No 710 Norte, Col El Limon, Paraiso, 86600, Mexico **(100%)**
Tel.: (52) 9333332919
Web Site: http://www.grupotmm.com
Sales Range: $25-49.9 Million
Emp.: 10
Sea Transportation-Freight
N.A.I.C.S.: 483111

TMM Car Carrier Ciudad de Mexico (1)
Avenida De La Cuspide 4755 5 Piso, CP 14010, Mexico, Mexico **(100%)**
Tel.: (52) 5556298866
Web Site: http://www.grupotmm.com.mx
Sales Range: $125-149.9 Million
Emp.: 300
N.A.I.C.S.: 483111

TMM Logistics Ciudad de Mexico (1)
Av De La Cuspide 4755 5 Piso Col Parques Del Pedregal, 14010, Mexico, Mexico **(100%)**
Tel.: (52) 5556298866
N.A.I.C.S.: 483111

Subsidiary (Domestic):

TMM Logistics Monterrey (2)
Av Manuel L Barragan No 4580, C Col Hidalgo, Monterrey, NL, Mexico **(100%)**
Tel.: (52) 81 83 31 71 22
Web Site: http://www.grupotmm.com
N.A.I.C.S.: 483111

Terminal Especializada de Contenedores (1)
Manzanillo-Santiago Highway S/N, Specialized Container Terminal, Manzanillo, Colima, Mexico **(100%)**
Tel.: (52) 3143311000
Web Site: https://www.ssamarine.com
Sales Range: $125-149.9 Million
Emp.: 300
N.A.I.C.S.: 483111

GRUPO TRADEBE MEDIOAMBIENTE S.L.

Av Barcelona 109 5 planta, 08970, Sant Joan Despi, Barcelona, Spain
Tel.: (34) 932058100
Web Site: http://www.tradebe.com
Waste Management, Remediation & Environmental Consulting Services
N.A.I.C.S.: 562910
Josep Creixell (Chm)

Subsidiaries:

Tradebe Brasil (1)
Avda Juscelino Kubitschek, 1726 11 andar conj 111/112, 04543-000, Vila Olimpia, Brazil
Tel.: (55) 11 305 304 77
Business Management Services
N.A.I.C.S.: 561110

Tradebe Environmental Services, LLC (1)
1433 E 83rd Ave Ste 200, Merrillville, IN 46410
Tel.: (219) 397-3951
Web Site: http://www.tradebeusa.com
Waste Management, Recycling & Treatment Services
N.A.I.C.S.: 562211
Jeff Beswick (CEO-Tradebe USA)

Subsidiary (Domestic):

Aaron Oil Company, LLC (2)
11 N Water St Ste 14250, Mobile, AL 36602
Tel.: (251) 479-1616
Web Site: http://www.aaronoil.com
Emp.: 100
Oil Collection & Recycling Services
N.A.I.C.S.: 213112
Daniel A. Cowart (Pres)

Treatment and Recycling of Wisconsin, LLC (2)
5611 W Hemlock St, Milwaukee, WI 53223
Tel.: (800) 388-7242
Web Site: http://www.tradebeusa.com
Treatment, Recycling & Other Waste Management Services
N.A.I.C.S.: 562998

United Oil Recovery, Inc. (2)
47 Gracey Ave, Meriden, CT 06451
Tel.: (203) 238-6745
Web Site: http://www.unitedindustrialservices.com
Sales Range: $25-49.9 Million
Emp.: 250
Refuse System
N.A.I.C.S.: 562920

Subsidiary (Domestic):

Norlite Corporation (3)
628 S Saratoga St, Cohoes, NY 12047-4644
Tel.: (518) 235-0030
Web Site: http://www.norliteagg.com
Sales Range: $50-74.9 Million
Emp.: 70
Ceramic Materials Mfr
N.A.I.C.S.: 212323
Tim Lachell (Mgr)

Tradebe S.a.r.l (1)
285 allee Marc Seguin, 26760, Beaumont, France
Tel.: (33) 4 75 80 11 00
Web Site: http://www.tradebe.fr
Business Management Services
N.A.I.C.S.: 561110

Tradebe Solvent Recycling Ltd. (1)
Middleton Road, Morecambe, LA3 3JW, Lancashire, United Kingdom
Tel.: (44) 1524 853053
Web Site: http://www.tradebe.com
Sales Range: $25-49.9 Million
Emp.: 200
Handling & Treatment of Solvent-Based By-Products
N.A.I.C.S.: 562219

Tradebe UK Limited (1)
Atlas House Third Avenue, Globe Business Park, Marlow, SL7 1EY, United Kingdom
Tel.: (44) 845 603 2893
Web Site: http://www.tradebe.co.uk
Waste Management Services
N.A.I.C.S.: 562219
Robin Randall (CEO)

Tradebe Usa Holdings, Inc (1)
1301 W 22nd Ste 500, Oak Brook, IL 60523
Tel.: (800) 388-7242
Web Site: http://www.tradebeusa.com
Waste Management Services
N.A.I.C.S.: 562219

GRUPO TRAXION, S. A. B. DE C. V.

Paseo de la Reforma 115 Floor 17, 11700, Lomas de Chapultepec, 11700, Mexico
Tel.: (52) 5550467900   MX
Web Site: https://43725142.hs-sites.com
Year Founded: 2011
TRAXION—(MEX)
Rev.: $1,227,461,440
Assets: $1,636,867,670
Liabilities: $962,459,447
Net Worth: $674,408,223
Earnings: $30,562,004
Emp.: 20,088
Fiscal Year-end: 12/31/22
Logistics & Transportation Services
N.A.I.C.S.: 541614
Bernardo Lijtszain Bimstein (Chm)

Subsidiaries:

Auto Express Frontera Norte, S. A. de C. V. (1)
Alfredo Nobel s/n Lots 2 3 and 4, Zona Industrial, 50071, Toluca, Edo de Mexico, Mexico
Tel.: (52) 7222133725
Web Site: https://www.afn.com.mx
Freight Transportation Services
N.A.I.C.S.: 488510

Autotransportes Miguel Meza Sanchez, S. A. P. I. de C. V. (1)
Real de los Reyes 285, Col Los Reyes Coyoacan Del Coyoacan, 04330, Coyoacan, Mexico
Tel.: (52) 56740301
Web Site: https://www.atmeza.com
Transportation Services
N.A.I.C.S.: 485999

Excelencia en Transporte de personal, S.A.P.I. de C.V. (1)
Calle Cipres 333 Colonia Atlampa, Cuauhtemoc Delegation, 06450, Mexico, Mexico
Tel.: (52) 5553404700
Web Site: https://utep.com.mx
Transportation Services
N.A.I.C.S.: 541614

Fundacion Traxion, A. C. (1)
Paseo de la Reforma No 115 piso 17 Colonia Lomas de Chapultepec C P, 11000, Mexico, Mexico
Tel.: (52) 5550467900
Web Site: https://fundaciontraxion.com
Environmental Consulting Services
N.A.I.C.S.: 541620

Traxion Solutions, S.A. de C.V. (1)
Paseo de la Reforma 115 17th and 18th floor, Lomas de Chapultepec, 11000, Mexico, Mexico
Tel.: (52) 5550467900
Web Site: https://traxion.global
Logistic Services
N.A.I.C.S.: 541614

V- Modal Mexicana, S.C. (1)
Manuel Gomez Morin 3870 Torre Lomas 4to piso Oficina 603 Centro Sur, 76090, Queretaro, Mexico
Tel.: (52) 4422099600
Web Site: https://www.vmodal.mx
Logistic Services
N.A.I.C.S.: 541614

GRUPO VASCONIA, S.A.B.

Av 16 de Septiembre 31 Col Santo Domingo, Mexico, Mexico
Tel.: (52) 5558990200
Web Site: https://www.grupovasconia.com
Year Founded: 1911
VASCONI—(MEX)
Rev.: $163,004,576
Assets: $211,029,693
Liabilities: $124,524,119
Net Worth: $86,505,574
Earnings: $1,291,120
Fiscal Year-end: 12/31/19
Aluminum Laminate Mfr & Whslr
N.A.I.C.S.: 331315
Emmanuel Reveles Ramirez (Dir-Admin & Fin)

GRUPO VILLAR MIR, S.A.U.

Torre Espacio Paseo de la Castellana 259 D, 28046, Madrid, Spain
Tel.: (34) 915567347   ES
Web Site: http://www.grupovillarmir.es
Year Founded: 1999
Holding Company Services
N.A.I.C.S.: 551112
Javier Lopez Madrid (Mng Dir)

Subsidiaries:

Ferroglobe PLC (1)
13 Chesterfield Street, London, W1J 5JN, United Kingdom **(57%)**
Tel.: (44) 7501308322
Web Site: https://www.ferroglobe.com
Rev.: $1,650,034,000
Assets: $1,758,770,000
Liabilities: $888,884,000
Net Worth: $869,886,000
Earnings: $98,478,000
Emp.: 3,403
Fiscal Year-end: 12/31/2023
Holding Company; Silicon Metals & Ferroalloys Mfr
N.A.I.C.S.: 551112
Javier Lopez Madrid (Chm & Exec Chm)

Subsidiary (US):

Globe Metallurgical, Inc. (2)
County Rd 32, Beverly, OH 45715
Tel.: (740) 984-2361
Web Site: http://www.glbsm.com
Silicon Metal Mfr
N.A.I.C.S.: 331410
Beau Carder (Engr-Mechanical)

Globe Specialty Metals, Inc. (2)
600 Brickell Ave Ste 3100, Miami, FL 33131 **(100%)**
Tel.: (786) 509-6900
Web Site: http://www.glbsm.com
Sales Range: $800-899.9 Million
Holding Company; Silicon Metal & Silicon-Based Alloys Mfr
N.A.I.C.S.: 551112
Alan Kestenbaum (Chm)

Norchem, Inc. (2)
985 Seaway Dr, Fort Pierce, FL 34949
Tel.: (772) 468-6110
Web Site: http://www.norchem.com
Chemical & Allied Products Merchant Whslr
N.A.I.C.S.: 424690
Dennis Pardikes (Pres)

Instituto de Gestion Sanitaria, S.A.U. (1)
Caleruega n 102-104 7 izq, 28033, Madrid, Spain
Tel.: (34) 91 774 70 00
Web Site: https://www.ingesan.es
Building Cleaning & Maintenance Services
N.A.I.C.S.: 561790

Obrascon Huarte Lain, S.A. (1)
Torre Espacio Paseo de la Castellana 259-D, 28046, Madrid, Spain **(51.12%)**
Tel.: (34) 913484100
Web Site: https://ohla-group.com
Rev.: $3,653,922,067
Assets: $3,599,395,077
Liabilities: $3,050,444,862
Net Worth: $548,950,215
Earnings: $6,685,065
Emp.: 15,283
Fiscal Year-end: 12/31/2023
Concession & Construction Services
N.A.I.C.S.: 237990
Jose Antonio de Cachavera Sanchez (Gen Mgr-Svcs)

Subsidiary (Domestic):

Asfaltos y Construcciones Elsan, S.A. (2)
Sor Angela de la Cruz 6, 28020, Madrid, Spain
Tel.: (34) 91 384 74 00
Web Site: http://www.elsan.es
Construction Engineering Services
N.A.I.C.S.: 541330

Catalana de Seguretat i Comunicacions, S.L. (2)
Crta Laurea Miro 401 Nave 8 Pol Industrial El Pla, Sant Feliu de Llobregat, Barcelona, 08980, Spain
Tel.: (34) 93 289 65 70
Web Site: http://www.grupocsc.es
Security System Installation Services
N.A.I.C.S.: 922160
Emilio Mariscal Fernandez (Mgr)

Comercial de Materiales de Incendios, S.L. (2)
Poligono el Rincon nave 44, 21007, Huelva, Spain
Tel.: (34) 959 233 101
Safety System Installation Services
N.A.I.C.S.: 922160

OHL Construccion Nacional Edificacion (2)
Torre Espacio Paseo de la Castellana 259 D, 28046, Madrid, Spain
Tel.: (34) 913484100
Civil Engineering Services
N.A.I.C.S.: 237990

Subsidiary (Domestic):

Agrupacion Guinovart Obras y Servicios Hispania, S.A. (3)
Torre Espacio Paseo de la Castellana 259 D, 28046, Madrid, Spain
Tel.: (34) 913484100

AND PRIVATE COMPANIES

Civil Engineering Services
N.A.I.C.S.: 237990

Nova Bocana Barcelona, S.A. (3)
Passeig de Joan de Borbo 99 101, 08039, Barcelona, Spain
Tel.: (34) 932257452
Civil Engineering Services
N.A.I.C.S.: 237990

Subsidiary (Domestic):

OHL Construccion Nacional Obra Civil (2)
Torre Espacio Paseo de la Castellana 259 D, 28046, Madrid, Spain
Tel.: (34) 913484100
Civil Engineering Services
N.A.I.C.S.: 237990

Subsidiary (Domestic):

Sociedad Anonima Trabajos y Obras (3)
Torre Espacio Paseo de la Castellana 259 D planta 8, 28046, Madrid, Spain
Tel.: (34) 91 348 4740
Web Site: http://www.sato.ohl.es
Offshore & Port Infrastructure Engineering & Construction Services
N.A.I.C.S.: 237990

Subsidiary (Domestic):

OHL Construction National Services (2)
Torre Espacio Paseo de la Castellana 259 D, 28046, Madrid, 28046, Spain
Tel.: (34) 913484100
Web Site: http://www.ohlconstruccion.com
Civil Engineering Services
N.A.I.C.S.: 237990

Subsidiary (Domestic):

PACSA, Servicios Urbanos y del Medio Natural, S.L. (3)
C / Felix Boix N 9, 28036, Madrid, Spain
Tel.: (34) 913532562
Web Site: http://www.grupopacsa.es
Civil Engineering Services
N.A.I.C.S.: 237990

Subsidiary (Domestic):

Ingenieria de los Recursos Naturales, S.A. (4)
Paseo de la Castellana 178 7 Dcha, 28046, Madrid, Spain
Tel.: (34) 353 25 62
Web Site: http://www.irena.es
Civil Engineering Services
N.A.I.C.S.: 237990

Subsidiary (Domestic):

OHL Industrial, S.L. (2)
Torre Espacio Paseo de la Castellana 259 D, 28046, Madrid, Spain
Tel.: (34) 91 348 4100
Web Site: http://www.ohlindustrial.com
Civil Engineering Services
N.A.I.C.S.: 237990

Obrascon Huerta Lain, Construccion Internacional S.L. (2)
Torre Espacio Paseo de la Castellana 259-D, Madrid, 28046, Spain
Tel.: (34) 913484320
Civil Engineering Services
N.A.I.C.S.: 237990

Subsidiary (Non-US):

CD-Telematika a.s. (3)
Pod Taborem 369/8a, 19100, Prague, 9, Czech Republic
Tel.: (420) 972225555
Web Site: http://www.cdt.cz
Civil Engineering Services
N.A.I.C.S.: 237990
Kornelie Schneiderova (Head-Acctg)

Subsidiary (Domestic):

Construcciones Enrique de Luis, S.A. (3)
Calle Madre Rafols 2 Ed Aida Planta 1 Oficina 5, 50004, Zaragoza, Spain
Tel.: (34) 976 447 244
Civil Engineering Services

N.A.I.C.S.: 237990

Subsidiary (Non-US):

OHL Andina, S.A. (3)
Monjitas 392-20, Santiago, Chile
Tel.: (56) 27319400
Civil Engineering Services
N.A.I.C.S.: 237990

OHL Central Europe, a.s. (3)
Olsanska 2643/1A, 130 80, Prague, 3, Czech Republic
Tel.: (420) 724337660
Web Site: http://www.ohl-central-europe.com
Civil Engineering Services
N.A.I.C.S.: 237990

OHL Colombia, S.A.S. (3)
Carrera 17 9309 Piso 8, Bogota, Colombia
Tel.: (57) 15188500
Construction Engineering Services
N.A.I.C.S.: 237990

OHL Construction Canada, Inc. (3)
275 Av Viger Est 2nd Floor, Montreal, H2X3R7, QC, Canada
Tel.: (514) 394-0865
Web Site: http://www.ohlcanada.com
Construction Engineering Services
N.A.I.C.S.: 237990

OHL Construction Pacific Pty Ltd (3)
Level 11 40 Creek Street, Brisbane, 4000, QLD, Australia
Tel.: (61) 7 30030335
Construction Services
N.A.I.C.S.: 237990
Leon Lindley (Mgr-Sys)

OHL Industrial Chile, S.A. (3)
C/Cerro El Plomo no 5855 Piso 15, Las Condes, Santiago, Chile
Tel.: (56) 22361610
Industrial Engineering Services
N.A.I.C.S.: 541330

Subsidiary (US):

OHL USA, Inc. (3)
9725 NW 117th Ave Ste 108, Miami, FL 33178
Tel.: (786) 418-3740
Web Site: http://www.ohlusa.com
Construction Engineering Services
N.A.I.C.S.: 237990

Subsidiary (Domestic):

Arellano Construction Company (4)
9675 NW 117th Ave, Miami, FL 33178
Tel.: (786) 418-3740
Construction Engineering Services
N.A.I.C.S.: 237990
Greter Alvarez (Mgr-Acctg)

Judlau Contracting, Inc. (4)
26-15 Ulmer St, College Point, NY 11356
Tel.: (718) 554-2320
Web Site: http://www.judlau.com
Construction Engineering Services
N.A.I.C.S.: 237990
Ashok Patel (CEO)

OHL Industrial USA, Inc. (4)
4020 S Industrial Dr Ste 160, Austin, TX 78744
Tel.: (512) 716-8960
Industrial Engineering Services
N.A.I.C.S.: 541330

Subsidiary (Non-US):

OHL Uruguay, S.A. (3)
Calle Rio Negro 1354 piso 5 escritorio 27, Montevideo, 11105, Uruguay
Tel.: (598) 2 901 96 26
Construction Engineering Services
N.A.I.C.S.: 237990

OHL ZS, a.s. (3)
Buresova 938/17, 602 00, Brno, Czech Republic
Tel.: (420) 541571111
Web Site: http://www.ohlzs.cz
Civil Engineering Services
N.A.I.C.S.: 237990
Roman Kocurek (CEO)

Branch (Domestic):

OHL ZS, a.s. - Ostrava (4)

Hlavkova 1, 702 04, Ostrava, Czech Republic
Tel.: (420) 596157225
Web Site: http://www.ohlzs.cz
Railway Construction, Repair & Maintenance Services
N.A.I.C.S.: 237990

Subsidiary (Non-US):

Slovenske Tunely, a.s. (3)
Lamacska cesta 99, 841 03, Bratislava, Slovakia
Tel.: (421) 259 101 513
Web Site: http://www.slovtunely.sk
Civil Engineering Services
N.A.I.C.S.: 237990
Milan Nedved (CEO)

Sociedad Concesionaria Centro de Justicia de Santiago, S.A. (3)
Manuel Rodriguez Sur N 2281, Santiago, Chile
Tel.: (56) 2 5982600
Web Site: http://www.concesionariacentrojusticia.cl
Emp.: 2,000
Civil Engineering Services
N.A.I.C.S.: 237990

Tomi-Remont a.s. (3)
Premyslovka 2514/4, Prostejov, Czech Republic
Tel.: (420) 582330876
Web Site: http://www.tomi-remont.cz
Civil Engineering Services
N.A.I.C.S.: 237990
Martin Dokoupil (Dir)

Subsidiary (Domestic):

Obrascon Huarte Lain, Desarrollos S. L. (2)
Torre Espacio Paseo de la Castellana 259D, 28046, Madrid, Spain
Tel.: (34) 913484100
Web Site: http://www.ohldesarrollos.com
Civil Engineering Services
N.A.I.C.S.: 237990

Terminal de Contenedores de Tenerife, S.A (2)
Nueva Terminal del Dique del Este Via de Servicio s/n, 38180, Santa Cruz de Tenerife, Spain
Tel.: (34) 922 990 430
Web Site: http://www.tctenerife.es
Cargo Handling Services
N.A.I.C.S.: 488320
Jose Ignacio Uriarte (Mng Dir)

GRUPO XTRA S.A. DE C.V.
Paseo de la Reforma 215, Colonia Lomas de Chapultepec, 11000, Mexico, DF, Mexico
Tel.: (52) 5552848500
Web Site: http://www.grupoxtra.com
Year Founded: 1988
Sales Range: $1-4.9 Billion
Emp.: 11,000
Holding Company; Textiles, Foods, Tourism, Real Estate
N.A.I.C.S.: 551112
Manuel Saba (Pres)

Subsidiaries:

Grupo Casa Saba S.A.B. de C.V. (1)
Paseo de la Reforma 215 Colonia Lomas de Chapultepec, Mexico, 11000, DF, Mexico
Tel.: (52) 55 5284 6600
Sales Range: $1-4.9 Billion
Emp.: 19,702
Pharmaceutical Products, Health & Beauty Aids, Non-Perishable Food Products, Consumer Products, Publications & Office Supplies Distr
N.A.I.C.S.: 424210
Manuel Saba Ades (Chm)

Harinas de Chihuahua, S.A. de C.V. (1)
Av la Junta 500 Antes Prolongacion Pacheco 508, Sector 02 Popular, Chihuahua, 31350, Mexico
Tel.: (52) 6144151200

Sales Range: $25-49.9 Million
Emp.: 160
Flour & Grain Products Producer
N.A.I.C.S.: 311211

Xtra Textil, S.A. de C.V. (1)
Av Paseo de la Reforma 215, Colonia Lomas de Chapultepec, Mexico, 11000, DF, Mexico
Tel.: (52) 5552848500
Textile Mfr & Distr
N.A.I.C.S.: 313310

GRUPO ZULIANO, C.A.
CC La Colina piso 1 Calle 84 entre Av 2A y 2B, Apartado 10057, Local 18 Sector Valle Frio, Maracaibo, Zulia, Venezuela
Tel.: (58) 2617924242
Web Site: https://www.grupozuliano.com.ve
Year Founded: 1970
Sales Range: Less than $1 Million
Emp.: 9
Petrochemical Products Mfr
N.A.I.C.S.: 325110
Gerardo Gonzalez (Pres)

GRUPONUEVA S.A.
3650 Avenida Apoquindo Piso 10, Las Condes, Santiago, Chile
Tel.: (56) 2 350 6140   CL
Web Site: http://www.gruponueva.com
Sales Range: $1-4.9 Billion
Holding Company: Forestry & Wood Derivatives
N.A.I.C.S.: 551112

Subsidiaries:

Masisa S.A. (1)
Apoquindo 3650 Piso 10, Las Condes, Santiago, Chile (65.94%)
Tel.: (56) 223506019
Web Site: https://www.masisa.com
Sales Range: $900-999.9 Million
Emp.: 5,150
Particle Board & Medium Density Fiberboard Mfr
N.A.I.C.S.: 322130
Eugenio Arteaga Infante (CFO)

Subsidiary (Non-US):

Maderas y Sinteticos Del Peru S.A.C. (2)
Jr Juno 102 Urb La Campina, Lima, Peru
Tel.: (51) 12523343
Wood Product Distr
N.A.I.C.S.: 424990

Subsidiary (Domestic):

Masisa Chile S.A. (2)
Ave Apoquindo 3650 Piso 10, Las Condes, Santiago, Chile
Tel.: (56) 22311010
Web Site: http://www.masisa.com
Sales Range: $600-649.9 Million
Emp.: 4,000
Activities for Forestry
N.A.I.C.S.: 115310

Subsidiary (Domestic):

Forestal Tornagaleones S.A. (3)
Jose Manuel Balmaceda 8050 Apdo 40-A, Valdivia, Santiago, Chile
Tel.: (56) 63214451
Forestry Services
N.A.I.C.S.: 113210

Subsidiary (Domestic):

Masisa Componentes SpA (2)
Bravo De Saravia 2550, Santiago, Chile
Tel.: (56) 24130964
Wood Products Mfr
N.A.I.C.S.: 321211

Subsidiary (Non-US):

Masisa PLC S.A.S. (2)
Av Cl 72 72A 54, Bogota, Colombia
Tel.: (57) 15879300
Wood Product Distr

GRUPONUEVA S.A.

GrupoNueva S.A.—(Continued)
N.A.I.C.S.: 424990

Subsidiary (US):

Masisa USA, Inc. (2)
900 Circle 75 Pkwy Ste 720, Atlanta, GA
30339-3084
Tel.: (770) 405-2600
Wood Products Sales
N.A.I.C.S.: 337110
Dan Schmidt (Pres)

Subsidiary (Non-US):

Oxinova C.A. (2)
Calle Cuchiveros sector Altavista Torre
Balear Piso 2 Ofic 2, Puerto Ordaz, Bolivar,
Venezuela
Tel.: (58) 2126207011
Web Site: http://www.oxinova.com
Wood Products Mfr
N.A.I.C.S.: 321211

GRUPPA KOMPANIY RUSA-GRO OOO

ul Valovaya 35 Business Center Wall
Street 5 floor office 256, 115054,
Moscow, Russia
Tel.: (7) 4953631661
Web Site: http://www.rusagrogroup.ru
Sugar, Oil & Other Agricultural Products
N.A.I.C.S.: 311314
Maxim Dmitrievich Basov (CEO)

Subsidiaries:

Belgorodsky Bacon (1)
49A Pushkina, Belgorod, 308015,
Russia **(100%)**
Tel.: (7) 4722 353566
Web Site: http://www.belbecon.ru
Pig Farming & Pig Fodder
N.A.I.C.S.: 112210

CJSC Rusagro-Aydar (1)
prospect B Khmelnitskogo 111, Belgorod,
308002, Russia
Tel.: (7) 472 385 43 38
Milk Farming Services
N.A.I.C.S.: 112120
Nikolay Guschin (Gen Dir)

Chaplyzhenky Elevator (1)
c Dolgoe Gubkinsky District, 309150, Belgorod, Russia **(100%)**
Tel.: (7) 47241 51676
Web Site: http://www.rusagrogroup.ru
Grain Elevators Mfr
N.A.I.C.S.: 111191
Victor Repin (Gen Dir)

Chernyansky Sugar (1)
Stroiteley 19, Chernyanka, 309560, Belgorod, Russia **(100%)**
Tel.: (7) 4723255991
Web Site: http://www.rusagrogroup.ru
Granulated & Dried Sugar Beet Pulp & Molasses Production
N.A.I.C.S.: 311313

LLC Agrotechnology (1)
ul Internatsionalnaya 16 a 8 floor, Tambov,
392000, Russia
Tel.: (7) 4752 49 25 78
Grain Storage Services
N.A.I.C.S.: 493130
Konstantin Beldushkin (Gen Dir)

LLC Zherdevsky Elevator (1)
Lineiny 21, Zherdevka, Tambov, Russia
Tel.: (7) 47535 5 21 40
Agricultural Product Mfr & Distr
N.A.I.C.S.: 111120
Alexander Esikov (Gen Dir)

Nezhegol-Agro (1)
Urozhainaya 20, 309292, Belgorod, Shebekino, Russia **(100%)**
Tel.: (7) 4724 828883
Web Site: http://www.rusagrogroup.ru
Grain Elevators Mfr
N.A.I.C.S.: 111199

Nika Sugar (1)
Pyatnitskoe, Volokonovsky area, 309665,
Belgorod, Russia **(100%)**
Tel.: (7) 4723556241

Mfr Pressed Powder Sugar & Pressed Refined Sugar
N.A.I.C.S.: 311314
Andrey Sibryaev (Gen Dir)

Nikiforovsky Elevator (1)
8 Yaroslavskaya Dmitrievka, 393002, Tambov, Nikiforovsky, Russia **(85.9%)**
Tel.: (7) 47536 38885
Web Site: http://www.rusagrogroup.ru
Grain Elevators
N.A.I.C.S.: 111199

Nikiforovsky Sugar (1)
r p Dmitrievka, Nikiforovskiy district,
393000, Tambov, Russia **(100%)**
Tel.: (7) 4753638817
Web Site: http://www.rusagrogroup.ru
Sugar Beet Production
N.A.I.C.S.: 311313

OJSC EZhK (1)
ul Titova 27, Ekaterinburg, 620085, Russia
Tel.: (7) 343 210 00 23
Margarine Mfr
N.A.I.C.S.: 311225
Dmitry Mitrofanov (Dir-Sls)

OOO Zarya (1)
ul Zavodskaya 28A, Zherdevka, Tambov,
393671, Russia
Tel.: (7) 4753 586 27
Sugar Mfr
N.A.I.C.S.: 311313
Konstantin Beldushkin (Gen Dir)

Poletaevskoe LLC (1)
s Poletaevo, Tambov, Russia
Tel.: (7) 4755 73 12 49
Sugar Mfr
N.A.I.C.S.: 311313

Rusagro-Invest (1)
111 Prospect B Khmelnitskogo, 308002,
Belgorod, Russia **(100%)**
Tel.: (7) 4722 353507
Web Site: http://www.rusagrogroup.ru
Agricultural Investments
N.A.I.C.S.: 523940

Rzhevsky Sugar (1)
s Rzhevka, 309261, Russia, Shebekinskiy, Russia **(100%)**
Tel.: (7) 4724 830398
Sugar & Beet Production
N.A.I.C.S.: 311314

Samaraagroprompererabotka
(SAPP) (1)
Severo-Zapadnaya 2, pgt Bezenchuk,
446252, Samara, Russia **(100%)**
Tel.: (7) 8467621064
Web Site: http://www.rusagrogroup.ru
Vegetable Oil & Fats Extraction & Production
N.A.I.C.S.: 311225

Tambovsky Bacon (1)
ul Internatsionalnaya 16a 7th Floor, Tambov, 392000, Russia **(100%)**
Tel.: (7) 4752 700112
Web Site: http://www.rusagrogroup.ru
Pig Breeding
N.A.I.C.S.: 112210
Maxim Basov (Gen Mgr)

Valuikisakhar Sugar (1)
Stepnoi 34, Valuiki town, 309994, Belgorod,
Russia **(100%)**
Tel.: (7) 4723566509
Web Site: http://www.rusagrogroup.ru
Sugar Beet Processing & Raw Cane Sugar
N.A.I.C.S.: 311313

Zherdevsky Sugar (1)
Internatsionalnaya St 1A, Zherdevka,
393671, Tambov, Russia **(100%)**
Tel.: (7) 4752422407
Web Site: http://www.rusagrogroup.ru
Mfr Sugar, Molasses, Crude Pulp & Sugar
Beet Granulated Pulp
N.A.I.C.S.: 311313

Znamensky Sugar (1)
Znamensky area, Znamenka, 393401, Tambov, Russia **(100%)**
Tel.: (7) 4755226262
Sugar Beet Processing
N.A.I.C.S.: 311313

GRUPPO COIN S.P.A.

Tel.: (39) 041 2398000
Web Site: http://www.gruppocoin.it
Year Founded: 1916
Sales Range: $1-4.9 Billion
Emp.: 9,498
Apparel, Accessories & Home Furnishing Store Operator & Franchiser
N.A.I.C.S.: 315990

GRUPPO FORMULA S.P.A.

Via G Di Vittorio, 10-20094, Milan,
Italy
Tel.: (39) 0245104111
Web Site: http://www.formula.it
Sales Range: $25-49.9 Million
Emp.: 100
Software
N.A.I.C.S.: 513210
Nicoloe Francesco Rienzi (Chm)

GRUPPO MINERALI MAFFEI S.P.A.

Piazza Martiri della Liberta 4, IT-28100, Novara, Italy
Tel.: (39) 0321 390251
Web Site:
http://www.gruppomineralimaffei.it
Sales Range: $100-124.9 Million
Holding Company; Quartz, Silica
Sand, Feldspar, Kaolin & Clay Mining
& Distr
N.A.I.C.S.: 551112
Giorgio Bozzola (CEO)

Subsidiaries:

Colombia Minerales Industriales
S.A. (1)
Carrera 46 No 22B-20, 577821, Bogota,
Colombia
Tel.: (57) 14856826
Web Site:
http://www.colombiaminerales.com.co
Silica Sand Mfr
N.A.I.C.S.: 212322

Czech Silicat s.r.o. (1)
Hasicska 1017, 357 31, Horni Slavkov,
Czech Republic
Tel.: (420) 725714652
Web Site: http://www.czechsilicat.cz
Chemical Products Mfr
N.A.I.C.S.: 325199
Miroslav Kolbasa (Dir-Exec)

Egyptian International Industrial Minerals S.a.e. (1)
Building in 10 - Block 1163 Ministries
Square, Sheraton Heliopolis Housing, Cairo,
Egypt
Tel.: (20) 26700905
Web Site: http://www.eiimtm.com
Silica Mfr
N.A.I.C.S.: 325180

Gruppo Minerali do Brasil Ltda (1)
Rodovia Vice Prefeito Hermenegildo Tonoli
2335, 13295-000, Itupeva, Brazil
Tel.: (55) 1144962259
Web Site:
http://www.gruppomineralidobrasil.com.br
Chemical Product Mfr & Distr
N.A.I.C.S.: 325199

Maffei Sarda Silicati S.p.A. (1)
Zona Ind San Lorenzo Str Prov Florinas,
Florinas, 07030, Sassari, Italy
Tel.: (39) 079438163
Sand Excavation Services
N.A.I.C.S.: 212390

Mexican Silicates S.A. de C.V. (1)
Av 20 de Noviembre numero 54 Colonia
Centro, 9000, Tlaxcala, Mexico
Tel.: (52) 2464666326
Web Site: http://www.mexicansilicates.com
Chemical Products Distr
N.A.I.C.S.: 424690

Mineral Resources de Guatemala
S.A. (1)
Diagonal 6 10-01 Zona 10 Oficina 1102,
Centro Gerencial Las Margaritas Torre II,
01010, Guatemala, Guatemala
Tel.: (502) 24925353

INTERNATIONAL PUBLIC

Web Site:
http://www.mineralresourcesguatemala.com
Chemical Products Distr
N.A.I.C.S.: 424690

Minerali Industriali Tunisia Sa (1)
El M'rakib Route de Haffouz, BP 85, Oueslatia, 3120, Kairouan, Tunisia
Tel.: (216) 77224356
Chemical Products Mfr
N.A.I.C.S.: 325199

Minerali Industriali EOOD,
Bulgaria. (1)
Nikola Petkov 41 a str, 5400, Sevlievo, Bulgaria
Tel.: (359) 67530914
Web Site: http://www.mib.bg
Emp.: 11,000
Bathroom Fitting & Accessory Mfr
N.A.I.C.S.: 326199

Minerali Industriali S.p.A. (1)
Piazza Martiri della Liberta 4, 28100, Novara, Italy
Tel.: (39) 0321377600
Web Site: http://www.mineraliindustriali.it
Quartz, Silica Sand, Feldspar, Kaolin & Clay
Mining & Distr
N.A.I.C.S.: 212390
Giorgio Bozzola (CEO)

Sasil S.p.A (1)
Via Liberta 8, Brusnengo, 13862, Biella,
Italy
Tel.: (39) 015985166
Web Site: http://www.sasil-life.com
Chemical Products Mfr
N.A.I.C.S.: 325199

Suez Company for Minerals (1)
Building n 1 Block 1156 Ministries Square
Sheraton Heliopolis Housing, 11361, Cairo,
Egypt
Tel.: (20) 222690977
Web Site: http://www.suezminerals.com
Glass Material Mfr
N.A.I.C.S.: 327215

GRUPPO MUTUIONLINE S.P.A

Via Desenzano 2, 20146, Milan, Italy
Tel.: (39) 0283443601
Web Site: https://www.gruppomol.it
MOL—(ITA)
Rev.: $318,324,189
Assets: $767,699,130
Liabilities: $476,812,594
Net Worth: $290,886,536
Earnings: $167,337,874
Emp.: 2,156
Fiscal Year-end: 12/31/20
Financial Services
N.A.I.C.S.: 523940
Alessandro Fracassi (CEO)

Subsidiaries:

65Plus S.r.l. (1)
Via Desenzano 2, 20126, Milan, MI, Italy
Tel.: (39) 0276002593
Web Site: https://www.65plus.it
Financial Consulting Services
N.A.I.C.S.: 523940

7Pixel S.r.l. (1)
Via Lanzoni 13, 27010, Giussano, Pavia,
Italy
Tel.: (39) 0290090634
Web Site: https://www.7pixel.it
Business Consulting Services
N.A.I.C.S.: 541618

Agenzia Italia S.p.A. (1)
Via Vittorio Alfieri 1, 31015, Conegliano, TV,
Italy
Tel.: (39) 04383681
Web Site: https://www.agita.it
Administrative Services
N.A.I.C.S.: 561110

Centro Finanziamenti S.p.A. (1)
Via Desenzano 2, 20146, Milan, Italy
Tel.: (39) 0800688525
Web Site: https://www.creditonline.it
Brokerage Services
N.A.I.C.S.: 425120

Centro Processi Assicurativi S.r.l. (1)
Via De Marini 53 C/O Torre Shipping Thir-

teenth Floor, 16149, Genoa, Italy
Tel.: (39) 028 344 6000
Web Site: https://www.cpa.it
Insurance Services
N.A.I.C.S.: 524210

Centro Servizi Asset Mangement S.r.l. (1)
Viale Sarca 222, 20126, Milan, Italy
Tel.: (39) 0283441
Brokerage Services
N.A.I.C.S.: 425120

Eagle & Wise Service S.r.l. (1)
Viale Sarca 222, 20125, Milan, Italy
Tel.: (39) 0287142000
Web Site: https://www.eaglewise.it
Real Estate Services
N.A.I.C.S.: 531390
Corrado Quarti *(CEO)*

EuroServizi per i Notai S.r.l. (1)
Via Desenzano 2, 20146, Milan, Italy
Tel.: (39) 0248983501
Brokerage Services
N.A.I.C.S.: 425120

Finprom Insurance S.R.L. (1)
Str Cocorilor n 24/A, 310426, Arad, Romania
Tel.: (40) 257304208
Insurance Services
N.A.I.C.S.: 524210

Finprom S.r.l. (1)
Street Cocorilor Nr 24/A, 310426, Arad, Romania
Tel.: (40) 257304208
Web Site: https://www.finprom.ro
Sales Range: $100-124.9 Million
Emp.: 360
Data Entry Outsourcing & Document Management Services
N.A.I.C.S.: 518210

Forensic Experts S.r.l. (1)
Tel.: (39) 05119983384
Web Site: https://www.forensicexperts.it
Brokerage Services
N.A.I.C.S.: 425120

Global Care S.R.L. (1)
Via Corsica 2 int18, 16128, Genoa, Italy
Tel.: (39) 010532803
Web Site: https://www.globalcare.srl
Health Care Srvices
N.A.I.C.S.: 621999

Green Call Service S.R.L. (1)
Via Italia 46, 20900, Seregno, MB, Italy
Tel.: (39) 03621867005
Web Site: https://www.greencall.it
Customer Care Services
N.A.I.C.S.: 541511

LeLynx S.A.S. (1)
34 quai de la Loire, 75019, Paris, France
Tel.: (33) 185098465
Web Site: https://www.lelynx.fr
Insurance Services
N.A.I.C.S.: 524210

Lercari International Ltd. (1)
New London House 6 New London Street, London, EC3R 7LP, United Kingdom
Tel.: (44) 2037419500
Insurance Services
N.A.I.C.S.: 524210

Lercari Motor S.R.L. (1)
Piazza della Repubblica 7/9, 20121, Milan, Italy
Tel.: (39) 0245413500
Financial Services
N.A.I.C.S.: 522320

Lercari S.r.l. (1)
Piazza della Repubblica 7/9, 20121, Milan, Italy
Tel.: (39) 0245413500
Insurance Services
N.A.I.C.S.: 524210

Luna Service S.R.L. (1)
Via Michele Migliarini 62, 00173, Rome, Italy
Tel.: (39) 03518349789
Web Site: https://lunaserviceroma.it
Hotel Services
N.A.I.C.S.: 721110

Quinservizi S.p.A. (1)
Via Romolo Ossani 14, 48018, Faenza, Ravenna, Italy
Tel.: (39) 0283440500
Web Site: https://www.quinservizi.it
Emp.: 500
Brokerage Services
N.A.I.C.S.: 425120

SOS Tariffe S.r.l. (1)
Via Desenzano 2, 20146, Milan, Italy
Tel.: (39) 025005111
Web Site: https://www.sostariffe.it
Mobile Network Operator
N.A.I.C.S.: 517121

San Filippo S.r.l. (1)
S Giorgio Park Industrial Zone Via Ungaretti 10N, 16157, Genoa, Italy
Tel.: (39) 0106980431
Web Site: https://www.oms-sanfilippo.it
Mechanical Component Mfr
N.A.I.C.S.: 333613

Sircus S.r.l. (1)
Via Roma 8a, 16121, Genoa, Italy
Tel.: (39) 010 544 6670
Industrial Equipment Mfr
N.A.I.C.S.: 333248

Sovime S.R.L. (1)
Via Pigna 104, 80128, Naples, Italy
Tel.: (39) 08119806317
Web Site: https://www.sovime.it
Real Estate Services
N.A.I.C.S.: 531390

Surf S.R.L. (1)
V Allende 10, 40026, Imola, BO, Italy
Tel.: (39) 0542643914
Web Site: https://www.surfsrl.it
Home Furnishing Mfr
N.A.I.C.S.: 321991

Trebi Generalconsult S.R.L. (1)
Via Elia Lombardini 13, 20143, Milan, MII, Italy
Tel.: (39) 025819131
Web Site: https://trebi.it
Information Technology Services
N.A.I.C.S.: 541511

GRUPPO RIELLO SISTEMI S.P.A.
Via Nazionale 10, Minerbe, 37046, Verona, Italy
Tel.: (39) 0442641800   IT
Web Site: http://www.riellosistemi.it
Year Founded: 1963
Sales Range: $100-124.9 Million
Emp.: 500
Holding Company
N.A.I.C.S.: 551112
Andrea Riello *(Pres & CEO)*

Subsidiaries:

Gruppo Riello Sistemi FRANCE (1)
Atemo Machine Outils ZAC Les Gatines 18 Avenue du Garigliano, 91601, Savigny-sur-Orge, Cedex, France
Tel.: (33) 1 69 44 00 00
Industrial Machinery Distr
N.A.I.C.S.: 423830

Gruppo Riello Sistemi Germany GmbH (1)
Burkhardt Weber Str 59, 72760, Reutlingen, Germany
Tel.: (49) 173 314 3091
Industrial Machinery Distr
N.A.I.C.S.: 423830

Gruppo Riello Sistemi North America (1)
3265 Jefferson Boulevard, Windsor, N8T 2W7, ON, Canada
Tel.: (519) 944-5600
Industrial Machinery Distr
N.A.I.C.S.: 423830

Mandelli Sistemi S.p.A. (1)
Via Caorsana 35, Piacenza, 29122, Italy   **(100%)**
Tel.: (39) 0523548548
Web Site: http://www.mandelli.com
Sales Range: $50-74.9 Million
Emp.: 150
Horizontal Machining Center Mfr
N.A.I.C.S.: 335999

Andrea Riello *(Pres)*

Riello Mandelli Machine Tools UK Ltd. (1)
Units 101 & 102 - Great Western Business Park Tolladine Road, Worcester, WR4 9PT, United Kingdom
Tel.: (44) 1905 612369
Industrial Machinery Distr
N.A.I.C.S.: 423830

Riello Sistemi (Shanghai) Trade Co., Ltd (1)
Room 203 Bldg 6 Lane 59 Shen Nan Road, Xin Zhuang Industry Zone, Shanghai, 201108, China
Tel.: (86) 21 34635799
Industrial Machinery Distr
N.A.I.C.S.: 423830
Stefano Baron *(Gen Mgr)*

GRUPPO WASTE ITALIA S.P.A.
Via Giovanni Bensi 12/3, 20152, Milan, Italy
Tel.: (39) 02 87211700   IT
Web Site: http://www.gruppowasteitalia.it
Year Founded: 1824
WIG—(ITA)
Holding Company; Industrial & Commercial Waste Management Services
N.A.I.C.S.: 551112
Marco Fiorentino *(VP)*

Subsidiaries:

Waste Italia S.p.A. (1)
Via Bensi 12/3, 20152, Milan, Italy **(100%)**
Tel.: (39) 02 413051
Web Site: http://www.wasteitalia.it
Industrial & Commercial Waste Management Services
N.A.I.C.S.: 562998
Giuseppe Maria Chirico *(Chm & CEO)*

GRUPUL EDITORILOR SI DIFUZORILOR DE PRESA SA
Bucharest Sector 1 Strada Teodosie Rudeanu No 6, Bucharest, Romania
Tel.: (40) 314251947
Web Site: http://www.gedp.ro
Sales Range: $1-9.9 Million
Emp.: 28
Newspaper Printing Services
N.A.I.C.S.: 323111

GRUSCHWITZ TEXTILWERKE AG
Memminger Strasse 68, 88299, Leutkirch, Germany
Tel.: (49) 756190980   De
Web Site: http://www.gruschwitz.com
Sales Range: $25-49.9 Million
Emp.: 129
Yarns, Strings & Fibers Mfr
N.A.I.C.S.: 313110

GRYPHON CAPITAL INCOME TRUST
Level 16 Governor Macquarie Tower 1 Farrer Place, Sydney, 2000, NSW, Australia
Tel.: (61) 282770000
GCI—(ASX)
Rev.: $35,827,991
Assets: $453,458,866
Liabilities: $3,482,238
Net Worth: $449,976,627
Earnings: $32,633,547
Fiscal Year-end: 06/30/24
Investment Trust Management Services
N.A.I.C.S.: 523940

GRZA TURIST A.D.
Branka Krsmanovica 14, Paracin, Serbia
Tel.: (381) 35 564 625
Year Founded: 1964
GRZA—(BEL)
Sales Range: Less than $1 Million
Home Management Services
N.A.I.C.S.: 721110
Radovan Stojanovic *(Exec Dir)*

GS CHAIN PLC
72 Charlotte St, London, W1T 4QQ, United Kingdom
Tel.: (44) 2038853142   UK
Web Site: https://www.gschain.world
Year Founded: 2021
GSC—(LSE)
Assets: $734,557
Liabilities: $730,828
Net Worth: $3,729
Earnings: ($868,773)
Emp.: 5
Fiscal Year-end: 06/30/23
Investment Management Service
N.A.I.C.S.: 523999
Sebastien Guerin *(Chief Operational Officer)*

GS HOLDINGS CORP.
GS Tower Nonhyun-ro 508, Gangnam-gu, Seoul, Korea (South)
Tel.: (82) 220051114
Web Site: http://www.gs.co.kr
078930—(KRS)
Rev.: $14,208,676,880
Assets: $22,518,695,560
Liabilities: $12,622,674,160
Net Worth: $9,896,021,400
Earnings: ($223,270,200)
Fiscal Year-end: 12/31/20
Holding Company
N.A.I.C.S.: 551112
Tae-Soo Huh *(Chm)*

Subsidiaries:

GS E&C Corp. (1)
Gran Seoul 33 Jong-ro, Jongno-gu, Seoul, Korea (South)
Tel.: (82) 221541114
Electric Power Distribution Services
N.A.I.C.S.: 221122
Byeong-Yong Lim *(Pres & CEO)*

GS EPS Co., Ltd. (1)
241 Bugok gongdan-ro Songak-eup, Dangjin, 31721, Chungnam, Korea (South)
Tel.: (82) 413512024
Web Site: https://www.gseps.com
Emp.: 285
Electric Power Distribution Services
N.A.I.C.S.: 221122
Eungsik Kim *(Pres & CEO)*

GS Energy Corporation (1)
Yeoksam-dong GS Tower 508 Nonhyeon-ro, Gangnam, Seoul, Korea (South)
Tel.: (82) 2 2005 0800
Energy Services
N.A.I.C.S.: 211130

Joint Venture (Domestic):

Boryeong LNG Terminal Co., Ltd. (2)
450 Ocheonhaean-ro, Boryeong, Chungcheongnam, Korea (South)   **(50%)**
Tel.: (82) 262639990
Electric Power Distribution Services
N.A.I.C.S.: 221122
SinDuk Kang *(CEO)*

Subsidiary (Domestic):

GS Caltex Corporation (2)
GS Tower 508 Nonhyeon-ro, Gangnam-gu, Seoul, 06141, Korea (South)
Tel.: (82) 220051114
Web Site: https://www.gscaltex.com
Rev.: $28,604,460,000
Assets: $17,568,080,000
Liabilities: $8,110,660,000
Net Worth: $9,457,420,000
Earnings: $389,580,000
Emp.: 3,000
Fiscal Year-end: 12/31/2019
Oil Refiner & Marketer
N.A.I.C.S.: 324110
Saehong Hur *(Pres & CEO)*

GS HOLDINGS CORP.

GS Holdings Corp.—(Continued)

Subsidiary (Non-US):

GS Caltex Singapore Pte., Ltd. (3)
8 Temasek Boulevard 26-03 Suntec Tower 3, Singapore, 038988, Singapore
Tel.: (65) 63336233
Web Site: http://www.gscaltex.com
Emp.: 24
Petroleum Whslr
N.A.I.C.S.: 213112
Halen Yong (Gen Mgr)

Subsidiary (Domestic):

GS EcoMetal Co., Ltd. (2)
75-34 Hwasan 1 Street, Onsan-Eup Uljugun, Ulsan, Korea (South)
Tel.: (82) 522375400
Web Site: https://i-web.kr
Emp.: 94
Petrochemical Products Mfr
N.A.I.C.S.: 324110
Choi Byung Min (CEO)

GS Mbiz Co., Ltd. (2)
19 Seonyu-ro 43-gil, Yeongdeungpo-gu, Seoul, 07210, Korea (South)
Tel.: (82) 234745500
Mobility Services
N.A.I.C.S.: 441330

GS POWER CO.,LTD (2)
897-2 Pyeongchon-Dong, Dongan-Gu, Anyang, 431-070, Gyeonggi, Korea (South) (51%)
Tel.: (82) 31420 2590
Web Site: http://www.gspower.co.kr
Oil & Petrochemical Business Services
N.A.I.C.S.: 213112

Incheon Total Energy Company (2)
37 Academy-ro 51 beon-gil, Yeonsu-gu, Incheon, Korea (South)
Tel.: (82) 15771079
Electric Power Distribution Services
N.A.I.C.S.: 221122
Taehyung Lee (CEO)

Inno Polytech Corporation (2)
130 Yongbong-ro Jisu-myeon, Jinju, Gyeongsangnam, Korea (South)
Tel.: (82) 7048326606
Web Site: http://innopolytech.co.kr
Resin Product Mfr
N.A.I.C.S.: 325211

Sangji Shipping Co., Ltd. (2)
129 Munsu-ro, Yeosu, Jeollanam-do, Korea (South)
Tel.: (82) 616502700
Chemical Products Mfr
N.A.I.C.S.: 325998
Kim Tae Young (CEO)

GS Engineering & Construction Corporation (1)
Gran Seoul 33 Jong-ro, Jongno-gu, Seoul, 03159, Korea (South)
Tel.: (82) 221541114
Web Site: https://www.gsenc.com
Rev.: $9,433,483,497
Assets: $12,998,055,007
Liabilities: $8,889,847,452
Net Worth: $4,108,207,554
Earnings: $260,222,925
Emp.: 5,422
Fiscal Year-end: 12/31/2022
Architectural Services, Civil Engineering & Construction Services
N.A.I.C.S.: 236210
Byeong-Yong Lim (Bd of Dirs & CEO)

Subsidiary (Non-US):

GS Construction Arabia Co., Ltd. (2)
6th Floor Al-Fardan Tower 7639 Prince Turki Bin Abdulaziz Street, PO Box 2920, Al Khobar, 31952, Saudi Arabia
Tel.: (966) 138825590
Architectural Services, Civil Engineering & Construction Services
N.A.I.C.S.: 237990

GS E&C India Pvt. Ltd. (2)
Udyog Vihar Phase 4 Plot No 288 A, Gurgaon, 122016, Haryana, India
Tel.: (91) 124 4537000
Architectural Services, Civil Engineering & Construction Services
N.A.I.C.S.: 237990

GS E&C Nanjing Co., Ltd. (2)
Heping Building 12th Floor, 22 Beijing East Road, Nanjing, 210008, China
Tel.: (86) 8651643828
Web Site: http://www.gsenc.com
Architectural Services, Civil Engineering & Construction Services
N.A.I.C.S.: 237990

GS E&C Thai Co., Ltd. (2)
246 Times Square Bldg 12th Floor Room 12-04 A Sukhumvit 12-14 Road, Kwaeng Klongtoey, Khet Klongtoey, Bangkok, 10110, Thailand
Tel.: (66) 2 653 0875
Architectural Services, Civil Engineering & Construction Services
N.A.I.C.S.: 237990

GS Inima Environment, S.A. (2)
Quintanavides Street 17, 28050, Madrid, Spain (100%)
Tel.: (34) 910505186
Web Site: http://www.inima.com
Sales Range: $150-199.9 Million
Emp.: 60
Construction & Maintenance of Water Desalination Plants & Other Water Treatment Plants
N.A.I.C.S.: 237990
Marta Verde Blazquez (Mng Dir)

Subsidiary (Non-US):

Ambient Servicos Ambientais de Ribeirao Preto, S.A. (3)
Rod Alexandra Balbo SP 328 km 3346, Ring Road North Contour, 14062-800, Ribeirao Preto, SP, Brazil
Tel.: (55) 1639628100
Web Site: http://www.ambient.com.br
Sales Range: $25-49.9 Million
Emp.: 49
Civil Engineering Services
N.A.I.C.S.: 237990

Subsidiary (Domestic):

Biorreciclaje de Cadiz, S.A. (3)
Federico Salmon 8, 28016, Madrid, Spain
Tel.: (34) 956423460
Civil Engineering Services
N.A.I.C.S.: 237990

Subsidiary (Non-US):

Desalari Ltda. (3)
Rivera Sur s/n Valle de Lluta Casilla 50D, Arica, Chile
Tel.: (56) 58217280
Web Site: http://www.desalari.cl
Civil Engineering Services
N.A.I.C.S.: 237990

Subsidiary (Domestic):

Gestion de Participes de Biorreciclaje, S.A. (3)
Ctra de Puerto Real a Paterna km 13.500, Medina-Sidonia, 11170, Spain
Tel.: (34) 956423460
Sales Range: $25-49.9 Million
Civil Engineering Services
N.A.I.C.S.: 237990

Inalia Cap Djinet, S.L. (3)
Ulises Edificio H 18, 28043, Madrid, Spain
Tel.: (34) 917036518
Engineeering Services
N.A.I.C.S.: 237990

Subsidiary (Non-US):

Inima CVV, S.A. (3)
Cerro el Plomo 5420 10th Commune of the Counts, Santiago, Chile
Tel.: (56) 228698086
Web Site: http://www.inima.com
Civil Engineering Services
N.A.I.C.S.: 237990

Inima Chile Ltda. (3)
Oficina Valparaiso 050 La Chimba Bajo, Antofagasta, Chile
Tel.: (56) 5521 4297
Civil Engineering Services
N.A.I.C.S.: 237990

Inversiones INIMA, S.A. (3)
Oficina Valparaiso 050 La Chimba Bajo, Antofagasta, Chile
Tel.: (56) 5521 4297
Investment Services
N.A.I.C.S.: 523999

Subsidiary (Domestic):

Tractament Metropolita de Fangs, S.L. (3)
Rambla Prim s/n, 08019, Barcelona, Spain
Tel.: (34) 934466617
Sales Range: $75-99.9 Million
Emp.: 54
Wastewater Treatment Facility
N.A.I.C.S.: 221320

Subsidiary (Non-US):

GS Nha Be Development One-Member LLC (2)
301 Nguyen Van Huong Street Thao Dien Ward, District 2, Ho Chi Minh City, Vietnam
Tel.: (84) 8 3519 2031
Architectural Services, Civil Engineering & Construction Services
N.A.I.C.S.: 237990

GS Phnom Penh Development Co., Ltd. (2)
132 Street Sothearos Sangkat Tonle Bassac, Khan Chamkarmon, Phnom Penh, Cambodia
Tel.: (855) 23 216 016
Architectural Services, Civil Engineering & Construction Services
N.A.I.C.S.: 237990

GS Saigon Development One-Member LLC (2)
301 Nguyen Van Huong Street Thao Dien Ward, District 2, Ho Chi Minh City, Vietnam
Tel.: (84) 8 3519 2031
Architectural Services, Civil Engineering & Construction Services
N.A.I.C.S.: 237990

GS Global Corp. (1)
10th Floor GS Tower 679 Yeoksam-dong, Gangnam-gu, Seoul, 6141, Korea (South)
Tel.: (82) 220055300
Web Site: http://www.gsgcorp.com
Sales Range: $750-799.9 Million
Emp.: 454
General Trading Services; Steel, Metal, Cement, Chemicals, Electronics & Other Industrial Products Whslr
N.A.I.C.S.: 425120
Taik-Keun Jung (Pres & CEO)

Subsidiary (Domestic):

GS Entec Corp. (2)
353 Yongjam-ro, Nam-gu, Ulsan, 44782, Korea (South)
Tel.: (82) 522317300
Chemical Product Mfr & Distr
N.A.I.C.S.: 325998
Jung-Hae Doh (CEO)

Subsidiary (Non-US):

GS Global Australia Pty., Ltd. (2)
suite 603 Level 6 132 Arthur Street, Sydney, 2060, NSW, Australia (100%)
Tel.: (61) 299540911
Web Site: http://www.gsgcorp.com
Sales Range: $25-49.9 Million
Emp.: 8
Construction Materials & Cement Products Distr
N.A.I.C.S.: 327310
Kenny Cho (Mng Dir)

GS Global Corporation-Kuala Lumpur (2)
Ste 1707 17th Fl Kenanga Intl Bldg, Jalan Sultan Ismail, Kuala Lumpur, 50250, Malaysia
Tel.: (60) 3 2162 3635
Web Site: http://www.gsgcorp.com
Sales Range: Less than $1 Million
Emp.: 5
International Concrete & Steel Trade Services
N.A.I.C.S.: 327331
Hyun-Min Shin (Gen Mgr)

GS Global Corporation-New Delhi (2)

INTERNATIONAL PUBLIC

Steel & Cement Distr
N.A.I.C.S.: 327331

GS Netvision Co., Ltd. (1)
18F GS Tower 508 Nonhyeon-ro, Gangnam-gu, Seoul, Korea (South)
Tel.: (82) 220063377
Digital Marketing Services
N.A.I.C.S.: 541613
Kim Jong Su (CEO)

GS Retail Co., Ltd. (1)
508 Nonhyeon-ro GS Tower 679 Yeoksamdong, Gangnam-gu, Seoul, Korea (South) (65.75%)
Tel.: (82) 220062088
Web Site: https://www.gsretail.com
Rev.: $8,610,670,678
Assets: $7,541,468,537
Liabilities: $4,151,324,410
Net Worth: $3,390,144,127
Earnings: $36,516,720
Emp.: 7,814
Fiscal Year-end: 12/31/2022
Convenience Stores Operating Services
N.A.I.C.S.: 445131

Subsidiary (Domestic):

GS Home Shopping, Inc. (2)
GS Tower 508 Nonhyeon-ro, Gangnam-gu, Seoul, 150-096, Korea (South)
Tel.: (82) 220051114
Web Site: http://company.gsshop.com
Rev.: $1,146,011,104
Assets: $1,451,676,305
Liabilities: $307,282,341
Net Worth: $1,144,393,964
Earnings: $115,139,200
Emp.: 1,011
Fiscal Year-end: 12/31/2020
Cable TV, Internet & Catalogue Shopping
N.A.I.C.S.: 516210
Yeon-Soo Huh (CEO)

Parnas Hotel Co., Ltd. (2)
521 Teheran-ro, Gangnam-gu, Seoul, Korea (South)
Tel.: (82) 25555656
Home Management Services
N.A.I.C.S.: 721110
Gwon Ik Beom (CEO)

GS Sports Corporation (1)
Seoul World Cup Stadium 240 World Cup-ro, Mapo-gu, Seoul, Korea (South)
Tel.: (82) 23065050
Sports Club Services
N.A.I.C.S.: 711211
Jang Kee Ju (CEO)

GS Teleservice Inc (1)
Tuna 7F 223 Buil-ro, Wonmi-gu, Seoul, Gyeonggi-do, Korea (South)
Tel.: (82) 6249000
Web Site: http://www.gstelesvc.com
Telemarketing Services
N.A.I.C.S.: 561422

XI S&D, Inc. (1)
Namsan Square 173 Toegye-ro, Jung-gu, Seoul, 04554, Korea (South)
Tel.: (82) 269107100
Web Site: https://www.xisnd.com
Housing Development Services
N.A.I.C.S.: 624229
Kim Hoan-Yeol (CEO)

Zeit O&M Co., Ltd. (1)
5F 40 Namdaemun 9-gil, Jung-gu, Seoul, 04522, Korea (South)
Tel.: (82) 264100333
Web Site: http://www.zeitonm.com
Chemical Products Mfr
N.A.I.C.S.: 325998
Park Seung-Bum (Pres & CEO)

GS HOLDINGS LIMITED

22 Sin Ming Lane Midview City 04-73, Singapore, 573969, Singapore
Tel.: (65) 66841014
Web Site: https://gsholdings.com.sg
43A—(CAT)
Rev.: $6,992,350
Assets: $3,407,559
Liabilities: $6,116,034
Net Worth: ($2,708,475)
Earnings: ($14,224,797)
Fiscal Year-end: 12/31/23

AND PRIVATE COMPANIES

Commercial Dishware Washing
N.A.I.C.S.: 561499
Pang Pok *(CEO)*

Subsidiaries:

GreatSolutions Pte. Ltd. (1)
8 Loyang Way 4, Singapore, 507604, Singapore
Tel.: (65) 66942668
Web Site: http://www.greatsolutions.com.sg
Dishware Washing Services
N.A.I.C.S.: 561790
Xiuling Xin *(Mgr-Corp Dev)*

Rasa Sayang Village Pte. Ltd. (1)
5 Changi Village Road 01-2063, Singapore, 500005, Singapore
Tel.: (65) 63868184
Web Site: http://rasa-sayang-village.business.site
Restaurant Services
N.A.I.C.S.: 722511

GS YUASA CORPORATION

1 Inobanba-cho Nishinosho Kisshoin, Minami-ku, Kyoto, 601-8520, Japan
Tel.: (81) 753121211
Web Site: https://www.gs-yuasa.com
6674—(TKS)
Rev.: $3,720,749,170
Assets: $4,340,542,430
Liabilities: $1,869,195,630
Net Worth: $2,471,346,800
Earnings: $211,943,040
Emp.: 12,892
Fiscal Year-end: 03/31/24
Holding Company; Battery Mfr & Whslr
N.A.I.C.S.: 551112
Toshiyuki Nakagawa *(VP)*

Subsidiaries:

Beijing Ri Jia Power Supply Co., Ltd. (1)
5A No 13 South Jingsheng Si Street Jinqiao Technical Manufacture Base, Tongzhou Park, Beijing, 101102, China
Tel.: (86) 10 60595892
Switchboard Apparatus Mfr
N.A.I.C.S.: 335313

Century Yuasa Batteries Pty Ltd (1)
49-65 Cobalt St, Brisbane, Carole Park, 4300, QLD, Australia
Tel.: (61) 733616166
Web Site: https://www.centurybatteries.com.au
Emp.: 25
Battery Mfr
N.A.I.C.S.: 335910

Subsidiary (Non-US):

Century Yuasa Batteries (NZ) Ltd (2)
259 Church Street, Onehunga, Auckland, 1061, New Zealand
Tel.: (64) 800939393
Web Site: https://www.cyb.co.nz
Sales Range: $25-49.9 Million
Battery Mfr
N.A.I.C.S.: 335910
Stu Stanners *(Gen Mgr)*

GS Battery (China) Co., Ltd. (1)
Wuxi National Hi-Tech Industrial Development Zone No 71-B, Wuxi, 214028, Jiangsu, China
Tel.: (86) 51085342011
Battery Mfr
N.A.I.C.S.: 335910

GS Battery (U.S.A.) Inc. (1)
1150 Northmeadow Pkwy Ste 110, Roswell, GA 30076-3886
Tel.: (678) 762-4818
Web Site: https://gsyuasa-es.com
Sales Range: $25-49.9 Million
Emp.: 25
Battery Mfr
N.A.I.C.S.: 335910

GS Battery Taiwan Co., Ltd. (1)
No 999 Zhongzheng North Road, Yongkang District, T'ainan, 710002, Taiwan
Tel.: (886) 62532191
Web Site: https://www.gs-battery.com.tw
Sales Range: $100-124.9 Million
Emp.: 620
Rechargeable Batteries Mfr & Distr
N.A.I.C.S.: 335910
Kazuhiko Noda *(Chm)*

GS KASEI KOGYO Co., Ltd. (1)
1400-1 Inokuchi, Takatsuki-cho, Nagahama, 529-0212, Shiga, Japan
Tel.: (81) 749854011
Web Site: http://www.gskasei.co.jp
Battery Mfr
N.A.I.C.S.: 335910

GS Yuasa Accounting Service Ltd. (1)
1 Inobabacho Kisshoinnishinosho, Minami-ku, Kyoto, 601-8310, Japan
Tel.: (81) 753252635
Finance & Accounting Services
N.A.I.C.S.: 541219

GS Yuasa Battery Ltd. (1)
1-7-13 Shiba Park, Minato-ku, Tokyo, 105-0011, Japan
Tel.: (81) 354025730
Web Site: https://gyb.gs-yuasa.com
Automotive Batteries Mfr & Distr
N.A.I.C.S.: 335910

GS Yuasa Battery Singapore Co., Pte. Ltd. (1)
11 Pioneer Walk, Singapore, 627826, Singapore
Tel.: (65) 62651566
Web Site: http://www.gs-yuasa.com
Sales Range: $25-49.9 Million
Emp.: 12
Battery Mfr
N.A.I.C.S.: 335910

GS Yuasa International Ltd. (1)
1 Inobanba-cho Nishinosho Kisshoin, Minami-ku, Kyoto, 601-8520, Japan
Tel.: (81) 753121211
Web Site: http://www.gs-yuasa.com
Electronic Parts & Equipment Whslr
N.A.I.C.S.: 423690
Kei Nishida *(Exec VP)*

Affiliate (Non-US):

AGM Batteries Ltd (2)
Denchi House Thurso Business Park, Thurso, KW14 7XW, United Kingdom (100%)
Tel.: (44) 1847867200
Web Site: http://www.agmbatteries.com
Sales Range: $50-74.9 Million
Emp.: 150
Storage Battery Mfr
N.A.I.C.S.: 335910

Joint Venture (Non-US):

Atlas Battery Ltd. (2)
D-181 Central Avenue, SITE, Karachi, 75730, Pakistan
Tel.: (92) 2132567990
Web Site: http://www.atlasbattery.com.pk
Rev.: $155,431,605
Assets: $67,054,735
Liabilities: $28,590,722
Net Worth: $38,464,013
Earnings: $4,281,404
Emp.: 346
Fiscal Year-end: 06/30/2022
Battery Mfr; Owned by GS Yuasa International Ltd. & by Atlas Group of Companies
N.A.I.C.S.: 335910
Ali H. Shirazi *(Pres & CEO)*

Fiamm-GS S.p.A. (2)
Viale Europa 63, 36075, Montecchio Maggiore, Italy
Tel.: (39) 0444709350
Batteries Mfr
N.A.I.C.S.: 335910

Subsidiary (Non-US):

GS Battery Vietnam Co., Ltd. (2)
No 18 No 3 street, Vietnam - Singapore Industrial Park Binh Hoa ward, Thuan An, Binh Duong, Vietnam
Tel.: (84) 2743756360
Storage Battery Mfr
N.A.I.C.S.: 335910

PT. GS Battery Inc. (2)
Jl Laksda Yos Sudarso Sunter, Jakarta, 14350, Indonesia
Tel.: (62) 216518979
Web Site: http://www.gs.astra.co.id
Sales Range: $350-399.9 Million
Emp.: 1,700
Storage Battery Mfr
N.A.I.C.S.: 335910

Shandong Huari Battery Co., Ltd. (2)
2nd Industry Road Shangqui, Zhangzhu, 250200, Shandong, China
Tel.: (86) 531 3256306
Web Site: http://www.huaribattery.com
Sales Range: $25-49.9 Million
Emp.: 100
Storage Battery Mfr
N.A.I.C.S.: 335910

GS Yuasa Lithium Power, Inc (1)
1150 Northmeadow Pkwy Ste 118, Roswell, GA 30076
Web Site: https://www.gsyuasa-lp.com
Sales Range: $25-49.9 Million
Emp.: 25
Battery Mfr
N.A.I.C.S.: 335910

GS Yuasa Power Electronics Ltd. (1)
55-2 Hatadacho Nishikyogoku Ukyo, Kyoto, 615-0824, Japan
Tel.: (81) 753120621
Power Supply Device Mfr
N.A.I.C.S.: 334419

GS Yuasa Technology Ltd. (1)
1-37 Nagatanocho, Fukuchiyama, 620-0853, Kyoto, Japan
Tel.: (81) 773202630
Web Site: https://www.gs-yuasa.com
Sales Range: $50-74.9 Million
Mfr & Sales of Batteries
N.A.I.C.S.: 335910

Global Battery Co., Ltd (1)
Global Bldg 708-8 Yeoksam Dong, Gangnam-gu, Seoul, 135-919, Korea (South)
Tel.: (82) 2 3451 6201
Web Site: http://www.gbattery.com
Battery Mfr
N.A.I.C.S.: 335910
Y. S. Park *(Gen Mgr)*

PT. Yuasa Battery Indonesia (1)
Jln MH Thamrin Kebon Nanas, PO Box 493, Pinang, Tangerang, 15143, Banten, Indonesia
Tel.: (62) 2155757205
Web Site: https://www.yuasabattery.co.id
Emp.: 150
Battery Mfr
N.A.I.C.S.: 335910
Shicato Yuasa *(Pres)*

Taiwan Yuasa Battery Co., Ltd. (1)
No 11 Ln 227 Fuying Rd, Xinzhuang Dist, New Taipei City, 242, Taiwan
Tel.: (886) 229018261
Web Site: https://www.yuasa.com.tw
Battery Mfr
N.A.I.C.S.: 335910

Tianjin Yuasa Batteries Co., Ltd. (1)
No 9 Saida 8th Road, Xiqing Economic Development Area, Tianjin, 300385, China
Tel.: (86) 2223888980
Web Site: http://www.yuasa.com.cn
Battery Mfr
N.A.I.C.S.: 335910

Yuasa (Tianjin) Technology Ltd. (1)
No 99 Haitong Avenue Export Processing Zone TEDA, Tianjin, China
Tel.: (86) 22 66230088
Web Site: http://www.yuasa-tech.com
Emp.: 1,500
Rechargeable Batteries Mfr & Distr
N.A.I.C.S.: 335910

Yuasa Battery (East Africa) Ltd. (1)
19 Vingunguti Industrial Area Nyerere Road, PO Box 40026, Dar es Salaam, Tanzania
Tel.: (255) 22 2864971
Web Site: http://www.synarge.com
Emp.: 103
Battery Mfr
N.A.I.C.S.: 335910

Shekhar Kanabar *(CEO)*

Yuasa Battery (Malaysia) Sdn. Bhd. (1)
Lot 1385 Kawasan Tikam Batu, 08600, Sungai Petani, Kedah, Malaysia
Tel.: (60) 44388806
Web Site: https://www.gs-yuasa.com.my
Sales Range: $25-49.9 Million
Emp.: 200
Battery Mfr
N.A.I.C.S.: 335910
Yussof Latiff *(Mng Dir)*

Plant (Domestic):

Yuasa Battery (Malaysia) Sdn. Bhd. - Manufacturing Plant (2)
Lot 1385 Kawasan Perusahaan Tikam Batu, 08600, Sungai Petani, Kedah, Malaysia
Tel.: (60) 4 4388806
Web Site: http://www.gs-yuasa.com.my
Sales Range: $50-74.9 Million
Emp.: 200
Battery Mfr
N.A.I.C.S.: 335910

Subsidiary (Domestic):

Yuasa Power Systems (M) Sdn Bhd (2)
Lot 10 Kawasan Perusahaan Tikam Batu, 08600, Sungai Petani, Kedah, Malaysia
Tel.: (60) 4 4387526
Sales Range: $25-49.9 Million
Emp.: 8
Industrial Battery Mfr
N.A.I.C.S.: 335910
Mohd Yussof Latiff *(Mng Dir)*

Yuasa Battery (Shunde) Co., Ltd. (1)
Fu'an Industrial Zone, Leliu Town Shunde District, Foshan, Guangdong, China
Tel.: (86) 75725639480
Web Site: https://www.yuasa-sd.com
Emp.: 800
Battery Mfr
N.A.I.C.S.: 335910

Yuasa Battery Europe Ltd. (1)
Unit 13 Hunts Rise South Marston Industrial Estate, Swindon, SN3 4TG, Wiltshire, United Kingdom
Tel.: (44) 8708500312
Web Site: http://www.yuasa-battery.co.uk
Sales Range: $25-49.9 Million
Emp.: 60
Battery Mfr
N.A.I.C.S.: 335910

Yuasa Membrane Systems Co., Ltd. (1)
4-8-1 Ohmori Kita, Ohta-ku, Tokyo, 143-0016, Japan
Tel.: (81) 354717310
Web Site: http://www.ymst.co.jp
Sales Range: $25-49.9 Million
Emp.: 31
Membrane Filtering System Mfr
N.A.I.C.S.: 339999
Shoji Ogura *(Pres)*

GS-ELEKTROANLAGENMONTAGE GMBH

Buhlaer Weg 6, 99759, Nordhausen, Germany
Tel.: (49) 3633844600
Web Site: http://www.gs-elektroanlagen.de
Year Founded: 1990
Rev.: $14,581,803
Emp.: 230
Electronic Components Mfr
N.A.I.C.S.: 335999
Peter Gornert *(Co-Partner)*

GSB FINANCE LIMITED

78/80 Ali Chambers Tamarind Lane Fort, Mumbai, 400 001, Maharastra, India
Tel.: (91) 2266338660
Web Site: https://www.gsbgroup.co.in
Year Founded: 2001
511543—(BOM)
Rev.: $390,588

GSB FINANCE LIMITED

GSB Finance Limited—(Continued)
Assets: $2,254,349
Liabilities: $1,524,230
Net Worth: $730,119
Earnings: $8,848
Fiscal Year-end: 03/31/23
Financial Services
N.A.I.C.S.: 523999
Giridharlal S. Biyani *(Chm & CFO)*

GSD HOLDING A.S.
Aydinevler Mahallesi Kaptan Rifat Sokak No 3, Kucukyali Maltepe, 34854, Istanbul, Turkiye
Tel.: (90) 216 587 9000 TR
Web Site: http://www.gsdholding.com.tr
Year Founded: 1986
Emp.: 120
Financial Holding Company
N.A.I.C.S.: 551111
Mehmet Turgut Yilmaz *(Chm)*

Subsidiaries:

GSD Denizcilik Gayrimenkul Insaat Sanayi Ve Ticaret AS (1)
Aydinevler Mahallesi Kaptan Rifat Sokak No 3, Istanbul, 34854, Turkiye
Tel.: (90) 2165879000
Rev.: $9,564,455
Assets: $43,485,753
Liabilities: $11,188,430
Net Worth: $32,297,324
Earnings: $6,615,558
Emp.: 10
Fiscal Year-end: 12/31/2022
Equipment Rental Services
N.A.I.C.S.: 532490
Mehmet Turgut Yilmaz *(Chm)*

GSD Dis Ticaret A.S. (1)
Aydinevler Mahallesi Kaptan Rifat Sokak No 3, Kucukyali Maltepe, 34854, Istanbul, Turkiye
Tel.: (90) 216 587 9000
Web Site: http://www.gsddisticaret.com.tr
International Trade Financing & Transaction Processing Services
N.A.I.C.S.: 522299
Mehmet Turgut Yilmaz *(Chm)*

GSD Egitim Vakfi (1)
Aydinevler Mahallesi Kaptan Rifat Sokak No 3, Kucukyali Maltepe, 34854, Istanbul, Turkiye
Tel.: (90) 216 587 9000
Educational Grantmaking Foundation
N.A.I.C.S.: 813211

GSD Egitim Vakfi Bahcelievler Ilkokulu (1)
Kocasinan Merkez Mh Karadeniz Cd No12, Bahcelievler, Turkiye
Tel.: (90) 2124512687
Web Site: http://www.gsd-ilkokulu.meb.k12.tr
Education Services
N.A.I.C.S.: 611310

GSD Yatirim Bankasi A.S. (1)
Aydinevler Mahallesi Kaptan Rifat Sokak No 3, Kucukyali Maltepe, 34854, Istanbul, Turkiye
Tel.: (90) 216 587 9000
Web Site: http://www.gsdbank.com.tr
Emp.: 130
Investment Banking
N.A.I.C.S.: 523150
Engin Kams *(Gen Mgr)*

Tekstil Faktoring A.S. (1)
Aydinevler Mahallesi Kaptan Rifat Sokak No 3, Kucukyali Maltepe, 34854, Istanbul, Turkiye
Tel.: (90) 216 587 9000
Web Site: http://www.tekstilfaktoring.com.tr
Credit Risk Protection & Short-Term Financing Services
N.A.I.C.S.: 522299

GSE CO., LTD.
412-30 Guamdumun-ro, Sacheon-eup, Sacheon, Gyeongsangnam-do, Korea (South)
Tel.: (82) 558550102
Web Site: http://www.yesgse.com
Year Founded: 1989
053050—(KRS)
Rev.: $132,398,250
Assets: $156,979,838
Liabilities: $89,008,304
Net Worth: $67,971,534
Earnings: $4,527,088
Emp.: 88
Fiscal Year-end: 12/31/22
Wireless Network Security Technology
N.A.I.C.S.: 334112
Su-Eun Yoo *(Chm)*

GSEVEN
205 Anupam BhawanCommercial Complex Near Akash Cinemas Azadpur, Delhi, India
Tel.: (91) 1147612345
Web Site: https://www.gseven.in
Year Founded: 2004
2937—(TPE)
Rev.: $102,667,825
Assets: $67,481,377
Liabilities: $44,518,203
Net Worth: $22,963,174
Earnings: $3,681,495
Fiscal Year-end: 12/31/20
Professional Training Services
N.A.I.C.S.: 611430
C. A. Dinesh Gupta *(Chm)*

GSG GROUP INC.
Haagwinde 20, 5262 KZ, Vught, Netherlands
Tel.: (31) 623407058 NV
Web Site: http://gsggroupinc.com
Year Founded: 2014
Assets: $200
Liabilities: $114,301
Net Worth: ($114,101)
Earnings: ($16,076)
Emp.: 1
Fiscal Year-end: 12/31/22
Ribbon Printing Services
N.A.I.C.S.: 313310
Gim Hooi Ooi *(CMO)*

GSH CORPORATION LIMITED
No 28-01 PLUS 20 Cecil Street, Singapore, 498796, Singapore
Tel.: (65) 68411000
Web Site: https://www.gshcorporation.com
BDX—(SES)
Rev.: $118,622,283
Assets: $923,642,354
Liabilities: $561,879,118
Net Worth: $361,763,235
Earnings: ($6,272,817)
Fiscal Year-end: 12/31/23
Electronic Products Sales
N.A.I.C.S.: 423620
Gilbert Guan Hui Ee *(CEO)*

Subsidiaries:

JEL Marketing (Vietnam) Joint Venture Co., Ltd. (1)
1st Floor 62A Pham Ngoc Thach Street, Ward 6 District 3, Ho Chi Minh City, Vietnam (49%)
Tel.: (84) 38 209 903
Web Site: http://www.icenter.com.vn
Photographic & Information Technology Products Distr
N.A.I.C.S.: 423620

Rainbow Properties Sdn Bhd (1)
1 Sutera Harbour Boulevard Sutera Harbour, 88100, Kota Kinabalu, Sabah, Malaysia
Tel.: (60) 88318888
Web Site: http://www.suteraatmantanani.com
Golf Course & Country Club Services
N.A.I.C.S.: 713910

Sutera Harbour Resort Sdn Bhd (1)
1 Sutera Harbour Boulevard Sutera Harbour, 88100, Kota Kinabalu, Sabah, Malaysia
Tel.: (60) 8 831 8888
Web Site: https://www.suteraharbour.com
Holding Company
N.A.I.C.S.: 551112
Gerard Tan *(Deputy CEO)*

GSI CREOS CORPORATION
16Fl Shiba-Koen First Bldg 3-8-2 Shiba, Minato-ku, Tokyo, 105-0014, Japan
Tel.: (81) 352111800 JP
Web Site: https://www.gsi.co.jp
Year Founded: 1931
8101—(TKS)
Rev.: $966,342,340
Assets: $497,970,960
Liabilities: $316,526,460
Net Worth: $181,444,500
Earnings: $13,345,590
Emp.: 658
Fiscal Year-end: 03/31/24
Textiles & Chemicals Mfr & Distr
N.A.I.C.S.: 313310
Tadaaki Yoshinaga *(Pres & CEO)*

Subsidiaries:

Beijing GSI Hosiery Co., Ltd. (1)
1 1st Road Niushan Industrial Zone, Shunyi, Beijing, 101301, China
Tel.: (86) 1069412634
Sales Range: $50-74.9 Million
Emp.: 200
Hosiery Mfr
N.A.I.C.S.: 315120

CITIC GSI Tomida Group Co., Ltd. (1)
The Business Building Second Happiness Village, Chayang District, Beijing, China
Tel.: (86) 1064673002
Textiles Mfr & Distr
N.A.I.C.S.: 313310

Central Scientific Commerce, Inc. (1)
1-28-6 Kameido, Koto-ku, Tokyo, 136-0071, Japan
Tel.: (81) 356278150
Web Site: https://cscjp.co.jp
Emp.: 58
Scientific & Analytical Instrument Whslr
N.A.I.C.S.: 423490

Creos Apparel Corporation (1)
7-22-17 Nishi-Gotanda, Shinagawa-ku, Tokyo, Japan
Tel.: (81) 334928481
Women Apparel Mfr & Whslr
N.A.I.C.S.: 315250

Daisan Shika Kogyo Co., Ltd. (1)
229-4 Fukawa, Kitakatsushikagun Sugitomachi, Saitama, Japan
Tel.: (81) 480365111
Paper Sleeve Mfr & Whslr
N.A.I.C.S.: 322220

G-Mark, Inc. (1)
2-3-1 Kudan Minami, Chiyoda-ku, Tokyo, Japan
Tel.: (81) 352111862
Firework & Furniture Whslr
N.A.I.C.S.: 423210

GSI (Shenzhen) Limited (1)
Room 922-923 9/F Shenzhen Kerry Center, 2008 Renminnan Road, Shenzhen, 518001, China
Tel.: (86) 75582306900
Textile Material Distr
N.A.I.C.S.: 424310

GSI ABROS Co., Ltd. (1)
9-9 Nihonbashi Hisamatsu-cho, Chuo-ku, Tokyo, 103-0005, Japan
Tel.: (81) 366619163
Web Site: https://gsi-abros.co.jp
Emp.: 14
Textile Material Distr
N.A.I.C.S.: 424310

GSI Creos (Beijing) Co., Ltd (1)
Web Site: http://www.gsi.co.jp

INTERNATIONAL PUBLIC

Textile Products Mfr & Distr
N.A.I.C.S.: 314999

GSI Creos (Thailand) Co., Ltd. (1)
62 The Millennia Tower 23rd Fl Room 2302 Soi Langsuan Lumpini, Patumwan, Bangkok, 10330, Thailand
Tel.: (66) 20553642
Textile Material Distr
N.A.I.C.S.: 424310

GSI Creos Brasil Ltda (1)
Avenida Paulista 2001 - Conjs 214 and 216, Cerqueira Cesar, 01311-931, Sao Paulo, Brazil
Tel.: (55) 1132664133
Web Site: https://gsi.com.br
Textile Products Distr
N.A.I.C.S.: 424350

GSI Creos Fiber & Textile Pinghu Co., Ltd. (1)
South Tower West-Gate No1888 Huanbei-2 Road, Pinghu Development Zone, Pinghu, 314200, Zhejiang, China
Tel.: (86) 57385079236
Textile Material Distr
N.A.I.C.S.: 424310

GSI Creos Korea Co., Ltd. (1)
Tel.: (82) 27774855
Web Site: http://www.gsi.co.jp
Sales Range: $25-49.9 Million
Emp.: 5
Textile Products Import & Distr
N.A.I.C.S.: 315250

GSI Europe-Import & Export GmbH (1)
Louise-Dumont Str 31, 40211, Dusseldorf, Germany (100%)
Tel.: (49) 2111665940
Web Site: https://www.gsieurope.de
Sales Range: $50-74.9 Million
Emp.: 9
Textile Mfr of Legwear, Innerwear & Outerwear Apparel
N.A.I.C.S.: 313310
Taijiro Uemura *(CEO)*

GSI Holding Corporation (1)
1065 Ave Of The Americas 32nd Fl, New York, NY 10018 (100%)
Tel.: (212) 684-5760
Web Site: http://www.gsicexim.com
Semiconductor Mfr
N.A.I.C.S.: 313310

Subsidiary (Domestic):

GSI Exim America Inc. (2)
1065 Avenue of the Americas, New York, NY 10018 (100%)
Tel.: (212) 684-5760
Web Site: https://www.gsiexim.com
Sales Range: $50-74.9 Million
Emp.: 16
Import & Export of Textiles
N.A.I.C.S.: 424690
Hiroyuki Matsuura *(Co-Pres)*

GSI Marulontex Co., Ltd. (1)
2nd floor FRAME Nihonbashi Building 9-9 Nihonbashi Hisamatsu-cho, Chuo-ku, Tokyo, 103-0005, Japan
Tel.: (81) 366616808
Web Site: https://www.marulon.co.jp
Emp.: 86
Textile & Fabric Finishing Mfr & Distr
N.A.I.C.S.: 313220

GSI Trading Hong Kong Limited (1)
Suite No 2B 9/F Tower 5 33 Canton Road, Tsimshatsui, Kowloon, China (Hong Kong) (100%)
Tel.: (852) 23170338
Web Site: http://www.gsi.co.jp
Sales Range: $50-74.9 Million
Emp.: 20
International Trading Services
N.A.I.C.S.: 425120

Gunsan Exportadora E Importadora Ltda. (1)
Av Paulista 2001 Fl 2 Rm 214 To 216, 01311, Sao Paulo, SP, Brazil (100%)
Tel.: (55) 1132664133
Web Site: https://www.dsi.so.jp
Sales Range: Less than $1 Million
Emp.: 4

AND PRIVATE COMPANIES

GSK PLC

Textile Mfr of Legwear, Innerwear & Outerwear Apparel
N.A.I.C.S.: 425120

Nisshin Kohgyo Corporation (1)
901-3 Kuriyama Hidaka-cho, Toyooka, Hyogo, Japan
Tel.: (81) 796440039
Textile Product Mfr & Whslr
N.A.I.C.S.: 314999

Office-Mate Corporation (1)
2-3-1 Kudan Minami, Chiyoda-ku, Tokyo, Japan
Tel.: (81) 352112185
Real Estate Manangement Services
N.A.I.C.S.: 531311

PT. GSI Creos Indonesia (1)
Plaza Sentral 10th Fl, Jl Jend Sudirman No 47, Jakarta, 12930, Indonesia
Tel.: (62) 215702195
Textile Material Distr
N.A.I.C.S.: 424310

Sakura Bussan Co., Ltd. (1)
7-5-4 Ginza Mori Building 5F S, Chuo-ku, Tokyo, 104-0061, Japan
Tel.: (81) 358600936
Web Site: https://sakura-bussan.co.jp
Printing & Packaging Product Mfr & Distr
N.A.I.C.S.: 326112

Sophia Corporation (1)
2117-7 Akasegawa, Akune, Kagoshima, Japan
Tel.: (81) 996731511
Textile Product Mfr & Whslr
N.A.I.C.S.: 314999

Tajima Gosen Co., Ltd. (1)
884 Nonosho Hidaka-cho, Toyooka, Hyogo, Japan
Tel.: (81) 796420912
Grey Yarn Whslr
N.A.I.C.S.: 424310

GSK PLC
980 Great West Road, Brentford, TW8 9GS, Middlesex, United Kingdom
Tel.: (44) 2080475000   UK
Web Site: https://www.gsk.com
Year Founded: 2000
GSK—(NYSE)
Rev.: $38,283,261,803
Assets: $74,482,453,926
Liabilities: $58,331,229,488
Net Worth: $16,151,224,438
Earnings: $6,220,651,351
Emp.: 70,244
Fiscal Year-end: 12/31/23
Biotechnology Research & Development Services
N.A.I.C.S.: 541714
Philip Thomson *(Pres-Global Affairs)*

Subsidiaries:

BELLUS Health Inc. (1)
275 Armand Frappier Blvd, Laval, H7V 4A7, QC, Canada
Tel.: (450) 680-4525
Web Site: http://www.bellushealth.com
Rev.: $16,000
Assets: $407,820,000
Liabilities: $16,808,000
Net Worth: $391,012,000
Earnings: ($76,080,000)
Emp.: 74
Fiscal Year-end: 12/31/2022
Biopharmaceutical Drugs for Central Nervous System Disorders
N.A.I.C.S.: 325412
Denis Garceau *(Sr VP-Drug Dev)*

Burroughs Wellcome (India) Ltd. (1)
252 Dr Annie Besant Road Worli, Mumbai, 400030, Maharashtra, India
Tel.: (91) 22 2495 9595
Pharmaceuticals Mfr
N.A.I.C.S.: 325412
D. S. Parekh *(Chm)*

Cellzome GmbH (1)
Meyerhofstrasse 1, 69117, Heidelberg, Germany
Tel.: (49) 6221137570

Pharmaceuticals Product Mfr
N.A.I.C.S.: 325412

Dealcyber Limited (1)
980 Great West Road, Brentford, TW8 9GS, Middlesex, United Kingdom
Group Property Management Services
N.A.I.C.S.: 531390

Domantis Ltd. (1)
980 Great West Road, Brentford, TW8 9GS, Middlesex, United Kingdom
Tel.: (44) 1223226900
Sales Range: $50-74.9 Million
Emp.: 68
Pharmaceuticals
N.A.I.C.S.: 325412

Duncan Pharmaceuticals Philippines Inc. (1)
2266 Chino Roces Avenue, Makati, 1231, Philippines
Tel.: (63) 28920761
Web Site: http://www.gsk.com.ph
Pharmaceuticals Mfr
N.A.I.C.S.: 325412

Etex Farmaceutica Limitada (1)
Av Andres Bello 2457 Costanera Center Torre 2 Piso 20, Providencia, 7510689, Santiago, Chile   (100%)
Tel.: (56) 23829000
Sales Range: $50-74.9 Million
Emp.: 120
Pharmaceuticals Mfr
N.A.I.C.S.: 325412

Eumecom Medizin Information Fortbilding GmbH (1)
Heiden Kanpsweg 82, 20097, Hamburg, Germany   (100%)
Tel.: (49) 4041523540
Sales Range: $25-49.9 Million
Emp.: 120
Pharmaceutical Research College
N.A.I.C.S.: 611310

Fixedspring Limited (1)
980 Great West Rd, Brentford, TW8 9GS, Mddx, United Kingdom
Pharmaceuticals Mfr
N.A.I.C.S.: 325412

GSK Azerbaijan (1)
Landmark 1 96 Nizami Street, Baku, AZ1010, Azerbaijan
Tel.: (994) 12 49766 01
Web Site: http://www.gsk.com
Sales Range: $25-49.9 Million
Emp.: 35
Pharmaceutical Products Distr
N.A.I.C.S.: 424210

GSK Belarus (1)
Office 400 7a Voronianskogo Street, 220039, Minsk, Belarus
Tel.: (375) 173742016
Sales Range: $25-49.9 Million
Emp.: 50
Pharmaceutical Products Distr
N.A.I.C.S.: 424210

GSK Business Service Centre Sdn Bhd (1)
Level 6 Quill 9 112 Jalan Professor Khoo Kay Kim, 46300, Petaling Jaya, Selangor, Malaysia
Tel.: (60) 376289000
Emp.: 1,000
Pharmaceuticals Product Mfr
N.A.I.C.S.: 339112

GSK CH Kazakhstan LLP (1)
32A Manas st, Almaty, 050008, Kazakhstan
Tel.: (7) 7272446999
Emp.: 130
Pharmaceuticals Product Mfr
N.A.I.C.S.: 339112

GSK Commercial Sp. z o.o. (1)
Tul Rzymowskiego 53, 02-697, Warsaw, Poland
Tel.: (48) 225769000
Pharmaceutical Products Distr
N.A.I.C.S.: 424210

GSK Consumer Healthcare (1)
Graha Paramita 5th floor Jalan Denpasar Raya Blok D-2 Kuningan, Jakarta, 12940, Indonesia
Tel.: (62) 212523490

Pharmaceutical Products Distr
N.A.I.C.S.: 424210
Brian McNamara *(CEO)*

GSK Consumer Healthcare Levice, s.r.o. (1)
Priemyselny Park Gena ul E Sachsa 4-6, Region Nitra, 934 01, Levice, Slovakia
Tel.: (421) 366293313
Pharmaceuticals Product Mfr
N.A.I.C.S.: 339112

GSK Consumer Healthcare Trinidad & Tobago Limited (1)
5th Floor Algico Plaza 91-93 St Vincent Street, Port of Spain, Trinidad & Tobago
Tel.: (868) 6277294
Pharmaceuticals Product Mfr
N.A.I.C.S.: 339112

GSK Cyprus (1)
Kennedy Avenue No 12-14 Fourth Floor, 1087, Nicosia, Cyprus
Tel.: (357) 80070017
Pharmaceutical Products Distr
N.A.I.C.S.: 424210

GSK Kazakhstan LLP (1)
273 N Nazarbayev avenue BU USKO Floor 3, 050059, Almaty, Kazakhstan
Tel.: (7) 7272582892
Emp.: 130
Pharmaceuticals Product Mfr
N.A.I.C.S.: 339112

GSK Macedonia (1)
Anton Popov 1/4 Mezzanine, 1000, Skopje, North Macedonia
Web Site: http://wwwgsk.com
Pharmaceutical Products Research Services
N.A.I.C.S.: 541715

GSK Malta (1)
1 1st floor De La Cruz Avenue, Qormi, QRM 2458, Malta
Tel.: (356) 80065004
Pharmaceutical Products Distr
N.A.I.C.S.: 424210

GSK Moldova (1)
60/2 Pushkin Street, Chisinau, MD- 2005, Moldova
Tel.: (373) 22234717
Sales Range: $25-49.9 Million
Emp.: 22
Pharmaceuticals Product Mfr
N.A.I.C.S.: 325412

GSK PSC Poland sp. z o.o. (1)
Ul Grunwaldzkiej 189, 60-322, Poznan, Poland
Tel.: (48) 618601000
Web Site: https://pl.gsk.com
Pharmaceutical Products Mfr & Distr
N.A.I.C.S.: 325412

GSK Services Sp. z o.o. (1)
ul Grunwaldzka 189, 60-322, Poznan, Poland
Tel.: (48) 618601000
Pharmaceutical Products Distr
N.A.I.C.S.: 424210

GSK Uzbekistan (1)
4a Afrosiab Street, 100031, Tashkent, Uzbekistan
Tel.: (998) 712525461
Sales Range: $25-49.9 Million
Emp.: 29
Pharmaceutical Products Research Services
N.A.I.C.S.: 541715
Leyli Mirzamukhamedova *(Country Mgr)*

GSK Vaccines GmbH (1)
Emil-von-Behring-Strasse 76, 35041, Marburg, Germany
Tel.: (49) 64213860
Pharmaceuticals Product Mfr
N.A.I.C.S.: 339112

GSK Vaccines Institute for Global Health S.r.l. (1)
Via Fiorentina 1, 53100, Siena, Italy
Tel.: (39) 0577243111
Pharmaceutical Product Mfr
N.A.I.C.S.: 339112

GSK d.o.o. (1)
Ameriska ulica 8, 1000, Ljubljana, Slovenia

Tel.: (386) 12802500
Pharmaceuticals Product Mfr
N.A.I.C.S.: 339112

Galvani Bioelectronics Limited (1)
Gunnels Wood Road, Stevenage, SG1 2NY, Hertfordshire, United Kingdom
Tel.: (44) 8003688514
Biochemical Product Mfr
N.A.I.C.S.: 325414
Adam Roth *(VP & Head-Bus Ops)*

Glaxo Finance Bermuda Limited (1)
PO Box HM 1072, Hamilton, HMEX, Bermuda
Tel.: (441) 2957237
Web Site: http://www.gsk.com
Group Finance Services
N.A.I.C.S.: 525990

Glaxo Wellcome (Kenya) Limited (1)
Dakar Road Industrial Area, PO Box 18288, Nairobi, Kenya   (100%)
Tel.: (254) 2532461
Sales Range: $50-74.9 Million
Emp.: 106
Pharmaceuticals Mfr & Distr
N.A.I.C.S.: 325412

Glaxo Wellcome Ceylon Limited (1)
121 Galle Rd, Kaldemulla, Moratuwa, Sri Lanka   (81%)
Tel.: (94) 112636341
Sales Range: $50-74.9 Million
Emp.: 200
Pharmaceuticals Mfr & Distr
N.A.I.C.S.: 325412
Stuart Chapman *(Mng Dir)*

Glaxo Wellcome International B.V. (1)
Huis Ter Heideweg 62, Zeist, 3705, Netherlands   (100%)
Tel.: (31) 306938100
Web Site: http://www.gsk.nl
Sales Range: $150-199.9 Million
Emp.: 400
Holding Company
N.A.I.C.S.: 551112

Subsidiary (Domestic):

Glaxo Wellcome Investments B.V. (2)
Huis Ter Heideweg 62, Zeist, 3705, Netherlands   (100%)
Tel.: (31) 306938100
Web Site: http://www.gsk.nl
Sales Range: $75-99.9 Million
Emp.: 200
Investment Management
N.A.I.C.S.: 523940

Glaxo Wellcome S.A. (1)
Salto 1105, Montevideo, 11200, Uruguay
Tel.: (598) 24198333
Web Site: http://www.gsk.com
Sales Range: $25-49.9 Million
Emp.: 21
Mfr of Pharmaceuticals
N.A.I.C.S.: 325412

Glaxo Wellcome Taiwan Limited (1)
24F No 66 Section 1 Zhong Xiao West Rd Shin Kong Mitsukoshi, Zhongzheng District, Taipei, 100, Taiwan   (100%)
Tel.: (886) 223818866
Sales Range: $50-74.9 Million
Emp.: 200
Pharmaceuticals Mfr & Distr
N.A.I.C.S.: 325412

GlaxoSmithKline (1)
5 Cresent Dr, Philadelphia, PA 19112   (100%)
Tel.: (215) 751-4000
Web Site: http://www.gsk.com
Pharmaceuticals Mfr
N.A.I.C.S.: 325412
Priti Hegde *(Mgr-Disease & Biomarker Transcriptomics)*

GlaxoSmithKline (1)
Sales Range: $200-249.9 Million
Emp.: 1,000
Pharmaceuticals Mfr & Distr
N.A.I.C.S.: 325412

GlaxoSmithKline (1)
5 Moore Drive PO Box 13398, Research Triangle Park, NC 27709-3398   (100%)

GSK PLC

GSK plc—(Continued)
Tel.: (919) 483-2100
Web Site: http://www.gsk.com
Sales Range: $1-4.9 Billion
Emp.: 4,500
Pharmaceuticals Mfr & Distr
N.A.I.C.S.: 325412

GlaxoSmithKline (1)
1500 K St NW Ste 650, Washington, DC 20005-1209 **(100%)**
Tel.: (202) 783-1277
Sales Range: $25-49.9 Million
Emp.: 25
Pharmaceuticals Mfr
N.A.I.C.S.: 325412

GlaxoSmithKline (1)
266 Kifissias Ave Halandri, 15232, Athens, Greece **(100%)**
Tel.: (30) 2106882100
Sales Range: $50-74.9 Million
Emp.: 200
Pharmaceuticals Mfr & Distr
N.A.I.C.S.: 325412

GlaxoSmithKline (1)
1 Pioneer Sector 1, Jurong, 628413, Singapore **(100%)**
Tel.: (65) 68612111
Web Site: http://www.gsk.com
Sales Range: $125-149.9 Million
Emp.: 500
Pharmaceuticals Mfr & Distr
N.A.I.C.S.: 325412

GlaxoSmithKline (1)
Stockley Park West, Uxbridge, UB11 1BT, Mddx, United Kingdom **(100%)**
Tel.: (44) 2089909000
Web Site: http://www.gsk.com
Sales Range: $450-499.9 Million
Emp.: 2,000
Pharmaceuticals Mfr
N.A.I.C.S.: 325412
Jonathan R. Symonds *(Chm)*

GlaxoSmithKline (1)
12 River Walk City West, Dublin, 24, Co Cork, Ireland **(100%)**
Tel.: (353) 14955000
Sales Range: $50-74.9 Million
Emp.: 150
N.A.I.C.S.: 325412

GlaxoSmithKline (1)
2200 Renaissance Blvd Ste 145, King of Prussia, PA 19406
Tel.: (610) 239-5200
Web Site: http://www.gsk.com
Sales Range: $25-49.9 Million
Emp.: 50
Pharmaceuticals Mfr & Distr
N.A.I.C.S.: 325412

GlaxoSmithKline (1)
65 Industrial St S, Clifton, NJ 07012-1709
Tel.: (973) 778-9000
Consumer Health Care Product Mfr
N.A.I.C.S.: 325620

GlaxoSmithKline (1)
6 Ridge Ct, Medford, NJ 08055-9700
Tel.: (856) 762-0300
Sales Range: $25-49.9 Million
Emp.: 3
Pharmaceuticals Distr
N.A.I.C.S.: 325412

GlaxoSmithKline (1)
1250 S Collegeville Rd, Collegeville, PA 19426-2990
Tel.: (610) 917-7000
Web Site: http://www.gsk.com
Sales Range: $350-399.9 Million
Emp.: 1,400
Biological Research
N.A.I.C.S.: 541720

GlaxoSmithKline (1)
2929 Walnut St Ste 1700, Philadelphia, PA 19104-2640
Tel.: (215) 823-3200
Testing Laboratories
N.A.I.C.S.: 541380

GlaxoSmithKline (1)
801 River Rd, Conshohocken, PA 19428-2631
Tel.: (610) 270-7125

Sales Range: $25-49.9 Million
Emp.: 200
Pharmaceuticals Mfr
N.A.I.C.S.: 541720
Kristen Neese *(VP-Comm)*

GlaxoSmithKline (1)
320 S Broadway, Saint Louis, MO 63102-2800
Tel.: (314) 621-2304
Sales Range: $150-199.9 Million
Emp.: 275
Pharmaceuticals Mfr
N.A.I.C.S.: 325412

GlaxoSmithKline (1)
184 Liberty Corner Rd, Warren, NJ 07509 **(100%)**
Tel.: (973) 889-2100
Web Site: http://www.gsk.com
Sales Range: $50-74.9 Million
Emp.: 400
Drug Store Operations
N.A.I.C.S.: 621511

GlaxoSmithKline (China) Investment Co. Ltd (1)
Tel.: (86) 1059252888 **(100%)**
Web Site: http://www.gsk-china.com
Sales Range: $125-149.9 Million
Emp.: 400
Pharmaceuticals Product Mfr
N.A.I.C.S.: 325412

GlaxoSmithKline (China) Limited (1)
9F Tower A Ocean International Centre No 56 Mid 4th East Ring Rd, Beijing, 100025, Chaoyang, China
Tel.: (86) 10 5925 2888
Web Site: http://www.gsk-china.com
Sales Range: $25-49.9 Million
Emp.: 100
Pharmaceuticals Mfr & Distr
N.A.I.C.S.: 325412

GlaxoSmithKline (China) R&D Co., Ltd. (1)
Tel.: (86) 2161590600
Web Site: http://www.gsk-china.com
Medical Research & Development Services
N.A.I.C.S.: 541715

GlaxoSmithKline (GSK) S.R.L. (1)
Opera Center 1 Costache Negri Street no 1-5 District 5, 050552, Bucharest, Romania
Tel.: (40) 213028208
Pharmaceuticals Product Mfr
N.A.I.C.S.: 325412

GlaxoSmithKline (Ireland) Limited (1)
12 Riverwalk Citywest Business Campus, Dublin, 24, Rathfarnham, Ireland
Tel.: (353) 14955000
Web Site: https://gskpro.com
Sales Range: $50-74.9 Million
Emp.: 150
Mfr of Pharmaceuticals
N.A.I.C.S.: 325412

GlaxoSmithKline (Malta) Limited (1)
1 1st Floor De La Cruz Avenue, Qormi, QRM 2458, Malta
Tel.: (356) 21238131
Pharmaceuticals Product Mfr
N.A.I.C.S.: 325412

GlaxoSmithKline (NZ) Ltd. (1)
(100%)
Tel.: (64) 93672900
Web Site: http://www.gsk.co.nz
Sales Range: $25-49.9 Million
Emp.: 60
Pharmaceuticals Mfr & Distr
N.A.I.C.S.: 325412

Division (Domestic):

GlaxoSmithKline (NZ) Ltd. Consumer Health Div. (2)
Level 11 Zurich House 21 Queen Street, Private Bag 106600, Auckland, 1010, New Zealand **(100%)**
Tel.: (64) 9367 2900
Web Site: http://www.gsk.co.nz
Sales Range: $25-49.9 Million
Pharmaceuticals & Toiletries Mfr & Distr
N.A.I.C.S.: 325412

GlaxoSmithKline (Proprietary) Limited (1)

57 Sloane St The Tempest Slashing Meadows, Bryanston, 2021, South Africa **(100%)**
Tel.: (27) 117456000
Web Site: http://www.gsk.com
Sales Range: $50-74.9 Million
Emp.: 250
Pharmaceuticals Mfr & Distr
N.A.I.C.S.: 325412

GlaxoSmithKline (Thailand) Limited (1)
55 Wave Place Building 12th Floor Wireless Road, Lumpini Patumwan, Bangkok, 10330, Thailand **(100%)**
Tel.: (66) 26593000
Web Site: https://gskpro.com
Sales Range: $125-149.9 Million
Emp.: 300
Mfr of Researched Pharmaceuticals
N.A.I.C.S.: 325412

GlaxoSmithKline (Tianjin) Co. Ltd. (1)
8 F N Tower Kerry Ctr 1 Guang Hua Rd, Chaoyang District, Beijing, 100020, China **(60%)**
Tel.: (86) 10 8529 6868
Web Site: http://www.gsk-china.com
Pharmaceuticals Mfr
N.A.I.C.S.: 325412

GlaxoSmithKline - Korea (1)
Web Site: http://www.gskkorea.co.kr
Pharmaceuticals Mfr & Distr
N.A.I.C.S.: 325412

GlaxoSmithKline AB (1)
Hemvarnsgatan 9, Box 516, 169 29, Solna, Sweden **(100%)**
Tel.: (46) 86389300
Sales Range: $25-49.9 Million
Emp.: 80
Pharmaceuticals Mfr & Distr
N.A.I.C.S.: 325412
Marine Stojanovic *(Mng Dir)*

GlaxoSmithKline AG (1)
Talstrasse 3, 3053, Munchenbuchsee, Switzerland **(100%)**
Tel.: (41) 318622111
Sales Range: $25-49.9 Million
Emp.: 100
Pharmaceuticals Mfr & Distr
N.A.I.C.S.: 325412

GlaxoSmithKline AS (1)
Drammensveien 288, 0283, Oslo, Norway **(100%)**
Tel.: (47) 22702000
Sales Range: $50-74.9 Million
Emp.: 140
Pharmaceuticals Mfr & Distr
N.A.I.C.S.: 325412

GlaxoSmithKline Algerie Spa (1)
Zone Industrielle Boudouaou Est 35 400, Boumerdes, Algeria
Tel.: (213) 21609525
Pharmaceuticals Product Mfr
N.A.I.C.S.: 325412

GlaxoSmithKline Algerie S.P.A. (1)
Zone Industrielle Boudouaou Est, 35 400, Boumerdes, Algeria
Tel.: (213) 24843220
Health & Medical Care Services
N.A.I.C.S.: 524114

GlaxoSmithKline Argentina SA (1)
Web Site: http://www.glaxosmithkline.com.ar
Sales Range: $200-249.9 Million
Emp.: 770
Pharmaceuticals Mfr & Distr
N.A.I.C.S.: 325412

GlaxoSmithKline Australia Pty Ltd. (1)
1061 Mtn Hwy, PO Box 168, Boronia, 3155, VIC, Australia **(100%)**
Tel.: (61) 397216000
Web Site: http://www.gsk.com
Sales Range: $200-249.9 Million
Emp.: 1,000
Pharmaceutical Mfr & Distr
N.A.I.C.S.: 325412

Subsidiary (Domestic):

GlaxoSmithKline Australia Pty. Ltd. - Consumer Healthcare Division (2)

INTERNATIONAL PUBLIC

82 Hughes Ave, Ermington, 2115, NSW, Australia
Tel.: (61) 296840888
Web Site: http://www.gsk.com.au
Sales Range: $125-149.9 Million
Emp.: 300
Pharmaceutical & Toiletries Mfr & Distr
N.A.I.C.S.: 325412

GlaxoSmithKline B.V. (1)
Huis Ter Heideweg 62, PO Box 780, 3705 LZ, Zeist, Netherlands **(100%)**
Tel.: (31) 0306938100
Web Site: http://www.gsk.nl
Sales Range: $125-149.9 Million
Emp.: 400
Pharmaceuticals Mfr & Distr
N.A.I.C.S.: 325412

GlaxoSmithKline Biologicals (Shanghai) Ltd (1)
277 Newton Road Zhangjiang High-tech Park, Pudong, Shanghai, 201203, China
Tel.: (86) 2150801010
Web Site: http://www.gsk-china.com
Sales Range: $25-49.9 Million
Emp.: 70
Biological Research & Development Services
N.A.I.C.S.: 541715

GlaxoSmithKline Biologicals Kft. (1)
Homoki Nagy Istvan utca 1, 2100, Godollo, Hungary
Tel.: (36) 28529960
Pharmaceuticals Product Mfr
N.A.I.C.S.: 325412

GlaxoSmithKline Biologicals S.A. (1)
89 Rue De IInstitut, Rixensart, 1330, Belgium **(100%)**
Tel.: (32) 26568111
Web Site: http://www.gsk-bio.com
Sales Range: $1-4.9 Billion
Emp.: 7,000
Vaccines Mfr
N.A.I.C.S.: 541715

Subsidiary (US):

GSK Biologicals (2)
553 Old Corvallis Rd, Hamilton, MT 59840-3607
Tel.: (406) 363-6214
Web Site: http://www.gsk.com
Sales Range: $10-24.9 Million
Emp.: 103
T-Cell Vaccines & Monoclonal Antibodies Developer
N.A.I.C.S.: 325414
James W. Young *(Chm)*

Subsidiary (Non-US):

GlaxoSmithKline (2)
2323 Du Parc Technologique Blvd, Sainte-Foy, G1P 4R8, QC, Canada
Tel.: (418) 650-0010
Web Site: http://www.gsk-bio.com
Sales Range: $200-249.9 Million
Emp.: 800
Pharmaceuticals Mfr
N.A.I.C.S.: 325412

Subsidiary (Domestic):

GlaxoSmithKline Biologicals Biotech S.A. (2)
89 De I Institut, Rixensart, 1330, Belgium
Tel.: (32) 26568111
Web Site: http://www.gskbio.com
Sales Range: $600-649.9 Million
Emp.: 5,000
Biotechnology Research
N.A.I.C.S.: 541714

GlaxoSmithKline Biologicals Manufacturing S.A. (2)
Rue de l Institut 89, 1330, Rixensart, Belgium
Tel.: (32) 26568111
Sales Range: $600-649.9 Million
Emp.: 4,000
N.A.I.C.S.: 541715

GlaxoSmithKline Biologicals S.A.S. (1)
637 Rue des Aulnois, 59230, Saint-Amand-les-Eaux, France

AND PRIVATE COMPANIES   GSK PLC

Tel.: (33) 327286400
Pharmaceuticals Product Mfr
N.A.I.C.S.: 325412

GlaxoSmithKline Brasil Ltda. (1)
Estrada dos Bandeirantes 8464, Rio de Janeiro, 22783-110, RJ, Brazil **(100%)**
Tel.: (55) 2132065050
Web Site: https://br.gsk.com
Rev.: $171,362,000
Emp.: 1,920
Pharmaceuticals Mfr
N.A.I.C.S.: 325412

GlaxoSmithKline Capital plc (1)
980 Great West Road, Brentford, TW8 9GS, United Kingdom
Tel.: (44) 2080475000
Emp.: 4,000
Financial Investment Services
N.A.I.C.S.: 523999

GlaxoSmithKline Chile Farmaceutica Limitada (1)
Av Andres Bello 2457 - Piso 20, Providencia, Santiago, Chile
Tel.: (56) 223829000
Pharmaceuticals Product Mfr
N.A.I.C.S.: 325412

GlaxoSmithKline Colombia S.A. (1)
(100%)
Mfr of Pharmaceuticals
N.A.I.C.S.: 325412

GlaxoSmithKline Consumer Healthcare (1)
1000 GSK Dr, Moon Township, PA 15108
Tel.: (412) 200-4000
Web Site: http://www.gsk.com
Sales Range: $600-649.9 Million
Emp.: 2,000
Consumer Healthcare Product Mfr
N.A.I.C.S.: 325412

GlaxoSmithKline Consumer Healthcare (Ireland) Limited (1)
Stonemasons Way, Rethfarnham, Dublin, Ireland
Tel.: (353) 1 4955000
Pharmaceuticals Product Mfr
N.A.I.C.S.: 325412

GlaxoSmithKline Consumer Healthcare (Pvt) Ltd (1)
World Trade Centre 34th Fl West Tower, Colombo, 100, Sri Lanka
Tel.: (94) 11 4790400
Emp.: 45
Pharmaceuticals Product Mfr
N.A.I.C.S.: 325412
Sunil Mehera *(Mng Dir)*

GlaxoSmithKline Consumer Healthcare (Thailand) Limited (1)
55 Wave Place Building 13th Floor Unit 13 05 and 13 06 Wireless Road, Lumpini Pathumwan, Bangkok, 10330, Thailand
Tel.: (66) 26593000
Pharmaceuticals Product Mfr
N.A.I.C.S.: 339112

GlaxoSmithKline Consumer Healthcare A/S (1)
Nykear 68, Brondby, DK2605, Denmark **(100%)**
Tel.: (45) 44868686
Web Site: http://www.glaxosmithkline.dk
Sales Range: $25-49.9 Million
Emp.: 60
Pharmaceuticals & Toiletries Mfr & Distr
N.A.I.C.S.: 325412
Karen Orgaard *(Partner-HR)*

GlaxoSmithKline Consumer Healthcare AB (1)
Hemvarnsgatan 9, 169 29, Solna, Sweden
Tel.: (46) 86389300
Emp.: 135
Pharmaceuticals Product Mfr
N.A.I.C.S.: 339112
Barbara Powell *(Mgr-Comm Consumer Healthcare)*

GlaxoSmithKline Consumer Healthcare Australia Pty Ltd (1)
82 Hughes Avenue, Ermington, 2115, NSW, Australia
Tel.: (61) 296840888
Pharmaceuticals Product Mfr

N.A.I.C.S.: 339112

GlaxoSmithKline Consumer Healthcare B.V. (1)
Huis ter Heideweg 62, 3705 LZ, Zeist, Netherlands
Tel.: (31) 306 93 87 00
Health Care Srvices
N.A.I.C.S.: 621999

GlaxoSmithKline Consumer Healthcare Colombia SAS (1)
Av Eldorado No 69B-45 9th Floor, Bogota Corporate Center, Bogota, Colombia
Tel.: (57) 14178686
Emp.: 350
Pharmaceuticals Product Mfr
N.A.I.C.S.: 339112

GlaxoSmithKline Consumer Healthcare Czech Republic s.r.o. (1)
Hvezdova 1734 2c, 140 00, Prague, Czech Republic
Tel.: (420) 222001111
Emp.: 500
Pharmaceuticals Product Mfr
N.A.I.C.S.: 339112
Miriam Kejzlarova *(Comm Mgr)*

GlaxoSmithKline Consumer Healthcare Finland Oy (1)
Piispansilta 9 A 4 Floor Iso Omena west wing, 02230, Espoo, Finland
Tel.: (358) 10303030
Emp.: 135
Pharmaceuticals Product Mfr
N.A.I.C.S.: 339112
Barbara Powell *(Comm Mgr)*

GlaxoSmithKline Consumer Healthcare Korea Co., Ltd. (1)
9th Floor 92 Hangang-daero Hangang-ro 2-ga LS Yongsan Tower, Yongsan-gu, Seoul, 04386, Korea (South)
Tel.: (82) 27094114
Web Site: http://kr.gsk.com
Pharmaceuticals Product Mfr
N.A.I.C.S.: 339112

GlaxoSmithKline Consumer Healthcare Pakistan Limited (1)
11-A 11th Floor Sky Tower East Wing HC-3 Block 4 Scheme-5, Dolmen City Clifton, Karachi, 75600, Pakistan
Tel.: (92) 21111475725
Pharmaceuticals Product Mfr
N.A.I.C.S.: 339112
Mashal Mohammad *(Sec)*

GlaxoSmithKline Consumer Healthcare S.A. (1)
Site Apollo Avenue Pascal 2-4-6, 1300, Wavre, Belgium
Tel.: (32) 10858600
Pharmaceuticals Product Mfr
N.A.I.C.S.: 339112

GlaxoSmithKline Consumer Healthcare S.p.A. (1)
Via Zambeletti, Baranzate Di Bollate, I 20021, Milan, Italy
Tel.: (39) 0238061
Web Site: http://www.gsk.it
Consumer Wellness & Brand Recognition
N.A.I.C.S.: 325412

GlaxoSmithKline Consumer Healthcare S.p.A. (1)
Via Zambeletti Snc, Baranzate, 20021, Milan, Italy
Tel.: (39) 0238061
Pharmaceuticals Product Mfr
N.A.I.C.S.: 325412

GlaxoSmithKline Consumer Healthcare Sdn. Bhd. (1)
Lot 89 Jalan Enggang Ulu Klang Industrial Estate, 54200, Ampang, Selangor Darul Ehsan, Malaysia **(100%)**
Tel.: (60) 374912020
Web Site: http://www.gks.com
Pharmaceuticals & Toiletries Mfr & Distr
N.A.I.C.S.: 325412

GlaxoSmithKline Consumer Healthcare Slovakia s. r. o. (1)
Galvaniho 7 A, 821 04, Bratislava, Slovakia
Tel.: (421) 248261111
Pharmaceuticals Product Mfr

N.A.I.C.S.: 339112

GlaxoSmithKline Consumer Healthcare Sp.z o.o. (1)
ul Rzymowskiego 53, 02-697, Warsaw, Poland
Tel.: (48) 22 576 90 00
Web Site: http://www.gsk.com.pl
Pharmaceuticals Product Mfr
N.A.I.C.S.: 325412

GlaxoSmithKline Consumer Nigeria plc (1)
1 Industrial Avenue, Ilupeju Ikeja, Lagos, Nigeria
Tel.: (234) 12711000
Pharmaceuticals Product Mfr
N.A.I.C.S.: 339112

GlaxoSmithKline Costa Rica S.A. (1)
400 metros Oeste de la Rotonda de la Bandera, Sabanilla, 10196 1000, San Jose, Costa Rica
Tel.: (506) 2066000
Pharmaceuticals Mfr & Distr
N.A.I.C.S.: 325412

GlaxoSmithKline Dungarvan Ltd. (1)
Knockbrack, Dungarvan, Waterford, Ireland **(100%)**
Tel.: (353) 5822500
Web Site: http://www.gsk.com
Sales Range: $200-249.9 Million
Emp.: 800
N.A.I.C.S.: 325412

GlaxoSmithKline EHF (1)
Thverholt 14, PO Box 5499, 105, Reykjavik, Iceland **(100%)**
Tel.: (354) 5303700
Web Site: http://www.gsk.is
Sales Range: $25-49.9 Million
Emp.: 9
Pharmaceuticals Mfr & Distr
N.A.I.C.S.: 325412

GlaxoSmithKline EOOD (1)
115G Tzarigradsko Shose Boulevard Floor 9, Sofia, 1784, Bulgaria
Tel.: (359) 29531034
Pharmaceuticals Product Mfr
N.A.I.C.S.: 325412

GlaxoSmithKline Ecuador S.A. (1)
Av 6 de Diciembre y Juan Boussingault Edificio T6 oficina 408, Quito, 170523, Ecuador
Tel.: (593) 22994700
Emp.: 140
Pharmaceutical Product Mfr & Distr
N.A.I.C.S.: 325412

GlaxoSmithKline Eesti OU (1)
Lootsa 8a, 11415, Tallinn, Estonia
Tel.: (372) 28002640
Pharmaceuticals Product Mfr
N.A.I.C.S.: 325412

GlaxoSmithKline Egypt (1)
Boomerang Bldg 5th District Area, PO Box 41, 11835, Cairo, Egypt **(100%)**
Tel.: (20) 226185000
Sales Range: $25-49.9 Million
Emp.: 100
Pharmaceuticals Mfr & Distr
N.A.I.C.S.: 325412
Amro Mandouh *(Gen Mgr-Middle East)*

GlaxoSmithKline El Salvador, S.A. de C.V. (1)
Edificio TWC 89 Av Norte y Calle El Mirador Torre 1 Nivel 2, Colonia Escalon, San Salvador, El Salvador
Tel.: (503) 21367801
Pharmaceuticals Mfr & Distr
N.A.I.C.S.: 325412

GlaxoSmithKline Export Limited Ghana (1)
PO Box CT 3067, Cantonments, Accra, Ghana
Tel.: (233) 302 215555
Pharmaceutical Products Distr
N.A.I.C.S.: 424210

GlaxoSmithKline Export Ltd. (1)
980 Great West Road, Brentford, TW8 9GS, Middlesex, United Kingdom **(100%)**
Tel.: (44) 80475000
Sales Range: $125-149.9 Million
Emp.: 300
Pharmaceuticals Distr

N.A.I.C.S.: 325412

GlaxoSmithKline Farmaceutica Ltda. (1)
Av Andres Bello 2457 - Piso 20 Oficinas 2001 2003 y 2004, Providencia, Santiago, Chile **(100%)**
Tel.: (56) 223829000
Sales Range: $25-49.9 Million
Emp.: 100
Pharmaceuticals Mfr & Distr
N.A.I.C.S.: 325412

GlaxoSmithKline Finance plc (1)
980 Great West Rd, Brentford, TW8 9GS, Middlesex, United Kingdom
Tel.: (44) 20 8047 5000
Web Site: http://www.gsk.com
Pharmaceuticals Product Mfr
N.A.I.C.S.: 325412

GlaxoSmithKline GmbH & Co. KG (1)
Prinzregentenplatz 9, 81675, Munich, Germany **(100%)**
Tel.: (49) 89360440
Web Site: https://de.gsk.com
Sales Range: $125-149.9 Million
Emp.: 450
Pharmaceuticals Mfr & Distr
N.A.I.C.S.: 325412

Subsidiary (Domestic):

GlaxoSmithKline Consumer Healthcare GmbH & Co KG (2)
Bussmatten 1, 77815, Bruhl, Germany **(100%)**
Tel.: (49) 7223760
Web Site: http://www.gsk-consumer.de
Sales Range: $50-74.9 Million
Emp.: 150
Pharmaceuticals & Toiletries Mfr & Distr
N.A.I.C.S.: 325412

GlaxoSmithKline Pharma GmbH (2)
Theresienhohe 11, 80339, Munich, Germany **(100%)**
Tel.: (49) 89360440
Web Site: http://www.glaxosmithkline.de
Sales Range: $50-74.9 Million
Emp.: 250
Pharmaceuticals Mfr & Distr
N.A.I.C.S.: 325412

GlaxoSmithKline Guatemala S.A. (1)
3ra Avenida 13-78 Zona 10 Torre Citibank Nivel 8, Guatemala, Guatemala
Tel.: (502) 23761930
Pharmaceuticals Product Mfr
N.A.I.C.S.: 339112

GlaxoSmithKline Healthcare AO (1)
premises III Room 9 floor 6 Presnenskaya nab 10, 123112, Moscow, Russia
Tel.: (7) 4957779850
Pharmaceuticals Product Mfr
N.A.I.C.S.: 339112

GlaxoSmithKline Holdings (Americas) Inc. (1)
1105 N Market St Ste 1300, Wilmington, DE 19801
Tel.: (302) 656-5280
Investment Management Service
N.A.I.C.S.: 551112

GlaxoSmithKline Holdings (One) Limited (1)
980 Great West Road, Brentford, TW8 9GS, Middlesex, United Kingdom
Tel.: (44) 2080475000
Emp.: 4,000
Investment Management Service
N.A.I.C.S.: 551112

GlaxoSmithKline Holdings Limited (1)
980 Great West Road, Brentford, TW8 9GS, Middlesex, United Kingdom
Tel.: (44) 2080472267
Investment Management Service
N.A.I.C.S.: 523999

GlaxoSmithKline Honduras S.A. (1)
Centro Corporativo los Proceres y Bulevar Morazan Avenida la Paz, Novacentro torre 2 Piso 9, Tegucigalpa, Honduras
Tel.: (504) 25401638
Pharmaceuticals Product Mfr

GSK plc—(Continued)
N.A.I.C.S.: 339112

GlaxoSmithKline Ilac Sanayi ve Ticaret AS (1)
Buyukdere Cad 1 Levent Plaza No 173 B Blok, Levent, 34394, Istanbul, Esentepe, Turkiye **(100%)**
Tel.: (90) 2123394400
Web Site: https://tr.gsk.com
Emp.: 600
Pharmaceuticals Mfr & Distr
N.A.I.C.S.: 325412

GlaxoSmithKline Ilaclari Sanayi ve Ticaret A.S. (1)
Buyukdere Cad 1 Levent Plaza B Blok No 173 Levent, Levent Istanbul, 34394, Istanbul, Turkiye
Tel.: (90) 2123394400
Pharmaceuticals Product Mfr
N.A.I.C.S.: 325412

GlaxoSmithKline Insurance Ltd. (1)
Armory Building, Reid Street, Hamilton, HM 12, Bermuda
Tel.: (441) 2957237
Group Insurance Services
N.A.I.C.S.: 524298

GlaxoSmithKline International (Luxembourg) S.A.R.L (1)
Route D arlon 53, Luxembourg, 8211, Luxembourg
Tel.: (352) 2534251
Investment Management Service
N.A.I.C.S.: 551112

GlaxoSmithKline Israel (1)
25 Bazel St, PO Box 10283, B28000FA, Petah Tiqwa, Israel **(100%)**
Tel.: (972) 39297100
Web Site: http://www.gsk.com
Sales Range: $50-74.9 Million
Emp.: 165
N.A.I.C.S.: 325412

GlaxoSmithKline K.K. (1)
(100%)
Tel.: (81) 357865000
Sales Range: $1-4.9 Billion
Emp.: 3,000
Pharmaceuticals Mfr & Distr
N.A.I.C.S.: 325412

GlaxoSmithKline Kft. (1)
Csorsz utsa 43, Budapest, 1124, Hungary
Tel.: (36) 1 225 5300
Web Site: http://www.gsk.hu
Pharmaceuticals Mfr & Distr
N.A.I.C.S.: 325412

GlaxoSmithKline Lietuva UAB (1)
Ukmerges g 120, LT-08105, Vilnius, Lithuania
Tel.: (370) 52649000
Pharmaceuticals Product Mfr
N.A.I.C.S.: 339112

GlaxoSmithKline Limited (1)
Tel.: (254) 206933200
Web Site: http://www.gsk.com
Research-Based Pharmaceuticals & healthcare Mfr & Distr
N.A.I.C.S.: 325412

GlaxoSmithKline Ltd. (1)
23/F Tower 6 The Gateway 9 Canton Road, Tsim Sha Tsui, Hong Kong, China (Hong Kong) **(100%)**
Tel.: (852) 31898989
Sales Range: $25-49.9 Million
Emp.: 50
Pharmaceuticals Mfr & Distr
N.A.I.C.S.: 325412

GlaxoSmithKline MDR-Boston Facility (1)
830 Winter St, Waltham, MA 02451-1420
Tel.: (781) 795-4100
Web Site: http://www.gsk.com
Sales Range: $25-49.9 Million
Emp.: 78
Pharmaceutical Discovey & Development
N.A.I.C.S.: 325412

GlaxoSmithKline Manufacturing S.p.A. (1)
Viale dell'Agricoltura 7, 37135, Verona, Italy
Tel.: (39) 0459218111
Emp.: 240
Pharmaceuticals Product Mfr
N.A.I.C.S.: 325412

GlaxoSmithKline Maroc S.A. (1)
42/44 Angle Boulevard Rachidi et Hamid El Ghazzali, Casablanca, Morocco
Pharmaceuticals Mfr & Distr
N.A.I.C.S.: 325412

GlaxoSmithKline Mexico S.A. de C.V. (1)
Tel.: (52) 54835200
Pharmaceuticals Mfr & Distr
N.A.I.C.S.: 325412

GlaxoSmithKline OTC Inc. (1)
PO Box 1217, Zebulon, NC 27597
Tel.: (919) 269-5000
Sales Range: $1-4.9 Billion
Emp.: 3,000
Pharmaceuticals Mfr & Distr
N.A.I.C.S.: 325412

GlaxoSmithKline Oral Care Plant (Ireland) (1)
Youghal Road Dungarvan, Dungarvan, Waterford, Ireland **(100%)**
Tel.: (353) 5822500
Web Site: http://www.gsk.com
Sales Range: $100-124.9 Million
Emp.: 700
Mfr of Dental Care Products
N.A.I.C.S.: 339114

GlaxoSmithKline Oy (1)
(100%)
Web Site: http://www.glaxosmithkline.fi
Sales Range: $25-49.9 Million
Emp.: 90
Pharmaceuticals Mfr & Distr
N.A.I.C.S.: 325412

GlaxoSmithKline Pakistan Ltd. (1)
35 Dockyard Rd W Whars, Karachi, 74000, Pakistan **(100%)**
Tel.: (92) 212315478
Sales Range: $450-499.9 Million
Emp.: 1,853
Pharmaceuticals Mfr & Distr
N.A.I.C.S.: 325412

GlaxoSmithKline Peru S.A. (1)
Av Victor Andres Belaunde N 147 via Principal N 133, Wework Torre Real 2 - Piso N 07 Office, 07-104, San Isidro, Lima, Peru
Tel.: (51) 12119700
Sales Range: $50-74.9 Million
Emp.: 120
Pharmaceuticals Mfr & Distr
N.A.I.C.S.: 325412

GlaxoSmithKline Pharma A/S (1)
Delta Park 37, Vallensbaek Strand, 2665, Brondby, Denmark **(100%)**
Tel.: (45) 36359100
Web Site: https://gskpro.com
Sales Range: $50-74.9 Million
Emp.: 145
Pharmaceuticals Mfr & Distr
N.A.I.C.S.: 325412

GlaxoSmithKline Pharma GmbH (1)
Web Site: http://www.gsk.com
Sales Range: $50-74.9 Million
Emp.: 150
Pharmaceuticals Mfr & Distr
N.A.I.C.S.: 325412

GlaxoSmithKline Pharmaceutical Sdn. Bhd. (1)
(100%)
Sales Range: $25-49.9 Million
Emp.: 100
Pharmaceuticals Mfr & Distr
N.A.I.C.S.: 325412

GlaxoSmithKline Pharmaceuticals Europe B.V. (1)
Huis Ter Heideweg 62, 3705 LZ, Zeist, Netherlands
Tel.: (31) 6938100
Holding Company
N.A.I.C.S.: 551112

GlaxoSmithKline Pharmaceuticals Ltd (1)
121 Galle Road Kaldemulla, Moratuwa, Sri Lanka
Tel.: (94) 117598373

Pharmaceuticals Product Mfr
N.A.I.C.S.: 325412

GlaxoSmithKline Pharmaceuticals Ltd. (1)
Dr Annie Besant Road, Mumbai, 400 030, India **(50.7%)**
Tel.: (91) 2224959595
Web Site: http://www.gsk-india.com
Sales Range: $150-199.9 Million
Emp.: 300
Pharmaceuticals Mfr & Distr
N.A.I.C.S.: 325412
Renu S. Karnad (Chm)

GlaxoSmithKline Pharmaceuticals S.A. (1)
Ul Drunwaldzai 189, 60322, Poznan, Poland **(100%)**
Tel.: (48) 225769000
Web Site: http://www.gsk.com.pl
Sales Range: $50-74.9 Million
Emp.: 200
Pharmaceuticals Mfr & Distr
N.A.I.C.S.: 325412

GlaxoSmithKline Pharmaceuticals S.A. (1)
Avenue Pascal 2-4-6, 1300, Wavre, Belgium
Tel.: (32) 10858500
Pharmaceuticals Product Mfr
N.A.I.C.S.: 325412

GlaxoSmithKline Pharmaceuticals Ukraine LLC (1)
Pavla Tychyny Avenue 1-V, 02152, Kiev, Ukraine
Tel.: (380) 445855185
Emp.: 400
Pharmaceutical Product Mfr & Distr
N.A.I.C.S.: 325412
Yana Syrovatka (Mgr-Comm & Govt Affairs)

GlaxoSmithKline Philippines, Inc. (1)
23rd Floor The Finance Centre 26th Street corner 9th Avenue, Bonifacio Global City, Taguig, 1634, Metro Manila, Philippines **(100%)**
Tel.: (63) 28920761
Web Site: http://www.gsk.com.ph
Sales Range: $200-249.9 Million
Emp.: 1,000
Pharmaceuticals Mfr & Distr
N.A.I.C.S.: 325412

GlaxoSmithKline Produtos Farmaceuticos Ltda. (1)
(100%)
Tel.: (351) 214129500
Web Site: http://www.gsk.com
Sales Range: $50-74.9 Million
Emp.: 18
Pharmaceuticals Mfr & Distr
N.A.I.C.S.: 325412

GlaxoSmithKline Pte. Ltd. (1)
Tel.: (65) 62328338
Sales Range: $125-149.9 Million
Emp.: 400
Pharmaceuticals Mfr & Distr
N.A.I.C.S.: 325412

Subsidiary (Domestic):

Glaxo Wellcome Manufacturing Pte Ltd (2)
1 Pioneer Sector 1 Jurong Industrial Estate, Jurong, Singapore, 628413, Singapore
Tel.: (65) 68612111
Pharmaceuticals Product Mfr
N.A.I.C.S.: 325412

Unit (Domestic):

GlaxoSmithKline Pte. Ltd. - Neural Pathways Discovery Performance Unit (2)
11 Biopolis Way Helios Bldg 03-01/02, Singapore, 138667, Singapore
Tel.: (65) 6398 3333
Pharmaceuticals Product Mfr
N.A.I.C.S.: 325412

Subsidiary (Domestic):

Glaxochem Pte Ltd (2)
23 Rochester Park, Singapore, 139234, Singapore
Tel.: (65) 68612111

Pharmaceutical Products Distr
N.A.I.C.S.: 325412

GlaxoSmithKline Puerto Rico (1)
PO Box 363461, San Juan, PR 00936-3461 **(100%)**
Tel.: (787) 774-1600
Pharmaceuticals Mfr & Distr
N.A.I.C.S.: 424210

GlaxoSmithKline Republica Dominicana S.A. (1)
Av Winston Churchill 95 Torre Blue Mall Piso 23, Horacio Fombona, Ens La Fe, Santo Domingo, Dominican Republic
Tel.: (809) 8299566335
Pharmaceuticals Mfr & Distr
N.A.I.C.S.: 325412

GlaxoSmithKline Research & Development Ltd. (1)
980 Great W Rd, Brentford, TW8 9GS, Middlesex, United Kingdom **(100%)**
Tel.: (44) 2080475000
Web Site: http://www.gsk.com
Sales Range: $700-749.9 Million
Emp.: 4,000
Pharmaceutical Research & Development
N.A.I.C.S.: 541715

GlaxoSmithKline S.A. (1)
(100%)
Sales Range: $200-249.9 Million
Emp.: 700
Pharmaceuticals Mfr & Distr
N.A.I.C.S.: 325412

Subsidiary (Domestic):

Duncan Farmaceutica, S.A. (2)
Parque Tecnologico De Madrid Calle Severo Ochoa 2, 28760, Tres Cantos, Madrid, Spain **(100%)**
Tel.: (34) 918070301
Web Site: http://www.esk.com
Sales Range: $200-249.9 Million
Emp.: 700
Pharmaceuticals Mfr
N.A.I.C.S.: 325412

GlaxoSmithKline S.A. (1)
Ave Fleming 20, 1300, Wavre, 1300, Belgium **(100%)**
Tel.: (32) 26562111
Web Site: http://www.gsk.com
Sales Range: $125-149.9 Million
Emp.: 1,000
Pharmaceuticals Mfr & Distr
N.A.I.C.S.: 325412

GlaxoSmithKline S.A.E. (1)
Boomerang Building No 46 Block J First Section City Centre, Fifth district, New Cairo, Cairo, Egypt
Tel.: (20) 226185000
Pharmaceuticals Product Mfr
N.A.I.C.S.: 325412

GlaxoSmithKline S.R.L. (1)
Str Dr Nicolae D Staicovici nr 2 Opera Center II etaj 4 sector 5, 050558, Bucharest, Romania **(100%)**
Tel.: (40) 800672524
Sales Range: $50-74.9 Million
Emp.: 200
Pharmaceuticals Mfr & Distr
N.A.I.C.S.: 325412

GlaxoSmithKline S.p.A. (1)
Viale dell Agricoltura 7, 37135, Verona, Italy **(100%)**
Tel.: (39) 0457741111
Sales Range: $125-149.9 Million
Emp.: 500
Pharmaceuticals Mfr & Distr
N.A.I.C.S.: 325412

GlaxoSmithKline SRO (1)
Hvezdova 1734 / 2c, 140 00, Prague, Czech Republic **(100%)**
Tel.: (420) 222001111
Sales Range: $50-74.9 Million
Emp.: 130
Pharmaceuticals Mfr & Distr
N.A.I.C.S.: 325412

GlaxoSmithKline Saudi Arabia (1)
3rd Fl Al Shehery Bookstore, PQ Box 309, Mussa Bin Nasser St, Riyadh, 11411, Olaya, Saudi Arabia **(49%)**
Tel.: (966) 14642826

AND PRIVATE COMPANIES — GSK PLC

Web Site: http://www.glaxowellcome.com.sa
Pharmaceuticals Mfr & Distr
N.A.I.C.S.: 325412

GlaxoSmithKline Services Unlimited (1)
980 Great West Road, Brentford, TW8 9GS, Middlesex, United Kingdom **(100%)**
Tel.: (44) 2080475000
Sales Range: $1-4.9 Billion
Emp.: 4,000
Pharmaceuticals Mfr
N.A.I.C.S.: 325412
Emma N. Walmsley *(CEO)*

GlaxoSmithKline Single Member A.E.B.E. (1)
Kifissias Avenue 266, Halandri, 15232, Athens, Greece
Tel.: (30) 2106882100
Emp.: 287
Pharmaceuticals Product Mfr
N.A.I.C.S.: 339112

GlaxoSmithKline Slovakia s.r.o. (1)
Galvaniho 7 / A, 831 03, Bratislava, Slovakia
Tel.: (421) 800500589
Pharmaceuticals Mfr & Distr
N.A.I.C.S.: 325412

GlaxoSmithKline South Africa (Pty) Limited (1)
Flushing Meadows Building The Campus 57 Sloane Street, Bryanston, 2021, South Africa
Tel.: (27) 117456000
Sales Range: $50-74.9 Million
Emp.: 167
Pharmaceuticals Product Mfr
N.A.I.C.S.: 325412

GlaxoSmithKline Trading Services Limited (1)
Unit 2500 Avenue 2000, Cork Airport Business Park, Cork, T12 P6PT, Ireland
Tel.: (353) 212407955
Pharmaceutical Products Distr
N.A.I.C.S.: 424210

GlaxoSmithKline Tunisia S.A.R.L. (1)
Les 4 R Rue du lac Lochness, Tunis, Tunisia
Tel.: (216) 71656035
Pharmaceuticals Product Mfr
N.A.I.C.S.: 339112

GlaxoSmithKline UK Limited (1)
980 Great West Road, Brentford, TW8 9GS, Middlesex, United Kingdom
Tel.: (44) 2080475000
Pharmaceuticals Product Mfr
N.A.I.C.S.: 325412

Subsidiary (Non-US):

GlaxoSmithKline Limited (2)
Likoni Road Industrial Area, PO Box 78392, 507, Nairobi, Kenya
Tel.: (254) 206933200
Sales Range: $125-149.9 Million
Emp.: 400
Pharmaceutical Products Distr
N.A.I.C.S.: 424210

GlaxoSmithKline Venezuela C.A. (1)
Web Site: http://www.gsk.com
Pharmaceuticals Mfr & Distr
N.A.I.C.S.: 325412

GlaxoSmithKline d.o.o (1)
Importanne Center Zmaja od Bosne 7-7a, Sarajevo, 71000, Bosnia & Herzegovina
Tel.: (387) 33959000
Pharmaceuticals Product Mfr
N.A.I.C.S.: 325412

GlaxoSmithKline d.o.o. (1)
Ulica Damira Tomljanovica Gavrana 15, Zagreb, 10020, Croatia
Tel.: (385) 16051999
Pharmaceuticals Product Mfr
N.A.I.C.S.: 325412

GlaxoSmithKline-Consumer Hungary Limited Liability Company (1)
Csorsz utca 43, 1124, Budapest, Hungary
Tel.: (36) 12255800
Pharmaceuticals Product Mfr
N.A.I.C.S.: 339112

Groupe GlaxoSmithKline SAS (1)
100 route de Versailles, 78163, Marly-le-Roi, France
Tel.: (33) 139178000
Web Site: http://www.gsk.fr
Pharmaceuticals Mfr & Distr
N.A.I.C.S.: 325412

Plant (Domestic):

GlaxoSmithKline - Evreux Plant (2)
23 rue Lavoisier ZI No 2, BP 118, 27091, Evreux, Cedex 9, France
Tel.: (33) 232235500
Web Site: http://www.gsk.fr
Sales Range: $400-449.9 Million
Emp.: 2,000
Pharmaceuticals Mfr
N.A.I.C.S.: 325412

Subsidiary (Domestic):

GlaxoSmithKline Sante Grand Public (2)
100 Rte De Versailles, 78163, Marly-le-Roi, Cedex, France
Tel.: (33) 139178000
Web Site: http://www.gsk.com
Sales Range: $50-74.9 Million
Emp.: 170
Pharmaceutical & Healthcare Products Mfr & Distr
N.A.I.C.S.: 325412

Laboratoire GlaxoSmithKline (2)
100 Route de Versailles, 78163, Marly-le-Roi, Cedex, France **(100%)**
Tel.: (33) 139178000
Web Site: http://www.gsk.com.fr
Sales Range: $200-249.9 Million
Emp.: 700
Pharmaceuticals Distr
N.A.I.C.S.: 424210

Horlicks Limited (1)
980 Great West Rd, Brentford, TW8 9GS, Mddx, United Kingdom
Web Site: http://www.horlicks.com
Powdered Drink Mfr
N.A.I.C.S.: 311514

Kemco Knoxville (1)
1704 Midpark Rd, Knoxville, TN 37921-5925
Tel.: (865) 558-3405
Sales Range: $25-49.9 Million
Emp.: 3
Pharmaceuticals Distr
N.A.I.C.S.: 493110

Laboratorios Farmaceuticos de Nicaragua, S.A. (1)
Kilometro 5 1/2 de la Carretera Norte, Blvd Pedro Joaquin Chamoro, Managua, Nicaragua
N.A.I.C.S.: 541715

Laboratorios Phoenix Sociedad Anonima Industrial Comercial y Financiera (1)
Gral Juan Gregorio Lemos 2809, Los Polvorines, B1613AUE, Buenos Aires, Argentina
Tel.: (54) 1144898300
Web Site: https://elea.com
Pharmaceuticals Product Mfr
N.A.I.C.S.: 325412

Nippon Wellcome KK (1)
Kobe Crystal Tower 1-3, Higashi-Kawasaki-cho 1-chome, Chuo-ku, Kobe, 650, Japan **(55%)**
Tel.: (81) 78 360 8900
Mfr of Pharmaceuticals
N.A.I.C.S.: 325412

PT GSK Consumer Healthcare Indonesia (1)
Graha Paramita 5th Floor Jl Denpasar Raya D2, Jakarta, 12940, Indonesia
Tel.: (62) 212523490
Pharmaceuticals Product Mfr
N.A.I.C.S.: 339112

PT Glaxo Wellcome Indonesia (1)
Jl Prof Dr Satrio No 164, Jakarta, 12930, Indonesia
Tel.: (62) 2125532350
Pharmaceuticals Product Mfr
N.A.I.C.S.: 339112

PT GlaxoSmithKline Indonesia (1)
Jalan Pulobuaran Raya Blok III DD 2 3 4, Kawasan Industri Pulogadung, 13930, Jakarta, Indonesia **(100%)**
Tel.: (62) 214603292
Web Site: http://www.gsk-indonesia.com
Sales Range: $125-149.9 Million
Emp.: 300
Pharmaceuticals Mfr & Distr
N.A.I.C.S.: 325412

Pharmlog Pharma Logistik GmbH (1)
Siemensstrasse 1, 59199, Bonen, Germany
Tel.: (49) 23839303
Web Site: https://www.pharmlog.com
Sales Range: $125-149.9 Million
Emp.: 385
Pharmaceuticals Mfr
N.A.I.C.S.: 325412
Hans-Peter Meid *(CEO & Mng Dir)*

SIA GlaxoSmithKline Latvia (1)
Duntes street 3, Riga, 1013, Latvia
Tel.: (371) 80205045
Sales Range: $50-74.9 Million
Emp.: 60
Pharmaceutical Products Distr
N.A.I.C.S.: 424210

SR One Limited (1)
200 Barr Harbor Dr Ste 250 4 Tower Bridge, West Conshohocken, PA 19428-3977
Tel.: (610) 567-1000
Web Site: http://www.srone.com
Sales Range: $50-74.9 Million
Emp.: 10
Venture Capital Investment Services
N.A.I.C.S.: 523999
Simeon J. George *(CEO)*

Sino-American Tianjin Smith Kline & French Laboratories Ltd (1)
Cheng Lin Zhuang Industrial District, Tianjin, 300163, China
Tel.: (86) 22 2470 0888
Pharmaceutical Products
N.A.I.C.S.: 325412

Sirtris Pharmaceuticals (1)
200 Technology Sq Ste 300, Cambridge, MA 02139
Tel.: (617) 252-6920
Web Site: http://www.sirtrispharma.com
Sales Range: $25-49.9 Million
Emp.: 39
Biopharmaceutical Developer
N.A.I.C.S.: 325412
Paul R. Schimmel *(Co-Founder)*

SmithKline Beecham (Cork) Limited (1)
Currabinny, Carrigaline, Cork, Ireland
Tel.: (353) 21 4378800
Web Site: http://www.gsk.ie
Emp.: 600
Pharmaceuticals Product Mfr
N.A.I.C.S.: 325412

SmithKline Beecham (Ireland) Limited (1)
Corrig Avenue, Dun Laoghaire, County Dublin, Ireland
Mfr of Pharmaceuticals
N.A.I.C.S.: 325412

SmithKline Beecham Consumer Brands Limited (1)
Corrig Avenue, Dun Laoghaire, County Dublin, Ireland
Mfr of Pharmaceuticals
N.A.I.C.S.: 325412

SmithKline Beecham Honduras S.A. (1)
Colonia Florencia Norte Boulevard a Suyapa, Tegucigalpa, Honduras
Pharmaceuticals Mfr & Distr
N.A.I.C.S.: 325412

SmithKline Beecham Limited (1)
980 Great West Road, Brentford, TW8 9GS, Middlesex, United Kingdom
Tel.: (44) 2080475000
Sales Range: $1-4.9 Billion
Emp.: 4,000
Pharmaceutical Product Mfr & Distr
N.A.I.C.S.: 325412
Emma N. Walmsley *(CEO)*

SmithKline Beecham de Panama S.A. (1)
c/o J Cain & Co Inc Edificio No 9106 France Field, Zona Libre de Colon, Colon, Panama
Pharmaceuticals Mfr & Distr
N.A.I.C.S.: 325412

Stafford Miller (Ireland) Limited (1)
Clocherane Youghal Road, Dungarvan, Co Waterford, Ireland
Tel.: (353) 5820200
Sales Range: $200-249.9 Million
Emp.: 800
Pharmaceuticals Product Mfr
N.A.I.C.S.: 325412

Stiefel GmbH & Co. KG (1)
Hochholzstrasse 40, Zillhausen, 72336, Balingen, Germany
Tel.: (49) 74359198585
Web Site: http://www.stiefelservice.de
Crane Mfr & Retailer
N.A.I.C.S.: 333923

Stiefel India Private Limited (1)
401 and 402 A Wing IV Floor Floral Deck Plaza Opp Rolta Bhavan, Central MIDC Road Andheri East, Mumbai, 400 093, India
Tel.: (91) 2228227009
Skin Care Product Mfr
N.A.I.C.S.: 325620

Stiefel Laboratories (U.K.) Ltd. (1)
980 Great West Road, Brentford, TW8 9GS, Middlesex, United Kingdom
Tel.: (44) 2080475000
Skin Care Product Mfr
N.A.I.C.S.: 325620

Stiefel Laboratories, Inc. (1)
255 Alhambra Cir Ste 1000, Coral Gables, FL 33134-7412
Tel.: (305) 443-3800
Web Site: http://www.stiefel.com
Sales Range: $900-999.9 Million
Emp.: 3,500
Pharmaceuticals Mfr
N.A.I.C.S.: 325412

Subsidiary (Non-US):

Stiefel Laboratories (Ireland) Limited (2)
12 Riverwalk Citywest Business Campus, Rathfarnham, Dublin, 24, Ireland
Tel.: (353) 14955000
Personal Care Product Mfr
N.A.I.C.S.: 325620

TESARO, Inc. (1)
1000 Winter St, Waltham, MA 02451
Tel.: (339) 970-0900
Web Site: http://www.tesarobio.com
Sales Range: $200-249.9 Million
Oncological Pharmaceutical Mfr
N.A.I.C.S.: 325412
Richard J. Rodgers *(Co-Founder)*

Subsidiary (Non-US):

TESARO Bio Spain, S.L.U. (2)
Camino de la Zarzuela 19 1 C, 28023, Madrid, Spain
Tel.: (34) 910480300
Web Site: http://www.tesarobio.es
Pharmaceutical Products Distr
N.A.I.C.S.: 424210
Jose Maria Maurer *(Fin Dir)*

ViiV HealthCare BV (1)
Van Asch van Wijckstraat 55H, 3811 LP, Amersfoort, Netherlands
Tel.: (31) 332081199
Medicine Research & Development Services
N.A.I.C.S.: 541714

ViiV Healthcare (1)
980 Great West Road, Brentford, TW8 9GS, Middlesex, United Kingdom
Tel.: (44) 2083806200
Web Site: https://www.viivhealthcare.com
Sales Range: $1-4.9 Billion
Emp.: 4,000
HIV Treatment Mfr; Joint Venture of Pfizer, Inc. & GlaxoSmithKline plc
N.A.I.C.S.: 325412

GSK PLC

INTERNATIONAL PUBLIC

GSK plc—(Continued)
Jill Anderson (CFO)

ViiV Healthcare Company (1)
251 Little Falls Dr, Wilmington, DE 19808
Medicine Research & Development Services
N.A.I.C.S.: 541714

ViiV Healthcare Pty Ltd (1)
Level 3 436 Johnston Street, Abbotsford, 3067, VIC, Australia
Tel.: (61) 397216161
Medicine Research & Development Services
N.A.I.C.S.: 621999

ViiV Healthcare S.r.l. (1)
Viale dell'Agricoltura 7, 37135, Verona, Italy
Tel.: (39) 0457741600
Medicine Research & Development Services
N.A.I.C.S.: 621999

ViiV Healthcare SAS (1)
23 rue Francois Jacob, 92500, Rueil-Malmaison, France
Tel.: (33) 139176900
Medicine Research & Development Services
N.A.I.C.S.: 621999

ViiV Healthcare ULC (1)
245 Armand-Frappier Boulevard, Laval, H7V 4A7, QC, Canada
Tel.: (450) 680-4810
Medicine Research & Development Services
N.A.I.C.S.: 621999

ViiVHIV Healthcare Unipessoal Lda (1)
R Dr Antonio Loureiro Borges n 3, Arquiparque-Miraflores, 1499-013, Alges, Portugal
Tel.: (351) 210940801
Web Site: https://viivexchange.com
Pharmaceutical Products Distr
N.A.I.C.S.: 424210

GSL GM CITY
1720 Bow Trail Southwest, Calgary, T3C 2E4, AB, Canada
Tel.: (403) 265-7690
Web Site: http://www.calgarygmc.ca
Year Founded: 1910
Sales Range: $125-149.9 Million
Emp.: 135
Car Dealer
N.A.I.C.S.: 441110
Robert Wolfe (Pres)

GSL SECURITIES LIMITED
1/25 and 1/26 1st Floor Tardeo Air-conditioned Market Society, Tardeo Road, Mumbai, 400034, Maharashtra, India
Tel.: (91) 2223516166
Web Site: https://www.gslsecurities.com
Year Founded: 1994
530469—(BOM)
Rev.: $27,780
Assets: $663,330
Liabilities: $11,870
Net Worth: $651,460
Earnings: ($13,524)
Emp.: 7
Fiscal Year-end: 03/31/23
Financial Management Services
N.A.I.C.S.: 523999
S. K. Bagrodia (Chm & Mng Dir)

GSN MASCHINEN-ANLAGEN-SERVICE GMBH
Benzstrasse 1, 72108, Rottenburg am Neckar, Germany
Tel.: (49) 745794840
Web Site: http://www.gsn-service.com
Year Founded: 1992
Rev.: $31,350,876
Emp.: 170

Industrial Equipment Mfr
N.A.I.C.S.: 333248
Meinrad Hirlinger (Mng Dir)

Subsidiaries:

GSN Maquinaria-Servicios-CNC, S.A. de C.V. (1)
Calle Pirineos No 515 Zona Industrial Benito Juarez, Bodega 31, Queretaro, 76120, Mexico
Tel.: (52) 4422095145
Web Site: http://www.gsn-mexico.com
Machine System Mfr
N.A.I.C.S.: 334511
Carlos Castro (Mng Dir)

GSN Retooling-Maintenance, Inc. (1)
5126 S Royal Atlanta Dr, Tucker, GA 30084
Tel.: (770) 349-6334
Emp.: 500
Machine Tools Mfr
N.A.I.C.S.: 333517

GSP AUTOMOTIVE GROUP WENZHOU CO., LTD.
No 1 Gaoxiang Road, High-tech Industrial Zone Ouhai, Wenzhou, 325006, China
Tel.: (86) 57786293313
Web Site: https://www.gspglobal.com
Year Founded: 1999
605088—(SHG)
Rev.: $412,964,922
Assets: $440,650,525
Liabilities: $201,677,341
Net Worth: $238,973,183
Earnings: $33,398,310
Emp.: 2,000
Fiscal Year-end: 12/31/22
Automotive Parts Mfr & Distr
N.A.I.C.S.: 336390
Jiaru Zhou (Chm)

Subsidiaries:

GSP Europe GmbH (1)
Leyboldstrasse 10, 50354, Hurth, Germany
Automobile Parts Mfr
N.A.I.C.S.: 336390

GSP Latin America Ltd. (1)
2600 S Douglas Rd PH 10, Coral Gables, FL 33134
Tel.: (305) 446-7702
Cv Axle & Joints Mfr
N.A.I.C.S.: 336350

GSP N.A. (1)
2725 New Cut Rd, Spartanburg, SC 29303
Tel.: (864) 578-6900
Web Site: https://www.gspnorthamerica.com
Automobile Parts Mfr & Distr
N.A.I.C.S.: 336390

GSP Nanjing Co., Ltd. (1)
No 59 Shuanghu Road, Gaochun District, Nanjing, China
Tel.: (86) 2556838033
Automobile Parts Mfr
N.A.I.C.S.: 336390

GSP FINANCE COMPANY (BANGLADESH) LIMITED
1 Paribagh Mymensingh Road, Dhaka, 1000, Bangladesh
Tel.: (880) 2223360506 BD
Web Site: https://www.gspfinance.com
Year Founded: 1995
GSPFINANCE—(CHT)
Rev.: $8,114,845
Assets: $110,280,791
Liabilities: $69,484,794
Net Worth: $40,795,998
Earnings: ($1,592,179)
Emp.: 31
Fiscal Year-end: 12/31/22
Financial Services
N.A.I.C.S.: 523999
Feroz U. Haider (Chm)

Subsidiaries:

GSP Investments Limited (1)
1 Paribagh Mymensingh Road, Dhaka, 1000, Bangladesh
Tel.: (880) 2223360506
Web Site: https://www.gsp-investments.com
Asset Management Services
N.A.I.C.S.: 523940
Asif Rahman (CEO)

GSP RESOURCE CORP.
1610 - 777 Dunsmuir St, Vancouver, V7Y 1K4, BC, Canada
Tel.: (604) 619-7469
Web Site: https://www.gspresource.com
GSRCF—(OTCIQ)
Rev.: $817
Assets: $2,049,495
Liabilities: $66,818
Net Worth: $1,982,677
Earnings: ($412,167)
Fiscal Year-end: 05/31/24
Metal Exploration Services
N.A.I.C.S.: 213114
Simon C. Dyakowski (Pres & CEO)

GSS ENERGY LTD.
Blk 4012 Ang Mo Kio Ave 10 05-01 Techplace 1, Singapore, 569628, Singapore
Tel.: (65) 62599133
Web Site: https://www.gssenergy.com.sg
Year Founded: 1979
41F—(CAT)
Rev.: $89,523,593
Assets: $78,857,835
Liabilities: $47,421,798
Net Worth: $31,436,037
Earnings: ($6,763,614)
Emp.: 482
Fiscal Year-end: 12/31/23
Automobile Equipment Mfr
N.A.I.C.S.: 336320
Yeung Kin Bond Sydney (CEO)

Subsidiaries:

Changzhou Giken Precision Co., Ltd. (1)
No 55 Keji Avenue, New District, Changzhou, 213031, Jiangsu, China
Tel.: (86) 51985105100
Web Site: http://www.giken.com.cn
Electronic Parts Mfr
N.A.I.C.S.: 334419

Giken Precision Engineering (S) Pte Ltd (1)
Blk 5046 01-541/549, Ang Mo Kio, Industrial Park 2, Singapore, 569549, Singapore
Tel.: (65) 64822323
Precision Parts Mfr
N.A.I.C.S.: 332721

GSS INFOTECH LIMITED
Ground Floor Wing-B N heights Plot No 12 TSIIC Software Units Layout, Madhapur Serilingampally Mandal Rangareddy District, Hyderabad, 500081, Telangana, India
Tel.: (91) 4044556600
Web Site: https://www.gssinfotech.com
GSS—(NSE)
Rev.: $27,163,254
Assets: $145,024,663
Liabilities: $56,061,539
Net Worth: $88,963,124
Earnings: $1,392,858
Emp.: 103
Fiscal Year-end: 03/31/22
IT Solutions & Services
N.A.I.C.S.: 541690
Bhargav Marepally (Founder, CEO & Mng Dir)

Subsidiaries:

Infospectrum Consulting Inc. (1)
1699 Wall St Ste 201, Mount Prospect, IL 60056
Tel.: (847) 640-3700
Web Site: http://www.isc-na.com
BPO & IT Consulting Services
N.A.I.C.S.: 541512

System Dynamix Corporation (1)
2842 Main St, Glastonbury, CT 06033
Tel.: (860) 633-7174
IT Consulting & Software Development Services
N.A.I.C.S.: 541511

GSTAAD CAPITAL CORP.
800 West Pender Street Suite 615, Vancouver, V6C 2V6, BC, Canada
Tel.: (604) 687-7767 BC
Year Founded: 2010
GTD.H—(TSXV)
Assets: $365,807
Liabilities: $5,524
Net Worth: $360,284
Earnings: ($32,943)
Fiscal Year-end: 06/30/22
Investment Services
N.A.I.C.S.: 523999
Jonathan Younie (CFO)

GSTECHNOLOGIES LTD.
11/125 St Georges Terrace, Perth, 6000, WA, Australia
Tel.: (61) 861898531 VG
Web Site: https://www.gstechnologies.co.uk
Year Founded: 2013
GST—(LSE)
Rev.: $1,554,000
Assets: $7,497,000
Liabilities: $1,250,000
Net Worth: $6,247,000
Earnings: ($1,223,000)
Emp.: 36
Fiscal Year-end: 03/31/24
Investment Management Service
N.A.I.C.S.: 523940
Tone Kay Kim Goh (Chm)

GT CAPITAL HOLDINGS, INC.
43rd Floor GT Tower International, 6813 Ayala Avenue, Corner HV Dela Costa Street, Makati, Philippines
Tel.: (63) 288364500
Web Site: https://www.gtcapital.com.ph
GTCAP—(PHI)
Rev.: $3,632,574,400
Assets: $8,144,593,600
Liabilities: $3,942,286,400
Net Worth: $4,202,307,200
Earnings: $228,446,400
Emp.: 19,510
Fiscal Year-end: 12/31/21
Holding Company
N.A.I.C.S.: 551112
Francisco C. Sebastian (Vice Chm)

Subsidiaries:

Federal Land, Inc. (1)
20th Floor GT Tower International, 6813 Ayala Ave cor HV Dela Costa, Makati, 1227, Philippines
Tel.: (63) 288836888
Web Site: http://federalland.ph
Real Estate Services
N.A.I.C.S.: 531311

Toyota Motor Philippines Corporation (1)
Toyota Special Economic Zone 4026, Metro, Santa Rosa, 1700, Philippines (51%)
Tel.: (63) 49 843 1156
Web Site: http://www.toyota.com.ph
Sales Range: $250-299.9 Million
Emp.: 1,902
CKD Unit Assembly & Sales
N.A.I.C.S.: 423120

AND PRIVATE COMPANIES

Alfred V. Ty *(Chm)*

Subsidiary (Domestic):

Lexus Manila, Inc. (2)
3402 8th Avenue cor 34th Street, North Bonifacio Global City, Taguig, 1634, Philippines
Tel.: (63) 288565050
Web Site: https://www.lexus.com.ph
Car Dealer Services
N.A.I.C.S.: 441110

Toyota Makati, Inc. (2)
Ayala Ave Metropolitan Ave, Santa Rosa-Tagaytay Highway, Makati, Metro Manila, Philippines
Tel.: (63) 88970333
Web Site: http://www.toyotamakati.com.ph
Car Dealer Services
N.A.I.C.S.: 441110

Toyota San Fernando Pampanga, Inc. (2)
Jose Abad Santos Avenue, San Fernando, 2000, Pampanga, Philippines
Tel.: (63) 9175109345
Web Site:
  https://www.toyotasanfernando.com.ph
Emp.: 250
Car Dealer Services
N.A.I.C.S.: 441110

Toyota Subic, Inc. (1)
Marshalling Yard Rizal Highway, Subic Gateway District Subic Bay Freeport Zone, Subic, 2222, Philippines
Tel.: (63) 472508008
Web Site: http://www.toyotasubic.com.ph
Car Dealer Services
N.A.I.C.S.: 441110

GT GROUP HOLDINGS LIMITED

Units 2502-5 25th Floor Harbour Centre 25 Harbour Road, Wanchai, China (Hong Kong)
Tel.: (852) 3 926 1888
Web Site: http://www.gtghl.com
Rev.: $7,184,283
Assets: $123,315,718
Liabilities: $176,880,537
Net Worth: ($53,564,819)
Earnings: ($69,526,310)
Emp.: 61
Fiscal Year-end: 12/31/19
Minerals Exploration & Sales
N.A.I.C.S.: 213115
Christine Shin Kwan Ng *(Exec Dir)*

Subsidiaries:

GT Capital Limited (1)
Ste 1502-1503 15 F Great Eagle Ctr 23 Harbour Rd, Wanchai, China (Hong Kong)
Tel.: (852) 31626688
Web Site: http://www.gtcapital.com.hk
Sales Range: $50-74.9 Million
Emp.: 10
Securities Brokerage Services
N.A.I.C.S.: 523150
Freddie Leung *(Mgr)*

Poly Metal and Minerals Limited (1)
Rm 1502-3 15 F Great Eagle Ctr 23 Harbour Rd, Wanchai, China (Hong Kong)
Tel.: (852) 31626666
Web Site: http://www.bejingyst.com
Sales Range: $50-74.9 Million
Emp.: 10
Iron Ore Processing Services
N.A.I.C.S.: 212210

GT STEEL CONSTRUCTION GROUP LIMITED

64 Woodlands Industrial Park E9, Singapore, 757833, Singapore
Tel.: (65) 63697205   Ky
Web Site: http://www.gt-steel.com.sg
Year Founded: 2003
8402—(HKG)
Rev.: $13,894,703
Assets: $14,108,084
Liabilities: $6,736,015
Net Worth: $7,372,069
Earnings: ($1,089,099)
Emp.: 119
Fiscal Year-end: 12/31/23
Construction Materials Mfr & Distr
N.A.I.C.S.: 332312
Cheng Yew Ong *(Founder, Chm & Compliance Officer)*

Subsidiaries:

G-Tech Metal Pte. Ltd. (1)
64 Woodlands Ind Park E9, Singapore, 757833, Singapore
Tel.: (65) 63697205
Steel Fabricator Mfr
N.A.I.C.S.: 332312

GT Steel Construction Group Limited - Singapore Factory (1)
110 Woodlands Industrial Park E3, Singapore, 757842, Singapore
Tel.: (65) 63655770
Structural Steel Mfr
N.A.I.C.S.: 332312

GTA FINANCECORP INC.

855 Brant Street, Burlington, L7R 2J6, ON, Canada
Tel.: (905) 681-1925   ON
Web Site:
  http://www.gtaresources.com
Year Founded: 2006
GTARF—(OTCIQ)
Assets: $83,436
Liabilities: $162,758
Net Worth: ($79,322)
Earnings: ($160,023)
Fiscal Year-end: 03/31/20
Investment Services
N.A.I.C.S.: 523999
Brian Crawford *(CFO)*

GTA FINANCECORP, INC.

855 Brant Street, Burlington, L7R 2J9, ON, Canada
Tel.: (905) 681-1925
Year Founded: 2006
Mining Exploration
N.A.I.C.S.: 212220
Peter M. Clausi *(Pres & CEO)*

GTG VENTURES, INC.

No 5 Sec 1 Wenxing Rd, Hsinchu County, Zhubei, 302, Taiwan
Tel.: (886) 36577555
Year Founded: 2005
GTGT—(OTCIQ)
Sales Range: Less than $1 Million
Telecommunication Servicesb
N.A.I.C.S.: 517810

GTG WELLNESS CO., LTD.

7 Dongwon-ro Bundang-gu, Seongnam, Gyeonggi-do, Korea (South)
Tel.: (82) 234625400
Web Site:
  http://www.gtgwellness.co.kr
219750—(KRS)
Rev.: $4,781,186
Assets: $27,244,932
Liabilities: $23,779,399
Net Worth: $3,465,533
Earnings: ($9,828,158)
Emp.: 50
Fiscal Year-end: 12/31/22
Medicinal Product Mfr
N.A.I.C.S.: 339112
Yoonsuk Han *(CEO)*

GTI ENERGY LTD

333c Charles St, North Perth, 6006, WA, Australia
Tel.: (61) 62851557   AU
Web Site:
  https://www.gtiresources.com.au
GTR—(ASX)
Rev.: $11,841
Assets: $14,522,670
Liabilities: $434,456
Net Worth: $14,088,214
Earnings: ($1,224,328)
Emp.: 2
Fiscal Year-end: 12/31/22
Mineral Properties Evaluation & Exploration Services
N.A.I.C.S.: 423520
Bruce Lane *(Exec Dir)*

GTI HOLDINGS LIMITED

Unit B 13/F Winsan Tower 98 Thomson Road, Wanchai, China (Hong Kong)
Tel.: (852) 2301 2238   Ky
Web Site:
  http://www.gtiholdings.com.hk
3344—(HKG)
Sales Range: $75-99.9 Million
Emp.: 2,500
Holding Company; Dyed Yarn & Knitted Sweaters Mfr
N.A.I.C.S.: 551112
Xiangbin Hao *(Exec Dir)*

Subsidiaries:

Chung Yick Textile Factory Limited (1)
Samarky Village Svay Toeu Commune Kampong Roung District, Svay Rieng, Cambodia
Tel.: (855) 67813888
Knit Cloth Mfr & Distr
N.A.I.C.S.: 315120

GTI TRANSPORT SOLUTIONS, INC.

5020 Fairway, Lachine, H8T 1B8, QC, Canada
Tel.: (514) 634-7655
Web Site: http://www.thegtigroup.com
Logistic Services
N.A.I.C.S.: 541614

Subsidiaries:

Jetco Delivery, Inc. (1)
5521 Harvey Wilson Dr, Houston, TX 77020
Tel.: (713) 676-1111
Web Site: http://www.jetcodelivery.com
Sales Range: $10-24.9 Million
Emp.: 130
Trucking Service
N.A.I.C.S.: 484110
Mauris Mattern *(Founder)*

GTL INFRASTRUCTURE LIMITED

Global Vision 3rd Floor Electronic SadanII, MIDC TTC Industrial Area Mahape, Navi Mumbai, 400710, Maharashtra, India
Tel.: (91) 2268293500
Web Site: https://www.gtlinfra.com
GTLINFRA—(NSE)
Rev.: $197,766,660
Assets: $879,969,090
Liabilities: $1,055,658,240
Net Worth: ($175,689,150)
Earnings: ($173,460,105)
Emp.: 636
Fiscal Year-end: 03/31/21
Telecom Infrastructure Services
N.A.I.C.S.: 517112
N. Balasubramanian *(Vice Chm)*

GTM HOLDINGS CORPORATION

9F 320 Zhong Xiao E Rd Sec.4, Taipei, 106, Taiwan
Tel.: (886) 227415000
Web Site: http://www.gtm.com.tw
Year Founded: 1951
1437—(TAI)
Rev.: $28,243,336
Assets: $421,984,647
Liabilities: $172,191,759
Net Worth: $249,792,888
Earnings: $18,774,420

GTPL HATHWAY LTD.

Emp.: 7
Fiscal Year-end: 12/31/23
Holding Company
N.A.I.C.S.: 551112
George Gu *(Chm & Gen Mgr)*

Subsidiaries:

GTM Textile Co., Ltd. (1)
10F-2 No 87 Zhengzhou Rd, Datong Dist, Taipei, 103, Taiwan
Tel.: (886) 225523466
Real Estate Development Services
N.A.I.C.S.: 531390

GTN INDUSTRIES LTD

GTN Industries House Plot No 29 Nagarjuna Hills Punjagutta, Hyderabad, 500082, Telangana, India
Tel.: (91) 4043407777
Web Site:
  https://www.gtnindustries.com
Rev.: $46,328,562
Assets: $46,981,973
Liabilities: $36,785,334
Net Worth: $10,196,639
Earnings: $971,146
Emp.: 1,460
Fiscal Year-end: 03/31/18
Cotton Yarn Mfr
N.A.I.C.S.: 313110
M. K. Patodia *(Chm & Mng Dir)*

GTN TEXTILES LIMITED

Door No VIII/911 Erumathala PO Aluva, Ernakulam, Kochi, 683112, Kerala, India
Tel.: (91) 4842661000
Web Site: https://www.gtntextiles.com
Year Founded: 1966
532744—(BOM)
Rev.: $1,199,928
Assets: $11,862,874
Liabilities: $10,989,437
Net Worth: $873,437
Earnings: ($2,153,648)
Emp.: 594
Fiscal Year-end: 03/31/23
Cotton Yarn & Processed Yarn Mfr & Distr
N.A.I.C.S.: 313110
Binod Kumar Patodia *(Chm & Mng Dir)*

GTPL HATHWAY LTD.

GTPL House Sindhu Bhavan Road Near Pakwan Cross Road, Bodakdev, Ahmedabad, 380059, India
Tel.: (91) 7961400000
Web Site: https://www.gtpl.net
Year Founded: 2006
540602—(BOM)
Rev.: $345,349,778
Assets: $321,146,144
Liabilities: $191,106,962
Net Worth: $130,039,182
Earnings: $28,719,737
Emp.: 706
Fiscal Year-end: 03/31/21
Broadband Access Services
N.A.I.C.S.: 519290
Anirudhsinh Noghubha Jadeja *(Mng Dir)*

Subsidiaries:

Airlink Communications Pvt. Ltd. (1)
1-2 1st Floor Annapurna Shopping Center Opp Dhanmora Complex, Adajan Patia, Surat, 395 009, India
Tel.: (91) 2616697777
Web Site: https://airlinkcpl.net
Data & Internet Services
N.A.I.C.S.: 517111

GTPL KCBPL Broadband Private Limited (1)
86 Golaghata Road Ganga Apartment 6th Floor, Kolkata, 700048, India

GTPL HATHWAY LTD.

GTPL Hathway Ltd.—(Continued)
Tel.: (91) 3366000000
Web Site: https://www.gtplkcbpl.com
Wired Telecommunication Services
N.A.I.C.S.: 517112
Anirudh Sinh Jadeja *(Chm)*

GTV ENGINEERING LTD.
216-218 New Industrial Area-II, Mandideep, Bhopal, 462 046, Madhya Pradesh, India
Tel.: (91) 7480401044
Web Site: https://www.gtv.co.in
539479—(BOM)
Rev.: $7,920,267
Assets: $6,842,628
Liabilities: $3,299,964
Net Worth: $3,542,664
Earnings: $78,396
Emp.: 22
Fiscal Year-end: 03/31/21
Power Plant Construction Services
N.A.I.C.S.: 237990
Mahesh Agrawal *(Mng Dir)*

GU, RENSOW LTD.
Shepherds Bldg, Rockley Rd, London, W14 0DA, United Kingdom
Tel.: (44) 2076031660
Web Site: http://www.gupuds.com
Sales Range: $25-49.9 Million
Emp.: 250
Pudding Mfr
N.A.I.C.S.: 311919
James Averdieck *(Founder & Mng Dir)*

GUALA CLOSURES S.P.A.
Via Rana 10/12-Zona Industriale D6, Spinetta Marengo, 15122, Turin, Alessandria, Italy
Tel.: (39) 01317531
Web Site: http://www.gualaclosures.com
Year Founded: 1954
GCL—(ITA)
Rev.: $950,838,550
Assets: $1,685,880,639
Liabilities: $931,616,663
Net Worth: $754,263,976
Earnings: $73,818,260
Emp.: 5,040
Fiscal Year-end: 12/31/22
Spirit & Wine Product Mfr
N.A.I.C.S.: 312140
Gabriele Del Torchio *(Chm & CEO)*

Subsidiaries:

Guala Closures (Chengdu) Co., Ltd. (1)
No 9-1 Gongye Avenue, Qionglai, 611530, Sichuan, China
Tel.: (86) 13568905359
Aluminium Products Mfr
N.A.I.C.S.: 327999

Guala Closures Deutschland GmbH (1)
Mainzer Strasse 185, 67547, Worms, Germany
Tel.: (49) 624140010
Web Site: https://www.gualaclosures.de
Emp.: 160
Aluminium Products Mfr
N.A.I.C.S.: 327999

Guala Closures North America, Inc. (1)
2300 S Watney Way, Fairfield, CA 94533
Tel.: (707) 425-2277
Packaging Machinery Distr
N.A.I.C.S.: 423840
Randy Weller *(Mgr-QA & CTS)*

Guala Closures Technologia Ukraine LLC (1)
18 Liniyna Str, 40007, Sumy, Ukraine
Tel.: (380) 542659192
Polymers Mfr
N.A.I.C.S.: 326140

Guala Closures Turkey Ambalaj ve Kapak Sistemleri Sanayi ve Ticaret Anonim Sirketi (1)
Ankara plant Neorama Plaza Kat 6 No 28, Sogutozu, 06510, Ankara, Turkiye
Tel.: (90) 5327157591
Packaging Services
N.A.I.C.S.: 561910

closurelogic GmbH (1)
Mainzer Strasse 185, 67547, Worms, Germany
Tel.: (49) 624140010
Emp.: 160
Metal Closure Mfr
N.A.I.C.S.: 332119

GUAN CHAO HOLDINGS LIMITED
Room 5705 57th Floor The Center 99 Queens Road, Central, China (Hong Kong)
Tel.: (852) 65909973
Web Site: http://www.guanchaoholdingsltd.com
Year Founded: 1989
1872—(HKG)
Rev.: $132,792,269
Assets: $116,385,840
Liabilities: $69,039,582
Net Worth: $47,346,258
Earnings: $3,725,296
Emp.: 93
Fiscal Year-end: 12/31/22
Automotive Retailer
N.A.I.C.S.: 441110
Vincent Tan *(Chm & CEO)*

GUAN CHONG BERHAD
Plo 273 Jalan Timah 2, 81700, Pasir Gudang, Pasir Gudang Johor, Malaysia
Tel.: (60) 72548888
Web Site: https://www.gcbcocoa.com
GCB—(KLS)
Rev.: $935,415,645
Assets: $774,682,399
Liabilities: $427,898,204
Net Worth: $346,784,195
Earnings: $31,197,981
Emp.: 1,268
Fiscal Year-end: 12/31/22
Cocoa Mfr
N.A.I.C.S.: 311352
Cheng Hia *(CFO)*

Subsidiaries:

Carlyle Cocoa Co., LLC (1)
23 Harbor View Dr, New Castle, DE 19720
Tel.: (302) 428-3800
Web Site: https://www.gcbcocoa.com
Cocoa Liquor & Cocoa Butter Mfr
N.A.I.C.S.: 311351

GCB Cocoa Singapore Pte. Ltd. (1)
2 Venture Drive 11-12 Vision Exchange, Singapore, 608526, Singapore
Tel.: (65) 62543752
Web Site: http://www.favorich.com
Cocoa Liquor & Cocoa Butter Mfr
N.A.I.C.S.: 311351
Elsa Tay *(Dir-Comml)*

Subsidiary (Non-US):

PT Asia Cocoa Indonesia (2)
JL Engku Putri Type 7A-F Kawasan Industri Tunas Centre, Batam, 29464, Indonesia
Tel.: (62) 7784043888
Cocoa Liquor & Cocoa Butter Mfr
N.A.I.C.S.: 311351

GCB Cocoa UK Limited (1)
Lower Road, Glemsford, Sudbury, CO10 7QR, Suffolk, United Kingdom
Tel.: (44) 1787703740
Web Site: https://www.gcbcocoa.co.uk
Cocoa Product Mfr
N.A.I.C.S.: 311351

GCB Foods Sdn. Bhd. (1)
725 Jalan Keluli 9, Pasir Gudang Industrial Estate, 81700, Pasir Gudang, Johor, Malaysia
Tel.: (60) 72552203
Web Site: http://www.gcbfoods.com
Chocolate & Beverage Mfr
N.A.I.C.S.: 311351

Guan Chong Cocoa Manufacturer Sdn. Bhd. (1)
PLO 273 Jalan Timah 2, 81700, Pasir Gudang, Johor, Malaysia
Tel.: (60) 72511588
Cocoa Liquor & Cocoa Butter Mfr
N.A.I.C.S.: 311351

GUANAJUATO SILVER COMPANY LTD.
Year Founded: 1978
VAN—(OTCIQ)
Rev.: $59,328
Assets: $1,813,388
Liabilities: $253,242
Net Worth: $1,560,146
Earnings: ($390,101)
Emp.: 2
Fiscal Year-end: 12/31/19
Oil & Gas Exploration & Development Services
N.A.I.C.S.: 211120
James Anderson *(Chm & CEO)*

GUANDAO PUER INVESTMENT CO., LTD.
32 Avenue Monterey, LU-2163, Luxembourg, Luxembourg
Tel.: (352) 27 44 96 57
Web Site: http://www.yngdsm.com
Year Founded: 2015
MLGDI—(EUR)
Sales Range: Less than $1 Million
Investment Management Service
N.A.I.C.S.: 525990

GUANFU HOLDINGS CO., LTD.
9F Building No 8 Chengfa New Era No 106 Yuanlin North Road, Shashi District, Jingzhou, 434000, Hubei, China
Tel.: (86) 7168029666
Web Site: http://www.guanfu.com
Year Founded: 2002
002102—(SSE)
Rev.: $1,721,344,716
Assets: $1,284,626,304
Liabilities: $720,913,284
Net Worth: $563,713,020
Earnings: $62,404,992
Fiscal Year-end: 12/31/22
Investment Services
N.A.I.C.S.: 523999
Wenchang Lin *(Chm)*

GUANGBO GROUP STOCK CO., LTD.
Chehe Shiqi Street, Haishu District, Ningbo, 315153, Zhejiang, China
Tel.: (86) 57428827003
Web Site: http://www.guangbo.net
Year Founded: 2001
002103—(SSE)
Rev.: $349,091,964
Assets: $283,727,340
Liabilities: $174,880,836
Net Worth: $108,846,504
Earnings: ($5,085,288)
Fiscal Year-end: 12/31/22
Office Stationery Mfr & Distr
N.A.I.C.S.: 322230
Wang Liping *(Chm)*

GUANGDONG ADVERTISING GROUP CO., LTD.
Block G Poly World Trade Center No 996 Xiaogang East Road, Haizhu Dist, Guangzhou, 510220, Guangdong, China
Tel.: (86) 2087617378
Year Founded: 1981

INTERNATIONAL PUBLIC

002400—(SSE)
Advertising Consulting Agency Services
N.A.I.C.S.: 541810
Dianlong Chen *(Chm)*

GUANGDONG ADWAY CONSTRUCTION (GROUP) HOLDINGS COMPANY LIMITED
3/F No 1 Building Pengyi Garden 1st BaGua Rd, Futian District, Shenzhen, 518029, Guangdong, China
Tel.: (86) 75582222269
Web Site: https://www.aidewei.cn
Year Founded: 1996
6189—(HKG)
Rev.: $139,507,409
Assets: $329,823,321
Liabilities: $184,254,130
Net Worth: $145,569,191
Earnings: ($50,827,137)
Emp.: 335
Fiscal Year-end: 12/31/20
Building Decoration Services
N.A.I.C.S.: 541310
Yujing Ye *(Founder, Chm & CEO)*

GUANGDONG ANJUBAO DIGITAL TECHNOLOGY CO., LTD.
Anjubao Technology Park No 6 Qiyun Road Science City, Guangzhou, 510663, China
Tel.: (86) 2082083888
Web Site: http://www.anjubao.com
Year Founded: 2004
300155—(CHIN)
Rev.: $61,350,588
Assets: $223,973,100
Liabilities: $31,074,732
Net Worth: $192,898,368
Earnings: ($6,574,932)
Fiscal Year-end: 12/31/22
Video Monitoring Systems & Communication Equipment Mfr
N.A.I.C.S.: 334310
Zhang Bo *(Chm & Gen Mgr)*

Subsidiaries:

Guangdong Anjubao Display Technology Co., Ltd. (1)
No 21 Nanxiang Second Road Science City, Display Science and Technology Industrial Park, Guangzhou, China
Tel.: (86) 2083931288
Web Site: https://www.ajbdp.com
Emp.: 500
Liquid Crystal Display Mfr & Distr
N.A.I.C.S.: 334419

GUANGDONG AOFEI DATA TECHNOLOGY CO., LTD.
South Communications Building 9th Floor No 1 Huajing Road, Tianhe District, Guangzhou, China
Tel.: (86) 4006283286
Web Site: https://www.ofidc.com
300738—(CHIN)
Rev.: $188,005,805
Assets: $1,209,707,352
Liabilities: $775,183,849
Net Worth: $434,523,504
Earnings: $19,906,049
Fiscal Year-end: 12/31/23
Computer System Integration Services
N.A.I.C.S.: 541512

GUANGDONG AVCIT TECHNOLOGY HOLDING CO., LTD.
AVCiT Tower No 83 Qide Road, Baiyun District, Guangzhou, 510440, China
Tel.: (86) 2089301789
Web Site: https://www.avcit.com
001229—(SSE)
Rev.: $27,490,320
Assets: $138,079,188

AND PRIVATE COMPANIES — GUANGDONG DONGFANG SCIENCE & TECHNOLOGY CO., LTD.

Liabilities: $9,013,680
Net Worth: $129,065,508
Earnings: $11,904,516
Fiscal Year-end: 12/31/22
Holding Company
N.A.I.C.S.: 551112
Fang Hua (Chm & Gen Mgr)

GUANGDONG BAOLIHUA NEW ENERGY STOCK CO., LTD.
Baolihua Comprehensive Building Xianggang Garden OCT, Meixian, Meizhou, 514788, Guangdong, China
Tel.: (86) 7532511298
Web Site: http://www.baolihua.com.cn
Year Founded: 1997
000690—(SSE)
Rev.: $1,321,866,000
Assets: $2,821,521,924
Liabilities: $1,236,671,280
Net Worth: $1,584,850,644
Earnings: $25,717,068
Fiscal Year-end: 12/31/22
Eletric Power Generation Services
N.A.I.C.S.: 221115
Zou Jinkai (Chm)

GUANGDONG BIOLIGHT MEDITECH CO., LTD.
2 Innovation First Road Technical Innovation Coast, Hi-tech Zone, Zhuhai, 519085, Guangdong, China
Tel.: (86) 7563399935
Web Site: https://www.blt.com.cn
Year Founded: 1993
300246—(CHIN)
Rev.: $166,191,480
Assets: $342,415,944
Liabilities: $131,473,368
Net Worth: $210,942,576
Earnings: $3,088,800
Emp.: 300
Fiscal Year-end: 12/31/22
Medical Instrument Mfr
N.A.I.C.S.: 339112
Jinyuan Yan (Chm & Pres)

GUANGDONG BOBAOLON CO., LTD.
Bobaolon Creative Industry Park Northern Dade Rd To The West, Southern Xinmei Rd Liushadong Street Puning City, Guangdong, 515300, China
Tel.: (86) 6632769999
Web Site: http://www.bobaolon.net
002776—(SSE)
Rev.: $16,042,104
Assets: $74,284,236
Liabilities: $167,587,056
Net Worth: ($93,302,820)
Earnings: ($114,838,776)
Emp.: 1,000
Fiscal Year-end: 12/31/22
Apparel Custom Designing Services
N.A.I.C.S.: 458110

Subsidiaries:

Shenzhen 1wor United Design Co. Ltd. (1)
Room A801 Floor 8/ Room 701 Floor 7 A District Junction of Langqin Rd, Chengshiliren Industrial Park and Dalang Street Longhua New District, Shenzhen, China
Tel.: (86) 75521002364
Men's Clothing Mfr
N.A.I.C.S.: 315250

GUANGDONG BRANDMAX MARKETING CO., LTD.
7F Tower B Pingyun Plaza No 163 West Pingyun Road Huangpu Avenue, Tianhe, Guangzhou, 510627, Guangdong, China
Tel.: (86) 2038205688
Web Site: http://www.brandmax.com
Year Founded: 2010
300805—(SSE)
Rev.: $305,346,132
Assets: $311,803,128
Liabilities: $102,497,616
Net Worth: $209,305,512
Earnings: ($20,725,848)
Fiscal Year-end: 12/31/22
Digital Marketing Services
N.A.I.C.S.: 541870
Dingjiao Liang (Chm)

GUANGDONG CHAMPION ASIA ELECTRONICS CO., LTD.
25 Digital Industrial Park, Sandong Town Huicheng District, Huizhou, 516003, Guangdong, China
Tel.: (86) 7522595831
Web Site: https://www.championasia.hk
Year Founded: 2009
603386—(SHG)
Rev.: $361,224,953
Assets: $501,264,897
Liabilities: $289,628,675
Net Worth: $211,636,222
Earnings: $22,832,662
Emp.: 1,500
Fiscal Year-end: 12/31/22
Printed Circuit Board Mfr & Distr
N.A.I.C.S.: 334412

GUANGDONG CHANT GROUP CO., LTD.
No 42 Gongye South Avenue, Xiaolan Town, Zhongshan, 528415, Guangdong, China
Tel.: (86) 76022583660
Web Site: http://www.chinachant.com
Year Founded: 1985
002616—(SSE)
Rev.: $474,111,528
Assets: $1,360,206,843
Liabilities: $1,012,677,393
Net Worth: $347,529,450
Earnings: $10,578,049
Fiscal Year-end: 12/31/22
Gas Grills & Gas Heating Appliances
N.A.I.C.S.: 335220

GUANGDONG CHAOHUA TECHNOLOGY CO., LTD.
Chaohua Industrial Park, Yanyang, Meizhou, 514759, Guagndong, China
Tel.: (86) 7538588528
Web Site: https://www.chaohuatech.com
002288—(SSE)
Rev.: $242,493,264
Assets: $429,649,272
Liabilities: $242,706,672
Net Worth: $186,942,600
Earnings: ($47,135,088)
Fiscal Year-end: 12/31/22
Electronic Components Mfr
N.A.I.C.S.: 334412
Jianfeng Liang (Chm)

Subsidiaries:

Guangzhou Taihua Multilayer Circuit Board Co., Ltd. (1)
o 1 Industrial Zone Lianglong West Street, Huashan Town Huadu District, Guangzhou, China
Tel.: (86) 2066803939
Emp.: 800
Multi Layer Circuit Board Mfr
N.A.I.C.S.: 334412

Huizhou Uniplus Electronics Co., Ltd. (1)
Daya Bay Economic and Technology Development Zone, Xiangshui Rever Industrial Park, Huizhou, Guangdong, China
Tel.: (86) 7525769188
Multi Layer Circuit Board Mfr
N.A.I.C.S.: 334412

Meizhou Chaohua CNC Technology Co., Ltd. (1)
Chaohua Industrial Park Yanyang, Meizhou, Guangdong, China
Tel.: (86) 7538588528
CNC Drilling Machine Mfr
N.A.I.C.S.: 333310

Meizhou Taihua Printed Circuit Board Co., Ltd. (1)
Ad9 Area Dongsheng Industrial Park, Meizhou, Guangdong, China
Tel.: (86) 7538588608
Multi Layer Circuit Board Mfr
N.A.I.C.S.: 334412

GUANGDONG CHJ INDUSTRY CO., LTD.
12F CHJ Plaza Office Building No 98 Nanbin Road, Haojiang District, Shantou, 515073, Guangdong, China
Tel.: (86) 75488781767
Web Site: http://www.chjchina.com
Year Founded: 2006
002345—(SSE)
Rev.: $620,204,364
Assets: $779,653,836
Liabilities: $275,404,428
Net Worth: $504,249,408
Earnings: $27,957,852
Emp.: 2,100
Fiscal Year-end: 12/31/22
Jewelry Designer, Mfr & Distr
N.A.I.C.S.: 339910
Chuangbin Liao (Chm, Pres & Gen Mgr)

GUANGDONG CREATE CENTURY INTELLIGENT EQUIPMENT GROUP CORPORATION LIMITED
Administrative Office Building Weifeng Road, Jinsheng Intelligent Manufacturing Industrial Park Dongcheng District, Dongguan, 523007, Guangdong, China
Tel.: (86) 76982288265
Web Site: http://www.januscn.com
Year Founded: 2003
300083—(SSE)
Rev.: $635,576,760
Assets: $1,235,317,824
Liabilities: $588,586,284
Net Worth: $646,731,540
Earnings: $47,038,212
Emp.: 2,000
Fiscal Year-end: 12/31/22
Communication Equipment Mfr & Distr
N.A.I.C.S.: 334290
Jun Xia (Chm)

GUANGDONG DCENTI AUTO-PARTS STOCK LIMITED COMPANY
No 2-4 Fu'an West Road, Dajiang Town, Taishan, Guangdong, China
Tel.: (86) 7505588101
Web Site: https://www.dcenti.cn
Year Founded: 2001
603335—(SHG)
Rev.: $235,510,456
Assets: $230,955,824
Liabilities: $139,297,284
Net Worth: $91,658,539
Earnings: ($5,396,850)
Emp.: 100
Fiscal Year-end: 12/31/22
Alloy Wheel Mfr & Distr
N.A.I.C.S.: 336390

GUANGDONG DELIAN GROUP CO., LTD.
No 386 Songgang Hongling 2nd Road, Shishan Town Nanhai District, Guangdong, 528200, Guangdong, China
Tel.: (86) 75763220244
Web Site: http://www.delian.cn
Year Founded: 1992
002666—(SSE)
Rev.: $685,420,164
Assets: $711,822,384
Liabilities: $237,611,556
Net Worth: $474,210,828
Earnings: $5,750,784
Emp.: 380
Fiscal Year-end: 12/31/22
Automotive Chemical Mfr
N.A.I.C.S.: 325998
Xu Tuanhua (Chm)

Subsidiaries:

DELIAN TRADING (HK) CO., LTD. (1)
Flat A 8/F 186-188 Nathan Rd TST, Kowloon, China (Hong Kong)
Tel.: (852) 21997555
Web Site: http://www.delian.cn
Sales Range: $50-74.9 Million
Emp.: 1
Automotive Chemical Distr
N.A.I.C.S.: 424690
Robert Kuok (Mgr)

SHANGHIA DELIAN CHEMICAL CO., LTD. (1)
No 199 Taitao Road Fangtia Dazhong Third Industry Zone, Anting Town Jiading District, Shanghai, China
Tel.: (86) 21 59507558
Automotive Chemical Mfr
N.A.I.C.S.: 325998

GUANGDONG DONGFANG SCIENCE & TECHNOLOGY CO., LTD.
No 2 Qiangshi Road, Shishan Town Nanhai District, Foshan, 518000, Guangdong, China
Tel.: (86) 75786692362
Web Site: https://www.vmtdf.com
Year Founded: 1996
002611—(SSE)
Rev.: $546,536,484
Assets: $972,772,632
Liabilities: $373,826,232
Net Worth: $598,946,400
Earnings: $62,784,072
Fiscal Year-end: 12/31/22
Corrugated Carton Machinery Mfr
N.A.I.C.S.: 333993
Yezhi Qiu (Gen Mgr)

Subsidiaries:

Dongfang Digicom Technology (Guangdong) Co., Ltd. (1)
No 2 Zhenqiangshi Road, Nanhai District, Foshan, 528225, China
Tel.: (86) 75786695482
Web Site: https://www.df-global.cn
Printing & Packaging Product Mfr & Distr
N.A.I.C.S.: 326112

Edf Europe S.r.l. (1)
Via della Meccanica 10, 40050, Argelato, BO, Italy
Tel.: (39) 0516631220
Web Site: https://www.edfeurope.com
Converting Machine Mfr
N.A.I.C.S.: 333243

QuantumCorrugated S.r.l. (1)
Via Lecco 72, 20871, Vimercate, MB, Italy
Tel.: (39) 03960871
Web Site: https://www.quantumcorrugated.com
Machinery Mfr & Distr
N.A.I.C.S.: 333248

Tiruna America Inc. (1)
1333 Parkview Rd, Green Bay, WI 54304
Tel.: (920) 338-6650
Web Site: https://www.tirunaamerica.com
Rolled Steel Shape Mfr & Distr
N.A.I.C.S.: 331221

Guangdong Dongfang Science & Technology Co., Ltd.—(Continued)

GUANGDONG DOWSTONE TECHNOLOGY CO., LTD.
Dowstone Office Building Yishui 3rd Road, Nanzhuang Town Chancheng District, Foshan, 528000, Guangdong, China
Tel.: (86) 75782106880
Web Site: https://www.dowstone.com.cn
Year Founded: 2007
300409—(CHIN)
Rev.: $963,443,052
Assets: $1,643,143,320
Liabilities: $748,187,388
Net Worth: $894,955,932
Earnings: $12,101,076
Emp.: 590
Fiscal Year-end: 12/31/22
Inorganic Non-Metallic Glazed Materials, Including Glaze, Pigments, Ceramic Ink & Auxiliary Materials
N.A.I.C.S.: 325130
Jihua Rong *(Chm & Pres)*

GUANGDONG DP CO., LTD.
16/F Yikai Building No 1637 Beitai Road Guangzhou Private Science Park, Baiyun, Guangzhou, 510450, Guangdong, China
Tel.: (86) 2037314588
Web Site: https://www.dp-light.com
Year Founded: 2002
300808—(SSE)
Rev.: $71,003,088
Assets: $193,544,208
Liabilities: $45,544,356
Net Worth: $147,999,852
Earnings: ($3,824,496)
Fiscal Year-end: 12/31/22
Lighting Product Mfr & Distr
N.A.I.C.S.: 335131
Chuguang Zhuo *(Board of Directors, Chm & Gen Mgr)*

GUANGDONG DTECH TECHNOLOGY CO., LTD.
Room 102 Building 2 No 12 Yihuan Road Chiling Industry, Houjie Town, Dongguan, 523960, Guangdong, China
Tel.: (86) 76989277168
Web Site: https://www.dtechs.cn
Year Founded: 2013
301377—(CHIN)
Rev.: $185,947,126
Assets: $447,808,970
Liabilities: $121,112,986
Net Worth: $326,695,985
Earnings: $30,888,437
Fiscal Year-end: 12/31/23
Industrial Machinery Mfr & Distr
N.A.I.C.S.: 333248
Hui Xu *(CFO)*

Subsidiaries:

Dongguan Chaozhi New Materials Co., Ltd. (1)
103 Room 2nd Bulidings No 12 First-Ring Road Chiling Industry, Houjie Town, Dongguan, China
Tel.: (86) 76989277168
Industrial Machinery Mfr
N.A.I.C.S.: 333248

Dongguan Dingtaixin Elec. Co., Ltd. (1)
Room 101 Building 1 No 12 First Ring Road Chiling Industry, Houjie Town, Dongguan, China
Tel.: (86) 76989277168
Industrial Machinery Mfr
N.A.I.C.S.: 333248

Guangdong UCAN Robot Technology Co., Ltd. (1)
101 Room 2nd Bulidings No 12 First-ring Road, Guangdong, China
Tel.: (86) 76989207168
Industrial Machinery Mfr
N.A.I.C.S.: 333924

Nanyang Dtech Co., Ltd. (1)
Intersection of Zhongxing Road & Heyuan Road, Xinye County, Nanyang, 473500, China
Tel.: (86) 76989277168
Industrial Machinery Mfr
N.A.I.C.S.: 333248

GUANGDONG ELLINGTON ELECTRONICS TECH CO., LTD.
88 Gaoping Industrial Zone Sanjiao Town, Zhongshan, 528445, Guangdong, China
Tel.: (86) 76085409988
Web Site: https://www.ellingtonpcb.com
Year Founded: 2000
603328—(SHG)
Rev.: $429,364,471
Assets: $691,660,818
Liabilities: $189,631,583
Net Worth: $502,029,235
Earnings: $37,703,269
Fiscal Year-end: 12/31/22
Circuit Board Mfr & Distr
N.A.I.C.S.: 334412

GUANGDONG ENPACK PACKAGING CO., LTD.
ENPACK Industrial Park Da'nan Road Haojiang District, Shantou, Guangdong, China
Tel.: (86) 75489816868
Web Site: https://www.enpackcorp.com.cn
002846—(SSE)
Rev.: $271,617,840
Assets: $382,787,964
Liabilities: $270,510,084
Net Worth: $112,277,880
Earnings: ($6,056,856)
Emp.: 1,083
Fiscal Year-end: 12/31/22
Metal Packaging Product Mfr & Distr
N.A.I.C.S.: 332431

GUANGDONG FAILONG CRYSTAL TECHNOLOGY CO., LTD.
No 68 HuangJiang DongHuan Road, HuangJiang Town, Dongguan, 523757, GuangDong, China
Tel.: (86) 76938879888
Web Site: https://www.dgylec.com
Year Founded: 2002
300460—(CHIN)
Rev.: $55,439,748
Assets: $271,539,216
Liabilities: $124,136,064
Net Worth: $147,403,152
Earnings: ($18,938,556)
Emp.: 900
Fiscal Year-end: 12/31/22
Piezoelectric Quartz Crystal Resonators
N.A.I.C.S.: 335999
Zhao Jiqing *(Chm & Gen Mgr)*

GUANGDONG FENGHUA ADVANCED TECHNOLOGY (HOLDING) CO., LTD.
Fenghua Road, Duanzhou District, Zhaoqing, 526020, Guangdong, China
Tel.: (86) 7582865325
Web Site: https://www.fhcomp.com
Year Founded: 1994
000636—(SSE)
Rev.: $543,899,772
Assets: $2,220,677,316
Liabilities: $534,342,744
Net Worth: $1,686,334,572
Earnings: $45,916,416
Fiscal Year-end: 12/31/22
Electric Equipment Mfr
N.A.I.C.S.: 334419
Li Cheng *(Chm)*

Subsidiaries:

FengHua Advanced Technology (HK) Ltd (1)
Rm 1606 Westley Square 48 Hoi Yuen Rd Kwun Tong, Kowloon, 15434, China (Hong Kong)
Tel.: (852) 25416302
Electronic Equipment Distr
N.A.I.C.S.: 423690

GUANGDONG FUXIN TECHNOLOGY CO., LTD.
No 20 Keyuan 3rd Road, Shunde High-tech Zone Ronggui, Foshan, 528305, Guangdong, China
Tel.: (86) 75728812666
Web Site: https://www.fuxin-cn.com
Year Founded: 2003
688662—(SHG)
Rev.: $70,385,174
Assets: $132,234,153
Liabilities: $29,725,165
Net Worth: $102,508,988
Earnings: $7,737,205
Fiscal Year-end: 12/31/22
Semiconductor Product Mfr & Distr
N.A.I.C.S.: 334413
Fulin Liu *(Chm & Gen Mgr)*

GUANGDONG GALANZ GROUP CO., LTD.
No 25 Ronggui Nan Rd, Shunde District, Foshan, 528305, Guangdong, China
Tel.: (86) 75728886389
Web Site: http://www.galanz.com
Sales Range: $1-4.9 Billion
Emp.: 28,000
Microwave Ovens, Air Conditioners & Household Appliances Mfr
N.A.I.C.S.: 335220
Leung Chiuyin *(Vice Chm & CEO)*

Subsidiaries:

Galanz (North America) Inc. (1)
115E Ogden Ave Ste117-368, Naperville, IL 60563
Tel.: (800) 562-0738
Household Appliance Distr
N.A.I.C.S.: 423620

GUANGDONG GANHUA SCIENCE & INDUSTRY CO LTD.
No 62 Ganhua Road, Pengjiang District, Jiangmen, 529030, Guangdong, China
Tel.: (86) 7503277650
Web Site: http://www.gdganhua.com
Year Founded: 1993
000576—(SSE)
Rev.: $62,531,352
Assets: $281,737,872
Liabilities: $30,565,080
Net Worth: $251,172,792
Earnings: $16,765,164
Fiscal Year-end: 12/31/22
Paper Products Mfr
N.A.I.C.S.: 322299
Hu Yuhuang *(Chm)*

GUANGDONG GENSHO LOGISTICS CO., LTD.
No 25 Dongzhong Road East Zone, Economic and Technological Development Zone, Guangzhou, 510530, Guangdong, China
Tel.: (86) 2082394665
Web Site: http://www.gsl.cc
Year Founded: 2005
603813—(SHG)
Rev.: $72,922,440
Assets: $186,523,436
Liabilities: $89,022,052
Net Worth: $97,501,384
Earnings: $5,286,748
Fiscal Year-end: 12/31/22
Logistic Services
N.A.I.C.S.: 541614
Junhua Yu *(Chm & Pres)*

GUANGDONG GOLDEN DRAGON DEVELOPMENT INC.
Golden Dragon Building No 1 Fangzheng 2nd Street, Qingyuan, 511518, Guangdong, China
Tel.: (86) 7633369393
Web Site: http://www.jlgf.com
Year Founded: 1997
000712—(SSE)
Rev.: $34,733,556
Assets: $3,168,052,992
Liabilities: $2,460,397,680
Net Worth: $707,655,312
Earnings: ($55,050,840)
Fiscal Year-end: 12/31/22
Tap Water Services
N.A.I.C.S.: 221310
Haimei Zhang *(CFO)*

GUANGDONG GOWORLD CO., LTD.
No 12 Longjiang Road Longhu District, Shantou, 515065, Guangdong, China
Tel.: (86) 75488192281
Web Site: http://www.gd-goworld.com
000823—(SSE)
Rev.: $936,872,352
Assets: $1,205,384,544
Liabilities: $494,501,436
Net Worth: $710,883,108
Earnings: $58,517,316
Fiscal Year-end: 12/31/22
Electronic Products Mfr
N.A.I.C.S.: 334419
Mo Yibin *(Chm)*

Subsidiaries:

China Circuit Technology (Shantou) Corporation (1)
Wangji Industrial Dist, Longhu, Shantou, 515065, Guangdong, China
Tel.: (86) 75488192282
Printed Circuit Board Mfr
N.A.I.C.S.: 334412

Shantou Goworld Display Co., Ltd. (1)
21Xingye Rd, Shantou, 515041, Guangdong, China
Tel.: (86) 75488192283
Web Site: https://www.goworld-lcd.com
Liquid Crystal Display Mfr & Distr
N.A.I.C.S.: 334419

GUANGDONG GREAT RIVER SMARTER LOGISTICS CO., LTD.
Building No 1 Songkeyuan Songshan Lake Science & Technology, Industry Park, Dongguan, 523000, Guangdong, China
Tel.: (86) 76986002930
Web Site: https://www.grsl.cn
Year Founded: 2012
002930—(SSE)
Logistics & Warehousing Services
N.A.I.C.S.: 541614
Haichuan Lin *(Chm & Pres)*

GUANGDONG GREEN PRECISION COMPONENTS CO., LTD.
Sandong Digital Industrial Park, Huizhou, 516025, Guangdong, China
Tel.: (86) 7523315828
Web Site: https://www.green-cpc.com
Year Founded: 2002

AND PRIVATE COMPANIES

300968—(SSE)
Rev.: $220,150,008
Assets: $329,403,672
Liabilities: $58,750,380
Net Worth: $270,653,292
Earnings: $16,269,552
Fiscal Year-end: 12/31/22
Electronic Products Mfr
N.A.I.C.S.: 334419
Baoyu Wu *(Chm & Gen Mgr)*

GUANGDONG GUANGHONG HOLDINGS CO., LTD.
37F South Tower Yuexiu City Plaza
No 437 Dongfeng Middle Road,
Guangzhou, 510030, Guangdong,
China
Tel.: (86) 2083603985
Web Site:
  http://www.ghkg000529.com
Year Founded: 1985
000529—(SSE)
Rev.: $479,873,160
Assets: $803,823,696
Liabilities: $376,204,608
Net Worth: $427,619,088
Earnings: $128,713,104
Fiscal Year-end: 12/31/22
Holding Company
N.A.I.C.S.: 551112
Cai Biao *(Chm)*

GUANGDONG GUANGHUA SCI-TECH CO., LTD.
No 295 Daxue Road, Shantou,
Guangdong, China
Tel.: (86) 75488213888
Web Site: https://www.ghtech.com
002741—(SSE)
Rev.: $463,647,132
Assets: $523,515,096
Liabilities: $274,911,624
Net Worth: $248,603,472
Earnings: $16,408,548
Emp.: 150
Fiscal Year-end: 12/31/22
Specialty Chemicals Mfr
N.A.I.C.S.: 325998

GUANGDONG GUANGZHOU DAILY MEDIA CO., LTD.
Room 3001 30F No 138 Fangyuan
Road, Haizhu District, Guangzhou,
510308, Guangdong, China
Tel.: (86) 2088630181
Web Site: http://www.gdgzrb.com
Year Founded: 1992
002181—(SSE)
Rev.: $76,678,056
Assets: $779,847,588
Liabilities: $149,438,952
Net Worth: $630,408,636
Earnings: $6,226,740
Fiscal Year-end: 12/31/22
Advertising Operator
N.A.I.C.S.: 541810
Li Guiwen *(Chm)*

GUANGDONG GUANHAO HIGH-TECH CO., LTD.
No 313 Donghai Road Donghai Island, Zhanjiang, 524072, Guangdong, China
Tel.: (86) 7593399898
Web Site: https://www.guanhao.com
Year Founded: 1993
600433—(SHG)
Rev.: $1,135,270,792
Assets: $1,389,848,424
Liabilities: $382,268,330
Net Worth: $1,007,580,095
Earnings: $54,349,556
Fiscal Year-end: 12/31/22
Paper Mfr
N.A.I.C.S.: 322220
Xie Xianlong *(Chm)*

Subsidiaries:
Zhuhai Shenglong Bar Code Technology Co., Ltd. (1)
Factory Building Floor 1-3 Building 6 No 2603 Lvyou Road, Zhuhai, Guangdong, China
Tel.: (86) 756 8529350
Web Site: http://www.zhsltm.com
Paper Products Mfr
N.A.I.C.S.: 322299
Niki Jiang *(Mgr-Sls)*

GUANGDONG HAID GROUP CO., LTD.
7th Floor Building 2 Haid Building No 42 Wanbo 4th Road, Nancun Town Panyu District, Guangzhou, Guangdong, China
Tel.: (86) 2039388960
Web Site: https://www.haid.com.cn
Year Founded: 1998
002311—(SSE)
Rev.: $14,702,044,968
Assets: $6,210,984,312
Liabilities: $3,494,227,464
Net Worth: $2,716,756,848
Earnings: $414,761,256
Emp.: 40,000
Fiscal Year-end: 12/31/22
Animal Feed Mfr
N.A.I.C.S.: 311119
Hua Xue *(Chm)*

Subsidiaries:
PT. Haida Agriculture Indonesia (1)
Jl Kraton Industri Raya No 4 Sawah Pejangkungan Kec Kraton, Pasuruan, 67151, Jawa Timur, Indonesia
Tel.: (62) 3436745868
Web Site: https://haida.co.id
Consultancy Services
N.A.I.C.S.: 541611

Sheng Long Bio-tech (India) Pvt. Ltd. (1)
Plot No A-11/1 Part A, Sipcot Industrial Park Thervoy Kandigai Gummidipoondi Taluk, Thiruvallur, 601 202, Tamilnadu, India
Tel.: (91) 67901001
Web Site: https://shenglongindia.com
Fish Product Mfr & Distr
N.A.I.C.S.: 311999

GUANGDONG HAOMEI NEW MATERIAL CO., LTD.
TaiJi Industrial City, High-tech Industrial Development Zone, Qingyuan, 511540, Guangdong, China
Tel.: (86) 7633699776
Web Site: https://www.haomei-alu.com
Year Founded: 2004
002988—(SSE)
Rev.: $759,926,232
Assets: $740,647,908
Liabilities: $433,475,172
Net Worth: $307,172,736
Earnings: ($15,643,368)
Fiscal Year-end: 12/31/22
Aluminium Products Mfr
N.A.I.C.S.: 331313
Weifeng Dong *(Chm & Gen Mgr)*

GUANGDONG HEC TECHNOLOGY HOLDING CO., LTD.
No 5 Industrial Zone Shangsha Village, Changan Town, Dongguan, 523871, China
Tel.: (86) 7695370225
Web Site: http://www.hec-al.com
600673—(SHG)
Rev.: $1,642,538,280
Assets: $3,438,143,645
Liabilities: $2,008,581,242
Net Worth: $1,429,562,403
Earnings: $174,561,847
Emp.: 12,000
Fiscal Year-end: 12/31/22

Electronic Component Mfr & Distr
N.A.I.C.S.: 334419
Li Yitao *(Board of Directors & Gen Mgr)*

Subsidiaries:
Yichang HEC Changjiang Pharmaceutical Co., Ltd (1)
Dong YangGuang Park Zhen An Road No 368 Shangsha Village Chang'an Town, Dongguan, China (50.04%)
Web Site: http://cj.hec.cn
Rev.: $525,791,261
Assets: $1,669,327,920
Liabilities: $817,099,780
Net Worth: $852,228,140
Earnings: $6,913,156
Emp.: 4,167
Fiscal Year-end: 12/31/2022
Pharmaceutical Product Mfr & Distr
N.A.I.C.S.: 325412
Juncai Jiang *(Bd of Dirs & Gen Mgr)*

GUANGDONG HIGH DREAM INTELLECTUALIZED MACHINERY CO., LTD.
No 3 Longzhan Road, Huanglong Beijiao Town, Shunde, Guangdong, China
Tel.: (86) 75722393573
Web Site: https://www.highdream.net
300720—(CHIN)
Rev.: $31,761,605
Assets: $92,102,984
Liabilities: $8,582,329
Net Worth: $83,520,656
Earnings: $5,096,770
Emp.: 480
Fiscal Year-end: 12/31/23
Automatic Weighing Instrument Mfr & Distr
N.A.I.C.S.: 334519

GUANGDONG HIGHSUN GROUP CO., LTD.
No 98 Donghua South Road, Yuexiu District, Guangzhou, 510100, Guangdong, China
Tel.: (86) 2028828222
Web Site: https://www.000861.com
Year Founded: 1991
000861—(SHG)
Rev.: $162,871,020
Assets: $1,245,663,900
Liabilities: $772,945,524
Net Worth: $472,718,376
Earnings: ($53,795,664)
Fiscal Year-end: 12/31/22
Property Management Services
N.A.I.C.S.: 531312
Jianming Shao *(Chm)*

GUANGDONG HOMA APPLIANCES CO., LTD.
No 54 Dongfu North Rd, Nantou, Zhongshan, 528427, Guangdong, China
Tel.: (86) 76023136888
Web Site: https://www.homa.cn
Year Founded: 2002
002668—(SSE)
Rev.: $1,550,806,941
Assets: $1,093,611,448
Liabilities: $862,474,246
Net Worth: $231,137,202
Earnings: ($12,243,011)
Fiscal Year-end: 12/31/21
Refrigerator Mfr & Distr
N.A.I.C.S.: 335220
Liu Xiangdong *(Pres)*

GUANGDONG HONG KONG GREATER BAY AREA HOLDINGS LTD.
Level 42 Block E China Resources Land Building, No18 First Dachong

GUANGDONG HONGTU TECHNOLOGY (HOLDINGS) CO., LTD.

Road Nanshan District, Shenzhen, PRC, China
Tel.: (86) 75582833533 Ky
Web Site: http://www.hydoo.com.cn
1396—(HKG)
Rev.: $444,798,432
Assets: $3,188,119,100
Liabilities: $2,694,668,558
Net Worth: $493,450,542
Earnings: ($242,755,391)
Emp.: 855
Fiscal Year-end: 12/31/22
Commercial Building Construction
N.A.I.C.S.: 236220
Dewen Wang *(Co-CEO)*

GUANGDONG HONGCHUAN SMART LOGISTICS CO., LTD.
Administrative Building of Sanjiang Company, Lishadao Chemical District Shatian Town, Dongguan, China
Tel.: (86) 76986002930
Web Site: http://www.grsl.cn
Year Founded: 2012
002930—(SSE)
Rev.: $177,346,260
Assets: $1,286,191,764
Liabilities: $906,545,952
Net Worth: $379,645,812
Earnings: $31,401,864
Fiscal Year-end: 12/31/22
Petrochemical Products Mfr
N.A.I.C.S.: 325110
Lin Haichuan *(Chm & Pres)*

GUANGDONG HONGDA HOLDINGS GROUP CO., LTD.
21F North Tower Jinbin Tengyue Building No 49-2 Huaxia Road, Tianhe District Zhujiang New City, Guangzhou, 510623, Guangdong, China
Tel.: (86) 2038092888
Web Site: http://www.hdbp.com
Year Founded: 2003
002683—(SSE)
Rev.: $1,427,705,136
Assets: $2,152,736,352
Liabilities: $1,151,873,892
Net Worth: $1,000,862,460
Earnings: $78,732,108
Emp.: 2,100
Fiscal Year-end: 12/31/22
Explosives Mfr
N.A.I.C.S.: 325920
Bingxu Zheng *(Chm)*

GUANGDONG HONGMING INTELLIGENT JOINT STOCK CO., LTD.
Niushanqiantou New Industrial Zone, Dongcheng District, Dongguan, 523127, Guangdong, China
Tel.: (86) 76922187143
Web Site:
  https://www.dghongming.com
Year Founded: 1999
301105—(CHIN)
Rev.: $32,313,060
Assets: $150,110,064
Liabilities: $21,427,848
Net Worth: $128,682,216
Earnings: $5,527,548
Fiscal Year-end: 12/31/22
Packaging Products Mfr
N.A.I.C.S.: 322220
Jin Jian *(Chm & Gen Mgr)*

GUANGDONG HONGTU TECHNOLOGY (HOLDINGS) CO., LTD.
No 168 Century Road, Jindu Town Gaoyao District, Zhaoqing, 526108, Guangdong, China
Tel.: (86) 7588512898
Web Site: https://www.ght-china.com

GUANGDONG HONGTU TECHNOLOGY (HOLDINGS) CO., LTD.

Guangdong Hongtu Technology (Holdings) Co., Ltd.—(Continued)
Year Founded: 2000
002101—(SSE)
Rev.: $936,713,700
Assets: $1,284,207,912
Liabilities: $549,212,508
Net Worth: $734,995,404
Earnings: $65,340,756
Fiscal Year-end: 12/31/22
Holding Company
N.A.I.C.S.: 551112
Dan Zhaoxue *(Chm)*

Subsidiaries:

Changchun Fawsn Swell Automotive Parts Co., Ltd. (1)
No 8858 Silicon Valley Street, Chaoyang Economic Development Zone, Changchun, China
Tel.: (86) 43181909026
Die Casting Product Mfr
N.A.I.C.S.: 331523

Chengdu Fuyi Swell Auto Parts Co., Ltd. (1)
No 168 Auto City Avenue, Chengdu Economic & Technological Development Zone, Chengdu, China
Tel.: (86) 2865316165
Die Casting Product Mfr
N.A.I.C.S.: 331523

Dongguan Swell Auto Parts Co., Ltd. (1)
3rd Floor Unit A Hanguang Building Haofeng Electroplating, Printing & Dyeing Professional Base Masan Village Mayong Town, Dongguan, China
Tel.: (86) 76981257236
Die Casting Product Mfr
N.A.I.C.S.: 331523

Foshan Fuyi Swell Auto Parts Co., Ltd. (1)
No 1 Building Qianjin Middle Road Hongsha High-tech Development Zone, Nanhai Science & Technology Industrial Park Nanhai District, Foshan, China
Tel.: (86) 75785862640
Die Casting Product Mfr
N.A.I.C.S.: 331523

Guangdong Yueke Finance Group Co., Ltd. (1)
No 63 Juxin Street, Haizhu District, Guangzhou, 510000, China
Tel.: (86) 2087680388
Web Site: https://www.gvcgc.com
Financial Services
N.A.I.C.S.: 523940

Swell-Marui (Guangzhou) Automobile Parts Co., Ltd. (1)
No 15 Jun Gong Road East Zone, Luo Gang District, Guangzhou, 510530, China
Tel.: (86) 2062959018
Web Site: https://www.swellmarui.com
Automobile Parts Mfr
N.A.I.C.S.: 336390

GUANGDONG HONGXING INDUSTRIAL CO., LTD.
4F Yueneng Building No 45 Tianhe Road, Yuexiu, Guangzhou, 510030, Guangdong, China
Tel.: (86) 75487818668
Web Site: https://www.hongxinggf.com
Year Founded: 2004
001209—(SSE)
Rev.: $186,444,180
Assets: $213,471,180
Liabilities: $40,353,768
Net Worth: $173,117,412
Earnings: ($2,104,596)
Fiscal Year-end: 12/31/22
Apparel Product Mfr & Distr
N.A.I.C.S.: 315990
Guo Wuwen *(Chm)*

GUANGDONG HOSHION INDUSTRIAL ALUMINIUM CO., LTD.
No 5 Meiyuan Road Qianlong Industrial Zone Sanxiang Town, Zhongshan, 528463, Guangdong, China
Tel.: (86) 76086893888
Web Site: http://www.hoshion.com
Year Founded: 2005
002824—(SSE)
Rev.: $421,097,508
Assets: $426,977,460
Liabilities: $199,327,284
Net Worth: $227,650,176
Earnings: $28,725,840
Emp.: 1,200
Fiscal Year-end: 12/31/22
Aluminum Product Mfr & Distr
N.A.I.C.S.: 331315
Jianxiang Li *(Chm & Gen Mgr)*

GUANGDONG HOTATA TECHNOLOGY GROUP CO., LTD.
No 12 No 14 Jinyang 2nd Road, Hualong Town Panyu District, Guangzhou, 511434, Guangdong, China
Tel.: (86) 2061960999
Web Site: http://www.hotata.com
Year Founded: 2005
603848—(SHG)
Rev.: $194,035,201
Assets: $396,137,673
Liabilities: $52,947,999
Net Worth: $343,189,674
Earnings: $30,689,966
Fiscal Year-end: 12/31/22
Home Product Mfr
N.A.I.C.S.: 332618
Shen Hanbiao *(Chm)*

GUANGDONG HUAFENG NEW ENERGY TECHNOLOGY CO., LTD.
Duanzhou Industrial City Duanzhou 1st Road, Gaoyao District, Zhaoqing, 526108, Guangdong, China
Tel.: (86) 7588610151
Web Site: https://www.c-hfcc.com
Year Founded: 1995
002806—(SSE)
Rev.: $92,371,968
Assets: $272,311,416
Liabilities: $104,852,124
Net Worth: $167,459,292
Earnings: ($1,349,244)
Fiscal Year-end: 12/31/22
Aluminum Foil Product Mfr & Distr
N.A.I.C.S.: 331315
Guoying Tan *(Chm)*

GUANGDONG HUATE GAS CO., LTD.
Jinshun Road, Heshun Lishui Nanhai, Foshan, 528244, Guangdong, China
Tel.: (86) 75785126928
Web Site: https://www.huategas.com
Year Founded: 1999
688268—(SHG)
Rev.: $253,163,664
Assets: $336,197,080
Liabilities: $113,593,962
Net Worth: $222,603,119
Earnings: $28,956,264
Fiscal Year-end: 12/31/22
Oil & Gas Distribution Services
N.A.I.C.S.: 221210
Pingxiang Shi *(Chm)*

Subsidiaries:

Chenzhou Xiangneng Semiconductor Gas Co., Ltd. (1)
Xiangwei 3rd Road High-tech Industrial Park, Suxian District, Chenzhou, Hunan, China
Tel.: (86) 7352652488
Semiconductor Gas Mfr & Distr
N.A.I.C.S.: 325120

Guangdong Southern-China Specialty Gases Institute Co., Ltd. (1)
No 38-36 Heshun Guanhe Road, Lishui Town Nanhai District, Foshan, 528241, Guangdong, China
Tel.: (86) 75785109801
Web Site: http://www.gdscsg.com
Gas Equipment Mfr & Distr
N.A.I.C.S.: 332420

Jiangxi Huate Electronic Chemical Co., Ltd. (1)
No 31 Xingyun Avenue Yongxiu Yunshan Economic Development Zone, Jiujiang, 330300, Jiangxi, China
Tel.: (86) 7923058988
Electronic Chemical Product Mfr & Distr
N.A.I.C.S.: 325998

GUANGDONG HUATIE TONGDA HIGH-SPEED RAILWAY EQUIPMENT CO., LTD.
A138 No 2 Xianglong Middle Road, Kaiping, 529300, Guangdong, China
Tel.: (86) 7502299580
Web Site: http://www.my0976.com
Year Founded: 1993
000976—(SSE)
Sales Range: $250-299.9 Million
Polyester Fiber Product Mfr
N.A.I.C.S.: 325220

GUANGDONG HUIYUN TITANIUM INDUSTRY CO., LTD.
Fuxing Road, Liudu Town Yunan County, Yunfu, 527500, Guangdong, China
Tel.: (86) 7666938666
Web Site: https://www.gdtitanium.com
Year Founded: 2003
300891—(SSE)
Rev.: $212,352,192
Assets: $343,683,756
Liabilities: $155,136,384
Net Worth: $188,547,372
Earnings: $1,989,468
Emp.: 1,000
Fiscal Year-end: 12/31/22
Construction Services
N.A.I.C.S.: 236220
Zhenguang Zhong *(Chm)*

GUANGDONG HYBRIBIO BIOTECH CO., LTD.
35 F Enterprise Square 2 3 Sheung Yuet Road, Kowloon Bay, China (Hong Kong)
Tel.: (852) 28518029
Web Site: https://www.hybribio.cn
300639—(CHIN)
Rev.: $155,562,318
Assets: $806,477,662
Liabilities: $88,320,654
Net Worth: $718,157,008
Earnings: $19,785,509
Emp.: 180
Fiscal Year-end: 12/31/23
Pharmaceutical Product Mfr & Distr
N.A.I.C.S.: 325413

GUANGDONG INSIGHT BRAND MARKETING GROUP CO., LTD.
501 Building No 26 Tianan Headquarters Center No 555 Panyu Avenue, Donghuan Street Panyu District, Guangzhou, 511400, Guangdong, China
Tel.: (86) 2022620010
Web Site: http://www.gdinsight.com
Year Founded: 2002
300781—(SSE)
Rev.: $68,164,200
Assets: $139,208,004
Liabilities: $33,680,556

INTERNATIONAL PUBLIC

Net Worth: $105,527,448
Earnings: $4,554,576
Fiscal Year-end: 12/31/22
Media Advertising Services
N.A.I.C.S.: 541840
Jianchao Wang *(Chm)*

GUANGDONG JADIETE HOLDINGS GROUP CO., LTD.
Room 4003-4008, Shenzhen Intl Chamber of Commerce Twr, Shenzhen, 518000, Guangdong, China
Tel.: (86) 7558 223 0001
Web Site: http://www.200168.com
200168—(SSE)
Rev.: $2,728,259
Assets: $73,646,444
Liabilities: $23,949,173
Net Worth: $49,697,271
Earnings: $198,680
Emp.: 77
Fiscal Year-end: 12/31/19
Real Estate Development Services
N.A.I.C.S.: 531311
Jincai Chen *(CFO & VP)*

GUANGDONG JIA YUAN TECHNOLOGY SHARES CO., LTD.
Eco-Industrial Park, Yanyang Town Mei County, Meizhou, 514759, Guangdong, China
Tel.: (86) 7532825818
Web Site: http://www.gdjygf.com
Year Founded: 2001
688388—(SHG)
Rev.: $651,574,694
Assets: $1,515,726,389
Liabilities: $476,200,647
Net Worth: $1,039,525,742
Earnings: $73,078,818
Fiscal Year-end: 12/31/22
Copper Product Mfr
N.A.I.C.S.: 331420
Pingyuan Liao *(Chm & Gen Mgr)*

GUANGDONG JIALONG FOOD CO., LTD.
1-6F Office Building of Guangdong Jialong Food Co Ltd, Yinggeshan Industrial Park Piwu Village Daba Town, Puning, 515345, Guangdong, China
Tel.: (86) 6632912816
Web Site: http://www.gdjlfood.com
Year Founded: 2002
002495—(SSE)
Rev.: $29,147,040
Assets: $172,355,040
Liabilities: $8,977,176
Net Worth: $163,377,864
Earnings: ($7,689,708)
Emp.: 400
Fiscal Year-end: 12/31/22
Chicken Products
N.A.I.C.S.: 112320
Ping Tao Lin *(Chm)*

GUANGDONG JIANGMEN CENTER FOR BIOTECH DEVELOPMENT CO., LTD.
No 135 Jianghai Third Road, Jianghai District, Jiangmen, Guangdong, China
Tel.: (86) 7503976036
Web Site: http://www.jmbiot.com
Year Founded: 1984
Pharmaceuticals Product Mfr
N.A.I.C.S.: 325412

GUANGDONG JIAYING PHARMACEUTICAL CO., LTD.
Zone B Dongsheng Industrial Park, Meizhou, 514000, Guangdong, China
Tel.: (86) 7536133081

AND PRIVATE COMPANIES

GUANGDONG KINLONG HARDWARE PRDCTS CO., LTD.

Web Site: https://www.gdjyzy.com.cn
002198—(SSE)
Rev.: $92,551,680
Assets: $118,869,660
Liabilities: $16,599,492
Net Worth: $102,270,168
Earnings: $6,167,772
Fiscal Year-end: 12/31/22
Pharmaceuticals Mfr
N.A.I.C.S.: 325412
Jianning Chen *(Chm)*

GUANGDONG JINGYI METAL CO., LTD.
Xihai Industrial Zone, Shunde District
Beijiao Town, Foshan, 528311,
Guangdong, China
Tel.: (86) 75726632838
Web Site:
 https://www.jingyimetal.com
Year Founded: 1999
002295—(SSE)
Rev.: $674,153,064
Assets: $321,583,392
Liabilities: $138,292,596
Net Worth: $183,290,796
Earnings: $4,064,580
Emp.: 9,201
Fiscal Year-end: 12/31/22
Copper Product Mfr
N.A.I.C.S.: 331529
Huang Yuhui *(Chm)*

Subsidiaries:

Foshan Shunde District Jingyi Wanxi
Copper Industry Co., Ltd. (1)
Inside of Xihai Indust Zone, Foshan,
Guangdong, China
Tel.: (86) 13802647400
Metal Development & Mfr
N.A.I.C.S.: 332999

Shunde Tube & Rod Technology Co.,
Ltd. (1)
Xihai Indust Park Beijiao Shunde, Foshan,
Guangdong, China
Tel.: (86) 75726668258
Web Site: http://www.guanbang.cn
Sales Range: $50-74.9 Million
Emp.: 4
Metal Development & Mfr
N.A.I.C.S.: 332999

GUANGDONG JINMA ENTERTAINMENT CORPORATION LIMITED
Yanjiang East 3rd Road Torch Development Zone, Zhongshan, Guangdong, China
Tel.: (86) 76028132780
Web Site:
 https://www.jinmarides.com
Year Founded: 1983
300756—(CHIN)
Rev.: $104,011,443
Assets: $297,252,150
Liabilities: $98,677,947
Net Worth: $198,574,203
Earnings: $6,502,312
Fiscal Year-end: 12/31/23
Amusement Park Rides Mfr
N.A.I.C.S.: 333310
Liu Xiwang *(Pres)*

GUANGDONG JINMING MACHINERY CO., LTD.
Hepu Road, Haojiang District, Shantou, 515098, Guangdong, China
Tel.: (86) 75488207788
Web Site: https://www.jmjj.com
Year Founded: 1987
300281—(CHIN)
Rev.: $66,326,364
Assets: $207,799,020
Liabilities: $29,835,000
Net Worth: $177,964,020
Earnings: ($221,832)
Emp.: 340

Fiscal Year-end: 12/31/22
Plastic Products & Molding Machine
Mfr
N.A.I.C.S.: 333248

Subsidiaries:

Guangdong Jinming Machinery Co.,
Ltd. (1)
B2 Rm 906 Tian Chuang Shi Yuan Bldg
312, Ya Yun Cun Hui Zhong Bei Li, Beijing,
China
Tel.: (86) 10 64801790
Plastic Products & Molding Machine Mfr
N.A.I.C.S.: 333248

Guangdong Jinming Machinery Co.,
Ltd. (1)
Rm 1308 South Tower Times New World
Center, 2191 Guang Yuan Dong Rd,
Guangzhou, China
Tel.: (86) 20 87643983
Plastic Products & Molding Machinery Mfr
N.A.I.C.S.: 333248

Guangdong Jinming Machinery Co.,
Ltd. (1)
Hepu Road, Haojiang District, Shantou,
515098, Guangdong, China
Tel.: (86) 7548 820 7788
Web Site: https://www.jmjj.com
Plastic Products & Molding Machinery Mfr
N.A.I.C.S.: 333248

GUANGDONG JOIN-SHARE FINANCING GUARANTEE INVESTMENT CO., LTD.
Room 4101-4110 Block 1 Join-Share
Intl Financing Ctr, Lecong Town
Shunde District, Foshan, Guangdong,
China
Tel.: (86) 75783303188   CN
Web Site: http://www.join-share.com
Year Founded: 2003
1543—(HKG)
Rev.: $44,613,785
Assets: $515,427,775
Liabilities: $185,352,991
Net Worth: $330,074,784
Earnings: $7,369,736
Emp.: 307
Fiscal Year-end: 12/31/22
Financial Support Services
N.A.I.C.S.: 523940
Liejin Wu *(Chm)*

GUANGDONG JUSHEN LOGISTICS COMPANY LIMITED
No 8 Jintai Road Danzao Logistics
Center, Danzao Town Nanhai District,
Foshan, 528216, Guangdong, China
Tel.: (86) 75785130718
Web Site: https://www.jushen.co
Year Founded: 2011
001202—(SSE)
Rev.: $114,414,164
Assets: $157,426,339
Liabilities: $45,200,014
Net Worth: $112,226,325
Earnings: $7,142,650
Fiscal Year-end: 12/31/21
Logistic Services
N.A.I.C.S.: 541614
Qi Lei *(Chm & Gen Mgr)*

GUANGDONG KANGHUA HEALTHCARE CO., LTD.
Unit 3207 Metroplaza Tower 2 223
Hing Fong Road, Kwai Fong, New
Territories, China (Hong Kong)
Tel.: (852) 24282880   CN
Web Site: http://www.kanghuagp.com
Year Founded: 2002
3689—(HKG)
Rev.: $259,126,873
Assets: $381,794,494
Liabilities: $170,842,511
Net Worth: $210,951,983
Earnings: $3,894,134
Emp.: 3,848

Fiscal Year-end: 12/31/22
Health Care Srvices
N.A.I.C.S.: 622110
Junyang Wang *(Chm & Exec Dir)*

GUANGDONG KINGSHINE ELECTRONIC TECHNOLOGY COMPANY LIMITED
No 9 Longshan 8th Road, Daya Bay
West District, Huizhou, 516083,
Guangdong, China
Tel.: (86) 7525181019
Web Site:
 http://www.kingshinepcb.com
Year Founded: 2001
300903—(SSE)
Rev.: $370,181,448
Assets: $871,062,660
Liabilities: $536,530,176
Net Worth: $334,532,484
Earnings: $7,032,636
Emp.: 2,300
Fiscal Year-end: 12/31/22
Electronic Product Mfr & Distr
N.A.I.C.S.: 334419
Xiaorong Zheng *(Chm & Gen Mgr)*

GUANGDONG KINGSTRONG TECHNOLOGY CO., LTD.
No 6 Bojin Road Hardware Industrial
Zone, Danzao Town Nanhai District,
Foshan, 528216, Guangdong, China
Tel.: (86) 75766823006
Web Site: https://www.king-strong.com
Year Founded: 1998
300629—(CHIN)
Rev.: $71,987,336
Assets: $276,403,533
Liabilities: $42,554,109
Net Worth: $233,849,424
Earnings: $19,605,193
Fiscal Year-end: 12/31/23
Superhard Material Product Mfr & Distr
N.A.I.C.S.: 327910
Wang Gang *(Chm & Gen Mgr)*

GUANGDONG KINLONG HARDWARE PRDCTS CO., LTD.
No 3 Jian Lang Rd Daping Tangxia
Town, Dongguan, 523722, Guangdong, China
Tel.: (86) 76982955232
Web Site: https://www.kinlong.com
002791—(SSE)
Rev.: $1,073,817,108
Assets: $1,480,678,056
Liabilities: $775,575,216
Net Worth: $705,102,840
Earnings: $9,204,624
Emp.: 13,000
Fiscal Year-end: 12/31/22
Home Furnishing Product Mfr
N.A.I.C.S.: 332510

Subsidiaries:

GuangDong Kin Long Hardware Pruducts (HK) Co., Ltd. (1)
9 San On Street, Tuen Mun, New Territories, China (Hong Kong)
Tel.: (852) 69565895
Building Accessory Product Mfr & Retailer
N.A.I.C.S.: 326199

Guangdong Kinex Hardware Products
Co., Ltd. (1)
No 10 Changtang Street, Daping Tangxia
Town, Dongguan, 523722, Guangdong,
China
Tel.: (86) 76982998666
Web Site: http://www.kinex.cn
Hardware Product Mfr
N.A.I.C.S.: 332510

Kin Long (Malaysia) Sdn. Bhd. (1)
B 812 Block B Kelana Square 17 Jalan SS
7/26 SS7, 47301, Petaling Jaya, Selangor,
Malaysia
Tel.: (60) 378063559
Web Site:
 https://kinlongmalaysia.business.site
Construction Materials Whslr
N.A.I.C.S.: 423390

Kin Long Construction Materials Trading L.L.C (1)
Warehouse DY 144, Al Jadaf, Dubai, United
Arab Emirates
Tel.: (971) 509341218
Building Accessory Product Mfr & Distr
N.A.I.C.S.: 327120

Kin Long Hardware (India) Private
Limited (1)
Sector 14, Gurgaon, 122003, Haryana, India
Tel.: (91) 1244201754
Web Site: https://kinlong-hardware.business.site
Hardware Fitting Mfr
N.A.I.C.S.: 332510

Kin Long Hardware (Thailand) Company Limited (1)
65 Soi Sukhumvit 42 Kluaynanthai
Sukhumvit Rd, Prakanõng Klongtoey, Bangkok, Thailand
Tel.: (66) 954650370
Building Accessory Product Mfr & Retailer
N.A.I.C.S.: 326199

Kin Long Industrial (Philippines)
Inc. (1)
Unit 2006-2007 Antel Global Corporate
Center, Dona Julia Vargas Avenue Ortigas
Center, Pasig, 1605, Metro Manila, Philippines
Tel.: (63) 289571518
Building Accessory Product Mfr & Distr
N.A.I.C.S.: 327120

Mayer & Co Beschlage GmbH (1)
Alpenstrasse 173, 5020, Salzburg, Austria
Tel.: (43) 66261960
Hardware Product Mfr
N.A.I.C.S.: 332510
Guido Felix *(Mng Dir)*

Mexico Kin Long S.A. de C.A. (1)
Calle 19 Numero 107 Piso Colonia San Pedro De Los Pinos, Alcaldia Benito Juarez,
03800, Mexico, Mexico
Tel.: (52) 5559672102
Building Accessory Product Mfr & Retailer
N.A.I.C.S.: 326199

Ningbo Kin Long Kexing Precision
Manufacturing Co., Ltd. (1)
two East Road No 8, Yinzhou District East
Industrial Zone Jiangshan town, Ningbo,
China
Tel.: (86) 57488451008
Web Site: https://www.kinlongkexing.net
Hardware Product Mfr
N.A.I.C.S.: 332510

PT. Kin Long Hardware
Indonesia (1)
Springhill Office Tower 8 Floor Unit 8A Jln
Benyamin Suaeb Ruas D7, Blok D6 RT
0031 RW 006 Kelurahan Pademangan
Timur Kecamatan Pademangan, Jakarta
Utara, 14410, Indonesia
Tel.: (62) 82124700768
Building Accessory Product Mfr & Distr
N.A.I.C.S.: 327120

Shenzhen Gemvary Technology Co.,
Ltd. (1)
1003 Bldg B SDGI Hi-tech Park, Nanshan
District, Shenzhen, China
Tel.: (86) 75586320888
Web Site: http://www.en.gemvary.com
Software Development Services
N.A.I.C.S.: 513210
Rufus Rongfu Wang *(CEO)*

Shenzhen Kin Long Hbs Intelligent
Technology Co., Ltd. (1)
Building B No 6 Huanping Rd, Gaoqiao
Community Longgang District, Shenzhen,
China
Tel.: (86) 4009319898
Web Site: https://en.klhbs.com
Security Door Lock Mfr & Distr

3157

GUANGDONG KINLONG HARDWARE PRDCTS CO., LTD.

Guangdong Kinlong Hardware Prdcts Co., Ltd.—(Continued)
N.A.I.C.S.: 332510

Viet Nam Kin Long Company Limited (1)
Lot A12/D7 Cau Giay New Urban Area, Dich Vong Ward Cau Giay District, Hanoi, Vietnam
Tel.: (84) 947680453
Building Accessory Product Mfr & Distr
N.A.I.C.S.: 327120

GUANGDONG KITECH NEW MATERIAL HOLDING CO., LTD.
No 323 Lianhai Road, Jianghai, Jiangmen, 529000, Guangdong, China
Tel.: (86) 7503096888
Web Site: https://www.qide.cn
Year Founded: 2007
300995—(SSE)
Rev.: $35,990,136
Assets: $106,862,652
Liabilities: $17,250,948
Net Worth: $89,611,704
Earnings: $2,302,560
Fiscal Year-end: 12/31/22
Holding Company
N.A.I.C.S.: 551112
Desheng Rao (Chm & Gen Mgr)

GUANGDONG LEADYO IC TESTING CO., LTD.
No 2 Xinfeng East 2nd Road Mowu Wanjiang Street, Dongguan, 523000, Guangdong, China
Tel.: (86) 76926382738
Web Site: http://www.leadyo.com
Year Founded: 2010
688135—(SHG)
Rev.: $63,521,874
Assets: $237,821,440
Liabilities: $85,228,332
Net Worth: $152,593,108
Earnings: $4,495,145
Emp.: 500
Fiscal Year-end: 12/31/22
Semiconductor Product Mfr
N.A.I.C.S.: 334413
Jiang Huang (Chm)

Subsidiaries:

Beijing Tongfang Microelectronics Co., Ltd. (1)
6th Floor West Block Building D No 1 Wangzhuang Road, Tsinghua Tongfang Hi-tech Plaza Haidian District, Beijing, 100083, China
Tel.: (86) 108 235 1818
Web Site: https://www.tsinghuaic.com
Electronic Components Mfr
N.A.I.C.S.: 335999

GUANGDONG LEARY NEW MATERIAL TECHNOLOGY CO., LTD.
Beishui Industry Park, Shunde, Foshan, 528325, Guangdong, China
Tel.: (86) 75766833180
Web Site: https://www.leary.net.cn
Year Founded: 2004
688683—(SHG)
Rev.: $66,805,072
Assets: $159,958,099
Liabilities: $18,170,638
Net Worth: $141,787,461
Earnings: $6,696,322
Fiscal Year-end: 12/31/22
Film Material Mfr
N.A.I.C.S.: 325992
Xiaoping Fan (Chm)

GUANGDONG LIANTAI ENVIRONMENTAL PROTECTION CO., LTD.
Longzhu Water Purification Plant Huangcuowei Zhongshan East Road, Shantou, 515041, Guangdong, China
Tel.: (86) 75488827725
Web Site: https://www.lt-hbgf.com
Year Founded: 2006
603797—(SHG)
Rev.: $137,821,989
Assets: $1,412,983,382
Liabilities: $1,000,291,664
Net Worth: $412,691,718
Earnings: $37,581,275
Fiscal Year-end: 12/31/22
Urban Sewage Treatment Services
N.A.I.C.S.: 221320
Huang Jianxun (Chm)

GUANGDONG LIANXUN PRECISION MANUFACTURING CO.,LTD.
Jinli High-Tech Zone, Zhaoqing, GuangDong, China
Tel.: (86) 7588568626
Web Site: https://www.baifeibu.com
Year Founded: 1998
Precision Machine Parts Mfr
N.A.I.C.S.: 333310

GUANGDONG LIFESTRONG PHARMACY CO., LTD.
No 08 Block 16 Chaoyang Road Jinyuan Industrial, Shantou, 515064, Guangdong, China
Tel.: (86) 75488119888
Web Site: https://www.wnqzy.com.cn
Year Founded: 1951
301111—(CHIN)
Rev.: $39,780,936
Assets: $120,331,224
Liabilities: $13,813,956
Net Worth: $106,517,268
Earnings: $4,692,168
Emp.: 100
Fiscal Year-end: 12/31/22
Pharmaceutical Product Mfr & Distr
N.A.I.C.S.: 325412

GUANGDONG LINGXIAO PUMP INDUSTRY CO., LTD.
No 117 Chunjiang Avenue, Yangchun, 529600, Guangdong, China
Tel.: (86) 6627707230
Web Site: https://www.lingxiao.com.cn
Year Founded: 1977
002884—(SSE)
Rev.: $208,277,784
Assets: $329,565,132
Liabilities: $19,240,416
Net Worth: $310,324,716
Earnings: $59,240,376
Fiscal Year-end: 12/31/22
Electric Pumps Mfr & Distr
N.A.I.C.S.: 333914
Wang Haibo (Chm & Gen Mgr)

GUANGDONG MARUBI BIO-TECHNOLOGY CO., LTD.
6th Floor South Tower Poly Weizuo Building 11 Xiancun Road, Zhujiang New City Tianhe District, Guangzhou, 510000, Guangdong, China
Tel.: (86) 2066378666
Web Site: http://www.marubi.cn
Year Founded: 2002
603983—(SHG)
Rev.: $243,132,997
Assets: $574,407,793
Liabilities: $117,744,986
Net Worth: $456,662,808
Earnings: $24,455,349
Fiscal Year-end: 12/31/22
Cosmetics Products Mfr
N.A.I.C.S.: 325620
Huaiqing Sun (Chm, CEO & Gen Mgr)

GUANGDONG MEIYAN JIXIANG HYDROPOWER CO., LTD.
No 58 Huanan Avenue, Meijiang District, Meizhou, 514071, Guangdong, China
Tel.: (86) 7532218286
Web Site: https://www.chinameiyan.com
Year Founded: 1993
600868—(SHG)
Rev.: $68,073,558
Assets: $407,352,629
Liabilities: $58,229,861
Net Worth: $349,122,768
Earnings: $8,287,419
Emp.: 300
Fiscal Year-end: 12/31/22
Electric Power Generation & Distribution Services
N.A.I.C.S.: 221111
Zhang Nengyong (Chm & Gen Mgr)

GUANGDONG MINGZHU GROUP CO., LTD.
No 99 Guanshan Road Xingning City, Meizhou, 514500, Guangdong, China
Tel.: (86) 7533327282
Web Site: https://www.gdmzh.com
Year Founded: 1994
600382—(SHG)
Rev.: $131,309,030
Assets: $585,769,284
Liabilities: $67,937,608
Net Worth: $517,831,676
Earnings: $41,539,614
Fiscal Year-end: 12/31/22
Metal Hardware Mfr
N.A.I.C.S.: 332510
Zhang Mei (Sec)

GUANGDONG MODERN HIGH-TECH FIBER CO., LTD.
Level 1 Annex Building Western Industrial Area, Jiedong District, Jieyang, 515500, Guangdong, China
Tel.: (86) 6633263998
Web Site: https://www.gdguangdong.com
Year Founded: 1993
300876—(SSE)
Rev.: $55,372,356
Assets: $173,657,952
Liabilities: $48,655,620
Net Worth: $125,002,332
Earnings: $6,966,648
Fiscal Year-end: 12/31/22
Polyolefin Fiber Product Mfr
N.A.I.C.S.: 325220
Qinghai Guo (Chm & Gen Mgr)

GUANGDONG NEDFON AIR SYSTEM CO., LTD.
No 15 Nanxing Road, Taicheng, Taishan, 529200, Guangdong, China
Tel.: (86) 7505605530
Web Site: https://www.nedfon.com
Year Founded: 1992
301043—(CHIN)
Rev.: $80,301,169
Assets: $157,933,042
Liabilities: $40,913,577
Net Worth: $117,019,464
Earnings: $13,550,817
Fiscal Year-end: 12/31/23
Ventilation System Product Mfr
N.A.I.C.S.: 335210
Qingquan Li (Chm & Gen Mgr)

GUANGDONG NEW GRAND PACKING CO.,LTD
Grand Long industrial park Second Road North Chaozhou Avenue, Northern Industrial District, Chaozhou, 521000, Guangdong, China
Tel.: (86) 7682399001
Web Site: https://www.newglp.com

INTERNATIONAL PUBLIC

Year Founded: 2006
002836—(SSE)
Rev.: $21,016,476
Assets: $71,091,540
Liabilities: $9,232,704
Net Worth: $61,858,836
Earnings: $13,250,952
Fiscal Year-end: 12/31/22
Printing Product Mfr & Distr
N.A.I.C.S.: 333310
Zhang Hongqing (Chm)

GUANGDONG ORIENT ZIRCONIC INDUSTRY SCIENCE & TECHNOLOGY CO., LTD.
Orient Zirconic Building Dingyang Road North, Yanhong Town Chenghai, Shantou, 515821, Guangdong, China
Tel.: (86) 75485506189
Web Site: http://www.orientzr.com
Year Founded: 1995
002167—(SSE)
Rev.: $200,183,387
Assets: $474,116,567
Liabilities: $284,337,367
Net Worth: $189,779,200
Earnings: ($10,748,948)
Fiscal Year-end: 12/31/23
Zirconium Products Mfr & Distr
N.A.I.C.S.: 325998
Jinpeng Wu (Deputy Gen Mgr)

GUANGDONG PAISHENG INTELLIGENT TECHNOLOGY CO., LTD.
North District 10, Dinghu District, Zhaoqing, 526070, Guangdong, China
Tel.: (86) 7582696038
Web Site: http://www.hongteo.com.cn
Year Founded: 2003
300176—(CHIN)
Rev.: $213,252,156
Assets: $304,309,980
Liabilities: $178,418,916
Net Worth: $125,891,064
Earnings: $1,492,452
Fiscal Year-end: 12/31/22
Aluminum Die-Castings
N.A.I.C.S.: 331523

GUANGDONG PAK CORPORATION CO. LTD.
No 293 Caixin Road Liangdibu Industrial Zone, Lanhe Town Nansha District, Guangzhou, 511480, Guangdong, China
Tel.: (86) 2028660333
Web Site: http://www.pak.com.cn
Year Founded: 1991
300625—(CHIN)
Rev.: $331,254,326
Assets: $477,289,902
Liabilities: $167,232,106
Net Worth: $310,057,795
Earnings: $28,857,249
Emp.: 4,000
Fiscal Year-end: 12/31/23
Lighting Product Mfr & Distr
N.A.I.C.S.: 335132
Zhang Yutao (Gen Mgr)

Subsidiaries:

PAK Lighting Australia Pty Ltd (1)
Unit 7/112 McEvoy St, Alexandria, 2015, NSW, Australia
Tel.: (61) 289648855
Web Site: http://www.paklighting.com.au
Lighting Product Distr
N.A.I.C.S.: 423610

GUANGDONG PIANO CUSTOMIZED FURNITURE CO., LTD.

AND PRIVATE COMPANIES

No 1 Haijing Road, Shiqi District, Zhongshan, 528400, Guangdong, China
Tel.: (86) 76023631781
Web Site: http://www.pianor.com
Year Founded: 2005
002853—(SSE)
Rev.: $203,813,064
Assets: $339,995,448
Liabilities: $162,835,920
Net Worth: $177,159,528
Earnings: $21,566,844
Fiscal Year-end: 12/31/22
Household Furniture Mfr & Distr
N.A.I.C.S.: 337126
Ma Libin *(Gen Mgr)*

GUANGDONG PROVINCIAL EXPRESSWAY DEVELOPMENT CO., LTD.
45F-46F Litong Square No 32 Zhujiang East Road, Zhujiang New Town Tianhe District, Guangzhou, 510623, Guangdong, China
Tel.: (86) 2029006999
Web Site: http://www.gpedcl.com
Year Founded: 1993
000429—(SSE)
Rev.: $585,275,652
Assets: $2,845,514,880
Liabilities: $1,249,321,320
Net Worth: $1,596,193,560
Earnings: $179,300,628
Fiscal Year-end: 12/31/22
Food Transportation Services
N.A.I.C.S.: 488490
Miao Deshan *(Chm)*

GUANGDONG QUANWEI TECHNOLOGY CO., LTD.
2nd Floor Yimao Building Building C No 999 Jinzhong Road, Changning District, Shanghai, 523187, Guangdong, China
Tel.: (86) 2162306166
Web Site:
http://www.guoligroup.com.cn
Year Founded: 2002
300716—(CHIN)
Rev.: $164,158,112
Assets: $155,085,160
Liabilities: $117,106,113
Net Worth: $37,979,048
Earnings: ($19,516,275)
Fiscal Year-end: 12/31/23
Polymer Material Mfr & Distr
N.A.I.C.S.: 325211
Chu Yifan *(Chm & Sec)*

GUANGDONG QUNXING TOYS JOINT-STOCK CO., LTD.
1F Building 2 Qunxing Industrial Park Qingping Road North Side, Linghai Industrial Zone Chenghai District, Shantou, Guangdong, China
Tel.: (86) 1062916232
Web Site:
http://www.qunxingtoys.com
Year Founded: 1996
002575—(SSE)
Rev.: $11,928,384
Assets: $115,403,184
Liabilities: $3,806,244
Net Worth: $111,596,940
Earnings: $1,586,520
Emp.: 1,250
Fiscal Year-end: 12/31/22
Electronic Toy Mfr
N.A.I.C.S.: 339930
Xiaodong Fan *(Chm)*

GUANGDONG REAL-DESIGN INTELLIGENT TECHNOLOGY CO., LTD.
No 1 Ruixiang Road Fengxiang Industrial Park, Daliang Town Shunde District, Foshan, 528300, Guangdong, China
Tel.: (86) 75729961812
Web Site: https://www.realdesign.com.cn
Year Founded: 1997
301135—(SSE)
Emp.: 2,000
Household Appliance Mfr & Distr
N.A.I.C.S.: 335220
Jiayi Liang *(CFO)*

GUANGDONG REDWALL NEW MATERIALS LIMITED
Technology Industrial Park, Shiwan Town Boluo County, Huizhou, 516127, Guangdong, China
Tel.: (86) 7526113900
Web Site: http://www.redwall.com.cn
Year Founded: 2005
002809—(SSE)
Rev.: $131,751,360
Assets: $281,645,208
Liabilities: $68,751,072
Net Worth: $212,894,136
Earnings: $12,628,980
Fiscal Year-end: 12/31/22
Concrete Admixture Mfr & Distr
N.A.I.C.S.: 327320
Liu Lianjun *(Chm & Pres)*

GUANGDONG RIFENG ELECTRIC CABLE CO., LTD.
Guangfeng Industrial Zone, West District, Zhongshan, 528401, Guangdong, China
Tel.: (86) 76088166388
Web Site: https://rfcable.com.cn
Year Founded: 2009
002953—(SSE)
Rev.: $495,060,228
Assets: $403,105,248
Liabilities: $214,031,376
Net Worth: $189,073,872
Earnings: $11,775,348
Emp.: 2,000
Fiscal Year-end: 12/31/22
Wire & Cable Mfr & Distr
N.A.I.C.S.: 331491
Jiujing Feng *(Chm)*

GUANGDONG RISING ASSETS MANAGEMENT CO., LTD.
17 Pearl River West Road Pearl River New Town, Tianhe District, Guangzhou, 510623, China
Tel.: (86) 20 8393 9933   CN
Web Site: http://www.gdrising.com.cn
Year Founded: 1999
Emp.: 2,400
Investment Holding Company
N.A.I.C.S.: 551112
Wei Zhu *(Chm)*

Subsidiaries:

Caledon Coal Pty. Ltd.   (1)
Level 3 15 Astor Terrace, Spring Hill, 4000, QLD, Australia
Tel.: (61) 733093100
Web Site: http://www.caledon.com.au
Sales Range: $50-74.9 Million
Emp.: 8
Coal Mining Services
N.A.I.C.S.: 213113
Mark Trevan *(Mng Dir)*

Guangdong Changsheng Enterprises Group Co., Ltd.   (1)
Xingcheng building 2th of 25 SiYou Xin Road, Guangzhou, 510600, China
Tel.: (86) 20 87369600
Real Estate Development Services
N.A.I.C.S.: 531390

Guangdong Dabaoshan Mine Co., Ltd.   (1)
Shaxi Town, Qujiang District, Shaoguan, 512128, Guangdong, China
Tel.: (86) 7516618321
Mineral Mining Services
N.A.I.C.S.: 212230

Guangdong Electronic Information Industrial Group Co., Ltd.   (1)
No 188 Yueken Road, Guangzhou, 510507, Guangdong, China
Tel.: (86) 20 87293998
Emp.: 5,000
Semiconductor Device Mfr & Distr
N.A.I.C.S.: 334413

Guangdong Ever-Rising Group Corporation Ltd.   (1)
floor 5/6 Yongsheng Building No 223 CuiQian South Road, Qianshan, Zhuhai, Guangdong, China
Tel.: (86) 756 8636114
Real Estate Development Services
N.A.I.C.S.: 531390

Guangdong Guangsheng Hotel Group Co., Ltd.   (1)
23rd Floor Asia International Hotel Huanshi Road East 326-1, Guangzhou, China
Tel.: (86) 20 61288888
Home Management Services
N.A.I.C.S.: 561110

Guangdong Guangsheng Metallurgy Co., Ltd.   (1)
11th Floor Yejin Building No 48 Zhongshaner Road, Guangzhou, China
Tel.: (86) 20 87766221
Iron Ore Mining Services
N.A.I.C.S.: 212210

Guangdong Guangsheng Power Fuel Co. Ltd.   (1)
Guangzhou yuexiu temple right road no 2 compound 3 floor, Guangzhou, China
Tel.: (86) 20 28992610
Coal Mining Services
N.A.I.C.S.: 212115
Guo Shisheng *(Pres)*

Guangdong Hongling Group Co., Ltd.   (1)
Honggui Building No 2068 Honggui Road, Luohu District, Shenzhen, 518008, China
Tel.: (86) 755 25865888
Real Estate Manangement Services
N.A.I.C.S.: 531210

Guangdong Huajian Enterprise Group Co., Ltd.   (1)
F19-20 No 233 Tianfu Road, Tianhe District, Guangzhou, 510630, China
Tel.: (86) 20 85613800
Emp.: 1,429
Property Management & Development Services
N.A.I.C.S.: 236116

Guangdong Province Guangsheng Assets Management Co., Ltd   (1)
20/F Grand Tower No 228 Tianhe Road, Guangzhou, 510620, China
Tel.: (86) 20 2886 1188
Asset Management Services
N.A.I.C.S.: 531390

Guangdong Rising Group Investment Co., Ltd   (1)
Zhongren Plaza No Zhongchen Road, Tianhe district, Guangzhou, 510515, China
Tel.: (86) 20 62806679
Real Estate Investment Services
N.A.I.C.S.: 531210

Guangdong Rising Mining Investment Development Co., Ltd.   (1)
53rd floor of GuangSheng International Building No17 West ZhuJiang Rd, TianHe District, Guangzhou, 510623, GuangDong, China
Tel.: (86) 20 38969031
Copper Mining Services
N.A.I.C.S.: 212230

Guangdong Shiliuye Construction Co., Ltd   (1)
No 319 Zhongcheng Road Shangyuangang, Tianhe District, Guangzhou, 510515, China
Tel.: (86) 20 87052716
Emp.: 3,000
Construction Engineering Services
N.A.I.C.S.: 541330

Guangzhou Digital Rise Co., Ltd.   (1)
6th Floor No 9 Mingyue Yi Road Guangzhou Da Dao Zhong, Guangzhou, 510600, Guangdong, China
Tel.: (86) 20 3874397
Web Site: http://www.digirise.com
Audio Streaming Services
N.A.I.C.S.: 518210

Guangzhou Rising Micro Electronics Co., Ltd.   (1)
Room 601-609 College of Science Guangdong University of Technology, Panyu District, Guangzhou, 510006, China
Tel.: (86) 20 85286631
Web Site: http://www.rising-ic.com
Communication Equipment Mfr
N.A.I.C.S.: 335929

PanAust Limited   (1)
Level 1 15 James Street Fortitude Valley, PO Box 2297, Brisbane, 4006, QLD, Australia
Tel.: (61) 731172000
Web Site: http://www.panaust.com.au
Sales Range: $650-699.9 Million
Emp.: 3,474
Copper & Gold Producer
N.A.I.C.S.: 212230
David Reid *(Gen Mgr-Ops)*

Subsidiary (Non-US):

Phu Bia Mining Limited   (2)
7th Floor Capital Tower 23 Singha Road, Saysetha Dist, Vientiane, Lao People's Democratic Republic
Tel.: (856) 21 268 000
Web Site: http://www.panaust.com
Copper & Gold Mining Services
N.A.I.C.S.: 212220

Rising Investment Co., Ltd.   (1)
Room 1206 12/F Bank of America Tower No 12 Harcourt Road, Hong Kong, China (Hong Kong)
Tel.: (852) 28992610
Investment Holding Services
N.A.I.C.S.: 523940

Rising Nonferrous Metals Co., Ltd.   (1)
4th Floor Chengguang Building No 613 Guangzhou North Avenue, Guangzhou, 510501, China
Tel.: (86) 2087649931
Web Site: http://www.gsysgf.com
Rev.: $3,210,141,837
Assets: $1,028,075,574
Liabilities: $527,486,170
Net Worth: $500,589,405
Earnings: $32,616,408
Fiscal Year-end: 12/31/2022
Non-ferrous Metal Mining Services
N.A.I.C.S.: 331410
Lan Yaping *(Chm)*

Shenzhen Changcheng Huihua Group Co., Ltd   (1)
26/F Shenzhen International Chamber of Commerce Tower Fuhua 3rd Road, Futian District, Shenzhen, China
Tel.: (86) 755 88315026
Property Development Services
N.A.I.C.S.: 236116

GUANGDONG RONGTAI INDUSTRY CO., LTD.
West side of Jiedong Economic Development Zone, Rongcheng District, Jieyang, 515500, Guangdong, China
Tel.: (86) 1081377507
Web Site: http://www.rongtai.com.cn
Year Founded: 1997
600589—(SHG)
Rev.: $59,118,705
Assets: $155,796,727
Liabilities: $249,829,178
Net Worth: ($94,032,451)
Earnings: ($104,661,012)
Emp.: 200
Fiscal Year-end: 12/31/22
Melamine Mateial Mfr & Distr
N.A.I.C.S.: 325211
Zhang Wei *(Chm & Gen Mgr)*

GUANGDONG SACA PRECI-

GUANGDONG SACA PRECI

GUANGDONG SACA PRECI—(CONTINUED)

SION MANUFACTURING CO., LTD.
No 3 Keye Road Industrial Park Beijiao Town Shunde district, Foshan, 528311, Guangdong, China
Tel.: (86) 75726332266
Web Site: http://www.sh-abc.cn
300464—(CHIN)
Rev.: $330,055,128
Assets: $321,659,208
Liabilities: $297,594,648
Net Worth: $24,064,560
Earnings: ($36,516,636)
Emp.: 790
Fiscal Year-end: 12/31/22
Precision Metal Fittings Mfr
N.A.I.C.S.: 332510
Gengxi Cai *(Chm & Gen Mgr)*

GUANGDONG SANHE PILE CO., LTD.
No 30 Tongxing East Road, Xiaolan Town, Zhongshan, 528414, Guangdong, China
Tel.: (86) 76028189998
Web Site: https://www.sanhepile.com
Year Founded: 2003
003037—(SSE)
Rev.: $933,637,536
Assets: $800,178,912
Liabilities: $548,311,140
Net Worth: $251,867,772
Earnings: $21,857,472
Emp.: 6,000
Fiscal Year-end: 12/31/22
Building Material Mfr & Distr
N.A.I.C.S.: 327120
Zelin Wei *(Chm)*

GUANGDONG SENSSUN WEIGHING APPARATUS GROUP LTD.
Baishawan Industrial Park east of Qiwan Road, Dong District, Zhongshan, 528403, Guangdong, China
Tel.: (86) 76023320821
Web Site: http://www.camry.com.cn
Year Founded: 1999
002870—(SSE)
Rev.: $676,285,740
Assets: $1,039,506,156
Liabilities: $655,128,864
Net Worth: $384,377,292
Earnings: $12,110,904
Fiscal Year-end: 12/31/22
Weighing Apparatus Mfr & Distr
N.A.I.C.S.: 333998
Liu Yuda *(Chm & Pres)*

GUANGDONG SHAONENG GROUP CO., LTD.
No 16 Wujiang Avenue, Wujiang District, Shaoguan, 512026, Guangdong, China
Tel.: (86) 7518153162
Web Site: https://www.shaoneng.com.cn
Year Founded: 1993
000601—(SSE)
Rev.: $540,346,248
Assets: $1,847,499,732
Liabilities: $1,161,703,296
Net Worth: $685,796,436
Earnings: ($10,426,104)
Fiscal Year-end: 12/31/22
Eletric Power Generation Services
N.A.I.C.S.: 221116
Hu Qijin *(Chm)*

GUANGDONG SHENGLU TELECOMMUNICATION TECH CO., LTD.
No 4 Jinye Second Road Xinan Industry, Sanshui District, Foshan, 528100, Guangdong, China
Tel.: (86) 75787744996
Web Site: https://www.shenglu.com
Year Founded: 1998
002446—(SSE)
Rev.: $199,766,736
Assets: $577,373,940
Liabilities: $135,921,240
Net Worth: $441,452,700
Earnings: $34,209,864
Emp.: 1,000
Fiscal Year-end: 12/31/22
Antennas & RF Microwave Components & Equipment Mfr
N.A.I.C.S.: 334220

GUANGDONG SHENLING ENVIRONMENTAL SYSTEMS CO., LTD.
No 8 Xinglong 10th Road Mechanical Equipment Park, Chencun Town Shunde District, Foshan, 528000, Guangdong, China
Tel.: (86) 75723832888
Web Site: https://www.shenling.com
Year Founded: 2000
301018—(CHIN)
Rev.: $353,689,351
Assets: $671,373,744
Liabilities: $323,382,915
Net Worth: $347,990,830
Earnings: $14,774,155
Fiscal Year-end: 12/31/23
Refrigeration Products Mfr
N.A.I.C.S.: 333415
Yingqi Cui *(Chm)*

GUANGDONG SHIRONGZHAOYE CO., LTD.
Building 17 Area 1 No 288 Zhufeng Avenue, Jinan Town Doumen District, Zhuhai, 519180, Guangdong, China
Tel.: (86) 7565888886
Web Site: http://www.shirongzhaoye.com
Year Founded: 2000
002016—(SSE)
Rev.: $116,714,520
Assets: $923,434,668
Liabilities: $273,570,804
Net Worth: $649,863,864
Earnings: $19,849,752
Fiscal Year-end: 12/31/22
Real Estate Development Services
N.A.I.C.S.: 531390
Zexin Zhou *(Chm, Acting Vice Chm & Chm)*

GUANGDONG SHUN AN DA PACIFIC CONTAINER CO., LTD.
Lelian Rd Leliu Shunde Dist, 528322, Foshan, Guangdong, China
Tel.: (86) 75725330157
Sales Range: $400-449.9 Million
Emp.: 1,200
Specialized Container Mfr
N.A.I.C.S.: 332439
Charles Panm *(Gen Mgr)*

GUANGDONG SHUNKONG DEVELOPMENT CO., LTD.
Floor 20 Building 1 Guanlv Road Real Estate Plaza Daliang Street, Shunde District, Foshan, 528300, Guangdong, China
Tel.: (86) 75722317888
Web Site: https://www.gdskfz.com
Year Founded: 1992
003039—(SSE)
Rev.: $185,276,052
Assets: $645,585,876
Liabilities: $213,816,564
Net Worth: $431,769,312
Earnings: $33,454,512

Fiscal Year-end: 12/31/22
Water Supply Services
N.A.I.C.S.: 221310
Haiyan Chen *(Chm & Gen Mgr)*

GUANGDONG SHUNNA ELECTRIC CO., LTD.
Xinye Building No 23 Xinyue Road Wusha Community Daliang Street, Shunde District, Foshan, 528333, Guangdong, China
Tel.: (86) 75722321218
Web Site: https://www.shunna.com.cn
Year Founded: 1992
000533—(SSE)
Rev.: $249,037,308
Assets: $358,210,944
Liabilities: $238,327,596
Net Worth: $119,883,348
Earnings: $4,422,600
Fiscal Year-end: 12/31/22
Household Electrical Appliance Mfr
N.A.I.C.S.: 335220
Huang Zhixiong *(Vice Chm)*

GUANGDONG SILVER AGE SCI & TECH CO., LTD.
Room 602 Building 1 No 13 Nange West Road, Daojiao Town, Dongguan, Guangdong, China
Tel.: (86) 76938855188
Web Site: https://www.silver3d.com
Year Founded: 1997
300221—(CHIN)
Rev.: $259,199,460
Assets: $248,896,908
Liabilities: $70,548,192
Net Worth: $178,348,716
Earnings: ($789,048)
Emp.: 640
Fiscal Year-end: 12/31/22
Plastics Product Mfr
N.A.I.C.S.: 326199
Songbin Tan *(Chm)*

GUANGDONG SITONG GROUP CO., LTD.
B11-4-1 South Area, Chaozhou Railway Station Developing Area, Chaozhou, 521031, Guangdong, China
Tel.: (86) 13828326131
Web Site: https://www.sitongceramics.com
Year Founded: 1997
603838—(SHG)
Rev.: $33,292,027
Assets: $156,426,477
Liabilities: $9,647,923
Net Worth: $146,778,555
Earnings: ($3,658,585)
Fiscal Year-end: 12/31/22
Ceramic Product Mfr & Distr
N.A.I.C.S.: 327110
Zhencheng Cai *(Chm, Vice Chm & Gen Mgr)*

GUANGDONG SONGFA CERAMICS CO., LTD.
No 20 Ruyi Road Industrial Park, Fengxi District, Chaozhou, 521031, Guangdong, China
Tel.: (86) 7682923128
Web Site: https://www.songfa.com
Year Founded: 2002
603268—(SHG)
Rev.: $38,023,956
Assets: $91,369,610
Liabilities: $61,838,675
Net Worth: $29,530,936
Earnings: ($23,946,863)
Fiscal Year-end: 12/31/22
Porcelain Mfr & Distr
N.A.I.C.S.: 327110
Lu Kun *(Chm)*

Subsidiaries:

Guangzhou Songfa Hotel Equipment Suppliers Co., Ltd. (1)
1511-1515 International Purchasing Center Pazhou Road East, Haizhou District, Guangzhou, China
Tel.: (86) 7682923710
Ceramic Products Mfr
N.A.I.C.S.: 327110

GUANGDONG SONGYANG RECYCLE RESOURCES CO., LTD.
Under The Town of Lian Li Industrial Zone, Chenghai, Shantou, Guangdong, China
Tel.: (86) 75485138388
Web Site: https://www.sypaper.cn
Year Founded: 2008
603863—(SHG)
Rev.: $130,303,639
Assets: $222,343,042
Liabilities: $96,389,668
Net Worth: $125,953,374
Earnings: ($38,922,334)
Fiscal Year-end: 12/31/22
Paper Products Mfr
N.A.I.C.S.: 322299
Zhuangpeng Wang *(Chm)*

GUANGDONG SOUTH NEW MEDIA CO., LTD.
Room 411 Zibian Building 25 No 686 Renmin North Road, Yuexiu District, Guangzhou, 510012, Guangdong, China
Tel.: (86) 2026188386
Web Site: http://www.snm.gd
Year Founded: 2010
300770—(SSE)
Rev.: $200,582,460
Assets: $615,826,692
Liabilities: $127,296,468
Net Worth: $488,530,224
Earnings: $97,061,328
Fiscal Year-end: 12/31/22
Media Advertising Services
N.A.I.C.S.: 541840
Fuqing Cai *(Chm)*

GUANGDONG SUNWILL PRECISING PLASTIC CO., LTD.
6 Keyuan 1st Road Shunde Ronggui high tech Development Zone, Foshan, 528305, Guangdong, China
Tel.: (86) 75728386388
Web Site: https://www.sunwill.com.cn
Year Founded: 1992
002676—(SSE)
Rev.: $294,889,140
Assets: $321,469,668
Liabilities: $158,559,336
Net Worth: $162,910,332
Earnings: $5,941,728
Emp.: 4,000
Fiscal Year-end: 12/31/22
Plastic Air Conditioning & Refrigeration Products Mfr
N.A.I.C.S.: 326199
Xianzhang Wang *(Chm)*

Subsidiaries:

Kunshan Sunwill Electric Appliances Co., Ltd. (1)
No 168 Dujuan Rd Japan Industrial Park Lujia Town, Kunshan, Suzhou, 215331, Jiangsu, China
Tel.: (86) 512 36802888
Electrical Appliance Mfr
N.A.I.C.S.: 335210
Shu Shi *(Mgr-Sls)*

Wuhan Sunwill Electric Co., Ltd. (1)
No 89 Checheng Rd Wuhan Economy & Technology Development Zone, Wuhan, 430056, Hubei, China
Tel.: (86) 27 84890996
Electrical Appliance Mfr

AND PRIVATE COMPANIES — GUANGDONG WENS DAHUANONG BIOTECHNOLOGY CO., LTD.

N.A.I.C.S.: 335210
Zhongshan Saitech Engineering Plastics Co., Ltd. (1)
Dayan Industrial Zone Huangpu Town, Zhongshan, 528429, Guangdong, China
Tel.: (86) 760 28163888
Plastic Product Mfr & Distr
N.A.I.C.S.: 326199

GUANGDONG TAIANTANG PHAMACEUTICAL CO., LTD.
Taiantang Qilin Garden No 28 Jieyang Road Jinping Industrial City, Jinping District, Shantou, 515021, Guangdong, China
Tel.: (86) 75488116065
Web Site: http://www.taiantang.net
Year Founded: 1995
002433—(SSE)
Rev.: $101,767,536
Assets: $921,377,808
Liabilities: $398,102,796
Net Worth: $523,275,012
Earnings: ($115,523,928)
Fiscal Year-end: 12/31/22
Pharmaceuticals Mfr
N.A.I.C.S.: 325412

GUANGDONG TAIENKANG PHARMACEUTICAL CO., LTD.
Wanji Industrial Zone, Longhu District, Shantou, 515065, Guangdong, China
Tel.: (86) 75489923979
Web Site: https://www.tai-kang.com.cn
Year Founded: 1999
301263—(CHIN)
Rev.: $110,000,592
Assets: $286,247,520
Liabilities: $25,951,536
Net Worth: $260,295,984
Earnings: $24,515,244
Fiscal Year-end: 12/31/22
Pharmaceutical Product Mfr & Distr
N.A.I.C.S.: 325412
Hanjie Zheng (Chm)

GUANGDONG TAPAI GROUP CO., LTD.
Ta Pai Building Ta Pai Avenue, Jiaocheng Town Jiaoling City, Meizhou, 514199, Guangdong, China
Tel.: (86) 7537887036
Web Site: https://www.tapai.com
Year Founded: 2007
002233—(SSE)
Rev.: $847,311,192
Assets: $1,802,720,556
Liabilities: $211,982,940
Net Worth: $1,590,737,616
Earnings: $37,375,884
Fiscal Year-end: 12/31/22
Cement Mfr
N.A.I.C.S.: 327310
Zhaohui Zhong (Chm)

GUANGDONG TECSUN SCIENCE & TECHNOLOGY CO., LTD.
3F and 4F and 2F Room 201 No 15 Ruanjian Road, Tianhe District, Guangzhou, 510663, Guangdong, China
Tel.: (86) 2029118777
Web Site: http://www.e-tecsun.com
Year Founded: 1999
002908—(SSE)
Rev.: $127,115,352
Assets: $209,746,368
Liabilities: $48,251,268
Net Worth: $161,495,100
Earnings: $15,971,904
Fiscal Year-end: 12/31/22
Electronic Component Mfr & Distr
N.A.I.C.S.: 334118

Xiaobin Guo (Chm, Pres & Gen Mgr)

GUANGDONG TENGEN INDUSTRIAL GROUP CO., LTD.
No 172 Shangyuan Road, Songgang Industrial Zone Qingxi Town, Dongguan, 523640, Guangdong, China
Year Founded: 2010
003003—(SSE)
Rev.: $204,175,296
Assets: $232,665,264
Liabilities: $63,813,204
Net Worth: $168,852,060
Earnings: ($471,744)
Emp.: 1,100
Fiscal Year-end: 12/31/22
Packaging Product Mfr & Distr
N.A.I.C.S.: 333993
Xiaowei Zhou (Chm & Gen Mgr)

GUANGDONG TIANAN NEW MATERIAL CO., LTD.
No 30 Xinyuan 1st Rd Jili Industrial Zone, Nanzhuang Town Chancheng District, Foshan, 528061, Guangdong, China
Tel.: (86) 75782012222 CN
Web Site: https://www.tianantech.com
Year Founded: 2000
603725—(SHG)
Rev.: $381,358,481
Assets: $402,125,382
Liabilities: $315,276,090
Net Worth: $86,849,292
Earnings: ($23,232,100)
Fiscal Year-end: 12/31/22
Automotive Interior Material Mfr & Distr
N.A.I.C.S.: 336360
Wu Qichao (Chm & Gen Mgr)

GUANGDONG TIANHE AGRICULTURAL MEANS OF PRODUCTION CO., LTD.
No 709 Dongfeng East Road, Yuexiu District, Guangzhou, 510080, Guangdong, China
Tel.: (86) 2087766490
Web Site: http://www.gd-tianhe.com
Year Founded: 2009
002999—(SSE)
Rev.: $2,036,339,136
Assets: $932,741,784
Liabilities: $730,534,896
Net Worth: $202,206,888
Earnings: $14,890,824
Emp.: 100
Fiscal Year-end: 12/31/22
Agriculture Product Distr
N.A.I.C.S.: 424690
Duanmu Zirong (Vice Chm)

GUANGDONG TIANYIMA INFORMATION INDUSTRY CO., LTD.
Room 2111-2112 West Tower Tianlan International Building No 20, Songshan Road South, Shantou, 515041, Guangdong, China
Tel.: (86) 75488880666
Web Site: https://www.tym.com.cn
Year Founded: 1998
301178—(CHIN)
Rev.: $61,666,488
Assets: $142,510,212
Liabilities: $24,682,320
Net Worth: $117,827,892
Earnings: $5,554,224
Fiscal Year-end: 12/31/22
Information Technology Services
N.A.I.C.S.: 541512
Mingling Lin (Chm)

GUANGDONG TLOONG TECHNOLOGY GROUP CO., LTD.
Jindu Industrial Park, Zhaoqing, 526108, Guangdong, China
Tel.: 7588288888
Web Site: http://www.tlym.cn
Year Founded: 1993
300063—(CHIN)
Rev.: $1,352,523,744
Assets: $469,828,944
Liabilities: $241,146,828
Net Worth: $228,682,116
Earnings: $14,455,584
Emp.: 350
Fiscal Year-end: 12/31/22
Printing Ink Mfr
N.A.I.C.S.: 325910
Chen Dongyang (CFO & Deputy Gen Mgr)

GUANGDONG TOPSTAR TECHNOLOGY CO., LTD.
No 2 Chuangxin Road Datanglang, Dalingshan Town, Dongguan, 523811, Guangdong, China
Tel.: (86) 13676260089
Web Site: https://www.topstarmachine.com
Year Founded: 2007
300607—(CHIN)
Rev.: $641,248,682
Assets: $999,083,755
Liabilities: $644,826,498
Net Worth: $354,257,258
Earnings: $12,399,504
Emp.: 3,000
Fiscal Year-end: 12/31/23
Industrial Robot Mfr & Distr
N.A.I.C.S.: 336110
Yongchong Zhou (CFO)

GUANGDONG TOPSTRONG LIVING INNOVATION & INTEGRATION CO., LTD.
No 429 Dongfu 3rd Road, Dongfeng Town, Zhongshan, 528425, Guangdong, China
Tel.: (86) 13432108267
Web Site: https://www.topstrong.net
Year Founded: 2002
300591—(CHIN)
Rev.: $180,896,754
Assets: $236,888,953
Liabilities: $133,829,205
Net Worth: $103,059,748
Earnings: $2,796,337
Fiscal Year-end: 12/31/23
Hardware Tool Mfr & Distr
N.A.I.C.S.: 332510
Xin Zhaolong (Chm & Gen Mgr)

GUANGDONG TRANSTEK MEDICAL ELECTRONICS CO., LTD
Zone A No 105 Dongli Road, Torch Development District, Zhongshan, 528437, Guangdong, China
Tel.: (86) 76088282982
Web Site: https://www.transtekcorp.com
Year Founded: 2002
300562—(CHIN)
Rev.: $124,547,556
Assets: $219,232,757
Liabilities: $74,980,864
Net Worth: $144,251,894
Earnings: $4,840,634
Fiscal Year-end: 12/31/23
Health Care Equipment Mfr & Distr
N.A.I.C.S.: 334510
David Pan (Chm)

GUANGDONG VANWARD NEW ELECTRIC CO., LTD.
No 13 Jianye Middle Road Ronggui High-tech Development Zone, Ronggui Shunde, Foshan, 528305, Guangdong, China
Tel.: 75728389929
Web Site: https://www.vanward.com
Year Founded: 1993
002543—(SSE)
Rev.: $930,544,524
Assets: $967,455,684
Liabilities: $361,201,464
Net Worth: $606,254,220
Earnings: $77,224,212
Fiscal Year-end: 12/31/22
Kitchen & Bathroom Appliances Mfr
N.A.I.C.S.: 335220
Yu Cong Louie Lu (Chm)

GUANGDONG VTR BIO-TECH CO., LTD.
No 8 Pingbei Rd 1 Science & Technology Industry Zone, Nanping, Zhuhai, 519060, Guangdong, China
Tel.: (86) 7568676888
Web Site: http://www.yiduoli.com
Year Founded: 1991
Emp.: 440
Feed Additive Mfr
N.A.I.C.S.: 311119
Shaomei Chen (Chm & Gen Mgr)

Subsidiaries:

Hunan Hong Ying Biotech Co., Ltd. (1)
Jiashan New Industrial Zone, Changde, Hunan, China (100%)
Tel.: (86) 7364227368
Feed Additive Distr
N.A.I.C.S.: 424910
Angel Lu (Mgr-Export)

GUANGDONG WANLIMA INDUSTRY CO LTD
1-3F Block F Poly World Trade Center No 1028 Xingang East Road, Haizhu District, Guangzhou, 510308, Guangdong, China
Tel.: (86) 2022319138
Web Site: https://www.wanlima.com.cn
Year Founded: 2002
300591—(CHIN)
Rev.: $87,030,229
Assets: $141,439,091
Liabilities: $70,091,819
Net Worth: $71,347,272
Earnings: ($10,078,212)
Fiscal Year-end: 12/31/23
Leather Mfr & Distr
N.A.I.C.S.: 316990
Lin Dazhou (Chm)

GUANGDONG WENKE GREEN TECHNOLOGY CORP., LTD.
14-16F Wenke Building No 101 Huabao Road, Pinghu Subdistrict Longgang District, Shenzhen, 518100, Guangdong, China
Tel.: (86) 75533052661
Web Site: http://www.wkyy.com
Year Founded: 1996
002775—(SSE)
Rev.: $128,851,131
Assets: $703,622,083
Liabilities: $671,056,795
Net Worth: $32,565,289
Earnings: ($51,799,330)
Fiscal Year-end: 12/31/22
Landscaping Services
N.A.I.C.S.: 561730
Congwen Li (Chm & Gen Mgr)

GUANGDONG WENS DAHUANONG BIOTECHNOLOGY CO., LTD.
No 6 Dongdi North Road, Xincheng Town Xinxing County, Yunfu, Guangdong, China

GUANGDONG WENS DAHUANONG BIOTECHNOLOGY CO., LTD.

Guangdong Wens Dahuanong Biotechnology Co., Ltd.—(Continued)
Tel.: (86) 766 2986988
Web Site: http://www.gddhn.com
Veterinary Pharmaceutical Mfr
N.A.I.C.S.: 325412

GUANGDONG XIANGLU TUNGSTEN CO. LTD
Guantang Industrial Zone, Chaoan, Chaozhou, Guangdong, China
Tel.: (86) 7686972888
Web Site: https://www.xl-tungsten.com
Year Founded: 1997
002842—(SSE)
Rev.: $234,966,420
Assets: $312,589,368
Liabilities: $178,295,364
Net Worth: $134,294,004
Earnings: ($5,792,904)
Fiscal Year-end: 12/31/22
Tungsten Product Mfr & Distr
N.A.I.C.S.: 331492
Chen Qifeng *(Chm)*

GUANGDONG XINBAO ELECTRICAL APPLIANCES HOLDINGS CO., LTD.
Longzhou Road Leliu Town, Shunde District, Foshan, 528322, Guangdong, China
Tel.: (86) 75725333888
002705—(SSE)
Rev.: $1,922,966,136
Assets: $1,806,180,012
Liabilities: $808,720,848
Net Worth: $997,459,164
Earnings: $134,979,156
Emp.: 28,000
Fiscal Year-end: 12/31/22
Electrical Appliance Mfr
N.A.I.C.S.: 335220
Jiangang Guo *(Chm)*

GUANGDONG XINHUI MEIDA NYLON CO., LTD.
Shangqiankou Jianghui Road, Xinhui District, Jiangmen, 529100, Guangdong, China
Tel.: (86) 7506107981
Web Site: http://www.meidanylon.com
Year Founded: 1984
000782—(SSE)
Rev.: $409,079,268
Assets: $441,962,352
Liabilities: $242,663,148
Net Worth: $199,299,204
Earnings: ($7,751,484)
Emp.: 3,500
Fiscal Year-end: 12/31/22
Chemical Fiber Mfr
N.A.I.C.S.: 325220
Min Guo *(Chm & Gen Mgr)*

GUANGDONG XIONGSU TECHNOLOGY GROUP CO., LTD.
Xiongsu Industrial Park Dungao Road Section Longgao Road, Jiujiang Town Nanhai District, Foshan, 528203, Guangdong, China
Tel.: (86) 75781868066
Web Site: http://www.xiongsu.cn
Year Founded: 2004
300599—(CHIN)
Rev.: $181,972,946
Assets: $373,723,784
Liabilities: $56,592,516
Net Worth: $317,131,268
Earnings: $3,773,794
Fiscal Year-end: 12/31/23
Plastic Pipe Fitting Mfr & Distr
N.A.I.C.S.: 326122
Ganxiong Huang *(Chm & Gen Mgr)*

GUANGDONG YANGSHAN UNITED PRECISION MANUFACTURING CO., LTD.
Dubu Town Industrial Park, Yangshan County, Qingyuan, 513125, Guangdong, China
Tel.: (86) 75726326360
Web Site: https://www.ysugroup.com
Year Founded: 2003
001268—(SSE)
Rev.: $90,850,222
Assets: $166,949,106
Liabilities: $31,150,800
Net Worth: $135,798,306
Earnings: $8,512,006
Fiscal Year-end: 12/31/23
Mechanical Product Mfr
N.A.I.C.S.: 333613
He Guijing *(Chm)*

GUANGDONG YANTANG DAIRY CO., LTD.
No 188 Xiangli Road, Huangpu District, Guangzhou, 510700, Guangdong, China
Tel.: (86) 2032631998
Web Site: https://www.yantangmilk.com
Year Founded: 1956
002732—(SSE)
Rev.: $263,276,676
Assets: $265,979,376
Liabilities: $87,219,288
Net Worth: $178,760,088
Earnings: $13,950,144
Emp.: 1,060
Fiscal Year-end: 12/31/22
Fluid Milk Mfr
N.A.I.C.S.: 311511
Feng Like *(Chm & Gen Mgr)*

GUANGDONG YUDEAN GROUP CO., LTD.
Yudean Plaza No 2 Tianhe Dong Road, Guangzhou, 510630, Guangdong, China
Tel.: (86) 20 85138888
Web Site: http://www.gdyd.com
Holding Company
N.A.I.C.S.: 551112
Li Zhuoxian *(Chm)*

Subsidiaries:

Guangdong Electric Power Development Co., Ltd. (1)
33-36F South Tower Yuedian Square No 2 TianHe East Road, Tian He East Road, Guangzhou, 510630, Guangdong, China
Tel.: (86) 2087570251
Web Site: http://www.ged.com.cn
Rev.: $7,393,617,036
Assets: $18,463,199,508
Liabilities: $14,430,556,296
Net Worth: $4,032,643,212
Earnings: ($421,750,368)
Emp.: 1,652
Fiscal Year-end: 12/31/2022
Power Plants, Transmission & Substation Projects Mfr & Operator
N.A.I.C.S.: 333613
Zheng Yunpeng *(Chm)*

GUANGDONG YUEHAI FEEDS GROUP CO., LTD.
No 22 Airport Road, Xiashan District, Zhanjiang, 524017, Guangdong, China
Tel.: (86) 7592323323
Web Site: https://www.yuehaifeed.com
Year Founded: 1994
001313—(SSE)
Rev.: $995,698,548
Assets: $638,564,472
Liabilities: $246,852,684
Net Worth: $391,711,788
Earnings: $16,155,828
Emp.: 3,400

Fiscal Year-end: 12/31/22
Feed Product Mfr & Distr
N.A.I.C.S.: 311119
Shixuan Zheng *(Chm & Pres)*

GUANGDONG YUEYUN TRANSPORTATION COMPANY LIMITED
8th Floor No 1731-1735 Airport Road, Baiyun District, Guangzhou, Guangdong, China
Tel.: (86) 2022353888 CN
Web Site: http://www.gdyueyun.com
Year Founded: 1999
3399—(HKG)
Rev.: $817,061,679
Assets: $1,293,870,534
Liabilities: $945,432,066
Net Worth: $348,438,469
Earnings: ($29,340,902)
Emp.: 17,073
Fiscal Year-end: 12/31/22
Logistics & Transportation Services
N.A.I.C.S.: 541614
Zhu Fang *(Chm)*

GUANGDONG ZHENYE TECHNOLOGY CO., LTD.
Number 6 Of Nanyan Road Songshan Lake, Dongguan, 523808, Guangdong, China
Tel.: (86) 76988985065
Web Site: https://www.zhengyekeji.com
Year Founded: 1997
300410—(CHIN)
Rev.: $139,067,604
Assets: $250,324,776
Liabilities: $160,977,024
Net Worth: $89,347,752
Earnings: ($14,229,540)
Emp.: 1,000
Fiscal Year-end: 12/31/22
Precision Inspection Equipment & Electronic Materials Mfr
N.A.I.C.S.: 334419
Dihua Xu *(Chm)*

GUANGDONG ZHONGSHENG PHARMACEUTICAL CO., LTD.
Information Industrial Park Xihu Industrial Zone, Shilong Town, Dongguan, 523325, Guangdong, China
Tel.: (86) 76986188130
Web Site: http://www.zspcl.com
Year Founded: 2001
002317—(SSE)
Rev.: $375,731,460
Assets: $810,849,312
Liabilities: $275,018,328
Net Worth: $535,830,984
Earnings: $45,215,820
Fiscal Year-end: 12/31/22
Pharmaceuticals Product Mfr
N.A.I.C.S.: 325412
Yong Hong Chen *(Chm & Gen Mgr)*

GUANGHE LANDSCAPE CULTURE COMMUNICATION CO., LTD.
No 289 Yingze Avenue, Taiyuan, 030001, Shanxi, China
Tel.: (86) 75523996252
600234—(SHG)
Rev.: $16,773,083
Assets: $118,978,807
Liabilities: $32,327,128
Net Worth: $86,651,679
Earnings: ($2,737,463)
Fiscal Year-end: 12/31/22
Video Product Mfr
N.A.I.C.S.: 333310
Dai Rong *(Sec & VP)*

GUANGHUI LOGISTICS CO., LTD.

INTERNATIONAL PUBLIC

Room 1701 No 2 Lujiang Road, Siming District, Xiamen, 361001, Fujian, China
Tel.: (86) 5922033603
600603—(SHG)
Rev.: $704,710,941
Assets: $3,047,613,000
Liabilities: $2,147,594,693
Net Worth: $900,018,307
Earnings: $76,032,988
Emp.: 494
Fiscal Year-end: 12/31/22
Holding Company
N.A.I.C.S.: 551112
Wenqiang Li *(Pres)*

GUANGLIAN AVIATION INDUSTRY CO., LTD.
No 3 Hanan Third Road Harbin Hanan Industrial New City, Core Area, Harbin, 150060, Heilongjiang, China
Tel.: (86) 45151910997
Web Site: http://www.guanglianhangkong.com
Year Founded: 2011
300900—(SSE)
Rev.: $93,175,056
Assets: $437,883,732
Liabilities: $178,671,636
Net Worth: $259,212,096
Earnings: $21,041,748
Emp.: 1,000
Fiscal Year-end: 12/31/22
Aircraft Parts Mfr & Distr
N.A.I.C.S.: 336413
Zengduo Wang *(Chm)*

GUANGSHEN RAILWAY COMPANY LIMITED
No 1052 Heping Road, Luohu District, Shenzhen, 518010, Guangdong, China
Tel.: (86) 75525588150 CN
Web Site: http://www.gsrc.com
Year Founded: 1984
601333—(SHG)
Rev.: $3,095,785,314
Assets: $5,730,578,285
Liabilities: $1,562,586,646
Net Worth: $4,167,991,640
Earnings: ($149,220,872)
Emp.: 40,616
Fiscal Year-end: 12/31/21
Passenger & Freight Transportation Services
N.A.I.C.S.: 482111
Lingling Hu *(Gen Mgr & Exec Dir)*

GUANGXI BOSSCO ENVIRONMENTAL PROTECTION TECHNOLOGY CO., LTD.
No 12 Kexing Road, Hi-tech Zone, Nanning, Guangxi, China
Tel.: (86) 7713299118
Web Site: https://www.bossco.cc
Year Founded: 1999
300422—(CHIN)
Rev.: $312,221,520
Assets: $1,684,668,024
Liabilities: $1,326,869,856
Net Worth: $357,798,168
Earnings: ($63,000,288)
Fiscal Year-end: 12/31/22
Waste Water Treatment Services
N.A.I.C.S.: 221320
Zhao Lie *(Chm-Supervisory Bd)*

Subsidiaries:

Beijing Bossco Environmental Protection Technology Co., Ltd (1)
Room 701 Marco Polo Office Tower 80 Anli Road Chaoyang District, Beijing, China
Tel.: (86) 1059636865
Environmental Engineering Services
N.A.I.C.S.: 541330

AND PRIVATE COMPANIES — GUANGXI RURAL INVESTMENT SUGAR INDUSTRY GROUP CO., LTD

Guangxi Bo Huan Environmental Consulting Company (1)
Room 1401 1402 1403Level 14 Building B3 De Li Dong Meng Guo Ji Wen, Hua Guang Chang 18 Foziling Road Qingxiu District, Nanning, China
Tel.: (86) 7715881118
Environmental Engineering Services
N.A.I.C.S.: 541330

Hezhou Bossco Environmental Investment & Construction Co., Ltd. (1)
No 39 Hezhou Blvd, Hezhou, Guangxi, China
Tel.: (86) 7745137127
Environmental Engineering Services
N.A.I.C.S.: 541330

Hunan Bossco Huayi Environment Engineering Co., Ltd (1)
707 Guang Fa Building No 2 Mid Renmin Road, Kunming, China
Tel.: (86) 87163130602
Environmental Engineering Services
N.A.I.C.S.: 541330

Luchuan Bossco Biotech Co., Ltd. (1)
No 186 Wenquan Blouleva rd East Wen Quan Zhi Xiang Square, Yan'an, Luchuan County, China
Tel.: (86) 7757279292
Environmental Engineering Services
N.A.I.C.S.: 541330

Sihong Bossco Water Co., Ltd (1)
Floor 11 No 14 North Renmin Rd, Sihong County, Suqian, Jiangsu, China
Tel.: (86) 52780795666
Environmental Engineering Services
N.A.I.C.S.: 541330

GUANGXI FENGLIN WOOD INDUSTRY GROUP CO., LTD.
No 1233 Yinhai Avenue, Lianggi ng District, Nanning, 530221, Guangxi, China
Tel.: (86) 7716114839
Web Site: http://www.fenglingroup.com
Year Founded: 2000
601996—(SHG)
Rev.: $288,195,640
Assets: $580,389,690
Liabilities: $185,352,051
Net Worth: $395,037,639
Earnings: $6,367,912
Fiscal Year-end: 12/31/22
Wood Panel Mfr & Whslr
N.A.I.C.S.: 321999
Liu Yichuan (Chm)

GUANGXI GUIDONG ELECTRIC POWER CO., LTD.
No 122 Songmuling Road Autonomous Region, Babu District, Hezhou, 542899, Guangxi, China
Tel.: (86) 7745297796
Web Site: http://www.gdep.com.cn
Year Founded: 1998
600310—(SHG)
Rev.: $2,447,849,851
Assets: $3,016,107,760
Liabilities: $2,382,090,394
Net Worth: $634,017,365
Earnings: ($31,312,191)
Fiscal Year-end: 12/31/22
Electric Power Generation & Distribution Services
N.A.I.C.S.: 221111
Tang Danzhong (Chm)

GUANGXI HUAXI NONFERROUS METALS CO., LTD
Floor 8-9 Building A Beibu Gulf Shipping Center No 12 Tiqiang Road, Zhuang Autonomous Region Liangqing District, Nanning, 530021, Guangxi, China
Tel.: (86) 7714821093
Web Site: http://www.nh.com.cn
Year Founded: 1998
600301—(SHG)
Rev.: $82,700,149
Assets: $65,449,103
Liabilities: $18,025,086
Net Worth: $47,424,017
Earnings: $2,544,750
Fiscal Year-end: 12/31/22
Chemical Products Mfr
N.A.I.C.S.: 325998
Cai Yong (Chm)

GUANGXI INVESTMENT GROUP CO., LTD.
Guangxi Investment Tower 109 Minzu Avenue, Nanning, 530028, China
Tel.: (86) 7715533156
Web Site: http://www.gig.cn
Sales Range: Less than $1 Million
Investment Services
N.A.I.C.S.: 523940
Liujiang Feng (Chm)

GUANGXI LIUGONG MACHINERY CO., LTD.
No 1 Liutai Road, Liuzhou, 545007, Guangxi, China
Tel.: (86) 7723886125   CN
Web Site: https://www.liugong.com
Year Founded: 1958
000528—(SSE)
Rev.: $3,717,755,496
Assets: $5,933,021,796
Liabilities: $3,521,679,876
Net Worth: $2,411,341,920
Earnings: $84,145,932
Emp.: 17,000
Fiscal Year-end: 12/31/22
Construction Machinery Mfr & Distr
N.A.I.C.S.: 333120
Zeng Guangan (Chm & CEO)

Subsidiaries:

Anhui LiuGong Crane Co., Ltd. (1)
No 18 Liugong Avenue, Bengbu, 233010, Anhui, China
Tel.: (86) 5524928535
Construction Machinery Mfr & Distr
N.A.I.C.S.: 333120

Dressta Co., Ltd. (1)
Grabskiego 48, 37-450, Stalowa Wola, Poland
Tel.: (48) 501802802
Web Site: https://dressta.com
Sales Range: $75-99.9 Million
Emp.: 115
Construction Equipment Sales
N.A.I.C.S.: 423810

LiuGong Construction Machinery N.A., LLC (1)
22220 Merchants Way Ste 100, Katy, TX 77449
Tel.: (281) 579-8882
Web Site: http://www.liugong.com
Construction Machinery Mfr
N.A.I.C.S.: 333120

LiuGong Dressta Machinery Sp. z o.o. (1)
ul Grabskiego 48, 37-450, Stalowa Wola, Poland
Tel.: (48) 501802802
Web Site: http://www.dressta.com
Construction Machinery Whslr
N.A.I.C.S.: 423810

LiuGong Machinery Asia Pacific Pte. Ltd. (1)
12 Joo Koon Circle, Singapore, 629044, Singapore
Tel.: (65) 6686 3566
Web Site: http://www.liugong.com
Construction Machinery Mfr & Distr
N.A.I.C.S.: 333120

LiuGong Machinery Europe B.V (1)
P J Oudweg 4, 1314 CH, Almere, Netherlands
Tel.: (31) 365290006
Web Site: https://liugong-europe.com
Construction Machinery Mfr & Distr
N.A.I.C.S.: 333120

LiuGong Machinery Hong Kong Co., Ltd. (1)
23/F Sing Ho Finance Building, 168 Gloucester Road, Wanchai, China (Hong Kong)
Tel.: (852) 39746912
Construction Machinery Mfr
N.A.I.C.S.: 333120

LiuGong Machinery Latin America, LTDA (1)
Parque Industrial Mogi Guacu na cidade de Mogi Guacu, Sao Paulo, 13849-226, Brazil
Tel.: (55) 1938512400
Construction Machinery Mfr & Distr
N.A.I.C.S.: 333120

LiuGong Machinery Middle East FZE (1)
RA08YB05, PO Box 263267, Jebel Ali, Dubai, United Arab Emirates
Tel.: (971) 48870641
Construction Machinery Mfr & Distr
N.A.I.C.S.: 333120

LiuGong Machinery Ru, LLC (1)
Putilkovo Village 69 km MKAD Office Complex Greenwood Building 17, Krasnogorskiy District, 143441, Moscow, Russia
Tel.: (7) 4952490406
Construction Machinery Mfr
N.A.I.C.S.: 333120

LiuGong Machinery South Africa (Pty) Ltd (1)
82 Pomona Rd Kempton Park, Johannesburg, 1619, South Africa
Tel.: (27) 119790971
Construction Machinery Mfr & Distr
N.A.I.C.S.: 333120

Liugong India Pvt. Ltd. (1)
101 Okhla Industrial Area Phase III, New Delhi, 110 020, India
Tel.: (91) 1147272200
Construction Machinery Mfr & Distr
N.A.I.C.S.: 333120

Liugong Machinery (Poland) sp. z o. o. (1)
Kwiatkowski 1 Street, 37-450, Stalowa Wola, Poland
Tel.: (48) 15 813 50 06
Web Site: http://www.liugongpl.com
Construction Machinery Mfr & Distr
N.A.I.C.S.: 333120
Zuozhou Tan (Chm)

Liuzhou Liugong Forklift Co., Ltd. (1)
No 1 Yanghe Avenue, Liuzhou, Guangxi, China
Tel.: (86) 7722040712
Web Site: http://en.lgforklift.cn
Electric Forklift Mfr
N.A.I.C.S.: 333924

Shanghai Jintai Engineering Machinery Co., Ltd. (1)
Road 45 Luopu, Anting, Shanghai, 201805, China
Tel.: (86) 2159577280
Web Site: https://www.jintai-sh.com
Construction Machinery Mfr
N.A.I.C.S.: 333120

GUANGXI LIUZHOU PHARMACEUTICAL CO., LTD.
No 68 Guantang, Liuzhou, 545001, Guangxi, China
Tel.: (86) 7722514508
Web Site: https://web.lzyy.cn
603368—(SHG)
Rev.: $2,675,017,458
Assets: $2,612,421,621
Liabilities: $1,718,726,775
Net Worth: $893,694,845
Earnings: $98,493,169
Fiscal Year-end: 12/31/22
Pharmaceutical Products Distr
N.A.I.C.S.: 424210
Chaoyang Zhu (Chm & Pres)

GUANGXI NANNING WATERWORKS CO., LTD.
No 4 Tiyu Road ASEAN Economic and Technological Development Zone, Nanning Overseas Chinese Investment Zone Wuming District, Nanning, 530029, Guangxi, China
Tel.: (86) 7714851348
Web Site: http://www.gxlcwater.com
Year Founded: 2006
601368—(SHG)
Rev.: $316,537,935
Assets: $2,713,765,612
Liabilities: $2,060,573,566
Net Worth: $653,192,046
Earnings: $23,002,982
Fiscal Year-end: 12/31/22
Sewage Treatment Services
N.A.I.C.S.: 221320
Binyuan Xu (Pres)

GUANGXI ORIENTAL INTELLIGENT MANUFACTURING TECHNOLOGY CO., LTD
No. 234 Linjiang Road Qixing District, Guilin, 541004, Guangxi, China
Tel.: (86) 7735820465
002175—(SSE)
Rev.: $37,883,612
Assets: $91,437,805
Liabilities: $23,849,621
Net Worth: $67,588,184
Earnings: $14,871,151
Fiscal Year-end: 12/31/22
Investment Services
N.A.I.C.S.: 523999
Zhongxin Dong (Deputy Gen Mgr)

GUANGXI RADIO & TV NETWORK CORPORATION
No 8 Jinghui Lane Yunjing Road Guangxi Zhuang Autonomous Region, Nanning, 530028, Guangxi, China
Tel.: (86) 7715905955
Web Site: http://www.96335.com
Year Founded: 2000
600936—(SHG)
Rev.: $235,943,829
Assets: $1,271,975,801
Liabilities: $958,775,145
Net Worth: $313,200,656
Earnings: ($145,600,542)
Emp.: 4,700
Fiscal Year-end: 12/31/22
Radio Station Services
N.A.I.C.S.: 516110
Xiangyang Xie (Chm)

GUANGXI RURAL INVESTMENT SUGAR INDUSTRY GROUP CO., LTD
No 30 Xiangzhu Avenue, Qingxiu District, Nanning, 530023, Guangxi, China
Tel.: (86) 7714914317
Web Site: http://www.nnsugar.com
Year Founded: 1999
000911—(SSE)
Rev.: $398,390,616
Assets: $627,356,340
Liabilities: $597,757,212
Net Worth: $29,599,128
Earnings: ($64,262,484)
Fiscal Year-end: 12/31/22
Sugar & Paper Product Mfr
N.A.I.C.S.: 311314
Luo Yingping (Chm)

Subsidiaries:

Nanning Qiaohong New Materials Co., Ltd. (1)
Nanning Overseas Chinese Investment Zone Lijian, Wumingli Jian, Nanning, China
Tel.: (86) 7716305580
Web Site: http://www.qiaohong-airlaid.com
Paper Products Mfr
N.A.I.C.S.: 322120

Guangxi Rural Investment Sugar Industry Group Co., Ltd—(Continued)

GUANGXI WUZHOU COMMUNICATIONS CO., LTD.
Modern International Mansion No 115-127 Minzu Avenue, Qingxiu District, Nanning, 530028, Guangxi, China
Tel.: (86) 7715568918
600368—(SHG)
Rev.: $236,787,801
Assets: $1,376,532,172
Liabilities: $585,791,819
Net Worth: $790,740,354
Earnings: $81,684,804
Fiscal Year-end: 12/31/22
Toll Collection Services
N.A.I.C.S.: 488490

GUANGXI WUZHOU ZHONGHENG GROUP CO., LTD.
No 1 Industrial Avenue Wuzhou Industrial Park, Wuzhou, 543000, Guangxi, China
Tel.: (86) 7743939039
Web Site: http://www.wz-zhongheng.com
Year Founded: 1993
600252—(SHG)
Rev.: $381,013,280
Assets: $1,649,959,586
Liabilities: $486,130,872
Net Worth: $1,163,828,713
Earnings: $11,095,180
Fiscal Year-end: 12/31/22
Pharmaceuticals Product Mfr
N.A.I.C.S.: 325412
Yang Jinhai *(Chm)*

GUANGXI XINXUNDA TECHNOLOGY GROUP CO., LTD.
Room 2501 Shenzhen Greater China International Exchange Plaza, No 1 Fuhua 1st Road Fuan Community Futian Subdistrict Futian District, Shenzhen, 518000, Guangdong, China
Tel.: (86) 75582731691
Web Site: http://www.gamexun.com
Year Founded: 2006
300518—(CHIN)
Rev.: $72,298,980
Assets: $273,673,296
Liabilities: $39,403,260
Net Worth: $234,270,036
Earnings: $8,101,080
Fiscal Year-end: 12/31/22
Online Game Development Services
N.A.I.C.S.: 541511
Wu Chenghua *(Chm)*

GUANGXI YUEGUI GUANGYE HOLDINGS CO., LTD.
No 100 Xingfu Road, Guigang, 510013, Guangxi, China
Tel.: (86) 2033970200
Web Site: http://www.yuegui.cn
Year Founded: 1993
000833—(SSE)
Rev.: $479,713,104
Assets: $760,805,136
Liabilities: $293,155,200
Net Worth: $467,649,936
Earnings: $41,481,180
Fiscal Year-end: 12/31/22
Sugar & Paper Product Mfr
N.A.I.C.S.: 311314
Liu Fuhua *(Chm)*

GUANGYUYUAN CHINESE HERBAL MEDICINE CO., LTD.
26th Floor Shanxi Wutong Building No 129 Changfeng Street, Xiaodian District, Taiyuan, 030000, Shanxi, China

Tel.: (86) 3517099061
Web Site: https://www.guangyuyuan.cn
Year Founded: 1996
600771—(SHG)
Rev.: $139,655,150
Assets: $381,845,136
Liabilities: $139,795,789
Net Worth: $242,049,347
Earnings: ($55,980,822)
Fiscal Year-end: 12/31/22
Pharmaceutical Product Mfr & Distr
N.A.I.C.S.: 325412
Li Xiaojun *(Chm)*

GUANGZHAO INDUSTRIAL FOREST BIOTECHNOLOGY GROUP LIMITED
6 Temasek Blvd 23-06 Suntec Tower Four, 038986, Singapore, Singapore
Tel.: (65) 62350255
Web Site: http://www.guangzhao.com
Sales Range: $1-9.9 Million
Forest Management Services
N.A.I.C.S.: 115310
Yong Hui Oh *(Exec Dir)*

Subsidiaries:

Shanghai Guangzhao Forestry Development Co., Ltd (1)
Room 603a-109 Building 2 No 351 Guoshoujing Road Zhangjiang, Shanghai, 201203, China
Tel.: (86) 2169156062
Plantation Farming Services
N.A.I.C.S.: 111421

Shanghai Guangzhao Plant Fast Growing Technology Co., Ltd (1)
No 138 Yulv Road Malu Town, Jiading District, Shanghai, 201801, China
Tel.: (86) 21 69156062
Saplings Distr
N.A.I.C.S.: 424910

GUANGZHENG EYE HOSPITAL GROUP CO., LTD.
No 266 Ronghe North Road, Urumqi Economic and Technological Development Zone, Xinjiang, 830012, China
Tel.: (86) 9913766551
Web Site: http://www.gzss.cc
Year Founded: 2001
002524—(SSE)
Rev.: $107,748,576
Assets: $218,665,980
Liabilities: $180,086,868
Net Worth: $38,579,112
Earnings: ($10,982,088)
Emp.: 660
Fiscal Year-end: 12/31/22
Steel Structure Products Mfr
N.A.I.C.S.: 331110
Zhou Yonglin *(Chm)*

GUANGZHOU AUTOMOBILE INDUSTRY GROUP CO., LTD.
23 15/F Chengyue Building No 448-458 Dongfeng Zhong Road, Guangzhou, 510030, Guangdong, China
Tel.: (86) 2083151380
Web Site: http://www.gaig.com.cn
Year Founded: 2000
Sales Range: $15-24.9 Billion
Automobile Mfr
N.A.I.C.S.: 336110
Fangyou Zhang *(Chm)*

Subsidiaries:

Denway Motors Ltd (1)
Room 801 Citicorp Centre 18 Whitefield Road, Causeway Bay, China (Hong Kong)
Tel.: (852) 25086228
Web Site: http://www.denway-motors.com
Sales Range: $75-99.9 Million
Emp.: 1,300

Holding Company; Motor Vehicles, Electrical Equipments & Parts Mfr
N.A.I.C.S.: 551112

Subsidiary (Non-US):

Baker and Priem Bull Bars Pty Limited (2)
58 Heathcote Road, Moorebank, 2170, New South Wales, Australia
Tel.: (61) 296011188
Web Site: http://www.bakerandpriem.com.au
Emp.: 3
Motor Vehicle Parts Mfr
N.A.I.C.S.: 423140
Mairo Collio *(Gen Mgr)*

GAC Changfeng Motor Co., Ltd. (1)
8th Floor Hualing Building No 111 Furong Middle Road, Changsha, 410011, Hunan, China (100%)
Tel.: (86) 73 1288 1959
Automobile Mfr
N.A.I.C.S.: 336110

Guangzhou Automobile Group Business Co., Ltd. (1)
No 54 Jinhui Building Yong Tai Rd, Guangzhou, 510095, China
Tel.: (86) 20 83589438
Automobile Parts Distr
N.A.I.C.S.: 423120

Guangzhou Automobile Group Company Limited (1)
GAC Center No 23 Xingguo Road Zhujiang New Town, Tianhe District, Guangzhou, 510623, Guangdong, China
Tel.: (86) 20 83151139
Web Site: https://www.gac.com.cn
Rev.: $15,444,903,755
Assets: $26,686,498,270
Liabilities: $9,515,253,384
Net Worth: $17,171,244,886
Earnings: $1,110,892,817
Emp.: 100,121
Fiscal Year-end: 12/31/2022
Automobile Parts Mfr
N.A.I.C.S.: 336110
Qinghong Zeng *(Chm)*

Guangzhou Automobile Group Component Co., Ltd. (1)
10F-12F Sunrish Plaza No 988 Guangzhou Da Dao Zhong, Tianhe District, Guangzhou, 510620, China
Tel.: (86) 20 83882608
Web Site: http://www.gacc.com.cn
Automobile Parts Mfr
N.A.I.C.S.: 336390

Guangzhou Guangyue Assets Management Co., Ltd. (1)
No 451 Shi Sha Rd, Shi Jin Town Baiyun District, Guangzhou, 510430, China
Tel.: (86) 20 36414330
Automobile Parts Mfr
N.A.I.C.S.: 336390

Guangzhou Motors Group Company (1)
No 352 Bin jiang Zhong Rd, Guangzhou, China
Tel.: (86) 20 84429542
Motorcycle Mfr
N.A.I.C.S.: 336991

Honda Automobile (China) Co., Ltd. (1)
No 363 Kaichuang Av Eastern Zone Guangzhou Economic and Technological, Guangzhou, 510760, China
Tel.: (86) 32288000 8105
Automobile Parts Mfr
N.A.I.C.S.: 336390

GUANGZHOU BAIYUN ELECTRIC EQUIPMENT CO., LTD.
No 18 Daling South Road Shenshan Industrial Zone, Jianggao Town Baiyun District, Guangzhou, 510460, Guangdong, China
Tel.: (86) 2086060164
Web Site: https://www.bydq.com
Year Founded: 1989
603861—(SHG)
Rev.: $486,502,511

Assets: $1,194,907,699
Liabilities: $772,328,649
Net Worth: $422,579,051
Earnings: $5,008,602
Fiscal Year-end: 12/31/22
Switchgear Control Equipment Mfr & Distr
N.A.I.C.S.: 335313
Mingcong Hu *(Pres & Gen Mgr)*

GUANGZHOU BAIYUN INTERNATIONAL AIRPORT COMPANY LIMITED
No 1 Joint-Stock Company Headquarters Office Building, South District, Guangzhou, 510470, Guangdong, China
Tel.: (86) 2036063595
Web Site: https://www.baiyunport.com
Year Founded: 2000
600004—(SHG)
Rev.: $557,522,770
Assets: $3,782,486,677
Liabilities: $1,338,318,971
Net Worth: $2,444,167,707
Earnings: ($150,397,126)
Fiscal Year-end: 12/31/22
Airport Operations
N.A.I.C.S.: 488119
Wang Xiaoyong *(Chm)*

GUANGZHOU BAIYUNSHAN PHARMACEUTICAL HOLDINGS COMPANY LIMITED
45ShaMian North Street, Liwan District, Guangzhou, 510130, Guangdong, China
Tel.: (86) 2066281011
Web Site: https://www.gybys.com.cn
600332—(SHG)
Rev.: $9,650,900,865
Assets: $10,043,436,523
Liabilities: $5,355,994,972
Net Worth: $4,687,441,551
Earnings: $544,343,931
Emp.: 28,048
Fiscal Year-end: 12/31/23
Holding Company
N.A.I.C.S.: 551112
Chuyuan Li *(Exec Dir)*

GUANGZHOU DEVELOPMENT GROUP INCORPORATED
31-32F No 3 Linjiang Avenue, Tianhe District, Guangzhou, 510623, Guangdong, China
Tel.: (86) 2037850968
Web Site: http://www.gdih.cn
Year Founded: 1997
600098—(SHG)
Rev.: $6,726,532,242
Assets: $8,699,678,517
Liabilities: $4,971,220,146
Net Worth: $3,728,458,371
Earnings: $190,081,621
Emp.: 4,630
Fiscal Year-end: 12/31/22
Electric Power Generation & Distribution Services
N.A.I.C.S.: 221118
Zhulin Wu *(Chm)*

Subsidiaries:

Guangxhou Gas Group Co., Ltd. (1)
Liwan Xiwan E Rd, Guangzhou, Guangdong, China
Tel.: (86) 2085515920
Web Site: http://www.gzgas.com
Gas Engineering Preparatory Services
N.A.I.C.S.: 237120
Qiao Wukang *(Gen Mgr)*

Subsidiary (Domestic):

Guangdong (Panyu) Petrochemical Storage & Transportation Ltd. (2)

No 1 Yuehai Road Huangge Town Panyu District, Guangzhou, 511455, Guangdong, China
Tel.: (86) 2066603088
Web Site: http://www.gdpec.com
Petrochemical Warehousing & Storage Services
N.A.I.C.S.: 493190
Huang Bo Heng *(Deputy Gen Mgr)*

GUANGZHOU DEVOTION THERMAL TECHNOLOGY CO., LTD.
No 5 Canglian 2nd Road, East District, Guangzhou, 510760, Guangdong, China
Tel.: (86) 2082268688
Web Site:
https://www.devotiongroup.com
Year Founded: 1993
300335—(CHIN)
Rev.: $160,484,220
Assets: $432,669,276
Liabilities: $146,345,940
Net Worth: $286,323,336
Earnings: $9,951,552
Emp.: 630
Fiscal Year-end: 12/31/22
Biomass Fuel Production
N.A.I.C.S.: 324199
Chang Yuanzheng *(Chm & Gen Mgr)*

GUANGZHOU ECHOM SCIENCE & TECHNOLOGY CO., LTD.
No 29 Kefeng Road Science City Hi-tech Industrial Development Zone, Guangzhou, 510663, Guangdong, China
Tel.: (86) 2032200889
Web Site: http://www.echom.com
Year Founded: 2007
002420—(SSE)
Rev.: $380,620,188
Assets: $293,239,440
Liabilities: $191,068,956
Net Worth: $102,170,484
Earnings: $5,965,596
Emp.: 2,000
Fiscal Year-end: 12/31/22
Television External Structure Components Mfr & Distr
N.A.I.C.S.: 334220
Xiong Haitao *(Chm & Vice Chm)*

GUANGZHOU FANGBANG ELECTRONICS CO., LTD.
6F Building A5 No 11 Kaiyuan Avenue, Guangzhou High-tech Industrial Development Zone, Guangzhou, 510635, Guangdong, China
Tel.: (86) 2082512686
Web Site: http://www.fbflex.com
Year Founded: 2010
688020—(SHG)
Rev.: $43,892,733
Assets: $276,297,498
Liabilities: $57,244,520
Net Worth: $219,052,979
Earnings: ($9,549,727)
Fiscal Year-end: 12/31/22
Electronic Product Mfr & Distr
N.A.I.C.S.: 334419
Zhi Su *(Chm & Gen Mgr)*

GUANGZHOU FRIENDSHIP GROUP CO., LTD.
No 369 Huanshi East Road, Yuexiu District, Guangzhou, 510095, Guangdong, China
Tel.: (86) 20 83483236
Web Site: http://www.cgzfs.com
Sales Range: $400-449.9 Million
Investment Services
N.A.I.C.S.: 455110
Xiangqian Fang *(Chm)*

GUANGZHOU FRONTOP DIGITAL CREATIVE TECHNOLOGY CO., LTD.
Building No 26 No 261 Wushan Road, Tianhe District, Guangzhou, 510000, Guangdong, China
Tel.: (86) 2029166030
Web Site: https://www.frontop.cn
Year Founded: 2002
301313—(CHIN)
Rev.: $85,559,760
Assets: $204,266,556
Liabilities: $58,475,196
Net Worth: $145,791,360
Earnings: $2,551,068
Emp.: 1,000
Fiscal Year-end: 12/31/22
Digital Marketing Services
N.A.I.C.S.: 541810
Wu Suiying *(Chm & Gen Mgr)*

GUANGZHOU GOALAND ENERGY CONSERVATION TECH CO., LTD.
No 3 Nanyun 5th Road Science City, Hi-tech Industrial Development Zone, Guangzhou, 510663, Guangdong, China
Tel.: (86) 2062800188
Web Site:
https://www.goaland.com.cn
Year Founded: 2001
300499—(CHIN)
Rev.: $80,749,713
Assets: $256,212,756
Liabilities: $58,239,010
Net Worth: $197,973,746
Earnings: ($4,482,650)
Fiscal Year-end: 12/31/23
Industrial Equipment Mfr
N.A.I.C.S.: 333415
Li Qi *(Chm)*

Subsidiaries:

Goaland Energy Conservation Tech USA Ltd. (1)
3301 San Gabriel Blvd, Rosemead, CA 91770
Tel.: (626) 766-1700
Cooling Equipment Distr
N.A.I.C.S.: 423730

Guangzhou Smart Grid Information Technology Co., Ltd. (1)
No 3 Nanyun Fifth Road Science City, Hi-Tech Industrial Development Zone, Guangzhou, China
Tel.: (86) 2066821212
Cooling Equipment Distr
N.A.I.C.S.: 423730

GUANGZHOU GRANDBUY CO., LTD.
No 12 Xihu Road, Yuexiu District, Guangzhou, 510030, Guangdong, China
Tel.: (86) 2083322348
Web Site:
https://www.grandbuy.com.cn
Year Founded: 2002
002187—(SSE)
Rev.: $686,810,124
Assets: $1,234,986,480
Liabilities: $674,550,396
Net Worth: $560,436,084
Earnings: ($20,123,532)
Fiscal Year-end: 12/31/22
General Merchandise Store Operator
N.A.I.C.S.: 455110
Wang Hui *(Chm)*

GUANGZHOU GREAT POWER ENERGY & TECHNOLOGY CO., LTD.
No 912 Shiliang Road, Shawan Town Panyu District, Guangzhou, 511483, Guangdong, China
Tel.: (86) 2039196888
Web Site: https://www.greatpower.net
Year Founded: 2001
300438—(CHIN)
Rev.: $1,272,964,680
Assets: $1,701,003,564
Liabilities: $1,115,829,000
Net Worth: $585,174,564
Earnings: $88,224,552
Emp.: 10,000
Fiscal Year-end: 12/31/22
Storage Battery Mfr
N.A.I.C.S.: 335910
Xinde Xia *(Chm)*

Subsidiaries:

Great Power (Zhuhai) Battery Co., Ltd. (1)
Xinqing 5th Road, Xinqing Science and Technology Industrial Park Doumen, Zhuhai, China
Tel.: (86) 7566333555
Battery Mfr
N.A.I.C.S.: 335910

Henan Great Power Energy & Technology Co., Ltd. (1)
At the intersection of Huaihe Rd & Zhongyuan Ave, Zhumadian, China
Tel.: (86) 3962709555
Battery Mfr
N.A.I.C.S.: 335910

Henan Great Power Energy Co., Ltd. (1)
At the Intersection of Huaihe Rd and Zhongyuan Ave, Zhumadian, China
Tel.: (86) 396 270 9555
Electronic Battery Mfr
N.A.I.C.S.: 335910

GUANGZHOU GRG METROLOGY & TEST CO., LTD.
No 8 Chuangyun Road, Panyu District, Guangzhou, 511450, Guangdong, China
Tel.: (86) 4006020999
Web Site: https://www.grgtmall.net
Year Founded: 2002
002967—(SSE)
Rev.: $365,610,192
Assets: $779,799,613
Liabilities: $279,277,418
Net Worth: $500,522,195
Earnings: $25,850,729
Emp.: 4,000
Fiscal Year-end: 12/31/22
Information Technology Services
N.A.I.C.S.: 541512
Yuezhen Huang *(Chm)*

GUANGZHOU GUANGRI STOCK CO., LTD.
22 23F Lingnan V Valley Gongkong Kechuang Building No 9 Jinsha Road, Haizhu District, Guangzhou, 510045, Guangdong, China
Tel.: (86) 2038371213
Web Site: https://www.guangrigf.com
600894—(SHG)
Rev.: $991,739,240
Assets: $1,804,600,512
Liabilities: $552,581,280
Net Worth: $1,252,019,232
Earnings: $71,949,075
Fiscal Year-end: 12/31/22
Elevator Mfr & Distr
N.A.I.C.S.: 333921

GUANGZHOU HAIGE COMMUNICATIONS GROUP INCORPORATED COMPANY
NO 88 Haiyun Road Science City High-tech Industrial Development Zone, Luogang District, Guangzhou, 510663, Guangdong, China
Tel.: (86) 2038699138
Web Site: http://www.haige.com
Year Founded: 2007
002465—(SSE)
Rev.: $788,431,644
Assets: $2,135,198,988
Liabilities: $553,823,244
Net Worth: $1,581,375,744
Earnings: $93,815,280
Emp.: 1,500
Fiscal Year-end: 12/31/22
Radio Communication Equipment Mfr
N.A.I.C.S.: 334220
Li Tiegang *(VP & Deputy Gen Mgr)*

GUANGZHOU HANGXIN AVIATION TECHNOLOGY CO., LTD.
No 1 Guangbao Road Science City, Luogang District, Guangzhou, 510663, Guangdong, China
Tel.: (86) 2066350888
Web Site: https://www.hangxin.com
Year Founded: 1994
300424—(CHIN)
Rev.: $196,127,568
Assets: $333,681,660
Liabilities: $226,170,360
Net Worth: $107,511,300
Earnings: $3,795,012
Fiscal Year-end: 12/31/22
Aviation Equipment Mfr
N.A.I.C.S.: 334511
Wang Lei *(Chm)*

GUANGZHOU HAOYANG ELECTRONIC CO., LTD.
No 109 Hai Yong Road, Shi Qi Town Pan Yu Zone, Guangzhou, 511450, Guangdong, China
Tel.: (86) 2039966388
Web Site: https://www.terbly.com
Year Founded: 2005
300833—(SSE)
Rev.: $171,667,080
Assets: $342,804,852
Liabilities: $38,653,524
Net Worth: $304,151,328
Earnings: $50,006,268
Fiscal Year-end: 12/31/22
Electronic Product Mfr & Distr
N.A.I.C.S.: 334419
Weikai Jiang *(Chm, Gen Mgr & Dir)*

GUANGZHOU HAOZHI INDUSTRIAL CO., LTD.
No 68 Hefeng Road, Huangpu District, Guangzhou, 511356, Guangdong, China
Tel.: (86) 2062257588
Web Site: https://www.haozhihs.net
Year Founded: 2006
300503—(CHIN)
Rev.: $140,889,438
Assets: $342,999,652
Liabilities: $187,753,247
Net Worth: $155,246,405
Earnings: ($27,320,534)
Emp.: 300
Fiscal Year-end: 12/31/23
Industrial Machinery Mfr
N.A.I.C.S.: 333248
Xiuqing Tang *(Chm & Deputy Gen Mgr)*

GUANGZHOU HENGYUN ENTERPRISES HOLDING LTD.
No 251 Kexue Avenue, Huangpu District, Guangzhou, 510670, Guangdong, China
Tel.: (86) 2082068252
Web Site:
http://www.hengyun.com.cn
Year Founded: 1993
000531—(SSE)
Rev.: $552,079,476
Assets: $2,104,775,712
Liabilities: $1,327,150,656
Net Worth: $777,625,056
Earnings: ($8,046,324)

GUANGZHOU HENGYUN ENTERPRISES HOLDING LTD.

Guangzhou Hengyun Enterprises Holding Ltd.—(Continued)
Fiscal Year-end: 12/31/22
Holding Company
N.A.I.C.S.: 551112
Xu Hongsheng (Chm)

GUANGZHOU HI-TARGET NAVIGATION TECH CO., LTD.
10th Floor Chuangxin Building Tian'An HQ Center, No 555 Panyu Avenue North Panyu Road Panyu District, Guangzhou, 511400, Guangdong, China
Tel.: (86) 2028688296
Web Site: https://en.hi-target.com.cn
Year Founded: 1999
300177—(CHIN)
Rev.: $185,110,380
Assets: $533,553,696
Liabilities: $210,100,176
Net Worth: $323,453,520
Earnings: ($15,403,284)
Emp.: 3,300
Fiscal Year-end: 12/31/22
Global Navigation Satellite System Software & Hardware Products
N.A.I.C.S.: 334220

GUANGZHOU HOLIKE CREATIVE HOME CO., LTD.
No 8 Lianyun Road Economic and Technological Development Zone, East Area, Guangzhou, 510665, Guangdong, China
Tel.: (86) 2089311886
Web Site: http://www.holike.com
Year Founded: 2007
603898—(SHG)
Rev.: $396,372,520
Assets: $615,144,039
Liabilities: $187,883,870
Net Worth: $427,260,169
Earnings: $60,521,301
Fiscal Year-end: 12/31/22
Household Furniture Mfr & Distr
N.A.I.C.S.: 337122
Hanbiao Shen (Chm, Pres & Gen Mgr)

GUANGZHOU HUAYAN PRECISION MACHINERY CO., LTD.
No 6 Chuangli Road Ningxi Street, Zengcheng Economic & Technological Development Zone, Guangzhou, 511340, Guangdong, China
Tel.: (86) 2032638568
Web Site: https://www.gzhuayan.com
Year Founded: 2002
301138—(CHIN)
Rev.: $76,503,960
Assets: $204,828,156
Liabilities: $46,365,696
Net Worth: $158,462,460
Earnings: $11,844,144
Fiscal Year-end: 12/31/22
Packaging Equipment Product Mfr
N.A.I.C.S.: 322220
Helin Bao (Chm)

GUANGZHOU JET BIO-FILTRATION CO., LTD.
No 1 DouTang Road, Yonghe Economic Zone, Guangzhou, 511356, China
Tel.: (86) 2032811888
Web Site: https://www.jetbiofil.com
Year Founded: 2001
688026—(SHG)
Rev.: $85,619,360
Assets: $225,389,820
Liabilities: $65,315,245
Net Worth: $160,074,575
Earnings: $12,314,793
Fiscal Year-end: 12/31/22
Application Development Services
N.A.I.C.S.: 541511
Jianhua Yuan (Chm)

GUANGZHOU JIACHENG INTERNATIONAL LOGISTICS CO., LTD.
No 8 Junma Avenue, Dongchong Town Nansha District, Guangzhou, 511475, Guangdong, China
Tel.: (86) 2034631836
Web Site: http://www.jiacheng88.com
Year Founded: 2000
603535—(SHG)
Rev.: $179,415,110
Assets: $536,014,459
Liabilities: $212,029,019
Net Worth: $323,985,439
Earnings: $24,026,736
Fiscal Year-end: 12/31/22
Professional Logistics Services
N.A.I.C.S.: 541614
Yanting Huang (Vice Chm)

GUANGZHOU JINYI MEDIA CORPORATION
Room 402-1 No 8-1 Huacheng Road, Tianhe District, Guangzhou, 510000, Guangdong, China
Tel.: (86) 2087548898
Web Site: http://www.jycinema.com
Year Founded: 2004
002905—(SSE)
Rev.: $120,180,996
Assets: $633,354,228
Liabilities: $612,500,616
Net Worth: $20,853,612
Earnings: ($53,538,732)
Fiscal Year-end: 12/31/22
Movie Screening Services
N.A.I.C.S.: 512131
Xiaowen Li (Chm)

GUANGZHOU JINZHONG AUTO PARTS MANUFACTURING CO., LTD.
Dongfeng Avenue West Xinhua Street, Huadu, Guangzhou, 510800, Guangdong, China
Tel.: (86) 2086733628
Web Site: https://www.gzjz-auto.com
Year Founded: 2004
301133—(CHIN)
Rev.: $130,435,098
Assets: $227,779,816
Liabilities: $81,538,958
Net Worth: $146,240,859
Earnings: $12,800,239
Fiscal Year-end: 12/31/23
Automobile Parts Mfr & Distr
N.A.I.C.S.: 336211
Hongping Xin (Chm)

GUANGZHOU JOINTAS CHEMICAL CO., LTD.
Building C, No. 62, Nanxiang 1st Road, High-Tech Industry Development Zone, Guangzhou, 510663, China
Tel.: (86) 2085576000253   CN
Web Site: https://www.jointas.com
Year Founded: 1989
002909—(SSE)
Rev.: $187,661,591
Assets: $276,929,675
Liabilities: $156,897,295
Net Worth: $120,032,380
Earnings: $1,442,352
Fiscal Year-end: 12/31/23
Adhesive Product Mfr & Distr
N.A.I.C.S.: 325520
Zhenfu Zou (Founder)

GUANGZHOU KDT MACHINERY CO., LTD
No 81 Ruixiang Street, Huangpu District, Guangzhou, 510530, Guangdong, China
Tel.: (86) 4009900083
Web Site: https://www.kdtmac.com
Year Founded: 2006
002833—(SSE)
Rev.: $298,699,596
Assets: $528,657,948
Liabilities: $158,864,004
Net Worth: $369,793,944
Earnings: $63,842,688
Fiscal Year-end: 12/31/22
Panel Furniture Machinery Mfr & Distr
N.A.I.C.S.: 333243
Lijun Xu (Deputy Gen Mgr-Finance & Dir-Fin)

Subsidiaries:

Chengdu KDT Machinery Co., Ltd   (1)
Dayi Industrial Development Zone, Chengdu, Sichuan, China
Tel.: (86) 2888373999
Industrial Machinery Distr
N.A.I.C.S.: 423830

KDT Europe Sp Z O O   (1)
Ul Wilenska 51 bud B lok 202, 05-200, Wolomin, Poland
Tel.: (48) 227639696
Web Site: http://www.kdteurope.com
Industrial Machinery Distr
N.A.I.C.S.: 423830

GUANGZHOU KINGMED DIAGNOSTICS CENTER CO., LTD.
3rd Floor Haizu Science & Technology Building 2429 Xingang Dong Road, Guangzhou, 510330, China
Tel.: (86) 20 2228 3222   CN
Web Site: http://www.kingmed.com.cn
Year Founded: 1994
Clinical Testing Laboratories Operator
N.A.I.C.S.: 541380
Yaoming Liang (Founder & CEO)

GUANGZHOU KINGMED DIAGNOSTICS GROUP CO., LTD.
3 Building 10 Luoxuan 3rd Road Guangzhou International Shengw, Guangzhou, 510000, China
Tel.: (86) 2022283222
603882—(SHG)
Rev.: $2,172,840,860
Assets: $1,950,255,375
Liabilities: $704,229,594
Net Worth: $1,246,025,781
Earnings: $386,491,042
Fiscal Year-end: 12/31/22
Health Care Srvices
N.A.I.C.S.: 621999
Yaoming Liang (Chm & Pres)

GUANGZHOU KINGTELLER TECHNOLOGY CO., LTD.
No 12 Ruifa Road Science City, Luogang District, Guangzhou, 510663, Guangdong, China
Tel.: (86) 2029087888
Web Site: https://www.kingteller.com.cn
Year Founded: 2001
002177—(SSE)
Rev.: $9,555,624
Assets: $242,611,200
Liabilities: $6,396,624
Net Worth: $236,214,576
Earnings: $7,605,468
Emp.: 2,500
Fiscal Year-end: 12/31/22
Automatic Teller Machine Distr
N.A.I.C.S.: 423420
Wenjiang Yang (Chm & Gen Mgr)

GUANGZHOU LBP MEDICINE

INTERNATIONAL PUBLIC

SCIENCE & TECHNOLOGY CO., LTD.
No 2 Kexin Street, Huangpu District, Guangzhou, 510663, Guangdong, China
Tel.: (86) 2032299997
Web Site: https://www.gzlbp.com
Year Founded: 2005
688393—(SHG)
Rev.: $71,236,320
Assets: $195,546,846
Liabilities: $23,930,759
Net Worth: $171,616,087
Earnings: $5,994,280
Fiscal Year-end: 12/31/22
Medical Product Mfr & Distr
N.A.I.C.S.: 339112
Xiangting Cai (Chm & Gen Mgr)

GUANGZHOU LINGNAN GROUP HOLDINGS COMPANY LIMITED
No 120 Liuhua Road, Guangzhou, 510016, Guangdong, China
Tel.: (86) 2086669900
Web Site: http://www.gzln.cn
Year Founded: 1993
000524—(SSE)
Rev.: $145,250,820
Assets: $419,301,792
Liabilities: $130,221,000
Net Worth: $289,080,792
Earnings: ($24,994,008)
Fiscal Year-end: 12/31/22
Restaurant Services
N.A.I.C.S.: 721110
Li Feng (Chm)

Subsidiaries:

LN Garden Hotel Company Ltd.   (1)
368 Huanshi Dong Lu, Guangzhou, 510064, China
Tel.: (86) 2083338989
Web Site: http://www2.gardenhotel.com
Hotel Operator
N.A.I.C.S.: 721110
Franco Io (Gen Mgr)

Liuhua Hotel Group Company Ltd.   (1)
194 Huanshi Road W, Guangzhou, 510017, China
Tel.: (86) 2086668800
Web Site: http://www.lh.com.cn
Hotel Operator
N.A.I.C.S.: 721110

GUANGZHOU LINGWE TECHNOLOGY CO., LTD.
R702 No 555 Panyu Avenue North, Communication Center Ecological Hi-Tech Park Panyu District, Guangzhou, 511493, China
Tel.: (86) 2039388561
Web Site: https://www.lingwe.com
Year Founded: 2007
301373—(SSE)
Rev.: $56,334,096
Assets: $101,269,116
Liabilities: $14,537,016
Net Worth: $86,732,100
Earnings: $12,774,996
Fiscal Year-end: 12/31/22
Silicon Product Mfr & Distr
N.A.I.C.S.: 325199
Yingni Hu (Chm)

GUANGZHOU LUXVISIONS INNOVATION TECHNOLOGY LIMITED
No 25 Guangpu West Road Science City, Guangzhou Hi-tech Industrial Development Zone, Guangzhou, China
Tel.: (86) 20 66615999
Web Site: http://www.luxvisions-inno.com

Camera Lenses Mfr
N.A.I.C.S.: 333310

GUANGZHOU MEADVILLE ELECTRONICS CO., LTD.
No 1 Xinle Road Science City Guangzhou, HiTech Industry Development Zone, Guangzhou, 510663, Guangdong, China
Tel.: (86) 2022217388
Printed Circuit Board Mfr
N.A.I.C.S.: 334412

GUANGZHOU METRO DESIGN & RESEARCH INSTITUTE CO., LTD.
No 204 Huanshi West Road, Yuexiu District, Guangzhou, 510010, Guangdong, China
Tel.: (86) 2083524958
Web Site: http://www.gmdi.cn
Year Founded: 1993
003013—(SSE)
Rev.: $347,666,904
Assets: $688,447,188
Liabilities: $380,962,764
Net Worth: $307,484,424
Earnings: $56,137,536
Fiscal Year-end: 12/31/22
Engineeering Services
N.A.I.C.S.: 541330
Xingzhong Nong (Chm & Sec-Party Committee)

GUANGZHOU PEARL RIVER INDUSTRIAL DEVELOPMENT HOLDINGS CO., LTD
30F Yide Center No 362 Dongfeng Middle Road, Yuexiu District, Guangzhou, 510030, China
Tel.: (86) 2083752439
Web Site: http://www.gzzjsy.com
Year Founded: 1985
600684—(SHG)
Rev.: $713,234,864
Assets: $4,528,691,210
Liabilities: $4,217,450,272
Net Worth: $311,240,938
Earnings: ($252,373,577)
Fiscal Year-end: 12/31/22
Real Estate Development Services
N.A.I.C.S.: 531390
Zhang Yan (Chm)

GUANGZHOU PEARL RIVER PIANO GROUP CO., LTD.
Building No 1 & Factory Building Self Numbered Building No 3, No 38 Xiangshan Avenue Yongning Street Zengcheng District, Guangzhou, 511340, Guangdong, China
Tel.: (86) 2081514020
Web Site: http://www.pearlriverpiano.com
Year Founded: 1956
002678—(SSE)
Rev.: $233,086,464
Assets: $718,522,272
Liabilities: $192,545,964
Net Worth: $525,976,308
Earnings: $17,304,300
Emp.: 4,000
Fiscal Year-end: 12/31/22
Piano Mfr
N.A.I.C.S.: 339992
Jianning Li (Chm)

GUANGZHOU PORT GROUP CO., LTD.
406 Riverside Road, Yuexiu District, Guangzhou, 510700, China
Tel.: (86) 2083770865
Web Site: http://www.gzport.com
Sales Range: $550-599.9 Million
Emp.: 14,000
Port Operations
N.A.I.C.S.: 488310
Houming Yan (CEO)

GUANGZHOU R&F PROPERTIES CO., LTD.
45-54/F R F Center 10 Huaxia Road, Zhujiang New Town, Guangzhou, China
Tel.: (86) 2038882777   CN
Web Site: https://www.rfchina.com
Year Founded: 1994
2777—(OTCIQ)
Rev.: $4,872,701,457
Assets: $51,080,103,013
Liabilities: $41,811,574,407
Net Worth: $9,268,528,605
Earnings: ($2,184,768,636)
Emp.: 27,162
Fiscal Year-end: 12/31/22
Comercial & Residential Property Developer
N.A.I.C.S.: 531190
Sze Lim Li (Co-Chm)

Subsidiaries:

R & F Properties (Cambodia) Co., Ltd.   (1)
380 Preah Monivong Blvd 93 Phnom Penh, 12300, Phnom Penh, Cambodia
Tel.: (855) 188882777
Web Site: http://www.rfcambodia.com
Real Estate Services
N.A.I.C.S.: 531390

R & F Property Pty Ltd   (1)
Level 52 Rialto Towers 525 Collins Street, Melbourne, 3000, VIC, Australia
Tel.: (61) 39 036 2777
Web Site: http://www.rfpropertyaustralia.com.au
Real Estate Services
N.A.I.C.S.: 531390
Vincent Chen (Deputy Gen Mgr)

R&F Property Australia Pty Ltd   (1)
20 Hockings Street, West End, 4101, QLD, Australia
Tel.: (61) 73 096 1300
Web Site: https://www.rfpropertyaustralia.com.au
Property Development Services
N.A.I.C.S.: 531390

GUANGZHOU RADIO GROUP CO., LTD.
163 Pingyun Road, West Huangpu Avenue, Guangzhou, 510656, China
Tel.: (86) 3869 9909   CN
Web Site: http://www.grg.com.cn
Year Founded: 1956
Sales Range: $1-4.9 Billion
Emp.: 7,000
Holding Company
N.A.I.C.S.: 551112
Youyong Zhao (Chm)

Subsidiaries:

GRG Banking Equipment Co., Ltd.   (1)
9 11 Kelin Road Science City, High-tech Industrial Development Zone, Guangzhou, 510663, Guangdong, China
Tel.: (86) 2062878545
Web Site: https://global.grgbanking.com
Rev.: $1,056,714,984
Assets: $2,833,860,276
Liabilities: $948,431,484
Net Worth: $1,885,428,792
Earnings: $116,157,132
Emp.: 24,000
Fiscal Year-end: 12/31/2022
Automated Teller Machine Mfr & Wholesale Distr
N.A.I.C.S.: 333998
Chen Jianliang (Chm)

GUANGZHOU RESTAURANT GROUP CO., LTD.
12F 13F Zibian Office Building Ximenkou Square 50 Zhongshan 7th Road, Liwan District, Guangzhou, 510665, Guangdong, China
Tel.: (86) 2081380909
Web Site: http://www.gzr.com.cn
Year Founded: 1992
603043—(SHG)
Rev.: $577,373,533
Assets: $820,876,245
Liabilities: $324,936,495
Net Worth: $495,939,750
Earnings: $73,061,394
Emp.: 100
Fiscal Year-end: 12/31/22
Restaurant Operators
N.A.I.C.S.: 722513
Xu Weibing (Chm)

GUANGZHOU RISONG INTELLIGENT TECHNOLOGY HOLDING CO., LTD.
No 188 Ruixiang Road, Huangpu, Guangzhou, 510535, China
Tel.: (86) 2066309188
Web Site: https://www.risongtc.com
Year Founded: 2012
688090—(SHG)
Rev.: $141,233,204
Assets: $249,347,115
Liabilities: $124,602,796
Net Worth: $124,744,319
Earnings: ($8,807,545)
Fiscal Year-end: 12/31/22
Holding Company
N.A.I.C.S.: 551112
Zhiqiang Sun (Chm & Pres)

Subsidiaries:

Guangzhou Risong Weldstone Intelligent Equipment Co., Ltd.   (1)
No 188 Ruixiang Road, Huangpu District, Guangzhou, 510535, China
Tel.: (86) 2066309188
Industrial Machinery Mfr
N.A.I.C.S.: 333248

Wuhan Risong Hokuto Automotive Equipment Co., Ltd.   (1)
No 701 Building Sixth Wanda Plaza, Economic Technological Development Area, Wuhan, China
Tel.: (86) 2750758866
Industrial Machinery Mfr
N.A.I.C.S.: 333248

GUANGZHOU RUOYUCHEN TECHNOLOGY CO., LTD.
25/F Poly Zhongyu Building No 319 Dashadong, Huangpu District, Guangzhou, 510725, Guangdong, China
Tel.: (86) 2031959063
Web Site: https://www.gzruoyuchen.com
Year Founded: 2011
003010—(SSE)
Rev.: $170,863,992
Assets: $168,906,816
Liabilities: $17,472,780
Net Worth: $151,434,036
Earnings: $4,739,904
Emp.: 1,000
Fiscal Year-end: 12/31/22
E Commerce Site Operator
N.A.I.C.S.: 334510
Yu Wang (Chm & Gen Mgr)

GUANGZHOU RURAL COMMERCIAL BANK CO., LTD.
No 9 Yingri Road, Huangpu District, Guangzhou, Guangdong, China
Tel.: (86) 2028019324   CN
Web Site: https://www.grcbank.com
Year Founded: 1998
1551—(HKG)
Rev.: $5,780,038,491
Assets: $181,939,860,711
Liabilities: $168,572,991,388
Net Worth: $13,366,869,323
Earnings: $451,305,245
Emp.: 13,620
Fiscal Year-end: 12/31/23
Commercial Banking Services
N.A.I.C.S.: 522110
Jikang Wang (Chm)

GUANGZHOU S.P.I DESIGN CO., LTD.
2-4F South Tower Huanhui Commercial Plaza No 1166 Xingang East Road, Haizhu, Guangzhou, 510000, Guangdong, China
Tel.: (86) 2037039822
Web Site: https://www.gz-spi.com
Year Founded: 2007
300844—(CHIN)
Rev.: $46,416,240
Assets: $145,398,240
Liabilities: $26,503,308
Net Worth: $118,894,932
Earnings: ($17,169,516)
Fiscal Year-end: 12/31/22
Engineeering Services
N.A.I.C.S.: 541330
Cai Bin (Chm & Gen Mgr)

GUANGZHOU SANFU NEW MATERIALS TECHNOLOGY CO., LTD.
No 57 Fenghuang Sanheng Road Sino-Singapore Guangzhou Knowledge City, Guangzhou, 510663, Guangdong, China
Web Site: http://www.gzsanfu.com.cn
Year Founded: 2009
688359—(SHG)
Rev.: $51,193,280
Assets: $105,923,938
Liabilities: $39,127,753
Net Worth: $66,796,185
Earnings: ($4,526,805)
Fiscal Year-end: 12/31/22
Chemical Product Mfr & Distr
N.A.I.C.S.: 325520
Wenlong Shangguan (Chm & Gen Mgr)

GUANGZHOU SEAGULL KITCHEN & BATH PRODUCTS CO., LTD.
No 363 Yushan W Rd Shatou, Panyu, Guangzhou, 511400, Guangdong, China
Tel.: (86) 2084896096
Web Site: https://www.seagullgroup.cn
Year Founded: 1958
002084—(SSE)
Rev.: $462,595,536
Assets: $588,853,044
Liabilities: $294,380,892
Net Worth: $294,472,152
Earnings: $6,656,364
Fiscal Year-end: 12/31/22
Heating Equipment Mfr
N.A.I.C.S.: 333414
Taiying Tang (Chm)

GUANGZHOU SHANGPIN HOME COLLECTION CO., LTD.
No 85 Huacheng Avenue Unit 01-05 Room 3501, Tianhe District, Guangzhou, 510000, Guangdong, China
Tel.: (86) 2085027987
Web Site: http://www.spzp.com
Year Founded: 2004
300616—(CHIN)
Rev.: $746,133,336
Assets: $1,148,650,308
Liabilities: $645,910,200
Net Worth: $502,740,108
Earnings: $6,500,520
Fiscal Year-end: 12/31/22
Furniture Product Mfr & Distr

GUANGZHOU SHANGPIN HOME COLLECTION CO., LTD.

Guangzhou Shangpin Home Collection Co., Ltd.—(Continued)
N.A.I.C.S.: 332510
Lianzhu Li *(Chm)*

GUANGZHOU SHIYUAN ELECTRONIC TECHNOLOGY CO., LTD.
No 6 4th Yunpu Road, Huangpu Industry District, Guangzhou, China
Tel.: (86) 2032210275
Web Site: https://www.cvte.com
Year Founded: 2005
2841—(SSE)
Rev.: $2,906,272,859
Assets: $2,789,722,821
Liabilities: $1,104,584,363
Net Worth: $1,685,138,458
Earnings: $286,943,218
Emp.: 5,400
Fiscal Year-end: 12/31/22
Electronic Components Mfr
N.A.I.C.S.: 334419
Xie Yong *(Sec)*

GUANGZHOU SHIYUAN ELECTRONICS CO., LTD
No 6 4th Yunpu Road, Huangpu Industry District, Guangzhou, China
Tel.: (86) 208 208 6168
Web Site: http://www.cvte.com
Year Founded: 2005
002841—(SSE)
Rev.: $2,440,241,370
Assets: $1,427,190,678
Liabilities: $708,953,175
Net Worth: $718,237,503
Earnings: $230,521,221
Emp.: 4,890
Fiscal Year-end: 12/31/19
Electronic Equipment Mfr & Distr
N.A.I.C.S.: 334419
Yong Xie *(Sec)*

Subsidiaries:

Guangzhou Shizhen Information Technology Co., Ltd. (1)
No 192 Kezhu Road Science Park, Guangzhou, 510663, China
Tel.: (86) 4001689545
Web Site: http://www.maxhub.vip
Peripheral Device Mfr
N.A.I.C.S.: 334118

GUANGZHOU SIE CONSULTING CO., LTD.
45th floor The Pinnacle No 17 the Pearl River West Road, Tianhe, Guangzhou, 510023, Guangdong, China
Tel.: (86) 2089814259
Web Site: https://www.chinasie.com
Year Founded: 2005
300687—(CHIN)
Rev.: $317,479,168
Assets: $527,776,739
Liabilities: $128,380,085
Net Worth: $399,396,654
Earnings: $35,832,733
Fiscal Year-end: 12/31/23
Information Technology Development Services
N.A.I.C.S.: 541512

GUANGZHOU TECH-LONG PACKAGING MACHINERY CO., LTD.
No 23 Yunpu 1 Road, Huangpu District, Guangzhou, 510530, Guangdong, China
Tel.: (86) 13622220030
Web Site: http://www.tech-long.com
Year Founded: 1998
002209—(SSE)
Rev.: $161,190,432
Assets: $242,004,672
Liabilities: $158,719,392
Net Worth: $83,285,280
Earnings: $3,137,940
Emp.: 340
Fiscal Year-end: 12/31/22
Liquid Packaging Mfr
N.A.I.C.S.: 333993

Subsidiaries:

Tech Long Europe GmbH (1)
Borsegasse 10/3, 1010, Vienna, Austria
Plastics Bottle Mfr
N.A.I.C.S.: 326160
Dominique Lipinski *(Mng Dir)*

Tech-Long Inc. (1)
3870 Lakefield Dr, Suwanee, GA 30024
Tel.: (770) 623-2688
Web Site: https://www.tech-long-intl.com
Packaging Equipment Distr
N.A.I.C.S.: 423840

GUANGZHOU TINCI MATERIALS TECHNOLOGY COMPANY LIMITED
No 8 Kangda Road Yunpu Industrial Zone, Dongcheng Huangpu District, Guangzhou, 510760, China
Tel.: (86) 2066601159
Web Site: http://www.tinci.com
Year Founded: 2000
002709—(SSE)
Rev.: $2,132,897,583
Assets: $3,319,792,576
Liabilities: $1,439,578,921
Net Worth: $1,880,213,655
Earnings: $261,771,890
Emp.: 6,800
Fiscal Year-end: 12/31/23
Chemical Products Mfr
N.A.I.C.S.: 325998

Subsidiaries:

Tianjin Tinci Materials Technology Co., Ltd. (1)
32 Shengda Rd 5th Branch Tianyuan Blvd, Xiqing Economy & Technology Developing Zone, Tianjin, 330380, China
Tel.: (86) 2258716582
Chemical Product Mfr & Distr
N.A.I.C.S.: 325998

Yichang Tinci Materials Technology Co., Ltd. (1)
West of Jianglin Road & south of Gangsheng Road, Yaojiagang Chemical Park Zhijiang, Yichang, 443000, China
Tel.: (86) 7174229899
Chemical Products Distr
N.A.I.C.S.: 424690

GUANGZHOU TONGDA AUTO ELECTRIC CO., LTD.
No 1112 Yunzheng Avenue, Baiyun District, Guangzhou, 510450, Guangdong, China
Tel.: (86) 2036471360
Web Site: https://www.tongda.cc
Year Founded: 1994
603390—(SHG)
Rev.: $66,986,497
Assets: $260,217,950
Liabilities: $40,481,897
Net Worth: $219,736,053
Earnings: ($14,668,318)
Fiscal Year-end: 12/31/23
Electrical Equipment Mfr & Distr
N.A.I.C.S.: 335999
Lina Chen *(Chm)*

GUANGZHOU WAHLAP TECHNOLOGY CORPORATION LIMITED
H1 Startoon City Yingxing East Road Donghuan Street, Panyu District, Guangzhou, 511400, China
Tel.: (86) 2039226222
Web Site: https://www.wahlap.com
Year Founded: 2010
301011—(CHIN)
Rev.: $114,968,943
Assets: $163,251,971
Liabilities: $65,982,352
Net Worth: $97,269,619
Earnings: $7,317,873
Fiscal Year-end: 12/31/23
Entertainment Product Mfr & Distr
N.A.I.C.S.: 339930
Benli Su *(Chm & Gen Mgr)*

GUANGZHOU WANBAO GROUP CO., LTD.
No 111 Jiangnan Mid Avenue, Guangzhou, 510220, China
Tel.: (86) 20 89010088
Web Site: http://www.gzwanbao.com
Compressor Mfr
N.A.I.C.S.: 333912
Qianding Zhou *(Gen Mgr)*

Subsidiaries:

ACC Compressors SpA (1)
11 Viale Lino Zanussi, Pordenone, 33170, Italy
Tel.: (39) 0434 379911
Web Site: http://www.the-acc-group.com
Sales Range: $800-899.9 Million
Emp.: 7,000
Household Refrigeration & Industrial Electrical Appliances Mfr
N.A.I.C.S.: 335220
Ramella Luca *(Owner)*

Subsidiary (Non-US):

ACC Germany GmbH (2)
Alter Postweg 75, 26133, Oldenburg, Germany
Tel.: (49) 4414010
Web Site: http://www.the-acc-group.com
Sales Range: $75-99.9 Million
Emp.: 150
Appliance Motor Mfr
N.A.I.C.S.: 423690

Appliances Components Companies Spain, S.A. (2)
Antoni Forrellad 2, 08912, Sant Quirze del Valles, Barcelona, Spain
Tel.: (34) 937106008
Appliance Motor Sales
N.A.I.C.S.: 423690

Shanghai Zanussi Elettromeccanica Co., Ltd. (2)
160 Basheng Road, Waigaoqiao Free Trade Zone, Shanghai, 200131, China
Tel.: (86) 2150481048
Web Site: http://www.highly.cc
Appliance Motor Sales
N.A.I.C.S.: 423690

GUANGZHOU WONDFO BIO-TECH CO., LTD.
No 8 Lizhishan Road, Science City Luogang District, Guangzhou, 510641, China
Tel.: (86) 4008308768
Web Site: https://en.wondfo.com
Year Founded: 1992
300482—(CHIN)
Rev.: $389,438,165
Assets: $812,946,368
Liabilities: $162,976,563
Net Worth: $649,969,804
Earnings: $68,681,953
Emp.: 3,000
Fiscal Year-end: 12/31/23
Pharmaceuticals Product Mfr
N.A.I.C.S.: 325412

Subsidiaries:

Wondfo USA Co., Ltd. (1)
545 Willowbrook Center Pkwy Ste B, Willowbrook, IL 60527
Tel.: (630) 468-2199
Web Site: https://www.wondfousa.com
Medical Instrument Mfr
N.A.I.C.S.: 339112

INTERNATIONAL PUBLIC

GUANGZHOU YUETAI GROUP CO., LTD.
4F No 170 Siyouxinma Road, Yuexiu District, Guangzhou, 510600, Guangdong, China
Tel.: (86) 20 87393888
Web Site: http://www.gzdh.com.cn
600393—(SHG)
Rev.: $462,082,892
Assets: $2,131,806,839
Liabilities: $1,340,455,739
Net Worth: $791,351,099
Earnings: ($139,889,923)
Fiscal Year-end: 12/31/20
Real Estate Manangement Services
N.A.I.C.S.: 531390

GUANGZHOU YUEXIU CAPITAL HOLDINGS GROUP CO., LTD.
63rd Floor Guangzhou International Finance Center, No 5 Zhujiang West Road Tianhe District, Guangzhou, 510623, Guangdong, China
Tel.: (86) 2088835125
Web Site: https://www.yuexiu-finance.com
Year Founded: 1992
000987—(SSE)
Holding Company
N.A.I.C.S.: 551112
Shuhui Wang *(Chm)*

GUANGZHOU ZHIGUANG ELECTRIC CO., LTD.
89 Ruihe Road, Huangpu District, Guangzhou, 510535, Guangdong, China
Tel.: (86) 2083909333
Web Site: https://www.gzzg.com.cn
Year Founded: 2002
002169—(SSE)
Rev.: $330,215,184
Assets: $903,729,528
Liabilities: $422,449,560
Net Worth: $481,279,968
Earnings: $5,936,112
Fiscal Year-end: 12/31/22
Electric Equipment Mfr
N.A.I.C.S.: 335999
Yongxi Li *(Chm & Pres)*

Subsidiaries:

Guangzhou Lingnan Cable Ltd. (1)
No 163 Renlv Road, Lanhe Town Nansha District, Guangzhou, 511480, China
Tel.: (86) 2084768952
Web Site: https://www.lncable.com
Electrical Equipment & Component Mfr
N.A.I.C.S.: 335999

Guangzhou Zhiguang Electric Ltd. (1)
51 Punan Road Yunpu Industrial Zone, Huangpu District, Guangzhou, China
Tel.: (86) 2032113398
Electrical Equipment & Component Mfr
N.A.I.C.S.: 335999

Guangzhou Zhiguang Energy Saving Co., Ltd. (1)
No 89 Ruihe Road, Huangpu, Guangzhou, China
Tel.: (86) 2083903333
Electrical Equipment & Component Mfr
N.A.I.C.S.: 335999

Hangzhou Zhiguang Yichuang Technologies Ltd. (1)
Room 1601 Building C Zijin Plaza 701 Gudun Road, Xihu District, Hangzhou, China
Tel.: (86) 57187382908
Electrical Equipment & Component Mfr
N.A.I.C.S.: 335999

GUANGZHOU ZHUJIANG BREWERY GROUP CO., LTD.
No 118 Modicesha Street Xingang

East Road, Haizhu District, Guangzhou, 510308, Guangdong, China
Tel.: (86) 2084206636
Web Site:
 https://www.zhujiangbeer.com
Year Founded: 1985
002461—(SSE)
Rev.: $691,910,856
Assets: $1,958,070,348
Liabilities: $600,503,436
Net Worth: $1,357,566,912
Earnings: $83,995,704
Emp.: 4,800
Fiscal Year-end: 12/31/22
Beer Breweries
N.A.I.C.S.: 312120
Wang Zhibin *(Chm)*

GUANWEI RECYCLING CORP.
Rong Qiao Economic Zone, Fuqing, 350301, Fujian, China
Tel.: (86) 591 85369 6197   NV
Web Site:
 http://www.guanweirecycling.com
Sales Range: $50-74.9 Million
Emp.: 540
Plastic Recycling & Manufacturing Services
N.A.I.C.S.: 423930
Min Chen *(Chm, Pres & CEO)*

GUANZE MEDICAL INFORMATION INDUSTRY (HOLDING) CO., LTD.
Room 501-A Block 10 Strategic Emerging Industry Base No 2966, Chunhui Road Jinan High-tech Zone, Shandong, China
Tel.: (86) 53158165902   Ky
Web Site:
 https://www.guanzegroup.com
Year Founded: 2020
2427—(HKG)
Rev.: $27,135,330
Assets: $50,210,441
Liabilities: $10,277,633
Net Worth: $39,932,808
Earnings: $2,801,598
Emp.: 43
Fiscal Year-end: 12/31/22
Holding Company
N.A.I.C.S.: 551112
Senquan Zhang *(Sec)*

GUARANTEE RV
34 Commercial Drive, Calgary, T3Z 2A7, AB, Canada
Tel.: (403) 273-1000
Web Site:
 https://www.guaranteerv.com
Year Founded: 1990
Sales Range: $10-24.9 Million
Emp.: 35
Recreational Vehicle Sales
N.A.I.C.S.: 441210
Charlie Cuffley *(Mgr-Sls)*

GUARANTEED INDUSTRIES LIMITED
5420 Rue Pare, Montreal, H4P 1R3, QC, Canada
Tel.: (514) 342-3400
Web Site:
 http://www.guaranteedindustry.com
Year Founded: 1957
Sales Range: $10-24.9 Million
Emp.: 75
Air Conditioning & Ventilation Contractors
N.A.I.C.S.: 238220
Robert Herard *(VP-Svc)*

GUARANTY TRUST BANK PLC
635 Akin Adesola Street Victoria Island, Lagos, Nigeria
Tel.: (234) 12715227
Web Site: http://www.gtbank.com
Year Founded: 1990
Rev.: $799,143,569
Assets: $10,299,437,430
Liabilities: $8,416,132,767
Net Worth: $1,883,304,662
Earnings: $53,936,703
Emp.: 5,606
Fiscal Year-end: 12/31/19
Banking Services
N.A.I.C.S.: 522110
Segun Fadahunsi *(Head-Sys & Control Div & Gen Mgr)*

Subsidiaries:

GTB Liberia Limited   (1)
United Nations Drive Clara Town, PO Box 0382, Bushrod Island, Monrovia, Montserrado, Liberia
Tel.: (231) 77499992
Web Site: http://www.gtbanklr.com
Commercial Banking Services
N.A.I.C.S.: 522110
Cathy Echeozo *(Dir-Nigerian)*

GTB Registrars Limited   (1)
7 Anthony Village Road, Lagos, Nigeria
Tel.: (234) 127160904
Web Site: http://www.gtbregistrars.com
Commericial Banking
N.A.I.C.S.: 522110

Guaranty Trust Bank (Gambia) Limited   (1)
56 Kairaba Avenue, Fajara KSMD, Banjul, Gambia   (70%)
Tel.: (220) 376371
Web Site: http://www.gambia.gtbplc.com
Banking Services
N.A.I.C.S.: 522110
Adesina Adebesin *(CEO & Mng Dir)*

Guaranty Trust Bank (Sierra Leone) Limited   (1)
12 Wilberforce Street, PO Box 1168, Freetown, Sierra Leone
Tel.: (232) 22228493
Web Site: http://www.gtb.sl
Nondepository Credit Intermediation
N.A.I.C.S.: 522299

Guaranty Trust Bank (UK) Limited   (1)
60-62 Margaret Street, London, W1W 8TF, United Kingdom
Tel.: (44) 2079479700
Web Site: http://www.gtbankuk.com
Banking Services
N.A.I.C.S.: 522110
Stuart Orton *(Exec Dir)*

Imperial Homes Mortgage Bank Limited   (1)
28 Saka Tinubu Street, Victoria Island, Lagos, Nigeria
Tel.: (234) 127161224
Web Site: http://www.gthomes.com
Sales Range: $50-74.9 Million
Emp.: 100
Mortgage Banking Services
N.A.I.C.S.: 522292

GUARANTY TRUST HOLDING COMPANY PLC
Plot 635 Akin Adesola, Victoria Island, Lagos, Nigeria
Tel.: (234) 12715227   NG
Web Site: https://www.gtcoplc.com
Year Founded: 1990
GTCO—(LSE)
Rev.: $393,058,086
Assets: $7,173,446,641
Liabilities: $6,080,079,502
Net Worth: $1,093,367,139
Earnings: $399,451,272
Emp.: 5,487
Fiscal Year-end: 12/31/23
Holding Company
N.A.I.C.S.: 551112
Segun Agbaje *(Grp CEO)*

Subsidiaries:

GTBank UK Ltd.   (1)
10 Great Castle Street, London, W1W 8LP, United Kingdom
Tel.: (44) 2079479700
Web Site: https://www.gtbankuk.com
Banking Product Services
N.A.I.C.S.: 521110

GUARARAPES CONFECCOES S.A.
Rua Lemos Monteiro n 120 Butanta, Sao Paulo, 05501-050, RN, Brazil
Tel.: (55) 1122812137
Web Site: https://ri.riachuelo.com.br
Year Founded: 1947
GUAR3—(BRAZ)
Rev.: $1,572,261,090
Assets: $2,551,378,706
Liabilities: $1,617,686,984
Net Worth: $933,691,722
Earnings: ($6,124,309)
Emp.: 35,000
Fiscal Year-end: 12/31/23
Apparel Mfr & Whslr
N.A.I.C.S.: 315250
Flavio Gurgel Rocha *(Dir-IR)*

GUARD THERAPEUTICS INTERNATIONAL AB
Nybrogatan 34 2 tr, 114 39, Stockholm, Sweden
Tel.: (46) 86706551
Web Site:
 https://www.guardtherapeutics.com
Year Founded: 1974
5LH0—(DEU)
Assets: $8,460,897
Liabilities: $1,836,520
Net Worth: $6,624,377
Earnings: ($11,249,429)
Emp.: 6
Fiscal Year-end: 12/31/23
Biotechnology Research & Development Services
N.A.I.C.S.: 541714
Karin Botha *(CFO)*

GUARDFORCE AI CO., LIMITED
96 Vibhavadi Rangsit Road, Talad Bangkhen Laksi, Bangkok, 10210, Thailand
Tel.: (66) 29736011   Ky
Web Site:
 http://www.guardforceai.com
Year Founded: 2018
GFAI—(NASDAQ)
Rev.: $34,477,948
Assets: $61,166,974
Liabilities: $42,034,672
Net Worth: $19,132,302
Earnings: ($18,564,794)
Emp.: 1,755
Fiscal Year-end: 12/31/22
Holding Company
N.A.I.C.S.: 551112
Terence Wing Khai Yap *(Chm)*

Subsidiaries:

Handshake Networking Co., Ltd.   (1)
Unit 501 Guardforce Centre 3 Hok Yuen Street East, Hung Hom, China (Hong Kong)
Tel.: (852) 21239193
Web Site: https://www.handshake.hk
Information Technology Consulting Services
N.A.I.C.S.: 518210

GUARDIAN CAPITAL GROUP LIMITED
Commerce Court West 199 Bay Street Suite 2700, PO Box 201, Toronto, M5L 1E8, ON, Canada
Tel.: (416) 364-8341   ON
Web Site:
 https://www.guardiancapital.com
Year Founded: 1962
GCAAF—(OTCIQ)
Rev.: $223,017,858
Assets: $1,117,623,879
Liabilities: $450,669,943
Net Worth: $666,953,936
Earnings: $149,212,087
Emp.: 662
Fiscal Year-end: 12/31/21
Diversified Financial & Investment Products & Services
N.A.I.C.S.: 523999
James S. Anas *(Chm)*

Subsidiaries:

Alexandria Bancorp Ltd   (1)
Flagship Building Suite 401 70 Harbour Drive, PO Box 2428, Seven Mile Beach, Georgetown, KY1-1105, Grand Cayman, Cayman Islands
Tel.: (345) 814 2900
Web Site:
 https://www.alexandriabancorp.com
Sales Range: $75-99.9 Million
Emp.: 9
Banking, Trust & Corporate Administration & Investment Management
N.A.I.C.S.: 522110
Robert F. Madden *(Mng Dir)*

Subsidiary (Domestic):

Alexandria Global Investment Management Ltd.   (2)
802 West Bay Road, PO Box 2428, KY1-1105, Georgetown, Cayman Islands
Tel.: (345) 945 1111
Web Site:
 http://www.alexandriabancorp.com
Sales Range: $50-74.9 Million
Emp.: 7
Investment Management Service
N.A.I.C.S.: 523999

Alexandria Trust Corporation   (1)
Suite 3 Courtyard Building The Courtyard Hastings Main Road, Christ Church, BB15156, Barbados
Tel.: (246) 228 8402
Web Site:
 https://www.alexandriabancorp.com
Investment Management Service
N.A.I.C.S.: 541611
Debbie McDonald *(Gen Mgr)*

Alta Capital Management, LLC   (1)
6440 S Wasatch Blvd Ste 260, Salt Lake City, UT 84121   (70%)
Tel.: (801) 274-6010
Web Site: https://www.altacapital.com
Portfolio Management
N.A.I.C.S.: 523940
Michael Tempest *(Chief Investment Officer & Mng Principal)*

GuardCap Asset Management Limited   (1)
6th Floor 11 Charles II Street St Jamess, London, SW1Y 4NS, United Kingdom
Tel.: (44) 207 907 2400
Web Site: https://www.guardcap.co.uk
Investment Banking Services
N.A.I.C.S.: 523999
Steve Bates *(Chief Investment Officer)*

Guardian Capital Advisors LP   (1)
Commerce Court West 199 Bay Street Suite 3100, PO Box 201, Toronto, M5L 1E8, ON, Canada
Tel.: (416) 947-3747
Web Site: http://www.gcaweb.com
Investment, Asset Management & Consulting Services
N.A.I.C.S.: 523940
Douglas G. Farley *(Sr VP & Portfolio Mgr)*

Guardian Capital Enterprises Limited   (1)
199 Bay St Ste 3100, Toronto, M5L 1E8, ON, Canada
Tel.: (416) 364-8341
Emp.: 100
Investment Advisory Services
N.A.I.C.S.: 523940

Guardian Capital LP   (1)
Commerce Court West Suite 3100, PO Box 201, Toronto, M5L 1E8, ON, Canada
Tel.: (416) 364-9634
Institutional Investment Management
N.A.I.C.S.: 523999

GUARDIAN CAPITAL GROUP LIMITED

Guardian Capital Group Limited—(Continued)

Brian P. Holland (Sr VP-Client Svc)

Guardian Smart Infrastructure Management Inc. (1)
Commerce Court West 199 Bay Street - Suite 2700, PO Box 201, Toronto, M5L 1E8, ON, Canada
Tel.: (416) 364-8341
Web Site: https://gsim.guardiancapital.com
Smart Infrastructure Application Services
N.A.I.C.S.: 541519

Subsidiary (Non-US):

Q-Free ASA (2)
Strindfjordvegen 1, Ranheim, 7053, Trondheim, Norway (100%)
Tel.: (47) 73826500
Web Site: http://www.q-free.com
Board Units Mfr
N.A.I.C.S.: 335312
Trond Valvik (Chm)

Subsidiary (Domestic):

Noca Holding AS (3)
String Fjordveien 1, 7053, Trondheim, Norway
Tel.: (47) 73826500
Web Site: http://www.noca.no
Sales Range: $50-74.9 Million
Emp.: 45
Management Services
N.A.I.C.S.: 523940

Subsidiary (Domestic):

Noca AS (4)
Stiklestadveien 1, Trondheim, 7041, Sor-Trondelag, Norway
Tel.: (47) 73809330
Web Site: http://www.noca.no
Sales Range: $25-49.9 Million
Emp.: 45
Electronic Components Mfr
N.A.I.C.S.: 334419
Frank Rudi (Mng Dir)

Subsidiary (US):

Open Roads Consulting, Inc. (3)
103 Watson Rd, Chesapeake, VA 23320
Tel.: (757) 546-3401
Web Site: http://www.openroadsconsulting.com
Sales Range: $10-24.9 Million
Emp.: 69
Process, Physical Distribution & Logistics Consulting Services
N.A.I.C.S.: 541614

Subsidiary (Non-US):

Q-Free (Bristol) UK Ltd. (3)
30 Lynx Crescent, Weston Industrial Estate, Weston-super-Mare, BS24 9BP, North Somerset, United Kingdom
Tel.: (44) 193 464 4299
Asset Management Services
N.A.I.C.S.: 523940
Gary Evans (Gen Mgr)

Subsidiary (US):

Q-Free America Inc. (3)
4660 La Jolla Village Dr Ste 100, San Diego, CA 92122
Traffic Management Services
N.A.I.C.S.: 488111

Subsidiary (Non-US):

Q-Free America Latina Ltda. (3)
Al Madeira 53 Cj 14, Alphaville, Barueri, 06454000, Brazil
Tel.: (55) 1141916345
Sales Range: $25-49.9 Million
Emp.: 10
Electronic Tolling Equipments Mfr
N.A.I.C.S.: 334511
Gino Olevato (Country Mgr)

Q-Free Australia Pty. Ltd. (3)
Level 7 107 Mount Street, North Sydney, Sydney, 2060, NSW, Australia
Tel.: (61) 280202650
Sales Range: $25-49.9 Million
Emp.: 15

Electronic Tolling Systems Installation Services
N.A.I.C.S.: 488490
Silje Troseth (Gen Mgr)

Q-Free Espana S.L.U. (3)
Calle Serrano 1 4th Floor, 28001, Madrid, Spain
Tel.: (34) 91 563 4415
Traffic Management Services
N.A.I.C.S.: 488111

Q-Free Malaysia Sdn. Bhd. (3)
19 2-3 Jalan PJU 8/5F Bandar Damansara Perdana, 47820, Petaling Jaya, Selangor Darul Ehsan, Malaysia
Tel.: (60) 377224457
Sales Range: $25-49.9 Million
Emp.: 8
Highway Toll Systems Operation Services
N.A.I.C.S.: 488490
Wisjnu Darma Setiawan (Gen Mgr)

Q-Free Netherlands B.V. (3)
Eursing 2, 9411 XC, Beilen, Netherlands
Tel.: (31) 59 354 2055
Web Site: https://www.intrada.q-free.com
Sales Range: $25-49.9 Million
Emp.: 20
Supplier of Road User Charging, Traffic Management Solutions & Video Identification Software
N.A.I.C.S.: 541511
Jos A.G. Nijhuis (Gen Mgr-Sls)

Q-Free Portugal Lda. (3)
Taguspark Av Prof Doutor Anibal Cavaco Silva Bloco B1 2B, 2740-120, Porto Salvo, Portugal
Tel.: (351) 214227170
Web Site: http://www.q-free.com
Sales Range: $25-49.9 Million
Emp.: 9
Electronic Toll Systems Installation & Support Services
N.A.I.C.S.: 488490

Q-Free Sverige AB (3)
Sundbybergsvagen 1, 171 73, Solna, Stockholm, Sweden
Tel.: (46) 851782080
Sales Range: $25-49.9 Million
Emp.: 12
Traffic Control Systems Distr
N.A.I.C.S.: 428830
Edvin Lundgren (Mgr)

Q-Free Thailand Co Ltd (3)
17 GEC Building 2nd Floor Zone A Soi Prasert-Manukitch 31, Prasert-Manukitch Road Ladprao, 10230, Bangkok, Thailand
Tel.: (66) 255320245
Web Site: http://www.q-free.com
Sales Range: $25-49.9 Million
Road Traffic Control Equipments Distr
N.A.I.C.S.: 423690

Q-Free Traffic Design d.o.o. (3)
Kamniska Ulica 50, 1000, Ljubljana, Slovenia
Tel.: (386) 1 300 9770
Web Site: https://www.traffic-design.si
Traffic Management Services
N.A.I.C.S.: 488111

Subsidiary (US):

TCS International, Inc. (3)
55 Union Ave, Sudbury, MA 01776
Tel.: (978) 443-2527
Web Site: https://www.tcsintl.com
Sales Range: $1-9.9 Million
Emp.: 15
Technological Parking Systems Designer & Consulting Services
N.A.I.C.S.: 541512

IDC Worldsource Insurance Network Inc. (1)
625 Cochrane Drive Suite 610, Markham, L3R 9R9, ON, Canada
Tel.: (905) 479-0888
Web Site: https://www.idcwin.ca
Investment Management Service
N.A.I.C.S.: 541611
Paul Brown (CEO & Chm)

Rae & Lipskie Investment Counsel Inc. (1)
20 Erb St West Suite 201, Waterloo, N2L 1T2, ON, Canada

Tel.: (519) 578-6849
Web Site: https://raelipskie.com
Investment Management Service
N.A.I.C.S.: 541513

Sterling Capital Management LLC (1)
4350 Congress St Ste 1000, Charlotte, NC 28209
Tel.: (704) 372-8670
Web Site: https://sterlingcapital.com
Sales Range: $25-49.9 Million
Emp.: 180
Investment Services
N.A.I.C.S.: 523150
Jeffrey J. Schappe (Mng Dir)

Division (Domestic):

Sterling Capital Management LLC (2)
434 Fayetteville St Ste 500, Raleigh, NC 27601
Tel.: (919) 716-9070
Web Site: http://www.sterlingcapital.com
Sales Range: $25-49.9 Million
Emp.: 35
Asset Management, Depository, Insurance & Investment Services
N.A.I.C.S.: 525990
Alexander W. McAlister (CEO)

Subsidiary (Domestic):

Sterling Capital Management LLC - Washington (3)
750 17th St NW Ste 450, Washington, DC 20006
Tel.: (202) 393-1777
Web Site: http://www.sterlingprivateclient.com
Emp.: 9
Financial Management Services
N.A.I.C.S.: 525990
Donald Harris (Mng Dir & Sr Portfolio Mgr)

Virginia Investment Counselors, Inc. (3)
500 E Main St Ste 200, Norfolk, VA 23510
Tel.: (757) 823-7800
Web Site: http://www.bbt.com
Rev.: $6,246,000
Emp.: 10
Money Management Services
N.A.I.C.S.: 525990

Worldsource Holding Corp (1)
625 Cochrane Dr Suite 700, Markham, L3R 9R9, ON, Canada
Tel.: (905) 940-5500
Web Site: http://www.worldsourcewealth.com
Sales Range: $50-74.9 Million
Emp.: 70
Holding Company
N.A.I.C.S.: 551112

Subsidiary (Domestic):

Worldsource Wealth Management Inc. (2)
625 Cochrane Suite 700, Markham, L3R 9R9, ON, Canada
Tel.: (905) 940-5500
Web Site: http://www.worldsourcewealth.com
Sales Range: $50-74.9 Million
Emp.: 70
Financial Advisory Distribution Network, including Mutual Funds, Securities & Insurance Products & Services
N.A.I.C.S.: 523150
John T. Hunt (Mng Dir)

Division (Domestic):

Worldsource Financial Management Inc. (3)
625 Cochrane Drive Suite 700, Markham, L3R 9R9, ON, Canada
Tel.: (905) 940-5500
Web Site: http://www.worldsourcewealth.com
Sales Range: $50-74.9 Million
Emp.: 65
Investment Services for Mutual Funds
N.A.I.C.S.: 523940
John Hunt (Pres)

Worldsource Insurance Network Inc. (3)
666 Burrard St Ste 2338, Vancouver, V6C 2X8, BC, Canada
Tel.: (604) 689-8289
Web Site: http://www.worldsourceinsurance.com
Sales Range: $50-74.9 Million
Emp.: 32
Insurance Investments
N.A.I.C.S.: 524210
Betsy Wan (VP-Ops-Western Canada)

Worldsource Securities Inc. (3)
625 Cochrane Drive Suite 700, Markham, L3R 9R9, ON, Canada
Tel.: (905) 940-5500
Web Site: http://www.worldsourcefinancial.com
Sales Range: $50-74.9 Million
Emp.: 65
Security Brokers
N.A.I.C.S.: 523150

GUARDIAN CONTROLS LTD.
149 Girinagar, Cochin, 682 020, India
Tel.: (91) 484 2316606
Web Site: http://www.guardiancontrols.com
Year Founded: 1985
Relay & Industrial Control Mfr
N.A.I.C.S.: 335314

GUARDIAN EXPLORATION INC.
538 Hurricane Drive Springbank Airport, Calgary, T3Z, AB, Canada
Tel.: (403) 730-6333
Web Site: http://www.guardianex.com
Year Founded: 1992
R6B—(DEU)
Rev.: $1,839
Assets: $446,179
Liabilities: $973,005
Net Worth: ($526,825)
Earnings: ($117,506)
Emp.: 1
Fiscal Year-end: 12/31/23
Natural Gas Exploration Service
N.A.I.C.S.: 211130
Graydon L. M. Kowal (CEO)

GUARDIAN GLOBAL SECURITY PLC
Audley House 13 Palace Street, London, SW1E5HX, United Kingdom
Tel.: (44) 2034118737   UK
Web Site: http://www.nu-oilandgas.com
Year Founded: 2007
NUOG—(AIM)
Assets: $2,270,380
Liabilities: $6,754,740
Net Worth: ($4,484,360)
Earnings: ($3,671,168)
Emp.: 5
Fiscal Year-end: 06/30/19
Oil & Gas Exploration Services
N.A.I.C.S.: 213112
David Lau (Sec)

GUARDIAN HOLDINGS LIMITED
1 Guardian Drive, Westmoorings, Trinidad & Tobago
Tel.: (868) 2266944   TT
Web Site: https://www.myguardiangroup.com
Year Founded: 1982
GHL—(TRI)
Rev.: $804,012,413
Assets: $5,142,178,640
Liabilities: $4,571,376,143
Net Worth: $570,802,496
Earnings: $103,616,399
Fiscal Year-end: 12/31/23
Offices of Other Holding Companies
N.A.I.C.S.: 551112
Peter Ganteaume (Deputy Chm)

AND PRIVATE COMPANIES

Subsidiaries:

Cassidy Davis Europe BV (1)
Nachtwachtlaan 20, Amsterdam, 1058, Netherlands
Tel.: (31) 205114880
Web Site: http://www.europe.jubileeinsurance.com
Emp.: 20
General Insurance Services
N.A.I.C.S.: 524210
Rogier Deweger *(Gen Mgr)*

Colrich (SAC) Ltd (1)
C-o Appleby, Spurling Hunter, Hamilton, Bermuda (100%)
Tel.: (441) 2952244
Holding Company
N.A.I.C.S.: 551112

Fatum General Insurance NV (1)
Cas Coraweg 2, Willemstad, 3002, Curacao
Tel.: (599) 9 777 7777
Web Site: http://www.nl.fatum.com
Sales Range: $100-124.9 Million
Emp.: 180
General Insurance Services
N.A.I.C.S.: 524210
Steven Martina *(Gen Mgr)*

Fatum Life NV (1)
Cas Coraweg 2, Postbus 3002, Willemstad, Curacao (99%)
Tel.: (599) 97777777
Web Site: http://www.fatum.com
Direct Life Insurance Carriers
N.A.I.C.S.: 524113
Steven Martina *(Mng Dir)*

Guardian Asset Management Ltd (1)
1 Guardian Dr, Westmoorings, Trinidad & Tobago (100%)
Tel.: (868) 632 6000
Web Site: http://www.guardianassetmanagement.com
Sales Range: $50-74.9 Million
Emp.: 60
Holding Company
N.A.I.C.S.: 551112
Brent Ford *(Mng Dir)*

Guardian General Insurance Ltd. (1)
30-34 Maraval Road, St Clair, Newtown, Trinidad & Tobago (100%)
Tel.: (868) 6229994
Web Site: http://www.guardiangenerallimited.com
Sales Range: $50-74.9 Million
Emp.: 32
Direct Life Insurance Carriers
N.A.I.C.S.: 524113
Randolph P. Richardson *(Branch Mgr)*

Guardian General Ltd (1)
Newtown Ctr 30-34 Maraval Road, Port of Spain, Trinidad & Tobago (100%)
Tel.: (868) 625 4445
Web Site: http://www.guardiangroup.com
Sales Range: $100-124.9 Million
Emp.: 250
Direct Life Insurance Carriers
N.A.I.C.S.: 524113

Guardian Life of the Caribbean Ltd (1)
1 Guardian Dr, Westmoorings, Trinidad & Tobago (100%)
Tel.: (868) 6325433
Web Site: http://www.gloc.biz
Direct Life Insurance Carriers
N.A.I.C.S.: 524113

La Societe de Promotion de la Pointe Simon et ses Environs (1)
42 Rue Garnier Pages, 97200, Fort-de-France, Martinique
Tel.: (596) 8 99 026 748
Real Estate Manangement Services
N.A.I.C.S.: 531390

NEM (West Indies) Insurance Ltd (1)
NEMWIL House, Princes Ct Keate St, Port of Spain, Trinidad & Tobago (100%)
Tel.: (868) 62347844
Insurance Agencies & Brokerages
N.A.I.C.S.: 524210

Trans-Nemwil Insurance (Grenada) Ltd (1)
PO Box 221, Theville, Saint George's, Grenada
Tel.: (473) 440 1585
Insurance Management Services
N.A.I.C.S.: 524298

West Indies Alliance Insurance Limited (1)
19 Dominica Drive, Kingston, 5, Jamaica
Tel.: (876) 929 8080
Web Site: http://www.wia.com.jm
Insurance Management Services
N.A.I.C.S.: 524298
Anne Reynolds *(Mgr-HR)*

Zenith Insurance Plc (1)
846-848 Europort, Gibraltar, Gibraltar (100%)
Tel.: (350) 48488
Web Site: http://www.zenith-insurance.co.uk
Sales Range: $50-74.9 Million
Emp.: 6
Direct Life Insurance Carriers
N.A.I.C.S.: 524113

GUAY INC.
1160 Bouvier Street, Quebec, G2K 1L9, QC, Canada
Tel.: (418) 628-8460
Web Site: http://www.gruesguay.com
Year Founded: 1964
Rev.: $72,492,767
Emp.: 450
Non Operated Cranes Rental Transport & Rigging Services
N.A.I.C.S.: 532412
Guillaume Gagnon *(Exec VP)*

GUBER A.D.
Svetog Save 89, 75420, Bratunac, Bosnia & Herzegovina
Tel.: (387) 56410660
GBUE—(BANJ)
Sales Range: Less than $1 Million
Emp.: 1
Real Estate Prorperty Leasing Services
N.A.I.C.S.: 531190

GUBRA A/S
Horsholm Kongevej 11B, 2970, Horsholm, Denmark
Tel.: (45) 31522650
Web Site: https://www.gubra.dk
Year Founded: 2008
GUBRA—(CSE)
Rev.: $29,663,151
Assets: $90,474,744
Liabilities: $21,070,597
Net Worth: $69,404,147
Earnings: ($6,442,390)
Emp.: 219
Fiscal Year-end: 12/31/23
Biotechnology Research & Development Services
N.A.I.C.S.: 541714
Jacob Jelsing *(Chm)*

GUBRE FABRIKALARI T.A.S.
Merdivenkoy Mah Bora Sk No 1 Kat, 12-30-31 Kadikoy, 34732, Istanbul, Turkiye
Tel.: (90) 2164685050
Web Site: http://www.gubretas.com.tr
GUBRF—(IST)
Rev.: $781,045,852
Assets: $644,234,613
Liabilities: $400,911,290
Net Worth: $243,323,324
Earnings: $23,392,755
Emp.: 1,639
Fiscal Year-end: 12/31/22
Chemical Fertiliser Mfr
N.A.I.C.S.: 325314
Fahrettin Poyraz *(Chm)*

GUD FILTERS PTY. LTD.
3 The Avenue East, Isipingo, 4110, South Africa
Tel.: (27) 31 910 3111
Web Site: http://www.gud.co.za
Sales Range: $250-299.9 Million
Emp.: 1,500
Automotive Filters Mfr
N.A.I.C.S.: 336310
Red Shuttleworth *(CEO)*

GUDECO ELEKTRONIK HANDELS GMBH
Siemensstra 22, 61267, Neu-Anspach, Germany
Tel.: (49) 60814040
Web Site: http://www.gudeco.de
Year Founded: 1979
Rev.: $18,346,020
Emp.: 54
Passive & Electromechanical Components Distr
N.A.I.C.S.: 423690
Michael Denner *(Co-Mng Dir)*

GUDEL GROUP AG
Gaswerkstrasse 26, Industrie Nord, 4900, Langenthal, Switzerland
Tel.: (41) 62 9169191 CH
Web Site: http://www.gudel.com
Year Founded: 1954
Sales Range: $125-149.9 Million
Emp.: 1,200
Components Mfr
N.A.I.C.S.: 334419
Manfred Fahrion *(Mng Dir)*

Subsidiaries:

Gudel Automation GmbH (1)
Industriestrasse 8, 86720, Nordlingen, Germany (100%)
Tel.: (49) 908129740
Web Site: http://www.de.gudel.com
Sales Range: $25-49.9 Million
Emp.: 80
Industrial Machinery Mfr
N.A.I.C.S.: 333248
Uwe Schaaf *(Gen Mgr)*

Gudel Controls GmbH (1)
Gewerbestrasse 4A, 83404, Ainring, Germany
Tel.: (49) 8654 4888 0
Web Site: http://www.abplan.de
Sales Range: $25-49.9 Million
Emp.: 45
Controls & Automation Packages for Automotive, Environmental, Wood Products & Paper Industries
N.A.I.C.S.: 334519
Manfred Resch *(CEO)*

Gudel GmbH (1)
Schoneringer Strasse 48, 4073, Wilhering, Austria
Tel.: (43) 7226206900
Industrial Supplies Whslr
N.A.I.C.S.: 423840

Gudel GmbH (1)
Rosenberger Strasse 1, 74706, Osterburken, Germany
Tel.: (49) 629164460
Industrial Supplies Whslr
N.A.I.C.S.: 423840
Erik Longin *(CFO)*

Gudel Inc. (1)
4881 Runway Blvd, Ann Arbor, MI 48108
Tel.: (734) 214-0000
Industrial Supplies Whslr
N.A.I.C.S.: 423840
Stuart Shepherd *(CEO)*

Gudel India Pvt. Ltd. (1)
Gat No 458/459 At Post Mauje Kasar Amboli Tal, Mulshi Pirangut Dist, Pune, 412 111, India
Tel.: (91) 2067910200
Web Site: http://www.gudel.com
Industrial Supplies Whslr
N.A.I.C.S.: 423840
Hrishikesh Kulkarni *(Mgr-Sls & Mktg)*

Gudel International Trading Co. Ltd. (1)
Block A 8 Floor C2 BLDG Block A 8 Floor C2 BLDG, Pudong, Shanghai, 201206, China
Tel.: (86) 2150550012
Web Site: http://www.gudel.com
Industrial Supplies Whslr
N.A.I.C.S.: 423840

Gudel Intralogistics GmbH (1)
Gewerbegebiet Salzhub 11, 83737, Miesbach, Germany
Tel.: (49) 806270750
Web Site: http://www.gudel-intralogistics.com
Logistics Consulting Servies
N.A.I.C.S.: 541614

Gudel Lineartec (U.K.) Ltd. (1)
Unit 5 Wickmans Drive Banner Lane, Coventry, CV4 9XA, West Midlands, United Kingdom
Tel.: (44) 2476695444
Industrial Supplies Whslr
N.A.I.C.S.: 423840

Gudel Lineartec Co. Ltd. (1)
No 99 An-Chai 8th St Hsin-Chu Industrial Park TW-Hu-Ko, Hsin-chu, Taiwan
Tel.: (886) 35978808
Industrial Supplies Whslr
N.A.I.C.S.: 423840

Gudel Lineartec Co., Ltd. (1)
19/28 Private Ville Hua Mak Road Hua Mak, Bang Kapi, Bangkok, 10240, Thailand
Tel.: (66) 23740709
Machine Component Distr
N.A.I.C.S.: 423840

Gudel Lineartec Inc. (1)
11-22 Songdo-dong, Yeonsu-Ku, Incheon, 406-840, Korea (South)
Tel.: (82) 328580541
Web Site: http://www.gudel.com
Industrial Supplies Whslr
N.A.I.C.S.: 423840

Gudel Otomasyon Ltd. Sti. (1)
Perpa Ticaret Merkezi B Blok Kat 11 No 1593 Okmeydani, 34384, Istanbul, Turkiye
Tel.: (90) 2122109590
Web Site: http://www.gudelotomasyon.com
Industrial Supplies Whslr
N.A.I.C.S.: 423840
Mecit Orter *(Mgr-Sls)*

Gudel S.r.l. (1)
Via per Cernusco 7, Bussero, 20060, Milan, Italy
Tel.: (39) 029217021
Web Site: http://www.gudel.com
Industrial Supply Distr
N.A.I.C.S.: 423840

Gudel SAS (1)
Tour de l'Europe 213 3 Bd de l'Europe a Mulhouse, 68100, Mulhouse, France
Tel.: (33) 130091545
Web Site: http://www.gudel.com
Industrial Supplies Whslr
N.A.I.C.S.: 423840

Gudel Sp. z o.o. (1)
ul Legionow 26/28, 43-300, Bielsko-Biala, Poland
Tel.: (48) 338190125
Web Site: http://www.gudel.com
Industrial Supplies Whslr
N.A.I.C.S.: 423840

Gudel Sumer SAS (1)
ZI Le Roqual, Carsac-Aillac, 24200, Sarlat-la-Caneda, France
Tel.: (33) 553303080
Web Site: http://www.gudel-sumer.com
Gear Box Mfr
N.A.I.C.S.: 336330

Gudel TSC S.A. de C.V. (1)
Gustavo M Garcia 308 Col Buenos Aires, 64800, Monterrey, Mexico
Tel.: (52) 8183742500
Web Site: http://www.gudel.com
Industrial Supplies Whslr
N.A.I.C.S.: 423840

Gudel a.s. (1)
Holandska 4, 63900, Brno, Czech Republic
Tel.: (420) 519323431
Web Site: http://www.gudel.com
Industrial Supplies Whslr
N.A.I.C.S.: 423840

GUDOU HOLDINGS LIMITED

GUDOU HOLDINGS LIMITED

Gudou Holdings Limited—(Continued)
19th Floor Tower One Of Tern Centre
No 237 Queens Road, Central, China
(Hong Kong)
Tel.: (852) 36282675   Ky
Web Site:
  http://www.gudouholdings.com
8308—(HKG)
Rev.: $19,495,819
Assets: $179,138,648
Liabilities: $109,829,355
Net Worth: $69,309,293
Earnings: $438,334
Emp.: 481
Fiscal Year-end: 12/31/20
Hotel Operator
N.A.I.C.S.: 721110
Chi Ming Hon *(Founder, Chm & CEO)*

GUELPH NISSAN
805 Woodlawn Rd W, Guelph, N1K
1E9, ON, Canada
Tel.: (519) 822-9200
Web Site:
  http://www.guelphinfinitinissan.com
Year Founded: 1980
New & Used Car Dealers
N.A.I.C.S.: 441110
Justine Baldwin *(Mgr-Parts)*

GUELPH TOOL INC.
39 Royal Road, Guelph, N1H 1G2,
ON, Canada
Tel.: (519) 822-5401
Web Site:
  https://www.guelphtoolinc.com
Year Founded: 1965
Rev.: $198,930,046
Emp.: 900
Metal Stampings & Other Industrial
Equipment Mfr
N.A.I.C.S.: 332999
Robert Ireland *(Pres)*

Subsidiaries:

Guelph Tool Sales Inc.   (1)
24150 Gibson Rd, Warren, MI 48089
Tel.: (586) 755-3333
Automobile Parts Distr
N.A.I.C.S.: 423120

GUELPH VOLKSWAGEN
359 Woodlawn Road West, Guelph,
N1H 7K9, ON, Canada
Tel.: (519) 824-9150
Web Site: http://www.gvw.ca
New & Used Car Dealers
N.A.I.C.S.: 441110
Jason Chow *(Principal)*

GUERBET SA
15 rue des Vanesses Zone Paris
Nord II, 93420, Villepinte, France
Tel.: (33) 145915000
Web Site: http://www.guerbet.com
GBT—(EUR)
Rev.: $812,945,176
Assets: $1,014,076,193
Liabilities: $604,438,809
Net Worth: $409,637,384
Earnings: $44,372,976)
Emp.: 2,839
Fiscal Year-end: 12/31/22
Pharmaceutical & Chemical Mfr
N.A.I.C.S.: 325412
Claire Corot *(Sr VP)*

Subsidiaries:

A Martins & Fernandes S.A   (1)
Rual Raul Mesnier du Ponsard 4 B,
1750-243, Lisbon, Portugal
Tel.: (351) 217573215
Web Site: http://www.guerbet.pt
Pharmaceutical Product Whslr
N.A.I.C.S.: 424210
Sonia Ferreira *(Dir-Technical)*

A. Martins & Fernandes   (1)
Rual Raul Mesnier du Ponsard 4-B, 1750,
Lisbon, Portugal
Tel.: (351) 217573215
Sales Range: $50-74.9 Million
Pharmaceuticals Whslr
N.A.I.C.S.: 424210

Guerbet AG   (1)
Thurgauerstr 32, 8050, Zurich, Switzerland
Tel.: (41) 432551800
Web Site: https://www.guerbet.com
Sales Range: $25-49.9 Million
Emp.: 8
Pharmaceuticals Mfr
N.A.I.C.S.: 325412

Guerbet Asia Pacific Ltd   (1)
Units 1502-03 15/F Tower A Cheung Kei
Center 18 Hung Luen Road, Hung Hom,
Kowloon, New Territories, China (Hong
Kong)
Tel.: (852) 31831500
Web Site: http://www.guerbet.com.hk
Sales Range: $25-49.9 Million
Pharmaceutical Preparation Mfr
N.A.I.C.S.: 325412
Danecki Guillaume *(Gen Mgr)*

Guerbet Colombia S.A.S.   (1)
Carrera 7 No 127 48 Of 1105, Teleport
Business Park, 110111, Bogota, Colombia
Tel.: (57) 16581246
Web Site: https://www.guerbet.com
Medical Equipment Mfr
N.A.I.C.S.: 339112
Daniel Aguia Murillejo *(Acct Mgr)*

Guerbet France, SA   (1)
Immeuble Rimbaud - 22 avenue des na-
tions, 93420, Villepinte, France
Tel.: (33) 145915000
Web Site: https://www.guerbet.com
Pharmaceutical Product Whslr
N.A.I.C.S.: 424210
Clement Cabanes *(Pres)*

Guerbet GmbH   (1)
Otto-Volger-Strasse 11, Taunus, 65843,
Sulzbach, Germany
Tel.: (49) 61967620
Web Site: https://www.guerbet.com
Sales Range: $25-49.9 Million
Pharmaceuticals Product Mfr
N.A.I.C.S.: 325412

Guerbet Grosshandel mit Phar-
mazeutischen Produkten
Ges.m.b.H.   (1)
Millennium Tower 23 Stock Handelskai 94-
96, 1200, Vienna, Austria
Tel.: (43) 17106206
Web Site: http://www.guerbet.com
Diagnostic Products Mfr
N.A.I.C.S.: 334510

Guerbet Ilac Tibbi A.S.   (1)
Kisikli Caddesi Haluk Turksoy Sok Isik
Plaza No 7 Floor 3 Flat 4, Altunizade Usku-
dar, 34662, Istanbul, Turkiye
Tel.: (90) 2166514744
Web Site: http://www.guerbet.com.tr
Pharmaceutical Product Whslr
N.A.I.C.S.: 424210

Guerbet Imaging Panama S. A.   (1)
Boulevard Ernesto Perez Balladares Zona
Libre de Colon, Colon, Panama
Tel.: (507) 4314392
Diagnostic Products Mfr
N.A.I.C.S.: 334510

Guerbet Japan KK   (1)
Kojimachi Annex 7F 4 5 10, Kojimachi
Chiyoda ku, Tokyo, 102 0083, Japan
Tel.: (81) 332885421
Pharmaceutical Products Distr
N.A.I.C.S.: 424210

Guerbet Korea Ltd.   (1)
6th floor IS Building 10 Teheran-ro 38-gil,
Gangnam-gu, Seoul, 06221, Korea (South)
Tel.: (82) 234531212
Web Site: https://www.guerbet.com
Medical Equipment Mfr
N.A.I.C.S.: 339112
Seung Ho Kang *(Gen Mgr)*

Guerbet LLC   (1)
214 Carnegie Ctr Ste 300, Princeton, NJ
08540
Tel.: (314) 376-4901
Web Site: https://www.guerbet.com
Pharmaceuticals Product Mfr
N.A.I.C.S.: 325412

Guerbet Laboratories Ltd.   (1)
Avon House 435 Stratford Road, Shirley,
Solihull, B90 4AA, United Kingdom
Tel.: (44) 1217338542
Web Site: https://www.guerbet.com
Pharmaceuticals Whslr
N.A.I.C.S.: 424210

Subsidiary (Domestic):

Guerbet Argentina Limited   (2)
Avon House 435 Stratford Road, Shirley,
B90 4AA, Solihull, United Kingdom
Tel.: (44) 121 733 8542
Pharmaceutical Product Whslr
N.A.I.C.S.: 424210

Branch (Non-US):

Guerbet Argentina Limited - Argentina
Branch Office   (3)
Calle Aguero 351, Ciudad Autonoma de
Buenos Aires, C1171ABC, Buenos Aires,
Argentina
Tel.: (54) 11 4863 5300
Pharmaceutical Product Whslr
N.A.I.C.S.: 424210

Guerbet Mexicana S. A. de C. V.   (1)
Insurgentes Sur 1647 Piso 15 Col San Jose
Insurgentes, Alcaldia Benito Juarez, CP
03900, Mexico, Mexico
Tel.: (52) 5554829200
Web Site: https://www.guerbet.com
Diagnostic Products Mfr
N.A.I.C.S.: 334510

Guerbet Nederland B.V.   (1)
Avelingen-West 70, 4202 MV, Gorinchem,
Netherlands
Tel.: (31) 183633688
Web Site: https://www.guerbet.com
Sales Range: $25-49.9 Million
Pharmaceutical Industry
N.A.I.C.S.: 325412

Guerbet Poland Sp. z o.o.   (1)
ul Aleje Jerozolimskie 162, 02-342, War-
saw, Poland
Tel.: (48) 223062242
Medical Equipment Mfr
N.A.I.C.S.: 339112
Wojewski Jaroslaw *(Reg Sls Mgr)*

Guerbet Produtos Radiologicos
Ltda.   (1)
Rua Andre Rocha 3 000, Jacarepagua, Rio
de Janeiro, 22710-568, RJ, Brazil
Tel.: (55) 2124449966
Diagnostic Products Mfr
N.A.I.C.S.: 334510

Guerbet S.p.A.   (1)
Via Larga 4, 20122, Milan, Italy
Tel.: (39) 0297168200
Web Site: https://www.guerbet.com
Pharmaceutical Industry
N.A.I.C.S.: 325412

Guerbet Taiwan Co., Ltd.   (1)
16th Floor No 35 Section 3 Minquan East
Road, Zhongshan District, Taipei, 10476,
Taiwan
Tel.: (886) 225061160
Web Site: https://www.guerbet.com
Sales Range: $25-49.9 Million
Pharmaceutical Industry
N.A.I.C.S.: 325412

Guerbet n.v.   (1)
EUROSTATION II Place Victor Horta 40/
40, 1060, Brussels, Belgium
Tel.: (32) 27262110
Web Site: https://www.guerbet.com
Chemical Products Distr
N.A.I.C.S.: 424690

Laboratorios Farmaceuticos Guerbet
S.A.   (1)
Paseo de la Castellana 91 3rd floor, 28046,
Madrid, Spain
Tel.: (34) 915045000
Web Site: https://www.guerbet.com
Sales Range: $25-49.9 Million
Pharmaceutical Industry
N.A.I.C.S.: 325412

INTERNATIONAL PUBLIC

Liebel-Flarsheim Ireland Limited   (1)
Damastown Mulhuddart, Dublin, 15, Ireland
Tel.: (353) 18207940
Pharmaceuticals Product Mfr
N.A.I.C.S.: 325412

Subsidiary (US):

Liebel-Flarsheim Company LLC   (2)
2111 E Galbraith Rd, Cincinnati, OH 45237
Tel.: (513) 761-2700
Web Site: http://www.liebel.com
Emp.: 100
Pharmaceuticals Product Mfr
N.A.I.C.S.: 325412
Bob McGraw *(Plant Mgr)*

Medex SA   (1)
240 allee Jacques Monod, 69792, Saint
Priest, France
Tel.: (33) 472792050
Web Site: http://www.medexbyguerbet.com
Pharmaceutical Product Whslr
N.A.I.C.S.: 424210
Christelle Reille *(Mgr-Chain Supply)*

Simafex   (1)
16 rue des Fours a Chaux, 17230, Marans,
France
Tel.: (33) 546011032
Web Site: http://www.simafex.com
Sales Range: $25-49.9 Million
Pharmaceutical Industry Ingredients Mfr
N.A.I.C.S.: 325411

GUERRERO EXPLORATION INC.
Suite 3300 - 205 5th Ave SW, Cal-
gary, T2P 2V7, AB, Canada
Tel.: (403) 705-2087   AB
Web Site: http://www.grxpl.com
Year Founded: 2010
Gold Exploration Services
N.A.I.C.S.: 212220
Michelle Robinson *(Pres & CEO)*

GUEST-TEK INTERACTIVE ENTERTAINMENT LTD.
777 8 Ave SW Suite 600, Calgary,
T2P 3R5, AB, Canada
Tel.: (403) 509-1010   AB
Web Site: https://www.guesttek.com
Year Founded: 1996
Sales Range: $25-49.9 Million
Emp.: 355
Hospitality Broadband Services
N.A.I.C.S.: 517112
Zoey Sachdeva *(CIO)*

Subsidiaries:

Guest-Tek Interactive Entertainment
Inc   (1)
3 Goodyear Ste B, Irvine, CA 92618-2049
Tel.: (949) 470-1891
Sales Range: $25-49.9 Million
Emp.: 12
IP Based Technology Solutions Provider
N.A.I.C.S.: 517121

Guest-Tek International Group
Ltd   (1)
Gainsborough House, 81 Oxford St, Lon-
don, W1D 2EU, United Kingdom
Tel.: (44) 2079035236
IP Based Technology Solutions Provider
N.A.I.C.S.: 517121

Subsidiary (Non-US):

Guest-Tek Interactive Entertainment
Sp. z o.o   (2)
Metropolitan Building Pilsudskiego Square 2
4th Floor, 00-073, Warsaw, Poland
Tel.: (48) 223351100
Web Site: http://www.guest-tek.com
Sales Range: $25-49.9 Million
Emp.: 100
IP Based Technology Solutions Provider
N.A.I.C.S.: 517121
Monika Dabrowska *(Gen Mgr)*

Telnet Corp.   (1)
659 D Lakeview Plz Blvd, Worthington, OH
43085
Tel.: (614) 842-2700

Web Site: http://www.telnetsolutions.com
Sales Range: $1-9.9 Million
Emp.: 50
Communication Equipment Mfr
N.A.I.C.S.: 423690
Russell Meccomb (CEO)

GUESTLOGIX INC.
111 Peter Street Suite 302, Toronto, M5V 2H1, ON, Canada
Tel.: (416) 642-0349 ON
Web Site: http://www.guestlogix.com
Year Founded: 2002
Sales Range: $25-49.9 Million
Emp.: 126
Travel Industry Onboard Retail Technology
N.A.I.C.S.: 334419
Louis Belanger-Martin (Chm)

GUFIC BIOSCIENCES LIMITED
37 1st Floor Kamala Bhavan II Swami Nityanand Road, Andheri East, Mumbai, 400 069, India
Tel.: (91) 2267261000
Web Site: https://gufic.com
509079—(BOM)
Rev.: $106,778,463
Assets: $71,171,332
Liabilities: $34,436,725
Net Worth: $36,734,607
Earnings: $13,082,174
Emp.: 1,382
Fiscal Year-end: 03/31/22
Pharmaceutical Products Mfr & Sales
N.A.I.C.S.: 325412
Jayesh P. Choksi (Chm & Mng Dir)

GUH HOLDINGS BERHAD
Plot 1240 1241 Bayan Lepas Free Industrial Zone Phase 3 Bayan Lepas, 11900, Penang, Malaysia
Tel.: (60) 46166333
Web Site: https://www.guh.com.my
GUH—(KLS)
Rev.: $58,379,259
Assets: $129,283,810
Liabilities: $27,160,847
Net Worth: $102,122,963
Earnings: ($907,513)
Fiscal Year-end: 12/31/22
Circuit Board Mfr
N.A.I.C.S.: 334412
Kenneth Bak Tee H'ng (CEO, Mng Dir-Grp & Co-Sec)

Subsidiaries:

GUH Circuit Industry (PG) Sdn. Bhd. (1)
Plot 1240 1241 Bayan Lepas FIZ Phase 3, 11900, Bayan Lepas, Penang, Malaysia
Tel.: (60) 46166333
Web Site: http://www.guh.com
Sales Range: $200-249.9 Million
Emp.: 680
Printed Circuit Board Mfr & Whslr
N.A.I.C.S.: 334412
Kok Siew Foong (Gen Mgr)

GUH Circuit Industry (Suzhou) Co., Ltd. (1)
588 Changjiang Road, Suzhou, Jiangsu, China
Tel.: (86) 51265369906
Sales Range: $200-249.9 Million
Emp.: 650
Circuit Board Mfr
N.A.I.C.S.: 334412

GUH Development Sdn. Bhd. (1)
45 Lorong Tangling Indah, Simpang Ampat, 14100, Penang, Malaysia
Tel.: (60) 45069333
Property Development Services
N.A.I.C.S.: 531390

GUH Electrical (BW) Sdn. Bhd. (1)
No 4935 Jalan Siram, 12100, Butterworth, Penang, Malaysia
Tel.: (60) 43329222
Web Site: http://www.guh.com.my
Sales Range: $50-74.9 Million
Emp.: 7
Electrical Appliance Whslr
N.A.I.C.S.: 423610
Wong Chee Ying (Branch Mgr)

GUH Plantations Sdn. Bhd. (1)
Plot 1240 1241 Bayan Lepas Free Industrial Zone Phase 3, 11900, Bayan Lepas, Penang, Malaysia
Tel.: (60) 46166335
Web Site: http://www.guh.com
Sales Range: $150-199.9 Million
Emp.: 800
Oil Palm Plantation Services
N.A.I.C.S.: 115112

GUH Properties Sdn. Bhd. (1)
32 33 Jalan MPK 6 Medan Perdagangan Kepayang, 70200, Seremban, Negeri Sembilan, Malaysia
Tel.: (60) 6333227
Real Estate Development Services
N.A.I.C.S.: 531390

Star Wheels Electronic Sdn. Bhd.
No 47-2F Second Floor Jalan Setia Perdana BD, Seria 88 Business Centre Setia Alam, 40170, Shah Alam, Selangor, Malaysia
Tel.: (60) 125833882
Web Site: https://starwheels.com.my
Electric Scooter Mfr
N.A.I.C.S.: 336320

Teknoserv Engineering Sdn. Bhd. (1)
27 Jalan Seerendah 26/40 Kawasan Perindustrian HICOM Seksen 26, 40400, Shah Alam, Selangor, Malaysia
Tel.: (60) 356142828
Waste Water Treatment Services
N.A.I.C.S.: 221320

GUHESWORI MERCHANT BANKING & FINANCE LIMITED
Pulchowk Harihar Bhawa Lalitpur, Patan, Nepal
Tel.: (977) 5450406
Web Site: https://www.gmbf.com.np
GMFILP—(NEP)
Rev.: $7,832,124
Assets: $69,231,300
Liabilities: $58,556,476
Net Worth: $10,674,824
Earnings: $485,780
Emp.: 220
Fiscal Year-end: 07/16/23
Banking Services
N.A.I.C.S.: 522110
Shreeman Shrestha (Chm)

GUI ZHOU TYRE CO., LTD.
No 41 Baihua Avenue, Yunyan District, Guiyang, 550201, Guizhou, China
Tel.: (86) 85184767826
Web Site: http://www.gztyre.com
Year Founded: 1996
000589—(SSE)
Rev.: $1,184,956,344
Assets: $2,212,925,832
Liabilities: $1,302,885,324
Net Worth: $910,040,508
Earnings: $60,202,116
Emp.: 7,000
Fiscal Year-end: 12/31/22
Tyre Product Mfr
N.A.I.C.S.: 336390
Huang Gege (Chm & Gen Mgr)

GUIDEDRAW LTD.
28 Chancery Lane, London, WC2A 1LB, United Kingdom
Web Site: http://www.framestore.com
Motion Picture Video & TV Post Production
N.A.I.C.S.: 512110

GUIDELINE GEO AB
Hemvarnsgatan 9, 172 66, Sundbyberg, Sweden
Tel.: (46) 855761300
Web Site: https://www.guidelinegeo.com
GO91—(DEU)
Sales Range: Less than $1 Million
Fiber Optic Electrical Equipment Mfr
N.A.I.C.S.: 335921
Mats Lundin (CFO)

Subsidiaries:

Guideline Geo Americas, Inc. (1)
1270 Drop Off Dr Unit B, Summerville, SC 29486
Tel.: (843) 852-5021
Mineral Exploration Services
N.A.I.C.S.: 213114

GUIDELINE GROUP INFORMATION TECHNOLOGIES LTD.
Iyad Harutzim 12, Tel Aviv, 6770005, Israel
Tel.: (972) 36388222
Web Site: https://www.guideline.co.il
Year Founded: 1981
GUID—(TAE)
Rev.: $20,080,527
Assets: $40,185,999
Liabilities: $9,665,148
Net Worth: $30,520,850
Earnings: $1,306,057
Fiscal Year-end: 12/31/22
Financial Management Services
N.A.I.C.S.: 541611

GUILBERT PROPRETE
134 avenue Henri Barbusse, 93140, Bondy, France
Tel.: (33) 148471402
Web Site: http://www.guilbert.net
Rev.: $20,200,000
Emp.: 1,100
Repair Services
N.A.I.C.S.: 561790
Georges Guilbert (Dir-Personnel)

GUILD ELECTRIC LTD.
470 Midwest Road, Toronto, M1P 4Y5, ON, Canada
Tel.: (416) 288-8222
Web Site: http://www.guildelectric.com
Year Founded: 1954
Rev.: $65,904,272
Emp.: 500
Electrical Contracting Services
N.A.I.C.S.: 238210
Gary Lengyel (CEO)

GUILD ESPORTS PLC
Sky Guild Gaming Centre 330 High Holborn, London, E1 6JT, United Kingdom UK
Web Site: https://www.guildesports.com
Year Founded: 2019
GILD—(LSE)
Rev.: $6,045,927
Assets: $16,378,176
Liabilities: $11,547,409
Net Worth: $4,830,768
Earnings: ($11,877,335)
Emp.: 36
Fiscal Year-end: 09/30/22
Sports Club Operator
N.A.I.C.S.: 713990
Jasmine Skee (CEO)

GUILDFORD MOTORS INC
13820 104 Ave, Surrey, V3T 1W9, BC, Canada
Tel.: (604) 584-1311
Web Site: http://www.vwsurrey.ca
Year Founded: 1974
Rev.: $14,260,750
Emp.: 33
New & Used Car Dealers
N.A.I.C.S.: 441110
Chun Pang Lum (Sec)

GUILIN FUDA CO., LTD.
Yang No 18 Road, Xicheng Economic Development Zone Yangtang Industrial district, Guilin, 541199, China
Tel.: (86) 7733681156
Web Site: https://www.glfoto.cn
Year Founded: 1995
603166—(SHG)
Rev.: $159,316,260
Assets: $455,643,377
Liabilities: $121,303,859
Net Worth: $334,339,518
Earnings: $9,208,864
Emp.: 2,600
Fiscal Year-end: 12/31/22
Automobile Parts Mfr & Distr
N.A.I.C.S.: 333612

Subsidiaries:

Guiln Fuda Alfing Large Cranksaft Co., Ltd. (1)
Yang No 18 Road, Yangtang Industrial District, Guilin, 541199, China
Tel.: (86) 773 368 1086
Web Site: https://www.alfingfuda.com
Crankshaft Mfr
N.A.I.C.S.: 336310

GUILIN LAYN NATURAL INGREDIENTS CORP.
19 South Renmin Road, Lingui County, Guilin, 541199, Guangxi, China
Tel.: (86) 7733568889
Web Site: https://www.layncorp.com
Year Founded: 1995
002166—(SSE)
Rev.: $196,663,896
Assets: $625,532,544
Liabilities: $188,432,244
Net Worth: $437,100,300
Earnings: $25,096,500
Fiscal Year-end: 12/31/22
Plant Extract Product Mfr
N.A.I.C.S.: 311942

Subsidiaries:

Layn Europe SRL (1)
Via Armando Magliotto 2 - Palazzina Locatelli Pt, Campus Universitario Di Savona, 17100, Savona, Italy
Tel.: (39) 0197703407
Food Whslr
N.A.I.C.S.: 424410
Luca Pennestri (Gen Mgr)

Layn USA, Inc. (1)
20250 Acacia St Ste 105, Newport Beach, CA 92660
Tel.: (949) 387-6840
Food Whslr
N.A.I.C.S.: 424410
Lori Farrow (Office Mgr)

GUILIN SANJIN PHARMACEUTICAL CO., LTD.
No 9 Renmin Nan Road, Lingui District, Guilin, 541004, Guangxi, China
Tel.: (86) 7735843251
Web Site: https://www.sanjin.com.cn
Year Founded: 1967
002275—(SSE)
Rev.: $275,146,092
Assets: $556,676,172
Liabilities: $161,684,640
Net Worth: $394,991,532
Earnings: $46,266,012
Fiscal Year-end: 12/31/22
Pharmaceuticals Mfr
N.A.I.C.S.: 325412
Xun Zou (Chm & Pres)

GUILIN SEAMILD FOODS CO., LTD.

GUILIN SEAMILD FOODS CO., LTD.

Guilin Seamild Foods Co., Ltd.—(Continued)
Community 9, High-Tech Development Zone, Guilin, 541004, Guangxi, China
Tel.: (86) 7735818688
Web Site: http://www.seamild.com.cn
Year Founded: 2001
002956—(SSE)
Rev.: $186,344,496
Assets: $269,719,632
Liabilities: $71,985,888
Net Worth: $197,733,744
Earnings: $15,272,712
Fiscal Year-end: 12/31/22
Oat Product Mfr
N.A.I.C.S.: 311230
Qingkui Xie *(Chm & Gen Mgr)*

GUILIN TOURISM CORPORATION LIMITED

No 27-2 Cuizhu Road, Guangxi Zhuang Autonomous Region, Guilin, 541002, Guangxi, China
Tel.: (86) 7733558976
Web Site: http://www.guilintravel.com
Year Founded: 1998
000978—(SSE)
Rev.: $18,171,972
Assets: $331,432,452
Liabilities: $151,414,380
Net Worth: $180,018,072
Earnings: ($39,581,568)
Fiscal Year-end: 12/31/22
Travel Services
N.A.I.C.S.: 561510
Shen Guangming *(Chm)*

GUILLEMOT CORPORATION S.A.

2 Rue du Chene Heleuc, BP 97143, 56910, Chantepie, Cedex, France
Tel.: (33) 299080880
Web Site: https://www.guillemot.com
GUL—(DEU)
Rev.: $29,936,241,050
Assets: $45,348,026,470
Liabilities: $35,390,072,930
Net Worth: $9,957,953,540
Earnings: $4,753,643,380
Emp.: 30,237
Fiscal Year-end: 12/31/23
Computer Equipment Designer & Mfr
N.A.I.C.S.: 334118

Subsidiaries:

Guillemot SA (1)
Dokter Hilaire Folletlaan 208, 1780, Wemmel, Belgium
Tel.: (32) 25828497
Web Site: http://www.thrustmaster.com
Sales Range: $50-74.9 Million
Emp.: 7
Computer Gaming Accessories Distr
N.A.I.C.S.: 423430

Guillemot Spain SL (1)
C/Maudes 51 8 planta, 28003, Madrid, Spain
Tel.: (34) 913956322
Web Site: http://www.thrustmaster.com
Emp.: 10
Computer Gaming Accessories Distr
N.A.I.C.S.: 423430
Eric Chulot *(Gen Mgr)*

GUINEA INSURANCE PLC

Guinea Insurance House 33 Ikorodu Road, Jibowu, Lagos, Nigeria
Tel.: (234) 12934575
Web Site: https://www.guineainsurance.com
Year Founded: 1958
GUINEAINS—(NIGE)
Rev.: $3,031,119
Assets: $9,474,886
Liabilities: $4,710,958
Net Worth: $4,763,929
Earnings: ($144,406)
Emp.: 67
Fiscal Year-end: 12/31/22
All Other Insurance Related Activities
N.A.I.C.S.: 524298
Isioma Omoshie-Okokuku *(Exec Dir-Mktg)*

GUINNESS NORTHERN COUNTIES LTD

Bower House 1 Stable Street Hollinwood, Oldham, OL9 7LH, United Kingdom
Tel.: (44) 1612197000
Web Site: http://www.guinnesspartnership.com
Sales Range: $75-99.9 Million
Emp.: 745
Elder People Housing & Health Care Services
N.A.I.C.S.: 621610
Neil Braithwaite *(Chm)*

Subsidiaries:

City Response Limited (1)
Irving Court Broadgate Oldham Broadway Business Park, Chadderton, Oldham, OL9 9XA, United Kingdom
Tel.: (44) 161 947 3550
Web Site: http://www.cityresponse.co.uk
Sales Range: $75-99.9 Million
Emp.: 30
Property Refurbishment Services
N.A.I.C.S.: 561990

Encore Homes Limited (1)
Bower House Unit 1 Stable Street, Chadderton, Oldham, OL9 7LH, Lancashire, United Kingdom
Tel.: (44) 1612 197000
Web Site: http://www.guinnesspartnership.com
Sales Range: $25-49.9 Million
Emp.: 400
Property Refurbishment Services
N.A.I.C.S.: 561990

GUIRENNIAO CO., LTD.

18F Xiang'an Business Bulding Sishui Dao, Huli District, Xiamen, China
Tel.: (86) 5925725650
603555—(SHG)
Rev.: $295,980,708
Assets: $425,858,655
Liabilities: $185,845,416
Net Worth: $240,013,238
Earnings: ($1,321,683)
Fiscal Year-end: 12/31/22
Sports Apparel Mfr
N.A.I.C.S.: 315250
Tianfu Lin *(Chm & Gen Mgr)*

GUIYANG LONGMASTER INFORMATION & TECHNOLOGY CO., LTD.

2nd Floor National Digital Content Industrial Park No 31, Changling South Road Guanshanhu District, Guiyang, 550025, Guizhou, China
Tel.: (86) 8513842119
Web Site: http://www.longmaster.com.cn
Year Founded: 1998
300288—(CHIN)
Rev.: $61,301,448
Assets: $259,633,296
Liabilities: $40,489,956
Net Worth: $219,143,340
Earnings: $9,868,716
Emp.: 580
Fiscal Year-end: 12/31/22
Computer Telephony Integration
N.A.I.C.S.: 541519

GUIYANG XINTIAN PHARMACEUTICAL CO., LTD.

No 114 Xintian Avenue, National Hi-Tech Industrial Development Zone, Guiyang, 550000, Guizhou, China
Tel.: (86) 85186298482
Web Site: http://www.gyxtyy.com
Year Founded: 1995
002873—(SSE)
Rev.: $152,708,868
Assets: $258,876,540
Liabilities: $100,336,860
Net Worth: $158,539,680
Earnings: $16,300,440
Emp.: 1,000
Fiscal Year-end: 12/31/22
Pharmaceutical Product Mfr & Distr
N.A.I.C.S.: 325412

GUIZHOU BAILING GROUP PHARMACEUTICAL CO., LTD.

Xihang Avenue Economic and Tchnlgcl Dvlpmnt Zn, Anshun, 561000, Guizhou, China
Tel.: (86) 85133411018
Web Site: https://www.gzbl.com
Year Founded: 1999
002424—(SSE)
Rev.: $497,034,252
Assets: $967,973,760
Liabilities: $406,809,000
Net Worth: $561,164,760
Earnings: $19,403,280
Fiscal Year-end: 12/31/22
Pharmaceutical Mfr & Whslr
N.A.I.C.S.: 325412
Wei Jiang *(Chm)*

GUIZHOU BROADCASTING & TV INFORMATION NETWORK CO., LTD.

No 36 Jinyang South Road, Guanshanhu District, Guiyang, 550081, Guizhou, China
Tel.: (86) 85184115592
Web Site: https://www.gzgdwl.com
Year Founded: 2008
600996—(SHG)
Rev.: $522,834,900
Assets: $2,529,804,771
Liabilities: $1,704,381,476
Net Worth: $825,423,295
Earnings: $1,567,440
Fiscal Year-end: 12/31/22
Television Broadcasting Services
N.A.I.C.S.: 516120
Chen Yu *(Chm & Sec-Party Committee)*

GUIZHOU CHANGZHENG TIANCHENG HOLDING CO., LTD.

No 1 Wuhan Road, Zunyi, 056300, Guizhou, China
Tel.: (86) 8528682211
Web Site: http://www.tckg.cn
600110—(SHG)
Rev.: $19,183,006
Assets: $185,949,944
Liabilities: $170,367,790
Net Worth: $15,582,154
Earnings: ($18,622,684)
Fiscal Year-end: 12/31/22
Holding Company
N.A.I.C.S.: 551112

GUIZHOU CHANHEN CHEMICAL CORPORATION

Longchang Town, Fuquan, Guizhou, China
Tel.: (86) 2883123199
Web Site: https://www.chanphos.com
002895—(SSE)
Rev.: $484,024,788
Assets: $1,423,436,976
Liabilities: $726,811,488
Net Worth: $696,625,488
Earnings: $106,392,312
Fiscal Year-end: 12/31/22
Phosphate Product Mfr & Distr
N.A.I.C.S.: 325312

Subsidiaries:

Guizhou Chanfert Enterprise Co., Ltd. (1)
Longchang Town, Fuquan, Guizhou, China
Tel.: (86) 2883123199
Web Site: https://www.chanphos.com
Chemical Products Distr
N.A.I.C.S.: 424690

GUIZHOU GAS GROUP CORPORATION, LTD.

No 298 Xintian Avenue, Yunyan District, Guiyang, 550004, Guizhou, China
Tel.: (86) 58185830557
Web Site: http://www.guizhougas.com
Year Founded: 2003
600903—(SHG)
Rev.: $865,308,661
Assets: $1,447,459,290
Liabilities: $928,680,602
Net Worth: $518,778,688
Earnings: $3,579,035
Fiscal Year-end: 12/31/22
Natural Gas Distribution Services
N.A.I.C.S.: 486210
Cheng Yang *(Pres)*

GUIZHOU GUIHANG AOTOMOTIVE COMPONENTS CO., LTD.

No 361 Pujiang Road, Xiaohe Economic and Technological Development Zone, Guiyang, 550009, Guizhou, China
Tel.: (86) 8513802670
Web Site: http://www.ghgf.com.cn
Year Founded: 1999
600523—(SHG)
Rev.: $302,317,550
Assets: $484,142,907
Liabilities: $78,951,230
Net Worth: $405,191,676
Earnings: $17,238,452
Emp.: 4,800
Fiscal Year-end: 12/31/22
Automotive Components Mfr
N.A.I.C.S.: 336320
Fengtao Ding *(Chm)*

GUIZHOU PANJIANG REFINED COAL CO., LTD.

Gangou Bridge Hongguo Economic Development Zone, Liupanshui, 553536, Guizhou, China
Tel.: (86) 8583703046
Web Site: http://www.pjgf.cn
Year Founded: 1999
600395—(SHG)
Rev.: $1,662,765,526
Assets: $4,218,283,855
Liabilities: $2,451,592,059
Net Worth: $1,766,691,796
Earnings: $308,047,414
Fiscal Year-end: 12/31/22
Coal Product Mfr & Distr
N.A.I.C.S.: 212114
Yang Dejin *(Vice Chm & Gen Mgr)*

GUIZHOU QIANYUAN POWER CO., LTD.

No 46 Dusi Viaduct Road, Nanming District, Guiyang, 550002, Guizhou, China
Tel.: (86) 85185218808
Web Site: http://www.gzqydl.cn
Year Founded: 1993
002039—(SSE)
Rev.: $366,882,048
Assets: $2,353,210,704
Liabilities: $1,452,380,436
Net Worth: $900,830,268
Earnings: $58,160,700
Fiscal Year-end: 12/31/22
Hydro Power Generation Services
N.A.I.C.S.: 221111

Yuandong Wu (Gen Mgr)

GUIZHOU REDSTAR DEVELOPMENT CO., LTD.
Dingqi Street, Zhenning County, Anshun, 561206, Guizhou, China
Tel.: (86) 85136780115
Web Site: https://www.hxfz.com.cn
Year Founded: 1993
600367—(SHG)
Rev.: $400,616,181
Assets: $401,945,586
Liabilities: $130,381,912
Net Worth: $271,563,674
Earnings: $30,166,147
Emp.: 1,056
Fiscal Year-end: 12/31/22
Chemical Product Mfr & Whslr
N.A.I.C.S.: 325180
Zhang Haijun (Chm)

Subsidiaries:

Chongqing Dazu Red Butterfly Strontium Industry Co., Ltd. (1)
Longshui Town, Dazu County, Chongqing, 402368, China
Tel.: (86) 234 362 4218
Inorganic Chemical Mfr
N.A.I.C.S.: 325180

Chongqing Dazu Red Butterfly Strontium Industry Co., Ltd. - Yongxi Factory (1)
Red Star community neighborhood committees, Yongxi Town Dazu County, Chongqing, 402367, China
Tel.: (86) 2343456638
Inorganic Chemical Mfr
N.A.I.C.S.: 325180

Guizhou Hongxing Development Co., Ltd. (1)
Dingqi Town, Zhenning County, Anshun, 561206, Guizhou, China
Tel.: (86) 8513 678 0115
Inorganic Chemical Mfr
N.A.I.C.S.: 325180

Guizhou Red Star Development Dragon Chemical Industry Co., Ltd. (1)
Tongping County Economic Development Zone, Tongren, 554001, Guizhou, China
Tel.: (86) 8563375412
Inorganic Chemical Mfr
N.A.I.C.S.: 325180

Guizhou Red Star Development Fanjingshan Cold Water Fisheries Co., Ltd. (1)
Tongjiang Village, Minxiao Town Jiangkou County, Tongren, 554400, Guizhou, China
Tel.: (86) 8566760333
Inorganic Chemical Mfr
N.A.I.C.S.: 325180

Guizhou Red Star Development Import & Export Co., Ltd. (1)
Inorganic Chemical Mfr
N.A.I.C.S.: 325180

Qingdao Hongxing Chemical Group Co., Ltd. (1)
No 8 Jiyang Road, Shibei District, Qingdao, China
Tel.: (86) 53282850016
Web Site: https://www.redstarchem.com
Chemical Products Mfr
N.A.I.C.S.: 325611

Qingdao Hongxing Chemical Group Inorganic New Material Technology Development Co., Ltd. (1)
No 43 North Fourth Road, Qingdao, 266043, China
Tel.: (86) 53284915015
Inorganic Chemical Mfr
N.A.I.C.S.: 325180

Qingdao Natural Pigments Limited (1)
No 43 North Fourth Road, Qingdao, 266043, China
Tel.: (86) 5328 491 5032
Inorganic Chemical Mfr

N.A.I.C.S.: 325180

Red Star Daqing Lvyou Natural Pigment Co., Ltd. (1)
Linyuan Park High-tech Zone, Daqing, 163515, Heilongjiang, China
Tel.: (86) 4596175057
Alcoholic Beverage Mfr & Distr
N.A.I.C.S.: 325193

GUIZHOU SANLI PHARMACEUTICAL CO., LTD.
Xiayun Industrial Park, Guian New District, Anshun, 561000, Guizhou, China
Tel.: (86) 85138113395
Web Site: https://www.gz-sanli.com
Year Founded: 1995
603439—(SHG)
Rev.: $168,664,823
Assets: $255,053,364
Liabilities: $81,207,107
Net Worth: $173,846,256
Earnings: $28,260,302
Fiscal Year-end: 12/31/22
Pharmaceutical Product Mfr & Distr
N.A.I.C.S.: 325412
Hai Zhang (Chm & Gen Mgr)

GUIZHOU SPACE APPLIANCE CO., LTD.
No 7 Honghe Road Economic and Technological Development Zone, Guiyang, 550009, China
Tel.: (86) 8518697168
002025—(SSE)
Rev.: $845,165,880
Assets: $1,399,573,188
Liabilities: $476,082,360
Net Worth: $923,490,828
Earnings: $77,983,776
Fiscal Year-end: 12/31/22
Electronic Products Mfr
N.A.I.C.S.: 334419
Wei Liang Yuan (Vice Chm)

GUIZHOU TAIYONG-CHANGZHENG TECHNOLOGY CO., LTD.
Middle section of Wuhan Road Waigaoqiao Industrial Park, Huichuan District, Zunyi, 563000, Guizhou, China
Tel.: (86) 75586966076
Web Site: http://www.taiyong.net
Year Founded: 2008
002927—(SSE)
Rev.: $125,761,896
Assets: $216,366,528
Liabilities: $71,154,720
Net Worth: $145,211,508
Earnings: $9,582,300
Fiscal Year-end: 12/31/22
Electrical Equipment Mfr & Distr
N.A.I.C.S.: 335311
Zhengqian Huang (Chm & Gen Mgr)

GUIZHOU TRANSPORTATION PLANNING SURVEY & DESIGN ACADEME CO., LTD.
No 100 Yangguan Avenue National High-tech Industrial Development Zone, Guiyang, 550081, China
Tel.: (86) 85185869235
Web Site: https://www.gzjtsjy.com
Year Founded: 1958
603458—(SHG)
Rev.: $302,650,312
Assets: $1,053,145,623
Liabilities: $571,336,417
Net Worth: $481,809,206
Earnings: $23,886,982
Fiscal Year-end: 12/31/22
Land Surveying Services
N.A.I.C.S.: 541370
Zhang Lin (Chm)

GUIZHOU WIRE ROPE INCORPORATED COMPANY
No 47 Taoxi Rd, Zunyi, 563000, Guizhou, China
Tel.: (86) 8528419247
Web Site: http://www.guizhouwirerope.com
Year Founded: 2000
600992—(SHG)
Rev.: $335,115,720
Assets: $469,080,528
Liabilities: $261,744,491
Net Worth: $207,336,037
Earnings: $3,237,161
Fiscal Year-end: 12/31/22
Steel Wire Rope Mfr
N.A.I.C.S.: 331110
Xianhong Ma (Chm)

GUIZHOU XINBANG PHARMACEUTICAL CO., LTD.
6th Floor Kekai No 1 Intersection of Hangtian Avenue Xintian Avenue, Wudang District, Guiyang, 550018, China
Tel.: (86) 85188660235
Web Site: https://www.xinbang.com
Year Founded: 1995
002390—(SSE)
Rev.: $891,544,212
Assets: $1,374,949,836
Liabilities: $383,016,816
Net Worth: $991,933,020
Earnings: $31,516,992
Emp.: 800
Fiscal Year-end: 12/31/22
Pharmaceuticals Mfr
N.A.I.C.S.: 325412
Ji Ann (Chm)

GUIZHOU YIBAI PHARMACEUTICAL CO., LTD.
No 220-1 Baiyun Avenue, Guiyang, 550008, China
Tel.: (86) 85184705590
Web Site: https://www.gzcci.com
Year Founded: 1995
600594—(SHG)
Rev.: $384,030,897
Assets: $683,159,373
Liabilities: $235,293,735
Net Worth: $447,865,638
Earnings: $(59,875,995)
Emp.: 9,000
Fiscal Year-end: 12/31/22
Pharmaceutical Product Mfr & Distr
N.A.I.C.S.: 325412
Qiling Dou (Chm)

GUJARAT ALKALIES & CHEMICALS LTD
PO Ranoli, 391350, Vadodara, 391350, Gujarat, India
Tel.: (91) 2656111000
Web Site: https://www.gacl.com
GUJALKALI—(NSE)
Rev.: $622,255,725
Assets: $1,137,693,375
Liabilities: $299,689,845
Net Worth: $838,003,530
Earnings: $55,913,130
Emp.: 1,553
Fiscal Year-end: 03/31/23
Caustic Soda Producer
N.A.I.C.S.: 325180
Sanjay S. Bhatt (Compliance Officer & Sec)

Subsidiaries:

Gacl-Nalco Alkalies & Chemicals Pvt. Ltd. (1)
Plot D-II/9, Tal Vagra Dist Bharuch, Gujarat, 392 130, India
Tel.: (91) 2652222435
Web Site: https://www.gnal.co.in
Chemical Products Mfr
N.A.I.C.S.: 325998

Milind Torawane (Chm)

GUJARAT AMBUJA EXPORTS LTD.
Ambuja Tower Opp Sindhu Bhavan Sindhu Bhavan Road Bodakdev P O Thaltej, Ahmedabad, 380054, Gujarat, India
Tel.: (91) 7961556677
Web Site: https://www.ambujagroup.com
Year Founded: 1983
GAEL—(NSE)
Rev.: $646,211,475
Assets: $295,179,885
Liabilities: $69,048,525
Net Worth: $226,131,360
Earnings: $46,146,555
Emp.: 2,649
Fiscal Year-end: 03/31/21
Agriculture Product Distr
N.A.I.C.S.: 424910
Manish Gupta (Chm & Mng Dir)

Subsidiaries:

Gujarat Ambuja Exports Ltd. - Akola Division (1)
Village Post Kanheri Gawali N H No 6 Akola-Balapur Road, Balapur, Akola, 444 302, Maharashtra, India
Tel.: (91) 7257285026
Edible Oil Mfr
N.A.I.C.S.: 311225

Gujarat Ambuja Exports Ltd. - Cotton Yarn Division (1)
1 Vrindavan Road, Dalpur Prantij Himmatnagar Sabarkantha, New Delhi, 383 006, Gujarat, India
Tel.: (91) 2772226252
Cotton Yarn Mfr
N.A.I.C.S.: 313110

Gujarat Ambuja Exports Ltd. - Kadi Division (1)
Kadi-Thore Road, Kadi, Mehsana, 382 715, Gujarat, India
Tel.: (91) 2764264013
Soyabean & Edible Oil Mfr
N.A.I.C.S.: 311224

Gujarat Ambuja Exports Ltd. - Karnataka Division (1)
Madli Cross P B Road, Hulsoggi Manakatti Shiggoan, New Delhi, 581 205, Karnataka, India
Tel.: (91) 836 2382432
Maize Flour Mfr
N.A.I.C.S.: 311211

Gujarat Ambuja Exports Ltd. - Mandsaur Division (1)
Survey No 41 Near Railway Crossing Mhow-Neemach RoadSurvey No 41 Near, Sondhani, New Delhi, Madhya Pradesh, India
Tel.: (91) 7422 300176
Edible Oil Mfr
N.A.I.C.S.: 311225

Gujarat Ambuja Exports Ltd. - Pithampur Division (1)
Plot No 414-417 Sector-III, Pithampur Industrial Area, Dhar, Madhya Pradesh, India
Tel.: (91) 7292 256790
Wheat Flour Mfr
N.A.I.C.S.: 311211

Gujarat Ambuja Exports Ltd. - Uttranchal Division (1)
C-50 Eldeco Sidcul Industrial Park, Udhamsingh Nagar, Sitarganj, 263153, Uttaranchal, India
Tel.: (91) 5948 256012
Maize Flour Mfr
N.A.I.C.S.: 311211

GUJARAT APOLLO INDUSTRIES LIMITED
Parishram 5-B Rashmi Society Mithakhali, Navrangpura, Ahmedabad, 380009, Gujarat, India
Tel.: (91) 7926444597

GUJARAT APOLLO INDUSTRIES LIMITED

Gujarat Apollo Industries Limited—(Continued)
Web Site: https://www.apollo.co.in
Year Founded: 1967
GUJAPOLLO—(NSE)
Rev.: $20,967,687
Assets: $83,865,708
Liabilities: $11,075,729
Net Worth: $72,789,980
Earnings: $6,088,160
Emp.: 91
Fiscal Year-end: 03/31/21
Road Construction Equipment Mfr & Sales
N.A.I.C.S.: 336999
Asit A. Patel (Mng Dir)

Subsidiaries:

Apollo Earthmovers Ltd. (1)
212-A GIDC Estate, Mehsana, 384002, Gujarat, India
Tel.: (91) 2762252362
Web Site: http://www.apollo.co.in
Sales Range: $50-74.9 Million
Emp.: 113
Construction Machinery Mfr
N.A.I.C.S.: 333120

Apollo Maschinenbau GmbH (1)
Gruenauer Fenn 44, 14712, Rathenow, Germany
Tel.: (49) 3385510200
Sales Range: $25-49.9 Million
Emp.: 2
Conveyor Equipment Mfr
N.A.I.C.S.: 333922
Klaus Sprehe (Gen Mgr)

GUJARAT CONTAINERS LIMITED

201/202 Alkapuri Arcade B Wing Opp Welcome Hotel, R C Dutt Road, Vadodara, 390005, India
Tel.: (91) 2652341265
Web Site: https://www.gujaratcontainers.com
Year Founded: 1992
513507—(BOM)
Rev.: $16,276,123
Assets: $7,352,916
Liabilities: $3,183,154
Net Worth: $4,169,762
Earnings: $1,330,088
Emp.: 100
Fiscal Year-end: 03/31/23
Barrel Mfr & Whslr
N.A.I.C.S.: 332439
Kiran Arvindlal Shah (Chm & Mng Dir)

Subsidiaries:

GUJARAT CONTAINERS LIMITED - Unit I (1)
Plant No 488 Baroda - Savli Highway, Tundav Savli, Vadodara, India
Tel.: (91) 2667 262084
Barrel Mfr
N.A.I.C.S.: 332439

GUJARAT CONTAINERS LIMITED - Unit II (1)
2/5 Phase 1 GIDC Near GNFC Corporate Office, Narmada Nagar, Bharuch, 392015, India
Tel.: (91) 2642 229478
Barrel Mfr
N.A.I.C.S.: 332439

GUJARAT COTEX LIMITED

Tel.: (91) 9327977729   In
Web Site: https://gujcotex.in
Year Founded: 1996
514386—(BOM)
Rev.: $1,994,365
Assets: $1,799,065
Liabilities: $953,864
Net Worth: $845,201
Earnings: $1,151
Emp.: 4
Fiscal Year-end: 03/31/23

Yarn Manufacturing
N.A.I.C.S.: 313110
Priyavanda S. Parekh (Chm)

GUJARAT CRAFT INDUSTRIES LIMITED

No 431 Santej-Vadsar Road, Tal Kalol, Gandhinagar, 382 721, Gujarat, India
Tel.: (91) 2764286131   In
Web Site: https://www.gujaratcraftindustry.com
Year Founded: 1984
526965—(BOM)
Rev.: $23,403,034
Assets: $14,935,229
Liabilities: $7,492,731
Net Worth: $7,442,499
Earnings: $1,034,588
Emp.: 84
Fiscal Year-end: 03/31/22
Polypropylene Fabric Mfr
N.A.I.C.S.: 313110
Rishab Ashok Chhajer (Mng Dir)

GUJARAT HOTELS LIMITED

WelcomHotel Vadodara R C Dutt Road Alkapuri, Vadodara, 390007, Gujarat, India
Tel.: (91) 2652330033
Web Site: https://www.gujarathotelsltd.in
Year Founded: 1982
507960—(BOM)
Rev.: $487,182
Assets: $5,319,077
Liabilities: $312,803
Net Worth: $5,006,274
Earnings: $371,089
Emp.: 145
Fiscal Year-end: 03/31/22
Home Management Services
N.A.I.C.S.: 721110

GUJARAT HYSPIN LIMITED

PO Box 22, Gondal, 360311, Gujarat, India
Tel.: (91) 2825297170
Web Site: http://www.gujarathyspin.com
Year Founded: 1994
540938—(BOM)
Rev.: $11,311,342
Assets: $4,271,593
Liabilities: $1,991,731
Net Worth: $2,279,863
Earnings: $20,155
Fiscal Year-end: 03/31/24
Textile Product Mfr & Distr
N.A.I.C.S.: 313110
Kaushik Dave (Mng Dir)

GUJARAT INDUSTRIES POWER COMPANY LIMITED

Post Ranoli, 391350, Vadodara, 391350, Gujarat, India
Tel.: (91) 2652232768   In
Web Site: https://www.gipcl.com
Year Founded: 1985
517300—(BOM)
Rev.: $191,603,617
Assets: $612,481,097
Liabilities: $175,709,229
Net Worth: $436,771,867
Earnings: $25,756,690
Emp.: 553
Fiscal Year-end: 03/31/22
Electric Power Generation
N.A.I.C.S.: 221122
N. K. Purohit (Gen Mgr-Mines)

GUJARAT INJECT (KERALA) LTD.

Building No XVII/1103 at Sarayu Arcade Satrapadi, Kanjikode, Palakkad, 678621, Kerala, India

Tel.: (91) 9898593314
Web Site: https://www.gujaratinject.in
Year Founded: 1991
524238—(BOM)
Rev.: $72,694
Assets: $36,351
Liabilities: $1,089,640
Net Worth: ($1,053,289)
Earnings: $4,921
Emp.: 4
Fiscal Year-end: 03/31/23
Pharmaceutical Product Mfr & Distr
N.A.I.C.S.: 325412
Murli Nair (CFO)

GUJARAT INTRUX LIMITED

Tel.: (91) 2827252851
Web Site: https://www.gujaratintrux.com
Year Founded: 1992
517372—(BOM)
Rev.: $6,278,688
Assets: $7,533,098
Liabilities: $570,589
Net Worth: $6,962,508
Earnings: $688,004
Emp.: 128
Fiscal Year-end: 03/31/23
Steel Casting Mfr
N.A.I.C.S.: 331513
Sanjay J. Vagadia (CFO)

GUJARAT INVESTA LIMITED

252 New Cloth Market O/s Raipur Gate, Ahmedabad, 380 002, Gujarat, India
Tel.: (91) 7922133383
Web Site: https://www.gujaratinvesta.com
Year Founded: 1993
531341—(BOM)
Rev.: $48,191
Assets: $1,441,993
Liabilities: $5,932
Net Worth: $1,436,061
Earnings: $4,278
Emp.: 5
Fiscal Year-end: 03/31/22
Financial Services
N.A.I.C.S.: 523999
Somna P. Agarwal (CEO)

GUJARAT LEASE FINANCING LIMITED

6th Floor Hasubhai Chambers Opp Town Hall Ellisbridge, Ahmedabad, 380 006, India
Tel.: (91) 7926575722
Web Site: http://www.gujaratleasefinancing.in
500174—(BOM)
Rev.: $39,940
Assets: $810,264
Liabilities: $1,413,580
Net Worth: ($603,316)
Earnings: ($11,220)
Emp.: 3
Fiscal Year-end: 03/31/22
Holding Company
N.A.I.C.S.: 551112
Anil K. Jhaveri (CEO)

GUJARAT MEDITECH LTD

17/A 4th Floor Sandesh Commercial Complex, Mirzapur Court, Ahmedabad, 380001, Gujarat, India
Tel.: (91) 79 30071204
Web Site: http://www.gujaratmeditech.com
Year Founded: 1991
Rev.: $116,918
Assets: $859,846
Liabilities: $185,033
Net Worth: $674,813
Earnings: $62
Fiscal Year-end: 03/31/18
Ophthalmic Glass Mfr & Distr

INTERNATIONAL PUBLIC

N.A.I.C.S.: 339115

GUJARAT METALLIC COAL & COKE LIMITED

155 Lenin Sarani 4th Floor Room No 402, Kolkata, 700 013, India
Tel.: (91) 3322155899
Web Site:
    http://www.gujaratmetallic.com
531881—(BOM)
Sales Range: Less than $1 Million
Emp.: 2
Coal Trading Services
N.A.I.C.S.: 423520
Sajjan Kumar Tailor (Mng Dir)

GUJARAT MINERAL DEVELOPMENT CORPORATION LIMITED

Khanij Bhavan 132 Feet Ring Road Near University Ground, Vastrapur, Ahmedabad, 380052, India
Tel.: (91) 7927913200
Web Site: https://www.gmdcltd.com
Year Founded: 1963
532181—(BOM)
Rev.: $466,999,916
Assets: $829,809,304
Liabilities: $134,613,440
Net Worth: $695,195,864
Earnings: $145,762,796
Emp.: 944
Fiscal Year-end: 03/31/23
Mineral Exploration Company
N.A.I.C.S.: 213115
Joel Evans (Sec)

GUJARAT NARMADA VALLEY FERTILIZERS & CHEMICALS LIMITED

PO Narmadanagar, 392015, Bharuch, 392015, Gujarat, India
Tel.: (91) 2642247001
Web Site: https://www.gnfc.in
500670—(BOM)
Rev.: $1,445,262,000
Assets: $1,596,504,000
Liabilities: $353,671,500
Net Worth: $1,242,832,500
Earnings: $200,928,000
Emp.: 2,504
Fiscal Year-end: 03/31/23
Fertilizer & Chemical Mfr
N.A.I.C.S.: 325311
Parikh D. V. (CFO)

Subsidiaries:

Gujarat Ncode Solutions Limited (1)
14th Floor Tower One Road 5C Zone 5, Gujarat International Finance Tech City, Gandhinagar, 382 355, Gujarat, India
Tel.: (91) 7966743289
Web Site: http://www.ncodesolutions.com
Chemical Products Mfr
N.A.I.C.S.: 325180
Anil Mukim (Chm)

GUJARAT NATURAL RESOURCES LIMITED

9th Floor Office No 906 907 908 909 910 ANAM 1, Nr Parimal Garden Ellisbridge, Ahmedabad, 380 006, Gujarat, India
Tel.: (91) 7940029806
Web Site: https://www.gnrl.in
513536—(BOM)
Rev.: $1,250,947
Assets: $20,391,253
Liabilities: $5,940,973
Net Worth: $14,450,279
Earnings: ($572,308)
Emp.: 5
Fiscal Year-end: 03/31/21
Oil & Gas Exploration Services
N.A.I.C.S.: 213112
Ashok C. Shah (Chm)

GUJARAT NRE COKE LTD.
22 Camac Street Block-C 5th Floor, Kolkata, 700 016, India
Tel.: (91) 3322891471 In
Web Site: http://www.gujaratnre.in
Year Founded: 1986
GUJNRECOKE—(NSE)
Metallurgical Coke Mfr
N.A.I.C.S.: 324199
Arun Kumar Jagatramka *(Chm & Mng Dir)*

GUJARAT ORGANICS LIMITED
3 A Barodawala Mansion 81 Dr A B Road Worli, Mumbai, 400 018, India
Tel.: (91) 22 2493 8687
Web Site:
http://www.gujaratorganics.com
Year Founded: 1978
Sales Range: $10-24.9 Million
Emp.: 110
Chemical Products Mfr
N.A.I.C.S.: 325199
Ashwin S. Dani *(Chm)*

GUJARAT PERSTORP ELECTRONICS LTD.
B 1 Sector 25 GIDC Electronics Estate, Gandhinagar, 382044, Gujarat, India
Tel.: (91) 7923242815
526385—(BOM)
Electronic Products Mfr
N.A.I.C.S.: 334419
Seema Thapar *(Sec)*

GUJARAT PETROSYNTHESE LTD
No 24 II Main Phase-I Doddanekkundi Industrial Area Mahadevapura Post, Bengaluru, 560 048, Karnataka, India
Tel.: (91) 8028524133
Web Site: https://www.gpl.in
Year Founded: 1996
506858—(BOM)
Rev.: $4,291,983
Assets: $6,583,832
Liabilities: $336,268
Net Worth: $6,247,564
Earnings: $133,333
Emp.: 31
Fiscal Year-end: 03/31/22
Polymer Blends Mfr
N.A.I.C.S.: 325211
R. M. Thakkar *(Founder)*

GUJARAT RAFFIA INDUSTRIES LIMITED
455 Santej - Vadsar Road Santej, Gandhinagar, 382 721, Gujarat, India
Tel.: (91) 7929702373
Web Site: https://www.griltarp.com
Year Founded: 1984
523836—(BOM)
Rev.: $5,337,602
Assets: $3,339,145
Liabilities: $886,028
Net Worth: $2,453,117
Earnings: $162,402
Emp.: 78
Fiscal Year-end: 03/31/21
Tarpaulin Bag Mfr
N.A.I.C.S.: 314910
Pradeep Ratanlal Bhutoria *(Chm & Mng Dir)*

GUJARAT SIDHEE CEMENT LIMITED
NK Mehta International House 2nd Floor 178 Backbay Reclamation, Mumbai, 400 020, India
Tel.: (91) 2266365444
Web Site: http://www.hathi-sidheecements.com

518029—(NSE)
Rev.: $96,978,541
Assets: $96,867,566
Liabilities: $32,001,005
Net Worth: $64,866,561
Earnings: $2,752,686
Emp.: 355
Fiscal Year-end: 03/31/22
Cement Mfr & Sales
N.A.I.C.S.: 327310
Mahendra Nanjibhai Mehta *(Chm)*

GUJARAT STATE FERTILIZERS & CHEMICALS LTD.
PO Fertilizernagar, 391 750, Vadodara, 391 750, Gujarat, India
Tel.: (91) 2652242451
Web Site:
https://www.gsfclimited.com
Year Founded: 1962
500690—(BOM)
Rev.: $1,264,795,609
Assets: $1,928,019,789
Liabilities: $320,900,034
Net Worth: $1,607,119,755
Earnings: $122,655,665
Emp.: 2,877
Fiscal Year-end: 03/31/22
Fertilizer Mfr
N.A.I.C.S.: 325314
V. D. Nanavaty *(CFO & Exec Dir-Fin)*

Subsidiaries:
GSFC Agrotech Limited (1)
Gatl Building 2nd Floor Opp Vishwa Mandir Fertilizernagar, PO Fertilizernagar Dist Vadodara, Gujarat, 391 750, India
Tel.: (91) 2653093661
Web Site: https://www.gsfcagrotech.com
Agricultural Chemical Product Mfr
N.A.I.C.S.: 325320

GUJARAT STATE FINANCIAL CORPORATION LTD.
Block No 10 Udyog Bhavan Sector-11 GH-4, Gandhinagar, 382 010, India
Tel.: (91) 7923256766
Web Site:
https://www.gsfc.gujarat.gov.in
Year Founded: 1960
532160—(BOM)
Rev.: $1,722,060
Assets: $404,168,496
Liabilities: $360,156,088
Net Worth: $44,012,408
Earnings: ($15,004,967)
Emp.: 24
Fiscal Year-end: 03/31/23
Financial Support Services
N.A.I.C.S.: 523999
Mamta Verma *(Mng Dir)*

GUJARAT STATE PETROLEUM CORPORATION LIMITED
GSPC Bhavan Sector 11, Gandhinagar, 382010, Gujarat, India
Tel.: (91) 7966701005 In
Web Site: http://www.gspcgroup.com
Sales Range: $600-649.9 Million
Holding Company; Petroleum & Natural Gas Exploration, Production & Distribution
N.A.I.C.S.: 551112
Sandeep Dave *(Officer-Compliance, Sec & Gen Mgr-Secretarial, Legal, HR & Comm)*

Subsidiaries:
GSPC LNG Limited (1)
B-103 Tower 2 Infocity, Gandhinagar, 382 009, Gujarat, India
Tel.: (91) 79 66708083
Natural Gas Distr
N.A.I.C.S.: 221210
D. J. Pandian *(Chm)*

GSPC Pipavav Power Company Limited (1)
Block No 15 3rd floor Udyog Bhavan Sector-11, Gandhinagar, 382011, Gujarat, India
Tel.: (91) 79 66701340
Web Site: http://www.gppc.co.in
Oil & Gas Exploration Services
N.A.I.C.S.: 211120
D. J. Pandian *(Sec)*

Guj Info Petro Limited (1)
3rd Floor Block-15 Udhyog Bhavan, Gandhinagar, 382011, India
Tel.: (91) 79 66701240
Web Site: http://www.gipl.in
Software Development Services
N.A.I.C.S.: 541511
Sudhir Mittal *(CEO)*

Gujarat Energy Research and Management Institute (1)
Block No 15 2nd Floor Udyong Bhavan Sector-11, Gandhinagar, 382011, Gujarat, India
Tel.: (91) 79 66701362
Web Site: http://www.germi.org
Oil & Gas Exploration, Research & Development Services
N.A.I.C.S.: 213112
Shri D.J. Pandian *(Vice Chm)*

Gujarat Gas Limited (1)
2 Shanti Sadan Society, Near Parimal Garden Ellisbridge, Ahmedabad, 380006, Gujarat, India (100%)
Tel.: (91) 7926462980
Web Site: www.gujaratgas.com
Rev.: $1,380,894,060
Assets: $1,157,483,145
Liabilities: $541,655,205
Net Worth: $615,827,940
Earnings: $174,408,780
Emp.: 1,050
Fiscal Year-end: 03/31/2021
Natural Gas Distribution Services
N.A.I.C.S.: 221210
Rajeshwari Sharma *(Officer-Compliance & Sec)*

GUJARAT TERCE LABORATORIES LIMITED
D/ 801 802 The First Behind Keshavbaug Party Plot, Near Shivalik High-Street Vastrapur, Ahmedabad, 380015, Gujarat, India
Tel.: (91) 9016093394
Web Site: https://www.gujaratterce.in
524314—(BOM)
Rev.: $5,520,019
Assets: $3,738,803
Liabilities: $2,573,871
Net Worth: $1,164,932
Earnings: $119,069
Emp.: 365
Fiscal Year-end: 03/31/22
Pharmaceutical Product Mfr & Distr
N.A.I.C.S.: 325412
Natwarbhai Purshottamdas Prajapati *(Founder, Chm, CEO & Mng Dir)*

GUJARAT THEMIS BIOSYN LIMITED
Themis House 11/12 Udyog Nagar SV Road, Goregaon West, Mumbai, 400 104, Maharashtra, India
Tel.: (91) 2267607080
Web Site: https://www.gtbl.in
Year Founded: 1981
506879—(BOM)
Rev.: $16,230,396
Assets: $16,721,359
Liabilities: $2,617,988
Net Worth: $14,103,371
Earnings: $5,954,703
Emp.: 105
Fiscal Year-end: 03/31/22
Pharmaceutical Preparation Mfr
N.A.I.C.S.: 325412
Dinesh Shantilal Patel *(Chm)*

GUJARAT TOOLROOM LIMITED
404 - 4th floor Samarth Co Op H Soc Nr Silicon Tower Nr Law Garden, Ahmedabad, 380006, India
Tel.: (91) 7227013356
Web Site:
https://www.gujarattoolroom.com
Year Founded: 1983
513337—(BOM)
Rev.: $290,150
Assets: $913,075
Liabilities: $151,346
Net Worth: $761,729
Earnings: $166,357
Fiscal Year-end: 03/31/23
Syringe Molding Mfr
N.A.I.C.S.: 333511
Vishal M. Shah *(Chm & Mng Dir)*

GUJCHEM DISTILLERIES INDIA LTD.
307 Third Floor Ashirwad Paras-1 Kanti Bharwad PMT, Opposite Andaz Party Plot Makarba, Ahmedabad, 380020, Gujarat, India
Tel.: (91) 9998860235
Web Site: https://gujchemdistillers.in
Year Founded: 1911
506640—(BOM)
Rev.: $34,524
Assets: $1,968,843
Liabilities: $1,444,302
Net Worth: $524,542
Earnings: $4,294
Emp.: 3
Fiscal Year-end: 03/31/23
Chemical Products Mfr
N.A.I.C.S.: 325199
Rajasvee Sagar Shah *(Chm & Mng Dir)*

GUJCHEM DISTILLERS INDIA LIMITED
National Chambers 2nd Floor Office No 6 Ashram Road, Ahmedabad, 380009, India
Tel.: (91) 79 2658 0893
Web Site:
http://www.gujchemdistillers.com
Sales Range: Less than $1 Million
Industrial Chemicals Mfr
N.A.I.C.S.: 325998
Hem Manish *(Mng Dir)*

GUK-FALZMASCHINEN GRIESSER & KUNZMANN GMBH & CO. KG
Bahnhofstr 4, 78669, Rottweil, Germany
Tel.: (49) 74267031
Web Site: http://www.guk-falzmaschinen.com
Year Founded: 1948
Sales Range: $25-49.9 Million
Emp.: 205
Folding Machines Mfr
N.A.I.C.S.: 333243
Ilse Reger *(Gen Mgr)*

GUL AHMED TEXTILE MILLS LTD.
Plot NoH-7 Landhi Industrial Area, Karachi, 75120, Pakistan
Tel.: (92) 21111486486
Web Site: https://www.gulahmed.com
GATM—(PSX)
Rev.: $499,789,309
Assets: $480,776,690
Liabilities: $327,646,804
Net Worth: $153,129,886
Earnings: $17,618,722
Emp.: 15,624
Fiscal Year-end: 06/30/23
Cotton & Fibre Mfr
N.A.I.C.S.: 313210
Mohammad Zaki Bashir *(CEO)*

GUL AHMED TEXTILE MILLS LTD.

Gul Ahmed Textile Mills Ltd.—(Continued)

Subsidiaries:

GTM (Europe) Limited (1)
Grane Road Mill Grane Road, Devonshire Street North, Haslingden, BB4 5ES, United Kingdom
Tel.: (44) 1612760882
Sales Range: $50-74.9 Million
Emp.: 5
Textile Distr
N.A.I.C.S.: 424310

GTM USA Corp. (1)
295 Bldg 5th Ave Ste 702, New York, NY 10016
Tel.: (212) 239-2700
Clothing Mfr
N.A.I.C.S.: 313310

Gul Ahmed International Limited FZC (1)
PO Box 8705, Sharjah Airport International Free Zone, Q4-029, Sharjah, United Arab Emirates
Tel.: (971) 65579483
Clothing Mfr
N.A.I.C.S.: 313310

GUL TECHNOLOGIES SINGAPORE LTD.

38 Jalan Pemimpin 07-08, Singapore, 577178, Singapore
Tel.: (65) 6861 6522   SG
Web Site: http://www.gultech.com
Year Founded: 1988
Sales Range: $200-249.9 Million
Printed Circuit Board Mfr
N.A.I.C.S.: 334412
Enk Ee Tan *(Vice Chm)*

Subsidiaries:

Gultech International Pte Ltd (1)
38 Jalan Pemimpin 07-08, Singapore, 577178, Singapore
Tel.: (65) 68616522
Web Site: http://www.gultech.com
Holding Company
N.A.I.C.S.: 551112

Subsidiary (Non-US):

Gultech (Suzhou) Electronics Co., Ltd. (2)
80 Su Hong Xi Road Suzhou Industrial Park, Suzhou, 215021, Jiangsu, China
Tel.: (86) 51267671711
Web Site: http://www.gultech.com
Sales Range: $400-449.9 Million
Printed Circuit Board Mfr
N.A.I.C.S.: 334412

Gultech (Wuxi) Electronics Co., Ltd. (2)
32 Chun Hui Dong Road Xishan Economic Development Zone, Wuxi, Jiangsu, China
Tel.: (86) 51088666888
Printed Circuit Board Mfr
N.A.I.C.S.: 334412

GULER YATIRIM HOLDING A.S.

Buyukdere Street Levent Plaza Block No 173 Interior Door No 30, Esentepe District Maslak, Istanbul, Turkiye
Tel.: (90) 2122902590   TR
Web Site: https://www.gulerholding.com.tr
Year Founded: 2006
GLRYH—(IST)
Rev.: $11,654,998
Assets: $266,720,498
Liabilities: $84,593,342
Net Worth: $182,127,155
Earnings: $4,016,565
Fiscal Year-end: 12/31/23
Holding Company
N.A.I.C.S.: 551112
Murat Guler *(Chm)*

GULF & PACIFIC EQUITIES CORP.

1240 Bay Street Suite 800, Toronto, M5R 2A7, ON, Canada
Tel.: (416) 968-3337
Web Site: https://www.gpequities.com
Year Founded: 1998
GUF—(TSXV)
Rev.: $3,354,787
Assets: $39,036,193
Liabilities: $22,436,246
Net Worth: $16,599,948
Earnings: $877,158
Fiscal Year-end: 12/31/22
Shopping Centers Development Services
N.A.I.C.S.: 236220
Anthony J. Cohen *(Pres & CEO)*

GULF AGENCY COMPANY LTD.

Jebel Ali Free Zone, PO Box 18006, Dubai, United Arab Emirates
Tel.: (971) 48811411
Web Site: http://www.gac.com
Year Founded: 1956
Sales Range: $1-4.9 Billion
Emp.: 9,000
Shipping, Logistics & Marine Services
N.A.I.C.S.: 488510
Bjorn Engblom *(Co-Exec Chm)*

Subsidiaries:

GAC (POLAND) SP. Z.O.O. (1)
Ul Storrady Swietoslawy 1B / 56, Szczecin, 71-602, Poland
Tel.: (48) 91 487 3754
Web Site: http://www.gac.com
Freight Transportation Services
N.A.I.C.S.: 483111
Klaus Holmager *(Bus Mgr-Logistics Svcs)*

GAC (TAIWAN) LTD. (1)
9F No 328 Chang Chun Road 104, Taipei, 10487, Taiwan
Tel.: (886) 2 2546 6950
Web Site: http://www.gac.com
Freight Transportation Services
N.A.I.C.S.: 483111
Kenny So *(Mng Dir)*

GAC Bunker Fuels (1)
Office No 4001 Jumeirah Business Center 1, PO Box 17041, Jumeirah Lakes Towers Cluster G, Dubai, 17041, United Arab Emirates
Tel.: (971) 43943402
Web Site: http://www.gac.com
Sales Range: $25-49.9 Million
Emp.: 9
Bunker Fuel Distr
N.A.I.C.S.: 457210
Martyn McMahon *(Mgr-Global Comml)*

GAC CARGO SYSTEMS (MALAYSIA) SDN. BHD (1)
B-801-2 Tower 2 Wisma AmFirst Jalan SS 7/15, Kelana Jaya, 47301, Petaling Jaya, Selangor, Malaysia
Tel.: (60) 3 7492 1000
Web Site: http://www.gac.com
Freight Transportation Services
N.A.I.C.S.: 483111
Surend Ckunjambo *(Dir-Project Logistics)*

GAC Denmark A/S (1)
St Kongensgade 77, 1264, Copenhagen, Denmark
Tel.: (45) 33 74 75 15
Web Site: http://www.gac.com
Sales Range: $25-49.9 Million
Emp.: 10
Freight Transportation Services
N.A.I.C.S.: 483111
Erik Thomsen *(Mng Dir)*

GAC ENERGY and MARINE SERVICES LTD (1)
16200 Central Green Blvd, Houston, TX 77032
Tel.: (713) 660-1650
Sales Range: $25-49.9 Million
Emp.: 80
Freight Transportation Services

N.A.I.C.S.: 483111
Yalonda Henderson *(VP-Ops)*

GAC FORWARDING & SHIPPING (SHANGHAI) LTD (1)
9F Hongyi Plaza 288 Jiujiang Road, Shanghai, 200001, China
Tel.: (86) 21 2310 8000
Web Site: http://www.gac.com
Emp.: 130
Freight Transportation Services
N.A.I.C.S.: 483111
Claus Schensema *(Mng Dir)*

GAC Ghana (1)
5th Floor Office & Retail Complex Movenpick Ambassador Hotel Ridge, PO Box CT8475, Accra, Ghana
Tel.: (233) 302 632184
Web Site: http://www.gac.com
Sales Range: $25-49.9 Million
Emp.: 5
Freight Transportation Services
N.A.I.C.S.: 483111
Neale Proctor *(Mng Dir)*

GAC Kazakhstan LLP (1)
19 Al-Farabi Avenue Business Centre Nurly Tau Almaty Building 1-B, Office 202, Almaty, 50059, Kazakhstan
Tel.: (7) 27 311 0590
Web Site: http://www.gac.com
Sales Range: $25-49.9 Million
Emp.: 6
Freight Transportation Services
N.A.I.C.S.: 483111
Jan Jiyenkulov *(Gen Dir)*

GAC LASER INTERNATIONAL LOGISTICS (PTY) LIMITED (1)
2 Baker Street Montague Gardens, Cape Town, 7447, South Africa
Tel.: (27) 21 528 3700
Web Site: http://www.gac.com
Sales Range: $25-49.9 Million
Emp.: 50
Freight Transportation Services
N.A.I.C.S.: 483111
Simon Hayes *(CEO)*

GAC LOGISTICS (UK) LTD (1)
Argonaut Park Galleymead Road, Colnbrook, Slough, SL3 0EN, United Kingdom
Tel.: (44) 1753 671671
Web Site: http://www.gac.com
Freight Transportation Services
N.A.I.C.S.: 483111
Herman Jorgensen *(Mng Dir-Grangemouth)*

GAC MARINE (1)
Mir 4 1958 Andaliba Street 70 Business Centre 405 4th floor, Ashgabat, 744017, Turkmenistan
Tel.: (993) 12 474 390
Web Site: http://www.gac.com
Freight Transportation Services
N.A.I.C.S.: 483111
Bayli Annakurbanov *(Mgr-Ops)*

GAC MARINE L.L.C. (1)
ICAD Industrial City of Abu Dhabi Zones Corp Sector M-41 Plot 29/30/31, PO Box 8101, Mussafah, Abu Dhabi, United Arab Emirates
Tel.: (971) 25014900
Web Site: http://www.gac.com
Freight Transportation Services
N.A.I.C.S.: 483111
Johan Fulke *(Mng Dir)*

GAC MARINE LOGISTICS INC. (1)
40th Floor Jumeirah Business Center 1 Jumeirah Lakes Towers, PO Box 17041, Dubai, 17041, United Arab Emirates
Tel.: (971) 4 435 3200
Web Site: http://www.gac.com
Sales Range: $25-49.9 Million
Emp.: 23
Freight Transportation Services
N.A.I.C.S.: 483111
Jan Kielmann *(Mng Dir)*

GAC NETHERLANDS LTD (1)
Sluisjesdijk 155, 3087 AG, Rotterdam, Netherlands
Tel.: (31) 10 495 1177
Web Site: http://www.gac.com
Sales Range: $25-49.9 Million
Emp.: 35
Freight Transportation Services
N.A.I.C.S.: 483111

INTERNATIONAL PUBLIC

Raymon Groen *(Sr Coord-Customs Clearance)*

GAC NORWAY AS (1)
Skoltegrunnskaien 1, Bergen, 5003, Norway
Tel.: (47) 99 202 560
Web Site: http://www.gac.com
Freight Transportation Services
N.A.I.C.S.: 483111
Ahmet Ozsoy *(Mng Dir)*

GAC Philippines, Inc (1)
7/F F&M Lopez Building II 109 Carlos Palanca St Legaspi Village, Makati, 1229, Metro Manila, Philippines
Tel.: (63) 2 892 2713
Web Site: http://www.gac.com
Emp.: 63
Freight Transportation Services
N.A.I.C.S.: 483111
Jake Cuerva *(Pres & Mng Dir)*

GAC SERVICES (JAPAN) LIMITED (1)
2-9-2 Higashi-Shinbashi, Minato-ku, Tokyo, 105-0021, Japan
Tel.: (81) 3 6450 1712
Web Site: http://www.gac.com
Emp.: 6
Freight Transportation Distr
N.A.I.C.S.: 483111
Yuichi Adachi *(Mgr-Mktg-Shipping)*

GAC SHIPPING (INDIA) PVT. LTD. (1)
GAC House Subramanian Road Willingdon Island, Kochi, 682003, India
Tel.: (91) 484 266 8372
Web Site: http://www.gac.com
Sales Range: $25-49.9 Million
Emp.: 50
Freight Transportation Services
N.A.I.C.S.: 483111
Roy Mathews *(Chm)*

GAC SHIPPING (S.A.) (PTY) LIMITED (1)
Fairweather House 176 Sir Lowry Rd, Cape Town, 8001, South Africa
Tel.: (27) 21 464 9700
Web Site: http://www.gac.com
Emp.: 18
Freight Transportation Services
N.A.I.C.S.: 483111
David Hitchman *(Mng Dir)*

GAC SHIPPING AND LOGISTICS LIMITED (1)
Office 5150 17 Butlerova str, 117342, Moscow, Russia
Tel.: (7) 4957480288
Web Site: http://www.gac.com
Sales Range: $25-49.9 Million
Emp.: 4
Freight Transportation Services
N.A.I.C.S.: 483111
Arkady Podkopaev *(Gen Mgr)*

GAC SHIPPING LIMITED (1)
284 Vauxhall Street, Colombo, 200, Sri Lanka
Tel.: (94) 114 797 900
Web Site: http://www.gac.com
Sales Range: $125-149.9 Million
Emp.: 350
Freight Transportation Services
N.A.I.C.S.: 483111
Preethilal Fernando *(CEO)*

GAC SHIPPING SA (1)
3 Konstantinou Paleologou Street, 185 35, Piraeus, Greece
Tel.: (30) 210 414 0400
Web Site: http://www.gac.com
Emp.: 70
Freight Transportation Services
N.A.I.C.S.: 483111
Constantinos Mouskos *(Gen Mgr)*

GAC SHIPPING SERVICES (NIGERIA) LTD. (1)
33A Marine Road, Lagos, Nigeria
Tel.: (234) 1 764 1303
Web Site: http://www.gac.com
Sales Range: $50-74.9 Million
Emp.: 200
Freight Transportation Services
N.A.I.C.S.: 483111
Robert Bal *(Mng Dir)*

AND PRIVATE COMPANIES

GAC Shipping (USA) Inc. (1)
250 Industrial Rd, Pascagoula, MS 39581
Tel.: (228) 712-9995
Sales Range: $25-49.9 Million
Emp.: 15
Freight Transportation Services
N.A.I.C.S.: 483111

GAC Sweden AB (1)
Lila Bommen 2, PO Box 11345, 40 427, Gothenburg, Sweden
Tel.: (46) 31 703 7800
Web Site: http://www.gac.com
Freight Transportation Services
N.A.I.C.S.: 483111
Ingela Berntson (Gen Mgr)

GAC TRANSFER SERVICES S.A. (1)
GAC Logistics Park Building CDC-1 Jebel Ali Free Zone, PO Box 29857, Dubai, United Arab Emirates
Tel.: (971) 4 881 1657
Web Site: http://www.ship-to-ship.com
Sales Range: $25-49.9 Million
Emp.: 5
Freight Transportation Services
N.A.I.C.S.: 483111
Ray Taylor (Gen Mgr)

GAC USA (1)
1 International Plz Ste 250, Philadelphia, PA 19113-1537
Tel.: (484) 953-3310
Web Site: http://www.gac.com
Emp.: 15
Freight Transportation Distr
N.A.I.C.S.: 483111
Darren Martin (Mng Dir-Shipping-North America)

GAC do Brasil Ltda (1)
Rua Dr Bacelar 368-3 Andar Vila Clementino, Sao Paulo, 04026-001, Brazil
Tel.: (55) 1150833999
Web Site: http://www.gac.com
Sales Range: $25-49.9 Million
Emp.: 50
Freight Transportation Services
N.A.I.C.S.: 483111
Rodrigo De Marco (Mng Dir)

GAC-Nurminen Navis Oy (1)
Pasilankatu 2, PO Box 505, Helsinki, 00241, Finland
Tel.: (358) 10 545 8800
Web Site: http://www.gac.com
Freight Forwarding Services
N.A.I.C.S.: 488510
Svante Eriksson (Mng Dir)

GULF AGENCY CO. (BAHRAIN) W.L.L. (1)
Office No 21 Building No 23Road 20 GLS Premises, PO Box 412, Muharraq, 224, Bahrain
Tel.: (973) 17 339 777
Web Site: http://www.gac.com
Sales Range: $50-74.9 Million
Emp.: 130
Freight Transportation Services
N.A.I.C.S.: 483111
Anil Kumar (Sr Mgr-Shipping)

GULF AGENCY CO. SHARJAH W.L.L. (1)
Al Ghanem Bussiness Centre 11Th Floor 1109, Corner of Al Arouba & Al Khan, Sharjah, 435, United Arab Emirates
Tel.: (971) 6 528 0070
Web Site: http://www.gac.com
Sales Range: $25-49.9 Million
Emp.: 60
Freight Transportation Services
N.A.I.C.S.: 483111
Pradeep Kumar (Gen Mgr)

GULF AGENCY COMPANY (AUSTRALIA) PTY LTD (1)
123 Clarence Street Suite 18 & 19 2F, Sydney, 2000, NSW, Australia
Tel.: (61) 2 8028 2400
Web Site: http://www.gac.com
Freight Forwarding Services
N.A.I.C.S.: 488510
Scott Henderson (Mng Dir)

GULF AGENCY COMPANY (CYPRUS) LTD (1)
83 Franklin Roosevelt Avenue, PO Box 51141, Limassol, 3502, Cyprus
Tel.: (357) 25 209 100
Web Site: http://www.gac.com
Sales Range: $25-49.9 Million
Emp.: 30
Freight Transportation Services
N.A.I.C.S.: 483111
Demetris Mouskos (Mng Dir)

GULF AGENCY COMPANY (EGYPT) LTD (1)
Villa No1 El Musheir Ahmed Ismail Street, Sheraton Heliopolis District, Cairo, Egypt
Tel.: (20) 2 2268 6230
Web Site: http://www.gac.com
Emp.: 300
Freight Transportation Services
N.A.I.C.S.: 483111
Mohammed Badawi (Mng Dir)

GULF AGENCY COMPANY (FUJAIRAH) PVT. WLL. (1)
Port of Fujairah, PO Box 590, Fujairah, United Arab Emirates
Tel.: (971) 92013501
Web Site: http://www.gac.com
Sales Range: $25-49.9 Million
Emp.: 50
Freight Transportation Services
N.A.I.C.S.: 483111
Ingemar Porathe (Gen Mgr-Shipping)

GULF AGENCY COMPANY (HONG KONG) LTD. (1)
12/F SML Tower 165 Hoi Bun Road, Kwun Tong, Kowloon, China (Hong Kong)
Tel.: (852) 2723 6306
Web Site: http://www.gac.com
Sales Range: $25-49.9 Million
Emp.: 70
Freight Transportation Services
N.A.I.C.S.: 483111
Alwyn Mendonca (Mng Dir)

GULF AGENCY COMPANY (JORDAN) LTD (1)
Isshakat Center 2nd Floor Mecca Street, PO Box 940173, Amman, 11194, Jordan
Tel.: (962) 6 580 8000
Web Site: http://www.gac.com
Emp.: 26
Freight Transportation Services
N.A.I.C.S.: 483111
Ghassoub Kawar (Mng Dir)

GULF AGENCY COMPANY (OMAN) L.L.C (1)
GAC Building Dohat Al Adab Street, Al Khuwair, Muscat, 112, Oman
Tel.: (968) 2447 7800
Web Site: http://www.gacworld.com
Sales Range: $125-149.9 Million
Emp.: 289
Freight Transportation Services
N.A.I.C.S.: 483111
Martyn McMahon (Mgr-Global Comml)

GULF AGENCY COMPANY (RAS AL KHAIMAH) L.L.C. (1)
GAC Building Al Muntaser Road Al Nakheel, PO Box 5162, Ras al Khaimah, 5162, United Arab Emirates
Tel.: (971) 7 227 2111
Web Site: http://www.gac.com
Sales Range: $25-49.9 Million
Emp.: 29
Freight Transportation Services
N.A.I.C.S.: 483111
Rajesh Moorjani (Gen Mgr)

GULF AGENCY COMPANY QATAR (W.L.L.) (1)
Standard Chartered Building 6th Floor Abdulla Bin Jassim Street, PO Box 6534, Doha, Qatar
Tel.: (974) 4420 5600
Web Site: http://www.gac.com
Freight Transportation Services
N.A.I.C.S.: 483111
Mikko Wieru (Gen Mgr)

GULF AGENCY COMPANY SAUDI ARABIA (1)
A H Algosaibi Building Opposite Dammam Sheraton Hotel Prince Mohammad, PO Box 335, Bin Fahd Street, Dammam, 31411, Saudi Arabia
Tel.: (966) 3 832 8762
Web Site: http://www.gac.com
Freight Transportation Services
N.A.I.C.S.: 483111
Gaurika Gurugamage (Asst Mgr-Ops-Offshore Projects)

GULF AGENCY DENIZCILIK A.S. (1)
Ataturk Bulvari Kordon Apt No 73 Kat1 No 1, Iskenderun, Türkiye
Tel.: (90) 3266139180
Web Site: http://www.gac.com
Sales Range: $50-74.9 Million
Emp.: 150
Freight Transportation Distr
N.A.I.C.S.: 483111
Raymond Makzume (Mng Dir)

NATIONAL SHIPPING GULF AGENCY COMPANY (ABU DHABI) LTD. L.L.C. (1)
Plot 211 Freeport Area, PO Box 377, Mina Zayed, Abu Dhabi, United Arab Emirates
Tel.: (971) 2 673 0500
Web Site: http://www.gac.com
Emp.: 200
Freight Transportation Services
N.A.I.C.S.: 483111
Ronnie Knowles (Mng Dir)

GULF AIR COMPANY B.S.C.
Gulf Air Bldg, Bahrain Intl Airport, Manama, 973, Bahrain
Tel.: (973) 17322200
Web Site: http://www.gulfair.com
Sales Range: $650-699.9 Million
Emp.: 5,000
Scheduled Air Transportation
N.A.I.C.S.: 481111
Hussain Abdul Rahman (Country Mgr)

Subsidiaries:

Gulf Air (1)
2603 Agusta Dr Ste 730, Houston, TX 77027-6495
Tel.: (713) 621-2771
Provider of Commercial Air Line Services
N.A.I.C.S.: 481111
Waleed Abdul Hameed Al Alawi (Deputy CEO)

GULF BANK K.S.C.P.
Mubarak Al Kabeer Street, PO Box 3200, Safat, 13032, Kuwait, 13032, Kuwait
Tel.: (965) 22449501 KW
Web Site: https://www.e-gulfbank.com
Year Founded: 1960
GBK—(KUW)
Rev.: $556,834,514
Assets: $21,466,540,586
Liabilities: $19,284,192,511
Net Worth: $2,182,348,075
Earnings: $137,867,770
Emp.: 1,506
Fiscal Year-end: 12/31/21
Banking Services
N.A.I.C.S.: 522110
Jasem Mustafa Boodai (Chm)

GULF BUSINESS MACHINES EC
MS Center 5th Floor Building 22 Avenue 58, PO Box 10554, Al Seef District, Manama, 436, Bahrain
Tel.: (973) 17584333
Web Site: http://www.gbm4ibm.com
Year Founded: 1990
Sales Range: $125-149.9 Million
Emp.: 850
Information Technology Solutions & Services
N.A.I.C.S.: 541512
Andreas Weiss (VP-Platforms Solutions-Dubai)

Subsidiaries:

GBM Pakistan Pvt. Ltd. (1)
Office 3-A 2nd Floor Khyber Plaza Fazal-e-Haq Road Blue Area, Islamabad, Pakistan
Tel.: (92) 51 2804391
Information Technology Consulting Services
N.A.I.C.S.: 541512
Rabika Meer (Mgr-Ops)

Gulf Business Machines (GBM) L.L.C. (1)
4th & 5th Floors Bin Hamoodah Golden Tower, PO Box 203, Khalifa Street, Abu Dhabi, United Arab Emirates
Tel.: (971) 26275165
Web Site: http://www.gbm4ibm.com
Sales Range: $50-74.9 Million
Emp.: 90
Computer Component Distr
N.A.I.C.S.: 423430

Gulf Business Machines (Oman) Co. L.L.C. (1)
PO Box 1476, Muttrah, 114, Oman
Tel.: (968) 567171
Web Site: http://www.ibm.com
Sales Range: $25-49.9 Million
Emp.: 35
Computer Component Distr
N.A.I.C.S.: 423430
Iyad Al Chammat (Country Gen Mgr)

Gulf Business Machines B.S.C. (C) (1)
Emarat Atrium Building Block B 3rd floor Sheikh Zayed Road, Dubai, United Arab Emirates
Tel.: (971) 43435353
Information Technology Consulting Services
N.A.I.C.S.: 541512
Miguel Khouri (Gen Mgr)

Gulf Business Machines Personal Systems Division (1)
Yellow Shed WB 4, PO Box 16829, Jebel Ali, United Arab Emirates
Tel.: (971) 48835652
Web Site: http://www.gbmme.com
Sales Range: $25-49.9 Million
Emp.: 18
Computer Component Distr
N.A.I.C.S.: 423430
Akram Ayyad (Gen Mgr)

Gulf Business Machines W.L.L. (1)
Al Dana Tower 6th Floor West Bay, PO Box 9307, Doha, Qatar
Tel.: (974) 44073111
Information Technology Consulting Services
N.A.I.C.S.: 541512
Syed Sharfuddin (Acct Mgr-Mktg)

GULF CABLE & ELECTRICAL INDUSTRIES CO. K.S.C.
Sulaibiya Area No 1 Khalaf Al-Ahmar Street Opposite to KPTC Warehouse, Sulaibiya Industrial Area, Kuwait, Kuwait
Tel.: (965) 24645500
Web Site: https://www.gulfcable.com
CABLE—(KUW)
Rev.: $249,337,600
Assets: $663,968,230
Liabilities: $53,950,623
Net Worth: $610,017,606
Earnings: $18,208,087
Emp.: 712
Fiscal Year-end: 12/31/20
Electrical Cables Mfr & Supplier
N.A.I.C.S.: 335921
Asaad Ahmad Omran Al-Banwan (Vice Chm)

Subsidiaries:

Care for Buildings and Cities Cleaning Contracting Company - WLL (1)
Block 1 Alsoor St Jasem Tower 13th Floor, Mirqab, Kuwait, Kuwait
Tel.: (965) 22960660
Web Site: https://www.care-kw.com
Cleaning Service
N.A.I.C.S.: 561720

GULF CAPITAL PJSC
Level 6-West Tower Abu Dhabi Mall,

GULF CAPITAL PJSC

Gulf Capital PJSC—(Continued)
PO Box 27522, Abu Dhabi, 27522, United Arab Emirates
Tel.: (971) 26716060   AE
Web Site: http://www.gulfcapital.com
Year Founded: 2006
Sales Range: $25-49.9 Million
Emp.: 80
Investment Management Service
N.A.I.C.S.: 523940
Kenneth A. Himmel *(Mng Partner)*

Subsidiaries:

Eclat Health Solutions Inc. (1)
4229 Lafayette Centre Dr Ste 1750, Chantilly, VA 20151-1269
Tel.: (703) 665-4499
Web Site: http://www.eclathealthsolutions.com
Scientific & Technical Consulting Services
N.A.I.C.S.: 541690
Jerry Jorgensen *(VP-Ops)*

GULF CEMENT COMPANY P.S.C.
PO Box 5295, Ras al Khaimah, United Arab Emirates
Tel.: (971) 72668222
Web Site: https://gulfcement.ae
Year Founded: 1977
GCEM—(ABU)
Rev.: $125,978,794
Assets: $230,231,336
Liabilities: $81,010,912
Net Worth: $149,220,424
Earnings: ($14,046,267)
Emp.: 500
Fiscal Year-end: 12/31/23
Cement Mfr
N.A.I.C.S.: 327310
Kayed Omar Saqer Mohamed Al-Qassimi *(Chm)*

GULF COMMERCIAL BANK
Al-Saadoun Street opposite to Al-Alawiyya Exchange, PO Box 3101, Baghdad, Iraq
Tel.: (964) 6868
Web Site: https://www.gcb.iq
Year Founded: 1999
BGUC—(IRAQ)
Rev.: $4,568,242
Assets: $349,896,824
Liabilities: $139,483,928
Net Worth: $210,412,896
Earnings: ($1,012)
Emp.: 384
Fiscal Year-end: 12/31/20
Commercial Banking Services
N.A.I.C.S.: 522110
Mohammed Saleh Fraaj *(Vice Chm)*

GULF CONSOLIDATED CONTRACTORS CO. LTD.
Automoto Mall Building-B Al-Khobar-Dammam Coastal Highway, PO Box 895, Dammam, 31421, Saudi Arabia
Tel.: (966) 138457777
Web Site: http://www.gccksa.com
Year Founded: 2006
Sales Range: $800-899.9 Million
Emp.: 4,000
Construction Contractors for Industrial Plants & Pipelines
N.A.I.C.S.: 237120
Aiman Rateb Mihyar *(CEO)*

GULF CORPORATION FOR TECHNOLOGY
Building 2038 Rd 4156 Block 341, Manama, Bahrain
Tel.: (973) 17239399
Web Site: http://www.gctbahrain.com
Year Founded: 1945
Sales Range: $10-24.9 Million
Emp.: 65

Pharmaceutical Products Sales & Distr; Medical, Scientific, Educational & Industrial Equipment & Supplies Sales & Distr
N.A.I.C.S.: 456110
Khalid B. Al Awadhi *(Chm & CEO)*

GULF ENERGY DEVELOPMENT PUBLIC COMPANY LIMITED
87 M Thai Tower Building All Seasons Place 11th Floor Witthayu Road, Lumphini Subdistrict Pathumwan District, Bangkok, 10330, Thailand
Tel.: (66) 20804499   TH
Web Site: https://www.gulf.co.th
Year Founded: 2011
GULF—(THA)
Rev.: $3,329,473,813
Assets: $13,414,123,775
Liabilities: $9,207,430,771
Net Worth: $4,206,693,005
Earnings: $584,267,300
Emp.: 1,212
Fiscal Year-end: 12/31/23
Eletric Power Generation Services
N.A.I.C.S.: 221118
Tanon Tantisunthorn *(Chief Corp Affairs Officer)*

GULF FRANCHISING HOLDING COMPANY K.S.C.C.
Al Sharqiya Tower 7th Floor Jaber Al Mubarak Street Block 2 Plot 7, PO Box 21839, Sharq, Kuwait, 13079, Kuwait
Tel.: (965) 22260449
Web Site: https://www.gfc.com.kw
Year Founded: 2001
GFC—(KUW)
Rev.: $10,624,279
Assets: $25,336,841
Liabilities: $18,409,917
Net Worth: $6,926,925
Earnings: ($958,224)
Emp.: 548
Fiscal Year-end: 12/31/21
Franchise Developer
N.A.I.C.S.: 561499

Subsidiaries:

Beit Dickson KSCC (1)
Hamad Al Mubarak street Block 7, Ras Salmiyah, Kuwait
Tel.: (965) 1858888
Pet Food Mfr
N.A.I.C.S.: 311119

Bon Sweets WLL (1)
Al Sharqiya Tower 7th Floor Jaber Al Mubarak Street Block 2 Plot 7, Al-Sharq, Kuwait
Tel.: (965) 1856666
Pet Food Mfr
N.A.I.C.S.: 311119

Computer Troubleshooters W.L.L. (1)
Sharq Ahmed Al Jaber St Al Diera Tower, PO Box 21839, Safat, 13079, Kuwait
Tel.: (965) 22459037
Web Site: https://www.cts.com.kw
Information Technology Consulting Services
N.A.I.C.S.: 541512

GULF GENERAL COOPERATIVE INSURANCE COMPANY
No 7698 Prince Al-Shuara st Al-Ruwais District Unit10, PO Box 1866, Jeddah, 21441, Saudi Arabia
Tel.: (966) 920012654
Web Site: https://www.ggi-sa.com
Year Founded: 2009
8260—(SAU)
Rev.: $68,978,003
Assets: $160,648,180
Liabilities: $89,293,428
Net Worth: $71,354,753
Earnings: ($27,780,296)
Emp.: 230

Fiscal Year-end: 12/31/22
Insurance Management Services
N.A.I.C.S.: 524298
Jamal Abdullah Al Dabbagh *(Chm)*

GULF GENERAL INVESTMENT COMPANY PSC
Al Fattan Plaza Building 4th Floor Airport Road, PO Box 22588, Dubai, United Arab Emirates
Tel.: (971) 42821888
Web Site: http://www.ggicouae.com
Year Founded: 1973
Rev.: $144,996,195
Assets: $1,342,000,200
Liabilities: $1,237,254,064
Net Worth: $104,746,136
Earnings: ($43,035,584)
Fiscal Year-end: 12/31/19
Real Estate Investment Services
N.A.I.C.S.: 531390
Majid Abdalla Juma Al Sari *(Vice Chm)*

Subsidiaries:

Dubai Al Ahlia Transport L.L.C (1)
PO Box 13408, Dubai, United Arab Emirates
Tel.: (971) 43408403
Web Site: http://www.date-dxb.com
Sales Range: $125-149.9 Million
Emp.: 286
Petroleum & Chemical Products Trucking Services
N.A.I.C.S.: 484230
P. K. Sunil *(Mgr-Maintenance)*

Gulf Dura Industries L.L.C (1)
PO Box 233249, Dubai, United Arab Emirates
Tel.: (971) 42578070
Web Site: http://www.gulfdura.com
Electro Mechanical Construction Materials Distr
N.A.I.C.S.: 423610

Gulf General Investment Company PSC - Real Estate Division (1)
Al Fattan Plz Bldg 3 Fl 313, Dubai, 22588, United Arab Emirates
Tel.: (971) 42821888
Sales Range: $25-49.9 Million
Emp.: 30
Real Estate Property Rental Services
N.A.I.C.S.: 531190

Gulf Prefab Houses Factory Ltd. (1)
PO Box 6058, Sharjah, United Arab Emirates
Tel.: (971) 65387993
Web Site: http://www.gulfab.com
Prefabricated Wood Building Mfr
N.A.I.C.S.: 321992

Horizon Metallic Industries L.L.C (1)
Third Indus St Indus Area 6, PO Box 33383, Near Gargash Enterprises, Sharjah, United Arab Emirates
Tel.: (971) 65441160
Sales Range: $25-49.9 Million
Emp.: 33
Steel Drums Mfr & Distr
N.A.I.C.S.: 332439

Lloyds Engineering Co. L.L.C (1)
PO Box 47337, Dubai, United Arab Emirates
Tel.: (971) 42591856
Web Site: http://www.lloydsengg.com
Sales Range: $25-49.9 Million
Emp.: 60
Steel Fabrication Services
N.A.I.C.S.: 332312
A. G. Rajesh *(Mng Dir)*

Middle East World Factories Equipment L.L.C (1)
Indus Area 11, PO Box 34203, Sharjah, United Arab Emirates
Tel.: (971) 65348088
Web Site: http://www.meequip.com
Sales Range: $25-49.9 Million
Emp.: 30
Industrial Machinery Retailer
N.A.I.C.S.: 423830

INTERNATIONAL PUBLIC

GULF GLASS FIBER TECHNOLOGICAL INDUSTRIES COMPANY
PO Box 11844, PO Box 11844, Al Jubayl, 31961, Saudi Arabia
Tel.: (966) 33586040
Web Site: http://www.fiber-tec.com
Year Founded: 1996
Sales Range: $25-49.9 Million
Emp.: 65
Glass Fiber, PTFE Coated Membrane & Fabrics Mfr
N.A.I.C.S.: 327212
Thomas John Kambiyil *(Gen Mgr-Sls & Mktg)*

GULF GLASS MANUFACTURING CO. K.S.C.
Mina Abdullah, PO Box 26996, Safat, Kuwait, 13130, Kuwait
Tel.: (965) 22285552   KW
Web Site: http://www.ggmc.com.kw
Year Founded: 1981
Emp.: 500
Glass Products Mfr
N.A.I.C.S.: 327215
Hussain Al-Shaikh *(Vice Chm & CEO)*

GULF HOTELS (OMAN) COMPANY LIMITED SAOG
Al Qurum, PO Box 1455, 112, Ruwi, Oman
Tel.: (968) 24660660
Year Founded: 1977
GHOS—(MUS)
Rev.: $9,014,541
Assets: $78,140,707
Liabilities: $16,958,946
Net Worth: $61,181,762
Earnings: ($1,811,200)
Emp.: 160
Fiscal Year-end: 12/31/21
Home Management Services
N.A.I.C.S.: 721110
Ali Ahmed Abdullah Al Najjar *(Chm)*

GULF HOTELS GROUP B.S.C.
PO Box 580, Manama, Bahrain
Tel.: (973) 17746446   BH
Web Site: https://www.gulfhotelsgroup.com
Year Founded: 1967
GHG—(BAH)
Rev.: $95,190,881
Assets: $296,529,760
Liabilities: $21,728,692
Net Worth: $274,801,069
Earnings: $17,689,226
Emp.: 960
Fiscal Year-end: 12/31/22
Hotel & Restaurant Management Services
N.A.I.C.S.: 721110
Farouk Yousuf Almoayyed *(Chm)*

Subsidiaries:

Bahrain Tourism Company B.S.C. (1) (100%)
PO Box 5831, Manama, Bahrain
Tel.: (973) 17530530
Web Site: http://www.alseyaha.com
Sales Range: $10-24.9 Million
Hotel Management & Tour Operating Services
N.A.I.C.S.: 721110

GHG Colombo Pvt. Ltd. (1)
No 415/1/G Sirimavo Bandaranayake Mawatha, 14, Colombo, Sri Lanka
Tel.: (94) 112339546
Web Site: https://www.ghgcolombo.com
Alcoholic Beverage Distr
N.A.I.C.S.: 424820

Gulf Court Hotel Business Bay LLC (1)
Al Abraj Street Business Bay, PO Box

AND PRIVATE COMPANIES

32300, Dubai, United Arab Emirates
Tel.: (971) 42473333
Web Site:
  https://www.gulfcourthotelbusiness.com
Home Management Services
N.A.I.C.S.: 721110

Gulf Hotel Laundry Services W.L.L (1)
PO Box 580, Manama, Bahrain
Tel.: (973) 17746394
Web Site: https://ghlsbahrain.com
Laundry Services
N.A.I.C.S.: 812320

Hospitality Resources S.P.C. (1)
Office No 106A Gulf exe offices 10-th floor Bldg 14 Rd 3801 block 338, PO Box 2661, Al Qudaybiyah, Manama, 2661, Bahrain
Tel.: (973) 17 710 123
Web Site:
  http://www.hospitalityresources.com.bh
Emp.: 5
Kitchen Equipment Whslr
N.A.I.C.S.: 423440
Fabian Gill (Gen mgr)

GULF INSURANCE CO.
Dar Al-Salam Bld Saadoon St, Baghdad, Iraq
Tel.: (964) 7901493449
Year Founded: 2004
Insurance Management Services
N.A.I.C.S.: 524298

GULF INTERNATIONAL BANK B.S.C.
Al Dowali Bldg 3 Palace Ave, PO Box 1017, Manama, Bahrain
Tel.: (973) 17534000
Web Site: http://www.gibonline.com
Sales Range: $200-249.9 Million
Emp.: 600
Banking Services
N.A.I.C.S.: 522110
Antoine L. Dijkstra (Mng Dir & Chief Investment/Treasury Officer)

Subsidiaries:

GIB Capital LLC (1)
3rd Floor NCCI South Tower King Fahad Road, PO Box 89589, Riyadh, 11673, Saudi Arabia
Tel.: (966) 11 218 0555
Web Site: http://www.gibcapital.com
Investment Banking Services
N.A.I.C.S.: 523150
Abdulla Al Zamil (Chm)

Gulf International Bank (UK) Ltd. (1)
One Knightsbridge, London, SW1X 7XS, United Kingdom (100%)
Tel.: (44) 2072593456
Sales Range: $50-74.9 Million
Emp.: 80
Banking Services
N.A.I.C.S.: 522110
Mark Watts (CEO & Mng Dir)

GULF INTERNATIONAL CHEMICALS SAOG
Road No 7 Rusayl Industrial Estate, PO Box 68, Muhafazat Masqat, Muscat, Oman
Tel.: (968) 24446800
Web Site: https://www.gicoman.com
Year Founded: 1996
GICI—(MUS)
Rev.: $4,363,727
Assets: $7,840,492
Liabilities: $948,926
Net Worth: $6,891,566
Earnings: $49,752
Emp.: 9
Fiscal Year-end: 12/31/21
Construction Materials Supplier
N.A.I.C.S.: 423320
Ahmed Zaid Al Muhrami (Chm)

GULF INTERNATIONAL SERVICES QSC
6th Floor Tower 10, PO Box 3212, QatarEnergy District, Doha, Qatar
Tel.: (974) 40132088
Web Site: https://www.gis.com.qa
Year Founded: 2008
GISS—(QE)
Rev.: $648,454,961
Assets: $2,826,710,013
Liabilities: $1,774,563,291
Net Worth: $1,052,146,722
Earnings: $114,041,410
Emp.: 1,000
Fiscal Year-end: 12/31/23
Investment Services
N.A.I.C.S.: 523999
Khalid Khalifa Al-Thani (Chm)

Subsidiaries:

Al Koot Insurance & Reinsurance Company P.J.S.C. (1)
Building No- 44 Street No- 840 Al Rawabi St, Doha, Qatar
Tel.: (974) 40402999
Web Site: https://www.alkoot.com.qa
Insurance Services
N.A.I.C.S.: 524210
Abdulrahman Ali Al-Abdulla (Chm)

Gulf Drilling International Limited Q.S.C. (1)
The Gate Mall Tower 3 10th 11th 12th Floors Maysaloun Street, PO Box 9072, Doha, Qatar
Tel.: (974) 44637333
Web Site: http://www.gdi.com.qa
Drilling Services
N.A.I.C.S.: 213111
Khalid Sultan Al Kuwari (Vice Chm)

GULF INVESTMENT HOUSE K.S.C.P.
Jawharat Al Khaleej Building Floor 8 Fahad Al Salem Street, Jibla, Kuwait, Kuwait
Tel.: (965) 22008440 KW
Web Site: https://www.gih.com.kw
Year Founded: 1998
GIH—(KUW)
Rev.: $12,745,760
Assets: $174,383,847
Liabilities: $12,176,372
Net Worth: $162,207,475
Earnings: $4,188,618
Emp.: 12
Fiscal Year-end: 12/31/22
Investment Services
N.A.I.C.S.: 523999
Yasser A. Joma'a (Deputy CEO)

Subsidiaries:

Afkar Holding Co. (1)
Fahad Al-Salem Street, Kuwait, Kuwait
Tel.: (965) 22008451
Web Site: https://afkarholding.com
Tissue Paper Mfr & Distr
N.A.I.C.S.: 322291

GULF KEYSTONE PETROLEUM LIMITED
Cedar House 3rd Floor Cedar House 3rd Floor, Hamilton, HM12, Bermuda
Tel.: (441) 2954630
Web Site:
  https://www.gulfkeystone.com
GKP—(LSE)
Rev.: $460,113,000
Assets: $744,357,000
Liabilities: $171,432,000
Net Worth: $572,925,000
Earnings: $266,094,000
Emp.: 600
Fiscal Year-end: 12/31/22
Oil & Gas Exploration Services
N.A.I.C.S.: 211120
Stuart Catterall (COO)

Subsidiaries:

Gulf Keystone Petroleum (UK) Limited (1)
6th Floor New Fetter Place 8-10 New Fetter Lane, Mayfair, London, EC4A 1AZ, United Kingdom
Tel.: (44) 207 514 1400
Web Site: http://www.gulfkeystone.co.uk
Sales Range: $50-74.9 Million
Emp.: 30
Oil & Gas Exploration Services
N.A.I.C.S.: 213112

Gulf Keystone Petroleum International Ltd. (1)
3rd Floor UB Centre, Bakhtyari, Erbil, Kurdistan, Iraq
Tel.: (964) 750 755 3111
Oil & Gas Exploration Services
N.A.I.C.S.: 213112
Ross Deutscher (Country Mgr)

GULF MANGANESE CORPORATION LIMITED
T4/152 Great Eastern Highway Ascot, South Perth, 6104, WA, Australia
Tel.: (61) 8 9367 9228 AU
Web Site:
  http://www.gulfmanganese.com
Rev.: $88,009
Assets: $15,809,476
Liabilities: $8,210,439
Net Worth: $7,599,036
Earnings: ($5,828,357)
Fiscal Year-end: 06/30/18
Mineral Exploration Services
N.A.I.C.S.: 212290
Hamish Bohannan (CEO & Mng Dir)

GULF MARINE SERVICES PLC
Office 403 International Tower 24th Karama Street, PO Box 46046, Abu Dhabi, United Arab Emirates
Tel.: (971) 25028888
Web Site: https://www.gmsplc.com
Year Founded: 1977
GMS—(LSE)
Rev.: $151,603,000
Assets: $668,332,000
Liabilities: $338,051,000
Net Worth: $330,281,000
Earnings: $42,068,000
Emp.: 660
Fiscal Year-end: 12/31/23
Marine Freight & Logistics Services
N.A.I.C.S.: 541614
Mansour Al Alami (Chm)

Subsidiaries:

Gulf Marine Saudi Arabia Co. Limited (1)
Tel.: (966) 138064070
Oil & Gas Exploration Services
N.A.I.C.S.: 213112

GULF MARKETING & SERVICES COMPANY LLC
B62 Bldg Maktoum Street, Apt 210 PO Box 5830, Dubai, United Arab Emirates
Tel.: (971) 4 228 2101
Web Site: http://www.gmasco.com
Year Founded: 1970
Emp.: 110
N.A.I.C.S.: 541810
Charles Awad (Mng Dir)

GULF MEDICAL PROJECTS COMPANY PJSC
Al Wahda Street Industrial Area 4, PO Box 5398, Sharjah, United Arab Emirates
Tel.: (971) 65095555 AE
Web Site: https://www.gmpc.ae
Year Founded: 1979
GMPC—(ABU)
Rev.: $155,117,774
Assets: $370,335,485
Liabilities: $50,063,448
Net Worth: $320,272,037
Earnings: $20,484,710

Fiscal Year-end: 12/31/23
Health Care Srvices
N.A.I.C.S.: 622110
Faisal Al Qasimi (Chm)

GULF MUSHROOM PRODUCTS CO. SAOG
PO Box 383, 320, Barka, Oman
Tel.: (968) 26884255
Web Site:
  http://www.gulfmushroom.com
Year Founded: 1997
GMPI—(MUS)
Rev.: $26,688,504
Assets: $46,730,715
Liabilities: $20,389,075
Net Worth: $26,341,640
Earnings: $3,598,234
Emp.: 363
Fiscal Year-end: 12/31/23
Mushroom Farming Services
N.A.I.C.S.: 111411
Abdullah Nasser Al Hadhrami (CEO)

GULF NAVIGATION HOLDING PJSC
39th Floor API Trio Tower Al Barsha 1, PO Box 49651, Dubai, United Arab Emirates
Tel.: (971) 44270104
Web Site: https://www.gulfnav.com
Year Founded: 2003
GULFNAV—(DFM)
Rev.: $28,733,936
Assets: $272,908,956
Liabilities: $110,734,046
Net Worth: $162,174,910
Earnings: $5,792,583
Emp.: 300
Fiscal Year-end: 12/31/23
Marine Transportation Services
N.A.I.C.S.: 483115
Ali Abouda (CFO)

Subsidiaries:

Gulf Navigation Polimar Maritime LLC (1)
39th Floor API Trio Tower Al Barsha 1, PO Box 49651, Dubai, United Arab Emirates
Tel.: (971) 44270104
Marine Shipping Services
N.A.I.C.S.: 488390

GULF NORTH AFRICA HOLDING CO. K.S.C.
Sharq Al Madina Tower Floor 14 Khaled Bin Al Waleed Street, PO Box 1246, Dasman, Kuwait, 15463, Kuwait
Tel.: (965) 22023750
Web Site:
  https://northafricaholding.com
Year Founded: 2006
GNAHC—(KUW)
Rev.: $10,198,479
Assets: $60,353,313
Liabilities: $12,034,863
Net Worth: $48,318,451
Earnings: $1,602,904
Emp.: 13
Fiscal Year-end: 12/31/21
Real Estate Investment Services
N.A.I.C.S.: 525990
Meshari Ayman Boodai (Chm)

GULF PAPER MANUFACTURING COMPANY K.S.C.
Shuaiba Industrial W Area Block 3, PO Box 7506, Fahaheel, 64006, Kuwait
Tel.: (965) 3262072 KW
Web Site: http://www.gulfpaper.com
Year Founded: 1979
Rev.: $30,000,000
Emp.: 400

GULF PAPER MANUFACTURING COMPANY K.S.C.

Gulf Paper Manufacturing Company K.S.C.—(Continued)
Facial Tissue Paper & Carton Paper Mfr
N.A.I.C.S.: 322299
Mohammed Saqer Al Maousherji *(Chm)*

GULF PETROLEUM INVESTMENT CO. S.A.K.C.
Sharq - Jaber Al-Mubarak St Behbhani Complex - 16th Floor, PO Box 1770, Al Safat, Kuwait, 13018, Kuwait
Tel.: (965) 22072083
Web Site:
https://www.petrogulf.com.kw
GPI—(KUW)
Rev.: $16,780,035
Assets: $156,834,646
Liabilities: $48,815,583
Net Worth: $108,019,062
Earnings: ($3,286,927)
Emp.: 145
Fiscal Year-end: 12/31/21
Oil & Gas Investments & Operations
N.A.I.C.S.: 213112
Jasim Al Hammad *(Chm)*

Subsidiaries:

Pyramid Drilling S.A.E. (1)
12 Road 83, Maadi, Cairo, 11431, Egypt
Tel.: (20) 223583249
Web Site: http://www.pyramiddrlg.com
Oil & Gas Drilling Services
N.A.I.C.S.: 213111
Alaaeddine Ali Hilal *(Mgr-Fin)*

Superior Oil field Services L.L.C. (1)
PO Box 41156, Abu Dhabi, United Arab Emirates
Tel.: (971) 2 644 6070
Web Site: https://www.superior.ae
Pumping Equipment Mfr
N.A.I.C.S.: 333914

GULF PHARMACEUTICAL INDUSTRIES P.S.C.
Airport Road Digdaga, PO Box 997, Ras al Khaimah, United Arab Emirates
Tel.: (971) 72461461
Web Site: https://www.julphar.net
Year Founded: 1980
JULPHAR—(ABU)
Rev.: $445,956,982
Assets: $668,091,477
Liabilities: $448,597,875
Net Worth: $219,493,601
Earnings: ($27,198,475)
Emp.: 2,323
Fiscal Year-end: 12/31/23
Pharmaceutical Mfr & Marketer
N.A.I.C.S.: 325412
Saqer Humaid Al Qasimi *(Chm)*

GULF PLASTICS INDUSTRIES COMPANY SAOG
PO Box 55, Rusayl, 124, Muscat, Oman
Tel.: (968) 24 446688   OM
Web Site:
http://www.gulfplasticoman.com
Year Founded: 1998
Plastics Product Mfr
N.A.I.C.S.: 326199
Asok Kumar *(Gen Mgr)*

GULF RESOURCES, INC.
Level 11 Vegetable Building Industrial Park of the East Shouguang City, Shouguang, 262700, Shandong, China
Tel.: (86) 5365670008   DE
Web Site:
https://www.gulfresourcesinc.com
GURE—(NASDAQ)
Rev.: $30,043,790
Assets: $226,671,708
Liabilities: $21,423,412
Net Worth: $205,248,296
Earnings: ($61,795,279)
Emp.: 380
Fiscal Year-end: 12/31/23
Bromine, Crude Salt & Chemicals Mfr & Distr
N.A.I.C.S.: 325199
Xiaobin Liu *(Chm & CEO)*

GULF ROCKS K.S.C.
Shawaft Bldg 4 2nd & 6th Fls Omar Bin Al-Khatab St, PO Box 1981, Safat, Kuwait, 13020, Kuwait
Tel.: (965) 22445005
Web Site: http://www.gulfrocks.com
Sales Range: $50-74.9 Million
Emp.: 210
Aggregates & Other Building Materials Mfr & Distr
N.A.I.C.S.: 444180
Shaheen Khaled Al Shaheen Al-Ghanim *(Chm & Mng Dir)*

GULF STONE COMPANY SAOG.
Industrial Estate Sultanate, PO Box 47, 327, Sohar, Oman
Tel.: (968) 26751675
Web Site: http://www.gulfstone-oman.com
Year Founded: 1999
GSCI—(MUS)
Rev.: $6,314,926
Assets: $13,090,809
Liabilities: $8,691,026
Net Worth: $4,399,783
Earnings: ($2,208,254)
Emp.: 122
Fiscal Year-end: 12/31/21
Flooring Tile & Stone Product Mfr
N.A.I.C.S.: 327991
Tareq Sulaiman Al Hougani *(Chm)*

GULF TOTAL TRACTEBEL POWER COMPANY
Najda Street, PO Box 6120, Abu Dhabi, United Arab Emirates
Tel.: (971) 2 694 3333
Web Site: http://www.adwea.ae
Sales Range: $75-99.9 Million
Emp.: 200
Electrical Generation & Water Desalination Services
N.A.I.C.S.: 221122
Frederic Henning *(Exec Mng Dir)*

GULF UNION ALAHLIA COOPERATIVE INSURANCE CO.
Salman Al Farisi St Al Khalidiyyah Al Janubiyyah, PO Box 5719, Dammam, 32221, Saudi Arabia
Tel.: (966) 38333544
Web Site:
https://www.gulfunion.com.sa
Year Founded: 2007
8120—(SAU)
Rev.: $115,938,556
Assets: $280,947,976
Liabilities: $191,735,264
Net Worth: $89,212,712
Earnings: $672,861
Emp.: 413
Fiscal Year-end: 12/31/22
Insurance Management Services
N.A.I.C.S.: 524298
Abdul Aziz Ali Al-Turki *(Chm)*

GULF WAREHOUSING COMPANY QSC
D Ring Road, PO Box 24434, Doha, Qatar
Tel.: (974) 44493000
Web Site:
https://www.gwclogistics.com
Year Founded: 2004
GWCS—(QE)
Rev.: $355,270,593
Assets: $1,182,775,222
Liabilities: $615,236,848
Net Worth: $567,538,374
Earnings: $63,049,360
Emp.: 2,600
Fiscal Year-end: 12/31/21
Warehousing & Logistics Consulting Services
N.A.I.C.S.: 493110
Fahad Hamad Jaseem Jabor Al-Thani *(Vice Chm)*

Subsidiaries:

GWC Global Transport LLC (1)
Al Makeen Building Airport Road, PO Box 11761, Dubai, United Arab Emirates
Tel.: (971) 4259 5322
Web Site: http://www.gulfwarehousing.com
Emp.: 15
Logistics Consulting Servies
N.A.I.C.S.: 541614
Arun Mathew *(Bus Mgr)*

GWC Marine Services W.L.L. (1)
D Ring Road Building No 90 Street No 250 Zone No 42, PO Box 7854, Al-Hilal, Doha, Qatar
Tel.: (974) 40119696
Web Site: https://www.gwcmarine.qa
Shipping Services
N.A.I.C.S.: 488330

LEDD Technologies W.L.L. (1)
92 D Ring Road, Al Hilal, Doha, Qatar
Tel.: (974) 40119777
Web Site: https://www.ledd.com
Supply Chain & Logistics Services
N.A.I.C.S.: 541614

GULFA GENERAL INVESTMENT COMPANY
PO Box 929, Ajman, United Arab Emirates
Tel.: (971) 67407100
Web Site: http://www.gulfa.ae
Year Founded: 1975
GULFA—(DFM)
Rev.: $3,823,382
Assets: $11,210,919
Liabilities: $2,459,121
Net Worth: $8,751,798
Earnings: ($1,142,477)
Emp.: 111
Fiscal Year-end: 12/31/19
Mineral Water Mfr
N.A.I.C.S.: 312112

GULFINVEST INTERNATIONAL K.S.C.C.
Al-Dhow Tower 22nd Floor Khaled Bin Al-Waleed Street, Sharq, Kuwait, Kuwait
Tel.: (965) 22255400
Web Site: http://www.gulfinvest.com
Investment & Financial Services
N.A.I.C.S.: 523999
Abdulmuhsen Sulaiman Al Meshaan *(Chm & Mng Dir)*

GULFSANDS PETROLEUM PLC
5th Floor 88 Kingsway, London, WC2B 6AA, United Kingdom
Tel.: (44) 20 7841 2727
Web Site: http://www.gulfsands.com
Oil & Gas Exploration Services
N.A.I.C.S.: 211120
John Bell *(Mng Dir)*

GULFSTREAM CAPITAL CORPORATION
Wildunger Strasse 1B Suite 61, 60487, Frankfurt, Germany
Tel.: (49) 6957801945   NV
Web Site:
http://www.gulfstreamcapital.com
Year Founded: 2010

INTERNATIONAL PUBLIC

Diamond Mining
N.A.I.C.S.: 212311
Harry Hohenstein *(Chm, Pres, CEO & CFO)*

GULFTAINER COMPANY LIMITED
PO Box 225, Sharjah, United Arab Emirates
Tel.: (971) 6 572 4201
Web Site: http://www.gulftainer.com
Year Founded: 1976
Sales Range: $300-349.9 Million
Emp.: 2,000
Container Terminals Manager & Operator
N.A.I.C.S.: 488310
Peter Richards *(Grp CEO)*

GULISTAN GROUP
2nd Floor Garden Heights 8-Aibak Block, New Garden Town, Lahore, Pakistan
Tel.: (92) 42 594 1819 23
Web Site: http://www.gulshan.com.pk
Year Founded: 1966
Sales Range: $1-4.9 Billion
Emp.: 10,000
Textile Products Mfr
N.A.I.C.S.: 314999

Subsidiaries:

Gulistan Spinning Mills Limited (1)
2nd Floor Finlay House, Unit Jamber Khurd Tehsil Chunian District I I Chundrigar Rd, Karachi, Pakistan
Tel.: (92) 212419943
Web Site: https://gulshan.com.pk
Sales Range: $10-24.9 Million
Emp.: 600
Spinning Mills
N.A.I.C.S.: 313110
Muhammad Akhtar Mirza *(Chm)*

Gulistan Textile Mills Limited (1)
2nd Floor Finlay House I I Chundrigar Road, Karachi, Pakistan
Tel.: (92) 2419943
Web Site: https://www.gulistan.com.pk
Rev.: $1,641,036
Assets: $14,357,649
Liabilities: $79,110,740
Net Worth: ($64,753,091)
Earnings: ($9,879,213)
Emp.: 7
Fiscal Year-end: 06/30/2019
Yarn Mfr
N.A.I.C.S.: 313110
Naseer Ahmed *(CEO)*

Paramount Spinning Mills Limited (1)
2nd Floor Finlay House I I Chundrigar Road, Karachi, Pakistan
Tel.: (92) 2132419947
Textile Mill Operator
N.A.I.C.S.: 313110
Nasir Mahmood *(CFO)*

GULLBERG & JANSSON AB
Hortensiagatan 7, 256 68, Helsingborg, Sweden
Tel.: (46) 423111500
Web Site:
https://www.gullbergjansson.se
Year Founded: 2002
Environmental Consulting Services
N.A.I.C.S.: 541620
Peter Back *(CEO)*

GULLEWA LIMITED
Suite 1 Level 2 Quantum House 49-51 York Street, Sydney, 2000, NSW, Australia
Tel.: (61) 293977555
Web Site: https://gullewa.com.au
GUL—(ASX)
Rev.: $3,297,605
Assets: $13,312,720
Liabilities: $370,463
Net Worth: $12,942,256

Earnings: $1,465,116
Emp.: 6
Fiscal Year-end: 06/30/24
Investments In Mining & Exploration
N.A.I.C.S.: 211130
David Deitz (CEO & Sec)

GULLIVER ENERGY LTD.
Koma 12 Menahem Begin 11, Ramat Gan, 5268104, Israel
Tel.: (972) 36120033
Year Founded: 1968
Rev.: $23,890
Assets: $866,080
Liabilities: $1,260,120
Net Worth: ($394,039)
Earnings: ($425,988)
Fiscal Year-end: 12/31/17
Oil & Gas Exploration Services
N.A.I.C.S.: 213112
Abraham Kremien (CEO)

GULSHAN POLYOLS LTD.
G-81 Preet Vihar, Delhi, 110092, India
Tel.: (91) 1149999200
Web Site: https://www.gulshanindia.com
GULPOLY—(NSE)
Rev.: $104,819,524
Assets: $67,770,325
Liabilities: $17,872,423
Net Worth: $49,897,903
Earnings: $8,525,176
Emp.: 427
Fiscal Year-end: 03/31/21
Specialty Chemicals Mfr
N.A.I.C.S.: 325180
Chandra Kumar Jain (Chm & Mng Dir)

GUMA GROUP
Venus Building 47 Landmarks Avenue, Samrand Kosmosdal, Centurion, 0157, South Africa
Tel.: (27) 12 657 3160
Web Site: http://www.guma.co.za
Holding Company
N.A.I.C.S.: 551112
Robert Matana Gumede (Chm)

Subsidiaries:

Gijima Group Limited (1)
47 Landmarks Ave Kosmosdal Samrand, PO Box 10629, Centurion, 0046, South Africa
Tel.: (27) 126755000
Web Site: http://www.gijima.com
Sales Range: $200-249.9 Million
Emp.: 2,318
Information & Communications Technology Services
N.A.I.C.S.: 811210
Robert Wellington Gumede (Chm)

Subsidiary (Domestic):

GijimaAst Electronic and Security Systems (Pty) Limited (2)
Block C Ast Group Ofc 47 Landsmarks Ave, Centurion, 0157, Gauteng, South Africa
Tel.: (27) 126755411
Security System Installation Services
N.A.I.C.S.: 238210

GijimaAst Holdings (Pty) Limited (2)
14 Cranbrook Park Cres, La Lucia, Durban, 4051, Kwazulu-Natal, South Africa
Tel.: (27) 126755000
Web Site: http://www.gijima.com
Sales Range: $350-399.9 Million
Emp.: 1,000
Mining Software Consulting Services
N.A.I.C.S.: 541512
Eileen Wilton (CEO)

Subsidiary (Non-US):

GijimaAst Information Technology Services (Pty) Limited (2)
2 Bismarck St, Windhoek, Namibia
Tel.: (264) 612853000

Web Site: http://www.gijima.com
Sales Range: $25-49.9 Million
Emp.: 65
Mining Software Consulting Services
N.A.I.C.S.: 541512
H. J. Villet (Mng Dir)

GUMI INC.
Sumitomo Fudosan Nishi-Shinjuku Building No 5 3F 4-34-7 Nishi-Shinjuku, Shinjuku-ku, Tokyo, 160-0023, Japan
Tel.: (81) 353585322
Web Site: https://www.gu3.co.jp
Year Founded: 2007
3903—(TKS)
Rev.: $79,756,260
Assets: $127,784,520
Liabilities: $46,864,900
Net Worth: $80,919,620
Earnings: ($39,223,740)
Emp.: 260
Fiscal Year-end: 04/30/24
Online Mobile Game Producer
N.A.I.C.S.: 513210
Hironao Kunimitsu (Founder & Chm)

GUN EI CHEMICAL INDUSTRY CO., LTD.
700 Yadooruicho, Takasaki, 370-0032, Gunma, Japan
Tel.: (81) 273531818
Web Site: https://www.gunei-chemical.co.jp
Year Founded: 1946
4229—(TKS)
Rev.: $200,349,100
Assets: $403,276,100
Liabilities: $70,918,690
Net Worth: $332,357,410
Earnings: $13,484,400
Fiscal Year-end: 03/31/24
Chemical Products Mfr
N.A.I.C.S.: 325211
Yoshikazu Arita (Chm)

Subsidiaries:

American GCI Resitop, Inc. (1)
1111 Plaza Dr Ste 646, Schaumburg, IL 60173
Tel.: (847) 278-1170
Web Site: https://american-gci.com
Chemical Products Mfr
N.A.I.C.S.: 325180

BIG Trading Co., Ltd. (1)
93 Okuda Nagare-machi, Inazawa, Aichi, Japan
Tel.: (81) 587220330
Temporary Help Service
N.A.I.C.S.: 561320

Gun Ei Chemical Industry Co., Ltd. - Shiga Plant (1)
1-4 Takamatsu-chou, Konan, 520-3211, Shiga, Japan
Tel.: (81) 748751241
Chemical Products Mfr
N.A.I.C.S.: 325211

Kynol Europa GmbH (1)
Borsteler Chaussee 55, 22453, Hamburg, Germany
Tel.: (49) 40 530 0450
Web Site: https://www.kynol.de
Carbon Products Mfr
N.A.I.C.S.: 335991
Julia Willer (Mng Dir)

Kynol Europa Import-Export GmbH (1)
Borsteler Chaussee 55, 22453, Hamburg, Germany
Tel.: (49) 405300450
Fiber Product Mfr
N.A.I.C.S.: 424690

Thai GCI Resitop Co., Ltd. (1)
12 i-4 Rd Tambol Map ta phut, PO Box 51, Amphur Muang Rayong, Rayong, 21150, Thailand
Tel.: (66) 38683223
Web Site: https://thaigci.wixsite.com

Synthetic Resin Mfr & Distr
N.A.I.C.S.: 325211
Katsuhiro Maruyama (Pres)

Tohoku U-Loid Industry Co., Ltd. (1)
14-453-5 Murasakino, Kitakami, 024-0004, Iwate, Japan (100%)
Tel.: (81) 197662031
Sales Range: $50-74.9 Million
Emp.: 38
Synthetic Resins, Wood Adhesives, Formalin & Other Chemical Products Mfr & Sales
N.A.I.C.S.: 325211

GUNAY BANK OJSC
Asiq Ali kuc 3A, AZ1072, Baku, Azerbaijan
Tel.: (994) 1546   Az
Web Site: http://www.gunaybank.com
Year Founded: 1992
GUNAB—(BAK)
Rev.: $1,902,907
Assets: $119,106,666
Liabilities: $88,973,226
Net Worth: $30,133,440
Earnings: $617,317
Fiscal Year-end: 12/31/19
Commercial Banking Services
N.A.I.C.S.: 522110
Mahmud Mammadov (Chm-Supervisory Bd)

GUNGHO ONLINE ENTERTAINMENT, INC.
Pacific Century Place Marunouchi 1-11-1 Marunouchi, Chiyoda-ku, Tokyo, 100-6221, Japan
Tel.: (81) 368951650   JP
Web Site: https://www.gungho.co.jp
Year Founded: 1998
3765—(TKS)
Rev.: $888,483,350
Assets: $1,191,439,050
Liabilities: $131,519,500
Net Worth: $1,059,919,550
Earnings: $116,509,970
Emp.: 1,475
Fiscal Year-end: 12/31/23
Online Videogame Developer & Whslr
N.A.I.C.S.: 513210
Hiroto Uehara (Auditor)

Subsidiaries:

GungHo Online Entertainment America, Inc. (1)
2101 Rosecrans Ave Ste 3220, El Segundo, CA 90245
Tel.: (310) 414-0888
Web Site: http://www.gunghoonline.com
Emp.: 30
Videogame Developer & Publisher
N.A.I.C.S.: 513210
Jun Iwasaki (Pres)

PlayPhone, Inc. (1)
3031 Tisch Way 110 Plaza W, San Jose, CA 95128 (70%)
Tel.: (408) 261-6200
Web Site: http://www.playphone.com
Mobile Gaming Software Developer
N.A.I.C.S.: 513210
Ron Czerny (Founder & CEO)

GUNGNIR RESOURCES INC.
Suite 404 1688 152nd Street, Surrey, V4A 4N2, BC, Canada
Tel.: (604) 683-0484   Ca
Web Site: https://www.gungnirresources.com
AMO1—(DEU)
Rev.: $89
Assets: $3,079,243
Liabilities: $39,374
Net Worth: $3,039,868
Earnings: ($704,264)
Fiscal Year-end: 12/31/21
Gold Mining Services
N.A.I.C.S.: 212220
Christopher C. Robbins (CFO)

GUNKUL ENGINEERING CO., LTD.
1177 8th Floor Pearl Bangkok Building Phahonyothin Road, Phayathai, Bangkok, 10400, Thailand
Tel.: (66) 22425800
Web Site: https://www.gunkul.com
Year Founded: 1982
GUNKUL—(THA)
Rev.: $225,861,972
Assets: $958,966,017
Liabilities: $550,557,194
Net Worth: $408,408,823
Earnings: $43,055,031
Emp.: 998
Fiscal Year-end: 12/31/23
Engineeering Services
N.A.I.C.S.: 541330
Gunkul Dhumrongpiyawut (Chm)

Subsidiaries:

Future Electrical Control Co., Ltd. (1)
1177 Pearl Bangkok Building 12A Floor Phaholyothin Road, Phayathai Phayathai, Bangkok, 10400, Thailand
Tel.: (66) 22425800
Web Site: https://www.future-electrical.com
Construction Services
N.A.I.C.S.: 541330

Future Energy Corporation Co., Ltd. (1)
956/1 Nakhonchaisri Road, Nakhonchaisri Sub-District Dusit District, Bangkok, Thailand
Tel.: (66) 22425800
Computer Program Services
N.A.I.C.S.: 541511

G.K. Assembly Co., Ltd. (1)
2 110/9-10 Maha Sawat, Bang Kruai District, Nonthaburi, 11130, Thailand
Tel.: (66) 298522503
Web Site: https://www.gunkul.com
Engineeering Services
N.A.I.C.S.: 541330

G.K. Real Estate (2564) Co., Ltd. (1)
1177 8th Floor Pearl Bangkok Building Phahonyothin Road, Phayathai Sub-District Phayathai District, Bangkok, Thailand
Tel.: (66) 22425800
Property Development Services
N.A.I.C.S.: 531390

G.K. Smart Farming Co., Ltd. (1)
1177 8th Floor Pearl Bangkok Building Phahonyothin Road, Phayathai Sub-District Phayathai District, Bangkok, Thailand
Tel.: (66) 22425800
Hemp & Cannabis Services
N.A.I.C.S.: 561730

G.K.Power Products Co., Ltd. (1)
1038 Nakhonchaisri Road, Nakornchaisri Sub-District Dusit District, Bangkok, Thailand
Tel.: (66) 22425800
Electrical System Equipment Mfr
N.A.I.C.S.: 335999

Greenovation Power Co., Ltd. (1)
1038 Nakornchaisri Road, Nakornchaisri Dusit, Bangkok, Thailand
Tel.: (66) 22425800
Web Site: https://www.gunkul.com
Engineeering Services
N.A.I.C.S.: 541330

K.N.P. Supply Co., Ltd. (1)
113/1 Pichai Road, Nakornchaisri Dusit, Bangkok, Thailand
Tel.: (66) 22425800
Web Site: https://www.gunkul.com
Engineeering Services
N.A.I.C.S.: 541330

NK Power Sola Co., Ltd. (1)
1038-1046 Nakornchaisri Road, Nakornchaisri Dusit, Bangkok, Thailand
Tel.: (66) 22425800
Web Site: https://www.gunkul.com
Engineeering Services
N.A.I.C.S.: 541330

GUNKUL ENGINEERING CO., LTD.

Gunkul Engineering Co., Ltd.—(Continued)

NKP Power Solar Co., Ltd. (1)
1177 8th Floor Pearl Bangkok Building Phahonyothin Road, Phayathai Sub-District Phayathai District, Bangkok, Thailand
Tel.: (66) 22425800
Electricity Product Mfr & Distr
N.A.I.C.S.: 335999

THCG Group Co., Ltd. (1)
1177 Pearl Bangkok Building 2nd Floor Room 203 204 Phaholyothin Road, Phayathai Phayathai, Bangkok, 10400, Thailand
Tel.: (66) 20238892
Web Site: https://www.thcggroup.com
Hemp Product Distr
N.A.I.C.S.: 493130

Thai Stick Herb Co., Ltd. (1)
1177 2nd Floor 12A01Room Pearl Bangkok Building Phahonyothin Road, Phayathai Sub-District Phayathai District, Bangkok, Thailand
Tel.: (66) 20238892
Hemp & Cannabis Services
N.A.I.C.S.: 561730

GUNN'S HOMEMADE CAKES & PASTRY LTD.
247 Selkirk Ave, Winnipeg, R2W 2L5, MB, Canada
Tel.: (204) 582-2364
Web Site:
http://www.gunnsbakery.com
Year Founded: 1937
Sales Range: $10-24.9 Million
Emp.: 80
Bakery Products Mfr & Distr
N.A.I.C.S.: 424420
Morris Gunn *(Founder)*

GUNNEBO AB
Johan pa Gardas Gata 7, PO Box 5181, SE-402 26, Gothenburg, Sweden
Tel.: (46) 102095020
Web Site: http://www.gunnebo.com
Year Founded: 1764
Rev.: $585,041,030
Assets: $590,935,380
Liabilities: $434,038,500
Net Worth: $156,896,880
Earnings: $4,822,650
Emp.: 4,256
Fiscal Year-end: 12/31/19
Security Systems & Products
N.A.I.C.S.: 561621
Robert Hermans *(Sr VP-Bus Unit Entrance Control)*

Subsidiaries:

A/S Gunnebo Nordic (1)
Horsvinget 7, 2630, Taastrup, Denmark
Tel.: (45) 70105600
Web Site: http://www.gunnebo.com
Bank Security & Cash Handling Services
N.A.I.C.S.: 561621

Gunnebo (Suisse) SA (1)
Route de Champ-Colin 2A, PO Box 2321, Nyon, 1260, Switzerland
Tel.: (41) 840888777
Web Site: http://www.gunnebo.ch
Emp.: 40
Bank Security & Cash Handling Services
N.A.I.C.S.: 561621
Jean-Gabriel Perreten *(Mgr)*

Gunnebo A/S (1)
Nydalsveien 16C, 0484, Oslo, Norway (100%)
Tel.: (47) 22021380
Web Site: http://www.gunnebolifting.com
Sales Range: $50-74.9 Million
Emp.: 10
Production of Industrial Fasteners
N.A.I.C.S.: 332618

Gunnebo Australia Pty Ltd (1)
Unit 8 16 Lexington Drive, Bella Vista, 2153, NSW, Australia
Tel.: (61) 298520700
Web Site: http://www.gunnebo.com.au
Bank Security & Cash Handling Services
N.A.I.C.S.: 561621

Gunnebo Baltic Sp z o o (1)
Ul Olsztynska 43, 11-130, Orneta, Poland (100%)
Tel.: (48) 600098586
Web Site: http://www.gunnebolifting.com
Sales Range: $50-74.9 Million
Emp.: 200
Miscellaneous Fabricated Wire Products
N.A.I.C.S.: 332618

Gunnebo CZ s.r.o. (1)
Za Trati 928/6 Cakovice, 196 00, Prague, Czech Republic
Tel.: (420) 266190200
Web Site: http://www.gunnebo.com
Bank Security & Cash Handling Services
N.A.I.C.S.: 561621

Gunnebo Canada Inc. (1)
9 Van Der Graaf Crt, Brampton, L6T 5E5, ON, Canada
Tel.: (905) 595-4140
Web Site: http://www.gunnebo.com
Sales Range: $25-49.9 Million
Emp.: 75
Bank Security & Cash Handling Services
N.A.I.C.S.: 561621
John Haining *(Pres)*

Gunnebo Deutschland GmbH (1)
Siemensstrasse 1, 85716, Unterschleissheim, Germany
Tel.: (49) 89 95 96 0
Web Site: http://www.gunnebo.com
Sales Range: $10-24.9 Million
Emp.: 50
Bank Security & Cash Handling Services
N.A.I.C.S.: 561621

Gunnebo Entrance Control Ltd. (1)
Kennicott House, Well Lane, Uckfield, WV11 1XR, East Sussex, United Kingdom
Tel.: (44) 3702240294
Web Site: http://www.gunnebo.com
Sales Range: $50-74.9 Million
Emp.: 120
Entrance Control Systems
N.A.I.C.S.: 334290

Gunnebo Entrance Control SARL (1)
20 Rue des Campanules Longes 77185, FR-94220, Charenton-du-Cher, France
Tel.: (33) 164801440
Sales Range: $25-49.9 Million
Emp.: 20
Entrance Control Systems
N.A.I.C.S.: 334290

Gunnebo Entrance Control, Inc. (1)
535 Getty Ct Ste F, Benicia, CA 94510
Tel.: (707) 748-0885
Web Site: http://www.gunnebo.us
Sales Range: $25-49.9 Million
Emp.: 12
Bank Security & Cash Handling Services
N.A.I.C.S.: 561621
Chris Wheeler *(Mgr-Ops)*

Gunnebo Espana SA (1)
Josep Pla 2 Edif B2 Pl 11-12, 08019, Barcelona, Spain
Tel.: (34) 933162600
Web Site: http://www.gunnebo.com
Bank Security & Cash Handling Services
N.A.I.C.S.: 561621
Jose Antonio Martinez Ortuno *(Mgr-Bus Dev-South America)*

Gunnebo Holding GmbH (1)
Siemensstr 1, Unterschleissheim, 85716, Germany
Tel.: (49) 8995960
Bank Security & Cash Handling Services
N.A.I.C.S.: 561621

Gunnebo India Ltd (1)
Unit No 102 1st Floor Akruti SMC LBS Marg, Khopat, Thane, 400 601, India
Tel.: (91) 22 67 80 35 00
Web Site: http://www.gunnebo.in
Sales Range: $25-49.9 Million
Emp.: 100
Bank Security & Cash Handling Services
N.A.I.C.S.: 561621

Gunnebo Indonesia (1)

Grha Gunnebo Indonesia Jl Salemba Raya No 32, Jakarta, 10430, Indonesia
Tel.: (62) 21 314 8383
Web Site: http://www.gunnebo.com
Sales Range: $25-49.9 Million
Emp.: 60
Bank Security & Cash Handling Services
N.A.I.C.S.: 561621
Stephen Hadiwibowo *(Mgr-Acct & Sls)*

Gunnebo Industries (1)
12 Vicars Pl, PO Box 6081, Wetherill Park, 2164, NSW, Australia (70%)
Tel.: (61) 297565544
Web Site: http://www.gunnebolifting.com
Sales Range: $25-49.9 Million
Emp.: 11
N.A.I.C.S.: 332618

Gunnebo Intrance Control S.p.A (1)
Via A Volta 15, 38015, Lavis, Italy (100%)
Tel.: (39) 0461248900
Web Site: http://www.italdis.com
Emp.: 70
Entrance Control Systems
N.A.I.C.S.: 334290
Henrik Lange *(Gen Mgr)*

Gunnebo Italia S.P.A (1)
Via Metallino 12, 200 90, Vimodrone, Milano, Italy
Tel.: (39) 02267101
Web Site: http://www.gunnebo.com
Bank Security & Cash Handling Services
N.A.I.C.S.: 561621

Gunnebo Johnson Corporation (1)
1240 N Harvard Ave, Tulsa, OK 74115-6103 (100%)
Tel.: (918) 832-8933
Web Site: http://www.gunnebojohnson.com
Sales Range: $50-74.9 Million
Emp.: 200
Mfr Blocks for the Crane Industry
N.A.I.C.S.: 333120

Gunnebo Ltd. (1)
Woolaston Rd Pk Farm N, Redditch, B98 7SG, Worcs, United Kingdom (100%)
Tel.: (44) 1527521550
Web Site: http://www.gunnebo.co.uk
Sales Range: $25-49.9 Million
Emp.: 15
Sales of Lifting & Fastening Systems
N.A.I.C.S.: 425120
Justin Wiglan *(Gen Mgr)*

Gunnebo Magyarorszag Kft. (1)
Kiss Erno utca 1-3, Budapest, 1046, Hungary
Tel.: (36) 14656080
Web Site: http://www.gunnebo.com
Sales Range: $25-49.9 Million
Emp.: 9
Bank Security & Cash Handling Services
N.A.I.C.S.: 561621
Estvan Rosman *(Gen Mgr)*

Gunnebo Middle East FZE (1)
Dubai Airport Free Zone East Wing 6A Office 816, PO Box 54435, Dubai, 54435, United Arab Emirates
Tel.: (971) 4 701 7837
Web Site: http://www.gunnebo.com
Sales Range: $25-49.9 Million
Emp.: 13
Bank Security & Cash Handling Services
N.A.I.C.S.: 561621
Jacob Touma *(Gen Mgr)*

Gunnebo Nederland BV (1)
Visseringweg 23, 1112 AS, Diemen, Netherlands
Tel.: (31) 203988988
Web Site: http://www.gunnebo.com
Emp.: 70
Bank Security & Cash Handling Services
N.A.I.C.S.: 561621

Gunnebo Nordic AB (1)
Askims Verkstadsvag 4, PO Box 9065, Gothenburg, 400 92, Sweden
Tel.: (46) 317277900
Web Site: http://www.gunnebo.com
Sales Range: $150-199.9 Million
Emp.: 800
Bank Security & Cash Handling Services
N.A.I.C.S.: 561621
Ben Morten *(Mng Dir)*

Gunnebo Nordic Oy (1)

Ayritie 4, 01510, Vantaa, Finland
Tel.: (358) 10 617 1700
Web Site: http://www.gunnebo.com
Bank Security & Cash Handling Services
N.A.I.C.S.: 561621

Gunnebo Osterreich GmbH (1)
Carlonestrasse 7 A, Ansfelden, 4052, Austria
Tel.: (43) 722982050
Sales Range: $25-49.9 Million
Emp.: 8
Bank Security & Cash Handling Services
N.A.I.C.S.: 561621
Thomas Haim *(Gen Mgr)*

Gunnebo Perimeter Protection AB (1)
Drakeg 5, Gothenburg, 41250, Sweden
Tel.: (46) 1 02 09 53 00
Bank Security & Cash Handling Services
N.A.I.C.S.: 561621

Gunnebo Polska SP. Z o.o. (1)
Ul Chopina 20-22, 62800, Kalisz, Poland
Tel.: (48) 627685570
Web Site: http://www.gunnebo.com
Sales Range: $10-24.9 Million
Emp.: 30
Bank Security & Cash Handling Services
N.A.I.C.S.: 561621

Gunnebo Portugal S.A. (1)
Av Infante D Henrique lote 306-2, 1950-421, Lisbon, Portugal
Tel.: (351) 218 315 600
Web Site: http://www.gunnebo.com
Bank Security & Cash Handling Services
N.A.I.C.S.: 561621

Gunnebo SafePay AB (1)
Fabriksgatan 10, Gothenburg, 412 50, Sweden
Tel.: (46) 317499050
Bank Security & Cash Handling Services
N.A.I.C.S.: 561621

Gunnebo Security (China) Co., Ltd (1)
Unit 1802B-1803 Lippo Plaza No 222 Huaihai Road M, Shanghai, 200021, China
Tel.: (86) 2154662978
Bank Security & Cash Handling Services
N.A.I.C.S.: 561621

Gunnebo Singapore Pte Ltd (1)
138 Robinson Rd 09-01 The Corporate Office, Singapore, 068906, Singapore
Tel.: (65) 63279119
Web Site: http://www.gunnebo.com
Sales Range: $25-49.9 Million
Emp.: 12
Bank Security & Cash Handling Services
N.A.I.C.S.: 561621
Elsie Tay *(Country Mgr)*

Gunnebo South Africa (Pty) Ltd (1)
105 Nagington Road, Private Bag X023, Wadeville, 1422, South Africa
Tel.: (27) 11 878 2300
Web Site: http://www.gunnebo.com
Sales Range: $25-49.9 Million
Emp.: 86
Bank Security & Cash Handling Services
N.A.I.C.S.: 561621
Martin Houseman *(Reg Dir-Africa)*

Gunnebo Treasury SA (1)
Faubourg Du Lac 2, Neuchatel, 2000, Switzerland
Tel.: (41) 327277570
Bank Security & Cash Handling Services
N.A.I.C.S.: 561621

Gunnebo UK Ltd (1)
First Floor Kennicott House Well Lane, Wednesfield, Wolverhampton, WV11 1XR, United Kingdom
Tel.: (44) 3702240294
Web Site: http://www.gunnebo.com
Sales Range: $25-49.9 Million
Emp.: 60
Bank Security & Cash Handling Services
N.A.I.C.S.: 561621
Paul Hutchinson *(Mng Dir)*

Gunnebo do Brasil Ltda (1)
Rua Guarani 485, Vila Conecicao, Sao Paulo, 09991-060, SP, Brazil
Tel.: (55) 1140559800

AND PRIVATE COMPANIES   GUNZE LIMITED

Web Site:
http://www.gunneboindustries.com
Sales Range: $25-49.9 Million
Emp.: 20
Sales of Lifting Equipment
N.A.I.C.S.: 333998

Hamilton Safe Co. (1)
7775 Cooper Rd, Cincinnati, OH 45242
Tel.: (513) 874-3733
Web Site: http://www.hamiltonsafe.com
Sales Range: $50-74.9 Million
Emp.: 220
Commercial & Institutional Security Products Mfr
N.A.I.C.S.: 332999
John Stroia (Pres)

GUNOSY INC.
2-24-12 Shibuya, Tokyo, Japan
Tel.: (81) 364554560
Web Site: https://gunosy.co.jp
6047—(TKS)
Rev.: $48,543,840
Assets: $74,950,790
Liabilities: $9,049,090
Net Worth: $65,901,700
Earnings: ($7,839,460)
Emp.: 50
Fiscal Year-end: 05/31/24
Software Application Developer
N.A.I.C.S.: 513210
Shinji Kimura (CEO & Chm)

GUNPOINT EXPLORATION LTD.
Suite 201 - 1512 Yew Street, Vancouver, V6K 3E4, BC, Canada
Tel.: (604) 731-2219
Web Site:
https://www.gunpointltd.com
Year Founded: 1989
CJIMF—(OTCIQ)
Rev.: $320,924
Assets: $5,661,104
Liabilities: $272,597
Net Worth: $5,388,507
Earnings: ($767,198)
Fiscal Year-end: 12/31/23
Mineral Exploration Services
N.A.I.C.S.: 213114
Marco Montecinos (VP)

GUNSYND PLC
78 Pall Mal St Jamess, London, SW1Y 5ES, United Kingdom
Tel.: (44) 2035826636   UK
Web Site: https://www.gunsynd.com
GUN—(AIM)
Assets: $2,794,050
Liabilities: $124,180
Net Worth: $2,669,870
Earnings: ($2,123,478)
Fiscal Year-end: 07/31/23
Investment Services
N.A.I.C.S.: 523999
Donald Strang (Exec Dir)

Subsidiaries:

Oscillate plc (1)
6th Floor 60 Gracechurch Street, London, EC3V 0HR, United Kingdom
Tel.: (44) 2037450281
Web Site: https://oscillateplc.com
Investment Management Service
N.A.I.C.S.: 541513

Rincon Resources Limited (1)
Unit 8 1200 Hay Street, West Perth, 6005, WA, Australia
Tel.: (61) 862434089
Web Site:
https://www.rinconresources.com.au
Zinc Mining Services
N.A.I.C.S.: 212230

Strategic Minerals Europe Ltd. (1)
365 Bay street suite 800, Toronto, M5H 2V1, ON, Canada
Tel.: (416) 361-3121
Web Site: https://www.strategicminerals.com

Raw Material & Metallic Mineral Whslr
N.A.I.C.S.: 423520

GUNTHER MELE LIMITED
30 Craig St, Brantford, N3R 7J1, ON, Canada
Tel.: (519) 756-4330
Web Site:
http://www.gunthermele.com
Year Founded: 1857
Sales Range: $25-49.9 Million
Emp.: 100
Mfr & Importer of Jewelry Packaging, Jewelry Boxes & Store Supplies
N.A.I.C.S.: 322212
Darrell King (Pres)

Subsidiaries:

Gunther Mele Packaging, Inc. (1)
1321 Millersport Hwy, Buffalo, NY 14221   (100%)
Tel.: (716) 821-1472
Web Site: http://www.gunthermele.com
Sales Range: $25-49.9 Million
Emp.: 4
Folding Paperboard Mfr
N.A.I.C.S.: 322212
Douglas King (CEO)

GUNVOR GROUP LTD.
48 Themistocles Dervis Street
Athienitis Centennial Bldg Suite 501, 1066, Nicosia, Cyprus
Tel.: (357) 24823420
Web Site:
http://www.gunvorgroup.com
Year Founded: 2000
Sales Range: $50-74.9 Billion
Emp.: 1,600
Holding Company; Petroleum & Coal Mining & Distr
N.A.I.C.S.: 551112
Torbjorn Tornqvist (Founder & CEO)

Subsidiaries:

Gunvor International B.V. (1)
Herengracht 498, 1017 CB, Amsterdam, Netherlands
Tel.: (31) 20 535 6089
Web Site: http://www.gunvorgroup.com
Holding Company; Regional Managing Office
N.A.I.C.S.: 551112

Subsidiary (Non-US):

Gunvor SA (2)
80-84 Rue du Rhone, Geneva, 1204, Switzerland
Tel.: (41) 22 718 7900
Web Site: http://www.gunvorgroup.com
Petroleum Bulk Trade Whslr
N.A.I.C.S.: 425120

Subsidiary (Non-US):

Gunvor Deutschland GmbH (3)
Schoberstrasse 3, 85055, Ingolstadt, Germany   (100%)
Tel.: (49) 84113301300
Web Site: http://www.gunvor-deutschland.de
Petroleum Wholesale Trade Distr
N.A.I.C.S.: 425120
Martin Schreiner (Mng Dir)

Subsidiary (Domestic):

Gunvor Raffinerie Ingolstadt GmbH (4)
Essostrasse 1, 85092, Kosching, Germany
Tel.: (49) 841 508 0
Web Site: http://www.gunvor-raffinerie-ingolstadt.de
Petroleum Refining Services
N.A.I.C.S.: 324110
Gerhard Fischer (Mgr-Refinery)

Subsidiary (Non-US):

Independent Belgian Refinery N.V. (2)
Scheldelaan 490, Antwerp, 2040, Belgium
Tel.: (32) 3 560 07 38
Web Site: http://www.ibrefinery.be

Sales Range: $50-74.9 Million
Emp.: 250
Petroleum Refining Services
N.A.I.C.S.: 324110
Luc Smets (Mgr-Refinery)

GUNZE LIMITED
Herbis Osaka Office Tower 2-5-25
Umeda, Kita-ku, Osaka, 530-0001, Japan
Tel.: (81) 663481313
Web Site: https://www.gunze.co.jp
Year Founded: 1896
3002—(TKS)
Rev.: $878,369,850
Assets: $1,070,628,310
Liabilities: $274,341,440
Net Worth: $796,286,870
Earnings: $33,770,490
Emp.: 1,449
Fiscal Year-end: 03/31/24
Apparel & Textile Mfr
N.A.I.C.S.: 315120
Toshiyasu Saguchi (Pres, Pres & Gen Mgr/Gen Mgr-Corp Strategy Dept)

Subsidiaries:

Ayabe Engineering Plastics Co., Ltd. (1)
8 Shiroyamacho, Ayabe, 623-8515, Kyoto, Japan
Tel.: (81) 773432319
Injection Molded Plastic Products Mfr
N.A.I.C.S.: 326121

Dalian Gunze Fashion Garments Co., Ltd. (1)
2-46 North East Dalian Economic Technological Development Area, Dalian Industrial Estate, Dalian, Liaoning, China
Tel.: (86) 41187615203
Fashion Apparels Mfr
N.A.I.C.S.: 315120

Elma Co., Ltd. (1)
10 Shindo Amarube-cho, Kameoka, 621-0806, Kyoto, Japan
Tel.: (81) 771250542
Sales Range: $50-74.9 Million
Emp.: 150
Electronic Components Mfr
N.A.I.C.S.: 334416

Fukushima Gravure Co., Ltd. (1)
88 Emukai Arai, Motomiya, 969-1104, Fukushima, Japan
Tel.: (81) 243362531
Plastic Films & Sheets Mfr
N.A.I.C.S.: 326113

Fukushima Plastics Co., Ltd. (1)
88 Emukai Arai, Motomiya, 969-1104, Fukushima, Japan
Tel.: (81) 243363931
Sales Range: $50-74.9 Million
Emp.: 104
Plastics Films Mfr
N.A.I.C.S.: 326111

G&U System Service, Ltd. (1)
3-14-24 Fukushima Osaka Fukushima Hanshin Building 8th floor, Fukushima-ku, Osaka, 553-0003, Japan   (49%)
Tel.: (81) 664584658
Web Site: https://www.guss.co.jp
Sales Range: $10-24.9 Million
Emp.: 74
Information Technology Services
N.A.I.C.S.: 541512

GGI Technology Ltd. (1)
Caiwu District of Wusha, Chang'an, Dongguan, Guangdong, China
Tel.: (86) 76985356948
Web Site: http://www.ggitech.com.cn
Sales Range: $100-124.9 Million
Emp.: 300
Touch Panels Mfr
N.A.I.C.S.: 334118

Guan Zhi Holdings Ltd. (1)
1502 16th Floor Metropolis Tower 10 Metropolis Drive, Hunghom, Kowloon, China (Hong Kong)
Tel.: (852) 31450238
Investment Management Service

N.A.I.C.S.: 523999

Gunze (Shanghai) International Trading Co., Ltd. (1)
Room 1603 T2 Office Bldg No 399 Yungu Rd, Jiading New City Jiading Dist, Shanghai, China
Tel.: (86) 2162518348
Sales Range: $50-74.9 Million
Emp.: 10
Thread Mfr
N.A.I.C.S.: 313110

Gunze Distribution Co., Ltd. (1)
521 Shimoishibashi, Shimotsuke, 329-0595, Tochigi, Japan
Tel.: (81) 285512600
Intimate Apparels Distr
N.A.I.C.S.: 424350
Takao Tomomatsu (Pres)

Gunze Electronics USA Corp. (1)
2113 Wells Branch Pkwy Ste 5400, Austin, TX 78728-6999
Tel.: (512) 990-3400
Web Site: https://www.gunzeusa.com
Emp.: 65
Touch Panels Mfr
N.A.I.C.S.: 334118

Gunze Engineering Co., Ltd. (1)
Web Site: http://www.gunze.co.jp
Industrial Engineering Services
N.A.I.C.S.: 541330

Gunze Green Co., Ltd. (1)
1-25-19 Nakouji, Amagasaki, 661-0974, Hyogo, Japan
Tel.: (81) 664945040
Web Site: http://www.gunzegreen.co.jp
Landscaping Services
N.A.I.C.S.: 561730

Gunze International Hong Kong Limited (1)
Unit 1502 15th Floor The Metropolis Tower 10 Metropolis Drive, Hunghom, Kowloon, China (Hong Kong)
Tel.: (852) 23142900
Web Site: http://www.gunze-intl.com
Emp.: 5
Hosiery & Underwear Distr
N.A.I.C.S.: 424350

Gunze International USA Inc. (1)
5W 37th St Ste 800, New York, NY 10018
Tel.: (212) 354-9060
Web Site: http://www.gunze-intl.com
Sales Range: $50-74.9 Million
Emp.: 3
Consumer Goods Whslr
N.A.I.C.S.: 424990
Yoshiyuki Hirano (Co-Pres)

Gunze Kobunshi Corporation (1)
3-17-1 Sakuradai, Isehara, 259-1132, Kanagawa, Japan
Tel.: (81) 463943711
Web Site: https://www.gunze.co.jp
Sales Range: $25-49.9 Million
Emp.: 89
Plastics Product Mfr
N.A.I.C.S.: 326199

Gunze Office Services Co., Ltd. (1)
Semba Center Bldg No6 2-3 Senbachuo, Chuo-ku, Osaka, 541-0055, Japan
Tel.: (81) 662450123
Office Support Services
N.A.I.C.S.: 561439

Gunze Packaging Systems Co., Ltd. (1)
Gunze Fukushima Bldg 2F 5-5-1 Fukushima, Fukushima-ku, Osaka, 553-0003, Japan
Tel.: (81) 663946111
Sales Range: $25-49.9 Million
Emp.: 20
Plastic Films Distr
N.A.I.C.S.: 325992

Gunze Plastics & Engineering Corporation (1)
1400 S Hamilton Cir, Olathe, KS 66061
Tel.: (913) 829-5577
Plastic Film Mfr & Distr
N.A.I.C.S.: 326113

Gunze Plastics & Engineering Corporation of America (1)

GUNZE LIMITED

Gunze Limited—(Continued)

1400 S Hamilton Cir, Olathe, KS 66061
Tel.: (913) 829-5577
Web Site: http://www.gunze.co.jp
Plastic Film Mfr & Distr
N.A.I.C.S.: 326113

Gunze Sports Co., Ltd. (1)
4-8-1 Tsukaguchi Honcho, Amagasaki, 661-0001, Hyogo, Japan
Tel.: (81) 664223911
Emp.: 127
Fitness Club & Swimming Pool Operation Services
N.A.I.C.S.: 713940

Hyogo Gunze Co., Ltd. (1)
1120 Kanki Higashikankicho, Kakogawa, 675-0057, Hyogo, Japan
Tel.: (81) 794323550
Innerwear Mfr
N.A.I.C.S.: 315210

Izumo Apparel Ltd. (1)
1315 Enyacho, Izumo, 693-0021, Shimane, Japan
Tel.: (81) 853214023
Yarn Mfr
N.A.I.C.S.: 313110

Keikyu Construction Co., Ltd. (1)
2-21-28 Takanawa Keikyu No 3 Building, Minato-ku, Tokyo, 108-0074, Japan
Tel.: (81) 3 3440 4501
Web Site: http://www.keikyu-kensetsu.co.jp
Railway Construction Services
N.A.I.C.S.: 237990

Kurayoshi Gunze Co., Ltd. (1)
1168 Fukuyoshi-cho, Kurayoshi, 682-0872, Tottori, Japan
Tel.: (81) 858227311
Innerwear Mfr
N.A.I.C.S.: 315210

Kyushu Gunze Co., Ltd. (1)
2738 Hosono, Kobayashi, 886-8511, Miyazaki, Japan
Tel.: (81) 984224771
Hosiery Mfr
N.A.I.C.S.: 315120

P.T. Gunze Socks Indonesia (1)
East Jakarta Industrial Park Plot 7H 1 Cikarang Selatan, Bekasi, 17550, West Java, Indonesia
Tel.: (62) 21 8970022
Web Site: http://www.gunze.co.id
Socks Mfr
N.A.I.C.S.: 315120
Tomio Suzuki (Pres)

Shanghai Gunze New Packaging Co., Ltd. (1)
No 285 Chengyuan Road, Pilot Free Trade Zone, Shanghai, 201206, China
Tel.: (86) 2158770595
Web Site: https://www.gunze-packaging.com
Emp.: 95
Plastics Films Mfr
N.A.I.C.S.: 326111

Tohoku Gunze Co., Ltd. (1)
10 Nakada, Sagae, 991-0041, Yamagata, Japan
Tel.: (81) 237864211
Sales Range: $50-74.9 Million
Emp.: 230
Innerwear Mfr
N.A.I.C.S.: 315210

Tsuyama Gunze Co., Ltd. (1)
2200 Ninomiya, Tsuyama, 708-0013, Okayama, Japan
Tel.: (81) 868280111
Web Site: http://www.gunze.co.jp
Emp.: 83
Yarn Throwing & Winding Services
N.A.I.C.S.: 313110

Yabu Apparel Ltd. (1)
186 Gakuonji Santocho, Asago, 669-5152, Hyogo, Japan
Tel.: (81) 796763650
Apparels Mfr
N.A.I.C.S.: 315210

Yokota Apparel Co., Ltd. (1)
98-2 Shimoyokota Okuizumo-cho, Nita-gun, Okuizumo, 699-1822, Shimane, Japan
Tel.: (81) 854520166
Intimate Apparel Mfr
N.A.I.C.S.: 315250

GUO ANDA CO., LTD.

The Hill Road 39, Fujian Irrigation Mechanical & Electrical Industrial Zone Jimei, Xiamen, 361023, China
Tel.: (86) 4008195119
Web Site: https://www.gad5119.com
Year Founded: 2008
300902—(SSE)
Rev.: $37,256,544
Assets: $132,113,592
Liabilities: $17,680,572
Net Worth: $114,433,020
Earnings: $2,121,444
Fiscal Year-end: 12/31/22
Fire Extinguishing Equipment Mfr & Distr
N.A.I.C.S.: 339999
Weiyi Hong (Chm & Gen Mgr)

GUOCHENG MINING CO., LTD.

Floor 16 Building 19 Block 16 No 188 South 4th Ring Road West, Fengtai District, Beijing, 100070, China
Tel.: (86) 1050955668
Web Site: http://www.jianxin0688.com
Year Founded: 1978
000688—(SSE)
Rev.: $217,208,628
Assets: $1,089,074,376
Liabilities: $636,028,848
Net Worth: $453,045,528
Earnings: $26,028,756
Fiscal Year-end: 12/31/22
Metal Products Mfr
N.A.I.C.S.: 331410
Cheng Wu (Chm)

GUOCHUANG SOFTWARE CO., LTD

No 355 Wenqu Road High-tech Zone, Hefei, 230088, Anhui, China
Tel.: (86) 55165396760
Web Site: http://www.kdgcsoft.com
Year Founded: 2000
300520—(CHIN)
Rev.: $354,222,975
Assets: $660,176,979
Liabilities: $372,743,046
Net Worth: $287,433,933
Earnings: ($53,569,537)
Fiscal Year-end: 12/31/23
Computer Software Solution Services
N.A.I.C.S.: 541511
Dong Yongdong (Chm & Gen Mgr)

GUODIAN NANJING AUTOMATION CO., LTD.

No 8 Xinghuo Road Nanjing High-tech Industrial Development Zone, Pukou Hi-tech District, Nanjing, 210032, Jiangsu, China
Tel.: (86) 2583410173
Web Site: http://www.sac-world.com
Year Founded: 1940
600268—(SHG)
Rev.: $983,889,462
Assets: $1,291,826,395
Liabilities: $778,504,283
Net Worth: $513,322,112
Earnings: $21,379,817
Fiscal Year-end: 12/31/22
Electrical Equipment Mfr & Distr
N.A.I.C.S.: 335999
Hailin Jing (Chm)

Subsidiaries:

Jiangsu Sunel Transformer Co., Ltd. (1)
No 9 East Road, Beitanghe Tianning Economic Development District, Changzhou, China
Tel.: (86) 51985350101
Web Site: http://www.sunel.com.cn
Transformer Mfr
N.A.I.C.S.: 335311

Wuhan Tianhe Technology Co., Ltd. (1)
3/F Building A Changyuan Building No 156 Zhongbei Road, Wuchang District, Wuhan, 430077, China
Tel.: (86) 2786791115
Web Site: http://www.en.t-he.net
Electrical Equipment & Component Mfr
N.A.I.C.S.: 335999

GUODIAN TECHNOLOGY & ENVIRONMENT GROUP CORPORATION LIMITED

Building 1 Yard 16 W 4th Ring Middle Road, Haidian District, Beijing, China
Tel.: (86) 1057659801
Web Site: http://www.khjt.com.cn
1296—(HKG)
Rev.: $2,393,826,274
Assets: $5,635,482,063
Liabilities: $4,387,718,680
Net Worth: $1,247,763,383
Earnings: ($6,807,580)
Emp.: 6,049
Fiscal Year-end: 12/31/20
Environmental Protection & Energy Saving Solution Supplier & Equipment Mfr
N.A.I.C.S.: 335311
Baoxing Luan (Chm-Supervisory Bd)

Subsidiaries:

Guodian United Power Technology (Baoding) Co., Ltd. (1)
88 Fengneng Street, Gaokai District, Baoding, 071051, China
Tel.: (86) 312 5927 000
Emp.: 4,000
Wind Turbine Development Services
N.A.I.C.S.: 221115

GUOEN HOLDINGS LIMITED

4/F KOHO 73-75 Hung To Road Kwun Tong, Kowloon, China (Hong Kong)
Tel.: (852) 39521100
Web Site: http://www.guruonline.com.hk
8121—(HKG)
Rev.: $20,092,117
Assets: $8,315,986
Liabilities: $5,311,654
Net Worth: $3,004,331
Earnings: ($3,998)
Emp.: 156
Fiscal Year-end: 03/31/22
Digital Marketing Services
N.A.I.C.S.: 541613
Shek Lun Yip (Co/Co-Founder, Chm, Chm, CEO & CEO)

Subsidiaries:

iMinds Interactive Limited (1)
4/F KOHO 73-75 Hung To Road, Kwun Tong, Kowloon, China (Hong Kong)
Tel.: (852) 39521311
Web Site: http://www.iminds.hk
Online Advertising Services
N.A.I.C.S.: 541810

GUOGUANG ELECTRIC COMPANY LIMITED

No 8 Jinghu Road Xinya Street, Huadu Region, Guangzhou, 510800, Guangdong, China
Tel.: (86) 2028609988 CN
Web Site: https://www.ggec.com
Year Founded: 1951
002045—(SSE)
Rev.: $841,518,288
Assets: $730,862,028
Liabilities: $427,561,524
Net Worth: $303,300,504
Earnings: $25,064,208
Emp.: 4,500
Fiscal Year-end: 12/31/22
Loudspeakers & Loudspeaker Boxes Mfr & Distr
N.A.I.C.S.: 334310
Hongda Lu (Chm)

Subsidiaries:

GGEC America, Inc. (1)
20450 Stevens Creek Blvd Ste 220, Cupertino, CA 95014 (100%)
Tel.: (408) 816-7788
Web Site: http://www.ggec.com
Emp.: 10
Audio Equipment Mfr & Distr
N.A.I.C.S.: 334310
Robert Tetzlaff (Pres & CEO)

GGEC Hong Kong Ltd. (1)
Flat 10-12 20/F Sterling Centre 11 Cheung Yue Street, Cheung Sha Wan, Kowloon, China (Hong Kong)
Tel.: (852) 25861700
Emp.: 20
Audio Equipment Mfr
N.A.I.C.S.: 334310
Danny Tsui (Gen Mgr)

GUOLIAN SECURITIES CO., LTD

No 8 Jinrong One Street, Wuxi, 214000, Jiangsu, China
Tel.: (86) 51082833209 CN
Web Site: http://www.glsc.com.cn
Year Founded: 1985
001456—(HKG)
Rev.: $410,912,744
Assets: $7,081,358,386
Liabilities: $5,458,225,601
Net Worth: $1,623,132,786
Earnings: $90,067,716
Emp.: 1,887
Fiscal Year-end: 12/31/20
Security Dealing Services
N.A.I.C.S.: 523150
Xiaobo Ge (Chm & Pres)

Subsidiaries:

Guolian Capital Co., Ltd. (1)
700 7th Floor No 8 Jinrong One Street, Wuxi, China
Tel.: (86) 51082725172
Emp.: 7
Financial Investment Services
N.A.I.C.S.: 523940
Zhengquan Li (Chm)

Hua Ying Securities Co., Ltd. (1)
Floor 15 19 Gao Lang Road East, the New District, Wuxi, 214028, China
Tel.: (86) 51085200510
Web Site: http://www.huayingsc.com
Emp.: 170
Underwriting Services
N.A.I.C.S.: 523150
Zhiying Chen (CFO)

GUOMAI CULTURE & MEDIA CO., LTD

Room 406 Building 2, Qianjiang Zhejiang Business Venture Capital Center Xihu District, Hangzhou, 310013, Zhejiang, China
Tel.: (86) 2164386485
Web Site: https://www.guomai.cc
Year Founded: 2012
301052—(CHIN)
Rev.: $67,340,239
Assets: $113,413,774
Liabilities: $18,876,704
Net Worth: $94,537,070
Earnings: $7,554,592
Fiscal Year-end: 12/31/23
Digital Marketing Services
N.A.I.C.S.: 541810
Jinbo Lu (Chm)

GUOMAI TECHNOLOGIES, INC.

No 116 East Riverside Avenue, Ma-

wei, Fuzhou, 350015, Fujian, China
Tel.: (86) 59187307399
Web Site: http://www.guomaitech.com
Year Founded: 2000
002093—(SSE)
Rev.: $72,242,820
Assets: $608,033,088
Liabilities: $110,858,436
Net Worth: $497,174,652
Earnings: $10,051,236
Fiscal Year-end: 12/31/22
Telecommunication Outsourcing Services
N.A.I.C.S.: 517810
Wei Chen *(Chm & Gen Mgr)*

GUOSEN SECURITIES CO. LTD.
Guosen Securities Building No 1012 Hongling Middle Road, Shenzhen, 518001, China
Tel.: (86) 75582130833
Web Site: https://www.guosen.com.cn
002736—(SSE)
Rev.: $2,228,958,108
Assets: $55,364,041,512
Liabilities: $40,357,383,300
Net Worth: $15,006,658,212
Earnings: $854,753,796
Fiscal Year-end: 12/31/22
Securities & Investment Brokerage
N.A.I.C.S.: 523150

GUOSHENG FINANCIAL HOLDING INC.
12th Floor Bank of Beijing Building 1115 Fenghuang Middle Avenue, Honggutan District, Nanchang, 330038, Guangdong, China
Tel.: (86) 79186267237
Web Site: https://www.gsfins.com
Year Founded: 1997
002670—(SSE)
Sales Range: Less than $1 Million
Home Appliance Wiring Parts & Components Mfr & Distr
N.A.I.C.S.: 332618
Chaodong Liu *(Chm)*

GUOTAI JUNAN SECURITIES (VIETNAM) CORP.
P9-10 1st floor Charm Vit tower 117 Tran Duy Hung, Cau Giay, Hanoi, Vietnam
Tel.: (84) 435730073
Web Site: http://www.vnsc.com.vn
IVS—(HNX)
Rev.: $3,317,548
Assets: $31,548,364
Liabilities: $436,555
Net Worth: $31,111,809
Earnings: $1,112,977
Emp.: 64
Fiscal Year-end: 12/31/23
Securities Dealing & Investment Banking
N.A.I.C.S.: 523150

GUOTAI JUNAN SECURITIES CO., LTD.
Guotai Junan Building No 768 Nanjing West Road, Jingan District, Shanghai, 200041, China
Tel.: (86) 2138676666
Web Site: https://www.gtja.com
Year Founded: 1999
2611—(HKG)
Rev.: $5,004,055,716
Assets: $128,129,497,729
Liabilities: $104,123,902,581
Net Worth: $24,005,595,148
Earnings: $1,297,926,396
Emp.: 15,000
Fiscal Year-end: 12/31/23

Financial Investment Services
N.A.I.C.S.: 523999
Song Wang *(Vice Chm & Pres)*
Subsidiaries:

Guotai Junan Allianz Fund Management Co., Ltd. (1)
9th Floor 1318 DBS Building Shanghai Lujiazui Rd, Shanghai, 200121, China
Tel.: (86) 2138784766
Web Site: http://www.vip-funds.com
Fund Management Services; Owned 33% by Allianz Global Investors AG & 67% by Guotai Junan Securities Co., Ltd.
N.A.I.C.S.: 525910

Guotai Junan Capital Limited (1)
27/F Low Block Grand Millennium Plaza 181 Queens Road Central, Hong Kong, China (Hong Kong)
Tel.: (852) 25097528
Financial Information Services
N.A.I.C.S.: 522320

Guotai Junan FX Limited (1)
27/F Low Block Grand Millennium Plaza 181 Queens Road Central, Hong Kong, China (Hong Kong)
Tel.: (852) 25099788
Foreign Currency Exchange Services
N.A.I.C.S.: 524210

Guotai Junan Financial Holdings Co., Ltd (1)
27/F Low Block Grand Millennium Plaza, Sheung Wan, Hong Kong, China (Hong Kong)
Tel.: (852) 25097546
Holding Company
N.A.I.C.S.: 551112

Guotai Junan Futures (Hong Kong) Limited (1)
27/F Low Block Grand Millennium Plaza 181 Queens Road Central, Hong Kong, China (Hong Kong)
Tel.: (852) 25099277
Futures Brokerage Services
N.A.I.C.S.: 524210

Guotai Junan Futures Co., Ltd. (1)
30F One Museum Place 669 Xinzha Rd, Jingan District, Shanghai, 200042, China
Tel.: (86) 2133038788
Web Site: https://en.gtjaqh.com
Future Investment Consulting & Asset Management Services
N.A.I.C.S.: 531390

Guotai Junan Innovation Investment Co., Ltd. (1)
31st Floor Bohua Plaza Lane 669 Xinzha Road, Jingan District, Shanghai, China
Tel.: (86) 2138675884
Web Site: https://www.gtjaiic.com
Financial Information Services
N.A.I.C.S.: 522320

Guotai Junan International Holdings Limited (1)
14/F Man Yee Building 68 Des Voeux Road, Central, China (Hong Kong)
Tel.: (852) 25097526
Web Site: https://www.gtja.com.hk
Rev.: $295,151,918
Assets: $12,043,023,465
Liabilities: $10,138,658,475
Net Worth: $1,904,364,990
Earnings: $10,587,855
Emp.: 625
Fiscal Year-end: 12/31/2022
Investment Banking & Securities Dealing
N.A.I.C.S.: 523150
Fung Yim *(Chm & CEO)*

Guotai Junan Securities (Hong Kong) Limited (1)
14/F Man Yee Building 68 Des Voeux Road Central, Hong Kong, China (Hong Kong)
Tel.: (852) 22500898
Web Site: https://www.gtjai.com
Wealth Management Services
N.A.I.C.S.: 525910

Guotai Junan Securities (Vietnam) Corporation (1)
P9-10 1st Floor Charmvit Tower 117 Tran Duy Hung, Trung Hoa Ward Cau Giay District, Hanoi, Vietnam

Tel.: (84) 2435730073
Web Site: https://gtjai.com.vn
Security Investment Consulting Services
N.A.I.C.S.: 541690

Guotai Junan Zhengyu Investment Co., Ltd. (1)
35th Floor Bohua Plaza No 669 Xinzha Road, Shanghai, 200041, China
Tel.: (86) 2138031809
Web Site: https://www.gtjazytz.com
Financial Information Services
N.A.I.C.S.: 522320

HuaAn Asset Management (Hong Kong) Limited (1)
Room 4702 47th Floor Central Plaza 18 Harbor Road, Chai Wan, China (Hong Kong)
Tel.: (852) 31901000
Web Site: https://huaan.com.hk
Asset Management Services
N.A.I.C.S.: 541618

HuaAn Funds Management Co., Ltd. (1)
31F Phase 2 Shanghai IFC 8 Century Avenue, Pudong District, Shanghai, 200120, China
Tel.: (86) 4008850099
Web Site: https://www.huaan.com.cn
Investment Management Service
N.A.I.C.S.: 525910

Shanghai Guotai Junan Securities Asset Management Co., Ltd. (1)
23F No 669 Xinzha Rd, Jingan District, Shanghai, China
Tel.: (86) 2138679666
Financial Information Services
N.A.I.C.S.: 522320

Virtual Mind Holding Company Limited (1)
Room 706 7/F Capital Centre 151 Gloucester Road, Wanchai, China (Hong Kong) (67.68%)
Tel.: (852) 21501000
Web Site: http://www.cefcfi.com.hk
Rev.: $11,426,550
Assets: $36,767,558
Liabilities: $10,081,808
Net Worth: $26,685,750
Earnings: ($8,399,063)
Emp.: 150
Fiscal Year-end: 12/31/2022
Women's Clothing Mfr
N.A.I.C.S.: 315250
Lin Guo *(Chm)*

GUOYUAN SECURITIES CO., LTD.
Building A Anhui International Financial Center No 18 Meishan Road, Hefei, 230001, Anhui, China
Tel.: (86) 4008888777
Web Site: https://www.gyzq.com.cn
Year Founded: 2001
000728—(SSE)
Rev.: $749,883,420
Assets: $18,179,083,260
Liabilities: $13,551,872,724
Net Worth: $4,627,210,536
Earnings: $243,287,928
Fiscal Year-end: 12/31/22
Security Brokerage Services
N.A.I.C.S.: 561612
Shen Hefu *(Chm)*

GURANS LIFE INSURANCE COMPANY LTD.
4th Floor Shree Raj Bhawan Tinkune, Kathmandu, Nepal
Tel.: (977) 1 5199310
Web Site: http://www.guranslife.com
GLICL—(NEP)
Sales Range: Less than $1 Million
Insurance Services
N.A.I.C.S.: 524298
Narayan Kumar Bhattarai *(CEO)*

GURIT HOLDING AG
Ebnaterstrasse 79, 9630, Wattwil, Switzerland

Tel.: (41) 443161555
Web Site: https://www.gurit.com
GURN—(SWX)
Rev.: $546,531,973
Assets: $330,486,096
Liabilities: $236,953,887
Net Worth: $93,532,209
Earnings: $4,742,097
Emp.: 2,295
Fiscal Year-end: 12/31/23
Plastics Material & Resin Manufacturing
N.A.I.C.S.: 325211
Rudolf Hadorn *(CEO)*
Subsidiaries:

China Techno Foam Co Ltd (1)
Economic & Technical Development Zone No 38 Kaituo Road, Qingdao, 266510, China
Tel.: (86) 532 8681 8444
Sales Range: $50-74.9 Million
Emp.: 12
Polyvinyl Chloride Foam Products Mfr
N.A.I.C.S.: 326150
Seshadri Srinivasan *(Gen Mgr)*

Fiberline Composites A/S (1)
Barmstedt Alle 5, 5500, Middelfart, Denmark (100%)
Tel.: (45) 70137713
Web Site: http://www.fiberline.com
Sales Range: $25-49.9 Million
Emp.: 220
Plastic Composite Profiles Mfr
N.A.I.C.S.: 326130
Stig Petersen *(Mgr-Sls)*

Gurit (1)
11 John Glenn Avenue, Auckland, 632, Albany, New Zealand (100%)
Tel.: (64) 94156262
Web Site: http://www.gurit.com
Emp.: 25
Marine Engineering & Shipbuilding
N.A.I.C.S.: 336611

Gurit (Asia Pacific) Ltd. (1)
11 John Glenn Avenue, Private Box 302-191, Rosedale, Auckland, 0632, New Zealand
Tel.: (64) 94156262
Sales Range: $25-49.9 Million
Emp.: 25
Marine Composite Material Mfr & Distr
N.A.I.C.S.: 336999

Gurit (Australia) Pty Ltd (1)
Unit 1A- 81 Bassett Street, 2103, Mona Vale, NSW, Australia (100%)
Tel.: (61) 299797248
Web Site: http://www.gurit.com
Sales Range: $25-49.9 Million
Emp.: 20
Plastics Product Mfr
N.A.I.C.S.: 326199

Gurit (Canada) Inc (1)
555 Boulevard Poirier, Magog, J1X 7L1, QC, Canada
Tel.: (819) 847-2182
Web Site: http://www.gurit.com
Sales Range: $100-124.9 Million
Emp.: 300
Fabricated Structural Metal Mfr
N.A.I.C.S.: 332312

Gurit (India) Pvt. Ltd (1)
Unit GB-140A GB-140B & GB-170 Greenbase Industrial and Logistic Park, Hiranandani Oradagam Vadakkupattu Village, Chennai, 603204, Aundh, India
Tel.: (91) 9043336865
Sales Range: $50-74.9 Million
Emp.: 9
Composite Materials Distr
N.A.I.C.S.: 423830
Gernot Becker *(Gen Mgr)*

Gurit (Kassel) GmbH (1)
Otto-Hahn-Strasse 5, 34123, Kassel, Germany (100%)
Tel.: (49) 561 998 5630
Web Site: http://www.gurit.com
Sales Range: $25-49.9 Million
Emp.: 80
Laminated Plastics Plate Sheet & Shape Mfr

GURIT HOLDING AG

Gurit Holding AG—(Continued)
N.A.I.C.S.: 326130

Gurit (Spain) Ltd (1)
Poligono Industrial Romica Calle Lisboa numero 5, 02007, Albacete, Spain.
Tel.: (34) 967254507
Web Site: http://www.es.gurit.com
Plastics Product Mfr
N.A.I.C.S.: 326199

Gurit (Tianjin) Composite Material Co., Ltd. (1)
No 1 Hengtong Road Yat Sen Park, WuQing District, Tianjin, 301726, China.
Tel.: (86) 2282106850
Plastic Material & Resin Mfr
N.A.I.C.S.: 325211

Gurit (UK) Limited (1)
St Cross Business Park, Newport, PO30 5WU, Isle of Wight, United Kingdom
Tel.: (44) 198 382 8000
Web Site: https://www.gurit.com
Sales Range: $125-149.9 Million
Emp.: 350
Synthetic Rubber Mfr
N.A.I.C.S.: 325212

Subsidiary (Domestic):

Gurit Composite Components Limited (2)
Saint Cross Business Park, Newport, PO30 5WU, Isle of Wight, United Kingdom
Tel.: (44) 1983828000
Sales Range: $25-49.9 Million
Emp.: 45
Automobile Parts Mfr
N.A.I.C.S.: 336390

Gurit (UK) Ltd (1)
St Cross Business Park, Isle of Wight, Newport, PO30 5WU, Hampshire, United Kingdom
Tel.: (44) 1983828000
Emp.: 10
Structural Engineering Services
N.A.I.C.S.: 541330

Gurit (USA) Inc (1)
115 Broadcommon Rd, Bristol, RI 02809 (100%)
Tel.: (401) 396-5008
Sales Range: $25-49.9 Million
Emp.: 1
Adhesive Mfr
N.A.I.C.S.: 325520

Gurit (Zullwil) AG (1)
Fabrikweg 54, Zullwil, Solothurn, 4234, Switzerland
Tel.: (41) 617950601
Web Site: http://www.gurit.com
Sales Range: $25-49.9 Million
Emp.: 30
Plastics Product Mfr
N.A.I.C.S.: 326199

Gurit Americas Inc. (1)
555 Boul Poirier, Magog, J1X 7L1, QC, Canada
Tel.: (819) 847-2182
Plastic Material & Resin Mfr
N.A.I.C.S.: 325211

Gurit Balsa, S.L. (1)
Avda Jaume I 76 4rta 1a, 17001, Girona, Spain
Tel.: (34) 972574514
Wind Energy Equipment Mfr
N.A.I.C.S.: 333611
Josep Fabregas (Head-Ops Excellence)

Gurit Composite Components Ltd. (1)
St Cross Business Park, Newport, PO30 5WU, United Kingdom
Tel.: (44) 1983828000
Wind Energy Equipment Mfr
N.A.I.C.S.: 333611
Andrew Ash (Mgr-MP&L)

Gurit Italy S.R.L. (1)
Via Torino N 105, 10088, Volpiano, TO, Italy
Tel.: (39) 0119952881
Wind Energy Equipment Mfr
N.A.I.C.S.: 333611

Gurit Scandinavia ApS (1)
Ndr Strandvej 119 Floor, 3150, Hellebaek, Denmark (100%)
Tel.: (45) 70255005
Business Support Services
N.A.I.C.S.: 561499

Gurit Services AG (1)
Thurgauerstrasse 54, 8050, Zurich, Switzerland (100%)
Tel.: (41) 443161550
Sales Range: $25-49.9 Million
Emp.: 12
Business Service Centers
N.A.I.C.S.: 561439

Gurit Tooling (Taicang) Co., Ltd. (1)
No 181 Changsheng North Road, Economic Development District, Taicang, 215400, Jiangsu, China
Tel.: (86) 51253370210
Sales Range: $200-249.9 Million
Emp.: 400
Wind Turbine Blade Mold Mfr
N.A.I.C.S.: 333511

JSB Group A/S (1)
Frejasvej 7, 6950, Ringkobing, Denmark
Tel.: (45) 9 732 0835
Web Site: http://www.jsbglobal.com
Wind Energy Equipment Mfr
N.A.I.C.S.: 333611
Johan Gralen (CTO)

GURKHAS FINANCE LIMITED
Dillibazar Charkhal Road, Kathmandu, Nepal
Tel.: (977) 14437401
Web Site: http://www.gurkhasfinance.com.np
Financial Services
N.A.I.C.S.: 523999
Mukunda Shrestha (COO & Sec)

GURKTALER AKTIENGESELLSCHAFT
Heiligenstadter Strasse 43, 1190, Vienna, Austria
Tel.: (43) 136708490
Web Site: https://gruppe.gurktaler.at
GAGS—(VIE)
Alcohol Producer
N.A.I.C.S.: 312140
Eduard Kranebitter (CEO)

GURU APP FACTORY CORP.
74 Norfolk House Rd, London, SW16 1JH, United Kingdom
Tel.: (44) 7944544871   NV
Web Site: https://guru-app.com
Year Founded: 2023
Rev.: $82,500
Assets: $68,190
Liabilities: $25,803
Net Worth: $42,387
Earnings: ($22,972)
Fiscal Year-end: 07/31/24
Software Development Services
N.A.I.C.S.: 541511

GURU ORGANIC ENERGY CORP.
135 Yorkville Avenue Suite 900, Toronto, M5R 3N5, ON, Canada
Tel.: (416) 972-9993
GURU—(TSX)
Rev.: $22,749,448
Assets: $51,120,994
Liabilities: $8,029,099
Net Worth: $43,091,895
Earnings: ($13,740,730)
Emp.: 70
Fiscal Year-end: 10/31/22
Business Consulting Services
N.A.I.C.S.: 522299

GURUM COMPANY INC.
6F 8 Seongnamdaero 331gil Bundang-gu, Seongnam, Gyeonggi-do, Korea (South)
Tel.: (82) 316079951
Web Site: http://www.gurumcompany.com
Year Founded: 2013
Game Development Services
N.A.I.C.S.: 513210

GURUNAVI, INC.
Hibiya Mitsui Tower 11th Floor 1-1-2 Yurakucho, Chiyoda-ku, Tokyo, 100-0006, Japan
Tel.: (81) 332158818   JP
Web Site: https://corporate.gnavi.co.jp
Year Founded: 1989
2440—(TKS)
Rev.: $85,811,020
Assets: $75,426,710
Liabilities: $34,861,140
Net Worth: $40,565,570
Earnings: ($2,399,430)
Emp.: 987
Fiscal Year-end: 03/31/24
Restaurant Search Engine
N.A.I.C.S.: 519290
Yohei Udagawa (Exec Officer-Restaurant Support)

GUS GROUP AG & CO KG
Bonner StraSSe 172-176, Cologne, 50968, Germany
Tel.: (49) 221 376 59 0
Web Site: http://www.gus-group.com
Software Mfr
N.A.I.C.S.: 513210
Dirk Bingler (Mng Dir)

Subsidiaries:

Blomesystem GmbH (1)
Strasse des Friedens 200, D-07548, Gera, Germany
Tel.: (49) 36552787800
Web Site: http://www.blomesystem.com
Laboratory Information Management Solutions
N.A.I.C.S.: 513210
Kristin Schumann (Mng Dir)

GUSBOURNE PLC
Kenardington Road, Appledore, Ashford, TN26 2BE, Kent, United Kingdom
Tel.: (44) 1622809763   UK
Web Site: https://www.gusbourne.com
Year Founded: 2008
GUS—(AIM)
Rev.: $8,656,905
Assets: $37,061,348
Liabilities: $20,135,067
Net Worth: $16,926,281
Earnings: ($3,187,326)
Emp.: 96
Fiscal Year-end: 12/31/22
Investment Management Service
N.A.I.C.S.: 523999
Andrew C. V. Weeber (Chm)

GUSHENGTANG HOLDINGS LIMITED
Room 005 No 419 Qingsha Road, Dongchong Town Nansha District, Guangzhou, China   Ky
Web Site: https://www.gstzy.cn
Year Founded: 2010
2273—(HKG)
Rev.: $321,686,835
Assets: $467,897,375
Liabilities: $148,601,434
Net Worth: $319,295,940
Earnings: $35,021,599
Emp.: 2,659
Fiscal Year-end: 12/31/23
Holding Company
N.A.I.C.S.: 551112
Jie Li (VP)

GUSTAFSON'S KIA

INTERNATIONAL PUBLIC

112 N Broadway Ave, Williams Lake, V2G 2X8, BC, Canada
Tel.: (250) 392-3035
Web Site: http://www.gustafsonskia.ca
Rev.: $13,347,016
Emp.: 30
New & Used Car Dealer
N.A.I.C.S.: 441110
William Cheung (Mgr-Fin Svcs)

GUTA-BANK JSC
Orlikov Per 5 Building 3, 107078, Moscow, Russia
Tel.: (7) 4957717444
Web Site: http://www.gutabank.ru
Commercial Banking Services
N.A.I.C.S.: 522110

GUTHRIE GTS LIMITED
1 Fifth Avenue 02-06/07 Guthrie House, Singapore, 268802, Singapore
Tel.: (65) 64662555   SG
Web Site: http://www.guthrie-gts.com
Year Founded: 1821
Sales Range: $200-249.9 Million
Property Development & Management Services
N.A.I.C.S.: 531311
Jerome Jansen (Sec)

Subsidiaries:

Craig Development Pte Ltd (1)
20 Craig Rd 02-K1 Craig Pl, Singapore, 089692, Singapore
Tel.: (65) 64385331
Web Site: http://www.guthrie-gts.com
Property Development Services
N.A.I.C.S.: 531210
Michael Leong (Mng Dir)

Guthrie Construction & Retrofitting (S) Pte Ltd (1)
Guthrie House 1 Fifth Avenue 02-06/07, Singapore, Singapore
Tel.: (65) 64662555
Construction & Retrofitting Consulting Services
N.A.I.C.S.: 236220
Harry Ong (Mng Dir)

Guthrie Consultancy Services Pte Ltd (1)
Guthrie House 02-06/07 1 Fifth Avenue, Singapore, 268802, Singapore
Tel.: (65) 64662555
Web Site: http://www.3-gts.com
Sales Range: $25-49.9 Million
Emp.: 60
Business Management Consulting Services
N.A.I.C.S.: 541611
Ben Yeo (Mng Dir)

Guthrie Engineering (S) Pte Ltd (1)
6 Aljunied Avenue 3,04-00, Singapore, 389322, Singapore
Tel.: (65) 67462222
Web Site: http://www.guthrie.com.sg
Sales Range: $25-49.9 Million
Emp.: 200
Mechanical & Electrical Engineering Services
N.A.I.C.S.: 541330
Tan Aik Khw (Mng Dir)

Subsidiary (Domestic):

Guthrie FMC Pte Ltd (2)
6 Aljunied Ave 3 03-01, Singapore, 389932, Singapore
Tel.: (65) 67451556
Web Site: http://www.guthrie.com.sg
Sales Range: $75-99.9 Million
Emp.: 200
Property & Facility Management Services
N.A.I.C.S.: 531312

Guthrie Marketing (S) Pte Ltd (1)
18 Soon Lee Road, Jurong, Singapore
Tel.: (65) 62621969
Bonded Warehousing Services
N.A.I.C.S.: 493110

AND PRIVATE COMPANIES

Guthrie Overseas Investments Pte Ltd (1)
1 Fifth Avenue 02-06/07 Guthrie House, Singapore, 268802, Singapore
Tel.: (65) 64662555
Web Site: http://www.guthrie-gts.com
Emp.: 50
Investment Management Service
N.A.I.C.S.: 523940

Guthrie PMS (S) Pte Ltd (1)
Guthrie House 1 Fifth Avenue Suite 02-06/07, Singapore, 268802, Singapore
Tel.: (65) 64662555
Sales Range: $50-74.9 Million
Emp.: 60
Property Management Services
N.A.I.C.S.: 531312

PT Guthrie Jaya Indah Island Resort (1)
Jalan Ir Sutami Patam Lestari, Sekupang, Batam, 24922, Riau Islands, Indonesia
Tel.: (62) 778 323702
Web Site: http://www.indahpuri.com
Sales Range: $25-49.9 Million
Emp.: 200
Golf Resort Operation Services
N.A.I.C.S.: 721110
Teresa Doong (Exec Dir)

GUTJAHR SYSTEMTECHNIK GMBH

Philipp-Reis-Str 5-7, D-64404, Bickenbach, Germany
Tel.: (49) 625793060
Web Site: http://www.gutjahr.com
Year Founded: 1989
Rev.: $16,711,431
Emp.: 47
Drainage Covering Services
N.A.I.C.S.: 339999
Walter Gutjahr (Founder)

GUTS GROUP INC.

6 PreedeePhanomyong 21 Sukhumvit 71, Phrakhanong Wattana, Bangkok, 10110, Thailand
Tel.: (66) 27629500
Web Site: http://www.gutsgroup.com
Year Founded: 1980
Sales Range: $200-249.9 Million
Emp.: 15,000
Security Services
N.A.I.C.S.: 561621
Vallop Kingchansilp (Pres & Mng Dir)

Subsidiaries:

GUTS INVESTIGATION CO., LTD. (1)
6 Preedee Phanomyong 21 Sukhumvit 71 Phrakhanong Wattana, Bangkok, 10110, Thailand
Tel.: (66) 2762 9500
Professional Investigation Services
N.A.I.C.S.: 561611

Subsidiary (Domestic):

GUTS Securitech Co., Ltd. (2)
6 Soi Pridi Banomyong 21 Sukhumvit 71 Rd North Prakanong Watthana, Bangkok, 10110, Thailand
Tel.: (66) 2762 9500
Web Site: http://www.gutssecuritech.com
Sales Range: $10-24.9 Million
Emp.: 30
Security System & Equipment Installation Services
N.A.I.C.S.: 561621
Ekachon Kingchansilp (Gen Mgr)

GUTS Operation Co., Ltd. (1)
6 Soi ChuleepornaSukhumvit 71 Rd, Phra Khanong Nua, 10110, Thailand
Tel.: (66) 23811728
Security Service Provider
N.A.I.C.S.: 561612

GUYANA FRONTIER MINING CORP.

Suite 1 246 E 1st Street, North Vancouver, V7L 1B3, BC, Canada
Tel.: (604) 558-0077 Ca
Web Site: http://www.guyanafrontier.com
Sales Range: Less than $1 Million
Mineral Exploration Services
N.A.I.C.S.: 213114
Evangelos F. Gnissios (Pres, CEO & Sec)

GUYANA GOLDSTRIKE INC.

510 - 580 Hornby Street, Vancouver, V6C 3B6, BC, Canada
Tel.: (877) 844-4661 BC
Web Site: http://www.guyanagoldstrike.com
Year Founded: 2006
GYA—(OTCIQ)
Assets: $93,955
Liabilities: $1,022,023
Net Worth: ($928,068)
Earnings: ($1,156,870)
Fiscal Year-end: 04/30/21
Marudi Gold Exploration & Development
N.A.I.C.S.: 212220
Scott Davis (CFO)

GUYOUNG TECH. CO., LTD

Dalsulgun Gujimyeon Gukkasandan-daero 39 rd 119, Daegu, Korea (South)
Tel.: (82) 535926111
Web Site: https://www.guyoungtech.com
Year Founded: 1989
053270—(KRS)
Rev.: $210,317,348
Assets: $184,171,685
Liabilities: $120,184,277
Net Worth: $63,987,408
Earnings: $3,049,391
Emp.: 282
Fiscal Year-end: 12/31/22
Automobile Parts Mfr
N.A.I.C.S.: 336211
Huihwa Lee (CEO)

Subsidiaries:

Guyoung Tech. Co., Ltd - Alabama Factory (1)
4988 Highway 31, Evergreen, AL 36401
Tel.: (251) 966-4880
Emp.: 300
Automobile Parts Distr
N.A.I.C.S.: 441330
Jong Young Lee (Gen Mgr)

Guyoung Tech. Co., Ltd - Daegu Plant (1)
2 Holim-dong, Dalseo-gu, Daegu, 42715, Korea (South)
Tel.: (82) 53 592 6111
Web Site: http://www.guyoungtech.com
Emp.: 300
Automobile Parts Distr
N.A.I.C.S.: 441330
Mia Kuratko (Gen Mgr)

Guyoung Tech. Co., Ltd - YEONG-CHEON PLANT (1)
150-7 Bukan-myun, Yeongcheon, 150-7, Gyeongsan buk-do, Korea (South)
Tel.: (82) 54 334 7384
Web Site: http://www.guyoungtech.com
Emp.: 200
Automobile Parts Distr
N.A.I.C.S.: 441330
Chee Hwa Lee (CEO)

GUYSON INTERNATIONAL LIMITED

Snaygill Industrial Estate, Keighley Road, Skipton, BD23 2QR, North Yorkshire, United Kingdom
Tel.: (44) 1756 799911
Web Site: http://www.guyson.co.uk
Year Founded: 1938
Sales Range: $10-24.9 Million
Emp.: 110
Blast Finishing, Spray Wash & Ultrasonic Cleaning Equipment Designer & Mfr; Hose & Couplings Supplier
N.A.I.C.S.: 333248
James R. F. Thomson (Owner)

Subsidiaries:

Guyson CN (1)
28 Suite Building ZhenXin Road, Xing An, Wuxi, 214000, Jiangsu, China
Tel.: (86) 510 82 79 01 20
Web Site: http://www.guyson.cn
Emp.: 1
Cleaning Equipment Whslr
N.A.I.C.S.: 423850

Guyson Corporation of U.S.A. (1)
13 Grande Blvd, Saratoga Springs, NY 12966-9090
Tel.: (518) 587-7894
Web Site: http://www.guyson.com
Blast Finishing, Spray Wash & Ultrasonic Cleaning Equipment Designer, Mfr & Whslr
N.A.I.C.S.: 333248
Steve Byrnes (Pres)

Guyson International Limited - Hose & Couplings Division (1)
Southview Business Park, Guiseley, Leeds, LS20 9PR, United Kingdom
Tel.: (44) 1943 870044
Web Site: http://www.guyson.co.uk
Emp.: 13
Ultrasonic Cleaning Equipment Design & Mfr
N.A.I.C.S.: 335999
Stev Sthosielv (Gen Mgr)

Guyson SA (1)
1 rue du Gue, 77990, Le Mesnil-Amelot, France
Tel.: (33) 1 60 27 25 00
Web Site: http://www.guyson.fr
Blast Finishing Equipment Sales & Service
N.A.I.C.S.: 423830

Guyson Sdn Bhd (1)
Shoplot 10 G/F Hotel Equatorial, 1 Jalan Bukit Jambul, 11900, Penang, Malaysia
Tel.: (60) 46 41 49 95
Web Site: http://www.guyson.co.uk
Blast Finishing Equipment Sales & Service
N.A.I.C.S.: 423830
Leong Keh (Gen Mgr)

GV FILMS LTD

408 Sagar Avenue 54B S V Road Andheri West, Mumbai, 400058, Maharashtra, India
Tel.: (91) 2226135910
Web Site: https://www.gvfilms.in
523277—(BOM)
Rev.: $66,626
Assets: $9,388,211
Liabilities: $6,210,177
Net Worth: $3,178,034
Earnings: ($286,445)
Emp.: 17
Fiscal Year-end: 03/31/21
Film Production & Distribution
N.A.I.C.S.: 512110
Ishari Kadhirvelan Ganesh (Chm)

GVIC COMMUNICATIONS CORP.

389 West 6th Avenue, Vancouver, V5Y 1L1, BC, Canada
Tel.: (604) 708-3264
Web Site: http://www.gviccommunications.ca
Year Founded: 2006
GCT—(TSX)
Rev.: $141,408,700
Assets: $203,781,882
Liabilities: $102,836,012
Net Worth: $100,945,869
Earnings: $27,886,876
Emp.: 1,384
Fiscal Year-end: 12/31/19
Newspaper Publishing Services
N.A.I.C.S.: 513110
Bruce W. Aunger (Sec)

GVK POWER AND INFRASTRUCTURE LIMITED

Subsidiaries:

Alta Newspaper Group Limited Partnership (1)
504 7 St S, Lethbridge, T1J 2H1, AB, Canada
Tel.: (403) 328-4411
Newspaper Publishers
N.A.I.C.S.: 513110

BIG Magazines Limited Partnership (1)
12 Concorde Pl Ste 800, North York, M3C 4J2, ON, Canada
Tel.: (416) 442-5600
Newspaper Publishers
N.A.I.C.S.: 513110

Canada's Outdoor Shows Limited Partnership (1)
160 Research Lane Unit 101, Guelph, N1G 5B2, ON, Canada
Tel.: (519) 822-2890
Web Site: http://www.canadasoutdoorshows.com
Trade Fair Management Services
N.A.I.C.S.: 561920
Doug Wagner (Pres)

Eco Log Environmental Risk Information Services Ltd. (1)
38 Lesmill Road Unit 2, Toronto, M3B 2T5, ON, Canada
Tel.: (416) 510-5204
Web Site: http://www.erisinfo.com
Emp.: 50
Newspaper Publishers
N.A.I.C.S.: 513110

Hawker Siddeley Canada Inc. (1)
Suite 640 3 Robert Speck Parkway, Mississauga, L4Z 2G5, ON, Canada
Tel.: (905) 897-7161
Newspaper Publishers
N.A.I.C.S.: 513110

Inceptus Media GP Inc. (1)
1 Place du Commerce Suite 315, Nuns, Montreal, H3E 1A2, QC, Canada
Tel.: (514) 767-3855
Web Site: http://www.inceptusmedia.com
Software Development Services
N.A.I.C.S.: 541512

JWP Publishing Limited Partnership (1)
6111 91 St NW, Edmonton, T6E 6V6, AB, Canada
Tel.: (780) 944-9333
Newspaper Publishers
N.A.I.C.S.: 513110

PrintWest Communications Ltd. (1)
1111 8 Ave, Regina, S4R 1E1, SK, Canada
Tel.: (306) 525-2304
Newspaper Publishers
N.A.I.C.S.: 513110

STP Publications Limited Partnership (1)
267 Esplanade W Suite 306, North Vancouver, V7M 1A5, BC, Canada
Tel.: (604) 983-3434
Newspaper Publishers
N.A.I.C.S.: 513110

Sunshine Coast Reporter Partnership (1)
5485 Wharf Road, PO Box 1388, Sechelt, V0N 3A0, BC, Canada
Tel.: (604) 885-4811
Web Site: http://www.coastreporter.net
Emp.: 17
Newspaper Publishers
N.A.I.C.S.: 513110
Peter Kvarnstrom (Publr)

Western Producer Publications Partnership (1)
2310 Millar Avenue, Saskatoon, S7K 2C4, SK, Canada
Tel.: (306) 665-3500
Newspaper Publishers
N.A.I.C.S.: 513110

GVK POWER AND INFRASTRUCTURE LIMITED

GVK POWER AND INFRASTRUCTURE LIMITED

GVK Power and Infrastructure Limited—(Continued)

Paigah House 156-159 SP Road, Secunderabad, 500003, Telangana, India
Tel.: (91) 402 790 2663   In
Web Site: http://www.gvk.com
Rev.: $625,668,540
Assets: $3,129,684,924
Liabilities: $2,951,088,828
Net Worth: $178,596,096
Earnings: ($43,653,828)
Emp.: 2,894
Fiscal Year-end: 03/31/19
Power Plant & Infrastructure Developer
N.A.I.C.S.: 237130
P. V. Rama Seshu *(Officer-Compliance, Sec & Asst VP)*

Subsidiaries:

GVK Airport Developers Private Limited   (1)
Darshak Chambers Plot No 32 Ground Floor House No 1-8-303/48/32, Street No 1 Penderghast Road, Secunderabad, 500003, Telangana, India
Tel.: (91) 4027902663
Web Site: https://www.gvk.com
Emp.: 170
Infrastructure Development Services
N.A.I.C.S.: 237310
G. V. Krishna Reddy *(Mng Dir)*

GVK Biosciences Pvt. Ltd.   (1)
Plot 28A IDA Nacharam, Hyderabad, 500 076, India
Tel.: (91) 40 66929999
Web Site: http://www.gvkbio.com
Emp.: 2,400
Contract Research Services to Pharmaceutical & Biotechnology Companies
N.A.I.C.S.: 541714
Manni Kantipudi *(CEO)*

Subsidiary (US):

Aragen Bioscience, Inc.   (2)
380 Woodview Ave, Morgan Hill, CA 95037   (65%)
Tel.: (408) 779-1700
Web Site: http://www.aragenbio.com
Sales Range: $1-9.9 Million
Emp.: 50
Research & Development in Biotechnology
N.A.I.C.S.: 541714
Malavika Ghosh *(VP-Vivo Svcs)*

GVK Industries Limited   (1)
Paigah House 156-159 SP Rd, Secunderabad, 500003, Andhra Pradesh, India
Tel.: (91) 4027902663
Web Site: http://www.gvk.com
Infrastructure Development Services
N.A.I.C.S.: 237990

GVK Jaipur Expressway Private Limited   (1)
Paigah House 156-159 SP Rd, Secunderabad, 500003, Telangana, India
Tel.: (91) 4027902663
Web Site: http://www.gvk.com
Highway Construction Services
N.A.I.C.S.: 237310

GVS S.P.A.

Via Roma 50, Zola Predosa, 40069, Bologna, Italy
Tel.: (39) 0516176311
Web Site: https://www.gvs.com
Year Founded: 1979
GVS—(ITA)
Rev.: $466,605,871
Assets: $1,061,000,432
Liabilities: $700,026,980
Net Worth: $360,973,451
Earnings: $14,722,642
Emp.: 4,386
Fiscal Year-end: 12/31/23
Application Development Services
N.A.I.C.S.: 541511
Grazia Valentini *(Founder)*

Subsidiaries:

GVS Argentina SA   (1)
Francisco Acuna de Figueroa 719 Piso 11 Of 57, 1416, Buenos Aires, Argentina
Tel.: (54) 1148614750
Electronic Components Mfr
N.A.I.C.S.: 334419

GVS Filtration Co., Ltd.   (1)
88 The ParQ Building 10 Floor Unit 10E03 Ratchadapisek Road, Klongtoei Sub-district Klongtoei District, Bangkok, 10110, Thailand
Tel.: (66) 826699590
Web Site: https://www.gvs.in.th
Electronic Components Mfr
N.A.I.C.S.: 334419

GVS Filtration Sdn. Bhd.   (1)
Lot No 10F-2B 10th Floor Tower 5 PFCC, Jalan Puteri 1/2 Bandar Puteri, 47100, Puchong, Selangor, Malaysia
Tel.: (60) 128818381
Web Site: https://www.gvs-lifesciences.my
Electronic Components Mfr
N.A.I.C.S.: 334419

GVS Japan KK   (1)
KKD Building 4F 7-10-12 Nishishinjuku, Shinjuku-ku, Tokyo, 160-0023, Japan
Tel.: (81) 359371447
Electronic Components Mfr
N.A.I.C.S.: 334419

GVS Korea Ltd.   (1)
315 Bricks Tower 368 Gyungchun-ro Gaundong, Namyangju, Gyunggi, Korea (South)
Tel.: (82) 315639873
Electronic Components Mfr
N.A.I.C.S.: 334419

GVS Microfiltrazione S.r.l.   (1)
Str Principala 320 ET1 Ciorani De Jos, Ciorani, Romania
Tel.: (40) 244463044
Electronic Components Mfr
N.A.I.C.S.: 334419

GVS Russia LLC   (1)
Profsoyuznaya st 25a of 102, Moscow, 117418, Russia
Tel.: (7) 4950045077
Web Site: https://gvsrus.ru
Electronic Components Mfr
N.A.I.C.S.: 334419

GVS Technology (Suzhou) Co., Ltd.   (1)
602 Changjiang Road SND, Fengqiao Civil-Run Sci-Tech Park, Suzhou, 215129, China
Tel.: (86) 51266619880
Web Site: https://www.gvs-lifesciences.cn
Electronic Components Mfr
N.A.I.C.S.: 334419

GW VITEK CO., LTD.

1101 244 Beotkkot-ro, Geumcheongu, Seoul, 153788, Korea (South)
Tel.: (82) 221403300
Web Site: https://www.gwvitek.com
036180—(KRS)
Rev.: $40,287,126
Assets: $49,790,305
Liabilities: $22,331,084
Net Worth: $27,459,221
Earnings: ($6,412,545)
Emp.: 117
Fiscal Year-end: 12/31/22
Scientific Laboratory Equipment Distr
N.A.I.C.S.: 423490

GWA GROUP LIMITED

Building 3B 188 Holt Street, Pinkenba, 4008, QLD, Australia
Tel.: (61) 731096000   AU
Web Site: http://www.gwagroup.com.au
Year Founded: 1989
GWAXF—(OTCIQ)
Rev.: $276,103
Assets: $440,628
Liabilities: $237,242
Net Worth: $203,386
Earnings: $25,795
Emp.: 504
Fiscal Year-end: 06/30/24
Building Fixtures & Fittings Distr
N.A.I.C.S.: 423720

Richard J. Thornton *(Bd of Dirs & Sec)*

Subsidiaries:

Caroma Industries Limited   (1)
39 Collins St, Alexandria, 2015, NSW, Australia
Sales Range: $25-49.9 Million
Emp.: 15
Bathroom Product Mfr
N.A.I.C.S.: 326199

Subsidiary (Non-US):

Caroma Industries (NZ) Limited   (2)
Web Site: http://www.caroma.co.nz
Sanitary Ware Mfr
N.A.I.C.S.: 327110

GWA Trading (Shanghai) Co., Ltd.   (1)
Rm 1503 15/F Block 2 Ganghui Office No 3 Hongqiao Road, Xujiahui Xuhui, Shanghai, 200030, China
Tel.: (86) 212 250 2100
Plumbing & Heating Equipment Distr
N.A.I.C.S.: 423720

Gainsborough Hardware Industries Limited   (1)
31-33 Alfred Street, Blackburn, 3130, VIC, Australia
Tel.: (61) 398771555
Web Site: http://www.gainsboroughhardware.com.au
Emp.: 500
Door & Access Systems Mfr
N.A.I.C.S.: 332321

Methven Limited   (1)
41 Jomac Place, Private Bag 19996, Avondale, Auckland, 1026, New Zealand   (100%)
Tel.: (64) 9 829 0429
Web Site: https://www.methven.com
Tap & Valve Mfr
N.A.I.C.S.: 332911
Phil Lough *(Chm)*

Sebel Furniture Holdings Pty Ltd   (1)
48 Airds Road, Minto, 2566, NSW, Australia
Tel.: (61) 130 066 4732
Web Site: https://www.sebelfurniture.com
Furniture Mfr
N.A.I.C.S.: 337121

GWANAK CONSTRUCTION AND EQUIPMENT SERVICE CO LTD

2F 293-19 Olympic-ro, Songpa-gu, Seoul, Korea (South)
Tel.: (82) 222407900
Web Site: https://www.gwan-ak.co.kr
Year Founded: 1998
Rev.: $6,152,571,227
Assets: $6,090,837,351
Liabilities: $4,080,585,462
Net Worth: $2,010,251,889
Earnings: $277,447,544
Fiscal Year-end: 12/31/19
Infrastructure Construction Services
N.A.I.C.S.: 238130

GWB IMMOBILIEN AG

Hauptstrasse 1a Siek, 22962, Hamburg, Germany
Tel.: (49) 410790800   De
G7B—(DEU)
Sales Range: Less than $1 Million
Commercial Building Construction Services
N.A.I.C.S.: 236220

GWR GROUP LIMITED

Level 4 46 Colin Street, West Perth, 6005, WA, Australia
Tel.: (61) 893226666
Web Site: https://www.gwrgroup.com.au
GWR—(ASX)
Rev.: $1,126,956
Assets: $27,884,189
Liabilities: $1,549,208

INTERNATIONAL PUBLIC

Net Worth: $26,334,981
Earnings: ($14,102,666)
Fiscal Year-end: 06/30/24
Metal Mineral Exploration
N.A.I.C.S.: 212290
Mark Pitts *(Sec)*

GXC COATINGS GMBH

Im Schleeke 27 31, 38642, Goslar, Lower Saxony, Germany
Tel.: (49) 532134300
Web Site: http://www.gxc-coatings.com
Year Founded: 1926
Sales Range: $75-99.9 Million
Emp.: 300
Glass Coating Mfr
N.A.I.C.S.: 327212

GXP GERMAN PROPERTIES AG

Oudenarder Str 16, 13347, Berlin, Germany
Tel.: (49) 3026391440
Web Site: http://www.gxpag.com
GXP1—(BER)
Sales Range: Less than $1 Million
Asset Management Services
N.A.I.C.S.: 523940
Itay Barlev *(CEO)*

GY COMMERCE CO LTD

35F Prime Center 85 Gwangnaru-ro 56-gil Gwangjin-gu, Seoul, Korea (South)
Tel.: (82) 269509500
Web Site: http://www.cycleloan.co.kr
Year Founded: 2006
Rev.: $3,631,117
Assets: $21,570,179
Liabilities: $21,284,481
Net Worth: $285,698
Earnings: ($8,437,735)
Emp.: 50
Fiscal Year-end: 12/31/19
Business Management Services
N.A.I.C.S.: 561110
Heung-Jae Lee *(CEO)*

GYAN DEVELOPERS & BUILDERS LIMITED

6 Gyan Kiran Hanumantha Rao Street North Usman Road, T Nagar, Chennai, 600 017, Tamil Nadu, India
Tel.: (91) 4424453762   In
Year Founded: 1992
530141—(BOM)
Rev.: $18,664
Assets: $662,537
Liabilities: $121,052
Net Worth: $541,484
Earnings: $10,789
Fiscal Year-end: 03/31/21
Real Estate Services
N.A.I.C.S.: 531390
T. Ashok Raj *(Mng Dir, Mng Dir & Mng Dir-Officer)*

GYARMATHY & PARTNERS LTD.

Tatra Utca 12/B, 1136, Budapest, Hungary
Tel.: (36) 13492954
Web Site: http://www.gyarmathy.hu
Year Founded: 1997
Logistics Consulting Servies
N.A.I.C.S.: 541614
Ildiko Tothne Hegyes *(Auditor)*

GYG PLC

Global Building Muelle Viejo Espigon Exterior, 07012, Palma de Mallorca, Spain
Tel.: (34) 971213305   UK
Web Site: http://www.gygplc.com
Year Founded: 1975

AND PRIVATE COMPANIES

GYG—(AIM)
Rev.: $72,340,880
Assets: $60,985,801
Liabilities: $44,421,756
Net Worth: $16,564,045
Earnings: $309,516
Emp.: 395
Fiscal Year-end: 12/31/20
Superyacht Refinishing Services
N.A.I.C.S.: 532284
Remy Millott (CEO)

Subsidiaries:

Pinmar USA, Inc. (1)
2010 Ave B, Riviera Beach, FL 33404
Tel.: (954) 760-9626
Boat Repair & Maintenance Services
N.A.I.C.S.: 811490

Pinmar Yacht Supply, S.L. (1)
Cami Escollera 5, 07012, Palma de Mallorca, Spain
Tel.: (34) 971713744
Web Site:
 http://www.pinmaryachtsupply.com
Yacht Goods Retailer
N.A.I.C.S.: 441222

GYLDENDAL A/S

Klareboderne 3, 1115, Copenhagen, K, Denmark
Tel.: (45) 33755555   DK
Web Site: https://www.gyldendal.dk
GYLD-B—(CSE)
Rev.: $102,103,862
Assets: $97,382,472
Liabilities: $50,028,215
Net Worth: $47,354,256
Earnings: ($8,772,844)
Emp.: 449
Fiscal Year-end: 12/31/22
Book Publisher, Printer, Distr & Retailer
N.A.I.C.S.: 513130
Poul Erik Toejner (Chm)

GYOR-SOPRON-EBENFURTI VASUT RT.

Szilagyi Dezso ter 1, H-1011, Budapest, Hungary
Tel.: (36) 2245899
Web Site: http://www.gysev.hu
Year Founded: 1872
Sales Range: $350-399.9 Million
Emp.: 1,800
Railway Operator
N.A.I.C.S.: 485112

GYRO COMMUNICATIONS LTD

10 Triton Street, London, NW1 3BF, United Kingdom
Tel.: (44) 20 7351 1550
Web Site: http://www.gyro.com
Sales Range: $100-124.9 Million
Emp.: 700
Advertising Services
N.A.I.C.S.: 541810
Christoph Becker (Chief Creative Officer & CEO-Global)

Subsidiaries:

Gyro Benelux B.V. (1)
Peperstraat 7, 1011 TJ, Amsterdam, Netherlands
Tel.: (31) 203 209 799
Advertising Services
N.A.I.C.S.: 541810
Michelle Henley (Exec Creative Dir & Gen Mgr)

Gyro Chicago (1)
20 W Kinzie Ste 1400, Chicago, IL 60654
Tel.: (312) 595-0203
Sales Range: $25-49.9 Million
Emp.: 40
Advertising Services
N.A.I.C.S.: 541810

Gyro Cincinnati (1)
7755 Montgomery Rd Ste 300, Cincinnati, OH 45236

Tel.: (513) 671-3811
Web Site: http://www.gyrohsr.com
Sales Range: $25-49.9 Million
Emp.: 130
Advertising Services
N.A.I.C.S.: 541810
Michael W. Hensley (Exec VP & Dir-Integrated Mktg Comm)

Gyro Denver (1)
World Trade Center 1625 Broadway Ste 2800, Denver, CO 80202
Tel.: (303) 294-9944
Sales Range: $25-49.9 Million
Emp.: 11
Advertising Services
N.A.I.C.S.: 541810

Gyro Deutschland GmbH (1)
Grosser Burstah 36-38, 20457, Hamburg, Germany
Tel.: (49) 40 38 68 74 0
Advertising Services
N.A.I.C.S.: 541810

Gyro Munich (1)
Auenstrasse 37, 80337, Munich, Germany
Tel.: (49) 89 76 77 34 0
Sales Range: $25-49.9 Million
Emp.: 15
Advertising Services
N.A.I.C.S.: 541810
Andrea Lichtenwimmer (Mng Dir)

Gyro New York (1)
115 Broadway 14th Fl, New York, NY 10006
Tel.: (212) 915-2490
Web Site: http://www.gyrohsr.com
Rev.: $100,000,000
Emp.: 250
Advertising Services
N.A.I.C.S.: 541810
Christoph Becker (CEO & Chief Creative Officer)

Gyro Paris (1)
20 Rue Mirabeau, 75016, Paris, France
Tel.: (33) 1 45 24 48 00
Web Site: http://www.gyro.com
Sales Range: $25-49.9 Million
Emp.: 20
Advertising Services
N.A.I.C.S.: 541810

Gyro Scandinavia AB (1)
Kungsgatan 15, Stockholm, 11143, Sweden
Tel.: (46) 8 462 49 00
Advertising Agencies
N.A.I.C.S.: 541810
Claes Buren (Gen Mgr)

GYROSCOPE THERAPEUTICS HOLDINGS PLC

Gyroscope Therapeutics Holdings plc, Stevenage, Hertfordshire, United Kingdom
Tel.: (44) 1438906770   UK
Year Founded: 2020
Emp.: 167
Holding Company
N.A.I.C.S.: 551112
Khurem Farooq (CEO)

GZP DOM A.D.

Preradoviceva 2a, Belgrade, Serbia
Tel.: (381) 11 6768 628
Year Founded: 1954
Sales Range: $1-9.9 Million
Emp.: 1
Building Construction Services
N.A.I.C.S.: 236116

H & R TRANSPORT LTD.

3601 2nd Ave N, Lethbridge, T1H 5K7, AB, Canada
Tel.: (403) 328-2345
Web Site: http://www.hrtrans.com
Year Founded: 1955
Truck Transportation Services
N.A.I.C.S.: 484122
Al Foder (Chm-Lethbridge)

H PIO CO., LTD.

115 Yangpyeong-ro, Yeongdeungpo-gu, Seoul, Korea (South)

Tel.: (82) 263912770
Web Site: https://www.denps.com
Year Founded: 2012
357230—(KRS)
Rev.: $150,315,425
Assets: $139,904,131
Liabilities: $15,920,179
Net Worth: $123,983,952
Earnings: $8,803,337
Emp.: 60
Fiscal Year-end: 12/31/22
Health Food Product Mfr
N.A.I.C.S.: 333241

H WORLD GROUP LIMITED

No 1299 Fenghua Road, Jiading District, Shanghai, 201803, China
Tel.: (86) 2161952011   CN
Web Site: https://ir.hworld.com
Year Founded: 2005
HTHT—(NASDAQ)
Rev.: $3,029,740,806
Assets: $8,796,521,932
Liabilities: $7,100,548,294
Net Worth: $1,695,973,638
Earnings: $571,970,536
Emp.: 26,985
Fiscal Year-end: 12/31/24
Economy Hotels Owner & Operator
N.A.I.C.S.: 721110
Qi Ji (Founder & Chm)

Subsidiaries:

Hotel Equipment & Design GmbH (1)
Lyoner Strasse 25, 60528, Frankfurt am Main, Germany
Tel.: (49) 696656403
Web Site: https://www.head-gmbh.com
Information Technology Services
N.A.I.C.S.: 541511
Lars Schmid (Mng Dir)

Intercity Hotel GmbH (1)
Lyoner Strasse 25, 60528, Frankfurt am Main, Germany
Tel.: (49) 696656404
Web Site: http://www.intercityhotel.com
Home Management Services
N.A.I.C.S.: 721110
Christian Kaschner (Mng Dir)

Jaz Hotel GmbH (1)
Lyoner Strasse 25, 60528, Frankfurt am Main, Germany
Tel.: (49) 696656401
Web Site: http://www.jaz-hotel.com
Hotel Operator
N.A.I.C.S.: 721110
Hasan Huseyin Yigit (Exec Dir)

MAXX Hotel GmbH (1)
Lyoner Strasse 25, 60528, Frankfurt am Main, Germany
Tel.: (49) 696656401
Hotel Operator
N.A.I.C.S.: 721110
Robert Boller (Mng Dir)

Sourcify GmbH (1)
Herriotstrasse 10, 60528, Frankfurt am Main, Germany
Tel.: (49) 6958809870
Web Site: https://www.sourcify.net
Information Technology Services
N.A.I.C.S.: 541511
Lars Schmid (Mng Dir)

Steigenberger Hotels Aktiengesellschaft (1)
Lyoner Strasse 25, 60528, Frankfurt am Main, Germany
Tel.: (49) 696656401
Web Site: https://hrewards.com
Hotel Operator
N.A.I.C.S.: 721110
Andre Witschi (Co-Chm)

Steigenberger Spa GmbH (1)
Lyoner Strasse 25, 60528, Frankfurt am Main, Germany
Tel.: (49) 69215908
Web Site:
 http://www.thespa.steigenberger.com
Hotel Operator

H&L GARAGES LIMITED

N.A.I.C.S.: 721110
H. Gehrmann (Mng Dir)

H&B DESIGN CO., LTD.

Space L Building 17 Dosan-daero 37-gil, Gangnam-gu, Seoul, Korea (South)
Tel.: (82) 28680246
Web Site:
 https://www.designcorp.co.kr
Year Founded: 2012
227100—(KRS)
Rev.: $9,862,811
Assets: $67,669,701
Liabilities: $36,780,778
Net Worth: $30,888,923
Earnings: ($5,924,978)
Emp.: 39
Fiscal Year-end: 12/31/22
Electronic Components Mfr
N.A.I.C.S.: 334419

H&G HIGH CONVICTION LIMITED

Level 5 107 Pitt Street, Sydney, 2000, NSW, Australia
Tel.: (61) 412308263
Web Site:
 https://www.hancockandgore.com.au
Year Founded: 2022
HCF—(ASX)
Rev.: $4,504,792
Assets: $45,782,096
Liabilities: $631,805
Net Worth: $45,150,290
Earnings: $5,329,595
Emp.: 274
Fiscal Year-end: 09/30/23
Investment Management Service
N.A.I.C.S.: 523999
Sandy Beard (Chm)

Subsidiaries:

Pegasus Health Group Pty. Ltd. (1)
1/30 Heathcote Road, Moorebank, 2170, NSW, Australia
Tel.: (61) 296016909
Web Site:
 https://www.pegasushealthcare.com
Pressuring Device Mfr & Distr
N.A.I.C.S.: 339113

H&H GROUP PLC

Borderway Mart, Rosehill Estate, Carlisle, CA1 2RS, United Kingdom
Tel.: (44) 1228406330   UK
Web Site:
 http://www.hhgroupplc.co.uk
Year Founded: 1892
Holding Company; Auction, Brokerage, Valuation & Real Estate Services
N.A.I.C.S.: 551112
Margaret Irving (Sec)

Subsidiaries:

Harrison & Hetherington Limited (1)
Borderway Mart, Rosehill Estate, Carlisle, CA1 2RS, United Kingdom
Tel.: (44) 12 2840 6200
Web Site:
 http://www.harrisonandhetherington.co.uk
Farmstock Auction, Brokerage & Valuation Services
N.A.I.C.S.: 424520
Brian Richardson (CEO)

John Swan Limited (1)
Auction Mart Newtown Saint Boswells, Melrose, TD6 0PP, Roxburghshire, United Kingdom
Tel.: (44) 1835 822 214
Web Site: http://www.johnswan.co.uk
Sales Range: $1-9.9 Million
Livestock Auctioning Services
N.A.I.C.S.: 424520

H&L GARAGES LIMITED

3191

H&L GARAGES LIMITED

H&L Garages Limited—(Continued)
Humber Rd, South Killingholme,
DN40 3DL, Lincs, United Kingdom
Tel.: (44) 1469571666 UK
Sales Range: $100-124.9 Million
Emp.: 300
New & Used Automobile Dealer
N.A.I.C.S.: 441110
Brett Whittingham *(Mng Dir)*

H&M HENNES & MAURITZ AB

Master Samuelsgatan 46A, SE-106
38, Stockholm, Sweden
Tel.: (46) 87965500 SE
Web Site: https://www.hm.com
Year Founded: 1947
HM.B—(OMX)
Rev.: $22,107,486,396
Assets: $16,978,373,467
Liabilities: $12,519,973,400
Net Worth: $4,458,400,067
Earnings: $817,012,747
Emp.: 101,103
Fiscal Year-end: 11/30/23
Clothing Product Mfr
N.A.I.C.S.: 315990
Karl-Johan Persson *(Chm)*

Subsidiaries:

FaBric Sales A/S (1)
Amagertorv 21, Copenhagen, 1160, Denmark
Tel.: (45) 70102331
Fabric Clothing Accessories Retailer
N.A.I.C.S.: 458110

Fabric Retail Glbl AB (1)
Sodra Larmgatan 11, Gothenburg, 411 16, Sweden
Tel.: (46) 313399630
Sales Range: $25-49.9 Million
Emp.: 85
Clothing Accessories Retailer
N.A.I.C.S.: 458110
Henrik Aaen *(Gen Mgr)*

Fabric Sales Norway AS (1)
Stortorvet 7, Oslo, 155, Norway
Tel.: (47) 22 79 55 61
Fabric Clothing Accessories Retailer
N.A.I.C.S.: 458110

H & M Hennes & Mauritz CZ, s.r.o. (1)
Vaclavske namesti 19, 110 00, Prague, Czech Republic
Tel.: (420) 800040464
Web Site: https://www2.hm.com
Clothing Accessories Retailer
N.A.I.C.S.: 458110

H & M Hennes & Mauritz LLP (1)
Etazh 9 Str 2 16 A Leningradskoe Shosse, Moscow, 125171, Russia
Tel.: (7) 4957899600
Web Site: http://www.hm.com
Emp.: 10
Clothing Accessories Retailer
N.A.I.C.S.: 458110

H & M Hennes & Mauritz Logistics AB Co. KG (1)
Tel.: (49) 403509550
Logistics Consulting Servies
N.A.I.C.S.: 541614

H & M Hennes & Mauritz Logistics GBC (1)
45 Rue Du Commandant Rolland, Le Bourget, 93350, France
Tel.: (33) 143117000
Logistics Consulting Servies
N.A.I.C.S.: 541614

H & M Hennes & Mauritz Logistics GBC NV (1)
Magdalenasteenweg 51, Brussels, 1000, Belgium
Tel.: (32) 22199270
Logistics Consulting Servies
N.A.I.C.S.: 541614

H & M Hennes & Mauritz Logistics Sp. z o.o. (1)
Magazynowa 3, Gadki, 62-023, Poland

Tel.: (48) 225517338
Logistics Consulting Servies
N.A.I.C.S.: 541614
Michael Schulz *(Gen Mgr)*

H & M Hennes & Mauritz Management B.V. (1)
Kalverstraat 112, Amsterdam, 1012 PK, Netherlands
Tel.: (31) 205567777
Web Site: http://www.hm.com
Sales Range: $25-49.9 Million
Emp.: 70
Clothing Apparel & Cosmetics Retailers
N.A.I.C.S.: 458110

H & M Hennes & Mauritz TR Tekstil ltd sirketi (1)
Abdi Ipekci Caddesi No 19/1 Kat 5, Nisantasi, Istanbul, 34367, Türkiye
Tel.: (90) 8503902900
Web Site: https://www2.hm.com
Sales Range: $100-124.9 Million
Emp.: 350
Clothing Accessories Retailer
N.A.I.C.S.: 458110
Goekce Kiziltepe *(Mgr-Store)*

H & M Hennes & Mauritz Vietnam LLC (1)
Metropolitan Building No 235 Dong Khoi Street, Ben Nghe Ward District 1, Ho Chi Minh City, Vietnam
Tel.: (84) 2862875147
Clothing Retailer
N.A.I.C.S.: 458110

H and M Hennes and Mauritz Proprietary Limited (1)
30 Chiappini Street, Cape Town, 8001, South Africa
Tel.: (27) 860690707
Clothing Retailer
N.A.I.C.S.: 458110

H&M Hennes & Mauritz (HK) Ltd (1)
Suite 1102 11th Floor Tower 6 China Hong Kong City 33 Canton Rd, Tsim Sha Tsui, Kowloon, China (Hong Kong)
Tel.: (852) 39737000
Web Site: http://www.hm.com
Mens & Boys Clothing & Furnishings Whslr
N.A.I.C.S.: 424350

H&M Hennes & Mauritz A.E. (1)
Pl Friendly Company 14, Kolonaki, 10674, Athens, Greece
Tel.: (30) 2103212920
Web Site: https://www2.hm.com
Sales Range: $50-74.9 Million
Emp.: 250
Family Clothing Stores
N.A.I.C.S.: 458110

H&M Hennes & Mauritz A/S (1)
Amagertorv 25 3 th, 1160, Copenhagen, Denmark
Tel.: (45) 70212200
Web Site: https://www2.hm.com
Sales Range: $400-449.9 Million
Emp.: 2,500
Family Clothing Stores
N.A.I.C.S.: 458110

H&M Hennes & Mauritz AS (1)
Karl Johans gate 16 C, 0154, Oslo, Norway
Tel.: (47) 63870000
Web Site: https://www.hm.com
Sales Range: $400-449.9 Million
Emp.: 3,500
Family Clothing Stores
N.A.I.C.S.: 458110
Lucas Seifert *(Gen Mgr)*

H&M Hennes & Mauritz B.V. & Co.KG (1)
Spitalerstrasse 12, 20095, Hamburg, Germany
Tel.: (49) 8006259900
Web Site: https://www2.hm.com
Men's Clothing Stores
N.A.I.C.S.: 458110

H&M Hennes & Mauritz Belgium NV (1)
Rue de la Madeleine 51, Magdalensteenweg 51, 1000, Brussels, Belgium
Tel.: (32) 22199870
Sales Range: $25-49.9 Million
Emp.: 50
Women's Clothing Store

N.A.I.C.S.: 458110

H&M Hennes & Mauritz Far East Ltd (1)
Twr 6 China Hong Kong City, 33 Canton Rd Tsim Sha Tsui, Kowloon, China (Hong Kong)
Tel.: (852) 27366688
Mens & Boys Clothing & Furnishings Whslr
N.A.I.C.S.: 424350

H&M Hennes & Mauritz GesmbH (1)
Kirchengasse 6/6, 1070, Vienna, Austria
Tel.: (43) 8006655900
Family Clothing Stores
N.A.I.C.S.: 458110

H&M Hennes & Mauritz Holding BV (1)
Kalverstraat 112 Kantoor, Amsterdam, 1012 PK, Netherlands
Tel.: (31) 205567777
Web Site: http://www.hm.com
Sales Range: $50-74.9 Million
Emp.: 70
Holding Company
N.A.I.C.S.: 551112

H&M Hennes & Mauritz Inc. (1)
1 Dundas St W 18th Fl Ste 1808, PO Box 47, Toronto, M5G 1Z3, ON, Canada
Tel.: (416) 623-4300
Web Site: http://www.hm.com
Sales Range: $25-49.9 Million
Emp.: 30
Family Clothing Stores
N.A.I.C.S.: 458110

H&M Hennes & Mauritz International B.V. (1)
Kalverstraat 112 Kantoor, 1012PK, Amsterdam, Netherlands
Tel.: (31) 205567777
Web Site: http://www.hm.com
Sales Range: $50-74.9 Million
Emp.: 65
Trusts Estates & Agency Accounts
N.A.I.C.S.: 525920

H&M Hennes & Mauritz LP (1)
Lighting Way 300 Ste 100, Secaucus, NJ 07094
Tel.: (212) 564-9922
Web Site: https://www2.hm.com
Sales Range: $50-74.9 Million
Emp.: 70
Home Furnishing Whslr
N.A.I.C.S.: 423220

H&M Hennes & Mauritz Netherlands BV (1)
Keizersgracht 271, 1016 ED, Amsterdam, Netherlands
Tel.: (31) 9001988
Web Site: https://www2.hm.com
Family Clothing Stores
N.A.I.C.S.: 458110
Leif Persson *(CFO)*

H&M Hennes & Mauritz OY (1)
Aleksanterinkatu 48B, 00100, Helsinki, Finland
Tel.: (358) 800114000
Web Site: https://www.hm.com
Sales Range: $200-249.9 Million
Emp.: 1,000
Women's Clothing Store
N.A.I.C.S.: 458110

H&M Hennes & Mauritz S.r.l. (1)
Via Turati 9, 20121, Milan, Italy
Tel.: (39) 0800599155
Web Site: https://www2.hm.com
Mens & Boys Clothing & Furnishings Whslr
N.A.I.C.S.: 424350

H&M Hennes & Mauritz SA (1)
Beethovenstrasse 41, Geneva, 1204, Switzerland
Tel.: (41) 223170909
Web Site: http://www.hm.com
Sales Range: $25-49.9 Million
Emp.: 30
Family Clothing Stores
N.A.I.C.S.: 458110

H&M Hennes & Mauritz SARL (1)
3 rue La Fayette, 75009, Paris, France
Tel.: (33) 805088888
Web Site: https://www2.hm.com

INTERNATIONAL PUBLIC

Sales Range: $800-899.9 Million
Emp.: 5,000
Family Clothing Stores
N.A.I.C.S.: 458110

H&M Hennes & Mauritz Sp.z o.o. (1)
ul Marszalkowska 194-122, 00-017, Warsaw, Poland
Tel.: (48) 800999888
Sales Range: $250-299.9 Million
Emp.: 1,000
Womens Childrens & Infants Clothing & Accessories Whslr
N.A.I.C.S.: 424320

H&M Hennes & Mauritz UK Ltd. (1)
1st Floor UK House 164-182 Oxford Street, London, W1D 1NN, United Kingdom
Tel.: (44) 447369000
Web Site: https://www2.hm.com
Clothing Mfr & Retailer
N.A.I.C.S.: 315990

H&M Hennes & Mauritz USA BV (1)
Kalverstraat 112, Amsterdam, 1012PK, Netherlands
Tel.: (31) 205567777
Web Site: http://www.hm.com
Emp.: 150
Trusts Estates & Agency Accounts
N.A.I.C.S.: 525920

H&M Hennes Ltd (1)
4th Floor 40 Argyll Street, 57 Rathbone Pl, London, W1F 7EB, United Kingdom
Tel.: (44) 2073232211
Sales Range: $100-124.9 Million
Emp.: 300
Women's Clothing Store
N.A.I.C.S.: 458110

H&M Rowells AB (1)
Hultagatan 47, Boras, 50189, Sweden
Tel.: (46) 33169700
Sales Range: $200-249.9 Million
Emp.: 700
Mail-Order Houses
N.A.I.C.S.: 333243

Hennes Mauritz (Shanghai) Commercial Ltd Co (1)
5th Fl 2 Twr Plz 66, 1366 W Nan Jing Rd Jing An Dis, 200040, Shanghai, China
Tel.: (86) 2123070200
Web Site: http://www.hm.com
Sales Range: $100-124.9 Million
Emp.: 300
Apparel Accessories & Apparel Mfr
N.A.I.C.S.: 315990

Impuls GmbH (1)
Komodienstrasse 11, 50667, Cologne, Germany
Tel.: (49) 221209060
Web Site: https://www.impuls-gmbh.com
Mental Health Care Services
N.A.I.C.S.: 621330

KE Persson AB (1)
Harvstigen 4, 64541, Strangnas, Sweden
Tel.: (46) 15210730
Web Site: http://www.kepab.com
Sales Range: $25-49.9 Million
Emp.: 4
Fabricated Pipe & Pipe Fitting Mfr
N.A.I.C.S.: 332996

Monki (1)
Sodra Larmgatan 11, 411 16, Gothenburg, Sweden
Tel.: (46) 844686900
Web Site: https://www.monki.com
Fabric Clothing Apparel Mfr
N.A.I.C.S.: 458110

Weekday Brands AB (1)
Forumgallerian, Uppsala, Sweden
Tel.: (46) 18126079
Web Site: http://www.weekday.se
Clothing Apparel Retailer
N.A.I.C.S.: 458110

H&R CENTURY UNION CORPORATION

Room 2201 Building 6 R And F
Ocean Plaza No 15 Beicheng Tianjie,
Jiangbei District, Chongqing, 400020,
China
Tel.: (86) 1065009170

AND PRIVATE COMPANIES

Web Site: https://www.huanruisj.com
000892—(SSE)
Rev.: $83,706,480
Assets: $321,812,244
Liabilities: $111,059,208
Net Worth: $210,753,036
Earnings: $2,520,180
Fiscal Year-end: 12/31/22
Media Services
N.A.I.C.S.: 513199
Zhong Junyan *(Chief Content Officer)*

H&R KGAA
Neuenkirchener Strasse 8, 48499, Salzbergen, Germany
Tel.: (49) 59769450
Web Site: https://www.hur.com
2HRA—(MUN)
Rev.: $1,492,719,246
Assets: $997,059,539
Liabilities: $541,139,151
Net Worth: $455,920,387
Earnings: $11,656,867
Emp.: 1,683
Fiscal Year-end: 12/31/23
Chemicals Mfr
N.A.I.C.S.: 325998
Niels Heinz Hansen *(Chm-Exec Bd & CEO)*

Subsidiaries:

GAUDLITZ GmbH (1)
Callenberger Str 42, D-96450, Coburg, Germany
Tel.: (49) 95616480
Web Site: https://www.gaudlitz.de
Emp.: 125
Engineering Plastic Product Mfr
N.A.I.C.S.: 325991

GAUDLITZ Precision Technology (Wuxi) Co., Ltd. (1)
No 67 Xuedian Road Block B State High-Tech Industry Development Zone, Wuxi, 214142, Jiangsu, China
Tel.: (86) 51085331177
Sales Range: $25-49.9 Million
Emp.: 95
Precision Plastic Parts Mfr
N.A.I.C.S.: 325211

GAUDLITZ Precision s.r.o. (1)
Borek 40, CZ-380 01, Dacice, Czech Republic
Tel.: (420) 384350300
Emp.: 99
Medical Device Mfr
N.A.I.C.S.: 339112

H&R ANZ Pty. Ltd. (1)
144-152 Fitzgerald Road North, Laverton, 3026, VIC, Australia
Tel.: (61) 393680088
Oil Refining Product Mfr
N.A.I.C.S.: 324110

H&R Benelux B.V. (1)
Thermiekstraat 2, NL-6361 HB, Nuth, Netherlands
Tel.: (31) 455656737
Sales Range: $25-49.9 Million
Emp.: 20
Aqualite Mfr
N.A.I.C.S.: 327993

H&R ChemPharm (Thailand) Ltd. (1)
B1 F5 Bangkok City Tower 179 S Sathorn Rd, Tungmahamek, Sathorn, 10120, Bangkok, Thailand
Tel.: (66) 23599003
Sales Range: $25-49.9 Million
Emp.: 16
Petrochemical Distr
N.A.I.C.S.: 324110

H&R ChemPharm (UK) Ltd. (1)
Dudley Rd, Tipton, DY4 8EH, West Midlands, United Kingdom
Tel.: (44) 1215220100
Sales Range: $25-49.9 Million
Emp.: 40
Petroleum Lubricants Mfr
N.A.I.C.S.: 325998

H&R ChemPharm GmbH (1)
Neuenkirchener Str 8, D-48499, Salzbergen, Germany
Tel.: (49) 59769450
Automotive Lubricant Distr
N.A.I.C.S.: 424720
Michael Bahre *(Mng Dir)*

H&R China (Daxie) Co., Ltd. (1)
99 Huandao Road North Daxie Development Zone, Ningbo, 315812, Zhejiang, China
Tel.: (86) 57455831758
Emp.: 118
Oil Refining Product Mfr
N.A.I.C.S.: 324110

H&R China (Fushun) Co., Ltd. (1)
No 3 Longxian Road, Dongzhou District, Fushun, 113004, Liaoning, China
Tel.: (86) 2453787688
Emp.: 92
Oil Refining Product Mfr
N.A.I.C.S.: 324110
Nicole Yuanyuan Ruan *(Sls Mgr)*

H&R China (Hong Kong) Co., Ltd. (1)
29-31/F The Gateway Tower 5 Harbour City 15 Canton Road, Tsim Sha Tsui, Kowloon, China (Hong Kong)
Tel.: (852) 31809348
Oil Refining Product Mfr
N.A.I.C.S.: 324110

H&R Group US, Inc. (1)
2925 Briarpark Dr Ste 200, Houston, TX 77042
Tel.: (713) 955-9230
Oil Refining Product Mfr
N.A.I.C.S.: 324110
Ana Maria Salcedo *(Ops Mgr)*

H&R Grundstucksverwaltungs GmbH (1)
Neuenkirchener Str 8, 48499, Salzbergen, Lower Saxony, Germany
Tel.: (49) 59769450
Sales Range: $100-124.9 Million
Emp.: 500
Land Management Services
N.A.I.C.S.: 237210

H&R Grundstucksverwaltungs-Beteiligungsgesellschaft mbH (1)
Neuenkirchener Str 8, 48499, Salzbergen, Lower Saxony, Germany
Tel.: (49) 59769450
Land Administration Services
N.A.I.C.S.: 237210
Frank Salevske *(Mgr)*

H&R InfoTech GmbH (1)
Am Sandtorkai 64, 20457, Hamburg, Germany
Tel.: (49) 405130930
Customized Software Development Services
N.A.I.C.S.: 541511

H&R International GmbH (1)
Am Sandtorkai 64, D-20457, Hamburg, Germany
Tel.: (49) 40432180
Emp.: 40
Chemicals Mfr
N.A.I.C.S.: 325998

H&R Lube Blending GmbH (1)
Neuenkirchener Str 8, 48499, Salzbergen, Niedersachsen, Germany
Tel.: (49) 59769450
Web Site: https://www.hur.com
Sales Range: $125-149.9 Million
Emp.: 400
Automotive Lubricant Mfr
N.A.I.C.S.: 324191
Dieter Pohl *(Mgr)*

H&R LubeTech GmbH (1)
Neuenkirchener Strasse 8, 48499, Salzbergen, Niedersachsen, Germany
Tel.: (49) 59769452 10
Web Site: http://www.hur-chempharm.de
Sales Range: $25-49.9 Million
Emp.: 29
Lubricants & Paraffins Product Testing Services
N.A.I.C.S.: 541380

H&R Olwerke Schindler GmbH (1)
Neuhofer Bruckenstr 127-52, 21107, Hamburg, Germany
Tel.: (49) 40325230
Oil Mfr
N.A.I.C.S.: 324191
Neil Hansen *(Mng Dir)*

H&R Singapore Pte. Ltd. (1)
9 Raffles Place 19-21 Republic Plaza, Singapore, 048619, Singapore
Tel.: (65) 66864689
Oil Refining Product Mfr
N.A.I.C.S.: 324110

H&R South Africa (Pty) Limited (1)
113 Trinidad Rd Island View, PO Box 21575, Bluff, Durban, 4052, Kwazulu-Natal, South Africa
Tel.: (27) 314668700
Sales Range: $25-49.9 Million
Emp.: 35
Petroleum & Agricultural Products Sales
N.A.I.C.S.: 424720

H&R South Africa GmbH (1)
Neuhofer Bruckenstr 127-152, 21107, Hamburg, Germany
Tel.: (49) 40325230
Sales Range: $75-99.9 Million
Emp.: 250
Petroleum Lubricant & Agricultural Chemicals Sales
N.A.I.C.S.: 424720

H&R South Africa Sales (Pty) Limited (1)
113 Trinidad Rd Island View, Bluff, Durban, 4052, KwaZulu-Natal, South Africa
Tel.: (27) 31 466 8700
Web Site: http://www.hur.com
Emp.: 35
Petroleum Lubricants Sales
N.A.I.C.S.: 424720
Clive Wood *(Gen Mgr)*

H&R WAX Malaysia Sdn. Bhd. (1)
Lot 5 Jalan Perusahaan Dua, MY-68100, Batu Caves, Selangor Darul Ehsan, Malaysia
Tel.: (60) 361896225
Web Site: https://www.hur.com
Petroleum Lubricants Sales
N.A.I.C.S.: 424720

HRI IT-Consulting GmbH (1)
Hafenweg 24, 48155, Munster, Germany
Tel.: (49) 512707760
Web Site: https://www.hri-itc.com
Information Technology Services
N.A.I.C.S.: 541511

PT HUR Sales Indonesia (1)
32nd Floor Suite SC-3206 Jl Letjen S Parman Kav 28, Tanjung Duren Selatan Grogol Petamburan, Jakarta Barat, 11470, Indonesia
Tel.: (62) 2139502245
Oil Refining Product Mfr
N.A.I.C.S.: 324110

H&R REAL ESTATE INVESTMENT TRUST
3625 Dufferin Street Suite 500, Toronto, M3K 1N4, ON, Canada
Tel.: (416) 635-7520 ON
Web Site: https://www.hr-reit.com
Year Founded: 1996
HR.UN—(OTCIQ)
Rev.: $859,475,390
Assets: $10,447,696,732
Liabilities: $5,698,168,981
Net Worth: $4,749,527,751
Earnings: ($488,580,015)
Emp.: 733
Fiscal Year-end: 12/31/20
Real Estate Investment Trust
N.A.I.C.S.: 525990
Thomas J. Hofstedter *(Pres & CEO)*

H&S HIGHTECH CORP.
62-7 Techno 1-ro Yuseong-gu, Daejeon, 34014, Korea (South)
Tel.: (82) 428661300
Web Site:
http://www.hnshightech.com
Year Founded: 1995
Emp.: 130

H+H INTERNATIONAL A/S

Telecommunication Component Mfr & Distr
N.A.I.C.S.: 334220
Jeong-Hee Kim *(Pres & CEO)*

Subsidiaries:

H&S HighTech Corp. - China Factory (1)
89 Huanhai Road, Yantai, Shandong, China
Tel.: (86) 5356872171
Electronic Components Mfr
N.A.I.C.S.: 334413

HnsPowerTech Corp. (1)
73 Haean-ro Danwon-gu, Ansan, Gyeonggi-do, Korea (South)
Tel.: (82) 3180847800
Web Site: http://www.hnspowertech.com
Emp.: 52
Inductor Power Product Mfr
N.A.I.C.S.: 334416
JinDong Kim *(Pres)*

H&T GROUP PLC
Times House Throwley Way, Sutton, SM1 4AF, Surrey, United Kingdom
Tel.: (44) 8001690780
Web Site: https://www.handt.co.uk
HAT—(AIM)
Rev.: $219,567,029
Assets: $266,811,411
Liabilities: $59,642,767
Net Worth: $207,168,644
Earnings: $18,823,529
Emp.: 1,335
Fiscal Year-end: 12/31/22
Holding Company
N.A.I.C.S.: 551112
John G. Nichols *(CEO)*

Subsidiaries:

Harvey & Thompson Ltd. (1)
Times House Throwley Way, Sutton, SM1 4AF, Surrey, United Kingdom
Tel.: (44) 800838973
Web Site:
http://www.harveyandthompson.co.uk
Sales Range: $25-49.9 Million
Emp.: 50
Pawn Broking Services
N.A.I.C.S.: 459999

H+H INTERNATIONAL A/S
Lautrupsgade 7 5th Floor, 2100, Copenhagen, Denmark
Tel.: (45) 35270200 DK
Web Site: https://www.hplush.com
Year Founded: 1909
HH—(CSE)
Rev.: $521,479,938
Assets: $542,605,374
Liabilities: $262,186,917
Net Worth: $280,418,457
Earnings: $45,868,241
Emp.: 1,739
Fiscal Year-end: 12/31/22
Aircrete Mfr
N.A.I.C.S.: 327331
Michael Troensegaard Andersen *(CEO)*

Subsidiaries:

H+H Danmark A/S (1)
Skanderborgvej 234, 8260, Viby, Denmark
Tel.: (45) 70240050
Web Site: https://www.hplush.dk
Aircrete Mfr
N.A.I.C.S.: 327331

H+H Deutschland GmbH (1)
Industriestrasse 3, 23829, Wittenborn, Germany
Tel.: (49) 45547000
Web Site: https://www.hplush.de
Emp.: 530
Aircrete Mfr
N.A.I.C.S.: 327331

Subsidiary (Domestic):

H+H Kalksandstein GmbH (2)

H+H INTERNATIONAL A/S

H+H International A/S—(Continued)

Malscher Str 17, D-76448, Durmersheim, Germany
Tel.: (49) 7245806203
Web Site: http://www.hplush.de
Sand-Lime Bricks Mfr
N.A.I.C.S.: 327120

Subsidiary (Non-US):

Hunziker Kalksandstein AG (2)
Aarauerstrasse 75, 5200, Brugg, Switzerland
Tel.: (41) 564605466
Web Site: https://www.hunziker-kalksandstein.ch
Concrete Block Mfr
N.A.I.C.S.: 327331

Subsidiary (Domestic):

KS-Quadro Bausysteme GmbH (2)
Malscher Strasse 17, 76448, Durmersheim, Germany
Tel.: (49) 172 726 7357
Web Site: https://www.ks-quadro.de
Concrete Block Mfr
N.A.I.C.S.: 327331

H+H Finland Oy (1)
Teikankaantie 256, 39500, Ikaalinen, Finland
Tel.: (358) 207 524 200
Web Site: http://www.HplusH.fi
Aircrete Mfr
N.A.I.C.S.: 327331

H+H Nederland B.V. (1)
Magnesiumstraat 1A, 6031 RV, Nederweert, Netherlands
Tel.: (31) 495 450 169
Web Site: http://www.HplusH.nl
Aircrete Mfr
N.A.I.C.S.: 327331

H+H Norge AS (1)
Messeveien 8, 2004, Lillestrom, Norway
Tel.: (47) 3220 6150
Web Site: http://www.HplusH.no
Aircrete Mfr
N.A.I.C.S.: 327331

H+H Polska Sp. z o.o. (1)
ul Kupiecka 6, 03-046, Warsaw, Poland
Tel.: (48) 225184000
Web Site: https://www.hplush.pl
Emp.: 600
Aircrete Mfr
N.A.I.C.S.: 327331

H+H Slovenska republika s.r.o. (1)
Polna 4/1967, 903 01, Senec, Slovakia
Tel.: (421) 245 258 601
Web Site: http://www.HplusH.sk
Aircrete Mfr
N.A.I.C.S.: 327331

H+H Sverige AB (1)
Mobilvagen 3, 246 43, Loddekopinge, Sweden
Tel.: (46) 40552300
Web Site: https://www.hplush.se
Aircrete Mfr
N.A.I.C.S.: 327331

H+H UK Limited (1)
Celcon House Ightham, Sevenoaks, TN15 9HZ, Kent, United Kingdom
Tel.: (44) 173 288 6333
Web Site: https://www.hhcelcon.co.uk
Sales Range: $50-74.9 Million
Emp.: 200
Building Product Mfr
N.A.I.C.S.: 236210

H-DO (THAILAND) LIMITED

35 Soi Sathorn 9 South Sathorn Road, Yannawa Sathorn, Bangkok, 10120, Thailand
Tel.: (66) 20111535
Web Site: http://www.h-do.co.th
Building Renovation Services
N.A.I.C.S.: 236118

H-FARM S.P.A.

Via Adriano Olivetti 1, 31056, Roncade, TV, Italy
Tel.: (39) 0422789611
Web Site: https://www.h-farm.com
Year Founded: 2005
FARM—(ITA)
Sales Range: $50-74.9 Million
Educational Support Services
N.A.I.C.S.: 611710
Riccardo Donadon *(Co-Founder, Pres & CEO)*

H-FARM SPA

Via Sile 41 Ca Tron, 31056, Roncade, Italy
Tel.: (39) 0422789611
Year Founded: 2005
Educational Support Services
N.A.I.C.S.: 611710
Riccardo Donadon *(Pres & CEO)*

H-ONE CO., LTD.

1-11-5 Sakuragi-cho, Omiya-ku, Saitama, 330-0854, Japan
Tel.: (81) 486430010   JP
Web Site: https://www.h1-co.jp
Year Founded: 1939
5989—(TKS)
Rev.: $1,537,693,656
Assets: $1,199,847,698
Liabilities: $832,784,702
Net Worth: $367,062,996
Earnings: ($143,085,523)
Emp.: 6,178
Fiscal Year-end: 03/31/24
Automobile Parts Mfr
N.A.I.C.S.: 336390
Mitsunori Tsukiji *(Mng Officer)*

Subsidiaries:

G-One Auto Parts De Mexico, S.A. De C.V. (1)
110 Av Amistad No 104, Zona Industrial, 38180, Apaseo el Grande, Guanajuato, Mexico
Tel.: (52) 4131586500
Web Site: https://www.g-one.com.mx
Automobile Body Frame Mfr & Distr
N.A.I.C.S.: 336211

GH Auto Parts Industries Inc (1)
No 5 Longhui Gongye Road, Huashan Town Huadu District, Guangzhou, 510880, Guangdong, China
Tel.: (86) 2086948151
Sales Range: $400-449.9 Million
Emp.: 1,200
Metal Stamping Mfr
N.A.I.C.S.: 332119

H-One Co. Ltd. - Kameyama Factory (1)
1701 Shimonosho-cho, Kameyama, 519-0197, Mie, Japan
Tel.: (81) 595821211
Sales Range: $200-249.9 Million
Emp.: 550
Automobile Parts Stamping & Welding Services
N.A.I.C.S.: 336370

H-One Co. Ltd. - Karasuyama Plant (1)
1657-1 Ishigami Nogami, Nasukarasuyama, 321-0634, Tochigi, Japan
Tel.: (81) 287831370
Sales Range: $25-49.9 Million
Emp.: 50
Automobile Parts Welding & Prototypes Mfr
N.A.I.C.S.: 336390
Ryupa Takasaki *(Mgr-Production)*

H-One Co. Ltd. - Koriyama Factory (1)
17 Shobuike Kikuta-machi, Koriyama, 963-0551, Fukushima, Japan
Tel.: (81) 249593005
Web Site: http://www.h1-co.jp
Emp.: 370
Automobile Metal Stampings Parts Mfr
N.A.I.C.S.: 336110

H-One Co. Ltd. - Maebashi Factory (1)
1170 Amakawa oshima-machi, Maebashi, 379-2154, Gunma, Japan
Tel.: (81) 272632111

Web Site: http://www.h1-co.jp
Emp.: 360
Automobile Metal Stampings Parts Mfr
N.A.I.C.S.: 336370
Atsushi Kaneda *(Pres & CEO)*

H-One India Pvt. Ltd (1)
Plot No 12 Udyog Vihar Surajpur Kasna Road, Gautam Budh Nagar, Noida, 201 306, UP, India
Tel.: (91) 1204380892
Web Site: https://www.h-oneindia.com
Emp.: 1,170
Metal Stamping Dies Mfr
N.A.I.C.S.: 336370

H-One Parts (Thailand) Co., Ltd. (1)
48 Moo 9 Rojana Road Tambol Tanu, Amphoe U-Thai Phranakorn, Ayutthaya, 13210, Thailand
Tel.: (66) 35330785
Sales Range: $200-249.9 Million
Emp.: 990
Automobile Framework Parts Mfr
N.A.I.C.S.: 336390

H-One Parts Sriracha Co., Ltd. (1)
789 Moo 1, T Nongkham, Si Racha, 20230, Chonburi, Thailand
Tel.: (66) 38296719
Web Site: http://www.h1sriracha.com
Automobile Framework Part Mfr
N.A.I.C.S.: 336110

KTH Leesburg Products, LLC (1)
405 Industrial Blvd, Leesburg, AL 35983
Tel.: (256) 526-3530
Emp.: 520
Automotive Vehicle Mfr
N.A.I.C.S.: 336110

Kalida Manufacturing, Inc. (1)
801 Ottawa St, Kalida, OH 45831
Tel.: (419) 532-2026
Automotive Vehicle Parts Mfr
N.A.I.C.S.: 336390

PT.H-One Gohi Prima Auto Technologies indonesia (1)
JL Inspeksi Tarum Bara Depan Peruri, Desa Parung Mulya Kecamatan Ciampel, Karawang, 41361, Indonesia
Tel.: (62) 2678630555
Emp.: 770
Automotive Vehicle Mfr
N.A.I.C.S.: 336110

QH Auto Parts Industries Inc. (1)
Jiafu Industrial Zone, Yinzhan Indusirialpark, Qingyuan, Guangdong, China
Tel.: (86) 7633697788
Emp.: 610
Automobile Body Frame Mfr & Distr
N.A.I.C.S.: 336211

WH Auto Parts Industries Inc. (1)
2 Mao dian shan Road Wuhan East Lake High Technology Development Zone, Automotive Electronics Industrial Park, Hubei, China
Tel.: (86) 2781291666
Emp.: 940
Automobile Body Frame Mfr & Distr
N.A.I.C.S.: 336211

H-SOURCE HOLDINGS LTD.

Suite 2250 1055 W Hastings St, Vancouver, V6E 2E9, BC, Canada
Tel.: (604) 688-9588   BC
Web Site: http://www.h-source.com
Year Founded: 2014
HSI—(CNSX)
Sales Range: Less than $1 Million
Holding Company
N.A.I.C.S.: 551112
John Kupice *(CEO)*

H. ALBERT GMBH

Doventorsdeich 17 / 21, Bremen, 28195, Germany
Tel.: (49) 421304040
Web Site: http://www.albert-gmbh.de
Year Founded: 1880
Rev.: $13,794,000
Emp.: 46
Ship & Industrial Equipments Distr
N.A.I.C.S.: 423860

Christiane Frenzel *(Sr Mgr-Sls)*

H. ASCHEHOUG & CO. W. NYGAARD AS

Sehesteds Gate 3, 0164, Oslo, Norway
Tel.: (47) 2240 0400   NO
Web Site: http://www.aschehoug.no
Year Founded: 1872
Book Publishers
N.A.I.C.S.: 513130
Mads Nygaard *(CEO & Publr)*

Subsidiaries:

De Norske Bokklubbene AS (1)
Gullhaug Torg 1, 0402, Oslo, Norway (48.5%)
Tel.: (47) 22028700
Web Site: http://www.bokklubben.no
Sales Range: $50-74.9 Million
Online & Mail Order Book Retailer
N.A.I.C.S.: 459210
Kari Moller *(CEO)*

H. CEGIELSKI - POZNAN S.A.

ul 28 Czerwca 1956 r nr 223 229, 61-485, Poznan, Poland
Tel.: (48) 618311350
Web Site: http://www.hcp.com.pl
Year Founded: 1846
Sales Range: $150-199.9 Million
Emp.: 600
Ship Building Machines & Equipment Mfr
N.A.I.C.S.: 333310
Wojciech Wieclawek *(Pres)*

H. GEIGER GMBH

Am Schotterwerk 1, 85125, Kinding, Germany
Tel.: (49) 8467150
Web Site: http://www.schotterwerk-geiger.com
Year Founded: 1929
Sales Range: $125-149.9 Million
Emp.: 280
Construction Materials Mfr
N.A.I.C.S.: 333120
Herbert Geiger *(Mng Partner)*

Subsidiaries:

Ingolstadter Asphaltmischwerke GmbH & Co. KG (1)
Ochsenschuttstr 3, 85053, Ingolstadt, Germany
Tel.: (49) 84591552
Construction Materials Distr
N.A.I.C.S.: 423320

Max Balz GmbH & Co. (1)
Kappel 1, 91788, Berlin, Germany
Tel.: (49) 914383510
Construction Materials Distr
N.A.I.C.S.: 423320

Pusch Bau GmbH & Co. KG (1)
Am Schotterwerk 1, 85125, Kinding, Germany
Tel.: (49) 8467150
Civil Engineering Services
N.A.I.C.S.: 541330

Zeidler & Wimmel Natursteinindustrie GmbH & Co. KG (1)
Konsul-Metzing-Str 7 9, 97268, Kirchheim, Germany
Tel.: (49) 936690690
Construction Materials Distr
N.A.I.C.S.: 423320

H. O. SCHLUTER GMBH & CO. KG

Hohensteinstrasse 4, Hanerau-Hademarschen, 25557, Schleswig, Holstein, Germany
Tel.: (49) 487296920
Web Site: http://www.ho-schlueter.de
Year Founded: 1957
Rev.: $42,022,680
Emp.: 150

AND PRIVATE COMPANIES

Metal & Plastic Products Mfr, Specializing in Windows, Doors & Facade Systems
N.A.I.C.S.: 332999
Sven Thomsen (Mng Dir)

H. SALB INTERNATIONAL
49 Rivalda Road, Toronto, M9M 2M4, ON, Canada
Tel.: (416) 746-1944
Web Site: http://www.hsalb.com
Year Founded: 1959
Rev.: $27,039,879
Emp.: 115
Used Clothes Recycling Services
N.A.I.C.S.: 314999
Farokh Ghadially (Gen Mgr)

H. STERN COM & IND., S.A.
11 3 CEP Rua Garcia D Avila, 22421 010, Rio de Janeiro, Brazil
Tel.: (55) 2121060000
Web Site: http://www.hstern.net
Sales Range: $125-149.9 Million
Emp.: 800
Mfr of Jewelry
N.A.I.C.S.: 339910
Roberto Stern (VP)

Subsidiaries:

H. Stern Jewelers, Inc. (1)
645 5th Ave, New York, NY 10022-5910
Tel.: (212) 688-0300
Sales Range: $75-99.9 Million
Emp.: 50
Retail Jewelry
N.A.I.C.S.: 458310

H.Stern Buenos Aires (1)
Florida 1001, Buenos Aires, 1005, Argentina
Tel.: (54) 11 43124595
Jewellery Distr
N.A.I.C.S.: 423940

H.Stern Israel (1)
Savionim Center Kiryat Savionim, 56450, Tel Aviv, Israel
Tel.: (972) 3 6323666
Jewellery Distr
N.A.I.C.S.: 423940

H.Stern Lima (1)
Calle Amador Merino Reyna 285 / of 701, San Isidro, Lima, 18, Peru
Tel.: (51) 1 2221808
Jewellery Distr
N.A.I.C.S.: 423940

H. WILSON INDUSTRIES LTD
1045 Memorial Dr Hwy 63 N, PO Box 5660, Fort McMurray, T9K 0K4, AB, Canada
Tel.: (780) 743-1881
Web Site: http://www.wilson-industries.com
Year Founded: 1977
Rev.: $10,000,000
Emp.: 60
Road Works, Water, Sewage & Related Construction Services
N.A.I.C.S.: 237110
Owes Holodniuk (Gen Mgr)

H.B. FENN AND COMPANY LTD.
34 Nixon Road, Bolton, L7E 1W2, ON, Canada
Tel.: (905) 857-7175
Web Site: http://www.hbfenn.com
Year Founded: 1977
Rev.: $35,615,880
Emp.: 225
Book Publisher & Distr
N.A.I.C.S.: 424920
Harold Fenn (Pres & CEO)

H.E.S. BEHEER N.V.
Elbeweg 115, PO Box 1192, 3198 LC, Europoort, Netherlands
Tel.: (31) 181258100
Web Site: http://www.hesbeheer.com
Year Founded: 1908
Sales Range: $100-124.9 Million
Logistic Services
N.A.I.C.S.: 541614
Harry F. C. van Rietschote (Gen Counsel)

Subsidiaries:

European Bulk Services (E.B.S.) B.V. (1)
Elbeweg 117, Europoort, 3198 LC, Rotterdam, Netherlands
Tel.: (31) 181 258121
Web Site: http://www.ebsbulk.nl
Dry Bulk Terminal Operator
N.A.I.C.S.: 488310
Sven Noordermeer (Mgr-Fin)

H.G. INFRA ENGINEERING LTD.
III Floor Sheel Mohar Plaza A-1 Tilak Marg C-Scheme, Jaipur, 302001, Rajasthan, India
Tel.: (91) 1414106040
Web Site: https://www.hginfra.com
Year Founded: 2003
541019—(BOM)
Rev.: $556,350,099
Assets: $590,693,364
Liabilities: $360,266,531
Net Worth: $230,426,833
Earnings: $59,132,066
Emp.: 4,034
Fiscal Year-end: 03/31/23
Construction Services
N.A.I.C.S.: 236220
Harendra Singh (Chm & Mng Dir)

H.H.V. WHITCHURCH & CO. LTD.
Old Street, PO Box 771, Roseau, Dominica
Tel.: (767) 4482181
Web Site: http://www.whitchurch.com
Year Founded: 1910
Sales Range: $100-124.9 Million
Emp.: 220
Insurance Services; Grocery Retailer/Whslr; Travel Agency; Shipping Services; Petroleum Distr
N.A.I.C.S.: 524210
Gerry Aird (Mng Dir)

Subsidiaries:

Millenium Freight Services (1)
Cnr Hanover St Kennedy Ave, Box 771, Roseau, Dominica
Tel.: (767) 448 2181
Freight Transportation Services
N.A.I.C.S.: 483111

H.I.S. CO., LTD.
Kamiyacho Trust Tower 5F 4-1-1 Toranomon, Minato-ku, Tokyo, 105-6905, Japan
Tel.: (81) 5017429955
Web Site: https://www.his.co.jp
Year Founded: 1980
9603—(TKS)
Rev.: $1,785,729,940
Assets: $3,129,143,140
Liabilities: $2,716,866,730
Net Worth: $412,276,410
Earnings: ($18,561,620)
Emp.: 11,816
Fiscal Year-end: 10/31/23
Travel Arrangement Services
N.A.I.C.S.: 561599
Hideo Sawada (Chm & CEO)

Subsidiaries:

Cruise Planet Co., Ltd. (1)
2-10-1 Yurakucho Tokyo Kotsu Kaikan Building 6F, Chiyoda-ku, Tokyo, 100-0006, Japan
Tel.: (81) 36 865 9600
Web Site: https://www.cruiseplanet.co.jp
Tour Operator Services
N.A.I.C.S.: 561520

Encore Cruises (1)
160 Bloor St E, Toronto, M4W 1B9, ON, Canada
Tel.: (416) 960-2516
Web Site: http://www.encorecruises.com
Cruise Planning & Booking Services
N.A.I.C.S.: 483112

Guam Reef Hotel, Inc. (1)
1317 Pale San Vitores Rd, Tumon, GU 96913
Tel.: (671) 646-6881
Web Site: https://guamreef.com
Hotel Operator
N.A.I.C.S.: 721110

H.I.S. Australia Pty. Ltd. (1)
Chevron Renaissance Shopping Centre Suite 8 Level 1 3240, Surfers Paradise Boulevard, Surfers Paradise, 4217, QLD, Australia
Tel.: (61) 75 584 8310
Travel Agency Services
N.A.I.C.S.: 561510

H.I.S. Canada Inc. (1)
636 Hornby Street, Vancouver, V6C 2G2, BC, Canada
Tel.: (604) 646-3756
Web Site: https://www.his-canada.com
Travel Agency Services
N.A.I.C.S.: 561510
Hideo Hatano (Pres)

H.I.S. Deutschland Touristik GmbH (1)
Grosse Eschenheimer Str 39 39a, 60313, Frankfurt am Main, Germany
Tel.: (49) 69 560 0510
Web Site: https://www.his-germany.de
Tour Operator Services
N.A.I.C.S.: 561520

H.I.S. Europe Italy S.R.L. (1)
Via Barberini 67 3 Piano, 00187, Rome, Italy
Tel.: (39) 0648 4591
Web Site: https://www.hisitaly.com
Tour Operator Services
N.A.I.C.S.: 561520

H.I.S. Europe Limited (1)
Vintners Place 68 Upper Thames Street, London, EC4V 3BJ, United Kingdom
Tel.: (44) 207 484 3333
Web Site: https://www.his-euro.co.uk
Tour Operator Services
N.A.I.C.S.: 561520

H.I.S. Hotel Holdings Co., Ltd. (1)
Kamiyacho Trust Tower 5F 4-3-1 Toranomon, Minato City, Tokyo, 105-0001, Japan
Tel.: (81) 501 743 0810
Web Site: https://www.hishotelgroup.com
Hotel Operator
N.A.I.C.S.: 721110
Yuji Iwama (CEO & Chm)

H.I.S. International Travel Pte. Ltd. (1)
100 Tras St 03-16/17/18 100AM Mall Next to Don Don Donki, Singapore, 079027, Singapore
Tel.: (65) 6 443 0815
Web Site: https://www.his.com.sg
Tour Operator Services
N.A.I.C.S.: 561520

H.I.S. Super Power Co., Ltd. (1)
4-1-1 Toranomon Kamiyacho TrastTower 5F, Minato-ku, Tokyo, 105-6905, Japan
Tel.: (81) 501 748 7111
Web Site: https://www.his-power.jp
Electric Power Distribution Services
N.A.I.C.S.: 221122
Hideo Sawada (Chm)

H.I.S. Tours Co., Ltd. (1)
Interchange 21 Building UL Floor Sukhumvit Road, Khlong Toei Nuea Subdistrict Watthana District, Bangkok, 10110, Thailand
Tel.: (66) 2 022 0933
Web Site: https://histours.co.th
Tour Operator Services
N.A.I.C.S.: 561520

H.I.S.-Merit Travel Inc. (1)
636 Hornby St, Vancouver, V6C 2G2, BC, Canada
Tel.: (778) 372-1000
Travel Services
N.A.I.C.S.: 561510

H.I.S.-Red Label Vacations Inc. (1)
5450 Explorer Dr Suite 302, Mississauga, L4W 5N1, ON, Canada
Tel.: (905) 283-6020
Web Site: https://www.redtag.ca
Tour Operator Services
N.A.I.C.S.: 561520

HIS (Hong Kong) Company Limited (1)
6/F The Cameron 33 Cameron Road, Tsim Sha Tsui, Kowloon, China (Hong Kong)
Tel.: (852) 3 961 6888
Web Site: https://www.his.com.hk
Tour Operator Services
N.A.I.C.S.: 561520

HIS International Tours France SAS (1)
14 rue Gaillon, 75002, Paris, France
Tel.: (33) 15 305 3403
Web Site: https://www.his-tours.fr
Tour Operator Services
N.A.I.C.S.: 561520

HIS Uluslararasi Turizm Seyahat Acentasi Limited Sirketi (1)
19 Mayis Mah Dr Husnu Ismet Ozturk SokakSisli Plaza E Blok No 15, Sisli, 34360, Istanbul, Türkiye
Tel.: (90) 212 703 3737
Web Site: https://his.com.tr
Tour Operator Services
N.A.I.C.S.: 561520

HTB Energy Co., Ltd. (1)
Tosei Tenjin Building 3-9-25 Tenjin, Chuo-ku, Fukuoka, 810-0001, Japan
Tel.: (81) 503 852 1193
Web Site: https://htb-energy.com
Electric Power Distribution Services
N.A.I.C.S.: 221122

Huis Ten Bosch Co., Ltd (1)
1-1 Huis Ten Bosch-Machi, Sasebo, 859-3292, Japan
Tel.: (81) 95 658 0080
Web Site: https://english.huistenbosch.co.jp
Emp.: 1,238
Tour Operator
N.A.I.C.S.: 561520

Japan Holiday Travel Co., Ltd. (1)
20F-Namba Skyo Bldg 5-1-60 Namba, Chuo-ku, Osaka, 542-0076, Japan
Tel.: (81) 66 634 1201
Web Site: https://www.jph.co.jp
Emp.: 139
Tour Operator Services
N.A.I.C.S.: 561520
Ikuyasu Go (Pres & CEO)

Jonview Canada Inc. (1)
5343 Dundas Street West 4th Floor, Toronto, M9B 6K5, ON, Canada
Tel.: (416) 323-9090
Web Site: https://www.jonview.com
Tour Operator Services
N.A.I.C.S.: 561520

Kyushu Sangyo Kotsu Holdings Co., Ltd. (1)
1-28 Shinshigai The Place Flower Field 4th Floor, Chuo-ku, Kumamoto, 860-0803, Japan
Tel.: (81) 96 325 8229
General Management Consulting Services
N.A.I.C.S.: 541611

Laguna Ten Bosch Co., Ltd. (1)
2-3 Kaiyocho, Gamagori, 443-0014, Aichi, Japan
Tel.: (81) 57 009 7117
Web Site: https://www.lagunatenbosch.co.jp
Theme Park Business Services
N.A.I.C.S.: 713110

Ohshu Express Ltd. (1)
23rd Floor Kamiyacho Trust Tower 4-1-1, Toranomon Minato-ku, Tokyo, 105-6923, Japan
Tel.: (81) 501 745 2929
Web Site: https://www.ohshu.

H.I.S. CO., LTD.

H.I.S. Co., Ltd.—(Continued)
Tour Operator Services
N.A.I.C.S.: 561520

Orion Tour Co., Ltd.
3-10-6 Higashinihonbashi Building 3rd Floor
Daiwa, Chuo-ku, Tokyo, 103-0004, Japan
Tel.: (81) 505 550 8772
Web Site: https://www.orion-tour.co.jp
Tour Operator Services
N.A.I.C.S.: 561520

SYS Inc. (1)
2nd 9th Building 3F 5-10-2 Minami Aoyama,
Minato-ku, Tokyo, 107-0062, Japan
Tel.: (81) 33 486 1070
Web Site: https://sys.ne.jp
Travel Agency Services
N.A.I.C.S.: 561510

The Watermark Hotel Nagasaki Co., Ltd. (1)
Huis Ten Bosch 7-9, Sasebo, 859-3243,
Nagasaki, Japan
Tel.: (81) 95 627 0505
Web Site:
https://www.watermarkhotelnagasaki.com
Hotel Operator
N.A.I.C.S.: 721110

Tour Wave Co., Ltd. (1)
2-5-1 Honcho Oak Sendai Building 2nd
Floor, Aoba-ku, Sendai, 980-0014, Miyagi,
Japan
Tel.: (81) 22 212 1980
Web Site: https://www.tourwave.net
Tour Operator Services
N.A.I.C.S.: 561520

H.P COTTON TEXTILE MILLS LTD.
F-0 The Mira Corporate Suites 1&2
Old Ishwar Nagar Mathura Road,
New Delhi, 110065, India
Tel.: (91) 1141540471
Web Site: https://www.hpthread.com
502873—(BOM)
Rev.: $11,747,190
Assets: $12,603,045
Liabilities: $10,831,275
Net Worth: $1,771,770
Earnings: ($2,466,555)
Emp.: 1,500
Fiscal Year-end: 03/31/23
Cotton Yarn Distr
N.A.I.C.S.: 424990
Kailash Kumar Agarwal *(Chm & Mng Dir)*

H.S. INDIA LTD.
Unit No 202 Morya Blue Moon Off
New Link Road Andheri West, Mumbai, 400053, Maharashtra, India
Tel.: (91) 2249240174
Web Site: https://www.hsindia.in
532110—(BOM)
Rev.: $1,432,856
Assets: $6,708,175
Liabilities: $3,011,354
Net Worth: $3,696,821
Earnings: ($196,128)
Emp.: 109
Fiscal Year-end: 03/31/21
Home Management Services
N.A.I.C.S.: 721110
Pushpendra Bansal *(CEO & Mng Dir)*

H.T.P. INVESTMENTS BV
Keizersgracht 560, 1017EM, Amsterdam, Netherlands
Tel.: (31) 113217017
Year Founded: 1990
Business Investments
N.A.I.C.S.: 523999
Klaas Meertens *(Co-Owner & Mng Partner)*

Subsidiaries:

Knaus Tabbert GmbH (1)
Helmut-Knaus-Str 1, 94118, Jandelsbrunn,
Germany
Tel.: (49) 8583 21 1
Web Site: http://www.knaus.de
Sales Range: $300-349.9 Million
Emp.: 120
Motorhomes, Travel Trailers & Campers Mfr
& Marketer
N.A.I.C.S.: 336214
Marc Hundsdorf *(Member-Mgmt Bd)*

Morelo Reisemobile GmbH (1)
Helmut-Reimann-Str 2, Schlusselfeld,
96132, Germany
Tel.: (49) 9552 92 96 0 0
Web Site: http://www.morelo-reisemobile.de
Sales Range: $25-49.9 Million
Emp.: 100
Motorhomes Mfr
N.A.I.C.S.: 336214
Jochen Reimann *(Mng Dir)*

Oyster Marine Ltd. (1)
Fox's Marina, Ipswich, IP2 8SA, Suffolk,
United Kingdom
Tel.: (44) 1473 688 888
Web Site: http://www.oystermarine.com
Sales Range: $50-74.9 Million
Emp.: 30
Cruising Yachts & Sailboats Mfr
N.A.I.C.S.: 336612
David Tydeman *(CEO)*

Subsidiary (Domestic):

Oyster Yachts Ltd. (2)
Foxs Marina, Ipswich, IP2 8NJ, Suffolk,
United Kingdom
Tel.: (44) 1473851436
Web Site: http://www.oysteryachts.com
Emp.: 3
Sailboats Mfr
N.A.I.C.S.: 336612
David Tydeman *(CEO)*

Oyster Yachts Southampton (2)
Saxon Wharf Lower York Street, Northam,
Southampton, SO14 5QF, Hampshire,
United Kingdom
Tel.: (44) 2380831000
Web Site: http://www.oysteryachts.com
Sales Range: $25-49.9 Million
Sailboats Mfr
N.A.I.C.S.: 336612
David Tydeman *(CEO)*

Subsidiary (US):

Oyster Yachts USA (2)
5 Marina Plz, Newport, RI 02840
Tel.: (401) 846-7400
Sales Range: $1-9.9 Million
Emp.: 5
Yachts Sales & Services
N.A.I.C.S.: 441222
Daniel Wurzbacher *(Mgr-Sls)*

H.T.U.P. PARK A.D.
Novosadskog sajma 35, 21000, Novi
Sad, Serbia
Tel.: (381) 214888888
Web Site:
http://www.hotelparkns.com
Year Founded: 1989
HPNS—(BEL)
Sales Range: Less than $1 Million
Emp.: 116
Home Management Services
N.A.I.C.S.: 721110

H.U. GROUP HOLDINGS, INC.
Akasaka Intercity AIR 1-8-1 Akasaka,
Minato-ku, Tokyo, 107-0052, Japan
Tel.: (81) 362790801
Web Site: https://www.hugp.com
Year Founded: 1950
4544—(TKS)
Rev.: $1,566,239,500
Assets: $1,922,511,890
Liabilities: $980,553,840
Net Worth: $941,958,050
Earnings: ($49,925,330)
Emp.: 5,295
Fiscal Year-end: 03/31/24
Holding Company
N.A.I.C.S.: 551112
Yoshihiro Ashihara *(Exec Officer-IVD)*

Subsidiaries:

Advanced Life Science Institute, Inc. (1)
51 Komiyamachi, Shinjuku-ku, Hachioji,
192-0031, Tokyo, Japan
Tel.: (81) 42 649 8230
Web Site: https://alsi-i.co.jp
Emp.: 10
Medical Product Mfr & Whslr
N.A.I.C.S.: 339112

CanAg Diagnostics (Beijing) Co., Ltd. (1)
Room 1151 Hotel Nikko New Century Beijing Office Tower Building, No 6 Southern
Road Capital Gym Haidian District, Beijing,
100044, China
Tel.: (86) 1085288156
Cancer Biomarker Assay Mfr
N.A.I.C.S.: 325413
Yuhui Duan *(Gen Mgr)*

Clinical Network G.K. (1)
Akasaka Intercity AIR 1-8 1 Akasaka,
Minato-ku, Tokyo, 107-0052, Japan
Tel.: (81) 5020005001
Web Site: https://www.cln-netgk.com
Emp.: 1,370
Transportation Services
N.A.I.C.S.: 485999

Fujirebio China Co., Ltd. (1)
Room3302 Building A Gubei Soho No 188
HongBaoShi Road, Shanghai, 201103,
China
Tel.: (86) 2162787686
Medicinal Product Mfr
N.A.I.C.S.: 339112

Fujirebio France SARL (1)
Les Conquerants 1 Avenue de l'Atlantique,
91976, Courtaboeuf, France
Tel.: (33) 169074834
Medicinal Product Mfr
N.A.I.C.S.: 339112

Fujirebio Germany GmbH (1)
Hans-Bockler-Allee 20, 30173, Hannover,
Germany
Tel.: (49) 5118573928
Medicinal Product Mfr
N.A.I.C.S.: 339112

Fujirebio Holdings, Inc. (1)
Akasaka Intercity AIR 1-8-1, Akasaka,
Minato-ku, Tokyo, 107-0052, Japan
Tel.: (81) 362790800
Medicinal Product Mfr
N.A.I.C.S.: 339112

Fujirebio Iberia SL (1)
Citypark Cornella Ctra l'Hospitalet 147-149
Edificio Atenas, PB 3-4, Citypark Cornella
Athens Building, 08940, Cornella de Llobregat, Barcelona, Spain
Tel.: (34) 932705300
Medicinal Product Mfr
N.A.I.C.S.: 339112
Rosana Isasi Martinez *(Mgr-Fin & Admin)*

Fujirebio Inc. (1)
Tel.: (81) 362790800
Sales Range: $200-249.9 Million
Emp.: 583
Diagnostic Products Research & Development Services
N.A.I.C.S.: 325412
Yoshihiro Ashihara *(Head-R&D Div)*

Subsidiary (Non-US):

Fujirebio Diagnostics AB (2)
Elof Lindalvs gata 13, PO Box 12132, 414
58, Gothenburg, Sweden
Tel.: (46) 31857030
Sales Range: $25-49.9 Million
Emp.: 45
Pharmaceutical Preparation Mfr
N.A.I.C.S.: 325412
Christina Hall *(Gen Mgr)*

Subsidiary (US):

Fujirebio Diagnostics Inc. (2)
201 Great Valley Pkwy, Malvern, PA 19355-1308
Tel.: (610) 240-3800
Sales Range: $75-99.9 Million
Emp.: 180
Mfr & Developer of Diagnostic Tests

INTERNATIONAL PUBLIC

N.A.I.C.S.: 423450
Monte Wiltse *(Pres & CEO)*

Subsidiary (Non-US):

Fujirebio Europe N.V. (2)
Technologiepark 6 follow section A7-A8,
9052, Gent, Belgium (100%)
Tel.: (32) 93291329
Web Site: http://www.fujirebio-europe.com
Diagnostic Medical Equipment Mfr
N.A.I.C.S.: 339112
Christiaan De Wilde *(CEO)*

Subsidiary (Non-US):

Innogenetics Diagnostica Iberia, S.L. (3)
Citypark Cornella Ctra l'Hospitalet 147-149
Edificio Atenas, PB 3-4, Cornella de Llobregat, 08940, Barcelona, Spain
Tel.: (34) 932705300
Diagnostic Medical Equipment Mfr
N.A.I.C.S.: 339112

Innogenetics S.r.l. (3)
Via Pontina km29, Pomezia, 00071, Rome,
Italy
Tel.: (39) 0696528700
Diagnostic Medical Equipment Mfr
N.A.I.C.S.: 339112
Macri Romano *(Mng Dir)*

Innogenetics SARL (3)
Les Conquerants Immeuble Le Kilimandjaro, 8/10 Avenue des Tropiques, Les
Ulis, 91976, France
Tel.: (33) 169074834
Web Site: http://www.fujiredio.com
Sales Range: $25-49.9 Million
Emp.: 7
Medical Diagnostic Equipment Mfr
N.A.I.C.S.: 339112
Christiaan De Wilde *(Gen Mgr)*

Subsidiary (US):

Innogenetics, Inc. (3)
1111 Alderman Dr, Alpharetta, GA 30005
Tel.: (678) 393-1672
Web Site: http://www.innogenetics.com
Sales Range: $25-49.9 Million
Emp.: 9
Diagnostic Medical Equipment Mfr
N.A.I.C.S.: 339112

Subsidiary (Non-US):

Instituto em Diagnostico Molecular Theranostica Ltda (3)
Avenida das Americas 500 BL20 SL 236,
Barra da Tijuca, Rio de Janeiro, Brazil
Tel.: (55) 2124831403
Sales Range: $25-49.9 Million
Emp.: 3
Medical Diagnostic Equipment Mfr
N.A.I.C.S.: 339112

Subsidiary (Non-US):

Fujirebio Taiwan, Inc. (2)
No 391 Sec 1 Heping W Rd, Dayuan District, Taoyuan, Taiwan
Tel.: (886) 33865117
Web Site: http://www.fujirebio.com.tw
Pharmaceutical Preparation Mfr
N.A.I.C.S.: 325412

Subsidiary (Domestic):

TFB, Inc (2)
18-2 Nishi Ikebukuro 1-Chome, Toshima-ku,
171-0021, Tokyo, Japan (100%)
Tel.: (81) 359511181
Web Site: http://www.tfb-net.com
Sales Range: $25-49.9 Million
Emp.: 100
Drugs & Druggists Sundries Whslr
N.A.I.C.S.: 424210
Yas Suzuki *(Mgr-Mktg)*

Fujirebio Italia S.r.L. (1)
Via Pontina km29, Roma, 00071, Pomezia,
Italy
Tel.: (39) 0696528700
Medicinal Product Mfr
N.A.I.C.S.: 339112
Tiziana Colangelo *(Mgr-Fin & Admin)*

Fujirebio US, Inc. (1)
205 Great Vly Pkwy, Malvern, PA 19355

Tel.: (610) 240-3800
Web Site: https://www.fujirebio.com
Medicinal Product Mfr
N.A.I.C.S.: 339112
Jenny Graham (CFO)

H.U. Cells, Inc. (1)
50 Fuchigami, Akiruno, Tokyo, 197-0833, Japan
Tel.: (81) 5020004558
Web Site: https://nucells.com
Medical Product Mfr & Whslr
N.A.I.C.S.: 339112

H.U. Frontier, Inc. (1)
1-8-1 Akasaka Akasaka Intercity AIR, Minato-ku, Tokyo, 107-0052, Japan
Tel.: (81) 5020005050
Web Site: https://huf.co.jp
Marketing Services
N.A.I.C.S.: 541613

H.U. Group Research Institute G.K. (1)
50 Fuchigami, Akiruno, Tokyo, Japan
Tel.: (81) 5020005697
Web Site: https://www.hugp.com
Life Science Research Services
N.A.I.C.S.: 621999
Kazuya Omi (Pres)

H.U. Wellness, Inc. (1)
Akasaka Intercity AIR 1-8-1 Akasaka, Minato-ku, Tokyo, 107-0052, Japan
Tel.: (81) 5020005003
Web Site: https://www.hugp.com
Emp.: 38
Health Care Srvices
N.A.I.C.S.: 621610

HOKUSHIN Clinical Laboratory, Inc. (1)
1-19 ARCS, Nagano, 380-0918, Japan
Tel.: (81) 262236366
Web Site: https://hokushin-cl.co.jp
Emp.: 125
Health Care Srvices
N.A.I.C.S.: 621999

Japan Clinical Laboratories, Inc. (1)
16-10 Ohashibeni Kumiyama cho, Kuse-gun, Kyoto, 613-0046, Japan
Tel.: (81) 756316181
Health Care Srvices
N.A.I.C.S.: 621999

KBBM, Inc. (1)
5th floor Pharmaceutical Research Building Kyoto University, 46 Yoshida Shimoadachi-cho Sakyo-ku, Kyoto, 606-8304, Japan
Tel.: (81) 757527510
Web Site: https://www.kyoto-bbm.com
Health Care Srvices
N.A.I.C.S.: 621999
Kunihiko Ogura (COO & Head-Sls Ops)

Nihon Rinsho, Inc. (1)
16-10 Ohashibe, Kumiyama-cho Kuse-gun, Kyoto, 613-0046, Japan
Tel.: (81) 756316185
Web Site: https://www.jcl.co.jp
Pharmaceutical Products Distr
N.A.I.C.S.: 423450

SRL & Shizuoka Cancer Center Collaborative Laboratories, Inc. (1)
1007 Shimonagakubo Nagaizumi-cho, Shizuoka Cancer Center Research Institute 1st floor Sunto-gun, Shizuoka, 411-0934, Japan
Tel.: (81) 559990505
Emp.: 14
Health Care Srvices
N.A.I.C.S.: 621999

SRL International, Inc. (1)
10F Shinjuku Mitsui Building 2-1-1 Nishishinjuku, Shinjuku-ku, Tokyo, 163-0408, Japan
Tel.: (81) 364539541
Web Site: https://srlinternational.co.jp
Health Care Services
N.A.I.C.S.: 621999

SRL Kitakanto Laboratory, Inc. (1)
141-15 Tsurumitsuji-cho, Maebashi, 379-2141, Gunma, Japan
Tel.: (81) 272656498
Web Site: https://www.gunrin.com
Emp.: 92
Health Care Srvices
N.A.I.C.S.: 621999

SRL, Inc. (1)
Akasaka Intercity AIR 1-8-1 Akasaka, Minato-ku, Tokyo, 107-0052, Japan
Tel.: (81) 362790900
Web Site: https://www.srl-group.co.jp
Sales Range: $200-249.9 Million
Emp.: 1,471
General Medical Services
N.A.I.C.S.: 621491
Takeo Takagi (Auditor)

Subsidiary (Domestic):

Fornet, Inc. (2)
5-5-19 Shinmachi, Hino, 191-0002, Japan
Tel.: (81) 425871311
Transportation Services
N.A.I.C.S.: 488999

Nihon Stery, Inc. (2)
Akasaka Intercity AIR 1-8-1 Akasaka, Minato-ku, Tokyo, 107-0052, Japan
Tel.: (81) 5020005500
Web Site: https://www.nihonstery.com
Emp.: 711
General Medical Services
N.A.I.C.S.: 621491

SRL Laboratories Create, Inc. (2)
3-21-18 Hyakunin-cho, Shinjuku-ku, Tokyo, 169-0073, Japan
Tel.: (81) 3 5332 6569
Web Site: http://www.srl-group.co.jp
General Medical Services
N.A.I.C.S.: 622110

SRL Medisearch Inc. (2)
Shinjuku Mitsui Building 2-1-1 Nishishinjuku, Shinjuku-ku, Tokyo, 163-0410, Japan
Tel.: (81) 5020005230
Web Site: https://www.srlmedi.com
Emp.: 200
Clinical Trial & Development Services
N.A.I.C.S.: 621491
Ikeoka Masahiro (Pres & CEO)

SRL Technosystem, Inc. (2)
5-4-2 Shinmachi, Hino, 191-0002, Japan
Tel.: (81) 425864415
Web Site: http://www.srl-tcs.co.jp
Business Software Development Services
N.A.I.C.S.: 541511

Division (Domestic):

SRL, Inc. - Akita Sales Division (2)
6-10-9 Sanno, Akita, 010-0951, Japan
Tel.: (81) 5020004686
Web Site: http://www.srl-group.co.jp
Sales Range: $25-49.9 Million
Emp.: 15
Pharmaceutical Products Distr
N.A.I.C.S.: 424210

SRL, Inc. - Aomori Sales Division (2)
2-2-3 Ekimae, Hirosaki, 036-8002, Aomori, Japan
Tel.: (81) 5020004670
Web Site: http://www.srl-group.co.jp
Pharmaceutical Products Distr
N.A.I.C.S.: 424210

SRL, Inc. - Asahikawa Sales Division (2)
22-2-1 10-jodori, Asahikawa, 078-8220, Hokkaido, Japan
Tel.: (81) 5020004672
Web Site: http://www.srl-group.co.jp
Pharmaceutical Products Distr
N.A.I.C.S.: 424210

SRL, Inc. - Atsugi Sales Division I (2)
3-1-1 Kotobukicho, Atsugi, 243-0003, Kanagawa, Japan
Tel.: (81) 5020004668
Web Site: http://www.srl-group.co.jp
Pharmaceutical Products Distr
N.A.I.C.S.: 424210

SRL, Inc. - Chiba I Sales Division (2)
1597-5 Takashinacho, Wakaba-ku, Chiba, 264-0024, Japan
Tel.: (81) 5020004798
Web Site: http://www.srl-group.co.jp
Pharmaceutical Products Distr
N.A.I.C.S.: 424210

SRL, Inc. - Chiba II Sales Division (2)
3-18-1 Nanatsugi-dai, Shiroi, 270-1436, Chiba, Japan
Tel.: (81) 474910391
Pharmaceutical Products Distr
N.A.I.C.S.: 424210

SRL, Inc. - Fukui Sales Division (2)
2-1301 Takayanagi, Fukui, 910-0837, Japan
Tel.: (81) 5020004778
Web Site: http://www.srl-group.co.jp
Pharmaceutical Products Distr
N.A.I.C.S.: 424210

SRL, Inc. - Fukuoka Nishi Sales Division (2)
1-5-28 Shimoyamato, Nishi-ku, Fukuoka, 819-0052, Japan
Tel.: (81) 5020004810
Web Site: http://www.srl-group.co.jp
Pharmaceutical Products Distr
N.A.I.C.S.: 424210

SRL, Inc. - Fukushima Chuo Sales Division (2)
209-10 Arai, Motomiya, 969-1104, Fukushima, Japan
Tel.: (81) 5020004710
Web Site: http://www.srl-group.co.jp
Pharmaceutical Products Distr
N.A.I.C.S.: 424210

SRL, Inc. - Gifu Sales Division (2)
3-42 Sodensakaemachi, Gifu, 502-0847, Japan
Tel.: (81) 5020004772
Web Site: http://www.srl-group.co.jp
Pharmaceutical Products Distr
N.A.I.C.S.: 424210

SRL, Inc. - Gunma Sales Division II (2)
141-15 Tsurukojimachi, Maebashi, 379-2141, Gumma, Japan
Tel.: (81) 5020004748
Web Site: http://www.srl-group.co.jp
Pharmaceutical Products Distr
N.A.I.C.S.: 424210

SRL, Inc. - Hachinohe Sales Division (2)
4-5-16 Ishido, Hachinohe, 039-1165, Aomori, Japan
Tel.: (81) 5020004674
Web Site: http://www.srl-group.co.jp
General Medical Services
N.A.I.C.S.: 622110

Subsidiary (Domestic):

SRL, Inc. - Hachioji Sales Division I (2)
5-4-2 Shinmachi, Hino, 191-0002, Japan
Tel.: (81) 425864415
Pharmaceutical Products Distr
N.A.I.C.S.: 424210

Division (Domestic):

SRL, Inc. - Hakodate Sales Division (2)
5-16 Tayacho, Hakodate, 040-0081, Hokkaido, Japan
Tel.: (81) 5020004750
Web Site: http://www.srl-group.co.jp
Pharmaceutical Products Distr
N.A.I.C.S.: 424210

SRL, Inc. - Hamamatsu Sales Division (2)
40-3 Sukenobucho, Nakaku, Hamamatsu, 430-0903, Shizuoka, Japan
Tel.: (81) 5020004630
Web Site: http://www.srl-group.co.jp
Pharmaceutical Products Distr
N.A.I.C.S.: 424210

SRL, Inc. - Himeji Sales Division (2)
140 Toyozawa-cho, Himeji, 670-0964, Hyogo, Japan
Tel.: (81) 79 289 0711
Web Site: http://www.srl-group.co.jp
Pharmaceutical Products Distr
N.A.I.C.S.: 424210

SRL, Inc. - Hiroshima Sales Division (2)
2-17-2 Dambara, Minami-ku, Hiroshima, 732-0811, Japan

Tel.: (81) 5020004716
Web Site: http://www.srl-group.co.jp
Pharmaceutical Products Distr
N.A.I.C.S.: 424210

SRL, Inc. - Ibaraki Sales Division II (2)
1-3-12 Higashihara, Mito, 310-0035, Ibaraki, Japan
Tel.: (81) 5020004752
Web Site: http://www.srl-group.co.jp
Pharmaceutical Products Distr
N.A.I.C.S.: 424210

Subsidiary (Domestic):

SRL, Inc. - Iwaki Sales Division (2)
3-4 Tairanakahirakubohosodamachi, Iwaki, 970-8008, Fukushima, Japan
Tel.: (81) 5020004714
General Medical Services
N.A.I.C.S.: 622110

Division (Domestic):

SRL, Inc. - Kagoshima Sales Division (2)
3-10 Kajiyacho, Kagoshima, 892-0846, Japan
Tel.: (81) 5020004831
Web Site: http://www.srl-group.co.jp
Pharmaceutical Products Distr
N.A.I.C.S.: 424210

SRL, Inc. - Kanazawa Sales Division (2)
839 Fukumasumachikita, Kanazawa, 920-0376, Ishikawa, Japan
Tel.: (81) 5020005118
Web Site: http://www.srl-group.co.jp
Pharmaceutical Products Distr
N.A.I.C.S.: 424210

SRL, Inc. - Kawagoe Sales Division I (2)
6-1 Kujiraishinden, Kawagoe, 350-0809, Saitama, Japan
Tel.: (81) 5020004684
Web Site: http://www.srl-group.co.jp
General Medical Services
N.A.I.C.S.: 622110

SRL, Inc. - Kenko Sales Division (2)
1-1-54 Fukuzaki, Minato-ku, Osaka, 552-0013, Japan
Tel.: (81) 665735114
Web Site: http://www.srl-group.co.jp
Sales Range: $25-49.9 Million
Emp.: 100
Pharmaceutical Products Distr
N.A.I.C.S.: 424210
Masashi Ogawa (CEO)

SRL, Inc. - Kenko Sales Division I (2)
2-9-14 Nishiki, Nerima-ku, Tokyo, 179-0082, Japan
Tel.: (81) 5020004838
Web Site: http://www.srl-group.co.jp
Pharmaceutical Products Distr
N.A.I.C.S.: 424210
Shinji Ogawa (Mng Dir)

SRL, Inc. - Kita Kanto Sales Division II (2)
2866-1 Takasagocho, Sano, 327-0022, Tochigi, Japan
Tel.: (81) 283216671
Web Site: http://www.srl-group.co.jp
Pharmaceutical Products Distr
N.A.I.C.S.: 424210

SRL, Inc. - Kitakyushu Sales Division (2)
5-3 Chayamachi, Yahatahigashi-ku, Kitakyushu, 805-0014, Fukuoka, Japan
Tel.: (81) 5020004806
Web Site: http://www.srl-group.co.jp
Pharmaceutical Products Distr
N.A.I.C.S.: 424210

SRL, Inc. - Kitami Sales Division (2)
1-1 Kita 2-jo Higashi, Kitami, 090-0022, Hokkaido, Japan
Tel.: (81) 157 25 6101
Web Site: http://www.srl-group.co.jp
General Medical Services
N.A.I.C.S.: 622110

SRL, Inc. - Kobe Sales Division V (2)

H.U. GROUP HOLDINGS, INC.

H.U. Group Holdings, Inc.—(Continued)
136-3 Kozubashi Tamatsu-cho, Nishi-ku,
Kobe, 651-2122, Hyogo, Japan
Tel.: (81) 5020004766
Web Site: http://www.srl-group.co.jp
General Medical Services
N.A.I.C.S.: 622110

Subsidiary (Domestic):

SRL, Inc. - Kochi Sales Division (2)
2-7-13 Kazurashima, Kochi, 781-8121, Japan
Tel.: (81) 5020004732
Pharmaceutical Products Distr
N.A.I.C.S.: 424210

Division (Domestic):

SRL, Inc. - Kofu Sales Division II (2)
3-32-12 Marunochi, Kofu, 400-0031, Yamanashi, Japan
Tel.: (81) 5020004795
Web Site: http://www.srl-group.co.jp
Pharmaceutical Products Distr
N.A.I.C.S.: 424210

Subsidiary (Domestic):

SRL, Inc. - Kumamoto Sales Division (2)
1-1-100 Nagamineminami, Higashi-ku, Kumamoto, 861-8039, Japan
Tel.: (81) 5020004816
Pharmaceutical Products Distr
N.A.I.C.S.: 424210

Division (Domestic):

SRL, Inc. - Kurume Sales Division VII (2)
133 Tenjimmachi, Kurume, 830-0033, Fukuoka, Japan
Tel.: (81) 5020005076
Web Site: http://www.srl-group.co.jp
Pharmaceutical Products Distr
N.A.I.C.S.: 424210

SRL, Inc. - Kushiro Sales Division (2)
3-19 Irie-cho, Kushiro, 085-0008, Hokkaido, Japan
Tel.: (81) 502 000 4680
Web Site: http://www.srl-group.co.jp
General Medical Services
N.A.I.C.S.: 622110

SRL, Inc. - Kyoto Sales Division (2)
425 Yamamotocho Gokomachi-Nijo Sagaru, Nakagyo-ku, Kyoto, 604-0933, Japan
Tel.: (81) 5020004775
Web Site: http://www.srl-group.co.jp
Pharmaceutical Products Distr
N.A.I.C.S.: 424210

Subsidiary (Domestic):

SRL, Inc. - Matsuyama Sales Division (2)
3-7-38 Minamiedo, Matsuyama, 7901-0062, Ehime, Japan
Tel.: (81) 5020004730
Pharmaceutical Products Distr
N.A.I.C.S.: 424210

Division (Domestic):

SRL, Inc. - Mie Sales Division (2)
4-6-6 Anotsudai, Tsu, 514-0131, Mie, Japan
Tel.: (81) 59 232 1205
Web Site: http://www.srl-group.co.jp
Pharmaceutical Products Distr
N.A.I.C.S.: 424210

Subsidiary (Domestic):

SRL, Inc. - Miyazaki Sales Division (2)
5744-3 Tayoshi, Miyazaki, 880-0911, Japan
Tel.: (81) 5020004742
Pharmaceutical Products Distr
N.A.I.C.S.: 424210

Division (Domestic):

SRL, Inc. - Morioka Sales Division (2)
1-57 Nakayashikicho, Morioka, 020-0141, Iwate, Japan
Tel.: (81) 5020004682

Pharmaceutical Products Distr
N.A.I.C.S.: 424210

SRL, Inc. - Nagano Sales Division II (2)
5-11-104 Kogandori, Suwa, 392-0027, Nagano, Japan
Tel.: (81) 266580800
Web Site: http://www.srl-group.co.jp
Pharmaceutical Products Distr
N.A.I.C.S.: 424210

Subsidiary (Domestic):

SRL, Inc. - Nagasaki Sales Division (2)
1765-1 Nakazatomachi, Nagasaki, 851-0103, Japan
Tel.: (81) 5020004812
Pharmaceutical Products Distr
N.A.I.C.S.: 424210

SRL, Inc. - Nagoya I Sales Division (2)
1-308 Yashirogaoka, Meito-ku, Nagoya, 465-0051, Aichi, Japan
Tel.: (81) 5020004756
Pharmaceutical Products Distr
N.A.I.C.S.: 424210

Division (Domestic):

SRL, Inc. - Nara Sales Division (2)
237-1 Shingacho, Kashihara, 634-0006, Nara, Japan
Tel.: (81) 5020004659
Web Site: http://www.srl-group.co.jp
Pharmaceutical Products Distr
N.A.I.C.S.: 424210

SRL, Inc. - Niigata Sales Division II (2)
16-4 Shinkocho, Chuo-ku, Niigata, 950-0965, Fukuoka, Japan
Tel.: (81) 502004796
Web Site: http://www.srl-group.co.jp
Pharmaceutical Products Distr
N.A.I.C.S.: 424210

SRL, Inc. - Noto Sales Division (2)
160-9 Ya Okawamachi, Hakui, 925-0015, Ishikawa, Japan
Tel.: (81) 767228050
Web Site: http://www.srl-group.co.jp
Pharmaceutical Products Distr
N.A.I.C.S.: 424210

SRL, Inc. - Oita Sales Division (2)
107-1 Miyoshi, Oita, 870-0030, Japan
Tel.: (81) 5020004734
Web Site: http://www.srl-group.co.jp
Pharmaceutical Products Distr
N.A.I.C.S.: 424210

SRL, Inc. - Okayama Sales Division (2)
3-14 Higashichuocho, Kita-ku, Okayama, 700-0835, Japan
Tel.: (81) 5020004698
Web Site: http://www.srl-group.co.jp
Pharmaceutical Products Distr
N.A.I.C.S.: 424210

SRL, Inc. - Okazaki Sales Division (2)
2-54-1 Koseidori Minami, Okazaki, 444-0044, Aichi, Japan
Tel.: (81) 5020004764
Web Site: http://www.srl-group.co.jp
Pharmaceutical Products Distr
N.A.I.C.S.: 424210

SRL, Inc. - Okinawa Sales Division VII (2)
26-1 Higashimachi, Naha, 900-0034, Okinawa, Japan
Tel.: (81) 988616131
Web Site: http://www.srl-group.co.jp
Pharmaceutical Products Distr
N.A.I.C.S.: 424210

SRL, Inc. - Osaka Chuo Sales Division (2)
1-1-54 Fukuzaki, Minato-ku, Osaka, 552-0013, Japan
Tel.: (81) 665735196
Web Site: http://www.srl-group.co.jp
Pharmaceutical Products Distr
N.A.I.C.S.: 424210

SRL, Inc. - Osaka Kita Sales Division (2)
1-1-8 Shinsenti Nishimachi, Toyonaka, 560-0083, Osaka, Japan
Tel.: (81) 5020004760
Web Site: http://www.srl-group.co.jp
Pharmaceutical Products Distr
N.A.I.C.S.: 424210

SRL, Inc. - Osaka Minami Sales Division (2)
3-2-13 Naka-Yasuicho, Sakai-ku, Sakai, 590-0063, Osaka, Japan
Tel.: (81) 722230236
Pharmaceutical Products Distr
N.A.I.C.S.: 424210

SRL, Inc. - Saga Sales Division (2)
4-2 Oroshihommachi, Saga, 849-0933, Japan
Tel.: (81) 50020004660
Web Site: http://www.srl-group.co.jp
Pharmaceutical Products Distr
N.A.I.C.S.: 424210

SRL, Inc. - Saitama Sales Division (2)
4-333-13 Sakuragicho, Omiya-ku, Saitama, 330-0854, Japan
Tel.: (81) 5020004612
Web Site: http://www.srl-group.co.jp
Pharmaceutical Products Distr
N.A.I.C.S.: 424210

SRL, Inc. - Sakata Sales Division (2)
14-2 Shimoyasucho, Sakata, 998-0012, Yamagata, Japan
Tel.: (81) 234227551
Web Site: http://www.srl-group.co.jp
General Medical Services
N.A.I.C.S.: 622110

SRL, Inc. - Sapporo Sales Division (2)
4-1-2 Kita 7-jounishi, Chuo-ku, Sapporo, 060-0807, Hokkaido, Japan
Tel.: (81) 5020004932
Web Site: http://www.srl-group.co.jp
Pharmaceutical Products Distr
N.A.I.C.S.: 424210

SRL, Inc. - Sasebo Sales Division (2)
1-4-10 Gonjoji, Sasebo, 859-3214, Nagasaki, Japan
Tel.: (81) 956393913
Web Site: http://www.srl-group.co.jp
Pharmaceutical Products Distr
N.A.I.C.S.: 424210

Subsidiary (Domestic):

SRL, Inc. - Sendai Sales Division (2)
2-1-65 Kakyoin, Aoba-ku, Sendai, 980-0013, Miyagi, Japan
Tel.: (81) 5020004690
Pharmaceutical Products Distr
N.A.I.C.S.: 424210

Division (Domestic):

SRL, Inc. - Shiga Sales Division (2)
1-1-12 Moriyamacho, Moriyama, 524-0022, Shiga, Japan
Tel.: (81) 5020004780
Web Site: http://www.srl-group.co.jp
Pharmaceutical Products Distr
N.A.I.C.S.: 424210

SRL, Inc. - Shimane Sales Division (2)
519-1 Isemiya-cho, Matsue, 690-0006, Shimane, Japan
Tel.: (81) 502 000 4725
Web Site: http://www.srl-group.co.jp
General Medical Services
N.A.I.C.S.: 622110

SRL, Inc. - Shizuoka Sales Division (2)
1-139 Chiyoda, Aoi-ku, Shizuoka, 420-0803, Japan
Tel.: (81) 5020005182
Web Site: http://www.srl-group.co.jp
Pharmaceutical Products Distr
N.A.I.C.S.: 424210

SRL, Inc. - Takamatsu Sales Division (2)
2078-10 Fuseishicho, Takamatsu, 761-8071, Kagawa, Japan
Tel.: (81) 5020004718
Web Site: http://www.srl-group.co.jp
Pharmaceutical Products Distr
N.A.I.C.S.: 424210

Subsidiary (Domestic):

SRL, Inc. - Tokushima Sales Division (2)
23-3-15 Atake, Tokushima, 770-0863, Japan
Tel.: (81) 5020004726
Pharmaceutical Products Distr
N.A.I.C.S.: 424210

SRL, Inc. - Tokyo I Sales Division (2)
1-26-2 Shinkawa, Chuo-ku, Tokyo, 104-0033, Japan
Tel.: (81) 5020004920
Pharmaceutical Products Distr
N.A.I.C.S.: 424210

Division (Domestic):

SRL, Inc. - Tokyo II Sales Division (2)
4-1-8 Konan, Minato-ku, Tokyo, 108-0075, Japan
Tel.: (81) 5020005013
Web Site: http://www.srl-group.co.jp
Pharmaceutical Products Distr
N.A.I.C.S.: 424210

SRL, Inc. - Tokyo III Sales Division (2)
5-4-2 Shimmachi, Hino-shi, Tokyo, 191-0002, Japan
Tel.: (81) 425864415
Web Site: http://www.srl-group.co.jp
Pharmaceutical Products Distr
N.A.I.C.S.: 424210

SRL, Inc. - Tokyo IV Sales Division (2)
1-12-1 Senju, Adachi-ku, Tokyo, 120-0034, Japan
Tel.: (81) 5020005082
Web Site: http://www.srl-group.co.jp
Pharmaceutical Products Distr
N.A.I.C.S.: 424210

SRL, Inc. - Tokyo V Sales Division (2)
2-9-14 Nisiki, Nerima-ku, Tokyo, 179-0082, Japan
Tel.: (81) 5020004838
Web Site: http://www.srl-group.co.jp
Pharmaceutical Products Distr
N.A.I.C.S.: 424210

SRL, Inc. - Tomakomai Sales Division (2)
3-2-13 Omotemachi, Tomakomai, 053-0022, Hokkaido, Japan
Tel.: (81) 144341170
Web Site: http://www.srl-group.co.jp
General Medical Services
N.A.I.C.S.: 622110

Subsidiary (Domestic):

SRL, Inc. - Toyama Sales Division VII (2)
33-3 Kamiiino, Toyama, 930-0827, Japan
Tel.: (81) 5020004782
Pharmaceutical Products Distr
N.A.I.C.S.: 424210

Division (Domestic):

SRL, Inc. - Tsukuba Sales Division II (2)
1-5-15 Minatomachi, Tsuchiura, 300-0034, Ibaraki, Japan
Tel.: (81) 5020004768
Web Site: http://www.srl-group.co.jp
Pharmaceutical Products Distr
N.A.I.C.S.: 424210

SRL, Inc. - Ueda Sales Division II (2)
200-1 Akiwa, Ueda, 386-0041, Nagano, Japan
Tel.: (81) 268 26 5121
Web Site: http://www.srl-group.co.jp

AND PRIVATE COMPANIES

Pharmaceutical Products Distr
N.A.I.C.S.: 424210

SRL, Inc. - Utsunomiya Sales Division II (2)
1557-1 Tsurutamachi, Utsunomiya, 320-0851, Tochigi, Japan
Tel.: (81) 5020004758
Web Site: http://www.srl-group.co.jp
Pharmaceutical Products Distr
N.A.I.C.S.: 424210

SRL, Inc. - Wakayama Sales Division (2)
3-1 Higashinunoecho, Wakayama, 640-8066, Japan
Tel.: (81) 734998389
Web Site: http://www.srl-group.co.jp
Pharmaceutical Products Distr
N.A.I.C.S.: 424210

SRL, Inc. - Yamagata Sales Division (2)
488-1 Urushiyama, Yamagata, 990-2161, Japan
Tel.: (81) 5020004696
Web Site: http://www.srl-group.co.jp
Pharmaceutical Products Distr
N.A.I.C.S.: 424210

Subsidiary (Domestic):

SRL, Inc. - Yamaguchi Sales Division (2)
2-21 Ogori Wakakusamachi, Yamaguchi, 754-0024, Japan
Tel.: (81) 839732801
General Medical Services
N.A.I.C.S.: 622110

Division (Domestic):

SRL, Inc. - Yokohama I Sales Division (2)
2-10-27 Kitasaiwai, Nishi-ku, Yokohama, 220-0004, Kanagawa, Japan
Tel.: (81) 5020004826
Web Site: http://www.srl-group.co.jp
Pharmaceutical Products Distr
N.A.I.C.S.: 424210

SRL, Inc. - Yokohama II Sales Division (2)
1-13-12 Shin-yokohama, Kohoku-ku, Yokohama, 222-0033, Kanagawa, Japan
Tel.: (81) 454765281
Pharmaceutical Products Distr
N.A.I.C.S.: 424210

SRL, Inc. - Yokosuka Sales Division I (2)
4-6 Ogawa-cho, Yokosuka, 238-0004, Kanagawa, Japan
Tel.: (81) 468242866
Web Site: http://www.srl-group.co.jp
Pharmaceutical Products Distr
N.A.I.C.S.: 424210

Selmesta Co., Ltd. (1)
No 12 4 25 Ishiwara, Sumida-ku, Tokyo, 130-8617, Japan
Tel.: (81) 336266555
Web Site: http://selmesta.co.jp
Health Care Srvices
N.A.I.C.S.: 621999

H.WESTON & SONS LTD
The Bounds, Much Macle, Ledbury, HR8 2NQ, Herefordshire, United Kingdom
Tel.: (44) 1531660233
Web Site: http://www.westons-cider.co.uk
Year Founded: 1878
Sales Range: $25-49.9 Million
Emp.: 166
Bottled Products Mfr
N.A.I.C.S.: 311999
Helen Thomas (Mng Dir)

H2 EQUITY PARTNERS B.V.
Oosteinde 19, 1017 WT, Amsterdam, Netherlands
Tel.: (31) 206790822   NI
Web Site: http://www.h2ep.nl
Year Founded: 1991
Emp.: 12
Privater Equity Firm
N.A.I.C.S.: 523999
Gert Jan van der Hoeven (Founder & Mng Partner)

Subsidiaries:

Agribio Holding B.V. (1)
Coldenhovelaan 6, De Lier, 2678 PS, Netherlands
Tel.: (31) 174530100
Web Site: http://www.agribioholding.com
Sales Range: $150-199.9 Million
Horticultural Product Distr
N.A.I.C.S.: 111422

Subsidiary (Non-US):

Barberet & Blanc S.A. (2)
Apdo Correos 38 Cno Viejo 205, 30890, Lumbreras, Murcia, Spain
Tel.: (34) 968402525
Web Site: http://www.barberet.es
Floriculture Production
N.A.I.C.S.: 111422

Subsidiary (Domestic):

Fides Holding B.V.
Coldenhovelaan 6, 2678 PS, De Lier, Netherlands
Tel.: (31) 174530100
Web Site: http://www.fides.nl
Emp.: 200
Floriculture Production
N.A.I.C.S.: 111422
Harry Kloppenburg (Dir)

Subsidiary (Non-US):

Japan Agribio Co., Ltd. (2)
1 5 11 Irifune, Chuo ku, Tokyo, 104 0042, Japan
Tel.: (81) 335236885
Web Site: http://www.japanagribio.co.jp
Sales Range: $50-74.9 Million
Plant Seed & Potted Plant Production & Sales
N.A.I.C.S.: 111422

JET Tageslicht & RWA GmbH (1)
Weidehorst 28, Hullhorst, 32609, Germany (100%)
Tel.: (49) 5744 503 0
Web Site: http://www.jet-gruppe.de
Sales Range: $125-149.9 Million
Emp.: 400
Commercial & Industrial Roof Dome, Lighting & Ventilation Products Mfr & Distr
N.A.I.C.S.: 332321
Gerard Vincent Kessels (Gen Mgr)

Subsidiary (Non-US):

BIK Bouwprodukten B.V. (2)
Van Roozendaalstraat 13, Spanbroek, 1715 EJ, Opmeer, Netherlands
Tel.: (31) 226 366 100
Web Site: http://www.bik.nl
Skylight & Light Domes Mfr
N.A.I.C.S.: 332321

Cox Building Products Limited (2)
CRH House Units 1-3 Prothero Industrial Estate, Bilport Lane, Wednesbury, WS10 0NT, W Midlands, United Kingdom
Tel.: (44) 121 530 4230
Web Site: http://www.coxbp.com
Skylight Mfr & Distr
N.A.I.C.S.: 332321
Chris Lister (Mgr-Sls)

Subsidiary (Domestic):

JET Brakel Aero GmbH (2)
Alte Hunxer Strasse 179, D-46562, Voerde, Germany
Tel.: (49) 281 404 0
Web Site: http://www.jet-gruppe.de
Aluminum Glazing Systems Mfr
N.A.I.C.S.: 332321

Subsidiary (Non-US):

Vaculux B.V. (2)
de Beverspijken 17, 5221 EE, 's-Hertogenbosch, Netherlands
Tel.: (31) 73 631 2420
Web Site: http://www.vaculux.nl
Commercial Skylight Mfr
N.A.I.C.S.: 332321

Motive Offshore Group Ltd (1)
Motive Base Cairnton Road Boyndie Drome, Banff, AB45 2LR, United Kingdom
Tel.: (44) 1261843537
Web Site: https://www.motive-offshore.com
Engineering Services & Energy Industry
N.A.I.C.S.: 541330

Subsidiary (Domestic):

Aquatic Engineering & Construction Limited (2)
Tern Place House Tern Place Bridge of Don, Aberdeen, AB23 8JX, United Kingdom
Tel.: (44) 1224452300
Web Site: http://www.aquaticsubsea.com
Sales Range: $50-74.9 Million
Emp.: 20
Oil & Gas Flexible Flowline, Cable & Wire Installation Services
N.A.I.C.S.: 213112
Martin Charles (CEO-Grp & Mng Dir-Grp)

Nottingham Rehab Limited (1)
Sherwood House Cartwright Way Forest Business Park, Bardon Hill, Coalville, LE67 1UB, Leics, United Kingdom
Tel.: (44) 3451218111
Web Site: http://www.nrshealthcare.co.uk
Home Health Care Equipment & Supplies Retailer
N.A.I.C.S.: 456199
Steve Kennedy (Comml Dir)

Parenco B.V. (1)
Industrieterrein Veerweg 1, 6871 AV, Renkum, Netherlands (100%)
Tel.: (31) 7 361 911
Web Site: http://www.parenco.com
Sales Range: $50-74.9 Million
Paper Mills
N.A.I.C.S.: 322120
Cornelis Feiter (Dir-Fin & IT)

Reparco Nederland B.V. (1)
Bijsterhuizen 11-07, Nijmegen, 6546 AR, Netherlands
Tel.: (31) 2434 35988
Web Site: http://www.reparco.net
Emp.: 5
Holding Company; Paper Recycling Services & Recovered Paper Whslr
N.A.I.C.S.: 551112
Kurt Martens (Mng Dir)

Subsidiary (Domestic):

Reparco Nijmegen B.V. (2)
Bijsterhuizen 11-07, 6546 AR, Nijmegen, Netherlands
Tel.: (31) 2434 35988
Web Site: http://www.reparco.net
Paper Recycling Services & Recovered Paper Whslr
N.A.I.C.S.: 562920

Reparco Randstad B.V. (2)
Saturnusstraat 26, 2516 AH, Hague, Netherlands
Tel.: (31) 703825444
Paper Recycling Services
N.A.I.C.S.: 562920

Reparco Renkum B.V. (2)
Bokkedijk 6a, Renkum, 6871 AB, Netherlands
Tel.: (31) 317318132
Paper Recycling Services
N.A.I.C.S.: 562920
Wille Verder (Gen Mgr)

Reparco Trading B.V. (2)
Bijsterhuizen 11-07, 6546 AR, Nijmegen, Netherlands
Tel.: (31) 2434 35999
Sales Range: $50-74.9 Million
Recycled Paper Wholesale Trade Agency
N.A.I.C.S.: 425120

Subsidiary (Non-US):

Reparco UK Ltd. (3)
Suite 29 Evans Business Centre Manchester Road, Bolton, BL3 2NZ, United Kingdom
Tel.: (44) 1204 548254
Web Site: http://www.reparco.com

H2APEX GROUP SCA

Sales Range: $50-74.9 Million
Emp.: 4
Recycled Paper Wholesale Trade Agency
N.A.I.C.S.: 425120
Patrick Kilcoyne (Mng Dir)

Smartwares (1)
Burg Stramanweg 103, 1101, Amsterdam, Netherlands
Tel.: (31) 26 319 4444
Web Site: http://www.smartwares.eu
Consumer Products Distr
N.A.I.C.S.: 423620
Gert Jan van der Hoeven (Chm)

H2APEX GROUP SCA
19 rue de Flaxweiler, 6776, Grevenmacher, Luxembourg
Tel.: (352) 28384720   LU
Web Site: https://h2apex.com
H2A—(DEU)
Rev.: $16,889,211
Assets: $135,168,882
Liabilities: $71,431,428
Net Worth: $63,737,454
Earnings: ($27,254,550)
Emp.: 81
Fiscal Year-end: 12/31/23
Electric Equipment Mfr
N.A.I.C.S.: 334419
Wolf-Gunter Freese (CEO & CFO)

Subsidiaries:

Inplastor Graphische Produkte Gesellschaft m.b.H. (1)
Leberstrasse 61, 1110, Vienna, Austria
Tel.: (43) 1 6041800
Web Site: http://www.inplastor.at
Plastic Card Mfr
N.A.I.C.S.: 326199

exceet Group AG (1)
Marktplatz 4, Saint Gallen, 9004, Switzerland
Tel.: (41) 499 93 33
Sales Range: $200-249.9 Million
Electronic Module Mfr
N.A.I.C.S.: 334419

Subsidiary (Domestic):

ECR AG
Riedstrasse 1, 6343, Rotkreuz, Switzerland
Tel.: (41) 41 798 48 84
Web Site: http://www.ecrag.ch
Electronic Components Mfr
N.A.I.C.S.: 334419

GS Swiss PCB AG (2)
Faennring 8, PO Box 61, 6403, Kussnacht, Switzerland
Tel.: (41) 854 48 00
Web Site: http://www.swisspcb.ch
Sales Range: $25-49.9 Million
Emp.: 180
Printed Circuit Board Mfr
N.A.I.C.S.: 334412

Subsidiary (Non-US):

exceet Card Group AG (2)
Senefelderstrasse 10, 33100, Paderborn, Germany
Tel.: (49) 5251 15 83 123
Web Site: http://www.exceet-card-group.com
Sales Range: $25-49.9 Million
Emp.: 42
Plastic Card Mfr
N.A.I.C.S.: 326199
Ulrich Reutner (Chm-Mgmt Bd)

Subsidiary (Non-US):

PPC B.V. (3)
Neutronstraat 8, 9743 AM, Groningen, Netherlands
Tel.: (31) 503687777
Web Site: https://www.ppc.nl
Sales Range: $25-49.9 Million
Emp.: 15
Plastic Card Mfr
N.A.I.C.S.: 326199

Subsidiary (Domestic):

exceet Card AG (3)

H2APEX GROUP SCA

H2APEX Group SCA—(Continued)

Edisonstrasse 3 Unterschleissheim, Unterschleissheim, Munich, 85716, Germany
Tel.: (49) 89 33034 0
Web Site: http://www.exceet-group-card.com
Sales Range: $25-49.9 Million
Smartcard Mfr
N.A.I.C.S.: 326199
Helmut Fischer (CFO)

Subsidiary (Non-US):

exceet Card Austria GmbH (3)
Industriezone 3, 6175, Kematen in Tirol, Austria
Tel.: (43) 5232 206 86
Sales Range: $25-49.9 Million
Plastic Card Mfr
N.A.I.C.S.: 326199

idvation GmbH (1)
Otto-Hesse-Strasse 19 / T5, 64293, Darmstadt, Germany
Tel.: (49) 6151 4923021
Web Site: http://www.idvation.com
Sales Range: $25-49.9 Million
Emp.: 5
Card Reader Mfr
N.A.I.C.S.: 334118

H2G GREEN LIMITED

39 Kaki Bukit Place, Singapore, 416217, Singapore
Tel.: (65) 67413939   SG
Web Site: https://h2g.green
Year Founded: 1998
5AI—(SES)
Rev.: $7,520,534
Assets: $24,899,067
Liabilities: $9,084,852
Net Worth: $15,814,215
Earnings: ($6,601,295)
Emp.: 63
Fiscal Year-end: 03/31/24
Holding Company
N.A.I.C.S.: 551112
Leow Sau Wan (Exec Dir)

H2O CREATIVE

Ashgrove House Monument Park, Chalgrove, Oxford, OX44 7RW, United Kingdom
Tel.: (44) 1865893425
Web Site: http://www.h2o-creative.com
Rev.: $19,483,893
Emp.: 60
Fiscal Year-end: 12/31/15
Holding Company
N.A.I.C.S.: 541820
Alan Brooks (Acct Dir)

Subsidiaries:

Aqua Eye Ltd (1)
Harts Barn Monmouth Road, Longhope, Mitcheldean, GL17 0QD, Gloucestershire, United Kingdom
Tel.: (44) 1452 225877
Web Site: http://www.aquaeye.co.uk
Software Development Services
N.A.I.C.S.: 541511
Kyron Venn (Mng Dir)

H2O Creative (1)
140 High Street, Swindon, SN4 7AY, Wiltshire, United Kingdom   (100%)
Tel.: (44) 1865 893425
Emp.: 50
Management Consulting Services
N.A.I.C.S.: 541618
Markus Murphy (Dir-Creative)

Orchid Field Marketing Ltd (1)
Room 25 Hampden House Monument Business Park, Chalgrove, OX44 7RW, Oxon, United Kingdom
Tel.: (44) 1865 893390
Web Site: http://www.orchid-fm.com
Marketing Consulting Services
N.A.I.C.S.: 541613
Lysa Campbell (Mng Dir)

H2O RETAILING CORP.

8-7 Kakuda-cho, Kita-ku, Osaka, Japan
Tel.: (81) 663611381   JP
Web Site: https://www.h2o-retailing.co.jp
Year Founded: 1929
8242—(TKS)
Rev.: $4,345,414,000
Assets: $4,693,688,290
Liabilities: $2,750,176,430
Net Worth: $1,943,511,860
Earnings: $144,792,050
Emp.: 34,624
Fiscal Year-end: 03/31/24
Department Store & Supermarket Owner & Operator
N.A.I.C.S.: 455110
Katsuhiro Hayashi (Exec VP)

Subsidiaries:

Asnas Co., Ltd. (1)
2nd Floor Commercial Building 5-6-10 Toyosaki, Kita-ku, Osaka, 531-0072, Japan
Tel.: (81) 664734106
Web Site: https://www.asnas.jp
Supermarket Management Services
N.A.I.C.S.: 445110

EveryD.com, Inc. (1)
1-16 Kamigofukumachi Matano Building 4F, Hakata-ku, Fukuoka, Japan
Tel.: (81) 927105170
Web Site: http://www.jp.everyd.com
Food Mfr & Whslr
N.A.I.C.S.: 311999

F.G.J Co., Ltd. (1)
2-12-5 Kita-Aoyama KRT Aoyama 4th Floor, Minato-ku, Tokyo, 107-0061, Japan
Tel.: (81) 364345370
Web Site: http://fgj.jp
Cosmetics Whslr
N.A.I.C.S.: 424210

H2O Communication Next Corporation (1)
H2O Tower 3F 2-5-2 Nishitenma, Kita-ku, Osaka, 530-0047, Japan
Tel.: (81) 663640110
Payment Processing Services
N.A.I.C.S.: 522320

H2O Shopping Center Development Co., Ltd. (1)
1-4-4 Hanazonominami, Nishinari-ku, Osaka, 557-0015, Japan
Tel.: (81) 666573325
Apparel Distr
N.A.I.C.S.: 424350

H2O Smile Co., Ltd. (1)
1-5-4 Nakatsu, Kita-ku, Osaka, 531-0071, Japan
Tel.: (81) 663775430
Light Work Services
N.A.I.C.S.: 238290

H2O System Co., Ltd. (1)
Nakatsu 1st Rich Building 2F 1-11-11 Nakatsu, Kita-ku, Osaka, 531-0071, Japan
Tel.: (81) 663131957
Data Processing Services
N.A.I.C.S.: 518210

Hankyu Act For (1)
1-5-4 Nakatsu, Kita-ku, Osaka, 531-0071, Japan   (100%)
Tel.: (81) 663775403
Business Accounting Services Contractor
N.A.I.C.S.: 541219

Hankyu Delica I, Inc. (1)
180 Furue-cho, Ikeda, 563-0015, Osaka, Japan
Tel.: (81) 727541001
Web Site: http://hankyudelica-i.co.jp
Food Mfr & Whslr
N.A.I.C.S.: 311999

Hankyu Eyewear Co Ltd (1)
8-7 Kakuda-cho Kita-ku, Osaka, Hankyu Terminal Bldg No 15, Osaka, 530-8611, Japan
Tel.: (81) 663672981
Web Site: http://www.h2o-retailing.co.jp
Sales Range: $25-49.9 Million
Emp.: 19
Sunglass Stores

N.A.I.C.S.: 327215
Masahiro Fujita (Pres)

Hankyu Food Process Co., Ltd. (1)
2-4-54 Nankohigashi, Suminoe-ku, Osaka, 559-0031, Japan
Tel.: (81) 647034471
Web Site: http://www.hankyu-fp.co.jp
Food Mfr & Whslr
N.A.I.C.S.: 311999

Hankyu Foods Inc (1)
22-5 Minamishodokoro-cho, Takatsuki, Osaka, 569-0063, Japan
Tel.: (81) 726686332
Web Site: http://www.hankyu-foods.co.jp
Mfr & Sales of Seaweed & Dried Food Products
N.A.I.C.S.: 311423

Subsidiary (Domestic):

Hankyu Bakery Co Ltd (2)
22-5 Minamishohocho, Takatsuki, 569-0063, Osaka, Japan   (100%)
Tel.: (81) 726627110
Web Site: https://www.hankyu-bakery.co.jp
Sales Range: $75-99.9 Million
Emp.: 300
Bread Mfr & Whslr
N.A.I.C.S.: 311812

Hankyu Delica Inc. (2)
180 Furue-cho, Ikeda, 563-0015, Osaka, Japan
Tel.: (81) 727541001
Web Site: http://www.hankyu-delica.co.jp
Contract Manufacturing, Sales & Marketing of Processed Foods
N.A.I.C.S.: 311991

Mameda Inc (2)
Nakatsu Kita-ku Osaka-Chome 32 Issue 1, Osaka, 531 0071, Japan
Tel.: (81) 663712751
Sales Range: $25-49.9 Million
Emp.: 100
Food Products Mfr
N.A.I.C.S.: 311991

Hankyu Hanshin Department Stores, Inc (1)
8-7 Kakudacho, Kita-Ku, Osaka, 530-8350, Japan
Tel.: (81) 663611381
Web Site: https://www.hankyu-dept.co.jp
Sales Range: $1-4.9 Billion
Emp.: 4,000
Department Stores
N.A.I.C.S.: 455110

Subsidiary (Domestic):

Heart Dining Inc (2)
6th floor H2O Juso Building Main Building 2-8-10 Nonakaminami, Yodogawa-ku, Osaka, 532-0022, Japan
Tel.: (81) 676330722
Web Site: https://www.heart-dining.co.jp
Sales Range: $25-49.9 Million
Emp.: 96
Cafe & Restaurant Services
N.A.I.C.S.: 722514

Hankyu Hello Dog Co., Ltd. (1)
14-1 Takamatsucho Nishinomiya Hankyu 4th floor, Nishinomiya, 663-8204, Hyogo, Japan
Tel.: (81) 798627290
Web Site: https://hankyu-hellodog.com
Emp.: 49
Pet Accessories Stores & Pet Hotels
N.A.I.C.S.: 812910

Hankyu Home Styling Co., Ltd. (1)
Nonaka Minami 2-8-10 Hankyu Interior Studio 1F 2F, Yodogawa-ku, Osaka, 532-0022, Japan
Tel.: (81) 663037151
Web Site: http://www.comfortq.com
Sales Range: $25-49.9 Million
Emp.: 27
Home Furnishing Goods Sales & Supply
N.A.I.C.S.: 423220
Kenji Matsumura (Pres)

Hankyu Job Yell Co Ltd (1)
9th floor Hankyu Terminal Building 1-1-4 Shibata, Kita-ku, Osaka, 530-0012, Japan
Tel.: (81) 663673244
Web Site: https://www.jobyell.co.jp

INTERNATIONAL PUBLIC

Emp.: 800
Temporary Staffing Services
N.A.I.C.S.: 561990

Hankyu Kensou Co., Ltd. (1)
2F H2O Nakatsu Building 1-5-4 Nakatsu, Kita Ward, Osaka, 531-0071, Japan
Tel.: (81) 642565011
Web Site: https://www.hankyu-kensou.co.jp
Construction Design Services
N.A.I.C.S.: 541330

Hankyu Kitchen Yell Kansai, Inc. (1)
8-7 Kakuda-cho, Kita-ku, Osaka, Japan
Tel.: (81) 120890581
Web Site: http://ec.k-yell.co.jp
Food Mfr & Whslr
N.A.I.C.S.: 311999

Hankyu Kitchen Yell, Inc (1)
8-7 Kakuda-cho, Kita-ku, Osaka, 530-0017, Japan
Tel.: (81) 727899358
Web Site: https://www.k-yell.co.jp
Sales Range: $75-99.9 Million
Emp.: 152
Independent Grocery Delivery Services
N.A.I.C.S.: 424410

Hankyu Maintenance Service Co Ltd (1)
Kita-Osaka Building 3F 3-20 Banzai-cho, Kita-ku, Osaka, 530-0028, Japan
Tel.: (81) 663614350
Web Site: https://www.hankyu-ms.co.jp
Emp.: 203
Building Maintenance Services
N.A.I.C.S.: 561790
Tomoyuki Ito (Pres)

Hankyu Oasis Co., Ltd. (1)
2-8-10 Nonakaminami, Yodogawa-ku, Osaka, 532-0022, Japan
Tel.: (81) 663037686
Web Site: http://www.hankyu-oasis.com
Supermarket Management Services
N.A.I.C.S.: 445110

Hankyu Quality Support (1)
Wako Building 2-2-17 Shibata, Kita-ku, Osaka, 530-0012, Japan
Tel.: (81) 664866955
Web Site: https://www.hankyu-qc.com
Sales Range: $25-49.9 Million
Emp.: 40
Quality Management Consultants
N.A.I.C.S.: 541611

Izumiya Card Co., Ltd. (1)
15th Floor Applause Tower 19-19 Chayamachi, Kita-ku, Osaka, 530-0013, Japan
Tel.: (81) 663773080
Web Site: https://www.izc.jp
Financial Services
N.A.I.C.S.: 522320

Izumiya Co., Ltd. (1)
1-4-4 Hanazono-Minami Nishinari-Ku, Nishinari-Ku, Osaka, 557 0015, Japan
Tel.: (81) 666573379
Web Site: http://www.izumiya.co.jp
Sales Range: $1-4.9 Billion
Emp.: 2,105
Supermarkets & Discount Stores
N.A.I.C.S.: 455219
Yonjo Haruya (Pres)

Kansai Super Premium Co.,Ltd. (1)
5-3-38 Chuo, Itami, 664-0851, Japan
Tel.: (81) 727756391
Logistic Services
N.A.I.C.S.: 541614

Oi Development Co Ltd (1)
50-5 Oi, Shinagawa-ku, Tokyo, 140-0014, Japan   (100%)
Tel.: (81) 337758411
Web Site: http://www.h2o-retailing.co.jp
Sales Range: $1-9.9 Million
Property Management Services
N.A.I.C.S.: 541618

Subsidiary (Domestic):

Hankyu Shopping Center Development Co Ltd (2)
1-4-4 Hanazono Minami, Nishinari Ward, Osaka, 104-0061, Japan
Tel.: (81) 335752011
Web Site: https://www.hankyu-scdev.jp

AND PRIVATE COMPANIES

Shopping Center
N.A.I.C.S.: 561439

Souq Company Co., Ltd. (1)
Hankyu Grand Builiding 8-47, Kakuda-cho Kita-ku, Osaka, 531-0017, Japan
Tel.: (81) 663139030
Grocery Products Retailer
N.A.I.C.S.: 445110

Sumire Agency, Inc. (1)
Nonakaminami 2 Chome Yodogawa ku 2 8 10, Hankyu No 6 Product Ctr, Osaka, 532 0022, Japan
Tel.: (81) 663037311
Life Insurance Agencies
N.A.I.C.S.: 524210

HA DO GROUP JOINT STOCK COMPANY
8 Lang Ha Street, Ba Dinh District, Hanoi, Vietnam
Tel.: (84) 2438310347
Web Site: https://www.hado.com.vn
Year Founded: 1990
HDG—(HOSE)
Rev.: $119,042,621
Assets: $594,860,102
Liabilities: $297,035,685
Net Worth: $297,824,418
Earnings: $35,691,189
Fiscal Year-end: 12/31/23
Real Estate Development Services
N.A.I.C.S.: 531390
Nguyen Trong Thong *(Chm)*

HA GIANG MINERAL MECHANICS JOINT STOCK COMPANY
No 390 Nguyen Trai Street, Ha Giang, Vietnam
Tel.: (84) 2193866708
Web Site: https://www.hgm.vn
Year Founded: 1996
HGM—(HNX)
Rev.: $17,568,200
Assets: $23,884,100
Liabilities: $4,131,000
Net Worth: $19,753,100
Earnings: $5,485,200
Fiscal Year-end: 12/31/23
Mineral Ore Exploration, Mining & Processing Services
N.A.I.C.S.: 212390

HA NOI - KINH BAC AGRICULTURE AND FOOD JOINT STOCK COMPANY
Floor 25 th Vlnaconex 9 Building HH 2-2 Block Me Tri, Nam Tu Liem, Hanoi, Vietnam
Tel.: (84) 4 37877290
Web Site: http://www.hakinvest.com.vn
Year Founded: 2009
Food Distr
N.A.I.C.S.: 424490
Quang Lu Duong *(Chm & Gen Dir)*

HA NOI BATTERY JOINT STOCK COMPANY
No 72 Phan Trong Tue Street, Van Dien Town Thanh Tri District, Hanoi, Vietnam
Tel.: (84) 2438615365
PHN—(HNX)
Rev.: $17,462,908
Assets: $7,143,215
Liabilities: $1,098,474
Net Worth: $6,044,740
Earnings: $2,102,848
Fiscal Year-end: 12/31/23
Battery Mfr
N.A.I.C.S.: 335910
Nguyen Thanh Hung *(Mgr)*

HA NOI SOUTH HOUSING AND URBAN DEVELOPMENT CORPORATION
Cau Giat industrial cluster, Duy Tien Town, Phu Ly, Ha Nam, Vietnam
Tel.: (84) 3513847756
Web Site: http://www.namhanoi.com.vn
NHA—(HOSE)
Rev.: $7,320,200
Assets: $68,474,000
Liabilities: $25,158,600
Net Worth: $43,315,400
Earnings: $603,700
Emp.: 190
Fiscal Year-end: 12/31/23
Construction & Real Estate Investment Services
N.A.I.C.S.: 531390
Nguyen Hong Thai *(Member-Mgmt Bd & Gen Mgr)*

HA NOI TRANSFORMER MANUFACTURING & ELECTRIC MATERIAL JOINT STOCK COMPANY
No 11-K2 Road-Cau Dien, Tu Liem Dist, Hanoi, Vietnam
Tel.: (84) 47644795
Web Site: http://www.ctbt.vn
BTH—(HNX)
Rev.: $98,500
Assets: $74,905,100
Liabilities: $47,302,000
Net Worth: $27,603,100
Earnings: $169,600
Fiscal Year-end: 12/31/22
Electric Equipment Mfr
N.A.I.C.S.: 334416

HA TAY PHARMACEUTICAL JOINT STOCK COMPANY
10A Quang Trung, Ha Dong, Hanoi, Vietnam
Tel.: (84) 2433522525
Web Site: https://www.hataphar.com.vn
DHT—(HNX)
Rev.: $64,374,560
Assets: $49,503,629
Liabilities: $19,369,818
Net Worth: $30,133,811
Earnings: $2,855,600
Fiscal Year-end: 12/31/21
Pharmaceutical Product Mfr & Distr
N.A.I.C.S.: 325412

HA TAY TRADING JOINT STOCK COMPANY
No 7 Tran Phu street, Van Quan ward Ha Dong district, Hanoi, Vietnam
Tel.: (84) 433547252
Web Site: https://www.thuongmaihatay.vn
Year Founded: 1958
HTT—(HNX)
Real Estate Lending Services
N.A.I.C.S.: 531190
Dao Van Chien *(Chm)*

HA TINH BOOK & EDUCATIONAL EQUIPMENT JOINT STOCK COMPANY
No 58 Phan Dinh Phung str, Ha Tinh, Vietnam
Tel.: (84) 393893399
Web Site: http://www.hbec.com.vn
HBE—(HNX)
Rev.: $1,976,715
Assets: $1,187,193
Liabilities: $116,992
Net Worth: $1,070,202
Earnings: $47,446
Fiscal Year-end: 12/31/20
Magazine Whslr
N.A.I.C.S.: 424920

Hung Dong *(Member-Mgmt Bd)*

HAAD THIP PUBLIC COMPANY LIMITED
87/1 Karnjanavanich Rd, T Banpru Hatyai, Songkhla, 90250, Thailand
Tel.: (66) 74210008
Web Site: https://www.haadthip.com
HTC—(THA)
Rev.: $229,637,399
Assets: $189,263,278
Liabilities: $74,556,442
Net Worth: $114,706,837
Earnings: $17,457,833
Emp.: 2,398
Fiscal Year-end: 12/31/23
Carbonated Drinks Bottler
N.A.I.C.S.: 312111
Charan Kullavanijaya *(Chm)*

Subsidiaries:

Haadthip Development Co., Ltd. (1)
87/1 Kanchanawanit Road, Ban Phru Subdistrict, Hat Yai, 90250, Songkhla, Thailand
Tel.: (66) 623101888
Web Site: https://www.haadthipdevelopment.com
Real Estate Development Services
N.A.I.C.S.: 531190

HAAF SPEDITION GMBH & CO. KG
Werkstrasse 4, 67354, Romerberg, Germany
Tel.: (49) 62328180
Web Site: http://www.haaf.de
Year Founded: 1949
Rev.: $31,897,694
Emp.: 150
Transportation Logistics Services
N.A.I.C.S.: 541614
Walter Haaf *(Founder)*

HAAKON INDUSTRIES (CANADA) LTD.
11851 Dyke Road, Richmond, V7A 4X8, BC, Canada
Tel.: (604) 273-0161
Web Site: https://www.haakon.com
Rev.: $52,792,974
Emp.: 450
Air Conditioning & Ventilating Equipment Mfr
N.A.I.C.S.: 333415
Robert Hole *(Owner & CEO)*

HAATZ INC.
202 Dongbu-daero Jinwi-myeon, Pyeongtaek, 17709, Gyeonggi-do, Korea (South)
Tel.: (82) 313707500
Web Site: https://www.haatz.com
Year Founded: 1988
066130—(KRS)
Rev.: $109,780,811
Assets: $103,252,997
Liabilities: $28,774,141
Net Worth: $74,478,857
Earnings: $3,523,780
Emp.: 218
Fiscal Year-end: 12/31/22
Kitchen Appliances Mfr
N.A.I.C.S.: 335210

HABA LABORATORIES, INC.
1-24-11 Kanda Sudacho, Chiyoda-ku, Tokyo, 101-0041, Japan
Tel.: (81) 352966250
Web Site: https://www.haba.com
Year Founded: 1976
4925—(TKS)
Rev.: $81,461,640
Assets: $82,168,910
Liabilities: $25,937,640
Net Worth: $56,231,270
Earnings: ($13,999,980)
Emp.: 673
Fiscal Year-end: 03/31/24
Cosmetic Product Mfr & Whslr
N.A.I.C.S.: 325620

Subsidiaries:

HABA Hong Kong Limited (1)
Sogo Causeway Bay Store B1/F, Hong Kong, China (Hong Kong)
Tel.: (852) 28313939
Web Site: http://www.haba.com.hk
Skin & Body Care Product Distr
N.A.I.C.S.: 424210

HABASIT AG
Roemerstrasse 1, 4153, Reinach, Basel, Switzerland
Tel.: (41) 617151515
Web Site: http://www.habasit.com
Year Founded: 1946
Sales Range: $700-749.9 Million
Emp.: 3,300
Conveyor Belting Mfr
N.A.I.C.S.: 326220
Thomas Habegger *(Chm)*

Subsidiaries:

Habasit (Australia) Pty Limited (1)
79b Egerton Street, Silverwater, 2128, NSW, Australia
Tel.: (61) 1300 945 455
Web Site: http://www.habasit.com.au
Sales Range: $50-74.9 Million
Emp.: 10
Conveyor Belting
N.A.I.C.S.: 326220

Habasit (Shanghai) Co. Ltd. (1)
No 8 Lane 195 Chedu Town Qianpu Road, Songjiang District, Shanghai, China
Tel.: (86) 215 4881218
Web Site: http://www.habasit.cn
Conveyor Belt Distr
N.A.I.C.S.: 423840
Li Bo *(Mgr-Fin & Admin)*

Habasit (UK) Limited (1)
Habegger House Keighley Road, Silsden, Keighley, BD20 0EA, W Yorkshire, United Kingdom
Tel.: (44) 8708359555
Web Site: http://www.habasit.co.uk
Sales Range: $75-99.9 Million
Emp.: 140
Conveyor Belts Mfr
N.A.I.C.S.: 326220

Subsidiary (Non-US):

Habasit GmbH (2)
Babenhauser Str 31, 64859, Eppertshausen, Germany
Tel.: (49) 60719690
Web Site: http://www.habasit.com
Sales Range: $125-149.9 Million
Emp.: 200
Conveyor Belts Mfr
N.A.I.C.S.: 326220
Jens Roth *(Mng Dir)*

Habasit AB (1)
Lillenorvej 69, DK-8340, Arhus, Malling, Denmark
Tel.: (45) 87818130
Web Site: http://www.habasit.dk
Sales Range: $50-74.9 Million
Emp.: 3
Conveyor Belts Mfr
N.A.I.C.S.: 326220

Habasit AB (1)
Kalle Bas Vag 1, PO Box 73, 438 05, Hindas, Sweden
Tel.: (46) 30122600
Web Site: http://www.habasit.se
Sales Range: $25-49.9 Million
Emp.: 40
Conveyor Belting
N.A.I.C.S.: 326220
Malgorzata Przybyszewska *(Mng Dir)*

Subsidiary (Non-US):

Habasit Norge A/S (2)
Jerikoveien 20, 1067, Oslo, Norway
Tel.: (47) 81558458
Web Site: http://www.habasit.no

HABASIT AG

Habasit AG—(Continued)
Sales Range: $25-49.9 Million
Emp.: 3
Conveyor Belts Mfr
N.A.I.C.S.: 326220
Bent Maehre *(Mgr-Sls)*

Habasit America, Inc. (1)
805 Satellite Blvd, Suwanee, GA 30024
Tel.: (678) 288-3600
Web Site: http://www.habasitusa.com
Sales Range: $50-74.9 Million
Emp.: 200
Mfr & Whslr of Industrial Solid Woven Synthetic & Rubber Belting
N.A.I.C.S.: 332618

Plant (Domestic):

Habasit America - Buffalo (2)
1400 Clinton St, Buffalo, NY 14206-2919
Tel.: (716) 824-8484
Web Site: http://www.habasitusa.com
Sales Range: $50-74.9 Million
Emp.: 200
Mfr & Whslr of Industrial Solid Woven Synthetic & Rubber Belting
N.A.I.C.S.: 332618
Vinod Chahal *(Mgr-Fabric Dev)*

Habasit America - Middletown (2)
150 Industrial Park Rd, Middletown, CT 06457
Tel.: (860) 632-2211
Web Site: http://www.habasitabt.com
Sales Range: $10-24.9 Million
Emp.: 100
Conveyor Belts Mfr
N.A.I.C.S.: 332618
Harry Cardillo *(Pres)*

Habasit America - Reading (2)
825 Morgantown Rd, Reading, PA 19607-9533
Tel.: (610) 373-1400
Web Site: http://www.habasitusa.com
Sales Range: $25-49.9 Million
Emp.: 100
Modular Plastic Conveyor Belting Mfr
N.A.I.C.S.: 326199

Habasit Argentina S.A. (1)
Indalecio Gomez Calle 4 No 3951 CP 1672 Villa Lynch San Martin, Buenos Aires, Argentina
Tel.: (54) 114 7559548
Web Site: http://www.habasit.com.ar
Conveyor Belt Distr
N.A.I.C.S.: 423840

Habasit Belgium N.V. (1)
Leuvensesteenweg 542, 1930, Zaventem, Belgium
Tel.: (32) 27250430
Web Site: http://www.habasit.com
Sales Range: $50-74.9 Million
Emp.: 7
Conveyor Belts Mfr
N.A.I.C.S.: 326220
Frank Smit *(Mng Dir)*

Habasit Canada Limited (1)
460 Michigan Drive, Oakville, L6L 0G7, ON, Canada
Tel.: (905) 827-4131
Web Site: https://www.habasit.com
Sales Range: $25-49.9 Million
Emp.: 23
Conveyor Belts Mfr
N.A.I.C.S.: 326220

Habasit Far East Pte. Ltd. (1)
9 Joo Koon Road, Singapore, 628973, Singapore
Tel.: (65) 68625566
Web Site: http://www.habasit.com.sg
Sales Range: $25-49.9 Million
Emp.: 30
Conveyor Belting
N.A.I.C.S.: 326220

Habasit France S.A.S. (1)
41 rue Alfred Kastler, ZAC de la Mer Rouge, F-68059, Mulhouse, France
Tel.: (33) 389338903
Web Site: http://www.habasit.fr
Sales Range: $50-74.9 Million
Emp.: 70
Conveyor Belts Mfr
N.A.I.C.S.: 326220

Habasit Gesellschaft m.b.H. (1)
Mlynska 326/13, 602 00, Brno, Czech Republic
Tel.: (420) 541 421651
Web Site: http://www.habasit.cz
Conveyor Belt Distr
N.A.I.C.S.: 423840

Habasit GmbH (1)
Hetmanekgasse 13, Postfach 44, 1230, Vienna, Austria
Tel.: (43) 169066
Web Site: http://www.habasit.at
Sales Range: $25-49.9 Million
Conveyor Belts Mfr
N.A.I.C.S.: 326220
Ulrich Buehrmann *(Mng Dir)*

Subsidiary (Non-US):

Habasit Bulgaria (2)
Juri Wenelin Str 18, BG-1000, Sofia, Bulgaria
Tel.: (359) 29890380
Web Site: http://www.habasit.bg
Conveyor Belting
N.A.I.C.S.: 326220

Habasit Hungaria Kft. (2)
Latohegyi u 4, Postfach 368, H-2501, Esztergom, Hungary
Tel.: (36) 33412607
Web Site: http://www.habasit.hu
Sales Range: $25-49.9 Million
Emp.: 40
Conveyor Belts Mfr
N.A.I.C.S.: 326220

Habasit Moscow (2)
Ul Kantemirovskaja 58, RUS-115477, Moscow, Russia
Tel.: (7) 4959561508
Web Site: http://www.habasit.ru
Sales Range: $25-49.9 Million
Emp.: 6
Conveyor Belting
N.A.I.C.S.: 326220

Habasit Polska Sp. z o.o. (2)
ul Budowlanych 11, 41-303, Dabrowa Gornicza, Poland
Tel.: (48) 326390240
Web Site: http://www.habasit.pl
Sales Range: $25-49.9 Million
Emp.: 20
Conveyor Belts Mfr
N.A.I.C.S.: 326220

Habasit Hispanica S.A. (1)
Zona Industrial Santiga Avda Castell de Barbera 34 Apartado, PO Box 180, 08210, Barbera del Valles, Spain
Tel.: (34) 937 191912
Web Site: http://www.habasit.es
Conveyor Belt Distr
N.A.I.C.S.: 423840
Xavier Pellise Canovas *(Key Acct Mgr)*

Habasit Italiana SpA (1)
Via Del Lavoro 50, 31016, Cordignano, Italy
Tel.: (39) 043 8911444
Conveyor Belt Distr
N.A.I.C.S.: 423840
Ugo Passadore *(Gen Mgr)*

Habasit Kayis San ve Tic. Ltd. (1)
Aydinli birlik Org San Bolgesi 4 Sok No 4, Istanbul, Türkiye
Tel.: (90) 212 6549404
Web Site: http://www.habasit.com.pr
Emp.: 25
Conveyor Belt Distr
N.A.I.C.S.: 423840
Umit Yanar *(Dir-Comml)*

Habasit Netherlands BV (1)
Sluiswachter 14, 3861 SN, Nijkerk, Netherlands
Tel.: (31) 332472030
Web Site: http://www.habasit.nl
Sales Range: $25-49.9 Million
Emp.: 30
Conveyor Belts Mfr
N.A.I.C.S.: 326220

Habasit Nippon Co. Ltd. (1)
460 Nagatanaka, Kinokawa, 649-6503, Wakayama-Ken, Japan
Tel.: (81) 736 736339
Web Site: http://www.habasit.co.jp
Conveyor Belt Distr

N.A.I.C.S.: 423840

Habasit Rossi (Taiwan) Limited (1)
No 71 Fu An Street, Tucheng, Taipei, Taiwan
Tel.: (886) 222 670538
Web Site: http://www.habasit.com.tw
Conveyor Belt Distr
N.A.I.C.S.: 423840
Lawrence Lan *(Mgr-Sls & Mktg)*

Habasit Ukraine LLC (1)
Gagarina Str 49 Village Agronomichne, 23227, Vinnytsia, Ukraine
Tel.: (380) 432 584735
Web Site: http://www.habasit.ua
Conveyor Belt Distr
N.A.I.C.S.: 423840
Alexander Detsyura *(Gen Mgr)*

Habasit do Brasil Ind. E Com. de Correias Ltda. (1)
Av Gupe 10767 Block A-3 Km 30 Rodavia Pres, Castello Branco Jardim Belval, CEP 06420-120, Sao Paulo, Brazil
Tel.: (55) 1147899022
Web Site: http://www.habasit.com.br
Sales Range: $25-49.9 Million
Emp.: 30
Conveyor Belts Mfr
N.A.I.C.S.: 326220

OOO Habasit Ltd. (1)
St Ozernaya 13a, 141727, Moscow, Dolgoprudny, Russia
Tel.: (7) 4959661566
Web Site: http://www.habasit.ru
Conveyor Belt Distr
N.A.I.C.S.: 423840

HABAU HOCH- UND TIEF- BAUGESELLSCHAFT M.B.H.

Greiner Strasse 63, A-4320, Perg, Austria
Tel.: (43) 7262 555 0   AT
Web Site: http://www.habau.com
Year Founded: 1988
Construction Services
N.A.I.C.S.: 236220
Hubert Wetschnig *(CEO)*

Subsidiaries:

MCE GmbH (1)
Lunzerstrasse 64, 4031, Linz, Austria   (100%)
Tel.: (43) 73290115843
Web Site: http://www.mce-hg.com
Complex Steel Structure Design, Assembly & Erection Services
N.A.I.C.S.: 238190
Dieter Reitz *(Mng Dir & Head-Rhein-Main Branch)*

HABERKORN HOLDING AG

Hohe Brucke, Wolfurt, 6961, Austria
Tel.: (43) 55746950
Web Site: http://www.haberkorn.com
Sales Range: $250-299.9 Million
Emp.: 1,400
Holding Company
N.A.I.C.S.: 551112
Fitz Gerald *(CEO & Mng Dir)*

Subsidiaries:

Haberkorn Eood (1)
ul Adam Mizkewitsch Nr 4a, 1360, Sofia, Bulgaria
Tel.: (359) 2 827 05 61
Web Site: http://www.haberkorn.bg
Industrial Supplies Whslr
N.A.I.C.S.: 423840

Haberkorn Sp. z o.o. (1)
ul Powstancow Slaskich 238, 44-348, Skrzyszow, Poland
Tel.: (48) 32 4597 999
Web Site: http://www.haberkorn.pl
Emp.: 30
Industrial Supplies Whslr
N.A.I.C.S.: 423840
Ewelina Thaut *(Mgr)*

Haberkorn d.o.o. (1)
Vodovodna ul 7, 2000, Maribor, Slovenia
Tel.: (386) 2 320 67 10

INTERNATIONAL PUBLIC

Web Site: http://www.haberkorn.si
Emp.: 25
Industrial Supplies Whslr
N.A.I.C.S.: 423840

Haberkorn s.r.o. (1)
Generala Vlacheho 305, 747 62, Mokre Lazce, Czech Republic
Tel.: (420) 553 757 111
Web Site: http://www.haberkorn.cz
Industrial Supplies Whslr
N.A.I.C.S.: 423840

Unico Haberkorn AG (1)
Musterplatzstrasse 3, 9442, Berneck, Switzerland
Tel.: (41) 71 74 74 920
Web Site: http://www.haberkorn.ch
Emp.: 50
Industrial Supplies Whslr
N.A.I.C.S.: 423840

HABIB BANK AG ZURICH

Weinbergstrasse 59, 8042, Zurich, Switzerland
Tel.: (41) 442694500   CH
Web Site:
https://www.habibbank.com
Year Founded: 1967
Banking Services
N.A.I.C.S.: 522110
Muhammed H. Habib *(Pres)*

Subsidiaries:

Habib Metropolitan Bank Limited (1)
Building II Chundrigar Road, Karachi, Pakistan
Tel.: (92) 21111141414
Web Site: https://www.habibmetro.com
Banking Services
N.A.I.C.S.: 522110

Subsidiary (Domestic):

First Habib Modaraba (2)
6th Floor HBZ Plaza Hirani Centre I Chundrigar Road, Karachi, Pakistan
Tel.: (92) 2132635949
Web Site: https://www.habibmodaraba.com
Rev.: $12,359,118
Assets: $73,892,216
Liabilities: $57,294,080
Net Worth: $16,598,136
Earnings: $1,869,374
Emp.: 81
Fiscal Year-end: 06/30/2023
Financial Services
N.A.I.C.S.: 523999
Muhammad Shoaib Ibrahim *(CEO)*

Habib Metropolitan Financial Services Limited (2)
1st Floor GPC II Block V Kehkashan Clifton, Karachi, Pakistan
Tel.: (92) 2135364665
Web Site: http://www.hmfs.com.pk
Financial Services
N.A.I.C.S.: 523999
Ather Husain Medina *(Head-Res)*

HABIB BANK LIMITED

Habib Bank Plaza I I Chundrigar Road, Karachi, 75650, Pakistan
Tel.: (92) 2132418000   PK
Web Site: https://www.hbl.com
Year Founded: 1947
HBL—(PSX)
Rev.: $1,064,005,846
Assets: $19,655,843,030
Liabilities: $18,355,880,666
Net Worth: $1,299,962,364
Earnings: $205,131,777
Emp.: 20,391
Fiscal Year-end: 12/31/23
Banking Services
N.A.I.C.S.: 522110

Subsidiaries:

HBL Asset Management Limited (1)
7th Floor Emerald Tower G-19 Block 5 Main Clifton Road Clifton, Karachi, Pakistan
Tel.: (92) 111425262
Web Site: http://www.hblasset.com

AND PRIVATE COMPANIES

Investment Advisory & Asset Management Services
N.A.I.C.S.: 523150
Noman Qurban *(CFO & Sec)*

Habib Allied International Bank Plc. (1)
379 Stratford Rd Sparkhill, Birmingham, B114JZ, United Kingdom **(90.5%)**
Tel.: (44) 1217731653
Web Site: http://www.habibbankuk.com
Sales Range: $50-74.9 Million
Emp.: 5
Bank Holding Company
N.A.I.C.S.: 551111

Subsidiary (Domestic):

Habibsons Bank Limited (2)
9 Portman St, London, W1H 6DZ, United Kingdom
Tel.: (44) 2078951100
Investment Banking Services
N.A.I.C.S.: 523150
Abbas Hasan *(Chm)*

Habib Finance International Limited (1)
Room 602 6/F Miramar Tower 132 Nathan Rd Tsim Sha Tsui, Kowloon, China (Hong Kong)
Tel.: (852) 25213099
Sales Range: $50-74.9 Million
Emp.: 10
Depository Credit Intermediation
N.A.I.C.S.: 522180
Tariq Hussain *(CEO)*

HABIB GROUP OF COMPANIES

4th Floor Imperial Court Dr Ziauddin Ahmed Rd, Karachi, 75530, Pakistan
Tel.: (92) 215680036
Sales Range: $75-99.9 Million
Emp.: 300
Manages & Operates Various Companies
N.A.I.C.S.: 551112

Subsidiaries:

Bank Al-Habib Limited (1)
126-C Old Bahawalpur Road, Multan, Pakistan
Tel.: (92) 2132446978
Web Site: http://www.bankalhabib.com
Rev.: $326,944,439
Assets: $8,366,454,877
Liabilities: $7,967,608,347
Net Worth: $398,846,530
Earnings: $72,074,097
Emp.: 11,315
Fiscal Year-end: 12/31/2019
Financial Services
N.A.I.C.S.: 522110

Habib IT Solutions PVT Ltd. (1)
3rd Floor, Imperial Court, Dr. Ziauddin Ahmed Road, Karachi, Pakistan
Tel.: (92) 21 111 111
Web Site: http://www.nvidia.in
Electronic Computer Mfr
N.A.I.C.S.: 334111

Habib Insurance Company Limited (1)
1st floor State Life Bldg No 6, Habib Square M A Jinnah Road, 74000, Karachi, Pakistan
Tel.: (92) 21111030303
Web Site: http://www.habibinsurance.net
Sales Range: $100-124.9 Million
Emp.: 150
Life & Health Insurance
N.A.I.C.S.: 524114
Tariq Awan *(Gen Mgr)*

Habib Sugar Mills Limited (1)
3rd Floor - Imperial Court Dr Ziauddin Ahmed Road, Karachi, 75530, Pakistan
Tel.: (92) 2135680036
Web Site: https://www.habib.com
Rev.: $70,979,025
Assets: $62,895,671
Liabilities: $22,707,762
Net Worth: $40,187,909
Earnings: $9,026,339
Emp.: 531
Fiscal Year-end: 09/30/2023

Sugar Mills
N.A.I.C.S.: 311314
Asghar D. Habib *(Chm)*

Habibsons Bank Limited (1)
2nd Floor Imperial Court Dr Ziauddin Ahmed Road, Karachi, Pakistan
Tel.: (92) 215687681
Financial Institution
N.A.I.C.S.: 522110
Muslim Habib *(Mng Dir)*

HABIB RICE PRODUCT LIMITED

2nd Floor UBL Building,II Chundrigar Road, Karachi, Pakistan
Tel.: (92) 853363963
Web Site: https://habibriceproducts.com
HAL—(KAR)
Rev.: $11,220,188
Assets: $8,363,206
Liabilities: $2,330,843
Net Worth: $6,032,363
Earnings: $884,928
Fiscal Year-end: 06/30/19
Food Products Mfr
N.A.I.C.S.: 311999

HABITAT

10 Hamada St, Herzliya Pituach, Israel
Tel.: (972) 99717000
Web Site: http://www.habitat.co.il
Kitchen Cabinet Mfr
N.A.I.C.S.: 337110

HABITAT BEAUJOLAIS VAL DE SAONE

13 rue Claude Bernard, 69400, Villefranche-sur-Saone, Rhone, France
Tel.: (33) 825815275
Web Site: http://www.habitatbvs.fr
Rev.: $24,000,000
Emp.: 90
Apartment Building Operator
N.A.I.C.S.: 531110
Pierre Alloin *(Chm)*

HABITAT DU GARD

92 bis Boulevard Jean Jaures, PO Box 47046, 30911, Nimes, Cedex 2, France
Tel.: (33) 466628100
Web Site: http://www.habitatdugard.org
Rev.: $22,100,000
Emp.: 300
Apartment Building Operator
N.A.I.C.S.: 531110
Marc Chavardes *(Technical Dir)*

HABITAT PROIECT S.A.

Bulevardul Copou Nr 4, 700505, Iasi, Romania
Tel.: (40) 232 267590
Web Site: http://www.habitatproiect.ro
Sales Range: Less than $1 Million
Emp.: 25
Office & Retail Space Rental Services
N.A.I.C.S.: 531120
Otilia Plesu *(Mgr)*

HABROK MINING PTY LTD.

63 Dowd Street, Welshpool, 6106, WA, Australia
Tel.: (61) 289200700
Web Site: http://habrokmining.com
Year Founded: 2019
Privater Equity Firm
N.A.I.C.S.: 523999
Matthew Bowles *(Mng Dir)*

HACHI-BAN CO., LTD.

1-12-18 Shinkanda, Kanazawa, 921-8582, Ishikawa, Japan

Tel.: (81) 762920888
Web Site: https://www.hachiban.co.jp
Year Founded: 1971
9950—(TKS)
Rev.: $50,388,030
Assets: $38,073,600
Liabilities: $15,705,360
Net Worth: $22,368,240
Earnings: $1,057,600
Emp.: 147
Fiscal Year-end: 03/31/24
Food Production & Restaurant Management
N.A.I.C.S.: 722513
Katsuji Goto *(Chm)*

Subsidiaries:

DOUBLE FLOWERING CAMMELIA CO., LTD (1)
30 Moo 4 Sarangphun Wangmung, Amphoe Bang Sao Thong, Saraburi, 18220, Thailand
Tel.: (66) 27063131
Soup Mfr & Whslr
N.A.I.C.S.: 311999

HACHIBAN Trading (Thailand) Co., Ltd. (1)
2 Premier Place 1st Floor Soi Premier 2, Nongbon Prawet, Bangkok, 10250, Thailand
Tel.: (66) 27440543
Web Site: https://www.hachiban-trading.co.th
Processed Food Product Mfr & Distr
N.A.I.C.S.: 311991

Thai Hachiban Co., Ltd. (1)
191-201 Soi Krasi, Talat Yot Phra Nakhon, Bangkok, 10200, Thailand
Tel.: (66) 22 808 2334
Web Site: https://www.hachiban.co.th
Restaurant Operators
N.A.I.C.S.: 722511

HACHIJUNI DC CARD CO., LTD.

1279-3 Minamiishidocho, Nagano, 380-0824, Japan
Tel.: (81) 262266611
Year Founded: 1982
Sales Range: $50-74.9 Million
Emp.: 69
Business Credit Card Services
N.A.I.C.S.: 522210

HACHIJUNI LEASE CO., LTD

218-14 Okada Nakagosho, Nagano, 380-0935, Japan
Tel.: (81) 262268282
Web Site: http://www.82lease.co.jp
Year Founded: 1974
Sales Range: $200-249.9 Million
Emp.: 135
Financial Lending Services
N.A.I.C.S.: 522220
Hirotoshi Mizusawa *(Pres)*

HACHSHARA INSURANCE COMPANY LTD.

6 Malakah St, PO Box 1877, Holon, 5811801, Israel
Tel.: (972) 37960000
Web Site: https://www.hcsra.co.il
ILDN—(TAE)
Rev.: $1,303,994,272
Assets: $9,393,611,319
Liabilities: $9,278,576,390
Net Worth: $115,034,929
Earnings: $19,757,767
Fiscal Year-end: 12/31/21
Property Insurance Services
N.A.I.C.S.: 524126

HACI OMER SABANCI HOLDING A.S.

Sabanci Center 4, Levent, 34330, Istanbul, Turkiye
Tel.: (90) 2123858080
Web Site: https://www.sabanci.com
Year Founded: 1967

SAHOL—(IST)
Rev.: $4,231,877,716
Assets: $67,715,750,892
Liabilities: $55,819,245,942
Net Worth: $11,896,504,950
Earnings: $476,512,177
Emp.: 60,000
Fiscal Year-end: 12/31/23
Holding Company
N.A.I.C.S.: 551112
Erol Sabanci *(Vice Chm)*

Subsidiaries:

Akcansa Cimento Sanayi ve Ticaret A.S. (1)
Barbaros Mahallesi Kardelen Sk No 2 D 124-125 Palladium Tower, Istanbul, Turkiye **(39.72%)**
Tel.: (90) 2165713000
Web Site: http://www.akcansa.com.tr
Rev.: $266,680,842
Assets: $329,686,733
Liabilities: $166,046,658
Net Worth: $163,640,074
Earnings: $15,596,433
Emp.: 967
Fiscal Year-end: 12/31/2020
Cement Mfr
N.A.I.C.S.: 327310
Hakan Gurdal *(Vice Chm)*

Bimsa Uluslararasi Is, Bilgi ve Yonetim Sistemleri A.S. (1)
Acarlar Is Merkezi D Blok Kat 3-4 Kavacik, Beykoz, 34805, Istanbul, Turkiye
Tel.: (90) 2164251050
Web Site: http://www.bimsa.com.tr
Business Management Consulting Services
N.A.I.C.S.: 541611

Brisa Bridgestone Sabanci Lastik Sanayi ve Ticaret A.S. (1)
Alikahya Fatih Mahallesi Sanayi Caddesi No 98 Izmit, 41310, Kocaeli, Turkiye **(100%)**
Tel.: (90) 2623164000
Web Site: http://www.brisa.com.tr
Sales Range: $450-499.9 Million
Emp.: 1,300
Tire Mfr & Distr
N.A.I.C.S.: 326211

Carrefour Sabanci Ticaret Merkezi AS CarrefourSA (1)
CarrefourSA Plaza Cevizli Mahallesi Tugay Yolu Caddesi No 67 A Blok B, Maltepe, Istanbul, Turkiye **(38.8%)**
Tel.: (90) 2166 55 0000
Web Site: http://www.carrefoursa.com
Sales Range: $125-149.9 Million
Emp.: 500
Supermarkets & Other Stores Operator
N.A.I.C.S.: 445110

Cimsa Cimento Sanayi ve Ticaret A.S. (1)
Kisikli Cad No 1 kat 23-24 Allianz Tower, Kucukbakkalkoy Mah, 34750, Istanbul, Turkiye **(54.54%)**
Tel.: (90) 2166515300
Web Site: http://www.cimsa.com.tr
Rev.: $265,077,149
Assets: $358,251,796
Liabilities: $169,573,345
Net Worth: $188,678,451
Earnings: $110,025,095
Emp.: 909
Fiscal Year-end: 12/31/2022
Cement & Ready-Mix Concrete Mfr
N.A.I.C.S.: 327310
Tamer Saka *(Chm)*

Subsidiary (Domestic):

Afyon Cimento Sanayi Turk A.S. (2)
Guvenevler Mahallesi Fatih, Cad 22, 03040, Afyonkarahisar, Turkiye
Tel.: (90) 27 2214 7200
Web Site: http://www.afyoncimento.com.tr
Sales Range: $250-299.9 Million
Emp.: 850
Cement Mfr
N.A.I.C.S.: 327310

Joint Venture (Domestic):

Oysa Cimento Sanayii A.S. (2)

3203

HACI OMER SABANCI HOLDING A.S.

Haci Omer Sabanci Holding A.S.—(Continued)
Karayilan Beldesi Bitisigi, PO Box 27, Iskenderun, 31201, Turkiye
Tel.: (90) 38823236
Sales Range: $50-74.9 Million
Emp.: 102
Hydraulic Cement Mfr
N.A.I.C.S.: 327310

Enerjisa Enerji A.S. (1)
Sabanci Center Kule 2 Kat 4, Levent, 34330, Istanbul, Turkiye **(50%)**
Tel.: (90) 2123858866
Web Site: http://www.enerjisa.com.tr
Holding Company; Electric Power Generation, Distr & Natural Gas Distr
N.A.I.C.S.: 551112
Yetik K. Mert *(CEO)*

Subsidiary (Domestic):

Enerjisa Baskent Elektrik Dagitim A.S. (2)
Sabanci Center Kule 2, Levent, 6520, Istanbul, Turkiye
Tel.: (90) 2123858828
Web Site: http://www.enerjisa.com.tr
Retail Electric Power Distr
N.A.I.C.S.: 221122

Enerjisa Electrik Enerjisi Toptan Satis A.S. (2)
Barbaros Mahallesi Begonya Sokak Nida Kule Atasehir Bati Sit No1/1, 34330, Istanbul, Turkiye
Tel.: (90) 2123858866
Web Site: http://www.enerjisa.com.tr
Electric Power Whslr & Natural Gas Distr
N.A.I.C.S.: 221122

Enerjisa Enerji Uretim A.S. (2)
Barbaros Mahallesi Begonya Sokak Nida Kule Atasehir Bati Sit No1/1, 34330, Istanbul, Turkiye
Tel.: (90) 212 385 88 66
Web Site: http://www.enerjisauretim.com.tr
Geothermal, Hydro & Wind Electric Power Generation Services
N.A.I.C.S.: 221118

Plant (Domestic):

Enerjisa Enerji Uretim A.S. - Canakkale Power Plant (3)
Mahmudiye Koyu, Ezine, 17600, Canakkale, Turkiye
Tel.: (90) 286 628 77 78
Web Site: http://www.enerjisauretim.com.tr
Geothermal & Wind Electric Power Generation Services
N.A.I.C.S.: 221116

Enerjisa Enerji Uretim A.S. - Kentsa Power Plant (3)
Sabanci Center Kule 2, Levent, 41220, Izmit, Turkiye
Tel.: (90) 2123858866
Web Site: http://www.enerjisauretim.com.tr
Emp.: 20
Geothermal Electric Power Generation Services
N.A.I.C.S.: 221116

Enerjisa Enerji Uretim A.S. - Mersin Power Plant (3)
Dagpazari Village Road 12 Km, Mut, Mersin, Turkiye
Tel.: (90) 3247910053
Web Site: http://www.enerjisauretim.com.tr
Geothermal Electric Power Generation Services
N.A.I.C.S.: 221116

Exsa Export Sanayi Mamulleri Satis ve Arastirma A.S. (1)
Kule 2 K 4 Sabanci Center, Istanbul, Turkiye
Tel.: (90) 2123858484
Textile Product Whslr
N.A.I.C.S.: 314999

I-Bimsa Uluslararasi Is Bilgi Veyonetim Sistemleri A.S. (1)
Acarlar yp Merkezi D Blok Kat 3-4 Kavacyk, Istanbul, 34805, Turkiye
Tel.: (90) 2164251050
Web Site: http://www.bimsa.com.tr
Sales Range: $50-74.9 Million
Emp.: 100

Business Information & Management Systems; Owned 50% by Haci Omer Sabanci Holding A.S. & 50% by International Business Machines Corporation
N.A.I.C.S.: 551112

Kordsa Teknik Tekstil A.S. (1)
Sanayi Mahallesi Teknopark Bulvari No1/1B, Pendik, 34906, Istanbul, Turkiye **(71,11%)**
Tel.: (90) 2163001000
Web Site: https://www.kordsa.com
Rev.: $614,991,131
Assets: $1,030,966,273
Liabilities: $586,551,224
Net Worth: $444,415,049
Earnings: $20,388,913
Emp.: 4,500
Fiscal Year-end: 12/31/2020
Textile Mfr
N.A.I.C.S.: 314999
Cevdet Alemdar *(Chm)*

Subsidiary (US):

Axiom Materials, Inc. (2)
2320 Pullman St, Santa Ana, CA 92705
Tel.: (949) 623-4400
Web Site: http://www.axiommaterials.com
Adhesives & Related Products Mfr
N.A.I.C.S.: 325520
John Adamo *(VP-Sls & Mktg)*

Fabric Development Inc. (2)
1217 Mill St, Quakertown, PA 18951
Tel.: (215) 536-1420
Web Site: http://www.fabricdevelopment.com
Specialty Broadwoven Fabrics, Including Twisted Weaves
N.A.I.C.S.: 313210

Kordsa, Inc. (2)
4501 N Access Rd, Chattanooga, TN 37415-9990
Tel.: (423) 643-8300
Nylon Industrial Yarn, Fabrics & Single End Cord Mfr
N.A.I.C.S.: 314994

Marsa Kraft Jacobs Suchard Sabanci Gida Sanayi Ve Ticaret A.S (1)
Kucukbakkalkoy Vedat Gunyol Cad Demir Sok No 1A, Atasehir, Istanbul, Turkiye
Tel.: (90) 2165701400
Web Site: http://www.marsa.com.tr
Sales Range: $25-49.9 Million
Emp.: 100
Food Products Mfr; Owned 51% by Haci Omer Sabanci Holding A.S. & 49% by Kraft Foods Inc
N.A.I.C.S.: 311224

Teknosa Ic ve Dis Ticaret A.S. (1)
Carrefoursa Plaza Tugay Yolu Cad No 67 Blok B, Cevizli Mah Maltepe, 34846, Istanbul, Turkiye
Tel.: (90) 2164683636
Web Site: https://www.teknosa.com
Sales Range: $650-699.9 Million
Electronic Product Whslr
N.A.I.C.S.: 449210
Max Roger Speur *(Chm)*

Temsa Global Sanayi ve Ticaret A.S. (1)
Omer Avni Mahallesi Inonu Caddesi No 50 Devres Han, Beyoglu, 34427, Istanbul, Turkiye
Tel.: (90) 2124030202
Web Site: http://www.temsa.com
Buses & Coaches Mfr
N.A.I.C.S.: 336110

Subsidiary (Non-US):

Temsa Europe NV (2)
Dellingstraat 32, 2800, Mechelen, Belgium
Tel.: (32) 15 44 00 00
Sales Range: $25-49.9 Million
Emp.: 9
Motor Vehicle Mfr & Distr
N.A.I.C.S.: 336890
Wim Vanhool *(Gen Mgr)*

Plant (Domestic):

Temsa Global Sanayi ve Ticaret A.S. - Adana Plant (2)
Mersin Yolu Uzeri 10 Km P K 480, 1323, Adana, Turkiye
Tel.: (90) 322 441 02 26
Buses & Coaches Mfr
N.A.I.C.S.: 336110

Yazaki Sabanci Otomotiv Kablo Donanimi San. Ve Tic. A.S. (1)
Topcu Sirti Mah Yazakisa Cad, Kuzuluk Akyazi, 544440, Sakarya, Turkiye
Tel.: (90) 2644378250
Sales Range: $200-249.9 Million
Emp.: 850
Motor Vehicle Wire Harnesses Mfr; Owned 75% by Yazaki Corporation & 25% by Haci Omer Sabanci Holding A.S.
N.A.I.C.S.: 336340

Yunsa Yunlu Sanayi Ve Ticaret A.S. (1)
Vadistanbul 1B Block Floor 23 Ayazaga Mah Azerbaycan Cad, 34396, Istanbul, Turkiye
Tel.: (90) 2123656500
Web Site: https://www.yunsa.com
Rev.: $39,534,780
Assets: $28,890,898
Liabilities: $17,597,002
Net Worth: $11,293,896
Earnings: $10,781,273
Emp.: 1,074
Fiscal Year-end: 12/31/2022
Fabric Product Mfr
N.A.I.C.S.: 313240
Hakan Konuskan *(Chief Supply Chain Officer)*

HACO N.V.
Hogeschuurstraat 2, 8850, Ardooie, Belgium
Tel.: (32) 51746454
Web Site: http://www.haco.com
Year Founded: 1965
Sales Range: $250-299.9 Million
Emp.: 1,800
Metal Forming & Woodworking Machinery Machine Control & Surfacing Installation Mfr
N.A.I.C.S.: 333517

Subsidiaries:

BLISS-BRET a.s. (1)
Street 1 maja 1850, 031 80, Liptovsky Mikulas, Slovakia
Tel.: (421) 907733082
Web Site: http://www.bliss-bret.com
Industrial Machinery Mfr
N.A.I.C.S.: 333310

BRET SA (1)
91 Route de Francheville, 27130, Verneuil-sur-Avre, France
Tel.: (33) 2 32 32 15 90
Web Site: http://www.bliss-bret.com
Emp.: 17
Industrial Machinery Mfr
N.A.I.C.S.: 333310
Peter Goegebeur *(Mgr)*

CHAMBON sas (1)
Rue de l Eglise, 39190, Cousance, France
Tel.: (33) 3 84 48 95 80
Web Site: http://www.chambon-sa.com
Industrial Equipment Mfr
N.A.I.C.S.: 333413

Chambon srl (1)
Calea Chisinaului 34, 700180, Iasi, Romania
Tel.: (40) 3 32 41 87 01
Web Site: http://www.chambon.ro
Emp.: 70
Industrial Machinery Mfr
N.A.I.C.S.: 333310
Alina Stefan *(Mgr)*

Clid Systemes sas (1)
ZI Rue Laennec, 59933, Armentieres, France
Tel.: (33) 475 55 01 15
Web Site: http://www.clid.fr
Emp.: 20
Industrial Equipment Mfr
N.A.I.C.S.: 333413
Alain Raygasse *(Gen Mgr)*

Elas nv (1)

INTERNATIONAL PUBLIC

Rue de l Abattoir 53, 7700, Mouscron, Belgium
Tel.: (32) 56 58 52 50
Industrial Machinery Mfr
N.A.I.C.S.: 333310

FAT S.A. (1)
281 Grabiszynska Street, 53-234, Wroclaw, Poland
Tel.: (48) 71 36 09 100
Web Site: http://www.fathaco.com
Industrial Machinery Mfr
N.A.I.C.S.: 333310
Sebastian Chomicz *(Dir-Sls)*

HACO (Ningbo) International Trading Co., LTD (1)
No 638 Fuchungjiang Road NETD, Beilun, Ningbo, 315800, China
Tel.: (86) 574 86837622
Industrial Equipment Mfr
N.A.I.C.S.: 333413

HACO - Mubea Systeme GmbH (1)
Christenfeld 13, 41379, Bruggen, Germany
Tel.: (49) 21 57 87 07 0
Web Site: http://www.de.haco.com
Industrial Machinery Mfr
N.A.I.C.S.: 333310

HACO Australia Perth (1)
7 35 Biscayne Way, Jandakot, 6164, WA, Australia
Tel.: (61) 8 9414 8009
Industrial Machinery Mfr
N.A.I.C.S.: 333310

HACO B.V (1)
Lange Voren 16, 5521 DD, Eersel, Netherlands
Tel.: (31) 161 45 48 74
Web Site: http://www.haco.com
Industrial Machinery Mfr
N.A.I.C.S.: 333310
Frank Havegeer *(Gen Mgr)*

HACO Canada Inc. (1)
2550 Dunwin Dr, Mississauga, L5L1J5, ON, Canada
Tel.: (905) 828-1087
Web Site: http://www.hacocanada.com
Industrial Machinery Mfr
N.A.I.C.S.: 333310
Francis Vanslambrouck *(Gen Mgr)*

HACO FAR EAST PTE Ltd (1)
Block 6015 Ang Mo Kio Industrial Park 3 01, 332, 569467, Singapore, Singapore
Tel.: (65) 29 75 662
Industrial Machinery Mfr
N.A.I.C.S.: 333310

HACO G. Kouzaris ltd. (1)
Miliaraki 23 25 K Patisia, Athens, Greece
Tel.: (30) 210 83 26 811
Industrial Equipment Mfr
N.A.I.C.S.: 333413

HACO Machinery Private Limited (1)
Plot No 122 B Sector 6 HSIIDC Industrial Growth Centre Bawal, 123501, Rewari, Haryana, India
Tel.: (91) 9813246805
Industrial Machinery Mfr
N.A.I.C.S.: 333310
Satya Prakash Yadav *(Sr Mgr)*

HACO SAS (1)
ZI Rue Laennec, 59930, La Chapelle, d Armentieres, France
Tel.: (33) 3 20 10 30 40
Web Site: http://www.haco.fr
Emp.: 20
Industrial Machinery Mfr
N.A.I.C.S.: 333310

HACO TRADING COMPANY nv (1)
Hogeschuurstraat 2, 8850, Ardooie, Belgium
Tel.: (32) 51 74 64 54
Web Site: http://www.hacotrading.be
Industrial Machinery Mfr
N.A.I.C.S.: 333310
Johan Calleeuw *(Accountant)*

HACO a.s. (1)
PO Box 76, 902 01, Senica, Slovakia
Tel.: (421) 802 51 08 50
Industrial Equipment Mfr
N.A.I.C.S.: 333413

HACO sl (1)
C Fornals N 9 Pol Ind Can Comelles, 08292, Barcelona, Esparreguera, Spain
Tel.: (34) 93 777 50 70
Industrial Machinery Mfr
N.A.I.C.S.: 333310

Haco (Australia) Pty Ltd (1)
70 Yellowbox Drv, Craigieburn, 3064, VIC, Australia
Tel.: (61) 3 9791 8255
Web Site: http://www.au.haco.com
Industrial Equipment Mfr
N.A.I.C.S.: 333413
Geoff Archer (Mgr-Sls)

Haco Machinery (Malaysia) Sdn Bhd (1)
No 30 Jalan Anggerik Mokara 31 47, 40460, Shah Alam, Selangor, Malaysia
Tel.: (60) 3 5122 1866
Industrial Equipment Mfr
N.A.I.C.S.: 333413

Haco-Atlantic, Inc. (1)
11629 N Houston Rosslyn Rd, Houston, TX 77086 **(100%)**
Tel.: (281) 445-3985
Web Site: http://www.hacoatlantic.com
Sales Range: $25-49.9 Million
Emp.: 12
Metal Forming Machinery Importer, Retailer & Servicer
N.A.I.C.S.: 423830
Daniel Kint (Gen Mgr)

Koluszky Foundry Sp. z.o.o. (1)
Ul 11 Listopada 65, 95-040, Koluszki, Poland
Tel.: (48) 447146200
Web Site: http://www.kfmhaco.com
Industrial Machinery Mfr
N.A.I.C.S.: 333310
Kamila Surmanska (Pres)

Robosoft nv (1)
Rozendaalstraat 6, 8900, Ieper, Belgium
Tel.: (32) 57 21 94 57
Web Site: http://www.robosoft.be
Industrial Machinery Mfr
N.A.I.C.S.: 333310

SIMA-SACA (1)
Boulevard Industriel 99, 7700, Mouscron, Belgium
Tel.: (32) 56 85 62 00
Web Site: http://www.sima.be
Industrial Equipment Mfr
N.A.I.C.S.: 333413
Ean Hason (Gen Mgr)

The Kingsland Engineering Co. Ltd (1)
Weybourne Road Sheringham, Norfolk, NR26 8HE, United Kingdom
Tel.: (44) 1263 822 153
Web Site: http://www.kingsland.com
Industrial Machinery Mfr
N.A.I.C.S.: 333310
Jonathan Battrick-Newall (Mgr-Svc)

s.c.m. BLISS SAS (1)
8 Avenue du Marechal Leclerc, BP 30, 21501, Montbard, France
Tel.: (33) 3 80 89 90 70
Industrial Machinery Mfr
N.A.I.C.S.: 333310

HADASIT BIO-HOLDINGS LTD.
Jerusalem Bio-Park 5th Floor Hadassah Ein-Kerem Campus, Jerusalem, 91120, Israel
Tel.: (972) 25722054
Web Site: https://www.hbl.co.il
Year Founded: 2005
HDST—(OTCIQ)
Emp.: 5
Biotechnology Investment Services
N.A.I.C.S.: 523999
Baruch Halpert (Chm)

HADCO LIMITED
JRJ Warehousing Compound Bhagoutie Trace, San Juan, Trinidad & Tobago
Tel.: (868) 6757628
Web Site: http://www.hadcoltd.com

Year Founded: 1992
Sales Range: $100-124.9 Million
Emp.: 500
Food & Electrical Distr
N.A.I.C.S.: 424420
John Hadad (Chm)

Subsidiaries:

G & M Warehousing Enterprises Limited (1)
Lot 33 Tissue Dr, Trincity, Trinidad & Tobago
Tel.: (868) 624 4347
Bonded Warehousing Services
N.A.I.C.S.: 493110

HD Cafe Ltd (1)
Ellerslie Plaza, Maraval, Port of Spain, Trinidad & Tobago
Tel.: (868) 622 8833
Web Site: http://www.hdcafett.com
Ice Cream Mfr & Distr
N.A.I.C.S.: 311520

Lighthouse Limited (1)
32-34 Dundonald Street, Port of Spain, Trinidad & Tobago
Tel.: (868) 625 4448
Web Site: http://www.lighthousett.com
Lighting Fixture Distr
N.A.I.C.S.: 423610

Nova Lighting Ltd (1)
18 Rust Street, Saint Clair, Port of Spain, Trinidad & Tobago
Tel.: (868) 628 5483
Web Site: http://www.novalightttt.com
Emp.: 19
Lighting Fixture Distr
N.A.I.C.S.: 423610
Maria Lalacksingh (Mgr)

PATCON Limited (1)
Shop 18 & 19 Ellerslie Plaza, Maraval, Port of Spain, Trinidad & Tobago
Tel.: (868) 628 5573
Web Site: http://www.peppercornstt.com
Gourmet Food Retailer
N.A.I.C.S.: 445298
Celeste Reece (Mgr)

HADLEY INDUSTRIES PLC
Downing St, PO Box 92, Smethwick, B66 2PA, West Midlands, United Kingdom
Tel.: (44) 121 555 1300
Web Site: http://www.hadleygroup.com
Year Founded: 1964
Sales Range: Less than $1 Million
Cold Rolled Metal Sections & Profiles Mfr
N.A.I.C.S.: 331221
Stewart Towe (Chm)

Subsidiaries:

EWS (Manufacturing) Limited (1)
Headway Road, Wolverhampton, WV10 6PZ, W Midlands, United Kingdom
Tel.: (44) 1902623333
Aluminium & Steel Spacer Tube Mfr
N.A.I.C.S.: 331318

Overeem B.V. (1)
Radonstraat 16, 6718 WS, Ede, Netherlands
Tel.: (31) 318697811
Web Site: http://www.overeembv.nl
Roll Formed Metal Products Mfr
N.A.I.C.S.: 332114

HADRIAN'S WALL SECURED INVESTMENTS LTD.
48 Gresham Street, London, EC2V 7AY, United Kingdom
Tel.: (44) 2030268620
Web Site: http://www.hadrianswallcapital.com
Year Founded: 2010
HWSL—(LSE)
Rev.: $14,544,819
Assets: $200,569,311
Liabilities: $20,733,845

Net Worth: $179,835,466
Earnings: $4,201,652
Fiscal Year-end: 06/30/19
Bank Financing Services
N.A.I.C.S.: 522299
Marc Bajer (CEO)

HAE IN CORP.
Hyein Building 86 Dongsanro, Seocho-Gu, Seoul, Korea (South)
Tel.: (82) 234984500
Web Site: https://www.haein.com
Year Founded: 1960
003010—(KRS)
Rev.: $136,548,642
Assets: $184,480,486
Liabilities: $101,608,413
Net Worth: $82,872,073
Earnings: ($1,590,838)
Emp.: 280
Fiscal Year-end: 12/31/22
Construction Equipment Mfr
N.A.I.C.S.: 333120
Kyung-Hie Won (Chm & CEO)

Subsidiaries:

Haein Resources Co., Ltd. (1)
93 Soegol 2-gil, Hupo-myeon Uljin-gun, Mungyeong, Gyeongsangbuk, Korea (South)
Tel.: (82) 547886051
Heavy Construction Equipment Mfr
N.A.I.C.S.: 333120

HAEDUK POWERWAY CO., LTD.
No 1608-1 songjeong-dong, Gangseo-Gu, Busan, 618-819, Korea (South)
Tel.: (82) 518310101
Web Site: http://www.haedukpw.com
Year Founded: 1978
102210—(KRS)
Rev.: $24,749,518
Assets: $89,075,449
Liabilities: $15,073,088
Net Worth: $74,002,361
Earnings: $5,412,955
Emp.: 65
Fiscal Year-end: 12/31/22
Rudder Assemblies Mfr & Sales
N.A.I.C.S.: 339999
Dong-Seok Im (Sr Mng Dir)

HAESUNG DS CO., LTD.
8F Haesung 2 Building 508 Teheran-ro, Gangnam-gu, Seoul, 06178, Korea (South)
Tel.: (82) 7047610000
Web Site: https://www.haesungds.com
Year Founded: 1984
195870—(KRS)
Rev.: $643,787,565
Assets: $505,923,801
Liabilities: $162,848,311
Net Worth: $343,075,491
Earnings: $122,259,421
Emp.: 1,392
Fiscal Year-end: 12/31/22
Semiconductor Product Mfr & Distr
N.A.I.C.S.: 334413
Andy Cho (CEO)

Subsidiaries:

HAESUNG DS Co., Ltd. - Changwon Factory (1)
726 Ungnam-ro Seongsan-gu, Changwon, 51552, Gyeongsangnam, Korea (South)
Tel.: (82) 7047610114
Semiconductor Components Mfr
N.A.I.C.S.: 334413

HAESUNG INDUSTRIAL CO., LTD.
19th Floor Haesung Bld 942 Daechi-dong, Gangnam-gu, Seoul, 135725, Korea (South)
Tel.: (82) 25281246
Web Site: http://www.haesungind.co.kr
034810—(KRS)
Rev.: $1,941,773,004
Assets: $2,012,101,500
Liabilities: $945,432,905
Net Worth: $1,066,668,596
Earnings: $81,621,508
Emp.: 68
Fiscal Year-end: 12/31/22
Real Estate Rental Services
N.A.I.C.S.: 531120

Subsidiaries:

Hankuk Paper Mfg Co Ltd (1)
18-19F Haesung 1 Building 942 Teheran-ro 504 Daechi-dong, Gangnam-gu, Korea (South)
Tel.: (82) 2 3475 7200
Web Site: http://www.hankukpaper.com
Sales Range: $650-699.9 Million
Emp.: 513
Paper Mfr
N.A.I.C.S.: 322120
Jae Ho Ahn (CEO)

Plant (Domestic):

Hankuk Paper Mfg Co Ltd - Onsan Plant (2)
40 Wonsan-ro Onsan-eup, Ulju-gun, Ulsan, Korea (South)
Tel.: (82) 522407700
Printing Paper Mfr
N.A.I.C.S.: 322120

Subsidiary (US):

Hankuk Paper USA, Inc. (2)
4801 Wilshire Blvd Ste 205, Los Angeles, CA 90010
Tel.: (323) 934-3602
Printing Paper Retailer
N.A.I.C.S.: 424110

Affiliate (Domestic):

Seha Corporation (2)
97 Biseul-ro 96-gil Sang-ri Yuga-myeon, Dalseong-gun, Daegu, Korea (South)
Tel.: (82) 536030600
Web Site: http://www.seha.co.kr
Rev.: $540,978,448
Assets: $529,770,918
Liabilities: $204,983,352
Net Worth: $324,787,566
Earnings: $10,922,868
Emp.: 780
Fiscal Year-end: 12/31/2022
Paper Products Mfr
N.A.I.C.S.: 322120

Subsidiary (Non-US):

Zhangjiagang Co., Ltd. (2)
Korea Industrial Center Bonghwangjin, Zhangjiagang, Jiangsu, China
Tel.: (86) 51258421922
Web Site: https://www.kookilpaper.cn
Emp.: 256
Special Paper Mfr & Distr
N.A.I.C.S.: 322120
Lee Bok Jin (CEO)

Keyang Electric Machinery Co., Ltd. (1)
Haesung II Bldg 2F 508 Teheran-ro, PO Box 06178, Gangnam-gu, Seoul, Korea (South) **(34%)**
Tel.: (82) 25596800
Web Site: http://www.keyang.co.kr
Rev.: $280,012,604
Assets: $228,224,344
Liabilities: $130,108,531
Net Worth: $98,115,813
Earnings: ($18,821,468)
Emp.: 727
Fiscal Year-end: 12/31/2022
Industrial Tools & Automotive Parts Mfr & Whslr
N.A.I.C.S.: 333517
Han-Soo Jung (CEO)

Subsidiary (Non-US):

Keyang Electric Machinery (Jiangsu) Co., Ltd. (2)

HAESUNG INDUSTRIAL CO., LTD.

Haesung Industrial Co., Ltd.—(Continued)

No 58 Zhujiang Road Economic Development Zone, Yancheng, Jiangsu, China
Tel.: (86) 51589969928
Machine Tools Mfr
N.A.I.C.S.: 333517

Keyang Electric Machinery (Suzhou) Co., Ltd. (2)
No 66 Dong Wu Nan Road Economic Development Zone, Wuzhong, Suzhou, Jiangsu, China
Tel.: (86) 51265613321
Machine Tools Mfr
N.A.I.C.S.: 333517

Plant (Domestic):

Keyang Electric Machinery Co., Ltd. - Ansan Plant (2)
9 Sandan-ro, Danwon-gu, Ansan, Gyeonggi-do, Korea (South)
Tel.: (82) 314905300
Machine Tools Mfr
N.A.I.C.S.: 333517

Keyang Electric Machinery Co., Ltd. - Cheonan Plant (2)
490-48 Yeonam-ro Seonghwan-eup, Seobuk-gu, Cheonan, Chungcheongnam, Korea (South)
Tel.: (82) 415800522
Machine Tools Mfr
N.A.I.C.S.: 333517

HAESUNG OPTICS CO., LTD.

66 Hyohaengro 184 Beon-gil Bongdam-eup, Hwaseong, 445896, Gyeonggi-do, Korea (South)
Tel.: (82) 312921555
Web Site: https://www.hso.co.kr
Year Founded: 1988
076610—(KRS)
Rev.: $125,639,371
Assets: $59,662,346
Liabilities: $31,646,672
Net Worth: $28,015,673
Earnings: ($13,326,112)
Emp.: 50
Fiscal Year-end: 12/31/22
Photographing Lenses & Prisms Mfr
N.A.I.C.S.: 333310
Eul Sung Lee *(Chm & Co-CEO)*

HAFA BATHROOM GROUP AB

Svarvaregatan 5, PO Box 525, 301 80, Halmstad, Sweden
Tel.: (46) 35 15 44 75
Web Site: http://www.hafabg.com
Year Founded: 2006
Bathroom Renovation Product Mfr
N.A.I.C.S.: 332913
Anders Hofstedt *(CEO)*

Subsidiaries:

Hafa Bathroom Group OY (1)
Valtakatu 34, 53100, Lappeenranta, Finland
Tel.: (358) 9 61 50 09 40
Sanitary Ware Mfr
N.A.I.C.S.: 332999

HAFFNER ENERGY SA

2 Place de la Gare, 51300, Vitry-le-Francois, France
Tel.: (33) 326749910
Web Site: https://www.haffner-energy.com
Year Founded: 2015
ALHAF—(EUR)
Natural Gas Distribution Services
N.A.I.C.S.: 221210
Marc Haffner *(Co-Founder, Deputy CEO & CTO)*

HAFIZ LIMITED

97 Alliance Building 2nd Floor Moolji Street Mereweather Tower, Karachi, 74000, Pakistan
Tel.: (92) 2132440371
Web Site: https://www.hafiztm.com
Year Founded: 1951
HAFL—(PSX)
Rev.: $117,755
Assets: $2,061,679
Liabilities: $57,022
Net Worth: $2,004,657
Earnings: $84,158
Emp.: 5
Fiscal Year-end: 06/30/23
Real Estate Lending Services
N.A.I.C.S.: 531190
Muhammad Shahid Siddiqui *(CFO)*

HAFSLUND ASA

Drammensveien 144, Skoyen, 0247, Oslo, Norway
Tel.: (47) 22435000
Web Site: http://www.hafslund.no
Year Founded: 1898
Rev.: $628,860,540
Assets: $1,864,196,180
Liabilities: $1,284,851,260
Net Worth: $579,344,920
Earnings: $524,962,900
Emp.: 1,136
Fiscal Year-end: 12/31/17
Hydroelectric Power Generation & District Heating Distr; Residential Security System Services
N.A.I.C.S.: 221122
Heidi Ulmo *(CFO)*

Subsidiaries:

Cumulus IT AS (1)
Hagalokkveien 1313, 1383, Asker, Norway
Tel.: (47) 45280700
Web Site: www.cumulus.no
Information Technology Consulting Services
N.A.I.C.S.: 541512

Fortum Distribution AS (1)
Post Box No 124, 1713, Gralum, Norway
Tel.: (47) 81544499
Electric Power Distribution
N.A.I.C.S.: 221122

Hafslund Driftssentral AS (1)
Noreveien 26, Oslo, 379, Norway
Tel.: (47) 22435000
Web Site: www.hafslund.no
Sales Range: $25-49.9 Million
Emp.: 60
Electrical Engineering Services
N.A.I.C.S.: 541330
Lise Heien Langaard *(Mng Dir)*

Hafslund Eiendom AS (1)
Drammensveien 144, Oslo, 277, Norway
Tel.: (47) 22435002
Electric Power Distr
N.A.I.C.S.: 221122
Hams Peter Rost *(Gen Mgr)*

Hafslund Energy Trading AS (1)
Drammensveien 144, Oslo, 277, Norway
Tel.: (47) 22435000
Sales Range: $75-99.9 Million
Emp.: 15
Electric Power Distribution Services
N.A.I.C.S.: 221122
Roger Lie *(Head-Trading)*

Hafslund Fakturaservice AS (1)
Drammensveien 144, Skoyen, Oslo, 277, Norway
Tel.: (47) 22435000
Web Site: http://www.hafslund.no
Sales Range: $50-74.9 Million
Emp.: 71
Business Support Services
N.A.I.C.S.: 561499
Thore Sveen *(Mng Dir)*

Hafslund Fjernvarme AS (1)
Drammensveien 144, 247, Oslo, Norway (100%)
Tel.: (47) 22435980
Web Site: http://www.hafslund.no
Sales Range: $100-124.9 Million
Emp.: 52
District Heating Power Generation & Distr
N.A.I.C.S.: 221122
Jan Presttun *(Mng Dir)*

Hafslund Hedging AS (1)
Drammensveien 144, Skoyen, 247, Oslo, Norway
Tel.: (47) 2243 5000
Web Site: http://www.hafslund.no
Sales Range: $75-99.9 Million
Emp.: 15
Electric Power Distr
N.A.I.C.S.: 221122

Hafslund Kundesenter AS (1)
Drammensveien 144, Skoyen, Oslo, Norway
Tel.: (47) 22435000
Web Site: http://www.hafslund.no
Sales Range: $10-24.9 Million
Emp.: 95
Customer Services
N.A.I.C.S.: 561499

Hafslund Nett AS (1)
Drammensveien 144, Oslo, 0247, Norway (100%)
Tel.: (47) 22435000
Web Site: http://www.hafslund.no
Sales Range: $550-599.9 Million
Emp.: 180
Power Generation Network
N.A.I.C.S.: 221122
Kristin Lian *(CEO & Sr VP-Networks)*

Hafslund Produksjon AS (1)
Kykkelstrudveien 100, 1815, Askim, Norway (100%)
Tel.: (47) 4722435000
Sales Range: $100-124.9 Million
Emp.: 21
Electric Power Generation
N.A.I.C.S.: 221118

Hafslund Strom AS (1)
Drammensveien 144, Skoyen, Oslo, 247, Norway
Tel.: (47) 22435000
Web Site: http://www.hafslund.no
Sales Range: $650-699.9 Million
Emp.: 75
Electric Power Sales & Distr
N.A.I.C.S.: 221122
Kari Ekelund Thorud *(Head-Mktg)*

Hallingkraft AS (1)
Sundrejordet 4, 3570, Bergen, Norway
Tel.: (47) 32086600
Web Site: http://www.hallingkraft.no
Sales Range: $75-99.9 Million
Emp.: 7
Electric Power Sales
N.A.I.C.S.: 221122

Inforum Norge AS (1)
Nordikle 88, Gressvik, 1620, Norway
Tel.: (47) 69355100
Electric Power Generation & Distribution Services
N.A.I.C.S.: 221118

NextNet AS (1)
Kaffegata 5, Flisa, 2270, Norway
Tel.: (47) 40 00 19 99
Web Site: www.nextnet.no
Emp.: 20
Internet Service Provider
N.A.I.C.S.: 517810
Bjoern Einar Kihl *(Office Mgr)*

NorgesEnergi AS (1)
Markensgate 34, 4612, Kristiansand, Norway
Web Site: http://www.norgesenergi.no
Sales Range: $75-99.9 Million
Emp.: 100
Electric Power Sales
N.A.I.C.S.: 221122
Gunnar Norheim *(Mng Dir)*

Policom AB (1)
Kungsgatan 12, Karlstad, 652 24, Sweden
Tel.: (46) 54570110
Electric Power Distr
N.A.I.C.S.: 221122

Total Energi AS (1)
PO Box 638, 6903, Floro, Norway
Tel.: (47) 57757950
Web Site: http://www.totalenergi.no
Electric Power Generation & Distribution Services
N.A.I.C.S.: 221118

HAGA S/A INDUSTRIA E COMERCIO

Av Eng Hans Gaiser 26 Centro, Nova Friburgo, 28605-220, RJ, Brazil
Tel.: (55) 2225258000
Web Site: https://www.haga.com.br
Year Founded: 1937
HAGA4—(BRAZ)
Rev.: $5,927,718
Assets: $12,714,740
Liabilities: $23,817,513
Net Worth: ($11,102,773)
Earnings: $511,976
Fiscal Year-end: 12/31/23
Lock Mfr & Whslr
N.A.I.C.S.: 332510
Jose Luiz Abicalil *(Chm, CEO, Officer-IR, Member-Exec Bd & CFO-Investor Relations)*

HAGAG GROUP REAL ESTATE ENTREPRENEURSHIP LTD.

Southern Tower 33rd Floor 30 Haarbaa St, Tel Aviv, 6473926, Israel
Tel.: (972) 36081936
Web Site: http://www.hagag-group.co.il
Year Founded: 1955
HGG—(TAE)
Rev.: $159,395,494
Assets: $1,052,282,067
Liabilities: $690,954,265
Net Worth: $361,327,802
Earnings: $74,281,253
Emp.: 2
Fiscal Year-end: 12/31/23
Other Activities Related to Real Estate
N.A.I.C.S.: 531390
Yitzhak Hagag *(Controller)*

HAGAR HF.

Holtavegur 10, 104, Reykjavik, Iceland
Tel.: (354) 5305500
Web Site: https://www.hagar.is
HAGA—(ICE)
Rev.: $1,244,219,446
Assets: $554,459,285
Liabilities: $352,046,532
Net Worth: $202,412,753
Earnings: $36,220,020
Emp.: 2,699
Fiscal Year-end: 02/28/24
General Merchandise Retailer Focusing on Food, Specialty & Pharmaceutical Products
N.A.I.C.S.: 445110
Finnur Arnason *(CEO)*

Subsidiaries:

Bananar ehf. (1)
Korngarour 1, 104, Reykjavik, Iceland
Tel.: (354) 5250100
Web Site: https://www.bananar.is
Grocery Distr
N.A.I.C.S.: 445110

Oliuverzlun Islands hf. (1)
Skutuvogur 5, 104, Reykjavik, Iceland
Tel.: (354) 5151000
Web Site: https://www.olis.is
Emp.: 390
Fuel Station Services
N.A.I.C.S.: 424720

HAGIHARA INDUSTRIES INC.

1-4 Nakadori Mizushima, Kurashiki, Okayama, Japan
Tel.: (81) 864400850
Web Site: https://www.hagihara.co.jp
Year Founded: 1962
7856—(TKS)
Rev.: $221,527,050
Assets: $300,842,880
Liabilities: $103,024,790
Net Worth: $197,818,090
Earnings: $22,106,620
Emp.: 1,297
Fiscal Year-end: 10/31/23

AND PRIVATE COMPANIES

Synthetic Resin Product Mfr & Whslr
N.A.I.C.S.: 325211
Kazushi Asano (Pres)
Subsidiaries:

Hagihana Machinery (Shanghai) Co., Ltd. (1)
428-3 Rongxing Road, Songjiang District, Shanghai, China
Tel.: (86) 215 778 4588
Web Site: https://www.hagihana.com
Yarn Machinery Mfr
N.A.I.C.S.: 333248
K. Asano (Pres)

Japan Fabweld Co., Ltd. (1)
1428-1 Yamaguchi, Kasaoka, 714-0007, Okayama, Japan
Tel.: (81) 86 565 1500
Sheet Metal Work Mfg
N.A.I.C.S.: 332999

PT. Hagihara Westjava Industries (1)
KIIC Block B-1 Jl Tol Jakarta-Cikampek Km47 Kawasan Industri KIIC, Jl Maligi I Lot B1 & B2, Karawang, 41361, West Java, Indonesia
Tel.: (62) 218901490
Web Site: http://hwi.co.id
Paper Bag Mfr & Distr
N.A.I.C.S.: 313110

Toyo Heisei Polymer Co., Ltd. (1)
2591 Shimoinayoshi, Kasumigaura, 315-0052, Ibaraki, Japan
Tel.: (81) 29 830 0234
Web Site: https://www.toyo-heisei.co.jp
Flat Yarn Product Mfr
N.A.I.C.S.: 314999
Yukihisa Shibata (Pres)

HAGIWARA ELECTRIC HOLDINGS CO., LTD.
Takaoka Park Building 2-2-1 Higashi Sakura, Higashi-ku, Nagoya, 461-8520, Japan
Tel.: (81) 529313511
Web Site: https://www.hagiwara.co.jp
Year Founded: 1948
7467—(TKS)
Rev.: $1,488,241,500
Assets: $791,256,660
Liabilities: $458,370,450
Net Worth: $332,886,210
Earnings: $29,222,810
Emp.: 736
Fiscal Year-end: 03/31/24
Electronic Device Mfr & Distr
N.A.I.C.S.: 334413
Mitsuo Iwai (Pres)
Subsidiaries:

Hagiwara (Shanghai) Co., Ltd. (1)
9F-F2 Huaxin Hai Xin Building 666 Fu Zhou Road, Shanghai, 200001, China
Tel.: (86) 2163507676
Electronic Component Mfr & Distr
N.A.I.C.S.: 334419

Hagiwara America, Inc. (1)
38777 W 6 Mile Rd Ste 307, Livonia, MI 48152
Tel.: (734) 462-0260
Web Site: https://www.hagiwara.co.jp
Electronic Equipment Distr
N.A.I.C.S.: 423690

Hagiwara Electric (Shanghai) Co., Ltd. (1)
F1 Floor 12 Huaxin Haixin Building No 666 Fuzhou Road, Huangpu District, Shanghai, 200001, China
Tel.: (86) 2163507676
Web Site: https://www.hagiwara.co.jp
Electronic Equipment Distr
N.A.I.C.S.: 423690

Hagiwara Electric (Thailand) Co., Ltd. (1)
25th Floor Unit 2503 Empire Tower 1 South Sathorn Road, Yannawa Sathorn, Bangkok, 10120, Thailand
Tel.: (66) 22863918
Web Site: https://www.hagiwara.co.jp
Electronic Equipment Distr
N.A.I.C.S.: 423690

Hagiwara Electric Europe GmbH (1)
Schadowstr 84, 40212, Dusseldorf, Germany
Tel.: (49) 2111793180
Web Site: https://www.hagiwara.co.jp
Electronic Equipment Distr
N.A.I.C.S.: 423690

Hagiwara Electric Korea Co., Ltd. (1)
713 Opulence Bldg Seocho-dong 254 Seocho-Daero, Seocho-gu, Seoul, 06647, Korea (South)
Tel.: (82) 262073660
Web Site: https://www.hagiwara.co.jp
Electronic Equipment Distr
N.A.I.C.S.: 423690

Hagiwara Electronics Co., Ltd. (1)
Takaoka Park Building 2-2-1 Higashi Sakura, Higashi-ku, Nagoya, 461-0005, Aichi, Japan
Tel.: (81) 529313125
Web Site: https://www.hagiwara.co.jp
Electronic Components Mfr
N.A.I.C.S.: 334419

Hagiwara Electronics India Private Limited (1)
1st Floor No 12 17th Main Road Off 100 Feet Road, HAL 2nd A Stage Indiranagar, Bengaluru, 560008, India
Tel.: (91) 8043024820
Web Site: https://www.hagiwara.co.jp
Electronic Components Mfr
N.A.I.C.S.: 334419

Hagiwara Engineering Co., Ltd. (1)
326 Sayamagahara, Iruma, 358-0032, Saitama, Japan
Tel.: (81) 429343411
Web Site: http://www.oec-inc.co.jp
Sales Range: $50-74.9 Million
Emp.: 83
Semiconductor Circuit Mfr
N.A.I.C.S.: 334413
Ken Yamauchi (Pres)

Hagiwara Hokuto Techno Co., Ltd. (1)
Takaoka Park Building 2-2-1 Higashi Sakura, Higashi-ku, Nagoya, 461-0005, Aichi, Japan
Tel.: (81) 529313671
Web Site: https://www.hagiwara.co.jp
Electronic Components Mfr
N.A.I.C.S.: 334419

Hagiwara Techno Solutions (Shanghai) Co., Ltd. (1)
Room 2111 Building A Far East International Plaza No 319 Xianxia Road, Changning District, Shanghai, China
Tel.: (86) 2163320188
Web Site: https://www.hagiwara.co.jp
Electronic Components Mfr
N.A.I.C.S.: 334419

Hagiwara Techno Solutions Co. Ltd. (1)
Takaoka KANAME Building 2-28-23 Izumi, Higashi-ku, Nagoya, 461-0001, Aichi, Japan
Tel.: (81) 529313110
Web Site: https://www.hagiwara.co.jp
Electronic Components Mfr
N.A.I.C.S.: 334419

Singapore Hagiwara Pte. Ltd. (1)
152 Beach Road 17-03 Gateway East, Singapore, 189721, Singapore
Tel.: (65) 62979303
Web Site: https://www.hagiwara.co.jp
Electronic Equipment Distr
N.A.I.C.S.: 423690

HAGLEITNER HYGIENE INTERNATIONAL GMBH
Lunastrasse 5, 5700, Zell am See, Austria
Tel.: (43) 504560　　　　　　　　　　AT
Web Site: http://www.hagleitner.com
Holding Company; Hygiene & Sanitary Products Mfr & Whslr
N.A.I.C.S.: 551112

Subsidiaries:

CARTEMANI s.r.l. (1)
Via E Fermi 34, 24035, Curno, Italy
Tel.: (39) 03562230
Chemical Products Distr
N.A.I.C.S.: 424690

HAGLEITNER HYGIENE BOSNE I HERCEGOVINE d.o.o. (1)
Ul Kninska bb, 74400, Derventa, Bosnia & Herzegovina
Tel.: (387) 53315048
Chemical Products Distr
N.A.I.C.S.: 424690

HAGLEITNER HYGIENE BULGARIA EOOD (1)
22 Zlaten rog 3 Stock Buro 6, 1407, Sofia, Bulgaria
Tel.: (359) 29630586
Chemical Products Distr
N.A.I.C.S.: 424690
Marcel Dogar (Country Mgr)

HAGLEITNER HYGIENE CESKO s.r.o. (1)
Nupaky 456, 251 01, Ricany, Czech Republic
Tel.: (420) 272680614
Chemical Products Distr
N.A.I.C.S.: 424690

HAGLEITNER HYGIENE DEUTSCHLAND GMBH (1)
Robert-Bosch-Str 12, Sauerlach, 82054, Munich, Germany
Tel.: (49) 8104629580
Chemical Products Distr
N.A.I.C.S.: 424690

HAGLEITNER HYGIENE HRVATSKA d.o.o. (1)
P P 1 Cvetkovic 85 a, 10450, Jastrebarsko, Croatia
Tel.: (385) 16272619
Chemical Products Distr
N.A.I.C.S.: 424690

HAGLEITNER HYGIENE ITALIA s.r.l. (1)
Via Josef-Maria-Pemter 9/a, 39044, Neumarkt, Italy
Tel.: (39) 0471052816
Chemical Products Distr
N.A.I.C.S.: 424690

HAGLEITNER HYGIENE MAGYARORSZAG Kft. (1)
Juharfa u 20, 9027, Gyor, Hungary
Tel.: (36) 96512400
Chemical Products Distr
N.A.I.C.S.: 424690

HAGLEITNER HYGIENE ROMANIA s.r.l. (1)
Sos Bucuresti Targoviste nr 12A, Ilfov, 077135, Mogosoaia, Romania
Tel.: (40) 213032160
Chemical Products Distr
N.A.I.C.S.: 424690
Cristian Cozma (Reg Mgr-Sls)

HAGLEITNER HYGIENE SLOVENSKO s.r.o. (1)
Dialnicna cesta 27, 903 01, Senec, Slovakia
Tel.: (421) 244441076
Chemical Products Distr
N.A.I.C.S.: 424690

HAGLEITNER HYGIENE SRBIJA d.o.o. (1)
Vojvodanska br 387, 11271, Surcin, Serbia
Tel.: (381) 114142770
Chemical Products Distr
N.A.I.C.S.: 424690

HAGLEITNER HYGIENE d.o.o. (1)
Potok pri Komendi 13, 1218, Komenda, Slovenia
Tel.: (386) 18343468
Chemical Products Distr
N.A.I.C.S.: 424690

HAGLEITNER ITALIA s.r.l. (1)
Via Latina 20, 00179, Rome, Italy
Tel.: (39) 0683512183
Chemical Products Distr
N.A.I.C.S.: 424690

HAHN & COMPANY

HAGLEITNER NWO DEUTSCHLAND GmbH (1)
Rontgenstrasse 34, 48432, Rheine, Germany
Tel.: (49) 1801973914
Chemical Products Distr
N.A.I.C.S.: 424690

HAGOROMO FOODS CORPORATION
Shizugin Chukyogin-Shizuokaekinan Building 3F 11-1, Minamicho Suruga-ku, Shizuoka, 422-8067, Japan
Tel.: (81) 542885200
Web Site: https://www.hagoromofoods.co.jp
Year Founded: 1931
2831—(TKS)
Rev.: $485,841,610
Assets: $438,679,260
Liabilities: $179,183,880
Net Worth: $259,495,380
Earnings: $11,560,890
Emp.: 694
Fiscal Year-end: 03/31/24
Food Products Mfr
N.A.I.C.S.: 311999
Yasuo Goto (Chm & Co-CEO)

Subsidiaries:

P.T. Aneka Tuna Indonesia (1)
Jl Surabaya-Malang Km 38 Gempol, Pasuruan, 67155, Jawa Timur, Indonesia
Tel.: (62) 343851361
Canned Food Distr
N.A.I.C.S.: 424490

HAGUE AND LONDON OIL PLC
Nieuwe Uitleg 24, 2514 BR, Hague, Netherlands
Tel.: (31) 703306688　　　　　　　　UK
Web Site: http://www.haloil.co.uk
Year Founded: 1999
Rev.: $39,475,900
Assets: $141,843,650
Liabilities: $137,195,586
Net Worth: $4,648,064
Earnings: ($714,305)
Emp.: 3
Fiscal Year-end: 12/31/18
Oil Exploration Services
N.A.I.C.S.: 211120
Andrew Cochran (Chm & Interim CEO)

HAHA GENERATION CORP.
6F No 364 Sec 5 Zhongxiao E Road, Xinyi District, Taipei, 11060, Taiwan
Tel.: (886) 227492597　　　　　　　　NV
Year Founded: 2014
Rev.: $11
Assets: $4,001
Liabilities: $68,497
Net Worth: ($64,496)
Earnings: ($31,405)
Fiscal Year-end: 12/31/20
Clothing Products Distr
N.A.I.C.S.: 424310
Fang-Ying Liao (Pres, CEO, CFO, Treas & Sec)

HAHN & COMPANY
21F Ferrum Tower 19 Eulji-ro 5-gil, Jung-gu, Seoul, Korea (South)
Tel.: (82) 2 566 0663
Web Site: http://hcompany.com
Year Founded: 2010
Privater Equity Firm
N.A.I.C.S.: 523910
Scott Sang-Won Hahn (CEO)

Subsidiaries:

Hanon Systems (1)
95 Sinilseo-ro, Daedeok-gu, Daejeon, 306-230, Korea (South)
Tel.: (82) 429306114

HAHN & COMPANY

Hahn & Company—(Continued)
Web Site: https://www.hanonsystems.com
Rev.: $6,617,467,049
Assets: $6,978,766,812
Liabilities: $5,161,079,501
Net Worth: $1,817,687,311
Earnings: $15,675,980
Emp.: 2,211
Fiscal Year-end: 12/31/2022
Automotive Climate-Control Components Mfr & Distr
N.A.I.C.S.: 336390
Yeo-Eul Yoon (Chm)

Subsidiary (Non-US):

Coclisa S.A. de C.V. (2)
Ave Laguna de Tamiahua No 7325, San Lorenzo, Ciudad Juarez, 32840, Chihuahua, Mexico
Tel.: (52) 656 6492322
Web Site: http://www.hanonsystems.com
Motor Vehicles & Parts Mfr
N.A.I.C.S.: 336110

Halla Visteon Climate Control (Nanchang) Co., Ltd. (2)
No 300 Industry Road No 1, Xiaolan Economy Development Zone, Nanchang, 330200, Jiangxi, China
Tel.: (86) 79185986663
Web Site: http://www.hanonsystems.com
Refrigeration & Heating Equipment Mfr
N.A.I.C.S.: 333415

Hanon Climate Systems India Private Limited (2)
SP-812-A Industrial Area Phase-II, Bhiwadi, Alwar, 301019, Rajasthan, India
Tel.: (91) 1493 221 426
Web Site: http://www.hanonsystems.com
Heater Cores Mfr
N.A.I.C.S.: 336390

Hanon Systems (Beijing) Co., Ltd. (2)
No 6 Caixiang West Rd Caiyuan Industrial Area, Nancai Town Shunyi District, Beijing, China
Tel.: (86) 10 8947 8080
Web Site: http://www.hanonsystems.com
Automotive Products Mfr
N.A.I.C.S.: 336390

Hanon Systems (Thailand) Co., Ltd. (2)
Eastern Seaboard Industrial Estate 64/4 Moo 4, T Pluakdaeng, Rayong, 21140, Thailand
Tel.: (66) 3895405059
Web Site: http://www.hanonsystems.co.th
Motor Vehicle Air Conditioning System Mfr
N.A.I.C.S.: 336390

Subsidiary (US):

Hanon Systems Alabama Corp. (2)
676 Hallabama Dr, Shorter, AL 36075
Tel.: (334) 466-5049
Web Site: http://www.hanonsystems.com
Automobile Air Conditioning Mfr
N.A.I.C.S.: 336390

Subsidiary (Non-US):

Hanon Systems Canada, Inc. (2)
360 University Ave, Belleville, K8N 5T6, ON, Canada
Tel.: (613) 969-1460
Web Site: http://www.hanonsystems.com
Air Conditioning Hoses & Cooling Modules Mfr
N.A.I.C.S.: 336390

Hanon Systems Portugal, S.A. (2)
Estrada Municipal 533, Algeruz San Pedro, 2950, Palmela, Portugal
Tel.: (351) 21 233 8800
Web Site: http://www.hanonsystems.com
Automotive Compressor Clutches Mfr
N.A.I.C.S.: 336390

Visteon Automotive Systems India Private Ltd. (2)
Keelakaranai Village Malrosapuram Post, Maraimalai Nagar Kancheepuram District, Chengalpattu, 603 204, India
Tel.: (91) 4427416500
Web Site: http://www.hanonsystems.com

Automotive Components Mfr
N.A.I.C.S.: 336390

Hotel Hyundai Co., Ltd. (1)
338 Bongmunno, Gyeongju, Gyeongsangbuk-do, Korea (South)
Tel.: (82) 54 748 2233
Web Site: http://www.hyundaihotel.com
Hotel Operations
N.A.I.C.S.: 721110

Unit (Domestic):

Hotel Hyundai Ulsan (2)
Ulsan Circular Road 875, Donggu, Ulsan, Korea (South)
Tel.: (82) 52 251 2233
Web Site: http://www.hyundaihotel.com
Hotel Operations
N.A.I.C.S.: 721110

Lutronic Corporation (1)
219 Sowon-ro, Deogyang-gu, Goyang, Gyeonggi-do, Korea (South)
Tel.: (82) 319083440
Web Site: http://www.international.lutronic.com
Rev.: $208,319,091
Assets: $183,435,288
Liabilities: $50,294,647
Net Worth: $133,140,641
Earnings: $24,712,064
Emp.: 277
Fiscal Year-end: 12/31/2023
Medical Instrument Mfr
N.A.I.C.S.: 339112
Haelyung Hwang (CEO)

Subsidiary (Non-US):

Lutronic Japan Co., Ltd. (2)
1-14-16 Hakata Ekimae Hakata Ekimae Center Building 9th floor, Hakata-ku, Fukuoka, 812-0011, Fukuoka prefecture, Japan
Tel.: (81) 924772755
Medical Treatment Services
N.A.I.C.S.: 621111

Lutronic Medical Systems Germany GmbH (2)
Esplanade 41, 20354, Hamburg, Germany
Tel.: (49) 40696399950
Medical Device Mfr
N.A.I.C.S.: 339112

Ssangyong Cement Industrial Co., Ltd. (1)
City Center Tower 34 Supyo-ro, Jung-gu, Seoul, 04555, Korea (South) (76.5%)
Tel.: (82) 222705114
Web Site: https://www.ssangyongcne.co.kr
Rev.: $1,507,187,692
Assets: $2,971,623,433
Liabilities: $1,749,684,327
Net Worth: $1,221,939,106
Earnings: $98,007,354
Emp.: 1,160
Fiscal Year-end: 12/31/2022
Cement Mfr
N.A.I.C.S.: 327310
Sa-Seung Hong (Chm)

Plant (Domestic):

Ssangyong Cement Industrial Co., Ltd. - Donghae Plant (2)
246 Hyoja-ro, Donghae, Gangwon-do, Korea (South)
Tel.: (82) 33 520 1114
Web Site: http://www.ssangyongcement.co.kr
Emp.: 431
Cement Mfr
N.A.I.C.S.: 327310

Unit (Domestic):

Ssangyong Cement Industrial Co., Ltd. - Ssangyong Technology Research Center (2)
99 Gajeong-ro, Yuseong-gu, Daejeon, Korea (South)
Tel.: (82) 428651500
Web Site: http://www.ssangyongcement.co.kr
Cement Products Research & Development Services
N.A.I.C.S.: 541715

Plant (Domestic):

Ssangyong Cement Industrial Co., Ltd. - Yeongwol Plant (2)
89 Ssangyong-ro Yeongwol-gun, Yongwol, Gangwon-do, Korea (South)
Tel.: (82) 33 370 8114
Web Site: http://www.ssangyongcement.co.kr
Emp.: 212
Cement Mfr
N.A.I.C.S.: 327310

HAHN GROUP GMBH

Liebshausener Str 3, 55494, Rheinbollen, Deutschland, Germany
Tel.: (49) 676490220
Web Site: http://www.hahn.group
Year Founded: 2017
Emp.: 350
Industrial Automation Solution Services
N.A.I.C.S.: 333318
Philipp Unterhalt (CEO & Mng Dir)

Subsidiaries:

Rei Automation, Inc. (1)
1240 Veterans Rd, Columbia, SC 29209
Tel.: (803) 791-8550
Web Site: http://www.reiautomation.com
Engineering Services
N.A.I.C.S.: 541330
Grant Phillips (Pres)

HAI AGROCHEM JOINT STOCK COMPANY

28 Mac Dinh Chi Street Da Kao ward, 1 District, Ho Chi Minh City, Vietnam
Tel.: (84) 2838292805
Web Site: http://www.congtyhai.com
HAI—(HOSE)
Rev.: $23,001,090
Assets: $126,567,069
Liabilities: $34,262,337
Net Worth: $92,304,732
Earnings: $256,509
Emp.: 134
Fiscal Year-end: 12/31/20
Pesticide Mfr
N.A.I.C.S.: 325320
Quach Thanh Dong (Mng Dir & Member-Exec Bd)

Subsidiaries:

HAI Agrochem Joint Stock Company (1)
120BEo Street 192, Teok Lork 3 Ward Tolkok District, Phnom Penh, Cambodia
Tel.: (855) 23880563
Agrochemical Product Mfr
N.A.I.C.S.: 325320

HAI DUONG PUMP MANUFACTURING JOINT STOCK COMPANY

No 2 Ngo Quyen Street, Cam Thuong Ward, Hai Duong, Vietnam
Tel.: (84) 2203853496
Web Site: https://hapuma.com
Year Founded: 1960
CTB—(HNX)
Rev.: $18,490,090
Assets: $22,541,268
Liabilities: $13,396,648
Net Worth: $9,144,620
Earnings: $1,357,190
Fiscal Year-end: 12/31/20
Pump & Valve Mfr
N.A.I.C.S.: 333914

HAI KWANG ENTERPRISE CORPORATION

No 12 Haihai 2nd Road, Xiaogang District, Kaohsiung, Taiwan
Tel.: (886) 78021011
Web Site: https://www.haikwang.com.tw

Year Founded: 1958
2038—(TAI)
Rev.: $306,258,826
Assets: $308,955,742
Liabilities: $179,499,421
Net Worth: $129,456,321
Earnings: $980,640
Emp.: 400
Fiscal Year-end: 12/31/23
Steel Bars & Billets Mfr & Sales
N.A.I.C.S.: 331221
Wei-Han Huang (Chm)

HAI LECK HOLDINGS LIMITED

47 Tuas View Circuit, Singapore, 637357, Singapore
Tel.: (65) 68622211
Web Site: https://www.haileck.com
BLH—(SES)
Rev.: $50,846,239
Assets: $99,227,121
Liabilities: $13,937,755
Net Worth: $85,289,366
Earnings: $3,178,214
Emp.: 2,200
Fiscal Year-end: 06/30/23
Civil Engineering Services
N.A.I.C.S.: 237990
Buck Poh Cheng (Chm)

Subsidiaries:

Hai Leck Engineering Pte Ltd (1)
47 Tuas View Circuit, 637 357, Singapore, Singapore
Tel.: (65) 68622211
Web Site: http://www.haileck.com
Scaffoldings & Civil Engineering Services
N.A.I.C.S.: 541330
Don Cheng (CEO)

Industrial Services Pte Ltd (1)
47 Tuas View Circuit, Singapore, 637357, Singapore
Tel.: (65) 68615122
Web Site: http://www.industrialservices.com.sg
Sales Range: $25-49.9 Million
Emp.: 100
Scaffolding Services
N.A.I.C.S.: 332323
Don Cheng (CEO)

Logthai-Hai Leck Engineering Co., Ltd. (1)
130/10 Noenpayom RD, Tumbon Maptaphut Aumphur Muangrayong, Rayong, 21150, Thailand
Tel.: (66) 38682297
Web Site: https://www.haileck-thailand.com
Scaffolding Services
N.A.I.C.S.: 332323

Tele-centre Services Pte. Ltd. (1)
56 Kallang Pudding Road 09-09 HH Kallang, Singapore, 349328, Singapore
Tel.: (65) 63377488
Web Site: https://www.tele-centre.com
Telecommunication Servicesb
N.A.I.C.S.: 517810

HAI MINH CORPORATION

561A Dien Bien Phu Street Ward 25, Binh Thanh District, Ho Chi Minh City, Vietnam
Tel.: (84) 835128668
Web Site: https://www.haiminh.com.vn
HMH—(HNX)
Rev.: $8,379,400
Assets: $22,255,900
Liabilities: $2,450,300
Net Worth: $19,805,600
Earnings: $196,200
Fiscal Year-end: 12/31/22
Freight Trucking & Inland Water Freight Transportation Services
N.A.I.C.S.: 484110

Subsidiaries:

Hai Minh Logistics Co.,Ltd. (1)

3rd Floor Hai Minh Building Km105 Nguyen Binh Khiem Street, Dong Hai 2 Ward Hai An District, Haiphong, Vietnam
Tel.: (84) 2253979946
Logistics Services Provider
N.A.I.C.S.: 541614

Hai Minh Port Service Joint Stock Company (1)
Lot KB3-02 Nam Dinh Vu Industrial Park Zone 1, Dong Hai 2 Ward Hai An District, Haiphong, Vietnam
Tel.: (84) 2253568683
Port Operator
N.A.I.C.S.: 488310

Nam Phat Logistics Co., Ltd. (1)
3rd Floor Hai Minh Building Km 105 Nguyen Binh Khiem Street, Dong Hai 2 Ward Hai An District, Haiphong, Vietnam
Tel.: (84) 2253825393
Freight Forwarding & Logistics Services
N.A.I.C.S.: 541614

Nam Phat Ltd (1)
74 Tran Hung Aao Str, Hai An District, Haiphong, Vietnam
Tel.: (84) 31 3825393
Freight Trucking Services
N.A.I.C.S.: 484121

HAI PHAT INVESTMENT JSC
5th Floors CT3 Tower-The Pride Building An Hung New Urban Area, La Khe Ward Ha Dong District, Hanoi, Vietnam
Tel.: (84) 432080666
Web Site: https://www.haiphat.com.vn
Year Founded: 2003
Real Estate Investment Services
N.A.I.C.S.: 531390
Do Quy Hai *(Chm)*

HAI PHONG ELECTRICAL MECHANICAL JSC
734 Nguyen Van Linh Street Niem Nghia Ward, Le Chan District, Haiphong, Vietnam
Tel.: (84) 2253835927
Web Site: https://www.hapemco.vn
DHP—(HNX)
Rev.: $10,472,981
Assets: $8,579,880
Liabilities: $1,990,252
Net Worth: $6,589,628
Earnings: $495,030
Emp.: 200
Fiscal Year-end: 12/31/21
Electrical Fan Mfr
N.A.I.C.S.: 333413

HAI PHONG ELECTRICITY WATER MACHINE ASSEMBLY JOINT STOCK
34 Thien Loi Street Nghia Xa Ward, Le Chan District, Haiphong, Vietnam
Tel.: (84) 2253856209
Web Site: https://diennuochp.com.vn
Year Founded: 1992
DNC—(HNX)
Rev.: $65,867,600
Assets: $12,238,500
Liabilities: $2,734,600
Net Worth: $9,503,900
Earnings: $2,919,400
Fiscal Year-end: 12/31/22
Electronic Cable Mfr
N.A.I.C.S.: 332618
Nguyen Van Thao *(Deputy Gen Dir)*

HAI PHONG HOANG HA PAPER JOINT STOCK COMPANY
No 194 Kieu Ha Dong Hai 2, Hai An district, Haiphong, Vietnam
Tel.: (84) 983239288
Web Site: https://hhppaper.com
Year Founded: 2012
Rev.: $14,729,952
Assets: $15,236,282
Liabilities: $6,790,280
Net Worth: $8,446,002
Earnings: $636,274
Fiscal Year-end: 12/31/19
Paperboard Mfr
N.A.I.C.S.: 322130
Nguyen Thi Thu Thuy *(Chm)*

HAI-O ENTERPRISE BERHAD
Wisma Hai-O Lot 11995 Batu 2 Jalan Kapar, 41400, Klang, Selangor, Malaysia
Tel.: (60) 333423322
Web Site: https://www.hai-o.com.my
HAIO—(KLS)
Rev.: $67,168,910
Assets: $91,946,145
Liabilities: $11,979,097
Net Worth: $79,967,048
Earnings: $9,635,822
Emp.: 504
Fiscal Year-end: 04/30/21
Pharmaceuticals Mfr
N.A.I.C.S.: 325412
Kai Hee Tan *(Chm)*

Subsidiaries:

Chop Aik Seng Sdn. Bhd. (1)
1195 Jln Kapar Batu 2, 41400, Kelang, Selangor, Malaysia
Tel.: (60) 3 33427768
Tea & Beverages Distr
N.A.I.C.S.: 311920

Grand Brands (M) Sdn. Bhd. (1)
Level 4 Wisma Hai-O Lot 11995 Batu 2 Jalan Kapar, 41400, Kelang, Selangor, Malaysia
Tel.: (60) 333432617
Web Site: http://www.hai-o.com.my
Sales Range: $25-49.9 Million
Emp.: 7
Transportation Services
N.A.I.C.S.: 488999

Hai-O Marketing Sdn. Bhd. (1)
Wawasan Hai-O Batu 3 1/4 Jalan Kapar, 41400, Kelang, Selangor, Malaysia
Tel.: (60) 333488588
Web Site: http://www.hai-omarketing.com.my
Sales Range: $25-49.9 Million
Emp.: 60
General Marketing Services
N.A.I.C.S.: 541613
Tham Yoke Lon *(Gen Mgr)*

Hai-O Medicine Sdn. Bhd. (1)
Wisma Hai-O Lot 11995 Batu 2 Jalan Kapar, 41400, Kelang, Selangor, Malaysia
Tel.: (60) 333436458
Medical Products Mfr & Distr
N.A.I.C.S.: 325412
Chai Meng Kow *(Mgr)*

Hai-O Raya Bhd. (1)
Wisma Hai-O Lot 11995 Batu 2 Jalan Kapar, 41400, Kelang, Selangor, Malaysia
Tel.: (60) 333433471
Web Site: http://www.hai-o.com.my
Sales Range: $75-99.9 Million
Emp.: 250
Confectioneries Distr
N.A.I.C.S.: 424450

Kinds Resource Sdn. Bhd. (1)
Lot 1388 Block A Batu 2 1/2 Jalan Kapar, 41400, Kelang, Selangor, Malaysia
Tel.: (60) 333431363
Web Site: http://www.hai-o.com.my
Sales Range: $50-74.9 Million
Emp.: 10
Botanical Herbs Distr
N.A.I.C.S.: 424210

PT. Hai-O Indonesia (1)
Rukan Mangga Dua Square Block E-2 Jalan Gunung Sahari Raya No 1, Jakarta, 14430, Indonesia
Tel.: (62) 216231
Web Site: http://www.hai-omarketing.com.my
Sales Range: $25-49.9 Million
Emp.: 10
General Marketing Services
N.A.I.C.S.: 541613

SG Global Biotech Sdn. Bhd. (1)
Wisma Hai-O Lot 11995 Batu 2 Jalan Kapar, 41400, Kelang, Selangor, Malaysia
Tel.: (60) 333423322
Sales Range: $25-49.9 Million
Emp.: 60
Pharmaceuticals Mfr
N.A.I.C.S.: 325412

Subsidiary (Domestic):

QIS Research Laboratory Sdn. Bhd. (2)
Wisma Hai-O Lot 11995 Jalan Kapar, 41400, Kelang, Selangor, Malaysia
Tel.: (60) 333424924
Sales Range: $10-24.9 Million
Emp.: 4
Testing & Laboratory Services
N.A.I.C.S.: 621511

Sea Gull Advertising Sdn. Bhd. (1)
Lot No 11995 Batu 2 Jalan Kapar, 41400, Selangor, Malaysia
Tel.: (60) 333431578
Web Site: http://www.hai-o.com.my
Sales Range: $25-49.9 Million
Emp.: 200
Advertising Services
N.A.I.C.S.: 541810

Vintage Wine Sdn. Bhd. (1)
Wisma Hai-O Lot 11995 Batu 2 Jalan Kapar, 41400, Kelang, Selangor, Malaysia
Tel.: (60) 333423322
Web Site: http://www.hai-o.com.my
Wine Distr
N.A.I.C.S.: 424820

HAIBO HEAVY ENGINERNG SCNC & TECH CO LTD
No 6 Huangjinqiao Industrial Park Zhengdian Street, Jiangxia District, Wuhan, 430207, Hubei, China
Tel.: (86) 2787028600
Web Site: https://www.haiod.com
Year Founded: 1994
300517—(CHIN)
Rev.: $58,477,033
Assets: $231,262,080
Liabilities: $81,397,342
Net Worth: $149,864,738
Earnings: $851,804
Fiscal Year-end: 12/31/23
Steel Product Mfr & Distr
N.A.I.C.S.: 331210
Haibo Zhang *(Chm)*

HAICHANG OCEAN PARK HOLDINGS LTD.
31st Floor Building A Foreshore Beach World Trade Centre, Phase I No 4 Lane 255 Dongyu Road Pudong New District, Shanghai, China   Ky
Web Site: http://www.haichangoceanpark.com
2255—(HKG)
Rev.: $376,927,242
Assets: $1,795,215,500
Liabilities: $1,208,349,344
Net Worth: $586,866,155
Earnings: $127,813,604
Emp.: 4,192
Fiscal Year-end: 12/31/21
Holding Company
N.A.I.C.S.: 551112
Xuguang Wang *(CEO)*

HAICHENG LINLI MINING CO., LTD.
Ding Village, Archway Town, Haicheng, 114207, Liaoning, China
Tel.: (86) 4123387338
Emp.: 100
Mineral Mining Services
N.A.I.C.S.: 212323

HAIDEMENOS S.A.
4 Archaiou Theatrou, Alimos, 17456, Athens, Greece
Tel.: (30) 210 9940944
Web Site: http://www.haidemenos.gr
Year Founded: 1995
Emp.: 166
Commercial Printing Services
N.A.I.C.S.: 323113
Haidemenos Stratos *(Pres & CEO)*

HAIDILAO INTERNATIONAL HOLDING LTD.
7th Floor No 1 Building Yard No 398 Zhongdong Rd, Dongxiaokou Town Chang Ping District, Beijing, 102218, China
Tel.: (86) 4009107107   Ky
Web Site: http://www.haidilao.com
Year Founded: 1994
6862—(HKG)
Rev.: $5,739,553,057
Assets: $3,416,731,004
Liabilities: $1,822,117,025
Net Worth: $1,594,613,979
Earnings: $622,424,540
Emp.: 153,747
Fiscal Year-end: 12/31/23
Holding Company
N.A.I.C.S.: 551112
Yong Zhang *(Chm)*

HAIER SMART HOME CO., LTD.
Haier Information Industry Park, Laoshan District, Qingdao, Shangdong, China
Tel.: (86) 53288931670   CN
Web Site: https://smart-home.haier.com
Year Founded: 1984
6690—(HKG)
Rev.: $34,189,304,343
Assets: $33,112,252,574
Liabilities: $19,814,471,179
Net Worth: $13,297,781,395
Earnings: $2,065,413,659
Emp.: 87,447
Fiscal Year-end: 12/31/22
Electronics Appliance Mfr
N.A.I.C.S.: 334419
Lixia Tan *(Vice Chm)*

Subsidiaries:

Candy Hoover Group S.r.l. (1)
Via Privata Eden Fumagalli, 20861, Brugherio, MB, Italy
Tel.: (39) 03920861
Web Site: http://www.candy-group.com
Household Appliances Mfr
N.A.I.C.S.: 335220
Beppe Fumagalli *(CEO)*

Subsidiary (Non-US):

Candy Hoover AG (2)
Riedstrasse 1, Cham, Switzerland
Tel.: (41) 41 785 40 40
Web Site: http://www.hoover.de
Household Appliance Distr
N.A.I.C.S.: 423620
Semmy Levit *(Mng Dir)*

Candy Hoover Austria GmbH (2)
Dominikanerbastei 4, 1010, Vienna, Austria
Tel.: (43) 18973300
Web Site: https://www.hoover.de
Household Appliance Distr
N.A.I.C.S.: 423620
Carmine Infante *(Mng Dir)*

Candy Hoover Belgium NV (2)
Haachtsesteenweg 162b, 1820, Melsbroek, Belgium
Tel.: (32) 27529410
Web Site: http://www.hoover.be
Household Appliance Distr
N.A.I.C.S.: 423620

Candy Hoover CR s.r.o. (2)
Futurama Business Park-Sokolovska 651 136a, 186 00, Prague, Karlin, Czech Republic
Tel.: (420) 257 530 418
Web Site: http://www.hoover.cz
Household Appliance Distr

HAIER SMART HOME CO., LTD.

Haier Smart Home Co., Ltd.—(Continued)
N.A.I.C.S.: 423620

Candy Hoover Electrodomesticos SA (2)
Passage tasso 8, 08009, Barcelona, Spain **(100%)**
Tel.: (34) 943037300
Web Site: http://www.hoover.es
Household Appliances
N.A.I.C.S.: 335220

Candy Hoover GmbH (2)
Pempelfurtstr 1, 40880, Ratingen, Germany
Tel.: (49) 2102 459 101
Web Site: http://www.candy.de
Household Appliance Distr
N.A.I.C.S.: 423620

Plant (Domestic):

Candy Hoover Group S.r.l. - Brugherio Plant (2)
Via Comolli, 20861, Brugherio, MB, Italy
Tel.: (39) 03920861
Web Site: http://www.candy.it
Vacuum Mfr
N.A.I.C.S.: 335220

Subsidiary (Non-US):

Candy Hoover Hungary Kft. (2)
Szekszardi u 16-18, 1138, Budapest, Hungary
Tel.: (36) 1798 4932
Web Site: http://www.hoover.hu
Household Appliance Distr
N.A.I.C.S.: 423620

Candy Hoover Nederland B.V. (2)
Postbus 763, 3800 AT, Amersfoort, Netherlands
Tel.: (31) 33 4224 000
Web Site: http://www.candy.nl
Household Appliance Distr
N.A.I.C.S.: 423620

Candy Hoover Polska Sp. z o.o. (2)
Ul zwirki Wigury 16A, 02-092, Warsaw, Poland
Tel.: (48) 224390586
Web Site: http://www.candy.pl
Household Appliance Distr
N.A.I.C.S.: 423620

Candy Hoover Portugal, Ltda. (2)
Duque de Palmela Street N 25 2nd Floor, 1250-097, Lisbon, Portugal **(100%)**
Tel.: (351) 213189700
Web Site: http://www.hoover.pt
Vacuum Cleaner Mfr
N.A.I.C.S.: 335210

Candy Hoover Romania S. R. L. (2)
Titeica Office Building Str Gheorghe Titeica nr 142 4th Floor, Sector 2, Bucharest, Romania
Tel.: (40) 21 318 32 97
Web Site: http://www.hoover.ro
Household Appliance Distr
N.A.I.C.S.: 423620

Hoover Ltd. (2)
Pentrebach Road, Merthyr Tydfil, CF48 4TU, Mid Glamorgan, United Kingdom **(100%)**
Tel.: (44) 1685721222
Web Site: http://www.hoover.co.uk
Household & Industrial Appliances Mfr
N.A.I.C.S.: 335220
Robert Mudie (Admin Dir-Grp Credit & Customer)

Subsidiary (Domestic):

Candy Domestic Appliances Limited (3)
Pentrebach Road, Merthyr Tydfil, CF48 4TU, Mid Glamorgan, United Kingdom **(100%)**
Tel.: (44) 1685 721 222
Web Site: http://www.candy-domestic.co.uk
Mfr of Household Appliances
N.A.I.C.S.: 335220

Subsidiary (Non-US):

Usines de Rosieres S.A.S. (2)
30 Rue Yves Lacelle, 18400, Lunery, France

Tel.: (33) 248557800
Household Appliances Mfr
N.A.I.C.S.: 335220

Carrier Refrigeration Benelux B.V. (1)
Beesdseweg 7, 4104 AW, Culemborg, Netherlands
Tel.: (31) 34 554 4444
Web Site: https://www.carrier.com
Refrigeration Equipment Distr
N.A.I.C.S.: 423740

Subsidiary (US):

Carrier Commercial Refrigeration, Inc. (2)
10 Farm Springs Road, Farmington, CT 06032-1981
Tel.: (860) 728-7000
Web Site: http://www.carrier.com
Refrigeration & Food Service Equipment, Hand & Hair Dryers Mfr
N.A.I.C.S.: 456120

Subsidiary (Domestic):

Beverage-Air Co. (3)
700 Buffington Rd, Spartanburg, SC 29303 **(100%)**
Tel.: (864) 580-5299
Web Site: http://www.beverage-air.com
Sales Range: $50-74.9 Million
Restaurant Equipment & Supplies; Maker of Dryers for Hands & Hair
N.A.I.C.S.: 333415

South-Town Refrigeration Inc. (3)
6325 Sanburg Rd Ste 800, Golden Valley, MN 55427 **(100%)**
Tel.: (763) 231-8300
Sales Range: $1-9.9 Million
Refrigeration Contractor
N.A.I.C.S.: 238220

Tyler Refrigeration Corp. (3)
1329 Lk St, Niles, MI 49120 **(100%)**
Tel.: (269) 683-2000
Commercial Refrigeration Units Designer Mfr
N.A.I.C.S.: 333415

Fisher & Paykel Appliances Holdings Ltd. (2)
78 Springs Road East Tamaki, Manukau, 2013, New Zealand
Tel.: (64) 92730600
Web Site: http://www.fisherpaykel.com
Sales Range: $800-899.9 Million
Emp.: 3,300
Manufactures, Assembles & Imports Home Appliances; Marketing of Consumer Electronics; Financial Services
N.A.I.C.S.: 335220

Subsidiary (US):

Dynamic Cooking Systems, Inc. (2)
5900 Skylab Rd, Huntington Beach, CA 92647
Tel.: (949) 790-8900
Web Site: http://www.fisherpaykel.com
Sales Range: $25-49.9 Million
Emp.: 57
Indoor & Outdoor Cooking Product Mfr
N.A.I.C.S.: 335220

Subsidiary (Domestic):

Equipment Finance Limited (2)
Private Bag 94013, South Auckland Mail Centre, Auckland, 2240, New Zealand
Tel.: (64) 95258580
Web Site: http://www.efl.co.nz
Financial Support Services
N.A.I.C.S.: 522299

Subsidiary (Non-US):

Fisher & Paykel (Singapore) Pte Limited (2)
150 Ubi Avenue 4 Ubi Biz Hub 03-01A, Singapore, 408825, Singapore
Tel.: (65) 67410777
Web Site: http://www.fisherpaykel.com.sg
Sales Range: $25-49.9 Million
Emp.: 40
Household Appliance Distr
N.A.I.C.S.: 423620

Fisher & Paykel Appliances (Thailand) Co., Ltd. (2)
Building K1 Crystal Design Center CDC Praditmanutham Road, Bangkok, 10230, Thailand
Tel.: (66) 21022285
Web Site: http://www.fisherpaykel.com
Emp.: 1,500
Household Appliances Mfr
N.A.I.C.S.: 335220

Fisher & Paykel Appliances Canada, Inc. (2)
4180 Sladeview Crescent Unit 4, Mississauga, L5L 0A1, ON, Canada
Tel.: (905) 569-4000
Web Site: http://www.fisherpaykel.ca
Sales Range: $50-74.9 Million
Emp.: 10
Household Appliance Distr
N.A.I.C.S.: 423220

Fisher & Paykel Appliances Italy S.p.A. (2)
Via Fabbian Matteo 7, 31030, Borso del Grappa, Treviso, Italy
Tel.: (39) 04239121
Web Site: http://www.elba-cookers.com
Sales Range: $75-99.9 Million
Emp.: 500
Cooking Equipment Mfr
N.A.I.C.S.: 333310

Fisher & Paykel Appliances Limited (2)
Ortensia Drive, Milton Keynes, MK17 8LX, Buckinghamshire, United Kingdom
Tel.: (44) 8000886605
Web Site: http://www.fisherpaykel.com
Household Appliance Distr
N.A.I.C.S.: 449210

Subsidiary (Non-US):

Fisher & Paykel Production Machinery Limited (2)
50-52 Allens Road, East Tamaki, Auckland, 1701, New Zealand
Tel.: (64) 92732750
Web Site: http://www.fisherpaykelpml.com
Sales Range: $25-49.9 Million
Emp.: 70
Special Purpose Industrial Machinery Distr
N.A.I.C.S.: 423830

Subsidiary (Non-US):

Fisher & Paykel Customer Services Pty Limited (2)
Weippin St, Cleveland, 4163, QLD, Australia
Tel.: (61) 738269100
Web Site: http://www.fisherpaykel.com
Household Appliance Distr
N.A.I.C.S.: 423620

Subsidiary (Domestic):

Fisher & Paykel Financial Services Limited (2)
31 Highbrook Drive, East Tamaki, Auckland, 2013, New Zealand
Tel.: (64) 95258550
Web Site: http://www.farmersfinancecard.co.nz
Sales Range: $75-99.9 Million
Emp.: 250
Financial Support Services
N.A.I.C.S.: 522299

Subsidiary (Non-US):

Fisher & Paykel Manufacturing Pty Limited (2)
Weippin Street, Cleveland, 4163, QLD, Australia
Tel.: (61) 732868888
Web Site: http://www.fisherpaykel.com.au
Sales Range: $25-49.9 Million
Emp.: 100
Household Appliances Mfr
N.A.I.C.S.: 449210
Craig Ibbitson (Mgr-Sls-WA)

Haier America Trading, LLC (1)
1800 Valley Rd, Wayne, NJ 07470
Tel.: (212) 594-3330
Web Site: http://www.haieramerica.com
Emp.: 100

INTERNATIONAL PUBLIC

Consumer Electronics & Appliances Rental
N.A.I.C.S.: 532210
Gina Copeland (Sr VP-Air Quality)

Haier Electronics Group Co., Ltd. (1)
Room 3513 35th Floor Central Centre 99 Queen's Road, Central, China (Hong Kong) **(100%)**
Tel.: (852) 21690000
Web Site: https://www.haier.hk
Rev.: $10,858,423,707
Assets: $5,732,284,345
Liabilities: $2,922,098,136
Net Worth: $2,810,186,209
Earnings: $1,075,835,245
Emp.: 16,775
Fiscal Year-end: 12/31/2019
Washing Machines & Water Heaters Mfr
N.A.I.C.S.: 335220

Haier US Appliance Solutions, Inc. (1)
Appliance Park AP3-225, Louisville, KY 40225
Tel.: (502) 452-4311
Web Site: http://www.geappliances.com
Emp.: 6,000
Household Appliance Mfr & Repair Services
N.A.I.C.S.: 335220
Marc Charnas (CFO & VP)

Subsidiary (Domestic):

Advanced Services, Inc. (2)
6419 Shelby View Dr Ste 110, Memphis, TN 38132
Tel.: (901) 387-4000
Web Site: https://www.asicontactcenters.com
Emp.: 650
Telephone Technical Support Services
N.A.I.C.S.: 561421

Roper Corporation (2)
Appliance Park Bldg 2 225, Louisville, KY 40225 **(100%)**
Tel.: (706) 638-5100
Electric & Gas Ranges, Surface Units & Ovens, Range Hoods & Microwaves Mfr
N.A.I.C.S.: 335220

Qingdao Haier Intelligent Electronics Co., Ltd.
Haier Information Industrial Complex No 1 Haier Road, Qingdao, 266101, China
Tel.: (86) 53288937058
Web Site: http://www.haier-lcd.com
Wireless Internet Services
N.A.I.C.S.: 517112
Jasmine Ren (Mgr-Mktg)

HAIHA CONFECTIONERY JOINT STOCK COMPANY

25 Truong Dinh, Hai Ba Trung, Hanoi, Vietnam
Tel.: (84) 438632956
Web Site:
https://www.haihaco.com.vn
Year Founded: 1960
HHC—(HNX)
Rev.: $35,692,343
Assets: $72,146,474
Liabilities: $47,448,104
Net Worth: $24,698,370
Earnings: $2,042,531
Fiscal Year-end: 12/31/23
Confectionery Mfr & Distr
N.A.I.C.S.: 311351
Linh Manh Le (Chm-Mgmt Bd)

HAIKE CHEMICAL GROUP LTD

Haike Building No 726 Beiyi Road, Dongying, Shandong, China
Tel.: (86) 546 7773577
Web Site:
http://www.haikechemical.com
HAIK—(LSE)
Sales Range: $100-124.9 Million
Petrochemical & Biochemical Products Mfr
N.A.I.C.S.: 325110
Xiaohong Yang (Chm)

AND PRIVATE COMPANIES
HAINAN DEVELOPMENT HOLDINGS NANHAI CO., LTD.

Subsidiaries:

Dongying Hi-Tech Spring Chemical Co., Ltd. (1)
Shengli Industrial Park Dongying D, Dongying, 257100, China
Tel.: (86) 5468182959
Web Site: http://www.chinadmc.com
Chemical Product Mfr & Distr
N.A.I.C.S.: 325320

Subsidiary (Non-US):

HaiKe Trading HongKong Limited (2)
OTB 160 Glourcester Road, Wanchai, China (Hong Kong)
Tel.: (852) 35247322
Web Site: http://www.haikechem.com
Chemical Products Distr
N.A.I.C.S.: 424690

HAIKUI SEAFOOD AG
c/o Norton Rose Fulbright LLP, Taunustor 1 TaunusTurm, 60310, Frankfurt am Main, Germany
Tel.: (49) 40 60 91 86 0
Web Site: http://www.haikui-seafood.com
Sales Range: $125-149.9 Million
Emp.: 666
Seafood Processing & Distribution
N.A.I.C.S.: 311710
Zhenkui Chen (CEO & Member-Mgmt Bd)

HAILAN HOLDINGS LIMITED
2/F No 1 Building Hampton By Hilton No 169 Yu Lin Road, Tianya District, Sanya, Hainan, China
Tel.: (86) 89888295758   Ky
Web Site:
  http://www.hailanholdings.com
2278—(HKG)
Rev.: $195,396,084
Assets: $1,221,275,297
Liabilities: $1,075,741,150
Net Worth: $145,534,147
Earnings: ($88,150,561)
Emp.: 222
Fiscal Year-end: 12/31/22
Residential Property Development Services
N.A.I.C.S.: 531210
Li Zhou (Chm & CEO)

HAILIANG EDUCATION GROUP INC.
1508 Binsheng Road, Binjiang District, Hangzhou, 310051, Zhejiang, China
Tel.: (86) 571 5812 1974   Ky
Web Site:
  http://www.hailiangeducation.com
HLG—(NASDAQ)
Rev.: $210,784,786
Assets: $501,116,663
Liabilities: $161,471,543
Net Worth: $339,645,121
Earnings: $36,582,411
Emp.: 5,171
Fiscal Year-end: 06/30/21
Private K-12 Educational Services
N.A.I.C.S.: 611110
Ping Huang (VP)

HAILIANG GROUP CO. LTD.
386 Jiefang Road, Diankou Down, Zhuji, 311814, Zhejiang, China
Tel.: (86) 575 8706 3555   CN
Web Site: http://www.hailiang.com
Year Founded: 1999
Sales Range: $5-14.9 Billion
Emp.: 12,000
Holding Company
N.A.I.C.S.: 551112
Cao Jianguo (Gen Mgr)

Subsidiaries:

Hailiang International Holdings Limited (1)
Office 18 6th Floor World-wide House No 19 Des Voeux Road, Central, China (Hong Kong)   (77.5%)
Tel.: (852) 36282461
Web Site: http://www.hailianghk.com
Rev.: $15,572,213
Assets: $54,378,495
Liabilities: $6,184,898
Net Worth: $48,193,598
Earnings: ($1,343,595)
Emp.: 214
Fiscal Year-end: 12/31/2022
Holding Company; Wireless Communications Equipment Mfr
N.A.I.C.S.: 551112
Jianguo Cao (Chm)

HAILIR PESTICIDES & CHEMICALS GROUP
216 Guocheng Road, Chengyang District, Qingdao, 266109, Shandong, China
Tel.: (86) 53258659175
Web Site: https://www.hailir.cn
Year Founded: 1999
603639—(SHG)
Rev.: $636,713,860
Assets: $819,599,349
Liabilities: $368,641,162
Net Worth: $450,958,187
Earnings: $64,585,390
Fiscal Year-end: 12/31/22
Pesticide Mfr & Distr
N.A.I.C.S.: 325320
Jiacheng Ge (Chm & Gen Mgr)

Subsidiaries:

Sinoagro Chemicals Co., Ltd. (1)
Room1705 No 1065 Zhong Shan Road West, Shanghai, 200051, China
Tel.: (86) 2160325568
Web Site: http://www.sinoagro.cn
Agricultural Pesticide Mfr & Distr
N.A.I.C.S.: 325320

HAILUN PIANO CO., LTD.
No 36 Longtanshan Road, Beilun District, Ningbo, 315806, Zhejiang, China
Tel.: (86) 57486813822
Web Site:
  http://www.hailunpiano.com
Year Founded: 2001
300329—(CHIN)
Rev.: $53,239,680
Assets: $197,787,096
Liabilities: $68,544,684
Net Worth: $129,242,412
Earnings: $1,168,128
Emp.: 800
Fiscal Year-end: 12/31/22
Piano Mfr
N.A.I.C.S.: 339992
Helen Chen (Chm)

HAIMA AUTOMOBILE CO., LTD.
No 12-8 Jinpan Road Jinpan Industrial Zone, Haikou, 570216, Hainan, China
Tel.: (86) 89866822672
Web Site: http://www.haima.com
Year Founded: 1988
000572—(SSE)
Rev.: $338,241,852
Assets: $884,345,904
Liabilities: $466,587,108
Net Worth: $417,758,796
Earnings: $221,045,760
Fiscal Year-end: 12/31/22
Automobile & Automobile Parts Mfr
N.A.I.C.S.: 336110
Zhu Jing (Chm)

HAIMO TECHNOLOGIES GROUP CORP.
No 593 Zhangsutan, Chengguan District, Lanzhou, 730010, Gansu, China
Tel.: (86) 9318553388
Web Site: http://www.haimotech.com
Year Founded: 1994
300084—(CHIN)
Rev.: $88,092,576
Assets: $290,164,680
Liabilities: $144,173,952
Net Worth: $145,990,728
Earnings: $1,961,388
Emp.: 1,000
Fiscal Year-end: 12/31/22
Meter Mfr
N.A.I.C.S.: 334514
Jianwen Dou (Chm)

Subsidiaries:

Haimo America, Inc. (1)
2901 Wilcrest Dr Ste 285, Houston, TX 77042
Tel.: (832) 831-6623
Web Site: https://goliveflo.com
Oil & Gas Machinery Equipment Mfr
N.A.I.C.S.: 333132

Haimo International FZE (1)
PO Box 17256, Jebel Ali Free Zone, Dubai, United Arab Emirates
Tel.: (971) 48860266
Sales Range: $25-49.9 Million
Emp.: 15
Electrical & Water Meters Distr
N.A.I.C.S.: 423610
Syed Zia (Gen Mgr)

Haimo Oilfield Services Co., Ltd. (1)
No 22 Keji 5th Rd, High-Tech Zone, Xi'an, 710065, Shaanxi, China
Tel.: (86) 298 985 1081
Oil & Gas Services
N.A.I.C.S.: 213112

Haimo Subsea Technololy (Shanghai) Co., Ltd. (1)
1st Floor Building 28 Lane 218 Haiji 6th Road, Lingang New Area of China Pilot Free Trade Zone, Shanghai, 201306, China
Tel.: (86) 215 828 1221
Marine Engineering Services
N.A.I.C.S.: 541330

Lanzhou Haimo Energy Technology Co., Ltd. (1)
No 593 Zhang Sutan, Chengguan District, Lanzhou, 730030, Gansu, China
Tel.: (86) 931 855 7780
Oil Field Equipment Mfr & Distr
N.A.I.C.S.: 333132

Xi'an Sitan Instrument Co., Ltd. (1)
No 22 Keji 5th Rd, High-Tech Zone, Xi'an, 710065, Shaanxi, China
Tel.: (86) 298 881 4516
Oil & Gas Recovery System Mfr
N.A.I.C.S.: 333132

HAINA INTELLIGENT EQUIPMENT INTERNATIONAL HOLDINGS LIMITED
Wuli Technology Park, Economic Development Area, Jinjiang, China
Tel.: (86) 59585717878   Ky
Web Site: http://www.haina-intelligent.com
Year Founded: 2011
1645—(HKG)
Holding Company
N.A.I.C.S.: 551112
Yiyuan Hong (Chm & CEO)

Subsidiaries:

Jinjiang Haina Machinery Company Limited (1)
Wuli Technology Park, Jinjiang, Fujian, China
Tel.: (86) 59585717878
Web Site: http://www.fjhaina.com
Baby Diaper Mfr
N.A.I.C.S.: 322291

HAINAN AIRPORT INFRASTRUCTURE CO LTD
42F Main Building 1 Hainan Building No 5 Guoxing Avenue, Meilan District, Haikou, 570206, Hainan, China
Tel.: (86) 89869960275
Web Site: http://www.zhuxin.biz
Year Founded: 1993
600515—(SHG)
Rev.: $659,972,145
Assets: $7,880,013,180
Liabilities: $4,537,242,988
Net Worth: $3,342,770,192
Earnings: $260,626,317
Fiscal Year-end: 12/31/22
Investment Services
N.A.I.C.S.: 523999
Yang Xiaobin (Chm)

HAINAN DADONGHAI TOURISM CENTRE (HOLDINGS) CO., LTD.
Dadonghai, Sanya, 572021, Hainan, China
Tel.: (86) 89888219888
200613—(SSE)
Rev.: $2,376,287
Assets: $14,928,782
Liabilities: $4,675,969
Net Worth: $10,252,813
Earnings: ($1,772,640)
Fiscal Year-end: 12/31/20
Hotel Operator
N.A.I.C.S.: 721110
Yuan Xiaoping (Chm & Gen Mgr)

HAINAN DEVELOPMENT HOLDINGS NANHAI CO., LTD.
17th Floor Xinbaohui Building No 2061 Nanhai Avenue, Nanshan District, Shenzhen, 518054, Guangdong, China
Tel.: (86) 75526067916
Web Site:
  http://www.sanxingglass.com
Year Founded: 1995
002163—(SSE)
Rev.: $507,690,612
Assets: $879,457,176
Liabilities: $666,975,816
Net Worth: $212,481,360
Earnings: ($20,307,456)
Fiscal Year-end: 12/31/22
Glass Products Mfr
N.A.I.C.S.: 327212
Wang Dongyang (Chm)

Subsidiaries:

AVIC (Hainan) Special Glass Material Co., Ltd. (1)
South First Ring Road, Laocheng Economic Development Zone, Luoyang, 571924, Hainan, China
Tel.: (86) 89867480159
Web Site: http://www.avicglass.com
Glass Product Mfr & Distr
N.A.I.C.S.: 327212

AVIC Sanxin Solar Glass Co., Ltd. (1)
West Laoshan Road Longzihu Disctrict, Bengbu, Anhui, China
Tel.: (86) 5523153791
Glass Products Mfr
N.A.I.C.S.: 327212

Guangdong AVIC Special Glass Technology Co., Ltd. (1)
Huangfengling Industrial Zone Luozu Village Shiyan Town Bao'an, Shenzhen, 518108, China
Tel.: (86) 75527633580
Web Site: http://www.avicsgt.com
Glass Products Mfr
N.A.I.C.S.: 327212

Guangdong Haikong Special Glass Technology Co., Ltd. (1)
Xiangshuihe Industrial Zone Daya Bay, Huizhou, 516081, Guangdong, China

HAINAN DEVELOPMENT HOLDINGS NANHAI CO., LTD.

Hainan Development Holdings Nanhai Co., Ltd.—(Continued)
Tel.: (86) 7525199008
Web Site: https://en.avicsgt.com
Building Construction Services
N.A.I.C.S.: 236220

Sanxin Facade Technology Ltd. (1)
Suite 1506 15/F Tower 6 China Hk City 33 Canton Road, Tsim Sha Tsui, Kowloon, China (Hong Kong)
Tel.: (852) 21211388
Web Site: http://www.sanxinfacade.com
Curtain Wall & Window Distr
N.A.I.C.S.: 423310

Shenzhen Sanxin Facade Engineering Co., Ltd. (1)
Room1001-1101 Block E Building 5 Software Industry Base Binhai Avenue, Nanshan District, Shenzhen, Guangdong, China
Tel.: (86) 75586284666
Web Site: https://www.sanxinfeng.com
Curtain Wall Mfr
N.A.I.C.S.: 332323

HAINAN DRINDA NEW ENERGY TECHNOLOGY CO., LTD.
Tel.: (86) 89866802555
Web Site: http://www.drinda.com.cn
002865—(SSE)
Rev.: $1,627,992,756
Assets: $1,332,297,720
Liabilities: $1,184,761,188
Net Worth: $147,536,532
Earnings: $100,659,780
Fiscal Year-end: 12/31/22
Automotive Parts Mfr & Distr
N.A.I.C.S.: 336360
Huang Falian *(CFO)*

HAINAN EXPRESSWAY CO., LTD.
Highway Building No 16 Lantian Road, Haikou, 570203, Hainan, China
Tel.: (86) 89866799790
Web Site: https://www.hi-expressway.com
Year Founded: 1993
000886—(SSE)
Rev.: $23,750,064
Assets: $473,755,932
Liabilities: $48,313,044
Net Worth: $425,442,888
Earnings: $35,123,868
Fiscal Year-end: 12/31/22
Food Transportation Services
N.A.I.C.S.: 488490
Chen Taifeng *(Chm & Sec-Party Committee)*

HAINAN HAIDE CAPITAL MANAGEMENT CO., LTD.
3rd Floor Guoxing Building No 22 Shouti South Road, Haidian District, Haikou, 100044, Hainan, China
Tel.: (86) 1068311860
Web Site: http://www.000567.com
Year Founded: 1992
000567—(SSE)
Rev.: $149,228,352
Assets: $1,115,024,508
Liabilities: $386,477,676
Net Worth: $728,546,832
Earnings: $98,299,656
Fiscal Year-end: 12/31/22
Real Estate Property Development Services
N.A.I.C.S.: 531311
Xinmin Zhu *(Chief Acctg Officer, Chm-Supervisory Bd & Deputy Gen Mgr)*

HAINAN HAIQI TRANSPORTATION GROUP CO., LTD.
Haiqi Building No 24 Haifu Road, Meilan District, Haikou, 570203, Hainan, China
Tel.: (86) 89865326058
Web Site: http://www.0898hq.com
Year Founded: 1985
603069—(SHG)
Rev.: $103,876,176
Assets: $292,184,910
Liabilities: $152,304,263
Net Worth: $139,880,646
Earnings: $5,509,142
Emp.: 3,500
Fiscal Year-end: 12/31/22
Logistics Consulting Servies
N.A.I.C.S.: 541614
Feng Xianyang *(Chm)*

HAINAN HAIYAO CO., LTD.
No 192 Nanhai Avenue, Xiuying District, Haikou, 570311, Hainan, China
Tel.: (86) 89836380609
Web Site: http://www.haiyao.com.cn
Year Founded: 1992
000566—(SSE)
Rev.: $249,778,620
Assets: $1,034,107,776
Liabilities: $705,967,704
Net Worth: $328,140,072
Earnings: $1,477,008
Fiscal Year-end: 12/31/22
Pharmaceuticals Mfr
N.A.I.C.S.: 325412
Wang Jianping *(Chm)*

HAINAN HULUWA PHARMACEUTICAL GROUP CO., LTD.
No 8 Yaogu 4th Road, Phase II Yaogu Industrial Park Haikou National High-tech Zone, Haikou, 570311, Hainan, China
Tel.: (86) 89868634767
Web Site: http://www.huluwayaoye.com
Year Founded: 2005
605199—(SHG)
Rev.: $212,712,529
Assets: $324,612,859
Liabilities: $182,069,555
Net Worth: $142,543,304
Earnings: $12,029,753
Fiscal Year-end: 12/31/22
Pharmaceutical Product Mfr & Distr
N.A.I.C.S.: 325412
Jingping Liu *(Chm & Gen Mgr)*

HAINAN JINGLIANG HOLDINGS CO., LTD.
Jing Liang Building No 16 East Third Ring Middle Road, Chaoyang District, Beijing, China
Tel.: (86) 1051672029
000505—(SSE)
Rev.: $1,805,244,948
Assets: $857,161,656
Liabilities: $370,997,172
Net Worth: $486,164,484
Earnings: $19,853,964
Fiscal Year-end: 12/31/22
Holding Company
N.A.I.C.S.: 551112
Shaoling Li *(Chm)*

HAINAN JINPAN SMART TECHNOLOGY CO., LTD.
No 168-39 Nanhai Avenue, Haikou, 570216, Hainan, China
Tel.: (86) 89866811301
Web Site: https://www.jst.com.cn
Year Founded: 1997
688676—(SHG)
Rev.: $666,282,156
Assets: $1,048,384,884
Liabilities: $644,850,334
Net Worth: $403,534,549
Earnings: $39,772,245
Fiscal Year-end: 12/31/22
Electrical Equipment Mfr & Distr
N.A.I.C.S.: 335999
Zhiyuan Li *(Chm)*

HAINAN MANASLU CORP.
B3406 34F West Tower Block B Guorui Building 11 Guoxing Avenue, Haikou, 570203, Hainan, China
Tel.: (86) 8986 531 5786
Year Founded: 2021
Emp.: 3
Investment Services
N.A.I.C.S.: 523999
Zhifan Zhou *(CEO & Chm)*

HAINAN MEILAN INTERNATIONAL AIRPORT COMPANY LIMITED
Meilan Airport Complex, Haikou, 571126, Hainan, China
Tel.: (86) 898966114 CN
Web Site: http://www.mlairport.com
Year Founded: 2000
0357—(HKG)
Rev.: $160,261,212
Assets: $1,493,793,003
Liabilities: $875,117,598
Net Worth: $618,675,405
Earnings: ($26,774,735)
Emp.: 1,296
Fiscal Year-end: 12/31/22
Airport Operations
N.A.I.C.S.: 488119
Zhoujin Xing *(Sec & Exec Dir)*

HAINAN POLY PHARM.CO.,LTD.
Guilingyang Economic Development Area, Yuhang, Haikou, 571127, Hainan, China
Tel.: (86) 89865714800
Web Site: https://www.hnpoly.com
Year Founded: 1992
300630—(CHIN)
Rev.: $253,610,136
Assets: $836,646,408
Liabilities: $443,174,004
Net Worth: $393,472,404
Earnings: $59,055,048
Fiscal Year-end: 12/31/22
Pharmaceutical Mfr & Distr
N.A.I.C.S.: 325412
Fan Minhua *(Gen Mgr)*

Subsidiaries:

Hainan Poly. Co., Ltd. (1)
Guilingyang Economic Development Area, Haikou, 571127, Hainan, China
Tel.: (86) 89865714800
Pharmaceuticals Product Mfr
N.A.I.C.S.: 325412

Zhejiang Poly. Co., Ltd. (1)
No 78 Xinzhou Road, Linping Yuhang, Hangzhou, 311103, Zhejiang, China
Tel.: (86) 57128971376
Pharmaceuticals Product Mfr
N.A.I.C.S.: 325412

HAINAN RUIZE NEW BUILDING MATERIAL CO.
20th Floor Sunshine Financial Plaza No 360-1 Yingbin Road, Jiyang District, Sanya, 572022, China
Tel.: (86) 89888703858
Web Site: https://www.hnruize.com
Year Founded: 2002
002596—(SSE)
Rev.: $271,381,968
Assets: $638,683,812
Liabilities: $430,088,724
Net Worth: $208,595,088
Earnings: ($69,319,692)
Fiscal Year-end: 12/31/22
Construction Material Mfr & Distr
N.A.I.C.S.: 327310

INTERNATIONAL PUBLIC

HAINAN SHENNONG SEED TECHNOLOGY CO., LTD.
Huiyuan Meilin Valley Comprehensive Office Building No 8 Meilin Road, Xiuying District, Haikou, 570311, Hainan, China
Tel.: (86) 89868512026
Web Site: https://www.hnsnkj.com.cn
Year Founded: 2000
300189—(CHIN)
Rev.: $23,483,273
Assets: $141,051,993
Liabilities: $20,453,350
Net Worth: $120,598,643
Earnings: ($5,073,755)
Fiscal Year-end: 12/31/23
Rice Farming & Distr
N.A.I.C.S.: 111160
Peijin Huang *(Chm)*

HAINAN SHUANGCHENG PHARMACEUTICALS CO., LTD.
No 16 Xingguo Road, Xiuying District, Haikou, 570314, Hainan, China
Tel.: (86) 89868635601
Web Site: https://www.shuangchengmed.com
Year Founded: 2000
002693—(SSE)
Rev.: $38,574,900
Assets: $127,907,208
Liabilities: $46,343,232
Net Worth: $81,563,976
Earnings: $1,265,004
Emp.: 330
Fiscal Year-end: 12/31/22
Pharmaceuticals Mfr
N.A.I.C.S.: 325412
Yu Xiaofeng *(Sec)*

HAINAN STRAIT SHIPPING CO., LTD.
14th Floor Port and Shipping Building No 157 Binhai Avenue, Haikou, 570311, Hainan, China
Tel.: (86) 89868668720
Web Site: https://www.hnss.net.cn
Year Founded: 2002
002320—(SSE)
Rev.: $416,071,188
Assets: $1,067,955,408
Liabilities: $170,795,196
Net Worth: $897,160,212
Earnings: $21,337,992
Emp.: 980
Fiscal Year-end: 12/31/22
Passenger & Freight Water Transportation Services
N.A.I.C.S.: 483212
Ye Wei *(Sec & Gen Mgr)*

HAINAN TRAFFIC ADMINISTRATION HOLDING CO., LTD.
17 F Jinling Building, Jinmao District, Haikou, China
Tel.: (86) 89868555399 CN
Holding Company
N.A.I.C.S.: 551112
Liang Tang *(Chm & Gen Mgr)*

Subsidiaries:

HNA Group Co., Ltd. (1)
Haihang Development Bldg No 29 Haixiu Rd, Haikou, 570203, Hainan, China
Tel.: (86) 89866739906
Web Site: http://www.hnagroup.com
Holding Company
N.A.I.C.S.: 551112
Chen Feng *(Co-Founder & Co-Chm)*

Subsidiary (Domestic):

Anqing Tianzhushan Airport Co., Ltd. (2)
Anqing Tianzhushan Airport Xiangshan Village, Yixiu District, Anqing, 246005, Anhui, China

AND PRIVATE COMPANIES — HAINAN TRAFFIC ADMINISTRATION HOLDING CO., LTD.

Tel.: (86) 556 5861057
Airport Management Services
N.A.I.C.S.: 488190

Baoji Shopping Mall Co., Ltd (2)
114 Jinger Road, Baoji, 721000, Shaanxi, China
Tel.: (86) 917 3215282
Shopping Mall Operator
N.A.I.C.S.: 531120

Beijing Capital Airlines Co., Ltd. (2)
HNA Plaza 2 Yi Dongsanhuan North Road, Chaoyang District, Beijing, 100027, China
Tel.: (86) 10 59156001
Aircraft Charter Services
N.A.I.C.S.: 481211

Beijing Grand-China Universe Media Inc. (2)
HongYuan Mansion 4 Jia Jiuxianqiao Road, Chaoyang District, Beijing, 100015, China
Tel.: (86) 10 84325605
Advetising Agency
N.A.I.C.S.: 541810

Beijing Joyful Journey Technologies Co., Ltd. (2)
Tower F Block 8 Qifa Mansion 2 Courtyard Sheng Gu Zhong Road, Chaoyang District, Beijing, 100029, China
Tel.: (86) 10 52902395
Software Development Services
N.A.I.C.S.: 541511

Beijing Vigor Tianbao International Studios Co., Ltd (2)
Jianxiang Plaza Jianxiang Bridge North 4th Road, Beijing, 100029, China
Tel.: (86) 10 82994949
Theater Operator
N.A.I.C.S.: 512131

Holding (Non-US):

CWT Limited (2)
38 Tanjong Penjuru, Singapore, 609039, Singapore
Tel.: (65) 6262 6888
Web Site: http://www.cwtlimited.com
Emp.: 6,000
Logistics Consulting Servies
N.A.I.C.S.: 541614
Pok Yen Loi *(Grp CEO)*

Subsidiary (Domestic):

Danzhou HNA Investment and Development Co., Ltd. (2)
168 Zhongxing Road, Danzhou, 571700, Hainan, China
Tel.: (86) 898 36780680
Investment Management Service
N.A.I.C.S.: 523940

Holding (Non-US):

Domaine Power Holdings Limited (2)
Unit 1705 - 07 17/F K11 Atelier Victoria Dockside 18 Salisbury Road, Tsim Sha Tsui, Kowloon, China (Hong Kong) **(80.86%)**
Tel.: (852) 26277016
Web Site: http://www.ktl.com.hk
Rev.: $17,478,467
Assets: $17,624,472
Liabilities: $1,118,386
Net Worth: $16,506,087
Earnings: ($10,117,578)
Emp.: 6
Fiscal Year-end: 03/31/2022
Holding Company; Fine Jewelry Distr
N.A.I.C.S.: 551112
Zhiyi Su *(Chm)*

Flughafen Frankfurt-Hahn GmbH (2)
Building 667, Hahn-Flughafen, D-55483, Kirchberg, Germany **(82.5%)**
Tel.: (49) 6543509113
Web Site: http://www.hahn-airport.de
Airport Operator
N.A.I.C.S.: 488119

Subsidiary (Domestic):

Gansu Airport Group Co., Ltd. (2)
203 Jiayuguan West Road, Lanzhou, 730020, Gansu, China
Tel.: (86) 931 8168019
Airport Management Services
N.A.I.C.S.: 488119

Grand China Project Logistics Co., Ltd (2)
Pufa Plaza 588 Pudong South Road, Shanghai, 200120, China
Tel.: (86) 21 60625231
Logistics Consulting Servies
N.A.I.C.S.: 541614

Guangdong HNA Lewanjia Supermarket Co., Ltd (2)
Area C Yunxing Wholesale Market Huanshi North Road, Meijiang District, Meizhou, 514087, Guangdong, China
Tel.: (86) 753 2593399
Supermarket Operator
N.A.I.C.S.: 445110

HNA Capital Holding Co., Ltd. (2)
21 & 23/F HNA Plaza Jia 26 Xiaoyun Road, Chaoyang District, Beijing, 100125, China
Tel.: (86) 1057583800
Web Site: http://www.hnacapital.com
Holding Company; Investment, Leasing, Insurance & Other Financial Services
N.A.I.C.S.: 551112

Subsidiary (Domestic):

HNA Capital Group Co., Ltd. (3)
21 & 23/F HNA Plaza Jia 26 Xiaoyun Road, Chaoyang District, Beijing, 100125, China
Tel.: (86) 10 57583800
Web Site: http://www.hnacapital.com
Investment, Leasing, Insurance & Other Financial Services
N.A.I.C.S.: 523150

Subsidiary (Domestic):

Bohai Leasing Co., Ltd. (4)
10th Floor Hongyuan Building No 4A Jiuxianqiao Road, Chaoyang District, Beijing, China
Tel.: (86) 1058102660
Web Site: https://www.bohaiholding.com
Rev.: $4,662,542,784
Assets: $36,213,012,295
Liabilities: $29,897,539,599
Net Worth: $6,315,472,696
Earnings: $177,405,156
Emp.: 530
Fiscal Year-end: 12/31/2023
Transportation Services
N.A.I.C.S.: 488510

Subsidiary (Non-US):

Avolon Holdings Limited (5)
Building 1 Shelbourne Road, Number One Ballsbridge, Dublin, 4, Ireland
Tel.: (353) 12315800
Web Site: http://www.avolon.aero
Sales Range: $600-649.9 Million
Aircraft Leasing Services
N.A.I.C.S.: 532411
Andy Cronin *(CEO)*

Seaco Global Ltd. (5)
4th Floor One Valentine Place, London, SE1 8QH, United Kingdom
Tel.: (44) 203 267 1352
Web Site: http://www.seacoglobal.com
Shipping Container Leasing, Sales & Support Services
N.A.I.C.S.: 532411
Jeremy Matthew *(CEO-Singapore)*

Subsidiary (US):

Seaco America LLC (6)
7200 NW 19 St Ste 500, Miami, FL 33126
Tel.: (305) 597-2120
Web Site: http://www.seacoglobal.com
Sales Range: $25-49.9 Million
Shipping Container Leasing, Sales & Support Services
N.A.I.C.S.: 532411

Subsidiary (Non-US):

Seaco Asia Pte Ltd. (6)
Fuji Xerox Towers #29-01, 80 Anson Road, Singapore, 79907, Singapore
Tel.: (65) 6595 1900
Web Site: http://www.seacoglobal.com
Sales Range: $25-49.9 Million
Shipping Container Leasing, Sales & Support Services
N.A.I.C.S.: 532411

Chris Jin *(Grp Deputy CEO)*

Subsidiary (Domestic):

Seaco British Isles Ltd. (6)
4th Floor One Valentine Place, London, SE1 8QH, United Kingdom
Tel.: (44) 203 267 1352
Shipping Container Leasing, Sales & Support Services
N.A.I.C.S.: 532411
Richard Fedden *(Reg Dir-Mktg)*

Subsidiary (Non-US):

Seaco China Ltd. (6)
Suite 812 Ocean Centre 5 Canton Road, Tsimshatsui, Kowloon, China (Hong Kong)
Tel.: (852) 2525 8613
Web Site: http://www.seacoglobal.com
Shipping Container Leasing, Sales & Support Services
N.A.I.C.S.: 532411

Seaco France SARL (6)
16 rue Antonin Raynaud, 92300, Levallois-Perret, France
Tel.: (33) 147459803
Web Site: http://www.seacoglobal.com
Sales Range: $50-74.9 Million
Emp.: 3
Shipping Container Leasing, Sales & Support Services
N.A.I.C.S.: 532411

Seaco Global Australia Pty. Ltd. (6)
Suite 1602 National Mutual Centre 44 Market Street, Sydney, 2000, NSW, Australia
Tel.: (61) 2 9290 1455
Web Site: http://www.seacoglobal.com
Shipping Container Leasing, Sales & Support Services
N.A.I.C.S.: 532411
Evette Murray *(Mktg Dir)*

Seaco International Leasing GmbH (6)
Am Sandtorpark 2, 20457, Hamburg, Germany
Tel.: (49) 408080310
Web Site: http://www.seacoglobal.com
Sales Range: $50-74.9 Million
Emp.: 10
Shipping Container Leasing, Sales & Support Services
N.A.I.C.S.: 532411
Markus Kaisel *(Mng Dir)*

Seaco Italia srl (6)
Via Aurelia 136, 57017, Livorno, Stagno, Italy
Tel.: (39) 0586950028
Web Site: http://www.seacoglobal.com
Sales Range: $1-9.9 Million
Emp.: 3
Shipping Container Leasing, Sales & Support Services
N.A.I.C.S.: 532411

Subsidiary (Domestic):

HNA Cargo Co., Ltd. (2)
Hna Plaza No 7 Guoxing Road, Meilan District, Haikou, 570206, Hainan, China
Tel.: (86) 898 66281765
Logistics Consulting Servies
N.A.I.C.S.: 541614

HNA Daji Investment & Development Co., Ltd. (2)
Tower A Qiaoyuan Park Crossroad of Tianshan Road & Panshan Road, Hedong District, Tianjin, 300162, China
Tel.: (86) 22 58159173
Investment Management Service
N.A.I.C.S.: 523940

Subsidiary (Non-US):

HNA Group (Hong Kong) Co., Ltd. (2)
The Center 99 Queen's Road, Central, China (Hong Kong)
Tel.: (852) 25680020
Aircraft Charter Services
N.A.I.C.S.: 481111

Subsidiary (Domestic):

HNA Property Management Co., Ltd. (2)
Property Building Sales Office Guoxing City Guoxing Road, Haikou, 570203, China
Tel.: (86) 898 66569800
Property Management Services
N.A.I.C.S.: 531390

HNA SAFE Car Rental Co., Ltd. (2)
168 Lantian Road, Haikou, 570203, Hainan, China
Tel.: (86) 898 66531051
Car Rental Services
N.A.I.C.S.: 532111

HNA Southern Tourism Holding Group Co., Ltd. (2)
HNA Plaza 8 Linhe Middle Road, Tianhe District, Guangzhou, 510610, China
Tel.: (86) 20 85501579
Travel Tour Operator
N.A.I.C.S.: 561520

HNA Technology Co., Ltd. (2)
4F Shanghai HNA Building 898 Puming Road, Pudong New Area, Shanghai, 200122, China
Tel.: (86) 2258679088
Web Site: http://www.hna-tic.com
Rev.: $20,629,112
Assets: $1,494,209,948
Liabilities: $493,970,864
Net Worth: $1,000,239,084
Earnings: $27,338,828
Emp.: 31,000
Fiscal Year-end: 12/31/2022
Investment Holding Company
N.A.I.C.S.: 551112

Subsidiary (US):

Ingram Micro Inc. (3)
3351 Michelson Dr Ste 100, Irvine, CA 92612
Tel.: (714) 566-1000
Web Site: http://www.ingrammicro.com
Information Technology Hardware, Software, Peripherals & Accessories Wholesale Distr
N.A.I.C.S.: 423420
Alain Monie *(Exec Chm)*

Subsidiary (Non-US):

ANOVO S.A. (4)
16 rue Joseph Cugnot, Industrielle de Bracheux, 60000, Beauvais, France
Tel.: (33) 344897900
Web Site: http://www.anovo.com
Electronics Equipment Repair & Recycling Services
N.A.I.C.S.: 811210

Subsidiary (Non-US):

A Novo Comlink Espana SL (5)
Parque Tecnologico de Andalucia, Charles Darwin S-N, 29590, Malaga, Spain
Tel.: (34) 952020020
Communication Equipment Mfr
N.A.I.C.S.: 334290

A Novo Polska Sp.zo.o. (5)
Fabryczna 20 C, Pietrzykowice, 55080, Warsaw, Poland
Tel.: (48) 71 316 96 54
Electronics Equipment Repair & Recycling Services
N.A.I.C.S.: 811210

Subsidiary (Non-US):

Aptec Holding Egypt LLC (4)
K30 Misr Ismailia Rd, PO Box 11822, Obour, Cairo, Egypt
Tel.: (20) 2 24772153
Web Site: http://www.eg.ingrammicro.com
Holding Company
N.A.I.C.S.: 551112
Mohammed Selim *(Country Mgr-Egypt & Libya Reg)*

Aptec Holdings Limited (4)
Floor 2 Bld 1 Innovation Hub Al Falak Street, PO Box 33550, Dubai Internet City, Dubai, United Arab Emirates
Tel.: (971) 43697111
Web Site: http://www.ae.ingrammicro.com
Holding Company
N.A.I.C.S.: 551112

Subsidiary (Non-US):

Ingram Micro Bilim Sistemleri A.S. (5)

HAINAN TRAFFIC ADMINISTRATION HOLDING CO., LTD.

Hainan Traffic Administration Holding Co., Ltd.—(Continued)
Azerbaycan Cd Vadi Istanbul 2B Blok D 4, Ayazaga mah Sariyer, 34485, Istanbul, Turkiye
Tel.: (90) 2124673800
Web Site: https://www.armada.com.tr
Computer Equipment Distr
N.A.I.C.S.: 423430
Francis Zoltan Lazar *(Chm, CEO, Mng Dir & Exec Dir)*

Subsidiary (Domestic):

CloudBlue Technologies, Inc. (4)
3351 Michelson Dr #100, Irvine, CA 92612
Tel.: (844) 957-2708
Web Site: http://www.cloudblue.com
Logistics Management Consulting Services
N.A.I.C.S.: 541614

Subsidiary (Non-US):

Ingram Macrotron GmbH (4)
Heisenbergbogen 3, Aschheim, 85609, Munich, Germany
Tel.: (49) 8942080
Computer Peripheral Equipment Distr
N.A.I.C.S.: 423430

Ingram Micro (China) Ltd (4)
9th Floor Pioneer Place No 33 Hoi Yuen Road, Kowloon, China (Hong Kong)
Tel.: (852) 25649200
Web Site: http://hk.ingrammicro.com
Computer & Computer Peripheral Equipment & Software Merchant Whslr
N.A.I.C.S.: 423420

Ingram Micro (India) Exports Pte Ltd (4)
205 Kallang Bahru, Singapore, 339341, Singapore
Tel.: (65) 6298 0888
Computer Equipment & Software Whslr
N.A.I.C.S.: 541519

Ingram Micro (NZ) Limited (4)
78 Apollo Drive, Rosedale, Auckland, 0632, New Zealand
Tel.: (64) 9 414 0100
Computer Related Products & Software Whslr
N.A.I.C.S.: 423430
Dan Meadows *(Mgr-Bus-Unified Comm)*

Ingram Micro (Shanghai) Commercial Factoring Co., Ltd. (4)
8-9F Building A 865 JiuXin Road, Shanghai, 201612, China
Tel.: (86) 2124016888
Electronic Equipment Whslr
N.A.I.C.S.: 423690

Ingram Micro (Thailand) Ltd (4)
1000/17-18 21-22 Liberty Plaza 12AB 14AB Fl Soi Sukhumvit 55, Sukhumvit Road Klongtonnua Wattana, Bangkok, 10110, Thailand
Tel.: (66) 27931888
Web Site: http://www.imonline.in.th
Computer Peripheral Equipment & Software Whslr
N.A.I.C.S.: 423430

Ingram Micro AB (4)
Gardsfogdevagen 7, 168 87, Bromma, Sweden
Tel.: (46) 84771500
Web Site: http://www.ingrammicro.se
Computer Services
N.A.I.C.S.: 541519
Christer Eklund *(Mng Dir)*

Subsidiary (Domestic):

Ingram Micro Americas Inc. (4)
3351 Michelson Dr Ste 100, Irvine, CA 92612-0697
Tel.: (714) 566-1000
Web Site: http://www.ingrammicro.com
Computer System Design Services
N.A.I.C.S.: 541512
Alain Monie *(CEO)*

Subsidiary (Non-US):

Ingram Micro ApS (4)
Kolding Apark 1 1tv, Kolding, 6000, Denmark
Tel.: (45) 73 30 30 30
Web Site: http://www.ingrammicro.dk
Industrial Machinery & Equipment Whslr
N.A.I.C.S.: 423830

Ingram Micro Argentina, S.A. (4)
Reconquista 661 Floor 4, Microcentro, Buenos Aires, C1003ABM, Argentina
Tel.: (54) 11 5238 1444
Web Site: http://cl.ingrammicro.com
Stationery & Office Supplies Whslr
N.A.I.C.S.: 424120

Ingram Micro Asia Ltd. (4)
205 Kallang Bahru, Singapore, 339341, Singapore
Tel.: (65) 62980888
Web Site: http://sg.ingrammicro.com
Electronic Store Operator
N.A.I.C.S.: 449210

Ingram Micro Asia Pacific Pte. Ltd (4)
205 Kallang Bahru, Singapore, 339341, Singapore
Tel.: (65) 6298 0888
Web Site: http://sg.ingrammicro.com
Computer Peripheral Equipment Distr
N.A.I.C.S.: 423430

Ingram Micro Australia Pty Ltd (4)
61 Dunning Ave, Rosebery, 2018, NSW, Australia
Tel.: (61) 293816000
Web Site: http://au.ingrammicro.com
Outsourced Logistics Services
N.A.I.C.S.: 541614

Ingram Micro BV (4)
Papendorpseweg 95, Utrecht, 3528 BJ, Netherlands
Tel.: (31) 302464001
Web Site: http://nl.ingrammicro.com
Computer Peripheral Equipment & Software Whslr
N.A.I.C.S.: 423430

Ingram Micro BVBA (4)
Hermeslaan 1b / 3rd floor, Diegem, B-1831, Belgium
Tel.: (32) 22549211
Web Site: http://be.ingrammicro.com
Personal Computer Distr
N.A.I.C.S.: 423430
Pascale Dries *(Sr Mgr-IS)*

Ingram Micro Brasil Ltda. (4)
Av Piracema1341, Barueri, 06460-030, Sao Paulo, Brazil
Tel.: (55) 1120784200
Web Site: http://br.ingrammicro.com
Computer Peripheral Equipment Distr
N.A.I.C.S.: 423430
Roberto Gero *(Dir-Advanced Computing)*

Ingram Micro CFS International B.V. (4)
Energieweg 2, 5145 NW, Waalwijk, Netherlands
Tel.: (31) 416 674 111
Web Site: http://www.ingrammicroservices.com
Holding Company; E-Commerce, Warehousing & Logistics Services
N.A.I.C.S.: 551112
Michiel Alting von Geusau *(Pres-Global Commerce & Lifecycle Svcs & Exec VP)*

Subsidiary (Domestic):

Best2Serve B.V. (5)
Energieweg 2, 5145 NW, Waalwijk, Netherlands
Tel.: (31) 207 660 3115
Web Site: http://www.best2serve.com
Payment Software Development Services
N.A.I.C.S.: 541511

Ingram Micro CFS Benelux B.V. (5)
Energieweg 2, 5145 NW, Waalwijk, Netherlands
Tel.: (31) 89 4208 0
Web Site: http://www.ingrammicroservices.com
Freight Transportation Arrangement
N.A.I.C.S.: 488510
Michiel Alting von Geusau *(Exec VP-Commerce & Lifestyle Svcs)*

Ingram Micro CFS Commerce B.V. (5)
Energieweg 2, 5145 NW, Waalwijk, Netherlands
Tel.: (31) 416 674 111
Payment Software Development Services
N.A.I.C.S.: 541511

Subsidiary (Non-US):

Ingram Micro CFS Fulfilment Ltd (5)
Windrush Industrial Park Burford Road, Witney, OX29 7EW, United Kingdom
Tel.: (44) 1993770600
Payment Software Development Services
N.A.I.C.S.: 541511

Ingram Micro CFS Germany GmbH (5)
Am Wall 21, 14979, Berlin, Germany
Tel.: (49) 33701 269 60001
Web Site: http://www.docdata.de
Ecommerce Services
N.A.I.C.S.: 425120

Subsidiary (Domestic):

Ingram Micro CFS E-Business GmbH (6)
Kesslerweg 6, 48155, Munster, Germany
Tel.: (49) 251 620 60 130
Software Development Services
N.A.I.C.S.: 541511

Ingram Micro CFS Fulfilment GmbH (6)
Am Wall 21, 14979, Berlin, Germany
Tel.: (49) 33701 269 60001
Software Development Services
N.A.I.C.S.: 541511

Subsidiary (Domestic):

Ingram Micro CFS eServices B.V. (5)
Energieweg 2, 5145NW, Waalwijk, Netherlands
Tel.: (31) 416631100
Web Site: http://www.ingrammicroservices.com
Freight Transportation Arrangement
N.A.I.C.S.: 488510

Subsidiary (Domestic):

Ingram Micro Consumer Electronics (4)
15880 N Greenway Hayden Loop Ste 150, Scottsdale, AZ 85260
Tel.: (480) 596-8636
Electronic Parts & Equipment Distr
N.A.I.C.S.: 423690

Ingram Micro Data Capture/POS Division (4)
3351 Michelson Dr Ste 100, Irvine, CA 92612
Tel.: (714) 566-1000
Web Site: http://www.corp.ingrammicro.com
Data Capture, Point-of-Sale, Bar Code & Mobile Computing Equipment Whslr
N.A.I.C.S.: 423420

Branch (Domestic):

Ingram Micro - Miami (5)
2000 NW 84th Ave, Miami, FL 33122
Tel.: (305) 593-5900
Web Site: http://www.mi.ingrammicro.com
Data Capture, Point-of-Sale, Bar Code & Mobile Computing Equipment Whslr
N.A.I.C.S.: 423420

Subsidiary (Non-US):

Ingram Micro Distribution GmbH (4)
Heisenbergbogen 3, PO Box 1264, Aschheim, 85609, Munich, Germany
Tel.: (49) 89 4208 0
Web Site: http://de.ingrammicro.eu
Computer & Computer Peripheral Equipment Merchant Whslr
N.A.I.C.S.: 423430
Alexander Maier *(VP)*

Ingram Micro GmbH (4)
Brunnmatt 14, 6330, Cham, Switzerland
Tel.: (41) 417843300
Web Site: http://www.ingrammicro.ch
Computer Peripheral Equipment Whslr
N.A.I.C.S.: 423430

Ingram Micro GmbH (4)
Guglgasse 7-9, 1030, Vienna, Austria
Tel.: (43) 140815430
Web Site: http://www.ingrammicro.at
Computer Peripheral Equipment Whslr
N.A.I.C.S.: 423430
Adolf Markones *(Exec Mng Dir)*

Ingram Micro Holdings (Australia) Pty Ltd (4)
61 Dunning Avenue, Rosebery, 2018, NSW, Australia
Tel.: (61) 293816000
Web Site: http://au.ingrammicro.com
Holding Company
N.A.I.C.S.: 551112

Ingram Micro Holdings Limited (4)
CBX II 406-432 Midsummer Boulevard, Milton Keynes, MK9 2EA, United Kingdom
Tel.: (44) 371 973 3000
Holding Company
N.A.I.C.S.: 551112

Subsidiary (Domestic):

Ingram Micro (UK) Limited (5)
CBX II 406-432 Midsummer Boulevard, Milton Keynes, MK9 2EA, Bucks, United Kingdom
Tel.: (44) 371 973 3000
Web Site: http://uk.ingrammicro.eu
Computer Related Equipment & Software Whslr
N.A.I.C.S.: 423430
Matthew Sanderson *(Mng Dir-UK & Ireland)*

Subsidiary (Non-US):

Ingram Micro Hosting B.V. (4)
Papendorpseweg 95, 3528 BJ, Utrecht, Netherlands
Tel.: (31) 302464001
Electronic Equipment Whslr
N.A.I.C.S.: 423690

Ingram Micro India Private Limited (4)
5th Floor Empire Plaza Building A LBS Marg, Vikhroli West, Mumbai, 400083, India
Tel.: (91) 22 6856 1001
Web Site: http://www.imonline.co.in
Data Processing, Hosting & Related Services
N.A.I.C.S.: 518210
Satheesh Kumar *(Sr Mgr)*

Ingram Micro India SSC Private Limited (4)
5th Floor Empire Plaza Building A LBS Marg, Vikhroli West, Mumbai, 400083, India
Tel.: (91) 22 6856 1001
Electronic Equipment Whslr
N.A.I.C.S.: 423690

Ingram Micro Israel Ltd (4)
3 Tevuot Haaretz Street, Tel Aviv, 69546, Israel
Tel.: (972) 36498140
Computer System Design Services
N.A.I.C.S.: 541512

Ingram Micro Istanbul Merkez (4)
Bayildim Cad Vanilya Sok No 2 D 3, Macka Besiktas, 34357, Istanbul, Turkiye
Tel.: (90) 2122590064
Web Site: http://www.tr.ingrammicro.com
Electronic Equipment Whslr
N.A.I.C.S.: 423690
Ali Baghdadi *(Sr VP & CEO-Ingram Micro META Reg)*

Ingram Micro Levant S.A.L. (4)
Jal el Dib, PO Box 901589, Beirut, Lebanon
Tel.: (961) 4718817
Web Site: http://www.lb.ingrammicro.com
Research & Development Services
N.A.I.C.S.: 541715
Elie Semaan *(Country Mgr)*

Ingram Micro Logistics LP (4)
55 Standish Court, Mississauga, L5R4A1, ON, Canada
Tel.: (905) 755-5000
Logistics Management Consulting Services
N.A.I.C.S.: 541614

Ingram Micro Malaysia Sdn Bhd (4)
Lot 4A 4th Floor Wisma Academy Jalan 19 1, 46300, Petaling Jaya, Selangor, Malaysia
Tel.: (60) 379528188

AND PRIVATE COMPANIES

Web Site: http://my.ingrammicro.com
Computer Peripheral Equipment Distr
N.A.I.C.S.: 423430

Ingram Micro Mexico LLC (4)
Calle 4 No 301 Letra C por 9 y 11 Col,
Santa Rita Cholul, Merida, 97138, Yucatan,
Mexico
Tel.: (52) 19991241920
Web Site: http://www.ingrammicro.com.mx
Electronic Equipment Whslr
N.A.I.C.S.: 423690

Ingram Micro Mexico, S.A. de C.V. (4)
Calle 4 No 301 Letter C por 9 y 11 Col
Santa Rita Cholul, Merida, 97138, Yucatan,
Mexico
Tel.: (52) 1999 124 1920
Web Site: http://www.ingrammicro.com.mx
Computer Peripheral Equipment Distr
N.A.I.C.S.: 423430

Subsidiary (Domestic):

Ingram Micro Mobility (4)
501 Airtech Pkwy, Plainfield, IN 46168
Tel.: (317) 707-2355
Web Site: http://www.ingrammicro.com
Wireless Device Distribution & Support Services
N.A.I.C.S.: 517810

Subsidiary (Domestic):

Actify LLC (5)
7635 Interactive Way Ste 200, Indianapolis, IN 46278
Tel.: (800) 467-0830
Web Site: http://www.actifywireless.com
Electronic Parts Whslr
N.A.I.C.S.: 423690

Subsidiary (Non-US):

Brightpoint NZ Limited (5)
25 Falcom Road, Manukau, Auckland, 2104, New Zealand
Tel.: (64) 99121280
Web Site: http://www.brightpointonline.co.nz
Mobile Phones & Wireless Accessories Distr
N.A.I.C.S.: 423690

Ingram Micro A/S (5)
Kolding Apark 1 1st Floor, 6000, Kolding, Denmark
Tel.: (45) 73303030
Web Site: http://www.ingrammicro.dk
Information Technology Hardware, Software, Peripherals & Accessories Wholesale Distr
N.A.I.C.S.: 423430

Ingram Micro AB (5)
Falkenbergsgatan 3, SE-41285, Gothenburg, Sweden
Tel.: (46) 317199100
Web Site: http://www.se-new.ingrammicro.com
Distribution & Value-added Logistics Services to the Wireless Communications Industry
N.A.I.C.S.: 423690

Ingram Micro GmbH (5)
Guglgasse 7-9, 1030, Vienna, Austria
Tel.: (43) 1 408 15 43 0
Web Site: http://at.ingrammicro.com
Information Technology Hardware, Software, Peripherals & Accessories Wholesale Distr
N.A.I.C.S.: 423430

Ingram Micro Mobility AS (5)
Brynsveien 12, 0667, Oslo, Norway
Tel.: (47) 230 50000
Web Site: http://www.ingrammicro.no
Information Technology Hardware, Software, Peripherals & Accessories Wholesale Distr
N.A.I.C.S.: 423430

Ingram Micro Mobility Philippines, Inc. (5)
Three World Square 22 Upper McKinley Road 12th Floor McKinley Hill, Taguig, Philippines
Tel.: (63) 2 669 2720
Mobile Phones & Wireless Accessories Distr

N.A.I.C.S.: 423690

Ingram Micro Slovakia, s. r. o (5)
Logistic Complex P3, DC7 1222, Bratislava Hall, 90055, Lozorno, Slovakia
Tel.: (421) 269203111
Web Site: http://www.sk.ingrammicro.eu
Mobile Phones & Wireless Accessories Distr
N.A.I.C.S.: 423690

Ingram Micro Southern Africa (Proprietary) Limited (5)
Building 5 Design Quarter District 128 Leslie Avenue, Fourways, Johannesburg, 2191, South Africa
Tel.: (27) 11 069 3600
Telecommunication Servicesb
N.A.I.C.S.: 517810

Subsidiary (Non-US):

Ingram Micro Mobility Finland Oy (4)
Vitikka 1 F, 02630, Espoo, Finland
Tel.: (358) 98874000
Web Site: http://www.ingrammicro.fi
Electronic Equipment Whslr
N.A.I.C.S.: 423690

Ingram Micro Oy (4)
Vitikka 1, 02630, Espoo, Finland
Tel.: (358) 9 887 4000
Web Site: http://www.ingrammicro.fi
Computer System Design Services
N.A.I.C.S.: 541512
Sami Elopuro (Country Mgr)

Ingram Micro S.A.C. (4)
Av Javier Prado Este 175 Office, San Isidro, 902-903, Lima, Peru
Tel.: (51) 12085500
Web Site: http://www.ingrammicro.com.pe
Mobile Phones & Wireless Accessories Distr
N.A.I.C.S.: 423690

Ingram Micro SL (4)
Calle Antonio Machado 78-80 Primera y segunda planta, Viladecans, 08840, Barcelona, Spain
Tel.: (34) 902 50 62 10
Web Site: http://www.ingrammicro.es
Computer Products Distr
N.A.I.C.S.: 423430

Ingram Micro SRL (4)
Viale delle Industrie 14/B, Settala, 20090, Milan, Italy
Tel.: (39) 0295181
Web Site: http://contentit.ingrammicro.eu
Computer System Design Services
N.A.I.C.S.: 541512

Ingram Micro Services, GmbH (4)
Heisenbergbogen 3, Dornach, 85609, Munich, Germany
Tel.: (49) 89 42 08 0
Web Site: http://www.datrepair.de
Electronic Equipment Whslr
N.A.I.C.S.: 423690

Ingram Micro Services Ltd. (4)
71 Bilton Way, Enfield, EN3 7EP, Mddx, United Kingdom
Tel.: (44) 2084438600
Electronics Equipment Repair & Recycling Services
N.A.I.C.S.: 811210

Ingram Micro Sp. z o.o. (4)
ul Krakowiakow 46, 02-255, Warsaw, Poland
Tel.: (48) 22 549 74 00
Web Site: http://pl.ingrammicro.eu
Mobile Device Distr
N.A.I.C.S.: 423690
Katarzyna Flis (Dir-Mktg-Advanced Solutions)

Subsidiary (Domestic):

Netxusa, Inc. (4)
8 Shelter Dr, Greer, SC 29650
Tel.: (864) 271-9868
Web Site: http://www.netxusa.com
Computer Systems Design
N.A.I.C.S.: 541512

ProMark Technology, Inc. (4)
10900 Pump House Rd Ste B, Annapolis Junction, MD 20701

Tel.: (240) 280-8030
Web Site: http://www.promarktech.com
Electronic Computer Mfr
N.A.I.C.S.: 334111

Shipwire, Inc. (4)
3131 Jat St Ste #210, Santa Clara, CA 95054
Tel.: (650) 561-4800
Web Site: http://www.shipwire.com
Logistics Management Consulting Services
N.A.I.C.S.: 541614

Subsidiary (Non-US):

SoftCom Group Inc. (4)
2610 88 Queens Quay, Toronto, M5J 0B8, ON, Canada
Tel.: (416) 957-7400
Software Publishing Services
N.A.I.C.S.: 513210

Subsidiary (Domestic):

HNA Topwin Futures Co., Ltd. (2)
Huaneng Building 2068 Shennan Middle Road, Shenzhen, 518031, China
Tel.: (86) 400 7700 999
Investment Management Service
N.A.I.C.S.: 523940

HNA Yajee Performing Arts International Co., Ltd. (2)
Zhengyici Peking Opera Theater 220 Qianmen West Heyan Street, Beijing, 100053, China
Tel.: (86) 10 83151650
Theater Operator
N.A.I.C.S.: 512131

Hainan Airlines Holding Co., Ltd. (2)
Hainan Airlines Haikou Meilan Base No 9 Meilan Airport Road, Meilan District, Haikou, 571126, Hainan, China
Tel.: (86) 89865801619
Web Site: http://www.hainanairlines.com
Rev.: $3,210,132,697
Assets: $19,391,244,210
Liabilities: $19,326,821,810
Net Worth: $64,422,400
Earnings: ($2,842,673,184)
Emp.: 10,000
Fiscal Year-end: 12/31/2022
Passenger Airline Operator
N.A.I.C.S.: 481111
Feng We (Vice Chm)

Subsidiary (Domestic):

Hainan Airlines Sales Co., Ltd. (3)
New HNA Plaza Guoxing Road, Haikou, 570203, Hainan, China
Tel.: (86) 898 68875473
Aircraft Charter Services
N.A.I.C.S.: 481211
Michael Tian (Mgr-Sls)

Subsidiary (Domestic):

Hainan BestChain Information System Co., Ltd (2)
Hainan Ecological Software Park, Hainan High-tech Demonstration Zone, Haikou, 571924, China
Tel.: (86) 898 68876000
Travel Tour Operator
N.A.I.C.S.: 561520

Hainan Golden Gulf Investment & Development Co., Ltd. (2)
Hainan Yingbin Hotel 9 Xisan Road, Daying Mountain Meilan District, Haikou, 570203, China
Tel.: (86) 898 65206063
Investment Management Service
N.A.I.C.S.: 523940

Hainan HNA Drink Co., Ltd (2)
Jinchang Road Haikou Meilan International Airport, Haikou, 571126, Hainan, China
Tel.: (86) 898 65751435
Aircraft Charter Services
N.A.I.C.S.: 481111

Hainan HNA Zhongmian Duty Free Co., Ltd (2)
Tower A Jingrui Plaza Guomao Road, Haikou, 570105, Hainan, China
Tel.: (86) 898 66519004
Airport Management Services
N.A.I.C.S.: 488190

HAINAN TRAFFIC ADMINISTRATION HOLDING CO., LTD.

Hainan Technik Co., Ltd. (2)
Meilan Base of HNA, Haikou, 571126, Hainan, China
Tel.: (86) 898 65756766
Airport Management Services
N.A.I.C.S.: 488190

Hainan eKing Technology Co., Ltd. (2)
eKing Technology Jialing International Building Guomao Road, Haikou, 570203, China
Tel.: (86) 898 68876001
Emp.: 600
Software Development Services
N.A.I.C.S.: 541511
Yanbing Yu (Chm & CEO)

Subsidiary (Non-US):

Hong Kong Airlines Limited (2)
11th Floor One Citygate 20 Tat Tung Road, Tung Chung, Lantau, China (Hong Kong)
Tel.: (852) 3151 1800
Web Site: http://www.hongkongairlines.com
Aircraft Charter Services
N.A.I.C.S.: 481211
Ben Wong Ching-ho (VP)

Joint Venture (Domestic):

SATS HK Limited (3)
Room 6T028 Passenger Terminal Building Hong Kong International Airport, Hong Kong, Lantau, China (Hong Kong) (51%)
Tel.: (852) 21168787
Web Site: http://www.sats.com.sg
Sales Range: $200-249.9 Million
Emp.: 800
Passenger & Ramp Handling Services Including Baggage Handling, Load Control & Flight Operations
N.A.I.C.S.: 488119
Joanne Cheung (Sr Mgr-Mktg)

Subsidiary (Non-US):

Hong Kong International Aviation Leasing Co., Ltd. (2)
26/F Three Pacific Place 1 Queen's Road East, Hong Kong, China (Hong Kong)
Tel.: (852) 31960917
Aircraft Leasing Services
N.A.I.C.S.: 532411

Subsidiary (Domestic):

Jiayu HNA Industry Development Co., Ltd. (2)
8/F Tobacco Bureau Fazhan Road, Jiayu County, Yuyue, 437200, Hubei, China
Tel.: (86) 715 6318211
Real Estate Development Services
N.A.I.C.S.: 531312

Lucky Air Co., Ltd. (2)
Lucky Air Building 296 Chuncheng Road, Guandu District, Kunming, 650200, Yunnan, China
Tel.: (86) 871 67128306
Web Site: http://www.luckyair.net
Aircraft Charter Services
N.A.I.C.S.: 481211

Manzhouli Xijiao Airport Co., Ltd. (2)
Manzhouli Xijiao Airport 9 kilometers, Manzhouli, 021400, Inner Mongolia, China
Tel.: (86) 470 6246017
Airport Management Services
N.A.I.C.S.: 488119

North-east HNA Investment Group Co., Ltd (2)
HNA Redbuds Hotel 5688 People's Avenue, Changchun, 130022, Jilin, China
Tel.: (86) 431 89680866
Investment Management Service
N.A.I.C.S.: 523940

Northwest HNA Property Co., Ltd. (2)
Tower D Wangzuo International Town 1 Tangyan Road, Gaoxin District, Xi'an, 710065, China
Tel.: (86) 29 88767657
Property Management Services
N.A.I.C.S.: 531312

Holding (Non-US):

SR Technics Holdco I GmbH (2)

HAINAN TRAFFIC ADMINISTRATION HOLDING CO., LTD.

Hainan Traffic Administration Holding Co., Ltd.—(Continued)

Flughofstrasse, 8302, Kloten, Switzerland
Tel.: (41) 58 688 6666
Holding Company; Civil Aircraft, Aircraft Engines & Components Mfr
N.A.I.C.S.: 551112
Jean-Marc Lenz (CEO)

Subsidiary (Non-US):

SR Technics Airfoil Services Ltd. (3)
Mahon Industrial Estate Blackrock, Cork, Ireland
Tel.: (353) 21 4521 200
Aircraft Maintenance Services
N.A.I.C.S.: 488190
Brendan Howley (COO)

Subsidiary (US):

SR Technics America Inc. (3)
645 Park of Commerce Way, Boca Raton, FL 33487
Tel.: (954) 278-3980
Web Site: http://www.srtechnics.com
Aircraft Maintenance Services
N.A.I.C.S.: 488190
Caroline Vandedrinck (Reg VP)

Subsidiary (Non-US):

SR Technics Australia Pty Ltd (3)
Amp Centre 27/50 Bridge Street, Sydney, 2000, NW, Australia
Tel.: (61) 45 1818 883
Web Site: http://www.srtechnics.com
Aircraft Maintenance Services
N.A.I.C.S.: 488190

SR Technics Malaysia Sdn Bhd (3)
No 3 Jalan Keluli 15/16 Section 15, 40200, Shah Alam, Selangor, Malaysia
Tel.: (60) 3 5520 8400
Web Site: http://www.srtechnics.com
Aircraft Maintenance Services
N.A.I.C.S.: 488190

SR Technics Malta Ltd. (3)
Gate 8 Triq Carmelo Caruana Safi, Valletta, SFI 1710, Malta
Tel.: (356) 79259994
Aircraft Maintenance Services
N.A.I.C.S.: 488190

Subsidiary (Domestic):

SR Technics Management AG (3)
Flughofstrasse, Zurich Airport, 8302, Kloten, Switzerland
Tel.: (41) 58 688 6666
Management Consulting Services
N.A.I.C.S.: 541618

Subsidiary (Non-US):

SR Technics Spain SA (3)
Calle Licoreres 10A, 07141, Marratxi, Baleares, Spain
Tel.: (34) 971795054
Web Site: http://www.srtechnics.com
Airport Operations
N.A.I.C.S.: 488119
Antonio Colella (Dir-Comml & Interim Gen Mgr)

Subsidiary (Domestic):

SR Technics Switzerland AG (3)
PO Box 8058, Zurich Airport, Zurich, Switzerland
Tel.: (41) 58 688 6666
Web Site: http://www.srtechnics.com
Emp.: 3,000
Aircraft, Aircraft Engine & Components Sales & Services
N.A.I.C.S.: 488190
Jean-Marc Lenz (CEO & COO)

Subsidiary (Non-US):

SR Technics UK Limited (3)
675/676 River Gardens, Feltham, TW14 0RB, United Kingdom
Tel.: (44) 2088311200
Web Site: http://www.srtechnics.com
Aeronautics
N.A.I.C.S.: 336413

Subsidiary (Domestic):

Sanya HNA Rea-estate Development Co., Ltd. (2)
HNA Real-estate Building 218 Fenghuang Road, Sanya, 572000, China
Tel.: (86) 898 38880700
Real Estate Development Services
N.A.I.C.S.: 531312

Sanya Phoenix International Airport Co., Ltd. (2)
Sanya Phoenix International Airport Phoenix Road 573, Sanya, 572000, Hainan, China
Tel.: (86) 898 88289006
Airport Management Services
N.A.I.C.S.: 488119
Qiu Huang (Pres)

Shandong HNA Business Development Co., Ltd (2)
6F HNA Wanbang Center 234 Yanan San Road, Shinan District, Qingdao, 266071, China
Tel.: (86) 532 58851111
Property Management Services
N.A.I.C.S.: 531312

Holding (Non-US):

Swissport International Ltd. (2)
PO Box Zurich-Airport, 8058, Glattbrugg, Switzerland (81%)
Tel.: (41) 438150000
Web Site: http://www.swissport.com
Sales Range: $1-4.9 Billion
Emp.: 62,000
N.A.I.C.S.: 488119
Joe Phelan (COO)

Subsidiary (Non-US):

Swissport Amsterdam B.V. (3)
Havenmeesterweg 21, 1118 CB, Schiphol, Netherlands
Tel.: (31) 207952432
Web Site: http://www.swissport.com
Emp.: 1,200
Aviation Ground Services
N.A.I.C.S.: 488119
Menno Biersma (CEO)

Swissport Belgium N. V. (3)
Brussels Airport Building 32 PB 3, Zaventem, 1930, Brussels, Belgium
Tel.: (32) 27883133
Web Site: http://www.swissport.com
Emp.: 1,492
Ground Handling Services
N.A.I.C.S.: 488119
Bertrand Vanden Broeck (Comml Dir)

Swissport Canada Handling Inc. (3)
PO Box 44641 YVR Domestic Terminal, Richmond, V7B 1W2, BC, Canada
Tel.: (604) 303-3758
Web Site: https://www.swissport.com
Emp.: 375
Aviation Ground Services
N.A.I.C.S.: 488190

Swissport Cargo Services, L.P. (3)
6500 Silver Dart Drive Core G, Mississauga, L5P 1A2, ON, Canada
Tel.: (905) 673-7292
Web Site: http://www.swissport.com
Airport Cargo Handling Services
N.A.I.C.S.: 488119
Paul Keery (Sr VP-Cargo North America)

Swissport Chile (3)
1850 Manuel Avalos Prado Aeropuerto Internacional A Merino Benitez, PO Box 4, Pudahuel, Santiago, Chile
Tel.: (56) 2 799 2145
Web Site: http://www.swissport.com
Emp.: 205
Aviation Ground Services
N.A.I.C.S.: 488190

Swissport Denmark (3)
Copenhagen Airport Terminal 2, DK 2770, Kastrup, Denmark
Tel.: (45) 32314047
Web Site: http://www.servisair.com
Aviation Ground Services
N.A.I.C.S.: 488190
Menno Biersma (CEO)

Swissport Finland Oy (3)
Teknikontie 7, 01530, Vantaa, Finland
Tel.: (358) 10 562 0500
Web Site: http://www.swissport.com
Emp.: 920
Aviation Ground Services
N.A.I.C.S.: 488190
Roland Etter (CEO)

Swissport Portugal (3)
Aeroporto de Lisboa Edificio Principal, Lisbon, 1700 007, Portugal
Tel.: (351) 939 495363
Web Site: http://www.swissport.com
Aviation Ground Services
N.A.I.C.S.: 488190
Marlene Tavares (Mgr-Traffic Rights)

Swissport Tanzania Plc. (3)
1st Floor-Swissport Freight Terminal, PO Box 18043, Julius Nyerere International Airport, Dar es Salaam, Tanzania
Tel.: (255) 222844610
Web Site: https://www.swissport.com
Rev.: $15,241,780
Assets: $20,332,550
Liabilities: $7,041,250
Net Worth: $13,291,300
Earnings: $993,730
Emp.: 265
Fiscal Year-end: 12/31/2019
Airport Ground-Handling Services
N.A.I.C.S.: 488119
Christoph Mueller (CEO-Interim)

Swissport Trinidad & Tobago (3)
Piarco International Airport, Piarco, Trinidad & Tobago
Tel.: (868) 299 0796
Web Site: http://www.swissport.com
Aviation Ground Services
N.A.I.C.S.: 488190
Eugene Shairsingh (CEO)

Subsidiary (US):

Swissport USA, Inc. (3)
44965 Aviation Dr Ste 200, Dulles, VA 20166-7557
Tel.: (703) 621-4216
Web Site: http://www.swissport.com
Airport Services
N.A.I.C.S.: 488119

Subsidiary (Domestic):

Swissport Fueling, Inc. (4)
4200 E Air Lane Sky Harbor International Airport, Phoenix, AZ 85034-3008
Tel.: (602) 273-3662
Web Site: http://www.swissport.com
Emp.: 160
Aircraft Fueling Services & Ground Support Equipment Refueling Services; Maintenance & Operation of Airport Fuel Storage & Distribution Systems
N.A.I.C.S.: 488119

Subsidiary (Domestic):

Tangshan Sannvhe Airport Co., Ltd. (2)
Tangshan Sannvhe Airport Sannvhe Village, Shigezhuang Town Fengrun, Tangshan, 063000, Hebei, China
Tel.: (86) 315 2521013
Airport Management Services
N.A.I.C.S.: 488119

Tianjin Airlines Co., Ltd. (2)
Tianjin Airlines Base 1196 Airport Road, Dongli, Tianjin, 300300, China
Tel.: (86) 22 58208888
Web Site: http://www.tianjin-air.com
Aircraft Charter Services
N.A.I.C.S.: 481211

Wanning HNA Dakangle Investment and Development Co., Ltd. (2)
Block 18 Wanning Xinglong Kangleyuan Hotel, Wanning, 573000, Hainan, China
Tel.: (86) 898 62576754
Investment Management Service
N.A.I.C.S.: 523940

Weifang Nanyuan Airport Co., Ltd. (2)
Weifang Nanyuan Airport 1 Airport Road, Kuiwen District, Weifang, 261052, Shandong, China
Tel.: (86) 536 8809534

INTERNATIONAL PUBLIC

Airport Management Services
N.A.I.C.S.: 488119

West Air Co., Ltd. (2)
Tower B Uranus Business Mansion 76 Xingguang Street, Hi-Tech Park New North Zone, Chongqing, 401121, China
Tel.: (86) 23 86068888
Web Site: http://www.westair.cn
Aircraft Charter Services
N.A.I.C.S.: 481211

Yichang Sanxia Airport Co., Ltd. (2)
Yichang Sanxia Airport 8 Airport Road, Xiaoting District, Yichang, 443007, Hubei, China
Tel.: (86) 717 6532518
Airport Management Services
N.A.I.C.S.: 488119

Yingkou Airport Co., Ltd. (2)
Yingkou Airport Cheng Fu Dong Li, Zhanqian District, Yingkou, 115000, Liaoning, China
Tel.: (86) 417 2903025
Airport Management Services
N.A.I.C.S.: 488119

Holding (Non-US):

myTECHNIC MRO Technic Servis A.S. (2)
Sabiha Gokcen International Airport, Pendik, 34912, Istanbul, Turkiye
Tel.: (90) 216 5880570
Web Site: http://www.mytechnic.aero
Airport Management Services
N.A.I.C.S.: 488119
Cem Ipek (VP)

HAINAN YEDAO (GROUP) CO., LTD.

No 2 Yaogu Erheng Road Yaogu Phase II, Xiuying District, Haikou, 570311, Hainan, China
Tel.: (86) 89866532925
Web Site: http://www.yedao.com
Year Founded: 1993
600238——(SHG)
Rev.: $127,688,278
Assets: $195,655,298
Liabilities: $114,936,610
Net Worth: $80,718,689
Earnings: ($9,214,049)
Fiscal Year-end: 12/31/21
Liquor Product Mfr & Distr
N.A.I.C.S.: 312120
Duan Shouqi (Chm)

HAINING CHINA LEATHER MARKET CO., LTD.

201 Haizhou West Road, Haining, 314400, Zhejiang, China
Tel.: (86) 57387217777
Web Site: http://www.chinaleather.com
Year Founded: 2007
002344——(SSE)
Rev.: $195,515,424
Assets: $1,937,150,748
Liabilities: $747,771,804
Net Worth: $1,189,378,944
Earnings: $37,926,252
Emp.: 370
Fiscal Year-end: 12/31/22
Leather Market Development & Leasing
N.A.I.C.S.: 531190
Yueming Zhang (Pres)

HAIPHONG SECURITIES JOINT STOCK COMPANY

No 24 Cu Chinh Lan, Hong Bang District, Haiphong, Vietnam
Tel.: (84) 313842335
Web Site: http://www.hpsc.com.vn
Year Founded: 2003
Securities Trading Services
N.A.I.C.S.: 523210

HAIRGROUP AG

AND PRIVATE COMPANIES

Himmelgeister Str 103-105, 40225, Dusseldorf, Germany
Tel.: (49) 211 17 48 0
Web Site: http://www.hairgroup.de
Sales Range: $150-199.9 Million
Emp.: 2,326
Hairdressing Industry
N.A.I.C.S.: 812111
Achim Mansen *(Chm-Mgmt Bd-Fin)*

HAIRHOUSE WAREHOUSE ONLINE PTY. LTD.
619 Doncaster Road, Doncaster, 3108, VIC, Australia
Tel.: (61) 398485566
Web Site:
http://www.hairwarehouse.com.au
Year Founded: 1992
Hair Care Products Distr
N.A.I.C.S.: 424210
Marie Morrell *(Owner)*

HAISAN RESOURCES BERHAD
Lot 506 Jalan Pelabuhan Utara Bandar Sultan Suleiman, 42000, Port Klang, Selangor Darul Ehsan, Malaysia
Tel.: (60) 3 3168 9626
Web Site: http://www.haisan.com
Year Founded: 2001
Investment Holding Company
N.A.I.C.S.: 551112
Bee Ling Lee *(VP-Temperature Controlled Logistics & IT)*

Subsidiaries:

Asia Mewah Resources Sdn. Bhd. (1)
No 39 Jln Mutiara Emas 5/19 Taman Mount Austin, 81100, Johor Bahru, Johor, Malaysia
Tel.: (60) 73576839
Block Ice Mfr
N.A.I.C.S.: 312113

Freeville (M) Sdn. Bhd. (1)
Lot 506 Jalan Pelabuhan Utara Bandar Sultan Suleiman, Port Klang, 42000, Selangor Darul Ehsan, Malaysia **(100%)**
Tel.: (60) 3 3168 9626
Web Site: http://www.haisan.com
Ice Sculpture Mfr
N.A.I.C.S.: 312113

Hai San & Sons Sdn. Bhd. (1)
Jln Pelabuhan, 46100, Port Klang, Selangor, Malaysia
Tel.: (60) 331688287
Sales Range: $25-49.9 Million
Emp.: 50
Ice Mfr & Distr
N.A.I.C.S.: 312113

Haisan Sdn. Bhd. (1)
Lot 506 Jalan Pelabuhan Utara Bandar Sultan Suleiman, Port Klang, 42000, Selangor, Malaysia
Tel.: (60) 331689626
Web Site: http://www.haisan.com
Sales Range: $25-49.9 Million
Emp.: 60
Industrial Engineering Services
N.A.I.C.S.: 541330
Jeremy Heng *(Mgr)*

IGLO (M) Sdn. Bhd. (1)
Lot 506 Jalan Pelabuhan Utara Bandar Sultan Suleiman, 42000, Port Klang, Selangor Darul Ehsan, Malaysia
Tel.: (60) 331665599
Web Site: http://www.iglo.com.my
Sales Range: $50-74.9 Million
Emp.: 200
Logistics & Warehousing Services
N.A.I.C.S.: 541614

IGLO (Shanghai) Co., Ltd. (1)
357 Jizhan Road, Minhang District, Shanghai, 201107, China
Tel.: (86) 2152968333
Cold Storage & Logistics Services
N.A.I.C.S.: 493120

Pontian Ice Factory Sdn. Bhd. (1)
Plo 37 Kawasan Perindustrian, Pontian, 82000, Johor, Malaysia
Tel.: (60) 76871419
Block Ice Mfr
N.A.I.C.S.: 312113

HAISCO PHARMACEUTICAL GROUP CO., LTD.
No 17 Sanxiang Avenue, Zedang Town, Chengdu, 856000, Sichuan, China
Tel.: (86) 8937834865
Web Site: http://www.haisco.com
Year Founded: 2000
002653—(SSE)
Rev.: $423,346,716
Assets: $848,852,784
Liabilities: $408,920,616
Net Worth: $439,932,168
Earnings: $38,890,800
Emp.: 6,000
Fiscal Year-end: 12/31/22
Drug Mfr
N.A.I.C.S.: 325412

Subsidiaries:

Liaoning Haisco Pharmaceutical Co., Ltd. (1)
Caozhuang Village, Caozhuang, Xingcheng, 125107, Liaoning, China
Tel.: (86) 4295693955
Pharmaceuticals Product Mfr
N.A.I.C.S.: 325412

HAISUNG TPC CO., LTD.
551 Neungheodaero Rd Lot 6 Block 132, Namdong-Gu Namdong Industrial Complex Gojan-Dong, Incheon, 405821, Korea (South)
Tel.: (82) 328203400
Web Site:
http://www.english.haisung.co.kr
Year Founded: 1991
059270—(KRS)
Emp.: 75
Transmission Component Mfr
N.A.I.C.S.: 336350
Gun-Bok Lee *(CEO)*

HAITAI CONFECTIONERY AND FOODS CO.,LTD.
Chonheung-ri Sungguheup, Yongsan-gu, Cheonan, Korea (South)
Tel.: (82) 27097766
Web Site: http://www.ht.co.kr
Year Founded: 1945
101530—(KRS)
Rev.: $452,734,385
Assets: $530,192,551
Liabilities: $335,477,602
Net Worth: $194,714,949
Earnings: ($1,724,389)
Emp.: 1,536
Fiscal Year-end: 12/31/22
Confectionery Mfr & Distr
N.A.I.C.S.: 311340
Kim Soo *(Sr Mgr)*

Subsidiaries:

Haitai Confectionery And Foods Co.,ltd. - Cheonan Factory (1)
67-26 Cheonheung 8-gil Seonggeo-eup Seobuk-gu, Cheonan, Chungcheongnam-do, Korea (South)
Tel.: (82) 416225805
Confectionary Product Mfr
N.A.I.C.S.: 311351

Haitai Confectionery And Foods Co.,ltd. - Chongju Factory (1)
Bokdae-dong 48 Kongdanro Heungduk-gu, Cheongju, Chungcheongnam-do, Korea (South)
Tel.: (82) 432661960
Snack Mfr
N.A.I.C.S.: 311919

Haitai Confectionery And Foods Co.,ltd. - Dague Factory (1)
541 Daekuyngro Hayang-eup, Gyeongsan, Kyungsangbuk-do, Korea (South)
Tel.: (82) 538528051
Bakery Products Mfr
N.A.I.C.S.: 311821

Haitai Confectionery And Foods Co.,ltd. - Kwangju Factory (1)
Yangsan-dong 222 Haseoro Bukgu, Kwangju, Korea (South)
Tel.: (82) 625717551
Confectionary Product Mfr
N.A.I.C.S.: 311351

HAITIAN ENERGY INTERNATIONAL LIMITED
Room 10 21/F Bldg B1 Phase 2 Wanda Plaza Financial Street Aojiang Road, Aofeng Community Taijiang District, Fuzhou, China
Tel.: (86) 591 8850 3331
Web Site: http://www.haitian-energy.com
Sales Range: $25-49.9 Million
Emp.: 222
Hydropower Plant Management & Operation
N.A.I.C.S.: 221111
Yang Lin *(Founder, Chm & CEO)*

HAITIAN INTERNATIONAL HOLDINGS LTD.
No 1688 Haitian Road Xiaogang Beilun, Ningbo, 315801, Zhejiang, China
Tel.: (86) 57486182786   Ky
Web Site: http://www.haitianinter.com
Year Founded: 2006
1882—(HKG)
Rev.: $1,728,069,314
Assets: $3,621,084,620
Liabilities: $1,228,668,620
Net Worth: $2,392,416,000
Earnings: $318,008,387
Emp.: 7,159
Fiscal Year-end: 12/31/22
Injection Moulding Machine Mfr & Distr
N.A.I.C.S.: 333248
Jingzhang Zhang *(Chm)*

Subsidiaries:

Absolute Haitian Corporation (1)
33 Southgate St, Worcester, MA 01610
Tel.: (508) 792-4305
Web Site: https://www.absolutehaitian.com
Plastic Injection Molding Machine Distr
N.A.I.C.S.: 423830

HT Korea Co., Ltd (1)
524 Anaji-ro, Geayang-gu, Incheon, Gyeonggi-do, Korea (South)
Tel.: (82) 323271891
Web Site: http://www.haitian.kr
Plastic Injection Molding Machine Mfr & Distr
N.A.I.C.S.: 333248

Haitian Huayuan (Japan) Machinery Co., Ltd (1)
6-1 Aburaya-cho 2-chome Room B-1 GIMUCO 2-6 Aburaya-cho, Minato-ku, Nagoya, 455-0815, Aichi, Japan
Tel.: (81) 523879805
Machinery Distr
N.A.I.C.S.: 423830

Haitian Huayuan Machinery (India) Private Limited (1)
Mascot Industrial Park Plot C 1 Kadi-Detroj Road, Jadavpura, Mehsana, 382 715, Gujarat, India
Tel.: (91) 8965958888
Web Site: https://haitianindia.com
Plastic Injection Molding Machine Distr
N.A.I.C.S.: 423830

Haitian Huayuan Middle East Makina Dis Ticaret Limited Sirketi (1)
Alkop San Sit B 6 Blok 8-9, Buyukcekmece, Istanbul, Turkiye
Tel.: (90) 2128581058

HAITIAN WATER GROUP CO., LTD.

Web Site: http://haitianinter.com
Emp.: 25
Plastic Injection Molding Machine Distr
N.A.I.C.S.: 423830

Haitian Huayuan South America Comercio De Maquinas Ltda. (1)
Av Bernardino de Lucca 128 Jardim Carambei, Sao Roque, 18132-295, SP, Brazil
Tel.: (55) 1147848888
Web Site: https://haitianbrazil.com
Plastic Injection Molding Machine Distr
N.A.I.C.S.: 423830

Haitian Iberica, S.L. (1)
Pol Ind Cova Solera Avda Can Sucarrats 94, Rubi, 08191, Barcelona, Spain
Tel.: (34) 936991423
Web Site: https://www.haitianiberica.com
Plastic Injection Molding Machine Distr
N.A.I.C.S.: 423830

Haitian International Germany GmbH (1)
Haitianstrasse 1, 92263, Ebermannsdorf, Germany
Tel.: (49) 943894390
Web Site: https://www.haitiangermany.com
Emp.: 100
Plastic Injection Molding Machine Mfr & Distr
N.A.I.C.S.: 333248

Haitian Middle East FZC (1)
Tel.: (971) 65622238
Plastic Injection Molding Machine Distr
N.A.I.C.S.: 423830

Haitian Plastics Machinery Group Co., Ltd. (1)
No 1688 Haitian Road Xiaogang, Beilun, Ningbo, 315801, China
Tel.: (86) 57486188888
Web Site: https://haitianpm.com
Injection Molding Machine Mfr
N.A.I.C.S.: 333248

Haitian Russia Ltd (1)
Volokolamskoye highway 116-4, 125371, Moscow, Russia
Tel.: (7) 4999555772
Web Site: https://haitian.ru
Plastic Injection Molding Machine Distr
N.A.I.C.S.: 423830

Huayuan (Vietnam) Machinery Co., Ltd. (1)
18 Dan Chu VSIP 2 IP, Hoa Phu Ward, Thu Dau Mot, Binh Duong, Vietnam
Tel.: (84) 2742220225
Web Site: https://www.haitianvietnam.com
Plastic Injection Molding Machine Mfr & Distr
N.A.I.C.S.: 333248

Ningbo Haitian Huayuan Machinery Co., Ltd (1)
Export Processing Zone Fuchun Middle Road, Beilun District, Ningbo, 315806, China
Tel.: (86) 57486182625
Plastic Injection Molding Machine Mfr & Distr
N.A.I.C.S.: 333248
Weiqun Chen *(Gen Mgr)*

Ningbo Zhafir Plastics Machinery Co., Ltd. (1)
No 98 Guanhai Road Chunxiao, Beilun, Ningbo, 315830, Zhejiang, China
Tel.: (86) 57486182985
Web Site: http://www.zhafir.com
Plastic Injection Molding Machine Mfr & Distr
N.A.I.C.S.: 333248

Zhafir Plastics Machinery GmbH (1)
Haitianstrasse 1, 92263, Ebermannsdorf, Germany
Tel.: (49) 943894120
Web Site: http://www.zhafir.com
Plastic Injection Molding Machine Mfr
N.A.I.C.S.: 333248

HAITIAN WATER GROUP CO., LTD.
No 506 South Section of Lakeside Road, Tianfu New District, Chengdu, 610000, Sichuan, China

HAITIAN WATER GROUP CO., LTD.

Haitian Water Group Co., Ltd.—(Continued)
Tel.: (86) 2889115006
Web Site:
http://www.haitianshuiwu.com
Year Founded: 2008
603759—(SHG)
Rev.: $166,696,007
Assets: $816,825,396
Liabilities: $477,484,830
Net Worth: $339,340,566
Earnings: $29,961,992
Fiscal Year-end: 12/31/22
Water Supply Services
N.A.I.C.S.: 221310
Gongquan Fei *(Board of Directors & Chm)*

HAITONG SECURITIES CO., LTD.
No 888 South Zhongshan Road,
Shanghai, 200011, China
Tel.: (86) 4008888001   CN
Web Site: https://www.htsec.com
Year Founded: 1988
6837—(HKG)
Rev.: $248,810,706
Assets: $3,775,784,589
Liabilities: $3,071,673,861
Net Worth: $704,110,727
Earnings: $19,171,163
Emp.: 356
Fiscal Year-end: 12/31/23
Financial Investment Services
N.A.I.C.S.: 523150
Xinjun Zhang *(CFO & Deputy Gen Mgr)*

Subsidiaries:

HFT Investment Management Co., Ltd.   (1)
36th 37th Floor Bank of East Asia Finance Tower 66, Hua Yuan Shi Qiao Road Pudong, Shanghai, 200120, China
Tel.: (86) 2138650999
Web Site: https://www.htfund.com
Emp.: 263
Investment Management Service
N.A.I.C.S.: 523940
Xiaofei Gu *(Mgr-Fund)*

Haitong Capital Investment Co., Ltd.   (1)
Unit 2607-2612 Haitong Securities Tower 689 Guangdong Rd, Huangpu District, Shanghai, 200021, China
Tel.: (86) 2163410311
Equity Fund Investment Services
N.A.I.C.S.: 523940

Haitong Futures Co., Ltd.   (1)
Unit 04 12th Floor 5th Floor 11th Floor No 799 Yanggao South Road, Pilot Free Trade Zone Floor 12, Shanghai, China
Tel.: (86) 2138917383
Web Site: https://www.htfutures.com
Commodity Futures Brokerage Services
N.A.I.C.S.: 523160

Haitong Innovation Securities Investment Co., Ltd.   (1)
Room 107N Building No 2 No 774 Changde Road, Jing'an District, Shanghai, China
Tel.: (86) 2123219000
Securities Investment Services
N.A.I.C.S.: 523150

Haitong International Holdings Limited   (1)
22F Li Po Chun Chambers 189 Des Voeux Road, Central, China (Hong Kong)
Tel.: (852) 39268888
Investment Holding Services
N.A.I.C.S.: 551112

Subsidiary (Domestic):

Haitong International Securities Group Limited   (2)
22/F Li Po Chun Chambers 189 Des Voeux Road, Central, China (Hong Kong)
Tel.: (852) 28484333
Web Site: http://www.htsec.com
Rev.: $196,719,878

Assets: $11,359,893,255
Liabilities: $8,722,070,235
Net Worth: $2,637,823,020
Earnings: ($833,915,025)
Emp.: 996
Fiscal Year-end: 12/31/2022
Financial Management Services
N.A.I.C.S.: 523999
Yong Lin *(Deputy Chm, CEO & Mng Dir)*

Subsidiary (Non-US):

Haitong Bank, S.A.   (3)
Edificio Quartzo Rua Alexandre Herculano 38, Herculano 38, 1269-180, Lisbon, Portugal
Tel.: (351) 213196900
Web Site: https://www.haitongib.com
Rev.: $90,348,065
Assets: $2,919,374,233
Liabilities: $2,230,053,368
Net Worth: $689,320,864
Earnings: $8,407,909
Emp.: 364
Fiscal Year-end: 12/31/2019
Investment Banking, Private Equity, Financial Advisory & Asset Management Services
N.A.I.C.S.: 523150
Alan do Amaral Fernandes *(Member-Exec Bd)*

Subsidiary (Non-US):

Haitong Banco de Investimento do Brasil S.A.   (4)
Av Brigadeiro Faria Lima 3729-9th Floor Itaim Bibi, 04538-905, Sao Paulo, Brazil   (80%)
Tel.: (55) 11 3074 7444
Web Site: http://www.haitongib.com.br
Investment Banking Services
N.A.I.C.S.: 523150
Alan Do Amaral Fernandes *(CEO)*

Branch (Non-US):

Haitong Bank, S.A. - Spain Branch   (4)
Calle Serrano 88, 28006, Madrid, Spain
Tel.: (34) 914005400
Web Site: http://www.haitongib.com
Investment Banking & Securities Brokerage Services
N.A.I.C.S.: 523150
Carolina Ibanez *(Sr Mng Dir)*

Haitong Bank, S.A. - Warsaw Branch   (4)
Zlota 59th Street Floor V, 00-120, Warsaw, Poland
Tel.: (48) 22 347 4000
Web Site: http://www.haitongib.com
Investment Banking & Securities Brokerage Services
N.A.I.C.S.: 523150

Subsidiary (Non-US):

Haitong Investment Ireland plc   (4)
4th Floor Spencer House Spencer Row Off Store Street, Dublin, D01 R9T8, Ireland
Tel.: (353) 18560699
Web Site: http://www.haitongib.com
Emp.: 3
Investment Banking & Securities Brokerage Services
N.A.I.C.S.: 523150

Haitong Securities (UK) Limited   (4)
1 Aldermanbury Square 3rd floor, London, EC2V 7HR, United Kingdom
Tel.: (44) 20 7456 9191
Web Site: http://www.haitongib.com
Investment Banking Services
N.A.I.C.S.: 523150
Paulo Araujo *(CEO)*

Subsidiary (Non-US):

Haitong International Holdings (UK) Limited   (3)
3F 1 Aldermanbury Square, London, EC2V 7HR, United Kingdom
Tel.: (44) 2074569191
Web Site: http://www.equities.htsec.com
Holding Company; Investment Advisory & Fund Management Services
N.A.I.C.S.: 551112

Subsidiary (Domestic):

Haitong International Securities (UK) Limited   (4)
3F 1 Aldermanbury Square, London, EC2V 7HR, United Kingdom
Tel.: (44) 2074569191
Web Site: http://equities.htsec.com
Investment Advisory & Fund Management Services
N.A.I.C.S.: 523940

Subsidiary (Non-US):

Haitong International Securities KK   (4)
2F BPR Place Kamiyacho 1-11-9 Azabudai, Minato-ku, Tokyo, 105-0001, Japan
Tel.: (81) 364027620
Web Site: http://equities.htsec.com
Investment Advisory & Fund Management Services
N.A.I.C.S.: 523940

IND-X Advisors Limited   (4)
801-04 Kinwick Centre 32 Hollywood Rd, Central, China (Hong Kong)
Tel.: (852) 2534 7426
Web Site: http://www.indxadvisors.com
Investment Research Advisory Services
N.A.I.C.S.: 523940
Richard Wallace *(Chm)*

Haitong UniTrust International Financial Leasing Co., Ltd.   (1)
No 599 South Zhongshan Road, Huangpu District, Shanghai, 200010, China
Web Site: http://www.utfinancing.com
Financial Lending Services
N.A.I.C.S.: 522220

Haitong-Fortis Private Equity Fund Management Co., Ltd.   (1)
Rm 4601 Tower 1Plaza 66 No 1266 Nanjing Rd W, Shanghai, 200040, China
Tel.: (86) 2162883005
Web Site: http://www.hffund.com.cn
Investment Management Service
N.A.I.C.S.: 523940
Baoguo Li *(Chm)*

Shanghai Haitong Securities Asset Management Company Limited   (1)
32nd Floor Haitong Securities Building No 689 Guangdong Road, Huangpu District, Shanghai, 200001, China
Tel.: (86) 2123154762
Web Site: https://www.htsamc.com
Security Asset Management Services
N.A.I.C.S.: 523940

Shanghai Weitai Properties Management Co., Ltd.   (1)
Level 3 No 689 Guangdong Road, Huangpu District, Shanghai, China
Tel.: (86) 2123219000
Real Estate Development Services
N.A.I.C.S.: 531390

Shanghai Zechun Investment & Development Co., Ltd.   (1)
Room 208B Building 8 No 108 Kayuan Second Road, Zhangjiang Hi-Tech Park, Shanghai, China
Tel.: (86) 2123219000
Real Estate Development Services
N.A.I.C.S.: 531390

HAIVISION SYSTEMS, INC.
2600 Blvd AlfredNobel, Montreal, H4S 0A9, QC, Canada
Tel.: (514) 334-5445
Web Site: https://www.haivision.com
Year Founded: 2004
HAI—(TSX)
Sales Range: $50-74.9 Million
Emp.: 150
Video Networking, Digital Signage & IP Video Distribution Solutions
N.A.I.C.S.: 334310
Lawrence Wilk *(VP-Fin)*

Subsidiaries:

CineMassive Displays, LLC   (1)
150 Ottley Dr NE, Atlanta, GA 30324-3925
Tel.: (855) 551-5080

INTERNATIONAL PUBLIC

Web Site: http://www.cinemassive.com
Computer Terminal & Other Computer Peripheral Equipment Mfr
N.A.I.C.S.: 334118
David Minnix *(CEO)*

Haivision Network Video - Internet Media Division   (1)
4005 Banister Ln Ste 200, Austin, TX 78704
Tel.: (512) 795-4228
Web Site: http://www.haivision.com
Sales Range: $25-49.9 Million
Emp.: 6
Internet Video Encoding & Video Streaming Software Developer
N.A.I.C.S.: 513210
Alan Haefs *(Dir-Sls)*

Haivision Network Video GmbH   (1)
Adolf-Steckel-Str 17, 24768, Rendsburg, Germany
Tel.: (49) 433146390040
Video Streaming Services
N.A.I.C.S.: 518210

Haivision Network Video Inc.   (1)
13975 Polo Trail Dr, Lake Forest, IL 60045
Tel.: (847) 362-6800
Rev.: $1,200,000
Emp.: 20
Video Networking, Digital Signage & IP Video Distribution Solutions
N.A.I.C.S.: 334310
Kathy Rodger *(Office Mgr)*

HAIWAN INTERNATIONAL DEVELOPMENT CO., LTD.
3F No 22 Dahe Road, West District, Taichung, Taiwan
Tel.: (886) 423026088
Year Founded: 1982
3252—(TPE)
Rev.: $17,976,925
Assets: $123,233,311
Liabilities: $61,003,596
Net Worth: $62,229,716
Earnings: $111,215
Fiscal Year-end: 12/31/22
Hotel & Restaurant Operator
N.A.I.C.S.: 722511

HAIXIN FOODS CO., LTD.
Building 1 No 150 Jianxin North Road, Jianxin Town Cangshan District, Fuzhou, 350008, Fujian, China
Tel.: (86) 59188202235
Web Site:
http://www.tengxinfoods.com.cn
Year Founded: 2005
002702—(SSE)
Rev.: $227,644,560
Assets: $247,953,420
Liabilities: $127,324,548
Net Worth: $120,628,872
Earnings: $8,876,088
Emp.: 1,030
Fiscal Year-end: 12/31/22
Frozen Food Products Mfr & Distr
N.A.I.C.S.: 311411
Yongzhuang Teng *(Chm & Interim Sec)*

HAIXIN GROUP COMPANY LTD.
688 Changxing Road, Dongjing Songjiang, Shanghai, 201619, China
Tel.: (86) 2157698100
Web Site: http://www.haixin.com
Year Founded: 1931
Sales Range: $200-249.9 Million
Emp.: 1,209
Textile & Knitware Mfr & Retailer
N.A.I.C.S.: 313290
Yang Aimin *(CFO)*

Subsidiaries:

Glenoit Fabrics HG Corp.   (1)
499 7Th Ave, New York, NY 10018
Tel.: (212) 764-3090
Sales Range: $125-149.9 Million
Emp.: 300

AND PRIVATE COMPANIES — HAKUDO CO., LTD.

Mfr of Fabrics for Clothing, Furnishings, Rugs & Textiles
N.A.I.C.S.: 459130
Gordon Sun *(Coord-Production)*

Haihao High Fashion Co., Ltd. (1)
Room 403 House 160, No 3 Xinjing New Residential A, Shanghai, China
Tel.: (86) 2157698935
Broadwoven Fabric Mills
N.A.I.C.S.: 313210

Haixin Ohtsu Co., Ltd. (1)
No 688 Caijiabang Road, Dongjing Town Songjiang Distri, Shanghai, China
Tel.: (86) 2157698608
Broadwoven Fabric Mills
N.A.I.C.S.: 313210

Haixin Plush Co., Ltd. (1)
No 999 Caijiabang Road, Dongjing Town Songjiang Distri, 201619, Shanghai, China
Tel.: (86) 2157698859
Web Site: http://www.haixinplush.com
Broadwoven Fabric Mills
N.A.I.C.S.: 313210

Haixin Toys Co., Ltd. (1)
178 Zhenye Rd Dongjing Town, Songjiang Industry Zone, Shanghai, 201619, Songjiang, China
Tel.: (86) 2157698100
Web Site: http://www.haixin.com.cn
Sales Range: $50-74.9 Million
Emp.: 200
Doll & Stuffed Toy Mfr
N.A.I.C.S.: 339930

HAJDUCICA A.D.
Valentova 1, Hajducica, Serbia
Tel.: (381) 13864125
Year Founded: 1987
HAJD—(BEL)
Rev.: $8,804,322
Assets: $10,975,624
Liabilities: $5,635,363
Net Worth: $5,340,261
Earnings: $28,666
Emp.: 53
Fiscal Year-end: 12/31/23
Cereal Crop Farming Services
N.A.I.C.S.: 111998

HAJI HUSEIN ALIREZA & CO. LTD.
PO Box 40, Jeddah, 21411, Saudi Arabia
Tel.: (966) 126049444
Web Site: http://www.hha.com.sa
Year Founded: 1906
Sales Range: $350-399.9 Million
Emp.: 1,200
Automotive Distr
N.A.I.C.S.: 441110
Husein A. Alireza *(CEO)*

Subsidiaries:

National Computer System Co. Ltd. (1)
PO Box 6256, Jeddah, 21442, Saudi Arabia
Tel.: (966) 2 644 4777
Web Site: http://www.natcom.com.sa
Sales Range: $75-99.9 Million
Emp.: 300
Information Technology Consulting Services
N.A.I.C.S.: 541512
Hekmat Q. M. Mahmoud *(Mgr-Bus Dev)*

HAJI MOHAMMAD ISMAIL MILLS LIMITED
409 Commerce Centre Hasrat Mohani Road, Karachi, 74200, Pakistan
Tel.: (92) 2132638521
Web Site: https://www.hmiml.com
Rev.: $2,261
Assets: $157,648
Liabilities: $1,137
Net Worth: $156,511
Earnings: ($26,020)
Emp.: 5
Fiscal Year-end: 06/30/19
Cotton Yarn Mfr

N.A.I.C.S.: 313110
Muhammad Sarfraz *(Sec)*

HAK ALGAHTANI GROUP OF COMPANIES
Khobar Dammam Hwy, PO Box 195, Al Khobar, 31952, Saudi Arabia
Tel.: (966) 38820222
Web Site: http://www.hakgroup.com
Year Founded: 1968
Rev.: $200,000,000
Emp.: 1,100
Electronics, Household Appliances & Communication Systems Sales
N.A.I.C.S.: 449210
Khalid H. Algahtani *(Pres & CEO)*

Subsidiaries:

Al Eman Printing Press Co (1)
First Industrial City, PO Box 195, Dammam, 31952, Saudi Arabia
Tel.: (966) 3 847 2141
Web Site: http://www.aleman.com.sa
Printing Services
N.A.I.C.S.: 323111

Arabian Food & Dairy Factories (1)
PO Box 195, Al Khobar, Saudi Arabia
Tel.: (966) 38576325
Dairy & Bakery Products
N.A.I.C.S.: 424430

Educational Technology Arabia Company Limited (1)
603 Cement Towers, Al Khobar, Saudi Arabia
Tel.: (966) 13 882 0198
Web Site: http://www.edutacs.com
Emp.: 15
Educational Support Services
N.A.I.C.S.: 611710
Mohammed Alam *(Gen Mgr)*

GH Transport Limited (1)
PO Box 39014, Dammam, Saudi Arabia
Tel.: (966) 38560004
Sales Range: $200-249.9 Million
Emp.: 540
Cargo Handling Services
N.A.I.C.S.: 488510

Gahtani International Maritime Agency (1)
PO Box 5564, Dammam, 31432, Saudi Arabia
Tel.: (966) 38347082
Sales Range: $200-249.9 Million
Emp.: 800
Transportation & Freight Services
N.A.I.C.S.: 488510
Raju Varghese *(Gen Mgr)*

HAKA Motors (1)
PO Box 195, Al Khobar, Saudi Arabia
Tel.: (966) 38670096
Web Site: http://www.hakamotors.com
Truck & Bus Sales
N.A.I.C.S.: 441227

Lazord (1)
PO Box 195, Al Khobar, Saudi Arabia
Tel.: (966) 38987363
Confectionery Mfr
N.A.I.C.S.: 311352

Rikaz Development Company (1)
Kingdom of saudi arabic Alkhobar highway, Al Khobar, Saudi Arabia
Tel.: (966) 13 8591999
Web Site: http://www.rikaz.com
Real Estate Development Services
N.A.I.C.S.: 531390

HAKATA TAKUMI KOUGEI INC.
2-12-40 Nakahata, Onojo, 816-0921, Fukuoka, Japan
Tel.: (81) 92 5817232
Web Site: http://www.takumikougei.jp
Year Founded: 2007
Sales Range: $1-9.9 Million
Textile Products Mfr
N.A.I.C.S.: 313220
Shigeru Sakai *(Chm)*

HAKERS ENTERPRISE CO., LTD.
9F-5 No 6 Sec 1 Jung-shing Rd, Wugu District, New Taipei City, 24872, Taiwan
Tel.: (886) 289769056
Web Site: https://www.haksport.com
Year Founded: 1986
4432—(TPE)
Rev.: $48,169,590
Assets: $47,806,335
Liabilities: $8,523,716
Net Worth: $39,282,619
Earnings: $5,386,080
Fiscal Year-end: 12/31/22
Sportswear Mfr
N.A.I.C.S.: 339920
Ying-Hsuan Chen *(Chm)*

HAKI SAFETY AB
Norra Vallgatan 70, 211 22, Malmo, Sweden
Tel.: (46) 40301210
Web Site: https://www.hakisafety.com
HAKI—(OMX)
Rev.: $109,387,732
Assets: $134,751,374
Liabilities: $77,795,574
Net Worth: $56,955,801
Earnings: $6,603,164
Emp.: 311
Fiscal Year-end: 12/31/22
Holding Company
N.A.I.C.S.: 551112

HAKIM OPTICAL LABORATORY LIMITED
128 Hazelton Avenue 2nd Floor, Toronto, M5R 2E5, ON, Canada
Tel.: (416) 924-8866
Web Site: http://www.hakimoptical.ca
Year Founded: 1967
Rev.: $55,000,000
Emp.: 600
Optical Stores
N.A.I.C.S.: 456130
Karim Hakim *(Founder)*

HAKKANI GROUP
2 Dhaka Trunk Road North Pahartali, Chittagong, Bangladesh
Tel.: (880) 243151463
Web Site: http://www.hakkanigroup.com
Holding Company
N.A.I.C.S.: 551112
M. A. Kader *(Chm)*

Subsidiaries:

Hakkani Corporation (1)
2 Dhaka Trunk Road North Pahartali, Chittagong, Bangladesh
Tel.: (880) 31 751463
Export, Import & Trade Services
N.A.I.C.S.: 561499

Hakkani Motors Ltd. (1)
2 Dhaka Trunk Road North Pahartali, Chittagong, Bangladesh
Tel.: (880) 31 751463
Automotive Services
N.A.I.C.S.: 423110

Hakkani Paper & Board Mills (Pvt.) Ltd. (1)
2 Dhaka Trunk Road North Pahartali, Chittagong, Bangladesh
Tel.: (880) 31 751463
Paper Products Mfr
N.A.I.C.S.: 322130

Hakkani Paper Mills (Pvt.) Ltd. (1)
3 Dhaka Trunk Road North Pahartali, Chittagong, Bangladesh
Tel.: (880) 31 751463
Paper Products Mfr
N.A.I.C.S.: 322299

Hakkani Pulp & Paper Mills Ltd. (1)
2 Dhaka Trunk Road North Pahartali, Chittagong, Bangladesh

Tel.: (880) 243151463
Web Site: https://www.hakkanigroup.com
Rev.: $6,243,562
Assets: $17,137,301
Liabilities: $11,945,756
Net Worth: $5,191,544
Earnings: ($285,484)
Emp.: 154
Fiscal Year-end: 06/30/2022
Pulp & Paper Mfr
N.A.I.C.S.: 322299

HAKKASAN LTD.
3rd Floor Elsley House 24-30 Great Titchfield Street, London, W1W 8BF, United Kingdom
Tel.: (44) 2072978901
Web Site: http://www.hakkasan.com
Year Founded: 1963
Restaurant
N.A.I.C.S.: 722511
Khalifa Bin Butti *(Chm)*

HAKKEN CAPITAL CORP.
4626 Lockehaven Place, Vancouver, V7G 2B8, BC, Canada
Tel.: (604) 612-5450
HAKK.P—(TSXV)
Assets: $276,107
Liabilities: $575
Net Worth: $275,532
Earnings: ($86,763)
Fiscal Year-end: 06/30/20
Business Consulting Services
N.A.I.C.S.: 522299
David Eto *(CEO)*

HAKKIM TEXTILE MILLS LIMITED
7-Farid Kot Link Road, Lahore, Pakistan
Tel.: (92) 573552
Textile Products Mfr
N.A.I.C.S.: 314999

HAKODATE KOKUSAI HOTEL, CO., LTD.
5-10 Ote-machi, Hakodate, 040-0064, Japan
Tel.: (81) 138230591
Hotel Services
N.A.I.C.S.: 721110

HAKUDO CO., LTD.
11F Mitsubishi Building 2-5-2 Marunouchi, Chiyoda-ku, Tokyo, Japan
Tel.: (81) 362122811
Web Site: https://www.hakudo.co.jp
Year Founded: 1932
7637—(TKS)
Rev.: $378,442,330
Assets: $277,719,150
Liabilities: $129,119,740
Net Worth: $148,599,410
Earnings: $12,664,760
Emp.: 751
Fiscal Year-end: 03/31/24
Aluminium Products Mfr
N.A.I.C.S.: 331315
Koji Tsunoda *(Pres & CEO)*

Subsidiaries:

Hakudo (Thailand) Co., Ltd. (1)
1 Vasu 1 Building Room 1101/4 11th Floor Soi Sukhumvit 25 Sukhumvit Rd, Klongtoey-Nua Watthana, Bangkok, 10110, Thailand
Tel.: (66) 20 543 7334
Web Site: https://www.fact-link.com
Metal Distr
N.A.I.C.S.: 423510
Yuichiro Akiyoshi *(Mgr Dir)*

Hakudo Co., Ltd. - Fukushima Plant (1)
Koriyama Industrial Estate No 2 2-10, Machikedai Koriyama, Fukushima, Japan
Tel.: (81) 249630541

HAKUDO CO., LTD.

Hakudo Co., Ltd.—(Continued)
Aluminium Products Mfr
N.A.I.C.S.: 331315

Hakudo Co., Ltd. - Kanagawa Plant (1)
2514 Toda, Atsugi, Kanagawa, Japan
Tel.: (81) 462290655
Aluminium Products Mfr
N.A.I.C.S.: 331315

Hakudo Co., Ltd. - Kyushu Plant (1)
669-1 Aza Enokimachi Sakainishimachi, Tosu, Saga, Japan
Tel.: (81) 942852107
Aluminium Products Mfr
N.A.I.C.S.: 331315

Hakudo Co., Ltd. - Shiga Plant (1)
3-3 Hino Industrial Estate No 2 Kitawaki, Gamo-gun, Hino, Shiga, Japan
Tel.: (81) 748532400
Aluminium Products Mfr
N.A.I.C.S.: 331315

Shanghai Hakudo Percision Materials Co., Ltd. (1)
No 1158 Jinyu Road, Songjiang District, Shanghai, 201699, China
Tel.: (86) 216 772 8910
Web Site: http://www.hakudo.com.cn
Precision Material Mfr & Distr
N.A.I.C.S.: 332721

HAKUHODO DY HOLDINGS INCORPORATED

Akasaka Biz Tower 5-3-1 Akasaka, Minato-ku, Tokyo, 107-6320, Japan
Tel.: (81) 364419033   JP
Web Site: https://www.hakuhodody-holdings.co.jp
Year Founded: 2003
HKUOF—(OTCIQ)
Rev.: $7,106,452,290
Assets: $7,359,395,550
Liabilities: $4,564,429,170
Net Worth: $2,794,966,380
Earnings: $222,341,700
Emp.: 28,836
Fiscal Year-end: 03/31/23
Holding Company; Advertising & Media Buying Agencies
N.A.I.C.S.: 551112
Mitsumasa Matsuzaki *(Sr Exec Corp Officer)*

Subsidiaries:

Cosmo Communications Inc. (1)
2-5-8 Kita-Aoyama Aoyama OM-SQUARE 4th floor, Minato-ku, Tokyo, 107-0061, Japan
Tel.: (81) 33 405 8111
Web Site: https://www.cosmo-com.jp
Sales Range: $50-74.9 Million
Emp.: 85
Advertising Agency
N.A.I.C.S.: 541810

D.A. Consortium, Inc. (1)
Yebisu Garden Place Tower 4-20-3 Ebisu, Shibuya-ku, Tokyo, 150-6033, Japan (100%)
Tel.: (81) 35 449 6360
Web Site: https://www.dac.co.jp
Emp.: 1,508
Online Advertising Business
N.A.I.C.S.: 541810
Masayu Shimada *(Pres & CEO)*

Daiko Advertising, Inc. (1)
AKASAKA-PARK Bldg 5-2-20 Akasaka, Minato-ku, Tokyo, 107-6107, Japan
Tel.: (81) 363648111
Web Site: http://www.daiko.co.jp
Sales Range: $10-24.9 Million
Emp.: 809
Advetising Agency
N.A.I.C.S.: 541810
Masahiro Takahashi *(Mng Exec Officer)*

Subsidiary (Domestic):

Ad Daiko Gifu Inc. (2)
8F G-front 9-20 Kandamachi, Gifu, 500-8833, Japan
Tel.: (81) 582645186
Advetising Agency
N.A.I.C.S.: 541810

Ad Daiko Nagoya Inc. (2)
Centirise Sakae 10th floor 3-3-21 Sakae, Naka-ku, Nagoya, 460-0008, Japan
Tel.: (81) 527708000
Web Site: http://www.addaiko.co.jp
Advetising Agency
N.A.I.C.S.: 541810

Asahi Area Advertising Inc. (2)
16F Nakanoshima Festivaltower 2-3-18 Nakanoshima, Kita-ku, Osaka, 530-0005, Japan
Tel.: (81) 6 6221 2923
Web Site: http://www.daiko.co.jp
Advertising Agency
N.A.I.C.S.: 541810

Asahi Area Advertising Wakayama Inc. (2)
2F Wakayama Asahi Bldg 17 Nanaban-cho, Wakayama, 640-8156, Japan
Tel.: (81) 734245111
Web Site: http://www.daiko.co.jp
Advertising Agencies
N.A.I.C.S.: 541810

Asahi Area Avertising Nara Inc. (2)
5F Nara Sanwatoyo Bldg 27-1 Nishimikado-Cho, Takama-cho, Nara, 630-8225, Japan
Tel.: (81) 742240376
Web Site: http://www.daiko.co.jp
Advertising Agencies
N.A.I.C.S.: 541810

D-CREATE Inc. (2)
12F Shiba Park Building B 2-4-1 Shibakoen, Minato-ku, Tokyo, 105-0001, Japan
Tel.: (81) 33 437 8855
Web Site: http://www.d-create.co.jp
Advertising Agencies
N.A.I.C.S.: 541810

Subsidiary (Non-US):

Daiko (Beijing) Advertising Co., Ltd. (2)
Room 702 ZhongYu Plaza No A6 Worker's Stadium North Road, Chaoyang District, Beijing, 100027, China
Tel.: (86) 1065889255
Web Site: http://www.daiko.co.jp
Advertising Services
N.A.I.C.S.: 541810
Hiroyuki Nanno *(Vice Chm & Mng Dir)*

Branch (Domestic):

Daiko Advertising, Inc. (2)
Nakanoshima Central Tower 2-2-7 Nakanoshima, Kita-ku, Osaka, 530-8263, Japan
Tel.: (81) 671748111
Web Site: http://www.daiko.co.jp
Emp.: 673
N.A.I.C.S.: 541810

Daiko Advertising, Inc. (2)
10F CentRise Sakae 3-3-21 Sakae Naka-ku, Nagoya, 460-0008, Japan
Tel.: (81) 527708000
Web Site: http://www.daiko.co.jp
N.A.I.C.S.: 541810
Shuichi Iwai *(Pres)*

Daiko Advertising, Inc. (2)
7F 57 Sankyo Building 1-13 Nishi 3-chome Kitanijyo, Chuo-ku, Sapporo, 060-0002, Japan
Tel.: (81) 112221544
Web Site: http://www.daiko.co.jp
Advetising Agency
N.A.I.C.S.: 541810
Soich Papodi *(Mgr)*

Daiko Advertising, Inc. (2)
Dai-ichi Aoba Bldg 1-1-6 Omachi, Aoba-ku, Sendai, 980-0804, Japan
Tel.: (81) 222216401
Web Site: http://www.daiko.co.jp
N.A.I.C.S.: 541810

Daiko Advertising, Inc. (2)
4F Asahi Seimei Building 1-1 Bandai 1-chome, Niigata, 950-0088, Japan
Tel.: (81) 252436286
Web Site: http://www.daiko.co.jp
N.A.I.C.S.: 541810

Subsidiary (Non-US):

Daiko Communications Asia Co., Ltd. (2)
17F Zoroastorian Building 101 Leighton Road, Causeway Bay, China (Hong Kong)
Tel.: (852) 28279688
Web Site: http://www.daiko.co.jp
Sales Range: $10-24.9 Million
Emp.: 10
N.A.I.C.S.: 541810

Subsidiary (Domestic):

Daiko Hokuriku Inc. (2)
8F Sumitomo Seimei Building 1-39 Takaokacho, Kanazawa, 920-0864, Japan
Tel.: (81) 762631476
Web Site: http://www.daiko.co.jp
N.A.I.C.S.: 541810

Daiko Kansai Inc. (2)
13F Nakanoshima Central Tower 2-2-7 Nakanoshima, Kita-ku, Osaka, 530-0005, Japan (100%)
Tel.: (81) 671748050
Web Site: http://kansai.daiko.co.jp
Advertising Agency
N.A.I.C.S.: 541810
Takao Imamura *(Pres)*

Daiko Kobe Inc. (2)
6F Nippon Life Sannomiya Station Building 7-1-1 Onoe-dori, Chuo-ku, Kobe, 651-0088, Japan
Tel.: (81) 78 265 0833
Web Site: https://www.daiko.co.jp
N.A.I.C.S.: 541810

Daiko Kyusyu Advertising Inc. (2)
11F Elle Gala 1-4-2 Tenjin, Chuo-ku, Fukuoka, 810-0001, Japan
Tel.: (81) 927627600
Web Site: http://www.daiko-kyushu.co.jp
Emp.: 92
Advetising Agency
N.A.I.C.S.: 541810

Daiko Mediax Inc. (2)
EDGE Yodoyabashi 9th floor 2-4-10 Imabashi, Chuo-ku, Osaka, 541-0042, Japan
Tel.: (81) 662025175
Web Site: http://www.d-mediax.com
Advertising Services
N.A.I.C.S.: 541810

Daiko Mie Inc. (2)
3F Yokkaichi-Sanko Building 3-12 Hamadacho, Yokkaichi, 510-0067, Japan
Tel.: (81) 593511171
Web Site: http://www.daiko.co.jp
N.A.I.C.S.: 541810

Daiko Ones Osaka Inc. (2)
1-2F Daiko Imabashi Bldg 2-4-10 Imabashi, Chuo-ku, Osaka, 541-0042, Japan
Tel.: (81) 671758710
Web Site: http://www.daiko.co.jp
Advertising Agency
N.A.I.C.S.: 541810

Daiko West Inc. (2)
4F Hiroshima Park Building 3-7-5, Otemachi Naka-ku, Hiroshima, 730-0051, Japan
Tel.: (81) 825457420
Web Site: http://www.daiko-west.co.jp
Advertising Agency
N.A.I.C.S.: 541810

Subsidiary (Non-US):

Shanghai Daiko Maocu Advertising Co., Ltd. (2)
Room 703 Silver Tower 218 South Xizang Road, Shanghai, 200021, China
Tel.: (86) 21 6334 3737
Web Site: http://www.daiko-kyushu.co.jp
N.A.I.C.S.: 541810

Shanghai Daiko Maocu Advertising Co., Ltd. (2)
Room 801-802 JianLiBao Building 410 Dong Feng Rd, Guangzhou, 510030, China
Tel.: (86) 20 8348 6861
Web Site: http://www.daiko.co.jp
N.A.I.C.S.: 541810

Hakuhodo Incorporated (1)
Akasaka Biz Tower 5-3-1 Akasaka, Minato-ku, Tokyo, 107-6322, Japan

INTERNATIONAL PUBLIC

Tel.: (81) 364418111
Web Site: http://www.hakuhodo.co.jp
Sales Range: $5-14.9 Billion
Emp.: 3,614
Advertising Agency
N.A.I.C.S.: 541810
Masayuki Mizushima *(Pres & CEO)*

Subsidiary (Non-US):

Agence 154 s.a. (2)
63, bd de Menilmontant, 75009, Paris, France
Tel.: (33) 1 53 04 40 00
Web Site: http://www.154.com
Rev.: $6,013,000
Emp.: 12
N.A.I.C.S.: 541810
Luc Duvoux *(Chm & Pres)*

Subsidiary (Domestic):

Backs Group Inc. (2)
14th floor of Rise Arena Building 4-5-2 Higashiikebukuro, Toshima-ku, Tokyo, 170-0013, Japan (94.36%)
Tel.: (81) 366265911
Web Site: https://www.backs.co.jp
Sales Range: $150-199.9 Million
Emp.: 249
Business-To-Consumer Retail Support Outsourcing Services
N.A.I.C.S.: 561499
Tsutomu Okada *(Pres)*

Subsidiary (Domestic):

Smart Communications Inc. (3)
1-19-19 Ebisu Ebisu Business Tower 14F, Shibuya-ku, Tokyo, 150-0013, Japan
Tel.: (81) 354229109
Web Site: http://www.smacom.co.jp
Sales Range: $25-49.9 Million
Emp.: 5
Telemarketing & Sales Support Services
N.A.I.C.S.: 561422

Subsidiary (Non-US):

Beijing Hakuhodo Co., Ltd. (2)
Unit 1206 1211 Tower B Pacific Century Place, Chaoyang District, Beijing, 100027, China
Tel.: (86) 1065802280
Advertising Services
N.A.I.C.S.: 541810
Osamu Takahashi *(Gen Mgr)*

Subsidiary (Domestic):

ChugokuShikoku Hakuhodo Inc. (2)
5th floor of Hiroshima Park Building 3-7-5 Otemachi, Naka-ku, Hiroshima, 730-0051, Japan
Tel.: (81) 822480401
Web Site: https://www.chugokushikoku.co.jp
Marketing, Branding & Advertising Services
N.A.I.C.S.: 541810
Shigemi Ikeda *(Pres)*

Digital Advertising Consortium, Inc. (2)
Yebisu Garden Place Tower 33F 4-20-3 Ebisu, Shibuya-ku, Tokyo, 150-6033, Japan
Tel.: (81) 35 449 6300
Web Site: https://www.dac.co.jp
Sales Range: $200-249.9 Million
Emp.: 1,508
Interactive Agencies
N.A.I.C.S.: 541810
Hirotake Yajima *(Pres & CEO)*

Subsidiary (Non-US):

Fischer Fala (2)
Rua Leopoldo Couto de Magalhaes 758 17th & 18th Floors, Sao Paulo, CEP 04542-000, SP, Brazil
Tel.: (55) 1137041411
Web Site: http://www.fischeramerica.com.br
Sales Range: $25-49.9 Million
Emp.: 115
N.A.I.C.S.: 541810

Foresight Research Co., Ltd. (2)
47 Manthana Village Soi Chimpli 14/2 Chimpli, Taling Chan, Bangkok, 10170, Thailand
Tel.: (66) 2 661 6093

HAKUHODO DY HOLDINGS INCORPORATED

Web Site:
  https://www.foresightresearch.co.th
Sales Range: $25-49.9 Million
Emp.: 35
N.A.I.C.S.: 541810
Busaba Pan-Anukul *(Mng Dir)*

Subsidiary (Domestic):

Fukushima Hakuhodo, Inc. (2)
7-3 Omachi Fukushima Center Building 8F, Fukushima, 960-8041, Japan
Tel.: (81) 245211133
Web Site: https://www.hakuhodo.co.jp
N.A.I.C.S.: 541810

G-plan, Inc. (2)
Matsushita Bldg 3-2 Kanda-Ogawacho 3-chome, Chiyoda-ku, Tokyo, 101-0052, Japan
Tel.: (81) 3 5283 5717
Web Site: http://www.gpoint.co.jp
N.A.I.C.S.: 541810

Subsidiary (Non-US):

Grebstad Hicks Communications Ltd. (2)
7/F The Broadway 54-62 Lockhart Road, Wanchai, China (Hong Kong) (60%)
Tel.: (852) 2810 0532
Web Site: http://ghcasia.com
Sales Range: Less than $1 Million
Emp.: 40
Advertising Agency
N.A.I.C.S.: 541810
Lynn Grebstad *(Co-Founder)*

Growww Media Co., Ltd. (2)
4th Fl No 285 Sec 4 Zhongxiao E Rd, Da'an Dist, Taipei, 106070, Taiwan
Tel.: (886) 226278806
Web Site: http://www.hakuhodo-global.com
Emp.: 700
Holding Company; Advertising & Public Relations Agencies
N.A.I.C.S.: 551112
Genki Tei *(CEO)*

Subsidiary (Domestic):

Interplan Group (3)
Rm 408 4F No 333 Sec 1 Keelung Rd, Taipei, 110, Taiwan
Tel.: (886) 227585450
Web Site: https://www.interplan.group
Emp.: 150
Convention & Trade Show Organizer
N.A.I.C.S.: 561920
Michael Tu *(Pres)*

Pilot Group (3)
3F No 27/29 Sec 1 An Ho Rd, Taipei, 106, Taiwan
Tel.: (886) 2 8773 2088
Web Site: http://www.pilotgp.com
Public Relations Agency
N.A.I.C.S.: 541820
Arthur Yang *(Founder & Chm)*

United Communication Group (3)
3rd Floor No 285 Section 4 Zhongxiao East Road, Daan District, Taipei, 106, Taiwan
Tel.: (886) 226278806
Web Site: https://www.ucgroup.com.tw
Emp.: 100
Advertising Agency
N.A.I.C.S.: 541810
Vince Cheng *(CEO)*

Subsidiary (Non-US):

Hakuhodo & Saigon Advertising Co., Ltd. (2)
10th Floor Tower 1-Saigon Centre 65 Le Loi, District 1, Ho Chi Minh City, Vietnam
Tel.: (84) 283 825 0140
Web Site: https://www.hakuhodo.vn
Advertising Agency
N.A.I.C.S.: 541810

Hakuhodo Australia Pty. Ltd. (2)
Level 5 Frank Hurley Grandstand Fox Studios Australia Driver Avenue, Moore Park, Sydney, 1363, NSW, Australia
Tel.: (61) 283533400
Web Site: http://www.hakuhodo.co.jp
Sales Range: $10-24.9 Million
Emp.: 30
Full Service
N.A.I.C.S.: 541810

Hakuhodo Bangkok Co., Ltd. (2)
16th Fl Tonson Tower 900 Ploenchit Road, Lumpini Pathumwan, Bangkok, 10330, Thailand
Tel.: (66) 22570533
Web Site: https://www.hakuhodo.co.jp
Sales Range: $25-49.9 Million
Emp.: 80
Full Service
N.A.I.C.S.: 541810

Subsidiary (Domestic):

Hakuhodo Co., Ltd. Tohoku (2)
4th Fl Koriyama Shokokaigisho Kaikan 1-3-8 Shimizudai, Koriyama, 963-8005, Japan
Tel.: (81) 24 934 5042
N.A.I.C.S.: 541810
Kazuo Asawa *(Pres)*

Subsidiary (Non-US):

Hakuhodo Communications, Inc. (2)
11th Fl No 367 Fuxing N Rd, Songshan, Taipei, Taiwan
Tel.: (886) 22 545 6622
Web Site: https://www.hakuhodo.co.jp
Sales Range: $10-24.9 Million
Emp.: 40
N.A.I.C.S.: 541810

Subsidiary (Domestic):

Hakuhodo Creative Vox, Inc. (2)
Net Akasaka Building 6F 3-13-16 Akasaka, Minato-ku, Tokyo, 107-0052, Japan
Tel.: (81) 36 441 4380
Web Site: https://hc-vox.co.jp
Advertising Agency
N.A.I.C.S.: 541810

Hakuhodo DY CAPCO (2)
2-14-27 Akasaka International Shin-Akasaka Building East Building 11F, Akasaka, Tokyo, 107-0052, Japan
Tel.: (81) 364416645
Web Site: http://www.hakuhodo-dy.capco.co.jp
Advertising Agency
N.A.I.C.S.: 541810

Hakuhodo DY Media Partners Inc. (2)
Akasaka Biz Tower 3-1 Akasaka 5-Chome, Minato-ku, Tokyo, 107-6321, Japan
Tel.: (81) 36 4418 111
Web Site:
  http://www.hakuhodody-media.co.jp
Rev.: $39,483,000
Emp.: 616
N.A.I.C.S.: 541810
Haruo Oki *(Mng Dir)*

Subsidiary (Domestic):

IREP Co., Ltd. (3)
4-20-3 Ebisu Ebisu Garden Place Tower 21F, Shibuya-ku, Tokyo, 150-6021, Japan
Tel.: (81) 354752720
Web Site: http://www.irep.co.jp
Emp.: 966
Marketing Consulting Services
N.A.I.C.S.: 327910
Atsushi Nagai *(CFO)*

Subsidiary (Domestic):

Frontier Digital Marketing Co., Ltd. (4)
Sanno Park Tower 3F 2-11-1, Nagatocho Chiyoda, Tokyo, Japan
Tel.: (81) 3 6205 3350
Web Site: http://www.frontierdm.com
Digital Marketing Services
N.A.I.C.S.: 541613
Sho Shimoda *(CEO)*

Subsidiary (Non-US):

Hakuhodo Deutschland GmbH (2)
Hanauer Landstrasse 172, 60314, Frankfurt am Main, Germany
Tel.: (49) 699494800
Web Site: https://www.hakuhodo.de
Advetising Agency
N.A.I.C.S.: 541810
Ryoichi Katsui *(Mng Dir)*

Branch (Domestic):

Hakuhodo Deutschland GmbH-Hamburg Office (3)
Valentinskamp 24, 20354, Hamburg, Germany
Tel.: (49) 403786100
Web Site: http://www.hakuhodo.de
Sales Range: $25-49.9 Million
Emp.: 20
N.A.I.C.S.: 541810

Hakuhodo Deutschland GmbH-Munich Office (3)
Thomas-Wimmer-Ring 17, 80539, Munich, Germany
Tel.: (49) 89551910
Web Site: http://www.hakuhodo.de
Sales Range: $10-24.9 Million
Emp.: 5
N.A.I.C.S.: 541810

Subsidiary (Domestic):

Hakuhodo Dy I.O Inc. (2)
5-6-15 Toyosu NBF Toyosu Garden Front 5th Floor, Koto-ku, Tokyo, 135-8617, Japan
Tel.: (81) 35 144 7150
Web Site: https://www.hio.co.jp
Advertising Services
N.A.I.C.S.: 541810

Hakuhodo Dy Total Support Inc. (2)
Heiwa No 1 Building 1-4-5 Hirakawacho, Chiyoda-ku, Tokyo, 102-0093, Japan
Tel.: (81) 36 261 4800
Web Site: https://www.hdy-ts.co.jp
Consulting Human Services
N.A.I.C.S.: 541612

Hakuhodo Erg, Inc. (2)
11th Floor Hakata Riverain East Site 2-1 Shimokawabata-machi, Hakata-ku, Fukuoka, 812-0027, Japan
Tel.: (81) 922633811
Sales Range: $25-49.9 Million
Emp.: 100
N.A.I.C.S.: 541810
Junji Narita *(Chm & CEO)*

Subsidiary (Non-US):

Hakuhodo France S.A. (2)
59 bd Exelmans, 75016, Paris, France
Tel.: (33) 140713500
Web Site: http://www.hakuhodo.fr
Sales Range: $25-49.9 Million
Emp.: 15
N.A.I.C.S.: 541810
Marc Desmazieres *(Dir-Creative)*

Hakuhodo Hong Kong Ltd. (2)
25th Fl Prosperity Millennia Plaza 663 Kings Road, North Point, China (Hong Kong)
Tel.: (852) 28651861
Web Site: http://www.hakuhodo.co.hk
Sales Range: $10-24.9 Million
Emp.: 40
Advertising Agency
N.A.I.C.S.: 541810

Subsidiary (Domestic):

Hakuhodo I.O. Co., Ltd. (2)
Akasaka Biz Tower 5-3-1 Akasaka, Minato-ku, Tokyo, 107-6320, Japan
Tel.: (81) 3 5446 6266
N.A.I.C.S.: 541810

Branch (Domestic):

Hakuhodo Inc. Chubu Office (2)
3-3-21 Sakae Centrise Sakae, Naka-ku, Nagoya, 460-0008, Japan
Tel.: (81) 522512125
Web Site: https://www.hakuhodo.co.jp
Full Service
N.A.I.C.S.: 541810

Hakuhodo Inc. Kansai Office (2)
2-2-7 Nakanoshima Nakanoshima Central Tower, Kita-ku, Osaka, 530-8262, Japan
Tel.: (81) 662295413
Web Site: https://www.hakuhodo.co.jp
Sales Range: $75-99.9 Million
Emp.: 300
Advertising Agency
N.A.I.C.S.: 541810

Hakuhodo Inc. Kyushu Office (2)
2-1-8 Shimokawabata-machi Hakata Riverain East Site, Hakata-ku, Fukuoka, 812-0027, Japan
Tel.: (81) 922634560

Web Site: http://www.hakuhodo.co.jp
Sales Range: $25-49.9 Million
Emp.: 100
Advertising Agency
N.A.I.C.S.: 541810
Junji Narita *(Chm & CEO)*

Subsidiary (Non-US):

Hakuhodo Malaysia Sdn. Bhd. (2)
7th Floor Building A Dataran PHB Saujana Resort Section U2, 40150, Shah Alam, Selangor, Malaysia
Tel.: (60) 37 848 3384
Web Site: https://www.hakuhodo.com.my
Sales Range: $10-24.9 Million
Emp.: 50
Advertising Agency
N.A.I.C.S.: 541810
Toru Watanade *(Mng Dir)*

Hakuhodo Percept Pvt. Ltd. (2)
Percept House No 2 Sant Nagar, New Delhi, 110 065, India
Tel.: (91) 11 4654 1000
Web Site: http://www.perceptindia.com
Sales Range: $25-49.9 Million
Emp.: 75
N.A.I.C.S.: 541810
Harindra Singh *(Vice Chm & Mng Dir)*

Hakuhodo Singapore Pte. Ltd. (2)
9 Kreta Ayer Road, Singapore, 088985, Singapore
Tel.: (65) 67345451
Web Site: https://www.hakuhodo.co.jp
Sales Range: $10-24.9 Million
Emp.: 35
Advertising Agency
N.A.I.C.S.: 541810

Subsidiary (Domestic):

Hakuhodo i-studio, Inc. (2)
1-10-1 Yurakucho Building, Chiyoda-ku Yurakucho, Tokyo, 100-0006, Japan
Tel.: (81) 35 219 7150
Web Site: https://www.i-studio.co.jp
Sales Range: $25-49.9 Million
Emp.: 285
Advertising Agency
N.A.I.C.S.: 541810

Joint Venture (Non-US):

Hakuhodo-Cheil, Inc. (2)
8th floor Dabo Building 20 Mapo-daero, Mapo-gu, Seoul, 04175, Korea (South)
Tel.: (82) 22 021 3600
Web Site: https://www.hakuhodocheil.co.kr
Advertising Agency
N.A.I.C.S.: 541810
Chun Hwan Kim *(Pres & CEO)*

Subsidiary (Domestic):

Hokkaido Hakuhodo, Inc. (2)
Maruito Sapporo Building 1-1 Kita 2 Jonishi, Chuo-ku, Sapporo, 060-0002, Japan
Tel.: (81) 112510176
Web Site:
  https://www.hokkaido.hakuhodo.co.jp
Sales Range: $10-24.9 Million
Emp.: 36
Marketing Branding & Advertising Services
N.A.I.C.S.: 541810

Hokuriku Hakuhodo, Inc. (2)
4-1 Minamicho Kanazawa New Grand Building, Kanazawa, 920-0919, Japan
Tel.: (81) 762225121
Web Site:
  https://www.hokuriku.hakuhodo.co.jp
Sales Range: $25-49.9 Million
Emp.: 20
Marketing Branding & Advertising Services
N.A.I.C.S.: 541810

Subsidiary (Non-US):

Integrated Communications Group Pte Ltd (2)
71 Neil Road, Singapore, 088900, Singapore
Tel.: (65) 63247955
Web Site: http://www.groupicg.com
Holding Company; Marketing Communications Services
N.A.I.C.S.: 551112
Kong Man Haw *(CEO & CFO)*

HAKUHODO DY HOLDINGS INCORPORATED

Hakuhodo DY Holdings Incorporated—(Continued)
Subsidiary (Domestic):

Moving Content Solutions Pte Ltd. (3)
71 Neil Road, Singapore, 088900, Singapore
Tel.: (65) 6 324 7955
Web Site: https://www.movingcontent.com
Logistics Consulting Servies
N.A.I.C.S.: 541614

Subsidiary (Non-US):

Origami Frontiers (3)
Room 701 Wise Logic Building 66 North Shanxi Road, Jingan District, Shanghai, 200041, China
Tel.: (86) 2118621032622
Web Site: http://www.origami-frontiers.com
Software Development Services
N.A.I.C.S.: 541511
James Ong (Founder & CEO)

Subsidiary (Domestic):

the thinc group (3)
243 Beach Road 02-01, Singapore, 189754, Singapore
Tel.: (65) 9 665 1496
Web Site: https://www.thethincgroup.com
Marketing Services
N.A.I.C.S.: 541613

Subsidiary (Non-US):

MJW Hakuhodo (2)
Level 5 The Frank Hurley Grandstand Driver Ave Fox Studios, Moore Park, Sydney, 2021, NSW, Australia
Tel.: (61) 2 8353 3400
Rev.: $43,000,000
Emp.: 48
Advetising Agency
N.A.I.C.S.: 541810

Branch (Domestic):

MJW Hakuhodo (3)
29-31 Victoria Avenue, Albert Park, 3206, VIC, Australia
Tel.: (61) 3 9686 5844
Sales Range: $25-49.9 Million
Emp.: 8
N.A.I.C.S.: 541810

Subsidiary (Non-US):

Media Intelligence Co., Ltd. (2)
130-132 Wireless Road 5th Fl Sindhorn Building Tower 2, Lumpini Pathumwan, Bangkok, 10330, Thailand
Tel.: (66) 2 651 5377
Web Site: http://www.mediaintelligence.co.th
Sales Range: $25-49.9 Million
Emp.: 60
Advetising Agency
N.A.I.C.S.: 541810

Media by Design (2)
Multimedia House Hill Street, Tunbridge Wells, TN1 2BY, Kent, United Kingdom
Tel.: (44) 18 9251 7777
Web Site: http://www.nexush.com
Sales Range: $25-49.9 Million
Emp.: 55
Media Buying Services, Planning & Consultation
N.A.I.C.S.: 541810
Ian Norman (Grp Mng Dir)

Nexus/H Ltd. (2)
Multimedia House Hill St, Tunbridge Wells, TN1 2BY, Kent, United Kingdom
Tel.: (44) 18 9251 7777
Web Site: http://www.nexush.co.uk
Sales Range: $25-49.9 Million
Emp.: 65
N.A.I.C.S.: 541810
Glenn Smith (Dir-Creative)

Subsidiary (Domestic):

Niigata Hakuhodo Inc. (2)
LEXN B 4F 1-12-8 Tenjin, Chuo-ku, Niigata, 950-0917, Japan
Tel.: (81) 252905555
Web Site: https://www.niigata.hakuhodo.co.jp
Sales Range: $25-49.9 Million
Emp.: 25
Advetising Agency
N.A.I.C.S.: 541810

Subsidiary (Non-US):

Shanghai Hakuhodo Advertising Co., Ltd. (2)
Unit 1706 17th Fl Office Tower 3 Raffles City Changning, No 1193 Changning Road Changning District, Shanghai, 200051, China
Tel.: (86) 215 230 6776
Web Site: https://www.hakuhodo.cn
Sales Range: $25-49.9 Million
Emp.: 100
Marketing & Media Partners
N.A.I.C.S.: 541840

Subsidiary (Domestic):

Shizuoka Hakuhodo Inc. (2)
11F Top Center Building 8-6 Tenma cho, Aoi-ku, Shizuoka, 420-0858, Japan
Tel.: (81) 546522800
Web Site: https://www.shizuoka.hakuhodo.co.jp
Sales Range: $25-49.9 Million
Emp.: 28
Advetising Agency
N.A.I.C.S.: 541810

Subsidiary (Non-US):

Spa-Hakuhodo Co., Ltd. (2)
8th Fl Rajapark Bldg 163 Sukhumvit 21 Rd, North Klong-Toey Wattana, Bangkok, 10110, Thailand
Tel.: (66) 22567007
Sales Range: $25-49.9 Million
Emp.: 120
N.A.I.C.S.: 541810

Taiwan Hakuhodo Media Inc. (2)
11th Fl No 367 Fuxing N Rd, Songshan Dist, Taipei, 10544, Taiwan
Tel.: (886) 225456622
Web Site: https://www.hakuhodo.co.jp
Sales Range: $25-49.9 Million
Emp.: 25
Full Service
N.A.I.C.S.: 541810

Subsidiary (Domestic):

Tohoku Hakuhodo Inc. (2)
4-1-25 Ichibancho JRE Higashi Nibancho Square 12F, Aoba-ku, Sendai, 980-0811, Japan
Tel.: (81) 222632211
Web Site: https://www.tohoku.hakuhodo.co.jp
Emp.: 91
Advetising Agency
N.A.I.C.S.: 541810
Shinobu Sasaki (Pres & Dir)

Sid Lee International LLC (1)
12102-1 Place Ville Marie, Montreal, H3B 3Y1, QC, Canada
Tel.: (514) 282-2200
Web Site: https://www.sidlee.com
Advetising Agency
N.A.I.C.S.: 541810
Jean-Francois Bouchard (Co-Founder & Chm)

Branch (Non-US):

SID LEE (2)
Gerard Doustraat 72-80, 1072VV, Amsterdam, Netherlands
Tel.: (31) 20 662303
Advertising Agencies
N.A.I.C.S.: 541810

SID LEE (2)
7 rue de Paradis, Ile-de-France, 75010, Paris, France
Tel.: (33) 1 44 88 83 90
Web Site: http://www.sidlee.com
Advetising Agency
N.A.I.C.S.: 541810
Johan Delpuech (Pres & Partner)

Branch (Domestic):

SID LEE (2)
55 Mill Street Building 5, Suite 500, Toronto, M5A 3C4, ON, Canada
Tel.: (416) 421-4200
Advetising Agency
N.A.I.C.S.: 541810
Eve Remillard-Larose (Mng Partner)

Branch (US):

SID LEE USA (2)
3601 South Congress Ste D-102, Austin, TX 78704
Tel.: (647) 283-3357
Advetising Agency
N.A.I.C.S.: 541810
Ethan Schmidt (Dir-Creative-New York)

SoldOut, Inc. (1)
Ryujinkan Head Office Building 3rd floor-6th floor 3-10, Kanda Surugadai Chiyoda-ku, Tokyo, 101-0062, Japan
Tel.: (81) 501 749 8000
Web Site: http://www.sold-out.co.jp
Rev.: $197,926,960
Assets: $65,310,960
Liabilities: $36,619,440
Net Worth: $28,691,520
Earnings: $1,684,320
Fiscal Year-end: 12/31/2020
Web Marketing Support Services
N.A.I.C.S.: 541613

Subsidiary (Domestic):

Search LIFE, Inc. (2)
3-4 Kanda Ryujinkan Head Office Building 4F, Chiyoda-ku, Tokyo, 101-0062, Japan
Tel.: (81) 5017498003
Web Site: http://www.searchlife.co.jp
Advertising Business Consulting Services
N.A.I.C.S.: 541810

The Red Peak Group LLC (1)
560 Broadway Ste 506, New York, NY 10012
Tel.: (212) 792-8930
Web Site: http://www.redpeakgroup.com
Emp.: 80
Advertising Agencies
N.A.I.C.S.: 541810
Steve Lipman (Dir-Production)

Yomiko Advertising Inc. (1)
Akasaka Park Building 5-2-2, Akasaka Minato-ku, Tokyo, 107-6105, Japan
Tel.: (81) 3 3589 8111
Web Site: http://www.yomiko.co.jp
Emp.: 670
Advetising Agency
N.A.I.C.S.: 541810
Daisuke Fujinuma (Pres & CEO)

Branch (Domestic):

Yomiko Advertising (2)
8th floor of Midosuji Mitsui Building 4-1-3 Bingomachi, Chuo-ku, Osaka, 541-0051, Japan
Tel.: (81) 66 205 7500
Web Site: https://www.yomiko.co.jp
Advetising Agency
N.A.I.C.S.: 541810

Yomiko Advertising (2)
2nd Fl Kitaichijo Mitsui Building 5-2-9 Kitaichijo-Nishi Chuo-ku, Sapporo, 060-0001, Hokkaido, Japan
Tel.: (81) 11 281 2341
N.A.I.C.S.: 541810

Yomiko Advertising (2)
4135 Ichi Bancho, Aoba-Ku, Sendai, 980-0811, Miyagi, Japan
Tel.: (81) 22 261 5959
Sales Range: $25-49.9 Million
Emp.: 10
N.A.I.C.S.: 541810
Takashi Matsuura (Branch Mgr)

Yomiko Advertising (2)
4th Fl Nakamachi Mitsui Building 9-12 Nakamachi, Naka-Ku, Hiroshima, 730-0037, Japan
Tel.: (81) 82 246 9211
N.A.I.C.S.: 541810
Yasunori Nakada (Chm)

Yomiko Advertising (2)
Yasuda Mitsui Fudosan Building 5th Fl 2-3-23 Hakata-ekimae, Hakato-Ku, Fukuoka, 812-0011, Japan
Tel.: (81) 92 451 1871
Advetising Agency

INTERNATIONAL PUBLIC

N.A.I.C.S.: 541810

Yomiko Advertising (2)
5th Fl Yomiuri Kachikawa Building, 1-27-10 Shibazaki-cho, Tachikawa, 190-2710, Tokyo, Japan
Tel.: (81) 425 24 0435
Web Site: http://www.yomiko.co.jp
Sales Range: $150-199.9 Million
Emp.: 590
N.A.I.C.S.: 541810
Yasunori Nakada (Pres & CEO)

HAKUTEN CORPORATION

20F Tokyo Square Garden 3-1-1 Kyobashi, Chuo-ku, Tokyo, 104-0031, Japan
Tel.: (81) 368218910
Web Site: https://www.hakuten.co.jp
Year Founded: 1967
2173—(TKS)
Rev.: $93,134,240
Assets: $54,359,030
Liabilities: $35,627,250
Net Worth: $18,731,780
Earnings: $4,807,020
Emp.: 478
Fiscal Year-end: 12/31/23
Events & Exhibitions Planner, Producer & Operator
N.A.I.C.S.: 561920
Atsushi Harada (Pres, COO & Dir)

Subsidiaries:

Nichinan Co., Ltd. (1)
1-14-13 Yoshiokahigashi, Ayase, 252-1125, Kanagawa, Japan
Tel.: (81) 46778889
Web Site: https://www.nichinan-group.com
Emp.: 750
Electric Equipment Mfr
N.A.I.C.S.: 335999

Sprasia, Inc. (1)
20F Tokyo Square Garden 3-1-1 Kyobashi, Chuo-ku, Tokyo, 104-0031, Japan
Tel.: (81) 368208620
Web Site: https://www.sprasia.co.jp
IT Support Services
N.A.I.C.S.: 541519

HAKUYOSHA COMPANY LTD.

2-11-8 Shimomaruko, Ota-ku, Tokyo, 146-0092, Japan
Tel.: (81) 357325111
Web Site: https://www.hakuyosha.co.jp
Year Founded: 1920
9731—(TKS)
Rev.: $306,798,480
Assets: $235,061,860
Liabilities: $175,718,560
Net Worth: $59,343,300
Earnings: $13,790,050
Emp.: 1,329
Fiscal Year-end: 12/31/23
Dry Cleaning Services
N.A.I.C.S.: 812320
Eiichi Igarashi (Pres, Co-CEO & Exec Officer)

Subsidiaries:

Dust-Tex Honolulu, Inc. (1)
220 Puuhale Rd Unit B1, Honolulu, HI 96819
Tel.: (808) 842-4811
Web Site: https://www.dusttexhonolulu.com
Linen Product Distr
N.A.I.C.S.: 423220

HAL MANN VELLA GROUP PLC

The Factory Mosta Road, Lija, LJA 9016, Malta
Tel.: (356) 21433636
Web Site: http://www.hmvellagroup.com
Year Founded: 1954
HM24A—(MAL)
Rev.: $31,025,120

AND PRIVATE COMPANIES — HAL TRUST N.V.

Assets: $151,996,720
Liabilities: $92,412,103
Net Worth: $59,584,617
Earnings: $1,462,457
Emp.: 184
Fiscal Year-end: 12/31/21
Construction Materials Mfr
N.A.I.C.S.: 327991
Martin Vella *(Chm)*

Subsidiaries:

Hal Mann Properties Ltd. (1)
The Factory Mosta Road, Lija, LJA 9016, Malta
Tel.: (356) 23310400
Web Site: https://www.hmvellaproperties.com
Real Estate Development Services
N.A.I.C.S.: 531390
Adrian Vella Petroni *(Dir-Properties)*

HAL OFFSHORE LIMITED
32 Corporate Avenue 4 Floor B wing Near Paper Box Industry Off, Mahakali Caves Road Andheri E, Mumbai, 400 093, India
Tel.: (91) 22 4236 9200
Web Site: http://www.haloffshore.in
Year Founded: 1998
Offshore Engineering Services
N.A.I.C.S.: 541330
Sanjeev Agrawal *(Chm)*

Subsidiaries:

Seamec Limited (1)
A-901-905 9th Floor 215 Atrium Andheri-Kurla Road, Andheri East, Mumbai, 400093, India (75%)
Tel.: (91) 2266941800
Web Site: https://www.seamec.in
Rev.: $40,381,341
Assets: $11,725,446
Liabilities: $2,655,921
Net Worth: $9,069,524
Earnings: $13,483,743
Emp.: 49
Fiscal Year-end: 03/31/2021
Offshore Oil Production Support Services
N.A.I.C.S.: 213112
S. N. Mohanty *(Compliance Officer, Pres-Legal & Corp Affairs & Sec)*

HAL TRUST N.V.
Johan van Walbeeckplein 11A, Willemstad, Curacao
Tel.: (599) 94615002
Web Site: http://www.halholding.com
Year Founded: 1977
HAL—(EUR)
Rev.: $14,414,615,302
Assets: $29,078,927,038
Liabilities: $11,558,229,387
Net Worth: $17,520,697,651
Earnings: $1,288,883,983
Emp.: 31,846
Fiscal Year-end: 12/31/23
Investment Trust
N.A.I.C.S.: 525920

Subsidiaries:

Atlas Professionals B.V. (1)
Wijkermeerstraat 32-34, 2131 HA, Hoofddorp, Netherlands
Tel.: (31) 235560420
Web Site: http://www.atlasprofessionals.com
Emp.: 283
Construction Services
N.A.I.C.S.: 236220

HAL Holding N.V. (1)
Johan van Walbeeckplein 11A, Willemstad, Curacao
Tel.: (599) 94615002
Web Site: https://www.halholding.com
Holding Company
N.A.I.C.S.: 551112
A. A. van 't Hof *(CFO & Member-Exec Bd)*

Subsidiary (Non-US):

HAL Investments BV (2)
Millennium Tower 31st Floor Weena 696, 3012 CN, Rotterdam, Netherlands **(100%)**
Tel.: (31) 102816500
Web Site: http://www.halinvestments.nl
Sales Range: $25-49.9 Million
Emp.: 35
Investment Services
N.A.I.C.S.: 523999
Caroline Veelenturf *(Office Mgr)*

Holding (Domestic):

Anthony Veder Group N.V. (3)
Parklaan 2, 3016 BB, Rotterdam, Netherlands
Tel.: (31) 10 4004800
Web Site: http://www.anthonyveder.com
Gas Transportation Services
N.A.I.C.S.: 213112

Holding (Non-US):

Atasun Optik A.S. (3)
Esentepe Mah Keskin Kalem Sk No 5 Sisli, 34394, Istanbul, Anadolu, Turkiye
Tel.: (90) 4446785
Web Site: http://www.atasunoptik.com.tr
Optical Goods Whslr
N.A.I.C.S.: 423460

AudioNova Denmark (3)
Amagerbrogade 264, Klampenborg, 2300, Copenhagen, Denmark
Tel.: (45) 88778057
Web Site: http://www.audionova.dk
Sales Range: $25-49.9 Million
Emp.: 15
Hearing Aid Product Distr
N.A.I.C.S.: 423450

AudioNova France (3)
Quai Charles de Gaulle 84, 69006, Lyon, France
Tel.: (33) 4 37 43 33 28
Hearing Aid Stores
N.A.I.C.S.: 456199

Holding (Domestic):

Broadview Holding B.V. (3)
Vd Does de Willeboissngl 13, 's-Hertogenbosch, 5211 CC, Netherlands
Tel.: (31) 73 687 5333
Investment Management Service
N.A.I.C.S.: 523999

Subsidiary (Non-US):

Broadview Industries AG (4)
Hengeler Mueller Benratherstrasse 18-20, 40213, Dusseldorf, Germany
Tel.: (49) 1706327310
Web Site: http://www.broadview-angebot.de
Investment Management Service
N.A.I.C.S.: 523999

Subsidiary (US):

Formica Corporation (4)
10155 Reading Rd, Cincinnati, OH 45241
Tel.: (513) 786-3400
Web Site: http://www.formica.com
High Pressure Laminates & Adhesives & Solid Surfacing Material Mfr
N.A.I.C.S.: 326130
Mitch Quint *(Pres-North America)*

Holding (Non-US):

Formica (Singapore) Pte. Ltd (5)
No 502/502A Sims Avenue, Singapore, 387567, Singapore
Tel.: (65) 6514 1313
Web Site: http://www.formica.com
Sales Range: $25-49.9 Million
Laminate Sheets Mfr
N.A.I.C.S.: 322220

Formica (Thailand) Co., Ltd. (5)
216/63-64 LPN Tower 15th Fl Nanglinchee Rd Chongnonsee, Yannawa, Bangkok, 10120, Thailand
Tel.: (66) 22854473
Web Site: http://www.formica.com
Construction Materials Mfr & Distr
N.A.I.C.S.: 327331

Plant (Domestic):

Formica (Thailand) Co., Ltd. - Phrapradaeng Factory (6)
51/27 Moo 2 Poochaosamingprai Rd, Bangyapraek, Phra Pradaeng, 10130, Samutprakarn, Thailand
Tel.: (66) 2 755 8525
Construction Materials Mfr
N.A.I.C.S.: 327331

Holding (Non-US):

Formica Asia Ltd. (5)
Room 1305-9 13/F Olympia Plaza 255 Kings Road, North Point, China (Hong Kong)
Tel.: (852) 25980117
Web Site: http://www.formica.com
Sales Range: $25-49.9 Million
Emp.: 45
Marketing & Sale of High Pressure Laminates & Other Surfacing Materials
N.A.I.C.S.: 326130

Formica Canada, Inc. (5)
25 Rue Mercier, Saint-Jean-sur-Richelieu, J3B 6E9, QC, Canada
Tel.: (450) 347-7541
Web Site: http://www.formica.com
Sales Range: $100-124.9 Million
Emp.: 350
High Pressure Laminate Mfr
N.A.I.C.S.: 322220

Formica Finance Limited (5)
Formica Building Coast Road, North Shields, NE29 8RE, Tyne and Wear, United Kingdom
Tel.: (44) 191 259 3100
Financial Management Services
N.A.I.C.S.: 523999
Melle De Pater *(Gen Mgr)*

Formica Holdco UK Limited (5)
Coast Rd, North Shields, NE29 8RE, Tyne and Wear, United Kingdom
Tel.: (44) 1912593100
Financial Management Services
N.A.I.C.S.: 523999

Formica IKI Oy (5)
Tehtaantie 2, 35990, Kolho, Finland
Tel.: (358) 3 580 001
Web Site: http://www.formica.com
Sales Range: $50-74.9 Million
Emp.: 163
Plastic Plate & Sheet Mfr
N.A.I.C.S.: 326199

Formica Ltd. (5)
Coast Rd, Tyne & Wear, North Shields, NE29 8RE, United Kingdom
Tel.: (44) 1916220096
Web Site: http://www.formica.com
Sales Range: $100-124.9 Million
Emp.: 450
High Pressure Laminate Mfr
N.A.I.C.S.: 326130
Bernie Davidson *(Plant Mgr)*

Formica Netherland B.V. (5)
Laan van Oversteen 14-B, Postbus 3131, 2280 GC, Rijswijk, Netherlands
Tel.: (31) 704134820
Web Site: http://www.formica.com
Sales Range: $10-24.9 Million
Emp.: 15
High Pressure Laminate Mfr
N.A.I.C.S.: 322220
Erik Bax *(CEO)*

Formica Norge A/S (5)
Fekjan 13 A, 1394, Nesbru, Norway
Tel.: (47) 66 98 48 00
Construction Material Mfr & Distr
N.A.I.C.S.: 333120

Formica S.A. (5)
Txomin Egileor, 54 48960, Bilbao, Spain
Tel.: (34) 944579600
Web Site: http://www.formica.com
Sales Range: $50-74.9 Million
Emp.: 250
High Pressure Laminate Mfr
N.A.I.C.S.: 326130

Formica S.A.S (5)
Le Botanic 40 Ave Lingenfeld, 77200, Torcy, France
Tel.: (33) 1 60 06 86 86
Web Site: http://www.formica.fr
Decorative Building Glassware Mfr
N.A.I.C.S.: 327212

Formica Skandinavien AB (5)
Florettgatan 22, 254 67, Helsingborg, Sweden
Tel.: (46) 42 38 48 00
Web Site: http://www.formica.es
Sales Range: $50-74.9 Million
Emp.: 10
Industrial Supplies Distr
N.A.I.C.S.: 423840
Anna-Lena Eskilssons *(Gen Mgr)*

Formica Societe Anonyme (5)
29 Rue De La Maison Rouge, Lognes, 77185, Paris, Cedex, France
Tel.: (33) 160068686
Web Site: http://www.formica.com
Sales Range: $25-49.9 Million
Emp.: 15
High Pressure Laminate Mfr
N.A.I.C.S.: 326130

Formica Switzerland AG (5)
Flughofstrasse 45, CH 8153, Rumlang, ZH, Switzerland
Tel.: (41) 448188818
Sales Range: $25-49.9 Million
Emp.: 2
Marketing & Sales of Laminates, Plastics, Plate Sheet & Profile Shapes
N.A.I.C.S.: 326130

Formica Taiwan (5)
6th Floor No 68-70 Section 3 Nanjing East Road, Zhongshan District, Taipei, Taiwan
Tel.: (886) 225151017
Web Site: http://www.formica.com
Sales Range: $25-49.9 Million
Emp.: 70
High-Pressure Decorative Laminate Mfr
N.A.I.C.S.: 326130

Formica Vertriebs GmbH (5)
11 Silver Fox Way Cobalt Business Park, NE-27, Newcastle, Germany
Tel.: (49) 1803676422
Web Site: http://www.formica-deutschland.de
Sales Range: $25-49.9 Million
Emp.: 12
High Pressure Laminate Mfr
N.A.I.C.S.: 424690

Formica de Mexico SA DE CV (5)
Viaducto Miguel Aleman No 55 Buenos Aires Cuauhtemoc, Mexico, 6780, Mexico
Tel.: (52) 5555303135
Building Materials Mfr
N.A.I.C.S.: 332311

Holding (Non-US):

Geers Hallokeszulek Kft (3)
Kesz Mester Udvarhaz Mester u 87, 1095, Budapest, Hungary
Tel.: (36) 1 433 0460
Hearing Aid Distr
N.A.I.C.S.: 423450

Holding (Domestic):

Koninklijke Ahrend N.V. (3)
Laarderhoogtweg 25, 1101 EB, Amsterdam, Netherlands (99%)
Tel.: (31) 880060000
Web Site: http://www.ahrend.com
Sales Range: $250-299.9 Million
Furniture Mfr
N.A.I.C.S.: 337214

Subsidiary (Domestic):

ASPA Benelux B.V. (4)
Elzenkade 1, PO Box 365, 3992 AD, Houten, Netherlands
Tel.: (31) 888455555
Web Site: http://www.aspa.nl
Office Furnishings Designer & Mfr
N.A.I.C.S.: 337214

Subsidiary (Non-US):

ASPA Belgium N.V. (5)
Rotterdamstraat 1, 1080, Brussels, Belgium
Tel.: (32) 22437910
Sales Range: $100-124.9 Million
Emp.: 6
Office Furnishings Marketer
N.A.I.C.S.: 423210

Subsidiary (Non-US):

TECHO, a. s. (4)

HAL TRUST N.V.

HAL Trust N.V.—(Continued)
U Tovaren 770 1b 102 00, Prague, 10,
Czech Republic
Tel.: (420) 267290111
Web Site: http://www.techo.com
Sales Range: $50-74.9 Million
Office Furniture Mfr
N.A.I.C.S.: 337214
Jiri Kejval *(Chm)*

Holding (Non-US):

MYLAPS Asia Pacific Lty Ltd (3)
Suite 3/292 Princes Highway, Carss Park,
Sydney, 2221, NSW, Australia
Tel.: (61) 2 9546 2606
Athletic Goods Mfr
N.A.I.C.S.: 339920

Holding (Domestic):

Mercurius Groep B.V. (3)
Langesteijn 102, 3342 LG, Hendrik-Ido-
Ambacht, Netherlands
Tel.: (31) 78 619 5000
Web Site: http://www.mercurius-group.nl
Holding Company
N.A.I.C.S.: 551112

Subsidiary (Domestic):

Belarto Group (4)
Westzijde 178, 1506 EK, Zaandam, Nether-
lands
Tel.: (31) 756476666
Web Site: http://www.belarto.nl
Holding Company; Announcement Cards &
Greeting Cards Publishing
N.A.I.C.S.: 551112

Subsidiary (Non-US):

Belarto Ltd (5)
31 Nottingham South & Wilford Industrial
Estate, West Bridgford, Nottingham, NG11
7EP, United Kingdom
Tel.: (44) 1159455873
Web Site: http://www.belarto.co.uk
Sales Range: $75-99.9 Million
Emp.: 10
Greeting Card Mfr
N.A.I.C.S.: 513191

Calligraphen AB (5)
Lundins Vag 1, 684 31, Munkfors, Sweden
Tel.: (46) 56353110
Web Site: http://www.calligraphen.se
Sales Range: $75-99.9 Million
Emp.: 14
Personalized Cards, Announcements, Invi-
tations & Party Items
N.A.I.C.S.: 323111
Anders Wejdenmark *(Co-Founder & CEO)*

Subsidiary (Non-US):

Calligraphen ApS (6)
Louisevej 42, 8220, Brabrand, Denmark
Tel.: (45) 86293967
Web Site: http://www.calligraphen.dk
Personalized Cards, Announcements, Invi-
tations & Party Items
N.A.I.C.S.: 323111

Calligraphen Oy (6)
Yrttipellontie 1, 90230, Oulu, Finland
Tel.: (358) 22306000
Web Site: http://www.calligraphen.fi
Sales Range: $10-24.9 Million
Personalized Cards, Announcements, Invi-
tations & Party Items
N.A.I.C.S.: 323111

Subsidiary (Non-US):

Edit'66 SAE (5)
c/Palautordera n 26, Poligono Industrial
Granollers, 08400, Barcelona, Spain
Tel.: (34) 938619222
Web Site: http://www.edit66.es
Sales Range: $75-99.9 Million
Emp.: 13
Greeting Card Catalog Printing
N.A.I.C.S.: 323111

Edit'66 SAS (5)
14 rue Beau de Rochas, 66330, Cabestany,
France
Tel.: (33) 468670222
Web Site: http://www.edit66.fr

Greeting Card Catalog Printing
N.A.I.C.S.: 323111

Exklusiv Kartenverlag GmbH (5)
Hirzenrott 6, Aachen, 52076, Germany
Tel.: (49) 240 894 980
Web Site: http://www.exklusivkarten.com
Greeting Card Mfr
N.A.I.C.S.: 513191

Subsidiary (Domestic):

Mercard Intercard BV (5)
Bruynvisweg 3, 1531 AX, Wormer, Nether-
lands
Tel.: (31) 756476666
Greeting Cards & Announcement Cards
Publishing
N.A.I.C.S.: 513191

Subsidiary (Non-US):

Mercard Intercard SA (5)
Koning Leopoldlaan 14/0-01, 9990, Brus-
sels, Belgium
Tel.: (32) 50710720
Web Site: http://www.belarto.be
Sales Range: $75-99.9 Million
Emp.: 6
Greeting Cards & Announcement Cards
Publishing
N.A.I.C.S.: 513191

Subsidiary (Domestic):

Floramedia Group B.V. (4)
Kleine Steng 1, 1551 NC, Westzaan, Neth-
erlands
Tel.: (31) 756476476
Web Site: http://www.floramedia.com
Sales Range: $25-49.9 Million
Supplier of Printed Plant Labels, Seed
Pockets & Plant Catalogues; Graphic De-
sign, Packaging & Labeling Services
N.A.I.C.S.: 323111

Subsidiary (Non-US):

Floramedia Austria GmbH (5)
Altmannsdorfer Anger 70/1A, 1120, Vienna,
Austria
Tel.: (43) 19826601
Web Site: http://www.floramedia.com
Sales Range: $100-124.9 Million
Supplier of Printed Plant Labels, Seed
Pockets & Plant Catalogues; Graphic De-
sign Services
N.A.I.C.S.: 323111
Johannes Lippitz *(Mng Dir)*

Floramedia Belgium n.v. (5)
Koning Leopoldlaan 14, 9990, Maldegem,
Belgium
Tel.: (32) 33211490
Web Site: http://www.floramedia.com
Sales Range: $100-124.9 Million
Supplier of Printed Plant Labels, Seed
Pockets & Plant Catalogues
N.A.I.C.S.: 323111

Floramedia Deutschland KG (5)
Steinbeisstrasse 9, 70736, Fellbach, Ger-
many
Tel.: (49) 7115185820
Web Site: http://www.floramedia.com
Sales Range: $100-124.9 Million
Supplier of Printed Plant Labels, Seed
Pockets & Plant Catalogues
N.A.I.C.S.: 323111

Floramedia Espana, S.A.U. (5)
C/ San Juan de Ribera 46, Alaquas, 46970,
Valencia, Spain
Tel.: (34) 963503288
Web Site: http://www.floramedia.com
Supplier of Printed Plant Labels, Seed
Pockets & Plant Catalogues
N.A.I.C.S.: 323111

Floramedia France (5)
Immeuble Le Britannia Bat C 20 boulevard
Eugene Deruelle, 69432, Lyon, Cedex,
France
Tel.: (33) 437484090
Web Site: http://www.floramedia.com
Sales Range: $100-124.9 Million
Supplier of Printed Plant Labels, Seed
Pockets & Plant Catalogues
N.A.I.C.S.: 323111

Floramedia Polska sp.z o.o. (5)

Pamietna 15D, 96-100, Skierniewice, Po-
land
Tel.: (48) 468348620
Web Site: http://www.floramedia.com
Supplier of Printed Plant Labels, Seed
Pockets & Plant Catalogues
N.A.I.C.S.: 323111
Wojciech Bogatko *(Dir)*

Floramedia Schweiz AG (5)
Farbhofstrasse 21, 8048, Zurich, Switzer-
land
Tel.: (41) 552202121
Web Site: http://www.floramedia.com
Sales Range: $100-124.9 Million
Supplier of Printed Plant Labels, Seed
Pockets & Plant Catalogues
N.A.I.C.S.: 323111
Luzza Cadonau *(Mng Dir)*

Floramedia UK Ltd (5)
Axis Two Brunel Way Severalls Business
Park, Middleborough, Colchester, CO4
9QX, Essex, United Kingdom
Tel.: (44) 1206771040
Web Site: http://www.floramedia.com
Sales Range: $100-124.9 Million
Supplier of Printed Plant Labels, Seed
Pockets & Plant Catalogues
N.A.I.C.S.: 323111
Nick Mathias *(Mng Dir)*

Subsidiary (Non-US):

Imprima iRooms Limited (4)
10th Floor 30 Crown Place, London, EC2A
4EB, United Kingdom
Tel.: (44) 2079654700
Virtual Data Rooms Provider
N.A.I.C.S.: 518210
Amir Khan *(Acct Dir)*

Subsidiary (Non-US):

Imprima (Deutschland) GmbH (5)
Bockenheimer Landstrasse 23, 60325,
Frankfurt am Main, Germany
Tel.: (49) 6991509800
Web Site: http://www.imprima.com
Virtual Data Room Provider
N.A.I.C.S.: 518210

Imprima (France) SARL (5)
32 Avenue de l Opera, 75002, Paris,
France
Tel.: (33) 176753291
Web Site: http://www.imprima.com
Virtual Data Rooms Provider
N.A.I.C.S.: 518210

Imprima (Nederland) B.V. (5)
De Boelelaan 7, 1083 HJ, Amsterdam,
Netherlands
Tel.: (31) 207155600
Web Site: http://www.imprima.com
Virtual Data Room Provider
N.A.I.C.S.: 518210

Joint Venture (Domestic):

**N.V. Nationale
Borg-Maatschappij** (3)
Keizersgracht 165, 1016 DP, Amsterdam,
Netherlands
Tel.: (31) 205533900
Web Site: http://www.nationaleborg.nl
Rev.: $579,698,529
Assets: $1,424,585,844
Liabilities: $1,367,820,626
Net Worth: $56,765,217
Earnings: $14,980,174
Emp.: 114
Fiscal Year-end: 12/31/2017
Non-Life Insurance & Reinsurance
N.A.I.C.S.: 524128
A. P. Jos C. Kroon *(CEO & Member-Mgmt Bd)*

Holding (Domestic):

**Orthopedie Investments Europe
B.V.** (3)
Weena 696, Rotterdam, 3012 CN, Nether-
lands
Tel.: (31) 102816500
Web Site: http://www.livit.nl
Financial Management Services
N.A.I.C.S.: 523999

PontMeyer B.V. (3)

INTERNATIONAL PUBLIC

Symon Spiersweg 17, 1506 RZ, Zaandam,
Netherlands **(67.9%)**
Tel.: (31) 756536292
Web Site: http://www.pontmeyer.nl
Sales Range: $350-399.9 Million
Timber Products & Building Materials Sup-
plier
N.A.I.C.S.: 444180

Trespa International B.V. (3)
Wetering 20, 6002 SM, Weert, Netherlands
Tel.: (31) 495458358
Web Site: https://www.trespa.com
Sales Range: $125-149.9 Million
Architectural Panels Mfr & Whslr
N.A.I.C.S.: 327390
Jan Horbach *(CEO)*

Holding (Non-US):

Royal Boskalis Westminster N.V. (2)
Rosmolenweg 20, 3356 LK, Papendrecht,
Netherlands
Tel.: (31) 786969000
Web Site: http://www.boskalis.com
Rev.: $3,950,328,081
Assets: $5,743,680,121
Liabilities: $2,950,540,686
Net Worth: $2,793,139,434
Earnings: $258,997,410
Emp.: 11,164
Fiscal Year-end: 12/31/2022
Maritime Infrastructure Construction & Main-
tenance Services
N.A.I.C.S.: 333120
P. A. M. Berdowski *(Chm-Mgmt Bd)*

Subsidiary (Domestic):

**Aannemingsmaatschappij Markus
B.V.** (3)
Kwadrantweg 7, 1042 AG, Amsterdam,
North Holland, Netherlands
Tel.: (31) 205874000
Web Site: http://www.markusbv.nl
Sales Range: $25-49.9 Million
Emp.: 100
Civil Engineering Services
N.A.I.C.S.: 541330
C. M. Nelis *(Principal)*

Subsidiary (Non-US):

Atlantique Dragage SARL (3)
9 Rue St Eloi, 78100, Saint Germain-en-
Laye, Yvelines, France
Tel.: (33) 139040490
Sales Range: $25-49.9 Million
Emp.: 10
Dredging Services
N.A.I.C.S.: 561990

BKI Gabon S.A. (3)
Route du Barracuda Boite Postale 336, Li-
breville, Gabon
Tel.: (241) 702186
Maritime Civil Engineering Services
N.A.I.C.S.: 541330

Subsidiary (Domestic):

**Baggermaatschappij Boskalis
B.V.** (3)
Rosmolenweg 20, PO Box 43, 3350 AA,
Papendrecht, Zuid-Holland, Netherlands
Tel.: (31) 786969000
Web Site: http://www.boskalis.com
Sales Range: $150-199.9 Million
Emp.: 800
Marine Engineering Services
N.A.I.C.S.: 541330

Subsidiary (Domestic):

Boskalis Infra B.V. (4)
Nijverheidstraat 68, 2901 AR, Capelle aan
den IJssel, South Holland, Netherlands
Tel.: (31) 104582022
Web Site: http://www.boskalis.nl
Civil Engineering Services
N.A.I.C.S.: 541330

Branch (Non-US):

Boskalis Argentina (3)
Av Alem Leandro 592 Floor 7, Buenos Ai-
res, Argentina
Tel.: (54) 1143125949
Emp.: 30
Dredging & Hydraulic Engineering Services
N.A.I.C.S.: 237990

AND PRIVATE COMPANIES · HAL TRUST N.V.

Subsidiary (Non-US):

Boskalis Australia Pty Ltd (3)
L 4 Loyal Insurance Bldg 131 St George Terrace, Perth, 6000, NSW, Australia
Tel.: (61) 294060400
Sales Range: $25-49.9 Million
Emp.: 20
Marine Engineering Services
N.A.I.C.S.: 541330
Wim Termijn *(Sec)*

Subsidiary (Domestic):

Boskalis B.V. (3)
Waalhaven East side 85, PO Box 4234, 3006 AE, Rotterdam, South Holland, Netherlands
Tel.: (31) 102888777
Web Site: http://www.boskalis.nl
Sales Range: $25-49.9 Million
Emp.: 90
Dredging Services
N.A.I.C.S.: 561990

Boskalis Dolman B.V. (3)
Rosmolenweg 20, PO Box 76, 3350 AB, Papendrecht, Zuid-Holland, Netherlands
Tel.: (31) 786969900
Web Site: http://www.boskalisdolman.nl
Sales Range: $10-24.9 Million
Emp.: 70
Soil Washing Services
N.A.I.C.S.: 562910

Subsidiary (Non-US):

Boskalis Dredging India Pvt. Ltd. (3)
23 Sangeeta Tagore Road, Santacruz West, Mumbai, 400 054, Maharashtra, India
Tel.: (91) 2226056699
Web Site: http://www.boskalis.com
Sales Range: $25-49.9 Million
Emp.: 4
Marine Engineering Services
N.A.I.C.S.: 541330

Subsidiary (Domestic):

Boskalis Environmental B.V. (3)
Rosmolenweg 20, 3356 LK, Papendrecht, Netherlands
Tel.: (31) 78 696 9000
Mineral Waste Stream Treatment Services
N.A.I.C.S.: 562998

Subsidiary (Non-US):

Boskalis Germany Holding GmbH (3)
Am Festungsgraben 10, 21079, Hamburg, Germany
Tel.: (49) 40 766 0940
Research & Development Services
N.A.I.C.S.: 541713

Boskalis Guyana Inc. (3)
1 Water Street Quarry Wharf, PO Box 101768, Kingston, Georgetown, Guyana
Tel.: (592) 229241
Web Site: http://www.boskalisguyana.com
Dredging Services
N.A.I.C.S.: 237990

Boskalis International (S) Pte Ltd (3)
23 Gul Rd, Singapore, 629356, Singapore
Tel.: (65) 67335622
Web Site: http://www.boskalis.com
Sales Range: $25-49.9 Million
Emp.: 20
Marine Engineering Services
N.A.I.C.S.: 541330

Subsidiary (Domestic):

Zinkcon Marine Singapore Pte. Ltd. (4)
23 Gul Road, Singapore, Singapore
Tel.: (65) 67333471
Web Site: http://www.boskalis.com
Sales Range: $25-49.9 Million
Emp.: 20
Marine Engineering Services
N.A.I.C.S.: 541330

Subsidiary (Non-US):

Boskalis International Uruguay S.A. (3)
Luis Alberto de Herrera 1248 World Trade Center Torre A, Officina 703, 11300, Montevideo, Uruguay
Tel.: (598) 2 628 5085
Maritime Civil Engineering Services
N.A.I.C.S.: 541330

Boskalis Italia S.r.l. (3)
Viale Castello Della Magliana 38, 00148, Rome, Italy
Tel.: (39) 068 880 4143
Maritime Civil Engineering Services
N.A.I.C.S.: 541330

Subsidiary (Domestic):

Boskalis Maritime Investments B.V. (3)
Rosmolenweg 20, 3356 LK, Papendrecht, South Holland, Netherlands
Tel.: (31) 786969011
Web Site: http://www.boskalis.com
Sales Range: $350-399.9 Million
Emp.: 750
Investment Management Service
N.A.I.C.S.: 523940

Boskalis Nederland B.V. (3)
Waalhaven Oostzijde 85 Havennummer 2204, 3087 BM, Rotterdam, Netherlands
Tel.: (31) 10 288 8777
Maritime Civil Engineering Services
N.A.I.C.S.: 541330

Boskalis Nederland Infra B.V. (3)
Opijnenstraat 2, 3087 CG, Rotterdam, Netherlands
Tel.: (31) 10 288 8777
Maritime Civil Engineering Services
N.A.I.C.S.: 541330

Boskalis Offshore B.V. (3)
Rosmolenweg 20, PO Box 43, 3350 AA, Papendrecht, South Holland, Netherlands
Tel.: (31) 786969011
Sales Range: $50-74.9 Million
Emp.: 1,000
Offshore Support Services
N.A.I.C.S.: 213112
J. F. A. de Blaeij *(Dir-Middle East)*

Boskalis Offshore Contracting B.V. (3)
Rosmolenweg 20, 3356 LK, Papendrecht, Netherlands
Tel.: (31) 78 696 9000
Maritime Civil Engineering Services
N.A.I.C.S.: 541330

Subsidiary (Non-US):

Boskalis Offshore GmbH (3)
Am Festungsgraben 10, 21079, Hamburg, Germany
Tel.: (49) 40 766 0940
Maritime Civil Engineering Services
N.A.I.C.S.: 541330

Subsidiary (Domestic):

Boskalis Offshore Heavy Marine Transport B.V. (3)
Rosmolenweg 20, 3356 LK, Papendrecht, Netherlands
Tel.: (31) 765484100
Web Site: https://boskalis.com
Sales Range: $50-74.9 Million
Emp.: 200
Marine Transportation Services
N.A.I.C.S.: 483111

Boskalis Offshore Marine Services B.V. (3)
Rosmolenweg 20, 3356 LK, Papendrecht, Netherlands
Tel.: (31) 78 696 9011
Maritime Civil Engineering Services
N.A.I.C.S.: 541330

Subsidiary (Non-US):

Boskalis Offshore Subsea Contracting Azerbaijan LLC (3)
Panorama Hotel VILLA 10 Selyan sossesi 12-ci Km Sixov, Baku, AZ1023, Azerbaijan
Tel.: (994) 51 414 3186
Maritime Civil Engineering Services
N.A.I.C.S.: 541330

Boskalis Offshore Transport Services N.V. (3)
Italielei nr 3, Box 3, 2000, Antwerp, Belgium
Tel.: (32) 3 212 2900

Maritime Civil Engineering Services
N.A.I.C.S.: 541330

Boskalis Panama S.A. (3)
Edificio Balboa Point 101 Banco Hipotecario Ave, Chile entre calle 40 y 41 Piso 4 Corregimiento Bella Vista, Panama, Panama
Tel.: (507) 317 7000
Maritime Civil Engineering Services
N.A.I.C.S.: 541330

Boskalis Polska Sp. z o.o. (3)
ul Langiewicza 28/2, 70-263, Szczecin, West Pomeranian, Poland
Tel.: (48) 914843464
Web Site: http://www.boskalis.pl
Sales Range: $25-49.9 Million
Dredging & Hydraulic Engineering Services
N.A.I.C.S.: 541330

Boskalis S.R.L. (3)
Floor 1 Room 3 22 Delfinului Street, 900389, Constanta, Romania
Tel.: (40) 72 132 8340
Maritime Civil Engineering Services
N.A.I.C.S.: 541330

Boskalis Smit India LLP (3)
702 Trade Centre Bandra Kurla Complex Bandra East, Mumbai, 400051, Maharashtra, India
Tel.: (91) 226 133 5900
Maritime Civil Engineering Services
N.A.I.C.S.: 541330

Boskalis South Africa (Pty) Ltd. (3)
9 Clive Street, Robindale, Randburg, 2194, Gauteng, South Africa
Tel.: (27) 118886218
Web Site: http://www.voskalis.nl
Sales Range: $25-49.9 Million
Emp.: 100
Marine Support Services
N.A.I.C.S.: 541330
John Armstrong *(Reg Mgr)*

Boskalis Sweden AB (3)
Spinnerivagen 1, PO Box 5068, 448 51, Tollered, Sweden
Tel.: (46) 31507330
Web Site: http://www.sweden.boskalis.com
Sales Range: $25-49.9 Million
Dredging Services
N.A.I.C.S.: 237990
Michael Tornqvist *(Reg Mgr)*

Subsidiary (Domestic):

Boskalis Transport B.V. (3)
Nijverheidstraat 68 2901 AR, PO Box 4290, Capelle aan den Ijssel, 3006 AG, Rotterdam, Netherlands
Tel.: (31) 10 458 2022
Mineral Waste Stream Treatment Services
N.A.I.C.S.: 562998

Subsidiary (Non-US):

Boskalis Westminster Contracting Limited (3)
Arch Makarios III Ave 224 Achilleos Building Block B 1st Floor 3030, PO Box 59603, 4011, Limassol, Cyprus
Tel.: (357) 2 576 0550
Maritime Civil Engineering Services
N.A.I.C.S.: 541330

Boskalis Westminster Dredging Ltd. (3)
224 Archbishop Makariou III Avenue Achilleos Block B 1st Floor, Limassol, CY-3030, Cyprus
Tel.: (357) 25760550
Dredging Services
N.A.I.C.S.: 237990

Boskalis Westminster Ltd. (3)
Westminster House Crompton Way Segensworth West, Fareham, PO15 5SS, Hampshire, United Kingdom
Tel.: (44) 1489885933
Web Site: http://www.boskalis.co.uk
Sales Range: $25-49.9 Million
Marine Engineering Services
N.A.I.C.S.: 541330

Subsidiary (Domestic):

Boskalis Zinkcon Ltd. (4)
Westminster House Crompton Way Segensworth West, Fareham, PO15 5SS, Hampshire, United Kingdom
Tel.: (44) 1489885922
Web Site: http://www.boskalis.com
Sales Range: $10-24.9 Million
Emp.: 40
Marine Engineering Services
N.A.I.C.S.: 541330

Llanelli Sand Dredging Ltd. (4)
Burry Port, WDA Industrial Estate, Llanelli, SA16 0NN, Carmarthenshire, United Kingdom
Tel.: (44) 1554832475
Web Site: http://www.llanellisand.co.uk
Sales Range: $50-74.9 Million
Sand & Gravel Dredging Services
N.A.I.C.S.: 212321

Rock Fall Company Ltd. (4)
Westminster House Crompton Way Segensworth West, Fareham, PO15 5SS, Ayrshire, United Kingdom
Tel.: (44) 156 385 1302
Web Site: http://www.rock-fall.com
Sales Range: $50-74.9 Million
Emp.: 6
Rock Drilling & Blasting Services
N.A.I.C.S.: 213111

Westminster Gravels Ltd. (4)
Westminster House Crompton Way, Fareham, PO15 5SS, Hampshire, United Kingdom
Tel.: (44) 1489885933
Web Site: http://www.bwlboskalis.com
Dredging Services
N.A.I.C.S.: 237990

Subsidiary (Non-US):

Boskalis Westminster Middle East Ltd. (3)
Achilleos Building First Floor 224 Arch Makarios III Avenue, Lemesos, CY-3030, Cyprus
Tel.: (357) 25760550
Emp.: 6
Dredging Services
N.A.I.C.S.: 237990

Subsidiary (Domestic):

Boskalis Westminster Shipping B.V. (3)
Rosmolenweg 20, 3356 LK, Papendrecht, Zuid-Holland, Netherlands
Tel.: (31) 786969900
Web Site: http://www.boskalisdolman.nl
Sales Range: $25-49.9 Million
Emp.: 50
Marine Support Services
N.A.I.C.S.: 541330

Subsidiary (Non-US):

Boskalis do Brasil Dragagem e Servicos Maritimos Ltda. (3)
Av Atlantica 1130 - 14 andar - Frente, Copacabana, Rio de Janeiro, 22021-000, Brazil
Tel.: (55) 2135903000
Web Site: http://www.boskalis.com
Dredging Services
N.A.I.C.S.: 237990

Coastal and Inland Marine Services Inc. (3)
PH Centro Comercial Ciudad Siglo XXI Avendida Ricardo J Alfaro y, Cl Juan Pablo II Bethania, Panama, Panama
Tel.: (507) 2600051
Sales Range: $25-49.9 Million
Emp.: 35
Dredging Services
N.A.I.C.S.: 237990

Codramex SA de CV (3)
Carretera Coatzacoalcos Minatitlan Km 5, Elvira Ochoa de Hernandez, Coatzacoalcos, Veracruz, Mexico
Tel.: (52) 9212118200
Dredging Services
N.A.I.C.S.: 237990

Subsidiary (Domestic):

Cofra B.V. (3)
Kwadrantweg 9 Port number 3374, Westpoort, 1042 AG, Amsterdam, Netherlands
Tel.: (31) 206934596

HAL TRUST N.V.

HAL Trust N.V.—(Continued)
Web Site: http://www.cofra.com
Sales Range: $25-49.9 Million
Dredging Services
N.A.I.C.S.: 561990

Subsidiary (Non-US):

Cofra Limited (3)
Orltons Barn Orltons Lane, Rusper, Horsham, RH12 4RN, United Kingdom
Tel.: (44) 129 387 1637
Maritime Civil Engineering Services
N.A.I.C.S.: 541330

Subsidiary (Domestic):

Dockwise Ltd. (3)
Lage Mosten 21, 4822 NJ, Breda, Netherlands
Tel.: (31) 76 548 41 00
Web Site: http://www.dockwise.com
Sales Range: $500-549.9 Million
Emp.: 428
Marine Transportation Services
N.A.I.C.S.: 483111

Subsidiary (Domestic):

Fairstar Heavy Transport N.V. (4)
Weena 690 Floor 20, 3012 CN, Rotterdam, Netherlands
Tel.: (31) 78 6969 000
Web Site: http://www.fairstar.com
Sales Range: $50-74.9 Million
Emp.: 80
Marine Heavy Transport Solutions
N.A.I.C.S.: 483111

Subsidiary (Domestic):

Fairstar Maritime Services BV (5)
Weena 690, PO Box 2225, 3012 NJ, Rotterdam, Netherlands
Tel.: (31) 104035333
Web Site: http://www.fairstar.com
Sales Range: $25-49.9 Million
Emp.: 35
Marine Shipping Services
N.A.I.C.S.: 488320

Subsidiary (Non-US):

Dragamex SA de CV (3)
Julio Verne 56 Floor 5, Miguel Hidalgo, 11560, Mexico, Mexico
Tel.: (52) 5552793630
Web Site: http://www.dragamex.net
Sales Range: $100-124.9 Million
Emp.: 300
Dredging Services
N.A.I.C.S.: 237990

Dragapor Dragagens de Portugal S.A. (3)
Av D Manuel I, 2890-014, Alcochete, Portugal
Tel.: (351) 212348240
Web Site: http://www.boskalis.com
Dredging Services
N.A.I.C.S.: 237990

Dravensa C.A. (3)
Urbanizacion Valle Abajo, Caracas, Venezuela
Tel.: (58) 212 215 3903
Maritime Civil Engineering Services
N.A.I.C.S.: 541330

Gardline Shipping Limited (3)
Endeavour House Admiralty Road Great Yarmouth, Norfolk, NR30 3NG, United Kingdom
Tel.: (44) 1493 845600
Web Site: http://www.gardline.com
Investment Management Service
N.A.I.C.S.: 523940

Subsidiary (Domestic):

Alicat Workboats Limited (4)
Southtown Road, Great Yarmouth, NR31 0JJ, Norfolk, United Kingdom
Tel.: (44) 1493655171
Web Site: http://www.alicatworkboats.com
Boat & Ship Building Services
N.A.I.C.S.: 336612
Steve Thacker (Gen Mgr)

Subsidiary (US):

Alpine Ocean Seismic Survey, Inc. (4)
155 Hudson Ave, Norwood, NJ 07648
Tel.: (201) 768-8000
Web Site: http://www.alpineocean.com
Geophysical Surveying Services
N.A.I.C.S.: 541370
Robert Mecarini (Pres)

Subsidiary (Domestic):

Applied Satellite Technology Ltd (4)
Satellite House Bessemer Way Harfreys Industrial Estate, Great Yarmouth, Norfolk, NR31 0LX, United Kingdom
Tel.: (44) 1493440011
Web Site: http://www.theastgroup.com
Satellite Communication Services
N.A.I.C.S.: 517410

Subsidiary (Non-US):

AST Distribution Asia Pte Ltd (5)
Blk 4 Kaki Bukit Ave 1 #07-08, 417939, Singapore, Singapore
Tel.: (65) 62916605
Satellite Communication Services
N.A.I.C.S.: 517410

Subsidiary (Domestic):

AST Marine Sciences Ltd (5)
Satellite House Bessemer Way Harfreys Industrial Estate, Great Yarmouth, Norfolk, NR31 0LX, United Kingdom
Tel.: (44) 1493440011
Satellite Communication Services
N.A.I.C.S.: 517410

Subsidiary (Non-US):

Applied Satellite Technology Australia Pty Ltd (5)
Satellite House 33a Walters Drive Osborne Park, Perth, 6017, WA, Australia
Tel.: (61) 892054000
Web Site: http://www.asta.net.au
Satellite Communication Services
N.A.I.C.S.: 517410

Subsidiary (Domestic):

Applied Satellite Technology Systems Ltd (5)
Systems House Woodside Road, Eastleigh, SO50 4ET, United Kingdom
Tel.: (44) 2380641144
Web Site: http://www.ast-systems.co.uk
Satellite Telecommunications
N.A.I.C.S.: 517410

Subsidiary (US):

Applied Satellite Technology Systems US LLC (5)
Fiesta Tech Center Ste 105, Gilbert, AZ 85233
Tel.: (480) 247-2439
Web Site: http://www.theastgroup.com
Satellite Communication Services
N.A.I.C.S.: 517410

Subsidiary (Domestic):

Castell SatCom Radio Ltd (5)
Unit 6 Centurion Park Kendal Road, Shrewsbury, SY1 4EH, United Kingdom
Tel.: (44) 8452939497
Web Site: http://www.castellsatcomradio.com
Satellite Communication Services
N.A.I.C.S.: 517410

Subsidiary (Domestic):

C A Design Services Ltd (4)
The Design Centre Hewett Road Gapton Hall, Great Yarmouth, NR31 0NN, Norfolk, United Kingdom
Tel.: (44) 1493440444
Web Site: http://www.cadesignservices.co.uk
Architectural Design & Engineering Services
N.A.I.C.S.: 541310
Clare Montgomery (Mktg Mgr)

Charity & Taylor (Electronic Services) Ltd (4)
Waterside House Falmouth, Penryn, TR10 8BE, United Kingdom
Tel.: (44) 1326653105
Web Site: http://www.charityandtaylor.com
Satellite Communication Services
N.A.I.C.S.: 517410

GSL Dardan Limited (4)
Quern House Mill Court Great Shelford, Cambridge, CB 22 5LD, United Kingdom
Tel.: (44) 1603447000
Web Site: http://www.dardansecurity.co.uk
Security Consulting Services
N.A.I.C.S.: 541690
Mark Duffy (Chm)

Howards (Estate Agents) Limited (4)
Colwyn House Sheepen Place, Colchester, CO3 3LD, United Kingdom
Tel.: (44) 1493665005
Web Site: http://www.howards.co.uk
Real Estate Consulting Service
N.A.I.C.S.: 531210
Chris Mitchell (Mng Dir)

Lankelma Ltd (4)
Coldharbour Barn Coldharbour Lane, Iden, TN31 7UT, East Sussex, United Kingdom
Tel.: (44) 1797280050
Web Site: http://www.lankelma.co.uk
Geophysical Surveying Services
N.A.I.C.S.: 541370
Eric Zon (Mng Dir)

Made By Prosper Limited (4)
1 Water End Barns Eversholt, Milton Keynes, MK17 9EA, United Kingdom
Tel.: (44) 1525309400
Web Site: http://www.prosper-design.com
Architectural Services
N.A.I.C.S.: 541310
Adam Taylor (Dir-Creative)

SEtech (Geotechnical Engineers) Ltd (4)
Endeavour House Admiralty Road, Great Yarmouth, NR30 3NG, Norfolk, United Kingdom
Tel.: (44) 1493845687
Web Site: http://www.setech-uk.com
Geophysical Surveying Services
N.A.I.C.S.: 541370

Titan Environmental Surveys Ltd (4)
Orion House Parc Crescent Waterton Industrial Estate, Bridgend, CF31 3BQ, United Kingdom
Tel.: (44) 1656673673
Web Site: http://www.titansurveys.com
Geophysical Surveying Services
N.A.I.C.S.: 541370

Subsidiary (Non-US):

HDC Wasserbau Nord GmbH (3)
Spaldingstrasse 218, 20097, Hamburg, Germany
Tel.: (49) 40235 167 2510
Maritime Civil Engineering Services
N.A.I.C.S.: 541330

Heinrich Hirdes GmbH (3)
Am Festungsgraben 10, 21079, Hamburg, Germany
Tel.: (49) 407660940
Web Site: http://www.hirdes.boskalis.com
Sales Range: $100-124.9 Million
Hydraulic Engineering Services
N.A.I.C.S.: 213112

Subsidiary (Domestic):

Heinrich Hirdes Kampfmittelraumung GmbH (4)
Bauhofstr 8B, 21079, Hamburg, Germany
Tel.: (49) 407660940
Web Site: http://www.heinrichherdes.de
Emp.: 150
Marine Support Services
N.A.I.C.S.: 541330

Subsidiary (Non-US):

Horizon Survey Company (FZE) (3)
SAIF Zone, PO Box 68785, Sharjah, United Arab Emirates
Tel.: (971) 6 557 3045
Web Site: https://www.horizon-geosciences.com
Marine Survey Services
N.A.I.C.S.: 488390

INTERNATIONAL PUBLIC

Subsidiary (Domestic):

Hydronamic B.V. (3)
Rosmolenweg 20, PO Box 209, 3356 LK, Papendrecht, Netherlands
Tel.: (31) 78 696 9099
Web Site: https://www.hydronamic.nl
Sales Range: $25-49.9 Million
Emp.: 50
Marine Engineering Services
N.A.I.C.S.: 541330

Subsidiary (Non-US):

Irish Dredging Company Ltd. (3)
Pembroke House Pembroke Street, Cork, Ireland
Tel.: (353) 214277399
Web Site: http://www.irishdredging.com
Sales Range: $25-49.9 Million
Dredging Services
N.A.I.C.S.: 237990

Subsidiary (Domestic):

J. van Vliet B.V. (3)
Keyboard Road 3, 1033 MZ, Amsterdam, Netherlands
Tel.: (31) 20 493 6370
Web Site: https://www.jvanvlietbv.nl
Civil Engineering Services
N.A.I.C.S.: 541330

Subsidiary (Non-US):

Nigerian Westminster Dredging & Marine Ltd. (3)
Plot 2 Kwara Street Osborne Estate, Ikoyi, Lagos, Nigeria
Tel.: (234) 13427531
Web Site: http://www.boskalis.com
Emp.: 600
Dredging & Marine Engineering Services
N.A.I.C.S.: 237990

P.T. Boskalis International Indonesia (3)
Office Tower Level 30 Unit D Jl Casablanca Raya Kav 88 Selatan, Kuningan, 12870, Jakarta, Indonesia
Tel.: (62) 2129820205
Web Site: http://www.boskalis.com
Sales Range: $25-49.9 Million
Marine Engineering Services
N.A.I.C.S.: 541330

Rever Offshore UK Limited (3)
1 Park Row, Leeds, LS1 5AB, Scotland, United Kingdom
Tel.: (44) 1224 857755
Subsea Construction; Offshore Operational & Maintenance Support
N.A.I.C.S.: 237990
Howard Woodcock (CEO)

Subsidiary (Non-US):

Bibby Offshore AS (4)
Moseidveien 1, 4033, Stavanger, Norway
Tel.: (47) 21 95 46 00
Web Site: http://www.bibbyoffshore.com
Maintenance Support Services
N.A.I.C.S.: 213112

Division (Non-US):

Bibby Offshore Limited (4)
29 Long Circular Road St James, Port of Spain, Trinidad & Tobago
Tel.: (868) 822 6060
Subsea Construction; Offshore Operational & Maintenance Support
N.A.I.C.S.: 237990

Subsidiary (Non-US):

Riovia S.A. (3)
Rivera 232, 70 000, Colonia del Sacramento, Uruguay
Tel.: (598) 45226688
Web Site: http://www.riovia.com
Sales Range: $25-49.9 Million
Emp.: 40
Dredging Services
N.A.I.C.S.: 237990

Subsidiary (Domestic):

SMIT Internationale N.V. (3)
Waalhaven Oostzijde 85, Rotterdam, 3087 BM, Netherlands

AND PRIVATE COMPANIES

Tel.: (31) 104549911
Web Site: http://www.smit.com
Sales Range: $800-899.9 Million
Emp.: 3,618
Harbor Towage, Marine Terminal Management, Wreck Removal & Barge Rental Services
N.A.I.C.S.: 488310

Joint Venture (Non-US):

Asian Lift Pte Ltd (4)
23 Gul Rd, Singapore, 629356, Singapore
Tel.: (65) 66684222
Web Site: http://www.asianlift.com.sg
Sales Range: $25-49.9 Million
Emp.: 10
Marine Heavy Lift Consulting Services
N.A.I.C.S.: 541620

Subsidiary (Domestic):

SMIT Harbour Towage Rotterdam B.V. (4)
Waalhaven Oostzijde 85, Havennummer 2204, 3087 BM, Rotterdam, Netherlands **(100%)**
Tel.: (31) 104549911
Web Site: http://www.smit.com
Sales Range: $100-124.9 Million
Emp.: 320
Freight Transportation Arrangement
N.A.I.C.S.: 488510

Subsidiary (US):

SMIT International (Americas) Inc. (4)
15402 Vantage Pkwy E Ste 316, Houston, TX 77032
Tel.: (281) 372-3500
Web Site: http://www.smit.com
Sales Range: $25-49.9 Million
Emp.: 9
Water Transportation Services
N.A.I.C.S.: 488390

Subsidiary (Domestic):

SMIT Logistics B.V. (4)
Waalhaven Oostzijde 85, Port No 2204, 3087BM, Rotterdam, Netherlands **(100%)**
Tel.: (31) 104549911
Web Site: http://www.smit.com
Sales Range: $100-124.9 Million
Emp.: 300
Freight Transportation Arrangement
N.A.I.C.S.: 488510

Subsidiary (Non-US):

Smit Lamnalco Towage (Australia) Pty. Ltd. (4)
Gate B51 Unit 5 11-13 Friendship Road, Port Botany, Sydney, 2036, NSW, Australia
Tel.: (61) 296950700
Web Site: http://www.smitlamnalco.com
Ship Management Services
N.A.I.C.S.: 532411

Subsidiary (Non-US):

Somague Engenharia, S.A. (3)
Rua Castillo 165 piso 1, Lisbon, 1070-050, Portugal
Tel.: (351) 219104000
Web Site: http://www.somague.pt
Public Utility Construction & Engineering Services
N.A.I.C.S.: 236620
Jose Maria Orihuela Uzal (Pres)

Subsidiary (US):

Stuyvesant Environmental Contracting, LLC (3)
212 Carnegie Ctr Ste 200, Princeton, NJ 08540
Tel.: (609) 897-0800
Maritime Civil Engineering Services
N.A.I.C.S.: 541330

Subsidiary (Non-US):

Terramare Oy (3)
Laurinmaenkuja 3 A, 00440, Helsinki, Uusimaa, Finland
Tel.: (358) 9613621
Web Site: http://www.terramare.boskalis.com

Sales Range: $50-74.9 Million
Marine Construction Services
N.A.I.C.S.: 237990
Hannu Tomperi (Mng Dir)

UAB Boskalis Baltic (3)
Sportininku str 36, Klaipeda, 92271, Lithuania
Tel.: (370) 46401633
Web Site: http://www.boskalis.com
Sales Range: $25-49.9 Million
Marine Engineering Services
N.A.I.C.S.: 541330

Subsidiary (Domestic):

Zandhandel J. van Vliet B.V. (3)
Toetsenbordweg 3, PO Box 37188, 1033 MZ, Amsterdam, Netherlands
Tel.: (31) 204936370
Web Site: http://www.jvanvlietbv.nl
Sales Range: $10-24.9 Million
Dredging Services
N.A.I.C.S.: 561990

Zinkcon International B.V. (3)
Rosmolenweg 20, 3356 LK, Papendrecht, Zuid-Holland, Netherlands
Tel.: (31) 786969099
Marine Engineering Services
N.A.I.C.S.: 541330

HAL Real Estate Inc. (1)
2025 1st Ave Ste 700, Seattle, WA 98121
Tel.: (206) 448-5080
Web Site: https://www.halrealestate.com
Real Estate Services
N.A.I.C.S.: 531390
Jonathan Manheim (Pres)

Timber & Building Supplies Holland N.V. (1)
Symon Spiersweg 17, 1506 RZ, Zaandam, Netherlands
Tel.: (31) 756536262
Web Site: http://www.tabsholland.nl
Construction Services
N.A.I.C.S.: 236220

HALA ENTERPRISES LIMITED
120 E-1 Gulberg 3, Hali Road, Lahore, 54660, Pakistan
Tel.: (92) 51449001721
Web Site: https://www.halaenterprises.com
Year Founded: 1974
HAEL—(PSX)
Rev.: $2,483,953
Assets: $2,529,951
Liabilities: $1,444,526
Net Worth: $1,085,425
Earnings: $50,485
Emp.: 131
Fiscal Year-end: 06/30/19
Towels Mfr
N.A.I.C.S.: 313210
Jillani Jahangir (CEO)

HALBERG A/S
Porthusvej 100, 5700, Svendborg, Denmark
Tel.: (45) 63 225 200   DK
Web Site: http://www.halberg-as.dk
Sales Range: $50-74.9 Million
Emp.: 216
Holding Company; Tobacco Products Mfr, Hotel Owner & Operator, Private Equity & Real Estate Investment Services
N.A.I.C.S.: 551112

Subsidiaries:

Halberg Kapital A/S (1)
Porthusvej 100, 5700, Svendborg, Denmark
Tel.: (45) 63 225 250
Web Site: http://www.halbergkapital.com
Emp.: 50
Privater Equity Firm
N.A.I.C.S.: 523999
Thomas Bastrup (Dir-Daily Mgmt)

HALCOM VIETNAM JSC
9th Floor Hoa Binh Tower No 106 Hoang Quoc Viet Str, Cau Giay Dist, Hanoi, Vietnam
Tel.: (84) 2435624709
Web Site: https://www.halcom.vn
Year Founded: 2001
HID—(HNX)
Investment Management Service
N.A.I.C.S.: 525990
Nguyen Quang Huan (Pres)

HALCYON COAST INVESTMENT (CANADA) LTD.
2111 Ottawa Avenue, West Vancouver, V7V 2S5, BC, Canada
Tel.: (604) 728-1829
Investment Holding Company
N.A.I.C.S.: 551112
Hai Zheng (Gen Mgr)

Subsidiaries:

Taian AGS Pipeline Construction Co., Ltd. (1)
East Panhe Street, Tai'an, 271000, Shandong, China **(60%)**
Tel.: (86) 538 822 3106
Web Site: http://www.taianags.com.cn
Pipeline Engineering & Construction Services
N.A.I.C.S.: 237120

HALCYON TECHNOLOGY PUBLIC COMPANY LIMITED
41 Moo 14 Bangchan Industrial Estate Soi 6 Serithai Road, Minburi, Bangkok, 10510, Thailand
Tel.: (66) 29063242
Web Site: https://www.halcyon.co.th
HTECH—(THA)
Rev.: $30,802,783
Assets: $52,081,394
Liabilities: $15,584,133
Net Worth: $36,497,260
Earnings: $974,720
Fiscal Year-end: 12/31/23
Cutting Tools & High Precision Parts Mfr
N.A.I.C.S.: 333515
Pete Rimchala (Mng Dir & Member-Exec Bd)

Subsidiaries:

Halcyon Metal Company Limited (1)
41 Mu 14 Bangchan Industrial Estate Soi 6 Serithai Road, Minburi, Bangkok, 10510, Thailand
Tel.: (66) 90 632 4250
Web Site: https://www.halcyon.co.th
High Precision Tools & Gauges Mfr
N.A.I.C.S.: 333310
Pete Rimchala (Mng Dir)

Halcyon Technology (M) Sdn. Bhd. (1)
Block A-6-11 Ativo Plaza No 1 Jalan PJU 9/1 Damansara Avenue PJU 9, Bandar Sri Damansara, 52200, Kuala Lumpur, Malaysia
Tel.: (60) 36 263 0313
Cutting Machinery Tool Mfr & Distr
N.A.I.C.S.: 333515

Halcyon Technology (Philippines) Inc. (1)
Orient Goldcrest Building 6 Unit 1 Lot 3281-J Phase 6, Laguna Technopark, Binan, Laguna, Philippines
Tel.: (63) 49 502 2295
Web Site: https://halcyonphilippines.com
Cutting Machine Tool Mfr
N.A.I.C.S.: 333515
Mamilcar P. Azarias (Pres)

PT HTECH Tools Indonesia (1)
Mintra Sunter Boulevard Blok B No 18 JI Yos Sudarso Kav 89, Jakarta Utara, 14350, Indonesia
Tel.: (62) 216 530 6109
Industrial Machinery Equipment Whslr
N.A.I.C.S.: 423830

HALDANE FISHER LTD.

HALDER VENTURES LIMITED

Shepherds Way Carnbane, Newry, BT35 6QQ, United Kingdom
Tel.: (44) 2830263201
Web Site: http://www.haldane-fisher.com
Year Founded: 1946
Sales Range: $75-99.9 Million
Emp.: 250
Building & Plumbing Product Distr
N.A.I.C.S.: 444180
Andrew Laird (Dir-HR)

Subsidiaries:

The Douglas Steam Saw Mill & Timber Company Limited (1)
Lake Road, Douglas, IM1 5AF, Isle of Man
Tel.: (44) 1624624466
Web Site: http://www.dssmltd.com
Sales Range: $25-49.9 Million
Emp.: 50
Lumber Distr
N.A.I.C.S.: 423990

HALDANE MCCALL PLC
Acclaim House 12 Mount Havelock, Douglas, 1MI 2QG, Isle of Man
Tel.: (44) 162 461 8444   IM
Web Site: http://www.haldanemccall.de
Year Founded: 2011
Sales Range: $25-49.9 Million
Emp.: 275
Holding Company; Hotels, Real Estate & Banking
N.A.I.C.S.: 551112

Subsidiaries:

Suru Group Ltd. (1)
2 Sobo Arobiodu Street GRA, PO Box 6897, Ikeja, Lagos, Nigeria
Tel.: (234) 8171886166
Web Site: http://www.surugroup.com
Holding Company
N.A.I.C.S.: 551111
Edward Ola Akinlade (Chm & Mng Dir)

Subsidiary (Domestic):

Suru Homes Ltd (2)
2 Sobo Arobiodu Street GRA, Ikeja, Lagos, Nigeria
Tel.: (234) 8171886166
Web Site: http://www.suruhomes.com
Residential Building Developer
N.A.I.C.S.: 531110
Nelson Akpodiogaga (Gen Mgr)

HALDER BETEILIGUNGS-BERATUNG GMBH
Solo West Guiollettstrasse 48, 60325, Frankfurt am Main, Germany
Tel.: (49) 69 242 5330   De
Web Site: http://www.halder.eu
Year Founded: 1991
Sales Range: $10-24.9 Million
Emp.: 14
Privater Equity Firm
N.A.I.C.S.: 523999
Paul De Ridder (Founder, CEO & Partner)

HALDER VENTURES LIMITED
Diamond Heritage Building 16 Strand Road Unit-1012 10th Floor, Kolkata, 700 001, India
Tel.: (91) 3366075557   In
Web Site: https://www.halderventure.in
Year Founded: 1924
539854—(BOM)
Rev.: $123,318,345
Assets: $36,637,829
Liabilities: $20,501,413
Net Worth: $16,136,416
Earnings: $3,079,481
Emp.: 16
Fiscal Year-end: 03/31/22
Agricultural Product Mfr & Distr
N.A.I.C.S.: 325320

HALDER VENTURES LIMITED

Halder Ventures Limited—(Continued)

Prabhat Kumar Halder *(CFO)*

HALDEX AB
Instrumentgatan 15, PO Box 507,
261 24, Landskrona, Sweden
Tel.: (46) 418476000 SE
Web Site: http://www.haldex.com
HLDX—(OMX)
Rev.: $563,032,960
Assets: $565,474,560
Liabilities: $366,484,160
Net Worth: $198,990,400
Earnings: $27,834,240
Emp.: 2,003
Fiscal Year-end: 12/31/21
Commercial Vehicle Systems, Hydraulic Systems, Garphyttan Wire & Traction Systems Mfr
N.A.I.C.S.: 336340
Walter Frankiewicz *(Exec VP-Americas)*

Subsidiaries:

Haldex ANAND India Ltd. (1)
B-71 MIDC Area Ambad, Nashik, 422010, Maharashtra, India
Tel.: (91) 2536699525
Motor Vehicles Mfr
N.A.I.C.S.: 336211

Haldex Brake Products AB (1)
Instrumentgatan 15, Box 501, 141 46, Landskrona, Sweden
Tel.: (46) 418 47 60 00
Automotive Brake System Mfr
N.A.I.C.S.: 336340
Paer Persson *(VP-HR)*

Haldex Brake Products Corporation (1)
10930 N Pomona Ave, Kansas City, MO 64153
Tel.: (816) 891-2470
Web Site: https://www.haldex.com
Emp.: 100
Commercial Vehicle Proprietary Products Supplier
N.A.I.C.S.: 336390

Division (Domestic):

Haldex Air Management (2)
10930 N Pomona Ave, Kansas City, MO 64153
Tel.: (816) 891-2470
Web Site: http://www.haldex.com
Vehicle Parts Mfr
N.A.I.C.S.: 336390

Plant (Domestic):

Haldex Brake Products Corporation - Little Rock Plant (2)
6800 Geyer Springs Rd, Little Rock, AR 72209
Tel.: (501) 221-4384
Web Site: http://www.haldex.com
Automotive Brake Products Mfr
N.A.I.C.S.: 336340
Ryle Vandervate *(Plant Mgr)*

Subsidiary (Non-US):

Haldex Limited (2)
500 Pinebush Road Unit 1, Cambridge, N1T 0A5, ON, Canada
Tel.: (519) 621-6722
Web Site: https://www.haldex.com
Automotive Brake Parts Distr
N.A.I.C.S.: 423120
Mark Weber *(Mgr-Sls & Distr-Canada)*

Haldex Brake Products GmbH (1)
Mittelgewannweg 27, Postfach 10 25 60, Heidelberg, DE-69015, Germany
Tel.: (49) 62217030
Web Site: http://www.brake-eu.haldex.com
Emp.: 180
Vehicle Parts Mfr
N.A.I.C.S.: 336390
Georg Haussler *(Pres)*

Haldex Brake Products Pty. Ltd. (1)
St Kilda Road Tower Suite 1104 1 Queens Road, Melbourne, 3004, VIC, Australia
Tel.: (61) 395797070
Garphyttan Wire & Traction System Mfr
N.A.I.C.S.: 336340

Haldex Concentric Plc. (1)
Unit 10 Gravelly Park Tyburn Road, Birmingham, B24 8HW, United Kingdom
Tel.: (44) 12 1327 2081
Sales Range: $50-74.9 Million
Emp.: 25
Air & Gas Compressor Mfr
N.A.I.C.S.: 333912
Wim Goossens *(Mng Dir)*

Haldex Espana S.A. (1)
Galileo Galilei num 7 2nd, 08403, Granollers, Spain
Tel.: (34) 93 840 7239
Web Site: http://www.haldex.com
Sales Range: $25-49.9 Million
Emp.: 22
Vehicle Parts Mfr
N.A.I.C.S.: 336390

Haldex Europe SAS (1)
30 rue du Ried, 67720, Weyersheim, France
Tel.: (33) 38 868 2200
Web Site: https://www.haldex.com
Sales Range: $25-49.9 Million
Emp.: 60
Vehicle Parts Mfr
N.A.I.C.S.: 336390

Haldex GmbH (1)
Heinrich-Fuchs-Str 96, 69126, Heidelberg, Germany
Tel.: (49) 6 221 7030
Web Site: http://www.haldex.com
Sales Range: $25-49.9 Million
Emp.: 100
Management Consulting Services
N.A.I.C.S.: 541611
Manfred Vogel *(Gen Mgr)*

Haldex Hungary Kft (1)
Dozsa Gyorgy Ut 93, Szentlorinckata, 2255, Hungary
Tel.: (36) 29631300
Automotive Parts Mfr & Distr
N.A.I.C.S.: 336390

Haldex India Limited (1)
B 71 MIDC Ambad, Nashik, 422010, India
Tel.: (91) 2536699501
Garphyttan Wire & Traction System Mfr
N.A.I.C.S.: 336340

Haldex Int Trading Co Ltd (1)
16 A Zhao Feng World Trade Building No 369 Jiang Su Road, Shanghai, 200050, China
Tel.: (86) 2152400338
Automobile Product Distr
N.A.I.C.S.: 423120

Haldex International Trading (Shanghai) Co., Ltd. (1)
16 A Zhao Feng World Trade Building No 369 Jiang Su Road, Shanghai, 200050, China
Tel.: (86) 215 240 0338
Web Site: http://www.haldex.com
Commercial Vehicle Proprietary Products Supplier
N.A.I.C.S.: 336390

Haldex Italia Srl. (1)
Via Angelo Agostoni 16, 20851, Lissone, MB, Italy
Tel.: (39) 03 947 1702
Web Site: http://www.haldex.com
Vehicle Parts Mfr
N.A.I.C.S.: 336390

Haldex Korea Ltd. (1)
601 Buryong building 6F 263 Cheonhodaero, Dongdaemun-gu, Seoul, 02603, Korea (South)
Tel.: (82) 22 636 7545
Web Site: http://www.hkr.haldex.com
Sales Range: $25-49.9 Million
Emp.: 7
Commercial Vehicle Proprietary Products Supplier
N.A.I.C.S.: 336390
J. D. Yoon *(Mng Dir)*

Haldex Limited (1)
Unit 1 Beaumont Square Durham Way South, Aycliffe Business Park, Newton Aycliffe, DL5 6XN, Durham, United Kingdom
Tel.: (44) 1325 310110
Motor Vehicle Parts Mfr
N.A.I.C.S.: 336390
Pram Mistry *(Gen Mgr)*

Haldex NV (1)
Molenstraat 5 Bus 1, Balegem, Gent, BE-9860, Belgium
Tel.: (32) 93639000
Web Site: http://www.haldex.com
Sales Range: $25-49.9 Million
Emp.: 5
Vehicle Parts Mfr
N.A.I.C.S.: 336390

Haldex Products de Mexico S.A. de C.V. (1)
Carretera Miguel Aleman KM205 Prologis Park Ed 2, 66627, Apodaca, NL, Mexico
Tel.: (52) 818 156 9500
Web Site: https://www.haldex.com
Sales Range: $100-124.9 Million
Emp.: 40
Automotive Braking System Mfr
N.A.I.C.S.: 336340

Haldex Russia OOO (1)
Warszawskoe Shosse 17 Building 2, 117105, Moscow, Russia
Tel.: (7) 4957475956
Web Site: http://www.haldex.com
Emp.: 3
Automotive Parts Mfr & Distr
N.A.I.C.S.: 336390

Haldex Sp. z.o.o. (1)
Ul Wodna 2 Kowale, 46-320, Praszka, Poland
Tel.: (48) 34 350 1100
Web Site: http://www.haldex.com
Automotive Braking Parts Distr
N.A.I.C.S.: 423120

Haldex Vehicle Products (Suzhou) Co. Ltd. (1)
No 6 Longpu Road SIP, Suzhou, 215126, Jiangsu, China
Tel.: (86) 5128 885 5301
Web Site: http://www.haldex.com
Emp.: 2,000
Motor Vehicle Parts Mfr
N.A.I.C.S.: 336390

Haldex Wien Ges.m.b.H. (1)
Leopoldigasse 13-17, A-1230, Vienna, Austria
Tel.: (43) 018651640
Web Site: http://www.brake-au.haldex.com
Sales Range: $25-49.9 Million
Emp.: 25
Vehicle Parts Mfr
N.A.I.C.S.: 336390

Haldex do Brasil Ind. e Comercio Ltda. (1)
Avenida Sebastiao Henrique da Cunha Pontes 8500-Galpao B Saida km156, Presidente Dutra-Chacaras Reunidas-Cond Centro Empres Century, Sao Jose dos Campos, 12238-365, SP, Brazil
Tel.: (55) 1239354000
Web Site: https://www.haldex.com
Vehicle Parts Mfr
N.A.I.C.S.: 336390

Subsidiary (Domestic):

Fabrica Brasileira de Freios S.A. (2)
Rua Anequira 167, Cordovil, Rio de Janeiro, Brazil
Tel.: (55) 2133415749
Vehicle Parts Mfr
N.A.I.C.S.: 336390

Haldex do Brasil Industria e Comercio Ltda. (1)
Avenida Sebastiao Henrique da Cunha Pontes 8500-Galpao B Saida Km 156, Presidente Dutra-Chacaras Reunidas-Cond Centro Empres Century, 12238-365, Sao Jose dos Campos, Sao Paulo, Brazil
Tel.: (55) 1239354020
Garphyttan Wire & Traction System Mfr
N.A.I.C.S.: 336340

HALDYN GLASS LTD.
B-1201 Lotus Corporate Park Off Western Express Highway, Goregoan East, Mumbai, 400 063, India
Tel.: (91) 2242878999
Web Site: https://www.haldynglass.com
515147—(BOM)
Rev.: $29,750,243
Assets: $27,560,196
Liabilities: $6,615,732
Net Worth: $20,944,464
Earnings: $1,613,976
Emp.: 351
Fiscal Year-end: 03/31/22
Glass Container Mfr
N.A.I.C.S.: 327213
N. D. Shetty *(Chm)*

HALEON PLC
Building 5 First Floor the Heights, Weybridge, KT13 0NY, Surrey, United Kingdom
Tel.: (44) 1932959500 UK
Web Site: https://www.haleon.com
Year Founded: 2022
HLN—(LSE)
Rev.: $14,266,599,344
Assets: $42,987,881,848
Liabilities: $21,870,739,712
Net Worth: $21,117,142,136
Earnings: $1,402,423,630
Emp.: 25,408
Fiscal Year-end: 12/31/23
Health Care Srvices
N.A.I.C.S.: 621610
Brian J. McNamara *(CEO)*

Subsidiaries:

GSK Consumer Healthcare Chile SpA (1)
Av Andres Bello 2457 Costanera Center Torre 2 Piso 20, Providencia Region Metropolitana de Santiago, Santiago, Chile
Tel.: (56) 223829000
Vaccine & Medicine Mfr
N.A.I.C.S.: 325412

Haleon Italy S.R.L. (1)
Via Monte Rosa 91, 20149, Milan, Italy
Tel.: (39) 0238061
Consumer Healthcare Product Mfr & Distr
N.A.I.C.S.: 325412

Haleon Netherlands B.V. (1)
Van Asch van Wijckstraat 55H, 3811 LP, Amersfoort, Netherlands
Tel.: (31) 332081100
Emp.: 200
Pharmaceutical Product Mfr & Distr
N.A.I.C.S.: 325412

Haleon New Zealand ULC (1)
12 Madden Street, Auckland, 1010, New Zealand
Tel.: (64) 800540144
Web Site: https://www.voltaren.co.nz
Pain Relief Product Mfr & Distr
N.A.I.C.S.: 325412

Haleon Pakistan Limited (1)
11-A 11th Floor Sky Tower East Wing HC-3 Block 4 Scheme-5, Dolmen City Clifton, Karachi, 75600, Pakistan
Tel.: (92) 21111425366
Web Site: https://www.haleon.pk
Consumer Healthcare Product Mfr & Distr
N.A.I.C.S.: 325412

HALEWOOD INTERNATIONAL LTD.
The Sovereign Distillery Wilson Rd, Huyton Business Park, Liverpool, L36 6AD, United Kingdom
Tel.: (44) 1514808800 UK
Web Site: http://www.halewood-int.com
Year Founded: 1978
Sales Range: $350-399.9 Million
Emp.: 1,500
Wine, Spirits & Specialty Drinks Distr
N.A.I.C.S.: 424820
Graham Oak *(Dir-Intl & Strategic)*

AND PRIVATE COMPANIES

Subsidiaries:

H&A Prestige Bottling Ltd. (1)
Ackhurst Business Park Ackhurst Road, Chorley, PR7 1NH, Lancashire, United Kingdom
Tel.: (44) 1257479100
Web Site:
http://www.hacontractbottling.co.uk
Spirit Bottle Mfr
N.A.I.C.S.: 327213
Richard Watson *(Mgr-Supply Chain)*

HALFORDS GROUP PLC
Icknield Street Drive Washford West, Redditch, B98 0DE, Worcestershire, United Kingdom
Tel.: (44) 1527517601
Web Site:
https://www.halfordscompany.com
Year Founded: 1892
HFD—(LSE)
Rev.: $1,859,533,312
Assets: $1,735,301,932
Liabilities: $987,198,212
Net Worth: $748,103,720
Earnings: $105,494,844
Emp.: 11,512
Fiscal Year-end: 04/01/22
Car Parts & Accessories, Cycles & Cycle Accessories Whslr
N.A.I.C.S.: 455219
Andy Randall *(COO)*

Subsidiaries:

Axle Group Holdings Limited (1)
26-32 Millbrae Rd, Langside, Glasgow, G42 9TU, United Kingdom
Tel.: (44) 1416323222
Holding Company
N.A.I.C.S.: 551112
Alan Revie *(Chm)*

Holding (Domestic):

National Tyre Services Ltd. (2)
Regent House, Heaton Lane, Stockport, SK4 1BS, Cheshire, United Kingdom
Tel.: (44) 1614291200
Web Site: http://www.national.co.uk
Sales Range: $25-49.9 Million
Emp.: 85
Automotive Maintenance Services & Tire & Automotive Parts Distr
N.A.I.C.S.: 441330

Stepgrades Motor Accessories Ltd. (2)
26 32 Millbrae Road, Langside, Glasgow, G42 9TU, United Kingdom
Tel.: (44) 1416323222
Web Site: http://www.viking.co.uk
Sales Range: $25-49.9 Million
Emp.: 50
General Automotive Maintenance Services & Tire Distr
N.A.I.C.S.: 811198
Kevin Peck *(Mng Dir)*

Constant Price Monitor Limited (1)
26-32 Millbrae Road, Langside, Glasgow, G42 9TU, United Kingdom
Tel.: (44) 8007310133
Web Site: https://www.tyre-shopper.co.uk
Automotive Tires Distr
N.A.I.C.S.: 423130

Halfords Finance Limited (1)
3 Great Cambridge Road, Enfield, EN11EL, United Kingdom (100%)
Tel.: (44) 2083660787
Financial Investment Activities
N.A.I.C.S.: 523999

Performance Cycling Limited (1)
Summer Lake Lake 11, Cerney Wick Lane South Cerney, Cirencester, GL7 5LW, Gloucestershire, United Kingdom
Tel.: (44) 1285851946
Web Site:
http://www.performancecycles.co.uk
Bicycle Retailer
N.A.I.C.S.: 459110
Andy Kirk *(Exec Dir)*

The Universal Tyre Company (Deptford) Limited (1)
Unit 8-9 Orbital One Green Street Green Road, Dartford, DA1 1QG, United Kingdom
Tel.: (44) 1322421980
Web Site: https://www.universal-tyres.co.uk
Automotive Tires Distr
N.A.I.C.S.: 423130

Tredz Limited (1)
Castell Close Swansea Retail Park, Llansamlet, Swansea, SA7 9FH, United Kingdom
Tel.: (44) 1792799508
Web Site: http://www.tredz.co.uk
Bicycle Retailer
N.A.I.C.S.: 459110

HALFORDS NEDERLAND BV
Palladiostraat 37, 3066 AH, Rotterdam, Netherlands
Tel.: (31) 854831810
Web Site: http://www.halfords.nl
Year Founded: 1976
Sales Range: $50-74.9 Million
Emp.: 135
Automobile & Bicycle Accessories Retailer
N.A.I.C.S.: 459110
Peter Jan Stormmesand *(CEO)*

HALFWAY MOTORS 1989 LTD
940 Memorial Avenue, Thunder Bay, P7B 4A2, ON, Canada
Tel.: (807) 345-2327
Web Site:
http://www.halfwaymotors.com
Rev.: $14,537,196
Emp.: 32
New & Used Car Dealers
N.A.I.C.S.: 441110
Daniel Trevisanutto *(Partner)*

HALI BUROMOBEL GMBH
Karl-Schachinger-Strasse 1, A-4070, Eferding, Austria
Tel.: (43) 7272 3731 0
Web Site: http://www.hali.at
Sales Range: $50-74.9 Million
Emp.: 245
Furniture Mfr
N.A.I.C.S.: 337214
Gunther Marchtrenker *(Mng Dir)*

HALIFAX CHRYSLER DODGE
12 Lakelands Boulevard, Halifax, B3S 1S8, NS, Canada
Tel.: (902) 455-0566
Web Site:
http://www.halifaxchrysler.ca
Year Founded: 1958
Sales Range: $25-49.9 Million
New & Used Car Dealers
N.A.I.C.S.: 441110

HALIFAX PORT AUTHORITY
1215 Marginal Road, Halifax, B3H 4P8, NS, Canada
Tel.: (902) 426-8222
Web Site:
https://www.portofhalifax.ca
Year Founded: 1984
Rev.: $12,109,399
Emp.: 60
Marine Cargo Services
N.A.I.C.S.: 488320
Karen Oldfield *(Pres & CEO)*

HALIFAX RACK & SCREW CUTTING CO. LTD.
Armytage Road, Brighouse, HD6 1QA, West Yorkshire, United Kingdom
Tel.: (44) 1484 714 667 UK
Web Site: http://www.halifaxrs.com
Year Founded: 1953
Gear Rack, Screw & Nut Mfr
N.A.I.C.S.: 332722

Dale Norman *(Sls Mgr)*

Subsidiaries:

Halifax Rack and Screw North America (1)
3786 Hopper Hill Rd, Cincinnati, OH 45255
Tel.: (513) 898-0745
Industrial Supplies Whslr
N.A.I.C.S.: 423840

HALK FINANSAL KIRALAMA A.S.
Buyukdere Cad No 78 Akabe Is Merkezi K 8 D 23-24, Sisli, Istanbul, 34394, Turkiye
Tel.: (90) 212 314 84 84
Web Site:
http://www.halkleasing.com.tr
HALKF—(IST)
Sales Range: Less than $1 Million
Financial Lending Services
N.A.I.C.S.: 533110

HALK GAYRIMENKUL YATIRIM ORTAKLIGI A.S.
Barbaros Mah Begonya Sk WBC is Merkezi No 2H, Atasehir, 34774, Istanbul, Turkiye
Tel.: (90) 2166001000
Web Site: https://www.halkgyo.com.tr
Year Founded: 2010
HLGYO—(IST)
Rev.: $53,462,574
Assets: $950,698,454
Liabilities: $270,699,448
Net Worth: $679,999,006
Earnings: $87,545,413
Emp.: 40
Fiscal Year-end: 12/31/23
Real Estate Investment Services
N.A.I.C.S.: 523999
Yasar Goktas *(Deputy Pres-Finance, Pres-Fin Affairs, Fund Mgmt, Sls, Mktg, HR, and Admin Affairs & Deputy)*

HALK VARLIK KIRALAMA AS
Barbaros Mahallesi Sebboy Sokak No 4/1, Atasehir, 34746, Istanbul, Turkiye
Tel.: (90) 2123148288
Web Site:
http://www.halkvarlikkiralama.com.tr
HLVKS—(IST)
Sales Range: Less than $1 Million
Real Estate Investment Services
N.A.I.C.S.: 531210
Himmer Karadag *(Chm)*

HALL CONSTRUCTION SERVICES LTD
Stotforth Hill House, Windlestone, Rushyford, DL17 0NF, Durham, United Kingdom
Tel.: (44) 1325311013
Web Site:
http://www.hallconstruction.uk.com
Year Founded: 1974
Rev.: $74,709,140
Emp.: 247
Construction Services
N.A.I.C.S.: 237990
Stephen Hall *(Founder)*

HALL LONGMORE (PROPRIETARY) LIMITED
2 Osborne Road, Wadeville, Germiston, 8024, South Africa
Tel.: (27) 11 874 7300
Web Site: http://www.hall-longmore.co.za
Year Founded: 1924
Emp.: 50
Steel Pole Mfr
N.A.I.C.S.: 331210
Ferdinand Fuhrmann *(Mng Dir)*

HALLA GROUP
Sigma Tower 7-19 Sincheon-dong, Songpa-gu, Seoul, Korea (South)
Tel.: (82) 2 3434 5114
Year Founded: 1962
Holding Company
N.A.I.C.S.: 551112
Mong-won Chung *(Chm)*

Subsidiaries:

HL Holdings Corporation (1)
343-1 Manho-Ri Poseung-Eup, Pyeongtaek, 451-821, Kyonggi-Do, Korea (South) (23.3%)
Tel.: (82) 234346363
Web Site: http://www.hallaholdings.com
Rev.: $979,540,356
Assets: $1,748,656,371
Liabilities: $977,670,171
Net Worth: $770,986,199
Earnings: $1,902,535
Emp.: 280
Fiscal Year-end: 12/31/2022
Holding Company; Automotive, Construction, Education & Sports Products & Services
N.A.I.C.S.: 551112

Affiliate (Domestic):

HL D&I Halla Corporation (2)
Olympic-ro, Songpagu, Seoul, Korea (South) (34.84%)
Tel.: (82) 234345114
Web Site: http://www.halla.co.kr
Rev.: $1,129,091,704
Assets: $1,278,912,517
Liabilities: $951,258,161
Net Worth: $327,654,357
Earnings: $19,251,401
Emp.: 1,165
Fiscal Year-end: 12/31/2022
Heavy Construction Services
N.A.I.C.S.: 237990
Mong-won Chung *(Chm)*

HL Mando Co, Ltd (2)
21 Pangyo-ro 255 beon-gil, Bundang-gu, Seongnam, Gyeonggi-do, Korea (South) (30.25%)
Tel.: (82) 262442114
Web Site: http://www.mando.om
Rev.: $5,764,897,666
Assets: $4,483,760,359
Liabilities: $2,739,797,091
Net Worth: $1,743,963,268
Earnings: $90,726,626
Emp.: 3,883
Fiscal Year-end: 12/31/2022
Automotive Brake, Steering & Suspension Components Mfr
N.A.I.C.S.: 336390
Mong-won Chung *(Chm & Co-CEO)*

Subsidiary (Domestic):

Halla Meister Ltd. (3)
14th FL Luther Convention Center 7-20 Sincheon-dong, Songpa-gu, Seoul, Korea (South)
Tel.: (82) 2 526 0500
Motor Vehicle Parts Distr
N.A.I.C.S.: 423110

Subsidiary (Non-US):

Halla Meister Shanghai Trading Co., Ltd. (4)
Room 2503 Innov Tower Block A 1801 Hongmei Rd, Shanghai, 200233, China
Tel.: (86) 21 6128 0090
Emp.: 15
Automobile Component Distr
N.A.I.C.S.: 423120
Hwang Ohoyoen *(Gen Mgr)*

Halla Meister Suzhou Logistics Co., Ltd (4)
No 328 Mayun Road, Suzhou, China
Tel.: (86) 512 6665 6114
Logistics Consulting Servies
N.A.I.C.S.: 541614

Subsidiary (US):

Meister Logistics Corporation America (4)
4201 Northpark Dr, Opelika, AL 36801

HALLA GROUP

Halla Group—(Continued)
Tel.: (334) 364-3706
Logistics Consulting Servies
N.A.I.C.S.: 541614

One Stop Undercar, Inc. (4)
2938 S Daimler St, Santa Ana, CA 92705
Tel.: (949) 955-2600
Web Site: http://www.onesps.com
Sales Range: $10-24.9 Million
Emp.: 50
Automotive Brakes
N.A.I.C.S.: 423120
Fred Myers (CEO)

Division (Domestic):

Mando Corporation - Iksan Division (3)
863 Palbong-dong, Iksan, 570-300, Jeollabuk-do, Korea (South)
Tel.: (82) 63 830 9114
Emp.: 526
Automotive Components Mfr
N.A.I.C.S.: 336340

Mando Corporation - Wonju Division (3)
5-22 Bangye-ri, Munmak-eup, Wonju, 220-805, Gangwon-do, Korea (South)
Tel.: (82) 33 730 6114
Emp.: 1,208
Automotive Components Mfr
N.A.I.C.S.: 336340

Uriman Inc. (1)
650 N Punete St, Brea, CA 92821
Tel.: (714) 257-2080
Web Site: http://www.uriman.com
Automobile Component Distr
N.A.I.C.S.: 423120
Brandon Song (Pres & CEO)

HALLENSTEIN GLASSON HOLDINGS LIMITED
Level 3 235-237 Broadway Newmarket, PO Box 91148, Auckland, 1023, New Zealand
Tel.: (64) 93062500
Web Site: https://www.hallensteinglasson.nz
HLG—(NZX)
Rev.: $245,042,464
Assets: $121,153,708
Liabilities: $63,545,455
Net Worth: $57,608,254
Earnings: $19,125,000
Emp.: 643
Fiscal Year-end: 08/01/23
Holding Company; Clothing Retailer
N.A.I.C.S.: 551112
Warren James Bell (Chm)

Subsidiaries:

Glassons Limited (1)
Level 3 235-237 Broadway Newmarket, Auckland, 1023, New Zealand
Tel.: (64) 33772203
Web Site: https://www.glassons.com
Clothing Retailer
N.A.I.C.S.: 458110

Hallenstein Bros Limited (1)
Level 3 235-237 Broadway, Auckland, 1023, New Zealand
Tel.: (64) 99762000
Web Site: https://www.hallenstein.com
Sales Range: $25-49.9 Million
Emp.: 30
Men's Clothing Stores
N.A.I.C.S.: 458110

Retail 161 Limited (1)
Level 3 237 Broadway Newmarket, Auckland, 1023, New Zealand
Tel.: (64) 93601530
Web Site: http://www.stormnz.com
Women's Apparel Retailer
N.A.I.C.S.: 424350

HALLMARK FORD SALES LIMITED
10025 152nd Street, Surrey, V3R 4G6, BC, Canada
Tel.: (604) 584-1222
Web Site: http://hallmarkford.autotrader.ca
Year Founded: 1984
Rev.: $34,224,910
Emp.: 72
New & Used Car Dealers
N.A.I.C.S.: 441110
Jeff Hall (Gen Mgr)

HALLMARK POULTRY PROCESSORS LTD.
1756 Pandora St, Vancouver, V5L 1M1, BC, Canada
Tel.: (604) 254-9885
Web Site: http://www.hallmarkpoultry.com
Rev.: $59,470,346
Emp.: 300
Poultry & Poultry Products Whslr
N.A.I.C.S.: 424440
Clifford Pollon (Pres)

Subsidiaries:

JD Sweid Foods Ltd. (1)
9696-199A Street, Langley, V1M 2X7, BC, Canada
Tel.: (604) 888-8662
Web Site: https://www.jdsweid.com
Emp.: 600
Meat Distr
N.A.I.C.S.: 424470

HALLOREN SCHOKOLADEN-FABRIK AG
Delitzscher Str 70, 06112, Halle, Germany
Tel.: (49) 34556420 De
Web Site: http://www.halloren.de
Year Founded: 1804
Sales Range: $125-149.9 Million
Emp.: 780
Chocolate Mfr & Distr
N.A.I.C.S.: 311351
Klaus Lelle (Chm-Exec Bd, CEO & Dir-Sls)

HALLVARSSON & HALVARSSON AB
Sveavagen 20, Stockholm, 103 59, Sweden
Tel.: (46) 84072000
Web Site: http://www.halvarsson.se
Sales Range: $25-49.9 Million
Emp.: 150
Communication Consulting Services
N.A.I.C.S.: 561499
Anders Halvarsson (Founding Partner)

HALMA PLC
Misbourne Court Rectory Way, Amersham, HP7 0DE, Bucks, United Kingdom
Tel.: (44) 1494721111 UK
Web Site: https://www.halma.com
Year Founded: 1894
HALMY—(OTCIQ)
Rev.: $2,570,904,950
Assets: $3,791,582,400
Liabilities: $1,596,814,962
Net Worth: $2,194,767,438
Earnings: $339,737,108
Emp.: 8,612
Fiscal Year-end: 03/31/24
Holding Company; Fire & Gas Detectors, Elevator Electronics, Water Purification, Process Safety, Resistors & Optics
N.A.I.C.S.: 551112
Jennifer Ward (Dir-Comm, Talent, and Culture-Grp)

Subsidiaries:

ASL Holdings Limited (1)
The Oaks Spring Hill Office Park Harborough Road, Pitsford, Northampton, NN6 9AA, United Kingdom
Tel.: (44) 1604883880
Web Site: https://www.aslh.co.uk
Information Technology Services
N.A.I.C.S.: 541511
Andy Walton (Ops Mgr)

Advanced Fire Systems Inc. (1)
4614 N Freya, Spokane, WA 99217
Tel.: (509) 489-5040
Web Site: https://www.advfiresystems.net
Plumbing, Heating & Air-Conditioning Contractors
N.A.I.C.S.: 238220
Bob Skelton (Owner)

Alicat BV (1)
Geograaf 24, 6921 EW, Duiven, Netherlands
Tel.: (31) 262031651
Mass Flow Meter & Pressure Controller Mfr
N.A.I.C.S.: 334514

Alicat Scientific India Private Limited (1)
101 Hamilton A Bldg Near Hiranandani Hospital Hiranandani Estate, Patli Pada Ghodbunder Road, Thane, 400 607, Maharashtra, India
Tel.: (91) 2246081434
Pressure Meter & Controller Mfr
N.A.I.C.S.: 334513

Ampac Europe Limited (1)
Unit 2 Waterbrook Estate Waterbrook Road, Alton, GU34 2UD, Hampshire, United Kingdom
Tel.: (44) 1420592070
Fire Detection Equipment Mfr & Distr
N.A.I.C.S.: 334290

Ampac NZ Limited (1)
Unit H 31 William Pickering Drive, Rosedale, Auckland, 0632, New Zealand
Tel.: (64) 94438072
Fire Detection Equipment Mfr & Distr
N.A.I.C.S.: 334290

Ampac Pty Limited (1)
7 Ledgar Road, Balcatta, Perth, 6021, WA, Australia
Tel.: (61) 892016100
Web Site: https://www.ampac.net
Fire Alarm Product Mfr & Distr
N.A.I.C.S.: 334519

Analytical Development Company Limited (1)
Global House Geddings Road, Hoddesdon, EN11 0NT, Herts, United Kingdom
Tel.: (44) 1992464527
Web Site: https://www.adc.co.uk
Infrared Gas Analyzer Mfr & Distr
N.A.I.C.S.: 334516

Apollo (Beijing) Fire Products Co. Ltd. (1)
E-F Area 3rd Floor Building 1 No 5 Xinghai Road, Beijing Economic-Technological Development Area, Beijing, 100176, China
Tel.: (86) 1059409111
Fire Detection Equipment Mfr
N.A.I.C.S.: 334290

Apollo Fire Detectors Limited (1)
36 Brookside Road, Havant, PO9 1JR, Hampshire, United Kingdom (100%)
Tel.: (44) 2392492412
Web Site: https://www.apollo-fire.co.uk
Sales Range: $100-124.9 Million
Emp.: 500
Smoke & Heat Detectors for Commercial Fire Alarm Systems
N.A.I.C.S.: 334290
Wendy Osborne (Dir-Talent & Culture)

Apollo Gesellschaft fur Meldetechnologie mbH (1)
Am Anger 31, 33332, Gutersloh, Germany
Tel.: (49) 52 413 3060
Web Site: https://www.apollo-feuer.de
Emp.: 6
Electrical Apparatus & Equipment Mfr
N.A.I.C.S.: 335999
Isa Oldemeyer (Gen Mgr)

Apollo GmbH (1)
Am Anger 31, D 33332, Gutersloh, Germany (100%)
Tel.: (49) 524133060

INTERNATIONAL PUBLIC

Sales Range: $25-49.9 Million
Emp.: 6
Smoke & Heat Detectors for Commercial Fire Alarm Systems
N.A.I.C.S.: 334290

Argus Security S.R.L. (1)
Via del Canneto 14, Muggia, 34015, Trieste, Italy
Tel.: (39) 0402396411
Web Site: https://www.argussecurity.it
Fire Detection Equipment Mfr
N.A.I.C.S.: 334290

Avire Elevator Technology India Pte. Ltd. (1)
Plot no A/147 Road Number 24, Wagle Industrial Estate, Thane, 400 604, India
Tel.: (91) 2241248000
Communication Product Mfr
N.A.I.C.S.: 334290

Avire Elevator Technology Shanghai Ltd. (1)
4th Floor G Building 1999-2059 Du Hui Road, Shanghai, 201108, China
Tel.: (86) 2164953748
Communication Product Mfr
N.A.I.C.S.: 334290

Avire Global Pte. Ltd. (1)
8 Admiralty Street 07-01/02 Admirax, Singapore, 757438, Singapore
Tel.: (65) 67764111
Communication Product Mfr
N.A.I.C.S.: 334290

Avire Limited (1)
Unit 2 The Switchback Gardner Road, Maidenhead, SL6 7RJ, Berks, United Kingdom
Tel.: (44) 1628540100
Communication Product Mfr
N.A.I.C.S.: 334290

Avire s.r.o. (1)
Okruzni 2615, 370 01, Ceske Budejovice, Czech Republic
Tel.: (420) 387005602
Web Site: https://www.avire-global.com
Communication Product Mfr
N.A.I.C.S.: 334290

Avo Photonics, Inc. (1)
120 Welsh Rd, Horsham, PA 19044
Tel.: (215) 441-0107
Web Site: https://www.avophotonics.com
Optoelectronic Device Mfr
N.A.I.C.S.: 334413
Joseph L. Dallas (Pres)

Beijing Ker'Kang Instrument Limited Company (1)
Unit 316 Area 1 Tower B Chuangxin Building 12 Hongda North Road, Beijing, 100176, China
Tel.: (86) 10 6787 0335
Web Site: http://www.crowcon.com
Industrial Machinery Mfr
N.A.I.C.S.: 333248
Jin Xu (Mng Dir)

Bureau d'Electronique appliquee S.A. (1)
Liege Science Park Allee des Noisetiers 5, 4031, Angleur, Belgium
Tel.: (32) 43616565
Web Site: https://eu.beasensors.com
Laser Equipment Distr
N.A.I.C.S.: 423690
Elmar Koch (CEO)

Business Marketers Group, Inc. (1)
N56 W 24720 N Corp Cir, Sussex, WI 53089
Tel.: (262) 246-8845
Telephone Apparatus Mfr
N.A.I.C.S.: 334210

CEF Safety Systems B.V. (1)
Delftweg 69, 2289 BA, Rijswijk, Netherlands (100%)
Tel.: (31) 703192129
Web Site: http://www.smithflow.com
Sales Range: $25-49.9 Million
Emp.: 5
Supplier of Machinery & Process Safety Systems in Germany & Benelux
N.A.I.C.S.: 238990
Mark Drunack (Controller-Fin)

AND PRIVATE COMPANIES   HALMA PLC

Cardio Dinamica Ltda. (1)
Av Paulista 509 Floor 1 Floor 2 Sets 201
212-214, Bela Vista, Sao Paulo, CEP
01311-910, SP, Brazil
Tel.: (55) 1138833000
Web Site: https://cardios.com.br
Fitness Equipment Installation Services
N.A.I.C.S.: 811210

Cardios Sistemas Comercial e Industrial Ltda. (1)
Av Paulista 509 Floor 1 Floor 2 Sets 201
212-214, Bela Vista, Sao Paulo, 01311-910,
SP, Brazil
Tel.: (55) 1138833030
Web Site: https://www.cardios.com.br
Cardiology Assessment Equipment Mfr
N.A.I.C.S.: 334510

Castell Safety International Limited (1)
The Castell Building 217 Kingsbury Road,
London, NW9 9PQ, United
Kingdom **(100%)**
Tel.: (44) 2082001200
Web Site: https://www.castell.com
Sales Range: $25-49.9 Million
Emp.: 55
Provider of Safety Systems for Controlling
the Use of & Access to Dangerous Machines
N.A.I.C.S.: 238990
Paul Roberts *(Engr-Sls & Mfg-Scotland & North England)*

Cranford Controls Limited (1)
Unit 2 Waterbrook Estate Waterbrook Road,
Alton, GU34 2UD, Hampshire, United Kingdom
Tel.: (44) 1420592444
Web Site: https://www.cranfordcontrols.com
Audible & Visual Warning Device Mfr & Distr
N.A.I.C.S.: 334310

Crowcon Detection Instruments Limited (1)
172 Brook Drive Milton Park, Abingdon,
OX14 4SD, Oxfordshire, United
Kingdom **(100%)**
Tel.: (44) 1235557700
Web Site: https://www.crowcon.com
Sales Range: $50-74.9 Million
Emp.: 160
Gas Detection Instruments
N.A.I.C.S.: 334511

Crowcon Detection Instruments Ltd. (1)
Vlambloem 129, Rotterdam, 3068 JG,
Netherlands **(100%)**
Tel.: (31) 104211232
Web Site: http://www.crowcon.com
Sales Range: $50-74.9 Million
Emp.: 14
Supplier of Gas Detection Instruments
N.A.I.C.S.: 213112

Dancutter A/S (1)
Livovej 1, 8800, Viborg, Denmark
Tel.: (45) 96512150
Web Site: https://dancutter.com
Pipeline Rehabilitation Equipment Mfr & Distr
N.A.I.C.S.: 333998

Diba Industries Ltd. (1)
2 College Business Park Coldhams Lane,
Cambridge, CB1 3HD, United
Kingdom **(100%)**
Tel.: (44) 1223472801
Web Site: https://www.arcmedgroup.com
Scientific Instrument Valves & Laboratory
Connectors, Columns & Fittings Mfr
N.A.I.C.S.: 334516
Gannon T. Gambeski *(Pres & CEO)*

Subsidiary (US):

Bio-Chem Fluidics Inc. (2)
85 Fulton St, Boonton, NJ 07005
Tel.: (973) 263-3001
Web Site: http://www.biochemfluidics.com
Emp.: 65
Fluid Handling Component Mfr & Distr
N.A.I.C.S.: 333248
Linsey Holden-Downes *(VP-Ops)*

Diba Industries, Inc. (1)
4 Precision Rd, Danbury, CT 06810
Tel.: (203) 744-0773
Web Site: http://www.dibaind.com
Medical Device Mfr
N.A.I.C.S.: 339112

Diba Japan KK (1)
2nd Floor Yaesu Fuji Building 5-3 Yaesu
1-chome, Chuo-ku, Tokyo, 103-0028, Japan
Tel.: (81) 3 5200 7660
Fluidic Device Mfr
N.A.I.C.S.: 334513

E-Motive Display Pte. Limited (1)
192 Pandan Loop, 05 01 Pantech Ind Complex, 128381, Singapore,
Singapore **(100%)**
Tel.: (65) 67764111
Web Site: http://www.emotivedisplay.com
Sales Range: $25-49.9 Million
Emp.: 45
Electronic Displays for Providing Information
to Elevator Passengers
N.A.I.C.S.: 334513

Elfab Limited (1)
Alder Road, W Chirton Industrial Est, North
Shields, NE29 8SD, Tyne And Wear, United
Kingdom **(100%)**
Tel.: (44) 1912931234
Web Site: http://www.elfab.com
Sales Range: $10-24.9 Million
Emp.: 75
Pressure Sensitive Relief Devices to Protect
Process Plants
N.A.I.C.S.: 334290

FFE Limited (1)
9 Hunting Gate, Hitchin, SG4 0TJ, Hertfordshire, United Kingdom
Tel.: (44) 1462444740
Web Site: https://ffeuk.com
Fire Detection Equipment Mfr & Distr
N.A.I.C.S.: 334290

Fire Fighting Enterprises Limited (1)
9 Hunting Gate, Hitchin, SG4 0TJ, Hertfordshire, United Kingdom **(100%)**
Tel.: (44) 1462444740
Web Site: https://www.ffeuk.com
Sales Range: $25-49.9 Million
Emp.: 30
Provider of Fire Extinguishing & Smoke Detection Services for the Industrial & Aviation
Industry
N.A.I.C.S.: 922160
Mark Osborne *(Mng Dir)*

Firetrace Aerospace, LLC (1)
8435 N 90th St Ste 2, Scottsdale, AZ 85258
Tel.: (480) 535-0693
Web Site: https://www.firetrace.com
Fire Detection Equipment Mfr & Distr
N.A.I.C.S.: 334290

FluxData Inc. (1)
176 Anderson Ave Ste F304, Rochester, NY 14607
Tel.: (727) 733-2447
Optical Sensing Product Mfr
N.A.I.C.S.: 333310

Fortress Interlocks Limited (1)
2 Inverclyde Drive, Wolverhampton, WV4
6FB, United Kingdom **(100%)**
Tel.: (44) 1902349000
Web Site: https://www.fortress-safety.com
Sales Range: $25-49.9 Million
Emp.: 60
Safety Systems for Controlling Access to
Dangerous Machines
N.A.I.C.S.: 238990
Jo Smith *(CEO)*

Fortress Interlocks Pty Limited (1)
12 Raylee Place, Lynbrook, Melbourne,
3975, VIC, Australia
Tel.: (61) 397715350
Sales Range: $25-49.9 Million
Emp.: 14
Safety & Control System Mfr
N.A.I.C.S.: 334513
Malcolm Sharp *(Mng Dir)*

Fortress Systems Pty Limited (1)
324 Governor Rd, PO Box 572, Braeside,
3195, VIC, Australia **(100%)**
Tel.: (61) 395874099
Web Site: http://www.fortressresistors.com
Sales Range: $25-49.9 Million
Emp.: 15
Machinery & Process Safety Systems &
High Power Electrical Resistors
N.A.I.C.S.: 334416

HWM-Water Limited (1)
Ty Coch House Llantarnam Park Way,
Cwmbran, NP44 3AW, United Kingdom
Tel.: (44) 1633489479
Web Site: https://www.hwmglobal.com
Monitoring & Telemetry Equipment Mfr &
Distr
N.A.I.C.S.: 334519

Halma Australasia Pty Ltd (1)
7 Ledgar Road, Balcatta, 6021, WA, Australia
Tel.: (61) 892016171
Fire Detection Equipment Mfr & Distr
N.A.I.C.S.: 334290

Halma Holdings Inc. (1)
3500 Quadrangle Blvd, Orlando, FL
32817 **(100%)**
Tel.: (513) 772-5501
Sales Range: $25-49.9 Million
Emp.: 10
Holding Company
N.A.I.C.S.: 551112
Arnold Moshier *(CFO)*

Subsidiary (Domestic):

Accudynamics LLC (2)
240 Kenneth Welch Dr, Lakeville, MA 02347-1348
Tel.: (508) 946-4545
Web Site: https://www.accudynamics.com
Electromechanical Component Mfr
N.A.I.C.S.: 334514
Michael McKenna *(Pres)*

Accutome, Inc. (2)
3222 Phoenixville Pike Bldg Ste 50,
Malvern, PA 19355
Tel.: (610) 353-4350
Web Site: https://www.keelerusa.com
Sales Range: $10-24.9 Million
Emp.: 28
Optical Instrument & Lens Mfr
N.A.I.C.S.: 333310
Brian Chandler *(Pres)*

Alicat Scientific, Inc. (2)
7641 N Business Park Dr, Tucson, AZ 85743
Tel.: (520) 290-6060
Web Site: https://www.alicat.com
Sales Range: $25-49.9 Million
Emp.: 60
Measuring Device Mfr
N.A.I.C.S.: 334513

Apollo America Inc. (2)
25 Corporate Dr, Auburn Hills, MI
48326 **(100%)**
Tel.: (248) 332-3900
Web Site: https://aaifire.com
Sales Range: $25-49.9 Million
Duct Detectors for Smoke Control Systems
N.A.I.C.S.: 334519
Dave Hall *(Product Mgr-Innovation)*

B.E.A. Inc. (2)
100 Enterprise Dr, Pittsburgh, PA 15275
Tel.: (412) 429-4100
Web Site: https://us.beasensors.com
Emp.: 75
Architectural Sensor Distr
N.A.I.C.S.: 423390
Tim Blanke *(Pres)*

CenTrak, Inc. (2)
826 Newtown-Yardley Rd, Newtown, PA 18940
Tel.: (215) 860-2928
Web Site: https://centrak.com
Sales Range: $1-9.9 Million
Emp.: 200
Clinical-Grade Real-Time Location Updates
with Room-Level & Bay-Level Accuracy of
Patients for Hospitals & Clinics
N.A.I.C.S.: 622110
Ari Naim *(Co-Founder)*

Subsidiary (Domestic):

Elpas, Inc. (3)
1880 Century Park E Ste 716, Los Angeles, CA 90067
Tel.: (310) 458-0458
Security Equipment Mfr
N.A.I.C.S.: 334290

Subsidiary (Domestic):

Electronic Micro Systems Inc. (2)
125 Ricefield Ln, Hauppauge, NY
11788-2007 **(100%)**
Tel.: (631) 864-4742
Web Site: http://www.emscomm.com
Sales Range: $25-49.9 Million
Elevator Controls & Emergency Communication Systems
N.A.I.C.S.: 238210
A. C. Ritter *(VP-Fin)*

Firetrace USA, LLC (2)
8435 N 90th St Ste 2, Scottsdale, AZ 85258
Tel.: (480) 645-9650
Web Site: https://www.firetrace.com
Sales Range: $25-49.9 Million
Fire Detection & Suppression Systems Mfr
N.A.I.C.S.: 922160

Fluid Conservation Systems Inc (2)
1960 Old Gatesburg Rd Ste 150, State College, PA 16803 **(100%)**
Tel.: (513) 831-9335
Web Site: https://www.fluidconservation.com
Sales Range: $25-49.9 Million
Emp.: 6
Mfr Water Leak Detectors.
N.A.I.C.S.: 333998

Keeler Instruments Inc. (2)
3222 Phoenixville Pike, Malvern, PA
19355 **(100%)**
Tel.: (610) 353-4350
Web Site: http://www.keelerusa.com
Sales Range: $25-49.9 Million
Emp.: 12
Optical Devices for Ophthalmics & Surgical
Procedures
N.A.I.C.S.: 423490

Kirk Key Interlock Company LLC (2)
9048 Meridian Cir NW, North Canton, OH 44720
Tel.: (234) 209-9301
Web Site: https://www.kirkkey.com
Sales Range: $25-49.9 Million
Emp.: 45
Hardware Mfr
N.A.I.C.S.: 332510

Labsphere, Inc. (2)
231 Shaker St, North Sutton, NH 03260
Tel.: (603) 927-4266
Web Site: https://www.labsphere.com
Sales Range: $25-49.9 Million
Emp.: 97
Electric Equipment Mfr
N.A.I.C.S.: 334419
Heather LaBelle *(VP-Ops)*

Marathon Sensors Inc. (2)
8904 Beckett, Cincinnati, OH
45069 **(100%)**
Tel.: (513) 772-1000
Web Site: http://www.marathonsensors.com
Sales Range: $25-49.9 Million
Emp.: 20
Sensors for Heat Treatment Processes &
Boiler Control
N.A.I.C.S.: 334513

Monitor Controls Inc (2)
125 Ricefield Ln, Hauppauge, NY
11788 **(100%)**
Tel.: (631) 543-4334
Web Site: http://www.januselevator.com
Sales Range: $25-49.9 Million
Mfr Elevator Fixtures
N.A.I.C.S.: 333921
Mike Byrne *(Pres)*

Nuvonic (2)
4215 Stuart Andrew Blvd Ste E, Charlotte,
NC 28217 **(100%)**
Tel.: (980) 256-5700
Web Site: https://www.nuvonicuv.com
Sales Range: $25-49.9 Million
Emp.: 12
Ultraviolet Light Equipment for Water Treatment
N.A.I.C.S.: 333310
Sandy Smith *(Mgr-Customer Svcs)*

Oklahoma Safety Equipment Co. Inc. (2)
1701 W Tacoma, Broken Arrow, OK 74013
Tel.: (918) 258-5626

HALMA PLC

Halma plc—(Continued)

Web Site: https://www.osecoelfab.com
Industrial Machinery Mfr
N.A.I.C.S.: 332911

Perma Pure Inc. LLC (2)
1001 New Hampshire Ave, Lakewood, NJ 08701 **(100%)**
Tel.: (732) 244-0010
Web Site: https://www.permapure.com
Sales Range: $25-49.9 Million
Gas Dryers for Treating Gas Samples Before Analysis
N.A.I.C.S.: 334516
Richard Curran *(Pres)*

Rohrback Cosasco Systems, Inc. (2)
11841 Smith Ave, Santa Fe Springs, CA 90670
Tel.: (562) 949-0123
Web Site: https://www.cosasco.com
Sales Range: $25-49.9 Million
Emp.: 50
Corrosion Monitoring Equipment Mfr
N.A.I.C.S.: 334513
Anupam Sangal *(VP-Supply Chain)*

Subsidiary (Non-US):

Rohrback Cosasco Systems UK Ltd. (3)
Misbourne Court Rectory Way, Claymore Drive Bridge of Don, Amersham, HP7 0DE, Buckinghamshire, United Kingdom
Tel.: (44) 1224825500
Web Site: http://www.cosasco.com
Emp.: 20
Corrosion Monitoring Equipment Mfr
N.A.I.C.S.: 334513
Dean Smith *(Gen Mgr)*

Halma India Private Ltd. (1)
Prestige Shantiniketan Gate No 2 Tower C 7th Floor, Whitefield Main Road Mahadevapura, Bengaluru, 560 048, Karnataka, India
Tel.: (91) 8067475300
Web Site: https://www.halma.in
Electrical & Electronic Component Mfr
N.A.I.C.S.: 335999

Halma Trading and Services India Pvt Ltd (1)
B1-401 Boomerang Chandivali Andheri East, Andheri East, Mumbai, 400072, India
Tel.: (91) 22 67080400
Web Site: http://www.halma.com
Sales Range: $25-49.9 Million
Emp.: 25
Electric Equipment Mfr
N.A.I.C.S.: 334419
Prasenjit Datta *(Mng Dir)*

Hanovia Limited (1)
780/781 Buckingham Avenue, Slough, SL1 4LA, Berkshire, United Kingdom **(100%)**
Tel.: (44) 1753515300
Web Site: http://www.weuvcare.com
Sales Range: $25-49.9 Million
Emp.: 55
Ultraviolet Light Equipment for Treating Drinking Water & Water Used in the Manufacture of Food, Drinks, Pharmaceuticals & Electronic Components
N.A.I.C.S.: 335139
John Ryan *(Mng Dir)*

Subsidiary (Non-US):

Berson Milieutechniek B.V. (2)
Tel.: (31) 402907777
Web Site: https://www.weuvcare.com
Ultraviolet Light Equipment Mfr
N.A.I.C.S.: 335139

Hydreka Enoveo SAS (1)
51 Avenue Rosa Parks, 69009, Lyon, France
Tel.: (33) 472531153
Water Measuring Product Mfr
N.A.I.C.S.: 334519

Hydreka S.A. (1)
51 Avenue Rosa Parks, 69009, Lyon, France **(100%)**
Tel.: (33) 472531153
Web Site: https://www.hydreka.com
Sales Range: $25-49.9 Million
Emp.: 35

Equipment & Software for Flow Analysis of Water & Sewerage Systems
N.A.I.C.S.: 334519

Hyfire Wireless Fire Solutions Ltd. (1)
Unit B12a Holly Farm Business Park, Honiley, CV8 1NP, Warwickshire, United Kingdom
Tel.: (44) 1926485282
Web Site: https://www.hyfirewireless.com
Fire Detection Equipment Mfr
N.A.I.C.S.: 334290
Robert Read *(Mgr-Technical)*

IZI Medical Products, LLC (1)
5 Easter Ct Ste J, Owings Mills, MD 21117
Tel.: (410) 594-9403
Web Site: https://www.izimed.com
Sales Range: $10-24.9 Million
Emp.: 35
Mfr of Medical Markers Used in Image Guided Surgery
N.A.I.C.S.: 339112
Greg Groenke *(CEO)*

InPipe GmbH (1)
Jagerwinkel 1a, 6991, Riezlern, Austria
Tel.: (43) 551730110
Pipeline Inspection Equipment Mfr
N.A.I.C.S.: 334519

Infinite Leap, Inc. (1)
826 Newtown-Yardley Rd, Newtown, PA 18940
Web Site: http://www.infiniteleap.net
Sales Range: $1-9.9 Million
Emp.: 31
Information Technology Services
N.A.I.C.S.: 541512
Mark Rheault *(Founder & CEO)*

Invenio Systems Limited (1)
Ty Coch House Llantarnam Park Way, Cwmbran, NP44 3AW, United Kingdom
Tel.: (44) 1633489479
Web Site: https://www.invenio-systems.co.uk
Water System Services
N.A.I.C.S.: 221310
Keith Hilson *(Dir-Bus Dev)*

Keeler Limited (1)
Clewer Hill Road, Windsor, SL4 4AA, Berks, United Kingdom **(100%)**
Tel.: (44) 1753857177
Web Site: https://www.keeler.co.uk
Sales Range: $25-49.9 Million
Emp.: 100
Provider of Ophthalmic Instruments for Diagnostic Assessment of Eye Conditions
N.A.I.C.S.: 339112

LAN Control Systems Limited (1)
Chelsea House Chelsea Street, New Basford, Nottingham, NG7 7HP, United Kingdom
Tel.: (44) 1159249537
Web Site: http://www.lancontrolsystems.com
Fire Alarm Management Services
N.A.I.C.S.: 561621

Langer Instruments Corporation (1)
7641 N Business Park Dr, Tucson, AZ 85743
Tel.: (929) 260-0623
Web Site: https://www.langerpump.com
Langer Instrument Mfr
N.A.I.C.S.: 339112

Limotec bvba (1)
Bosstraat 21, Vichte, 8570, Anzegem, Belgium
Tel.: (32) 56650660
Web Site: http://www.limotec.be
Fire Detection Equipment Mfr
N.A.I.C.S.: 334290

Maxtec LLC (1)
2305 S 1070 W, Salt Lake City, UT 84119
Tel.: (385) 549-8000
Web Site: https://www.maxtec.com
Oxygen Analyzer Distr
N.A.I.C.S.: 423450

Medicel AG (1)
Dornierstrasse 11, 9423, Altenrhein, Switzerland
Tel.: (41) 717271050
Web Site: https://www.medicel.com
Emp.: 88

Medical Device Mfr
N.A.I.C.S.: 339112
Volker Dockhorn *(CEO)*

Memco Limited (1)
Memco House Waldeck Rd, Maidenhead, SL6 8BR, United Kingdom **(100%)**
Tel.: (44) 1628770734
Web Site: http://www.memco.co.uk
Sales Range: $10-24.9 Million
Emp.: 60
Infrared Safety Systems for Elevator Doors
N.A.I.C.S.: 333921

MicroSurgical Technology, Inc. (1)
8415 154th Ave NE, Redmond, WA 98052
Tel.: (425) 556-0544
Web Site: https://www.microsurgical.com
Ophthalmic Product Mfr
N.A.I.C.S.: 339115

Mini-Cam Limited (1)
Unit 4 Yew Tree Way Stonecross Park, Golborne, Warrington, WA3 3JD, United Kingdom
Tel.: (44) 1942270524
Web Site: http://www.minicam.co.uk
Pipeline Inspection Equipment Mfr & Distr
N.A.I.C.S.: 334519
Tom Davies *(Mng Dir)*

Navtech Radar Limited (1)
Home Farm, Ardington, Wantage, OX12 8PD, Oxfordshire, United Kingdom
Tel.: (44) 1235832419
Web Site: https://www.navtechradar.com
Radar Product Mfr
N.A.I.C.S.: 334511
Phil Avery *(Mng Dir)*

NovaBone Products, LLC (1)
13510 NW US Hwy 441, Alachua, FL 32615
Tel.: (904) 807-0140
Web Site: https://novabone.com
Sales Range: $1-9.9 Million
Emp.: 26
Medical, Dental, Hospital Equipment & Supplies Mfr & Merchant Whslr
N.A.I.C.S.: 339112
Arthur Wotiz *(Owner & Pres)*

Subsidiary (Non-US):

NovaBone Products - International (2)
Central Plaza 10th Floor #1037, Shanghai, 200020, China
Tel.: (86) 21 63915870
Medical, Dental, Hospital Equipment & Supplies Merchant Whslr
N.A.I.C.S.: 423450

Ocean Insight, Inc. (1)
830 Douglas Ave, Dunedin, FL 34698
Tel.: (727) 733-2447
Web Site: http://www.oceanoptics.com
Sales Range: $10-24.9 Million
Emp.: 250
Analytical Instruments
N.A.I.C.S.: 334516

Subsidiary (Domestic):

International Light Technologies, Inc. (2)
10 Technology Dr, Peabody, MA 01960
Tel.: (978) 818-6180
Web Site: http://www.intl-lighttech.com
Rev.: $3,300,000
Emp.: 21
Totalizing Fluid Meter & Counting Device Mfr
N.A.I.C.S.: 334514
Emilio Petriella *(Pres)*

Subsidiary (Non-US):

Ocean Optics BV (2)
Geograaf 24, 6921 EW, Duiven, Netherlands
Tel.: (31) 263190500
Optical Sensing Product Mfr
N.A.I.C.S.: 333310

Ocean Optics Germany (1)
Maybachstrasse 11, 73760, Ostfildern, Germany
Tel.: (49) 711 34 16 96 0
Web Site: http://oceanoptics.com

INTERNATIONAL PUBLIC

Sales Range: $25-49.9 Million
Emp.: 25
Electric Equipment Mfr
N.A.I.C.S.: 334419

Palintest Limited (1)
Palintest House Kingsway Team Valley, Gateshead, NE11 0NS, Tyne & Wear, United Kingdom **(100%)**
Tel.: (44) 1914910808
Web Site: https://www.palintest.com
Sales Range: $25-49.9 Million
Emp.: 80
Provider of Instruments for Analysing Water & Measuring Environmental Pollution
N.A.I.C.S.: 334516

Palmer Environmental Limited (1)
Misbourne Court Rectory Way, Amersham, HP7 0DE, Buckinghamshire, United Kingdom **(100%)**
Tel.: (44) 1633489479
Web Site: http://www.hwm-water.com
Sales Range: $25-49.9 Million
Emp.: 120
Instruments for Detecting & Locating Water Leaks from Underground Pipes
N.A.I.C.S.: 334511

PeriGen Inc. (1)
100 Regency Forest Dr Ste 200, Cary, NC 27518
Tel.: (984) 208-4250
Web Site: http://www.perigen.com
Software Publisher
N.A.I.C.S.: 513210
Natan Blanks *(Sr VP)*

Ramtech Electronics Limited (1)
Ramtech House Castle Marina Road, Castlebridge Office Village, Nottingham, NG7 1TN, United Kingdom
Tel.: (44) 1159578282
Web Site: https://ramtechglobal.com
Emp.: 70
Electronic Product Distr
N.A.I.C.S.: 423690

Robutec AG (1)
Dornierstrasse 11, 9423, Altenrhein, Switzerland
Tel.: (41) 717271050
Web Site: http://www.robutec.ch
Medical Device Mfr
N.A.I.C.S.: 339112
Bedros Malyano *(Mgr-Quality)*

Rudolf Riester GmbH (1)
Bruckstr 31, 72417, Jungingen, Germany
Tel.: (49) 747792700
Web Site: https://www.riester.de
Sales Range: $50-74.9 Million
Emp.: 150
Diagnostic Instrument Mfr & Distr
N.A.I.C.S.: 334510
Dominik Beck *(CEO & Mng Dir)*

S.E.R.V. Trayvou Interverrouillage SA (1)
1ter Rue du Marais - Bat B, 93106, Montreuil, Cedex, France **(100%)**
Tel.: (33) 0148181515
Web Site: http://www.servtrayvou.com
Sales Range: $25-49.9 Million
Emp.: 35
Safety Systems for Controlling Access to Dangerous Machines
N.A.I.C.S.: 238990

Sensit Technologies LLC (1)
851 Transport Dr, Valparaiso, IN 46383-8432
Tel.: (219) 465-2700
Web Site: https://www.gasleaksensors.com
Analytical Laboratory Instrument Mfr
N.A.I.C.S.: 334516
Peter Karlsson *(Mgr-Sls)*

Sensitron S.r.l. (1)
Viale della Repubblica 48, 20007, Cornaredo, MI, Italy
Tel.: (39) 0293548155
Web Site: https://www.sensitron.it
Gas Detector Distr
N.A.I.C.S.: 423690

Sensorex Corporation (1)
11751 Markon Dr, Garden Grove, CA 92841
Tel.: (714) 895-4344
Web Site: https://www.sensorex.com

AND PRIVATE COMPANIES

Monitoring Products Mfr
N.A.I.C.S.: 334519

Sofis BV (1)
J Keplerweg 14, 2408 AC, Alphen aan den Rijn, Netherlands
Tel.: (31) 172471339
Web Site: https://www.sofisglobal.com
Emp.: 100
Mechanical Valve Mfr
N.A.I.C.S.: 332919

Sofis GmbH (1)
Hahnenkammstrasse 12, 63811, Stockstadt, Germany
Tel.: (49) 6027405120
Mechanical Valve Mfr
N.A.I.C.S.: 332919

Sofis Limited (1)
Unit 7B West Station Business Park Spital Road, Maldon, CM9 6FF, Essex, United Kingdom (100%)
Tel.: (44) 1376517901
Web Site: https://www.sofisglobal.com
Safety Systems for Controlling Valves on Oil Rigs & Chemical Plants
N.A.I.C.S.: 332911

Subsidiary (Non-US):

Netherlocks Safety Systems (2)
J Keplerweg 14, 2408 AC, Alphen aan den Rijn, Netherlands
Tel.: (31) 172471339
Safety Controlling Valves Mfr
N.A.I.C.S.: 332911

Static Systems Group Limited (1)
Heath Mill Road, Wombourne, WV5 8AN, Staffordshire, United Kingdom
Tel.: (44) 1902895551
Web Site: https://www.staticsystems.co.uk
Hospital Equipment Mfr & Distr
N.A.I.C.S.: 339112

SunTech Medical Devices (Shenzhen) Co. Ltd. (1)
105 HuanGuan South Road Suite 15 2 3/F DaHe Community Guanlan, LongHua District, Shenzhen, 518110, Guangdong, China
Tel.: (86) 75529588810
Medical Device Mfr
N.A.I.C.S.: 339112
Robert Sweitzer (Pres)

Suntech Medical, Inc. (1)
5827 S Miami Blvd Ste 100, Morrisville, NC 27560-8394
Tel.: (919) 654-2300
Web Site: https://www.suntechmed.com
Medical Device Distr
N.A.I.C.S.: 423450
Robert Sweitzer (Pres)

T.L. Jones Limited (1)
BDO Christchurch Limited 287-293 Durham Street, PO Box 1151, Christchurch Central, Christchurch, 8013, New Zealand (100%)
Tel.: (64) 6433494456
Web Site: http://www.tljones.com
Sales Range: $25-49.9 Million
Emp.: 12
Infrared Safety Systems for Elevator Doors
N.A.I.C.S.: 238990

TeDan Surgical Innovations, Inc (1)
11333 Chimney Rd, Houston, TX 77035-2901
Tel.: (713) 726-0846
Web Site: http://www.tedansurgical.com
Surgical & Medical Instrument Mfr
N.A.I.C.S.: 339112

Volk Optical Inc. (1)
7893 Enterprise Dr, Mentor, OH 44060-5309 (100%)
Tel.: (440) 942-6161
Web Site: https://www.volk.com
Sales Range: $25-49.9 Million
Emp.: 50
Ophthalmic Lenses as Aids to Diagnosis & Surgery
N.A.I.C.S.: 339115
Gary D. Webel (Officer-Data Protection)

HALMAN-ALDUBI INVESTMENT HOUSE LTD.
26 Harokmim St, Holon, 5885849, Israel
Tel.: (972) 3 6121700
Web Site: http://www.halmanaldubi.com
Year Founded: 1990
HAIN—(TAE)
Sales Range: $25-49.9 Million
Emp.: 15
Investment Services
N.A.I.C.S.: 523999
Uri Aldubi (Founder & Chm)

HALMEK HOLDINGS CO., LTD.
4-1-1 Kagurazaka, Shinjuku-ku, Tokyo, 162-0825, Japan
Tel.: (81) 332611321
Web Site: https://www.halmek-holdings.co.jp
Year Founded: 1989
7119—(TKS)
Rev.: $207,653,150
Assets: $132,953,540
Liabilities: $83,014,990
Net Worth: $49,938,550
Earnings: $3,146,360
Emp.: 900
Fiscal Year-end: 03/31/24
Holding Company
N.A.I.C.S.: 551112
Fuminori Ishii (CFO)

HALMONT PROPERTIES CORPORATION
51 Yonge Street Suite 4000, Toronto, M5E 1J1, ON, Canada
Tel.: (647) 448-7147 Ca
Web Site: https://www.halmontproperties.ca
Year Founded: 2000
HMT—(TSXV)
Rev.: $8,776,399
Assets: $172,246,322
Liabilities: $85,788,736
Net Worth: $86,457,586
Earnings: $4,777,384
Fiscal Year-end: 12/31/20
Real Estate Services
N.A.I.C.S.: 531190

HALO COLLECTIVE INC.
504 - 100 Park Royal West, Vancouver, V7T 1A2, BC, Canada
Tel.: (541) 816-4810
Web Site: https://haloco.com
Year Founded: 2015
HCANF—(OTCEM)
Rev.: $36,179,930
Assets: $104,796,919
Liabilities: $38,340,440
Net Worth: $66,456,479
Earnings: ($96,908,560)
Emp.: 230
Fiscal Year-end: 12/31/21
Cannabis Product Mfr
N.A.I.C.S.: 325411
Katharyn Field (Chm & CEO)

HALO FOOD CO. LIMITED
Level 5 126 Phillip St, Sydney, 2000, NSW, Australia
Tel.: (61) 395876483
Web Site: https://www.keytonedairy.com
HLF—(ASX)
Rev.: $45,913,893
Assets: $67,782,327
Liabilities: $25,658,428
Net Worth: $42,123,899
Earnings: ($5,721,640)
Fiscal Year-end: 03/31/22
Dairy Products Mfr
N.A.I.C.S.: 311511
Danny Rotman (CEO)

Subsidiaries:

Omniblend Pty. Ltd. (1)
26-28 Bond St, Mordialloc, 3195, VIC, Australia
Tel.: (61) 393586388
Web Site: http://www.omniblend.com.au
Blending & Packing Services
N.A.I.C.S.: 561910

HALO TECHNOLOGIES HOLDINGS LTD.
Level 4 10 Barrack Street, Sydney, 2000, NSW, Australia
Tel.: (61) 1300348007 AU
Web Site: https://www.halo-technologies.com
Year Founded: 2017
HAL—(ASX)
Rev.: $9,281,439
Assets: $303,902,237
Liabilities: $292,274,720
Net Worth: $11,627,517
Earnings: ($4,697,578)
Fiscal Year-end: 12/31/23
Holding Company
N.A.I.C.S.: 551112
George Paxton (CEO)

HALONG CANNED FOOD JOINT STOCK CORPORATION
No 71 Le Lai Street May Chai Ward, Ngo Quyen District, Haiphong, Vietnam
Tel.: (84) 313836692
Web Site: https://www.canfoco.com.vn
Year Founded: 1957
CAN—(HNX)
Rev.: $30,553,178
Assets: $16,597,420
Liabilities: $10,344,372
Net Worth: $6,253,048
Earnings: $497,243
Emp.: 1,000
Fiscal Year-end: 12/31/23
Frozen Food Product Mfr
N.A.I.C.S.: 311412
Thi Thu Nga Pham (Deputy Gen Dir)

HALOPOLYMER KIROVO-CHEPETSK LLC
2 Pozharny Lane, Kirovo-Chepetsk, Kirov, Russia
Tel.: (7) 8336169495
Web Site: http://www.halopolymer.com
Emp.: 100
Electric Power Distribution Services
N.A.I.C.S.: 221330
Artyom Gnevnov (CEO)

HALOPOLYMER PERM, OJSC
98 Lasvinskaya St, Perm, Russia
Tel.: (7) 3422506180
Web Site: http://www.halopolymer.com
Emp.: 100
Electric Power Distribution Services
N.A.I.C.S.: 221330
Maxim Shaybakov (Gen Dir)

HALOWS CO., LTD
3270-1 Hayashima Hayashima-Cho Tsukubo-Gun, Okayama, 701-0393, Japan
Tel.: (81) 864831011
Web Site: https://www.halows.com
Year Founded: 1958
2742—(TKS)
Rev.: $1,234,823,030
Assets: $706,695,220
Liabilities: $388,927,210
Net Worth: $317,768,010
Earnings: $32,498,480
Emp.: 1,127
Fiscal Year-end: 02/29/20
Supermarket Chain Store
N.A.I.C.S.: 445110
Toshiyuki Sato (Pres & CEO)

HALS-DEVELOPMENT JSC
Bolshaya Tatarskaya 35/4, 115184, Moscow, Russia
Tel.: (7) 495 589 22 22 RU
Web Site: http://en.hals-development.ru
HALS—(RUS)
Sales Range: $50-74.9 Million
Real Estate Development Services
N.A.I.C.S.: 531390
Andrey Puchkov (Co-Chm)

HALSE MARTIN CONSTRUCTION CO LTD
1636 McGuire Avenue, North Vancouver, V7P 3B1, BC, Canada
Tel.: (604) 980-4811
Web Site: https://www.halse-martin.com
Year Founded: 1944
Rev.: $28,664,701
Emp.: 16
Building Construction Services
N.A.I.C.S.: 236220
Roy Reichgeld (Principal)

HALSNOY DOKK AS
Roysanesveien 24, 5457, Hoylandsbygdi, Norway
Tel.: (47) 5348 2900 NO
Web Site: http://www.halsnoydokk.no
Year Founded: 2006
Sales Range: $10-24.9 Million
Emp.: 25
Ship Building & Repair Services
N.A.I.C.S.: 336611
Frode Gronstol (Mng Dir)

HALSSEN & LYON GMBH
Pickhuben 9, 20457, Hamburg, Germany
Tel.: (49) 40361430 De
Web Site: http://www.haelssen-lyon.de
Year Founded: 1879
Sales Range: $50-74.9 Million
Tea Product Mfr
N.A.I.C.S.: 311920
Dietmar Scheffler (Mng Dir)

Subsidiaries:

Haelssen & Lyon North America Corporation (1)
39 W 38th St Ste 11 E, New York, NY 10016
Tel.: (212) 480-5721
Tea Distr
N.A.I.C.S.: 424490
Beau Bernstein (Dir-Mktg)

HALTEC HALLENSYSTEME GMBH
Hauptstrasse 287, 58675, Hemer, Germany
Tel.: (49) 237294970
Web Site: http://www.haltec.net
Year Founded: 1996
Rev.: $28,967,400
Emp.: 113
Hall & Tent Construction Services
N.A.I.C.S.: 236220
Thomas Arens (Mng Dir)

Subsidiaries:

HALTEC Hale Sp. z o.o. (1)
ul Fabianowska 151/153, 62-052, Komorniki, Poland
Tel.: (48) 618219097
Web Site: http://www.haltec.pl
Building Construction Services
N.A.I.C.S.: 236220

HALTEC Hallensysteme AG (1)
Stadtbachstrasse 42a, 3012, Bern, Switzerland
Tel.: (41) 313004161
Web Site: http://www.haltec.ch
Building Construction Services
N.A.I.C.S.: 236220

HALTEC HALLENSYSTEME GMBH

HALTEC Hallensysteme GmbH—(Continued)

HALTEC Hallensysteme GmbH (1)
Wiener Strasse 131, 4020, Linz, Austria
Tel.: (43) 7323716210
Web Site: http://www.haltec.at
Building Construction Services
N.A.I.C.S.: 236220

HALTEC Nederland B.V. (1)
Demmersweg 43-12, 7556 BN, Hengelo, Netherlands
Tel.: (31) 742420005
Web Site: http://www.haltec.nl
Emp.: 140
Building Construction Services
N.A.I.C.S.: 236220

HALTEC SAS (1)
Rue de l'Industrie ZA Les Plaines, 26320, Saint-Marcel-les-Valence, France
Tel.: (33) 967373943
Building Construction Services
N.A.I.C.S.: 236220

HALTON HILLS HYDRO INC.

43 Alice Street, Acton, L7J 2A9, ON, Canada
Tel.: (519) 853-3700
Web Site:
https://www.haltonhillshydro.com
Year Founded: 1888
Sales Range: $25-49.9 Million
Electric Power Services
N.A.I.C.S.: 221122
David Smelsky (CFO)

HALWANI BROS

PO Box 690, Jeddah, 21421, Saudi Arabia
Tel.: (966) 26366667
Web Site: http://www.halwani.com.sa
Year Founded: 1830
6001—(SAU)
Rev.: $273,115,948
Assets: $269,288,708
Liabilities: $153,658,434
Net Worth: $115,630,273
Earnings: $777,866
Emp.: 1,200
Fiscal Year-end: 12/31/22
Food Products Mfr
N.A.I.C.S.: 311991

HALYK BANK OF KAZAKHSTAN JSC

40 Al Farabi Ave, A26M3K5, Almaty, Kazakhstan
Tel.: (7) 7272590777   KZ
Web Site: https://www.halykbank.kz
Year Founded: 1923
H4L1—(DEU)
Rev.: $2,729,392,693
Assets: $32,000,742,364
Liabilities: $27,727,154,421
Net Worth: $4,273,587,943
Earnings: $1,238,209,382
Emp.: 16,325
Fiscal Year-end: 12/31/22
Commercial Banking Services
N.A.I.C.S.: 522110
Alexander Pavlov (Chm)

Subsidiaries:

CJSC Halyk Leasing (1)
104 Office 531 Seifullin Str, Almaty, Kazakhstan
Tel.: (7) 3272587960
Business Credit Institution
N.A.I.C.S.: 522299

CJSC Kazteleport (1)
39A Chailovsky Str, Almaty, 480000, Kazakhstan
Tel.: (7) 3272590449
Development Telecommunication Network
N.A.I.C.S.: 517810

HSBK Europe B.V. (1)
Schouwburgplein 30-34, PostBus 21153, Rotterdam, 3012 CL, Zuid-Holland, Netherlands
Tel.: (31) 0182391907
Sales Range: $1-9.9 Million
Trust Management
N.A.I.C.S.: 523991

Halyk Finance JSC (1)
109 Abay Ave 5th Floor, A05A1B9, Almaty, Kazakhstan
Tel.: (7) 727 357 31 77
Web Site: http://www.halykfinance.kz
Commercial Banking Services
N.A.I.C.S.: 522110
Farkhad Okhonov (Deputy CEO)

JSC Altyn Bank (1)
43 Dostyk Ave, A25D9H3, Almaty, Kazakhstan (100%)
Tel.: (7) 7273565777
Web Site: http://altyn-i.kz
Emp.: 500
International Banking
N.A.I.C.S.: 522299
Murat B. Baisynov (Member-Mgmt Bd)

JSC Halyk Global Markets (1)
N Nazarbayev Avenue 240 G BC CDC One 10-11 Floors, A26F8D4, Almaty, Kazakhstan
Tel.: (7) 727 339 9555
Web Site: https://www.halykgm.kz
Financial Investment Services
N.A.I.C.S.: 523999

JSCB Tenge Bank (1)
Parkentskaya Street 66 Landmark Parkent Market, Yashnabod District, 100007, Tashkent, Uzbekistan
Tel.: (998) 71 203 0065
Web Site: https://www.tengebank.uz
Financial Services
N.A.I.C.S.: 523150

Kazakhintrakh JSC (1)
109 v Abay avenue, 050008, Almaty, Kazakhstan
Tel.: (7) 8 727 259 98 99
Web Site: http://www.kazakhintrakh.kz
Insurance Management Services
N.A.I.C.S.: 524298
Erlan Kambetbaev (Chm-Mgmt Bd & CEO)

Kazkommertsbank JSC (1)
135/8 Gagarin Ave, Almaty, 050060, Kazakhstan
Tel.: (7) 727 2 585 185
Web Site: http://www.qazkom.kz
Rev.: $984,592,070
Assets: $10,758,877,780
Liabilities: $9,951,776,380
Net Worth: $807,101,400
Earnings: ($1,132,042,940)
Fiscal Year-end: 12/31/2017
Commercial Banking Services
N.A.I.C.S.: 522110
Ulf Wokurka (Chm-Mgmt Bd)

Subsidiary (Non-US):

Commercial Bank Moskommertsbank LLC (2)
20 Malaya Ordynka Str Bldg 1, 119017, Moscow, Russia
Tel.: (7) 4953632222
Web Site: http://www.moskb.ru
Commercial Banking Services
N.A.I.C.S.: 522110
Murat U Koshenov (Chm)

Subsidiary (Domestic):

JSC Insurance Company Kazkommerts Policy (2)
125/185 Baizakov Str, Almaty, 050026, Kazakhstan
Tel.: (7) 7272584808
Web Site: http://www.kkp.kz
General Insurance Services
N.A.I.C.S.: 524210
Kamilya Arstanbekova (Chm)

Subsidiary (Non-US):

Kyrgyzkommertsbank OJSC (2)
720011 101 Shopokov St, 720011, Bishkek, Kyrgyzstan
Tel.: (996) 312333000
Web Site: http://www.kkb.kg
Rev.: $125,546,000
Assets: $2,799,627,000
Liabilities: $2,034,910,000
Net Worth: $764,717,000
Earnings: $156,023,000

Emp.: 152
Fiscal Year-end: 12/31/2017
Commercial Banking Services
N.A.I.C.S.: 522110
Hideo Sawada (Chm)

HAMA FINANCIAL INSTITUTION LIMITED

Tripureshwor, PO Box 1425, Kathmandu, Nepal
Tel.: (977) 1 4249503
Web Site:
http://www.hamafinance.com.np
Year Founded: 2006
Financial Services
N.A.I.C.S.: 523999
Rajan Krishna Shrestha (Chm)

HAMA GMBH & CO KG

Dresdner Str 9, 86653, Monheim, Germany
Tel.: (49) 90 91 502 0   De
Web Site: http://www.hama.com
Year Founded: 1923
Emp.: 2,500
Consumer Electronics, Computer & Communication Accessories & Gaming Accessories Mfr & Distr
N.A.I.C.S.: 334118
Christoph Thomas (CEO)

Subsidiaries:

Companhia Hama Portugal, LDA (1)
Av Do Forte 4-4A Fraccao G, 2790 071, Carnaxide, Portugal
Tel.: (351) 21 469 37 70
Web Site: http://www.hama.pt
Consumer Electronics, Computer & Communication Accessories & Gaming Accessories Distr
N.A.I.C.S.: 423690
Filipe Barbosa (Mng Dir)

Hama (UK) Ltd. (1)
Unit 4 Cherrywood, Chineham Business Park, Basingstoke, RG24 8WF, United Kingdom
Tel.: (44) 1256 374700
Web Site: http://www.hama.co.uk
Consumer Electronics, Computer & Communication Accessories & Gaming Accessories Distr
N.A.I.C.S.: 423690
Phil Pace (Acct Mgr-Natl)

Hama B.V. (1)
Herengracht 282, 1016 BX, Amsterdam, Netherlands
Tel.: (31) 857606770
Web Site: http://nl.hama.com
Consumer Electronics, Computer & Communication Accessories & Gaming Accessories Distr
N.A.I.C.S.: 423690
Dave van der Zanden (Mng Dir)

Hama Distribution Romania SRL (1)
7 Cedrilor Street 1st Floor 5 District, 050865, Bucharest, Romania
Tel.: (40) 21 4104625
Web Site: http://www.hama-distribution.ro
Consumer Electronics, Computer & Communication Accessories & Gaming Accessories Distr
N.A.I.C.S.: 423690

Hama EURL (1)
15 rue de la Briqueterie, 77470, Poincy, France
Tel.: (33) 1 603250 00
Web Site: http://www.hama.fr
Consumer Electronics, Computer & Communication Accessories & Gaming Accessories Distr
N.A.I.C.S.: 423690
Sebastien Fournee (Mgr-Trade Mktg & Mdsg)

Hama Kft. (1)
Zador u 18, 1181, Budapest, Hungary
Tel.: (36) 1 2971040
Web Site: http://www.hama.hu
Consumer Electronics, Computer & Communication Accessories & Gaming Accessories Distr

INTERNATIONAL PUBLIC

N.A.I.C.S.: 423690
Otto Prohaszka (Mng Dir)

Hama NV (1)
Vantegemstraat 1, 9230, Wetteren, Belgium
Tel.: (32) 9 27260 00
Web Site: http://www.hama.be
Consumer Electronics, Computer & Communication Accessories & Gaming Accessories Distr
N.A.I.C.S.: 423690
Regis Vermeire (Dir-Sls)

Hama Polska Sp. z.o.o. (1)
Robakowo ul Poznanska 5, 62 023, Gadki, Poland
Tel.: (48) 61873 1010
Web Site: http://www.hama.pl
Consumer Electronics, Computer & Communication Accessories & Gaming Accessories Distr
N.A.I.C.S.: 423690
Rafal Myczkowski (VP)

Hama Slovakia spol.s.r.o. (1)
Bratislavska 87, 902 01, Rezinok, Slovakia
Tel.: (421) 33 6481184
Web Site: http://www.hama.sk
Consumer Electronics, Computer & Communication Accessories & Gaming Accessories Distr
N.A.I.C.S.: 423690
Tomas Jurenka (Product Mgr)

Hama Technics AG (1)
Brunnenstrasse 1, 8604, Volketswil, Switzerland
Tel.: (41) 43 355 34 40
Web Site: http://www.hamatechnics.ch
Consumer Electronics, Computer & Communication Accessories & Gaming Accessories Distr
N.A.I.C.S.: 423690
Reto Schaller (Acct Mgr)

Hama Technics Handels GmbH (1)
Georg-Sigl-Strasse 3, 2384, Breitenfurt, Austria
Tel.: (43) 2239 4777 0
Web Site: http://www.hama.at
Consumer Electronics, Computer & Communication Accessories & Gaming Accessories Distr
N.A.I.C.S.: 423690

Hama Technics S.L. (1)
Carrer 27 del BZ 71 A 79, Consorcio de la Zona Franca, 08040, Barcelona, Spain
Tel.: (34) 902 474 249
Web Site: http://www.hama.es
Consumer Electronics, Computer & Communication Accessory & Gaming Accessory Distr
N.A.I.C.S.: 423690
Elisabeth Diaz Guerrero (Mgr-Mdsg)

Hama spol. s r.o. (1)
Ksirova 150, 61900, Brno, Czech Republic
Tel.: (420) 543 538134
Web Site: http://www.hama.cz
Consumer Electronics, Computer & Communication Accessories & Gaming Accessories Distr
N.A.I.C.S.: 423690

HAMADAN GLASS COMPANY LLP

No 2-Hafez Jonobi St-Gazali St Shahid Barati Ave, 11318-47113, Tehran, 11318 47113, Iran
Tel.: (98) 52206670
Web Site:
https://www.hamadanglass.com
Year Founded: 1975
SHMD—(THE)
Sales Range: Less than $1 Million
Emp.: 476
Glass Products Mfr
N.A.I.C.S.: 327215
Mohammad Zarrabieh (Chm)

HAMAGA AS

Ratajova 1113/8, 14800, Prague, 4, Czech Republic
Tel.: (420) 244 402 838
Real Estate & Tourism Services
N.A.I.C.S.: 531390

AND PRIVATE COMPANIES

Michal Snobr *(CEO)*
Subsidiaries:

JRC Czech, a.s. (1)
Naskove 1100/3, 150 00, Prague, Czech Republic
Tel.: (420) 212249520
Web Site: http://www.jrc.cz
Sales Range: $10-24.9 Million
Emp.: 102
Retailer of PC Game Video Game & Gaming Accessory
N.A.I.C.S.: 423430
Mark Merka *(CEO)*

HAMAI CO., LTD.
5-5-15 Nishi-gotanda, Shinagawa-ku, Tokyo, 141-0031, Japan
Tel.: (81) 334910131   JP
Web Site: https://www.hamai.com
Year Founded: 1921
6131—(TKS)
Rev.: $57,870,550
Assets: $67,382,340
Liabilities: $46,144,410
Net Worth: $21,237,930
Earnings: $4,613,780
Emp.: 115
Fiscal Year-end: 03/31/24
Milling Machines, Machine Tools, Semiconductors & Front Lapping Machines Mfr
N.A.I.C.S.: 333517
Komei Muto *(Pres)*

Subsidiaries:

Hamai Co., Ltd. - Ashikaga Factory (1)
1480 Fukutomi-shin-machi, Ashikaga, 326-0332, Tochigi, Japan
Tel.: (81) 284 71 3951
Web Site: http://www.hamai.com
Sales Range: $75-99.9 Million
Precision Machine Tool Mfr & Whslr
N.A.I.C.S.: 423830

HAMAI INDUSTRIES LIMITED
7-7-7 Nishitotanda, Shinagawa-ku, Tokyo, 141-8512, Japan
Tel.: (81) 334926655
Web Site: https://www.hamai-net.com
Year Founded: 1927
6497—(TKS)
Rev.: $78,925,880
Assets: $149,584,820
Liabilities: $38,732,670
Net Worth: $110,852,150
Earnings: $6,444,810
Emp.: 332
Fiscal Year-end: 12/31/23
Precision Machine Equipment Mfr & Sales
N.A.I.C.S.: 423830
Saburo Hamai *(Chm)*

Subsidiaries:

Hamai Fuchu Factory Ltd. (1)
1-3 Nishihara-cho, Fuchu, 183-0046, Tokyo, Japan
Tel.: (81) 42 362 6515
Precision Machine Equipment Mfr
N.A.I.C.S.: 333248

Hamai Otaki Factory Ltd. (1)
880 Yokoyama, Otaki-machi, Isumi, 298-0206, Chiba, Japan
Tel.: (81) 470 82 2061
Precision Machine Equipment Mfr
N.A.I.C.S.: 332216

HAMAK GOLD LIMITED
Pasea Estate Road Town, PO Box 958, Tortola, VG1110, Virgin Islands (British)
Tel.: (284) 4942011   UK
Web Site: https://www.hamakminingco.com
Year Founded: 2021
HAMA—(LSE)

Assets: $1,552,000
Liabilities: $411,000
Net Worth: $1,141,000
Earnings: ($3,731,000)
Emp.: 8
Fiscal Year-end: 12/31/22
Mineral Exploration Services
N.A.I.C.S.: 213115
Amara Kamar *(Chm)*

HAMAKYOREX CO., LTD.
1701-1 Terawaki-cho, Chuo-ku, Hamamatsu, 430-0841, Shizuoka, Japan
Tel.: (81) 534440055
Web Site: https://www.hamakyorex.co.jp
Year Founded: 1971
9037—(TKS)
Rev.: $929,180,920
Assets: $1,023,836,120
Liabilities: $391,715,210
Net Worth: $632,120,910
Earnings: $54,896,050
Emp.: 5,778
Fiscal Year-end: 03/31/24
Automobile Freight Transportation Services
N.A.I.C.S.: 484110
Masataka Osuka *(CEO)*

HAMAMA MEIR TRADING (1996) LTD.
Champion Tower 30 Sheshet Hayamim St, Bnei Brak, 5120261, Israel
Tel.: (972) 35195555
Web Site: https://www.hamama.biz
Year Founded: 1996
HMAM—(TAE)
Rev.: $75,179,720
Assets: $48,641,248
Liabilities: $24,488,189
Net Worth: $24,153,059
Earnings: $847,355
Emp.: 60
Fiscal Year-end: 12/31/23
Packaged Frozen Food Merchant Wholesalers
N.A.I.C.S.: 424420

HAMAMATSU PHOTONICS K.K.
325-6 Sunayama-cho, Naka-ku, Hamamatsu, 430-8587, Shizuoka, Japan
Tel.: (81) 534522141
Web Site: http://www.hamamatsu.com
Year Founded: 1953
6965—(TKS)
Rev.: $1,570,045,050
Assets: $2,856,709,890
Liabilities: $587,491,580
Net Worth: $2,269,218,310
Earnings: $303,629,250
Emp.: 4,071
Fiscal Year-end: 09/30/23
Photodiodes, Phototransistors & Other Optical Semiconductor Products Mfr
N.A.I.C.S.: 334413
Tadashi Maruno *(Pres, CEO & Mng Dir)*

Subsidiaries:

Beijing Hamamatsu Photon Techniques, Inc. (1)
11-18 Building No 188 Western Road South 4th Ring Road, Fengtai District, Beijing, 100070, China
Tel.: (86) 106 370 6370
Web Site: http://www.bhphoton.com
Sales Range: $25-49.9 Million
Emp.: 40
Semiconductor & Related Device Mfr
N.A.I.C.S.: 334413

Hamamatsu Corporation (1)
360 Foothill Rd, Bridgewater, NJ 08807

Tel.: (908) 231-0960
Web Site: https://www.hamamatsu.com
Sales Range: $600-649.9 Million
Emp.: 180
Photosensitive Devices & Special Lamps Mfr
N.A.I.C.S.: 423690
Leo Kohyama *(Mgr-Mktg Comm)*

Hamamatsu Corporation - Factory (1)
360 Foothill Rd, Bridgewater, NJ 08807
Tel.: (908) 231-0960
Web Site: http://www.hamamatsu.com
Emp.: 70
Semiconductor Devices Mfr
N.A.I.C.S.: 334413
Tom Baker *(Gen Mgr)*

Hamamatsu Electronic Press Co., Ltd. (1)
1359-11 Mukokasa Takenouchi, Iwata, 438-0013, Shizuoka, Japan
Tel.: (81) 538866740
Emp.: 47
Precision Parts Mfr
N.A.I.C.S.: 332721

Hamamatsu Photonics (China) Co., Ltd. (1)
Room 1201 Building B Jiaming Center No 27 Dongsanhuan North Road, Chaoyang District, Beijing, 100020, China
Tel.: (86) 1065866006
Web Site: https://www.hamamatsu.com.cn
Photomultiplier Tube Mfr
N.A.I.C.S.: 335139

Hamamatsu Photonics Deutschland GmbH (1)
Arzbergerstr 10, 82211, Herrsching am Ammersee, Germany
Tel.: (49) 8 152 3750
Web Site: https://www.hamamatsu.com
Sales Range: $50-74.9 Million
Emp.: 80
Electronic Parts & Equipment Whslr
N.A.I.C.S.: 423690

Hamamatsu Photonics France S.A.R.L. (1)
19 Rue du Saule Trapu, Parc du Moulin de, 91882, Massy, Cedex, France
Tel.: (33) 16 953 7100
Web Site: http://www.sales.hamamatsu.com
Sales Range: $25-49.9 Million
Emp.: 35
Electronic Parts & Equipment Whslr
N.A.I.C.S.: 423690

Hamamatsu Photonics Italia S.R.L. (1)
Strada della Moia 1 int 6, Arese, 20020, Milan, Italy
Tel.: (39) 029 358 1733
Web Site: https://www.hamamatsu.com
Sales Range: $25-49.9 Million
Emp.: 18
Electronic Parts & Equipment Whslr
N.A.I.C.S.: 423690

Hamamatsu Photonics K.K. - Electron Tube Division (1)
314-5 Shimokanzo, Iwata, 438-0193, Shizuoka, Japan
Tel.: (81) 53 962 3151
Web Site: http://www.hamamatsu.com
Semiconductor Equipment Mfr
N.A.I.C.S.: 334413

Hamamatsu Photonics K.K. - Solid State Division (1)
1126-1 Ichino-cho, Higashi-ku, Hamamatsu, 435-8558, Shizuoka, Japan
Tel.: (81) 534343311
Semiconductor Equipment Mfr
N.A.I.C.S.: 334413

Hamamatsu Photonics K.K. - Systems Division (1)
812 Joko-cho, Higashi-ku, Hamamatsu, 431-3196, Shizouka, Japan
Tel.: (81) 53 435 1560
Web Site: http://www.hamamatsu.com
Semiconductor Equipment Mfr
N.A.I.C.S.: 334413

Hamamatsu Photonics Norden AB (1)

HAMAMATSU PHOTONICS K.K.

Torshamnsgatan 35, 164 40, Kista, Sweden
Tel.: (46) 85 090 3100
Web Site: http://www.hamamatsu.com
Sales Range: $25-49.9 Million
Emp.: 20
Electrical Apparatus & Equipment Wiring Supplies & Construction Material Whslr
N.A.I.C.S.: 423610

Hamamatsu Photonics Taiwan Co., Ltd. (1)
13F-1 No101 Section 2 Gongdao 5th Road, East Dist, Hsinchu, 300046, Taiwan
Tel.: (886) 36590080
Photomultiplier Tube Mfr
N.A.I.C.S.: 335139

Hamamatsu Photonics UK Limited (1)
2 Howard Court 10 Tewin Road, Welwyn Garden City, AL7 1BW, Hertfordshire, United Kingdom
Tel.: (44) 1707294888
Web Site: http://www.hamamatsu.co.uk
Sales Range: $25-49.9 Million
Emp.: 30
Medical Dental & Hospital Equipment & Supplies Whslr
N.A.I.C.S.: 423450

Iwata Grand Hotel Inc. (1)
2280 Iwai, Iwata, 438-0016, Shizuoka Prefecture, Japan
Tel.: (81) 538341211
Web Site: https://www.iwata-gh.co.jp
Sales Range: $10-24.9 Million
Emp.: 60
Hotels & Motels
N.A.I.C.S.: 721110

Koso Corporation (1)
677-1 Kakeshita, Iwata, 438-0124, Shizuoka, Japan
Tel.: (81) 539635051
Emp.: 205
Electric Device Mfr
N.A.I.C.S.: 334419

NKT Photonics A/S (1)
Blokken 84, DK 3460, Birkerod, Denmark
Tel.: (45) 43483900
Web Site: http://www.nktphotonics.com
Sales Range: $25-49.9 Million
Emp.: 60
Mfr of Fiber Laser Systems & Fiber-Based Measuring Equipment
N.A.I.C.S.: 333310
Christian V. Poulsen *(CTO)*

Photochemical Co., Ltd. (1)
5319-1 Haga, 701-1221, Okayama, Japan
Tel.: (81) 862869777
Semiconductor & Related Device Mfr
N.A.I.C.S.: 334413

Photonics Management Corp. (1)
360 Foothill Rd, Bridgewater, NJ 08807
Tel.: (908) 231-0960
Web Site: http://www.usa.hamamatsu.com
Sales Range: $75-99.9 Million
Emp.: 200
Electronic Parts & Equipment Whslr
N.A.I.C.S.: 423690
Tom Baker *(Gen Mgr)*

Subsidiary (Domestic):

Energetiq Technology, Inc. (2)
205 Lowell St, Wilmington, MA 01887
Tel.: (781) 939-0763
Web Site: https://www.energetiq.com
Broadband Light Sources Mfr
N.A.I.C.S.: 334413
Paul A. Blackborow *(CEO)*

Takaoka Electronics Co., Ltd. (1)
2-14-18 Takaoka Nishi, Naka-ku, Hamamatsu, 433-8118, Shizuoka, Japan
Tel.: (81) 534371361
Web Site: https://www.takaokadenshi.co.jp
Emp.: 165
Photomultiplier Tube Mfr
N.A.I.C.S.: 335139

Universal Spectrum Corporation (1)
250 Wood Ave, Middlesex, NJ 08846
Tel.: (732) 805-1965
Web Site: http://www.unispeccorp.com
Electronic Parts & Equipment Whslr
N.A.I.C.S.: 423690

HAMAT GROUP LTD.

Hamamatsu Photonics K.K.—(Continued)

HAMAT GROUP LTD.
Hamat Service Center Hayozma 41, PO Box 6555, Ashdod, 7752475, Israel
Tel.: (972) 502597836 **TR**
Web Site: https://www.hamat.co.il
Year Founded: 1944
HAMAT—(TAE)
Rev.: $267,261,772
Assets: $423,657,405
Liabilities: $275,725,925
Net Worth: $147,931,480
Earnings: $11,411,797
Emp.: 200
Fiscal Year-end: 12/31/23
Plumbing Fixture Fitting & Trim Manufacturing
N.A.I.C.S.: 332913

HAMATON AUTOMOTIVE TECHNOLOGY CO., LTD.
No 12 East Zhenxiong Road Linping Yuhang, Hangzhou, Zhejiang, China
Tel.: (86) 57189361220
Web Site: https://www.hamaton.com
Year Founded: 1993
300643—(CHIN)
Rev.: $150,374,136
Assets: $199,234,395
Liabilities: $48,765,411
Net Worth: $150,468,985
Earnings: $16,876,506
Fiscal Year-end: 12/31/23
Automotive Tool Mfr & Distr
N.A.I.C.S.: 333991

HAMAYUU CO., LTD.
1-13-3 Yamate-dori, Showa-Ku, Nagoya, 466-0815, Japan
Tel.: (81) 528320005
Web Site: https://www.hamayuu.co.jp
Year Founded: 1967
7682—(TKS)
Restaurant Operators
N.A.I.C.S.: 722511
Nagayoshi Hayashi *(Pres)*

HAMBORNER REIT AG
Goethestrasse 45, 47166, Duisburg, Germany
Tel.: (49) 203544050
Web Site: http://www.hamborner.de
HABA—(STU)
Rev.: $107,090,438
Assets: $1,390,535,290
Liabilities: $879,419,383
Net Worth: $511,115,908
Earnings: $14,364,343
Emp.: 46
Fiscal Year-end: 12/31/22
Real Estate Investment Trust
N.A.I.C.S.: 525990
Claus-Matthias Boge *(Deputy Chm-Supervisory Bd)*

Subsidiaries:

Hambornberg Immobilien- und Verwaltungs-GmbH **(1)**
Goethestr 45, Duisburg, 47166, Nordrhein-Westfalen, Germany
Tel.: (49) 203544050
Sales Range: $50-74.9 Million
Emp.: 24
Commercial Real Estate Management Services
N.A.I.C.S.: 531210

HAMBRO PERKS ACQUISITION COMPANY LIMITED
Floor 2 Trafalgar Court, PO Box 286, Saint Peter Port, Guernsey **GG**
Web Site:
https://www.hambroperks.com
Year Founded: 2021
HPA1—(LSE)

Investment Management Service
N.A.I.C.S.: 523999
Dominic Perks *(CEO)*

HAMBURGER HAFEN UND LOGISTIK AG
Bei St Annen 1, 20457, Hamburg, Germany
Tel.: (49) 4030880
Web Site: https://www.hhla.de
HHFA—(DEU)
Rev.: $1,597,046,000
Assets: $3,322,836,358
Liabilities: $2,492,770,273
Net Worth: $830,066,085
Earnings: $22,033,245
Emp.: 6,789
Fiscal Year-end: 12/31/23
Container Terminals Management
N.A.I.C.S.: 322211
Roland Lappin *(CFO & Member-Exec Bd)*

Subsidiaries:

ARS-UNIKAI GmbH **(1)**
Sachsenbrucke Schuppen 48, 20457, Hamburg, Germany
Tel.: (49) 4072002100
Transportation Logistics Services
N.A.I.C.S.: 541614

Bionic Production GmbH **(1)**
Vor Dem Neuen Tore 18, 21339, Luneburg, Germany
Tel.: (49) 41312300230
Web Site: https://bionicproduction.com
Software Development Services
N.A.I.C.S.: 541511

CTD Container-Transport-Dienst GmbH **(1)**
Reiherdamm 44, 20457, Hamburg, Germany **(100%)**
Tel.: (49) 407411640
Web Site: https://www.ctd.de
Sales Range: $25-49.9 Million
Emp.: 49
Container Transportation & Trucking Services
N.A.I.C.S.: 484121
Ralph Frankenstein *(Mng Dir)*

Combisped Hanseatische Spedition GmbH **(1)**
Steinbruckerstrasse 1, 23556, Lubeck, Germany
Tel.: (49) 4 518 8040
Web Site: https://www.combisped.de
Container Trucking Services
N.A.I.C.S.: 484121
Thomas Dreyer *(Mgr)*

CuxPort GmbH **(1)**
Neufelder Schanze 4, 27472, Cuxhaven, Germany
Tel.: (49) 4 721 7480
Web Site: https://www.cuxport.de
Cargo & Container Handling Equipment Distr
N.A.I.C.S.: 488320
Peter Zint *(Mng Dir)*

Fischmarkt Hamburg-Altona Gesellschaft mit beschrankter Haftung **(1)**
Grosse Elbstr 137, 22767, Hamburg, Germany
Tel.: (49) 4030887800
Web Site: https://www.fischmarkt-hamburg.de
Sales Range: $25-49.9 Million
Emp.: 42
Fresh & Frozen Seafood Sales
N.A.I.C.S.: 424460

GHL Gesellschaft fur Hafen- und Lagereiimmobilien-Verwaltung Block D mbH **(1)**
Bei St Annen 1, 20457, Hamburg, Germany
Tel.: (49) 403 0880
Web Site: https://hhla.de
Port Operation Services
N.A.I.C.S.: 488310

GHL Zweite Gesellschaft fur Hafen- und Lagereiimmobilien-Verwaltung

mbH **(1)**
Bei St Annen 1, Hamburg, Germany
Tel.: (49) 4030881
Real Estate Manangement Services
N.A.I.C.S.: 531312

HCC Hanseatic Cruise Centers GmbH **(1)**
Dessauer Strasse 10, 20457, Hamburg, Germany
Tel.: (49) 4072002100
Sales Range: $25-49.9 Million
Emp.: 50
Cruise Lining Services
N.A.I.C.S.: 483112

HCCR Hamburger Container- und Chassis-Reparatur-Gesellschaft mbH **(1)**
Altenwerder Damm 22, 21129, Hamburg, Germany
Tel.: (49) 40740050
Web Site: https://www.hccr.de
Sales Range: $50-74.9 Million
Emp.: 250
Containers Trading & Maintenance Services
N.A.I.C.S.: 484110

HHLA Container Terminal Burchardkai GmbH **(1)**
Waltershofer Damm, 21129, Hamburg, Germany
Tel.: (49) 4030880
Sales Range: $200-249.9 Million
Emp.: 1,000
Containers Handling Services
N.A.I.C.S.: 488320
Heinrich Goller *(Mng Dir)*

HHLA Container Terminal Tollerort GmbH **(1)**
Am Vulkanhafen 30, 20457, Hamburg, Germany
Tel.: (49) 4030880
Containers Handling Services
N.A.I.C.S.: 488320

HHLA Container Terminals GmbH **(1)**
Bei St Annen 1, 20457, Hamburg, Germany
Tel.: (49) 4030882303
Web Site: http://www.hhla.com
Sales Range: $1-4.9 Billion
Emp.: 4,700
Container Terminal Operation Services
N.A.I.C.S.: 484121

HHLA Container-Terminal Altenwerder GmbH **(1)**
Am Ballinkai 1, 21129, Hamburg, 21129, Germany
Tel.: (49) 4030880
Web Site: http://www.hhl.de
Sales Range: $125-149.9 Million
Emp.: 400
Cargo & Containers Handling Services
N.A.I.C.S.: 488320

HHLA Frucht- und Kuhl-Zentrum GmbH **(1)**
Dessauer St 10, 20457, Hamburg, Germany
Tel.: (49) 4030887352
Sales Range: $25-49.9 Million
Emp.: 75
Cold Warehousing Storage Services
N.A.I.C.S.: 493120

HHLA Intermodal GmbH **(1)**
Bei St Annen 1, 20457, Hamburg, Germany
Tel.: (49) 4030880
Web Site: http://www.hhla.de
Sales Range: $1-4.9 Billion
Emp.: 4,000
Rail Transportation Services
N.A.I.C.S.: 482111

HHLA Intermodal Verwaltung GmbH **(1)**
Bei St Annen 1, 20457, Hamburg, Germany
Tel.: (49) 4030881
Sales Range: $50-74.9 Million
Emp.: 10
Real Estate Asset Management Services
N.A.I.C.S.: 531390

HHLA Logistics Altenwerder GmbH & Co. KG **(1)**
Bei St Annen 1, 20457, Hamburg, Germany

INTERNATIONAL PUBLIC

Tel.: (49) 4030884710
Logistics Distribution Services
N.A.I.C.S.: 541614

HHLA Logistics Altenwerder Verwaltungsgesellschaft mbH **(1)**
Bei St Annen 1, 20457, Hamburg, Germany
Tel.: (49) 4030881
Logistics Distribution Services
N.A.I.C.S.: 541614

HHLA Logistics GmbH **(1)**
Bei St Annen 1, 20457, Hamburg, Germany
Tel.: (49) 4030887000
Web Site: http://www.hhla-logistics.de
Sales Range: $25-49.9 Million
Emp.: 105
Logistics Distribution Services
N.A.I.C.S.: 541614
Jurgen H Frank *(Mng Dir)*

HHLA Next GmbH **(1)**
Bei St Annen 1, 20457, Hamburg, Germany
Tel.: (49) 4030880
Web Site: https://hhla-next.de
Logistics Consulting Servies
N.A.I.C.S.: 541614

HHLA PLT Italy S.r.l. **(1)**
Via Degli Alti Forni Snc, 34145, Trieste, Italy
Tel.: (39) 0409858400
Web Site: https://www.hhla-plt.it
Port Terminal Services
N.A.I.C.S.: 488310

HHLA Project Logistics LLC **(1)**
47 Agmashenebeli Str, 4400, Poti, Georgia
Tel.: (995) 493221085
Logistic Services
N.A.I.C.S.: 541614
Korneli Korchilava *(Mng Dir)*

HHLA TK Estonia AS **(1)**
Veose 16, 74115, Maardu, Estonia
Tel.: (372) 6319205
Web Site: https://www.hhla-tk.ee
Cargo & Container Handling Equipment Distr
N.A.I.C.S.: 488320
Vladimir Popov *(Chm)*

HHLA TK Estonia AS **(1)**
3 Ravala Avenue, 10143, Tallinn, Estonia
Tel.: (372) 6319205
Web Site: http://www.tk.ee
Cargo & Container Handling Equipment Distr
N.A.I.C.S.: 488320
Vladimir Popov *(Chm)*

HPC Hamburg Port Consulting GmbH **(1)**
Breite Str 61, 22767, Hamburg, Germany
Tel.: (49) 40740080
Web Site:
https://www.hamburgportconsulting.com
Sales Range: $25-49.9 Million
Emp.: 80
Port Management Consulting Services
N.A.I.C.S.: 541611
Sven Daniels *(Partner & Head-Market Segment Marine Container Terminals)*

HPTI Hamburg Port Training Institute GmbH **(1)**
Uberseezentrum Schumacherwerder, 20457, Hamburg, Germany
Tel.: (49) 40788780
Web Site: http://www.hpti.de
Sales Range: $10-24.9 Million
Emp.: 10
Transport Training & Seminar Programme Services
N.A.I.C.S.: 611430
Wolfhard H. Arlt *(Mng Dir)*

HVCC Hamburg Vessel Coordination Center GmbH **(1)**
Bei St Annen 1, 20457, Hamburg, Germany
Tel.: (49) 4080884395
Web Site: https://www.hvcc-hamburg.de
Feeder Vessel & Barger Mfr
N.A.I.C.S.: 336611
Gerald Hirt *(Mng Dir)*

LLC Ukrainian Intermodal Company **(1)**
1-A Mytna Square Marine Plaza Centre Office 307 / 308, 65026, Odessa, Ukraine
Tel.: (380) 482390477

AND PRIVATE COMPANIES

Web Site: https://uic-llc.com
Port Terminal Services
N.A.I.C.S.: 488310

METRANS (Danubia) Kft. (1)
1211 Budapest Salak ut 37, Budapest, Hungary
Tel.: (36) 18141200
Web Site: https://www.metrans.hu
Container Terminal Equipment Distr
N.A.I.C.S.: 488310

METRANS Adria D.O.O. (1)
Ankaranska cesta 7B, 6000, Koper, Slovenia
Tel.: (386) 56304022
Web Site: https://www.metrans.si
Sales Range: $25-49.9 Million
Emp.: 8
Container Trucking Services
N.A.I.C.S.: 484121

METRANS DYKO Rail Repair Shop s.r.o. (1)
Podleska 926/5, Uhrineves, 140 00, Prague, 10, Czech Republic
Tel.: (420) 326597111
Web Site: https://www.dyko.cz
Emp.: 180
Railway Vehicles Repair Services
N.A.I.C.S.: 488210

METRANS Rail (Deutschland) GmbH (1)
Grimmaische Str 13-15, 04109, Leipzig, Germany
Tel.: (49) 4030093490
Web Site: https://www.metransrail.de
Emp.: 310
Truck Transportation
N.A.I.C.S.: 484110

METRANS Railprofi Austria GmbH (1)
Karl Mierka Strasse 7-9, 3500, Krems an der Donau, Austria
Tel.: (43) 6649155880
Web Site: https://www.railprofi.com
Rail Freight Transportation Services
N.A.I.C.S.: 488210

METRANS a.s. (1)
Podleska 926, 104 00, Prague, 10, Czech Republic
Tel.: (420) 267293102
Web Site: https://metrans.eu
Container Trucking Services
N.A.I.C.S.: 484110

Subsidiary (Non-US):

METRANS (Danubia) a.s. (2)
Povodska 18, 92901, Dunajska Streda, Slovakia
Tel.: (421) 313234101
Sales Range: $50-74.9 Million
Emp.: 200
Cargo Shipping Services
N.A.I.C.S.: 483111
Peter Kiss *(Mgr-Sls)*

SC Container Terminal Odessa (1)
Odessa Port 1 Tamozhennaya pl, 65026, Odessa, Ukraine
Tel.: (380) 487294550
Web Site: https://www.cto.od.ua
Sales Range: $125-149.9 Million
Emp.: 400
Port Container Terminal Operation Services
N.A.I.C.S.: 488310
Yarovaya Svetlana *(VP)*

SC Container Terminal Odessa (1)
Odessa Port 1 Tamozhennaya Pl, Odessa, 65026, Ukraine
Tel.: (380) 48 729 4550
Web Site: www.cto.od.ua
Cargo & Container Handling Equipment Distr
N.A.I.C.S.: 488320
Anastas Kokkin *(Gen Dir)*

SCA Service Center Altenwerder GmbH (1)
Am Ballinkai 1, Hamburg, 21129, Germany
Tel.: (49) 40533092515
Containers Repair & Maintenance Services
N.A.I.C.S.: 811310

Service Center Burchardkai GmbH (1)

Bei St Annen 1, 20457, Hamburg, Germany
Tel.: (49) 4030880
Container Trucking Services
N.A.I.C.S.: 484121

TIP Zilina, s.r.o. (1)
Povodska Cesta 18, PO Box 191, 929 01, Dunajska Streda, Slovakia
Tel.: (421) 918759229
Web Site: https://www.terminalzilina.sk
Container Terminal Equipment Distr
N.A.I.C.S.: 488310
Peter Aufricht *(Mng Dir & Mgr-Terminal)*

Third Element Aviation GmbH (1)
Bronninghauser Str 38, 33729, Bielefeld, Germany
Tel.: (49) 52125270844
Web Site: https://3rd-element.com
Drone Mfr
N.A.I.C.S.: 336411

UNIKAI Hafenbetrieb GmbH (1)
Buchheisterstr 74, 20457, Hamburg, Germany
Tel.: (49) 4031182390
Sales Range: $25-49.9 Million
Emp.: 2
Cargo Containers Handling Services
N.A.I.C.S.: 488320

UNIKAI Lagerei- und Speditionsgesellschaft mbH (1)
Dessauer Strasse 10, 20457, Hamburg, Germany
Tel.: (49) 4072002100
Web Site: https://www.unikai.de
Sales Range: $25-49.9 Million
Emp.: 400
Vehicle Freight Forwarding Services
N.A.I.C.S.: 488510

Ulrich Stein Gesellschaft mit beschrankter Haftung (1)
Dessauer Strasse 10, 20457, Hamburg, Germany
Tel.: (49) 4072002100
Sales Range: $25-49.9 Million
Emp.: 20
Fruits Transportation & Cold Storage Services
N.A.I.C.S.: 493130

iSAM Automation Canada Corp. (1)
290 Newport Drive, Port Moody, V3H 5N2, BC, Canada
Tel.: (604) 492-2976
Software Development Services
N.A.I.C.S.: 541511

iSAM North America Corp. (1)
500 Broadcast Dr, Mobile, AL 36606
Tel.: (251) 338-2528
Web Site: https://www.isamamerica.com
Software Development Services
N.A.I.C.S.: 541511

HAMBURGER SPARKASSE AG
Adolphsplatz 3, Hamburg, 20457, Germany
Tel.: (49) 4035790
Web Site: http://www.haspa.de
Sales Range: $1-4.9 Billion
Emp.: 5,894
Banking Services
N.A.I.C.S.: 522110
Harald Vogelsang *(Member-Mgmt Bd)*

HAMEE CORP.
Square O2 2-12-10 Sakaemachi, Odawara, 250-0011, Kanagawa, Japan
Tel.: (81) 465228057
Web Site: https://hamee.co.jp
3134—(TKS)
Rev.: $116,415,320
Assets: $95,924,320
Liabilities: $28,786,550
Net Worth: $67,137,770
Earnings: $7,409,810
Emp.: 463
Fiscal Year-end: 04/30/24
Mobile Phone Accessory Online Retailer; Cloud Managerial System Software

N.A.I.C.S.: 513210
Atsushi Higuchi *(Founder & Chm)*

Subsidiaries:

Hamee India Pvt. Ltd. (1)
316 Bestech ChambersNear Bank of Maharastra Sushant Lok 1, Gurgaon, 122002, Haryana, India
Tel.: (91) 1244105983
Web Site: http://www.hamee-india.com
Phone Accessory Distr
N.A.I.C.S.: 423690

Hamee Korea Co., Ltd. (1)
12F C-dong BYC High City 131 Gasan Digital 1-ro, Geumcheon-gu, Seoul, 08506, Korea (South)
Tel.: (82) 27577343
Web Site: http://www.hamee.co.kr
Phone Accessory Distr
N.A.I.C.S.: 423690

Hamee Shanghai Trade Co., Ltd. (1)
Building 48 No 142 Lane 88 Yunping Road Jiading Distric, Shanghai, China
Tel.: (86) 2139598768
Phone Accessory Distr
N.A.I.C.S.: 423690

Hamee Taiwan, Corp. (1)
11011 Rm 5C14 5F No 5 Sec 5 Xinyi Rd Xinyi Dist, Taipei, Taiwan
Tel.: (886) 227203817
Phone Accessory Distr
N.A.I.C.S.: 423690

Hamee US, Corp. (1)
385 Van Ness Ave Ste 100, Torrance, CA 90501
Tel.: (760) 571-9622
Web Site: http://www.hamee.com
Phone Accessory Distr
N.A.I.C.S.: 423690

HAMELIN GOLD LIMITED
Suite 2 1 Alvan Street, Subiaco, 6008, WA, Australia
Tel.: (61) 894869455 AU
Web Site: https://www.hamelingold.com.au
Year Founded: 2021
HMG—(ASX)
Rev.: $66,512
Assets: $16,257,835
Liabilities: $288,389
Net Worth: $15,969,446
Earnings: ($648,331)
Fiscal Year-end: 06/30/23
Gold Exploration Services
N.A.I.C.S.: 212220
Dan Travers *(Sec)*

HAMELN GROUP GMBH
Langes Feld 13, 31789, Hameln, Germany
Tel.: (49) 5151581237 De
Web Site: http://www.hameln-group.com
Holding Company; Pharmaceutical Products & Services
N.A.I.C.S.: 551112
Christoph Kerstein *(Mng Dir)*

Subsidiaries:

Hameln Phama Plus GmbH (1)
Langes Feld 13, 31789, Hameln, Germany
Tel.: (49) 5151 581 540
Web Site: http://www.hameln-plus.com
Emp.: 30
Parenteral Products Marketer
N.A.I.C.S.: 424210
Wolf-Christian Kanzelmeyer *(Mng Dir)*

Hameln Pharmaceuticals Ltd. (1)
Nexus Gloucester Business Park, Gloucester, GL3 4AG, United Kingdom
Tel.: (44) 1452 621661
Web Site: http://www.hameln.co.uk
Emp.: 20
Pharmaceutical Products Distr
N.A.I.C.S.: 424210
Stephen Watkin *(Mng Dir)*

HAMID FABRICS LTD.

Hamid Tower 7th Floor 24 Gulshan C/A Circle-2, Dhaka, 1212, Bangladesh
Tel.: (880) 288345645
Web Site: https://www.hfl.com.bd
Year Founded: 1995
HFL—(DHA)
Rev.: $25,025,897
Assets: $45,334,136
Liabilities: $14,010,407
Net Worth: $31,323,729
Earnings: $155,448
Emp.: 1,336
Fiscal Year-end: 06/30/23
Solid Dyed Fabric Product Mfr
N.A.I.C.S.: 313310
Abdullah Al Mahmud Mahin *(CEO & Mng Dir)*

HAMID TEXTILE MILLS LIMITED
142 D Model Town, Lahore, Pakistan
Tel.: (92) 494528177
Web Site: https://www.hamid-textile.com
Year Founded: 1987
HATM—(PSX)
Rev.: $2,027,314
Assets: $2,515,579
Liabilities: $1,075,662
Net Worth: $1,439,917
Earnings: $26,586
Emp.: 47
Fiscal Year-end: 06/30/23
Textile Products Mfr
N.A.I.C.S.: 314999
Khawar Almas Khawaja *(Co-Chm)*

HAMILTON & COMPANY LIMITED
Empire House, A K Nayak Marg, Fort, Mumbai, 400 001, India
Tel.: (91) 02222077391
Consumer Specialties
N.A.I.C.S.: 532289

Subsidiaries:

S&S Power Switchgear Limited (1)
Plot No14 Cmda Industrial Area-II Maraimalai Nagar, Chithamanur Village, Kanchipuram, 603209, India **(74.98%)**
Tel.: (91) 4447431625
Web Site: https://www.sspower.com
Switchgear Mfr
N.A.I.C.S.: 335313
Ashok Kumar Vishwakarma *(CEO & Mng Dir)*

HAMILTON & SPILL LTD
11300 River Rd, Richmond, V6X 1Z5, BC, Canada
Tel.: (604) 276-9555
Year Founded: 1974
Rev.: $43,896,000
Emp.: 80
Furniture Mfr
N.A.I.C.S.: 337126
Rick Verjee *(Pres)*

HAMILTON GLOBAL OPPORTUNITIES PLC
30-35 Pall Mall, London, SW1Y 5LP, United Kingdom
Tel.: (44) 2070622401
Web Site: https://www.hamiltongo.eu
Year Founded: 2009
ALHGO—(EUR)
Rev.: $347,370
Assets: $18,393,138
Liabilities: $723,422
Net Worth: $17,669,716
Earnings: $1,643,417
Emp.: 4
Fiscal Year-end: 12/31/22
Miscellaneous Financial Investment Activities
N.A.I.C.S.: 523999

HAMILTON GLOBAL OPPORTUNITIES PLC

Hamilton Global Opportunities Plc—(Continued)

Gustavo Perrotta (CEO)

Subsidiaries:

Gauzy Ltd. (1)
14 Hathiya Street, Tel Aviv, 6816914, Israel
Tel.: (972) 722500385
Web Site: https://www.gauzy.com
Emp.: 48
Light Control Glass Product Mfr & Distr
N.A.I.C.S.: 327215

HAMILTON INSURANCE GROUP, LTD.

Wellesley House North 1st Floor 90 Pitts Bay Road, Pembroke, HM08, Bermuda
Tel.: (441) 4055200
Web Site: http://www.hamiltongroup.com
Year Founded: 2013
Insurances Services & Holding Company
N.A.I.C.S.: 551112
Jonathan Reiss (Pres-Strategic Partnerships)

Subsidiaries:

Ironshore Europe DAC (1)
2 Shelbourne Buildings Shelbourne Rd, Ballsbridge, Dublin, Ireland (100%)
Tel.: (353) 1 232 1900
Web Site: http://www.ironshore.com
General Insurance Services
N.A.I.C.S.: 524210
Fiona Marry (CEO)

Pembroke Managing Agency Limited (1)
Level 3 8 Fenchurch Place, London, EC3M 4AJ, United Kingdom
Tel.: (44) 20 7337 4400
Web Site: http://www.ironshore.com
Specialty Insurance Services
N.A.I.C.S.: 524298
Tim Glover (CEO)

HAMILTON RENTALS LTD.

Unit 2 The Maple Centre Downmill Road, Bracknell, RG12 1QS, Berks, United Kingdom
Tel.: (44) 1344456600 UK
Web Site: http://www.hamilton.co.uk
Sales Range: $25-49.9 Million
Emp.: 70
Personal Computer, Server & Audio-Visual Equipment Rental & Services
N.A.I.C.S.: 532420

HAMM CONSTRUCTION LTD.

126 English Cr, Saskatoon, S7K 8A5, SK, Canada
Tel.: (306) 931-6626
Web Site: http://www.hammconstruction.ca
Year Founded: 1970
Rev.: $18,300,882
Emp.: 124
Underground Infrastructure Services
N.A.I.C.S.: 237110
Robert Hamm (Founder)

HAMMER METALS LIMITED

Unit 1 & 2 28-30 Mayfair Street, West Perth, 6005, WA, Australia
Tel.: (61) 863691195 AU
Web Site: https://www.hammermetals.com.au
HMX—(ASX)
Rev.: $118,231
Assets: $24,530,956
Liabilities: $559,739
Net Worth: $23,971,217
Earnings: $4,187,089
Emp.: 2
Fiscal Year-end: 06/30/24
Gold Ore & Silver Ore Mining
N.A.I.C.S.: 212220
Mark Pitts (Sec)

Subsidiaries:

Hammer Metals Australia Pty. Ltd. (1)
Unit 1 & 2 28-30 Mayfair Street, West Perth, 6005, WA, Australia
Tel.: (61) 863691195
Web Site: https://www.hammermetals.com.au
Polyhedral Mining Services
N.A.I.C.S.: 213114

HAMMER RETEX AG

Sinserstrasse 67, 6330, Cham, Switzerland
Tel.: (41) 417851851
Web Site: http://www.hammerretex.ch
Sales Range: $10-24.9 Million
Emp.: 60
Real Estate Agency
N.A.I.C.S.: 531210
Claude Ebnoether (CEO)

HAMMERHEAD ENERGY INC.

Eighth Avenue Place East Tower Suite 2700 525 8th Avenue SW, Calgary, T2P 1G1, AB, Canada
Web Site: https://www.hhres.com
Year Founded: 2009
HHRS—(NASDAQ)
Rev.: $578,993,590
Assets: $1,381,603,483
Liabilities: $378,229,251
Net Worth: $1,003,374,232
Earnings: $176,091,228
Emp.: 84
Fiscal Year-end: 12/31/22
Oil & Gas Exploration Services
N.A.I.C.S.: 237120
Michael Kohut (CFO)

HAMMERSON PLC

Marble Arch House 66 Seymour Street, London, W1H 5BX, United Kingdom
Tel.: (44) 2078871000 UK
Web Site: https://www.hammerson.com
Year Founded: 1942
HMSO—(LSE)
Rev.: $183,020,656
Assets: $6,671,700,308
Liabilities: $2,943,401,188
Net Worth: $3,728,299,120
Earnings: ($582,597,652)
Emp.: 494
Fiscal Year-end: 12/31/21
Real Estate Investment Trust
N.A.I.C.S.: 531390
Jean-Philippe Mouton (Mng Dir-France)

Subsidiaries:

Dundrum Town Centre Management Limited (1)
Dundrum Town Centre Sandyford Road, Dundrum, Dublin, 16, Ireland
Tel.: (353) 12991700
Web Site: https://www.dundrum.ie
Shopping Mall Services
N.A.I.C.S.: 531120

Forum Steglitz 2 GmbH (1)
Schlossstrasse 1, Center Management Schlossstrasse, 12163, Berlin, Germany
Tel.: (49) 30 792 9060
Web Site: https://www.forum-steglitz.de
Sales Range: $100-124.9 Million
Emp.: 250
Investment Advice
N.A.I.C.S.: 523940

Hammerson (Brent Cross) Ltd (1)
Kings Place 90 York Way, London, N1 9GE, United Kingdom
Tel.: (44) 2078871000
Web Site: http://www.hammerson.com
Sales Range: $75-99.9 Million
Emp.: 150
Real Estate Agents & Brokers
N.A.I.C.S.: 531210

Hammerson Group Management Ltd (1)
Kings Place 90, London, N1 9GA, United Kingdom
Tel.: (44) 2078871000
Web Site: http://www.hammerson.com
Sales Range: $75-99.9 Million
Emp.: 200
Real Estate Agents & Brokers
N.A.I.C.S.: 531210

Hammerson International Holdings Ltd (1)
10 Grosvenor St, London, W1K 4BJ, United Kingdom
Tel.: (44) 2078871000
Web Site: http://www.hammerson.com
Sales Range: $75-99.9 Million
Emp.: 180
Real Estate Agents & Brokers
N.A.I.C.S.: 531210

Hammerson Marketing et Communication SAS (1)
Tel.: (33) 156693000
Leasing Non-Residential Real Estate Services
N.A.I.C.S.: 531120

Hammerson Oracle Investments Ltd (1)
10 Grosvenor St, W1K4BJ, London, United Kingdom
Tel.: (44) 2078871000
Web Site: http://www.hammerson.com
Sales Range: $50-74.9 Million
Emp.: 150
Real Estate Agents & Brokers
N.A.I.C.S.: 531210

Hammerson Property Ltd (1)
90 York Way, London, United Kingdom
Tel.: (44) 2078871000
Sales Range: $75-99.9 Million
Emp.: 120
Real Estate Agents & Brokers
N.A.I.C.S.: 531210

Hammerson SAS (1) (100%)
Tel.: (33) 156693000
Sales Range: $50-74.9 Million
Emp.: 100
Real Estate Property Lessors
N.A.I.C.S.: 531190

Subsidiary (Domestic):

Bercy Hammerson France (2)
23 rue des Capucines 48 Rue, Cambon, 44 rue Washington, 75001, Paris, France (100%)
Tel.: (33) 156693000
Web Site: https://www.hammerson.fr
Sales Range: $50-74.9 Million
Emp.: 100
Real Estate Property Lessors
N.A.I.C.S.: 531190

Subsidiary (Non-US):

Hammerson Centre Commercial Italie SAS (2)
Tel.: (33) 156693000
Sales Range: $50-74.9 Million
Emp.: 100
Real Estate Property Lessors
N.A.I.C.S.: 531190

Subsidiary (Domestic):

Hammerson Madeleine SAS (2)
48 R Cambon 75001, 44 Rue Washington, 75408, Paris, France (100%)
Tel.: (33) 156693000
Sales Range: $50-74.9 Million
Emp.: 100
Real Estate Property Lessors
N.A.I.C.S.: 531190

Lxb Holdings Limited (1)
6 Cavendish Place, W1G9NB, London, United Kingdom
Tel.: (44) 8707703069
Web Site: http://www.lxbproperties.com
Real Estate Investment Company
N.A.I.C.S.: 531190

INTERNATIONAL PUBLIC

Union Square Developments Limited (1)
12 Upper Level Mall Union Square Guild Square, Aberdeen, AB11 5RG, United Kingdom
Tel.: (44) 1224254300
Web Site: https://www.unionsquareaberdeen.com
Software Development Services
N.A.I.C.S.: 541511

West Quay Shopping Centre Ltd (1)
Management Suite 8-10 Portland Terrace, Southampton, SO14 7EG, United Kingdom
Tel.: (44) 2380336828
Web Site: https://www.west-quay.co.uk
Emp.: 50
Shopping Center Management Services
N.A.I.C.S.: 531120
Andy Collyer (Gen Mgr)

HAMMOND MANUFACTURING CO. LTD.

394 Edinburgh Rd North, Guelph, N1H 1E5, ON, Canada
Tel.: (519) 822-2960 Ca
Web Site: https://www.hammfg.com
Year Founded: 1944
HMFAF—(OTCIQ)
Rev.: $179,933,769
Assets: $143,123,935
Liabilities: $68,367,810
Net Worth: $74,756,125
Earnings: $13,693,346
Emp.: 900
Fiscal Year-end: 12/31/23
Mfr of Electrical & Electronic Products, Racks, Transformers, Outlet Strips & Surge Suppressors
N.A.I.C.S.: 334513
Robert F. Hammond (Chm & CEO)

Subsidiaries:

Hammond Electronics Limited (1)
1 Onslow Close Kingsland Business Park, Basingstoke, RG24 8QL, Hampshire, United Kingdom
Tel.: (44) 125 681 2812
Web Site: http://www.hammond-electronics.co.uk
Sales Range: $50-74.9 Million
Emp.: 10
Electronic Parts Whslr
N.A.I.C.S.: 423620

Hammond Electronics Pty. Limited (1)
11 13 Port Rd, Queenstown, Adelaide, 5014, SA, Australia
Tel.: (61) 882402244
Sales Range: $25-49.9 Million
Emp.: 1
Electrical Products Mfr
N.A.I.C.S.: 335139
Pat Cicricookfrn (Mng Dir)

Hammond Manufacturing Company Inc (1)
475 Cayuga Rd, Cheektowaga, NY 14225
Tel.: (716) 630-7030
Web Site: https://www.hammfg.com
Sales Range: $25-49.9 Million
Emp.: 30
Electronic Parts Whslr
N.A.I.C.S.: 423620
Robert F. Hammond (Chm & CEO)

Les Fabrications Hammond Quebec Inc (1)
985 Rue Bergar Laval, Quebec, H7L 4Z6, QC, Canada
Tel.: (450) 975-1884
Web Site: http://www.hammondmfg.com
Sales Range: $50-74.9 Million
Emp.: 5
Electronic Parts Whslr
N.A.I.C.S.: 423620

HAMMOND POWER SOLUTIONS INC.

595 Southgate Drive, Guelph, N1G 3W6, ON, Canada
Tel.: (519) 822-2441

AND PRIVATE COMPANIES — **HAMPTON HILL MINING NL**

Web Site:
https://america.hammondpower.com
HMDPF—(OTCIQ)
Rev.: $297,424,421
Assets: $183,913,246
Liabilities: $85,344,401
Net Worth: $98,568,845
Earnings: $11,871,881
Emp.: 1,400
Fiscal Year-end: 12/31/21
Industrial Machinery & Equipment Merchant Whslr
N.A.I.C.S.: 423830
William G. Hammond *(Chm & CEO)*

Subsidiaries:

Delta Transformers Inc. (1)
3850 Java Place suite 200, Brossard, J4Y 0C4, QC, Canada
Tel.: (450) 449-9774
Web Site: http://www.delta.xfo.com
Emp.: 14
Transformer Mfr
N.A.I.C.S.: 335311
Dell Hammond *(Pres)*

Euroelettro Hammond S.p.A (1)
Via dell'Agricoltura 8/F ZI vingla schiatti 12, 36040, Meledo di Sarego, VI, Italy
Tel.: (39) 0444 822 000
Web Site: http://www.euroelettro.com
Industrial Machinery & Equipment Sales
N.A.I.C.S.: 423830

HPS s.r.l. (1)
Via Cimarosa 102/104, 57124, Livorno, Italy
Tel.: (39) 0586 851807
Web Site: http://www.h-p-s.it
Emp.: 13
Industrial Supplies Whslr
N.A.I.C.S.: 423840

Hammond Power Solutions S.A. de C.V. (1)
Ave Avante 810 Parque Industrial Guadalupe, 67190, Guadalupe, CP 67190, Nuevo Leon, Mexico
Tel.: (52) 11528184797115
Industrial Machinery & Equipment Sales
N.A.I.C.S.: 423830

Hammond Power Solutions, Inc. (1)
1100 Lk St, Baraboo, WI 53913-2866
Tel.: (608) 356-3921
Web Site:
https://americas.hammondpower.com
Industrial Machinery & Equipment Sales
N.A.I.C.S.: 423830

Mesta Electronics Inc (1)
11020 Parker Dr, North Huntingdon, PA 15642
Tel.: (412) 754-3000
Web Site: http://www.mesta.com
Rev.: $2,100,000
Emp.: 17
Semiconductor & Related Device Mfr
N.A.I.C.S.: 334413
Peter Leventopoulos *(Gen Mgr)*

HAMON & CIE S.A.
Axisparc Rue Andre Dumont 6, BE-1435, Mont-Saint-Guibert, Belgium
Tel.: (32) 10390400
Web Site: http://www.hamon.com
HAMO—(EUR)
Rev.: $318,688,976
Assets: $364,051,564
Liabilities: $387,103,173
Net Worth: ($23,051,608)
Earnings: ($52,404,088)
Emp.: 1,264
Fiscal Year-end: 12/31/20
Power Boiler, Heat Exchangers, Dry Cooling Systems & Chimneys Mfrs
N.A.I.C.S.: 332410
Quentin Biart *(CFO-Grp)*

Subsidiaries:

Hamon Corporation (1)
58 E Main St, Somerville, NJ 08876
Tel.: (908) 685-4000
Web Site: http://www.hamonusa.com

Sales Range: $25-49.9 Million
Emp.: 56
Gasket, Packing & Sealing Device Mfr
N.A.I.C.S.: 339991
Robert Recio *(Gen Counsel & Exec VP)*

Subsidiary (Domestic):

Hamon Deltak, Inc. (2)
13330 12th Ave N, Plymouth, MN 55441-4510
Tel.: (763) 557-7440
Web Site: http://www.hamonusa.com
Sales Range: $75-99.9 Million
Heat Recovery Steam Generators & Energy Conversion Systems Designer & Mfr
N.A.I.C.S.: 332410

HAMPDEN HOLDINGS LIMITED
Hampden House, Great Hampden, Great Missenden, HP16 9RD, Buckinghamshire, United Kingdom
Tel.: (44) 1494488888   UK
Web Site: http://www.hampden.co.uk
Year Founded: 1995
Sales Range: $1-4.9 Billion
Holding Company; Insurance Administrative & Claims Support Services
N.A.I.C.S.: 551112
Tim Oliver *(Chm)*

Subsidiaries:

Hampden Capital Plc (1)
85 Gracechurch Street, London, EC3V 0AA, United Kingdom
Tel.: (44) 2078636500
Web Site: http://www.hampden.co.uk
Emp.: 40
Holding Company; Insurance Company Support Services
N.A.I.C.S.: 551112
Neil Smith *(CEO)*

Subsidiary (Domestic):

Hampden Agencies Limited (2)
85 Gracechurch Street, London, EC3V 0AA, United Kingdom
Tel.: (44) 2078636500
Sales Range: $10-24.9 Million
Emp.: 40
Insurance Underwriting Agency Support Services
N.A.I.C.S.: 561499
David Cant *(Dir-Fin)*

Nomina Plc (2)
40 Gracechurch Street, London, EC3V 0BT, United Kingdom
Tel.: (44) 2078636500
Web Site: http://www.hampden.co.uk
Corporate Management & Administrative Support Services
N.A.I.C.S.: 561499
Jeremy Evans *(CEO)*

Hampden Plc (1)
Hampden House, Great Hampden, Great Missenden, HP16 9RD, Bucks, United Kingdom
Tel.: (44) 1494488888
Web Site: http://www.hpcgroup.co.uk
Sales Range: $50-74.9 Million
Emp.: 40
Holding Company; Insurance Run-off Companies Owner & Administrator
N.A.I.C.S.: 551112
Steven Harris *(Sec)*

Subsidiary (Non-US):

Hampden Insurance Group BV (2)
K P van der Mandelelaan 90, PO Box 8524, 3009 AM, Rotterdam, Netherlands
Tel.: (31) 10 2121000
Web Site: http://www.hampden.eu
Reinsurance Services
N.A.I.C.S.: 524130
Gerrit M. van Dijk *(Gen Dir)*

Seymour Taylor Audit Limited (1)
57 London Road, High Wycombe, HP11 1BS, Bucks, United Kingdom
Tel.: (44) 1494552100
Web Site: http://www.stca.co.uk

Sales Range: $25-49.9 Million
Emp.: 40
Accounting, Auditing, Tax & Payroll Services
N.A.I.C.S.: 541211
Simon Turner *(Mng Dir)*

HAMPIDJAN HF
Skarfagardar 4, 104, Reykjavik, Iceland
Tel.: (354) 5303300
Web Site: http://www.hampidjan.is
Year Founded: 1934
Sales Range: $50-74.9 Million
Emp.: 500
Fishing Gear Mfr
N.A.I.C.S.: 339920
Vilhjalmur Vilhjalmsson *(Chm)*

Subsidiaries:

Cosmos Trawl A/S (1)
Notkajen 2, PO Box 89, 9850, Hirtshals, Denmark
Tel.: (45) 98941977
Web Site: http://www.cosmostrawl.dk
Fishing Equipment Distr
N.A.I.C.S.: 423910
Thorleif Gronkjaer *(Mgr-Sls)*

Hampidjan Australia Pty Ltd (1)
5 Leda Drive, Burleigh Heads, 4220, QLD, Australia
Tel.: (61) 755255555
Web Site: http://www.hampidjan.com.au
Fishing Equipment Distr
N.A.I.C.S.: 423910

Hampidjan Baltic UAB (1)
Pakruojo g 34, 76126, Siauliai, Lithuania
Tel.: (370) 41507600
Fishing Equipment Distr
N.A.I.C.S.: 423910
Hjortur Eruensson *(Gen Mgr)*

Hampidjan Canada Ltd. (1)
527-531 Conception Bay Highway, PO Box 580, Spaniard's Bay, A0A 3X0, NL, Canada
Tel.: (709) 786-0855
Web Site: https://www.hampidjan.ca
Fishing Equipment Distr
N.A.I.C.S.: 423910

Hampidjan New Zealand Ltd (1)
82 Vickerman Street, PO Box 5087, Port Nelson, Nelson, New Zealand
Tel.: (64) 35487942
Web Site: http://www.hamidjan.co.nz
Fishing Equipment Distr
N.A.I.C.S.: 423910
Karen Culley *(Mng Dir)*

Hampidjan Russia Ltd. (1)
Survorova 57 Office 102 105, 236000, Kaliningrad, Russia
Tel.: (7) 4012691586
Fishing Equipment Distr
N.A.I.C.S.: 423910

Hampidjan USA Inc. (1)
8300 Military Rd S Unit 100, Seattle, WA 98108-3952
Tel.: (800) 385-5224
Fishing Equipment Distr
N.A.I.C.S.: 423910

Swan Net Gundry Ltd. (1)
41 Great Republic Dr, Gloucester, MA 01930
Tel.: (978) 282-1662
Web Site:
http://www.usa.swannetgundry.com
Aquaculture Product Distr
N.A.I.C.S.: 424910

Subsidiary (Non-US):

Coastal Cages Ltd. (2)
Ballymoon Kilcar Co, Donegal, Ireland
Tel.: (353) 749738406
Aquaculture Product Distr
N.A.I.C.S.: 424910

HAMPSON INDUSTRIES PLC
7 Harbour Buildings Waterfront West Dudley Road, Brierley Hill, DY5 1LN, United Kingdom
Tel.: (44) 1384485345

Web Site:
http://www.hampsongroup.com
Sales Range: $300-349.9 Million
Emp.: 75,183
Aerospace & Automotive Engineering Products Mfr
N.A.I.C.S.: 541330
Malcolm Dolan *(Sec)*

Subsidiaries:

Hampson Precision Automotive (India) Private Limited (1)
Survey No 40/41 Village Thonnachi Kuppe Kasaba Hobli, Nelamangala Taluk Tumkur Rd, 562123, Bengaluru, India   (97.5%)
Tel.: (91) 8022995001
Web Site: http://www.hampson-autoindia.com
Sales Range: $25-49.9 Million
Emp.: 130
Automotive Mechanical & Electrical Repair & Maintenance
N.A.I.C.S.: 811114

HAMPTON ASSOCIATES LTD.
11 Victoria Street, Aberdeen, AB10 1XB, United Kingdom
Tel.: (44) 1224620562
Web Site:
http://www.hamptonassociates.com
Emp.: 13
Advertising Agencies
N.A.I.C.S.: 541810
Erik Porter *(Principal-Creative)*

HAMPTON BAY CAPITAL, INC.
65 Queen Street West Suite 1125, Toronto, M5H 2M5, ON, Canada
Tel.: (514) 866-6743
LHI—(TSXV)
Rev.: $4,123
Assets: $824,978
Liabilities: $42,405
Net Worth: $782,573
Earnings: ($182,854)
Fiscal Year-end: 12/31/19
Financial Investment Services
N.A.I.C.S.: 523999
Guy Charette *(Sec)*

HAMPTON FINANCIAL CORPORATION
141 Adelaide Street W Suite 1800, Toronto, M5H 3L5, ON, Canada
Tel.: (416) 862-7800   ON
Web Site:
https://hamptonfinancialcorp.com
Year Founded: 2014
HFC—(TSXV)
Rev.: $12,384,275
Assets: $13,704,763
Liabilities: $14,997,872
Net Worth: ($1,293,109)
Earnings: $1,011,488
Fiscal Year-end: 08/31/21
Investment Services
N.A.I.C.S.: 523999
Olga Juravlev *(Acting CFO)*

Subsidiaries:

Hampton Securities Limited (1)
141 Adelaide Street W Suite 1800, Toronto, M5H 3L5, ON, Canada
Tel.: (416) 862-7800
Web Site:
https://www.hamptonsecurities.com
Investment Services
N.A.I.C.S.: 523999
Olga Juravlev *(CFO)*

HAMPTON HILL MINING NL
Level 2 9 Havelock St, West Perth, 6005, WA, Australia
Tel.: (61) 894818444
Web Site:
http://www.hamptonhill.com.au
Sales Range: Less than $1 Million
Gold & Base Metal Exploration

HAMPTON HILL MINING NL

Hampton Hill Mining NL—(Continued)
N.A.I.C.S.: 213114
Joshua Norman Pitt *(Chm)*

HAMPTON STEEL LTD.
34-42 Sanders Road Finedon Road Industrial Estate, Wellingborough, NN8 4NL, Northants, United Kingdom
Tel.: (44) 1933 233333
Web Site:
  http://www.hamptonsteel.co.uk
Year Founded: 1991
Steel Wire Fencing & Related Products Mfr
N.A.I.C.S.: 331222
Mark Johnson *(Mng Dir)*

HAMRO BIKAS BANK LIMITED
Bidur-3 Battar, Siddharthanagar, Nepal
Tel.: (977) 10561777
Web Site: http://www.hamrobank.com
Sales Range: Less than $1 Million
Commercial Banking Services
N.A.I.C.S.: 522110
Hari Prasad *(Chm)*

HAN KOOK CAPITAL CO., LTD.
11F East 170 Eulji-ro, Jung-gu, Seoul, Kangnam-Gu, Korea (South)
Tel.: (82) 15222299
Web Site:
  https://www.hankookcapital.co.kr
Year Founded: 1989
023760—(KRS)
Sales Range: $75-99.9 Million
Emp.: 103
Financial Management Services; Lease, Venture Capital, Credits, Factoring & Corporate restructuring
N.A.I.C.S.: 523999
Sang Chun Lee *(Pres & CEO)*

HAN SUNG ENTERPRISE CO., LTD.
638 Yeongdong-daero, Gangnam-gu, Seoul, Korea (South)
Tel.: (82) 514107100
Web Site: https://www.hsep.com
Year Founded: 1963
003680—(KRS)
Rev.: $224,079,803
Assets: $180,182,793
Liabilities: $140,081,400
Net Worth: $40,101,393
Earnings: $1,084,690
Emp.: 683
Fiscal Year-end: 12/31/22
Seafood Product Mfr
N.A.I.C.S.: 311710
Woo-Kun Lim *(Chm & CEO)*

Subsidiaries:

Han Sung Enterprise Co., Ltd. - Danggiin Factory **(1)**
Hamdeok Town, Dangjin, 106-25, Chungcheongnam, Korea (South)
Tel.: (82) 514107100
Fishery & Seafood Production Mfr
N.A.I.C.S.: 311710

Han Sung Enterprise Co., Ltd. - Guryongpo Factory **(1)**
181 1 Lee, Nam-gu Guryongpoeup Byeongpo, Pohang, 181 1, Korea (South)
Tel.: (82) 5427667924
Fishery & Seafood Production Mfr
N.A.I.C.S.: 311710

Pacific Giant, Inc. **(1)**
4625 District Blvd, Vernon, CA 90058
Tel.: (323) 587-5000
Web Site: http://www.pacificgiant.com
Seafood Product Whslr
N.A.I.C.S.: 424460

HAN'S LASER TECHNOLOGY INDUSTRY GROUP CO., LTD.
Han s Laser Building No 9988 Shennan Avenue, Nanshan District, Shenzhen, 518057, China
Tel.: (86) 4006664000
Web Site: https://www.hanslaser.net
Year Founded: 1996
002008—(SSE)
Rev.: $2,100,549,672
Assets: $4,480,449,012
Liabilities: $2,316,049,632
Net Worth: $2,164,399,380
Earnings: $169,844,688
Emp.: 10,746
Fiscal Year-end: 12/31/22
Laser Processing Equipment Mfr
N.A.I.C.S.: 335139

Subsidiaries:

Baublys Laser GmbH **(1)**
Mauserstrasse 19, 71640, Ludwigsburg, Germany
Tel.: (49) 714185350
Web Site: https://www.baublys.de
Sales Range: $10-24.9 Million
Laser System Mfr
N.A.I.C.S.: 335999

Control Laser Corporation **(1)**
8251 Presidents Dr Ste 16, Orlando, FL 32809
Tel.: (407) 926-3500
Web Site: https://www.controllaser.com
Sales Range: $25-49.9 Million
Industrial Laser Systems Mfr
N.A.I.C.S.: 335999

HANA FINANCIAL GROUP, INC.
66 Eulji-ro, Jung-gu, Seoul, 04538, Korea (South)
Tel.: (82) 220021110
Web Site: https://www.hanafn.com
Year Founded: 1991
086790—(KRS)
Rev.: $9,273,240,280
Assets: $423,488,237,840
Liabilities: $394,415,972,880
Net Worth: $29,072,264,960
Earnings: $2,470,087,760
Emp.: 12,195
Fiscal Year-end: 12/31/20
Commercial Banking Services
N.A.I.C.S.: 551111
Jun-seong Han *(Deputy Pres & Chief Innovation Officer)*

Subsidiaries:

Banco KEB Hana do Brasil S.A. **(1)**
Av Dr Chucri Zaidan 940 18th Floor-conj 181, Vila Cordeiro, Sao Paulo, 04583-906, Brazil
Tel.: (55) 1151881120
Web Site: http://www.bancokebhana.com.br
Banking Services
N.A.I.C.S.: 522110

Hana Alternative Asset Management Co., Ltd. **(1)**
21F 66 Eulji-ro, Jung-gu, Seoul, Korea (South)
Tel.: (82) 221906500
Web Site: http://www.hana-aamc.com
Asset Management Services
N.A.I.C.S.: 523940
Yoon Ho Kim *(Mng Dir-Real Estate Investment Div 1)*

Hana Asia Limited **(1)**
Rm 1703a 17 F International Commerce Ctr 1 Austin Rd W, Tsim Sha Tsui, Kowloon, China (Hong Kong)
Tel.: (852) 25223646
Financial Management Services
N.A.I.C.S.: 523999

Hana Asset Trust Co., Ltd. **(1)**
127 Teheran-ro, Gangnam-gu, Seoul, Korea (South)
Tel.: (82) 232874600
Web Site: http://www.hanatrust.com
Real Estate Services
N.A.I.C.S.: 531390

Lee Eun-Hyung *(CEO)*

Hana Capital Co., Ltd. **(1)**
7th Floor Nara Building 1328-3 Seochodong, Seocho-gu, Seoul, 137-858, Korea (South)
Tel.: (82) 220371111
Web Site: http://www.hanacapital.co.kr
Financial Services
N.A.I.C.S.: 921130

Hana Daetoo Securities Co., Ltd. **(1)**
27-3 Yeouido-dong, Yeongdeungpo-gu, Seoul, 150 705, Korea (South)
Tel.: (82) 237717114
Web Site: http://www.hanaw.com
Emp.: 1,500
Asset Management Services
N.A.I.C.S.: 523150
Kim Jung-Tae *(Chm)*

Hana F&I, Inc. **(1)**
11th Floor 66 Eulji-ro, Jung-gu, Seoul, 04538, Korea (South) **(59.6%)**
Tel.: (82) 237082114
Web Site: http://www.hanafni.com
Financial Investment Services
N.A.I.C.S.: 523999

Hana Financial Investment Co., Ltd. **(1)**
82 Uisadang-daero, Yeongdeungpo-gu, Seoul, Korea (South)
Tel.: (82) 237717114
Financial Investment Services
N.A.I.C.S.: 523999
Lee Eun-Hyung *(Pres & CEO)*

Hana HSBC Life Insurance Co., Ltd. **(1)**
17th Floor Hanabank Building 101-1, Ulchiro 1-ka Chung-ku, Seoul, 100-191, Korea (South)
Tel.: (82) 237097300
Life Insurance Products & Services
N.A.I.C.S.: 524113

Hana I&S **(1)**
265-2 Seohyun-Dong Bundang-Gu, Seongnam, 463-050, Kyungki-Do, Korea (South)
Tel.: (82) 2 2151 6476
Web Site: http://www.hanains.com
Information Technology Consulting Services
N.A.I.C.S.: 541512

Hana Institute of Finance **(1)**
27-3 Youido-Dong, Yeongdeungpo-Gu, Seoul, 150 705, Korea (South)
Tel.: (82) 241 3 36 83
Web Site: http://www.hanaif.re.kr
Sales Range: $25-49.9 Million
Emp.: 15
Financial Consulting Services
N.A.I.C.S.: 541611
Heung Sik Choe *(Pres)*

Hana Insurance Co., Ltd. **(1)**
117 Changgyeonggung-ro, Jongno-gu, Seoul, Korea (South)
Tel.: (82) 266708400
General Insurance Services
N.A.I.C.S.: 524210
Kwon Tae-Gyun *(Pres & CEO)*

Hana SK Card **(1)**
140 Da-Dong Jung-Gu, Seoul, 100-714, Korea (South)
Tel.: (82) 1 599 1155
Web Site: http://www.hanaskcard.com
Credit Card Management Services
N.A.I.C.S.: 522210

Hana Savings Bank Co., Ltd. **(1)**
16th Floor 127 Teheran-ro, Gangnam-gu, Seoul, 06133, Korea (South)
Tel.: (82) 18991122
Web Site: http://www.hanasavings.com
Banking Services
N.A.I.C.S.: 522110

Hana TI Co., Ltd. **(1)**
5th Floor Hana Financial Group Integrated Data Center Vision Center, 167 Eco-ro Seogu, Incheon, 22742, Korea (South)
Tel.: (82) 221516400
Web Site: http://www.hanati.co.kr
Financial Services
N.A.I.C.S.: 523999
Park Geun-Young *(Pres & CEO)*

Hana Ventures LLC **(1)**

INTERNATIONAL PUBLIC

8F 509 Teheran-ro, Gangnam-Gu, Seoul, 06169, Korea (South)
Tel.: (82) 220066000
Web Site: http://www.hanaventures.co.kr
Financial Investment Services
N.A.I.C.S.: 523999
Alex Kim *(Pres & CEO)*

KEB Hana Bank **(1)**
181 Euljiro 2-ga Jung-gu, PO Box 2924, Seoul, 100-793, Korea (South) **(60%)**
Tel.: (82) 2 3708 2144
Web Site: http://www.kebhana.com
Sales Range: $1-4.9 Billion
Banking, Investment & Credit Card Services
N.A.I.C.S.: 551111

Subsidiary (Non-US):

Banco KEB do Brasil S.A. **(2)**
Av Doutor Chucri Zaidan 940 Torre II 18 Andar Cj 181 Vila Cordeiro, Sao Paulo, 04583 110, Brazil
Tel.: (55) 11 5188 1122
Banking Services
N.A.I.C.S.: 522110

Hana Bank (China) Co., Ltd. **(2)**
Building 7 Daojiayuan 11-Floor, Chaoyang District, Beijing, 100025, China **(100%)**
Tel.: (86) 1066581111
Web Site: http://www.hanabank.cn
Commercial Banking Services
N.A.I.C.S.: 522110

KEB Asia Finance Limited **(2)**
Suites 1001-04 Level 10 1 Pacific Place, 88 Queensway, Hong Kong, China (Hong Kong)
Tel.: (852) 3589 7500
Banking Services
N.A.I.C.S.: 522110

KEB Australia Ltd. **(2)**
Suite 902 Level 12 The Chifley Tower, 2 Chifley Square, Sydney, 2000, NSW, Australia
Tel.: (61) 2 9231 6333
Banking Services
N.A.I.C.S.: 522110

Subsidiary (Domestic):

KEB Capital Inc. **(2)**
10th Floor Hanwi Building 70 Da-dong, Jung-gu, Seoul, 100-182, Korea (South)
Tel.: (82) 52314662
Investment Services
N.A.I.C.S.: 523999

KEB Futures Co., Ltd. **(2)**
11th Floor Yuhwa Building 23-7 Yeouidodong, Yeongdeungpo-gu, Seoul, Korea (South)
Tel.: (82) 57773117
Investment Services
N.A.I.C.S.: 523999

KEB Investors Services Company **(2)**
6th Floor Hanwi Building 70 Da-dong, Jung-gu, Seoul, Korea (South)
Tel.: (82) 2 6714 4615
Web Site: http://www.kebis.co.kr
Investment Services
N.A.I.C.S.: 523999
Anne Yung Hyun *(Pres)*

Subsidiary (US):

KEB LA Financial Corp. **(2)**
777 S Figueroa St Ste 3000, Los Angeles, CA 90017
Tel.: (213) 683-0830
Web Site: http://www.kebhana.com
Emp.: 14
Banking Services
N.A.I.C.S.: 522110
Seockjoo Yune *(CFO & Sr VP)*

KEB NY Financial Corp. **(2)**
460 Park Ave 14th Fl, New York, NY 10022
Tel.: (212) 838-4949
Banking Services
N.A.I.C.S.: 522110
Thomas W. Toomey *(Chm & CEO)*

KEB USA International Corp. **(2)**
460 Park Ave 15th Fl, New York, NY 10022
Tel.: (212) 838-4949
Banking Services

N.A.I.C.S.: 522110

Subsidiary (Non-US):

Korea Exchange Bank (Deutschland) AG (2)
Bockenheimer Landstrasse 51-53, 60325, Frankfurt am Main, Germany
Tel.: (49) 69 7129 0
Emp.: 23
Banking Services
N.A.I.C.S.: 522110
Thomas Alfoldi (Chm)

Korea Exchange Bank of Canada (2)
4950 Yonge Street Suite 1101, Toronto, M2N 6K1, ON, Canada
Tel.: (416) 222-5200
Banking Services
N.A.I.C.S.: 522110

PT Bank KEB Hana Indonesia (2)
Wisma GKBI 20th Floor Suite 2002, PO Box 2317, Jalan Jenderal Sudirman No 28, Jakarta, 10210, Indonesia (69%)
Tel.: (62) 21 574 1030
Web Site: http://www.hanabank.co.id
Commericial Banking
N.A.I.C.S.: 522110

KEB Hana Card Co., Ltd. (1)
66 Eulji-ro, Jung-gu, Seoul, Korea (South)
Tel.: (82) 15443500
Web Site: http://eng.hanacard.co.kr
Credit Card Issuing Services
N.A.I.C.S.: 522210

PT. Bank KEB Hana (1)
Mangkuluhur City Tower One Jln Jend Gatot Subroto Kav 1-3, Jakarta, 12930, Indonesia
Tel.: (62) 215220222
Web Site: http://www.hanabank.co.id
Commercial Banking Services
N.A.I.C.S.: 522110
Park Jong Jin (Pres)

HANA MATERIALS INC.
50 3Gongdan 3-ro, Seobuk-gu, Cheonan, 31093, Chungcheongnam, Korea (South)
Tel.: (82) 414101015
Web Site: https://en.hanamts.com
Year Founded: 2007
166090—(KRS)
Rev.: $235,717,815
Assets: $367,873,230
Liabilities: $139,635,308
Net Worth: $228,237,922
Earnings: $61,463,470
Emp.: 754
Fiscal Year-end: 12/31/22
Diode Mfr
N.A.I.C.S.: 334413
Kim Hyun Joo (Chm & CEO)

HANA MICROELECTRONICS PUBLIC COMPANY LIMITED
65/98 Soi Vibhavadi-Rangsit 64 Junction 2 Kwang Talad Bangkhen, Khet Laksi, Bangkok, 10210, Thailand
Tel.: (66) 25511297
Web Site:
    https://www.hanagroup.com
Year Founded: 1978
HANA—(THA)
Rev.: $777,444,896
Assets: $1,030,650,435
Liabilities: $179,800,244
Net Worth: $850,850,190
Earnings: $51,394,428
Emp.: 3,139
Fiscal Year-end: 12/31/23
Electronics Mfr
N.A.I.C.S.: 334419
D. Scott Worthington (VP-Engrg)

Subsidiaries:

HANA Microelectronics, Inc. (1)
5255 Stevens Creek Blvd Ste122, Santa Clara, CA 95051
Tel.: (408) 452-7474
Electronic Components Distr
N.A.I.C.S.: 423690

Hana Microdisplay Technologies, Inc. (1)
2061 Case Pkwy S, Twinsburg, OH 44087 (100%)
Tel.: (330) 405-4600
Web Site: http://www.hanaoh.com
Sales Range: $25-49.9 Million
Emp.: 30
Microdisplay Mfr
N.A.I.C.S.: 334419
D. Scott Worthington (VP-Mfg Engrg)

Hana Microelectronics (Jiaxing) Co., Ltd. (1)
No 18 Hana Road Xin Cheng Industrial Park, Xiuzhou District, Jiaxing, 314000, ZheJiang Province, China (100%)
Tel.: (86) 57383528000
Emp.: 1,400
Microelectronics Mfr
N.A.I.C.S.: 334418

Hana Microelectronics Public Co., Ltd. (1)
65/98 Soi Vibhavadi-Rangsit 64 Junction 2, Kwang Talad Bamgkhen Bangkok, Lamphun, 93022-750, Thailand (100%)
Tel.: (66) 255112978
Web Site: http://www.hanaus.com
Sales Range: $900-999.9 Million
Emp.: 3,000
Microelectronics Mfr
N.A.I.C.S.: 334418
Wing Keung Chow (VP & Gen Mgr-Lamphun Operation)

Hana Semiconductor (Ayutthaya) Co., Ltd. (1)
Hi-Tech Industrial Estate Authority of Thailand 100 Moo 1 T Baan-Len, A Bang Pa-In KM 59 Asia Road, Ayutthaya, 13160, Thailand (100%)
Tel.: (66) 35350803
Sales Range: $800-899.9 Million
Emp.: 3,400
Semiconductor Assembly & Testing
N.A.I.C.S.: 334413

Hana Semiconductor (BKK) Co., Ltd. (1)
65/98 Soi Vibhavadi-Rangsit 64 Junction 2, Kwang Talad Bangkhen Khet Laksi, Bangkok, 10210, Thailand (100%)
Tel.: (66) 25511297
Web Site: http://www.hanaus.com
Sales Range: $100-124.9 Million
Emp.: 500
Semiconductor Assembly
N.A.I.C.S.: 334413

Omac Sales Limited (1)
Rm E F 16 F Fook Indl Bldg 41-45 Kwai Fung Crescent, Kwai Chung, China (Hong Kong)
Tel.: (852) 23452528
Sales Range: $50-74.9 Million
Emp.: 9
Electronic Components Distr
N.A.I.C.S.: 423690
Terry Chow (Gen Mgr)

HANA MICRON INC.
77 Yeonamyulgeum-ro, Eumbong-myeon, Asan, 336-864, Chungcheongnam-do, Korea (South)
Tel.: (82) 414237777
Web Site:
    https://www.hanamicron.com
Year Founded: 2001
067310—(KRS)
Rev.: $686,001,650
Assets: $1,080,740,426
Liabilities: $706,279,122
Net Worth: $374,461,304
Earnings: $44,662,848
Emp.: 978
Fiscal Year-end: 12/31/22
Semiconductor Product Mfr
N.A.I.C.S.: 334413
Lee Dong-Cheol (CEO)

Subsidiaries:

HT Micron (1)

Av Unisinos 1550, Sao Leopoldo, 93022-000, Rio Grande do Sul, Brazil
Tel.: (55) 5130818650
Web Site: https://www.htmicron.com.br
Semiconductor Product Mfr
N.A.I.C.S.: 334413
Ricardo Felizzola (CEO)

Hana WLS Inc. (1)
Production Line 4 77 Yeonamyulgeum-ro, Eumbong-myeon, Asan, Chungcheongnam-do, Korea (South)
Tel.: (82) 414237777
Web Site: https://hanawls.com
Semiconductor Machinery Mfr
N.A.I.C.S.: 333242
Shin Tae-Hee (CEO)

HANA MUST SEVEN SPECIAL PURPOSE ACQUISITION COMPANY
82 Uisadang-Daero, Yeongdeungpo-Gu, Seoul, 07321, Korea (South)
Tel.: (82) 237713497
Year Founded: 2020
372290—(KRS)
Emp.: 1
Financial Services
N.A.I.C.S.: 523999
Ha-Yong Song (Mgr)

HANA MUST SPECIAL PURPOSE ACQUISITION COMPANY
100 Eulji-ro Jung-gu, Seoul, Korea (South)
Tel.: (82) 2 3771 3635
Investment Services
N.A.I.C.S.: 523999
Kwak Je-Hoon (CEO)

HANA PHARM CO., LTD.
10F Ek-Tower 407 Teheran-Ro, Gangnam-Gu, Seoul, Korea (South)
Tel.: (82) 25777667
Web Site: https://www.hanaph.co.kr
Year Founded: 1978
293480—(KRS)
Rev.: $161,718,109
Assets: $265,354,815
Liabilities: $59,494,377
Net Worth: $205,860,438
Earnings: $18,643,607
Emp.: 674
Fiscal Year-end: 12/31/22
Pharmaceuticals Product Mfr
N.A.I.C.S.: 325412
Younha Lee (CEO)

HANALL BIOPHARMA CO., LTD.
12 Bongeunsa-ro 114-gil, Gangnam-gu, Seoul, Korea (South)
Tel.: (82) 216445515
Web Site: https://hanall.com
Year Founded: 1973
009420—(KRS)
Rev.: $84,366,486
Assets: $163,717,095
Liabilities: $34,664,390
Net Worth: $129,052,705
Earnings: $192,880
Emp.: 317
Fiscal Year-end: 12/31/22
Pharmaceuticals Product Mfr
N.A.I.C.S.: 325412
Jae-chun Yoon (Chm, Chm & Co-CEO)

Subsidiaries:

HanAll BioPharma Co., Ltd. - Business Development Division (1)
6th Fl I-Space Building 11-10 Sincheon-Dong, Songpa-Gu, Seoul, 138-240, Korea (South)
Tel.: (82) 2 2204 1753
Web Site: http://www.hanall.co.kr
Pharmaceutical Products Distr
N.A.I.C.S.: 424210

Sung-Wuk Kim (CEO)

HanAll BioPharma Co., Ltd. - International Exports Division (1)
Dancrshil 6th Fl I-Space Building Sincheon-Dong, Songpa-Gu, Seoul, 138-240, Korea (South)
Tel.: (82) 2 2204 1872
Pharmaceutical Products Distr
N.A.I.C.S.: 424210

HANAN MOR GROUP - HOLDING LTD.
1 Hapatish Street, Ness Ziona, 74047, Israel
Tel.: (972) 89305959
Web Site: http://www.hmg.co.il
CILO—(TAE)
Rev.: $110,589,859
Assets: $828,122,932
Liabilities: $862,888,783
Net Worth: ($34,765,851)
Earnings: ($237,792,509)
Fiscal Year-end: 12/31/23
Residential Property Managers
N.A.I.C.S.: 531311
Avi Maor (CEO)

HANATOUR SERVICE, INC.
1 Gongpyeong-dong, Jongno-gu, Seoul, Korea (South)
Tel.: (82) 221271000
Web Site:
    http://globalflight.hanatour.com
Year Founded: 1993
039130—(KRS)
Rev.: $88,181,578
Assets: $349,314,381
Liabilities: $272,843,217
Net Worth: $76,471,164
Earnings: ($49,527,050)
Emp.: 1,184
Fiscal Year-end: 12/31/22
Travel Agency
N.A.I.C.S.: 561510
Woong Bi Kim (Mgr)

Subsidiaries:

Hanatour Japan Co., Ltd. (1)
2-3-15 Shinjuku, Shinjuku-ku, Tokyo, 160-0022, Japan
Tel.: (81) 366294766
Web Site: https://www.hanatourjapan.jp
Rev.: $36,541,860
Assets: $68,624,110
Liabilities: $55,500,520
Net Worth: $13,123,590
Earnings: $8,656,890
Emp.: 68
Fiscal Year-end: 12/31/2023
Tourism & Travelling Services
N.A.I.C.S.: 561520
Byung-Chan Lee (CEO)

HANBIT SOFT INC.
Room 1506 15th floor 186 Gasan digital 1-ro, Geumcheon-gu, Seoul, 8502, Korea (South)
Tel.: (82) 7040508000
Web Site: https://www.hanbitsoft.com
Year Founded: 1999
047080—(KRS)
Rev.: $43,192,173
Assets: $33,702,503
Liabilities: $14,635,154
Net Worth: $19,067,348
Earnings: $1,559,420
Emp.: 78
Fiscal Year-end: 12/31/22
Online Game & Entertainment Software Publisher
N.A.I.C.S.: 513210
Yoo Ra Kim (CEO)

HANCAP AB
Montorgatan 9, 30262, Halmstad, Sweden
Tel.: (46) 35 172300
Web Site: http://www.hancap.se

HANCAP AB

Hancap AB—(Continued)
Holding Company; Windows & Conservatories Mfr
N.A.I.C.S.: 551112

HANCHANG CORPORATION
1052 Jungang-daero, Yeonje-gu, Busan, Korea (South)
Tel.: (82) 28506500
Web Site:
 https://www.hanchang.co.kr
Year Founded: 1967
005110—(KRS)
Rev.: $68,523,714
Assets: $87,039,922
Liabilities: $69,131,883
Net Worth: $17,908,039
Earnings: ($1,435,022)
Emp.: 34
Fiscal Year-end: 12/31/22
Communication Equipment Mfr & Distr
N.A.I.C.S.: 334290
Seung Hwan Choi (CEO)

HANCHANG INDUSTRY CO., LTD.
227-14 Amsogogae-ro Yanggam-myeon, Hwaseong, 18635, Gyeonggi-do, Korea (South)
Tel.: (82) 313532970
Web Site: http://www.hanchem.com
Year Founded: 1985
079170—(KRS)
Rev.: $76,163,109
Assets: $57,570,929
Liabilities: $10,166,019
Net Worth: $47,404,910
Earnings: $4,694,315
Emp.: 83
Fiscal Year-end: 12/31/22
Mineral Product Mfr & Sales
N.A.I.C.S.: 327999
Chang-Won Lee (CEO)

HANCHANG PAPER CO., LTD
270 Yongdang-dong, Yangsan, Gyeognam-do, Korea (South)
Tel.: (82) 553702000
Web Site: https://hanchangpaper.com
Year Founded: 1973
009460—(KRS)
Rev.: $164,846,328
Assets: $217,108,900
Liabilities: $132,408,469
Net Worth: $84,700,431
Earnings: $966,991
Emp.: 217
Fiscal Year-end: 12/31/22
Paper Products Mfr
N.A.I.C.S.: 322299
Kil-Su Kim (CEO)

HANCOCK & GORE LTD.
Level 5 107 Pitt Street, PO Box 1445, Sydney, 2000, NSW, Australia
Tel.: (61) 286674660 **AU**
Web Site:
 https://www.hancockandgore.com
Year Founded: 1904
HNG—(ASX)
Rev.: $4,706,083
Assets: $47,827,805
Liabilities: $660,037
Net Worth: $47,167,768
Earnings: $5,567,741
Emp.: 274
Fiscal Year-end: 09/30/23
Investment Services
N.A.I.C.S.: 523999
Kevin J. Eley (Chm)

Subsidiaries:

Aarque Graphics NZ Ltd (1)
2 A Waipareira Ave, Henderson, Henderson, 0654, New Zealand (50%)
Tel.: (64) 98372144
Web Site: http://www.aarque.co.nz
Sales Range: $10-24.9 Million
Emp.: 60
Imaging Equipment & Associated Consumer Products Distr
N.A.I.C.S.: 423420

BLC Cosmetics Pty Ltd (1)
Level 2 68-72 Waterloo Road, Macquarie Park, 2113, NSW, Australia (60%)
Tel.: (61) 286674695
Web Site: http://www.blccosmetics.com
Sales Range: $10-24.9 Million
Emp.: 10
Beauty & Skin Care Products Importer & Distr
N.A.I.C.S.: 424990

BOC Ophthalmic Instruments Pty Ltd (1)
Unit C/28-32 Egerton Street, Silverwater, 2128, NSW, Australia (50%)
Tel.: (61) 296437888
Web Site:
 http://www.bocinstruments.com.au
Sales Range: $25-49.9 Million
Emp.: 12
Ophthalmic Equipment Importer & Distr
N.A.I.C.S.: 423450
Tony Cosentino (Mng Dir)

Baker & McAuliffe Holdings Pty Ltd (1)
Suite A2 3 15-21 Doody St, Alexandria, 2015, NSW, Australia
Tel.: (61) 29 571 8800
Web Site: https://www.jsblighting.com.au
Emp.: 14
Electronic Product Distr
N.A.I.C.S.: 423690

Biante Pty Limited (1)
PO Box 185, Belmont, 6984, WA, Australia
Tel.: (61) 894795130
Web Site: http://www.biante.com.au
Online Model Cars Retailer
N.A.I.C.S.: 336370

Createc Pty Ltd (1)
25 South Street, Rydalmere, 2116, NSW, Australia (50%)
Tel.: (61) 288450200
Web Site: http://www.anitech.com.au
Sales Range: $50-74.9 Million
Emp.: 70
Imaging Equipment & Associated Consumer Products Supplier & Services; Owned 50% by HGL Limited & 50% by Chris Wagstaff (CEO)
N.A.I.C.S.: 423430

GAMA Healthcare Australia Pty Ltd. (1)
Suite 1 33-37 Duerdin Street, Notting Hill, 3168, VIC, Australia (85%)
Tel.: (61) 397696600
Web Site: https://gamahealthcare.com.au
Pharmacy Products & Promotional Solutions Importer & Distr
N.A.I.C.S.: 424210

Hamlon Pty Ltd (1)
Level 2 68-72 Waterloo Road, Macquarie Park, 2086, NSW, Australia (100%)
Tel.: (61) 299757655
Web Site: http://www.icandycreative.com.au
Sales Range: $25-49.9 Million
Emp.: 45
Price Ticketing, Shelf Management, Merchandising & Promotional Display Products Importer & Distr
N.A.I.C.S.: 423490

JSB Lighting (1)
22-38 Yurong St, Darlinghurst, 2037, NSW, Australia (100%)
Tel.: (61) 295718800
Web Site: http://www.jsblighting.com.au
Sales Range: $25-49.9 Million
Emp.: 20
Commercial Lighting Equipment Importer & Distr
N.A.I.C.S.: 423610
Dudley Hewitt (CEO)

Kinsole Pty Ltd (1)
Unit 2 21 Binney Road, Kings Park, 2148, NSW, Australia (50%)
Tel.: (61) 29 621 3066
Web Site: https://www.xln.com.au
Patchwork & Quilting Fabrics Importer & Distr
N.A.I.C.S.: 424990

Mountcastle Pty Ltd (1)
95-103 Hyde Rd, Yeronga, 4104, QLD, Australia (89.7%)
Tel.: (61) 738485855
Web Site: http://www.mountcastle.com.au
Sales Range: $25-49.9 Million
Emp.: 100
Headwear Importer, Distr & Mfr
N.A.I.C.S.: 315990

The Point-of-Sale Centre (New Zealand) Ltd (1)
Unit 1 7 Henry Rose Place, Albany, 0632, Auckland, New Zealand
Tel.: (64) 800502050
Web Site: http://www.spos.co.nz
Sales Range: $25-49.9 Million
Emp.: 10
Marketing & Retail Solutions
N.A.I.C.S.: 541613

HANCOCK PROSPECTING PTY. LTD.
28-42 Ventnor Avenue, West Perth, 6005, WA, Australia
Tel.: (61) 894298222
Web Site:
 http://www.hancockprospecting.com
Year Founded: 1952
Iron Ore Mining Services
N.A.I.C.S.: 212210
Gina Rinehart (Chm)

Subsidiaries:

Azure Minerals Limited (1)
Level 1 34 Colin Street, West Perth, 6005, WA, Australia
Tel.: (61) 894812555
Web Site: http://www.azureminerals.com.au
Rev.: $1,261
Assets: $21,660,083
Liabilities: $1,871,557
Net Worth: $19,788,526
Earnings: ($15,341,107)
Emp.: 10
Fiscal Year-end: 06/30/2022
Minerals Exploration
N.A.I.C.S.: 213115

Subsidiary (Non-US):

Minera Piedra Azul, S.A. de C.V. (2)
Ave Javier De Leon 707 Col Pitic, Hermosillo, Sonora, Mexico
Tel.: (52) 6622855350
Web Site: http://www.azureminerals.com
Mineral Exploration Services
N.A.I.C.S.: 213115

HANCOM LIFECARE INC.
53 Jungbudaero 1960Beon-Gil Yangji-Myun, Cheoin-Gu, Yongin, 17160, Gyeonggi-do, Korea (South)
Tel.: (82) 15662601
Web Site:
 http://www.hancomlifecare.com
Year Founded: 1971
372910—(KRS)
Emp.: 268
Protecting Product Mfr
N.A.I.C.S.: 339113
Joonseok Woo (CEO)

HANCOM WITH INC.
4Fl Hancom Tower 49 Daewangpangyoro 644 Beongil, Bundang-gum, Seongnam, 13493, Gyeonggido, Korea (South)
Tel.: (82) 316226300
Web Site:
 https://www.hancomwith.com
054920—(KRS)
Rev.: $22,017,580
Assets: $172,534,416
Liabilities: $62,134,328
Net Worth: $110,400,088

INTERNATIONAL PUBLIC

Earnings: $4,662,048
Emp.: 33
Fiscal Year-end: 12/31/22
Software Publishing Services
N.A.I.C.S.: 513210
Hyun Soo Kim (Co-CEO)

Subsidiaries:

Hancom GMD Inc. (1)
5F Hancom Tower 644-gil 49 Daewangpangyo-ro, Bundang-gu, Seongnam, Gyeonggi-do, Korea (South) (35.7%)
Tel.: (82) 31 622 6111
Web Site: http://www.hancomgmd.com
Rev.: $9,881,098
Assets: $61,307,318
Liabilities: $19,922,060
Net Worth: $41,385,259
Earnings: $1,406,937
Emp.: 44
Fiscal Year-end: 12/31/2018
Semiconductor Mfr
N.A.I.C.S.: 334413

HANCOM, INC.
Hancom Tower 49 Daewangpangyo-ro 644 Beon-gil Sampyeong-dong, Bundang-gu, Seongnam, 13494, Gyeonggi-do, Korea (South)
Tel.: (82) 316273001
Web Site: http://www.hancom.com
Year Founded: 1990
030520—(KRS)
Rev.: $185,620,445
Assets: $532,978,685
Liabilities: $164,078,341
Net Worth: $368,900,344
Earnings: $12,815,720
Emp.: 414
Fiscal Year-end: 12/31/22
Software Development Services
N.A.I.C.S.: 513210

Subsidiaries:

APS Korea, Inc. (1)
368-1 Gojan-Dong Namdong-Gu, Incheon, 405-816, Korea (South)
Tel.: (82) 31 710 0791
Web Site: http://www.aps-korea.co.kr
Industrial Equipment Mfr
N.A.I.C.S.: 333242

Subsidiary (Non-US):

APS Ireland, Inc. (2)
Unit 26A Waterford Industrial Estate Cork Road, Waterford, Ireland
Tel.: (353) 51357834
Spray Coating Services
N.A.I.C.S.: 332812
Michael O'Sullivan (Plant Mgr)

Subsidiary (US):

APS Materials, Inc. (2)
4011 Riverside Dr, Dayton, OH 45405
Tel.: (937) 278-6547
Web Site: https://apsmaterials.com
Spray Coating Services
N.A.I.C.S.: 332812

Durecom Co., Ltd. (1)
14-2LT 15BL 450-2 Moknae-dong Danwon-gu, Ansan, Gyeonggi-do, Korea (South)
Tel.: (82) 31 412 4001
Web Site: http://www.durecom.com
Remote Meter Reader Mfr
N.A.I.C.S.: 334514
Gui Il Jung (CEO)

Global Cathodic Protection, Inc. (1)
9300 Lawndale St Ste A, Houston, TX 77012
Tel.: (713) 784-9588
Web Site: https://www.globalcorrosion.com
Engineeering Services
N.A.I.C.S.: 541330
Baker Davis (Dir-Projects)

Hancom FinTech, Inc. (1)
5 FL Hancom Tower 49 Daewangpangyo-ro 644 Beon-gil Sampyeong-dong, Bundang-gu, Seongnam, Gyeonggi-do, Korea (South)

Tel.: (82) 316277112
Web Site: http://www.dreamsead.com
Crowdfunding Services
N.A.I.C.S.: 561499
Yun-Seong Ji (CEO)

Hancom Interfree, Inc. (1)
Unit 207 Floor 2 35 Techno 9-ro, Yuseong-gu, Daejeon, Korea (South)
Tel.: (82) 316277900
Web Site: http://www.interfree.com
Application Software Development Services
N.A.I.C.S.: 513210

Hancom MDS (Shenzhen) Technology Ltd. Co. (1)
17B East side 17th Floor DaQing Building No 6027 Shennan Road, Tian'an shequ Shatou Sub-District Futian District, Shenzhen, 518000, China
Tel.: (86) 75523945779
Software Development Services
N.A.I.C.S.: 541511

Hancom Talkafe Inc. (1)
1F 49 Daewangpangyo-ro 644th gil Sampyeong-dong Hancom Tower, Bundang-gu, Seongnam, Gyeonggi-do, Korea (South)
Tel.: (82) 316277799
Web Site: http://www.talkafe.net
Application Software Development Services
N.A.I.C.S.: 513210
Eun-Jin Jun (Pres)

MDS China Holding Co., Ltd. (1)
21st Floor Taiyau building 181 Johnston Road, Wanchai, 999077, China (Hong Kong)
Tel.: (852) 25414188
Information Technology Services
N.A.I.C.S.: 541511

MDS Pacific India Pvt., Ltd. (1)
116 2nd Floor West of Chord Road 1st Block 2nd Stage Rajajinagar, Bengaluru, 560086, India
Tel.: (91) 8041239727
Information Technology Services
N.A.I.C.S.: 541511

iText Software Corp. (1)
265 Medford St Ste 401, Somerville, MA 02143
Tel.: (617) 982-2646
Software Development Services
N.A.I.C.S.: 541511
Bruno Lowagie (CEO)

Subsidiary (Non-US):

iText Software Asia Pte. Ltd. (2)
Robinson Road 71, Singapore, 068895, Singapore
Tel.: (65) 31571294
Software Development Services
N.A.I.C.S.: 541511

iText Software BVBA (2)
AA Tower Technologiepark-Zwijnaarde 122, 9052, Zwijnaarde, Belgium
Tel.: (32) 92980231
Software Development Services
N.A.I.C.S.: 541511
Nathan Voogt (Mgr-EMEA North)

HAND ENTERPRISE SOLUTIONS CO., LTD.
No 33 Huilian Road, Qingpu District, Shanghai, 201707, China
Tel.: (86) 2167002300
Web Site: https://www.hand-china.com
Year Founded: 1996
300170—(CHIN)
Rev.: $422,165,952
Assets: $816,615,540
Liabilities: $260,807,040
Net Worth: $555,808,500
Earnings: $61,462,908
Emp.: 10,056
Fiscal Year-end: 12/31/22
IT Consulting Services
N.A.I.C.S.: 541519
Diqing Chen (Chm)

Subsidiaries:

Hand Enterprise USA, Inc. (1)
1900 Mccarthy Blvd Ste 445, Milpitas, CA 95035
Tel.: (408) 649-3797
Web Site: https://www.hand-us.com
Business Management Services
N.A.I.C.S.: 561110

HANDA MINING CORPORATION
Suite 1500 701 West Georgia St, Vancouver, V7Y 1C6, BC, Canada
Tel.: (604) 601-6926   BC
Web Site: https://www.handamining.com
Year Founded: 2009
HAND—(TSXV)
Rev.: $262
Assets: $20,733
Liabilities: $566,174
Net Worth: ($545,441)
Earnings: ($1,460,273)
Fiscal Year-end: 01/31/20
Copper Mining Services
N.A.I.C.S.: 212230
Jan Petrus Nelson (Chm & CEO)

HANDAL ENERGY BERHAD
C L29 07 KL Trillion 338 Jalan Tun Razak, 50400, Kuala Lumpur, Malaysia
Tel.: (60) 327335555   MY
Web Site: https://www.haenergy.com.my
Year Founded: 1988
HANDAL—(KLS)
Rev.: $13,077,062
Assets: $22,486,636
Liabilities: $14,082,718
Net Worth: $8,403,918
Earnings: ($9,692,733)
Emp.: 118
Fiscal Year-end: 12/31/22
Holding Company; Construction Equipment & Cranes
N.A.I.C.S.: 551112
Mallek Rizal Mohsin (Vice Chm)

Subsidiaries:

Simflexi Sdn. Bhd. (1)
Unit 9-6 and 7-6 Level 6 Galleria Cyberjaya Jalan Teknokrat 6 Cyber 5, 63000, Cyberjaya, Selangor, Malaysia
Tel.: (60) 383280560
Web Site: http://www.simflexi.com
Engineeering Services
N.A.I.C.S.: 541330

HANDAN XURI COMMERCIAL & INDUSTRIAL CO., LTD.
No 385 Heping Road, Handan, 056001, Hebei, China
Tel.: (86) 3108120845
Web Site: http://www.e-xuri.com
Year Founded: 1992
Sales Range: $50-74.9 Million
Emp.: 280
Industrial Sewing Thread Mfr
N.A.I.C.S.: 313110
Weishan Dong (Pres & Gen Mgr)

HANDENI GOLD INC.
Plot 82A ITV Road, PO Box 33507, Dar es Salaam, Tanzania
Tel.: (255) 222700084   NV
Web Site: http://www.handenigold.com
Year Founded: 2004
HNDI—(OTCEM)
Sales Range: Less than $1 Million
Gold Mining Services
N.A.I.C.S.: 212220
Reginald Mengi (Chm)

HANDOK CLEAN TECH CO., LTD.
13 Techno 8-Ro, Yuseong-Gu, Daejeon, 34028, Korea (South)
Tel.: (82) 426715671
Web Site: https://www.hdctech.co.kr
Year Founded: 1990
256150—(KRS)
Rev.: $45,367,382
Assets: $45,357,355
Liabilities: $4,343,514
Net Worth: $41,013,840
Earnings: $3,884,944
Emp.: 224
Fiscal Year-end: 12/31/22
Filtering Mfr
N.A.I.C.S.: 333413
Ko In Sun (CEO)

HANDOK INC.
132 Teheran-ro, Gangnam-gu, Seoul, 06235, Korea (South)
Tel.: (82) 25275114
Web Site: https://www.handok.co.kr
Year Founded: 1954
002390—(KRS)
Rev.: $417,063,270
Assets: $668,138,432
Liabilities: $375,254,848
Net Worth: $292,883,585
Earnings: $8,194,278
Emp.: 964
Fiscal Year-end: 12/31/22
Pharmaceuticals Product Mfr
N.A.I.C.S.: 325412
Jin-ki Baik (Co-CEO & VP)

Subsidiaries:

Handok Inc. - Handok Eumseong Factory (1)
78 Daepungsandan-ro Daeso-myeon, Eumseong, 27670, Chungcheongbuk-do, Korea (South)
Tel.: (82) 435301114
Pharmaceuticals Product Mfr
N.A.I.C.S.: 325412

Theravalues Corporation (1)
1F Kioicho Bldg 3-12 Kioicho, Chiyoda-ku, Tokyo, 102-0094, Japan
Tel.: (81) 332347677
Turmeric Powder Distr
N.A.I.C.S.: 424490

HANDS CORPORATION LTD.
50 Gajeong-ro 37 beon-gil, Seo-gu, Incheon, Korea (South)
Tel.: (82) 328709600
Web Site: https://www.handscorp.co.kr
Year Founded: 1972
143210—(KRS)
Rev.: $596,921,209
Assets: $661,605,544
Liabilities: $512,245,632
Net Worth: $149,359,912
Earnings: ($59,837,579)
Emp.: 882
Fiscal Year-end: 12/31/22
Aluminum Wheel Mfr & Distr
N.A.I.C.S.: 336390
Hyun-Chang Seung (Chm & CEO)

Subsidiaries:

Hands Corporation Ltd. - Hands 1 Plant (1)
53 Glipa-ro Nam-gu, Incheon, 22121, Korea (South)
Tel.: (82) 328701500
Aluminum Alloy Wheel Mfr
N.A.I.C.S.: 336390

Hands Corporation Ltd. - Hands 2 Plant (1)
50 Gajeong-ro 37beon-gil Seo-gu, Incheon, 22836, Korea (South)
Tel.: (82) 328701300
Aluminum Alloy Wheel Mfr
N.A.I.C.S.: 336390

Hands Corporation Ltd. - Hands 3 Plant (1)
865 Baekbeom-ro Seo-gu, Incheon, 22841, Korea (South)
Tel.: (82) 328701700
Aluminum Alloy Wheel Mfr
N.A.I.C.S.: 336390

Hands Corporation Ltd. - Hands 5 Plant (1)
178-10 Gajwa-dong Seo-gu, Incheon, 22840, Korea (South)
Tel.: (82) 328701400
Aluminum Alloy Wheel Mfr
N.A.I.C.S.: 336390

Hands Corporation Ltd. - Hands 6 Plant (1)
682 Ssangsong-ri Mado-myeon, Hwaseong, 18542, Gyeonggi, Korea (South)
Tel.: (82) 313708000
Aluminum Alloy Wheel Mfr
N.A.I.C.S.: 336390

Hands Corporation Ltd. - Hands Mechanic Plant (1)
557-2 Sibjeong-dong Bupyeong-gu, Incheon, 21449, Korea (South)
Tel.: (82) 7046162372
Aluminum Alloy Wheel Mfr
N.A.I.C.S.: 336390

Hands Corporation Ltd. - Hands Thumb Plant (1)
178-379 Gajwa-dong Seo-gu, Incheon, 22845, Korea (South)
Tel.: (82) 328706724
Aluminum Alloy Wheel Mfr
N.A.I.C.S.: 336390

Qingdao Donghwa Castings Co., Ltd (1)
Pingying Road Tonghe District Pingdu, Qingdao, Shandong, China
Tel.: (86) 53287314988
Aluminum Alloy Wheel Distr
N.A.I.C.S.: 423120

HANDS FORM HOLDINGS LIMITED
Room 9 2/F Hang Bong Commercial Centre 28 Shanghai Street, Jordan, Kowloon, China (Hong Kong)
Tel.: (852) 21274675   Ky
Web Site: http://www.handsform.com
Year Founded: 1989
1920—(HKG)
Rev.: $15,620,918
Assets: $15,801,840
Liabilities: $2,441,625
Net Worth: $13,360,215
Earnings: ($7,165,883)
Emp.: 16
Fiscal Year-end: 12/31/22
Holding Company
N.A.I.C.S.: 551112
Adam Kwok Fai Cheung (Exec Dir)

HANDSMAN CO., LTD.
2080 Yoshio-cho, Miyakonojo, 885-0006, Japan
Tel.: (81) 986380847
Web Site: https://www.handsman.co.jp
Year Founded: 1914
76360—(TKS)
Sales Range: Less than $1 Million
Retail Store Operator
N.A.I.C.S.: 459999
Seiji Ozono (Pres & CEO)

HANDSOME CORP.
Handsome Bldg 523 Dosan-daero, Gangnam-gu, Seoul, 06013, Korea (South)
Tel.: (82) 18005700
Web Site: https://www.handsome.co.kr
Year Founded: 1987
020000—(KRS)
Rev.: $1,182,884,031
Assets: $1,292,176,787
Liabilities: $267,087,100
Net Worth: $1,025,089,688
Earnings: $92,576,337
Emp.: 1,578
Fiscal Year-end: 12/31/22

HANDSOME CORP.

Handsome Corp.—(Continued)
Men & Women Apparel Mfr
N.A.I.C.S.: 315250
Min Duk Kim (CEO)

HANDY NETWORK INTERNATIONAL CO., LTD.
4-3-10 Minoh Noguchi Building 3F, Minoh, Osaka, Japan
Tel.: (81) 72 725 3388
Web Site: http://www.hni.co.jp
Year Founded: 1987
Healthcare Equipment Whslr & Mfr
N.A.I.C.S.: 423440
Tetsuro Haruyama (Dir)

HANDYSOFT, INC.
4F 41-22 Burim-ro 170beon-gil, Dongan-gu, Anyang, Gyeonggi-do, Korea (South)
Tel.: (82) 7044839000
Web Site:
 https://www.handysoft.co.kr
Year Founded: 2009
220180—(KRS)
Rev.: $25,399,054
Assets: $60,022,870
Liabilities: $9,273,972
Net Worth: $50,748,898
Earnings: $99,074
Emp.: 106
Fiscal Year-end: 12/31/22
Software Publisher
N.A.I.C.S.: 513210
Lee Joon Hee (CEO)

HANEDA ZENITH HOLDINGS CO., LTD.
4F Kojimachi M-Square 5-7-2 Kojimachi, Chiyoda-ku, Tokyo, 102-0083, Japan
Tel.: (81) 3 3556 2801
Web Site: http://www.zenith-haneda.co.jp
Year Founded: 2014
Holding Company; Concrete Pipes & Other Concrete Products Mfr
N.A.I.C.S.: 551112
Satoshi Takane (Vice Chm)

HANERGY HOLDING GROUP LIMITED
No 0 A Anli Road, Chaoyang District, Beijing, 100031, China
Tel.: (86) 10 8391 4567
Web Site: http://www.hanergy.eu
Year Founded: 1994
Sales Range: $5-14.9 Billion
Emp.: 15,000
Renewable Energy Power Generation; Solar Energy Technology Mfr
N.A.I.C.S.: 551112
Hejun Li (Chm)

Subsidiaries:

Hanergy America Solar Solutions (1)
1350 Bayshore Hwy Ste 825, Burlingame, CA 94010
Tel.: (650) 288-3722
Web Site: http://www.hanergyamerica.com
Renewable Energy Power Generation; Solar Energy Technology Mfr
N.A.I.C.S.: 221118

Subsidiary (Domestic):

MiaSole, Inc. (2)
2590 Walsh Ave, Santa Clara, CA 95051 (100%)
Tel.: (408) 919-5700
Web Site: http://www.miasole.com
Photovoltaic Solar Panels Mfr
N.A.I.C.S.: 221114
Jie Zhang (CEO)

Hanergy Solar Power (Europe) B. V. (1)
World Trade Center Tower H Zuidplein 138, 1077 XV, Amsterdam, Netherlands
Tel.: (31) 20 6753588
Web Site: http://www.hanergy.eu
Renewable Energy Power Generation; Solar Energy Technology Mfr
N.A.I.C.S.: 221118

Hanergy Solar Power (Italy) s.r.l. (1)
Lungotevere Mellini n 27, Rome, 00193, Italy
Tel.: (39) 0632652798
Web Site: http://www.hanergy.com
Emp.: 15
Renewable Energy Power Generation; Solar Energy Technology Mfr
N.A.I.C.S.: 221118
Jarno Montella (CEO)

HANEXPRESS CO., LTD.
2/3/4F 317 Hyoreong-ro, Seocho-gu, Seoul, Korea (South)
Tel.: (82) 234005474
Web Site: https://www.hanex.co.kr
Year Founded: 1979
014130—(KRS)
Rev.: $658,187,061
Assets: $312,895,323
Liabilities: $232,088,331
Net Worth: $80,806,993
Earnings: $6,552,839
Emp.: 427
Fiscal Year-end: 12/31/22
Logistic Services
N.A.I.C.S.: 541614
Jae-Heon Lee (CEO)

Subsidiaries:

Han Express Energy Sdn. Bhd. (1)
Lot 196 and 126 Block 11 Engkilo Land District, Off Sibu Sungai Maaw Road Sg Sadit, 96000, Sibu, Sarawak, Malaysia
Tel.: (60) 84227058
Wood Product Mfr & Distr
N.A.I.C.S.: 321999

Han Express Vietnam Co., Ltd. (1)
6F TNR TOWER 180-192 Nguyen Cong Tru, Nguyen Thai Binh ward District 1, Ho Chi Minh City, Vietnam
Tel.: (84) 2839152031
Warehousing Services
N.A.I.C.S.: 493110

HanExpress Logistics (Ningbo) Co., Ltd (1)
No 55 Huandao North Road Development Zone, Ningbo, Zhejiang, China
Tel.: (86) 57486751301
Logistics Consulting Servies
N.A.I.C.S.: 541614

HANEY BUILDERS' SUPPLIES (1971) LTD.
22740 Dewdney Trunk Road, Maple Ridge, V2X 3K2, BC, Canada
Tel.: (604) 463-6206
Web Site:
 https://www.haneybuilders.com
Year Founded: 1938
Rev.: $15,164,694
Emp.: 50
Lumber Yard Supplier
N.A.I.C.S.: 444180
Tom Stinson (Owner)

HANG CHI HOLDINGS LIMITED
Room D 35/F T G Place 10 Shing Yip Street, Kwun Tong, Kowloon, China (Hong Kong)
Tel.: (852) 21571216
Web Site: http://www.shuionnc.com
Year Founded: 1993
8405—(HKG)
Rev.: $24,612,728
Assets: $43,017,353
Liabilities: $16,095,600
Net Worth: $26,921,753
Earnings: $4,922,775
Emp.: 437
Fiscal Year-end: 12/31/22
Home Care Services
N.A.I.C.S.: 621610
Pui Shan Leung (CFO & Sec)

Subsidiaries:

Shui Jun Nursing Centre (Yau Tong) Company Limited (1)
Shop G67 & Shop B 1/F Ka Fat Shopping Centre Ka Wing Street, Yau Tong Centre, Kowloon, China (Hong Kong)
Tel.: (852) 2 379 6081
Web Site: http://www.shuionnc.com
Health Care Srvices
N.A.I.C.S.: 622110

Shui On Nursing Centre (Kwai Shing E.) Co., Limited (1)
Rooms G01 101 201 301 and 401 Sing Hei House Car Park Building, Kwai Shing East Estate, Kwai Chung, New Territories, China (Hong Kong)
Tel.: (852) 21550993
Health Care Srvices
N.A.I.C.S.: 622110

HANG FUNG INTERNATIONAL INDUSTRIAL CO., LTD.
Unit 13 8/F Harbour Centre Tower1 1 Hok Cheung ST, Hunghom, Kowloon, China (Hong Kong)
Tel.: (852) 2580 6006
Web Site:
 http://www.hangfungint.com
Year Founded: 1980
Emp.: 500
Packaging Mfr
N.A.I.C.S.: 326112
Freeman Leung (Gen Mgr)

Subsidiaries:

Sydek Hang Fung Trading Co., Ltd. (1)
Room 813 8th Fl Tower 1, 1 Hok Cheung St Harbour Ctr, Kowloon, China (Hong Kong)
Tel.: (852) 26359208
Packaging Material Whslr
N.A.I.C.S.: 423840

Subsidiary (Non-US):

Sydek Hang Fung Precise Package (Shanghai) Co., Ltd. (2)
2/F TenMa Pudong Building 438 Fu Te Dong Yi Rd Shanghai Outer Gaoqiao, Free Trade Zone D12-12, Shanghai, 200131, China
Tel.: (86) 21 5866 6009
Web Site: http://www.hangfungint.com
Sales Range: $25-49.9 Million
Emp.: 7
Industrial Packaging Mfr
N.A.I.C.S.: 326112

Sydek Hang Fung Precision (Suzhou) Co., Ltd. (2)
269 He Feng Road Xu Kou Wu Zhong, Suzhou, Jiangsu, China
Tel.: (86) 512 6656 3230
Industrial Packaging Mfr
N.A.I.C.S.: 326112

HANG JIN TECHNOLOGY CO., LTD.
No 1 Huagong Street, Lianshan District, Huludao, 430014, Liaoning, China
Tel.: (86) 4292709027
Web Site:
 http://www.fangdachemical.com
Year Founded: 1997
000818—(SSE)
Rev.: $602,584,164
Assets: $718,112,304
Liabilities: $179,144,784
Net Worth: $538,967,520
Earnings: $32,259,708
Fiscal Year-end: 12/31/22
Chemical Products Mfr
N.A.I.C.S.: 325998
Weidong Cai (Chm & Gen Mgr)

HANG LUNG GROUP LIMITED

INTERNATIONAL PUBLIC

28th Floor Standard Chartered Bank Building, 4 Des Voeux Road, Central, China (Hong Kong)
Tel.: (852) 28790111
Web Site: http://www.hanglung.com
Year Founded: 1960
0010—(OTCIQ)
Rev.: $1,398,264,470
Assets: $28,951,141,897
Liabilities: $9,114,854,244
Net Worth: $19,836,287,653
Earnings: $612,803,047
Emp.: 4,224
Fiscal Year-end: 12/31/22
Property Development & Hotel Management Services
N.A.I.C.S.: 531390
Ronnie Chichung Chan (Chm)

Subsidiaries:

AP City Limited (1)
28th-Floor Standard Chartered Bank Building, Central, China (Hong Kong) (100%)
Tel.: (852) 28790111
Sales Range: $200-249.9 Million
Emp.: 400
Investment Advice
N.A.I.C.S.: 523940
Ronnie Chichung Chan (Chm)

AP Joy Limited (1)
28th-Floor Standard Chartered Bank Bldg, Central, China (Hong Kong) (100%)
Tel.: (852) 28790111
Web Site: https://www.hanglung.com
Land Subdivision
N.A.I.C.S.: 237210

AP Properties Limited (1)
28th-Floor Standard Chartered Bank Building, Central, China (Hong Kong) (100%)
Tel.: (852) 28790111
Sales Range: $50-74.9 Million
Emp.: 200
Land Subdivision
N.A.I.C.S.: 237210
Ronnie Chichung Chan (Chm)

AP Success Limited (1)
28th-Fl Standard Chartered Bank Bldg, Central, China (Hong Kong) (100%)
Tel.: (852) 28790111
Web Site: https://www.hanglung.com
Investment Advice
N.A.I.C.S.: 523940

AP Universal Limited (1)
28th-Floor Standard Chartered Bank Bldg, Central, China (Hong Kong) (100%)
Tel.: (852) 28790111
Investment Advice
N.A.I.C.S.: 523940
Cheong Ho Hau (Exec Dir)

AP Win Limited (1)
28Fl Standard Chartered Bank Bldg, Central, China (Hong Kong) (100%)
Tel.: (852) 28790111
Web Site: https://www.hanglung.com
Land Subdivision
N.A.I.C.S.: 237210

AP World Limited (1)
28th-Floor Standard Chartered Bank Bldg, Central, China (Hong Kong) (100%)
Tel.: (852) 28790111
Web Site: https://www.hanglung.com
Land Subdivision
N.A.I.C.S.: 237210

Bonna Estates Company Limited (1)
28th-Floor Standard Chartered Bank Bldg, Central, China (Hong Kong) (100%)
Tel.: (852) 28790111
Real Estate Property Lessors
N.A.I.C.S.: 531190

Caddo Enterprises, Limited (1)
28th-Floor Standard Chartered Bank Building, Central, China (Hong Kong) (100%)
Tel.: (852) 28790111
Web Site: https://www.hanglung.com
Real Estate Property Lessors
N.A.I.C.S.: 531190

Dokay Limited (1)
28th-Floor Standard Chartered Bank Building, Central, China (Hong Kong) (100%)

AND PRIVATE COMPANIES

Tel.: (852) 28790111
Real Estate Property Lessors
N.A.I.C.S.: 531190

Fu Yik Company Limited (1)
28th-Floor Standard Chartered Bank Bldg,
Central, China (Hong Kong) **(100%)**
Tel.: (852) 28790111
Web Site: https://www.hanglung.com
Real Estate Property Lessors
N.A.I.C.S.: 531190

Gowily Limited (1)
28th-Floor Standard Chartered Bank Bldg,
Central, China (Hong Kong) **(100%)**
Tel.: (852) 28790111
Real Estate Property Lessors
N.A.I.C.S.: 531190

Grand Hotel Group Limited (1)
28th-Floor Standard Chartered Bank Bldg,
Central, China (Hong Kong) **(100%)**
Tel.: (852) 28790111
Management Consulting Services
N.A.I.C.S.: 541618
Ronnie Chichung Chan *(Chm)*

HLP (China) Limited (1)
28th-Floor Standard Chartered Bank Building, Central, China (Hong Kong) **(100%)**
Tel.: (852) 28790111
Web Site: https://www.icris.cr.gov.hk
Holding Company
N.A.I.C.S.: 551112

HLP Treasury Services Limited (1)
28th-Floor Standard Chartered Bank Building, Central, China (Hong Kong) **(100%)**
Tel.: (852) 28790111
Web Site: https://www.hanglung.com
Holding Company
N.A.I.C.S.: 551112

Hang Chui Company Limited (1)
28th-Fl Standard Chartered Bank Bldg,
Central, China (Hong Kong) **(100%)**
Tel.: (852) 28790111
Web Site: https://www.hanglung.com
Real Estate Property Lessors
N.A.I.C.S.: 531190

Hang Far Company Limited (1)
28th-Floor Standard Chartered Bank Building, Central, China (Hong Kong) **(100%)**
Tel.: (852) 28790111
Holding Company
N.A.I.C.S.: 551112
Ronnie Chichung Chan *(Chm)*

Hang Fine Company Limited (1)
28th-Floor Standard Chartered Bank Bldg,
Central, China (Hong Kong) **(100%)**
Tel.: (852) 28790111
Web Site: https://www.hanglung.com
Real Estate Property Lessors
N.A.I.C.S.: 531190

Hang Kwok Company Limited (1)
28th-Floor Standard Chartered Bank Bldg, 4
Des Voeux Rd, Central, China (Hong Kong) **(100%)**
Tel.: (852) 28790111
Web Site: https://www.hantlunt.com
Real Estate Property Lessors
N.A.I.C.S.: 531190
Hau Cheong Ho *(Exec Dir)*

Hang Lung (Administration) Limited (1)
28th-Floor Standard Chartered Bank Building, Central, China (Hong Kong) **(100%)**
Tel.: (852) 28790111
Web Site: https://www.hanglung.com
Real Estate Agents & Brokers
N.A.I.C.S.: 531210

Hang Lung Financial Services Limited (1)
28/F Standard Chartered Bank Bldg 4 Des
Voeux Rd C, Central District, Hong Kong,
China (Hong Kong)
Tel.: (852) 28790111
Web Site: https://www.hanglung.com
Financial Management Services
N.A.I.C.S.: 523999

Hang Lung Project Management Limited (1)
28th-Floor Standard Chartered Bank Bldg,
Central, China (Hong Kong) **(100%)**
Tel.: (852) 28790111

Sales Range: $150-199.9 Million
Emp.: 1,000
Management Consulting Services
N.A.I.C.S.: 541618
Ronnie Chichung Chan *(Chm)*

Hang Lung Properties Limited (1)
28 F Standard Chartered Bank Building 4
Des Voeux Road, Central, China (Hong Kong) **(62.01%)**
Tel.: (852) 28790111
Web Site: https://www.hanglung.com
Rev.: $1,322,351,017
Assets: $27,181,617,187
Liabilities: $8,887,497,284
Net Worth: $18,294,119,902
Earnings: $561,938,477
Fiscal Year-end: 12/31/2022
Real Estate Investment Trust
N.A.I.C.S.: 525990
Cheong Ho Hau *(CFO & Sec)*

Hang Lung Property Management Limited (1)
28/F Standard Chartered Bank Building 4
Des Voeux Road, Central, China (Hong Kong) **(100%)**
Tel.: (852) 28790111
Web Site: https://www.hanglung.com
Real Estate Agents & Brokers
N.A.I.C.S.: 531210

Hang Lung Real Estate Agency Limited (1)
28th-Floor Standard Chartered Bank Bldg,
Central, China (Hong Kong) **(100%)**
Tel.: (852) 28790111
Web Site: https://www.hanglung.com
Real Estate Agents & Brokers
N.A.I.C.S.: 531210
Ronnie Chichung Chan *(Chm)*

Hang Lung Treasury Limited (1)
28/F Standard Chartered Bank Bldg 4 Des
Voeux Rd C, Central District, Hong Kong,
China (Hong Kong)
Tel.: (852) 28790111
Financial Management Services
N.A.I.C.S.: 523999
Ronnie Chan *(Chm)*

Hebo Limited (1)
28/F Standard Chartered Bank Bldg 4 Des
Voeux Rd, Central District, Hong Kong,
China (Hong Kong)
Tel.: (852) 28790111
Web Site: https://www.hanglung.com
Real Estate Development Services
N.A.I.C.S.: 531390

Hoi Sang Limited (1)
28th-Floor Standard Chartered Bank Bldg,
Central, China (Hong Kong) **(100%)**
Tel.: (852) 28790111
Web Site: https://www.hanglung.com
Holding Company
N.A.I.C.S.: 551112

Lockoo Limited (1)
28th-Floor Standard Chartered Bank Bldg,
Central, China (Hong Kong) **(100%)**
Tel.: (852) 28790111
Sales Range: $200-249.9 Million
Emp.: 1,000
Land Subdivision
N.A.I.C.S.: 237210

Mansita Limited (1)
28th-Fl Standard Chartered Bank Bldg,
Central, China (Hong Kong) **(100%)**
Tel.: (852) 28790111
Real Estate Property Lessors
N.A.I.C.S.: 531190

Modalton Limited (1)
28th-Floor Standard Chartered Bank Bldg,
Central, China (Hong Kong) **(100%)**
Tel.: (852) 28790111
Web Site: https://www.hunglung.com
Investment Advice
N.A.I.C.S.: 523940

Ottringham Limited (1)
28th-Floor Standard Chartered Bank Bldg,
Central, China (Hong Kong) **(100%)**
Tel.: (852) 28790111
Web Site: http://www.hanglung.com
Real Estate Property Lessors
N.A.I.C.S.: 531190

Palex Limited (1)

28th-Floor Standard Chartered Bank Bldg,
Central, China (Hong Kong) **(100%)**
Tel.: (852) 28790111
Investment Advice
N.A.I.C.S.: 523940
Ronnie Chichung Chan *(Chm)*

Park-In Commercial Centre (1)
56 Dundas St, Mongkok, Kowloon, China
(Hong Kong) **(100%)**
Tel.: (852) 2775 8111
Web Site: http://www.hanglung.com
Commercial & Residential Car Parks
N.A.I.C.S.: 812930

Pocaliton Limited (1)
28th-Floor Standard Chartered Bank Bldg,
Central, China (Hong Kong) **(100%)**
Tel.: (852) 28790111
Web Site: https://www.hanglung.com
Real Estate Property Lessors
N.A.I.C.S.: 531190
Ronnie Chichung Chan *(Chm)*

Rioloy Limited (1)
21st-Floor Standard Chartered Bank Bldg,
Central, China (Hong Kong) **(100%)**
Tel.: (852) 28790111
Real Estate Property Lessors
N.A.I.C.S.: 531190
Ronnie Chichung Chan *(Chm)*

Tegraton Limited (1)
28th-Floor Standard Chartered Bank Bldg,
Central, China (Hong Kong) **(100%)**
Tel.: (852) 28790111
Investment Advice
N.A.I.C.S.: 523940
Ronnie Chichung Chan *(Chm)*

Wililoy Limited (1)
28th-Floor Standard Chartered Bank Bldg,
Central, China (Hong Kong) **(100%)**
Tel.: (852) 28790111
Holding Company
N.A.I.C.S.: 551112

HANG PIN LIVING TECHNOLOGY COMPANY LIMITED
25th & 26th Floor 238 Des Voeux
Road, Central, China (Hong Kong)
Tel.: (852) 2 111 9823 BM
Web Site: http://www.hk01682.com
Year Founded: 1988
1682—(HKG)
Rev.: $15,779,284
Assets: $17,428,294
Liabilities: $4,942,385
Net Worth: $12,485,909
Earnings: ($1,634,564)
Emp.: 22
Fiscal Year-end: 03/31/22
Investment Holding Company
N.A.I.C.S.: 551112
Kai Yeung Lam *(CEO)*

HANG SANG (SIU PO) INTERNATIONAL HOLDING COMPANY LIMITED
16 Cheung Yue Street Block C 5/F
Gee Hing Chang Industrial Building,
Cheung Sha Wan, Kowloon, China
(Hong Kong)
Tel.: (852) 23851067 Ky
Web Site:
  http://www.hangsangpress.com
3626—(HKG)
Rev.: $9,739,280
Assets: $11,477,801
Liabilities: $2,743,534
Net Worth: $8,734,268
Earnings: ($494,638)
Emp.: 78
Fiscal Year-end: 06/30/22
Apparel Labeling Services
N.A.I.C.S.: 561910
Samson Man wai Fung *(Co-Founder, Chm & CEO)*

Subsidiaries:

Alpha Prime Foods Limited (1)
16 Cheung Yue Street Block A 4 Floor, Gee
Hing Chang Industrial Building Cheung Sha

Wan, Kowloon, China (Hong Kong)
Tel.: (852) 23856388
Web Site: https://alphaprimefoods.com
Frozen Seafood Distr
N.A.I.C.S.: 424460

HANG TAI YUE GROUP HOLDINGS LIMITED
9/F HKHC Tower No 241-243 Nathan
Road, Jordan, Kowloon, China (Hong Kong)
Tel.: (852) 25492038 Ky
Web Site: http://www.hangtaiyue.com
8081—(HKG)
Rev.: $17,132,558
Assets: $75,840,825
Liabilities: $38,112,938
Net Worth: $37,727,888
Earnings: $1,265,438
Emp.: 110
Fiscal Year-end: 12/31/22
Investment Holding Company
N.A.I.C.S.: 551112
Ching Yee Lam *(CEO & Sec)*

Subsidiaries:

Epro Systems (HK) Limited (1)
Unit 301 3/F Hing Yip Commercial Centre
272-284 Des Voeux Road, Central, China
(Hong Kong)
Tel.: (852) 23763373
Web Site: http://www.epro.com.hk
Software Development Services
N.A.I.C.S.: 513210

HANG XANH MOTORS SERVICE JOINT STOCK COMPANY
333 Dien Bien Phu, Ward 15 Binh
Thanh District, Ho Chi Minh City,
Vietnam
Tel.: (84) 2835120026
Web Site:
  https://www.haxaco.com.vn
Year Founded: 2000
HAX—(HOSE)
Rev.: $164,055,186
Assets: $82,659,066
Liabilities: $34,702,101
Net Worth: $47,956,965
Earnings: $1,526,707
Fiscal Year-end: 12/31/23
Automobile Repair & Maintenance
Services
N.A.I.C.S.: 811114
Do Tien Dung *(Exec Dir)*

HANG YICK HOLDINGS COMPANY LIMITED
Unit B Upper G/F Stage 4 Yau Tong
Industrial Bldg, 18-20 Sze Shan
Street Yau Tong, Kowloon, China
(Hong Kong)
Tel.: (852) 23468162 Ky
Web Site: http://www.hy-engineering.com
Year Founded: 1982
1894—(HKG)
Rev.: $23,575,260
Assets: $24,160,740
Liabilities: $2,473,245
Net Worth: $21,687,495
Earnings: ($2,473,883)
Emp.: 274
Fiscal Year-end: 03/31/23
Construction Steel & Metal Product
Mfr
N.A.I.C.S.: 332999
Pui Sun Lee *(Chm & CEO)*

Subsidiaries:

Huizhou Hengyi Wujin Zhipin Limited (1)
Chongkai High-Tach Industrial Development
Zone, Lilian Village Lilin Town, Huizhou,
516035, Guangdong, China
Tel.: (86) 7523855820
Construction & Engineering Services
N.A.I.C.S.: 541330

3245

Hang Yick Holdings Company Limited—(Continued)

HANG ZHOU YITONG NEW MATERIALS CO., LTD.
Daciyan Town, Jiande, 311613, Zhejiang, China
Tel.: (86) 57164560598
Web Site: http://www.hzytxc.com
Year Founded: 2000
300930—(SSE)
Rev.: $54,326,376
Assets: $118,890,720
Liabilities: $6,572,124
Net Worth: $112,318,596
Earnings: $12,855,024
Fiscal Year-end: 12/31/22
Metal Parts Mfr & Distr
N.A.I.C.S.: 332119
Zhirong Wang *(Chm & Gen Mgr)*

HANGJI GLOBAL LIMITED
15 Ayion Omologiton Avenue, Nicosia, 1080, Cyprus
Tel.: (357) 8444031915
Web Site:
  http://www.hangjiglobal.com
Engineeering Services
N.A.I.C.S.: 541330

HANGXIAO STEEL STRUCTURE CO., LTD.
Ruifeng international business building, No 258 Zhonghezhong Road, Hangzhou, 310003, Zhejiang, China
Tel.: (86) 57187246788
Web Site: https://www.hxss.com.cn
Year Founded: 1985
600477—(SHG)
Rev.: $1,394,930,848
Assets: $1,955,965,050
Liabilities: $1,191,114,162
Net Worth: $764,850,888
Earnings: $37,607,474
Emp.: 6,000
Fiscal Year-end: 12/31/22
Steel Structural Product Mfr
N.A.I.C.S.: 331221
Single Silverwood *(Chm)*

Subsidiaries:

Guangdong Hangxiao Steel Structure Co., Ltd. (1)
Pingsha Industrial Zone, Jinwan District, Zhuhai, China
Tel.: (86) 75 6772 3888
Structured Steel Products Mfr
N.A.I.C.S.: 331221

Hangzhou Hangxiao Steel Structure Co. Ltd. (1)
Hongken Farm Xinjie Town, Xiaoshan, Hangzhou, 311217, Zhejiang, China
Tel.: (86) 57 1826 14788
Structured Steel Products Mfr
N.A.I.C.S.: 331221

Hebei Hangxiao Steel Structure Co., Ltd. (1)
North Ring Road, Yutian County, Tangshan, 064100, Hebei, China
Tel.: (86) 3156182200
Web Site: http://www.hbhxsteel.com
Steel Structural Product Mfr
N.A.I.C.S.: 331221

Henan Hangxiao Steel Structure Co., Ltd. (1)
Qianlou Village Matun Town Mengjin, Luoyang, Henan, China
Tel.: (86) 379 67895588
Structured Steel Products Mfr
N.A.I.C.S.: 331221

Shandong Hangxiao Steel Structure Co., Ltd. (1)
No 8 Rd 2 Qi Jiaozhouwan Industry Park, Qingdao, 266300, Shandong, China
Tel.: (86) 532 87273788
Steel Structural Product Mfr
N.A.I.C.S.: 331221

Zhejiang Headerboard Building Materials Co., Ltd. (1)
5F Ruifeng International Business Plaza No 258 Middle Zhonghe Road, Hangzhou, 310003, China
Tel.: (86) 571 87040819
Web Site: http://www.headerboard.com
Steel Bar Mfr
N.A.I.C.S.: 331221
Scott She *(Gen Mgr)*

HANGZHOU ADVANCE GEAR-BOX GROUP CO., LTD.
No 45 Xiaojin Road, Xiaoshan District, Hangzhou, 311203, Zhejiang, China
Tel.: (86) 57183802671
Web Site:
  http://www.chinaadvance.com
Year Founded: 1960
601177—(SHG)
Rev.: $308,327,540
Assets: $623,503,862
Liabilities: $311,843,493
Net Worth: $311,660,369
Earnings: $29,396,489
Emp.: 2,600
Fiscal Year-end: 12/31/22
Metallurgical Product Mfr
N.A.I.C.S.: 332117
Yang Shuiyu *(Chm)*

Subsidiaries:

Hangzhou Advance Forging Co., Ltd. (1)
189 Kanshan Road Kanshan, Hangzhou, 311243, Zhejiang, China
Tel.: (86) 57182588999
Forging Machine Mfr
N.A.I.C.S.: 333517

Hangzhou Advance Foundry Co., Ltd. (1)
Xianghu Farm, Xiaoshan, Hangzhou, 311258, Zhejiang, China
Tel.: (86) 571 82763818
Metallurgical Product Mfr
N.A.I.C.S.: 332117

Hangzhou Advance General Machinery Co., Ltd. (1)
No 178 Xiaojin road, Xiaoshan, Hangzhou, 312003, Zhejiang, China (62.61%)
Tel.: (86) 571 82674705
Metallurgical Product Mfr
N.A.I.C.S.: 332117

Hangzhou Advance Masson Marine Transmission Co., Ltd. (1)
North of No 7 Road Xiaoshan Economic & Technological Development Zone, Qiaonan District, Hangzhou, 311215, China
Tel.: (86) 57122852888
Marine Transmission Mfr
N.A.I.C.S.: 333618

Hangzhou Advance Wind-Power Gearbox Co., Ltd. (1)
Yaqian Industrial Park, Xiaoshan District, Hangzhou, 311209, China
Tel.: (86) 57183877812
Wind Power Gearbox Mfr
N.A.I.C.S.: 333611

Hangzhou Haveco Automotive Transmission Co., Ltd. (1)
No 45 Xianghu Road, Xiaoshan, Hangzhou, 311203, China
Tel.: (86) 57182672380
Automotive Transmission Parts Mfr
N.A.I.C.S.: 336350
Lin Zhang *(Dir-Sls)*

Shaoxing Advance Gearbox Co., Ltd. (1)
No 603 Jingshui Road Kedong Hi-tech Zone, Keqiao Town, Shaoxing, 312030, Zhejiang, China
Tel.: (86) 575 4815218
Industrial Machinery Mfr & Distr
N.A.I.C.S.: 333248

HANGZHOU ALLTEST BIO-TECH CO., LTD.
550 Yinhai Street, Hangzhou Economy & Technology Development Area, Hangzhou, 310018, China
Tel.: (86) 57156267891
Web Site: https://www.alltests.com.cn
Year Founded: 2009
688606—(SHG)
Rev.: $475,754,961
Assets: $659,841,137
Liabilities: $74,243,632
Net Worth: $585,597,505
Earnings: $166,300,655
Fiscal Year-end: 12/31/22
Medical Product Mfr & Distr
N.A.I.C.S.: 339112
Fei Gao *(Chm & Gen Mgr)*

HANGZHOU ANYSOFT INFORMATION TECH CO LTD
No 101 Qinguo Street, Fuyang District, Hangzhou, 311400, Zhejiang, China
Tel.: (86) 57188939703
Web Site: http://www.anysoft.cn
Year Founded: 2002
300571—(CHIN)
Rev.: $269,105,742
Assets: $489,938,908
Liabilities: $268,307,841
Net Worth: $221,631,067
Earnings: ($5,462,924)
Fiscal Year-end: 12/31/23
Mobile Telecommunications Services
N.A.I.C.S.: 517810
Qing Guo *(Chm & Gen Mgr)*

HANGZHOU ARCVIDEO TECHNOLOGY CO., LTD.
Danghong Building No 309 Zhongchuang Road, Binjiang District, Hangzhou, 310012, Zhejiang, China
Tel.: (86) 57187767690
Web Site: https://www.arcvideo.cn
Year Founded: 2010
688039—(SHG)
Rev.: $46,534,330
Assets: $228,154,830
Liabilities: $35,341,558
Net Worth: $192,813,272
Earnings: ($13,841,797)
Fiscal Year-end: 12/31/22
Information Technology Services
N.A.I.C.S.: 541512
Yanlong Sun *(Chm & Gen Mgr)*

HANGZHOU BINJIANG REAL ESTATE GROUP CO., LTD.
No 38 Qingchun East Road, Hangzhou, 310016, Zhejiang, China
Web Site: http://www.binjiang.com.cn
002244—(SSE)
Rev.: $9,753,348,956
Assets: $40,157,251,828
Liabilities: $32,063,703,450
Net Worth: $8,093,548,377
Earnings: $350,179,816
Fiscal Year-end: 12/31/23
Real Estate Property Development Services
N.A.I.C.S.: 531110
Jinxing Qi *(Chm)*

HANGZHOU BIO-SINCERITY PHARMA-TECH CO., LTD.
No 159 Lvzhou Road Donghu Street, Linping District, Hangzhou, 311103, Zhejiang, China
Tel.: (86) 57187923909
Web Site: https://www.hzbio-s.com
Year Founded: 2011
301096—(CHIN)
Rev.: $85,280,364
Assets: $411,329,880
Liabilities: $62,820,576
Net Worth: $348,509,304
Earnings: $27,260,064

INTERNATIONAL PUBLIC

Fiscal Year-end: 12/31/22
Pharmaceutical Product Mfr & Distr
N.A.I.C.S.: 325412
Jinfang Lou *(Chm & Gen Mgr)*

HANGZHOU CABLE CO., LTD.
No 18 Yongtong Road Dongzhou Street, Fuyang District, Hangzhou, 311401, Zhejiang, China
Tel.: (86) 57163167793
Web Site: http://www.hzcables.com
Year Founded: 2002
603618—(SHG)
Rev.: $1,140,274,618
Assets: $1,341,355,082
Liabilities: $916,672,283
Net Worth: $424,682,799
Earnings: $15,245,927
Fiscal Year-end: 12/31/21
Wire & Cable Mfr & Distr
N.A.I.C.S.: 335999
Hua Jianfei *(Chm)*

HANGZHOU CENTURY CO., LTD.
528 Xingqi Road, Yuhang Economic Development Area, Hangzhou, 311106, China
Tel.: (86) 57128818756
Web Site: https://www.century-cn.com
Year Founded: 2003
300078—(CHIN)
Rev.: $155,688,156
Assets: $512,267,652
Liabilities: $325,372,788
Net Worth: $186,894,864
Earnings: ($123,764,004)
Fiscal Year-end: 12/31/22
Electronic Article Surveillance Products Mfr
N.A.I.C.S.: 334310
Xianhong Ma *(Chm)*

Subsidiaries:

Century Retail Europe B.V. (1)
Enterseweg 15, 7471 SB, Goor, Netherlands
Tel.: (31) 623170728
Web Site: https://www.century-eu.com
Security Detection Product Mfr
N.A.I.C.S.: 334511

HANGZHOU CHANG CHUAN TECHNOLOGY CO., LTD.
No 410 Jucai Road, Binjiang District, Hangzhou, 310051, Zhejiang, China
Tel.: (86) 57185096193
Web Site: http://www.hzcctech.com
Year Founded: 2008
300604—(CHIN)
Rev.: $250,016,483
Assets: $831,238,163
Liabilities: $342,445,027
Net Worth: $488,793,135
Earnings: $6,360,730
Emp.: 3,000
Fiscal Year-end: 12/31/23
Semiconductor Equipment Mfr & Distr
N.A.I.C.S.: 334515
Yi Zhao *(Chm, Pres & Gen Mgr)*

HANGZHOU CHUHUAN SCIENCE & TECHNOLOGY COMPANY LIMITED
Room 601 Building 5 No 108 Xiangyuan Road, Gongshu District, Hangzhou, 310015, Zhejiang, China
Tel.: (86) 57188054639
Web Site: https://www.hzctkj.com
Year Founded: 2005
001336—(SSE)
Rev.: $62,980,875
Assets: $158,659,548
Liabilities: $52,128,096
Net Worth: $106,531,452
Earnings: $5,219,931

AND PRIVATE COMPANIES

HANGZHOU HIKVISION DIGITAL TECHNOLOGY CO., LTD.

Fiscal Year-end: 12/31/23
Water Treatment Equipment Distr
N.A.I.C.S.: 423850
Budong Chen *(Chm)*

HANGZHOU CNCR-IT CO., LTD.
No 259 IoT Street Xixing Street, Binjiang District, Hangzhou, 310051, Zhejinag, China
Tel.: (86) 57186791278
Web Site: http://www.cncr-it.com
Year Founded: 2000
300250—(CHIN)
Rev.: $50,619,816
Assets: $109,884,060
Liabilities: $29,482,596
Net Worth: $80,401,464
Earnings: ($15,932,592)
Emp.: 130
Fiscal Year-end: 12/31/22
Data Communication & Network Access Equipment Mfr
N.A.I.C.S.: 334220
Hong Aijin *(Chm)*

HANGZHOU COCO HEALTHCARE PRODUCTS CO., LTD.
No 2 Huaqiao Road West Industrial Park, Linan District, Hangzhou, 311300, Zhejiang, China
Tel.: (86) 4008260630
Web Site: https://www.cocohealthcare.com
Year Founded: 2001
301009—(CHIN)
Rev.: $152,321,746
Assets: $280,565,788
Liabilities: $76,395,056
Net Worth: $204,170,732
Earnings: $2,842,944
Fiscal Year-end: 12/31/23
Sanitary Product Mfr & Distr
N.A.I.C.S.: 322291

HANGZHOU DADI HAIYANG ENVIRONMENTAL PROTECTION CO., LTD.
No 111 Lingang Road Renhe Street, Yuhang District, Hangzhou, 311107, Zhejiang, China
Tel.: (86) 57188522803
Web Site: https://www.hzddhy.com
Year Founded: 2003
301068—(CHIN)
Rev.: $112,327,020
Assets: $172,960,164
Liabilities: $62,611,380
Net Worth: $110,348,784
Earnings: $7,758,504
Fiscal Year-end: 12/31/22
Hazardous Waste Collection Services
N.A.I.C.S.: 562112
Weizhong Tang *(Chm)*

HANGZHOU DPTECH TECHNOLOGIES CO., LTD.
18th Floor DPtech Building No 595 Yueming Road, Binjiang District, Hangzhou, 310051, Zhejiang, China
Tel.: (86) 57128280909
Web Site: https://www.dptech.com
Year Founded: 2008
300768—(SSE)
Rev.: $125,399,664
Assets: $514,831,356
Liabilities: $66,288,456
Net Worth: $448,542,900
Earnings: $21,026,304
Fiscal Year-end: 12/31/22
Software Development Services
N.A.I.C.S.: 541511
Shusheng Zheng *(Chm & Pres)*

HANGZHOU ELECTRONIC SOUL NETWORK TECHNOLOGY CO., LTD.
Dianhun Building NO 435 Bin'an Road Xixing Street, Binjiang District, Hangzhou, 310051, Zhejiang, China
Tel.: (86) 57156683882
Web Site: https://www.dianhun.cn
Year Founded: 2008
603258—(SHG)
Rev.: $111,002,992
Assets: $406,184,206
Liabilities: $67,274,485
Net Worth: $338,909,721
Earnings: $28,226,648
Fiscal Year-end: 12/31/22
Online Game Development Services
N.A.I.C.S.: 513210

HANGZHOU EVERFINE PHOTO-E-INFO CO., LTD.
No 669 Binkang Road, Binjiang District, Hangzhou, 310053, Zhejiang, China
Tel.: (86) 57186698333
Web Site: https://www.everfine.net
Year Founded: 2003
300306—(CHIN)
Rev.: $61,941,672
Assets: $237,923,244
Liabilities: $25,422,228
Net Worth: $212,501,016
Earnings: $11,233,404
Emp.: 480
Fiscal Year-end: 12/31/22
Light Emitting Diode & Lighting Photoelectric Detection Equipment Mfr
N.A.I.C.S.: 334419
Pan Jiangen *(Chm & Gen Mgr)*

HANGZHOU FIRST APPLIED MATERIAL CO., LTD.
8 Fusite Street, Lin'an, 311300, Hangzhou, China
Tel.: (86) 57163812086
Web Site: https://www.firstpvm.com
Year Founded: 2003
603806—(SHG)
Rev.: $2,650,400,312
Assets: $2,835,334,897
Liabilities: $868,259,855
Net Worth: $1,967,075,042
Earnings: $221,631,172
Emp.: 599
Fiscal Year-end: 12/31/22
Plastic Material Mfr & Distr
N.A.I.C.S.: 325211
Jianhua Lin *(Pres)*

HANGZHOU FREELY COMMUNICATION CO., LTD.
Building A Zongheng Communication No 190 Xietong Road, Binjiang District, Hangzhou, 310051, Zhejiang, China
Tel.: (86) 57187672346
Web Site: http://www.freelynet.com
Year Founded: 2006
603602—(SHG)
Rev.: $159,185,632
Assets: $223,406,530
Liabilities: $118,094,203
Net Worth: $105,312,327
Earnings: $3,046,469
Fiscal Year-end: 12/31/22
Communication Network Services
N.A.I.C.S.: 517810
Weifeng Su *(Chm)*

HANGZHOU GAOXIN RUBBER & PLASTIC MATERIALS CO., LTD.
10 Longhang Road Jingshan Town, Yuhang District, Hangzhou, 311116, Zhejiang, China
Tel.: (86) 57188581338
300478—(CHIN)
Rev.: $54,728,803
Assets: $48,063,555
Liabilities: $35,067,213
Net Worth: $12,996,342
Earnings: $3,330,680
Fiscal Year-end: 12/31/23
Polymer Cable Mfr & Distr
N.A.I.C.S.: 332618
Xiangjiang Li *(Chm)*

HANGZHOU GREENDA ELECTRONIC MATERIALS CO., LTD.
No 9936 Hongshiwu Road, Qiantang District, Hangzhou, 311228, Zhejiang, China
Tel.: (86) 57186630720
Web Site: https://www.greendachem.com
Year Founded: 2001
603931—(SHG)
Rev.: $119,002,956
Assets: $218,090,565
Liabilities: $29,775,105
Net Worth: $188,315,459
Earnings: $22,940,546
Fiscal Year-end: 12/31/22
Electronic Product Mfr & Distr
N.A.I.C.S.: 334419
Huier Jiang *(Chm)*

HANGZHOU HAOYUE PERSONAL CARE CO., LTD.
No 3 Fengdu Road, Pingyao Town Yuhang District, Hangzhou, 311115, Zhejiang, China
Tel.: (86) 57189190009
Web Site: http://www.hz-haoyue.com
Year Founded: 2008
605009—(SHG)
Rev.: $393,440,266
Assets: $584,725,312
Liabilities: $161,554,012
Net Worth: $423,171,300
Earnings: $59,372,450
Emp.: 800
Fiscal Year-end: 12/31/22
Sanitary Paper Product Mfr & Distr
N.A.I.C.S.: 322291
Zhibiao Li *(Chm & Gen Mgr)*

HANGZHOU HESHUN TECHNOLOGY CO., LTD.
Renkang Road Qianjiang Economic Development Zone, Yuhang District, Hangzhou, 313219, Zhejiang, China
Tel.: (86) 5728358620
Web Site: https://www.hzhssy.com
Year Founded: 2003
301237—(SSE)
Rev.: $70,695,612
Assets: $226,219,500
Liabilities: $15,646,176
Net Worth: $210,573,324
Earnings: $9,175,140
Fiscal Year-end: 12/31/22
Film Product Mfr
N.A.I.C.S.: 325992
Heqiang Fan *(Chm & Gen Mgr)*

HANGZHOU HIKVISION DIGITAL TECHNOLOGY CO., LTD.
No 555 Qianmo Road, Binjiang District, Hangzhou, 310051, China
Tel.: (86) 57188075998
Web Site: https://www.hikvision.com
002415—(SSE)
Rev.: $11,676,551,564
Assets: $16,740,352,900
Liabilities: $6,495,343,283
Net Worth: $10,245,009,617
Earnings: $1,802,362,825
Emp.: 58,284
Fiscal Year-end: 12/31/22
Digital Video Surveillance Products
N.A.I.C.S.: 334310

Subsidiaries:

EZVIZ Europe B.V. (1)
Dirk Storklaan 3, 2132 PX, Hoofddorp, Netherlands
Tel.: (31) 202040128
Web Site: http://www.ezviz.eu
Electronic Security Equipment Distr
N.A.I.C.S.: 423690

Hangzhou Hikrobot Technology Co., Ltd. (1)
Tel.: (86) 57188967998
Emp.: 1,200
Industrial Equipment Mfr & Distr
N.A.I.C.S.: 333248

Hikvision (Malaysia) Sdn. Bhd. (1)
301 Level 3 of Menara LGB No 1 Jalan Wan Kadir, Taman Tun Dr Ismail, 60000, Kuala Lumpur, Malaysia
Tel.: (60) 327224000
Video Surveillance Product Mfr
N.A.I.C.S.: 334310

Hikvision Australia PTY Co., Ltd. (1)
Unit 14a 2 Eden Park Dr, Macquarie Park, 2113, NSW, Australia
Tel.: (61) 1300976305
Video Surveillance Product Mfr
N.A.I.C.S.: 334310

Hikvision Azerbaijan Limited Liability (1)
Landmark III Building 90A Nizami Street, Baku, Azerbaijan
Tel.: (994) 123101333
Video Surveillance Product Mfr
N.A.I.C.S.: 334310

Hikvision Canada Inc. (1)
4848 Levy Street, Saint Laurent, H4R 2P1, QC, Canada
Video Surveillance Product Mfr
N.A.I.C.S.: 334310

Hikvision Czech s.r.o. (1)
BETA Building Vyskocilova 1481/4, Prague, Czech Republic
Tel.: (420) 296182640
Video Surveillance Product Mfr
N.A.I.C.S.: 334310

Hikvision Deutschland GmbH (1)
Werner-Heisenberg Strasse 2b, 63263, Neu-Isenburg, Germany
Tel.: (49) 69401507290
Video Surveillance Product Mfr
N.A.I.C.S.: 334310

Hikvision Europe B.V. (1)
Dirk Storklaan 3, 2132 PX, Hoofddorp, Netherlands
Tel.: (31) 235542770
Sales Range: $25-49.9 Million
Emp.: 16
Video Surveillance Products Distr
N.A.I.C.S.: 423410
Jiangfeng Zhi *(Gen Mgr)*

Hikvision FZE (1)
52nd Floor Almas Tower Jumeirah Lakes Towers, Dubai, United Arab Emirates
Tel.: (971) 44432090
Video Surveillance Product Mfr
N.A.I.C.S.: 334310

Hikvision France SAS (1)
6 Rue Paul Cezanne, 93360, Neuilly-Plaisance, France
Tel.: (33) 185330450
Video Surveillance Product Mfr
N.A.I.C.S.: 334310

Hikvision Italy S.R.L (1)
Via Abruzzo 12, 31029, Vittorio Veneto, TSF, Italy
Tel.: (39) 04386902
Video Surveillance Product Mfr
N.A.I.C.S.: 334310

Hikvision Kazakhstan Limited Liability Partnership (1)
Dostyk ave 38 of 303c, 050010, Almaty, Kazakhstan
Tel.: (7) 7272917588
Video Surveillance Product Mfr
N.A.I.C.S.: 334310

Hikvision Korea Limited (1)
14-1 Pangyoyeok-ro 192beon-gil, Bundang-

HANGZHOU HIKVISION DIGITAL TECHNOLOGY CO., LTD.

Hangzhou Hikvision Digital Technology Co., Ltd.—(Continued)
gu, Seongnam, Gyeonggi-do, Korea (South)
Tel.: (82) 16618138
Video Surveillance Product Mfr
N.A.I.C.S.: 334310

Hikvision LLC (1)
Leningradsky prospect 72 building 4 Floor 9, 125315, Moscow, Russia
Tel.: (7) 4956696799
Web Site: http://hikvision.ru
Video Surveillance Product Mfr
N.A.I.C.S.: 334310

Hikvision Mexico S.A.de C.V. (1)
PlaZa Carso Tower II Lake Zurich 219 Floor 4 Col Ampliacion Granad, Miguel Hidalgo, 11529, Mexico, Mexico
Tel.: (52) 5526240110
Video Surveillance Product Mfr
N.A.I.C.S.: 334310

Hikvision New Zealand Limited (1)
Unit 1B 93-95 Ascot Avenue, Greenlane, Auckland, New Zealand
Tel.: (64) 92173127
Video Surveillance Product Mfr
N.A.I.C.S.: 334310

Hikvision Pakistan (SMC-Private) Limited (1)
Suit 1102 11th Floor Emerald Tower Clifton Block 5, Karachi, Pakistan
Tel.: (92) 2135147526
Video Surveillance Product Mfr
N.A.I.C.S.: 334310

Hikvision Poland Spolka Z Ograniczona Odpowiedzialnoscia (1)
Business Garden Building B3 ul Zwirki i Wigury 16B, 02-092, Warsaw, Poland
Tel.: (48) 224600150
Video Surveillance Product Mfr
N.A.I.C.S.: 334310

Hikvision Singapore Pte. Ltd. (1)
438B Alexandra Road 06-04 Alexandra Technopark Tower B, Singapore, 119968, Singapore
Tel.: (65) 66844718
Video Surveillance Product Mfr
N.A.I.C.S.: 334310

Hikvision South Africa (Pty) Co., Ltd. (1)
Building 2 Waverley Office Park 39 Scott Street, Bramley, Johannesburg, South Africa
Tel.: (27) 877018113
Video Surveillance Product Mfr
N.A.I.C.S.: 334310

Hikvision Spain, S.L. (1)
Almazara, Tres Cantos, 928760, Madrid, Spain
Tel.: (34) 917371655
Video Surveillance Product Mfr
N.A.I.C.S.: 334310

Hikvision Technology Egypt JSC (1)
office 202- South building Better home Cairo Business Plaza, New Cairo, Cairo, Egypt
Tel.: (20) 223066117
Video Surveillance Product Mfr
N.A.I.C.S.: 334310

Hikvision Technology Israel Co., Ltd. (1)
1st Hasadna St, Or Yehuda, Israel
Tel.: (972) 795555590
Video Surveillance Product Mfr
N.A.I.C.S.: 334310

Hikvision Turkey Technology & Security Systems Commerce Corporation (1)
Fatih Sultan Mehmet Mah Poligon Cad Buyaka 2 Site 3 Block 8C 102, Umraniye, Istanbul, Turkiye
Tel.: (90) 2165217070
Video Surveillance Product Mfr
N.A.I.C.S.: 334310

Hikvision UK Limited (1)
4 The Square Stockley Park, Uxbridge, UB11 1ET, United Kingdom
Tel.: (44) 1628902140
Video Surveillance Product Mfr
N.A.I.C.S.: 334310

Hikvision USA, Inc. (1)
18639 Railroad St, City of Industry, CA 91748
Tel.: (909) 895-0400
Video Surveillance Product Mfr
N.A.I.C.S.: 334310

Hikvision do Brasil Comercio de Equipamentos de Seguranca Ltda. (1)
Praca Professor Jose Lannes 40-15 andar, Cidade Moncoes, Sao Paulo, 04571-030, SP, Brazil
Tel.: (55) 40204458
Video Surveillance Product Mfr
N.A.I.C.S.: 334310

LLC Hikvision Tashkent (1)
Centre-4 21A Hikvision Business Centre, Yunusabad District, 100017, Tashkent, Uzbekistan
Tel.: (998) 712335550
Video Surveillance Product Mfr
N.A.I.C.S.: 334310

PT. Hikvision Technology Indonesia (1)
APL Tower Floor 22nd Unit 9 Jl Lt Gen S Parman Kav 28, Jakarta, 11470, Indonesia
Tel.: (62) 2129339366
Video Surveillance Product Mfr
N.A.I.C.S.: 334310

Prama Hikvision Indian Private Limited (1)
S18th Floor Near Oberoi Mall Off W.E Highway, Oberoi Commerz II International Business Park Goregaon East, Mumbai, 400063, India
Tel.: (91) 2240419900
Web Site: http://www.hikvisionindia.com
CCTV Camera Mfr
N.A.I.C.S.: 333310

Pyronix Limited (1)
Secure House Braithwell Way, Hellaby, Rotherham, S66 8QY, United Kingdom
Tel.: (44) 1709700100
Web Site: https://www.pyronix.com
Electronic Security Equipment Mfr
N.A.I.C.S.: 334419

SIA BK Latvia (1)
Katlakalna 6D, Riga, 1073, Latvia
Tel.: (371) 66119360
Web Site: https://www.bklatvia.lv
Electronic Security Equipment Distr
N.A.I.C.S.: 423690
Andrejs Sakels *(Sls Mgr)*

ZAO Hikvision (1)
Helsingforskaya st 2A, Saint Petersburg, Russia
Tel.: (7) 8123131963
Electronic Security Equipment Mfr
N.A.I.C.S.: 334419

HANGZHOU HOPECHART IOT TECHNOLOGY CO., LTD.
Hongquan Building No 35 Qizhi Street, Binjiang District, Hangzhou, 310051, Zhejiang, China
Tel.: (86) 57189775590
Web Site: http://www.hopechart.com
Year Founded: 2009
688288—(SHG)
Rev.: $33,654,077
Assets: $138,246,938
Liabilities: $25,003,920
Net Worth: $113,243,018
Earnings: ($14,888,550)
Emp.: 600
Fiscal Year-end: 12/31/22
Application Development Services
N.A.I.C.S.: 541511
Junqiang He *(Chm & Gen Mgr)*

HANGZHOU HOTA M & E HOLDINGS CO., LTD.
No 1201 Tonghui North Road, Ningwei Subdistrict Xiaoshan District, Hangzhou, 311215, Zhejiang, China
Tel.: (86) 57122821056
Web Site: https://www.hota.com.cn
Year Founded: 1995
001225—(SSE)
Rev.: $53,062,680
Assets: $220,917,651
Liabilities: $21,708,476
Net Worth: $199,209,176
Earnings: $15,667,332
Fiscal Year-end: 12/31/23
Holding Company
N.A.I.C.S.: 551112
Qing Xu *(Chm)*

HANGZHOU HUAGUANG ADVANCED WELDING MATERIALS CO., LTD.
Building 3 No 82 Qihang Road Renhe Street, Yuhang District, Hangzhou, 311107, Zhejiang, China
Tel.: (86) 57188764399
Web Site: http://www.cn-huaguang.com
Year Founded: 1997
688379—(SHG)
Rev.: $171,336,972
Assets: $236,940,514
Liabilities: $111,066,172
Net Worth: $125,874,342
Earnings: $1,224,035
Fiscal Year-end: 12/31/22
Electrical Equipment Mfr & Distr
N.A.I.C.S.: 335999
Limei Jin *(Chm & Gen Mgr)*

HANGZHOU HUAWANG NEW MATERIAL TECHNOLOGY CO., LTD.
No 18 Binhe North Rd Qingshanhu Street, Linan, Hangzhou, 311305, Zhejiang, China
Tel.: (86) 57163753803
Web Site: https://www.hwpaper.cn
Year Founded: 2009
605377—(SHG)
Rev.: $482,470,785
Assets: $774,959,141
Liabilities: $267,563,537
Net Worth: $507,395,604
Earnings: $65,613,848
Fiscal Year-end: 12/31/22
Paper Products Mfr
N.A.I.C.S.: 322299
Zhengliang Tou *(Board of Directors & Chm)*

HANGZHOU HUAXING CHUANGYE COMMUNICATION TECHNOLOGY STOCK CO., LTD.
No 550 Jucai Road Changhe Street, Binjiang District, Hangzhou, 310052, Zhejiang, China
Tel.: (86) 57189910606
Web Site: https://www.hxcy.com.cn
Year Founded: 2003
300025—(CHIN)
Rev.: $94,965,156
Assets: $131,620,788
Liabilities: $37,052,964
Net Worth: $94,567,824
Earnings: $1,959,984
Emp.: 652
Fiscal Year-end: 12/31/22
Mobile Communication Technology Services
N.A.I.C.S.: 517112
Zhu Dongcheng *(Chm)*

HANGZHOU HUNING ELEVATOR PARTS CO., LTD.
Zhongtai Industrial Park, Shuita Village Zhongtai Township Yuhang District, Hangzhou, 311121, Zhejiang, China
Tel.: (86) 57188637676
Web Site: https://en.hzhuning.com

INTERNATIONAL PUBLIC

Year Founded: 2004
300669—(CHIN)
Rev.: $52,932,515
Assets: $145,815,836
Liabilities: $20,925,437
Net Worth: $124,890,399
Earnings: $6,843,254
Emp.: 170
Fiscal Year-end: 12/31/23
Elevator Parts Mfr & Distr
N.A.I.C.S.: 333921
Zou Jiachun *(Chm & Gen Mgr)*

HANGZHOU IECHO SCIENCE & TECHNOLOGY CO., LTD.
No 1 Building No 1 Weiye Road, Binjiang, Hangzhou, 310053, Zhejiang, China
Tel.: (86) 57186609565
Web Site: https://www.iechosoft.com
Year Founded: 2005
688092—(SHG)
Rev.: $41,705,764
Assets: $87,791,769
Liabilities: $12,563,624
Net Worth: $75,228,145
Earnings: $6,368,684
Emp.: 400
Fiscal Year-end: 12/31/22
Information Technology Services
N.A.I.C.S.: 541512
Xiaowei Fang *(Chm)*

HANGZHOU INNOVER TECHNOLOGY CO., LTD.
No 1186-1 Binan Road, Binjiang District, Hangzhou, 310052, Zhejiang, China
Tel.: (86) 4000081000
Web Site: https://www.innover.com.cn
Year Founded: 1991
002767—(SSE)
Rev.: $78,993,252
Assets: $152,103,744
Liabilities: $38,521,548
Net Worth: $113,582,196
Earnings: $4,690,764
Emp.: 500
Fiscal Year-end: 12/31/22
Gas Measuring Instrument Mfr
N.A.I.C.S.: 334515
Shi Yimin *(Chm)*

HANGZHOU IRON & STEEL CO., LTD.
No 178 Banshan Road, Gongshu District, Hangzhou, 310022, Zhejiang, China
Tel.: (86) 57188132917
Web Site: http://www.hzsteel.com
Year Founded: 2003
600126—(SHG)
Rev.: $6,082,819,835
Assets: $4,017,560,925
Liabilities: $1,182,768,786
Net Worth: $2,834,792,139
Earnings: $67,369,957
Emp.: 16,900
Fiscal Year-end: 12/31/22
Iron & Steel Product Mfr & Distr
N.A.I.C.S.: 331110
Wu Dongming *(Chm)*

HANGZHOU JIEBAI GROUP CO., LTD.
36-37F Kunhe Center No 208 North Huancheng Road, Xiacheng District, Hangzhou, 310006, Zhejiang, China
Tel.: (86) 57185153911
Web Site: https://www.jiebai.com
Year Founded: 1918
600814—(SHG)
Rev.: $326,233,117
Assets: $1,338,722,934
Liabilities: $687,889,919

Net Worth: $650,833,016
Earnings: $53,709,298
Fiscal Year-end: 12/31/21
Departmental Store Operator
N.A.I.C.S.: 455110
Bi Ling *(Chm)*

HANGZHOU JIZHI MECHA-TRONIC CO., LTD.
No 1-1 Qixian Rd Liangzhu Street, Yuhang District, Hangzhou, 311100, Zhejiang, China
Tel.: (86) 57187203495
Web Site: http://www.zjjizhi.com
Year Founded: 2007
300553—(CHIN)
Rev.: $35,904,651
Assets: $149,213,039
Liabilities: $47,990,342
Net Worth: $101,222,698
Earnings: $4,610,570
Fiscal Year-end: 12/31/23
Automatic Balancing Machine Mfr & Distr
N.A.I.C.S.: 333310
Lou Rongwei *(Chm & Gen Mgr)*

HANGZHOU JUHESHUN NEW MATERIAL CO., LTD.
No 389 Weishi Road, Linjiang High-tech Industrial Park, Hangzhou, 311228, Zhejiang, China
Tel.: (86) 57182955559
Web Site: http://www.jhspa6.com
Year Founded: 2013
605166—(SHG)
Rev.: $847,597,664
Assets: $560,620,738
Liabilities: $311,394,676
Net Worth: $249,226,062
Earnings: $34,003,953
Fiscal Year-end: 12/31/22
Polyamide Product Mfr
N.A.I.C.S.: 325211
Changbao Fu *(Chm)*

HANGZHOU KELIN ELECTRIC CO., LTD.
Building 7 No 1418-41 Moganshan Road, Hangzhou, 310011, Zhejiang, China
Tel.: (86) 57188409181
Web Site: https://www.kelinpower.com
Year Founded: 2002
688611—(SHG)
Rev.: $26,677,530
Assets: $123,228,210
Liabilities: $8,808,949
Net Worth: $114,419,261
Earnings: $8,000,287
Fiscal Year-end: 12/31/22
Electrical Equipment Mfr & Distr
N.A.I.C.S.: 335999
Dong Xie *(Chm & Gen Mgr)*

HANGZHOU LANDSCAPE ARCHITECTURE DESIGN INSTITUTE CO., LTD.
9F South Building Building No 2 Xixi Century Center, No 136 Shuanglong Street Xihu District, Hangzhou, 310030, Zhejiang, China
Tel.: (86) 57187980956
Web Site: http://www.hzyly.com
Year Founded: 2001
300649—(CHIN)
Rev.: $43,565,370
Assets: $153,765,875
Liabilities: $77,501,952
Net Worth: $76,263,923
Earnings: $1,315,863
Fiscal Year-end: 12/31/23
Landscape Management Services
N.A.I.C.S.: 541320
He Wei *(Board of Directors & Chm)*

HANGZHOU LANDSCAPING CO., LTD.
8th Floor Office Building No 226 Kaixuan Road, Jianggan District, Hangzhou, 310016, Zhejiang, China
Tel.: (86) 57186020323
Web Site: http://www.hzyllh.com
Year Founded: 1992
605303—(SHG)
Rev.: $72,215,526
Assets: $398,040,290
Liabilities: $203,368,726
Net Worth: $194,671,564
Earnings: ($36,736,980)
Fiscal Year-end: 12/31/22
Landscaping Services
N.A.I.C.S.: 561730
Guanghong Wu *(Chm & CEO)*

HANGZHOU LIANLUO INTERACTIVE INFORMATION TECHNOLOGY CO., LTD.
18F Xintu Building No 451 Wulianwang Street, Binjiang District, Hangzhou, 310051, Zhejiang, China
Tel.: (86) 57128280882
Web Site: http://www.lianluo.com
002280—(SSE)
Rev.: $1,764,649,692
Assets: $1,305,543,096
Liabilities: $1,133,168,400
Net Worth: $172,374,696
Earnings: ($131,449,500)
Fiscal Year-end: 12/31/22
Software Applications Distr, Research & Development
N.A.I.C.S.: 513210
Zhi Yong Xu *(Chm)*

HANGZHOU LION ELECTRONICS CO., LTD.
No 199 20th Street, Economic and Technological Development Zone, Hangzhou, 310018, Zhejiang, China
Tel.: (86) 57186597238
Web Site: http://www.li-on.com
Year Founded: 2002
605358—(SHG)
Rev.: $409,155,969
Assets: $2,603,243,982
Liabilities: $1,224,332,689
Net Worth: $1,378,911,292
Earnings: $96,565,702
Fiscal Year-end: 12/31/22
Electronic Product Mfr & Distr
N.A.I.C.S.: 334419
Minwen Wang *(Chm)*

HANGZHOU MDK OPTO ELECTRONIC CORP., LTD.
No 15 Xinchao Road, Chang'an Tow, Haining, 310018, Jiaxing, China
Tel.: (86) 57156700355
Web Site: https://www.chinamdk.com
Year Founded: 2010
688079—(SHG)
Rev.: $58,088,183
Assets: $268,033,386
Liabilities: $44,438,987
Net Worth: $223,594,399
Earnings: $3,101,310
Fiscal Year-end: 12/31/22
Electronic Product Mfr & Distr
N.A.I.C.S.: 334419
Wenzhi Ge *(Chm & Gen Mgr)*

Subsidiaries:

China Investment Information Services Co., Ltd. (1)
Suite 2501-03 Great Eagle Centre 23 Harbour Road, Wanchai, China (Hong Kong)
Tel.: (852) 25010600
Web Site: https://www.ciis.com.hk
Software Development Services
N.A.I.C.S.: 541511

HANGZHOU MEIBAH PRECISION MACHINERY CO., LTD.
Building 2 LOFT49 Tong Yi Road, Hangzhou, 310015, China
Tel.: (86) 571 8998 1320
Web Site: http://www.meibah.com
Emp.: 125
High Precision Control Valves Mfr for Auto Industry
N.A.I.C.S.: 332999
Thomas Wu *(Sls Mgr)*

Subsidiaries:

Schumag AG (1)
Nerscheider Weg 170, D-52076, Aachen, Germany
Tel.: (49) 2408120
Web Site: https://www.schumag.de
Rev.: $47,532,888
Assets: $42,988,400
Liabilities: $42,128,632
Net Worth: $859,768
Earnings: $736,944
Emp.: 456
Fiscal Year-end: 12/31/2021
Mfr of Precision-Products for the Automobile Industry
N.A.I.C.S.: 336390
Karl Josef Libeaux *(Vice Chm)*

Subsidiary (Non-US):

Schumag Romania S.R.L. (2)
Loc Chisoda DN 59 Km 8+550 M Stanga, 307221, Timisoara, Romania
Tel.: (40) 256273966
Web Site: http://www.schumag.de
Sales Range: $25-49.9 Million
Emp.: 100
Automobile Parts Mfr
N.A.I.C.S.: 336390

HANGZHOU NBOND NONWOVEN CO.,LTD
No 8 Changda Road/No 16 Hongda Road, National Economic and Technological Development Zone Linping District, Hangzhou, 311102, Zhejiang, China
Tel.: (86) 57189170665
Web Site: https://www.nbond.cn
Year Founded: 2002
603238—(SHG)
Rev.: $223,155,017
Assets: $318,212,697
Liabilities: $104,555,108
Net Worth: $213,657,589
Earnings: $5,296,590
Fiscal Year-end: 12/31/22
Non Wovens Material Mfr & Distr
N.A.I.C.S.: 313230
Ren Jianhua *(Chm)*

Subsidiaries:

Hangzhou Bonyee Daily Necessity Technology Co., Ltd. (1)
16 Hongda Road, Town of Canal Yuhang district, Hangzhou, 311102, Zhejiang, China
Tel.: (86) 5718 917 0008
Web Site: https://www.bonyee.com
Wet Wipe Mfr
N.A.I.C.S.: 313230

HANGZHOU ONECHANCE TECHNOLOGY CORP.
No 520 Kejiyuan Road, Baiyang Subdistrict Qiantang New District, Hangzhou, 310018, Zhejiang, China
Tel.: (86) 57185088289
Web Site: http://www.topwinchance.com
Year Founded: 2012
300792—(SSE)
Rev.: $216,025,056
Assets: $477,993,204
Liabilities: $72,174,024
Net Worth: $405,819,180
Earnings: $25,277,616
Emp.: 1,500
Fiscal Year-end: 12/31/22

E Commerce Site Operator
N.A.I.C.S.: 541511
Zhenyu Lin *(Chm & Gen Mgr)*

HANGZHOU OXYGEN PLANT GROUP CO., LTD.
Hongyuan Building No 592 Zhongshan North Road, Gongshu District, Hangzhou, 310014, Zhejiang, China
Tel.: (86) 57185869000
Web Site: https://www.hangyang.com
Year Founded: 1950
002430—(SSE)
Rev.: $1,797,570,684
Assets: $2,701,078,380
Liabilities: $1,443,185,640
Net Worth: $1,257,892,740
Earnings: $169,926,120
Emp.: 1,500
Fiscal Year-end: 12/31/22
Air & Compressor Machinery Mfr
N.A.I.C.S.: 333912
Zheng Wei *(Chm)*

HANGZHOU PINMING SOFTWARE CO., LTD.
Block C 5F Building B Tiantang Software Park No 3 Xidoumen Road, Xihu, Hangzhou, 310012, Zhejiang, China
Tel.: (86) 57156928512
Web Site: http://www.pinming.cn
Year Founded: 2011
688109—(SHG)
Rev.: $61,085,513
Assets: $133,310,235
Liabilities: $18,012,323
Net Worth: $115,297,912
Earnings: ($7,863,916)
Emp.: 1,000
Fiscal Year-end: 12/31/22
Software Development Services
N.A.I.C.S.: 541511
Xujun Mo *(Chm)*

HANGZHOU PREVAIL OPTOELECTRONIC EQUIPMENT CO., LTD.
No 11809 Jianshe 4th Road, Guali Town Xiaoshan District, Hangzhou, 311241, Zhejiang, China
Tel.: (86) 57182559907
Web Site: https://www.prevail-catv.com
Year Founded: 2001
300710—(CHIN)
Rev.: $50,452,273
Assets: $125,954,845
Liabilities: $29,805,297
Net Worth: $96,149,548
Earnings: ($1,398,669)
Fiscal Year-end: 12/31/23
Testing Equipment Mfr
N.A.I.C.S.: 334515
Lei Qianguo *(Chm & Gen Mgr)*

HANGZHOU RADICAL ENERGY SAVING TECHNOLOGY CO., LTD.
No 89 Chunchao Road Qiaonan Area, Xiaoshan Economic & Technological Development Zone, Hangzhou, 311231, Zhejiang, China
Tel.: (86) 57122806161
Web Site: https://www.radical.cn
Year Founded: 2002
300652—(CHIN)
Rev.: $91,817,453
Assets: $236,251,283
Liabilities: $50,068,316
Net Worth: $186,182,967
Earnings: $16,955,438
Fiscal Year-end: 12/31/23
Automotive Bearing Mfr & Distr
N.A.I.C.S.: 336310

HangZhou Radical Energy Saving Technology Co., Ltd.—(Continued)

HANGZHOU RAYCLOUD TECHNOLOGY CO., LTD.
11F Main Building Hengxin Building No 588 Jiangnan Avenue, Binjiang District, Hangzhou, 310052, Zhejiang, China
Tel.: (86) 57181025116
Web Site: http://www.raycloud.com
Year Founded: 2013
688365—(SHG)
Rev.: $69,352,195
Assets: $184,678,046
Liabilities: $62,384,143
Net Worth: $122,293,904
Earnings: ($25,114,499)
Fiscal Year-end: 12/31/22
Software Development Services
N.A.I.C.S.: 541511
Guanghua Tan (Chm & Gen Mgr)

HANGZHOU ROBAM APPLIANCES CO., LTD.
No 592 Linping Av. Yuhang Economic Development Zone, Hangzhou, 311112, Zhejiang, China
Tel.: (86) 57186280607
Web Site:
https://www.robamworld.com
Year Founded: 1979
002508—(SSE)
Rev.: $1,442,118,600
Assets: $2,111,592,132
Liabilities: $727,493,832
Net Worth: $1,384,098,300
Earnings: $220,764,960
Fiscal Year-end: 12/31/22
Cooking Appliance Mfr
N.A.I.C.S.: 335220
Ren Jianhua (Chm)

Subsidiaries:

Robam Appliances Pvt. Ltd. (1)
Tel.: (91) 2241313119
Web Site: http://www.robamindia.com
Kitchen Product Mfr
N.A.I.C.S.: 333994

Robam Malaysia Sdn Bhd (1)
6A Jalan Mesra 1 Taman Mesra Batu Tiga, 40150, Shah Alam, Selangor, Malaysia
Tel.: (60) 355245587
Web Site: http://www.robammalaysia.com
Dishwasher Mfr
N.A.I.C.S.: 335220

HANGZHOU SECK INTELLIGENT TECHNOLOGY CO., LTD.
No 47 Haoshantou Pingyao Town, Yuhang, Hangzhou, 311121, China
Tel.: (86) 57188911100
Web Site: https://www.seck.com.cn
Year Founded: 1999
300897—(SSE)
Rev.: $79,206,660
Assets: $172,864,692
Liabilities: $42,285,672
Net Worth: $130,579,020
Earnings: $11,368,188
Fiscal Year-end: 12/31/22
Software Development Services
N.A.I.C.S.: 541511
Bingjiong Qian (Chm)

HANGZHOU SF INTRA-CITY INDUSTRIAL CO., LTD.
Floor 21-22 Shunfeng Headquarters Building No 3076 Xinghai Road, Nanshan District, Shenzhen, Guangdong, China   CN
Year Founded: 2016
9699—(HKG)
Rev.: $1,715,138,458
Assets: $581,481,364
Liabilities: $168,724,662

Net Worth: $412,756,701
Earnings: $8,979,979
Emp.: 2,041
Fiscal Year-end: 12/31/23
Logistic Services
N.A.I.C.S.: 541614
Hey Man Chan (CFO)

HANGZHOU SHENHAO TECHNOLOGY CO., LTD.
No 5 Yuda Road, Yuhang Subdistrict Yuhang District, Hangzhou, 311121, Zhejiang, China
Tel.: (86) 57188720409
Web Site:
http://www.shenhaoinfo.com
Year Founded: 2002
300853—(SSE)
Rev.: $54,962,388
Assets: $310,222,224
Liabilities: $124,666,776
Net Worth: $185,555,448
Earnings: ($9,120,384)
Emp.: 500
Fiscal Year-end: 12/31/22
E Commerce Site Operator
N.A.I.C.S.: 334510
Rushen Chen (Chm)

HANGZHOU SHUNWANG TECHNOLOGY CO., LTD.
Building No 1-No. 6 Shunwang Canal International No 555 Huzhou Street, Gongshu District, Hangzhou, 310015, Zhejiang, China
Tel.: (86) 57187205808
Web Site: http://www.shunwang.com
Year Founded: 2005
300113—(CHIN)
Rev.: $201,833,303
Assets: $344,673,838
Liabilities: $50,091,232
Net Worth: $294,582,606
Earnings: $23,874,652
Fiscal Year-end: 12/31/23
Information Technology Services
N.A.I.C.S.: 541512
Yong Hua (Chm, Pres & Gen Mgr)

HANGZHOU SILAN MICROELECTRONICS CO., LTD.
No 4 HuangGuShan Road, Hangzhou, 310012, Zhejiang, China
Tel.: (86) 57188210880
Web Site: https://www.silan.com.cn
Year Founded: 1997
600460—(SHG)
Rev.: $1,162,821,105
Assets: $2,375,635,420
Liabilities: $1,242,547,666
Net Worth: $1,133,087,754
Earnings: $147,759,319
Fiscal Year-end: 12/31/22
Semiconductor Device Mfr & Whslr
N.A.I.C.S.: 334413
Xiangdong Chen (Chm)

Subsidiaries:

Chendu Perfect Technology Co., Ltd. (1)
No 9 Shixin Road Concentrated Industrial Development Zone, Chengdu-Aba Huaikou Town Jintang County, Chengdu, China
Tel.: (86) 2884925088
Web Site: https://www.perfect-cd.com
Semiconductor Mfr & Distr
N.A.I.C.S.: 334413

Hangzhou Multi-Color Optoelectrical Co., Ltd. (1)
No 300 Number 10 Road Economic and Technology Development Zone, Hangzhou, 310018, Zhejiang, China
Tel.: (86) 57186708389
Web Site: http://www.mc-oe.com
LCD Products Mfr
N.A.I.C.S.: 339950

Hangzhou Silan Azuer Co., Ltd. (1)

No 300 No 10 Road East HETZ, Hangzhou, Zhejiang, China
Tel.: (86) 57186708306
Light Emitting Diode Chip Mfr & Distr
N.A.I.C.S.: 334413

Hangzhou Silan Integrated Circuit Co., Ltd. (1)
No 308 10 Road East HETZ, Hangzhou, 310018, China
Tel.: (86) 57 1867 14088
Semiconductor Devices Mfr
N.A.I.C.S.: 334413
ZhouMiao Gao (Sr VP)

Hangzhou Silan Optronics Technology Co., Ltd (1)
No 500 Bingkang Road, Hangzhou, 310052, Zhejiang, China
Tel.: (86) 57186627052
Web Site: http://www.slopto.com.cn
Semiconductor Device Mfr & Distr
N.A.I.C.S.: 334413

Hangzhou Youwang Electronics Co., Ltd. (1)
No 1 Chengye Road, Binjiang District, Hangzhou, 310053, China
Tel.: (86) 57186673988
Web Site: http://www.youwang.com.cn
Integrated Circuits Mfr
N.A.I.C.S.: 334413

Xiamen Silan Advanced Compound Semiconductor Co., Ltd. (1)
No 99 Lanying Road, Haicang District, Xiamen, Fujian, China
Tel.: (86) 5923568999
Light Emitting Diode Chip Mfr & Distr
N.A.I.C.S.: 334413

Xiamen Silan Microchip Manufacturing Co., Ltd. (1)
No 89 Lanying Road, Haicang District, Xiamen, Fujian, China
Tel.: (86) 5923533162
Semiconductor Circuit Mfr & Distr
N.A.I.C.S.: 334413

HANGZHOU STAR SHUAIER ELECTRIC APPLIANCE CO., LTD.
No 99jiao Jie Ling Shou Xiang Town, Fuyang, Hangzhou, 311422, Zhejiang, China
Tel.: (86) 57163410817
Web Site:
https://www.hzstarshuaier.com
Year Founded: 2002
002860—(SSE)
Rev.: $273,680,316
Assets: $349,340,472
Liabilities: $150,438,600
Net Worth: $198,901,872
Earnings: $16,723,044
Emp.: 220
Fiscal Year-end: 12/31/22
Electrical Power Equipment Mfr & Distr
N.A.I.C.S.: 335311

HANGZHOU STEAM TURBINE CO., LTD.
1188 Dongxin Road, Hangzhou, 310022, Zhejiang, China
Tel.: (86) 57185780114
Web Site: https://en.htc.cn
Year Founded: 1958
200771—(SSE)
Rev.: $20,143,206,252
Assets: $35,553,636,612
Liabilities: $26,223,076,620
Net Worth: $9,330,559,992
Earnings: $195,865,020
Fiscal Year-end: 12/31/22
Steam Turbine Mfr
N.A.I.C.S.: 333611

HANGZHOU SUNRISE TECHNOLOGY COMPANY LIMITED
No 1099 Cangxing Jie Cangqian

Street, Yuhang District, Hangzhou, 310030, Zhejiang, China
Tel.: (86) 57189935888
Web Site:
https://www.sunhopesmart.com
Year Founded: 2001
300360—(CHIN)
Rev.: $211,487,328
Assets: $566,904,312
Liabilities: $131,272,596
Net Worth: $435,631,716
Earnings: $66,278,628
Emp.: 1,240
Fiscal Year-end: 12/31/22
Electricity Energy Metering Instruments & Power Information Collection Systems Mfr
N.A.I.C.S.: 334515
Yang Guang (Chm & Gen Mgr)

HANGZHOU TIANMUSHAN PHARMACEUTICAL ENTERPRISE CO., LTD.
No 18 Shangyang Road, Linan District, Hangzhou, 311200, Zhejiang, China
Tel.: (86) 57163722229
Web Site: https://www.hztmyy.com
Year Founded: 1958
600671—(SHG)
Rev.: $15,290,430
Assets: $42,097,508
Liabilities: $41,468,558
Net Worth: $628,950
Earnings: ($9,485,466)
Fiscal Year-end: 12/31/22
Pharmaceutical Product Mfr & Distr
N.A.I.C.S.: 325412
Liu Jiayong (Chm)

HANGZHOU TIANYUAN PET PRODUCTS CO., LTD.
No 291 Ningqiao Avenue, Tangqi Town Yuhang District, Hangzhou, 311100, Zhejiang, China
Tel.: (86) 57128886888
Web Site:
https://www.tianyuanpet.com
Year Founded: 2003
301335—(CHIN)
Rev.: $286,876,267
Assets: $361,957,703
Liabilities: $89,166,915
Net Worth: $272,790,788
Earnings: $10,812,268
Fiscal Year-end: 12/31/23
Pet Product Mfr & Distr
N.A.I.C.S.: 311119
Yuanchao Xue (Chm, Pres & Gen Mgr)

HANGZHOU TIGERMED CONSULTING CO., LTD.
Fl15 Dongguan Plaza No 618 Jiangnan Avenue, Binjiang District, Hangzhou, 310051, Zhejiang, China
Tel.: (86) 57128887227
Web Site:
http://www.tigermedgrp.com
Year Founded: 2004
3347—(HKG)
Rev.: $994,800,128
Assets: $3,853,490,004
Liabilities: $669,073,673
Net Worth: $3,184,416,331
Earnings: $320,288,904
Emp.: 9,233
Fiscal Year-end: 12/31/22
Pharmaceuticals & Health Care Products Researcher & Developer
N.A.I.C.S.: 541715
Jiansong Yang (Chief Scientific Officer & Sr VP)

Subsidiaries:

Acme Bioscience, Inc. (1)

AND PRIVATE COMPANIES

3941 E Bayshore Rd, Palo Alto, CA 94303
Tel.: (650) 969-8000
Biological Testing Services
N.A.I.C.S.: 541380
Jason Zhang *(Founder & CEO)*

BRI Biopharmaceutical Research Inc. (1)
101 - 8898 Heather Street, Vancouver, V6P 3S8, BC, Canada
Tel.: (604) 432-9237
Web Site: http://www.bripharm.com
Clinical Research Services
N.A.I.C.S.: 541715

Beijing Canny Consulting Inc. (1)
Room 703 Union Plaza No 20 Chaoyangmenwai Street, Chaoyang District, Beijing, 100022, China
Tel.: (86) 4008770626
Web Site: https://www.bj-canny.com
Pharmaceutical Consultant Services
N.A.I.C.S.: 456110

Beijing Yaxincheng Medical InfoTech Co. Ltd. (1)
Room 102 Building 1 PeKing House No 20A Xidawanglu, Chaoyang District, Beijing, China
Tel.: (86) 1056291011
Web Site: https://www.yaxincheng.com
Pharmaceutical Translation Services
N.A.I.C.S.: 541930
Yingchun Fu *(Co-Founder & Chm)*

DreamCIS Inc. (1)
130 Sajik-ro Jeokseon-Hyundai B/D 10F, Jongno-gu, Seoul, Korea (South)
Tel.: (82) 22 010 4500
Web Site: https://www.dreamcis.com
Clinical Research Services
N.A.I.C.S.: 541715

Frontage Holdings Corporation (1)
Level 54 Hopewell Centre 183 Queens Road East, Hong Kong, KY1-1111, China (Hong Kong) **(50.71%)**
Rev.: $250,360,000
Assets: $550,594,000
Liabilities: $214,746,000
Net Worth: $335,848,000
Earnings: $25,900,000
Emp.: 1,698
Fiscal Year-end: 12/31/2022
Holding Company
N.A.I.C.S.: 551112
Son Li *(Founder)*

Subsidiary (US):

Frontage Laboratories, Inc. (2)
700 Pennsylvania Dr, Exton, PA 19341
Tel.: (610) 232-0100
Web Site: http://www.frontagelab.com
Emp.: 50
Pharmaceutical Preparation Mfr
N.A.I.C.S.: 325412
Song Li *(Co-Founder & CEO)*

Subsidiary (Domestic):

Concord Biosciences LLC (3)
10845 Wellness Way, Concord, OH 44077
Tel.: (440) 357-3200
Commercial Research Laboratory Pharmaceuticals
N.A.I.C.S.: 541715

Ocean Ridge Biosciences, Inc. (3)
10475 Riverside Dr Ste 1, Palm Beach Gardens, FL 33410-4208
Tel.: (561) 223-3152
Web Site: http://www.oceanridgebio.com
Research & Development in Biotechnology
N.A.I.C.S.: 541714
David Willoughby *(Founder)*

Frontage Laboratories (Shanghai) Co., Ltd. (1)
1227 Zhangheng Rd Building 2 Zhangjiang High-Tech Park, Shanghai, 201203, China
Tel.: (86) 2150796268
Clinical Research Services
N.A.I.C.S.: 541715

Hangzhou Simo Co., Ltd. (1)
Room 1705 Baoyichuangyi Plaza No 3760 Nanhuan Rd, Binjiang District, Hangzhou, 310053, China
Tel.: (86) 571 28887227
Web Site: http://www.simochina.com
Emp.: 60
Pharmaceutical Research & Development Services
N.A.I.C.S.: 541715

Jiaxing Clinflash Computer Technology Co., Ltd. (1)
Floor 5 Tigermed Plaza No 28 Huixin Road, Nanhu District, Jiaxing, 314006, Zhejiang, China
Tel.: (86) 4008038655
Web Site: https://www.clinflash.com
Clinical Research Services
N.A.I.C.S.: 541715

MacroStat (China) Clinical Research Co., Ltd (1)
498 Guoshoujing Road Suite 106-119 Block 1 Zhang Jiang High-Tech Park, Shanghai, 201203, China
Tel.: (86) 215 0276030
Web Site: http://www.macrostat.com
Pharmaceutical Research & Development Services
N.A.I.C.S.: 541715
Bing Zhang *(Co-Partner)*

Marti Farm Ltd. (1)
Lascinska Cesta 40, 10000, Zagreb, Croatia
Tel.: (385) 15588297
Web Site: https://martifarm.com
Pharmaceuticals Mfr
N.A.I.C.S.: 325412

Opera Contract Research Organization SRL. (1)
10th Cozia Street, 300209, Timisoara, Romania
Tel.: (40) 744100196
Web Site: https://operacro.com
Contract Research Services
N.A.I.C.S.: 541715

Taizhou Tigermed-Jyton Medical Tech. Co., Ltd. (1)
Suite 808 Union Plaza No 20 Chaoyangmenwai Street, Chaoyang District, Beijing, China
Tel.: (86) 106 588 9599
Web Site: https://en.jtmedical.com
Research & Development Services
N.A.I.C.S.: 541715
Peng Yifei *(Gen Mgr)*

HANGZHOU TODAYTEC DIGITAL CO., LTD.
600 KangXin Rd Hang Zhou Qianjiang Economic Development Zone, Linping District, Hangzhou, 311106, Zhejiang, China
Tel.: (86) 57186358910
Web Site:
    https://www.todaytec.com.cn
Year Founded: 2002
300743—(CHIN)
Rev.: $90,723,302
Assets: $128,646,376
Liabilities: $41,939,468
Net Worth: $86,706,908
Earnings: $7,837,119
Fiscal Year-end: 12/31/23
Thermal Imaging Product Mfr & Distr
N.A.I.C.S.: 326140
Han Qiong *(Chm, Pres & Gen Mgr)*

Subsidiaries:

Todaytec Canada Inc. (1)
250 Chrysler Drive Unit 2, Brampton, L6S 6B6, ON, Canada
Tel.: (416) 520-2536
Web Site: https://www.todaytec.ca
Inked Ribbon Mfr
N.A.I.C.S.: 339940

Todaytec India Private Limited (1)
C149 Phase 1, Okhla Industrial Are, New Delhi, India
Tel.: (91) 1141670109
Thermal Transfer Ribbon Mfr
N.A.I.C.S.: 339940

Todaytec Industria de Codigos de Barras Ltda. (1)
Rua Acara - 200 Bloco 2/B, Manaus, 69075-030, Brazil

Tel.: (55) 9232373870
Thermal Transfer Ribbon Mfr
N.A.I.C.S.: 339940

HANGZHOU WAHAHA GROUP CO., LTD.
No 160 Qingtai Street, Hangzhou, 310009, China
Tel.: (86) 57186032866
Web Site: http://www.wahaha.com.cn
Year Founded: 1987
Emp.: 300
Food & Beverage Mfr
N.A.I.C.S.: 311999

HANGZHOU WEIGUANG ELECTRONIC CO., LTD.
NO 365 Xingzhong Road Linping Region, Hangzhou, 311100, Zhejiang, China
Tel.: (86) 57186240288
Web Site: https://en.wgmotor.com
Year Founded: 2009
002801—(SSE)
Rev.: $169,149,708
Assets: $248,645,592
Liabilities: $33,319,728
Net Worth: $215,325,864
Earnings: $43,233,372
Fiscal Year-end: 12/31/22
Fan Motor Mfr & Distr
N.A.I.C.S.: 335210
He Ping *(Chm)*

HANGZHOU WENSLI SILK CULTURE CO., LTD.
Room 501 5th Floor Building 2 No 68, Tiancheng Road, Hangzhou, 310021, Zhejiang, China
Tel.: (86) 57186847618
Web Site: https://www.wensli.cn
Year Founded: 2007
301066—(CHIN)
Rev.: $77,075,388
Assets: $116,186,616
Liabilities: $26,944,164
Net Worth: $89,242,452
Earnings: $(224,640)
Fiscal Year-end: 12/31/22
Textile Product Mfr & Distr
N.A.I.C.S.: 314999
Jianhua Li *(Chm)*

HANGZHOU XILI INTELLIGENT TECHNOLOGY CO., LTD.
No 173 LiangFu Road Zhuantang Street, Xihu District, Hangzhou, 310024, Zhejiang, China
Tel.: (86) 57156660370
Web Site: http://www.cnxili.com
Year Founded: 1999
688616—(SHG)
Rev.: $76,144,901
Assets: $141,606,738
Liabilities: $34,483,616
Net Worth: $107,123,122
Earnings: $8,934,831
Fiscal Year-end: 12/31/22
Electrical Equipment Mfr & Distr
N.A.I.C.S.: 335999
Yiran Song *(Chm)*

HANGZHOU XZB TECH CO.,LTD
No 18 Longtan Road Cangqian Street, Yuhang District, Hangzhou, China
Tel.: (86) 57188620919
Web Site: https://www.xzbco.com
Year Founded: 2002
603040—(SHG)
Rev.: $73,963,450
Assets: $180,004,116
Liabilities: $20,346,614
Net Worth: $159,657,503
Earnings: $21,868,774

Fiscal Year-end: 12/31/22
Automotive Parts Mfr & Distr
N.A.I.C.S.: 336310

HANGZHOU YOUNGSUN INTELLIGENT EQUIPMENT CO., LTD.
No 2 Xiyuan 7 Rd, West Lake Science & Technology Development Area, Hangzhou, 310030, Zhejiang, China
Tel.: (86) 57187978016
Web Site:
    https://www.youngsunpack.com
Year Founded: 2002
603901—(SHG)
Rev.: $385,951,148
Assets: $894,401,394
Liabilities: $523,850,820
Net Worth: $370,550,574
Earnings: $38,422,833
Fiscal Year-end: 12/31/22
Packing Equipment Mfr
N.A.I.C.S.: 339991
Jie Lv *(Vice Chm)*

HANGZHOU ZHENGQIANG CORPORATION LIMITED
Xiaoshan Litoujin Industrial Area, Hangzhou, 311201, Zhejiang, China
Tel.: (86) 57182392329
Web Site:
    https://www.zhengqiang.com
Year Founded: 1997
301119—(CHIN)
Rev.: $58,790,690
Assets: $163,089,985
Liabilities: $26,174,225
Net Worth: $136,915,760
Earnings: $13,650,549
Emp.: 515
Fiscal Year-end: 12/31/23
Automobile Parts Mfr & Distr
N.A.I.C.S.: 336211
Zhengqing Xu *(Chm)*

HANGZHOU ZHONGHENG ELECTRIC CO., LTD.
69 Dongxin Avenue Zhonhen Building, Hangzhou, China
Tel.: (86) 57186698999
Web Site: https://www.hzzh.com
Year Founded: 1996
002364—(SSE)
Rev.: $225,917,640
Assets: $459,621,864
Liabilities: $143,387,712
Net Worth: $316,234,152
Earnings: $(7,837,128)
Emp.: 400
Fiscal Year-end: 12/31/22
Electric Power Products Mfr
N.A.I.C.S.: 335311
Guoding Zhu *(Chm)*

HANGZHOU ZHONGTAI CRYOGENIC TECHNOLOGY CORPORATION
No 228 Golf Road, Dongxing District, Hangzhou, 311402, Zhejiang, China
Tel.: (86) 57163415978
Web Site:
    https://www.zhongtaihangzhou.com
Year Founded: 2006
300435—(CHIN)
Rev.: $457,201,368
Assets: $657,605,520
Liabilities: $261,337,752
Net Worth: $396,267,768
Earnings: $39,025,584
Emp.: 430
Fiscal Year-end: 12/31/22
Cryogenic Technology Equipment Mfr
N.A.I.C.S.: 333415
Youchun Zhang *(Chm)*

Hangzhou Zhongtai Cryogenic Technology Corporation—(Continued)

HANGZHOU ZHONGYA MACHINERY CO., LTD.
No 398 North Xueyuan Road, Gongshu District, Hangzhou, 310011, Zhejiang, China
Tel.: (86) 57188237000
Web Site: https://en.zhongyagroup.com
Year Founded: 1999
300512—(CHIN)
Rev.: $143,437,245
Assets: $385,964,705
Liabilities: $157,019,566
Net Worth: $228,945,140
Earnings: $5,784,808
Emp.: 1,300
Fiscal Year-end: 12/31/23
Packaging Equipment Mfr & Distr
N.A.I.C.S.: 333993
Shi Zhongwei *(Chm)*

HANHUA FINANCIAL HOLDING CO., LTD.
No 1 Dongzhimen Beizhongjie Street B, Dongcheng District, Beijing, China
Tel.: (86) 1057766666
Web Site: https://www.hanhua.com
3903—(HKG)
Rev.: $64,431,385
Assets: $1,612,298,142
Liabilities: $493,360,124
Net Worth: $1,118,938,018
Earnings: $7,305,854
Emp.: 914
Fiscal Year-end: 12/31/22
Financial Services Holding Company; Investment Management & Consulting Services
N.A.I.C.S.: 551112
Guoxiang Zhang *(Chm & Exec Dir)*

HANIL CHEMICAL IND. CO., LTD.
47 Sandan 3-ro 6-gil, Seongmunmyeon, Dangjin, Chungcheongnam-do, Korea (South)
Tel.: (82) 234484257
Web Site: https://www.hanzinc.com
Year Founded: 1972
007770—(KRS)
Rev.: $119,896,749
Assets: $120,543,192
Liabilities: $29,311,589
Net Worth: $91,231,604
Earnings: $3,066,546
Emp.: 124
Fiscal Year-end: 12/31/22
Chemical Products Mfr
N.A.I.C.S.: 325180
Sung-Jin Yoon *(CEO)*

HANIL FEED CO., LTD.
213 Hagal-Dong, Giheung-gu, Yongin, Gyeonggi-do, Korea (South)
Tel.: (82) 312804000
Web Site: https://www.hanilfeed.com
Year Founded: 1963
005860—(KRS)
Rev.: $313,178,805
Assets: $144,110,533
Liabilities: $102,256,605
Net Worth: $41,853,927
Earnings: ($10,802,089)
Emp.: 84
Fiscal Year-end: 12/31/22
Animal Feed Mfr
N.A.I.C.S.: 311119

HANIL FORGING INDUSTRIAL CO., LTD.
42 Seongju-ro 97beon-gil, Seongsan-gu, Changwon, Gyeongnam, Korea (South)
Tel.: (82) 435365181
Web Site: https://www.hifg.co.kr
Year Founded: 1966
024740—(KRS)
Rev.: $136,038,601
Assets: $198,043,712
Liabilities: $109,486,523
Net Worth: $88,557,189
Earnings: $5,274,716
Emp.: 135
Fiscal Year-end: 12/31/22
Automobile Parts Mfr
N.A.I.C.S.: 336390
Joon-Suk Hong *(Chm)*

Subsidiaries:

Hanil Forging Industrial Co., Ltd. - Jincheon Factory (1)
566-40 87th Subaji Road, Duksan-Myun, Jincheon, Chungcheongbuk-do, Korea (South)
Tel.: (82) 435365181
Motor Vehicle Parts Mfr
N.A.I.C.S.: 336390

Hanil Forging Industrial Co., Ltd. - Thailand Factory (1)
Eastern Seaboard Industrial Estate Rayong Thailand 300/47 Moo1, Tamnbon Tasith, Pluak Daeng, 21140, Rayong, Thailand
Tel.: (66) 38954961
Motor Vehicle Parts Mfr
N.A.I.C.S.: 336390

HANIL HOLDINGS CO., LTD
9F hanilcement building 275 Hyoryeong-ro, Seocho-dong Seocho-gu, 1587, Seoul, 1587, Korea (South)
Tel.: (82) 25507901
Web Site: https://www.hanil.com
Year Founded: 1961
003300—(KRS)
Rev.: $1,507,624,197
Assets: $2,506,587,712
Liabilities: $936,414,294
Net Worth: $1,570,173,419
Earnings: $68,683,260
Emp.: 26
Fiscal Year-end: 12/31/22
Holding Company
N.A.I.C.S.: 551112
Huh Gi Ho *(Co-CEO)*

Subsidiaries:

Hanil Cement Co., Ltd. (1)
9th floor Hanil Cement Building 1587 Seocho-dong, Seocho-gu, Seoul, 06654, Korea (South) (51.46%)
Tel.: (82) 25507901
Fiscal Year-end: 12/31/2018
Holding Company
N.A.I.C.S.: 551112

Subsidiary (Domestic):

Hanil Hyundai Cement Co., Ltd. (2)
6th floor Hanil Cement Building 1587 Seocho-dong, Seocho-gu, Seoul, Korea (South)
Tel.: (82) 25202114
Web Site: https://www.hdcement.co.kr
Rev.: $361,372,183
Assets: $497,879,652
Liabilities: $218,783,254
Net Worth: $279,096,399
Earnings: $27,385,023
Emp.: 437
Fiscal Year-end: 12/31/2022
Cement Mfr
N.A.I.C.S.: 327310
Gi-Ho Huh *(Chm)*

Hanil Networks Co., Ltd. (1)
Wooduk Bldg 13th 330 Gangnam-daero, Gangnam-gu, Seoul, Korea (South) (50.1%)
Tel.: (82) 234669100
Web Site: https://www.hanilnetworks.com
Rev.: $91,001,698
Assets: $106,554,512
Liabilities: $40,854,088
Net Worth: $65,700,424
Earnings: $5,590,617
Emp.: 181
Fiscal Year-end: 12/31/2023

Information Technology Equipment Whslr
N.A.I.C.S.: 423430

HANIL IRON & STEEL CO., LTD.
28 Toegye-ro 27-gil, Jung-gu, Seoul, Korea (South)
Tel.: (82) 222676161
Web Site: https://www.hanilsteel.co.kr
Year Founded: 1957
002220—(KRS)
Rev.: $195,760,890
Assets: $260,131,863
Liabilities: $126,265,334
Net Worth: $133,866,529
Earnings: ($1,154,354)
Emp.: 124
Fiscal Year-end: 12/31/22
Iron & Steel Product Mfr
N.A.I.C.S.: 331110
Jung-Hun Um *(Chm & CEO)*

HANIL VACUUM CO., LTD.
73B/12L 643-11 Gojan-Dong, Namdong-Gu, Incheon, Korea (South)
Tel.: (82) 328219300
Web Site: https://www.vacuum-coater.com
Year Founded: 1988
123840—(KRS)
Rev.: $5,298,119
Assets: $47,195,167
Liabilities: $18,337,995
Net Worth: $28,857,172
Earnings: ($45,638,733)
Emp.: 84
Fiscal Year-end: 12/31/22
Vacuum Deposition Apparatus Mfr
N.A.I.C.S.: 333310

HANISON CONSTRUCTION HOLDINGS LIMITED
22/F Kings Wing Plaza 1 3 On Kwan Street, Shek Mun, Sha Tin, New Territories, China (Hong Kong)
Tel.: (852) 2 414 3889
Web Site: http://www.hanison.com
0896—(HKG)
Rev.: $187,222,209
Assets: $1,048,628,166
Liabilities: $515,024,363
Net Worth: $533,603,803
Earnings: $35,467,694
Emp.: 485
Fiscal Year-end: 03/31/21
Building Construction Services
N.A.I.C.S.: 236220
Stewart Sue Toa Wong *(Mng Dir)*

Subsidiaries:

Care & Health Limited (1)
Unit 1 6/F Block B Shatin Ind Centre 5-7 Yuen Shun Circuit, Sha Tin, NT, China (Hong Kong)
Tel.: (852) 23688680
Web Site: http://www.careandhealth.com.hk
Healthcare Product Distr
N.A.I.C.S.: 423450

Million Hope Industries Limited (1)
Office A 20/F Kings Wing Plaza 1 3 On Kwan Street, Shek Mun, Sha Tin, NT, China (Hong Kong)
Tel.: (852) 26930276
Web Site: http://www.millionhope.com.hk
Aluminium Fixture Mfr
N.A.I.C.S.: 331524

Sure Promise Limited (1)
Flat/RM 7A G/F Allway Gardens Phase2 187-195 Tsuen King Circuit, Tsuen Wan, China (Hong Kong)
Tel.: (852) 3 565 5761
Web Site: https://www.surepromise.com
Ecommerce Services
N.A.I.C.S.: 423690

HANJIA DESIGN GROUP CO., LTD.
No 501 Hushu South Road, Hangzhou, 310005, Zhejiang, China
Tel.: (86) 57189975173
Web Site: https://www.cnhanjia.com
Year Founded: 1993
300746—(CHIN)
Rev.: $320,271,674
Assets: $375,127,833
Liabilities: $195,193,465
Net Worth: $179,934,368
Earnings: $1,538,364
Emp.: 1,400
Fiscal Year-end: 12/31/23
Architectural Design Services
N.A.I.C.S.: 541310
Cen Zhengping *(Chm)*

HANJIN HEAVY INDUSTRIES & CONSTRUCTION CO., LTD.
50 Gangbyeonyeok-ro, Gwangjin-gu, Seoul, Korea (South)
Tel.: (82) 220492395
Web Site: http://www.hhic-holdings.com
Year Founded: 1937
003480—(KRS)
Rev.: $1,327,259,029
Assets: $1,905,865,980
Liabilities: $1,620,108,220
Net Worth: $285,757,760
Earnings: ($37,231,121)
Emp.: 2,227
Fiscal Year-end: 12/31/22
Investment Management Service
N.A.I.C.S.: 523940

Subsidiaries:

HHIC-Hong Kong Ltd. (1)
Room 1601 Office Tower Convention Plaza 1 Harbour Road, Wanchai, China (Hong Kong)
Tel.: (852) 2238 0602
Ship Building Services
N.A.I.C.S.: 336611

Hanjin Heavy Industries & Construction Co., Ltd. - Dadaepo Factory (1)
66 Dadae-ro 605 beon-gil, Saha-gu, Busan, Korea (South)
Tel.: (82) 51 260 3114
Ship Building Services
N.A.I.C.S.: 336611

Hanjin Heavy Industries & Construction Co., Ltd. - Yuldo Factory (1)
133 Bukhang-ro 309 beon-gil, Seo-gu, Incheon, Korea (South)
Tel.: (82) 32 580 9114
Ship Building Services
N.A.I.C.S.: 336611

HANJIN KAL CORP.
117 Seosomun-ro, Jung-gu, Seoul, 04515, Korea (South)
Tel.: (82) 27266166
Web Site: https://www.hanjinkal.co.kr
Year Founded: 2013
180640—(KRS)
Rev.: $153,657,775
Assets: $3,002,864,535
Liabilities: $1,027,028,673
Net Worth: $1,975,835,862
Earnings: $505,888,912
Emp.: 29
Fiscal Year-end: 12/31/22
Holding Company
N.A.I.C.S.: 551112
Walter Cho *(Co-Chm & Co-CEO)*

Subsidiaries:

JungSeok Enterprise Co., Ltd. (1)
Tel.: (82) 27266311
Web Site: http://www.jungseok.co.kr
Parking Management Services
N.A.I.C.S.: 812930

HANJIN TRANSPORTATION CO., LTD.

63 Namdaemun-ro, Jung-Gu, Seoul, Korea (South)
Tel.: (82) 27285114
Web Site: http://www.hanjin.co.kr
Year Founded: 1945
002320—(KRS)
Rev.: $2,185,505,807
Assets: $3,139,482,630
Liabilities: $1,962,610,915
Net Worth: $1,176,871,714
Earnings: $36,508,885
Emp.: 1,510
Fiscal Year-end: 12/31/22
Transportation, Delivery & Logistics Services
N.A.I.C.S.: 492110
Shin Young-Hwan *(Exec VP)*

Subsidiaries:

Hanjin Global Logistics (Dalian) Co., Limited (1)
RM 2305 Hongyubld No 68 Renmin St, Zhongshan Dist, Dalian, China
Tel.: (86) 41182766797
Logistic Services
N.A.I.C.S.: 488999

Hanjin Global Logistics (Guangzhou) Co., Limited (1)
Rm 2505 South Tower Jinbintengyue Bldg 49 Huaxia Rd, Zhujiangxincheng Tianhe, Guangzhou, China
Tel.: (86) 2038031096
Logistic Services
N.A.I.C.S.: 488999

Hanjin Global Logistics (Hong Kong) Limited (1)
Unit 02 14/F Texaco Centre 126-140 Texaco Road, Tsuen Wan, China (Hong Kong)
Tel.: (852) 31535294
Logistic Services
N.A.I.C.S.: 488999

Hanjin Global Logistics (Shanghai) Co., Limited (1)
RM 2501 Zhongrong Hengrui International Plaza East Building No 620, Zhangyang Road Pudong, Shanghai, China
Tel.: (86) 2168862890
Logistic Services
N.A.I.C.S.: 488999

Hanjin Global Logistics (Shenzhen) Co., Limited (1)
9F Tower B Hong Long Century Plaza Intersection of Shennan, Middle Road and Heping Road Luohu District, Shenzhen, China
Tel.: (86) 75523982542
Logistic Services
N.A.I.C.S.: 488999

Qingdao Hanjin Luhai International Logistics Co., Limited (1)
RM606 6th Floor Building A Yihe International Mansion No 10, Hongkong Middle Road, Qingdao, China
Tel.: (86) 53285023351
Logistic Services
N.A.I.C.S.: 488999

HANJOO METAL CO., LTD.
34-5 Hwasan 2-Gil Onsan-eup Uljugun, Ulsan, Korea (South)
Tel.: (82) 522311001
Web Site:
https://www.hanjoolightmetal.com
Year Founded: 1987
Aluminum Molded Automotive Parts Mfr
N.A.I.C.S.: 331523
Sam Soon Jeong *(CEO)*

HANJUNGNCS CO., LTD.
379 Yeongcheon Industrial Complex Road, Yeongcheon, Gyeongbuk, Korea (South)
Tel.: (82) 543375050
Web Site: https://www.hjncs.com
Year Founded: 1995
Automobile Parts Mfr
N.A.I.C.S.: 336390

Hwan Sik Kim *(CEO)*

HANKOOK & COMPANY CO., LTD.
286 Pangyo-Ro, Bundang-Gu, Seongnam, 13494, Gyeonggi-do, Korea (South)
Tel.: (82) 3151787000
Web Site:
https://www.hankookcompany.com
Year Founded: 1941
000240—(KRS)
Rev.: $840,552,056
Assets: $3,299,494,924
Liabilities: $341,604,576
Net Worth: $2,957,890,348
Earnings: $125,680,499
Emp.: 1,048
Fiscal Year-end: 12/31/22
Storage Battery Mfr
N.A.I.C.S.: 335910
Seongha Yoon *(Mgr-Comm Team)*

Subsidiaries:

Asia Pacific Division Pte Ltd. (1)
Jl Sultan Iskandar Muda Gandaria 8 Office Tower 22nd Floor, Kebayoran Lama, Jakarta Selatan, 12240, Jakarta, Indonesia
Tel.: (62) 2129303860
Battery Mfr & Distr
N.A.I.C.S.: 335910

Hankook Tire Co., Ltd. (1)
Av Vitacura 2771 Oficina 1304, Las Condes, 7550134, Santiago, Chile
Tel.: (56) 225968460
Web Site: https://www.hankooktire.com
Tire Mfr & Distr
N.A.I.C.S.: 326211

HANKOOK COSMETICS MANUFACTURING CO., LTD.
35 Cheonggyecheon-ro, Jongno-gu, Seoul, 03188, Korea (South)
Tel.: (82) 27243700
Web Site: https://www.hkcosm.com
Year Founded: 1962
003350—(KRS)
Rev.: $79,673,635
Assets: $63,404,765
Liabilities: $27,168,326
Net Worth: $36,236,439
Earnings: $3,093,315
Emp.: 186
Fiscal Year-end: 12/31/22
Cosmetics Products Mfr
N.A.I.C.S.: 325620
Lim Jin Seo *(Dir)*

Subsidiaries:

Hankook Cosmetics Co., Ltd. (1)
35 Cheonggyecheon-ro, Jongno-gu, 03188, Korea (South)
Tel.: (82) 800232221
Web Site: https://www.ihkcos.com
Rev.: $50,657,801
Assets: $33,681,524
Liabilities: $16,490,626
Net Worth: $17,190,898
Earnings: $320,697
Emp.: 49
Fiscal Year-end: 12/31/2022
Cosmetic Product Whslr
N.A.I.C.S.: 424210
Yong Joon Lee *(CEO)*

HANKOOK FURNITURE CO., LTD.
120 Hakdong-ro, Gangnam-gu, Seoul, 135822, Korea (South)
Tel.: (82) 226007000
Web Site:
http://www.koreafurniture.com
004590—(KRS)
Rev.: $77,390,047
Assets: $162,655,515
Liabilities: $33,280,202
Net Worth: $129,375,314
Earnings: $9,043,001

Emp.: 57
Fiscal Year-end: 12/31/22
Furniture Mfr & Whslr
N.A.I.C.S.: 337121

HANKOOK TECHNOLOGY INC.
30 Sowol-ro 2-gil, Jung-gu, Seoul, Korea (South)
Tel.: (82) 221067500
Web Site: https://www.myht.co.kr
Year Founded: 1997
053590—(KRS)
Rev.: $234,649,399
Assets: $249,625,745
Liabilities: $210,093,512
Net Worth: $39,532,233
Earnings: ($14,233,317)
Emp.: 33
Fiscal Year-end: 12/31/22
Power Generating Equipment Mfr
N.A.I.C.S.: 237130
Han Glennsang *(Exec Dir)*

HANKOOK TIRE & TECHNOLOGY CO., LTD.
286 Pangyo-ro, Bundang-gu, Seongnam, 13494, Gyeonggi-do, Korea (South)
Tel.: (82) 3151787000 KR
Web Site:
https://www.hankooktire.com
Year Founded: 1941
161390—(KRS)
Rev.: $6,438,353,729
Assets: $9,649,906,310
Liabilities: $2,842,237,317
Net Worth: $6,807,668,993
Earnings: $541,329,061
Emp.: 6,986
Fiscal Year-end: 12/31/22
Tires, Inner Tubes & Related Products Mfr & Distr
N.A.I.C.S.: 326211
Soo-il Lee *(Chm, Vice Chm & Co-CEO)*

Subsidiaries:

Atlasbx Co., Ltd. (1)
185 Daejeon-ro 1331beon-gil, Daedeok-gu, Daejeon, Korea (South)
Tel.: (82) 426204242
Rev.: $587,123,925
Assets: $437,960,072
Liabilities: $155,496,756
Net Worth: $282,463,316
Earnings: $44,976,132
Emp.: 839
Fiscal Year-end: 12/31/2018
Storage Battery Mfr
N.A.I.C.S.: 335910

Hankook Car & Life Co., Ltd. (1)
286 Pangyo-ro, Bundang-gu, Seongnam, 13494, Gyeonggi-do, Korea (South)
Tel.: (82) 3151787000
Tire Mfr & Distr
N.A.I.C.S.: 326211

Hankook Donggeurami Partners Co., Ltd. (1)
40 Daedeok-daero 1447beon-gil, Daedeok-gu, Daejeon, 34300, Korea (South)
Tel.: (82) 429301244
Tire Mfr & Distr
N.A.I.C.S.: 326211

Hankook Engineering Works Co., Ltd. (1)
30 Daehwa-ro 52beon-gil, Daedeok-gu, Daejeon, Korea (South)
Tel.: (82) 426322446
Engineering Consulting Services
N.A.I.C.S.: 541330

Hankook France SARL (1)
Batiment Organdi 1 esplanade Miriam Makeba, 69100, Villeurbanne, France
Tel.: (33) 47 269 7640
Web Site: https://www.hankooktire.com
Sales Range: $25-49.9 Million
Emp.: 42
Rubber Tire Mfr

N.A.I.C.S.: 326211

Hankook Networks America, Inc. (1)
Ste 2950 International Blvd, Clarksville, TN 37043
Intelligence Logistics Services
N.A.I.C.S.: 541614

Hankook Networks Co., Ltd. (1)
4F 286 Pangyo-ro, Bundang-gu, Seongnam, 13494, Gyeonggi-do, Korea (South)
Tel.: (82) 3151788200
Intelligence Logistics Services
N.A.I.C.S.: 541614

Hankook Precision Works Co., Ltd. (1)
45 Munpyeongseo-ro, Daedeok-gu, Daejeon, Korea (South)
Tel.: (82) 429309000
Tire Mold Mfr
N.A.I.C.S.: 333248

Hankook Steel Co., Ltd. (1)
228 Jangbaek-ro Gunbuk-myeon, Gunbuk-myeon, Haman, Gyeongsangnam-do, Korea (South)
Tel.: (82) 555857001
Web Site: https://www.hascokorea.co.kr
Rev.: $41,702,636
Assets: $36,850,685
Liabilities: $14,015,557
Net Worth: $22,835,128
Earnings: $1,320,355
Emp.: 44
Fiscal Year-end: 12/31/2022
Cast Steel Mfr
N.A.I.C.S.: 331513
Mangyu Ha *(CEO)*

Hankook Tire America Corp. (1)
1450 Vly Rd, Wayne, NJ 07470
Tel.: (973) 633-9000
Web Site: http://www.hankooktireusa.com
Sales Range: $50-74.9 Million
Emp.: 80
Tire Distr; Regional Managing Office
N.A.I.C.S.: 423130
Justin Shellaway *(Gen Counsel-Corp Strategy-Nashville)*

Subsidiary (Non-US):

Hankook Tire Canada Corp. (2)
30 Resolution Drive, Brampton, L6W 0A3, ON, Canada
Tel.: (905) 463-9802
Web Site: https://www.hankooktire.com
Sales Range: $25-49.9 Million
Emp.: 10
Tire Distr
N.A.I.C.S.: 423130

Branch (Non-US):

Hankook Tire Co., Ltd. - Panama Office (2)
Proconsa Piso 11 Fl Office Amb, Panama, Panama (100%)
Tel.: (507) 2633008
Sales Range: $25-49.9 Million
Emp.: 5
Tire Distr
N.A.I.C.S.: 423130
James Kang *(Gen Mgr)*

Subsidiary (Non-US):

Hankook Tire do Brasil Ltda. (2)
Rua George Ohm 230 - CJ 82 Brooklin, Sao Paulo, 04576-020, Brazil
Tel.: (55) 1130450544
Sales Range: $25-49.9 Million
Emp.: 10
Tire Distr
N.A.I.C.S.: 423130

Hankook Tire Austria GmbH (1)
Concorde Business Park2/F/9, 2320, Schwechat, Austria
Tel.: (43) 17062526
Tire Mfr & Distr
N.A.I.C.S.: 326211

Hankook Tire Budapest Kereskedelmi Kft (1)
IP West Building Budafoki str 91-93, 1117, Budapest, Hungary
Tel.: (36) 14643660
Web Site: https://www.hankooktire.com

HANKOOK TIRE & TECHNOLOGY CO., LTD.

Hankook Tire & Technology Co., Ltd.—(Continued)
Sales Range: $25-49.9 Million
Emp.: 25
Tire Mfr & Distr
N.A.I.C.S.: 326211
Kang Soo (Mgr-Fin)

Hankook Tire Ceska Republika s.r.o. (1)
Jihlavska 1558/21, Michle, 140 00, Prague, Czech Republic
Tel.: (420) 244914901
Tire Mfr & Distr
N.A.I.C.S.: 326211

Hankook Tire Co., Ltd. (1)
Blg 3A Tower Maadi Star Towers Cornich Nile Maadi, Fl 22 Flat left Elevator, Cairo, Egypt
Tel.: (20) 225260010
Tire Mfr & Distr
N.A.I.C.S.: 326211

Hankook Tire Co., Ltd. (1)
PO Box 5922, Jeddah, 21432, Saudi Arabia
Tel.: (966) 126806160
Tire Mfr & Distr
N.A.I.C.S.: 326211

Hankook Tire Co., Ltd. (1)
Office 2407 24F No 333 Keelung Rd Sec 1, Taipei, Taiwan
Tel.: (886) 227577327
Tire Mfr & Distr
N.A.I.C.S.: 326211

Hankook Tire Colombia Ltda. (1)
Calle 100 No 19 -54 Office 301, Bogota, Colombia
Tel.: (57) 17434545
Tire Mfr & Distr
N.A.I.C.S.: 326211

Hankook Tire DE Mexico, S.A. DE C.V (1)
Av Paseo de las Palmas no 735 7 Piso Col Lomas de Chapultepec III, seccion Delegacion Miguel Hidalgo, 11000, Mexico, Mexico
Tel.: (52) 5555351058
Tire Mfr & Distr
N.A.I.C.S.: 326211

Hankook Tire Europe GmbH (1)
Siemensstrasbe 14, 63263, Neu-Isenburg, Germany (100%)
Tel.: (49) 61024318000
Web Site: https://www.hankooktire.com
Sales Range: $50-74.9 Million
Emp.: 40
Tire Mfr & Distr
N.A.I.C.S.: 326211
Han-Jun Kim (Pres)

Subsidiary (Non-US):

Hankook Espana S.A. (2)
Calle Teide 3 3 planta Oficina 3, San Sebastian de los Reyes, 28703, Madrid, Spain
Tel.: (34) 914905088
Web Site: https://www.hankooktire.com
Tires
N.A.I.C.S.: 326211

Subsidiary (Domestic):

Hankook Reifen Deutschland GmbH (2)
Siemensstrasse 14, 63263, Neu-Isenburg, Germany (100%)
Tel.: (49) 61024318000
Web Site: https://www.hankooktire.com
Sales Range: $25-49.9 Million
Emp.: 28
Tire Distr
N.A.I.C.S.: 423130

Subsidiary (Non-US):

Hankook Tire France SARL (2)
Le Patio 35-37 Rue Louis Guerin, 69100, Villeurbanne, France
Tel.: (33) 472697640
Web Site: http://www.hankooktire.com
Emp.: 40
Tire Distr
N.A.I.C.S.: 423130

Hankook Tire Italia S.R.L. (2)
Edison Park Center Edificio A Viale T Edison n 110, Sesto San Giovanni, 20099, San Donato Milanese, Italy
Tel.: (39) 022434161
Sales Range: $50-74.9 Million
Emp.: 33
Tire Distr
N.A.I.C.S.: 423130

Hankook Tyre U.K. Ltd. (2)
Fawsley Drive, Heartlands Business Park, Daventry, NN11 8UG, Northamptonshire, United Kingdom (100%)
Tel.: (44) 1327304100
Web Site: https://www.hankooktire.com
Sales Range: $25-49.9 Million
Emp.: 49
Tire Distr
N.A.I.C.S.: 423130
Chang Yool Han (Mng Dir)

Hankook Tire Japan Corp. (1)
9th Fl Naniwasuji Honmachi Mid Bldg 2-3-2 Utsubo-Honmachi, Nishi-Ku, Osaka, Japan
Tel.: (81) 648038871
Tire Mfr & Distr
N.A.I.C.S.: 326211

Hankook Tire Malaysia SDN. BHD. (1)
32-01 a Premier Suite Menara 1MK Kompleks 1 Mont' Kiara No 1, Jalan Kiara Mont' Kiara, 50480, Kuala Lumpur, Malaysia
Tel.: (60) 362061875
Tire Mfr & Distr
N.A.I.C.S.: 326211

Hankook Tire Middle East & Africa FZE (1)
Office 1607 and 1608 Tower A JAFZA One, Jebel Ali Freezone, Dubai, United Arab Emirates
Tel.: (971) 43321330
Tire Mfr & Distr
N.A.I.C.S.: 326211

Hankook Tire Netherlands B.V (1)
Siriusdreef 35-37, 2132 WT, Hoofddorp, Netherlands
Tel.: (31) 23 554 1550
Web Site: https://www.hankooktire.com
Sales Range: $25-49.9 Million
Emp.: 14
Tire Mfr & Distr
N.A.I.C.S.: 326211

Hankook Tire Panama Ltda. (1)
Oceania Business Plaza Torre 1000 Oficina 18A, Punta Pacifico, Panama, Panama
Tel.: (507) 2633008
Tire Mfr & Distr
N.A.I.C.S.: 326211

Hankook Tire Polska Sp. z o.o. (1)
ul Komitetu Obrony Robotnikow 48, 02-146, Warsaw, Poland
Tel.: (48) 223955885
Tire Mfr & Distr
N.A.I.C.S.: 326211

Hankook Tire Rus LLC (1)
Business Center Alcon 5th floor Bld 1 Leningradsky Prospect 72, 125315, Moscow, Russia
Tel.: (7) 4952680100
Web Site: http://www.hankooktire.com
Sales Range: $25-49.9 Million
Emp.: 21
Rubber Tire Mfr
N.A.I.C.S.: 326211

Hankook Tire Sweden AB (1)
Kanalvagen 12, 194 61, Upplands Vasby, Sweden
Tel.: (46) 101302100
Tire Mfr & Distr
N.A.I.C.S.: 326211

Hankook Tire Thailand Co., Ltd. (1)
No 140 One Pacific Place Building 15 Floor Room 1505-1506 Sukhumvit Rd, Klongtoey, Bangkok, 10110, Thailand
Tel.: (66) 26533790
Tire Mfr & Distr
N.A.I.C.S.: 326211

Hankook Tire Ukraine LLC (1)
Business Center Horizon Park Mykola Hrinchenko Bld 4V, Kiev, 03038, Ukraine
Tel.: (380) 443591420
Tire Mfr & Distr
N.A.I.C.S.: 326211

Hankook Tire Vietnam Co., Ltd. (1)
Unit 605 6th Floor Center Point Building 106 Nguyen Van Troi, Ward 8 Phu Nhuan District, Ho Chi Minh City, Vietnam
Tel.: (84) 2862730103
Tire Mfr & Distr
N.A.I.C.S.: 326211

Hankook Tire d.o.o (1)
Milentija Popovica 5v 7th Floor app 24, 11070, Novi Beograd, Serbia
Tel.: (381) 117455291
Tire Mfr & Distr
N.A.I.C.S.: 326211

Hankook Tires India LLP (1)
The Unit Number 703 705 Palm Spring Plaza Golf Course Road Sector-54, Gurgaon, Haryana, India
Tel.: (91) 1244758040
Tire Mfr & Distr
N.A.I.C.S.: 326211

Hankook Tyre Australia Pty. Ltd. (1)
Building A Level 3 11 Talavera Road, Macquarie Park, 2113, NSW, Australia (100%)
Tel.: (61) 298701200
Web Site: https://www.hankooktire.com.au
Sales Range: $25-49.9 Million
Emp.: 20
Tire Distr
N.A.I.C.S.: 423130
Pauo Park (CEO)

PT. Hankook Tire Sales Indonesia (1)
Jl Sultan Iskandar Muda Gandaria 8 Office tower 22nd Floor, Kebayoran Lama, Jakarta Selatan, 12240, Jakarta, Indonesia
Tel.: (62) 2129303860
Tire Mfr & Distr
N.A.I.C.S.: 326211

HANKUK CARBON CO., LTD.
85 Chunhwa-ro Bubuk-myeon, Bubuk-myeon, Miryang, Gyeongsangnam-do, Korea (South)
Tel.: (82) 553508888
Web Site: https://www.hcarbon.com
Year Founded: 1984
017960—(KRS)
Rev.: $283,230,754
Assets: $448,950,898
Liabilities: $138,954,169
Net Worth: $309,996,729
Earnings: $15,540,088
Emp.: 492
Fiscal Year-end: 12/31/22
Electronic Board Mfr
N.A.I.C.S.: 334418
Moon-Soo Jo (Co-CEO)

Subsidiaries:

HANKUK CARBON Co., Ltd. Hamyang Plant (1)
100 Saneopdanji-ro, Sudong, Gyeongsangdo, Korea (South)
Tel.: (82) 55 964 1551
Electronic Board Mfr
N.A.I.C.S.: 334418

Hankuk Advanced Materials Co., Ltd. (1)
85 Chunhwa-ro, Bubuk-myeon, Miryang, Kyungsangnam-do, Korea (South)
Tel.: (82) 55 350 8888
Web Site: https://www.hamaterials.com
Carbon Fabric Mfr
N.A.I.C.S.: 314999

Korea Composites Inc. (1)
1317-21 Seosam-ro Chukdong-myeon, Sacheon, 52509, Gyeongsangnam, Korea (South)
Tel.: (82) 558502700
Web Site: https://kci.so
Aircraft Part Mfr
N.A.I.C.S.: 336413

HANKUK GLASS INDUSTRIES INC.
10F 211 Teheran-ro, Gangnam-gu, Seoul, Korea (South)
Tel.: (82) 2 3706 9114
Web Site: http://www.hanglas.co.kr
Year Founded: 1957
Rev.: $324,700,838
Assets: $801,699,959
Liabilities: $134,108,603
Net Worth: $667,591,356
Earnings: $131,077,407
Emp.: 300
Fiscal Year-end: 12/31/17
Glass Products Mfr
N.A.I.C.S.: 327211
Yong-seong Lee (CEO)

HANKUK PACKAGE CO., LTD.
17 Haesung Building 504 Teheran-ro, Gangnam-gu, Seoul, 06178, Gyeonggi-do, Korea (South)
Tel.: (82) 25658600
Web Site: https://www.hkpak.co.kr
Year Founded: 1993
037230—(KRS)
Rev.: $166,683,897
Assets: $142,317,375
Liabilities: $90,883,965
Net Worth: $51,433,411
Earnings: ($8,132,308)
Emp.: 350
Fiscal Year-end: 12/31/22
Milk Packaging Services
N.A.I.C.S.: 322130
Jinwoo Jung (CEO)

HANKUK STEEL WIRE CO., LTD.
Sinpyeong-dong 27 Hasinbeonyeongro, Saha-gu, Busan, Korea (South)
Tel.: (82) 512004400
Web Site: http://www.ehansun.co.kr
Year Founded: 1990
025550—(KRS)
Rev.: $188,287,425
Assets: $195,477,391
Liabilities: $105,526,060
Net Worth: $89,951,331
Earnings: $11,477,947
Emp.: 191
Fiscal Year-end: 12/31/22
Steel Pole Mfr
N.A.I.C.S.: 331110
Jye Hoon Lee (Co-Chm & CEO)

HANKYU HANSHIN HOLDINGS INC.
1-16-1 Shibata, Kita-ku, Osaka, 530-0012, Japan
Tel.: (81) 663735001   JP
Web Site: https://www.hankyu-hanshin.co.jp
Year Founded: 2006
9042—(TKS)
Rev.: $6,594,208,710
Assets: $20,179,867,300
Liabilities: $13,104,311,780
Net Worth: $7,075,555,520
Earnings: $448,164,610
Fiscal Year-end: 03/31/24
Holding Company
N.A.I.C.S.: 551112
Kazuo Sumi (Chm, Chm & CEO/CEO-Grp)

Subsidiaries:

Alna Sharyo Co., Ltd. (1)
1-2 Hankyu shojaku, Settsu, 566-0013, Osaka, Japan
Tel.: (81) 663831811
Web Site: https://alna-sharyo.co.jp
Railroad Equipment Mfr
N.A.I.C.S.: 336510

Bay Communications Inc. (1)
4th floor Hanshin Noda Center Building 1-1-31 Ebie, Fukushima-ku, Osaka, 553-0001, Japan
Tel.: (81) 664501173
Web Site: https://www.baycom.jp
Cable & Pay Television Services
N.A.I.C.S.: 516210

AND PRIVATE COMPANIES — HANKYU HANSHIN HOLDINGS INC.

Eki Retail Service Hankyu Hanshin Co., Ltd. (1)
1-16-1 Shibata, Kita-ku, Osaka, 530-0012, Japan
Tel.: (81) 663735346
Web Site: http://www.ers.hankyu-hanshin.co.jp
Food Product Retailer
N.A.I.C.S.: 445110

HHE (Deutschland) GmbH (1)
Cargo City Sued Geb 570, 60549, Frankfurt am Main, Germany
Tel.: (49) 699686410
Logistic Services
N.A.I.C.S.: 488510

HHE (USA) Inc. (1)
989 AEC Dr, Wood Dale, IL 60191
Tel.: (630) 285-7100
Transportation & Logistics Services
N.A.I.C.S.: 541614

Hankyu Corporation (1)
1 16 1 Shibata, Kita Ku, Osaka, 530 8389, Japan
Tel.: (81) 663735085
Web Site: http://www.hankyu.co.jp
Sales Range: $1-4.9 Billion
Emp.: 13,500
Passenger Railway Operator & Real Estate Developer
N.A.I.C.S.: 485112

Subsidiary (Domestic):

Hankyu Advertising Agency Inc. (2)
1-4-8 Shibata 9th floor Kita Hankyu Building, Kita-ku, Osaka, 530-0012, Japan
Tel.: (81) 663736801
Web Site: https://www.hankyu-ad.jp
Emp.: 94
Advertising Agency Services
N.A.I.C.S.: 541810

Hankyu Bus Co., Ltd. (2)
5-1-24 Shonainishimachi Toyonaka, Osaka, 561-8461, Japan
Tel.: (81) 668663112
Web Site: http://www.bus.hankyu.co.jp
Food Transportation Services
N.A.I.C.S.: 488490
Manami Ishikawa (Mgr-Sls)

Hankyu Business Associate Co., Ltd. (2)
1-16-1 Shibata, Kita-ku, Osaka, 530-0012, Japan
Tel.: (81) 663735185
Web Site: https://www.hhba.hankyu-hanshin.co.jp
Sales Range: $100-124.9 Million
Emp.: 260
Data Processing Hosting Services
N.A.I.C.S.: 518210

Hankyu Community Service Co., Ltd. (2)
Hankyu Terminal Building 15th Floor, Osaka, Japan
Tel.: (81) 663736315
Building Inspection Services
N.A.I.C.S.: 541350

Hankyu Facilities Co., Ltd. (2)
Hankyu Terminal Bldg 15th Fl, Osaka, Japan
Tel.: (81) 663736300
Real Estate Agents & Brokers
N.A.I.C.S.: 531210

Subsidiary (Non-US):

Hankyu International Transport (Deutschland) GmbH (2)
Im Taubengrund 35, 65451, Kelsterbach, Germany
Tel.: (49) 610776070
Web Site: http://www.hankyu.com
Sales Range: $25-49.9 Million
Emp.: 50
Local Freight Trucking
N.A.I.C.S.: 484110

Hankyu International Transport (Netherlands) B.V. (2)
Prestwickweg 2, 1118 LB, Schiphol, Netherlands
Tel.: (31) 205005300
Web Site: http://www.eu-hh-express.com
Sales Range: $25-49.9 Million
Emp.: 30
Freight Transportation Arrangement
N.A.I.C.S.: 488510

Hankyu International Transport (Taiwan) Ltd. (2)
14F No 37 Sec 3 Minquan East Road, Zhongshan District, Taipei, 104, Taiwan
Tel.: (886) 225063232
Web Site: http://www.hankyu.com.tw
Marine Cargo Handling
N.A.I.C.S.: 488320

Subsidiary (Domestic):

Hankyu Investment Partners, Inc. (2)
Tamura Koma Bldg 5th Fl, Osaka, Japan
Tel.: (81) 662668955
Web Site: http://www.hankyu-ip.com
Financial Investment
N.A.I.C.S.: 523999
Kazuo Sumi (Pres)

Hankyu REIT, Inc. (2)
19-19 Chayamachi Kita-ku, Osaka, 5300013, Japan
Tel.: (81) 663766821
Web Site: http://www.hankyu-reit.jp
Sales Range: $50-74.9 Million
Emp.: 23
Real Estate Investment Trust
N.A.I.C.S.: 525990
Tamio Uda (Dir-Supervisory)

Hankyu Realty Co., Ltd. (2)
Hankyu Terminal Bldg 1-1-4 Shibata, ku, Osaka, Japan
Tel.: (81) 663133340
Web Site: https://hhp-en.com
Sales Range: $150-199.9 Million
Emp.: 900
Nonresidential Buildings Lessors
N.A.I.C.S.: 531120

Hankyu Taxi Inc. (2)
1-9-10 Airport, Ikeda, 563-0034, Osaka, Japan
Tel.: (81) 661527450
Web Site: https://www.hankyu-taxi.co.jp
Sales Range: $400-449.9 Million
Emp.: 1,200
Taxi Service
N.A.I.C.S.: 485310

Hankyu Travel Support Co., Ltd. (2)
2-5-25 Umeda, Kita-ku, Osaka, 530-0001, Japan
Tel.: (81) 647955740
Web Site: https://www.hts-net.co.jp
Sales Range: $25-49.9 Million
Emp.: 1,180
Travel Agencies
N.A.I.C.S.: 561510

Iina Dining Co., Ltd. (2)
3-7-36 Jusohonmachi 13th Building 2nd floor, Yodogawa-ku, Osaka, 532-0024, Japan
Tel.: (81) 663071391
Web Site: http://www.iina-dining.co.jp
Sales Range: $75-99.9 Million
Emp.: 750
Food Mfr
N.A.I.C.S.: 311999

Takarazuka Creative Arts Co., Ltd. (2)
1-1-57 Sakaemachi, Takarazuka, 665-0845, Hyogo, Japan (100%)
Tel.: (81) 797836000
Web Site: http://www.tca-pictures.net
Emp.: 136
Musical, Television & Magazine Production & Distribution
N.A.I.C.S.: 512250
Kenji Takada (Pres)

Takarazuka Stage Co., Ltd. (2)
1-1-57 Sakaemachi, Takarazuka, 665-0845, Hyogo, Japan
Tel.: (81) 797856230
Web Site: https://www.takarazuka-butai.co.jp
Emp.: 449
Motion Picture Theaters Not Drive-Ins
N.A.I.C.S.: 512131

Hankyu Hanshin Clean Service Co., Ltd. (1)
1-12-39 Umeda Shinhankyu Bldg 7f, Kita-Ku, Osaka, 530-0001, Japan
Tel.: (81) 663439057
Business Support Services
N.A.I.C.S.: 561499

Hankyu Hanshin Express Co., Ltd. (1)
9th floor Herbis Osaka 2-5-25, Umeda Kita-ku, Osaka, 530-0001, Japan
Tel.: (81) 647955811
Web Site: https://www.hh-express.com
Sales Range: $1-4.9 Billion
Emp.: 3,475
Transportation & Logistics Services
N.A.I.C.S.: 488999
Seisaku Okafuji (Chm & CEO)

Subsidiary (US):

Hankyu Hanshin Express (USA) Inc. (2)
1561 Beachey Pl, Carson, CA 90746-4005
Tel.: (310) 884-2400
Web Site: https://www.hhe-global.com
Freight Transportation Arrangement
N.A.I.C.S.: 488510

Hankyu Hanshin Express Southeast Asia Pte. Ltd. (1)
01-10 Changi Cargo Agents Megaplex 1 119 Airport Cargo Road, Singapore, 918104, Singapore
Tel.: (65) 64223808
Logistics Transportation Services
N.A.I.C.S.: 488510

Hankyu Hanshin Financial Support Co., Ltd. (1)
1-16-1 Shibata, Kita-Ku, Osaka, 530-0012, Japan
Tel.: (81) 663735067
Financial Management Services
N.A.I.C.S.: 523999

Hankyu Hanshin Hotels Co., Ltd. (1)
1-1-35 Shibata, Kita-ku, Osaka, 530-8310, Japan
Tel.: (81) 663725231
Sales Range: $500-549.9 Million
Emp.: 2,000
Hotel Services
N.A.I.C.S.: 721110

Subsidiary (Domestic):

Amanohashidate Hotel Co., Ltd. (2)
310 Monju, Miyazu, 626-0001, Kyoto, Japan
Tel.: (81) 772224111
Web Site: https://www.amanohashidate-htl.co.jp
Sales Range: $10-24.9 Million
Emp.: 100
Hotels & Motels
N.A.I.C.S.: 721110

Arima View Hotel Co., Ltd. (2)
Arima-cho ikenoziri 292-2, Kitaku, Kobe, 651-1401, Hyogo, Japan
Tel.: (81) 789042295
Web Site: http://www.arima-view.com
Emp.: 100
Hotels & Motels
N.A.I.C.S.: 721110

Hankyu Hanshin Restaurants Co., Ltd. (2)
Chayamachi 19-19 Kita-ku, Kita-Ku, Osaka, 530-0013, Japan
Tel.: (81) 664852660
Restaurant Operating Services
N.A.I.C.S.: 722511

Hanshin Hotel Systems Co., Ltd. (2)
2-5-25 Umeda, Kita-Ku, Osaka, 530-0001, Japan
Tel.: (81) 663437000
Web Site: http://www.ritz-carlton.co.jp
Emp.: 500
Restaurant Operating Services
N.A.I.C.S.: 722511
Hiroyuki Hashimoto (Pres)

Hotel New Hankyu Kochi Co., Ltd. (2)
4-2-50 Honmachi, Kochi, 780-8561, Japan
Tel.: (81) 888731111
Web Site: http://www.crownpalais.jp
Emp.: 100

Hotels & Motels
N.A.I.C.S.: 721110
Yamasaki Lkumichiuo (Pres)

Hankyu Hanshin Marketing Solutions Inc. (1)
Umeda Center Bldg 26F 2-4-12 Nakazaki-Nishi, Kita-ku, Osaka, 530-0015, Japan
Tel.: (81) 663736801
Web Site: https://www.hhms.co.jp
Emp.: 290
Advertising Services
N.A.I.C.S.: 541810
Yoshiaki Miyake (Chm)

Hankyu Hanshin Security Service Co., Ltd. (1)
1-12-39 Umeda Shinhankyu Bldg 12f, Kita-Ku, Osaka, 530-0001, Japan
Tel.: (81) 663439059
Security System Services
N.A.I.C.S.: 561621

Hankyu Hanshin Techno Service Co., Ltd. (1)
1-12-39 Umeda Shinhankyu Bldg 12f, Kita-Ku, Osaka, 530-0001, Japan
Tel.: (81) 663439173
Business Support Services
N.A.I.C.S.: 561499

Hankyu Kanko Bus Co., Ltd. (1)
7-7-19 Nakatsu, Kita-ku, Osaka, 531-0071, Japan
Tel.: (81) 664587101
Web Site: http://www.hankyu.k-bus.co.jp
Bus Rental Services
N.A.I.C.S.: 532120

Hankyu Retails Corporation (1)
1-16-1 Shibata, Kita-Ku, Osaka, 530-0012, Japan
Tel.: (81) 663735342
Web Site: http://www.hankyu-retails.co.jp
Emp.: 200
Convenience Store Operating Retailer
N.A.I.C.S.: 445131
Sakira Bara (Mgr)

Hankyu Sekkei Consultant Co., Ltd. (1)
4th Floor Kitahankyu Building 1-4-8 Shibata, Kita-ku, Osaka, 530-0012, Japan
Tel.: (81) 663592752
Web Site: http://www.sekkei.hankyu.co.jp
Railway Construction Services
N.A.I.C.S.: 237990

Hanshin Bus Co., Ltd. (1)
108-1 Oshokawata-cho, Amagasaki, 660-0072, Hyogo, Japan
Tel.: (81) 664161351
Web Site: http://www.hanshin-bus.co.jp
Emp.: 539
Passenger Bus Rental Services
N.A.I.C.S.: 532120

Hanshin Contents Link Corporation (1)
Hanshin Noda Center Building 10F 1-1-31 Ebie, Fukushima-ku, Osaka, 553-0001, Japan
Tel.: (81) 6 6347 6514
Web Site: http://www.hcl-c.com
Music Entertainment Services
N.A.I.C.S.: 711320
Masato Kitaguchi (Pres & CEO)

Hanshin Electric Railway Co., Ltd. (1)
1-1-24 Ebie, Fukushima-ku, Osaka, 553-8553, Japan
Tel.: (81) 664572123
Emp.: 1,500
Passenger Railway & Bus Services; Residential & Commercial Property Development; Stadium & Tourist Attraction Operator; Travel Services
N.A.I.C.S.: 561599

Subsidiary (Domestic):

Chuo Densetsu Co., Ltd. (2)
1-1-31 Ebie, Fukushima-Ku, Osaka, 553-0001, Japan (75%)
Tel.: (81) 664538720
Web Site: https://www.cde.co.jp
Emp.: 253
Construction Equipment Whslr
N.A.I.C.S.: 423390

HANKYU HANSHIN HOLDINGS INC.

Hankyu Hanshin Holdings Inc.—(Continued)

Hanshin Tigers Baseball Club (2)
2-33 Koshiencho, Nishinomiya, 663-8152, Hyogo, Japan
Tel.: (81) 798488455
Web Site: https://hanshintigers.jp
Professional Basketball Team
N.A.I.C.S.: 711211

Hanshin Real Estate Co., Ltd. (1)
1-1-31 Ebie Hanshin Noda Center Bldg 17f, Fukushima-Ku, Osaka, 553-0001, Japan (100%)
Tel.: (81) 6 4798 7601
Web Site: http://www.hanshin.co.jp
Real Estate Manangement Services
N.A.I.C.S.: 531390

Hanshin Taxi Co., Ltd. (1)
1-12 1-1 Naruohama, Nishinomiya, 663-8142, Hyogo, Japan
Tel.: (81) 798466023
Web Site: https://www.hanshin-taxi.co.jp
Emp.: 450
Taxi Service
N.A.I.C.S.: 485310

High Security System Co., Ltd. (1)
5-6-16 Fukushima Hanshinsugimura Bldg Minamito 5f, Fukushima-Ku, Osaka, 553-0003, Japan
Tel.: (81) 669407068
Security System Services
N.A.I.C.S.: 561621

Hokushinkyuko Railway Co., Ltd. (1)
27 Ohashi Shitani, Yamada-cho Kita-ku, Kobe, 651-1243, Japan
Tel.: (81) 78 581 1070
Web Site: http://www.hokushinkyuko.co.jp
Emp.: 64
Rail Transportation Services
N.A.I.C.S.: 488210
Hideshiko Tatsuma (Pres)

Itec Hankyu Hanshin Co., Ltd. (1)
Hanshin Noda Center Building 1-1-31 Ebie, Fukushima-Ku, Osaka, 553-0001, Japan
Tel.: (81) 664565200
Web Site: https://www.itec.hankyu-hanshin.co.jp
Emp.: 1,219
Information Technology Consulting Services
N.A.I.C.S.: 541512

Kita-Osaka Kyuko Railway Co., Ltd. (1)
2-4-1 Terauchi, Toyonaka, 561-0872, Osaka, Japan
Tel.: (81) 668650601
Web Site: http://www.kita-kyu.co.jp
Rail Transportation Services
N.A.I.C.S.: 488210

Nose Electric Railway Co., Ltd. (1)
Hirano 1-chome 35th number 2, Kawanishi, 666-0121, Hyogo, Japan
Tel.: (81) 727927200
Web Site: http://www.noseden.hankyu.co.jp
Emp.: 116
Electric Rail Transportation Services
N.A.I.C.S.: 488210
Masakazu Jonan (Pres)

Osaka Diamond Chikagai Co., Ltd. (1)
1-chome Umeda Diamond Underground Street No 1, Kita-Ku, Osaka, 530-0001, Japan
Tel.: (81) 663488931
Web Site: http://www.diamor.jp
Real Estate Manangement Services
N.A.I.C.S.: 531390

Sanyo Jidosha Unso Co., Ltd. (1)
3-1-22 Nishikonoike-cho, Higashiosaka, 578-0976, Osaka, Japan
Tel.: (81) 643090526
Web Site: http://www.sanyoju.co.jp
Emp.: 729
Logistics Consulting Servies
N.A.I.C.S.: 541614

Umeda Arts Theater Co., Ltd. (1)
Hankyu Chayamachi Building 19-1 Chayamachi, Kita-ku, Osaka, 530-0013, Japan
Tel.: (81) 663773800
Web Site: https://www.umegei.com

Theater Operating Services
N.A.I.C.S.: 512131

Wellness Hanshin Inc. (1)
17-28 Koshien 7bancho B107, Nishinomiya, 663-8177, Hyogo, Japan
Tel.: (81) 798 40 5070
Web Site: http://www.wellness-h.com
Fitness Club Services
N.A.I.C.S.: 713940

HANLA IMS CO., LTD.
115 Hwajeonsanda 1 Il-ro, Ganseo-gu, Busan, Korea (South)
Tel.: (82) 516017000
Web Site: https://www.hanlaims.com
Year Founded: 1989
092460—(KRS)
Rev.: $75,654,668
Assets: $137,182,243
Liabilities: $62,654,384
Net Worth: $74,527,859
Earnings: $6,187,968
Emp.: 197
Fiscal Year-end: 12/31/22
Monitoring Device Mfr
N.A.I.C.S.: 334519
Seok Jun Ji (Co-CEO)

Subsidiaries:

Hanla M&E Co., Ltd. (1)
Room 711 OuYin Business B/D No 1369 Wuzhong Road, Shanghai, 201103, China
Tel.: (86) 2154843251
Measuring Equipment Distr
N.A.I.C.S.: 423830

HANLEY ECONOMIC BUILDING SOCIETY
Hanley Economic Building Society Granville House Forge Lane, Stoke-on-Trent, ST1 5TB, United Kingdom
Tel.: (44) 1782 255000
Web Site: http://www.thehanley.co.uk
Rev.: $12,763,180
Assets: $586,251,098
Liabilities: $549,452,849
Net Worth: $36,798,250
Earnings: $918,120
Emp.: 57
Fiscal Year-end: 08/31/19
Mortgage Lending & Other Financial Services
N.A.I.C.S.: 522310
David Lownds (Head-Sls, Mktg & Bus Dev)

HANMA TECHNOLOGY GROUP CO., LTD.
Economic & Technological Development Zone, Ma'anshan, 243061, Anhui, China
Tel.: (86) 5558323386
Web Site: https://www.camc-global.com
Year Founded: 1970
600375—(SHG)
Rev.: $481,417,392
Assets: $1,363,695,372
Liabilities: $1,331,416,233
Net Worth: $32,279,139
Earnings: ($205,883,459)
Emp.: 4,000
Fiscal Year-end: 12/31/22
Automobile Parts Mfr
N.A.I.C.S.: 336211

HANMAN FIT LIMITED
702 Concord CHS No 10 N S Road, JVPD Scheme Juhu Circule Vile Parle West, Mumbai, 400056, Maharashtra, India
Tel.: (91) 222 671 4225
538731—(BOM)
Rev.: $82,618
Assets: $774,239
Liabilities: $438,456
Net Worth: $335,783

Earnings: ($248,779)
Fiscal Year-end: 03/31/21
Fitness Facilities Operator
N.A.I.C.S.: 713940
Ankush Gupta (CEO)

HANMI PHARMACEUTICAL CO., LTD.
14 Wiryeseong-daero, Songpa-gu, 05545, Seoul, 05545, Korea (South)
Tel.: (82) 24109114   KR
Web Site: https://www.hanmipharm.com
Year Founded: 1973
128940—(KRS)
Rev.: $1,021,296,242
Assets: $1,476,157,256
Liabilities: $702,080,390
Net Worth: $774,076,865
Earnings: $77,895,134
Emp.: 2,297
Fiscal Year-end: 12/31/22
Pharmaceutical Products Mfr & Sales
N.A.I.C.S.: 325412
Sung-Ki Lim (Founder)

Subsidiaries:

Beijing Hanmi Pharmaceutical Co., Ltd. (1)
No 10 Tianzhu West Road, Tianzhu Airport Industrial Zone A Shunyi District, Beijing, 101312, China
Tel.: (86) 80429898
Web Site: http://www.bjhanmi.com.cn
Pharmaceutical Products Distr
N.A.I.C.S.: 424210
Hanmi Pharm. (Pres)

Hanmi Fine Chemical Co., Ltd (1)
57 Gyeongje-ro, Siheung, 429-848, Gyeonggi-do, Korea (South)
Tel.: (82) 314992541
Web Site: http://www.hanmifc.co.kr
Emp.: 20
Active Pharmaceutical Ingredients Mfr
N.A.I.C.S.: 325412
Dae Chul Yoon (CEO)

Hanmi IT Co., Ltd. (1)
45 Bangi Dong Hanmi Tower 6th Floor, SongPaGu, Seoul, 138-724, Korea (South)
Tel.: (82) 2 410 0573
Web Site: http://www.hanmiit.net
Sales Range: $25-49.9 Million
Emp.: 100
Information Technology Consulting Services
N.A.I.C.S.: 541512
Jung Hoon Lee (CEO)

Hanmi Japan Pharmaceutical Co., Ltd (1)
Aspa Nihonbashi Office Nihonbashi-Hongoku-cho 2-1-1, Chuo-ku, Tokyo, 103-0021, Japan
Tel.: (81) 8033556790
Pharmaceuticals Product Mfr
N.A.I.C.S.: 325412

HANMI SCIENCE CO., LTD.
14 Wiryeseong-daero, Songpa-gu, Seoul, Korea (South)
Tel.: (82) 24109114
Web Site: https://hanmi.co.kr
Year Founded: 1973
008930—(KRS)
Rev.: $802,323,580
Assets: $851,132,947
Liabilities: $295,251,254
Net Worth: $555,881,693
Earnings: $53,083,747
Emp.: 428
Fiscal Year-end: 12/31/22
Holding Company
N.A.I.C.S.: 551112
Jong Su Woo (Pres)

HANMI SEMICONDUCTOR CO., LTD.
14 Gajwa-ro 30 Beon-gil, Seo-gu, Incheon, Korea (South)
Tel.: (82) 325719100

INTERNATIONAL PUBLIC

Web Site: https://www.hanmisemi.com
Year Founded: 1980
042700—(KRS)
Rev.: $251,263,109
Assets: $349,317,085
Liabilities: $50,112,873
Net Worth: $299,204,212
Earnings: $70,762,850
Emp.: 643
Fiscal Year-end: 12/31/22
Semiconductor Equipment Mfr
N.A.I.C.S.: 334413
Noh-Kwon Kwak (Founder & Chm)

Subsidiaries:

Nanotec International GmbH (1)
Kreuzhofstr 10, 81476, Munich, Germany
Tel.: (49) 897557322
Web Site: https://www.nanotec-gmbh.de
Sales Range: $25-49.9 Million
Emp.: 4
Semiconductor Mfr
N.A.I.C.S.: 334413

PTS Progressive Engineering Co., Ltd. (1)
55/77-79 Soi Ngamwongwan 32 Toongsonghong, Laksi, Bangkok, 10210, Thailand
Tel.: (66) 25803997
Web Site: https://www.ptsprogressive.com
Sales Range: $25-49.9 Million
Emp.: 60
Semiconductor Equipments Mfr & Distr
N.A.I.C.S.: 334413

Premtek International Inc. (1)
4F No 47 Ln 2 Kuang-Fu Rd Sec 2, Hsin-chu, Taiwan
Tel.: (886) 35722000
Web Site: http://www.premtek.com.tw
Sales Range: $50-74.9 Million
Emp.: 70
Semiconductor Equipment Distr
N.A.I.C.S.: 423690
Danny Huang (CEO)

Prime e-Tech International Pte. Ltd. (1)
3 Lorong Bakar Batu 07-02 Union Industrial Center, Singapore, 348741, Singapore
Tel.: (65) 67873132
Web Site: https://www.ptisemi.com
Emp.: 10
Semiconductor Materials Mfr & Distr
N.A.I.C.S.: 423690

RNM Dynamics (Phils) Inc. (1)
Unit 7 Fl Richville Corporate Tower Madrigal Bus Park, Alabang, Muntinlupa, 1780, Philippines
Tel.: (63) 28427545
Web Site: http://www.rnmdynamics.com
Sales Range: $25-49.9 Million
Emp.: 35
Semiconductor Materials Mfr & Distr
N.A.I.C.S.: 423690
Ferdinand G. Bercenio (Founder & Pres)

Tek India (1)
310 Manish Chambers Sonawala Rd Goregaon E, Mumbai, 400 063, Maharashtra, India
Tel.: (91) 2226850069
Sales Range: $25-49.9 Million
Emp.: 6
Semiconductor Equipments Mfr & Distr
N.A.I.C.S.: 334413

Division (Domestic):

Tek India - Productronics (2)
No 17 Dalvi Bldg Aarey Road Goregaon East, Mumbai, 400063, Maharashtra, India
Tel.: (91) 8108375236
Web Site: http://www.productronics.in
Sales Range: $25-49.9 Million
Emp.: 6
Electric Equipment Mfr
N.A.I.C.S.: 336320

HANMIGLOBAL CO., LTD.
9F / 11F City Airport Tower Building 36 Teheran-ro 87-gil, Gangnam-gu, Seoul, 6164, Korea (South)
Tel.: (82) 234296300

AND PRIVATE COMPANIES

HANNSTAR DISPLAY CORPORATION

Web Site: https://www.hmglobal.com
Year Founded: 1996
053690—(KRS)
Rev.: $287,175,786
Assets: $286,136,759
Liabilities: $136,842,190
Net Worth: $149,294,568
Earnings: $20,650,653
Emp.: 1,013
Fiscal Year-end: 12/31/22
Construction Engineering Services
N.A.I.C.S.: 237990

Subsidiaries:

Ecosian Co., Ltd. (1)
8th floor 1st Baeksang Star Tower 65 Digital 9-gi, Geumcheon-gu, Seoul, 8511, Korea (South)
Tel.: (82) 226219800
Web Site: https://www.ecosian.com
Building Design Services
N.A.I.C.S.: 541310

HanmiGlobal Construction Consulting (Shanghai) Co., Ltd. (1)
Room 2602 Building B The Place No 100 Zunyi Road, Shanghai, 200051, China
Tel.: (86) 2163858713
Construction Services
N.A.I.C.S.: 236220

HanmiGlobal Consulting (Shanghai) Co., Ltd. (1)
Room 803 Shanghai Square No 138Â Huai-hai Road Middle, Shanghai, 200021, China
Tel.: (86) 21 6385 8713
Construction Engineering Services
N.A.I.C.S.: 541330

HanmiGlobal India Private Ltd. (1)
208 2nd Fl Worldmark 1 Asset 11 Aerocity NH-8, New Delhi, 110 037, India
Tel.: (91) 9650865553
Construction Services
N.A.I.C.S.: 236220

HanmiGlobal Saudi (LLC) (1)
Tel.: (966) 112938267
Construction Engineering Services
N.A.I.C.S.: 541330

HanmiGlobal UK Limited (1)
Peterbridge House 3 The Lagkes, Northampton, NN4 7HB, Northamptonshire, United Kingdom
Tel.: (44) 1293555545
Construction Services
N.A.I.C.S.: 236220

HanmiGlobal Vietnam Co., Ltd. (1)
173 / 36/ 12D1 Duong Quang Ham P 5 Q, Go Vap, Ho Chi Minh City, Vietnam
Tel.: (84) 98 9964 460
Construction Engineering Services
N.A.I.C.S.: 541330

K2 Consultancy Group Limited (1)
4th Floor 7 Holyrood Street, London, SE1 2EL, United Kingdom
Tel.: (44) 1293555545
Web Site: https://www.k2consultancy.com
Management Consultancy Services
N.A.I.C.S.: 541611

OTAK JAPAN Inc. (1)
4F Kato Building Shiba-daimon 2-9-14, Minato-ku, Tokyo, 105-0012, Japan
Tel.: (81) 364590728
Web Site: https://www.otakjapan.co.jp
Construction Management Services
N.A.I.C.S.: 236220

Tarr Whitman Group, LLC (1)
11241 Willows Rd NE Ste 200, Redmond, WA 98052
Tel.: (425) 822-4446
Construction Services
N.A.I.C.S.: 236220

HANNA CAPITAL CORP.
1800-130 King St, Toronto, M5X 1E3, ON, Canada
Tel.: (416) 945-6630   NV
Web Site: http://hannacapitalcorp.com
Year Founded: 2004
A2PTXY—(DEU)
Assets: $1,011,056
Liabilities: $171,049
Net Worth: $840,007
Earnings: $55,946
Fiscal Year-end: 06/30/22
Metal Mineral Mining Services
N.A.I.C.S.: 212290
Herbert M. Brugh *(Pres & CEO)*

HANNAN METALS LTD.
1305 - 1090 West Georgia Street, Vancouver, V6E 3V7, BC, Canada
Tel.: (604) 699-0202
Web Site: https://www.hannanmetals.com
Year Founded: 2017
C8MQ—(DEU)
Rev.: $62,282
Assets: $8,551,843
Liabilities: $254,068
Net Worth: $8,297,775
Earnings: ($1,245,693)
Fiscal Year-end: 05/31/23
Mineral Exploration Services
N.A.I.C.S.: 213114
Lars Dahlenborg *(Pres)*

HANNANS LIMITED
Level 11 London House 216 St Georges Tce, Perth, 6000, WA, Australia
Tel.: (61) 893243388   AU
Web Site: http://www.hannansreward.com
RIL—(ASX)
Rev.: $127,046
Assets: $9,959,209
Liabilities: $77,301
Net Worth: $9,881,908
Earnings: ($1,637,175)
Fiscal Year-end: 06/30/24
Gold & Base Metal Exploration Services
N.A.I.C.S.: 213114
Damian Hicks *(Co-Founder)*

HANNET CO., LTD.
281 Dongmak-ro, Mapo-ku, Seoul, Korea (South)
Tel.: (82) 221256000
Web Site: https://www.hannet.net
Year Founded: 1997
052600—(KRS)
Rev.: $16,845,065
Assets: $36,979,358
Liabilities: $9,523,240
Net Worth: $27,456,118
Earnings: $1,505,067
Emp.: 81
Fiscal Year-end: 12/31/22
Value-Added Network Services
N.A.I.C.S.: 541990
Seon-Jong Kim *(Board of Directors & CEO)*

HANNING & KAHL GMBH & CO KG
Rudolf-Diesel-Strasse 6, Oerlinghausen, 33813, Germany
Tel.: (49) 5202707600
Web Site: http://www.hanning-kahl.com
Year Founded: 1898
Rev.: $62,073,000
Emp.: 350
Rail Technology Equipments Mfr
N.A.I.C.S.: 488210
Andreas Reschke *(Mng Dir)*

Subsidiaries:

HANNING & KAHL L.P. (1)
114 DeKalb St Unit C, Bridgeport, PA 19405
Tel.: (610) 239-1620
Rail Equipment Distr
N.A.I.C.S.: 423510

HANNO WERK GMBH & CO. KG
Hanno-Ring 3-5, 30880, Laatzen, Germany
Tel.: (49) 510270000
Web Site: http://www.hanno.com
Year Founded: 1895
Rev.: $28,421,616
Emp.: 150
Sealing & Insulating Services
N.A.I.C.S.: 423840
Reinhard Vogelei *(Mgr-Works)*

HANNONG CHEMICALS INC
587 Soryong-dong, Gunsan, 573-400, Jeollabuk-do, Korea (South)
Tel.: (82) 634626018
Web Site: https://www.hannong.co.kr
Year Founded: 1976
011500—(KRS)
Rev.: $183,645,026
Assets: $172,893,445
Liabilities: $55,856,090
Net Worth: $117,037,355
Earnings: $6,574,127
Emp.: 208
Fiscal Year-end: 12/31/22
Surfactants & Other Chemical Related Services
N.A.I.C.S.: 325199
Eung Sang Kim *(CEO)*

HANNOVER FINANZ GMBH
Gunther Wagner Allee 13, 30177, Hannover, Germany
Tel.: (49) 511280070   De
Web Site: https://www.hannoverfinanz.de
Year Founded: 1979
Privater Equity Firm
N.A.I.C.S.: 523999
Steffen Frenzel *(Partner-Accounting)*

Subsidiaries:

FMW Industrieanlagenbau GmbH (1)
Kirchstetten 100, 3062, Saint Polten, Austria   **(67.96%)**
Tel.: (43) 274382450
Web Site: http://www.fmw.co.at
Sales Range: $50-74.9 Million
Pulp, Paper, Biomass & Mineral Technologies Designer, Mfr, Installation & Support Services
N.A.I.C.S.: 333248
Michael Mittag *(CEO)*

Subsidiary (Non-US):

Cimprogetti S.p.A. (2)
Via Pasubio 5, Dalmine, 24044, BG, Italy
Tel.: (39) 0354550111
Web Site: http://www.cimprogetti.com
Sales Range: $10-24.9 Million
Lime Industry Process Furnace Designer & Mfr
N.A.I.C.S.: 333994
Pierluigi Rizzi *(Pres, CEO & Mng Dir)*

Presswerk Krefeld GmbH & Co. KG (1)
Idastrasse 60, 47809, Krefeld, Germany
Tel.: (49) 2151 5810
Web Site: http://www.pwk-automotive.com
Automotive Linkage & Suspension Components Mfr & Whslr
N.A.I.C.S.: 336330

SIMPLON Fahrrad GmbH (1)
Oberer Achdamm 22, 6971, Hard, Austria
Tel.: (43) 5574 72 564 0
Web Site: http://www.simplon.com
Sports Bicycle Mfr
N.A.I.C.S.: 336991
Ulrich Mogwitz *(Mgr-Investment)*

HANNSTAR BOARD CORPORATION
No 9 Gongye 4th Rd, Guanyin Dist, Taoyuan, 328, Taiwan
Tel.: (886) 34838500   TW
Web Site: https://tw.hannstarboard.com
Year Founded: 1989
5469—(TAI)
Rev.: $1,405,400,941
Assets: $2,564,003,043
Liabilities: $1,108,999,042
Net Worth: $1,455,004,000
Earnings: $148,338,756
Emp.: 14,062
Fiscal Year-end: 12/31/23
Printed Circuit Board Mfr & Distr
N.A.I.C.S.: 334412
Zhi-Zhong Zhou *(CFO)*

HANNSTAR BOARD INTERNATIONAL HOLDINGS LIMITED
No 97 of Chengjiang Eastern Rd, Jiangyin, Jiangsu, China
Tel.: (86) 51086197999   CN
Web Site: http://www.hannstarboard.com
Year Founded: 2006
Holding Company; Printed Circuit Board Sales
N.A.I.C.S.: 551112
Kevin Chen *(Section Mgr)*

HANNSTAR DISPLAY CORPORATION
4F No 15 Ln 168 Xingshan Rd, Neihu Dist, Taipei, 11469, Taiwan
Tel.: (886) 255550077
Web Site: https://www.hannstar.com
Year Founded: 1998
6116—(TAI)
Rev.: $403,968,885
Assets: $1,721,075,968
Liabilities: $353,286,000
Net Worth: $1,367,789,968
Earnings: ($152,963,891)
Emp.: 2,657
Fiscal Year-end: 12/31/23
Thin Film Transistor Liquid Crystal Display Products Mfr
N.A.I.C.S.: 334412
Yu-Chi Chiao *(Chm & Pres-Acting)*

Subsidiaries:

HannStar Display (Nanjing) Corporation (1)
No 18 Heng Fei Road Nanjing Economic & Technology Development Zone, Nanjing, 210038, China
Tel.: (86) 2585803888
Liquid Crystal Display Mfr
N.A.I.C.S.: 334419

HannStar Display Corporation - Neihu Plant (1)
4F No 15 Ln 168 Xing Shan Rd Neihu Dist, Taipei, 114, Taiwan
Tel.: (886) 255550077
Liquid Crystal Display Mfr
N.A.I.C.S.: 334419

HannStar Display Corporation - Tainan Plant (1)
No 35 Nanke 2nd Rd Xinshi District Tainan Science Park, Tainan City, 741, Taiwan
Tel.: (886) 65052880
Liquid Crystal Display Mfr
N.A.I.C.S.: 334419

Hannspree, Inc. (1)
4F No 15 Ln 168 Xing Shan Rd, Neihu District, Taipei, 114, Taiwan
Tel.: (886) 255555577
Visual Electronics Mfr
N.A.I.C.S.: 334118

Subsidiary (Non-US):

Hannspree Display Technology (Nanjing) Inc. (2)
33 Heng Fei Road Nanjing Economic and Technology Development Zone, Nanjing, 210038, China
Tel.: (86) 2585803888
Liquid Crystal Display Mfr
N.A.I.C.S.: 334419

3257

HANNSTAR DISPLAY CORPORATION

HannStar Display Corporation—(Continued)

Hannspree Europe Holdings B.V. (2)
Newtonweg 25, 5928 PN, Venlo, Netherlands (100%)
Tel.: (31) 77 3275835
Web Site: http://www.hannspree.eu
Holding Company; Regional Managing Office; Computer Monitor Whslr
N.A.I.C.S.: 551112

Subsidiary (Non-US):

Hannspree Europe GmbH (3)
Meerbuscher Strasse 72, 40670, Meerbusch, Germany
Tel.: (49) 2159 81457 0
Web Site: http://www.hannspree.eu
Computer Monitor Whslr
N.A.I.C.S.: 423430

HANNSTOUCH SOLUTION INC.
No 7 Beiyuan 1st Road, Shanhua Dist, T'ainan, 741, Taiwan
Tel.: (886) 65053959
Web Site:
https://www.hannstouch.com
Year Founded: 1999
3049—(TAI)
Rev.: $43,553,614
Assets: $458,688,952
Liabilities: $150,315,505
Net Worth: $308,373,447
Earnings: ($31,105,234)
Emp.: 269
Fiscal Year-end: 12/31/23
Thin Film Transistor Liquid Crystal Display Panels Mfr
N.A.I.C.S.: 334118
YuChi Chiao (Co-Chm)

HANOI - HAI DUONG BEER JSC
Den Thanh street, Binh Han dist, Hai Duong, Vietnam
Tel.: (84) 3203852319
Web Site:
http://www.hadubeco.com.vn
Year Founded: 1991
HAD—(HNX)
Rev.: $5,062,614
Assets: $3,593,520
Liabilities: $714,106
Net Worth: $2,879,413
Earnings: $126,032
Emp.: 280
Fiscal Year-end: 12/31/21
Beer Mfr
N.A.I.C.S.: 312120
Tran Huy Loan (Vice Chm & Member-Mgmt Bd)

HANOI BEER ALCOHOL & BEVERAGE JOINT STOCK CORPORATION
183 Hoang Hoa Tham Street, Ba Dinh, Hanoi, Vietnam
Tel.: (84) 2438453843
Web Site: https://habeco.com.vn
Year Founded: 1890
Beer & Ale Merchant Whslr
N.A.I.C.S.: 424810

HANOI BEER TRADING JSC
183 Hoang Hoa Tham, Ba Dinh District, Hanoi, Vietnam
Tel.: (84) 37281476
Web Site:
https://www.biahoihanoi.com.vn
HAT—(HNX)
Rev.: $123,408,200
Assets: $19,652,400
Liabilities: $12,754,900
Net Worth: $6,897,500
Earnings: $2,483,100
Emp.: 70
Fiscal Year-end: 12/31/23

Beer Producer & Distr; Wine & Soft Drink Distr
N.A.I.C.S.: 312120
Hung Manh Nguyen (Chm-Mgmt Bd)

Subsidiaries:

C.K.H. Food Trading Pte. Ltd. (1)
15 Jalan Tepong 02-20, Singapore, 619336, Singapore
Tel.: (65) 62612682
Web Site: https://ckhfoodtrading.com
Emp.: 1,000
Food Products Distr
N.A.I.C.S.: 424420

Tipex Pte Ltd. (1)
348 Jalan Boon Lay, Singapore, 619529, Singapore
Tel.: (65) 62687600
Web Site: https://www.tipex.com.sg
Tissue Paper Mfr & Distr
N.A.I.C.S.: 333243

HANOI EDUCATION DEVELOPMENT & INVESTMENT JSC
HEID Office Building 12 Lang Ha, Thanh Cong Ward Ba Dinh District, Hanoi, Vietnam
Tel.: (84) 2435123939
Web Site: https://heid.vn
Year Founded: 2007
EID—(HNX)
Rev.: $43,370,251
Assets: $26,220,586
Liabilities: $9,055,884
Net Worth: $17,164,703
Earnings: $2,960,302
Fiscal Year-end: 12/31/23
Education Development Services
N.A.I.C.S.: 611710

HANOI INVESTMENT GENERAL CORPORATION
14th floor Peakview building 36 Hoang Cau O Cho Dua Ward, Dong Da, Hanoi, Vietnam
Tel.: (84) 2435537188
Web Site: http://www.hanic.com.vn
SHN—(HNX)
Rev.: $585,360,300
Assets: $570,979,200
Liabilities: $412,588,500
Net Worth: $158,390,700
Earnings: $254,100
Fiscal Year-end: 12/31/22
Nitrogenous Fertilizer Import & Export Services
N.A.I.C.S.: 325311

HANOIMILK JSC
Km9 Thang Long Noi Bai Expressway Quang Minh Industrial Park, Me Linh District, Hanoi, Vinh Phuc, Vietnam
Tel.: (84) 2438866567
Web Site: https://hanoimilk.com
Year Founded: 2001
HNM—(HNX)
Rev.: $28,790,931
Assets: $28,152,125
Liabilities: $9,773,134
Net Worth: $18,378,990
Earnings: $1,385,844
Emp.: 343
Fiscal Year-end: 12/31/23
Milk Production Services
N.A.I.C.S.: 112120
Ha Quang Tuan (Chm-Mgmt Bd & Gen Mgr)

HANOVER ACCEPTANCES LIMITED
16 Hans Road, London, SW3 1RT, United Kingdom
Tel.: (44) 20 7581 1477
Web Site:
http://www.hanoveracceptance.com
Year Founded: 1974

Sales Range: $1-4.9 Billion
Emp.: 1,766
Investment Management Service
N.A.I.C.S.: 523940
Manfred S. Gorvy (Chm)

Subsidiaries:

African Realty Trust (Pty) Ltd. (1)
LetabaDrft Loerie St, Agatha, Tzaneen, Limpopo, South Africa
Tel.: (27) 153044000
Fruit Farming Services
N.A.I.C.S.: 111320

HANOVER INVESTORS MANAGEMENT LLP
25 Savile Row, London, W1S 2ER, United Kingdom
Tel.: (44) 20 7766 8400
Web Site:
http://www.hanoverinvestors.com
Privater Equity Firm
N.A.I.C.S.: 523999
Fred Lundqvist (Partner)

Subsidiaries:

Kalibrate Technologies Ltd. (1)
First Floor 196 Deansgate, Manchester, M3 3WF, United Kingdom
Tel.: (44) 161 609 4000
Web Site: http://www.kalibrate.com
Petroleum Retail Industry Software & Consulting Services
N.A.I.C.S.: 513210
Mark Hawtin (Chief Comml Officer)

Subsidiary (US):

Intalytics, Inc. (2)
5 Research Dr, Ann Arbor, MI 48108
Tel.: (734) 623-7710
Web Site: http://www.intalytics.com
Professional, Scientific & Technical Services
N.A.I.C.S.: 541990
Dave Huntoon (Co-Founder & Mng Dir)

Knowledge Support Systems Inc. (2)
Ste 200 25 B Hanover Rd, Florham Park, NJ 07932
Tel.: (973) 549-1850
Pricing Analytics, Price Management, Rules-Based Pricing & Optimization Technology & Services
N.A.I.C.S.: 541613
Bob Stein (Pres & CEO)

Trade Area Systems Inc. (2)
1 W Exchange St Ste 4B, Providence, RI 02903
Tel.: (508) 223-3003
Web Site: http://www.tradeareasystems.com
Mobile Application Development Services
N.A.I.C.S.: 541511
Bill Dakai (Founder & Pres)

HANP INC.
282 yongmong-ri duksan-myun, Jincheon, Chungcheongbuk-do, Korea (South)
Tel.: (82) 435367561
Web Site: http://www.hanp.co.kr
Year Founded: 1994
066110—(KRS)
Rev.: $2,338,268
Assets: $88,038,888
Liabilities: $47,305,708
Net Worth: $40,733,181
Earnings: $6,291,763
Emp.: 39
Fiscal Year-end: 12/31/21
Digital Output Device Part Mfr
N.A.I.C.S.: 334419
Yong-Hyun Wi (CEO)

HANPIN ELECTRON CO., LTD.
No 256 Sec 3 Chung Cheng Rd, Jen Teh Hsiang, Tainan, Taiwan
Tel.: (886) 62791717
Web Site: https://www.hanpin.com.tw
2488—(TAI)
Rev.: $80,511,263
Assets: $113,035,020

INTERNATIONAL PUBLIC

Liabilities: $32,243,565
Net Worth: $80,791,455
Earnings: $11,482,618
Emp.: 636
Fiscal Year-end: 12/31/23
Musical Instrument Mfr
N.A.I.C.S.: 339992

Subsidiaries:

HANPIN BVI INTL CO., LTD. (1)
Unit U 4/F Valiant Industrial Centre No 2-12 Au Pui Wan Street, Fo Tan, Sha Tin, New Territories, China (Hong Kong)
Tel.: (852) 28815068
Web Site: http://www.hanpin.com.tw
Emp.: 2
Audio Equipment Mfr
N.A.I.C.S.: 334310

Hanchih Electronics (Shenzhen) Co., Ltd. (1)
100 Xingye 1st Rd Fenghuang Industrial District Fuyong, Baoan, Shenzhen, Guandong, China
Tel.: (86) 755 2737 8666
Web Site: http://www.hanpin.com.tw
Audio Equipment Mfr
N.A.I.C.S.: 334310

Hanpin BVI International Co., Ltd. (1)
Unit U 4/F No 2-12 Au Pui Wan Street, Valiant Industrial Centre Fotan, Sha Tin, New Territories, China (Hong Kong)
Tel.: (852) 28815068
Audio Equipment Mfr
N.A.I.C.S.: 334310

HANRYU HOLDINGS, INC.
160 Yeouiseo-ro, Yeongdeungpo-gu, Seoul, 07231, Korea (South)
Tel.: (82) 25648588
Web Site:
https://www.hanryuholdings.com
Year Founded: 2021
HRYU—(NASDAQ)
Rev.: $794,166
Assets: $20,544,956
Liabilities: $7,476,491
Net Worth: $13,068,465
Earnings: ($9,407,635)
Emp.: 52
Fiscal Year-end: 12/31/23
Holding Company
N.A.I.C.S.: 551112
Dae-Hwan Son (COO)

HANS BIOMED CORPORATION
7 Jeongui-ro 8-gil Songpa-gu, Seoul, 05836, Korea (South)
Tel.: (82) 2 466 2266
Web Site:
http://www.hansbiomed.com
Year Founded: 1993
042520—(KRS)
Rev.: $54,370,190
Assets: $119,088,971
Liabilities: $75,314,060
Net Worth: $43,774,911
Earnings: ($20,355,612)
Emp.: 288
Fiscal Year-end: 09/30/21
Medical & Surgical Instrument Mfr
N.A.I.C.S.: 339112
Ho Chan Hwang (CEO)

Subsidiaries:

HansBiomed China, Inc. (1)
No 1439 Wuzhong Road, Shanghai, China
Tel.: (86) 2154371030
Skin Graft Product Distr
N.A.I.C.S.: 423450

HansBiomed USA, Inc. (1)
Ave Ste 4, Englewood Cliffs, NJ 07632
Tel.: (201) 224-2333
Web Site: https://www.hansbiomed.com
Skin Graft Product Distr
N.A.I.C.S.: 423450

AND PRIVATE COMPANIES

HANS ENERGY COMPANY LIMITED
Unit 2608 26/F Harbour Centre 25 Harbour Road, Wanchai, China (Hong Kong)
Tel.: (852) 29220600 Ky
Web Site: http://www.hansenergy.com
0554—(HKG)
Rev.: $88,593,503
Assets: $252,032,948
Liabilities: $98,137,133
Net Worth: $153,895,815
Earnings: $213,180
Emp.: 172
Fiscal Year-end: 12/31/22
Oil & Petrochemical Products Terminal, Transshipment & Storage Services
N.A.I.C.S.: 424710
Lei Zhang (COO)

HANS ENG CO., LTD.
Road 29 Noksan Industrial Complex 381, Songjeong-dong, Busan, Korea (South)
Tel.: (82) 51 831 77 00 KR
Web Site: http://www.hanseng.co.kr
Year Founded: 1968
Childrens Toys & Recreational Products Mfr & Sales
N.A.I.C.S.: 339930
Sang Nam Han (Co-CEO)

HANS HEPP GMBH & CO. KG
Georgswerder Damm 16, 20539, Hamburg, Germany
Tel.: (49) 407804680 De
Web Site: http://www.hanshepp.de
Year Founded: 1936
Sales Range: $10-24.9 Million
Dressings & First-Aid Material Mfr
N.A.I.C.S.: 339113
Christian Beckmann (Gen Mgr & Dir)

HANS LUTZ MASCHINENFABRIK GMBH & CO. KG
Gutenbergstrasse 19, Reinbek, 21465, Germany
Tel.: (49) 40727690
Web Site: http://www.lutz-aufzuege.de
Year Founded: 1927
Rev.: $18,828,810
Emp.: 200
Marine Elevators Mfr
N.A.I.C.S.: 333921
Hans Martin Lutz (Chm)

HANS-GUNTER BERNER GMBH & CO. KG
Hasenholz 10, 24161, Altenholz, Germany
Tel.: (49) 431329932
Web Site: http://www.h-g-Berner.de
Rev.: $13,550,700
Emp.: 30
Nutrient Concentrates Mfr
N.A.I.C.S.: 311999
Frauke Berner (Mng Dir)

HANS-JURGEN KEIL ANLAGENBAU GMBH & CO. KG
Zum Welplager Moor 8, 49163, Hunteburg, Germany
Tel.: (49) 547592000
Web Site: http://www.keil-anlagenbau.de
Year Founded: 1973
Sales Range: $10-24.9 Million
Emp.: 126
Storage Tank Mfr & Distr
N.A.I.C.S.: 423840
Jens Bothe (CFO)

HANSA BIOPHARMA AB
Scheelevagen 22, SE-223 63, Lund, Sweden
Tel.: (46) 46165670
Web Site: https://www.hansabiopharma.com
HNSA—(OMX)
Rev.: $14,473,105
Assets: $158,045,651
Liabilities: $101,575,768
Net Worth: $56,469,883
Earnings: ($57,239,971)
Emp.: 144
Fiscal Year-end: 12/31/22
Biopharmaceutical Product Mfr
N.A.I.C.S.: 325412
Emanuel Bjorne (VP-Bus Dev)

HANSA CHEMIE INTERNATIONAL AG
Zumikerstrasse 16a, Zollikon, CH-8702, Zurich, Switzerland
Tel.: (41) 434994310
Web Site: http://www.hansainternational.ch
Holding Company
N.A.I.C.S.: 551112
Khodayar Alambeigi (Pres & Exec Dir)

Subsidiaries:

Hansa Chemie Holland BV (1)
Spoorstraat 44, NL-5911 KJ, Venlo, Netherlands
Tel.: (31) 773200878
Web Site: http://www.hansainternational.de
Chemical Products Distr
N.A.I.C.S.: 325998

Savanna AG (1)
Kloter Rechtsanwalte, Rietstrasse 50 Zollikon, Zurich, CH-8702, Switzerland
Tel.: (41) 434994310
Web Site: http://www.hansagroup.de
Sales Range: $25-49.9 Million
Emp.: 50
Chemical Products Mfr
N.A.I.C.S.: 325998

Venanco AG (1)
Ihlggsersse 23, CH-8832, Wollerau, Switzerland
Tel.: (41) 41417920688
Web Site: http://www.hansainternational.ch
Chemical Products Mfr
N.A.I.C.S.: 325998

HANSA INVESTMENT COMPANY LIMITED
Clarendon House 2 Church Street, PO Box HM666, Hamilton, HM CX, Bermuda
Tel.: (441) 2076475750 BM
Web Site: https://www.hansaicl.com
Year Founded: 1912
HANA—(LSE)
Rev.: $9,820,752
Assets: $574,309,519
Liabilities: $531,431
Net Worth: $573,778,087
Earnings: $115,402,676
Fiscal Year-end: 03/31/24
Investment Trust Services
N.A.I.C.S.: 523999
Jonathan Davie (Chm)

HANSA LUFTBILD AG
Nevinghoff 20, 48147, Munster, Germany
Tel.: (49) 25123300
Web Site: http://www.hansaluftbild.de
Sales Range: $10-24.9 Million
Emp.: 60
Real Estate Manangement Services
N.A.I.C.S.: 531390
Paul Hartfiel (Member-Mgmt Bd)

HANSAE YES24 HOLDINGS CO., LTD.
6F 30 Eunhang-ro, Yeongdeungpo-gu, Seoul, 07242, Korea (South)
Tel.: (82) 237790800
Web Site: https://www.hansaeyes24.com
Year Founded: 1982
016450—(KRS)
Rev.: $2,548,061,080
Assets: $1,562,351,189
Liabilities: $924,577,260
Net Worth: $637,773,930
Earnings: $37,952,322
Emp.: 30
Fiscal Year-end: 12/31/22
Holding Company
N.A.I.C.S.: 551112
Dong-Nyung Kim (Chm & CEO)

Subsidiaries:

Hansae Co., Ltd. (1)
29 Eunhaeng-ro 5th floor Jeongwoo Building, Yeongdeungpo-gu, Seoul, 150739, Korea (South) (64.68%)
Tel.: (82) 237790779
Web Site: http://www.hansae.com
Rev.: $1,691,051,823
Assets: $950,474,973
Liabilities: $538,529,641
Net Worth: $411,945,331
Earnings: $65,682,187
Emp.: 514
Fiscal Year-end: 12/31/2022
Apparels Mfr
N.A.I.C.S.: 315250
Ik Whan Kim (CEO)

HANSAEMK CO.,LTD.
MK Bldg 633 Nonhyeon-Ro, Gangnam-Gu, Seoul, 135826, Korea (South)
Tel.: (82) 221425000
Web Site: https://www.hansaemk.com
Year Founded: 1995
069640—(KRS)
Rev.: $214,469,001
Assets: $177,599,666
Liabilities: $147,082,893
Net Worth: $30,516,774
Earnings: ($29,836,308)
Emp.: 294
Fiscal Year-end: 12/31/22
Apparel Mfr & Store Operator
N.A.I.C.S.: 458110
Mun-hwan Kim (CEO)

HANSAMATRIX AS
Akmenu iela 72, Ogre, 5001, Latvia
Tel.: (371) 65049088
Web Site: http://www.hansamatrix.com
Year Founded: 2018
HMX1R—(RSE)
Rev.: $27,560,443
Assets: $33,384,865
Liabilities: $23,274,526
Net Worth: $10,110,339
Earnings: $232,805
Emp.: 204
Fiscal Year-end: 12/31/19
Aircraft Mfr
N.A.I.C.S.: 336411
Zanda Lapane (CEO)

Subsidiaries:

SIA HansaMatrix Innovation (1)
Ziedleju 1, Marupe, LV-2167, Latvia
Tel.: (371) 67550500
Optical Product Mfr
N.A.I.C.S.: 333310

SIA HansaMatrix Ventspils (1)
Vatp-1, Ventspils, LV-3602, Latvia
Tel.: (371) 63620900
Optical Product Mfr
N.A.I.C.S.: 333310

HANSAPOST OU
Luite 19a, 11313, Tallinn, Estonia
Tel.: (372) 611 5511

Web Site: http://www.hansapost.ee
Online Store
N.A.I.C.S.: 455110

Subsidiaries:

Hobby Hall Suomi Oy (1)
PL 9210 Juurakkokuja 4, 01510, Vantaa, Finland
Tel.: (358) 985668000
Web Site: http://www.hobbyhall.fi
Online Store
N.A.I.C.S.: 449210

HANSAPRINT OY
Artukaistentie 10, 20240, Turku, Finland
Tel.: (358) 10 542 2
Web Site: http://www.hansaprint.com
Year Founded: 1996
Sales Range: $1-4.9 Billion
Emp.: 500
Newspaper Printing Services
N.A.I.C.S.: 323111
Heikki Ketonen (Exec VP-Print)

Subsidiaries:

Hansaprint Elanders Kft (1)
Puskas Tivadar u 6, 2900, Komárom, Hungary
Tel.: (36) 34 889 100
Web Site: http://www.hansaprint.com
Magazine Printing Services
N.A.I.C.S.: 323111

HANSARD GLOBAL PLC
Hansard International 55 Athol Street, Box 192, Douglas, IM99 1QL, Isle of Man
Tel.: (44) 1624688000
Web Site: https://www.hansard.com
HSD—(LSE)
Rev.: $70,737,212
Assets: $1,737,881,600
Liabilities: $1,702,716,652
Net Worth: $35,164,948
Earnings: $6,109,740
Emp.: 192
Fiscal Year-end: 06/30/20
Long-Term Investment Products & Services
N.A.I.C.S.: 522180
Gordon S. Marr (CEO)

Subsidiaries:

Hansard Europe Designated Activity Company (1)
Ground Floor 6 Exchange Place IFSC 1, Dublin, D01 T9C2, Ireland
Tel.: (353) 12112800
Life Assurance Financial Services
N.A.I.C.S.: 524113

Hansard Europe Limited (1)
Ground Floor 6 Exchange Place IFSC, Dublin, Ireland
Tel.: (353) 12112800
Web Site: https://www.hansard.com
Sales Range: $50-74.9 Million
Emp.: 10
Fire Insurance Services
N.A.I.C.S.: 524113

HANSCO CAPITAL CORP.
890 West Pender Street Suite 600, Vancouver, V6C 1K4, BC, Canada
Tel.: (604) 357-1030
HCO.P—(TSXV)
Assets: $255,748
Liabilities: $29,023
Net Worth: $226,726
Earnings: ($50,062)
Fiscal Year-end: 09/30/21
Business Consulting Services
N.A.I.C.S.: 522299

HANSELLS MASTERTON LTD.
160 State Highway 2 Rd 11, Masterton, 5810, New Zealand
Tel.: (64) 63700200

HANSELLS MASTERTON LTD.

Hansells Masterton Ltd.—(Continued)

Web Site:
http://www.hansellsmasterton.co.nz
Food Packaging & Mfr
N.A.I.C.S.: 311999
Alan Stewart *(Exec Chm)*

Subsidiaries:

Naturalac Nutrition Limited (1)
Level 2 18 Normanby Road Mount Eden
Symonds Street, PO Box 8645, Auckland, 1024, New Zealand
Tel.: (64) 96385320
Web Site: http://www.horleys.com
Sales Range: $25-49.9 Million
Emp.: 11
Dietary Supplement Products Mfr
N.A.I.C.S.: 311999

HANSEN TECHNOLOGIES LIMITED

2 Frederick Street, Doncaster, 3108, VIC, Australia
Tel.: (61) 398403000 AU
Web Site: https://www.hansencx.com
HSN—(ASX)
Rev.: $237,335,736
Assets: $378,493,588
Liabilities: $153,370,058
Net Worth: $225,123,530
Earnings: $14,065,171
Emp.: 1,584
Fiscal Year-end: 06/30/24
Holding Company; Billing Systems & Customer Care Software Publisher & Services
N.A.I.C.S.: 551112
Darren Meade *(Head-Delivery)*

Subsidiaries:

Hansen Corporation Europe Limited (1)
Third Floor Harlequin House 7 High Street, 13 The Causeway, Teddington, TW11 8EE, Middlesex, United Kingdom
Tel.: (44) 2086148700
Sales Range: $50-74.9 Million
Emp.: 18
Billing Systems & Customer Care Software Distr & Services
N.A.I.C.S.: 423430
Scott Weir *(Chief Info & Security Officer)*

Hansen Corporation Investments Pty Limited (1)
2 Frederick Street, Doncaster, 3108, VIC, Australia
Tel.: (61) 398403000
Software Development Services
N.A.I.C.S.: 518210

Hansen Corporation Pty. Ltd. (1)
2 Frederick Street, Doncaster, Melbourne, 3108, VIC, Australia (100%)
Tel.: (61) 39 840 3000
Web Site: http://www.hsntech.com
Sales Range: $75-99.9 Million
Emp.: 170
Billing Systems & Customer Care Software Publisher & Services
N.A.I.C.S.: 513210

Hansen Corporation USA Limited (1)
621 17th St Ste 1401, Denver, CO 80293 (100%)
Tel.: (303) 296-0211
Web Site: http://www.hsntech.com
Billing Systems & Customer Care Software Distr & Services
N.A.I.C.S.: 423430

Hansen New Zealand Limited (1)
Level 7 67 Symonds St, Auckland, 1010, New Zealand
Tel.: (64) 93730400
Emp.: 55
Billing Systems & Customer Care Software Distr & Services
N.A.I.C.S.: 423430
Raymond Hayter *(Country Mgr)*

Hansen Technologies (Shanghai) Company Limited (1)
Room 3-135 3F No 333 North Chendgu Road, Jingan District, Shanghai, 200000, China
Tel.: (86) 2152289700
Information Technology & Software Product Services
N.A.I.C.S.: 541512

Hansen Technologies CDE Limited (1)
Third Floor Harlequin House 7 High Street, Teddington, TW11 8EE, United Kingdom
Tel.: (44) 2086148700
Software Development Services
N.A.I.C.S.: 541511

Hansen Technologies Canada, Inc. (1)
55 York Street Suite 1100, Toronto, M5J 1R7, ON, Canada
Tel.: (416) 943-9696
Software Development Services
N.A.I.C.S.: 518210

Hansen Technologies Denmark A/S (1)
Norre Havnegade 43, 6400, Sonderborg, Denmark
Tel.: (45) 73425050
Software Development Services
N.A.I.C.S.: 518210

Hansen Technologies Norway AS (1)
Karenslyst alle 49, 0279, Oslo, Norway
Tel.: (47) 57739970
Software Development Services
N.A.I.C.S.: 518210

Hansen Technologies Sweden AB (1)
Isafjordsgatan 5, 164 40, Kista, Sweden
Tel.: (46) 925320300
Software Development Services
N.A.I.C.S.: 518210

Hansen Technologies Vietnam LLC (1)
100 Xuan Thuy Street, Thao Dien Ward Thu Duc City, Ho Chi Minh City, Vietnam
Tel.: (84) 2862735007
Software Development Services
N.A.I.C.S.: 518210

Sigma Systems Group (USA) Inc. (1)
7173 S Havana St Ste 100-91, Centennial, CO 80112
Web Site: https://sigmasys.com
Financial Investment Services
N.A.I.C.S.: 523999

Sigma Systems Japan K.K. (1)
1-14-11 Shin-Kitano, Yodogawa-ku, Osaka, 532-0025, Japan
Tel.: (81) 668860588
Web Site: https://www.sigma-system.co.jp
Software Design Mfr
N.A.I.C.S.: 541511

HANSEN YUNCKEN PTY LTD

Level 1 191 Fullarton Road Dulwich, Adelaide, 5065, SA, Australia
Tel.: (61) 882297300
Web Site:
http://www.hansenyuncken.com.au
Sales Range: $150-199.9 Million
Emp.: 300
Building Construction Services
N.A.I.C.S.: 236220
Peter Salveson *(CEO)*

HANSETANK SPEDITION GMBH

Wragekamp 3, 22397, Hamburg, Germany
Tel.: (49) 4052988230
Web Site: http://www.hansetank.com
Year Founded: 1997
Rev.: $10,345,500
Emp.: 13
Liquid Goods Transportation Services
N.A.I.C.S.: 541614
Thomas Pollakowski *(Co-CEO)*

HANSHANG GROUP CO., LTD.

No 134 Hanyang Avenue, Wuhan, 430050, Hubei, China
Tel.: (86) 2768849119
Web Site: http://www.whhsg.com
Year Founded: 1990
600774—(SHG)
Rev.: $194,731,458
Assets: $491,103,602
Liabilities: $240,356,755
Net Worth: $250,746,846
Earnings: $12,423,289
Fiscal Year-end: 12/31/22
Departmental Store Operator
N.A.I.C.S.: 455110
Yan Zhi *(Chm)*

HANSHIN CONSTRUCTION CO., LTD.

82 Deokpyeong-ro, Baegam-myeon Cheoin-gu, Yongin, 17172, Gyeonggi-do, Korea (South)
Tel.: (82) 313345344
Web Site: https://www.hanshinc.com
Year Founded: 1950
004960—(KRS)
Rev.: $936,931,559
Assets: $1,801,988,347
Liabilities: $1,244,579,054
Net Worth: $557,409,292
Earnings: $34,861,168
Emp.: 996
Fiscal Year-end: 12/31/22
Construction & Engineering Services
N.A.I.C.S.: 541330
Yong-Sun Choi *(Chm)*

HANSHIN MACHINERY CO., LTD.

singil-dong, Danwon-gu, Ansan, 1122-6, Gyeonggi, Korea (South)
Tel.: (82) 314913911
Web Site: https://www.hanshin.co.kr
Year Founded: 1969
011700—(KRS)
Rev.: $42,982,646
Assets: $88,758,567
Liabilities: $17,468,673
Net Worth: $71,289,894
Earnings: ($3,631,265)
Emp.: 90
Fiscal Year-end: 12/31/22
Air Compressor Product Mfr & Whslr
N.A.I.C.S.: 333912
Hwang Yun Ho *(Asst Mgr)*

HANSLER INDUSTRIES

580 King Street West, Brockville, K6V 3T5, ON, Canada
Tel.: (613) 342-4450
Web Site: http://www.hansler.ca
Year Founded: 1953
Sales Range: $25-49.9 Million
Emp.: 70
Heavy Equipment Rental & Leasing Services
N.A.I.C.S.: 532490
Dwayne Sakaluk *(VP)*

Subsidiaries:

Hansler Manutention, Inc (1)
10145 Cote de Liesse, Dorval, H9P 1A3, QC, Canada
Tel.: (514) 636-0453
Web Site: http://www.hanslermanutention.ca
Sales Range: $25-49.9 Million
Emp.: 12
Lift Trucks Rental & Leasing Services
N.A.I.C.S.: 333924
John Brinkworth *(Dir-Fin)*

HANSOL GROUP

21st Fl Hansol Bldg 736 1 Yeoksam Dong, Gangnam Gu, Seoul, 135 080, Korea (South)
Tel.: (82) 232877114
Web Site: http://www.hansol.co.kr
Year Founded: 1965

INTERNATIONAL PUBLIC

Sales Range: $700-749.9 Million
Emp.: 3,500
Holding Company; Paper Manufacturing; Chemicals; Information Publishing; Construction; Finance
N.A.I.C.S.: 551112
Dong-Kil Cho *(Chm)*

Subsidiaries:

Hansol Chemical Co. Ltd. (1)
18th Floor Hansol Bldg, 736-1 Yeoksam 1-dong Gangnam-g, Seoul, Korea (South)
Tel.: (82) 232876714
Web Site: http://www.hansolchemical.com
Inorganic Dye & Pigment Mfr
N.A.I.C.S.: 325130

Hansol Development Co. Ltd. (1)
Chijong-myon, Wonju, Kangwon-do, Korea (South)
Tel.: (82) 337697777
Hardwood Veneer & Plywood Mfr
N.A.I.C.S.: 321211

Hansol EME Co. Ltd. (1)
7th Floor First Tower 266-1 Seohyeon-dong, Bundang-gu, Seongnam, Gyeonggi, Korea (South)
Tel.: (82) 317785516
Web Site: http://www.hansoleme.com
Sales Range: $200-249.9 Million
Emp.: 600
Pulp Mill
N.A.I.C.S.: 322110

Hansol Homedeco Co. Ltd. (1)
27F 15 Boramae-ro 5-gil, Dongjak-gu, Seoul, 156-714, Korea (South)
Tel.: (82) 807772299
Web Site:
https://www.hansolhomedeco.com
Rev.: $217,378,691
Assets: $245,053,831
Liabilities: $127,379,136
Net Worth: $117,674,695
Earnings: ($3,733,417)
Emp.: 303
Fiscal Year-end: 12/31/2022
Hardwood Veneer & Plywood Mfr
N.A.I.C.S.: 321211
Gyeong-Rok Kim *(CEO)*

Hansol LCD Inc. (1)
11th Floor Hansol Building 736-1 Yeoksam-dong, Gangnuam-gu, Seoul, 135-080, Korea (South)
Tel.: (82) 232877903
Web Site: http://www.hansollcd.co.kr
Computer Terminal Mfr
N.A.I.C.S.: 334118

Hansol Logistics Co., Ltd. (1)
22nd floor Pine Avenue Building B Euljiro2-ga 100 Euljiro, Jung-gu, Seoul, Korea (South)
Tel.: (82) 232877400
Web Site: https://www.hansollogistics.com
Mail-Order Houses
N.A.I.C.S.: 332999
Gyu-Ho Hwang *(Chm & CEO)*

Hansol PNS Co., Ltd. (1)
5F Ilheung Bldg 213 Toegye-ro, Jung-gu, Seoul, 04557, Korea (South)
Tel.: (82) 27725100
Web Site: http://www.hansolpns.com
Rev.: $241,026,726
Assets: $103,502,441
Liabilities: $64,307,685
Net Worth: $39,194,756
Earnings: $1,358,724
Emp.: 263
Fiscal Year-end: 12/31/2022
Paper Product Whslr & Computer Software Development Services
N.A.I.C.S.: 424110
Jeong Seongwon *(Sr Mgr)*

Hansol Paper Co., Ltd. (1)
21st Fl Hansol Bldg, 736-1 Yeoksam Dong Gongnam Gu, Seoul, 135-080, Korea (South) (100%)
Tel.: (82) 232877114
Web Site: http://www.hansolpaper.co.kr
Sales Range: $200-249.9 Million
Emp.: 1,000
Wood-Free Paper, Coated Paper & White Board
N.A.I.C.S.: 322120

Hansol Telecom Co. Ltd. (1)
13th Floor KTF Bldg, 1321-11 Seocho-dong Seocho-gu, Seoul, Korea (South)
Tel.: (82) 234881813
Web Site: http://www.hansoltelecom.co.kr
Wired Telecommunications Carriers
N.A.I.C.S.: 517111

NexG Co., Ltd. (1)
16F Nuikkumsquare Business Center, 396 World Cup Buk-Ro Mapo-Gu, Seoul, 03925, Korea (South)
Tel.: (82) 2 60053000
Web Site: http://www.nexg.net
Software Development Services
N.A.I.C.S.: 541511
Kyung Hoon Lee (CEO)

HANSOL INTICUBE CO., LTD.
14th floor Business Tower Nurikum Square Building, 396 World Cupbuk-ro Mapo-gu, Seoul, Korea (South)
Tel.: (82) 260053000
Web Site:
https://www.hansolinticube.com
Year Founded: 2003
070590—(KRS)
Rev.: $45,365,393
Assets: $30,538,828
Liabilities: $12,694,543
Net Worth: $17,844,284
Earnings: ($4,453,106)
Emp.: 237
Fiscal Year-end: 12/31/22
Communication Service
N.A.I.C.S.: 517112
Hyung Jun Kim (CEO)

HANSOL IONES CO., LTD
71-29 Barangongdan-ro 4-gil Hyangnam-eup, Hwaseong, Gyeonggi-do, Korea (South)
Tel.: (82) 312387785
Web Site: https://hansoliones.com
Year Founded: 1993
114810—(KRS)
Rev.: $125,720,784
Assets: $174,390,788
Liabilities: $58,715,509
Net Worth: $115,675,279
Earnings: $21,699,257
Emp.: 551
Fiscal Year-end: 12/31/22
Flat Panel Display & Semiconductor Parts Mfr
N.A.I.C.S.: 334413
Park In-Rae (CEO)

HANSOL TECHNICS CO., LTD.
5 Fl Fine Avenue Bldg B 100 Eulji-ro, Jung-Gu, Seoul, 04551, Korea (South)
Tel.: (82) 232877903
Web Site:
https://www.hansoltechnics.com
Year Founded: 2015
004710—(KRS)
Rev.: $1,263,549,394
Assets: $822,164,098
Liabilities: $484,663,964
Net Worth: $337,500,134
Earnings: $25,025,063
Emp.: 610
Fiscal Year-end: 12/31/22
Electronic Components Mfr
N.A.I.C.S.: 334419
Park Hyun Soon (CEO)

HANSONGNEOTECH CO., LTD.
36-1 1gongdan-ro 7-gil, Gumi, Gyeongsangbuk-do, Korea (South)
Tel.: (82) 544629930
Web Site: https://hsneotech.com
Year Founded: 2015
226440—(KRS)
Rev.: $21,230,736
Assets: $42,899,963
Liabilities: $24,177,207
Net Worth: $18,722,755
Earnings: ($14,914,222)
Emp.: 90
Fiscal Year-end: 12/31/22
Financial Investment Management Services
N.A.I.C.S.: 523940

HANSSAK CO., LTD.
401-403 27 Digital-ro 34 gil, Guro-gu, Seoul, Korea (South)
Tel.: (82) 220821200
Web Site: https://www.hanssak.co.kr
Year Founded: 1992
430690—(KRS)
Software Development Services
N.A.I.C.S.: 541511

HANSSEM CO., LTD.
15418/144 Beonyeong 2-ro, Danwon-gu, Ansan, Gyeonggi, Korea (South)
Tel.: (82) 269083114
Web Site: https://www.hanssem.com
Year Founded: 1973
009240—(KRS)
Rev.: $1,534,694,952
Assets: $843,454,208
Liabilities: $501,810,974
Net Worth: $341,643,234
Earnings: ($54,702,925)
Emp.: 2,269
Fiscal Year-end: 12/31/22
Kitchen & Interior Furniture Mfr
N.A.I.C.S.: 337122
Seung-Su Kang (Chm & CEO)

Subsidiaries:

Hanssem (Shanghai) Home Furnishings Co., Ltd. (1)
1F L102 and 2F Center88 88 Changning Rd, Changning District, Shanghai, China
Tel.: (86) 4000063388
Wooden Furniture Mfr
N.A.I.C.S.: 337122

Hanssem Co., Ltd. - Ansan Plant 1 (1)
52 Sandan-ro 19beon-gil, Danwon-gu, Ansan, Gyeonggi-do, Korea (South)
Tel.: (82) 314890611
Wooden Furniture Mfr
N.A.I.C.S.: 337122

Hanssem Co., Ltd. - Ansan Plant 2 (1)
144 Beonnyeong 2-ro, Danwon-gu, Ansan, Gyeonggi-do, Korea (South)
Tel.: (82) 314961101
Wooden Furniture Mfr
N.A.I.C.S.: 337122

Hanssem Co., Ltd. - Ansan Plant 3 (1)
131 Beonnyeong 2-ro, Danwon-gu, Ansan, Gyeonggi-do, Korea (South)
Tel.: (82) 3180412621
Wooden Furniture Mfr
N.A.I.C.S.: 337122

Hanssem Co., Ltd. - Siheung Plant 1 (1)
2127-11 Suin-ro, Siheung, Gyeonggi-do, Korea (South)
Tel.: (82) 314122401
Wooden Furniture Mfr
N.A.I.C.S.: 337122

Hanssem Co., Ltd. - Siheung Plant 2 (1)
22-11 Oido-ro, Siheung, Gyeonggi-do, Korea (South)
Tel.: (82) 314122420
Wooden Furniture Mfr
N.A.I.C.S.: 337122

Hanssem Corporation (1)
200 Helen St, South Plainfield, NJ 07080
Tel.: (908) 754-4949
Household Product Whslr
N.A.I.C.S.: 423620

Plant (Domestic):

Hanssem Corporation - New Jersey Plant 2 (2)
157 Helen St, South Plainfield, NJ 07080
Tel.: (908) 753-1143
Wooden Furniture Mfr
N.A.I.C.S.: 337122

Hanssem Inc. (1)
1F Toei Bldg 2-2-7 Koraibashi, Chuo-ku, Osaka, 541-0043, Japan
Tel.: (81) 662235051
Wooden Furniture Mfr
N.A.I.C.S.: 337122

HANSTONE GOLD CORP.
1100 - 1111 Melville Street, Vancouver, V6E3V6, BC, Canada
Tel.: (777) 896-7778
Web Site:
https://www.hanstonegold.com
HANCF—(OTCIQ)
Rev.: $540
Assets: $1,301,618
Liabilities: $756,114
Net Worth: $545,503
Earnings: ($1,066,137)
Fiscal Year-end: 12/31/22
Mineral Exploration Services
N.A.I.C.S.: 213115
Robert Quinn (VP)

HANTANG CULTURE & EDUCATION HOLDING GROUP LIMITED
Room C08 3/F Desun International Education Plaza No 1-27 Desheng Road, Panyu District, Guangzhou, 511400, China
Tel.: (86) 13510193139 NV
Year Founded: 2019
Rev.: $4,471
Assets: $3,977
Liabilities: $22,937
Net Worth: ($18,960)
Earnings: ($70,010)
Emp.: 3
Fiscal Year-end: 03/31/20
Education Services
N.A.I.C.S.: 611710
Jingyi Liao (Pres)

HANTOP INC.
598-7 Daeyeon3-dong, Nam-gu, Busan, Korea (South)
Tel.: (82) 516262841
Web Site: http://www.ynam.co.kr
Year Founded: 1959
002680—(KRS)
Rev.: $76,028,127
Assets: $109,659,998
Liabilities: $71,156,334
Net Worth: $38,503,664
Earnings: ($5,144,084)
Emp.: 119
Fiscal Year-end: 12/31/22
Flour & Animal Feed Mfr
N.A.I.C.S.: 311211
Sin-Woo Kang (CEO)

HANUNG TOYS AND TEXTILES LIMITED
E-93 2nd Floor Greater Kailash Enclave I, New Delhi, 110048, India
Tel.: (91) 1126241572
Web Site: http://www.hanung.com
Year Founded: 1990
Rev.: $2,073,538
Assets: $96,604,995
Liabilities: $424,969,199
Net Worth: ($328,364,204)
Earnings: ($16,194,080)
Emp.: 147
Fiscal Year-end: 03/31/17
Stuffed Toy Mfr
N.A.I.C.S.: 339930

Subsidiaries:

Cody Direct Corp. (1)
230 5th Ave Ste 1411, New York, NY 10001
Tel.: (646) 649-2568
Web Site: http://www.codydirect.com
Home Furnishing Distr
N.A.I.C.S.: 423220
Ginger Bouler (Mgr-Customer Svc)

HANVEY GROUP HOLDINGS LTD.
Unit 1503-6 15/F Tower 1 Ever Gain Plaza No 88 Container Port Road, Kwai Chung, New Territories, China (Hong Kong)
Tel.: (852) 24892318 Ky
Web Site:
http://www.hanveygroup.com.hk
Year Founded: 1986
8219—(HKG)
Rev.: $26,375,765
Assets: $28,522,508
Liabilities: $23,496,158
Net Worth: $5,026,351
Earnings: ($360,112)
Emp.: 119
Fiscal Year-end: 12/31/21
Watch Product Mfr & Distr
N.A.I.C.S.: 339910
Clement Sin Cheong Cheuk (Founder, Chm & CEO)

HANWA CO., LTD.
Ginza Shochiku Square 1-13-1 Tsukiji, Chuo-ku, Tokyo, 104-8429, Japan
Tel.: (81) 335442171 JP
Web Site: https://www.hanwa.co.jp
Year Founded: 1947
8078—(TKS)
Rev.: $16,075,387,800
Assets: $7,713,777,460
Liabilities: $5,355,560,810
Net Worth: $2,358,216,650
Earnings: $253,936,370
Emp.: 5,508
Fiscal Year-end: 03/31/24
Iron & Steel Product Mfr
N.A.I.C.S.: 423510
Hironari Furukawa (Pres)

Subsidiaries:

Alcecap S.A.S. (1)
Calle 64A No 97A-50, Bogota, DC, Colombia
Tel.: (57) 3188001897
Steel Product Mfr & Distr
N.A.I.C.S.: 331110

Chang Fu Stainless Steel Center (Suzhou) Co., Ltd. (1)
No 7 Guangzhou East Road, Taicang Economic Development Zone, Taicang, 215400, Jiangsu, China
Tel.: (86) 51253590800
Web Site: https://www.cfs-sz.com.cn
Steel Product Distr
N.A.I.C.S.: 423510

Daiko Sangyo Co., Ltd. (1)
Yusen Building 3rd Floor 3-9 Kaigan Dori, Naka-ku, Yokohama, 231-0002, Kanagawa, Japan
Tel.: (81) 452122061
Web Site: http://www.daiko-yokohama.co.jp
Emp.: 20
Logistic Services
N.A.I.C.S.: 488510
Hisao Hirama (Pres)

Daikoh Owano Co.,Ltd. (1)
No 1-41 Nankohigashi 8-chome, Suminoe-ku, Osaka, 559-0031, Japan
Tel.: (81) 666125781
Web Site: https://daikoh-owano.co.jp
Emp.: 98
Steel Product Mfr & Distr
N.A.I.C.S.: 331110

Daikoh Steel Co., Ltd. (1)
8-1-41 Nanko-higashi, Suminoe-ku, Osaka, 559-0031, Japan
Tel.: (81) 666125781
Web Site: http://www.daikohsteel.co.jp
Steel Processing Services
N.A.I.C.S.: 331110

HANWA CO., LTD.

Hanwa Co., Ltd.—(Continued)

Daisun Co., Ltd. (1)
Daisan Building 3F 4-5-7 Tachiuriboi, Nishi-ku, Osaka, 550-0012, Japan
Tel.: (81) 665433711
Web Site: https://www.daisun.co.jp
Emp.: 36
Steel Products Mfr
N.A.I.C.S.: 332312

Dongguan Tetsuwa Metals Co., Ltd. (1)
Longxi Industrial Area, Zhouxi Nancheng District, Dongguan, 523077, Guangdong, China
Tel.: (86) 76922401299
Metal Products Mfr
N.A.I.C.S.: 332999

East Japan Foods Co.,Ltd. (1)
4-3-30 Kazuma, Minami, Ishinomaki, 986-0042, Japan
Tel.: (81) 225948377
Web Site: https://www.hfoods.jp
Emp.: 117
Seafood Product Mfr & Distr
N.A.I.C.S.: 311710

FABCON Kyushu Corporation (1)
293-3 Koga, Chikuzen-cho, Chikushino, 818-0047, Fukuoka, Japan
Tel.: (81) 925556652
Web Site: http://www.fabcon-k.com
Emp.: 25
Fabricated Steel Product Mfr
N.A.I.C.S.: 332312

Fas-Link Co., Ltd. (1)
3-5-27 Nonko-minami, Suminoe-ku, Osaka, 559-0032, Japan
Tel.: (81) 665690500
Web Site: http://www.fas-link.com
Screws Mfr & Whslr
N.A.I.C.S.: 332722

Fukuoka Kogyo Co., Ltd. (1)
2-3-10 Fujisaki, Sawara Ward, Fukuoka, 814-0013, Okayama, Japan
Tel.: (81) 928215131
Web Site: https://fukuoka-kogyo.co.jp
Industrial Equipment Distr
N.A.I.C.S.: 423840

Guangzhou Hanwa Trading Co., Ltd. (1)
Unit 3701-3704 Profit Plaza No 76 Westhuangpu Road, Guangzhou, 510623, Guangdong, China
Tel.: (86) 2087320451
Steel Product Distr
N.A.I.C.S.: 423510

HALOS Corporation (1)
4th Fl Hanwa Bekkan No 2 Builldlinig 1-7-3 Shintomi, Chuo-ku, Tokyo, 104-0041, Japan (100%)
Tel.: (81) 335522698
Web Site: http://www.halos.co.jp
Emp.: 679
Amusement Machines Mfr
N.A.I.C.S.: 339999
Fuji Imaizumi (CEO)

HANWA (KOREA) CO., LTD. (1)
Room 3205 Korea World Trade Tower Samseong-Dong 511 Yeongdong-Daero, Gangnam-Gu, Seoul, 6164, Korea (South)
Tel.: (82) 25515387
Sales Range: $25-49.9 Million
Emp.: 20
Ferro Alloy Mfr
N.A.I.C.S.: 331110
Shuhei Nishioka (Pres)

HANWA CANADA CORP. (1)
Ste 502 1001 West Broadway, Vancouver, V6H 4B1, BC, Canada
Tel.: (604) 876-1175
Sales Range: $50-74.9 Million
Emp.: 6
Seafood Whslr
N.A.I.C.S.: 424420

HANWA CO., (HONG KONG) LTD. (1)
Suite 1504 15/F 12 Taikoo Wan Road, Tai Koo Shing Island East, Taikoo Shing, China (Hong Kong)
Tel.: (852) 25450110

Emp.: 16
Seafood Whslr
N.A.I.C.S.: 424420
Tesu Kikuchi (Dir)

HANWA INDIA PRIVATE LTD. (1)
Kanakia wall street Office No 908 9th floor B-wing Andheri Kurla road, Chakala Andheri East, Mumbai, 400093, Maharashtra, India
Tel.: (91) 2240191300
Sales Range: $50-74.9 Million
Emp.: 8
Steel Product Distr
N.A.I.C.S.: 423510

HANWA SINGAPORE (PRIVATE) LTD. (1)
1 Raffles Place 11-61 One Raffles Place Tower 2, Singapore, 048616, Singapore
Tel.: (65) 65367822
Web Site: http://www.hanwa.co.jp
Steel Product Distr
N.A.I.C.S.: 331110

HANWA STEEL SERVICE (THAILAND) CO., LTD. (1)
700/625 Moo 4 700/630 Moo 5 Tambol Baankao, Amphur Panthong, Chon Buri, 20160, Thailand
Tel.: (66) 38210200
Sales Range: $50-74.9 Million
Emp.: 200
Steel Forging Mfr
N.A.I.C.S.: 331110

HANWA THAILAND CO., LTD. (1)
24th Fl Unit 2401-2 Q House Lumpini Bldg No 1 South Sathorn Rd, Tungmahamek Sathorn, Bangkok, 10120, Thailand
Tel.: (66) 23438877
Web Site: https://hkt.hanwa.co.th
Sales Range: $25-49.9 Million
Emp.: 30
Seafood Distr
N.A.I.C.S.: 424460

Hanwa (Beijing) Co., Ltd. (1)
Suite A101 10/F Twin Towers East B12 Jianguomenwai Ave, Chao Yang District, Beijing, China
Tel.: (86) 1051235113
Steel Product Distr
N.A.I.C.S.: 423510

Hanwa (Dalian) Co., Ltd. (1)
Senmao Building 12F 147 Zhongshan Road, Xigang District, Dalian, 116011, Liaoning, China
Tel.: (86) 41183686954
Steel Product Distr
N.A.I.C.S.: 423510

Hanwa (Malaysia) Sdn. Bhd. (1)
Lot 19-5 Level 19 Menara Hap Seng 2 No 1 Jaran P Ramlee, 50250, Kuala Lumpur, Malaysia
Tel.: (60) 320222308
Steel Product Distr
N.A.I.C.S.: 423510

Hanwa (Qingdao) Co., Ltd. (1)
Unit 1006-7 Shangri-la Centre Office No 9 Hongkong Middle Road, Qingdao, 266071, Shandong, China
Tel.: (86) 53285779990
Steel Product Distr
N.A.I.C.S.: 423510

Hanwa Alpha Business Co., Ltd. (1)
14th Floor Ginza Shochiku Square 1-13-1 Tsukiji, Chuo-ku, Tokyo, 104-8429, Japan
Tel.: (81) 335442401
Web Site: https://www.hanwa.co.jp
Life & Casualty Insurance Services
N.A.I.C.S.: 524113

Hanwa American Corp. (1)
Parker Plz 12th Fl 400 Kelby St, Fort Lee, NJ 07024
Tel.: (201) 363-4500
Web Site: http://www.hanwa.com
Sales Range: $25-49.9 Million
Emp.: 30
Import & Export Wholesale Machinery, Scrap & Timber, Petroleum Products & Seafood
N.A.I.C.S.: 423510

Hanwa American Corp. (1)
18100 Von Karman Ste 480, Irvine, CA 92612-0169 (100%)

Tel.: (949) 955-2780
Web Site: http://www.hanwa.com
Sales Range: $10-24.9 Million
Emp.: 6
Import & Export of Iron, Steel, Non-Ferrous Metals, Machinery, Oil, Seafood, Logs, Fuels & Chemicals
N.A.I.C.S.: 423510

Hanwa Chile Limitada (1)
Apoquindo 5583 Oficina 92, Las Condes, Santiago, Chile
Tel.: (56) 222475125
Steel Product Distr
N.A.I.C.S.: 423510
Marcial Gonzalez Donoso (Deputy Mgr)

Hanwa Co., Ltd. (1)
2nd Floor West Tower Nelson Mandela Square Maude Street, Sandton, 2196, South Africa
Tel.: (27) 118815966
Steel Product Distr
N.A.I.C.S.: 423510

Hanwa Co., Ltd. (1)
Unit 7 9 11th Floor HAGL Myanmar Centre Tower 1 192, Kaba Aye Pagoda Road Bahan Township, Yangon, Myanmar
Tel.: (95) 19345379
Steel Product Distr
N.A.I.C.S.: 423510
Lisa Lin (Asst Mgr)

Hanwa Co., Ltd. (1)
14th Floor 6788 Ayala Avenue Oledan Square Metro Manila, Makati, 1226, Philippines
Tel.: (63) 288175624
Steel Product Distr
N.A.I.C.S.: 423510

Hanwa Co., Ltd. (1)
7th Floor 55Strand, London, WC2N 5LS, United Kingdom
Tel.: (44) 2078394448
Steel Product Distr
N.A.I.C.S.: 423510
Toshiyuki Tanaka (Mgr)

Hanwa Daisun Co., Ltd. (1)
1-13-1 Tsukiji, Chuo-ku, Tokyo, 104-0045, Japan
Tel.: (81) 362640130
Web Site: https://hanwadaisun.co.jp
Steel Product Distr
N.A.I.C.S.: 423510

Hanwa Eco Steel Co., Ltd. (1)
4th floor Shinkamagaya F Tower 2-8-17 Shinkamagaya, Kamagaya, 273-0107, Chiba, Japan
Tel.: (81) 474048514
Web Site: https://www.hanwaeco.co.jp
Steel Products Mfr
N.A.I.C.S.: 331110

Hanwa Europe B.V. (1)
WTC Tower-A Level3 Strawinskylaan 305, 1077 XX, Amsterdam, Netherlands
Tel.: (31) 205752460
Seafood Whslr
N.A.I.C.S.: 424420

Hanwa Europe B.V. (1)
Wipplingerstrasse 34 Top 174, 1010, Vienna, Austria
Tel.: (43) 15320165
Steel Product Distr
N.A.I.C.S.: 423510

Hanwa Fellows Engineering (China) Co., Ltd. (1)
16F SMEG Plaza 1386 Hong Qiao Road, Chang Ning District, Shanghai, 200336, China
Tel.: (86) 2162375032
Steel Product Distr
N.A.I.C.S.: 423510

Hanwa Fellows Engineering (Thailand) Co., Ltd. (1)
16th Floor Unit 14B Bubhajit Building 20 North Sathorn Rd, Silom, Bangkok, 10500, Thailand
Tel.: (66) 22347897
Steel Product Distr
N.A.I.C.S.: 423510

Hanwa Foods Co., Ltd. (1)

INTERNATIONAL PUBLIC

1-7-4 Shintomi, Chuo-ku, Tokyo, 104-0041, Japan
Tel.: (81) 362283401
Web Site: https://www.hanwafoods.co.jp
Emp.: 27
Seafood Product Distr
N.A.I.C.S.: 424460

Hanwa Logistics Group Co., Ltd. (1)
3-7-2 Akanehama, Narashino, 275-0024, Chiba, Japan (100%)
Tel.: (81) 474548001
Web Site: http://www.hanwa.co.jp
Emp.: 57
Warehousing & Logistics Services
N.A.I.C.S.: 493110
Takuya Hadano (Dir)

Hanwa Logistics Nagoya Co., Ltd. (1)
13 Kaneoka, Tobishima-mura, Ama, 490-1445, Aichi, Japan
Tel.: (81) 567552691
Web Site: http://www.hanwa.co.jp
Sales Range: $50-74.9 Million
Emp.: 52
Warehousing & Logistics Services
N.A.I.C.S.: 531130

Hanwa Logistics Osaka Co., Ltd. (1)
1-65 Chikkoyawata-machi, Sakai-ku, Sakai, 590-0901, Osaka, Japan
Tel.: (81) 722252720
Web Site: http://www.hanwa.co.jp
Sales Range: $25-49.9 Million
Emp.: 37
Freight Forwarding Services
N.A.I.C.S.: 488510

Hanwa Logistics Tokyo Co., Ltd. - Sendai Factory (1)
2-3 Matsuzakadaira, Taiwa-cho Kurokawa-gun, Miyagi, 981-3408, Japan
Tel.: (81) 22 347 1675
Web Site: http://www.hanwa.co.jp
Steel Shapes Mfr
N.A.I.C.S.: 331221

Hanwa Metals Co., Ltd. (1)
SBS Logicom Nangang Logistics Center 1F 2-5-8 Nanko-minami, Suminoe-ku, Osaka, 559-0032, Japan
Tel.: (81) 647034172
Metal Product Distr
N.A.I.C.S.: 423510

Hanwa Mexicana, S.A. De C.V. (1)
Paseo de la Reforma 255 Piso 11-A Col, Cuauhtemoc, 06500, Mexico, Mexico
Tel.: (52) 5552559934
Steel Product Distr
N.A.I.C.S.: 423510

Hanwa Middle East Fze (1)
Dubai Airport FreeZone East Wing Building No 6E Office No 549, PO Box 293873, PO Box 293873, Dubai, United Arab Emirates
Tel.: (971) 47017565
Steel Product Distr
N.A.I.C.S.: 423510

Hanwa Smc Steel Service Ha Noi Co., Ltd. (1)
Lot 47 Quang Minh Industrial Zone, Quang Minh Town Me Linh District, Hanoi, Vietnam
Tel.: (84) 2435251522
Steel Product Distr
N.A.I.C.S.: 423510

Hanwa Steel Centre (M) Sdn. Bhd. (1)
Plot 33 Jalan Perusahaan Bukit Minyak, Bukit Minyak Industrial Park, 14000, Bukit Mertajam, Penang, Malaysia (56%)
Tel.: (60) 45070033
Web Site: http://www.hanwa-hscm.com.my
Stainless Steel Processing Services
N.A.I.C.S.: 331110

Hanwa Steel Service (Dongguan) Co., Ltd. (1)
No 42 Weijian Road, Chashan Town, Dongguan, 523391, Guangdong, China
Tel.: (86) 76981821000
Steel Product Distr
N.A.I.C.S.: 423510

Hanwa Steel Service Ltd. (1)
Omi-Mizuguchi 2nd Techno Park 32-2 Hinokigaoka, Minakuchi-cho, Koka, 528-0068,

AND PRIVATE COMPANIES

Shiga, Japan
Tel.: (81) 748638211
Web Site: https://www.hanwa.co.jp
Emp.: 78
Industrial Machinery Services
N.A.I.C.S.: 811310

Hanwa Steel Service Mexicana, S.A. De C.V. (1)
Celaya No 105 P I amistad, Parque Industrial Amistad Bajio Guanajuato, 38160, Apaseo el Grande, Mexico
Tel.: (52) 4131586600
Web Site: https://www.hanwa.mx
Steel Product Distr
N.A.I.C.S.: 423510

Hanwa Trading (Shanghai) Co., Ltd. (1)
16F SMEG Plaza 1386 Hong Qiao Road, Chang Ning District, Shanghai, 200336, China
Tel.: (86) 2162375260
Steel Product Distr
N.A.I.C.S.: 423510

Hanwa Vietnam Co., Ltd. (1)
Unit 4-1 19th Floor A & B Tower 76 Le Lai Street, Ben Thanh Ward District 1, Ho Chi Minh City, Vietnam
Tel.: (84) 2838225715
Steel Product Distr
N.A.I.C.S.: 423510
Shota Ayabe *(Deputy Gen Mgr)*

Hirouchi Atsuen Kogyo Co., Ltd. (1)
4-8-16 Shiginonishi, Joto-ku, Osaka, 536-0014, Japan
Tel.: (81) 669632201
Web Site: http://www.hirouchi.jp
Steel Products Mfr
N.A.I.C.S.: 332312

Hirouchi Steel Co., Ltd. (1)
551-1 Korigawa, Yao, 581-0872, Japan
Tel.: (81) 729401171
Steel Product Mfr & Distr
N.A.I.C.S.: 331110

Hokuriku Column Co., Ltd. (1)
2-33-5 Ariiso, Imizu, 933-0251, Toyama, Japan
Tel.: (81) 766861171
Steel Products Mfr
N.A.I.C.S.: 332312

Izumo Tec Co., Ltd. (1)
4-4-7 Kitakyuhoji-cho 7F VPO Honmachi Central, Chuo-ku, Osaka, 541-0057, Japan
Tel.: (81) 662431068
Web Site: https://www.izumo-t.co.jp
Emp.: 22
Construction Services
N.A.I.C.S.: 236220

Japanlife Co., Ltd. (1)
Kinshicho Prime Tower 6th floor 1-5-7 Kameido, Koto-ku, Tokyo, 136-0071, Japan
Tel.: (81) 362606301
Web Site: https://www.japanlife.co.jp
Construction Equipment Mfr
N.A.I.C.S.: 333120

Kaneki Co., Ltd. (1)
17-2 Ichida Gionda Kumiyama-cho, Kusegun, Kyoto, Japan
Tel.: (81) 774435425
Web Site: https://www.kaneki-kyoto.jp
Emp.: 96
Steel Products Mfr
N.A.I.C.S.: 332312

MS Hiyoshi Kouzai Co., Ltd. (1)
4-5-33 Kitamura, Imabari, 799-1502, Ehime, Japan
Tel.: (81) 898355803
Steel Products Mfr
N.A.I.C.S.: 332312

Maruhon Honma Suisan Co., Ltd. (1)
5-4-7 Hachikengojyohigashi, Nishi-ku, Sapporo, 063-0865, Hokkaido, Japan
Tel.: (81) 117563011
Web Site: https://www.honma-suisan.co.jp
Sea Food Product Services
N.A.I.C.S.: 424460

Matsuoka Kozai Co., Ltd. (1)
76-1 Konan-cho Nojiri, Koka, 520-3307, Shiga, Japan

Tel.: (81) 748863003
Logistic Services
N.A.I.C.S.: 488510

Metaltech Co., Ltd. (1)
4-29-9 Midori, Sumida-ku, Tokyo, 130-0021, Japan
Tel.: (81) 336338541
Web Site: https://www.metaltech.co.jp
Emp.: 57
Metal Products Mfr
N.A.I.C.S.: 332999

NST Saigon Coil Center Co., Ltd. (1)
No 3 VSIP Street 8, Vietnam-Singapore Industrial Park Binh Hoa Ward Thuan An Town, Binh Dong, Vietnam
Tel.: (84) 2743784460
Web Site: https://nstsaigon.vn
Steel Product Distr
N.A.I.C.S.: 423510

Nikko Kinzoku Co., Ltd. (1)
1071 Tanoura, Moji-ku, Kitakyushu, 801-0803, Fukuoka, Japan
Tel.: (81) 933320731
Construction Materials Distr
N.A.I.C.S.: 423390

Owano Shoten Co., Ltd. (1)
8-1-103 Nanko-higashi, Suminoe-ku, Osaka, 559-0031, Japan
Tel.: (81) 666137708
Logistic Services
N.A.I.C.S.: 488510

PT HANWA STEEL SERVICE INDONESIA (1)
MM2100 Industrial Town Blok QQ-5, West Cikarang, Bekasi, 17520, West Java, Indonesia
Tel.: (62) 2189981791
Sales Range: $25-49.9 Million
Emp.: 92
Steel Processing Services
N.A.I.C.S.: 331110

PT. Hanwa Indonesia (1)
Jakarta Mori Tower 15th Floor Jl Jendral Sudirman Kav 40 - 41, Jakarta, 10210, Indonesia
Tel.: (62) 2125098028
Web Site: http://www.hanwa.co.id
Steel Product Distr
N.A.I.C.S.: 423510

PT. Hanwa Royal Metals (1)
Jl Mayjen Sungkono Desa Prambangan Kec Kebomas Kab Gresik, Surabaya, 61161, Jawa Timur, Indonesia
Tel.: (62) 313988262
Metal Products Mfr
N.A.I.C.S.: 332999
Ardian Com *(Asst Mgr)*

Pcm Processing (Thailand) Ltd. (1)
700/614 M 7 Donhuaroh Amata, Chonburi Industrial Estate Muangchonburi, Chon Buri, 20000, Thailand
Tel.: (66) 38 193 2902
Web Site: https://www.pcm-pro.com
Emp.: 121
Steel Products Mfr
N.A.I.C.S.: 332312
Pajongjit Changsanoh *(Sls Mgr)*

Ri Hong Stainless (Shanghai) Co., Ltd. (1)
No 118 Liuhua Road, Putuo District, Shanghai, 200331, China
Tel.: (86) 66278333
Web Site: https://www.rihongs.com
Steel Product Distr
N.A.I.C.S.: 423510

S.K. Engineering Co., Ltd. (1)
16th Fl Ginza Shochiku Square Bldg 1-13-1 Tsukiji, Chuo-ku, Tokyo, 104-8429, Japan
Tel.: (81) 335445101
Web Site: http://www.hanwa.co.jp
Construction Engineering Services
N.A.I.C.S.: 541330

San Diego Vista Steel Service Corporation (1)
8753 Kerns St, San Diego, CA 92154-6213
Tel.: (619) 671-9247
Web Site: https://www.sdvssc.com
Emp.: 25

Steel Coils Mfr
N.A.I.C.S.: 332613
Makoto Takahashi *(Pres)*

San Ei Metal Co., Ltd. (1)
Tel.: (81) 647070301
Web Site: http://www.san-ei-metal.co.jp
Metal Products Mfr
N.A.I.C.S.: 332999

Santo Steel Co., Ltd. (1)
3-4-3 Kawara-machi, Chuo-ku, Osaka, 541-0048, Japan
Tel.: (81) 662210791
Reinforcing Bars Mfr
N.A.I.C.S.: 331110

Sanyo Kouzai Co., Ltd. (1)
2-1-13 Minamiyoshijima, Naka-ku, Hiroshima, 730-0826, Japan
Tel.: (81) 822430288
Web Site: https://www.sanyo-kouzai.co.jp
Emp.: 78
Steel Products Mfr
N.A.I.C.S.: 332312

Seattle Shrimp & Seafood Company, Inc. (1)
801 S Fidalgo St Ste 100, Seattle, WA 98108
Tel.: (206) 805-5000
Web Site: http://www.seattleshrimp.com
Sea Food Product Services
N.A.I.C.S.: 424460
Atsushige Amano *(Pres)*

Seibu Service Co., Ltd. (1)
17 Sumiyoshihama-cho, Higashinada-ku, Kobe, 658-0042, Hyogo, Japan
Tel.: (81) 788573818
Web Site: https://www.seibu-recycle.co.jp
Emp.: 45
Industrial Disposal Services
N.A.I.C.S.: 561990

Seiki Co., Ltd. (1)
1-20 Nakata Tomiki Taketoyo-cho, Chitagun, Chita, 470-2531, Aichi, Japan
Tel.: (81) 569727551
Web Site: https://www.seiki-japan.com
Aluminum Cane Product Mfr
N.A.I.C.S.: 331315

Showa Metal Co., Ltd. (1)
6-26 Higashi-ogishim, Kawasaki-ku, Kawasaki, 210-0869, Kanagawa, Japan **(97%)**
Tel.: (81) 442771431
Web Site: https://www.sk-showa.co.jp
Sales Range: $25-49.9 Million
Emp.: 56
Recycles & Distributes Titanium & Other Rare Metal Scraps
N.A.I.C.S.: 331492

Siam Hanwa Co., Ltd. (1)
24th Floor Unit 2401-2402 Q house Lumpini Building, 1 South Sathorn Road Tungmahamek Sathorn, Bangkok, 10120, Thailand
Tel.: (66) 23438877
Steel Product Distr
N.A.I.C.S.: 423510

Sodensha Co., Ltd. (1)
18-1 Amida Furukawakamizone, Osaki, 989-6264, Miyagi, Japan
Tel.: (81) 229272165
Web Site: https://sodensha.jp
Emp.: 40
Industrial Equipment Distr
N.A.I.C.S.: 423840

Sohbi Craft Poland Sp.Z o.o. (1)
Pomeranian Special Economic Zone-Crystal Park Ostaszewo 57h, 87-148, Lysomice, Poland
Tel.: (48) 56 649 5600
Web Site: https://www.sohbi.pl
Metal Products Mfr
N.A.I.C.S.: 332999
Jakub Gutkowski *(Mgr-Sls Section)*

Sohbi Kohgei (Phils) Inc. (1)
Special Economic Zone Lima Technology Center, Lipa, 4217, Batangas, Philippines
Tel.: (63) 43 981 3830
Web Site: https://www.sohbi.ph
Metal Products Mfr
N.A.I.C.S.: 332999
Marlon Lat *(Mgr-HRGA)*

Stainless Pipe Kogyo Co., Ltd. (1)

4-16-8 Mokuzaidori, Mihara-ku, Sakai, 587-0042, Osaka, Japan
Tel.: (81) 723612882
Web Site: http://www.sutepai.co.jp
Steel Products Mfr
N.A.I.C.S.: 332312

Subaru Steel Co., Ltd. (1)
1-chome 4 Chome Nearly 38 Citizen New Namba Bldg Hikaru 11 Order, Minato-cho Naniwa-ku Xinhua, Osaka, 556-0017, Japan
Tel.: (81) 666352330
Web Site: http://www.subarusteel.co.jp
Steel Products Mfr
N.A.I.C.S.: 332312

Taiwan Hanwa Kogyo Co., Ltd. (1)
Rm 5 7F No 57 Fuxing N Rd, Songshan Dist, Taipei, 10595, Taiwan
Tel.: (886) 227213229
Steel Product Distr
N.A.I.C.S.: 423510

Taiyokozai Co., Ltd. (1)
4F HK Yodoyabashi Garden Avenue 4-3-9 Fushimicho, Chuo-ku, Osaka, 541-0044, Japan
Tel.: (81) 662210220
Web Site: https://www.taiyokozai.co.jp
Steel Sheet Mfr
N.A.I.C.S.: 332322

Tanaka Steel Trading Co., Ltd. (1)
150 Shimokawasaki, Hanyu, 348-8525, Japan
Tel.: (81) 485621212
Web Site: https://tanaka-th.co.jp
Steel Product Distr
N.A.I.C.S.: 423510

Tekken Industry Company (1)
2-10-2 Takase, Maruoka-cho, Sakai, 910-0355, Fukui, Japan
Tel.: (81) 776668215
Web Site: https://www.tekken-ind.co.jp
Emp.: 57
Steel Products Mfr
N.A.I.C.S.: 332312

Tohan Steel Co., Ltd. (1)
1-17-1 Hinode, Funabashi, 273-0015, Chiba, Japan
Tel.: (81) 474318201
Web Site: https://tohansteel.co.jp
Sales Range: $25-49.9 Million
Emp.: 80
Reinforcing Bars Mfr
N.A.I.C.S.: 332111

Toyo Energy Co., Ltd. (1)
4-3-9 Fushimi-cho HK Yodoyabashi Garden Avenue 6th floor, Chuo-ku, Osaka, 541-0044, Japan
Tel.: (81) 662010681
Web Site: https://www.toyo-e.co.jp
Sales Range: $5-14.9 Billion
Emp.: 63
Petroleum Product Distr
N.A.I.C.S.: 424720

Wing Co., Ltd. (1)
Web Site: http://www.wing1964.co.jp
Steel Products Mfr
N.A.I.C.S.: 332312

Wuhan Fubohe Auto Parts Co., Ltd. (1)
No 1 Boqi Road, Caidian District, Wuhan, 430100, China
Tel.: (86) 2769813302
Automobile Parts Mfr
N.A.I.C.S.: 336390

HANWANG TECHNOLOGY CO., LTD.

3rd Floor Building 5 No 8 Dongbeiwang West Road, Haidian District, Beijing, 100193, China
Tel.: (86) 1082786816
Web Site: http://www.hanvon.com
Year Founded: 2005
002362—(SSE)
Rev.: $196,631,604
Assets: $283,526,568
Liabilities: $61,542,936
Net Worth: $221,983,632
Earnings: ($19,035,432)

HANWANG TECHNOLOGY CO., LTD.

INTERNATIONAL PUBLIC

Hanwang Technology Co., Ltd.—(Continued)
Emp.: 759
Fiscal Year-end: 12/31/22
Computer & Electronics Mfr
N.A.I.C.S.: 334118
Liu Yingjian *(Chm)*

Subsidiaries:

Hanvon C-PEN Technology Co., Ltd. (1)
Hanwang Building Zhongguancun Software Park Building 5, Dongbeiwang West Road
No 8 Haidian District, Beijing, 100193, China
Tel.: (86) 1082786849
Web Site: https://qy.hw99.com
Integrated Chip Mfr
N.A.I.C.S.: 334413

Hanvon Manufacturer Co., Ltd (1)
No 1 Hanwang Road Dongyanjiao, Beijing, 101601, China
Tel.: (86) 1061592777
Computer Peripheral Equipment Mfr
N.A.I.C.S.: 334118

Hanvon Technology (Deutschland) GmbH (1)
Wollgrasweg 9 Kayhude, Halle, 23863, Germany
Tel.: (49) 4535298852
Computer Peripheral Equipment Distr
N.A.I.C.S.: 423430

Hanvon Technology Company Ltd (1)
Room 1501-08 Millennuium City 5 418 Kwun Tong Road Kwun Tong, Kowloon, China (Hong Kong)
Tel.: (852) 21521189
Web Site: http://www.hanvon.com.hk
Computer Peripheral Equipment Distr
N.A.I.C.S.: 423430

HANWEI ELECTRONICS GROUP CORPORATION

No 169 Xuesong Road, National High-Tech zone, Zhengzhou, 450001, China
Tel.: (86) 37167169070
Web Site: https://www.hwsensor.com
Year Founded: 1998
300007—(CHIN)
Rev.: $322,156,993
Assets: $872,475,212
Liabilities: $424,432,418
Net Worth: $448,042,794
Earnings: $18,423,307
Fiscal Year-end: 12/31/23
Gas Sensor & Instrument Mfr
N.A.I.C.S.: 334519
Hongjun Ren *(Chm)*

HANWEI ENERGY SERVICES CORP.

595 Howe Street Suite 902, Vancouver, V6C 2T5, BC, Canada
Tel.: (604) 685-2239 BC
Web Site:
  http://www.hanweienergy.com
Year Founded: 2005
HE—(TSX)
Rev.: $7,466,863
Assets: $15,355,374
Liabilities: $15,511,830
Net Worth: ($156,456)
Earnings: ($1,095,192)
Emp.: 123
Fiscal Year-end: 03/31/21
Fiberglass-Reinforced Plastic Pipes Mfr
N.A.I.C.S.: 326122
Fulai Lang *(Chm, Pres & CEO)*

HANWHA ACE SPECIAL PURPOSE ACQUISITION 2ND CO., LTD.

56 Yeoui-daero, Yeongdeungpo-gu, Seoul, Korea (South)
Tel.: (82) 237727762
Year Founded: 2015
Financial Investment Management Services
N.A.I.C.S.: 523940
Sang-Man Lee *(CEO)*

HANWHA ENGINE CO., LTD.

67 Gongdan-ro, Seongsan-gu Sinchon-dong, Changwon, Gyeongsangnam-do, Korea (South)
Tel.: (82) 552606000 KR
Web Site: https://www.hanwha-engine.com
Year Founded: 1983
082740—(KRS)
Rev.: $586,174,264
Assets: $733,428,636
Liabilities: $563,441,626
Net Worth: $169,987,010
Earnings: ($30,888,925)
Emp.: 775
Fiscal Year-end: 12/31/22
Marine Diesel Engines Mfr
N.A.I.C.S.: 333618
Ryu Moon Ghee *(CEO)*

Subsidiaries:

HSD Marine Industry(Dalian) Co., Ltd. (1)
No 31 Haiqing Road, Development Area, Dalian, China
Tel.: (86) 41187517987
Web Site: http://www.hsdengine.com
Marine Engine Mfr
N.A.I.C.S.: 333618

HANWHA GROUP

1 Janggyo-dong, Jung-gu, Seoul, 100-797, Korea (South)
Tel.: (82) 27291881
Web Site: http://www.hanwha.co.kr
Year Founded: 1952
Sales Range: $1-9.9 Million
Emp.: 50,000
Holding Company; Diversified Trading, Chemicals, Engineering & Financial Services
N.A.I.C.S.: 551112
Seung-Youn Kim *(Chm)*

Subsidiaries:

Asan Techno Valley Co., Ltd. (1)
Seyoung Building 15th Floor 199 Gwongwang-ro, Paldal-gu, Suwon, Gyeonggi-do, Korea (South)
Tel.: (82) 31 8014 7000
Web Site: http://www.atv21.co.kr
Construction Engineering Services
N.A.I.C.S.: 541330

Dream Pharma Corp. (1)
6th FL Sogong-Dong Hanwha Bldg 109 Sogong-Ro, Jung-Gu, Seoul, 100-755, Korea (South)
Tel.: (82) 2 728 7407
Web Site: http://www.dreampharma.co.kr
Pharmaceuticals Product Mfr
N.A.I.C.S.: 325412

Gimhae Techno Valley Co., Ltd. (1)
Jeongwu Building 5th Floor 55 Naeoejungang-ro, Gimhae, Gyeongsangnam-do, Korea (South)
Tel.: (82) 55 320 5700
Web Site: http://www.gtv21.co.kr
Construction Engineering Services
N.A.I.C.S.: 541330

Hancomm Inc. (1)
Hanwha Life Building 92 Sejong-daero, Jung-gu, Seoul, Korea (South)
Tel.: (82) 2 3119 114
Web Site: http://www.hancomm.co.kr
Advertising Agency Services
N.A.I.C.S.: 541810

Hanwha Advanced Materials Co., Ltd. (1)
Hanwha Building Janggyo-dong 1, Jung-gu, Seoul, 100-797, Korea (South)
Tel.: (82) 2729 5700
Web Site: http://www.hwam.co.kr
Specialty Engineered Materials & Products Mfr
N.A.I.C.S.: 339999

Subsidiary (Non-US):

Hanwha Advanced Materials (Beijing) Co., Ltd. (2)
Zhongguancun Science Park East Sector Changping Zone 4 Lixiang Road, Beijing, 102200, China
Tel.: (86) 10 6073 5588
Automotive Components Mfr
N.A.I.C.S.: 336370

Hanwha Advanced Materials (Shanghai) Co., Ltd. (2)
Jiading Industrial Zone 1201 Xingrong Road, Shanghai, 201807, China
Tel.: (86) 21 3996 3996
Automotive Components Mfr
N.A.I.C.S.: 336370

Subsidiary (US):

Hanwha Advanced Materials Alabama LLC (2)
4400 N Park Dr, Opelika, AL 36801
Tel.: (334) 741-7725
Web Site: http://www.hanwhaus.com
Automotive Components Mfr
N.A.I.C.S.: 336370
Lee Sun-seok *(CEO)*

Subsidiary (Non-US):

Hanwha Advanced Materials Czech s.r.o. (2)
Priborska 280, 739 42, Frydek-Mistek, Chlebovice, Czech Republic
Tel.: (420) 552 304 608
Web Site: http://www.hanwhacz.cz
Thermoplastic Product Mfr
N.A.I.C.S.: 325211

Hanwha Aerospace Co., Ltd. (1)
1204 Changwon-daero, Seongsan-gu Changwon-si Gyeongsangnam-do, Busan, Korea (South)
Tel.: (82) 552602114
Web Site:
  http://www.hanwhaaerospace.com
Rev.: $5,015,877,662
Assets: $11,625,650,618
Liabilities: $8,616,108,632
Net Worth: $3,009,541,986
Earnings: $116,605,441
Emp.: 1,931
Fiscal Year-end: 12/31/2022
Security Imaging Mfr
N.A.I.C.S.: 334610
Hyun-Woo Shin *(Chm & CEO)*

Subsidiary (US):

174 Power Global Corporation (2)
300 Spectrum Center Drive Suite 1020, Irvine, CA 92618
Tel.: (949) 748-5970
Web Site: http://www.174powerglobal.com
Solar Power Generato
N.A.I.C.S.: 221122
Henry Yun *(Pres)*

Subsidiary (Domestic):

OnForce Solar, Inc. (3)
728 E 136th St, Bronx, NY 10454
Tel.: (800) 786-4028
Web Site: http://www.onforcesolar.com
Finances, Designs, Engineers, Installs & Maintains Solar Energy Systems for Commercial, Industrial & Residential Customers
N.A.I.C.S.: 221118
Charles Feit *(CEO)*

Joint Venture (Non-US):

Dyna-Mac Holdings Ltd. (2)
45 Gul Road, Singapore, 629350, Singapore
Tel.: (65) 64150880
Web Site: https://www.dyna-mac.com
Rev.: $291,729,910
Assets: $261,406,498
Liabilities: $208,169,355
Net Worth: $53,237,143
Earnings: $21,730,667
Emp.: 949
Fiscal Year-end: 12/31/2023
Offshore Oil & Gas Engineering & Construction Services
N.A.I.C.S.: 237990
Tjew Yok Lim *(COO)*

Subsidiary (Domestic):

Dyna-Mac Engineering Services Pte Ltd (3)
45 Gul Road, Singapore, 629350, Singapore
Tel.: (65) 64150880
Sales Range: $200-249.9 Million
Emp.: 700
Oil & Gas Line Construction Engineering Services
N.A.I.C.S.: 237120

Dyna-Mac Offshore Services Pte. Ltd. (3)
45 Gul Road, Singapore, 629350, Singapore
Tel.: (65) 67625816
Emp.: 500
Marine Engineering Services
N.A.I.C.S.: 541330
Desmond Lim *(CEO)*

Haven Automation Industries (S) Pte. Ltd. (3)
84 Tuas Avenue 11, Singapore, 639098, Singapore
Tel.: (65) 68610880
Sales Range: $75-99.9 Million
Emp.: 150
Ship Building & Repair Services
N.A.I.C.S.: 336611

Subsidiary (US):

Hanwa Aerospace USA (2)
5 McKee Pl, Cheshire, CT 06410
Tel.: (203) 806-2090
Web Site:
  http://www.hanwhaaerospaceusa.com
Sales Range: $100-124.9 Million
Tools, Fixtures, Jet Engine Components, Injection Molds, Gages & Spindles Designer & Mfr
N.A.I.C.S.: 333515
Terry Bruni *(Pres & COO)*

Subsidiary (Domestic):

Apex Machine Tool Company, Inc. (3)
1790 New Britain Ave, Farmington, CT 06032 (100%)
Tel.: (860) 677-2884
Web Site: http://www.apexmachinetool.com
Sales Range: $10-24.9 Million
Emp.: 240
Engineeering Services
N.A.I.C.S.: 541330

Unit (Domestic):

EDAC Aero Rotating Components (3)
275 Richard St, Newington, CT 06111
Tel.: (860) 667-2134
Web Site: http://www.edacaero.com
Sales Range: $25-49.9 Million
Emp.: 120
Aircraft Engine Engineering, Manufacturing & Repair Services
N.A.I.C.S.: 336412

Subsidiary (Domestic):

Flanagan Brothers, Inc. (3)
81 National Dr, Glastonbury, CT 06033 (100%)
Tel.: (860) 633-9474
Web Site:
  http://www.flanaganindustries.com
Rev.: $8,000,000
Emp.: 90
Mfr of Aerospace & Land-Based Gas Turbine Components
N.A.I.C.S.: 336413
Micheal Flanagan *(VP)*

Hanwha Asset Management Co., Ltd. (1)
korea Life 63 Building 60 Youido-Dong, Yeongdeungpo-gu, Seoul, 7345, Korea (South)
Tel.: (82) 2 6950 0000
Web Site: http://www.hanwhafund.co.kr

AND PRIVATE COMPANIES — HANWHA GROUP

Emp.: 200
Asset Management Services
N.A.I.C.S.: 531390
Kim Dong Hyun (CEO)

Hanwha Azdel, Inc. (1)
2000 Enterprise Dr, Forest, VA 24551
Tel.: (434) 385-6524
Web Site: http://www.azdel.com
Thermoplastic Composite Sheets Mfr
N.A.I.C.S.: 326130
George Bondurant (Gen Mgr)

Hanwha Corporation (1)
86 Cheonggyecheon-ro, Jung-gu, Seoul, Korea (South)
Tel.: (82) 27291881
Web Site: https://www.hanwha.com
Rev.: $39,439,167,644
Assets: $155,677,559,640
Liabilities: $131,035,887,653
Net Worth: $24,641,671,986
Earnings: $1,213,956,475
Emp.: 5,124
Fiscal Year-end: 12/31/2023
Explosives & Guided Weapons Mfr; Food & Industrial Raw Materials Whslr
N.A.I.C.S.: 325920
Seung Youn Kim (Chm)

Affiliate (Non-US):

Amru and Hanwha International Co., Ltd. (2)
15 Phum Boeung Salang Sangkat Russei Keo Khan Russei Keo, Phnom Penh, Cambodia
Tel.: (855) 23 990 987
Machine Tools Mfr
N.A.I.C.S.: 333517

Subsidiary (Non-US):

Hanwha (H.K.) Co., Ltd. (2)
Unit 2709 The Center 99 Queens Road, Central, Central, China (Hong Kong)
Tel.: (852) 2529 9325
Web Site: http://www.hanwha.co.kr
Emp.: 3
Machine Tools Mfr
N.A.I.C.S.: 333517
Jh Ban (Gen Mgr)

Hanwha China (2)
Beijing Kerry Center South Tower 10th Floor 1 Guanghua Road, Chaoyang, Beijing, 100020, China
Tel.: (86) 10 6583 777
Machine Tools Mfr
N.A.I.C.S.: 333517

Hanwha Europe GmbH (2)
Mergenthaller Allee 79-81, Eschborn, 65760, Germany
Tel.: (49) 619650160
Web Site: http://www.hanwha.de
Chemical Products
N.A.I.C.S.: 325998

Hanwha Internacional do Brasil Ltda. (2)
Centro Profissional Shopping Morumbi Av Roque Petroni, Junior 1089 Conj-1003, Sao Paulo, 04707-000, Brazil
Tel.: (55) 11 3033 5940
Metal Mining Services
N.A.I.C.S.: 213114

Hanwha International (S) Pte Ltd. (2)
4 Shenton Way 15-05/06 SGX 2 Center, Singapore, 068807, Singapore
Tel.: (65) 6227 3139
Machine Tools Mfr
N.A.I.C.S.: 333517

Hanwha International India Pvt. Ltd. (2)
No 35 3rd Floor Maker Chamber III Nariman Point, Mumbai, 400021, India
Tel.: (91) 22 2204 3720
Machine Tools Mfr
N.A.I.C.S.: 333517
Young Chung Chu (Mng Dir)

Subsidiary (US):

Hanwha International LLC (2)
2559 Golden Plz Route 30, Cranbury, NJ 08512
Tel.: (609) 655-2500
Bearings, Irons, Livestock, Petrochemicals & Plastic Products Importer & Exporter
N.A.I.C.S.: 425120
Jason Kim (Gen Mgr)

Subsidiary (Non-US):

Hanwha Japan Co., Ltd. (2)
Hanwha Building 8F 10-1 Shiba-4 chome, Minato-Ku, Tokyo, 108, Japan
Tel.: (81) 354415900
Web Site: http://www.hanwha-japan.com
Petrochemicals, Bearings, IT, Plastic Products & Machinery Equipment Importer & Exporter
N.A.I.C.S.: 425120

Subsidiary (US):

Universal Bearings, Inc. (2)
431 N Birkey Dr, Bremen, IN 46506
Tel.: (574) 546-2261
Web Site: http://www.univbrg.com
Emp.: 300
Loose Needle Rollers & Related Products Mfr
N.A.I.C.S.: 332991
Youn Kim (Pres)

Hanwha Defense Systems Co., Ltd. (1)
799 Gongdan-ro, Seongsan-gu, Changwon, Gyeongsangnam-do, Korea (South)
Tel.: (82) 55 280 6114
Web Site: http://www.hanwha-defensesystems.co.kr
Sales Range: $550-599.9 Million
Armored Vehicles & Weapon Systems Developer & Mfr
N.A.I.C.S.: 561499
Seungwoo Kim (Mgr-Personal Info)

Hanwha Development Co., Ltd. (1)
Seoul Plaza Hotel 119 Sogong Ro, Jung-gu, Seoul, 100 864, Korea (South) **(53.8%)**
Tel.: (82) 27712200
Web Site: http://www.hoteltheplaza.com
Hotel Operator
N.A.I.C.S.: 721110
Yuji Hirahara (Gen Mgr)

Subsidiary (US):

Hanwha America Development Inc. (2)
225 N Columbus Dr Ste 100, Chicago, IL 60610
Tel.: (312) 469-8093
Machine Tools Mfr
N.A.I.C.S.: 333517

Subsidiary (Non-US):

Hanwha Canada Development Inc. (2)
2860 Innovation Drive, London, N6M-0C5, ON, Canada
Tel.: (519) 457-8325
Machine Tools Mfr
N.A.I.C.S.: 333517

Hanwha Energy Corp. (1)
9F Hanwha Bldg 86 Cheonggyecheon-ro, Jung-Gu, Seoul, Korea (South)
Tel.: (82) 2 279 3099
Web Site: http://www.hec.hanwha.co.kr
Electric Power Distribution Services
N.A.I.C.S.: 221122
Kwon-Hyek Woong (CEO)

Hanwha Engineering & Construction Corp. (1)
Hanwha Building 3F-5F 1 Janggyo-Dong, Jung-Gu, Seoul, 100-797, Korea (South) **(100%)**
Tel.: (82) 27292255
Web Site: http://www.hwenc.com
Engineering & Construction Services
N.A.I.C.S.: 541330

Subsidiary (Non-US):

Hanwha Saudi Contracting Co., Ltd. (2)
31952 Eastern Cement Tower Suite 506 King Fahd Road, PO Box 31156, Khobar-Dammam Highway, Al Khobar, Saudi Arabia
Tel.: (966) 3 881 2193
Web Site: http://www.hwenc.com
Machine Tools Mfr

N.A.I.C.S.: 333517
Saji Mohammed (Asst Mgr-HR)

Hanwha General Chemical Co., Ltd. (1)
86 Chenggyecheon-ro, Jung-ku, Seoul, Korea (South)
Tel.: (82) 27292700
Web Site: http://www.hanwhasolutions.com
Rev.: $8,172,826,155
Assets: $13,485,770,827
Liabilities: $8,492,742,226
Net Worth: $4,993,028,601
Earnings: ($214,023,899)
Emp.: 2,464
Fiscal Year-end: 12/31/2019
Chemicals & Chemical Products Mfr
N.A.I.C.S.: 325998
Seon Choi (Pres)

Subsidiary (US):

Ansaldo Energy Inc. (2)
188 Route 10 West, Suite 321, East Hanover, NJ 07936
Tel.: (973) 781-1500
Power Generation & Plant Engineering Services
N.A.I.C.S.: 541330

Subsidiary (Non-US):

Hanwha Chemical (Ningbo) Co., Ltd. (2)
No 55 Huandao North Road Daxie Development Zone, Ningbo, 315812, Zhejiang, China
Tel.: (86) 574 8675 1088
Chemical Products Mfr
N.A.I.C.S.: 325998
Lin Cheng (Deputy Mgr)

Hanwha Chemical (Thailand) Co., Ltd. (2)
377 Moo 17 Bangsaothong, Samut Prakan, 10540, Thailand
Tel.: (66) 23153207
Web Site: http://www.hanwha.th.com
Emp.: 200
PVC Products Mfr
N.A.I.C.S.: 326122

Hanwha Chemical Malaysia Sdn. Bhd. (2)
Suite No 22 04 Level 22 Menara Citibank 165, Jalan Ampang, 50450, Kuala Lumpur, Malaysia
Tel.: (60) 19 228 1601
Chemical Products Mfr
N.A.I.C.S.: 325998

Hanwha Chemical Trading (Shanghai) Co., Ltd. (2)
Dawning Center East Tower 19th Floor 500 Hongbaoshi Road, Changning, Shanghai, 201103, China
Tel.: (86) 21 6278 5556
Chemical Products Mfr
N.A.I.C.S.: 325998

Subsidiary (Domestic):

Hanwha Galleria Co., Ltd. (2)
8th Fl Taepyeongno 2Ga 92 SejongDaero, Jung-gu, Seoul, 100-733, Korea (South)
Tel.: (82) 2 410 7114
Web Site: http://www.hanwhagalleria.co.kr
Departmental Store Operator
N.A.I.C.S.: 455110
Kang Shin-ho (Asst Mgr)

Subsidiary (Domestic):

Hanwha Galleria Timeworld Co., Ltd. (3)
211 Daedeok-daero, Seo-gu, Daejeon, Korea (South) **(98.3%)**
Tel.: (82) 42 480 000
Departmental Store Operator
N.A.I.C.S.: 455110

Subsidiary (Domestic):

Hanwha Q CELLS Co., Ltd. (2)
Hanwha Building 86 Cheonggyecheon-ro Jung-gu, Seoul, 04541, Korea (South) **(49.58%)**
Tel.: (82) 27292512
Web Site: http://www.hanwha-qcells.com

Sales Range: $1-4.9 Billion
Photovoltaic Cell Mfr
N.A.I.C.S.: 334413
Nam Seong-woo (Chm & CEO)

Subsidiary (Non-US):

Hanwha Q CELLS GmbH (3)
OT Thalheim Sonnenallee 17-21, 06766, Bitterfeld-Wolfen, Germany
Tel.: (49) 349466990
Web Site: http://www.q-cells.com
Sales Range: $1-4.9 Billion
Emp.: 1,500
Solar Cells Developer & Mfr
N.A.I.C.S.: 335999
Andreas von Zitzewitz (Mng Dir & COO)

Subsidiary (Non-US):

Hanwha Q CELLS Australia Pty. Ltd. (4)
Level 2 56 Berry Street, North Sydney, 2060, NSW, Australia
Tel.: (61) 2 9455 0017
Solar Equipment Mfr
N.A.I.C.S.: 333414

Hanwha Q CELLS Japan Co., Ltd. (4)
Hanwha Bldg 8F 10-1 Shiba-4 chome, Minato-ku, Tokyo, Japan
Tel.: (81) 3 5441 5900
Solar Equipment Mfr
N.A.I.C.S.: 333414

Hanwha Q CELLS Malaysia (4)
Lot 1 Jalan SP 2 Seksyen 2 Selangor Science Park 2, 63300, Cyberjaya, Selangor, Malaysia
Tel.: (60) 3 83 15 00 00
Solar Equipment Mfr
N.A.I.C.S.: 333414

Subsidiary (US):

Hanwha Q CELLS USA Corp. (4)
8001 Irvine Ctr Dr Ste 1250, Irvine, CA 92618
Tel.: (949) 748-5996
Web Site: http://www.q-cells.us
Solar Equipment Mfr
N.A.I.C.S.: 333414

Subsidiary (Non-US):

Q-Cells Asia Ltd. (4)
Rm 1308 13 F Nan Fung Tower, 173 Des Voeux Rd, Central, China (Hong Kong)
Tel.: (852) 2541 5688
Photovoltaic Cells Mfr & Whslr
N.A.I.C.S.: 334413

Holding (US):

Hanwha Solar America LLC (3)
2424 Walsh Ave, Santa Clara, CA 95051
Tel.: (408) 841-4161
Solar Equipment Mfr
N.A.I.C.S.: 333414

Subsidiary (Non-US):

Hanwha SolarOne (Shanghai) Co., Ltd. (3)
Room 605-606 Yongda International Tower 2277 Longyang Road, Shanghai, 201204, China
Tel.: (86) 21 6278 5556
Solar Equipment Mfr
N.A.I.C.S.: 333414
Jun Xi (Sr Mgr-Mktg Comm)

Hanwha SolarOne GmbH (3)
Oskar Messter Strasse 13, 85737, Ismaning, Germany
Tel.: (49) 89 2175 667 30
Solar Equipment Mfr
N.A.I.C.S.: 333414

Hanwha SolarOne Technology Co., Ltd. (3)
No 66 Dapu Road Lianyungang ECO & TECH Development Zone, Lianyungang, China
Tel.: (86) 518 8115 1158
Solar Equipment Mfr
N.A.I.C.S.: 333414

Jiangsu Linyang Solarfun Co., Ltd. (3)

HANWHA GROUP

Hanwha Group—(Continued)

No 666 Linyang Rd, Qidong, Nantong, China
Tel.: (86) 51383307688
Semiconductor & Device Mfr
N.A.I.C.S.: 334413

Subsidiary (Domestic):

KPX Fine Chemical Co., Ltd. (2)
425 Wol Ha-Dong, Yeosu, Jeonnam, Korea (South)
Tel.: (82) 61 688 4800
Basic Chemicals Mfr
N.A.I.C.S.: 325199
Eui-Nam Kwak *(CEO)*

Subsidiary (US):

Power Systems Mfg., LLC (2)
1440 W Indiantown Rd, Jupiter, FL 33458-7925
Tel.: (561) 354-1100
Web Site: http://www.psm.com
Aftermarket Services for Gas Turbine Power Plant Mfr
N.A.I.C.S.: 333618
Alexander Hoffs *(Pres)*

Joint Venture (Domestic):

Yeochun NCC Co., Ltd. (2)
Centropolis B 7F 26 Ujeongguk-ro, Jongno-gu, Seoul, 03161, Korea (South)
Tel.: (82) 26 370 5300
Web Site: https://www.yncc.co.kr
Emp.: 981
Petrochemical Mfr; Owned 50% by Hanwha Chemical Corporation & 50% by Daelim Industrial Co., Ltd.
N.A.I.C.S.: 325110

Hanwha Hotels & Resorts Co., Ltd. (1)
86 Cheonggyecheon-ro, Jung-Gu, Seoul, Korea (South)
Tel.: (82) 2 729 3849
Web Site: http://www.hwrc.co.kr
Hotel Operator
N.A.I.C.S.: 721110
Kyung Sup Byun *(Mgr)*

Hanwha Life Insurance Co., Ltd. (1)
63 Hanwha Life Building 60 Youido-dong, Yongdungpo-gu, Seoul, Korea (South)
Tel.: (82) 27896114
Web Site: http://www.hanwhalife.com
Sales Range: $5-14.9 Billion
Emp.: 5,000
Life Insurance Products & Services
N.A.I.C.S.: 524113
Nam-Gyu Cha *(Pres & CEO)*

Subsidiary (Domestic):

Hanwha General Insurance Co., Ltd. (2)
56 Yeoui-daero, Yeongdeungpo-gu, Seoul, Korea (South) (52.22%)
Tel.: (82) 2 316 0565
Web Site: http://www.hwgeneralins.com
General Insurance Products & Services
N.A.I.C.S.: 524126
Myungjun Shim *(Head-Investment & Fin Div)*

Subsidiary (Non-US):

Hanwha Life Co., Ltd (2)
City Tower Level 6 40 Basinghall Street, London, EC2V 5DE, United Kingdom
Tel.: (44) 207 826 4021
General Insurance Services
N.A.I.C.S.: 524210

Hanwha Life Insurance Vietnam Ltd. (2)
14th floor Fideco Tower 81-85 Ham Nghi St Dist 1, Ho Chi Minh City, Vietnam
Tel.: (84) 8 3914 9100
Web Site: http://www.korealife.com.vn
Emp.: 210
General Insurance Services
N.A.I.C.S.: 524210
Seung Joo Yeo *(Chm)*

Subsidiary (US):

Hanwha Life Investment (America) Ltd. (2)

575 Lexington Ave Ste 2860, New York, NY 10022
Tel.: (212) 308-7501
Investment Management Service
N.A.I.C.S.: 523940
Calvin Kang *(Portfolio Mgr)*

Subsidiary (Non-US):

PT. Hanwha Life Insurance (2)
Ratu Plaza Jl Jend Sudirman Kav 9, Jakarta, 10270, Indonesia
Tel.: (62) 21 8378 0882
General Insurance Services
N.A.I.C.S.: 524210

Hanwha Machinery Co., Ltd. (1)
59 Sung San-Dong, Changwon, 641-315, Kyungsangnam-Do, Korea (South)
Tel.: (82) 552808988
Web Site: http://www.hanwhatechm.co.kr
Industrial Furnaces, Factory Automation Systems & Machine Tools Mfr
N.A.I.C.S.: 333994

Subsidiary (US):

Hanwha Machinery America Inc. (2)
9750 S Oakwood Park Dr, Franklin, WI 53132
Tel.: (414) 421-2300
Web Site: http://www.hanwhamachinery.com
Machine Tools Mfr
N.A.I.C.S.: 333517
Bob Erickson *(Reg Mgr-Sls)*

Hanwha Polydreamer Co., Ltd. (2)
Pureun Building 7th Floor 581 Gangnam-daero, Seocho-gu, Seoul, Korea (South)
Tel.: (82) 2 3014 0500
Web Site: http://www.hwpd.net
Packaging Materials Mfr
N.A.I.C.S.: 326112
Jae Kyung Kim *(Gen Mgr)*

Hanwha Resort Co., Ltd. (1)
Hanwha Building 8th Floor 1 Janggyo-dong, Jung-gu, 100797, Seoul, Korea (South)
Tel.: (82) 27293456
Web Site: http://www.hanwharesort.co.kr
Resorts, Condominiums, Theme Parks & Golf Courses Operator
N.A.I.C.S.: 713990

Hanwha S&C Co., Ltd. (1)
Hanwha S&C 19F/20F Hanwha Building Janggyo-dong 1, Jung-gu, Seoul, Korea (South)
Tel.: (82) 2 729 2100
Web Site: http://www.hsnc.co.kr
Information Technology Services
N.A.I.C.S.: 541512
Wan-Kyu Eo *(Mgr)*

Hanwha Savings Bank (1)
139 Bucheorno, Wonmi-gu, Bucheon, Gyeonggi-do, Korea (South)
Tel.: (82) 32 657 5000
Web Site: http://www.hanwhasbank.com
Commercial Banking Services
N.A.I.C.S.: 522110
Seok Kyeon Kim *(Exec VP)*

Hanwha Securities Co., Ltd. (1)
23 5 Youngdeungpo Ku, Yoido-Dong, Seoul, Korea (South)
Tel.: (82) 237727000
Web Site: http://www.koreastock.co.kr
Sales Range: $200-249.9 Million
Emp.: 1,100
Securities Brokerage & Dealing Services
N.A.I.C.S.: 523150
Lee Yongho *(Pres)*

Subsidiary (Non-US):

Hanwha Bank Hungary Ltd. (2)
Rakoczi ut 1-3, 1088, Budapest, Hungary
Tel.: (36) 014299400
Web Site: http://www.hanwhabank.hu
Sales Range: $50-74.9 Million
Emp.: 55
Banking Services
N.A.I.C.S.: 522110

Holding (Domestic):

Hanwha Investment Trust Management Co., Ltd. (2)
23-5 9th Floor Hanwha Securities Co Ltd Building, Yoido-dong, Youngdeungpo-ku,

Seoul, Korea (South) (38%)
Tel.: (82) 237726000
Web Site: http://www.koreatrust.co.kr
Investment Services
N.A.I.C.S.: 523999

Hanwha Solutions Corp. (1)
86 Cheonggyecheon-ro, Jung-gu, Seoul, 04541, Korea (South)
Tel.: (82) 260490520
Web Site: http://www.hanwhasolutions.com
Solar Modules & Cells Mfr
N.A.I.C.S.: 221114
Koo Yung Lee *(Chm)*

Hanwha Stores Co., Ltd. (1)
7-11 Floor Hanvit Plaza Building Shinchun-dong, Songpa-gu, Seoul, Korea (South)
Tel.: (82) 24107114
Web Site: http://www.galleria.co.kr
Departmental Store Operator
N.A.I.C.S.: 455110

Hanwha TechM Co., Ltd. (1)
59 Seongsan-dong, Seongsan-gu, Changwon, Korea (South)
Tel.: (82) 5 5280 8841
Web Site: http://www.hanwhatechm.co.kr
Machine Tools Mfr
N.A.I.C.S.: 333517
Young-Ho Cho *(Dir-Quality)*

Subsidiary (Non-US):

Hanwha TechM (Suzhou) Co., Ltd. (2)
North Side of Sigang Segment Zhangyang Road, Zhangjiagang Economic and Technology Development Zone, Zhangjiagang, 215600, Jiangsu, China
Tel.: (86) 512 8959 8910
Machine Tools Mfr
N.A.I.C.S.: 333517

Plant (Domestic):

Hanwha TechM Co., Ltd. - Asan 1 Plant (2)
144 Asan Valley South Road, Dunpomyeon, Ansan, 31409, Chungnam, Korea (South)
Tel.: (82) 41 538 7777
Emp.: 415
Hydraulic Equipment Mfr
N.A.I.C.S.: 333998
Kim Yong Chul *(Pres)*

Hanwha TechM Co., Ltd. - Changwon Plant (2)
9 Sungsanpaechong-ro, Sungsan-gu, Changwon, Kyungnam, Korea (South)
Tel.: (82) 55 280 4694
Machine Tools Mfr
N.A.I.C.S.: 333517

Subsidiary (US):

Hanwha TechM USA LLC (2)
1500 E Highwood, Pontiac, MI 48340
Tel.: (248) 588-1242
Machine Tools Mfr
N.A.I.C.S.: 333517

PT. Hanwha Mining Services (1)
Menara Citicon Unit F2 11th Floor JL Letjen S Parman Kav 72, Jakarta, 11410, Indonesia
Tel.: (62) 21 2930 8840 1
Metal Mining Services
N.A.I.C.S.: 213114

HANWHA INVESTMENT & SECURITIES CO., LTD.

1st floor Hanwha Investment & Securities Building 56 Yeoui-daero, Yeongdeungpo-gu, Seoul, 07325, Korea (South)
Tel.: (82) 337750775
Web Site:
https://www.hanwhawm.com
Year Founded: 1962
003530—(KRS)
Rev.: $1,670,265,613
Assets: $9,567,887,119
Liabilities: $8,338,977,322
Net Worth: $1,228,909,797
Earnings: ($43,345,229)

INTERNATIONAL PUBLIC

Emp.: 1,129
Fiscal Year-end: 12/31/22
Investment Management Service
N.A.I.C.S.: 523999
Jin-hyeong Joo *(Exec Dir)*

HANWHA OCEAN CO., LTD.

Geoje-daero, 3370, Geoje, 3370, Gyeongsangnam-do, Korea (South)
Tel.: (82) 221290114 KR
Web Site:
https://www.hanwhaocean.com
Year Founded: 1973
042660—(KRS)
Rev.: $3,727,735,241
Assets: $9,384,755,289
Liabilities: $8,813,361,817
Net Worth: $571,393,472
Earnings: ($1,338,245,069)
Emp.: 8,629
Fiscal Year-end: 12/31/22
Shipbuilding, Repair & Heavy Construction Services
N.A.I.C.S.: 336611
Sung Geun Lee *(Pres & CEO)*

Subsidiaries:

DSME E&R Ltd. (1)
201 Panam-Techno Twn, 239-2 Panam-dong Dong-gu, Daejeon, 300-832, Korea (South)
Tel.: (82) 422730021
Web Site: http://www.dsme.enr.co.kr
Sonar Systems & Underwater Cameras Mfr
N.A.I.C.S.: 334511

Dyna-Mac Holdings Ltd. (1)
45 Gul Road, Singapore, 629350, Singapore
Tel.: (65) 64150880
Web Site: https://www.dyna-mac.com
Rev.: $291,729,910
Assets: $261,406,498
Liabilities: $208,169,355
Net Worth: $53,237,143
Earnings: $21,730,667
Emp.: 949
Fiscal Year-end: 12/31/2023
Offshore Oil & Gas Engineering & Construction Services
N.A.I.C.S.: 237990
Tjew Yok Lim *(COO)*

Subsidiary (Domestic):

Dyna-Mac Engineering Services Pte Ltd (2)
45 Gul Road, Singapore, 629350, Singapore
Tel.: (65) 64150880
Sales Range: $200-249.9 Million
Emp.: 700
Oil & Gas Line Construction Engineering Services
N.A.I.C.S.: 237120

Dyna-Mac Offshore Services Pte. Ltd. (2)
45 Gul Road, Singapore, 629350, Singapore
Tel.: (65) 67625816
Emp.: 500
Marine Engineering Services
N.A.I.C.S.: 541330
Desmond Lim *(CEO)*

Haven Automation Industries (S) Pte. Ltd. (2)
84 Tuas Avenue 11, Singapore, 639098, Singapore
Tel.: (65) 68610880
Sales Range: $75-99.9 Million
Emp.: 150
Ship Building & Repair Services
N.A.I.C.S.: 336611

Samwoo Heavy Industries Co., Ltd. (2)
111 Yulchonsandan 3-ro Gwangyang-eup, Gwangyang, Jeollanam, Korea (South)
Tel.: (82) 617803000
Web Site: https://www.idssw.co.kr
Emp.: 950
Ship Mfr
N.A.I.C.S.: 336611

AND PRIVATE COMPANIES / HAO WEN HOLDINGS LIMITED

Shinhan Machinery Co., Ltd. (1)
117 Woobong-Ri, Onsan-Eup Ulju-Gun, Ulsan, 689 890, Korea (South)
Tel.: (82) 522405000
Web Site: http://www.shinerpia.com
Sales Range: $200-249.9 Million
Emp.: 1,000
Ship Building Services
N.A.I.C.S.: 336611
Ryu Wan-Soo *(Pres & CEO)*

HANWHA SOLUTIONS CORPORATION
Hanwha building 86 Cheonggyecheon-ro, Jung-Gu, Seoul, Korea (South)
Tel.: (82) 27292700
Web Site:
  http://www.hcc.hanwha.co.kr
Year Founded: 1974
009830—(KRS)
Rev.: $10,472,578,196
Assets: $18,278,911,916
Liabilities: $10,687,980,750
Net Worth: $7,590,931,166
Earnings: $280,739,757
Emp.: 6,773
Fiscal Year-end: 12/31/22
Organic Petrochemical Mfr
N.A.I.C.S.: 325110
Kim Eui-Yeol *(Assoc Mgr)*

HANWHA SYSTEMS CO., LTD.
Hanwha Bldg 14F 86 Cheonggyecheon-Ro, Jung-Gu, Seoul, 04541, Korea (South)
Tel.: (82) 27293030
Web Site:
  https://www.hanwhasystems.com
Year Founded: 1995
272210—(KRS)
Rev.: $1,678,197,799
Assets: $3,026,296,446
Liabilities: $1,477,760,251
Net Worth: $1,548,536,195
Earnings: ($58,718,297)
Emp.: 4,307
Fiscal Year-end: 12/31/22
Communication Equipment Distr
N.A.I.C.S.: 423690
Song-Jae In *(Sr Mgr)*

HANYANG DIGITECH CO., LTD.
332-7 Samsung 1-ro, Hwaseong, Gyeonggi-do, Korea (South)
Tel.: (82) 316955000
Web Site:
  https://www.hanyangdgt.com
Year Founded: 2004
078350—(KRS)
Rev.: $371,818,429
Assets: $179,283,620
Liabilities: $85,818,176
Net Worth: $93,465,443
Earnings: $28,517,333
Emp.: 58
Fiscal Year-end: 12/31/22
Semiconductor Module Mfr
N.A.I.C.S.: 334413
Hyung-Youk Kim *(Chm & CEO)*

HANYANG ENG CO., LTD.
72 Yeongtong-ro 26beon-gil, Hwaseong, Gyeonggi, Korea (South)
Tel.: (82) 316950000
Web Site:
  https://www.hanyangeng.co.kr
Year Founded: 1982
045100—(KRS)
Rev.: $891,938,673
Assets: $561,098,551
Liabilities: $198,808,404
Net Worth: $362,290,147
Earnings: $53,515,875
Emp.: 1,073
Fiscal Year-end: 12/31/22

Chemical Equipment Mfr
N.A.I.C.S.: 333248
Kim Yun-Sang *(CEO)*
Subsidiaries:

Hanyang (Xian) Engineering Co., Ltd. (1)
Room 706 Building A Yanxiang City Plaza No 56 Jinye 1 Road, High-tech Zone, Xi'an, China
Tel.: (86) 2981154808
Civil Engineering Services
N.A.I.C.S.: 541330

Hanyang Construction(Dalian) Co., Ltd. (1)
No 127 Liaohe Road Wanda Plaza Building 4 Room 915, Development Zones, Dalian, Liaoning, China
Tel.: (86) 41187536190
Civil Engineering Services
N.A.I.C.S.: 541330

Hanyang Navicom Co., Ltd (1)
Techon 1 Ro 61-7 714 Gwanpyeong -Dong, Yuseng-gu, Daejeon, Korea (South)
Tel.: (82) 42 363 9000
Web Site: http://www.hanyangnav.co.kr
Communication Equipment Mfr
N.A.I.C.S.: 334220
S. M. Lee *(Pres & CEO)*

HANYANG SECURITIES CO., LTD.
Gukjegeumyung-ro 6 yuk-gil 7, Yeongdeungpo-gu, Seoul, Korea (South)
Tel.: (82) 237705462
Web Site: https://www.hygood.co.kr
Year Founded: 1956
001750—(KRS)
Rev.: $882,544,522
Assets: $1,187,283,941
Liabilities: $824,368,289
Net Worth: $362,915,652
Earnings: $18,986,313
Emp.: 471
Fiscal Year-end: 12/31/22
Trading & International Banking Services
N.A.I.C.S.: 522110
Jae-Taek Im *(Board of Directors, Pres & CEO)*

HANYU GROUP JOINT-STOCK CO., LTD.
No 336 Qinglan Road, High-tech Development Zone, Jiangmen, 529040, Guangdong, China
Tel.: (86) 7503839060
Web Site:
  https://www.idearhanyu.com
Year Founded: 2002
300403—(CHIN)
Rev.: $148,482,828
Assets: $315,825,588
Liabilities: $57,996,432
Net Worth: $257,829,156
Earnings: $28,668,276
Emp.: 1,330
Fiscal Year-end: 12/31/22
Household Drainage Pumps Mfr
N.A.I.C.S.: 333914
Cao Yang *(Chm-Supervisory Bd)*

HANZA AB
Torshamnsgatan 35, 164 40, Kista, Sweden
Tel.: (46) 86246200
Web Site: https://www.hanza.com
Year Founded: 2008
HANZA—(OMX)
Rev.: $411,281,203
Assets: $290,765,784
Liabilities: $157,245,818
Net Worth: $133,519,966
Earnings: $21,244,069
Emp.: 2,800
Fiscal Year-end: 12/31/23

Contract Manufacturing Services
N.A.I.C.S.: 339999
Erik Stenfors *(Pres & CEO)*
Subsidiaries:

HANZA Alfaram Electric (Suzhou) Co., Ltd. (1)
3rd Floor Building 1 Area B No 20 Huayun Road, Dongfang Industrial Park Suzhou Industrial Park, Suzhou, Jiangsu, China
Tel.: (86) 51262868001
Industrial Machinery Mfr
N.A.I.C.S.: 314999
Rainer Olesk *(Pres)*

HANZA Czech Republic s.r.o (1)
Obornik 2247/31i, 78901, Zabreh, Czech Republic
Tel.: (420) 732284547
Industrial Machinery Mfr
N.A.I.C.S.: 314999
Josef Pernica *(Acct Mgr)*

HANZA Electric (Suzhou) Co. Ltd. (1)
Dongfang Industrial Park Area B Building 1 3rd Floor No 20 Huayun Road, Suzhou Industrial Park, Jiangsu, China
Tel.: (86) 51262868001
Cluster & Electronics Product Mfr
N.A.I.C.S.: 334419

HANZA Elektromekan AB (1)
Brannaregatan 3, Box 904, 672 29, Arjang, Sweden
Tel.: (46) 86246200
Industrial Machinery Mfr
N.A.I.C.S.: 314999
Veronica Svensson *(Sls Dir)*

HANZA GmbH (1)
Leverkuser Strasse 65, 42897, Remscheid, Germany
Tel.: (49) 21915761809
Industrial Machinery Mfr
N.A.I.C.S.: 314999

HANZA Levyprofiili Oy (1)
Kuhasalontie 18, 80220, Joensuu, Finland
Tel.: (358) 13220050
Steel Products Mfr
N.A.I.C.S.: 331110

HANZA Mechanics Kunovice s.r.o (1)
Osvobozeni 1486, 68604, Kunovice, Czech Republic
Tel.: (420) 601585010
Steel Products Mfr
N.A.I.C.S.: 331110

HANZA Mechanics Narva AS (1)
Kulgu 5, 20104, Narva, Estonia
Tel.: (372) 7468800
Industrial Machinery Mfr
N.A.I.C.S.: 314999
Liivar Kongi *(Pres)*

HANZA Mechanics Sweden AB (1)
Industrigatan 8, Box 904, 672 21, Arjang, Sweden
Tel.: (46) 86246200
Industrial Machinery Mfr
N.A.I.C.S.: 314999
Ola Svensson *(Acct Mgr)*

HANZA Mechanics Tartu AS (1)
Silikaadi 5, 60534, Tartu, Estonia
Tel.: (372) 7468800
Web Site: https://tartu.hanza.com
Industrial Machinery Mfr
N.A.I.C.S.: 314999
Liivar Kongi *(Pres)*

HANZA Mechanics Toreboda (1)
Verkstadsgatan 2, Box 93, Toreboda, 545 31, Sweden (100%)
Tel.: (46) 50618400
Sales Range: $10-24.9 Million
Emp.: 85
Mechanical Component Mfr
N.A.I.C.S.: 332999
Jonas Lundin *(Mgr-Site)*

Unit (Domestic):

HANZA Mechanics - Arjang (2)
Industrigatan 8, Box 904, SE-672 21, Arjang, Sweden
Tel.: (46) 57314300

Mechanical Component Mfr
N.A.I.C.S.: 332999
Ola Svensson *(Mgr-Site)*

HANZA Metalliset Oy (1)
Ahjotie 3, 79700, Heinavesi, Finland
Tel.: (358) 405515255
Industrial Machinery Mfr
N.A.I.C.S.: 314999
Tuomo Pasanen *(Mgr)*

HANZA Poland Sp. z.o.o (1)
Aleje Jerozolimskie 38, 56-120, Brzeg Dolny, Poland
Tel.: (48) 603755288
Industrial Machinery Mfr
N.A.I.C.S.: 314999
Pawel Filarowski *(Pres)*

HANZA Tech Solutions GmbH (1)
Kopenhagener Str 11, 48163, Munster, Germany
Tel.: (49) 25019208440
Steel Products Mfr
N.A.I.C.S.: 331110

HANZA Toolfac Oy (1)
Teollisuuskatu 7, 74120, Iisalmi, Finland
Tel.: (358) 207412740
Industrial Machinery Mfr
N.A.I.C.S.: 314999
Juhani Niiranen *(Pres)*

HAO BAI INTERNATIONAL (CAYMAN) LIMITED
Unit A 7/F Wah Shing Ind Building 18 Cheung Shun Street Lai Chi Kok, Hong Kong, China (Hong Kong)
Tel.: (852) 23888311   Ky
Web Site:
  http://www.harmonyasia.com
Year Founded: 2006
8431—(HKG)
Rev.: $1,988,490
Assets: $10,727,595
Liabilities: $10,614,630
Net Worth: $112,965
Earnings: ($4,228,410)
Emp.: 11
Fiscal Year-end: 03/31/23
Water Circulation Management Services
N.A.I.C.S.: 237110

HAO TIAN INTERNATIONAL CONSTRUCTION INVESTMENT GROUP LIMITED
50 Ko Po Sha Tau Kok Road, Fanling, China (Hong Kong)
Tel.: (852) 26744184   Ky
Web Site:
  http://www.chimkeegroup.com.hk
Year Founded: 1962
1341—(HKG)
Rev.: $28,375,600
Assets: $378,040,380
Liabilities: $167,416,040
Net Worth: $210,624,340
Earnings: ($53,139,760)
Emp.: 127
Fiscal Year-end: 03/31/22
Holding Company
N.A.I.C.S.: 551112
James Yiu Chi Tang *(Exec Dir)*

HAO WEN HOLDINGS LIMITED
Level 12 Infinitus Plaza 199 Des Voeux Road Central, Sheung Wan, China (Hong Kong)
Tel.: (852) 21559506   Ky
Web Site: http://www.tricor.com.hk
Year Founded: 2000
8019—(HKG)
Rev.: $8,762,083
Assets: $50,633,856
Liabilities: $9,204,343
Net Worth: $41,429,513
Earnings: ($7,413,260)
Emp.: 26
Fiscal Year-end: 12/31/22
Pharmaceutical Product Mfr & Distr

HAO WEN HOLDINGS LIMITED

Hao Wen Holdings Limited—(Continued)
N.A.I.C.S.: 325412

HAO YONG AUTOMOTIVE CONTROLS LTD.
No 75 Yangwei Road Baizhou Bianzhou, Baizhou Bianzhou Dongcheng Street, Dongguan, Guangdong, China
Tel.: (86) 76981029888
Web Site: https://www.haoyong-auto.com
Year Founded: 2004
Automotive Components Mfr
N.A.I.C.S.: 336310

HAOERSAI TECHNOLOGY GROUP CORP., LTD.
22F Building No 3 Nuode Center No 128 South Sihuan West Road, Fengtai District, Beijing, 100070, China
Tel.: (86) 1088578857
Web Site: http://www.haoersai.com
Year Founded: 2000
002963—(SSE)
Rev.: $57,145,608
Assets: $297,121,500
Liabilities: $85,217,184
Net Worth: $211,904,316
Earnings: ($21,908,016)
Emp.: 600
Fiscal Year-end: 12/31/22
Construction Services
N.A.I.C.S.: 236220
Baolin Dai (Chm & Gen Mgr)

HAOMA MINING NL
401 Collins Street, Melbourne, 3000, VIC, Australia
Tel.: (61) 396296888
Web Site: http://www.haoma.com.au
Sales Range: Less than $1 Million
Gold Mining & Mineral Exploration
N.A.I.C.S.: 212220
James Andrew Wallace (Sec)

HAOXIANGNI HEALTH FOOD CO., LTD.
intersection of S102 Provincial Road and Zhonghua Road, Xuedian Town, Xinzheng, Henan, China
Tel.: (86) 4006919999
Web Site: https://www.haoxiangni.cn
Year Founded: 1992
002582—(SSE)
Rev.: $196,628,796
Assets: $734,268,132
Liabilities: $146,014,596
Net Worth: $588,253,536
Earnings: $26,636,688)
Fiscal Year-end: 12/31/22
Dehydrated Fruit & Candy Mfr
N.A.I.C.S.: 311423
Mingxia Luo (CFO & Deputy Gen Mgr)

HAOYUN TECHNOLOGIES CO., LTD.
Room 101 Building No 22 Tian an Headquarters Center No 555, Panyu Avenue North Donghuan Street Panyu District, Guangzhou, 511400, Guangdong, China
Tel.: (86) 2034831515
Web Site: http://www.haoyuntech.com
300448—(SSE)
Rev.: $62,777,052
Assets: $222,014,520
Liabilities: $16,932,240
Net Worth: $205,082,280
Earnings: $2,900,664
Fiscal Year-end: 12/31/22
Financial Security System Development Services
N.A.I.C.S.: 541511

Qingjiang Mao (Chm)

HAOYUN TECHNOLOGY CO., LTD.
Room 101 Building No 22 Tian an Headquarters Center, No 555 Panyu Avenue North Donghuan Street, Panyu District, Guangzhou, 511400, Guangdong, China
Tel.: (86) 2034831515
Web Site: http://www.haoyuntech.com
300448—(CHIN)
Rev.: $62,777,052
Assets: $222,014,520
Liabilities: $16,932,240
Net Worth: $205,082,280
Earnings: $2,900,664
Emp.: 1,100
Fiscal Year-end: 12/31/22
Financial Security Products
N.A.I.C.S.: 513210
Qingjiang Mao (Chm)

HAP SENG CONSOLIDATED BERHAD
21st Floor Menara Hap Seng Jalan P Ramlee, 50250, Kuala Lumpur, Malaysia
Tel.: (60) 321725228   MY
Web Site: https://www.hapseng.com.my
Year Founded: 1976
HAPSENG—(KLS)
Rev.: $1,504,866,878
Assets: $3,947,988,360
Liabilities: $2,044,449,101
Net Worth: $1,903,539,259
Earnings: $224,948,783
Emp.: 9,983
Fiscal Year-end: 12/31/22
Investment Holding Company
N.A.I.C.S.: 551112
Edward Ming Foo Lee (Mng Dir-Grp & Mng Dir-Grp)

Subsidiaries:

Gres Universal Pte. Ltd.   (1)
105 Eunos Avenue 3, Singapore, 409836, Singapore
Tel.: (65) 65381588
Web Site: https://www.gres.com.sg
Building Materials Distr
N.A.I.C.S.: 423390

Hafary Balestier Showroom Pte. Ltd.   (1)
560 Balestier Rd, Singapore, 329876, Singapore
Tel.: (65) 62501369
Building Materials Distr
N.A.I.C.S.: 423390

Hafary Holdings Limited   (1)
105 Eunos Avenue 3, Singapore, 409836, Singapore
Tel.: (65) 63832314
Web Site: https://www.hafary.com.sg
Rev.: $171,492,842
Assets: $357,192,305
Liabilities: $261,884,420
Net Worth: $95,307,885
Earnings: $30,368,856
Emp.: 929
Fiscal Year-end: 12/31/2023
Tiles, Flooring & Sanitary Ware Mfr & Distr
N.A.I.C.S.: 327120
Kok Ann Low (CEO)

Hap Seng Credit Sdn. Bhd.   (1)
18th Floor Menara Hap Seng No 1 and 3 Jalan P Ramlee, 50250, Kuala Lumpur, Malaysia
Tel.: (60) 321169000
Financial Services
N.A.I.C.S.: 522110

Hap Seng Fertilizers Sdn. Bhd.   (1)
4th Floor Menara Hap Seng Jalan P Ramlee, 50250, Kuala Lumpur, Malaysia
Tel.: (60) 321725666
Agricultural Supply Retailer

N.A.I.C.S.: 424910

Hap Seng Land Sdn. Bhd.   (1)
19th Floor Menara Hap Seng Jalan P Ramlee, Letter Box No 81, Jalan P Ramlee, 50250, Kuala Lumpur, Malaysia
Tel.: (60) 21169333
Web Site: https://www.hapsengland.com
Property Development & Investment Services
N.A.I.C.S.: 531120
Sam Wong (Deputy Mgr-Sls)

Hap Seng Plantations Holdings Berhad   (1)
21st Floor Menara Hap Seng Jalan P Ramlee, 50250, Kuala Lumpur, Malaysia   (52.36%)
Tel.: (60) 321725228
Web Site: http://www.hapsengplantations.com.my
Rev.: $172,392,381
Assets: $512,281,270
Liabilities: $103,974,180
Net Worth: $408,307,090
Earnings: $44,511,111
Emp.: 7,747
Fiscal Year-end: 12/31/2022
Holding Company; Oil Palm Farming & Palm Oil Marketing Services
N.A.I.C.S.: 551112
Edward Ming Foo Lee (Mng Dir)

Hap Seng Properties Development Sdn. Bhd.   (1)
13-0 Lorong Plaza Kingfisher 6 Plaza Kingfisher, 88450, Kota Kinabalu, Sabah, Malaysia
Tel.: (60) 88433711
Property Development & Investment Services
N.A.I.C.S.: 531120

Hap Seng Realty (KK I) Sdn. Bhd.   (1)
L08-01 Level 8 Plaza Shell No 29 Jalan Tunku Abdul Rahman, 88000, Kota Kinabalu, Sabah, Malaysia
Tel.: (60) 88355816
Property Development & Investment Services
N.A.I.C.S.: 531120

Hap Seng Star Sdn. Bhd.   (1)
GF-01 Menara Hap Seng 3, No 1 Jalan PRamlee, 50250, Kuala Lumpur, Malaysia
Tel.: (60) 321169228
Web Site: https://www.hapseng.mercedes-benz.com.my
Car Services
N.A.I.C.S.: 441110
Lee Kian Hock (Principal)

Hap Seng Trucks Distribution Sdn. Bhd.   (1)
No 1 Jalan Kinrara 2 Taman Perindustrian Bandar Kinrara, 47180, Puchong, Selangor, Malaysia
Tel.: (60) 380829120
Web Site: http://www.trucksdistribution.com.my
Daimler Truck Distr
N.A.I.C.S.: 423110
Ooi Dee Kai (Deputy Mgr)

MML (Shanghai) Trading Co., Ltd.   (1)
5F 989 Hu Qing Ping Road, Min Hang District, Shanghai, 201105, China
Tel.: (86) 2131198888
Porcelain Tiles Mfr
N.A.I.C.S.: 327120

MML Marketing Pte. Ltd.   (1)
105 Eunos Avenue 3 6th Floor, Singapore, 409836, Singapore
Tel.: (65) 63584415
Porcelain Tiles Mfr
N.A.I.C.S.: 327120
Raymond Ang (Mgr-Sls)

Malaysian Mosaics Sdn. Bhd.   (1)
1A Jalan 205 Off Jalan Tandang, PO Box 456 Jalan Sultan, 46050, Petaling Jaya, Selangor, Malaysia
Tel.: (60) 300888182
Web Site: http://mymml.com
Mosaic & Ceramic Tiles Mfr
N.A.I.C.S.: 327120

INTERNATIONAL PUBLIC

Menara Hap Seng Sdn. Bhd.   (1)
3rd Floor Menara Hap Seng Jalan P Ramlee, PO Box 81, 50250, Kuala Lumpur, Malaysia
Tel.: (60) 163701005
Property Development & Investment Services
N.A.I.C.S.: 531120
Chayenne Wong (Mgr)

Surface Project Pte. Ltd.   (1)
105 Eunos Avenue 3, Singapore, 409836, Singapore
Tel.: (65) 63835001
Web Site: https://www.surface-project.com.sg
Building Materials Whslr
N.A.I.C.S.: 423320
Sharon Khoo (Mgr-Sls)

Surface Stone Pte. Ltd.   (1)
105 Eunos Ave 3, Singapore, 409836, Singapore
Tel.: (65) 62817800
Web Site: https://www.surfacestone.com.sg
Marble & Granite Stone Distr
N.A.I.C.S.: 423320

Wood Culture Pte. Ltd.   (1)
11 Changi North Way, Singapore, 498796, Singapore
Tel.: (65) 66862133
Web Site: https://www.woodculture.com.sg
Home Furnishing Whslr
N.A.I.C.S.: 423220

HAPACO GROUP JOINT STOCK COMPANY
Floor 5 6 Buildings Khanh Hoi Lot 2/3c Le Hong Phong, Ngo Quyen District, Haiphong, Vietnam
Tel.: (84) 313556002
Web Site: https://www.hapaco.vn
HAP—(HOSE)
Rev.: $12,351,595
Assets: $52,540,588
Liabilities: $2,927,631
Net Worth: $49,612,958
Earnings: $754,413
Emp.: 563
Fiscal Year-end: 12/31/23
Paper Products Mfr
N.A.I.C.S.: 322299
Duong Hien Vu (Chm)

HAPBEE TECHNOLOGIES INC.
Suite 2250 1055 W Hastings Street, Vancouver, V6E 2E9, BC, Canada
Tel.: (831) 292-4356   BC
Web Site: https://www.hapbee.com
Year Founded: 2019
HAPBF—(OTCQB)
Rev.: $939,489
Assets: $2,797,657
Liabilities: $2,777,634
Net Worth: $20,023
Earnings: ($3,674,034)
Emp.: 3
Fiscal Year-end: 12/31/22
Health Care Srvices
N.A.I.C.S.: 621610

HAPPIEST MINDS TECHNOLOGIES PVT. LTD.
SMILES 1 3rd 4th Floor SJR Equinox Sy No 47 8 Hosur Road, Doddathogur Village Begur Hobli Electronics City Phase 1, Bengaluru, 560 100, India
Tel.: (91) 8039653000
Web Site: http://www.happiestminds.com
Professional, Scientific & Technical Services
N.A.I.C.S.: 541990
Ashok Soota (Chm)

HAPPINESS AND D CO., LTD.
Toka Bldg 4F 1-16-1 Ginza, Chuo-ku, Tokyo, 104-0061, Japan
Tel.: (81) 335627521

AND PRIVATE COMPANIES

Web Site: https://www.happiness-d.co.jp
Year Founded: 1990
3174—(TKS)
Sales Range: $125-149.9 Million
Emp.: 445
Luxury Brand Retailer
N.A.I.C.S.: 459999
Yasuo Den *(Pres)*

HAPPINET CORPORATION
Komagata CA Bldg 2-4-5 Komagata, Taito-ku, Tokyo, 111-0043, Japan
Tel.: (81) 338470521
Web Site: https://www.happinet.co.jp
Year Founded: 1969
7552—(TKS)
Rev.: $2,316,547,210
Assets: $749,673,150
Liabilities: $410,586,760
Net Worth: $339,086,390
Earnings: $43,500,410
Emp.: 964
Fiscal Year-end: 03/31/24
Toy Mfr & Whslr
N.A.I.C.S.: 339930
Kazuhiko Note *(Chm, CEO & Exec Officer)*

Subsidiaries:

Happinet Logistics Service Corporation (1)
17-18 Futamatashinmachi, Ichikawa, 272-0002, Chiba, Japan
Tel.: (81) 473188161
Logistics Consulting Servies
N.A.I.C.S.: 541614
Katsuya Tsuda *(Pres)*

Happinet Marketing Corporation (1)
Komagata CA Bldg 2-4-5, Komagata Taito-ku, Tokyo, 111-0043, Japan
Tel.: (81) 338473341
Toy Distr
N.A.I.C.S.: 423920
Atsushi Suzuki *(Pres)*

Happinet Phantom Studios Corporation (1)
9F A-Place Yoyogi 5-23-15, Sendagaya Shibuya-ku, Tokyo, 151-0051, Japan
Tel.: (81) 362764035
Web Site: https://happinet-phantom.com
Film Production Services
N.A.I.C.S.: 512110

Happinet Vending Service Corporation (1)
Komagata CA Bldg 2-4-5 Komagata, Taito-ku, Tokyo, 111-0043, Japan
Tel.: (81) 338476769
Web Site: http://www.happinet.co.jp
Emp.: 100
Welding Machine Distr
N.A.I.C.S.: 423440
Kentaro Tsujii *(Pres)*

HAPPY BELLY FOOD GROUP INC.
Suite 400 -1681 Chestnut Street, Vancouver, V6J 4M6, BC, Canada
Tel.: (604) 682-2928
Web Site: https://happybellyfg.com
W3J—(DEU)
Rev.: $66,461
Assets: $1,064,361
Liabilities: $224,465
Net Worth: $839,896
Earnings: ($5,344,010)
Fiscal Year-end: 12/31/19
Online Shopping Services
N.A.I.C.S.: 445110
Shawn Moniz *(CEO)*

HAPPY CREEK MINERALS LTD.
1200 - 750 West Pender Street, Vancouver, V6C 2T8, BC, Canada
Tel.: (604) 590-1525
Web Site: https://www.happycreekmineral.com
Year Founded: 2004
HPYCF—(OTCIQ)
Assets: $13,951,114
Liabilities: $826,832
Net Worth: $13,124,282
Earnings: ($481,233)
Fiscal Year-end: 01/31/24
Mineral Exploration Services
N.A.I.C.S.: 213114
David Blann *(Founder, Pres & CEO)*

HAPPY FORGING LIMITED
BXXIX-2254/1 Kanganwal Road, PO Jugiana, Ludhiana, 141120, Punjab, India
Tel.: (91) 1615217162
Web Site: https://www.happyforgingsltd.com
Year Founded: 1979
544057—(BOM)
Rev.: $145,715,185
Assets: $160,730,762
Liabilities: $40,949,214
Net Worth: $119,781,548
Earnings: $8,644,881
Emp.: 3,029
Fiscal Year-end: 03/31/23
Automotive Products Mfr
N.A.I.C.S.: 336330

HAPPY VALLEY NUTRITION LIMITED
Ground Floor 96 St Georges Bay Road, Parnell, Auckland, 1052, New Zealand
Tel.: (64) 98841470 NZ
Web Site: https://www.hvn.co.nz
Year Founded: 2016
HVM—(ASX)
Rev.: $1,438,000
Assets: $19,753,393
Liabilities: $14,305,817
Net Worth: $5,447,575
Earnings: ($4,134,732)
Fiscal Year-end: 06/30/22
Dairy Products Distr
N.A.I.C.S.: 424430
Richard Chew *(CFO)*

HAPPYDOO SA
Parc Innolin 3 Rue du Golf, 33706, Merignac, Cedex, France
Tel.: (33) 556347525 FR
Year Founded: 2001
MLHAP—(EUR)
Sales Range: Less than $1 Million
Emp.: 17
Business Services
N.A.I.C.S.: 561499
Daniel Droetto *(CEO)*

HAPPYNEURON SAS
66 bd Niels Bohr, BP 2132, 69603, Villeurbanne, France
Tel.: (33) 4 78 89 75 40 FR
Web Site: http://www.scientifictraining.com
Cognitive Therapy Solutions
N.A.I.C.S.: 541715
Bernard Croisile *(Chief Scientific Officer)*

HAPVIDA PARTICIPACOES E INVESTIMENTOS S.A.
Av Heraclito Graca n 406, Fortaleza, 60140-061, Ceara, Brazil
Tel.: (55) 8532559005
Web Site: https://ri.hapvida.com.br
Year Founded: 1979
HAPV3—(BRAZ)
Rev.: $4,964,120,996
Assets: $13,082,737,716
Liabilities: $4,277,900,174
Net Worth: $8,804,837,541
Earnings: ($135,509,551)
Fiscal Year-end: 12/31/23
Supplementary Health Care Services
N.A.I.C.S.: 524114
Jorge Fontoura Pinheiro Koren de Lima *(CEO)*

Subsidiaries:

Notre Dame Intermedica Participacoes S.A. (1)
Av Paulista 867 Bela Vista, Sao Paulo, 01311-100, Brazil
Tel.: (55) 1131552000
Web Site: http://www.gndi.com.br
Sales Range: $1-4.9 Billion
Health Care Srvices
N.A.I.C.S.: 621491
Christopher Riley Gordon *(Pres)*

Subsidiary (Domestic):

Hospital e Maternidade Samaritano Ltda. (2)
Rodrigues Pacheco Street 145, Sorocaba, Sao Paulo, Brazil
Tel.: (55) 1532194464
Web Site: http://www.samaritano.med.br
Hospital Services
N.A.I.C.S.: 622110

HARADA INDUSTRY CO., LTD.
Omori Bellport B-4F 6-26-2 Minami-Ohi, Shinagawa-ku, Tokyo, 140-0013, Japan
Tel.: (81) 337654321
Web Site: https://www.harada.com
Year Founded: 1958
6904—(TKS)
Rev.: $310,623,730
Assets: $248,522,780
Liabilities: $169,777,850
Net Worth: $78,744,930
Earnings: $5,849,850
Fiscal Year-end: 03/31/24
Automotive Antennas Mfr & Sales
N.A.I.C.S.: 441330
Shoji Harada *(Chm)*

Subsidiaries:

DALIAN HARADA INDUSTRY CO., LTD. (1)
No 101 Jin Ma Road Economic and Technical Development Zone, Dalian, 116600, Liaoning, China
Tel.: (86) 41187612111
Web Site: http://www.harada.cn
Wireless Communication Equipment Mfr & Distr
N.A.I.C.S.: 334220

HARADA ASIA-PACIFIC LTD. (1)
23/13 Sorachai Building 12th Floor Sukhumvit 63 Rd Klongton-Nua, Wattana, Bangkok, 10110, Thailand
Tel.: (66) 27141400
Automobile Parts Distr
N.A.I.C.S.: 423110
Yoicehi Kakamiao *(Gen Mgr)*

HARADA AUTOMOTIVE ANTENNA (PHILIPPINES), INC. (1)
Block 12 Lots 3 4 First Cavite Industrial Estate, Langkaan, Dasmarinas, 4126, Cavite, Philippines
Tel.: (63) 464021105
Web Site: http://www.harada.com
Wireless Communication Equipment Distr
N.A.I.C.S.: 423690

HARADA COMMUNICATION SYSTEMS CO., LTD. (1)
5-7 Takinoshita-machi, Nagaoka, 940-0026, Niigata, Japan
Tel.: (81) 258 52 5353
Wireless Antenna Mfr & Distr
N.A.I.C.S.: 334220

HARADA INDUSTRIES (EUROPE) LIMITED (1)
Bell Heath Way Woodgate Business Park Clapgate Lane, Birmingham, B32 3BZ, United Kingdom
Tel.: (44) 1214232222
Web Site: http://www.harada.co.uk
Wireless Communication Equipment Distr
N.A.I.C.S.: 423690

HARADA INDUSTRIES (MEXICO), S.A.DE C.V. (1)
Av Central Km 3 1 Libramiento a Tequisquiapan Zona Industrial, Valle de Oro San Juan del Rio, 76803, Queretaro, Mexico
Tel.: (52) 4272725083
Antenna Mfr & Distr
N.A.I.C.S.: 334220

HARADA INDUSTRIES VIETNAM LIMITED (1)
Long Binh Techno Park Loteco Epz, Long Binh Ward, Bien Hoa, Dong Nai, Vietnam
Tel.: (84) 2513892001
Antenna Mfr & Distr
N.A.I.C.S.: 334220
Shintaro Hirano *(Mgr)*

HARADA INDUSTRY OF AMERICA, INC. (1)
22925 Venture Dr, Novi, MI 48375-4181
Tel.: (248) 374-9000
Web Site: http://www.harada.com
Wireless Communication Equipment Distr
N.A.I.C.S.: 423690

SHANGHAI HARADA NEW AUTOMOTIVE ANTENNA CO., LTD. (1)
No 333 2nd JinYuan Road, JiangQiao Town JiaDing District, Shanghai, China
Tel.: (86) 2139556548
Antenna Mfr & Distr
N.A.I.C.S.: 334220

HARALD QUANDT HOLDING GMBH
Am Pilgerrain 17, 61352, Bad Homburg, Germany
Tel.: (49) 6172 402 0 De
Web Site: http://www.haraldquandt.de
Investment Holding Company
N.A.I.C.S.: 551112
Bernhard Oberhofer *(Co-CEO)*

Subsidiaries:

HQ Capital GmbH & Co. KG (1)
Am Pilgerrain 17, 61352, Bad Homburg, Germany
Tel.: (49) 6172 402 800
Web Site: http://www.hqcapital.com
Holding Company; Private Equity & Real Estate Investment Services
N.A.I.C.S.: 551112
Thomas Jetter *(Chm-Supervisory Bd)*

Subsidiary (Domestic):

HQ Capital (Deutschland) GmbH (2)
Am Pilgerrain 17, 61352, Bad Homburg, Germany
Tel.: (49) 6172 402 801
Web Site: http://www.hqcapital.com
Emp.: 89
Private Equity & Real Estate Investment Firm
N.A.I.C.S.: 523999

Subsidiary (US):

HQ Capital Private Equity LLC (2)
1290 Ave of the Americas 10th Fl, New York, NY 10104
Tel.: (212) 863-2300
Web Site: http://www.hqcapital.com
Privater Equity Firm
N.A.I.C.S.: 523999

HQ Capital Real Estate L.P. (2)
1185 Avenue of the Americas 10th Fl, New York, NY 10104
Tel.: (212) 843-6100
Web Site: http://www.hqcapital.com
Real Estate Investment & Property Management Services
N.A.I.C.S.: 531390

Subsidiary (Domestic):

HQ Equita GmbH (2)
Inge Quandt Haus Am Pilgerrain 15, 61352, Bad Homburg, Germany
Tel.: (49) 6172 9441 0
Web Site: http://www.hqequita.com

HARALD QUANDT HOLDING GMBH

Harald Quandt Holding GmbH—(Continued)
Sales Range: $25-49.9 Million
Emp.: 14
Privater Equity Firm
N.A.I.C.S.: 523999
Hans J. Moock *(Partner & Mng Dir)*

Subsidiary (Domestic):

EBERTLANG Distribution GmbH   (3)
Garbenheimer Strasse 36, D-35578,
Wetzlar, Germany
Tel.: (49) 6441671180
Web Site: http://www.ebertlang.com
Sales Range: $1-9.9 Million
Computer Products & Software Distr
N.A.I.C.S.: 423430
Steffen Ebert *(Founder & Co-CEO)*

Muegge GmbH   (3)
Hochstrasse 4-6, 64385, Reichelsheim,
Germany
Tel.: (49) 616493070
Web Site: http://www.muegge.de
Industrial Microwave Products Mfr & Consulting Services
N.A.I.C.S.: 334419
Klaus Martin Baumgaertner *(CEO)*

Subsidiary (US):

Gerling Applied Engineering, Inc.   (4)
1064 Woodland Ave Ste U, Modesto, CA 95351
Tel.: (209) 527-8960
Web Site: http://www.muegge-gerling.com
Emp.: 11
Electronic Components Mfr
N.A.I.C.S.: 334419
John F. Gerling *(Pres)*

HARANGA RESOURCES LIMITED
Suite 3 9 Hampden Road, Nedlands, 6009, WA, Australia
Tel.: (61) 130 066 0448
Web Site: http://www.haranga.com
Rev.: $607
Assets: $155,008
Liabilities: $183,842
Net Worth: ($28,834)
Earnings: ($4,353,547)
Fiscal Year-end: 12/31/17
Iron Exploration & Mining Services
N.A.I.C.S.: 212210
Nerida Schmidt *(Sec)*

HARBIN AIR CONDITIONING CO., LTD.
No 7 Dianchi Street Centralized District Yingbin Road, High-Tech Developing Zone, Harbin, 150078, Heilongjiang, China
Tel.: (86) 45158699963
Web Site: https://www.hac.com.cn
Year Founded: 1952
600202—(SHG)
Rev.: $154,873,583
Assets: $345,255,913
Liabilities: $228,814,387
Net Worth: $116,441,526
Earnings: $5,258,907
Fiscal Year-end: 12/31/22
Air Cooling Condenser Mfr & Distr
N.A.I.C.S.: 333415
Ding Sheng *(Chm)*

HARBIN BANK CO., LTD.
No 888 Shangjiang Avenue, Daoli District, Harbin, 150010, China
Tel.: (86) 45186779933
Web Site: https://www.hrbcb.com.cn
Year Founded: 1997
6138—(HKG)
Rev.: $3,659,526,983
Assets: $100,067,720,782
Liabilities: $91,177,504,751
Net Worth: $8,890,216,031
Earnings: $100,034,579
Emp.: 6,825
Fiscal Year-end: 12/31/22

Banking Services
N.A.I.C.S.: 522110

HARBIN BOSHI AUTOMATION CO., LTD.
No 9 Donghu Street Central District Yingbin Road, Harbin Development Zone, Harbin, 150078, Heilongjiang, China
Tel.: (86) 45184367031
Web Site: https://www.boshi.cn
Year Founded: 1997
002698—(SSE)
Rev.: $302,386,500
Assets: $873,325,908
Liabilities: $403,450,632
Net Worth: $469,875,276
Earnings: $62,483,616
Emp.: 500
Fiscal Year-end: 12/31/22
Packaging & Rubber Processing Equipment
N.A.I.C.S.: 333993
Deng Xijun *(Chm & Gen Mgr)*

HARBIN CHURIN GROUP JOINTSTOCK CO., LTD.
No 319 Dongdazhi Street, Nangang District, Harbin, 150001, Heilongjiang, China
Tel.: (86) 4515 364 4632
Web Site: http://www.qlgroup.com
Rev.: $47,937,040
Assets: $202,826,091
Liabilities: $435,317,713
Net Worth: ($232,491,622)
Earnings: ($75,865,309)
Fiscal Year-end: 12/31/19
Departmental Store Operator
N.A.I.C.S.: 455110
Ya Li *(Chm)*

HARBIN DONGAN AUTO ENGINE CO., LTD.
No 6 Zhengyi South Road, Central District, Harbin, 150069, Heilongjiang, China
Tel.: (86) 45156186616
Web Site: https://www.daae.com.cn
Year Founded: 1948
600178—(SHG)
Rev.: $809,697,737
Assets: $1,055,768,688
Liabilities: $589,166,880
Net Worth: $466,601,808
Earnings: $15,223,558
Emp.: 4,000
Fiscal Year-end: 12/31/22
Automobile Engine Parts Mfr & Distr
N.A.I.C.S.: 336310
Libao Chen *(Chm)*

HARBIN ELECTRIC CORPORATION
1399 Chuangxinyi Road the Science & Technology Innovation Base, Songbei District, Harbin, 150028, China
Tel.: (86) 451 5859 8107   CN
Web Site: http://en.harbin-electric.com
Emp.: 25,500
Power Generation Equipment Mfr & Whslr
N.A.I.C.S.: 332410
Zefu Si *(Chm)*

Subsidiaries:

Harbin Electric Company Limited   (1)
No 1399 Chuangxinyi Road the Science and Technology Innovation Base, Songbei District, Harbin, 150028, Heilongjiang, China   (50.93%)
Tel.: (86) 45158598000
Web Site: https://www.harbin-electric.com
Rev.: $3,507,790,303
Assets: $8,885,007,687
Liabilities: $7,147,717,468

Net Worth: $1,737,290,218
Earnings: $18,171,729
Emp.: 13,500
Fiscal Year-end: 12/31/2022
Power Plant Equipment Mfr & Distr
N.A.I.C.S.: 333611
Ze-fu Si *(Chm)*

Subsidiary (Domestic):

HE Harbin Power Plant Valve Co., Ltd.   (2)
No 6 Hanan 3rd Road, the core area of Hanan Industrial New City, Harbin, China
Tel.: (86) 45187373552
Web Site: http://www.hvc.cc
Valve Mfr
N.A.I.C.S.: 332919

Harbin Boiler Company Limited   (2)
three power Road 309, Xiangfang District, Harbin, Heilongjiang, China   (89.63%)
Tel.: (86) 45182198888
Web Site: http://www.hbc.com.cn
Electric Equipment Mfr
N.A.I.C.S.: 335999

Harbin Electric (H.E) Corporation   (2)
No 1399 Chuangxinyi Road the Science and Technology Innovation Base, Songbei, Harbin, 150028, China
Tel.: (86) 45158598000
Web Site: http://www.en.harbin-electric.com
Electric Equipment Mfr
N.A.I.C.S.: 335999
Si Zefu *(Chm)*

Harbin Electric International Co., Ltd.   (2)
No 1299 Chuangxinyi Road, Songbei, Harbin, 150028, China
Tel.: (86) 45158591111
Web Site: http://www.china-hei.com
Electric Equipment Mfr
N.A.I.C.S.: 335999
Guo Yu *(Chm)*

Harbin Electric Machinery Co., Ltd.   (2)
No 99 Sandadongli Road, Xiangfang District, Harbin, 150040, China
Tel.: (86) 45182872091
Web Site: http://www.hec-china.com
Electric Equipment Mfr
N.A.I.C.S.: 335999
Wang Gui *(Pres)*

Nantong Hemeijia Obstetrics & Gynecology Hospital Co. Ltd.   (1)
200 meters west of Xianfeng Primary School, Tongzhou District, Nantong, China
Tel.: (86) 4008163120
Web Site: https://www.nthmj.com
Obstetric & Gynecology Hospital Services
N.A.I.C.S.: 621111

HARBIN ELECTRIC GROUP JIAMUSI ELECTRIC MACHINE CO., LTD.
NO 247 changan east road, Qianjin District, Jiamusi, 154002, China
Tel.: (86) 4548848800   CN
Web Site: https://www.jemlc.com
000922—(SSE)
Rev.: $495,561,129
Assets: $879,832,424
Liabilities: $463,889,607
Net Worth: $415,942,817
Earnings: $48,615,668
Fiscal Year-end: 12/31/22
Electric Equipment Mfr
N.A.I.C.S.: 336320
Qingyong Liu *(Chm)*

HARBIN GLORIA PHARMACEUTICAL CO., LTD.
No 29 Beijing Road Limin economic and Technological Development Zone, Hulan District, Harbin, 101318, China
Tel.: (86) 1068002437
Web Site: http://www.gloria.cc
Year Founded: 2008
002437—(SSE)
Rev.: $436,356,180

INTERNATIONAL PUBLIC

Assets: $572,016,276
Liabilities: $332,839,260
Net Worth: $239,177,016
Earnings: ($40,902,732)
Emp.: 2,427
Fiscal Year-end: 12/31/22
Pharmaceuticals Mfr
N.A.I.C.S.: 325412
Dongxu Wang *(Chm)*

HARBIN GONG DA HIGH-TECH ENTERPRISE DEVELOPMENT CO., LTD.
No 118 Xidazhi Street, Nangang District, Harbin, 150006, Heilongjiang, China
Tel.: (86) 451 86269018
600701—(SHG)
Rev.: $112,053,196
Assets: $603,463,118
Liabilities: $1,166,749,179
Net Worth: ($563,286,061)
Earnings: ($552,340,771)
Fiscal Year-end: 12/31/19
Food Products Mfr
N.A.I.C.S.: 311224
Ren Huiyun *(Pres)*

HARBIN HATOU INVESTMENT CO., LTD.
27 Kunlun Street Mall Longshun, Nangang District, Harbin, 150028, Heilongjiang, China
Tel.: (86) 45151939831
600864—(SHG)
Rev.: $359,725,902
Assets: $4,812,052,963
Liabilities: $3,129,430,932
Net Worth: $1,682,622,031
Earnings: ($136,801,899)
Fiscal Year-end: 12/31/22
Electric Power Generation & Distribution Services
N.A.I.C.S.: 221112
Hongbo Zhao *(Chm)*

HARBIN JIUZHOU GROUP CO., LTD.
No 609 Jiuzhou Road, Songbei District, Harbin, 150027, Heilongjiang, China
Tel.: (86) 45158771318
Web Site: http://www.jze.com.cn
Year Founded: 1997
300040—(CHIN)
Rev.: $186,951,024
Assets: $1,063,131,264
Liabilities: $657,488,988
Net Worth: $405,642,276
Earnings: $20,728,656
Emp.: 680
Fiscal Year-end: 12/31/22
Power Transmitting & Converting Set Equipment
N.A.I.C.S.: 335311
Li Yin *(Chm)*

HARBIN MEDISAN PHARMACEUTICAL CO., LTD.
The middle part of Beijing Road Limin Development Zone, Harbin, 150025, Heilongjiang, China
Tel.: (86) 45185608888
Web Site: https://www.medisan.com.cn
Year Founded: 1996
002900—(SSE)
Rev.: $144,388,764
Assets: $460,061,316
Liabilities: $171,961,920
Net Worth: $288,099,396
Earnings: $4,241,484
Fiscal Year-end: 12/31/22
Chemical Preparation Mfr & Distr
N.A.I.C.S.: 325411
Qin Jianfei *(Chm & Pres)*

AND PRIVATE COMPANIES

HARBOUR EQUINE HOLDINGS LIMITED

HARBIN PHARMACEUTICAL GROUP SANJING PHARMACEUTICAL CO., LTD
No 418 Hayao Road, Daoli District, Harbin, 150071, Heilongjiang, China
Tel.: (86) 45184600888
Web Site: http://www.sanjing.com.cn
Year Founded: 1950
600829—(SHG)
Rev.: $1,353,609,471
Assets: $991,043,895
Liabilities: $645,289,772
Net Worth: $345,754,122
Earnings: $36,987,903
Fiscal Year-end: 12/31/22
Pharmaceutical Product Whslr
N.A.I.C.S.: 424210
Weidong Zhu *(Chm, Pres & Gen Mgr)*

HARBIN SAYYAS WINDOWS CO., LTD.
No 9 Xinnong Road, Wanggang Town & Nangang District, Harbin, 150088, Heilongjiang, China
Tel.: (86) 4006700999
Web Site: https://www.sayyas.net
Year Founded: 1998
301227—(CHIN)
Rev.: $132,344,662
Assets: $318,370,422
Liabilities: $58,769,676
Net Worth: $259,600,746
Earnings: $20,558,831
Fiscal Year-end: 12/31/23
Wood Windows Mfr & Distr
N.A.I.C.S.: 321911
Yunlong Ding *(Chm)*

HARBIN VITI ELECTRONICS CO., LTD.
No 11 West Haping Road, High-tech Development District, Harbin, 150060, Heilongjiang, China
Tel.: (86) 45187101777
Web Site: https://www.viti.net.cn
Year Founded: 2000
603023—(SHG)
Rev.: $10,413,524
Assets: $113,560,041
Liabilities: $6,305,196
Net Worth: $107,254,845
Earnings: $618,588
Fiscal Year-end: 12/31/22
Automotive Parts Mfr & Distr
N.A.I.C.S.: 336390
Zhen Hua Chen *(Founder, Chm & Pres)*

HARBIN XINGUANG OPTIC-ELECTRONICS TECHNOLOGY CO., LTD.
No 1294 Chuangxin Road, Songbei District, Harbin, 150028, Heilongjiang, China
Tel.: (86) 45158627230
Web Site: http://www.xggdkj.com
Year Founded: 2007
688011—(SHG)
Rev.: $21,041,762
Assets: $190,504,422
Liabilities: $22,591,581
Net Worth: $167,912,840
Earnings: ($3,463,907)
Emp.: 550
Fiscal Year-end: 12/31/22
Electronic Product Mfr & Distr
N.A.I.C.S.: 334419
Weimin Kang *(Chm & Gen Mgr)*

HARBINGER GROUP INC.
139 Siddhant Survey No 97/6 Off Paud Road, Kothrud, Pune, 411038, India
Tel.: (91) 2025284201

Web Site:
http://www.harbingergroup.com
Year Founded: 1990
Sales Range: $75-99.9 Million
Emp.: 500
Computer Software Services
N.A.I.C.S.: 513210
Vikas Joshi *(Chm & Mng Dir)*

Subsidiaries:

Harbinger Knowledge Products Pvt. Ltd. (1)
139 Siddhant Survey 97/6 Off Paud Road, Kothrud, Pune, 411038, India
Tel.: (91) 20 2528.4201
Web Site:
  http://www.harbingerknowledge.com
Software Publisher
N.A.I.C.S.: 513210
Jayant Kulkarni *(Exec Dir)*

Harbinger Knowledge Products, Inc. (1)
16770 NE 79th St Ste 100, Redmond, WA 98052
Tel.: (425) 861-8400
Web Site:
  http://www.harbingerknowledge.com
Software Publisher
N.A.I.C.S.: 513210
Seema Chaudhary *(Pres)*

HARBOES BRYGGERI A/S
Spegerborgvej 34, 4230, Skaelskor, Denmark
Tel.: (45) 58168888   DK
Web Site: https://www.harboe.com
Year Founded: 1883
HARB.B—(OMX)
Rev.: $234,292,105
Assets: $188,678,311
Liabilities: $76,282,148
Net Worth: $112,396,163
Earnings: $66,028
Emp.: 504
Fiscal Year-end: 04/30/22
Alcoholic & Non-Alcoholic Beverage Mfr
N.A.I.C.S.: 312120
Bernhard Griese *(Chm)*

Subsidiaries:

AS Viru Olu (1)
Rakvere mnt 7, Laane-Virumaa, 45301, Haljala, Estonia
Tel.: (372) 3295000
Web Site: http://www.wiru.ee
Beer Mfr
N.A.I.C.S.: 312120

Darguner Brauerei GmbH (1)
Brewery Street 3, 17159, Dargun, Germany
Tel.: (49) 399593010
Web Site: https://www.darguner.com
Beer Mfr
N.A.I.C.S.: 312120

Gourmet Bryggeriet ApS (1)
Spegerborgvej 34, 4230, Skaelskor, Denmark
Tel.: (45) 58168888
Web Site:
  http://www.gourmetbryggeriet.com
Beer Mfr
N.A.I.C.S.: 312120

Harboe Sverige AB (1)
Byggvagen 4, 443 61, Stenkullen, Sweden
Tel.: (46) 30224160
Beer & Soft Drink Distr
N.A.I.C.S.: 424490

HARBOR STAR SHIPPING SERVICES INC.
2224 A Bonifacio Street corner Pres Sergio Osmena Highway, Bangkal, Makati, 1233, Philippines
Tel.: (63) 285531502
Web Site:
  https://www.harborstar.com.ph
TUGS—(PHI)
Rev.: $39,714,263

Assets: $129,152,312
Liabilities: $102,966,783
Net Worth: $26,185,529
Earnings: ($3,286,635)
Emp.: 607
Fiscal Year-end: 12/31/21
Harbor Assistance, Lighterage, Towage, Salvage & Other Marine Services
N.A.I.C.S.: 488390
Ignatius A. Rodriguez *(Officer-Corp Information)*

HARBOUR DIGITAL ASSET CAPITAL LIMITED
19/F Yat Chau Building 262 Des Voeux Road, Central, China (Hong Kong)
Tel.: (852) 39727192
Web Site: http://www.unity913.com
0913—(HKG)
Rev.: $219,683
Assets: $23,777,475
Liabilities: $178,883
Net Worth: $23,598,593
Earnings: ($5,620,200)
Emp.: 15
Fiscal Year-end: 12/31/22
Securities
N.A.I.C.S.: 525990

HARBOUR ENERGY PLC
4th Floor Saltire Court 20 Castle Terrace, Edinburgh, EH1 2EN, United Kingdom
Tel.: (44) 2073990910   UK
Web Site:
  http://www.harbourenergy.com
PMOIF—(OTCIQ)
Rev.: $3,715,000,000
Assets: $9,897,000,000
Liabilities: $8,357,000,000
Net Worth: $1,540,000,000
Earnings: $32,000,000
Emp.: 1,716
Fiscal Year-end: 12/31/23
Holding Company; Oil & Gas Exploration & Production
N.A.I.C.S.: 551112
Linda Zarda Cook *(CEO)*

Subsidiaries:

Chrysaor Holding Limited (1)
Brettenham House, Lancaster Place, London, WC2E 7EN, United Kingdom
Tel.: (44) 207 660 5555
Web Site: http://www.chrysaor.com
Holding Company
N.A.I.C.S.: 551112
Phil Kirk *(CEO)*

Subsidiary (Domestic):

Chrysaor E&P Limited (2)
Brettenham House, Lancaster Place, London, WC2E 7EN, United Kingdom
Tel.: (44) 203 696 2700
Petroleum & Natural Gas Extraction
N.A.I.C.S.: 211130
Phil Kirk *(CEO)*

Subsidiary (Domestic):

Chrysaor Production (U.K.) Limited (3)
Brettenham House Lancaster Place, London, WC2E 7EN, United Kingdom (100%)
Tel.: (44) 2074086000
Web Site: http://www.conocophillips.co.uk
Sales Range: $150-199.9 Million
Emp.: 43
Petroleum & Associated Businesses
N.A.I.C.S.: 324110
Terri King *(Pres)*

PCO Trading Ltd (1)
23 Lwr Belgrave Street, London, SW1W0NR, United Kingdom (100%)
Tel.: (44) 2077301111
Sales Range: $25-49.9 Million
Emp.: 50
Petroleum & Petroleum Products Whslr

N.A.I.C.S.: 424720

Premier Oil Exploration Ltd (1)
23 Lower Belgrave Street, London, SW1W 0NR, United Kingdom (100%)
Tel.: (44) 207 730 1111
Web Site: https://www.harbourenergy.com
Sales Range: $50-74.9 Million
Emp.: 90
Crude Petroleum & Natural Gas Extraction
N.A.I.C.S.: 211120

Premier Oil Far East Limited (1)
435 Orchard Road 22-02 Wisma Atria, Singapore, 238877, Singapore
Tel.: (65) 68380115
Oil & Gas Exploration Services
N.A.I.C.S.: 211120

Premier Oil Group Ltd (1)
23 Lwr Belgrave St, London, Sw1W 0NR, United Kingdom (100%)
Tel.: (44) 2077301111
Sales Range: $50-74.9 Million
Emp.: 60
Oil & Gas Field Exploration Services
N.A.I.C.S.: 213112

Premier Oil Holdings Ltd (1)
23 Lwr Belgrave St, London, SW1 W0NR, United Kingdom (100%)
Tel.: (44) 2077301111
Web Site: http://www.premier-oil.com
Sales Range: $50-74.9 Million
Emp.: 100
Petroleum & Petroleum Products Whslr
N.A.I.C.S.: 424720

Premier Oil Natuna Sea BV (1)
The Jakarta Stock Exchange Bldg, Tower 1 10th Fl - Sudirman, Jakarta, 12190, Indonesia
Tel.: (62) 215151800
Web Site: http://www.premier-oil.com
Oil & Gas Field Exploration Services
N.A.I.C.S.: 213112

Premier Oil UK Ltd (1)
Prime Four Kingswells, Aberdeen, AB15 8PU, United Kingdom
Tel.: (44) 122 461 8900
Web Site: http://www.premier-oil.com
Sales Range: $50-74.9 Million
Emp.: 100
Oil & Gas Exploration Services
N.A.I.C.S.: 213112

Premier Oil Vietnam Offshore BV (1)
18/F Kumho Asiana Plaza Saigon No 39 Le Duan Street Ward Ben Nghe, District 1, Ho Chi Minh City, 70000, Vietnam
Tel.: (84) 839105788
Oil & Gas Exploration Services
N.A.I.C.S.: 213112

Premier Oil do Brasil Petroleo e Gas Ltda. (1)
Rua Lauro Muller 116-Sala 2006 Torre Rio Sul Shopping 20 andar, Botafogo, Rio de Janeiro, 22290-906, Brazil
Tel.: (55) 2135507000
Oil & Gas Exploration Mfr
N.A.I.C.S.: 324110
Francisco Santos *(CFO & Dir-Fin)*

Premier Pict Petroleum Ltd (1)
23 Lwr Belgrave St, London, SW1W0NR, United Kingdom (100%)
Tel.: (44) 2077301111
Web Site: http://www.premier-oil.com
Sales Range: $50-74.9 Million
Emp.: 100
Oil & Gas Field Exploration Services
N.A.I.C.S.: 213112

HARBOUR EQUINE HOLDINGS LIMITED
5th Floor Caltex House 158 Hennessy Road, Wanchai, China (Hong Kong)   Ky
Web Site:
  https://www.harbourequine.com
Year Founded: 1978
8377—(HKG)
Rev.: $9,837,821
Assets: $17,608,350
Liabilities: $8,846,996
Net Worth: $8,761,353

HARBOUR EQUINE HOLDINGS LIMITED

Harbour Equine Holdings Limited—(Continued)
Earnings: ($2,954,158)
Emp.: 141
Fiscal Year-end: 12/31/22
Holding Company
N.A.I.C.S.: 551112
Yiu Tung Chan *(Exec Dir)*

Subsidiaries:

Harbour Racing Limited (1)
5/F Caltex House 258 Hennessy Road,
Wanchai, China (Hong Kong)
Tel.: (852) 28689866
Web Site:
https://www.harbourbloodstock.com
Equine Management Services
N.A.I.C.S.: 112920

LMP International Limited (1)
19/F Aubin House No 171 - 172 Gloucester Road, Wanchai, China (Hong Kong)
Tel.: (852) 28110963
Web Site: https://www.lmp-intl.com
Interior Decoration Services
N.A.I.C.S.: 541410

Tseyu International Trading Company Limited (1)
Unit 1302 13/F New East Ocean Centre No 9 Science Museum Road, Tsim Sha Tsui East, Kowloon, China (Hong Kong)
Tel.: (852) 23916748
Web Site: https://www.tseyu.com.hk
Elastic Filament Thread Mfr & Distr
N.A.I.C.S.: 313110

HARBOUR MARINE PRODUCTS INC.
2165 Commissioner Street, Vancouver, V5L 1A4, BC, Canada
Tel.: (604) 255-9992
Year Founded: 1996
Seafood Product Distr
N.A.I.C.S.: 424420
Joe Cook *(Plant Mgr)*

HARBOUR-LINK GROUP BERHAD
Wisma Harbour Parkcity Commerce Square Jalan Tun Ahmad Zaidi, 97000, Bintulu, Sarawak, Malaysia
Tel.: (60) 86318998
Web Site:
https://www.harbour.com.my
HARBOUR—(KLS)
Rev.: $213,112,442
Assets: $230,322,983
Liabilities: $47,942,837
Net Worth: $182,380,146
Earnings: $37,052,073
Emp.: 861
Fiscal Year-end: 06/30/23
Marine Services
N.A.I.C.S.: 483113
M. Chandrasegaran *(Co-Sec)*

Subsidiaries:

Eastern Soldar (Singapore) Pte. Ltd. (1)
8 Chia Ping Road 06-20 Jtc Flatted Factory, Singapore, 619973, Singapore
Tel.: (65) 62617309
Sales Range: $25-49.9 Million
Emp.: 2
Mechanical Engineering Services
N.A.I.C.S.: 541330
Arnold Khew *(Mgr)*

Eastern Soldar Engineering & Construction Sdn. Bhd. (1)
Lot 17239 Oakland Industrial Park, Jalan Haruan2, 70200, Seremban, Negeri Sembilan, Malaysia
Tel.: (60) 67646699
Sales Range: $50-74.9 Million
Emp.: 70
Oil & Gas Support Services
N.A.I.C.S.: 213112
Toh Guan Seng *(Mng Dir)*

Subsidiary (Domestic):

ESE Energy Sdn. Bhd. (2)
B-3A-5 Setiawalk Perslaran Wawasan, Pusat Bandar Puchong, 47160, Puchong, Selangor, Malaysia
Tel.: (60) 358853180
Web Site: https://www.eseenergy.my
Sales Range: $25-49.9 Million
Emp.: 60
Mechanical & Civil Engineering Services
N.A.I.C.S.: 541330
David Toh *(Mng Dir)*

Harbour Agencies (Sarawak) Sdn. Bhd. (1)
Wisma Harbour Pk City Commercer Sq, Jalan Tun Ahmad Zaidi, PO Box 62095, 97000, Bintulu, Sarawak, Malaysia
Tel.: (60) 89752311
Freight Forwarding & Shipping Services
N.A.I.C.S.: 483111

Subsidiary (Domestic):

Harbour Agencies (Sabah) Sdn. Bhd. (2)
Room 903 9th Floor Wisma Khoo Siak Chiew, PO Box 2280, 90725, Sandakan, Sabah, Malaysia
Tel.: (60) 89225561
Sales Range: $25-49.9 Million
Emp.: 5
Freight Forwarding & Shipping Services
N.A.I.C.S.: 488510
Eleen Foo *(Mgr)*

Harbour Agencies (Sibu) Sdn. Bhd. (1)
2nd Fl No 41 43 Jalan Mahsuri, 96000, Sibu, Sarawak, Malaysia
Tel.: (60) 84341558
Sales Range: $25-49.9 Million
Emp.: 15
Freight Forwarding & Shipping Services
N.A.I.C.S.: 483111
Harris Hii *(Gen Mgr)*

Harbour Services Corporation Sdn. Bhd. (1)
Wisma Harbour Park City Commerce Square Jalan Tun Ahmad Zaidi, 97000, Bintulu, Sarawak, Malaysia
Tel.: (60) 86318998
Web Site: http://www.harbour.com.my
Sales Range: $125-149.9 Million
Emp.: 300
Freight Forwarding & Shipping Services
N.A.I.C.S.: 483111

Harbour-Link Lines (JB) Sdn. Bhd. (1)
28 01 Jalan Molek 1 28 Taman Molek, 81100, Johor Bahru, Johor Darul Takzim, Malaysia
Tel.: (60) 73562800
Sales Range: $25-49.9 Million
Emp.: 10
Freight Forwarding & Shipping Services
N.A.I.C.S.: 488510
Douglas Choo *(Gen Mgr)*

Harbour-Link Lines (PK) Sdn. Bhd. (1)
B-9-2 North Tower BBT One Lebuh Batu Nilam 1, Bandar Bukit Tinggi, 41200, Port Klang, Selangor Darul Ehsan, Malaysia
Tel.: (60) 333252010
Sales Range: $25-49.9 Million
Emp.: 19
Shipping Services
N.A.I.C.S.: 488330

Harbour-Link Logistics Sdn. Bhd. (1)
Wisma Harbour Park City Commerce Square, Bintulu, 97000, Sarawak, Malaysia
Tel.: (60) 86332815
Web Site: http://www.harbour.com.my
Sales Range: $50-74.9 Million
Emp.: 200
Freight Forwarding & Shipping Services
N.A.I.C.S.: 483111

Subsidiary (Domestic):

Harbour-Link Logistics (S) Sdn. Bhd. (2)
Lot 19 Jalan 1G Industrial Zone 4, KKIP Selatan Jalan Sepangar, 88460, Kota Kinabalu, Sabah, Malaysia
Tel.: (60) 88492791
Web Site: http://www.harbour.com.my
Sales Range: $25-49.9 Million
Emp.: 15
Freight Forwarding & Shipping Services
N.A.I.C.S.: 483111
Roffiah Idris *(Mgr-Logistics)*

HARBOURVEST GLOBAL PRIVATE EQUITY LIMITED
BNP Paribas House St Julian s Avenue, Saint Peter Port, GY1 1WA, Guernsey
Tel.: (44) 1481750800 GY
Web Site: https://www.hvpe.com
Year Founded: 2007
HVPE—(LSE)
Rev.: $3,693,000
Assets: $3,839,505,000
Liabilities: $1,579,000
Net Worth: $3,837,926,000
Earnings: ($10,674,000)
Emp.: 1,000
Fiscal Year-end: 01/31/23
Privater Equity Firm
N.A.I.C.S.: 523999
Ed Warner *(Chm)*

HARBOURVIEW AUTOHAUS LTD.
4921 Wellington Road, Nanaimo, V9T 2H5, BC, Canada
Tel.: (250) 751-1221
Web Site:
https://www.harbourviewvw.com
Year Founded: 1983
Rev.: $17,388,990
Emp.: 35
New & Used Car Dealers
N.A.I.C.S.: 441110
Sjon Wynia *(Gen Mgr)*

HARBRIDGE + CROSS LIMITED
350 Creditstone Road Suite 202, Concord, L4K 3Z2, ON, Canada
Tel.: (416) 213-7165
Web Site:
http://www.harbridgeandcross.com
Year Founded: 1967
Sales Range: $10-24.9 Million
General Contracting Services
N.A.I.C.S.: 236220
Sam Kumar *(Pres)*

HARCOURTS INTERNATIONAL LTD
31 Amy Johnson Place, Eagle Farm, 4009, QLD, Australia
Tel.: (61) 738393226
Web Site: http://harcourts.net
Sales Range: $15-24.9 Billion
Emp.: 3,100
Real Estate Services
N.A.I.C.S.: 531390
Paul Wright *(Co-Owner)*

HARD OFF CORPORATION CO., LTD.
3-1-13 Shinei-cho, Shibata, 957-0063, Niigata, Japan
Tel.: (81) 254244344
Web Site: https://www.hardoff.co.jp
Year Founded: 1972
2674—(TKS)
Rev.: $198,994,050
Assets: $152,684,390
Liabilities: $40,321,000
Net Worth: $112,363,390
Earnings: $13,834,730
Fiscal Year-end: 03/31/24
Used Merchandise Store Operator
N.A.I.C.S.: 459510
Taro Yamamoto *(Pres)*

INTERNATIONAL PUBLIC

HARD-CO CONSTRUCTION LTD.
625 Conlin Road, Whitby, L1R 2W8, ON, Canada
Tel.: (905) 655-2001
Web Site: http://www.hard-co.com
Year Founded: 1992
Rev.: $15,794,694
Emp.: 110
Highway & Street Construction Services
N.A.I.C.S.: 237310
Barry Harding *(Co-Founder)*

Subsidiaries:

Hard-Co Sand & Gravel Ltd. (1)
4900 Thickson Rd N, Whitby, L1R 2W9, ON, Canada
Tel.: (905) 655-9954
Stone Distr
N.A.I.C.S.: 238140

HARDCASTLE & WAUD MANUFACTURING COMPANY LIMITED
C-101 1st Floor 247 Park C-101 1st Floor 247 Park, Lal Bahadur Shastri Marg, Mumbai, 400083, India
Tel.: (91) 2249186000
Web Site: https://www.hawcoindia.in
509597—(BOM)
Rev.: $595,710
Assets: $5,942,181
Liabilities: $452,744
Net Worth: $5,489,437
Earnings: $173,606
Emp.: 6
Fiscal Year-end: 03/31/22
Industrial Lubricants Mfr
N.A.I.C.S.: 325199
Banwari Lal Jatia *(Mng Dir)*

HARDCORE DISCOVERIES LTD.
1095 West Pender Street Suite 305, Vancouver, V6E 2M6, BC, Canada
Tel.: (604) 331-1213
Web Site: https://thecse.com
HARD—(CNSX)
Assets: $155,371
Liabilities: $472,724
Net Worth: ($317,352)
Earnings: ($1,197,856)
Fiscal Year-end: 12/31/22
Mineral Exploration Services
N.A.I.C.S.: 213115
Grant Hendrickson *(Pres & CEO)*

HARDEN TECHNOLOGIES INC.
Building 8 No 6 Jingye Road, Torch Development Zone, Zhongshan, 528400, China
Tel.: (86) 76089935422 VG
Year Founded: 2010
HAHA—(BZX)
Rev.: $21,141,677
Assets: $26,605,213
Liabilities: $16,072,667
Net Worth: $10,532,546
Earnings: $604,733
Emp.: 219
Fiscal Year-end: 12/31/23
Recycling Equipment Mfr
N.A.I.C.S.: 333310
Chunmei Lei *(CFO)*

HARDIDE PLC
9 Longlands Road, Bicester, OX26 5AH, Oxfordshire, United Kingdom
Tel.: (44) 1869353830
Web Site: https://www.hardide.com
HDD—(AIM)
Rev.: $5,683,644
Assets: $11,027,628
Liabilities: $6,170,490

Net Worth: $4,857,138
Earnings: ($2,479,518)
Fiscal Year-end: 09/30/22
Tungsten Carbide-Based Coatings
N.A.I.C.S.: 325510
Ian Eggleton (Mgr-Engineering)

Subsidiaries:

Hardide Coatings Incorporated (1)
444 Hollie Dr, Martinsville, VA 24112
Tel.: (832) 491-4720
Web Site: https://hardide.com
Tungsten Carbide Coatings Mfr
N.A.I.C.S.: 325180

Hardide Coatings Limited (1)
9 Longlands Road, Bicester, OX26 5AH, Oxfordshire, United Kingdom
Tel.: (44) 1869353830
Web Site: https://www.hardide.com
Sales Range: $25-49.9 Million
Emp.: 25
Tungsten Carbide Coatings
N.A.I.C.S.: 331492

HARDIE GRANT PUBLISHING PTY. LTD.

Ground Floor Building 1 658 Church St, 658 Church St, Richmond, 3121, VIC, Australia
Tel.: (61) 3 8520 6444
Web Site:
  http://www.hardiegrant.com.au
Year Founded: 1997
Sales Range: $25-49.9 Million
Emp.: 100
Book, Magazine & Internet Publisher
N.A.I.C.S.: 513130
John Gerahty (Chm)

HARDT GROUP GLOBAL MANAGEMENT AG

Grabenstrasse 42, 6301, Zug, Switzerland
Tel.: (41) 41 7297 982
Web Site: http://www.hardtgroup.com
Real Estate Investment Management Services
N.A.I.C.S.: 523999
Alexander Schweickhardt (Co-Founder & CEO)

Subsidiaries:

HARDT GROUP Advisors, Inc. (1)
99 Park Ave Ste 1550, New York, NY 10016
Tel.: (212) 523-0211
Real Estate Investment Management Services
N.A.I.C.S.: 523999

HARDT GROUP GmbH (1)
Graben 12, 1010, Vienna, Austria
Tel.: (43) 1 513 011 11
Real Estate Investment Management Services
N.A.I.C.S.: 523999

HARDWOODS DISTRIBUTION INC.

20161 86th Avenue Building B- Suite 340, Langley, V2Y 2C1, BC, Canada
Tel.: (604) 881-1988 Ca
Web Site: https://adentragroup.com
Year Founded: 2011
HDI—(TSX)
Rev.: $974,182,671
Assets: $458,381,660
Liabilities: $219,515,591
Net Worth: $238,866,069
Earnings: $29,415,293
Emp.: 1,329
Fiscal Year-end: 12/31/20
Hardwood Lumber, Plywood, Melamine, Particleboard & Specialty Products Distr
N.A.I.C.S.: 423310
Robert J. Brown (Pres & CEO)

Subsidiaries:

Downes & Reader Hardwood Co., Inc. (1)
60 Evans Dr, Stoughton, MA 02072
Tel.: (781) 341-4092
Lumber, Plywood, Millwork & Wood Panel Merchant Whslr
N.A.I.C.S.: 423310
Patrick Amato (Sls Mgr)

Hardwoods Specialty Products US LP (1)
6400 Sycamore Canyon Blvd, Riverside, CA 92507
Tel.: (951) 653-9433
Hardwood Distr
N.A.I.C.S.: 423310

Subsidiary (Domestic):

Aura Hardwood Lumber Inc. (2)
620 Quinn Ave, San Jose, CA 95112
Tel.: (408) 275-1990
Web Site: https://www.aurahardwoods.com
Lumber, Plywood & Millwork
N.A.I.C.S.: 423310
Kellen Aura (Pres)

Diamond Hardwoods & Architectural Products, Inc. (2)
2534 San Benito St, Fresno, CA 93721
Tel.: (559) 264-4888
Web Site:
  http://www.diamondhardwood.com
Sales Range: $1-9.9 Million
Emp.: 10
Lumber, Plywood, And Millwork, Nsk
N.A.I.C.S.: 423310

Far West Plywood Company (2)
18450 Parthenia Pl, Northridge, CA 91325
Tel.: (818) 885-1511
Web Site: http://www.farwestplywood.com
Sales Range: $10-24.9 Million
Emp.: 15
Lumber, Plywood, Millwork & Wood Panel Merchant Whslr
N.A.I.C.S.: 423310
Janet Armstrong (Pres)

Novo Building Products, LLC (2)
8181 Logistic Dr, Zeeland, MI 49464
Web Site: https://www.novobp.com
Specialty Building Products Mfr & Distr
N.A.I.C.S.: 321999
Rochelle L. Grace (Dir-Talent & OD)

Subsidiary (Domestic):

L.J. Smith Inc. (3)
35280 Scio-Bowerston Rd, Bowerston, OH 44695-9726
Tel.: (740) 269-2221
Web Site: https://www.ljsmith.com
Sales Range: $25-49.9 Million
Emp.: 250
Provider of Millwork Services
N.A.I.C.S.: 321918
Carla Gowins (Coord-HR)

Southwest Moulding Co. (3)
9209 Old Hickory Trl Ste 180, Dallas, TX 75237 (100%)
Tel.: (214) 630-8961
Web Site:
  https://www.southwestmoulding.com
Sales Range: $50-74.9 Million
Emp.: 140
Moulding & Millwork Distr
N.A.I.C.S.: 423310

Tenon USA, Inc (3)
200 Westgate Cir Ste 402, Annapolis, MD 21401 (100%)
Tel.: (410) 571-0844
Sales Range: $25-49.9 Million
Emp.: 100
Activities for Forestry
N.A.I.C.S.: 115310

The Empire Company, LLC (3)
8181 Logistics Dr, Zeeland, MI 49464-9378 (100%)
Tel.: (616) 772-7272
Web Site: http://www.empireco.com
Sales Range: $50-74.9 Million
Emp.: 180
Mouding & Millwork Distr
N.A.I.C.S.: 423310

Thomas H. Highley (CEO)

Hardwoods of Michigan, Inc. (1)
430 Division St, Clinton, MI 49236-9702
Tel.: (517) 456-7431
Web Site: http://www.hmilumber.com
Sales Range: $50-74.9 Million
Emp.: 120
Lumber Drying & Processing; Sawmill
N.A.I.C.S.: 321999

Subsidiary (Domestic):

Tri-County Logging, Inc. (2)
430 Division St, Clinton, MI 49236
Tel.: (517) 456-7431
Web Site: http://www.hmilumber.com
Sales Range: $50-74.9 Million
Emp.: 85
Producer of Lumber
N.A.I.C.S.: 321113

Division (Domestic):

Walker Lumber Company, Inc. (2)
148 Tipple Ln, Woodland, PA 16881-0060
Tel.: (814) 857-7642
Web Site: http://www.wlci.us
Sales Range: $25-49.9 Million
Emp.: 50
Sawmill & Dry Kiln
N.A.I.C.S.: 423310

Mid-Am Building Supply, Inc. (1)
1615 Omar Bradley Dr, Moberly, MO 65270
Tel.: (660) 263-2140
Web Site: http://www.midambuilding.com
Sales Range: $125-149.9 Million
Emp.: 300
Building Supplies Distr
N.A.I.C.S.: 423310
Richard Knaebel (VP-Ops)

Pacific Mutual Door Company (1)
1525 W 31st St, Kansas City, MO 64108
Tel.: (816) 531-0161
Web Site:
  https://www.pacificmutualdoor.com
Sales Range: $100-124.9 Million
Emp.: 175
Doors, Windows & Related Building Materials Whslr
N.A.I.C.S.: 423310

Subsidiary (Domestic):

Hardman Wholesale LLC (2)
404 N First St, Osborne, KS 67473-1841
Tel.: (785) 346-2131
Sales Range: $10-24.9 Million
Emp.: 50
Lumber, Plywood & Millwork Whslr
N.A.I.C.S.: 423310
Rusty Berry (Branch Mgr)

Warren Brothers Sash & Door Company (2)
700 Massman Dr, Nashville, TN 37210-3724 (100%)
Tel.: (615) 885-0355
Web Site: http://warrenbros.com
Sales Range: $25-49.9 Million
Lumber, Plywood & Millwork Whslr
N.A.I.C.S.: 423310

Rugby Holdings LLC (1)
1 Pillsbury St Ste 302, Concord, NH 03301
Tel.: (603) 369-4710
Holding Company
N.A.I.C.S.: 551112

Subsidiary (Domestic):

River City Millwork, Inc. (2)
200 Quaker Rd, Rockford, IL 61104
Tel.: (815) 965-9439
Web Site: http://www.rivercitymillwork.com
Rev.: $5,000,000
Emp.: 21
Lumber, Plywood, Millwork & Wood Panel Merchant Whslr
N.A.I.C.S.: 423310
Bill Sarbaugh (Pres)

Rugby IPD Corp. (2)
1 Pillsbury St Ste 302, Concord, NH 03301
Tel.: (603) 369-4710
Web Site: http://www.rugbyabp.com
Industrial Building Materials Distr
N.A.I.C.S.: 423310
Ann Stroehlein (Controller)

Subsidiary (Domestic):

Albuquerque Hardwood Lumber Company (3)
4100 2nd St NW, Albuquerque, NM 87107
Tel.: (505) 344-8856
Lumber, Plywood, Millwork & Wood Panel Merchant Whslr
N.A.I.C.S.: 423310

F.W. Honerkamp, Co. Inc. (3)
500 Oak Point Ave, Bronx, NY 10474
Tel.: (718) 589-9700
Web Site: http://www.honerkamp.com
Industrial Building Materials Distr
N.A.I.C.S.: 423310

HARDWYN INDIA LIMITED

B-101 Mayapuri Ind Area Phase-1, New Delhi, 110064, India
Tel.: (91) 9212373715
Web Site: https://www.hardwyn.com
HARDWYN—(NSE)
Rev.: $20,042,505
Assets: $50,676,108
Liabilities: $4,963,710
Net Worth: $45,712,398
Earnings: $1,401,836
Emp.: 69
Fiscal Year-end: 03/31/23
Hardware Mfr
N.A.I.C.S.: 332510
Swaranjit Singh Sayal (Chm)

HARDY CAPITAL CORPORATION

Guiness Tower Suite 2390 - 1055 West Hastings Penthouse, Vancouver, V6E 2E9, BC, Canada
Tel.: (604) 235-5550
Web Site:
  http://www.hardycapital.com
Equity Investment Firm
N.A.I.C.S.: 523999
Roger Hardy (Chm & CEO)

Subsidiaries:

ShoeMe Technologies Ltd. (1)
Suite 206 1715 Cook Street, Vancouver, V5Y 3J6, BC, Canada
Tel.: (866) 440-7948
Web Site: http://www.shoeme.ca
Sales Range: $150-199.9 Million
Emp.: 250
Online Shoe Retailer
N.A.I.C.S.: 458210
Sean C. Clark (Co-Founder & Pres)

Affiliate (US):

Gerler & Son, Inc. (2)
1730 Minor Ave Ste 700, Seattle, WA 98101
Tel.: (206) 812-7800
Web Site: http://www.onlineshoes.com
Online Shoe Retailer
N.A.I.C.S.: 458210
Dave Martine (Gen Mgr)

HAREL INSURANCE INVESTMENTS & FINANCIAL SERVICES LTD.

Abba Hillel 3, Ramat Gan, 5252202, Israel
Tel.: (972) 37547111
Web Site: https://pr.harel-group.co.il
HARL—(TAE)
Rev.: $6,744,211,268
Assets: $39,261,970,609
Liabilities: $36,834,499,214
Net Worth: $2,427,471,395
Earnings: $134,482,946
Emp.: 5,000
Fiscal Year-end: 12/31/23
Investment Management Service
N.A.I.C.S.: 523999
Nir Cohen (CEO)

Subsidiaries:

Hamishmar Insurance Agency Ltd. (1)

HAREL INSURANCE INVESTMENTS & FINANCIAL SERVICES LTD.

Harel Insurance Investments & Financial Services Ltd.—(Continued)
3 Abba Hillel Street, PO Box 1954, Ramat Gan, 52118, Israel
Tel.: (972) 37547000
Web Site: http://www.harel-group.co.il
General Insurance Services
N.A.I.C.S.: 524113

Harel (UK) Ltd. (1)
107 Leadenhall Street, London, EC3A 4AF, United Kingdom
Tel.: (44) 2079775293
Emp.: 10
Insurance Brokerage Services
N.A.I.C.S.: 524210
Sammy Bassat *(Mgr)*

Harel Finance Operating Services Ltd. (1)
7 Jabotinsky, Ramat Gan, 52520, Israel
Tel.: (972) 37546029
Web Site: http://www.harel-group.co.il
Financial Investment Advisory Services
N.A.I.C.S.: 523940

Harel Hamishmar Computers Ltd. (1)
3 Aba H Silver Road, PO Box 1956, Ramat Gan, 61015, Israel
Tel.: (972) 37547804
Emp.: 339
Information Technology & Data Processing Services
N.A.I.C.S.: 541519
Moshe Nissan *(Mgr)*

Harel Insurance Company Ltd. (1)
3 Abba Hillel St, 1951, Ramat Gan, 52811, Israel
Tel.: (972) 37547777
Emp.: 2,884
General Insurance Services
N.A.I.C.S.: 524113

Subsidiary (Domestic):

E.M.I. - Ezer Mortgage Insurance Company Ltd. (2)
3 Abba Hillel St, Har Hotzvim, Ramat Gan, 5211802, Israel
Tel.: (972) 25414444
Web Site: http://www.emiltd.com
Emp.: 6
Mortgage Insurance Services
N.A.I.C.S.: 524126
Tsila Daskal *(CEO)*

Harel Insurance, Financing & Issuing Ltd. (2)
3 Aba Hillel Silver, Ramat Gan, 52118, Israel
Tel.: (972) 37547575
Web Site: http://www.harel-group.co.il
Emp.: 5,000
Insurance Services
N.A.I.C.S.: 524210
Michelle Sibnoy *(Mgr-Insurance)*

Yeelim Insurance Agency Ltd. (2)
13 Idelson, Tel Aviv, 63140, Israel
Tel.: (972) 36216500
General Insurance Services
N.A.I.C.S.: 524210

Harel Mutual Funds Ltd. (1)
7 Jabotinsky, Ramat Gan, 52520, Israel
Tel.: (972) 37546110
Web Site: http://www.pia.co.il
Sales Range: $200-249.9 Million
Emp.: 300
Mutual Fund Management Services
N.A.I.C.S.: 523940
Shimon Alkabetz *(CEO)*

Interasco Societe Anonyme General Insurance Company (1)
Vas Georgiou Street 44 Kalvou Street, Chalandri, 15233, Athens, Greece
Tel.: (30) 2106793100
Web Site: https://www.interasco.gr
Insurance Services
N.A.I.C.S.: 524210

Israel Infrastructure Fund (1)
Adgar 360 26th Floor 2 Hashlosha St, Tel Aviv, 6706054, Israel (39%)
Tel.: (972) 3 711 0700
Web Site: http://www.iif.co.il

Investment Fund
N.A.I.C.S.: 525990
Yaron Kestenbaum *(Co-Founder & Mng Partner)*

Madanes Insurance Agency Ltd. (1)
2 Hashlosha St, Tel Aviv, 6706054, Israel
Tel.: (972) 36380400
Web Site: http://www.madanesglobal.com
Emp.: 420
Insurance Services
N.A.I.C.S.: 524210
Shuki Madanes *(Founder & Chm)*

Turk Nippon Sigorta A.S. (1)
Altunizade Mah Mahir iz Cad No 24, Uskudar, 34662, Istanbul, Turkiye (100%)
Tel.: (90) 2165541100
Web Site: https://www.turknippon.com
Emp.: 100
General Insurance Services
N.A.I.C.S.: 524113
Yona Yair Hamburger *(VP)*

Yedidim Pension Arrangements Insurance Agency Ltd. (1)
12 Hahilazon st, Ramat Gan, 5252276, Israel
Tel.: (972) 36386216
Web Site: https://www.yedidim-health.co.il
Sales Range: $100-124.9 Million
Emp.: 200
Insurance Advisory Services
N.A.I.C.S.: 524298

HAREL MALLAC & CO. LTD.
18 Edith Cavell Street, 11302, Port Louis, Mauritius
Tel.: (230) 2073000
Web Site:
https://www.harelmallac.com
Year Founded: 1830
HML.N0000—(MAU)
Rev.: $97,736,456
Assets: $101,404,310
Liabilities: $67,567,671
Net Worth: $33,836,639
Earnings: $335,250
Emp.: 918
Fiscal Year-end: 12/31/23
Holding Company
N.A.I.C.S.: 551112
Antoine Louis Harel *(Chm)*

Subsidiaries:

Archemics Ltd (1)
Motorway M2 Bois Marchand, 21401, Terre Rouge, Mauritius
Tel.: (230) 2491991
Web Site: https://archemics.mu
Sales Range: $25-49.9 Million
Emp.: 200
Industrial Adhesives Mfr
N.A.I.C.S.: 325520
Olivier Maujean *(Gen Mgr)*

Harel Mallac Bureautique Ltd (1)
18 Edith Cavell St, Port Louis, Mauritius
Tel.: (230) 2073000
Web Site: http://www.harelmallac.com
Sales Range: $50-74.9 Million
Emp.: 60
Office Equipments Mfr
N.A.I.C.S.: 423420

Harel Mallac Engineering Ltd (1)
Pailles Rd, Les Pailles, Port Louis, Mauritius
Tel.: (230) 2073000
Web Site: http://www.harelmallac.com
Sales Range: $25-49.9 Million
Emp.: 50
Agro Industrial Equipments Mfr
N.A.I.C.S.: 334514
Michel Pilot *(Mng Dir)*

Harel Mallac Outsourcing Ltd (1)
18 Edith Cavell St, Port Louis, Mauritius
Tel.: (230) 2073000
Web Site: http://www.harelmallac.com
Sales Range: $25-49.9 Million
Emp.: 75
IT Service Company
N.A.I.C.S.: 541512

Harel Mallac Technologies Ltd (1)
1st floor Block A Phoenix Central Pont Fer,
Phoenix, 73524, Mauritius
Tel.: (230) 207 3300
Web Site:
https://www.harelmallactechnologies.com
Sales Range: $50-74.9 Million
Emp.: 165
Information Technology Service Provider
N.A.I.C.S.: 519290
Alain Ah-Sue *(Mng Dir)*

Harel Mallac Travel and Leisure Ltd (1)
18 Edith Cavell St, PO Box 36, Port Louis, Mauritius
Tel.: (230) 2073016
Web Site: http://www.harelmallactravel.com
Emp.: 15
Travel Agency Services
N.A.I.C.S.: 561510
Andre Nairac *(Gen Mgr)*

The Mauritius Chemical & Fertilizer Industry Limited (1)
Chaussee tronelin Sorg, PO Box 344, Chaussee Tromelin Fort George, Port Louis, Mauritius
Tel.: (230) 2163965
Web Site: http://www.mcfigroup.intnet.mu
Sales Range: $50-74.9 Million
Emp.: 200
NPK Blended Fertilizers Mfr
N.A.I.C.S.: 325311

HARFANG EXPLORATION INC.
1100 av des Canadiens-de-Montreal suite 300, Montreal, H3B 2S2, QC, Canada
Tel.: (514) 940-0670 BC
Web Site:
https://www.harfangexploration.com
Year Founded: 2010
HAR—(TSXV)
Rev.: $47,078
Assets: $2,991,931
Liabilities: $243,655
Net Worth: $2,748,275
Earnings: ($945,749)
Fiscal Year-end: 01/31/20
Gold Mining Exploration Company
N.A.I.C.S.: 212220
Ian Campbell *(Pres & CEO)*

Subsidiaries:

LaSalle Exploration Corp. (1)
2080-777 Hornby Street, Vancouver, V6Z 1S4, BC, Canada
Tel.: (604) 647-3966
Web Site: http://www.lasallecorp.com
Rev.: $17,405
Assets: $4,101,130
Liabilities: $466,493
Net Worth: $3,634,637
Earnings: ($36,098)
Fiscal Year-end: 12/31/2020
Mineral Exploration Services
N.A.I.C.S.: 213115

NewOrigin Gold Corp. (1)
110 Yonge Street Suite 1601, Toronto, M5C 1T4, ON, Canada
Tel.: (905) 727-1779
Web Site: https://www.neworigingold.com
Rev.: $71,951
Assets: $52,494
Liabilities: $247,830
Net Worth: ($195,337)
Earnings: ($57,359)
Fiscal Year-end: 06/30/2024
Explorer of Gold & Base Metal Properties
N.A.I.C.S.: 212220
Robert I. Valliant *(Founder, Pres & CEO)*

HARGREAVE HALE AIM VCT PLC
Talisman House Boardmans Way, Blackpool, FY4 5FY, United Kingdom
Tel.: (44) 1253376622 UK
Web Site:
https://www.hargreaveaimvcts.co.uk
Year Founded: 2004
HHV—(LSE)
Rev.: $98,260,912
Assets: $312,473,827
Liabilities: $1,606,183

Net Worth: $310,867,644
Earnings: $92,149,814
Fiscal Year-end: 09/30/21
Portfolio Management & Investment Advice
N.A.I.C.S.: 523940
Oliver Bedford *(Mgr-Lead)*

HARGREAVES LANSDOWN PLC
One College Square South Anchor Road, Bristol, BS1 5HL, United Kingdom
Tel.: (44) 1179009000
Web Site: https://www.hl.co.uk
Year Founded: 1981
HRGLF—(OTCIQ)
Rev.: $70,737,212
Assets: $1,737,881,600
Liabilities: $1,702,716,652
Net Worth: $35,164,948
Earnings: $6,109,740
Emp.: 1,586
Fiscal Year-end: 06/30/20
Investment Products
N.A.I.C.S.: 523940
Ruchir Rodrigues *(Chief Comml Officer & Chief Client Officer)*

Subsidiaries:

HL Tech Sp. z o.o. (1)
Mennica Legacy Tower Prosta 20 Floor 2, 00-850, Warsaw, Poland
Tel.: (48) 519018500
Web Site: https://www.hltech.com
Information Technology Services
N.A.I.C.S.: 541519
Tomasz Krzyzak *(Mgr)*

Hargreaves Lansdown Asset Management Ltd (1)
1 College Square S Anchor Road, Bristol, BS1 5HL, United Kingdom
Tel.: (44) 1179889880
Web Site:
http://www.hargreaveslansdown.co.uk
Financial Consulting Services
N.A.I.C.S.: 523999

Hargreaves Lansdown EBT Trustees Ltd (1)
1 College Square S, Anchor Rd, Bristol, BS1 5HL, United Kingdom
Tel.: (44) 1179889880
Web Site:
http://www.hargreaveslansdown.co.uk
Emp.: 900
Employee Benefit Services
N.A.I.C.S.: 525120
Ian Gorham *(CEO)*

Hargreaves Lansdown Fund Managers Ltd (1)
1 College Sq S Anchor Rd, Bristol, BS1 5HL, United Kingdom
Tel.: (44) 1179889880
Web Site: http://www.hl.co.uk
Sales Range: $350-399.9 Million
Emp.: 650
Investment & Fund Management Services
N.A.I.C.S.: 523999
Alison Zobel *(Sec)*

Hargreaves Lansdown Nominees Ltd (1)
One College Square South Anchor Road, Bristol, BS1 5HL, United Kingdom
Tel.: (44) 1179809800
Web Site:
http://www.hargreaveslansdown.co.uk
Sales Range: $350-399.9 Million,
Emp.: 600
Personal Financial Services
N.A.I.C.S.: 523999
Ian Goram *(CEO)*

Hargreaves Lansdown Pensions Direct Ltd (1)
1 College Square S Anchor Rd, Bristol, PS1 5HL, United Kingdom
Tel.: (44) 1179809800
Web Site: http://www.hl.co.uk
Sales Range: $350-399.9 Million
Emp.: 600
Pension Broking Services

AND PRIVATE COMPANIES

N.A.I.C.S.: 525110
Ian Gorham *(CEO)*

Hargreaves Lansdown Pensions Trustees Ltd (1)
1 College Sq S Anchor Rd, Bristol, BS1 5HL, United Kingdom
Tel.: (44) 1179889880
Web Site: http://www.hl.co.uk
Sales Range: $350-399.9 Million
Emp.: 600
Pensions & Funds Services
N.A.I.C.S.: 525110
Amy Watson *(Mgr-HR)*

Hargreaves Lansdown Stockbrokers Ltd (1)
1 College Square S Anchor Rd, Bristol, BS1 5HL, United Kingdom
Tel.: (44) 8453651254
Web Site: http://www.hl.co.uk
Sales Range: $350-399.9 Million
Emp.: 650
Stock Broking Services
N.A.I.C.S.: 523150
Ian Gorham *(Mng Dir)*

Hargreaves Lansdown Trustee Company Ltd (1)
One College Square South Anchor Road, Bristol, BS1 5HL, United Kingdom
Tel.: (44) 1179889880
Web Site: http://www.hl.co.uk
Sales Range: $350-399.9 Million
Emp.: 900
Personal Financial Services
N.A.I.C.S.: 523999
Ian Gorham *(Mng Dir)*

HARGREAVES SERVICES PLC
Dawn Hedley West Terrace, Esh Winning, Durham, DH7 9PT, United Kingdom
Tel.: (44) 1913734485
Web Site: https://www.hsgplc.co.uk
HSP—(AIM)
Rev.: $266,536,756
Assets: $377,291,836
Liabilities: $134,802,085
Net Worth: $242,489,751
Earnings: $13,494,094
Fiscal Year-end: 05/31/24
Mineral Mining & Energy Industry Support Services
N.A.I.C.S.: 561499
Gordon F. C. Banham *(CEO-Grp)*

Subsidiaries:

Access Services (HK) Limited (1)
Room 1117 Tuen Mun Central Square No 22 Hoi Wing Road, Tuen Mun, China (Hong Kong)
Tel.: (852) 24088670
Web Site: http://www.as.hargreaves.asia
Construction Services
N.A.I.C.S.: 236220

Hargreaves Industrial Services (HK) Limited (1)
Room 1117 Tuen Mun Central Square No 22 Hoi Wing Road, Tuen Mun, China (Hong Kong)
Tel.: (852) 23252909
Web Site: http://www.his.hargreaves.asia
Construction Services
N.A.I.C.S.: 236220

Hargreaves Power Services (HK) Limited (1)
Room 1117 Tuen Mun Central Square No 22 Hoi Wing Road, Tuen Mun, China (Hong Kong)
Tel.: (852) 23113191
Web Site: http://www.hps.hargreaves.asia
Overhead Line Maintenance Services
N.A.I.C.S.: 237160

HARI GOVIND INTERNATIONAL LIMITED
125 Wardhman Nagar Nr, Radha Krishna Mandir, Nagpur, 440008, India
Tel.: (91) 2228520461
Web Site: https://www.hgil.in

531971—(BOM)
Assets: $635,454
Liabilities: $207,422
Net Worth: $428,032
Earnings: ($13,189)
Fiscal Year-end: 03/31/23
Textile Products Mfr
N.A.I.C.S.: 314999
Jugalkishore H. Maniyar *(Chm & Mng Dir)*

HARIA EXPORTS LIMITED
Haria Center 8 Subhash Road, Vile Parel E, Mumbai, 400 057, India
Tel.: (91) 2261546154
Web Site:
 https://www.hariaexports.com
512604—(BOM)
Rev.: $152,780
Assets: $1,911,976
Liabilities: $1,993
Net Worth: $1,909,983
Earnings: $67,128
Fiscal Year-end: 03/31/22
Garment Supply & Notebook Mfr
N.A.I.C.S.: 314999
Kantilal L. Haria *(Chm & Mng Dir-Haria Group)*

Subsidiaries:

Haria Apparels Limited (1)
8 Subhash Road Haria Centre, Vile Parle East, Mumbai, 400069, Maharashtra, India
Tel.: (91) 2240973000
Web Site: https://www.hariaapparels.com
Rev.: $2,945,714
Assets: $3,002,749
Liabilities: $2,156,706
Net Worth: $846,043
Earnings: $103,145
Fiscal Year-end: 03/31/2019
Textile Product Mfr & Whslr
N.A.I.C.S.: 313240
Kantilal L. Haria *(Chm, Mng Dir & Compliance Officer)*

HARIBO GMBH & CO. KG
Hans-Riegel-Strasse 1, 53129, Bonn, Germany
Tel.: (49) 2285370
Web Site: http://www.haribo.com
Year Founded: 1920
Sales Range: $800-899.9 Million
Emp.: 7,000
Candy Mfr
N.A.I.C.S.: 311340
Hans Riegel Jr. *(Founder)*

Subsidiaries:

HARIBO AUSTRALIA Pty Limited (1)
Unit 16 76 Reserve Road, Artarmon, 2064, NSW, Australia
Tel.: (61) 2 8424 7600
Web Site: http://www.haribo.com
Candy Mfr
N.A.I.C.S.: 311340

HARIBO BELGIE B.V.B.A. (1)
Duffelsesteenweg 233 Kontich, Antwerp, 2550, Belgium
Tel.: (32) 3 450 73 70
Web Site: http://www.haribo.com
Emp.: 80
Candy Mfr
N.A.I.C.S.: 311340
Maret Wonderland *(Brand Mgr)*

HARIBO Dunhills (Pontefract) PLC (1)
26 Front Street, Pontefract, WF8 1NJ, United Kingdom
Tel.: (44) 1977 600266
Candy Distr
N.A.I.C.S.: 424450

HARIBO Espana S.A.U (1)
Ctra Girona- Banyoles 14, Cornella del Terri, 17844, Girona, Spain
Tel.: (34) 972595000
Web Site: http://www.haribo.com
Candy Distr

N.A.I.C.S.: 424450
HARIBO Espana S.A.U. (1)
Ctra Girona- Banyoles 14, Cornella del Terri, 17844, Madrid, Spain
Tel.: (34) 972595000
Candy Distr
N.A.I.C.S.: 424450
Dolors Berengui *(Product Mgr)*

HARIBO Hungaria Kft. (1)
Szeder u 5, 8248, Nemesvamos, Hungary
Tel.: (36) 88 520 500
Web Site: http://www.haribo.com
Candy Distr
N.A.I.C.S.: 424450

HARIBO ITALIA S.p.A. (1)
Viale delle Industrie 10/13, Arese, 20020, Milan, Italy
Tel.: (39) 02 48 210 0
Web Site: http://www.haribo.com
Candy Distr
N.A.I.C.S.: 424450
Stefano Rondena *(Acct Mgr-Natl & Area Mgr)*

HARIBO Ireland Ltd. (1)
2nd Floor 15 Earl Street, Dundalk, A91R5CC, Louth, Ireland
Tel.: (353) 42 933 0580
Web Site: http://www.haribo.com
Emp.: 8
Candy Distr
N.A.I.C.S.: 424450
Roy Goodwin *(Gen Mgr)*

HARIBO Konfety OOO (1)
Business Club ALEX 3/5 Suschtschewskij Wal, Moscow, 127018, Russia
Tel.: (7) 495 225 26 36
Web Site: http://www.haribo-shop.ru
Candy Distr
N.A.I.C.S.: 424450

HARIBO Lakrids A/S (1)
Praestovej 55, 4640, Fakse, Denmark
Tel.: (45) 56 76 22 00
Web Site: http://www.haribo.com
Emp.: 380
Candy Distr
N.A.I.C.S.: 424450
Rene Wayert *(Mgr-Logistics & Warehouse)*

HARIBO Lakrids Oy Ab (1)
Manttaalitie 5-7 E, 01530, Vantaa, Finland
Tel.: (358) 98700420
Web Site: http://www.haribo.fi
Emp.: 9
Candy Distr
N.A.I.C.S.: 424450
Marika Ojapalo *(Mgr-Mktg)*

HARIBO Lakris AS (1)
Grini Naeringspark 6, PB 39, 1332, Osteras, Norway
Tel.: (47) 67 15 55 00
Web Site: http://www.haribo.com
Candy Distr
N.A.I.C.S.: 424450

HARIBO Lakrits AB (1)
Moersaregatan 14, 250 22, Helsingborg, Sweden
Tel.: (46) 42 38 89 80
Web Site: http://www.haribo.com
Candy Distr
N.A.I.C.S.: 424450
Kenneth Magnusson *(Mgr-Property Maintenance)*

HARIBO Lakritzen - Hans Riegel Betriebsges.m.b.H. (1)
Industriezeile 68, 4017, Linz, Austria
Tel.: (43) 732 774691 0
Web Site: http://www.haribo.com
Candy Distr
N.A.I.C.S.: 424450

HARIBO Ricqles-Zan S.A. (1)
67 boulevard du Capitaine Geze, 13014, Marseille, France
Tel.: (33) 4 91 61 53 00
Web Site: http://www.haribo.com
Candy Distr
N.A.I.C.S.: 424450
David Saladin *(Mgr-Supply Chain)*

HARIBO Sekerleme San. Ve Tic. Ltd. Sti. (1)
Omerli Mah Adnan Kahveci Cad No 21,

HARIM HOLDINGS CO., LTD.

Hadimkoy, 34555, Istanbul, Turkiye
Tel.: (90) 212 866 36 00
Web Site: http://www.haribo.com
Candy Distr
N.A.I.C.S.: 424450

HARIBO of America Inc. (1)
1825 Woodlawn Dr Ste 204, Baltimore, MD 21207
Tel.: (410) 265-8890
Web Site: http://www.haribo.com
Sales Range: $25-49.9 Million
Emp.: 105
Candy Mfr
N.A.I.C.S.: 311340
Christian Jegen *(Pres & CEO)*

Haribo Nederland B.V. (1)
Riethil 1, 4825 AP, Breda, Netherlands
Tel.: (31) 76 5878950
Web Site: http://www.haribo.com
Candy Distr
N.A.I.C.S.: 424450
Jos Meulenbroek *(Dir-Sls)*

HARIG CRANKSHAFTS LIMITED
C-49 Phase 2 Distt Gautam Budh Nagar, Noida, 201305, Uttar Pradesh, India
Tel.: (91) 1202562415
500178—(BOM)
Auto Ancillary Product Mfr & Distr
N.A.I.C.S.: 336330
Deshbir Singh *(Mng Dir)*

HARIM HOLDINGS CO., LTD.
121 Jungang-ro, Iksan, 54596, Jeollabuk-do, Korea (South)
Tel.: (82) 638514599   KR
Web Site:
 https://www.harimholdings.co.kr
Year Founded: 2011
003380—(KRS)
Rev.: $10,565,652,018
Assets: $10,177,314,025
Liabilities: $6,296,766,887
Net Worth: $3,880,547,138
Earnings: $436,449,696
Emp.: 69
Fiscal Year-end: 12/31/22
Holding Company
N.A.I.C.S.: 551112
Hong-Kuk Kim *(Board of Directors, Chm & CEO)*

Subsidiaries:

Allen Harim Foods LLC (1)
29984 Pinnacle Way, Millsboro, DE 19966
Tel.: (302) 629-9136
Web Site: https://allenharimllc.com
Chicken Product Distr
N.A.I.C.S.: 424440
Mickey Baugher *(CEO)*

Harim Co., Ltd. (1)
14 Mangseong-ro, Mangseong-myeon, Iksan, 54517, Jeollabuk-do, Korea (South)
Tel.: (82) 638602114
Web Site: https://www.harim.com
Rev.: $1,030,011,512
Assets: $697,841,698
Liabilities: $466,897,569
Net Worth: $230,944,129
Earnings: $3,836,388
Emp.: 2,686
Fiscal Year-end: 12/31/2022
Poultry Processing & Whslr
N.A.I.C.S.: 311615
Hong-Kuk Kim *(Board of Directors, Chm & CEO)*

Jeil Feed Co., Ltd. (1)
240 Daejeon-ro 1331 Beon-gil, Daeduk-gu, Daejeon, 54596, Korea (South)
Tel.: (82) 426244101
Web Site: https://www.jeilfeed.co.kr
Sales Range: $650-699.9 Million
Emp.: 386
Livestock Feed Mfr & Whslr
N.A.I.C.S.: 311119
Cheon-nyeon Kwon *(CEO)*

HARIM HOLDINGS CO., LTD.

Harim Holdings Co., Ltd.—(Continued)

Subsidiary (Domestic):

Korea Thumb Vet Co., Ltd. (2)
470-15 Seonhwa-ro, Iksan, Jeollabuk-do, Korea (South)
Tel.: (82) 638311275
Web Site: https://www.thumbvet.com
Pet Food Distr
N.A.I.C.S.: 424490

NS Home Shopping Co., Ltd. (1)
NS Home Shopping Bldg 15 Pangyo-ro 228beon-gil, Bundang-gu, Seongnam, Gyeonggi-do, Korea (South)
Tel.: (82) 2 6336 1234
Web Site: http://pr.nsmall.com
Emp.: 497
Home Shopping Services
N.A.I.C.S.: 455219
Sang-Cheol Do (CEO)

Subsidiary (Non-US):

NS International China Co., Ltd (2)
Room No 920 Xuanrun Building Wuzhong Road 1100 Minhang District, Shanghai, 201103, China
Tel.: (86) 2134666991
Home Shopping Services
N.A.I.C.S.: 455219

HARIMA B-STEM CORPORATION

Yokohama Landmark Tower 16th floor 2-2-1 Minatomirai, Nishi-ku, Yokohama, 220-8116, Kanagawa, Japan
Tel.: (81) 452243550
Web Site: https://www.bstem.co.jp
Year Founded: 1961
9780—(TKS)
Rev.: $241,990,320
Assets: $118,550,960
Liabilities: $50,132,720
Net Worth: $68,418,240
Earnings: $7,627,840
Emp.: 4,246
Fiscal Year-end: 03/31/22
Property Management Services
N.A.I.C.S.: 531311
Yoshihisa Ohtori (Pres & CEO)

HARIMA CHEMICALS GROUP, INC.

Keihanshin Yodoyabashi Bldg 5th floor 4-4-7 Imabashi, Chuo-ku, Osaka, 541-0042, Japan
Tel.: (81) 662012461
Web Site: https://www.harima.co.jp
Year Founded: 1947
4410—(TKS)
Rev.: $610,301,300
Assets: $651,633,630
Liabilities: $381,410,220
Net Worth: $270,223,410
Earnings: ($7,674,210)
Emp.: 1,734
Fiscal Year-end: 03/31/24
Chemical Coatings & Plastic Resins Mfr
N.A.I.C.S.: 325998
Eiketsu Ro (Mng Dir)

Subsidiaries:

Cenxi Donglin Rosin Co., Ltd. (1)
Hexi Development Zone, Shuiwen Town, Cenxi, 543204, Guangxi, China
Tel.: (86) 774 835 8386
Web Site: http://www.harima.co.jp
Gum Rosin & Turpentine Oil Mfr & Sales
N.A.I.C.S.: 325998

Dongguan Hanghua-Harima Paper Chemicals Co., Ltd. (1)
No 11 Weisi Road, District No 3 Changping Zone Eastern Industrial Park Changping Town, Dongguan, 523560, Guangdong, China
Tel.: (86) 769 8255 0101
Web Site: http://www.harima.co.jp
Paper Chemicals Mfr & Sales
N.A.I.C.S.: 325998

Hangzhou Hanghua-Harima Chemicals Co., Ltd.
No 87 Hongda Road, Qiaonan District Xiaoshan Economic and Technological Development Zone, Hangzhou, 311231, Zhejiang, China (56.07%)
Tel.: (86) 57182696228
Paper Chemicals Mfr & Sales
N.A.I.C.S.: 325998

Harima Chemicals (Shanghai) Co., Ltd. (1)
Suite 09 15th Floor SML Center No 610 Xujiahui Road, Shanghai, 200025, China
Tel.: (86) 216 135 7778
Business Management Services
N.A.I.C.S.: 541611

Harima Chemicals, Inc. (1)
No 10 5th Floor Lane39 Chung Sun N Rd Sec 2, Taipei, 10450, Taiwan
Tel.: (886) 22 537 3192
Ink Resin Mfr & Distr
N.A.I.C.S.: 325910

Harima Kasei Polymer Co., Ltd. (1)
Yodoyabashi Bldg 5F 4-4-7 Imabashi, Chuo-ku, Osaka, 541 0042, Japan (100%)
Tel.: (81) 6 6201 2461
Web Site: http://www.harima.co.jp
Ink Resins & Adhesive Resins Mfr & Sales
N.A.I.C.S.: 325998

Harima M.I.D., Inc. (1)
Keihanshin Yodoyabashi Bldg 5th floor 4-4-7 Imabashi, Chuo-ku, Osaka, 541-0042, Japan (75%)
Tel.: (81) 662012461
Web Site: http://www.harima.co.jp
Chemicals Mfr
N.A.I.C.S.: 325199

Harima Trading, Inc. (1)
Keihanshin Yodoyabashi Bldg 5th floor 4-4-7 Imabashi, Chuo-ku, Osaka, 541-0042, Japan
Tel.: (81) 662012461
Web Site: http://www.harima.co.jp
Emp.: 6
Real Estate Manangement Services
N.A.I.C.S.: 531390

Harima USA, Inc. (1)
1965 Evergreen Blvd Ste 400, Duluth, GA 30096 (100%)
Tel.: (770) 813-1720
Web Site: http://www.harima.co.jp
Sales Range: $25-49.9 Million
Emp.: 4
Chemicals Mfr & Sales
N.A.I.C.S.: 325998

Harima do Brasil Industria Quimica Ltda. (1)
Rua Maestro Cardim 1191 - 6 andar Conj 61/62, Bela Vista, Sao Paulo, 01323-001, Brazil (87.2%)
Tel.: (55) 1133734100
Web Site: https://www.harima.com.br
Sales Range: $25-49.9 Million
Emp.: 60
Chemicals Mfr
N.A.I.C.S.: 325998
Tetsunori Kawakami (Pres)

Harimatec Czech s.r.o. (1)
(100%)
Tel.: (420) 284688922
Web Site: http://www.harimatec.eu
Emp.: 10
Chemicals Mfr
N.A.I.C.S.: 325998

Harimatec Hangzhou Co., Ltd. (1)
No 15 Gaoxin 5 Road Hongda Road Qiaonan-Qu, Xiaoshan Economic and Technological Development Zone, Hangzhou, 311231, Zhejiang, China (85%)
Tel.: (86) 571 2286 8518
Web Site: http://www.harima.co.jp
Emp.: 2
Lead-Free Solder Paste & Electronic Materials Mfr & Sales
N.A.I.C.S.: 325998

Harimatec Inc. (1)
1965 Evergreen Blvd Ste 400, Duluth, GA 30096
Tel.: (678) 325-2926
Web Site: https://www.harimatec.com

Sales Range: $25-49.9 Million
Emp.: 6
Adhesive Mfr
N.A.I.C.S.: 325211
Yoshiaki Koike (CEO)

Harimatec Malaysia Sdn. Bhd. (1)
Lot 62049 Jalan Portland Tasek Industrial Estate, 31400, Ipoh, Perak, Malaysia (85%)
Tel.: (60) 55464427
Web Site: http://www.harima.co.jp
Lead-Free Solder Paste & Electronic Materials Mfr & Marketer
N.A.I.C.S.: 325998

Lawter (N.Z.) Ltd. (1)
211 Totara Street, Mount Maunganui, 3116, New Zealand
Tel.: (64) 75727089
Web Site: http://www.lawter.com
Emp.: 7
Mfr of Adhesive Resins, Ink Resins & Turpentine Oil
N.A.I.C.S.: 325998

Lawter Argentina S.A. (1)
Tel.: (54) 1147178900
Web Site: http://www.lawter.com
Emp.: 15
Chemicals Mfr
N.A.I.C.S.: 325998

Lawter BVBA (1)
Haven 1520, Ketenislaan 1C, 9130, Kallo, Belgium (100%)
Tel.: (32) 35709494
Sales Range: $50-74.9 Million
Emp.: 160
Ink Resins & Adhesive Resins Mfr & Sales
N.A.I.C.S.: 325998

Lawter Chemicals (Shanghai) Co., Ltd. (1)
Suite 07 15th floor SML Center No 610 Xujiahui Road, Shanghai, 200025, China
Tel.: (86) 2123295201
Web Site: http://www.harima.co.jp
Chemicals Mfr
N.A.I.C.S.: 325998

Lawter Maastricht B.V. (1)
Ankerkade 81, 6222 NL, Maastricht, Netherlands
Tel.: (31) 43 352 5354
Web Site: http://www.lawter.com
Emp.: 44
Adhesive Resins, Ink Resins & Other Chemicals Mfr
N.A.I.C.S.: 325998
Piet Geuze (Gen Mgr)

Lawter, Inc. (1)
200 N LaSalle St Ste 2600, Chicago, IL 60601
Tel.: (312) 662-5700
Web Site: https://www.lawter.com
Emp.: 30
Ink & Adhesive Resins Mfr
N.A.I.C.S.: 325180
Ichiro Taninaka (Pres & CEO)

Division (Domestic):

Lawter Inc. - R&D (2)
1202 E Parker St, Baxley, GA 31513
Tel.: (912) 367-3616
Web Site: http://www.lawter.com
Resin Mfr
N.A.I.C.S.: 325194

Nanning Harima Chemicals Co., Ltd. (1)
No 6 Dongling Road, Nanning Economic and Technological Development Area, Nanning, 530031, Guangzi, China (95%)
Tel.: (86) 2123295201
Ink Resins & Adhesive Resins Mfr & Sales
N.A.I.C.S.: 325998

Nippon Filler Metals, Ltd. (1)
487 Sekiyado Motomachi, Noda, 270-0203, Chiba, Japan
Tel.: (81) 47 196 2551
Web Site: http://www.n-fillermetals.co.jp
Emp.: 30
Soldering Paste & Soldering Materials Mfr & Sales
N.A.I.C.S.: 325998

Plasmine Technology, Inc. (1)

INTERNATIONAL PUBLIC

3298 Summit Blvd 35, Pensacola, FL 32503-4350
Tel.: (850) 438-8550
Web Site: http://www.plasmine.com
Sales Range: $25-49.9 Million
Emp.: 10
Chemicals Mfr
N.A.I.C.S.: 325180
Steven Violette (Pres)

Plant (Domestic):

Plasmine Technology, Inc. - Bay Minette (2)
251 Newport Pkwy, Bay Minette, AL 36507
Tel.: (251) 937-2771
Web Site: http://www.plasmine.com
Sales Range: $25-49.9 Million
Plastics Material & Resin Mfr
N.A.I.C.S.: 325211

Seven Rivers, Inc. (1)
3-5-1 Tomonishi, Asaminami-ku, Hiroshima, 731-3169, Japan (100%)
Tel.: (81) 828489111
Industrial Detergents & Cleaning Equipment Mfr & Sales
N.A.I.C.S.: 325611

Xinyi Rihong Plastic Chemical Co., Ltd. (1)
No 220 Industry Road, Xinyi, 525300, Guangdong, China (80%)
Tel.: (86) 668 888 7766
Web Site: http://www.harima.co.jp
Ink Resins & Adhesive Resins Mfr & Sales
N.A.I.C.S.: 325998

Xinyi Zhonglin Rosin Co., Ltd. (1)
220 Industry Road, Xinyi, 525300, Guangdong, China (81%)
Tel.: (86) 668 888 5999
Web Site: http://www.harima.co.jp
Gum Rosin & Turpentine Oil Mfr & Sales
N.A.I.C.S.: 325998

HARIMA-KYOWA CO., LTD.

313 Sho Shikahigashicho, Himeji, 671-0218, Hyogo, Japan
Tel.: (81) 792535217
Web Site: https://www.harimakb.co.jp
Year Founded: 1951
7444—(TKS)
Rev.: $407,063,630
Assets: $219,048,790
Liabilities: $59,357,800
Net Worth: $159,690,990
Earnings: $9,293,660
Emp.: 1,193
Fiscal Year-end: 03/31/24
Sanitary Good Whslr
N.A.I.C.S.: 424210
Shinya Tsuda (Pres & CEO)

HARIOM PIPE INDUSTRIES LIMITED

SAMARPAN 34174122 Pillar No 125, Attapur, Hyderabad, 500 048, Telangana, India
Tel.: (91) 9948387000
Web Site: https://www.hariompipes.com
Year Founded: 2007
HARIOMPIPE—(NSE)
Rev.: $77,268,785
Assets: $85,029,015
Liabilities: $40,047,707
Net Worth: $44,981,308
Earnings: $5,540,195
Emp.: 328
Fiscal Year-end: 03/31/23
Iron & Steel Mfr
N.A.I.C.S.: 331210
Amitabh Bhattacharya (CFO)

HARISH TEXTILE ENGINEERS LTD.

19 Parsi Panchayat Road, Andheri East, Mumbai, 400069, India
Tel.: (91) 2228367151
Web Site: https://www.harishtextile.com

Year Founded: 1964
542682—(BOM)
Rev.: $14,649,344
Assets: $10,765,700
Liabilities: $9,459,491
Net Worth: $1,306,209
Earnings: $65,902
Emp.: 154
Fiscal Year-end: 03/31/22
Wood Products Mfr
N.A.I.C.S.: 321999
Venugopal Iyer *(Mgr)*

HARISON TOSHIBA LIGHTING CORP.
5-2-1 Asahi-Machi, Imabari, 794 8510, Japan
Tel.: (81) 898239800
Web Site: http://www.htl.co.jp
Year Founded: 1944
Sales Range: $100-124.9 Million
Emp.: 700
Lighting Products
N.A.I.C.S.: 335132
Toshiharu Sakurai *(Pres & CEO)*

Subsidiaries:

Harison Toshiba USA Inc. (1)
31555 W 14 Mile Rd Ste 201, Farmington Hills, MI 48334-1287
Tel.: (661) 257-7901
Web Site: http://www.harison-toshiba.com
Rev.: $38,344,200
Emp.: 30
Light Bulbs & Related Supplies
N.A.I.C.S.: 423610

HARIYANA METALS INDUSTRIES LIMITED
Old Motor Stand Itwari, Nagpur, 440 008, India
Tel.: (91) 7122766301
Web Site: https://www.hariyanaventures.in
Year Founded: 1974
506024—(BOM)
Rev.: $351,966
Assets: $571,683
Liabilities: $337,495
Net Worth: $234,189
Earnings: ($102,239)
Emp.: 15
Fiscal Year-end: 03/31/24
Business Development Services
N.A.I.C.S.: 523991
Ritesh Ojha *(Compliance Officer & Sec)*

HARIYANA SHIP BREAKERS LTD.
156 Maker Chambers VI 220 Jamnalal Bajaj Marg, Nariman Point, Mumbai, 400 021, India
Tel.: (91) 2222043211
526931—(BOM)
Rev.: $22,714,665
Assets: $37,036,859
Liabilities: $18,456,684
Net Worth: $18,580,175
Earnings: $1,309,758
Emp.: 12
Fiscal Year-end: 03/31/21
Sponge Iron Mfr & Whslr
N.A.I.C.S.: 331210
Shanti Sarup Reniwal *(Chm)*

HARJU ELEKTER AS
Paldiski mnt 31, 76606, Keila, Estonia
Tel.: (372) 6747400
Web Site: http://www.harjuelekter.ee
Year Founded: 1983
Sales Range: $50-74.9 Million
Emp.: 200
Electric Equipment Mfr
N.A.I.C.S.: 333992

Andres Allikmae *(Chm-Mgmt Bd & CEO)*

Subsidiaries:

AS Harju Elekter Teletehnika (1)
Paldiski mnt 31, 76606, Keila, Estonia
Tel.: (372) 6747495
Emp.: 80
Sheet Metal Product Mfr & Distr
N.A.I.C.S.: 332322
Urmas Paisnik *(Mng Dir)*

Rifas UAB (1)
Tinklu st 35 R, Panevezys, Lithuania
Tel.: (370) 45 58 27 28
Web Site: http://www.rifas.lt
Emp.: 91
Cabinet Door & Panel Mfr
N.A.I.C.S.: 337122
Aidas Setikas *(CEO)*

Subsidiary (Domestic):

Automatikos Iranga UAB (2)
Drujos g 2, Vilnius, 11342, Lithuania
Tel.: (370) 45510400
Web Site: http://www.ak-rele.lt
Rev.: $57,932,000
Emp.: 82
Industrial Automation Control System Mfr
N.A.I.C.S.: 334513

Satmatic OY (1)
Sammontie 9, 28400, Ulvila, Finland
Tel.: (358) 2 5379 800
Web Site: http://www.satmatic.fi
Emp.: 100
Electric Equipment Mfr
N.A.I.C.S.: 335999
Simo Puustelli *(Mng Dir)*

Subsidiary (Domestic):

Finnkumu Oy (2)
PL 40, Kurikka, 61301, Finland
Tel.: (358) 400367761
Web Site: http://www.finnkumu.fi
Electric Power Equipment Mfr
N.A.I.C.S.: 334515

HARKEL OFFICE FURNITURE LTD.
1743 Creditstone Road, Vaughan, L4K 5X7, ON, Canada
Tel.: (905) 417-5335
Web Site: http://harkeloffice.com
Year Founded: 1979
Sales Range: $10-24.9 Million
Office Furniture Mfr
N.A.I.C.S.: 337211
Marc Klerer *(Mktg Mgr)*

HARLAND & WOLFF GROUP HOLDINGS PLC
18 King William Street, London, EC4N 7BP, United Kingdom
Tel.: (44) 2890511415 UK
Web Site: http://www.infrastrata.co.uk
Year Founded: 2007
HARL—(AIM)
Rev.: $35,306,535
Assets: $84,143,637
Liabilities: $145,200,465
Net Worth: ($61,056,828)
Earnings: ($88,812,589)
Emp.: 267
Fiscal Year-end: 12/31/22
Gas Storage & Petroleum Exploration Services
N.A.I.C.S.: 486210
John MacInnes Wood *(CEO)*

Subsidiaries:

Harland & Wolff (Appledore) Limited (1)
Wooda Road, Appledore, North Devon, EX39 1UZ, United Kingdom
Tel.: (44) 3301240427
Marine Engineering Services
N.A.I.C.S.: 541330

Harland & Wolff (Belfast) Limited (1)
Queens Island, Belfast, BT3 9DU, United Kingdom

Tel.: (44) 3301240427
Marine Engineering Services
N.A.I.C.S.: 541330

Harland & Wolff (Methil) Limited (1)
Wellesley Road, Leven, KY8 3RA, United Kingdom
Tel.: (44) 3301240427
Marine Engineering Services
N.A.I.C.S.: 541330

Islandmagee Energy Limited (1)
8 Portmuck Road, Islandmagee Co Antrim, Larne, BT40 3TW, United Kingdom
Tel.: (44) 2893321384
Web Site: https://www.islandmageeenergy.com
Natural Gas Storage Facility Services
N.A.I.C.S.: 221210

Islandmagee Storage Limited (1)
1st Floor The Arena Building 85 Ormeau Road, Belfast, BT7 1SH, United Kingdom **(100%)**
Tel.: (44) 28 90 438 009
Web Site: http://www.islandmageestorage.com
Natural Gas Storage Services
N.A.I.C.S.: 493190

HARMONEY CORP LIMITED
Level 36 Governor Philip Tower 1 Farrer Place, Sydney, 2000, NSW, Australia
Tel.: (61) 1300042766 AU
Web Site: https://www.harmoney.com.au
Year Founded: 2014
HMY—(ASX)
Rev.: $69,813,523
Assets: $512,304,884
Liabilities: $477,255,656
Net Worth: $35,049,227
Earnings: ($4,942,948)
Emp.: 88
Fiscal Year-end: 06/30/23
Financial Investment Services
N.A.I.C.S.: 523999

HARMONIC DRIVE SYSTEMS INC.
Minamioi 6-25-3, Shinagawa-ku, Tokyo, 140-0013, Japan
Tel.: (81) 354717800 JP
Web Site: https://www.hds.co.jp
Year Founded: 1970
6324—(TKS)
Rev.: $368,811,560
Assets: $787,528,620
Liabilities: $262,688,010
Net Worth: $524,840,610
Earnings: ($163,967,660)
Emp.: 1,349
Fiscal Year-end: 03/31/24
Precision Speed Reducer Mfr
N.A.I.C.S.: 333612
Mitsumasa Ito *(Chm)*

Subsidiaries:

HD Logistics, Inc. (1)
1856-1 Hotakamaki, Azumino, 399-8305, Nagano, Japan
Tel.: (81) 263 83 8700
Logistics Consulting Servies
N.A.I.C.S.: 541614

Harmonic AD, Inc. (1)
4034 Toyoshina, Azumino, 399-8205, Nagano, Japan
Tel.: (81) 263716330
Emp.: 61
Speed Reducer Mfr
N.A.I.C.S.: 333612
Tetsuo Ikuta *(Pres)*

Harmonic Drive L.L.C. (1)
42 Dunham Ridge, Beverly, MA 01915 **(100%)**
Tel.: (978) 532-1800
Gear Mfr
N.A.I.C.S.: 333612

Harmonic Drive SE (1)

Hoenbergstrasse 14, 65555, Limburg, Germany **(74.7%)**
Tel.: (49) 643150080
Web Site: http://www.harmonicdrive.de
Emp.: 175
Gearing & Motion Control Product Mfr
N.A.I.C.S.: 333612
Ekrem Sirman *(Pres, CEO & Member-Mgmt Bd)*

Subsidiary (Non-US):

Harmonic Drive Espana, S.L.U. (2)
Poligono Industrial Leguizamon C/ Araba n 1 2 planta - Oficinas 08, 48450, Etxebarri, Vizcaya, Spain
Tel.: (34) 944266415
Web Site: http://www.harmonicdrive.de
Motion Control Component Distr
N.A.I.C.S.: 423840
Fernando Aramendia *(Dir)*

Harmonic Drive France SAS (2)
26 rue Emile Decorps Immeuble Pixel, 69100, Villeurbanne, France
Tel.: (33) 437 23 66 30
Web Site: http://www.harmonicdrive.de
Motion Control Component Distr
N.A.I.C.S.: 423840
Laurent Noraz *(Gen Mgr)*

Harmonic Drive UK Limited (2)
Unit 36 Wolseley Court Staffordshire Technology Park, Great Britain, Stafford, ST18 0GA, United Kingdom
Tel.: (44) 1785245190
Web Site: http://www.harmonicdrive.de
Motion Control Component Distr
N.A.I.C.S.: 423840
Graham Mackrell *(Mng Dir)*

Subsidiary (Domestic):

Micromotion GmbH (2)
An der Fahrt 13, 55124, Mainz, Germany
Tel.: (49) 6131 66927 0
Web Site: http://www.micromotion-drives.com
Motion Control Component Mfr
N.A.I.C.S.: 333612
Reinhard Degen *(Member-Mgmt Bd)*

Harmonic Drive Systems (Shanghai) Co., Ltd. (1)
Rm206 1 No 641 Tianshan Rd, Changning District, Shanghai, 200336, China
Tel.: (86) 2162375656
Web Site: http://www.harmonicdrive.net.cn
Gear Whslr
N.A.I.C.S.: 423840
Tetsuo Ikuta *(Chm)*

Harmonic Precision Corporation (1)
Head office factory 4020-18 Oaza Wada, Matsumoto, 390-1242, Nagano, Japan **(100%)**
Tel.: (81) 263402272
Roller Bearing Mfr
N.A.I.C.S.: 332991
Tetsuaki Maruyama *(Dir)*

Ome Iron Casting Co., Ltd. (1)
3-11-1 Nagaoka Mizuho-cho, Nishitama-gun, Tokyo, 190-1232, Japan
Tel.: (81) 42 555 3100
Web Site: https://ome-chuuzou.com
Emp.: 17
Machine Equipment Parts Mfr
N.A.I.C.S.: 336390
Takuro Miyoshi *(Pres)*

SAMICK ADM CO., LTD. (1)
Dalseong 2chadong 2-ro 66 Guji-Myeon, Dalseong-gun, Daegu, Korea (South) **(51%)**
Tel.: (82) 536156810
Web Site: https://www.hds.co.jp
Precision Planetary Gears Mfr
N.A.I.C.S.: 333612
Isao Miura *(Pres)*

Winbel Co., Ltd. (1)
8172-60 Akaho, Komagane, 399-4117, Nagano, Japan
Tel.: (81) 26 581 6300
Web Site: https://www.winbel.co.jp
Emp.: 41
Motor Mfr & Distr
N.A.I.C.S.: 335312
Masaru Aruga *(Pres)*

HARMONICARE MEDICAL HOLDINGS LTD.

Harmonicare Medical Holdings Ltd.—(Continued)

HARMONICARE MEDICAL HOLDINGS LTD.
Xiaoguanbeili No 2 Beiyuan Road, Chaoyang District, Beijing, 100029, China
Tel.: (86) 1057960505   Ky
Web Site: http://www.hemeiyl.com
Rev.: $141,903,386
Assets: $280,554,276
Liabilities: $37,621,593
Net Worth: $242,932,683
Earnings: $4,520,205
Emp.: 3,724
Fiscal Year-end: 12/31/17
Holding Company
N.A.I.C.S.: 551112
Yuming Lin (Founder, Chm & Pres)

Subsidiaries:

Harbin Electrical Machinery Company Limited (1)
No 99 Sandadongli Road, Xiangfang District, Harbin, China
Tel.: (86) 45182872573
Web Site: https://hec-china.com
Turbo Generator Mfr
N.A.I.C.S.: 333611
Wang Gui (Pres & CEO)

HARMONY CAPITAL SERVICES LIMITED
Office no 8A 8th Floor Astral Centre, 470-B N M Joshi Marg Chinchpokli-West, Mumbai, 400 011, India
Tel.: (91) 2223001206
Web Site: https://www.hcsl.co.in
Year Founded: 1994
530055—(BOM)
Rev.: $646
Assets: $180,629
Liabilities: $606
Net Worth: $180,022
Earnings: ($7,854)
Fiscal Year-end: 03/31/21
Financial Management Services
N.A.I.C.S.: 523999
Asutosh Raulo (Mng Dir)

HARMONY GOLD MINING COMPANY LIMITED
Tel.: (27) 114112000   ZA
Web Site: https://www.harmony.co.za
Year Founded: 1950
HMY—(NYSE)
Rev.: $3,409,205,714
Assets: $3,358,161,219
Liabilities: $1,083,709,619
Net Worth: $2,274,451,600
Earnings: $482,562,102
Emp.: 34,913
Fiscal Year-end: 06/30/24
Gold Exploration & Mining Services
N.A.I.C.S.: 212220
Johannes Van Heerden (CEO-South-East Asia)

Subsidiaries:

ARMGold/Harmony Freegold Joint Venture Company (Proprietary) Limited (1)
Cnr Woord Ave & Main Reef Road, Johannesburg, 1760, South Africa
Tel.: (27) 114112000
Gold Mining Services
N.A.I.C.S.: 212220

Big Bell Gold Operations Pty Ltd (1)
PO Box 40, Perth, 6640, WA, Australia
Tel.: (61) 8 99572399
Sales Range: $25-49.9 Million
Emp.: 260
Mineral Mining & Exploration
N.A.I.C.S.: 327999

Harmony Gold (Australia) Pty. Ltd. (1)
Ste 5 11 Collins Rd, Perth, 6005, WA, Australia **(100%)**
Tel.: (61) 892113100
Web Site: http://www.harmonygold.com.au
Sales Range: $25-49.9 Million
Emp.: 12
Holding Company
N.A.I.C.S.: 551112

Harmony Gold (PNG Services) (Proprietary) Limited (1)
Level 2 189 Coronation Drive, Milton, 4064, QLD, Australia
Tel.: (61) 733203700
Web Site: http://www.harmony.co.za
Sales Range: $50-74.9 Million
Emp.: 45
Gold Mining Services
N.A.I.C.S.: 212220

Harmony Gold Mines (1)
Private Bag X1012, Evander, 2280, Mpumalanga, South Africa **(100%)**
Tel.: (27) 176201600
Web Site: http://www.harmony.co.za
Sales Range: $1-4.9 Billion
Emp.: 5,000
Provider of Gold Mine Exploration & Development Services
N.A.I.C.S.: 212220

Kalahari Goldridge Mining Co Ltd (1)
Spanover Farm, PO Box 101331448111, Mareetsane, Mafikeng, 2715, North West Province, South Africa **(100%)**
Tel.: (27) 183321100
Sales Range: $100-124.9 Million
Emp.: 200
Provider of Gold Mine Exploration & Development Services
N.A.I.C.S.: 212220

Randfontein Estates Limited (1)
Cnr Main Reef Road & Ward Avenue, Randfontein, 1759, South Africa
Tel.: (27) 114112000
Gold Mining Services
N.A.I.C.S.: 212220
Alida Clarke (Mgr-HR)

HARMONYCHAIN AS
St Olavs gate 21B, 165, Oslo, Norway
Tel.: (47) 92011397
Web Site: https://www.harmonychain.com
Year Founded: 2017
HMONY—(EUR)
Software Development Services
N.A.I.C.S.: 541511
Ola Stene Johansen (CEO)

HARN ENGINEERING SOLUTIONS PUBLIC COMPANY LIMITED
9/20-22 Soi Soonvijai Rama 9 Road Bangkapi, Huaykwang, Bangkok, 10310, Thailand
Web Site: http://www.harn.co.th
HARN—(THA)
Rev.: $38,715,188
Assets: $51,203,479
Liabilities: $10,825,730
Net Worth: $40,377,748
Earnings: $3,303,729
Emp.: 240
Fiscal Year-end: 12/31/23
Fire Protection, Sanitary, Air-Conditioning Systems & Firefighting System Valves & Equipment
N.A.I.C.S.: 922160
Wirat Sukchai (CEO & Mng Dir)

HARN LEN CORPORATION BHD
6th Floor Johor Tower 15 Jalan Gereja, 80100, Johor Bahru, Johor, Malaysia
Tel.: (60) 72221777
Web Site: https://www.harnlen.com.my
HARNLEN—(KLS)
Rev.: $59,325,031
Assets: $94,191,934
Liabilities: $25,372,807
Net Worth: $68,819,127
Earnings: $562,860
Emp.: 667
Fiscal Year-end: 05/31/23
Palm Oil Plantation & Oil Milling Operations
N.A.I.C.S.: 311224
Siew Kim Fong (Co-Sec)

HARNOIS GROUPE PETROLIER INC.
80 Route 158, Saint-Thomas, J0K 3L0, QC, Canada
Tel.: (450) 759-7979
Web Site: http://www.harnoisgroupe.com
Petroleum Product Distr
N.A.I.C.S.: 424720
Serge Harnois (Pres & CEO)

HAROON OILS LIMITED
11 Dockyard Road West Wharf Industrial Area, PO Box 4992, Karachi, 74000, Pakistan
Tel.: (92) 212314068
Web Site: http://www.haroonoils.com
Sales Range: $1-9.9 Million
Emp.: 110
Petroleum Oil & Grease Mfr
N.A.I.C.S.: 324191
Amber H. Saigol (Chm)

HARP INTERNATIONAL LIMITED
Gellihirion Industrial Estate, Pontypridd, CF37 5SX, Rhondda Cynon Taff, United Kingdom
Tel.: (44) 1443 842 255
Web Site: http://www.harpintl.com
Year Founded: 1991
Sales Range: $25-49.9 Million
Refrigeration & Air Conditioning Services
N.A.I.C.S.: 423730
Bryan J. Davies (Mng Dir)

Subsidiaries:

Harp Middle East L.L.C (1)
PO Box 48598, Sharjah, United Arab Emirates
Tel.: (971) 6 534 4794
Web Site: http://www.harpmiddleeast.com
Refrigeration & Air Conditioning Equipment Distr
N.A.I.C.S.: 423730

Harp USA Inc. (1)
101 NE 3rd Ave Ste 1500, Fort Lauderdale, FL 33301
Tel.: (954) 332-3582
Web Site: http://www.harp.us.com
Refrigeration & Air Conditioning Equipment Distr
N.A.I.C.S.: 423730

HARPENDEN BUILDING SOCIETY
Mardall House 9-11 Vaughan Road, Harpenden, AL5 4HU, Hertfordshire, United Kingdom
Tel.: (44) 1582 765411
Web Site: http://www.harpendenbs.co.uk
Year Founded: 1953
Rev.: $9,269,077
Assets: $388,670,363
Liabilities: $351,761,939
Net Worth: $36,908,424
Earnings: $727,938
Emp.: 44
Fiscal Year-end: 12/31/19
Mortgage Lending & Other Financial Services
N.A.I.C.S.: 522310
Stephen J. Richardson (Chm)

INTERNATIONAL PUBLIC

HARPER MACLEOD LLP
The Cadoro 45 Gordon St, Glasgow, G1 3PE, United Kingdom
Tel.: (44) 141 221 8888   UK
Web Site: http://www.harpermacleod.co.uk
Year Founded: 2004
Law firm
N.A.I.C.S.: 541110
Martin Darroch (CEO)

HARPIA OMEGA PARTICIPACOES S.A.
Av Brigadeiro Faria Lima 3477 - 14 Andar, 4538133, Sao Paulo, Brazil
Tel.: (55) 1133832277
Financial Investment Services
N.A.I.C.S.: 523999
Claudio Eugenio Stiller Galeazzi (Chm)

HARRIS MAZDA
2525 Bowen Road, Nanaimo, V9T 3L2, BC, Canada
Tel.: (250) 758-9125
Web Site: https://www.harrismazda.ca
Year Founded: 1970
Sales Range: $10-24.9 Million
Emp.: 40
New & Used Car Dealers
N.A.I.C.S.: 441110

HARRIS SCARFE AUSTRALIA PTY LTD.
77-90 Rundle Mall Levels 1 & 2 Rundle Place Shopping Centre, Adelaide, 5000, SA, Australia
Tel.: (61) 882034444   AU
Web Site: http://www.harrisscarfe.com.au
Year Founded: 1849
Sales Range: $150-199.9 Million
Emp.: 2,000
Discount Department Store Owner & Operator
N.A.I.C.S.: 455110
Steve Mavro (CFO)

HARRIS TECHNOLOGY GROUP LIMITED
124 Abbott Rd, Hallam, 3803, VIC, Australia
Tel.: (61) 1300139999   AU
Web Site: https://www.ht8.com.au
HT8—(ASX)
Rev.: $11,156,945
Assets: $4,881,792
Liabilities: $3,829,567
Net Worth: $1,052,224
Earnings: ($939,366)
Emp.: 28
Fiscal Year-end: 06/30/24
Online Shopping
N.A.I.C.S.: 459999
Garrison Huang (CEO & Mng Dir)

HARRISONS HOLDINGS (MALAYSIA) BERHAD
Unit 9A 9th Floor Wisma Bumi Raya 10 Jalan Raja Laut, 50350, Kuala Lumpur, Malaysia
Tel.: (60) 326983733
Web Site: https://www.harrisons.com.my
5008—(KLS)
Rev.: $460,130,159
Assets: $194,498,624
Liabilities: $105,625,185
Net Worth: $88,873,439
Earnings: $14,387,513
Emp.: 1,803
Fiscal Year-end: 12/31/22
Shipping Handling Services
N.A.I.C.S.: 483111
Kong Choon Low (CFO & Co-Sec)

AND PRIVATE COMPANIES

Subsidiaries:

Harrisons Peninsular Sdn. Bhd. (1)
9 Jalan 222, 46100, Petaling Jaya, Malaysia
Tel.: (60) 379567266
Chemical & Allied Product Whslr
N.A.I.C.S.: 424690

Harrisons Sabah Sdn. Bhd. (1)
19 Jalan Haji Saman, PO Box No 10022, 88800, Kota Kinabalu, Malaysia
Tel.: (60) 193558180
Chemical & Allied Product Whlsr
N.A.I.C.S.: 424690

Subsidiary (Domestic):

Harrisons Travel Sdn. Bhd. (2)
19 Jalan Haji Saman, PO Box 10022, 88800, Kota Kinabalu, Malaysia
Tel.: (60) 88215011
Chemical & Allied Product Whlsr
N.A.I.C.S.: 424690

Harrisons Trading (Peninsular) Sdn Bhd (1)
Lot C-14 Block C MAS Cargo Freight Forwarders Complex, 64000, Kuala Lumpur, Malaysia
Tel.: (60) 387873382
Sales Range: $25-49.9 Million
Emp.: 5
Building Materials Distr
N.A.I.C.S.: 444180
Pannir Salvam (Mgr)

Subsidiary (Domestic):

Harrisons Marketing & Services Sdn Bhd (2)
9 Jalan 222, 46100, Petaling Jaya, Selangor, Malaysia
Tel.: (60) 379567266
Sales Range: $50-74.9 Million
Emp.: 4
Wine & Food Products Distr
N.A.I.C.S.: 424820

Harrisons Trading (Sabah) Sdn Bhd (1)
19 Jalan Haji Saman, PO Box 10022, 88800, Kota Kinabalu, Sabah, Malaysia
Tel.: (60) 193558180
Sales Range: $50-74.9 Million
Emp.: 200
Engineering & Building Materials Distr
N.A.I.C.S.: 444180

Subsidiary (Domestic):

Harrisons Sarawak Sdn Bhd (2)
Lot 8939-8941 3rd Floor 21/2 Mile Jalan Pending, 93450, Kuching, Sarawak, Malaysia (100%)
Tel.: (60) 82334000
Web Site: https://www.harrisons.com.my
Building Materials Distr
N.A.I.C.S.: 444180

HARRISONS MALAYALAM LIMITED
241624 Bristow Road, Willingdon Island, Cochin, 682003, India
Tel.: (91) 4842668023
Web Site:
https://www.harrisonmalayalam.com
500467—(BOM)
Rev.: $59,214,795
Assets: $53,382,819
Liabilities: $34,658,714
Net Worth: $18,724,105
Earnings: $2,130,136
Emp.: 7,350
Fiscal Year-end: 03/31/23
Rubber, Pepper, Tea, Pineapple & Other Crop Production
N.A.I.C.S.: 326299
V. Venugopal (Mgr)

HARRODS LTD.
87-135 Brompton Road, Knightsbridge, London, SW1X 7XL, United Kingdom
Tel.: (44) 2077301234
Web Site: http://www.harrods.com
Year Founded: 1849
Sales Range: $750-799.9 Million
Emp.: 4,000
Department Stores
N.A.I.C.S.: 455110
Michael Ward (Mng Dir)

Subsidiaries:

Air Harrods Ltd (1)
1st Ave London Stansted Airport, Stansted, CM24 1QQ, United Kingdom
Tel.: (44) 1279660800
Web Site: http://www.airharrods.com
Sales Range: $25-49.9 Million
Emp.: 15
Helicopter Charter Service
N.A.I.C.S.: 481112
Paul Norton (Mng Dir)

Harrods Aviation (1)
First Avenue London Stansted Airport, Stansted, CM24 1QQ, United Kingdom
Tel.: (44) 1279665398
Web Site: http://www.harrodsaviation.com
Emp.: 250
Aircraft Services
N.A.I.C.S.: 481111
Fiona Robinson (Mgr-Mktg)

Harrods Bank Ltd (1)
87-135 Brompton Rd, Knightsbridge, London, SW1X 7XL, United Kingdom
Tel.: (44) 2072256789
Web Site: http://www.harrodsbank.co.uk
Sales Range: $50-74.9 Million
Emp.: 20
Bank
N.A.I.C.S.: 523150

Harrods Casino (1)
87-135 Brompton Rd, Knightsbridge, London, SW1X 7XL, United Kingdom
Tel.: (44) 20 7930 6229
Web Site: http://www.harrods-casino.com
Casino
N.A.I.C.S.: 713210

Harrods Estates (1)
82 Brompton Road, Knightsbridge, London, SW3 1ER, United Kingdom
Tel.: (44) 2072256506
Web Site: http://www.harrodsestates.com
Sales Range: $25-49.9 Million
Emp.: 50
Real Estate Services
N.A.I.C.S.: 531210
Julian Cook (Mng Dir)

PL Management Ltd (1)
68 Hammersmith Road, London, W14 8YW, United Kingdom
Tel.: (44) 20 3626 7565
Web Site: http://www.plmanagement.co.uk
Residential Development Services
N.A.I.C.S.: 531311

HARRY BARLOW LTD.
20 Hanson St, London, W1W 6UF, United Kingdom
Tel.: (44) 207 436 2701
Web Site:
http://www.harrybarlow.com
Year Founded: 1998
Sales Range: $10-24.9 Million
Emp.: 10
Government/Political/Public Affairs
N.A.I.C.S.: 541810
Harry J. Barlow (Dir-Govt Affairs)

HARRY ROSEN INC.
77 Bloor St W Ste 1600, Toronto, M5S 1M2, ON, Canada
Tel.: (416) 935-9200
Web Site: http://www.harryrosen.com
Year Founded: 1954
Sales Range: $200-249.9 Million
Emp.: 800
Apparel & Footwear Retailer
N.A.I.C.S.: 458110
Jeff Farbstein (Exec VP & Gen Mdse Mgr)

HARRYS MANUFACTURING INC.
1070-1055 West Hastings Street, Vancouver, V6E 2E9, BC, Canada
Tel.: (604) 565-5100   BC
Web Site: http://www.harrysmfg.com
Year Founded: 2007
WSRRF—(OTCIQ)
Rev.: $17,528
Assets: $70,334
Liabilities: $251,448
Net Worth: ($181,114)
Earnings: ($485,007)
Fiscal Year-end: 07/31/23
Tobacco Mfr
N.A.I.C.S.: 312230
Michael Young (CFO)

Subsidiaries:

Harrys International Manufacturing Inc. (1)
101-2445 Ware Street, Abbotsford, V2S 3E3, BC, Canada
Tel.: (604) 308-1602
Cigarette Mfr
N.A.I.C.S.: 312230

HARSHA ENGINEERS INTERNATIONAL LIMITED
Sarkhej Bavla Road Changodar, Ahmedabad, 382213, Gujarat, India
Tel.: (91) 2717618200
Web Site:
https://www.harshaengineers.com
Year Founded: 1972
543600—(BOM)
Rev.: $167,113,482
Assets: $173,267,790
Liabilities: $44,765,901
Net Worth: $128,501,888
Earnings: $14,780,888
Emp.: 602
Fiscal Year-end: 03/31/23
Precision Product Mfr
N.A.I.C.S.: 332721

Subsidiaries:

Harsha Engineers Europe SRL (1)
Str Hermann Oberth Nr 28 Hala 4, Ghimbav, 507075, Brasov, Romania
Tel.: (40) 372779900
Bearing Cage & Stamped Component Mfr
N.A.I.C.S.: 331222

Harsha Precision Bearing Components (China) Co. Ltd. (1)
No 10 Fuhua Road, Bixi District, Changshu, 215536, Jiangsu, China
Tel.: (86) 51252265381
Steel & Polyamide Bearing Cage Mfr
N.A.I.C.S.: 331222

HARSON TRADING (CHINA) CO., LTD.
No 1008 Huaan Road Caoan Economic and Technological Development Zone, Huaqiao Town, Kunshan, 215332, Jiangsu, China
Tel.: (86) 51257606227
Web Site:
http://www.harsongroup.com
Year Founded: 2006
603958—(SHG)
Rev.: $136,690,898
Assets: $177,441,694
Liabilities: $28,308,612
Net Worth: $149,133,082
Earnings: ($6,669,231)
Fiscal Year-end: 12/31/20
Shoe Mfr & Distr
N.A.I.C.S.: 316990
Yuzhen Chen (Chm)

HART STORES INC.
900 Place Paul-Kane, Laval, H7C 2T2, QC, Canada
Tel.: (450) 661-4155   Ca
Web Site: http://www.hartstores.com

HARTAMAS GROUP BHD.

Year Founded: 1960
Sales Range: $50-74.9 Million
Departmental Store Operator
N.A.I.C.S.: 455110
Franco Messina (CFO & VP-Fin)

HARTALEGA HOLDINGS BERHAD
C-G-9 Jalan Dataran SD1 Dataran SD PJU 9, Bandar Sri Damansara, 52200, Kuala Lumpur, Malaysia
Tel.: (60) 362771733
Web Site:
https://www.hartalega.com.my
Year Founded: 1998
HARTA—(KLS)
Rev.: $509,972,063
Assets: $1,122,733,757
Liabilities: $136,836,825
Net Worth: $985,896,931
Earnings: ($50,541,799)
Emp.: 7,562
Fiscal Year-end: 03/31/23
Holding Company; Glove Mfr
N.A.I.C.S.: 551112
Kam Hon Kuan (Chm)

Subsidiaries:

MUN (Australia) Pty Limited (1)
Suite 305 51 Rawson Street, Epping, 2121, NSW, Australia
Tel.: (61) 298687708
Web Site: http://www.munglobal.com.au
Medical Gloves Mfr
N.A.I.C.S.: 339113

MUN Global Sdn. Bhd. (1)
C-G-9 Jalan Dataran SD1 Dataran SD PJU 9, Bandar Sri Damansara, 52200, Kuala Lumpur, Malaysia
Tel.: (60) 362771733
Web Site: http://m.munglobal.com
Medical Gloves Mfr
N.A.I.C.S.: 339113

MUN Health Product (India) Pvt Ltd (1)
No A-6 Unit 38-22-137, Kaparada Industrial Estate, Visakhapatnam, 530007, Andhra Pradesh, India
Tel.: (91) 8912955744
Medical Gloves Mfr
N.A.I.C.S.: 339113

HARTAMAS GROUP BHD.
Level 13 Block A Menara Prima Jalan PJU 1/37 Dataran Prima, 47301, Petaling Jaya, Selangor, Malaysia
Tel.: (60) 378395555
Web Site: http://www.hartamas.com
Year Founded: 1996
Sales Range: $75-99.9 Million
Emp.: 75
Hotel Resort Ownership & Operations; Investment Holding Company
N.A.I.C.S.: 551112
Eric Lim (Mng Dir)

Subsidiaries:

Hartamas Real Estate Sdn. Bhd. (1)
Level 13 Block A Menara Prima Jalan PJU 1/37, Dataran Prima, 47301, Petaling Jaya, Selangor Darul Ehsan, Malaysia
Tel.: (60) 378395555
Web Site: http://www.hartamas.com
Real Estate Property Management Services
N.A.I.C.S.: 531311
Tay Lee Chin (Co-Founder)

Subsidiary (Domestic):

HARTAMAS REAL ESTATE (KD) SDN BHD (2)
No 13-1 Street Wing Sun Suria Avenue Persiaran Mahogani, Kota Damansara Darul Ehsan, 47810, Petaling Jaya, Selangor, Malaysia
Tel.: (60) 3 6143 3555
Real Estate Development Services
N.A.I.C.S.: 531210

HARTAMAS GROUP BHD.

Hartamas Group Bhd.—(Continued)

HARTAMAS REAL ESTATE (OUG) SDN BHD (2)
Unit 4-2 Commerce One Lorong 2/137C
Jalan Klang Lama, Wilayah Persekutuan,
58200, Kuala Lumpur, Malaysia
Tel.: (60) 3 77858888
Real Estate Development Services
N.A.I.C.S.: 531210
Desmond Tho (Branch Mgr)

HARTAMAS REAL ESTATE (SETIA ALAM) SDN BHD (2)
2A-1 Jalan Setia Dagang AL U13/AL
Seksyen U13, Setia Alam Darul Ehsan,
40170, Shah Alam, Selangor, Malaysia
Tel.: (60) 3 3362 1186
Real Estate Development Services
N.A.I.C.S.: 531210

HARTCO INC.
9393 Louis-H-Lafontaine, Montreal,
H1J 1Y8, QC, Canada
Tel.: (514) 354-3810 QC
Web Site: http://www.hartco.com
Year Founded: 1976
Sales Range: $200-249.9 Million
Information Technology Solutions
N.A.I.C.S.: 541512
Michael Lemieux (CFO & VP-Fin)

HARTE GOLD CORP.
161 Bay St Suite 2400, Toronto,
M5J2S1, ON, Canada
Tel.: (416) 368-0999 ON
Web Site: http://www.hartegold.com
HRT—(DEU)
Rev.: $38,074,516
Assets: $93,947,750
Liabilities: $107,854,456
Net Worth: ($13,906,707)
Earnings: ($47,124,244)
Emp.: 92
Fiscal Year-end: 12/31/19
Gold Mining Services
N.A.I.C.S.: 212220
Joseph Conway (Chm)

HARTMAN FIJNMECHANISCHE INDUSTRIE B.V.
Industrieweg 25, 7141 CX, Groenlo,
Netherlands
Tel.: (31) 544 47 50 00 NI
Web Site: http://www.hfibv.nl
High Precision Turned Products Mfr
N.A.I.C.S.: 332721
Marcel Duistermaat (Engr-Sls)

HARTMANN TRESORE AG
Pamplonastrasse 2, 33106, Paderborn, Germany
Tel.: (49) 52511744410
Web Site: http://www.hartmann-tresore.com
Year Founded: 1983
Sales Range: $10-24.9 Million
Emp.: 45
Safe & Cabinet Mfr & Distr
N.A.I.C.S.: 332999
Christoph Hartmann (Co-Founder & Chm)

Subsidiaries:

HARTMANN TRESORE France S.A.R.L. (1)
3 rue de la Louviere, BP 77, 78512, Rambouillet, Cedex, France
Tel.: (33) 134571155
Security System Mfr
N.A.I.C.S.: 337215

HARTMANN TRESORE Italia Srl (1)
Via Benedetto Brin 12, 20149, Milano, Italy
Tel.: (39) 0243981634
Web Site: http://www.casseforti.it
Security System Mfr
N.A.I.C.S.: 337215

HARTMANN TRESORE Middle East LLC (1)
Gold & Diamond Park Sheikh Zayed Road,
PO Box 102 761, Dubai, United Arab Emirates
Tel.: (971) 43808099
Web Site: http://www.safes.ae
Security System Mfr
N.A.I.C.S.: 337215

HARTMANN TRESORE Polska Sp. z o.o. (1)
ul Marynarska 19 A, 02-674, Warsaw, Poland
Tel.: (48) 225954090
Web Site: http://www.hartmann-tresore.pl
Security System Mfr
N.A.I.C.S.: 337215

HARTMANN TRESORE Schweiz AG (1)
Pflanzschulstrasse 3, Postfach 185, 8411,
Winterthur, Switzerland
Tel.: (41) 443503955
Web Site: http://www.hartmann-tresore.ch
Security System Mfr
N.A.I.C.S.: 337215
Stefan Schurch (Bus Mgr)

HARTSHEAD RESOURCES NL
333C Charles Street, Perth, 6006,
WA, Australia
Tel.: (61) 892262011 AU
Web Site: https://hartshead-resources.com.au
PGNYF—(OTCIQ)
Rev.: $2,424
Assets: $3,665,858
Liabilities: $666,454
Net Worth: $2,999,403
Earnings: ($2,812,100)
Fiscal Year-end: 06/30/22
Oil Exploration
N.A.I.C.S.: 211120
Nathan Lude (Exec Dir)

HARTWELL PLC
Wootton Business Park Besselsleigh
Road, Wootton, OX13 6FD, Oxon,
United Kingdom
Tel.: (44) 1865861300
Web Site: http://www.hartwell.co.uk
Emp.: 700
Car Dealership Owner & Operator
N.A.I.C.S.: 441110
Kevin Godfrey (Mng Dir)

HARTWICK O'SHEA & CARTWRIGHT LIMITED
3245 American Drive, Mississauga,
L4V 1B8, ON, Canada
Tel.: (905) 672-5100
Web Site: http://www.hocltd.com
Year Founded: 1974
Rev.: $24,829,200
Emp.: 85
Freight & Logistics Services
N.A.I.C.S.: 488510

Subsidiaries:

HOC USA Inc. (1)
400 Riverwalk Pkwy Ste 200 B,
Tonawanda, NY 14150
Tel.: (716) 877-0475
Freight Forwarding Services
N.A.I.C.S.: 488510
Sam Lombardo (VP)

HARUYAMA HOLDINGS INC.
1-2-3 Omotemachi, Kita-ku,
Okayama, 700-0822, Japan
Tel.: (81) 862267114
Web Site: https://www.haruyama.co.jp
Year Founded: 1974
7416—(TKS)
Rev.: $237,398,150
Assets: $312,586,900
Liabilities: $154,317,060
Net Worth: $158,269,840
Earnings: $2,677,050
Emp.: 1,207
Fiscal Year-end: 03/31/24
Holding Company; Suburban Suit Specialty Stores
N.A.I.C.S.: 551112
Hiroaki Nakamura (Pres & CEO)

HARVARD INTERNATIONAL LTD.
Harvard House The Waterfront, Elstree Road, Elstree, WD6 3BS, Herts, United Kingdom
Tel.: (44) 2082387650
Web Site: http://www.harvardplc.com
Sales Range: $75-99.9 Million
Emp.: 86
Electronic Appliance Distr
N.A.I.C.S.: 423620
Robert Thompson (Dir-Fin)

Subsidiaries:

Alba Broadcasting Corporation Limited (1)
Harvard House The Waterfront Elstree Road, Elstree, Borehamwood, WD6 3BS, Herts, United Kingdom
Tel.: (44) 20 82387650
Sales Range: $25-49.9 Million
Emp.: 40
Consumer Electronic Products Distr
N.A.I.C.S.: 423620

Alba Radio Limited (1)
Harvard House The Waterfront Elstree Road Elstree, WD6 3BS, Herts, United Kingdom (100%)
Tel.: (44) 2082387650
Sales Range: $75-99.9 Million
Electrical Appliance Television & Radio Set Whslr
N.A.I.C.S.: 423620

Bush Australia Pty Limited (1)
9-4 Ave of the Americas, Newington, 2127, NSW, Australia (100%)
Tel.: (61) 297143434
Web Site: http://www.bushaustralia.com.au
Sales Range: $25-49.9 Million
Emp.: 15
Electrical Apparatus & Equipment Wiring Supplies & Equipment Whslr
N.A.I.C.S.: 423610

Grundig Australia PTY Limited (1)
PO Box 6287, Silverwater, 1811, NSW, Australia
Tel.: (61) 297143434
Web Site: http://www.grundig.net.au
Sales Range: $25-49.9 Million
Emp.: 16
Consumer Electronics Distr
N.A.I.C.S.: 423620

Harvard International (Hong Kong) Limited (1)
13/f Railway Plz 39 Chatham Rd S, Tsim Tsa Tsui, Kowloon, China (Hong Kong)
Tel.: (852) 27352161
Consumer Electronics Distr
N.A.I.C.S.: 423620

Harvard Maritime Limited (1)
13th Floor Railway Plaza, 39 Chatham Rd, S Tsim Sha Tsui, Kowloon, China (Hong Kong) (100%)
Tel.: (852) 27352161
Web Site: http://www.harvardplc.com
Procurement, Shipping, Manufacturing & Quality Control
N.A.I.C.S.: 335999

Roadstar Deutschland GmbH (1)
Fester Str 48, 40882, Ratingen, Germany (100%)
Tel.: (49) 210274560
Electronic Parts & Equipment Whslr
N.A.I.C.S.: 423690

Roadstar Italia SpA (1)
Via Matteotti 39, Cernobbio, 22012, Como, Italy (100%)
Tel.: (39) 031342584
Web Site: http://www.roadstar.com
Electronic Parts & Equipment Whslr
N.A.I.C.S.: 423690

Roadstar Management SA (1)

INTERNATIONAL PUBLIC

Via Passeggiata 7, 6883, Novazzano, Switzerland (100%)
Tel.: (41) 916975105
Web Site: http://www.roadstar.com
Sales Range: $50-74.9 Million
Emp.: 6
Electronic Parts & Equipment Whslr
N.A.I.C.S.: 423690

HARVATEK CORPORATION
No 18 Lane 522 Section 5 Zhonghua Road, Hsin-chu, 30094, Taiwan
Tel.: (886) 35399889
Web Site: https://www.harvatek.com
Year Founded: 1995
6168—(TAI)
Rev.: $66,486,737
Assets: $131,252,587
Liabilities: $24,001,373
Net Worth: $107,251,214
Earnings: $3,001,373
Emp.: 515
Fiscal Year-end: 12/31/23
Electronic Components Mfr
N.A.I.C.S.: 334419

Subsidiaries:

Yangzhou YoungTek Electronics Ltd. (1)
Building 4 No 122 Jinshan Road, Yangzhou Economic & Technological Development Zone, Yangzhou, China
Tel.: (86) 51485160317
Electronic Product Mfr & Distr
N.A.I.C.S.: 335999

HARVEST CAPITAL MANAGEMENT PUBLIC LTD.
9 Soteris Michaelides Str Hawaii Green House 2 Off 32, 3035, Limassol, Cyprus
Tel.: (357) 99 303035
HCM—(CYP)
Sales Range: Less than $1 Million
Financial Services
N.A.I.C.S.: 523999
Nikolaos Poukis (Chm)

HARVEST HEALTHCARE LEADERS INCOME ETF
610 Chartwell Rd Suite 204, Oakville,
L6J 4A5, ON, Canada
Tel.: (416) 649-4541 ON
Year Founded: 2014
HHL—(TSX)
Rev.: $23,334,714
Assets: $394,860,133
Liabilities: $4,364,901
Net Worth: $390,495,232
Earnings: $18,954,483
Fiscal Year-end: 12/31/20
Investment Services
N.A.I.C.S.: 523999
Michael Kovacs (Pres & CEO)

HARVEST MINERALS LIMITED
22 Lindsay Street, Perth, 6000, WA, Australia
Tel.: (61) 892001847
Web Site: http://www.harvestminerals.net
HMI—(AIM)
Rev.: $5,623,964
Assets: $7,008,700
Liabilities: $675,165
Net Worth: $6,333,535
Earnings: $128,967
Fiscal Year-end: 12/31/22
Fertilizer Products Developer
N.A.I.C.S.: 212390
Brian McMaster (Exec Chm & Chm)

HARVEST MIRACLE CAPITAL BERHAD
Unit C-01-2 Block C Plaza Glomac
No 6 Jalan SS7/19 Kelana Jaya,

AND PRIVATE COMPANIES

47301, Petaling Jaya, Selangor, Malaysia
Tel.: (60) 378052188 MY
Web Site: https://www.hmcap.my
HM—(KLS)
Rev.: $28,116,424
Assets: $87,201,139
Liabilities: $26,476,623
Net Worth: $60,724,516
Earnings: ($1,756,113)
Fiscal Year-end: 03/31/23
Information Technology Services
N.A.I.C.S.: 541512
Ooi Jin Tan *(Chm)*

Subsidiaries:

Open Adventure Sdn. Bhd. (1)
Menara Luxor Level 9 6B Persiaran Tropicana, Tropicana Golf and Country Resort, 47410, Petaling Jaya, Selangor, Malaysia
Tel.: (60) 378052588
Web Site:
  http://www.openadventure.com.my
Software Development Services
N.A.I.C.S.: 541511

Super Kian Holdings Sdn. Bhd. (1)
9 02 9th Floor Persoft Tower 6B Persiaran Tropicana Tropicana Golf, Petaling Jaya, 47410, Malaysia
Tel.: (60) 378052188
Property Construction Services
N.A.I.C.S.: 236220
Yow Weng Weng *(Gen Mgr)*

Viewnet Computer System Sdn. Bhd. (1)
Lot 3-1T-013 3rd Floor Plaza Low Yat, Jalan Bukit Bintang, 55100, Kuala Lumpur, Malaysia
Tel.: (60) 126890929
Web Site: https://www.viewnet.com.my
Information Technology Products Distr
N.A.I.C.S.: 423430
Simon Pang *(Founder)*

Subsidiary (Domestic):

PC Zone Computer Trading (M) Sdn. Bhd. (2)
Low Yatt Plaza Lot2-42 2nd Floor, No 7 Jalan 1/77 Off Jalan Bukit Bintang, 55100, Kuala Lumpur, Malaysia
Tel.: (60) 327156881
Web Site: http://www.pczonecomputer.com
Information Technology Products Distr
N.A.I.C.S.: 423430

HARVEST PORTFOLIOS GROUP INC.
710 Dorval Drive Suite 209, Oakville, L6K 3V7, ON, Canada
Tel.: (416) 649-4541
Web Site:
  http://www.harvestportfolios.com
Year Founded: 2009
Sales Range: $50-74.9 Million
Emp.: 10
Asset Management & Investment Services
N.A.I.C.S.: 523940
Nick Bontis *(Member-Exec Bd)*

Subsidiaries:

Australian REIT Income Fund (1)
610 Chartwell Rd Suite 204, Oakville, L6J 4A5, ON, Canada
Tel.: (416) 649-4541
Web Site: http://www.harvestportfolios.com
Rev.: $3,312,872
Assets: $10,831,621
Liabilities: $2,925,822
Net Worth: $7,905,799
Earnings: $2,797,993
Fiscal Year-end: 12/31/2019
Closed-End Investment Fund
N.A.I.C.S.: 525990
Michael Kovacs *(Founder, Pres, CEO & Sec)*

Brand Leaders Income Fund (1)
610 Chartwell Rd Suite 204, Oakville, L6J 4A5, ON, Canada
Tel.: (416) 649-4541
Web Site: http://harvestportfolios.com
Rev.: $406,689
Assets: $3,480,551
Liabilities: $38,796
Net Worth: $3,441,755
Earnings: $251,635
Fiscal Year-end: 12/31/2020
Closed-End Investment Fund
N.A.I.C.S.: 525990
Daniel Lazzer *(CFO)*

Energy Leaders Income Fund (1)
710 Dorval Drive Suite 209, Oakville, L6K 3V7, ON, Canada
Tel.: (416) 649-4541
Web Site: http://www.harvestportfolios.com
Sales Range: Less than $1 Million
Closed-End Investment Fund
N.A.I.C.S.: 525990
Michael Kovacs *(Pres, CEO)*

Global Telecom & Utilities Income Fund (1)
610 Chartwell Rd Suite 204, Oakville, L6J 4A5, ON, Canada
Tel.: (416) 649-4541
Web Site: http://harvestportfolios.com
Rev.: $392,033
Assets: $2,669,586
Liabilities: $18,475
Net Worth: $2,651,110
Earnings: $255,046
Fiscal Year-end: 12/31/2019
Closed-End Investment Fund
N.A.I.C.S.: 525990
Caroline Grimont *(VP-Mktg)*

Harvest Sustainable Income Fund (1)
Suite 209 710 Dorval Drive, Oakville, L6K 3V7, ON, Canada
Tel.: (416) 649-4541
Sales Range: $1-9.9 Million
Closed-End Investment Fund
N.A.I.C.S.: 525990
Mary Medeiros *(VP-Ops)*

HARVEST TECHNOLOGY GROUP LTD.
7 Turner Avenue, Bentley, 6102, WA, Australia
Tel.: (61) 894820500 AU
Web Site:
  http://www.sharkmitigation.com
Year Founded: 2011
HTG—(ASX)
Rev.: $6,524,851
Assets: $18,848,521
Liabilities: $6,715,942
Net Worth: $12,132,579
Earnings: ($7,844,758)
Fiscal Year-end: 06/30/21
Software Development Services
N.A.I.C.S.: 513210
Ilario Faenza *(Mng Dir)*

HARVEST TECHNOLOGY PLC
Nineteen Twenty Three Valletta Road, Marsa, MRS 3000, Malta
Tel.: (356) 21445566
Web Site: https://www.harvest.tech
Year Founded: 1923
HRV—(MAL)
Rev.: $19,341,723
Assets: $27,786,044
Liabilities: $11,329,520
Net Worth: $16,456,523
Earnings: $3,308,288
Emp.: 125
Fiscal Year-end: 12/31/21
Information Technology Management Services
N.A.I.C.S.: 541512
Juanito Camilleri *(Chm)*

Subsidiaries:

APCO Systems Limited (1)
Nineteen Twenty Three Valletta Road, Marsa, MRS 3000, Malta
Tel.: (356) 21445566
Web Site: http://www.apcopay.com
Ecommerce Services
N.A.I.C.S.: 541511

HARVEST VINCCLER, S.C.A.
Alirio Ugarte Ave Bldg Harvest Vinccler Fl 1, Maturin, 6201, Monagas, Venezuela
Tel.: (58) 2916401700 VE
Sales Range: $150-199.9 Million
Oil & Natural Gas Property Investment, Development & Production
N.A.I.C.S.: 211120
Mauricio DiGirolamo *(Gen Mgr)*

HARVEY NICHOLS GROUP LIMITED
361 - 365 Chiswick High Road, London, W4 4HS, United Kingdom
Tel.: (44) 2072355000
Web Site:
  http://www.harveynichols.com
Clothing & Accessories Retailer
N.A.I.C.S.: 458110
Manju Malhotra *(COO)*

HARVEY NORMAN HOLDINGS LTD
B1 Richmond Road, Homebush, 2140, NSW, Australia
Tel.: (61) 292016111
Web Site:
  https://www.harveynorman.com.au
HNORF—(OTCIQ)
Rev.: $1,871,900,366
Assets: $5,293,714,588
Liabilities: $2,264,247,453
Net Worth: $3,029,467,135
Earnings: $238,800,747
Emp.: 6,500
Fiscal Year-end: 06/30/24
General Merchandise Retailer
N.A.I.C.S.: 455219
Martin Anderson *(Gen Mgr-Advertising)*

Subsidiaries:

Arisit Pty Limited (1)
40-50 Mark Anthony Drive, Dandenong South, 3175, VIC, Australia
Tel.: (61) 1300762219
Web Site: https://www.arisit.com
Electrical Appliance Retailer
N.A.I.C.S.: 449210

Harvey Norman Croatia d.o.o. (1)
Velimira Skorpika 34, 10000, Zagreb, Croatia
Tel.: (385) 15566200
Web Site: http://www.harveynorman.hr
Electrical Appliance Retailer
N.A.I.C.S.: 449210

Harvey Norman Singapore Pte. Limited (1)
315 Outram Road 01-01/02 Tan Boon Liat Building, Singapore, 169074, Singapore
Tel.: (65) 18003119989
Web Site: http://www.harveynorman.com.sg
Electrical Appliance Retailer
N.A.I.C.S.: 449210

Harvey Norman Trading (Ireland) Limited (1)
Brent House Swords Business Park, Swords, Dublin, K67 Y2V0, Ireland
Tel.: (353) 18704700
Web Site: http://www.harveynorman.ie
Electrical Appliance Retailer
N.A.I.C.S.: 449210

Harvey Norman Trading d.o.o. (1)
Letaliska cesta 3D, 1000, Ljubljana, Slovenia
Tel.: (386) 802225
Web Site: https://www.harveynorman.si
Electrical Appliance Retailer
N.A.I.C.S.: 449210

Pertama Holdings Limited (1)
315 Outram Road, Singapore, 169074, Singapore (100%)
Tel.: (65) 62256006
Web Site: http://www.harveynorman.com.sg
Consumer Electronic Products Mfr & Distr
N.A.I.C.S.: 423620
Chun Onn Poon *(CFO & Sec)*

Space Furniture Pte Limited (1)
77 Bencoolen St, Singapore, 189653, Singapore
Tel.: (65) 64150000
Web Site: http://www.spacefurniture.com.sg
Furniture Retailer
N.A.I.C.S.: 449110

HARVIA OYJ
Teollisuustie 1-7, PO Box 12, 40951, Muurame, Finland
Tel.: (358) 207464000
Web Site: https://www.harvia.fi
Year Founded: 1950
HARVIA—(HEL)
Rev.: $186,065,185
Assets: $225,338,873
Liabilities: $119,203,540
Net Worth: $106,135,333
Earnings: $30,291,388
Emp.: 633
Fiscal Year-end: 12/31/22
Household Appliance Mfr & Distr
N.A.I.C.S.: 335210
Tapio Pajuharju *(CEO)*

Subsidiaries:

Almost Heaven Saunas LLC (1)
11261 James St, Holland, MI 49424
Web Site: https://www.almostheaven.com
Sauna Models Constructor
N.A.I.C.S.: 812199
Rick Mouw *(Founder)*

Damo Wellness Romania Srl (1)
Str Stadionului Nr 4, 535500, Gheorgheni, Romania
Tel.: (40) 366401344
Web Site: https://www.sauna.ro
Spa Product Mfr
N.A.I.C.S.: 326191

Domo Wellness Romania Srl (1)
Str Stadionului Nr 4, Harghita, Gheorgheni, 535500, Romania
Tel.: (40) 366401344
Web Site: https://www.sauna.ro
Spa Operator
N.A.I.C.S.: 812199
Delia Stoica *(Production Mgr)*

EOS Saunatechnik GmbH (1)
Schneiderstriesch 1, 35759, Driedorf, Germany
Tel.: (49) 2775820
Web Site: https://www.eos-sauna.com
Mechanical Component Mfr
N.A.I.C.S.: 335210
Rainer Kunz *(CEO & Mng Dir)*

Subsidiary (Domestic):

Kusatek GmbH (2)
Schneiderstriesch 1, 35759, Driedorf, Germany
Tel.: (49) 27755776512
Web Site: https://www.kusatek.de
Spa Operator
N.A.I.C.S.: 812199

Spatronic GmbH (2)
Schneiderstriesch 1, 35759, Driedorf, Germany
Tel.: (49) 277582850
Web Site: https://www.spatronic.de
Electrical Equipment Distr
N.A.I.C.S.: 423610

Kirami Oy (1)
Villilantie 2, 32730, Sastamala, Finland
Tel.: (358) 105742172
Web Site: https://www.kirami.com
Copper Product Mfr & Distr
N.A.I.C.S.: 331420

Sauna-Eurox Oy (1)
Suontaantie 2 B, 29100, Luvia, Finland
Tel.: (358) 26349600
Web Site: https://www.saunagranit.com
Synthetic Stone Mfr
N.A.I.C.S.: 327991

Saunamax Oy (1)
Fluorescent Tube 4, 00750, Helsinki, Finland
Tel.: (358) 504004770

HARVIA OYJ

Harvia Oyj—(Continued)

Web Site: http://www.saunamax.fi
Real Estate Development Services
N.A.I.C.S.: 531390

Sentiotec GmbH (1)
Wartenburger Strasse 31, 4840, Vocklabruck, Austria
Tel.: (43) 76722290010
Web Site: https://www.sentiotec.com
Spa Operator
N.A.I.C.S.: 812199
Markus Wormanseder *(CEO & Mng Dir)*

HARWOOD CAPITAL LLP
6 Stratton Street, London, W1J 8LD, United Kingdom
Tel.: (44) 20 7640 3200
Web Site:
http://www.harwoodcapital.co.uk
Year Founded: 2003
Investment Management Service
N.A.I.C.S.: 523999
J. J. Brade *(Partner)*

Subsidiaries:

Crest Foods Co. Inc. (1)
905 Main St, Ashton, IL 61006
Tel.: (815) 453-7411
Web Site: http://www.crestfoods.com
Sales Range: $25-49.9 Million
Emp.: 850
Dairy Stabilizers, Manufacturing & Contract Packaging
N.A.I.C.S.: 333241
Jeffrey Meiners *(Pres)*

GTL Resources PLC (1)
107 Cheapside, London, EC2V 6DN, United Kingdom
Tel.: (44) 1642794000
Web Site: http://www.gtlresources.com
Sales Range: $25-49.9 Million
Emp.: 73
Ethanol Producer
N.A.I.C.S.: 325193
Richard Ruebe *(CEO)*

Journey Group plc (1)
Building One The Square Southall Lane, Heston, UB2 5NH, United Kingdom
Tel.: (44) 2086061300
Web Site: http://www.journeygroup.plc.uk
Catering, Travel Supplies & Cabin Management Services
N.A.I.C.S.: 488190
Stephen Yapp *(Chm)*

Subsidiary (US):

Air Fayre CA Inc. (2)
20051 S Vermont Ave, Los Angeles, CA 90502
Tel.: (310) 808-1061
Web Site: http://www.airfayre.com
Emp.: 200
Airline Logistics Services
N.A.I.C.S.: 488190
Darryl Terrell *(Mgr-Supply Chain)*

Air Fayre USA Inc. (2)
20051 S Vermont Ave, Los Angeles, CA 90502
Tel.: (310) 808-1061
Airline Logistics Services
N.A.I.C.S.: 488190

Subsidiary (Non-US):

Encompass Supply Chain Management (Canada) Inc. (2)
380 Courtney Park Dr E Unit C, Mississauga, L5T 2S5, ON, Canada
Tel.: (905) 698-1125
Oil Transportation Services
N.A.I.C.S.: 488190

MNH Sustainable Cabin Services Pty Sydney - Australasia (2)
Suite 705 247 Coward Street, Mascot, 2020, NSW, Australia
Tel.: (61) 2 9691 3763
Web Site: http://www.mnhscs.com
Waste Management Services
N.A.I.C.S.: 562998

Subsidiary (Domestic):

Watermark Group Services (UK) Limited (2)
Unit 1 3 The Heston Centre International Avenue, Hounslow, TW5 9NJ, Middlesex, United Kingdom
Tel.: (44) 2086062000
Management Consulting Services
N.A.I.C.S.: 541618

Oryx International Growth Fund Limited (1)
BNP Paribas House 1, 1 St Julian's Avenue, Saint Peter Port, GY1 1WA, Guernsey
Tel.: (44) 1481 750 858
Web Site:
http://www.oryxinternationalfund.co.uk
Financial Investment Services
N.A.I.C.S.: 523150
Nigel Cayzer *(Chm)*

Source BioScience Limited (1)
1 Orchard Place Nottingham Business Park, Nottingham, NG8 6PX, United Kingdom
Tel.: (44) 115 973 9012
Web Site: http://www.sourcebioscience.com
Emp.: 200
Diagnostic & Screening Services
N.A.I.C.S.: 621511

HARWORTH GROUP PLC
Advantage House Poplar Way, Rotherham, S60 5TR, South Yorkshire, United Kingdom
Tel.: (44) 1143493131
Web Site:
https://www.harworthgroup.com
HWG—(LSE)
Rev.: $149,191,704
Assets: $1,034,812,095
Liabilities: $250,071,658
Net Worth: $784,740,436
Earnings: $127,612,103
Emp.: 91
Fiscal Year-end: 12/31/21
Property Development Services
N.A.I.C.S.: 531390
Chris Birch *(Gen Counsel & Sec)*

Subsidiaries:

Harworth Insurance Company Limited (1)
Harworth Park Blyth Road, Harworth, Doncaster, DN11 8DB, S Yorkshire, United Kingdom
Tel.: (44) 1302751751
Insurance Services
N.A.I.C.S.: 524128
David Carr *(Admin Mgr)*

Mining Services Limited (1)
Harworth Pk Blyth Rd, Doncaster, TN11 8DB, United Kingdom **(100%)**
Tel.: (44) 1302751751
Web Site: http://www.ukcoal.co.uk
Commercial & Industrial Machinery & Equipment Rental & Leasing
N.A.I.C.S.: 532490

UK Coal Mining Limited (1)
Thoresby Colliery, NG219PS, Nottingham, United Kingdom **(100%)**
Tel.: (44) 1623822238
Web Site: http://www.ukcoal.com
Bituminous Coal Underground Mining
N.A.I.C.S.: 212115
Stewart Hoult *(Mng Dir)*

HARYANA CAPFIN LIMITED
Plot No 30 Institutional Area Sector-44, Gurgaon, 122 002, Haryana, India
Tel.: (91) 4624000
Web Site:
https://www.haryanacapfin.com
532855—(BOM)
Rev.: $282,023
Assets: $24,629,514
Liabilities: $4,480,722
Net Worth: $20,148,792
Earnings: $149,222

Emp.: 8
Fiscal Year-end: 03/31/22
Financial Investment Services
N.A.I.C.S.: 523999
Rajender Singh *(CFO)*

HARYANA FINANCIAL CORPORATION LTD.
30 Bays Building Ground Floor, Sector 17-C, Chandigarh, 160017, India
Tel.: (91) 1722702755
Web Site: https://hfcindia.org.in
Year Founded: 1951
530927—(BOM)
Sales Range: Less than $1 Million
Financial Support Services
N.A.I.C.S.: 523999
Rajesh Khullar *(Chm)*

HARYANA LEATHER CHEMICALS LTD.
1405 B Signature Towers South City I, Gurgaon, 122001, Haryana, India
Tel.: (91) 1242739000
Web Site:
https://www.leatherchem.com
524080—(BOM)
Rev.: $5,233,736
Assets: $5,140,202
Liabilities: $705,629
Net Worth: $4,434,573
Earnings: $223,131
Emp.: 90
Fiscal Year-end: 03/31/23
Specialty Chemicals Mfr
N.A.I.C.S.: 325998
Pankaj Jain *(Vice Chm & Mng Dir)*

HARYANA TEXPRINTS (OVERSEAS) LTD.
Plot No 3 Sector 25, Faridabad, 121004, Haryana, India
Tel.: (91) 129 4180900
Web Site:
http://www.haryanatexprints.com
Year Founded: 1992
Rev.: $11,896,500
Assets: $6,871,748
Liabilities: $5,144,882
Net Worth: $1,726,867
Earnings: $188,297
Emp.: 146
Fiscal Year-end: 03/31/16
Textile Products Mfr
N.A.I.C.S.: 313310
Narayan Prasad Jhanwar *(Mng Dir)*

HAS LIFESTYLE LIMITED
35-B Khatau Bldg 2nd Floor, Alkesh Dinesh Modi Marg Fort, Mumbai, 400 001, India
Tel.: (91) 2230266060
Web Site:
http://www.hasjuicebar.com
Year Founded: 2007
Juice Bar Operator
N.A.I.C.S.: 722515
Aarti Pandey *(Sec)*

HASCOL PETROLEUM LIMITED
Office 29 29th floor Sky Towers-West Wing A Dolmen City, Abdul Sattar Edhi Avenue Block-4, Karachi, Pakistan
Tel.: (92) 111757757
Web Site: https://www.hascol.com
Year Founded: 2001
HASCOL—(LAH)
Rev.: $1,169,882,724
Assets: $563,848,288
Liabilities: $621,308,499
Net Worth: ($57,460,211)
Earnings: ($166,646,341)
Emp.: 617
Fiscal Year-end: 12/31/19

INTERNATIONAL PUBLIC

Oil Marketing Services
N.A.I.C.S.: 213112
Zeeshan Ul Haq *(Sec)*

HASEE COMPUTER CO., LTD.
Hasee Industrial Park Ban Xue gang Industrial Area, Longgang District, Shenzhen, China
Tel.: (86) 75584710000
Web Site: http://www.hasee.com
Year Founded: 1995
Sales Range: $650-699.9 Million
Emp.: 3,000
Computers & Computer Peripherals Mfr
N.A.I.C.S.: 334111
Haijun Wu *(Chm)*

HASEEB WAQAS GROUP OF COMPANIES
6 F Model Town, Lahore, 54000, Pakistan
Tel.: (92) 4235917321
Web Site: http://www.hwgc.com.pk
Year Founded: 1992
Holding Company
N.A.I.C.S.: 551112

Subsidiaries:

Abdullah Sugar Mills Limited (1)
Hujra Chunian Road, Merajabad Distt Okara, Dipalpur, Pakistan
Tel.: (92) 444 561023 4
Sugar Mfr
N.A.I.C.S.: 311314

Haseeb Waqas Sugar Mills Ltd. (1)
6-F Model Town, Lahore, Pakistan
Tel.: (92) 4235917321
Web Site: https://www.hwgc.com.pk
Assets: $22,233,107
Liabilities: $19,511,940
Net Worth: $2,721,168
Earnings: ($1,656,275)
Emp.: 340
Fiscal Year-end: 09/30/2023
Sugar Mfr
N.A.I.C.S.: 311314
Haseeb Ilyas *(CEO)*

HASEGAWA CO., LTD.
7F Koraku International Building 1-5-3 Koraku, Bunkyo-ku, Tokyo, 112-0004, Japan
Tel.: (81) 570017676
Web Site: https://www.hasegawa.jp
Year Founded: 1929
8230—(TKS)
Rev.: $191,586,560
Assets: $177,734,480
Liabilities: $82,028,320
Net Worth: $95,706,160
Earnings: $6,843,760
Emp.: 1,098
Fiscal Year-end: 03/31/22
Religious Goods Store Operator
N.A.I.C.S.: 459999

HASEKO CORPORATION
2-32-1 Shiba, Minato-ku, Tokyo, 105-8507, Japan
Tel.: (81) 334565451
Web Site: https://www.haseko.co.jp
Year Founded: 1937
1808—(TKS)
Rev.: $7,234,122,810
Assets: $8,931,636,910
Liabilities: $5,552,300,850
Net Worth: $3,379,336,060
Earnings: $370,411,180
Emp.: 2,576
Fiscal Year-end: 03/31/24
Real Estate Manangement Services
N.A.I.C.S.: 531190
Noriaki Tsuji *(Chm)*

Subsidiaries:

Century Life Co., Ltd. (1)
4-2-3 Shiba, Minato-ku, Tokyo, Japan

3282

AND PRIVATE COMPANIES

Tel.: (81) 120580731
Web Site: http://www.centurylife.co.jp
Nursing Home Services
N.A.I.C.S.: 621610

Foris Corporation (1)
9F Haseko Minamisagocho Ekimae Building 3-3-9 Shinsuna, Koto-ku, Tokyo, 136-0075, Japan
Tel.: (81) 366602581
Web Site: https://www.foris-group.co.jp
Sales Range: $50-74.9 Million
Emp.: 108
Household Furniture Mfr & Engineering Services
N.A.I.C.S.: 337126

Furusato. Co., Ltd. (1)
15-1 Omiya-cho Komoriyama Building 5th floor, Saiwai-ku, Kawasaki, Kanagawa, Japan
Tel.: (81) 442711187
Web Site: http://www.furusato.net
Emp.: 662
Outpatient Care Services
N.A.I.C.S.: 621498

HOSODA CORPORATION (1)
3-35-21 Asagayaminami, Suginami-Ku, Tokyo, Japan **(89.73%)**
Tel.: (81) 332201111
Web Site: https://www.hosoda.co.jp
Emp.: 185
Construction & Real Estate Services
N.A.I.C.S.: 237990
Kenichi Abe *(Pres)*

Haseko America, Inc. (1)
91-1001 Kaimalie St Ste 205, Ewa Beach, HI 96706-6250 **(100%)**
Tel.: (808) 689-7772
Web Site: http://www.haseko.com
Emp.: 65
Real Estate Development & Operation
N.A.I.C.S.: 237210
Tsutomu Sagawa *(Pres)*

Haseko Anesis Corporation (1)
3-8-2 Shiba, Minato-Ku, Tokyo, 105-0014, Japan
Tel.: (81) 334571248
Web Site: https://www.haseko.co.jp
Interior Design Services
N.A.I.C.S.: 541410

Subsidiary (Domestic):

Haseko Systems Inc. (2)
2-32-1 Shiba, Minato-ku, Tokyo, 105-0014, Japan **(100%)**
Tel.: (81) 33 456 6014
Web Site: https://www.haseko.co.jp
Emp.: 374
Information Processing Services
N.A.I.C.S.: 519290
Yukinari Takami *(Mng Exec Officer)*

Haseko Business Proxy, Inc. (1)
Shiba Koen First Building 3-8-2 Shiba, Minato-ku, Tokyo, 105-0014, Japan
Tel.: (81) 54190628
Web Site: https://www.haseko-hbp.co.jp
Emp.: 127
Real Estate Services
N.A.I.C.S.: 531390

Haseko Community Okinawa Inc. (1)
Arte Building Naha 5th Floor 3-15-9 Kumoji, Naha, 900-0015, Okinawa Prefecture, Japan
Tel.: (81) 988602401
Building Management Services
N.A.I.C.S.: 561790

Haseko Community, Inc. (1)
4 6 6 Shiba, Minato Ku, Tokyo, 108 8383, Japan
Tel.: (81) 334571222
Rev.: $379,049,000
Emp.: 300
Repair Work & Refinishing Buildings; Management & Maintenance of Condominium
N.A.I.C.S.: 238390

Haseko Furnishing Co.,Ltd. (1)
3-3-9 Shinsuna Hasekonan Sunamachi Station Front Building 9F, Koto-ku, Tokyo, 136-0075, Japan
Tel.: (81) 366602581
Web Site: https://www.haseko-hfs.co.jp

Emp.: 117
Furniture Product Mfr & Distr
N.A.I.C.S.: 321999

Haseko Intech, Inc. (1)
2-6-1 Shiba Hase Ko Shiba 2 Building 4th floor, Minato-ku, Tokyo, 105-0014, Japan
Tel.: (81) 354445361
Web Site: http://www.haseko-intech.com
Emp.: 60
Residential Building Remodeling Services
N.A.I.C.S.: 236118

Haseko Livenet, Inc. (1)
Shiba Koen First Building 3-8-2 Shiba, Minato-ku, Tokyo, 105-0014, Japan
Tel.: (81) 354199100
Web Site: https://www.haseko-hln.com
Emp.: 512
Condominium Rental Management
N.A.I.C.S.: 531311

Haseko Property Management Holdings Inc. (1)
Shiba 2-6-1 Haseko Shiba 2 Building, Minato-ku, Tokyo, 105-0014, Japan
Tel.: (81) 334571225
Web Site: https://www.haseko-hkh.co.jp
Emp.: 112
Property Management Services
N.A.I.C.S.: 531311

Haseko Reform Inc. (1)
2-6-1 Shiba, Minato-ku, Tokyo, 105-0014, Japan
Tel.: (81) 334571264
Interior Remodeling Services
N.A.I.C.S.: 236118

Haseko Senior Holdings Co., Ltd. (1)
Komoriyama Building 15-1 Omiya-cho, Saiwai-ku, Kawasaki, 212-0014, Japan
Tel.: (81) 442711187
Web Site: http://www.haseko-senior.co.jp
Nursing Home Services
N.A.I.C.S.: 621610

Haseko Senior Well Design Co., Ltd. (1)
Daiyu Building 2F 2-9-10 Shiba, Minato-ku, Tokyo, 105-0014, Japan
Tel.: (81) 354276480
Web Site: https://www.haseko-senior.co.jp
Emp.: 1,860
Nursing Care Services
N.A.I.C.S.: 623110

Haseko Urban Co., Ltd. (1)
32 1 Shiba 2 Chome, Minato Ku, Tokyo, 105-8507, Japan **(100%)**
Tel.: (81) 334565451
Web Site: http://www.haseko.co.jp
Sales Range: Less than $1 Million
Emp.: 3
Development & Sales of Condominium Apartments for Investors
N.A.I.C.S.: 531311

Haseko Urbest, Inc. (1)
2-6-1 Shiba 6th Floor Hase Koshiba 2 Building, Minato Ku, Tokyo, 105-8545, Japan
Tel.: (81) 354405800
Web Site: https://www.haseko-urbest.com
Emp.: 701
Sale & Resale of Condominiums
N.A.I.C.S.: 531311

Joint Property Co., Ltd. (1)
2-31-19 Banzai building first floor, Minato Ku, Tokyo, 105-0014, Japan
Tel.: (81) 354188200
Web Site: https://www.joint-property.co.jp
Emp.: 47
Real Estate Services
N.A.I.C.S.: 531390

Seikatsu Kagaku Un-Ei Co., Ltd. (1)
4-2-3 Shiba, Minato-ku, Tokyo, 108-0014, Japan
Tel.: (81) 354273177
Web Site: http://www.seikatsu-kagaku.co.jp
Nursing Home Services
N.A.I.C.S.: 621610

Sohgoh Real Estate Co., Ltd. (1)
Banzai Building 4th Floor 2-31-19, Minato-ku, Tokyo, 105-0014, Japan
Tel.: (81) 366322900

Web Site: https://www.sohgohreal.co.jp
Emp.: 65
Real Estate Services
N.A.I.C.S.: 531390

HASGO GROUP LTD.
Haseley Business Ctr, Warwick, CV35 7LS, United Kingdom
Tel.: (44) 2476247213
Year Founded: 2000
Holding Company; Engineering Services
N.A.I.C.S.: 551112

Subsidiaries:

MCT ReMan Ltd. (1)
Winterstoke Road, Weston-super-Mare, BS24 9AT, North Somerset, United Kingdom
Tel.: (44) 1934428000
Web Site: http://www.mctreman.com
Sales Range: $50-74.9 Million
Emp.: 110
Remanufacturer of Manual Transmissions
N.A.I.C.S.: 336350
Andy Cook *(Dir-Comml)*

HASGROVE PLC
4th Floor Station House Stamford New Road, Altrincham, WA14 1EP, Cheshire, United Kingdom
Tel.: (44) 161 927 3222 UK
Web Site: http://www.hasgrove.com
Year Founded: 2004
Emp.: 100
Holding Company; Advertising Services
N.A.I.C.S.: 551112
Paul Antony Sanders *(Grp CEO)*

Subsidiaries:

Landmarks SA (1)
28 Rue Du Belvedere, 1150, Brussels, Belgium **(100%)**
Tel.: (32) 2 779 95 49
Web Site: http://www.landmarks.be
Business Support Services
N.A.I.C.S.: 561499
Ian Martin *(Dir-Digital)*

Odyssey Interactive Limited (1)
5th Floor Station House Stamford New Road, Altrincham, WA14 1EP, Cheshire, United Kingdom **(100%)**
Tel.: (44) 161 927 3222
Web Site: http://www.interact-intranet.co.uk
Sales Range: $25-49.9 Million
Emp.: 30
Software Publisher
N.A.I.C.S.: 513210

The Chase Creative Consultants Limited (1)
1 N Parade Parsonage Gardens, Manchester, M3 2NH, United Kingdom **(100%)**
Tel.: (44) 1618325575
Web Site: http://www.thechase.co.uk
Sales Range: $25-49.9 Million
Emp.: 30
N.A.I.C.S.: 541810
Bev Hutchinson *(Dir-Client Svcs)*

HASH SPACE ACQUISITION CORP.
Haiyi Lu 17-3-102, Qianzhangshu Tongzhou District, Beijing, China
Tel.: (86) 165959908 Ky
Year Founded: 2021
Emp.: 2
Investment Services
N.A.I.C.S.: 523999
Haiyi Lu *(Chm & CEO)*

HASHIMI CAN COMPANY LIMITED
B/24 Sindh Industrial Trading Estate, Karachi, 75700, Pakistan
Tel.: (92) 212563170
Web Site: https://www.hashimican.bizland.com

META—(PSX)
Rev.: $1,831
Assets: $2,941
Liabilities: $9,943
Net Worth: ($7,002)
Earnings: ($217,251)
Emp.: 10
Fiscal Year-end: 06/30/23
Tin Container Cans Mfr
N.A.I.C.S.: 332431

HASHIMOTO SOGYO HOLDINGS CO., LTD.
14-7 Nihonbashi Kodenmacho, Chuo-ku, Tokyo, 103-0001, Japan
Tel.: (81) 336659001
Web Site: https://www.hat-hd.co.jp
Year Founded: 1938
7570—(TKS)
Rev.: $1,028,734,130
Assets: $528,773,560
Liabilities: $322,415,970
Net Worth: $206,357,590
Earnings: $17,245,490
Fiscal Year-end: 03/31/24
Industrial Equipment Distr
N.A.I.C.S.: 423830
Teiichi Sakata *(Exec VP)*

HASHWANI GROUP
First Floor The Cotton Exchange Building I I Chundrigar Road, Karachi, Pakistan
Tel.: (92) 21 3241294649
Web Site:
http://www.hashwanigroup.com
Holding Services
N.A.I.C.S.: 551112
Akbar Ali Hashwani *(Chm)*

Subsidiaries:

Landmark Spinning Industries Limited (1)
The Cotton Exchange Building 1st Floor I I Chundrigar Road, Karachi, 75350, Pakistan
Tel.: (92) 2132412946
Web Site:
https://www.landmarkspinning.com
Assets: $473,064
Liabilities: $914,182
Net Worth: ($441,118)
Earnings: ($44,348)
Emp.: 3
Fiscal Year-end: 06/30/2023
Cotton Yarn Mfr
N.A.I.C.S.: 313110
Amin A. Hashwani *(CEO)*

HASSO PLATTNER VENTURES AFRICA (PTY) LTD.
First Floor Old Warehouse Building Black River Park, 2 Fir Street Observatory, Cape Town, 7925, South Africa
Tel.: (27) 21 486 1060
Web Site: http://www.hp-ventures.co.za
Privater Equity Firm
N.A.I.C.S.: 523999
Marc Balkin *(Partner)*

Subsidiaries:

MineRP (1)
Ground Floor 267 West Avenue, Centurion, 0157, South Africa
Tel.: (27) 879803100
Web Site: http://www.minerp.com
Sales Range: $150-199.9 Million
Emp.: 200
Mining Management Software Solutions
N.A.I.C.S.: 541511

Subsidiary (Non-US):

GIJIMAAST Americas Incorporated (2)
432 Westmount Ave Unit AB, Sudbury, P3A 5Z8, ON, Canada
Tel.: (705) 525-4774
Web Site: http://www.gijimaast.ca

HASSO PLATTNER VENTURES AFRICA (PTY) LTD.

Hasso Plattner Ventures Africa (Pty) Ltd.—(Continued)
Sales Range: $25-49.9 Million
Emp.: 10
Mining Software Consulting Services
N.A.I.C.S.: 541511

GijimaAst (Pty) Limited (2)
2 44 Denis St, Subiaco, 6008, WA, Australia
Tel.: (61) 863801719
Sales Range: $25-49.9 Million
Emp.: 6
Mining Software Consulting Services
N.A.I.C.S.: 541512

HASSO PLATTNER VENTURES MANAGEMENT GMBH
Rudolf-Breitscheid-Strabe 187, Potsdam, 14482, Germany
Tel.: (49) 331 97992 101
Web Site: http://www.hp-ventures.com
Year Founded: 2005
Sales Range: $10-24.9 Million
Emp.: 200
Venture Capital Investment Firm
N.A.I.C.S.: 523999
Rouven Westphal (Co-Mng Dir)

HASTI FINANCE LIMITED
No 14 Imperial Hotel Complex Near Albert Cinema Hall Whannels Road, Egmore, Chennai, 600 008, Tamil Nadu, India
Tel.: (91) 8655458399
Web Site:
https://www.hastifinance.com
Year Founded: 1994
531387—(BOM)
Rev.: $122,800
Assets: $2,659,527
Liabilities: $158,313
Net Worth: $2,501,214
Earnings: ($40,961)
Emp.: 3
Fiscal Year-end: 03/31/23
Financial Services
N.A.I.C.S.: 523999
Nitin Prabhudas Somani (Mng Dir)

HASTINGS TECHNOLOGY METALS LIMITED
Level 3 5 Mill Street, PO Box 6, 167 St Georges Terrace, Perth, 6000, WA, Australia
Tel.: (61) 861176118
Web Site:
https://www.hastingstechmetal.com
Year Founded: 2006
HAS—(ASX)
Rev.: $3,721,631
Assets: $320,515,013
Liabilities: $122,587,229
Net Worth: $197,927,784
Earnings: ($22,563,898)
Emp.: 3
Fiscal Year-end: 06/30/24
Other Metal Ore Mining
N.A.I.C.S.: 212290
Guy Robertson (Fin Dir & Co-Sec)

Subsidiaries:

Hastings Technology Metals Pte Ltd (1)
10 Anson Road 19-02 International Plaza, Singapore, 079903, Singapore
Tel.: (65) 62209220
Web Site: https://hastingstechmetals.com
Metal Products Mfr
N.A.I.C.S.: 332999

HAT SICAF S.P.A
Corso Europa 22, 20122, Milan, Italy
Tel.: (39) 02 89286200
Web Site: http://www.hat.it
Privater Equity Firm
N.A.I.C.S.: 523999

Ignazio Castiglioni (CEO)

Subsidiaries:

Orizzonte SGR S.p.A. (1)
Piazza Castello 113, 10121, Turin, Italy (70%)
Tel.: (39) 011 19703670
Web Site: http://www.orizzontesgr.it
Privater Equity Firm
N.A.I.C.S.: 523999
Aldo Napoli (VP & Pres-Exec Committee)

HATCH LTD.
Sheridan Science & Technology Park 2800 Speakman Drive, Mississauga, L5K 2R7, ON, Canada
Tel.: (905) 855-7600
Web Site: http://www.hatch.com
Year Founded: 1955
Sales Range: $600-649.9 Million
Emp.: 6,000
Engineering, Consulting & Other Services
N.A.I.C.S.: 541330
Kurt A. Strobele (Chm)

Subsidiaries:

Hatch Associates Pty. Ltd. (1)
152 Wharf St, PO Box 425, Brisbane, 4000, QLD, Australia (100%)
Tel.: (61) 738347777
Web Site: http://www.hatch.com.au
Sales Range: $150-199.9 Million
Emp.: 600
Engineering Services
N.A.I.C.S.: 541330

Hatch IAS (1)
7000 Industrial Blvd, Aliquippa, PA 15001
Tel.: (724) 375-5500
Web Site: http://www.hatchias.com
Industrial Automation Services
N.A.I.C.S.: 541512
Nigel Blackmore (Mgr-Sls)

HATCH64
468 Queen St E Suite 500, Toronto, M5A 1T7, ON, Canada
Tel.: (416) 363-1388
Web Site: http://hatch64.com
Year Founded: 1964
Emp.: 28
Advertising & Media Representation Agency
N.A.I.C.S.: 541810
Cynthia Jollymore (VP-Sls-Atlantic Canada, Manitoba & Saskatchewan)

HATCHASIA INC.
31st Street Corner 2nd Avenue Bonifacio Technology Center, Bonifacio Global City, Taguig, Philippines
Tel.: (63) 2 956 7777
Web Site: http://www.hatchasia.com
N.A.I.C.S.:
Kirk A. Arambulo (Pres & CEO)

Subsidiaries:

Silver Heritage Group Limited (1)
6/F The Phoenix 23 Luard Road, Wanchai, China (Hong Kong)
Tel.: (852) 21101684
Web Site: http://www.silverheritage.com.au
Casino Operator
N.A.I.C.S.: 721120
Paul Simmons (Sr VP-Casino Ops)

HATCHER GROUP LTD.
18/F Prosperity Tower 39 Queen's Road, Central, China (Hong Kong)
Tel.: (852) 2 200 7600 Ky
Web Site: http://www.vbg-group.com
Year Founded: 2016
8365—(HKG)
Rev.: $4,278,009
Assets: $8,957,016
Liabilities: $4,146,191
Net Worth: $4,810,825
Earnings: ($2,590,950)
Emp.: 18

Fiscal Year-end: 09/30/21
Financial Advisory Services
N.A.I.C.S.: 523940
Letty Ho Yan Wan (Chm)

Subsidiaries:

Baron Global Financial Canada Ltd. (1)
2250 - 1055 West Hastings Street, Vancouver, V6E 2E9, BC, Canada
Tel.: (604) 688-9588
Web Site: http://www.barongroupintl.com
Financial Services
N.A.I.C.S.: 523940
David Eaton (Chm)

VBG Consulting (Beijing) Co., Ltd. (1)
Rm 2-510 Building 1 Donggang Xinzuo 56 Fuqian Street, Nan faxin Shunyi District, Beijing, 101300, China
Tel.: (86) 1085911136
Financial Services
N.A.I.C.S.: 523940

HATEKS HATAY TEKSTIL ISLETMELERI A.S.
Otencay District E-5 Highway Street Outer Door No 21, Antakya, Hatay, Turkiye
Tel.: (90) 3264512400
Web Site: https://www.hateks.com.tr
Year Founded: 1973
HATEK—(IST)
Rev.: $24,767,275
Assets: $65,404,458
Liabilities: $26,619,455
Net Worth: $38,785,003
Earnings: ($5,163,275)
Fiscal Year-end: 12/31/23
Textile Product Mfr & Whslr
N.A.I.C.S.: 314999
Abud Abdo (Chm)

HATENA CO., LTD.
Aoyama Sunlight Building 3F 6-5-55 Minamiaoyama, Minato-ku, Tokyo, 107-0062, Japan
Tel.: (81) 752410170
Web Site: https://hatena.ne.jp
3930—(TKS)
Sales Range: Less than $1 Million
Data Processing Services
N.A.I.C.S.: 541513
Yoshiomi Kurisu (Pres)

HATHEWAY (TRACADIE) LTEE
3318 rue La Chapelle, Tracadie-Sheila, E1X 1G5, NB, Canada
Tel.: (506) 395-2208
Web Site: http://www.hatheway.com
Year Founded: 2001
Rev.: $49,477,473
Emp.: 200
New & Used Car Dealers
N.A.I.C.S.: 441110
Ian Hatheway (Owner & Pres)

HATHWAY BHAWANI CABLETEL & DATACOM LIMITED
1st Floor B Wing Jaywant Apartment Above SBI Bank 63 Tardeo Road, Santacruz East, Mumbai, 400034, India
Tel.: (91) 2223535107
Web Site:
https://www.hathwaybhawani.com
509073—(BOM)
Rev.: $426,317
Assets: $357,985
Liabilities: $113,909
Net Worth: $244,076
Earnings: $23,164
Emp.: 13
Fiscal Year-end: 03/31/23
Internet Providing Services
N.A.I.C.S.: 517111
Vatan Pathan (CEO)

INTERNATIONAL PUBLIC

HATHWAY CABLE & DATACOM LTD.
802 8th Floor Interface-11, Link Road, Malad West, Mumbai, 400064, India
Tel.: (91) 2268768200
Web Site: https://www.hathway.com
Year Founded: 1959
HATHWAY—(NSE)
Rev.: $255,831,030
Assets: $616,854,420
Liabilities: $71,135,610
Net Worth: $545,718,810
Earnings: $34,568,625
Emp.: 343
Fiscal Year-end: 03/31/21
Cable TV & Internet Services
N.A.I.C.S.: 516210
Sridhar Gorthi (Chm)

HATSUHO SHOUJI CO., LTD.
2nd Floor Maruyama Nissay Building 2-14-21 Nishiki, Naka-ku, Nagoya, 460-0003, Aichi, Japan
Tel.: (81) 522221066
Web Site: https://www.hatsuho.co.jp
Year Founded: 1958
74250—(TKS)
Rev.: $210,056,161
Assets: $139,471,424
Liabilities: $81,539,478
Net Worth: $57,931,946
Earnings: $5,642,550
Emp.: 255
Fiscal Year-end: 12/31/22
Steel Product Distr
N.A.I.C.S.: 423390
Satoru Saito (Pres)

HATSUN AGRO PRODUCTS LTD
Plot No 14 Tamil Nadu Housing Board A Road, Sholinganallur, Chennai, 600119, India
Tel.: (91) 4424501622
Web Site: https://www.hap.in
531531—(BOM)
Rev.: $990,652,654
Assets: $511,987,558
Liabilities: $315,335,229
Net Worth: $196,652,329
Earnings: $22,639,371
Emp.: 10,905
Fiscal Year-end: 03/31/23
Fluid Milk Mfrs
N.A.I.C.S.: 311514
R. G. Chandramogan (Chm)

HATTEN LAND LIMITED
53 Mohamed Sultan Road 3-01, Singapore, 238993, Singapore
Tel.: (65) 64700619 SG
Web Site:
https://www.hattenland.com.sg
Year Founded: 1993
PH0—(CAT)
Rev.: $7,768,677
Assets: $240,150,476
Liabilities: $223,284,656
Net Worth: $16,865,820
Earnings: ($7,277,249)
Emp.: 129
Fiscal Year-end: 06/30/23
Property Developer
N.A.I.C.S.: 531311
Siong Foh Chong (Head-Dev Mgmt)

HATTINGTON CAPITAL LLP
22-23 Old Burlington Street Fourth Floor, London, W1S 2JJ, United Kingdom
Tel.: (44) 20 3006 8440 UK
Web Site: http://www.hattington.com
Year Founded: 2013

AND PRIVATE COMPANIES

Private Equity & Real Estate Investment Firm
N.A.I.C.S.: 523999
Subsidiaries:

Dobbies Garden Centres Limited (1)
Melville Nursery, Lasswade, EH18 1AZ, United Kingdom
Tel.: (44) 1316631941
Web Site: http://www.dobbies.com
Garden Center Operator
N.A.I.C.S.: 444240
Matthew Bailey *(Mgr-Store)*

Subsidiary (Domestic):

Dobbies Grovelands (2)
166 Hyde End Road, Shinfield, RG29ER, Reading, United Kingdom
Tel.: (44) 01189884822
Web Site: http://www.dobbies.com
Nursery & Garden Centers
N.A.I.C.S.: 444240
Paul Hilliam *(Mgr-Store)*

Edinburgh Butterfly & Insect World (2)
Melville Nurseries, Lasswade, EH18 1AZ, Midlothian, United Kingdom
Tel.: (44) 1316634932
Web Site: http://www.edinburgh-butterfly-world.co.uk
All Other Amusement & Recreation Industries
N.A.I.C.S.: 713990
Andrew McDonald *(Gen Mgr)*

HATTON PLANTATIONS PLC
168 2nd Floor Negombo Road, Peliyagoda, Wattala, Sri Lanka
Tel.: (94) 114537700
Web Site: https://hattonplantations.lk
Year Founded: 2017
HPL—(COL)
Rev.: $25,658,330
Assets: $23,652,778
Liabilities: $8,588,396
Net Worth: $15,064,382
Earnings: $5,557,581
Emp.: 5,329
Fiscal Year-end: 03/31/23
Tea Mfr
N.A.I.C.S.: 311920
Menaka Athukorala *(Mng Dir)*

HAUHINCO MASCHINENFABRIK G. HAUSHERR JOCHUMS GMBH & CO. KG
Beisenbruchstrasse 10, 45549, Sprockhovel, Germany
Tel.: (49) 23247050
Web Site: http://www.hauhinco.de
Year Founded: 1908
Rev.: $24,230,000
Emp.: 104
Hydraulics Mfr
N.A.I.C.S.: 333248
Andrej Dyck *(Mgr-Sls-GUS Reg)*

Subsidiaries:

Hauhinco LP (1)
1325 Evans City Rd, Evans City, PA 16033
Tel.: (724) 789-7050
Web Site: http://www.hauhinco.com
Construction Machinery & Equipment Distr
N.A.I.C.S.: 423810
Ron Osselborn *(Pres)*

HAULOTTE GROUP SA
Rue Emile Zola BP 9, FR-42420, Lorette, France
Tel.: (33) 477292424
Web Site: http://www.haulotte.com
PIG—(EUR)
Rev.: $656,428,880
Assets: $748,684,439
Liabilities: $534,113,965
Net Worth: $214,570,473
Earnings: ($16,492,553)
Emp.: 1,900
Fiscal Year-end: 12/31/22

People & Material Lifting Equipment & Earth Moving Equipment Mfr
N.A.I.C.S.: 333120
Pierre Saubot *(Chm)*

Subsidiaries:

Acarlar Dis Ticaret Ve Makina Sanayi A S. (1)
Anadolu Mah Kanuni Cad No 30, Orhanli Beldesi Tuzla, 34956, Istanbul, Turkiye
Tel.: (90) 2165814949
Web Site: https://www.acarlarmakine.com
Boom Lift Equipment Distr
N.A.I.C.S.: 423830
Serkan Acar *(Gen Mgr)*

Bil-Jax, Inc. (1)
125 Taylor Pkwy, Archbold, OH 43502-9122
Tel.: (419) 445-8915
Web Site: http://www.biljax.com
Sales Range: $50-74.9 Million
Emp.: 125
Scaffolding Services
N.A.I.C.S.: 332323

Farissia BTP Eurl (1)
Zone d'activite 29 N 3, Zeralda, Algiers, Algeria
Tel.: (213) 23208215
Web Site: http://www.farissiabtp.dz
Boom Lift Sale & Rental Services
N.A.I.C.S.: 532490

Haulotte Argentina S.A. (1)
Ruta Panamericana Km 34 300 Ramal Escobar, Grand Bourg, 1615, Buenos Aires, Argentina
Tel.: (54) 8002200920
Web Site: https://www.haulotte.com.ar
Industrial Machinery Equipment Distr
N.A.I.C.S.: 423830

Haulotte Australia Pty Ltd. (1)
51 Portlink Drive, Dandenong South, 3175, VIC, Australia
Tel.: (61) 1300207683
Web Site: https://www.haulotte.com.au
Emp.: 1,500
Material Lifting Equipment Mfr
N.A.I.C.S.: 333998

Haulotte Chile Spa (1)
Panamericana Norte height Km 21 5 Cruce c/Lo Pinto Hill, Colina, 9361433, Santiago, Chile
Tel.: (56) 223727630
Web Site: https://www.haulotte-chile.com
Scaffold & Event Product Mfr
N.A.I.C.S.: 332323
Ernesto Martinez *(Sls Mgr)*

Haulotte Do Brazil Ltd.a (1)
Av Alameda Caiapos 589, Sao Paulo, CEP 06460-110, Brazil
Tel.: (55) 1141964300
Web Site: https://www.haulotte.com.br
Material Lifting Equipment Mfr
N.A.I.C.S.: 333998
Marcelo Nottolini Racca *(Gen Mgr)*

Haulotte France Sarl. (1)
601 rue Nicephore Niepce Parc des Lumieres, 69800, Saint Priest, France
Tel.: (33) 472880570
Web Site: https://www.haulotte.fr
Emp.: 62
Industrial Machinery Equipment Distr
N.A.I.C.S.: 423830
Laurent Royannez *(Gen Mgr)*

Haulotte Hubarbeitsbuhnen GmbH (1)
Ehrenkirchener Strasse 2, DE-79427, Eschbach, Germany
Tel.: (49) 763450670
Web Site: https://www.haulotte.de
Material Lifting Equipment Mfr
N.A.I.C.S.: 333998
Alexandre Saubot *(Dir-Publication)*

Haulotte Iberica S.L (1)
C/ Argentina N 13 P I La Garena, Alcala de Henares, 28806, Madrid, Spain
Tel.: (34) 912158444
Web Site: https://www.haulotte.com.es
Material Lifting Equipment Mfr
N.A.I.C.S.: 333998
Mariola Enciso *(Controller-Fin)*

Haulotte India Private Limited (1)
Unit No 1205 12th Floor Bhumiraj Costarica, Navi Mumbai, 400705, Maharashtra, India
Tel.: (91) 2266739531
Web Site: https://www.haulotte.in
Material Lifting Equipment Mfr
N.A.I.C.S.: 333998
Vijisha Nair *(Coord-Sls)*

Haulotte Italia S.R.L. (1)
Via Lombardia 15, 20098, San Giuliano Milanese, Italy
Tel.: (39) 0298970110
Web Site: https://www.haulotte.it
Material Lifting Equipment Mfr
N.A.I.C.S.: 333998

Haulotte Mexico S.A. de C.V. (1)
Calle 40 Sur esq 13 Este, Civac, CP 62578, Jiutepec, Morelos, Mexico
Tel.: (52) 7773215907
Web Site: https://www.haulotte.com.mx
Material Lifting Equipment Mfr
N.A.I.C.S.: 333998

Haulotte Middle East FZE (1)
Dubai Airport Free Zone, PO Box 293881, Dubai, United Arab Emirates
Tel.: (971) 42997735
Web Site: https://www.haulotte.ae
Material Lifting Equipment Mfr
N.A.I.C.S.: 333998
Azzam Hunjul *(Mng Dir)*

Haulotte Netherlands B.V (1)
Koopvaardijweg 26, 4906 CV, Oosterhout, Netherlands
Tel.: (31) 162670707
Web Site: https://www.haulotte.nl
Material Lifting Equipment Mfr
N.A.I.C.S.: 333998
Govert Van Oord *(Gen Mgr)*

Haulotte North America Manufacturing L.L.C (1)
3409 Chandler Creek Rd, Virginia Beach, VA 23453
Tel.: (757) 689-2146
Web Site: https://www.haulotte-usa.com
Scaffold & Event Product Mfr
N.A.I.C.S.: 332323
Claude Fuger *(Mng Dir)*

Haulotte Polska Sp. z o.o. (1)
Ul Graniczna 22, Janki, 05-090, Raszyn, Poland
Tel.: (48) 227200880
Web Site: https://www.haulotte.pl
Material Lifting Equipment Mfr
N.A.I.C.S.: 333998

Haulotte Scandinavia AB (1)
Taljegardsgatan 12, 431 53, Molndal, Sweden
Tel.: (46) 317443290
Web Site: http://www.haulotte.se
Material Lifting Equipment Mfr
N.A.I.C.S.: 333998
Robert Magnusson *(Gen Mgr)*

Haulotte Shanghai Co., Ltd. (1)
7 Workshop No 191 Hua Jin Road, Minhang District, Shanghai, 201108, China
Tel.: (86) 2164426610
Material Lifting Equipment Mfr
N.A.I.C.S.: 333998
Rachel Chang *(Mgr-Credit-Asia Pacific)*

Haulotte Singapore Pte Ltd. (1)
51 Changi Business Park Central 2 09-10/11, Singapore, 486066, Singapore
Tel.: (65) 65466150
Web Site: https://www.haulotte.sg
Material Lifting Equipment Mfr
N.A.I.C.S.: 333998
John Chan *(Mgr-Svc-Asia)*

Haulotte Trading (Shanghai) Co., Ltd. (1)
Shanghai Huajin Road No 7 191 Factory Building, Minhang District, Shanghai, 201108, China
Tel.: (86) 2164426610
Web Site: http://www.haulotte.cn
Material Lifting Equipment Mfr
N.A.I.C.S.: 333998
Rachel Chang *(Mgr-Credit)*

Haulotte UK Ltd. (1)

HAVELL'S INDIA LTD.
1 Gravelly Way, Four Ashes, Wolverhampton, WV10 7GW, United Kingdom
Tel.: (44) 1216199753
Web Site: https://www.haulotte.co.uk
Material Lifting Equipment Mfr
N.A.I.C.S.: 333998
Natalie Reynolds *(Gen Mgr)*

Haulotte Vostok OOO (1)
Ryabinovaya str 61A bld 1, Moscow, 121471, Russia
Tel.: (7) 4952215302
Web Site: https://www.haulotte.ru
Material Lifting Equipment Mfr
N.A.I.C.S.: 333998

Michael Raymond Nigeria Ltd. (1)
7Abraham Avenue By Emmanuel Plaza Junction Off Elioparanwo Road, Port Harcourt, Nigeria
Tel.: (234) 7015859099
Web Site: http://www.mrnigltd.com
Construction Services
N.A.I.C.S.: 236220

Pie Tnufa Ltd. (1)
Hamaayan St 4, Modi'in-Maccabim-Re'ut, Israel
Tel.: (972) 86187977
Web Site: http://www.pietnufa.com
Mini Crane Lifting Product Distr
N.A.I.C.S.: 423830

Sterling Access CC (1)
Marelden Industrial Park Stand 81 Walter Sisulu Road, eMalahleni, Mpumalanga, 1035, South Africa
Tel.: (27) 799069763
Web Site: http://www.sterlingaccess.co.za
Boom Lift Equipment Distr
N.A.I.C.S.: 423830
Duanne Bodenstein *(Owner)*

HAUS TALK, INC.
Unit 701 Orient Square Bldg Emerald Ave, Ortigas Center, Pasig, Philippines
Tel.: (63) 286348712 PH
Web Site: https://www.haustalk.com.ph
Year Founded: 2004
HTI—(PHI)
Rev.: $18,953,297
Assets: $90,632,365
Liabilities: $27,369,774
Net Worth: $63,262,591
Earnings: $4,381,094
Emp.: 118
Fiscal Year-end: 12/31/23
Real Estate Development Services
N.A.I.C.S.: 531390
Terence Restituto D. Madlambayan *(Chm)*

HAUTE-NORMANDIE VEHICULES INDUSTRIELS
Rouen Multimarchandises Ii Rue Du Clos Tellier, 76800, Saint Etienne-du-Rouvray, France
Tel.: (33) 235644242
Web Site: http://www.vehicules-industriels.net
Rev.: $23,500,000
Emp.: 43
New & Used Car Dealers
N.A.I.C.S.: 441110
Bruno Dufrechou *(Mgr-Pur)*

HAUTECOEUR FRANCE
1D rue du General de Gaulle, BP 14121, Dinsheim sur Bruche, 67124, Molsheim, France
Tel.: (33) 388494300
Web Site: http://www.hautecoeur.com
Rev.: $23,100,000
Emp.: 50
Furniture Designer & Mfr
N.A.I.C.S.: 337126
Marie-Elisabeth Strub *(Pres)*

HAVELL'S INDIA LTD.
QRG Towers 2D Sec-126 Express

HAVELL'S INDIA LTD.

Havell's India Ltd.—(Continued)
Way, Noida, 201304, UP, India
Tel.: (91) 1204771000
Web Site: https://www.havells.com
Year Founded: 1958
HAVELLS—(BOM)
Rev.: $1,924,502,580
Assets: $1,436,418,165
Liabilities: $617,023,680
Net Worth: $819,394,485
Earnings: $163,318,155
Emp.: 5,970
Fiscal Year-end: 03/31/22
Electrical & Power Distribution Equipment Mfr
N.A.I.C.S.: 335999
Anil Rai Gupta *(Chm & Mng Dir)*

Subsidiaries:

Havell's Holdings International,
LLC (1)
4 Manhattanville Rd, Purchase, NY 10577
Tel.: (914) 417-6900
Web Site: http://www.havells-sylvania.com
Sales Range: $600-649.9 Million
Holding Company; Lighting Fixtures Mfr
N.A.I.C.S.: 551112

Subsidiary (Domestic):

CML Innovative Technologies (2)
147 Central Ave, Hackensack, NJ 07601-3426
Tel.: (201) 489-8989
Web Site: http://www.cml-it.com
Sales Range: $350-399.9 Million
Emp.: 1,800
LED Lighting Fixtures & Miniature Lighting Components Mfr
N.A.I.C.S.: 335139
Don Faul *(VP)*

Division (Non-US):

Sylvania Europe Holding Co. Ltd.
(German Branch) (2)
Am Prime Parc 17, D-65479, Raunheim, Germany
Tel.: (49) 6142913670
Web Site: http://www.havells-sylvania.com
Holding Company
N.A.I.C.S.: 551112

Subsidiary (Domestic):

Havell's Sylvania (Germany)
GmbH (3)
Graf-Zeppelin-Strasse 9-12, D-91056, Erlangen, Germany
Tel.: (49) 9131793500
Web Site: http://www.sylvania-lighting.de
Sales Range: $150-199.9 Million
Emp.: 580
Residential, Industrial & Commercial Lighting Fixtures Mfr
N.A.I.C.S.: 335131

Subsidiary (Non-US):

Havell's Sylvania Netherlands
b.v. (3)
PO Box 5651, 4801 EB, Breda, Netherlands
Tel.: (31) 767504444
Web Site: http://www.havells-sylvania.com
Sales Range: $1-9.9 Million
Emp.: 75
Residential Lighting Fixture Mfr
N.A.I.C.S.: 335131

Havell's Sylvania-Concord:marlin (3)
Avis Way, Newhaven, BN9 0ED, E Sussex, United Kingdom
Tel.: (44) 1273515811
Web Site: http://www.concordmarlin.com
Sales Range: $100-124.9 Million
Emp.: 250
High-End Architectural Lighting Fixtures Mfr
N.A.I.C.S.: 335132
Bridget Anderson *(Mgr-Fin)*

SLI France S.A. (3)
11 rue de Victor Grignard, F-42000, Saint Etienne, France
Tel.: (33) 4 7792 2730
Web Site: http://www.havells-sylvania.com

Residential, Commercial & Industrial Lighting Fixtures Mfr
N.A.I.C.S.: 335131

SLI Sylvania S.A. (3)
Los Llanos de Jerez 17, 28820, Coslada, Spain (100%)
Tel.: (34) 916699000
Web Site: http://www.havells-sylvania.com
Sales Range: $25-49.9 Million
Emp.: 50
Lighting Fixtures Whslr
N.A.I.C.S.: 423620
Eduardo Fuentes *(Mgr-Mktg)*

Sylvania N.V. (3)
Industrie Park 13, Tienen, 3300, Belgium
Tel.: (32) 16800211
Web Site: http://www.havells-sylvania.com
Sales Range: $125-149.9 Million
Emp.: 40
Halogen Lighting Fixtures Mfr
N.A.I.C.S.: 335131
John Deriks *(Plant Mgr)*

Havell's India Ltd. - Alwar Works (1)
A-461/462 MIA, Alwar, 301030, Rajasthan, India
Tel.: (91) 144 3048100
Electric Equipment Mfr
N.A.I.C.S.: 335999

Havell's India Ltd. - Faridabad
Works (1)
14/3 Mathura Road, Faridabad, India
Tel.: (91) 129 3056100
Electric Equipment Mfr
N.A.I.C.S.: 335999

Havell's India Ltd. - Haridwar
Works (1)
Plot No 2A Sector 10 Sidcul Industrial Area, Haridwar, 249403, Uttarakhand, India
Tel.: (91) 1334308202
Electric Equipment Mfr
N.A.I.C.S.: 335999

Havells Sylvania (Guangzhou) Enterprise Ltd (1)
11th Floor No 163 Pingyun Road West
Huangpu Ave, Tianhe District, Guangzhou, 510656, China
Tel.: (86) 20 3815 1138
Web Site: http://www.havells-sylvania.com
Electric Equipment Mfr
N.A.I.C.S.: 335999

Havells Sylvania Argentina S.A. (1)
Arias 3751-Piso 21, C1430CRG, Buenos Aires, Argentina
Tel.: (54) 1145464200
Web Site: http://www.sylvania.com.ar
Emp.: 2
Lighting Equipment Mfr & Distr
N.A.I.C.S.: 335139
Alejandro Saraintaris *(Office Mgr)*

Havells Sylvania Belgium
B.V.B.A. (1)
Noorderlaan 105c, Antwerp, 2030, Belgium
Tel.: (32) 3 610 44 44
Sales Range: $25-49.9 Million
Emp.: 45
Electric Equipment Mfr
N.A.I.C.S.: 335999
Marc Elst *(Gen Mgr)*

Havells Sylvania Brasil Iluminacao
Ltda. (1)
Avenida Adolfo Pinheiro Nr 1000 Cj 002 Edificio Bueno de Moraes, Sao Paulo, Brazil
Tel.: (55) 1131332419
Web Site: http://www.sylvania.com.br
Sales Range: Less than $1 Million
Emp.: 25
Lighting Equipment Mfr & Distr
N.A.I.C.S.: 335139

Havells Sylvania Colombia S.A. (1)
Calle 57B Sur No 72 A 23, Bogota, Colombia
Tel.: (57) 1 7825200
Electric Equipment Mfr
N.A.I.C.S.: 335999

Havells Sylvania Costa Rica S.A. (1)
Zona Industrial de Pavas,), San Jose, Costa Rica
Tel.: (506) 22 107 678

Web Site: http://www.havells-sylvania.com
Electric Equipment Mfr
N.A.I.C.S.: 335999
Mauricio Ulloa *(Controller-Fin)*

Havells Sylvania Dubai FZCO (1)
Dubai Air Port Free Zone ILU-I15, PO Box 54350, Dubai, 54350, United Arab Emirates
Tel.: (971) 42998141
Sales Range: $25-49.9 Million
Emp.: 15
Lighting Fixture Mfr
N.A.I.C.S.: 335132

Havells Sylvania Europe Ltd (1)
Longbow House 14-20 Chiswell Street, London, EC1Y 4TW, United Kingdom
Tel.: (44) 2070119700
Web Site: http://www.havells-sylvania.com
Sales Range: $50-74.9 Million
Emp.: 150
Electrical Component Mfr
N.A.I.C.S.: 335999

Havells Sylvania Fixtures UK
Ltd. (1)
Avis Way, Newhaven, Newhaven, BN9 0ED, East Sussex, United Kingdom
Tel.: (44) 870 606 2030
Web Site: http://www.havells-sylvania.com
Sales Range: $50-74.9 Million
Emp.: 200
Electric Equipment Mfr
N.A.I.C.S.: 335999
Malcolm James *(Gen Mgr)*

Havells Sylvania France S.A.S. (1)
Le Signac 1-3 Avenue du General de Gaulle, 92230, Gennevilliers, France
Tel.: (33) 1 55 51 11 00
Electric Equipment Mfr
N.A.I.C.S.: 335999

Havells Sylvania Greece
A.E.E.E. (1)
Menelaou 153, Argyroupolis, 164 51, Athens, Greece
Tel.: (30) 2109966561
Web Site: http://www.havells-sylvania.com
Sales Range: $25-49.9 Million
Emp.: 10
Electric Equipment Mfr
N.A.I.C.S.: 335999
Alex Liakatas *(Gen Mgr)*

Havells Sylvania Guatemala S.A. (1)
20 Calle Final Km 6 8 Carretera a Muxbal Conplejo Pradera Ofibodegas, Bodega 18, Guatemala, 1012, Guatemala
Tel.: (502) 2 387 5323
Electric Equipment Mfr
N.A.I.C.S.: 335999
Jose Luis Perez *(Gen Mgr)*

Havells Sylvania Italy S.p.A. (1)
Piazza Don Enrico Mapelli 75, Sesto San Giovanni, Italy
Tel.: (39) 02 24 12 58 11
Web Site: http://www.havells-sylvania.com
Electrical Component Mfr
N.A.I.C.S.: 335999

Havells Sylvania Lighting France
SAS (1)
1 Av du Gal de Gaulle, 92230, Gennevilliers, France
Tel.: (33) 155 511 100
Web Site: http://www.havells-sylvania.com
Sales Range: $100-124.9 Million
Emp.: 300
Lighting Fixture Mfr
N.A.I.C.S.: 335132
Julien Arnal *(Pres)*

Havells Sylvania N.V. (1)
De Los Jazmines N53-147 y Pasaje San Carlos Sector Brasilia 2, Quito, Ecuador
Tel.: (593) 2 328 4407
Web Site: http://www.havells-sylvania.com
Emp.: 35
Electrical Equipment Distr
N.A.I.C.S.: 335999
Hector Herrera *(Branch Mgr)*

Havells Sylvania Spain Logistics
S.L. (1)
Caleruega 102, Madrid, 28033, Spain
Tel.: (34) 916699000
Logistic Services

INTERNATIONAL PUBLIC

N.A.I.C.S.: 541614

Havells Sylvania Spain S.A. (1)
Caleruega 102, Caleruega 102, Madrid, Spain
Tel.: (34) 916699000
Web Site: http://www.havells-sylvania.com
Sales Range: $25-49.9 Million
Emp.: 50
Electric Equipment Mfr
N.A.I.C.S.: 335999

Havells Sylvania Sweden A.B. (1)
Uppkoparvagen 7, 120 44, Arsta, Sweden
Tel.: (46) 855632200
Sales Range: $25-49.9 Million
Emp.: 13
Electric Equipment Mfr
N.A.I.C.S.: 335999
Daniel Selea *(Gen Mgr)*

Havells Sylvania Switzerland
A.G. (1)
Schaffhauserstrasse 470, 8052, Zurich, Switzerland
Tel.: (41) 443053180
Web Site: http://www.havells-sylvania.com
Electric Equipment Mfr
N.A.I.C.S.: 335999

Havells Sylvania Tunisia
S.A.R.L. (1)
Zone Industriel El Baten, BP 203A, 3140, Al Qayrawan, Tunisia
Tel.: (216) 77306625
Web Site: http://www.havells-sylvania.com
Sales Range: $50-74.9 Million
Emp.: 250
Electric Equipment Mfr
N.A.I.C.S.: 335999
John Derikx *(Mng Dir)*

Havells Sylvania UK Ltd. (1)
Avis Way, Newhaven, Lewes, BN9 0ED, East Sussex, United Kingdom
Tel.: (44) 870 606 2030
Web Site: http://www.havells-sylvania.com
Emp.: 200
Electric Equipment Mfr
N.A.I.C.S.: 335999

Havells Sylvania Venezuela C.A. (1)
Carretera Nacional Guarenas-Guatire, Las Flores Local D, Guatire, 1221, Estado Miranda, Venezuela
Tel.: (58) 212 381 0452
Web Site: http://www.havells-sylvania.com
Emp.: 3
Electric Equipment Mfr
N.A.I.C.S.: 335999
Desmond Boo *(Office Mgr)*

HAVELLANDISCHE EISEN-BAHN AG

Schonwalder Allee 51, 13587, Berlin, Germany
Tel.: (49) 303759810
Web Site: http://www.hvle.de
Year Founded: 1892
Rev.: $23,725,680
Emp.: 190
Private Railway Services
N.A.I.C.S.: 482111
Martin Wischner *(Member-Exec Bd)*

Subsidiaries:

Bossdorf & Kerstan GmbH (1)
Bahnhofstr 1, 15907, Lubben, Spreewald, Germany
Tel.: (49) 3546179240
Web Site: http://www.buk-eisenbahn.de
Railway Freight Transportation Services
N.A.I.C.S.: 482111

Kompetenznetz Rail Berlin Brandenburg GmbH (1)
Adlerstrasse 2 Geb 61, 14774, Brandenburg, Germany
Tel.: (49) 338180402410
Web Site: http://www.knrbb.de
Railway Freight Transportation Services
N.A.I.C.S.: 482111
Michael Kluge *(Project Mgr)*

Rail & Logistik Center Wustermark
GmbH & Co. KG (1)

Bahnhofstrasse 2, 14641, Wustermark, Germany
Tel.: (49) 3323422430
Web Site: http://www.rlcw.de
Logistics Consulting Servies
N.A.I.C.S.: 541614

HAVELOCK EUROPA PLC
Havelock House John Smith Business Park Grantsmuir Road, Kirkcaldy, KY2 6NA, United Kingdom
Tel.: (44) 1592 643883
Web Site:
   http://www.havelockeuropa.com
Rev.: $76,241,716
Assets: $38,428,664
Liabilities: $31,605,538
Net Worth: $6,823,125
Earnings: $149,201
Emp.: 414
Fiscal Year-end: 12/31/16
Educational & Retail Interiors Designer, Mfr & Installer; Point of Sale Merchandising Displays Printer
N.A.I.C.S.: 541410
Shaun Allen Ormrod (CEO)

Subsidiaries:

ESA McIntosh Limited (1)
Mitchelston Dr, Kirkcaldy, KY1 3LX, Fife, United Kingdom
Tel.: (44) 1592656200
Web Site: http://www.esamcintosh.co.uk
Sales Range: $50-74.9 Million
Emp.: 250
Furniture Mfr
N.A.I.C.S.: 337127
Lynda Dean (Project Coord)

Stage Systems Limited (1)
Prince William Rd, Loughborough, LE11 5GU, Leics, United Kingdom
Tel.: (44) 1509611021
Web Site: http://www.stagesystems.co.uk
Sales Range: $25-49.9 Million
Emp.: 28
Design & Installation of Stage Systems
N.A.I.C.S.: 541410
Edward Fuller (Gen Mgr)

TeacherBoards (1985) Limited (1)
Airedale Business Ctr, Skipton, BD23 2TZ, North Yorkshire, United Kingdom
Tel.: (44) 1756700501
Web Site: http://www.teacherboards.co.uk
Sales Range: $25-49.9 Million
Emp.: 54
Teaching Equipment Mfr
N.A.I.C.S.: 337127
Belinda Chapman (Mgr-Sls)

HAVELSAN HAVA ELEKTRONIK SANAYI VE TICARET AS
Mustafa Kemal Mahallesi 2120 Cad No 39, Cankaya, 06510, Ankara, Turkiye
Tel.: (90) 312 219 57 87
Web Site: http://www.havelsan.com.tr
Year Founded: 1982
Sales Range: $125-149.9 Million
Emp.: 1,140
Navigation System & Equipment Mfr
N.A.I.C.S.: 334511
Ahmet Hamdi Atalay (CEO & Gen Mgr)

Subsidiaries:

Quantum3d Inc. (1)
1759 McCarthy Blvd, Milpitas, CA 95035
Tel.: (408) 600-2562
Web Site: http://www.quantum3d.com
Emp.: 50
Real-Time Visual Computing Solutions Developer & Mfr
N.A.I.C.S.: 334413
Murat Kose (CFO & COO)

HAVILA HOLDING AS
Mjolstadnesvegen 24, 6092, Fosnavag, Norway

Tel.: (47) 70084500 NO
Web Site: http://www.havila.no
Holding Company Freight Shipping & Ship Building Service
N.A.I.C.S.: 551112
Per Rolf Saevik (Owner)

Subsidiaries:

Fjord1 ASA (1)
Strandavegen 15, 6905, Floro, Norway
Tel.: (47) 57757000
Web Site: https://www.fjord1.no
Rev.: $264,169,222
Assets: $949,631,535
Liabilities: $712,243,396
Net Worth: $237,388,140
Earnings: $12,702,106
Emp.: 1,201
Fiscal Year-end: 12/31/2021
Tour Management Services
N.A.I.C.S.: 713990
Dagfinn Neteland (CEO)

Subsidiary (Domestic):

Bolsones Verft AS (2)
Fannestrandvegen 66, 6416, Molde, Norway
Tel.: (47) 71206400
Web Site: http://www.bolsonesverft.no
Shipyard Building Services
N.A.I.C.S.: 237990

Havila Shipping ASA (1)
(50.5%)
Tel.: (47) 70080900
Web Site: https://www.havilashipping.no
Sales Range: $50-74.9 Million
Emp.: 544
Offshore Marine Services
N.A.I.C.S.: 483111
Njal Saevik (CEO)

HAVILA KYSTRUTEN AS
Mjolstadnesvegen, 6092, Fosnavag, Norway
Tel.: (47) 70007070
Web Site:
   https://www.havilavoyages.com
Year Founded: 1975
HKY—(EUR)
Rev.: $5,207,058
Assets: $388,812,247
Liabilities: $272,673,024
Net Worth: $116,139,223
Earnings: ($12,856,554)
Emp.: 310
Fiscal Year-end: 12/31/21
Transportation Services
N.A.I.C.S.: 488510
Arne Johan Dale (CFO)

HAVILAH RESOURCES LIMITED
PO Box 3, Adelaide, 5063, SA, Australia
Tel.: (61) 871113627 AU
Web Site: https://www.havilah-resources.com.au
Year Founded: 1996
HAV—(ASX)
Rev.: $5,875
Assets: $35,801,125
Liabilities: $1,134,006
Net Worth: $34,667,119
Earnings: $3,722,143
Fiscal Year-end: 07/31/24
Gold & Metals Exploration
N.A.I.C.S.: 212220
Christopher William Giles (Dir-Technical)

Subsidiaries:

Geothermal Resources Limited (1)
31 Flemington Street, Glenside, 5065, SA, Australia
Tel.: (61) 883389292
Web Site:
   http://www.havilah-resources.com.au
Rev.: $82,918
Assets: $2,326,073
Liabilities: $703,378

Net Worth: $1,622,696
Earnings: ($160,638)
Emp.: 3
Geothermal Energy Exploration
N.A.I.C.S.: 237130

Neo Oil Pty Ltd (1)
99 Bathhurst Street, Sydney, 2000, NSW, Australia
Tel.: (61) 416267645
Precious Metal Exploration Services
N.A.I.C.S.: 213114

HAVIX CORPORATION
3-5-7 Fukumitsu-Higashi, Gifu, 502-0813, Japan
Tel.: (81) 582963911
Web Site: https://www.havix.co.jp
Year Founded: 1950
3895—(TKS)
Rev.: $87,278,440
Assets: $86,557,950
Liabilities: $42,066,040
Net Worth: $44,491,910
Earnings: $4,455,140
Emp.: 204
Fiscal Year-end: 03/31/24
Fabric & Paper Mfr & Distr
N.A.I.C.S.: 313230

HAVN LIFE SCIENCES, INC.
605-130 Brew Street, Port Moody, V3H 0E3, BC, Canada
Tel.: (604) 370-9520
Web Site: https://www.havnlife.com
HAVN—(CNSX)
Sales Range: Less than $1 Million
Biotechnology Research & Development Services
N.A.I.C.S.: 541714
Vic Neufeld (Chm)

HAVSFRUN INVESTMENT AB
Nybrogatan 6, PO Box 5855, 10240, Stockholm, Sweden
Tel.: (46) 850677700
Web Site: https://www.havsfrun.se
Year Founded: 1987
HAVB—(OMX)
Rev.: $1,063,063
Assets: $12,878,511
Liabilities: $121,760
Net Worth: $12,756,751
Earnings: ($471,119)
Emp.: 3
Fiscal Year-end: 12/31/22
Investment Services
N.A.I.C.S.: 523999
Jonas Israelsson (CEO)

Subsidiaries:

Havsfrun Capital AB (1)
Strandvagen 1, 114 51, Stockholm, Sweden
Tel.: (46) 850677700
Sales Range: $50-74.9 Million
Emp.: 6
Mutual Fund Management Services
N.A.I.C.S.: 525910
Claes Werkell (CEO)

HAW PAR CORPORATION LIMITED
401 Commonwealth Drive 03-03 Haw Par Technocentre, Singapore, 149598, Singapore
Tel.: (65) 63379102
Web Site: https://www.hawpar.com
Year Founded: 1969
HAWPY—(OTCIQ)
Rev.: $164,483,049
Assets: $2,226,533,365
Liabilities: $48,319,590
Net Worth: $2,178,213,775
Earnings: $90,425,022
Emp.: 469
Fiscal Year-end: 12/31/20
Pharmaceuticals Mfr & Trader; Leisure Products Sales & Services; Property Manager

N.A.I.C.S.: 325412
Ee Lim Wee (Pres & CEO)

Subsidiaries:

Brunswick Haw Par Holdings Pte Ltd. (1)
401 Commonwealth Drive, 03-03 Haw Par Technocentre, Singapore, 149598, Singapore (100%)
Tel.: (65) 63379102
Web Site: http://www.hawpar.com
Sales Range: $25-49.9 Million
Emp.: 200
Business Support Services
N.A.I.C.S.: 561499

Haw Par Healthcare Limited (1)
401 Commonwealth Drive 03-03 Haw Par Technocentre, Singapore, 149598, Singapore (100%)
Tel.: (65) 63379102
Web Site: https://www.tigerbalm.com
Sales Range: $50-74.9 Million
Emp.: 300
Mfr of Health Products
N.A.I.C.S.: 621410

Subsidiary (Non-US):

Tiger Balm (Malaysia) Sdn Bhd (2)
Plot 95 No 6 Jalan Firma 1 1, Tebrau Industrial Estate, 81100, Johor Bahru, Malaysia (100%)
Tel.: (60) 73549616
Sales Range: $25-49.9 Million
Emp.: 30
Mfr of Pharmaceuticals
N.A.I.C.S.: 325412

Xiamen Tiger Medicals Co., Ltd. (2)
No 289 Yang Guang West Road, Hai Cang District, 361 006, Xiamen, 361027, China (100%)
Tel.: (86) 5925620201
Web Site: https://www.hawpar.com
Sales Range: $25-49.9 Million
Emp.: 50
Pharmaceutical Preparation Manufacturing
N.A.I.C.S.: 325412

Haw Par Land (M) Sdn. Bhd. (1)
9th Fl Menara Haw Par Lot 242 Jalan Sultan Ismail, Jalan Sultan Ismail, 50250, Kuala Lumpur, Malaysia
Tel.: (60) 320701855
Web Site: http://www.hawpar.com
Sales Range: $25-49.9 Million
Emp.: 5
N.A.I.C.S.: 325412

Haw Par Land (Malaysia) Sdn. Bhd. (1)
9th Floor Menara Haw Par Jalan Sultan Ismail, 50250, Kuala Lumpur, Malaysia
Tel.: (60) 320701855
Herbal Product Mfr
N.A.I.C.S.: 325411

Haw Par Leisure Pte Ltd (1)
401 Commonwealth Drive 03-03 Haw Par Technocentre, Singapore, 149598, Singapore
Tel.: (65) 63379102
Herbal Product Mfr
N.A.I.C.S.: 325411

Haw Par Properties (Singapore) Private Limited (1)
401 Commonwealth Dr, 03 03 Haw Par Techno Ctr, Singapore, 149598, Singapore (100%)
Tel.: (65) 63379102
Sales Range: $50-74.9 Million
Emp.: 25
Provider of Real Estate Services
N.A.I.C.S.: 531210

Haw Par Securities (Private) Limited (1)
401 Commonwealth Drive, 03-03 Haw Par Technocentre, Singapore, 149598, Singapore (100%)
Tel.: (65) 63379102
Sales Range: $10-24.9 Million
Emp.: 50
Provider of Business Services
N.A.I.C.S.: 561499

Underwater World Pattaya Ltd. (1)

HAW PAR CORPORATION LIMITED

Haw Par Corporation Limited—(Continued)
22/22 Moo 11 Sukhumvit Road, Nongprue,
Bang Lamung, 20150, Chonburi, Thailand
Tel.: (66) 38756878
Web Site:
https://www.underwaterworldpattaya.com
Aquarium Services
N.A.I.C.S.: 711219

**Underwater World Singapore Pte.
Ltd.**
80 Siloso Rd, Sentosa, Singapore, 098969,
Singapore (100%)
Tel.: (65) 62750030
Web Site:
http://www.underwaterworld.com.sg
Sales Range: $25-49.9 Million
Emp.: 80
Operator of a Marine Tourist Park
N.A.I.C.S.: 561499

HAWA ENGINEERS LTD.
Plot No 129 B/h Kashiram Textile Mill
Narol Road, Ahmedabad, 382 405,
Gujarat, India
Tel.: (91) 7925320781
Web Site:
https://www.hawaengltd.com
539176—(BOM)
Rev.: $12,279,518
Assets: $6,298,417
Liabilities: $4,329,041
Net Worth: $1,969,376
Earnings: $83,738
Emp.: 87
Fiscal Year-end: 03/31/23
Industrial Valve Mfr
N.A.I.C.S.: 332911
Aslam Fazlurrehman Kagdi *(Chm,
Co-Mng Dir & CFO)*

HAWE HYDRAULIK SE
Einsteinring 17, 85609, Munich, Germany
Tel.: (49) 893791001000
Web Site: http://www.hawe.com
Pumps & Hydraulics Mfr
N.A.I.C.S.: 333996
Karl Haeusgen *(CEO & Member-
Mgmt Bd)*

Subsidiaries:

HAWE Finland Oy (1)
Kellonsoittajantie 2, 02770, Espoo, Finland
Tel.: (358) 108212600
Industrial Pump & Motor Distr
N.A.I.C.S.: 423120
Mikko Vainio *(Mng Dir)*

HAWE Hidraulica, S.L.U. (1)
Polig Ind Almeda c/ del Progres 139-141,
Cornella de Llobregat, 08940, Barcelona,
Spain
Tel.: (34) 934751370
Industrial Pump & Motor Distr
N.A.I.C.S.: 423120

HAWE Hidravlika d.o.o. (1)
Petrovce 225, 3301, Ljubljana, Slovenia
Tel.: (386) 37134880
Industrial Pump & Motor Distr
N.A.I.C.S.: 423120
Kristian Les *(Gen Mgr)*

HAWE Holding GmbH (1)
Rm 1908 Landmark Tower 1 8 North Dong-
sanhuan Rd, 100004, Beijing, China
Tel.: (86) 1065907173
Industrial Pump & Motor Distr
N.A.I.C.S.: 423120

**HAWE Hydraulics Australia PTY
Ltd** (1)
5/ 83-85 Montague Street, Wollongong,
2500, NSW, Australia
Tel.: (61) 242257222
Industrial Pump & Motor Distr
N.A.I.C.S.: 423120

HAWE Hydraulics Pvt. Ltd. (1)
No 68 Industrial Suburb 2nd Stage, Yesh-
wanthpur, Bengaluru, 560 022, India
Tel.: (91) 8041952000
Industrial Pump & Motor Distr

N.A.I.C.S.: 423120
R. Mohan Raj *(Gen Mgr)*

**HAWE Hydraulik Singapore Pte.
Ltd.** (1)
25 International Business Park 01-59/60
German Centre, Singapore, 609916, Singapore
Tel.: (65) 65628361
Industrial Pump & Motor Distr
N.A.I.C.S.: 423120

HAWE Italiana S.r.l. (1)
Via C Cantu 8, Cinisello Balsamo, 20092,
Milan, Italy
Tel.: (39) 0239975100
Industrial Pump & Motor Distr
N.A.I.C.S.: 423120
Mauro Lanzani *(Mgr-Sls)*

HAWE Japan Ltd. (1)
2-2 Yoshimoto-cho Nakagawa-ku, Nagoya,
454-0825, Japan
Tel.: (81) 523651655
Industrial Pump & Motor Distr
N.A.I.C.S.: 423120
Hirokazu Saito *(Gen Mgr)*

HAWE Korea Co., Ltd. (1)
27 1-gil 4-sandan Jiksan-eup, Seobuk-gu,
Cheonan, 331-814, South Chungcheong,
Korea (South)
Tel.: (82) 415853800
Industrial Pump & Motor Distr
N.A.I.C.S.: 423120

HAWE North America, Inc. (1)
9009 Perimeter Woods Dr, Charlotte, NC
28216
Tel.: (704) 509-1599
Web Site: http://www.haweusa.com
Emp.: 79
Pumps & Hydraulics Mfr
N.A.I.C.S.: 333996
Jean McAllister *(CFO)*

**HAWE Oil-Hydraulic Technology
(Shanghai) Co., Ltd.** (1)
155 Jindian Road, Pudong, 201206, Shanghai, China
Tel.: (86) 2158999678
Industrial Pump & Motor Distr
N.A.I.C.S.: 423120
Cheng'en Zhou *(VP)*

HAWE Osterreich GmbH (1)
Keltenstrasse 5, 3100, Saint Polten, Austria
Tel.: (43) 274224577
Industrial Pump & Motor Distr
N.A.I.C.S.: 423120
Anton Vertetics *(Acct Mgr)*

HAWE-HYDRATEC AG (1)
Dorfstrasse 37, 6035, Perlen, Switzerland
Tel.: (41) 417474000
Industrial Pump & Motor Distr
N.A.I.C.S.: 423120
Herr Kurt Hess *(Mng Dir)*

HAWE-Otelec S.A.S. (1)
2 Rue Parc des Vergers Parc d'activites
des Vergers, 91250, Tigery, France
Tel.: (33) 169471010
Industrial Pump & Motor Distr
N.A.I.C.S.: 423120

HAWE S.A.
Franciszka Nullo Str 2, 00-486, Warsaw, Poland
Tel.: (48) 225015500
Web Site: http://www.hawesa.pl
Telecommunication Servicesb
N.A.I.C.S.: 517810
Pawel Sobkow *(Chm-Mgmt Bd)*

HAWESKO HOLDING AG
Elbkaihaus Grosse Elbstrasse 145d,
22767, Hamburg, Germany
Tel.: (49) 4030392100
Web Site: https://www.hawesko-
holding.com
HAW—(DEU)
Rev.: $724,672,998
Assets: $468,043,384
Liabilities: $321,696,525
Net Worth: $146,346,859
Earnings: $28,235,485

Emp.: 1,261
Fiscal Year-end: 12/31/22
Holding Company; Wine & Champagne Whslr, Mail Order &
E-Commerce Sales
N.A.I.C.S.: 551112
Thomas R. Fischer *(Deputy Chm-
Supervisory Bd)*

Subsidiaries:

**Alexander Baron von Essen Wein-
handels GmbH** (1)
Konigswintererstr 552, 53227, Bonn, Germany
Tel.: (49) 22844960
Web Site:
http://www.selectionalexandervonessen.de
Sales Range: $50-74.9 Million
Emp.: 2
Speciality Wines & Spirits Sales
N.A.I.C.S.: 424820

**CWD Champagner- und Wein-
Distributionsgesellschaft mbH &
Co. KG** (1)
Koenigswinterer Str 552, 53227, Hamburg,
Germany
Tel.: (49) 228 449 6666
Web Site: https://www.cwdwein.de
Sales Range: $25-49.9 Million
Emp.: 20
Wine Distr
N.A.I.C.S.: 424820
Oliver Thieme *(Mng Dir)*

Carl Tesdorpf GmbH (1)
Friesenweg 4, 22763, Hamburg, Germany
Tel.: (49) 45 179 9270
Web Site: https://www.tesdorpf.de
Sales Range: $25-49.9 Million
Emp.: 20
Wine Distr
N.A.I.C.S.: 424820
Carl Johann Tesdorpf *(Founder)*

**Chateaux et Domaines Weinhan-
delsgesellschaft mbH** (1)
Friedrichshof - Giesdorfer Allee 103, 50997,
Cologne, Germany
Tel.: (49) 223 689 0240
Web Site: https://www.c-und-d.de
Sales Range: $50-74.9 Million
Emp.: 4
Speciality Wines Sales
N.A.I.C.S.: 424820
Michel Cuvelier *(Co-CEO)*

**Deutschwein Classics GmbH &
Co. KG** (1)
Koenigswinterer Str 552, 53227, Bonn, Germany
Tel.: (49) 2 284 4960
Web Site:
https://www.deutschweinclassics.de
Sales Range: $50-74.9 Million
Emp.: 4
Wine Distr
N.A.I.C.S.: 424820
Pascal Dautel *(Mng Dir)*

**Gebruder Josef und Matthaus Ziegler
GmbH** (1)
Hauptstrasse 26, 97896, Freudenberg, Germany
Tel.: (49) 93 759 2880
Web Site: https://www.brennerei-ziegler.de
Wine Products Whslr
N.A.I.C.S.: 445320

Globalwine AG (1)
Raffelstrasse 25, 8045, Zurich, Switzerland
Tel.: (41) 44 450 1616
Web Site: https://www.globalwine.ch
Emp.: 25
Wine Whslr
N.A.I.C.S.: 327910
Geri Theiler *(CEO)*

Subsidiary (Domestic):

Vogel Vins SA (2)
Route du Signal 81, Grandvaux, 1091,
Cully, Switzerland
Tel.: (41) 21 799 9966
Web Site: https://www.vogel-vins.ch
Wine Products Whslr
N.A.I.C.S.: 445320

INTERNATIONAL PUBLIC

**Grand Cru Select Weinhandelsgesell-
schaft mbH** (1)
Griegstrasse 75 Haus 23, 22763, Hamburg,
Germany
Tel.: (49) 40607728400
Wine Products Whslr
N.A.I.C.S.: 445320

**Hanseatisches Wein- und Sekt-
Kontor HAWESKO GmbH & Co.
KG** (1)
Friesenweg 24, 22763, Hamburg, Germany
Tel.: (49) 4122504433
Web Site: https://www.hawesko.de
Sales Range: $50-74.9 Million
Emp.: 100
Champagne & Speciality Wines Sales
N.A.I.C.S.: 424820
Gerd Stemmann *(Mng Dir)*

**IWL Internationale Wein Logistik
GmbH** (1)
Hamburger Strasse 14-20, 25436, Tornesch, Germany
Tel.: (49) 412250400
Sales Range: $250-299.9 Million
Emp.: 656
Wine Distr
N.A.I.C.S.: 424820
Frank Gobels *(Mng Dir)*

**Jacques Wein-Depot Wein-
Einzelhandel GmbH** (1)
Bilker Allee 49, 40219, Dusseldorf, Germany
Tel.: (49) 211390020
Web Site: https://www.jacques.de
Sales Range: $25-49.9 Million
Emp.: 53
Wine Retailer
N.A.I.C.S.: 445320
Dirk Schwiegelshohn *(Mgr-Mktg)*

**Le Monde des Grands Bordeaux
Chateau Classic s.a.r.l.** (1)
40-44 Rte De Lesparre, 33340, Saint-
Christoly-Medoc, Gironde, France
Tel.: (33) 556731500
Web Site: http://www.chateauclassic.com
Sales Range: $25-49.9 Million
Emp.: 15
Speciality Wines Sales
N.A.I.C.S.: 424820

**The Wine Company Hawesko
GmbH** (1)
Friesenweg 24, 22763, Hamburg, Germany
Tel.: (49) 412 250 4466
Web Site: https://www.the-wine-company.se
Wine Products Whslr
N.A.I.C.S.: 445320
Kathrin Kochanski *(Mktg Mgr-Intl)*

**Verwaltungsgesellschaft Han-
seatisches Wein- und Sekt-Kontor
HAWESKO m.b.H.** (1)
Plan 5, 20095, Hamburg, Germany
Tel.: (49) 4122504433
Sales Range: $250-299.9 Million
Emp.: 656
Wine Distr
N.A.I.C.S.: 424820

**Wein & Co. Handelsgesellschaft
m.b.H** (1)
Autoallee 7 / Top 25 Sud, 2334, Vosendorf,
Austria
Tel.: (43) 50 706 3070
Web Site: https://www.weinco.at
Wine Products Whslr
N.A.I.C.S.: 445320

Wein & Vinos GmbH (1)
Hardenbergstr 9a, 10623, Berlin, Germany
Tel.: (49) 303 150 6080
Web Site: https://www.vinos.de
Wine Products Whslr
N.A.I.C.S.: 445320

**Wein Wolf Holding GmbH & Co.
KG** (1)
Konigswinterer Str 552, 53227, Bonn, Germany
Tel.: (49) 2 284 4960
Web Site: https://www.weinwolf.de
Sales Range: $50-74.9 Million
Emp.: 100
Holding Company
N.A.I.C.S.: 551112

Berndt G. Siebdrat *(Founder & Mng Dir)*
Subsidiary (Domestic):

Wein Wolf Import GmbH & Co. Vertriebs KG (2)
Konigswinterer Strasse 552, 53227, Bonn, Nordrhein-Westfalen, Germany
Tel.: (49) 22844960
Web Site: http://www.weinwolf.de
Sales Range: $25-49.9 Million
Emp.: 76
International Wines Import & Sales
N.A.I.C.S.: 424820

Wein Wolf Import GmbH & Co. Vertriebs KG (1)
Munchner Bundesstrasse 107, 5020, Salzburg, Austria
Tel.: (43) 6624214640
Web Site: https://www.wein-wolf.at
Sales Range: $25-49.9 Million
Emp.: 20
Wine Products Whslr
N.A.I.C.S.: 424820
Christine Stelzer *(Mng Dir)*

WeinArt Handelsgesellschaft mbH (1)
Winkeler Str 93, 65366, Geisenheim, Germany
Tel.: (49) 67 227 1080
Web Site: https://www.weinart.de
Wine Products Whslr
N.A.I.C.S.: 445320

Weinland Ariane Abayan GmbH & Co. KG (1)
Erikastrasse 67, 20251, Hamburg, Germany
Tel.: (49) 404800350
Web Site: https://www.abayan.de
Sales Range: $50-74.9 Million
Emp.: 14
Wines Import & Distr
N.A.I.C.S.: 424820
Anton A. Rossner *(Mng Dir)*

Wine Dock GmbH (1)
Friesenweg 4 House 14, 22763, Hamburg, Germany
Tel.: (49) 4122504404
Web Site: http://www.wine-dock.de
Wine Products Whslr
N.A.I.C.S.: 445320

WirWinzer GmbH (1)
Widenmayerstr 18 / RGB, 80538, Munich, Germany
Tel.: (49) 8941 613 7060
Web Site: https://www.wirwinzer.de
Wine Products Whslr
N.A.I.C.S.: 445320
Sebastian Zellner *(Founder & CEO)*

HAWKEYE ELECTRONIC SECURITY LTD.
14 Belmont Rd, Kingston, 5, Jamaica
Tel.: (876) 9601791
Web Site: http://www.hawkeye.com.jm
Year Founded: 1988
Sales Range: $10-24.9 Million
Emp.: 100
Electronic Security Systems
N.A.I.C.S.: 561621
Rockey Allen *(Mgr-Ops)*

HAWKEYE GOLD & DIAMOND INC.
M 202 - 1985 Alberni Street, Vancouver, V6G 0A2, BC, Canada
Tel.: (778) 379-5393   Ca
Web Site: https://www.hawkeyegold.com
Year Founded: 1988
HGT0—(DEU)
Assets: $24,136
Liabilities: $1,022,815
Net Worth: ($998,679)
Earnings: ($517,578)
Fiscal Year-end: 05/31/24
Mineral Exploration Services
N.A.I.C.S.: 213114
Greg Neeld *(Pres & CEO)*

HAWKINS COOKERS LIMITED
F 101 Maker Tower Cuffe Parade, Mumbai, 400 005, India
Tel.: (91) 2222186607
Web Site: https://www.hawkinscookers.com
508486—(BOM)
Rev.: $131,568,678
Assets: $55,931,244
Liabilities: $26,832,201
Net Worth: $29,099,043
Earnings: $11,450,480
Emp.: 595
Fiscal Year-end: 03/31/22
Kitchenware Equipment Mfr & Whslr
N.A.I.C.S.: 335220
Hutoxi Bhesania *(Sec)*

HAWKSFORD INTERNATIONAL
Rathbone House 15 Esplanade, Saint Helier, JE1 1RB, Jersey
Tel.: (44) 1534740000
Web Site: http://www.rathbonetrust.com
Sales Range: $125-149.9 Million
Emp.: 300
International Trust Service
N.A.I.C.S.: 523991
Steve Spybey *(Dir-Ops)*

HAWSONS IRON LIMITED
Level 21 12 Creek Street Adelaide Street, PO Box 10919, Brisbane, 4000, QLD, Australia
Tel.: (61) 732202022   AU
Web Site: https://hawsons.com.au
HIO—(ASX)
Rev.: $39,483
Assets: $42,171,210
Liabilities: $1,516,039
Net Worth: $40,655,171
Earnings: ($2,430,885)
Fiscal Year-end: 06/30/24
Mineral Exploration Services
N.A.I.C.S.: 213115
Michael Harvey *(CFO & Sec)*

HAWTAI MOTOR GROUP LIMITED
A9 Lishuiqiao, Chaoyang District, Beijing, 102218, China
Tel.: (86) 10 6497 8745
Web Site: http://en.hawtaimotor.com
Sales Range: $1-4.9 Billion
Emp.: 7,000
Holding Company; Motor Vehicle & Motor Vehicle Components Designer, Mfr & Whslr
N.A.I.C.S.: 551112
Xiangyin Wang *(Pres)*
Subsidiaries:

Rongcheng Hawtai Automobile Co., Ltd. (1)
A9 Lishuiqiao, Chaoyang District, Beijing, 102218, China
Tel.: (86) 10 6497 8666
Web Site: http://www.hawtaimotor.com
Motor Vehicle & Motor Vehicle Components Designer, Mfr & Whslr
N.A.I.C.S.: 336110
Xiangyin Wang *(Pres)*

HAWTHORN RESOURCES CORP.
625 Howe St Suite 1180, Vancouver, V6C 2T6, BC, Canada
Tel.: (778) 869-1741
Year Founded: 2020
HWTN—(CNSX)
Mineral Exploration Services
N.A.I.C.S.: 212390

HAWTHORN RESOURCES LIMITED
Level 23 Rialto Tower South 525 Collins Street, Melbourne, 3000, VIC, Australia
Tel.: (61) 396055950
Web Site: https://www.hawthornresources.com
HAW—(ASX)
Rev.: $449,774
Assets: $10,371,994
Liabilities: $1,094,516
Net Worth: $9,277,478
Earnings: ($358,568)
Emp.: 7
Fiscal Year-end: 06/30/24
Gold Exploration
N.A.I.C.S.: 213114
Mourice Garbutt *(Sec)*

HAXC HOLDINGS (BEIJING) CO., LTD.
Bldg 105 A No 17 Jingsheng S 4th Street Zhongguancun Science Park, Jinqiao Science & Technology Industrial Base Tongzhou Park, Beijing, 101102, China
Tel.: (86) 1056940328
Web Site: https://www.haxc.com.cn
Year Founded: 2013
300928—(SSE)
Rev.: $125,023,392
Assets: $190,510,164
Liabilities: $7,780,968
Net Worth: $182,729,196
Earnings: $6,538,428
Fiscal Year-end: 12/31/22
Holding Company
N.A.I.C.S.: 551112
Pan He *(Chm & Gen Mgr)*

HAY TOR CAPITAL LLP
Fifth Floor 22-23 Old Burlington Street, London, W1S 2JJ, United Kingdom
Tel.: (44) 2074794980
Web Site: http://www.haytorcapital.com
Year Founded: 2011
Privater Equity Firm
N.A.I.C.S.: 523999
John Ashdown *(Mng Partner)*
Subsidiaries:

NeoNet AB (1)
Olof Palmes Gata 31, Stockholm, 111 22, Sweden (60%)
Tel.: (46) 84541500
Web Site: http://www.neonet.com
Sales Range: $50-74.9 Million
Emp.: 60
Developer of Electronic Trading Software
N.A.I.C.S.: 513210
Patrik Nylander *(Mgr-Risk)*

HAYAKAWA DENSEN KOGYO CO., LTD.
422 Nishi-Nobusue, Hyogo-ku, Himeji, 670 0971, Japan
Tel.: (81) 792963221   JP
Web Site: http://www.hdk-corp.com
Year Founded: 1964
Sales Range: $25-49.9 Million
Emp.: 10,300
Holding Company; Printed Circuit Assembly & Wire Harness Mfr
N.A.I.C.S.: 551112
Masao Hayakawa *(Chm)*
Subsidiaries:

Thai Wire & Cable Services Co., Ltd. (1)
8/3 Moo 2 Bangna-Trad Km 41 Bangwua, Bangpakong, Chachoengsao, 24180, Thailand (82%)
Tel.: (66) 38538944
Electronic Wire Harness Mfr
N.A.I.C.S.: 334419

HAYASHI TELEMPU CO., LTD.
1-4-5 Kamimaezu, Naka-Ku, Nagoya, 460-0013, Japan
Tel.: (81) 523222121   JP
Web Site: http://www.hayatele.co.jp
Sales Range: $500-549.9 Million
Emp.: 1,741
Automotive Components Mfr
N.A.I.C.S.: 336110
Takao Hayashi *(Pres)*
Subsidiaries:

Amtex Inc. (1)
1500 Kingsview Dr, Lebanon, OH 45036-8389
Tel.: (513) 932-9319
Web Site: http://www.amtexna.com
Sales Range: $50-74.9 Million
Emp.: 250
Automotive & Apparel Trimmings
N.A.I.C.S.: 336360
Pat Kiernan *(Plant Mgr)*

HAITEX Co., Ltd. (1)
MarunouchiKS Bldg 10F 2-18-25, Marunouchi Naka-ku, Nagoya, 460-0002, Aichi, Japan
Tel.: (81) 52 203 9777
Web Site: http://www.haitex.hayatele.co.jp
Emp.: 146
Information Technology Consulting Services
N.A.I.C.S.: 541512

Hayashi Canada Inc. (1)
300 Dunn Road, Stratford, N5A 6S4, ON, Canada
Tel.: (519) 271-5600
Emp.: 160
Automotive Products Mfr
N.A.I.C.S.: 336390

Hayashi Telempu Co., Ltd. - Hamamatsu Plant (1)
2520 Yamashina, Fukuroi, Shizuoka, Japan
Tel.: (81) 538 43 1221
Automotive Products Mfr
N.A.I.C.S.: 336390

Hayashi Telempu Co., Ltd. - Main Plant (1)
100-2 Machiyahora, Kamekubi-cho, Toyota, Aichi, Japan
Tel.: (81) 565 45 7171
Automotive Products Mfr
N.A.I.C.S.: 336390

Hayashi Telempu Co., Ltd. - Mizushima Plant (1)
2115-1 Tsurushinden, Tsurajima-cho, Kurashiki, Okayama, Japan
Tel.: (81) 86 446 4614
Automotive Products Mfr
N.A.I.C.S.: 336390

Hayashi Telempu Co., Ltd. - Nagoya Plant (1)
4-20 Douzen-cho, Minami-ku, Nagoya, Aichi, Japan
Tel.: (81) 52 811 8181
Automotive Products Mfr
N.A.I.C.S.: 336390

Hayashi Telempu Co., Ltd. - Toyohashi Plant (1)
3-37 Akemi-cho, Toyohashi, Aichi, Japan
Tel.: (81) 532 23 2811
Automotive Products Mfr
N.A.I.C.S.: 336390

Hayashi Telempu North America Corporation (1)
14328 Genoa Ct, Plymouth, MI 48170
Tel.: (734) 456-5221
Automotive Products Mfr
N.A.I.C.S.: 336390
Ben Probert *(Mgr-Pur)*
Plant (Domestic):

Hayashi Telempu North America Corporation - Alabama Plant (2)
3711 Industrial Ct, Jasper, AL 35501
Tel.: (205) 221-1005
Automotive Products Mfr
N.A.I.C.S.: 336390

Hayashi Telempu North America Corporation - Kentucky Plant (2)
110 Fortune Dr, Frankfort, KY 40601

Hayashi Telempu Co., Ltd.—(Continued)
Tel.: (502) 605-9998
Automotive Products Mfr
N.A.I.C.S.: 336390

Hayashi Telempu North America Corporation - Ohio Plant (2)
1500 Kingsview Dr, Lebanon, OH 45036
Tel.: (513) 932-9319
Automotive Products Mfr
N.A.I.C.S.: 336390

Hayatele Kanto Co., ltd. (1)
957 Kamikawai, Nasukarasuyama, Tochigi, Japan
Tel.: (81) 287 88 6171
Automotive Products Mfr
N.A.I.C.S.: 336390

Hayatele Kyushu K.K. (1)
1230-2 Aza-Furuko-Otsu Oaza-Kuma, Shiota-cho, Ureshino, Saga, Japan
Tel.: (81) 954 66 5711
Automotive Products Mfr
N.A.I.C.S.: 336390

Hayatele Touhoku Co., Ltd. (1)
87-1 Aza-Tsurugasawa Takizawa, Ichinoseki, Iwate, Japan
Tel.: (81) 191 31 8177
Automotive Products Mfr
N.A.I.C.S.: 336390

HAYASHIKANE SANGYO CO., LTD.
2-4-8 Yamato-machi, Shimonoseki, 750-8608, Yamaguchi, Japan
Tel.: (81) 832660210
Web Site: https://www.hayashikane.co.jp
Year Founded: 1941
2286—(TKS)
Rev.: $313,155,360
Assets: $191,974,230
Liabilities: $118,649,500
Net Worth: $73,324,730
Earnings: $4,950,890
Emp.: 342
Fiscal Year-end: 03/31/24
Food Product Mfr & Distr
N.A.I.C.S.: 311710
Tetsuji Nakabe (Pres)

HAYAT COMMUNICATIONS CO. K.S.C.C.
Hayat Communications Al Argan Business Park Kuwait Free Trade Zone, PO Box 1668, Safat, 13017, Kuwait, 13017, Kuwait
Tel.: (965) 22024444
Web Site: https://www.hayat.com
Year Founded: 1997
HAYATCOMM—(KUW)
Rev.: $86,931,376
Assets: $93,638,289
Liabilities: $62,046,508
Net Worth: $31,591,781
Earnings: ($5,886,129)
Emp.: 1,100
Fiscal Year-end: 12/31/22
Electrical & Communication Equipment Mfr & Distr
N.A.I.C.S.: 334290
Imad Habib Jawhar Hayat (Vice Chm & CEO)

Subsidiaries:

Hayat Commications (MEA) FZCO (1)
Jebel Ali Free Zone, PO Box 18050, Dubai, United Arab Emirates
Tel.: (971) 44871006
Wireless Telecommunication Services
N.A.I.C.S.: 517112

Hayat Commications Company W.L.L. (1)
Villa 1834 Road 2739 Block 327, 71439, Adliya, Bahrain
Tel.: (973) 17180366
Wireless Telecommunication Services
N.A.I.C.S.: 517112

HAYAT PHARMACEUTICAL INDUSTRIES
PO Box 1564, Amman, 11118, Jordan
Tel.: (962) 64162607
Web Site: https://www.hayatpharma.com
Year Founded: 1994
HPIC—(AMM)
Rev.: $23,385,616
Assets: $46,000,266
Liabilities: $8,660,339
Net Worth: $37,339,928
Earnings: $4,951,464
Emp.: 208
Fiscal Year-end: 12/31/20
Pharmaceutical Products Marketing & Mfr
N.A.I.C.S.: 424210
Maher M. Kurdi (Chm)

HAYCO MANUFACTURING LTD.
3002 Citicorp Centre 18 Whitfield Road, Causeway Bay, China (Hong Kong)
Tel.: (852) 21689200
Web Site: http://www.hayco.com.hk
Year Founded: 1983
Rev.: $12,800,000
Emp.: 90
Industrial Mold Mfr
N.A.I.C.S.: 333511
Christopher Hay (CEO)

HAYDALE GRAPHENE INDUSTRIES PLC
Clos Fferws Parc Hendre Capel Hendre, Ammanford, SA18 3BL, Carmarthenshire, United Kingdom
Tel.: (44) 1269842946
Web Site: https://www.haydale.com
Year Founded: 2003
HAYD—(AIM)
Rev.: $3,938,746
Assets: $19,636,704
Liabilities: $10,067,494
Net Worth: $9,569,211
Earnings: ($6,529,275)
Emp.: 60
Fiscal Year-end: 06/30/22
Holding Company; Graphene & Other Nanomaterial Products Mfr
N.A.I.C.S.: 551112
Patrick Carter (CFO)

Subsidiaries:

Haydale Ltd. (1)
Clos Fferws Parc Hendre Capel Hendre, Ammanford, SA18 3BL, Carmarthenshire, United Kingdom
Tel.: (44) 1269842946
Chemical Products Mfr
N.A.I.C.S.: 325199

Haydale Technologies Korea Co., Ltd. (1)
3317 33rd Fl World Trade Tower 511 Youngdong Street, Ganganam-gu, Seoul, Korea (South)
Tel.: (82) 260072033
Chemical Products Mfr
N.A.I.C.S.: 325199

Haydale Technologies Thailand Ltd. (1)
Unit 510 -515 INC2 Tower D 141 Mu9 Phaholyothin Road, Thailand Science Park Khlong Luang District, Pathumthani, 12120, Thailand
Tel.: (66) 21178071
Chemical Products Mfr
N.A.I.C.S.: 325199

Haydale Technologies, Inc. (1)
1446 S Buncombe Rd, Greer, SC 29651
Tel.: (864) 877-0123
Holding Company; Graphene & Other Nanomaterial Products Mfr
N.A.I.C.S.: 551112

Subsidiary (Domestic):

Haydale Ceramic Technologies, LLC (2)
1446 S Buncombe Rd, Greer, SC 29651
Tel.: (864) 877-0123
Emp.: 40
Graphene & Other Nanomaterial Products Mfr
N.A.I.C.S.: 335991

HAYDARI CONSTRUCTION COMPANY LIMITED
Mezzanine Floor UBL Building I I Chundrigar Road, Karachi, Pakistan
Tel.: (92) 32411247
Construction Engineering Services
N.A.I.C.S.: 541330

HAYEL SAEED ANAM GROUP OF COMPANIES
PO Box 5302, Taiz, Yemen
Tel.: (967) 4212334
Web Site: http://www.hsagroup.com
Year Founded: 1938
Sales Range: $1-4.9 Billion
Emp.: 17,500
Diversified Holding & Trading Company; Agricultural Services; Animal Development; Fisheries
N.A.I.C.S.: 551112
Ali Mohamed Saeed (Co-Founder & Chm-Supervisory Bd)

Subsidiaries:

Al Alam Industrial Company LLC (1)
PO Box 4432, Aden, Yemen
Tel.: (967) 2 821614
Web Site: http://www.alalam-ic.com
Plastics Bag Mfr
N.A.I.C.S.: 322220
Ali Mohammed Saeed (Chm)

Al Tawfiq Co For Plastic & Woven Sacks Industries Ltd. (1)
PO Box 32368, Jeddah, 21428, Saudi Arabia
Tel.: (966) 2 6081033
Web Site: http://www.apws.com.sa
Plastics Bag Mfr
N.A.I.C.S.: 322220
Yassin Al Aghbari (Mng Dir)

Al-Jazira Marine Resources Company Ltd. (1)
PO Box 3258, Hodeidah, Yemen
Tel.: (967) 3 263310
Frozen Seafood Mfr
N.A.I.C.S.: 311412

Alsaeed Trading Company Ltd. (1)
PO Box 5351, Taiz, Yemen
Tel.: (967) 4232727
Web Site: http://www.alsaeedtrading.com
Sales Range: $75-99.9 Million
Emp.: 110
Consumer Goods Distr
N.A.I.C.S.: 423990

Arabia Felix Industrial Ltd. (1)
PO Box 5568, Taiz, Yemen
Tel.: (967) 4 218229
Pesticide Mfr
N.A.I.C.S.: 325320

Artex Trading Company Ltd. (1)
60th Road, PO Box 3803, Sana'a, Yemen
Tel.: (967) 1 454980
Web Site: http://www.artexyemen.com
Emp.: 40
Electrical Home Appliances Distr
N.A.I.C.S.: 423620
Esam AL Haiki (Mng Dir)

Arwa Mineral Water Company (1)
PO Box 883, Sana'a, Yemen
Tel.: (967) 1370255
Web Site: http://www.shamlan-water.com
Sales Range: $100-124.9 Million
Emp.: 375
Mineral Water Producer
N.A.I.C.S.: 312111

Cepac Ltd (1)
Meadows Road Brookfield Park Manvers, Wath Upon Dearne, Rotherham, S63 5DJ, United Kingdom
Tel.: (44) 1709 511666
Web Site: http://www.cepac.co.uk
Corrugated Packaging Material Mfr & Distr
N.A.I.C.S.: 322211
Richard Walton (Dir-Ops)

Frimex Investment Llc (1)
1102 Reem Tower Maktum St, Deira, Dubai, 4397, United Arab Emirates
Tel.: (971) 42234636
Emp.: 20
Investment Management Service
N.A.I.C.S.: 523940
Sushi Shakir (Founder & CTO)

General Industries & Packages Company (1)
PO Box 6328, Taiz, Yemen
Tel.: (967) 4 218027
Web Site: http://www.genpackhsa.com
Food Products Mfr
N.A.I.C.S.: 311999
Abdulsalam Abdulsalam (Mgr-R&D)

Global Intertrade Group (1)
11 Aflaton St, Cairo, Egypt
Tel.: (20) 2 24156186
Industrial Supplies Whslr
N.A.I.C.S.: 423840

Hayel Saeed Anam & Associates Welfare Corporation (1)
PO Box 5962, Taiz, Yemen
Tel.: (967) 4 212120
Fund Management Services
N.A.I.C.S.: 525120

Hi-pack Group for Packaging Solution (1)
Zone A6, 10th of Ramadan City, Egypt
Tel.: (20) 15 411066
Web Site: http://www.hipackgroup.com
Industrial Supplies Whslr
N.A.I.C.S.: 423840
Fathy Gaafar (Mgr-Bus Dev)

Longulf Trrading (UK) Ltd. (1)
Prince Albert House 2 Kingsmill Terrace, London, NW8 6BN, United Kingdom
Tel.: (44) 2077227733
Web Site: http://www.longulf.com
Sales Range: $50-74.9 Million
Emp.: 60
Raw Material Distr
N.A.I.C.S.: 423990
Dirhem Abdo Saeed (Mng Dir)

MASS Advertising Agency Ltd. (1)
Alhoban Road, PO Box 4863, Taiz, Yemen
Tel.: (967) 4218086
Web Site: http://www.massyemen.com
Sales Range: $25-49.9 Million
Emp.: 200
Advertising Services
N.A.I.C.S.: 541810

Middle East Shipping Company Ltd. (1)
Hayel Saeed Building Al Tahrir Street, PO Box 3700, Hodeidah, Yemen
Tel.: (967) 3203977
Web Site: http://www.mideastshipping.com
Sales Range: $50-74.9 Million
Emp.: 142
Freight Transportation Services
N.A.I.C.S.: 488510

Middle East Trading Co. (1)
Anam Building Al-Mugamma Street, PO Box 5927, Taiz, Yemen
Tel.: (967) 4231634
Web Site: http://www.metcotrading.com
Sales Range: $150-199.9 Million
Emp.: 600
Consumer Goods Importer & Distr
N.A.I.C.S.: 424990

Natco Al Razi Company (1)
PO Box 186, Sana'a, Yemen
Tel.: (967) 01272986
Web Site: http://www.natco-razi.com.ye

AND PRIVATE COMPANIES

Sales Range: $25-49.9 Million
Emp.: 49
Pharmaceutical Products Distr
N.A.I.C.S.: 424210

National Biscuits & Confectionery Company Ltd. (1)
PO Box 30972, Jeddah, 21487, Saudi Arabia
Tel.: (966) 126360606
Web Site: http://www.nbcc.com.sa
Confectionary Product Mfr
N.A.I.C.S.: 311824
Shajahan Sulaiman *(Mgr-Customer Svc)*

National Company for Sponge and Plastic Industry Ltd. (1)
PO Box 6714, Taiz, Yemen
Tel.: (967) 4218070
Web Site: http://www.ncspi.com
Sales Range: $1-4.9 Billion
Emp.: 2,800
Foam & Plastic Products
N.A.I.C.S.: 326199

National Dairy and Food Company Ltd. (1)
PO Box 6520, Taiz, Yemen
Tel.: (967) 4218017
Web Site: http://www.nadfood.com
Sales Range: $75-99.9 Million
Emp.: 1,500
Dairy Products Producer.
N.A.I.C.S.: 112120

National Products Marketing Company (1)
PO Box 6006, Al-Akaba, Taiz, Yemen
Tel.: (967) 4 215171
Web Site: http://www.npmc.biz
Food Products Distr
N.A.I.C.S.: 424490
A. S. Mutahar Saeed *(Gen Mgr)*

National Trading Co. (1)
PO Box 1108, Sana'a, Yemen
Tel.: (967) 1204227
Sales Range: $25-49.9 Million
Emp.: 48
Electrical Goods Importer & Distr
N.A.I.C.S.: 423610

PT Pacific Palmindo Industry (1)
Jl Pulau Bawean KIM - II Mabar, Medan, 20242, Indonesia
Tel.: (62) 61 6871122
Oil Refinery Services
N.A.I.C.S.: 324110
Abdullah Mugbil *(Gen Mgr)*

Pacific Inter-link Sdn Bhd (1)
31st Floor Menara Dato Onn Putra World Trade Centre, 45 Jalan Tun Ismai, 50480, Kuala Lumpur, Malaysia
Tel.: (60) 3 4042 3933
Web Site: http://www.pilgroup.com
Emp.: 140
Commodity Trading Services
N.A.I.C.S.: 523160
Milind Jadhav *(CFO)*

United Carton Industries Company Ltd. (1)
Phase 5 Industrial Area, PO Box 31503-21418, Jeddah, 21418, Saudi Arabia
Tel.: (966) 122244100
Web Site: http://www.ucic.com.sa
Corrugated Packaging Material Mfr
N.A.I.C.S.: 322211
Mohnish Rikhy *(Pres)*

United Feed Company (1)
PO Box 8680, Jeddah, 21487, Saudi Arabia
Tel.: (966) 2 6426033
Animal Food Distr
N.A.I.C.S.: 424910

United Industries Co (1)
PO Box 5302, Taiz, Yemen
Tel.: (967) 4218082
Sales Range: $25-49.9 Million
Emp.: 250
Cigarette Mfr
N.A.I.C.S.: 312230

United Insurance Co. (1)
Al-Saeed Building Al-Zubairy Str, PO Box 1883, Sana'a, Yemen
Tel.: (967) 1214232
Web Site: http://www.uicyemen.com

Sales Range: $50-74.9 Million
Emp.: 100
Insurance Services
N.A.I.C.S.: 524298

Widyan Trading Company Ltd. (1)
PO Box 70161, Aden, Yemen
Tel.: (967) 2 240500
Building Materials Distr
N.A.I.C.S.: 423390

Yemen Company For Flour Mills & Silos- Hodeidah (1)
PO Box 4200, Hodeidah, Yemen
Tel.: (967) 3 211901
Web Site: http://www.ycfmshod.com
Wheat Flour Mfr & Distr
N.A.I.C.S.: 311211

Yemen Company For Packaging Material Industry (1)
PO Box 4102, Taiz, Yemen
Tel.: (967) 4 218458
Web Site: http://www.ycpmiyemen.com
Packaging Materials Mfr
N.A.I.C.S.: 326112
Shihab Saeed Abdu Saeed *(Gen Mgr)*

Yemen Company for Ghee and Soap Industry Ltd. (1)
PO Box 5273, Taiz, Yemen
Tel.: (967) 4350270
Web Site: http://www.ycgsi.com
Sales Range: $150-199.9 Million
Emp.: 1,000
Cooking Oil & Soap Producer
N.A.I.C.S.: 311225

Yemen Company for Industry and Commercial Ltd. (1)
PO Box 5423, Taiz, Yemen
Tel.: (967) 4218060
Web Site: http://www.ycic.com
Sales Range: $750-799.9 Million
Emp.: 2,600
Biscuits & Confectionery Mfr
N.A.I.C.S.: 311340

Yemen Lubricants Manufacturing Company Ltd. (1)
PO Box 6583, Taiz, Yemen
Tel.: (967) 4 350287
Lubricant Mfr
N.A.I.C.S.: 333914

Yemen Travel Agencies (1)
PO Box 12363, Sana'a, Yemen
Tel.: (967) 1 272865
Travel Services
N.A.I.C.S.: 561510

HAYLEYS FABRIC PLC
Narthupana Estate, Neboda, Sri Lanka
Tel.: (94) 342297100
Web Site: https://www.hayleysfabric.com
Year Founded: 1993
MGT.N0000—(COL)
Rev.: $166,631,461
Assets: $118,949,509
Liabilities: $90,650,830
Net Worth: $28,298,679
Earnings: $1,133,052
Emp.: 2,776
Fiscal Year-end: 03/31/23
Textile Products Mfr
N.A.I.C.S.: 313310
Rohan Goonetilleke *(Mng Dir & CEO)*

HAYLEYS LEISURE PLC
Level 27 East Tower World Trade Center Echelon Square, Colombo, Sri Lanka
Tel.: (94) 114767800
Web Site:
  https://www.amayaresorts.com
Year Founded: 1981
CONN—(COL)
Rev.: $5,098,580
Assets: $18,005,317
Liabilities: $13,897,675
Net Worth: $4,107,642
Earnings: ($2,744,351)

Emp.: 333
Fiscal Year-end: 03/31/23
Hotel & Restaurant Operator
N.A.I.C.S.: 721110

HAYLEYS PLC
No 400 Deans Road, PO Box 70, 10, Colombo, 10, Sri Lanka
Tel.: (94) 112627000   LK
Web Site: https://www.hayleys.com
Year Founded: 1952
HAYL—(COL)
Rev.: $1,622,552,115
Assets: $1,373,928,874
Liabilities: $965,464,918
Net Worth: $408,463,956
Earnings: $92,115,109
Emp.: 31,483
Fiscal Year-end: 03/31/23
Diversified Holding Company
N.A.I.C.S.: 551112
A. Mohan Pandithage *(Co-Chm & CEO)*

Subsidiaries:

Advantis Intasl Bangladesh (Pvt) Ltd. (1)
Sheba House 6th Floor Plot 34 Road 46, Gulshan-2, Dhaka, 1212, Bangladesh
Tel.: (880) 298875214
Web Site: https://advantis.world
Logistic Services
N.A.I.C.S.: 541614

Advantis Kusuhara Sedate Myanmar (Pvt) Ltd. (1)
Room No 902/B 9th Floor Mahar Nawarat Condominium 50th Street, Between Maha Bandula Road and Merchant Road Botahtaung Township, Yangon, Myanmar
Tel.: (95) 1 901 0188
Logistic Services
N.A.I.C.S.: 541614

Advantis Sabang Raya Lines Pte. Ltd. (1)
No 448 Serangoon Road 03-01, Singapore, 218138, Singapore
Tel.: (65) 63910039
Emp.: 1,200
Logistic Services
N.A.I.C.S.: 541614

Alumex PLC (1)
Pattiwila Road, Sapugaskanda, Makola, Sri Lanka
Tel.: (94) 112400332
Web Site: https://www.alumexgroup.com
Building Materials Whslr
N.A.I.C.S.: 423390
D. W. P. N. Dediwela *(Mng Dir)*

Alutec Anodising & Machine Tools (Pvt) Ltd. (1)
Pattiwila Road Sapugaskanda, Makola, 11640, Sri Lanka
Tel.: (94) 11 240 0332
Web Site: http://www.alumexgroup.com
Sales Range: $100-124.9 Million
Emp.: 650
Aluminum Extrusion Product Mfr
N.A.I.C.S.: 331318
Mohan Pandithage *(Chm)*

Blue Diamonds Jewellery Worldwide PLC (1)
49 Ring Road Phase 1 I P Z, Katunayake, Sri Lanka
Tel.: (94) 114335000
Jewelry Whslr
N.A.I.C.S.: 423940

Bonterra Ltd. (1)
No 400 Deans Road, 10, Colombo, Sri Lanka
Tel.: (94) 112628951
Web Site: https://bonterraerosion.com
Organic Chemical Product Mfr
N.A.I.C.S.: 325199

CMA Ships Lanka (Pvt) Ltd. (1)
Level 5 Hnb Towers 479 T B Jayah Mawatha 10, Colombo, Sri Lanka
Tel.: (94) 112686610
Web Site: https://www.cma-cgm.com
Maritime Transportation Services

HAYLEYS PLC

N.A.I.C.S.: 488390
Cooray Danuka *(Fin Mgr)*

Dipped Products PLC (1)
400 Deans Road, 10, Colombo, 10, Sri Lanka
Tel.: (94) 112683964
Web Site: https://www.dplgroup.com
Rev.: $266,633,308
Assets: $209,682,714
Liabilities: $98,117,486
Net Worth: $111,565,228
Earnings: $28,302,733
Emp.: 18,208
Fiscal Year-end: 03/31/2023
Rubber Glove Mfr
N.A.I.C.S.: 315990
A. M. Pandithage *(Chm)*

Subsidiary (Non-US):

Icoguanti S.p.A. (2)
Corso Caronara 10A, 16125, Genoa, Italy
Tel.: (39) 010218298
Web Site: http://www.icoguanti.it
Sales Range: $25-49.9 Million
Emp.: 15
Rubber Gloves & Labels Importer & Distr
N.A.I.C.S.: 315990

Subsidiary (Domestic):

Kelani Valley Plantations Limited (2)
No 400 Deans Road, 10, Colombo, Sri Lanka
Tel.: (94) 112627700
Web Site: https://www.kvpl.com
Sales Range: $150-199.9 Million
Emp.: 1,000
Forest Products
N.A.I.C.S.: 113210

Neoprex Limited (2)
400 Deans Road, Colombo, 10, Sri Lanka
Tel.: (94) 0112683964
Sales Range: $1-4.9 Billion
Emp.: 16,930
Surgical Supplies Mfr
N.A.I.C.S.: 339113

Texnil Limited (2)
400 Deans Road, Colombo, 10, Sri Lanka
Tel.: (94) 0112683964
Sales Range: $200-249.9 Million
Emp.: 1,000
Rubber Products Mfr
N.A.I.C.S.: 326299

Venigros Limited (2)
400 Deans Road, Colombo, 10, Sri Lanka
Tel.: (94) 0112683964
Web Site: http://www.dplgroup.com
Sales Range: $200-249.9 Million
Emp.: 1,000
Rubber Products Mfr
N.A.I.C.S.: 326299

Energynet (Pvt) Ltd. (1)
180 Deans Road, 10, Colombo, Sri Lanka
Tel.: (94) 114336677
Web Site: https://www.energynetlk.com
Renewable Energy Services
N.A.I.C.S.: 221118
Hasith Premathilake *(Mng Dir)*

Eurocarb Products Ltd. (1)
Unit 1 Point 4 Second Way, Avonmouth, Bristol, BS11 8DF, United Kingdom
Tel.: (44) 1179820333
Activated Carbon Mfr & Distr
N.A.I.C.S.: 325998

HJS Condiments Limited (1)
Block 61 62 63, Biyagama Export Processing Zone, Biyagama, Sri Lanka
Tel.: (94) 112465271
Food & Beverage Services
N.A.I.C.S.: 722310

Haycarb Holdings Australia (Pty) Ltd. (1)
U 6 22-26 Bunney Rd, Oakleigh, 3167, VIC, Australia
Tel.: (61) 385550680
Sales Range: $50-74.9 Million
Emp.: 6
Investment Management Service
N.A.I.C.S.: 523999
Jerry Perera *(Gen Mgr)*

Haychem (Bangladesh) Ltd. (1)

HAYLEYS PLC

Hayleys PLC—(Continued)
Building B Apartment B-1 C-3 House CEN
B-11 Road 99, Gulshan-2, Dhaka, 1212,
Bangladesh
Tel.: (880) 241080651
Web Site: https://haychembd.com
Agricultural Services
N.A.I.C.S.: 115116
Abeyakumar Mohan Pandithage *(Chm)*

Haylex B.V. (1)
Riverside Business Centre River Lawn
Road, Tonbridge, TN9 1EP, Kent, United
Kingdom **(100%)**
Tel.: (44) 1732783547
Sales Range: $50-74.9 Million
Emp.: 5
Durable Goods Whslr
N.A.I.C.S.: 423990

Hayleys Advantis Ltd (1)
1st Floor Thurburn Wing 400 Deans Road,
01010, Colombo, Sri Lanka
Tel.: (94) 112167000
Web Site: https://www.hayleysadvantis.com
Sales Range: $450-499.9 Million
Emp.: 1,200
Support Activities for Water Transportation
N.A.I.C.S.: 488390

Subsidiary (Domestic):

Civaro Lanka (Pvt) Limited. (2)
No 50 Foster Lane, Colombo, 10, Sri Lanka
Tel.: (94) 11 4732800
Web Site: http://www.civaro.com
Sales Range: $50-74.9 Million
Emp.: 250
Logistics & Freight Transportation Services
N.A.I.C.S.: 488510
Ashan Fernando *(Deputy Gen Mgr)*

Hayleys Agriculture Holdings Limited (1)
No 25 Foster Lane, 10, Colombo, Sri Lanka
Tel.: (94) 112688960
Web Site:
https://www.hayleysagriculture.com
Frozen Specialty Food Mfr & Exporter
N.A.I.C.S.: 311412

Hayleys Agro Products Limited (1)
25 Foster Lane, PO Box 70, Colombo,
01000, Sri Lanka **(100%)**
Tel.: (94) 112688960
Web Site: http://www.hayleysagriculture.com
Pesticide & Agricultural Chemical Mfr
N.A.I.C.S.: 325320
J. Dharmasena *(Mng Dir)*

Subsidiary (Domestic):

Agro Technica Ltd. (2)
No 25 Foster Lane, Colombo, Sri Lanka
Tel.: (94) 112688960
Agricultural Products & Fertilizer Mfr
N.A.I.C.S.: 325320
Mohammed Amjad Rajap *(Dir)*

Subsidiary (Non-US):

Hayleys Agro Bio-tech (Pvt) Ltd. (2)
Tel.: (94) 112628200
Web Site:
http://www.hayleysagrobiotech.com
Biotechnology Research Services
N.A.I.C.S.: 541714
Rizvi Zaheed *(Mng Dir)*

Subsidiary (Domestic):

Hayleys Agro Farms (Pvt) Ltd. (2)
400 Deans Road, Colombo, Sri Lanka
Tel.: (94) 112 688960
Agricultural Farming Services
N.A.I.C.S.: 111998

Hayleys Agro Fertilizers (Pvt) Ltd. (2)
No 25 Foster Lane, 10, Colombo, Sri Lanka
Tel.: (94) 112688960
Chemical Fertiliser Mfr
N.A.I.C.S.: 325312

Hayleys Business Solutions International (Pvt) Ltd. (1)
No 25 Foster Lane, 10, Colombo, Sri Lanka
Tel.: (94) 112628700
Business Support Services
N.A.I.C.S.: 561499

Hayleys Consumer Products Ltd. (1)
No 25 Foster Lane, 10, Colombo, Sri Lanka
Tel.: (94) 112166200
Fast-Moving Consumer Goods Distr
N.A.I.C.S.: 424490

Hayleys Electronics Ltd. (1)
180 Deans Road, PO Box 70, 10, Colombo,
Sri Lanka
Tel.: (94) 112448518
Emp.: 100
Electrical Contractor
N.A.I.C.S.: 238210

Hayleys Engineering Ltd (1)
25 Foster Ln, PO Box 70, Colombo, Sri
Lanka **(100%)**
Tel.: (94) 112688960
Sales Range: $150-199.9 Million
Emp.: 1,000
Engineeering Services
N.A.I.C.S.: 541330

Hayleys Group Services Ltd. (1)
(100%)
Tel.: (94) 112627650
Web Site: http://www.hayleysplc.com
Sales Range: $25-49.9 Million
Emp.: 8
Chemical Product & Preparation Mfr
N.A.I.C.S.: 325998

Hayleys Industrial Solutions Limited (1)
25 Foster Lane, PO Box 70, Colombo, Sri
Lanka **(100%)**
Tel.: (94) 112688960
Electric Power Generation
N.A.I.C.S.: 221118

Hayleys Lifesciences (Pvt) Ltd. (1)
No 25 Foster Lane, 10, Colombo, Sri Lanka
Tel.: (94) 115311311
Medical Equipment Distr
N.A.I.C.S.: 423450

Hayleys Photoprint Ltd (1)
No 400 Deans Road, Colombo, 10, Sri
Lanka **(100%)**
Tel.: (94) 112696331
Web Site: http://www.hayleys.com
Photographic & Photocopying Equipment
Mfr
N.A.I.C.S.: 333310
Mervyn DeSilva *(CEO)*

Hayleys Travels (Pvt) Ltd. (1)
No 400 Deans Road, Colombo, 10, Sri
Lanka
Tel.: (94) 112168103
Web Site:
https://inbound.hayleystravels.com
Travel Arrangement Services
N.A.I.C.S.: 561599

Haymark Inc. (1)
220 Spring Hill Dr Ste 220, Spring, TX
77386
Tel.: (281) 292-8678
Web Site: http://www.haymarkusa.com
Emp.: 2
Activated Carbon Mfr
N.A.I.C.S.: 325998

Infocraft Ltd. (1)
400 Deans Road, Colombo, 10, Sri Lanka
Tel.: (94) 11 2667357
Web Site: http://www.infocraft.lk
Computer Related Services
N.A.I.C.S.: 541519

Mabroc Teas (Pvt) Ltd. (1)
Tel.: (94) 117878000
Web Site: http://www.mabrocteas.com
Emp.: 180
Tea Products Mfr & Distr
N.A.I.C.S.: 311920
Niran Ranatunga *(Mng Dir)*

Millennium Transportation Pvt Ltd (1)
No 108 YMBA Building Sir Baron
Jayathileke Mw, Colombo, 20621, Sri Lanka
Tel.: (94) 112325832
Web Site:
http://www.millenniumtransportation.com
Sales Range: $25-49.9 Million
Emp.: 7
Oil Transportation Services
N.A.I.C.S.: 488190

One World Logistics Maldives (Pvt) Ltd. (1)
04th Floor Ma Bodudhaharaage Keneeree
Magu, Chandanee Magu, Male, 20191,
Maldives
Tel.: (960) 3011888
Transportation Services
N.A.I.C.S.: 541614
A. K. M. Kamrul Ahasan *(Head)*

PT Mapalus Makawanua Charcoal Industry (1)
Jl Raya Manado Bitung Km 35 Tanjung
Merah, Sulawesi, 95547, Indonesia
Tel.: (62) 43838873
Charcoal Mfr
N.A.I.C.S.: 325998

Puritas (Pvt) Ltd. (1)
No 25 Foster Lane, 10, Colombo, Sri Lanka
Tel.: (94) 112683963
Web Site: https://www.puritas.lk
Sales Range: $75-99.9 Million
Emp.: 20
Sewage & Waste Water Treatment Services
N.A.I.C.S.: 221320

Ravi Industries Ltd. (1)
Industrial Equipment Mfr
N.A.I.C.S.: 333248

Singer (Sri Lanka) PLC (1)
(61.73%)
Tel.: (94) 112316316
Web Site: https://www.singersl.com
Rev.: $182,308,291
Assets: $262,301,230
Liabilities: $222,056,286
Net Worth: $40,244,944
Earnings: $319,333
Emp.: 2,986
Fiscal Year-end: 03/31/2023
Home Appliance & Electronics Mfr
N.A.I.C.S.: 335220
H. Viresh Gomes *(Head-Financial Services)*

Subsidiary (Domestic):

Singer Industries (Ceylon) PLC (2)
No-2 5th Lane, Rathmalana, Colombo, Sri
Lanka
Tel.: (94) 2634416
Rev.: $5,020,409
Assets: $12,526,853
Liabilities: $3,626,344
Net Worth: $8,900,509
Earnings: $493,200
Emp.: 72
Fiscal Year-end: 03/31/2022
Cabinet & Stand Mfr
N.A.I.C.S.: 337126
A. M. Pandithage *(Chm)*

Singer Business School (Pvt) Ltd. (1)
No 112 Havelock Road, 5, Colombo, Sri
Lanka
Tel.: (94) 115400400
Web Site: https://singerfashionacademy.com
Training Education Services
N.A.I.C.S.: 611430

Sri Lanka Institute of Nanotechnology (Pvt) Ltd. (1)
Tel.: (94) 114650500
Nanotechnology Research Services
N.A.I.C.S.: 541713
Eugene Maheshi Fernando *(Asst Mgr-Business Development)*

The Kingsbury PLC (1)
48 Janadhipathi Mawatha, 1, Colombo, 5,
Sri Lanka
Tel.: (94) 112421221
Web Site:
https://www.thekingsburyhotel.com
Rev.: $10,755,263
Assets: $22,899,004
Liabilities: $16,902,821
Net Worth: $5,996,183
Earnings: $(2,270,768)
Emp.: 718
Fiscal Year-end: 03/31/2022
Hotel Owner & Operator
N.A.I.C.S.: 721110
L. T. Samarawickrama *(Mng Dir)*

Total Transport Solutions Maldives (Pvt) Ltd. (1)
04th - 05th Floor Ma Bodudhaharaage,

INTERNATIONAL PUBLIC

Chandhanee Magu, Male, 20002, Maldives
Tel.: (960) 3011888
Logistic Services
N.A.I.C.S.: 541614

Toyo Cushion Lanka (Pvt) Ltd. (1)
Broadwoven Fabric Mills
N.A.I.C.S.: 313210

Volanka Exports Limited (1)
25 Foster Lane, 10, Colombo, Sri Lanka
Tel.: (94) 11 22682583
Web Site: http://www.volanka.com
Fibres, Oils & Dyed Fabrics
N.A.I.C.S.: 314994

Volanka Insurance Services (Pvt) Ltd. (1)
400 Deans Road, Colombo, 10, Sri Lanka
Tel.: (94) 11 2696336
Web Site: http://www.hayleys.com
Emp.: 2
Insurance Management Services
N.A.I.C.S.: 524298
Dhammika Siriwardena *(Mng Dir)*

Volanka Ltd (1)
193 Minuwangoda Road, Kotugoda, Sri
Lanka
Tel.: (94) 112232475
Web Site: http://www.volanka.com
Commercial & Service Industry Machinery
Mfr
N.A.I.C.S.: 333310

HAYMARKET GROUP LIMITED
174 Hammersmith Road, London, W6
7JP, United Kingdom
Tel.: (44) 2082674210 UK
Web Site: http://www.haymarket.com
Sales Range: $450-499.9 Million
Holding Company; Magazines Publisher & Media Services
N.A.I.C.S.: 551112
Rupert Heseltine *(Chm)*

Subsidiaries:

Haymarket Media (India) Pvt Ltd (1)
85 Podar Centre Parel Post Office Lane off
Dr Ambedkar Road, Mumbai, 400 013, India
Tel.: (91) 22 24962730
Media Advertising Services
N.A.I.C.S.: 541840
Kangkan Sarma *(Natl Mgr-Sls)*

Haymarket Media Asia Pte Ltd (1)
21 Media Circle 05-05 Infinite Studios, Singapore, 138562, Singapore
Tel.: (65) 6224 6101
Web Site: http://www.haymarket.com
Emp.: 35
Media Advertising Services
N.A.I.C.S.: 541840

Haymarket Media GmbH & Co. KG (1)
Frankfurter Str 3d, 38122, Braunschweig,
Germany
Tel.: (49) 531 38004 0
Web Site: http://www.haymarket.de
Media Advertising Services
N.A.I.C.S.: 541840
Brian Freeman *(Mng Dir)*

Haymarket Media Group Ltd. (1)
174 Hammersmith Road, London, W6 7JP,
United Kingdom
Tel.: (44) 2082674210
Web Site: http://www.haymarket.com
Sales Range: $75-99.9 Million
Emp.: 250
Magazine Publisher
N.A.I.C.S.: 513120
Kevin Costello *(CEO)*

Subsidiary (Domestic):

Haymarket Exhibitions Ltd. (2)
22 Bute Gardens, London, W6 7HN, United
Kingdom
Tel.: (44) 2083072300
Web Site: http://www.haymarketgroup.com
Exhibition Organizer
N.A.I.C.S.: 561920

Subsidiary (Non-US):

Haymarket Media Limited (2)

AND PRIVATE COMPANIES

HAYS PLC

23/F The Centrium 60 Wyndham Street, Central, China (Hong Kong)
Tel.: (852) 3118 1500
Media Advertising Services
N.A.I.C.S.: 541840

Subsidiary (US):

Haymarket Media, Inc. (2)
114 W 26th St 4th Fl, New York, NY 10001
Tel.: (646) 638-6000
Web Site: http://www.haymarket.com
Sales Range: $25-49.9 Million
Emp.: 100
Trade Journal Publisher
N.A.I.C.S.: 513120
Lee Maniscalco (CEO)

Unit (Domestic):

McKnight's Long Term Care News & Assisted Living (3)
900 Skokie Blvd Ste 114, Northbrook, IL 60062
Tel.: (847) 784-8706
Web Site: http://www.mcknights.com
Emp.: 8
Medical Trade Journal Publisher
N.A.I.C.S.: 513120
John O'Connor (VP, Assoc Publr & Dir-Editorial)

HAYS PLC

4th floor 20 Triton Street, London, NW1 3BF, United Kingdom
Tel.: (44) 2039782520   UK
Web Site: https://www.haysplc.com
Year Founded: 1987
HAS—(LSE)
Rev.: $8,945,881,308
Assets: $2,820,527,528
Liabilities: $1,739,510,864
Net Worth: $1,081,016,664
Earnings: $209,360,424
Emp.: 13,234
Fiscal Year-end: 06/30/22
Holding Company; Specialist Staffing Services
N.A.I.C.S.: 551112
Paul Venables (Grp Dir-Fin)

Subsidiaries:

3 Story Software LLC (1)
63 Bridge St, New Milford, CT 06776
Tel.: (860) 799-6366
Web Site: https://www.3storysoftware.com
Software Development Services
N.A.I.C.S.: 541511
Joseph Marsh (Sr VP)

HAYS Life Sciences UK (1)
4th floor 20 Triton Street, London, NW1 3BF, United Kingdom
Tel.: (44) 2034650090
Web Site: http://www.hays.co.uk
Pharmaceutical Human Resource Consulting Services
N.A.I.C.S.: 541612

Hays (Schweiz) AG (1)
Sihlstrasse 37, 8001, Zurich, Switzerland
Tel.: (41) 44 225 5000
Web Site: https://www.hays.ch
Sales Range: $25-49.9 Million
Emp.: 25
Specialist Recruitment Services
N.A.I.C.S.: 561311
Marc Lutz (Mng Dir)

Hays (Switzerland) Ltd. (1)
Rue Kleberg 6, 1201, Geneva, Switzerland
Tel.: (41) 229016000
Web Site: https://www.hays.ch
Sales Range: $25-49.9 Million
Emp.: 20
Specialist Recruitment Services
N.A.I.C.S.: 561311

Hays AG (1)
Willy-Brandt-Platz 1-3, 68161, Mannheim, Germany
Tel.: (49) 6 211 7880
Web Site: https://www.hays.de
Sales Range: $75-99.9 Million
Emp.: 400
Specialist Recruitment Services
N.A.I.C.S.: 561311

Klaus Breitschopf (Chm-Exec Bd)

Hays BV (1)
Ellen Pankhurststraat 1G, 5032 MD, Tilburg, Netherlands
Tel.: (31) 134686669
Web Site: https://www.hays.nl
Emp.: 200
Human Resource Consulting Services
N.A.I.C.S.: 541612

Hays Belgium NV (1)
Noordersingel 23, 2140, Antwerp, Belgium
Tel.: (32) 3 202 7970
Web Site: http://www.hays.be
Emp.: 40
Human Resource Consulting Services
N.A.I.C.S.: 541612
Robby Vanuxem (Mng Dir)

Hays Business Solutions Private Limited (1)
11th Floor Building 9B DLF Cyber City, Gurgaon, 122002, Haryana, India
Tel.: (91) 1244752500
Web Site: https://hbs.hays.in
Placement Recruitment Services
N.A.I.C.S.: 561311

Hays Colombia SAS (1)
Highway Nte 27 108, Bogota, Cundinamarca, Colombia
Tel.: (57) 15142482
Web Site: https://www.hays.com.co
Emp.: 10,000
Placement Recruitment Services
N.A.I.C.S.: 561311

Hays Czech Republic, s.r.o. (1)
Olivova 4/2096, 110 00, Prague, Czech Republic
Tel.: (420) 22 888 7915
Web Site: https://www.hays.cz
Sales Range: $10-24.9 Million
Emp.: 40
Specialist Staffing Services
N.A.I.C.S.: 561311
Kristyna Kralova (Mgr-Mktg & PR)

Hays Executive SASU (1)
147 Boulevard Haussmann, 75008, Paris, France
Tel.: (33) 14 299 1669
Web Site: https://www.hays-executive.com
Emp.: 250
Human Resource Consulting Services
N.A.I.C.S.: 541612

Hays FZ-LLC (1)
Block No 19 Knowledge Village, Dubai, 500340, United Arab Emirates
Tel.: (971) 4 559 5800
Web Site: http://www.hays.ae
Sales Range: $25-49.9 Million
Emp.: 40
Human Resource Consulting Services
N.A.I.C.S.: 541612

Hays Healthcare Limited (1)
6th Floor Valentines House 51-69 Ilford Hill, Ilford, IG1 2DG, Essex, United Kingdom
Tel.: (44) 20 8477 3666
Web Site: http://www.hays.com
Sales Range: $25-49.9 Million
Emp.: 40
Health Care Staff Recruiting Services
N.A.I.C.S.: 541612

Hays Holding GmbH (1)
Willy-Brandt-Platz 1-3, 68161, Mannheim, Germany
Tel.: (49) 62117880
Web Site: https://www.hays.de
Placement Recruitment Services
N.A.I.C.S.: 561311
Dirk Hahn (Co-Mng Dir)

Hays Holdings BV (1)
PO Box 4065, 5004 JB, Tilburg, Netherlands
Tel.: (31) 135910160
Sales Range: $50-74.9 Million
Emp.: 23
Investment Management Service
N.A.I.C.S.: 523999

Hays Holdings Limited (1)
20 Triton Street, London, NW1 3BF, United Kingdom
Tel.: (44) 2073832266
Web Site: http://www.hays.com

Emp.: 60
Holding Company
N.A.I.C.S.: 551112

Hays Hong Kong Limited (1)
6604-06 66/F ICC 1 Austin Road West, Kowloon, China (Hong Kong)
Tel.: (852) 2 521 8884
Web Site: https://m.hays.com.hk
Human Resource Consulting Services
N.A.I.C.S.: 541612

Hays Hungary Kft (1)
Szabadsag ter 7 Bank Center Granit torony, 1054, Budapest, Hungary
Tel.: (36) 704122206
Web Site: http://www.hays.hu
Sales Range: $25-49.9 Million
Emp.: 3
Human Resource Consulting Services
N.A.I.C.S.: 541612

Hays International Holdings Limited (1)
250 Euston Road, London, NW1 2AF, United Kingdom
Tel.: (44) 20 7383 2266
Web Site: http://www.hays.co.uk
Emp.: 6
Investment Management Service
N.A.I.C.S.: 523999

Hays Nord Est SASU (1)
Vauban building 4 Passage Lucilline, 76000, Rouen, France
Tel.: (33) 232125050
Web Site: http://www.hays.fr
Sales Range: $25-49.9 Million
Emp.: 8
Human Resource Consulting Services
N.A.I.C.S.: 541612
Raphaelle Martel (Mgr)

Hays Osterreich GmbH (1)
Europaplatz 3/5, 1150, Vienna, Austria
Tel.: (43) 15 353 4430
Web Site: https://www.hays.at
Sales Range: $25-49.9 Million
Emp.: 13
Specialist Recruitment Services
N.A.I.C.S.: 561311
Mark Frost (Mng Dir)

Hays Ouest SASU (1)
36 Boulevard Gabriel Guist Hau, 44000, Nantes, France
Tel.: (33) 251831620
Web Site: http://www.hays.fr
Emp.: 15
Human Resource Consulting Services
N.A.I.C.S.: 541612

Hays Overseas (Portugal) SGPS LDA (1)
Avenida da Republica 90 1st Floor Fraction 4, Lisbon, 1600-206, Portugal
Tel.: (351) 21 782 6560
Web Site: https://www.hays.pt
Emp.: 40
Human Resource Consulting Services
N.A.I.C.S.: 541612
Paula Batista (Mng Dir)

Hays Overseas Holdings Limited (1)
250 Euston Road, London, NW1 2AF, United Kingdom
Tel.: (44) 20 7383 2266
Web Site: http://www.hays.com
Emp.: 6
Investment Management Service
N.A.I.C.S.: 523999
Jacek Tarkowski (CEO)

Hays Personnel Espana Empresa de Trabojo Temporal SA (1)
Plaza Colon 2 - Torre 1 Plt Sexta, Madrid, 28046, Spain
Tel.: (34) 914430750
Web Site: http://www.hays.es
Human Resource Consulting Services
N.A.I.C.S.: 541612

Hays Personnel Services Espana SA (1)
Torre 2 planta 3, Madrid, 28046, Spain
Tel.: (34) 914430750
Web Site: http://www.hays.es
Human Resource Consulting Services
N.A.I.C.S.: 541612

Hays Poland Sp z.o.o (1)
ul Marszalkowska 126/134, 00-008, Warsaw, Poland
Tel.: (48) 22 584 5650
Web Site: http://www.hays.pl
Sales Range: $25-49.9 Million
Emp.: 11
Human Resource Consulting Services
N.A.I.C.S.: 541612
Michal Mlynarczyk (Mng Dir)

Hays Professional Solutions Osterreich GmbH (1)
Europaplatz 3/5, 1150, Vienna, Austria
Tel.: (43) 153534430
Placement Recruitment Services
N.A.I.C.S.: 561311

Hays Resource Management Japan K.K. (1)
Izumi Garden Tower 28th Floor 1-6-1 Roppongi, Minato-Ku, Tokyo, 106-6028, Japan
Tel.: (81) 33 560 1188
Web Site: https://www.hays.co.jp
Emp.: 100
Human Resource Consulting Services
N.A.I.C.S.: 541612

Hays S.A. de C.V. (1)
Av Paseo de las Palmas 405 Lomas - Viceroys Lomas de Chapultepec, Miguel Hidalgo, 11000, Mexico, Mexico
Tel.: (52) 5552492500
Web Site: https://www.hays.com.mx
Sales Range: $25-49.9 Million
Emp.: 16
Human Resource Consulting Services
N.A.I.C.S.: 541612
Gerardo Kanahuati (Gen Mgr)

Hays S.a.r.l (1)
65 Avenue de la Gare, 1611, Luxembourg, Luxembourg
Tel.: (352) 268654
Web Site: https://www.hays.lu
Sales Range: $25-49.9 Million
Emp.: 6
Human Resource Consulting Services
N.A.I.C.S.: 541612

Hays S.r.l (1)
Corso Italia 13, 20122, Milan, Italy
Tel.: (39) 0288 8931
Web Site: http://www.hays.it
Emp.: 60
Human Resource Consulting Services
N.A.I.C.S.: 541612

Hays SASU (1)
147 Boulevard Haussmann, 75008, Paris, France
Tel.: (33) 153732222
Web Site: https://www.hays.fr
Recruiting Services
N.A.I.C.S.: 561311

Hays Services NV (1)
Brugsesteenweg 255, 8500, Kortrijk, Belgium
Tel.: (32) 56230460
Web Site: http://www.hays.be
Emp.: 150
Human Resource Consulting Services
N.A.I.C.S.: 541612

Hays Slovakia s.r.o. (1)
Sturova 3, 811 02, Bratislava, Slovakia
Tel.: (421) 2 35 035 020
Web Site: http://www.hays.sk
Specialist Recruitment Services
N.A.I.C.S.: 561311

Hays Social Care Limited (1)
4th floor 20 Triton Street, London, NW1 3BF, West Yorkshire, United Kingdom
Tel.: (44) 1132345435
Professional Training Services
N.A.I.C.S.: 611430

Hays Solutions S.r.l (1)
Corso Italy 13, 20122, Milan, Italy
Tel.: (39) 0288893300
Web Site: http://www.hays-itservices.it
Placement Recruitment Services
N.A.I.C.S.: 561311

Hays Specialist Recruitment (Australia) Pty Limited (1)
Level 13 Chifley Tower 2 Chifley Square, Sydney, 2000, NSW, Australia

HAYS PLC

Hays PLC—(Continued)
Tel.: (61) 28 226 9600
Web Site: https://www.hays.com.au
Sales Range: $700-749.9 Million
Specialist Recruitment Services
N.A.I.C.S.: 561311

Hays Specialist Recruitment (Holdings) Limited
3rd Floor 14 St Georges Square, Huddersfield, HD1 1JF, West Yorkshire, United Kingdom
Tel.: (44) 1484517968
Web Site: http://www.hays.co.uk
Emp.: 9
Investment Management Service
N.A.I.C.S.: 523999

Hays Specialist Recruitment (Shanghai) Co. Limited
Unit 1205-1212 HKRI Centre One HKRI Taikoo Hui 288 Shimen Road No 1, Shanghai, 200041, China
Tel.: (86) 212 322 9686
Web Site: http://www.hays.cn
Human Resource Consulting Services
N.A.I.C.S.: 541612
Sean Ng *(Gen Mgr)*

Hays Specialist Recruitment Belgium (1)
Hays Brussels Avenue Louise, 1050, Brussels, Belgium
Tel.: (32) 2 541 1650
Web Site: https://www.hays.be
Sales Range: $25-49.9 Million
Emp.: 20
Specialist Recruitment Services
N.A.I.C.S.: 561311
Nathalie Alhadess *(Mng Dir)*

Hays Specialist Recruitment Brazil (1)
Av das Americas 3500, Barra da Tijuca, Rio de Janeiro, 13025-170, Brazil
Tel.: (55) 2124306600
Web Site: https://www.hays.com.br
Sales Range: $10-24.9 Million
Emp.: 30
Specialist Staffing Services
N.A.I.C.S.: 561311

Hays Specialist Recruitment Canada (1)
8 King Street East 20th Floor, Toronto, M5C 1B5, ON, Canada
Tel.: (416) 367-4297
Web Site: https://www.hays.ca
Sales Range: $10-24.9 Million
Emp.: 50
Specialist Recruitment Services
N.A.I.C.S.: 561311
Rowan Ogrady *(Pres)*

Hays Specialist Recruitment Denmark (1)
Kgs Nytorv 8, Copenhagen, Denmark
Tel.: (45) 33193200
Web Site: https://www.hays.dk
Sales Range: $25-49.9 Million
Emp.: 15
Specialist Staffing Services
N.A.I.C.S.: 561311

Hays Specialist Recruitment Dubai UAE (1)
Block No 19, Knowledge Village, 500340, Dubai, United Arab Emirates
Tel.: (971) 4 559 5800
Web Site: https://www.hays.ae
Sales Range: $25-49.9 Million
Emp.: 50
Specialist Staffing Services
N.A.I.C.S.: 561311
Chris Greaves *(Mng Dir)*

Hays Specialist Recruitment France (1)
147 bd Haussemann, 11 avenue Delcasse, 75008, Paris, France
Tel.: (33) 142991670
Web Site: http://www.hays.fr
Specialist Recruitment Services
N.A.I.C.S.: 561311

Hays Specialist Recruitment Hong Kong (1)
6604-06 66/F ICC 1 Austin Road West, Kowloon, China (Hong Kong)
Tel.: (852) 2 521 8884
Web Site: https://www.hays.com.hk
Sales Range: $25-49.9 Million
Emp.: 60
Specialist Staffing Services
N.A.I.C.S.: 561311

Hays Specialist Recruitment Hungary (1)
Szabadsag ter 7 Bank Center, 1054, Budapest, Hungary
Tel.: (36) 1 501 2400
Web Site: https://www.hays.hu
Sales Range: $25-49.9 Million
Emp.: 25
Specialist Recruitment Services
N.A.I.C.S.: 561311

Hays Specialist Recruitment Ireland (1)
26/27a Grafton Street, Dublin, Ireland
Tel.: (353) 1 571 0010
Web Site: https://www.hays.ie
Sales Range: $10-24.9 Million
Emp.: 50
Specialist Staffing Services
N.A.I.C.S.: 561311
Richard Eardley *(Mng Dir)*

Hays Specialist Recruitment Italy (1)
Hays Via Leonida Bissolati 76, 00187, Rome, Italy
Tel.: (39) 06 420 3841
Web Site: https://www.hays.it
Sales Range: $25-49.9 Million
Emp.: 3
Specialist Staffing Services
N.A.I.C.S.: 561311
Carlos Manuel Soave *(Mng Dir)*

Hays Specialist Recruitment Japan KK (1)
Izumi Garden Tower 28th Floor 1-6-1 Roppongi, Minato-ku, Tokyo, 106-6028, Japan
Tel.: (81) 33 560 1188
Web Site: https://www.hays.co.jp
Specialist Staffing Services
N.A.I.C.S.: 561311

Hays Specialist Recruitment Limited (1)
250 Euston Road, London, NW1 2AF, United Kingdom
Tel.: (44) 20 7383 2266
Web Site: http://www.hays.co.uk
Emp.: 65
Human Resource Consulting Services
N.A.I.C.S.: 541612

Hays Specialist Recruitment Luxembourg (1)
Hays 65 Avenue de la Gare, 1611, Luxembourg, Luxembourg
Tel.: (352) 268654
Web Site: https://www.hays.lu
Sales Range: $25-49.9 Million
Emp.: 15
Specialist Staffing Services
N.A.I.C.S.: 561311
Leslie Boutin-Sossah *(Assoc Dir)*

Hays Specialist Recruitment Netherlands (1)
Ellen Pankhurststraat 1G, 5032 MD, Tilburg, Netherlands
Tel.: (31) 134686669
Web Site: https://www.hays.nl
Sales Range: $25-49.9 Million
Emp.: 20
Specialist Recruitment Services
N.A.I.C.S.: 561311

Hays Specialist Recruitment New Zealand (1)
Level 12 PWC Tower 188 Quay Street, Auckland, 1010, New Zealand
Tel.: (64) 9 377 4774
Web Site: https://www.hays.net.nz
Sales Range: $10-24.9 Million
Emp.: 35
Specialist Staffing Services
N.A.I.C.S.: 561311
Jason Walker *(Mng Dir)*

Hays Specialist Recruitment Portugal (1)
Avenida da Republica 90 1 Fraccao 4, 1600-206, Andar, Portugal
Tel.: (351) 21 782 6560
Web Site: https://m.hays.pt
Sales Range: $10-24.9 Million
Emp.: 50
Specialist Staffing Services
N.A.I.C.S.: 561311

Hays Specialist Recruitment Private Limited (1)
2nd Floor A Wing Fortune 2000 Bandra Kurla Complex Bandra E, Mumbai, 400 051, India
Tel.: (91) 22 42 482500
Web Site: http://www.hays.in
Sales Range: $25-49.9 Million
Emp.: 25
Human Resource Consulting Services
N.A.I.C.S.: 541612

Hays Specialist Recruitment Pte Limited (1)
27-20 UOB Plaza 2 80 Raffles Place, Singapore, 048624, Singapore
Tel.: (65) 62234535
Emp.: 12,000
Specialist Recruitment Services
N.A.I.C.S.: 561311

Hays Specialist Recruitment Spain (1)
Paseo de la Castellana 81 10th floor, 28046, Madrid, Spain
Tel.: (34) 90 110 0099
Web Site: https://www.hays.es
Sales Range: $25-49.9 Million
Emp.: 55
Specialist Recruitment Services
N.A.I.C.S.: 561311

Hays Specialist Recruitment Sweden (1)
Hays Sturegallerian Stureplan 4C, Stureplan 4C, 114 35, Stockholm, Sweden
Tel.: (46) 86576100
Web Site: https://www.hays.se
Sales Range: $10-24.9 Million
Emp.: 50
Specialist Recruitment Services
N.A.I.C.S.: 561311

Hays Specialist Recruitment Warsaw (1)
ul Marszalkowska 126/134, 00-008, Warsaw, Poland
Tel.: (48) 22 584 5650
Web Site: https://m.hays.pl
Sales Range: $25-49.9 Million
Emp.: 80
Specialist Staffing Services
N.A.I.C.S.: 561311

Hays Sud Ouest SASU (1)
23 Rue La Fayette, 31000, Toulouse, France
Tel.: (33) 534445092
Web Site: http://www.hays.fr
Emp.: 600
Human Resource Consulting Services
N.A.I.C.S.: 541612
Emmanuel Arribat *(Office Mgr)*

Hays Talent Solutions Espana S.L. (1)
Calle Valencia 307 - 313, 08009, Barcelona, Spain
Tel.: (34) 934760103
Web Site: https://www.haystalentsolutions.com
Recruitment Services
N.A.I.C.S.: 561311

Hays Talent Solutions GmbH (1)
Volklinger Strasse 33, 40221, Dusseldorf, Germany
Tel.: (49) 2111793880
Web Site: http://www.hays.de
Sales Range: $25-49.9 Million
Emp.: 100
Human Resource Consulting Services
N.A.I.C.S.: 541612

Hays Technology Solutions GmbH (1)
Willy-Brandt-Platz 1-3, 68161, Mannheim, Germany
Tel.: (49) 62117880
Placement Recruitment Services
N.A.I.C.S.: 561311
Markus Auer *(Co-Mng Dir)*

INTERNATIONAL PUBLIC

Hays Technology Solutions Romania S.R.L. (1)
Premium Plaza 63-69 Dr Iacob Felix Street 7th floor, 011033, Bucharest, Romania
Tel.: (40) 724832298
Web Site: https://www.hays.ro
Recruitment Services
N.A.I.C.S.: 561311

Hays Travail Temporaire Luxembourg S.a.r.l (1)
15 Boulevard du Jazz, Belvaux, 4370, Sanem, Luxembourg
Tel.: (352) 2610601
Web Site: http://www.hays.lu
Placement Recruitment Services
N.A.I.C.S.: 561311

HaysP - Recrutamento, Seleccao e Empresa de Trabalho Temporario, Unipessoal, LDA (1)
Avenida Da Republica 90 1 Fraccao 4, Lisbon, 1600-206, Portugal
Tel.: (351) 910654994
Web Site: http://www.hays.pt
Sales Range: $25-49.9 Million
Emp.: 5
Human Resource Consulting Services
N.A.I.C.S.: 541612

Veredus Corp. (1)
4300 W Cypress St Ste 900, Tampa, FL 33607
Tel.: (813) 936-7004
Web Site: http://www.vereduscorp.com
Employment Agencies
N.A.I.C.S.: 561311
Dan Rodriguez *(CEO & Mng Dir)*

HAZAMA ANDO CORPORATION

1-9-1 Higashi-Shinbashi, Minato-ku, Tokyo, 105-7360, Japan
Tel.: (81) 335756001
Web Site: http://www.ad-hzm.co.jp
Year Founded: 1889
1719 (TKS)
Rev.: $2,605,186,080
Assets: $2,208,698,450
Liabilities: $1,187,651,750
Net Worth: $1,021,046,700
Earnings: $91,733,580
Emp.: 3,375
Fiscal Year-end: 03/31/24
Contracting & Civil Engineering Services
N.A.I.C.S.: 541330
Masato Fukutomi *(Pres)*

Subsidiaries:

Aoyama Kiko Co., Ltd. (1)
2-45 Yamanaka, Kitamoto, 364-0004, Saitama, Japan **(100%)**
Tel.: (81) 485919725
Web Site: http://www.aoyamakiko.co.jp
Emp.: 121
Construction Engineering Services
N.A.I.C.S.: 541330
Hiromitsu Maehara *(Pres)*

Geoscape Corporation (1)
2-2-5 Toranomon Kyodo Tsushin Kaikan 2F, Minato-ku, Tokyo, 105-0001, Japan
Tel.: (81) 335885990
Landscape Design Services
N.A.I.C.S.: 541320

Hazama Ando Thailand Co., Ltd. (1)
159 Serm-Mit Tower Building 15th Floor Sukhumvit Road 21 Soi Asoke, North Klongtoey Wattana, Bangkok, 10110, Thailand
Tel.: (66) 26652980
Construction Services
N.A.I.C.S.: 236220

Hazama Corporation (1)
Ste 220 1045 W Redondo Beach Blvd, Gardena, CA 90247-4163
Tel.: (310) 352-3066
Engineeering Services
N.A.I.C.S.: 541330

Hazama Corporation (1)
Hamburgo 206 Int 203, Mexico, 06600, DF, Mexico **(100%)**

Tel.: (52) 5555259311
Web Site: http://www.hazama.com
Sales Range: $25-49.9 Million
Emp.: 50
N.A.I.C.S.: 541330

Hazama Kogyo Co., Ltd. (1)
1-38-4 Kameido Asahiseimeikoto Building 6F, Koto-ku, Tokyo, 136-0071, Japan
Tel.: (81) 356267130
Construction Materials Whslr
N.A.I.C.S.: 423320

Hazama Philippines, Inc. (1)
Unit 304 Seddco I Bldg 120 Valero St Salcedo Vlg, 1229, Manila, Makati City, Philippines (100%)
Tel.: (63) 2 810 7651
Sales Range: $25-49.9 Million
Emp.: 5
N.A.I.C.S.: 541330

PT. Hazama Ando Murinda (1)
MidPlaza 1 Building 16th Floor Jl Jend Sudirman Kav 10-11, Jakarta, 10220, Indonesia
Tel.: (62) 215735774
Construction Services
N.A.I.C.S.: 236220

Vietnam Development Construction Co. Ltd. (1)
18th Floor Harbour View Tower 35 Nguyen Hue Street, District 1, Ho Chi Minh City, Vietnam
Tel.: (84) 2838299533
Construction Services
N.A.I.C.S.: 236220

HAZELDENE'S CHICKEN FARM PTY. LTD.
74 Hazeldene's Rd, Lockwood, 3551, VIC, Australia
Tel.: (61) 354311300
Web Site:
   http://www.hazeldenes.com.au
Year Founded: 1957
Emp.: 700
Poultry Farming Services
N.A.I.C.S.: 112990
John Hazeldene (Exec Dir)

HAZER GROUP LIMITED
Level 9 99 St Georges Tce, Perth, 6000, WA, Australia
Tel.: (61) 893293358
Web Site:
   https://www.hazergroup.com.au
HZR—(ASX)
Rev.: $994,365
Assets: $20,716,176
Liabilities: $11,175,604
Net Worth: $9,540,573
Earnings: ($12,576,876)
Fiscal Year-end: 06/30/22
Materials Recovery Facilities
N.A.I.C.S.: 562920
Andrew Cornejo (CTO)

HAZOOR MULTI PROJECTS LIMITED
C45 4th Floor plot210 C Wing Mittal Tower, Barrister Rajanai Patel Marg Nariman Point, Mumbai, 400002, Maharashtra, India
Tel.: (91) 2222000525
Web Site:
   https://www.hazoormultiproject.com
Year Founded: 1992
532467—(BOM)
Rev.: $93,063,151
Assets: $30,316,346
Liabilities: $20,566,472
Net Worth: $9,749,874
Earnings: $5,464,868
Emp.: 9
Fiscal Year-end: 03/31/23
Real Estate Development Services
N.A.I.C.S.: 531390
Dineshkumar Agrawal (CFO)

HB ESTATE DEVELOPERS LTD.
Plot No 31 Echelon Institutional Area Sector - 32, Gurgaon, 122001, Haryana, India
Tel.: (91) 1244675500   In
Web Site: http://www.hbestate.com
Year Founded: 1996
532334—(BOM)
Rev.: $7,098,832
Assets: $72,284,653
Liabilities: $50,755,338
Net Worth: $21,529,315
Earnings: ($2,139,301)
Emp.: 234
Fiscal Year-end: 03/31/22
Real Estate Investment & Development Services
N.A.I.C.S.: 531390
Lalit Bhasin (Chm & Mng Dir)

HB GLOBAL LIMITED
Weifang Road Juxian Industry Garden, Rizhao, Shandong, China
Tel.: (86) 6336175066
Web Site: http://www.hbglobal.asia
HBGLOB—(KLS)
Rev.: $10,532,095
Assets: $37,426,340
Liabilities: $9,008,501
Net Worth: $28,417,839
Earnings: ($23,219,152)
Fiscal Year-end: 12/31/22
Investment Holding Services
N.A.I.C.S.: 551112
Hengbao Shen (Founder & CEO)

HB GRANDI HF
Nordurgardur 1, 101, Reykjavik, Iceland
Tel.: (354) 5501000
Web Site: http://www.hbgrandi.com
Sales Range: $125-149.9 Million
Emp.: 900
Fishing & Fish Processing Services
N.A.I.C.S.: 311710
Kristjan Loftsson (Chm)

HB LEASING & FINANCE COMPANY LIMITED
Plot No 31 Echelon Institutional Area Sector - 32, Gurgaon, 122001, Haryana, India
Tel.: (91) 1244675500   In
Web Site: https://www.hbleasing.com
Year Founded: 1982
508956—(BOM)
Rev.: $74,841
Assets: $402,852
Liabilities: $91,090
Net Worth: $311,762
Earnings: $27,135
Emp.: 2
Fiscal Year-end: 03/31/22
Financial Lending Services
N.A.I.C.S.: 522220
Lalit Bhasin (Chm)

HB PORTFOLIO LTD.
Plot No 31 Echelon Institutional Area Sector - 32, Gurgaon, 122001, Haryana, India
Tel.: (91) 1244675500   In
Web Site:
   https://www.hbportfolio.com
Year Founded: 1994
532333—(BOM)
Rev.: $2,534,964
Assets: $29,562,651
Liabilities: $1,499,149
Net Worth: $28,063,502
Earnings: $881,397
Emp.: 6
Fiscal Year-end: 03/31/22
Merchant & Investment Banking Services

N.A.I.C.S.: 523150
Lalit Bhasin (Chm)

HB SOLUTION CO., LTD.
33 Techno 8-ro, Yuseong-gu, Daejeon, 305-500, Korea (South)
Tel.: (82) 429303900
Web Site: http://www.kmac.com
Year Founded: 1996
297890—(KRS)
Rev.: $143,889,415
Assets: $164,556,080
Liabilities: $54,876,617
Net Worth: $109,679,463
Earnings: $33,435,356
Emp.: 276
Fiscal Year-end: 12/31/22
Precision Analysis & Measurement Equipment Mfr
N.A.I.C.S.: 334515

Subsidiaries:

K-MAC Technology Corp. (1)
4F No 69 Ln 76 Ruiguang Rd, Neihu Dist, Taipei, 114, Taiwan
Tel.: (886) 287912656
Semiconductor Equipment Mfr
N.A.I.C.S.: 333242

HB SOLUTION CO., LTD.
77-26 Yeonamyulgeum-Ro Eumbong-Myun, Asan, 31413, South Choongcheong, Korea (South)
Tel.: (82) 415498850
Web Site: https://www.hb-solution.co.kr
Year Founded: 2001
297890—(KRS)
Rev.: $139,245,788
Assets: $159,245,494
Liabilities: $53,105,628
Net Worth: $106,139,866
Earnings: $32,356,323
Emp.: 276
Fiscal Year-end: 12/31/22
Display Component Mfr
N.A.I.C.S.: 334419
Heung-Geun Lee (Co-CEO)

HB STOCKHOLDINGS LIMITED
Plot No 31 Echelon Institutional Area Sector - 32, Gurgaon, 122001, Haryana, India
Tel.: (91) 1244675500   In
Web Site:
   https://www.hbstockholdings.com
Year Founded: 1985
532216—(BOM)
Rev.: $2,418,896
Assets: $9,649,922
Liabilities: $262,813
Net Worth: $9,387,109
Earnings: $2,072,897
Emp.: 7
Fiscal Year-end: 03/31/22
Securities Investment Services
N.A.I.C.S.: 523999
Mahesh Kumar Gupta (CFO)

HB TECHNOLOGY INC.
Sandong-ro 87, Eumbong-myeon, Asan, 31419, Chungcheongnamdo, Korea (South)
Tel.: (82) 415328730
Web Site:
   https://www.hbtechnology.co.kr
Year Founded: 1997
078150—(KRS)
Rev.: $113,557,812
Assets: $237,158,254
Liabilities: $78,980,298
Net Worth: $158,177,956
Earnings: $20,869,495
Emp.: 419
Fiscal Year-end: 12/31/22
Semiconductor & Display Equipment Mfr

N.A.I.C.S.: 334419
Sung-Joon Moon (CEO)

Subsidiaries:

HB Technology Inc. - Cheonan-si Plant (1)
Pungsesandan-ro 50 Pungse-myeon, Dongnam-gu, Cheonan, Chungcheongnam-Do, Korea (South)
Tel.: (82) 415328730
Semiconductor & Related Device Mfr
N.A.I.C.S.: 334413

HBF HEALTH LTD.
570 Wellington Street, Perth, 6000, WA, Australia
Tel.: (61) 892656111
Web Site: http://www.hbf.com.au
Year Founded: 1941
Sales Range: $5-14.9 Billion
Emp.: 850
Health Insurance Services
N.A.I.C.S.: 524114
Tony Iannello (Chm)

Subsidiaries:

HealthGuard Health Benefits Fund Ltd (1)
130 Egan Street, PO Box 513, Kalgoorlie, 6433, WA, Australia
Tel.: (61) 1300 308 712
Web Site: http://www.gmfhealth.com.au
Health Insurance Services
N.A.I.C.S.: 524114

HBIS GROUP CO., LTD.
No 385 Sports South Avenue, Shijiazhuang, 050023, Hebei, China
Tel.: (86) 31166778886
Web Site: https://www.hbisco.com
Year Founded: 1944
000709—(SSE)
Rev.: $19,864,605,353
Assets: $35,061,894,287
Liabilities: $25,860,385,786
Net Worth: $9,201,508,501
Earnings: $193,156,056
Emp.: 127,000
Fiscal Year-end: 12/31/22
Iron & Steel Products Smelting & Processing
N.A.I.C.S.: 331314
Yong Yu (Pres)

Subsidiaries:

Chengde Vanadium & Titanium New Materials Co., Ltd. (1)
No 1 of Gangcheng road, Luanhe town Shuangluan district, Chengde, 067102, Hebei, China
Tel.: (86) 3144076988
Steel Foundry Mfr
N.A.I.C.S.: 331513

Duferco International Trading Holding SA (1)
Via Bagutti 9, 6900, Lugano, Switzerland
Tel.: (41) 918225600
Emp.: 300
Steel Product Distr
N.A.I.C.S.: 423510

DufercoSteel Processing (Pty) Ltd (1)
1 Potassium Street Bay, Saldanha, 7395, South Africa
Tel.: (27) 227097000
Web Site: http://www.duferco.co.za
Steel Product Mfr & Distr
N.A.I.C.S.: 331110

HBIS Beijing International Trade Co., Ltd. (1)
16th Floor World Trade Mansion No 92 Jianguo Rd, Chaoyang District, Beijing, 100002, China
Tel.: (86) 1085897800
Steel Distr
N.A.I.C.S.: 423510

HBIS Carbon Assets Management Co., Ltd. (1)

HBIS GROUP CO., LTD.

HBIS Group Co., Ltd.—(Continued)
No 385 South Tiyu Street, Shijiazhuang, 050023, Hebei, China
Tel.: (86) 31166778692
Asset Management Services
N.A.I.C.S.: 523940

HBIS Commercial Factoring Co., Ltd. (1)
No 385 Tiyu South Street, Shijiazhuang, 050023, Hebei, China
Tel.: (86) 31166778847
Financial Management Services
N.A.I.C.S.: 523940

HBIS Digital Technology Co., Ltd. (1)
Tel.: (86) 31188990020
Web Site: https://www.hbisdt.com
Digital Platform Services
N.A.I.C.S.: 518210
Li Yiren *(Chm)*

HBIS Duferco International Trading Holding S.A. (1)
6 Rue Guillaume Schneider, 2522, Luxembourg, Luxembourg
Tel.: (352) 449846
Steel & Raw Material Distr
N.A.I.C.S.: 423390

HBIS Financial Leasing Co., Ltd. (1)
No 385 Tiyu South Street, Shijiazhuang, 050023, Hebei, China
Tel.: (86) 31166778625
Financial Lending Services
N.A.I.C.S.: 522220

HBIS Group Chengde Iron & Steel Company (1)
No 1 of Gangcheng Road, Luanhe town Shuangluan district, Chengde, 067102, Hebei, China
Tel.: (86) 3144076988
Vanadium Product Mfr
N.A.I.C.S.: 332999

HBIS Group Electricity Sales Co., Ltd. (1)
No 385 South Tiyu Street, Shijiazhuang, 050023, Hebei, China
Tel.: (86) 31166778853
Electric Power Distribution Services
N.A.I.C.S.: 221122

HBIS Group Finance Co., Ltd. (1)
No 385 Tiyu South Street, Shijiazhuang, 050023, Hebei, China
Tel.: (86) 31167807666
Financial Management Services
N.A.I.C.S.: 523940

HBIS Group Financial Management Cloud Technology Co., Ltd. (1)
No 385 South Tiyu Street, Shijiazhuang, 050023, Hebei, China
Tel.: (86) 31166508771
Financial Sharing Services
N.A.I.C.S.: 518210

HBIS Group Handan Iron & Steel Company (1)
No 232 FuXing Road, Handan, 056015, Hebei, China
Tel.: (86) 3106072141
Web Site: http://www.hdgt.com.cn
Steel Product Mfr & Distr
N.A.I.C.S.: 331110

HBIS Group Hengstrip Company (1)
29 Yuhua West Road, Hengshui, 053000, Hebei, China
Tel.: (86) 3182123762
Web Site: http://www.hsbbco.cn
Steel Products Mfr
N.A.I.C.S.: 331110

HBIS Group Investment Holding Co., Ltd. (1)
No 385 South Tiyu Street, Shijiazhuang, 050023, Hebei, China
Tel.: (86) 31166778747
Fund Management Services
N.A.I.C.S.: 523940

HBIS Group Purchasing Corporation (1)
No 385 Sports South Street, Shijiazhuang, 050023, Hebei, China
Tel.: (86) 31166778901
Steel Product Distr
N.A.I.C.S.: 423510

HBIS Group Sales Corporation (1)
No 385 Sports South Street, Shijiazhuang, 050023, Hebei, China
Tel.: (86) 4006010666
Steel Product Distr
N.A.I.C.S.: 423510

HBIS Group Shijiazhuang Iron & Steel Company (1)
363 Heping E Road, Shijiazhuang, 050031, Hebei, China
Tel.: (86) 31186913693
Steel Products Mfr
N.A.I.C.S.: 331110

HBIS Group Supply Chain Management Co., Ltd. (1)
No 385 Tiyu South Street, Shijiazhuang, 050023, Hebei, China
Tel.: (86) 31166778674
Bulk Commodity Logistics Services
N.A.I.C.S.: 484110

HBIS Group Tangshan Iron & Steel Company (1)
No 9 Binhe Road, Tangshan, 063000, Hebei, China
Tel.: (86) 3152702409
Web Site: http://www.tangsteel.com
Emp.: 33,000
Steel Product Mfr & Distr
N.A.I.C.S.: 331110
Wang Lanyu *(Chm & Sec)*

HBIS Group Wuyang Iron & Steel Company (1)
West Section of Hubin Avenue, Wugang, Shaoyang, Henan, China
Tel.: (86) 3758111139
Web Site: http://en.wygt.cn
Emp.: 10,000
Steel Plate Mfr & Distr
N.A.I.C.S.: 332312
Deng Jianjun *(Chm & Sec)*

HBIS Group Xuanhua Construction Machinery Co., Ltd. (1)
No 21 Fucheng South Street, Xuanhua District, Zhangjiakou, 075105, Hebei, China
Tel.: (86) 3133186077
Heavy Machinery Equipment Mfr & Distr
N.A.I.C.S.: 333120

HBIS Group Xuanhua Iron & Steel Company (1)
No 93 Xuanfu Street, Xuanhua District, Zhangjiakou, 075103, Hebei, China
Tel.: (86) 3138674421
Web Site: http://www.xuangang.com.cn
Steel Products Mfr
N.A.I.C.S.: 331110

HBIS Industrial Technology Service Co., Ltd. (1)
No 385 Tiyu South Street, Shijiazhuang, 050023, Hebei, China
Tel.: (86) 31167807666
Steel Products Mfr
N.A.I.C.S.: 331110

HBIS Limited (1)
No 385 Sports South Avenue, Shijiazhuang, 050023, Hebei, China
Tel.: (86) 31166770709
Steel Mfrs
N.A.I.C.S.: 331110

HBIS Mining (1)
Block B No 599 Ronghuaxi Road, Tangshan, 063000, Hebei, China
Tel.: (86) 3152793029
Mining Equipment & Iron Powder Mfr
N.A.I.C.S.: 333131

HBIS Sales Co. Ltd. (1)
No 385 Sports South Avenue, Shijiazhuang, 050023, Hebei, China
Tel.: (86) 4006010666
Steel Mfrs
N.A.I.C.S.: 331110

HBIS Serbia Iron & Steel d.o.o. (1)
Bulevar Mihajla Pupina 6, Novi Beograd, 11000, Belgrade, Serbia
Tel.: (381) 26692099
Web Site: http://www.hbisserbia.rs
Emp.: 5,000
Steel Product Mfr & Distr
N.A.I.C.S.: 331110

HBIS Serbia Ltd. (1)
Bulevar Mihajla Pupina 6, Novi Beograd, 11000, Belgrade, Serbia
Tel.: (381) 26695217
Web Site: https://hbisserbia.rs
Emp.: 5,000
Iron & Flat Steel Mfr
N.A.I.C.S.: 331210

Hansteel Company Ltd. (1)
Rm 1017-1020 Tongye Building 32 Tieling Road, Shanghai, 200092, China
Tel.: (86) 2165022290
Web Site: https://www.hansteel.net
Fabricated Steel Mfr
N.A.I.C.S.: 332312

Palabora Mining Co. Ltd. (1)
1 Copper Road, Phalaborwa, 1389, South Africa **(26.07%)**
Tel.: (27) 15 780 2911
Web Site: http://www.palabora.com
Sales Range: $1-4.9 Billion
Emp.: 1,800
Copper Mining
N.A.I.C.S.: 212230
Jinghua Han *(Chm & CEO)*

Subsidiary (Non-US):

Palabora Asia Pte Limited (2)
101 Thomson Rd, 21 04 United Sq, Singapore, 307591, Singapore
Tel.: (65) 62514744
Web Site: http://www.palabora.com
Sales Range: $25-49.9 Million
Emp.: 9
Metal Whslr
N.A.I.C.S.: 423510

Palabora Europe Limited (2)
3000 Cathedral Hil, Guildford, GU2 7YB, Surrey, United Kingdom
Tel.: (44) 1483 246636
Web Site: http://www.palabora.com
Sales Range: $25-49.9 Million
Emp.: 5
Metal Whslr
N.A.I.C.S.: 423510
Richard Knight *(Bus Mgr)*

Subsidiary (US):

Palabora US (2)
1000 Cobb Pl Ste 100, Kennesaw, GA 30144
Tel.: (770) 590-7970
Web Site: http://www.palabora.us
Sales Range: $25-49.9 Million
Emp.: 5
Ore Mining
N.A.I.C.S.: 423520
Sandra Delarm *(Gen Mgr)*

Qingdao HBIS New Material Technology Co., Ltd. (1)
No 107 Qianwangang Road, Huangdao Zone, Qingdao, 266510, Shandong, China
Tel.: (86) 53286831737
Steel Products Mfr
N.A.I.C.S.: 331110

South Africa Palabora Copper (Pty) Limited (1)
1 Copper Road, PO Box 65, Phalaborwa, 1389, Limpopo, South Africa
Tel.: (27) 157802911
Web Site: http://www.palabora.com
Refined Copper Mfr & Distr
N.A.I.C.S.: 331410
Jinghua Han *(Chm)*

Tangsteel Company Ltd. (1)
No 9 Binhe Road, Tangshan, 063000, Hebei, China
Tel.: (86) 3152702409
Web Site: https://www.tangsteel.com
Emp.: 33,000
Steel Mfrs
N.A.I.C.S.: 331110

Tie Tie Intelligence Logistics Co., Ltd. (1)
No 385 South Tiyu Street, Shijiazhuang, 050023, Hebei, China
Tel.: (86) 4006568111

INTERNATIONAL PUBLIC

Integrated Logistics Services
N.A.I.C.S.: 541614

Tie Tie IoT Technology Co., Ltd. (1)
No 385 Tiyu South Street, Shijiazhuang, 050023, Hebei, China
Tel.: (86) 4000608111
E-Commerce Platform Services
N.A.I.C.S.: 334511

HBIS RESOURCES CO., LTD.

No 21 Dongsheng Road, Xuanhua District, Zhangjiakou, 075105, Hebei, China
Tel.: (86) 31166500923
Web Site: https://www.hbiszy.com
Year Founded: 1999
000923—(SSE)
Rev.: $709,455,240
Assets: $2,167,794,252
Liabilities: $492,916,320
Net Worth: $1,674,877,932
Earnings: $93,547,116
Fiscal Year-end: 12/31/22
Construction Machinery Product Mfr
N.A.I.C.S.: 333120
Wang Yaobin *(Chm)*

HBL POWER SYSTEMS LTD.

No 8-2-601 Road No 10 Banjara Hills, Hyderabad, 500034, Telangana, India
Tel.: (91) 4066167777
Web Site: https://www.hbl.in
HBLPOWER—(NSE)
Rev.: $170,704,743
Assets: $154,601,442
Liabilities: $36,423,769
Net Worth: $118,177,673
Earnings: $12,817,691
Emp.: 1,663
Fiscal Year-end: 03/31/22
Automobile Batteries Mfr
N.A.I.C.S.: 335910
Kavita Prasad *(Exec Dir)*

Subsidiaries:

HBL Germany GmBH (1)
Emilienstrasse 24a, 08056, Zwickau, Germany
Tel.: (49) 37530355394
Web Site: https://www.hblpower.de
Storage Battery Mfr
N.A.I.C.S.: 335910

HBL Hong Kong Ltd. (1)
Rm 1417 Block A Hoi Luen Ctr 55 Hoi Yuen Rd, Kwun Tong Dist, Kowloon, China (Hong Kong)
Tel.: (852) 27502287
Batteries Mfr
N.A.I.C.S.: 335910

HBM HEALTHCARE INVESTMENTS AG

Bundesplatz 1, CH-6300, Zug, Switzerland
Tel.: (41) 417107577
Web Site: https://www.hbmhealthcare.com
HBMN—(SWX)
Rev.: $138,580,931
Assets: $2,002,847,007
Liabilities: $113,861,419
Net Worth: $1,888,985,588
Earnings: ($1,200,665)
Emp.: 700
Fiscal Year-end: 03/31/24
Privater Equity Firm
N.A.I.C.S.: 523999
Andreas Wicki *(CEO)*

Subsidiaries:

HBM Healthcare Investments (Cayman) Ltd. (1)
Governors Square, Suite #4-212-2 23 Lime Tree Bay Avenue West Bay, Georgetown, KY11204, Cayman Islands
Tel.: (345) 946 8002
Web Site: http://www.hbmbioventures.com

AND PRIVATE COMPANIES

HBM Partners Ltd. (1)
Investment Management Service
N.A.I.C.S.: 523999
Bundesplatz 1, 6300, Zug, Switzerland
Tel.: (41) 43 888 7171
Web Site: https://www.hbmpartners.com
Bond Investment Services
N.A.I.C.S.: 523999
Stanislas Poniatowski (Chm)

HBOIL JSC
110 Sonsgolon SHD 20-Horoo, 18135, Ulaanbaatar, Mongolia
Tel.: (976) 88119740
Web Site: http://www.hboil.mn
HBO—(MONG)
Sales Range: Less than $1 Million
Petroleum Refinery Services
N.A.I.C.S.: 324110

HBP ENERGY CORP.
4703 Central Plaza 18 Harbour Rd, Wanchai, China (Hong Kong)
Tel.: (852) 37963738
Year Founded: 2012
HBPE—(OTCIQ)
Sales Range: Less than $1 Million
Investment Management Service
N.A.I.C.S.: 523940

HBS REALTORS PVT. LTD.
505 Ceejay House Dr Annie Besant Road, Worli, Mumbai, 400 018, India
Tel.: (91) 2266210000
Web Site: http://www.hbsrealtors.com
Real Estate Support Services
N.A.I.C.S.: 531390
Hitesh Lalchandani (Head-Sls)

HC BERLIN PHARMA AG
Kurfurstendamm 190-192, D-10707, Berlin, Germany
Tel.: (49) 30700159660
Emp.: 10
Pharmaceuticals Mfr
N.A.I.C.S.: 325412
Ottmar W. Geiger (Member-Exec Bd)

HC GROUP, INC.
7/F Tower A1 Junhao Central Park Plaza No 10 Chaoyang Park South Road, Beijing, 100026, China
Tel.: (86) 1001065920172
Web Site: http://www.hcgroup.com
2280—(HKG)
Rev.: $2,355,895,854
Assets: $934,763,263
Liabilities: $474,443,752
Net Worth: $460,319,512
Earnings: ($32,308,286)
Emp.: 1,028
Fiscal Year-end: 12/31/22
Business Information Services
N.A.I.C.S.: 519290
Wee Ong Lee (CFO)

Subsidiaries:

HC Group Search Inc. (1)
1111 Bagby St Ste 1910, Houston, TX 77002
Tel.: (832) 460-7373
Web Site: https://www.hcgroup.global
Cutting Machine Mfr & Distr
N.A.I.C.S.: 333515

HC Group Search Ltd. (1)
25 Wilton Road Victoria Suite 451-452, London, SW1V 1LW, United Kingdom
Tel.: (44) 2073927777
Staffing & Recruitment Services
N.A.I.C.S.: 541612

HC Group Search Pte. Ltd. (1)
Level 57 Republic Plaza Raffles Place, Singapore, 048619, Singapore
Tel.: (65) 31587410
Staffing & Recruitment Services
N.A.I.C.S.: 541612

HC SEMITEK CORPORATION
8 Binhu Road East Lake Hi-tech Development Zone, Wuhan, 430223, Hubei, China
Tel.: (86) 2781929000
Web Site: https://www.hcsemitek.com
Year Founded: 2005
300323—(CHIN)
Rev.: $330,639,192
Assets: $1,555,508,448
Liabilities: $673,584,444
Net Worth: $881,924,004
Earnings: ($20,648,628)
Emp.: 800
Fiscal Year-end: 12/31/22
Light Emitting Diode (LED) Wafers & Chips Mfr
N.A.I.C.S.: 334413
Zhang Zhaohong (Chm)

HC SLINGSBY PLC
Otley Road, Baildon, Shipley, BD17 7LW, West Yorkshire, United Kingdom
Tel.: (44) 3301220712
Web Site: https://www.slingsby.com
SLNG—(AIM)
Rev.: $28,822,305
Assets: $20,165,429
Liabilities: $14,754,881
Net Worth: $5,410,548
Earnings: $292,806
Fiscal Year-end: 12/31/23
Range Of Industrial & Commercial Equipment Primarily Consisting Of Incidental Purchasing Supplies
N.A.I.C.S.: 423490
Dominic S. Slingsby (Chm & Dir-Ops)

Subsidiaries:

ESE Direct Limited (1)
Wensum Works 150 Northumberland Street, Norfolk, Norwich, NR2 4EE, United Kingdom
Tel.: (44) 160 362 9956
Web Site: https://www.esedirect.co.uk
Industrial & Commercial Equipment Distr
N.A.I.C.S.: 423440
Mark Wilson (Sls Mgr)

HC SURGICAL SPECIALISTS LIMITED
9 Raffles Place 26-01 Republic Plaza Tower 1, Singapore, 48619, Singapore
Tel.: (65) 62050345   SG
Web Site: https://www.hcsurgical.com
Year Founded: 2015
1B1—(SES)
Rev.: $13,938,496
Assets: $20,632,827
Liabilities: $9,907,373
Net Worth: $10,725,454
Earnings: $2,918,859
Emp.: 67
Fiscal Year-end: 05/31/24
Health Care Srvices
N.A.I.C.S.: 621999
Sieu Min Heah (CEO)

Subsidiaries:

CKH (Mt A) Pte. Ltd. (1)
3 Mount Elizabeth, Singapore, 228510, Singapore
Tel.: (65) 62540284
General Surgical Services
N.A.I.C.S.: 622110

Julian Ong Endoscopy & Surgery Pte. Ltd. (1)
Blk 710A Ang Mo Kio Ave 8 01-2629, Singapore, 561710, Singapore (51%)
Tel.: (65) 66940449
Web Site: https://drjulianong.sg
Health Care Srvices
N.A.I.C.S.: 621112

LAI BEC Pte. Ltd. (1)
3 Mt Elizabeth 05-06 Mt Elizabeth Medical Centre, Singapore, 228510, Singapore
Tel.: (65) 67370027
Health Care Srvices
N.A.I.C.S.: 621112

HCD INVESTMENT PRODUCING & TRADING JOINT STOCK CO
No 122B Quang Trung Str, Quang Trung Ward, Hai Duong, Vietnam
Tel.: (84) 2433518419
HCD—(HNX)
Plastic Materials Mfr
N.A.I.C.S.: 325211
Nguyen Duc Dung (Chm)

HCH. KETTELHACK GMBH & CO. KG
Birkenallee 183, Rheine, 48432, Germany
Tel.: (49) 59718640
Web Site: http://www.kettelhack.de
Year Founded: 1874
Rev.: $41,382,000
Emp.: 211
Textile Products Supplier
N.A.I.C.S.: 313310
Jan Kettelhack (Mng Dir)

HCI HAMMONIA SHIPPING AG
Burchardstrasse 8, D-20095, Hamburg, Germany
Tel.: (49) 40888810
Web Site: http://www.hci-hammonia-shipping.de
Sales Range: $75-99.9 Million
Freight Shipping Services
N.A.I.C.S.: 488510
Karsten Liebing (Member-Mgmt Bd)

Subsidiaries:

MS HAMMONIA BAVARIA Schiffahrts GmbH & Co. KG (1)
Elbchaussee 370, 22609, Hamburg, Germany
Tel.: (49) 40381080
Web Site: http://www.hammonia-reederei.de
Sales Range: $25-49.9 Million
Emp.: 70
Marine Shipping Services
N.A.I.C.S.: 488510
Karsten Liebing (Gen Mgr)

MS HAMMONIA MASSILIA Schiffahrts GmbH & Co. KG (1)
Burchardstrasse 8, D-20095, Hamburg, Germany
Tel.: (49) 40 88 88 10
Marine Passenger Transport Services
N.A.I.C.S.: 483112

MS HAMMONIA ROMA Schiffahrts GmbH & Co. KG (1)
Elbchaussee 370, 22609, Hamburg, Germany
Tel.: (49) 40381080
Cargo Handling Services
N.A.I.C.S.: 488320

MS HAMMONIA TEUTONICA Schiffahrts GmbH & Co. KG (1)
Elbchaussee 370, Hamburg, 22609, Germany
Tel.: (49) 40381080
Marine Shipping Services
N.A.I.C.S.: 488510

HCK CAPITAL GROUP BERHAD
Level 39 - 42 HCK Tower No 8 Jalan Damansara Empire City PJU 8, 47820, Petaling Jaya, Selangor Darul Ehsan, Malaysia
Tel.: (60) 379688668   MY
Web Site: https://www.hckgroup.my
Year Founded: 1999
HCK—(KLS)
Rev.: $38,850,370
Assets: $179,918,730
Liabilities: $127,348,360
Net Worth: $52,570,370
Earnings: $2,526,138
Fiscal Year-end: 12/31/22
Holding Company; Real Estate, Media, Food & Beverage, Hospitality & Technology
N.A.I.C.S.: 551112
Clement Chii Kok Hii (Founder & Chm)

Subsidiaries:

HCK Communications Sdn. Bhd. (1)
Wisma HCK No 6 Jalan 19/1B Seksyen 19, 46300, Petaling Jaya, Selangor, Malaysia
Tel.: (60) 79688668
Web Site: http://www.hckgroup.my
Emp.: 80
Media Holding Company
N.A.I.C.S.: 551112

HCL INFOSYSTEMS LIMITED

HCL INFOSYSTEMS LIMITED
A-11 First Floor Sector 3, Noida, 201 301, Uttar pradesh, India
Tel.: (91) 1202526490   In
Web Site: https://www.hclinfosystems.in
Year Founded: 1976
500179—(BOM)
Rev.: $15,148,770
Assets: $67,055,625
Liabilities: $96,418,140
Net Worth: ($29,362,515)
Earnings: $3,346,980
Emp.: 179
Fiscal Year-end: 03/31/22
Holding Company; Information Technology Products & Services
N.A.I.C.S.: 551112
Sushil Kumar Jain (Compliance Officer & Sec)

Subsidiaries:

HCL Avitas Private Limited (1)
Unit No 9 Suncity Business Tower Golf Course Road Sector 54, Gurgaon, 122 003, India
Tel.: (91) 1244502700
Information Technology Consulting Services
N.A.I.C.S.: 541512

HCL Comnet Limited (1)
Shop No 117 4th Floor Nelson Tower Wing Nelson Manickam Aminjikarai, Chennai, 600 029, India
Tel.: (91) 4449908801
Information Technology Consulting Services
N.A.I.C.S.: 541512

Subsidiary (Domestic):

HCL Comnet Systems and Services Limited (2)
806 Siddarth 96 Nehru Place, Delhi, 110 019, India
Tel.: (91) 1126444812
Information Technology Consulting Services
N.A.I.C.S.: 541512

HCL Learning Limited (1)
G - 8 & 9 Sector -3, Noida, 201 301, India
Tel.: (91) 9250003050
Web Site: http://www.hcllearning.com
Emp.: 120
Information Technology Training Services
N.A.I.C.S.: 541512

HCL Services Limited (1)
D-233 Sector-63, Noida, 201301, India
Tel.: (91) 860 180 3333
Web Site: http://www.hclservices.in
Information Technology Consulting Services
N.A.I.C.S.: 541512
Biswanath Bhattacharya (CEO)

Subsidiary (US):

HCL Touch Inc. (2)
203 N LaSalle St Ste 2100, Chicago, IL 60601
Tel.: (855) 425-2273
Information Technology Consulting Services
N.A.I.C.S.: 541512

HCL Talent Care Private Limited (1)
Sunnyside East Wing 2nd Floor 8/17 Sha-

3297

HCL INFOSYSTEMS LIMITED

HCL Infosystems Limited—(Continued)
fee Mohammed Road Nungambakkam,
Chennai, 600 034, India
Tel.: (91) 4440010600
Web Site: http://www.hcltalentcare.com
Information Technology Training Services
N.A.I.C.S.: 541512

HCL TECHNOLOGIES LTD.
Technology Hub SEZ Plot No 3A Sector 126, Noida, 201304, India
Tel.: (91) 1204306000
Web Site: https://www.hcltech.com
Year Founded: 1991
532281—(BOM)
Rev.: $10,415,769,000
Assets: $11,765,481,000
Liabilities: $3,564,288,000
Net Worth: $8,201,193,000
Earnings: $1,524,568,500
Emp.: 168,977
Fiscal Year-end: 03/31/21
Management Cousulting Service
N.A.I.C.S.: 541611
Rahul Singh *(COO)*

Subsidiaries:

AXON Group Limited (1)
Axon Centre Church Rd, Egham, TW20 9QB, Surrey, United Kingdom
Tel.: (44) 1784480800
Web Site: http://www.hcl-axon.com
Sales Range: $400-449.9 Million
Emp.: 8,500
Holding Company; Information Technology Systems Design, Support & Consulting Services
N.A.I.C.S.: 551112

Subsidiary (Domestic):

AXON Solutions Limited (2)
AxonCentre Church Rd, Egham, TW20 9QB, Surrey, United Kingdom
Tel.: (44) 1784480800
Web Site: http://www.hcl-axon.com
Sales Range: $100-124.9 Million
Emp.: 500
Information Technology Systems Design, Support & Consulting Services
N.A.I.C.S.: 541519
Stephen Cardell *(Pres)*

Subsidiary (Non-US):

AXON Solutions Sdn Bhd (2)
Level 5E-1B Enterprise 4 Technology Park
Malaysia, Bukit Jalil, 57000, Kuala Lumpur, Malaysia
Tel.: (60) 389941089
Web Site: http://www.hcl-axon.com
Sales Range: $75-99.9 Million
Emp.: 400
Technical Consulting
N.A.I.C.S.: 541611
Sheila Kaur *(Mng Dir)*

Actian Corporation (1)
2600 Great America Way Ste 401, Santa Clara, CA 95054 **(80%)**
Tel.: (650) 587-5500
Web Site: https://www.actian.com
Data Management Solutions
N.A.I.C.S.: 513210
Melissa Ribeiro *(Chief People Officer)*

Subsidiary (Non-US):

Actian Europe Limited (2)
Axon Centre Church Road, Egham, TW20 9QB, Surrey, United Kingdom
Tel.: (44) 17 5355 9500
Web Site: http://www.actian.com
Data Management Solutions
N.A.I.C.S.: 513210

Actian Germany GmbH (2)
Weimarer Str 1a, D-98693, Ilmenau, Germany
Tel.: (49) 367767850
Data Management Solutions
N.A.I.C.S.: 513210

Versant GmbH (2)
Halenreie 42, Hamburg, 22359, Germany **(100%)**

Tel.: (49) 40 60990 0
Web Site: http://www.actian.com
Designs, Develops, Markets & Supports Database Management Systems
N.A.I.C.S.: 541512

BigFix, Inc. (1)
1480 64th St Ste 200, Emeryville, CA 94608
Tel.: (510) 652-6700
Web Site: http://support.bigfix.com
Sales Range: $25-49.9 Million
Emp.: 200
Enterprise Systems & Security Management Solutions
N.A.I.C.S.: 513210

Butler America Aerospace LLC (1)
2 Trap Falls Rd Ste 204, Shelton, CT 06484
Tel.: (203) 926-2700
Web Site: https://butler.com
Airforce Defense Services
N.A.I.C.S.: 928110

Geometric Limited (1)
Unit No 703-A 7th floor B Wing Reliable Tech Park, Airoli Navi, Mumbai, 400 708, India
Tel.: (91) 22 6705 6500
Web Site: http://www.geometricglobal.com
Holding Company; Engineering Solutions Software Developer, Publisher & Distr
N.A.I.C.S.: 551112
Shashank Patkar *(Chief Transformation Officer)*

Subsidiary (US):

Geometric Americas, Inc. (2)
50 Kirts Blvd Ste A, Troy, MI 48084
Tel.: (248) 404-3500
Web Site: http://www.geometricglobal.com
Engineering Solutions Software Developer & Distr
N.A.I.C.S.: 513210

Branch (Domestic):

Geometric Americas, Inc. Scottsdale (3)
15974 N 77th St Ste 103, Scottsdale, AZ 85260-1790
Tel.: (480) 367-0132
Web Site: http://www.geometricglobal.com
CAM Programming Software Developer & Marketer
N.A.I.C.S.: 513210
Samantha Keane *(Coord-Sls)*

Subsidiary (Non-US):

Geometric China Inc. (2)
23B The World Square 855 South Pudong Rd, Pudong New Area, Shanghai, China
Tel.: (86) 2168881896
Web Site: http://www.geometricglobal.com
Engineering Solutions Software Developer & Distr
N.A.I.C.S.: 513210

Geometric Europe GmbH (2)
Frankfurter Ring 17, 80807, Munich, Germany
Tel.: (49) 89 37 42 665 00
Web Site: http://www.geometricglobal.com
Engineering Solutions Software Developer & Distr
N.A.I.C.S.: 513210

Subsidiary (Non-US):

Geometric SRL (3)
Parcul Mic Street 19-21 bl 2sc A Mezzanine, Brasov, 500386, Romania
Tel.: (40) 268 312 680
Web Site: http://www.geometricglobal.com
Engineering Software Development Services
N.A.I.C.S.: 541511

Subsidiary (Non-US):

Geometric Japan K.K. (2)
Hikari Bldg 9F 1-43-7 Yoyogi, Shibuya-Ku, Tokyo, 151-0053, Japan
Tel.: (81) 353043766
Web Site: http://www.geometricglobal.com
Engineering Solutions Software Developer & Distr
N.A.I.C.S.: 513210

HCL America, Inc. (1)
621 Capitol Mall Ste 2200, Sacramento, CA 95814
Tel.: (408) 733-0480
Web Site: https://www.hcltech.com
Rev.: $4,009,000,000
Assets: $2,802,000,000
Liabilities: $1,247,000,000
Net Worth: $1,555,000,000
Earnings: $131,000,000
Emp.: 300
Fiscal Year-end: 03/31/2024
Software Development & Consulting Services
N.A.I.C.S.: 541618

Division (Domestic):

HCL America, Inc. (2)
15 Exchange Pl Ste 730, Jersey City, NJ 07302
Tel.: (201) 680-7000
Web Site: http://www.hcltech.com
Sales Range: $25-49.9 Million
Technology Consulting
N.A.I.C.S.: 541690

Subsidiary (Domestic):

HCL Expense Management Services Inc. (2)
201 State Rt 17 12, Rutherford, NJ 07070
Tel.: (201) 933-2200
Web Site: http://www.controlpointsolutions.com
Sales Range: $10-24.9 Million
Emp.: 8
Telecommunications Expense Management Solutions
N.A.I.C.S.: 561499

HCL Technologies (Mass) Inc. (2)
400 Crown Colony Dr Ste 500, Quincy, MA 02169
Tel.: (617) 328-7131
Web Site: http://www.hcltech.com
Sales Range: $10-24.9 Million
Emp.: 6
Computer Software & Consulting Services
N.A.I.C.S.: 423430

PowerTeam, Inc. (2)
718 Washington Ave N ste 101, Minneapolis, MN 55401
Tel.: (612) 339-3355
Web Site: http://www.powerobjects.com
Sales Range: $25-49.9 Million
Emp.: 250
Computer System Design Services
N.A.I.C.S.: 541512
Alex Fagundes *(Dir & Chief Architect)*

HCL Argentina S.A. (1)
Avenida Cordoba 657 Piso 4 Oficina A, Buenos Aires, 1054, Argentina
Tel.: (54) 1143113004
Software Development Services
N.A.I.C.S.: 541511

HCL Australia Services Pty. Ltd. (1)
Level 8 1 Pacific Highway, North Sydney, 2060, NSW, Australia **(100%)**
Tel.: (61) 280815800
Web Site: http://www.hcltech.com
Sales Range: $25-49.9 Million
Emp.: 10
Software Development & Consulting Services
N.A.I.C.S.: 541512

Branch (Domestic):

HCL Australia Services Pty. Ltd. (2)
Level 8 11 Queens Road, Melbourne, 3004, VIC, Australia **(100%)**
Tel.: (61) 385069600
Web Site: http://www.hcltech.com
Sales Range: $25-49.9 Million
Emp.: 10
Software Development & Consulting Services
N.A.I.C.S.: 541512

Subsidiary (Non-US):

HCL New Zealand Ltd. (2)
Level 16 157 Lambton Quay, Wellington, 6011, New Zealand
Tel.: (64) 44626898
Web Site: http://www.hcl.com

INTERNATIONAL PUBLIC

Sales Range: $25-49.9 Million
Software Development & Consulting Services
N.A.I.C.S.: 541512

Branch (Domestic):

HCL New Zealand Ltd. (3)
Level 12 48 Emily Place, Auckland, 1010, New Zealand
Tel.: (64) 93699500
Web Site: http://www.hcl.com
Sales Range: $25-49.9 Million
Emp.: 14
Software Development & Consulting Services
N.A.I.C.S.: 541512
Anand Gupta *(CEO)*

HCL Axon (Pty) Ltd. (1)
The Boulevard Business Park Block B Ground Floor Searle Street, Woodstock, Cape Town, 7925, South Africa
Tel.: (27) 21 404 0000
Software Development Services
N.A.I.C.S.: 541511
Suman Roy *(Mng Dir)*

HCL BPO Services (NI) Limited (1)
Unit 2 6 Boucher Business Centre Apollo Road, Belfast, BT12 6HP, United Kingdom
Tel.: (44) 2890344120
Business Process Outsourcing Services
N.A.I.C.S.: 561499

HCL Bermuda Limited (1)
Appleby Cannon'S Court 22 Victoria Street, Hamilton, HM12, Pembroke, Bermuda
Tel.: (441) 295 2244
Software Development Services
N.A.I.C.S.: 541511

HCL Client/Server Applications Division (1)
3 Udyog Vihar Phase 1, Gurgaon, 122 016, Haryana, India **(100%)**
Tel.: (91) 124 643 9900
Web Site: http://www.hcltech.com
Software Development & Consulting Services
N.A.I.C.S.: 541512

HCL Core Technologies Division (1)
50 53 Greams Rd, Chennai, 600 006, India **(100%)**
Tel.: (91) 4428293298
Web Site: http://www.hcltech.com
Sales Range: $75-99.9 Million
Emp.: 450
Provider of Software Development & Consulting Services
N.A.I.C.S.: 541512
Ramamurthy Vaidyanathan *(Exec VP)*

HCL EAS Limited (1)
Axoncentre Church Rd, Egham, TW20 9QB, Surrey, United Kingdom
Tel.: (44) 1784 480 800
Information Technology Consulting Services
N.A.I.C.S.: 541512

HCL Great Britain Ltd. (1)
Axon Centre 4-12 Church Road, Egham, SL6 4FJ, Surrey, United Kingdom **(100%)**
Tel.: (44) 2071058610
Web Site: http://www.hcltech.com
Sales Range: $25-49.9 Million
Emp.: 30
Provider of Software Development & Consulting Services
N.A.I.C.S.: 541512
Rajiv Govil *(Dir-HR)*

HCL Hong Kong SAR Ltd (1)
20/F Tai Yip Building 141 Thomson Road, Wanchai, China (Hong Kong) **(100%)**
Tel.: (852) 22139205
Web Site: http://www.hcltech.com
Sales Range: $750-799.9 Million
Emp.: 55
Software Development & Consulting Services
N.A.I.C.S.: 541512

HCL Insurance BPO Services Ltd. (1)
HCL House 28-36 Eastern Road, Romford, RM1 3PJ, United Kingdom
Tel.: (44) 17 0875 8000
Emp.: 200

AND PRIVATE COMPANIES

Business Process Outsourcing Services
N.A.I.C.S.: 561499

HCL Japan Ltd. (1)
10F Sumitomo Fudosan Kudanshita Bldg,
3-5 Jimboucho Kanda Chiyoda-ku, Tokyo,
101 0051, Japan **(100%)**
Tel.: (81) 352262641
Web Site: http://www.hcljapan.jp
Sales Range: $75-99.9 Million
Emp.: 260
Software Development, Web Solutions &
Consulting Services
N.A.I.C.S.: 541512

HCL Netherlands B.V. (1)
Prinses Margrietplantsoen 50 9th Floor Unit
9 02/E Tower, 2595 BR, Hague,
Netherlands **(100%)**
Tel.: (31) 703012410
Web Site: http://www.hcltech.com
Sales Range: $75-99.9 Million
Emp.: 258
Provider of Software Development & Consulting Services
N.A.I.C.S.: 541512

**HCL Networking Products
Division** (1)
49 50 Nelson Manickam Rd, No 4 Moores
Rd Egmore, Chennai, 600 029,
India **(100%)**
Tel.: (91) 423741939
Web Site: http://www.hcltech.com
Sales Range: $75-99.9 Million
Emp.: 500
Provider of Software Development & Consulting Services
N.A.I.C.S.: 541512

HCL Poland Sp.z.o.o. (1)
Krakow Business Park ul Krakowska 280,
Zabierzow, 32-080, Poland
Tel.: (48) 12 390 9000
Web Site: http://www.hcltech.com
Sales Range: $75-99.9 Million
Emp.: 800
Software Development Services
N.A.I.C.S.: 541511

**HCL Technologies (Shanghai)
Limited** (1)
4th floor Block B 399 ShengXia Road Yaxin
Science & Technology Park, Pudong New
Area, Shanghai, 201210, China
Tel.: (86) 2120743888
Web Site: http://www.hcltech.com
Computer Software Development Services
N.A.I.C.S.: 541511

**HCL Technologies (Singapore)
Ltd.** (1)
8 Shenton Way 33 03 Temasek Tower, Singapore, 068811, Singapore
Tel.: (65) 62738288
Sales Range: $150-199.9 Million
Emp.: 1,000
Information Technology Services
N.A.I.C.S.: 541512

**HCL Technologies BPO Services
Ltd** (1)
Unit-2 Block-1 No 84 Greams Road, Thousand Lights, Chennai, 600 006, India
Tel.: (91) 44 6622 5522
Business Process Outsourcing Services
N.A.I.C.S.: 561499

**HCL Technologies Belgium
SA/NV** (1)
Rue des Colonies 11 Kolonienstraat, 1000,
Brussels, Belgium **(100%)**
Tel.: (32) 25176087
Sales Range: $25-49.9 Million
Emp.: 3
Software Development & Consulting Services
N.A.I.C.S.: 541512

**HCL Technologies Denmark
ApS.** (1)
Tuborg Boulevard 12 3rd Floor, 2900, Hellerup, Denmark
Tel.: (45) 3694 4405
Emp.: 10
Software Development Services
N.A.I.C.S.: 541511

HCL Technologies Europe Ltd. (1)
InSitu Centre 17 Ave Didier Daurat, BP 51,
31702, Blagnac, France
Tel.: (33) 534604546
Sales Range: $25-49.9 Million
Provider of Software Development & Consulting Services
N.A.I.C.S.: 541512

HCL Technologies GmbH (1)
Frankfurter Strasse 63 69, 65760, Eschborn, Germany **(100%)**
Tel.: (49) 6196769970
Sales Range: $25-49.9 Million
Emp.: 120
Provider of Software Development & Consulting Services
N.A.I.C.S.: 541512

HCL Technologies Norway AS (1)
Fridtjof Nansensvei 14, 0369, Oslo, Norway
Tel.: (47) 99 500 107
Software Development Services
N.A.I.C.S.: 541511

HCL Technologies Sweden AB (1)
Stureplan 4C 4th Fl, 11435, Stockholm,
Sweden **(100%)**
Tel.: (46) 8398842
Web Site: http://www.hcltechnologies.se
Provider of Software Development & Consulting Services
N.A.I.C.S.: 541512

**Sankalp Semiconductor Private
Limited** (1)
401E B Wing East Special Economic Zone,
20 & 21 Sarjapura Outer Ring Road, Bengaluru, 560103, Karnataka, India
Tel.: (91) 8049356500
Web Site: https://www.sankalpsemi.com
Semiconductor Mfr & Distr
N.A.I.C.S.: 334413

Sankalp USA Inc. (1)
2225 E Bayshore Rd Ste 200, Palo Alto, CA
94303
Tel.: (650) 549-7940
Semiconductor Mfr & Distr
N.A.I.C.S.: 334413

**Sankguj Semiconductor Private
Limited** (1)
Plot No 9 Survey No 89 Aryabhatta Tech
Park, Navanagar, Hubli, 580 025, India
Tel.: (91) 8363980300
Web Site: https://www.sankalpsemi.com
Semiconductor Mfr & Distr
N.A.I.C.S.: 334413

TELERx Marketing, Inc. (1)
410 Horsham Rd, Horsham, PA 19044-2205
Web Site: http://www.c3isolutions.com
Customer Care Contact Center Outsourcing
N.A.I.C.S.: 541613
Robert Piwko (Exec VP-Global Acct Mgmt)

Subsidiary (Domestic):

C3i, Inc. (2)
2200 Rennaissance Blvd Ste 370, King of
Prussia, PA 19406
Tel.: (267) 942-3300
Web Site: http://www.c3i-inc.com
Sales Range: $25-49.9 Million
Emp.: 80
Office Computer Automation Systems Integration
N.A.I.C.S.: 541512
Joel H. Morse (Pres)

Global Safety Surveillance, Inc. (2)
150 Clove Rd Ste 2, Little Falls, NJ 07424
Tel.: (973) 812-7575
Sales Range: $1-9.9 Million
Emp.: 85
Technology Enabled Solutions & Services
for Global Drug Safety
N.A.I.C.S.: 541519
Craig Hatton (Dir-Comml Solutions)

HCP PLASTENE BULKPACK LTD.

H B Jirawala House 13 Nav Bharat
society, Usmanpura, Ahmedabad,
380013, Gujarat, India
Tel.: (91) 7927561000
Web Site: https://hpbl.in
Year Founded: 1984
526717—(BOM)
Rev.: $779,592
Assets: $9,710,555
Liabilities: $19,810,231
Net Worth: ($10,099,676)
Earnings: ($2,826,041)
Emp.: 3
Fiscal Year-end: 03/31/20
Polypropylene Woven Sacks Mfr
N.A.I.C.S.: 314910
Manoj M. Somani (Chm & Mng Dir)

HCR CO., LTD.

6F Building 102 Yard A 10 North
Jiuxianqiao Road, Chaoyang District,
Beijing, 100016, China
Tel.: (86) 1052027125
Web Site: https://www.hcr.com.cn
Year Founded: 2008
688500—(SHG)
Rev.: $69,954,019
Assets: $170,535,990
Liabilities: $36,560,020
Net Worth: $133,975,970
Earnings: ($26,554,877)
Fiscal Year-end: 12/31/22
Information Technology Services
N.A.I.C.S.: 541512
Long Zhao (Chm & Gen Mgr)

HCS BETEILIGUNGSGESELLSCHAFT MBH

Bockenheimer Landstrasse 2-4,
60306, Frankfurt am Main, Germany
Tel.: (49) 69264846280
Web Site: http://www.hcs-beteiligungen.de
Investment Services
N.A.I.C.S.: 523999

Subsidiaries:

AGO AG Energie + Anlagen (1)
Am Goldenen Feld 23, 95326, Kulmbach,
Germany **(70%)**
Tel.: (49) 9221 6020
Web Site: http://www.ago.ag
Sales Range: $75-99.9 Million
Emp.: 179
Project Development, Power Facility Maintenance & Operation & Consulting Services
for Energy Industry
N.A.I.C.S.: 333613
Gunther Hein (Member-Exec Bd)

Subsidiary (Non-US):

AGO Energy (Pty) Ltd. (2)
Unit 6 Beach Blvd, Table View, 7441, Western Cape, South Africa **(100%)**
Tel.: (27) 83 492 8755
Web Site: http://www.ago-energy.co.za
Energy Supply Systems Mfr
N.A.I.C.S.: 237130
Uwe Kern (Co-Mng Dir)

Subsidiary (Domestic):

**Fittings GmbH Formstucke +
Anlagen** (2)
Justus-Liebig-Strasse 24, 99087, Erfurt,
Germany **(75%)**
Tel.: (49) 361 65 34 021
Pipe System Mfr
N.A.I.C.S.: 332996

HCT CO., LTD.

74 Seoicheon-ro 578beongil Majangmyeon, Icheon, Gyeonggi-do, Korea
(South)
Tel.: (82) 316456300
Web Site: http://www.hct.co.kr
Year Founded: 2000
072990—(KRS)
Rev.: $51,477,009
Assets: $101,683,370
Liabilities: $43,222,892
Net Worth: $58,460,479
Earnings: $4,225,177
Emp.: 410
Fiscal Year-end: 12/31/22
Scientific Inspection Services
N.A.I.C.S.: 541990
Bong-Jai Huh (Pres & CEO)

Subsidiaries:

HCT America LLC (1)
1726 Ringwood Ave, San Jose, CA 95131
Tel.: (510) 933-8848
Web Site: https://hctamerica.com
Wireless Testing & Certification Services
N.A.I.C.S.: 541380

HD DUNAV AD

Stoyan Kyalachev 6 P K 31, 3000,
Vratsa, 3000, Bulgaria
Tel.: (359) 877088458
Web Site: https://www.holding-dunav.com
HDDV—(BUL)
Sales Range: Less than $1 Million
Holding Company
N.A.I.C.S.: 551112
Radoslava Penkova (Dir-IR)

HD HYUNDAI CO., LTD

50 Techno sunhwan-ro 3-gil, Yugaeup Dalseong-gun Daegu, 43022,
Daejeon, Korea (South)
Tel.: (82) 5315889997
Web Site: https://www.hd-hyundai.com
267250—(KRS)
Rev.: $25,906,047
Assets: $32,950,403
Liabilities: $22,013,904
Net Worth: $10,936,500
Earnings: $171,131
Emp.: 51
Fiscal Year-end: 12/31/21
Holding Company
N.A.I.C.S.: 551112
Kwon Oh-Gap (Chm & CEO)

HD HYUNDAI ENERGY SOLUTIONS CO.,LTD.

477 Bundangsuseo-ro, Bundang-gu,
Seongnam, Gyeonggi-do, Korea
(South)
Tel.: (82) 15225001
Web Site: https://www.hyundai-es.co.kr
Year Founded: 2016
322000—(KRS)
Rev.: $755,351,121
Assets: $500,717,511
Liabilities: $208,081,586
Net Worth: $292,635,925
Earnings: $46,487,972
Emp.: 248
Fiscal Year-end: 12/31/22
Semiconductor Device Mfr & Distr
N.A.I.C.S.: 334413

HD HYUNDAI INFRACORE CO., LTD.

489 Injung-ro, Dong-gu, Incheon, Korea (South)
Tel.: (82) 322111114
Web Site: https://www.hd-infracore.com
Year Founded: 1937
042670—(KRS)
Rev.: $3,647,939,056
Assets: $3,633,024,039
Liabilities: $2,378,947,624
Net Worth: $1,254,076,415
Earnings: $176,234,684
Emp.: 4,465
Fiscal Year-end: 12/31/22
Construction Machinery Mfr
N.A.I.C.S.: 333120
Cho Young Cheul (Pres & Exec Dir)

Subsidiaries:

**Doosan Infracore America
Corporation** (1)
2905 Shawnee Industrial Way, Suwanee,
GA 30024

HD HYUNDAI INFRACORE CO., LTD.

HD Hyundai Infracore Co., Ltd.—(Continued)
Tel.: (770) 831-2200
Web Site: http://usa.doosaninfracore.co.kr
Construction Equipment Mfr
N.A.I.C.S.: 333120

Subsidiary (Domestic):

Bobcat Company (2)
250 E Beaton Dr, West Fargo, ND 58078-6000
Tel.: (701) 241-8700
Web Site: https://www.bobcat.com
Sales Range: $1-4.9 Billion
Farm & Industrial Equipment Mfr
N.A.I.C.S.: 333111

Doosan Infracore Germany GmbH (1)
Hans-Boeckler-Strasse 27-29, 40764, Langenfeld, Germany
Tel.: (49) 2173 85090
Industrial Machinery Mfr
N.A.I.C.S.: 333248

Doosan Infracore India Private Co., Ltd. (1)
No 67 3RD Floor Tnpl Building, Guindy, Chennai, 600032, India
Tel.: (91) 42223900
Construction Equipment Mfr
N.A.I.C.S.: 333120

Doosan Infracore XinJiang Machinery Co., Ltd. (1)
No 178 Hetanbei Road, Wurumuqi, Xinjiang, China
Tel.: (86) 9914697217
Forklift & Other Hydraulic Excavator Mfr
N.A.I.C.S.: 333924

Geith International Ltd (1)
Unit 5/6 C Swords Business Campus, Swords Co Dublin, Meath, K67 F5P7, Ireland
Tel.: (353) 16502100
Web Site: https://www.geith.com
Sales Range: $50-74.9 Million
Emp.: 140
Construction & Excavation Attachment Mfr
N.A.I.C.S.: 333120
Andrew Bacom *(Mng Dir)*

Subsidiary (Non-US):

Agent Commercial France de Geith International Ltd. (2)
11 Rue Champ Lyon, 69800, Saint Priest, Dolin, France
Tel.: (33) 800916626
Web Site: http://www.geith.com
Heavy Equipment Attachment Mfr
N.A.I.C.S.: 333120

Subsidiary (US):

Geith Inc. (2)
2905 Shawnee Industrial Way, Suwanee, GA 30024
Web Site: http://www.geith.com
Heavy Equipment Attachment Mfr
N.A.I.C.S.: 333120

Subsidiary (Non-US):

Geith International Ltd. (2)
Unit 6 3 Heol Y Gamlas, Parc Nantgarw, Cardiff, CF15 7QU, United Kingdom
Tel.: (44) 2039361232
Web Site: http://www.geith.com
Sales Range: $25-49.9 Million
Emp.: 4
Heavy Equipment Attachment Mfr
N.A.I.C.S.: 333120
Robert Welsh *(Mgr-Sls)*

Global Parts, S.r.l (2)
Via Lamarmora 12, Livorno, Italy
Tel.: (39) 0586903076
Web Site: https://www.globalparts.it
Construction & Excavation Attachment Mfr
N.A.I.C.S.: 333120

HDC HOLDINGS CO., LTD.
8th 9th Floors HDC IPARK Mall 55 Hangang-daero 23-gil, Yongsan-gu, Seoul, 04377, Korea (South)
Tel.: (82) 220089114
Web Site: https://www.hdc-dvp.com
Year Founded: 1986
012630—(KRS)
Rev.: $3,869,472,456
Assets: $8,891,325,730
Liabilities: $5,184,538,371
Net Worth: $3,706,787,359
Earnings: ($3,920,316)
Emp.: 13
Fiscal Year-end: 12/31/22
Construction Engineering Services
N.A.I.C.S.: 541330
Ik-Hoon Choi *(Chm, CEO & Exec Dir)*

HDC HYUNDAI DEVELOPMENT COMPANY
8th 9th floors HDC IPARK Mall 55 Hangang-daero 23-gil, Yongsan-gu, Seoul, 04377, Korea (South)
Tel.: (82) 220089114
Web Site: https://www.hdc-dvp.com
Year Founded: 2018
294870—(KRS)
Rev.: $2,529,795,825
Assets: $5,626,962,509
Liabilities: $3,401,226,437
Net Worth: $2,225,736,072
Earnings: $38,631,496
Emp.: 1,830
Fiscal Year-end: 12/31/22
Construction Engineering Services
N.A.I.C.S.: 541330
Choi Ik Hoon *(Chm, Pres, CEO & Exec Dir)*

Subsidiaries:

Hotel HDC Co., Ltd. (1)
4th Floor 421 Yeongdong-daero, Gangnam-gu, Seoul, Korea (South)
Tel.: (82) 220164511
Web Site: https://www.hdc-hotel.com
Emp.: 596
Hotel Services
N.A.I.C.S.: 721110

HDC HYUNDAI ENGINEERING PLASTICS CO., LTD.
1221-32 Daehoman-ro, Seokmunmyeon, Dangjin, 343-856, Chungcheongnam-do, Korea (South)
Tel.: (82) 413500500
Web Site: https://www.hdc-hyundaiep.com
Year Founded: 2000
089470—(KRS)
Rev.: $802,189,963
Assets: $462,754,276
Liabilities: $222,325,490
Net Worth: $240,428,787
Earnings: $8,828,263
Emp.: 374
Fiscal Year-end: 12/31/22
Plastic Materials Mfr
N.A.I.C.S.: 326199
Joong Kyu Chung *(CEO)*

HDC LABS CO., LTD.
HDC Labstower 346 Hyoryeong-ro, Seocho-gu, Seoul, 06722, Gyeonggi, Korea (South)
Tel.: (82) 18991909
Web Site: http://www.hdc-icontrols.com
Year Founded: 1999
039570—(KRS)
Rev.: $482,477,551
Assets: $302,437,720
Liabilities: $96,429,507
Net Worth: $205,808,213
Earnings: $9,820,340
Emp.: 5,404
Fiscal Year-end: 12/31/22
Electronic Components Mfr
N.A.I.C.S.: 334419
Seong Eun Kim *(CEO)*

HE BEI CHENG DE LOLO COMPANY LIMITED
No 8 West Area Hi-tech Industrial Development Zone, Chengde, 067000, Hebei, China
Tel.: (86) 3142059888
Web Site: http://www.lolo.com.cn
Year Founded: 1997
000848—(SSE)
Rev.: $377,959,608
Assets: $535,308,696
Liabilities: $143,071,812
Net Worth: $392,236,884
Earnings: $84,505,356
Emp.: 800
Fiscal Year-end: 12/31/22
Vegetable Beverage Mfr
N.A.I.C.S.: 311421
Liang Qichao *(Chm, Vice Chm, Pres & Gen Mgr)*

HEAD B.V.
Prins Bernhardplein 200, 1097, Amsterdam, Netherlands
Tel.: (31) 206251291   NI
Web Site: http://www.head.com
Sales Range: $400-449.9 Million
Sports Equipment & Apparel Mfr
N.A.I.C.S.: 339920
Ralf Bernhart *(Deputy Chm-Mgmt Bd)*

Subsidiaries:

Concept Systems Inc. (1)
136 E State St, Ithaca, NY 14850
Tel.: (607) 272-1206
Web Site: https://www.conceptsystems.com
Management Consulting Services
N.A.I.C.S.: 541618
Mary Kane *(Pres)*

HTM USA Holdings Inc. (1)
3125 Sterling Cir Ste 101, Boulder, CO 80301
Tel.: (800) 874-3235
Sport Equipment Distr
N.A.I.C.S.: 423910

Head Canada Inc. (1)
935A Southgate Drive Unit 4, PO Box 3620, Guelph, N1L 0B9, ON, Canada
Tel.: (519) 822-1576
Sport Equipment Distr
N.A.I.C.S.: 423910

Head France S.A.S. (1)
Zone Artisanale les Condamines, BP 29, Bresson, 38321, France
Tel.: (33) 476626900
Emp.: 50
Sport Equipment Distr
N.A.I.C.S.: 423910
Nicolas Saur *(Gen Mgr)*

Head Germany GmbH (1)
Velaskostrasse 8, Feldkirchen, 85622, Germany
Tel.: (49) 899099950
Sport Equipment Distr
N.A.I.C.S.: 423910
Tassilo Weinzierl *(Mgr-Product Category)*

Head Holding Unternehmensbeteiligung GmbH (1)
Tyroliapl 1, 1010, Vienna, Austria
Tel.: (43) 1 701790
Holding Company
N.A.I.C.S.: 551112

Head Japan Co., Ltd. (1)
3-27 Kanda-Jimbocho, Chiyoda-ku, Tokyo, 101-0051, Japan
Tel.: (81) 332217921
Sport Equipment Distr
N.A.I.C.S.: 423910

Head Spain S.A. (1)
Roger 65-67 5, 08028, Barcelona, Spain
Tel.: (34) 934092080
Sport Equipment Distr
N.A.I.C.S.: 423910

Head Sport GmbH (1)
Wuhrkopfweg 1, 6921, Kennelbach, Austria
Tel.: (43) 55746080
Sport Equipment Distr
N.A.I.C.S.: 423910

Head Technology GmbH (1)
Widmaierstr 144, 70567, Stuttgart, Germany
Tel.: (49) 71112173261
Sport Equipment Distr
N.A.I.C.S.: 423910

Head UK Ltd (1)
2 Beezon Road, Kendal, LA9 6BW, United Kingdom
Tel.: (44) 1539724740
Sport Equipment Distr
N.A.I.C.S.: 423910

Head/Penn Racquet Sports (1)
306 S 45th Ave, Phoenix, AZ 85043-3913
Tel.: (602) 269-1492
Web Site: http://www.pennracquet.com
Sales Range: $200-249.9 Million
Emp.: 800
Tennis Balls, Racquetballs & Accessories Mfr & Marketer
N.A.I.C.S.: 339920

Mares (1)
Salita Bonsen 4, 16035, Rapallo, Italy
Tel.: (39) 01852011
Web Site: http://www.mares.com
Sales Range: $50-74.9 Million
Emp.: 170
Sporting & Athletic Equipment
N.A.I.C.S.: 339920
Gerald Skrobanek *(Gen Mgr)*

Mares America (1)
1 Selleck St, Norwalk, CT 06855-1120
Tel.: (203) 855-0631
Web Site: http://www.mares.com
Sales Range: $25-49.9 Million
Emp.: 10
Diving Equipment Mfr
N.A.I.C.S.: 339920

Subsidiary (Domestic):

Dacor Corporation (2)
Shore Pointe 1 Selleck St, Norwalk, CT 06855
Tel.: (203) 852-7079
Sales Range: $25-49.9 Million
Scuba Equipment Mfr
N.A.I.C.S.: 339920

Mares Asia Pacific Ltd. (1)
Unit 1502-03 15/F Park Building 476 Castle Peak Road, Kowloon, China (Hong Kong)
Tel.: (852) 23070310
Sport Equipment Distr
N.A.I.C.S.: 423910

SSI International (HK) Ltd. (1)
Unit A 5/F Eastern Flower Centre 22-24 Cameron Road, Tsim Sha Tsui, Kowloon, China (Hong Kong)
Tel.: (852) 23070310
Sport Equipment Distr
N.A.I.C.S.: 423910

SSI International GmbH (1)
Johann-Hollfritsch-Str 6, 90530, Wendelstein, Germany
Tel.: (49) 91299099380
Web Site: http://www.divessi.com
Sporting Goods Mfr
N.A.I.C.S.: 339920

Tyrolia Technology GmbH (1)
DI Christoph Wurm Tyroliaplatz 1, Schwechat, Austria
Tel.: (43) 1701790
Web Site: http://www.tyrolia-technology.com
Machine Tools Mfr
N.A.I.C.S.: 333517

HEAD INVEST OY
Rantakatu 4, 90100, Oulu, Finland
Tel.: (358) 201432300   FI
Web Site: http://www.headinvest.fi
Sales Range: $200-249.9 Million
Emp.: 302
Investment Holding Company
N.A.I.C.S.: 551112
Pekka Sipola *(CFO)*

Subsidiaries:

Head Asset Management Oy (1)
Etelaesplanadi 24 A, 00130, Helsinki, Finland
Tel.: (358) 9 25115 20
Web Site: http://www.headassetmanagement.fi

AND PRIVATE COMPANIES — HEADWATER EXPLORATION INC.

Securities Brokerage Services
N.A.I.C.S.: 523150

JOT Automation Ltd. (1)
Elektroniikkatie 17, Oulu, 90590, Finland
Tel.: (358) 103015000
Web Site: http://www.jotautomation.com
Testing & Production Automation Equipment Mfr
N.A.I.C.S.: 333248
Jiafu Wu *(Chm)*

Subsidiary (Non-US):

JOT Automation Beijing Ltd. (2)
Building A Da Chen Park No 10 Jing Yuan Street, Economic & Technological Development Area, 100176, Beijing, China
Tel.: (86) 10 5979 0809
Industrial Machinery & Equipment Distr
N.A.I.C.S.: 423830
Xu Mingshuo *(Mgr-Sls)*

Subsidiary (US):

JOT Automation Inc. (2)
9465 Customhouse Plz SE B & C, San Diego, CA 92514
Tel.: (858) 255-8808
Industrial Machinery & Equipment Distr
N.A.I.C.S.: 423830

Subsidiary (Non-US):

JOT Automation Italy S.R.L (2)
Via Piero Gobetti 23n, 52100, Arezzo, Italy
Tel.: (39) 0575 325 41
Industrial Machinery & Equipment Distr
N.A.I.C.S.: 423830

JOT Automation Kft. (2)
Regi Veszpremi ut 7, 9028, Gyor, Hungary
Tel.: (36) 30 268 7940
Industrial Machinery & Equipment Distr
N.A.I.C.S.: 423830

JOT Automation Vietnam Ltd. (2)
7th Floor Plaschem Building 562 Nguyen Van Cu Str, Long Bien Dist, Hanoi, Vietnam
Tel.: (84) 4 36522326
Industrial Machinery & Equipment Distr
N.A.I.C.S.: 423830
Luu Anh Tinh *(Engr-Svc)*

OUJOT Eesti (2)
Kaabli 11, EE-10112, Tallinn, Estonia
Tel.: (372) 667 0800
Web Site: http://www.jotautomation.com
Emp.: 15
Industrial Machinery & Equipment Distr
N.A.I.C.S.: 423830

Proventia Group Oy (1)
Tietotie 1, FIN-90460, Oulunsalo, Finland
Tel.: (358) 207810200
Web Site: http://www.proventia.com
Holding Company; Exhaust Purification Systems Developer & Mfr
N.A.I.C.S.: 551112
Jari Ensio Lotvonen *(CEO)*

Subsidiary (Domestic):

Proventia Emission Control Oy (2)
Tietotie 1, 90460, Oulunsalo, Finland
Tel.: (358) 207 810 200
Web Site: http://www.proventia.com
Exhaust Purification System Developer & Mfr
N.A.I.C.S.: 333413
Jari Ensio Lotvonen *(Pres & CEO)*

Subsidiary (Non-US):

Proventia GmbH (2)
Zurcherstrasse 46, Winterthur, 8400, Switzerland
Tel.: (41) 52 264 5060
Web Site: http://www.pure-clean-air.com
Emp.: 60
Exhaust Purification Systems Whslr
N.A.I.C.S.: 423830

HEADHUNTER GROUP PLC
9/10 Godovikova St, 129 085, Moscow, 129085, Russia
Tel.: (7) 4959746427   CY
Web Site: https://www.hh.ru
Year Founded: 2014
HHR—(NASDAQ)
Rev.: $243,607,159
Assets: $321,944,854
Liabilities: $229,491,017
Net Worth: $92,453,837
Earnings: $49,724,424
Emp.: 1,473
Fiscal Year-end: 12/31/22
Online Recruitment Services
N.A.I.C.S.: 561311
Mikhail Zhukov *(CEO)*

HEADLAM GROUP PLC
Gorsey Lane, PO Box 1, Coleshill, Birmingham, B46 1JU, United Kingdom
Tel.: (44) 1675433000
Web Site: https://www.headlam.com
HEAD—(LSE)
Rev.: $827,123,024
Assets: $634,598,328
Liabilities: $335,899,928
Net Worth: $298,698,400
Earnings: ($27,561,716)
Emp.: 2,498
Fiscal Year-end: 12/31/20
Floor Covering Distr
N.A.I.C.S.: 449121
Stephen G. Wilson *(CEO)*

Subsidiaries:

Belcolor AG (1)
Sonneggstrasse 24A, 9642, Ebnat, Sankt Gallen, Switzerland
Tel.: (41) 719926161
Web Site: http://www.belcolorfoto.ch
Sales Range: $25-49.9 Million
Emp.: 20
Photofinishing Services
N.A.I.C.S.: 812921

CECO (Flooring) Limited (1)
Carryduff Business Park 8 Comber Road, Carryduff, Belfast, BT8 8AN, United Kingdom
Tel.: (44) 2890817272
Construction Materials Distr
N.A.I.C.S.: 423310

Cheshires of Nottingham (1)
Concord House Dabell Ave, Blenhiem Industrial Estate, Nottingham, NG6 8WA, United Kingdom
Tel.: (44) 1159770278
Web Site: http://www.cheshires-sales.co.uk
Sales Range: $25-49.9 Million
Emp.: 50
Marketing & Order Consulting Services
N.A.I.C.S.: 541613

Dersimo BV (1)
Noordzee 12, 3144 DB, Maassluis, Netherlands
Tel.: (31) 10 591 4070
Web Site: https://www.dersimo.nl
Construction Materials Distr
N.A.I.C.S.: 423310

Headlam BV (1)
Bettinkhorst 4, 7207 BP, Zutphen, Netherlands
Tel.: (31) 57 558 1822
Web Site: https://www.headlam.nl
Emp.: 70
Construction Materials Distr
N.A.I.C.S.: 423310

Hfd Ltd (1)
Gorsey Ln, Birmingham, B46 1LW, United Kingdom
Tel.: (44) 1675433000
Web Site: http://www.headlam.com
Sales Range: $25-49.9 Million
Emp.: 13
Home Furnishing Whslr
N.A.I.C.S.: 423220

LMS SA (1)
7 rue du Fosse Blanc, BP 64, 92230, Gennevilliers, France
Tel.: (33) 141325333
Web Site: http://www.lamaisondusol.com
Sales Range: $75-99.9 Million
Emp.: 25
Carpet Distr
N.A.I.C.S.: 423220

Lethem-Vergeer B.V. (1)
Bettinkhorst 4, 7207 BP, Zutphen, Netherlands (50%)
Tel.: (31) 575581822
Web Site: http://www.lethem.nl
Sales Range: $50-74.9 Million
Emp.: 100
Home Furnishing Whslr
N.A.I.C.S.: 423220
Anthony Graham *(Mng Dir)*

Rackhams Limited (1)
6 Jubilee Avenue, Highams Park Industrial Estate, London, E4 9JD, United Kingdom
Tel.: (44) 2085319225
Web Site: http://www.ackhamsflooring.b2b-payments.co.uk
Construction Materials Distr
N.A.I.C.S.: 423310

HEADLAND CAPITAL PARTNERS LIMITED
2301 Henley Building 5 Queens Road, Central, China (Hong Kong)
Tel.: (852) 37988388
Web Site: http://www.hpef.com
Year Founded: 1865
Sales Range: $25-49.9 Million
Emp.: 45
Privater Equity Firm
N.A.I.C.S.: 523999
George Raffini *(Chm)*

Subsidiaries:

Headland Capital Partners (India) Private Limited (1)
The Capital 701 Plot No C-70 G Block B-Wing 7th Floor, Bandra Kurla Complex, Mumbai, 400 051, India
Tel.: (91) 22 3953 7447
Sales Range: $50-74.9 Million
Emp.: 5
Investment Advisory Services
N.A.I.C.S.: 523940

Headland Capital Partners (Shanghai) Limited (1)
Room 1503 1788 Nanjing Road West, Shanghai, 200040, China
Tel.: (86) 21 3256 9922
Investment Advisory Services
N.A.I.C.S.: 523940

Headland Investment Consulting (Shanghai) Corporation Limited (1)
13A 21st Floor HSBC Building Shanghai IFC 8 Century Avenue, Pudong, Shanghai, 200120, China
Tel.: (86) 21 6841 3396
Web Site: http://www.headlandcp.com
Investment Advisory Services
N.A.I.C.S.: 523940

Kreuz Holdings Limited (1)
12 International Business Park Swiber IBP 01-03/04, Singapore, 609920, Singapore
Tel.: (65) 6505 0900
Web Site: http://www.kreuzsubsea.com
Sales Range: $150-199.9 Million
Offshore Oil & Gas Equipment Construction, Installation & Support Services
N.A.I.C.S.: 237120
Sheldon Richard Hutton *(VP-Installations)*

Subsidiary (Non-US):

Kreuz Engineering Ltd. (2)
FI 15 A2 Main Office Tower Financial Park Labuan Complex, Jalan Merdeka, 87000, Labuan, Malaysia
Tel.: (60) 87453288
Offshore Marine Engineering Services
N.A.I.C.S.: 213112

Subsidiary (Domestic):

Kreuz International Pte Ltd (2)
12 International Business Park Cyberhub@ IBP 03-02, Singapore, 609920, Singapore
Tel.: (65) 65050600
Web Site: http://www.kreuzinternational.com
Sales Range: $25-49.9 Million
Offshore Engineering Services
N.A.I.C.S.: 541330

Subsidiary (Non-US):

Kreuz Offshore Contractors Ltd. (2)
FI 15 A2 Main Office Tower Financial Park Labuan Complex, Jalan Merdeka, 87000, Labuan, Malaysia
Tel.: (60) 87453288
Offshore Marine Engineering Services
N.A.I.C.S.: 541330

Subsidiary (Domestic):

Kreuz Offshore Marine Pte Ltd (2)
12 International Business Park Cyberhub IBP 03-02, Singapore, Singapore
Tel.: (65) 65050600
Offshore Marine Engineering Services
N.A.I.C.S.: 541330
Darren Chee Neng Yeo *(Mng Dir)*

Kreuz Shipbuilding & Engineering Pte Ltd (2)
23 Tuas Crescent, Singapore, Singapore
Tel.: (65) 65774800
Web Site: http://www.swiber.com
Sales Range: $75-99.9 Million
Ship Building & Repair Services
N.A.I.C.S.: 336611
Stephen Church *(VP-Fleet Mgmt & Yard Svcs)*

Kreuz Subsea Pte. Ltd. (2)
12 International Business Park Cyber Ibp 01-30/04, Singapore, 609920, Singapore
Tel.: (65) 65050900
Web Site: http://www.kreuzsubsea.com
Sales Range: $25-49.9 Million
Emp.: 20
Pipeline Installation & Marine Support Services
N.A.I.C.S.: 237120
Lesley Rebello *(Engr)*

HEADSENT AB
Regeringsgatan 30-32, PO Box 7715, 103 95, Stockholm, Sweden
Tel.: (46) 84585350
HEAD—(OMX)
Rev.: $22,816,752
Assets: $16,069,390
Liabilities: $6,613,074
Net Worth: $9,456,317
Earnings: ($3,468,293)
Emp.: 78
Fiscal Year-end: 12/31/20
Financial Consulting Services
N.A.I.C.S.: 541611

HEADSUP ENTERTAINMENT INTERNATIONAL, INC.
246 Stewart Green Southwest Suite 1739, Calgary, T3H 3C8, AB, Canada
Tel.: (403) 269-9039
Web Site: http://www.headsupentertain.com
HDUP—(OTCIQ)
Rev.: $55,000
Assets: $1,109,000
Liabilities: $626,000
Net Worth: $483,000
Earnings: ($42,000)
Fiscal Year-end: 01/31/21
Entertainment Services
N.A.I.C.S.: 711130
Doug Wilson *(Pres & CEO)*

HEADWATER EQUIPMENT SALES LTD
1954 Riveridge Rd, PO Box 1533, Lethbridge, T0L 0V0, AB, Canada
Tel.: (403) 327-3681
Web Site: http://www.hwequipment.com
Year Founded: 1997
Rev.: $11,177,266
Emp.: 30
Industrial Equipment Distr
N.A.I.C.S.: 423840
Mike Stringer *(Owner)*

HEADWATER EXPLORATION INC.

HEADWATER EXPLORATION INC.

Headwater Exploration Inc.—(Continued)
301 5475 Spring Garden Road, Halifax, B3J 3T2, NS, Canada
Tel.: (902) 429-4511 AB
Web Site: http://www.corridor.ca
CDH—(TSX)
Sales Range: $1-9.9 Million
Emp.: 10
Pipeline Transporting Natural Gas Services
N.A.I.C.S.: 211120
J. Douglas Foster *(Chm)*

HEADWATERS CO., LTD.
2-16-6 Shinjuku East Square Bldg 7F, Shinjuku-Ku, Tokyo, 160-0022, Japan
Tel.: (81) 353639361
Web Site:
  https://www.headwaters.co.jp
Year Founded: 2005
4011—(TKS)
Rev.: $16,413,350
Assets: $9,174,460
Liabilities: $2,360,970
Net Worth: $6,813,490
Earnings: $496,300
Fiscal Year-end: 12/31/23
Software Development Services
N.A.I.C.S.: 541511
Yosuke Shinoda *(Founder, Chm & Pres)*

HEADWAY ADVANCED MATERIALS INC.
71 Guang Fu Road Hsinchu Industrial Park, Hsinchu, Taiwan
Tel.: (886) 35977800
Web Site:
  https://www.headway.com.tw
Year Founded: 1976
1776—(TAI)
Rev.: $39,468,163
Assets: $54,913,403
Liabilities: $22,563,752
Net Worth: $32,349,650
Earnings: $979,627
Fiscal Year-end: 12/31/23
Plastic Resin Mfr & Distr
N.A.I.C.S.: 325211
Zhao Weijun *(Pres)*

Subsidiaries:

Fo-Shan City Shanshui Lianmei Chemical Co., Ltd. (1)
No 32-1 Datang Industrial Park, Sanshui District, Foshan, Guangdong, China
Tel.: (86) 75787273699
Polyurethane Resin Mfr
N.A.I.C.S.: 325211

Headway Advanced Materials (Shanghai) Co., Ltd. (1)
No 88 Chugong Road Zhelin Town Fengxian District, Shanghai, China
Tel.: (86) 2137593199
Polyurethane Resin Mfr
N.A.I.C.S.: 325211

Headway Advanced Materials (Vietnam) Co., Ltd. (1)
319B Road Nhon Trach 5 Industrial Park, Nhon Trach, Dong Nai, Vietnam
Tel.: (84) 613560236
Polyurethane Resin Mfr
N.A.I.C.S.: 325211

Headway Polyurethane Co., Ltd. (1)
No 9 Siwei Rd, Hukou, 303, Hsinchu, Taiwan
Tel.: (886) 35977738
Polyurethane Products Mfr
N.A.I.C.S.: 325211

Hong Yu Materials Co., Ltd. (1)
No 41 Ln 88 Sec 2 Zhongxing Rd Zhudong Township, Hsinchu, 310, Taiwan
Tel.: (886) 35828886
Chemical Material Distr
N.A.I.C.S.: 424690

Shanghai Hui Yu Fine Chemicals Co., Ltd. (1)
No 45 Zhouzhu Road Zhoupu Town Nanhui District, Shanghai, China
Tel.: (86) 2158112756
Running Track Mfr
N.A.I.C.S.: 339920

Shanghai Xin Yu Resin Co., Ltd. (1)
No 388 Xinxu Road Xinbang Town Songjiang District, Shanghai, China
Tel.: (86) 2157892258
Resin Product Mfr & Distr
N.A.I.C.S.: 325211

Yu Cheng Materials Co., Ltd. (1)
No 71 Guangfu Rd, Hukou, 303, Hsinchu, Taiwan
Tel.: (886) 35978899
Polyurethane Products Mfr
N.A.I.C.S.: 325211

HEAG SUDHESSISCHE ENERGIE AG
Frankfurter Strasse 110, 64293, Darmstadt, Germany
Tel.: (49) 61517010 De
Web Site: http://www.entega.ag
Year Founded: 2003
Sales Range: $1-4.9 Billion
Emp.: 2,360
Utilities Supplier; Heating & Power Services
N.A.I.C.S.: 926130
Andreas Niedermaier *(Gen Mgr)*

Subsidiaries:

COUNT + CARE GmbH (1)
Landwehrstrasse 55, 64293, Darmstadt, Germany (75%)
Tel.: (49) 61514047000
Web Site: http://www.countandcare.de
Sales Range: $250-299.9 Million
Emp.: 350
Energy Sector Infrastructure Management
N.A.I.C.S.: 221121
Volker Abert *(Mng Dir)*

ENTEGA Haustechnik GmbH & Co. KG (1)
Dornheimer Weg 24, Darmstadt, 64289, Germany
Tel.: (49) 61519702000
Web Site: http://www.entega-haustechnik.de
Sales Range: $50-74.9 Million
Emp.: 120
Heating & Electrical Installation & Maintenance Service
N.A.I.C.S.: 238220
Michael Boddeker *(Mng Dir)*

NATURpur Energie AG (1)
Frankfurter Strasse 110, 64293, Darmstadt, Germany
Tel.: (49) 61517013401
Web Site: http://www.naturpur-ag.de
Emp.: 1
Renewable Energy Power Generation
N.A.I.C.S.: 221118

e-ben GmbH & Co. KG (1)
Hauptstrasse 21, 64625, Bensheim, Germany
Tel.: (49) 1801002300
Web Site: http://www.eben.de
Renewable Energy Generation & Distr
N.A.I.C.S.: 221118

HEALING TOUCH HOLDINGS, INC.
140 Paya Lebar Road AZ Building 09-26, Singapore, 409015, Singapore
Tel.: (65) 68505050 DE
Web Site:
  http://www.healingtouchspa.com
Year Founded: 2010
Sales Range: $1-9.9 Million
Spa & Beauty Care Services
N.A.I.C.S.: 713940
Sing Wei Lung *(Chm, CEO, Treas & Sec)*

HEALIOS K.K.

Hibiya Mitsui Tower 12F WORK STYLING 1-1-2 Yurakucho, Chiyoda-ku, Tokyo, 100-0006, Japan
Tel.: (81) 357778308
Web Site: https://www.healios.co.jp
Year Founded: 2011
4593—(TKS)
Rev.: $857,890
Assets: $107,448,950
Liabilities: $80,031,920
Net Worth: $27,417,030
Earnings: ($27,105,070)
Emp.: 60
Fiscal Year-end: 12/31/23
Ophthalmological Surgery Adjuvants Mfr
N.A.I.C.S.: 339112
Hardy Tadahisa S. Kagimoto *(Pres & CEO)*

Subsidiaries:

Athersys, Inc. (1)
3201 Carnegie Ave, Cleveland, OH 44115-2634
Tel.: (216) 431-9900
Web Site: https://www.athersys.com
Rev.: $5,325,000
Assets: $27,731,000
Liabilities: $51,582,000
Net Worth: ($23,851,000)
Earnings: ($72,534,000)
Emp.: 24
Fiscal Year-end: 12/31/2022
Pharmaceutical Preparation Manufacturing
N.A.I.C.S.: 325412
Laura K. Campbell *(Sr VP-Fin)*

Subsidiary (Domestic):

ABT Holding Company (2)
3201 Carnegie Ave, Cleveland, OH 44115-2634
Tel.: (216) 431-9900
Web Site: http://www.athersys.com
Sales Range: $250-299.9 Million
Holding Company
N.A.I.C.S.: 551112

Subsidiary (Non-US):

ReGenesys BVBA (3)
Gaston Geenslaan 1, 3001, Heverlee, Belgium
Tel.: (32) 16751355
Web Site: https://regenesys.eu
Sales Range: $25-49.9 Million
Emp.: 13
Research & Development Laboratories
N.A.I.C.S.: 541715
Bart Vaes *(Assoc Dir)*

HEALIUS LIMITED
Level 22 Liberty Place 161 Castlereagh Street, St Leonards, Sydney, 2000, NSW, Australia
Tel.: (61) 294329400 AU
Web Site:
  https://www.healius.com.au
Year Founded: 1994
HLS—(ASX)
Rev.: $1,165,998,927
Assets: $1,991,720,077
Liabilities: $1,296,808,221
Net Worth: $694,911,856
Earnings: ($424,679,485)
Emp.: 10,610
Fiscal Year-end: 06/30/24
Health Care Srvices
N.A.I.C.S.: 622110
Maxine Jaquet *(CEO & Mng Dir)*

Subsidiaries:

Abbott Pathology Pty Ltd (1)
46 Sir Donald Bradman Drive, Mile End, Adelaide, 5031, SA, Australia
Tel.: (61) 881597900
Web Site:
  https://www.abbottpathology.com.au
Medical Pathology Services
N.A.I.C.S.: 621511
Madelyn Duckmanton *(CEO)*

Adora Fertility Pty Ltd (1)

INTERNATIONAL PUBLIC

Level 5 28 Foveaux Street, Surry Hills, 2010, NSW, Australia
Tel.: (61) 291389800
Web Site: https://www.adorafertility.com.au
Women Healthcare Services
N.A.I.C.S.: 621610
Paul Atkinson *(Natl Dir-Medical & Specialist-Fertility & Obstetrician)*

Agilex Biolabs Pty. Ltd. (1)
31 Dalgleish Street, Thebarton, SA, Australia
Tel.: (61) 883028787
Web Site: https://www.agilexbiolabs.com
Emp.: 100
Biotech Clinical Trial Services
N.A.I.C.S.: 541714

Albany Day Hospital Pty Ltd (1)
6 Lubich Way, Mira Mar, Albany, 6330, WA, Australia
Tel.: (61) 861461466
Web Site:
  https://www.albanydayhospital.com.au
Hospital Care Services
N.A.I.C.S.: 622110

Austrials Pty Ltd (1)
Level 3 Westside Private Hospital 32 Morrow St, Taringa, Brisbane, 4068, QLD, Australia
Tel.: (61) 732785255
Web Site: https://www.austrials.com.au
Emp.: 1,000
Medical Research Services
N.A.I.C.S.: 541715

Bourke Street Clinic Pty Ltd (1)
421 Bourke St, Surry Hills, 2010, NSW, Australia
Tel.: (61) 293320400
Web Site:
  https://www.thebourkestreetclinic.com.au
Medical Practice Services
N.A.I.C.S.: 621111

Cooper Street Clinic Pty Ltd (1)
1 Cooper St, Double Bay, 2028, NSW, Australia
Tel.: (61) 293285444
Web Site:
  https://www.cooperstreetclinic.com.au
Medical Practice Services
N.A.I.C.S.: 621111

Healius Pathology Pty. Ltd. (1)
Level 22 161 Castlereagh Street, Sydney, NSW, Australia
Tel.: (61) 294329523
Emp.: 7,600
Medical Pathology Laboratory Services
N.A.I.C.S.: 621511

Healthcare Imaging Services (Victoria) Pty Ltd (1)
Suite 1.02 71 Queens Road, Melbourne, 3008, VIC, Australia
Tel.: (61) 399182950
Diagnostic Imaging Services
N.A.I.C.S.: 621512

Healthcare Imaging Services Pty Ltd (1)
Level 6 203 Pacific Highway, Saint Leonards, 2065, NSW, Australia
Tel.: (61) 294329400
Web Site:
  http://www.healthcareimaging.com.au
Diagnostic Imaging Services
N.A.I.C.S.: 621512

Subsidiary (Domestic):

Campbelltown MRI Pty Ltd (2)
12-14 Warby St, Campbelltown, 2560, NSW, Australia
Tel.: (61) 246258531
Diagnostic Imaging Services
N.A.I.C.S.: 621512

Subsidiary (Domestic):

Queensland Diagnostic Imaging Pty Ltd (3)
11 Riverview Place Metroplex On Gateway, Murarrie, 4172, QLD, Australia
Tel.: (61) 738394244
Web Site: http://www.qdi.com.au
Diagnostic Imaging Services
N.A.I.C.S.: 621512

Montserrat DH Pty Ltd (1)
32 Morrow Street, Taringa, Brisbane, 4068, QLD, Australia
Tel.: (61) 738336701
Web Site: https://www.montserrat.com.au
Hospital Care Services
N.A.I.C.S.: 622110
Shane Kosanic (CFO)

Pacific Medical Centres Pty Ltd (1)
23 27 First Ave, Blacktown, 2148, NSW, Australia
Tel.: (61) 86028888
Web Site:
https://www.pacificmedicalcentre.com.au
Genaral Health Care Services
N.A.I.C.S.: 621999

Park Family Practice Services Pty Ltd (1)
34 Waverley St, Bondi Junction, 2022, NSW, Australia
Tel.: (61) 293895988
Web Site:
https://www.parkfamilypractice.com.au
Medical Practice Services
N.A.I.C.S.: 621111

Toowoomba Diagnostic Imaging Pty. Ltd. (1)
881 Ruthven St, Toowoomba, QLD, Australia
Tel.: (61) 745292222
Web Site: https://www.toowoombadi.com.au
Medical Diagnostic Imaging Centre Services
N.A.I.C.S.: 621512

Whitsunday Radiology Pty. Ltd. (1)
Suite 14 230 Shute Harbour Rd, Cannonvale, QLD, Australia
Tel.: (61) 749464633
Web Site:
https://whitsundayradiology.com.au
Radiological Laboratory Services
N.A.I.C.S.: 621512

HEALTH AND HAPPINESS (H&H) INTERNATIONAL HOLDINGS LIMITED
Suites 4007-09 40/F One Island East Taikoo Place 18 Westlands Road, Quarry Bay, Hong Kong, China (Hong Kong)
Tel.: (852) 2038189999   Ky
Web Site: http://www.hh.global
Year Founded: 1999
1112—(HKG)
Rev.: $1,793,738,326
Assets: $2,943,208,710
Liabilities: $2,080,892,549
Net Worth: $862,316,161
Earnings: $85,894,333
Emp.: 3,328
Fiscal Year-end: 12/31/22
Pediatric Nutritional Products Mfr; Baby Care Products Mfr; Pediatric & Baby Care Information Services
N.A.I.C.S.: 325411
Fei Luo (Chm)

Subsidiaries:

Biostime Hong Kong Limited (1)
Rm 3508 35/F Shun Tak Ctr West Twr, Central, China (Hong Kong)
Tel.: (852) 25772888
Holding Company
N.A.I.C.S.: 551112

Health & Happiness (H&H) Trading India Private Limited (1)
No 6/12 Primrose Road, Gurappa Avenue, Bengaluru, 560025, Karnataka, India
Tel.: (91) 8001003817
Web Site: https://www.swisse.co.in
Skin Care Products Distr
N.A.I.C.S.: 456120

Healthy Times. Inc. (1)
13200 Kirkham Way Ste 104, Poway, CA 92064-7126
Tel.: (858) 513-1550
Web Site: http://www.healthytimes.com
Baby Care Product Mfr
N.A.I.C.S.: 311514

Solid Gold Pet, LLC (1)
15455 Conway Rd Ste 100, Chesterfield, MO 63017
Web Site: http://www.solidgoldpet.com
Pet Food Distr
N.A.I.C.S.: 424490

Swisse Wellness Pty Ltd (1)
381 Great South Road, Ellerslie, Auckland, New Zealand
Tel.: (64) 508794773
Nutritional Food Distr
N.A.I.C.S.: 456191
Kimberly Weld (VP-North America)

Swisse Wellness Pty Ltd (1)
Level 7 88 Langridge Street, Collingwood, Melbourne, 3066, VIC, Australia
Tel.: (61) 800794773
Web Site: https://swisse.com.au
Pharmaceutical Product Mfr & Distr
N.A.I.C.S.: 325411

HEALTH AND PLANT PROTEIN GROUP LIMITED
Tel.: (61) 730674828   AU
Web Site: https://www.hppgroup.com
HPP—(ASX)
Rev.: $172,277
Assets: $4,182,056
Liabilities: $74,787
Net Worth: $4,107,269
Earnings: ($534,860)
Emp.: 1
Fiscal Year-end: 06/30/24
Ginger Production, Processing & Distribution
N.A.I.C.S.: 311423
Albert Tse (Exec Chm)

Subsidiaries:

Buderim Ginger (Overseas) Holdings Pty Ltd (1)
50 Pioneer Rd, Yandina, 4561, QLD, Australia
Tel.: (61) 754467100
Sales Range: $25-49.9 Million
Emp.: 80
Ginger Supplies
N.A.I.C.S.: 111419

Subsidiary (Non-US):

Frespac Ginger (Fiji) Ltd (2)
Lot 14 Wailada, PO Box 15128, Lami, Suva, Fiji
Tel.: (679) 3362863
Web Site: http://www.buderimginger.com
Sales Range: $25-49.9 Million
Ginger Supplies
N.A.I.C.S.: 111419
Sathish Kumar (Mgr-Factory)

Buderim Ginger America, Inc. (1)
850 Montgomery Ste 350, San Francisco, CA 94133
Tel.: (201) 560-1170
Confectionery Ginger Mfr
N.A.I.C.S.: 111419

Buderim Macadamias Pty Ltd (1)
1 Northcott Crescent, PO Box 344, Alstonville, 2477, NSW, Australia
Tel.: (61) 266286185
Web Site: http://www.agrimac.com.au
Sales Range: $10-24.9 Million
Emp.: 50
Macadamia Nut Farming Services
N.A.I.C.S.: 111335

GLM Trading Ltd. (1)
11 Manvers Street, Bath, BA1 1JQ, United Kingdom
Tel.: (44) 12 254 0055
Crop Protection Services
N.A.I.C.S.: 111419

GS Hall & Company Limited (1)
Shortland Street, PO Box 536, Auckland, 1140, New Zealand
Tel.: (64) 9 270 0725
Web Site: https://www.gshall.co.nz
Food Products Mfr
N.A.I.C.S.: 311942
Paul Cheater (Dir-Operations)

Macfarms, LLC (1)
89-406 Mamalahoa Hwy, Captain Cook, HI 96704
Tel.: (808) 328-2435
Web Site: http://www.macfarms.com
Sales Range: $25-49.9 Million
Emp.: 150
Macadamia Nut Farming Services
N.A.I.C.S.: 111335
Mark Crawford (VP)

Star Marketing Ltd. (1)
3289 - 190 St, Surrey, V3Z 1A7, BC, Canada
Tel.: (778) 574-0778
Web Site: https://starmarketingcanada.com
Food Products Distr
N.A.I.C.S.: 424490
Kyle Leslie (Pres)

HEALTH BIOSCIENCES SPA
Via di Santa Cornelia 5, 00060, Formello, Italy
Tel.: (39) 0640411918
Web Site: http://www.health-biosciences.com
CORN—(VIE)
Sales Range: Less than $1 Million
Real Estate Investment Services
N.A.I.C.S.: 531210

Subsidiaries:

Be Health SpA (1)
Via di Santa Cornelia 5, 00060, Formello, RM, Italy
Tel.: (39) 0640412639
Web Site: http://www.behealthglobal.com
Health Care Products Mfr
N.A.I.C.S.: 339112

Health Pharma SpA (1)
Via di Santa Cornelia 5, 00060, Formello, RM, Italy
Tel.: (39) 0640412640
Web Site: http://www.healthpharma.it
Health Care Products Mfr
N.A.I.C.S.: 339112

HEALTH EMPIRE CORPORATION PUBLIC COMPANY LIMITED
No 51 Major Tower Building Rama 9-Ramkhamhaeng 20th Floor, Room No Office 2 Rama 9 Road Huamark Subdistrict Bangkapi District, Bangkok, 10240, Thailand
Tel.: (66) 25145000
Web Site:
https://www.healthempire.co.th
Year Founded: 1990
HEALTH—(THA)
Rev.: $731,843
Assets: $22,194,363
Liabilities: $1,848,727
Net Worth: $20,345,635
Earnings: ($7,720,400)
Fiscal Year-end: 12/31/23
Audio & Video Media Producer & Distr
N.A.I.C.S.: 512120

HEALTH ITALIA S.P.A.
Via Di Santa Cornelia 9, 00060, Formello, RM, Italy
Tel.: (39) 0661566722
Web Site: https://www.healthitalia.it
HI—(ITA)
Sales Range: Less than $1 Million
Healtcare Services
N.A.I.C.S.: 621491
Roberto Anzanello (Chm)

HEALTHBANK HOLDINGS LIMITED
31 Jurong Port Road South Wing 02-20, Jurong Logistics Hub, Singapore, 619115, Singapore
Tel.: (65) 62611212
Web Site: https://www.smjf.com.sg
40B—(CAT)
Rev.: $31,831
Assets: $3,574,789
Liabilities: $140,423
Net Worth: $3,434,366
Earnings: ($5,081,972)
Emp.: 5
Fiscal Year-end: 12/31/23
Carpet Sales & Distr
N.A.I.C.S.: 423220
Peng Fei (CEO & Exec Dir)

HEALTHBEACON PLC
Unit 20 Naas Road Business Park, Muirfield Drive, Dublin, D12WD85, Ireland
Tel.: (353) 14508480   IE
Web Site:
https://www.healthbeacon.com
Year Founded: 2013
HBCN—(EUR)
Rev.: $2,719,323
Assets: $40,460,682
Liabilities: $4,516,238
Net Worth: $35,944,444
Earnings: ($10,082,622)
Emp.: 57
Fiscal Year-end: 12/31/21
Medical Technology Services
N.A.I.C.S.: 541511
Kieran Daly (CTO)

HEALTHCARE & MEDICAL INVESTMENT CORPORATION
Tel.: (81) 352822922
Web Site: http://www.hcm3455.co.jp
Year Founded: 2014
34550—(TKS)
Sales Range: Less than $1 Million
Real Estate Related Services
N.A.I.C.S.: 531390
Seiji Yoshioka (Pres)

HEALTHCARE ACTIVOS YIELD SOCIMI, S.A.
Paseo de la Castellana 45, 28046, Madrid, Spain
Tel.: (34) 910616184   ES
Web Site:
https://www.healthcareactivos.com
Year Founded: 2019
MLHAY—(EUR)
Rev.: $22,636,860
Assets: $465,333,953
Liabilities: $233,354,685
Net Worth: $231,979,268
Earnings: $6,536,999
Fiscal Year-end: 12/31/21
Investment Management Service
N.A.I.C.S.: 523999
Albert Fernandez (CEO)

HEALTHCARE AI ACQUISITION CORP.
190 Elgin Avenue, Georgetown, KY1-9008, Cayman Islands
Tel.: (345) 8158548   Ky
Web Site:
https://www.nuvocares.com
Year Founded: 2021
HAIA—(NASDAQ)
Rev.: $14,002,297
Assets: $223,672,996
Liabilities: $232,383,132
Net Worth: ($8,710,136)
Earnings: $12,796,243
Emp.: 2
Fiscal Year-end: 12/31/22
Investment Services
N.A.I.C.S.: 523999
Xiaocheng Peng (CFO)

HEALTHCARE AT HOME LTD.
Fifth Avenue Centrum 100, Burton-on-Trent, DE14 2WS, Staffordshire, United Kingdom
Tel.: (44) 3331039499
Web Site: http://www.hah.co.uk

HEALTHCARE AT HOME LTD.

Healthcare at Home Ltd.—(Continued)
Year Founded: 1992
Sales Range: $1-4.9 Billion
Emp.: 1,295
Women Healthcare Services
N.A.I.C.S.: 621610
Mike Gordon (Chm)

Subsidiaries:

High Tech Home Care AG (1)
Buonaserstrasse 30, Rotkreuz, 6343, Zug, Switzerland
Tel.: (41) 417499900
Web Site: http://www.hthc.ch
Women Healthcare Services
N.A.I.C.S.: 621610

HEALTHCARE CO., LTD.
No 999 Gaonan Road, Dingyan Town, Rugao, 226521, Jiangsu, China
Tel.: (86) 51368169482
Web Site: http://www.hkfoam.com
Year Founded: 2003
603313—(SHG)
Rev.: $1,125,621,156
Assets: $1,274,224,995
Liabilities: $844,432,065
Net Worth: $429,792,929
Earnings: $5,806,832
Fiscal Year-end: 12/31/22
Mattress Mfr & Distr
N.A.I.C.S.: 337910
Zhang Gen Ni (Chm & Pres)

HEALTHCARE GLOBAL ENTERPRISES LIMITED
HCG Towers No 8 P Kalinga Rao Road Sampangi Rama Nagar, Bengaluru, 560027, India
Tel.: (91) 7406499999
Web Site: https://www.hcgoncology.com
Year Founded: 1989
539787—(BOM)
Rev.: $192,526,425
Assets: $302,964,890
Liabilities: $182,337,929
Net Worth: $120,626,961
Earnings: $5,313,263
Emp.: 5,679
Fiscal Year-end: 03/31/22
Healthcare Services
N.A.I.C.S.: 621491
B. S. Ajai Kumar (Founder, Chm & CEO)

Subsidiaries:

APEX HCG Oncology Hospitals LLP (1)
Holy Cross Road IC Colony-Borivali West, Opposite Dharmendra Building Off Borivali Dahisar Link Road, Mumbai, 400103, India
Tel.: (91) 2233696999
Cancer Hospital Services
N.A.I.C.S.: 622310

Cancer Care Kenya Limited (1)
Shivachi Road Parklands, Nairobi, Kenya
Tel.: (254) 203740132
Web Site: http://www.cancercarekenya.com
Cancer Treatment Services
N.A.I.C.S.: 622310

HCG EKO Oncology LLP (1)
Plot DG 4 Premises No. 03-358, Action Area 1D New Town, Kolkata, 700 156, India (100%)
Tel.: (91) 6358888825
Web Site: https://www.hcgoncology.com
Cancer Care Services
N.A.I.C.S.: 621491

Triesta Sciences, Inc. (1)
P Kalinga Rao Road Sambangi Ram Nagara, Bengaluru, 560027, India
Tel.: (91) 8040206106
Web Site: http://triesta.com
Laboratory Services
N.A.I.C.S.: 541380

HEALTHCARE SPECIAL OPPORTUNITIES FUND
130 King Street West Suite 2130, Toronto, M5X 1E2, ON, Canada
Tel.: (416) 362-4141
MDS.UN—(TSX)
Fiscal Year-end: 12/31/20
Investment Management Service
N.A.I.C.S.: 525990
Michael B. Decter (Mgr-Fund)

HEALTHCO HEALTHCARE & WELLNESS REIT
Level 7 1 Macquarie Place, Sydney, 2000, NSW, Australia
Tel.: (61) 1300466326   AU
Web Site: https://www.hmccapital.com.au
Year Founded: 2021
HCW—(ASX)
Rev.: $43,750,408
Assets: $1,124,405,034
Liabilities: $499,576,188
Net Worth: $624,828,845
Earnings: $13,822,782
Fiscal Year-end: 06/30/23
Property Management Services
N.A.I.C.S.: 531311
Joseph Carrozzi (Chm)

HEALTHCONN CORP.
5F No 54 Sec 1 Zhongxiao E Rd, Zhongzheng Dist, Taipei, 100, Taiwan
Tel.: (886) 255696199
Web Site: https://www.healthconn.com
Year Founded: 2009
6665—(TAI)
Health Care Srvices
N.A.I.C.S.: 621610
Martin Chiang (Dir-Bus Admin)

HEALTHY LIFE AGRITEC LIMITED
SH-B/09 New Heera Panna CHS LTD Gokul Village Shanti Park, Mira Road East, Thane, 401107, Maharashtra, India
Tel.: (91) 8355891669
Web Site: https://www.healthylifeagritec.com
Year Founded: 2019
543546—(BOM)
Rev.: $12,927,295
Assets: $3,271,183
Liabilities: $345,519
Net Worth: $2,925,664
Earnings: $181,164
Emp.: 8
Fiscal Year-end: 03/31/23
Fire Insurance Services
N.A.I.C.S.: 524113

HEALTHYDAYS GROUP PLC
6 New Street Square, New Fetter Lane, London, EC4A 3BF, United Kingdom
Tel.: (44) 1142760000   UK
Year Founded: 2007
Sales Range: $1-9.9 Million
Emp.: 10
Holding Company; Healthcare Products
N.A.I.C.S.: 551112
Amer Deen (CEO)

HEALWELL AI INC.
460 College St Suite 301, Toronto, M6G 1A1, ON, Canada
Tel.: (905) 960-6717   ON
Web Site: https://www.mcionehealth.com
Year Founded: 2012
AIDX—(TSX)
Rev.: $39,703,612
Assets: $34,039,234
Liabilities: $23,972,710
Net Worth: $10,066,524
Earnings: ($15,643,620)
Emp.: 600
Fiscal Year-end: 12/31/22
Healthcare Technology Services
N.A.I.C.S.: 541511

Subsidiaries:

Intrahealth Systems Limited (1)
19 Como St Takapuna, Auckland, 0622, New Zealand
Tel.: (64) 94807442
Web Site: https://www.intrahealth.com
Healthcare Software Solution Services
N.A.I.C.S.: 541511

HEAR ATLAST HOLDINGS, INC.
44 Greystone Crescent, Georgetown, L7G 1G9, ON, Canada
Tel.: (416) 918-6987   NV
Web Site: http://www.hearatlastholdings.com
HRAL—(OTCIQ)
Assets: $0
Liabilities: $3,040,000
Net Worth: ($3,040,000)
Earnings: ($104,000)
Emp.: 1
Fiscal Year-end: 03/31/23
Hearing Aids & Other Related Products Retailer
N.A.I.C.S.: 456199

HEAR.COM N.V.
Amsterdamsestraatweg 421, 3551 CL, Utrecht, Netherlands
Tel.: (31) 558080140   NI
Year Founded: 2020
Emp.: 1,388
Holding Company
N.A.I.C.S.: 551112
Paul Crusius (Co-CEO)

HEARMEOUT LIMITED
Level 2 50 Kings Park Road, West Perth, 6005, WA, Australia
Tel.: (61) 863778043   AU
Web Site: http://www.hearmeoutapp.com
Year Founded: 2014
Rev.: $9,225
Assets: $2,337,438
Liabilities: $224,555
Net Worth: $2,112,883
Earnings: ($4,699,747)
Fiscal Year-end: 12/31/17
Mobile Application Development Services
N.A.I.C.S.: 513210
Peter Webse (Sec)

HEART OF ENGLAND CO-OPERATIVE SOCIETY LIMITED
22 Abbey Street, Nuneaton, CV11 5BU, Warks, United Kingdom
Tel.: (44) 2476382331
Web Site: http://www.21stcentury.coop
Sales Range: $150-199.9 Million
Emp.: 500
Grocery, Travel, Postal & Funeral Service Cooperative
N.A.I.C.S.: 424410
Ali Kurji (CEO)

HEARTLAND BANK LIMITED
Level 3 Heartland House 35 Teed Street, Newmarket, 1023, Auckland, New Zealand
Tel.: (64) 508432785   NZ
Web Site: http://www.heartland.co.nz
HBL—(NZX)
Rev.: $315,616,029
Assets: $4,632,012,560
Liabilities: $4,015,383,373

INTERNATIONAL PUBLIC

Net Worth: $616,629,187
Earnings: $57,337,321
Emp.: 535
Fiscal Year-end: 06/30/23
Commercial Banking & Mortgage Lending Services
N.A.I.C.S.: 522110
Christopher Patrick Francis Flood (Co-CEO)

Subsidiaries:

MARAC Finance & Lending (1)
Heartland House 35 Teed Street, Newmarket, 1023, New Zealand
Tel.: (64) 95200097
Web Site: http://www.marac.co.nz
Financial Services
N.A.I.C.S.: 522320
Jeff Greenslade (CEO)

HEARTLAND FORD SALES, INC.
101 Southridge Boulevard, Fort Saskatchewan, T8L 0P6, AB, Canada
Tel.: (888) 467-9158
Web Site: http://www.heartlandfordsales.com
Year Founded: 2011
Car Dealership
N.A.I.C.S.: 441110
Shilene Blades (Mgr-Svc)

HEARTLAND GROUP HOLDINGS LIMITED
Level 3 35 Teed Street, Newmarket, Auckland, 1023, New Zealand   NZ
Web Site: https://www.heartlandgroup.info
Year Founded: 2018
HGH—(NZX)
Rev.: $315,616,029
Assets: $4,632,012,560
Liabilities: $4,015,383,373
Net Worth: $616,629,187
Earnings: $57,337,321
Emp.: 535
Fiscal Year-end: 06/30/23
Holding Company
N.A.I.C.S.: 551112
Jeff Greenslade (CEO)

Subsidiaries:

Challenger Bank Limited (1)
Flinders Lane, PO Box 297, Melbourne, 8009, VIC, Australia
Tel.: (61) 1300221479
Web Site: https://challenger.com.au
Banking & Asset Management Services
N.A.I.C.S.: 541513
Christopher Patrick Francis Flood (Acting CEO)

HEARTS AND MINDS INVESTMENTS LIMITED
Level 8 210 George Street, Sydney, 2000, NSW, Australia
Tel.: (61) 292909600   AU
Web Site: https://www.heartsandminds.com.au
HM1—(ASX)
Rev.: $55,670,185
Assets: $487,785,431
Liabilities: $22,102,004
Net Worth: $465,683,428
Earnings: $34,006,918
Fiscal Year-end: 06/30/24
Investment Management Service
N.A.I.C.S.: 525910
Chris Cuffe (Chm)

HEATEC JIETONG HOLDINGS LTD
10 Tuas South Street 15, Singapore, 637076, Singapore
Tel.: (65) 68611433
Web Site: https://www.heatecholdings.com

AND PRIVATE COMPANIES

Year Founded: 1990
5OR—(CAT)
Rev.: $18,983,907
Assets: $19,137,668
Liabilities: $10,155,752
Net Worth: $8,981,915
Earnings: ($657,745)
Emp.: 380
Fiscal Year-end: 12/31/23
Heat Transfer & Piping Systems
N.A.I.C.S.: 333415
Jenson Soon (Gen Mgr)

Subsidiaries:

Heatec Jietong Pte. Ltd. (1)
10 Tuas South Street 15, Singapore, 637076, Singapore
Tel.: (65) 68611433
Heat Exchanger Mfr
N.A.I.C.S.: 332410

Subsidiary (Domestic):

Chem-Grow Pte. Ltd. (2)
No 15 Tuas Link 3, Singapore, 638529, Singapore
Tel.: (65) 62658751
Web Site: https://www.chemgrow.com
Chemical Cleaning Services
N.A.I.C.S.: 213112

Subsidiary (Non-US):

Heatec Guangzhou Co., Ltd. (2)
No 35 Yuan Hui Li Xin Hua Road, Huangpu, Guangzhou, China
Tel.: (86) 2082038152
Heat Exchanger Mfr & Distr
N.A.I.C.S.: 332410

Heatec Shanghai Co., Ltd. (2)
No 318 Chen Yin Road, Baoshan Urban Industrial Park, Shanghai, 200444, China
Tel.: (86) 2165481188
Web Site: http://www.heatec.com.cn
Heat Exchanger Mfr
N.A.I.C.S.: 332410

Heatec Veslink Marine Services Corp. (1)
Werehouse 1 Guillermo Cpd Sta Rosa 1, Marilao, Bulacan, 3019, Philippines
Tel.: (63) 442486203
Pipeline Restoration & Installation Services
N.A.I.C.S.: 237120
Diosa Villena (Accountant)

HEATHERBRAE INC
140 12371 Horseshoe Way, Richmond, V7A 4X6, BC, Canada
Tel.: (604) 277-2315
Web Site: http://www.heatherbrae.com
Year Founded: 1990
Rev.: $24,609,980
Emp.: 150
Building Construction Services
N.A.I.C.S.: 238190
Michael Knight (Pres & Principal)

HEATHPATCH LTD.
Dairy Farm Office Semer, Ipswich, IP7 6RA, United Kingdom
Tel.: (44) 1449 741481
Web Site: http://www.heathpatch.co.uk
Holding Services
N.A.I.C.S.: 551112

Subsidiaries:

Material Change Limited (1)
The Amphenol Building Rutherford Drive, Wellingborough, NN8 6AX, United Kingdom
Tel.: (44) 1933 408190
Web Site: http://www.material-change.com
Emp.: 2
Farm Supplies Distr
N.A.I.C.S.: 424910
Ed Bastow (Mng Dir)

HEAVEN-SENT CAPITAL MANAGEMENT GROUP CO. LTD.
17th Floor Huantai Building 12A Zhongguancun South Street, Haidian District, Beijing, 100081, China
Tel.: (86) 10 6212 5588
Web Site: http://www.ggttvc.com
Privater Equity Firm
N.A.I.C.S.: 523999
Baohong Yu (Pres)

Subsidiaries:

Zhejiang Silicon Paradise Asset Management Group Co., Ltd. (1)
Xixi National Wetland Park Fudi Causeway No 8 Tianmushan Road, West Lake District, Hangzhou, 310002, China
Tel.: (86) 57187083018
Fund Management Services
N.A.I.C.S.: 523999
Qi Hao Huang (Mgr-Investment)

HEAVY ENGINEERING INDUSTRIES & SHIPBUILDING CO. K.S.C.
Safat, PO Box 21998, 13080, Kuwait, 13080, Kuwait
Tel.: (965) 24835488   KW
Web Site: https://www.heisco.com
Year Founded: 1974
SHIP—(KUW)
Rev.: $402,042,107
Assets: $573,926,803
Liabilities: $344,090,052
Net Worth: $229,836,751
Earnings: $18,289,593
Emp.: 12,201
Fiscal Year-end: 12/31/22
Ship Building & Engineering Services
N.A.I.C.S.: 336611
Salem Abdulhadi Marafi (Deputy CEO-Shipyard Operation)

Subsidiaries:

Gulf Dredging and General Contracting Company KSE (1)
Gate 7 Shuwaikh Port End of Gazali St, PO Box 24054, Kuwait, Safat, Kuwait
Tel.: (965) 24624400
Web Site: https://www.gulfdredging.com
Sales Range: $50-74.9 Million
Emp.: 250
Heavy & Civil Engineering Construction
N.A.I.C.S.: 237990

Heavy Engineering Industries & Shipbuilding Co. K.S.C. - Industrial Contracts Division (1)
PO Box 10155, Shuaiba, Kuwait, Kuwait
Tel.: (965) 23253000
Web Site: http://www.heisco.com
Ship Building & Repairing Services
N.A.I.C.S.: 336611

HEAVY MINERALS LIMITED
Level 8 London House 216 St Georges Terrace, Perth, 6000, WA, Australia
Tel.: (61) 894810389   AU
Web Site: https://www.heavyminerals.com
Year Founded: 2021
HVY—(ASX)
Rev.: $17,826
Assets: $2,307,977
Liabilities: $49,570
Net Worth: $2,258,406
Earnings: ($763,987)
Fiscal Year-end: 06/30/23
Mineral Exploration Services
N.A.I.C.S.: 212390

HEAVY RARE EARTHS LIMITED
Level 21 459 Collins Street, Melbourne, 3000, VIC, Australia
Tel.: (61) 386303321   AU
Web Site: https://www.hreltd.com.au
Year Founded: 2021
HRE—(ASX)
Rev.: $18,454
Assets: $3,627,667
Liabilities: $113,137
Net Worth: $3,514,530
Earnings: ($1,169,858)
Fiscal Year-end: 06/30/23
Rare Earth Exploration Services
N.A.I.C.S.: 212290

HEBA FASTIGHETS AB
Timmermansgatan 31, 118 55, Stockholm, 118 55, Sweden
Tel.: (46) 84424440
Web Site: https://www.hebafast.se
HEBA.B—(OMX)
Sales Range: $25-49.9 Million
Emp.: 31
Real Estate Development Services
N.A.I.C.S.: 531390
Helena Elfstadius (Head-Property)

HEBEI CHANGSHAN BIO-CHEMICAL PHARMACEUTICAL CO. LTD.
No 71 Menglong Street, South District Zhengding County High-tech Industrial Development Zone, Shijiazhuang, 050800, Hebei, China
Tel.: (86) 31189190165
Web Site: https://www.hbcsbio.com
Year Founded: 2000
300255—(CHIN)
Rev.: $328,006,692
Assets: $847,426,320
Liabilities: $418,641,912
Net Worth: $428,784,408
Earnings: $2,458,404
Fiscal Year-end: 12/31/22
Pharmaceuticals Product Mfr
N.A.I.C.S.: 325412

Subsidiaries:

Changshan Biochemical Pharmaceutical (Jiangsu) Co., Ltd. (1)
18 Guoxiang Road, Wujin Economic Development Zone, Changzhou, 213149, Jiangsu, China
Tel.: (86) 51986567888
Emp.: 100
Pharmaceuticals Mfr
N.A.I.C.S.: 325412

Changshan ConjuChem Biological Pharmaceutical R&D Co., Ltd. (1)
North of Yinchuan Street, Zhengding New District, Shijiazhuang, Hebei, China
Tel.: (86) 31189190272
Pharmaceuticals Mfr
N.A.I.C.S.: 325412

Hebei Changshan Kaikude Biotechnology Co., Ltd. (1)
19 Zhaopu Street, North District High-tech Industrial Development Zone Zhengding County, Shijiazhuang, Hebei, China
Tel.: (86) 31189198555
Pharmaceuticals Mfr
N.A.I.C.S.: 325412

Hebei Changshan Kaila Biotechnology Co., Ltd. (1)
No 9 Fuqiang Road, Zhengding County, Shijiazhuang, Hebei, China
Tel.: (86) 31188712901
Pharmaceuticals Mfr
N.A.I.C.S.: 325412

Hebei Changshan Kailuonite Biotechnology Co., Ltd. (1)
North of Yinchuan Street, Zhengding New District, Shijiazhuang, Hebei, China
Tel.: (86) 31189190235
Pharmaceuticals Mfr
N.A.I.C.S.: 325412

Hebei Changshan Long Kang Biotechnology Co., Ltd. (1)
North of Yinchuan Street, Zhengding New District, Shijiazhuang, Hebei, China
Tel.: (86) 31189190198
Pharmaceuticals Mfr
N.A.I.C.S.: 325412

Hebei Meishan Polysaccharide & Polypeptide Technology Co., Ltd. (1)
North of Yinchuan Street, Zhengding New District, Shijiazhuang, Hebei, China
Tel.: (86) 31189190198
Polysaccharide & Polypeptide Mfr
N.A.I.C.S.: 326150

Long Kang Medical Investment Management Hebei Co., Ltd. (1)
North of Yinchuan Street, Zhengding New District, Shijiazhuang, Hebei, China
Tel.: (86) 31189190198
Medical Investment Management Services
N.A.I.C.S.: 541611

Shijiazhuang Changshan Pharmacy Co., Ltd. (1)
29 Heping West Road, Xinhua District, Shijiazhuang, Hebei, China
Tel.: (86) 31189150116
Pharmaceuticals Mfr
N.A.I.C.S.: 325412

HEBEI CHENGXIN CO., LTD.
South Yuanzhao Road, Yuanshi County, Shijiazhuang, 51130, Hebei, China
Tel.: (86) 31184635784
Web Site: http://www.hebeichengxin.com
Year Founded: 1990
Sales Range: $1-4.9 Billion
Emp.: 5,500
Chemical Products Mfr
N.A.I.C.S.: 325998
Xianying Chu (Pres)

HEBEI CONSTRUCTION GROUP CORPORATION LIMITED
125 Lugang Road, Jingxiu District, Baoding, Hebei, China
Tel.: (86) 3123311000   CN
Web Site: https://www.hebjs.com.cn
Year Founded: 1952
1727—(HKG)
Rev.: $5,616,844,927
Assets: $9,495,511,740
Liabilities: $8,629,598,250
Net Worth: $865,913,490
Earnings: $44,287,636
Emp.: 9,104
Fiscal Year-end: 12/31/22
Civil Engineering Services
N.A.I.C.S.: 541330
Yongjian Liu (VP)

HEBEI GONGDA KEYA ENERGY TECHNOLOGY CO., LTD.
Building No 9 Runjiang Headquarters International No 455, Yuhua East Road High-tech Zone, Shijiazhuang, 050000, Hebei, China
Tel.: (86) 31183839905
Web Site: https://www.gdkeya.com
Year Founded: 2002
301197—(CHIN)
Rev.: $49,558,997
Assets: $232,247,134
Liabilities: $44,472,073
Net Worth: $187,775,061
Earnings: $7,845,619
Fiscal Year-end: 12/31/23
Software Development Services
N.A.I.C.S.: 541511
Chengying Qi (Chm)

HEBEI HENGSHUI LAOBAIGAN LIQUOR CO., LTD.
No 809 Renmin East Road, Hengshui, 053000, Hebei, China
Tel.: (86) 3182122755
Web Site: http://www.hengshuilaobaigan.net
Year Founded: 1999

HEBEI HENGSHUI LAOBAIGAN LIQUOR CO., LTD.

Hebei Hengshui Laobaigan Liquor Co., Ltd.—(Continued)
600559—(SHG)
Rev.: $653,295,408
Assets: $1,252,036,445
Liabilities: $641,786,118
Net Worth: $610,250,327
Earnings: $99,346,577
Fiscal Year-end: 12/31/22
Liquor Product Mfr & Distr
N.A.I.C.S.: 312130
Yanlong Liu (Chm)

HEBEI HUATONG WIRES & CABLES GROUP CO., LTD.
No 111 Huatong Street, Fengnan Economic Development District, Tangshan, 063000, Hebei, China
Tel.: (86) 3155092086
Web Site: https://www.htwirecable.com
Year Founded: 2002
605196—(SHG)
Rev.: $729,072,111
Assets: $764,386,810
Liabilities: $416,686,098
Net Worth: $347,700,712
Earnings: $36,063,004
Emp.: 800
Fiscal Year-end: 12/31/22
Wire & Cable Mfr
N.A.I.C.S.: 331491
Wendong Zhang (Chm)

HEBEI HUIJIN GROUP CO., LTD.
No 209 Xiangjiang Road, High-tech Industrial Development Zone, Shijiazhuang, 050035, Hebei, China
Tel.: (86) 31166858090
Web Site: https://en.hjjs.com
Year Founded: 2005
300368—(CHIN)
Rev.: $81,015,012
Assets: $473,417,568
Liabilities: $379,089,828
Net Worth: $94,327,740
Earnings: ($39,553,488)
Emp.: 600
Fiscal Year-end: 12/31/22
Banking Industry Machinery & Equipment Mfr
N.A.I.C.S.: 333248
Mao Shiquan (Chm)

HEBEI JIANXIN CHEMICAL CO., LTD.
Jianxin Building No 8 Qingchi Street, Cangzhou, 061000, Hebei, China
Tel.: (86) 3173560511
Web Site: https://www.jianxinchemical.com
Year Founded: 2003
300107—(CHIN)
Rev.: $104,242,788
Assets: $234,048,204
Liabilities: $28,981,368
Net Worth: $205,066,836
Earnings: $8,602,308
Emp.: 350
Fiscal Year-end: 12/31/22
Chemicals Mfr
N.A.I.C.S.: 325998
Zhu Shouchen (Chm)

HEBEI LIHUA HAT MANUFACTURING GROUP CO., LTD.
No 2 Lihua Road, Dingxing, Hebei, China
Tel.: (86) 312 692 3013
Web Site: http://www.lihuahats.com
Year Founded: 1985
Emp.: 1,800
Holding Company; Hat Mfr & Whslr
N.A.I.C.S.: 551112
Jushan Liu (Founder & Chm)

Subsidiaries:

Dingxing Lida Hat Making Co., Ltd. (1)
No 3 Lihua Road, Dingxing, Hebei, China
Tel.: (86) 3126923013
Web Site: http://www.lihuahats.com
Sales Range: $250-299.9 Million
Hat Mfr & Whslr
N.A.I.C.S.: 315990

HEBEI SAILHERO ENVIRONMENTAL PROTECTION HIGH-TECH CO., LTD.
No 251 Xiangjiang Road, Shijiazhuang, 050035, Hebei, China
Tel.: (86) 31185323900
Web Site: https://en.sailhero.com
Year Founded: 1996
300137—(CHIN)
Rev.: $141,541,452
Assets: $327,466,152
Liabilities: $55,369,548
Net Worth: $272,096,604
Earnings: ($18,938,556)
Fiscal Year-end: 12/31/22
Environmental Monitoring & Control Instruments Mfr
N.A.I.C.S.: 334512
Yao Guorui (Chm)

Subsidiaries:

Beijing Sailhero Zhongrun Science and Technology Co., Ltd. (1)
Room 403 Unit 3 Building A Chegongzhuang Street, West District, Beijing, 100044, China
Tel.: (86) 1088393818
Web Site: http://www.sailhero.com.cn
Environmental Monitoring Equipment Mfr & Distr
N.A.I.C.S.: 334519

Sailbri Cooper Inc. (1)
10300 SW Nimbus Ave Ste PB, Tigard, OR 97223
Tel.: (503) 670-8127
Web Site: https://www.sci-monitoring.com
Holding Company; Air Monitoring Instrumentation Mfr
N.A.I.C.S.: 551112
Krag Petterson (VP-Mktg & Sls)

Subsidiary (Domestic):

Cooper Environmental Services, LLC (2)
10300 SW Nimbus Ave Suite P-B, Beaverton, OR 97008
Tel.: (503) 670-8127
Web Site: http://www.cooperenvironmental.com
Pollution Monitoring Technologies Developer & Mfr
N.A.I.C.S.: 334519
John A. Cooper (Pres)

Sunset Laboratory, Inc. (2)
10180 SW Nimbus Ave Ste J/5, Tigard, OR 97223-4341
Tel.: (503) 624-1100
Air Monitoring Instrumentation Mfr
N.A.I.C.S.: 334519
Joshua Dixon (VP-East Coast Office)

HEBEI SINOPACK ELECTRONIC TECHNOLOGY CO., LTD.
No 21 Changsheng Street Economic Development Zone, Luquan Economic Development Zone, Shijiazhuang, 050200, Hebei, China
Tel.: (86) 31183933966
Web Site: https://www.sinopack.com.cn
Year Founded: 2009
003031—(SSE)
Rev.: $183,209,364
Assets: $249,831,972
Liabilities: $73,537,308
Net Worth: $176,294,664
Earnings: $20,871,864

Emp.: 290
Fiscal Year-end: 12/31/22
Electronic Product Mfr & Distr
N.A.I.C.S.: 334419
Qiang Wang (Chm)

HEBEI YANGYUAN ZHIHUI BEVERAGE CO., LTD.
No 6 New District Road, Hengshui Economic Development Zone North District, Hengshui, 053000, Hebei, China
Tel.: (86) 3182329090
Web Site: https://www.hbyangyuan.com
Year Founded: 1997
603156—(SHG)
Rev.: $831,564,883
Assets: $2,115,008,218
Liabilities: $497,924,542
Net Worth: $1,617,083,676
Earnings: $206,984,630
Fiscal Year-end: 12/31/22
Walnut Beverage Mfr & Distr
N.A.I.C.S.: 311511
Yao Kuizhang (Chm)

HEBEI YICHEN INDUSTRIAL GROUP CORPORATION LIMITED
No 1 Yichen North Street Gaocheng District, Shijiazhuang, Hebei, China
Tel.: (86) 31188929020
Web Site: http://www.hbyc.com.cn
Year Founded: 2001
1596—(HKG)
Rev.: $176,660,574
Assets: $504,798,074
Liabilities: $157,551,395
Net Worth: $347,246,679
Earnings: $22,767,149
Emp.: 1,369
Fiscal Year-end: 12/31/22
Rail Fastening System Product Mfr & Distr
N.A.I.C.S.: 331110
Fengxuan Zhang (Deputy Gen Mgr)

HEBERT KANNEGIESSER GMBH
Kannegiesserring 8, 32602, Vlotho, Germany
Tel.: (49) 5733120
Web Site: http://www.kannegiesser.com
Year Founded: 1948
Laundry Equipment Mfr
N.A.I.C.S.: 333310
Martin Kannegiesser (Co-Mng Dir)

Subsidiaries:

Herbert Kannegiesser Ges. mbH (1)
Webergasse 18, 1200, Vienna, Austria
Tel.: (43) 1 3 32 88 88
Laundry Equipment Mfr
N.A.I.C.S.: 333310

Kannegiesser Aue GmbH (1)
Herbert Kannegiesser Strasse 4 Gewerbegebiet Am Gerichtsberg, Schneeberg, Bad Schlema, Germany
Tel.: (49) 3772 3713 0
Laundry Equipment Mfr
N.A.I.C.S.: 333310

Kannegiesser Augsburg GmbH (1)
Wasserturmstrasse 51, 86199, Augsburg, Germany
Tel.: (49) 821 9070 0
Laundry Equipment Mfr
N.A.I.C.S.: 333310

Kannegiesser Australia Pty Ltd. (1)
Unit 13 5 Hudson Ave, Castle Hill, 2154, NSW, Australia
Tel.: (61) 2 96 34 82 22
Laundry Equipment Mfr
N.A.I.C.S.: 333310

Kannegiesser Benelux B.V. (1)

INTERNATIONAL PUBLIC

Geurdeland 1, 6673 DR, Andelst, Netherlands
Tel.: (31) 488 470 650
Web Site: http://www.kannegiesser.de
Laundry Equipment Distr
N.A.I.C.S.: 423850

Kannegiesser ETECH, Inc. (1)
2425 109th St, Grand Prairie, TX 75050
Tel.: (972) 602-8766
Web Site: http://www.kannegiesser-usa.com
Laundry Washing & Drying Services
N.A.I.C.S.: 423850
Phil Hart (Pres & CEO)

Subsidiary (Domestic):

ETECH Systems, Inc. (2)
2090 Elm St SE, Minneapolis, MN 55414
Tel.: (612) 722-1366
Web Site: http://news.etechsystems.com
Material Handling Systems Software & Services
N.A.I.C.S.: 541511

Kannegiesser Espana, S.L. (1)
C/Cadiz 15 Pol Ind Siemens, Cornella de Llobregat, 08940, Barcelona, Spain
Tel.: (34) 93 435 77 00
Web Site: http://www.kannegiesser.es
Emp.: 10
Laundry Equipment Distr
N.A.I.C.S.: 423850
Carsten Osingnann (Gen Mgr)

Kannegiesser France S.A. (1)
21 rue des Peupliers, 92752, Nanterre, France
Tel.: (33) 155 669 420
Web Site: http://www.kannegiesser.fr
Laundry Equipment Distr
N.A.I.C.S.: 423850

Kannegiesser GmbH (1)
Voss Strasse 12, 31157, Sarstedt, Germany
Tel.: (49) 5066 9020 0
Laundry Equipment Mfr
N.A.I.C.S.: 333310

Kannegiesser Italia S.R.L. (1)
Via Cesare Pavese 1/3, Opera, Milan, Italy
Tel.: (39) 02 57 60 60 00
Web Site: http://www.kannegiesser.it
Emp.: 19
Laundry Equipment Mfr
N.A.I.C.S.: 333310
Alessandro Rolli (CEO)

Kannegiesser UK Ltd. (1)
Beaumont Road Industrial Estate, Banbury, OX16 1QZ, Oxon, United Kingdom
Tel.: (44) 1295 221 221
Web Site: http://www.kannegiesser.co.uk
Laundry Equipment Distr
N.A.I.C.S.: 423850
Martin McGeever (Dir-Engrg, Health & Safety)

Pharmagg Systemtechnik GmbH (1)
Hingster Strasse 5, 27318, Hoya, Germany
Tel.: (49) 4251 9320 0
Laundry Equipment Mfr
N.A.I.C.S.: 333310

HEBSON HOLDINGS PLC
27 Theodorou Mavrosavva, Nicosia, Cyprus
Tel.: (357) 22558888
Holding Company
N.A.I.C.S.: 551112

HEC INFRA PROJECTS LTD.
Sigma-1 Corporates Corporate House No 6 Sindhu, Sindhu Bhavan Road Near Mann Party Plot Cross Road Bodakdev, Ahmedabad, 380054, Gujarat, India
Tel.: (91) 7940086771
Web Site: https://www.hecprojects.in
Year Founded: 2005
HECPROJECT—(NSE)
Rev.: $6,363,635
Assets: $10,167,112
Liabilities: $6,552,881
Net Worth: $3,614,232
Earnings: $94,515
Emp.: 38

AND PRIVATE COMPANIES

HEFEI MEYER OPTOELECTRONIC TECHNOLOGY INC.

Fiscal Year-end: 03/31/23
Waste Management Services
N.A.I.C.S.: 221310
Jeel Patel *(Chief Compliance Officer & Sec)*

HEC PHARM CO., LTD.
Dong Yang Guang Park Shangsha, Changan Dongguan, Guangdong, 523871, China
Tel.: (86) 769 853 158 88   CN
Web Site: http://www.hecpharm.com
Year Founded: 1992
Pharmaceuticals Product Mfr
N.A.I.C.S.: 325412

HECKLER AG
Gartenstrasse 37 39, 75223, Niefern-Oschelbronn, Germany
Tel.: (49) 72339300
Web Site: http://www.heckler.de
Year Founded: 1950
Rev.: $38,255,315
Emp.: 150
Extrusion Parts & Machine Tool Mfr
N.A.I.C.S.: 333517
Claudio Sandrini *(Member-Mgmt Bd)*

Subsidiaries:

HECKLER Romania S.R.L.   (1)
Sat Selimbar Str Mihai Viteazu 11, Selimbar, 557260, Sibiu, Romania
Tel.: (40) 269206492
Automotive Spare Parts Distr
N.A.I.C.S.: 423120

Zi Kaltumformung GmbH   (1)
Ursprunger Strasse 26-28, 09353, Zwickau, Germany
Tel.: (49) 372341980
Diesel Engine Mfr
N.A.I.C.S.: 336310
Michael Rebholz *(CEO)*

HECTO FINANCIAL CO., LTD.
9th-10th floor Yeoksam-dong Taekwang Tower, 6 Teheran-ro 34-gil Gangnam-gu, Seoul, 06220, Korea (South)
Tel.: (82) 16005220
Web Site:
https://www.hectofinancial.co.kr
Year Founded: 2000
234340—(KRS)
Rev.: $99,135,173
Assets: $258,176,320
Liabilities: $148,218,070
Net Worth: $109,958,250
Earnings: $9,232,185
Emp.: 174
Fiscal Year-end: 12/31/22
Financial Services
N.A.I.C.S.: 523150
Jong Won Choi *(CEO)*

HECTO INNOVATION CO., LTD
12th & 13th floors Taekwang Tower 6 Teheran-ro 34-gil, Gangnam-gu, Seoul, 06220, Korea (South)
Tel.: (82) 29294463
Web Site:
https://www.hectoinnovation.co.kr
Year Founded: 2009
214180—(KRS)
Rev.: $201,695,752
Assets: $404,064,096
Liabilities: $187,306,834
Net Worth: $216,757,262
Earnings: $24,679,901
Emp.: 143
Fiscal Year-end: 12/31/22
Mobile Phone Security Software
N.A.I.C.S.: 513210

HEDEF GIRISIM SERMAYESI YATI ORTAK
Dr Adnan Buyukdeniz Cad No 4/2 Cessas Plaza Kat 3 D 7, Inkilap Mh Umraniye, 34676, Istanbul, Turkiye
Tel.: (90) 2169705757
Web Site: https://hedefgirisim.com.tr
Year Founded: 2012
HDFGS—(IST)
Sales Range: Less than $1 Million
Investment Management Service
N.A.I.C.S.: 523940
Namik Kemal Gokalp *(Chm)*

HEDOSOPHIA EUROPEAN GROWTH
2 Soho Place, London, W1D 3BG, United Kingdom
Web Site:
https://www.hedosophiagrowth.eu
Year Founded: 2012
HEGA—(EUR)
Rev.: $8,954,384
Assets: $548,045,522
Liabilities: $559,943,348
Net Worth: ($11,897,826)
Earnings: ($75,312,012)
Fiscal Year-end: 12/31/21
Investment Management Service
N.A.I.C.S.: 523999
Ian Osborne *(CEO)*

HEEL CANADA INC.
11025 LH Lafontaine, Anjou, H1J 2Z4, QC, Canada
Tel.: (514) 353-4335
Web Site: http://www.heel.ca
Sales Range: $1-9.9 Million
Emp.: 40
Homeopathic Medicine Mfr
N.A.I.C.S.: 325412

HEERA ISPAT LTD.
Block No 0-104 Ganesh Homes Near Pramukh Bunglow, Behind Sahajannd Homes Chenpur Road New Ranip, Usmanpura, Ahmedabad, 382470, Gujarat, India
Tel.: (91) 7927550140   In
Web Site: http://www.heeraispat.com
Year Founded: 1992
526967—(BOM)
Assets: $4,668
Liabilities: $33,811
Net Worth: ($29,143)
Earnings: ($14,360)
Emp.: 2
Fiscal Year-end: 03/31/22
Steel Product Mfr & Whslr
N.A.I.C.S.: 331110

HEERIM ARCHITECTS & PLANNERS CO., LTD.
12F Gangdong Tower 39 Sangil ro 6 gil, Gangdong-gu, Seoul, 05288, Korea (South)
Tel.: (82) 234109000
Web Site: https://www.heerim.com
Year Founded: 1970
037440—(KRS)
Rev.: $169,558,562
Assets: $152,730,337
Liabilities: $100,520,953
Net Worth: $52,209,384
Earnings: $5,487,507
Emp.: 1,407
Fiscal Year-end: 12/31/22
Architectural Services
N.A.I.C.S.: 541310
Young Kyoon Jeong *(Chm & CEO)*

Subsidiaries:

P2 LED Cube   (1)
5F Gangdong Tower 39 Sangil-ro 6-gil, Gangdong gu, Seoul, 05288, Korea (South)
Tel.: (82) 234449711
Web Site: https://www.p2ledcube.com
Sales Range: $25-49.9 Million
Emp.: 8
Architectural Lighting System Design & Installation Services

N.A.I.C.S.: 541490

HEETON HOLDINGS LIMITED
60 Paya Lebar Road 0836 Paya Lebar Square, Singapore, 779088, Singapore
Tel.: (65) 64561188
Web Site: https://www.heeton.com
5DP—(SES)
Rev.: $51,395,137
Assets: $736,668,938
Liabilities: $419,996,970
Net Worth: $316,671,968
Earnings: ($4,981,444)
Emp.: 345
Fiscal Year-end: 12/31/23
Property Development Services
N.A.I.C.S.: 531311
Vince Giap Eng Toh *(Deputy Chm)*

Subsidiaries:

Econolodge Co., Ltd.   (1)
484 Moo 10 Pattaya 2nd Road Soi 15, Pattaya, Chon Buri, Thailand
Tel.: (66) 38425050
Construction Services
N.A.I.C.S.: 236220

Heeton Estate Pte Ltd   (1)
60 Sembawang Road 01-01/02/03/04 Hong Heng Mansion, Singapore, Singapore
Tel.: (65) 67897772
Sales Range: $50-74.9 Million
Emp.: 6
Real Estate Manangement Services
N.A.I.C.S.: 531210

Heeton SG50 Limited   (1)
Heeton UK Adam House 7-10 Adam Street The Strand, London, WC2N 6AA, United Kingdom
Tel.: (44) 2075209032
Construction Services
N.A.I.C.S.: 236220

HEFAL SERWIS S.A.
Ul Marklowicka 30A, Wodzislaw Slaski, 44-370, Poland
Tel.: (48) 324560262
Web Site: http://www.hefalserwis.pl
Year Founded: 2000
Building Construction Services
N.A.I.C.S.: 236210
Leszek Koloczek *(Chm)*

HEFEI CHANG QING MACHINERY CO., LTD.
No 18 Dongyou Road, Hefei, 230022, Anhui, China
Tel.: (86) 55163475077
Web Site: http://www.hfcqjx.com
Year Founded: 2004
603768—(SHG)
Rev.: $444,115,751
Assets: $589,746,058
Liabilities: $325,062,223
Net Worth: $264,683,835
Earnings: $13,522,584
Fiscal Year-end: 12/31/22
Automotive Welding Part Mfr & Distr
N.A.I.C.S.: 336310
Yinghong Wu *(Chm & Gen Mgr)*

HEFEI DEPARTMENT STORE GROUP CO., LTD.
No 596 Huangshan Road, Shushan District, Hefei, 230031, Anhui, China
Tel.: (86) 55165771035
Web Site: http://www.hfbh.com.cn
Year Founded: 1996
000417—(SSE)
Rev.: $884,785,356
Assets: $1,833,865,488
Liabilities: $1,103,841,648
Net Worth: $730,023,840
Earnings: $23,532,444
Fiscal Year-end: 12/31/22
Departmental Store Operator
N.A.I.C.S.: 455110

Shen Xiaogen *(Chm)*

HEFEI FENGLE SEED CO., LTD.
No 6500 Changjiang West Road, Hefei, 231283, Anhui, China
Tel.: (86) 55162239888
Web Site: http://www.fengle.com.cn
Year Founded: 1984
000713—(SSE)
Rev.: $421,938,504
Assets: $410,528,196
Liabilities: $126,324,900
Net Worth: $284,203,296
Earnings: $8,256,924
Fiscal Year-end: 12/31/22
Agricultural Chemical Product Mfr
N.A.I.C.S.: 325320
Feng Yue *(Chm)*

HEFEI JIANGHANG AIRCRAFT EQUIPMENT CO., LTD.
No 35 Yanan Road, Baohe Industrial Zone, Hefei, 230051, Anhui, China
Tel.: (86) 55163499099
Web Site: http://www.jianghang.com
Year Founded: 2007
688586—(SHG)
Rev.: $156,535,961
Assets: $505,734,082
Liabilities: $174,267,527
Net Worth: $331,466,555
Earnings: $34,256,336
Emp.: 1,300
Fiscal Year-end: 12/31/22
Aircraft Parts Mfr & Distr
N.A.I.C.S.: 336413
Zuming Song *(Chm)*

HEFEI LIFEON PHARMACEUTICAL CO., LTD.
No 126 Science Avenue High-tech Industrial Development Zone, Hefei, 230088, Anhui, China
Tel.: (86) 55165350399
Web Site: https://www.lifeon.cn
Year Founded: 2002
003020—(SSE)
Rev.: $362,139,336
Assets: $297,895,104
Liabilities: $90,072,216
Net Worth: $207,822,888
Earnings: $29,429,244
Emp.: 700
Fiscal Year-end: 12/31/22
Pharmaceutical Product Mfr & Distr
N.A.I.C.S.: 325412
Junqiu Ji *(Chm)*

HEFEI METALFORMING INTELLIGENT MANUFACTURING CO., LTD.
No 123 Ziyun Road Economic and Technological Development Area, Hefei, 230601, Anhui, China
Tel.: (86) 55165160108
Web Site: https://www.hfmpress.com
Year Founded: 1951
603011—(SHG)
Rev.: $243,515,418
Assets: $561,615,767
Liabilities: $254,873,736
Net Worth: $306,742,031
Earnings: $1,838,299
Fiscal Year-end: 12/31/22
Machine Tools Mfr
N.A.I.C.S.: 333517
Lanjun Zhang *(Deputy Gen Mgr)*

HEFEI MEYER OPTOELECTRONIC TECHNOLOGY INC.
No 668 West Wangjiang Rd Hightech Industry Development Zone, Hefei, 230088, Anhui, China
Tel.: (86) 55165306653
Web Site: https://www.meyerop.com

HEFEI MEYER OPTOELECTRONIC TECHNOLOGY INC.

Hefei Meyer Optoelectronic Technology Inc.—(Continued)
Year Founded: 1993
002690—(SSE)
Rev.: $297,263,304
Assets: $465,414,768
Liabilities: $93,464,280
Net Worth: $371,950,488
Earnings: $102,507,444
Emp.: 600
Fiscal Year-end: 12/31/22
Optoelectronic Detection & Classification Equipment Mfr
N.A.I.C.S.: 333248
Ming Tian (Chm)

HEFEI TAIHE OPTOELECTRONIC TECHNOLOGY CO., LTD

No 66 Yulan Avenue Taohua Industrial Park Expansion Zone, Economic and Technological Development Zone, Hefei, Anhui, China
Tel.: (86) 55165399166
Web Site:
  https://www.chinacolorsort.com
Year Founded: 2004
603656—(SHG)
Rev.: $67,300,291
Assets: $186,202,327
Liabilities: $48,706,627
Net Worth: $137,495,700
Earnings: $3,027,473
Fiscal Year-end: 12/31/22
Food Machinery Mfr & Distr
N.A.I.C.S.: 333241

HEFEI URBAN CONSTRUCTION DEVEL CO., LTD.

Floor 9-14 Building A Amber Five Rings International, No 100 Qianshan Road Shushan District, Hefei, 230031, Anhui, China
Tel.: (86) 55162661906
Web Site: https://www.hucd.cn
Year Founded: 1999
002208—(SSE)
Rev.: $565,233,552
Assets: $4,696,228,368
Liabilities: $3,375,593,676
Net Worth: $1,320,634,692
Earnings: $46,938,528
Fiscal Year-end: 12/31/22
Residential Building Leasing Services
N.A.I.C.S.: 531110
Xiaoyi Wang (Chm)

HEFFNER MOTORS LIMITED

3131 King St E, Kitchener, N2A 1B1, ON, Canada
Tel.: (519) 748-9666
Web Site: http://www.heffner.ca
Year Founded: 1963
Sales Range: $10-24.9 Million
Emp.: 100
New & Used Car Dealers
N.A.I.C.S.: 441110
John Heffner Jr. (Pres)

HEG LIMITED

Bhilwara Towers A-12 Sector 1, Noida, 201301, Delhi, India
Tel.: (91) 1204390300
Web Site: https://www.hegltd.com
509631—(BOM)
Rev.: $351,675,870
Assets: $776,947,080
Liabilities: $192,604,230
Net Worth: $584,342,850
Earnings: $72,667,140
Emp.: 842
Fiscal Year-end: 03/31/23
Graphite Electrode Mfr
N.A.I.C.S.: 335991
Ravi Jhunjhunwala (Chm, CEO & Mng Dir)

HEHEIST CO., LTD.

580-1 Imafuku, Kawagoe, 350-1151, Saitama, Japan
Tel.: (81) 492737000
Web Site: https://www.hephaist.co.jp
Year Founded: 1962
6433—(TKS)
Rev.: $26,542,560
Assets: $47,393,280
Liabilities: $16,049,440
Net Worth: $31,343,840
Earnings: $2,100,560
Fiscal Year-end: 03/31/22
System Product Mfr
N.A.I.C.S.: 541519
Hirota Ozaki (Pres)

Subsidiaries:

HEPHAIST SEIKO (SHANGHAI) Co., Ltd. (1)
2623 New Town Center Building 83 Loushanguan Road, Shanghai, 200336, China
Tel.: (86) 21 3133 2623
Industrial Supplies Whslr
N.A.I.C.S.: 423840

HEPHAIST SEIKO Co., Ltd. - Akita Factory (1)
454 Shimoda Toyoiwakoyama, Akita-shi, Akita, 010-1653, Japan
Tel.: (81) 188280111
Web Site: https://www.hephaist.co.jp
Motion Bearing Mfr
N.A.I.C.S.: 333613

HEIAN CEREMONY SERVICE CO., LTD.

1-35 Sakuragaoka, Hiratsuka, 254-0053, Kanagawa, Japan
Tel.: (81) 463342771
Web Site: https://www.heian-group.co.jp
Year Founded: 1969
2344—(TKS)
Rev.: $66,607,183
Assets: $224,757,122
Liabilities: $88,199,513
Net Worth: $136,557,610
Earnings: $5,867,194
Fiscal Year-end: 03/31/24
Wedding & Funeral Services
N.A.I.C.S.: 812990
Hideyuki Soma (Pres)

HEIDELBERG INNOVATION FONDS MANAGEMENT GMBH

Walehofer Str 11-5, 69123, Heidelberg, Germany
Tel.: (49) 0622164680 De
Web Site: http://www.hd-innovation.de
Year Founded: 1997
Sales Range: $50-74.9 Million
Emp.: 7
Investment Services for Healthcare & Pharmaceutical Industries
N.A.I.C.S.: 523999
Ulrich Abshagen (Founder & Mng Partner)

HEIDELBERG MATERIALS AG

Berliner Strasse 6, 69120, Heidelberg, Germany
Tel.: (49) 62214810 De
Web Site:
  https://www.heidelbergmaterial.com
Year Founded: 1873
HEI—(MUN)
Rev.: $23,377,317,312
Assets: $39,155,924,705
Liabilities: $20,123,770,874
Net Worth: $19,032,153,831
Earnings: $2,129,254,843
Emp.: 51,573
Fiscal Year-end: 12/31/23
Cement, Ready Mixed Concrete, Concrete Products, Aggregates, Sand-Lime Bricks, Lime & Other Building Materials Mfr
N.A.I.C.S.: 327310
Hakan Gurdal (Member-Mgmt Bd)

Subsidiaries:

A1 Services (Manchester) Limited (1)
Mayo House 4 Overman Way Agecroft Commerce Park, Swinton, Manchester, M27 8BQ, United Kingdom
Tel.: (44) 1617362020
Web Site:
  https://www.recycling.heidelberg.co.uk
Emp.: 3,500
Construction & Civil Engineering Services
N.A.I.C.S.: 541330

ARC Slimline Limited (1)
Hanson House 14 Castle Hill, Maidenhead, SL6 4JJ, United Kingdom
Tel.: (44) 1454314400
Investment Management Service
N.A.I.C.S.: 523940

Akcansa Cimento Sanayi ve Ticaret A.S. (1)
Barbaros Mahallesi Kardelen Sk No 2 D 124-125 Palladium Tower, Istanbul, Turkiye (39.72%)
Tel.: (90) 2165713000
Web Site: http://www.akcansa.com.tr
Rev.: $266,680,842
Assets: $329,686,733
Liabilities: $166,046,658
Net Worth: $163,640,074
Earnings: $15,596,433
Emp.: 967
Fiscal Year-end: 12/31/2020
Cement Mfr
N.A.I.C.S.: 327310
Hakan Gurdal (Vice Chm)

Alex Fraser Asphalt Pty. Ltd. (1)
Level 1 50 Parkwest Drive, Derrimut, 3026, VIC, Australia
Tel.: (61) 136135
Web Site: https://alexfraser.com.au
Readymix Concrete Mfr
N.A.I.C.S.: 327320
Peter Murphy (Mng Dir)

Alexandre Limited (1)
Hanson House 14 Castle Hill, Maidenhead, SL6 4JJ, United Kingdom
Tel.: (44) 20 7245 1245
Management Consulting Services
N.A.I.C.S.: 541618

Allied Ready Mix Concrete Limited (1)
13980 Mitchell Rd, Richmond, V6V 1M8, BC, Canada
Tel.: (604) 324-8191
Sales Range: $25-49.9 Million
Emp.: 25
Readymix Concrete Mfr
N.A.I.C.S.: 327320
Tyler Thorson (Mgr)

Unit (Non-US):

Castle Cement Ltd. - Padeswood Works (2)
Padeswood Works Chester Road, Mold, CH7 4HB, Flintshire, United Kingdom
Tel.: (44) 124 455 0330
Web Site: http://www.castlecement.com
Sales Range: $50-74.9 Million
Cement Mfr & Distr
N.A.I.C.S.: 327310

Hanson Cement - Ribblesdale Works (2)
Ribblesdale Works West Bradford Road, West Bradford Road, Clitheroe, BB7 4QF, Lancashire, United Kingdom
Tel.: (44) 120 042 2401
Web Site: http://www.castlecement.com
Sales Range: $100-124.9 Million
Emp.: 420
Cement Mfr & Distr
N.A.I.C.S.: 327310
Gary Young (Plant Mgr)

Hanson Cement Ltd. (2)
Ketton Works, Ketco Avenue, Stamford, PE9 3SX, Rutland, United Kingdom
Tel.: (44) 1780720501
Web Site: http://www.heidelbergcement.com

INTERNATIONAL PUBLIC

Sales Range: $100-124.9 Million
Emp.: 360
Cement Mfr & Distr
N.A.I.C.S.: 327310
Mark Hickingbottom (Comml Dir-Natl-Bulk Products)

Amey Roadstone International Limited (1)
Higham Road, Wellingborough, NN9 6QF, United Kingdom
Tel.: (44) 1933626309
Investment Management Service
N.A.I.C.S.: 523940

Aridos Sanz S.L.U. (1)
Ctra Segovia Km 8 3 PPG Front Suitable, Post 12, 47193, Valladolid, Spain
Tel.: (34) 983401068
Mining & Quarrying Services
N.A.I.C.S.: 212311

Aridos Velilla, S.A. (1)
Finca Velilla S/N, 45270, Mocejon, Spain
Tel.: (34) 925 59 01 88
Cement Mfr
N.A.I.C.S.: 327310

B.V. Betoncentrale BEMA (1)
Laanenderweg 43, 1812 PW, Alkmaar, Netherlands
Tel.: (31) 72 540 01 41
Cement Mfr
N.A.I.C.S.: 327310

B.V. Betoncentrale De Schelde (1)
Van Konijnenburgweg 46, 4612 PL, Bergen-op-Zoom, Netherlands
Tel.: (31) 164 23 36 69
Sales Range: $25-49.9 Million
Emp.: 10
Cement Mfr
N.A.I.C.S.: 327310

B.V. Bouwgrondstoffen A.G.M. (1)
Amerikahavenweg 12, 1045 AD, Amsterdam, Netherlands
Tel.: (31) 20 6147821
Construction Materials Whslr
N.A.I.C.S.: 423320

B.V. Mortel Installatie Assen (1)
Wenkebachstraat 11, 9403 BG, Assen, Netherlands
Tel.: (31) 592602000
Web Site: http://www.megamix.nl
Sales Range: $25-49.9 Million
Emp.: 10
Readymix Concrete Mfr
N.A.I.C.S.: 327320

BEKTAS Group LLP (1)
76 Zhibek Zholy Ave, Almaty, Kazakhstan
Tel.: (7) 727 273 06 03
Readymix Concrete Mfr & Distr
N.A.I.C.S.: 327320

BETOTECH, s.r.o. (1)
Beroun 660, 266 01, Beroun, Czech Republic
Tel.: (420) 777090042
Web Site: https://www.betotech.cz
Aggregate, Cement & Concrete Testing Services
N.A.I.C.S.: 541380

BM Valla ehf (1)
Breiohofoi 3, 110, Reykjavik, Iceland
Tel.: (354) 4125000
Web Site: https://www.bmvalla.is
Construction Materials Whslr
N.A.I.C.S.: 423320

BT Poznan Sp. z.o.o. (1)
Gnieznienska 61, Janikowo, 62006, Poland
Tel.: (48) 61 878 03 24
Cement Mfr
N.A.I.C.S.: 327310

Bath and Portland Stone (Holdings) Limited (1)
Avon Mill Lane, Keynsham, Bristol, BS31 2UG, Avon, United Kingdom
Tel.: (44) 1179869631
Investment Management Service
N.A.I.C.S.: 523940

Bausteinwerk Bott - Blasberg G.m.b.H. & Co. Kommanditgesellschaft (1)

AND PRIVATE COMPANIES

HEIDELBERG MATERIALS AG

Darmstadter Str 5, 64625, Bensheim, Germany
Tel.: (49) 625 11 30 30
Marble & Stone Distr
N.A.I.C.S.: 423320

BayKaz Beton LLP (1)
76 Zhibek Zholy Ave, Almaty, Kazakhstan
Tel.: (7) 727 273 06 03
Readymix Concrete Mfr & Distr
N.A.I.C.S.: 327320

Beton de Liege SA (1)
Rue de l'Ile Monsin 12, 4020, Liege, Belgium
Tel.: (32) 4 240 36 01
Readymix Concrete Mfr
N.A.I.C.S.: 327320

Betong Ost AS (1)
Marvegen 14, PO Box 1223, 2206, Kongsvinger, Norway
Tel.: (47) 6 288 8111
Web Site: https://www.betongost.no
Construction Materials Distr
N.A.I.C.S.: 423320

Betong Sor AS (1)
Lilleakerveien 2 B, PO Box 203, Lilleaker, 0216, Oslo, Norway
Tel.: (47) 22878300
Cement Mfr
N.A.I.C.S.: 327310

Betontir S.p.A. (1)
Corso Di Francia 200, 00191, Rome, Italy
Tel.: (39) 0632493432
Construction Management Services
N.A.I.C.S.: 541330

Betotech Baustofflabor GmbH (1)
Berliner Strasse 6, 69120, Heidelberg, Germany
Tel.: (49) 62214810
Web Site: https://www.betotech.de
Readymix Concrete Mfr
N.A.I.C.S.: 327320
Markus Pfeuffer (Mng Dir)

Betotech GmbH (1)
Schulstrasse 24, 72654, Neckartenzlingen, Germany
Tel.: (49) 7127954684
Web Site: https://www.beto-tec.de
Readymix Concrete Mfr
N.A.I.C.S.: 327320

Betotech Verwaltungs-GmbH (1)
Berliner Str 10, 69120, Heidelberg, Germany
Tel.: (49) 6221 481554
Administrative Management Services
N.A.I.C.S.: 541611

Bickleylake Limited (1)
1 Grosvenor Place, London, SW1X 7JH, Middlesex, United Kingdom
Tel.: (44) 20 7245 1245
Investment Management Service
N.A.I.C.S.: 523940

Birchwood Omnia Limited (1)
The Ridge Chipping Sodbury, Bristol, BS37 6AY, United Kingdom
Tel.: (44) 1454316000
Cement Mfr
N.A.I.C.S.: 327310

Bitumix Granite Sdn Bhd (1)
No 1550 Jln Pelabuhan Batu 14 Kampung Selamat, 26080, Kuantan, Malaysia
Tel.: (60) 95837851
Granite Quarrying Services
N.A.I.C.S.: 212313

Bjorgun ehf (1)
Vioinesvegur 22, Alfsnesvik, 162, Reykjavik, Iceland
Tel.: (354) 5635600
Web Site: https://www.bjorgun.is
Emp.: 30
Shipping Rescue Services
N.A.I.C.S.: 488330
Sveinbjorn Guomundsson (Mgr-Production)

British Agricultural Services Limited (1)
1 Grosvenor Place, London, SW1X 7JH, United Kingdom
Tel.: (44) 2072451245
Agricultural Consulting Services
N.A.I.C.S.: 541690

Butra HeidelbergCement Sdn. Bhd. (1)
Tel.: (673) 27713958
Web Site: https://www.bruneicement.com
Readymix Concrete Mfr
N.A.I.C.S.: 327320

CBR Asset Management Belgium S.A. (1)
Chaussee de La Hulpe 185, 1170, Brussels, 1170, Belgium
Tel.: (32) 2 678 32 11
Sales Range: $100-124.9 Million
Emp.: 250
Asset Management Services
N.A.I.C.S.: 523940
Daniel Gauthier (CEO)

CBR International Services S.A. (1)
Chaussee De La Hulpe 185, Brussels, 1170, Belgium
Tel.: (32) 26783211
Emp.: 250
Cement & Additive Distr
N.A.I.C.S.: 423320
Daniel Gauthier (CEO)

CBR Portland B.V. (1)
Sint Teunislaan 1, 5231 BS, 's-Hertogenbosch, Netherlands
Tel.: (31) 736401170
Construction Materials Distr
N.A.I.C.S.: 423320

CGF Capital B.V. (1)
Strawinskylaan 3105 Atriu, 1077 ZX, Amsterdam, Netherlands
Tel.: (31) 204064444
Financial Management Services
N.A.I.C.S.: 523999

CHB P H R Limited (1)
South Mall, London, United Kingdom
Tel.: (44) 20 8803 9984
Investment Management Service
N.A.I.C.S.: 523940

Cadman (Black Diamond), Inc. (1)
26111 SE Green Valley Rd, Black Diamond, WA 98010
Tel.: (425) 961-7100
Web Site: http://www.cadman.com
Emp.: 30
Readymix Concrete Mfr
N.A.I.C.S.: 327320
Bill Sayer (VP-Aggregate)

Cadman (Rock), Inc. (1)
19603 SR 203, Monroe, WA 98272
Tel.: (425) 867-1234
Web Site: http://www.cadman.com
Emp.: 30
Construction Sand & Gravel Quarrying Services
N.A.I.C.S.: 212321
Dave Warner (Gen Mgr)

Cadman (Seattle), Inc. (1)
5225 E Marginal Way S, Seattle, WA 98134
Tel.: (425) 961-7100
Web Site: http://www.cadman.com
Emp.: 10
Readymix Concrete Mfr
N.A.I.C.S.: 327320
Ed Richardson (Branch Mgr)

Calaveras Standard Materials (1)
2002 E Mcfadden Ave, Santa Ana, CA 92705-4766
Tel.: (714) 973-3000
Readymix Concrete Mfr
N.A.I.C.S.: 327320

Calumite Limited (1)
Brigg Road, Scunthorpe, DN16 1AW, North Lincolnshire, United Kingdom
Tel.: (44) 1724282211
Web Site: https://calumite.co.uk
Sales Range: $25-49.9 Million
Emp.: 7
Glass Raw Material Mfr
N.A.I.C.S.: 327215

Subsidiary (Non-US):

Calumite s.r.o. (2)
Lihovarska 636/44, Kuncicky, 718 00, Ostrava, Czech Republic
Tel.: (420) 596238908
Web Site: https://www.calumite.cz
Sales Range: $25-49.9 Million
Blast Furnace Slag Mfr
N.A.I.C.S.: 327992

Cantera El Hoyon, S.A. (1)
Principe De Vergara 43, 28001, Madrid, Spain
Tel.: (34) 915 78 64 00
Construction Materials Distr
N.A.I.C.S.: 423320

Canteras Mecanicas Carcaba, S.A.U. (1)
Santa Marina De Piedramuelle S/N, 33193, Oviedo, Spain
Tel.: (34) 985780914
Mining & Quarrying Services
N.A.I.C.S.: 212311

Carpat Beton S.R.L. (1)
Str Palas Sola 104, Constanta, Romania
Tel.: (40) 241 616 697
Readymix Concrete Mfr
N.A.I.C.S.: 327320

Carpat Beton Servicii Pompe SRL (1)
Soseaua Bucuresti-Targoviste 4, Mogosoaia, 77135, Romania
Tel.: (40) 21 350 43 66
Concrete Products Mfr
N.A.I.C.S.: 327390

Carpat Cemtrans S.R.L. (1)
Bucharest Business Park 1A Bucuresti Ploiesti Rd, 013681, Bucharest, Romania
Tel.: (40) 21 311 5975
Web Site: http://www.heidelbergcement.ro
Cargo Handling Services
N.A.I.C.S.: 488320
Florian Aldea (Country Mgr)

Carpatcement Holding S.A. (1)
Str Principala 1 Soimus, Chiscadaga, Soimus, 337457, Romania
Tel.: (40) 25423 70 02
Web Site: http://www.heidelbergcement.ro
Investment Management Service
N.A.I.C.S.: 523999
Bohdan Arnautu (Mgr-Comm)

Castle Building Products Limited (1)
North Farm Workshops Wallingford Road, North Moreton, Didcot, OX11 9BE, Oxon, United Kingdom
Tel.: (44) 1491826522
Web Site: https://www.cbpoxon.com
Construction Materials Distr
N.A.I.C.S.: 423320

Castle Cement (Chatburn) Limited (1)
Ribblesdale Works, Clitheroe, BB7 4QF, Lancashire, United Kingdom
Tel.: (44) 1200422401
Cement Mfr
N.A.I.C.S.: 327310
Gary Young (Plant Mgr)

Castle Cement (Ribblesdale) Limited (1)
Ribblesdale Works West Bradford Road, Clitheroe, BB7 4QF, Lancashire, United Kingdom
Tel.: (44) 1200422401
Web Site: https://www.heidelbergcement.com
Cement Mfr
N.A.I.C.S.: 327310

Castle Cement Limited (1)
Park Square 3160 Solihull Parkway, Birmingham Businees Park, Birmingham, B37 7YN, United Kingdom (100%)
Tel.: (44) 01216064000
Sales Range: $450-499.9 Million
Emp.: 1,200
Cement Mfr & Distr
N.A.I.C.S.: 327310

Cava delle Capannelle S.R.L. (1)
Via Parco del Serio 759, 24050, Grassobbio, Italy
Tel.: (39) 035525092
Web Site: https://www.cavacapannelle.com
Building Material Mfr & Distr
N.A.I.C.S.: 327320

Cementrum I B.V. (1)
Sint Teunislaan 1, 's-Hertogenbosch, 5231 BS, Netherlands
Tel.: (31) 73 640 1170
Cement Mfr
N.A.I.C.S.: 327310

Cementrum II B.V. (1)
Sint Teunislaan 1, 5231 BS, 's-Hertogenbosch, Netherlands
Tel.: (31) 73 6401170
Cement Mfr
N.A.I.C.S.: 327310

Cemitaly S.p.A. (1)
I Lab Kilometro Rosso Via Stezzano 87, 24126, Bergamo, Italy
Tel.: (39) 035396111
Web Site: https://www.cemitaly.it
Readymix Concrete Mfr
N.A.I.C.S.: 327320

Ceskomoravsky Cement, A.S. (1)
Mokra 359, 664 04, Mokra-Horakov, Czech Republic (82.4%)
Tel.: (420) 544122111
Web Site: https://www.heidelbergcement.cz
Mfr of Cement, Lime Products, Plasters & Morters
N.A.I.C.S.: 327310
Pavel Tehnik (Dir-Cement & Aggregate Sls)

Ceskomoravsky beton, a.s. (1)
Beroun 660, 266 01, Beroun, Czech Republic
Tel.: (420) 311644005
Investment Management Service
N.A.I.C.S.: 523940

Ceskomoravsky sterk, a.s. (1)
Mokra 359, 664 04, Mokra-Horakov, Czech Republic
Tel.: (420) 544122111
Aggregate Mfr
N.A.I.C.S.: 327992
Pavla Stavinohova (Chm-)

Chemical Manufacture and Refining Limited (1)
Lime Kiln Works, Rye, TN31 7TE, United Kingdom
Tel.: (44) 1797223936
Industrial Chemicals Mfr
N.A.I.C.S.: 325180

Cimenteries CBR S.A. (1)
Chaussee De La Hulpe 185, Brussels, 1170, Belgium (100%)
Tel.: (32) 26783211
Web Site: http://www.cbr.be
Sales Range: $50-74.9 Million
Emp.: 250
Mfr & Sales of Cement, Concrete, Aggregates, Lime
N.A.I.C.S.: 325520
Bernard Ortegat (Dir-Comm)

Affiliate (Non-US):

China Century Cement Ltd. (2)
Room 1506-1507 Teem Tower Teemall, 208 Tianhe Rd Tianhe District, 510620, Guangzhou, Guangdong, China (50%)
Tel.: (86) 2038102676
Web Site: http://www.heidelbergcement.com
Mfr of Cement & Ready-Mix Concrete Products
N.A.I.C.S.: 327310

Subsidiary (Non-US):

ENCI Holding N.V. (2)
Sint Teunislaan 1, 's-Hertogenbosch, 6212 NA, Netherlands (100%)
Tel.: (31) 736401170
Web Site: http://www.enci.nl
Sales Range: $10-24.9 Million
Emp.: 80
Holding Company; Cement Mfr
N.A.I.C.S.: 551112

Subsidiary (Domestic):

ENCI-Maasbricht B.V. (3)
Lage Kanaaldijk 115, 6212 NA, Maastricht, Netherlands (74.99%)
Tel.: (31) 433297777
Web Site: http://www.enci.nl
Mfr of Cement
N.A.I.C.S.: 327310

Mebin B.V. (3)
Pettelaarpark 30, 5216 PD, 's-

HEIDELBERG MATERIALS AG
INTERNATIONAL PUBLIC

Heidelberg Materials AG—(Continued)

Hertogenbosch, Netherlands **(74.99%)**
Tel.: (31) 736401160
Web Site: http://www.mebin.nl
Mfr of Ready-Mixed Concrete
N.A.I.C.S.: 327320
Roberd Laar Vande *(Gen Mgr)*

Subsidiary (Non-US):

HC Trading B.V. **(2)**
Meydan Sok No 1 Kat 25 Beybi GIZ Plaza,
Maslak, 34398, Istanbul, Turkiye **(100%)**
Tel.: (90) 2123650202
Web Site: http://www.hctrading.com
Sales Range: $50-74.9 Million
Emp.: 110
Cement & Related Products Trading Services
N.A.I.C.S.: 425120

HeidelbergCement China **(2)**
Room 1506-1507 Teem Tower Teemall, 208
Tianhe Road, Guangzhou, 510620, Tianhe,
China
Tel.: (86) 2038102676
Web Site: http://www.heidelbergcement.com
Mfr of Cement & Cement Products
N.A.I.C.S.: 327310

Subsidiary (Domestic):

Inter-Beton S.A. **(2)**
Chaissee de la Hulpe 185, Brussels, 1170,
Belgium **(48.29%)**
Tel.: (32) 26783348
Web Site: http://www.interbeton.be
Sales Range: $100-124.9 Million
Mfr of Ready-Mixed Concrete
N.A.I.C.S.: 327320
Johan Baeten *(Mgr-Mktg)*

Subsidiary (Non-US):

Limay Grinding Mill Corporation Co.
Ltd. **(2)**
Unit 2012 Herrera Tower Herrera Corner
Valero Street, Salcedo Village, Makati, Manila, Philippines
Tel.: (63) 2 845 19 54
Mfr of Cement
N.A.I.C.S.: 327310

Sterkovny a piskovny Brno A.S. **(2)**
Prikop 15-17, CZ-65745, Brno, Czech
Republic **(99.5%)**
Mfr of Aggregates
N.A.I.C.S.: 333120

Ciments du Maroc SA **(1)**
621 boulevard Panoramique, 20 150, Casablanca, Morocco **(62.34%)**
Tel.: (212) 52 285 9450
Web Site: https://www.cimentsdumaroc.com
Emp.: 720
Cement Mfr
N.A.I.C.S.: 327310

Cimgabon S.A. **(1)**
Siege, Libreville, Gabon
Tel.: (241) 70 20 25
Sales Range: $150-199.9 Million
Emp.: 350
Cement Distr
N.A.I.C.S.: 423320

Cindercrete Products Limited **(1)**
Highway 1 East, Regina, S4P 3A1, SK,
Canada
Tel.: (306) 789-2636
Web Site: https://www.cindercrete.com
Concrete Product Distr
N.A.I.C.S.: 423320
Rob McMillan *(Mgr-Concrete)*

City of London Heliport Limited **(1)**
1 Grosvenor Place, London, SW1X 7JH,
United Kingdom
Tel.: (44) 2072451245
Investment Management Service
N.A.I.C.S.: 523940

Civil and Marine (Holdings)
Limited **(1)**
Purfleet Works London Road West Thurrock, Grays, RM20 3NL, United Kingdom
Tel.: (44) 1708406813
Web Site: https://www.hanson.co.uk
Emp.: 25
Investment Management Service
N.A.I.C.S.: 523940

Closed Joined Stock Company Construction Materials **(1)**
Thekhnicheskaya str 2, Sterlitamak,
453110, Russia
Tel.: (7) 3473 29 90 91
Cement Mfr
N.A.I.C.S.: 327310

Coln Gravel Company Limited **(1)**
Claydon Pike, Cirencester, GL7 3DT,
United Kingdom
Tel.: (44) 1367 252239
Construction Materials Whslr
N.A.I.C.S.: 423390

Concrete Italia S.r.l. **(1)**
Via Berna 9, 00144, Rome, Italy
Tel.: (39) 0645426711
Web Site: https://www.concreteitalia.it
Emp.: 60
Financial Consulting Services
N.A.I.C.S.: 541611

Concrete Recyclers Australia Pty.
Ltd. **(1)**
Tel.: (61) 28 832 7400
Web Site: https://www.concreterecyclers.com.au
Readymix Concrete Mfr
N.A.I.C.S.: 327320
Scott Lawson *(Mgr-Sls)*

Conservation Resources Company,
Inc. **(1)**
5990 Potters Ln, Pipersville, PA 18947
Tel.: (215) 766-7000
Web Site: https://conservationresources.co
Drainage & Erosion Control Product Distr
N.A.I.C.S.: 423390

Contiga AB **(1)**
Tel.: (46) 10 471 4000
Web Site: https://www.contiga.se
Prefabricated Steel & Concrete Product
Distr
N.A.I.C.S.: 423390
Filip Sten *(Mng Dir)*

Contiga AS **(1)**
Peer Gynts Vei 1, 1535, Moss, Norway
Tel.: (47) 2 324 8900
Web Site: https://www.contiga.no
Prefabricated Steel & Concrete Product
Distr
N.A.I.C.S.: 423390

Contiga Tinglev A/S **(1)**
Mads Clausens Vej 58, 6360, Tinglev, Denmark
Tel.: (45) 7 217 1000
Web Site: https://www.contiga.dk
Concrete Product Distr
N.A.I.C.S.: 423320

Cradley Special Brick Company
Limited **(1)**
Overend Road Corngreaves Trading Estate,
Cradley Heath, B64 7DD, West Midlands,
United Kingdom
Tel.: (44) 138 463 7174
Web Site: https://www.cradleystore.co.uk
Concrete Brick Mfr & Distr
N.A.I.C.S.: 327120

Crispway Limited **(1)**
The Ridge Chipping Sodbury, Bristol, BS37
6AY, Avon, United Kingdom
Tel.: (44) 2072451245
Management Consulting Services
N.A.I.C.S.: 541618

DK Beton A/S **(1)**
Fredensvej 40, 4100, Ringsted, Denmark
Tel.: (45) 7 021 9600
Web Site: https://www.dkbeton.dk
Emp.: 10
Concrete Product Mfr & Distr
N.A.I.C.S.: 327320
Niels Sondergaard *(CEO)*

DK Cement A/S **(1)**
Tronholmen 55, Randers, 8960, Denmark
Tel.: (45) 7024 1400
Emp.: 3
Cement Mfr
N.A.I.C.S.: 327310
Torben Hansen *(Gen Mgr)*

DUPAMIJ Holding GmbH **(1)**

Birgelfeld 81, 47546, Kalkar, Nordrhein-Westfalen, Germany
Tel.: (49) 2824 2434
Investment Management Service
N.A.I.C.S.: 523999

Desimpel Brick Limited **(1)**
Hanson Bricks Stewartby, Bedford, MK43
9LZ, United Kingdom
Tel.: (44) 8705258258
Construction Materials Distr
N.A.I.C.S.: 423320

Donau Kies Verwaltungs GmbH **(1)**
Alte Worther Str 45, 94315, Straubing, Germany
Tel.: (49) 99312497
Investment Management Service
N.A.I.C.S.: 523940

Duna-Drava Cement Kft. **(1)**
Kohidpart dulo 2, 2600, Vac,
Hungary **(50%)**
Tel.: (36) 2 751 1600
Web Site: https://www.duna-drava.hu
Emp.: 700
Mfr of Cement
N.A.I.C.S.: 327310
Janos Szarkandi *(Chm, Pres, CEO & Gen Mgr)*

E Sub Limited **(1)**
1 Grosvenor Place, London, SW1X 7JH,
United Kingdom
Tel.: (44) 2072451245
Investment Management Service
N.A.I.C.S.: 523940

Eckhard Garbe GmbH **(1)**
Wiesendamm 32, 13597, Berlin, Germany
Tel.: (49) 3070193220
Web Site: https://eg.garbe-gruppe.de
Construction & Civil Engineering Services
N.A.I.C.S.: 541330

Enci B.V. **(1)**
Pettelaarpark 30, 5216 PD, 's-Hertogenbosch, Netherlands
Tel.: (31) 73 640 1180
Web Site: http://www.enci.nl
Cement Products & Services
N.A.I.C.S.: 327310
Rob Aarts *(Acct Mgr)*

Etablissement F.S. Bivois SARL **(1)**
25 Rue de Gerstheim, 67100, Strasbourg,
France
Tel.: (33) 388847575
Web Site: https://www.bivois.fr
Emp.: 5
Cement Mfr
N.A.I.C.S.: 327310

Exakt Kiesaufbereitung-Gesellschaft
mit beschrankter Haftung & Co
Kommanditgesellschaft
Alt-Enginger-Weg 60, 33106, Paderborn,
Germany
Tel.: (49) 5254 51 35
Gravel Mining Services
N.A.I.C.S.: 212321

Fertigbeton (FBU) GmbH **(1)**
Unterwittbacher Str, 97892, Kreuzwertheim,
Germany
Tel.: (49) 93425840
Building Concrete Product Distr
N.A.I.C.S.: 423320

Formpave Limited **(1)**
Tufthorn Avenue, Gloucestershire, Coleford,
GL16 8PR, United Kingdom
Tel.: (44) 1594 836 999
Web Site: http://www.formpave.co.uk
Emp.: 40
Concrete Block Mfr
N.A.I.C.S.: 327331

Foundamental GmbH **(1)**
Budapester Str 5, 10787, Berlin, Germany
Tel.: (49) 15221482769
Web Site: https://www.foundamental.com
Readymix Concrete Mfr
N.A.I.C.S.: 327320

Garkalnes Grants SIA **(1)**
Vidzemes Soseja 1, Garkalne, LV-2167,
Latvia **(100%)**
Tel.: (371) 29 400 351
Construction Materials Whslr
N.A.I.C.S.: 423320

Janis Liepa *(Dir)*

Gorazdze Cement S.A. **(1)**
ul Cementowa 1, Chorula, 47-316, Gorazdze, Poland
Tel.: (48) 77 777 8000
Web Site: https://www.gorazdze.pl
Sales Range: $300-349.9 Million
Emp.: 1,500
Cement & Ready-Mix Concrete Mfr & Aggregates Mining
N.A.I.C.S.: 327310

Subsidiary (Domestic):

Gorazdze Beton Sp. z o.o. **(2)**
ul Torunska 111, 85-844, Bydgoszcz, Poland
Tel.: (48) 77 777 9730
Web Site: http://www.gorazdze.pl
Sales Range: $50-74.9 Million
Emp.: 200
Readymix Concrete Mfr
N.A.I.C.S.: 327320

Gorazdze Kruszywa **(2)**
1 Cementowa Street, 47-316, Gorazdze,
Poland **(100%)**
Tel.: (48) 777778600
Holding Company; Aggregates Mining
N.A.I.C.S.: 551112
Aleksander Rys *(Member-Mgmt Bd)*

Granor S.A.S. **(1)**
Port fluvial Loos Sequedin Rue de la Deule,
59120, Loos, France
Tel.: (33) 3 20 93 56 97
Cement Mfr
N.A.I.C.S.: 327310

Greenwoods (St Ives) Limited **(1)**
Greenwoods Cemas House New Road, St
Ives, Huntingdon, PE27 5BG, Cambridgeshire, United Kingdom
Tel.: (44) 1480494455
Web Site: https://www.greenwoodsfca.co.uk
Financial Consulting Services
N.A.I.C.S.: 541611

Greystone Ambient & Style GmbH &
Co. KG **(1)**
Ueckermunder Strasse 27, 17367, Eggenstein, Germany
Tel.: (49) 397792990
Web Site: http://www.greystone-as.de
Building Materials Distr
N.A.I.C.S.: 444180

Gulf Coast Stabilized Materials
LLC **(1)**
10621 Clodine Rd, Richmond, TX 77407
Tel.: (281) 491-7376
Readymix Concrete Mfr
N.A.I.C.S.: 327320
Chris Harmon *(Mgr-Sls)*

HBMA Holdings LLC **(1)**
300 E John Carpenter Freeway Ste 1645,
Irving, TX 75062
Tel.: (972) 653-6141
Investment Management Service
N.A.I.C.S.: 523999

HC Asia Holding GmbH **(1)**
Berliner Ste 6, 69120, Heidelberg, Germany
Tel.: (49) 6221 372430
Investment Management Service
N.A.I.C.S.: 523940

HC Betons SIA **(1)**
Kronu Iela 5, Riga, LV-1035, Latvia
Tel.: (371) 6 737 4662
Web Site: https://www.hcbetons.lv
Emp.: 55
Concrete Product Distr
N.A.I.C.S.: 423320
Janis Pocs *(Mng Dir)*

HC Betoon AS **(1)**
Peterburi Tee 75, Tallinn, 13816, Estonia
Tel.: (372) 620 9620
Web Site: https://www.betoon.ee
Ready Mix Concrete Mfr & Distr
N.A.I.C.S.: 327320

HC Italia SRL **(1)**
Via Isaac Newton 9, 20090, Assago, Mi,
Italy
Tel.: (39) 025 830 4686
Web Site: https://www.hcitaliasrl.com
Urodynamic Equipment Mfr

AND PRIVATE COMPANIES

HEIDELBERG MATERIALS AG

N.A.I.C.S.: 334510

HC Materialen B.V. (1)
Sint Teunislaan 1, 5231 BS, 's-Hertogenbosch, Netherlands
Tel.: (31) 736401120
Web Site: http://www.enci.nl
Sales Range: $50-74.9 Million
Emp.: 100
Construction Materials Whslr
N.A.I.C.S.: 423390

HC Trading Malta Limited (1)
St Georges Building No 1 Level 4 Elija Zammit Street, San Giljan, STJ 3151, Malta
Tel.: (356) 22484800
Emp.: 15
Construction Materials Whslr
N.A.I.C.S.: 423390
Jan Eriksson *(Gen Dir)*

HCT Asia Services Pte. Ltd. (1)
60 Anson Road 06-01, Mapletree Anson, Singapore, 079914, Singapore
Tel.: (65) 65345240
Web Site: http://www.heidelbergcement.com
Construction Materials Whslr
N.A.I.C.S.: 423320

HCT Services Asia Pte. Ltd. (1)
60 Anson Road Mapletree Anson 06-01, Singapore, 079914, Singapore
Tel.: (65) 65345240
Cement Mfr
N.A.I.C.S.: 327310

HIPS (Trustees) Limited (1)
Valley House, Bedford, MK43 0PP, Bedfordshire, United Kingdom
Tel.: (44) 1525840809
Sales Range: $50-74.9 Million
Emp.: 4
Pension Fund Management Services
N.A.I.C.S.: 525110

HK Holdings (No.1) Limited (1)
1 Grosvenor Place, London, SW1X 7JH, United Kingdom
Tel.: (44) 2072451245
Investment Management Service
N.A.I.C.S.: 523940

HM Gorazdze Prefabrykacja Sp.z.o.o. (1)
Ul Domaniewska 47, 02-672, Warsaw, Poland
Tel.: (48) 226222209
Web Site: https://precon.com.pl
Building Material Mfr & Distr
N.A.I.C.S.: 327310

HM Trading Global GmbH (1)
Berliner Strasse 6, 69120, Heidelberg, Germany
Tel.: (49) 622148133001
Construction Material Mfr & Distr
N.A.I.C.S.: 327390

HPL Estates Limited (1)
1 Grosvenor Place, London, SW1X 7JH, United Kingdom
Tel.: (44) 2072451245
Investment Management Service
N.A.I.C.S.: 523940

Hampshire Properties LLC (1)
1650 Willow Lawn Dr Ste 301, Richmond, VA 23230
Tel.: (804) 414-0537
Web Site: https://www.hampshirepropertiesllc.com
Real Estate Services
N.A.I.C.S.: 531210

Hanson Limited (1)
The Ridge, Chipping Sodbury, BS37 6AY, Bristol, United Kingdom **(100%)**
Tel.: (44) 1454316000
Web Site: https://www.hanson.co.uk
Sales Range: $5-14.9 Billion
Emp.: 250
Holding Company; Cement, Concrete & Other Building Products Mfr & Distr; Aggregates Mining & Quarrying
N.A.I.C.S.: 551112
Daniel Cooper *(CEO)*

Joint Venture (Non-US):

Alliance Construction Materials Ltd. (2)

1901A One Harbourfront 18 Tak Fung Street, Hung Hom, China (Hong Kong) **(50%)**
Tel.: (852) 2 862 2200
Web Site: https://www.concrete.hk
Sales Range: $75-99.9 Million
Emp.: 240
Construction Materials Mfr & Distr
N.A.I.C.S.: 238110

Subsidiary (Non-US):

Hanson (Israel) Ltd. (1)
 (100%)
Tel.: (972) 3 576 4242
Web Site: https://hanson.co.il
Sales Range: $75-99.9 Million
Asphalt & Ready-Mix Concrete Mfr & Aggregates Mining
N.A.I.C.S.: 327320

Subsidiary (Domestic):

Hanson Aggregates (North) Limited (2)
Pottal Pool Pit, Stafford, ST19 5RR, Staffordshire, United Kingdom
Tel.: (44) 1785712607
Readymix Concrete Mfr
N.A.I.C.S.: 327320

Subsidiary (Non-US):

Hanson Aggregates Holding Nederland B.V. (2)
Amerikahavenweg 11, 1045 AA, Amsterdam, Netherlands
Tel.: (31) 20 6147928
Investment Management Service
N.A.I.C.S.: 523940

Hanson Aggregates Nederland B.V. (2)
Amerikahavenweg 11, 1045 AA, Amsterdam, Netherlands
Tel.: (31) 206 14 79 28
Construction Materials Whslr
N.A.I.C.S.: 423320

Subsidiary (Domestic):

Hanson Aggregates South Wales Holdings Limited (2)
Old Station Yard, Penrith, CA11 0DE, United Kingdom
Tel.: (44) 1931717200
Dimension Stone Mining & Quarrying Services
N.A.I.C.S.: 212311

Hanson Amalgamated Industries Limited (2)
Hanson House 14 Castle Hill, Maidenhead, SL6 4JJ, United Kingdom
Tel.: (44) 1628774100
Web Site: http://www.hanson.co.uk
Emp.: 12
Construction Materials Distr
N.A.I.C.S.: 423320
Patrick Iasaogi *(Gen Mgr)*

Subsidiary (Non-US):

Hanson Australia (Holdings) Pty. Limited (2)
Level 10 35 Clarence St, Sydney, 2000, NSW, Australia
Tel.: (61) 293234000
Web Site: https://www.hanson.com.au
Sales Range: $900-999.9 Million
Emp.: 20
Holding Company; Aggregates Quarrying & Concrete Mfr
N.A.I.C.S.: 551112

Subsidiary (Domestic):

Alex Fraser Pty Limited (3)
50 Parkwest Drive, Derrimut, 3026, VIC, Australia
Tel.: (61) 39 371 8000
Web Site: https://www.alexfraser.com.au
Waste Management Services
N.A.I.C.S.: 562998

Plant (Domestic):

Alex Fraser Pty Limited - Asphalt - Laverton Plant (4)
9-19 Alex Fraser Drive, Laverton, 3026,

VIC, Australia
Tel.: (61) 3 8360 6000
Asphalt Product Mfr
N.A.I.C.S.: 324121

Joint Venture (Domestic):

Cement Australia Holdings Pty. Ltd. (3)
18 Station Avenue, Darra, 4076, QLD, Australia **(50%)**
Tel.: (61) 1300236368
Web Site: https://www.cementaustralia.com.au
Cement & Cement Related Products Mfr, Distr & Marketer; Raw Construction Materials Mining
N.A.I.C.S.: 327310
Rob Davies *(CEO & Mng Dir)*

Plant (Domestic):

Cement Australia Holdings Pty Ltd - Bulwer Island Plant (4)
77 Pamela St, Pinkenba, 4008, QLD, Australia
Tel.: (61) 736327813
Web Site: http://www.cementaustralia.com.au
Cement Mfr
N.A.I.C.S.: 327310

Cement Australia Holdings Pty Ltd - Gladstone Plant (4)
Landing Rd, PO Box 285, Gladstone, 4680, QLD, Australia
Tel.: (61) 74 970 1100
Web Site: http://www.cementaustralia.com.au
Cement Mfr
N.A.I.C.S.: 327310

Cement Australia Holdings Pty Ltd - Railton Plant (4)
101 Cement Works Rd, Railton, 7305, TAS, Australia
Tel.: (61) 36 491 0111
Web Site: https://www.cementaustralia.com.au
Construction Material & Cement Mfr & Whslr
N.A.I.C.S.: 327310

Subsidiary (Domestic):

Geocycle Pty. Ltd. (4)
92 Ordish Rd, Dandenong South, Melbourne, 3175, VIC, Australia
Tel.: (61) 130 065 7057
Web Site: https://www.cementaustralia.com.au
Waste Management Services
N.A.I.C.S.: 562920

Subsidiary (Domestic):

Hanson Australia Pty Limited (3)
Level 14 35 Clarence Street, Sydney, 2000, NSW, Australia
Tel.: (61) 293234000
Web Site: https://www.hanson.com.au
Readymix Concrete & Aggregate Mfr
N.A.I.C.S.: 327320
Phil Schacht *(CEO)*

Division (Domestic):

Hanson Construction Materials Pty Ltd. (3)
Lot 10 Palmer Crescent, Bunbury, 6230, WA, Australia
Tel.: (61) 897260233
Web Site: https://www.hanson.com.au
Sales Range: $25-49.9 Million
Emp.: 30
Construction Materials
N.A.I.C.S.: 236220

Subsidiary (Domestic):

Pioneer North Queensland Pty Ltd (4)
Lot 5 Maconachie Street, Woree, Cairns, 4870, QLD, Australia
Tel.: (61) 740478300
Web Site: https://www.pnq.com.au
Sales Range: $25-49.9 Million
Construction Material Mfr & Distr
N.A.I.C.S.: 324121

Subsidiary (Domestic):

Hymix Australia Pty. Ltd. (3)
4 Bailey Crescent, Southport, 4215, QLD, Australia
Tel.: (61) 130 004 9649
Web Site: https://www.hymix.com.au
Sales Range: $125-149.9 Million
Emp.: 300
Readymix Concrete Mfr
N.A.I.C.S.: 327320

Joint Venture (Domestic):

Metromix Pty. Ltd. (3)
Level 4 107 Phillip Street, Parramatta, 2150, NSW, Australia **(50%)**
Tel.: (61) 29 849 7400
Web Site: https://www.metromix.com.au
Aggregates & Construction Sand Mining & Quarry Operations; Concrete Mfr
N.A.I.C.S.: 212319
John Bailey *(Sls Mgr-Concrete-Sydney)*

Subsidiary (Non-US):

Hanson Australia Cement Pty Limited (2)
Level 10 35 Clarence Street, Sydney, 2000, NSW, Australia
Tel.: (61) 29 323 4000
Web Site: https://www.hanson.com.au
Emp.: 24
Cement Mfr
N.A.I.C.S.: 327310

Hanson Australia Investments Pty Limited (2)
L 10 35 Clarence St, Sydney, 2000, NSW, Australia
Tel.: (61) 293234000
Emp.: 20
Investment Management Service
N.A.I.C.S.: 523940
Kevin Gluskie *(CEO)*

Subsidiary (Domestic):

Hanson Bath and Portland Stone Limited (2)
Hanson Bath Portland Stone Avon Mill Lane, Keynsham, Bristol, BS31 2UG, United Kingdom
Tel.: (44) 1179869631
Web Site: https://www.heidelbergcement.com
Natural Limestone & Masonry Products Distr
N.A.I.C.S.: 424910

Hanson Batteries Limited (2)
Hanson House 14 Castle Hill, Maidenhead, SL6 4JJ, United Kingdom
Tel.: (44) 1628774100
Investment Management Service
N.A.I.C.S.: 523940

Subsidiary (Non-US):

Hanson Beton Nederland B.V. (2)
Harmonieplein 117, 3603 BS, Maarssen, Netherlands **(100%)**
Tel.: (31) 346581880
Web Site: http://www.hansonbeton.nl
Ready-Mix Concrete Mfr & Aggregates Mining
N.A.I.C.S.: 327320

Hanson Brick Limited (2)
5155 Dundas Streets West, Burlington, L7R 3Y2, ON, Canada
Tel.: (905) 335-3401
Bricks Mfr
N.A.I.C.S.: 327331

Hanson Building Materials Cartage Sdn Bhd (2)
W501 5Th Floor West Tower Wisma Consplant 1 No 2 Jalan Ss 16/4, Subang Jaya, 47500, Selangor, Malaysia
Tel.: (60) 46425175
Sales Range: $550-599.9 Million
Emp.: 2,000
Construction Materials Whslr
N.A.I.C.S.: 423320
John Thornton *(Pres)*

Subsidiary (Domestic):

Hanson Building Materials Europe Limited (2)

HEIDELBERG MATERIALS AG

Heidelberg Materials AG—(Continued)

Hanson House 14 Castle Hill, Maidenhead, SL6 4JJ, United Kingdom
Tel.: (44) 1628774100
Web Site: https://www.hanson.co.uk
Emp.: 70
Construction Materials Distr
N.A.I.C.S.: 423320
Daniel Cooper *(Mng Dir)*

Subsidiary (Non-US):

Hanson Building Materials Industries Sdn Bhd (2)
W501 Level 5 West Tower Wisma Consplant 1 2 Jalan Ss16/4, Subang Jaya, 47500, Selangor, Malaysia
Tel.: (60) 3.5885 8888
Construction Materials Whslr
N.A.I.C.S.: 423320

Subsidiary (Domestic):

Hanson Building Materials Limited (2)
Crossway Blvd, Greenhithe, DA9 9BT, United Kingdom
Tel.: (44) 1322620300
Construction Materials Distr
N.A.I.C.S.: 423320

Subsidiary (Non-US):

Hanson Building Materials Malaysia Sdn Bhd (2)
W501 5th Floor West Tower Wisma Consplant No 2 Jalan SS 16/4, Subang Jaya, 47500, Malaysia
Tel.: (60) 358858888
Readymix Concrete Mfr
N.A.I.C.S.: 327320

Hanson Building Materials Manufacturing Sdn Bhd (2)
W501 5Th Floor West Tower Wisma Cosplant 1 No 2 Jalan Ss16/4, Subang Jaya, 47500, Selangor, Malaysia
Tel.: (60) 72528949
Readymix Concrete Mfr
N.A.I.C.S.: 327320
Ng Tiam Soon *(Plant Mgr)*

Hanson Building Materials Production Sdn Bhd (2)
W501 5th Floor West Tower Wisma Consplant No 2 Jalan Ss 16/4, Subang Jaya, 47500, Malaysia
Tel.: (60) 79329641
Readymix Concrete Mfr & Distr
N.A.I.C.S.: 327320

Hanson Building Materials Services Sdn Bhd (2)
Krystal Point Complex Block B 303-4-1 Jalan Sultan Azlan Shah, Sungai Nibong, 11900, Penang, Malaysia
Tel.: (60) 4 642 5175
Web Site: http://www.hanson.com
Emp.: 200
Ready Mix Concrete Whslr
N.A.I.C.S.: 423320
S. H. Peoh *(Gen Mgr)*

Hanson Building Materials-KTPC Sdn Bhd (2)
W501 Level 5 West Tower Wisma Consplant 1 No 2 Jalan Ss16/4, Subang Jaya, 47500, Selangor, Malaysia
Tel.: (60) 7 252 8949
Concrete Mfr
N.A.I.C.S.: 327320

Hanson Concrete (M) Sdn Bhd (2)
Jln Minyak Beku Batu 2 1/2, 83000, Batu Pahat, Malaysia
Tel.: (60) 7 434 2631
Readymix Concrete Mfr
N.A.I.C.S.: 327320

Subsidiary (Domestic):

Hanson Crewing Services Limited (2)
21/8 Second Floor Arena Court MCrown Lane, Maidenhead, SL6 4JJ, Berkshire, United Kingdom
Tel.: (44) 7441904939
Web Site: https://hansoncrewing.uk
Administrative Management Services

N.A.I.C.S.: 541611

Subsidiary (Non-US):

Hanson Finance Australia Ltd (2)
Level 10 35 Clarence Street, Sydney, 2000, NSW, Australia
Tel.: (61) 293234000
Emp.: 20
Financial Management Services
N.A.I.C.S.: 523999
Phil Schacht *(CEO)*

Subsidiary (Domestic):

Hanson Finance Limited (2)
Hanson House 14 Castle Hill, Maidenhead, SL6 4JJ, United Kingdom
Tel.: (44) 1628774100
Web Site: https://www.heidelbergcement.com
Emp.: 50
Financial Management Services
N.A.I.C.S.: 523999
Patrick O'Shea *(CEO)*

Hanson Financial Services Limited (2)
Hanson House 14 Castle Hill, Maidenhead, SL6 4JJ, United Kingdom
Tel.: (44) 1628774100
Web Site: https://www.hanson.co.uk
Emp.: 3,500
Financial Management Services
N.A.I.C.S.: 523999

Hanson Foods Limited (2)
30-40 Vale Royal, London, N7 9AP, United Kingdom
Tel.: (44) 2076092299
Food Products Mfr
N.A.I.C.S.: 311999

Subsidiary (Non-US):

Hanson Hispania S.A. (2)
C/ Cardenal Marcelo Spinola 42 Planta Primera, 28016, Madrid, Spain **(100%)**
Tel.: (34) 91 593 5800
Web Site: https://www.hanson.es
Sales Range: $25-49.9 Million
Emp.: 38
Concrete Mfr & Aggregates Mining
N.A.I.C.S.: 327390

Subsidiary (Domestic):

Hanson Industrial (Engineering Holdings) Limited (2)
Hanson House 14 Castle Hill, Maidenhead, SL6 4JJ, United Kingdom
Tel.: (44) 1628774100
Web Site: https://www.hanson.co.uk
Emp.: 70
Investment Management Service
N.A.I.C.S.: 523940
Patrick O'Shea *(Gen Mgr)*

Hanson Industrial Limited (2)
Hanson House 14 Castle Hill, Maidenhead, SL6 4JJ, Berkshire, United Kingdom
Tel.: (44) 1628774100
Web Site: https://www.hanson.co.uk
Emp.: 60
Investment Management Service
N.A.I.C.S.: 523940
Patrick O'Shea *(CEO)*

Hanson International Holdings Limited (2)
Hanson House 14 Castle Hill, Maidenhead, SL6 4JJ, United Kingdom
Tel.: (44) 1628774100
Web Site: https://www.hanson.co.uk
Emp.: 60
Investment Management Service
N.A.I.C.S.: 523940
Patrick O'Shea *(CEO)*

Subsidiary (Non-US):

Hanson Island Management Limited (2)
Lancaster Court, Saint Peter Port, GY1 1WJ, Guernsey
Tel.: (44) 1481712269
Sales Range: $25-49.9 Million
Emp.: 4
Management Consulting Services
N.A.I.C.S.: 541618

Subsidiary (Domestic):

Hanson LHA Limited (2)
Hanson House 14 Castle Hill, Maidenhead, SL6 4JJ, United Kingdom
Tel.: (44) 1628774100
Investment Management Service
N.A.I.C.S.: 523940

Subsidiary (Non-US):

Hanson Landfill Services Pty Ltd (2)
55 Bridge Inn Road, Wollert, 3750, VIC, Australia
Tel.: (61) 394081299
Web Site: https://www.hansonlandfill.com.au
Sales Range: $25-49.9 Million
Emp.: 20
Waste Disposal Services
N.A.I.C.S.: 562212

Subsidiary (Domestic):

Hanson Marine Limited (2)
Hanson House 14 Castle Hill, Maidenhead, SL6 4JJ, United Kingdom
Tel.: (44) 1628774100
Construction Sand & Gravel Quarrying Services
N.A.I.C.S.: 212321
Daniel Cooper *(Gen Mgr)*

Hanson Peabody Limited (2)
14 Castle Hill, SL6 4JJ, Maidenhead, Berks, United Kingdom
Tel.: (44) 1628774100
Web Site: https://www.hanson.co.uk
Emp.: 60
Cement Mfr
N.A.I.C.S.: 327310
Patrick O'Shei *(Gen Mgr)*

Subsidiary (Non-US):

Hanson Pipe & Precast Quebec Ltd. (2)
1331 Av de la Gare, Mascouche, J7K 3G6, QC, Canada
Tel.: (450) 474-6189
Concrete Pipe Mfr
N.A.I.C.S.: 327332

Hanson Precast Pty Ltd (2)
214 Riverstone Parade, PO Box 121, Riverstone, 2765, NSW, Australia
Tel.: (61) 2 9627 2666
Web Site: http://www.hanson.com.au
Sales Range: $25-49.9 Million
Emp.: 150
Architectural Consulting Services
N.A.I.C.S.: 541310
John Hewitt *(Mgr)*

Plant (Domestic):

Hanson Precast Pty Ltd - Mulgrave Factory (3)
63 Railway Road, North, Mulgrave, 2756, NSW, Australia
Tel.: (61) 2 4577 5844
Web Site: http://www.hanson.com.au
Architectural Consulting Services
N.A.I.C.S.: 541310

Subsidiary (Non-US):

Hanson Pty Limited (2)
L 6 35 Clarence St, Sydney, 2000, NSW, Australia
Tel.: (61) 293234000
Readymix Concrete & Aggregate Mfr.
N.A.I.C.S.: 327320
Phil Serchuk *(CEO)*

Hanson Quarry Products (Batu Pahat) Sdn Bhd (2)
Taman Ampang Jaya, Batu Pahat, 83000, Malaysia
Tel.: (60) 74341754
Construction Sand & Gravel Quarrying Services
N.A.I.C.S.: 212321

Hanson Quarry Products (Holdings) Sdn Bhd (2)
W501 5th Floor West Tower Wisma Consplant 1 No 2 Jalan SS16/4, Subang Jaya, 47500, Malaysia
Tel.: (60) 358858888
Investment Management Service

INTERNATIONAL PUBLIC

N.A.I.C.S.: 523999

Hanson Quarry Products (Israel) Ltd (2)
5 Jabotinsky, POB 3540, Ramat Gan, Israel
Tel.: (972) 35764242
Limestone Mining & Quarrying Services
N.A.I.C.S.: 212312

Hanson Quarry Products (Kuantan) Sdn Bhd (2)
No 1550 Jln Pelabuhan Batu 14 Kampung Selamat, 26080, Kuantan, Malaysia
Tel.: (60) 9 583 4532
Limestone Quarrying Services
N.A.I.C.S.: 212311

Hanson Quarry Products (Kulai) Sdn Bhd (2)
Batu 22 Off Kulai Main Road, Kulai, 81000, Malaysia
Tel.: (60) 6 553 2162
Construction Sand & Gravel Quarrying Services
N.A.I.C.S.: 212321

Hanson Quarry Products (Perak) Sdn Bhd (2)
3/4 Mile Jalan Teluk Muroh, Lumut, 32200, Perak, Malaysia
Tel.: (60) 6 553 2162
Industrial Gas Mfr
N.A.I.C.S.: 325120

Hanson Quarry Products (Rawang) Sdn Bhd (2)
Ct No 17208 Lot 1506 Mukim Rawang Sungai Samak, Daerah Ulu Selangor, Rawang, 48000, Malaysia
Tel.: (60) 6 553 2162
Construction Sand & Gravel Quarrying Services
N.A.I.C.S.: 212321

Hanson Quarry Products (Segamat) Sdn Bhd (2)
No 1908 Lbr Segamat-kuantan Batu 3 1/4, Segamat, 85000, Johor, Malaysia
Tel.: (60) 79312986
Web Site: https://www.hanson.com
Emp.: 20
Construction Materials Whslr
N.A.I.C.S.: 423320
Keong Kong Wai *(Mgr-Sls)*

Hanson Quarry Products (Terengganu) Sdn Bhd (2)
No 2701 Kampung Santong, 23100, Paka, Malaysia
Tel.: (60) 98276526
Construction Sand & Gravel Quarrying Services
N.A.I.C.S.: 212321

Subsidiary (Domestic):

Hanson Quarry Products Europe Ltd. (2)
Ridgewood House The Ridge, Chipping Sodbury, BS37 6AY, Bristol, United Kingdom
Tel.: (44) 1454316000
Web Site: https://www.hanson.co.uk
Sales Range: $250-299.9 Million
Emp.: 100
Aggregates & Crushed Stone Mining, Quarrying & Distribution
N.A.I.C.S.: 212319
Clare Mayo *(Dir-HR)*

Division (Domestic):

Hanson Aggregates Limited (3)
Hanson House 14 Castle Hill, Maidenhead, SL6 4JJ, Berkshire, United Kingdom
Tel.: (44) 1628774100
Web Site: https://www.hanson.co.uk
Aggregates & Crushed Stone Mining, Quarrying & Distribution
N.A.I.C.S.: 212319

Unit (Domestic):

Hanson Aggregates UK - South West (4)
The Ridge, Chipping Sodbury, BS37 6AY, Bristol, United Kingdom
Tel.: (44) 1454316000
Web Site: http://www.hanson.biz

AND PRIVATE COMPANIES

Sales Range: $200-249.9 Million
Emp.: 300
Aggregates & Crushed Stone Mining, Quarrying & Distribution
N.A.I.C.S.: 212319

Subsidiary (Non-US):

Hanson Quarry Products Sdn. Bhd. (2)
W501 5th Floor West Tower, 2 Jalan SS 16/4, 47500, Subang Jaya, Malaysia (100%)
Tel.: (60) 350358888
Web Site: https://www.hanson.my
Sales Range: $50-74.9 Million
Emp.: 1,000
Aggregates Mining & Building Materials Distr
N.A.I.C.S.: 212319

Subsidiary (Domestic):

Hanson Quarry Products Ventures Limited (2)
Hanson House 14 Castle Hill, Maidenhead, SL6 4JJ, United Kingdom
Tel.: (44) 1628774100
Investment Management Service
N.A.I.C.S.: 523940

Hanson RBS Trustees Limited (2)
Hanson House 14 Castle Hill, Maidenhead, SL6 4JJ, United Kingdom
Tel.: (44) 1628774100
Investment Management Service
N.A.I.C.S.: 523940

Hanson Retail Limited (2)
Hanson House 14 Castle Hill, Maidenhead, SL6 4JJ, United Kingdom
Tel.: (44) 1628774100
Construction Materials Distr
N.A.I.C.S.: 423320

Hanson TIS Holdings Limited (2)
Hanson House 14 Castle Hill, Maidenhead, SL6 4JJ, United Kingdom
Tel.: (44) 1628774100
Investment Management Service
N.A.I.C.S.: 523940

Hanson TIS Limited (2)
6 Inchcape Road, Wallasey, CH45 8JR, United Kingdom
Tel.: (44) 1516912101
Construction Materials Distr
N.A.I.C.S.: 423320

Hanson Thermalite Limited (2)
Motherwell Way, Grays, RM20 3LB, United Kingdom
Tel.: (44) 1708682200
Concrete Brick & Block Mfr
N.A.I.C.S.: 327120

Subsidiary (US):

Heidelberg Materials US, Inc. (2)
300 E John Carpenter Fwy, Irving, TX 75062
Tel.: (972) 653-5500
Web Site: https://www.heidelbergmaterials.us
Readymix Concrete & Aggregate Mfr
N.A.I.C.S.: 327320
Carol Lowry *(Gen Counsel & VP)*

Subsidiary (Domestic):

Aaron Concrete Contractors LP (3)
4108 Nixon Ln, Austin, TX 78725
Tel.: (512) 926-7326
Web Site: https://www.aaronconcrete.com
Rev.: $15,293,000
Emp.: 150
Concrete Work
N.A.I.C.S.: 238110

Bach Plumbing & Heating Company of Clayton, Inc. (3)
11176 County Route 9, Clayton, NY 13624
Tel.: (315) 686-3083
Web Site: http://www.bachandco.com
Sales Range: $1-9.9 Million
Emp.: 40
Specialty Trade Contractors
N.A.I.C.S.: 238990
Darice Bach *(Gen Mgr)*

Hanson Aggregates North America (3)
8505 Freeport Pkwy Ste 600, Irving, TX 75063-2505
Tel.: (972) 621-0345
Web Site: http://www.hanson.biz
Sales Range: $1-4.9 Billion
Ready-Mix Concrete & Asphalt Operations
N.A.I.C.S.: 327320

Subsidiary (Domestic):

Hanson Aggregates BMC, Inc. (4)
1401 Route 610, Woodbine, NJ 08270-3203
Tel.: (609) 861-0080
Aggregate Mfr
N.A.I.C.S.: 327992

Hanson Aggregates Davon LLC (4)
1111 E Main St, Chillicothe, OH 45601
Tel.: (740) 773-2172
Readymix Concrete Mfr
N.A.I.C.S.: 327320

Hanson Aggregates East LLC (4)
2101 Gateway Ctr Blvd Ste 205, Morrisville, NC 27560
Tel.: (919) 380-2500
Construction Aggregate Mfr
N.A.I.C.S.: 327992

Hanson Aggregates LLC (4)
8505 Freeport Pkwy 500, Irving, TX 75063
Tel.: (972) 621-0345
Readymix Concrete Mfr
N.A.I.C.S.: 327320

Hanson Aggregates Mid-Pacific, Inc. (4)
Pine Hollow Rd, Clayton, CA 94517
Tel.: (925) 672-4955
Construction Materials Whslr
N.A.I.C.S.: 423320

Hanson Aggregates Midwest LLC (4)
13526 Overstake Rd, Winchester, OH 45697-9644
Tel.: (937) 442-6009
Emp.: 30
Limestone Mining & Quarrying Services
N.A.I.C.S.: 212312
Dennis Dolan *(Pres)*

Hanson Aggregates Pacific Southwest, Inc. (4)
9229 Harris Plant Rd, San Diego, CA 92163
Tel.: (858) 277-5481
Ready Mix Concrete Mfr & Distr
N.A.I.C.S.: 327320

Subsidiary (Domestic):

Cadman, Inc. (5)
7554 185th Ave NE, Redmond, WA 98052
Tel.: (425) 867-1234
Web Site: http://www.cadman.com
Ready Mixed Cement Producers; Sand & Gravel Distributor
N.A.I.C.S.: 327320
Kyle Hasu *(Sls Mgr)*

Campbell Concrete & Materials, L.P. (5)
16155 Park Row Ste 120, Houston, TX 77084-6971 (100%)
Tel.: (972) 653-5500
Ready-Mix Concrete Mfr & Aggregates Processor
N.A.I.C.S.: 327320

Continental Florida Materials, Inc. (5)
2802 Eisenhower Blvd, Fort Lauderdale, FL 33316-0100 (100%)
Tel.: (954) 523-8442
Web Site: http://www.lehighcement.com
Import Terminals for Cement
N.A.I.C.S.: 423320
Dennis Willover *(Office Mgr)*

Subsidiary (Non-US):

Lehigh Cement (5)
12640 Inland Way, Edmonton, T5V 1K2, AB, Canada (100%)
Tel.: (780) 420-2500
Web Site: http://www.lehighcement.net
Cement Mfr
N.A.I.C.S.: 327310

HEIDELBERG MATERIALS AG

James M. Derkatch *(CEO)*

Subsidiary (Domestic):

Lehigh Cement Co. (5)
66 Demarest Rd, Sparta, NJ 07871
Tel.: (610) 562-3000
Web Site: https://www.lehighhanson.com
Cement Mfr & Distr
N.A.I.C.S.: 327310
Bill Trautz *(Plant Mgr)*

Subsidiary (Non-US):

Lehigh Hanson Canada (5)
12640 Inland Way, Edmonton, T5V 1K2, AB, Canada (55%)
Tel.: (780) 420-2500
Web Site: http://www.lehighhansoncanada.com
Mfr of Cement, Ready-Mix Concrete, Concrete Products & Aggregates
N.A.I.C.S.: 327310
Andrew Thompson *(Bus Mgr)*

Division (Domestic):

Lehigh Northeast Cement Co. (5)
313 Warren St, Glens Falls, NY 12801
Tel.: (518) 792-1137
Web Site: http://www.lehighcement.com
Mfr of Cement
N.A.I.C.S.: 327310

Lehigh Southwest Cement Company (5)
12667 Alcosta Blvd Ste 400, San Ramon, CA 94583 (100%)
Tel.: (925) 244-6500
Web Site: https://www.lehighsw.com
Emp.: 30
Cement Mfr
N.A.I.C.S.: 327310
Jon Morrish *(Pres)*

Subsidiary (Domestic):

Standard Concrete Products, Inc. (5)
2002 E McFadden Ave Ste 150, Santa Ana, CA 92705 (100%)
Tel.: (714) 245-1550
Web Site: http://www.standard-concrete.com
Readymix Concrete Mfr
N.A.I.C.S.: 327320

Joint Venture (Domestic):

Texas Lehigh Cement Company LP (5)
701 Cement Plant Rd, Buda, TX 78610-0610
Tel.: (512) 295-6111
Web Site: https://www.texaslehigh.com
Construction & Well Cements Mfr; Owned 50% by Eagle Materials Inc. & 50% by Lehigh Cement Company
N.A.I.C.S.: 327310

Subsidiary (Domestic):

Hanson Aggregates Pennsylvania LLC (4)
7660 Imperial Way, Allentown, PA 18195-1016
Tel.: (800) 523-5488
Sales Range: $100-124.9 Million
Emp.: 150
Sand & Gravel Mining Services
N.A.I.C.S.: 212321

Hanson Aggregates Southeast LLC (4)
2310 Park lake Dr Ste 550, Atlanta, GA 30305
Tel.: (770) 491-2777
Web Site: http://www.hanson.com
Sales Range: $25-49.9 Million
Emp.: 7
Readymix Concrete Mfr
N.A.I.C.S.: 327320
Brent Brown *(Mgr-Sls)*

Hanson Aggregates WRP, Inc. (4)
2050 Woodland Rd, Davis, OK 73030
Tel.: (580) 369-3773
Sales Range: $50-74.9 Million
Emp.: 20
Crushed Stone & Rock Quarrying Services
N.A.I.C.S.: 212312

Tim Nichols *(Mgr)*

Hanson Material Service (4)
470 W 172nd St, Thornton, IL 60476 (100%)
Tel.: (312) 372-3600
Web Site: http://www.lehighhanson.com
Sales Range: $150-199.9 Million
Aggregates Mining & Quarrying
N.A.I.C.S.: 212319
Toby Breedlove *(VP & Gen Mgr)*

Subsidiary (Domestic):

Hanson Brick East, LLC (3)
7400 Carmel Executive Park Ste 200, Charlotte, NC 28226
Tel.: (704) 341-8750
Web Site: http://www.hansonbrick.com
Sales Range: $400-449.9 Million
Concrete Block Mfr
N.A.I.C.S.: 327120
Charlie Ward *(Sr VP & Gen Mgr)*

Unit (Domestic):

Hanson Concrete Products (3)
3500 Maple Ave Ste 1500, Dallas, TX 75219-3935
Tel.: (214) 525-5500
Web Site: http://www.hanson.biz
Sales Range: $50-74.9 Million
Emp.: 120
Concrete Pipe Mfr
N.A.I.C.S.: 238110

Hanson Concrete Products (3)
2900 Terminal Ave, Richmond, VA 23234-1632
Tel.: (804) 233-5471
Web Site: http://www.hanson.biz
Sales Range: $25-49.9 Million
Emp.: 50
Concrete Pipe Mfr
N.A.I.C.S.: 238110

Subsidiary (Domestic):

Lehigh Cement Company LLC (3)
7660 Imperial Way, Allentown, PA 18195-1016 (100%)
Tel.: (610) 366-4600
Web Site: http://www.lehighhanson.com
Cement & Concrete Products Mfr
N.A.I.C.S.: 327310

Subsidiary (Domestic):

Calaveras Materials Inc. (4)
7673 N Ingram Ave Ste 103, Fresno, CA 93711
Tel.: (559) 277-7060
Web Site: http://www.lehighsw.net
Sales Range: $25-49.9 Million
Emp.: 6
Readymix Concrete Mfr
N.A.I.C.S.: 327320
Ozzie Diaz *(Area Mgr)*

Plant (Domestic):

Calaveras Materials Inc. - Central Avenue Plant (5)
2095 E Central Ave, Fresno, CA 93725
Tel.: (559) 233-3338
Web Site: http://www.lehighsw.net
Sales Range: $25-49.9 Million
Emp.: 6
Readymix Concrete Mfr
N.A.I.C.S.: 327320
Ozzy Diaz *(Area Mgr)*

Calaveras Materials Inc. - Hughson Plant (5)
1100 Lowe Rd, Hughson, CA 95326
Tel.: (209) 883-0448
Web Site: http://www.lehighsw.net
Sales Range: $25-49.9 Million
Emp.: 6
Asphalt & Aggregate Mfr
N.A.I.C.S.: 324121
Ramie Stone *(Gen Mgr)*

Calaveras Materials Inc. - Lathrop Plant (5)
1945 Lathrop Rd, Lathrop, CA 95330
Tel.: (800) 676-3201
Readymix Concrete Mfr
N.A.I.C.S.: 327320

HEIDELBERG MATERIALS AG

INTERNATIONAL PUBLIC

Heidelberg Materials AG—(Continued)

Calaveras Materials Inc. - River Rock Plant (5)
12523 N Hwy 59, Merced, CA 95348
Tel.: (209) 563-6370
Web Site: http://www.lehighsw.net
Readymix Concrete Mfr
N.A.I.C.S.: 327320

Calaveras Materials Inc. - San Andreas Plant (5)
2288 Pool Sta Rd, San Andreas, CA 95249
Tel.: (209) 754-1899
Web Site: http://www.lehighsw.net
Emp.: 4
Readymix Concrete Mfr
N.A.I.C.S.: 327320
Vince Fisher *(Plant Mgr)*

Calaveras Materials Inc. - Thorne Avenue Plant (5)
410 N Thorne Ave, Fresno, CA 93706
Tel.: (559) 268-5654
Web Site: http://www.lehighsw.net
Readymix Concrete Mfr
N.A.I.C.S.: 327320
Ozzie Diaz *(Gen Mgr)*

Subsidiary (Domestic):

Lehigh Northwest Cement Company (4)
2115 N 30th St Ste 202, Tacoma, WA 98403
Tel.: (253) 682-0279
Web Site: http://www.lehighnw.com
Emp.: 5
Cement Mfr & Distr
N.A.I.C.S.: 327310

Subsidiary (Domestic):

The SEFA Group Inc. (3)
217 Cedar Rd, Lexington, SC 29073
Tel.: (803) 794-3230
Web Site: http://www.sefagroup.com
Rev.: $12,000,000
Emp.: 78
Scrap & Waste Materials
N.A.I.C.S.: 423930
Gregg T. Hendrix *(Pres & CEO)*

Joint Venture (Domestic):

Midland Quarry Products Ltd. (2)
Leicester Road, Whitwick, LE67 5GR, Leicestershire, United Kingdom
Tel.: (44) 3301232058
Web Site: https://www.mqp.co.uk
Sales Range: $50-74.9 Million
Emp.: 30
Aggregates & Crushed Stone Mining & Quarry Operations; Owned 50% by Anglo American plc & 50% by Hanson Limited
N.A.I.C.S.: 212319
Phil Bradshaw *(Dir-Ops)*

Subsidiary (Non-US):

Rocla Pty Limited (2)
Level 4 68 Waterloo Road, Macquarie Park, 2113, NSW, Australia
Tel.: (61) 289860900
Web Site: http://www.rocla.com.au
Concrete Products Mfr
N.A.I.C.S.: 327390
Craig Donaldson *(Reg Sls Mgr)*

Heidelberg Cement, Inc. (1)
7660 Imperial Way, Allentown, PA 18195 **(100%)**
Tel.: (610) 366-4600
Web Site: http://www.lehighhanson.com
Holding Company; Cement Mfr
N.A.I.C.S.: 551112

Heidelberg Materials Alkmaar Beton B.V. (1)
Laanenderweg 43, 1812 PW, Alkmaar, Netherlands
Tel.: (31) 639841576
Construction Material Mfr & Distr
N.A.I.C.S.: 327120

Heidelberg Materials Beton DE GmbH (1)
Am Remsufer 10, 71686, Remseck am Neckar, Germany
Tel.: (49) 7146283960

Building Material Mfr & Distr
N.A.I.C.S.: 327310

Heidelberg Materials Betong Norge AS (1)
Lilleakerveien 2A, 0283, Oslo, Norway
Tel.: (47) 934468740
Web Site:
  https://www.betong.heidelbergmaterials.no
Construction Material Mfr & Distr
N.A.I.C.S.: 327120

Heidelberg Materials Betong Sverige AB (1)
Marieviksgatan 25, 117 43, Stockholm, Sweden
Tel.: (46) 86256200
Web Site:
  https://www.betong.heidelbergmaterials.se
Construction Material Mfr & Distr
N.A.I.C.S.: 327120

Heidelberg Materials Betoon AS (1)
Peterburi tee 75, 13816, Tallinn, Estonia
Tel.: (372) 6209620
Web Site:
  https://www.betoon.heidelbergmaterials.ee
Construction Material Mfr & Distr
N.A.I.C.S.: 327120

Heidelberg Materials Cement Sverige AB (1)
Marieviksgatan 25, Box 47210, 100 74, Stockholm, Sweden
Tel.: (46) 86256800
Web Site:
  https://www.cement.heidelbergmaterials.se
Construction Material Mfr & Distr
N.A.I.C.S.: 327120

Heidelberg Materials Digital Hub Brno, s.r.o. (1)
Skrobarenska 511/3, Trnita, 617 00, Brno, Czech Republic
Tel.: (420) 544137503
Web Site: https://www.digitalhubbrno.cz
Building Material Mfr & Distr
N.A.I.C.S.: 327310

Heidelberg Materials Digital Hub Varna EAD (1)
Osmi Primorski polk Blvd 115 4th floor, 9002, Varna, Bulgaria
Tel.: (359) 884166105
Web Site: https://www.digitalhubvarna.com
Construction Material Mfr & Distr
N.A.I.C.S.: 327120

Heidelberg Materials France S.A.S. (1)
Tour Alto - 4 place des Saisons, 92400, Courbevoie, France
Tel.: (33) 134777800
Web Site: https://www.heidelbergmaterials.fr
Construction Material Mfr & Distr
N.A.I.C.S.: 327120

Heidelberg Materials Hispania Cementos, S.A. (1)
C/ Cardenal Marcelo Spinola 42 1, 28016, Madrid, Spain
Tel.: (34) 952209192
Web Site: https://www.cementosrezola.es
Construction Material Mfr & Distr
N.A.I.C.S.: 327120

Heidelberg Materials Kazakhstan LLP (1)
Bogenbay Batyr street building 142 office 801, 050000, Almaty, Kazakhstan
Tel.: (7) 7059263192
Web Site: https://www.cem.kz
Emp.: 1,200
Construction Material Mfr & Distr
N.A.I.C.S.: 327120

Heidelberg Materials Kunda AS (1)
Jaama 2, 44106, Kunda, Estonia
Tel.: (372) 3229900
Web Site:
  https://www.kunda.heidelbergmaterials.ee
Emp.: 51,000
Construction Material Mfr & Distr
N.A.I.C.S.: 327390

Heidelberg Materials Latvija Betons SIA (1)
Kronu iela 5, Riga, 1035, Latvia
Tel.: (371) 65588888

Web Site: https://www.betons.heidelbergmaterials.lv
Emp.: 55
Construction Material Mfr & Distr
N.A.I.C.S.: 327390

Heidelberg Materials Latvija SSC SIA (1)
Kronu iela 5, Riga, LV-1035, Latvia
Tel.: (371) 65588888
Web Site: https://www.betons.heidelbergmaterials.lv
Emp.: 55
Construction Material Mfr & Distr
N.A.I.C.S.: 327120

Heidelberg Materials Lietuva Cementas UAB (1)
Svepelio str 5, Klaipeda Free Economic Zone, LT-94103, Klaipeda, Lithuania
Tel.: (370) 69466166
Web Site:
  https://www.cementas.heidelberg.lt
Construction Material Mfr & Distr
N.A.I.C.S.: 327120

Heidelberg Materials Miljo AS (1)
Kompveien 1353, N-1930, Aurskog, Norway
Tel.: (47) 63862620
Web Site:
  https://www.miljo.heidelbergmaterials.no
Construction Material Mfr & Distr
N.A.I.C.S.: 327120

Heidelberg Materials Mineralik DE GmbH (1)
Peter-Schuhmacher-Strasse 8, 69181, Leimen, Germany
Tel.: (49) 622148141140
Building Material Mfr & Distr
N.A.I.C.S.: 327310

Heidelberg Materials Nederland Beton B.V. (1)
Pettelaarpark 30, PO Box 3232, 5203 DE, 's-Hertogenbosch, Netherlands
Tel.: (31) 732066000
Web Site: https://www.mebinshop.nl
Construction Material Mfr & Distr
N.A.I.C.S.: 327120

Heidelberg Materials Norway AS (1)
Lilleakerveien 2A, Postboks 143, Lilleaker, 0216, Oslo, Norway
Tel.: (47) 22878500
Building Material Mfr & Distr
N.A.I.C.S.: 327310

Heidelberg Materials Precast Abetong AB (1)
Taptogrand 6, Box 24, 351 03, Vaxjo, Sweden
Tel.: (46) 47096500
Web Site:
  https://www.precastabetong.heidelberg.se
Building Material Mfr & Distr
N.A.I.C.S.: 327310

Heidelberg Materials Precast Contiga AB (1)
Vintergatan 7, Norra Industriomrade, 761 50, Norrtalje, Sweden
Tel.: (46) 104714000
Web Site:
  https://www.precastcontiga.heidelberg.se
Building Material Mfr & Distr
N.A.I.C.S.: 327310

Heidelberg Materials Precast Denmark A/S (1)
Mads Clausens Vej 58, 6360, Tinglev, Denmark
Tel.: (45) 72171000
Web Site:
  https://precast.heidelbergmaterials.dk
Construction Material Mfr & Distr
N.A.I.C.S.: 327390

Heidelberg Materials Prefab Norge AS (1)
Peer Gynts vei 1, 1535, Moss, Norway
Tel.: (47) 23248900
Web Site:
  https://www.prefab.heidelbergmaterials.no
Construction Material Mfr & Distr
N.A.I.C.S.: 327120

Heidelberg Materials Romania S.A. (1)
SOS Bucharest-Ploiesti 1A building C2 et 1

sector 1, Bucharest Business Park, 013681, Bucharest, Romania
Tel.: (40) 213115976
Web Site: https://www.heidelbergmaterials.ro
Construction Material Mfr & Distr
N.A.I.C.S.: 327120

Heidelberg Materials UK Limited (1)
Second Floor Arena Court Crown Lane, Maidenhead, SL6 8QZ, United Kingdom
Tel.: (44) 1628774100
Web Site:
  https://www.heidelbergmaterials.co.uk
Construction Material Mfr & Distr
N.A.I.C.S.: 327120

Heidelberg Materials- Helwan Cement S.A.E. (1)
Kafr Elw Helwan, Cairo, Egypt
Tel.: (20) 19083
Construction Material Mfr & Distr
N.A.I.C.S.: 327120

Heidelberg Materials- Tourah Cement S.A.E. (1)
Corniche El-Nil Helwan Road Tourah 269, Cairo, Egypt
Tel.: (20) 19083
Construction Material Mfr & Distr
N.A.I.C.S.: 327120

HeidelbergCement Asia Pte Ltd (1)
60 Anson Road Mapletree Anson #06-01, Singapore, 79914, Singapore
Tel.: (65) 64385606
Web Site: http://www.heidelbergcement.com
Cement Mfr & Distr
N.A.I.C.S.: 327310
Marda R. Saturno *(Dir-HR-Asia-Oceania)*

HeidelbergCement Bangladesh Limited (1)
Symphony Plot No SE F 9 Road No - 142 6th Floor Gulshan Avenue South, Dhaka, 1212, Bangladesh
Tel.: (880) 258811691
Web Site:
  https://www.heidelbergcementbd.com
Sales Range: $150-199.9 Million
Emp.: 260
Cement Mfr & Distr
N.A.I.C.S.: 327310
Md. Emdadul Haque *(Sec)*

HeidelbergCement Central Europe East Holding B.V. (1)
Sint Teunislaan 1, 5231 BS, 's-Hertogenbosch, Netherlands
Tel.: (31) 736401150
Investment Management Service
N.A.I.C.S.: 523940

HeidelbergCement Grundstucksgesellschaft mbH & Co. KG (1)
Berliner Strasse 6, 69120, Heidelberg, Germany
Tel.: (49) 62214810
Web Site: http://www.heidelbergcement.com
Real Estate Manangement Services
N.A.I.C.S.: 531390

HeidelbergCement Grundstucksverwaltungsgesellschaft mbH (1)
Berliner Str 6, 69120, Heidelberg, Germany
Tel.: (49) 6221 4810
Emp.: 800
Real Estate Manangement Services
N.A.I.C.S.: 531390
Bernd Scheifele *(Mng Dir)*

HeidelbergCement India Ltd. (1)
Plot Number 68 2nd Floor Sector 44, Gurgaon, 122 002, Haryana, India **(68.55%)**
Tel.: (91) 1244503700
Web Site: https://www.mycemco.com
Rev.: $295,267,245
Assets: $388,399,830
Liabilities: $184,483,845
Net Worth: $203,915,985
Earnings: $42,990,675
Emp.: 1,121
Fiscal Year-end: 03/31/2021
Cement Mfr
N.A.I.C.S.: 327310
Anil Kumar Sharma *(CFO)*

HeidelbergCement Miljo AB (1)
Anstagatan 6, 702 32, Orebro, Sweden
Tel.: (46) 19 766 2460

AND PRIVATE COMPANIES

HEIDELBERG MATERIALS AG

Web Site: https://www.hcmiljo.se
Construction Raw Material Mfr & Distr
N.A.I.C.S.: 327331
Anders Jansson *(Head-Ops & Dir-Mktg)*

Plant (Domestic):

HeidelbergCement Miljo AB - Production Plant (2)
Skolgatan 6, Box 102, 624 22, Slite, Sweden
Tel.: (46) 49 828 1321
Web Site: https://www.hcmiljo.se
Emp.: 300
Cement Mfr
N.A.I.C.S.: 327310
Ker Morken *(Gen Mgr)*

HeidelbergCement Netherlands Holding B.V. (1)
Sint Teunislaan 1, 's-Hertogenbosch, 5231 BS, Netherlands
Tel.: (31) 73 640 1170
Web Site: http://www.heidelbergcement.com
Investment Management Service
N.A.I.C.S.: 523940

HeidelbergCement Northern Europe AB (1)
Annetorpsvagen 100, PO Box 60066, 21610, Malmo, Sweden **(100%)**
Tel.: (46) 40165000
Sales Range: $25-49.9 Million
Emp.: 60
Cement Mfr
N.A.I.C.S.: 327310

Affiliate (Non-US):

A/S Scancem Chemicals (2)
Industriveien 12, PO Box 1273, N 1471, Lorenskog, Norway **(100%)**
Tel.: (47) 67978400
Mfr of Cement
N.A.I.C.S.: 327310

Subsidiary (Domestic):

Abetong AB (2)
Taptogrand 6, PO Box 24, 351 03, Vaxjo, Sweden **(100%)**
Tel.: (46) 4 709 6500
Web Site: https://www.abetong.se
Concrete Products
N.A.I.C.S.: 327332
Gunnrar Syvertsem *(Mng Dir)*

Subsidiary (Domestic):

Abetong AB (3)
Falkenbergsvagen 59, 311 50, Falkenberg, Sweden **(100%)**
Tel.: (46) 3 465 5400
Web Site: https://www.abetong.se
Sales Range: $50-74.9 Million
Emp.: 125
Produces Concrete Products
N.A.I.C.S.: 327332

Subsidiary (Domestic):

Abetong Teknik AB (4)
Taptogrand 6, Box 24, 351 03, Vaxjo, Sweden **(100%)**
Tel.: (46) 47096500
Web Site: https://www.abetong.se
Sales Range: $25-49.9 Million
Emp.: 55
Mfr of Cement
N.A.I.C.S.: 327310
Filip Sten *(Pres)*

Meag Va-System AB (4)
Grunnebo, 462 93, Vanersborg, Sweden **(100%)**
Tel.: (46) 104552420
Web Site: http://www.meag.se
Sales Range: $25-49.9 Million
Emp.: 7
Mfr of Cement
N.A.I.C.S.: 327310

Affiliate (Non-US):

Alrashid-Abetong Co. Ltd. (3)
Rashid Tower 3rd Floor Dhabab St, PO Box 6058, Al Maather Area, Riyadh, 11442, Saudi Arabia **(45%)**
Tel.: (966) 464 5541
Web Site: https://www.alrashidabetong.com

Concrete Assemby Plants, Ready-Mix Concrete
N.A.I.C.S.: 327320

Mastrak Sdn Bhd (3)
No 7 Jalan 5/76 B Desa Pandan, 55100, Kuala Lumpur, Malaysia
Tel.: (60) 39815371
Mfr of Railroad Sleepers
N.A.I.C.S.: 336510

Subsidiary (Domestic):

Betongindustri AB (2)
Marieviksgatan 25, 117 43, Stockholm, Sweden **(100%)**
Tel.: (46) 8 625 6200
Web Site: https://www.betongindustri.se
Sales Range: $25-49.9 Million
Emp.: 200
Concrete Products
N.A.I.C.S.: 327332
Hans Fredrick Myklestu *(Pres)*

Cementa AB (Malmo) (2)
Ivagen 1, PO Box 30022, Malmo, 2119, Sweden **(100%)**
Tel.: (46) 40361500
Web Site: http://www.cementa.se
Sales Range: $25-49.9 Million
Emp.: 20
Portland Cement
N.A.I.C.S.: 327310
Ronny Andersson *(Head-Res & Innovation)*

Cementa AB (Stockholm) (2)
Marieviksgatan 25, Box 47210, 100 74, Stockholm, Sweden **(100%)**
Tel.: (46) 8 625 6800
Web Site: https://www.cementa.se
Sales Range: $25-49.9 Million
Emp.: 30
Portland Cement
N.A.I.C.S.: 327310
Jan Gange *(CEO)*

Cementa Research AB (2)
Fkeppirgatan 1, Box 102, S 624 22, Slite, Sweden **(100%)**
Tel.: (46) 498281000
Sales Range: $25-49.9 Million
Emp.: 30
Cement Manufacturing
N.A.I.C.S.: 327310
Jan Gange *(Gen Mgr)*

Subsidiary (Non-US):

Gyproc Oy (2)
Kalkkiperreri, FIN 08700, Virkkala, Finland **(100%)**
Tel.: (358) 193451442
Sales Range: $25-49.9 Million
Emp.: 20
Mfr of Plasterboard
N.A.I.C.S.: 327420

NorBetong a.s. (2)
Lilleakerveien 2A, Lilleaker, 0283, Oslo, Norway **(100%)**
Tel.: (47) 22878300
Web Site: http://www.norbetong.no
Sales Range: $25-49.9 Million
Emp.: 15
Ready Mixed Concrete
N.A.I.C.S.: 327320
Bjorn Styrmo *(Dir-Fin)*

NorStone a.s. (2)
Roynebergveien 24, Royneberg, 4052, Oslo, Norway **(100%)**
Tel.: (47) 5 167 6100
Web Site: http://www.norstone.no
Emp.: 120
Aggregates
N.A.I.C.S.: 333131
Kjell Ateland *(Mng Dir)*

Sand & Grus AB Jehander (2)
(100%)
Tel.: (46) 8 625 6300
Web Site: https://www.jehander.se
Sales Range: $25-49.9 Million
Emp.: 20
Aggregates
N.A.I.C.S.: 333131
Per Astrom *(Mng Dir & VP)*

Subsidiary (Domestic):

Norrkopings Sand AB (3)

Finspangsvagen 490, 605 98, Norrkoping, Sweden
Tel.: (46) 11331300
Sales Range: $50-74.9 Million
Emp.: 13
Producer of Gravel & Crushed Stone
N.A.I.C.S.: 212321

Unit (Domestic):

Sand & Grus Jehander (3)
Liljeholmsvagen 30, Box 47124, Stockholm, 10074, Sweden
Tel.: (46) 86256300
Web Site: http://www.heidelbergcement.com
Sales Range: $25-49.9 Million
Emp.: 11
Wholesale of Construction Materials
N.A.I.C.S.: 444180
Par Astrom *(CEO)*

Subsidiary (Non-US):

Scancem International ANS (2)
Lilleakerveien 2B, 0283, Oslo, Norway **(100%)**
Tel.: (47) 22013300
Web Site: http://www.hcafrica.com
Sales Range: $25-49.9 Million
Emp.: 50
Mfr of Cement
N.A.I.C.S.: 327310
Jean Marc Junon *(Chm)*

Subsidiary (Non-US):

Cimbenin S.A. (3)
PO Box 1124, Cotonou, Benin **(55.9%)**
Tel.: (229) 21330732
Sales Range: $75-99.9 Million
Cement Grinding
N.A.I.C.S.: 212312

Ciments du Togo, S.A. (3)
PO Box 1687, Lome, Togo **(99.6%)**
Tel.: (228) 22270859
Web Site: https://www.heidelbergcement.com
Cement Grinding Mill
N.A.I.C.S.: 327310

Ghacem Ltd. (3)
Opposite E P Church Madina-Adenta Road, PO Box 1891, Accra, Ghana **(93.1%)**
Tel.: (233) 201000730
Sales Range: $75-99.9 Million
Cement Grinding
N.A.I.C.S.: 212312

Affiliate (Non-US):

Nova Cimangola S.a.r.l. (3)
Avenida 4 de Fevereiro nr 42 2 Piso, 1A e 2A Andar, Caixa Postal 2532, Luanda, Angola **(24.5%)**
Tel.: (244) 94 064 2172
Web Site: https://www.cimangola.com
Cement Mfr
N.A.I.C.S.: 327310

Subsidiary (Non-US):

Sierra Leone Cement Corp. Ltd. (3)
1 Betts Street, PO Box 592, Cline Town, Freetown, Sierra Leone **(50%)**
Tel.: (232) 30232232
Web Site: http://www.hcafrica.com
Sales Range: $25-49.9 Million
Cement Grinding & Supplier
N.A.I.C.S.: 327310

Tanzania Portland Cement Company Ltd. (3)
Tegeta Wazo Hill, PO Box 1950, Dar es Salaam, Tanzania **(65.05%)**
Tel.: (255) 746810930
Web Site: https://www.twigacement.com
Rev.: $149,996,073
Assets: $147,185,158
Liabilities: $47,651,644
Net Worth: $99,533,513
Earnings: $25,672,412
Emp.: 283
Fiscal Year-end: 12/31/2019
Cement Mfr & Distr
N.A.I.C.S.: 327310
Ahmed Elsawy *(Plant Mgr)*

HeidelbergCement Norway a.s. (1)
Lilleakerveien 2A, 0216, Oslo, Norway
Tel.: (47) 2 287 8500

Web Site: https://www.hc-ne.com
Cement Mfr
N.A.I.C.S.: 327310
Vetle Houg *(Mgr-Comm)*

HeidelbergCement Pumps & Trucks AS (1)
Morbjergaenget 19, 4000, Roskilde, Denmark
Tel.: (45) 70211188
Web Site: http://www.hcpumps.dk
Engineering Equipment Distr
N.A.I.C.S.: 423490

HeidelbergCement Romania SA (1)
SOS Bucharest-Ploiesti 1A Bucharest Business Park C2 building, et 1 sector 1, 013681, Bucharest, Romania
Tel.: (40) 21 311 5976
Web Site: https://www.heidelbergcement.ro
Emp.: 1,100
Cement Mfr
N.A.I.C.S.: 327310
Vladimir Bota *(Mgr-IT)*

HeidelbergCement Shared Service Centre AB (1)
Lilleakerveien 2 B, 216, Oslo, Norway
Tel.: (47) 22878500
Cement Mfr
N.A.I.C.S.: 327310

HeidelbergCement Shared Services GmbH (1)
Peter-Schuhmacher-Strasse 8, Leimen, 69181, Germany
Tel.: (49) 6221 481 34518
Emp.: 150
Readymix Concrete Mfr
N.A.I.C.S.: 327320
Ralf Hoelscher *(Gen Mgr)*

HeidelbergCement Sweden AB (1)
Liljeholmsvagen 30, Stockholm, 117 61, Sweden
Tel.: (46) 858796900
Investment Management Service
N.A.I.C.S.: 523999

HeidelbergCement Technology Center GmbH (1)
Rohrbacherstrasse 95, D-69181, Leimen, Germany **(100%)**
Tel.: (49) 6221481341
Web Site: http://www.heidelbergcement.com
Sales Range: $50-74.9 Million
Emp.: 120
Cement Plant Technical & Operational Services
N.A.I.C.S.: 541990

HeidelbergCement UK Holding II Limited (1)
Hanson House 14 Castle Hill, Maidenhead, SL6 4JJ, United Kingdom
Tel.: (44) 1628 774131
Investment Management Service
N.A.I.C.S.: 523940

HeidelbergCement UK Limited (1)
Hanson House 14 Castle Hill, Maidenhead, SL6 4JJ, United Kingdom
Tel.: (44) 1628 774100
Readymix Concrete Mfr
N.A.I.C.S.: 327320

Heidelbergcement International Holding GmbH (1)
Berliner Str 6, 69120, Heidelberg, Germany
Tel.: (49) 62214810
Web Site: http://www.heidelbergcement.com
Investment Management Service
N.A.I.C.S.: 327910

Heidelberger Beton Aschaffenburg Verwaltungs-GmbH (1)
Hafenrandstrasse 15, 63741, Aschaffenburg, Germany
Tel.: (49) 6021 84660
Concrete Products Mfr
N.A.I.C.S.: 327320

Heidelberger Beton Donau-Iller Verwaltungs-GmbH (1)
Gewerbestr 3, 89275, Elchingen, Germany
Tel.: (49) 7308817111
Construction Materials Whslr
N.A.I.C.S.: 423320

Heidelberger Beton Donau-Naab GmbH & Co. KG (1)

HEIDELBERG MATERIALS AG
INTERNATIONAL PUBLIC

Heidelberg Materials AG—(Continued)
Tel.: (49) 947160470
Emp.: 50
Concrete Mfr
N.A.I.C.S.: 327320

Heidelberger Beton Elster-Spree GmbH & Co. KG (1)
Drewitzer Strasse 18, 03042, Cottbus, Germany
Tel.: (49) 355726831
Readymix Concrete Mfr
N.A.I.C.S.: 327320

Heidelberger Beton GmbH (1)
Berliner Strasse 10, D-69120, Heidelberg, Germany (100%)
Tel.: (49) 62214819626
Web Site: http://www.heidelberger-beton.de
Readymix Concrete Mfr
N.A.I.C.S.: 327320
Michael Gieding (Mng Dir)

Heidelberger Beton Inntal GmbH & Co. KG (1)
Schneiderwimm 122, 84503, Altotting, Germany
Tel.: (49) 8671926880
Readymix Concrete Mfr
N.A.I.C.S.: 327320

Heidelberger Beton Kurpfalz GmbH & Co. KG (1)
Hermann-Wittmann-Str 1, 69214, Eppelheim, Germany
Tel.: (49) 622179200
Readymix Concrete Mfr
N.A.I.C.S.: 327320

Heidelberger Beton Rhein-Nahe GmbH & Co.KG (1)
Felix-Wankel-Strasse 2, 55545, Bad Kreuznach, Germany
Tel.: (49) 671 89400 10
Cement Mfr
N.A.I.C.S.: 327310

Heidelberger Beton Schwandorf GmbH (1)
Regensburger Strasse Flr-Nr 543, Schwandorf, 92421, Germany
Tel.: (49) 9471 6047 0
Web Site: http://www.heidelberger-beton.de
Emp.: 10
Construction Materials Whslr
N.A.I.C.S.: 423320
Jochen Heller (Gen Mgr)

Subsidiary (Domestic):

Baustoffwerke Dresden GmbH & Co. KG (2)
Radeburger Strasse 30, 01129, Dresden, Germany (51%)
Tel.: (49) 351 817 8771
Web Site: https://www.hplush.de
Concrete, Gypsum & Limestone Products Mfr
N.A.I.C.S.: 327390
Ralph Nagel (Reg Mgr-Sls)

Heidelberger Beton Zwickau GmbH & Co. KG (1)
Planitzer Strasse 2, 8056, Zwickau, Germany
Tel.: (49) 375 27005 0
Readymix Concrete Mfr
N.A.I.C.S.: 327320

Heidelberger Beton Zwickau Verwaltungs-GmbH (1)
Muldestr 0, 08056, Zwickau, Germany
Tel.: (49) 375 27 00 50
Readymix Concrete Mfr
N.A.I.C.S.: 327320

Heidelberger Betonelemente Verwaltungs-GmbH (1)
Gewerbeallee 2 6, 9224, Mittelbach, Germany
Tel.: (49) 371 271070
Concrete Products Mfr
N.A.I.C.S.: 327390

Heidelberger Betonpumpen Rhein-Main-Nahe GmbH & Co, KG (1)
Felix-Wankel-Strasse 2, 55545, Bad Kreuznach, Germany
Tel.: (49) 671 48359 66

Readymix Concrete Mfr
N.A.I.C.S.: 327320

Heidelberger Betonpumpen Rhein-Main-Nahe Verwaltungs-GmbH (1)
Dieselstr 20, 60314, Frankfurt, Germany
Tel.: (49) 671 483590
Concrete Pipe Mfr
N.A.I.C.S.: 327332

Heidelberger Betonpumpen Simonis GmbH & Co. KG (1)
Zum Grenzgraben 27, Ubstadt-Weiher, 76698, Karlsruhe, Germany
Tel.: (49) 7251969740
Readymix Concrete Mfr
N.A.I.C.S.: 327320

Heidelberger Fliessestrich Sudwest GmbH (1)
Hermann Wittmann Strasse 1, 69214, Eppelheim, Germany
Tel.: (49) 6221792075
Readymix Concrete Mfr
N.A.I.C.S.: 327320

Heidelberger KS Beteiligungen Deutschland Verwaltungsgesellschaft mbH (1)
Berliner Str 6, 69120, Heidelberg, Germany
Tel.: (49) 6221 4810
Investment Management Service
N.A.I.C.S.: 523940

Heidelberger Sand und Kies Handel & Logistik GmbH (1)
Ruhrallee 311, Essen, 45136, Germany
Tel.: (49) 201 8126550
Gravel & Sand Mining Services
N.A.I.C.S.: 212321

Heidelberger Sand und Kies Handels- und Vertriebs-GmbH (1)
Berliner Str 6, 69120, Heidelberg, Germany
Tel.: (49) 6221 4819040
Construction Materials Distr
N.A.I.C.S.: 423320

Heidelberger Weserkies Verwaltungs-GmbH (1)
Arberger Hafendamm 15, 28309, Bremen, Germany
Tel.: (49) 421 43570 0
Concrete Block Mfr
N.A.I.C.S.: 327331

Helwan Cement Company S.A.E. (1)
Kafr Elw 16, Helwan, Cairo, Egypt
Tel.: (20) 22 501 0771
Web Site: https://www.suezcement.com.eg
Cement Mfr
N.A.I.C.S.: 327310

Hormigones y Aridos, S.A. (1)
Paraje Andaroleta S/N, Zaramillo, 48820, Spain
Tel.: (34) 946 693 089
Readymix Concrete & Aggregate Mfr
N.A.I.C.S.: 327320

Houserate Limited (1)
1 Grosvenor Pl, SW1X 7HJ, London, United Kingdom - England
Tel.: (44) 2072451245
Investment Management Service
N.A.I.C.S.: 523940

Intercom S.r.l. (1)
Via Della Gora 13, Montespertoli, 50025, Florence, Italy
Tel.: (39) 057 167 1096
Web Site: https://www.intercomsas.it
Leather Goods Mfr
N.A.I.C.S.: 316990

International Trading and Finance (ITF) B.V. (1)
Sint Teunislaan 1, 5231 BS, 's-Hertogenbosch, Netherlands
Tel.: (31) 736401170
Financial Management Services
N.A.I.C.S.: 523999

Irvine - Whitlock Limited (1)
Brickstone House, Priory Business Park, Bedford, MK43 3JW, United Kingdom
Tel.: (44) 123 483 2300
Web Site: https://www.irvine-whitlock.co.uk

Sales Range: $100-124.9 Million
Emp.: 150
Brickwork Contractor
N.A.I.C.S.: 238990

Italcementi S.p.A (1)
Via G Camozzi 124, 24121, Bergamo, Italy (100%)
Tel.: (39) 035396111
Web Site: https://www.italcementi.it
Holding Company; Cement Mfr
N.A.I.C.S.: 551112

Subsidiary (Domestic):

Calcementi Jonici S.r.l. (2)
Contrada Limarri-Zona Industriale, Marina, 89048, Siderno, RC, Italy
Tel.: (39) 096 438 2811
Web Site: https://www.calcementi.it
Construction Raw Material Mfr
N.A.I.C.S.: 423320

Calcestruzzi S.p.A (2)
Via Stezzano 87, 24126, Bergamo, Italy
Tel.: (39) 03 539 6111
Web Site: https://www.calcestruzzi.it
Ready-Mixed Concrete Materials Mfr
N.A.I.C.S.: 327320
Cono Giuseppe Federico (Pres)

Subsidiary (Non-US):

Ciments Francais S.A. (2)
Tour Ariane 5 place de la Pyramide, Quartier Villon, 92800, Puteaux, Cedex, France
Tel.: (33) 1 42 91 75 00
Cement, Ready-Mixed Concrete, Other Concrete Products, Bags & Transportation
N.A.I.C.S.: 327310
Jean-Paul Meric (Chm)

Subsidiary (Domestic):

Ciments Calcia S.a.s. (3)
Les Technodes, 78931, Guerville, Cedex, France
Tel.: (33) 134777840
Cement Mfr & Distr
N.A.I.C.S.: 327310
Bruno Pillon (Pres)

Subsidiary (Domestic):

Socli S.a.s. (4)
2 Quartier Castans, 65370, Izaourt, France
Tel.: (33) 562993399
Web Site: https://www.socli.fr
Binders & Mortars Mfr & Whslr
N.A.I.C.S.: 327390

Subsidiary (Non-US):

Compagnie Financiere des Ciments SA (3)
Grand Route 260, Gaurain - Ramecroix, B 7530, Tournai, Belgium
Tel.: (32) 69252511
Financial & Public Relations Services
N.A.I.C.S.: 921130

Subsidiary (Domestic):

Eurarco France S.A. (3)
Chemin Barre Mer Saint Firmin les Crotoy, 80550, Le Crotoy, France
Tel.: (33) 322279233
Cement Mfr & Distr
N.A.I.C.S.: 327310

Granulats Ouest - GO (3)
54 Port Des Monards, 17120, Barzan, France
Tel.: (33) 546904078
Construction Materials Distr
N.A.I.C.S.: 423390

Immobiliere Des Technodes (3)
Rue des Technodes, 78930, Guerville, France
Tel.: (33) 134777777
Web Site: https://www.cimengs-calcia.fr
Sales Range: $150-199.9 Million
Emp.: 500
Real Estate Agents & Managers
N.A.I.C.S.: 531210

Unibeton S.A.S. (3)
Les Technodes, 78931, Guerville, Cedex, France
Tel.: (33) 130987200

Web Site: http://www.unibeton.fr
Emp.: 611
Ready-Mix Concrete Product Mfr
N.A.I.C.S.: 327320

Division (Domestic):

Unibeton Est (4)
ZI Avenue des Erables, BP 50013, 54181, Heillecourt, Cedex, France
Tel.: (33) 383515270
Readymix Concrete Mfr
N.A.I.C.S.: 327320
Patrick Perron (Dir-Comml)

Unibeton Ile de France (4)
Les Technodes-Bat F, 78931, Guerville, Cedex, France
Tel.: (33) 134777850
Readymix Concrete Mfr
N.A.I.C.S.: 327320
Laurent Armand (Reg Dir)

Unibeton Mediterranee (4)
Z A du Berthoire 21 avenue Fernand Julien, 13410, Lambesc, France
Tel.: (33) 442927170
Readymix Concrete Mfr
N.A.I.C.S.: 327320
Phillippe Chaize (Reg Dir)

Unibeton Ouest Pays de Loire (4)
3 rue du Charron CS 20375, 44816, Saint-Herblain, Cedex, France
Tel.: (33) 240924391
Readymix Concrete Mfr
N.A.I.C.S.: 327320
William de Warren (Reg Dir)

Unibeton Sud Ouest (4)
162 BC du Haut Leveque, 33608, Pessac, France
Tel.: (33) 556151015
Readymix Concrete Mfr
N.A.I.C.S.: 327320
Pascal Barylo (Reg Dir)

Subsidiary (Non-US):

Devnya Cement JSC (2)
Industrial Zone, 9160, Devnya, Bulgaria
Tel.: (359) 5 199 7323
Web Site: https://www.devnyacement.bg
Cement Mfr
N.A.I.C.S.: 327310

Gacem Company Limited (2)
Kanifing Industrial Estate, Banjul, Gambia
Tel.: (220) 395 2002
Cement Distr
N.A.I.C.S.: 423390

Halyps Building Materials S.A. (2)
17th klm National Road Athens - Korinthos, Aspropyrgos, 19300, Athens, Greece
Tel.: (30) 2105518100
Web Site: http://www.halyps.gr
Sand & Crushed Stone Quarrying; Concrete Mfr
N.A.I.C.S.: 327320
Silvio Thiede (Mng Dir)

Subsidiary (Domestic):

IMES S.r.l. (2)
Via Andriano 20, Terlano, 39018, Bolzano, Italy
Tel.: (39) 0471257147
Web Site: https://imes.it
Financial Management Services
N.A.I.C.S.: 523999

Subsidiary (Non-US):

Interbulk Trading S.A. (2)
Via Giuseppe Bagutti 5, Caselle, Lugano, 6904, Switzerland
Tel.: (41) 91 9113700
Construction Materials Distr
N.A.I.C.S.: 423390

Subsidiary (Domestic):

Intertrading S.r.l. (2)
Via Manzoni 6, Arosio, 22060, Como, Italy
Tel.: (39) 03 175 8075
Web Site: https://www.intertradingsrl.it
Construction Materials Mfr
N.A.I.C.S.: 423390

HEIDELBERG MATERIALS AG

Subsidiary (Non-US):

Italcementi Finance (2)
Tour Ariane, 92088, Paris, France
Tel.: (33) 142917582
Web Site:
https://www.italcementifinance.com
Sales Range: $50-74.9 Million
Emp.: 1
Financial Treasury Services
N.A.I.C.S.: 523999
Marc Pasquiou (Grp Treas)

Subsidiary (Domestic):

Italcementi Ingegneria S.r.l. (2)
Via Gabriele Camozzi 124, 24121, Bergamo, Italy
Tel.: (39) 035396111
Construction Engineering Services
N.A.I.C.S.: 541330

Subsidiary (Non-US):

Jalaprathan Cement Public Company Limited (2)
23 124 128 Soi Soonvijai Rama 9 Rd, Bangkapi Huay Kwang, Bangkok, 10310, Thailand
Tel.: (66) 2 080 0333
Web Site: https://www.asiacement.co.th
Cement Mfr
N.A.I.C.S.: 327310

Subsidiary (US):

Lehigh Hanson ECC, Inc. (2)
3251 Bath Pike, Nazareth, PA 18064-8928 (100%)
Tel.: (610) 837-6725
Concrete & Cement Production
N.A.I.C.S.: 327310
Alexander Carr (Pres)

Subsidiary (Non-US):

Cambridge Aggregates Inc. (2)
1102 Cedar Creek Road, Cambridge, N1R 5Y2, ON, Canada
Tel.: (226) 581-3076
Web Site: https://www.lehighhanson.com
Construction Materials Whslr
N.A.I.C.S.: 423320

Plant (Non-US):

Hanson Ready Mix, Inc. - Arnprior Plant (3)
482 Russet Drive, Arnprior, K7S 3G8, ON, Canada
Readymix Concrete Mfr
N.A.I.C.S.: 327320
Tony Johnson (Plant Mgr)

Hanson Ready Mix, Inc. - Ashton Plant (3)
1535 Ashton Station Road, Ashton, K0A 1B0, ON, Canada
Tel.: (613) 257-2613
Readymix Concrete Mfr
N.A.I.C.S.: 327320

Hanson Ready Mix, Inc. - Aylmer Plant (3)
1301 Chemin Pink, Gatineau, J9J 395, QC, Canada
Tel.: (819) 682-1155
Readymix Concrete Mfr
N.A.I.C.S.: 327320
Pierre Parisien (Mgr-Sls)

Plant (Domestic):

Hanson Ready Mix, Inc. - Braddock Plant (3)
17th St, Braddock, PA 15104
Tel.: (412) 271-1612
Readymix Concrete Mfr
N.A.I.C.S.: 327320

Hanson Ready Mix, Inc. - Charleston Plant (3)
1011 Bullitt St, Charleston, WV 25301
Tel.: (304) 346-8131
Readymix Concrete Mfr
N.A.I.C.S.: 327320

Hanson Ready Mix, Inc. - Huntington Plant (3)
6700 Kyle Ln, Huntington, WV 25702

Tel.: (304) 733-5676
Readymix Concrete Mfr
N.A.I.C.S.: 327320

Plant (Non-US):

Hanson Ready Mix, Inc. - Ottawa (3)
2787 Sheffield Road, Ottawa, K1B 3V8, ON, Canada
Tel.: (613) 748-6650
Ready Mix Concrete Whslr
N.A.I.C.S.: 327320

Plant (Domestic):

Hanson Ready Mix, Inc. - Ottawa Plant (4)
2787 Sheffield Road, Ottawa, K1B 3V8, ON, Canada
Tel.: (613) 748-6650
Readymix Concrete Mfr
N.A.I.C.S.: 327320
Tony Johnson (Plant Mgr)

Plant (Domestic):

Hanson Ready Mix, Inc. - Parkersburg Plant (3)
316 Murray Ln, Parkersburg, WV 26101
Tel.: (304) 422-4841
Readymix Concrete Mfr
N.A.I.C.S.: 327320

Plant (Non-US):

Hanson Ready Mix, Inc. - Pembroke Plant (3)
2065 Petawawa Boulevard, Pembroke, K8A 7G8, ON, Canada
Tel.: (613) 735-0631
Readymix Concrete Mfr
N.A.I.C.S.: 327320
Tony Johnson (Plant Mgr)

Plant (Domestic):

Hanson Ready Mix, Inc. - Pittsburgh Plant (3)
2220 2nd Ave, Pittsburgh, PA 15219-3107
Tel.: (412) 431-6001
Readymix Concrete Mfr
N.A.I.C.S.: 327320

Hanson Ready Mix, Inc. - State College (3)
123 Hawbaker Industrial Dr, State College, PA 16803
Tel.: (866) 505-2776
Readymix Concrete Mfr
N.A.I.C.S.: 327320

Plant (Non-US):

Hanson Ready Mix, Inc. - Thurso Plant (3)
355 Rue Galipeau, Thurso, J0X 3B0, QC, Canada
Readymix Concrete Mfr
N.A.I.C.S.: 327320
Pierre Parisien (Mgr-Sls)

Plant (Domestic):

Hanson Ready Mix, Inc. - Winfield Plant (3)
Scary Creek Industrial Park, Winfield, WV 25213
Tel.: (866) 505-2776
Readymix Concrete Mfr
N.A.I.C.S.: 327320

Hanson Ready Mix, Inc. - Wheeling Plant (3)
1601 W Baltimore, McMechen, WV 26040
Tel.: (866) 505-2776
Readymix Concrete Mfr
N.A.I.C.S.: 327320

Lehigh Cement - Indiana Plant (3)
301 E Hwy 31, Speed, IN 47172 (100%)
Tel.: (812) 246-5472
Cement Production
N.A.I.C.S.: 327310

Subsidiary (Non-US):

Saarlandische Zement Gesellschaft GmbH (2)
Am Zementwerk 14, 66130, Saarbrucken, Germany

Tel.: (49) 681 87 80 98
Cement Additives Mfr
N.A.I.C.S.: 327310

Sable Classifie et Equipement de Wilson Ltee (2)
180 Ch McCrank RR 1, Alcove, La Peche, J0X 1A0, QC, Canada
Tel.: (819) 456-2341
Emp.: 5
Construction Material Mfr & Distr
N.A.I.C.S.: 327331
Daniel Cloutier (Gen Mgr)

Plant (Non-US):

Shymkent Cement JSC (2)
Koikeldy Batyr Str 22, Shymkent, 160015, Kazakhstan (99.84%)
Tel.: (7) 7252 48 00 39
Readymix Concrete Mfr
N.A.I.C.S.: 327320

Subsidiary (Domestic):

Silos Granari della Sicilia S.r.l. (2)
Via Sant Elia Zona Ind Ie, Corato, 70033, Bari, Italy
Tel.: (39) 0809172500
Web Site: http://www.silosgranari.it
Grain Storage Services
N.A.I.C.S.: 493130

Subsidiary (Non-US):

Sociedad Financiera y Minera S.A. (2)
Carretera de Almeria Km 8, 29720, Malaga, Spain
Tel.: (34) 952209100
Web Site: http://www.fym.es
Concrete Products Mfr
N.A.I.C.S.: 327390

Sociedad Financiera y Minera, SA (2)
Ctra de Almeria, 29720, Malaga, Spain
Tel.: (34) 95 220 9100
Web Site: https://www.fym.es
Cement Mfr
N.A.I.C.S.: 327310

Subsidiary (Domestic):

Hormigones y Minas S.A. (3)
Carretera De Almeria Km 8, Malaga, 29720, Spain
Tel.: (34) 952209100
Cement Mfr
N.A.I.C.S.: 327310

Plant (Domestic):

Sociedad Financiera y Minera S.A. - Anorga Cement Factory (3)
Avda Anorga 36, 20018, San Sebastian, Spain
Tel.: (34) 943362040
Cement Mfr
N.A.I.C.S.: 327310

Sociedad Financiera y Minera S.A. - Arrigorriaga Cement Factory (3)
Barrio Arane sn, 48480, Arrigorriaga, Bizkaia, Spain
Tel.: (34) 94 671 03 11
Cement Mfr
N.A.I.C.S.: 327310

Sociedad Financiera y Minera S.A. - Kukularra Plant (3)
Barrio Sakoni sn, Erandio, 48480, Vizcaya, Spain
Tel.: (34) 900 210 363
Concrete Products Mfr
N.A.I.C.S.: 327390

Sociedad Financiera y Minera S.A. - Malaga Cement Factory (3)
Carretera de Almeria Km 8, 29720, Malaga, Spain
Tel.: (34) 95 220 91 00
Cement Mfr
N.A.I.C.S.: 327310
Arnold Macburnie (Gen Mgr)

Subsidiary (Non-US):

Societe Internationale Italcementi (Luxembourg) S.A. (2)

534 Rue de Neudorf, 2220, Luxembourg, Luxembourg
Tel.: (352) 270422
Sales Range: $25-49.9 Million
Emp.: 2
Construction Materials Distr
N.A.I.C.S.: 423390
Monica Porfilio (Gen Mgr)

Zuari Cement (2)
Adventz Centre 2nd & 3rd Floor No 28 Cubbon Road, Bengaluru, 560001, India
Tel.: (91) 804 119 4408
Web Site: https://www.zuaricements.com
Cement Mfr
N.A.I.C.S.: 327310
Jamshed Naval Cooper (Mng Dir)

Joseph Wones (Holdings) Limited (1)
Southgate House Southgate Avenue, Stevenage, SG1 1HG, United Kingdom
Tel.: (44) 2072451245
Investment Management Service
N.A.I.C.S.: 523940

Kalksandsteinwerk Amberg GmbH & Co. KG (1)
Schafhofer Weg 8, 92263, Ebermannsdorf, Germany
Tel.: (49) 94 38 94 00 0
Web Site: http://www.kalksandstein-amberg.de
Construction Materials Distr
N.A.I.C.S.: 423320

Kamenivo Slovakia a.s. (1)
PO Box 24, Hrabove, Bytca, 014 01, Slovakia
Tel.: (421) 415078217
Web Site: https://www.ksas.sk
Sand & Gravel Mining Services
N.A.I.C.S.: 212321

Kazakhstan Cement Holding B.V. (1)
Sint Teunislaan 1, 5231BS, 's-Hertogenbosch, Netherlands
Tel.: (31) 736401170
Investment Management Service
N.A.I.C.S.: 523940

Kieswerk Maas-Roeloffs GmbH & Co. KG (1)
Taubensterz 5, Kalkar, 47546, Germany
Tel.: (49) 2824 2434
Emp.: 7
Limestone Mining & Quarrying Services
N.A.I.C.S.: 212311
Kai Artus (Gen Mgr)

Kieswerk Maas-Roeloffs Verwaltungsgesellschaft mbH (1)
Taubensterz 5, Kalkar, 47546, Germany
Tel.: (49) 2824 2434
Business Support Services
N.A.I.C.S.: 561499

Kieswerke Andresen GmbH (1)
Tarbeker Landstr 7, Damsdorf, 23824, Germany
Tel.: (49) 4323 9055 0
Web Site: http://www.die-kieswerke.de
Emp.: 20
Gravel & Sand Mining Services
N.A.I.C.S.: 212321
Lutje Andresen (Gen Mgr)

Kieswerke Flemmingen GmbH (1)
Flemmingener Weg 1, OT Niedersteinbach, 09322, Penig, Germany
Tel.: (49) 344978110
Concrete Products Mfr
N.A.I.C.S.: 327390

Kieswerke Kieser GmbH & Co. KG (1)
Schlegelstrasse 5, 99867, Gotha, Germany
Tel.: (49) 362 140 9912
Web Site: https://www.kieswerke-kieser.de
Construction Materials Distr
N.A.I.C.S.: 423320

Kivel Properties Limited (1)
20 Manvers Street, Bath, BA1 1PX, United Kingdom
Tel.: (44) 2072451245
Real Estate Management Services
N.A.I.C.S.: 531390

HEIDELBERG MATERIALS AG   INTERNATIONAL PUBLIC

Heidelberg Materials AG—(Continued)

Kommanditbolaget Cementen (1)
Kaskog 20, Kista, Sweden
Tel.: (46) 73 533 65 43
Cement Mfr
N.A.I.C.S.: 327310

Kunda Nordic Cement Corp. (1)
Jaama 2, Kunda, 44106, Estonia
Tel.: (372) 3229900
Web Site: http://www.heidelbergcement.com
Sales Range: $50-74.9 Million
Emp.: 180
Cement Mfr
N.A.I.C.S.: 327310
Meelis Einstein *(Mng Dir)*

LLC HeidelbergCement Rus (1)
Tel.: (7) 4951233218
Web Site: https://heidelbergcement.ru
Sales Range: $25-49.9 Million
Emp.: 30
Cement Mfr & Distr
N.A.I.C.S.: 327310

LLC KaliningradCement (1)
126 Off 15 1812 Goda Str, Kaliningrad, 236016, Russia
Tel.: (7) 4012582821
Commercial Seaport Terminal Services
N.A.I.C.S.: 488310

La Cimenterie de Lukala S.A.R.L. (1)
Building du 30 Juin, Kinshasa, Congo, Democratic Republic of
Tel.: (243) 817005793
Cement Mfr
N.A.I.C.S.: 327310

Labske sterkopisky a beton s.r.o. (1)
Piskovna, Chotikov, 330 17, Czech Republic
Tel.: (420) 377 821 578
Construction Materials Distr
N.A.I.C.S.: 423320

Leamaat Omikron B.V. (1)
Sint Teunislaan 1, 5231 BS, 's-Hertogenbosch, Netherlands
Tel.: (31) 736401207
Construction Materials Whslr
N.A.I.C.S.: 423390

Leca (Great Britain) Limited (1)
The Ridge Chipping Sodbury, Bristol, BS37 6AY, United Kingdom
Tel.: (44) 1787477112
Investment Management Service
N.A.I.C.S.: 523940

Lehigh Hanson Materials Limited (1)
12640 Inland Way, Edmonton, T5V 1K2, AB, Canada
Tel.: (780) 420-2500
Web Site: http://www.lehighhansoncanada.com
Sales Range: $450-499.9 Million
Emp.: 2,000
Concrete Pipe Mfr
N.A.I.C.S.: 327332
Chris Ward *(CEO)*

Lehigh Northwest Marine, LLC (1)
300 E John Carpenter Freeway, Irving, TX 75062
Tel.: (972) 653-5500
Investment Management Service
N.A.I.C.S.: 523940

Lehigh Realty Company (1)
403 Joan Ave N Ste B, Lehigh Acres, FL 33971
Tel.: (239) 369-2018
Web Site: http://www.lehighrealty.com
Real Estate Services
N.A.I.C.S.: 531210

Liberia Cement Corporation Ltd. (1)
Bushroda Island Somalia Drive, Monrovia, Liberia
Tel.: (231) 6515186
Cement Mfr & Distr
N.A.I.C.S.: 327310

Limited Liability Company Heidelberg-Beton Ukraine (1)
Aktsionerna St 1a, Krivoy Rog, 50006, Ukraine
Tel.: (380) 564044495

Construction Materials Whslr
N.A.I.C.S.: 423320

Lindustries Limited (1)
4Th Floor Saltire Court 20 Castle Terrace, Edinburgh, EH1 2EN, United Kingdom
Tel.: (44) 2072451245
Investment Management Service
N.A.I.C.S.: 523940

Lithonplus GmbH & Co. KG (1)
Karl-Losch-Strasse 3, 67360, Lingenfeld, Germany
Tel.: (49) 6344949125
Web Site: https://www.lithon.de
Concrete Products Mfr & Distr
N.A.I.C.S.: 327331

London Brick Engineering Limited (1)
Stewart Ho, Bedford, MK43 9LZ, United Kingdom
Tel.: (44) 8705 258258
Concrete Block Mfr
N.A.I.C.S.: 327331

MM MAIN-MORTEL Verwaltungsgesellschaft mbH (1)
Hafenrandstr 15, 63741, Aschaffenburg, Germany
Tel.: (49) 602184660
Management Consulting Services
N.A.I.C.S.: 541618

MM Main-Mortel GmbH & Co.KG (1)
Seligenstadter Strasse 1a, 63811, Stockstadt, Germany
Tel.: (49) 60279796100
Readymix Concrete Mfr
N.A.I.C.S.: 327320

Malmo-Limhamns Jarnvagsaktiebolag (1)
Karlbergsvagen 25, Box 47210, Stockholm, 10074, Sweden
Tel.: (46) 40 361590
Rail Transportation Services
N.A.I.C.S.: 488210

Marples Ridgway Limited (1)
Hanson House 14 Castle Hill, Maidenhead, SL6 4JJ, United Kingdom
Tel.: (44) 2072451245
Investment Management Service
N.A.I.C.S.: 523940

Mayco Mix Ltd. (1)
1125 Cedar Road, PO Box 542, Nanaimo, V9X 1K9, BC, Canada
Tel.: (250) 722-0064
Web Site: http://www.maycomix.com
Emp.: 20
Ready Mix Concrete Mfr & Distr
N.A.I.C.S.: 327320
Doug Lum *(Mgr)*

Mebin Leeuwarden B.V. (1)
Schenkenschans 3a, Postbus 70196, Leeuwarden, 9704 AD, Netherlands
Tel.: (31) 58 212 67 43
Sales Range: $50-74.9 Million
Emp.: 10
Cement Mfr & Distr
N.A.I.C.S.: 327310

Mediterranean Carriers, Inc. (1)
Arias Fabrega & Fabrega, Panama, C081601098, Panama
Tel.: (507) 2057000
Web Site: https://www.arafa.com
Emp.: 212
Human Resource Consulting Services
N.A.I.C.S.: 541612
Arus Gawear *(Mgr)*

Melbourne Concrete Pty. Ltd. (1)
PO Box 6481, West Footscray, Melbourne, 3012, VIC, Australia
Tel.: (61) 393102609
Web Site: https://www.melbourneconcrete.com.au
Readymix Concrete Mfr
N.A.I.C.S.: 327320
Glenn Williams *(Mng Dir)*

Meppeler Betoncentrale B.V. (1)
Meursingeweg 4, 7941 EP, Meppel, Netherlands
Tel.: (31) 505515110
Ready Mix Concrete Mfr & Distr
N.A.I.C.S.: 327320

Meriwether Ready Mix, Inc. (1)
105 Liberty Park Rd, Griffin, GA 30224
Tel.: (770) 229-8409
Web Site: http://www.meriwetherreadymix.com
Rev.: $3,000,000
Emp.: 10
Brick, Stone & Related Construction Material Merchant Whslr
N.A.I.C.S.: 423320
Johnnie Bertram *(Pres)*

Mibau Baustoffhandel GmbH (1)
Gewerbestrasse 3, Cadenberge, 21781, Cuxhaven, Germany
Tel.: (49) 477793390
Concrete Material Mfr
N.A.I.C.S.: 324121

Mibau Holding GmbH (1)
Gewerbestrasse 3, Cadenberge, 21781, Cuxhaven, Germany
Tel.: (49) 4777933931
Web Site: https://www.mibau-stema.com
Concrete Material Mfr
N.A.I.C.S.: 324121

N.V. Silicaatsteen (1)
Staatstuinwijk 36, B-3600, Gent, Belgium
Tel.: (32) 89355901
Mfr of Calcium Silicate Blocks & Slabs
N.A.I.C.S.: 327331

National Brick Company Limited (1)
Unicorn House Wellington Street, Ripley, DE5 3DZ, United Kingdom
Tel.: (44) 1773570575
Concrete Block Mfr
N.A.I.C.S.: 327331

National Star Limited (1)
Hanson House 14 Castle Hill, Maidenhead, SL6 4JJ, United Kingdom
Tel.: (44) 2072451245
Investment Management Service
N.A.I.C.S.: 523940

Norbetong Pumping AS (1)
Lilleakerveien 2B, Oslo, 0283, Norway
Tel.: (47) 22 87 83 00
Concrete Pumping Services
N.A.I.C.S.: 238110

Norcem a.s. (1)
Fakturamottak, Postboks 143, Lilleaker, 0216, Oslo, Norway (100%)
Tel.: (47) 2 287 8400
Web Site: http://www.norcem.no
Sales Range: $25-49.9 Million
Emp.: 12
Cement Hydraulic
N.A.I.C.S.: 327310
Gunnar Syvertsen *(Gen Mgr)*

Nord-fosen Pukkverk AS (1)
Hopen, 7740, Steinsdalen, Norway
Tel.: (47) 72 57 78 90
Web Site: http://www.heidelbergcement.com
Sales Range: $25-49.9 Million
Emp.: 11
Construction Gravel & Sand Distr
N.A.I.C.S.: 423320

Norsk Stein AS (1)
Jelsavegen 512, 4234, Jelsa, Norway
Tel.: (47) 52792900
Concrete Material Distr
N.A.I.C.S.: 423320
Marie Reumont *(Dir-Production)*

OJSC Cesla (1)
22 Liter B 10th Krasnoarmeyskaya Str, Saint Petersburg, 190103, Russia
Tel.: (7) 8126796288
Cement Mfr
N.A.I.C.S.: 327310

OOO Norcem Kola (1)
82 Lenina ave, 183038, Murmansk, Russia
Tel.: (7) 815 269 0170
Web Site: https://www.heidelbergcement.ru
Sales Range: $25-49.9 Million
Emp.: 15
Construction Materials Whslr
N.A.I.C.S.: 423320
Ivan Fursa *(Gen Mgr)*

Open Joint Stock Company Gurovo-Beton (1)
3 Zheleznodorozhnaya str Tula Region,

Aleksinsky District, 301382, Novogurovsky, Russia
Tel.: (7) 48753 200 05
Web Site: http://www.heidelbergcement.com
Emp.: 150
Cement Distr
N.A.I.C.S.: 423320
Jan Nie Schwietz *(Gen Mgr)*

Open Joint-Stock Company Slantsy Cement Plant Cesla (1)
1 Kingiseppskoe ch, Leningrad region, Slantsy, 188560, Leningrad, Russia
Tel.: (7) 8137472341
Web Site: http://www.heidelbergcement.com
Cement Mfr
N.A.I.C.S.: 327310

Oswald Tillotson Limited (1)
1 Grosvenor Place, London, SW1X 7JH, United Kingdom
Tel.: (44) 2072451245
Cement Mfr
N.A.I.C.S.: 327310

P.T. Semen Grobogan (1)
Desa Sugihmanik Kec Tanggungharjo Kab Grobogan, Jawa Tengah, 58166, Indonesia
Tel.: (62) 8112898568
Web Site: https://semen-grobogan.com
Building Material Mfr & Distr
N.A.I.C.S.: 327310

PREFA Grygov a.s. (1)
V Podlesi 258, Grygov, 783 73, Olomouc, Czech Republic
Tel.: (420) 585111030
Web Site: http://www.prefagrygov.cz
Construction Building Material Distr
N.A.I.C.S.: 423320

PT Multi Bangun Galaxy (1)
Jl Raya Lembar, Gerung, Indonesia
Tel.: (62) 370 681668
Management Consulting Services
N.A.I.C.S.: 541618

PT Pionirbeton Industri (1)
Jl Rawa Sumur IV Block BB9A-B, Pulogadung Industrial Estate, East Jakarta, 13930, Indonesia
Tel.: (62) 214 683 6344
Web Site: https://www.pionirbeton.co.id
Readymix Concrete Mfr
N.A.I.C.S.: 327320
Ivana Lim *(Mgr-Pur)*

Paderborner Transport-Beton-Gesellschaft mit beschrankter Haftung (1)
Alt-Enginger-Weg 2, Elsen, 33106, Paderborn, Germany
Tel.: (49) 52549559018
Readymix Concrete Mfr
N.A.I.C.S.: 327320

Paderborner Transport-Beton-Gesellschaft mit beschrankter Haftung & Co. K.-G. (1)
Burnerstr Str 66, 59590, Geseke, Nordrhein-Westfalen, Germany
Tel.: (49) 2942 97740
Construction Goods Transportation Services
N.A.I.C.S.: 488999

Pencrete Limited (1)
Hanson House 14 Castle Hill, Maidenhead, SL6 4JJ, United Kingdom
Tel.: (44) 2072451245
Investment Management Service
N.A.I.C.S.: 523940

Pioneer Aggregates (UK) Limited (1)
Bulls Lodge Quarry Generals Lane, Chelmsford, CM3 3HR, United Kingdom
Tel.: (44) 1245451644
Aggregate Mfr
N.A.I.C.S.: 327992

Pioneer Asphalts (U.K.) Limited (1)
Westbury Quarries, Wells, BA5 3BZ, United Kingdom
Tel.: (44) 1749870272
Asphalt Mfr
N.A.I.C.S.: 324121

Pioneer International Investments Limited (1)
Hanson House 14 Castle Hill, Maidenhead, SL6 4JJ, United Kingdom

AND PRIVATE COMPANIES — HEIDELBERG MATERIALS AG

Tel.: (44) 20 7734 2042
Investment Management Service
N.A.I.C.S.: 523940

Plzenske sterkopisky s.r.o. (1)
Krimice 61, 322 00, Plzen, Czech Republic
Tel.: (420) 602 28 97 09
Construction Materials Whslr
N.A.I.C.S.: 423390

Precon Polska Sp.z o.o. (1)
ul Domaniewska 47, 02-672, Warsaw, Poland
Tel.: (48) 22 622 2209
Web Site: https://www.precon.com.pl
Precast Concrete Mfr
N.A.I.C.S.: 327390

RST Ralf Schmidt Tiefbau, Kabel & Kabelrohrverlegung GmbH (1)
Heidering 12 Platz 1 und Verwaltung Heidering 18 Platz 2 und Logistik, 16727, Velten, Germany
Tel.: (49) 3304244300
Web Site: https://rst-tiefbau.de
Construction & Civil Engineering Services
N.A.I.C.S.: 541330

RWG I Abbruch und Tiefbau GmbH (1)
Wiesendamm 32, 13597, Berlin, Germany
Tel.: (49) 3070193220
Web Site: https://at.garbe-gruppe.de
Demolition & Civil Engineering Services
N.A.I.C.S.: 541330

RWG I/Schicht Baustoffaufbereitung, Logistik + Entsorgung GmbH (1)
Wiesendamm 32, 13597, Berlin, Germany
Tel.: (49) 3070193220
Web Site: https://schicht.garbe-gruppe.de
Logistics & Container Services
N.A.I.C.S.: 541614

Recem S.A. (1)
Rue de Merl 74, 2146, Luxembourg, 2146, Luxembourg
Tel.: (352) 496951
Web Site: http://www.marsh.com
Emp.: 35
Business Support Services
N.A.I.C.S.: 561499
Claude Weber (Gen Mgr)

Redbank Manufacturing Company Limited (1)
Atherstone Road, Measham, Swadlincote, DE12 7EL, Derbyshire, United Kingdom
Tel.: (44) 1530 270333
Sales Range: $25-49.9 Million
Emp.: 60
Concrete Products Mfr
N.A.I.C.S.: 327390
Peter Cobb (Gen Mgr-Sls)

Rederij Cement-Tankvaart B.V. (1)
Keizersveer 3c, 4941 TA, Raamsdonksveer, Netherlands
Tel.: (31) 115680911
Web Site: https://www.rctbv.nl
Inland Freight Water Transport Services
N.A.I.C.S.: 483211

Rempel Bros. Concrete Ltd. (1)
8955 Shaughnessy Street, PO Box 2300, Vancouver, V6P 3Y7, BC, Canada
Tel.: (604) 525-9344
Web Site: http://www.rempelbros.com
Concrete Product Mfr & Distr
N.A.I.C.S.: 327320
Andrew Porth (Mgr-Sls)

Renor AS (1)
Kompveien 1353, Aurskog, 1930, Norway
Tel.: (47) 63 86 26 20
Emp.: 30
Waste Management Services
N.A.I.C.S.: 562998

Roewekamp GmbH (1)
Buschgrundstr 8, 45894, Gelsenkirchen, Germany
Tel.: (49) 209 93 06 80
Construction Materials Distr
N.A.I.C.S.: 423320

Roewekamp GmbH & Co Kommanditgesellschaft (1)
Buschgrundstr 8, 45894, Gelsenkirchen, Germany

Tel.: (49) 209 9332596
Construction Materials Distr
N.A.I.C.S.: 423320

Rostocker Zementumschlagsgesellschaft mbH (1)
Ost-West-Strasse 12, 18147, Rostock, Germany
Tel.: (49) 3816730042
Web Site: https://www.rzu-gmbh.de
Concrete Material Mfr
N.A.I.C.S.: 324121

SABIA spol. s.r.o. (1)
Masarykova 190, 411 56, Bohusovice nad Ohri, Czech Republic
Tel.: (420) 416 738 985
Construction Materials Distr
N.A.I.C.S.: 423320

SEFA Transportation, LLC (1)
219 Cedar Rd, Lexington, SC 29073
Tel.: (803) 358-1368
Web Site: https://sefatransportation.com
Fly Ash & Cement Transporting Services
N.A.I.C.S.: 532411

SER Sanierung im Erd- und Ruckbau GmbH (1)
Lichtenbergerstrasse 26, 74076, Heilbronn, Germany
Tel.: (49) 7131594900
Web Site: https://www.ser-gmbh.net
Construction Material Mfr & Distr
N.A.I.C.S.: 327390

SIA SBC (1)
Zeltinu Street 130, Marupes region, Marupes, 2167, Latvia
Tel.: (371) 6 740 8383
Web Site: https://www.sbc.lv
Fabricated Steel Mfr
N.A.I.C.S.: 332312
Victor Kurmelov (Mgr-Storage)

SJP 1 Limited (1)
City House 1/3 City Road, Newcastle, United Kingdom
Tel.: (44) 2072451245
Real Estate Development Services
N.A.I.C.S.: 531390

SMW Sand und Mortelwerk Verwaltungs-GmbH (1)
Karl-Marx-Str 98, Konigs Wusterhausen, 15751, Germany
Tel.: (49) 3375 578110
Emp.: 9
Construction Materials Whslr
N.A.I.C.S.: 423320
Siegfried Kaden (Mgr-Sls)

SP Bohemia, k.s. (1)
V Lukash 132, 267 01, Kraluv Dvur, Czech Republic
Tel.: (420) 601267600
Web Site: https://www.spbohemia.cz
Construction Sand & Gravel Mining Services
N.A.I.C.S.: 212321

SPRL Ferme de Wisempierre (1)
Rue de Wisempierre 1, Tournai, Belgium
Tel.: (32) 69844157
Investment Management Service
N.A.I.C.S.: 523940

SSR Schadstoffsanierung Rostock GmbH (1)
Wiesendamm 32, 13597, Berlin, Germany
Tel.: (49) 3070193270
Web Site: https://ssr.garbe-gruppe.de
Construction & Concrete Services
N.A.I.C.S.: 238110

Sagrex B.V. (1)
Laarstraat 5, 6653 KG, Deest, Netherlands
Tel.: (31) 487 516344
Web Site: http://www.sagrex.nl
Sales Range: $50-74.9 Million
Emp.: 7
Construction Materials Whslr
N.A.I.C.S.: 423320

Sagrex France S.A.S. (1)
Boulevard Henri Barbusse 6, 60150, Thourotte, France
Tel.: (33) 344239393
Web Site: https://www.granor.fr
Highway Construction Services
N.A.I.C.S.: 237310

Sagrex Holding B.V. (1)
Laarstraat 5, 6653 KG, Deest, Netherlands
Tel.: (31) 736401121
Web Site: http://www.sagrex.be
Investment Management Service
N.A.I.C.S.: 523999

Sagrex Productie B.V. (1)
Sint Teunislaan 1, 5231 BS, 's-Hertogenbosch, Netherlands
Tel.: (31) 736401170
Construction Materials Distr
N.A.I.C.S.: 423320

Samuel Wilkinson & Sons Limited (1)
Wellington Street, Derby, DE1 2LZ, United Kingdom
Tel.: (44) 870 525 8258
Investment Management Service
N.A.I.C.S.: 523940

Sandwerke Biesern GmbH (1)
Dittmannsdorfer Str 110, 09322, Penig, Germany
Tel.: (49) 37381 94721
Construction Materials Distr
N.A.I.C.S.: 423320

Scancem Central Africa Holding 1 AB (1)
Storgatan 33, 352 30, Vaxjo, Sweden
Tel.: (46) 47096590
Investment Management Service
N.A.I.C.S.: 523940

Scancem Central Africa Holding 3 AB (1)
Box 47055, 100 74, Stockholm, Sweden
Tel.: (46) 858796900
Investment Management Service
N.A.I.C.S.: 523999

Scancem International DA (1)
Lilleakerveien 2A, PO Box 17, Lilleaker, 0283, Oslo, Norway
Tel.: (47) 22013300
Web Site: https://www.heidelbergcement.com
Cement Mfr
N.A.I.C.S.: 327310

Seagoe Concrete Products Limited (1)
The Ridge Chipping Sodbury, Bristol, BS37 6AY, United Kingdom
Tel.: (44) 1454316000
Readymix Concrete Mfr
N.A.I.C.S.: 327320

Second City Properties Limited (1)
Hanson House 14 Castle Hill, Maidenhead, SL6 4JJ, United Kingdom
Tel.: (44) 2072451245
Investment Management Service
N.A.I.C.S.: 523940

Sementsverksmidjan ehf (1)
Manabraut 20, 300, Akranes, Iceland
Tel.: (354) 4305000
Web Site: https://www.sement.is
Cement Mfr
N.A.I.C.S.: 327310

Severoceske piskovny a sterkovny s.r.o. (1)
Roztyly 3, 438 01, Zatec, Czech Republic
Tel.: (420) 474 392 093
Construction Sand & Gravel Mining Services
N.A.I.C.S.: 212321

Shapedirect Limited (1)
1 Grosvenor Place, London, SW1X 7JH, United Kingdom
Tel.: (44) 2072451245
Investment Management Service
N.A.I.C.S.: 523940

Sherman Industries LLC (1)
246 Steele Station Rd, Rainbow City, AL 35906
Tel.: (256) 413-0377
Web Site: http://www.lehighhanson.com
Readymix Concrete Mfr
N.A.I.C.S.: 327320

Sola Betong AS (1)
Risavika Havnering 215, 4056, Tananger, Norway
Tel.: (47) 51644949

Web Site: https://www.sola-betong.no
Cement Mfr
N.A.I.C.S.: 327310

South Coast Basalt Pty Ltd (1)
Level 10 35 Clarence Street, Sydney, 2000, NSW, Australia
Tel.: (61) 293234000
Construction Materials Distr
N.A.I.C.S.: 423320

South Valley Materials, Inc. (1)
7761 Hanford Armona Rd, Hanford, CA 93230
Tel.: (559) 277-7060
Ready Mix Concrete Distr
N.A.I.C.S.: 423320

Plant (Domestic):

South Valley Materials, Inc. - Coalinga Plant (2)
38930 Hwy 33, Coalinga, CA 93210
Tel.: (559) 935-0764
Web Site: http://www.lehighsw.net
Readymix Concrete Mfr
N.A.I.C.S.: 327320

South Valley Materials, Inc. - Exeter Plant (2)
1132 N Belmont Rd, Exeter, CA 93221
Tel.: (559) 594-4142
Web Site: http://www.lehighsw.net
Sales Range: $25-49.9 Million
Emp.: 9
Readymix Concrete Mfr
N.A.I.C.S.: 327320

South Valley Materials, Inc. - Porterville Plant (2)
22157 Ave 152, Porterville, CA 93257
Tel.: (559) 784-6725
Web Site: http://www.lehighsw.net
Readymix Concrete Mfr
N.A.I.C.S.: 327320

South Valley Materials, Inc. - Tulare Plant (2)
3450 S Blackstone Ave, Tulare, CA 93274
Tel.: (559) 686-6171
Web Site: http://www.lehighsw.net
Concrete Mfr
N.A.I.C.S.: 327320

St Edouard S.a.r.l. (1)
14 Rue de la Prairie, 88100, Saint-Die-des-Vosges, France
Tel.: (33) 3 29 56 20 00
Construction Materials Distr
N.A.I.C.S.: 423320

Stahlsaiten Betonwerke GmbH (1)
Neubeckumer Str 92, 59320, Ennigerloh, Germany
Tel.: (49) 2524 290
Concrete Mfr
N.A.I.C.S.: 327320

Stema Shipping A/S (1)
Sydhavn 4 1 tv, 6200, Aabenraa, Denmark
Tel.: (45) 74627972
Concrete Material Mfr
N.A.I.C.S.: 324121

Stema Shipping France S.a.s. (1)
648 Chemin de la Breteque, 76230, Bois-Guillaume, France
Tel.: (33) 235650265
Concrete Material Mfr
N.A.I.C.S.: 324121

Structherm Holdings Limited (1)
Bent Ley Road Meltham, Meltham, HD9 4AP, West Yorkshire, United Kingdom
Tel.: (44) 1484850098
Web Site: http://www.structherm.co.uk
Sales Range: $50-74.9 Million
Emp.: 15
Investment Management Service
N.A.I.C.S.: 523999
Lawrie Newton (Mgr-Technical Sls-Central Reg)

Structherm Limited (1)
Bent Ley Rd, Meltham, Holmfirth, HD9 4AP, West Yorkshire, United Kingdom
Tel.: (44) 148 485 0098
Web Site: https://www.structherm.co.uk
Sales Range: $25-49.9 Million
Emp.: 15
Construction Engineering Services

HEIDELBERG MATERIALS AG

INTERNATIONAL PUBLIC

Heidelberg Materials AG—(Continued)
N.A.I.C.S.: 237990
David Harrison *(Mng Dir)*

Suez Cement Company (S.A.E.) (1)
K30 Maadi/Ain Sokhna Road, Cairo, 2691, Egypt
Tel.: (20) 225222000
Web Site:
https://www.heidelbergmaterials.eg
Rev.: $402,074,253
Assets: $500,136,287
Liabilities: $334,386,682
Net Worth: $165,749,605
Earnings: ($73,344,278)
Emp.: 1,421
Fiscal Year-end: 12/31/2019
Cement Mfr & Distr
N.A.I.C.S.: 327310

Subsidiary (Domestic):

Tourah Portland Cement Company (2)
Corniche El-Nil Helwan Road Tourah, PO Box 269, Cairo, Egypt **(66.12%)**
Tel.: (20) 2 27004316
Web Site: http://www.tourahcement.com.eg
Sales Range: $125-149.9 Million
Cement Mfr
N.A.I.C.S.: 327310
Omar Khorshid *(Dir-Technical)*

Suncoast Asphalt Pty. Ltd. (1)
187-193 Potassium St, Narangba, 4504, QLD, Australia
Tel.: (61) 733853300
Web Site:
https://www.suncoastasphalt.com.au
Emp.: 60
Readymix Concrete Mfr
N.A.I.C.S.: 327320

Svabo Kaross & Hydraulservice AB (1)
Kabelvagen 19, 291 62, Kristianstad, Sweden
Tel.: (46) 4 420 8140
Web Site: https://www.svabo.se
Sales Range: $25-49.9 Million
Emp.: 15
Hydraulic Handling & Lifting Contract Services
N.A.I.C.S.: 238290

TBG BAK s.r.o. (1)
Vodni 177, Trutnov, 541 01, Czech Republic
Tel.: (420) 499 800 111
Sales Range: $50-74.9 Million
Emp.: 100
Construction Materials Whslr
N.A.I.C.S.: 423320

TBG BETONMIX a. s. (1)
Jihlavska 709/51, 642 00, Brno, Czech Republic
Tel.: (420) 547427570
Web Site: https://www.transportbeton.cz
Readymix Concrete Mfr
N.A.I.C.S.: 327320
Radek Klimus *(Chm)*

TBG BETONPUMPY MORAVA s.r.o. (1)
Jihlavska 709/51, 642 00, Brno, Czech Republic
Tel.: (420) 547427582
Readymix Concrete Mfr
N.A.I.C.S.: 327320

TBG Ilm-Beton GmbH & Co. KG (1)
Feldstr 40, 99310, Rudisleben, Germany
Tel.: (49) 3628662616
Readymix Concrete Mfr
N.A.I.C.S.: 327320

TBG Transportbeton Elster-Spree Verwaltungs-GmbH (1)
Drewitzer Str 18, 03042, Cottbus, Germany
Tel.: (49) 355 726831
Business Management Consulting Services
N.A.I.C.S.: 541618

TBG Transportbeton Franken Geschaftsfuhrung GmbH (1)
Schwabacher Str 500, 90763, Furth, Germany
Tel.: (49) 911 9287 0

Concrete Mfr & Distr
N.A.I.C.S.: 327320

TBG Transportbeton GmbH & Co. KG (1)
Liebigstrasse 3 Ellmendingen, 75210, Keltern, Germany
Tel.: (49) 723693510
Web Site: https://www.tbg-ellmendingen.de
Ready Mix Concrete Distr
N.A.I.C.S.: 423320

TBG Transportbeton Kurpfalz GmbH & Co. KG (1)
Hermann-Wittmann-Strasse 1, Postfach 12 67, 69209, Eppelheim, Germany
Tel.: (49) 6221 79 20 0
Web Site: http://www.tbg-kurpfalz-beton.de
Sales Range: $25-49.9 Million
Emp.: 25
Ready Mix Concrete Mfr & Distr
N.A.I.C.S.: 327320
Alexander Humberg *(Gen Mgr)*

TBG Transportbeton Mainfranken Geschaftsfuhrungs GmbH (1)
Hans-Kleider Strasse 9, 97337, Dettelbach, Germany
Tel.: (49) 9324 30350
Sales Range: $25-49.9 Million
Emp.: 10
Readymix Concrete Mfr
N.A.I.C.S.: 327320
Thomas Wittmann *(Gen Mgr)*

TBG Transportbeton Reichenbach GmbH & Co. KG (1)
Alte Ziegelei 6 Vogtland, 08468, Reichenbach, Germany
Tel.: (49) 376513247
Readymix Concrete Mfr
N.A.I.C.S.: 327320

TBG Transportbeton Reichenbach Verwaltungs-GmbH (1)
Alte Ziegelei 6, Reichenbach, 8468, Germany
Tel.: (49) 3671576190
Investment Management Service
N.A.I.C.S.: 523999
Ralf Doehler *(Office Mgr)*

TBG Transportbeton Saalfeld Verwaltungs-GmbH (1)
Remschutzer Strasse 52, 07318, Saalfeld, Germany
Tel.: (49) 3671 57619 0
Web Site: http://www.betonwelt.de
Concrete Product Transportation Services
N.A.I.C.S.: 488999

TBG Transportbeton Schwarzenberg Verwaltungs-GmbH (1)
Strasse der Einheit 57, 08340, Schwarzenburg, Germany
Tel.: (49) 3774 51210
Web Site: http://www.heidelbergcement.com
Ready Mix Concrete Mfr & Distr
N.A.I.C.S.: 327320

TBG WIKA-Beton Verwaltungs-GmbH (1)
Auf Der Halloh 1, 21684, Stade, Germany
Tel.: (49) 4141 80390
Construction Materials Distr
N.A.I.C.S.: 423320

TBG ZNOJMO s. r. o. (1)
Dyje C Ev 502, 669 02, Dobsice, Czech Republic
Tel.: (420) 515 222 660
Web Site: http://www.heidelbergcement.com
Concrete Product Mfr & Distr
N.A.I.C.S.: 327390

TBH Transportbeton Hamburg GmbH & Co. KG (1)
Einsiedeldeich 15, 20539, Hamburg, Germany
Tel.: (49) 40 781107 0
Concrete Products Mfr
N.A.I.C.S.: 327390

TBH Transportbeton Hamburg Verwaltungs-GmbH (1)
Einsiedeldeich 15, 20539, Hamburg, Germany
Tel.: (49) 4078876270

Sales Range: $25-49.9 Million
Emp.: 30
Ready Mix Concrete Mfr & Distr
N.A.I.C.S.: 327320
Walter Heidelberg *(Gen Mgr)*

TBM Transportbeton-Gesellschaft mbH Marienfeld & Co. KG (1)
Max-Planck-Str 22 Marienfeld, 33428, Harsewinkel, Germany
Tel.: (49) 524 780 0078
Web Site: https://www.tbm-beton.de
Ready Mix Concrete Distr
N.A.I.C.S.: 423320

TBM Transportbeton-Gesellschaft mit beschrankter Haftung Marienfeld (1)
Max-Planck-Str 22, 33428, Cologne, Germany
Tel.: (49) 524780008
Construction Materials Distr
N.A.I.C.S.: 423320

TMC Pioneer Aggregates Limited (1)
Bulls Lodge Quarry Generals Lane, Boreham, CM3 3HR, Chelmsford, United Kingdom - England
Tel.: (44) 1245451644
Aggregate Mfr
N.A.I.C.S.: 327992

TRANS-SERVIS, Spol. S r.o. (1)
Kraluv Dvur 253, Beroun District, 267 01, Kraluv Dvur, Czech Republic
Tel.: (420) 602229267
Concrete Products Mfr
N.A.I.C.S.: 327390

Tanah Merah Quarry Sdn Bhd (1)
W501 Level 5 West Tower Wisma Consplant 1 No 2 Jalan Ss16/4, Subang Jaya, 47500, Selangor, Malaysia
Tel.: (60) 66674408
Emp.: 6
Gravel & Sand Mining Services
N.A.I.C.S.: 212321
Yong Jun Kang *(Mgr)*

The Holms Sand & Gravel Company (1985) (1)
Hanson House 14 Castle Hill, Maidenhead, SL6 4JJ, United Kingdom
Tel.: (44) 1454314400
Construction Sand & Gravel Mining Services
N.A.I.C.S.: 212321

The Pinden Plant & Processing Co. Limited (1)
Pinden Quarry, Dartford, DA2 8EA, United Kingdom
Tel.: (44) 1474707827
Concrete Products Mfr
N.A.I.C.S.: 327390

Tillotson Commercial Motors Limited (1)
1 Grosvenor Place, SW1X 7JH, London, United Kingdom - England
Tel.: (44) 2072451245
Investment Management Service
N.A.I.C.S.: 523940

Tinglev Elementfabrik GmbH (1)
Am Gewerbepark 8A, Altlandsberg, 15345, Brandenburg, Germany
Tel.: (49) 3 343 9860
Web Site: https://www.tinglev-elementfabrik.de
Emp.: 91
Foundation Component & Beam Mfr
N.A.I.C.S.: 327390

Transportbeton Bad Waldsee Geschaftsfuhrungs GmbH (1)
Deisenfangstr 43, 88212, Ravensburg, Baden-Wurttemberg, Germany
Tel.: (49) 7524 912591
Concrete Mfr & Distr
N.A.I.C.S.: 327320

Tulacement Limited Liability Company (1)
3 Zheleznodorozhnaya str, Aleksinsky District, Novogurovsky, 301382, Tula, Russia
Tel.: (7) 4875320000
Web Site: http://www.heidelbergcement.com
Cement Mfr
N.A.I.C.S.: 327310

UAB Gerdukas (1)
Technikos str 7K, 51209, Kaunas, Lithuania
Tel.: (370) 3 738 0832
Web Site: https://www.gerdukas.lt
Sales Range: $25-49.9 Million
Emp.: 15
Readymix Concrete Mfr
N.A.I.C.S.: 327320

UAB HC Betonas (1)
Technikos Str 7k, LT-51209, Kaunas, Lithuania
Tel.: (370) 837380832
Precast Concrete Mfr
N.A.I.C.S.: 327390

UAB Heidelberg Cement Klaipeda (1)
Svepeliu g 5, Klaipedos laisvoji ekonomine zona, Klaipeda, 94102, Lithuania
Tel.: (370) 6 098 8808
Web Site: https://www.gerdukas.lt
Sales Range: $25-49.9 Million
Emp.: 23
Concrete Products Mfr
N.A.I.C.S.: 327390
Povilas Bradulskis *(Gen Mgr)*

UDS (No 3) Limited (1)
Hanson House 14 Castle Hill, Maidenhead, SL6 4JJ, United Kingdom
Tel.: (44) 2072451245
Investment Management Service
N.A.I.C.S.: 523940

VAPIS stavebni hmoty s.r.o. (1)
V Lukach 132, 267 01, Beroun, Czech Republic
Tel.: (420) 311 644 705
Concrete Block Mfr
N.A.I.C.S.: 327331

Verwaltungsgesellschaft Baustoffwerke Dresden mbH (1)
Radeburger Str 30, 01129, Dresden, Germany
Tel.: (49) 351 817870
Construction Materials Distr
N.A.I.C.S.: 423320

Visionrefine Limited (1)
The Ridge Chipping Sodbury, Bristol, BS37 6AY, United Kingdom
Tel.: (44) 1454316000
Investment Management Service
N.A.I.C.S.: 523940

WIKA Stade GmbH u. Co. KG (1)
Auf Der Halloh 1, 21684, Stade, Germany
Tel.: (49) 414 18 03 90
Web Site: http://www.heidelbergcement.de
Emp.: 50
Construction Materials Whslr
N.A.I.C.S.: 423320
Bernd Klose *(Mng Dir)*

Walhalla Kalk GmbH & Co. KG (1)
Donaustaufer Strasse 207, 93055, Regensburg, Germany **(79.9%)**
Tel.: (49) 9 414 0250
Web Site: https://www.walhalla-kalk.de
Sales Range: $25-49.9 Million
Emp.: 120
Lime & Lime Products Mfr
N.A.I.C.S.: 327410
Johann Spangler *(Mgr-Sales)*

Walhalla Kalk Verwaltungsgesellschaft mbH (1)
Donaustaufer Str 207, 93055, Regensburg, Germany
Tel.: (49) 941 4025 0
Web Site: http://www.walhalla-kalk.de
Emp.: 100
Management Consulting Services
N.A.I.C.S.: 541618
Wolfgang Wegner *(Gen Mgr)*

Waterfall Quarries Pty Limited (1)
Pyrenees Highway, Carisbrook, 3464, VIC, Australia
Tel.: (61) 354642415
Construction Sand & Gravel Quarrying Services
N.A.I.C.S.: 212321

Welbecson Group Limited (1)
1 Grosvenor Place, London, SW1X 7JH, United Kingdom
Tel.: (44) 2072451245

AND PRIVATE COMPANIES

Investment Management Service
N.A.I.C.S.: 523940

betotech Munchen Verwaltungs GmbH (1)
Zamilastr 9, Munich, 81677, Germany
Tel.: (49) 89 9939300
Web Site: http://www.heidelbergcement.de
Administrative Management Services
N.A.I.C.S.: 541611

HEIDELBERG PHARMA AG
Gregor Mendel Strasse 22, 68526, Ladenburg, Germany
Tel.: (49) 620310090   De
Web Site: https://www.heidelberg-pharma.com
Year Founded: 1997
HPHA—(DEU)
Rev.: $18,546,441
Assets: $77,660,925
Liabilities: $23,195,976
Net Worth: $54,464,949
Earnings: ($22,459,969)
Emp.: 95
Fiscal Year-end: 11/30/23
Cancer Treatment Development Services
N.A.I.C.S.: 541715
Georg F. Baur *(Deputy Chm-Supervisory Bd)*

HEIDELBERGER BETEILIGUNGSHOLDING AG
Ziegelhaeuser Landstrasse 3, 69120, Heidelberg, Germany
Tel.: (49) 62216492430
Web Site: https://www.heidelberger-beteiligungsholding.de
HDD—(DEU)
Rev.: $9,160,602
Assets: $30,438,715
Liabilities: $12,477,811
Net Worth: $17,960,905
Earnings: ($4,132,039)
Fiscal Year-end: 12/31/20
Financial Investment Services
N.A.I.C.S.: 523940
Eva Katheder *(Chm-Supervisory Bd)*

HEIDELBERGER DRUCKMASCHINEN AG
Kurfuersten-Anlage 52-60, 69115, Heidelberg, Germany
Tel.: (49) 62219200
Web Site: https://www.heidelberg.com
HDD—(MUN)
Rev.: $2,584,707,950
Assets: $2,281,449,940
Liabilities: $1,712,706,270
Net Worth: $568,743,670
Earnings: $42,089,190
Emp.: 9,592
Fiscal Year-end: 03/31/24
Printing Machinery Mfr
N.A.I.C.S.: 333248
Dirk Kaliebe *(CFO, Member-Mgmt Bd & Head-Fin Svcs)*

Subsidiaries:

BluePrint Products N.V. (1)
Zwaluwbeekstraat 14, 9150, Kruibeke, Belgium
Tel.: (32) 37780337
Printing Chemical Product Mfr
N.A.I.C.S.: 325998
Kris Temmerman *(Mng Dir)*

Cerm N.V. (1)
Siemenslaan 17, Oostkamp, 8020, Brugge, Belgium
Tel.: (32) 50833883
Software Development Services
N.A.I.C.S.: 541511
Nico Delaere *(Mgr-IT Support)*

Docufy GmbH (1)
Kirschackerstrasse 27, 96052, Bamberg, Germany
Tel.: (49) 951208596
Software Development Services
N.A.I.C.S.: 541511
Ingo Buchardt *(Head-Sls)*

Gallus Druckmaschinen GmbH (1)
Steinbruchstrasse 5, Oberkleen, 35428, Langgons, Germany
Tel.: (49) 64479250
Printing Machinery Mfr
N.A.I.C.S.: 333248

Gallus Ferd. Ruesch AG (1)
Harzbuchelstrasse 34, 9016, Saint Gallen, Switzerland
Tel.: (41) 712428686
Web Site: https://www.gallus-group.com
Printing Machinery Mfr
N.A.I.C.S.: 333248
Frank Schaum *(Head-Bus Unit Label)*

Heidelberg Asia Pte Ltd. (1)
159 Kampong Ampat 05-02 KA Place, Singapore, 368328, Singapore
Tel.: (65) 69295320
Web Site: https://www.heidelberg.com
Sales Range: $25-49.9 Million
Emp.: 40
Commercial Printing Services
N.A.I.C.S.: 323111

Heidelberg Baltic Finland OU (1)
Karjavalja tn 10, 12918, Tallinn, Estonia
Tel.: (372) 6161390
Web Site: https://www.heidelberg.com
Printing Machinery & Equipment Mfr
N.A.I.C.S.: 333248
Liina Kivi *(Controller-Fin)*

Heidelberg Benelux B.V. (1)
Mollerusweg 102, 2031 BZ, Haarlem, Netherlands
Tel.: (31) 235121511
Printing Machinery Mfr
N.A.I.C.S.: 333248
Edwin Gronert *(Mgr-Back Office Sls)*

Heidelberg Benelux BVBA (1)
Kareelovenlaan 5 Avenue du Four a Briques, 1140, Brussels, Belgium
Tel.: (32) 27273111
Printing Machinery Mfr
N.A.I.C.S.: 333248
Edwin Huyghebaert *(CFO)*

Heidelberg Canada Graphic Equipment Ltd. (1)
5900 Keaton Crescent, Mississauga, L5R 3K2, ON, Canada   (100%)
Tel.: (905) 362-4400
Web Site: http://www.heidelberg.com
Sales Range: $75-99.9 Million
Emp.: 120
Distr of Printing Presses
N.A.I.C.S.: 423830

Heidelberg Catering Services GmbH (1)
Gutenbergring 19, 69168, Wiesloch, Germany
Tel.: (49) 6222825054
Emp.: 50
Catering Services
N.A.I.C.S.: 722320

Heidelberg China Ltd. (1)
Room 301 3rd Floor Building 10 Hengtong International Business Park, No 10 Jiuxianqiao Road Chaoyang District, Beijing, 100015, China
Tel.: (86) 1059624288
Web Site: http://www.heidelberg.com
Computer Peripheral Equipment Distr
N.A.I.C.S.: 423430

Heidelberg France S.A.S. (1)
13 Rue Charles Cros, 93294, Tremblay-en-France, Cedex, France
Tel.: (33) 149894200
Computer Peripheral Equipment Distr
N.A.I.C.S.: 423430

Heidelberg Grafik Ticaret Servis Limited Sirketi (1)
Yalcin Kores Cad No22 Erdinc Buildings A Block 1 Tower 4 Floor, Gunesli, 34212, Istanbul, Turkiye
Tel.: (90) 2124103700
Web Site: https://www.heidelberg.com
Emp.: 62

Printing Machinery Mfr
N.A.I.C.S.: 333248

Heidelberg Graphic Equipment (Shanghai) Co. Ltd. (1)
No 9928 Songze Road Qingpu Industrial Zone, Shanghai, 201700, China
Tel.: (86) 2139203000
Sales Range: $50-74.9 Million
Emp.: 410
Computer Peripheral Equipment Distr
N.A.I.C.S.: 423430

Heidelberg Graphic Equipment Limited (1)
1 Furzeground Way Stockley Park, Uxbridge, London, UB11 1EZ, United Kingdom   (100%)
Tel.: (44) 8448922010
Web Site: https://www.heidelberg.com
Sales Range: $50-74.9 Million
Emp.: 150
Mfr of Printing Presses
N.A.I.C.S.: 333248
Ryan Miles *(Mng Dir)*

Heidelberg Graphic Equipment Ltd. (1)
Unit 4/ 19-23 Geddes Street, PO Box 750, Mulgrave, 3170, VIC, Australia   (100%)
Tel.: (61) 300135135
Web Site: https://www.heidelberg.com
Sales Range: $75-99.9 Million
Emp.: 68
Distr of Printing Presses
N.A.I.C.S.: 423830

Subsidiary (Non-US):

Heidelberg Graphic Equipment Ltd. (2)
2c William Pickering Drive Rosedale, Albany, Auckland, 0632, New Zealand   (100%)
Tel.: (64) 94141124
Web Site: https://www.heidelberg.com
Sales Range: $25-49.9 Million
Emp.: 15
Mfr of Printing Presses
N.A.I.C.S.: 333248

Heidelberg Graphic Systems Southern Africa (Pty) Ltd (1)
Unit 4 Galaxy Park 17 Galaxy Avenue, Linbro Business Park, Johannesburg, 2090, South Africa
Tel.: (27) 115744000
Web Site: https://www.heidelberg.com
Sales Range: $50-74.9 Million
Emp.: 68
Computer Peripheral Equipment Distr
N.A.I.C.S.: 423430

Heidelberg Graphics (Thailand) Ltd. (1)
163 Ocean Insurance Bldg 19th Fl Surawongse Rd Suriyawongse, Bangrak, Bangkok, 10500, Thailand
Tel.: (66) 24915000
Printing Machinery Mfr
N.A.I.C.S.: 333248

Heidelberg Graphics Taiwan Ltd. (1)
16F No 655 Ban-Nan Road, Zhong-He District, New Taipei City, 23557, Taiwan
Tel.: (886) 222277200
Printing Machinery Mfr
N.A.I.C.S.: 333248

Heidelberg Hellas A.E.E. (1)
P Bakogianni 26, 144 51, Metamorfosis, Greece
Tel.: (30) 2102805500
Printing Equipment Whslr
N.A.I.C.S.: 423830
Michael Zervogiannakis *(VP)*

Heidelberg India Private Ltd. (1)
333 GST Road, Chrompet, Chennai, 600044, Tamil Nadu, India
Tel.: (91) 4443472000
Web Site: https://www.heidelbergindia.com
Printing Machinery Mfr
N.A.I.C.S.: 333248
Rajendra Prasad *(Mktg Mgr)*

Heidelberg International Ltd. A/S (1)
Industriparken 20 C, Ballerup, Denmark
Tel.: (45) 4487 8200
Bookbinding Machines Manufacturing

N.A.I.C.S.: 333248

Heidelberg Italia S.r.L. (1)
Via Trento 61, 20021, Ospiate di Bollate, MI, Italy
Tel.: (39) 0235003500
Printing Machinery Mfr
N.A.I.C.S.: 333248
Mauro Antonini *(Sls Mgr)*

Heidelberg Japan K.K. (1)
3-31-8 Higashi-Shinagawa, Shinagawa-ku, Tokyo, 140-8541, Japan
Tel.: (81) 357157255
Web Site: http://www.heidelberg.com
Sales Range: $125-149.9 Million
Emp.: 300
Commercial Printing Services
N.A.I.C.S.: 323111

Heidelberg Korea Ltd. (1)
Shinwon Plaza Building 85 Dokseodang-ro, Yongsan-gu, Seoul, 04419, Korea (South)
Tel.: (82) 2 795 8822
Web Site: http://www.heidelberg.com
Emp.: 70
Commercial Printing Services
N.A.I.C.S.: 323111

Heidelberg Magyarorszag Kft. (1)
Kek Duna u 5, Budakalasz, 2011, Budapest, Hungary
Tel.: (36) 26540520
Printing Machinery Mfr
N.A.I.C.S.: 333248
Boglarka Bodnar *(Head-Fin & Acctg)*

Heidelberg Malaysia Sdn Bhd (1)
Office Suite B-08-06 Block B Level 8 Sky Park One City Jalan USJ25/1, 47650, Subang Jaya, Selangor, Malaysia
Web Site: http://www.heidelberg.com.jp
Commercial Printing Services
N.A.I.C.S.: 323111

Heidelberg Manufacturing Deutschland GmbH (1)
Industriegebiet Egelsee, Amstetten, 73340, Tubingen, Germany
Tel.: (49) 7331310
Emp.: 850
Printing Machinery Mfr
N.A.I.C.S.: 333248

Heidelberg Mexico S. de R.L. de C.V. (1)
German Centre Av Santa Fe No 170 8 Piso Col Lomas de Santa Fe, Alvaro Obregon, 01219, Mexico, Mexico
Tel.: (52) 5550106210
Web Site: http://www.heidelberg.com
Commercial Printing Services
N.A.I.C.S.: 323111

Heidelberg Philippines, Inc. (1)
3rd Floor Molave Building 2231 Chino Roces Avenue, Makati, 1231, Philippines
Tel.: (63) 288575188
Printing Services
N.A.I.C.S.: 323111
Dennis Canoza *(Fin Mgr)*

Heidelberg Polska Sp z.o.o. (1)
ul East Sun 8, 02-226, Warsaw, Poland
Tel.: (48) 225789777
Sales Range: $75-99.9 Million
Emp.: 120
Computer Peripheral Equipment Distr
N.A.I.C.S.: 423430
Krzysztof Pindral *(Mng Dir)*

Heidelberg Postpress Deutschland GmbH (1)
Austr 50, 71642, Ludwigsburg, Germany   (100%)
Tel.: (49) 71415010
Web Site: http://www.heidelberg.com
Sales Range: $200-249.9 Million
Emp.: 160
Mfr of Paper Folders, Mailers, Bindery & Book Binding
N.A.I.C.S.: 322130

Subsidiary (US):

Baumfolder Corporation (2)
1660 Campbell Rd, Sidney, OH 45365   (50%)
Tel.: (937) 492-1281
Sales Range: $50-74.9 Million
Emp.: 135

HEIDELBERGER DRUCKMASCHINEN AG

Heidelberger Druckmaschinen AG—(Continued)
Mfr of Paper Folding Machines, Paper Cutters, Paper Drills, Gluers & Bindery
N.A.I.C.S.: 333243

Heidelberg Praha spol s.r.o. (1)
Safrankova 1243 / 3, 155 00, Prague, 5, Czech Republic
Tel.: (420) 225993111
Sales Range: $25-49.9 Million
Emp.: 40
Industrial Machinery Equipment Whslr
N.A.I.C.S.: 423830

Heidelberg Print Finance Americas, Inc (1)
2 International Dr 101, Portsmouth, NH 03801-6810
Tel.: (603) 433-8165
Sales Range: $50-74.9 Million
Emp.: 3
Computer Peripheral Equipment Distr
N.A.I.C.S.: 423430

Heidelberg Schweiz AG (1)
Brunnmattstrasse 20, 3001, Bern, Switzerland
Tel.: (41) 313850111
Web Site: http://www.heidelberg.com
Sales Range: $75-99.9 Million
Emp.: 160
Computer Peripheral Equipment Distr
N.A.I.C.S.: 423430

Heidelberg Slovensko s.r.o. (1)
Vajnorska 100 B, 831 04, Bratislava, Slovakia
Tel.: (421) 263810630
Industrial Machinery Whslr
N.A.I.C.S.: 423830
Jan Prochazka *(Mgr-Svcs)*

Heidelberg Spain S.L.U. (1)
Carretera de L Hospitalet 98-108, Cornella de Llobregat, 08940, Barcelona, Spain
Tel.: (34) 934758000
Printing Product Whslr
N.A.I.C.S.: 424110

Heidelberg Sverige AB (1)
Limhamnsgardens alle 27, 216 16, Limhamn, Sweden
Tel.: (46) 855566800
Web Site: http://www.heidelberg.com
Computer Peripheral Equipment Distr
N.A.I.C.S.: 423430

Heidelberg USA, Inc. (1)
1000 Gutenberg Dr, Kennesaw, GA 30144-7028 **(100%)**
Tel.: (770) 419-6500
Web Site: https://www.heidelberg.com
Sales Range: $300-349.9 Million
Emp.: 1,000
Distr of Printing Presses
N.A.I.C.S.: 423830

Heidelberg Web Carton Converting GmbH (1)
Am Forst 17, 92637, Weiden, Germany
Tel.: (49) 96139393
Emp.: 150
Printing Machinery & Equipment Mfr
N.A.I.C.S.: 333248

Heidelberg do Brasil Sistemas Graficos e Servicos Ltda (1)
Alameda Africa 734/756 Polo Empresarial Tambore, Santana de Parnaiba, 06543-306, SP, Brazil
Tel.: (55) 1155254500
Computer Peripheral Equipment Distr
N.A.I.C.S.: 423430

Heidelberger CIS OOO (1)
Smolnaya street 14 Business center floors 11 - 12, 125493, Moscow, Russia
Tel.: (7) 4959950490
Web Site: http://www.heidelberg.com
Printing Machinery & Supplies Whslr
N.A.I.C.S.: 423830

Heidelberger Druckmaschinen Austria Vertriebs-GmbH (1)
Karl-Farkas-Gasse 22, 1030, Vienna, Austria
Tel.: (43) 1601400
Printing Equipment Whslr
N.A.I.C.S.: 423830

Heidelberger Druckmaschinen Osteuropa Vertriebs-GmbH 4 (1)
Hebbelplatz 7, Vienna, 1100, Austria
Tel.: (43) 160 56 10
Industrial Machinery Equipment Whslr
N.A.I.C.S.: 423830

Heidelberger Druckmaschinen Ukraina Ltd. (1)
9 Stepana Bandery Avenue Office 3 403, 04073, Kiev, Ukraine
Tel.: (380) 444597050
Printing Machinery Mfr
N.A.I.C.S.: 333248

Heidelberger Druckmaschinen Vertrieb Deutschland GmbH (1)
Gutenbergring 19, 69168, Wiesloch, Germany
Tel.: (49) 62228267456
Web Site: https://www.heidelberg.com
Computer Peripheral Equipment Distr
N.A.I.C.S.: 423430

Menschick Trockensysteme GmbH (1)
Benzstrasse 56, 71272, Renningen, Germany
Tel.: (49) 71593049
Nozzle & Hot Air Dryer Mfr
N.A.I.C.S.: 335220

P.T. Heidelberg Indonesia (1)
Mulia Business Park Building E Jl MT Haryono Kav 58-60, Jakarta, 12780, Indonesia
Tel.: (62) 2127536800
Printing Equipment Whslr
N.A.I.C.S.: 423830
Niklas Kumpf *(Pres)*

Press Parts Outlet GmbH (1)
Karl-Farkas-Gasse 22, 1030, Vienna, Austria
Tel.: (43) 6644361002
Web Site: https://press-parts-outlet.com
Graphic Machinery Whslr
N.A.I.C.S.: 423830

Print Finance Vermittlung GmbH (1)
Kurfursten-anlage 52-60, Heidelberg, 69115, Germany
Tel.: (49) 6221924550
Web Site: http://www.heidelberger.com
Sales Range: $50-74.9 Million
Emp.: 1,000
Computer Peripheral Equipment Distr
N.A.I.C.S.: 423430
Alexander Mueller *(Mng Dir)*

Shenzhen Heidelberg NetworX Technology Co., Ltd. (1)
Room 1801 Block 1 Building B Smart Plaza No 4068 Qiaoxiang Road, Nanshan District, Shenzhen, China
Tel.: (86) 400 993 0080
Web Site: https://www.boxuni.com
Printing Services
N.A.I.C.S.: 323111

HEIJMANS N.V.

Graafsebaan 65, 5248 JT, Rosmalen, Netherlands NI
Web Site: http://www.heijmans.nl
HJN1—(DEU)
Rev.: $2,337,252,456
Assets: $1,474,332,708
Liabilities: $1,050,823,491
Net Worth: $423,509,217
Earnings: $65,937,741
Emp.: 5,487
Fiscal Year-end: 12/31/23
Engineering & Construction Services
N.A.I.C.S.: 237310
Ron Icke *(Vice Chm-Supervisory Bd)*

Subsidiaries:

Bouwcombinatie Intermezzo V.O.F. (1)
Graafsebaan 65, 5248 JT, Rosmalen, Noord-Brabant, Netherlands
Tel.: (31) 735435111
Sales Range: $300-349.9 Million
Emp.: 600
Property Development Services
N.A.I.C.S.: 531210

Breijn B.V. (1)
Graafsebaan 67, 5248 JT, Rosmalen, Noord-Brabant, Netherlands
Tel.: (31) 735435873
Web Site: http://www.breijn.nl
Sales Range: $75-99.9 Million
Emp.: 300
Construction Engineering Services
N.A.I.C.S.: 541330
Edwin van Osch *(Mgr-Geodesy)*

Burgers Ergon B.V. (1)
Boschdijk 780, PO Box 266, 5624 CL, Eindhoven, North Brabant, Netherlands
Tel.: (31) 402197197
Web Site: http://www.burgers-ergon.nl
Sales Range: $350-399.9 Million
Emp.: 1,300
Civil Engineering Services
N.A.I.C.S.: 541330

CMG Gesellschaft fur Baulogistik GmbH (1)
Robert-Bosch-Strasse 7-9, 48153, Munster, Germany
Tel.: (49) 2516 080 1801
Web Site: http://www.cmg-baulogistik.de
Construction Equipment Rental Services
N.A.I.C.S.: 238910

Dynniq Energy B.V. (1)
Grote Esch 816, 2841 MJ, Moordrecht, Netherlands
Tel.: (31) 202143520
Web Site: https://www.dynniq-energy.com
Eletric Power Generation Services
N.A.I.C.S.: 486210

Heijmans Bestcon B.V. (1)
Kanaaldijk 19, 5683 CR, Best, Netherlands
Tel.: (31) 49 936 6366
Web Site: http://www.bestcon.nl
Sales Range: $50-74.9 Million
Emp.: 26
Precast Concrete Products Mfr
N.A.I.C.S.: 327390
Ronald Keurntjes *(Mng Dir)*

Heijmans Beton- en Waterbouw B.V. (1)
Graafsebaan 67, 5248 JT, Rosmalen, Noord-Brabant, Netherlands
Tel.: (31) 735436611
Web Site: http://www.heijmansbetonenwaterbouw.nl
Sales Range: $400-449.9 Million
Emp.: 1,200
Civil Engineering Services
N.A.I.C.S.: 237990

Heijmans Energie B.V. (1)
Graafsebaan 65, 5248 JT, Rosmalen, Netherlands
Tel.: (31) 735436611
Real Estate Construction & Technology Services
N.A.I.C.S.: 531320

Heijmans Infra Geintegreerde Projecten B.V. (1)
Graafsebaan 67, 5248 JT, Rosmalen, Netherlands
Tel.: (31) 735435111
Web Site: http://www.heijmans.nl
Civil Engineering Services
N.A.I.C.S.: 541330
T. Hillen *(Gen Mgr)*

Heijmans Nederland B.V. (1)
Graafsebaan 65, 5248 JT, Rosmalen, Netherlands
Tel.: (31) 735435111
Web Site: https://www.heijmans.nl
Sales Range: $1-4.9 Billion
Emp.: 7,000
Industrial Building Construction Services
N.A.I.C.S.: 236210

Heijmans Techniek en Mobiliteit B.V. (1)
Ertveldweg 31-33, 5231 XA, Den Bosch, North Brabant, Netherlands
Tel.: (31) 736484111
Web Site: http://www.heijmanstechniekenmobiliteit.nl
Sales Range: $50-74.9 Million
Emp.: 200
Highway Construction & Maintenance Services
N.A.I.C.S.: 237310

INTERNATIONAL PUBLIC

Heijmans Technische Infra B.V. (1)
Beurdsestraat 30, 5211 JB, 's-Hertogenbosch, Netherlands **(100%)**
Tel.: (31) 786801801
Public Works Contractor; Public Lighting & Traffic Management Services
N.A.I.C.S.: 238210

Heijmans Vastgoed B.V. (1)
Oostmaaslaan 71, 3063 AN, Rotterdam, Netherlands
Tel.: (31) 102510350
Sales Range: $50-74.9 Million
Emp.: 60
Residential Property Development Services
N.A.I.C.S.: 531210
Dick Laheij *(Dir-Dev)*

Heijmans Vastgoed Participaties B.V. (1)
Roosevelttweg 11-1e verd, 1314 SJ, Almere, Utrecht, Netherlands
Tel.: (31) 334224600
Sales Range: $75-99.9 Million
Emp.: 130
Real Estate Property Development Services
N.A.I.C.S.: 531210

Heijmans Vastgoed Realisatie B.V. (1)
Graafsebaan 65, 5248 JT, Rosmalen, Noord-Brabant, Netherlands
Tel.: (31) 735435111
Commercial Property Development Services
N.A.I.C.S.: 531210

Heijmans Woningbouw B.V. (1)
Graafsebaan 65, 5248 JT, Rosmalen, Netherlands
Tel.: (31) 735435111
Web Site: https://www.heijmans.nl
Sales Range: $75-99.9 Million
Emp.: 120
Residential Property Development & Construction Services
N.A.I.C.S.: 236116

Heijmans Woningbouw B.V. (1)
Graafsebaan 65, 5248 JT, Rosmalen, Netherlands
Tel.: (31) 735435111
Web Site: https://www.heijmans.nl
Sales Range: $75-99.9 Million
Emp.: 120
Residential Property Development & Construction Services
N.A.I.C.S.: 236116

Subsidiary: (Domestic)

Heijmans Burgh Haamstede B.V. (2)
De Roterij 24, Burgh, 4328 BA, Haamstede, Zeeland, Netherlands
Tel.: (31) 111651710
Web Site: http://www.heijmansburgh.nl
Sales Range: $25-49.9 Million
Emp.: 60
Housing Building Construction Services
N.A.I.C.S.: 236116

Reukers B.V. (2)
Parallelweg 8, 7141 DC, Groenlo, Gelderland, Netherlands
Tel.: (31) 544478888
Web Site: http://www.reukers.nl
Sales Range: $25-49.9 Million
Emp.: 45
Real Estate Property Development Services
N.A.I.C.S.: 531210

Walcherse Bouwunie B.V. (2)
Molenstraat 4, 4364 AA, Grijpskerke, Zeeland, Netherlands
Tel.: (31) 118595900
Web Site: http://www.heijmansbouwzeeland.com
Sales Range: $75-99.9 Million
Real Estate Property Development Services
N.A.I.C.S.: 531210

Heijmans Woningbouw B.V. (1)
Graafsebaan 65, 5248 JT, Rosmalen, Netherlands
Tel.: (31) 735435111
Web Site: https://www.heijmans.nl
Sales Range: $75-99.9 Million
Emp.: 120
Residential Property Development & Construction Services
N.A.I.C.S.: 236116

AND PRIVATE COMPANIES

Heijmans Woningbouw B.V. (1)
Graafsebaan 65, 5248 JT, Rosmalen, Netherlands
Tel.: (31) 735435111
Web Site: https://www.heijmans.nl
Sales Range: $75-99.9 Million
Emp.: 120
Residential Property Development & Construction Services
N.A.I.C.S.: 236116

Subsidiary (Domestic):

Heijmans Burgh Haamstede B.V. (2)
De Roterij 24, Burgh, 4328 BA, Haamstede, Zeeland, Netherlands
Tel.: (31) 111651710
Web Site: http://www.heijmansburgh.nl
Sales Range: $25-49.9 Million
Emp.: 60
Housing Building Construction Services
N.A.I.C.S.: 236116

Reukers B.V. (2)
Parallelweg 8, 7141 DC, Groenlo, Gelderland, Netherlands
Tel.: (31) 544478888
Web Site: http://www.reukers.nl
Sales Range: $25-49.9 Million
Emp.: 45
Real Estate Property Development Services
N.A.I.C.S.: 531210

Walcherse Bouwunie B.V. (2)
Molenstraat 4, 4364 AA, Grijpskerke, Zeeland, Netherlands
Tel.: (31) 118595900
Web Site: http://www.heijmansbouwzeeland.com
Sales Range: $75-99.9 Million
Real Estate Property Development Services
N.A.I.C.S.: 531210

Oevermann Hochbau GmbH (1)
Teutoburger Weg 5, 33332, Gutersloh, Germany
Tel.: (49) 524186090
Web Site: http://www.oevermann.com
Sales Range: $50-74.9 Million
Emp.: 250
Civil Engineering & Construction Services
N.A.I.C.S.: 236116

Oevermann Ingenieurbau GmbH (1)
Robert-Bosch-Str 7-9, 48153, Munster, Nordrhein-Westfalen, Germany
Tel.: (49) 25176010
Web Site: http://www.oevermann.com
Construction Engineering Services
N.A.I.C.S.: 541330

Oevermann Verkehrswegebau GmbH (1)
Robert Bosch Strasse 7-9, 48153, Munster, Nordrhein-Westfalen, Germany
Tel.: (49) 2517601301
Construction Engineering Services
N.A.I.C.S.: 541330

Partners in Bouwen (1)
Handelsweg 2, 1271 EJ, Huizen, Netherlands
Tel.: (31) 355263136
Web Site: http://www.vosenteeuwissen.nl
Residential Property Development Services
N.A.I.C.S.: 531210
Erik Vos *(Mng Dir)*

Wegenbouwmaatschappij J. Heijmans B.V. (1)
Graafsebaan 67, 5248 JT, Rosmalen, Noord-Brabant, Netherlands
Tel.: (31) 735436600
Housing Building Construction Services
N.A.I.C.S.: 236116

HEILONGJIANG AGRICLTURE COMPANY LIMITED
No 263 Hanshui Road, Nangang District, Harbin, 150090, Heilongjiang, China
Tel.: (86) 45155195980
Web Site: http://www.hacl.cn
Year Founded: 1998
600598—(SHG)
Rev.: $598,324,709
Assets: $1,155,224,229
Liabilities: $179,312,730
Net Worth: $975,911,499
Earnings: $136,930,941
Fiscal Year-end: 12/31/22
Agricultural Product Production & Distr
N.A.I.C.S.: 111199
Ma Zhongzhi *(Gen Mgr & Dir)*

HEILONGJIANG INTERCHINA WATER TREATMENT CO., LTD.
10F InterChina Business Building No 33 Dengshikou Avenue, Dongcheng District, Beijing, 100006, China
Tel.: (86) 1051695607
Web Site: http://www.interchina.com
600187—(SHG)
Rev.: $40,378,787
Assets: $564,501,675
Liabilities: $117,972,504
Net Worth: $446,529,171
Earnings: ($16,259,345)
Fiscal Year-end: 12/31/22
Sewage Treatment Services
N.A.I.C.S.: 221320
Jun Yin *(Chm)*

HEILONGJIANG TRANSPORT DEVELOPMENT CO., LTD.
No 1688 Qunli 5th Avenue, Daoli District, Harbin, 150070, Heilongjiang, China
Tel.: (86) 45151688007 CN
Web Site: http://www.hljjt.com
Year Founded: 2010
601188—(SHG)
Rev.: $61,112,259
Assets: $733,722,678
Liabilities: $71,144,050
Net Worth: $662,578,628
Earnings: $17,313,623
Emp.: 454
Fiscal Year-end: 12/31/22
Real Estate & Transportation Services
N.A.I.C.S.: 531390
Yisong Sun *(Chm)*

HEILONGJIANG ZBD PHARMACEUTICAL CO., LTD.
No 72 Hongxing Street, Hulin Town, Jixi, 158400, Heilongjiang, China
Tel.: (86) 45186811969
Web Site: https://www.zbdzy.com
Year Founded: 1996
603567—(SHG)
Rev.: $592,404,223
Assets: $1,639,236,760
Liabilities: $641,434,683
Net Worth: $997,802,077
Earnings: $26,028,854
Fiscal Year-end: 12/31/22
Pharmaceutical Product Mfr & Distr
N.A.I.C.S.: 325412
Xiuping Ge *(CFO)*

HEIMAR HF.
Hagasmari 1, IS-201, Kopavogur, Iceland
Tel.: (354) 5128900
Web Site: https://www.reginn.is
Year Founded: 2009
REGINN—(ICE)
Rev.: $100,694,343
Assets: $1,409,625,786
Liabilities: $987,333,723
Net Worth: $422,292,063
Earnings: $27,905,277
Emp.: 28
Fiscal Year-end: 12/31/23
Commercial Property Mgr & Leasing Services
N.A.I.C.S.: 531312
Tomas Kristjansson *(Chm)*

Subsidiaries:

Kvikmyndahollin ehf. (1)
Borgantun 25/105, Reykjavik, Iceland
Tel.: (354) 5128906
Real Estate Manangement Services
N.A.I.C.S.: 531390

HEIMSTADEN AB
Ostra Promenaden 7 A, 211 28, Malmo, Sweden
Tel.: (46) 770111050 SE
Web Site: https://corporate.heimstaden.com
Year Founded: 1998
HEIM-PREF—(OMX)
Rev.: $1,428,624,950
Assets: $34,374,666,329
Liabilities: $21,455,974,224
Net Worth: $12,918,692,105
Earnings: ($2,369,646,052)
Emp.: 1,967
Fiscal Year-end: 12/31/23
Real Estate Manangement Services
N.A.I.C.S.: 531190
Magnus Nordholm *(Deputy CEO & Head-ECM & Partners)*

HEINKEL PROCESS TECHNOLOGY GMBH
Ferdinand-Porsche-Strasse 8, 74354, Besigheim, Germany
Tel.: (49) 714396920
Web Site: http://www.heinkel.com
Year Founded: 1884
Sales Range: $10-24.9 Million
Emp.: 150
Centrifuge Mfr
N.A.I.C.S.: 333998
Thomas G. Kleiner *(Mng Dir)*

Subsidiaries:

Heinkel Filtering Systems Inc. (1)
520 Sharptown Rd, Swedesboro, NJ 08085-1731 (100%)
Tel.: (856) 467-3399
Web Site: http://www.heinkel.com
Marketing & Sales of Industrial Centrifuges & Filter Presses
N.A.I.C.S.: 333998
Alan Ferraro *(Pres)*

HEINRICH BAUER VERLAG KG
Burchardstrasse 11, 20077, Hamburg, Germany
Tel.: (49) 4030190 De
Web Site: http://www.bauermedia.com
Year Founded: 1875
Sales Range: $1-4.9 Billion
Emp.: 8,700
Multimedia Holding Company; Periodical & Internet Publishing; Radio & Television Broadcasting Stations Operator
N.A.I.C.S.: 551112
John Mulvey *(Editor-MOJO)*

Subsidiaries:

Bauer Media AS (1)
Jernbanetorget 4A, 0154, Oslo, Norway
Tel.: (47) 22023200
Web Site: http://www.bauermedia.no
Media Services
N.A.I.C.S.: 541840

Bauer Media ApS (1)
Mileparken 20A, 2740, Skovlunde, Denmark
Tel.: (45) 33119000
Web Site: http://www.bauermedia.dk
Marketing & Advertising Services
N.A.I.C.S.: 541613
Rune Schwartz *(Mgr-Innovation)*

Bauer Media France SNC (1)
7 rue Watt, 75013, Paris, France
Tel.: (33) 140227500
Web Site: http://www.bauermedia.fr
Publishing Services
N.A.I.C.S.: 323111

Bauer Media Group AB (1)
Gjorwellsgatan 30, 112 60, Stockholm, Sweden
Tel.: (46) 84503300
Web Site: http://www.bauermedia.se
Media Services
N.A.I.C.S.: 541840

Bauer Media Oy (1)
Tallberginkatu 1 C, 00180, Helsinki, Finland
Tel.: (358) 207474000
Web Site: http://www.bauermedia.fi
Media Services
N.A.I.C.S.: 541840
Sampsa Savolainen *(Sls Dir)*

Bauer Print Ciechanow Sp. z o.o. (1)
ul Niechodzka 25, Ciechanow, 06-400, Warsaw, Poland
Tel.: (48) 236731900
Commercial Printing Services
N.A.I.C.S.: 323111

Bauer Print Wykroty Sp. z o.o. (1)
ul Wyzwolenia 54, Wykroty Nowogrodziec, 59-730, Boleslawiec, Poland
Tel.: (48) 757350888
Commercial Printing Services
N.A.I.C.S.: 323111
Robert Zagdanski *(Mgr-Prepress & Engraving)*

H. Bauer Publishing Ltd. (1)
Academic House 24-28 Oval Rd, London, NW1 7DT, United Kingdom
Tel.: (44) 2072418000
Web Site: http://www.bauer.co.uk
Sales Range: $125-149.9 Million
Emp.: 300
Magazine Publishing & Radio Broadcasting Services
N.A.I.C.S.: 513120
Julia Toni *(Head-Digital Mktg)*

Subsidiary (Domestic):

Bauer Consumer Media Ltd. (2)
Endeavour House, 189 Shaftesbury Avenue, London, WC2 8JG, United Kingdom
Tel.: (44) 2074379011
Web Site: http://www.bauermedia.co.uk
Emp.: 650
Magazine Publisher
N.A.I.C.S.: 513120
Paul Keenan *(CEO)*

Unit (Domestic):

Bauer Specialist Media (3)
Media House, Lynchwood, Peterborough, PE2 6EA, United Kingdom
Tel.: (44) 1733468000
Web Site: http://www.bauer.co.uk
Sales Range: $200-249.9 Million
Emp.: 650
Automotive, Specialty & Hobbies Magazine Publisher
N.A.I.C.S.: 513120
Rob Munro-Hall *(Mng Dir)*

Joint Venture (Domestic):

Box Television Ltd. (3)
Mappin House 4, Winsley Street, London, W1W 8HF, United Kingdom (50%)
Tel.: (44) 2071828000
Web Site: http://www.boxtv.co.uk
Sales Range: $25-49.9 Million
Emp.: 60
Cable Television Broadcasting
N.A.I.C.S.: 516210
Matt Rennie *(Mng Dir)*

Subsidiary (Domestic):

Choice Publishing Ltd (3)
1st Floor 2 Kings Street, Peterborough, PE1 1LT, United Kingdom
Tel.: (44) 1733555123
Web Site: http://www.choicemag.co.uk
Sales Range: $25-49.9 Million
Emp.: 8
Magazine Publisher
N.A.I.C.S.: 513120

Subsidiary (Non-US):

Bauer Media Group (2)
54-58 Park St, Sydney, 2000, NSW, Australia (100%)
Tel.: (61) 292828000

HEINRICH BAUER VERLAG KG

Heinrich Bauer Verlag KG—(Continued)
Web Site: http://www.bauermedia.com.au
Magazine Publisher & Distr
N.A.I.C.S.: 513120
Andrew Stedwell (CFO)

Subsidiary (Non-US):

Bauer Digital KG (3)
Messberg 1, 20067, Hamburg, Germany
Tel.: (49) 40 3019 1792
Web Site: http://www.bauermedia.com
Emp.: 140
Digital Advertising Services
N.A.I.C.S.: 541850
Sven-Olof Reimers (Co-Mng Dir)

Bauer Media AB (3)
Gjorwellsgatan 30, 100 26, Stockholm, Sweden
Tel.: (46) 8 450 3300
Web Site: http://www.bauermedia.se
Radio Broadcasting Stations
N.A.I.C.S.: 516110
Staffan Rosell (CEO)

Bauer Media New Zealand (3)
90 Wellesley Street West, Westhaven, Auckland, 1010, New Zealand **(100%)**
Tel.: (64) 93082700
Web Site: http://www.bauermedia.co.nz
Sales Range: $125-149.9 Million
Emp.: 400
Magazine Publisher Services
N.A.I.C.S.: 513120
Brendon Hill (CEO)

Bauer Media Polska sp. z o.o. (3)
ul Motorowa 1, 04-035, Warsaw, Poland
Tel.: (48) 22 517 03 81
Web Site: http://www.bauer.pl
Magazine Publisher
N.A.I.C.S.: 513120

Bauer Media SK v.o.s. (3)
Digital Park II, Einsteinova ul 23, 851 01, Bratislava, Slovakia
Tel.: (421) 2 33 33 57 00
Web Site: http://www.bauermedia.sk
Magazine Publisher
N.A.I.C.S.: 513120
Samkova Romana (Mgr)

Bauer Media v.o.s. (3)
Moulikova 1b/3286, 150 00, Prague, Czech Republic
Tel.: (420) 2 25 00 81 11
Web Site: http://www.bauermedia.cz
Magazine Publisher
N.A.I.C.S.: 513120
Vit Fiala (Dir-Advertisement)

Bauer Sichuan Culture Service Co.Ltd. (3)
Room 1808 LT Square No 500 North Chengdu Road, 200003, Shanghai, China
Tel.: (86) 21 63 60 63 09
Web Site: http://www.smartshe.com
Newspaper & Magazine Publisher
N.A.I.C.S.: 513110

Division (Domestic):

Bauer Trader Media (3)
73 Atherton Rd, Oakleigh, 3166, VIC, Australia **(100%)**
Tel.: (61) 395674200
Web Site: http://www.traderclassifieds.com.au
Emp.: 200
Classifieds Magazine Publisher & Distr
N.A.I.C.S.: 513120
Keith Falconer (CEO)

Subsidiary (Non-US):

Bauer Vertriebs KG (3)
Brieffach 4000, 20086, Hamburg, Germany
Tel.: (49) 40 3019 0
Newspaper & Magazine Publisher
N.A.I.C.S.: 513110
Anke Schneider (Mgr-CRM)

Subsidiary (Domestic):

Pacific Magazines Pty. Ltd. (3)
Media City 8 Central Avenue, Eveleigh, Sydney, 2015, NSW, Australia
Tel.: (61) 293942000
Web Site: http://www.pacificmags.com.au
Sales Range: $200-249.9 Million
Emp.: 700
Magazine Publisher
N.A.I.C.S.: 513120
Gereurd Roberts (CEO)

Subsidiary (Non-US):

Phoenix Press Ltd L.P. (3)
ul Sw Antoniego 7, 50-073, Wroclaw, Poland
Tel.: (48) 71 344 98 13
Web Site: http://www.phoenix.pl
Newspaper & Magazine Publisher
N.A.I.C.S.: 513110

bookandsmile (3)
Inselstrasse 20, 04103, Leipzig, Germany
Tel.: (49) 341 30 89 51 21
Web Site: http://www.billigflieger.de
Online Travel Ticket Booking Services
N.A.I.C.S.: 513130
Michael Rehs (CEO)

Subsidiary (US):

Bauer Publishing USA (2)
270 Sylvan Ave, Englewood Cliffs, NJ 07632
Tel.: (201) 569-6699
Web Site: http://www.bauerpublishing.com
Sales Range: $25-49.9 Million
Emp.: 300
Magazine Publisher
N.A.I.C.S.: 513120
Dennis Cohen (Sr VP-Subscriptions & Licensing)

Unit (Domestic):

In Touch Weekly (3)
270 Sylvan Ave, Englewood Cliffs, NJ 07632
Tel.: (201) 569-6699
Web Site: http://www.intouchweekly.com
Magazine
N.A.I.C.S.: 513130
Jo Piazza (Exec Dir-News)

Subsidiary (Domestic):

Bauer Radio Ltd. (2)
Castle Quay, Castlefield, Manchester, M15 4PR, United Kingdom
Tel.: (44) 1612885000
Web Site: http://www.key103.co.uk
Sales Range: $25-49.9 Million
Emp.: 100
Radio Station Operator
N.A.I.C.S.: 516110
Steve Parkinson (Mng Dir-London)

Subsidiary (Domestic):

Absolute Radio Ltd. (3)
1 Golden Square, London, W1F 9DJ, United Kingdom
Tel.: (44) 2074341215
Web Site: http://www.absoluteradio.co.uk
Sales Range: $25-49.9 Million
Emp.: 100
Radio Broadcasting Services
N.A.I.C.S.: 516110
Cat Martin (Dir-Comm)

Key 103 (3)
Castle Quay, Castlefield, Manchester, M15 4PR, United Kingdom
Tel.: (44) 1612885000
Web Site: http://www.key103.co.uk
Sales Range: $50-74.9 Million
Radio Stations
N.A.I.C.S.: 516110
Kate Cocker (Controller-Content)

Kiss 100 (3)
Mappin House 4 Winsley Street, London, W1W 8HF, United Kingdom
Tel.: (44) 2071828000
Web Site: http://www.kissfm.com
Sales Range: $25-49.9 Million
Emp.: 50
Radio Stations
N.A.I.C.S.: 516110
Steve Parkinson (Mng Dir)

Metro Radio (3)
55 Degrees N Pilgrim St, Newcastle upon Tyne, NE1 6BF, United Kingdom
Tel.: (44) 1912306100
Web Site: http://www.metroradio.co.uk
Sales Range: $25-49.9 Million
Emp.: 54
Radio Stations
N.A.I.C.S.: 516110

Radio Aire Ltd (3)
51 Burley Rd, Leeds, LS3 1LR, W Yorkshire, United Kingdom
Tel.: (44) 1132835500
Web Site: http://www.radioaire.com
Sales Range: $25-49.9 Million
Emp.: 25
Radio Stations
N.A.I.C.S.: 516110

Radio City Ltd. (3)
Saint Johns Beacon, 1 Houghton Street, Liverpool, L1 1RL, United Kingdom
Tel.: (44) 1514726800
Web Site: http://www.radiocity.co.uk
Sales Range: $25-49.9 Million
Emp.: 60
Radio Station Services
N.A.I.C.S.: 516110
Chris Rick (Controller-Program)

TFM Radio (3)
55 degrees N Pilgrim St, Thornaby, Newcastle, NE1 6BL, United Kingdom
Tel.: (44) 1912306100
Web Site: http://www.tfmradio.co.uk
Radio Stations
N.A.I.C.S.: 516110
Dominic Mennelly (Dir-Station)

Viking Radio Ltd. (3)
The Boathouse, Commercial Rd, Hull, HU1 2SG, Yorkshire, United Kingdom
Tel.: (44) 1482325141
Web Site: http://www.vikingfm.co.uk
Sales Range: $25-49.9 Million
Emp.: 25
Radio Stations
N.A.I.C.S.: 516110

Subsidiary (Domestic):

Frontline Limited (2)
Mitgata House 117 Park Road, Peterborough, PE1 1TN, United Kingdom
Tel.: (44) 1733555161
Web Site: http://www.frontlineltd.co.uk
Sales Range: $50-74.9 Million
Emp.: 120
Magazine Distribution
N.A.I.C.S.: 513120

Heinrich Bauer Produktions KG (1)
Burchardstrasse 11, 20077, Hamburg, Germany
Tel.: (49) 4030192499
Commercial Printing Services
N.A.I.C.S.: 323111

HEINRICH DE FRIES GMBH

Gauss Str 20, 40235, Dusseldorf, Germany
Tel.: (49) 21123070
Web Site: http://www.hadef.com
Year Founded: 1904
Rev.: $24,829,200
Emp.: 115
Hoist Winches & Cranes Mfr
N.A.I.C.S.: 333924
Wolfgang Reinecke (Gen Mgr-Sls Dept)

Subsidiaries:

HADEF France Manutention et Levage Industriel SARL (1)
ZAC Bois St Pierre, 38280, Janneyrias, France
Tel.: (33) 478900411
Web Site: http://www.hadef.fr
Industrial Machinery Whslr
N.A.I.C.S.: 423830

LM MASKIN AS (1)
Hasleveien 15, 0571, Oslo, Norway
Tel.: (47) 23392250
Web Site: http://www.lm-maskin.no
Industrial Machinery Whslr
N.A.I.C.S.: 423830

Traditie N. V. (1)
Hijstraditie Bettoweg 19, 3125 AB, Schiedam, Netherlands
Tel.: (31) 104151266

Web Site: http://www.hadef.nl
Industrial Machinery Whslr
N.A.I.C.S.: 423830

HEINRICH DEHN INTERNATIONALE SPEDITION GMBH

Liebigstrasse 92, Hamburg, 22113, Germany
Tel.: (49) 40736200
Web Site: http://www.heinrich-dehn.de
Year Founded: 1818
Rev.: $45,520,200
Emp.: 111
Freight Forwarding Transportation Services
N.A.I.C.S.: 481112
Frank Gutzeit (Mng Dir)

HEINRICH GEUTHER KINDER-MOBEL UND -GERATE GMBH & CO. KG

Steinach 1, 96268, Kronach, Germany
Tel.: (49) 9266800
Web Site: http://www.geuther.de
Rev.: $24,224,020
Emp.: 120
Kids Furniture Mfr
N.A.I.C.S.: 339930
Elisabeth Bauer (Mng Dir)

HEINRICH HAGNER GMBH & CO.

Farinastrasse 1-9, Freudenstadt, 72250, Germany
Tel.: (49) 74418650
Web Site: http://www.chh-cosmetic.de
Year Founded: 1942
Rev.: $44,140,800
Emp.: 83
Cosmetics Products Mfr
N.A.I.C.S.: 325411
Thomas Foth (Mng Dir)

HEINRICH HUHN GMBH + CO.KG

Hauptstrasse 44, Drolshagen, 57489, Germany
Tel.: (49) 2763810
Web Site: http://www.heinrich-huhn.de
Year Founded: 1912
Rev.: $68,432,210
Emp.: 285
Metal Stamping Mfr
N.A.I.C.S.: 332119

Subsidiaries:

HUHN PressTech, spol. s r. o. (1)
Skolska 1604/30, 952 01, Vrable, Slovakia
Tel.: (421) 377768611
Metal Stamping Mfr
N.A.I.C.S.: 332119

HEINRICH KUPER GMBH & CO. KG

Heinrich Kuper Strasse 10 15, Rietberg, 33397, Germany
Tel.: (49) 52449840
Web Site: http://www.kuper.de
Year Founded: 1933
Rev.: $70,561,139
Emp.: 220
Industrial Machinery & Equipment Mfr
N.A.I.C.S.: 333248
Holger Schrmeisser (Gen Mgr)

HEINRICH RENNER GMBH

Kamptalstrasse 64, 3550, Langenlois, Austria
Tel.: (43) 27342218 AT
Web Site: http://www.derrenner.at
Year Founded: 1922
Emp.: 100
Metal & Glass Processing Services

AND PRIVATE COMPANIES

N.A.I.C.S.: 332999
Andreas Renner (Mng Dir)

HEINRICH SCHMIDT GMBH & CO. KG
Balhorner Feld 2, 33106, Paderborn, Germany
Tel.: (49) 525152660
Web Site: http://www.schmidt-paderborn.de
Year Founded: 1885
Sales Range: $10-24.9 Million
Commercial Vehicle Distr
N.A.I.C.S.: 423110
Ulrich Schmidt (Mng Partner)

HEINZ SOYER BOLZEN-SCHWEISSTECHNIK GMBH
Inninger Strasse 14, 82237, Starnberg, Germany
Tel.: (49) 81538850
Web Site: http://www.soyer-shop.de
Year Founded: 1970
Rev.: $14,581,803
Emp.: 58
Stud Welding Equipment Mfr
N.A.I.C.S.: 333992
Heinz Soyer Jun (Co-Mng Dir)

Subsidiaries:

Soyer Magyarorszag Kft. (1)
Baber u 14, 8000, Szekesfehervar, Hungary
Tel.: (36) 22504427
Web Site: http://www.soyer.hu
Winding Machinery Distr
N.A.I.C.S.: 423830

HEINZ-GLAS GMBH & CO. KGAA
Glashuttenplatz 1-7, 96355, Tettau, Germany
Tel.: (49) 9269 77 0
Web Site: http://www.heinz-glas.com
Year Founded: 1982
Glass Mfr
N.A.I.C.S.: 238150

HEINZE GRUPPE GMBH
Eupener Str 35, 32051, Herford, Germany
Tel.: (49) 5221 186 0   De
Web Site: http://www.heinze-gruppe.de
Emp.: 1,100
Holding Company; Industrial Products & Services
N.A.I.C.S.: 551112
Jennifer Tietjen (CFO)

Subsidiaries:

Heinze Kunststofftechnik GmbH & Co. KG (1)
Eupener Str 35, 32051, Herford, Germany
Tel.: (49) 5221 186 0
Web Site: http://www.heinze-gruppe.de
Sales Range: $150-199.9 Million
Emp.: 320
Refined Surface Plastic Product Mfr
N.A.I.C.S.: 326199
Jorg Tilmes (Mng Dir)

HEINZEL HOLDING GMBH
Wagramer Strasse 28-30, 1220, Vienna, Austria
Tel.: (43) 1 260 11 490
Web Site:
http://www.heinzelgroup.com
Rev.: $2,265,798,180
Assets: $1,523,398,191
Liabilities: $657,898,712
Net Worth: $865,499,479
Earnings: $95,805,143
Emp.: 2,551
Fiscal Year-end: 12/31/19
Pulp & Paper Mfr
N.A.I.C.S.: 322110

Alfred Hannes Heinzel (Chm-Supervisory Bd)

Subsidiaries:

AS Estonian Cell (1)
Jaama 21, Viru-Nigula Vald Laane-Virumaa, 44106, Kunda, Estonia
Tel.: (372) 687 00 00
Web Site: http://www.estoniancell.ee
Sales Range: $75-99.9 Million
Emp.: 99
Pulp Mfr
N.A.I.C.S.: 322110
Lauri Raid (CTO)

Austrian Recycling s.r.o. (1)
Temelin 127, 373 01, Temelin, Czech Republic
Tel.: (420) 385310847
Web Site: https://austrian-recycling.com
Disposal Raw Material Recovery Services
N.A.I.C.S.: 562920
Michael Gavrilovic (Mng Dir)

Chiemgau Recycling GmbH (1)
Am Baumgarten 4, 83064, Raubling, Germany
Tel.: (49) 8035968760
Web Site: https://chiemgau-recycling.de
Material Recovery Services
N.A.I.C.S.: 562920

EUROPAPIER SRBIJA d.o.o. (1)
Sinjska 41 H, 11000, Belgrade, Serbia
Tel.: (381) 11 7150 850
Pulp & Paper Distr
N.A.I.C.S.: 424990

Europapier International AG (1)
Autokaderstrasse 86-96, 1211, Vienna, Austria
Tel.: (43) 1277780
Web Site: http://www.europapier.at
Sales Range: $550-599.9 Million
Emp.: 100
Paper Whslr
N.A.I.C.S.: 424130
Helmut Limbeck (CEO)

Subsidiary (Non-US):

Europapier Adria d.o.o. (2)
Slavonska avenija 65, 10360, Sesvete, Croatia
Tel.: (385) 1 2050 333
Web Site: http://www.europapier.hr
Sales Range: $25-49.9 Million
Emp.: 17
Tape Distr
N.A.I.C.S.: 424110

Europapier Alpe d.o.o. (2)
Leskoskova cesta 14, 1000, Ljubljana, Slovenia
Tel.: (386) 1 54 72 100
Web Site: http://www.europapier.si
Tape Distr
N.A.I.C.S.: 424110

Europapier Bohemia spol. s r.o. (2)
K Perovne 1384/13, 102 00, Prague, Czech Republic
Tel.: (420) 274009111
Web Site: http://www.europapier.cz
Tape Distr
N.A.I.C.S.: 424110

Europapier Budapest Kft. (2)
Campona u 1 Harbor Park DC3 epulet, 1225, Budapest, Hungary
Tel.: (36) 13717900
Web Site: http://www.europapier.hu
Tape Distr
N.A.I.C.S.: 424110

Europapier Bulgaria EOOD (2)
148 Kliment Ochridski Blvd, Sofia, 1756, Bulgaria
Tel.: (359) 2 961 98 98
Web Site: http://www.europapier.bg
Tape Distr
N.A.I.C.S.: 424110
Ivailo Vatsov (Dir-Sls & Mktg)

Europapier CIS OOO (2)
st Bolshaya Pereyaslavskaya 46 bldg 2, 129110, Moscow, Russia
Tel.: (7) 4957870150
Web Site: http://www.europapier.ru
Tape Distr

N.A.I.C.S.: 424110

Europapier Dunav d.o.o. (2)
Batajnicki drum 6f, 11080, Zemun, Belgrade, Serbia
Tel.: (381) 117150850
Web Site: http://www.europapier.rs
Sales Range: $25-49.9 Million
Tape Distr
N.A.I.C.S.: 424110
Dragutin Ilic (Mng Dir)

Europapier Hercegtisak d.o.o. (2)
Varazdinska 2a, 88220, Siroki Brijeg, Bosnia & Herzegovina
Tel.: (387) 739700730
Web Site: http://www.europapier.ba
Tape Distr
N.A.I.C.S.: 424110

Europapier Romania Srl (2)
A1 Business Park - Cladirea F1 Autostrada Bucuresti - Pitesti Km 13, Dragomiresti - Vale, Dragomiresti-Deal, 077096, Romania
Tel.: (40) 21 352 5605
Web Site: http://www.europapier.ro
Tape Distr
N.A.I.C.S.: 424110
Adrian Ungureanu (CEO & Mng Dir)

Europapier Slovensko, s.r.o. (2)
Panonska cesta 40, 852 45, Bratislava, Slovakia
Tel.: (421) 8501112312
Web Site: http://www.europapier.sk
Emp.: 60
Tape Distr
N.A.I.C.S.: 424110
Josef Misof (Mng Dir)

Europapier-Impap Sp. z o.o. (2)
Aleje Jerozolimskie 142 A, 02-305, Warsaw, Poland
Tel.: (48) 22 35 69 200
Web Site: http://www.europapier-online.pl
Tape Distr
N.A.I.C.S.: 424110
Marek Cholewa (CEO)

Europapier Polska Sp.z.o.o. (1)
Aleje Jerozolimskie 142A, Blonie, 02-305, Warsaw, Poland
Tel.: (48) 221200000
Web Site: https://www.europapier.pl
Paper & Forest Product Mfr
N.A.I.C.S.: 322299

Heinzel Sales Asia Pacific Sdn. Bhd. (1)
Jalan Stesen Sentral 5, 50470, Kuala Lumpur, Malaysia
Tel.: (60) 322609275
Pulp & Paper Mfr
N.A.I.C.S.: 322110
Thomas Bauer (Mng Dir)

Heinzel Sales Canada Inc. (1)
Suite 300 440 Cambie Street, Vancouver, V6B 2N5, BC, Canada
Tel.: (604) 200-8700
Pulp & Paper Mfr
N.A.I.C.S.: 322110
Matthew Burke (Sls Dir)

LLC Europapier (1)
ul Bolshaya Pereyaslavskaya 46 4 floor, 129110, Moscow, Russia
Tel.: (7) 4957870150
Web Site: http://europapier.ru
Pulp & Paper Distr
N.A.I.C.S.: 424990

Laakirchen Papier AG (1)
Schillerstrasse 5, 4663, Laakirchen, Austria
Tel.: (43) 76138800
Web Site:
http://laakirchen.heinzelpaper.com
Sales Range: $250-299.9 Million
Tape Distr
N.A.I.C.S.: 424110
Franz Baldauf (CFO)

Joint Venture (Domestic):

Bunzl & Biach Ges.m.b.H (2)
Steinheilgasse 5, 1210, Vienna, Austria (51%)
Tel.: (43) 1250610
Web Site: https://www.bunzl-biach.at
Waste Paper Product Distr
N.A.I.C.S.: 424130

HEINZEL HOLDING GMBH

Andreas Mang (Mng Dir)

Subsidiary (Non-US):

Heinzel Graphic Paper Italia S.r.l. (2)
Via Palmanova 67/B, IT-20132, Milan, Italy
Tel.: (39) 02 2818 141
Emp.: 12
Tape Distr
N.A.I.C.S.: 424110
Carlo Varini (Mng Dir)

Heinzel Graphic Paper Polska Sp. z.o.o. (2)
Ul Gwiazdzista 15 a-8, 01-651, Warsaw, Poland
Tel.: (48) 22 832 52 80
Tape Distr
N.A.I.C.S.: 424110
Tadeusz Misko (Mng Dir)

North Rim Pulp & Paper Inc. (1)
Suite 300 - 440 Cambie Street, Vancouver, V6B 2N5, BC, Canada
Tel.: (604) 200-8700
Web Site: http://www.nrppi.com
Emp.: 20
Pulp Mfr
N.A.I.C.S.: 322110
Ken Grenier (Founder & Pres)

Raubling Papier GmbH (1)
Rosenheimer Str 37, 83064, Raubling, Germany
Tel.: (49) 80359090
Web Site: https://raubling.heinzelpaper.com
Pulp Mfr
N.A.I.C.S.: 322110
Christoph Wochinger (Co-CEO)

UPM-Kymmene (Austria) GmbH (1)
Marxergasse 1B, 1030, Vienna, Austria
Tel.: (43) 17074951
Web Site: http://www.upm.com
Sales Range: $50-74.9 Million
Emp.: 10
N.A.I.C.S.: 322120
Mattias Sparr (Gen Mgr)

Subsidiary (Domestic):

Steyrermuhl Sagewerksgesellschaft m.b.H. Nfg KG (2)
Fabriksplatz 1, 4662, Steyrermuhl, Austria
Tel.: (43) 761389000
Sales Range: $100-124.9 Million
Sawmill & Paper Mill Operator
N.A.I.C.S.: 561110

Plant (Domestic):

UPM-Kymmene (Austria) GmbH - Steyrermuhl Paper Mill (3)
Fabriksplatz 1, 4662, Steyrermuhl, Austria
Tel.: (43) 7613 8900 0
Sales Range: $125-149.9 Million
Emp.: 430
Newsprint & Uncoated Magazine Paper Mill
N.A.I.C.S.: 322120
Ernst Spitzbart (Dir)

UPM-Kymmene (Austria) GmbH - Steyrermuhl Sawmill (3)
Fabriksplats 1, 4662, Steyrermuhl, Austria
Tel.: (43) 7613 8900 425
Sales Range: $25-49.9 Million
Emp.: 90
Sawmills
N.A.I.C.S.: 321113

Wilfried Heinzel AG (1)
Wagramer Strasse 28-30, 1220, Vienna, Austria
Tel.: (43) 1260110
Web Site: http://www.heinzelsales.com
Sales Range: $400-449.9 Million
Emp.: 137
Pulp & Paper Distr
N.A.I.C.S.: 424110
Dietmar Geigl (CFO & Member-Mgmt Bd)

Subsidiary (Non-US):

Heinzel Deutschland GmbH (2)
Bahnhofstrasse 38, 65185, Wiesbaden, Germany
Tel.: (49) 611 50 59 69 0
Web Site: http://www.heinzel.com
Pulp & Paper Distr

HEINZEL HOLDING GMBH

Heinzel Holding GmbH—(Continued)
N.A.I.C.S.: 424990

Subsidiary (US):

Heinzel Import-Export, Inc. **(2)**
220 E 42nd St Ste 3010, New York, NY 10017
Tel.: (212) 953-3200
Sales Range: $25-49.9 Million
Emp.: 6
Pulp & Paper Distr
N.A.I.C.S.: 424110

Subsidiary (Non-US):

Heinzel Sales France S.A.S. **(2)**
20 Rue d Armenonville, Neuilly sur Seine, 92200, Paris, France
Tel.: (33) 1 40 88 93 20
Pulp & Paper Distr
N.A.I.C.S.: 424990

Heinzel Sales Italy S.r.l. **(2)**
Via Benadir 5, 20132, Milan, Italy
Tel.: (39) 02 669 3692
Pulp & Paper Distr
N.A.I.C.S.: 424990
Carlo Varini *(Co-Mng Dir)*

Zellstoff Pols AG **(1)**
Dr Luigi Angeli Strasse 9, 8761, Pols, Austria
Tel.: (43) 35798181
Web Site: http://www.zellstoff-poels.at
Sales Range: $300-349.9 Million
Pulp & Paper Mfr
N.A.I.C.S.: 322110
Ilse Ranser *(Mgr-HR)*

HEIQ PLC

15 Whitehall, London, SW1A 2DD, United Kingdom
Tel.: (44) 2073895010 UK
Web Site: https://www.heiq.com
HEIQ—(AIM)
Rev.: $47,202,000
Assets: $71,143,000
Liabilities: $30,804,000
Net Worth: $40,339,000
Earnings: ($29,814,000)
Emp.: 202
Fiscal Year-end: 12/31/22
Investment Services
N.A.I.C.S.: 523999
Richard Lockwood *(Founder)*

Subsidiaries:

Chem-Tex Laboratories, Inc. **(1)**
PO Box 5228, Concord, NC 28027
Tel.: (704) 795-9322
Web Site: http://www.chemtexlaboratories.com
Chemicals Mfr
N.A.I.C.S.: 325998
Collette Martin *(Office Mgr)*

Chrisal N.V. **(1)**
Priester Daensstraat 9, 3920, Lommel, Belgium
Tel.: (32) 11548000
Textile Chemical Mfr & Distr
N.A.I.C.S.: 325199

Heiq (China) Material Tech Ltd. **(1)**
Room 2313 Xuhui Commercial Mansion No 168 Yude Road, Shanghai, China
Tel.: (86) 2154655700
Textile Products Mfr
N.A.I.C.S.: 313310

Heiq Aeoniq GmbH **(1)**
Industriestrasse 35, 3130, Herzogenburg, Austria
Tel.: (43) 6643984251
Textile Products Mfr
N.A.I.C.S.: 313310

Heiq Chemtex Inc. **(1)**
PO Box 5228, Concord, NC 28027
Tel.: (704) 795-9322
Web Site: https://www.chemtexlaboratories.com
Textile & Paper Chemical Mfr
N.A.I.C.S.: 313310

Heiq Company Limited **(1)**
No 14 & 16 Ln 50 Wufu 1st Rd, Luzhu District, Taoyuan, 33850, Taiwan
Tel.: (886) 33120561
Textile Products Mfr
N.A.I.C.S.: 313310

Heiq Iberia Unipessoal Lda. **(1)**
Tecmaia Rua Eng Frederico Ulrich 2650, Moreira, 4470-605, Maia, Portugal
Tel.: (351) 229443523
Textile Chemical Mfr & Distr
N.A.I.C.S.: 325199

Heiq Materials AG **(1)**
Ruetistrasse 12, Schlieren, 8952, Zurich, Switzerland
Tel.: (41) 562506850
Web Site: https://www.heiq.com
Textile Chemical Mfr & Distr
N.A.I.C.S.: 325199

Heiq RAS AG **(1)**
Rudolf Vogt Strasse 8-10, 93053, Regensburg, Germany
Tel.: (49) 94160717300
Textile Chemical Mfr & Distr
N.A.I.C.S.: 325199

Life Material Technologies Limited **(1)**
222 Lumpini Building 2 247 Rajdamri Road, Lumpini Phatumwan, Bangkok, 10330, Thailand
Tel.: (66) 26519322
Web Site: https://www.life-natural.com
Textile Products Mfr
N.A.I.C.S.: 313310

HEITECH PADU BERHAD

Level 15 HeiTech Village Persiaran Kewajipan USJ1 UEP, 47600, Subang Jaya, Selangor Darul Ehsan, Malaysia
Tel.: (60) 86013000
Web Site: https://www.heitech.com.my
HTPADU—(KLS)
Rev.: $62,191,111
Assets: $62,850,794
Liabilities: $42,357,460
Net Worth: $20,493,333
Earnings: ($2,124,656)
Emp.: 529
Fiscal Year-end: 12/31/22
IT Solutions & Services
N.A.I.C.S.: 541690
Mohammad Hilmey Mohammad Taib *(Deputy Chm & Pres)*

Subsidiaries:

Bodynet Ltd **(1)**
9 Cartwright Court Bradley Business Park, Huddersfield, HD2 1GN, United Kingdom
Tel.: (44) 127 421 4250
Web Site: https://www.bodynet.co.uk
Software Developing Services
N.A.I.C.S.: 541511

Cinix 1 Pty. Ltd. **(1)**
Tel.: (61) 73 445 1800
Web Site: https://www.cinix1.com.au
Computer Repair Services
N.A.I.C.S.: 811210

Dapat Vista (M) Sdn. Bhd. **(1)**
Unit 2-1 Level 2 The Podium Tower 3 UOA Business Park, No 1 Jalan Pengaturcara U1/51A Seksyen U1, 40150, Shah Alam, Selangor, Malaysia
Tel.: (60) 378062755
Web Site: http://www.dapat.com
Data Development Services
N.A.I.C.S.: 518210
Zulzaha Shaari *(Head-Corp Svcs, Attracts, Manages & Retains Talent)*

Duta Technic Sdn. Bhd. **(1)**
26 Jalan Opera B U2/B, Taman TTDI Jaya Seksyen U2, 40150, Shah Alam, Selangor, Malaysia
Tel.: (60) 378311648
Web Site: https://www.duta-technic.com
Civil Engineering Services
N.A.I.C.S.: 541330
Azhar Ismail *(Exec Dir)*

Educational Trend Sdn. Bhd. **(1)**
Level 14 Heitech Vlg Persiaran Kewajipan USJ 1, UEP Subang Jaya, 47600, Subang Jaya, Selangor, Malaysia
Tel.: (60) 380235562
Web Site: http://www.edutrend.com
Sales Range: $10-24.9 Million
Emp.: 30
Educational Support Services
N.A.I.C.S.: 611710

HeiTech Managed Services Sdn. Bhd. **(1)**
HeiTech Village 2 No 1 Jalan Astaka U8/81, Seksyen U8, 40150, Shah Alam, Selangor Darul Ehsan, Malaysia
Tel.: (60) 380268126
Web Site: https://hms.heitech.com.my
Sales Range: $25-49.9 Million
Computer Network Design Services
N.A.I.C.S.: 541512

HeiTech i-Solutions Sdn. Bhd. **(1)**
Ground Fl HeiTech Vlg Persiaran Kewajipan, USJ 1 UEP Subang Jaya, 47600, Subang Jaya, Selangor, Malaysia
Tel.: (60) 386013000
Web Site: http://www.heitech.com
Sales Range: $75-99.9 Million
Financial Management Services
N.A.I.C.S.: 541611

Inter-City MPC (M) Sdn. Bhd. **(1)**
No 12 Jalan Anggerik Mokara 31/59 Seksyen 31, Kota Kemuning, 40460, Shah Alam, Selangor, Malaysia
Tel.: (60) 351229745
Web Site: https://www.intercity.com.my
Sales Range: $10-24.9 Million
Business Process Outsourcing Services
N.A.I.C.S.: 561499

Motordata Research Consortium Sdn. Bhd. **(1)**
No 7 Jalan Pelukis U1/46A, Temasya Glenmarie, 40150, Shah Alam, Selangor, Malaysia
Tel.: (60) 355681988
Web Site: https://www.mrc.com.my
Sales Range: $25-49.9 Million
Database Management Services
N.A.I.C.S.: 541513
Steve Miller *(CEO)*

Tekkis Sdn. Bhd. **(1)**
Level 15 Persiaran Kewajipan USJ 1, Menara HeiTech Village UEP, 47600, Subang Jaya, Selangor, Malaysia
Tel.: (60) 173420811
Web Site: https://www.tekkis.com.my
Digital Payment Services
N.A.I.C.S.: 522320

HEITKAMP & THUMANN KG

Konigsallee 4, 40212, Dusseldorf, Germany
Tel.: (49) 21179540
Web Site: http://www.ht-group.com
Sales Range: $400-449.9 Million
Emp.: 932
Holding Company
N.A.I.C.S.: 551112
Dietmar Schmitz *(Mng Dir-Compliance)*

Subsidiaries:

Doby Verrolec Ltd **(1)**
Unit 4 Harelaw Industrial Estate, Stanley, DH9 8UJ, Durham, United Kingdom
Tel.: (44) 1207 238844
Web Site: http://www.dobyverrolec.com
Emp.: 40
Plumbing Fixture Mfr
N.A.I.C.S.: 332913
Malcolm Moss *(Mng Dir)*

Doby Verrolec fze **(1)**
Hamriyah Free Zone Authority Warehouse Ref WN13 / WN14, PO Box 42978, Sharjah, United Arab Emirates
Tel.: (971) 6526 1502
Industrial Supplies Whslr
N.A.I.C.S.: 423840
Dean Clarke *(Mgr-Production)*

Dongguan Heitkamp & Thumann Metal Products Ltd. **(1)**
Hongtu High & New Technology Development Zone, Nancheng District, Dongguan, 523080, Guangdong, China
Tel.: (86) 769 22401 768
Industrial Supplies Whslr
N.A.I.C.S.: 423880

H&T Marsberg GmbH & Co. KG. **(1)**
Am Meilenstein 8-19, 34431, Marsberg, Germany
Tel.: (49) 2991 980 0
Industrial Supplies Whslr
N.A.I.C.S.: 423840

H&T Waterbury Inc. **(1)**
984 Waterville St, Waterbury, CT 06710
Tel.: (203) 574-2240
Industrial Supplies Whslr
N.A.I.C.S.: 423840
Kevin Korn *(Mgr-CI & EHS)*

Heitkamp & Thumann (S) PTE Ltd. **(1)**
27 Senoko South Road Woodlands East Industrial Estate, 758082, Singapore, Singapore
Tel.: (65) 6756 1366
Industrial Supplies Whslr
N.A.I.C.S.: 423840

Presspart Manufacturing Ltd. **(1)**
Whitebirk Industrial Estate, Blackburn, BB1 5RF, United Kingdom **(100%)**
Tel.: (44) 1254582233
Web Site: http://www.presspart.com
Sales Range: $50-74.9 Million
Emp.: 250
Metal Stampings & Structural Metalwork Mfr
N.A.I.C.S.: 332119

Subsidiary (Non-US):

novelex AG **(2)**
Ipsachstrasse 14, CH 2560, Nidau, Switzerland
Tel.: (41) 323327332
Web Site: http://www.forteq.com
Sales Range: $50-74.9 Million
Emp.: 75
Plastic Mfr
N.A.I.C.S.: 326199
Baet Wasser *(Mng Dir)*

Presspart Manufacturing S.A. **(1)**
Avda del Foix s/n Parque Empresarial El Foix, L Arboc, 43720, Tarragona, Spain
Tel.: (34) 977 16 75 26
High Precision Metal Stampings Mfr
N.A.I.C.S.: 332119

Thumann & Heitkamp Hong Kong Ltd. **(1)**
11/F AXA Centre 151 Gloucester Road, Wanchai, China (Hong Kong)
Tel.: (852) 3752 1812
Industrial Supplies Whslr
N.A.I.C.S.: 423840
Wellman Kwan *(Dir-Fin Controlling-Asia Pacific)*

Westfalia Brasil Componentes Metalicos Ltda. **(1)**
Av Prof Manoel Cesar Ribeiro, Pindamonhangaba, 12311-010, Sao Paulo, Brazil
Tel.: (55) 12 3644 8800
Metal Hose Distr
N.A.I.C.S.: 423840
Flavio Crovador Marques *(Mgr-Sls)*

Westfalia Metal Components India Pvt. Ltd. **(1)**
A-25 MIDC Phase 1 Chakan Taluka, Khed District, Pune, 410 501, Maharashtra, India
Tel.: (91) 2135 615200
Metal Hose Distr
N.A.I.C.S.: 423840
Vaibhav Joshi *(Mng Dir)*

Westfalia Metal Components Shanghai Co. Ltd. **(1)**
No 239 North Hongxiang Road Wanxiang Town, Pudong New District, Shanghai, 201313, China
Tel.: (86) 21 6045 5969
Metal Stamping Mfr
N.A.I.C.S.: 336370
Mingli Ndabaneze *(Mgr-Maintenance)*

Westfalia Metal s.r.o. **(1)**
Brnenska 61, 69301, Hustopece, Czech Republic

AND PRIVATE COMPANIES

Tel.: (420) 515 151 311
Metal Hose Distr
N.A.I.C.S.: 423840
Rostislav Antos *(Mgr-Lean)*

Westfalia Metallschlauchtechnik GmbH & Co. KG (1)
Am Schwanenweiher 1, 57271, Hilchenbach, Germany
Tel.: (49) 2733 283 100
Web Site: http://www.ht-ac.com
Emp.: 200
Metal Stamping Mfr
N.A.I.C.S.: 336370
Stefan Hauk *(Mng Dir)*

Westfalia Presstechnik GmbH & Co. KG (1)
Gewerbering 26, 8451, Crimmitschau, Germany
Tel.: (49) 3762 9400 0
Metal Stamping Mfr
N.A.I.C.S.: 336370

Westfalia Shanghai Trading Co. Ltd. (1)
Beijing East Road No 668 Room 20 G
Shanghai High-Tech King City, West Tower, Shanghai, 20001, China
Tel.: (86) 21 515712 46
Metal Hose Distr
N.A.I.C.S.: 423840

Westfalia, Inc. (1)
625 Middle St, Bristol, CT 06010
Tel.: (860) 314-2920
Emp.: 30
Metal Hose Distr
N.A.I.C.S.: 423840
Bob Whelan *(Dir-Fin)*

HEIWA CORPORATION
1-16-1 Higashi-Ueno, Taito-ku, Tokyo, 110-0015, Japan
Tel.: (81) 338390077
Web Site: https://www.heiwanet.co.jp
Year Founded: 1949
6412—(TKS)
Rev.: $901,478,410
Assets: $2,829,271,690
Liabilities: $1,248,258,840
Net Worth: $1,581,012,850
Earnings: $109,798,710
Emp.: 506
Fiscal Year-end: 03/31/24
Holding Company
N.A.I.C.S.: 551112
Katsuya Minei *(Pres)*

Subsidiaries:

PGM Holdings K.K. (1)
1-3F NBF Takanawa Bldg 1-3-13 Takanawa, Minato-ku, Tokyo, 108-0074, Japan (100%)
Tel.: (81) 3 64088800
Web Site: http://www.pacificgolf.co.jp
Rev.: $652,614,960
Assets: $2,369,437,560
Liabilities: $1,510,621,560
Net Worth: $858,816,000
Earnings: $50,932,560
Fiscal Year-end: 12/31/2013
Holding Company
N.A.I.C.S.: 551112
Kotaro Tanaka *(Pres)*

HEIWA PAPER CO., LTD.
1-22-11 Shinkawa, Chuo-ku, Tokyo, 104-0033, Japan
Tel.: (81) 332068501
Web Site: https://www.heiwapaper.co.jp
Year Founded: 1946
9929—(TKS)
Rev.: $106,579,640
Assets: $124,492,740
Liabilities: $57,744,960
Net Worth: $66,747,780
Earnings: $898,960
Emp.: 157
Fiscal Year-end: 03/31/24
Paper Product Mfr & Whslr
N.A.I.C.S.: 322299

Yoshio Seike *(Pres)*

HEIWA REAL ESTATE CO. LTD.
1-10 Kabutocho Nihonbashi, Chuo-ku, Tokyo, 103-8222, Japan
Tel.: (81) 336660181
Web Site: https://www.heiwa-net.co.jp
8803—(NGO)
Rev.: $319,222,740
Assets: $2,856,047,610
Liabilities: $2,000,494,530
Net Worth: $855,553,080
Earnings: $65,512,290
Emp.: 96
Fiscal Year-end: 03/31/23
Building Leasing & Asset Development Services
N.A.I.C.S.: 531110
Kazuo Yamada *(Mng Exec Officer-Dev Promo Dept)*

Subsidiaries:

Heiwa Real Estate Asset Management Co., Ltd. (1)
5-1 Nihonbashi-kabutocho, Chuo-ku, Tokyo, 103-0026, Japan
Tel.: (81) 336698771
Real Estate Services
N.A.I.C.S.: 531390
Yasutaka Watanabe *(Gen Mgr)*

Heiwa Service Co., Ltd. (1)
1-10 Nihonbashi Kabutocho, Chuo-ku, Tokyo, 103-0026, Japan (100%)
Tel.: (81) 336660188
Web Site: http://www.heiwaservice.com
Emp.: 50
Construction Services
N.A.I.C.S.: 237990
Koji Itabashi *(Pres)*

HEIWA REAL ESTATE REIT-,INC.
9-1 Nihonbashi-kabutocho, Chuo-ku, Tokyo, Japan
Tel.: (81) 336698771
Web Site: http://www.heiwa-re.co.jp
Year Founded: 2002
89660—(TKS)
Sales Range: Less than $1 Million
Real Estate Related Services
N.A.I.C.S.: 531390
Aya Motomura *(Exec Dir)*

HEIWADO CO., LTD.
1 Nishiimacho, Hikone, 522-8511, Shiga, Japan
Tel.: (81) 749269534 JP
Web Site: https://www.heiwado.jp
Year Founded: 1957
8276—(TKS)
Rev.: $3,016,256,160
Assets: $2,194,078,490
Liabilities: $859,272,550
Net Worth: $1,334,805,940
Earnings: $48,098,560
Fiscal Year-end: 02/29/24
Supermarkets & Department Stores Owner & Operator
N.A.I.C.S.: 445110
Masashi Hiramatsu *(Pres & CEO)*

HEKI CO., LTD.
2-6-12 Matsuyama, Okinawa, 900-0032, Okinawa, Japan
Tel.: (81) 988631533
Web Site: https://www.heki.co.jp
Year Founded: 2005
3039—(TKS)
Sales Range: $1-9.9 Million
Restaurant Operators
N.A.I.C.S.: 722511
Tomoko Kaneshiro *(Pres & CEO)*

HEKTAR REAL ESTATE INVESTMENT TRUST

D1 U3 10 Solaris Dutamas No 1 Jalan Dutamas 1 Sri Hartamas, 50480, Kuala Lumpur, 50480, Malaysia
Tel.: (60) 0362055570 MY
Web Site: https://www.hektarreit.com
Year Founded: 2006
HEKTAR—(KLS)
Rev.: $24,856,318
Assets: $261,482,898
Liabilities: $134,930,186
Net Worth: $126,552,713
Earnings: $15,798,022
Emp.: 234
Fiscal Year-end: 12/31/22
Real Estate Investment Trust Services
N.A.I.C.S.: 531110
Martin Chen *(Deputy Gen Mgr-Legal)*

HEKTAS TICARET T.A.S.
Gebze Osb Neighborhood 700 Street No 711/1, 41480, Gebze, Kocaeli, Turkiye
Tel.: (90) 2627511412
Web Site: https://www.hektas.com.tr
Year Founded: 1956
HEKTS—(IST)
Rev.: $204,517,584,760
Assets: $862,074,499,305
Liabilities: $861,819,156,056
Net Worth: $255,343,248
Earnings: ($30,291,852,052)
Emp.: 621
Fiscal Year-end: 12/31/23
Agrochemical Mfr
N.A.I.C.S.: 325320
Musa Levent Ortakcier *(Gen Mgr)*

HELABA LANDESBANK HESSEN-THURINGEN
Main Tower Neue Mainzer Strasse 52-58, 60311, Frankfurt am Main, Germany
Tel.: (49) 69913201
Web Site: http://www.helaba.de
Year Founded: 1953
Rev.: $4,424,566,860
Assets: $231,842,376,080
Liabilities: $222,088,395,480
Net Worth: $9,753,980,600
Earnings: $537,532,800
Emp.: 6,283
Fiscal Year-end: 12/31/19
Commericial Banking
N.A.I.C.S.: 522110
Gerhard Grandke *(Chm-Supervisory Bd)*

Subsidiaries:

1822direkt Gesellschaft der Frankfurter Sparkasse mbH (1)
Borsigallee 19, 60388, Frankfurt am Main, Germany
Tel.: (49) 69941700
Web Site: http://www.1822direkt.de
Real Estate Support Services
N.A.I.C.S.: 531390

BM H Beteiligungs Managementgesellschaft Hessen mbH (1)
Schumannstrasse 4-6, 60825, Frankfurt am Main, Germany
Tel.: (49) 691338507840
Web Site: http://www.bmh-hessen.de
Sales Range: $50-74.9 Million
Emp.: 10
Investment Management Service
N.A.I.C.S.: 523999
Juergen Zabel *(Mgr)*

BWT-Beteiligungsgesellschaft fur den Wirtschaftsaufbau Thuringens mbH (1)
Main Tower Neue Mainzer Strasse 52-58, 60311, Frankfurt am Main, Germany
Tel.: (49) 6991324333
Web Site: http://www.helaba.de
Management Consulting Services
N.A.I.C.S.: 541611

Uwe Ehrhardt *(Mng Dir)*

Banque LBLux S.A. (1)
3 rue Jean Monnet, L-2180, Luxembourg, Luxembourg
Tel.: (352) 424341
Web Site: http://www.lblux.lu
Sales Range: $75-99.9 Million
Emp.: 150
Private & Corporate Banking Services
N.A.I.C.S.: 522110

Burogebaude Darmstadter Landstrasse GmbH & Co. KG (1)
Neue Mainzer Str 52-58, 60311, Frankfurt am Main, Germany
Tel.: (49) 69913201
Property Management Services
N.A.I.C.S.: 531311

DIV Deutsche Immobilienfonds GmbH (1)
Wolfratshauser Strasse 49, 82049, Pullach, Germany
Tel.: (49) 89211040
Web Site: http://www.div.de
Financial & Leasing Services
N.A.I.C.S.: 561499

DKB Wohnimmobilien Beteiligungs GmbH & Co. KG (1)
Jagerallee 23, 14469, Potsdam, Brandenburg, Germany
Tel.: (49) 3312903560
Real Estate Support Services
N.A.I.C.S.: 531390

Dexia Kommunalbank Deutschland AG (1)
Charlottenstrasse 82, Berlin, 10969, Germany
Tel.: (49) 30255980
Web Site: http://www.dexia.de
Public Finance Services
N.A.I.C.S.: 921130
Laurent Fritsch *(Chief Risk and Operational Officer)*

FRAWO Frankfurter Wohnungs- und Siedlungs-Gesellschaft mbH (1)
Westerbachstrasse 33, Frankfurt am Main, Germany
Tel.: (49) 69975510
Real Estate Support Services
N.A.I.C.S.: 531390

Family Office der Frankfurter Bankgesellschaft AG (1)
Junghofstrasse 24, 60311, Frankfurt am Main, Germany
Tel.: (49) 692999276800
Web Site: http://www.familyoffice-fbg.com
Advisory & Risk Management Services
N.A.I.C.S.: 541618

Frankfurter Bankgesellschaft (Schweiz) AG (1)
Borsenstrasse 16, 8001, Zurich, Switzerland
Tel.: (41) 442654444
Web Site: http://www.frankfurter-bankgesellschaft.ch
Sales Range: $10-24.9 Million
Investment Banking Services
N.A.I.C.S.: 523150
Holger May *(Member-Mgmt Bd)*

GGM Gesellschaft fur Gebaude Management mbH (1)
Speicherstrasse 55, 60327, Frankfurt am Main, Germany
Tel.: (49) 6991732900
Web Site: http://www.ggm-re.de
Sales Range: $50-74.9 Million
Property Management Services
N.A.I.C.S.: 531311

GHT Gesellschaft fur Projektmanagement Hessen-Thuringen mbH (1)
Standeplatz 17, 34117, Kassel, Germany
Tel.: (49) 561918990
Web Site: http://www.ght-projektmanagement.de
Emp.: 12
Building Construction Services
N.A.I.C.S.: 236220
Juergen Wiegel *(Mgr)*

GWH Bauprojekte GmbH (1)
Westerbachstrasse 33, 60489, Frankfurt am Main, Germany

HELABA LANDESBANK HESSEN-THURINGEN

Helaba Landesbank Hessen-Thuringen—(Continued)
Tel.: (49) 69975512200
Web Site: http://www.gwh-bauprojekte.de
Real Estate Services
N.A.I.C.S.: 531390

GWH Immobilien Holding GmbH (1)
Westerbachstrasse 33, 60489, Frankfurt am Main, Germany
Tel.: (49) 69975510
Real Estate Services
N.A.I.C.S.: 531390

GWH WertInvest GmbH (1)
Westerbachstrasse 33, 60489, Frankfurt am Main, Germany
Tel.: (49) 6966819930
Web Site: http://www.gwh-wertinvest.de
Real Estate Consulting Service
N.A.I.C.S.: 531390
Neda Valad (Mgr-Fund)

Galerie Lippe GmbH & Co. KG (1)
Kahlenstr 2-4, 59555, Lippstadt, Germany
Tel.: (49) 7656302103
Web Site: http://www.lippegalerie.de
Shopping Centre Services
N.A.I.C.S.: 531120

Gemeinnutzige Wohnungsgesell-schaft mbH Hessen (1)
Westerbachstrasse 33, 60489, Frankfurt am Main, Germany
Tel.: (49) 69975510
Web Site: http://www.gwh.de
Sales Range: $50-74.9 Million
Emp.: 100
Real Estate Services
N.A.I.C.S.: 531390

Grundstucksverwaltungs gesellschaft (1)
Specher Str 55, 60327, Frankfurt am Main, Germany
Tel.: (49) 6991732224
Real Estate Manangement Services
N.A.I.C.S.: 531390

HANNOVER LEASING Wachstumswerte Asien 1 GmbH & Co. KG (1)
Wolfratshauser Str 49, Pullach, 82049, Bavaria, Germany
Tel.: (49) 89211040
Web Site: http://www.hannover-leasing.de
Financial Management Services
N.A.I.C.S.: 523999

Hafenbogen GmbH & Co. KG (1)
Neue Mainzer Strasse 82, 60311, Frankfurt am Main, Germany
Tel.: (49) 69870085410
Web Site: http://www.hafenbogen.de
Real Estate Agency Services
N.A.I.C.S.: 531390

Hannover Leasing GmbH & Co. KG (1)
Wolfratshauser Strasse 49, 82049, Pullach, Germany
Tel.: (49) 89211040
Web Site: https://www.hannover-leasing.de
Financial Services
N.A.I.C.S.: 561499
Axel Wieandt (Chm)

Haus am Brusseler Platz GmbH & Co. KG (1)
Speicherstrasse 55, 60327, Frankfurt am Main, Germany
Tel.: (49) 6991732726
Flexible Office Design Services
N.A.I.C.S.: 541410

Helaba Asset Services (1)
4th Floor La Touche House, Dublin, Ireland
Tel.: (353) 16460902
Real Estate Agency Services
N.A.I.C.S.: 531210
Patrick Smyth (Co-Mng Dir)

Helaba Beteiligungs-Management Gesellschaft mbH (1)
Schumannstrasse 5-6, 60325, Frankfurt am Main, Germany
Tel.: (49) 699720870
Business Support Services
N.A.I.C.S.: 561499

Helaba Digital GmbH & Co. KG (1)
Neue Mainzer Strasse 52-58 Main Tower, 60311, Frankfurt am Main, Germany
Tel.: (49) 6991320
Real Estate Investment Services
N.A.I.C.S.: 531390
Philipp Kaiser (Mng Dir)

Helaba Dublin Landesbank Hessen-Thuringen International (1)
5 Georges Dock IFSC, PO Box 3137, Dublin, Ireland
Tel.: (353) 16460902
Web Site: http://www.helaba.ie
Sales Range: $25-49.9 Million
Emp.: 33
Financial Services
N.A.I.C.S.: 522320
Paul Murray (Mng Dir)

Helaba Gesellschaft fur Immobilienbewertung mbH (1)
Main Tower Neue Mainzer Strasse 52-58, 60311, Frankfurt, Germany
Tel.: (49) 69829035700
Web Site: http://www.hib-Immobewertung.de
Emp.: 24
Real Estate Agency Services
N.A.I.C.S.: 531210

Helaba International Finance plc (1)
5 Georges Dock, PO Box 3137, Dublin, 1, Ireland
Tel.: (353) 16460900
Web Site: http://www.helaba.ie
Sales Range: $10-24.9 Million
Emp.: 25
Management Services
N.A.I.C.S.: 561110

Helaba Invest Kapitalanlagegesellschaft mbH (1)
Junghofstrasse 24, Frankfurt am Main, 60311, Germany
Tel.: (49) 69299700
Web Site: http://www.helaba-invest.de
Sales Range: $75-99.9 Million
Investment Company
N.A.I.C.S.: 523940
Uwe Trautmann (COO)

Helaba Landesbank Hessen Thuringen (1)
3rd Floor 95 Queen Victoria Street, London, EC4V 4HN, United Kingdom
Tel.: (44) 2073344500
Web Site: http://www.helaba.de
Sales Range: $50-74.9 Million
Emp.: 75
Public Finance & Investment Services
N.A.I.C.S.: 523940

Helaba Landesbank Hessen-Thuringen Girozentrale (1)
Bonifaciusstrasse 16, Erfurt, 99084, Germany (100%)
Tel.: (49) 3612177100
Web Site: http://www.helaba.de
Sales Range: $50-74.9 Million
Emp.: 100
Investment Banking Services
N.A.I.C.S.: 523150
Herbert Hans Gruentker (CEO)

Innovationsfonds Hessen GmbH & Co. KG (1)
Main Tower Neue Mainzer Strasse 52-58, 60311, Frankfurt am Main, Germany
Tel.: (49) 699720870
Financial Services
N.A.I.C.S.: 561499

Komuno GmbH (1)
Stresemannallee 30, 60596, Frankfurt am Main, Germany
Tel.: (49) 69667789580
Web Site: http://www.komuno.de
Financial Services
N.A.I.C.S.: 523999
Robert Wassmer (Mng Dir)

LBS Immobilien GmbH (1)
Gesellschaft Neue Mainzer Strasse 52 58, 5860311, Frankfurt am Main, Germany
Tel.: (49) 6960509222
Web Site: http://www.lbsi.de
Sales Range: $25-49.9 Million
Emp.: 40
Real Estate Services
N.A.I.C.S.: 531210

OFB Beteiligungen GmbH (1)
Speicherstr 55, Frankfurt am Main, 60327, Hessen, Germany
Tel.: (49) 6991732296
Web Site: http://www.ofb.de
Emp.: 60
Financial Management Services
N.A.I.C.S.: 523999

OFB GKH Gesellschaft fur Kommunalbau In Hessen mbH (1)
Speicherstrasse 55, Frankfurt, 60327, Germany
Tel.: (49) 699173202
Web Site: http://www.ofb.de
Sales Range: $25-49.9 Million
Emp.: 40
Banking
N.A.I.C.S.: 522110

OFB Projektentwicklung GmbH (1)
Speicherstrasse 55, 60327, Frankfurt am Main, Germany
Tel.: (49) 699173201
Web Site: http://www.ofb.de
Sales Range: $75-99.9 Million
Real Estate Development Services
N.A.I.C.S.: 531390
Klaus Kirchberger (CEO & Member-Mgmt Bd)

Palladium Praha s.r.o. (1)
namesti Republiky 1, 110 00, Prague, Czech Republic
Tel.: (420) 225770250
Web Site: http://www.palladiumpraha.cz
Shopping Center Operating Services
N.A.I.C.S.: 561439
Karolina Peterkova (Dir-Mktg)

S-Beteiligungsgesellschaft Hessen-Thuringen mbH (1)
Main Tower Neue Mainzer Strasse 52 58, D-60297, Frankfurt am Main, Germany
Tel.: (49) 699720870
Web Site: http://www.helaba.de
Sales Range: $50-74.9 Million
Emp.: 4
Financial Services
N.A.I.C.S.: 522320

SQO Stadt Quartier Offenburg GmbH & Co. KG (1)
Speicherstrasse 55, 60327, Frankfurt am Main, Germany
Tel.: (49) 699173201
All Other Product Retailer
N.A.I.C.S.: 455219

Sparkassen-Immobilien-Vermittlungs-GmbH (1)
Main Tower Neue Mainzer Strasse 52-58, 60311, Frankfurt am Main, Germany
Tel.: (49) 696050920
Web Site: http://www.sparkassen.immo
Real Estate Services
N.A.I.C.S.: 531390

Systeno GmbH (1)
Eschborner Landstrasse 122, 60489, Frankfurt am Main, Germany
Tel.: (49) 6940127912120
Web Site: http://www.systeno.de
Housing Heat Supply Services
N.A.I.C.S.: 238220

TE Kronos GmbH (1)
Neue Mainzer Str 52-58, 60311, Frankfurt, Hessen, Germany
Tel.: (49) 69913201
Web Site: http://www.helaba.de
Financial Management Services
N.A.I.C.S.: 523999
Hans-Dieter Brenner (Chm)

Vermogensverwaltung Emaillierwerk GmbH (1)
Petersberger Str 34, Fulda, 36037, Hessen, Germany
Tel.: (49) 3612271055
Holding Company
N.A.I.C.S.: 551112

HELBOR EMPREENDIMENTOS S.A.

Av Paulista 1294 13th floor Bela Vista, Mogi das Cruzes, 01310 915, SP, Brazil
Tel.: (55) 1131741211

Web Site: http://www.helbor.com.br
Year Founded: 1977
HBOR3—(BRAZ)
Rev.: $228,113,363
Assets: $1,087,017,364
Liabilities: $663,428,773
Net Worth: $423,588,591
Earnings: $30,897,016
Fiscal Year-end: 12/31/23
Real Estate Development Services
N.A.I.C.S.: 531390
Henry Borenstein (Vice Chm & CEO)

Subsidiaries:

SPE HB Brokers - Gestao Imobiliaria Ltda. (1)
Av Paulista 1294 13 Andar Edificio Eluma I Bela Vista, Sao Paulo, Brazil
Tel.: (55) 1136745500
Web Site: https://hbbrokers.com.br
Real Estate Manangement Services
N.A.I.C.S.: 531210

HELEN OF TROY LIMITED

Clarendon House 2 Church Street, Hamilton, Bermuda
Tel.: (441) 9152258000 **BM**
Web Site:
https://www.helenoftroy.com
Year Founded: 1968
HELE—(NASDAQ)
Rev.: $2,072,667,000
Assets: $2,913,715,000
Liabilities: $1,424,904,000
Net Worth: $1,488,811,000
Earnings: $143,273,000
Emp.: 1,903
Fiscal Year-end: 02/28/23
Housewares, Health & Home, Nutritional Supplements & Beauty Products Designer, Developer & Marketer
N.A.I.C.S.: 335210
Gary B. Abromovitz (Deputy Chm)

Subsidiaries:

HOT (UK) Limited (1)
1-4 Jessops Riverside-800 Brightside Lane, Sheffield, SR 2RX, United Kingdom
Tel.: (44) 1142420405
Web Site: http://www.hot-europe.com
Sales Range: $100-124.9 Million
Emp.: 50
Personal Care Products Retailer
N.A.I.C.S.: 335210

Healthy Directions, LLC (1)
6710A Rockledge Dr Ste 500, Bethesda, MD 20817
Tel.: (301) 340-2100
Web Site: http://www.healthydirections.com
Sales Range: $125-149.9 Million
Emp.: 130
Health Newsletter Publisher & Branded Nutritional Supplements Marketer
N.A.I.C.S.: 513199
Ben Teicher (Pres)

Helen of Troy Canada, Inc. (1)
3380 South Service Rd, Burlington, ON, Canada
Tel.: (905) 637-4987
Web Site: http://www.hotca.ca
Healthcare Device Mfr
N.A.I.C.S.: 334512

Helen of Troy L.P. (1)
1 Helen of Troy Plz, El Paso, TX 79912
Tel.: (915) 225-8000
Web Site: http://www.hotus.com
Emp.: 500
Healthcare Device & Home Comfort Product Mfr
N.A.I.C.S.: 334512

Helen of Troy Texas Corporation (1)
12 S 6th St, Minneapolis, MN 55402
Tel.: (612) 333-0977
Household Appliance Whslr
N.A.I.C.S.: 423620

Division (Domestic):

Helen of Troy Consumer Products Division (2)
1 Helen Of Troy Plz, El Paso, TX 79912-1148

AND PRIVATE COMPANIES

HELICAL PLC

Tel.: (915) 225-8000
Web Site: http://www.hotus.com
Sales Range: $100-124.9 Million
Emp.: 500
Marketer & Distributor for Vidal Sassoon Products, Handheld Dryers, Curling Irons, Brush Irons & Hairsetters
N.A.I.C.S.: 335210

Helen of Troy Professional Salon Division (2)
1 Helen Of Troy Plz, El Paso, TX 79912-1148
Tel.: (915) 225-8000
Web Site: http://www.hotus.com
Sales Range: $150-199.9 Million
Emp.: 500
Marketer & Distributor of Beauty & Barber Supplies
N.A.I.C.S.: 335210

Idelle Labs, Ltd. (1)
39 Old Ridgeburry Rd, Danbury, CT 06810
Tel.: (203) 797-0350
Sales Range: $1-9.9 Million
Household Appliance Whslr
N.A.I.C.S.: 423620

KAZ Hausgerate GmbH (1)
Sandleitengasse 15-17, 1160, Vienna, Austria
Tel.: (43) 17203883
Emp.: 2
Healthcare & Home Environment Product Mfr
N.A.I.C.S.: 334512

Kaz Canada, Inc. (1)
510 Bronte St South, Milton, L9T 2X6, ON, Canada
Tel.: (905) 876-3130
Web Site: http://www.kaz.com
Healthcare Device Mfr
N.A.I.C.S.: 334512

Kaz Consumer Products, S.L.U. (1)
C/Josefa Valcarcel 8- 2 Piso, 28027, Madrid, Spain
Tel.: (34) 913202884
Healthcare Devices & Home Comfort Product Operator
N.A.I.C.S.: 334512

Kaz Europe Sarl (1)
Place Chauderon 18, 1003, Lausanne, Switzerland
Tel.: (41) 216440110
Healthcare Device & Home Comfort Product Mfr
N.A.I.C.S.: 334512

Kaz France SAS (1)
Inter Centre d'Affaires 35 Rue des Chantiers, 78000, Versailles, France
Tel.: (33) 130849751
Healthcare Device & Home Comfort Product Mfr
N.A.I.C.S.: 334512

Kaz Home Appliance (Shenzhen) Company Limited (1)
Flat 4B & 4C Productivity Building 2nd High Technology Road, Science and Industry Park-Nanshan District, Shenzhen, China
Tel.: (86) 75583433838
Healthcare Devices & Home Comfort Product Operator
N.A.I.C.S.: 334512

Kaz, Inc. (1)
400 Donald Lynch Blvd, Marlborough, MA 01752
Tel.: (508) 490-7000
Web Site: http://www.kaz.com
Sales Range: $300-349.9 Million
Emp.: 150
Electric Vaporizers; Electric Heating Pads; Private-Label Heating Products; Electric Humidifiers; Home Steam Baths & Saunas & Heating Caps Mfr
N.A.I.C.S.: 335210
Jon Kosheff (Pres)

Subsidiary (Domestic):

Kaz USA, Inc. (2)
250 Turnpike Rd, Southborough, MA 01772
Tel.: (973) 455-2000
Web Site: http://www.kaz.com
Healthcare Devices & Home Comfort Product Operator

N.A.I.C.S.: 334512

OXO International Inc. (1)
1331 S 7th St Bldg 1, Chambersburg, PA 17201
Tel.: (212) 242-3333
Web Site: http://www.oxo.com
Sales Range: $25-49.9 Million
Emp.: 115
Kitchenware, Cleaning Supplies & Hardware Mfr
N.A.I.C.S.: 332510

Steel Technologies, LLC (1)
700 N Hurstbourne Pkwy Ste 400, Louisville, KY 40222
Tel.: (502) 245-2110
Web Site: http://steeltechnologies.com
Emp.: 1,013
Fiscal Year-end: 09/30/2006
Beauty & Nutritional Supplement Product Whslr
N.A.I.C.S.: 456120
Thad Solomon (Pres)

Steel Technology, LLC (1)
525 NW York Dr, Bend, OR 97703
Web Site: http://www.hydroflask.com
Sales Range: $50-74.9 Million
Emp.: 24
Stainless Steel Insulated Hydration Containers Mfr
N.A.I.C.S.: 332439

HELENS INTERNATIONAL HOLDINGS COMPANY LIMITED
Building B2 Guanggu Chongwen Centre Phase I No 792 Gaoxin Avenue, East Lake New Technology Development Zone, Wuhan, Hubei, China   Ky
Web Site: https://www.helensbar.com
Year Founded: 2009
9869—(HKG)
Rev.: $167,342,296
Assets: $299,759,637
Liabilities: $47,571,029
Net Worth: $252,188,608
Earnings: $24,991,693
Emp.: 2,779
Fiscal Year-end: 12/31/23
Holding Company
N.A.I.C.S.: 551112
Bingzhong Xu (Founder)

HELESI PLC
Industrial Zone of Tseri, Nicosia, PC 2480, Cyprus
Tel.: (357) 22 382070
Web Site: http://www.helesi.com
Sales Range: $25-49.9 Million
Emp.: 290
Plastics Product Mfr
N.A.I.C.S.: 333248
Athanasios Andrianopoulos (CEO)

Subsidiaries:

Helesi Italia S.r.l. (1)
Via Giovanni XXII n106, 41012, Carpi, Italy
Tel.: (39) 0522 732146
Sales Range: $25-49.9 Million
Emp.: 100
Plastics Product Mfr
N.A.I.C.S.: 326199
Athanasios Andrianopulos (Pres)

Helesi Plc - Komotini Plant (1)
Indus Zone O T 29, 69100, Komotini, Rhodope, Greece
Tel.: (30) 2531082579
Wheeled Bins Mfr
N.A.I.C.S.: 326199

Helesi S.A. (1)
Markopoulo Indus Park, Ntorovateza, 19003, Markopoulon, Greece
Tel.: (30) 2299082709
Injection Molded Plastic Products Mfr
N.A.I.C.S.: 326199

HELGELAND SPAREBANK
Tel.: (47) 75119000

HELG—(OSL)
Sales Range: Less than $1 Million
Commercial Banking Services
N.A.I.C.S.: 522110
Hanne Johansen Nordgaard (CEO)

HELI-LYNX HELICOPTER SERVICES INC.
684 Mud Street East, Stoney Creek, L8J 3C9, ON, Canada
Tel.: (905) 643-7334
Web Site: http://www.helilynx.com
Year Founded: 2002
Rev.: $10,010,262
Emp.: 50
Helicopter Services & Mfr
N.A.I.C.S.: 336411
Matt Trahearn (Founder & Dir-Maintenance)

HELIA GROUP LIMITED
Level 26 101 Miller Street, North Sydney, 2060, NSW, Australia
Tel.: (61) 1300655422
Web Site: https://helia.com.au
0GI0—(DEU)
Rev.: $213,588,606
Assets: $2,350,675,011
Liabilities: $1,401,923,282
Net Worth: $948,751,729
Earnings: $124,687,652
Emp.: 232
Fiscal Year-end: 12/31/22
Mortgage & Nonmortgage Loan Brokers
N.A.I.C.S.: 522310
Ian MacDonald (Chm)

HELIAD AG
Ulmenstrasse 37-39, 60325, Frankfurt am Main, Germany
Tel.: (49) 6971912800
Web Site: https://heliad.com
Year Founded: 2003
A7A—(DEU)
Rev.: $971,406
Assets: $100,750,215
Liabilities: $19,229,415
Net Worth: $81,520,800
Earnings: ($17,231,411)
Emp.: 8
Fiscal Year-end: 12/31/23
Asset Management Services
N.A.I.C.S.: 523940
Axel-Gunter Benkner (Chm-Supervisory Bd)

Subsidiaries:

Heliad Equity Partners GmbH & Co. KGaA (1)
Gruneburgweg 18, 60322, Frankfurt am Main, Germany
Tel.: (49) 69719159650
Web Site: http://www.heliad.com
Sales Range: Less than $1 Million
Investment Holding Company
N.A.I.C.S.: 523999
Volker Rofalski (Chm-Supervisory Bd)

Subsidiary (Non-US):

R. Hasler AG (2)
Bahnhofstrasse 15, Mohlin, 4313, Aargau, Switzerland
Tel.: (41) 628717267
Investment Management Service
N.A.I.C.S.: 523999

HELIATEK GMBH
Treidlerstrasse 3, 1139, Dresden, Germany
Tel.: (49) 351 21 30 34 30
Web Site: http://www.heliatek.com
Emp.: 63
Solar Film Mfr
N.A.I.C.S.: 334419
Thibaud Le Seguillon (CEO)

HELICAL PLC
5 Hanover Square, London, W1S 1HQ, United Kingdom
Tel.: (44) 2076290113   UK
Web Site: https://www.helical.co.uk
Year Founded: 1919
HLCL—(LSE)
Rev.: $52,402,561
Assets: $1,386,253,844
Liabilities: $560,541,491
Net Worth: $825,712,353
Earnings: $24,271,960
Emp.: 28
Fiscal Year-end: 03/31/21
Property Development & Investment Services
N.A.I.C.S.: 531390
Gerald Kaye (CEO)

Subsidiaries:

61 Southwark Street Ltd (1)
61 Southwark St, London, SE1 0HL, United Kingdom
Tel.: (44) 2079221281
Web Site: http://www.hashdownphillips.com
Property Management & Investment Services
N.A.I.C.S.: 531312

Albion Land (Bushey Mill) Ltd (1)
No 500 Sq, London, W1S 1HQ, United Kingdom
Tel.: (44) 2076290113
Web Site: http://www.helical.co.uk
Sales Range: $25-49.9 Million
Emp.: 26
Property Management & Investment Services
N.A.I.C.S.: 531312
Duncan Walker (Mgr)

Helical (Bramshott Place) Ltd (1)
11-15 Farm St, London, W1J 5RS, United Kingdom
Tel.: (44) 2088039588
Property Management & Investment Services
N.A.I.C.S.: 531311

Helical (Cardiff) Ltd (1)
5 Hanover Square, London, W1S 1HQ, United Kingdom
Tel.: (44) 2076290113
Sales Range: $25-49.9 Million
Emp.: 30
Property Management & Investment Services
N.A.I.C.S.: 531312

Helical (Crawley) Ltd (1)
5 Hanover Square, London, W1S 1HQ, United Kingdom
Tel.: (44) 2076290113
Web Site: http://www.helical.co.uk
Emp.: 25
Property Management & Investment Services
N.A.I.C.S.: 531312

Helical (Hailsham) Ltd (1)
50 Hanover Sq, London, W1S 1HQ, United Kingdom
Tel.: (44) 2076290113
Web Site: http://www.helical.co.uk
Property Management & Investment Services
N.A.I.C.S.: 531312
Michelle Slade (Mng Dir)

Helical (Sevenoaks) Ltd (1)
11-15 Farm St, London, W1J 5RS, United Kingdom
Tel.: (44) 2076290113
Web Site: http://www.helical.co.uk
Sales Range: $25-49.9 Million
Emp.: 35
Property Management & Investment Services
N.A.I.C.S.: 531312

Helical Bar (Rex House) Ltd (1)
No 5 Hanover Square, London, W1F1HQ, United Kingdom
Tel.: (44) 2076290113
Web Site: http://www.helical.co.uk
Emp.: 30
Property Management & Investment Services

HELICAL PLC

Helical Plc—(Continued)
N.A.I.C.S.: 531311

Helical Bar (Wales) Ltd (1)
Grosvenor House 8 Park Grove, Cardiff, CF10 3BN, South Glamorgan, United Kingdom
Tel.: (44) 2920223123
Sales Range: $25-49.9 Million
Emp.: 5
Building Construction Services
N.A.I.C.S.: 236116
Richard Morgan (Office Mgr)

Helical Bar Developments (South East) Ltd (1)
5 Hanover Square, London, W1S 1HQ, United Kingdom
Tel.: (44) 2076290113
Web Site: http://www.helical.co.uk
Sales Range: $25-49.9 Million
Emp.: 26
Property Management & Investment Services
N.A.I.C.S.: 531312

Helical Retail Ltd (1)
Desford Hall, Leicester, LE9 9JJ, United Kingdom
Tel.: (44) 1455828771
Property Management & Investment Services
N.A.I.C.S.: 531312

Helical Wroclaw Sp. z o.o. (1)
Ul Szpitalna 8 4, 00 031, Warsaw, Poland
Tel.: (48) 228265617
Property Management & Investment Services
N.A.I.C.S.: 531312

HELICAL TECHNOLOGY LIMITED

Dock Road, Lytham Saint Anne's, FY8 5AQ, Lancashire, United Kingdom
Tel.: (44) 3333 44 45 46
Web Site: http://www.helical-technology.com
Year Founded: 1962
Sales Range: $50-74.9 Million
Emp.: 213
Actuator Mfr
N.A.I.C.S.: 333995
Alistair Morris (Mng Dir)

Subsidiaries:

Helical Auto-Technology Pvt Ltd (1)
Office/Works Gat No 115 116 117 Ambedwet, Mulshi, Pune, 412 108, India
Tel.: (91) 2067960600
Actuator Mfr
N.A.I.C.S.: 333995
Parikshit Kulkarni (Asst Mgr-Production, Plng & Control)

HELIJET INTERNATIONAL INC.

5911 Airport Road South, Vancouver International Airport, Richmond, V7B 1B5, BC, Canada
Tel.: (604) 273-4688   Ca
Web Site: https://www.helijet.com
Year Founded: 1987
Rev.: $30,438,158
Assets: $17,942,002
Liabilities: $16,577,692
Net Worth: $1,364,310
Earnings: $124,414
Emp.: 130
Fiscal Year-end: 08/31/18
Helicopter & Turbo-Prop Airplane Charter Services
N.A.I.C.S.: 481211
Daniel A. J. Sitnam (Pres & CEO)

Subsidiaries:

Pacific Heliport Services (1)
455 West Waterfront Road, Vancouver, V6B 5E8, BC, Canada
Tel.: (604) 688-4246
Web Site: http://www.pacificheliportservices.com

Sales Range: $25-49.9 Million
Emp.: 12
Charter Helicopter Services
N.A.I.C.S.: 481112

HELIO S.A.

Tel.: (48) 227257181
Web Site: https://www.helio.pl
Year Founded: 1992
HEL—(WAR)
Rev.: $84,085,158
Assets: $54,180,286
Liabilities: $24,309,655
Net Worth: $29,870,631
Earnings: $3,482,822
Emp.: 100
Fiscal Year-end: 06/30/22
Fruits & Nuts Producer
N.A.I.C.S.: 111336
Leszek Pawel Wasowicz (Chm-Mgmt Bd & CEO)

HELIOGRAPH HOLDING GMBH

Konrad-Zuse-Bogen 18, D-82152, Krailling, Germany
Tel.: (49) 89785960
Web Site: http://www.heliograph-holding.com
Gravure Cylinder Making Equipment Mfr
N.A.I.C.S.: 333248
Rolf Pfiffner (Mng Dir)

HELIOS & MATHESON INFORMATION TECHNOLOGY LIMITED

Ascendas International Tech Park 4th Floor Crest Phase II CSIR Road, Taramani, Chennai, 600 113, Tamilnadu, India
Tel.: (91) 44 43750000
Web Site: http://www.heliosmatheson.com
Year Founded: 1991
Sales Range: $100-124.9 Million
Software Development Services
N.A.I.C.S.: 541511
Diwakar Sai Yerra (Sec)

HELIOS D,D

Radnicka 101, 75290, Banovici, Bosnia & Herzegovina
Tel.: (387) 35 880 400
Web Site: http://www.helios.com.ba
Year Founded: 1971
HELSRK1—(SARE)
Sales Range: Less than $1 Million
Emp.: 75
Metal Processing Services
N.A.I.C.S.: 332811
Fadil Halilovic (Member-Mgmt Bd)

HELIOS ENERGY LTD.

Tel.: (61) 1300291195
Web Site: https://www.heliosenergyltd.com
HE8—(ASX)
Rev.: $94,113
Assets: $31,375,786
Liabilities: $1,210,129
Net Worth: $30,165,658
Earnings: ($3,310,653)
Fiscal Year-end: 06/30/24
Metal Mineral Exploration Services
N.A.I.C.S.: 212290

Subsidiaries:

Helios Energy USA Ltd. (1)
7114 Sleepy Hollow Rd, Fairview, TN 37062
Web Site: https://www.heliosenergyus.com
Solar Energy Services
N.A.I.C.S.: 221114
Chris Nelson (CEO)

HELIOS INVESTMENT PARTNERS LLP

2nd Floor 12 Charles II Street, London, SW1Y 4QU, United Kingdom
Tel.: (44) 207 484 7700   UK
Web Site: http://www.heliosinvestment.com
Year Founded: 2004
Rev.: $3,000,000,000
Equity Investment Firm
N.A.I.C.S.: 523999
Tope Lawani (Founder & Mng Partner)

Subsidiaries:

Helios Fairfax Partners Corporation (1)
95 Wellington Street West Suite 800, Toronto, M5J 2N7, ON, Canada   (45.9%)
Tel.: (416) 646-3556
Web Site: http://www.fairfaxafrica.ca
Rev.: $12,036,000
Assets: $488,333,000
Liabilities: $13,737,000
Net Worth: $474,596,000
Earnings: ($71,687,000)
Emp.: 13
Fiscal Year-end: 12/31/2023
Holding Company
N.A.I.C.S.: 551112
Michael Wilkerson (Vice Chm)

Telkom Kenya Limited (1)
Telkom Plaza Ralph Bunche Road, PO Box 30301-00100, Nairobi, Kenya   (60%)
Tel.: (254) 20 4952000
Web Site: http://www.orange-tkl.co.ke
Telephone Communications
N.A.I.C.S.: 517111
Eddy Njoroge (Chm)

HELIOS TECHNO HOLDING CO., LTD.

703 Mikage Toyotomi-cho, Himeji, 679-2122, Hyogo, Japan
Tel.: (81) 792639500
Web Site: https://www.heliostec-hd.co.jp
Year Founded: 1976
6927—(TKS)
Rev.: $71,857,310
Assets: $138,142,390
Liabilities: $31,371,060
Net Worth: $106,771,330
Earnings: $15,143,510
Fiscal Year-end: 03/31/24
Holding Company
N.A.I.C.S.: 551112
Yoshihisa Sato (Pres)

Subsidiaries:

Leadtech Co., Ltd. (1)
4-6 Chubu Industrial Park, Iwaki, 972-8338, Fukushima, Japan
Tel.: (81) 246722720
Web Site: https://www.leadtech.jp
Emp.: 29
Semiconductor Mfr & Distr
N.A.I.C.S.: 334413

Lux Co., Ltd. (1)
703 Mikage Toyotomicho, Himeji, 679-2122, Hyogo, Japan
Tel.: (81) 792653369
Web Site: https://www.luxnet.co.jp
Emp.: 25
Lighting Lamp Retailer
N.A.I.C.S.: 423610

Nakan Techno Co., Ltd. (1)
2071 Oht, Sakura, 285-0808, Chiba, Japan
Tel.: (81) 434812230
Web Site: http://www.nakan-techno.co.jp
Emp.: 138
Printing Machinery & Equipment Mfr
N.A.I.C.S.: 333248
Yoshihisa Sato (Pres)

Phoenix Electric Co., Ltd. (1)
703 Mikage Toyotomi-cho, Himeji, 679-2122, Hyogo, Japan
Tel.: (81) 792645711
Web Site: https://www.phoenix-elec.co.jp

INTERNATIONAL PUBLIC

Emp.: 173
Halogen Lamp Mfr & Retailer
N.A.I.C.S.: 335139
Hiroya Tahara (Pres)

HELIOS TOWERS PLC

Bridgwater Road, Bristol, BS13 8AE, United Kingdom
Tel.: (44) 2078713670   UK
Web Site: https://www.heliostowers.com
Year Founded: 2009
HTWS—(LSE)
Rev.: $560,700,000
Assets: $2,144,400,000
Liabilities: $2,095,100,000
Net Worth: $49,300,000
Earnings: ($171,400,000)
Fiscal Year-end: 12/31/22
Telecommunication Servicesb
N.A.I.C.S.: 517810
Kash Pandya (CEO)

Subsidiaries:

HTG Managed Services Limited (1)
31 Akosombo Road Airport Residential Area, Accra, Ghana
Tel.: (233) 242435581
Telecommunication Servicesb
N.A.I.C.S.: 517810

HELIOS UNDERWRITING PLC

33 Cornhill 1st Floor, London, EC3V 3ND, United Kingdom
Tel.: (44) 2078636655   UK
Web Site: https://www.huwplc.com
HUW—(AIM)
Rev.: $308,779,349
Assets: $747,979,046
Liabilities: $600,064,378
Net Worth: $147,914,668
Earnings: ($4,187,074)
Emp.: 3
Fiscal Year-end: 12/31/22
Holding Company; Insurance Underwriting Services
N.A.I.C.S.: 551112
Nigel John Hanbury (CEO)

Subsidiaries:

Hampden Corporate Member Limited (1)
Hampden House, Great Hampden, Great Missenden, HP16 9RD, Bucks, United Kingdom
Tel.: (44) 1494488888
Sales Range: $50-74.9 Million
Emp.: 30
Insurance Underwriting Services
N.A.I.C.S.: 524292

HELIOSPECTRA AB

Johan Willins gata 8 416 64, SE-1458, Gothenburg, Sweden
Tel.: (46) 31406710
Web Site: https://www.heliospectra.com
HELIO—(OMX)
Rev.: $3,505,371
Assets: $4,996,426
Liabilities: $3,836,639
Net Worth: $1,159,787
Earnings: ($2,252,268)
Emp.: 11
Fiscal Year-end: 12/31/23
Electric Lamp Mfr
N.A.I.C.S.: 335139
Andreas Gunnarsson (Chm)

Subsidiaries:

Heliospectra Inc. (1)
1005 Northgate Dr Ste 325, San Rafael, CA 94903
Electric Lamp Mfr
N.A.I.C.S.: 335139

HELIOSTAR METALS LTD.

595 Burrard Street Suite 1723, Vancouver, V7X 1J1, BC, Canada
Tel.: (604) 484-7855 BC
Web Site:
https://www.heliostarmetals.com
Year Founded: 1983
HSTXF—(OTCQX)
Rev.: $1,355
Assets: $9,512,364
Liabilities: $1,470,120
Net Worth: $8,042,244
Earnings: ($9,744,276)
Fiscal Year-end: 03/31/22
Mineral Exploration Services
N.A.I.C.S.: 213114
Jacques Vaillancourt *(Chm)*

Subsidiaries:

Redstar Gold USA Inc. (1)
5301 Longley Ln Ste 122, Reno, NV 89511
Tel.: (775) 828-4010
Sales Range: $50-74.9 Million
Emp.: 1
Gold Exploration Services
N.A.I.C.S.: 213114

HELIQWEST AVIATION INC
37-27018 Sh 633, PO Box 97, Sturgeon, T8T 0E3, AB, Canada
Tel.: (780) 458-3005
Web Site: https://www.heliqwest.com
Rev.: $11,201,340
Emp.: 50
Aircraft Maintenance & Services
N.A.I.C.S.: 336413

HELIUM ONE GLOBAL LTD.
Kilwa House 369 Toure Drive, PO Box 23197, Dar es Salaam, Tanzania VG
Web Site: http://www.helium-one.com
Year Founded: 2015
Oil & Gas Dtr
N.A.I.C.S.: 237120
David Minchin *(CEO)*

Subsidiaries:

Attis Oil and Gas Limited (1)
C/o The Clubhouse 8st Jamess Square St Jamess, London, SW1Y 4J, United Kingdom
Tel.: (44) 207 236 1177
Web Site: http://www.mayanenergy.co.uk
Sales Range: Less than $1 Million
Emp.: 5
Oil & Gas Exploration
N.A.I.C.S.: 211120
Charles Ainslie Wood *(Chm)*

HELIX BIOPHARMA CORP.
Bay Adelaide Centre North Tower 40 Temperance Street Suite 2700, PO Box 4, Toronto, M5H 0B4, ON, Canada
Tel.: (604) 684-2181
Web Site:
https://www.helixbiopharma.com
HBP—(TSX)
Assets: $3,179,968
Liabilities: $4,269,684
Net Worth: ($1,089,716)
Earnings: ($6,287,967)
Emp.: 10
Fiscal Year-end: 07/31/21
Pharmaceutical Developer & Mfr
N.A.I.C.S.: 325412
Slawomir Majewski *(Chm)*

Subsidiaries:

PharmaDerm Laboratories Ltd. (1)
305 Industrial Pkwy S Unit 3, Aurora, L4G 6X7, ON, Canada
Tel.: (905) 841-2300
Web Site: http://www.biochipnet.com
Pharmaceuticals
N.A.I.C.S.: 325412

HELIX RESOURCES LIMITED
Level 4 225 St Georges Terrace, Perth, 6000, WA, Australia
Tel.: (61) 893212644 AU
Web Site:
https://www.helixresources.com.au
HLX—(ASX)
Rev.: $139,028
Assets: $21,876,749
Liabilities: $609,407
Net Worth: $21,267,342
Earnings: ($1,180,933)
Emp.: 1
Fiscal Year-end: 06/30/24
Iron Ore, Uranium & Gold Exploration
N.A.I.C.S.: 212210
Benjamin Donovan *(Sec)*

HELIXMITH CO., LTD.
21 Magokjungang 8-ro 7-gil, Gangseo-gu, Seoul, 07794, Korea (South)
Tel.: (82) 221027200
Web Site: https://www.helixmith.com
Year Founded: 1996
084990—(KRS)
Rev.: $2,147,299
Assets: $194,865,421
Liabilities: $28,826,583
Net Worth: $166,038,837
Earnings: ($33,030,559)
Emp.: 111
Fiscal Year-end: 12/31/22
Biological Product Mfr
N.A.I.C.S.: 325414
Sunyoung Kim *(Founder & CEO)*

HELKAMA-AUTO OY
Lautamiehentie 3, 02770, Espoo, Finland
Tel.: (358) 104362300 FI
Web Site: http://www.helkama-auto.fi
Year Founded: 1905
Sales Range: $150-199.9 Million
Emp.: 91
Automobile Whslr
N.A.I.C.S.: 423110
Maija Koskela *(CEO)*

HELLA GMBH & CO. KGAA
Rixbecker Strasse 75, 59552, Lippstadt, Germany
Tel.: (49) 2941380 De
Web Site: https://www.hella.com
Year Founded: 1899
HLE—(LUX)
Rev.: $8,780,336,522
Assets: $7,795,132,547
Liabilities: $4,601,161,973
Net Worth: $3,193,970,574
Earnings: $291,333,370
Emp.: 37,448
Fiscal Year-end: 12/31/23
Automobile Product Distr
N.A.I.C.S.: 423120
Rolf Breidenbach *(Chm-Mgmt Bd, Pres, CEO & Mng Dir)*

Subsidiaries:

AutoMester Danmark ApS (1)
Hvidkaervej 23 D, 5250, Odense, Denmark
Tel.: (45) 6 341 8988
Web Site: https://www.automester.dk
Automotive Spare Parts Distr
N.A.I.C.S.: 423120

Beifang HELLA Automotive Lighting Ltd. (1)
No 339 North Shenwei Road Yanjiao, Economic and Technological Development Zone, Sanhe, 65201, Hebei, China
Tel.: (86) 1089492600
Rev.: $5,017,320
Emp.: 366
Automotive Spare Parts Distr
N.A.I.C.S.: 423120

Changchun HELLA Automotive Lighting Ltd. (1)
No 593 Kunshan Road Changchun Economic and Technical Development Zone, Changchun, 130033, China
Rev.: $28,474,920
Emp.: 1,369
Automobile Spare Parts Mfr
N.A.I.C.S.: 336390

Docter Optics Asia Ltd. (1)
No 711 Shinwon Plaza 85 Dokseodang-ro, Yongsan-gu, Seoul, 04419, Korea (South)
Tel.: (82) 15225416
Optical Component Mfr
N.A.I.C.S.: 333310

Docter Optics SE (1)
Mittelweg 29, 07806, Neustadt, Germany
Tel.: (49) 36481270
Web Site: https://www.docteroptics.com
Optical Product Mfr
N.A.I.C.S.: 327215
Henry Steger *(Dir-Sls & Mktg)*

Subsidiary (US):

Docter Optics Inc. (2)
1425 W Elliot Rd Ste A-105, Gilbert, AZ 85233
Tel.: (480) 844-7585
Optical Product Distr
N.A.I.C.S.: 456130

Electra Hella's S.A. (1)
Doiranis 139 & Skra, 17672, Kallithea, Greece
Tel.: (30) 21095316905
Automotive Spare Parts Distr
N.A.I.C.S.: 423120

FWB Kunststofftechnik GmbH (1)
Blocksbergstrasse 175, 66955, Pirmasens, Germany
Tel.: (49) 63312620
Web Site: https://fwb-gmbh.de
Emp.: 200
Injection Molding Mfr
N.A.I.C.S.: 333511

HELLA (Xiamen) Automotive Electronics Co. Ltd. (1)
No 36 Second East Haijing Road, Amoy Expore Processing Zone, 361026, Xiamen, China
Tel.: (86) 5923162888
Rev.: $6,266,763
Emp.: 315
Automotive Spare Parts Mfr & Distr
N.A.I.C.S.: 336390
Gareth Hughes *(Gen Mgr)*

HELLA (Xiamen) Electronic Device Co., Ltd (1)
1446 XinJicheng Road, Huli, Xiamen, 360000, Fujian, China
Tel.: (86) 5923380001
Rev.: $1,519,857
Emp.: 114
Automotive Spare Parts Distr
N.A.I.C.S.: 423120

HELLA A/S (1)
Lundsbjerg Industrievej 13, 6200, Aabenraa, Denmark
Tel.: (45) 73303600
Emp.: 12
Automotive Spare Parts Distr
N.A.I.C.S.: 423120

HELLA Aglaia Mobile Vision GmbH (1)
Ullsteinstrasse 140, 12109, Berlin, Germany
Tel.: (49) 3020004290
Web Site: https://www.hella-aglaia.com
Software Development Services
N.A.I.C.S.: 541511
Thomas Schilling *(Chm)*

HELLA Asia Singapore Pte. Ltd. (1)
No 2 International Business Park 02-12 The Strategy, Singapore, 609930, Singapore
Tel.: (65) 68547300
Emp.: 49
Automotive Spare Parts Distr
N.A.I.C.S.: 423120

HELLA Australia Pty Ltd. (1)
4 Hargrave Place, Mentone, 3194, VIC, Australia
Tel.: (61) 395819333
Web Site: https://www.hella.com
Emp.: 515
Automotive Spare Parts Distr
N.A.I.C.S.: 423120

HELLA Automotive Sales, Inc. (1)
201 Kelly Dr, Peachtree City, GA 30269
Tel.: (770) 631-7500
Automobile Equipment Mfr
N.A.I.C.S.: 336110

HELLA Autotechnik Nova s.r.o. (1)
Druzstevni 338/16, 78985, Mohelnice, Czech Republic
Tel.: (420) 583498111
Emp.: 3,100
Automotive Spare Parts Distr
N.A.I.C.S.: 423120
Tomas Linhart *(CFO)*

HELLA CZ. s.r.o. (1)
Revolucni 785, 285 22, Zruc nad Sazavou, Czech Republic
Tel.: (420) 32 753 6425
Web Site: http://www.hella.cz
Emp.: 12
Automotive Spare Parts Distr
N.A.I.C.S.: 423120
Gelu Manta *(Dir-Mgmt)*

HELLA Centro Corporativo Mexico S.A. de C.V. (1)
Privada Cumbres de Acultzingo 202 Los Pirules, 54040, Tlalnepantla, Estado de Mexico, Mexico
Tel.: (52) 5553211300
Automotive Spare Parts Distr
N.A.I.C.S.: 423120

HELLA Changchun Tooling Co., Ltd. (1)
Tel.: (86) 43185078736
Rev.: $244,350
Emp.: 187
Automobile Spare Parts Mfr
N.A.I.C.S.: 336390

HELLA Corporate Center (China) Co., Ltd. (1)
7F New Bund Center No 555 West Haiyang Road, Pudong New Area, Shanghai, 201203, China
Tel.: (86) 2160586800
Automotive Spare Parts Distr
N.A.I.C.S.: 423120

HELLA Distribution GmbH (1)
Overhagener Weg 14, 59597, Erwitte, Germany
Tel.: (49) 2941389927
Web Site: http://www.hella.de
Emp.: 480
Automotive Spare Parts Distr
N.A.I.C.S.: 423120
Thomas Ladzik *(Mgr-Quality)*

HELLA Electronics Engineering GmbH (1)
Blumenstrasse 16A, 93055, Regensburg, Germany
Tel.: (49) 941599380
Web Site: http://www.hella.com
Emp.: 70
Automobile Spare Parts Mfr
N.A.I.C.S.: 336390
Moritz Schmidt *(Mng Dir)*

HELLA Engineering France S.A.S. (1)
6 Impasse Alice Guy, 31300, Toulouse, France
Tel.: (33) 561163257
Emp.: 87
Automotive Spare Parts Distr
N.A.I.C.S.: 423120

HELLA Fahrzeugkomponenten GmbH (1)
Dortmunder Strasse 5, 28199, Bremen, Germany
Tel.: (49) 4 215 9510
Web Site: https://www.hella.com
Emp.: 500
Automobile Spare Parts Mfr
N.A.I.C.S.: 336390

HELLA Fahrzeugteile Austria GmbH (1)
Fabriksgasse 2, 7503, Grosspetersdorf, Austria
Tel.: (43) 33629001
Emp.: 500
Automotive Spare Parts Distr
N.A.I.C.S.: 423120
Reinhard Pinzker *(Acct Mgr)*

HELLA GMBH & CO. KGAA

Hella GmbH & Co. KGaA—(Continued)

HELLA Fast Forward Shanghai Co., Ltd. (1)
Unit 4 building 15 No 56 Antuo Road, Jiading District, Shanghai, 201805, China
Tel.: (86) 2160958789
Automotive Electronic Component Mfr
N.A.I.C.S.: 336320

HELLA Finance Nederland (1)
Celsiusbaan 2, 3439 NC, Nieuwegein, Netherlands
Tel.: (31) 306095611
Automotive Spare Parts Distr
N.A.I.C.S.: 423120

HELLA Gutmann Holding GmbH (1)
Am Krebsbach 2, 79241, Ihringen, Germany
Tel.: (49) 2941380
Automobile Spare Parts Mfr
N.A.I.C.S.: 336390

Subsidiary (Domestic):

HELLA Gutmann Anlagenvermietung GmbH (2)
Gerberstr 2, 79206, Breisach, Baden-Wurttemberg, Germany
Automobile Spare Parts Mfr
N.A.I.C.S.: 336390

Subsidiary (Non-US):

HELLA Gutmann Solutions International AG (2)
Sonnenbergstrasse 11, 6052, Hergiswil, Switzerland
Tel.: (41) 416304560
Web Site: http://www.swiss.hella-gutmann.com
Automobile Spare Parts Mfr
N.A.I.C.S.: 336390

HGS-LITO Kft. (2)
Cziraki u 26-32, 1163, Budapest, Hungary
Tel.: (36) 702601327
Automotive Diagnostic Equipment Mfr
N.A.I.C.S.: 334515

HELLA Gutmann Mobility GmbH (1)
Gutenbergstr 4, 10587, Berlin, Germany
Tel.: (49) 3055578840
Optical Component Mfr
N.A.I.C.S.: 333310

HELLA Gutmann Solutions A/S (1)
Lundborgvej 16, 8800, Viborg, Denmark
Tel.: (45) 86602888
Web Site: https://www.hella-gutmann.dk
Automobile Spare Parts Mfr
N.A.I.C.S.: 336390
Bertz Thomsen *(Mng Dir-Sls, Mktg & Economy)*

HELLA Handel Austria GmbH (1)
Deutschstrasse 6, 1239, Vienna, Austria
Tel.: (43) 1614600
Automotive Spare Parts Distr
N.A.I.C.S.: 423120

HELLA Hungaria Kft. (1)
Forgach u 17, 1139, Budapest, Hungary
Tel.: (36) 14502150
Emp.: 10
Automotive Spare Parts Distr
N.A.I.C.S.: 423120

HELLA India Automotive Private Limited (1)
9th K M Mile Stone Gurgaon Farookhnagar Road, Gurgaon, 122001, Haryana, India
Tel.: (91) 1244425700
Emp.: 98
Automotive Spare Parts Distr
N.A.I.C.S.: 423120
Naveen Gautam *(Mng Dir)*

HELLA India Automotive Private Limitited (1)
9th KM Mile Stone Gurgaon Farookhnagar Road, Village Dhankot Distt, Gurgaon, 122001, Haryana, India
Tel.: (91) 1244991700
Emp.: 1,600
Automotive Electronic Component Mfr
N.A.I.C.S.: 336320

HELLA Induperm A/S (1)
Kobenhavnsvej 1, 4800, Nykobing, Denmark
Tel.: (45) 54860200
Automotive Spare Parts Distr
N.A.I.C.S.: 423120
Matthias Schroeter *(Mng Dir)*

HELLA Innenleuchten-Systeme Bratislava, s.r.o. (1)
Tehelna 8, 841 07, Bratislava, Slovakia
Tel.: (421) 269204100
Automotive Spare Parts Distr
N.A.I.C.S.: 423120
Ivan Drgon *(Coord-Logistics)*

HELLA Innenleuchten-Systeme GmbH (1)
Maienbuhlstrasse 7, 79677, Wembach, Germany
Tel.: (49) 76 738 2070
Web Site: http://www.hella.com
Emp.: 700
Automobile Spare Parts Mfr
N.A.I.C.S.: 336390
Thomas Weier *(Head-Pur & Logistics)*

HELLA Ireland Limited (1)
Woodford Business Park Santry Unit 6 1, Dublin, Ireland
Tel.: (353) 18620000809
Automotive Spare Parts Distr
N.A.I.C.S.: 423120
Mannix Kennedy *(Dir-Sls)*

HELLA Japan Inc. (1)
Kosugi bldg 9F / 10F 1-28-11, Shinjuku-ku, Tokyo, 160-0022, Japan
Tel.: (81) 345783000
Automotive Spare Parts Distr
N.A.I.C.S.: 423120

HELLA Korea Inc. (1)
10F 41 Mapo-daero 4da-gil, Mapo-gu, Seoul, 04177, Korea (South)
Tel.: (82) 221779600
Automotive Spare Parts Distr
N.A.I.C.S.: 423120

HELLA Lighting Finland Oy (1)
Inkereentie 566, 24280, Salo, Finland
Tel.: (358) 104764400
Automotive Spare Parts Distr
N.A.I.C.S.: 423120
Kimmo Suupohja *(Mng Dir)*

HELLA Middle East FZE (1)
LOB 19 Office 502, PO Box 17002, Dubai, United Arab Emirates
Tel.: (971) 48996000
Rev.: $5,443,600
Emp.: 18
Automotive Spare Parts Distr
N.A.I.C.S.: 423120

HELLA Polska Sp. z o.o. (1)
Al Wyscigowa 6, 02-681, Warsaw, Poland
Tel.: (48) 225141760
Automotive Spare Parts Distr
N.A.I.C.S.: 423120
Michal Koszalka *(Mng Dir)*

HELLA Romania s.r.l. (1)
Hella street no 3, Ghiroda, 307200, Timisoara, Romania
Tel.: (40) 372881100
Automotive Spare Parts Distr
N.A.I.C.S.: 423120
Razvan Cighi *(Head-Sls)*

HELLA S.A. (1)
Avda de los Artesanos 24, Tres Cantos, 28760, Madrid, Spain
Tel.: (34) 918061919
Automotive Spare Parts Distr
N.A.I.C.S.: 423120
Luis Puchades Baixauli *(Mgr-Comml)*

HELLA S.A.S. (1)
11 avenue Albert Einstein Le Coudray, BP 7, 93155, Le Blanc-Mesnil, Cedex, France
Tel.: (33) 149395900
Automotive Spare Parts Distr
N.A.I.C.S.: 423120

HELLA S.p.A. (1)
Via B Buozzi 5, 20090, Settala, MI, Italy
Tel.: (39) 0298 8351
Web Site: http://www.hella.it
Automotive Spare Parts Distr
N.A.I.C.S.: 423120
Daniela Copetti *(Acct Mgr)*

HELLA Saturnus Slovenija d.o.o. (1)
Letaliska c 17, 1001, Ljubljana, Slovenia
Tel.: (386) 15203333
Web Site: http://www.hella-saturns.si
Automobile Spare Parts Mfr
N.A.I.C.S.: 336390

HELLA Shanghai Electronics Co., Ltd. (1)
411 Jianye Road, Pudong New Area, Shanghai, 201201, China
Tel.: (86) 2161606888
Sales Range: $300-349.9 Million
Emp.: 1,600
Automobile Spare Parts Mfr
N.A.I.C.S.: 336390
James Lee *(Project Mgr)*

HELLA Slovakia Front-Lighting s.r.o. (1)
Kocovce 228, 916 31, Nove Mesto nad Vahom, Slovakia
Tel.: (421) 327705111
Automotive Spare Parts Distr
N.A.I.C.S.: 423120

HELLA Slovakia Lighting s.r.o. (1)
Hrezdovska 1629/16, 957 04, Banovce nad Bebravou, Slovakia
Tel.: (421) 387628110
Electronic Product Mfr & Distr
N.A.I.C.S.: 334111

HELLA Slovakia Signal-Lighting s.r.o. (1)
Hrezdovska 1629/16, 957 04, Banovce nad Bebravou, Slovakia
Tel.: (421) 387628110
Automotive Spare Parts Distr
N.A.I.C.S.: 423120

HELLA Trading (Shanghai) Co., Ltd. (1)
11th Floor Building 2 No 58 Haiqu Road, Zhang Jiang Hi-Tech Park Pudong District, Shanghai, 200072, China
Tel.: (86) 2180267162
Sales Range: $25-49.9 Million
Emp.: 280
Automotive Spare Parts Distr
N.A.I.C.S.: 423120

HELLA UK Holdings Limited (1)
Unit 6 Appletree Industrial Estate Appletree Road, Chipping Warden, OX17 1LL, Oxon, United Kingdom
Tel.: (44) 1295662400
Web Site: https://www.hella.co.uk
Emp.: 50
Automotive Spare Parts Distr
N.A.I.C.S.: 423120

HELLA Ventures, LLC (1)
306 Cambridge Ave, Palo Alto, CA 94040
Tel.: (734) 414-0932
Web Site: https://www.hellaventures.com
Private Equity Services
N.A.I.C.S.: 523999
Martin Rudigier *(Principal)*

HELLA Vietnam Company Limited (1)
Golden Tower 10th floor 06 Nguyen Thi Minh Khai, District 1, Ho Chi Minh City, Vietnam
Tel.: (84) 862879555
Automotive Spare Parts Distr
N.A.I.C.S.: 423120
Timo Krokowski *(Mng Dir)*

HELLA Werkzeug Technologiezentrum GmbH (1)
Beckumer Strasse 130, 59555, Lippstadt, Germany
Automobile Spare Parts Mfr
N.A.I.C.S.: 336390

HELLA do Brazil Automotive Ltda. (1)
Rua Bom Pastor 2224-15th floor, Ipiranga, Sao Paulo, 04203-002, Brazil
Tel.: (55) 1126277801
Automotive Spare Parts Distr
N.A.I.C.S.: 423120
Miriam Niestadtkotter *(Product Mgr & Mgr-Supply Chain)*

HELLA-New Zealand Limited (1)
81-83 Ben Lomond Crescent, Pakuranga, Auckland, 2010, New Zealand
Tel.: (64) 9 577 0000
Web Site: https://www.hella.co.nz
Automobile Spare Parts Mfr
N.A.I.C.S.: 336390
Bryan Wild *(Mgr-Quality Assurance)*

Hella Inc (1)
201 Kelly Dr, Peachtree City, GA 30269
Tel.: (770) 631-7500
Web Site: http://www.hellausa.com
Emp.: 100
Automotive Spare Parts Distr
N.A.I.C.S.: 423120

Subsidiary (Domestic):

HELLA Corporate Center USA, Inc. (2)
15951 Technology Dr, Northville, MI 48168
Tel.: (734) 414-0900
Emp.: 350
Automotive Spare Parts Distr
N.A.I.C.S.: 423120
Mike Thompson *(Dir-Fin)*

Hella Mining LLC (2)
2580 Ruby Vista Dr, Elko, NV 89801
Tel.: (775) 738-7440
Automotive Spare Parts Distr
N.A.I.C.S.: 423120

Hella KGaA Hueck & Co. - Nellingen Plant (1)
Amstetterstrasse 32, 89191, Nellingen, Germany
Tel.: (49) 733796150
Automobile Spare Parts Mfr
N.A.I.C.S.: 336390

Hella KGaA Hueck & Co. - Plant 4 (1)
Romerstrasse 66, 59075, Hamm, Bockum-Hovel, Germany
Tel.: (49) 23817980
Automobile Spare Parts Mfr
N.A.I.C.S.: 336390

Hella KGaA Hueck & Co. - Plant 5 (1)
Berghauser Strasse 30, 45663, Recklinghausen, Germany
Tel.: (49) 23613070
Automobile Spare Parts Mfr
N.A.I.C.S.: 336390

Hella-Bekto Industries d.o.o. (1)
Ibrahima Popovica bb, 73000, Gorazde, Bosnia & Herzegovina
Tel.: (387) 62994155
Automotive Spare Parts Distr
N.A.I.C.S.: 423120

Intermobil Otomotiv Mumessillik Ve Ticaret A.S. (1)
Halide Edip Adivar Mahallesi Darulaceze Caddesi Akin Plaza No 3/83, Sisli, 34382, Istanbul, Turkiye
Tel.: (90) 2123142000
Web Site: https://www.intermobil.com.tr
Emp.: 1,954
Automotive Spare Parts Mfr & Distr
N.A.I.C.S.: 336390

Manufacturas y Accesorios Electricos S.A. (1)
Calle de la Solana 15, Torrejon de Ardoz, Madrid, Spain
Tel.: (34) 918061919
Automotive Spare Parts Distr
N.A.I.C.S.: 423120

Sistemas Iluminacion S.A. de C.V. (1)
Cumbres de Maltrata Hab Loma Bonita, 54040, Tlalnepantla, Mexico
Tel.: (52) 5555146180
Automotive Spare Parts Distr
N.A.I.C.S.: 423120

TecMotive GmbH (1)
Ullsteinstrasse 140, 12109, Berlin, Germany
Tel.: (49) 3058595780
Web Site: https://www.tecmotive.com
Technical Field Services
N.A.I.C.S.: 541330

The Drivery GmbH (1)
Mariendorfer Damm 1, 12099, Berlin, Germany
Tel.: (49) 1747842385

AND PRIVATE COMPANIES

Web Site: https://www.thedrivery.com
Mobility Innovation & Marketplace Services
N.A.I.C.S.: 926120
Timon Rupp *(Founder, CEO & Gen Mgr)*

UAB HELLA Lithuania (1)
Oro parko str 6 Kaunas FEZ, Kaunas district, 54460, Kaunas, Lithuania
Tel.: (370) 65658585
Optical Component Mfr
N.A.I.C.S.: 333310
Jurgita Macijauskiene *(Head-HR)*

UCANDO GmbH (1)
Gutenbergstrasse 4, 10587, Berlin, Germany
Tel.: (49) 3055578840
Automobile Spare Parts Mfr
N.A.I.C.S.: 336390
Frank Feichtinger *(Mng Dir)*

UCANDO Sp. z o.o. (1)
ul Stanieẃicka 22, 03-310, Warsaw, Poland
Tel.: (48) 22 100 1307
Web Site: https://www.ucando.pl
Automotive Spare Parts Distr
N.A.I.C.S.: 423120
Frank Feichtinger *(Mng Dir)*

avitea GmbH (1)
Sudstrasse 8 - 8a, 59557, Lippstadt, Germany
Tel.: (49) 29 418 2830
Web Site: https://www.avitea.de
Employment Placement Agencies
N.A.I.C.S.: 561311

avitea Industrieservice GmbH (1)
Sudstrasse 8-8a, 59557, Lippstadt, Germany
Tel.: (49) 2941660050
Web Site: https://www.avitea-industrieservice.de
Emp.: 700
Logistic Services
N.A.I.C.S.: 541614

HELLA INDIA LIGHTING LTD.
6A 6th Floor Platinum Tower 184 Udyog Vihar Phase-1, Gurgaon, 122016, Haryana, India
Tel.: (91) 18001035405
Web Site: http://www.hella.com
Year Founded: 1959
Automobile Parts Mfr
N.A.I.C.S.: 336320
Narender Jain *(CFO)*

HELLA INFRA MARKET PRIVATE LIMITED
Opal Square 4th Floor Plot No C-1 SG Barve Road, Opp Railadevi TMC Office Wagle Estate, Thane, 400604, Maharashtra, India
Tel.: (91) 9606350000 In
Web Site: https://infra.market
Construction Materials Mfr & Distr
N.A.I.C.S.: 423390

HELLENIC BANK PUBLIC COMPANY LTD.
Corner Limassol Avenue and 200 Athalassa Avenue, 2025, Strovolos, 2025, Cyprus
Tel.: (357) 22500000
Web Site: https://www.hellenicbank.com
Year Founded: 1976
HB—(CYP)
Rev.: $733,325,974
Assets: $22,145,849,435
Liabilities: $20,483,024,619
Net Worth: $1,662,824,815
Earnings: $403,401,038
Emp.: 2,256
Fiscal Year-end: 12/31/23
Banking Services
N.A.I.C.S.: 522110
Andrew Charles Wynn *(Vice Chm)*

Subsidiaries:

Hellenic Alico Life Insurance Company Ltd (1)
38 Kennedy Ave, PO Box 20672, 1662, Nicosia, Cyprus (72.5%)
Tel.: (357) 22450650
Sales Range: $50-74.9 Million
Emp.: 7
Commericial Banking
N.A.I.C.S.: 522110

Hellenic Bank (Investments) Ltd (1)
31 Kyriacou Matsi Str 2nd Fl, PO Box 24747, 1082, Nicosia, Cyprus
Tel.: (357) 22500100
Web Site: http://www.hellenicbank.com
Sales Range: $50-74.9 Million
Emp.: 15
Investment Banking & Securities Dealing
N.A.I.C.S.: 523150

Hellenic Bank Trust and Finance Corp. Ltd (1)
Corner 200 Limassol Ave and Athalassas Ave, 2025, Strovolos, Cyprus
Tel.: (357) 22500821
Web Site: http://www.hellenicbank.com
Financial Investment
N.A.I.C.S.: 523999

Pancyprian Insurance Company Ltd (1)
Pancyprian Tower, 66 Grivas Dhigenis Ave, 1095, Nicosia, Cyprus
Tel.: (357) 22743743
Sales Range: $50-74.9 Million
Emp.: 80
Commericial Banking
N.A.I.C.S.: 522110

HELLENIC COMPANY FOR TELECOMMUNICATIONS & TELEMATIC APPLICATIONS S.A.
Atthidon Street 4, 17671, Kallithea, Greece
Tel.: (30) 2109559000 GR
Web Site: https://www.forthnet.gr
Year Founded: 1995
HTO—(ATH)
Rev.: $3,708,995,278
Assets: $5,366,251,612
Liabilities: $3,381,601,547
Net Worth: $1,984,650,065
Earnings: $417,239,159
Emp.: 10,590
Fiscal Year-end: 12/31/22
Internet & Other Telecommunication Services
N.A.I.C.S.: 517112
Dimitris Tzelepis *(CEO-Interim & CFO)*

HELLENIC EXCHANGES- ATHENS STOCK EXCHANGE S.A.
110 Atainon Avenue, 10442, Athens, Greece
Tel.: (30) 2103366800
Web Site: https://www.athexgroup.gr
EXAE—(ATH)
Rev.: $39,347,075
Assets: $392,975,394
Liabilities: $283,605,655
Net Worth: $109,369,739
Earnings: $8,864,667
Emp.: 236
Fiscal Year-end: 12/31/22
Holding Company; Stock Exchanges
N.A.I.C.S.: 551112
Sokrates Lazaridis *(CEO)*

Subsidiaries:

Athens Exchange S.A. (1)
110 Athinon Ave, 104 42, Athens, Greece
Tel.: (30) 2103366496
Web Site: http://www.athexgroup.gr
Sales Range: $25-49.9 Million
Emp.: 132
Stock Exchange
N.A.I.C.S.: 523210

HELLENIC FABRICS S.A.
26 Komninon St, 54624, Thessaloniki, Greece
Tel.: (30) 2310366886
Sales Range: $5-14.9 Billion
Emp.: 356
Denim Fabrics Production Services
N.A.I.C.S.: 313220
Ioannis Christos Akkas *(Chm)*

Subsidiaries:

Kilkis Spinning Mills S.A. (1)
Neasanta, 61100, Kilkis, Greece
Tel.: (30) 2310366700
Web Site: http://www.kellinicfabric.gr
Sales Range: $25-49.9 Million
Emp.: 185
Cotton Yarn Mfr
N.A.I.C.S.: 313110
John Andrias *(Mng Dir)*

Thessaly Cotton Ginning S.A (1)
Grammatiko, Sofadhes, 43300, Karditsa, Greece
Tel.: (30) 2443029100
Web Site: http://www.hellanicfabrics.com
Sales Range: $25-49.9 Million
Emp.: 70
Ginned Cotton Mfr
N.A.I.C.S.: 115111
John Accas *(Gen Mgr)*

HELLENIC FISHFARMING S.A.
5c Pentelis Avenue, Halandri, 152 34, Athens, Greece
Tel.: (30) 210 6131666
Web Site: http://www.helfish.gr
Year Founded: 1987
Emp.: 310
Fish Farming & Processing Services
N.A.I.C.S.: 112511
Ioannis Aristeidis Katsivelis *(Chm & Mng Dir)*

Subsidiaries:

ASTERIAS S.A. (1)
3 Botassi, Piraeus, 18537, Greece
Tel.: (30) 210 4287949
Emp.: 1
Fish Farming & Processing Services
N.A.I.C.S.: 112511
Christof Sarmas *(Mgr)*

KALLONI S.A. (1)
PO Box 312, Kimmeria, 67100, Xanthi, Greece
Tel.: (30) 25410 29992
Web Site: http://www.kalloni.gr
Fish Farming & Processing Services
N.A.I.C.S.: 112511
Panagioti Zacharopoulos *(Mgr-Sls)*

HELLENIC TELECOMMUNICATIONS ORGANIZATION S.A.

HELLENIC TELECOMMUNICATIONS ORGANIZATION S.A.
99 Kifissias Avenue Maroussi, 15124, Athens, Greece
Tel.: (30) 2103243523 GR
Web Site: http://www.cosmote.gr
Year Founded: 1949
HTO—(ATH)
Rev.: $3,729,009,281
Assets: $5,395,208,288
Liabilities: $3,399,848,910
Net Worth: $1,995,359,378
Earnings: $419,490,611
Emp.: 11,020
Fiscal Year-end: 12/31/22
Local, Long-Distance & Mobile Telecommunications & Internet Services
N.A.I.C.S.: 517111
Michael Tsamaz *(Chm & CEO)*

Subsidiaries:

Cosmo-One Hellas Market Site S.A. (1)
Olympics 26, 14122, Iraklion, Greece (61.74%)
Tel.: (30) 210 2723 810
Web Site: http://www.cosmo-one.gr
Emp.: 26
Electronic Auctions
N.A.I.C.S.: 455219

Cosmote E-Value S.A. (1)
6 - 8 Megalou Vasileiou Street Kerameikos, 118 54, Athens, Greece
Tel.: (30) 2108198800
Web Site: http://www.cosmote-evalue.gr
Telecommunication Servicesb
N.A.I.C.S.: 517810
Athanasios Tom Stratos *(CEO)*

Cosmote Global Solutions S.A. (1)
Airport Plaza Stockholm Building 2nd Floor Leonardo da Vincilaan 19A, 1831, Diegem, Belgium
Tel.: (32) 23009111
Web Site: http://www.cosmote-gs.com
IT Services
N.A.I.C.S.: 541519

Cosmote Mobile Telecommunications SA (1)
98 Kifissias Av, 15124, Maroussi, Athens, Greece (100%)
Tel.: (30) 6971013888
Web Site: http://www.cosmote.gr
Sales Range: $1-4.9 Billion
Emp.: 7,500
Mobile Telecommunications Services
N.A.I.C.S.: 517112

Subsidiary (Domestic):

Germanos S.A. (2)
23rd Klm Athens Lamia National Road, Agios Stefanos, Greece
Tel.: (30) 2106242000
Web Site: http://www.e-germanos.gr
Telecommunication Servicesb
N.A.I.C.S.: 517810

Subsidiary (Non-US):

Germanos Telecom Romania S.A. (3)
Sos Bucuresti Ploiesti, No 7 Sect 1, 013692, Bucharest, Romania (99.02%)
Tel.: (40) 214077331
Web Site: http://www.germanos.ro
Telecommunications
N.A.I.C.S.: 517810

Germanos Telecom S.A. (3)
Vidoe Smileski Bato No 4, 1000, Skopje, North Macedonia (99.03%)
Tel.: (389) 22400510
Telecommunications
N.A.I.C.S.: 517810

Subsidiary (Non-US):

SC Cosmote Romanian Mobile Telecommunications S.A. (2)
3 19G sector 6 Atriom Bldg, 011141, Bucharest, Romania (86.2%)
Tel.: (40) 214040432
Web Site: http://www.cosmote.ro
Sales Range: $150-199.9 Million
Emp.: 1,000
Telecommunications
N.A.I.C.S.: 517810

Sunlight Romania S.R.L. Filiala (2)
B-dul Preciziei 11 Sector 6, 007000, Bucharest, Romania
Tel.: (40) 214077357
Web Site: http://www.sunlight.ro
Emp.: 20
Software Reproducing
N.A.I.C.S.: 334610

HELLASCOM S.A. (1)
26 Olympias Street, 141 22, Iraklion, Greece (100%)
Tel.: (30) 2106386800
Web Site: http://www.hellascom.com
Sales Range: $25-49.9 Million
Emp.: 30
Telecommunications Networks Design, Planning & Construction
N.A.I.C.S.: 517810

OTE Academy S.A. (1)
Pelica & Spartis 1, 15122, Maroussi, Greece (100%)
Tel.: (30) 2106114400
Web Site: http://www.oteacademy.gr
Sales Range: $25-49.9 Million
Emp.: 45
Telecommunications
N.A.I.C.S.: 517810
Christos Vakalis *(Mng Dir)*

HELLENIC TELECOMMUNICATIONS ORGANIZATION S.A.

Hellenic Telecommunications Organization S.A.—(Continued)

OTE Estate S.A. (1)
99 Kifissias Ave, 15124, Athens, Greece
Tel.: (30) 2106372700
Web Site: http://www.ote-estate.gr
Sales Range: $50-74.9 Million
Emp.: 64
Real Estate Development & Management Services
N.A.I.C.S.: 531390

OTE International Solutions S.A. (1)
6-8 Agisilaou Str, 15123, Maroussi, Athens, Greece **(100%)**
Tel.: (30) 210 87 62 500
Web Site: http://www.oteglobe.gr
Sales Range: $50-74.9 Million
Emp.: 120
Telecommunication Servicesb
N.A.I.C.S.: 517810
Dino Andreou (CEO)

OTE Plus Technical & Business Solutions S.A. (1)
90 Marinou Antipa str, N Iraklio, Athens, 14121, Greece **(100%)**
Tel.: (30) 2102781700
Web Site: http://www.oteplus.gr
Emp.: 60
Information Technology Consulting Services
N.A.I.C.S.: 541690
Olga Tamvaka (Gen Mgr)

HELLENIC TELEVISION LTD.
Unit 1 20 Brook Road Wood Green, London, N22 6TR, United Kingdom
Tel.: (44) 2082927073 UK
Web Site: http://www.hellenictv.net
Year Founded: 1982
Broadcast Television Services
N.A.I.C.S.: 334220
Christaki Fella (CEO)

Subsidiaries:

CYTA (UK) Ltd (1)
10 Ashfield Parade, London, NW3 2BH, United Kingdom
Tel.: (44) 2088825830
Web Site: http://www.cytauk.com
Emp.: 15
Telecommunications Products & Services
N.A.I.C.S.: 517810
Serg Sergiu (Mng Dir)

HELLENIQ ENERGY HOLDINGS S.A
8A Chimarras str, 151 25, Maroussi, Greece
Tel.: (30) 2106302000 GR
Web Site: https://www.helleniqenergy.gr
Year Founded: 1998
98LQ—(LSE)
Rev.: $17,819,389
Assets: $2,705,391
Liabilities: $167,429
Net Worth: $2,537,963
Earnings: $1,099,248
Emp.: 3,519
Fiscal Year-end: 12/31/22
Holding Company
N.A.I.C.S.: 551112
Ioannis Papathanasiou (Chm)

Subsidiaries:

Blue Circle Engineering Limited (1)
3 Ellispontou, Strovolos, 2015, Nicosia, Cyprus
Tel.: (357) 22441415
Web Site: https://www.bluecircle.com.cy
Liquid Petroleum Gas Distr
N.A.I.C.S.: 424710

HELLENIQ ENERGY HOLDINGS S.A.
8A Chimarras str, GR 151 25, Maroussi, Greece
Tel.: (30) 2106302000
Web Site: http://www.helpe.gr
Year Founded: 1998

ELPE—(ATH)
Rev.: $15,657,314,915
Assets: $9,240,233,110
Liabilities: $6,296,782,862
Net Worth: $2,943,450,248
Earnings: $965,873,084
Emp.: 3,519
Fiscal Year-end: 12/31/22
Oil & Gas Production Services
N.A.I.C.S.: 211120
Andreas Shiamishis (CEO)

Subsidiaries:

Asprofos Engineering S.A. (1)
284 El Venizelou Avenue Kallithea, 176 75, Athens, Greece **(100%)**
Tel.: (30) 2109491600
Web Site: http://www.asprofos.gr
Sales Range: $75-99.9 Million
Emp.: 400
Engineeering Services
N.A.I.C.S.: 541330

Diaxon ABEE (1)
Industial Area of Komotini Section 45, 69100, Komotini, Greece **(100%)**
Tel.: (30) 2531082360
Sales Range: $50-74.9 Million
Emp.: 130
Petroleum Refining Services
N.A.I.C.S.: 324110
S. Pilitsis (Plant Mgr)

Diaxon SA (1)
8A Chimarras Str, 15125, Maroussi, Greece
Tel.: (30) 2106302228
Web Site: https://www.diaxon.gr
Polypropylene Film Mfr
N.A.I.C.S.: 326113
Georgios Zagliverinos (Chm & CEO)

EKO Serbia AD (1)
Tosin Bunar 274 a, Novi Beograd, Serbia
Tel.: (381) 112061500
Web Site: https://www.ekoserbia.com
Gas Station Services
N.A.I.C.S.: 457120
Vera Zivkovic (Mgr-HR)

EL.P.ET Balkaniki S.A. (1)
Chimarras St, 151 24, Maroussi, Greece **(100%)**
Tel.: (30) 2105533094
Web Site: http://www.elpet-balkaniki.gr
Petroleum & Petroleum Products Distr
N.A.I.C.S.: 424720

Subsidiary (Non-US):

Okta A.D. (2)
1 Str 25 Miladinovci, PO Box 66, Ilinden, 1000, Skopje, North Macedonia **(81.51%)**
Tel.: (389) 22532000
Web Site: https://www.okta-elpe.com
Sales Range: $200-249.9 Million
Emp.: 800
Oil Refinery
N.A.I.C.S.: 324110

Subsidiary (Domestic):

Vardax S.A. (2)
7th KM National Road Thessaloniki-Veroia, Echedoros, 57008, Thessaloniki, Greece **(100%)**
Tel.: (30) 2310750810
Web Site: https://www.vardax.gr
Sales Range: $25-49.9 Million
Emp.: 15
Crude Oil Pipeline Services
N.A.I.C.S.: 486110

ELPET Valkaniki SA (1)
199 Kifissias Avenue, 151 24, Athens, Greece
Tel.: (30) 2106839483
Petroleum Refining Services
N.A.I.C.S.: 324110

Eko ABEE (1)
2 Messogion Ave chimras 8 A, 15125, Athens, Greece **(100%)**
Tel.: (30) 2107705401
Web Site: http://www.eko.gr
Sales Range: $250-299.9 Million
Emp.: 800
Petroleum Product Distr
N.A.I.C.S.: 424720

George Georgiou (Chm & Mng Dir)

Subsidiary (Non-US):

Eko Bulgaria EAD (2)
Lachezar Stanchev St No 3 Litex Tower complex fl 9, Izgrev district, 1756, Sofia, Bulgaria **(100%)**
Tel.: (359) 24485500
Web Site: https://www.eko.bg
Sales Range: $50-74.9 Million
Emp.: 60
Petroleum Products Distr; Gas Station Developer & Operator
N.A.I.C.S.: 424720

Eko Georgia Ltd (2)
74 I Chavchavadge Ave 8th Fl, Tbilisi, 380062, Georgia **(97.4%)**
Tel.: (995) 032292364
Web Site: http://www.ekogeorgia.ge
Sales Range: $25-49.9 Million
Emp.: 17
Petroleum & Petroleum Products Importer, Exporter, Distr & Sales
N.A.I.C.S.: 424720

Eko Yu AD (2)
Tosin Donar 274A, 11000, Novi Beograd, Serbia **(100%)**
Tel.: (381) 112061500
Web Site: http://www.ekoserbia.com
Sales Range: $25-49.9 Million
Emp.: 40
Petroleum Products Distr; Gas Station Developer & Operator
N.A.I.C.S.: 424720

Hellenic Petroleum Cyprus Ltd. (2)
Ellispondou 3, Strovolos, Nicosia, Cyprus **(100%)**
Tel.: (357) 22477000
Web Site: http://www.eko.com.cy
Emp.: 55
Lubricant Product Distr
N.A.I.C.S.: 457210
George Gregoras (Mng Dir)

Global Petroleum Albania Sh.A (1)
Rruga e Kavajes 59, Tirana Tower, Tirana, Albania **(100%)**
Tel.: (355) 4235263
Web Site: http://www.global-alb.com
Petroleum Products Wholesale & Retail Importer
N.A.I.C.S.: 424720

Hellenic Petroleum International AG (1)
Wagramer Strasse19, 1220, Vienna, Austria **(100%)**
Tel.: (43) 126983710
Web Site: http://www.helpe.gr
Petroleum Production
N.A.I.C.S.: 211120
Andreas Shiamishis (Chm-Supervisory Bd)

Helpe Arta Preveza SA (1)
Gravias 4A, 15125, Maroussi, Greece
Tel.: (30) 2106302000
Web Site: http://www.helpe-artapreveza.gr
Hydrocarbon Mfr
N.A.I.C.S.: 325110

Jugopetrol AD (1)
Stanka Dragojevica bb, 81000, Podgorica, Montenegro **(54%)**
Tel.: (382) 20401800
Web Site: https://www.jugopetrol.co.me
Rev.: $184,099,987
Assets: $137,270,834
Liabilities: $21,671,178
Net Worth: $115,599,656
Earnings: $6,789,404
Fiscal Year-end: 12/31/2021
Petroleum & Petroleum Products Retailer, Distr & Warehouser; Hydrocarbon Exploration & Production Services
N.A.I.C.S.: 424720

HELLIX VENTURES INC.
125A - 1030 Denman Street, Vancouver, V6G 2M6, BC, Canada
Tel.: (604) 683-6657 AB
Web Site: http://www.hellixventures.com
Sales Range: Less than $1 Million
Emp.: 2

INTERNATIONAL PUBLIC

Oil & Gas Exploration & Development Services
N.A.I.C.S.: 211120
Frank Underhill (Pres)

HELLMA GMBH & CO. KG
Klosterrunsstrasse 5, 79379, Mullheim, Germany
Tel.: (49) 76311820 De
Web Site: http://www.hellma-analytics.com
Year Founded: 1922
Rev.: $18,346,020
Emp.: 210
Cells & Optical Components Distr
N.A.I.C.S.: 423460
Lutz Mayer (Mng Dir)

Subsidiaries:

Hellma (Asia Pacific) Pte Ltd (1)
21 Biopolis Road 03-01A, Nucleos, Singapore, 138567, Singapore
Tel.: (65) 63974129
Web Site: http://www.hellma-asia.com
Optical Goods Distr
N.A.I.C.S.: 423460
Sharon Tong (Mgr-Sls)

Hellma Axiom, Inc. (1)
1451 Edinger Ave Ste A, Tustin, CA 92780-6250
Tel.: (949) 757-9300
Web Site: http://www.goaxiom.com
Optical Instrument & Lens Mfr
N.A.I.C.S.: 333310
Walter M. Doyle (Owner)

Hellma Benelux BVBA (1)
Hogen Akkerhoekstraat 14, 9150, Kruibeke, Belgium
Tel.: (32) 38773327
Web Site: http://www.hellma.be
Optical Goods Distr
N.A.I.C.S.: 423460

Hellma Canada Limited (1)
7321 Victoria Park Avenue, Markham, L3R 2Z8, ON, Canada
Tel.: (905) 604-5013
Optical Goods Distr
N.A.I.C.S.: 423460

Hellma Italia S.R.L. (1)
Via Gioacchino Murat 38, 20159, Milan, Italy
Tel.: (39) 0226116419
Web Site: http://www.hellma.it
Optical Goods Distr
N.A.I.C.S.: 423460

Hellma Materials GmbH (1)
Moritz-von-Rohr-Strasse 1, 07745, Jena, Germany
Tel.: (49) 364128770
Web Site: http://www.hellma-materials.com
Emp.: 73
Optical Goods Distr
N.A.I.C.S.: 423460

Subsidiary (Domestic):

Photonic Sense Gmbh (2)
Am Goldberg 3, 99817, Eisenach, Germany
Tel.: (49) 369173180
Web Site: http://www.photonic-sense.com
Semiconductor Devices Mfr
N.A.I.C.S.: 334413

Hellma Optik GmbH (1)
Muhlenstrasse 30, 07745, Jena, Germany
Tel.: (49) 3641310780
Web Site: http://www.hellma-optics.com
Optical Goods Distr
N.A.I.C.S.: 423460
Oliver Falkenstorfer (Mng Dir)

Hellma Schweiz AG (1)
Schwantenmos 15, 8126, Zumikon, Switzerland
Tel.: (41) 449182379
Web Site: http://www.hellma.ch
Optical Goods Distr
N.A.I.C.S.: 423460
Pascal Giger (Product Mgr)

Hellma UK Ltd (1)
Cumberland House 24-28 Baxter Avenue,

AND PRIVATE COMPANIES

Southend-on-Sea, SS2 6HZ, Essex, United Kingdom
Tel.: (44) 1702335266
Web Site: http://www.hellma.co.uk
Optical Goods Distr
N.A.I.C.S.: 423460
Ray Wood *(Mgr-Technical Sls)*

Hellma USA Inc. (1)
80 Skyline Dr, Plainview, NY 11803
Tel.: (516) 939-0888
Web Site: http://www.hellmausa.com
Optical Goods Distr
N.A.I.C.S.: 423460

Hellma-France S.A.R.L. (1)
35 rue de Meaux, 75019, Paris, France
Tel.: (33) 142080128
Optical Goods Distr
N.A.I.C.S.: 423460

HELLMANN WORLDWIDE LOGISTICS GMBH & CO. KG

Elbestrasse 1, 49090, Osnabruck, Germany
Tel.: (49) 5416050
Web Site: http://www.hellmann.net
Year Founded: 1871
Sales Range: $1-4.9 Billion
Emp.: 8,652
Air, Sea & Road Freight Transportation; Warehousing, Logistics, Supply Chain Management & Customs Brokerage Services
N.A.I.C.S.: 488510
Jost J. Hellmann *(Mng Partner)*

Subsidiaries:

ATS-Hellmann Worldwide Logistics Ltd. (1)
Steinackerstrasse 28, Zurich, 8302, Switzerland
Tel.: (41) 44 815 80 00
Freight Forwarding & Shipping Services
N.A.I.C.S.: 488510
Claudio Gugger *(Mgr-Air Export)*

Hellmann East Europe LLC (1)
Mezhyhirskogo Spasa str 6D off 1, Vyshgorod, Kiev, 07300, Ukraine
Tel.: (380) 44 339 99 93
Freight Forwarding & Shipping Services
N.A.I.C.S.: 488510
Aleksandra Kacharskaya *(Mgr-OPS Dept)*

Hellmann East Europe Overseas Ltd (1)
1/20 Marazlievskaya 213 Office, 65014, Odessa, Ukraine
Tel.: (380) 48 737 30 40
Web Site: http://www.hellmann.com
Emp.: 20
Freight Forwarding & Shipping Services
N.A.I.C.S.: 488510
Alexey Azarov *(Dir-Admin)*

Hellmann East Europe SOOO (1)
Olshevskogo Str building 22 office 31, 220073, Minsk, Belarus
Tel.: (375) 17 202 59 85
Freight Forwarding & Shipping Services
N.A.I.C.S.: 488510
Anna Milutina *(Head-Road Dept)*

Hellmann Network Inc. (1)
1870 Rhapta Road Westlands, Nairobi, Kenya
Tel.: (254) 20 5225739
Freight Forwarding & Shipping Services
N.A.I.C.S.: 488510

Hellmann Perishable Logistics (1)
Aeroporto Internacional de Sao Paulo-Ed, Teca - sala 2 17, Guarulhos, 07190-971, Brazil
Tel.: (55) 11 2445 5130
Freight Forwarding & Shipping Services
N.A.I.C.S.: 488510
Camela Atouguia *(Gen Mgr)*

Hellmann Perishable Logistics (1)
2nd Freight Avenue Cargo Village JKIA Int Airport, Nairobi, Kenya
Tel.: (254) 723 701 276
Freight Forwarding & Shipping Services
N.A.I.C.S.: 488510

Hellmann Perishable Logistics (1)
Almacen Fiscalizado WEC 24 Aduana del, Aeropuerto Internacional, Mexico, Mexico
Tel.: (52) 55 5786 8180
Freight Forwarding & Shipping Services
N.A.I.C.S.: 488510
Mario Camacho *(Product Mgr-HPL)*

Hellmann Saudi Arabia LLC (1)
Sakura Plaza Madinah Road, Salama District, Jeddah, 23525, Saudi Arabia
Tel.: (966) 126 977 422
Freight Forwarding & Shipping Services
N.A.I.C.S.: 488510
Aflak Kandak *(Supvr-Ops)*

Hellmann Worldwide Logistics (Cambodia) LLC (1)
Intelligent Office Center IOC No 254 3rd Floor, Unit F3 R05 Monivong Blvd Sangkat Boeung Rang Khan Daun Penh, Phnom Penh, Cambodia
Tel.: (855) 23 985 185
Freight Forwarding & Shipping Services
N.A.I.C.S.: 488510
Kosal Yien *(Mgr-Ops)*

Hellmann Worldwide Logistics (China) Ltd. (1)
No 328 Haitian 1 Road, Shanghai, 201202, China
Tel.: (86) 21 2898 0000
Freight Forwarding & Shipping Services
N.A.I.C.S.: 488510
Astor Yu *(Mgr-Airfreight Ops)*

Hellmann Worldwide Logistics (Cuba) GmbH (1)
Zona Especial de Desarrollo y de Actividades Logisticas, Carretera Aerocaribbean Km 1 5 Wajay, Havana, Cuba
Tel.: (53) 7 670 0841
Freight Forwarding & Shipping Services
N.A.I.C.S.: 488510
Maximo Lopez *(Gen Mgr)*

Hellmann Worldwide Logistics (Pty) Ltd (1)
48 Electron Avenue, Isando, 1600, South Africa
Tel.: (27) 119287000
Web Site: http://www.hellmann.net
Sales Range: $50-74.9 Million
Emp.: 150
Air, Sea & Road Freight Transportation; Warehousing, Logistics, Supply Chain Management & Customs Brokerage Services
N.A.I.C.S.: 488510
Vino Nunco *(COO-Africa)*

Hellmann Worldwide Logistics (Pty) Ltd. (1)
5 Von Braun Street, Windhoek, Namibia
Tel.: (264) 61 371 100
Freight Forwarding & Shipping Services
N.A.I.C.S.: 488510
Karin Fischer *(Branch Mgr)*

Hellmann Worldwide Logistics (Pvt) Ltd (1)
D 38 Block-5 Clifton, Karachi, 75600, Pakistan
Tel.: (92) 21111495725
Web Site: http://www.hellmann.net
Sales Range: $50-74.9 Million
Emp.: 60
Air, Sea & Road Freight Transportation; Warehousing, Logistics, Supply Chain Management & Customs Brokerage Services
N.A.I.C.S.: 488510
Asad Nihal *(Mng Dir)*

Hellmann Worldwide Logistics (Pvt) Ltd (1)
No 50/25 A Sir James Peiris Mawatha, 00200, Colombo, Sri Lanka
Tel.: (94) 11 4456700
Freight Forwarding & Shipping Services
N.A.I.C.S.: 488510
I. J. Rathnayaka *(Asst Mgr-IT)*

Hellmann Worldwide Logistics (Shanghai) Ltd. (1)
22F 1 Prime 360 Wu Jin Rd, Shanghai, 200080, China
Tel.: (86) 2123200399
Web Site: http://www.hellmann.net
Sales Range: $300-349.9 Million
Emp.: 545

Sea Freight Transportation; Warehousing, Logistics, Supply Chain Management & Customs Brokerage Services
N.A.I.C.S.: 488510
Ben Hui *(Sr VP)*

Hellmann Worldwide Logistics (T) Ltd. (1)
Samora Avenue Harbour View Tower 7th Floor Room 701, Dar es Salaam, 15072, Tanzania
Tel.: (255) 22 2122630
Freight Forwarding & Shipping Services
N.A.I.C.S.: 488510
David Haule *(Supvr-Sea Freight)*

Hellmann Worldwide Logistics (Vietnam) Co., Ltd (1)
Unit 408 - 4th Floor SCSC Building 30 Phan Thuc Duyen Street, Tan Binh District, Ho Chi Minh City, Vietnam
Tel.: (84) 8 39487186
Freight Forwarding & Shipping Services
N.A.I.C.S.: 488510
Nancy Truc *(Mgr-Air Freight)*

Hellmann Worldwide Logistics A/S (1)
Lergravsvej 53, 2300, Copenhagen, Denmark
Tel.: (45) 44 88 10 50
Freight Forwarding & Shipping Services
N.A.I.C.S.: 488510
Christian Maersk *(Gen Mgr)*

Hellmann Worldwide Logistics AS (1)
Kirstinehoej 17 1st Floor, Kastrup, DK 2770, Copenhagen, Denmark
Tel.: (45) 44881050
Web Site: http://www.hellmann.net
Sales Range: $75-99.9 Million
Emp.: 8
Air, Sea & Road Freight Transportation; Warehousing, Logistics, Supply Chain Management & Customs Brokerage Services
N.A.I.C.S.: 488510

Hellmann Worldwide Logistics B.V. (1)
Hoeksteen 157, Hoofddorp, 2132 MX, Netherlands
Tel.: (31) 206557400
Web Site: http://www.hellmann.net
Sales Range: $50-74.9 Million
Emp.: 100
Air, Sea & Road Freight Transportation; Warehousing, Logistics, Supply Chain Management & Customs Brokerage Services
N.A.I.C.S.: 488510
Remko Boogaard *(Branch Mgr & Mgr-Export)*

Hellmann Worldwide Logistics Co., Ltd. (1)
193/105 Lake Rajada Office Complex Building 25th Floor Unit C Ratchada, Klongtoey District, 10110, Bangkok, Thailand
Tel.: (66) 2 6619638
Web Site: http://www.hellmann.com
Emp.: 50
Freight Forwarding & Shipping Services
N.A.I.C.S.: 488510
Hendrik van Asselt *(Country Mgr)*

Hellmann Worldwide Logistics Do Brasil Ltda. (1)
Av Chucri Zaidan 80 9th Floor, Sao Paulo, 04583 909, Brazil
Tel.: (55) 1145015600
Web Site: http://www.hellmann.net
Sales Range: $50-74.9 Million
Emp.: 90
Freight Forwarding Services, Storage & Warehousing
N.A.I.C.S.: 488510
Valeria Rossi *(Mgr-Export-Sea Freight & Air Freight)*

Hellmann Worldwide Logistics GmbH (1)
Wilhelm-Spazier-Strasse 2, 5020, Salzburg, Austria
Tel.: (43) 6628249730
Web Site: http://www.hellmann.net
Sales Range: $25-49.9 Million
Emp.: 41
Freight Forwarding Services, Storage & Warehousing

N.A.I.C.S.: 488510
Thomas Schrotter *(Mng Dir)*

Hellmann Worldwide Logistics Inc. (1)
1375 Cardif Blvd Unit 1, Mississauga, L5S 1R1, ON, Canada
Tel.: (905) 564-6620
Web Site: http://www.hellmann.net
Sales Range: $50-74.9 Million
Emp.: 25
Air, Sea & Road Freight Transportation; Warehousing, Logistics, Supply Chain Management & Customs Brokerage Services
N.A.I.C.S.: 488510
Mike Amberg *(Mgr-IT)*

Hellmann Worldwide Logistics Inc. (1)
10th Floor Jae Young Building 678-10 Deong Chon 3 Dong, Kang Seo-Ku, Seoul, 157 033, Korea (South)
Tel.: (82) 236638363
Web Site: http://www.hellmann.net
Sales Range: $50-74.9 Million
Emp.: 80
Air, Sea & Road Freight Transportation; Warehousing, Logistics, Supply Chain Management & Customs Brokerage Services
N.A.I.C.S.: 488510
C. S. Yoo *(Pres)*

Hellmann Worldwide Logistics India Private Limited (1)
1st Floor Infotech Center 14/2 Milestone Old Gurgaon Road, Udyog Vihar, 122016, Gurgaon, India
Tel.: (91) 1244516700
Web Site: http://www.hellmann.net
Sales Range: $200-249.9 Million
Emp.: 370
Air Sea & Road Freight Transportation Warehousing Logistics Supply Chain Management & Customs Brokerage Distr
N.A.I.C.S.: 488510
Perminder Singh Sandhu *(Head-HR & Admin)*

Hellmann Worldwide Logistics Kazakhstan LLP (1)
5 Valikhanova str, 050016, Almaty, Kazakhstan
Tel.: (7) 727 234 77 80
Web Site: http://www.hellman.net
Emp.: 7
Freight Forwarding & Shipping Services
N.A.I.C.S.: 488510
Vladimir Khan *(Gen Dir)*

Hellmann Worldwide Logistics Kft. (1)
Lorinci ut 61 Airport Business Park Bldg B/1, 2220, Vecses, Hungary
Tel.: (36) 29 55 33 55
Web Site: http://www.hellman.com
Freight Forwarding & Shipping Services
N.A.I.C.S.: 488510
Denes Szigeti *(Mgr-Airfreight)*

Hellmann Worldwide Logistics LLC (1)
Jebel Ali Free Zone South Zone, PO Box 27974, Dubai, United Arab Emirates
Tel.: (971) 4 8994111
Freight Forwarding & Shipping Services
N.A.I.C.S.: 488510
Anna Paetzold *(Gen Mgr-HR & Bus Intelligence)*

Hellmann Worldwide Logistics LLP (1)
Suite 07 01A Nan Wah Building 4 Changi South Lane, 71 Alps Avenue Suite 02-03, Singapore, 498745, Singapore
Tel.: (65) 65454003
Web Site: http://www.hellmann.net
Sales Range: $50-74.9 Million
Emp.: 53
Air, Sea & Road Freight Transportation; Warehousing, Logistics, Supply Chain Management & Customs Brokerage Services
N.A.I.C.S.: 488510
Michael W. Thomas *(CEO-South East Asia)*

Hellmann Worldwide Logistics Limited (1)
4 Richard Pearse Road Christchurch Airport, 8053, Christchurch, New Zealand
Tel.: (64) 3 964 6949

HELLMANN WORLDWIDE LOGISTICS GMBH & CO. KG

Hellmann Worldwide Logistics GmbH & Co. KG—(Continued)
Web Site: http://www.hellmann.net
Emp.: 13
Freight Forwarding & Shipping Services
N.A.I.C.S.: 488510
Brendan Bingham *(Mgr-Warehouse)*

Hellmann Worldwide Logistics Ltd. (1)
Unit 2 G/F Blk A Tonic Industrial Centre 26 Kai Cheung Road, Kowloon Bay, China (Hong Kong)
Tel.: (852) 36268000
Web Site: http://www.hellmann.net
Sales Range: $200-249.9 Million
Emp.: 292
Storage Warehousing & Freight Forwarding Distr
N.A.I.C.S.: 488510
Mark Hellmann *(Pres & CEO-East Asia)*

Hellmann Worldwide Logistics Ltd. (1)
Kuhlmann House Lancaster Way, Fradley Park, Lichfield, WS13 8SX, United Kingdom
Tel.: (44) 1543443300
Web Site: http://www.hellmann.net
Sales Range: $50-74.9 Million
Emp.: 60
Air, Sea & Road Freight Transportation; Warehousing, Logistics, Supply Chain Management & Customs Brokerage Services
N.A.I.C.S.: 488510
Andy Connor *(Mng Dir)*

Division (Domestic):

Hellmann Perishable Logistics (2)
Hellmann House Lakeside Industrial Estate, Colnbrook Bypass, Colnbrook, SL3 0EL, Berks, United Kingdom
Tel.: (44) 1753681994
Web Site: http://www.hellmann.net
Freight Forwarding Services for Perishables
N.A.I.C.S.: 488510

Hellmann Worldwide Logistics Ltd. (1)
12 Gausul Azam Avenue Sector 13 Uttara, 1230, Dhaka, Bangladesh
Tel.: (880) 2 8959308
Freight Forwarding & Shipping Services
N.A.I.C.S.: 488510
Abu Sayeed Khan *(Gen Mgr-Airfreight Ops & CSSV)*

Hellmann Worldwide Logistics Ltd. (1)
66 Omaya Bin Abed Shamas Str Abdali Area, 11190, Amman, Jordan
Tel.: (962) 6 5686864
Freight Forwarding & Shipping Services
N.A.I.C.S.: 488510
Aref Hallak *(Branch Mgr)*

Hellmann Worldwide Logistics Ltd. (1)
36 Bis St Louis Street, Port Louis, Mauritius
Tel.: (230) 211 1390
Emp.: 17
Freight Forwarding & Shipping Services
N.A.I.C.S.: 488510
Aboobakar Yousuf *(Gen Mgr)*

Hellmann Worldwide Logistics Ltd. (1)
, 2022, Mangere, New Zealand
Tel.: (64) 9 921 2600
Freight Forwarding & Shipping Services
N.A.I.C.S.: 488510
Andrea Nielsen *(Mgr-Client Ops)*

Hellmann Worldwide Logistics Ltd. (1)
10F No 25 Sec 1 Chang An E Road, 10441, Taipei, Taiwan
Tel.: (886) 2 25239111
Freight Forwarding & Shipping Services
N.A.I.C.S.: 488510
Aaron Cheng *(Gen Mgr)*

Hellmann Worldwide Logistics Ltd. (1)
Damascus Tower 20th Floor Office No 9, PO Box 2711, Almarjeh Street, Damascus, Syria
Tel.: (963) 11 2312030
Freight Forwarding & Shipping Services

N.A.I.C.S.: 488510
Amer Issa *(Mgr-Comml)*

Hellmann Worldwide Logistics Ltd. Sti (1)
Mermerciler Sanayii Sitesi 7 Cadde No 4, Beylikduzu, 34520, Istanbul, Turkiye
Tel.: (90) 212 875 3044
Freight Forwarding & Shipping Services
N.A.I.C.S.: 488510
Cem Akgul *(Mng Dir)*

Hellmann Worldwide Logistics Ltda. (1)
Isidora Goyenechea 3600 Of 201, Las Condes, Santiago, Chile
Tel.: (56) 27156200
Web Site: http://www.hellmann.net
Sales Range: $50-74.9 Million
Emp.: 40
Air, Sea & Road Freight Transportation; Warehousing, Logistics, Supply Chain Management & Customs Brokerage Services
N.A.I.C.S.: 488510
Carolina Cortes *(Mgr-Projects & Ops)*

Hellmann Worldwide Logistics Madagascar SARL (1)
Immeuble TECNO MOBILE 2 eme etage Lot 001 A, Bis Ambohibao Antehiroka, 101, Antananarivo, Madagascar
Tel.: (261) 20 22 444 66
Freight Forwarding & Shipping Services
N.A.I.C.S.: 488510
Adriana Rajemiarison *(Mgr-Sls)*

Hellmann Worldwide Logistics N.V. (1)
Ankerrui 18 2th Floor, 2000, Zaventem, Belgium
Tel.: (32) 32023262
Web Site: http://www.hellmann.net
Sales Range: $50-74.9 Million
Emp.: 17
Air, Sea & Road Freight Transportation; Warehousing, Logistics, Supply Chain Management & Customs Brokerage Services
N.A.I.C.S.: 485999
Fred Dalle *(Mng Dir)*

Hellmann Worldwide Logistics OU (1)
Punane 42, 13619, Tallinn, Estonia
Tel.: (372) 6112850
Freight Forwarding & Shipping Services
N.A.I.C.S.: 488510
Priit Tomson *(Mgr-Sls)*

Hellmann Worldwide Logistics Polska spolka z ograniczona odpowiedzialnoscia (1)
ul Sokolowska 10, 05-090, Raszyn, Poland
Tel.: (48) 22 717 97 97
Freight Forwarding & Shipping Services
N.A.I.C.S.: 488510
Beata Kwolik *(Dir-Ops)*

Hellmann Worldwide Logistics Pty Ltd (1)
Airgate Business Park 289 Coward Street, Mascot, 2020, NSW, Australia
Tel.: (61) 296677555
Web Site: http://www.hellmann.net
Sales Range: $100-124.9 Million
Emp.: 200
Air, Sea & Road Freight Transportation; Warehousing, Logistics, Supply Chain Management & Customs Brokerage Services
N.A.I.C.S.: 488510
Ray Vella *(Mng Dir)*

Hellmann Worldwide Logistics S.A. (1)
Reconquista 656 2nd Floor Office A, Buenos Aires, C1003ABN, Argentina
Tel.: (54) 1155522044
Web Site: http://www.hellmann.net
Sales Range: $50-74.9 Million
Emp.: 50
Air, Sea & Road Freight Transportation; Warehousing, Logistics, Supply Chain Management & Customs Brokerage Services
N.A.I.C.S.: 488510
Lucas MacGaw *(Pres & CEO)*

Division (Domestic):

Hellmann Perishable Logistics (2)

Edificio Corporativo Piso 2 Of 211 Aeropuerto Internacional de Ezeiza, Ministro Pistarini, 1043, Buenos Aires, Argentina
Tel.: (54) 1154805510
Sales Range: $25-49.9 Million
Emp.: 50
Freight Forwarding Services for Perishables
N.A.I.C.S.: 488510

Hellmann Worldwide Logistics S.A. (1)
ZAL II C Cal Pi de LOlla 16-18, El Prat de Llobregat, 08820, Barcelona, Spain
Tel.: (34) 932643870
Web Site: http://www.hellmann.net
Sales Range: $50-74.9 Million
Emp.: 80
Air, Sea & Road Freight Transportation; Warehousing, Logistics, Supply Chain Management & Customs Brokerage Services
N.A.I.C.S.: 488510
Miguel Pujol *(Gen Mgr)*

Hellmann Worldwide Logistics S.A. de C.V. (1)
Norte 3 No 90 Bodega F Col Federal Del, Venustiano Carranza, Mexico, 15700, Mexico
Tel.: (52) 5550101200
Web Site: http://www.hellmann.net
Sales Range: $100-124.9 Million
Emp.: 120
Air, Sea & Road Freight Transportation; Warehousing, Logistics, Supply Chain Management & Customs Brokerage Services
N.A.I.C.S.: 488510
Gerhard Allgaeuer *(Pres & CEO-Latin America)*

Hellmann Worldwide Logistics S.A.C. (1)
Avn Elmer Faucett 2851 Oficina 323 Callao, Callao 1, Callao, 4, Peru
Tel.: (51) 16136800
Web Site: http://www.hellmann.net
Sales Range: $25-49.9 Million
Emp.: 65
Air, Sea & Road Freight Transportation; Warehousing, Logistics, Supply Chain Management & Customs Brokerage Services
N.A.I.C.S.: 488510
Carlos Augusto Dammert *(Pres)*

Hellmann Worldwide Logistics S.R.O. (1)
Zdebradska 94 Jazlovice, 251 01, Ricany, Czech Republic
Tel.: (420) 323 209 225
Freight Forwarding & Shipping Services
N.A.I.C.S.: 488510
David Gurin *(Mgr-Seafreight Product)*

Hellmann Worldwide Logistics S.p.A. (1)
Via E Montale 18, 20090, Novegro di Segrate, Milan, Italy
Tel.: (39) 027562781
Web Site: http://www.hellmann.net
Sales Range: $50-74.9 Million
Emp.: 50
Air, Sea & Road Freight Transportation; Warehousing, Logistics, Supply Chain Management & Customs Brokerage Services
N.A.I.C.S.: 488510
Daniela Coppola *(Mgr-PR, HR & Mktg)*

Hellmann Worldwide Logistics SIA (1)
K Ulmana gatve 2 k-1-5, 1004, Riga, Latvia
Tel.: (371) 67409944
Web Site: http://www.hellmann.net
Freight Forwarding & Shipping Services
N.A.I.C.S.: 488510
Natalja Haritona *(Mgr-Acctg Dept)*

Hellmann Worldwide Logistics SRL (1)
Airport Plaza Building 1A Drumul Garii Odai Street, Entrance B Rooms 210-211, Otopeni, 75100, Romania
Tel.: (40) 21 3000 244
Freight Forwarding & Shipping Services
N.A.I.C.S.: 488510
Silvio Wollmann *(Mgr-Airfreight)*

Hellmann Worldwide Logistics Sdn. Bhd. (1)
Suite D-5-2 3 & 3A Level 5 Block D Sky-Park One City, Jalan USJ 25/1, 47650,

Subang Jaya, Malaysia
Tel.: (60) 3 5115 9932
Freight Forwarding & Shipping Services
N.A.I.C.S.: 488510
Andrew Lim *(Mgr-Bus Dev)*

Hellmann Worldwide Logistics UAB (1)
Dariaus ir Gireno str 81, 2189, Vilnius, Lithuania
Tel.: (370) 52 499 110
Web Site: http://www.hellmann.com
Emp.: 55
Freight Forwarding & Shipping Services
N.A.I.C.S.: 488510
Edvard Ostrouch *(Mgr-Sls-Russia & CIS)*

Hellmann Worldwide Logistics WLL (1)
Office 22 Ground Floor Waha Mall Dajeej, PO Box 601, Al Farwaniyah, 81017, Kuwait
Tel.: (965) 2434 8299
Freight Forwarding & Shipping Services
N.A.I.C.S.: 488510
Meera Castelino *(Mgr-Customer Support & Pricing)*

Hellmann Worldwide Logistics Zambia Limited (1)
Stand No 174 Luanshya Road Light Industrial Area, 10101, Lusaka, Zambia
Tel.: (260) 211 238325
Freight Forwarding & Shipping Services
N.A.I.C.S.: 488510
Armand Posthumus *(Mgr-Ops)*

Hellmann Worldwide Logistics sarl (1)
Machkas Center Phoenicia Avenue Ain el Mreisseh, PO Box 13-5313, 7th floor Office No 704 Ras Beirut, Beirut, 20340716, Lebanon
Tel.: (961) 1 365765
Freight Forwarding & Shipping Services
N.A.I.C.S.: 488510
Faouzi S. Bayoud *(Gen Mgr)*

Hellmann Worldwide Logistics, Inc. (1)
10450 Doral Blvd, Doral, FL 33178
Tel.: (305) 406-4500
Web Site: http://www.hellmann.net
Sales Range: $350-399.9 Million
Emp.: 724
Air, Sea & Road Freight Transportation; Warehousing, Logistics, Supply Chain Management & Customs Brokerage Services
N.A.I.C.S.: 488510
Julian M. Riches *(CFO)*

Division (Domestic):

Hellmann Perishable Logistics Inc. (2)
10450 Doral Blvd, Doral, FL 33178
Tel.: (305) 594-4995
Web Site: http://www.hellmann.net
Emp.: 30
Freight Forwarding Services for Perishables
N.A.I.C.S.: 488510
Ambre Valdes Gine *(Mgr-Perishable Logistics)*

OOO Hellmann East Europe (1)
Urzhumskaya str 4 bld 14, 129343, Moscow, Russia
Tel.: (7) 495 775 14 97
Freight Forwarding & Shipping Services
N.A.I.C.S.: 488510
Evgeniya Malysheva *(Head-Fin Dept)*

HELLO GROUP INC.

20th Floor Block B Tower 2 Wangjing SOHO No 1 Futongdong Street, Chaoyang District, Beijing, 100102, China
Tel.: (86) 1057310567   Ky
Web Site: https://ir.hellogroup.com
MOMO—(NASDAQ)
Rev.: $1,946,406,192
Assets: $2,425,251,024
Liabilities: $750,567,976
Net Worth: $1,674,683,048
Earnings: $227,406,998
Emp.: 1,705
Fiscal Year-end: 12/31/22
Mobile Applications
N.A.I.C.S.: 513210

Yan Tang *(Chm)*

HELLO PAL INTERNATIONAL, INC.
550 Denman Street Suite 200, Vancouver, V6G 3H1, BC, Canada
Tel.: (604) 683-0911
Web Site: https://www.hellopal.com
Motor Vehicle Part & Accessory Mfr
N.A.I.C.S.: 336390
K. L. Wong *(Founder & Chm)*

HELLOWORLD TRAVEL LIMITED
Level 10 338 Pitt Street, Sydney, 2000, NSW, Australia
Tel.: (61) 282294000 AU
Web Site:
https://www.helloworldlimited.com
HLO—(ASX)
Rev.: $152,382,478
Assets: $410,021,366
Liabilities: $190,773,236
Net Worth: $219,248,129
Earnings: $20,518,830
Emp.: 652
Fiscal Year-end: 06/30/24
Travel Services
N.A.I.C.S.: 561510
Andrew Burnes *(CEO & Mng Dir)*

Subsidiaries:

Entertainment Logistix Pty. Ltd. (1)
10/3-13 Marigold St, Revesby, NSW, Australia
Tel.: (61) 300722746
Web Site:
https://entertainmentlogistix.com.au
Entertainment Logistics Services
N.A.I.C.S.: 541614

Harvey World Travel Group Pty. Ltd. (1)
Level 3 77 Berry Street, North Sydney, 2060, NSW, Australia
Tel.: (61) 282294144
Web Site: http://www.harveyworld.com.au
Travel Services
N.A.I.C.S.: 561510
Glenn Buckingham *(Mgr-Network Dev)*

Harvey World Travel Southern Africa (Pty) Limited (1)
The Travel Campus 26 Girton Road, Parktown, 2193, South Africa **(50%)**
Tel.: (27) 871101890
Web Site: https://www.harveyworld.co.za
Travel Services
N.A.I.C.S.: 561510

Show Group Enterprises Pty Ltd (1)
Level 3 4A Lord St, Botany, 2019, NSW, Australia
Tel.: (61) 293529999
Web Site: http://www.showgroup.com.au
Logistics & Travel Services & Freight Forwarder to the Sports, Film, Arts & Entertainment Industries
N.A.I.C.S.: 488510
John Kline *(Head-Freight & Logistics)*

Stella Travel Services (Australia) Pty Ltd (1)
Level 3 77 Berry Street, North Sydney, 2060, NSW, Australia
Tel.: (61) 282294000
Travel Agency
N.A.I.C.S.: 561510

The AOT Group Pty. Ltd. (1)
179 Normanby Road, South Melbourne, 3205, VIC, Australia
Tel.: (61) 398677233
Web Site: http://www.aot.com.au
Emp.: 570
Holding Company; Tour Operator & Travel Services
N.A.I.C.S.: 551112
Andrew Burnes *(Co-Owner & CEO)*

Subsidiary (Non-US):

AOT Business Consulting (Shanghai) Inc. (2)
66 Shanxi North Road 17F Unit 17 Wise Logic Building, Shanghai, China
Tel.: (86) 21 6271 7055
Tour Operator
N.A.I.C.S.: 561520

ATS Pacific (NZ) Ltd (2)
Level 5 Chorus House 66 Wyndam Street, Auckland, 1010, New Zealand
Tel.: (64) 9 918 7120
Web Site: http://www.atspacific.co.nz
Emp.: 45
Tour Operator
N.A.I.C.S.: 561520
Stuart Neels *(Gen Mgr)*

ATS Pacific Fiji Limited (2)
PO Box 9172, Nadi Airport, Nadi, Fiji
Tel.: (679) 672 2811
Web Site: https://www.atspacific.com.fj
Tour Operator
N.A.I.C.S.: 561520
Leigh Howard *(Gen Mgr-Fiji)*

Subsidiary (Domestic):

Australian Online Travel Pty. Ltd. (2)
Level 10 338 Pitt Street, Sydney, 2000, NSW, Australia
Tel.: (61) 282294811
Web Site: http://www.aot.com.au
Travel Arrangement Services
N.A.I.C.S.: 561599

Division (Domestic):

Travelmate.com.au Pty. Ltd. (3)
Level 15 32 Turbot St, Brisbane, 4000, QLD, Australia
Tel.: (61) 1300666787
Web Site: http://www.travelmate.com.au
Travel Agencies
N.A.I.C.S.: 561510

Subsidiary (Domestic):

Sunlover Holidays Pty Ltd (2)
Level 15 32 Turbot St, Brisbane, 4000, QLD, Australia
Tel.: (61) 30 073 0039
Web Site:
https://www.sunloverholidays.com.au
Tour Operator
N.A.I.C.S.: 561520

Williment Travel Group Limited (1)
Classic House Level 10 15 Murphy Thorndon, Wellington, 6011, New Zealand
Tel.: (64) 4 380 2500
Web Site: http://www.williment.co.nz
Sports Tour Operating Services
N.A.I.C.S.: 561520
Adair Cameron *(Gen Mgr-Event)*

HELLYER MILL OPERATIONS PTY LTD.
PO Box 1467, Burnie, 7320, TAS, Australia
Tel.: (61) 364391464
Metal Exploration Services
N.A.I.C.S.: 213114

HELM AG
Nordkanalstrasse 28, 20097, Hamburg, Germany
Tel.: (49) 4023750
Web Site: http://www.helmag.com
Year Founded: 1900
Sales Range: $5-14.9 Billion
Emp.: 1,366
Chemicals, Pharmaceuticals, Nutrition Products, Plastics, Crop Protection & Fertilizers Marketer & Distr
N.A.I.C.S.: 424690
Hans-Christian Sievers *(Chm-Exec Bd)*

Subsidiaries:

HELM AGRO US, INC. (1)
8275 Tournament Dr Ste 340, Memphis, TN 38125
Tel.: (901) 312-1525
Web Site: http://www.helmagro.com
Sales Range: $25-49.9 Million
Emp.: 12
Industrial Chemical Whslr
N.A.I.C.S.: 424690

HELM ANDINA LTDA. (1)
Carrera 11 A No 93-67 Oficina 404, Bogota, Colombia
Tel.: (57) 1 621 52 64
Web Site: http://www.helmandina.com
Sales Range: $25-49.9 Million
Emp.: 15
Agricultural Chemical Distr
N.A.I.C.S.: 424690
Holger Berg *(Mng Dir)*

HELM ARGENTINA S.R.L. (1)
Valentin Virasoro 2669 P 1, Beccar, P1643HDA, Pila, Buenos Aires, Argentina
Tel.: (54) 11 4719 7377
Web Site: http://www.helmargentina.com
Sales Range: $25-49.9 Million
Emp.: 15
Industrial Chemical Whslr
N.A.I.C.S.: 424690

HELM AUSTRIA GES.M.B.H. (1)
Am Heumarkt 7 / 2 / 3 / 23, 1030, Vienna, Austria
Tel.: (43) 1 5133810
Web Site: http://www.helmaustria.com
Sales Range: $50-74.9 Million
Emp.: 3
Industrial Chemical Whslr
N.A.I.C.S.: 424690

HELM CHEMICALS B.V. (1)
Hoorn 75, Alphen aan den Rijn, 2404, Netherlands
Tel.: (31) 172 467100
Web Site: http://www.helm-chemicals.eu
Sales Range: $25-49.9 Million
Emp.: 35
Industrial Chemical Whslr
N.A.I.C.S.: 424690
Stephane Deltour *(Acct Mgr)*

HELM CHINA LTD. (1)
Room 905 Kerry Center Office Bldg 1515 Nanjing Road West, Shanghai, 200040, China
Tel.: (86) 21 6320 0808
Web Site: http://www.helmchina.com
Sales Range: $25-49.9 Million
Emp.: 23
Industrial Chemical Whslr
N.A.I.C.S.: 424690
Bernard Chambres *(Mng Dir)*

HELM D3 SAS (1)
Les Ocres de l Arbois Bat B Parc de la Duranne 495 Rue Rene Descartes, 13857, Aix-en-Provence, Cedex 3, France
Tel.: (33) 442 654065
Web Site: http://www.helmd3.com
Industrial Chemical Whslr
N.A.I.C.S.: 424690

HELM DE MEXICO, S.A. (1)
Proton No 2 Parque Industrial Naucalpan, 53489, Naucalpan, Mexico
Tel.: (52) 55 5228 9900
Web Site: http://www.helmmexico.com
Rev.: $14,949,200
Emp.: 219
Industrial Chemical Whslr
N.A.I.C.S.: 424690
Stefan Stietzel *(Mng Dir)*

HELM DUNGEMITTEL GMBH (1)
Nordkanalstr 28, 20097, Hamburg, Germany
Tel.: (49) 40 23750
Web Site: http://www.helmag.com
Sales Range: $25-49.9 Million
Emp.: 600
Fertilizer Whslr
N.A.I.C.S.: 424690

HELM ENGRAIS FRANCE S.A.R.L. (1)
Espace 21 Bat 6 31 Place Ronde, Paris, 92986, France
Tel.: (33) 1 55230670
Sales Range: $50-74.9 Million
Emp.: 4
Industrial Chemical Whslr
N.A.I.C.S.: 424690
Chapelier Frederic *(Mgr)*

HELM FERTILIZER CORP (1)
Ste 330 4042 Park Oaks Blvd, Tampa, FL 33610
Tel.: (813) 621-8846
Fertilizer Distr
N.A.I.C.S.: 424910
Dale Miller *(Pres)*

HELM FERTILIZER GREAT BRITAIN LTD. (1)
Suite A The Exchange Station Parade GB, Harrogate, HG1 1TS, North Yorkshire, United Kingdom
Tel.: (44) 1423 527777
Emp.: 5
Industrial Chemical Whslr
N.A.I.C.S.: 424690

HELM FERTILIZER HELENA TERMINAL INC. (1)
Helena Slackwater Harbor, West Helena, AR 72390
Tel.: (870) 338-8177
Fertilizer Distr
N.A.I.C.S.: 424910

HELM FERTILIZER TERMINAL INC. (1)
1421 Channel Ave, Memphis, TN 38113
Tel.: (901) 948-3303
Fertilizer Distr
N.A.I.C.S.: 424910

HELM FRANCE S.A.R.L. (1)
Espace 21 Bat 6 31 Place Ronde, La Defense, 92986, Paris, France
Tel.: (33) 1 46 96 04 40
Web Site: http://www.helmfrance.com
Sales Range: $25-49.9 Million
Emp.: 15
Industrial Chemical Whslr
N.A.I.C.S.: 424690
Luc Francille *(Gen Mgr)*

HELM GREAT BRITAIN LTD. (1)
The Harlequin Building 65 Southwark Street, London, SE1 0HR, United Kingdom
Tel.: (44) 2076200756
Web Site: http://www.helmgreatbritain.com
Sales Range: $25-49.9 Million
Emp.: 17
Industrial Chemical Whslr
N.A.I.C.S.: 424690

HELM HONG KONG LTD. (1)
1301 China Resources Building 26 Harbour Road, Wanchai, China (Hong Kong)
Tel.: (852) 2827 8068
Web Site: http://www.helmhongkong.com
Sales Range: $25-49.9 Million
Emp.: 20
Industrial Chemical Whslr
N.A.I.C.S.: 424690

HELM IBERICA, S.A. (1)
Carretera Fuencarral N 24 Edificio Europa 1 Portal 2 Planta 1-3, 28108, Alcobendas, Spain
Tel.: (34) 91 657 43 70
Web Site: http://www.helmiberica.com
Emp.: 25
Industrial Chemical Whslr
N.A.I.C.S.: 424690

HELM ITALIA S.R.L. (1)
Via Vittor Pisani 22, 20124, Milan, Italy
Tel.: (39) 02 67444 1
Web Site: http://www.helmitalia.com
Emp.: 17
Chemicals Mfr
N.A.I.C.S.: 325199

HELM JAPAN LTD. (1)
3-2-11 Nishi-Shinjuku, Shinjuku-ku, Tokyo, 160-0023, Japan
Tel.: (81) 3 5322 6116
Web Site: http://www.helm-japan.com
Sales Range: $50-74.9 Million
Emp.: 5
Industrial Chemical Whslr
N.A.I.C.S.: 424690

HELM KIMYA LTD. SIRKETI (1)
Bueyuekdere Caddesi 108 Enka Han Kat 5, Esentepe, Istanbul, 34394, Turkiye
Tel.: (90) 212 336 68 50
Web Site: http://www.helm.com.tr
Sales Range: $25-49.9 Million
Emp.: 20
Industrial Chemical Whslr
N.A.I.C.S.: 424690
Matches Deewane *(Gen Mgr)*

HELM KOREA LTD. (1)

HELM AG

HELM AG—(Continued)
909B CCMM Building 101 Yeouigongwon-ro Youngdeungpo-gu, Gangnam District, Seoul, 150-968, Korea (South)
Tel.: (82) 2 5084400
Web Site: http://www.helmkorea.com
Sales Range: $50-74.9 Million
Emp.: 8
Industrial Chemical Whslr
N.A.I.C.S.: 424690
Jimmy Lee *(Mng Dir)*

HELM POLSKA SP. Z O.O (1)
Ul Domaniewska 42, 02-672, Warsaw, Poland
Tel.: (48) 22 6543500
Web Site: http://www.helmpolska.pl
Sales Range: $25-49.9 Million
Emp.: 24
Industrial Chemical Whslr
N.A.I.C.S.: 424690

HELM PORTUGAL, LDA. (1)
Estrada Nacional 10-Km 140 260, 2695-066, Bobadela, Portugal
Tel.: (351) 21 9948300
Web Site: http://www.helmportugal.com
Sales Range: $25-49.9 Million
Emp.: 30
Industrial Chemical Whslr
N.A.I.C.S.: 424690

HELM SKANDINAVIEN A/S (1)
Winghouse Orestads Boulevard 73, 2300, Copenhagen, Denmark
Tel.: (45) 3586 0910
Web Site: http://www.helmas.dk
Sales Range: $25-49.9 Million
Emp.: 23
Industrial Chemical Whslr
N.A.I.C.S.: 424690
Jorn Erhardsen *(Mng Dir)*

HELM U.S. CORPORATION (1)
1110 Centennial Ave, Piscataway, NJ 08854-4169
Tel.: (732) 981-1116
Web Site: http://www.helmus.com
Sales Range: $25-49.9 Million
Emp.: 30
Industrial Chemical Distr
N.A.I.C.S.: 424690
Phillip Mangold *(Pres)*

KRAEFT LOGISTIK GMBH (1)
Nordersand 2, Hamburg, 20457, Germany
Tel.: (49) 403174694
Web Site: http://www.kraeftlogistik.com
Sales Range: $25-49.9 Million
Emp.: 15
Warehousing & Distribution Services
N.A.I.C.S.: 493110
Hans-Otto Biermann *(Mng Dir)*

MIDER-HELM METHANOL Vertriebs GmbH (1)
Nordkanalstr 28, Hamburg, 20097, Germany
Tel.: (49) 40 23752550
Sales Range: $50-74.9 Million
Emp.: 3
Industrial Chemical Whslr
N.A.I.C.S.: 424690

S.A. HELM BENELUX N.V. (1)
Fountain Plaza Belgicastraat 1 B11, Zaventem, 1930, Belgium
Tel.: (32) 2 672 68 69
Web Site: http://www.helmbenelux.be
Sales Range: $50-74.9 Million
Emp.: 5
Industrial Chemical Whslr
N.A.I.C.S.: 424690
Luc Martens *(Gen Mgr)*

HELMA EIGENHEIMBAU AG
Zum Meersefeld 4, 31275, Lehrte, Germany
Tel.: (49) 513288500
Web Site: https://www.helma.de
Year Founded: 1980
H5E—(DEU)
Rev.: $326,408,275
Assets: $484,992,445
Liabilities: $350,458,666
Net Worth: $134,533,779
Earnings: $2,270,667
Emp.: 362
Fiscal Year-end: 12/31/22
Residential Building Construction Services
N.A.I.C.S.: 236115
Gerrit Janssen *(Chm-Mgmt Bd & CEO)*

Subsidiaries:

HELMA Ferienimmobilien GmbH (1)
Zum Meersefeld 4, 31275, Lehrte, Germany
Tel.: (49) 513288500
Real Estate Agency Services
N.A.I.C.S.: 531210

Hausbau Finanz GmbH (1)
Zum Meersefeld 4, 31275, Lehrte, Germany
Tel.: (49) 51328850230
Real Estate Agency Services
N.A.I.C.S.: 531210

HELMHOLTZ-ZENTRUM HEREON
Max-Planck-Strasse 1, 21502, Geesthacht, Germany
Tel.: (49) 4152870
Emp.: 1,012
Scientific Research & Development Services
N.A.I.C.S.: 541715

HELNAN INTERNATIONAL HOTELS A/S
Strandvejen 25, 8000, Arhus, C, Denmark
Tel.: (45) 86144411
Web Site: http://www.helnan.dk
Year Founded: 1982
Hotel Operator
N.A.I.C.S.: 721110
Enan Galaly *(Founder & Pres)*

Subsidiaries:

Helnan Marina Hotel (1)
Kystvej 32, DK-8500, Grena, Denmark
Tel.: (45) 86322500
Web Site: http://www.helnan.info.dk
N.A.I.C.S.: 483111

HELPAGE FINLEASE LTD.
S-191 C 3rd Floor Manak Complex School Block Shakarpur, New Delhi, 110 092, India
Tel.: (91) 1145578607
Web Site: https://www.helpagefinlease.com
539174—(BOM)
Rev.: $335,915
Assets: $5,207,824
Liabilities: $3,472,783
Net Worth: $1,735,041
Earnings: $72,975
Emp.: 12
Fiscal Year-end: 03/31/23
Financial Support Services
N.A.I.C.S.: 523999
Sidharth Goyal *(Mng Dir)*

HELSTON GARAGES GROUP
85 Meneage Street, Helston, TR13 8RD, Cornwall, United Kingdom
Tel.: (44) 1326 330 640
Web Site: http://www.helstongarages.co.uk
Year Founded: 1960
Sales Range: $500-549.9 Million
Emp.: 764
New & Used Car Dealer
N.A.I.C.S.: 441110

HELTOR LIMITED
Old Newton Road Heathfield, Newton Abbot, TQ12 6RW, Devon, United Kingdom
Tel.: (44) 1626832516
Web Site: http://www.heltor.co.uk
Rev.: $47,299,137
Emp.: 63
Fuel Distribution Services
N.A.I.C.S.: 485991
John Piller *(Mgr-Distr)*

HELUKABEL GMBH
Dieselstr 8-12, 71282, Hemmingen, Germany
Tel.: (49) 715092090
Web Site: http://www.helukabel.com
Year Founded: 1978
Rev.: $375,305,701
Emp.: 524
Cable & Wire Mfr & Distr
N.A.I.C.S.: 332618
Helmut Luksch *(Co-Mng Dir)*

Subsidiaries:

HELUKABEL (Thailand) Co. Ltd. (1)
38/25 Moo 10 Bangkrang, Muang, Nonthaburi, Thailand
Tel.: (66) 292735703
Web Site: http://www.helukabel.co.th
Cable Distr
N.A.I.C.S.: 423610

HELUKABEL (UK) Ltd. (1)
Unit 6 Wrynose Rd Old Hall Industrial Estate, Bromborough, Wirral, CH62 3QD, Merseyside, United Kingdom
Tel.: (44) 1513450808
Web Site: http://www.helukabel.co.uk
Cable Distr
N.A.I.C.S.: 423610
Adam Parry *(Mng Dir)*

HELUKABEL AB (1)
Spjutvagen 1, 175 61, Jarfalla, Sweden
Tel.: (46) 855774280
Web Site: http://www.helukabel.se
Cable Distr
N.A.I.C.S.: 423610

HELUKABEL AG (1)
Gräbackerstrasse 60, 8957, Spreitenbach, Switzerland
Tel.: (41) 564181515
Web Site: http://www.helukabel.ch
Cable Distr
N.A.I.C.S.: 423610

HELUKABEL Austria GmbH (1)
Pummerinplatz 1, 4490, Sankt Florian, Austria
Tel.: (43) 7224905550
Web Site: http://www.helukabel.at
Cable Distr
N.A.I.C.S.: 423610

HELUKABEL B.V. (1)
De Kempen 4, Budel, 6021 PG, Eindhoven, Netherlands
Tel.: (31) 495499049
Web Site: http://www.helukabel.nl
Cable Distr
N.A.I.C.S.: 423610

HELUKABEL Belgium BVBA. (1)
Z 1 Researchpark 310, 1731, Zellik, Belgium
Tel.: (32) 24810020
Web Site: http://www.helukabel.be
Cable Distr
N.A.I.C.S.: 423610
Nicolas Willems *(Acct Mgr)*

HELUKABEL CZ s.r.o. (1)
Dul MAX 39, Libusin, 27306, Kladno, Czech Republic
Tel.: (420) 312672620
Web Site: http://www.helukabel.cz
Cable Distr
N.A.I.C.S.: 423610

HELUKABEL Canada Inc. (1)
3650 Odyssey Drive Unit 4 - 5, Mississauga, L5M 0Y9, ON, Canada
Tel.: (289) 444-5040
Web Site: https://www.helukabel.ca
Cable Distr
N.A.I.C.S.: 423610

HELUKABEL France Sarl. (1)
Z A du Pont d'Aspach 3 Rue DMC-B P 30, 68520, Burnhaupt-le-Haut, France
Tel.: (33) 389627562
Web Site: http://www.helukabel.fr
Cable Distr
N.A.I.C.S.: 423610

INTERNATIONAL PUBLIC

HELUKABEL INDIA PVT.LTD. (1)
F-305 Kailash Complex Hiranandani Gardens Link Road, Vikhroli West, Mumbai, 400 079, India
Tel.: (91) 2225185841
Web Site: http://www.helukabel.in
Cable Distr
N.A.I.C.S.: 423610

HELUKABEL Int Trading (SHANGHAI) Co., Ltd. (1)
Room 1103 Hongjia Building 388 Fushan Road, Pu Dong, 200122, Shanghai, China
Tel.: (86) 2158693999
Web Site: http://www.helukabel.com.cn
Cable Distr
N.A.I.C.S.: 423610
Holge Wennrich *(Mng Dir)*

HELUKABEL Italia S.r.l. (1)
Via Val D Ossola 7-13, 20871, Vimercate, MB, Italy
Tel.: (39) 0396081503
Web Site: http://www.helukabel.it
Cable Distr
N.A.I.C.S.: 423610

HELUKABEL KOREA Co., Ltd. (1)
521-17 Daejeo 2 Dong Gang-seo Gu, Busan, Korea (South)
Tel.: (82) 519728646
Web Site: http://www.helukabel.co.kr
Cable Distr
N.A.I.C.S.: 423610

HELUKABEL Kablo San. ve Tic. Ltd. Sti. (1)
Yakuplu Merkez Mah Hurriyet Bulvari 228 Sokak No 24 Kaymakamlik Yani, Beylikduzu, 34524, Istanbul, Turkiye
Tel.: (90) 2125024195
Web Site: http://www.helukabel.com.tr
Cable Distr
N.A.I.C.S.: 423610

HELUKABEL MALAYSIA SDN BHD (1)
W-2-1-1 Axis Technologiy Centre No 13 Jalan 225 Seksyen 51A, 46100, Petaling Jaya, Selangor, Malaysia
Tel.: (60) 79691180
Web Site: http://www.helukabel.com.my
Cable Distr
N.A.I.C.S.: 423610

HELUKABEL Polska Sp.z o.o. (1)
Krze Duze 2, 96325, Zyrardow, Poland
Tel.: (48) 468580100
Web Site: http://www.helukabel.pl
Cable Distr
N.A.I.C.S.: 423610

HELUKABEL Russia (1)
Klutschevaja ul 30 lit A office 413, Saint Petersburg, 195221, Russia
Tel.: (7) 8124491060
Web Site: http://www.helukabel.ru
Cable Distr
N.A.I.C.S.: 423610

HELUKABEL Singapore Pte. Ltd. (1)
159 Sin Ming Road 02-01 Amtech Building, Singapore, 575625, Singapore
Tel.: (65) 65546170
Web Site: http://www.helukabel.com.sg
Cable Distr
N.A.I.C.S.: 423610
Irwan Susanto *(Area Mgr)*

HELUKABEL South Africa (Pty) Ltd. (1)
164 Gigantic Road Northlands Business Park, Randburg, 2169, South Africa
Tel.: (27) 114628752
Web Site: http://www.helukabel.co.za
Cable Distr
N.A.I.C.S.: 423610
Doug Gunnewegh *(Mng Dir)*

HELUKABEL USA, Inc. (1)
1490 Crispin Dr, Elgin, IL 60123
Tel.: (847) 930-5118
Web Site: http://www.helukabel.com
Cable Distr
N.A.I.C.S.: 423610

Helusta UAB (1)
Laisves a 16, 35200, Panevezys, Lithuania
Tel.: (370) 45436323
Web Site: http://www.helusta.lt

AND PRIVATE COMPANIES

Cable Distr
N.A.I.C.S.: 423610

Kabelmat Wickeltechnik GmbH. (1)
Steinbuckelweg 25, 72293, Glatten, Germany
Tel.: (49) 744396700
Web Site: http://www.kabelmat.com
Cable Distr
N.A.I.C.S.: 423610
Horst Schoch *(Mng Dir)*

PT Helukabel Indonesia (1)
Gedung Wisma Abadi Block C3 4th Floor Jl
Kyai Caringin 29-31, Jakarta, 10160, Indonesia
Tel.: (62) 213848872
Web Site: http://www.helukabel.co.id
Cable Distr
N.A.I.C.S.: 423610

Robotec Systems GmbH (1)
Carl-Friedrich-Gauss-Str 7, 47475, Kamp-Lintfort, Germany
Tel.: (49) 2842921480
Web Site: http://www.robotec-systems.de
Cable Distr
N.A.I.C.S.: 423610

HELVAR MERCA OY AB
Kalevankatu 4, 00101, Helsinki, Finland
Tel.: (358) 956549301 FI
Web Site:
  http://www.helvarmerca.com
Year Founded: 1901
Sales Range: $200-249.9 Million
Emp.: 700
N.A.I.C.S.: 551112
Gerhard Wendt *(Chm)*

Subsidiaries:

Electrosonic, Inc. (1)
10320 Bren Rd E, Minnetonka, MN 55343
Tel.: (952) 931-7500
Web Site: http://www.electrosonic.com
Sales Range: $25-49.9 Million
Emp.: 28
Large Screen Image Processing Equipment Mfr
N.A.I.C.S.: 334310
Steve Leyland *(Chm)*

Fastems Oy AB (1)
Tuotekatu 4, Tampere, 33840, Finland (100%)
Tel.: (358) 32685111
Web Site: http://www.fastems.com
Sales Range: $50-74.9 Million
Emp.: 200
Mfr of Factory Automation Systems
N.A.I.C.S.: 334512
Mikko Nyman *(CEO)*

Subsidiary (Non-US):

FASTEMS K.K. (2)
Office La Mer 2F Sgami-Ono 8-4-2, Minami-ku Kanagawa Pref, Sagamihara, 252-0303, Japan
Tel.: (81) 8035551283
Industrial Automation Machinery Distr
N.A.I.C.S.: 423610
Toshio Hanibuchi *(Mgr-Sls)*

Subsidiary (US):

FASTEMS LLC (2)
9850 Windisch Rd, West Chester, OH 45069
Tel.: (513) 779-4614
Industrial Automation Machinery Distr
N.A.I.C.S.: 423610
Tyrone Brown *(Mgr-Svc)*

Subsidiary (Non-US):

Fastems AB (2)
Bultgatan 40, PO Box 513, 442 15, Kungalv, Sweden
Tel.: (46) 303246900
Industrial Automation Machinery Distr
N.A.I.C.S.: 423610
Kent Andersson *(Mgr-Svc)*

Fastems S.r.l. (2)
Via Bruno Buozzi 61, San Donato Milanese, 20097, Milan, Italy
Tel.: (39) 0236572723
Industrial Automation Machinery Distr
N.A.I.C.S.: 423610
Jonne Riikonen *(Mgr-Svc)*

Fastems Systems GmbH (2)
Gewerbering 5, 47661, Issum, Germany
Tel.: (49) 283592440
Industrial Automation Machinery Distr
N.A.I.C.S.: 423610

Helvar Oy AB (1)
Yrittajantie 23, PO Box 100, 03601, Karkkila, Finland (100%)
Tel.: (358) 956541
Web Site: http://www.helvar.com
Sales Range: $50-74.9 Million
Emp.: 250
Supplier of Magnetic & Electronic Ballasts to the Lighting Industry
N.A.I.C.S.: 335139

Subsidiary (Non-US):

HELVAR GMBH (2)
Philip-Reis-Strasse 4-8, 63150, Heusenstamm, Germany
Tel.: (49) 6104780750
Lighting Equipment Distr
N.A.I.C.S.: 423610
Oliver Weiss *(Mgr-Sls)*

Helvar AB (2)
Asogatan 155, 116 32, Stockholm, Sweden
Tel.: (46) 854523970
Lighting Equipment Distr
N.A.I.C.S.: 423610
Patrik Frithiof *(Mgr-Country)*

Helvar Kft. (2)
Lomb u 31/b, 1139, Budapest, Hungary
Tel.: (36) 12393136
Lighting Equipment Distr
N.A.I.C.S.: 423610

Helvar Lighting (Suzhou) Co., Ltd. (2)
15F International Building 2 Suzhou Avenue West SIP, Suzhou, 215021, China
Tel.: (86) 51267633078
Lighting Equipment Distr
N.A.I.C.S.: 423610

Helvar Ltd (2)
Hawley Mill Hawley Road, Dartford, Kent, DA2 7SY, United Kingdom
Tel.: (44) 1322617200
Lighting Equipment Distr
N.A.I.C.S.: 423610
Elliet Jones *(Mgr-Sls)*

Helvar Srl (2)
Via W Tobagi 26/1, Peschiera Borromeo, 20068, Milan, Italy
Tel.: (39) 0255301033
Lighting Equipment Distr
N.A.I.C.S.: 423610
Fabio Marcomin *(Mgr-Sls)*

Mercantile Oy AB (1)
Hakkilankaari 2, 1380, Vantaa, Finland (100%)
Tel.: (358) 934501
Web Site: http://www.mercantile.fi
Sales Range: Less than $1 Million
Emp.: 90
Wholesale Distr of Industrial Supplies
N.A.I.C.S.: 425120

Orum Oy AB (1)
Lantinen Teollisuuskatu 2, Espoo, FIN 02920, Finland (100%)
Tel.: (358) 1056941
Web Site: http://www.orum.fi
Sales Range: $50-74.9 Million
Emp.: 150
Importer & Wholesaler of Automotive Parts & Accessories
N.A.I.C.S.: 336340
Kauko Mannerjarei *(Gen Mgr)*

Qualitron Oy AB (1)
Vitikka 4, Espoo, 2630, Finland (100%)
Tel.: (358) 10 328 7500
Web Site: http://www.qualitron.fi
Sales Range: $1-9.9 Million
Emp.: 17
Marketing of Systems Integration of Television Production, Video & Audio Technology
N.A.I.C.S.: 512110
Matti Saarinen *(Head-Mktg & Sls)*

HELVETIA HOLDING AG
Dufourstrasse 40, 9001, Saint Gallen, Switzerland
Tel.: (41) 582801000 CH
Web Site: https://www.helvetia.com
Year Founded: 1996
HELN—(SWX)
Rev.: $11,957,760,532
Assets: $68,120,953,437
Liabilities: $62,918,625,277
Net Worth: $5,202,328,160
Earnings: $681,152,993
Emp.: 12,628
Fiscal Year-end: 12/31/22
Holding Company; Insurance Products & Services
N.A.I.C.S.: 551112
Doris Russi Schurter *(Chm)*

Subsidiaries:

Acierta Asistencia, S.A. (1)
Avenida de Burgos 109, 28050, Madrid, Spain
Tel.: (34) 910551693
Web Site: https://www.aciertaasistencia.es
Real Estate Services
N.A.I.C.S.: 531390

Atlanto AG (1)
Dufourstrasse 40, 9001, Saint Gallen, Switzerland
Tel.: (41) 582805980
Web Site: https://www.atlanto.ch
Financial Services
N.A.I.C.S.: 522320

C.V. Sanchinarro, S.L. (1)
Calle Principe Carlos 44, 28050, Madrid, Spain
Tel.: (34) 917503184
Veterinary Clinic Services
N.A.I.C.S.: 541940

Europaische Reiseversicherungs AG (1)
St Alban-Anlage 56, 4002, Basel, Switzerland
Tel.: (41) 58 275 22 10
Web Site: http://www.erv.ch
Travel Insurance Services
N.A.I.C.S.: 524298

Finovo AG (1)
Grosspeteranlage 29, 4052, Basel, Switzerland
Tel.: (41) 445125656
Web Site: https://www.finovo.ch
Pension Fund & Insurance Services
N.A.I.C.S.: 524292
Martin Diethelm *(CTO)*

Grupo TH Mantenimiento, S.L. (1)
C/ Forja N 15 Nave 5, Torrejon de Ardoz, 28850, Madrid, Spain
Tel.: (34) 916778852
Web Site: https://th-mantenimiento.com
Air Conditioning & Refrigeration Equipment Mfr
N.A.I.C.S.: 333415

Helvetia Asset Management AG (1)
Steinengraben 41, 4002, Basel, Switzerland
Tel.: (41) 582801900
Web Site: https://www.helvetia.com
Real Estate Services
N.A.I.C.S.: 531210

Helvetia Assurances S.A. (1)
25 Quai Lamande, 76600, Le Havre, France
Tel.: (33) 232929292
Web Site: https://www.helvetia.com
Motor Vehicle Insurance Services
N.A.I.C.S.: 524298

Branch (Domestic):

Helvetia Assurances S.A. - Le Havre (2)
25 Quai LaMande, BP 1403, Le Havre, 76067, France
Tel.: (33) 232929292
Sales Range: $100-124.9 Million
Emp.: 240
Transportation Insurance Services
N.A.I.C.S.: 524128

HELVETIA HOLDING AG

Helvetia Compagnie Suisse d'Assurances SA (1)
2 rue Sainte-Marie, 92415, Courbevoie, France
Tel.: (33) 1 47 89 90 00
Web Site: http://www.helvetia.com
General Insurance Services
N.A.I.C.S.: 524298

Helvetia Compania Suiza Sociedad Anonima de Seguros y Reaseguros (1)
Paseo de Cristobal Colon 26, E-41001, Seville, Spain (100%)
Tel.: (34) 954593230
Web Site: https://www.helvetia.es
Insurance Services
N.A.I.C.S.: 524298

Helvetia Consulta AG (1)
St Alban-Anlage 26, CH-4002, Basel, Switzerland
Tel.: (41) 582802056
Travel Insurance Services
N.A.I.C.S.: 524210

Helvetia Consulta Gesellschaft fur Vorsorgeberatung AG (1)
St Alban-Anlage 26, 4002, Basel, Switzerland
Tel.: (41) 582802056
Web Site: http://www.helvetia.com
Sales Range: $25-49.9 Million
Risk Managemeng Srvices
N.A.I.C.S.: 541611

Helvetia Consulting AG (1)
Dufourstrasse 40, CH-9001, Saint Gallen, Switzerland
Tel.: (41) 582805363
Web Site: https://www.helvetia-consulting.ch
Consulting Services
N.A.I.C.S.: 541611
Andreas Bolzern *(Mng Dir)*

Helvetia Investment Foundation (1)
St Alban-Anlage 26, 4002, Basel, Switzerland
Tel.: (41) 582802173
Web Site: http://www.helvetia-anlagestifunt.ch
Sales Range: $50-74.9 Million
Investment Services
N.A.I.C.S.: 523999
Dunja Schwander *(Mng Dir)*

Helvetia Italia Assicurazioni S.p.A. (1)
Via GB Cassinis 21, 20139, Milan, Italy
Tel.: (39) 0253511
Fire Insurance Services
N.A.I.C.S.: 524114

Helvetia Latin America LLC (1)
1395 Brickell Ave Ste 680, Miami, FL 33131
Tel.: (305) 503-5166
Web Site: https://www.helvetia.com
General Insurance Brokerage & Services
N.A.I.C.S.: 524210
Leonardo Morales *(Sr VP & Head-Marine & Art)*

Helvetia Leben Maklerservice GmbH (1)
Weissadlergasse 2, 60311, Frankfurt am Main, Germany
Tel.: (49) 691332575
Web Site: https://www.helvetia.com
Fire Insurance Services
N.A.I.C.S.: 524114

Helvetia Schweizerische Lebensversicherungsgesellschaft AG (1)
St Alban-Anlage 26, CH-4002, Basel, Switzerland
Tel.: (41) 582801000
Fire Insurance Services
N.A.I.C.S.: 524114

Helvetia Schweizerische Versicherungsgesellschaft AG (1)
Berliner Strasse 56-58, 60311, Frankfurt am Main, Germany
Tel.: (49) 6913320
Fire Insurance Services
N.A.I.C.S.: 524113

Subsidiary (Domestic):

Helvetia Schweizerische Lebensversicherungs AG (2)

HELVETIA HOLDING AG

Helvetia Holding AG—(Continued)
Weissadlergasse 2, 60311, Frankfurt am Main, Germany **(100%)**
Tel.: (49) 6913320
Sales Range: $150-199.9 Million
Life Insurance Products & Services
N.A.I.C.S.: 524113

Helvetia Versicherungs-AG (2)
Berliner Strasse 56-58, 60311, Frankfurt am Main, Germany
Tel.: (49) 6913320
General Insurance Services
N.A.I.C.S.: 524298
Burkhard Gierse *(Member-Mgmt Bd)*

Helvetia Swiss Insurance Company (Labuan Branch) Ltd. (1)
Suite 1303 Level 13 The Gardens South Tower Mid Valley City, Lingkaran Syed Putra, 59200, Kuala Lumpur, Federal Territory, Malaysia
Tel.: (60) 3 2282 6689
Web Site: http://www.helvetia.com
General Insurance Brokerage & Services
N.A.I.C.S.: 524210

Helvetia Swiss Insurance Company Ltd (1)
Dufourstrasse 40, CH-9001, Saint Gallen, Switzerland
Tel.: (41) 582801000
Web Site: https://www.helvetia.com
Emp.: 100
General Insurance Services
N.A.I.C.S.: 524210

Helvetia Swiss Insurance Company in Liechtenstein Ltd. (1)
Herrengasse 11, 9490, Vaduz, Liechtenstein
Tel.: (423) 231 12 25
General Insurance Brokwerage & Services
N.A.I.C.S.: 524210

Helvetia Swiss Life Insurance Company Ltd (1)
St Alban Anlage 26, 4002, Basel, Switzerland
Tel.: (41) 58 280 1000
Web Site: http://www.helvetia.com
Fire Insurance Services
N.A.I.C.S.: 524113

Helvetia Versicherungen (1)
Saint Alban-Anlage 26, 4002, Basel, Switzerland **(100%)**
Tel.: (41) 582801000
Web Site: http://www.helvetia.ch
Sales Range: $700-749.9 Million
Emp.: 2,500
Insurance Services
N.A.I.C.S.: 524298
Philipp Gmur *(CEO)*

Helvetia Versicherungen AG (1)
Hoher Markt 10-11, 1010, Vienna, Austria
Tel.: (43) 502221000
Web Site: https://www.helvetia.com
Sales Range: $100-124.9 Million
Insurance Services
N.A.I.C.S.: 524298
Thomas Neusiedler *(Chm)*

Helvetia Vita - Compagnia Italo Svizzera Di Assicurazioni Sulla Vita S.p.A. (1)
Via GB Cassinis 21, 20139, Milan, Italy
Tel.: (39) 0253511
Fire Insurance Services
N.A.I.C.S.: 524114

Helvetic Warranty GmbH (1)
Industriestrasse 12, 8305, Dietlikon, Switzerland
Tel.: (41) 449086414
Web Site: https://helvetic-warranty.ch
Insurance Services
N.A.I.C.S.: 524298

Helvitia Vita Compagnia SA (1)
Via G B Cassinis 21, 20139, Milan, Italy **(100%)**
Tel.: (39) 02 53 511
Web Site: http://www.helvetia.com
Holding Company; Life Insurance Products & Services
N.A.I.C.S.: 551112

Subsidiary (Domestic):

Italo Svizzera di Assicurazioni sulla Vita S.p.A. **(2)**

Via GB Cassinis 21, 20139, Milan, Italy **(100%)**
Tel.: (39) 0253511
Web Site: http://www.helvetia.com
Life Insurance Products & Services
N.A.I.C.S.: 524113

Jalsosa, S.L. (1)
Camino de Fitena s/n, Pinos Puente, 18240, Granada, Spain
Tel.: (34) 958459050
Web Site: https://jalsosa.com
Health Care Product Mfr & Distr
N.A.I.C.S.: 325620

Layertex S.L. (1)
Cami del Mig 88, Poligono Industrial Les Corts Cabrera de Mar, 08304, Barcelona, Spain
Tel.: (34) 937547405
Web Site: https://www.layertex.com
Health Care Products Mfr
N.A.I.C.S.: 325620

Smart Insurance & IT Solutions GmbH (1)
Salztorgasse 5/3 Stock, 1010, Vienna, Austria
Tel.: (43) 502221919
Web Site: https://www.smart-versicherung.at
Insurance Brokerage Services
N.A.I.C.S.: 524210
Thomas Stellfeld *(Mng Dir)*

SmartLife Care AG (1)
Zurichstrasse 44, 8306, Bruttisellen, Switzerland
Tel.: (41) 848656565
Web Site: https://www.smartlife-care.ch
Fire Insurance Services
N.A.I.C.S.: 524114
Jens Wohler *(COO)*

fairchcek Schadenservice GmbH (1)
Dorfplatz 4, Stattegg, 8046, Graz, Austria
Tel.: (43) 316890685
Web Site: https://faircheck.at
Property Management Services
N.A.I.C.S.: 531312

HEM HOLDINGS & TRADING LTD.

601/602 A Fairlink Centre, Off Andheri Link Road Andheri West, Mumbai, 400053, Maharashtra, India
Tel.: (91) 2240034768
Web Site: https://www.hemholdings.com
Year Founded: 1982
505520—(BOM)
Rev.: $15,255
Assets: $296,014
Liabilities: $4,589
Net Worth: $291,424
Earnings: ($1,634)
Fiscal Year-end: 03/31/23
Holding Company
N.A.I.C.S.: 551112
P. V. S. Chandra Sekharam *(CFO)*

HEMANG RESOURCES LIMITED

Plot No 4 6th Avenue Harington Road Chetpet, Chennai, 600031, Tamil Nadu, India
Tel.: (91) 45590053
Web Site: http://www.bhatiacoalindia.com
Year Founded: 1979
531178—(BOM)
Rev.: $10,740,475
Assets: $9,886,968
Liabilities: $7,276,255
Net Worth: $2,610,713
Earnings: $2,664,617
Fiscal Year-end: 03/31/22
Financial Services
N.A.I.C.S.: 523999
Komal Jitendra Thakker *(CEO)*

HEMANT SURGICAL INDUSTRIES LIMITED

502 5th Floor Ecstasy City Of Joy Commercial Complex JSD Road, Mulund West, Mumbai, 400080, Maharashtra, India
Tel.: (91) 8425840446
Web Site: https://www.hemantsurgical.com
Year Founded: 1985
543916—(BOM)
Medical Product Distr
N.A.I.C.S.: 423450
HansKumar Shah *(CEO)*

HEMARAJ LEASEHOLD REAL ESTATE INVESTMENT TRUST

27th Fl UM Tower 9 Ramkhamhaeng Rd, Suangluang, Bangkok, 10250, Thailand
Tel.: (66) 27173901
Web Site: http://www.hemarajreit.com
WHAIR—(THA)
Rev.: $25,453,379
Assets: $382,686,977
Liabilities: $135,280,051
Net Worth: $247,406,926
Earnings: $16,379,495
Fiscal Year-end: 12/31/23
Real Estate Investment Trust Services
N.A.I.C.S.: 531190
Kanchana Ouaoborm *(Mng Dir)*

HEMAS HOLDINGS PLC

75 Braybrooke Place, 2, Colombo, Sri Lanka
Tel.: (94) 114731731
Web Site: https://www.hemas.com
HHL—(COL)
Rev.: $379,280,230
Assets: $327,878,176
Liabilities: $197,654,812
Net Worth: $130,223,365
Earnings: $16,872,551
Emp.: 4,739
Fiscal Year-end: 03/31/23
Holding Company
N.A.I.C.S.: 551112
Roy Joseph *(Member-Exec Bd, Mng Dir & Hemas Manufacturing Pvt Ltd)*

Subsidiaries:

ACX International (Pte) Ltd (1)
Tel.: (94) 114529529
Sales Range: $25-49.9 Million
Emp.: 50
Freight Transportation Services
N.A.I.C.S.: 488510
Harin Gomes *(Gen Mgr)*

Atlas Axillia Co. (Pvt) Ltd. (1)
Tel.: (94) 115320320
Web Site: http://www.atlas.lk
Stationery Product Mfr & Retailer
N.A.I.C.S.: 322230
Asitha Samaraweera *(Mng Dir)*

Diethelm Travel Sri Lanka (1)
Level 6 Hemas House No 75 Braybrooke Place, 00200, Colombo, Sri Lanka
Tel.: (94) 112313131
Sales Range: $10-24.9 Million
Emp.: 50
Travel Agency Services
N.A.I.C.S.: 561520
Harith Perera *(Mng Dir)*

Evergreen Shipping Agency Lanka (Pvt) Ltd. (1)
Level 9 Parkland No 33 Park Street, 02, Colombo, Western, Sri Lanka
Tel.: (94) 117441000
Web Site: http://www.evergreen-line.com
Cargo Handling Services
N.A.I.C.S.: 488320

Far Shipping Lanka (Pvt) Ltd. (1)
No 36 Hemas Building Sir Razeek Fareed Mawatha, 01, Colombo, Sri Lanka
Tel.: (94) 1148958069
Shipping Agency Services
N.A.I.C.S.: 488510

Forbes Air Services (Pvt) Ltd. (1)

INTERNATIONAL PUBLIC

Hemas House 75 Braybrooke Place, 02, Colombo, Sri Lanka
Tel.: (94) 114704070
Airline Services
N.A.I.C.S.: 481111

Healthnet International (Pvt) Ltd. (1)
30/4 Park Road, 5, Colombo, Sri Lanka
Tel.: (94) 112795795
Web Site: https://www.healthnet.lk
Pharmacy Product Retailer
N.A.I.C.S.: 456110

Hemas Air Services (Pte) Ltd (1)
Hemas Bldg, 75 York St, Colombo, 01, Sri Lanka
Tel.: (94) 11 2343711
Airline Services
N.A.I.C.S.: 561599

Hemas Air Services (Pvt.) Ltd. (1)
N0 30/1 Sir Razik Fareed Mawatha, Colombo, 01, Sri Lanka
Tel.: (94) 11 234 2291
Web Site: https://www.hemas.com
Sales Range: $10-24.9 Million
Emp.: 45
Airline Services
N.A.I.C.S.: 561599
Dushy Jayaweera *(Mng Dir)*

Hemas Developments (Pte) Ltd (1)
No 75 Braybrooke Place, 02, Colombo, Sri Lanka
Tel.: (94) 112348853
Sales Range: $10-24.9 Million
Emp.: 10
Healtcare Services
N.A.I.C.S.: 621491

Hemas Hospitals (Pvt) Ltd. (1)
389 Negombo Road, Wattala, Sri Lanka
Tel.: (94) 117888888
Web Site: http://www.hemashospitals.com
Hospital Services
N.A.I.C.S.: 622110

Hemas Manufacturing (Pte) Ltd (1)
75 Braybrooke Place, 02, Colombo, Sri Lanka
Tel.: (94) 114731731
Sales Range: $25-49.9 Million
Emp.: 50
Baby Care Products Mfr & Whslr
N.A.I.C.S.: 424350

Hemas Maritime (Pvt) Ltd. (1)
No 33 Park Street, 02, Colombo, Sri Lanka
Tel.: (94) 117441000
Cargo Handling Services
N.A.I.C.S.: 488320

Hemas Pharmaceuticals (Pvt.) Ltd. (1)
No 12 Glen Aber Place, 03, Colombo, Sri Lanka
Tel.: (94) 114766666
Sales Range: $200-249.9 Million
Emp.: 1,400
Pharmaceuticals Product Mfr
N.A.I.C.S.: 325412
Kasturi Chellaraja Wilson *(Mng Dir)*

Hemas Power Limited (1)
Tel.: (94) 114731731
Web Site: http://www.hemas.com
Sales Range: $75-99.9 Million
Emp.: 20
Power Generation Services
N.A.I.C.S.: 221118
Kishan Nanayakkara *(Mng Dir)*

Hemas Surgicals & Diagnostics (Pvt.) Ltd. (1)
Tel.: (94) 114766666
Web Site: http://www.hemashealthcare.com
Sales Range: $125-149.9 Million
Emp.: 650
Pharmaceutical Product Whslr
N.A.I.C.S.: 325412

Hemas Travels (Pte) Ltd (1)
Hemas Building 36 Sir Razik Fareed Mawatha, Colombo, Sri Lanka
Tel.: (94) 114704705
Web Site: https://www.acorntravels.lk
Emp.: 80
Travel Services
N.A.I.C.S.: 561510

Mazu Shipping (Pvt) Ltd. (1)

36 Sir Razik Fareed Mawatha, 01, Colombo, Sri Lanka
Tel.: (94) 114731731
Shipping Agency Services
N.A.I.C.S.: 488510

Morison Limited (1)
Hemas House 3rd Floor 75 Braybrook place, 02, Colombo, Sri Lanka
Tel.: (94) 112904222
Web Site: https://www.morison.lk
Emp.: 500
Pharmaceuticals Product Mfr
N.A.I.C.S.: 325412
Dinesh Athapaththu *(Mng Dir)*

Serendib Leisure Management Ltd. (1)
3rd Floor Hemas House 75 Braybrooke Place, 02, Colombo, Sri Lanka
Tel.: (94) 114626626
Web Site: https://vouchers.serendibleisure.com
Sales Range: $10-24.9 Million
Emp.: 40
Home Management Services
N.A.I.C.S.: 721110

Skynet Worldwide Express (Pvt.) Ltd. (1)
Tel.: (94) 114731600
Web Site: https://www.skynetworldwide.net
Sales Range: $10-24.9 Million
Emp.: 50
Courier Service
N.A.I.C.S.: 492110

HEMCHECK SWEDEN AB
Universitetsgatan 2, Karlstad, 651 88, Sweden
Tel.: (46) 702880826
Web Site: http://www.hemcheck.com
BIOVIT—(OMX)
Rev.: $123,634
Assets: $2,477,357
Liabilities: $143,303
Net Worth: $2,334,055
Earnings: ($1,395,562)
Emp.: 2
Fiscal Year-end: 12/31/22
Biotechnology Research & Development Services
N.A.I.C.S.: 541714
Joen Averstad *(CEO)*

HEMERIA SASU
8 Impasse Boudeville, 31100, Toulouse, France
Tel.: (33) 5 6143 5800 FR
Web Site: http://www.hemeria-sas.com
Year Founded: 2019
Space Technology Engineering & Mfr
N.A.I.C.S.: 336419

HEMIJSKA INDUSTRIJA VRANJE A.D.
Omladinskih brigada 11, 17500, Vranje, Serbia
Tel.: (381) 17401007
Web Site: https://www.hiv.co.rs
Year Founded: 1957
HIVR—(BEL)
Rev.: $2,138,956
Assets: $2,723,981
Liabilities: $1,286,123
Net Worth: $1,437,857
Earnings: $1,053
Emp.: 60
Fiscal Year-end: 12/31/23
Plastics Product Mfr
N.A.I.C.S.: 326199
Rade Novkovic *(CEO)*

HEMISPHERE ENERGY CORPORATION
Suite 501 905 West Pender Street, Vancouver, V6C 1L6, BC, Canada
Tel.: (604) 685-9255
Web Site: https://www.hemisphereenergy.ca
Year Founded: 1978
HME—(OTCIQ)
Rev.: $13,264,940
Assets: $41,053,310
Liabilities: $28,295,776
Net Worth: $12,757,535
Earnings: ($325,357)
Emp.: 8
Fiscal Year-end: 12/31/20
Oil & Gas Exploration Services
N.A.I.C.S.: 213112
Charles N. O'Sullivan *(Founder & Chm)*

HEMISPHERE FASHION GROUP
Hompeschstrasse 3, 81675, Munich, Germany
Tel.: (49) 893300710
Web Site: http://www.hemisphere.de
Year Founded: 1985
Rev.: $10,345,500
Emp.: 6
Textile Products Mfr
N.A.I.C.S.: 314999
Peter Lochmann *(Founder)*

HEMISPHERE PROPERTIES INDIA LIMITED
Room No 144 C-Wing Nirman Bhawan Maulana Azad Road, New Delhi, 110001, India
Tel.: (91) 9310531098
Web Site: https://www.hpil.co.in
543242—(BOM)
Rev.: $49,823
Assets: $147,225,255
Liabilities: $95,815,602
Net Worth: $51,409,654
Earnings: ($1,017,389)
Emp.: 2
Fiscal Year-end: 03/31/21
Property Management Services
N.A.I.C.S.: 531311
D. Thara *(Chm & Mng Dir)*

HEMMERLIN S.A.
12 rue des Cevennes, 68392, Sausheim, Cedex, France
Tel.: (33) 389619419 FR
Web Site: http://www.hemmerlin.com
Year Founded: 1982
Rev.: $30,800,000
Emp.: 170
Transportation Services
N.A.I.C.S.: 484230
Gilbert Hemmerlin *(Pres)*

Subsidiaries:

HEMMERLIN ROMANIA DUNAROM SPED. S.R.L. (1)
Sat Teghes Comuna Domnesti T61 P217/4 217/3 Lot 15 Etaj 1 Camera 18, Domnesti, Ilfov, Romania
Tel.: (40) 737 049 738
General Trucking Services
N.A.I.C.S.: 484121

HEMMERLIN SWISS AG (1)
Impasse du Nouveau-Marche 1, 1723, Marly, Switzerland
Tel.: (41) 26 435 35 55
General Trucking Services
N.A.I.C.S.: 484121

Hemmerlin Polska Sp. z o.o. (1)
ul Stary Rynek 38-39, 61-772, Poznan, Poland
Tel.: (48) 61 874 16 14
Web Site: http://www.hemmerlin.com.pl
General Trucking Services
N.A.I.C.S.: 484121

HEMO ORGANIC LIMITED
8-A Gulnar Chinar-Gulnar Apartment Anand - V V Nagar Road, Anand, 388 001, Gujarat, India
Tel.: (91) 2692248535
Web Site: https://www.hemoorganicltd.com
524590—(BOM)
Rev.: $1,102
Assets: $31,854
Liabilities: $22,872
Net Worth: $8,982
Earnings: ($6,535)
Emp.: 5
Fiscal Year-end: 03/31/21
Pharmaceuticals Product Mfr
N.A.I.C.S.: 325412
Vishwambar Kameshwar Singh *(Mng Dir)*

HEMOGENYX PHARMACEUTICALS PLC
6th Floor 60 Gracechurch Street, London, EC3V 0HR, United Kingdom
Tel.: (44) 1727627627 UK
Web Site: https://hemogenyx.com
Year Founded: 2012
HEMO—(LSE)
Rev.: $13,379
Assets: $8,953,054
Liabilities: $4,858,734
Net Worth: $4,094,320
Earnings: ($5,032,797)
Emp.: 14
Fiscal Year-end: 12/31/22
Pharmaceutical Product Mfr & Distr
N.A.I.C.S.: 325412
Vladislav Sandler *(CEO)*

HEMOPLAST JSC
Majakovsky street 57, Belgorod-Dniestrovsky, Odessa, 67700, Ukraine
Tel.: (380) 484931562
Web Site: http://www.hemoplast.ua
Year Founded: 1973
HEMO—(UKR)
Sales Range: Less than $1 Million
Medical Laboratory Product Mfr
N.A.I.C.S.: 334516
Ruslan Petrovich Zozulya *(Co-Chm)*

HEMOSTEMIX INC.
707 7th Ave SW Suite 1150, Calgary, T2P 3H6, AB, Canada
Tel.: (905) 580-4170
Web Site: https://www.hemostemix.com
Year Founded: 2014
HMTXF—(OTCQB)
Assets: $1,817,298
Liabilities: $2,676,786
Net Worth: ($859,488)
Earnings: ($6,077,140)
Fiscal Year-end: 12/31/20
Biotechnology Research & Development Services
N.A.I.C.S.: 541714
Thomas Smeenk *(Founder, Pres & CEO)*

HEMOTEQ AG
Adenauerstrasse 15, Wurselen, 52146, Germany
Tel.: (49) 2405 455 000 De
Web Site: http://www.hemoteq.de
Year Founded: 1999
Sales Range: $10-24.9 Million
Emp.: 100
Specialty Medical Coatings Developer & Mfr
N.A.I.C.S.: 325510
Michael Hoffmann *(Co-Founder & CEO)*

HEMPEL A/S
Lundtoftegardsvej 91, 2800, Lyngby, Denmark
Tel.: (45) 4593 3800 DK
Web Site: http://www.hempel.com
Year Founded: 1915
Rev.: $1,717,865,240
Assets: $1,455,818,000
Liabilities: $904,846,880
Net Worth: $550,971,120
Earnings: $55,993,000
Emp.: 6,219
Fiscal Year-end: 12/31/19
Protective Coatings Mfr
N.A.I.C.S.: 325510
Mark Rees *(VP-Middle East)*

Subsidiaries:

Crown Paints Ltd. (1)
Crown House Hollins Road, Darwen, Lancaster, BB3 0BG, United Kingdom
Tel.: (44) 1254704951
Web Site: http://www.crownpaint.co.uk
Sales Range: $250-299.9 Million
Emp.: 1,400
Decorative Coatings Mfr & Whslr
N.A.I.C.S.: 325510

Hempel (China) Ltd. (1)
Unit 1509-16 15th Fl BEA Tower Millennium City 5, 418 Kwun Tong Rd, Kowloon, China (Hong Kong)
Tel.: (852) 28577663
Web Site: http://www.hempel.hk
Sales Range: $50-74.9 Million
Emp.: 60
Protective Coatings Mfr & Whslr
N.A.I.C.S.: 325510

Hempel (USA) Inc. (1)
600 Conroe Park N Dr, Conroe, TX 77303
Tel.: (936) 523-6000
Web Site: http://www.hempel.com
Decorative Coatings Mfr & Whslr
N.A.I.C.S.: 325510
Peter Kirkegaard *(Chief People & Culture Officer & Exec VP)*

Jones-Blair Company, LLC (1)
2728 Empire Central, Dallas, TX 75235 (100%)
Tel.: (214) 353-1600
Web Site: http://www.jones-blair.com
High Performance Coatings Developer, Mfr & Marketer
N.A.I.C.S.: 325510
Jeff Powell *(Pres)*

Division (Domestic):

Neogard Construction Coatings (2)
2728 Empire Central, Dallas, TX 75235
Tel.: (214) 353-1600
Web Site: http://www.neogard.us
Polymeric & Elastomeric Coatings Mfr
N.A.I.C.S.: 325510
Steve Dillon *(Acct Mgr-Territory)*

HEMPRO A.D.
Terazije 8, Belgrade, Serbia
Tel.: (381) 11 244 7715
Web Site: http://www.hempro.co.rs
Year Founded: 1945
Chemical Product Export & Trading
N.A.I.C.S.: 325998

HEMPTOWN ORGANICS CORP.
#750 - 1095 West Pender Street, Vancouver, V6E 2M6, BC, Canada
Tel.: (778) 908-2730 BC
Web Site: http://hemptownusa.com
Year Founded: 2014
Hemp-derived Cannabidiol (CBD) Products
N.A.I.C.S.: 111419
Rod Wolterman *(Founder & Chm)*

Subsidiaries:

Kirkman Group, Inc. (1)
6400 SW Rosewood St, Lake Oswego, OR 97035
Tel.: (503) 694-1600
Web Site: http://www.kirkmangroup.com
Nutritional Supplements Mfr
N.A.I.C.S.: 325412
Michael Schaeffer *(CEO)*

Hemptown Organics Corp.—(Continued)

HENAN ANCAI HI-TECH CO., LTD.
South Section of Zhongzhou Road, Anyang, 455000, Henan, China
Tel.: (86) 3723732533
Web Site: https://www.acht.com.cn
Year Founded: 1987
600207—(SHG)
Rev.: $581,858,035
Assets: $1,037,344,824
Liabilities: $579,810,329
Net Worth: $457,534,495
Earnings: $10,881,407
Emp.: 2,400
Fiscal Year-end: 12/31/22
Glass Product Mfr & Distr
N.A.I.C.S.: 327212
He Yimin *(Chm)*

HENAN BCCY ENVIRONMENTAL ENERGY CO., LTD.
10F Kailin Building Ruyi Hexi 2nd Street Ruyi West Road, Zhengdong New District, Zhengzhou, 450000, Henan, China
Tel.: (86) 37163969330
Web Site:
https://www.bccynewpower.com
Year Founded: 2009
300614—(SSE)
Rev.: $62,472,384
Assets: $263,807,388
Liabilities: $53,096,472
Net Worth: $210,710,916
Earnings: $5,290,272
Fiscal Year-end: 12/31/22
Energy Distribution Services
N.A.I.C.S.: 221122
Gonghai Chen *(Chm & Gen Mgr)*

HENAN CARVE ELECTRONICS TECHNOLOGY CO., LTD.
Shanan Industrial Agglomeration Zone, Shenqiu County, Zhoukou, 466300, Henan, China
Tel.: (86) 3945280985
Web Site: https://www.carve.com.cn
Year Founded: 2009
301182—(CHIN)
Rev.: $70,838,820
Assets: $162,300,996
Liabilities: $25,402,572
Net Worth: $136,898,424
Earnings: $4,534,920
Emp.: 2,000
Fiscal Year-end: 12/31/22
Electronic Component Mfr & Distr
N.A.I.C.S.: 334419
Haigang Chen *(Chm)*

HENAN COMMUNICATIONS PLANNING AND DESIGN INSTITUTE CO., LTD
No 9 Zeyu Street, Zhengdong New District, Zhengzhou, 451450, Henan, China
Tel.: (86) 37162037987
Web Site: https://www.hnrbi.com
Year Founded: 1964
300732—(CHIN)
Rev.: $325,071,588
Assets: $950,734,007
Liabilities: $532,340,462
Net Worth: $418,393,545
Earnings: $16,962,509
Fiscal Year-end: 12/31/23
Civil Engineering Services
N.A.I.C.S.: 237310
Xingwen Chang *(Chm)*
Subsidiaries:
Henan Gaojian Project Management Co., Ltd. (1)
No 9 Zeyu Street, Zhengdong New District,
Zhengzhou, Henan, China
Tel.: (86) 37162037039
Engineeering Services
N.A.I.C.S.: 541330
Zhang Jianping *(Chm)*

Henan Province Academy of Engineering Detect Cross Reinforcement Ltd. (1)
No 70 Mid Longhai Road, Erqi District, Zhengzhou, Henan, China
Tel.: (86) 37156598133
Engineering Services
N.A.I.C.S.: 541330
Yang Lei *(Chm)*

HENAN DAYOU ENERGY CO., LTD.
No 6 Qianqiu Road, Yima, Sanmenxia, 472300, Henan, China
Tel.: (86) 3985887735
Web Site: https://dyny.hnecgc.com.cn
Year Founded: 1998
600403—(SHG)
Rev.: $1,205,837,109
Assets: $3,130,600,239
Liabilities: $1,915,409,148
Net Worth: $1,215,191,091
Earnings: $218,391,442
Fiscal Year-end: 12/31/22
Coal Exploitation & Distribution Services
N.A.I.C.S.: 423520
Ren Chunxing *(Chm)*

HENAN ENERGY & CHEMICAL INDUSTRY GROUP CO., LTD.
Guo Long Mansion, Zhengzhou, 450046, Henan, China
Tel.: (86) 37169337002 CN
Sales Range: Less than $1 Million
Holding Company; Coal Mining & Chemicals Mfr
N.A.I.C.S.: 551112
Xiang'en Chen *(Chm & CEO)*

HENAN HENGXING SCIENCE & TECHNOLOGY CO., LTD.
NO 121 Yiluo North Road, Kangdian Town, Gongyi, 451253, Henan, China
Tel.: (86) 37168716999
Web Site:
https://www.hengxingsteelwire.com
Year Founded: 1995
002132—(SSE)
Rev.: $620,205,768
Assets: $1,129,008,348
Liabilities: $602,773,704
Net Worth: $526,234,644
Earnings: $26,319,384
Emp.: 2,200
Fiscal Year-end: 12/31/22
Metal Products Mfr
N.A.I.C.S.: 331222
Xie Xiaobo *(Chm)*

HENAN HUANGHE WHIRLWIND CO., LTD.
Intersection of Qilihe North Road and Xinyi Road, Zhengzhou, 461500, Henan, China
Tel.: (86) 15538112502
Web Site:
https://www.huanghewhirlwind.com
Year Founded: 1978
600172—(SHG)
Rev.: $338,391,210
Assets: $1,352,772,392
Liabilities: $890,585,561
Net Worth: $462,186,832
Earnings: $4,326,974
Fiscal Year-end: 12/31/22
Cutting Tool Mfr
N.A.I.C.S.: 333515
Li Ge *(Chm)*

HENAN HUAYING AGRICULTURE DEVELOPMENT CO., LTD.
308 Yuejin East Road, Huangchuan County, Henan, 465150, China
Tel.: (86) 3763119902
Web Site: https://www.hua-ying.com
Year Founded: 2002
002321—(SSE)
Rev.: $406,929,744
Assets: $495,443,520
Liabilities: $304,366,140
Net Worth: $191,077,380
Earnings: ($83,821,608)
Fiscal Year-end: 12/31/22
Poultry Services
N.A.I.C.S.: 311615
Xu Shuijun *(Chm)*

HENAN JINDAN LACTIC ACID TECHNOLOGY CO., LTD.
No 08 Jindan Avenue, Dancheng County, Zhoukou, 477150, Henan, China
Tel.: (86) 37160136136
Web Site:
https://www.jindanlactic.com
Year Founded: 2006
300829—(SSE)
Rev.: $215,460,648
Assets: $351,890,136
Liabilities: $135,362,448
Net Worth: $216,527,688
Earnings: $18,565,092
Fiscal Year-end: 12/31/22
Acid Product Mfr
N.A.I.C.S.: 325199
Peng Zhang *(Chm)*

HENAN JINMA ENERGY COMPANY LIMITED
West Ring Of The South Road, Jiyuan, 459000, Henan, China
Tel.: (86) 3916038000 CN
Web Site: https://www.hnjmny.com
Year Founded: 2003
6885—(HKG)
Rev.: $1,747,789,618
Assets: $1,576,843,913
Liabilities: $913,246,121
Net Worth: $663,597,792
Earnings: $80,138,074
Emp.: 2,848
Fiscal Year-end: 12/31/22
Fuel Product Mfr & Distr
N.A.I.C.S.: 324199
Chiu Fai Yiu *(Chm & Exec Dir)*

HENAN KEDI DAIRY INDUSTRY CO., LTD.
No 18 Industrial Avenue Industrial Concentrated Area, Yucheng County, Shangqiu, 476343, China
Tel.: (86) 370 421 8588
Web Site: http://www.kedidairy.com
002770—(SSE)
Rev.: $72,908,043
Assets: $370,463,312
Liabilities: $323,939,564
Net Worth: $46,523,749
Earnings: ($195,088,421)
Fiscal Year-end: 12/31/20
Dairy Product Production & Distr
N.A.I.C.S.: 112120
Qinghai Zhang *(Chm)*

HENAN LANTIAN GAS CO., LTD.
No 68 Jiefang Road, Zhumadian, 463000, Henan, China
Tel.: (86) 3963811051
Web Site: http://www.hnltrq.com.cn
Year Founded: 2002
605368—(SHG)
Rev.: $667,419,508
Assets: $877,142,317
Liabilities: $356,906,389
Net Worth: $520,235,928
Earnings: $83,154,048
Fiscal Year-end: 12/31/22
Oil & Gas Distribution Services
N.A.I.C.S.: 221210
Qiyong Chen *(Chm & Gen Mgr)*

HENAN LILIANG DIAMOND CO., LTD.
Room 11A No 8 of Inner Ring Road, ZhengDong District, Zhengzhou, 450000, China
Tel.: (86) 3707396698
Web Site: https://www.llgem.com
Year Founded: 2010
301071—(CHIN)
Rev.: $105,910,380
Assets: $921,203,082
Liabilities: $170,860,816
Net Worth: $750,342,265
Earnings: $51,228,267
Fiscal Year-end: 12/31/23
Diamond Product Mfr & Distr
N.A.I.C.S.: 333514
Zengming Shao *(Chm)*

HENAN LINGRUI PHARMACEUTICAL CO., LTD.
No 59 Jiefang Road, Xin County, Xinyang, 465550, Henan, China
Tel.: (86) 3762988888
Web Site: https://www.lingruius.com
Year Founded: 1992
600285—(SHG)
Rev.: $421,461,453
Assets: $609,951,331
Liabilities: $250,742,733
Net Worth: $359,208,598
Earnings: $65,332,444
Fiscal Year-end: 12/31/22
Pharmaceutical Product Mfr & Distr
N.A.I.C.S.: 325412
Xiong Wei *(Chm & Pres)*

HENAN MINGTAI ALUMINUM CO., LTD.
Huiguo Town Development Zone, Gongyi, 451283, Henan, China
Tel.: (86) 37167898155
Web Site: http://www.hngymt.com
Year Founded: 1997
601677—(SHG)
Rev.: $3,900,471,129
Assets: $2,661,214,131
Liabilities: $886,948,415
Net Worth: $1,774,265,716
Earnings: $224,441,811
Emp.: 3,100
Fiscal Year-end: 12/31/22
Aluminium Products Mfr
N.A.I.C.S.: 331315
Ting Yi Ma *(Chm)*

HENAN NEWLAND PHARMACEUTICAL CO., LTD.
East side of the southern section of Weiwu Road, Changge, 461500, Henan, China
Tel.: (86) 3746103777
Web Site:
https://www.newlandpharma.com
Year Founded: 2005
301277—(CHIN)
Rev.: $88,081,344
Assets: $215,341,308
Liabilities: $24,511,032
Net Worth: $190,830,276
Earnings: $18,574,920
Fiscal Year-end: 12/31/22
Pharmaceutical Product Mfr & Distr
N.A.I.C.S.: 325412
Xie Jianzhong *(Chm)*

HENAN QINGSHUIYUAN TECHNOLOGY CO., LTD.

AND PRIVATE COMPANIES

100 meters west of the intersection of Kegong Road and Wenbo Road, Huling High-tech Zone, Jiyuan, 459000, Henan, China
Tel.: (86) 3916089345
Web Site: https://www.qywt.com.cn
Year Founded: 1995
300437—(CHIN)
Rev.: $253,382,688
Assets: $439,523,604
Liabilities: $213,027,516
Net Worth: $226,496,088
Earnings: ($6,169,176)
Emp.: 350
Fiscal Year-end: 12/31/22
Phosphonates Mfr
N.A.I.C.S.: 325998
Wang Zhiqing *(Chm & Pres)*

HENAN REBECCA HAIR PRODUCTS CO., LTD.
No 666 Rebecca Avenue, Xuchang, 461100, Henan, China
Tel.: (86) 3745136699
Web Site: http://www.rebecca.com.cn
Year Founded: 1990
600439—(SHG)
Rev.: $176,614,678
Assets: $737,561,172
Liabilities: $340,417,687
Net Worth: $397,143,485
Earnings: $4,770,946
Emp.: 11,000
Fiscal Year-end: 12/31/22
Hair Product Mfr & Whslr
N.A.I.C.S.: 339999
Zheng Wenqing *(Chm & Gen Mgr)*

HENAN SENYUAN ELECTRIC CO., LTD.
West side of the southern section of Weiwu Road, Changge, 461500, Henan, China
Tel.: (86) 3746108288
Web Site: http://www.hnsyec.com
Year Founded: 2000
002358—(SSE)
Rev.: $337,895,064
Assets: $880,998,768
Liabilities: $446,398,992
Net Worth: $434,599,776
Earnings: $5,359,068
Emp.: 10,000
Fiscal Year-end: 12/31/22
Electric Device Mfr
N.A.I.C.S.: 335999
Zhao Zhongting *(Chm)*

Subsidiaries:

Ruzhou Xintai Solar Power Technological Development Co.,Ltd. (1)
Mangchuan Town, Ruzhou, Henan, China
Tel.: (86) 13867597895
Electrical Equipment & Vehicle Mfr
N.A.I.C.S.: 336320

Zhengzhou Senyuan New Energy Technology Co., Ltd. (1)
No 56 Jingbei 5th Road, Economic and Technological Development Zone, Zhengzhou, China
Tel.: (86) 37167386666
Web Site: en.hnsyxnykj.cn
Electrical Mfr & Distr
N.A.I.C.S.: 335999

Zhenzhou Senyuan New Energy Technology Co., Ltd. (1)
Tel.: (86) 37167391111
Electrical Equipment & Component Mfr
N.A.I.C.S.: 335999

HENAN SHEN HUO COAL INDUSTRY & ELECTRICITY POWER CO., LTD.
No 17 Guangming Road, Dongcheng District Yongcheng City, Henan, 476600, China

Tel.: (86) 3705982722
000933—(SSE)
Rev.: $5,995,620,540
Assets: $8,491,024,152
Liabilities: $5,517,169,632
Net Worth: $2,973,854,520
Earnings: $1,062,996,480
Fiscal Year-end: 12/31/22
Coal Mining Services
N.A.I.C.S.: 324199

HENAN SHIJIA PHOTONS TECHNOLOGY CO., LTD.
No 201 Yanhe Road, National Economic Development Zone, Hebi, Henan, China
Tel.: (86) 3922298000
Web Site: https://www.sjphotons.com
Year Founded: 2010
688313—(SHG)
Rev.: $126,818,027
Assets: $221,103,521
Liabilities: $51,966,617
Net Worth: $169,136,904
Earnings: $9,026,555
Fiscal Year-end: 12/31/22
Optical Communication Product Mfr & Distr
N.A.I.C.S.: 335929
Haiquan Ge *(Chm & Gen Mgr)*

Subsidiaries:

Henan Jake New Material Co., Ltd. (1)
No 166 Dongyang Avenue, Dongyang Industrial Zone, Hebi, China
Tel.: (86) 3922167167
Logic Controller Optical Cable Services
N.A.I.C.S.: 541715

Henan Shijia Communication Technology Co., Ltd. (1)
No 201 Yanhe Road, Qibin District, Hebi, Henan, China
Tel.: (86) 3922168136
Logic Controller Optical Cable Services
N.A.I.C.S.: 541715

Henan Shijia Electronic Technology Co., Ltd. (1)
No 201 Yanhe Road, Qibin District, Hebi, Henan, China
Tel.: (86) 3922168061805
Logic Controller Optical Cable Services
N.A.I.C.S.: 541715

Henan Shijia Optoelectronic Devices Co., Ltd. (1)
No 201 Yanhe Road, Qibin District, Hebi, Henan, China
Tel.: (86) 392 229 8000
Logic Controller Optical Cable Services
N.A.I.C.S.: 541715

Optic River Communication Ltd. (1)
Building 4 Kukeng Community Guanlan Street, Instrument World Industrial Park Longhua District, Shenzhen, 518108, Guangdong, China
Tel.: (86) 75586181805
Web Site: https://www.orclink.net
Logic Controller Optical Cable Services
N.A.I.C.S.: 541715

Shenzhen Shijia Optical Cable Technology Co., Ltd. (1)
Building 4 No 306 Guiyue Road Guanlan Street, Longhua Distric, Shenzhen, China
Tel.: (86) 75521037248
Web Site: https://en.sjfiber.com
Fiber Optic Cable Mfr
N.A.I.C.S.: 335921

Shijia U.S. (1)
46750 Fremont Blvd Ste 208, Fremont, CA 94538
Tel.: (510) 270-8809
Fiber Optic Cable Distr
N.A.I.C.S.: 423610

Wuhan Shijia Photoelectric Technology Co., Ltd. (1)
Donghu New Technology Development Zone, Wuhan, China
Tel.: (86) 3922298000

Logic Controller Optical Cable Services
N.A.I.C.S.: 541715

Wuxi Jake Plastic Industry Co., Ltd. (1)
No 39 Yanqiao Road, Yanqiao supporting area Huishan Economic Development Zone, Wuxi, China
Tel.: (86) 51083572589
Logic Controller Optical Cable Services
N.A.I.C.S.: 541715

HENAN SPLENDOR SCIENCE & TECHNOLOGY CO., LTD.
No 188 Science Avenue High-tech Industrial Development Zone, Zhengzhou, 450001, Henan, China
Tel.: (86) 37167371035
Web Site: https://www.hhkj.cn
Year Founded: 2001
002296—(SSE)
Rev.: $91,521,144
Assets: $344,604,780
Liabilities: $89,288,784
Net Worth: $255,315,996
Earnings: $14,601,600
Emp.: 360
Fiscal Year-end: 12/31/22
Railway Signal Communication Products Mfr
N.A.I.C.S.: 488210
Haiying Li *(Chm)*

HENAN TALOPH PHARMACEUTICAL STOCK CO., LTD.
No 8 Jinsuo Road Hi-Tech Industrial Development Zone, Zhengzhou, 450001, Henan, China
Tel.: (86) 37167993688
Web Site: https://www.taloph.com
Year Founded: 1993
600222—(SHG)
Rev.: $275,281,480
Assets: $505,465,848
Liabilities: $278,848,398
Net Worth: $226,617,450
Earnings: ($10,128,484)
Fiscal Year-end: 12/31/22
Pharmaceutical Product Mfr & Distr
N.A.I.C.S.: 325412
Yin Hui *(Chm)*

HENAN THINKER AUTOMATIC EQUIPMENT CO., LTD.
No 63 Dulan Street High-tech Zone, Zhengzhou, 450001, Henan, China
Tel.: (86) 37160671600
Web Site: https://www.hnthinker.com
Year Founded: 1992
603508—(SHG)
Rev.: $149,831,061
Assets: $673,235,550
Liabilities: $50,575,688
Net Worth: $622,659,862
Earnings: $48,631,626
Emp.: 900
Fiscal Year-end: 12/31/22
Automation Monitoring Equipment Mfr
N.A.I.C.S.: 334419
Xin Li *(Chm)*

HENAN TONG-DA CABLE CO., LTD.
Room 2103 Missun Center No 33 East Jinshui Road, Zhengzhou, 450003, Henan, China
Tel.: (86) 37160311151
Web Site: https://www.tddlcable.com
Year Founded: 2011
002560—(SSE)
Rev.: $772,757,388
Assets: $734,520,852
Liabilities: $378,985,932
Net Worth: $355,534,920
Earnings: $17,102,124
Emp.: 800
Fiscal Year-end: 12/31/22

Aluminum & Steel Reinforced Conductor Mfr
N.A.I.C.S.: 335931
Ma Hongju *(Chm)*

HENAN TOPFOND PHARMACEUTICAL CO.,LTD.
No 2 Guangming Road, 463000, Zhumadian, Henan, China
Tel.: (86) 3963823555   CN
Web Site: http://www.topfond.com
Year Founded: 1969
Sales Range: $400-449.9 Million
Emp.: 5,000
Pharmaceuticals Product Mfr
N.A.I.C.S.: 325412
Yincong Yan *(Vice Chm & Deputy Gen Mgr)*

HENAN XINNING MODERN LOGISICS CO., LTD.
No 760 Yangguang West Road, Zhangpu Town, Kunshan, 215326, Jiangsu, China
Tel.: (86) 51257120911
Web Site: https://www.xinning.com.cn
Year Founded: 1997
300013—(CHIN)
Rev.: $93,549,924
Assets: $106,621,164
Liabilities: $100,353,708
Net Worth: $6,267,456
Earnings: ($224,640)
Fiscal Year-end: 12/31/22
Electronic Component Warehousing Services
N.A.I.C.S.: 493110
Tian Xu *(Chm)*

HENAN XINYE TEXTILE CO., LTD.
No 15 Shuyuan Road Chengguang Town, Xinye County, Nanyang, 473500, Henan, China
Tel.: (86) 37766221824
Web Site: http://www.xinye-tex.com
002087—(SSE)
Rev.: $483,098,148
Assets: $948,827,412
Liabilities: $850,345,236
Net Worth: $98,482,176
Earnings: ($197,792,712)
Fiscal Year-end: 12/31/22
Textile Products Mfr
N.A.I.C.S.: 314999
Xue Zhu Wei *(Chm)*

HENAN YICHENG NEW ENERGY CO., LTD.
Fine Chemical Industry Park, Kaifeng, 450018, Henan, China
Tel.: (86) 37189988671
Web Site: http://www.ycne.com.cn
Year Founded: 1992
300080—(SSE)
Rev.: $1,578,820,464
Assets: $1,887,836,652
Liabilities: $977,564,484
Net Worth: $910,272,168
Earnings: $67,790,736
Fiscal Year-end: 12/31/22
Crystalline Silicon Carbide Engineering Ceramic Products & Carbon & Oxide Micropowder Mfr
N.A.I.C.S.: 325998
Wang Anle *(Chm)*

HENAN YINGE INDUSTRIAL INVESTMENT CO., LTD.
95 Renmindong Road, Xuchang, 462000, Henan, China
Tel.: (86) 395 235 5301
Web Site: http://www.yinge.com.cn
Rev.: $288,946,447
Assets: $630,845,016
Liabilities: $449,673,405

Henan Yinge Industrial Investment Co., Ltd.—(Continued)
Net Worth: $181,171,612
Earnings: ($93,043,978)
Emp.: 5,139
Fiscal Year-end: 12/31/19
Paper Products Mfr & Sales
N.A.I.C.S.: 322291
Qi Gu (Chm)

HENAN YUGUANG GOLD & LEAD CO., LTD
No 1 Jingliang South Street, Jiyuan, 459000, Henan, China
Tel.: (86) 3916699888
Web Site: https://www.yggf.com.cn
Year Founded: 2000
600531—(SHG)
Rev.: $3,806,580,932
Assets: $1,939,389,005
Liabilities: $1,327,545,728
Net Worth: $611,843,277
Earnings: $59,662,208
Emp.: 3,600
Fiscal Year-end: 12/31/22
Nonferrous Metal Mfr & Distr
N.A.I.C.S.: 331410
Zhao Jingang (Chm)

HENAN YUNENG HOLDINGS CO., LTD.
8-12F Tower B Investment Mansion, Zhengzhou, 450008, Henan, China
Tel.: (86) 37169515111
Web Site: http://www.yuneng.com.cn
001896—(SSE)
Rev.: $1,838,889,000
Assets: $4,325,295,780
Liabilities: $3,758,404,104
Net Worth: $566,891,676
Earnings: ($300,523,392)
Fiscal Year-end: 12/31/22
Holding Company
N.A.I.C.S.: 551112
Shuying Zhao (Chm)

HENAN ZHONGFU INDUSTRY CO., LTD.
No 31 Xinhua Road, Gongyi, 451200, Henan, China
Tel.: (86) 37164569099
Web Site: https://www.zfsy.com.cn
Year Founded: 1993
600595—(SHG)
Rev.: $2,459,341,830
Assets: $3,396,468,404
Liabilities: $1,372,358,501
Net Worth: $2,024,109,903
Earnings: $147,414,033
Fiscal Year-end: 12/31/22
Aluminium Products Mfr
N.A.I.C.S.: 331315
Ma Wenchao (Chm)

HENAN ZHONGYUAN EXPRESSWAY COMPANY LIMITED
No 100 Nongye East Road, Zhengdong New District, Zhengzhou, 450016, Henan, China
Tel.: (86) 37167717696
Web Site: http://www.zygs.com
Year Founded: 2000
600020—(SHG)
Rev.: $1,040,435,323
Assets: $6,979,243,733
Liabilities: $5,206,863,870
Net Worth: $1,772,379,863
Earnings: $19,724,782
Fiscal Year-end: 12/31/22
Transportation Maintenance Services
N.A.I.C.S.: 488490
Liu Jing (Chm)

HENDALE CAPITAL
Unit 12A 12/F On Hing Building 1 On Hing Terrace, Central, Hong Kong, China (Hong Kong)
Tel.: (852) 2840 0776
Web Site: http://www.hendale.com
Year Founded: 2015
Holding Company
N.A.I.C.S.: 551112
Henry Lee (Mng Partner)

HENDERSON DIVERSIFIED INCOME TRUST PLC
Bnp House Anley Street, Saint Helier, JE2 3QE, Jersey
Tel.: (44) 1534815200
HDIV—(LSE)
Sales Range: Less than $1 Million
Investment Trust Management Services
N.A.I.C.S.: 523940

HENDERSON EUROPEAN TRUST PLC
201 Bishopsgate, London, EC2M 3AE, United Kingdom
Tel.: (44) 2078181818 UK
Web Site: http://www.janushenderson.com
HET—(LSE)
Rev.: $27,180,287
Assets: $459,223,950
Liabilities: $55,033,424
Net Worth: $404,190,526
Earnings: $22,730,028
Fiscal Year-end: 09/30/20
Investment Management Service
N.A.I.C.S.: 525990
Victoria K. Hastings (Chm)

HENDERSON FAR EAST INCOME LIMITED
IFC1 The Esplanade, Saint Helier, JE1 4BP, Jersey
Tel.: (44) 2078181818
Web Site: https://www.janushenderson.com
HFL—(NZX)
Rev.: $47,123,201
Assets: $496,589,245
Liabilities: $39,593,537
Net Worth: $456,995,708
Earnings: $70,992,174
Fiscal Year-end: 08/31/23
Investment Services
N.A.I.C.S.: 523940
Michael Kerley (Portfolio Mgr)

HENDERSON HIGH INCOME TRUST PLC
201 Bishopsgate, London, EC2M 3AE, United Kingdom
Tel.: (44) 2078181818 UK
Web Site: http://www.janushenderson.com
HHI—(LSE)
Assets: $319,011,825
Liabilities: $60,911,565
Net Worth: $258,100,260
Earnings: ($13,273,590)
Fiscal Year-end: 12/31/22
Investment Management Trust Services
N.A.I.C.S.: 523940
Jeremy Rigg (Chm)

HENDERSON LAND DEVELOPMENT CO. LTD.
71/F Two International Finance Centre 8 Finance Street, Central, China (Hong Kong)
Tel.: (852) 29088111 HK
Web Site: https://www.hld.com
Year Founded: 1976
0012—(HKG)
Rev.: $3,257,752,500
Assets: $67,548,225,000
Liabilities: $23,541,345,000
Net Worth: $44,006,880,000
Earnings: $1,211,632,500
Emp.: 9,950
Fiscal Year-end: 12/31/22
Investment Holding, Infrastructure Investment & Construction Services
N.A.I.C.S.: 551112
Margaret Pui Man Lee (Sr Gen Mgr-Portfolio Leasing Dept)

Subsidiaries:

E Man Construction Company Limited (1)
29/F AIA Tower 183 Electric Road, North Point, China (Hong Kong)
Tel.: (852) 29082222
Property Development Services
N.A.I.C.S.: 531390
Wong Wing Hoo Billy (Gen Mgr)

Hang Yick Properties Management Limited (1)
21/F Two Portside 9 Pat Tat Street, San Po Kong, Kowloon, China (Hong Kong)
Tel.: (852) 25455109
Web Site: https://www.hy.com.hk
Property Management Services
N.A.I.C.S.: 531312

Henderson Investment Limited (1)
8 Finance St 71-76th Fl 2nd International, Central, 852, China (Hong Kong)
Tel.: (852) 29088888
Web Site: https://www.hilhk.com
Sales Range: $400-449.9 Million
Emp.: 10,000
Land Subdivision
N.A.I.C.S.: 237210
Shau-Kee Lee (Pres)

Hong Kong & China Gas Company Limited (1)
9/F Lee Theatre Causeway Bay, Hong Kong, China (Hong Kong) (41.5%)
Tel.: (852) 25761535
Web Site: https://www.towngas.com
Rev.: $7,280,930,898
Assets: $20,700,806,421
Liabilities: $11,624,586,246
Net Worth: $9,076,220,175
Earnings: $916,495,201
Emp.: 54,080
Fiscal Year-end: 12/31/2023
Natural Gas Distr
N.A.I.C.S.: 221210
Alfred Wing-kin Chan (Mng Dir)

Subsidiary (Non-US):

Anhui Province Natural Gas Development Co., Ltd. (2)
Xinneng Building No 9 Dalian Road Baohe Industrial Zone, Hefei, 230051, Anhui, China
Tel.: (86) 55162225677
Rev.: $832,187,472
Assets: $843,138,462
Liabilities: $414,217,641
Net Worth: $428,920,821
Earnings: $36,265,320
Fiscal Year-end: 12/31/2022
Natural Gas Pipeline Construction Services
N.A.I.C.S.: 237120

ECO Energy Company Limited (2)
140-2 Kye-Dong, Chongno-Gu, Seoul, Korea (South) (100%)
Tel.: (82) 27465604
Industrial Building Construction Mfr
N.A.I.C.S.: 236210

Subsidiary (Domestic):

Starmax Assets Limited (2)
25th Floor 363 Java Rd, North Point, China (Hong Kong) (100%)
Tel.: (852) 29633990
Sales Range: $25-49.9 Million
Emp.: 20
Residential Remodeler
N.A.I.C.S.: 236118

Towngas Enterprise Limited (2)
15 Floor 363 Java Road, North Point, China (Hong Kong) (100%)
Tel.: (852) 29632181
Web Site: http://www.towngasavenue.com

INTERNATIONAL PUBLIC

Sales Range: $25-49.9 Million
Emp.: 150
Restaurant
N.A.I.C.S.: 722511
Vivin Kan (Mgr-Bus Dev)

Towngas International Company Limited (2)
Ground Floor, GTO Box 134, Quarry Bay, China (Hong Kong) (100%)
Tel.: (852) 29633388
Web Site: http://www.towngas.com
Sales Range: $100-124.9 Million
Emp.: 300
Pipeline Transportation of Refined Petroleum Products
N.A.I.C.S.: 486910

Towngas Telecommunications Fixed Network Limited (2)
21st Floor, 363 Java Road, North Point, China (Hong Kong) (100%)
Tel.: (852) 29633666
Web Site: http://www.towngastelecom.com
Sales Range: $25-49.9 Million
Emp.: 40
Telecommunications
N.A.I.C.S.: 517810
Jason Wong (Gen Mgr)

Subsidiary (Domestic):

HDC Data Centre Limited (3)
17th Fl Well Tech Ctr 9 Pat Tat Street San Po Kong, 9 Pat Tat St San Po Kong, Kowloon, China (Hong Kong) (100%)
Tel.: (852) 29633541
Web Site: http://www.hdcdatacentre.com
Sales Range: $25-49.9 Million
Emp.: 10
Data Processing Hosting & Related Services
N.A.I.C.S.: 518210

Subsidiary (Domestic):

U-Tech Engineering Company Limited (2)
6/F 100 To Kwa Wan Road Town, Kowloon, China (Hong Kong) (100%)
Tel.: (852) 27655666
Sales Range: $25-49.9 Million
Emp.: 100
Engineeering Services
N.A.I.C.S.: 541330
Richard Lau (Gen Mgr)

Affiliate (Non-US):

Wuhan Natural Gas Company Limited (2)
5th Floor Building A, International Mansion No 1 Sha, Wuhan, Hubei, China (49%)
Tel.: (86) 2785511333
Web Site: http://www.whng.com.cn
Natural Gas Distribution
N.A.I.C.S.: 221210

Hong Kong Ferry (Holdings) Co. Ltd. (1)
98 Tam Kon Shan Road TYTL 102 Ngau Kok Wan, Tsing Yi, New Territories, China (Hong Kong)
Tel.: (852) 23944294
Web Site: https://www.hkf.com
Rev.: $35,780,580
Assets: $960,664,178
Liabilities: $40,336,410
Net Worth: $920,327,768
Earnings: $165,639,840
Emp.: 250
Fiscal Year-end: 12/31/2022
Ferry Service
N.A.I.C.S.: 483212
Peter Wai Kuen Yuen (Sec)

Subsidiary (Domestic):

HYFCO Development Company Limited (2)
98 Tam Kon Shan Road, Ngau Kok Wan North, Tsing Yi, China (Hong Kong)
Tel.: (852) 23952859
Sales Range: $150-199.9 Million
Real Estate Investment Trust
N.A.I.C.S.: 525990
MA Chi-Wai (Mgr)

HYFCO Estate Management And Agency Limited (2)

98 Tam Kon Shan Road TYTL 102, Ngau Kok Wan North, Tsing Yi, New Territories, China (Hong Kong)
Tel.: (852) 2 394 4294
Sales Range: $150-199.9 Million
Residential Property Managers
N.A.I.C.S.: 531311

HYFCO Trading And Investments Company Limited (2)
98 Tam Kon Shan Road TYTL 102, Ngau Kok Wan North, Tsing Yi, New Territories, China (Hong Kong)
Tel.: (852) 2 394 4294
Web Site: https://www.hkf.com
Sales Range: $25-49.9 Million
Emp.: 100
Petroleum Lubricating Oil & Grease Mfr
N.A.I.C.S.: 324191
David Ho *(Mgr)*

The Hong Kong Shipyard Limited (2)
98 Tam Kon Shan Road TYTL 102, Ngau Kok Wan North, Tsing Yi, New Territories, China (Hong Kong)
Tel.: (852) 2 436 1138
Sales Range: $25-49.9 Million
Emp.: 100
Ship Building & Repairing
N.A.I.C.S.: 336611
MA Chi-Wai *(Mgr)*

The Hongkong And Yaumati Ferry Company Limited (2)
98 Tam Kon Shan Road TYTL 102, Ngau Kok Wan North, Tsing Yi, New Territories, China (Hong Kong)
Tel.: (852) 2 563 9305
Web Site: https://www.hkf.com
Emp.: 210
Deep Sea Freight Transportation
N.A.I.C.S.: 483111

Megastrength Security Services Company Limited (1)
18/F 78 Hung To Road, Kwun Tong, Kowloon, China (Hong Kong)
Tel.: (852) 27528833
Web Site: https://www.msshk.com
Emp.: 1,500
Security Services
N.A.I.C.S.: 561612

Miramar Hotel and Investment Company, Limited (1)
15/F Miramar Tower 132 Nathan Road, Tsimshatsui, Kowloon, China (Hong Kong)
Tel.: (852) 23155555
Sales Range: $25-49.9 Million
Emp.: 200
Hotels & Motels
N.A.I.C.S.: 721110
Ka Shing Lee *(CEO & Chm)*

Well Born Real Estate Management Limited (1)
8/F Golden Centre 188 Des Voeux Road, Sheung Wan, Central, China (Hong Kong)
Tel.: (852) 28511396
Web Site: https://www.wb.com.hk
Property Management Services
N.A.I.C.S.: 531312

HENDERSON OPPORTUNITIES TRUST PLC
201 Bishopsgate, London, EC2M 3AE, United Kingdom
Tel.: (44) 2078181818 UK
Year Founded: 2006
HOT—(LSE)
Assets: $121,292,586
Liabilities: $28,712,592
Net Worth: $92,579,994
Earnings: ($37,985,310)
Fiscal Year-end: 10/31/22
Investment Management Service
N.A.I.C.S.: 525990

HENDERSON PARK CAPITAL PARTNERS UK LLP
42-44 Grosvenor Garden, London, SW1W 0EB, United Kingdom
Tel.: (44) 2037271000
Privater Equity Firm

N.A.I.C.S.: 523999
Nicholas Weber *(Founder & CEO)*

Subsidiaries:

Green REIT plc (1)
32 Molesworth Street, Dublin, 2, Ireland
Tel.: (353) 1 2418400
Web Site: http://www.greenpropertyreit.com
Real Estate Investment Trust
N.A.I.C.S.: 525990
Gary Kennedy *(Chm)*

HENDERSON SMALLER COMPANIES INVESTMENT TRUST PLC
201 Bishopsgate, London, EC2M 3AE, United Kingdom
Tel.: (44) 800832832 UK
Year Founded: 1917
HSL—(LSE)
Assets: $1,187,448,944
Liabilities: $207,536,736
Net Worth: $979,912,208
Earnings: ($226,273,784)
Fiscal Year-end: 05/31/22
Investment Management Service
N.A.I.C.S.: 525990
Neil Hermon *(Mgr-Fund)*

HENDRIX GENETICS B.V.
Spoorstraat 69, 5831 CK, Boxmeer, Netherlands
Tel.: (31) 485 801 911 NI
Web Site: http://www.hendrix-genetics.com
Animal Genetics Research & Breeding Farms Operator
N.A.I.C.S.: 115210
Ronald de Haan *(Mng Dir-Layers)*

Subsidiaries:

Landcatch Natural Selection Limited (1)
Ormsary Fish Farm, Lochgilphead, PA31 8PE, Argyll, United Kingdom
Tel.: (44) 1880 770 720
Web Site: http://www.hendrix-genetics.com
Emp.: 30
Finfish Farming & Fish Hatchery Operator
N.A.I.C.S.: 112511
Neil Manchester *(Mng Dir)*

HENDY GROUP LTD.
School Lane Chandlers Ford Industrial Estate, Eastleigh, SO53 4DG, Hampshire, United Kingdom
Tel.: (44) 844 5399301
Web Site: http://www.hendy.co.uk
Year Founded: 1898
Sales Range: $350-399.9 Million
Emp.: 697
New & Used Car Dealer
N.A.I.C.S.: 441110
Paul A. Hendy *(CEO)*

HENG HUP HOLDINGS LTD.
No 264 Jalan Satu A, Kampung Baru Subang, Shah Alam, Selangor, Malaysia
Tel.: (60) 378452292
Web Site: http://www.henghup.com
1891—(HKG)
Rev.: $293,204,834
Assets: $83,175,011
Liabilities: $36,899,434
Net Worth: $46,275,577
Earnings: $1,793,209
Emp.: 323
Fiscal Year-end: 12/31/23
Scrap Ferrous Metal Distr
N.A.I.C.S.: 423510
Kok Chin Sia *(Chm & CEO)*

HENG SHENG HOLDING GROUP LTD.
6 3 F Lladro Centre 72-80 Hoi Yuen Road, Kwun Tong, China (Hong Kong)
Tel.: (852) 221255058
Web Site: https://www.hsfamilyent.com
Year Founded: 1995
900270—(KRS)
Rev.: $96,450,018
Assets: $283,407,590
Liabilities: $44,002,879
Net Worth: $239,404,711
Earnings: ($1,432,455)
Emp.: 1,704
Fiscal Year-end: 12/31/22
Holding Company
N.A.I.C.S.: 551112
Li Liangwei *(CFO)*

HENG TAI CONSUMABLES GROUP LIMITED
31st Floor Guangdong Finance Building 88 Connaught Road West, Sheung Wan, China (Hong Kong)
Tel.: (852) 26280077 Ky
Web Site: https://www.hengtai.com.hk
Year Founded: 1986
0197—(HKG)
Rev.: $64,647,098
Assets: $157,943,233
Liabilities: $14,988,379
Net Worth: $142,954,854
Earnings: ($26,976,941)
Emp.: 284
Fiscal Year-end: 06/30/22
Packaged Food Distr
N.A.I.C.S.: 311991
Horris Siu hong Wong *(CFO & Sec)*

Subsidiaries:

Golden Harvest (Macao Commercial Offshore) Limited (1)
Ctro Cml Praia Grande, Macau, China (Macau)
Tel.: (853) 28355763
Agricultural Products Sourcing & Distr
N.A.I.C.S.: 424480

Golden Sector Agro-Development Limited (1)
29th Fl Guangdong Finance Bldg 88 Connaught Rd West, Hong Kong, Sheung Wan, China (Hong Kong)
Tel.: (852) 2628 0077
Web Site: http://www.hengtai.com.hk
Fresh Produce Products Sales
N.A.I.C.S.: 424480

Golden Sector Limited (1)
Rm 304 A Sunbeam Ctr 27 Shing Yip St, Kwun Tong, Kowloon, China (Hong Kong)
Tel.: (852) 35251122
Web Site: http://www.goldensector.com.hk
Dried & Preserved Food Export Services
N.A.I.C.S.: 424490
Peter Ling-Ming Hung *(Gen Mgr)*

Heng Yui (Macao) Commercial Offshore Limited (1)
Ctro Cml Praia Grande 7th Fl D, Macau, China (Macau)
Tel.: (853) 28330037
Food & Beverages Distr
N.A.I.C.S.: 424490

Hongkang (Jiujiang) Agricultural Development Co., Ltd. (1)
Nong Ye Ke Ji Shi Fan Yuan, Qiu Jin Zhen, Jiujiang, Jiangxi, China
Tel.: (86) 792 3115041
Agricultural Products Cultivation Services & Sales
N.A.I.C.S.: 115112

Nexus Logistics (International) Limited (1)
29F Guangdong Finance Building 88 Connaught Road West, Sheung Wan, China (Hong Kong) (100%)
Tel.: (852) 24262018
Web Site: http://www.nexuslogistics.com.hk
Sales Range: $25-49.9 Million
Warehousing & Transportation Services
N.A.I.C.S.: 481212

Sino Wealth Securities Limited (1)
Unit 1904 19/F Emperor Group Centre 288 Hennessy Road, Wanchai, China (Hong Kong)
Tel.: (852) 21101190
Web Site: https://www.sinowealthsec.com
Securities Brokerage Services
N.A.I.C.S.: 523150

Sui Tai & Associates Limited (1)
31 Fl Guang Dong Finance Building 88 Connaught Road W, Hong Kong, China (Hong Kong)
Tel.: (852) 26280077
Administrative Services
N.A.I.C.S.: 541611

Triglory (H.K.) Limited (1)
29th Rd 25 F Guangdong Fin Bldg 88 Connaught Rd W, Sheung Wan, China (Hong Kong)
Tel.: (852) 31820286
Cosmetics Distr
N.A.I.C.S.: 424210

HENG XIN CHINA HOLDINGS LIMITED
Suite 3604 36/F Central Plaza, Wanchai, China (Hong Kong)
Tel.: (852) 3678 5500 BM
Web Site: http://www.hengxinchina.com.hk
Year Founded: 2002
Sales Range: $1-9.9 Million
Investment Management Service
N.A.I.C.S.: 523999
Kam Fai Tse *(Sec)*

Subsidiaries:

JTI Securities Limited (1)
Room 1101 11th Floor 88 Gloucester Road, Wanchai, China (Hong Kong)
Tel.: (852) 25889088
Web Site: http://www.jtisec.com.hk
Security Trading Services
N.A.I.C.S.: 523150

HENGAN INTERNATIONAL GROUP CO. LTD.
Hengan Industrial City Anhai Town, Jinjiang, 362261, Fujian, China
Tel.: (86) 59585708888 CN
Web Site: http://www.hengan.com
Year Founded: 1985
1044—(OTCIQ)
Rev.: $3,427,920,693
Assets: $6,808,794,119
Liabilities: $3,796,459,688
Net Worth: $3,012,334,432
Earnings: $706,059,399
Emp.: 25,000
Fiscal Year-end: 12/31/20
Mfr & Distr of Personal Care Hygiene Products
N.A.I.C.S.: 812199
Man Bok Sze *(Chm)*

Subsidiaries:

Carefeel Cotton Industries (M) Sdn. Bhd. (1)
No 8 & 10 Jalan Pusat BCH 1C Bandar Country Homes, 48000, Rawang, Selangor, Malaysia
Tel.: (60) 367331188
Web Site: http://www.carefeelcotton.com
Cotton Product Mfr
N.A.I.C.S.: 314999
Sharon The *(Officer-Admin)*

Fujian Hengan Holding Co., Ltd. (1)
11f Hengan Industrial Area, Anhai Town Jinjiang, Quanzhou, 362200, Fujian, China
Tel.: (86) 5958 518 1260
Web Site: https://hadiaper.diytrade.com
Sanitary Napkin Mfr & Distr
N.A.I.C.S.: 322291

Hengan Pharmacare Company Limited (1)
Flat Q & R 10/F Block 2 Kinho Ind Bldg 14-24 Au Pui Wan Street, Fotan, Sha Tin, New Territories, China (Hong Kong)
Tel.: (852) 26042317

HENGAN INTERNATIONAL GROUP CO. LTD.

Hengan International Group Co. Ltd.—(Continued)
Web Site: http://www.banitore.com.hk
First Aid Product Distr
N.A.I.C.S.: 424210

Sunway Kordis (Shanghai) Limited (1)
777 Xinji Road Qingpu Industrial Zone, Shanghai, 201707, China
Tel.: (86) 2159703600
Web Site: http://www.sunkor.com.cn
Food Wrap Film & Plastic Bag Mfr
N.A.I.C.S.: 326111

Wang-Zheng Berhad (1)
No 1 Jalan Utarid U519 Section U5, 40150, Shah Alam, Selangor Darul Ehsan, Malaysia (50.45%)
Tel.: (60) 378013333
Web Site: https://www.wangzhengberhad.com
Rev.: $56,781,647
Assets: $57,355,963
Liabilities: $15,111,466
Net Worth: $42,244,497
Earnings: $1,376,175
Fiscal Year-end: 12/31/2022
Investment Holding Company; Disposable Fibre-Based Products & Processed Paper Mfr & Distr
N.A.I.C.S.: 551112
Kheng Jiu Goh (CEO & Mng Dir)

Subsidiary (Domestic):

Modern Alpine Sdn. Bhd. (2)
1 Jalan Utarid U5/19 Section U5, Shah Alam, 40150, Selangor Darul Ehsan, Malaysia
Tel.: (60) 378013288
Web Site: http://www.wangzhengberhad.com
Paper Sales & Marketing Services
N.A.I.C.S.: 322130

New Top Win Corporation Sdn. Bhd. (2)
No 1 Jalan Utarid U5/90 Section U5, Mutiara Subang, Shah Alam, 40150, Selangor Darul Ehsan, Malaysia
Tel.: (60) 378013388
Web Site: http://www.wangzhengberhad.com
Paper Converters & Distr
N.A.I.C.S.: 322120

Quality Hero Corporation Sdn. Bhd. (2)
No 1 Jln Utarid U5/19, 40150, Shah Alam, Selangor Darul Ehsan, Malaysia
Tel.: (60) 378013333
Web Site: https://www.qualityhero.com
Diapers & Sanitary Napkins Mfr
N.A.I.C.S.: 322291
Simon Wan Huat Tan (Exec Dir)

Wang-Zheng Corporation Sdn. Bhd. (2)
1 Jalan Utarid U5/19, Mutiara Subang, 40150, Selangor Darul Ehsan, Malaysia
Tel.: (60) 378013243
Web Site: http://www.wangzhengberhad.com
Disposable Products Whslr
N.A.I.C.S.: 424990

HENGBAO CO., LTD.
No 5 Financial Street 8th Floor Block B Xinsheng Building, Xicheng District, Beijing, 100033, China
Tel.: (86) 1066017777
Web Site: https://www.hengbao.com
Year Founded: 1996
002104—(SSE)
Rev.: $145,134,288
Assets: $319,073,040
Liabilities: $44,449,236
Net Worth: $274,623,804
Earnings: $11,500,164
Fiscal Year-end: 12/31/22
Card Product Mfr
N.A.I.C.S.: 326199
Jing Qian (Chm & Gen Mgr)

Subsidiaries:

Hengbao International Pte Ltd. (1)
300 Beach Road 34-06 The Concourse, Singapore, 199555, Singapore
Tel.: (65) 62988348
Emp.: 8
Information Technology Support Services
N.A.I.C.S.: 541512
David Tang (Dir-Bus Dev)

HENGDELI HOLDINGS LIMITED
Room 301 3/F Lippo Sun Plaza 28 Canton Road, Tsim Sha Tsui, Kowloon, China (Hong Kong)
Tel.: (852) 23750788 Ky
Web Site: http://www.hengdeligroup.com
3389—(OTCIQ)
Rev.: $143,897,596
Assets: $488,174,983
Liabilities: $42,362,788
Net Worth: $445,812,195
Earnings: ($12,203,561)
Emp.: 1,596
Fiscal Year-end: 12/31/22
Watch Retailer & Distr
N.A.I.C.S.: 423940
Yonghua Huang (Exec Dir)

HENGDIAN ENTERTAINMENT CO., LTD.
Business Building, Hengdian Film and Television Industry Experimental Zone Hengdian Town, Dongyang, 322118, Zhejiang, China
Tel.: (86) 57986587877
Web Site: http://www.hengdianfilm.com
Year Founded: 2008
603103—(SHG)
Rev.: $200,328,687
Assets: $634,655,048
Liabilities: $469,782,191
Net Worth: $164,872,857
Earnings: ($44,567,074)
Emp.: 50,000
Fiscal Year-end: 12/31/22
Film Production Services
N.A.I.C.S.: 512110
Zhang Yibing (Chm)

HENGDIAN GROUP DMEGC MAGNETICS CO., LTD.
Dongci Building No 233 Huaxia Avenue Hengdian, Dongyang, 322118, Zhejiang, China
Tel.: (86) 57986551999
Web Site: http://www.chinadmegc.com
Year Founded: 1999
002056—(SSE)
Rev.: $2,730,869,856
Assets: $2,472,428,556
Liabilities: $1,381,323,996
Net Worth: $1,091,104,560
Earnings: $234,365,508
Emp.: 18,000
Fiscal Year-end: 12/31/22
Electronic Components Mfr
N.A.I.C.S.: 334419
Shijin He (Chm & CEO)

Subsidiaries:

DMEGC Germany GmbH (1)
Kaiserleistrasse 41-43, 63067, Offenbach, Germany
Tel.: (49) 6980907408
Web Site: https://www.dmegc.de
Fabricated Metal Products Mfr
N.A.I.C.S.: 332999
Gu Ying (Gen Mgr)

DMEGC Japan Corporation Limited (1)
9th floor Shiba Shimura Building 2-3-12 Shiba, Minato-Ku, Tokyo, 105-0014, Japan
Tel.: (81) 367226601

Web Site: https://www.dmegc.jp
Electronic Components Mfr
N.A.I.C.S.: 334419

DMEGC Solar USA, LLC (1)
3655 Torrance Blvd Ste 410, Torrance, CA 90503
Tel.: (310) 543-8788
Web Site: http://www.dmegcsolar.com
Electronic Components Mfr
N.A.I.C.S.: 334419

DMEGC UK Solar PV (1)
152 City Rd, London, EC1V 2NX, United Kingdom
Tel.: (44) 7471466526
Electronic Components Mfr
N.A.I.C.S.: 334419

HENGDIAN GROUP TOSPO LIGHTING CO LTD
Hengdian Electronic Industrial Park, Jinhua, 322118, Zhejiang, China
Tel.: (86) 57986555001
Web Site: https://www.tospolighting.com.cn
Year Founded: 1996
603303—(SHG)
Rev.: $653,827,974
Assets: $705,592,668
Liabilities: $238,223,602
Net Worth: $467,369,066
Earnings: $47,804,417
Fiscal Year-end: 12/31/22
Lighting Product Mfr & Distr
N.A.I.C.S.: 335132
Ni Qiang (Chm)

Subsidiaries:

Zhejiang Hengdian Tospo Imp.&Exp. Co. Ltd. (1)
8/F T1 Hengdian Center No 136 Fuchun Road, Shangcheng District, Hangzhou, 310016, Zhejiang, China
Tel.: (86) 571876328002800
Automotive Parts Mfr & Distr
N.A.I.C.S.: 336390

HENGERDA NEW MATERIALS (FUJIAN) CO., LTD.
Xindu Plant No 228 Tingdaowei, Xindu Village Xindu Town Licheng District, Putian, 351142, Fujian, China
Tel.: (86) 5942999566
Web Site: https://www.hengerda.com
Year Founded: 1995
300946—(SSE)
Rev.: $67,796,352
Assets: $173,204,460
Liabilities: $24,247,080
Net Worth: $148,957,380
Earnings: $13,371,696
Fiscal Year-end: 12/31/22
Metalworking Machinery Equipment Mfr
N.A.I.C.S.: 333519
Zhenghua Lin (Chm & Gen Mgr)

HENGFENG INFORMATION TECHNOLOGY CO. LTD.
Building 5 Innovation Park Keji East Road Wulongjiang Middle Avenue, Shangjie Town Minhou County, Fuzhou, 350117, Fujian, China
Tel.: (86) 59187733307
Web Site: http://www.i-hengfeng.com
Year Founded: 1995
300605—(SSE)
Rev.: $72,341,100
Assets: $162,081,972
Liabilities: $84,600,828
Net Worth: $77,481,144
Earnings: $5,519,124
Fiscal Year-end: 12/31/22
Construction Services
N.A.I.C.S.: 541330
Yinbao Zhao (CFO & Fin Dir)

INTERNATIONAL PUBLIC

HENGGUANG HOLDING CO., LIMITED
1666 Chenglong Road Section 2 Building 2 5th Floor, Longquanyi District, Chengdu, 61000, Sichuan, China
Tel.: (86) 400 028 1990 Ky
Year Founded: 2004
Rev.: $21,883,400
Assets: $8,595,656
Liabilities: $2,903,897
Net Worth: $5,691,759
Earnings: $45,718
Emp.: 99
Fiscal Year-end: 12/31/20
Holding Company
N.A.I.C.S.: 551112
Zhang Jiulin (CEO & Chm)

HENGLI GROUP CO.,LTD.
1 Hengli Road, Suzhou, 215226, China
Tel.: (86) 512 6383 8999
Web Site: http://www.hengli.com
Year Founded: 1994
Sales Range: Less than $1 Million
Emp.: 120,000
Weaving & Yarn Mfr
N.A.I.C.S.: 333248
Chen Jianhua (CEO)

HENGLI INDUSTRIAL DEVELOPMENT GROUP CO., LTD.
No 116 Zaozishan Road, Yueyang Economic and Technological Development Zone, Yueyang, 414000, Hunan, China
Tel.: (86) 7308245282
Web Site: http://www.hlsyfzjt.com
Year Founded: 1993
000622—(SSE)
Rev.: $34,577,712
Assets: $45,895,356
Liabilities: $17,625,816
Net Worth: $28,269,540
Earnings: ($1,861,704)
Fiscal Year-end: 12/31/22
Automotive Air Conditioner Mfr
N.A.I.C.S.: 333415
Weijin Ma (Chm)

HENGLI PETROCHEMICAL CO., LTD.
Level 41 Dalian Wanda Center 6 Xing Gang Road, Zhong Shan District, Dalian, Liaoning, China
Tel.: (86) 41186641378
Web Site: https://www.dlrpm.com
600346—(SHG)
Rev.: $31,221,912,155
Assets: $33,896,838,634
Liabilities: $26,466,815,934
Net Worth: $7,430,022,700
Earnings: $325,489,769
Fiscal Year-end: 12/31/22
Rubber & Plastic Machinery Mfr & Whslr
N.A.I.C.S.: 333248

HENGLIN HOME FURNISHINGS CO., LTD.
No 378-380 Jiaxi Road, Anji County, Huzhou, 313300, Zhejiang, China
Tel.: (86) 5725518666
Web Site: https://www.henglin.com
Year Founded: 1998
603661—(SHG)
Rev.: $914,695,498
Assets: $1,234,542,142
Liabilities: $768,981,456
Net Worth: $465,560,686
Earnings: $49,541,741
Emp.: 4,500
Fiscal Year-end: 12/31/22
Office Furniture Mfr & Distr
N.A.I.C.S.: 337214

HENGST SE & CO. KG
Nienkamp 55-85, 48147, Munster, Germany
Tel.: (49) 251 20202 0
Web Site: http://www.hengst.com
Year Founded: 1958
Sales Range: $450-499.9 Million
Emp.: 3,000
Automotive Filter Mfr
N.A.I.C.S.: 333413
Jens Rottgering *(Owner & Chm)*

Subsidiaries:

Delbag GmbH (1)
Shamrockring 1, 44623, Herne, Germany
Tel.: (49) 23231476001
Filtration Products Mfr
N.A.I.C.S.: 333413

Delbag S.A.S. (1)
1 Rue des Campanules, 77185, Lognes, France
Tel.: (33) 160049332
Filtration Products Mfr
N.A.I.C.S.: 333413

Delbag s.r.o. (1)
Slovanska 781, Liberec XXV-Vesec, 463 12, Liberec, Czech Republic
Tel.: (420) 481688516
Filtration Products Mfr
N.A.I.C.S.: 333413

Hengst Asia Pacific Pte. Ltd. (1)
25 Bukit Batok Crescent 10-10 The Elitist, Singapore, 658066, Singapore
Tel.: (65) 68182880
Automobile Parts Distr
N.A.I.C.S.: 423120
Frank Maergner *(Dir-Sls)*

Hengst Filter Systems (Kunshan) Co., Ltd. (1)
1858 North Jin Sha Jiang Road, Kunshan, 215300, Jiang Su, China
Tel.: (86) 51257723700
Automobile Parts Distr
N.A.I.C.S.: 423120

Hengst Industria de Filtros Ltda. (1)
Rua Dona Francisca 7337, 89219-600, Joinville, Santa Catarina, Brazil
Tel.: (55) 4730279070
Automobile Parts Distr
N.A.I.C.S.: 423120
Luiz Mirara *(Mng Dir & Pres)*

Hengst Middle East FZE (1)
PO Box 371242, Dubai Airport Free Zone DAFZA, Dubai, United Arab Emirates
Tel.: (971) 42323215
Filtration Products Mfr
N.A.I.C.S.: 333413

Hengst Poland Sp. z o.o. (1)
Czachorowo 59, 63-800, Gostyn, Poland
Tel.: (48) 656154230
Automobile Parts Distr
N.A.I.C.S.: 423120

Hengst SE & Co. KG - Berlin Plant (1)
Mandelstrasse 16, 10409, Berlin, Germany
Tel.: (49) 30421896
Automobile Parts Distr
N.A.I.C.S.: 423120

Hengst SE & Co. KG - Nordwalde Plant (1)
Industriestrasse 6-8, 48356, Nordwalde, Germany
Tel.: (49) 257395870
Automobile Parts Distr
N.A.I.C.S.: 423120

Hengst of North America, Inc. (1)
29 Hengst Blvd, Camden, SC 29020
Tel.: (803) 432-5992
Web Site: http://www.hengst.com
Sales Range: $1-9.9 Million
Emp.: 70
Automotive Filter Mfr
N.A.I.C.S.: 333413
Stephen Geppert *(Dir-Ops)*

Hengst-Luman India Pvt. Ltd. (1)
G-10 Udyog Nagar, New Delhi, 110041, India
Tel.: (91) 1125472564
Automobile Parts Distr
N.A.I.C.S.: 423120

HENGTAI SECURITIES CO., LTD
3rd 4th & 12th Floor Building B Desheng International Center, Xicheng District No 83 Deshengmenwai Street, Beijing, 100033, China
Tel.: (86) 956088 CN
Web Site: https://www.cnht.com.cn
1476—(HKG)
Rev.: $382,653,882
Assets: $4,355,383,219
Liabilities: $3,206,103,077
Net Worth: $1,149,280,142
Earnings: ($210,827,448)
Emp.: 2,918
Fiscal Year-end: 12/31/22
Security Brokerage Services
N.A.I.C.S.: 523150
Zhu Yanhui *(Chm & Exec Dir)*

Subsidiaries:

Hengtai Capital Investment Co., Ltd. (1)
Room 201 Block A 1 Qianwan First Road, Qianhai Shenzhen-Hong Kong Cooperation Zone, Shenzhen, Guangdong, China
Tel.: (86) 75583700311
Financial Consulting Services
N.A.I.C.S.: 541611

Subsidiary (Domestic):

Shanghai Hongdian Investment Management Co., Ltd. (2)
Room 1009 No 99 Huangpu Road Hongkou District, Shanghai, China
Tel.: (86) 2133821309
Investment Management Service
N.A.I.C.S.: 523940

Shanghai Yingwo Investment Management Co., Ltd. (2)
Room 358 Building 3 No 806 Fengzhen Road Hongkou District, Shanghai, China
Tel.: (86) 1056673933
Investment Management Service
N.A.I.C.S.: 523940
Zhuang Niu *(Exec Dir)*

Hengtai Changcai Securities Co., Ltd. (1)
NO 3333 Xiantai Street, Economic and Technological Development Zone, Changchun, 130000, Jilin, China
Tel.: (86) 43180524609
Web Site: https://www.cczq.net
Securities Brokerage Services
N.A.I.C.S.: 523150

Hengtai Futures Co., Ltd. (1)
Unit 201 2nd Floor No 120 Lane 91 Ashan Road, Pudong New District, Shanghai, China
Tel.: (86) 2168405668
Web Site: https://www.htqhedu.com
Futures Brokerage Services
N.A.I.C.S.: 523160

Subsidiary (Domestic):

Hengtai Yingwo Asset Management Co., Ltd. (2)
1/F No 251 Block 1 Yaohua Road Pilot Free Trade Zone, Shanghai, China
Tel.: (86) 2168402780
Investment Management Service
N.A.I.C.S.: 523940
Fu Lixin *(Exec Dir)*

Hengtai Pioneer Investments Co., Ltd. (1)
Building 5 No 25 Shuntong Road Shunyi District, Beijing, China
Tel.: (86) 1083270868
Investment Management Service
N.A.I.C.S.: 523940

Subsidiary (Domestic):

Beijing Hengtai Hengzhong Information Service Co., Ltd. (2)
Room 615 Building C No 33 Finance Street Xicheng District, Beijing, China
Tel.: (86) 1083270999
Investment Management Service
N.A.I.C.S.: 523940

Beijing Hengtai Hongze Investment Co., Ltd. (2)
F2-1 B 701-2 7/F No 2 and 4 Wudinghou Street Xicheng District, Beijing, China
Tel.: (86) 1056765390
Investment Management Service
N.A.I.C.S.: 523940
Lihui Wu *(Exec Dir)*

New China Fund Management Co., Ltd. (1)
11th Floor New Era Building No 26 Pinganli West Street, Xicheng District, Beijing, 100044, China
Tel.: (86) 2363710818
Web Site: https://www.ncfund.com.cn
Fund Management Services
N.A.I.C.S.: 523940

Subsidiary (Domestic):

Beijing New China Fushi Asset Management Co., Ltd. (2)
Room 3-01 Building 6 Ronghuiyuan Airport Economic Core Zone, Shunyi District, Beijing, China
Tel.: (86) 105801085
Asset Management Services
N.A.I.C.S.: 531390

HENGTONG LOGISTICS CO., LTD.
Comprehensive Logistics Park East of Yanwei Road, Hebao Village Longkou Economic Development Zone Yantai, Longkou, 265700, China
Tel.: (86) 5358806203
Web Site: http://www.lkhengtong.com
Year Founded: 2007
603223—(SHG)
Rev.: $739,827,719
Assets: $639,542,456
Liabilities: $115,115,869
Net Worth: $524,426,587
Earnings: $14,552,502
Emp.: 1,600
Fiscal Year-end: 12/31/22
Transportation Management Consulting Services
N.A.I.C.S.: 541614
Zhendong Liu *(Chm)*

HENGTONG OPTIC-ELECTRIC CO., LTD.
No 2288 Zhongshan North Road, Wujiang District, Suzhou, 215200, Jiangsu, China
Tel.: (86) 51263430985
Web Site: http://www.htgd.com.cn
Year Founded: 1993
600487—(SHG)
Rev.: $6,523,543,297
Assets: $7,817,035,314
Liabilities: $4,039,814,254
Net Worth: $3,777,221,060
Earnings: $222,328,974
Fiscal Year-end: 12/31/22
Fiber Optic Cable Mfr
N.A.I.C.S.: 335921
Jianlin Qian *(Board of Directors & Chm)*

HENGXIN SHAMBOLA CULTURE CO., LTD.
11th Floor North District Newton Office Area Landianchang South Road, Haidian District, Beijing, 100097, China
Tel.: (86) 1088846823
Web Site: http://www.hxgro.com
Year Founded: 2001
300081—(CHIN)
Rev.: $56,678,336
Assets: $270,636,402
Liabilities: $79,902,627
Net Worth: $190,733,774
Earnings: ($39,625,063)
Fiscal Year-end: 12/31/23
Mobile Communication Equipment Distr
N.A.I.C.S.: 423690
Xianmin Meng *(Chm & Pres)*

HENGXIN TECHNOLOGY LTD.
5 Tampines Central 1 06-05 Tampines Plaza 2, Singapore, 529541, Singapore
Tel.: (65) 62369353 SG
Web Site: https://www.hengxin.com.sg
1085—(HKG)
Rev.: $317,732,816
Assets: $598,277,604
Liabilities: $212,563,098
Net Worth: $385,714,506
Earnings: $14,672,535
Emp.: 936
Fiscal Year-end: 12/31/23
Communication Equipment Mfr
N.A.I.C.S.: 334220
Guoqiang Xu *(Exec Dir)*

Subsidiaries:

Jiangsu Hengxin Technology Co., Ltd. (1)
No 138 Taodu Road, Dingshu Town, Yixing, 214222, Jiangsu, China
Tel.: (86) 51087497938
Web Site: https://www.hengxin.com
Cable Product Mfr & Distr
N.A.I.C.S.: 334220
Zhi Cheng *(Engr-Mechanical)*

HENGXING GOLD HOLDING COMPANY LIMITED
43F Fortune Centre No 100 Lujiangdao Road, Siming District, Xiamen, China
Tel.: (86) 5922969521
Web Site: http://www.hxgoldholding.com
2303—(HKG)
Rev.: $120,976,168
Assets: $175,318,965
Liabilities: $23,563,418
Net Worth: $151,755,547
Earnings: $30,701,246
Emp.: 392
Fiscal Year-end: 12/31/19
Gold Mining
N.A.I.C.S.: 212220
Xiping Ke *(Founder, Chm & Pres)*

HENGYI INTERNATIONAL INDUSTRIES GROUP, INC.
No1 Xinhua Road, He Ping District, Tianjin, 300021, China
Tel.: (86) 2258900299
Year Founded: 2009
Hotel & Restaurant Operator
N.A.I.C.S.: 721110
Yijun Hu *(CEO)*

HENGYI PETROCHEMICAL CO., LTD.
No 260 Shixin North Road, Xiaoshan District, Hangzhou, 311215, Zhejiang, China
Tel.: (86) 57182797888
Web Site: https://www.hengyishihua.com
000703—(SSE)
Rev.: $21,347,857,908
Assets: $15,719,857,920
Liabilities: $11,134,653,660
Net Worth: $4,585,204,260
Earnings: ($151,568,820)
Fiscal Year-end: 12/31/22
Industrial Chemical Product Mfr & Distr
N.A.I.C.S.: 325211
Xianshui Fang *(Vice Chm)*

Hengyi Petrochemical Co., Ltd.—(Continued)

HENINGER TOYOTA
3640 Macleod Trail South, Calgary,
T2G 2P9, AB, Canada
Tel.: (403) 243-8000
Web Site:
http://www.heningertoyota.com
Year Founded: 1957
Rev.: $49,384,732
Emp.: 96
New & Used Car Dealers
N.A.I.C.S.: 441110
Dave Verboom *(Mgr-Fixed Ops)*

HENKEL + GERLACH GMBH & CO. KG
Carl-Zeiss-Str 32, 28816, Stuhr, Germany
Tel.: (49) 42156910 De
Web Site: http://www.henkel-gerlach.de
Year Founded: 1927
Sales Range: $25-49.9 Million
Emp.: 60
Electronic Equipment & Device Mfr
N.A.I.C.S.: 335931
Walter Peterhans *(Mng Dir)*

Subsidiaries:

Torsit BV (1)
Mame Curiestraat, 3846BW, Harderwijk, Netherlands
Tel.: (31) 313410156
Web Site: http://www.torsit.nl
Mfr of Hoisting & Lifting Equipment
N.A.I.C.S.: 333923

HENKEL AG & CO. KGAA
Henkelstrasse 67, 40589, Dusseldorf, Germany
Tel.: (49) 2117970 De
Web Site: https://www.henkel.com
Year Founded: 1876
HEN3—(MUN)
Rev.: $23,748,659,180
Assets: $35,023,587,360
Liabilities: $13,032,289,220
Net Worth: $21,991,298,140
Earnings: $1,454,900,660
Emp.: 48,900
Fiscal Year-end: 12/31/23
Holding Company; Laundry & Home Cleaning Products, Adhesive Technologies, Cosmetics & Toiletries Mfr
N.A.I.C.S.: 551112
Simone Bagel-Trah *(Chm-Supervisory Bd)*

Subsidiaries:

Aislantes Nacionales S.A. (1)
Av Senator Jaime Guzman 220, Quilicura, Santiago, Chile
Tel.: (56) 225403000
Web Site: http://www.aislantesnacionales.cl
Construction Adhesive Mfr
N.A.I.C.S.: 325520

Ashwa Technologies Co. Ltd. (1)
Jeddah Industrial Area Phase 2 Opposite Fine Tissues, PO Box 6420, Jeddah, Saudi Arabia
Tel.: (966) 26373969
Sales Range: $450-499.9 Million
Emp.: 1,995
Adhesive & Sealant Mfr
N.A.I.C.S.: 325520

CHEMOFAST Anchoring GmbH (1)
Hanns-Martin-Schleyer-Str 23, 47877, Wilich, Germany
Tel.: (49) 21 548 1230
Web Site: https://chemofast.com
Sales Range: $25-49.9 Million
Emp.: 85
Resin Mortar Mfr
N.A.I.C.S.: 325998
Ralf Jungermann *(Co-Mng Dir)*

Chengdu Henkel Adhesive Technologies Co., Ltd. (1)
No 218 Long an Road, Longquanyi District, Chengdu, 610100, China
Tel.: (86) 2888456694
Adhesive Product Mfr
N.A.I.C.S.: 325520

Chengdu Henkel Adhesive Techonologies Co. Ltd. (1)
No 218 Long'An Road, Longquanyi, Chengdu, 610100, China
Tel.: (86) 2888456694
Adhesive Product Mfr
N.A.I.C.S.: 325520

Clynol GmbH (1)
Hohenzollernring 127-129, Hamburg, 22763, Germany
Tel.: (49) 40882402
Web Site: http://www.clynol.com
Hair Care Products Mfr
N.A.I.C.S.: 325620
Linton Husbands *(Mgr-Natl Sls)*

Cordes & Co. GmbH (1)
Weissenfelder Strasse 1, 21698, Harsefeld, Germany (100%)
Tel.: (49) 4 164 8160
Web Site: https://www.cordes.eu
Sales Range: $25-49.9 Million
Emp.: 550
Mfr of Chemicals; Printing Ink, Plastic Coatings for the Wallpaper & Paper Industries
N.A.I.C.S.: 325910
Martin Cordes *(Owner)*

Elch GmbH (1)
Henkelstr 67, Dusseldorf, 40589, Nordrhein-Westfalen, Germany
Tel.: (49) 2117970
Web Site: http://www.henkel.com
Emp.: 550
Soap & Detergent Products Mfr
N.A.I.C.S.: 325611

Forstverwaltung Brannenburg GmbH & Co. OHG (1)
Bahnhofstr 74, 83098, Brannenburg, Germany
Tel.: (49) 80341824
Forestry Services
N.A.I.C.S.: 115310

GPM-Henkel Ltd. (1)
Dali Industrial Area 1 Lefkosias Street, Nicosia, 2540, Cyprus
Tel.: (357) 22884444
Web Site: http://www.henkel.com
Chemical Product Whslr
N.A.I.C.S.: 424690

Hans Schwarzkopf & Henkel GmbH & Co. KG (1)
Hohenzollernring 127-129, 22763, Hamburg, Germany (100%)
Tel.: (49) 408 824 2201
Web Site: http://www.schwarzkopf.com
Sales Range: $125-149.9 Million
Emp.: 280
Mfr & Marketing of Hair & Skin Care Products
N.A.I.C.S.: 325620

Henkel & Cie AG (1)
Salinenstrasse 61, 4133, Pratteln, Switzerland (100%)
Tel.: (41) 61 825 7000
Web Site: http://www.henkel.ch
Sales Range: $50-74.9 Million
Emp.: 110
Production & Sale of Detergents, Cosmetics, Adhesives, Industrial & Organic Chemicals
N.A.I.C.S.: 325611

Division (Domestic):

Henkel & Cie AG - Laesser Klebstoffe Division (2)
Gosgerstrasse 81, 5015, Erlenbach, Switzerland
Tel.: (41) 62 844 1414
Web Site: https://www.henkel.com
Sales Range: $25-49.9 Million
Emp.: 60
Personal Care Products
N.A.I.C.S.: 812199
John Pierre De Smeet *(Mng Dir)*

Henkel (Jiangsu) Auto Parts Co., Ltd. (2)
Qunyi Village, Danbei Town, Danyang, 212322, Jiangsu, China
Tel.: (86) 51186089356
Adhesive Product Mfr
N.A.I.C.S.: 325520

Henkel (Siam) Adhesive Technologies Ltd. (1)
The Offices at Central World 35th Floor 999/9 Rama 1 Road, Pathumwan District, Bangkok, 10330, Thailand
Tel.: (66) 22098000
Adhesive Product Mfr
N.A.I.C.S.: 325520
Cholapob Krongthong *(Head-Strategy & Mktg Grp)*

Henkel Adhesive Technologies (Malaysia) Holdings B.V. (1)
Brugwal 11, Nieuwegein, 3432 NZ, Utrecht, Netherlands
Tel.: (31) 306073911
Investment Management Service
N.A.I.C.S.: 523999

Henkel Adhesives Technologies India Private Limited (1)
L and T Seawoods Grand Central Tower 1 401 B Wing 4th Floor Seawoods, Navi Mumbai, 400706, Maharashtra, India
Tel.: (91) 227 130 1112
Web Site: https://www.henkel.in
Adhesive Product Mfr
N.A.I.C.S.: 325520
Sundar Iyer *(CFO)*

Henkel Anand India Pvt. Ltd. (1)
Plot No C-22 SIPOT Industrial Park Irungattukottai, Sriperumbudur Taluk, Chennai, 602 105, India
Tel.: (91) 4447109700
Emp.: 44
Chemical Products Mfr
N.A.I.C.S.: 325998

Henkel Argentina S.A. (1)
Nicolas Avellaneda 1357, San Isidro, B1642EYA, San Isidro, Buenos Aires, Argentina (100%)
Tel.: (54) 1140010100
Web Site: https://www.henkel.com.ar
Sales Range: $25-49.9 Million
Emp.: 70
Production & Sale of Adhesives for the Industry & Trade, Industrial Chemicals, Products for Textile, Leather & Cosmetics Production
N.A.I.C.S.: 325520
Julio Munoz *(Pres)*

Henkel Asia-Pacific Ltd. (1)
18 Fl Island Pl Tower, 510 Kings Rd, North Point, China (Hong Kong) (100%)
Tel.: (852) 22330000
Web Site: http://www.henkel.com
Sales Range: $50-74.9 Million
Emp.: 100
Holding Company; Regional Managing Office
N.A.I.C.S.: 551112

Subsidiary (Non-US):

Henkel (China) Co., Ltd. (2)
Room 801 Taiyanggong Building No 12A Taiyanggong Middle Road, Chaoyang District, Beijing, 100028, China
Tel.: (86) 108 429 9188
Web Site: https://www.henkel.ch
Adhesives & Coatings Mfr
N.A.I.C.S.: 325520

Subsidiary (Domestic):

Ablestik (Shanghai) Ltd. (3)
No 332 Meigui S Rd Waigaoqiao Free Trade Zone, Shanghai, 200131, China
Tel.: (86) 2138984800
Adhesive Mfr
N.A.I.C.S.: 325520
Allen Wu *(Mgr)*

Affiliate (Domestic):

Changchun Henkel Surface Technologies Co. Ltd. (3)
6077 Chaoda Road, 130062, Changchun, China
Tel.: (86) 4315556077

Sales Range: $25-49.9 Million
Emp.: 100
Adhesives & Sealants Mfr
N.A.I.C.S.: 325520

Subsidiary (Domestic):

Guangzhou Henkel Surface Technologies Co. Ltd. (3)
9 NanYun Er Lu GZ Science City, Guangzhou, 510663, China
Tel.: (86) 20 32122 800
Adhesive Mfr
N.A.I.C.S.: 325520

Subsidiary (Domestic):

Henkel Adhesives Technologies (Guangdong) Co. Limited (4)
The Fifth Industry Zone Nanshan, Humen Town, Dongguan, 523932, Guangdong, China
Tel.: (86) 7698 556 3700
Web Site: https://www.henkel.com
Sales Range: $75-99.9 Million
Emp.: 380
Mfr of Adhesives
N.A.I.C.S.: 325520

Affiliate (Domestic):

Guangzhou National Adhesives Co. Ltd. (3)
No 33 Liye Rd, Panyu, 511453, Dongyong, China
Tel.: (86) 2084906257
Sales Range: $25-49.9 Million
Emp.: 70
Chemical Products
N.A.I.C.S.: 325998

Guilin Henkel Detergents & Cleaning Products Co. Ltd. (3)
9 Xiangrenshan Road, Guilin, 541003, Guangxi, China
Tel.: (86) 7733603081
N.A.I.C.S.: 325211

Subsidiary (Domestic):

Henkel (China) Investment Co. Ltd. (3)
Building 7 Shangpu Center No 99 Jiangwancheng Road, Yangpu District, Shanghai, 200438, China
Tel.: (86) 212 891 8000
Web Site: https://www.henkel.cn
Adhesive Mfr
N.A.I.C.S.: 325520

Subsidiary (Non-US):

Henkel Adhesive Technologies Sdn. Bhd. (3)
Lot 8 & 10 Jalan Tukul 16/5, 40000, Shah Alam, Selangor, Malaysia
Tel.: (60) 355191105-
Web Site: http://www.henkel.com
Emp.: 10
Adhesive Mfr
N.A.I.C.S.: 325520

Subsidiary (Domestic):

Henkel Adhesives Co., Ltd. (3)
Xiapeng Industrial Zone Dongxia North Road, Shantou, 515065, Guangdong, China (100%)
Tel.: (86) 7548 834 7510
Web Site: http://www.henkelasia.com
Sales Range: $50-74.9 Million
Emp.: 120
Plastic Materials Mfr
N.A.I.C.S.: 325211

Henkel Chemical Technologies (Shanghai) Ltd. (3)
No 36 Pugong Road, Fengxian District Shanghai Chemical Industry Zone, Shanghai, 201507, China
Tel.: (86) 216 758 3300
Web Site: http://www.henkel.cn
Adhesive Mfr
N.A.I.C.S.: 325520

Henkel Cosmetics (Zhaoqing) Co. Ltd. (3)
No 1 Duan Zhou Rd, Zhaoqing, 526060, Guangdong, China
Tel.: (86) 758 272 8344

AND PRIVATE COMPANIES

HENKEL AG & CO. KGAA

Web Site: http://www.henkel.com
Plastic Materials
N.A.I.C.S.: 325211

Subsidiary (Non-US):

Henkel Dongsung (Thailand) Ltd. (3)
212 Moo 1 Teparak Road, Bangsaothong, Samut Prakan, 10540, Thailand
Tel.: (66) 23154622
Web Site: http://www.henkel.com
Sales Range: $25-49.9 Million
Emp.: 52
Adhesive Mfr
N.A.I.C.S.: 325520

Henkel Dongsung Vietnam Co. Ltd. (3)
No 7 Road 9A Bien Hoa II Industrial Park, Bien Hoa, Dong Nai, Vietnam
Tel.: (84) 61 3835461
Adhesive Mfr
N.A.I.C.S.: 325520

Henkel Hong Kong Holding Ltd. (3)
9/F 169 Electric Road, Hong Kong, 510620, China (Hong Kong)
Tel.: (852) 2122330000
Web Site: http://www.henkel.com
Investment Management Service
N.A.I.C.S.: 523999

Subsidiary (Domestic):

Henkel Hong Kong Ltd. (4)
Unit 1601-6 Level 16 Metroplaza Tower 1 No 223 Hing Fong Road, Kwai Fong, New Territories, China (Hong Kong)
Tel.: (852) 02968 2977
Web Site: http://www.henkel.com
Adhesive Mfr
N.A.I.C.S.: 325520

Subsidiary (Domestic):

Henkel Loctite (China) Co. Ltd. (3)
No 90 ZhuJiang Road, Economic and Technological Development Zone, Yantai, 264006, Shandong, China
Tel.: (86) 535 637 2999
Web Site: https://www.henkel.cn
Sales Range: $50-74.9 Million
Emp.: 200
Adhesive & Sealant Mfr
N.A.I.C.S.: 325520

Henkel Xianghua Adhesives Co. Ltd. (3)
No 115 Yingjun Rd, Zhangjiang Town, 201210, Shanghai, China
Tel.: (86) 21 5857 0626
Adhesive Mfr
N.A.I.C.S.: 325520

Affiliate (Domestic):

Shanghai Henkel Chemicals Co., Ltd. (3)
1610 Gulanglu, Shanghai, 200333, China
Tel.: (86) 2162505288
Sales Range: $25-49.9 Million
Emp.: 100
Plastic Materials
N.A.I.C.S.: 325211

Tianjin Henkel Detergents & Cleaning Products Co. Ltd. (3)
No 7 Jinchi Road, Dongli District, Tianjin, 300163, China
Tel.: (86) 4343321242
Detergents & Cleaning Products
N.A.I.C.S.: 325611

Subsidiary (Non-US):

Yamahatsu (Thailand) Co. Ltd. (3)
600/48 Moo 11 Sukhaphiban 8 Road, Nong Kham Subdistrict, Si Racha, 20230, Chonburi, Thailand
Tel.: (66) 3 832 0100
Web Site: https://www.henkel.co.th
Soap & Detergent Products Mfr
N.A.I.C.S.: 325611

Subsidiary (Non-US):

Henkel (Malaysia) Sdn. Bhd. (2)
Unit 2 01 2 02 Level 2 Mercu 3 Jalan Bangsar KL Eco City, Jalan Pantai Bahru, 59200, Kuala Lumpur, Malaysia (100%)
Tel.: (60) 32 246 1000

Web Site: https://www.henkel.com
Sales Range: $25-49.9 Million
Emp.: 80
Sales of Adhesives & Sealants
N.A.I.C.S.: 325520
Lai Yuan Kieng *(Bus Mgr)*

Henkel (Thailand) Ltd. (2)
The offices at Centralworld 35 Floor 999 9 Rama 1 Rd, Patumwan Patumwan, Bangkok, 10330, Thailand
Tel.: (66) 2 209 8000
Web Site: http://www.henkel.co.th
Adhesive Mfr
N.A.I.C.S.: 325520
Surachet Tanwongsval *(Pres)*

Henkel Australia Pty. Ltd. (2)
135-141 Canterbury Road, PO Box 63, Kilsyth, 3137, VIC, Australia (100%)
Tel.: (61) 39 728 7200
Web Site: https://www.henkel.com.au
Sales Range: $50-74.9 Million
Sales of Chemical Products
N.A.I.C.S.: 424690
Daniel Rudolph *(Pres)*

Subsidiary (Domestic):

Henkel Finance Australia L.P. (3)
135 141 Canterbury Rd, Kilsyth, 3137, VIC, Australia
Tel.: (61) 407833993
Financial Management Services
N.A.I.C.S.: 523999

Subsidiary (Non-US):

Henkel New Zealand Ltd. (3)
2 Allens Road, East Tamaki, Auckland, 2163, New Zealand (100%)
Tel.: (64) 9 250 9900
Web Site: https://www.henkel.com.au
Sales Range: $25-49.9 Million
Emp.: 400
Production & Sale of Specialty Chemicals
N.A.I.C.S.: 325998
Daniel Rudolph *(Pres)*

Subsidiary (Non-US):

Henkel Home Care Korea Ltd. (2)
5th floor Union Steel Building 890 Daechi-dong, Gangnam-gu, Seoul, 135-524, Korea (South)
Tel.: (82) 2 560 8400
Web Site: https://www.henkelhomecare.co.kr
Sales Range: $25-49.9 Million
Emp.: 5
Soap & Detergent Products Mfr
N.A.I.C.S.: 325611
Cheon Soo Kim *(Pres)*

Plant (Domestic):

Henkel Home Care Korea Ltd. - Ansan Plant (3)
20 Ho 18 Block 610-3 Sukgok-dong, Danwon-ku, Ansan, 428-833, Korea (South)
Tel.: (82) 31 491 6861
Adhesive Mfr
N.A.I.C.S.: 325520

Subsidiary (Non-US):

Henkel Japan Ltd. (2)
Tokyo Sphere Tower Tennoz 14th Floor, Shinagawa-ku, Tokyo, 140-0002, Japan
Tel.: (81) 35 769 6427
Web Site: https://www.henkel.co.jp
Chemical Products Mfr
N.A.I.C.S.: 325998

Subsidiary (Domestic):

Henkel Ablestik Japan Ltd. (3)
27-7 Shin Isogo-cho, Isogo-ku, Yokohama, 235-0017, Kanagawa, Japan
Tel.: (81) 45 758 1800
Web Site: http://www.henkel.co.jp
Soap & Detergent Products Mfr
N.A.I.C.S.: 325611

Subsidiary (Non-US):

Henkel Korea Ltd. (3)
Henkel Tower 1st 8th 10th 13th floor 41, Mapo-daero 4-da-gil Mapo-dong 418 Mapo-gu, Seoul, 04177, Korea (South)
Tel.: (82) 232791700

Web Site: https://www.henkel.co.kr
Sales Range: $25-49.9 Million
Chemical Products Mfr
N.A.I.C.S.: 325998

Subsidiary (Domestic):

Henkel Loctite Korea Ltd. (3)
8th Floor Kumho Electric Building 418 Mapo-Dong, Mapo-Ku, 121-734, Seoul, Korea (South)
Tel.: (82) 232791700
Web Site: http://www.henkelkorea.com
Sales Range: $25-49.9 Million
Emp.: 100
Adhesive & Sealant Mfr
N.A.I.C.S.: 325520

Subsidiary (Domestic):

Henkel Loctite Hong Kong Limited (2)
9/F 169 Electric Road, North Point, China (Hong Kong)
Tel.: (852) 22330000
Web Site: http://www.loctite.com
Sales Range: $25-49.9 Million
Emp.: 60
Mfr & Distributor of Adhesives & Sealants; Gum & Wood Chemicals
N.A.I.C.S.: 325520

Subsidiary (Non-US):

Henkel Hakusui Corporation (3)
14Fl Sphere Tower Tennoz 2-2-8 Higashishinagawa, Osaka, 550-0015, Japan (60%)
Tel.: (81) 357696427
Web Site: http://www.henkel.co.jp
Production & Sale of Chemical Products
N.A.I.C.S.: 424690

Subsidiary (Non-US):

Henkel Singapore Pte. Ltd. (2)
Techno Centre 401 Commonwealth Drive 03-01/02, Haw Par, Singapore, 149598, Singapore (100%)
Tel.: (65) 6 266 0100
Web Site: http://www.henkel.com
Sales Range: $25-49.9 Million
Emp.: 70
Production & Sale of Metal Chemicals
N.A.I.C.S.: 325199

Henkel Taiwan Ltd. (2)
10th Floor No 866 Zhongzheng Road, Zhonghe District, New Taipei City, 23586, Taiwan (100%)
Tel.: (886) 28 978 9788
Web Site: https://www.henkel.tw
Sales Range: $25-49.9 Million
Emp.: 100
Production & Sale of Textile, Leather, Paper & Specialty Chemicals Products; Additives for Lacquer & Paint
N.A.I.C.S.: 325998

Branch (Domestic):

Henkel Taiwan Ltd. - P'ingchen (3)
No 1 Kung Yeh 1 Rd Ping Cheng Ind Pk, P'ingchen, 326, Taoyuan Hsien, Taiwan
Tel.: (886) 34696550
Sales Range: $25-49.9 Million
Supplier of Adhesives
N.A.I.C.S.: 325520

Subsidiary (Non-US):

Henkel Technologies (Korea) Ltd. (3)
258 - 6 Yongwon-Ri Seongnam-Myeon, Dongnam-Gu, Cheonan, 330-891, Chungchongnam-Do, Korea (South)
Tel.: (82) 415530948
Adhesive Mfr
N.A.I.C.S.: 325520

Plant (Domestic):

Henkel Technologies (Korea) Ltd. - Busan Plant (3)
472 Shinpyung-Dong, Saha-Ku, Busan, 604-030, Korea (South)
Tel.: (82) 51 200 4800
Web Site: http://www.henkel.com
Adhesive Mfr
N.A.I.C.S.: 325520
Arnold Nan *(Gen Mgr)*

Henkel Technologies (Korea) Ltd. - Chunan Plant (3)
258-6 Yongwon-ri Seongnam-myoun, Cheohan, 330-891, Choongnam, Korea (South)
Tel.: (82) 41 553 0948
Emp.: 7
Adhesive Mfr
N.A.I.C.S.: 325520
Herald Park *(Plant Mgr)*

Henkel Technologies (Korea) Ltd. - Eumsung Plant (3)
128 Daegeunlo Geumwang-eup, Oseon-ri, Eumseong, 369-906, Chuncheingbuk-do, Korea (South)
Tel.: (82) 43 880 9000
Web Site: http://www.henkel.co.kr
Emp.: 150
Silicone Products Mfr
N.A.I.C.S.: 327910
Herald Heynsergpark *(Plant Mgr)*

Subsidiary (Non-US):

Henkel Vietnam Co. Ltd. (2)
Suite 1001 10th Floor Centre Point Building 106 Nguyen Van Troi Ward 8, Phu Nhuan District, Ho Chi Minh City, Vietnam
Tel.: (84) 8 39977334
Emp.: 30
Cosmetic Products Mfr & Distr
N.A.I.C.S.: 325620
Frank Ennenbach *(Gen Mgr)*

Plant (Domestic):

Henkel Vietnam Co. Ltd. - Binh Duong Cosmetics Plant (3)
Lot G1 Viet Huong Industrial Park, Highway No 13, Thuan An, Binh Duong, Vietnam
Tel.: (84) 650747122
Web Site: http://www.henkel.com
Sales Range: $50-74.9 Million
Chemical Products Mfr
N.A.I.C.S.: 325998

Affiliate (Non-US):

National Adhesives Co. Ltd. (2)
N5 6 Sukaphilbal 2 Rd Bangchan Industrial Estate, Minburi, Bangkok, 10510, Thailand
Tel.: (66) 251700459
Sales Range: $25-49.9 Million
Emp.: 100
Mfr of Adhesives & Specialty Synthetic Polymers
N.A.I.C.S.: 325520

Subsidiary (Non-US):

PT Henkel Indonesien (2)
Nissi Bintaro Campus 3rd Floor Jl Tegal Rotan Raya No 78, Bintaro, Tangerang, 15413, Banten, Indonesia
Tel.: (62) 212 758 6900
Web Site: https://www.henkel.co.id
Emp.: 360
Chemical Products Mfr
N.A.I.C.S.: 325998

Henkel BH d.o.o. (1)
Trg Solidarnosti 2A, 71000, Sarajevo, Bosnia & Herzegovina
Tel.: (387) 33778700
Web Site: http://www.henkel.com
Sales Range: $25-49.9 Million
Emp.: 15
Adhesive Mfr
N.A.I.C.S.: 325520

Henkel Balti (1)
Sopruse pst 145, 13417, Tallinn, Estonia
Tel.: (372) 6999070
Sealant & Adhesive Mfr
N.A.I.C.S.: 325520

Henkel Balti Operations OU (1)
Savi 12, 80010, Parnu, Estonia
Tel.: (372) 6999070
Adhesive Product Mfr
N.A.I.C.S.: 325520

Henkel Bautechnik (Ukraina) TOB (1)
St Novopromyslova 2, 07301, Vyshgorod, Kyiv, Ukraine
Tel.: (380) 80 030 8405
Web Site: https://www.ceresit.ua
Waterproof Cement Mfr
N.A.I.C.S.: 327310

HENKEL AG & CO. KGAA

INTERNATIONAL PUBLIC

Henkel AG & Co. KGaA—(Continued)

Henkel Bautechnik Kazakhstan LLP (1)
Masanchi Str 78, 050012, Almaty, Kazakhstan
Tel.: (7) 727244230
Adhesive Product Mfr
N.A.I.C.S.: 325520
Anara Mukan Jr. *(Product Mgr)*

Henkel Belgium N.V. (1)
Esplanade 1, PO Box 101, 1020, Brussels, Belgium **(100%)**
Tel.: (32) 2 421 2711
Web Site: https://www.henkel.be
Sales Range: $125-149.9 Million
Emp.: 300
Mfr of Detergents, Adhesives, Industrial & Organic Chemicals, Cosmetics
N.A.I.C.S.: 325520

Subsidiary (Domestic):

Henkel Electronic Materials (Belgium) N.V. (2)
Nijverheidsstraat 7, 2260, Westerlo, Belgium
Tel.: (32) 1457 5611
Web Site: http://www.henkel.com
Sales Range: $25-49.9 Million
Emp.: 100
Adhesive Mfr
N.A.I.C.S.: 325520
Jelle Geukens *(Plant Mgr)*

Henkel Belgium Operations N.V. (1)
Anderlechtstraat 33, 1620, Drogenbos, Belgium
Tel.: (32) 23704431
Adhesive Product Mfr
N.A.I.C.S.: 325520
Mark Devos *(Ops Mgr)*

Henkel Canada Corporation (1)
2515 Meadowpine Boulevard, Mississauga, L5N 6C3, ON, Canada
Tel.: (905) 814-6511
Web Site: http://www.henkel-northamerica.com
Sales Range: $25-49.9 Million
Emp.: 100
Mfr of Chemicals
N.A.I.C.S.: 325998

Division (Domestic):

Henkel Adhesive Technologies Canada (2)
2515 Meadowpine Boulevard, Mississauga, L5N 6C3, ON, Canada
Tel.: (905) 814-6511
Web Site: https://www.henkel-northamerica.com
Adhesives & Sealants Mfr & Whslr
N.A.I.C.S.: 325520
Rose Doldo *(Mgr)*

Subsidiary (Domestic):

Henkel Consumer Goods Canada, Inc. (2)
2515 Meadowpine Blvd, Mississauga, L5N 6C3, ON, Canada
Tel.: (905) 814-6511
Web Site: http://www.henkel.com
Sales Range: $25-49.9 Million
Emp.: 10
Soap & Detergent Mfr
N.A.I.C.S.: 325611
Stacey Brown *(Mgr-Sls)*

Henkel Capital S.A. de C.V. (1)
Boulevard Magnocentro No 8 Centro Urbano Interlomas, Huixquilucan, 52760, Mexico, Mexico
Tel.: (52) 553 300 3000
Web Site: https://www.henkel.mx
Sales Range: $125-149.9 Million
Emp.: 300
Chemical Products Mfr
N.A.I.C.S.: 325998

Branch (Domestic):

Henkel Capital S.A. de C.V. (2)
Av Chapultepec No 2244 Col Bueno Aires, Monterrey, CP 64800, Nuevo Leon, Mexico
Tel.: (52) 818 359 8800
Web Site: https://www.henkel.mx

Sales Range: $25-49.9 Million
Emp.: 80
Adhesives & Specialty Synthetic Polymers Mfr
N.A.I.C.S.: 325520
Tomas Gonzales *(Plant Mgr)*

Henkel Central Asia & Caucasus TOO (1)
78 Masanchi Str Crossino Schevchenko, 050012, Almaty, 050012, Kazakhstan
Tel.: (7) 727 244 3399
Web Site: http://www.henkel.com
Emp.: 100
Cosmetics Products Mfr
N.A.I.C.S.: 325520
Agul Amamkeldiyeza *(Gen Dir)*

Subsidiary (Domestic):

Henkel Bautechnik Kazakhstan TOO (2)
78 Masanchi Str Crossino Schevchenko, 50012, Almaty, Kazakhstan
Tel.: (7) 727 244 2343
Sales Range: $25-49.9 Million
Emp.: 4
Construction Materials Distr
N.A.I.C.S.: 423320
Nurgul Khmeeyirod *(Dir-Plant)*

Subsidiary (Non-US):

Henkel Bautechnik TAA (2)
Stroitelnaya Str 1-1, Zaslavl, 223036, Minsk, Belarus
Tel.: (375) 17 544 70 88
Adhesive Mfr
N.A.I.C.S.: 325520

Henkel Centroamericana S.A. (1)
Interamericas World Financial Center Torre Norte Nivel 15, Diagonal 6 10-50 Zona 10, Guatemala, 2625, CA, Guatemala
Tel.: (502) 2 421 1600
Web Site: https://www.henkel.com
Plastic Materials
N.A.I.C.S.: 325211

Henkel Chembond Surface Technologies Ltd. (2)
Chembond Centre EL-71 MIDC Mahape, Vashi Navi, Mumbai, 400705, India
Tel.: (91) 22 392 130 00
Sales Range: $25-49.9 Million
Emp.: 66
Production of Protective Preparations for Cloth & Leather Products
N.A.I.C.S.: 313320

Henkel Chile S.A. (1)
Avenida Laguna Sur 9551, Parque Industrial Puerto Comuna de Pudahuel, Santiago, 9060987, Chile **(100%)**
Tel.: (56) 2 381 7200
Web Site: https://www.henkel.cl
Emp.: 180
Mfr & Distr of Adhesives & Sealants
N.A.I.C.S.: 325520

Subsidiary (Domestic):

Henkel Chile Ltda. (2)
Avenida Laguna Sur 9551 Parque Industrial Puerto, Comuna de Pudahuel, 9060987, Santiago, Chile
Tel.: (56) 23817200
Web Site: https://www.henkel.cl
Emp.: 180
Adhesive Mfr
N.A.I.C.S.: 325520

Henkel Colombiana S.A. (1)
Calle 17 No 68b-97, Industrial Zone of Montevideo, Bogota, Colombia **(100%)**
Tel.: (57) 142 3900
Web Site: https://www.henkel.com.co
Sales Range: $150-199.9 Million
Emp.: 300
Sale of Specialty Chemicals Products
N.A.I.C.S.: 424690

Henkel Costa Rica Ltda. (1)
1km Este del Aeropuerto Internacional Juan Santa Maria Rio Segundo, PO Box 83-4050, San Joaquin de Flores, 20109, Alajuela, Costa Rica
Tel.: (506) 4 037 4900
Web Site: https://www.henkel.com

Sales Range: $25-49.9 Million
Emp.: 58
Chemical Products Mfr
N.A.I.C.S.: 325998

Henkel Denmark A/S (1)
Industriparken 21 A, 2750, Ballerup, Denmark
Tel.: (45) 4 330 1300
Web Site: https://www.henkel.dk
Adhesive Product Mfr
N.A.I.C.S.: 325520

Henkel Detergents Saudi Arabia Ltd. (1)
PO Box 25790, Second Industrial Zone-D, 11476, Riyadh, Saudi Arabia
Tel.: (966) 112652655
Sales Range: $125-149.9 Million
Emp.: 380
Chemical Products Mfr
N.A.I.C.S.: 325998

Henkel Eastern Europe GmbH (1)
Erdberg strasse 29, 1030, Vienna, Austria **(100%)**
Tel.: (43) 1711040
Web Site: http://www.henkel.com
Sales Range: $200-249.9 Million
Emp.: 750
Mfr & Distributor of Adhesives & Sealants
N.A.I.C.S.: 325520
Rainer M. Haertel *(Mng Dir)*

Subsidiary (Non-US):

Henkel Balti OU (2)
Soprues Pst 145, 13417, Tallinn, Estonia
Tel.: (372) 699 9070
Web Site: https://www.henkel.com
Sales Range: $25-49.9 Million
Emp.: 60
Chemical Products Trader
N.A.I.C.S.: 424690

Henkel Bulgaria EOOD (2)
Business Park Sofia Building 2 floor 4, 1766, Sofia, Bulgaria
Tel.: (359) 2 806 3900
Web Site: http://www.henkel.bg
Sales Range: $50-74.9 Million
Emp.: 160
Chemical Products Mfr
N.A.I.C.S.: 325998
Nicolae Olteanu *(Pres)*

Subsidiary (Domestic):

Henkel Central Eastern Europe GmbH (2)
Erdbergstrasse 29, 1030, Vienna, Austria **(100%)**
Tel.: (43) 171 1040
Web Site: https://www.henkel.at
Sales Range: $25-49.9 Million
Emp.: 60
Mfr of Cosmetics & Perfumes
N.A.I.C.S.: 325620

Subsidiary (Domestic):

Henkel Austria Group (3)
Erdbergstrasse 29, A-1030, Vienna, Austria **(100%)**
Tel.: (43) 1711040
Web Site: http://www.henkel.co.at
Detergents, Cosmetics, Adhesives, Cleaning Products & Chemicals Mfr
N.A.I.C.S.: 325611
Michael Sgiarovello *(Head-Corp Comm)*

Subsidiary (Non-US):

Henkel CR spol.s.r.o. (3)
Boudnikova 2514/5, 180 00, Prague, Czech Republic
Tel.: (420) 22 010 1101
Web Site: https://www.henkel.cz
Plastic Materials
N.A.I.C.S.: 325211
Jaroslava Haid-Jarkova *(Gen Mgr)*

Henkel Croatia d.o.o. (3)
Budmanijeva 1, 10 000, Zagreb, Croatia **(100%)**
Tel.: (385) 1 600 8222
Web Site: https://www.henkel.hr
Sales Range: $25-49.9 Million
Emp.: 65
Plastic Materials
N.A.I.C.S.: 325211

Zeljko Smodlaka *(Chm)*

Henkel Magyarorszag Kft. (3)
David Ferenc Utca 6, 1113, Budapest, Hungary **(100%)**
Tel.: (36) 1 372 5555
Web Site: https://www.henkel.hu
Emp.: 1,000
Production & Sale of Detergents, Cosmetics & Adhesives
N.A.I.C.S.: 325611
Agnes Sabian *(Gen Mgr)*

Henkel Slovenija d.o.o. (3)
Industrijska Ulica 23, 2000, Maribor, Slovenia
Tel.: (386) 22222100
Chemical Products Mfr
N.A.I.C.S.: 325998
Mark Mintas *(Pres)*

Henkel Slovensko spol. s.r.o. (3)
Tel.: (421) 23 331 9111
Web Site: https://www.henkel.sk
Sales Range: $125-149.9 Million
Chemical Products Distr
N.A.I.C.S.: 325998

Subsidiary (Non-US):

Henkel Hellas SA (2)
Kyprou 23, Moschato, 183 46, Athens, Greece
Tel.: (30) 2104897200
Web Site: https://www.henkel.gr
Sales Range: $100-124.9 Million
Emp.: 300
Adhesives Production & Sales
N.A.I.C.S.: 325520

Henkel Merima a.d. (2)
Savska 28, 37000, Krusevac, Serbia
Tel.: (381) 37415415
Web Site: http://www.henkel.com
Chemical Products Mfr
N.A.I.C.S.: 325998

Henkel Polska S.A. (2)
ul Domaniewska 41, 02-672, Warsaw, Poland **(100%)**
Tel.: (48) 22 565 6000
Web Site: https://www.henkel.pl
Sales Range: $200-249.9 Million
Plastic Materials
N.A.I.C.S.: 325211
Janusz Golebiowski *(Chm & Fin Dir)*

Henkel Romania Srl (2)
Str Ionita Vornicul Nr 1-7 Sector 2, 20325, Bucharest, Romania **(100%)**
Tel.: (40) 21 203 2600
Web Site: https://www.henkel.ro
Emp.: 200
Plastic Materials
N.A.I.C.S.: 325211

OOO Henkel RUS (2)
46 Stroiteley Avenue, Saratov Region, 413116, Engels, Russia
Tel.: (7) 4957455588
Web Site: https://www.henkel.ru
Sales Range: $400-449.9 Million
Adhesive & Sealant Mfr
N.A.I.C.S.: 325520
Alexey Ananishnov *(Gen Mgr)*

OOO Henkel Sud (2)
c/o ERA AG Ul Prospekt Stroitelej 48, 413116, Engels, Russia
Tel.: (7) 8451124693
Web Site: http://www.henkel.com
Sales Range: $50-74.9 Million
Emp.: 200
Plastic Materials
N.A.I.C.S.: 325211

Rilken Cosmetics Industry S.A. (2)
Kitmou 23, 18346, Moschato, Greece **(51%)**
Tel.: (30) 2106249800
Web Site: http://www.Henkel.gr
Sales Range: $100-124.9 Million
Emp.: 367
Cosmetics Mfr
N.A.I.C.S.: 325620

Henkel Ecuatoriana S.A. (1)
Ed Alpallana II 6th floor La Alpallana, E7-212 and Diego de Almagro, Quito, Ecuador
Tel.: (593) 2 250 8773
Web Site: http://www.henkel.com

AND PRIVATE COMPANIES

HENKEL AG & CO. KGAA

Chemical Products Mfr
N.A.I.C.S.: 325998

Henkel Egypt for Industry & Trade SAE (1)
12 Kamal El-Din Hussien Street Behind Fairmont Towers Hotel, Heliopolis, Cairo, Egypt
Tel.: (20) 226969100
Adhesive Product Mfr
N.A.I.C.S.: 325520

Henkel Finland Oy (1)
Ayritie 12a, 01510, Vantaa, Finland
Tel.: (358) 2 012 2311
Web Site: https://www.henkel.fi
Adhesive Product Mfr
N.A.I.C.S.: 325520
Sanna Helsto *(Mgr-Trade Brand)*

Henkel France Operations S.A. (1)
33 route de Gallardon, 28230, Epernon, France
Tel.: (33) 237188600
Adhesive Product Mfr
N.A.I.C.S.: 325520

Henkel France S.A. (1)
161 Rue de Silly, 92100, Boulogne-Billancourt, France
Tel.: (33) 14 684 9000
Web Site: https://www.henkel.fr
Sales Range: $50-74.9 Million
Emp.: 1,100
Production & Sale of Detergents & Household Cleansers, Adhesives & Cosmetics
N.A.I.C.S.: 325611
Natalie Taboo *(Dir-Media)*

Subsidiary (Domestic):

Henkel Loctite France SAS (2)
161 Rue Decsilly Boulogne Billencourt, 92000, Senlis, France
Tel.: (33) 146849000
Sales Range: $50-74.9 Million
Emp.: 200
Adhesives & Sealants Mfr
N.A.I.C.S.: 325520

Henkel Technologies France SAS (2)
299 Rue Grange Morin Zone Industrielle Nord, BP 438, Arnas, 69655, Villefranche-sur-Saone, France
Tel.: (33) 474023800
Emp.: 13
Adhesive Mfr
N.A.I.C.S.: 325520

Henkel Genthin GmbH (1)
Ziegelei 56, Postfach 43, 39307, Genthin, Germany **(100%)**
Tel.: (49) 39338850
Web Site: http://www.henkel-genthin.de
Sales Range: $125-149.9 Million
Emp.: 350
Mfr of Pharmaceuticals, Soap & Detergents
N.A.I.C.S.: 325412

Henkel Global Supply Chain B.V. (1)
Gustav Mahlerlaan 2970, 1081 LA, Amsterdam, Netherlands
Tel.: (31) 205174000
Adhesive Product Mfr
N.A.I.C.S.: 325520

Henkel IP Management and IC Services GmbH (1)
Alfred-Nobel-Str 10, Monheim, 40789, Germany
Tel.: (49) 7362810
Adhesive Mfr
N.A.I.C.S.: 325520

Henkel Iberica Portugal, Unipessoal Lda. (1)
Rua D Nuno Alvares Pereira N 4 and 4A, Poligono das Actividades Economicas Parque Oriente - Blocks 1 and 2, 2695-167, Bobadela, Portugal
Tel.: (351) 21 957 8100
Web Site: https://www.henkel.pt
Chemical Products Mfr
N.A.I.C.S.: 325998

Henkel Iberica S.A. (1)
Bilbao 72-84, 08005, Barcelona, Spain **(80%)**
Tel.: (34) 93 290 4000

Web Site: https://www.henkel.es
Sales Range: $200-249.9 Million
Emp.: 600
Production & Sale of Detergents & Household Cleansers, Adhesives, Industrial & Organic Chemicals
N.A.I.C.S.: 325611
Luis Carlos Lacorte *(Pres)*

Subsidiary (Domestic):

Henkel Loctite Espana, S.A. (2)
Poligono Industrial Alparrache Camino Villaviciosa, Parc 18 20 Navalcarnero, 28600, Madrid, Spain **(100%)**
Tel.: (34) 918609000
Web Site: http://www.loctite.es
Sales Range: $25-49.9 Million
Emp.: 40
Mfr & Distributor of Adhesives & Sealants
N.A.I.C.S.: 325520

Henkel Industrie AG (1)
Ostad Motahari, PO Box 1875, Miramad 8th St No 11, 3117, Tehran, Iran **(49%)**
Tel.: (98) 2188757141
Web Site: http://www.henkel.com
Production & Sale of Specialty Chemicals
N.A.I.C.S.: 325998

Henkel Ireland Ltd. (1)
Tallaght Business Park Whitestown, Tallaght, Dublin, Ireland
Tel.: (353) 1 404 6444
Web Site: http://www.henkel.com
Emp.: 500
Adhesive Mfr
N.A.I.C.S.: 325520
Karl Callaghan *(Mgr-Engrg)*

Henkel Italia Operations S.r.l. (1)
Via Puccini 65/67, Casarile, 20080, Milan, Italy
Tel.: (39) 02900181
Web Site: https://www.henkel.it
Adhesive Product Mfr
N.A.I.C.S.: 325520

Henkel Italia S.r.l. (1)
Via C Amoretti 78, 20157, Milan, Italy
Tel.: (39) 0235 7921
Web Site: https://www.henkel.it
Adhesive Product Mfr
N.A.I.C.S.: 325520
Mara Panajia *(Gen Mgr)*

Henkel Jamaica Limited (1)
36-38 Red Hills Road, Kingston, 10, Jamaica
Tel.: (876) 9297980
Sales Range: $25-49.9 Million
Emp.: 16
Production & Sale of Adhesives for the Industry & Trade, Industrial Chemicals, Products for the Textile, Leather & Paper Production
N.A.I.C.S.: 325520

Henkel Jebel Ali FZCO (1)
Block F 4th Floor Silicon Oasis, PO Box 341044, Dubai, United Arab Emirates
Tel.: (971) 4 389 3333
Web Site: https://www.henkel-gcc.com
Emp.: 1,600
Adhesive Product Mfr
N.A.I.C.S.: 325520

Henkel Kenya Ltd. (1)
Outer Ring Road, PO Box 40050, 00100, Nairobi, Kenya **(55%)**
Tel.: (254) 20 245 1638
Web Site: https://www.henkel.com
Production & Sale of Adhesives, Cosmetics, Industrial Chemicals, Textile & Leather Treatment Products
N.A.I.C.S.: 325520

Henkel La Luz S.A. (1)
KM 18 5 Carretera Vieja Antigua 16-81 Zona 1, Mixco, Guatemala
Tel.: (502) 2 203 8444
Web Site: https://www.henkel.com
Emp.: 20
Soap & Detergent Mfr
N.A.I.C.S.: 325611
Luis Salazar *(Gen Mgr)*

Henkel Latvia SIA (1)
Gustava Zemgala Gatve 76 B2, LV-1039, Riga, Latvia
Tel.: (371) 67819310

Adhesive Product Mfr
N.A.I.C.S.: 325520
Anete Kaulina *(Acct Mgr)*

Henkel Lebanon S.A.L. (1)
Henkel Building Zouk Mosbeth, Beirut, Lebanon
Tel.: (961) 9 220374
Web Site: http://www.henkel.com
Sales Range: $25-49.9 Million
Emp.: 100
Chemical Products Mfr
N.A.I.C.S.: 325998

Henkel Loctite Deutschland GmbH (1)
Gutenbergstrasse 3, 85748, Garching, Germany **(100%)**
Tel.: (49) 8992681583
Web Site: http://www.loctite.de
Sales Range: $25-49.9 Million
Emp.: 100
Mfr & Distributor of Adhesives & Sealants
N.A.I.C.S.: 325520

Henkel Loctite-KID GmbH (1)
Heydstrasse 10, 58093, Hagen, Germany
Tel.: (49) 23 31 62 83 90
Web Site: http://www.henkel-loctite-kid.de
Sales Range: $25-49.9 Million
Emp.: 4
Automobile Parts Mfr
N.A.I.C.S.: 336390
Markus Alterauge *(Member-Mgmt Bd)*

Henkel Ltd. (1)
Wood Lane End, Hemel Hempstead, HP2 4RQ, Herts, United Kingdom **(100%)**
Tel.: (44) 144 227 8000
Web Site: https://www.henkel.co.uk
Sales Range: $25-49.9 Million
Emp.: 75
Production & Sale of Organic Chemicals, Adhesives & Industrial Chemicals
N.A.I.C.S.: 325998

Subsidiary (Domestic):

Multicore Solders Ltd. (2)
Technologies House Kelsey Ho Wood Lane End, Hemel Hempstead, HP2 4RQ, Hertfordshire, United Kingdom
Tel.: (44) 1442 278000
Web Site: http://www.henkel.com
Emp.: 5
Soldering Wire & Nonferrous Metal Mfr
N.A.I.C.S.: 331491

Henkel Ltda. (1)
Av Prof Vernon Krieble 91, Itapevi, 06696-070, Sao Paulo, Brazil **(100%)**
Tel.: (55) 1132057001
Web Site: http://www.henkel.com.br
Sales Range: $150-199.9 Million
Emp.: 900
Consumer Adhesives, Technology of Industrial Adhesives, Sealants, Surface Treatment & Hair Care
N.A.I.C.S.: 424690
Julio M. Kampff *(Pres)*

Subsidiary (Domestic):

Henkel Loctite Brasil Ltda. (2)
Av Prof Vernon Kriebel 91, 06696-070, Sao Paulo, Itapevi, Brazil **(100%)**
Tel.: (55) 11 3205 7000
Web Site: http://www.henkel.com.br
Sales Range: Less than $1 Million
Emp.: 350
Mfr & Distr of Adhesives & Sealants
N.A.I.C.S.: 325520

Henkel Management AG (1)
Henkelstr 67, Dusseldorf, 40589, Germany
Tel.: (49) 2117970
Business Management Consulting Services
N.A.I.C.S.: 541611
Kathrin Menges *(Exec VP-HR & Infrastructure Svcs)*

Henkel Maribor d.o.o. (1)
Industrijska Ulica 23, 2506, Maribor, Slovenia
Tel.: (386) 2 222 2100
Web Site: https://www.henkel.si
Emp.: 670
Adhesive Product Mfr
N.A.I.C.S.: 325520
Matej Ribic *(Mgr-Material Mgmt)*

Henkel Mexicana S.A. de C.V. (1)
Calzada Ermita Ixtapalapa 66 Miravalle, Benito Juarez, Mexico, 55090, Ecatapec, Mexico **(100%)**
Tel.: (52) 52431670
Web Site: http://www.henkel.com
Sales Range: $125-149.9 Million
Emp.: 400
Production of Petrochemicals
N.A.I.C.S.: 325110

Henkel Nederland B.V. (1)
Brugwal 11, 3432 NZ, Nieuwegein, Netherlands **(100%)**
Tel.: (31) 30 607 3911
Web Site: https://www.henkel.nl
Sales Range: $125-149.9 Million
Emp.: 200
Production & Sale of Detergents, Cosmetics & Adhesives
N.A.I.C.S.: 325611

Subsidiary (Domestic):

Loctite (Overseas) Ltd. (2)
Brugwal 11, 3432 NZ, Nieuwegein, Netherlands
Tel.: (31) 306073860
Web Site: http://www.henkle.com
Adhesives & Sealants Mfr
N.A.I.C.S.: 325520

Loctite International B.V. (2)
Brugwal 11, 3432 NZ, Nieuwegein, Netherlands
Tel.: (31) 306073870
Web Site: http://www.loctite.com
Sales Range: $50-74.9 Million
Emp.: 200
Adhesives & Sealants Mfr
N.A.I.C.S.: 325520

Turco Nederland B.V. (2)
Astronaut 36, 3824 MJ, Amersfoort, Netherlands
Tel.: (31) 334511720
Real Estate Services
N.A.I.C.S.: 531390

Subsidiary (Domestic):

Turco Produkten B.V. (3)
Astronaut 36, 3824 MJ, Amersfoort, Netherlands
Tel.: (31) 334511720
Sales Range: $25-49.9 Million
Emp.: 15
Chemical Products Mfr
N.A.I.C.S.: 325998

Henkel Nederland Operations B.V. (1)
Haven Noordzijde 6, 9679 TC, Scheemda, Netherlands
Tel.: (31) 597670500
Web Site: https://www.henkel.nl
Adhesive Product Mfr
N.A.I.C.S.: 325520
Jos De Jonge *(Plant Mgr)*

Henkel Norden AB (1)
Gustavslundsvagen 151A, Box 151 22, 167 15, Bromma, Sweden **(100%)**
Tel.: (46) 10 480 7500
Web Site: https://www.henkel.se
Sales Range: $25-49.9 Million
Emp.: 100
Plastic Materials
N.A.I.C.S.: 325211
Robert Larsen *(Pres & Dir-HR & Compliance)*

Subsidiary (Domestic):

Henkel Adhesive Technologies Norden AB (2)
Torsgatan 12, Norrkoping, 600 12, Sweden
Tel.: (46) 104807800
Sales Range: $25-49.9 Million
Emp.: 80
Adhesive Mfr
N.A.I.C.S.: 325520
Robert Larsen *(Mng Dir)*

Henkel Surface Technologies Nordic Ab (2)
Argongatan 10, 43124, Molndal, Sweden **(100%)**
Tel.: (46) 31679500
Web Site: http://www.henkel-spm.se

HENKEL AG & CO, KGAA

Henkel AG & Co. KGaA—(Continued)
Production & Sale of Adhesives for the Industry & Trade
N.A.I.C.S.: 325520

Henkel Norden Oy (1)
Ayritie 12 A, 01510, Vantaa, Finland
Tel.: (358) 20122311
Sales Range: $25-49.9 Million
Emp.: 83
Chemical Products Mfr
N.A.I.C.S.: 325998
Alan Friis *(Dir-Sls)*

Subsidiary (Domestic):

Henkel Makroflex Oy (2)
Makrotie 1, Oitti, 12100, Finland
Tel.: (358) 1978 601
Web Site: http://www.makroflex.ee
Plastic Materials Mfr
N.A.I.C.S.: 325211

Henkel Norge AB (1)
Karenslyst Alle 8b, 0604, Oslo,
Norway (100%)
Tel.: (47) 23371520
Web Site: http://www.henkel.no
Emp.: 15
Marketing of Adhesives for Industry & Trade
N.A.I.C.S.: 424690

Henkel Oberflachentechnik GmbH (1)
Henkelstrasse 67, 40589, Dusseldorf, Germany
Tel.: (49) 2117973000
Sales Range: $50-74.9 Million
Emp.: 165
Chemical Products Mfr
N.A.I.C.S.: 325998

Henkel PDC Egypt SAE (1)
12 Kamal El-Din Hussien Street Behind
Sheraton Heliopolis Hotel, Cairo, EG003,
Egypt
Tel.: (20) 222684860
Soap & Detergent Mfr
N.A.I.C.S.: 325611

Subsidiary (Non-US):

Henkel Algerie S.p.A. (2)
22 Rue Ahmed Ouaked Bois Des Cars Iii,
Dely-Ibrahim, 16320, Algiers, Algeria
Tel.: (213) 2191 8607
Web Site: http://www.henkel.com
Detergent & Laundry Care Products Mfr
N.A.I.C.S.: 325611

Henkel Alki Distribution S.A.R.L. (2)
Rue Des Metals, Ariana, Tunisia
Tel.: (216) 70837740
Soap & Detergent Mfr
N.A.I.C.S.: 325611

Henkel Arabia for Home and Personal Care Products Co. Ltd. (2)
2nd Industrial Area Zone D, Riyadh, 11476,
Saudi Arabia
Tel.: (966) 12652655
Soap & Detergent Mfr
N.A.I.C.S.: 325611

Henkel Industrial Adhesives Pakistan Pvt. Ltd. (2)
2nd Floor 17-N, Johar Town, Lahore, Pakistan
Tel.: (92) 4235316432
Adhesive Mfr
N.A.I.C.S.: 325520
Shahbaz Sair *(Country Mgr)*

Henkel Jordan PSC (2)
Next To Marka Bridge And Toyota Spare
Parts Warehouse, PO Box 7809, Marka,
Amman, 11118, Jordan
Tel.: (962) 6 489 1961
Web Site: http://www.henkel.com
Detergent & Laundry Products Mfr
N.A.I.C.S.: 325611

Henkel Saudi Arabia Detergents Co. Ltd. (2)
New Industrial City 2nd Zone-D, PO Box
25790, 11476, Riyadh, Saudi Arabia
Tel.: (966) 1 265 2655
Soap & Detergent Mfr
N.A.I.C.S.: 325611

Henkel Trading Maghreb S.A.R.L.
Rte De Gabes Km 3, BP 144, 3028, Sfax,
Tunisia
Tel.: (216) 74453229
Web Site: http://www.henkel.com
Chemical Products Mfr
N.A.I.C.S.: 325998
Karray Lassaad *(Mgr)*

Jasminal S.A.R.L. (2)
Rue Commandant Bejaoui Cite Taieb, Sfax,
3000, Tunisia
Tel.: (216) 74 228 001
Chemical Products Mfr
N.A.I.C.S.: 325998

Henkel Peruana S.A. (1)
Carretera Central Km 3 7, Ate-Vitarte, Lima,
Peru
Tel.: (51) 14360396
Chemical Products Mfr
N.A.I.C.S.: 325998

Henkel Philippines Inc. (1)
LSL Building Diode Street, Light Industry &
Science Park of the Philippines, Cabuyao,
4025, Laguna, Philippines
Tel.: (63) 495431088
Web Site: https://www.henkel.com
Sales Range: $50-74.9 Million
Emp.: 103
Production & Sale of Specialty Chemicals
N.A.I.C.S.: 325998

Henkel Polska Operations Sp. z o.o. (1)
ul Domaniewska 41, 02-672, Warsaw, Poland
Tel.: (48) 225656000
Adhesive Product Mfr
N.A.I.C.S.: 325520

Henkel Polybit Industries Ltd. (1)
Industrial Area - II, PO Box 5911, Dammam,
31432, Saudi Arabia
Tel.: (966) 138084061
Adhesive Product Mfr
N.A.I.C.S.: 325520

Henkel Republica Dominicana SRL (1)
Calle Haim Lopez Penha 21 Ensanche
Paraiso, Santo Domingo, Dominican Republic
Tel.: (809) 2892810
Adhesive Product Mfr
N.A.I.C.S.: 325520

Henkel S.p.A. (1)
Via G Barella No 6, 20157, Milan,
Italy (100%)
Tel.: (39) 02357921
Web Site: http://www.henkel.it
Sales Range: $125-149.9 Million
Emp.: 500
Production Sale of Detergents, Adhesives,
Cosmetics, Industrial Chemicals; Sale of
Textile Chemicals
N.A.I.C.S.: 325611

Subsidiary (Domestic):

Henkel Loctite Italia S.p.A. (2)
Via G Barella No 78 Carrella amoretti,
20157, Milan, Italy (100%)
Tel.: (39) 02357921
Web Site: http://www.henkel.it
Emp.: 68
Mfr & Distributor of Adhesives & Sealants
N.A.I.C.S.: 325520
Alberto Jackie *(Mgr-Mktg)*

Loctite Italia S.p.A. (2)
Via Barrella 6, 20157, Milan, Ferentino,
Italy (100%)
Tel.: (39) 0235792807
Web Site: http://www.henkel.it
Production & Sale of Detergents
N.A.I.C.S.: 325611

Henkel Soad Ltd. (1)
4 Arie Regev Street, PO Box 8167,
4209001, Netanya, Israel
Tel.: (972) 9 886 2600
Web Site: http://www.henkel.co.il
Sales Range: $25-49.9 Million
Emp.: 67
Chemical Products
N.A.I.C.S.: 325998

Henkel South Africa (Pty.) Ltd. (1)
4th Floor Douglas Roberts Centre 22 Skeen
Boulevard, Bedfordview, 2007, Gauteng,
South Africa (50%)
Tel.: (27) 11 617 2400
Web Site: https://www.henkel.com
Production & Sale of Industrial Chemicals,
Cosmetics, Textile & Fatty Acids Products
N.A.I.C.S.: 325998
David Berman *(Mng Dir)*

Henkel Srbija d.o.o. (1)
Bulevar Oslobodenja 383, 11040, Belgrade,
Serbia
Tel.: (381) 11 207 2200
Web Site: https://www.henkel.rs
Sales Range: $50-74.9 Million
Emp.: 130
Soap & Detergent Products Mfr
N.A.I.C.S.: 325611
Georg Grassl *(Gen Mgr)*

Plant (Domestic):

Henkel Srbija d.o.o. - Indjija Plant (2)
Save Kovacevica bb, 22000, Indija, Serbia
Tel.: (381) 22520120
Soap & Detergent Products Mfr
N.A.I.C.S.: 325611

Henkel Srbija d.o.o. - Krusevac Plant (2)
Savska 28, 37000, Krusevac, Serbia
Tel.: (381) 37 415 415
Web Site: http://www.henkel.com
Soap & Detergent Products Mfr
N.A.I.C.S.: 325611

Henkel Surface Technologies GmbH (1)
Collardinstrasse 2, 35745, Herborn,
Germany (100%)
Tel.: (49) 27779160
Web Site: http://www.henkel.com
Sales Range: $50-74.9 Million
Emp.: 120
Chemicals for Metal Finishing
N.A.I.C.S.: 325998

Unit (US):

Henkel Surface Technologies (2)
32100 Stephenson Hwy, Madison Heights,
MI 48071-5514
Tel.: (248) 583-9300
Web Site:
http://www.automotive.henkel.com
Sales Range: $125-149.9 Million
Adhesive Sealants & Surface Treatments
Mfr
N.A.I.C.S.: 325998
Keena Toth *(Mgr-Comm)*

Henkel Surface Technologies (2)
421 London Rd, Delaware, OH 43015-2493
Tel.: (614) 363-1351
Web Site: http://www.arkema-inc.com
Sales Range: $25-49.9 Million
Emp.: 46
Aviation & Performance Chemicals Mfr
N.A.I.C.S.: 325998

Henkel Sweden Operations AB (1)
Torsgatan 12, PO Box 120 33, 600 12,
Norrkoping, Sweden
Tel.: (46) 104807800
Adhesive Product Mfr
N.A.I.C.S.: 325520
Joakim Svensk *(Plant Mgr)*

Henkel Switzerland Operations AG (1)
Gosgerstrasse 81, Erlinsbach, 5015, Solothurn, Switzerland
Tel.: (41) 628441414
Adhesive Product Mfr
N.A.I.C.S.: 325520

Henkel Teroson GmbH (1)
Henkel Teroson Str 57, Heidelberg, 69123,
Germany (100%)
Tel.: (49) 62217040
Web Site: http://www.henkel.de
Sales Range: $200-249.9 Million
Emp.: 600
Plastic Materials
N.A.I.C.S.: 325211
Gegen Diaper *(Mng Dir)*

INTERNATIONAL PUBLIC

Henkel Tunisie S.A. (1)
Residence Les Jardins du Lac Imm Idriss
Les Berges du Lac 2, PO Box 419, 1053,
Tunis, Tunisia
Tel.: (216) 7 119 6120
Web Site: http://en.henkel-mea.com
Emp.: 378
Laundry & Home Care & Adhesives Technologies
N.A.I.C.S.: 325998

Henkel Ukraine TOW (1)
Saksaganskogo street 120 Europa Plaza,
01032, Kiev, Ukraine
Tel.: (380) 442475100
Web Site: http://www.henkel.ua
Soap & Detergent Products Mfr
N.A.I.C.S.: 325611
Toere Birol *(Gen Mgr)*

Henkel Venezolana S.A. (1)
Calle 2 Carretera Nacional, Guacara - San
Joaquin Zona Industrial Pruinca, Guacara,
Estado de Carabobo, Venezuela (44.9%)
Tel.: (58) 245 560 2611
Web Site: http://www.henkel.com
Sales Range: $50-74.9 Million
Emp.: 101
Production & Sale of Adhesives for the Industry & Trade, Industrial Chemicals, Products for Textile, Leather & Cosmetics Production
N.A.I.C.S.: 325520

Subsidiary (Domestic):

Henkel Loctite de Venezuela, C.A. (2)
Piso 8 Officina 85 Av Principal de Altamira
sur, Caracas, 1062, Venezuela
Tel.: (58) 2123623131
Web Site: http://www.loctite.com.ve
Adhesives Mfr & Distr
N.A.I.C.S.: 325520

Henkel Wasch- und Reinigungsmittel GmbH (1)
Henkel Strasse 67, 40589, Dusseldorf,
Germany (100%)
Tel.: (49) 2117970
Sales Range: $1-4.9 Billion
Emp.: 5,500
Personal Care Products
N.A.I.C.S.: 812199

Henkel of America Inc. (1)
1 Henkel Way, Rocky Hill, CT 06067-3581
Tel.: (610) 270-8100
Sales Range: $1-4.9 Billion
Industrial Organic Chemicals Mfr
N.A.I.C.S.: 325199
Paul R. Berry *(Sr VP, Sec & Dir)*

Subsidiary (Non-US):

Henkel Puerto Rico, Inc. (2)
Tel.: (630) 696-0610
Web Site: http://www.henkel.com
Adhesive Mfr
N.A.I.C.S.: 325520
Rosa Davila *(Dir-Ops)*

Subsidiary (Domestic):

Henkel US Operations Corporation (2)
1 Henkel Way, Rocky Hill, CT
06067-3582 (100%)
Tel.: (860) 571-5100
Web Site: http://www.henkelna.com
Industrial Chemicals, Adhesives, Resins &
Fatty Acids, Resins Derivatives, Water
Treatment Polymers Retailer & Mfr
N.A.I.C.S.: 325199
Marcy L. Tenaglia *(Sr VP-Legal)*

Subsidiary (Domestic):

Acheson Ventures, LLC (3)
405 Water St Ste200, Port Huron, MI
48060-3456
Tel.: (810) 966-0900
Web Site:
https://www.achesonventures.com
Sales Range: $250-299.9 Million
Emp.: 750
Specialty Lubricants, Chemicals & Spray
Equipment Mfr
N.A.I.C.S.: 325998

AND PRIVATE COMPANIES

HENKEL AG & CO. KGAA

Holding (Non-US):

Acheson Colloiden (4)
Rocafort 241 243, 08029, Barcelona, Spain
Tel.: (34) 933638970
Web Site: http://www.achesonindustries.com
Sales of Specialty Lubricants
N.A.I.C.S.: 425120

Acheson Colloids Company (4)
Prince Rock, Plymouth, PL4 0SP, United Kingdom
Tel.: (44) 752218788
Web Site: http://www.achesonindustries.com
Sales Range: $25-49.9 Million
Emp.: 4
Mfr & Sales of Lubricants.
N.A.I.C.S.: 324191

Acheson France S.A. (4)
ZI Ouest Rue Georges Besse, PO Box 68, 67152, Erstein, France
Tel.: (33) 388590123
Web Site: http://www.achesonindustries.com
Sales Range: $25-49.9 Million
Emp.: 40
Sales of Lubricants.
N.A.I.C.S.: 425120

Acheson Industries (Europe) Ltd. (4)
Sun Life House, 85 Queens Rd, Reading, RG1 4PT, Berks, United Kingdom
Tel.: (44) 1189588844
Web Site: http://www.achesonindustries.com
Lubricant Mfr
N.A.I.C.S.: 324191

Acheson Italiana s.r.l. (4)
Via Roma 29, Mezzago, 20050, Milan, Italy
Tel.: (39) 0039620811
Web Site: http://www.ici.com
Sales Range: $1-9.9 Million
Emp.: 7
Sales of Lubricants.
N.A.I.C.S.: 425120

Acheson do Brasil Ind. e Com Ltda. (4)
Rua Howard A Acheson Jr 279, Jardim Da Gloria, 06711 280, Cotia, SP, Brazil
Tel.: (55) 146124000
Web Site: http://www.achesonindustries.com
Mfr & Sale of Lubricants.
N.A.I.C.S.: 324191

Division (Domestic):

Henkel Corporation, Ontario (4)
Francis Industrial Park 1496 E Francis St, Ontario, CA 91761
Tel.: (909) 947-2228
Web Site: http://www.henkel.com
Sales Range: $25-49.9 Million
Emp.: 15
Inks & Coatings for Electronics Industry Mfr
N.A.I.C.S.: 325910

Holding (Non-US):

Henkel Nederland B.V., Scheemda (4)
Haven Noordzijde 6, PO BOX 1, 9679 ZD, Scheemda, Netherlands
Tel.: (31) 597670500
Sales Range: $25-49.9 Million
Emp.: 90
Lubricant Mfr
N.A.I.C.S.: 324191

Sociedad de Comercio, Acheson Colloids (4)
Ave Francisco Bilbao, Las Condes, 8268, Santiago, Chile
Tel.: (56) 22119240
Web Site: http://www.ici.com
Adhesives, Specialty Synthetic Polymers & Starches Mfr
N.A.I.C.S.: 325520

Subsidiary (Domestic):

Alterna Holdings Corp. (3)
2029 Century Park E Ste 1300, Los Angeles, CA 90067
Tel.: (310) 275-1175
Web Site: http://www.alternahaircare.com
Sales Range: $10-24.9 Million
Hair Care Products Developer & Marketer
N.A.I.C.S.: 424210
Michael Shaun Corby *(Creative Dir-Global)*

Dexter Hysol Aerospace LLC (3)
2850 Willow Pass Rd, Pittsburg, CA 94565
Tel.: (925) 458-8000
Metal Valve & Pipe Fitting Mfr
N.A.I.C.S.: 332919

Dial International, Inc. (3)
271a Crossway Rd, Tallahassee, FL 32305
Tel.: (480) 754-3425
Sales Range: $25-49.9 Million
Emp.: 10
Soap Mfr
N.A.I.C.S.: 325611

Emerson & Cuming (3)
869 Washington St, Canton, MA 02021-2592
Tel.: (978) 436-9700
Sales Range: $50-74.9 Million
Emp.: 210
Polymer Designer & Mfr
N.A.I.C.S.: 325520
Carolyn Sutton *(Mgr-Credit & Collections)*

Branch (Non-US):

Emerson & Cuming (4)
Berga Alle 1, S 254 52, Helsingborg, Sweden
Tel.: (46) 42200986
Sales Range: $25-49.9 Million
Emp.: 1
Mfr of Electrical & Engineering Materials.
N.A.I.C.S.: 335999

Henkel Electronics Materials N.V. (4)
Nijverheidsstraat 7, Westerlo, B 2260, Belgium
Tel.: (32) 014575611
Web Site: http://www.henkel-adhesives.com
Adhesive Mfr
N.A.I.C.S.: 325520

Subsidiary (Domestic):

Henkel Adhesives Corporation (3)
25817 Clawiter Rd, Hayward, CA 94545-3217 (100%)
Tel.: (510) 786-3700
Web Site: http://www.henkeladhesives.com
Sales Range: $25-49.9 Million
Emp.: 35
Mfr of Adhesives
N.A.I.C.S.: 325520

Subsidiary (Domestic):

Henkel Consumer Adhesives, Inc. (4)
26235 1st St, Westlake, OH 44145
Tel.: (866) 591-2178
Developer & Marketer of Home & Office Repair & Adhesive Products
N.A.I.C.S.: 322220
John Kahl *(CEO)*

Loctite Puerto Rico, Inc. (4)
PO Box 669, Sabana Grande, PR 00637-0669 (100%)
Tel.: (787) 873-6500
Web Site: http://www.loctite.com
Adhesives & Sealants
N.A.I.C.S.: 325520
Rosa Davila *(Gen Mgr)*

Resin Technology Group LLC (4)
28 Norfolk Ave, South Easton, MA 02375-1907
Tel.: (508) 230-8070
Adhesive Mfr
N.A.I.C.S.: 325520

Sovereign Specialty Chemicals, Inc. (4)
2200 Renaissance Blvd Ste 200, King of Prussia, PA 19406-2755
Tel.: (312) 223-7970
Web Site: http://www.sovereignsc.com
Developer, Producer & Distributor of Adhesives, Sealants & Coatings
N.A.I.C.S.: 325520

Subsidiary (Domestic):

Henkel Technologies (5)
6315 Wiehe Rd, Cincinnati, OH 45237-4213
Tel.: (513) 351-1300
Web Site: http://www.imperialadhesives.com
Rev.: $40,000,000
Emp.: 8

Mfr of Industrial Adhesives
N.A.I.C.S.: 325520

Sovereign Specialty Chemicals (5)
123 W Bartges St, Akron, OH 44311-1034
Tel.: (330) 374-2900
Rev.: $30,000,000
Emp.: 104
Mfr of Adhesives & Sealants
N.A.I.C.S.: 325520

Subsidiary (Domestic):

Henkel Consumer Goods Inc. (3)
7201 E Henkel Way, Scottsdale, AZ 85255
Tel.: (480) 754-3425
Web Site: http://www.henkel-northamerica.com
Emp.: 550
Consumer Products Mfr; Beauty Care, Laundry & Home Care Products Mfr
N.A.I.C.S.: 325611
Valerie Pochron *(Asst Gen Counsel)*

Henkel Consumer Goods, Inc. (3)
200 Elm St, Stamford, CT 06902-3800 (100%)
Tel.: (475) 210-0230
Web Site: http://www.henkelna.com
Sales Range: $50-74.9 Million
Emp.: 50
Personal Care Products
N.A.I.C.S.: 325620
Frank Steinert *(Sr VP & Head-HR-North America)*

Henkel Electronic Materials LLC (3)
14000 Jamboree Rd, Irvine, CA 92606
Tel.: (714) 368-8000
Web Site: http://www.henkel.com
Emp.: 180
Printed Circuit Assembly Mfr
N.A.I.C.S.: 334418
Neil Poole *(CFO)*

Henkel Laboratories (3)
20021 Susana Rd, Rancho Dominguez, CA 90221
Tel.: (310) 764-4600
Web Site: http://www.henkel.com
Sales Range: $50-74.9 Million
Emp.: 170
Electronic & Engineering Materials Mfr
N.A.I.C.S.: 325520

Subsidiary (Non-US):

Ablestik Malaysia (4)
Lot 8 And 10 Jalan Tukul 16 5, 40000, Shah Alam, Selangor Darul Ehsan, Malaysia
Tel.: (60) 355191105
Sales Range: $25-49.9 Million
Emp.: 100
Electronic & Engineering Materials
N.A.I.C.S.: 335999

Henkel Ablestik Korea Ltd. (4)
Dae Ryung Techno Town II 6th Floor Gasan-dong, Kumchun-gu, Seoul, 569-21, Korea (South)
Tel.: (82) 66758000
Mfr of Electronic & Engineering Products
N.A.I.C.S.: 335999

Henkel Ltd., Linton (4)
Premier House, Station Road, Linton, CB21 4NW, Cambridgeshire, United Kingdom
Tel.: (44) 1223 893771
Web Site: http://www.henkel.com
Sales Range: $25-49.9 Million
Emp.: 30
Semi-Conductive Adhesives Mfr
N.A.I.C.S.: 325520

Division (Domestic):

Henkel US Operations Corporation - TCLAD Division (3)
1600 Orrin Rd, Prescott, WI 54021-2000
Tel.: (715) 262-5898
Insulated Metal Substrate Mfr
N.A.I.C.S.: 334419

Subsidiary (Domestic):

HenkelOrbseal (3)
201 Hwy 10 E, Richmond, MO 64085
Tel.: (816) 776-5024
Web Site: https://www.henkel-northamerica.com

Sales Range: $125-149.9 Million
Emp.: 300
Automotive Sealants & Adhesives
N.A.I.C.S.: 325520
Brad Holder *(Plant Mgr)*

Kenra Professional, LLC (3)
5800 Bristol Pkwy 7th Fl, Culver City, CA 90230-7600
Tel.: (317) 356-6491
Web Site: http://www.kenraprofessional.com
Professional Hair Care Products Developer, Mfr & Distr
N.A.I.C.S.: 325620
Jen Norman *(VP-Sls & Bus Dev)*

Magna-Tech Manufacturing Corporation (3)
3416 S Hoyt Ave, Muncie, IN 47302-2081
Tel.: (765) 284-5050
Web Site: http://www.loctiteimpregnation.com
Sales Range: $1-9.9 Million
Emp.: 110
Metal Coating, Engraving (except Jewelry & Silverware) & Allied Services to Mfr
N.A.I.C.S.: 332812
Chris Russell *(VP-Sls & Mktg)*

Sexy Hair Concepts, LLC (3)
21551 Prairie St, Chatsworth, CA 91311
Tel.: (818) 435-0800
Web Site: http://www.sexyhair.com
Hair Care Products Designer & Marketer
N.A.I.C.S.: 424210
Mark Milner *(CFO)*

Sonderhoff USA LLC (3)
1895 Big Timber Rd Unit B, Elgin, IL 60123
Tel.: (847) 888-1110
Polymer Sealing & Potting System Mfr
N.A.I.C.S.: 325520

Sovereign Chemicals Company (3)
4040 Embassy Pkwy Ste 190, Akron, OH 44333
Tel.: (330) 542-8400
Web Site: http://www.henkel.com
Chemical & Allied Products Merchant Whslr
N.A.I.C.S.: 424690

The Bergquist Company (3)
18930 W 78th St, Chanhassen, MN 55317
Tel.: (952) 835-2322
Web Site: http://www.henkel.com
Sales Range: $150-199.9 Million
Emp.: 1,000
Thermal-Management Solutions for Electronics Industry
N.A.I.C.S.: 334419
Terry Solberg *(Dir-Product Mgmt)*

Plant (Domestic):

The Bergquist Company - Cannon Falls Facility (4)
301 Washington St W, Cannon Falls, MN 55009
Tel.: (507) 263-3766
Web Site: http://www.bergquistcompany.com
Thermal Management Materials Mfr
N.A.I.C.S.: 334419

Subsidiary (Non-US):

The Bergquist Company GmbH (4)
Verbindungsweg 42, 25469, Halstenbek, Germany (100%)
Tel.: (49) 4101 8030
Web Site: http://www.bergquistcompany.eu
Sales Range: $10-24.9 Million
Emp.: 25
Thermal-Management Solutions for Electronics Industry
N.A.I.C.S.: 334419
Peter Schuett *(Mgr-Inside Sls)*

The Bergquist Company Korea, Ltd. (4)
Dongil Techno Town #5303 202-6 Anyang 7 Dong, Manan-gu, Anyang, 430-817, Gyeonggi-do, Korea (South)
Tel.: (82) 31 448 0382
Web Site: http://www.bergquistcompany.co.kr
Sales Range: $10-24.9 Million
Emp.: 22
Thermal Management Materials Mfr
N.A.I.C.S.: 334419

HENKEL AG & CO. KGAA

Henkel AG & Co. KGaA—(Continued)

The Bergquist Company Shenzhen Ltd. (4)
Room 401-1 Type A Block E4 TCL Science Park No 1001, Zhongshan Park Road Xili Nanshan District Heao Henggang Long-gang, Shenzhen, 518055, China
Tel.: (86) 75533209328
Adhesive Product Mfr
N.A.I.C.S.: 325520

The Bergquist Company Zhuhai Ltd. (4)
Block 1 No 524 Anji East Road Jin Wan Qu, Sanzao Town, Zhuhai, 519040, Guang-dong, China
Tel.: (86) 7567683388
Adhesive Product Mfr
N.A.I.C.S.: 325520

Subsidiary (Domestic):

Tweezerman International (3)
2 Tri Harbor Ct, Port Washington, NY 11050-4617
Tel.: (516) 676-7772
Web Site: https://www.tweezerman.com
Sales Range: $75-99.9 Million
Emp.: 175
Grooming & Beauty Products
N.A.I.C.S.: 423850
Juergen Bosse *(Pres & CEO)*

Zotos International, Inc. (3)
100 Tokeneke Rd, Darien, CT 06820
Tel.: (203) 655-8911
Web Site: http://www.zotos.com
Beauty Aid Products Mfr & Distr
N.A.I.C.S.: 325620
Jodi Cioffi *(Sr Mgr-Comm)*

Subsidiary (Domestic):

Joico Laboratories Inc. (4)
488 E Santa Clara Ste 301, Arcadia, CA 91006
Tel.: (626) 321-4100
Web Site: http://www.joico.com
Sales Range: $50-74.9 Million
Salon Products & Services
N.A.I.C.S.: 325620
Angelia Polsinelli *(Sr Dir-North American Education)*

Henkel-Storitve d.o.o. (1)
Industrijska Ulica 23, 2000, Maribor, Slovenia
Tel.: (386) 2 222 25 31
Emp.: 42
Adhesive Mfr
N.A.I.C.S.: 325520
Gregor Majcen *(Gen Mgr)*

Indola GmbH (1)
Hohenzollernring 127, Hamburg, 22763, Germany
Tel.: (49) 40882403
Web Site: http://www.indola.com
Cosmetic Products Mfr & Distr
N.A.I.C.S.: 325620

OOO Henkel Rus (1)
Business center Europe House Kolokolnikov pereulok 11, 107045, Moscow, Russia
Tel.: (7) 4957455588
Detergent & Laundry Products Mfr
N.A.I.C.S.: 325611

Subsidiary (Domestic):

OOO Henkel Bautechnik (2)
Krasnoarmeyskaya Building 1A, 140413, Kolomna, Russia
Tel.: (7) 496 615 2444
Adhesive Mfr
N.A.I.C.S.: 325520

Persil-Altersunterstutzung GmbH (1)
Erdbergstrasse 29, Vienna, 1030, Austria
Tel.: (43) 171104421
Investment Management Service
N.A.I.C.S.: 523999
Gunter Thumser *(Mng Dir)*

Piidea Canada Ltd. (1)
2515 Meadowpine Blvd, Mississauga, L5N 6C3, ON, Canada
Salon Operator
N.A.I.C.S.: 812112

Pritt Produktionsgesellschaft GmbH (1)
Sichelstrasse 1, 30453, Hannover, Germany (100%)
Tel.: (49) 51121400
Web Site: http://www.henkel.com
Sales Range: $50-74.9 Million
Emp.: 200
Plastic Materials
N.A.I.C.S.: 325211
Frank Peekhaus *(Mng Dir)*

Purbond AG (1)
Industriestrasse 17a, 6203, Sempach, Switzerland
Tel.: (41) 41 469 68 60
Wood Component Engineering Services
N.A.I.C.S.: 541330
Walter Stampfli *(Gen Mgr)*

Roof Care Co. (1)
PO Box 1813, Umm al-Quwain, United Arab Emirates
Tel.: (971) 6 767 0666
Web Site: https://www.roof-care.com
Water Proofing Product Mfr
N.A.I.C.S.: 325510

Schwarzkopf & Henkel GmbH (1)
Henkelstrasse 67, 40589, Dusseldorf, Germany
Tel.: (49) 211790
Web Site: http://www.schwarzkopf.com
Emp.: 530
Beauty Care Services
N.A.I.C.S.: 812112

Subsidiary (Non-US):

Schwarzkopf & Henkel K.K. (2)
Sphere Tower Tennoz 2-2-8 Higashi-Shinagawa, Shinagawa-ku, Tokyo, 140-0002, Japan (49%)
Tel.: (81) 35 783 2075
Web Site: https://www.schwarzkopf-henkel.jp
Sales Range: $25-49.9 Million
Emp.: 50
Production & Sale of Dentifrice & Synthetic Detergents, Shoe Specialty Chemicals
N.A.I.C.S.: 325611

Subsidiary (Domestic):

Schwarzkopf & Henkel Production Management GmbH (2)
Henkelstr 67, Dusseldorf, 40589, Germany
Tel.: (49) 2117972000
Business Management Consulting Services
N.A.I.C.S.: 541611

Subsidiary (Non-US):

Schwarzkopf S.A. (2)
161 Rue De Silly, 92100, Boulogne-Billancourt, France
Tel.: (33) 1 46 84 98 98
Beauty Care Services
N.A.I.C.S.: 812112

Subsidiary (US):

Schwarzkopf, Inc. (2)
600 Corporate Pointe Ste 1100, Culver City, CA 90230
Tel.: (310) 641-4600
Sales Range: $50-74.9 Million
Hair Care Products Mfr
N.A.I.C.S.: 325620
Hans Van Bylen *(Exec VP)*

Seal for Life Industries, LLC (1)
Gasselterstraat 20, Stadskanaal, 9503 JB, Groningen, Netherlands
Tel.: (31) 599696170
Emp.: 380
Industrial Chemicals & Machinery & Equipment Whslr
N.A.I.C.S.: 423330

Subsidiary (US):

Highland International, Inc. (2)
PO Box 3564, Boone, NC 28607
Tel.: (828) 265-2513
Web Site: http://www.highland-international.com
Paint, Varnish & Supplies Whslr
N.A.I.C.S.: 424950
Joel White *(Founder & Pres)*

Lifelast Inc. (2)
2119 SE Columbia Way Ste 280, Vancouver, WA 98661-8037
Tel.: (360) 254-0563
Web Site: http://www.lifelast.com
Plastics Material & Resin Mfr
N.A.I.C.S.: 325211
Stan Buratto *(Pres)*

U.S. Coatings LLC (2)
2355 Weldon Pkwy, Saint Louis, MO 63146
Tel.: (314) 205-1500
Web Site: http://www.uscoatings.com
Spice & Extract Mfr
N.A.I.C.S.: 311942
Janet McKemie *(Office Mgr)*

Sonderhoff (Suzhou) Sealing System Co., Ltd. (1)
No 1 Lansheng Road Suzhou Industrial Park, Suzhou, 215126, China
Tel.: (86) 51282272800
Polymer Sealing & Potting System Mfr
N.A.I.C.S.: 325520

Sonderhoff Chemicals GmbH (1)
Richard-Byrd-Strasse 26, 50829, Cologne, Germany
Tel.: (49) 221956850
Polymer Sealing & Potting System Mfr
N.A.I.C.S.: 325520

Sonderhoff Engineering GmbH (1)
Dr Walter Zumtobel Strasse 15, 6850, Dornbirn, Austria
Tel.: (43) 5572398810
Polymer Sealing & Potting System Mfr
N.A.I.C.S.: 325520

Sonderhoff Holding GmbH (1)
Richard-Byrd-Strasse 26, 50829, Cologne, Germany
Tel.: (49) 221956850
Web Site: http://www.sonderhoff.com
Polymer Sealing & Potting System Mfr
N.A.I.C.S.: 325520
Kai Ethner *(Mng Dir)*

Sonderhoff Italia S.r.l. (1)
Via della Foppa 2/5, 23848, Oggiono, Italy
Tel.: (39) 034126551
Polymer Sealing & Potting System Mfr
N.A.I.C.S.: 325520

Sonderhoff Polymer-Services Austria GmbH (1)
Allgaustrasse 3, 6912, Horbranz, Austria
Tel.: (43) 5572398810902
Polymer Sealing & Potting System Mfr
N.A.I.C.S.: 325520

Sonderhoff Services GmbH (1)
Mathias-Bruggen-Strasse 124-128, 50829, Cologne, Germany
Tel.: (49) 2219565260
Polymer Sealing & Potting System Mfr
N.A.I.C.S.: 325520

Thera Cosmetic GmbH (1)
Henkelstrasse 67, 40589, Dusseldorf, Germany (100%)
Tel.: (49) 2117970
Sales Range: $1-4.9 Billion
Emp.: 6,000
Cosmetic & Hygienic Soaps
N.A.I.C.S.: 325611

Turk Henkel Kimya Sanayi ve Ticaret A.S. (1)
Fatih Sultan Mehmet Mah Poligon Cad, No 8 Buyaka Iki Sitesi C Blok Kat 10-14 Tepeustu Umraniye, 34771, Istanbul, Turkiye
Tel.: (90) 2165794000
Web Site: https://www.henkel.com.tr
Production & Sale of Detergents
N.A.I.C.S.: 325611

Union Tecnico Comercial S.R.L. (1)
Los Telares 239 Vulcano-Ate, Lima, 15012, Peru
Tel.: (51) 16129600
Web Site: http://www.utecotec.com
Emp.: 50
Electricity & Gas Distribution Services
N.A.I.C.S.: 213112
Harry Braun *(Pres)*

HENKELHAUSEN GMBH & CO. KG

INTERNATIONAL PUBLIC

Hafenstrasse 51, 47809, Krefeld, Germany
Tel.: (49) 2151 574 0 De
Web Site: http://www.henkelhausen.de
Diesel & Gas Engine Sales & Services
N.A.I.C.S.: 423120
Lutz Goebel *(Mng Dir)*

HENNEO MEDIA, SA

Paseo de la Independencia 29, 50001, Zaragoza, Spain
Tel.: (34) 976 765 000 ES
Web Site: http://www.henneo.com
Year Founded: 1895
Broadcasting Media Services
N.A.I.C.S.: 516120
Ignacio Martinez de Albornoz *(Head-Corp Dev)*

Subsidiaries:

Heraldo de Aragon SA (1)
Paseo Independencia 29, 50001, Zaragoza, Spain
Tel.: (34) 976 76 50 00
Web Site: http://www.heraldo.es
Newspapers
N.A.I.C.S.: 513110
Pilar De Yarza *(Pres)*

Subsidiary (Domestic):

20 Minutos Espana S.L. (2)
Condesa de Venadito 1 2 Planta, Madrid, 28027, Spain
Tel.: (34) 91 701 56 00
Web Site: http://www.20minutos.es
Newspaper Printing & Publishing Services
N.A.I.C.S.: 513110
Hector Maria Benito *(Dir-Ops)*

HENNGE K.K.

Daiwa Shibuya Square 16-28 Nanpeidai-Cho, Shibuya-Ku, Tokyo, 150-0036, Japan
Tel.: (81) 364153660
Web Site: https://www.hennge.com
Year Founded: 1996
4475—(TKS)
Rev.: $48,041,840
Assets: $44,631,550
Liabilities: $27,509,200
Net Worth: $17,122,350
Earnings: $3,608,810
Fiscal Year-end: 09/30/23
Software Development Services
N.A.I.C.S.: 541511
Kazuhiro Ogura *(CEO)*

HENRY BOOT PLC

4 Charles Street Isaacs Building, Sheffield, S1 2HS, United Kingdom
Tel.: (44) 1142555444 UK
Web Site:
https://www.henryboot.co.uk
BOOT—(LSE)
Rev.: $313,087,517
Assets: $694,929,974
Liabilities: $212,551,066
Net Worth: $482,378,908
Earnings: $41,627,695
Emp.: 496
Fiscal Year-end: 12/31/21
Holding Company; Land Development, Commercial Construction & Property Management Services
N.A.I.C.S.: 551112
E. Jamie Boot *(Chm)*

Subsidiaries:

Banner Plant Limited (1)
Isaacs Building 4 Charles Street, Sheffield, S1 2HS, United Kingdom (100%)
Tel.: (44) 1246299400
Web Site: https://www.bannerplant.co.uk
Sales Range: $50-74.9 Million
Emp.: 90
Mechanical Plant & Power Tool Sales & Rental

AND PRIVATE COMPANIES

N.A.I.C.S.: 423810
Jon Fisher *(Mng Dir)*

First National Housing Trust Limited (1)
Banner Cross Hall Ecclesall Road South, Sheffield, S11 9PD, United Kingdom (100%)
Tel.: (44) 114 255 5444
Web Site: http://www.henryboot.co.uk
Sales Range: $25-49.9 Million
Emp.: 45
Real Estate Development Services
N.A.I.C.S.: 531390

HENRY BOOT 'K' LTD (1)
Tel.: (44) 1142555444
Sales Range: $25-49.9 Million
Emp.: 40
Property Development Services
N.A.I.C.S.: 531312

Hallam Land Management Limited (1)
Isaacs Building 4 Charles Street, Sheffield, S1 2HS, United Kingdom (100%)
Tel.: (44) 1142555444
Web Site: https://www.hallamland.co.uk
Real Estate Development Services
N.A.I.C.S.: 531390
Nick Duckworth *(Mng Dir)*

Henry Boot Construction (UK) Limited (1)
Callywhite Lane, Dronfield, S18 2XN, Derbyshire, United Kingdom (100%)
Tel.: (44) 124 641 0111
Web Site: https://www.henrybootconstruction.co.uk
Sales Range: $50-74.9 Million
Emp.: 250
Construction Services
N.A.I.C.S.: 236210

Henry Boot Developments Limited (1)
Floors 5-7 Isaacs Building Charles Street, Sheffield, S1 2HS, United Kingdom (100%)
Tel.: (44) 1143504477
Web Site: https://hbd.co.uk
Sales Range: $50-74.9 Million
Emp.: 60
Real Estate Development Services
N.A.I.C.S.: 531390
Ed Hutchinson *(Mng Dir)*

Henry Boot Estates Limited (1)
Banner Cross Hall, Sheffield, S11 9PD, United Kingdom (100%)
Tel.: (44) 1142555444
Web Site: http://www.hallamland.co.uk
Real Estate Development Services
N.A.I.C.S.: 531390

Henry Boot Projects Limited (1)
Banner Cross Hall Ecclesall Road South, Sheffield, S11 9PD, United Kingdom
Tel.: (44) 1142555444
Property Development Services
N.A.I.C.S.: 531312
Edward Boot *(Mng Dir)*

Henry Boot Tamworth Limited (1)
Banner Cross Hall Ecclesall Road South, Sheffield, S11 9PD, United Kingdom
Tel.: (44) 1142555444
Web Site: https://www.henryboot.co.uk
Real Estate Development Services
N.A.I.C.S.: 531390

Road Link (A69) Limited (1)
Stocksfield Hall, Stocksfield, NE43 7TN, Northumberland, United Kingdom
Tel.: (44) 1661842842
Sales Range: $50-74.9 Million
Emp.: 5
Property Development Services
N.A.I.C.S.: 531390

St John's Manchester Limited (1)
Bonded Warehouse 18 Lower Byrom Street, Manchester, M3 4AP, United Kingdom
Tel.: (44) 1618348640
Web Site: https://www.stjohnsmanchester.com
Property Development Services
N.A.I.C.S.: 531390

HENRY HEYINK CONSTRUCTION LTD.
275 Colborne St, PO Box 1341, Chatham, N7M 5R9, ON, Canada
Tel.: (519) 354-4593
Web Site: https://www.heyink.on.ca
Year Founded: 1979
Rev.: $13,131,663
Emp.: 45
General Contracting & Building Construction Services
N.A.I.C.S.: 236220
Henry Heyink *(Pres)*

HENRY LAMOTTE GMBH
Merkurstrasse 47, Bremen, 28197, Germany
Tel.: (49) 4215239470 De
Web Site: http://www.lamotte.de
Year Founded: 1925
Sales Range: $125-149.9 Million
Emp.: 200
Holding Company; Food & Oil Products Mfr, Processor, Packager & Whslr
N.A.I.C.S.: 551112
Otto Lamotte *(Mng Dir-Oils Div)*

Subsidiaries:

Henry Lamotte Food GmbH (1)
Merkurstrasse 47, D-28197, Bremen, Germany
Tel.: (49) 4215239470
Web Site: http://www.lamotte-food.de
Sales Range: $50-74.9 Million
Emp.: 60
Frozen Fruit, Vegetable & Fish Packaging & Whslr; Ethnic Food Specialties & Ingredients Mfr & Distr
N.A.I.C.S.: 311411
Henry Lamotte *(Mng Dir)*

Henry Lamotte Oils GmbH (1)
Merkurstrasse 47, 28197, Bremen, Germany
Tel.: (49) 4215239460
Sales Range: $25-49.9 Million
Emp.: 100
Oils, Fats, Waxes & Related Specialties Mfr
N.A.I.C.S.: 311225
Otto Lamotte *(Mng Dir)*

Henry Lamotte SERVICES GmbH (1)
Merkurstrasse 47, 28197, Bremen, Germany
Tel.: (49) 4215239480
Web Site: http://www.lamotte-services.de
Emp.: 70
Natural Oil Mfr
N.A.I.C.S.: 111120
Harald Schiff *(Mng Dir)*

HENSALL DISTRICT CO-OPERATIVE, INC.
1 Davidson Dr, Hensall, ON, Canada
Tel.: (519) 262-3002
Web Site: https://hensallco-op.ca
Emp.: 100
Animal Nutrition, Freight Forwarding, Logistics & Crop Services
N.A.I.C.S.: 111998
Brad Chandler *(CEO)*

Subsidiaries:

Gentec Inc. (1)
1955 Grandview Dr N, Twin Falls, ID 83301
Tel.: (208) 734-6604
Rev.: $1,100,000
Emp.: 13
Research & Development in Biotechnology
N.A.I.C.S.: 541714

HENSOLDT AG
Willy-Messerschmitt-Strasse 3, 82024, Taufkirchen, Germany
Tel.: (49) 89515180 De
Web Site: https://www.hensoldt.net
Year Founded: 2017
HAG—(DEU)
Rev.: $2,038,856,386

Assets: $3,929,793,576
Liabilities: $3,020,200,906
Net Worth: $909,592,670
Earnings: $61,816,978
Emp.: 6,907
Fiscal Year-end: 12/31/23
Defence & Security Sensor Solution Services
N.A.I.C.S.: 561621
Johannes P. Huth *(Chm)*

Subsidiaries:

Antycip Iberica SL (1)
Planta 1 - Oficina S14 Ctra BV-1274 Km 1, 08225, Terrassa, Barcelona, Spain
Tel.: (34) 937001451
Microelectronic & Electronic Testing Product Mfr
N.A.I.C.S.: 334419

Antycip Technologies S.A.S. (1)
9 Rue du Perou, 91300, Massy, France
Tel.: (33) 170260825
Web Site: http://www.antycip.com
Microelectronic & Electronic Testing Product Mfr
N.A.I.C.S.: 334419

EuroAvionics Schweiz AG (1)
Gerbegasslein 1, 4450, Sissach, Switzerland
Tel.: (41) 612611009
Aircraft Flight Instrument Mfr
N.A.I.C.S.: 334511

EuroAvionics US Holdco. Inc. (1)
2480 Fruitville Rd, Sarasota, FL 34237
Tel.: (941) 306-1328
Aircraft Flight Instrument Mfr
N.A.I.C.S.: 334511

HENSOLDT Cyber GmbH (1)
Willy-Messerschmitt-Strasse 3, 82024, Taufkirchen, Germany
Tel.: (49) 89515181871
Web Site: https://www.hensoldt-cyber.com
Information Technology Services
N.A.I.C.S.: 541511
Marian Rachow *(Mng Dir)*

HENSOLDT Holding Germany GmbH (1)
Willy-Messerschmitt-Strasse 3, 82024, Taufkirchen, Germany
Tel.: (49) 89515180
Web Site: http://www.hensoldt.net
Holding Company
N.A.I.C.S.: 551112
Jack Artman *(VP & Head-M&A)*

Subsidiary (Domestic):

EuroAvionics GmbH (2)
Karlsruher Strasse 91, 75179, Pforzheim, Germany
Tel.: (49) 72 31 58 678 0
Web Site: http://www.euroavionics.com
Aircraft Equipment Distr
N.A.I.C.S.: 423860

Subsidiary (US):

EuroAvionics USA LLC (3)
2480 Fruitville Rd, Sarasota, FL 34237
Tel.: (941) 306-1328
Web Site: http://www.euroavionicsusa.com
Aircraft Engineering Services
N.A.I.C.S.: 488190
Raymond Toves *(Founder & CEO)*

Subsidiary (Non-US):

Kelvin Hughes Limited (2)
Voltage 6 Mollison Avenue, Enfield, EN3 7XQ, United Kingdom
Tel.: (44) 1992805200
Web Site: https://uk.hensoldt.net
Naval & Maritime Navigational Radar & Systems
N.A.I.C.S.: 334511
Russell Gould *(CEO)*

Subsidiary (Non-US):

A/S Kelvin Hughes (3)
World Trade Center Borupvang 3, 2750, Ballerup, Denmark
Tel.: (45) 86112888
Web Site: http://www.kelvinhughes.com

HENSOLDT AG

Marine Navigation Equipment Mfr
N.A.I.C.S.: 334511

Kelvin Hughes (Nederland) B.V. (3)
Tel.: (31) 104724050
Web Site: http://www.kelvinhughes.com
Navigational Equipment
N.A.I.C.S.: 334511
Bruce N. de Bies *(Bus Mgr)*

Kelvin Hughes (Singapore) Pte. Ltd. (3)
20 Harbour Drive #07-07 PSA Vista, Singapore, 117612, Singapore
Tel.: (65) 6331 4268
Web Site: http://www.kelvinhughes.com
Marine Navigation Equipment
N.A.I.C.S.: 334511

Subsidiary (Non-US):

Nexeya SAS (2)
Centrale Parc Bat 2 Avenue Sully Prudhomme, 92298, Chatenay-Malabry, Cedex, France
Tel.: (33) 1 41 87 30 00
Web Site: http://www.nexeya.com
Sales Range: $125-149.9 Million
Emp.: 887
Holding Company; Industrial Engineering Services & Products Mfr
N.A.I.C.S.: 551112
Philippe Gautier *(CEO)*

Subsidiary (Domestic):

Nexeya France SAS (3)
6 rue des Freresw Boude, BP 70439, ZI Thibaud, 31104, Toulouse, Cedex 1, France
Tel.: (33) 5 6143 5800
Web Site: http://www.nexeya-france-sas.com
Industrial Engineering Services & Products Mfr
N.A.I.C.S.: 334511

HENSOLDT Optronics (Pty) Ltd. (1)
Denel Office Park Nellmapius Drive, Irene, 0157, South Africa
Tel.: (27) 126740215
Aviation & Aerospace Product Mfr
N.A.I.C.S.: 336411

HENSOLDT Optronics GmbH (1)
Carl-Zeiss-Strasse 22, 73447, Oberkochen, Germany
Tel.: (49) 736495570
Aviation & Aerospace Product Mfr
N.A.I.C.S.: 336411

HENSOLDT Private Ltd. (1)
The Hive 4th Floor VR Bengaluru No 11B Sy No 40/9 Devasandra, Industrial Area Second Stage KR Puram Hobli, Bengaluru, 560048, India
Tel.: (91) 7760989500
Aviation & Aerospace Product Mfr
N.A.I.C.S.: 336411

HENSOLDT Sensors GmbH (1)
Willy-Messerschmitt-Strasse 3, 82024, Taufkirchen, Germany
Tel.: (49) 89515180
Aviation & Aerospace Product Mfr
N.A.I.C.S.: 336411

HENSOLDT do Brasil Seguranca e Defesa Electronica e Optica Ltda (1)
Rua Joaquim Floriano 466 conjunto 1715 Edificio Brascan Century Office, Itaim Bibi, Sao Paulo, 04534-002, Brazil
Tel.: (55) 1155555421
Aviation & Aerospace Product Mfr
N.A.I.C.S.: 336411

Hensoldt Australia Pty Ltd (1)
Unit 4 50 Collie St, Fyshwick, 2609, ACT, Australia
Tel.: (61) 262594400
Aviation & Aerospace Product Mfr
N.A.I.C.S.: 336411

Hensoldt France S.A.S. (1)
115 avenue de Dreux ZAC Sainte-Apolline, 78970, Plaisir, France
Tel.: (33) 180829250
Aviation & Aerospace Product Mfr
N.A.I.C.S.: 336411

Hensoldt Singapore Pte Ltd. (1)
10 Kallang Avenue 09-14 Aperia Tower 2,

HENSOLDT AG

HENSOLDT AG—(Continued)
Singapore, 339510, Singapore
Tel.: (65) 63314268
Aviation & Aerospace Product Mfr
N.A.I.C.S.: 336411

Hensoldt Space Consulting S.A.S. (1)
1 Rond-Point du General Eisenhower Golf Park Batiment F, 31100, Toulouse, France
Tel.: (33) 531224300
Web Site: https://en.hensoldt-space-consulting.com
Emp.: 20
Engineering Consulting Services
N.A.I.C.S.: 541330
Nicolas Mayordomo *(CEO)*

Midi Ingenierie S.A.S. (1)
Golf Park Building F 1 Roundabout of General Eisenhower, 31100, Toulouse, France
Tel.: (33) 561399618
Web Site: https://www.midi-ingenierie.com
Integrated Electronic Component Mfr
N.A.I.C.S.: 334111

Nexeya Canada Inc. (1)
400 Alden Road, Markham, L3R 4C1, ON, Canada
Tel.: (905) 475-2607
Web Site:
 https://www.nexeyatesolutions.com
Aviation & Aerospace Product Mfr
N.A.I.C.S.: 336411

Nexeya USA Inc. (1)
241 Rudoph Dr, Beaufort, NC 28516
Tel.: (252) 723-9191
Aviation & Aerospace Product Mfr
N.A.I.C.S.: 336411

Penser Maitriser Technicite Logistique - P.M.T.L S.A.S. (1)
Chemin Grand, 32430, Cologne, France
Tel.: (33) 562067275
Web Site: http://www.pmtl.fr
Emp.: 55
Aviation & Aerospace Product Mfr
N.A.I.C.S.: 336411

HENZETEAM GMBH

Im Schwenkrain 8, 70376, Stuttgart, Germany
Tel.: (49) 711518200
Web Site: http://www.henze.de
Rev.: $26,528,736
Emp.: 35
Logistic Services
N.A.I.C.S.: 541614
Ernst V. Bock *(Mng Dir)*

HEP TECH CO., LTD.

No 20 Jingke 7th Rd, Nantun Dist, Taichung, 408, Taiwan
Tel.: (886) 435009325
Web Site: http://www.hepgroup.net
Year Founded: 2002
3609—(TPE)
Rev.: $20,455,966
Assets: $37,797,147
Liabilities: $26,184,472
Net Worth: $11,612,675
Earnings: ($6,614,147)
Emp.: 500
Fiscal Year-end: 12/31/23
Electronic Parts Mfr
N.A.I.C.S.: 334419
Jui-Chien Chen *(Chm)*

Subsidiaries:

HEP GmbH (1)
Ramsloh 10, 58579, Schalksmuhle, Germany
Tel.: (49) 23 555 0919
Web Site: https://www.hepgmbh.de
Electronic Lighting Component Mfr
N.A.I.C.S.: 335132

HEPAHOPE KOREA, INC.

9Floor CCMM Building 12 Yeouido-Dong, Seoul, 150-860, Youngdeungpo-Gu, Korea (South)
Tel.: (82) 27861474
Web Site: http://www.hepahope.co.kr
Sales Range: $1-9.9 Million
Emp.: 12
Artificial Liver, Related Products & Medical Device Mfr
N.A.I.C.S.: 325414
Seong Su Park *(CEO)*

HEPCO HEAVY EQUIPMENT PRODUCTION COMPANY

No 102 Somaye Ave, PO Box 15872-1814, Tehran, Iran
Tel.: (98) 21 88303820
Web Site: http://www.hepcoir.com
Construction Machinery Mfr
N.A.I.C.S.: 333120

HEPHAESTUS HOLDINGS LIMITED

Flat A-G 15/F 15 Chong Yip Street Kwun Tong, Kowloon, China (Hong Kong)
Tel.: (852) 27639980   Ky
Web Site:
 http://www.unionasiahk.com
8173—(HKG)
Rev.: $6,671,491
Assets: $7,617,430
Liabilities: $1,445,995
Net Worth: $6,171,435
Earnings: $535,396
Emp.: 59
Fiscal Year-end: 03/31/22
Holding Company
N.A.I.C.S.: 551112
Alex Kam-fai Lee *(Exec Dir)*

HEPITES SA

Str Henri Coanda Nr 5, Galati, Romania
Tel.: (40) 236 425361
Sales Range: $1-9.9 Million
Emp.: 156
Pharmaceutical Preparation Whslr
N.A.I.C.S.: 456110

HEPWORTH PME LLC

Nad Al Hammar Street Rashidiya, PO Box 2345, Dubai, United Arab Emirates
Tel.: (971) 42894670
Web Site: http://www.hepworth.ae
Sales Range: $25-49.9 Million
Emp.: 450
PVC Pipe Mfr
N.A.I.C.S.: 326122

Subsidiaries:

Hepworth PME Qatar WLL (1)
PO Box 50207, Mesaieed, Qatar
Tel.: (974) 44506810
Plastic Product Distr
N.A.I.C.S.: 424610
Clifford Monteiro *(Mgr-Fin)*

Hepworth WLL (1)
Building 1 Avenue, PO Box 143, 0010, Manama, Bahrain
Tel.: (973) 17672050
Plastic Product Distr
N.A.I.C.S.: 424610

HER CHEE INDUSTRIAL CO., LTD.

No 2 Yi-Kung 2 Rd Road Yi-Chu Industrial Area, Yi-Chu Hsiang, Hsien, Taiwan
Tel.: (886) 53426621
Web Site:
 https://www.hercheemoto.en.com
Year Founded: 1976
8937—(TPE)
Rev.: $6,631,492
Assets: $43,334,303
Liabilities: $20,633,430
Net Worth: $22,700,872
Earnings: $55,342
Emp.: 100
Fiscal Year-end: 12/31/22
Automobile Mfr & Distr
N.A.I.C.S.: 336110
Xie Jing-Jing *(Chm)*

HERA S.P.A.

Viale Carlo Berti Pichat nr 2/4, 40127, Bologna, Italy
Tel.: (39) 051287111
Web Site: http://www.gruppohera.it
HER—(ITA)
Rev.: $21,672,782,215
Assets: $18,474,530,542
Liabilities: $14,541,118,066
Net Worth: $3,933,412,476
Earnings: $329,484,136
Emp.: 9,025
Fiscal Year-end: 12/31/22
Natural Gas Distr
N.A.I.C.S.: 221210
Tomaso Tommasi di Vignano *(Chm)*

Subsidiaries:

A.C.R. di Reggiani Albertino S.p.A. (1)
Via Statale Nord 162, 41037, Mirandola, MO, Italy
Tel.: (39) 0535615311
Web Site: https://www.acrreggiani.it
Environmental Consulting Services
N.A.I.C.S.: 541620

ASA Spa (1)
Via Del Gazometro 9, 57122, Livorno, LI, Italy
Tel.: (39) 0800139139
Web Site: https://www.asaspa.it
Landfill Management Services
N.A.I.C.S.: 562212

AcegasApsAmga S.p.A. (1)
Via del Teatro 5, 34121, Trieste, Italy
Tel.: (39) 0407793111
Web Site: https://www.acegasapsamga.it
Environmental Services
N.A.I.C.S.: 541620

Akhea Consortium (1)
Viale Berti Pichat no 2 4, 40127, Bologna, Italy
Tel.: (39) 0542 68 79 11
Solid Waste Treatment Services
N.A.I.C.S.: 562212

Akron Spa (1)
Via Molino Rosso 8, 40026, Imola, Bologna, Italy
Tel.: (39) 0542640375
Web Site: http://www.akron-ambiente.it
Hazardous Waste Disposal Services
N.A.I.C.S.: 562211

Aliplast France Recyclage S.A.S. (1)
3 Rue du Ried, 67610, La Wantzenau, France
Tel.: (33) 390297110
Plastic Recycling Distr
N.A.I.C.S.: 423930

Aliplast Iberia SL (1)
Pol Ind El Colomer c/Castilla Leon 19 Apartado de Correos 382, Onda, 12200, Valencia, Castellon, Spain
Tel.: (34) 964506270
Plastics Product Mfr
N.A.I.C.S.: 326199

Aliplast Spa (1)
Via Delle Fornaci 14 Ospedaletto D, Istrana, 31036, Treviso, TV, Italy
Tel.: (39) 0422837090
Web Site: https://www.aliplastspa.com
Emp.: 1,400
Plastics Product Mfr
N.A.I.C.S.: 326199

AresGas Ead (1)
36 Alabin Str Fl 2, 1301, Sofia, Bulgaria
Tel.: (359) 29390970
Web Site: https://www.aresgas.bg
Natural Gas Distr
N.A.I.C.S.: 221210

Centuria RIT s.c.a.r.l. (1)
Via dell Arrigoni 60, 47522, Cesena, Forli-Cesena, Italy
Tel.: (39) 0547415080

INTERNATIONAL PUBLIC

Web Site: http://www.centuria-agenzia.it
Sales Range: $25-49.9 Million
Emp.: 10
Agrofood Development Consulting Services
N.A.I.C.S.: 541690

F.lli Franchini S.R.L. (1)
Via Covignano 201/a, 47923, Rimini, Italy
Tel.: (39) 0541796311
Web Site: https://www.fllifranchini.com
Electrical System Installation Services
N.A.I.C.S.: 238210

Hera Comm Mediterranea S.r.l. (1)
Zona Indus Aversa Nord, Carinaro, Caserta, Italy
Tel.: (39) 0815028334
Web Site:
 http://www.heracommmediterranea.it
Energy Development Services
N.A.I.C.S.: 561990

Hera Comm S.p.A. (1)
Via Molino Rosso 8, 40026, Imola, BO, Italy
Tel.: (39) 0542843111
Web Site: https://heracomm.gruppohera.it
Energy Transition Services
N.A.I.C.S.: 221118

Hera Energie Bologna S.r.l. (1)
Via dell Elettricista 2, 40138, Bologna, Italy
Tel.: (39) 051560633
Web Site: http://www.heraenergie.it
Heating & Airconditioning Contract Services
N.A.I.C.S.: 238220

Hera Luce S.r.l. (1)
Tel.: (39) 0541908911
Web Site: https://www.heraluce.it
Sales Range: $25-49.9 Million
Emp.: 20
Lighting Systems Installation Services
N.A.I.C.S.: 238210

Hera Servizi Energia Srl (1)
Via Augusto Righi 1, Forli, Italy
Tel.: (39) 051560633
Web Site: http://www.hse.gruppohera.it
Energy Efficiency Services
N.A.I.C.S.: 213112

Hera Trading S.r.l. (1)
Tel.: (39) 0542843160
Sales Range: $50-74.9 Million
Emp.: 44
Natural Gas Producer & Distr
N.A.I.C.S.: 211130
Stavros Papageorgiou *(CEO)*

Herambiente Spa (1)
Viale Berti Pichat 2/4, 40127, Bologna, Italy
Tel.: (39) 0512871111
Water & Energy Services
N.A.I.C.S.: 221310

Primagas Ad (1)
Tsar Simeon I street 25 floor 7, 9000, Varna, Bulgaria
Tel.: (359) 52920920
Web Site: https://primagas-bg.com
Natural Gas Distribution Services
N.A.I.C.S.: 221210

Recycla S.p.A. (1)
Via Ponte Giulio 62 Industrial Area, 33085, Maniago, PN, Italy
Tel.: (39) 0427735611
Web Site: https://www.recycla.it
Waste Management Services
N.A.I.C.S.: 562998

Sinergia S.r.l. (1)
Via Serio 29, Albino, 24021, Bergamo, Italy
Tel.: (39) 0350527200
Web Site: http://www.sinergia-it.com
Energy Maintenance Services
N.A.I.C.S.: 541690

Sotris Spa (1)
SS 309 Km 2600 N 272, Ravenna, 48100, Italy
Tel.: (39) 0544453895
Sales Range: $25-49.9 Million
Emp.: 10
Solid Waste Treatment Services
N.A.I.C.S.: 562211

Tiepolo S.R.L. (1)
Via J Ressel 6, San Dorligo della Valle, 34018, Trieste, Italy
Tel.: (39) 040280750

AND PRIVATE COMPANIES

Web Site: https://www.tiepolosrl.it
Electronic Services
N.A.I.C.S.: 238210

Uniflotte Srl (1)
Carlo Berti Pichat 2/4, 40126, Bologna, Italy
Tel.: (39) 0514224480
Web Site: https://www.uniflotte.it
Car & Truck Vehicle Distr
N.A.I.C.S.: 441120

Vallortigara Servizi Ambientali S.p.A. (1)
Via dell'Artigianato 21, 36036, Torrebelvicino, VI, Italy
Tel.: (39) 0445660455
Web Site: https://www.vallortigara.it
Waste Management Services
N.A.I.C.S.: 562998

HERACLES SA

231 rue Saint-Honore, 75001, Paris, France
Tel.: (33) 1 55 34 73 03
Web Site: http://www.1855.com
Emp.: 40
Wine Producer & E-Commerce Retailer
N.A.I.C.S.: 312130
Lucie Delaruelle *(Mgr-Press Rels)*

HERAEUS HOLDING GMBH

Heraeusstrasse 12-14, Postfach 1561, D-63450, Hanau, Germany
Tel.: (49) 61 81 35 0   De
Web Site: http://www.heraeus.com
Year Founded: 1851
Sales Range: $1-4.9 Billion
Emp.: 12,477
Holding Company; Metal Processing Services; Dental Health & Aesthetics, Medical Technology, Quartz Glass Technology, Sensors & Specialty Lighting Products Mfr
N.A.I.C.S.: 551112
Jurgen Heraeus *(Chm-Supervisory Bd)*

Subsidiaries:

Heraeus Amba Australia Pty. Ltd. (1)
Unit 3 41-49 Norcal Road, Nunawading, 3131, VIC, Australia
Tel.: (61) 3 9874 7455
Web Site: http://www.heraeusamba.com
Emp.: 3
Optical Instrument Mfr
N.A.I.C.S.: 333310
Tess Fitzpatrick *(Mng Dir)*

Heraeus Amba Ltd. (1)
Thorpe Way, Banbury, OX16 4ST, United Kingdom
Tel.: (44) 1295 272666
Web Site: http://www.heraeusamba.com
Ultraviolet Lamp Mfr
N.A.I.C.S.: 335139

Heraeus CZ s.r.o. (1)
Zeleznobrodska 367/27, 197 00, Prague, Czech Republic
Tel.: (420) 22 22 12 660
Emp.: 4
Medical Equipment Mfr
N.A.I.C.S.: 334510
Tomas Rubes *(Country Mgr)*

Heraeus Catalysts (Danyang) Co. Ltd. (1)
8 ShengChang Xi Road Danyang Development Zone, Danyang, 212310, Jiangsu, China
Tel.: (86) 511 86997599
Web Site: http://www.heraeus-catalysts-china.com
Motorcycle Catalyst Mfr
N.A.I.C.S.: 336390

Heraeus Deutschland GmbH & Co. KG (1)
Heraeusstrasse 12-14, D-63450, Hanau, Germany
Tel.: (49) 6181350
Web Site: https://www.heraeus-electronics.com
Chemical Products Mfr
N.A.I.C.S.: 325998

Heraeus Drijfhout BV (1)
Hoogoorddreef 123, 1101 BB, Amsterdam, Netherlands
Tel.: (31) 20 56 48 626
Web Site: http://www.heraeus-drijfhout.nl
Emp.: 4
Metal Mining Services
N.A.I.C.S.: 212290
Eleonore Hemsen *(Gen Mgr)*

Heraeus Electro-Nite (Aust.) Pty. Ltd. (1)
3 Resolution Drive, Unanderra, 2526, NSW, Australia
Tel.: (61) 242 729 777
Web Site: http://www.heraeus.com
Measuring Instrument Distr
N.A.I.C.S.: 423830

Heraeus Electro-Nite (U.K.) Ltd. (1)
Carlisle Close, Derbyshire, Chesterfield, S41 9ED, United Kingdom
Tel.: (44) 1246 459 100
Web Site: http://www.eelectro-nite.com
Emp.: 55
N.A.I.C.S.: 423830
Mark Lee *(Mng Dir)*

Heraeus Electro-Nite AB (1)
Sodra Kungsvagen 66 S, 181 32, Lidingo, Sweden
Tel.: (46) 8 544 806 50
Emp.: 4
Measuring Instrument Distr
N.A.I.C.S.: 423830

Heraeus Electro-Nite Canada Ltd. (1)
327 Glover Road, Stoney Creek, L8E 5M2, ON, Canada
Tel.: (800) 290-0100
Measuring Instrument Distr
N.A.I.C.S.: 423830

Heraeus Electro-Nite Chelyabinsk LLC (1)
ul 2 Paveletskaya 36, 454047, Chelyabinsk, Russia
Tel.: (7) 351 725 7612
Measuring Instrument Distr
N.A.I.C.S.: 423830

Heraeus Electro-Nite Espana, S.L. (1)
Poligono de Asipo Calle A No 22, Llanera, 33428, Asturias, Spain
Tel.: (34) 985 264 801
Measuring Instrument Distr
N.A.I.C.S.: 423830

Heraeus Electro-Nite France S.A.R.L. (1)
Alle des Coteaux, BP 90025, F-57971, Yutz, Cedex, France
Tel.: (33) 38 256 35 41
Web Site: http://www.heraeus-electro-nite.com
Measuring Instrument Distr
N.A.I.C.S.: 423830
Jan Doets *(Mng Dir)*

Heraeus Electro-Nite Instrumentos Ltda. (1)
Rua Blindex 134, Piraporinha, Diadema, 09950-080, Brazil
Tel.: (55) 11 3579 9300
Measuring Instrument Distr
N.A.I.C.S.: 423830

Heraeus Electro-Nite International N.V. (1)
Centrum-Zuid 1105, 3530, Houthalen, Belgium (100%)
Tel.: (32) 11600211
Web Site: http://www.heraeus.com
Sales Range: $75-99.9 Million
Emp.: 500
Mfr of Measuring Probes & Instrumentation for Molten Metal Control
N.A.I.C.S.: 334519
Jan Doets *(CEO & Member-Mgmt Bd)*

Heraeus Electro-Nite Italy S.R.L. (1)
Via Ciucani 21, Ornago, 20060, Milan, Italy
Tel.: (39) 039 62861
Web Site: http://www.electro-nite.it
Measuring Instrument Distr
N.A.I.C.S.: 423830

Heraeus Electro-Nite Japan Ltd. (1)
28-23 Onitaka 3-chome, Ichikawa, Chiba, 272-0015, Japan
Tel.: (81) 47 370 4181
Measuring Instrument Distr
N.A.I.C.S.: 423830

Heraeus Electro-Nite Mexicana S.A. de C.V. (1)
Av Delta No 1400, Ramos Arizpe, 25903, COAH, Mexico
Tel.: (52) 844 866 9090
Web Site: http://www.electronite.com
Emp.: 200
Chemical Products Mfr
N.A.I.C.S.: 325998

Heraeus Electro-Nite Polska Sp. z o.o. (1)
Ul Kombajnistow 2, 41200, Sosnowiec, Poland
Tel.: (48) 32 363 00 00
Chemical Products Mfr
N.A.I.C.S.: 325998

Heraeus Electro-Nite Shenyang Co. Ltd. (1)
No 26 No 7 St, Shenyang, 110027, Liaoning, China
Tel.: (86) 2425292288
Chemical Products Mfr
N.A.I.C.S.: 325998

Heraeus Electro-Nite Taiwan Ltd. (1)
14 Donglin Rd, Siaogang, Kaohsiung, Taiwan
Tel.: (886) 78719600
Chemical Products Mfr
N.A.I.C.S.: 325998

Heraeus Electro-Nite Ukraina LLC (1)
16-a Kiyashka Str, Zaporizhzhya, 69041, Ukraine
Tel.: (380) 61 220 56 39
Web Site: http://www.heraeus-electro-nite.com
Emp.: 7
Chemical Products Mfr
N.A.I.C.S.: 325998
Azar Enkou *(Mng Dir)*

Heraeus Inc. (1)
540 Madison Ave Fl 16, New York, NY 10022-3249 (100%)
Tel.: (212) 752-2705
Web Site: http://www.heraeus.com
Sales Range: $25-49.9 Million
Emp.: 18
Precious Metals
N.A.I.C.S.: 331221
Uve Kupka *(Pres)*

Subsidiary (Domestic):

Heraeus Electro-Nite Co., LLC (2)
1 Summit Sq 1st Fl Ste 100, Langhorne, PA 19047 (100%)
Tel.: (215) 944-9000
Web Site: http://www.electro-nite.com
Sales Range: $75-99.9 Million
Emp.: 450
Mfr of Heating Sensors
N.A.I.C.S.: 334512

Branch (Domestic):

Heraeus Electro-Nite (3)
3 Fountain Ave, Ellwood City, PA 16117-2448 (100%)
Tel.: (724) 758-4541
Web Site: http://www.electro-nite.com
Sales Range: $25-49.9 Million
Emp.: 150
Heating Sensors Mfr
N.A.I.C.S.: 334512
Deb Smalley *(Office Mgr)*

Subsidiary (Domestic):

Heraeus Materials Technology North America LLC (2)
301 N Roosevelt Ave, Chandler, AZ 85226
Tel.: (480) 961-9200
Web Site: http://www.heraeus-hmtna.com
Chemical Products Mfr
N.A.I.C.S.: 325998

Heraeus Metal Processing, LLC (2)
15524 Carmenita Rd, Santa Fe Springs, CA 90670-5610
Tel.: (562) 921-7464
Web Site: http://www.heraeus.de
Sales Range: $50-74.9 Million
Metal Stamping
N.A.I.C.S.: 331492
Sam Cuellar *(Mgr-Analytical Svcs)*

Heraeus Metals New York LLC (2)
540 Madison Ave, New York, NY 10022
Tel.: (212) 752-2180
Steel Products Mfr
N.A.I.C.S.: 331110
Artin Janian *(VP-Fin & Ops)*

Heraeus Precious Metals Management Inc. (2)
540 Madison Ave, New York, NY 10022-3213 (100%)
Tel.: (212) 752-2180
Sales Range: $25-49.9 Million
Emp.: 15
Metal Refining Services
N.A.I.C.S.: 423940
Artin Janian *(Sr VP-Fin & Ops)*

Subsidiary (Domestic):

Heraeus Precious Metals North America Daychem LLC (3)
970 Industrial Park Dr, Vandalia, OH 45377
Tel.: (937) 264-1000
Web Site: http://www.daychem.com
Sales Range: $1-9.9 Million
Emp.: 15
Industrial Organic Chemicals
N.A.I.C.S.: 325199

Subsidiary (Domestic):

Heraeus Precious Metals North America Conshohocken LLC (2)
24 Union Hill Rd, West Conshohocken, PA 19428
Tel.: (617) 828-4478
Chemical Products Mfr
N.A.I.C.S.: 325998

Heraeus Kulzer Australia Pty. Ltd. (1)
18/175 Gibbes St, Roseville, 2069, NSW, Australia
Tel.: (61) 1800 226 521
Chemical Products Mfr
N.A.I.C.S.: 325998

Heraeus Ltd. (1)
Heraeus Technology Centre 30 On Chuen Street, On Lok Tsuen Fanling, Hong Kong, China (Hong Kong)
Tel.: (852) 2675 1200
Web Site: http://www.heraeus.com.hk
Chemical Products Mfr
N.A.I.C.S.: 325998

Heraeus Materials S.A. (1)
Avenue des Sciences 2D, Y-Parc, Yverdon-les-Bains, 1400, Switzerland
Tel.: (41) 24 424 98 98
Chemical Products Mfr
N.A.I.C.S.: 325998

Heraeus Materials Singapore Pte. Ltd. (1)
Block 5000 Ang Mo Kio Avenue 5, Singapore, 569881, Singapore
Tel.: (65) 6571 7888
Electronic Industry Assembly & Packaging Technology Mfr
N.A.I.C.S.: 334418

Heraeus Materials Technology Shanghai Ltd. (1)
1 Guang Zhong Road, Zhuanqiao, Shanghai, 201108, Minhang, China
Tel.: (86) 21 33575688
Web Site: http://www.heraeus-hmts.com
Chemical Products Mfr
N.A.I.C.S.: 325998

Heraeus Materials Technology Taiwan Ltd. (1)
4F-5 No 408 Rui-Guang Road, Nei-Hu, Taipei, 11492, Taiwan
Tel.: (886) 226271111
Web Site: http://www.heraeus.com.tw
Chemical Products Mfr
N.A.I.C.S.: 325998

HERAEUS HOLDING GMBH

Heraeus Holding GmbH—(Continued)

Heraeus Medical Australia Pty Limited (1)
Building 3 Level 2, 35-41 Waterloo Road, Macquarie Park, 2113, NSW, Australia
Tel.: (61) 800226521
Precious Metal Mining Services
N.A.I.C.S.: 212290
Susan Tye *(Country Mgr)*

Heraeus Medical GmbH (1)
Heraeusstrasse 12-14, D-63450, Hanau, Germany
Tel.: (49) 6181354510
Web Site: http://www.heraeus-medicalcomponents.com
Sales Range: $150-199.9 Million
Emp.: 350
Media Holding Company
N.A.I.C.S.: 551112

Subsidiary (US):

Heraeus Medical Components Caribe (2)
415 Rd 693, Dorado, PR 00646-4802
Tel.: (787) 626-0260
Web Site: http://www.heraeus.com
Medical Equipment Components Mfr
N.A.I.C.S.: 923120
Manuel Santiago *(VP & Mgr)*

Heraeus Medical Components, Inc. (2)
5030 Centerville Rd, Saint Paul, MN 55127
Tel.: (651) 792-8500
Web Site: http://heraeus-medicalcomponents.com
Medical Device & Equipment Mfr
N.A.I.C.S.: 423450
Keith Forster *(Gen Mgr)*

Heraeus Metal Processing, Ltd. (1)
Bay 75 Shannon Industrial Estate, County Clare, Shannon, Ireland
Tel.: (353) 61 472099
Web Site: http://www.heraeus-catalysts.com
Emp.: 15
Steel Products Mfr
N.A.I.C.S.: 331110
Andrew Walsh *(Mng Dir)*

Heraeus Metals (Shanghai) Co., Ltd. (1)
No 1 Guang Zhong Road, Zhuanqiat Town Mining District, Shanghai, 201108, China
Tel.: (86) 2133575679
Steel Products Mfr
N.A.I.C.S.: 331110

Heraeus Metals Hong Kong Ltd. (1)
18 Sung On Street, Hunghom, Kowloon, China (Hong Kong)
Tel.: (852) 2773 1733
Web Site: http://www.heraeus.com.hk
Steel Products Mfr
N.A.I.C.S.: 331110

Heraeus Oriental HiTec Co. Ltd. (1)
587-122 Hakik-Dong, Nam-Ku, Incheon, 402-040, Korea (South)
Tel.: (82) 3 2830 8500
Emp.:130
Silo Mfr
N.A.I.C.S.: 331420
Pyoung Gil Kim *(Mgr-Production)*

Heraeus Quartz UK Ltd. (1)
Neptune Road, Wallsend, NE28 6DD, United Kingdom
Tel.: (44) 191 262 5311
Chemical Products Mfr
N.A.I.C.S.: 325998

Heraeus Quarzglas GmbH & Co. KG (1)
Reinhard-Heraeus Ring 29, Kleinostheim, 63801, Germany (100%)
Tel.: (49) 6181356453
Web Site: http://www.heraeus-quarzglas.com
Sales Range: $200-249.9 Million
Emp.: 450
Quartz Glass for Chemical Industry, Fiber Optic Products, Optics & Lamps & Semiconductor Industry
N.A.I.C.S.: 333242
Heinz Fabian *(Gen Mgr)*

Division (US):

Heraeus Quartz America, LLC (2)
100 Heraeus Blvd, Buford, GA 30518 (100%)
Tel.: (678) 714-4350
Sales Range: $25-49.9 Million
Emp.: 15
Optical Materials Distr & Sales
N.A.I.C.S.: 333310

Heraeus Recycling Technology (Taicang) Co., Ltd. (1)
Xinjian Yuewang, Shaxi Town, Taicang, 215437, China
Tel.: (86) 512 5373 7666
Web Site: http://www.heraeus.com
Emp.: 40
Chemical Products Mfr
N.A.I.C.S.: 325998
Zhou Aii *(Mgr)*

Heraeus S.A. (1)
c/ Forjadores 16, Boadilla del Monte, 28660, Madrid, Spain
Tel.: (34) 91 358 19 96
Web Site: http://www.heraeus.es
Emp.: 20
Chemical Products Distr
N.A.I.C.S.: 424690
Enrique Fraile *(Gen Mgr)*

Heraeus S.p.A. (1)
Via dei Chiosi 11, Cavenago, 20873, Cavenago di Brianza, Italy
Tel.: (39) 02 957591
Web Site: http://www.heraeus.it
Metal Product Distr
N.A.I.C.S.: 423510

Heraeus Sensor Technology GmbH (1)
Reinhard-Heraeus-Ring 23, 63801, Kleinostheim, Germany
Tel.: (49) 6181 35 80 98
Chemical Products Mfr
N.A.I.C.S.: 325998

Heraeus ShinEtsu Quartz China Inc. (1)
Room 1702 No 620 Zhangyang Road East building of Zhongrong Henrul Inte, Pudong District, 200122, Shanghai, China
Tel.: (86) 21 6867 2266 809
Chemical Products Mfr
N.A.I.C.S.: 325998

Heraeus South Africa (Pty.) Ltd. (1)
29 Atlas Road, Anderbolt, Boksburg, 1508, Dunswart, South Africa
Tel.: (27) 11 9184374
Chemical Products Mfr
N.A.I.C.S.: 325998

Heraeus Zhaoyuan Changshu Ltd. (1)
Huangpujiang Road Southeast, Economic Development Zone, Changshu, Jiangsu, China
Tel.: (86) 512 5235 2388
Chemical Products Mfr
N.A.I.C.S.: 325998

Heraeus Zhaoyuan Precious Metal Materials Co. Ltd. (1)
No 9 South Ankang Road, Zhaoyuan, China
Tel.: (86) 5358236744
Precious Metal Mining Services
N.A.I.C.S.: 212290

Heraeus Precious Metals GmbH & Co. KG (1)
Heraeusstrasse 12-14, 63450, Hanau, Germany (100%)
Tel.: (49) 6181350
Metals-Contacts Technology, Materials Technology; Chemicals-Precious Metal Recycling, Metal Compounds & Baths, Catalysts, Thick Film, Ceramic Colours, Trading-Precious Metals Trading & Procurement
N.A.I.C.S.: 325998

Division (Domestic):

Heraeus Contact Materials Division (2)
Heraeussrt 12-14, Hanau, 63450, Germany
Tel.: (49) 6181350
Web Site: http://www.heraeus-contactmaterials.com

Sales Range: $1-4.9 Billion
Emp.: 3,500
Assembly & Packaging Technology Materials Mfr
N.A.I.C.S.: 334418
Roland Cerner *(Mng Dir)*

Subsidiary (Non-US):

Heraeus Materials Singapore Pte. Ltd. - Contact Materials (3)
26 Pioneer Crescent #06-11/12 West Park Bizcentral, Singapore, 628558, Singapore
Tel.: (65) 6556 3530
Web Site: http://www.heraeus-contactmaterials.com
Sales Range: $50-74.9 Million
Emp.: 180
Specialty Bonding Wire Mfr
N.A.I.C.S.: 332618

Woojin Electro-Nite Inc. (1)
292 Osan-ri, Dongtan-myeon, Hwaseong, 445813, Korea (South)
Tel.: (82) 3 1379 3114
Web Site: http://www.woojinhen.com
Sensor & Measuring Instrument Mfr
N.A.I.C.S.: 334413

HERALD HOLDINGS LIMITED

3110 31/F Tower Two Lippo Centre
89 Queensway, Hong Kong, China (Hong Kong)
Tel.: (852) 2 522 6181
Web Site:
http://www.heraldgroup.com.hk
0114—(HKG)
Rev.: $151,569,815
Assets: $125,428,278
Liabilities: $44,062,535
Net Worth: $81,365,743
Earnings: ($7,634,197)
Emp.: 6,026
Fiscal Year-end: 03/31/22
Toys & Gift Products Distr
N.A.I.C.S.: 459420
Kam-Hung Shum *(Mng Dir)*

Subsidiaries:

Herald Datanetics Limited (1)
Unit 1028 10/Fl One Island South 2 Heung Yip Road, Wong Chuk Hang, Hong Kong, China (Hong Kong)
Tel.: (852) 25524171
Web Site: http://www.heralddata.com
Sales Range: $200-249.9 Million
Emp.: 450
Tape Heads & Fibre Optic Components Mfr
N.A.I.C.S.: 334513

Herald Electronics Limited (1)
Unit B 2nd Fl Tai Tak Indus Bldg 2-12 Kwai Fat Rd, Kwai Chung, New Territories, China (Hong Kong)
Tel.: (852) 24264221
Web Site: http://www.heraldelectronics.com
Electronic Timepieces Mfr
N.A.I.C.S.: 334519

Herald Engineering Services Inc. (1)
16230 Monterey Rd Ste 200, Morgan Hill, CA 95037-5456
Tel.: (408) 782-0845
Electrical Engineering Services
N.A.I.C.S.: 541330

Herald Houseware Limited (1)
Unit B 6F Tai Tak Indus Bldg 2-12 Kwai Fat Rd, Kwai Chung, China (Hong Kong)
Tel.: (852) 24108873
Housewares Whslr
N.A.I.C.S.: 423220

Herald Investments (China) Company Limited (1)
7B Blk A No 1068 Xi Kang Road, Shanghai, China
Tel.: (86) 2152521460
Investment Management Service
N.A.I.C.S.: 523999

Herald Metal and Plastic Works Limited (1)
1/F Pat Tat Industrial Building 1 Pat Tat Street, San Po Kong, Kowloon, China (Hong Kong)

Tel.: (852) 27268111
Web Site: http://www.heraldtoy.com.hk
Toy Mfr
N.A.I.C.S.: 339930

Herald Technology Inc. (1)
328 N Pine St, Florence, AL 35630
Tel.: (256) 764-0641
Web Site: https://www.heraldtech.net
Information Technology Services
N.A.I.C.S.: 541511

Pilot Housewares (U.K.) Limited (1)
Unit H Daniels Way Watnall Road, Hucknall, Nottingham, NG15 7LN, United Kingdom
Tel.: (44) 1159633966
Web Site: http://www.pilothousewares.co.uk
Sales Range: $25-49.9 Million
Emp.: 11
Cooking Utensil Distr
N.A.I.C.S.: 423220

Ventura Watch AG (1)
Glarnerstrasse 25, 8854, Siebnen, Switzerland
Tel.: (41) 554401571
Watch Retailer
N.A.I.C.S.: 458310

Zeon Far East Limited (1)
Unit A 6F Tai Tak Indus Bldg 2-12 Kwai Fat Rd, Kwai Chung, New Territories, China (Hong Kong)
Tel.: (852) 24123178
Clocks & Watches Whslr
N.A.I.C.S.: 423940

Zeon Limited (1)
Units 1 2 Phoenix Park Apsley Way, London, NW2 7LN, United Kingdom
Tel.: (44) 2082081833
Web Site: http://www.zeonltd.co.uk
Sales Range: $50-74.9 Million
Emp.: 100
Watches & Consumer Electronic Product Distr
N.A.I.C.S.: 423620

Zhuhai Herald Datanetics Limited (1)
No 1 Pingxi 6th Road, Nanping Science and Technology Industrial Park, Zhuhai, 519060, Guangdong, China
Tel.: (86) 7568920600
Computer Product Mfr
N.A.I.C.S.: 334111

HERALD INVESTMENT MANAGEMENT LIMITED

10-11 Charterhouse Square, London, EC1M 6EE, United Kingdom
Tel.: (44) 2075536300 UK
Web Site: http://www.heralduk.com
Year Founded: 1993
Sales Range: $50-74.9 Million
Emp.: 10
Investment Fund Management Services
N.A.I.C.S.: 523940
Katie Potts *(Founder & Mng Dir)*

HERAMED LIMITED

Suite 201/697 Burke Road, Camberwell, 3124, VIC, Australia
Tel.: (61) 272511888 AU
Web Site: https://www.hera-med.com
Year Founded: 2011
HMD—(ASX)
Rev.: $402,897
Assets: $2,014,361
Liabilities: $1,547,662
Net Worth: $466,699
Earnings: ($4,502,770)
Fiscal Year-end: 12/31/23
Software Development Services
N.A.I.C.S.: 541511
Ady Jakubovitz *(VP)*

HERANBA INDUSTRIES LIMITED

2Nd Floor A-Wing Fortune Avirahi Jambli Gali Jain Derasar Lane, Borivali West, Mumbai, 400092, India

AND PRIVATE COMPANIES

Tel.: (91) 2250705050
Web Site: https://www.heranba.co.in
Year Founded: 1996
543266—(BOM)
Rev.: $200,617,190
Assets: $145,867,995
Liabilities: $48,344,478
Net Worth: $97,523,517
Earnings: $9,034,526
Emp.: 700
Fiscal Year-end: 03/31/22
Agrochemical Mfr
N.A.I.C.S.: 325320
Sadashiv K. Shetty *(Chm)*

HERANTIS PHARMA PLC
Bertel Jungin Aukio 1, FIN-02600, Espoo, Finland
Tel.: (358) 92221195
Web Site: https://www.herantis.com
HRTIS—(OMX)
Rev.: $145,694
Assets: $6,725,809
Liabilities: $6,790,866
Net Worth: ($65,056)
Earnings: ($10,062,837)
Emp.: 10
Fiscal Year-end: 12/31/22
Pharmaceutical Mfr, Developer & Researcher
N.A.I.C.S.: 325412
Timo Veromaa *(Chm)*

HERB SHAW & SONS LIMITED
31 Sharon Street, Pembroke, K8A 7J5, ON, Canada
Tel.: (613) 732-9989
Web Site: http://www.shawlumber.ca
Year Founded: 1847
Plywood Products Mfr
N.A.I.C.S.: 321212
John Shaw *(Pres)*

HERBAL DISPATCH INC.
Suite 800 543 Granville Street, Vancouver, V6C 1X8, BC, Canada
Tel.: (778) 386-6151
Web Site: https://herbaldispatch.com
Year Founded: 2015
HA9—(DEU)
Rev.: $268,743
Assets: $5,867,000
Liabilities: $1,230,018
Net Worth: $4,636,982
Earnings: ($3,409,176)
Fiscal Year-end: 12/31/22
Cannabis Product Mfr
N.A.I.C.S.: 325412
Philip Campbell *(CEO)*

Subsidiaries:

Coco Pure Beverage Corp. (1)
105-23000 Fraserway Way, Richmond, V6V 3C7, BC, Canada
Tel.: (778) 999-4477
Web Site: https://www.cocospure.com
Nutritional Beverage Mfr & Distr
N.A.I.C.S.: 311514

HERBALIFE NUTRITION LTD.
Ugland House South Church Street, PO Box 309GT, Georgetown, Cayman Islands
Tel.: (345) 2137450500   Ky
Web Site: http://www.herbalife.com
Year Founded: 1980
HLF—(NYSE)
Rev.: $5,062,400,000
Assets: $2,809,400,000
Liabilities: $3,869,700,000
Net Worth: ($1,060,300,000)
Earnings: $142,200,000
Emp.: 9,200
Fiscal Year-end: 12/31/23
Weight Management, Nutritional Supplement, Energy, Fitness & Personal Care Products Sales

N.A.I.C.S.: 424210
John G. DeSimone *(CFO)*

Subsidiaries:

Dexma Sensors S.L. (1)
C/ Napols 189 Bajos D, 08013, Barcelona, Spain
Tel.: (34) 931810195
Web Site: https://www.dexma.com
Software Development Services
N.A.I.C.S.: 541511

Frilo Software GmbH (1)
Stuttgarter Strasse 40, 70469, Stuttgart, Germany
Tel.: (49) 711810020
Web Site: https://www.frilo.eu
Software Development Services
N.A.I.C.S.: 541511

Graphisoft Italia S.R.L. (1)
Via Rossignago 2/a, 30038, Spinea, Venice, Italy
Tel.: (39) 0418943500
Web Site: https://graphisoft.com
Software Development Services
N.A.I.C.S.: 541511

HBL Products S.A. (1)
Route de Meyrin 123, 1219, Chatelaine, Switzerland
Tel.: (41) 223609360
Supplementary Product Mfr
N.A.I.C.S.: 311999

HBL, Ltd. (1)
New Hay Smeaton Lane Stretton Under Fosse, Rugby, CV230PS, United Kingdom
Tel.: (44) 7977273707
Courier Service
N.A.I.C.S.: 492110
Howard Luis *(Gen Mgr)*

HLF Colombia Ltd. (1)
Calle 185 N 45-03 Centro Comercial Santafe Centro, Empresarial Plaza Brasil Piso 8, 111166, Bogota, Colombia
Tel.: (57) 6017428500
Web Site: https://www.herbalife.com.co
Nutritional Supplement & Personal Care Product Retailer
N.A.I.C.S.: 456191

Herbalife (Cambodia) Co., Ltd. (1)
Lot No A2-6 & A6 Street 169 Sangkat Veal Vong Khan 7 Makara, Phnom Penh, Cambodia
Tel.: (855) 23999268
Web Site: http://www.herbalife.com.kh
Emp.: 10
Healthcare Product Distr
N.A.I.C.S.: 621399

Herbalife Bela, LLC (1)
Bldg 29-91A Prityckogo str, 220092, Minsk, Belarus
Tel.: (375) 172379691
Supplementary Product Mfr
N.A.I.C.S.: 311999

Herbalife Bolivia, Ltda. (1)
Parque Industrial Manzana 8A, Santa Cruz, Bolivia
Tel.: (591) 33644070
Web Site: http://www.herbalife.com.bo
Supplementary Product Mfr
N.A.I.C.S.: 311999

Herbalife Czech Republic, s.r.o (1)
Web Site: http://www.herbalife.cz
Supplementary Product Mfr
N.A.I.C.S.: 311999

Herbalife Del Ecuador, S.A. (1)
Av 10 de Agosto N 52-107 Y, Cap Ramon Borja, Quito, Ecuador
Web Site: http://www.herbalife.com.ec
Nutritional Supplement & Personal Care Product Retailer
N.A.I.C.S.: 456191

Herbalife Internacional de Mexico, S.A. de C.V (1)
Calzada Gonzalez Gallo 383, 44460, Guadalajara, Mexico
Tel.: (52) 13337705400
Web Site: http://www.herbalife.com.mx
Supplementary Product Mfr
N.A.I.C.S.: 311999

Herbalife Internaitonal (Thailand), Ltd. (1)
93/1 Or GPF Wittayu Room 114/1 and 212 Wireless Road, Lumpini Pathumwan, Bangkok, 10330, Thailand
Tel.: (66) 26601600
Web Site: https://www.herbalife.co.th
Sales Range: $25-49.9 Million
Emp.: 40
Nutritional Supplement & Personal Care Product Retailer
N.A.I.C.S.: 456191
Jirata Rornes *(Mgr-Sls)*

Herbalife International (Thailand), Ltd. (1)
93/1 GPF Wittayu Towers Tower B Unit 114/1 & 212 Wireless Road, Lumpini Pathumwan, Bangkok, 10330, Thailand
Tel.: (66) 26601600
Web Site: http://www.herbalife.co.th
Supplementary Product Mfr
N.A.I.C.S.: 311999

Herbalife International Del Ecuador, S.A. (1)
Av 10 de Agosto N 52-107 y Cap, Ramon Borja, Quito, Ecuador
Web Site: http://www.herbalife.com.ec
Supplementary Product Mfr.
N.A.I.C.S.: 311999

Herbalife International Do Brasil Ltda. (1)
Rua Werner Von Siemens n 111 Building 19 - Space 03 - 2nd Floor, Lapa de Baixo, Sao Paulo, 05069-010, Brazil
Tel.: (55) 1138797822
Web Site: https://www.herbalife.com.br
Nutritional Supplement & Personal Care Product Retailer
N.A.I.C.S.: 456191

Herbalife International Finland OY (1)
PO Box 211, 00131, Helsinki, Finland
Tel.: (358) 972519555
Web Site: http://www.herbalife.fi
Nutritional Supplement & Personal Care Product Retailer
N.A.I.C.S.: 456191

Herbalife International Greece S.A. (1)
110 Pentelis str, Marousi, 15126, Athens, Greece
Tel.: (30) 2155003057
Web Site: https://wellness.com.gr
Sales Range: $25-49.9 Million
Emp.: 23
Nutritional Supplement & Personal Care Product Distr
N.A.I.C.S.: 456191

Herbalife International RS LLC (1)
PO Box 17, 129110, Moscow, Russia
Tel.: (7) 4957295030
Web Site: http://www.herbalife.ru
Sales Range: $50-74.9 Million
Emp.: 200
Nutritional Supplement & Personal Care Product Retailer
N.A.I.C.S.: 456191

Herbalife International South Africa, Ltd. (1)
32 Woodlands Office Park Woodlands Drive, Woodmead, Johannesburg, 1685, South Africa
Tel.: (27) 115541000
Emp.: 65
Nutritional Supplement & Personal Care Product Retailer
N.A.I.C.S.: 456191

Herbalife International del Colombia (1)
Tel.: (57) 16726969
Web Site: http://www.herbalife.com.co
Supplementary Product Mfr
N.A.I.C.S.: 311999

Herbalife International of America, Inc. (1)
800 W Olympic Blvd Ste 406, Los Angeles, CA 90015
Tel.: (310) 410-9600
Web Site: https://support.herbalife.com

Sales Range: $1-4.9 Billion
Emp.: 2,450
Retailer of Nutritional Products, Weight Loss & Health Supplements, Skin Care, Hair Care & Suntan Products
N.A.I.C.S.: 424210

Subsidiary (Non-US):

Herbalife (N.Z.) Limited (2)
Level 2 8 Pacific Rise, Mount Wellington, Auckland, New Zealand
Tel.: (64) 95742080
Web Site: http://www.herbalife.com
Sales Range: $25-49.9 Million
Emp.: 10
Markets & Distributes Weight Management Products, Dietary Supplements & Personal Care Products
N.A.I.C.S.: 456199

Herbalife (U.K.) Limited (2)
The Atrium 1 Harefield Road, Uxbridge, UB8 1HB, Middlesex, United Kingdom
Tel.: (44) 2035350908
Web Site: https://www.herbalife.co.uk
Sales Range: $150-199.9 Million
Nutritional Supplements Mfr & Distr
N.A.I.C.S.: 456199

Herbalife Australasia Pty. Ltd. (2)
Unit G/5 Butler Boulevard Burbridge Business Park Adelaide Airport, Adelaide Airport, Adelaide, 5950, SA, Australia
Tel.: (61) 881540200
Web Site: http://www.herbalife.com.au
Sales Range: $10-24.9 Million
Emp.: 30
Sales of Nutritional Supplements
N.A.I.C.S.: 456191

Subsidiary (Domestic):

Herbalife China, LLC (2)
1800 Century Park E, Los Angeles, CA 90067
Tel.: (310) 410-9600
Supplementary Product Mfr
N.A.I.C.S.: 311999

Subsidiary (Non-US):

Herbalife Denmark ApS (2)
Hovedvagtsgade 6, PO Box 52, 1103, Copenhagen, Denmark
Tel.: (45) 38487766
Sales Range: $150-199.9 Million
Markets & Distributes Weight Management, Dietary Supplements & Personal Care Products
N.A.I.C.S.: 456199

Herbalife Europe Limited (2)
The Atrium 1 Harefield Road, Uxbridge, UB8 1HB, Middlesex, United Kingdom
Tel.: (44) 1895819000
Sales Range: $100-124.9 Million
Emp.: 150
Markets & Distributes Weight Management Products, Dietary Supplements & Personal Care Products
N.A.I.C.S.: 456199

Herbalife International Argentina, S.A. (2)
Debenedetti 3895 1429, Olivos, Buenos Aires, Argentina
Tel.: (54) 1147118500
Web Site: http://www.herbalife.com
Sales Range: $10-24.9 Million
Emp.: 50
Markets & Distributes Weight Management Products, Dietary Supplements & Personal Care Products
N.A.I.C.S.: 456191

Subsidiary (Domestic):

Herbalife International Communications, Inc. (2)
1800 Century Park E, Los Angeles, CA 90067
Tel.: (310) 410-9600
Nutritional Supplement & Personal Care Product Retailer
N.A.I.C.S.: 456191

Subsidiary (Non-US):

Herbalife International Deutschland GmbH (2)

HERBALIFE NUTRITION LTD.

Herbalife Nutrition Ltd.—(Continued)

Grafenhauser Strasse 85, 64293, Darmstadt, Germany
Tel.: (49) 61518605500
Web Site: https://www.herbalife.de
Sales Range: $50-74.9 Million
Emp.: 70
Markets & Distributes Weight Management Products, Dietary Supplements & Personal Care Products
N.A.I.C.S.: 456199

Herbalife International Espana, S.A. (2)
C/ Arequipa 1, 28043, Madrid, Spain
Tel.: (34) 915152130
Sales Range: $25-49.9 Million
Emp.: 25
Markets & Distributes Weight Management Products, Dietary Supplements & Personal Care Products
N.A.I.C.S.: 456199

Herbalife International France S.A. (2)
3 Rue Alexandre Volta, BP 81020, 67451, Mundolsheim, Cedex, France
Tel.: (33) 388103900
Web Site: https://www.herbalifefrance.fr
Sales Range: $50-74.9 Million
Emp.: 40
Markets & Distributes Weight Management Products, Dietary Supplements & Personal Care Products
N.A.I.C.S.: 456199
Daniel Durand *(Gen Mgr)*

Herbalife International Israel Ltd. (2)
Tel.: (972) 39431111
Sales Range: $10-24.9 Million
Emp.: 22
Markets & Distributes Weight Management Products, Dietary Supplements & Personal Care Products
N.A.I.C.S.: 456191

Herbalife International Luxembourg Netherlands Branch (2)
Spurkterweg 16, 5804 AP, Venray, Netherlands
Tel.: (31) 478556060
Sales Range: $50-74.9 Million
Emp.: 155
Markets & Distributes Weight Management Products, Dietary Supplements & Personal Care Products
N.A.I.C.S.: 456191

Herbalife International Philippines (2)
26F The Trade Financial Tower Bldg 32nd St corner 7th Ave, The Fort Bonifacio Global City, Taguig, 1634, Philippines
Tel.: (63) 285552828
Web Site: https://www.herbalife.com.ph
Sales Range: $25-49.9 Million
Emp.: 18
Markets & Distributes Weight Management Products, Dietary Supplements & Personal Care Products
N.A.I.C.S.: 456199

Herbalife International de Mexico, S.A.de C.V. (2)
Av Federalismo 635 -C, Col Mexicaltzingo, 44180, Guadalajara, Jalisco, Mexico
Tel.: (52) 13338373800
Sales Range: $75-99.9 Million
Emp.: 150
Markets & Distributes Weight Management Products, Dietary Supplements & Personal Care Products
N.A.I.C.S.: 456199

Branch (Domestic):

Herbalife International of America, Inc. - Torrance (2)
950 W 190th St, Torrance, CA 90502
Tel.: (310) 410-9600
Web Site: http://www.herbalife.com
Sales Range: $500-549.9 Million
Emp.: 800
Nutritional Supplements, Weight Loss Products, Skin Care & Hair Care Products Sales
N.A.I.C.S.: 424490

Subsidiary (Non-US):

Herbalife International, S.A.-Portugal (2)

Av Infante D Henrique 347, 1800-218, Lisbon, Portugal
Tel.: (351) 217714400
Sales Range: $150-199.9 Million
Markets & Distributes Weight Management Products, Dietary Supplements & Personal Care Products
N.A.I.C.S.: 456199

Herbalife International-Hong Kong (2)
8th Floor Tower 2 China Hong Kong City 33 Canton Road, Tsimshatsui, Kowloon, China (Hong Kong)
Tel.: (852) 28341821
Web Site: http://www.company.herbalife.com.hk
Sales Range: $150-199.9 Million
Markets & Distributes Weight Management Products, Dietary Supplements & Personal Care Products
N.A.I.C.S.: 456199

Herbalife Italia S.p.A. (2)
Via Amsterdam 125, 00144, Rome, Italy
Tel.: (39) 0652304444
Web Site: https://www.herbalife.it
Sales Range: $25-49.9 Million
Emp.: 50
Sales of Nutritional Supplements, Weight Loss Products, Skin Care & Hair Care Products
N.A.I.C.S.: 456191

Herbalife Of Canada Ltd. (2)
120 4550-25th Street SE, Calgary, T2B 3P1, AB, Canada
Tel.: (403) 204-2264
Web Site: http://www.herbalife.ca
Sales Range: $50-74.9 Million
Emp.: 50
Markets & Distributes Weight Management Products, Dietary Supplements & Personal Care Products
N.A.I.C.S.: 456199

Herbalife Polska sp.z.o.o (2)
Janki Ul Falencka 1 B, 05 090, Raszyn, Poland
Tel.: (48) 227037600
Web Site: http://www.herbalife.pl
Sales Range: $25-49.9 Million
Emp.: 20
Markets & Distributes Weight Management Products, Dietary Supplements & Personal Care Products
N.A.I.C.S.: 456199

Herbalife of Japan K.K. (2)
2-9-11 Akasaka, Minato-ku, Tokyo, 107-8546, Japan
Tel.: (81) 355490111
Web Site: https://www.herbalife.co.jp
Sales Range: $200-249.9 Million
Emp.: 50
Sales of Nutritional Supplements, Weight Loss Products, Skin Care & Hair Care Products
N.A.I.C.S.: 456191

Vida Herbal Suplementos Alimenticios, C.A. (Venezuela) (2)
Edificio Playdeca Final Calle Bolivar, Baruta, Caracas, 1080, Estado Miranda, Venezuela
Tel.: (58) 2129434611
Sales Range: $200-249.9 Million
Markets & Distributes Weight Management Products, Dietary Supplements & Personal Care Products
N.A.I.C.S.: 456191

Herbalife International of Hong Kong Limited (2)
8/F Tower 2 China Hong Kong City 33 Canton Road Tsimshatsui, Central, Kowloon, China (Hong Kong)
Tel.: (852) 27378688
Web Site: http://www.herbalife.com
Nutritional Supplement & Personal Care Product Mfr & Distr
N.A.I.C.S.: 456191

Herbalife International of Israel (1990) Ltd. (1)
Derech Hamakabin Str bld 46, Rishon le Zion, 75359, Israel
Tel.: (972) 39431155
Nutritional Supplement & Personal Care Product Distr

N.A.I.C.S.: 456191

Herbalife Kazakhstan LLP (1)
Tel.: (7) 88000805030
Web Site: http://www.herbalifekazakhstan.com
Sales Range: $25-49.9 Million
Emp.: 7
Nutritional Supplement & Personal Care Product Mfr & Distr
N.A.I.C.S.: 456191

Herbalife Norway Products AS (1)
Fornebuveien 46-48, 1366, Lysaker, Norway
Web Site: http://www.herbalife.no
Nutritional Supplement & Personal Care Product Retailer
N.A.I.C.S.: 456191

Herbalife Paraguay S.R.L. (1)
Av Eusebio Ayala N casi Profesor Conradi, 4657, Asuncion, Paraguay
Tel.: (595) 215182000
Web Site: http://www.herbalife.com.py
Nutritional Supplement & Personal Care Product Retailer
N.A.I.C.S.: 456191

Herbalife Peru S.R.L. (1)
Av Del Ejercito 530, Miraflores, Lima, Peru
Tel.: (51) 15122300
Web Site: https://www.herbalife.com.pe
Nutritional Supplement & Personal Care Product Retailer
N.A.I.C.S.: 456191

Herbalife RO S.R.L. (1)
COCOR STORE ground floor Bd I Bratianu no 29-33 sector 3, 031041, Bucharest, Romania
Tel.: (40) 213102410
Nutritional Supplement & Personal Care Product Distr
N.A.I.C.S.: 456191

Herbalife Slovakia, s.r.o. (1)
Web Site: http://www.skherbalife.sk
Supplementary Product Mfr
N.A.I.C.S.: 311999

Herbalife Taiwan, Inc. (1)
16th Floor No 8 Section 7 Citizen Avenue, Nangang District, Taipei, Taiwan
Tel.: (886) 281705268
Web Site: https://www.herbalife.com.tw
Sales Range: $25-49.9 Million
Emp.: 100
Nutritional Supplement & Personal Care Product Distr
N.A.I.C.S.: 456191

Herbalife Vietnam SMLLC (1)
26 Tran Cao Van Street, Vo Thi Sau Ward District 3, Ho Chi Minh City, Vietnam
Tel.: (84) 2838279191
Web Site: https://www.herbalife-vietnam.com
Emp.: 40
Nutritional Supplement & Personal Care Product Retailer
N.A.I.C.S.: 456191

Herbalife of Ghana Limited (1)
Tel.: (233) 302819240
Web Site: http://www.herbalifeghana.com
Emp.: 17
Nutritional Supplement & Personal Care Product Retailer
N.A.I.C.S.: 456191

I.C.S. Herbalife MA, S.R.L. (1)
Str Ismail 81/1 Business Centre Panorama et 2, 2001, Chisinau, Moldova
Tel.: (373) 22265888
Web Site: http://www.herbalife.md
Supplementary Product Mfr
N.A.I.C.S.: 311999

Scia NV (1)
Corda 2 Kempische Steenweg 309/0.03, 3500, Hasselt, Belgium
Tel.: (32) 11948610
Web Site: https://www.scia.net
Software Development Services
N.A.I.C.S.: 541511

Solibri Benelux B.V. (1)
Polarisavenue 130, 2132 JX, Hoofddorp, Netherlands
Tel.: (31) 233038505

INTERNATIONAL PUBLIC

Software Development Services
N.A.I.C.S.: 541511

Spacewell International NV, (1)
Sneeuwbeslaan 20 Bus 3, Wilrijk, 2610, Antwerp, Belgium
Tel.: (32) 38290495
Web Site: https://spacewell.com
Software Development Services
N.A.I.C.S.: 541511

HERBAPOL LUBLIN S.A.

Ul Diamentowa 25, 20 954, Lublin, Poland
Tel.: (48) 817441221
Web Site: http://www.herbapol.com.pl
Sales Range: $100-124.9 Million
Emp.: 500
Herbal Products
N.A.I.C.S.: 325412
Roman Gorny *(Pres & CEO)*

HERBICIDES PRODUCTION COMPANY

No 41-2nd Floor-Shariati St Dastgerdi St Zafar, Tehran, Iran
Tel.: (98) 21 22900132
Web Site: http://www.hpc-co.com
Year Founded: 1366
Emp.: 45
Agricultural Chemical Mfr
N.A.I.C.S.: 325320
Zain-Ulabdeen Emanlu *(Chm)*

HERBOS-INVEST D.D.

Kneza Branimira br 2, 88000, Mostar, Bosnia & Herzegovina
Tel.: (387) 3 632 6316
Web Site: http://www.herbos.ba
HBINRK1—(SARE)
Rev.: $11,058
Assets: $1,135,951
Liabilities: $142,421
Net Worth: $993,530
Earnings: ($7,319)
Emp.: 1
Fiscal Year-end: 12/31/20
Financial Services
N.A.I.C.S.: 523999

HERBSTREITH & FOX KG PEKTIN-FABRIKEN

Turnstrasse 37, 75305, Neuenburg, Germany
Tel.: (49) 7082 7913 0
Web Site: http://www.herbstreith-fox.de
Year Founded: 1934
Rev.: $38,623,200
Emp.: 187
Pectin Mfr
N.A.I.C.S.: 311999
Gerhard F. Fox *(Chm & Gen Partner)*

Subsidiaries:

Herbafood Ingredients GmbH (1)
Phobener Chaussee 12, 14542, Werder, Germany
Tel.: (49) 3327785202
Web Site: http://www.herbafood.de
Food Products Distr
N.A.I.C.S.: 424490
David Gebhardt *(Mgr-Sls & Technical Svc)*

Herbstreith & Fox Inc. (1)
570 Taxter Rd, Elmsford, NY 10523
Tel.: (914) 345-9501
Web Site: http://www.herbstreith-fox.com
Food Products Distr
N.A.I.C.S.: 424490

Herbstreith & Fox Kft. (1)
Donati u 9 - 11, 1015, Budapest, Hungary
Tel.: (36) 12240161
Web Site: http://www.herbstreith-fox.hu
Food Products Distr
N.A.I.C.S.: 424490

HERCEGOVINA A.D.

AND PRIVATE COMPANIES

HERITAGE GROUP LTD.

Sutjeska 2, Ravni Topolovac, Zitiste, Serbia
Tel.: (381) 23 829 311
Year Founded: 1989
Sales Range: Less than $1 Million
Cereal Crop Farming Services
N.A.I.C.S.: 111998

HERCEGOVINA AUTO D.D.
Bisce Polje BB, 88 000, Mostar, Bosnia & Herzegovina
Tel.: (387) 36576489
Web Site: http://www.hercegovinaauto.ba
HRCAR—(SARE)
Rev.: $2,781,148
Assets: $6,819,103
Liabilities: $2,047,678
Net Worth: $4,771,425
Earnings: $29,975
Emp.: 45
Fiscal Year-end: 12/31/21
Automotive Distr
N.A.I.C.S.: 423110

HERCEGOVINAPUTEVI A.D.
Nemanjina 5, 89000, Trebinje, Bosnia & Herzegovina
Tel.: (387) 59261050
HGPT—(BANJ)
Sales Range: $1-9.9 Million
Emp.: 91
Highway Construction Services
N.A.I.C.S.: 237990
Trifko Curtovic (Chm-Mgmt Bd)

HERCULES SILVER CORP.
100 King Street West Suite 1600, Toronto, M5X 1G5, ON, Canada
Tel.: (786) 633-1756
BIG—(TSXV)
Rev.: $143,622
Assets: $19,519,510
Liabilities: $381,283
Net Worth: $19,138,227
Earnings: ($7,320,653)
Fiscal Year-end: 12/31/23
Investment Fund Management Services
N.A.I.C.S.: 523940

HERCULES SITE SERVICES PLC
Hercules Court Lakeside Business Park Broadway Lane, South Cerney, Cirencester, GL7 5XZ, United Kingdom
Tel.: (44) 1793336851 UK
Web Site: https://www.hercules-construction.co.uk
Year Founded: 2008
HERC—(AIM)
Rev.: $67,274,329
Assets: $46,020,696
Liabilities: $36,736,482
Net Worth: $9,284,214
Earnings: $435,627
Emp.: 153
Fiscal Year-end: 09/30/22
Commercial & Institutional Building Construction
N.A.I.C.S.: 236220

HEREN HEALTH CO., LTD.
No 625 Xinlian Road Xixing Street, Binjiang District, Hangzhou, 310051, Zhejiang, China
Tel.: (86) 57181397006
Web Site: http://www.herenit.com
Year Founded: 2010
300550—(CHIN)
Rev.: $61,868,686
Assets: $202,595,626
Liabilities: $50,411,046
Net Worth: $152,184,580
Earnings: $5,509,517
Fiscal Year-end: 12/31/23

Medical Information Services
N.A.I.C.S.: 519290
Chenhui Zhao (Chm & Gen Mgr)

HERENCIA RESOURCES PLC.
7/6 Richardson Street, West Perth, 6005, WA, Australia
Tel.: (61) 8 9481 4204 UK
Web Site: http://www.herenciaresources.com
Assets: $7,781,468
Liabilities: $3,694,468
Net Worth: $4,087,000
Earnings: ($847,969)
Emp.: 16
Fiscal Year-end: 12/31/17
Mineral Exploration & Development Services
N.A.I.C.S.: 213115
David Little (Sec)

HERGOTT FARM EQUIPMENT LTD.
Hwy 5 East, PO Box 1240, Humboldt, S0K 2A0, SK, Canada
Tel.: (306) 682-2592
Web Site: http://www.hergottcaseih.com
Year Founded: 1944
Farm Equipment Distr
N.A.I.C.S.: 423820
Dave Hergott (Mgr-Parts)

HERIGE SA
Route de la Roche-sur-Yon BP 7, 85260, L'Herbergement, France
Tel.: (33) 251080808 FR
Web Site: http://www.groupe-herige.fr
ALHRG—(EUR)
Sales Range: $700-749.9 Million
Pre-Cast, Ready-Mix Concrete & Building Joinery Products & Equipment Mfr & Distr
N.A.I.C.S.: 327320
Caroline Lutinier (Head-Grp Comm)

HERIOT REIT LTD.
Suite 1-Ground Floor 3 Melrose Boulevard, Melrose Arch, Johannesburg, 2196, South Africa
Tel.: (27) 116841570
Web Site: http://www.heriotreit.com
Year Founded: 1998
Rev.: $33,651,068
Assets: $338,415,346
Liabilities: $125,067,863
Net Worth: $213,347,483
Earnings: $15,214,204
Fiscal Year-end: 06/30/19
Asset Management Services
N.A.I.C.S.: 523940
Richard Herring (CEO)

HERITAGE BANK LIMITED
6th Floor 400 Ruthven St, PO Box 190, Toowoomba, 4350, QLD, Australia
Tel.: (61) 746909000
Web Site: http://www.heritage.com.au
Rev.: $262,031,727
Assets: $7,094,422,312
Liabilities: $6,689,560,274
Net Worth: $404,862,038
Earnings: $30,431,845
Emp.: 774
Fiscal Year-end: 06/30/19
Financial & Banking Services
N.A.I.C.S.: 522110
Kerry J. Betros (Chm)

HERITAGE BRANDS LIMITED
30 Bando Road, Springvale, 3171, VIC, Australia
Tel.: (61) 1300650981 AU
Web Site: https://www.heritagebrands.com.au

HBA—(NSXA)
Rev.: $37,016,651
Assets: $31,561,280
Liabilities: $14,551,327
Net Worth: $17,009,953
Earnings: $81,464
Fiscal Year-end: 07/31/21
Cosmetic Product Whslr
N.A.I.C.S.: 424210
Constantine Gendis (CEO & Mng Dir)

HERITAGE CANNABIS HOLDINGS CORP.
77 Bloor Street West, Toronto, M5S 1M2, ON, Canada
Tel.: (647) 660-2560 BC
Web Site: https://www.heritagecann.com
Year Founded: 2007
HERTF—(OTCQB)
Rev.: $31,756,523
Assets: $42,175,424
Liabilities: $26,429,124
Net Worth: $15,746,300
Earnings: ($15,174,167)
Emp.: 158
Fiscal Year-end: 10/31/23
Investment Services
N.A.I.C.S.: 523999
Donald Ziraldo (Chm)

HERITAGE FOODS LTD.
H No 8229382A1286 Plot No 1286, Road No 1 & 65 Jubilee Hills, Hyderabad, 500 082, Telangana, India
Tel.: (91) 4023391221
Web Site: https://www.heritagefoods.in
HERITGFOOD—(NSE)
Rev.: $367,533,212
Assets: $123,202,170
Liabilities: $33,446,049
Net Worth: $89,756,121
Earnings: $13,115,739
Emp.: 3,009
Fiscal Year-end: 03/31/22
Dairy, Fruits, Vegetables, Bakery Products Mfr & Supplier
N.A.I.C.S.: 311511
Umakanta Barik (Officer-Compliance & Sec)

Subsidiaries:

Heritage Foods India Ltd. - Dairy Division (1)
6-3-541/C Panjagutta, Hyderabad, 500 082, Telangana, India
Tel.: (91) 4023391221
Web Site: http://www.heritagefoods.in
Sales Range: $75-99.9 Million
Emp.: 500
Milk Processing & Milk Products Mfr & Distr
N.A.I.C.S.: 311511

Heritage Nutrivet Limited (1)
Part -B of 3rd Floor H No 8-2 293/82/A/1286 Plot No 1286, Road No 1 & 65 Jubilee Hills, Hyderabad, 500 033, Telangana, India
Tel.: (91) 4023391221
Web Site: https://www.heritagenutrivet.in
Cattle Feed Product Mfr & Distr
N.A.I.C.S.: 311119
Brahmani Nara (Mng Dir)

HERITAGE GROUP LTD.
Heritage Hall Le Marchant Street, PO Box 225, Saint Peter Port, GY1 4HY, Guernsey
Tel.: (44) 1481 716000
Web Site: http://www.heritage.co.gg
Sales Range: $75-99.9 Million
Emp.: 200
Insurance & Financial Services; Fund Administration, Fiduciary, Corporate & Trust Services
N.A.I.C.S.: 523999
Richard Tee (CEO)

Subsidiaries:

Better Capital LLP (1)
Third Floor 39-41 Charing Cross Road, London, WC2H 0AR, United Kingdom
Tel.: (44) 20 7440 0840
Web Site: http://www.bettercapital.co.uk
Emp.: 20
Privater Equity Firm
N.A.I.C.S.: 523999
Jon Moulton (Chm)

Holding (Domestic):

CAV Aerospace Ltd. (2)
Unit 24 Medomslay Road, Consett, DH8 6SR, County Durham, United Kingdom
Tel.: (44) 1207 582811
Web Site: http://www.cav-aerospace.net
Aircraft Part Mfr
N.A.I.C.S.: 336413

Clarity Commerce Solutions Ltd. (2)
Unit 1 Beechwood Lime Tree Way, Chineham Business Park, Basingstoke, RG24 8WA, Hants, United Kingdom
Tel.: (44) 1256365150
Web Site: http://www.omnicogroup.com
Sales Range: $25-49.9 Million
Software Management Solutions for the Entertainment, Ticketing, Hospitality & Leisure Sectors
N.A.I.C.S.: 423430
Bill Henry (CEO)

Subsidiary (Domestic):

Baron LRMS Limited (3)
Springfield Mills Spa Street, Ossett, WF50HW, West Yorkshire, United Kingdom
Tel.: (44) 8448044120
Business Support Services
N.A.I.C.S.: 561499

Subsidiary (US):

Clarity Commerce Solutions, Inc. (3)
355 Inverness Dr S Ste A, Englewood, CO 80112-5816
Tel.: (303) 649-9818
Web Site: http://www.claritycommerce.com
Sales Range: $1-9.9 Million
Emp.: 25
Software Management Solutions for the Entertainment, Ticketing, Hospitality & Leisure Sectors
N.A.I.C.S.: 423430

Subsidiary (Domestic):

Clarity Retail Systems Plc (3)
Ground Floor 200 Cedarwood Chineham Business Park, Basingstoke, RG24 8WD, Hampshire, United Kingdom (100%)
Tel.: (44) 1256365150
Web Site: http://www.omnicogroup.com
Sales Range: $25-49.9 Million
Emp.: 60
Software Publisher Services
N.A.I.C.S.: 513210
William Henry (CEO)

Cyntergy Services Limited (3)
33 Hanworth Road, Sunbury, TW16 5DA, Middlesex, United Kingdom
Tel.: (44) 1932 778000
Web Site: http://www.cyntergyservicesltd.com
Sales Range: $10-24.9 Million
Emp.: 100
Information Technology Support Services
N.A.I.C.S.: 541513
Stephen Rose (Dir-Ops)

Holding (Domestic):

Spicers Ltd. (2)
Sawston, Cambridge, CB22 3JG, United Kingdom
Tel.: (44) 844 2380000
Web Site: http://www.spicers.co.uk
Office Supplies & Equipment Distr
N.A.I.C.S.: 423420
Shirley Irons (Dir-HR)

Subsidiary (Domestic):

OfficeTeam Group Limited (3)
Unit 4 500 Purley Way, Croydon, CR0 4NZ, Surrey, United Kingdom
Tel.: (44) 2087743415

3361

HERITAGE GROUP LTD.

Heritage Group Ltd.—(Continued)
Web Site: http://www.officeteam.co.uk
Emp.: 250
Office Supplies Distr & Business Support Services
N.A.I.C.S.: 424120
Jeff Whiteway *(CEO)*

Subsidiary (Non-US):

Spicers (Ireland) Limited (3)
40-60 Kingswood Road Citywest Business Campus, Saggart, Dublin, 24, Ireland
Tel.: (353) 12457777
Web Site: http://www.spicers.ie
Sales Range: $50-74.9 Million
Emp.: 60
Office Supplies & Equipment Distr
N.A.I.C.S.: 423420
Martin Everard *(Mng Dir)*

Heritage International Fund Services (Malta) Limited (1)
SmartCity Malta SCM 01 Suite 502, Ricasoli, Kalkara, SCM 1001, Malta
Tel.: (356) 2090 8900
Financial Services
N.A.I.C.S.: 523999

HERITAGE MINING LTD.
300-1055 West Hastings St, Vancouver, V6E 2E9, BC, Canada
Tel.: (905) 505-0918   BC
Web Site:
   https://www.heritagemining.ca
Year Founded: 2019
HML—(CNSX)
Assets: $1,227,914
Liabilities: $147,717
Net Worth: $1,080,197
Earnings: ($2,149,250)
Fiscal Year-end: 12/31/22
Metal Exploration Services
N.A.I.C.S.: 213114
Patrick Mohan *(Chm)*

HERITAGE OIL PLC
4th Fl Windward House La Route de la Liberation, Saint Helier, JE2 3BQ, Jersey
Tel.: (44) 1534835400
Web Site:
   http://www.heritageoilplc.com
Sales Range: $1-9.9 Million
Emp.: 139
Oil & Gas Exploration
N.A.I.C.S.: 211120
Michael John Hibberd *(Chm)*

Subsidiaries:

Heritage Oil Corporation (1)
633 6th Ave SW Ste 2000, Calgary, T2P 2Y5, AB, Canada
Tel.: (403) 234-9974
Web Site: http://www.heritageoilltd.com
Sales Range: $1-9.9 Million
Oil & Gas Exploration, Development & Production
N.A.I.C.S.: 211120
Michael John Hibberd *(Chm)*

Subsidiary (Non-US):

Heritage Oil & Gas Limited (2)
St No 30 House 24 Sector F-6 1, Islamabad, Pakistan
Tel.: (92) 512825011
Web Site: http://www.heritageoilplc.com
Oil & Gas Development & Production Services
N.A.I.C.S.: 211120

HERITAGE POULTRY LTD.
20 Woodslee Avenue, Paris, N3L 4A5, ON, Canada
Tel.: (519) 442-7812
Web Site:
   http://www.heritagepoultry.com
Year Founded: 1998
Rev.: $16,258,706
Emp.: 70
Poultry Services
N.A.I.C.S.: 311615
Rodolfo Martinez *(Pres)*

HERKULES CAPITAL AS
Haakon VIIs gt 5B, 0161, Oslo, Norway
Tel.: (47) 22090600   NO
Web Site:
   http://www.herkulescapital.no
Sales Range: $10-24.9 Million
Emp.: 25
Privater Equity Firm
N.A.I.C.S.: 523999
Gert W. Munthe *(Founder, Chm & Partner)*

Subsidiaries:

Aibel AS (1)
Vestre Svanholmen 14, 4068, Stavanger, Norway (50%)
Tel.: (47) 85270000
Web Site: http://www.aibel.com
Sales Range: $1-4.9 Billion
Emp.: 1,500
Oil & Gas Production Facilities Support Services
N.A.I.C.S.: 213112
Mads Andersen *(Pres & CEO)*

Bandak Group (1)
Heroya Naeringspark Tormod Gjestlandsveg 16, 3936, Porsgrunn, Norway
Tel.: (47) 35 10 11 11
Web Site: http://www.bandakgroup.com
Oil & Gas Field Equipment Mfr
N.A.I.C.S.: 333914

European House of Beds AB (1)
Axel Danielssons Vag 267, 215 82, Malmo, Sweden
Tel.: (46) 40374735
Web Site:
   http://www.europeanhouseofbeds.com
Sales Range: $50-74.9 Million
Mattress Mfr
N.A.I.C.S.: 337910
Pia Rasmussen *(Owner & CEO)*

Intelecom Group AS (1)
Brynsveien 13, PO Box 124 Bryn, Oslo, 0667, Norway
Tel.: (47) 03050
Web Site: http://www.intele.com
Sales Range: $75-99.9 Million
Holding Company; Cloud-Based Multi-Channel Communication System Management Services
N.A.I.C.S.: 551112
Knut-Hakon Nilsen *(CFO)*

Subsidiary (Non-US):

Intelecom Danmark AS (2)
Digevej 114, 2300, Copenhagen, Denmark
Tel.: (45) 70807080
Information Technology Consulting Services
N.A.I.C.S.: 541511
Bettina Lip *(Mgr-Customer Svc)*

Intelecom Sweden AB (2)
Gustavslundsvagen 145, 16751, Bromma, Sweden
Tel.: (46) 840004000
Web Site: http://www.imtelecom.se
Emp.: 15
Information Technology Consulting Services
N.A.I.C.S.: 541511
Johan Josdal *(Partner & Acct Mgr)*

Intelecom UK Ltd. (2)
10 Greycoat Place, London, SW1P 1SB, United Kingdom
Tel.: (44) 845 080 3070
Web Site: http://www.intele.com
Cloud-Based Multi-Channel Communication System Management Services
N.A.I.C.S.: 517810

HERKULES S.A.
ul Annopol 5, 03-236, Warsaw, Poland
Tel.: (48) 22913111111
Web Site: https://www.herkules-polska.pl
HRS—(WAR)
Sales Range: Less than $1 Million

Crane Rental Services
N.A.I.C.S.: 532490
Marta Towpik *(CEO)*

Subsidiaries:

Generation Mining Ltd. (1)
100 King Street West Suite 7010, PO Box 70, Toronto, M5X 1B1, ON, Canada
Tel.: (416) 640-0280
Web Site: https://www.genmining.com
Rev.: $187,382
Assets: $18,480,628
Liabilities: $36,281,925
Net Worth: ($17,801,297)
Earnings: ($41,540,704)
Emp.: 17
Fiscal Year-end: 12/31/2022
Mineral Exploration Services
N.A.I.C.S.: 213114
Brian Jennings *(CFO)*

PGMB Budopol S.A. (1)
Opolska 6, 41-800, Zabrze, Poland
Tel.: (48) 427137652
Web Site: https://pgmb-budopol.pl
Construction Services
N.A.I.C.S.: 236220

Viatron S.A. (1)
Plac Kaszubski 8 / 505, 81-350, Gdynia, Poland
Tel.: (48) 587835095
Web Site: https://www.viatron.pl
Wind Electric Power Generation Services
N.A.I.C.S.: 221115

HERM. DAUELSBERG GMBH & CO. KG
Am Wall 128 134, 28195, Bremen, Germany
Tel.: (49) 4213093303
Web Site: http://www.dauelsberg.de
Year Founded: 1857
Rev.: $120,366,444
Emp.: 35
Ship Owning & Broker Services
N.A.I.C.S.: 488330
Klaus F. Bunnemann *(Co-Owner & Mng Dir)*

HERMANN LANGE GMBH & CO. KG
Herforder Str 333, 33609, Bielefeld, Germany
Tel.: (49) 52178700
Web Site:
   http://www.hermannlange.de
Rev.: $25,105,080
Emp.: 50
Women Apparel Distr
N.A.I.C.S.: 458110
Reinhard Schnier *(Mng Dir)*

HERMANN SCHWELLING MASCHINENBAU GMBH & CO. KG
Austrasse 1-9, 88699, Frickingen, Germany
Tel.: (49) 75 54 2100 0   De
Web Site: http://www.hsm.eu
Year Founded: 1971
Emp.: 700
Shredding, Cutting & Compacting Equipment Designer, Mfr & Whslr
N.A.I.C.S.: 335999
Hermann Schwelling *(Mng Dir)*

HERMES CENTRE JOINT STOCK COMPANY
20a Naran Road, Bayangol District Hermes Centre, Ulaanbaatar, Mongolia
Tel.: (976) 11301577
HRM—(MONG)
Rev.: $550,718
Assets: $3,192,591
Liabilities: $78,531
Net Worth: $3,114,060
Earnings: $311,604
Fiscal Year-end: 12/31/19

Home Furnishing & Furniture Mfr
N.A.I.C.S.: 449129

HERMES INTERNATIONAL SCA
24 rue du faubourg Saint-Honore, 75008, Paris, France
Tel.: (33) 140174920   FR
Web Site:
   https://www.finance.hermes.com
Year Founded: 1837
HESAF—(OTCIQ)
Sales Range: $5-14.9 Billion
Personal Care Product Distr
N.A.I.C.S.: 423940
Guillaume de Seynes *(Exec VP-Mfg Div & Equity Investments)*

Subsidiaries:

Hermes Argentina Srl (1)
Av Alvear 1901, Buenos Aires, Argentina
Tel.: (54) 1148041209
Clothing Accessory & Jewelry Retailer
N.A.I.C.S.: 458110

Hermes Asia Pacific Limited (1)
Shop G24 Sogo Department Store 555 Hennessy Road, Causeway Bay, China (Hong Kong)
Tel.: (852) 25755424
Clothing Accessory & Jewelry Retailer
N.A.I.C.S.: 458110

Hermes Benelux Nordics SA (1)
50 Boulevard de Waterloo, 1000, Brussels, Belgium
Tel.: (32) 25112062
Clothing Accessory & Jewelry Retailer
N.A.I.C.S.: 458110

Hermes China Co. Ltd. (1)
G/F Shanghai Plaza 66 No 1266 Nanjing Xi Road, Shanghai, 200040, China
Tel.: (86) 2162880328
Clothing Accessory & Jewelry Retailer
N.A.I.C.S.: 458110

Hermes Denmark ApS (1)
4 Hojbro Plads, Copenhagen, 1200, Denmark
Tel.: (45) 33112424
Clothing Accessory & Jewelry Retailer
N.A.I.C.S.: 458110

Hermes Do Brasil Industria E Comercio Ltda. (1)
Av Magalhaes de Castro 12 000 Loja 32 Piso Terreo, Sao Paulo, 05502-001, Brazil
Tel.: (55) 1135524500
Clothing Accessory & Jewelry Retailer
N.A.I.C.S.: 458110

Hermes GmbH (1)
Maximilianstrasse 8, Munich, 80539, Germany
Tel.: (49) 892919703
Clothing Accessory & Jewelry Retailer
N.A.I.C.S.: 458110

Hermes Grece S.A. (1)
Stadiou 4 and Voukourestiou 1, Athens, 105 64, Greece
Tel.: (30) 2103233715
Clothing Accessory & Jewelry Retailer
N.A.I.C.S.: 458110

Hermes Immobilier Geneve SA (1)
39 Rue du Rhone, Geneva, Switzerland
Tel.: (41) 228190719
Clothing Accessory & Jewelry Retailer
N.A.I.C.S.: 458110

Hermes India Retail & Distributors Private Limited (1)
G8-G9 Yashwant Place Commercial Complex, Chanakyapuri, New Delhi, 110021, India
Tel.: (91) 1126885501
Clothing Accessory & Jewelry Retailer
N.A.I.C.S.: 458110

Hermes Internacional Portugal Lda (1)
Largo do Chiado 9, Lisbon, 1200-108, Portugal
Tel.: (351) 213242070
Clothing Accessory & Jewelry Retailer

AND PRIVATE COMPANIES — HERO CORP.

N.A.I.C.S.: 458110

Hermes Italie S.P.A. (1)
Via Gastone Pisoni 2, 20121, Milan, Italy
Tel.: (39) 0289087333
Clothing Accessory & Jewelry Retailer
N.A.I.C.S.: 458110

Hermes Japon Co., Ltd. (1)
4-1 Ginza 5-chome, Chuo-ku, Tokyo, 104-0061, Japan
Tel.: (81) 332896811
Clothing Accessory & Jewelry Retailer
N.A.I.C.S.: 458110

Hermes Prague, A.S. (1)
Parizska 120/12, Prague, 110 00, Czech Republic
Tel.: (420) 224817545
Clothing Accessory & Jewelry Retailer
N.A.I.C.S.: 458110

Hermes Sellier SAS (1)
24 rue du Faubourg Saint-Honore, 75008, Paris, France
Tel.: (33) 149923892
Apparel & Footwear Whslr
N.A.I.C.S.: 424340

Hermes de Paris Mexico, S.A. de C.V. (1)
Av Presidente Masaryk 422-A Col Polanco, Miguel Hidalgo, Mexico, 11560, Mexico
Tel.: (52) 5552822118
Clothing Accessory & Jewelry Retailer
N.A.I.C.S.: 458110

Hermes of Paris, Inc. (1)
55 E 59th St, New York, NY 10022-1199
Tel.: (212) 759-7585
Web Site: http://www.hermes.com
Sales Range: $150-199.9 Million
Emp.: 350
Jewelry & Luxury Goods Sales
N.A.I.C.S.: 423940
Robert B. Chavez *(Pres & CEO)*

Holding Textile Hermes SAS (1)
16 chemin des Muriers, 69310, Pierre-Benite, France
Tel.: (33) 472395000
Web Site: http://www.holding-textile-hermes.com
Textile Design Services
N.A.I.C.S.: 541490

J.L. & Company Limited (1)
Northampton Site/Ready-To-Wear Westminster Works Oliver Street, Northampton, NN3 7JL, United Kingdom
Tel.: (44) 1604715011
Shoe Mfr
N.A.I.C.S.: 316210

John Lobb SAS (1)
32 rue de Mogador, 1741, Paris, France
Tel.: (33) 143475814
Web Site: http://www.johnlobb.com
Shoe Mfr
N.A.I.C.S.: 316210

HERMES MUSIC S.A. DE C.V.
Naranjo 76, Santa Maria la Ribera, Mexico, 06400, Distrito Federal, Mexico
Tel.: (52) 5550022200
Web Site: http://www.hermes-music.com.mx
Sales Range: $75-99.9 Million
Emp.: 300
Musical Instrument Distr
N.A.I.C.S.: 459140
Juan Cordoba Perches *(Gen Mgr)*

Subsidiaries:

Hermes Trading Co. Inc. (1)
830 N Cage Blvd, Pharr, TX 78577-3106
Tel.: (956) 781-8472
Web Site: http://www.hermes-music.com
Sales Range: $75-99.9 Million
Emp.: 114
Musical Instrument Sales
N.A.I.C.S.: 459140
Jorge Saavedra *(Pres)*

HERMES SCHLEIFMITTEL GMBH & CO. KG
Luruper Hauptstrasse 106, 22547, Hamburg, Germany
Tel.: (49) 4083300
Web Site: http://www.hermes-schleifmittel.com
Year Founded: 1927
Sales Range: $25-49.9 Million
Emp.: 180
Abrasive Products
N.A.I.C.S.: 327910
Jan Cord Becker *(CEO)*

Subsidiaries:

Hermes Abrasives (Canada) Ltd. (1)
160 Brunel Road, Mississauga, L4Z 1T5, ON, Canada
Tel.: (905) 890-2000
Abrasive Product Distr
N.A.I.C.S.: 423840

Hermes Abrasives (Shanghai) Co., Ltd. (1)
No 98 Tian Ying Rd Factory No 3 Qingpu Industrial Zone, Qingpu, Shanghai, 201712, China
Tel.: (86) 21 6922 5522
Web Site: http://www.hermesabrasives.com.cn
Motor Vehicle Parts Mfr
N.A.I.C.S.: 336390

Hermes Abrasives Ltd. (1)
524 Viking Dr, Virginia Beach, VA 23452
Tel.: (757) 486-6623
Web Site: http://www.hermesabrasives.com
Coated Abrasive Products
N.A.I.C.S.: 327910
Robert Bishop *(Controller)*

Hermes Schleifkorper GmbH (1)
Lohrmannstrasse 21, 01237, Dresden, Germany
Tel.: (49) 351 28 01 0
Web Site: http://www.hermes-schleifkoerper.de
Abrasive Product Mfr & Distr
N.A.I.C.S.: 327910
Axel Krupp *(Mng Dir)*

HERMES TRANSPORTES BLINDADOS SA
Av Produccion Nacional N 278-Urbanizacion La Villa, Chorrillos, Lima, Peru
Tel.: (51) 6174000
Web Site: https://www.hermes.com.pe
Year Founded: 1985
HERMESC1—(LIM)
Rev.: $115,712,088
Assets: $436,234,583
Liabilities: $224,453,620
Net Worth: $211,780,962
Earnings: $22,060,022
Fiscal Year-end: 12/31/23
Security & Investigation Services
N.A.I.C.S.: 561611
Gonzalo De La Puente Wiese *(Chm)*

HERMITAGE OFFSHORE SERVICES LTD.
LOM Building 27 Reid Street, Hamilton, HM 11, Bermuda
Tel.: (441) 298 3535   MH
Web Site: http://www.hermitage-offshore.com
Year Founded: 2013
Rev.: $20,654,000
Assets: $191,074,000
Liabilities: $137,010,000
Net Worth: $54,064,000
Earnings: ($197,294,000)
Emp.: 7
Fiscal Year-end: 12/31/18
Deep Sea Freight Transportation
N.A.I.C.S.: 483111
Marianne Lie *(Vice Chm)*

HERNER GLAS - BERND HOFFBAUER GMBH
Am Trimbuschhof 16 20, 44628, Herne, Germany
Tel.: (49) 232317750
Web Site: http://www.hernerglas.de
Rev.: $20,691,000
Emp.: 90
Lighting Glasses Mfr
N.A.I.C.S.: 335131
Bernd Hoffbauer *(Mng Dir)*

HERO AG
Niederlenzer Kirchweg 6, PO Box 36, Lenzburg, LE4 9JQ, Switzerland
Tel.: (41) 628855111
Web Site: http://www.hero.ch
Year Founded: 1886
Sales Range: $1-4.9 Billion
Emp.: 4,000
Holding Company; Food Products Mfr & Distr
N.A.I.C.S.: 551112
Arend Oetker *(Owner)*

Subsidiaries:

Beech-Nut Nutrition Corporation (1)
13023 Tesson Ferry Rd Ste 105, Saint Louis, MO 63128-3480
Tel.: (314) 436-7667
Web Site: http://www.beechnut.com
Sales Range: $25-49.9 Million
Emp.: 36
Baby Food Mfr
N.A.I.C.S.: 311422

Bempfinger Lebensmittel GmbH (1)
Mittelstadter Strasse 48, Bempflingen, Munich, 72658, Baden Wurttemberg, Germany (100%)
Tel.: (49) 7123381310
Web Site: http://www.bempflinger.de
Sales Range: $25-49.9 Million
Emp.: 70
N.A.I.C.S.: 236220
Martin Renner *(Pres)*

Capfruit S.A. (1)
ZA Rapon, Anneyron, 26140, Paris, France (100%)
Tel.: (33) 475314022
Web Site: http://www.capfruit.com
Sales Range: $25-49.9 Million
Emp.: 40
Supplier of Fruit Purees, Coulis, Decoration Fruits & Frozen Fruit for Culinary Arts
N.A.I.C.S.: 311411

Citron Export Inc. (1)
PO Box 1025, Adjuntas, PR 00601-1025 (100%)
Tel.: (787) 829-2610
Sales Range: $25-49.9 Million
Emp.: 28
N.A.I.C.S.: 236220

Hero Benelux B.V. (1)
Teterubgsedik 279, 4817 ME, Breda, Netherlands (100%)
Tel.: (31) 765798000
Web Site: http://www.herobenelux.nl
Sales Range: $75-99.9 Million
Emp.: 188
Food Manufacturing & Distribution
N.A.I.C.S.: 311999
Jop Peek *(Mng Dir)*

Hero Czech s.r.o. (1)
Radlicka 751/113e, 158 00, Prague, Czech Republic
Tel.: (420) 227 031 311
Web Site: http://firma.hero.cz
Emp.: 60
Food Manufacturing & Distribution
N.A.I.C.S.: 311999
Vladmir Kucera *(Gen Mgr)*

Hero Espana, S.A. (1)
Avda De Murcia 1, 30820, Alcantarilla, Murcia, Spain (100%)
Tel.: (34) 968898900
Web Site: http://www.hero.es
Food Manufacturing & Distribution
N.A.I.C.S.: 311999
Jose Antonio Cano Turpin *(Mgr-Production)*

Hero Italia SpA (1)
Via Leoni 4, Verona, 37121, Italy (100%)
Tel.: (39) 0458090911

Web Site: http://www.hero.it
Sales Range: $25-49.9 Million
Emp.: 22
Food Manufacturing & Distribution
N.A.I.C.S.: 311999
Robert Lehner *(CEO)*

Hero Polska Sp. z o.o. (1)
ul Pilchowicka 9/11, 02-175, Warsaw, Poland (100%)
Tel.: (48) 225742320
Web Site: http://www.hero.pl
Sales Range: $25-49.9 Million
Emp.: 1
Food Manufacturing & Distribution
N.A.I.C.S.: 311999
Monika Brazdova *(CFO)*

Hero Portugal Lda. (1)
Avda Leran Aeras 6 A Kuintaeranp, Alsragede, 2610 097, Amadora, Portugal (100%)
Tel.: (351) 214721880
Web Site: http://www.hero.pt
Sales Range: $25-49.9 Million
Emp.: 50
Food Mfr & Distr
N.A.I.C.S.: 311999
Miguel Rodregues *(Gen Mgr)*

Hero Slovakia s.r.o. (1)
Mugrasova 2, 949 01, Nitra, Slovakia
Tel.: (421) 377 784 005
Web Site: http://www.hero.cz
Emp.: 50
Food Manufacturing & Distribution
N.A.I.C.S.: 311999

Juver Alimentacion SA (1)
C Jesus Aguilar Arnat 40, E 30110, Churra, Murcia, Spain
Tel.: (34) 968356900
Food Manufacturing & Distribution
N.A.I.C.S.: 311999

HERO CORP.
34 Community Centre Basant Lok, Vasant Vihar, New Delhi, India
Tel.: (91) 11 2614 2451
Web Site: http://www.herogroup.com
Year Founded: 1956
Sales Range: $1-4.9 Billion
Emp.: 30,000
Holding Company
N.A.I.C.S.: 551112
Brijmohan Lall Munjal *(Chm & Mng Dir)*

Subsidiaries:

Hero Eco Limited (1)
80 Coleman Street, London, EC2R 5BJ, United Kingdom
Tel.: (44) 1242 807 420
Electric Cycles & Scooters Mfr
N.A.I.C.S.: 336991
Arindam Ganguli *(CEO-A2B Ebike)*

Hero MotoCorp Ltd. (1)
The Grand Plaza Plot No 2 Nelson Mandela Road, Vasant Kunj -Phase -II, New Delhi, 110070, India
Tel.: (91) 1146044200
Web Site: https://www.heromotocorp.com
Rev.: $4,302,082,785
Assets: $3,152,616,285
Liabilities: $1,028,729,520
Net Worth: $2,123,886,765
Earnings: $400,770,825
Emp.: 8,793
Fiscal Year-end: 03/31/2021
Motorcycles & Parts Mfr
N.A.I.C.S.: 336991
Pawan Munjal *(Chm, CEO & Mng Dir)*

Majestic Auto Ltd. (1)
A-110 Sector-4, Noida, 201301, India
Tel.: (91) 1204540909
Web Site: https://www.majesticauto.in
Rev.: $9,551,001
Assets: $91,082,191
Liabilities: $32,438,297
Net Worth: $58,643,894
Earnings: $2,976,874
Emp.: 19
Fiscal Year-end: 03/31/2021
Bicycle Components Mfr
N.A.I.C.S.: 336991

HERO CORP.

Hero Corp.—(Continued)

Mahesh Chander Munjal *(Chm & Co-Mng Dir)*

Munjal Auto Industries Limited (1)
2nd Floor Tower C Unitech Business Zone, Nirvana Country South City 2 Sector 50, Gurgaon, 122018, India
Tel.: (91) 1244057891
Web Site: https://www.munjalauto.com
Rev.: $292,070,292
Assets: $122,284,153
Liabilities: $78,308,043
Net Worth: $43,976,109
Earnings: $2,790,142
Emp.: 946
Fiscal Year-end: 03/31/2021
Automotive Components Mfr
N.A.I.C.S.: 336110
Sudhir Kumar Munjal *(Chm & Mng Dir)*

Munjal Showa Limited (1)
9-11 Maruti Industrial Area Sector-18, Gurgaon, 122015, Haryana, India
Tel.: (91) 1244783000
Web Site: http://www.munjalshowa.net
Rev.: $151,169,234
Assets: $97,189,401
Liabilities: $19,107,955
Net Worth: $78,081,446
Earnings: $3,825,094
Emp.: 2,412
Fiscal Year-end: 03/31/2023
Mfr of Shock Absorbers & Gas Springs for 2- & 4-Wheeled Vehicles
N.A.I.C.S.: 336390
Yogesh Chander Munjal *(Chm & Co-Mng Dir)*

Shivam Autotech Ltd. (1)
10 1st Floor Emaar Digital Greens Tower A Sector 61, Golf Course Extension Road, Gurgaon, 122102, Haryana, India
Tel.: (91) 1244698700
Web Site: https://www.shivamautotech.com
Rev.: $67,011,699
Assets: $100,247,102
Liabilities: $84,819,680
Net Worth: $15,427,421
Earnings: ($3,074,744)
Emp.: 879
Fiscal Year-end: 03/31/2021
Motorcycle Parts Mfr
N.A.I.C.S.: 336991
Davendra Ujlayan *(VP-Fin)*

HEROES TECHNOLOGY LTD.
25 Horsell Road, The Orangery, London, N5 1XL, United Kingdom
Tel.: (44) 2035142292   UK
Web Site: https://makeheroes.co
Year Founded: 2020
Ecommerce Services
N.A.I.C.S.: 425120
Alessio Bruni *(Co-Founder)*

Subsidiaries:

Magmatic Limited (1)
Trunki Towers Shaftesbury Chapel Union Road, Bristol, BS2 0LP, United Kingdom
Tel.: (44) 1179542780
Web Site: http://www.trunki.com
Sales Range: $10-24.9 Million
Emp.: 21
Children's Plastic Travel Bag & Toy Mfr
N.A.I.C.S.: 326199
Rob Law *(Gen Mgr)*

Subsidiary (US):

Trunki Inc. (2)
1000 N W St Ste 1200, Wilmington, DE 19801
Web Site: http://www.trunki.com
Children's Travel Bag Whslr
N.A.I.C.S.: 423990

HERON RESOURCES LIMITED
Level 8 309 Kent Street Suite 2, Sydney, 2000, NSW, Australia
Tel.: (61) 2 9119 8111   AU
Web Site:
http://www.heronresources.com.au
Rev.: $834,019
Assets: $210,821,137
Liabilities: $120,176,079
Net Worth: $90,645,058
Earnings: ($28,665,357)
Emp.: 21
Fiscal Year-end: 06/30/19
Base & Precious Metal Exploration Services
N.A.I.C.S.: 213114
David von Perger *(Gen Mgr-Exploration & Geology)*

HEROSE GMBH
Elly-Heuss-Knapp-Strasse 12, 23843, Bad Oldesloe, Germany
Tel.: (49) 45315090
Web Site: http://www.herose.com
Year Founded: 1873
Rev.: $50,852,937
Emp.: 300
Industrial Valve Mfr
N.A.I.C.S.: 332911
Dirk M. Zschalich *(Chm & Mng Dir)*

Subsidiaries:

HEROSE Trading Co., Ltd. (1)
Wanda Road 41-16 Building 33 Jingang Industry Park, Dalian Economy & Technology Development Zone, Dalian, 116600, China
Tel.: (86) 41166164388
Web Site: http://www.herose.cn
Fitting & Valve Distr
N.A.I.C.S.: 423720

Herose Iberica sl (1)
Deu i Mata 117-121 1-5, 08029, Barcelona, Spain
Tel.: (34) 930028328
Web Site: http://www.herose.es
Fitting & Valve Distr
N.A.I.C.S.: 423720
Xavier Greoles Sole *(Head-Production Engrg)*

Herose Limited (1)
3 Lindley Road, Finningley, Doncaster, DN9 3DQ, United Kingdom
Tel.: (44) 1302773114
Web Site: http://www.herose.co.uk
Fitting & Valve Distr
N.A.I.C.S.: 423720
Keith Stewart *(Mng Dir)*

HEROUX-DEVTEK INC.
1111 Saint Charles Street West Suite 600 West Tower, Longueuil, J4K 5G4, QC, Canada
Tel.: (450) 679-5450   Ca
Web Site:
   https://www.herouxdevtek.com
Year Founded: 1942
5D6—(DEU)
Rev.: $465,221,478
Assets: $673,286,399
Liabilities: $355,904,215
Net Worth: $317,382,183
Earnings: $28,271,553
Emp.: 1,800
Fiscal Year-end: 03/31/24
Precision Parts Mfr for Information Technology, Gas Turbines & Aircraft
N.A.I.C.S.: 336412
Gilles Labbe *(Chm)*

Subsidiaries:

APPH Ltd. (1)
8 Pembroke Court Manor Park, Runcorn, WA7 1TG, Cheshire, United Kingdom   (100%)
Tel.: (44) 192 853 0530
Web Site: https://www.apph.com
Sales Range: $75-99.9 Million
Emp.: 390
Aircraft Landing Gear, Hydraulic Systems & Other Components Mfr, Repair & Overhaul Services
N.A.I.C.S.: 336413

Subsidiary (Domestic):

APPH (Bolton) Ltd. (2)
Great Bank Road, Wingates Industrial Park, Westhoughton, BL5 3XU, Lancs, United Kingdom   (100%)
Tel.: (44) 192 853 0530
Web Site: http://www.apphltd.co.uk
Sales Range: $25-49.9 Million
Emp.: 18
Aerospace Filters Mfr
N.A.I.C.S.: 336413

APPH Aviation Services Ltd. (2)
1 Rokeby Court Eastgate Way, Runcorn, WA7 1RW, Cheshire, United Kingdom   (100%)
Tel.: (44) 1928579791
Web Site: http://www.apphltd.co.uk
Sales Range: $25-49.9 Million
Emp.: 46
Aircraft Landing Gear, Hydraulic Systems & Flight Controls Maintenance, Repair & Overhaul Services
N.A.I.C.S.: 336413
Ken Livingston *(Gen Mgr)*

APPH Nottingham Ltd. (2)
Urban Road, Kirkby in Ashfield, NG17 8AP, Notts, United Kingdom
Tel.: (44) 1623754355
Sales Range: $25-49.9 Million
Emp.: 70
Precision Machined Aircraft Components & Sub-Assemblies Mfr
N.A.I.C.S.: 336413
Gaetan Roy *(Gen Mgr)*

Subsidiary (US):

APPH Wichita, Inc. (2)
1445 Sierra Dr, Wichita, KS 67209
Tel.: (316) 943-5752
Aircraft Landing Gear & Hydraulic Systems Design, Development, Testing & Repair Services
N.A.I.C.S.: 336413
James Meier *(Mgr-Production)*

Beaver Aerospace & Defense, Inc. (1)
11850 Mayfield, Livonia, MI 48150
Tel.: (734) 853-5003
Web Site: http://www.beaver-online.com
Custom Ball Screws & Electromechanical Actuation Systems Design & Mfr
N.A.I.C.S.: 332722

HDI Landing Gear USA, Inc. (1)
663 Montgomery Ave, Springfield, OH 45506
Tel.: (937) 325-1586
Web Site: http://www.herouxdevtek.com
Aircraft Landing Gear Mfr
N.A.I.C.S.: 336413
Fred Gagne *(Gen Mgr)*

Heroux-Devtek - Longueuil Plant (1)
755 Rue Thurber, Longueuil, J4H 3N2, QC, Canada
Tel.: (450) 679-5450
Web Site: http://www.herouxdevtek.com
Sales Range: $200-249.9 Million
Emp.: 400
Aircraft Landing Gear Components Mfr
N.A.I.C.S.: 336413
Gaetan Roy *(VP)*

Heroux-Devtek - Scarborough Plant (1)
1480 Birchmount Road, Scarborough, M1P 2E3, ON, Canada
Tel.: (416) 757-2366
Web Site: http://www.herouxdevtek.com
Sales Range: $25-49.9 Million
Emp.: 52
Aerostructure Components Mfr
N.A.I.C.S.: 336413
Michael Secord *(Plant Mgr)*

HEROZ, INC.
7F PMO Tamachi 5-31-17 Shiba, Minato-Ku, Tokyo, 108-0014, Japan
Tel.: (81) 364352495
Web Site: https://www.heroz.co.jp
Year Founded: 2009
4382—(TKS)
Rev.: $31,999,010
Assets: $50,837,510
Liabilities: $16,842,280
Net Worth: $33,995,230
Earnings: ($7,495,740)

INTERNATIONAL PUBLIC

Fiscal Year-end: 04/30/24
Software Development Services
N.A.I.C.S.: 541511
Tomohiro Takahashi *(COO)*

HERSTAL, S.A.
Voie de Liege 33, 4040, Herstal, Belgium
Tel.: (32) 4 240 8111   BE
Web Site: http://www.fnherstal.com
Year Founded: 1889
Sales Range: $250-299.9 Million
Emp.: 2,500
Small Arm & Ammunition For Defense & Law Enforcement Hunting & Shooting Arm & Ammunition Archery Accessory Outdoor Equipment Mfr
N.A.I.C.S.: 332994
Philippe Claessen *(CEO)*

Subsidiaries:

Browning International S.A. (1)
Parc Industriel Des Hauts Sarts, Herstal, 4040, Liege, Belgium   (100%)
Tel.: (32) 42405211
Web Site: http://www.browningint.com
Sales Range: $25-49.9 Million
Emp.: 60
Sporting Goods; Hunting, Shooting & Archery; Outdoor Goods
N.A.I.C.S.: 339920

Browning Viana Fabrica De Armas E Artigos De Desporto Sa (1)
Lugar de Morenos s/n, 4935-231, Neiva, Portugal
Tel.: (351) 258359000
Hunting Equipment Distr
N.A.I.C.S.: 423910

FN Herstal Far East & Australasia Pte. Ltd. (1)
51 Goldhill Plaza 17-06, Singapore, 308900, Singapore
Tel.: (65) 62526612
Small Calibre Firearm Mfr & Distr
N.A.I.C.S.: 332994

FN Herstal S.A. (1)
33 Rue Voie De Liege, Herstal, 4040, Liege, Belgium   (100%)
Tel.: (32) 42408811
Web Site: http://www.fnherstal.com
Sales Range: Less than $1 Million
Emp.: 1,200
Mfr Small Arms, Ammunitions, Weapons Systems, Engineering
N.A.I.C.S.: 332994

Subsidiary (US):

FN America, Inc. (2)
7918 Jones Branch Dr Ste 400, McLean, VA 22102
Tel.: (703) 288-3500
Web Site: http://www.fnhusa.com
Firearms Mfr, Marketing & Sales
N.A.I.C.S.: 332994
Mark Cherpes *(Pres & CEO)*

Subsidiary (Domestic):

FN America, LLC (3)
797 Old Clemson Rd, Columbia, SC 29229-4203
Tel.: (540) 288-8002
Web Site: http://www.fnmfg.com
Small Arms Mfr
N.A.I.C.S.: 332994
Greg Butler *(COO)*

Subsidiary (Non-US):

FNH UK Limited (2)
Unit 6 Lakeside Business Park Swan Lane, Sandhurst, GU47 9DN, Berks, United Kingdom
Tel.: (44) 1252 874177
Web Site: http://www.manroy.com
Sales Range: $10-24.9 Million
Emp.: 60
Weapons & Related Accessories Mfr
N.A.I.C.S.: 332994
Glyn P. Bottomley *(CEO)*

AND PRIVATE COMPANIES

Subsidiary (Domestic):

Manroy Engineering Ltd. (3)
Hobbs Lane Beckley, Rye, TN31 6TS, East Sussex, United Kingdom
Tel.: (44) 1797260553
Web Site: http://www.manroy.com
Emp.: 100
Weapons & Accessories Mfr
N.A.I.C.S.: 332994
Mike Bayne *(Dir-Technical)*

Noptel Oy (1)
Teknologiantie 2, 90590, Oulu, Finland
Tel.: (358) 401814351
Web Site: http://www.noptel.fi
Emp.: 70
Optoelectronic Product Mfr
N.A.I.C.S.: 334413
Markku Koskinen *(CEO)*

U.S. Repeating Arms Company (1)
344 Winchester Ave, New Haven, CT 06511-1918
Tel.: (203) 789-5000
Web Site: http://www.winchester-guns.com
Sales Range: $100-124.9 Million
Emp.: 450
Mfr of Firearms
N.A.I.C.S.: 332994

HERTI AD

38 Antim Privi Street, 9700, Shumen, Bulgaria
Tel.: (359) 54823012
Web Site: https://www.herti.bg
Year Founded: 1993
HERT—(BUL)
Rev.: $42,774,430
Assets: $31,292,726
Liabilities: $15,162,139
Net Worth: $16,130,587
Earnings: $3,533,633
Emp.: 463
Fiscal Year-end: 12/31/23
Aluminium Pilfer-Proof Closures Mfr
N.A.I.C.S.: 331318
Alexander Blagoev Yulianov *(Chm)*

Subsidiaries:

HERTI UK Ltd. (1)
Astra House The Common, Cranleigh, GU6 8RZ, Surrey, United Kingdom
Tel.: (44) 1483266617
Web Site: https://www.herti.co.uk
Aluminium Pilfer Proof Closure Distr
N.A.I.C.S.: 423510
Pavel Zahariev *(Dir-Sls)*

Herti France (1)
281 rue Alexandre Richetta, 69 400, Villefranche-sur-Saone, France
Tel.: (33) 474661442
Web Site: https://www.herti.fr
Aluminium Pilfer Proof Closure Distr
N.A.I.C.S.: 423510

Herti Germany GmbH (1)
Ginsheimer Str, Gustavsburg, 65462, Ginsheim, Germany
Tel.: (49) 61345705055
Web Site: https://www.hertigermany.de
Aluminium Pilfer Proof Closure Distr
N.A.I.C.S.: 423510

Herti Group International (1)
168 Stirbei Voda street 20 B block 6th ap 1st District, 010121, Bucharest, Romania
Tel.: (40) 314072531
Web Site: https://herti.ro
Plastic Mfr
N.A.I.C.S.: 326199

Intertechservice Ltd. (1)
Yuri Gagarin Ave 23 office 314, 196135, Saint Petersburg, Russia
Tel.: (7) 8126768620
Web Site: http://www.intertechservice.com
Aluminum Extruded Product Mfr
N.A.I.C.S.: 331318

Tihert - EAD (1)
38 Antim I Str, 9700, Shumen, Bulgaria
Tel.: (359) 53232844
Web Site: https://tihert.bg
Machine Tool Distr
N.A.I.C.S.: 423830

HERTZ LITHIUM INC.

1500-1055 West Georgia Street, Vancouver, V6E 3N9, BC, Canada
Tel.: (604) 805-4602
Web Site: https://hertz-energy.com
Year Founded: 2019
HZLIF—(OTCIQ)
Lithium Product Mfr
N.A.I.C.S.: 325180
Kal Malhi *(CEO)*

HERZOG & DE MEURON BASEL LTD.

Rheinschanze 6, Basel, 4056, Switzerland
Tel.: (41) 61 385 5757
Web Site: http://www.herzogdemeuron.com
Year Founded: 1978
Sales Range: $25-49.9 Million
Emp.: 360
Architectural & Engineering Services
N.A.I.C.S.: 541310
Jacques Herzog *(Founder & Partner)*

HESAI GROUP

Building A No 658 Zhaohua Road, Changning District, Shanghai, 201702, China
Tel.: (86) 2131588240
Web Site: https://www.hesaitech.com
Year Founded: 2021
HSAI—(NASDAQ)
Rev.: $184,261,071
Assets: $588,233,861
Liabilities: $1,070,106,429
Net Worth: ($481,872,568)
Earnings: ($114,476,061)
Emp.: 1,020
Fiscal Year-end: 12/31/22
Software Development Services
N.A.I.C.S.: 541511

HESS GROUP AG

Steinholzli, CH 3097, Bern, Switzerland
Tel.: (41) 319703131
Web Site: https://thehessgroup.ch
Sales Range: $100-124.9 Million
Emp.: 500
Holding Company; Investment, Real Estate & Wineries
N.A.I.C.S.: 551112
Donald Hess *(Founder & Pres)*

HESTA AG

Baarerstrasse 101, 6302, Zug, Switzerland
Tel.: (41) 41 767 20 88
Year Founded: 1938
Sales Range: $25-49.9 Million
Emp.: 4
Holding Company
N.A.I.C.S.: 551112
Debby Blakey *(CEO)*

Subsidiaries:

Hesta Beteiligungs-GmbH (1)
Schutzen Strasse 24, 78315, Radolfzell, Germany (100%)
Tel.: (49) 77329409990
Sales Range: $75-99.9 Million
Real Estate Investment Services
N.A.I.C.S.: 523999

Hesta Immobilien GmbH (1)
Schutzenstrasse 24, 78315, Radolfzell, Germany (100%)
Tel.: (49) 77329409990
Web Site: http://www.hesta-immobilien.de
Sales Range: $50-74.9 Million
Emp.: 9
Real Estate Brokerage Services
N.A.I.C.S.: 531390
Arnold Kannenberg *(Mng Dir)*

HESTER BIOSCIENCES LIMITED

Pushpak 1st Floor Motilal Hirabhai Road Panchvati Circle, Ahmedabad, 380006, Gujarat, India
Tel.: (91) 7926445107
Web Site: https://www.hester.in
HESTERBIO—(NSE)
Rev.: $33,953,966
Assets: $76,734,977
Liabilities: $40,235,832
Net Worth: $36,499,145
Earnings: $5,389,566
Emp.: 584
Fiscal Year-end: 03/31/22
Poultry Vaccines Mfr
N.A.I.C.S.: 325414
Rajiv Gandhi *(CEO & Mng Dir)*

Subsidiaries:

Hester Biosciences Nepal Private Limited (1)
Arun Plaza 2nd Floor HIM Service Building, Sundhara, Kathmandu, 44600, Nepal
Tel.: (977) 14218322
Web Site: https://www.hester.com.np
Animal Vaccine Mfr
N.A.I.C.S.: 325412

HETMOS MOSTAR HOTELI D.D.

Mostarskog bataljona bb, Mostar, 88000, Bosnia & Herzegovina
Tel.: (387) 36 500 100
Web Site: http://www.bristol.ba
HETMRK1—(SARE)
Rev.: $187,081
Assets: $5,450,190
Liabilities: $2,180,124
Net Worth: $3,270,065
Earnings: ($301,348)
Emp.: 11
Fiscal Year-end: 12/31/20
Home Management Services
N.A.I.C.S.: 721110

HETTICH HOLDING GMBH & CO. OHG

Vahrenkampstrasse 12-16, 32278, Kirchlengern, Germany
Tel.: (49) 5223770
Web Site: http://www.corporate.hettich.com
Year Founded: 1930
Sales Range: $1-4.9 Billion
Emp.: 5,800
Holding Company; Furniture & Specialty Hardware Mfr & Distr
N.A.I.C.S.: 551112
Andreas Hettich *(Chm-Mgmt Bd)*

Subsidiaries:

Druck- und Spritzgusswerk Hettich GmbH & Co. KG (1)
Siegener Str 37, 35066, Frankenberg, Germany
Tel.: (49) 6451 741 0
Hardware Mfr & Distr
N.A.I.C.S.: 332510

HETTICH TR MOBILYA TEKNIK MALZEMELERI SAN. VE TIC. LTD. STI. (1)
Serifali mah Turker cad No 2, 34775, Istanbul, Turkiye
Tel.: (90) 216 365 46 51
Web Site: http://www.hettich.com
Emp.: 30
Hardware Distr
N.A.I.C.S.: 423710

Herrajes Hettich, S.A. de C.V. (1)
Paseo de la Reforma 107 3o piso Col Tabacalera Del Cuauhtemoc, 06030, Mexico, Mexico
Tel.: (52) 55 55922212
Hardware Distr
N.A.I.C.S.: 423710

Hettich (UK) Ltd (1)
Unit 200 Metroplex Business Park Broadway, Salford, M50 2UE, Manchester, United Kingdom
Tel.: (44) 161 872 9552
Web Site: http://www.hettich.com
Emp.: 30
Hardware Distr
N.A.I.C.S.: 423710
Chris Mortimer *(Mgr-Sls)*

Hettich America, L.P. (1)
6225 Shiloh Rd, Alpharetta, GA 30005-2206 (100%)
Tel.: (770) 887-3733
Web Site: http://www.hettichamerica.com
Sales Range: $25-49.9 Million
Emp.: 30
Furniture Hardware Mfr & Distr
N.A.I.C.S.: 332510

Hettich Australia Pty Ltd (1)
1 Herbert Place, Smithfield, 2164, NSW, Australia
Tel.: (61) 2 9616 7700
Hardware Distr
N.A.I.C.S.: 423710

Hettich CR k.s. (1)
Jihlavska 3, 591 01, Zdar nad Sazavou, Czech Republic
Tel.: (420) 566 692 111
Hardware Mfr
N.A.I.C.S.: 332510

Hettich Canada L.P. (1)
90 Snow Blvd, Concord, L4K 4A2, ON, Canada
Tel.: (905) 660-1390
Hardware Distr
N.A.I.C.S.: 423710
Gary Schaab *(Mgr-Ops)*

Hettich France SCS (1)
ZAC de Montevrain-Val d Europe 1 rue de Berlin Montevrain, 77772, Marne-la-Vallee, Cedex, France
Tel.: (33) 1 60 27 23 60
Hardware Distr
N.A.I.C.S.: 423710

Hettich Franke GmbH & Co. KG (1)
Hinter dem Ziegelwasen 6/1, D-72336, Balingen, Germany
Tel.: (49) 743330830
Web Site: http://www.hettich-franke.com
Sales Range: $50-74.9 Million
Emp.: 120
Adjustable Fittings Mfr
N.A.I.C.S.: 332510

Hettich FurnTech GmbH & Co. KG (1)
Gerhard-Luking-Strasse 10, 32602, Vlotho, Germany
Tel.: (49) 5733 798 0
Hardware Mfr & Distr
N.A.I.C.S.: 332510

Hettich Hardware Accessories (Shanghai) Co. Ltd (1)
Number 55 Xiya Road, Pudong, 200131, Shanghai, China
Tel.: (86) 21 61054588
Hardware Distr
N.A.I.C.S.: 423710

Hettich Iberia S.L. en Com. (1)
Pol Ind Etxezarreta 3, 20749, Aizarnazabal, Gipuzkoa, Spain
Tel.: (34) 943 897 020
Hardware Distr
N.A.I.C.S.: 423710

Hettich Italia Srl (1)
Via del Lavoro 25, Cimavilla di Codogne, 31013, Codogne, Italy
Tel.: (39) 0438 4781
Web Site: http://www.hettich.it
Hardware Distr
N.A.I.C.S.: 423710
Martina Dal Bianco *(Mgr-Mktg)*

Hettich Japan K.K. (1)
Surugadai Yagi Bldg 2F 3-8-5 Kanda Ogawamachi, Chiyoda-ku, Tokyo, 101-0052, Japan
Tel.: (81) 3 5283 2941
Hardware Distr
N.A.I.C.S.: 423710

Hettich Logistik Service GmbH & Co. KG (1)
In Deler Lovage 50, 32257, Bunde, Germany

HETTICH HOLDING GMBH & CO. OHG

Hettich Holding GmbH & Co. oHG—(Continued)
Tel.: (49) 522 37 70
Hardware Mfr & Distr
N.A.I.C.S.: 332510

Hettich Marketing- und Vertriebs GmbH & Co. KG (1)
Industriestrasse 83-87, 32139, Spenge, Germany
Tel.: (49) 5225 8794 0
Hardware Mfr & Distr
N.A.I.C.S.: 332510

Hettich Middle East JLT. (1)
3203 Swiss Tower JLT, PO Box 115081, Dubai, 115081, United Arab Emirates
Tel.: (971) 4 3695336
Hardware Distr
N.A.I.C.S.: 423710
Parameswaran K. A. (Mng Dir)

Hettich Polska Sp. z o.o. (1)
ul Wierzbowa 48, Lusowo, 62-080, Tarnowo Podgorne, Poland
Tel.: (48) 61 816 83 00
Web Site: http://www.hettich.com
Emp.: 10
Hardware Distr
N.A.I.C.S.: 423710
Beata Lasota (Mng Dir)

Hettich SR s.r.o. (1)
Holleho 11, 911 05, Trencin, Slovakia
Tel.: (421) 32 65 83 885
Hardware Distr
N.A.I.C.S.: 423710

Hettich Singapore (S.E.A.) Pte Ltd (1)
33 Ubi Rd 1 #01-77 Oxly Bishub, Singapore, 408729, Singapore
Tel.: (65) 64626771
Web Site: http://www.hettich.com
Hardware Distr
N.A.I.C.S.: 423710
Michael Saravanan (Dir-Comml)

Hettich Skandinaviska AB (1)
Bultvagen 4, Box 9048, 550 09, Jonkoping, Sweden
Tel.: (46) 36 312330
Hardware Distr
N.A.I.C.S.: 423710

Hettich Strothmann GmbH & Co. KG (1)
UIndustriestrasse 7F, D-33397, Rietberg, Germany
Tel.: (49) 52449230
Web Site: http://www.hettich.com
Furniture Handles Mfr
N.A.I.C.S.: 332510

Hettich-ONI GmbH & Co. KG (1)
Industriestrasse 11, 32602, Vlotho, Germany
Tel.: (49) 5228 790
Hardware Mfr & Distr
N.A.I.C.S.: 332510

Paul Hettich GmbH & Co. KG (1)
Vahrenkampstrasse 12-16, D-32278, Kirchlengern, Germany (100%)
Tel.: (49) 5223770
Web Site: http://www.hettich.com
Hardware Mfr & Dist
N.A.I.C.S.: 332510

HEUNG-A LOGISTICS CO., LTD

11F Gyeonggi Bldg 115 Samgak-Dong, Chung-Gu, Seoul, 100-200, Korea (South)
Tel.: (82) 2 730 8865
Emp.: 100
Logistics Consulting Servies
N.A.I.C.S.: 541614

HEUNG-A SHIPPING COMPANY LIMITED

5th floor8 Cheonggyecheon-ro, Junggu, Seoul, 138-200, Korea (South)
Tel.: (82) 234493000 KR
Web Site: https://heung-a.com
Year Founded: 1961
003280—(KRS)
Rev.: $136,418,680
Assets: $243,184,971
Liabilities: $139,406,239
Net Worth: $103,778,733
Earnings: $18,262,200
Emp.: 353
Fiscal Year-end: 12/31/22
International Maritime Transportation Services Including Container & Tanker Services
N.A.I.C.S.: 483111

Subsidiaries:

Heung-A (M) Sdn. Bhd. (1)
Suite P2.01 Level P2 Menara Trend Intan Millenium Square No 68, Klang, Kuala Lumpur, 41300, Malaysia
Tel.: (60) 333451199
Web Site: http://www.heung-a.co.kr
Emp.: 24
Marine Shipping Services
N.A.I.C.S.: 483111

Heung-A (Singapore) Pte Ltd. (1)
79 Anson Road Anson 23-05, Singapore, 079906, Singapore
Tel.: (65) 65119100
Web Site: http://www.heung-a.co.kr
Marine Shipping Services
N.A.I.C.S.: 483111
Alex Chew (Office Mgr)

Heung-A Shipping (China) Co.,Ltd. (1)
12th Fl Gangtai Plaza 700 Yanan E Road, Shanghai, 200001, China
Tel.: (86) 21 5385 1133
Web Site: http://www.heung-a.co.kr
Sales Range: $25-49.9 Million
Emp.: 15
Marine Shipping Services
N.A.I.C.S.: 483111
Eric Huang (Mgr-Sls)

Heung-A Shipping (Thailand) Co., Ltd. (1)
8F U-Chuliang Bldg 968 Rama 4 Road, Silom Bangrak, Bangkok, 10500, Thailand
Tel.: (66) 26375400
Web Site: http://www.heung-a.co.kr
Sales Range: $25-49.9 Million
Emp.: 50
Marine Shipping Services
N.A.I.C.S.: 483111
Somkiat Tantaranukul (Gen Mgr)

Heung-A Shipping Vietnam Co., Ltd. (1)
2nd Floor 11 Nguyen Cong Tru Street 1st District, Ho Chi Minh City, Vietnam
Tel.: (84) 8 38210806
Web Site: http://www.heung-a.co.kr
Marine Shipping Services
N.A.I.C.S.: 483111

Heung-a Logistics (Shanghai) Co., Ltd. (1)
3PL Service 19th Phase 2 East Ocean Center, 618 Yan An E Road, Shanghai, 200001, China
Tel.: (86) 21 5385 5188
Sea Freight Transportation Services
N.A.I.C.S.: 483111

HEUNGGU OIL CO., LTD.

5 Dongdeok-ro 35-gil, Jung-gu, Daegu, Korea (South)
Tel.: (82) 534243395
Year Founded: 1996
24060—(KRS)
Rev.: $108,900,799
Assets: $69,722,708
Liabilities: $10,278,875
Net Worth: $59,443,834
Earnings: $1,972,170
Emp.: 69
Fiscal Year-end: 12/31/22
Petroleum Product Distr
N.A.I.C.S.: 424720
Dong-Hong Seo (Vice Chm)

HEUNGKUK FIRE & MARINE INSURANCE CO., LTD.

68 Saemunan-ro, Jongno-gu, Seoul, 03184, Korea (South)
Tel.: (82) 220026000
Web Site: https://www.heungkukfire.co.kr
Year Founded: 1948
000540—(KRS)
Rev.: $2,103,911,410
Assets: $9,798,955,390
Liabilities: $7,750,656,820
Net Worth: $2,048,298,570
Earnings: $163,721,970
Fiscal Year-end: 12/31/22
General Insurance Services
N.A.I.C.S.: 524210
Jung Won Kwon (CEO)

HEUNGKUK METALTECH CO., LTD.

357 Asanvalley-ro, Dunpo-myeon, Asan, 31409, Chungnam, Korea (South)
Tel.: (82) 415467771
Web Site: https://www.heungkuk.co.kr
Year Founded: 1974
010240—(KRS)
Rev.: $103,203,900
Assets: $90,223,165
Liabilities: $19,611,860
Net Worth: $70,611,305
Earnings: $6,557,849
Emp.: 102
Fiscal Year-end: 12/31/22
Industrial Parts Mfr
N.A.I.C.S.: 332991
Myung-Joon Ryoo (CEO)

Subsidiaries:

Hk Tracks (Wuxi) Co. Ltd. (1)
16 S Factory 108 Xixian Rd Meicun-zhen, Wuxi New District, Jiangsu, China
Tel.: (86) 51088558235
Construction Machinery Parts Mfr
N.A.I.C.S.: 333120

HEURTEY PETROCHEM SA

8 Cours Louis Lumiere, 94306, Vincennes, Cedex, France
Tel.: (33) 141938000
Web Site: http://www.heurtey.com
Rev.: $341,357,244
Assets: $429,468,518
Liabilities: $333,692,557
Net Worth: $95,775,961
Earnings: ($7,560,922)
Emp.: 868
Fiscal Year-end: 12/31/16
Tubular Process Fired Heaters, Cracking Furnaces & Reformers Mfr
N.A.I.C.S.: 333994

Subsidiaries:

Heurtey Petrochem Brasil Ltda. (1)
Av Presidente Wilson 231 - 9 Andar Centro, Rio de Janeiro, 20030-021, RJ, Brazil
Tel.: (55) 2131493266
Industrial Process Furnace Mfr
N.A.I.C.S.: 333994

Heurtey Petrochem GmbH (1)
Ziegelstr 4, 27386, Hemslingen, Germany
Tel.: (49) 42661440
Web Site: http://www.heurtey.com
Sales Range: $25-49.9 Million
Emp.: 4
Oil Refinery & Petrochemical Plant Furnace Mfr
N.A.I.C.S.: 333414

Heurtey Petrochem India Pvt Ltd (1)
A-301 Boomerang Main Chandivali Farm Road Near Chandivali Studio, Andheri E, Mumbai, 400 072, India
Tel.: (91) 2267740000
Web Site: http://www.heurtey.com
Sales Range: $25-49.9 Million
Emp.: 100
Oil Refinery & Petrochemical Plant Furnace Mfr

INTERNATIONAL PUBLIC

N.A.I.C.S.: 333414
M. Suresh (Gen Mgr)

Heurtey Petrochem Manufacturing S.A. (1)
39 Santierului Street, 120226, Buzau, Romania
Tel.: (40) 238402500
Industrial Process Furnace Mfr
N.A.I.C.S.: 333994
Ionescu Anca Cristina (Project Mgr)

Heurtey Petrochem Romania Srl (1)
39 St Santierului, 120226, Buzau, Romania
Tel.: (40) 238402500
Web Site: http://www.heurtey.com
Sales Range: $25-49.9 Million
Emp.: 15
Oil Refinery & Petrochemical Plant Furnace Mfr
N.A.I.C.S.: 333994

Heurtey Petrochem South Africa (PTY) LTD (1)
19 Polo Crescent Woodhead Office Park, PO Box 3186, Woodmean, Johannesburg, South Africa
Tel.: (27) 11 209 10 60
Web Site: http://www.heurtey.com
Oil Refinery & Petrochemical Plant Furnace Mfr
N.A.I.C.S.: 333994

L.L.C. Heurtey Petrochem Rus (1)
Renaissance Plaza 69-71 Marata Street, 191119, Saint Petersburg, Russia
Tel.: (7) 8124487680
Industrial Process Furnace Mfr
N.A.I.C.S.: 333994
Korkunov Kyrill (Gen Mgr)

Petro-Chem Development Company, Inc. (1)
12012 Wickchester Ln Ste 550, Houston, TX 77079
Tel.: (713) 524-6670
Web Site: http://www.petro-chemusa.com
Refinery Heaters & Waste Heat Boilers Mfr
N.A.I.C.S.: 333994
Christopher C Eley (CEO)

Subsidiary (Non-US):

Heurtey Petrochem Technology (Beijing) Ltd. (2)
Room 1701 Tower A Guancheng Building No 12 Taiyanggongzhong Rd, Chaoyang District, Beijing, PR, China
Tel.: (86) 10 842 98068
Web Site: http://www.petro-chemusa.com
Oil Refinery & Petrochemical Plant Furnace Mfr
N.A.I.C.S.: 333994

Subsidiary (Domestic):

Petro-Chem Development Company, Inc. (2)
7666 E 61st St Ste 400, Tulsa, OK 74133
Tel.: (918) 254-8000
Web Site: http://www.petro-chemusa.com
Mfr of Refinery Heaters & Waste Heat Boilers
N.A.I.C.S.: 333994

Subsidiary (Non-US):

Petro-Chem Korea Co. Ltd. (2)
Rm 1501 Kolon Digital Tower Aston 505 14 Gasan Dong, Seoul, 153 801, Korea (South)
Tel.: (82) 220827970
Web Site: http://www.petro-chem.co.kr
Sales Range: $25-49.9 Million
Emp.: 22
Oil Refinery & Petrochemical Plant Furnace Mfr
N.A.I.C.S.: 333994

HEVEA B.V.

Boeierstraat 12, Raalte, 8102, Netherlands
Tel.: (31) 572341550 NI
Web Site: http://www.dunlopboots.com
Year Founded: 1904
Sales Range: $1-9.9 Million
Emp.: 100

Safety, Work Boots & Outdoor Shoes Mfr
N.A.I.C.S.: 316210
Allard Bijlsma *(CEO)*

Subsidiaries:

Wear Well Footwear Limited (1)
Unit 9 Gr Is Enterprise Pk, Ballincollig, Cork, Ireland
Tel.: (353) 214876222
Sales Range: $50-74.9 Million
Emp.: 6
Work Boots & Outdoor Shoes Sales
N.A.I.C.S.: 424340

HEVEABOARD BERHAD
Lot 1942 Batu 3 Jalan Tampin, 73400, Gemas, Negeri Sembilan Daru, Malaysia
Tel.: (60) 79484745
Web Site: https://www.heveaboard.com.my
HEVEA—(KLS)
Rev.: $64,527,863
Assets: $109,114,230
Liabilities: $18,723,335
Net Worth: $90,390,945
Earnings: ($818,024)
Emp.: 1,790
Fiscal Year-end: 12/31/23
Particleboard Mfr
N.A.I.C.S.: 321219
Hau Chun Yoong *(Mng Dir)*

Subsidiaries:

HeveaGro Sdn. Bhd. (1)
Lot 2133 Batu 3 Jalan Tampin, 73400, Gemas, Negeri Sembilan, Malaysia
Tel.: (60) 79482893
Web Site: http://www.hevea.com.my
Fresh & Organic Mushroom Mfr
N.A.I.C.S.: 311421

HeveaMart Sdn. Bhd. (1)
Lot 1942 Batu 3 Jalan Tampin, 73400, Gemas, Negeri Sembilan, Malaysia
Tel.: (60) 79484745
Web Site: http://www.heveaboard.com.my
Emp.: 400
Particleboard Mfr
N.A.I.C.S.: 321999

HeveaPac Sdn. Bhd. (1)
PT 403 406 & 414 Kawasan Perindustrian Sg Gadut KM 11 Jalan Tampin, 71450, Seremban, Negeri Sembilan, Malaysia
Tel.: (60) 66793775
Web Site: http://www.heveapac.com.my
Sales Range: $400-449.9 Million
Emp.: 2,000
Furniture Mfr
N.A.I.C.S.: 337121

HEVOL SERVICES GROUP CO. LIMITED
16th Floor Block D Newlogo International Building No 18A, Zhongguancun South Street Haidian District, Beijing, China   Ky
Web Site: https://www.hevolwy.com.cn
Year Founded: 2002
6093—(HKG)
Rev.: $181,834,709
Assets: $228,798,322
Liabilities: $121,173,986
Net Worth: $107,624,335
Earnings: $15,802,780
Emp.: 4,849
Fiscal Year-end: 12/31/23
Property Management Services
N.A.I.C.S.: 531311
Hongfang Hu *(CFO)*

HEW-KABEL HOLDING GMBH
Klingsiepen 12, 51688, Wipperfurth, Germany
Tel.: (49) 22676830
Web Site: https://hew-kabel.com
Emp.: 100

Holding Company
N.A.I.C.S.: 551112

Subsidiaries:

HEW-KABEL GmbH & Co. KG (1)
Klingsiepen 12, 51688, Wipperfurth, Germany
Tel.: (49) 22676830
Web Site: http://www.hew-kabel.com
Sales Range: $50-74.9 Million
Emp.: 300
Special Cable & Wire Mfr
N.A.I.C.S.: 335929
Rainer Flohr *(Mng Dir)*

Habia Kabel GmbH (1)
Oststrasse 91, 22844, Norderstedt, Germany
Tel.: (49) 405353500
Web Site: http://www.habia.com
Emp.: 80
Current-Carrying Wiring Device Mfr
N.A.I.C.S.: 335931

HEWLAND ENGINEERING LTD
Waltham Rd, White Waltham, SL6 3LR, Berkshire, United Kingdom
Tel.: (44) 1628827600
Web Site: http://www.hewland.com
Year Founded: 1957
Sales Range: $10-24.9 Million
Emp.: 133
Engineeering Services
N.A.I.C.S.: 541330
William Hewland *(Pres)*

HEXAGON AB
Lilla Bantorget 15, SE-111 23, Stockholm, Sweden
Tel.: (46) 86012620   SE
Web Site: https://www.hexagon.com
Year Founded: 1992
HEXA.B—(OTCIQ)
Rev.: $4,623,586,656
Assets: $13,146,589,664
Liabilities: $5,839,544,256
Net Worth: $7,307,045,408
Earnings: $767,281,528
Emp.: 20,343
Fiscal Year-end: 12/31/20
Multidimensional Measurement Instruments, Metal Products, Robotic & Automotive Components & Rubber Wheels & Gaskets Mfr
N.A.I.C.S.: 334513
Norbert Hanke *(Interim CEO)*

Subsidiaries:

Autonomoustuff LLC (1)
306 Erie Ave, Morton, IL 61550
Tel.: (309) 291-0966
Web Site: http://www.autonomoustuff.com
Electrical Apparatus & Related Equipment Merchant Whslr
N.A.I.C.S.: 423610

Brown & Sharpe Qianshao (1)
11 Luoyang Road, Qingdao, 266045, China
Tel.: (86) 532 486 2324
Web Site: http://www.hexagon.com
Sales Range: $100-124.9 Million
Emp.: 500
Mfr of Aircraft Engines & Parts
N.A.I.C.S.: 336412

Catavolt, Inc. (1)
555 North Point Center East Suite 550, Alpharetta, GA 30022
Tel.: (800) 939-6812
Web Site: http://www.catavolt.com
Software Publisher
N.A.I.C.S.: 513210
Francisco Daffre *(VP-Professional Svcs)*

Hexagon Measurement Technologies (1)
4th Floor 1 Riverside Manbre Road, London, W6 9WA, United Kingdom
Tel.: (44) 2086007230
Web Site: http://www.hexagonmt.com
Sales Range: $25-49.9 Million
Emp.: 25

Macro & Micro Multidimensional Measurement Equipment Mfr
N.A.I.C.S.: 334519

Division (Domestic):

Hexagon Metrology Services Ltd. (2)
Cedar House, 78 Portsmouth Road, Cobham, KT11 1AN, Surrey, United Kingdom   (100%)
Tel.: (44) 20 7068 6540
Web Site: http://www.hexagonmetrology.net
Sales Range: $25-49.9 Million
Portable Measurement Systems, Laser Trackers, Coordinate Measuring Machines & Engineering Software Developer & Mfr
N.A.I.C.S.: 334519
Norbert Hanke *(Pres)*

Division (US):

Brown & Sharpe Inc (3)
250 Circuit Dr, North Kingstown, RI 02852
Tel.: (401) 886-2000
Web Site: http://www.hexagonmi.com
Provider of Industrial Instruments
N.A.I.C.S.: 333517
Jack Rosignal *(VP-Sls)*

Subsidiary (Non-US):

Hexagon Metrology France S.A. (3)
Immeuble Le Viking, 32 Ave De La Baltique, 91978, Courtaboeuf, Cedex, France   (100%)
Tel.: (33) 169291200
Web Site: http://www.hexagonnmetrology.com
Sales Range: $25-49.9 Million
Mfr of Weights & Measuring Devices
N.A.I.C.S.: 334519

Hexagon Metrology GmbH (3)
Siegmund-Hiepe-Str 2-12, 35578, Wetzlar, Germany   (100%)
Tel.: (49) 64412070
Web Site: https://www.hexagonmi.com
Sales Range: $50-74.9 Million
Emp.: 400
Mfr of Weights & Measuring Devices
N.A.I.C.S.: 334519
Per Holmberg *(Pres)*

Hexagon Metrology Nordic AB (3)
Filargatan 3, 63181, Eskilstuna, Sweden   (100%)
Tel.: (46) 16160800
Web Site: http://www.hexagonmetrology.com
Sales Range: $10-24.9 Million
Emp.: 60
Mfr of Measuring & Controlling Devices
N.A.I.C.S.: 334519

Division (Non-US):

Leica Geosystems AG Metrology Division (3)
Moenchmattweg 5, Unterentfelden, 5035, Switzerland
Tel.: (41) 627376767
Sales Range: $50-74.9 Million
Emp.: 70
Developer of Three Dimensional Spatial Measurement & Analysis Instruments
N.A.I.C.S.: 334513
Duncan Redgewell *(Gen Mgr)*

Subsidiary (Domestic):

Vero Software Ltd. (3)
Hadley House, Bayshill Road, Cheltenham, GL50 3AW, Gloucestershire, United Kingdom
Tel.: (44) 1242542040
Web Site: http://www.verosoftware.com
Sales Range: $10-24.9 Million
Emp.: 30
Designs, Develops & Supplies Software Enabling Mechanical Design & Manufacturing Software (CAD/CAM Software)
N.A.I.C.S.: 513210
Steve Sivitter *(CEO)*

Subsidiary (Non-US):

Vero China (4)
Room 2010 No 69 Dongfang Rd, Pudong New Area, Shanghai, 200120, China
Tel.: (86) 216 375 6598
Web Site: http://www.vero-china.com.cn

Designs, Develops & Supplies Computer Aided Design & Computer Aided Manufacturing Software
N.A.I.C.S.: 541511

Vero France (4)
Parc Technoland ZI Champ Dolin, 1 Allee des Abruzzes, 69800, Saint Priest, France
Tel.: (33) 472793999
Web Site: http://www.vero-software.fr
Designs, Develops & Supplies Computer Aided Design & Computer Aided Manufacturing Software
N.A.I.C.S.: 541511

Vero Italia Srl (4)
Via Prelle 30, 10090, Romano Canavese, Turin, Italy
Tel.: (39) 0125717111
Web Site: http://www.vero.it
Emp.: 40
Designs, Develops & Supplies Computer Aided Design & Computer Aided Manufacturing Software
N.A.I.C.S.: 541511

Branch (Domestic):

Vero Italia Srl (5)
Viale San Marco 38, 30020, Marcon, Italy
Tel.: (39) 0415951523
Web Site: http://www.vero.it
Sales Range: $25-49.9 Million
Emp.: 7
Designs, Develops & Supplies Computer Aided Design & Computer Aided Manufacturing Software
N.A.I.C.S.: 541511

Vero Italia Srl (5)
Via Caboto 8b, 20025, Legnano, MI, Italy
Tel.: (39) 0331 937711
Web Site: http://www.vero.it
Designs, Develops & Supplies Computer Aided Design & Computer Aided Manufacturing Software
N.A.I.C.S.: 541511

Subsidiary (Non-US):

Vero Japan K.K. (4)
Kamiyacho Plaza Bldg 3F 4-1-14 Toranomon, Minato-ku, Tokyo, 105-0001, Japan
Tel.: (81) 3 5777 2045
Web Site: http://www.verosoftware.com
Designs, Develops & Supplies Computer Aided Design & Computer Aided Manufacturing Software
N.A.I.C.S.: 541511

Vero Software GmbH (4)
Parkstrasse 18, Remscheid, Germany
Tel.: (49) 2191 609290
Software Developer & Marketer
N.A.I.C.S.: 513210
Michel Reuter *(Mgr-Mktg)*

Subsidiary (US):

Vero USA Inc. (4)
28345 Beck Rd Ste 310, Wixom, MI 48393-4744
Tel.: (248) 869-4040
Web Site: http://www.veroint.com
Designs, Develops & Supplies Computer Aided Design & Computer Aided Manufacturing Software
N.A.I.C.S.: 541511
Richard Smith *(Pres)*

Division (Non-US):

Leica Geosystems AG (2)
Heinrich Wild Strasse, 9435, Heerbrugg, Switzerland
Tel.: (41) 71 727 3131
Web Site: https://www.leica-geosystems.com
Developer of Surveying & Spatial Imaging & Analysis Technologies
N.A.I.C.S.: 541360
Johannes Schwarz *(Exec VP-Geosystems)*

Subsidiary (Non-US):

Leica Geosystems Ltd. (3)
Unit # 1, 3761 Victoria Park Avenue, Scarborough, ON M1W, ON, Canada
Tel.: (416) 497-2460
Web Site: http://www.leica-geosystems.com

HEXAGON AB

Hexagon AB—(Continued)
Sales Range: $25-49.9 Million
Emp.: 10
Supplier of Image Processing & Digital Mapping Technologies
N.A.I.C.S.: 333310

Subsidiary (US):

Leica Geosystems, Inc. (3)
5051 Peachtree Corners Cir Ste 250, Norcross, GA 30092
Tel.: (770) 326-9500
Web Site: http://www.leica-geosystems.us
Sales Range: $25-49.9 Million
Emp.: 60
Developer of Surveying & Spatial Imaging & Analysis Technologies
N.A.I.C.S.: 334519

Subsidiary (Domestic):

Leica Geosystems GR, LLC (4)
5051 peach tree conor cir, Norcross, GA 30092
Tel.: (770) 326-9500
Web Site: http://www.leica-geosystems.com
Sales Range: $10-24.9 Million
Emp.: 35
Mfr of Global Positioning Systems, Levels, Construction Site Lasers & Machine Guidance Systems
N.A.I.C.S.: 541360

Branch (Domestic):

Leica Geosystems, Inc. - Costa Mesa (4)
201 Paularino Ave, Costa Mesa, CA 92626
Tel.: (714) 546-0606
Web Site: http://www.leica-geosystems.com
Sales Range: $10-24.9 Million
Emp.: 35
Developer of Surveying & Spatial Imaging & Analysis Technologies
N.A.I.C.S.: 334519

Subsidiary (US):

Mintec, Inc. (3)
3544 E Fort Lowell Rd, Tucson, AZ 85716
Tel.: (520) 795-3891
Web Site: http://www.hexagonmining.com
Emp.: 140
Mining Software Developer
N.A.I.C.S.: 513210
John Davies (Pres)

Division (Non-US):

NovAtel Inc. (2)
10921 14th Street NE, Calgary, T3K 2L5, AB, Canada
Tel.: (403) 295-4500
Web Site: https://www.novatel.com
Sales Range: $50-74.9 Million
Global Positioning Systems & Components Mfr
N.A.I.C.S.: 334511

Division (Domestic):

Veripos Inc. (2)
Veripos House 1B Farburn Terrace Dyce, Aberdeen, AB21 7DT, United Kingdom
Tel.: (44) 122 496 5800
Web Site: https://www.veripos.com
Sales Range: $25-49.9 Million
Emp.: 115
Global Positioning Devices Mfr
N.A.I.C.S.: 334511

Intergraph Corporation (1)
305 intergraph way, Madison, AL 35758
Tel.: (256) 730-2000
Web Site: http://www.intergraph.com
Sales Range: $550-599.9 Million
Emp.: 3,500
Spatial Information Management Software & Services
N.A.I.C.S.: 513210
Warren D. Fletcher (Pres-Security)

Subsidiary (Non-US):

Atheeb Intergraph Saudi Company - Riyadh (2)
Al-Mousa Center Building Tower B 5th Fl, Room 251 Along Olaya Road, 11524, Riyadh, Saudi Arabia
Tel.: (966) 14622335
Web Site: http://www.atheeb.com
Sales Range: $25-49.9 Million
Emp.: 80
Provider of Software Services
N.A.I.C.S.: 541511

Subsidiary (Domestic):

Augusta Systems, Inc. (2)
3592 Collins Ferry Rd Ste 200, Morgantown, WV 26505
Tel.: (304) 599-3200
Web Site: http://www.augustasystems.com
Sales Range: $1-9.9 Million
Emp.: 25
Computer Networking Services
N.A.I.C.S.: 541519

Subsidiary (Non-US):

Credent Technology Asia Pte. Ltd. (2)
85 Science Park Drive 02-01 The Cavendish, 02 01 The Cavendish, Singapore, 118259, Singapore
Tel.: (65) 6 779 0177
Web Site: https://www.credent-asia.com
Sales Range: $25-49.9 Million
Emp.: 75
Graphic Equipment Mfr
N.A.I.C.S.: 325992

CyberMAK Information Systems W.L.L. (2)
Block 14 Hamad Al-Sagar Street Qibla Kharafi Tower, Building No 6 Floor 14, Kuwait, 13009, Kuwait
Tel.: (965) 2 232 3344
Web Site: https://www.cybermak.net
Sales Range: $25-49.9 Million
Emp.: 20
Information Management Software
N.A.I.C.S.: 449210

Division (Domestic):

Hexagon PPM (2)
305 Intergraph Way, Madison, AL 35758
Web Site: https://hexagonppm.com
Industrial Facility Design, Construction & Operation Software & Technologies
N.A.I.C.S.: 513210
Mattias Stenberg (Pres)

Unit (Domestic):

Hexagon PPM - CADWorx & Analysis Solutions (3)
7840 N Sam Houston Pkwy W Ste 100, Houston, TX 77064
Tel.: (281) 890-4566
Web Site: http://www.coade.com
Engineering Software
N.A.I.C.S.: 513210

Subsidiary (Non-US):

Intergraph (Austria) GmbH (2)
Margaretenstrasse 70 / I / 1, 1050, Vienna, Austria
Tel.: (43) 19 610 5670
Web Site: http://www.intergraph.com
Sales Range: $25-49.9 Million
Emp.: 23
GIS & Mapping Solutions & Services
N.A.I.C.S.: 334610
Ola Rollen (CEO)

Intergraph (Espana) S.A. (2)
Calle Gobelas 21 planta baja izqda La Florida, 28023, Madrid, Spain
Tel.: (34) 91 708 8800
Web Site: http://www.intergraph.com
Sales Range: $25-49.9 Million
Emp.: 48
Distribution of Graphic Equipment
N.A.I.C.S.: 325992

Intergraph (Espana) S.A. (2)
Carrer de Nicaragua 46 1 1, 8029, Barcelona, Spain
Tel.: (34) 93 321 2020
Web Site: http://www.intergraph.com
Sales Range: $25-49.9 Million
Emp.: 5
Distribution of Graphic Equipment
N.A.I.C.S.: 325992

Intergraph (Finland) Oy (2)
Keilaranta 8, 02150, Espoo, Finland
Tel.: (358) 9804641
Web Site: http://www.intergraph.fi
Sales Range: $25-49.9 Million
Emp.: 8
Mapping, GIS Applications, Process Power & Offshore Applications Services
N.A.I.C.S.: 449210

Intergraph (India) Private Ltd. (2)
1 8 446 and 447 South P Road, Secunderabad, 500 003, Andhra Pradesh, India
Tel.: (91) 4027905378
Web Site: http://www.intergraph.com
Sales Range: $75-99.9 Million
Emp.: 425
Provider of Software Development, Customization, Integration & Maintenance Services for Engineering, Mapping, Enterprise, Internet Commerce & Web Applications
N.A.I.C.S.: 334610

Intergraph (Shenzhen) Company Ltd. (2)
Room 1101-1107 11th Fl Tower A Glendale Plz, Chaoyang District, Beijing, 100022, China
Tel.: (86) 1057601688
Web Site: http://www.intergraph.com.cn
Sales Range: $25-49.9 Million
Emp.: 100
GIS & Mapping Solutions & Services
N.A.I.C.S.: 334610
Welch Sun (Gen Mgr)

Intergraph (Sverige) A.B. (2)
Hammarbacken 10, PO Box 420, SE 19124, Sollentuna, Sweden
Tel.: (46) 8925400
Web Site: http://www.intergraph.se
Sales Range: $25-49.9 Million
Emp.: 20
Provider of GIS & Power & Process Software
N.A.I.C.S.: 449210

Intergraph (Switzerland) AG (2)
Neumattstrasse 24, Dietikon, 8953, Switzerland
Tel.: (41) 433224646
Web Site: http://www.intergraph.ch
Sales Range: $25-49.9 Million
Emp.: 25
Graphic Equipment Mfr
N.A.I.C.S.: 325992

Intergraph (UK) Limited (2)
100 Delta Business Park Great Western Way, Swindon, SN5 7XP, Wiltshire, United Kingdom
Tel.: (44) 179 361 9999
Web Site: http://www.intergraph.com
Sales Range: $25-49.9 Million
Emp.: 115
GIS & Process, Power & Offshore Software Services
N.A.I.C.S.: 449210

Intergraph Belgium NV/SA (2)
Tennessee House Riverside Business Park Boulevard International 55 E, 1070, Brussels, Belgium
Tel.: (32) 2 559 1600
Web Site: http://www.intergraph.com
Sales Range: $25-49.9 Million
Emp.: 60
Distribution of Graphic Software - Geographical Information Systems, Digital Mapping & Other Services
N.A.I.C.S.: 334610

Intergraph Benelux B.V. (2)
Siriusdreef 2, 2132 WT, Hoofddorp, Netherlands
Tel.: (31) 235666666
Web Site: http://www.intergraph.nl
Sales Range: $25-49.9 Million
Emp.: 100
GIS & Process & Power Software Mfr
N.A.I.C.S.: 449210

Subsidiary (Domestic):

Intergraph European Manufacturing L.L.C. (3)
Siriusdreef 2, PO Box 333, 2130 WT, Hoofddorp, Netherlands
Tel.: (31) 235666666
Web Site: http://www.intergraph.com
Sales Range: $25-49.9 Million
Emp.: 75
Mfr Facility

INTERNATIONAL PUBLIC

N.A.I.C.S.: 449210

Subsidiary (Non-US):

Intergraph CR spol s.r.o. (2)
Prosecka 851, 19000, Prague, Czech Republic
Tel.: (420) 234707820
Web Site: http://www.intergraph.com
Sales Range: $10-24.9 Million
Emp.: 40
Provider of GIS & Mapping Solutions & Services
N.A.I.C.S.: 541360

Intergraph Canada Ltd. (2)
10921 -14 Street NE, Calgary, T3K 2L5, AB, Canada
Tel.: (403) 569-5500
Web Site: http://www.intergraph.ca
Sales Range: $25-49.9 Million
Emp.: 125
Information Management Software Mfr
N.A.I.C.S.: 449210

Intergraph Consulting Pvt Ltd. (2)
1-8-446 447 SP Road, 500 003, Secunderabad, India
Tel.: (91) 40 27905378
Computer & Software Mfr
N.A.I.C.S.: 449210

Intergraph Corp. (N.Z.) Limited (2)
342 Lambton Quay Level 14, Wellington, 6011, New Zealand
Tel.: (64) 4 914 1200
Web Site: http://www.intergraph.com
Sales Range: $25-49.9 Million
Emp.: 30
GIS Software & Services
N.A.I.C.S.: 334610

Intergraph Corp. (NZ) Limited (2)
Level 7 Telco Bldg 16 Kingston St, Auckland, 1010, New Zealand
Tel.: (64) 9 976 8900
Web Site: http://www.intergraph.com
Sales Range: $10-24.9 Million
Emp.: 26
IT Software Services
N.A.I.C.S.: 541511

Intergraph Corp. Pty. Ltd. (2)
32 Walker Street Level 4, North Sydney, 2060, NSW, Australia
Tel.: (61) 29 956 4000
Web Site: http://www.intergraph.com
Sales Range: $10-24.9 Million
Emp.: 30
Software Services
N.A.I.C.S.: 541511

Intergraph Corp. Pty. Ltd. (2)
Technology Park Ste 4, 18 Brodie Hall Dr, Bentley, 6102, WA, Australia
Tel.: (61) 864652000
Web Site: http://www.intergraph.com
Sales Range: $25-49.9 Million
Emp.: 20
Provider of Software Services
N.A.I.C.S.: 541511

Intergraph Corporation Taiwan (2)
No 54 Section 4 Minsheng E Rd, Songshan District, Taipei, 105, Taiwan
Tel.: (886) 22 716 4458
Web Site: http://www.intergraph.com.tw
Sales Range: $25-49.9 Million
Emp.: 10
Distribution of Graphic Equipment
N.A.I.C.S.: 325992

Intergraph Danmark A/S (2)
Borupvang 2B 1 th, 2750, Ballerup, Denmark
Tel.: (45) 3 619 2000
Web Site: http://www.intergraph.dk
Sales Range: $25-49.9 Million
Geographical Information Systems Solutions & Process, Power & Offshore Solutions
N.A.I.C.S.: 334610

Intergraph Deutschland GmbH (2)
Reichenbachstrasse 3, D 85737, Ismaning, Germany
Tel.: (49) 89961060
Web Site: http://www.intergraph.de
Sales Range: $25-49.9 Million
Emp.: 200
GIS & Mapping Solutions

AND PRIVATE COMPANIES

N.A.I.C.S.: 334610

Intergraph France S.A. (2)
5 Rue Le Corbusier, BP 50238, Parc Silic,
94528, Rungis, France
Tel.: (33) 14 560 3000
Web Site: http://www.intergraph.com
Sales Range: $25-49.9 Million
Emp.: 55
Distribution of Graphic Equipment Software
N.A.I.C.S.: 334610

Intergraph Hong Kong Limited (2)
Suite 1130 11/F Ocean Centre, Harbour
City, Kowloon, China (Hong Kong)
Tel.: (852) 2593 1638
Web Site: http://www.intergraph.com.hk
CAD/CAE & System Integration Solutions
N.A.I.C.S.: 541512

Intergraph Israel Software Development Center Ltd (2)
4 HaHaroshet str, Nesher, 36881, Israel
Tel.: (972) 48779191
Web Site: http://www.intergraph.com
Sales Range: $25-49.9 Million
Emp.: 100
Information Management Software
N.A.I.C.S.: 449210

Intergraph Italia LLC (2)
Strada 7 Palazzo R1, Milanofiori, 20089,
Milan, Rozzano, Italy
Tel.: (39) 0257 5451
Web Site: http://www.intergraph.it
Sales Range: $25-49.9 Million
Emp.: 60
GIS & Process & Building Software
N.A.I.C.S.: 449210

Intergraph Korea, Ltd. (2)
15th Floor Hongwoo Building Seocho 2
Dong, Seocho Gu, 137 070, Seoul, Korea
(South)
Tel.: (82) 234890300
Web Site: http://www.intergraph.co.kr
Sales Range: $25-49.9 Million
Emp.: 46
Information Management Software
N.A.I.C.S.: 449210

Intergraph Norge AS (2)
Nesoyveien 4, N 1377, Billingstad, Norway
Tel.: (47) 66985858
Web Site: http://www.intergraph.no
Sales Range: $10-24.9 Million
GIS & Process Power & Offshore Services
N.A.I.C.S.: 440210

Intergraph Polska Sp. Z o.o. (2)
ul Stawki 40, 01-040, Warsaw, Poland
Tel.: (48) 224958800
Web Site: http://www.intergraph.pl
Sales Range: $25-49.9 Million
Emp.: 60
Graphic Equipment Mfr
N.A.I.C.S.: 325992

Intergraph Servicios de Venezuela, C.A. (2)
CCCT Torre C Piso 11 Oficina C1102 Chuao, Caracas, 1064-A, Venezuela
Tel.: (58) 2129595344
Web Site: http://www.intergraph.com.ve
Sales Range: $25-49.9 Million
Emp.: 15
Software Services
N.A.I.C.S.: 541511

Intergraph Systems (Shenzhen) Co. Ltd (2)
15th fl rm #1501 Yong An dong li Jian Guo
Men, Beijing, 100022, Chaoyang District,
China
Tel.: (86) 10 5760 1688
Web Site: http://www.intergraph.com.cn
Sales Range: $25-49.9 Million
Emp.: 20
GIS & Mapping Solutions & Services
N.A.I.C.S.: 334610

Intergraph de Mexico S.A. de C.V. (2)
Durango No 263 Piso 7 Col Roma Norte,
Mexico, 6700, DF, Mexico
Tel.: (52) 55 5525 5554
Emp.: 60
Software Services
N.A.I.C.S.: 541511
Adrian Hernandez Lopez *(Mgr-Mktg)*

Luciad NV (1)
Arenberg Science Park Gaston Geenslaan
11, 3001, Leuven, Belgium
Tel.: (32) 1623 9591
Web Site: http://www.luciad.com
Geospatial Application Software Developer
& Services
N.A.I.C.S.: 513210
Lode Missiaen *(Founder)*

Subsidiary (US):

Luciad, Inc. (2)
2200 Pennsylvania Ave NW, Washington,
DC 20037
Tel.: (202) 507-5895
Web Site: http://www.luciad.com
Geospatial Application Software Developer
& Services
N.A.I.C.S.: 513210
Demetreus Lancsweert *(Country Mgr)*

MSC Software Corporation (1)
4675 MacArthur Ct, Newport Beach, CA
92660
Tel.: (714) 540-8900
Web Site: http://www.mscsoftware.com
Simulation Software Solutions
N.A.I.C.S.: 513210
John Janevic *(COO)*

Subsidiary (Non-US):

ICSA (Ingenieria y Computacion, S.A.) (2)
Carril Rodriguez Pena 2451, Godoy Cruz,
Mendoza, M5503ADA, Argentina
Tel.: (54) 2614136200
Web Site: http://www.icsaautomation.com
Industrial Automation; Control, Protection,
Automation & Power Generation
N.A.I.C.S.: 221118

MSC Software GmbH (2)
Am Moosfeld 13, 81829, Munich, Germany
Tel.: (49) 8921093224
Web Site: http://www.mscsoftware.com
Computer-Aided Engineering (CAE) Software Supplier & Comprehensive Finite Element Analysis (FEA) Program
N.A.I.C.S.: 513210

Subsidiary (Non-US):

MSC.Software AB (3)
Hangpilsgatan 6, 426 77, Frolunda, Sweden
Tel.: (46) 317485990
Web Site: http://www.mscsoftware.com
Virtual Development Application Developer,
Marketer & Servicer
N.A.I.C.S.: 541511

MSC.Software Benelux B.V. (3)
Gentseweg 15, 2803 PC, Gouda, Netherlands
Tel.: (31) 18 253 6444
Web Site: https://www.mscsoftware.com
Computer-Aided Engineering (CAE) Software Supplier & Comprehensive Finite Element Analysis (FEA) Program
N.A.I.C.S.: 513210

MSC.Software Ltd. (3)
4 Archipelago Lyon Way, Frimley, GU16
7ER, Surrey, United Kingdom
Tel.: (44) 127 690 3120
Web Site: https://www.mscsoftware.com
Supplier of Computer-Aided Engineering
(CAE) Software & Comprehensive Finite
Element Analysis (FEA) Program
N.A.I.C.S.: 513210

Branch (Domestic):

MSC.Software Ltd. (4)
Suite A2 Fourth Floor Steam Mill Business
Centre Steam Mill Street, Chester, CH3
5AN, Cheshire, United Kingdom
Tel.: (44) 1276672280
Web Site: http://www.mscsoftware.com
Virtual Development Application Developer,
Marketer & Servicer
N.A.I.C.S.: 541512

Subsidiary (Non-US):

MSC.Software S.r.l. (3)
Via Nazionale 74, Tavagnacco, 33010,
Udine, Italy
Tel.: (39) 0432576711
Web Site: http://www.mscsoftware.com
Virtual Development Application Developer,
Marketer & Servicer
N.A.I.C.S.: 541512

Branch (Domestic):

MSC.Software s.r.l. (4)
Corso d'Italia 45, 00198, Rome, Italy
Tel.: (39) 068 440 4511
Web Site: https://www.mscsoftware.com
Computer-Aided Engineering (CAE) Software Supplier & Comprehensive Finite Element Analysis (FEA) Program
N.A.I.C.S.: 513210

Subsidiary (Non-US):

MSC.Software Sarl (3)
Europarc Immeuble Jupiter B10 4 Rue du
professeur Pierre Vellas, 31300, Toulouse,
France
Tel.: (33) 17 997 2692
Web Site: https://www.mscsoftware.com
Computer-Aided Engineering (CAE) Software Supplier & Comprehensive Finite Element Analysis (FEA) Program
N.A.I.C.S.: 513210

Branch (Domestic):

MSC.Software Sarl - Saint-Fons (4)
87 avenue des Freres Perret, 69192, Saint-Fons, France
Tel.: (33) 17 997 2692
Web Site: https://www.mscsoftware.com
Computer-Aided Engineering (CAE) Software Supplier & Comprehensive Finite Element Analysis (FEA) Program
N.A.I.C.S.: 513210

Subsidiary (Non-US):

MSC.Software Simulating Reality S.A. (3)
Avda De Manoteras 32 Edificio A- 1 Planta,
28050, Madrid, Spain
Tel.: (34) 91 556 0919
Web Site: http://www.mscsoftware.com
Computer-Aided Engineering (CAE) Software Supplier & Comprehensive Finite Element Analysis (FEA) Program
N.A.I.C.S.: 513210

MSC.Software s.r.o. (3)
Prikop 4, 60200, Brno, Czech Republic
Tel.: (420) 545176106
Web Site: http://www.mscsoftware.com
Virtual Development Application Developer,
Marketer & Servicer
N.A.I.C.S.: 541512

MSI Engineering Software Ltd. (3)
14 Imber St Kiryat-Arie, PO Box 3769,
4951148, Petah Tiqwa, Israel
Tel.: (972) 89353230
Web Site: http://www.msi.co.il
Computer-Aided Engineering (CAE) Software & Comprehensive Finite Element
Analysis (FEA) Program Supplier
N.A.I.C.S.: 513210

OOO MSC.Software RUS (3)
2nd Zvenigoro skaya st 13 building 43 office 521, 123022, Moscow, Russia
Tel.: (7) 495 363 0683
Web Site: http://www.mscsoftware.com
Virtual Product Development Software Publisher
N.A.I.C.S.: 513210

Omega Vision 2000 s.a. (3)
Vas Sofias 115, 11521, Athens, Greece
Tel.: (30) 210777 031 6317
Web Site: https://www.ovision.gr
Integrated Computer Solutions & Product
Data Management
N.A.I.C.S.: 513210

Branch (Domestic):

MSC.Software Corp. - Ann Arbor (2)
4675 MacArthur Ct, Ann Arbor, MI 48104
Tel.: (714) 540-8900
Web Site: http://www.mscsoftware.com
Software Developer
N.A.I.C.S.: 513210

Subsidiary (Non-US):

MSC.Software Japan Ltd. (2)
Shinjuku First West 8F 23-7 Nishi Shinjuku

HEXAGON COMPOSITES ASA

1-Chome, Shinjuku-Ku, Tokyo, 160-0023,
Japan
Tel.: (81) 36 911 1200
Web Site: http://www.mscsoftware.com
Computer-Aided Engineering (CAE) Software Supplier & Comprehensive Finite Element Analysis (FEA) Program
N.A.I.C.S.: 513210

Branch (Domestic):

MSC.Software Japan Ltd. - Osaka Office (3)
Mainichi Intecio Bldg 17th floor 3-4-5,
Umeda Kita-ku, Osaka, 530-0001, Japan
Tel.: (81) 66 343 5831
Web Site: http://www.mscsoftware.co.jp
Computer-Aided Engineering (CAE) Software & Comprehensive Finite Element
Analysis (FEA) Program
N.A.I.C.S.: 513210

Branch (Non-US):

MSC.Software Ltd. - Beijing Office (2)
Unit 03-06 Floor14 BlockA Juanshi Tiandi
Plaza No 50, Wangjing West Road Chaoyang District, Beijing, 100102, China
Tel.: (86) 108 260 7000
Web Site: http://www.mscsoftware.com.cn
Software Distr
N.A.I.C.S.: 423430

MSC.Software Ltd. - Chengdu Office (2)
14F/1-2-2 Chuan Xin Mansion Hong Zhao
Bi No 18 Sec 2 Ren Min S Road, Chengdu,
610016, Sichuan, China
Tel.: (86) 288 619 9275
Web Site: http://www.mscsoftware.com
Supplier of Computer-Aided Engineering
(CAE) Software & Comprehensive Finite
Element Analysis (FEA) Program
N.A.I.C.S.: 513210

OxBlue Corporation (1)
1777 Ellsworth Industrial Blvd NW, Atlanta,
GA 30318-7666
Tel.: (404) 917-0200
Web Site: https://www.oxblue.com
Radio, Television Broadcasting & Wireless
Communications Equipment Mfr
N.A.I.C.S.: 334220
Bryan Mattern *(Co-Founder & CTO)*

Qognify, Inc. (1)
1 Blue Hill Plz 10th Fl, Pearl River, NY
10965-3100
Tel.: (845) 201-5600
Web Site: http://www.qognify.com
Computer Software Developer
N.A.I.C.S.: 541512
Steve Shine *(Pres & CEO)*

Subsidiary (Domestic):

On-Net Surveillance Systems Inc. (2)
1 Blue Hill Plz 7th Fl, Pearl River, NY
10965
Tel.: (845) 369-6400
Web Site: http://www.onssi.com
Custom Computer Programming Services
N.A.I.C.S.: 541511
Gadi Piran *(Founder, Pres & CTO)*

Tesa Technology UK Ltd (1)
Metrology House Halesfield 13, Telford, TF7
4PL, United Kingdom (100%)
Tel.: (44) 1952681349
Web Site: http://www.tesatechnology.com
Sales Range: Less than $1 Million
Emp.: 2
Mfr of Metrology Equipment
N.A.I.C.S.: 333517

Thermopylae Sciences + Technology (1)
1911 N Fort Myer Dr Ste 700, Arlington, VA
22209
Tel.: (703) 740-8768
Web Site: https://www.t-sciences.com
Computer Related Services
N.A.I.C.S.: 541519
A.J. Clark *(Pres)*

HEXAGON COMPOSITES ASA

3369

HEXAGON COMPOSITES ASA

Hexagon Composites ASA—(Continued)

Korsegata 4B, PO Box 836, 6002, Alesund, Norway
Tel.: (47) 70304450   **NO**
Web Site:
https://www.hexagongroup.com
HXGCF—(OTCIQ)
Rev.: $508,890,537
Assets: $631,915,391
Liabilities: $315,959,170
Net Worth: $315,956,221
Earnings: ($92,523,104)
Emp.: 1,149
Fiscal Year-end: 12/31/23
Holding Company; Filament-Wound Composite Cylinder Designer & Mfr
N.A.I.C.S.: 551112
Knut Trygve Flakk (Chm)

Subsidiaries:

Agility Fuel Solutions Holdings Inc.   **(1)**
3335 Susan St Ste 100, Costa Mesa, CA 92626   **(100%)**
Tel.: (949) 236-5520
Web Site:
http://www.agilityfuelsolutions.com
Emp.: 415
Holding Company; Natural Gas Solutions; Composite Fuel Cylinder Designer & Mfr
N.A.I.C.S.: 551112
Andrew Griffiths (CFO)

Subsidiary (Domestic):

Agility Fuel Solutions LLC   **(2)**
3335 Susan St Ste 100, Costa Mesa, CA 92626
Tel.: (949) 236-5520
Web Site:
http://www.agilityfuelsolutions.com
Natural Gas Solutions; Composite Fuel Cylinder Designer & Mfr
N.A.I.C.S.: 333995
Andrew Griffiths (CFO)

Hexagon Digital Wave, LLC   **(1)**
13760 E Arapahoe Rd, Centennial, CO 80112
Tel.: (303) 790-7559
Web Site: https://www.hexagondigitalwave.com
Measuring & Controlling Device Mfr
N.A.I.C.S.: 334519
Daniel Derrickson (Controller)

Hexagon Lincoln, Inc.   **(1)**
5150 NW 40th St, Lincoln, NE 68524   **(100%)**
Tel.: (402) 470-8450
Web Site: http://www.hexagonlincoln.com
Sales Range: $25-49.9 Million
Emp.: 100
Filament-Wound High-Pressure Cylinder Designer & Mfr
N.A.I.C.S.: 333995
Jack Schimenti (Pres)

Hexagon Raufoss AS   **(1)**
Raufoss Industrial Park B306, PO Box 74, Raufoss, 2831, Norway   **(100%)**
Tel.: (47) 61154020
Web Site: https://www.hexagonraufoss.com
Sales Range: $75-99.9 Million
Emp.: 12
Filament-Wound High-Pressure Cylinder Designer & Mfr
N.A.I.C.S.: 333995

Wystrach GmbH   **(1)**
Industriestrasse 60, 47652, Weeze, Germany
Tel.: (49) 283791350
Web Site: https://www.wystrach.gmbh
Flow Control Equipment Mfr
N.A.I.C.S.: 332919

HEXAGON ENERGY MATERIALS LIMITED

45 Ventnor Ave, West Perth, 6005, WA, Australia
Tel.: (61) 862440349
Web Site:
https://hxgenergymaterials.com.au
Year Founded: 2001
HXG—(ASX)
Rev.: $470,839
Assets: $2,709,087
Liabilities: $1,840,902
Net Worth: $868,185
Earnings: ($1,038,664)
Fiscal Year-end: 06/30/24
Graphite Mining Services
N.A.I.C.S.: 212390
Ian Gregory (Sec)

HEXAGON HOLDINGS BERHAD

A11-0-2 Megan Salak Pk, Jalan 2/125E Taman Desa Petaling, 57100, Kuala Lumpur, Malaysia
Tel.: (60) 390515999
Sales Range: $100-124.9 Million
Plant & Process Engineering Services
N.A.I.C.S.: 541330
Enk Purn Tan (Co-Sec)

Subsidiaries:

Advance Metal Substrate Technology Sdn. Bhd.   **(1)**
PT 1481 Jalan Emas 1 Nilai Industrial Estate, 71800, Nilai, Negeri Sembilan, Malaysia
Tel.: (60) 67990150
Web Site: http://www.amst.com.my
Sales Range: $50-74.9 Million
Emp.: 250
Lead Frames Mfr
N.A.I.C.S.: 332999

Darwin International Trading (Shanghai) Co. Ltd.   **(1)**
Building 2 No 528 Qinzhou Road, 200233, Shanghai, China
Tel.: (86) 2154975577
Web Site: http://www.darwinco.net
Sales Range: $50-74.9 Million
Emp.: 25
Trading & Engineering Services
N.A.I.C.S.: 425120
Zhao Jone (Mgr-Mktg)

Hexagon Distributors Sdn. Bhd.   **(1)**
Lot 1903A Jalan KPB 7 Kawasan Perindustrian Kg Baru Balakong, 43300, Seri Kembangan, Selangor, Malaysia
Tel.: (60) 389618066
Web Site:
http://www.hexagondistributors.com
Sales Range: $50-74.9 Million
Emp.: 115
Polymer Composites Mfr
N.A.I.C.S.: 325211

Subsidiary (Domestic):

Hexagon Composite Sdn. Bhd.   **(2)**
Lot 1903A Jalan KPB 7 Kawasan Perindustrian Kg Baru Balakong, 43300, Seri Kembangan, Selangor, Malaysia
Tel.: (60) 389618066
Web Site:
http://www.hexagoncomposite.com
Sales Range: $25-49.9 Million
Emp.: 40
Polymer Composites Mfr & Distr
N.A.I.C.S.: 325211

Hexagon Shop System Sdn. Bhd.   **(1)**
PT 3266 Jalan AM 1 Arab-Malaysian Industrial Park, 71800, Nilai, Negeri Sembilan, Malaysia
Tel.: (60) 67942000
Web Site:
http://www.hexagonshopsystem.com
Sales Range: $75-99.9 Million
Emp.: 350
Shop Interiors Designing & Installation Services
N.A.I.C.S.: 541410

Hexagon Tower (Tianjin) Engineering Co., Ltd.   **(1)**
Suite 1416 Buynow Building No 308 Anshan West Road, Nankai District, Tianjin, China
Tel.: (86) 2258892290
Web Site: http://www.hexagon-tower.com
Engineering Services
N.A.I.C.S.: 541330

Hexagon Tower Philippines Inc.   **(1)**
Room 201 Jemco Building C Raymundo Avenue, Rosario, Pasig, 1609, Philippines
Tel.: (63) 26436270
Web Site: http://www.hexagon-tower.com
Industrial Engineering Services
N.A.I.C.S.: 541330

Hexagon-Tatsuno Engineering Sdn. Bhd.   **(1)**
Lot 1903 A Kawasan Perindustrian Balakong, 43300, Seri Kembangan, Selangor, Malaysia
Tel.: (60) 389618066
Web Site: http://www.hexagontatsuno.com
Petroleum & Industrial Equipment Installation & Maintenance Services
N.A.I.C.S.: 237120

Polymer Composite Asia Sdn. Bhd.   **(1)**
PT 3266 Jalan AM 1 Arab-Malaysian Industrial Park, 71800, Nilai, Negeri Sembilan, Malaysia
Tel.: (60) 67942000
Web Site:
http://www.polymercompositeasia.com
Sales Range: $50-74.9 Million
Emp.: 250
Polymer Products Mfr & Distr
N.A.I.C.S.: 326199

Subsidiary (Non-US):

Hexagon Midco India Pvt. Ltd.   **(2)**
Near Jain Ashram Station Road Vatva, Ahmedabad, 382445, Gujarat, India
Tel.: (91) 7925899999
Plant Engineering Services
N.A.I.C.S.: 541330

Subsidiary (Domestic):

Hexagon Vetec Sdn. Bhd.   **(2)**
PT 3266 Jalan AM 1 Arab-Malaysian Industrial Park, 71800, Nilai, Negeri Sembilan, Malaysia
Tel.: (60) 67942000
Sales Range: $75-99.9 Million
Emp.: 350
Metal Products Mfr
N.A.I.C.S.: 332999
Alan Loi (Gen Mgr)

Subsidiary (Non-US):

Polymer Composite Asia (Shanghai) Co. Ltd   **(2)**
1056 Maoting Road Chedun Songjiang Area, 201611, Shanghai, China
Tel.: (86) 2157776190
Web Site: http://www.hexagon-tower.com
Sales Range: $25-49.9 Million
Emp.: 30
Polymer Product Mfr
N.A.I.C.S.: 326140

HEXAGON PURUS ASA

Korsegata 4B, 6002, Aalesund, Norway
Tel.: (47) 70304450
Web Site:
https://www.hexagongroup.com
Year Founded: 1963
HPUR—(OSL)
Rev.: $479,060,318
Assets: $593,764,641
Liabilities: $296,883,706
Net Worth: $296,880,935
Earnings: ($86,937,188)
Emp.: 1,156
Fiscal Year-end: 12/31/23
Hydrogen Fuel Mfr
N.A.I.C.S.: 825120
David Bandele (CFO)

HEXATRONIC GROUP AB

Sofierogatan 3A, SE-412 51, Gothenburg, Sweden
Tel.: (46) 317973100
Web Site:
https://hexatronicgroup.com
Year Founded: 1972

INTERNATIONAL PUBLIC

HTRO—(OMX)
Rev.: $621,025,223
Assets: $692,011,577
Liabilities: $429,280,583
Net Worth: $262,730,994
Earnings: $74,273,886
Emp.: 1,696
Fiscal Year-end: 12/31/22
Cabling, Interconnect & Fiber Systems Mfr & Distr
N.A.I.C.S.: 335921
Henrik Larsson Lyon (CEO)

Subsidiaries:

Apticom S.R.L.   **(1)**
Rue Santos-Dumont 1, 6041, Gosselies, Belgium
Tel.: (32) 71420531
Communication Network Services
N.A.I.C.S.: 516210

Blue Diamond Industries LLC   **(1)**
2117 W Winchester Ave, Middlesboro, KY 40965
Tel.: (606) 248-8078
Web Site: http://www.bdiky.com
Rev.: $8,200,000
Emp.: 50
All Other Plastics Product Mfr
N.A.I.C.S.: 326199

Edugrade AB   **(1)**
Hastaholmen 4, 824 44, Hudiksvall, Sweden
Tel.: (46) 650553430
Web Site: https://edugrade.com
Professional Training Services
N.A.I.C.S.: 611430

Edugrade SE   **(1)**
Hastaholmen 4, 824 44, Hudiksvall, Sweden
Tel.: (46) 650553430
Web Site: https://edugrade.com
Educational Support Services
N.A.I.C.S.: 611710

Endor ehf.   **(1)**
Suourlandsbraut 8, Selfoss, 108, Reykjavik, Iceland
Tel.: (354) 5124600
Web Site: https://www.endor.is
Emp.: 11
Information Technology Management Services
N.A.I.C.S.: 541512
Hannes Hjalti Gilbert (Engr-Sys)

Gordon Franks Training Ltd.   **(1)**
Crossway 156 Great Charles Street Queensway, Birmingham, B3 3HN, United Kingdom
Tel.: (44) 1213333001
Web Site: https://www.wearegft.co.uk
Professional & Management Training Services
N.A.I.C.S.: 611430

H. Weterings-Plastics B.V.   **(1)**
Galgeweg 42, 2691 MG, 's-Gravenzande, Netherlands
Tel.: (31) 174629664
Web Site: https://en.weteringsplastics.nl
Plastics Product Mfr
N.A.I.C.S.: 326112

Hexatronic Australia Pty. Ltd.   **(1)**
Unit 2 40 Borthwick Ave, Murarrie, 4172, QLD, Australia
Tel.: (61) 733995280
Telecommunication & Information Services
N.A.I.C.S.: 517810

Hexatronic Cables & Interconnect AB   **(1)**
Kabelvagen 1, 824 82, Hudiksvall, Sweden
Tel.: (46) 104530200
Fiber Optic Cable Mfr
N.A.I.C.S.: 335921

Hexatronic Canada Inc   **(1)**
62 Railside Rd Unit 5, Toronto, M3A 1A3, ON, Canada
Tel.: (416) 391-0033
Web Site: https://toronics.com
Fiber Optic Cable Mfr & Distr
N.A.I.C.S.: 335921

Hexatronic Fiberoptic AB   **(1)**

Skalholtsgatan 10, 16440, Kista, Sweden
Tel.: (46) 104249800
Web Site: https://www.hexatronic.com
Telecommunication Servicesb
N.A.I.C.S.: 517111

Hexatronic GmbH (1)
Otto-Hahn-Str 4a, 22941, Bargteheide, Germany
Tel.: (49) 45325036961
Web Site: https://www.hexatronic.com
Fibre Optic Cable Mfr & Distr
N.A.I.C.S.: 335921
David Dumke *(Dir-Product Development)*

Hexatronic New Zealand Ltd. (1)
15 John Seddon Drive, Porirua, Wellington, 5022, New Zealand
Tel.: (64) 42382228
Web Site: https://www.hexatronic.co.nz
Fiber Optic Cable Distr
N.A.I.C.S.: 423610
John Witkowski *(Country Mgr)*

Hexatronic Security & Surveillance AB (1)
Vikdalsgrand 10A, 131 52, Nacka, Sweden
Tel.: (46) 102522775
Fibre Optic Cable Mfr & Distr
N.A.I.C.S.: 335921
Jawad Saadi *(Mng Dir)*

Hexatronic UK Ltd. (1)
Unit B Quay West Hardway, Hardway, Gosport, PO12 4LJ, Hampshire, United Kingdom
Tel.: (44) 2392580555
Web Site: https://www.hexatronic.com
Fibre Optic Cable Mfr & Distr
N.A.I.C.S.: 335921
Kieran Stone *(CTO)*

Impact Data Solutions Limited (1)
West Wing Beech House Ancells Business Park, Fleet, GU51 2UN, Hampshire, United Kingdom **(90%)**
Tel.: (44) 1252896910
Web Site: http://www.impactds.com
Emp.: 275
Infrastructure Developing Services
N.A.I.C.S.: 518210
Nathan Rawles *(Sls Dir-EMEA)*

KNET Co. Ltd. (1)
A-604 551-17 Yangcheon-ro, Gayang-dong Gangseo-gu, Seoul, 07532, Korea (South)
Tel.: (82) 220635400
Web Site: https://www.e-knet.com
Polyethylene Pipe Product Mfr & Distr
N.A.I.C.S.: 326122

Mccom, Ltd. (1)
2500 E Randol Mill Rd Ste 200, Arlington, TX 76011
Tel.: (972) 445-8668
Web Site: http://www.usnet-1.com
Sales Range: $10-24.9 Million
Telecommunications Resellers
N.A.I.C.S.: 517121
Dustin McLeod *(CEO)*

Mpirical Limited (1)
3-4-3 Storey House White Cross, Lancaster, LA1 4XQ, United Kingdom
Tel.: (44) 1524844669
Web Site: https://www.mpirical.com
Training & Coaching Services
N.A.I.C.S.: 611430

Opternus Components GmbH (1)
Bahnhofstrasse 5, 22941, Bargteheide, Germany
Tel.: (49) 453220440
Web Site: https://www.opternus.de
Fiber Optic Cable Connector Mfr
N.A.I.C.S.: 334417

Opternus GmbH (1)
Bahnhofstrasse 5, 22941, Bargteheide, Germany
Tel.: (49) 453220440
Web Site: https://www.opternus.de
Fibre Optic Cable Mfr & Distr
N.A.I.C.S.: 335921

Optical Solutions (Sydney City) Pty. Ltd. (1)
8 Rachael Close, Silverwater, 2128, NSW, Australia
Tel.: (61) 293951400
Fiber Optic Cable Distr

N.A.I.C.S.: 423610

Optical Solutions (Victoria) Pty. Ltd. (1)
Unit 3 30 Prohasky Street, Port Melbourne, 3207, VIC, Australia
Tel.: (61) 396464166
Fiber Optic Cable Distr
N.A.I.C.S.: 423610

Optical Solutions (WA) Pty. Ltd. (1)
23 Brennan Way, Belmont, 6104, WA, Australia
Tel.: (61) 893617000
Fiber Optic Cable Distr
N.A.I.C.S.: 423610

Optical Solutions Australia (ACT) Pty. Limited (1)
22 Isa Street, Fyshwick, 2609, ACT, Australia
Tel.: (61) 261624600
Fiber Optic Cable Distr
N.A.I.C.S.: 423610

Optical Solutions Australia (Queensland) Pty Limited (1)
Unit 2 40 Borthwick Ave, Murarrie, 4172, QLD, Australia
Tel.: (61) 733995280
Fiber Optic Cable Distr
N.A.I.C.S.: 423610

P.T. KNET Indonesia (1)
Grand wijaya centre blok G no 2 jl Wijaya II, Kebayoran Baru, Jakarta, 12160, Indonesia
Tel.: (62) 2172797570
Telecommunication Servicesb
N.A.I.C.S.: 517111

PQMS Ltd. (1)
Sole End Industrial Estate Astley Lane, Bedworth, CV12 0NE, United Kingdom
Tel.: (44) 2476316789
Web Site: https://www.pqmstraining.co.uk
Management Consultancy Services
N.A.I.C.S.: 541611

Proximion AB (1)
Skalholtsgatan 10, 164 40, Kista, Sweden
Tel.: (46) 87504888
Web Site: https://www.proximion.com
Fibre Optic Cable Mfr & Distr
N.A.I.C.S.: 335921
Johan Pejnefors *(CEO)*

Rochester Wire & Cable LLC (1)
751 Old Brandy Rd, Culpeper, VA 22701
Tel.: (540) 825-2111
Web Site: http://www.rochestercables.com
Cable Wire Mfr
N.A.I.C.S.: 332618

Smart Awards Ltd. (1)
Beechwood House Tanners Lane, Berkswell, Coventry, CV7 7DA, United Kingdom
Tel.: (44) 2476421125
Web Site: https://www.smartawards.co.uk
Telecommunication Servicesb
N.A.I.C.S.: 513199

TK kontor Freitag GmbH (1)
Ilsahl 1, 24536, Neumunster, Germany
Tel.: (49) 15202932390
Web Site: https://tk-kontor-freitag.de
Engineering Consulting Services
N.A.I.C.S.: 541330

Tech Optics First Company Ltd. (1)
Units 6&7 Tannery Road, Tonbridge, TN9 1RF, Kent, United Kingdom
Tel.: (44) 1732770456
Web Site: https://www.techoptics.com
Fiber Optic Cable Mfr
N.A.I.C.S.: 335921

Tech Optics Ltd. (1)
Unit 6 Tannery Road, Tonbridge, TN9 1RF, Kent, United Kingdom
Tel.: (44) 1732770466
Web Site: https://www.techoptics.com
Fibre Optic Cable Mfr & Distr
N.A.I.C.S.: 335921

homeway GmbH (1)
Liebigstrasse 6, 96465, Neustadt bei Coburg, Germany
Tel.: (49) 9568897930
Web Site: https://www.homeway.de
Household Appliances Mfr

N.A.I.C.S.: 335220

HEXICON AB
Ostra Jarnvagsgatan 27, 111 20, Stockholm, Sweden
Tel.: (46) 850235177
Web Site: https://www.hexicongroup.com
Year Founded: 2009
HEXI—(OMX)
Rev.: $534,809
Assets: $46,984,555
Liabilities: $46,809,407
Net Worth: $175,148
Earnings: ($17,545,684)
Emp.: 28
Fiscal Year-end: 12/31/23
Renewable Energy Services
N.A.I.C.S.: 221210
Hans Uthmann *(Chm)*

HEXIMA LIMITED
Level 4 LIMS2 La Trobe University, Melbourne, 3086, VIC, Australia
Tel.: (61) 3 9479 1210
Web Site: http://www.hexima.com.au
Rev.: $2,413,124
Assets: $4,044,080
Liabilities: $2,765,372
Net Worth: $1,278,708
Earnings: ($2,036,196)
Emp.: 50
Fiscal Year-end: 06/30/19
Insect Resistance, Fungal Resistance & Gene Delivery Technology
N.A.I.C.S.: 541715
Marilyn A. Anderson *(Chief Science Officer)*

HEXING ELECTRICAL CO LTD
No 1418-35 Moganshan Road Shangcheng Industrial Park, Hangzhou, China
Tel.: (86) 4009955981
Web Site: https://electric.hxgroup.com
603556—(SHG)
Rev.: $464,685,193
Assets: $1,129,616,224
Liabilities: $290,719,864
Net Worth: $838,896,360
Earnings: $93,264,393
Fiscal Year-end: 12/31/22
Electric Meter Product Mfr & Distr
N.A.I.C.S.: 335311

HEXIS AG
Zum Pk 5, PO Box 3068, 8404, Winterthur, Switzerland
Tel.: (41) 522626311
Web Site: http://www.hexis.com
Sales Range: $75-99.9 Million
Emp.: 32
Fuel Cell Research & Development Services
N.A.I.C.S.: 541715
Andreas Mai *(Co-CEO)*

Subsidiaries:

HEXIS GmbH (1)
Schulthaissstrasse 15, Konstanz, 78462, Germany
Tel.: (49) 7531 3631911
Web Site: http://www.hexis.com
Sales Range: $25-49.9 Million
Emp.: 8
Fuel Cell Mfr
N.A.I.C.S.: 334413
Mike Hellwig *(Mgr-Sls)*

HEXONIA GMBH
Van-der-Upwich-Str 40, 41334, Nettetal, Germany
Tel.: (49) 21538031600
Web Site: https://hexonia.de
Year Founded: 2005
Emp.: 250

Industrial Material Mfr
N.A.I.C.S.: 331222

HEXPOL AB
Skeppsbron 3, SE-211 20, Malmo, Sweden
Tel.: (46) 40254660
Web Site: https://www.hexpol.com
Year Founded: 1893
HPOL.B—(OMX)
Rev.: $1,638,801,920
Assets: $1,840,111,840
Liabilities: $725,155,200
Net Worth: $1,114,956,640
Earnings: $172,010,720
Emp.: 4,550
Fiscal Year-end: 12/31/20
Rubber Compound & Gasket Mfr
N.A.I.C.S.: 326291
Georg Brunstam *(Pres & CEO)*

Subsidiaries:

Almaak international GmbH (1)
Elbestrasse 29, 47800, Krefeld, Germany
Tel.: (49) 21514960
Web Site: https://almaak.de
Emp.: 200
Plastics Product Mfr
N.A.I.C.S.: 326199

Berwin Group Limited (1)
Broadway Globe Lane Industrial Estate, Dukinfield, SK16 4UJ, Cheshire, United Kingdom
Tel.: (44) 161 342 1150
Web Site: https://www.hexpol.com
Sales Range: $1-9.9 Million
Emp.: 248
Rubber Products Mfr
N.A.I.C.S.: 314994

Subsidiary (Domestic):

Flexi-Cell (UK) Ltd. (2)
Broadway Globe Lane Industrial Estate, Dukinfield, SK16 4UJ, Cheshire, United Kingdom
Tel.: (44) 1613421150
Rubber Compound & Gasket Mfr
N.A.I.C.S.: 326291

Berwin Industrial Polymers Limited (1)
Church Road, Lydney, GL15 5FG, Gloucestershire, United Kingdom
Tel.: (44) 1594846551
Rubber Products Mfr
N.A.I.C.S.: 326291

Gislaved Gummi AB (1)
Abjornsgatan 9, 332 36, Gislaved, Sweden
Tel.: (46) 37184800
Web Site: https://www.gislavedgummi.com
Emp.: 700
Plate Heat Exchanger Gasket, Customized Rubber Compounds & Extruded Profile Mfr
N.A.I.C.S.: 326299
Stefan Rydh *(Dir-Sls & Mktg)*

Subsidiary (Non-US):

Gislaved Gummi (Qingdao) Co., Ltd. (2)
899 Fenghuangshan Road, Huangdao, Qingdao, 266431, China
Tel.: (86) 53281731167
Industrial Gasket Mfr & Distr
N.A.I.C.S.: 339991
David Jia *(Pres)*

Gislaved Gummi Lanka (Pvt) Ltd. (2)
371 Colombo Road, Bokundara, Piliyandala, 10300, Sri Lanka
Tel.: (94) 114212722
Industrial Gasket Mfr & Distr
N.A.I.C.S.: 339991
Roger Jonsson *(Pres)*

HEXPOL Compounding (Qingdao) Co., Ltd. (1)
Fenghuangshan Road CN, Huangdao, Qingdao, 266431, China
Tel.: (86) 53281731118
Rubber Products Mfr
N.A.I.C.S.: 326291

HEXPOL AB

HEXPOL AB—(Continued)

HEXPOL Compounding CA Inc. (1)
491 Wilson Way, City of Industry, CA 91744
Tel.: (626) 961-0311
Rubber Compound & Gasket Mfr
N.A.I.C.S.: 326291

HEXPOL Compounding HQ SA (1)
Gewerbestrasse 8, 4700, Eupen, Belgium
Tel.: (32) 87596150
Rubber Products Mfr
N.A.I.C.S.: 326291

HEXPOL Compounding HQ Sprl (1)
Industriestrasse 36, 4700, Eupen, Belgium
Tel.: (32) 87595430
Web Site:
http://www.hexpolcompounding.com
Rubber Products Mfr
N.A.I.C.S.: 326291

HEXPOL Compounding Lesina s.r.o (1)
Skaina, 351 34, Lesina, Czech Republic
Tel.: (420) 354524911
Web Site:
http://www.hexpolcompounding.com
Engineered Rubber Product Mfr
N.A.I.C.S.: 326299

HEXPOL Compounding S.L.U. (1)
Ctra Molins de Reia Caldes Km 13 2, 08191, Rubi, Spain
Tel.: (34) 936998611
Rubber Products Mfr
N.A.I.C.S.: 326291

HEXPOL Compounding Sprl (1)
Industriestrasse 36, 4700, Eupen, Belgium
Tel.: (32) 8 759 5430
Web Site: http://www.hpc-hq.com
Rubber Compound Mfr
N.A.I.C.S.: 326299

Subsidiary (Non-US):

Chase Elastomer (UK) Ltd. (2)
Unit 3 Fifth Avenue Tameside Park, Dukinfield, SK16 4PP, Cheshire, United Kingdom
Tel.: (44) 1613434433
Web Site: http://www.chaseuk.com
Rubber Compound Mfr & Distr
N.A.I.C.S.: 326299

HEXPOL Compounding (Foshan) Co., Ltd. (2)
No 3 Xinhui Road Wusha Daliang, Shunde District, Foshan, 528333, Guangdong, China
Tel.: (86) 75722915100
Web Site: http://www.hexpoltpe.com
Rubber Compound Mfr
N.A.I.C.S.: 326299
Gareth Jefferson (Gen Mgr)

HEXPOL Compounding GmbH (2)
Ottostrasse 34, 41836, Huckelhoven, Germany
Tel.: (49) 243397550
Web Site:
http://www.hexpolcompounding.com
Emp.: 180
Rubber Compound Mfr
N.A.I.C.S.: 326299

Subsidiary (Domestic):

Muller Kunststoffe GmbH (3)
Grunewaldstr 13, 96215, Lichtenfels, Germany
Tel.: (49) 9571 94894 0
Web Site: http://www.hexpoltpe.com
Emp.: 120
Plastics Product Mfr
N.A.I.C.S.: 326199

Stellana Deutschland GmbH (3)
Am Appenstedter Waldchen 7, 21217, Seevetal, Germany
Tel.: (49) 4070388470
Thermoplastic & Polyurethane Wheel Mfr
N.A.I.C.S.: 325211
Hans-Joachim Schnur (Mgr-Export)

Subsidiary (US):

HEXPOL Compounding LLC (2)
14330 Kinsman Rd, Burton, OH 44021 (100%)
Tel.: (440) 834-4644

Web Site:
http://www.hexpolcompounding.com
Rubber Compound Products Mfr
N.A.I.C.S.: 326291
Tracy Garrison (Pres, CEO & Head-NAFTA Ops)

Subsidiary (Domestic):

Chase Elastomer Corporation (3)
635 Tower Dr, Kennedale, TX 76060
Tel.: (817) 483-9797
Web Site:
http://www.hexpolcompounding.com
Rubber Compound Distr
N.A.I.C.S.: 424690

GoldKey Processing, Inc. (3)
14910 Madison Rd, Middlefield, OH 44062
Tel.: (440) 632-0901
Web Site:
https://www.goldkeyprocessing.com
Rubber Compound Mfr & Distr
N.A.I.C.S.: 326299

Subsidiary (Non-US):

HEXPOL Compounding (UK) Ltd. (3)
Broadway Globe Lane Industrial Estate, Dukinfield, SK16 4UJ, Cheshire, United Kingdom
Tel.: (44) 1613421150
Rubber Compound & Gasket Mfr
N.A.I.C.S.: 326291
Anthony Hallworth (Mgr-Sls)

Subsidiary (Domestic):

HEXPOL Compounding NC Inc. (3)
280 Crawford Rd, Statesville, NC 28625
Tel.: (704) 872-1585
Web Site:
http://www.hexpolcompounding.com
Emp.: 60
Rubber Compound Products Mfr
N.A.I.C.S.: 326299
Randy Simpson (COO)

Subsidiary (Non-US):

HEXPOL Compounding S.A. de C.V. (3)
Avenida Japon 302 Parque Industrial San Francisco, San Fransisco de los Romo, 20304, Aguascalientes, Mexico
Tel.: (52) 4491393270
Web Site:
http://www.hexpolcompounding.com
Rubber Compound Mfr
N.A.I.C.S.: 326299

Subsidiary (Domestic):

HEXPOL Compounding Queretaro S.A. de C.V. (4)
La Noria 115 Parque Industrial Queretaro, Santa Rosa Jauregui, 76220, Queretaro, Mexico
Tel.: (52) 4422113500
Web Site:
http://www.hexpolcompounding.com
Rubber Compound Mfr
N.A.I.C.S.: 326299

Subsidiary (Domestic):

Portage Precision Polymers, Inc. (3)
215 W Lake St, Ravenna, OH 44266
Tel.: (330) 296-6327
Web Site: http://www.p3mixing.com
Sales Range: $25-49.9 Million
Rubber Products Mfr
N.A.I.C.S.: 326299
Lisa Zavara (Mgr-HR)

Robbins LLC (3)
3415 Thompson St, Muscle Shoals, AL 35661
Tel.: (256) 383-5441
Web Site: https://www.robbinsllc.com
Sales Range: $100-124.9 Million
Emp.: 240
Tire Retreading & Custom-Mixed Rubber Compound Mfr
N.A.I.C.S.: 326212
Peggy McCollum (Mgr-Customer Svc)

Subsidiary (Non-US):

HEXPOL Compounding s.r.o. (2)

Sumperska 1344, 78391, Unicov, Czech Republic
Tel.: (420) 585004011
Web Site:
http://www.hexpolcompounding.com
Emp.: 100
Rubber Compound Mfr
N.A.I.C.S.: 326299

HEXPOL TPE AB (2)
Gamla Ornasgatan 15, Box 51, 662 22, Amal, Sweden
Tel.: (46) 53 260 7500
Web Site: https://www.hexpoltpe.com
Thermoplastic Elastomers Products Mfr
N.A.I.C.S.: 326199
Klas Dannas (Mgr-Research & Development-Global)

HEXPOL TPE Ltd (2)
Don Street, Middleton, Manchester, M24 2GG, United Kingdom
Tel.: (44) 161 654 6616
Web Site: https://www.hexpoltpe.com
Thermoplastic Polymer Products Mfr
N.A.I.C.S.: 326199
Mark Griffiths (Mgr-Manufacturing-Research & Development)

HEXPOL Services Compounding S.A de C.V (1)
Avenida Japon 302, Parque Industrial San Francisco San Francisco de los Romo, 20304, Aguascalientes, Mexico
Tel.: (52) 4491393270
Rubber Products Mfr
N.A.I.C.S.: 326291
Salvador Vazquez Mireles (Mgr-Bus Dev)

HEXPOL TPE GmbH (1)
Plant 1 Grunewaldstr 13, 96215, Lichtenfels, Germany
Tel.: (49) 9571948940
Plastic Product Mfr & Distr
N.A.I.C.S.: 326199

Kirkhill Manufacturing Company Inc. (1)
2500 E Thompson St, Long Beach, CA 90805
Tel.: (562) 803-1117
Rubber Compound & Gasket Mfr
N.A.I.C.S.: 326291

MESGO Asia KAUCUK A.S. (1)
TOSB Otomotiv Yan Sanayi Ihtisas Organize Sanayi Bolgesi 4 Cad No 3/1, Sekerpinar, 41420, Cayirova, Kocaeli, Turkiye
Tel.: (90) 2626582223
Rubber Products Mfr
N.A.I.C.S.: 326299

MESGO SpA (1)
Via Virgilio 16, 24060, Gorlago, BG, Italy
Tel.: (39) 035 425 2000
Web Site: https://www.mesgo.it
Emp.: 50
Synthetic Rubber Mfr
N.A.I.C.S.: 325212

Subsidiary (Domestic):

MESGO Iride Colors Srl (2)
Via Borgo S Siro 66, 27026, Garlasco, PV, Italy
Tel.: (39) 0382816611
Emp.: 47
Color Pigments Mfr
N.A.I.C.S.: 325130

Subsidiary (Domestic):

3A MCOM Srl (3)
Zona Industriale 4, Grigno, 38055, Trento, Italy
Tel.: (39) 0382816611
Rubber Compound & Gasket Mfr
N.A.I.C.S.: 326291
Daniele Batti (Mgr-Production)

McCann Plastics LLC (1)
5600 Mayfair Rd, North Canton, OH 44720
Tel.: (330) 499-1515
Web Site: http://www.mccannplastics.com
Plastic Product Mfr & Distr
N.A.I.C.S.: 326199

Mesgo Asia Kaucuk San. Ve Tic. Ltd. (1)
TOSB Otomotiv Yan Sanayi Ihtisas Organize Sanayi Bolgesi 4 Cad No 3/1, Sekerpi-

INTERNATIONAL PUBLIC

nar, Cayirova, Kocaeli, Turkiye
Tel.: (90) 2626582223
Silicon Compound Mfr
N.A.I.C.S.: 325180

Preferred Compounding Corp. (1)
1020 Lambert St, Barberton, OH 44203-1612
Tel.: (330) 798-4790
Web Site: http://www.preferredperforms.com
Rubber Compounding & Products Mfr
N.A.I.C.S.: 326299
Kenneth L. Bloom (Pres & CEO)

Plant (Domestic):

Preferred Compounding Corp. - Tallapoosa (2)
101 Stoffel Dr, Tallapoosa, GA 30176
Tel.: (770) 574-2321
Web Site: http://www.preferredperforms.com
Rubber Compounding & Products Mfr
N.A.I.C.S.: 326299

Subsidiary (Domestic):

Trostel Ltd. (2)
901 Maxwell St, Lake Geneva, WI 53147-1003
Tel.: (262) 248-4481
Gaskets, Packing & Sealing Devices Mfr
N.A.I.C.S.: 339991
Greg Vassmer (VP-Sls & Engrg)

RheTech Engineered Plastics Ltd. (1)
1500 E N Territorial Rd, Withmore Lake, MI 48189
Plastics Product Mfr
N.A.I.C.S.: 326199

RheTech LLC (1)
1500 E N Territorial Rd, Whitmore Lake, MI 48189
Tel.: (734) 769-0585
Web Site: https://www.rhetech.com
Thermoplastic Mfr
N.A.I.C.S.: 325211

RheTech Thermocolor LLC (1)
2901 W Monroe St, Sandusky, OH 44870
Tel.: (419) 626-5677
Thermoplastic Mfr
N.A.I.C.S.: 325211

Rhetech, Inc. (1)
1500 E N Territorial Rd, Whitmore Lake, MI 48189
Tel.: (734) 769-0585
Web Site: https://www.rhetech.com
Thermoplastic Alloys, Compounds & Concentrates Mfr
N.A.I.C.S.: 325991

Stellana (Qingdao) Co., Ltd. (1)
899 Fenghuangshan Road, Huangdao, Qingdao, 266431, China
Tel.: (86) 53281731167
Rubber Compound & Gasket Mfr
N.A.I.C.S.: 326291
Edmund Li (Reg Dir-Sls & Mktg)

Stellana AB (1)
Roforsvagen 23, PO Box 54, 695 32, Laxa, Sweden
Tel.: (46) 584444800
Web Site: https://www.stellana.se
Sales Range: $25-49.9 Million
Emp.: 85
Rubber Wheel Mfr
N.A.I.C.S.: 326299

Subsidiary (Non-US):

Elastomeric Engineering Co. Ltd. (2)
51-54 IDB Industrial Estate, Horana, Sri Lanka
Tel.: (94) 4212722
Web Site: http://www.elastomericgroup.com
Rubber Wheel, Tire & Gasket Mfr
N.A.I.C.S.: 326299

Plant (US):

Stellana U.S. Inc. (2)
999 Wells St, Lake Geneva, WI 53147
Tel.: (262) 348-5575
Web Site: http://www.stellana.us
Sales Range: $25-49.9 Million
Emp.: 50
Polyurethane Tire & Wheel Mfr

N.A.I.C.S.: 326150
Michael Scoon *(Mgr-Sls & Mktg)*

Union de Industrias C.A., S.A. (1)
Carretera de Alfaro S/N, 31591, Cornella de Llobregat, Navarre, Spain
Tel.: (34) 948780025
Web Site: https://www.unicamezclas.com
Rubber Products Mfr
N.A.I.C.S.: 326299

Vicom 2002 S.L. (1)
C/ Sumoi 7-9, Poligono Industrial Clot de Moja Olerdola, 08734, Barcelona, Spain
Tel.: (34) 938199447
Web Site: https://www.vicom2002.es
Thermoplastic Mfr
N.A.I.C.S.: 325211

HEXTAR GLOBAL BERHAD
No 64 Jalan Bayu Laut 4/KS09 Kota Bayuemas, 41200, Klang, 41200, Selangor, Malaysia
Tel.: (60) 330033333 MY
Web Site: https://hextarglobal.com
5151—(KLS)
Rev.: $145,633,145
Assets: $191,260,936
Liabilities: $134,832,106
Net Worth: $56,428,829
Earnings: $14,728,768
Emp.: 755
Fiscal Year-end: 12/31/23
Holding Company; Agrochemicals, Horticultural Products, Cotton & Paper Based Products Mfr & Distr
N.A.I.C.S.: 551112

Subsidiaries:

Halex Biotechnologies Sdn. Bhd. (1)
Lot 650 & 651 Ban Foo Village Mukim Plentong, Ulu Tiram, 81800, Johor, Malaysia
Tel.: (60) 7 865 0523
Horticultural Product Distr
N.A.I.C.S.: 424930

Halex Industries (M) Sdn. Bhd. (1)
Lot PTB 264 Jalan Tun Mutalib Satu Kawasan Industri Bandar Tenggara, 81440, Kulai, Johor Bahru, Malaysia
Tel.: (60) 7 896 6985
Chemical Products Mfr
N.A.I.C.S.: 325199

Halex Woolton (M) Sdn. Bhd. (1)
Lot 142 Jalan Kota Tinggi Bt 12 1/2 Mukim of Plentong, Ulu Tiram, 81800, Johor, Malaysia
Tel.: (60) 7 861 8311
Textile Products Mfr
N.A.I.C.S.: 313240

Hextar Rubber Sdn. Bhd. (1)
28 Lorong Tapah Off Jalan Goh Hock Huat, Klang, 41400, Selangor, Malaysia
Rubber Mfr
N.A.I.C.S.: 325212
Choo Meng Ong *(Owner)*

Subsidiary (Domestic):

Hextar Healthcare Berhad (2)
Lot 138201 Off 3/4 Mile Jalan Bercham Kawasan Perindustrian Bercham, 31400, Ipoh, Perak Darul Ridzuan, Malaysia **(50.18%)**
Tel.: (60) 55482723
Web Site: https://www.rubberex.com.my
Rev.: $37,029,934
Assets: $146,485,124
Liabilities: $18,539,704
Net Worth: $127,945,421
Earnings: ($11,785,276)
Emp.: 814
Fiscal Year-end: 12/31/2022
Glove Mfr
N.A.I.C.S.: 339113
Chin Leng Khoo *(Mng Dir)*

HEXTAR HOLDINGS SDN. BHD.
Lot 5 Jalan Perigi Nenas 7/3 Fasa 1A Pulau Indah Industrial Park, 42920, Port Klang, Selangor Darul Ehsan, Malaysia
Tel.: (60) 331013333 MY
Web Site:
  http://www.hextargroup.com
Year Founded: 2006
Engineeering Services
N.A.I.C.S.: 551112
Chooi Keng Lee *(Mng Dir-Pesticides)*

Subsidiaries:

Hextar Chemicals Sdn. Bhd. (1)
Lot 5 Jalan Perigi Nenas 7/3 Fasa 1A, Pulau Indah Industrial Park, 42920, Port Klang, Selangor Darul Ehsan, Malaysia
Tel.: (60) 3 3101 3333
Web Site: http://www.hextargroup.com
Pesticides & Other Agricultural Chemicals Mfr & Whslr
N.A.I.C.S.: 325320
Chooi Keng Lee *(Mng Dir)*

Hextar Fertilizers Sdn. Bhd. (1)
Lot 5 Jalan Perigi Nenas 7/3 Fasa 1A, Pulau Indah Industrial Park, 42920, Port Klang, Selangor Darul Ehsan, Malaysia
Tel.: (60) 331013333
Web Site: http://www.hextargroup.com
Fertilizer Mfr & Whslr
N.A.I.C.S.: 325314
Benny Ang *(Mng Dir)*

Hextar Technologies Solutions Bhd (1)
No 64 Jalan Bayu Laut 4/KS9 Kota Bayuemas, 41200, Port Klang, Selangor Darul Ehsan, Malaysia
Tel.: (60) 330033338
Web Site: https://www.complete-group.com
Rev.: $34,367,572
Assets: $33,089,964
Liabilities: $7,068,397
Net Worth: $26,021,568
Earnings: $795,479
Emp.: 107
Fiscal Year-end: 03/31/2023
Logistic Services
N.A.I.C.S.: 541614
Hee Ling Law *(Mng Dir)*

HEXTAR INDUSTRIES BERHAD
No 64 Jalan Bayu Laut 4/KS09 Kota Bayuemas, 41200, Klang, Selangor, Malaysia
Tel.: (60) 330033333
Web Site:
  https://hextarindustries.com
HEXIND—(KLS)
Rev.: $272,106,032
Assets: $186,384,762
Liabilities: $112,172,275
Net Worth: $74,212,487
Earnings: $20,749,418
Emp.: 319
Fiscal Year-end: 12/31/22
Quarry Equipment Distr
N.A.I.C.S.: 423810
Choun Sien Chan *(Chm)*

Subsidiaries:

PK Fertilizers (Sarawak) Sdn. Bhd. (1)
PKF Building No 12938 Jalan BBN 1/7D, 71800, Nilai, Negeri Sembilan, Malaysia
Tel.: (60) 67997788
Web Site: http://www.pkfert-sk.com
Household Fertilizer Mfr
N.A.I.C.S.: 325311
Terence Tang *(Reg Sls Mgr)*

SCH Corporation Sdn Bhd (1)
Lot 35 Jalan CJ 1/1 Kawasan Perusahaan Cheras Jaya, 43200, Cheras, Selangor, Malaysia
Tel.: (60) 390822681
Web Site: http://www.schgroup.com.my
Quarry Industrial Equipment Distr
N.A.I.C.S.: 423810

Subsidiary (Domestic):

Sin Chee Heng (Butterworth) Sdn. Bhd. (2)
22 Lorong Industri Ringan 1 Kawasan Industri Ringan Juru, 14100, Simpang Empat, Penang, Malaysia
Tel.: (60) 45180633
Quarry & Heavy Industrial Machinery Equipment Mfr
N.A.I.C.S.: 333131

Sin Chee Heng (Kuantan) Sdn. Bhd. (2)
No 1 3 Jalan Industri Tanah Putih Baru 5 Batu 3, Jalan Gambang, 25150, Kuantan, Pahang, Malaysia
Tel.: (60) 95148685
Quarry & Heavy Industrial Machinery Equipment Mfr
N.A.I.C.S.: 333131

Sin Chee Heng Sdn. Bhd. (2)
Lot 35 Jalan CJ 1/1 Kawasan Perusahaan Cheras Jaya, 43200, Cheras, Selangor, Malaysia
Tel.: (60) 390822481
Quarry & Heavy Industrial Machinery Equipment Mfr
N.A.I.C.S.: 333131

Subsidiary (Domestic):

Sin Chee Heng (Johore) Sdn. Bhd. (3)
No 106 Jalan Lagenda 6 Taman Lagenda Putra, 81000, Kulai, Johor, Malaysia
Tel.: (60) 167143286
Quarry & Heavy Industrial Machinery Equipment Mfr
N.A.I.C.S.: 333131

Sin Chee Heng (Sabah) Sdn. Bhd. (3)
DBKK No 32 Lot 37 Bigwheel Industrial Park, Jalan Tuaran, 88450, Kota Kinabalu, Sabah, Malaysia
Tel.: (60) 168334001
Quarry & Heavy Industrial Machinery Equipment Mfr
N.A.I.C.S.: 333131

Sin Chee Heng (Sarawak) Sdn. Bhd. (3)
SL10 Lot 594 Block 23B KNLD Batu 8 Jalan Batu Kitang, 93250, Kuching, Sarawak, Malaysia
Tel.: (60) 82618955
Quarry & Heavy Industrial Machinery Equipment Mfr
N.A.I.C.S.: 333131

TK Rentals Sdn. Bhd. (1)
No 22 Jalan Industri Taming Mas, Pusat Industri Taming Mas, 43300, Seri Kembangan, Selangor, Malaysia
Tel.: (60) 389619988
Web Site: http://www.tkrentals.com
Lifting Equipment Mfr
N.A.I.C.S.: 333923

HEXZA CORPORATION BERHAD
Lot 6 & 20 Persiaran Tasek Kawasan Perindustrian Tasek, 31400, Ipoh, Perak Darul Ridzuan, Malaysia
Tel.: (60) 52917823
Web Site: https://www.hexza.com.
Year Founded: 1969
HEXZA—(KLS)
Rev.: $12,700,649
Assets: $77,026,237
Liabilities: $1,834,213
Net Worth: $75,192,024
Earnings: $1,273,668
Fiscal Year-end: 06/30/23
Formaldehyde Mfr
N.A.I.C.S.: 325199
Keng Yuen Leong *(Deputy Chm)*

Subsidiaries:

Chemical Industries (Malaya) Sdn. Bhd. (1)
Lot 6 and 20 Persiaran Tasek Perindustrian Tasek, 31400, Ipoh, Perak Darul Ridzuan, Malaysia
Tel.: (60) 52913128
Web Site: https://www.cim-malaysia.com
Sales Range: $25-49.9 Million
Emp.: 60
Methanol Mfr
N.A.I.C.S.: 325193
See Cheng Lim *(Deputy Gen Mgr)*

Hexza-Mather Sdn. Bhd. (1)
Lot 6 and 20 Persiaran Tasek, Kawasan Perindustrian Tasek, 31400, Ipoh, Perak Darul Ridzuan, Malaysia
Tel.: (60) 5 291 3128
Web Site: https://www.hexza.com.my
Sales Range: $25-49.9 Million
Emp.: 30
Wine Coolers Mfr
N.A.I.C.S.: 312130

Hexzachem Sarawak Sdn. Bhd. (1)
Lot 799 Block 7 MTLD, Demak Laut Industrial Park, 93050, Kuching, Sarawak, Malaysia **(100%)**
Tel.: (60) 82439021
Web Site: http://www.hexza.com.my
Sales Range: $50-74.9 Million
Emp.: 60
Formaldehyde & Formaldehyde-Based Resins Mfr
N.A.I.C.S.: 325520

Hexzachem Sarawak Sdn. Bhd. (1)
Lot 799 Block 7 MTLD, Demak Laut Industrial Park, 93050, Kuching, Sarawak, Malaysia **(100%)**
Tel.: (60) 82439021
Web Site: http://www.hexza.com.my
Sales Range: $50-74.9 Million
Emp.: 60
Formaldehyde & Formaldehyde-Based Resins Mfr
N.A.I.C.S.: 325520

Hexzachem Sarawak Sdn. Bhd. (1)
Lot 799 Block 7 MTLD, Demak Laut Industrial Park, 93050, Kuching, Sarawak, Malaysia **(100%)**
Tel.: (60) 82439021
Web Site: http://www.hexza.com.my
Sales Range: $50-74.9 Million
Emp.: 60
Formaldehyde & Formaldehyde-Based Resins Mfr
N.A.I.C.S.: 325520

Hexzachem Sarawak Sdn. Bhd. (1)
Lot 799 Block 7 MTLD, Demak Laut Industrial Park, 93050, Kuching, Sarawak, Malaysia **(100%)**
Tel.: (60) 82439021
Web Site: http://www.hexza.com.my
Sales Range: $50-74.9 Million
Emp.: 60
Formaldehyde & Formaldehyde-Based Resins Mfr
N.A.I.C.S.: 325520

Norsechem Marketing Sdn. Bhd. (1)
Lot 6 and 20 Persiaran Tasek, Kawasan Perindustrian Tasek, 31400, Ipoh, Perak Darul Ridzuan, Malaysia
Tel.: (60) 52913128
Industrial Chemical Distr
N.A.I.C.S.: 424690

Norsechem Resins Sdn. Berhad (1)
Lot 6 & 20 Persiaran Tasek Kawasan Perindustrian Tasek, 31400, Ipoh, Perak Darul Ridzuan, Malaysia
Tel.: (60) 52917823
Synthetic Resins Mfr & Distr
N.A.I.C.S.: 325211

Summit Development Corporation Sdn. Bhd. (1)
Lot 6 and 20 Persiaran Tasek, Kawasan Perindustrian Tasek, 31400, Ipoh, Perak Darul Ridzuan, Malaysia
Tel.: (60) 5 291 7823
Web Site: http://www.hexza.com.my
Sales Range: $50-74.9 Million
Emp.: 4
Property Management Services
N.A.I.C.S.: 531311

HEY-SONG CORPORATION
3rd Floor No 296 Section 4 Xinyi Road, Taipei, Taiwan
Tel.: (886) 227062191
Web Site:
  https://www.heysong.com.tw
1234—(TAI)
Rev.: $300,277,957
Assets: $682,664,156
Liabilities: $72,902,087
Net Worth: $609,762,069

HEY-SONG CORPORATION

Hey-Song Corporation—(Continued)
Earnings: $31,016,285
Emp.: 568
Fiscal Year-end: 12/31/23
Beverages Mfr
N.A.I.C.S.: 311421

Subsidiaries:

HeySong Food (Suzhou) Co., Ltd. (1)
No 888 Jinfeng S Rd, Mudu Town Wuzhong District, Suzhou, 215101, Jiangsu, China
Tel.: (86) 51266556699
Soft Drinks Mfr
N.A.I.C.S.: 312111

HEYBRYAN MEDIA, INC.
501-318 Homer Street, Vancouver, V6B 2V2, BC, Canada
Tel.: (604) 283-7049
Web Site:
http://www.heybryanmedia.com
HEY—(CNSX)
Rev.: $13,581
Assets: $3,320,868
Liabilities: $584,845
Net Worth: $2,736,023
Earnings: ($3,568,260)
Fiscal Year-end: 12/31/19
Software Development Services
N.A.I.C.S.: 541511
Lance Montgomery *(Founder & CEO)*

HEYL CHEMISCH-PHARMAZEUTISCHE FABRIK GMBH UND CO. KG
Goerzallee 253, 14167, Berlin, Germany
Tel.: (49) 30816960
Web Site: http://www.heyl-berlin.de
Year Founded: 1926
Rev.: $11,449,020
Emp.: 18
Pharmaceutical Ingredient Mfr
N.A.I.C.S.: 325412
Eduard Heyl *(Mng Dir)*

Subsidiaries:

Heyltex Corporation (1)
925 S Mason Rd PMB 242, Katy, TX 77450
Tel.: (281) 395-7040
Web Site: http://www.heyltex.com
Pharmaceutical Products Distr
N.A.I.C.S.: 424210
Alexander Heyl *(CEO)*

Laborchemie Apolda GmbH (1)
Utenbacher Str 72, 99510, Apolda, Germany
Tel.: (49) 3644875237
Web Site: http://www.laborchemie.de
Pharmaceuticals Product Mfr
N.A.I.C.S.: 325412
Michael Frey *(Head-Sls & Bus Dev)*

HEZHONG INTERNATIONAL (HOLDING) LIMITED
Block A Room 503 Dachong Business Center, Hi-Tech Park Nanshan District, Shenzhen, 518000, Guangdong, China
Tel.: (86) 755 86535407 Ky
Year Founded: 2018
Rev.: $34,399,362
Assets: $15,278,384
Liabilities: $4,760,601
Net Worth: $10,517,783
Earnings: $4,265,884
Emp.: 327
Fiscal Year-end: 06/30/18
Holding Company
N.A.I.C.S.: 551112
Zhaobin Wen *(Chm)*

HF COMPANY
Node Park Touraine, 37310, Tauxigny, France
Tel.: (33) 247343838 FR

Web Site:
https://www.hfcompany.com
Year Founded: 1996
HF—(EUR)
Sales Range: $50-74.9 Million
Electronic Equipment & Wiring Supplies Distr
N.A.I.C.S.: 334419
Yves Bouget *(Pres)*

Subsidiaries:

Avidsen (1)
32 rue Augustin Fresnel, 37170, Chambray les Tours, France
Tel.: (33) 2 47 34 30 60
Web Site: http://www.avidsen.com
Electronic & Telecommunications Equipment Mfr & Distr
N.A.I.C.S.: 334419

LEA Networks, LLC (1)
5500 W Touhy Ave Ste P, Skokie, IL 60077
Tel.: (847) 673-1853
Web Site: http://www.lea-networks.com
Splitters/Filters & Surge Protection & Connectivity Systems for Telecommunications Industry
N.A.I.C.S.: 423610
Yves Dubois *(CEO)*

Metronic SAS (1)
100 rue Gilles de Gennes Node Park Touraine, BP 1, 37310, Tauxigny, France
Tel.: (33) 2 47 34 11 44
Web Site: http://www.metronic.com
Mfr of Digital Set Top Boxes
N.A.I.C.S.: 334419
Eric Tabone *(Pres)*

HF GROUP PLC
Rehani House Koinange /Kenyatta Avenue St, PO Box 30088, 100, Nairobi, Kenya
Tel.: (254) 709438888
Web Site: https://www.hfgroup.co.ke
Year Founded: 1965
HFCK—(NAI)
Rev.: $40,641,496
Assets: $467,779,526
Liabilities: $400,403,557
Net Worth: $67,375,969
Earnings: $2,949,962
Emp.: 565
Fiscal Year-end: 12/31/23
Mortgage Banking Services
N.A.I.C.S.: 522292
Kaushik Manek *(Chm-Interim)*

HFB FINANCIAL PLANNING LTD.
No 1 Mill The Wharf, Shardlow, Derby, DE72 2GH, United Kingdom
Tel.: (44) 1332 987 624 UK
Web Site:
http://www.hfbfinancial.co.uk
Year Founded: 2013
Financial Planning & Advisory Services
N.A.I.C.S.: 523940
Michael James Speakman *(Dir-Fin Plng)*

HFBG HOLDING B.V.
Taurusavenue 18, 2132 LS, Hoofddorp, Netherlands
Tel.: (31) 235685630
Web Site: https://headfirst.group
Rev.: $2,782,938,234
Assets: $662,011,514
Liabilities: $506,734,112
Net Worth: $155,277,402
Earnings: $40,657,152
Emp.: 467
Fiscal Year-end: 12/31/23
Holding Company
N.A.I.C.S.: 551112
Marion van Happen *(CEO)*

Subsidiaries:

Impellam Group plc (1)

800 The Boulevard Capability Green, Luton, LU1 3BA, Bedfordshire, United Kingdom
Tel.: (44) 1582692692
Web Site: http://www.impellam.com
Rev.: $2,458,217,622
Assets: $1,389,926,786
Liabilities: $1,091,012,371
Net Worth: $298,914,416
Earnings: $31,810,149
Emp.: 3,064
Fiscal Year-end: 12/30/2022
Holding Company; Staffing & Business Support Services
N.A.I.C.S.: 551112
Julia Robertson *(CEO)*

Subsidiary (Domestic):

Austin Benn Ltd. (2)
800 The Boulevard, Capability Green, Luton, LU1 3BA, Beds, United Kingdom
Tel.: (44) 1582 692 932
Web Site: http://www.austinbenn.co.uk
Sales Professional Recruitment Services
N.A.I.C.S.: 561311

Subsidiary (Non-US):

Bartech Technical Services of Canada Limited (2)
160 Traders Blvd East Suite 112, Mississauga, L4Z 3K7, ON, Canada
Tel.: (905) 502-9914
Staffing & Recruiting Services
N.A.I.C.S.: 561312

Subsidiary (Domestic):

Blue Arrow Ltd. (2)
800 The Boulevard, Capability Green, Luton, LU1 3BA, Bedfordshire, United Kingdom
Tel.: (44) 1582401636
Web Site: http://www.bluearrow.co.uk
Staffing Services
N.A.I.C.S.: 541612

ABC Contract Services Ltd. (3)
800 The Boulevard, Capability Green, Luton, LU1 3BA, Bedfordshire, United Kingdom
Tel.: (44) 1582692692
Web Site:
http://www.abccontractservices.co.uk
Architecture & Design Professional Employment Agency
N.A.I.C.S.: 561311

Blue Arrow Recruitment Solutions Ltd. (3)
800 The Boulevard, Capability Green, Luton, LU1 3SY, Beds, United Kingdom
Tel.: (44) 1582401636
Web Site: http://www.bluearrow.co.uk
Sales Range: $25-49.9 Million
Recruitment & Workforce Management Consutancy & Support Services
N.A.I.C.S.: 541618

Subsidiary (US):

CORESTAFF Services, LP (2)
4801 Woodway Dr Ste 290, Houston, TX 77056-3415
Tel.: (713) 438-1300
Web Site: http://www.corestaff.com
Sales Range: $50-74.9 Million
Emp.: 75
Holding Company; Staffing Services
N.A.I.C.S.: 551112

Division (Domestic):

CORESTAFF Support Services, Inc. (3)
4801 Woodway Dr Ste 290, Houston, TX 77056-3415
Tel.: (713) 438-1300
Web Site: http://www.corestaff.com
Sales Range: $10-24.9 Million
Emp.: 40
Staffing Services
N.A.I.C.S.: 561311

Subsidiary (Domestic):

Carbon60 Limited (2)
Buckingham House Buckingham Street,

INTERNATIONAL PUBLIC

Aylesbury, HP20 2LA, Bucks, United Kingdom
Tel.: (44) 1296311411
Web Site: https://www.carbon60global.com
Sales Range: $10-24.9 Million
Telecommunications & Information Technology Professional Recruiting Services
N.A.I.C.S.: 561311
Paul Nolan *(Mng Dir)*

Career Teachers Limited (2)
9 Devonshire Square, Spitalfields, London, EC2M 4HP, United Kingdom
Tel.: (44) 2071053499
Web Site: http://www.careerteachers.co.uk
Staffing & Recruiting Services
N.A.I.C.S.: 561311

Carlisle Cleaning Services Ltd. (2)
Personnel House 99 Bridge Road East, Welwyn Garden City, AL7 1JN, Herts, United Kingdom
Tel.: (44) 1707824200
Web Site: http://www.carlislecleaning.co.uk
Cleaning & Janitorial Staffing Services
N.A.I.C.S.: 561311

Carlisle Events Services Limited (2)
Wallace House 4 Falcon Way Shire Park, Welwyn Garden City, AL7 1TW, Middlesex, United Kingdom
Tel.: (44) 208 782 7393
Web Site:
http://www.carlislesupportservices.com
Sales Range: $50-74.9 Million
Emp.: 5
Event Management Services
N.A.I.C.S.: 711310

Carlisle Security Services Ltd. (2)
800 The Boulevard Capability Green Luton, Welwyn Garden City, AL7 1JN, Herts, United Kingdom
Tel.: (44) 1707294785
Web Site:
http://www.carlislesupportservice.co.uk
Sales Range: $50-74.9 Million
Emp.: 150
Security Professional Leasing Services
N.A.I.C.S.: 561330

Carlisle Staffing plc (2)
5th Floor 5 Devonshire Square, London, EC2M 4YD, United Kingdom
Tel.: (44) 20 7562 1770
Web Site: http://www.carlislems.co.uk
Recruitment Process Outsourcing Services
N.A.I.C.S.: 561311

Chadwick Nott (2)
4th Floor 9 Devonshire Square, London, EC2M 4HP, United Kingdom
Tel.: (44) 2030964540
Web Site: http://www.chadwicknott.co.uk
Legal Professional Recruitment Services
N.A.I.C.S.: 561311

Comensura Ltd. (2)
First Floor Mulberry House Parkland Square, 750 Capability Green, Luton, LU1 3LU, Bedfordshire, United Kingdom
Tel.: (44) 2039127412
Web Site: https://www.comensura.com
Sales Range: $25-49.9 Million
Emp.: 45
Management Consultancy & Business Support Services
N.A.I.C.S.: 541611

Subsidiary (Non-US):

Comensura Pty Limited (2)
Suite 1403 Level 14 309 Kent Street, Sydney, 2000, NSW, Australia
Tel.: (61) 1300598505
Web Site: https://www.comensura.com
Staffing & Recruiting Services
N.A.I.C.S.: 561312

Global Medics NZ Limited (2)
Level 3 Tower 2 DLA Piper Tower 205 Queen Street, Auckland, 1010, New Zealand
Tel.: (64) 92812455
Web Site: https://www.globalmedics.com
Staffing & Recruiting Services
N.A.I.C.S.: 561312

Global Medics Pty Limited (2)
Level 2 14 Martin Place, Sydney, 2000, NSW, Australia

Tel.: (61) 282482900
Staffing & Recruiting Services
N.A.I.C.S.: 561312

Subsidiary (US):

Guidant Group, Inc. (2)
1775 Saint James Pl Ste 236, Houston, TX 77056-3416
Tel.: (713) 438-1775
Web Site: http://www.guidantgroup.com
Sales Range: $25-49.9 Million
Emp.: 25
Management Consultancy & Business Support Services
N.A.I.C.S.: 541611
Simon Blockley *(Mng Dir)*

Subsidiary (Non-US):

Healthlink New Zealand Group Limited (2)
Level 3 13-15 Teed St, Newmarket, Auckland, 1023, New Zealand
Tel.: (64) 95202371
Web Site: http://nz.healthlink.net
Information Technology & Services
N.A.I.C.S.: 541511
Mariie Fane *(Mgr-Client-Pathology & Radiology)*

Irish Recruitment Consultants Limited (2)
Unit 9 Blackrock Business Park, Blackrock, Dublin, A94 E4X2, Ireland
Tel.: (353) 16610644
Web Site: https://www.irishrecruitment.ie
Employment Agency Services
N.A.I.C.S.: 561311

Litmus Solutions Pty. Ltd. (2)
Level 2 14 Martin Place, Sydney, 2000, NSW, Australia
Tel.: (61) 282482960
Leading Management Services
N.A.I.C.S.: 541618

Subsidiary (Domestic):

Lorien Resourcing Limited - London (2)
107 Leadenhall Street 3rd Floor, London, EC3A 4AF, United Kingdom
Tel.: (44) 2076541000
Web Site: http://www.lorienresourcing.co.uk
Sales Range: $450-499.9 Million
Recruitment & Staffing Consulting Services
N.A.I.C.S.: 561499

Subsidiary (Domestic):

Lorien Resourcing Limited - Leeds (3)
West One 114 Wellington Street, Leeds, LS1 1BA, United Kingdom
Tel.: (44) 207 654 1000
Web Site: http://www.lorienglobal.com
Recruitment & Staffing Consulting Services
N.A.I.C.S.: 561499

Lorien Resourcing Limited - Manchester (3)
Lowry House 17 Marble Street, Manchester, M2 3AW, United Kingdom
Tel.: (44) 1618882500
Web Site: http://www.lorienglobal.com
Recruitment & Staffing Consulting Services
N.A.I.C.S.: 561499

Subsidiary (Non-US):

Medacs Healthcare Australia (Pty) Limited (2)
Level 2 14 Martin Place, PO Box 1448, Neutral Bay, Sydney, 2000, NSW, Australia
Tel.: (61) 1800059790
Web Site: http://apac.medacs.com
Health Care Employees Staffing Services
N.A.I.C.S.: 561320

Medacs Healthcare Limited (2)
Level 3 Tower 2 DLA Piper Tower 205 Queen Street, Mount Eden, Auckland, New Zealand
Tel.: (64) 96308300
Web Site: http://www.medacs.com
Medical Staffing Services
N.A.I.C.S.: 561320

Subsidiary (Domestic):

Medacs Healthcare plc (2)
800 The Boulevard, Capability Green, Luton, LU1 3BA, Beds, United Kingdom
Tel.: (44) 1582692692
Web Site: http://www.medacs.co.uk
Healthcare Staffing Services
N.A.I.C.S.: 561311

PRN Recruitment Ltd. (2)
High Street House New Market Street, Skipton, BD23 2HU, North Yorkshire, United Kingdom
Tel.: (44) 8000 379 090
Web Site: http://www.prnrecruitment.co.uk
Sales Range: $25-49.9 Million
Emp.: 5
Medical Professional Recruitment Agency
N.A.I.C.S.: 561311

SRG (2)
Buckland House Waterside Drive Langley Business Park, Slough, SL3 6EZ, Berks, United Kingdom
Tel.: (44) 1753589600
Web Site: http://www.srgtalent.com
Sales Range: $25-49.9 Million
Scientific, Engineering & Clinical Industries Recruiting & Outsourcing Services
N.A.I.C.S.: 561311
Audrey McCulloch *(Dir-Ops)*

Division (Domestic):

SRG Clinical (3)
5th Floor Devonshire Square, London, EC2M 4YD, United Kingdom
Tel.: (44) 2075621795
Web Site: http://www.srgclinical.com
Emp.: 25
Clinical Research Professional Recruitment & Consulting Services
N.A.I.C.S.: 561311

SRG Engineering (3)
8th Floor Furness House Furness Quay, Salford, M50 3XZ, Manchester, United Kingdom
Tel.: (44) 1618682200
Web Site: http://www.srgengineering.co.uk
Sales Range: $10-24.9 Million
Emp.: 50
Engineering Professional Recruitment & Staffing Services
N.A.I.C.S.: 561311

Division (US):

SRG Woolf Group, Inc. (3)
5315 Highgate Dr Ste 202, Durham, NC 27713
Tel.: (919) 425-0155
Web Site: http://www.srgwoolf.com
Sales Range: $25-49.9 Million
Emp.: 4
Pharmaceutical Staffing & Recruitment Services
N.A.I.C.S.: 561311

Subsidiary (US):

The Bartech Group, Inc. (2)
27777 Franklin Rd Ste 600, Southfield, MI 48034
Tel.: (800) 824-2962
Web Site: http://www.bartechgroup.com
Emp.: 150
Workforce Management & Staffing Services
N.A.I.C.S.: 561320
David W. Barfield *(CEO)*

Subsidiary (Domestic):

Younifi Limited (2)
800 The Boulevard Capability Green, Luton, LU1 3BA, United Kingdom
Tel.: (44) 8450754600
Web Site: https://www.younifi.co.uk
Staffing & Recruiting Services
N.A.I.C.S.: 561312

HFCL LIMITED
8 Commercial Complex Masjid Moth, Greater Kailash II, New Delhi, 110048, India
Tel.: (91) 1135209400
Web Site: https://www.hfcl.com
HFCL—(NSE)
Rev.: $608,665,785
Assets: $711,956,700
Liabilities: $449,403,045
Net Worth: $262,553,655
Earnings: $33,611,760
Emp.: 1,753
Fiscal Year-end: 03/31/21
Telecom Equipment Mfr
N.A.I.C.S.: 334417
Manoj Baid *(Sec & Sr VP)*

Subsidiaries:

DragonWave HFCL India Private Limited (1)
8 Commercial Complex Masjid Moth, Greater Kailash -2, New Delhi, 110048, India
Tel.: (91) 11 428233000
Broadband Wireless Microwave Equipment Developer, Mfr & Marketer
N.A.I.C.S.: 334220

HTL Limited (1)
No 57 GST Road Guindy, Chennai, 600032, India
Tel.: (91) 4422501020
Web Site: https://htllimited.com
Telecommunications Equipment Mfr
N.A.I.C.S.: 334290

HFO TELECOM AG
Ziegeleistrasse 2, 95145, Hof, Germany
Tel.: (49) 92869404100
Web Site: http://www.hfo-telecom.de
Year Founded: 1997
Emp.: 115
Telecommunication Services b
N.A.I.C.S.: 517111
Achim Hager *(CEO & Mng Dir)*

HFR INC.
Hana EZ Tower 5F 10 Seongnam-daero 43beon-gil, Bundang-gu, Seongnam, 13636, Gyeonggi, Korea (South)
Tel.: (82) 317127768
Web Site: https://www.hfrnet.com
Year Founded: 2015
230240—(KRS)
Rev.: $289,363,307
Assets: $245,634,457
Liabilities: $105,152,531
Net Worth: $140,481,926
Earnings: $54,175,891
Emp.: 179
Fiscal Year-end: 12/31/22
Optical & Radio Networking Services
N.A.I.C.S.: 517810
Jong Min Cheong *(CEO)*

HFX HOLDING CORP.
885 West Georgia Street Suite 1500, Vancouver, V6C 3E8, BC, Canada
Tel.: (604) 215-1568
Year Founded: 2010
HXC—(TSXV)
Assets: $3,256
Liabilities: $184,551
Net Worth: ($181,295)
Earnings: ($29,454)
Fiscal Year-end: 10/31/22
Investment Management Service
N.A.I.C.S.: 523940

HG METAL MANUFACTURING LIMITED
28 Jalan Buroh, Singapore, 619484, Singapore
Tel.: (65) 62682828
Web Site: https://www.hgmetal.com
Year Founded: 1971
BTG—(SES)
Rev.: $113,424,979
Assets: $103,808,225
Liabilities: $24,159,661
Net Worth: $79,648,565
Earnings: $343,104
Emp.: 191
Fiscal Year-end: 12/31/23
Steel Product Mfr & Distr
N.A.I.C.S.: 331110
Woon Hong Wee *(Co-Sec)*

Subsidiaries:

HG Construction Steel Pte Ltd. (1)
Tel.: (65) 62682828
Steel Products Mfr & Distr
N.A.I.C.S.: 331110

HG Metal Manufacturing Sdn. Bhd. (1)
Level 16 Surian Tower No 1 Jalan PJU 7/3, Mutiara Damansara, 47810, Petaling Jaya, Selangor, Malaysia
Tel.: (60) 3 7949 6000
Steel Products Mfr
N.A.I.C.S.: 331110

HG Metal Pte Ltd (1)
28 Jalan Buroh, Singapore, 619484, Singapore
Tel.: (65) 62682828
Web Site: http://www.hgmetal.com
Steel Products Mfr & Distr
N.A.I.C.S.: 332996

HG Yangon Company Limited (1)
No 856 Nilar Street, 36 Ward North Dagon Township, Yangon, Myanmar
Tel.: (95) 1581436
Metal Products Mfr
N.A.I.C.S.: 332812

Jin Heng Li Hardware Sdn Bhd (1)
AL 209 Lot 2243, Sungai Buloh, 47000, Selangor, Malaysia (100%)
Tel.: (60) 3 6156 8760
Steel Products Whslr
N.A.I.C.S.: 423510

Niho (Singapore) Pte Ltd (1)
13 Jalan Terusan, Singapore, 619293, Singapore
Tel.: (65) 62682828
Web Site: http://www.hgmetal.com
Emp.: 6
Seal Products Distr
N.A.I.C.S.: 423840

Oriental Metals Pte Ltd (1)
28 Jalan Buroh, Jurong Town, Singapore, 619484, Singapore
Tel.: (65) 6 268 2828
Web Site: https://www.hgmetal.com
Steel Products Mfr
N.A.I.C.S.: 332323

PT HG Metal Distribution Indonesia (1)
Jl Melawai VII No 10, Kebayoran Baru, Jakarta, 12160, Selatan, Indonesia
Tel.: (62) 21 7236791
Steel Product Distr
N.A.I.C.S.: 423510

HG SEMICONDUCTOR LIMITED
2nd Floor and North side of the 3rd Floor No 8 Pinggong Er Road, Nanping Technology Industrial Park, Zhuhai, China
Tel.: (86) 7568699668 Ky
Web Site: http://www.lighting-hg.com
Year Founded: 2010
6908—(HKG)
Rev.: $12,287,527
Assets: $100,850,443
Liabilities: $15,214,165
Net Worth: $85,636,278
Earnings: ($14,220,695)
Emp.: 237
Fiscal Year-end: 12/31/22
Light Emitting Diode Product Mfr & Distr
N.A.I.C.S.: 334413
Yi Wen Zhao *(Co-Founder, Chm & CEO)*

HG TECHNOLOGIES CO., LTD.
No 8 Shangbi East Street Economic

HG TECHNOLOGIES CO., LTD.

HG Technologies Co., Ltd.—(Continued)
Development Zone, Handan, 056000, Hebei, China
Tel.: (86) 3108066668
Web Site: http://www.hg-oa.com
Year Founded: 2000
300847—(SSE)
Rev.: $152,366,292
Assets: $197,360,280
Liabilities: $19,410,300
Net Worth: $177,949,980
Earnings: $15,261,480
Fiscal Year-end: 12/31/22
Information Technology Services
N.A.I.C.S.: 541512
Haijun Zhang *(Chm)*

HGCAPITAL TRUST PLC

2 More London Riverside, London, SE1 2AP, United Kingdom
Tel.: (44) 2083960930   UK
Web Site:
    https://www.hgcapitaltrust.com
Year Founded: 2000
HGT—(LSE)
Rev.: $33,511,245
Assets: $1,390,826,740
Net Worth: $1,752,838,244
Earnings: $22,821,915
Fiscal Year-end: 12/31/20
Private Equity Investment Trust
N.A.I.C.S.: 525990
Roger Mountford *(Chm)*

Subsidiaries:

HgCapital LLP   (1)
2 More London Riverside, London, SE1 2AP, United Kingdom
Tel.: (44) 2070897888
Web Site: http://www.hgcapital.com
Private Equity & Investment Management Firm
N.A.I.C.S.: 523999
Stephen Bough *(Deputy Chm)*

Joint Venture (Domestic):

Argus Media Limited   (2)
Lacon House 84 Theobald's Road, London, WC1X 8NL, United Kingdom
Tel.: (44) 2077804200
Web Site: http://www.argusmedia.com
Emp.: 850
Price & Availability Information for Energy Related Products
N.A.I.C.S.: 519290
Adrian Binks *(Chm & CEO)*

Subsidiary (Non-US):

Argus Media Ltd. - Japan   (3)
22 Malacca St, 10-02 Royal Brothers Bldg, Singapore, 48980, Singapore
Tel.: (65) 65333638
Web Site: http://www.argusmediagroup.com
Sales Range: $25-49.9 Million
Emp.: 20
Price & Availability Information for Energy Related Products
N.A.I.C.S.: 519290

Argus Media Ltd. - Russia   (3)
Ul Prechistenka 40/2 Entr 2 Fl 7, 119034, Moscow, Russia
Tel.: (7) 959337571
Web Site: http://www.argus.ru
Sales Range: $25-49.9 Million
Emp.: 100
Price & Availability Information for Energy Related Products
N.A.I.C.S.: 519290

Subsidiary (US):

Argus Media, Inc.   (3)
2929 Allen Pkwy Ste 700, Houston, TX 77019   (100%)
Tel.: (713) 622-3996
Web Site: http://www.argusmediagroup.com
Sales Range: $25-49.9 Million
Emp.: 100
Price & Availability Information for Energy Related Products
N.A.I.C.S.: 513199

Euan Craik *(CEO)*

Branch (Domestic):

Argus Media, Inc. - New York   (4)
500 5th Ave Ste 2410, New York, NY 10110
Tel.: (646) 376-6130
Web Site: http://www.argusmedia.com
Sales Range: $25-49.9 Million
Emp.: 17
Price & Availability Information for Energy Related Products
N.A.I.C.S.: 513199
Miles Weigel *(Gen Mgr)*

Argus Media, Inc. - Washington, D.C.   (4)
1012 14th St NW Ste 1500, Washington, DC 20005
Tel.: (202) 775-0240
Web Site: http://www.argusmedia.com
Price & Availability Information for Energy Related Products
N.A.I.C.S.: 711510

Subsidiary (Domestic):

DeWitt & Company Incorporated   (4)
601 Sawyer St Ste 750, Houston, TX 77007
Tel.: (713) 360-7500
Web Site: http://www.dewittworld.com
Sales Range: $10-24.9 Million
Emp.: 50
Petrochemical Consulting Services
N.A.I.C.S.: 541690
Charles Venezia *(VP-Benzene & Derivatives)*

Subsidiary (US):

Mercaris Company   (3)
8070 Georgia Ave, Silver Spring, MD 20910
Tel.: (240) 354-7114
Web Site: https://mercaris.com
Information Services
N.A.I.C.S.: 519290
Kellee James *(Founder & CEO)*

TABrewer Consulting, Inc.   (3)
363 Wycliffe Dr, Houston, TX 77079-7146
Tel.: (713) 562-1109
Business Consulting Services
N.A.I.C.S.: 541611

Holding (Domestic):

Boosey & Hawkes Limited   (2)
Aldwych House 71-91 Aldwych, London, WC2B 4HN, United Kingdom
Tel.: (44) 2070547200
Web Site: http://www.boosey.com
Sales Range: $350-399.9 Million
Holding Company; Music Publisher
N.A.I.C.S.: 551112
John B. Minch *(CEO)*

Subsidiary (Non-US):

Boosey & Hawkes Bote & Bock GmbH & Co.   (3)
Lutzowufer 26, Berlin, 10787, Germany
Tel.: (49) 3025001300
Web Site: http://www.boosey.com.de
Sales Range: $25-49.9 Million
Emp.: 30
Music Publisher & Sheet Music Retailer
N.A.I.C.S.: 512230
Winfried Jacobs *(Mng Dir)*

Subsidiary (Domestic):

Boosey & Hawkes Music Publishers Ltd.   (3)
Aldwych House 71-91 Aldwych, London, WC2B 4HN, United Kingdom
Tel.: (44) 2070547200
Web Site: http://www.boosey.com
Emp.: 80
Music Publishers
N.A.I.C.S.: 512230
John B. Minch *(CEO)*

Subsidiary (US):

Boosey & Hawkes, Inc.   (3)
35 E 21st St, New York, NY 10010-6212
Tel.: (212) 358-5300
Web Site: http://www.boosey.com
Sales Range: $25-49.9 Million
Emp.: 30
Music Publishers

N.A.I.C.S.: 512230

Holding (Non-US):

Esendex   (2)
Via Castelnuovo 4, 44121, Ferrara, Italy
Tel.: (39) 0532207296
Web Site: https://www.esendex.it
SMS Messaging & Emailing Services
N.A.I.C.S.: 517810
Giorgio Nani *(CEO)*

F24 AG   (2)
Isarwinkel 14, 81379, Munich, Germany
Tel.: (49) 89 23236380
Web Site: http://www.f24.com
Rev.: $7,987,228
Assets: $6,385,427
Liabilities: $3,738,262
Net Worth: $2,647,165
Earnings: $536,838
Emp.: 37
Fiscal Year-end: 12/31/2015
Application Service Provider
N.A.I.C.S.: 518210
Ralf Meister *(Co-Founder)*

Subsidiary (Non-US):

F24 Czech Republic s.r.o.   (3)
Vaclavske nam 19/832, 110 00, Prague, Czech Republic
Tel.: (420) 234 656 124
Security Alert & Crisis Management Services
N.A.I.C.S.: 561621
Michael Funk *(Mng Dir)*

F24 France SARL   (3)
60 Avenue Charles de Gaulle CS 60016, 92573, Neuilly-sur-Seine, Cedex, France
Tel.: (33) 1 72 74 55 07
Web Site: http://www.f24.com
Sales Range: $25-49.9 Million
Emp.: 3
Security Alert & Crisis Management Services
N.A.I.C.S.: 561621
David Ebel *(Mng Dir)*

F24 SERVICIOS DE COMUNICACION, S.L.U.   (3)
Edif Atica 5 planta 2 Avda Europa 26, Pozuelo de Alarcon, 28224, Madrid, Spain
Tel.: (34) 911 845 925
Sales Range: $25-49.9 Million
Emp.: 4
Security Alert & Crisis Management Services
N.A.I.C.S.: 561621
Juan Manuel Gil Bote *(Mng Dir)*

Subsidiary (US):

F24 United States, Inc.   (3)
1330 Avenue of the Americas Ste 23A, New York, NY 10019
Tel.: (212) 653-0948
Sales Range: $25-49.9 Million
Emp.: 4
Software Development Services
N.A.I.C.S.: 541511
Robert F. Mattes *(Mng Dir)*

Holding (Non-US):

Intelerad Medical Systems Inc.   (2)
800 De Maisonneuve E. Blvd., 12th fl, Montreal, H2L 4L8, QC, Canada
Tel.: (514) 931-6222
Web Site: http://www.intelerad.com
Sales Range: $10-24.9 Million
Image Archiving & Communications Systems
N.A.I.C.S.: 513210
Jean-Baptiste Brian *(Chm)*

Subsidiary (US):

Lumedx Corp.   (3)
555 12th St, Oakland, CA 94607
Tel.: (510) 419-1000
Web Site: http://www.lumedx.com
Sales Range: $1-9.9 Million
Emp.: 90
Custom Computer Programming Services
N.A.I.C.S.: 541511
Chris Winquist *(COO)*

PenRad Technologies, Inc.   (3)
114 Commerce Cir, 55313, Buffalo, MN

INTERNATIONAL PUBLIC

Tel.: (763) 475-3388
Web Site: http://www.penrad.com
Whol Medical/Hospital Equipment
N.A.I.C.S.: 423450
Greg Gustafson *(Founder, Pres & CEO)*

lifeIMAGE, Inc.   (3)
300 Washington St 1 Gateway Ctr Ste 507, Newton, MA 02458
Tel.: (617) 244-8411
Web Site: http://www.lifeimage.com
Software Publisher
N.A.I.C.S.: 513210
Matthew A. Michela *(Pres & CEO)*

Holding (Domestic):

IntelliFlo Limited   (2)
Third Floor Drapers Court Kingston Hall Road, Kingston upon Thames, KT12BQ, United Kingdom
Tel.: (44) 8452303800
Web Site: http://www.intelliflo.com
Sales Range: $10-24.9 Million
Emp.: 50
Financial Services Software Developer
N.A.I.C.S.: 513210
Nick Eatock *(Founder & Chm)*

Iris Software Group Ltd.   (2)
Riding Court House, Datchet, SL3 9JT, Berkshire, United Kingdom
Tel.: (44) 1753212200
Web Site: http://www.iris.co.uk
Sales Range: $125-149.9 Million
Emp.: 160
Computer Software & Consulting Services
N.A.I.C.S.: 513210
Nick Discombe *(Chm)*

Subsidiary (US):

Apex Software Technologies, LLC   (3)
500 Colonial Ctr Pkwy Ste 650, Roswell, GA 30076
Tel.: (878) 645-3150
Web Site: http://www.apexhcm.com
Sales Range: $1-9.9 Million
Emp.: 50
Software Development Services
N.A.I.C.S.: 541511
Robert Digby *(CEO)*

Subsidiary (Non-US):

Exchequer Enterprise Software (New Zealand) Limited   (3)
45 Bath St, Private Bag 93219, Parnell, Auckland, New Zealand
Tel.: (64) 93075978
Software Developer
N.A.I.C.S.: 513210

Exchequer Software Ltd   (3)
Unit F6 Riverview Business Pk Nangor Rd Riverview Business Park, Nangor Road, 12, Dublin, Ireland
Tel.: (353) 1 450 6820
Web Site: http://www.exchequer.ie
Emp.: 26
Software Developer
N.A.I.C.S.: 513210

IRIS Enterprise Software (Australia) Pty Ltd   (3)
277 Liverpool Street, Sydney, 2010, Australia
Tel.: (61) 2 9380 6220
Software Developer
N.A.I.C.S.: 513210
Michelle Nielsen *(Gen Mgr)*

Information Technology Services (ITS) Ltd   (3)
Mriehel Bypass, Regional Road, Mriehel, BKR 3000, Malta
Tel.: (356) 21 344111
Web Site: http://www.firstsource.com
Software Developer
N.A.I.C.S.: 513210

Subsidiary (Domestic):

KashFlow Software Ltd   (3)
Ivybridge House 1 Adam Street, London, WC2N 6LE, United Kingdom
Tel.: (44) 800 848 8301
Web Site: http://www.kashflow.com

AND PRIVATE COMPANIES — HGCAPITAL TRUST PLC

Sales Range: $1-9.9 Million
Emp.: 25
Online Accounting Software Publisher
N.A.I.C.S.: 513210
Lord Young *(Chm)*

Subsidiary (Non-US):

LANWorks Pte Ltd (3)
6 Commonwealth Lane, 01-01 GMTI Building, Singapore, 149845, Singapore
Tel.: (65) 6304 7500
Software Developer
N.A.I.C.S.: 513210

Modfin Systems Pty Ltd (3)
Brooklyn Square, 309 Veale St, Pretoria, Nieuw Muckleneuk, South Africa
Tel.: (27) 12 460 0285
Software Developer
N.A.I.C.S.: 513210

Subsidiary (US):

OneAdvanced, Inc. (3)
3200 Windy Hill Rd Ste 230 W, Atlanta, GA 30339
Tel.: (770) 933-1965
Web Site: https://www.oneadvanced.com
Sales Range: $25-49.9 Million
Emp.: 10
Software Developer
N.A.I.C.S.: 513210
Gordon Wilson *(CEO)*

Subsidiary (Domestic):

Transoft Group Ltd. (3)
Transoft House 5J Langley Business Centre, Station Rd, Langley, SL3 8DS, Slough, United Kingdom
Tel.: (44) 1753378000
Web Site: http://www.transoft.com
Sales Range: $25-49.9 Million
Emp.: 20
Software Developer
N.A.I.C.S.: 513210
Tim Jones *(Mng Dir)*

Holding (Non-US):

MOBILITY CONCEPT GMBH (2)
Grunwalder Weg 34, Oberhaching, 82041, Germany
Tel.: (49) 89 63266 0
Web Site: http://www.mobility-concept.de
Fleet Leasing Services
N.A.I.C.S.: 532112
Rudolf Rizzolli *(CEO)*

Holding (Domestic):

NetNames Holdings Limited (2)
Prospero House 3rd Floor, 241 Borough High Street, London, SE1 1GA, United Kingdom
Tel.: (44) 207 015 9200
Web Site: http://www.netnames.com
Sales Range: $100-124.9 Million
Holding Company; Web Hosting & Domain Name Management Services
N.A.I.C.S.: 551112
Gary McIlraith *(CEO)*

Subsidiary (Non-US):

Ascio GmbH (3)
Landshuter Allee 14, 80637, Munich, Germany
Tel.: (49) 8938329120
Web Site: http://www.ascio.com
Sales Range: $50-74.9 Million
Emp.: 50
Web Hosting & Internet Domain Management Services
N.A.I.C.S.: 518210
Bojan Stopic *(Mgr-Sls)*

Subsidiary (Domestic):

Envisional Limited (3)
Betjeman House 104 Hills Rd, Cambridge, CB2 1LQ, Cambridgeshire, United Kingdom
Tel.: (44) 1223372400
Web Site: http://www.envisional.com
Sales Range: $25-49.9 Million
Emp.: 27
Online Data Monitoring Services
N.A.I.C.S.: 518210
David Franklin *(Gen Mgr)*

Subsidiary (Non-US):

NetNames A/S (3)
Arne Jacobsens Alle 15, 2300, Copenhagen, Denmark
Tel.: (45) 33 88 63 00
Web Site: http://www.netnames.com
Internet Domain Names Management Services
N.A.I.C.S.: 518210
Jorgen Christensen *(Mng Dir)*

NetNames AS (3)
CJ Hambros Plass 2c, 2 etasje, 0164, Oslo, Norway
Tel.: (47) 21549800
Web Site: http://www.netnames.com
Sales Range: $25-49.9 Million
Emp.: 2
Internet Domain Managing Services
N.A.I.C.S.: 518210

Subsidiary (US):

NetNames Inc. (3)
55 Broad St 11th Fl, New York, NY 10004
Tel.: (212) 627-4599
Web Site: http://www.netnames.com
Sales Range: $100-124.9 Million
Emp.: 10
Internet Domain Managing Services
N.A.I.C.S.: 518210
Francisco Navaro *(Dir-Mktg)*

Holding (Non-US):

P&I Personal & Informatik AG (2)
Kreuzberger Ring 56, D-65205, Wiesbaden, Germany
Tel.: (49) 61171470
Web Site: http://www.pi-ag.com
Rev.: $152,015,410
Assets: $224,191,990
Liabilities: $151,008,875
Net Worth: $73,183,116
Earnings: $74,471,023
Emp.: 430
Fiscal Year-end: 03/31/2019
Human Resource Data Management Software, Consulting & Outsourcing Services
N.A.I.C.S.: 561499
Vasilios Triadis *(Chm-Mgmt Bd)*

Subsidiary (Non-US):

P&I Personal & Informatik AG (3)
Seestrasse 185, CH-8800, Thalwil, Switzerland **(100%)**
Tel.: (41) 44 722 7575
Web Site: http://www.pi-ag.com
Human Resource Data Management Software Whslr, Consulting & Outsourcing Services
N.A.I.C.S.: 423430

P&I Personal & Informatik GmbH (3)
Ares Tower Donau-City-Strasse 11, A-1220, Vienna, Austria **(100%)**
Tel.: (43) 1 260 390
Web Site: http://www.pi-ag.com
Human Resource Data Management Software Whslr, Consulting & Outsourcing Services
N.A.I.C.S.: 423430
Philipp Schinko *(Mng Dir-Sls & Mktg)*

P&I Personal & Informatik s.r.o. (3)
Sliezska 1, SK-831 03, Bratislava, Slovakia **(100%)**
Tel.: (421) 252636161
Web Site: http://www.pi-ag.com
Human Resource Data Management Software Whslr, Consulting & Outsourcing Services
N.A.I.C.S.: 423430
Tibor Tildi *(Sls Mgr)*

Holding (Non-US):

Raet B.V. (2)
Plotterweg 38, 3821 BB, Amersfoort, Netherlands
Tel.: (31) 33 4506 506
Web Site: http://www.raet.nl
Human Resource & Payroll Business Process Outsourcing Services
N.A.I.C.S.: 561499
Sander Odijk *(Dir-Partnership & Strategic Alliances)*

Register S.p.A (2)
Viale della Giovine Italy 17, 50122, Florence, Italy **(100%)**
Tel.: (39) 055200211
Web Site: http://www.dada.eu
Internet Hosting & Content Services
N.A.I.C.S.: 517810
Claudiota Corbetta *(CEO)*

Subsidiary (Non-US):

Namesco Ltd (3)
Acton House Perdiswell Park, Worcester, WR3 7GD, United Kingdom
Tel.: (44) 345 363 3630
Web Site: http://www.names.co.uk
Internet Broadcasting Services
N.A.I.C.S.: 516210

Nominalia Internet S.L. (3)
Carrer d ulldecona 21 Planta 1, Catalunya, Barcelona, 08038, Spain
Tel.: (34) 93 288 40 62
Web Site: http://www.nominalia.com
Web Hosting Services
N.A.I.C.S.: 518210

Holding (US):

Sovos Compliance, LLC (2)
200 Ballardvale St 4th Fl, Wilmington, MA 01887
Tel.: (866) 890-3970
Web Site: http://www.sovos.com
Sales Range: $50-74.9 Million
Tax & Accounting Software
N.A.I.C.S.: 541511
John Gledhill *(VP-Corp Dev)*

Subsidiary (Domestic):

1099 Pro, Inc. (3)
23901 Calabasas Rd Ste 2080, Calabasas, CA 91302-4104
Tel.: (818) 876-0200
Web Site: http://www.1099pro.com
Computer And Software Stores, Nsk
N.A.I.C.S.: 449210
Ray Stewart *(CEO)*

Aatrix Software, Inc. (3)
2100 Library Cir, Grand Forks, ND 58201
Tel.: (701) 746-6801
Web Site: http://www.aatrix.com
Rev.: $9,459,676
Emp.: 40
Software Reproducing
N.A.I.C.S.: 334610

Joint Venture (Non-US):

Visma AS (2)
Karenlyst Alle 56, 0277, Oslo, Norway **(31.3%)**
Tel.: (47) 46404000
Web Site: http://www.visma.com
Rev.: $1,706,404,419
Assets: $4,273,388,164
Liabilities: $2,705,806,114
Net Worth: $1,567,582,050
Earnings: $112,499,095
Emp.: 11,175
Fiscal Year-end: 12/31/2019
Business Software Developer
N.A.I.C.S.: 513210
Oystein Moan *(Chm & Co-CEO)*

Subsidiary (Domestic):

Visma Mamut AS (3)
Karenslyst Alle 56, 0277, Oslo, Norway
Tel.: (47) 46404000
Web Site: http://www.visma.no
Integrated Customer Relationship Management Accounting Personnel & E-commerce Software Mfr
N.A.I.C.S.: 513210
Kenneth Lovold *(Mng Dir)*

Subsidiary (Non-US):

Mamut AB (4)
Kungsgatan 24, Stockholm, Sweden
Tel.: (46) 084116190
Sales Range: $25-49.9 Million
Emp.: 30
Software Reproducing
N.A.I.C.S.: 334610

Mamut Aps (4)
Arne Jacobsens Alle 15, 2300, Copenhagen, Denmark
Tel.: (45) 80390002
Web Site: http://www.mamut.dk
Sales Range: $25-49.9 Million
Emp.: 15
Computer & Computer Peripheral Equipment & Software Merchant Whslr
N.A.I.C.S.: 423430
Michael Brahe *(Pres)*

Subsidiary (Domestic):

Mamut Norge AS (4)
Pilestredet 75 C, Oslo, Norway
Tel.: (47) 23203500
Web Site: http://www.mamut.com
Computer & Computer Peripheral Equipment & Software Merchant Whslr
N.A.I.C.S.: 423430

Subsidiary (Non-US):

Mamut Software Ltd. (4)
90 Long Acre Covent Garden, London, WC2E 9RZ, United Kingdom
Tel.: (44) 2071530900
Web Site: http://www.visma.co.uk
Computer & Computer Peripheral Equipment & Software Merchant Whslr
N.A.I.C.S.: 423430

Ideagen PLC (1)
1 Mere Way Ruddington Fields Business Park, Ruddington, NG11 6JS, Nottinghamshire, United Kingdom
Tel.: (44) 1629 699100
Web Site: http://www.ideagen.com
Rev.: $89,126,172
Assets: $292,239,726
Liabilities: $121,693,801
Net Worth: $170,545,925
Earnings: $845,860
Emp.: 612
Fiscal Year-end: 04/30/2021
Software Applications
N.A.I.C.S.: 513210
David Hornsby *(Chm)*

Subsidiary (Domestic):

Ideagen Capture Limited (2)
78 Macrae Road, Avon, Bristol, BS20 0DD, United Kingdom
Tel.: (44) 1629 699 100
Web Site: http://www.ideagenplc.com
Emp.: 4
Software Development Services
N.A.I.C.S.: 541511

Subsidiary (US):

InspectionXpert Corporation (2)
1 Glenwood Ave WeWork 5th Fl, Raleigh, NC 27603
Tel.: (984) 275-3449
Web Site: https://www.inspectionxpert.com
Computer-aided Design & Drafting & In Process Inspection Software Publisher
N.A.I.C.S.: 513210
Mari Luke *(Mgr-Mktg)*

Subsidiary (Domestic):

Ninian Solutions Ltd. (2)
2 Leman Street 2nd Floor Aldgate Tower, London, E1 8FA, United Kingdom
Tel.: (44) 870 977 2212
Web Site: https://www.huddle.com
Online Content Management Services
N.A.I.C.S.: 513199
Mark Wrighton *(CEO)*

Pentana Limited (2)
Gatehouse Fretherne Road, Welwyn Garden City, AL8 6RD, Hertfordshire, United Kingdom
Tel.: (44) 1707 373335
Web Site: http://www.ideagenplc.com
Information Technology Consulting Services
N.A.I.C.S.: 541512
Ken Ebbage *(Dir)*

Subsidiary (US):

Pentana Inc. (3)
113 Molesey Hurst, Williamsburg, VA 23188
Tel.: (800) 350-8034
Web Site: http://www.pentana.com
Information Technology Consulting Services
N.A.I.C.S.: 541512

HGCAPITAL TRUST PLC

HgCapital Trust plc—(Continued)

Subsidiary (Domestic):

Plumtree Group Limited (2)
Ergo House Mere Way Ruddington Fields Business Park, Nottingham, NG11 6JS, United Kingdom
Tel.: (44) 1159376661
Information Technology Consulting Services
N.A.I.C.S.: 541512

Subsidiary (US):

Qualtrax Inc. (2)
105 Industrial Dr, Christiansburg, VA 24073-2536
Tel.: (540) 382-4234
Web Site: http://www.qualtrax.com
Electronic Computer Mfr
N.A.I.C.S.: 334111
William T. Fleshman Jr. *(VP)*

HGEARS AG
Brambach 38, 78713, Schramberg, Germany
Tel.: (49) 74225660
Web Site: https://www.hgears.com
Year Founded: 1958
HGEA—(DEU)
Rev.: $121,384,632
Assets: $147,577,164
Liabilities: $67,991,582
Net Worth: $79,585,582
Earnings: ($14,886,682)
Emp.: 663
Fiscal Year-end: 12/31/23
Power Train Parts Mfr
N.A.I.C.S.: 336350

Subsidiaries:

hGears (Suzhou) Co., Ltd. (1)
9 Yangpu Road Suzhou Industrial Park, Suzhou, 215126, Jiangsu, China
Tel.: (86) 51262816628
Sports Car Mfr & Distr
N.A.I.C.S.: 336390

hGears Padova S.p.A. (1)
Via Lussemburgo, 35127, Padova, Italy
Tel.: (39) 0498537301311
Web Site: https://hgears.com
Emp.: 300
Precision Turned Parts & Gear Kit Mfr
N.A.I.C.S.: 332721

HGH HOLDINGS LTD.
EMS Building 60 Benoi Road No 03-02, Singapore, 629906, Singapore
Tel.: (65) 62687112
Web Site:
https://www.hghholdings.com.sg
Year Founded: 1995
5GZ—(CAT)
Rev.: $15,174,036
Assets: $48,804,532
Liabilities: $13,803,216
Net Worth: $35,001,316
Earnings: ($245,304)
Emp.: 81
Fiscal Year-end: 12/31/23
Loudspeaker Parts Mfr
N.A.I.C.S.: 332722

HGV HAMBURGER GESELLSCHAFT FUR VERMOGENS- UND BETEILIGUNGSMANAGEMENT MBH
Gustav-Mahler-Platz 1 Colonnaden, 20354, Hamburg, Germany
Tel.: (49) 40 32 32 23 0
Web Site: http://www.hgv.hamburg.de
Holding Company
N.A.I.C.S.: 551112
Peter Tschentscher *(Chm)*

Subsidiaries:

Stromnetz Hamburg GmbH (1)
Bramfelder Chaussee 130, 22177, Hamburg, Germany
Tel.: (49) 404 920200
Web Site: http://www.stromnetz-hamburg.de
Electric Power Distribution Services
N.A.I.C.S.: 221122

HH BIOTECHNOLOGY HOLDINGS COMPANY
C Site 25-26F Presidential Building No 69 Heping North Street, Heping District, Shenyang, 110003, China
Tel.: (86) 2422813888   NV
Web Site:
http://www.greatchinaholdings.com
HHBT—(OTCEM)
Sales Range: $1-9.9 Million
Emp.: 121
Nutritional Products Development Services
N.A.I.C.S.: 311911
Peng Jiang *(Chm)*

HH GLOBAL GROUP LIMITED
Grove House Guildford Road, Leatherhead, KT22 9DF, Surrey, United Kingdom
Tel.: (44) 208 770 7300   UK
Web Site: http://www.hhglobal.com
Holding Company
N.A.I.C.S.: 551112
Robert MacMillan *(CEO)*

Subsidiaries:

Adare International Limited (1)
Lilly House Priestley Road, Basingstoke, RG24 9LZ, United Kingdom
Tel.: (44) 1256631600
Web Site: http://www.adareinternational.net
Emp.: 600
Marketing Services
N.A.I.C.S.: 561499
Andrew Dutton *(CEO)*

HH Associates US, Inc. (1)
400 Lakeview Pkwy, Vernon Hills, IL 60061-1854
Tel.: (847) 216-6303
Web Site: http://www.hhglobal.com
Professional, Scientific & Technical Services
N.A.I.C.S.: 541990
Tony Massey *(CMO)*

InnerWorkings, Inc. (1)
203 N La Salle St Ste 1800, Chicago, IL 60601
Tel.: (312) 642-3700
Web Site: http://www.inwk.com
Rev.: $1,157,834,000
Assets: $629,283,000
Liabilities: $451,031,000
Net Worth: $178,252,000
Earnings: ($10,075,000)
Emp.: 2,100
Fiscal Year-end: 12/31/2019
Print Management & Promotional Material Distribution Services
N.A.I.C.S.: 323120
Mike Perez *(Pres & CEO)*

Subsidiary (Non-US):

Cirqit De Honduras S. de R.L. De C.V. (2)
Centro Comercial Plaza Millenium, Tegucigalpa, 22250465, Honduras
Tel.: (504) 22631365
Computer Hardware & Software Whslr
N.A.I.C.S.: 423430

Cirqit S.A. (2)
Av Shirys N36-120 entre Naciones Unidas y Suecia, Edificio Allure Park Oficina 15B, Quito, Ecuador
Tel.: (593) 23324293
Web Site: http://www.inwk.com
Marketing Consulting Services
N.A.I.C.S.: 541613

Cirqit de Costa Rica S.A. (2)
200 E De Plaza Mayor Rohrmoser, Alajuela, Costa Rica
Tel.: (506) 22962202
Advertising Agency Services
N.A.I.C.S.: 541810

Subsidiary (Domestic):

DB Studios, Inc. (2)
17032 Murphy Ave, Irvine, CA 92614
Tel.: (949) 833-0100
Web Site: http://www.dbstudios.com
Graphic Design & Production Services
N.A.I.C.S.: 541430

Subsidiary (Non-US):

EYELEVEL Retail Solutions Consultoria Ltda (2)
Rua Capitao Souza Franco 848 Cj 93, Curitiba, 80730-420, Brazil
Tel.: (55) 4191234594
Marketing Consulting Services
N.A.I.C.S.: 541613

EYELEVEL Solutions LTD. (2)
Rankin House Knowlhill Business Parc, Roebuck Way, Milton Keynes, MK5 8GB, United Kingdom
Tel.: (44) 7714255185
Marketing Consulting Services
N.A.I.C.S.: 541613

EYELEVEL s.r.o. (2)
Logistic terminal Nupaky 148, Ricany, 25101, Czech Republic
Tel.: (420) 777054632
Web Site: http://www.eyelevel.com
Marketing Consulting Services
N.A.I.C.S.: 541613

Subsidiary (Domestic):

EYELEVEL, Inc. (2)
6720 N Basin Ave, Portland, OR 97217
Tel.: (503) 831-9366
Web Site: http://www.eyelevel.com
Emp.: 25
Marketing Consulting Services
N.A.I.C.S.: 541613

Subsidiary (Non-US):

Eyelevel Distribution Services (2)
Logistic Terminal Nupaky 148, Ricany, Prague, Prague, Czech Republic
Tel.: (420) 323627911
Web Site: http://www.eyelevel.com
Emp.: 300
Real Estate Prorperty Leasing Services
N.A.I.C.S.: 531190

INWK Mexico S de R.L. De C.V. (2)
Lope De Vega 107 Chaputlepec Morales Miguel Hidalgo, Cuajimalpa de Morelos Districto Federal, 05100, Mexico, Mexico
Tel.: (52) 5536220905
Marketing Consulting Services
N.A.I.C.S.: 541613

INWK Panama S.A. (2)
Av Samuel Lewis Y Calle Gerardo, Ortega, Panama, Panama
Tel.: (507) 62452778
Marketing Consulting Services
N.A.I.C.S.: 541613

InnerWorkings Andina S.A.S. (2)
Carrera 11B 99-25 Floor 12 Office 114, Bogota, Colombia
Tel.: (57) 3116476638
Marketing Consulting Services
N.A.I.C.S.: 541613
Reyner Aponte *(Acct Mgr)*

InnerWorkings Asia Pacific (2)
801 Pacific House 20 Queens Road Central, Hong Kong, China (Hong Kong)
Tel.: (852) 92587626
Marketing Consulting Services
N.A.I.C.S.: 541613

InnerWorkings Belgium SPRL/BVBA (2)
Avenue Charles-Quint 584, 1082, Brussels, Belgium
Tel.: (32) 486658127
Advertising Agency Services
N.A.I.C.S.: 541810

InnerWorkings Brasil Gerenciamento de Impressoes (2)
Av Magalhaes De Castro 4800, Edif Capital Building Torre 1 Andar 13 Conj 134 Cidade Jardim, Sao Paulo, 05676-900, Brazil
Tel.: (55) 56276680
Advertising Agency Services
N.A.I.C.S.: 541810

InnerWorkings Canada (2)

INTERNATIONAL PUBLIC

511 Millway Avenue, Concord, L4K 3V4, ON, Canada
Tel.: (905) 761-7726
Emp.: 10
Advertising Agency Services
N.A.I.C.S.: 541810
Fred Pall *(Gen Mgr)*

InnerWorkings Colombia S.A.S. (2)
Calle 90 No 19 41 Of 203, Bogota, 110221, Cundinamarca, Colombia
Tel.: (57) 16354467
Marketing Consulting Services
N.A.I.C.S.: 541613

InnerWorkings Danmark A/S (2)
Havnegade 100, 5000, Odense, Denmark
Tel.: (45) 29480021
Commercial Printing Services
N.A.I.C.S.: 323113

InnerWorkings Deutschland Gmbh (2)
Robert Bosch Strasse 31, Waldstetten, 78550, Germany
Tel.: (49) 71719226945
Printing Machinery Rental & Distr
N.A.I.C.S.: 532420

InnerWorkings Dubai (2)
Reef Tower 9th Floor Office 30-34 Jumeira Lake Towers, Dubai, Dubai, United Arab Emirates
Tel.: (971) 1506527743
Marketing Consulting Services
N.A.I.C.S.: 541613

InnerWorkings Europe Limited (2)
5 Cranbrook Way, Solihull, B90 4GT, West Midlands, United Kingdom
Tel.: (44) 1216282900
Web Site: http://www.inwk-wbs.co.uk
Emp.: 67
Marketing Consulting Services
N.A.I.C.S.: 541613

InnerWorkings France (2)
Place De Seine Batiment B 159 Rue Anatole France, 92300, Levallois-Perret, France
Tel.: (33) 177358475
Marketing Consulting Services
N.A.I.C.S.: 541613
Cendrine Montousse *(CEO)*

InnerWorkings India Private Limited (2)
Level 2 Kalpataru Synergy Opposite Grand Hyatt, Santacruz East, Mumbai, 400055, India
Tel.: (91) 39537100
Marketing Consulting Services
N.A.I.C.S.: 541613

InnerWorkings Nederland BV (2)
Hogehilweg 16, 1101 CD, Amsterdam, Netherlands
Tel.: (31) 486658127
Marketing Consulting Services
N.A.I.C.S.: 541613

InnerWorkings Peru S.A.C. (2)
Av Ricardo Rivera Navarrete Nor 765 Piso 2, Magdalena del Mar, 15001, Lima, Peru
Tel.: (51) 16282027
Web Site: http://www.inwk.com
Marketing Consulting Services
N.A.I.C.S.: 541613

InnerWorkings Rus LLC (2)
2-ya Zvenigorodskaya Street 13 Block 43, 123022, Moscow, Russia
Tel.: (7) 4959662141
Advertising Related Services
N.A.I.C.S.: 541890

InnerWorkings Russia LLA (2)
2-ya Zvenigorodskaya street 13 Block 43 Office 409, Moscow, 123022, Russia
Tel.: (7) 4959662141
Marketing Consulting Services
N.A.I.C.S.: 541613

InnerWorkings Singapore Private Limited (2)
3 Raffles Place 06-01 Bharat Buildings, Singapore, 048617, Singapore
Tel.: (65) 96542844
Marketing Consulting Services
N.A.I.C.S.: 541613

Branch (Domestic):

InnerWorkings, Inc. - Cincinnati Office (2)

AND PRIVATE COMPANIES

7141 E Kemper Rd, Cincinnati, OH 45249
Tel.: (513) 984-9500
Web Site: http://www.inwk.com
Emp.: 15
Print Management & Promotional Material Distribution Services
N.A.I.C.S.: 323120

InnerWorkings, Inc. - East Brunswick Office (2)
7 Joanna Ct, East Brunswick, NJ 08816
Tel.: (732) 651-8822
Web Site: http://www.inwk.com
Print Management & Promotional Material Distribution Services
N.A.I.C.S.: 323120

InnerWorkings, Inc. - New York City Office (2)
1440 Broadway 22nd Fl, New York, NY 10018
Tel.: (212) 213-0900
Web Site: http://www.inwk.com
Emp.: 19
Commercial Printing Services
N.A.I.C.S.: 323111

Subsidiary (Domestic):

Lightning Golf and Promotions, Inc. (2)
11419 Cronridge Dr Ste 12, Owings Mills, MD 21117
Tel.: (410) 356-1300
Web Site: http://www.inwk.com
Emp.: 10
Promotional Material Distribution Services
N.A.I.C.S.: 541870

Madden Communications Inc. (2)
901 Mittel Dr, Wood Dale, IL 60191-1118
Tel.: (630) 787-2200
Web Site: http://www.madden.com
Sales Range: $25-49.9 Million
Emp.: 165
Commercial Printing, Lithographic Services
N.A.I.C.S.: 323111

Subsidiary (Non-US):

Merchandise Mania Limited (2)
Unit 231 A 52 Upper Street Islington Green, London, N1 0QH, United Kingdom
Tel.: (44) 2087360270
Web Site: http://www.merchandisemania.co.uk
Emp.: 8
Gifts & Promotional Product Distr
N.A.I.C.S.: 459420
Simon Dipple *(Mng Dir)*

Subsidiary (Domestic):

Overseas Printing Corporation (2)
655 Montgomery St Ste 1710, San Francisco, CA 94111
Tel.: (415) 835-9999
Web Site: http://www.overseasprinting.com
Emp.: 5
International Book & Commercial Printing Services
N.A.I.C.S.: 323117

Subsidiary (Non-US):

PPA International Limited (2)
Flat A 20/F Richwealth Industrial Building 77-87 Wang Lung Street, Tsuen Wan, New Territories, China (Hong Kong)
Tel.: (852) 31883622
Web Site: http://www.inwk.com
Paper Packaging Material Mfr
N.A.I.C.S.: 322220

Subsidiary (Domestic):

Print Systems, Inc. (2)
1415 Plainfield Ave Ne, Grand Rapids, MI 49505-4966
Tel.: (616) 458-8284
Web Site: http://www.inwk.com
Emp.: 10
Commercial Printing Services
N.A.I.C.S.: 323113

Subsidiary (Non-US):

Productions Graphics Agencement et Volume (2)
31 Rue Saint Jacques, 76600, Le Havre, France

Tel.: (33) 235511511
Graphic Design & Production Services
N.A.I.C.S.: 541430

Professional Packaging Services Limited (2)
Home Farm Unit D The Granary The Avenue Apperley Lane, Bradford, BD17 7RH, West Yorkshire, United Kingdom
Tel.: (44) 1274659530
Web Site: http://www.p-p-s-ltd.com
Emp.: 15
Paper Packaging Material Mfr
N.A.I.C.S.: 322220

Subsidiary (Domestic):

Screened Images, Inc. (2)
7 Joanna Ct Ste H, East Brunswick, NJ 08816
Tel.: (732) 651-8181
Emp.: 30
Commercial Screen Printing Services
N.A.I.C.S.: 323113

HH&L ACQUISITION CO.
8 Connaught Place One Exchange Square Suite 3508, Central, China (Hong Kong)
Tel.: (852) 37522870   Ky
Web Site: http://www.hopuhl.com
Year Founded: 2020
HHLA—(NYSE)
Rev.: $22,163,807
Assets: $420,157,231
Liabilities: $432,477,867
Net Worth: ($12,320,636)
Earnings: $17,691,841
Emp.: 3
Fiscal Year-end: 12/31/22
Investment Holding Company
N.A.I.C.S.: 551112
Kenneth W. Hitchner *(Chm)*

HHG CAPITAL CORPORATION
40/F Montery Plaza 15 Chong Yip Street, Kowloon, 999077, China (Hong Kong)
Tel.: (852) 39985110   VG
Year Founded: 2020
HHGC—(NASDAQ)
Rev.: $507,209
Assets: $34,678,996
Liabilities: $36,145,409
Net Worth: ($1,466,413)
Earnings: ($46,734)
Emp.: 2
Fiscal Year-end: 12/31/22
Investment Services
N.A.I.C.S.: 523999
Kin Sze *(Chm & CEO)*

HHRG BERHAD
No 2945 Plot A2 Jalan Sungai Baong Kawasan Perindustrian, Perabut Sungai Baong Mukim 5, 14200, Penang, Sungai Jawi, Malaysia
Tel.: (60) 45825888
Web Site: https://hhrg.com.my
Year Founded: 2011
HHRG—(KLS)
Rev.: $26,311,443
Assets: $56,589,779
Liabilities: $13,131,455
Net Worth: $43,458,323
Earnings: $1,662,620
Fiscal Year-end: 03/31/24
Biomass Materials & Mattress & Bedding Accessories Mfr
N.A.I.C.S.: 313110
Choon Seng H'ng *(Mng Dir)*

Subsidiaries:

Fibre Star (M) Sdn.Bhd. (1)
3843 MK 11 Luar Desa Jawi, Seberang Perai Selatan, 14200, Sungai Jawi, Penang, Malaysia
Tel.: (60) 45826605
Web Site: http://www.fibrestar.com.my
Mattress & Related Product Mfr

N.A.I.C.S.: 337910

HK Fibre Sdn. Bhd. (1)
Lot 344 & 345 Kg Kemayang Tawang, Bachok, 16020, Kelantan, Malaysia
Tel.: (60) 97766088
Coconut Biomass Material Mfr
N.A.I.C.S.: 311225

HK Gua Musang Sdn. Bhd. (1)
Lot 551 Gua Musang Industrial Area Gua Musang City, Gua Musang District, 18300, Kelantan, Malaysia
Tel.: (60) 99123177
Coconut Biomass Material Mfr
N.A.I.C.S.: 311225

HK Kitaran Sdn. Bhd. (1)
No 2945 Jalan Sungai Baong Kawasan Perindustrian Perabut Sungai Baong, Mukim 5 Sungai Jawi, 14200, Sungai Bakap, Penang, Malaysia
Tel.: (60) 45825888
Coconut Biomass Material Mfr
N.A.I.C.S.: 311225

HHY FUND
Level 15 90 Collins St, Melbourne, 3000, VIC, Australia
Tel.: (61) 396544477
Investment Management Service
N.A.I.C.S.: 525990
Tristan Darwin *(Mgr-Fund)*

HI AI 1ST SPECIAL PURPOSE ACQUISITION CO
Hi Investment Securities Bldg 61 Yeouinaru-ro Yeongdeungpo-gu, Seoul, 07327, Korea (South)
Tel.: (82) 221229690
Emp.: 2
Financial Investment Management Services
N.A.I.C.S.: 523940
Jong-Hyuk Choi *(CEO)*

HI AIR KOREA CO., LTD.
204 Gomo-ro 324beon-gil, Gimhae, Gyeonsangnam, Korea (South)
Tel.: (82) 55 340 5000
Web Site: http://www.hiairkorea.co.kr
Year Founded: 1988
Sales Range: $300-349.9 Million
Ventilation Equipment Mfr
N.A.I.C.S.: 333413
K. B. Kim *(Chm & CEO)*

Subsidiaries:

Novenco A/S (1)
Industrivej 22 Ydernaes, DK 4700, Naestved, Denmark
Tel.: (45) 70124222
Web Site: http://www.novencogroup.com
Sales Range: $150-199.9 Million
Emp.: 600
Ventilation & Air Handling Equipment & Fire Fighting Systems Engineering, Mfr & Distr
N.A.I.C.S.: 333415
Lars Knaack *(CFO)*

Subsidiary (Non-US):

Novenco B.V. (2)
Bergweg Zuid 115, 2661 CS, Bergschenhoek, Netherlands
Tel.: (31) 0105242424
Web Site: http://www.novenco.nl
Sales Range: $25-49.9 Million
Emp.: 50
Industrial & Commercial Ventilation & Air Handling Equipment Whslr & Installer
N.A.I.C.S.: 333415
Ruud Zanderk *(Mng Dir)*

HI GOLD OCEAN KMARIN NO.12 SHIP INVESTMENT COMPANY
Jeju Province small medium Business Center 473 Yeonsam-ro, Jeju, 690824, Jeju Special Self-Go, Korea (South)
Tel.: (82) 220904625

172580—(KRS)
Rev.: $6,840,989
Assets: $31,535,074
Liabilities: $4,071,360
Net Worth: $27,463,714
Earnings: ($1,201,845)
Emp.: 4
Fiscal Year-end: 12/31/20
Investment Management Service
N.A.I.C.S.: 523999
Ju-Sig Cheon *(CEO)*

HI REAL SPA
Via Carlo Porta 1, 20121, Milan, Italy
Tel.: (39) 0287166507
Web Site: http://www.hireal.it
Sales Range: $10-24.9 Million
Emp.: 65
Hotel Investment Services
N.A.I.C.S.: 525990

HI SHARP ELECTRONICS CO., LTD.
No 673 Changxing Rd, Bade, Taoyuan, 334, Taiwan
Tel.: (886) 33653121
Web Site: https://www.hisharp.com
Year Founded: 1987
3128—(TPE)
Rev.: $33,508,770
Assets: $38,997,030
Liabilities: $19,306,507
Net Worth: $19,690,523
Earnings: $2,425,976
Fiscal Year-end: 12/31/22
Automobile Parts Mfr
N.A.I.C.S.: 336110
Sung-Kui Chiang *(Pres)*

Subsidiaries:

Home Automation (FE) Pte. Ltd. (1)
80 Genting Ln 08-07, Ruby Industrial Complex, Singapore, 349565, Singapore
Tel.: (65) 67438797
Web Site: https://homeautomation.com.sg
Security System Services
N.A.I.C.S.: 561621

Securevision, W.S Gauci Ltd. (1)
Wignacourt Street, Birkirkara, BKR 4714, Malta
Tel.: (356) 21444398
Web Site: https://www.securevision.com.mt
Investment & Financial Services
N.A.I.C.S.: 522320

Wave Sine Technology Ltd. (1)
24/2 Green Road, Dhanmondi, Dhaka, 1205, Bangladesh
Tel.: (880) 244612808
Web Site: https://wavesinebd.com
Security System Services
N.A.I.C.S.: 561621

HI SPECIAL PURPOSE ACQUISITION COMPANY
61 Yeouinaru-ro, Yeongdeungpo-gu, Seoul, Korea (South)
Tel.: (82) 221229226
Year Founded: 2014
Assets: $9,801,644
Liabilities: $1,103,551
Net Worth: $8,698,095
Earnings: $2,062
Financial Investment Management Services
N.A.I.C.S.: 523940

HI SUN TECHNOLOGY (CHINA) LIMITED
Room 2515 25/F Sun Hung Kai Centre 30 Harbour Road, Wanchai, China (Hong Kong)
Tel.: (852) 25888800   BM
Web Site: http://www.hisun.com.hk
0818—(HKG)
Rev.: $437,672,820
Assets: $1,460,552,153
Liabilities: $497,381,198

HI SUN TECHNOLOGY (CHINA) LIMITED

Hi Sun Technology (China) Limited—(Continued)
Net Worth: $963,170,955
Earnings: $142,113,285
Emp.: 2,782
Fiscal Year-end: 12/31/22
Information Technology Services
N.A.I.C.S.: 541512
Yuk Fung Cheung *(Chm)*

Subsidiaries:

Hangzhou PAX Electronic Technology Limited (1)
No 500 12 Hao Street Economic development zone, Xiasha, Hangzhou, China
Tel.: (86) 57186717908
Web Site: https://www.paxhz.com
Electric Equipment Mfr
N.A.I.C.S.: 334515

Megahunt Technologies Inc. (1)
North Side 4F Block 2 Yard 20 Suzhou Ave, Haidian District, Beijing, China
Tel.: (86) 1082618165
Web Site: https://www.megahuntmicro.com
Semiconductor Product Mfr & Distr
N.A.I.C.S.: 334413

HI-CLEARANCE, INC.

8F-2 No 2 Lane 609 Sec 5 Chung Hsin Rd, Sanchong Dist, New Taipei City, 241, Taiwan
Tel.: (886) 229953318
Web Site:
https://www.hiclearance.com.tw
Year Founded: 1989
1788—(TPE)
Rev.: $146,630,616
Assets: $140,971,110
Liabilities: $64,695,338
Net Worth: $76,275,772
Earnings: $11,456,962
Fiscal Year-end: 12/31/22
Medical Equipment & Device Mfr
N.A.I.C.S.: 339112

Subsidiaries:

P.T. Hiclearance Medical Indonesia (1)
Jl Cakung Industri Selatan 1 No 12 Rorotan, Kec Cilincing, Jakarta Utara, Indonesia
Tel.: (62) 214613070
Web Site: https://hiclearance.co.id
Surgical Equipment Services
N.A.I.C.S.: 621493

Renalysis Medical Care Co. Ltd. (1)
9F-2 No 2 Lane 609 Sec 5 Chung Hsin Rd, Sanchong Dist, New Taipei City, 241, Taiwan
Tel.: (886) 222781236
Haemodialysis Product Mfr & Distr
N.A.I.C.S.: 334510

Taicha Medical Corp. (1)
17F Building 1 No 18 Taigu Road Pilot Free Trade Zone, Shanghai, China
Tel.: (86) 2160276738
Haemodialysis Product Mfr & Distr
N.A.I.C.S.: 334510

HI-GREEN CARBON LIMITED

G-557 Lodhika Industrial Estate Metoda G I D C Gate No 3 Metoda, Rajkot, 360021, Gujarat, India
Tel.: (91) 9227874044
Web Site:
https://www.higreencarbon.com
Year Founded: 2011
HIGREEN—(NSE)
Rev.: $9,519,991
Assets: $5,418,338
Liabilities: $2,467,580
Net Worth: $2,950,758
Earnings: $1,501,833
Emp.: 32
Fiscal Year-end: 03/31/23
Rubber Product Distr
N.A.I.C.S.: 423930

HI-KALIBRE EQUIPMENT LTD.

7321-68 Ave NW, Edmonton, T6B 3T6, AB, Canada
Tel.: (780) 435-1111
Web Site: https://www.hikalibre.com
Year Founded: 1986
Blowout Prevention Equipment Mfr
N.A.I.C.S.: 333413
Patrick Rabby *(Pres)*

HI-KLASS TRADING & INVESTMENT LIMITED

24 Veer Nariman Road Rehman Building 2Nd Floor Office No 15 Fort, Mumbai, 400001, Maharashtra, India
Tel.: (91) 9874385558
Web Site: https://www.hiklass.co.in
Year Founded: 1992
542332—(BOM)
Rev.: $29,663
Assets: $526,130
Liabilities: $1,263
Net Worth: $524,867
Earnings: $86
Emp.: 2
Fiscal Year-end: 03/31/22
Financial Services
N.A.I.C.S.: 523999
Suresh Tarachand Jain *(Mng Dir)*

HI-LAI FOODS CO., LTD.

21F-1 No 266 Cheng-Kung 1st Road, 80146, Kaohsiung, Taiwan
Tel.: (886) 72135788
1268—(TPE)
Rev.: $117,464,716
Assets: $196,392,709
Liabilities: $138,535,253
Net Worth: $57,857,456
Earnings: $4,066,285
Fiscal Year-end: 12/31/22
Restaurant Operators
N.A.I.C.S.: 722511
Tsung-Cheng Lai *(Chm)*

HI-LEX CORPORATION

1-12-28 Sakaemachi, Takarazuka, 665-0845, Hyogo, Japan
Tel.: (81) 797852500
Web Site: https://www.hi-lex.co.jp
Year Founded: 1946
7279—(TKS)
Rev.: $2,117,237,070
Assets: $1,992,247,460
Liabilities: $636,788,350
Net Worth: $1,355,459,110
Earnings: ($21,206,190)
Emp.: 12,446
Fiscal Year-end: 10/31/23
Remote Control Cables & Accessories Mfr
N.A.I.C.S.: 335314
Makoto Teraura *(Chm)*

Subsidiaries:

CHONGQING HI-LEX CABLE SYSTEM GROUP CO., LTD (1)
No 6 Yunrui Street New North Zone, Chongqing, 401120, China
Tel.: (86) 2367410898
Rev.: $141,000,000
Emp.: 1,133
Control Cables Mfr
N.A.I.C.S.: 331318

Changchun Hi-Lex Auto Cable Co. Ltd. (1)
No 2723 Chaoqun Street High New Technology Development Zone, Changchun, Jilin, China
Tel.: (86) 43189685711
Automotive Products Mfr
N.A.I.C.S.: 336390

Chongqing Hi-Lex Control Cable System Co Ltd. (1)
No C29 Economy Development Yard, Yubei District, Chongqing, 400020, China
Tel.: (86) 2367463128
Automotive Products Mfr
N.A.I.C.S.: 336390

DAE DONG HI-LEX INC (1)
43 Namdongdong-ro 78beon-gil, Namdonggu, Incheon, 405-821, Korea (South)
Tel.: (82) 32 818 7631
Web Site: http://www.hi-lex.co.jp
Emp.: 211
Automotive Control Cable Mfr
N.A.I.C.S.: 336390

DAE DONG SYSTEM CO., LTD (1)
3LT 3BL Namdong-Daero, Namdong-gu, Incheon, 405-100, Korea (South)
Tel.: (82) 32 813 8171
Web Site: https://www.dds.co.kr
Emp.: 256
Automotive Control Cable Mfr
N.A.I.C.S.: 336390

DAEDONG HI-LEX OF AMERICA, INC (1)
1195 County Rd 177, Cusseta, AL 36852
Tel.: (334) 756-5338
Web Site: http://www.hi-lex.co.jp
Emp.: 66
Motor Vehicle Parts Distr
N.A.I.C.S.: 423140

Daedong Door Inc. (1)
64 Cheomdan-daero 124 beon-gil, Yeonsugu, Incheon, 21991, Korea (South)
Tel.: (82) 327169480
Car Cable Mfr
N.A.I.C.S.: 336320

Guangdong Hi Lex Cable System Co, Ltd. (1)
7 Xinxiang Road, Xintang Zengcheng, Guangzhou, China
Tel.: (86) 2082686600
Automotive Products Mfr
N.A.I.C.S.: 336390

HI Lex Do Brasil Ltda. (1)
Alameda Ulderico Ferrari 100 + Itaim Guacu, Itu, 13312-655, SP, Brazil
Tel.: (55) 1140130055
Automotive Products Mfr
N.A.I.C.S.: 336390

HI-LEX Czech, s.r.o. (1)
Prumyslova zona Joseph 163, 435 01, Havran, Czech Republic
Tel.: (420) 602614263
Web Site: https://www.hi-lex.com
Transmission Cable Mfr
N.A.I.C.S.: 336320

HI-LEX Europe GmbH (1)
Athenstrasse 2, 97424, Schweinfurt, Germany
Tel.: (49) 9721388840
Automotive Products Mfr
N.A.I.C.S.: 336390

HI-LEX HUNGARY Kft (1)
Ipari park 3, 2651, Retsag, Nograd, Hungary
Tel.: (36) 3 555 1200
Web Site: https://hi-lex.co.hu
Emp.: 250
Motor Vehicle Parts Whslr
N.A.I.C.S.: 423140

HI-LEX Hungary Cable System Manufacturing LLC (1)
Ipari Park 3, 2651, Retsag, Hungary
Tel.: (36) 35551200
Automotive Products Mfr
N.A.I.C.S.: 336390

HI-LEX KANTO, INC (1)
1523 Kobayashi, Mobara, 297-0074, Chiba, Japan
Tel.: (81) 47 524 5155
Web Site: http://www.hi-lex.co.jp
Control Cables Mfr
N.A.I.C.S.: 332618

HI-LEX VIETNAM CO., LTD (1)
Lot C8 Nhat Ban IZ Haiphong IZ, Anduong, Haiphong, Vietnam
Tel.: (84) 2253743058
Rev.: $15,000,000
Emp.: 481
Automotive Control Cable Mfr
N.A.I.C.S.: 336390

Hi-Lex Italy S.p.A. (1)
Via S Rufino 29, 16043, Chiavari, GE, Italy
Tel.: (39) 0185368905
Automotive Products Mfr

INTERNATIONAL PUBLIC

Hangzhou HI-LEX Cable Systems Co., Ltd. (1)
No 3998 Jiangdong 3rd Road, Dajiangdong Industry Cluster Zone, Hangzhou, China
Tel.: (86) 57183811961
Automotive Products Mfr
N.A.I.C.S.: 336390

Hi-Lex America, Inc. (1)
5200 Wayne Rd, Battle Creek, MI 49037-1092
Tel.: (269) 968-0781
Web Site: http://www.hi-lex.com
Sales Range: $75-99.9 Million
Emp.: 460
Remote Control Cables & Accessories Mfr
N.A.I.C.S.: 335314

Hi-Lex Auto Parts Spain, S.L. (1)
Londres 20 Granollers, Granollers, 08401, Barcelona, Spain
Tel.: (34) 935809835
Automotive Products Mfr
N.A.I.C.S.: 336390

Hi-Lex Cable System Co.,Ltd. (1)
Baglan Energy Park Central Av, Port Talbot, SA12 7AX, United Kingdom
Tel.: (44) 1639825300
Web Site: http://www.hi-lex.co.jp
Motorcycle Bicycle & Parts Mfr
N.A.I.C.S.: 336991

Hi-Lex Controls, Inc. (1)
152 Simpson Dr, Litchfield, MI 49252
Tel.: (517) 542-2955
Web Site: http://www.hi-lex.com
Sales Range: $150-199.9 Million
Emp.: 500
Relays & Industrial Controls Mfr
N.A.I.C.S.: 336390
Shoichi Hirai *(Pres & CEO)*

Hi-Lex Corporation - KAIBARA PLANT (1)
1700 Azaminamiida, Kaibara Kaibara-cho, Tanba, 669-3309, Hyogo, Japan
Tel.: (81) 79 572 2130
Web Site: http://www.hi-lex.co.jp
Industrial Machinery Mfr
N.A.I.C.S.: 333248

Hi-Lex Corporation - MIKKABI PLANT (1)
310 Ushi Mikkabi-cho, Kita-Ku, Hamamatsu, 431-1404, Shizuoka, Japan
Tel.: (81) 535252111
Emp.: 120
Control Cables Mfr
N.A.I.C.S.: 332618

Hi-Lex Corporation - SANDA PLANT (1)
4-3-9 Miwa, Sanda, 669-1513, Hyogo, Japan
Tel.: (81) 79 563 3001
Web Site: http://www.hi-lex.co.jp
Control Cables Mfr
N.A.I.C.S.: 332618

Hi-Lex Corporation - SANDA-NISHI PLANT (1)
14-4 Technopark, Sanda, 669-1339, Hyogo, Japan
Tel.: (81) 795682480
Control Cables Mfr
N.A.I.C.S.: 332618

Hi-Lex India (P) Ltd. (1)
Plot No - 398 Sector - 8 IMT Manesar, Gurgaon, 122050, Haryana, India
Tel.: (91) 124 456 5000
Web Site: https://www.hi-lex.co.in
Transmission Cable Distr
N.A.I.C.S.: 423610
Y. Fukuda *(CEO & Mng Dir)*

Hi-Lex Mexicana S.A. DE C.V. (1)
Av Penuelas 9 Fracc Ind, San Pedrito, 76148, Queretaro, Mexico
Tel.: (52) 442 238 4100
Web Site: https://www.hi-lex.com.mx
Emp.: 1,200
Motor Vehicle Supplies & New Parts Whslr
N.A.I.C.S.: 423120

Hi-Lex Miyagi, Inc. (1)
1 Shin-Teraura Ohayashi Wakayanagi, Kuri-

hara, 989-5509, Miyagi, Japan
Tel.: (81) 228322077
Automotive Products Mfr
N.A.I.C.S.: 336390

Hi-Lex Rus LLC (1)
Building 5/1 3rd Magistral Str, Samara region, 445043, Togliatti, Russia
Tel.: (7) 8482525690
Web Site: http://www.hi-lex.com.ru
Car Cable Mfr
N.A.I.C.S.: 336320

Hi-Lex Saitama, Inc. (1)
100 Kyouei, Honjo, 367-0037, Saitama, Japan
Tel.: (81) 49 521 2611
Web Site: http://www.hi-lex.co.jp
Motor Vehicle Parts Mfr
N.A.I.C.S.: 336390

Hi-Lex Serbia d.o.o. (1)
Dimitrija Davidovica bb, 22000, Sremska Mitrovica, Serbia
Tel.: (381) 222150226
Web Site: https://www.hi-lex.com
Transmission Cable Mfr
N.A.I.C.S.: 336320

Hi-Lex Shimane, Inc. (1)
1820-16 Shimoko-Cho, Hamada, 697-0006, Shimane, Japan
Tel.: (81) 85 523 5855
Web Site: http://www.hi-lex.co.jp
Sales Range: $50-74.9 Million
Emp.: 200
Motor Vehicle Parts Mfr
N.A.I.C.S.: 336390

Izushi Cable, Inc. (1)
1031 Hinobe Izushi-Cho, Toyooka, Toyooka, 668-0246, Hyogo, Japan
Tel.: (81) 79 652 6003
Web Site: http://www.hi-lex.co.in
Cable Networks
N.A.I.C.S.: 516210

Jiangsu Dae Dong Hi-Lex Inc. (1)
No 31 Xinyuan Road Yancheng Economic Development Zone, Yancheng, Jiangsu, China
Tel.: (86) 51588148888
Automotive Products Mfr
N.A.I.C.S.: 336390

Jiangsu Daedong Door Inc. (1)
No 12 Yuefeng Rd, Zhangjiagang, 215600, Jiangsu, China
Tel.: (86) 51289598786
Automotive Products Mfr
N.A.I.C.S.: 336390

PT. Hi-Lex Cirebon (1)
Jl Nyi Gede Cangkring No 70 Desa panembahan Kec Plered, PO Box 981, Cirebon, 45100, West Java, Indonesia
Tel.: (62) 2318309780
Automotive Products Mfr
N.A.I.C.S.: 336390

PT. Hi-Lex Indonesia Cikarang Factory (1)
Jl Trembesi 1Blok F16 No 001 Delta Silicon2 Lippo, Cikarang Desa Cicau-Kecamatan Cikarang Pusat, Bekasi, Indonesia
Tel.: (62) 2129288411
Automotive Products Mfr
N.A.I.C.S.: 336390

PT.HI-LEX INDONESIA (1)
Jl Bouraq No 35 Kelurahan Karang Anyar Kecamatan, Neglasari, Tangerang, 15121, Banten, Indonesia
Tel.: (62) 215522331
Rev.: $65,000,000
Emp.: 56
Control Cables Mfr
N.A.I.C.S.: 335921

PT.Hi-Lex Parts Indonesia (1)
Jl Bouraq No 35, PO Box 126, Ds Karanganyar kec Neglasari, Tangerang, Banten, Indonesia
Tel.: (62) 21 552 2325
Web Site: https://site-hilex.hi-lexindonesia.com
Relay & Industrial Control Mfr
N.A.I.C.S.: 335314

Sun Medical Technology Research Corp. (1)
2990 Shiga, Suwa, 392-0012, Nagano, Japan
Tel.: (81) 266541900
Automotive Products Mfr
N.A.I.C.S.: 336390

TSK (KOREA) CO., LTD (1)
974-6 Yang-deok Dong, Masan Hoe-Won Gu, Changwon, 630-728, Gyeong Nam, Korea (South)
Tel.: (82) 55 293 1473
Emp.: 246
Control Cables Mfr
N.A.I.C.S.: 335921

YANTAI TSK CABLE SYSTEM CO., LTD (1)
Yantai Export Processing Zone E2, Yantai, Shandong, China
Tel.: (86) 535 687 7215
Web Site: http://www.hi-lex.co.jp
Emp.: 227
Control Cables Mfr
N.A.I.C.S.: 335921

HI-P INTERNATIONAL LIMITED
11 International Business Park Jurong East, Singapore, 609926, Singapore
Tel.: (65) 62685459
Web Site: http://www.hi-p.com
Rev.: $1,013,634,203
Assets: $957,264,577
Liabilities: $516,727,996
Net Worth: $440,536,581
Earnings: $59,520,953
Fiscal Year-end: 12/31/19
Precision Plastic Injection Molding Tools Mfr
N.A.I.C.S.: 333248
Wan Mei Chan *(Co-Sec)*

Subsidiaries:

Hi-P (Chengdu) Mold Base Manufacturing Co., Ltd. (1)
B2 B4 unit Mold Industrial Park Encircle RD, West Park of Chengdu Hi-Tec Zone Hongguang Town, Chengdu, China
Tel.: (86) 2886180336
Mold Mfr
N.A.I.C.S.: 333511

Hi-P (Chengdu) Precision Plastic Manufacturing Co., Ltd. (1)
B2 B4 unit Mold Industrial Park Encircle RD, West Park of Chengdu Hi-Tec Zone Hongguang Town, Chengdu, China
Tel.: (86) 2886180336
Mold Mfr
N.A.I.C.S.: 333511

Hi-P (Shanghai) Housing Appliance Co., Ltd. (1)
No 366 Jinzang Road, Pudong New Area, Shanghai, China
Tel.: (86) 2161870588
Injection Molded Plastic Products Mfr
N.A.I.C.S.: 326199

Hi-P (Shanghai) Technology Co., Ltd. (1)
No4 Factory Lane 955 Jinhai Road Pudong New Area Shanghai, Pudong New Area, Shanghai, 201206, China
Tel.: (86) 2161016466
Emp.: 2,000
Injection Molded Plastic Products Mfr
N.A.I.C.S.: 326199

Hi-P (Suzhou) Electronics Technology Co., Ltd. (1)
No 86 Liufeng Road Hedong Industrial Park Guoxiang Street, Suzhou, Jiangsu, China
Tel.: (86) 51267867100
Printed Circuit Board Mfr
N.A.I.C.S.: 334412

Hi-P (Thailand) Co., Ltd. (1)
7/132 Moo 4 Amata City Industrial Estate T Mabyangporn, Pluak Deang, Rayong, Thailand
Tel.: (66) 386504328
Mold Mfr & Whslr
N.A.I.C.S.: 333511
Thinnakorn Kettoom *(Asst Mgr-HR)*

Hi-P (Tianjin) Technology Co., Ltd. (1)
The No 29 3th Street Xinye Factory 7 Western TEDA, Tianjin, China
Tel.: (86) 2265272666
Electrical & Telecommunication Equipment Product Whslr
N.A.I.C.S.: 423690

Hi-P (Xiamen) Precision Plastic Manufacturing Co., Ltd. (1)
Plant D No 04 Plot Export Processing Zone, Xiamen, Fujian, China
Tel.: (86) 5926881747
Injection Molded Plastic Products Mfr
N.A.I.C.S.: 326199

Hi-P Electronics Pte. Ltd. (1)
12 Ang Mo Kio Street 64 03-01 UE Biz Hub Central Blk A, Singapore, 569088, Singapore
Tel.: (65) 66435200
Electric Component Whslr
N.A.I.C.S.: 423690
C. S. Chan *(Sr Mgr)*

Hi-P Lens Technology (Shanghai) Co., Ltd. (1)
No 4 Workshop Lane 955 Jinhai Road, Pudong New Area, Shanghai, China
Tel.: (86) 2161016466
Optical Lens Mfr
N.A.I.C.S.: 333310

Hi-P Management Services Pte. Ltd. (1)
11 International Business Park, Jurong East, Jurong, Singapore
Tel.: (65) 65656682
Business Management Services
N.A.I.C.S.: 561110

Hi-P North America, Inc. (1)
1100 Nerge Rd, Elk Grove Village, IL 60007
Tel.: (847) 996-3000
Web Site: http://www.hi-p.com
Sales Range: $25-49.9 Million
Emp.: 10
Engineering Consulting Services
N.A.I.C.S.: 541330

Hi-P Poland Sp. z o.o. (1)
Ul Magazynowa 8, Bielany Wroclawskie, 55-040, Kobierzyce, Lower Silesian, Poland
Tel.: (48) 71 710 0505
Web Site: http://www.hi-p.pl
Emp.: 300
Molds & Plastic Molded Parts Mfr & Sales
N.A.I.C.S.: 333511
Krzysztof Moczulski *(Gen Mgr)*

Hi-P Tianjin Electronics Co., Ltd. (1)
No 156 Nanhai Road Jintin Industrial Park, Factory No 31 TEDA, Tianjin, China
Tel.: (86) 2266201216
Injection Molded Plastic Products Mfr
N.A.I.C.S.: 326199

HI-TEC SPORTS PLC
Aviation Way, Southend-on-Sea, SS2 6GH, Essex, United Kingdom
Tel.: (44) 1702541741
Web Site: http://www.hi-tecsports.com
Year Founded: 1974
Sales Range: $25-49.9 Million
Emp.: 180
Mfr of Athletic Footwear
N.A.I.C.S.: 339920
Frank Van Wezel *(Chm)*

Subsidiaries:

HI-TEC Espana S.A. (1)
Elche Parque Empresarial C/ Antoni Gaudi N 12, Torrellano Elche, 03203, Alicante, Spain
Tel.: (34) 965 681 423
Web Site: http://www.hi-tec.com
Footwear Distr
N.A.I.C.S.: 424340

Hi-Tec Nederland BV (1)
Paasheuvelweg 22A, 1105 BJ, Amsterdam, Netherlands
Tel.: (31) 20 711 84 88
Web Site: http://www.hi-tec.nl
Footwear Distr
N.A.I.C.S.: 424340

Hi-Tec Sports Canada Ltd. (1)
2585 Dunwin Drive, Mississauga, L5L 3N9, ON, Canada
Tel.: (800) 465-5766
Web Site: http://www.hi-tec.com
Footwear Distr
N.A.I.C.S.: 424340

Hi-Tec Sports USA, Inc. (1)
4801 Stoddard Rd, Modesto, CA 95356-9318 **(100%)**
Tel.: (209) 545-1111
Web Site: http://www.hi-tec.com
Sales Range: $50-74.9 Million
Emp.: 80
Mfr of Outdoor Rugged Footwear
N.A.I.C.S.: 424340
Frank Van Wezel *(Chm)*

HiTech Sports Pty Ltd (1)
PO Box 38, Wilston, Brisbane, 4051, QLD, Australia
Tel.: (61) 7 3168 2978
Web Site: http://www.hitechsports.com.au
Emp.: 25
Footwear Distr
N.A.I.C.S.: 424340

HI-TECH GEARS LTD
14th Floor Tower-B Millennium Plaza Sushant Lok-I Sector-27, Gurgaon, 122009, Haryana, India
Tel.: (91) 1244715100
Web Site: https://www.hitechgears.com
Year Founded: 1986
HITECHGEAR—(NSE)
Rev.: $103,198,505
Assets: $125,884,259
Liabilities: $82,103,795
Net Worth: $43,780,464
Earnings: $3,929,426
Emp.: 679
Fiscal Year-end: 03/31/21
Auto Component Mfr
N.A.I.C.S.: 335139
Pranav Kapuria *(Mng Dir)*

Subsidiaries:

Teutech Industries Inc. (1)
361 Speedvale Ave W, Guelph, N1H 1C7, ON, Canada
Tel.: (519) 836-3180
Electronic Product Mfr & Distr
N.A.I.C.S.: 335999

HI-TECH LUBRICANTS LTD.
1A Danepur Road G O R1, Lahore, Pakistan
Tel.: (92) 42363118813
Web Site: https://www.hitechlubricants.com
Year Founded: 1997
HTL—(PSX)
Rev.: $63,376,148
Assets: $43,755,424
Liabilities: $22,013,160
Net Worth: $21,742,264
Earnings: ($888,520)
Emp.: 576
Fiscal Year-end: 06/30/23
Lubricant Oil Mfr
N.A.I.C.S.: 324191
Shaukat Hassan *(Chm)*

Subsidiaries:

Haut Buys (Pvt) Ltd (1)
43-D Block N Gulberg II, Lahore, Pakistan
Tel.: (92) 4235246577
Web Site: https://hautbuys.com
Consumer Goods Product Mfr
N.A.I.C.S.: 311999

Pak Agro Packaging (Private) Limited (1)
Suite 08 2nd Floor 1-A Plaza F-10 Markaz, Islamabad, Pakistan
Tel.: (92) 512213012
Web Site: http://www.pakagro.com
Emp.: 150
Agro Equipment Mfr

HI-TECH LUBRICANTS LTD.

Hi-Tech Lubricants Ltd.—(Continued)
N.A.I.C.S.: 333111
Khalid Butt (CEO)

HI-TECH PIPES LTD.
505 Pearls Omaxe Tower Netaji Subhash Place, New Delhi, 110034, India
Tel.: (91) 1148440050
Web Site: https://www.hitechpipes.in
Year Founded: 1986
HITECH—(NSE)
Rev.: $183,105,277
Assets: $81,802,211
Liabilities: $53,793,326
Net Worth: $28,008,885
Earnings: $3,112,596
Emp.: 525
Fiscal Year-end: 03/31/21
Steel Products Mfr
N.A.I.C.S.: 331110

HI-TECH STEEL SERVICES LTD.
Bold Industrial Park Neills Road St Helens, Saint Helens, WA9 4TU, Merseyside, United Kingdom
Tel.: (44) 1744 818 767
Web Site: http://www.hitechsteels.com
Year Founded: 1992
Sales Range: $50-74.9 Million
Emp.: 75
Steel Products Mfr
N.A.I.C.S.: 331221
Ian Gorman (Mng Dir)

HI-TECH WINDING SYSTEMS LTD.
08 / Gokul Complex Opp Nagri Hospital Gujarat College Road Ellisbridge, Ahmedabad, 380006, Gujarat, India
Tel.: (91) 7043230374
Web Site: https://www.hitechwinding.com
Year Founded: 1988
541627—(BOM)
Rev.: $9,245
Assets: $506,546
Liabilities: $10,243
Net Worth: $496,302
Earnings: $177
Fiscal Year-end: 03/31/23
Paper Tube & Cone Mfr
N.A.I.C.S.: 322219
Hariprasad Khetan (Exec Dir)

HI-VIEW RESOURCES INC.
Suite 170-422 Richards Street, Vancouver, V6B 2Z4, BC, Canada
Tel.: (604) 377-8994   BC
Web Site: https://hiviewresources.com
Year Founded: 2021
HVW—(CNSX)
Mineral Exploration Services
N.A.I.C.S.: 212220
Howard Milne (Pres & CEO)

HIAG IMMOBILEN HOLDING AG
Aeschenplatz 7, 4052, Basel, Switzerland
Tel.: (41) 616065500
Web Site: https://www.hiag.com
Year Founded: 1876
HIAG—(SWX)
Rev.: $160,199,668
Assets: $2,382,072,746
Liabilities: $1,097,144,050
Net Worth: $1,284,928,696
Earnings: $55,821,251
Emp.: 81
Fiscal Year-end: 12/31/23
Other Activities Related to Real Estate
N.A.I.C.S.: 531390
Felix Grisard (Chm)

Subsidiaries:

Doka Schweiz AG (1)
Industriestrasse 24, 8155, Niederhasli, Switzerland
Tel.: (41) 43 411 2040
Web Site: https://www.doka.com
Sales Range: $50-74.9 Million
Emp.: 50
Construction Materials Whslr
N.A.I.C.S.: 423390
Stephan Zeidler (Gen Mgr)

Hiag Handel Immobilien AG (1)
Morxstrasse 98, Fullinsdorf, 4125, Riehen, Switzerland
Tel.: (41) 562688411
Sales Range: $50-74.9 Million
Emp.: 10
Residential Property Managers
N.A.I.C.S.: 531311

Hiag Holding AG (1)
Ibelweg 18, Zug, 6300, Switzerland   (100%)
Tel.: (41) 417662410
Web Site: http://www.hiag.com
Sales Range: $50-74.9 Million
Emp.: 8
Open-End Investment Funds
N.A.I.C.S.: 525910

Hiag Immobilien Schweiz AG (1)
Aeschenplatz 7, 4052, Basel, Switzerland   (100%)
Tel.: (41) 616065500
Web Site: https://www.hiag.com
Open-End Investment Funds
N.A.I.C.S.: 525910

Jaeger et Bosshard SA (1)
Route des Jeunes 32, PO Box 735, 1212, Lancy, Switzerland
Tel.: (41) 223423444
Web Site: https://www.jaeger-bosshard.ch
Waste Management Services
N.A.I.C.S.: 562998

Jago AG (1)
Industriestrasse 21, Kleindottingen, Basel, 5314, Switzerland
Tel.: (41) 562688131
Web Site: http://www.jago.ch
Sales Range: $50-74.9 Million
Emp.: 8
Construction Materials Whslr
N.A.I.C.S.: 423390
Markus Hober (Mgr)

HIAP HOE LIMITED
18 Ah Hood Road 13-51 Hiap Hoe Building At Zhongshan Park, Singapore, 329983, Singapore
Tel.: (65) 62502200   SG
Web Site: https://www.hiaphoe.com
Year Founded: 1994
5JK—(SES)
Rev.: $84,743,850
Assets: $1,203,705,193
Liabilities: $656,200,245
Net Worth: $547,504,948
Earnings: $4,177,544
Emp.: 434
Fiscal Year-end: 12/31/23
Property Development & Management Services
N.A.I.C.S.: 531210
Ho Beng Teo (CEO)

Subsidiaries:

Golden Bay Realty (Private) Limited (1)
400 Orchard Road Unit 0625 Orchard Towers, Singapore, 238875, Singapore
Tel.: (65) 67366028
Emp.: 1
Property Development Services
N.A.I.C.S.: 236115
Patrick Tan (Gen Mgr)

Super Funworld Pte Ltd (1)
1 Yuan Ching Road, Jurong Town, Singapore, 618640, Singapore
Tel.: (65) 62661000
Property Investment Services
N.A.I.C.S.: 531390

HIAP HUAT HOLDINGS BHD
Lot 102521 Jalan Sungai Pinang 5/3 Taman Perindustrian, Pulau Indah, 42920, Klang, Selangor, Malaysia
Tel.: (60) 333849368
Web Site: https://www.hiaphuat.com
HHHCORP—(KLS)
Rev.: $18,977,152
Assets: $28,098,335
Liabilities: $8,082,649
Net Worth: $20,015,686
Earnings: $1,728,153
Fiscal Year-end: 12/31/23
Chemical Waste Management
N.A.I.C.S.: 562112
Say Hwa Chan (Mng Dir)

Subsidiaries:

Lab Master Sdn. Bhd. (1)
Lot 102521 Jalan Sungai Pinang 5/3 Pulau Indah Mukim, Daerah Klang, 42920, Klang, Selangor, Malaysia
Tel.: (60) 321069866
Web Site: http://www.labmaster.com.my
Medical Laboratory Services
N.A.I.C.S.: 621511

HIAP SENG ENGINEERING LIMITED
4 Benoi Place, Singapore, 629925, Singapore
Tel.: (65) 6861 0667
Web Site: http://www.hiapseng.com
Rev.: $103,069,209
Assets: $66,169,449
Liabilities: $61,263,620
Net Worth: $4,905,829
Earnings: ($28,882,079)
Emp.: 1,000
Fiscal Year-end: 03/31/19
Engineering Procurement & Construction Services
N.A.I.C.S.: 541330
Hak Jin Tan (CFO & Co-Sec)

Subsidiaries:

Asia Process Industries Pte. Ltd. (1)
21 Tuas Crescent, Singapore, 638715, Singapore
Tel.: (65) 68978082
Engineeering Services
N.A.I.C.S.: 541330

HS Compression & Process Pte Ltd (1)
19 Tuas Crescent, Singapore, 638713, Singapore
Tel.: (65) 68631105
Web Site: http://www.hiapseng.com
Sales Range: $25-49.9 Million
Emp.: 90
Industrial Engineering Services
N.A.I.C.S.: 541330

Hiap Seng Engineering (M) Sdn. Bhd. (1)
No 482 S/L 4206 Parkcity Commercial Square Phase 6, Jalan Tun Ahmad Zaidi, 97000, Bintulu, Sarawak, Malaysia
Tel.: (60) 86333931
Engineeering Services
N.A.I.C.S.: 541330

Hiap Seng Engineering (Thailand) Co., Ltd. (1)
27/58 M8 Tambon Bueng, Si Racha, 20230, Chonburi, Thailand
Tel.: (66) 38320999
Web Site: http://www.hiapseng-thailand.com
Steel Products Mfr
N.A.I.C.S.: 332999
Richard Tan (Mng Dir)

Hiap Seng-Sanko TPM Pte. Ltd. (1)
4 Benoi Place, Singapore, 629925, Singapore
Tel.: (65) 68978082
Engineering Services
N.A.I.C.S.: 541330

INTERNATIONAL PUBLIC

Subsidiary (Domestic):

ProEn Scaffold Pte. Ltd. (2)
No 5 Soon Lee Street 03-30 Pioneer Point, Singapore, 627607, Singapore
Tel.: (65) 67107125
Web Site: http://www.proen.com.sg
Petrochemical Products Mfr
N.A.I.C.S.: 325110
Quek Hung Ling (Gen Mgr)

HIAP TECK VENTURE BERHAD
Lot 6096 Jalan Haji Abdul Manan, Batu 5 1/2 Off Jalan Meru, 41050, Kelang, Selangor Darul Ehsan, Malaysia
Tel.: (60) 333778888
Web Site: https://www.htgrp.com.my
HIAPTEK—(KLS)
Rev.: $335,493,757
Assets: $400,509,630
Liabilities: $128,337,778
Net Worth: $272,171,852
Earnings: $6,736,508
Emp.: 636
Fiscal Year-end: 07/31/23
Steel Pole Mfr
N.A.I.C.S.: 331210
Tien Seng Law (Deputy Chm)

Subsidiaries:

Alpine Pipe Manufacturing Sdn Bhd (1)
Lot 6085 Jalan Haji Abdul Manan Batu 5 1/2 Jalan Meru, 41050, Klang, Selangor Darul Ehsan, Malaysia
Tel.: (60) 333778688
Web Site: https://alpinepipe.com
Sales Range: $100-124.9 Million
Emp.: 405
Pipes & Rolled Steel Sheets Mfr
N.A.I.C.S.: 331110
Law Sook Teng (Mng Dir)

Hiap Teck Hardware Sdn Bhd (1)
Lot 6096 Jalan Haji Abdul Manan Batu 5 1/2 Off Jalan Meru, 41050, Klang, Selangor Darul Ehsan, Malaysia
Tel.: (60) 33 377 8888
Web Site: https://hiapteck.com
Sales Range: $100-124.9 Million
Emp.: 500
Steel Door Mfr
N.A.I.C.S.: 332321

Huatraco Scaffold Sdn Bhd (1)
Lot 6096 Jalan Haji Abdul Manan Batu 5 1/2 off Jalan Meru, 41050, Klang, Selangor Darul Ehsan, Malaysia
Tel.: (60) 33 377 8999
Web Site: https://huatraco.com
Sales Range: $25-49.9 Million
Emp.: 150
Scaffolds Mfr
N.A.I.C.S.: 332999

Subsidiary (Domestic):

Huatraco Industries Sdn Bhd (2)
6088 Jalan Haji Abdul Manan Batu 5 1/2, 41050, Kelang, Selangor, Malaysia
Tel.: (60) 333928336
Web Site: http://www.huatraco.com
Sales Range: $25-49.9 Million
Emp.: 15
Pipes Mfr
N.A.I.C.S.: 327332
George Teh (Gen Mgr)

Huatraco Scaffold System Sdn Bhd (2)
Lot 6096 Jalan Haji Abdul Manan Batu 5 1/2 off Jalan Meru, 41050, Klang, Selangor, Malaysia
Tel.: (60) 333778999
Web Site: https://huatraco.com
Scaffolds Mfr & Distr
N.A.I.C.S.: 332999

HIAP TONG CORPORATION LTD.
22 Soon Lee Road, Singapore, 628082, Singapore

Tel.: (65) 67795050 SG
Web Site: https://www.hiaptong.com
Year Founded: 1978
5PO—(CAT)
Rev.: $73,239,718
Assets: $145,741,386
Liabilities: $76,378,659
Net Worth: $69,362,727
Earnings: $10,258,614
Fiscal Year-end: 03/31/23
Hydraulic Lifting & Haulage Services
N.A.I.C.S.: 333120
Lim San Ong *(Exec Dir)*

HIBERNIAN FOOTBALL CLUB LTD.
Easter Road Stadium 12 Albion Place, Edinburgh, EH7 5QG, United Kingdom
Tel.: (44) 1316612159
Web Site: http://www.hibernian.co.uk
Year Founded: 1875
Sales Range: $10-24.9 Million
Emp.: 83
Soccer Team
N.A.I.C.S.: 711211
Rod Petrie *(Chm)*

HIBINO CORPORATION
3-5-14 Konan, Minato-ku, Tokyo, 108-0075, Japan
Tel.: (81) 337404391
Web Site: https://www.hibino.co.jp
Year Founded: 1964
2469—(TKS)
Rev.: $333,745,510
Assets: $269,879,690
Liabilities: $197,923,230
Net Worth: $71,956,460
Earnings: $10,754,470
Emp.: 1,600
Fiscal Year-end: 03/31/24
Audio & Video Equipment Mfr & Whslr
N.A.I.C.S.: 334310
Hiroaki Hibino *(Chm)*

Subsidiaries:

Eightythree Corporation (1)
Kennedy House Ginza 7-2 Ginza Corridor Street B1F, Chuo-ku, Tokyo, 104-0061, Japan
Tel.: (81) 33 572 8391
Web Site: https://www.kennedyhouse-ginza.com
Restaurant Operators
N.A.I.C.S.: 722511

Electori Co., Ltd. (1)
2-7-70 Coast, Minato-ku, Tokyo, 105-0022, Japan
Tel.: (81) 35 419 1590
Web Site: https://www.electori.co.jp
Audio Equipment Distr
N.A.I.C.S.: 423620

First Engineering Co., Ltd. (1)
3-2-5 Nihonbashi Ningyo-cho, Chuo-ku, Tokyo, 103-0013, Japan
Tel.: (81) 3 5623 2321
Web Site: http://www.first-eng.co.jp
Audio Equipment Mfr & Distr
N.A.I.C.S.: 334310

Hibino Asia Pacific (Shanghai) Limited (1)
R/N 215 No 3 Bldg D1 International Creative Space 909 Tianyaoqiao-Lu, Shanghai, 200030, China
Tel.: (86) 2154198591
Audio Equipment Mfr & Distr
N.A.I.C.S.: 334310

Hibino Asia Pacific Limited (1)
Office C 28/F Plaza 88 No 88 Yeung Uk Road, Mongkok, Tsuen Wan, New Territories, China (Hong Kong)
Tel.: (852) 26377368
Web Site: https://www.hibino.com.hk
Video & Audio Equipment Distr
N.A.I.C.S.: 423990

Hibino Besco Corporation (1)
2-9-23 Shinonome, Koto-ku, Tokyo, 104-0043, Japan
Tel.: (81) 364572371
Web Site: http://www.besco.co.jp
Emp.: 12
Video & Audio Equipment Rental Services
N.A.I.C.S.: 532282
Yoshito Nakajima *(Pres)*

Hibino Imagineering Corporation (1)
2-7-70 Kaigan, Minato-ku, Tokyo, 105-0022, Japan
Tel.: (81) 354189500
Sales Range: $10-24.9 Million
Cinema Projection System Whslr
N.A.I.C.S.: 423410

Hibino Lighting Inc. (1)
2-7-70 Kaigan, Minato-ku, Tokyo, 105-0022, Japan
Tel.: (81) 35 419 1571
Web Site: https://www.hibinolighting.co.jp
Lighting Equipment Distr
N.A.I.C.S.: 423610

Hibino Media Technical Corporation (1)
6F 2-9-23 Shinonome, Koto-ku, Tokyo, 135-0062, Japan
Tel.: (81) 364572063
Web Site: https://www.media-t.co.jp
Video & Audio Equipment Mfr & Distr
N.A.I.C.S.: 334310

Hibino Spacetech Corporation (1)
2-7-70 Kaigan, Minato-ku, Tokyo, 105-0022, Japan
Tel.: (81) 35 419 1576
Web Site: https://www.hibino-spacetech.co.jp
Real Estate Services
N.A.I.C.S.: 531390

Hibino USA, Inc. (1)
6 Venture Ste 225, Irvine, CA 92618
Tel.: (949) 538-2400
Web Site: http://www.hibino.co.jp
Video & Audio Systems Operator & Rental Services
N.A.I.C.S.: 512199

Subsidiary (Domestic):

TLS Productions, Inc. (2)
78 Jackson Plz, Ann Arbor, MI 48103 (80%)
Tel.: (810) 220-8577
Web Site: http://www.tlsproductionsinc.com
Commercial, Industrial & Institutional Electric Lighting Fixture Mfr
N.A.I.C.S.: 335132
Beatrice Barnett *(Project Mgr)*

Nippon Environment Amenity Co., Ltd. (1)
3-5-23 Takanawa KDX Takanawadai Building 7th Floor, Minato-ku, Tokyo, 108-0074, Japan
Tel.: (81) 35 421 7520
Web Site: https://www.nea-ltd.com
Emp.: 113
Acoustic Product Mfr & Distr
N.A.I.C.S.: 334510

Sama Sound Inc. (1)
03147 11th Floor 457 Samil-daero, Jongno-gu Gyeongun-dong, Seoul, Korea (South)
Tel.: (82) 2 734 0631
Web Site: https://www.samasound.co.kr
Sound System Distr
N.A.I.C.S.: 512240

HIBISCUS PETROLEUM BERHAD
2nd Floor Syed Kechik Foundation Building Jalan Kapas, Bangsar, 59100, Kuala Lumpur, Malaysia
Tel.: (60) 320921300
Web Site: https://www.hibiscuspetroleum.com
HIBISCS—(KLS)
Rev.: $496,260,317
Assets: $1,311,857,778
Liabilities: $742,596,614
Net Worth: $569,261,164
Earnings: $84,765,714
Emp.: 824
Fiscal Year-end: 06/30/23
Oil & Gas Exploration & Production
N.A.I.C.S.: 211120
Kenneth Gerard Pereira *(Mng Dir)*

Subsidiaries:

SEA Hibiscus Sdn Bhd (1)
27th Floor Menara LGB Jalan Wan Kadir, Taman Tun Dr Ismail, 60000, Kuala Lumpur, Malaysia
Tel.: (60) 377100030
Oil & Gas Exploration Services
N.A.I.C.S.: 213112

HIBIYA ENGINEERING LTD
3-5-27 Mita, Minato-ku, Tokyo, 108-6312, Japan
Tel.: (81) 334541385
Web Site: https://www.hibiya-eng.co.jp
1982—(TKS)
Rev.: $553,666,820
Assets: $649,273,860
Liabilities: $187,142,320
Net Worth: $462,131,540
Earnings: $31,728,000
Emp.: 966
Fiscal Year-end: 03/31/24
Construction Business
N.A.I.C.S.: 238220
Yuuji Yamauchi *(Mng Exec Officer)*

Subsidiaries:

Hibiya Tsushou Co., Ltd. (1)
3-5-27 Mita Sumitomo Realty & Development Mita Twin Building, West Building Minato-Ku, Tokyo, 108-6312, Japan
Tel.: (81) 334547541
Web Site: http://www.tsushou.co.jp
Sales Range: $75-99.9 Million
Emp.: 71
Industrial & Commercial Machinery Whslr
N.A.I.C.S.: 423830
Takayuki Nohara *(Pres & CEO)*

NIKKEY Company Limited (1)
3-20-14 Higashi-Gotanda, Shinagawa-Ku, Tokyo, 141-0022, Japan
Tel.: (81) 364296717
Web Site: https://www.nikkey.co.jp
Emp.: 67
Scrap & Waste Material Whslr
N.A.I.C.S.: 562998

HIBIYA-KADAN FLORAL CO., LTD.
1-6-30 3rd Floor LB, Minato-ku, Tokyo, 106-8587, Japan
Tel.: 3 5444 8700 JP
Web Site: http://www.hibiya.co.jp
Year Founded: 1950
Flower & Flower Arrangement Services
N.A.I.C.S.: 424930
Miyajima Hiroaki *(Pres)*

Subsidiaries:

Odakyu Landflora Co., Ltd. (1)
1-1-18 Chitosedai, Setagaya-ku, Tokyo, 157-0071, Japan
Tel.: (81) 354908787
Web Site: http://www.odakyu-florist.co.jp
Sales Range: $25-49.9 Million
Emp.: 230
Flower & Flower Arrangement Services
N.A.I.C.S.: 424930
Kanno Shoji *(Pres)*

HIBLEAD INC.
3 Chome-23-17 Takanawa Minato-ku, Tokyo, 108-0074, Japan
Tel.: (81) 354228743
Web Site: http://www.hiblead.co.jp
Information Technology Support Services
N.A.I.C.S.: 541512

HIBU GROUP 2013 LIMITED
One Reading Central Forbury Road, Reading, RG1 3YL, United Kingdom
Tel.: (44) 118 358 3300 UK
Web Site: https://www.yellgroup.com
Year Founded: 2013
Holding Company; Telephone Directories Publisher
N.A.I.C.S.: 551112
Richard Hanscott *(CEO-UK)*

Subsidiaries:

hibu (UK) Limited (1)
One Reading Central Forbury Road, Reading, RG1 3YL, Berks, United Kingdom
Tel.: (44) 118 358 3300
Web Site: http://www.yell.com
Telephone Directories Publisher & Advertising Services
N.A.I.C.S.: 513140
Richard Hanscott *(CEO)*

HICHAIN LOGISTICS CO., LTD.
111 Quanhai Road, Wujiang Economic and Technological Development Zone, Suzhou, 518052, Jiangsu, China
Tel.: (86) 4006018333
Web Site: https://www.hichain.com
Year Founded: 2011
300873—(SSE)
Rev.: $252,770,544
Assets: $521,418,924
Liabilities: $135,349,812
Net Worth: $386,069,112
Earnings: $50,289,876
Fiscal Year-end: 12/31/22
Freight Transportation Services
N.A.I.C.S.: 488510
Chen Liang *(Chm & Gen Mgr)*

HICL INFRASTRUCTURE PLC
30 Gresham Street, London, EC2V 7QP, United Kingdom
Tel.: (44) 2075974000 GY
Web Site: https://www.hicl.com
Year Founded: 2006
HICL—(LSE)
Rev.: $504,800,296
Assets: $4,290,259,428
Liabilities: $1,086,176
Net Worth: $4,289,173,252
Earnings: $500,591,364
Fiscal Year-end: 03/31/22
Other Financial Vehicles
N.A.I.C.S.: 525990
Ian Russell *(Chm)*

Subsidiaries:

Prima 200 Limited (1)
5 The Triangle Wildwood Drive, Worcester, WR5 2QX, United Kingdom
Tel.: (44) 844 875 2402
Web Site: https://www.prima200.co.uk
Property Funding Management Services
N.A.I.C.S.: 531390

RWF Health & Community Developers Limited (1)
Suite A 30A Church Road, Tunbridge Wells, TN1 1JP, Kent, United Kingdom
Tel.: (44) 189 268 1063
Web Site: https://www.rwf-hcdl.co.uk
Property Management Services
N.A.I.C.S.: 531311
Paul Evans *(Gen Mgr)*

HICLASST, INC.
Smetanova 88/20, Retenice, 415 03, Teplice, Czech Republic
Tel.: (420) 775 321 8230 NV
Web Site: http://www.hiclasst.com
Year Founded: 2016
Assets: $2,403
Liabilities: $23,776
Net Worth: ($21,373)
Earnings: ($12,774)
Fiscal Year-end: 11/30/18
Online Shopping Services
N.A.I.C.S.: 455110
Patrik Wiedemann *(Pres, CEO, CFO, Chief Acctg Officer & Sec)*

HICONICS ECO-ENERGY TECHNOLOGY CO., LTD.

Hiclasst, Inc.—(Continued)

HICONICS ECO-ENERGY TECHNOLOGY CO., LTD.
No 3 Boxing 2nd Road, Beijing Economic and Technological Development Zone Hekang New Energy, Beijing, 100176, China
Tel.: (86) 1059180000
Web Site: https://www.hiconics.com
Year Founded: 2003
300048—(CHIN)
Rev.: $210,029,956
Assets: $445,932,297
Liabilities: $203,288,495
Net Worth: $242,643,802
Earnings: ($31,005,282)
Emp.: 1,000
Fiscal Year-end: 12/31/23
Variable Frequency Drive (VFD) Designer & Mfr
N.A.I.C.S.: 335311
Yongjun Fu (Chm)

HIDAY HIDAKA CORP.
Saitama Mongai Square 10th floor
118 Daimoncho 2-chome, Omiya-ku, Saitama, 330-0846, Japan
Tel.: (81) 0486448030 JP
Web Site: https://hidakaya.hiday.co.jp
Year Founded: 1983
7611—(TKS)
Sales Range: $300-349.9 Million
Emp.: 747
Restaurant Operators
N.A.I.C.S.: 722511
Tadashi Kanda (Exec Chm)

HIDAYAT YAKIN SDN. BHD.
2046 Taman Sari Jalan Hospital Kota Bharu, 15200, Kota Baharu, Kelantan, Malaysia
Tel.: (60) 97487223 MY
Year Founded: 1994
Sales Range: $10-24.9 Million
Rubber Tree Cultivation
N.A.I.C.S.: 111421
Murthadha Abu Bakar Alhabshi (Co-Owner)

HIDEEP INC.
10th floor Hi-Deep DTC Tower 49 Daewangpangyo-ro 644beon-gil, Bundang-gu, Seongnam, Gyeonggi-do, Korea (South)
Tel.: (82) 317175775
Web Site: https://www.hideep.com
Year Founded: 2010
365590—(KRS)
Emp.: 51
Software Development Services
N.A.I.C.S.: 541511
Beomgyu Koh (CEO)

HIDILI INDUSTRY INTERNATIONAL DEVELOPMENT LIMITED
Unit 1605 16/F Block B Century Center of Air China, 1 Hangkong Road Wuhou, Chengdu, 617000, China
Tel.: (86) 28 6168 9138 Ky
Web Site: http://www.hidili.com.cn
Sales Range: $100-124.9 Million
Emp.: 5,153
Coal Mining & Related Services
N.A.I.C.S.: 212115
Yang Xian (Founder & Chm)

HIDIS GMBH
Luxemburger Strasse 14, D-44789, Bochum, Germany
Tel.: (49) 20655167994 De
Web Site: http://www.hidis.de
Year Founded: 2003
Outsource Distribution Services
N.A.I.C.S.: 561499

Sascha Arndt (Mng Dir)

HIDONG ESTATE PLC
Third Floor Standard Bank Chambers Beach Street, 10300, Penang, Malaysia UK
Year Founded: 1923
HID—(LSE)
Rev.: $17,011
Assets: $3,031,523
Liabilities: $28,695
Net Worth: $3,002,828
Earnings: ($16,907)
Fiscal Year-end: 03/31/22
Rubber Products Mfr
N.A.I.C.S.: 326220

HIDRA STIL D.D.
Industrijska br 4, 76 100, Brcko, Bosnia & Herzegovina
Tel.: (387) 49590470
Web Site: http://www.hidrastil.ba
Sales Range: Less than $1 Million
Sanitary Ware Mfr
N.A.I.C.S.: 326191

HIDRIA D.O.O.
Nazorjeva 6a, 1000, Ljubljana, Slovenia
Tel.: (386) 53756301
Web Site: http://www.hidria.com
Holding Company; Power Tools; Industrial Components & Systems; Automotive Products; Air Conditioning, Heating & Ventilation
N.A.I.C.S.: 551112
Edvard Svetlik (Chm-Supervisory Bd)

Subsidiaries:

Hidria AET d.o.o. (1)
Poljubinj 89a, 5220, Tolmin, Slovenia
Tel.: (386) 5 382 1000
Automotive Equipment Mfr & Whslr
N.A.I.C.S.: 336320
Rudi Kragelj (Mgr-Sls & Dev)

Hidria BH d.o.o. (1)
Dzemala Bijedica 129, 71000, Sarajevo, Bosnia & Herzegovina
Tel.: (387) 33 721 710
Ventilation System Whslr
N.A.I.C.S.: 423730

Hidria Bausch Gmbh (1)
Industriestr 12, 71665, Vaihingen, Germany
Tel.: (49) 7042 94 23 0
Web Site: http://www.bausch.de
Automotive Equipment Mfr & Whslr
N.A.I.C.S.: 336320
Christof Droste (Co-Mng Dir)

Hidria Bausch Kft (1)
Karacsondi ut hrsz 11234/17, 3200, Gyongyos, Hungary
Tel.: (36) 1 206 6266 130
Automotive Equipment Mfr & Whslr
N.A.I.C.S.: 336320

Hidria C.Z. (1)
Drahobejlova 54, 19000, Prague, Czech Republic
Tel.: (420) 2 6631 5776
Ventilation System Whslr
N.A.I.C.S.: 423730

Hidria GIF GmbH (1)
Bruhlstrasse 7, 79112, Freiburg, Germany
Tel.: (49) 76 64 9302 0
Ventilation System Mfr & Whslr
N.A.I.C.S.: 336320

Hidria Heatec d.o.o. (1)
Vojkova 58, 1000, Ljubljana, Slovenia
Tel.: (386) 1 300 5293
Heating Equipment Whslr
N.A.I.C.S.: 423720

Hidria IMP Klima d.o.o. (1)
Godovic 150, 5275, Idrija, Slovenia
Tel.: (386) 5 374 3000
Automotive Equipment Mfr & Whslr
N.A.I.C.S.: 336320

Hidria LC d.o.o. (1)

Slovenska cesta 29, 5281, Ljubljana, Slovenia
Tel.: (386) 5 375 6609
Logistics Consulting Servies
N.A.I.C.S.: 541614
Vojka Tusar (Project Mgr)

Hidria Podgorica d.o.o. (1)
Ivana Vojusevica 26, 81000, Podgorica, Montenegro
Tel.: (382) 81 202 255
Ventilation System Whslr
N.A.I.C.S.: 423730

Hidria Polska Sp. z o.o. (1)
ul Warszawska 44, 06-100, Pultusk, Poland
Tel.: (48) 23 692 07 47
Ventilation System Whslr
N.A.I.C.S.: 423730

Hidria Rotomatika d.o.o. (1)
Spodnja Kanomlja 23, Spodnja Idrija, 5281, Idrija, Slovenia
Tel.: (386) 5 375 6000
Automotive Equipment Mfr & Whslr
N.A.I.C.S.: 336320
Martin Hladnik (Gen Mgr)

Hidria Tehnoloski center d. o. o. (1)
Smarska cesta 4b, 6000, Koper, Slovenia
Tel.: (386) 8 202 82 44
Web Site: http://www.hidria.com
Emp.: 30
Automotive Equipment Whslr
N.A.I.C.S.: 423830
Igor Rupnik (Dir)

Hidria USA Inc. (1)
202 Beechtree Business Park, Greenville, SC 29605
Tel.: (864) 277-7709
Electric Motor & Fan Whslr
N.A.I.C.S.: 423830

Hidria d.o.o.e.l. (1)
Belasica 2, 1000, Skopje, North Macedonia
Tel.: (389) 2 3078 035
Ventilation System Whslr
N.A.I.C.S.: 423730

Suzhou Hidria Diesel Cold Start Technologies Co., Ltd. (1)
No 9 Yang Zhou Road New & High Tech Industrial Park, Changshu, 215500, China
Tel.: (86) 512 52866681
Automotive Equipment Mfr & Whslr
N.A.I.C.S.: 336320

Tomos d.o.o. (1)
Smarska Cesta 4, Koper, 6000, Slovenia
Tel.: (386) 56684400
Web Site: http://www.tomos.si
Sales Range: $100-124.9 Million
Emp.: 450
Motorcycle Mfr
N.A.I.C.S.: 336991

Subsidiary (US):

HT USA Inc. (2)
202 Beechtree Blvd, Greenville, SC 29605-5100
Tel.: (864) 277-7709
Web Site: http://www.tomosusa.com
Rev.: $13,000,000
Emp.: 7
Export/Import Manufacturing
N.A.I.C.S.: 522299

HIDROBIRO A.D.
Bulevar Oslobodenja 57a, Novi Sad, Serbia
Tel.: (381) 64 2253256
Year Founded: 1957
Sales Range: Less than $1 Million
Emp.: 2
Engineering & Technical Consulting Services
N.A.I.C.S.: 541690

HIDROELEKTRA NISKO-GRADNJA D.D.
Zeleni trg 6a, 10000, Zagreb, Croatia
Tel.: (385) 1 61 99 555
Web Site: http://www.hidroelektra-niskogradnja.hr
Year Founded: 1946
Civil Engineering Services

INTERNATIONAL PUBLIC

N.A.I.C.S.: 541330

HIDROELEKTRANE NA DRINI A.D.
Andricgrad Complex, 73240, Visegrad, RS, Bosnia & Herzegovina
Tel.: (387) 58635200
Web Site: https://www.henadrini.com
Year Founded: 1989
HEDR-R-A—(BANJ)
Sales Range: Less than $1 Million
Electronic Services
N.A.I.C.S.: 221111
Darko Andric (Head-IT Dept)

HIDROELEKTRANE NA VRBASU A.D
Svetog Save 13, 70260, Mrkonjic Grad, Bosnia & Herzegovina
Tel.: (387) 50225300
Web Site:
  https://www.henavrbasu.com
Year Founded: 1975
HELV-R-A—(BANJ)
Sales Range: Less than $1 Million
Hydroelectric Power Generation Services
N.A.I.C.S.: 221111
Tomislav Todorovic (Chm-Supervisory Bd)

HIDROGRADEVINAR A.D.
Promenade 13, Sremska Mitrovica, Serbia
Tel.: (381) 22621936
Year Founded: 1991
HIDG—(BEL)
Rev.: $1,057,781
Assets: $1,319,101
Liabilities: $469,956
Net Worth: $849,145
Earnings: ($160,521)
Emp.: 42
Fiscal Year-end: 12/31/23
Hydraulic Structure Construction Services
N.A.I.C.S.: 237990
Milorad Kovacevic (Exec Dir)

HIDROGRADNJA A.D.
Dvorska 2, Vrsac, Serbia
Tel.: (381) 60 0909 092
Year Founded: 1989
Sales Range: Less than $1 Million
Emp.: 1
Hydraulic Structure Construction Services
N.A.I.C.S.: 237990

HIDROGRADNJA D.D. SARAJEVO
Hamdije Kresevljakovica 19, 71000, Sarajevo, Bosnia & Herzegovina
Tel.: (387) 33 205 569
Web Site: http://www.hidrogradnja.ba
Year Founded: 1947
HDGSR—(SARE)
Sales Range: $1-9.9 Million
Emp.: 724
Construction Services
N.A.I.C.S.: 541330
Mirsad Agovic (Chm-Supervisory Bd)

HIDROPNEVMOTEHNIKA AD
3 Inzhener Feliks Vozheli Str, 6100, Kazanlak, Bulgaria
Tel.: (359) 43162228
Web Site: https://www.hpt-bg.com
Year Founded: 1963
HPT—(BUL)
Sales Range: Less than $1 Million
Hydraulic & Pneumatic Mfr
N.A.I.C.S.: 339999

HIDROSTAL S.A.

Av Portada del Sol 722, Casilla, 36, Lima, Peru
Tel.: (51) 13191000
Web Site:
https://www.hidrostal.com.pe
Year Founded: 1955
HIDROSI1—(LIM)
Sales Range: Less than $1 Million
Hydro Electric Motor Mfr & Distr
N.A.I.C.S.: 333996

HIDROTEHNIKA-HIDROENERGETIKA A.D.
Brace Krsmanovica 13, Belgrade, Serbia
Tel.: (381) 112181888
Web Site:
https://www.hidroenergetika.rs
Year Founded: 1946
HDRT—(BEL)
Rev.: $14,413,252
Assets: $16,282,322
Liabilities: $10,272,393
Net Worth: $6,009,930
Earnings: $319,549
Emp.: 117
Fiscal Year-end: 12/31/22
Hydro-Energetic Structures Construction Services
N.A.I.C.S.: 237110
Predrag Radulovic *(Asst Gen Mgr-Implementation & Realization)*

HIFAB GROUP AB
Sveavagen 167, PO Box 19090, 10432, Stockholm, Sweden
Tel.: (46) 104766000   SE
Web Site: https://www.hifab.se
HIFAB.B—(OMX)
Rev.: $28,908,745
Assets: $15,104,854
Liabilities: $9,470,155
Net Worth: $5,634,700
Earnings: $1,194,189
Emp.: 206
Fiscal Year-end: 12/31/23
Civil Engineering & Construction Services
N.A.I.C.S.: 237990
Kristian Henninge *(Mgr-Market-South)*

Subsidiaries:

Hifab International AB   (1)
Sveavagen 167, Box 19090, 104 32, Stockholm, Sweden
Tel.: (46) 104766000
Civil Construction Services
N.A.I.C.S.: 237990

Hifab Oy   (1)
Saterinkatu 6 6th floor, 02600, Espoo, Finland
Tel.: (358) 40 134 0173
Web Site: https://www.hifab.se
Emp.: 1
Civil Construction Services
N.A.I.C.S.: 237990

HIFLY AIRLINES
Iua latino Coelho Rua Latino Coelho n0 1 Hi Fly Building -132, 1350-047, Lisbon, Portugal
Tel.: (351) 210046743
Web Site: http://www.hifly.aero
Year Founded: 1988
Sales Range: $150-199.9 Million
Emp.: 571
Airline Services
N.A.I.C.S.: 481111

HIGASHI TWENTY ONE CO., LTD.
3-1-9 Uchikubojicho, Chuo-ku, Osaka, 540-0013, Japan
Tel.: (81) 669455611
Web Site: https://www.e-higashi.co.jp
9029—(TKS)
Rev.: $268,597,350
Assets: $168,786,350
Liabilities: $87,410,640
Net Worth: $81,375,710
Earnings: $9,954,660
Emp.: 1,495
Fiscal Year-end: 03/31/24
Logistic Services
N.A.I.C.S.: 541614
Shigemi Kanamori *(Chm)*

HIGASHIMARU CO., LTD.
20 Inogakura Ijuincho, Hioki, 899-2594, Japan
Tel.: (81) 992733859
Web Site: https://www.k-higashimaru.co.jp
2058—(FKA)
Rev.: $109,248,480
Assets: $116,953,760
Liabilities: $66,588,720
Net Worth: $50,365,040
Earnings: $29,040
Emp.: 178
Fiscal Year-end: 03/31/22
Fish Feed Product Distr
N.A.I.C.S.: 445250
Kichitaro Higashi *(Founder & Chm)*

HIGGSTEC, INC.
No 22 Dingping Rd, Suao Township, Yilan, 270008, Taiwan
Tel.: (886) 39908282
Web Site:
https://www.higgstec.com.tw
Year Founded: 2002
5220—(TPE)
Rev.: $30,503,424
Assets: $44,820,342
Liabilities: $18,550,886
Net Worth: $26,269,456
Earnings: $3,577,807
Fiscal Year-end: 12/31/22
Electronic Components Mfr
N.A.I.C.S.: 334419
Heng-Ming Yeh *(Chm)*

HIGH ARCTIC ENERGY SERVICES INC.
Calgary Place I Suite 2350 330 - 5th Ave SW, Calgary, T2P 0L4, AB, Canada
Tel.: (403) 508-7836
Web Site: https://www.haes.ca
Year Founded: 1993
6LQ0—(DEU)
Rev.: $46,766,847
Assets: $92,983,211
Liabilities: $17,975,632
Net Worth: $75,007,580
Earnings: $(9,691,210)
Emp.: 202
Fiscal Year-end: 12/31/23
Oil Field Services
N.A.I.C.S.: 213111
Michael Rupert Binnion *(Chm)*

Subsidiaries:

High Arctic Energy Services LP   (1)
Suite 500 700-2nd Street SW, Calgary, T2P 2W1, AB, Canada
Tel.: (403) 508-7836
Web Site: http://www.haes.ca
Sales Range: $100-124.9 Million
Emp.: 200
Oil & Gas Field Drilling Services
N.A.I.C.S.: 213111

High Arctic Energy Services PNG Limited   (1)
Section 216 Lot 4 Magemage Garden Kitogara St, Port Moresby, Papua New Guinea
Tel.: (675) 3233649
Sales Range: $50-74.9 Million
Emp.: 200
Oil & Gas Field Drilling Services
N.A.I.C.S.: 327910

HIGH COUNTRY CHEVROLET LTD.
702 11th Ave SE, High River, T1V 1M3, AB, Canada
Tel.: (403) 652-2000
Web Site:
http://www.highcountrychev.com
Year Founded: 1983
Rev.: $17,040,246
Emp.: 25
New & Used Car Dealers
N.A.I.C.S.: 441110
Chad Turner *(Mgr-Sls-New & Used Cars)*

HIGH FASHION INTERNATIONAL LIMITED
2/F CITIC Telecom Tower 93 Kwai Fuk Road, Kwai Chung, NT, China (Hong Kong)
Tel.: (852) 26155188
Web Site:
http://www.highfashion.com.hk
0608—(HKG)
Rev.: $448,214,138
Assets: $794,016,578
Liabilities: $393,922,470
Net Worth: $400,094,108
Earnings: $19,812,863
Emp.: 5,000
Fiscal Year-end: 12/31/22
Apparel & Accessories Mfr
N.A.I.C.S.: 315990
Patricia Siu Hang So *(Exec Dir)*

Subsidiaries:

August Silk Inc.   (1)
499 7th Ave, New York, NY 10018-6803
Web Site: http://www.augustsilk.com
Women's Clothing Retailer
N.A.I.C.S.: 424350

High Fashion (China) Co., Ltd.   (1)
N Side Hongda Rd, Xiao Shan, Hangzhou, 311231, Zhejiang, China
Tel.: (86) 57182695661
Sales Range: $750-799.9 Million
Emp.: 5,000
Garments Mfr
N.A.I.C.S.: 315210

High Fashion (UK) Limited   (1)
Unit 25 Point Bus Park Rockingham Road, Market Harborough, LE16 7QU, Leicestershire, United Kingdom
Tel.: (44) 8451302460
Web Site: http://www.highfashion.com
Sales Range: $25-49.9 Million
Emp.: 20
Garment Trading Services
N.A.I.C.S.: 315210

High Fashion Garments Company Limited   (1)
11F High Fashion Ctr 1-11 Kwai Hei St, Kwai Chung, New Territories, China (Hong Kong)
Tel.: (852) 26155188
Apparels Mfr
N.A.I.C.S.: 315210

High Fashion Garments, Inc.   (1)
50 Enterprise, Edison, NJ 07094
Tel.: (732) 287-9118
Fashion Apparels Whslr
N.A.I.C.S.: 424310

High Fashion Knit Company Limited   (1)
11F High Fashion Ctr 1-11 Kwai Hei St, Kwai Chung, New Territories, China (Hong Kong)
Tel.: (852) 26155188
Sales Range: $50-74.9 Million
Emp.: 100
Fashion Garments Whslr
N.A.I.C.S.: 424350

Rosso Amaranto S.r.l   (1)
Via Marconi 16, 22070, Beregazzo con Figliaro, Italy
Tel.: (39) 031988573
Web Site: http://www.rossoamaranto.com
Graphic Design Services
N.A.I.C.S.: 541430

HIGH FINANCE LTD.
77 Gracechurch Street, London, EC3V 0AS, United Kingdom
Tel.: (44) 207 337 8800
Web Site: http://www.hfg.co.uk
Year Founded: 2002
Sales Range: $10-24.9 Million
Emp.: 40
Employee Recruitment Services
N.A.I.C.S.: 561311
Shaun Rogers *(Chm)*

Subsidiaries:

Hfg (singapore) Pte. Ltd.   (1)
37th Floor 50 Raffles Place, Singapore, 048623, Singapore
Tel.: (65) 68297153
Life & Health Insurance Services
N.A.I.C.S.: 524210

HIGH GROUND ENTERPRISE LIMITED
No 2 Heera Panna Mall 2nd Floor Behind Oshiwara Police Station Oshiwar, Andheri West, Mumbai, 400053, India
Tel.: (91) 22 4222 9700   In
Web Site:
http://www.highgroundenterprise.com
Year Founded: 1986
Rev.: $83,742,691
Assets: $53,541,447
Liabilities: $35,186,824
Net Worth: $18,354,623
Earnings: $2,485,477
Emp.: 90
Fiscal Year-end: 03/31/18
Film Production Services
N.A.I.C.S.: 512110

HIGH LINER FOODS INCORPORATED
100 Battery Point, PO Box 910, Lunenburg, B0J 2C0, NS, Canada
Tel.: (902) 634-8811   NS
Web Site:
https://www.highlinerfoods.com
Year Founded: 1899
HLF—(TSX)
Rev.: $942,224,000
Assets: $820,494,000
Liabilities: $552,324,000
Net Worth: $268,170,000
Earnings: $10,289,000
Emp.: 1,200
Fiscal Year-end: 12/28/19
Frozen Seafood Products Mfr
N.A.I.C.S.: 445250
Robert L. Pace *(Chm)*

Subsidiaries:

High Liner Foods (USA) Incorporated   (1)
18 Electronics Ave, Danvers, MA 01923   (100%)
Tel.: (978) 777-2660
Web Site: http://www.highlinerfoodsusa.com
Sales Range: $25-49.9 Million
Emp.: 250
Frozen Seafood Products Mfr
N.A.I.C.S.: 311710
Peter B. Brown *(Pres & COO)*

Subsidiary (Domestic):

Rubicon Resources, LLC   (2)
5730 Uplander Way Ste 200, Culver City, CA 90230
Tel.: (310) 887-3883
Web Site: http://www.rubiconresources.com
General Line Groceries Whslr
N.A.I.C.S.: 424410

HIGH PEAK ROYALTIES LIMITED
Suite 305 35 Lime Street, Sydney, 2000, NSW, Australia
Tel.: (61) 282960011   AU

HIGH PEAK ROYALTIES LIMITED

High Peak Royalties Limited—(Continued)
Web Site:
https://www.highpeak.com.au
HPR—(ASX)
Rev.: $735,300
Assets: $7,021,279
Liabilities: $852,654
Net Worth: $6,168,624
Earnings: ($128,649)
Emp.: 1
Fiscal Year-end: 06/30/24
Resources Investment Holding Company
N.A.I.C.S.: 551112
Andrew Carroll *(Chm)*

HIGH PERFORMANCE REAL ESTATE INVESTMENTS COMPANY PLC
Gardens street - PC Plaza Complex Office 301, PO Box 3778, Amman, 11953, Jordan
Tel.: (962) 65537223
Year Founded: 2006
HIPR—(AMM)
Rev.: $13,822
Assets: $12,144,200
Liabilities: $748,358
Net Worth: $11,395,842
Earnings: ($132,552)
Emp.: 5
Fiscal Year-end: 12/31/20
Real Estate Development Services
N.A.I.C.S.: 531390
Mustafa Abu Ghali *(Gen Mgr)*

HIGH POWER LIGHTING CORP.
5F No 173-8 Yung-Fong Road, Tu Cheng Dist, New Taipei City, 236, Taiwan
Tel.: (886) 282628886
Web Site:
https://www.hplighting.com.tw
Year Founded: 2005
6559—(TAI)
LED Chip Mfr
N.A.I.C.S.: 334413
Wu Ming-Chang *(VP)*

HIGH QUALITY FOOD S.P.A.
Via di Pietralata 179, 00158, Rome, Italy
Tel.: (39) 0662272725
Web Site: https://www.hqf.it
Year Founded: 2003
HQF—(ITA)
Packaged Product Mfr & Distr
N.A.I.C.S.: 311514
Simone Cozzi *(Pres & CEO)*

HIGH RIVER FORD
1103 11th Ave SE, High River, T1V 1M3, AB, Canada
Tel.: (403) 652-2134
Web Site:
http://www.highriverford.com
New & Used Car Dealers
N.A.I.C.S.: 441110
Matt Christie *(Mgr-Fin Svcs)*

HIGH STREET FILATEX LTD
B-17 IInd Floor 22 Godam Industrial Area, Jaipur, 302006, Rajasthan, India
Tel.: (91) 1414025431
Web Site:
https://www.highstreetfilatex.in
Year Founded: 1994
531301—(BOM)
Rev.: $2,150
Assets: $308,464
Liabilities: $438,431
Net Worth: ($129,967)
Earnings: $30,791
Emp.: 2

Fiscal Year-end: 03/31/21
Knitted Socks Mfr
N.A.I.C.S.: 315120
Bhagwan Singh *(Chm)*

HIGH TECH PHARM CO., LTD.
280 Sinnae-ro Daeso-Myeon, Eumseong, 27663, Chungcheongbuk-do, Korea (South)
Tel.: (82) 438830012
Web Site: https://www.htpharm.com
Year Founded: 1998
106190—(KRS)
Rev.: $78,960,510
Assets: $101,398,923
Liabilities: $24,745,785
Net Worth: $76,653,138
Earnings: $4,504,539
Emp.: 99
Fiscal Year-end: 12/31/22
Pharmaceutical & Medicinal Products Mfr
N.A.I.C.S.: 325412

HIGH TECHNOLOGY SYSTEMS LTD.
43 R Section Six Zahraa el Maadi Main Road, PO Box 50, New Maadi, 11742, Cairo, Egypt
Tel.: (20) 227549607
Web Site: http://www.hiteknofal.com
Year Founded: 1987
Sales Range: $1-9.9 Million
Emp.: 300
Cable & Telecommunication Product Designer Mfr
N.A.I.C.S.: 335921
Mohamed Nofal *(Founder & CEO)*

HIGH TIDE, INC.
112 11127 15 Street NE, Calgary, T3K 2M4, AB, Canada
Web Site:
https://www.hightideinc.com
HITI—(NASDAQ)
Rev.: $654,646,866
Assets: $313,317,502
Liabilities: $133,884,264
Net Worth: $179,433,238
Earnings: ($54,973,965)
Emp.: 1,550
Fiscal Year-end: 10/31/23
Tobacco Product Mfr & Distr
N.A.I.C.S.: 312230
Raj Grover *(Founder, Pres & CEO)*

Subsidiaries:

Canna Cabana Inc. (1)
10828 124 Street NW, Edmonton, T5M 0H3, AB, Canada
Tel.: (780) 758-3700
Web Site: http://www.cannacabana.com
Cannabis Retailer
N.A.I.C.S.: 459999

DHC Supply, LLC (1)
1667 W 9th St, Long Beach, CA 90813
Tel.: (805) 625-9420
Web Site: http://www.dailyhighclub.com
Sales Range: $1-9.9 Million
Emp.: 10
Construction Materials Distr
N.A.I.C.S.: 423390
Harrison Baum *(CEO)*

NuLeaf Naturals, LLC (1)
1550 Larimer St Ste 964, Denver, CO 80202 (80%)
Tel.: (720) 372-4842
Web Site: https://www.nuleafnaturals.com
Sales Range: $10-24.9 Million
Emp.: 40
Health Care Products Mfr
N.A.I.C.S.: 325411
Jaden Barnes *(Co-Founder & CEO)*

RGR Canada Inc. (1)
112 11127 15th Street NE, Calgary, T3K 2M4, AB, Canada
Web Site: http://www.valiantdist.ca
Smoking Product Whslr

N.A.I.C.S.: 424940
Smoke Cartel, Inc. (1)
1313 Rogers St, Savannah, GA 31405
Tel.: (912) 319-7199
Web Site: http://www.smokecartel.com
Assets: $2,148,000
Liabilities: $2,202,000
Net Worth: ($54,000)
Earnings: ($1,676,000)
Emp.: 7
Fiscal Year-end: 12/31/2019
Glass Products Mfr
N.A.I.C.S.: 327212
Sean Geng *(Chm & COO)*

HIGH-5 CONGLOMERATE BERHAD
High-5 Complex Lot 72 Persiaran Jubli Perak, Seksyen 21, 40300, Shah Alam, Selangor Darul Ehsan, Malaysia
Tel.: (60) 3519 22888
Web Site: http://www.high5.com.my
Sales Range: $25-49.9 Million
Bakery Products Mfr
N.A.I.C.S.: 311812
Loon Foo Siew *(Sec)*

HIGH-GRADE BRICK-TILE JOINT STOCK COMPANY
Cay Cham Hamlet, Tan Uyen, Binh Duong, Vietnam
Tel.: (84) 6503658278
Web Site:
https://www.gachngoicaocap.com
Year Founded: 2006
MCC—(HNX)
Rev.: $1,638,144
Assets: $3,718,286
Liabilities: $876,935
Net Worth: $2,841,351
Earnings: $85,588
Fiscal Year-end: 12/31/21
Tiles & Bricks Mfr & Distr
N.A.I.C.S.: 327331

HIGH-TECH METALS LIMITED
22 Townshend Road, Subiaco, 6008, WA, Australia
Tel.: (61) 893880051
Web Site:
https://www.hightechmetals.com.au
Year Founded: 2022
HTM—(ASX)
Rev.: $66,938
Assets: $2,488,009
Liabilities: $167,686
Net Worth: $2,320,323
Earnings: ($492,509)
Fiscal Year-end: 06/30/24
Support Activities for Metal Mining
N.A.I.C.S.: 213114

HIGH-TEK HARNESS ENTERPRISE CO., LTD.
4Fl No 16 Lane 50 Sec 3 Nan-Kang Rd, Taipei, Taiwan
Tel.: (886) 227825881
Web Site: https://www.high-tek.com.tw
Year Founded: 1984
3202—(TPE)
Rev.: $129,635,025
Assets: $147,416,784
Liabilities: $80,771,973
Net Worth: $66,644,811
Earnings: $1,457,993
Emp.: 6
Fiscal Year-end: 12/31/22
Coaxial Cable Mfr
N.A.I.C.S.: 335929
Hsiao-Chin Wei *(Chm)*

HIGH-TOUCH COMMUNICATIONS INC.

INTERNATIONAL PUBLIC

372 Ste-Catherine St W Ste 320, Montreal, H3B 1A2, QC, Canada
Tel.: (514) 739-2461
Web Site: http://www.hightouch.com
Year Founded: 1982
Sales Range: $10-24.9 Million
Emp.: 20
Advertising Agencies
N.A.I.C.S.: 541810
Tom Kouri *(Pres)*

HIGHBANK RESOURCES LTD.
Suite 615 - 800 West Pender St, Vancouver, V6C 2V6, BC, Canada
Tel.: (604) 683-6648
Web Site:
https://highbankresources.com
Year Founded: 1980
HBK—(TSXV)
Assets: $158,348
Liabilities: $7,556,914
Net Worth: ($7,398,566)
Earnings: ($6,598,442)
Fiscal Year-end: 12/31/21
Metals & Mineral Mining, Exploration & Development Services
N.A.I.C.S.: 212290
Gary Musil *(CFO & Sec)*

HIGHBROAD ADVANCED MATERIAL (HEFEI) CO., LTD.
No 699 Dayu Road, Xinzhan District, Hefei, 230012, Anhui, China
Tel.: (86) 55164369688
Web Site: https://www.hibr.com.cn
Year Founded: 2009
301321—(CHIN)
Rev.: $309,883,860
Assets: $544,264,812
Liabilities: $341,414,892
Net Worth: $202,849,920
Earnings: ($7,630,740)
Fiscal Year-end: 12/31/22
Electronic Component Mfr & Distr
N.A.I.C.S.: 334419
Zhaozhong Wang *(Chm & Gen Mgr)*

HIGHBURY FORD SALES LIMITED
1365 Dundas St, London, N5W 3B5, ON, Canada
Tel.: (519) 455-1800
Web Site:
https://www.highburyford.com
Year Founded: 1975
New & Used Car Dealers
N.A.I.C.S.: 441110
Peter Sandor *(Ops Mgr)*

HIGHCO S.A.
365 Avenue Archimede, 13290, Aix-en-Provence, France
Tel.: (33) 442245824
Web Site: https://www.highco.com
Year Founded: 1990
HCO—(EUR)
Sales Range: $150-199.9 Million
Marketing Consultancy Services
N.A.I.C.S.: 541613
Cecile Collina-Hue *(Mng Dir & Member-Mgmt Bd)*

Subsidiaries:

Capitaldata Sas (1)
8 Rue de la Rochefoucauld, CS 30500, 75427, Paris, Cedex, France
Tel.: (33) 177756767
Marketing & Advertising Services
N.A.I.C.S.: 541810

High Connexion Srl (1)
Via Risorgimento 93, Alzate Brianza, 22040, Milan, Como, Italy
Tel.: (39) 0318820250
Web Site: http://www.highconnexion.it
Network Communication Services
N.A.I.C.S.: 517111

AND PRIVATE COMPANIES

High Connexion, S.A.S (1)
9 Avenue des Saules, 69600, Oullins, France
Tel.: (33) 1 70 99 36 60
Web Site: http://www.highconnexion.com
Telecommunication Servicesb
N.A.I.C.S.: 517112
Chloe Bernard (Acct Mgr-Wholesale & Billing Solutions)

HighCo BENELUX (1)
Kruiskouter 1, 1730, Asse, Belgium
Tel.: (32) 2467 3333
Marketing Consultancy Services
N.A.I.C.S.: 541613

HighCo BOX, S.A.S (1)
8 rue de la Rochefoucauld, 75 427, Paris, Cedex, France
Tel.: (33) 1 77 75 67 67
Web Site: http://www.highco-box.fr
Marketing Consultancy Services
N.A.I.C.S.: 541613

HighCo DATA, S.A.S (1)
110 avenue Galilee, BP 70392, 13799, Aix-en-Provence, Cedex, France
Tel.: (33) 4 42 24 85 00
Web Site: http://www.highco-data.fr
Marketing Consultancy Services
N.A.I.C.S.: 541613

HighCo MRM (1)
Barberton House Farndon Road, Market Harborough, LE16 9NR, Leicestershire, United Kingdom
Tel.: (44) 1858 410 510
Web Site: http://www.highco-mrm.com
Emp.: 120
Marketing Consultancy Services
N.A.I.C.S.: 541613
Peter Kerr (Mng Dir)

HighCo SPAIN (1)
Edif El Torreon C / Anochecer 2, 28223, Pozuelo de Alarcon, Spain
Tel.: (34) 913 512 856
Web Site: http://www.highco.com
Marketing Consultancy Services
N.A.I.C.S.: 541613
Harrald Zwart (Mng Dir)

Highco Data Benelux NV (1)
Kruiskouter 1, 1730, Asse, Belgium
Tel.: (32) 23520390
Web Site: http://www.highco-data.be
Marketing & Advertising Services
N.A.I.C.S.: 541810
David Vigneron (Mng Dir & Dir-Publ)

Highco Editing SAS (1)
365 Avenue Archimede, CS 60 346, 13799, Aix-en-Provence, Cedex, France
Tel.: (33) 442245824
Marketing & Advertising Services
N.A.I.C.S.: 541810

Highco Mindoza SAS (1)
365 Avenue Archimede, 13799, Aix-en-Provence, France
Tel.: (33) 442248552
Web Site: http://www.mindoza.fr
Marketing & Advertising Services
N.A.I.C.S.: 541810
Jeremie Dupuis (Dir-UX)

Highco Shelf Service NV (1)
Z1 Research Park 50, 1731, Zellik, Belgium
Tel.: (32) 28974933
Web Site: http://www.highcoshelf.be
Emp.: 200
Marketing & Advertising Services
N.A.I.C.S.: 541810
Gerrit Van Reeth (CEO)

Highco Shopper SAS (1)
8 Rue de la Rochefoucauld, CS 30500, 75427, Paris, Cedex, France
Tel.: (33) 177756500
Network Communication Services
N.A.I.C.S.: 517111

Highco Shopper SL (1)
Edif El Torreon C / Anochecer 2, 28223, Pozuelo de Alarcon, Spain
Tel.: (34) 913512856
Marketing & Advertising Services
N.A.I.C.S.: 541810

Integral Shopper Fz LLC (1)
Dubai Media City Bldg 8 Office 510, PO Box 502068, Dubai, United Arab Emirates
Tel.: (971) 44574279
Web Site: http://www.integralshopper.com
Consumer Goods Retailer
N.A.I.C.S.: 532289
Antoine Achkar (Mng Dir)

Milky JSC (1)
8 Rue de la Rochefoucauld, CS 30500, 75427, Paris, Cedex, France
Tel.: (33) 147749458
Marketing & Advertising Services
N.A.I.C.S.: 541810

Useradgents Sas (1)
8 Rue de la Rochefoucauld, 75009, Paris, France
Tel.: (33) 177756590
Web Site: http://www.useradgents.com
Mobile Application Services
N.A.I.C.S.: 541511

HIGHCON SYSTEMS LTD.
2 Nahal Snir Street, PO Box 13200, Yavne, 8122503, Israel
Tel.: (972) 89101705
Web Site: https://www.highcon.net
Year Founded: 2009
HICN—(TAE)
Rev.: $8,374,000
Assets: $33,931,000
Liabilities: $37,333,000
Net Worth: ($3,402,000)
Earnings: ($24,190,000)
Fiscal Year-end: 06/30/23
Industrial Machinery Distr
N.A.I.C.S.: 423830
Shlomo Nimrodi (CEO)

HIGHCROFT INVESTMENTS PLC
Thomas House Langford Locks, Langford Lane, Kidlington, OX5 1HR, Oxon, United Kingdom
Tel.: (44) 1865840023
Web Site:
  http://www.highcroftplc.com
HCFT—(LSE)
Rev.: $7,079,020
Assets: $108,885,382
Liabilities: $37,973,996
Net Worth: $70,911,386
Earnings: $8,982,580)
Emp.: 7
Fiscal Year-end: 12/31/22
Real Estate Investment Services
N.A.I.C.S.: 523999
David Kingerlee (Exec Dir)

Subsidiaries:

Rodenhurst Estates Limited (1)
Thomas House Langford Locks, Kidlington, OX5 1HR, United Kingdom
Tel.: (44) 1865 840 000
Web Site: http://www.kingerlee.co.uk
Emp.: 120
Real Estate Manangement Services
N.A.I.C.S.: 531390
Michael Puttick (Mng Dir)

HIGHER EDUCATION & VOCATIONAL BOOK JSC
25 Han Thuyen str, Hai Ba Trung dist, Hanoi, Vietnam
Tel.: (84) 48256547
HEV—(HNX)
Rev.: $1,374,437
Assets: $903,711
Liabilities: $271,587
Net Worth: $632,124
Earnings: $78,772
Fiscal Year-end: 12/31/20
Education Development Services
N.A.I.C.S.: 611710
Pham Gia Tri (Mgr)

HIGHER WAY ELECTRONIC CO., LTD.
14F-6 No 925 Sec 4 Taiwan Boulevard, Xitun Dist, Taichung, 407, Taiwan
Tel.: (886) 423550011
Web Site:
  https://www.higherway.com.tw
Year Founded: 1991
3268—(TPE)
Rev.: $38,459,181
Assets: $29,138,761
Liabilities: $13,000,969
Net Worth: $16,137,792
Earnings: $1,603,195
Fiscal Year-end: 12/31/22
Electric Equipment Mfr
N.A.I.C.S.: 334419
Hanson Hung (Pres)

HIGHEST PERFORMANCES HOLDINGS INC.
61F Pearl River Tower No 15 Zhujiang West Road Zhujiang New Town, Tianhe, Guangzhou, 5162, Guangdong, China
Tel.: (86) 2028381666
Web Site: https://www.puyiwm.com
Year Founded: 2010
HPH—(NASDAQ)
Rev.: $163,104,000
Assets: $588,657,000
Liabilities: $225,421,000
Net Worth: $363,236,000
Earnings: ($70,463,000)
Emp.: 230
Fiscal Year-end: 06/30/24
Holding Company
N.A.I.C.S.: 551112
Haifeng Yu (Founder & Chm)

HIGHFIELD RESOURCES LIMITED
169 Fullarton Road, Dulwich, 5065, SA, Australia
Tel.: (61) 881335000
Web Site:
  http://www.highfieldresources.com
HFR—(ASX)
Assets: $112,130,673
Liabilities: $13,510,977
Net Worth: $98,619,696
Earnings: ($3,864,972)
Emp.: 29
Fiscal Year-end: 12/31/22
Potash Exploration Services
N.A.I.C.S.: 212390
Katelyn Adams (Sec)

Subsidiaries:

Geoalcali SLU (1)
Avenida Carlos III 13 1B, 31002, Pamplona, Navarra, Spain
Tel.: (34) 948050577
Web Site: http://www.geoalcali.com
Potash Mining Services
N.A.I.C.S.: 212390

HIGHGOLD MINING, INC.
320-800 West Pender Street, Vancouver, V6C 2V6, BC, Canada
Tel.: (604) 629-1165
Web Site:
  http://www.highgoldmining.com
HGMIF—(OTCQX)
Rev.: $107,944
Assets: $31,538,652
Liabilities: $697,651
Net Worth: $30,841,001
Earnings: ($577,948)
Fiscal Year-end: 12/31/20
Gold Exploration Services
N.A.I.C.S.: 212220
Darwin Green (Founder, Pres & CEO)

HIGHLAND CHEVROLET BUICK GMC CADILLAC
15783 Yonge Street, Aurora, L4G 1P4, ON, Canada
Tel.: (905) 727-9444
Web Site:
  http://www.highlandgm.com
Rev.: $38,789,240
Emp.: 80
New & Used Car Dealer
N.A.I.C.S.: 441110
Ron Vande Beek (VP)

HIGHLAND COPPER COMPANY INC.
Royal Centre 1055 West Georgia Street Suite 1500, Vancouver, V6E 4N7, BC, Canada
Tel.: (450) 677-2455 BC
Web Site:
  https://www.highlandcopper.com
Year Founded: 2006
HI—(DEU)
Assets: $58,625,096
Liabilities: $5,915,942
Net Worth: $52,709,154
Earnings: $24,197,120
Fiscal Year-end: 06/30/24
Copper Exploration Services
N.A.I.C.S.: 212230
David A. Fennell (Chm)

Subsidiaries:

Keweenaw Copper Co. (1)
56730 Calumet Ave Ste J, Calumet, MI 49913
Tel.: (906) 337-5988
Web Site:
  http://www.keweenawcopperco.com
Copper Exploration Services
N.A.I.C.S.: 213114
Angel Peters (Office Mgr)

HIGHLAND FOUNDRY LTD.
9670 187th Street, Surrey, V4N 3N6, BC, Canada
Tel.: (604) 888-8444
Web Site:
  http://www.highlandfoundry.com
Rev.: $20,027,235
Emp.: 130
Steel Foundry Services
N.A.I.C.S.: 331513
Kim Morgan (VP-Sls & Mktg)

HIGHLAND FUELS LTD.
Affric House Beechwood Park, Inverness, IV2 3BW, United Kingdom
Tel.: (44) 1463220223
Web Site:
  http://www.highlandfuels.co.uk
Year Founded: 1957
Sales Range: $250-299.9 Million
Emp.: 139
Fuel Distribution Services
N.A.I.C.S.: 457210
George Shand (Mng Dir)

HIGHLAND HELICOPTERS LTD.
4240 Agar Drive, Richmond, V7B 1A3, BC, Canada
Tel.: (604) 273-6161
Web Site: https://www.highland.ca
Year Founded: 1959
Helicopter Services
N.A.I.C.S.: 488190
Dan Kolshuk (Dir-Maintenance)

HIGHLANDER SILVER CORP.
605 – 130 Brew Street, Port Moody, V3H 0E3, BC, Canada
Tel.: (211) 6042837630 BC
HLSCF—(OTCIQ)
Rev.: $14,614
Assets: $391,559
Liabilities: $177,442
Net Worth: $214,117
Earnings: ($4,190,535)

HIGHLANDER SILVER CORP.

Highlander Silver Corp.—(Continued)
Fiscal Year-end: 09/30/23
Mineral Exploration Services
N.A.I.C.S.: 213115
Stephen Brohman *(CFO)*

HIGHLIGHT COMMUNICATIONS AG
Netzibodenstrasse 23b, 4133, Pratteln, Switzerland
Tel.: (41) 618169696
Web Site: https://www.highlight-communications.ch
Year Founded: 1983
HLG—(MUN)
Rev.: $465,060,431
Assets: $661,008,395
Liabilities: $486,221,619
Net Worth: $174,786,776
Earnings: ($11,712,061)
Emp.: 1,524
Fiscal Year-end: 12/31/23
Financial Holding Services
N.A.I.C.S.: 551112
Bernhard Burgener *(Chm)*

Subsidiaries:

Constantin Film AG (1)
Feilitzschstrasse 6, 80802, Munich, Germany
Tel.: (49) 894444600
Web Site: https://constantin.film
Film Production & Distribution Services
N.A.I.C.S.: 512110

Subsidiary (Domestic):

Constantin Entertainment GmbH (2)
Carl-Zeiss-Ring 3, 85737, Ismaning, Germany
Tel.: (49) 89444488440
Web Site: https://www.constantin-entertainment.de
Emp.: 300
TV Entertainment Services
N.A.I.C.S.: 512110

Constantin Music GmbH (2)
Feilitzschstr 6, 80802, Munich, Germany
Tel.: (49) 894444600
Web Site: https://constantin-music.de
Music Recording Services
N.A.I.C.S.: 512290

Olga Film GmbH (2)
Tengstrasse 20, 80798, Munich, Germany
Tel.: (49) 892782950
Web Site: https://www.olgafilm.de
Film Production & Distribution Services
N.A.I.C.S.: 512110

Rat Pack Filmproduktion GmbH (2)
Beethovenplatz 2, 80336, Munich, Germany
Tel.: (49) 89121148700
Web Site: https://www.ratpack-film.de
Film Production & Distribution Services
N.A.I.C.S.: 512110

Constantin Film und Entertainment AG (1)
Bertastrasse 1, 8003, Zurich, Switzerland
Tel.: (41) 442131350
Web Site: http://www.lajulie.ch
Musical Troop Services
N.A.I.C.S.: 711130

Hager Moss Film GmbH (1)
Rambergstrasse 5, 80799, Munich, Germany
Tel.: (49) 892060800
Web Site: https://hagermoss.de
Film Production & Distribution Services
N.A.I.C.S.: 512110

Leitmotif Creators GmbH (1)
Munchener Strasse 101g, 85737, Ismaning, Germany
Tel.: (49) 89996334400
Web Site: https://www.leitmotif.vision
Film Production & Distribution Services
N.A.I.C.S.: 512110

Magic Sports Media GmbH (1)
Munchener Str 101g, 85737, Ismaning, Germany
Tel.: (49) 89960662554
Web Site: https://www.magicsportsmedia.de
Sport Media Services
N.A.I.C.S.: 711211
Colin Clegg *(Head-Key Acctg & Intl)*

Mythos Film Produktions-GmbH & Co. KG (1)
Bleibtreustrasse 15, 10623, Berlin, Germany
Tel.: (49) 30887144817
Web Site: http://www.mythos-film.de
Film Production & Distribution Services
N.A.I.C.S.: 512110

Sport1 GmbH (1)
Munchener Str 101 g, 85737, Ismaning, Germany
Tel.: (49) 89960660
Web Site: https://www.sport1.de
Sport & Recreation Instruction Services
N.A.I.C.S.: 611620

Sport1 Media GmbH (1)
Munchener Str 101 g, 85737, Ismaning, Germany
Tel.: (49) 89960660
Web Site: https://business.sport1.de
Advertising Services
N.A.I.C.S.: 541810

TEAM Marketing AG (1)
Alpenquai 30, 6005, Lucerne, Switzerland
Tel.: (41) 413681818
Web Site: http://team.ch
Marketing Services
N.A.I.C.S.: 541613

HIGHLIGHT EVENT & ENTERTAINMENT AG
Netzibodenstrasse 23b, 4133, Pratteln, Switzerland
Tel.: (41) 412260597   CH
Web Site: https://www.hlee.ch
HLEE—(SWX)
Rev.: $580,966,741
Assets: $908,958,980
Liabilities: $653,086,475
Net Worth: $255,872,506
Earnings: ($23,337,029)
Emp.: 1,352
Fiscal Year-end: 12/31/22
Holding Company
N.A.I.C.S.: 551112
Bernhard Burgener *(Pres)*

Subsidiaries:

Chameleo GmbH (1)
Parkstr 22, 80339, Munich, Germany
Tel.: (49) 8918905670
Web Site: https://www.chameleo.ch
Consulting Services
N.A.I.C.S.: 541618

Highlight Event AG (1)
Hirschengraben 31, Emmen, 6003, Lucerne, Switzerland
Tel.: (41) 412260590
Web Site: https://www.highlightevent.ch
Entertainment Services
N.A.I.C.S.: 711130

PSSST Film GmbH (1)
Landsberger Strasse 146 Rgb, 80339, Munich, Germany
Tel.: (49) 8985636006
Web Site: https://www.pssst-film.com
Film Production Services
N.A.I.C.S.: 512110

HIGHMARK INTERACTIVE INC.
10 Kingsbridge Garden Circle Suite 700, Mississauga, L5R 3K7, ON, Canada
Tel.: (416) 558-8907
CROW.P—(TSXV)
Assets: $1,532,590
Liabilities: $25,304
Net Worth: $1,507,285
Earnings: ($240,535)
Fiscal Year-end: 12/31/20
Business Consulting Services
N.A.I.C.S.: 522299

HIGHNOON LABORATORIES LIMITED
17 5 KM Multan Road, Lahore, 53700, Pakistan
Tel.: (92) 42111000465
Web Site: https://www.highnoon-labs.com
Year Founded: 1984
HINOON—(KAR)
Rev.: $58,267,142
Assets: $30,470,835
Liabilities: $8,266,579
Net Worth: $22,204,255
Earnings: $6,443,889
Emp.: 1,825
Fiscal Year-end: 12/31/19
Pharmaceutical Preparations
N.A.I.C.S.: 325412
Tausif Ahmad Khan *(Chm)*

Subsidiaries:

Curexa Health (Private) Limited (1)
Plot No 517, Sundar Industrial Estate, Lahore, Pakistan
Tel.: (92) 42352986814
Web Site: https://www.curexa.com.pk
Pharmaceuticals Product Mfr
N.A.I.C.S.: 325412

HIGHPOWER INTERNATIONAL, INC.
Building 1 68 Xinxia Road Pinghu Town, Longgang District, Shenzhen, 518111, Guangdong, China
Tel.: (86) 75589686533   DE
Web Site: http://www.highpowertech.com
Nickel Metal Hydride Rechargeable Batteries & Related Products Developer, Mfr & Marketer
N.A.I.C.S.: 335910
Sunny Pan *(CFO)*

Subsidiaries:

Hong Kong Highpower International Co., Ltd. (1)
Room 2003 20/F Prosperity Place No 6 Shing Yip Street, Kwun Tong, Kowloon, China (Hong Kong)
Tel.: (852) 35650188
Lithium Battery Mfr & Distr
N.A.I.C.S.: 335910

Hong Kong Highpower Technology Co., Ltd. (1)
Room 4 13/F Tai Ping Indl Center Block 4 51 A Ting Kok Road, Tai Po, New Territories, China (Hong Kong)
Tel.: (852) 26639955
Rechargeable Lithium Batteries Mfr
N.A.I.C.S.: 335910

Icon Energy System (Shenzhen) Co., Ltd. (1)
Block A 4/F Jinmeiwei Industrial Park, Guanlan Hi-tech Industrial Park Shangkeng Community Baoan District, Shenzhen, 518110, China
Tel.: (86) 75589686903
Web Site: http://www.iconergy.com
Lithium Battery Mfr & Distr
N.A.I.C.S.: 335910

Shenzhen Highpower Technology Co., Ltd. (1)
Building 1 68 Xinxia Road, Pinghu Town Longgang District, Guangdong, Shenzhen, 518111, China
Tel.: (86) 75589686533
Web Site: http://www.highpowertech.com
Battery Mfr & Distr
N.A.I.C.S.: 335910
George Pan *(Chm & CEO)*

HIGHROCK RESOURCES LTD.
200 - 82 Richmond Street, Toronto, M5C 1P1, ON, Canada
Tel.: (437) 677-5075   BC
Web Site:
https://highrockresources.ltd
Year Founded: 2021

INTERNATIONAL PUBLIC

HRK—(CNSX)
Assets: $227,421
Liabilities: $90,197
Net Worth: $137,223
Earnings: ($163,817)
Fiscal Year-end: 01/31/24
Mineral Exploration Services
N.A.I.C.S.: 213115
Derrick Dao *(CEO)*

HIGHSUN HOLDING GROUP CO., LTD.
Wenwusha Town Binhai Industrial Zone, Changle, China
Tel.: (86) 59127908888
Web Site:
http://www.highsunchina.com
Year Founded: 1984
Holding Company
N.A.I.C.S.: 551112
Chen Jianlong *(Chm & CEO)*

Subsidiaries:

Fibrant Holding B.V. (1)
Poststraat 1, 6135 KR, Sittard, Netherlands   (100%)
Tel.: (31) 46 477 0035
Web Site: http://www.fibrant52.com
Emp.: 1,200
Holding Company; Specialty Chemicals Mfr & Distr
N.A.I.C.S.: 551112
Ed Sheu *(Chm)*

Subsidiary (Domestic):

Fibrant B.V. (2)
Postraat 1, 6135 KR, Sittard, Netherlands   (100%)
Tel.: (31) 464770035
Web Site: http://www.fibrant52.com
Specialty Chemicals Mfr & Distr
N.A.I.C.S.: 325998
Ed Sheu *(Chm)*

Subsidiary (US):

Fibrant, LLC (2)
1408 Columbia Nitrogen Dr, Augusta, GA 30901
Tel.: (706) 849-6600
Web Site: http://www.fibrant52.com
Chemical Performance Products & Services
N.A.I.C.S.: 325998
Bill Powers *(VP-US Ops)*

HIGHTECH PAYMENT SYSTEMS S A
Casablanca Nearshore Park Shore 1 1100 boulevard Al Qods, Sidi Maarouf, 20270, Casablanca, Morocco
Tel.: (212) 529 045 000
Web Site: http://www.hps-worldwide.com
Rev.: $47,756,454
Assets: $71,976,885
Liabilities: $47,822,481
Net Worth: $24,154,404
Earnings: $5,819,068
Emp.: 373
Fiscal Year-end: 12/31/16
Electronic Financial Payment Services
N.A.I.C.S.: 522320
Abdeslam Alaoui Smaili *(CEO)*

Subsidiaries:

HPS Europe (1)
Hps-65-67 Rue Du Faubourg St Honore 4th Floor, 75008, Paris, France
Tel.: (33) 158180134
Information Technology Consulting Services
N.A.I.C.S.: 541512

HIGHTEL TOWERS SPA
Via della Stazione di San Pietro 65, 165, Rome, Italy
Tel.: (39) 0645553140
Web Site: http://www.hightel.it
Year Founded: 2011

Telecommunication Equipment Provider
N.A.I.C.S.: 517810
Nicola Parmeggiani (CEO)

HIGHTEX GMBH
Nordstrasse 10, 83253, Rimsting, Germany
Tel.: (49) 8051 68880
Web Site: http://www.hightex-membrane.de
Year Founded: 1948
Sales Range: $25-49.9 Million
Emp.: 20
Membrane Structure Installation & Construction Services
N.A.I.C.S.: 237990
Klaus-Micheal Koch (CEO)

HIGHVISTA GOLD INC.
4 King Street West Suite 1505, Toronto, M5H 1B6, ON, Canada
Tel.: (416) 682-2674
Web Site: http://www.highvistagold.com
Year Founded: 2009
HVV.H—(TSXV)
Assets: $1,622
Liabilities: $1,552,284
Net Worth: ($1,550,662)
Earnings: ($161,098)
Fiscal Year-end: 03/31/22
Gold Exploration Services
N.A.I.C.S.: 212220
John L. Burns (Pres & CEO)

HIGHWAY 50 GOLD CORP.
Suite 1570 200 Burrard Street, Vancouver, V6C 3L6, BC, Canada
Tel.: (604) 681-4462
Web Site: https://www.highway50gold.com
Year Founded: 2004
HGGCF—(OTCIQ)
Assets: $941,045
Liabilities: $303,933
Net Worth: $637,112
Earnings: ($3,265,298)
Fiscal Year-end: 12/31/23
Mineral Exploration Services
N.A.I.C.S.: 213114
Gordon P. Leask (Pres & CEO)

HIGHWAY CAPITAL PLC
Eden House Reynolds Road, Beaconsfield, HP9 2FL, Bucks, United Kingdom
Tel.: (44) 20 3427 3382
Year Founded: 1994
Emp.: 4
Investment & Financial Services
N.A.I.C.S.: 523999
Maciej Szytko (Sec)

HIGHWAY HOLDINGS LIMITED
Suite 1801 Level 18 Landmark North 39 Lung Sum Avenue, Sheung Shui, New Territories, China (Hong Kong)
Tel.: (852) 23444248
Web Site: https://www.highwayholdings.com
Year Founded: 1990
HIHO—(NASDAQ)
Rev.: $6,321,000
Assets: $13,883,000
Liabilities: $5,667,000
Net Worth: $8,216,000
Earnings: ($978,000)
Emp.: 142
Fiscal Year-end: 03/31/24
OEM & ODM Equipment Mfr
N.A.I.C.S.: 332313
Roland W. Kohl (Founder, Chm & CEO)

Subsidiaries:
Golden Bright Plastic Manufacturing Company Limited (1)
Suite No 810 Level 8 Landmark North 39 Lung Sum Avenue, Sheung Shui, New Territories, China (Hong Kong)
Tel.: (852) 23444248
Web Site: http://www.goldenbright.net
Plastics Product Mfr
N.A.I.C.S.: 326199
Will Holder (Gen Mgr)

Hi-Lite Camera Company Limited (1)
Suite 810 Level 8 Landmark North 39 Lung Sum Avenue, Sheung Shui, New Territories, China (Hong Kong)
Tel.: (852) 24940923
Camera Mfr
N.A.I.C.S.: 333310

Kayser Limited (1)
Room 810 8/f Landmark North 39 Lung Sum Avenue, Sheung Shui, New Territories, China (Hong Kong)
Tel.: (852) 23444248
Electronic Components Mfr
N.A.I.C.S.: 334419

Nissin Precision Metal Manufacturing Limited (1)
Suite 810 Level 8 Landmark North 39 Lung Sum Avenue, Sheung Shui, New Territories, China (Hong Kong)
Tel.: (852) 23444248
Web Site: http://www.highwayholdings.com
Sales Range: $25-49.9 Million
Emp.: 15
Precision Metal Products Mfr
N.A.I.C.S.: 332721

HIGHWAY INSURANCE HOLDINGS PLC
Highway House, Brentwood, CM14 4EJ, Essex, United Kingdom
Tel.: (44) 8712221110
Web Site: http://www.highway-insurance.co.uk
Year Founded: 1995
Sales Range: $450-499.9 Million
Emp.: 768
Holding Company; Insurance
N.A.I.C.S.: 551112
Philip John Lampshire (Sec)

Subsidiaries:
A Quote Insurance Services Limited (1)
Barrett House, Savoy Close, Andover, SP10 2HZ, United Kingdom
Tel.: (44) 1264337447
Web Site: http://www.aquote.co.uk
Insurance Broking Services
N.A.I.C.S.: 524210

Direct Motorline Limited (1)
4th Floor West Crown House, Crown Street, Ipswich, IP1 3HS, United Kingdom
Tel.: (44) 8712221110
Motor Insurance Telebroker
N.A.I.C.S.: 524210

Elite Underwriting Limited (1)
Lincoln House, 6 Church Street, Aylesbury, HP20 2QS, United Kingdom
Tel.: (44) 8706006061
Web Site: http://www.eliteunderwriting.co.uk
Insurance Underwriters
N.A.I.C.S.: 524128

HIGHWEALTH CONSTRUCTION CORP.
10th Floor No 267 Lequn 2nd Road, Zhongshan District, Taipei, 10462, Taiwan
Tel.: (886) 227555899
Web Site: https://www.highwealth.com.tw
2542—(TAI)
Rev.: $1,441,093,278
Assets: $7,419,298,618
Liabilities: $5,544,307,322
Net Worth: $1,874,991,296

Earnings: $288,921,765
Emp.: 1,426
Fiscal Year-end: 12/31/23
Construction Engineering Services
N.A.I.C.S.: 237990
Chih-Lung Cheng (Chm)

HIGHWOOD ASSET MANAGEMENT LTD.
1100 250 2nd Street, Calgary, T2P 0C1, AB, Canada
Tel.: (403) 719-0499
Web Site: https://highwoodmgmt.com
Year Founded: 2012
HAM—(TSXV)
Rev.: $23,013,113
Assets: $51,356,682
Liabilities: $43,719,282
Net Worth: $7,637,400
Earnings: ($7,262,688)
Emp.: 6
Fiscal Year-end: 12/31/20
Oil & Gas Distribution Services
N.A.I.C.S.: 221210
Kelly McDonald (VP)

Subsidiaries:
Boulder Energy Ltd. (1)
540 222 3rd Avenue SW, Calgary, T2P 0B4, AB, Canada
Tel.: (403) 767-3060
Web Site: http://www.boulderenergy.ca
Petroleum Exploration
N.A.I.C.S.: 211120
Martin Cheyne (CEO)

HIGIJENA A.D.
Jovana Hranilovica 50, Novi Sad, Serbia
Tel.: (381) 21 6334 150
Year Founded: 1994
Sales Range: Less than $1 Million
Building Cleaning Services
N.A.I.C.S.: 561790

HIKAL LIMITED
Great Eastern Chambers Sector 11 CBD Belapur, Navi Mumbai, 400 614, India
Tel.: (91) 2230973100
Web Site: https://www.hikal.com
Year Founded: 1988
HIKAL—(NSE)
Rev.: $243,203,645
Assets: $286,011,870
Liabilities: $150,112,343
Net Worth: $135,899,526
Earnings: $9,397,758
Emp.: 2,015
Fiscal Year-end: 03/31/23
Pharmaceutical & Agrochemical Products Developer, Mfr & Marketer
N.A.I.C.S.: 325998
Sameer Hiremath (CEO & Co-Mng Dir)

Subsidiaries:
Acoris Research Limited (1)
603 A-Wing Great Eastern Chambers, CBD Belapur, Navi Mumbai, 400 614, Maharashtra, India
Tel.: (91) 2227574276
Web Site: http://www.acorisresearch.com
Sales Range: $50-74.9 Million
Emp.: 110
Medicine Ingredients Mfr
N.A.I.C.S.: 325411

Medipharma Ltd (1)
Mayfield Industrial Way, Weyhill, Andover, FP118HU, Hampshire, United Kingdom
Tel.: (44) 1264339770
Web Site: http://www.medipharma.co.uk
Sales Range: $25-49.9 Million
Emp.: 30
Medicine Ingredients Mfr
N.A.I.C.S.: 325411
Jalal Janmohamed (Mng Dir)

HIKARI BUSINESS FORM CO., LTD.
22nd floor Shinjuku Sumitomo Building 261 NishiShinjuku, Shinjuku-Ku, Tokyo, 163-0261, Japan
Tel.: (81) 333481431
Web Site: https://www.hikaribf.co.jp
Year Founded: 1968
39480—(TKS)
Sales Range: Less than $1 Million
Emp.: 381
Commercial Printing Services
N.A.I.C.S.: 323111
Yasuhiro Matsumoto (Pres & CEO)

HIKARI FURNITURE CO., LTD.
4-7-1 Higashiogu Arakawa-Ku, Tokyo, 116-0012, Japan
Tel.: (81) 338000111
Web Site: http://www.hikari-ss.co.jp
Furniture Mfr & Distr
N.A.I.C.S.: 337126
Sadaji Yasuoka (Pres)

HIKARI HEIGHTS-VARUS CO., LTD.
1-15 Minami 19-jo Nishi 11-chome, Jonishi Chuo-Ku, Sapporo, 064-0919, Japan
Tel.: (81) 115208668
Web Site: https://www.varus.co.jp
2137—(SAP)
Sales Range: Less than $1 Million
Women Healthcare Services
N.A.I.C.S.: 621610
Chieka Mori (Chm & Pres)

HIKARI HOLDINGS CO., LTD.
1223-14 Kasaharacho Tajimi, Gifu, 507-0901, Japan
Tel.: (81) 572561212
Web Site: https://www.h-holdings.jp
Year Founded: 2015
1445—(TKS)
Rev.: $35,244,880
Assets: $23,396,560
Liabilities: $21,054,000
Net Worth: $2,342,560
Earnings: ($842,160)
Fiscal Year-end: 08/31/22
Holding Company
N.A.I.C.S.: 551112
Yasufumi Hashiba (Chm)

HIKARI TSUSHIN, INC.
Hikari West Gate Bldg 1-4-10 Nishi-Ikebukuro, Toshima-ku, Tokyo, 171-0021, Japan
Tel.: (81) 359513718
Web Site: https://www.hikari.co.jp
Year Founded: 1988
9435—(TKS)
Rev.: $3,978,876,280
Assets: $13,741,899,160
Liabilities: $8,326,663,270
Net Worth: $5,415,235,890
Earnings: $807,907,250
Emp.: 4,149
Fiscal Year-end: 03/31/24
Copiers, Facsimiles, Telephone & Other Office Equipment Sales; Telecommunications & Internet Services; Medical Insurance Products; Venture Capital & Private Equity Financial Services
N.A.I.C.S.: 517112
Yasumitsu Shigeta (Chm & Chm)

Subsidiaries:
CHIC Holdings, Inc. (1)
2-12-5 Yotsuya, Shinjuku-ku, Tokyo, Japan (99.99%)
Tel.: (81) 3 5312 2303
Web Site: http://www.chic-holdings.jp
Private Equity
N.A.I.C.S.: 523999
Yasushi Fukuchi (Pres & CEO)

HIKARI TSUSHIN, INC.

Hikari Tsushin, Inc.—(Continued)

Frontier Co., Ltd. (1)
57-1 Ototsu Komatsu-cho, Saijo, 799-1106, Ehime, Japan
Tel.: (81) 898769200
Web Site: https://www.frontier-jp.com
Extruded Moldings, Plastic Ladder & Filter Material Mfr; Waste Water Treatment Services
N.A.I.C.S.: 562998

Hikari Private Equity Inc (1)
3-13-5 Minami Ikebukuro, Toshima-ku, 171-0022, Tokyo, Japan
Tel.: (81) 359518497
Web Site: http://www.hpe.co.jp
Financial Investment Activities
N.A.I.C.S.: 523999

IE Group, Inc. (1)
1-4-10 Nishiikebukuro, Toshima-ku, Tokyo, 171-0021, Japan
Tel.: (81) 359513515
Web Site: https://www.ie-group.co.jp
Emp.: 488
Office Equipment Distr
N.A.I.C.S.: 423420
Junya Mori (CEO)

Intea Holdings Inc. (1)
Building 3F Shinkawa Iwade Chuo Ward, 1-26-9 Shinkawa, Tokyo, 104-0033, Japan
Tel.: (81) 362220610
Web Site: http://www.inteahd.co.jp
Sales Range: $50-74.9 Million
Holding Company
N.A.I.C.S.: 551112
Akitoshi Okawa (CEO)

NFC Holdings, Inc. (1)
5F H&I Bldg 5-17-18 Shinjuku, Shinjuku-ku, Tokyo, 160-022, Japan (74.34%)
Tel.: (81) 362330300
Web Site: http://www.newton-fc.com
Rev.: $258,227,200
Assets: $303,297,750
Liabilities: $205,178,750
Net Worth: $98,119,000
Earnings: $25,153,310
Emp.: 2,411
Fiscal Year-end: 03/31/2020
Life Insurance Brokerage
N.A.I.C.S.: 524210
Kazuhiro Chubachi (Chm & Pres)

Premium Water Holdings, Inc. (1)
5F Jingumae 123 Building 1-23-26 Jingumae, Shibuya-ku, Tokyo, 150-0001, Japan
Tel.: (81) 368640980
Web Site: https://www.premiumwater-hd.co.jp
Rev.: $532,620,580
Assets: $657,073,660
Liabilities: $506,563,960
Net Worth: $150,509,700
Earnings: $38,185,970
Emp.: 848
Fiscal Year-end: 03/31/2024
Holding Company; Mineral Water Producer
N.A.I.C.S.: 551112
Yohei Hagio (Pres)

SBI-Hikari P.E. Co., Ltd. (1)
Izumi Garden Tower 1-6-1 Roppongi, Minato-ku, Tokyo, Japan (14.91%)
Tel.: (81) 3 6629 0100
Web Site: http://www.sbigroup.co.jp
Operates & Manages Venture Capital Funds
N.A.I.C.S.: 523999

Telecom Service Co., Ltd. (1)
Hikari Westgate Building 6F 1-4-10 Nishiikebukuro, Toshima-ku, Tokyo, 171-0021, Japan
Tel.: (81) 120945821
Web Site: http://www.telecom-service.net
Sales Range: $100-124.9 Million
Emp.: 806
Telecommunication Servicesb
N.A.I.C.S.: 517810

e-machitown Co., Ltd. (1)
Minami Ikebukuro Building, 3-13-15 Minami-Ikebukuro Toshima-ku, Tokyo, 171-0022, Japan (81.9%)
Tel.: (81) 359137555
Web Site: http://corp.emachi.co.jp
Sales Range: $25-49.9 Million
Emp.: 420
Internet-Related & Advertising Services

N.A.I.C.S.: 541890
Toshiaki Sakari (Pres)

HIKMA PHARMACEUTICALS PLC

1 New Burlington Place, London, W1S 2HR, United Kingdom
Tel.: (44) 2073992760   UK
Web Site: https://www.hikma.com
Year Founded: 1978
HIK—(LSE)
Rev.: $2,875,000,000
Assets: $4,680,000,000
Liabilities: $2,471,000,000
Net Worth: $2,209,000,000
Earnings: $192,000,000
Emp.: 9,100
Fiscal Year-end: 12/31/23
Generic Pharmaceutical Products Mfr
N.A.I.C.S.: 325412
Mazen Darwazah (Pres, Vice Chm & MENA)

Subsidiaries:

Al Jazeerah Pharmaceutical Industries Ltd. (1)
Tel.: (966) 114173731
Pharmaceuticals Product Mfr
N.A.I.C.S.: 325412

Arab Pharmaceutical Manufacturing Co. (1)
Buhairah Area, PO Box 42, As Salt, 19110, Balqa, Jordan
Tel.: (962) 53492200
Web Site: http://www.apm.com.jo
Pharmaceuticals Product Mfr
N.A.I.C.S.: 325412

Hikma Emerging Markets & Asia Pacific FZ LLC (1)
Premises 202-204 Floor 2 Building 26, PO Box 505088, Dubai Health Care City, Dubai, United Arab Emirates
Tel.: (971) 45127500
Pharmaceuticals Product Mfr
N.A.I.C.S.: 325412

Hikma Farmaceutica S.A. (1)
Estrada Rio Da Mo No 8 8A 8B - Fervença, Terrugem, 2705-906, Sintra, Portugal
Tel.: (351) 219608410
Sales Range: $125-149.9 Million
Emp.: 300
Pharmaceuticals Product Mfr
N.A.I.C.S.: 325412

Hikma Italia S.p.A. (1)
Tel.: (39) 03821751801
Web Site: https://www.hikma.com
Pharmaceuticals Product Mfr
N.A.I.C.S.: 325412

Hikma Liban S.A.R.L (1)
Bir Hassan Embassies street Al Saria Building, PO Box 14-6696, Beirut, Lebanon
Tel.: (961) 1833467
Pharmaceuticals Product Mfr
N.A.I.C.S.: 325412

Hikma Pharma Algeria S.A.R.L (1)
Zone d Activite 15/16, Staoueli, Algiers, Algeria
Tel.: (213) 23209100
Web Site: https://www.hikma.com
Pharmaceuticals Product Mfr
N.A.I.C.S.: 325412

Hikma Pharma GmbH (1)
Lochhamer Strasse 13, 82152, Martinsried, Germany
Tel.: (49) 89454500
Web Site: https://www.hikma.com
Sales Range: $25-49.9 Million
Emp.: 20
Pharmaceuticals Product Mfr
N.A.I.C.S.: 325412

Hikma Pharma SAE (1)
6 October City 2nd Industrial Zone plot 1, Cairo, 11511, Egypt
Tel.: (20) 238331691
Pharmaceuticals Product Mfr
N.A.I.C.S.: 325412

Hikma Pharmaceuticals LLC (1)
Al-Bayader King Adbullah The Second Street Facing Al-Ahli Club, PO Box 182400, Amman, Jordan
Tel.: (962) 65802900
Pharmaceuticals Product Mfr
N.A.I.C.S.: 325412

Hikma Pharmaceuticals USA Inc. (1)
246 Industrial Way W, Eatontown, NJ 07724
Tel.: (732) 542-1191
Pharmaceuticals Product Mfr
N.A.I.C.S.: 325412

Hikma Slovakia s.r.o. (1)
Seberiniho 1, 821 03, Bratislava, Slovakia
Tel.: (421) 255648971
Pharmaceuticals Product Mfr
N.A.I.C.S.: 325412

Hikma Speciality USA Inc. (1)
5865 Ridgeway Center Pkwy Ste 300, Memphis, TN 38120
Tel.: (901) 820-4477
Web Site: http://www.hikma-specialty.com
Pharmaceuticals Product Mfr
N.A.I.C.S.: 325412

Pharma Ixir Co. Ltd. (1)
Buri Al Lamab Area Block 9 Building No 98, Khartoum, Sudan
Tel.: (249) 183251134
Pharmaceuticals Product Mfr
N.A.I.C.S.: 325412

SPA Al Dar Al Arabia pour la Fabrication de Medicaments (1)
Zone d Activite El Boustane N 78, Sidi Abdellah Al Rahmania, Algiers, Algeria
Tel.: (213) 21100280
Pharmaceuticals Product Mfr
N.A.I.C.S.: 325412

STE D'Industriee Pharmaceutique Ibn Al Baytar (1)
11 Rue Charguia 1-2035, Carthage, 8610, Tunis, Tunisia
Tel.: (216) 71807777
Pharmaceuticals Product Mfr
N.A.I.C.S.: 325412

STE Medicef (1)
Avenue Habib Bourguiba, Sidi Thabet, 2020, Ariana, Tunisia
Tel.: (216) 71552292
Pharmaceuticals Product Mfr
N.A.I.C.S.: 325412

Savannah Pharmaceutical Industries Co. Ltd. (1)
Buri Al Lamab Area Block 9 Building No 98, Khartoum, Sudan
Tel.: (249) 155777073
Pharmaceuticals Product Mfr
N.A.I.C.S.: 325412

Societe de Promotion Pharmaceutique du Maghreb S.A. (1)
Rue 7 zone industrielle du Sahel, BP 96/97, 26400, Had Soualem, Morocco (94.1%)
Tel.: (212) 522964567
Web Site: http://www.promopharm.co.ma
Sales Range: $50-74.9 Million
Emp.: 300
Pharmaceuticals Mfr
N.A.I.C.S.: 325412
Araidah Mamoun (Chm & CEO)

Thymoorgan Pharmazie GmbH (1)
Schiffgraben 23, 38690, Goslar, Germany
Tel.: (49) 532477010
Web Site: https://www.thymoorgan.de
Pharmaceuticals Product Mfr
N.A.I.C.S.: 325412

West-Ward Pharmaceuticals Corp. (1)
401 Industrial Way W, Eatontown, NJ 07724 (100%)
Tel.: (732) 542-1191
Web Site: http://www.west-ward.com
Generic Pharmaceutical Products Mfr
N.A.I.C.S.: 325412

HIL INDUSTRIS BERHAD

Lot 3 Jalan Lada Sulah 16/11 Section 16, 40000, Shah Alam, Selangor Darul Ehsan, Malaysia
Tel.: (60) 355100501   MY
Web Site: https://www.hil.com.my

INTERNATIONAL PUBLIC

Year Founded: 1969
HIL—(KLS)
Rev.: $35,913,263
Assets: $101,226,738
Liabilities: $13,530,775
Net Worth: $87,695,963
Earnings: $4,889,364
Fiscal Year-end: 12/31/22
Injection Molding Services
N.A.I.C.S.: 333248
Milton Norman Kwee Leong Ng (Mng Dir)

Subsidiaries:

Hil Medic Sdn. Bhd. (1)
Lot 3 Jalan Lada Sulah 16/11 Section 16, 40000, Shah Alam, Selangor, Malaysia
Tel.: (60) 355100501
Web Site: https://hilmedic.com.my
Software Development Services
N.A.I.C.S.: 513210

HILAL CEMENT COMPANY K.S.C.C.

Al Marzouq Tower 19th Floor abu Baker al Siddiq St Qibla Area, PO Box 20732, Safat, Kuwait, 13068, Kuwait
Tel.: (965) 22278804
Web Site: http://www.hilalcement.com
HCC—(KUW)
Rev.: $62,845,326
Assets: $65,882,363
Liabilities: $25,531,753
Net Worth: $40,350,610
Earnings: ($4,060,308)
Emp.: 43
Fiscal Year-end: 12/31/19
Cement Mfr
N.A.I.C.S.: 327310
Sayed Salah Sayed Hashim Al-Tabtabaei (Chm)

HILAN LTD.

8 Meitav Street, Tel Aviv, 6789809, Israel
Tel.: (972) 36383341
Web Site: https://www.hilan.co.il
HLAN—(TAE)
Rev.: $715,236,071
Assets: $648,266,601
Liabilities: $643,951,088
Net Worth: $4,315,513
Earnings: $59,990,882
Fiscal Year-end: 12/31/23
Software Publisher
N.A.I.C.S.: 513210
Avraham Baum (Chm)

Subsidiaries:

Hashavshevet Ltd. (1)
3 Beit Hillel St, Tel Aviv, 67017, Israel
Tel.: (972) 35631919
Web Site: https://h-erp.co.il
Software Development Services
N.A.I.C.S.: 513210

Ness Technologies Israel Ltd. (1)
Ness Tower Atidim Industrial Park, Kiryat Atidim, Tel Aviv, 61580, Israel
Tel.: (972) 3 7666800
Web Site: http://www.ness-tech.co.il
Sales Range: $200-249.9 Million
Emp.: 2,500
IT Services
N.A.I.C.S.: 541512
Shacar Efal (Pres & CEO)

Payday LLC (1)
365 Edwin Dr, Virginia Beach, VA 23462
Tel.: (757) 523-0605
Web Site: https://paydaypayroll.com
Software Development Services
N.A.I.C.S.: 541511

QlikTech International Ltd. (1)
Atir Yeda 1 2 Building 7 Floor, Kefar Sava, 4464301, Israel
Tel.: (972) 98993000
Data Processing Services

HILBER SOLAR GMBH
Trins 128, 6150, Steinach, Austria
Tel.: (43) 52755100
Web Site: http://www.hilbersolar.at
Year Founded: 2003
Sales Range: $25-49.9 Million
Emp.: 200
Photovoltaic Tracking System Mfr
N.A.I.C.S.: 333248

HILBROY ADVISORY INC.
14 rue Begin, Montreal, H4R 1X1, QC, Canada
Tel.: (514) 334-3131
Web Site: http://www.hilbroyadvisory.com
Advisory & Investment Consulting Services
N.A.I.C.S.: 523940
Fred Dasilva *(Pres, Treas & Sec)*

HILDEBRAND MOTORS LTD.
6401 46th Street, Olds, T4H 1L7, AB, Canada
Tel.: (403) 556-3371
Web Site: http://www.oldsgm.com
Year Founded: 1984
Rev.: $15,493,488
Emp.: 28
New & Used Car Dealers
N.A.I.C.S.: 441110
Alan Conway *(Mgr-Parts)*

HILI PROPERTIES PLC
Nineteen Twenty Three Valletta Road, Marsa, MRS 3000, Malta
Tel.: (356) 25681200
Web Site: http://www.hiliproperties.com
HP25A—(MAL)
Rev.: $10,121,360
Assets: $256,328,625
Liabilities: $120,140,243
Net Worth: $136,188,382
Earnings: $3,892,537
Emp.: 15
Fiscal Year-end: 12/31/21
Real Estate Agency Services
N.A.I.C.S.: 531210
Richard Abdilla Castillo *(Chm & Mng Dir)*

Subsidiaries:

Hili Premier Estate Romania SRL (1)
4-8 Nicolae Titulescu Road America House Building, West Wing Office no 1 7th floor, Bucharest, Romania
Tel.: (40) 212026800
Real Estate Development Services
N.A.I.C.S.: 531390

HILI VENTURES LTD
1923 Valleta Road, Marsa, MRS 3000, Malta
Tel.: (356) 25 68 1200
Web Site: http://hiliventures.com
Year Founded: 1923
Holding Company
N.A.I.C.S.: 551112
Steve Tarr *(Chm)*

Subsidiaries:

Motherwell Bridge Industries Limited (1)
Hal Far Industrial Estate, Hal Far BBG, 3000, Hal Far, Malta
Tel.: (356) 21 657 800
Steel Fabrication & Engineering Services; Construction & Maintenance of Port Handling Equipment
N.A.I.C.S.: 541330
Noeleen Mallia *(Coord-Recruitment)*

Subsidiary (Non-US):

Techniplus S.A.R.L. (2)
Zone Chantier Naval Port de Casablanca Boulevard des Almohades, Casablanca, 2030, Morocco
Tel.: (212) 5 22 30 60 69
Web Site: http://www.techniplus.net
Material Handling Equipment Sales & Maintenance Services
N.A.I.C.S.: 811310
Thomas Descamps *(Mng Dir)*

HILIKS TECHNOLOGIES LTD.
A 704 7th Floor Bonanza Building Sahar Plaza Complex M V Road, JB Nagar Marol JB Nagar Metro Station Andheri East, Mumbai, 400059, Maharashtra, India
Tel.: (91) 7799169999
Web Site: https://hiliks.com
539697—(BOM)
Rev.: $1,377,747
Assets: $1,885,290
Liabilities: $1,101,794
Net Worth: $783,496
Earnings: $27,465
Fiscal Year-end: 03/31/21
Financial Support Services
N.A.I.C.S.: 523999
Rajeev Ramachandra Padhye *(Exec Dir)*

HILL & SMITH PLC
Westhaven House Arleston Way, Shirley, Solihull, B90 4LH, West Midlands, United Kingdom
Tel.: (44) 1217047430
Web Site: https://hsgroup.com
Year Founded: 1824
HILS—(LSE)
Rev.: $896,774,060
Assets: $878,037,524
Liabilities: $442,888,264
Net Worth: $435,149,260
Earnings: $32,585,280
Emp.: 4,400
Fiscal Year-end: 12/31/20
Holding Company; Building, Construction & Industrial Products Manufacturing; Steel Supplier
N.A.I.C.S.: 551112
Derek W. Muir *(CEO)*

Subsidiaries:

ATA Hill & Smith AB (1)
Staffans Vag 7, 192 78, Sollentuna, Sweden
Tel.: (46) 8988070
Web Site: http://www.ata.se
Road & Bridge Railing Parts Mfr
N.A.I.C.S.: 237310

ATA Hill & Smith AS (1)
Arboalleen 17, 3048, Drammen, Norway
Tel.: (47) 32269300
Web Site: http://www.ata.no
Road & Bridge Railing Parts Mfr
N.A.I.C.S.: 237310

ATG Access Ltd. (1)
CoBaCo House North Florida Road Haydock Industrial Estate, Haydock, WA11 9TP, United Kingdom
Tel.: (44) 8456757574
Web Site: http://www.atgaccess.com
Engineeering Services
N.A.I.C.S.: 541330

Access Design & Engineering Limited (1)
Marsh Road Cleveland, Middlesbrough, TS1 5JS, United Kingdom
Tel.: (44) 1952588788
Web Site: http://www.access-design.co.uk
Steel Mfrs
N.A.I.C.S.: 332313

Ash Plastic Products Limited (1)
City House Ettingshall Road, Wolverhampton, WV2 2JP, West Midlands, United Kingdom
Tel.: (44) 1902450300
Web Site: http://www.ashplastics.co.uk
Packaging Machinery Mfr
N.A.I.C.S.: 333993

David Archer *(Mng Dir)*

Asset International Ltd (1)
Stephenson St, Newport, NP19 4XH, United Kingdom (100%)
Tel.: (44) 1633271906
Web Site: http://www.assetint.co.uk
Sales Range: $25-49.9 Million
Emp.: 50
Fabricated Structural Metal Mfr
N.A.I.C.S.: 332312
Richard McTavish *(Mng Dir)*

Barkers Engineering Ltd (1)
Etna Works Duke St, Fenton, Stoke-on-Trent, ST4 3NS, United Kingdom
Tel.: (44) 1782319264
Web Site: http://barkersfencing.com
Sales Range: $25-49.9 Million
Emp.: 100
Ornamental & Architectural Metal Work Mfr
N.A.I.C.S.: 332323

Bergen Pipe Supports (India) Private Limited (1)
720 Bellerica Road Sector-22 Sri City DTZ, Varadaiahpalem Taluk, Chittoor, 517541, Andhra Pradesh, India
Tel.: (91) 8576305660
Fabricated Equipment Mfr
N.A.I.C.S.: 332313
Jeetinder Chopra *(Mng Dir)*

Bergen Pipe Supports, Inc. (1)
225 Merrimac St, Woburn, MA 01801
Tel.: (781) 935-9550
Plastics Pipe & Pipe Fitting Mfr
N.A.I.C.S.: 326122
Mike Spellman *(Grp CEO)*

Berry Systems (1)
Springvale Bus and Industrial Pk, WV140QL, Bilston, United Kingdom (100%)
Tel.: (44) 1902491100
Web Site: http://www.berrysystems.co.uk
Sales Range: $25-49.9 Million
Emp.: 50
Fabricated Structural Metal Mfr
N.A.I.C.S.: 332312

Birtley Building Products Ltd (1)
Mary Avenue, Birtley, DH3 1JF, United Kingdom (100%)
Tel.: (44) 1914106631
Web Site: http://www.birtley-building.co.uk
Sales Range: $50-74.9 Million
Emp.: 120
Fabricated Structural Metal Mfr
N.A.I.C.S.: 332312

Birtley Group Limited (1)
Mary Avenue, Birtley, DH3 1JF, Durham, United Kingdom
Tel.: (44) 8451215376
Wood Window & Door Mfr
N.A.I.C.S.: 321911

British Pipe Supports (Jingjiang) Limited (1)
West End of Fuyang Road South Developing District, Jingjiang, 214500, Jiangsu, China
Tel.: (86) 523 8462 1530
Web Site: http://www.hsholdings.co.uk
Sales Range: $25-49.9 Million
Emp.: 100
Commercial Pipe Fitting Mfr
N.A.I.C.S.: 332919

CPK Manufacturing LLC (1)
2188 Del Franco St Ste 70, San Jose, CA 95131
Tel.: (408) 971-4019
Web Site: http://www.cpkmfg.net
CNC Machine Mfr
N.A.I.C.S.: 332710

Capital Steel Service, LLC. (1)
82 Stokes Ave, Trenton, NJ 08638
Tel.: (609) 882-6983
Web Site: http://www.capitalsteelservice.com
Sales Range: $1-9.9 Million
Emp.: 11
Fabricated Structural Metal Mfr
N.A.I.C.S.: 332312
Craig Yemola *(VP)*

Conimast International SAS (1)
ZI La Sauniere, BP 70, 89600, Saint Florentin, France
Tel.: (33) 38 643 8200
Web Site: https://www.conimast.fr
Sales Range: $50-74.9 Million
Emp.: 20
Street Light Post Mfr
N.A.I.C.S.: 332312

Creative Pultrusions Inc. (1)
214 Industrial Ln, Alum Bank, PA 15521
Tel.: (814) 839-4186
Web Site: http://www.creativepultrusions.com
Sales Range: $25-49.9 Million
Emp.: 150
Supplier of Plastic Products
N.A.I.C.S.: 326199
Perci Fungaroli *(Dir-Materials & Fin)*

Subsidiary (Domestic):

Kenway Corporation (2)
681 Riverside Dr, Augusta, ME 04330
Tel.: (207) 622-6229
Web Site: http://www.kenway.com
Plastics Pipe & Pipe Fitting Mfr
N.A.I.C.S.: 326122
Ian Kopp *(Pres & COO)*

ET Techtonics, Inc. (1)
214 Industrial Ln, Alum Bank, PA 15521
Tel.: (814) 839-4189
Web Site: http://www.ettechtonics.com
Road & Bridge Railing Parts Mfr
N.A.I.C.S.: 237310

Hardstaff Barriers Limited (1)
Hillside Gotham Road, Kingston-on-Soar, Nottingham, NG11 0DF, United Kingdom
Tel.: (44) 115 983 2304
Web Site: https://www.hardstaffbarriers.com
Barrier Product Mfr
N.A.I.C.S.: 334511
Kathryn Cooper *(Mgr-Svcs)*

Hill & Smith Infrastructure Products India Private Limited (1)
335 Udyog Vihar Phase IV, Gurgaon, 122015, Haryana, India
Tel.: (91) 124 4383721
Web Site: http://www.hsipi.in
Galvanizing Metals Mfr
N.A.I.C.S.: 332812

Hill & Smith Ltd (1)
Springvale Business and Industrial Park, Bilston, WV140QL, United Kingdom (100%)
Tel.: (44) 1902499400
Web Site: http://www.hill-smith.co.uk
Sales Range: $50-74.9 Million
Emp.: 150
Fabricated Structural Metal Mfr
N.A.I.C.S.: 332312
Mark Tonks *(Mng Dir)*

Hill & Smith Pty Limited (1)
Unit 1 242 New Cleveland Road, Tingalpa, 4173, QLD, Australia
Tel.: (61) 1300277683
Web Site: http://www.hsroads.com.au
Concrete Products Mfr
N.A.I.C.S.: 327390

Hill & Smith, Inc. (1)
987 Buckeye Park Rd, Columbus, OH 43207
Tel.: (614) 340-6294
Web Site: http://www.hillandsmith.com
Road & Bridge Railing Parts Mfr
N.A.I.C.S.: 237310

Joseph Ash Ltd (1)
The Alcora Building 2 Mucklow Hill, Halesowen, B62 8DG, United Kingdom
Tel.: (44) 1215042560
Web Site: http://www.josephash.co.uk
Sales Range: $25-49.9 Million
Emp.: 20
Tank Component Mfr
N.A.I.C.S.: 336992

Lionweld Kennedy Flooring Ltd (1)
Marsh Road, Middlesbrough, TS1 5JS, Cleveland, United Kingdom
Tel.: (44) 1642245151
Web Site: http://www.lk-uk.com
Sales Range: $25-49.9 Million
Emp.: 90
Alumina Refining
N.A.I.C.S.: 331313

HILL & SMITH PLC

Hill & Smith PLC—(Continued)

Mallatite Ltd (1)
Hardwick View Road, Holmewood Industrial Estate, Chesterfield, S425SA, United Kingdom
Tel.: (44) 1246593280
Web Site: http://www.mallatite.co.uk
Sales Range: $25-49.9 Million
Emp.: 55
Lighting Equipment Mfr
N.A.I.C.S.: 335139
Alan Paterson (Mng Dir)

National Signal, Inc. (1)
2440 Artesia Ave, Fullerton, CA 92833
Tel.: (888) 994-0300
Web Site: http://www.nationalsignalinc.net
Sales Range: $1-9.9 Million
Emp.: 50
Communication Equipment Mfr
N.A.I.C.S.: 334290
Mark Fernandez (Pres)

Novia Associates, Inc. (1)
1 Northwestern Dr, Salem, NH 03079
Tel.: (603) 898-8600
Web Site: http://www.cp-novia.com
Vibration Isolation Hanger Mfr
N.A.I.C.S.: 332618
Brad Forsythe (Gen Mgr)

Novia Corporation, Inc. (1)
1 Northwestern Dr, Salem, NH 03079
Tel.: (603) 898-8600
Web Site: https://www.cp-novia.com
Pipe Fitting Distr
N.A.I.C.S.: 423720

Optimum Barriers (1)
Springvale Business and Industrial Park, Bilston, Wolverhampton, WV14 0QL, United Kingdom (100%)
Tel.: (44) 1902403197
Web Site: http://www.optimumbarriers.co.uk
Sales Range: $25-49.9 Million
Emp.: 10
Industrial Building Construction
N.A.I.C.S.: 236210

Parking Facilities Ltd. (1)
Unit One Kingsbury Link Trinity Road, Tamworth, B78 2EX, Staffordshire, United Kingdom
Tel.: (44) 1827870250
Web Site: https://www.parkingfacilities.co.uk
Parking Control Equipment Mfr
N.A.I.C.S.: 334514

Pipe Supports Asia Ltd (1)
26/5 Moo 9 Soi Bangchalong Bangna-Trad km 18 2, Bangchalong, Bang Phli, 10540, Samut Prakarn, Thailand
Tel.: (66) 2 312 7685
Web Site: http://www.pipesupports.com
Industrial Pipe Distr
N.A.I.C.S.: 423830

Pipe Supports Ltd (1)
Unit 22 West Stone Berry Hill Industrial Estate, Droitwich, WR9 9AS, United Kingdom
Tel.: (44) 1905795500
Web Site: http://www.pipesupports.com
Sales Range: $25-49.9 Million
Emp.: 60
Fabricated Pipe & Pipe Fitting Mfr
N.A.I.C.S.: 332996

Premier Galvanizing Limited (1)
Unit 25 Stoneferry Business Park Foster Street, Hull, HU8 8BT, East Yorkshire, United Kingdom
Tel.: (44) 148 258 7587
Web Site: https://www.premiergalvanizing.co.uk
Metal Galvanizing & Coating Mfr
N.A.I.C.S.: 332812

Prolectric Services Limited (1)
Unit 35 Hither Green, Industrial Estate, Clevedon, BS21 6XU, North Somerset, United Kingdom
Tel.: (44) 1275400570
Web Site: https://www.prolectric.co.uk
Solar Electric Power Generation Services
N.A.I.C.S.: 221114

Redman Fisher Engineering Ltd (1)
Marsh Road Teesside, Middlesbrough, TS1 5JS, United Kingdom (100%)
Tel.: (44) 1952685110
Web Site: http://www.redmanfisher.com
Sales Range: $25-49.9 Million
Emp.: 100
Sheet Metal Work Mfg
N.A.I.C.S.: 332322

Techspan Systems (1)
Griffin Lane Aylesbury, Buckingham, HP19 8BP, United Kingdom (100%)
Tel.: (44) 1296673000
Web Site: http://www.techspan.co.uk
Sales Range: $25-49.9 Million
Emp.: 35
Electronic Components Mfr
N.A.I.C.S.: 334419

Tegrel Limited (1)
Tundry Way, Tyne and Wear, Blaydon, NE21 5TT, United Kingdom
Tel.: (44) 1914146111
Web Site: http://www.tegrel.co.uk
Sheet Steel Mfr
N.A.I.C.S.: 332312
David Oliphant (Mgr-Sys)

United Fiberglass of America, Inc. (1)
907 Wheel St, Springfield, OH 45503
Tel.: (937) 325-7305
Web Site: http://www.unitedfiberglass.com
Sales Range: $1-9.9 Million
Emp.: 25
Noncurrent-Carrying Wiring Devices, Nsk
N.A.I.C.S.: 335932

V&S Columbus Galvanizing LLC (1)
987 Buckeye Park Rd, Columbus, OH 43207
Tel.: (614) 443-4621
Road & Bridge Railing Parts Mfr
N.A.I.C.S.: 237310
Rich Collins (Sr Mgr-Sls & Mktg)

V&S Memphis Galvanizing LLC (1)
3348 Fite Rd, Millington, TN 38053
Tel.: (901) 358-4899
Road & Bridge Railing Parts Mfr
N.A.I.C.S.: 237310

V&S New York Galvanizing LLC (1)
272 Corporate Dr, Owego, NY 13827
Tel.: (607) 304-2399
Building Material Mfr & Distr
N.A.I.C.S.: 327120

Varley and Gulliver Ltd (1)
Ridgacre Road, Sparkbrook, West Bromwich, B71 1BB, United Kingdom (100%)
Tel.: (44) 1217732441
Web Site: http://www.v-and-g.co.uk
Sales Range: $25-49.9 Million
Emp.: 50
Fabricated Structural Metal Mfr
N.A.I.C.S.: 332312

Voigt & Schweitzer LLC (1)
987 Buckeye Park Rd, Columbus, OH 43207
Tel.: (614) 449-8281
Web Site: http://www.hotdipgalvanizing.com
Rev.: $17,400,000
Emp.: 200
Galvanizing Services
N.A.I.C.S.: 332812
Brian Miller (Pres)

Subsidiary (Domestic):

Korns Galvanizing Co., Inc. (2)
75 Bridge St, Johnstown, PA 15902
Tel.: (814) 535-3293
Web Site: http://www.kornsgalvanizing.com
Rev.: $1,900,000
Emp.: 25
Metal Coating, Engraving, except Jewelry & Silverware & Allied Services to Manufacturers
N.A.I.C.S.: 332812
John Sheehan (Chm)

V&S Amboy Galvanizing LLC (2)
1190 Amboy Ave, Perth Amboy, NJ 08861
Tel.: (732) 442-7555
Web Site: http://www.hotdipgalvanizing.com
Sales Range: $25-49.9 Million
Emp.: 50
Metal Products Galvanizing Services
N.A.I.C.S.: 332812
Bob Messler (VP-Ops-Galvanizing)

V&S Bristol Galvanizing LLC (2)
14781 Industrial Park Rd, Bristol, VA 24202
Tel.: (276) 466-5558
Web Site: http://www.galvanizing.com
Sales Range: $10-24.9 Million
Emp.: 17
Galvanizing Services
N.A.I.C.S.: 332812
Tracey Wright (Plant Mgr)

V&S Columbus Galanizing LLC (2)
1000 Buckeye Park Rd, Columbus, OH 43207
Tel.: (614) 443-4621
Web Site: http://www.hotdipgalvanizing.com
Sales Range: $1-9.9 Million
Emp.: 65
Galvanizing Services
N.A.I.C.S.: 332812
Paul Shope (Plant Mgr)

V&S Delaware Galvanizing LLC (2)
511 Carroll Dr, New Castle, DE 19720
Tel.: (302) 322-1420
Web Site: http://www.hotdipgalvanizing.com
Metal Products Galvanizing Services
N.A.I.C.S.: 423510

V&S Detroit Galvanizing LLC (2)
12600 Arnold, Redford, MI 48239
Tel.: (313) 535-2600
Web Site: http://www.hotdipgalvanizing.com
Rev.: $1,800,000
Emp.: 30
Galvanizing Services
N.A.I.C.S.: 332812

V&S Lebanon Galvanizing LLC (2)
153 Micro Dr, Jonestown, PA 17038
Tel.: (717) 861-7777
Web Site: http://www.hotdipgalvanizing.com
Metal Products Galvanizing Services
N.A.I.C.S.: 423510

V&S Schuler Engineering Inc. (2)
2240 Allen Ave SE, Canton, OH 44707
Tel.: (330) 452-5200
Rev.: $3,700,000
Emp.: 60
Fabricated Structural Metal
N.A.I.C.S.: 332312
Greg Shaheen (Dir-Ops)

V&S Schuler Tubular Products LLC (2)
420 E Frankfort St, Muskogee, OK 74403
Tel.: (918) 687-7701
Web Site: http://www.vsschuler.com
Rev.: $2,400,000
Emp.: 30
Fabricated Structural Metal
N.A.I.C.S.: 332312

V&S Taunton Galvanizing, LLC (2)
585 John Hancock Rd, Taunton, MA 02780
Tel.: (508) 828-9499
Web Site: http://www.hotdipgalvanizing.com
Sales Range: $25-49.9 Million
Emp.: 30
Steel Products Galvanizing Services
N.A.I.C.S.: 423510

HILL INCORPORATED

150 Duncan Mill Rd Unit 2, Toronto, M5G 1V2, ON, Canada
Tel.: (416) 543-4904
Web Site: https://hillincorporated.com
Year Founded: 2008
HSEEF—(TSXV)
Rev.: $1,918,630
Assets: $2,256,841
Liabilities: $2,206,287
Net Worth: $50,554
Earnings: ($1,187,909)
Fiscal Year-end: 06/30/24
Alcoholic Beverage Product Distr
N.A.I.C.S.: 424820
Matthew Jewell (CFO)

HILLCREST ENERGY TECHNOLOGIES LTD.

Suite 1170 - 1040 West Georgia Street, Vancouver, V6E 4H1, BC, Canada
Tel.: (713) 626-9564   BC
Web Site: https://hillcrestenergy.tech
Year Founded: 2006

INTERNATIONAL PUBLIC

HLRTF—(OTCQB)
Rev.: $151,051
Assets: $2,048,660
Liabilities: $1,202,456
Net Worth: $846,205
Earnings: ($6,098,500)
Fiscal Year-end: 12/31/23
Oil & Gas Exploration & Production Services
N.A.I.C.S.: 211120
Donald Currie (CEO)

HILLCREST VOLKSWAGEN (1979) LTD

3154 Robie Street, Halifax, B3K 4P9, NS, Canada
Tel.: (902) 453-2790
Web Site: http://www.hillcrestvw.com
Year Founded: 1979
New & Used Car Dealers
N.A.I.C.S.: 441110
Mike Currie (Gen Mgr-Sls)

HILLGROVE RESOURCES LIMITED

Ground Floor 57 King William Road, PO Box 372, Unley, 5061, SA, Australia
Tel.: (61) 870701698
Web Site: https://www.hillgroveresources.com
HGO—(ASX)
Rev.: $530,618
Assets: $68,833,867
Liabilities: $31,454,942
Net Worth: $37,378,925
Earnings: ($11,121,177)
Emp.: 208
Fiscal Year-end: 12/31/23
Gold, Copper & Other Metal Mining Services
N.A.I.C.S.: 212220
Derek Carter (Chm)

HILLHOUSE INVESTMENT MANAGEMENT LIMITED

1 Exchange Square 8 Connaught Place Suite 1606, Hong Kong, China (Hong Kong)
Tel.: (852) 21791988   HK
Web Site: http://www.hillhousecap.com
Year Founded: 2005
Asset Management Services
N.A.I.C.S.: 525990
Lei Zhang (Founder & CEO)

Subsidiaries:

Belle International Holdings Limited (1)
19/F Belle Tower No 8 Lanxiang 1st ST, Yuehai Sub-district Nanshan District, Shenzhen, China (57.6%)
Tel.: (86) 75582877388
Web Site: http://www.belleintl.com
Sales Range: $5-14.9 Million
Holding Company; Footwear Mfr & Sales
N.A.I.C.S.: 551112
Baijiao Sheng (CEO)

Subsidiary (Non-US):

Belle Worldwide Limited (2)
9 F Belle Twr 918 Cheung Sha Wan Rd, Cheung Sha Wan, Kowloon, China (Hong Kong)
Tel.: (852) 27414760
Footwear Poducts Mfr & Whslr
N.A.I.C.S.: 316210

Subsidiary (Domestic):

Guangzhou Taobo Sports Development Company Limited (2)
No 81 Xihu Rd, Yuexiu Dist, Guangzhou, 510030, Guangdong, China
Tel.: (86) 2061273333
Sportswear Mfr
N.A.I.C.S.: 315210

AND PRIVATE COMPANIES

Subsidiary (Non-US):

Lai Wah Footwear Trading
Limited (2)
9 F Belle Tower 918 Cheung Sha Wan Rd,
Cheung Sha Wan, Kowloon, China (Hong
Kong)
Tel.: (852) 27414760
Leather Footwear Whslr
N.A.I.C.S.: 424340

Millie's Company Limited (2)
9/F Belle Tower 918 Cheung Sha Wan
Road, Cheung Sha Wan, Kowloon, China
(Hong Kong)
Tel.: (852) 24221268
Emp.: 200
Womens Clothing & Footwear Whslr
N.A.I.C.S.: 424340
Candy Hon *(Gen Mgr)*

Mirabell International Holdings
Limited (2)
9th Fl Belle Tower 918 Cheung Sha Wan
Rd, Kowloon, China (Hong Kong)
Tel.: (852) 24898131
Web Site: http://www.mirabell.com.hk
Footwear Mfr & Whslr
N.A.I.C.S.: 316210
Baijiao Sheng *(Exec Dir)*

Subsidiary (Domestic):

Mirabell Footwear Limited (3)
9 F Belle Tower 918 Cheung Sha Wan Rd,
Kowloon, China (Hong Kong)
Tel.: (852) 24898131
Footwear Whslr
N.A.I.C.S.: 424340

Subsidiary (Non-US):

Senses Marketing International
Limited (2)
10 F Belle Tower 918 Cheung Sha Wan Rd,
Cheung Sha Wan, Kowloon, China (Hong
Kong)
Tel.: (852) 28861208
Footwear Whslr
N.A.I.C.S.: 424340

Staccato Footwear Company
Limited (2)
Belle Tower 10F 918 Cheung Sha Wan
Road, Cheung Sha Wan, Kowloon, China
(Hong Kong)
Tel.: (852) 27414760
Footwear Products Whslr
N.A.I.C.S.: 424340

Blue Insurance Limited (1)
Suite 1701 City Plaza One 1111 King's
Road, Taikoo Shing, Hong Kong, China
(Hong Kong) (80%)
Tel.: (852) 35509600
Web Site: http://www.blue.com.hk
Sales Range: $50-74.9 Million
Emp.: 100
Life Insurance Products & Services
N.A.I.C.S.: 524113
Trevor Bull *(CEO/Mng Dir-India)*

HILLS LIMITED
Unit 1 Building F 3-29 Birnie Avenue,
Lidcombe, 2141, NSW, Australia
Tel.: (61) 292165510
Web Site:
https://corporate.hills.com.au
HIL—(ASX)
Rev.: $139,689,085
Assets: $73,973,935
Liabilities: $48,205,843
Net Worth: $25,768,093
Earnings: ($7,927,690)
Fiscal Year-end: 06/30/21
Holding Company; Technology &
Communications Solutions
N.A.I.C.S.: 551112
David Chambers *(Chm)*

Subsidiaries:

Extensia Pty. Ltd. (1)
Level 7 344 Queen Street, GPO Box 710,
Brisbane, QLD, Australia
Tel.: (61) 732920255
Web Site: https://extensia.com.au
Health Care Information Services
N.A.I.C.S.: 524114

Hills Industries Antenna & TV
Systems (1)
U1 Building F 3-29 Birnie Ave, Lidcombe,
2210, NSW, Australia
Tel.: (61) 297175290
Web Site: http://www.hillsantenna.com.au
Sales Range: $25-49.9 Million
Emp.: 35
Provider of Household Audio & Video
Equipment
N.A.I.C.S.: 334310

Hills Industries Direct Alarm
Supplies (1)
12 Wiggs Rd, Riverwood, 2210, NSW,
Australia (100%)
Tel.: (61) 297175222
Web Site: http://www.hioos.com.au
Sales Range: $25-49.9 Million
Emp.: 35
Providers of Household Audio & Video
Equipment
N.A.I.C.S.: 334310

Pacific Communications Pty. Ltd. (1)
Unit 10 331 Ingles St Port, Melbourne,
3207, VIC, Australia
Tel.: (61) 396760222
Web Site: http://www.pacom.com.au
Sales Range: $25-49.9 Million
Emp.: 35
Providers of Household Audio & Video
Equipment
N.A.I.C.S.: 334310
Joe Abiad *(Dir-Fin & Agency Ops)*

Subsidiary (Non-US):

Gencom Technologies Ltd. (2)
7 Airborne Road, Rosedale, Auckland,
0632, New Zealand (100%)
Tel.: (64) 9 913 7500
Web Site: https://www.gencom.com
Sales Range: $25-49.9 Million
Emp.: 15
Media Technology Solutions
N.A.I.C.S.: 334310

General Communications (2)
189 Willis St, Wellington, New Zealand
Tel.: (64) 9397100
Web Site: http://www.hills.com.au
Providers of Household Audio & Video
Equipment
N.A.I.C.S.: 334310

HILLS WASTE SOLUTIONS LIMITED
Wiltshire House County Park Business Centre Shrivenham Road, Swindon, SN1 2NR, United Kingdom
Tel.: (44) 01793 714950
Web Site: http://www.hills-waste.co.uk
Waste Management & Recycling Services
N.A.I.C.S.: 562998
Alan Pardoe *(Chm)*

Subsidiaries:

Able Waste Management Ltd. (1)
The Recycling Center Hallen Industrial Estate, Bristol, BS10 7SE, United Kingdom
Tel.: (44) 0117 982 9882
Web Site: http://www.ablewaste.co.uk
Recyclable Material Merchant Whslr
N.A.I.C.S.: 423930
Art Lynds *(Mgr)*

HILLSTONE NETWORKS CO., LTD.
181 Jingrun Road, Science and Technology Town, Suzhou, 215000, China
Tel.: (86) 51266806966
Web Site:
https://www.hillstonenet.com
Year Founded: 2011
688030—(SHG)
Rev.: $113,948,092
Assets: $297,095,203
Liabilities: $111,673,346
Net Worth: $185,421,857
Earnings: ($25,623,323)
Emp.: 2,000
Fiscal Year-end: 12/31/22
Information Technology Services
N.A.I.C.S.: 541512
Dongping Luo *(Chm & Gen Mgr)*

HILONG HOLDING LIMITED
No 1825 Luodong Road Baoshan Industrial Zone, Shanghai, 200949, China
Tel.: (86) 2133851886
Web Site:
http://www.hilonggroup.com
1623—(HKG)
Rev.: $524,545,351
Assets: $1,095,264,191
Liabilities: $624,225,841
Net Worth: $471,038,350
Earnings: $20,463,862
Emp.: 3,245
Fiscal Year-end: 12/31/22
Oilfield Equipment & Services
N.A.I.C.S.: 333132
Jun Zhang *(Chm)*

Subsidiaries:

Hilong Drill Pipe (Wuxi) Co., Ltd. (1)
No 217 Xitai Road, Meicun Xinwu District,
Wuxi, 214112, China
Tel.: (86) 51085366075
Oil & Gas Equipment Mfr & Distr
N.A.I.C.S.: 333132

Hilong Energy Limited (1)
Rm 3206 32/F Times Sq Twr 1, Causeway
Bay, China (Hong Kong)
Tel.: (852) 25060885
Holding Company
N.A.I.C.S.: 551112

Hilong Marine Engineering (Hong
Kong) Limited (1)
RM 1008 Sino Life Insurance Building No
707 Zhang Yang Rd, Pudong Xin District,
Shanghai, 200120, China
Tel.: (86) 2158301130
Oil & Gas Field Drilling Services
N.A.I.C.S.: 213111

Hilong Oil Service & Engineering Co.,
Ltd. (1)
Floor 20 Office Building No 1, Shimao International Center 13 North Gongti Road Chaoyang District, Beijing, 100027, China
Tel.: (86) 1084059090
Oil & Gas Field Drilling Services
N.A.I.C.S.: 213111
Dai Daliang *(Gen Mgr)*

Subsidiary (Non-US):

Hilong (Colombia) Oil Service & Engineering Co., Ltd. (2)
Cra 11AN 97 A-19 Ofic 402 Edif IQ, Bogota,
Colombia
Tel.: (57) 3202163992
Oil & Gas Field Drilling Services
N.A.I.C.S.: 213111

Hilong Oil Service & Engineering Ecuador Cia. Ltda. (2)
Av De los shyris 344 y Eloy Alfaro, Edificio
Parque CentralPiso 4 OF 403, Quito, Ecuador
Tel.: (593) 23823946
Oil & Gas Field Drilling Services
N.A.I.C.S.: 213111
Shao Guo Wei *(Mgr-Fin)*

Hilong Oil Service & Engineering Nigeria Ltd. (2)
NO 34 Woke Road Off Sani Abacha road
GRA Phase 3, Port Harcourt, Nigeria
Tel.: (234) 8063721583
Oil & Gas Field Drilling Services
N.A.I.C.S.: 213111

Hilong Oil Service & Engineering
Pakistan (Private) Limited (2)
House No 25 Khayaban-e Hafiz Phase V
DHA, Karachi, Pakistan
Tel.: (92) 2135853397
Oil & Gas Field Drilling Services
N.A.I.C.S.: 213111

HILONG HOLDING LIMITED

Xuefeng Chen *(Deputy Gen Mgr)*

Hilong Petroleum Company LLC (1)
24FR Plot 6 ICAD 1, Musaffah, 108704,
Abu Dhabi, United Arab Emirates
Tel.: (971) 25512513
Oilfield Equipment Services
N.A.I.C.S.: 213112
Willis Yan *(Sr Mgr-Sls)*

Hilong Petroleum Pipe Company
LLC (1)
24FR Plot 6 Industrial City Of Abu Dhabi
ICAD-I Mussafah, PO Box 108704, Abu
Dhabi, United Arab Emirates
Tel.: (971) 25512513
Web Site: https://www.hilonguae.com
Oil & Gas Equipment Mfr & Distr
N.A.I.C.S.: 333132
Gilbert Talion *(Coord-Logistics)*

Hilong Petropipe Co., Ltd. (1)
1103 17th Ave, Nisku, T9E 0N1, AB,
Canada
Tel.: (780) 979-0731
Pipe Coating Services & Oil Gas Equipment
Distr
N.A.I.C.S.: 332812
Paul Klotz *(Mgr)*

Hilong USA LLC. (1)
10333 Richmond Ave Ste 615, Houston, TX
77042
Tel.: (713) 339-3678
Web Site: https://hilonggroup.com
Oil & Gas Equipment Distr
N.A.I.C.S.: 423830

Jiangsu TSC Coating Co., Ltd. (1)
No 18 Zhanghang Road Dawn Industrial
Park, Taizhou, 225532, Jiangsu, China
Tel.: (86) 52388680186
Pipe Coating Services
N.A.I.C.S.: 332812

Nantong Hilong Steel Pipe Co.,
Ltd. (1)
No 899 East Road Three factory Sanchang
Town, Haimen, 226126, Jiangsu, China
Tel.: (86) 51382658629
Emp.: 170
Steel Mfr & Distr
N.A.I.C.S.: 331210

Shanghai Tube-Cote Petroleum Pipe
Coating Co., Ltd. (1)
No 669 Jinle Road Yuepu Industrial Zone,
Baoshan District, Shanghai, 200941,
China (51%)
Tel.: (86) 2166932885
Pipe Coating Services
N.A.I.C.S.: 332812
Cao Yuhong *(Gen Mgr)*

Sichuan Hilong Petroleum Technology Co., Ltd. (1)
Xingye Road Airport Industrial Park, Gaoping District, Nanchong, 637100, Sichuan,
China
Tel.: (86) 8176077766
Pipe Coating Services
N.A.I.C.S.: 332812

Texas Internal Pipe Coating, LLC (1)
8463 Hwy 75 S, Madisonville, TX 77864
Tel.: (936) 348-2508
Web Site:
https://www.texasinternalpipecoating.com
Emp.: 125
Pipe Coating Services
N.A.I.C.S.: 332812
Rhonda Lechuga *(Dir-Customer Svc)*

Tianjin Tube-Cote Petroleum Pipe
Coating Co., Ltd. (1)
Nanhai anti Lu Xi standard factory building
6 No 8 Chuangye Road, Nangang Industrial
Zone, Tianjin, 300280, China
Tel.: (86) 2263117161
Pipe Coating Services
N.A.I.C.S.: 332812

Trade House Hilong-Rus Co.
Ltd. (1)
Str Vernadskogo d 29 floor 17 office 1701,
119331, Moscow, Russia
Tel.: (7) 49331977
Oil & Gas Equipment Distr
N.A.I.C.S.: 423830

HILTI AG

HILTI AG
Feldkircherstrasse 100, PO Box 333,
9494, Schaan, Liechtenstein
Tel.: (423) 234 2111
Web Site: http://www.hilti.com
Year Founded: 1941
Rev.: $6,234,990,848
Assets: $6,568,942,016
Liabilities: $3,195,139,328
Net Worth: $3,373,802,688
Earnings: ($608,794,112)
Emp.: 30,000
Fiscal Year-end: 12/31/19
Fastening, Drilling Equipment & Construction Tools Mfr & Marketer
N.A.I.C.S.: 333517
Christoph Loos *(CEO & Member-Exec Bd)*

Subsidiaries:

Hilti (Aust.) Pty. Ltd. **(1)**
PO Box 3217, 2138, Rhodes, NSW,
Australia **(100%)**
Tel.: (61) 287481000
Web Site: http://www.hilti.com.au
Sales Range: $50-74.9 Million
Emp.: 160
Tool Mfr & Distr
N.A.I.C.S.: 333991

Hilti (Bulgaria) EOOD **(1)**
ul Business Park Sofia 4, 1766, Sofia,
Bulgaria **(100%)**
Tel.: (359) 29760011
Web Site: http://www.hilti.bg
Tool Mfr & Distr
N.A.I.C.S.: 333991

Hilti (Canada) Corporation **(1)**
2360 Meadowpine Boulevard, Mississauga,
L5N 6S2, ON, Canada **(100%)**
Web Site: http://www.hilti.ca
Sales Range: $25-49.9 Million
Tool Mfr & Distr
N.A.I.C.S.: 333991

Hilti (China) Ltd. **(1)**
8th Floor Building 2 Global Metropolis Plaza
58 Yaoyuan Road, Pudong New Area,
Shanghai, 200233, China
Tel.: (86) 4008202585
Web Site: http://www.hilti.cn
Sales Range: $100-124.9 Million
Hand & Power Tools Mfr
N.A.I.C.S.: 333991

Hilti (Fastening Systems) Ltd. **(1)**
North City Business Park Finglas 11, Dublin, Ireland
Tel.: (353) 1850287387
Web Site: http://www.hilti.ie
Sales Range: $25-49.9 Million
Tool Mfr & Distr
N.A.I.C.S.: 333991
Martin Idbarnt *(Gen Mgr)*

Hilti (Gt. Britain) Limited **(1)**
Unit 2 Lapwing Centre 4 Hagley Rd, Manchester, M5 3EY, Salford, United
Kingdom **(100%)**
Tel.: (44) 844 815 6290
Web Site: http://www.hilti.co.uk
Sales Range: $200-249.9 Million
Emp.: 2
Tool Mfr & Distr
N.A.I.C.S.: 333991

Hilti (Hong Kong) Ltd. **(1)**
701 2704 7 Fl Tower 8 Manulife Financial
Center, 223 Wai Yip Kwntong, Kowloon,
China (Hong Kong) **(100%)**
Tel.: (852) 82288118
Sales Range: $25-49.9 Million
Emp.: 90
Tool Mfr & Distr
N.A.I.C.S.: 333991

Hilti (Japan) Ltd. **(1)**
2 6 20 Chigasaki Minami Tsuzuki Ward, Yokohama, 224 8550, Japan **(100%)**
Tel.: (81) 459436211
Web Site: http://www.hilti.co.jp
Sales Range: $25-49.9 Million
Emp.: 100
Tool Mfr & Distr

Hilti (Korea) Company Ltd. **(1)**
407 Shingal Ri Kihung up, Seoul, 137-896,
Yongin kun, Korea (South)
Tel.: (82) 312818040
Web Site: http://www.hilti.co.kr
Sales Range: $50-74.9 Million
Emp.: 150
Tool Mfr & Distr
N.A.I.C.S.: 333991
Susan Yeon *(Gen Mgr)*

Hilti (Malaysia) Sdn. Bhd. **(1)**
9 Jalan PJS 11 20, Petaling Jaya, 46150,
Bandar Sunway, Malaysia
Tel.: (60) 356338583
Web Site: http://www.hilti.my
Sales Range: $25-49.9 Million
Emp.: 53
Tool Mfr & Distr
N.A.I.C.S.: 333991

Hilti (Philippines), Inc. **(1)**
9/F Cyberscape Beta Topaz & Ruby Road,
Ortigas Center, Pasig, 1605,
Philippines **(100%)**
Tel.: (63) 287847100
Web Site: http://www.hilti.com.ph
Sales Range: $25-49.9 Million
Emp.: 250
Tool Mfr & Distr
N.A.I.C.S.: 333991

Hilti (Poland) Sp. zo.o. **(1)**
ul Pulawska 491, 02-844, Warsaw, Poland
Tel.: (48) 801888801
Web Site: http://www.hilti.pl
Sales Range: $50-74.9 Million
Tool Mfr & Distr
N.A.I.C.S.: 333991
Tomas Trocil *(Gen Dir)*

Hilti (Portugal), Productos e Servicos
Lda. **(1)**
Rua da Lionesa 446 Ed C39 Apartado
4085, Leca do Balio, 4465-671, Matosinhos, Portugal **(100%)**
Tel.: (351) 808200111
Web Site: http://www.hilti.pt
Sales Range: $25-49.9 Million
Tool Mfr & Distr
N.A.I.C.S.: 333991
Francesco Bandini *(Chm)*

Hilti (Schweiz) AG **(1)**
Soodstrasse 61, 8134, Adliswil,
Switzerland **(100%)**
Tel.: (41) 844848485
Web Site: http://www.hilti.ch
Sales Range: $50-74.9 Million
Tool Mfr & Distr
N.A.I.C.S.: 333991

Hilti (South Africa) Pty. Ltd. **(1)**
72 Gazelle Ave Corp Pk, Johannesburg,
1685, South Africa **(100%)**
Tel.: (27) 112373000
Web Site: http://www.za.hilti.com
Sales Range: $50-74.9 Million
Emp.: 200
Tool Mfr & Distr
N.A.I.C.S.: 333991
Birk Dijkstra *(Gen Mgr)*

Hilti (Suomi) Oy **(1)**
Virkatie 3, PO Box 164, 01510, Vantaa,
Finland **(100%)**
Tel.: (358) 207999200
Web Site: http://www.hilti.fi
Sales Range: $25-49.9 Million
Emp.: 85
Tool Mfr & Distr
N.A.I.C.S.: 333991

Hilti (Ukraine) Ltd. **(1)**
street Vincent Hvoyka bldg 15/15, Kiev,
04080, Ukraine **(100%)**
Tel.: (380) 443905566
Web Site: http://www.hilti.ua
Sales Range: $25-49.9 Million
Emp.: 85
Tool Mfr & Distr
N.A.I.C.S.: 333991

Hilti AG, Werk Thuringen **(1)**
Werkstr 13, A-6712, Thuringen, Austria
Tel.: (43) 24513211
Tool Mfr & Distr
N.A.I.C.S.: 333991

Hilti Albania Shpk **(1)**
Karburant ELDA Rruga e Durresit, Laprake,
Tirana, Albania
Tel.: (355) 4 2 413 906
Civil Engineering Services
N.A.I.C.S.: 541330

Hilti Argentina, S.A. **(1)**
Profesor Manuel Garcia 4760, AR
B1605BIB, Buenos Aires, Olive Trees, Argentina
Tel.: (54) 47214400
Tool Mfr & Distr
N.A.I.C.S.: 333991

Hilti Austria GmbH **(1)**
Altmannsdorfer Strasse 165, PO Box 316,
Vienna, 1230, Austria **(100%)**
Tel.: (43) 1661010
Web Site: http://www.hilti.at
Sales Range: $100-124.9 Million
Emp.: 325
Tool Mfr
N.A.I.C.S.: 333991
Manfred Gutternigg *(CEO)*

Hilti BY FLLC **(1)**
Business Center A100 Gintovta str 1-3,
Minsk, 220125, Belarus
Tel.: (375) 17 286 38 18
Civil Engineering Services
N.A.I.C.S.: 541330

Hilti Bahrain W.L.L. **(1)**
Shop Z55 Road 2403 Sitra Highway Area
West Al Ekr 624, PO Box 11401, Manama,
Bahrain
Tel.: (973) 17 701031
Civil Engineering Services
N.A.I.C.S.: 541330

Hilti Belgium N.V. **(1)**
Bettegem 12, Z 4 Broekooe 220 1730,
1731, Asse, Belgium **(100%)**
Tel.: (32) 24677911
Web Site: http://www.hilti.be
Sales Range: $50-74.9 Million
Emp.: 200
Tool Mfr & Distr
N.A.I.C.S.: 333991
Tuillaume Lafond *(Gen Mgr)*

Hilti CR Spol. s.r.o. **(1)**
Uhrineveska 734, PO Box 29, Pruhonice,
252 43, Prague, Czech Republic **(100%)**
Tel.: (420) 261195333
Web Site: http://www.hilti.cz
Sales Range: $1-9.9 Million
Emp.: 200
Tool Mfr & Distr
N.A.I.C.S.: 333991
Joses Zeitler *(Gen Mgr)*

Hilti Caribe Inc. **(1)**
PO Box 194949 380 Juan Calas F St Ste
13, San Juan, PR 00919-4949
Tel.: (787) 281-6160
Sales Range: $25-49.9 Million
Emp.: 36
Tool Mfr & Distr
N.A.I.C.S.: 333991

Hilti Chile Limitada **(1)**
Av El Salto 4001, 8580641, Huechuraba,
Santiago, Chile **(100%)**
Tel.: (56) 226553000
Web Site: http://www.hilti.cl
Sales Range: $50-74.9 Million
Tool Mfr & Distr
N.A.I.C.S.: 333991

Hilti Colombia S.A. **(1)**
Calle 26 13A 37, Bogota,
Colombia **(100%)**
Tel.: (57) 3810132
Sales Range: $25-49.9 Million
Emp.: 28
Tool Mfr & Distr
N.A.I.C.S.: 333991

Hilti Complete Systems UAB **(1)**
Verkiu g 29 22 corp, Vilnius, 06327,
Lithuania **(100%)**
Tel.: (370) 52722452
Sales Range: $25-49.9 Million
Emp.: 9
Tool Mfr & Distr
N.A.I.C.S.: 333991
Arnoldas Paplauskas *(Mgr-Fin)*

Hilti Construction Equipments
EURL **(1)**
85 Rue Boudjemaa Moghni El Magharia
Hussein Dey, 16 040, Algiers, Algeria
Tel.: (213) 21 771 444
Civil Engineering Services
N.A.I.C.S.: 541330

Hilti Croatia d.o.o. **(1)**
Ljudevita Posavskog 29, 10360, Sesvete,
Croatia **(100%)**
Tel.: (385) 12030777
Web Site: http://www.hilti.hr
Sales Range: Less than $1 Million
Emp.: 20
Tool Mfr & Distr
N.A.I.C.S.: 333991

Hilti Denmark A/S **(1)**
Stamholmen 157 1st floor, 2650, Hvidovre,
Denmark **(100%)**
Tel.: (45) 44888080
Web Site: http://www.hilti.dk
Sales Range: $25-49.9 Million
Tool Mfr
N.A.I.C.S.: 333991

Hilti Deutschland GmbH **(1)**
Hiltistr 2, 86916, Kaufering, Germany
Tel.: (49) 8191900
Web Site: http://www.hilti.de
Tool Mfr
N.A.I.C.S.: 333991

Hilti Distribution Ltd. **(1)**
Business Pk ZAO Greenwood MKAD 69 km
Bldg 3, Moscow, 143441, Russia **(100%)**
Tel.: (7) 4957925252
Web Site: http://www.hilti.ru
Tool Mfr & Distr
N.A.I.C.S.: 333991
Vladimir Mosny *(Gen Mgr)*

Hilti Eesti OU **(1)**
Mustamae tee 46, 10621, Tallinn, Estonia
Tel.: (372) 6260080
Web Site: http://www.hilti.ee
Sales Range: $25-49.9 Million
Emp.: 12
Tool Mfr
N.A.I.C.S.: 333991

Hilti Entwicklung Befestigungstechnik
GmbH **(1)**
Hiltistrabe 2, Kaufering, 86916,
Germany **(100%)**
Tel.: (49) 8191900
Web Site: http://www.hilti.de
Sales Range: $100-124.9 Million
Emp.: 350
Tool Mfr & Distr
N.A.I.C.S.: 333991
Jochen Olbert *(Gen Mgr)*

Hilti Entwicklung Elektrowerzeuge
GmbH **(1)**
Hiltistrasse 2, 86916, Kaufering, Germany
Tel.: (49) 8008885522
Web Site: http://www.hilti.de
Tool Mfr & Distr
N.A.I.C.S.: 333991

Hilti Espanola S.A. **(1)**
Fuente de la Mora 2 Edificio I, 28050, Madrid, Spain
Tel.: (34) 902100475
Web Site: http://www.hilti.es
Sales Range: $25-49.9 Million
Emp.: 100
Tool Mfr & Distr
N.A.I.C.S.: 333991
Lorent Gimenez *(Gen Mgr)*

Hilti Far East Private Ltd. **(1)**
No 20 Harbour Drive 06 06 PSA Vista, Singapore, 117612, Singapore **(100%)**
Tel.: (65) 67777887
Web Site: http://www.hilti.com.sg
Sales Range: $10-24.9 Million
Tool Mfr & Distr
N.A.I.C.S.: 333991

Hilti France S.A. **(1)**
1 rue Jean Mermoz, Rond Pt Merantais,
78778, Magny-les-Hameaux, Cedex,
France **(100%)**
Tel.: (33) 825010505
Web Site: http://www.hilti.fr
Sales Range: $400-449.9 Million
Tool Mfr & Distr
N.A.I.C.S.: 333991

Hilti Hellas S.A. **(1)**

132 Kymis Avenue, 15123, Maroussi,
Greece **(100%)**
Tel.: (30) 2102880600
Web Site: http://www.hilti.gr
Sales Range: $25-49.9 Million
Tool Mfr & Distr
N.A.I.C.S.: 333991
Stamatina K. Zoi *(Mgr-Fin)*

Hilti Holding GmbH (1)
Altmannsdorferstr 165, Postfach 316, 1230,
Vienna, Austria
Tel.: (43) 166101
Web Site: http://www.hilti.at
Tool Mfr & Distr
N.A.I.C.S.: 333991

Hilti Hungaria Szolgaltato Kft. (1)
Bojtar U 58-62, PF 140, Obuda, 1037, Budapest, Hungary
Tel.: (36) 80445844
Web Site: http://www.hilti.hu
Tool Mfr & Distr
N.A.I.C.S.: 333991

Hilti India Private Limited (1)
F 90/4 Okhla Industrial Area, Phase 1, New
Delhi, India
Tel.: (91) 1142701111
Web Site: http://www.hilti.in
Sales Range: $200-249.9 Million
Emp.: 600
Tool Mfr & Distr
N.A.I.C.S.: 333991

**Hilti Insaat Malzemeleri Ticaret
A.S.** (1)
Yukari Dudullu Mh Tavukcu Yolu Cd Sehit
Sk, Form Plaza No 24, Istanbul, 347750,
Umraniye, Turkiye
Tel.: (90) 2165286800
Web Site: http://www.hilti.com.tr
Sales Range: $50-74.9 Million
Emp.: 120
Tool Mfr & Distr
N.A.I.C.S.: 333991
Mehmet Kalay *(Gen Mgr)*

Hilti Italia S.p.A. (1)
Piazza Montanelli 20, 20099, Sesto San
Giovanni, MI, Italy
Tel.: (39) 022126274
Web Site: http://www.hilti.it
Sales Range: $200-249.9 Million
Power Tools Mfr & Whslr
N.A.I.C.S.: 333991

Hilti Kunststofftechnik GmbH (1)
Martin Hilti Way 1, 89278, Nersingen, Germany
Tel.: (49) 73088160
Web Site: http://www.hilti.de
Sales Range: $50-74.9 Million
Emp.: 200
Tool Mfr & Distr
N.A.I.C.S.: 333991

Hilti Maroc S.A. (1)
6 Allee des Cypres, Ain Sebaa, Casablanca, Morocco
Tel.: (212) 522 67 58 00
Civil Engineering Services
N.A.I.C.S.: 541330

Hilti Mexicana, S.A. de C.V. (1)
Col Los Morales Polanco Jaime Blames 8,
Oficina 102 1Er PisoDel Miguel, Mexico,
11510, Mexico **(100%)**
Tel.: (52) 5553871600
Web Site: http://www.lag.hilti.com
Sales Range: $50-74.9 Million
Emp.: 150
Tool Mfr & Distr
N.A.I.C.S.: 333991

Hilti Middle East FZE (1)
Roundabout 8 WC-1 Jebel Ali Free Zone,
PO Box 16792, Dubai, United Arab Emirates
Tel.: (971) 4 8060 300
Civil Engineering Services
N.A.I.C.S.: 541330

Hilti Nederland B.V. (1)
Leeuwenhoekstraat 4, 2652 XL, Berkel en
Rodenrijs, Netherlands **(100%)**
Tel.: (31) 105191111
Web Site: http://www.hilti.nl
Sales Range: $50-74.9 Million
Tool Mfr & Distr
N.A.I.C.S.: 333991

Hilti Qatar W.L.L. (1)
Al Mamoura complex 2nd, Doha, 24097,
Qatar
Tel.: (974) 4406 3600
Civil Engineering Services
N.A.I.C.S.: 541330

Hilti Romania S.R.L. (1)
Equest Logistic Center, Dragomiresti-Deal,
077096, Ilfov, Romania
Tel.: (40) 21 352 3000
Civil Engineering Services
N.A.I.C.S.: 541330
Calin Oana Raluca *(Mgr-Tool Svc)*

Hilti SMN doo (1)
Banatska 83C, Zemun, Serbia
Tel.: (381) 11 655 68 96
Civil Engineering Services
N.A.I.C.S.: 541330

Hilti Services Limited (1)
Mukusalas Street 42A, Riga, 1004,
Latvia **(100%)**
Tel.: (371) 67600673
Web Site: http://www.hilti.lv
Sales Range: $25-49.9 Million
Tool Mfr & Distr
N.A.I.C.S.: 333991

Hilti Slovakia Spol. s.r.o. (1)
Galvaniho, Bratislava, 821 04, Slovakia
Tel.: (421) 248221211
Web Site: http://www.hilti.sk
Sales Range: $50-74.9 Million
Emp.: 250
Tool Mfr & Distr
N.A.I.C.S.: 333991
Marek Kis-Bandi *(Gen Mgr)*

Hilti Slovenija d.o.o. (1)
Brodisce 18, Ljubljana, 1236, Trzin,
Slovenia **(100%)**
Tel.: (386) 802522
Web Site: http://www.hilti.si
Sales Range: $1-9.9 Million
Tool Mfr & Distr
N.A.I.C.S.: 333991

Hilti Svenska AB (1)
Testvagen 1, PO Box 123, 232 22, Arlov,
Sweden
Tel.: (46) 20555999
Web Site: http://www.hilti.se
Sales Range: $50-74.9 Million
Tool Mfr & Distr
N.A.I.C.S.: 333991

Hilti Systems BH Sarajevo d.o.o. (1)
Dobrinjska 7, 71000, Sarajevo, Bosnia &
Herzegovina
Tel.: (387) 33 761 100
Web Site: http://www.hilti.group
Emp.: 8
Civil Engineering Services
N.A.I.C.S.: 541330

Hilti Taiwan Co., Ltd. (1)
4F No 2 Section 2, Taipei, 104,
Taiwan **(100%)**
Tel.: (886) 800 221036
Web Site: http://www.hilti.com.tw
Sales Range: $50-74.9 Million
Emp.: 200
Tool Mfr & Distr
N.A.I.C.S.: 333991

Hilti Vietnam Co. Ltd (1)
40 Hoa Dao Street, Phu Nhuan, Ho Chi
Minh City, Vietnam
Tel.: (84) 8 3930 4091
Emp.: 40
Civil Engineering Services
N.A.I.C.S.: 541330
Binh Le An *(Mgr-HR)*

Hilti do Brasil Comercial Ltda. (1)
Al Rio Negro 500 Tower A 9th Floor, Alphaville Industrial, Barueri, 06454-000, Sao
Paulo, Brazil
Tel.: (55) 1141349050
Web Site: http://www.hilti.com.br
Sales Range: $50-74.9 Million
Hand & Power Tools Mfr
N.A.I.C.S.: 333991

Hilti, Inc. (1)
5825 S 129th E Ave Ste F, Tulsa, OK
74134
Tel.: (918) 252-6000
Web Site: http://www.us.hilti.com

Sales Range: $200-249.9 Million
Mfr of Anchors, Direct Fastening Systems &
Drilling Systems
N.A.I.C.S.: 333991
Avi Kahn *(CEO-North America)*

Hilti-Syria L.L.C. (1)
Artoz, Judaydat Artuz, Syria
Tel.: (963) 11 680 8066
Civil Engineering Services
N.A.I.C.S.: 541330

**Inversiones Hilti de Venezuela
S.A.** (1)
Edificio Segre Piso 2 Ala Norte Calle Pascuale, Giorgio 3ra Transversal, Caracas, VE
1071, Los Ruices, Venezuela
Tel.: (58) 2122034200
Web Site: http://www.hilti.com
Sales Range: $25-49.9 Million
Emp.: 32
Tool Mfr & Distr
N.A.I.C.S.: 333991

P.T. Hilti Nusantara (1)
Building 111 GCS Cilandak Commercial Estate Jl Raya Cilandak KKO, 12075, Jakarta,
Indonesia
Tel.: (62) 21 789 0850
Civil Engineering Services
N.A.I.C.S.: 541330
Jeffry Lukita *(Product Mgr)*

HILTON FOOD GROUP PLC
2-8 The Interchange Latham Road,
Huntingdon, PE29 6YE, Cambridgeshire, United Kingdom
Tel.: (44) 1480383333
Web Site:
  https://www.hiltonfoods.com
Year Founded: 1994
HFG—(LSE)
Rev.: $5,078,976,418
Assets: $1,641,305,498
Liabilities: $1,232,038,954
Net Worth: $409,266,544
Earnings: $47,625,549
Fiscal Year-end: 12/31/23
Meat Packing
N.A.I.C.S.: 311612
Robert Watson *(Chm)*

Subsidiaries:

HFG Sverige AB (1)
Hacksta Industri Omrade Saltangsvagen
53, 721 32, Vasteras, Sweden
Tel.: (46) 214703000
Web Site:
  http://www.hiltonfoodgroupplc.com
Sales Range: $100-124.9 Million
Emp.: 300
Meat Packing Services
N.A.I.C.S.: 311611
Wim Kole *(CEO)*

Hilton Foods Limited Sp. z.o.o. (1)
ul Strefowa 31, 43-100, Tychy, Poland
Tel.: (48) 327789709
Web Site: http://www.hiltonfoods.pl
Sales Range: $75-99.9 Million
Emp.: 800
Meat Packing Services
N.A.I.C.S.: 424420

Hilton Meats (Retail) Limited (1)
Unit 2 8 The Interchange Latham Rd,
Huntingdon, PE29 6YE, Cambridgeshire,
United Kingdom
Tel.: (44) 1480383333
Sales Range: $100-124.9 Million
Emp.: 800
Chilled Beef & Lamb Production Services
N.A.I.C.S.: 311611
Frank McMyler *(Mng Dir)*

Hilton Meats Zaandam B.V. (1)
Grote Tocht 31, 1507 CG, Zaandam, 1507
CG, Netherlands
Tel.: (31) 756594702
Sales Range: $25-49.9 Million
Emp.: 250
Food Production
N.A.I.C.S.: 311999
Vincent Sereuder *(Mgr-Production)*

HILTON HOMES LTD.
Suite 201 1615 St Marys Rd, Winnipeg, R2M 3W8, MB, Canada
Tel.: (204) 254-8790
Web Site:
  https://www.hiltonhomes.ca
Year Founded: 1985
Rev.: $10,000,000
Emp.: 5
Home Construction & Building Services
N.A.I.C.S.: 444110
Issy Kahanovitch *(Mgr-Production)*

HILTON METAL FORGING LTD.
303 Tanishka Building Akurli Road
Kandivali East, Mumbai, 400101, Maharshtra, India
Tel.: (91) 2240426565
Web Site:
  https://www.hiltonmetal.com
Year Founded: 1997
HILTON—(NSE)
Rev.: $6,510,791
Assets: $15,423,804
Liabilities: $9,538,634
Net Worth: $5,885,170
Earnings: ($2,671,537)
Emp.: 137
Fiscal Year-end: 03/31/21
Forging Services
N.A.I.C.S.: 332111
Yuvraj Hiralal Malhotra *(Chm & Mng Dir)*

HILZINGER HOLDING GMBH
Carl-Benz-Str 4, 77731, Willstatt,
Germany
Tel.: (49) 78529190
Web Site: http://www.hilzinger.de
Sales Range: $250-299.9 Million
Emp.: 700
Holding Company; Windows & Doors
Mfr
N.A.I.C.S.: 551112
Helmut Hilzinger *(Mng Dir)*

Subsidiaries:

**hilzinger Fenster + Tueren
GmbH** (1)
Carl-Benz-Strasse 4, 77731, Willstatt, Germany
Tel.: (49) 78529190
Web Site: http://www.hilzinger.de
Sales Range: $100-124.9 Million
Emp.: 1,200
Windows & Doors Mfr & Supplier
N.A.I.C.S.: 321911
Helmut Hilzinger *(Mng Dir)*

HIM GMBH
Waldstrasse 11, Biebesheim am
Rhein, 64584, Germany
Tel.: (49) 62588950
Web Site: http://www.him.de
Year Founded: 1972
Rev.: $116,225,708
Emp.: 331
Waste Management Services
N.A.I.C.S.: 562211
Andreas Ellerkmann *(Chm)*

HIM INTERNATIONAL MUSIC, INC.
15F No 135 Sec 2 Jian Guo N Rd,
Taipei, Taiwan
Tel.: (886) 225121919
Web Site: https://www.him.com.tw
8446—(TPE)
Rev.: $28,057,593
Assets: $97,736,297
Liabilities: $46,164,556
Net Worth: $51,571,741
Earnings: $9,808,211
Fiscal Year-end: 12/31/22
Music Publishers
N.A.I.C.S.: 512230
Yen Ching Lu *(Chm)*

HIM TEKNOFORGE LIMITED

HIM International Music, Inc.—(Continued)

HIM TEKNOFORGE LIMITED
Vill Billanwali Sai Road, Baddi, 173205, HP, India
Tel.: (91) 8527661999
Web Site:
https://www.himteknoforge.com
Year Founded: 1973
505712—(BOM)
Rev.: $49,483,988
Assets: $45,522,894
Liabilities: $24,760,566
Net Worth: $20,762,328
Earnings: $1,280,607
Emp.: 1,191
Fiscal Year-end: 03/31/23
Auto & Tracker Components Mfr
N.A.I.C.S.: 336110
Rajiv Aggarwal *(Co-Mng Dir)*

HIMACHAL FIBRES LIMITED
Plot No 43-44 Industrial Area, Barotiwala Distt, Solan, 174103, HP, India
Tel.: (91) 1614684000
Web Site:
https://www.himachalfibre.com
Year Founded: 1980
514010—(BOM)
Rev.: $2,072,750
Assets: $7,500,504
Liabilities: $3,972,505
Net Worth: $3,528,000
Earnings: ($687,737)
Emp.: 296
Fiscal Year-end: 03/31/21
Yarn & Cotton Mfr
N.A.I.C.S.: 313110
Gian Chand Thakur *(Exec Dir)*

HIMACS, LTD.
Queen's Tower C 2-3-5 Minatomirai, Nishi-ku, Yokohama, 220-6221, Kanagawa, Japan
Tel.: (81) 452016655
Web Site: https://www.himacs.jp
Year Founded: 1976
4299—(TKS)
Rev.: $114,729,770
Assets: $89,829,900
Liabilities: $17,549,550
Net Worth: $72,280,350
Earnings: $7,826,240
Emp.: 903
Fiscal Year-end: 03/31/24
Software Development Services
N.A.I.C.S.: 541511
Tsuyoshi Nakajima *(Pres & CEO)*

HIMADRI SPECIALTY CHEMICAL LTD.
Ruby House 8 India Exchange Place 2nd Fl, Kolkata, 700 001, India
Tel.: (91) 3322304363
Web Site: https://www.himadri.com
Year Founded: 1987
500184—(BOM)
Rev.: $573,274,870
Assets: $502,064,609
Liabilities: $191,159,746
Net Worth: $310,904,862
Earnings: $29,464,754
Emp.: 895
Fiscal Year-end: 03/31/23
Carbon Chemical Company
N.A.I.C.S.: 335991
Shyam Sundar Choudhary *(Co-Founder)*

HIMALAYA DRUG COMPANY
Makali, Bengaluru, 562 123, India
Tel.: (91) 8023714444
Web Site:
http://www.himalayahealthcare.com
Year Founded: 1930
Sales Range: $350-399.9 Million
Emp.: 1,200

Pharmaceuticals, Personal Care, Well-Being & Animal Health Products Mfr
N.A.I.C.S.: 325412
Philip Haydon *(CEO)*

Subsidiaries:

SIA The Himalaya Drug Company (1)
Elizabetes str 11-10, Riga, 1010, Latvia
Tel.: (371) 67854168
Web Site: http://www.himalayadirect.com
Herbal Product Distr
N.A.I.C.S.: 424210
Natalija Berzina *(Acct Mgr-Trade Mktg)*

The Himalaya Drug Company (Pty) Ltd (1)
Yellow Wood Place Woodmead Business Park 145 Western Service Road, Sandton, Woodmead, 2191, South Africa
Tel.: (27) 116564284
Herbal Product Distr
N.A.I.C.S.: 424210

The Himalaya Drug Company FZCO (1)
Dubai Airport Free Zone Authority Phase-4 Block B 4th Floor, PO Box 54637, Dubai, United Arab Emirates
Tel.: (971) 42045455
Web Site: http://www.himalayaherbals.com
Herbal Product Distr
N.A.I.C.S.: 424210

The Himalaya Drug Company L.L.C. (1)
1101 Gillingham Ln, Sugar Land, TX 77478
Tel.: (713) 863-1622
Web Site: http://www.himalayausa.com
Herbal Product Distr
N.A.I.C.S.: 424210

The Himalaya Drug Company Pte Ltd (1)
9 Temasek Boulevard 24-01 Suntec Tower 2, Singapore, 038989, Singapore
Tel.: (65) 65353067
Herbal Product Distr
N.A.I.C.S.: 424210
Jay Kumar Parla *(Head-Ops & Scientific Svcs)*

HIMALAYA FOOD INTERNATIONAL LIMITED
Village Shubh Khera, Paonta Sahib, Shimla, 173025, Himachal Pardesh, India
Tel.: (91) 1704223494
Web Site:
https://himalayafoodcompany.com
526899—(BOM)
Rev.: $7,949,760
Assets: $37,159,395
Liabilities: $28,695,030
Net Worth: $8,464,365
Earnings: $343,980
Emp.: 83
Fiscal Year-end: 03/31/21
Food Products Mfr
N.A.I.C.S.: 311412
Man Mohan Malik *(Co-Founder, Chm, CEO & Mng Dir)*

HIMALAYA SHIPPING LTD.
2nd Floor S E Pearman Bldg 9 Parla-Ville Road, Hamilton, HM 11, Bermuda
Tel.: (441) 4791831590   BM
Web Site: https://www.himalaya-shipping.com
Year Founded: 2021
HSHP—(NYSE)
Assets: $177,800,000
Liabilities: $87,500,000
Net Worth: $90,300,000
Earnings: ($2,000,000)
Fiscal Year-end: 12/31/22
Marine Shipping Services
N.A.I.C.S.: 488510
Herman Billung *(CEO)*

HIMALAYAN BANK LIMITED
Kamaladi, PO Box 20590, Kathmandu, Nepal
Tel.: (977) 14227749   NP
Web Site:
https://www.himalayanbank.com
Year Founded: 1993
HBL—(NEP)
Rev.: $87,337,636
Assets: $1,510,914,132
Liabilities: $1,331,417,661
Net Worth: $179,496,470
Earnings: $26,272,257
Emp.: 1,018
Fiscal Year-end: 07/15/21
Investment & Banking Services
N.A.I.C.S.: 523150
Maheshwor P. Joshi *(Officer-Grievance, Head-Legal & Share Dept & Asst Gen Mgr)*

HIMALAYAN DISTILLERY LIMITED
Jawalakhel Lalitpur, Patan, Nepal
Tel.: (977) 15422028
Web Site:
https://www.himalayandistillery.com
Year Founded: 1999
HDL—(NEP)
Rev.: $42,376,087
Assets: $26,968,722
Liabilities: $2,357,184
Net Worth: $24,611,538
Earnings: $4,948,215
Fiscal Year-end: 07/16/23
Beverages Mfr & Whslr
N.A.I.C.S.: 339999
Akhileswar Prashad Singh *(Chm)*

HIMALAYAN EVEREST INSURANCE LIMITED
HGI House Babar Mahal, GPO Box 148, Kathmandu, Nepal
Tel.: (977) 15245090
Web Site: https://www.hei.com.np
Year Founded: 1993
HEI—(NEP)
Insurance Services
N.A.I.C.S.: 524298
Nura Kumari Sharma *(Dir-Pub)*

Subsidiaries:

Everest Insurance Company Ltd. (1)
Hattisar, PO Box 10675, Kathmandu, Nepal
Tel.: (977) 1 4444717
Web Site: http://www.everestinsurance.com
Sales Range: $1-9.9 Million
Insurance Services
N.A.I.C.S.: 524298
Roshan Kumar Shrestha *(Head-Mktg)*

HIMARAYA CO., LTD.
1-1-1 Ezoe, Gifu, 500-8630, Japan
Tel.: (81) 582716622
Web Site: https://hmry.jp
Year Founded: 1982
7514—(TKS)
Rev.: $363,944,640
Assets: $216,101,460
Liabilities: $113,608,300
Net Worth: $102,493,160
Earnings: $1,281,320
Emp.: 737
Fiscal Year-end: 08/31/24
Sports Apparel Distr
N.A.I.C.S.: 424350
Yusaku Komori *(Chm & CEO)*

HIMATSINGKA SEIDE LIMITED
10/24 Kumara Krupa Road High Grounds, Bengaluru, 560 001, Karnataka, India
Tel.: (91) 8042578000
Web Site:
https://www.himatsingka.com
Year Founded: 1985

INTERNATIONAL PUBLIC

HIMATSEIDE—(NSE)
Rev.: $330,047,491
Assets: $663,531,563
Liabilities: $489,799,221
Net Worth: $173,732,342
Earnings: $7,682,957
Emp.: 7,114
Fiscal Year-end: 03/31/23
Decorative & Fashion Fabric Wear Designer
N.A.I.C.S.: 313210
Shrikant Himatsingka *(CEO-Grp & Mng Dir)*

Subsidiaries:

Himatsingka America Inc. (1)
261 5th Ave Ste 1400, New York, NY 10016
Tel.: (212) 545-8929
Fabric Sales
N.A.I.C.S.: 313210

Himatsingka Linens (1)
10/24 Kumara Krupa Road High Grounds, Bengaluru, 560 001, Karnataka, India
Tel.: (91) 8022378000
Web Site: http://www.himatsingka.com
Sales Range: $25-49.9 Million
Fabrics & Yarn Products Distr
N.A.I.C.S.: 313210

Himatsingka Singapore Pte. Ltd. (1)
1 Nassim Road 01-04, Singapore, 258 458, Singapore
Tel.: (65) 6838 0976
Fabrics Mfr
N.A.I.C.S.: 313210

HIMAX TECHNOLOGIES, INC.
No 26 Zilian Road, Xinshi District, T'ainan, 744092, Taiwan
Tel.: (886) 65050880   Ky
Web Site: https://www.himax.com.tw
HIMX—(NASDAQ)
Rev.: $945,428,000
Assets: $1,643,404,000
Liabilities: $779,702,000
Net Worth: $863,702,000
Earnings: $49,421,000
Emp.: 2,164
Fiscal Year-end: 12/31/23
Semiconductor Developer
N.A.I.C.S.: 334413
Biing-Seng Wu *(Co-Founder & Chm)*

Subsidiaries:

CM Visual Technology Corp. (1)
No 13 Mujhagang West Rd, Shanhua Dist, Tainan City, 741, Taiwan
Tel.: (886) 6 588 9933
Web Site: https://www.cmvt.com.tw
Omni Wide Film Product Mfr
N.A.I.C.S.: 334419

Himax Analogic, Inc. (1)
10F No 1 Xiangyang Rd, Taipei, 10046, Taiwan
Tel.: (886) 22 370 3999
Integrated Circuit Distr
N.A.I.C.S.: 423690

Himax Display (USA) Inc. (1)
1901 S Bascom Ave Ste 300, Campbell, CA 95008
Tel.: (408) 877-4223
Semiconductor Product Distr
N.A.I.C.S.: 423690

Himax IGI Precision Ltd. (1)
4611 E Lake St, Minneapolis, MN 55406
Tel.: (612) 721-6283
Semiconductor Product Mfr
N.A.I.C.S.: 334413

Himax Imaging, Inc. (1)
36 Discovery Ste 270, Irvine, CA 92618
Tel.: (949) 585-9838
Web Site: http://www.himaximaging.com
Emp.: 50
Computer Peripherals Mfr
N.A.I.C.S.: 334118

Himax Imaging, Ltd. (1)
17F No 285 Section 2 Guangfu Road, Hsinchu, 30071, Taiwan
Tel.: (886) 3 516 3277

AND PRIVATE COMPANIES

Semiconductor Product Mfr & Distr
N.A.I.C.S.: 334413

Himax Media Solutions, Inc. (1)
10F No 1 Xiangyang Rd, Taipei, 10046, Taiwan
Tel.: (886) 22 370 3999
Semiconductor Product Distr
N.A.I.C.S.: 423690
Norman Hung *(VP-Sales-Marketing)*

Himax Technologies (Shenzhen) Co., Ltd. (1)
Web Site: http://www.himax.com.tw
Computer Peripherals Mfr
N.A.I.C.S.: 334118

Himax Technologies (Suzhou) Co., Ltd. (1)
Web Site: http://www.himax.com
Computer Peripherals Mfr
N.A.I.C.S.: 334118

Himax Technologies Japan Ltd. (1)
Purosu Nishishinbashi Bldg 3F 2-4-3 Nish-ishinbashi, Minato-ku, Tokyo, 105-0003, Japan
Tel.: (81) 35 510 5385
Semiconductor Mfr
N.A.I.C.S.: 334413

Himax Technologies Korea Ltd. (1)
E-202 Y-Mall 210 GwangJang Road 1767 Jangjae ri, Baebang town, Asan, 336-747, Chungcheongnam-do, Korea (South)
Tel.: (82) 41 560 6666
Semiconductor Mfr
N.A.I.C.S.: 334413

HIMILE MECHANICAL SCIENCE & TECHNOLOGY CO., LTD

No 1 Himile Road Mishui Science & Technology Industry Zone, Gaomi, Weifang, 261500, Shandong, China
Tel.: (86) 5362361008
Web Site: https://www.haomaikeji.com
Year Founded: 1995
002595—(SSE)
Rev.: $932,569,092
Assets: $1,206,350,496
Liabilities: $175,331,520
Net Worth: $1,031,018,976
Earnings: $168,508,080
Emp.: 7,562
Fiscal Year-end: 12/31/22
Industrial Machinery Mfr
N.A.I.C.S.: 333248
Tang Lixing *(Chm-Supervisory Bd)*

Subsidiaries:

Himile (Liaoning) Science & Technology Co., Ltd. (1)
No 22 Zhongyang Road Yilu Industry Zone, Tieling, 112611, Liaoning, China
Tel.: (86) 2478715833
Industrial Machinery Mfr
N.A.I.C.S.: 333248

Himile (Thailand) Co., Ltd. (1)
No 7/407 M 6 Mabyangpom, Pluakdaeng, Rayong, 21140, Thailand
Tel.: (66) 38020118
Industrial Machinery & Equipment Distr
N.A.I.C.S.: 423830

Himile Europe, LLC (1)
Amerikai fasor 9, 8000, Szekesfehervar, Hungary
Tel.: (36) 303209139
Web Site: https://himile.eu
Industrial Machinery & Equipment Distr
N.A.I.C.S.: 423830

Himile Mechanical Science & Technology (Kunshan) Co., Ltd. (1)
No 9 Qiaocheng Road, Kunshan, 215300, Jiangsu, China
Tel.: (86) 51257716591
Industrial Machinery Mfr
N.A.I.C.S.: 333248

Himile Mold (Tianjin) Co., Ltd. (1)
No 15 Huaxing Road Huaming Industrial Park, Dongli District, Tianjin, 300300, China

Tel.: (86) 2259652369
Industrial Machinery Mfr
N.A.I.C.S.: 333248

HIMMER AG

Steinerne Furt 95, 86176, Augsburg, Germany
Tel.: (49) 82172000
Web Site: http://www.himmer.de
Rev.: $13,393,974
Emp.: 101
Printing Services
N.A.I.C.S.: 323111
Marcus Fischer *(CEO)*

HIMS CO., LTD.

126 Namdongseo-Ro Gojan-Dong, Namdong-Gu, Incheon, Korea (South)
Tel.: (82) 328212511
Web Site: https://www.hims.co.kr
Year Founded: 1999
238490—(KRS)
Rev.: $24,191,321
Assets: $60,994,446
Liabilities: $13,490,658
Net Worth: $47,503,788
Earnings: ($6,630,874)
Emp.: 230
Fiscal Year-end: 12/31/22
Display Component Mfr
N.A.I.C.S.: 334419
J. H. Kim *(CEO)*

HIN SANG GROUP (INTERNATIONAL) HOLDING CO. LTD.

Unit 1213-1215 12/F Seapower Tower Concordia Plaza, 1 Science Museum Road Tsim Sha Tsui, Kowloon, China (Hong Kong)
Tel.: (852) 2 798 9901 Ky
Web Site: http://www.hinsanggroup.com
Year Founded: 1996
6893—(HKG)
Rev.: $15,548,023
Assets: $89,482,584
Liabilities: $50,556,420
Net Worth: $38,926,164
Earnings: ($1,690,283)
Emp.: 262
Fiscal Year-end: 03/31/22
Holding Company
N.A.I.C.S.: 551112
Siu Hin Pang *(Co-Founder, Chm & CEO)*

Subsidiaries:

Hin Sang Hong Company Limited (1)
Units 1213-1215 12/F Seapower Tower Concordia Plaza No 1, Science Museum Road Tsim Sha Tsui, Kowloon, China (Hong Kong)
Tel.: (852) 27989901
Food Supplement Distr
N.A.I.C.S.: 456191
Selina Wong *(Mgr-HR & Admin)*

Tai Wo Tong Company Limited (1)
No 24 Nga Tsin Long Road, Kowloon, China (Hong Kong)
Tel.: (852) 26232006
Web Site: http://www.taiwotang1932.com
Bakery Goods Retailer
N.A.I.C.S.: 445291

HINCKLEY AND RUGBY BUILDING SOCIETY

Upper Bond Street, Hinckley, LE10 1NZ, Leicestershire, United Kingdom
Tel.: (44) 800 434 6343
Web Site: http://www.hrbs.co.uk
Rev.: $22,953,000
Assets: $1,094,688,904
Liabilities: $1,038,071,066
Net Worth: $56,617,837
Earnings: $664,981
Emp.: 95

Fiscal Year-end: 11/30/19
Mortgage Lending
N.A.I.C.S.: 522310
Lisa M. Bengi *(Head-HR)*

HIND ALUMINIUM INDUSTRIES LIMITED

B-1 Tulsi Vihar Dr Annie Besant Road, Worli Naka, Mumbai, 400 018, Maharashtra, India
Tel.: (91) 2240457100
Web Site: https://www.associatedgroup.com
Year Founded: 1973
531979—(BOM)
Rev.: $3,502,249
Assets: $10,815,141
Liabilities: $3,673,870
Net Worth: $7,141,271
Earnings: ($454,927)
Emp.: 10
Fiscal Year-end: 03/31/22
Aluminium Products Mfr
N.A.I.C.S.: 331313
Shailesh Daga *(Mng Dir)*

HIND COMMERCE LIMITED

307 Arun Chambers Tardeo Road, Mumbai, 400 034, India
Tel.: (91) 2240500100
Web Site: https://www.hindcommerce.com
Year Founded: 1984
538652—(BOM)
Rev.: $54,640
Assets: $1,821,510
Liabilities: $78,554
Net Worth: $1,742,957
Earnings: $11,471
Emp.: 3
Fiscal Year-end: 03/31/23
Yarn & Fabric Trading Services
N.A.I.C.S.: 424990
Umesh R. Lahoti *(Mng Dir)*

HIND RECTIFIERS LIMITED

Lake Road Bhandup W, Mumbai, 400 078, India
Tel.: (91) 2249601775
Web Site: https://www.hirect.com
Year Founded: 1958
504036—(BOM)
Rev.: $50,838,661
Assets: $33,601,277
Liabilities: $18,935,785
Net Worth: $14,665,492
Earnings: $1,064,495
Emp.: 375
Fiscal Year-end: 03/31/22
Railway Transportation Equipment Mfr
N.A.I.C.S.: 336999
S. K. Nevatia *(Chm & Mng Dir)*

HIND SECURITIES & CREDITS LIMITED

D-16 Ground Floor Udyog Nagar Nangloi, Delhi, 110041, India
Tel.: (91) 989 942 5575
Web Site: http://www.supersecurities.in
Rev.: $456,597
Assets: $3,278,499
Liabilities: $2,462,393
Net Worth: $816,106
Earnings: $8,077
Emp.: 3
Fiscal Year-end: 03/31/19
Financial Support Services
N.A.I.C.S.: 523999
Jagdish Rai Bansal *(Chm & Mng Dir)*

HIND SYNTEX LIMITED

Plot No 2 3 4 & 5 Sector A Industrial Growth Centre, Pillukhedi, Rajgarh, 465667, Madhya Pradesh, India

Tel.: (91) 73752444350
Web Site: http://www.hindgroupindia.com
Year Founded: 1983
Rev.: $6,848,392
Assets: $3,441,545
Liabilities: $2,787,932
Net Worth: $653,613
Earnings: ($434,746)
Emp.: 779
Fiscal Year-end: 03/31/18
Synthetic Blended Yarn Product Mfr
N.A.I.C.S.: 313110
Balesh Kumar Bagree *(CFO)*

Subsidiaries:

Dewas Soya Ltd. (1)
Plot No 96 and 97 Agra-Bombay Road, Industrial Area No 3, Dewas, 455001, MP, India
Tel.: (91) 7272258807
Cigarette Filters Mfr
N.A.I.C.S.: 312230
Sanjay Tiwari *(Sec)*

HINDCON CHEMICALS LIMITED

Vashudha 62 B Braunfeld Row, Kolkata, 700027, India
Tel.: (91) 3324490839
Web Site: https://www.hindcon.com
Year Founded: 1947
HINDCON—(NSE)
Rev.: $10,404,580
Assets: $6,430,382
Liabilities: $1,294,503
Net Worth: $5,135,879
Earnings: $522,259
Emp.: 115
Fiscal Year-end: 03/31/23
Chemicals Mfr
N.A.I.C.S.: 325998
Sanjay Goenka *(Mng Dir)*

HINDOOSTAN MILLS LIMITED

Shivsagar Estate D Block 8th floor Dr Annie Besant Road, Worli, Mumbai, 400 018, India
Tel.: (91) 2261240700
Web Site: https://www.hindoostan.com
Year Founded: 1873
509895—(BOM)
Rev.: $14,027,559
Assets: $10,353,539
Liabilities: $3,685,950
Net Worth: $6,667,588
Earnings: ($928,869)
Emp.: 399
Fiscal Year-end: 03/31/23
Spinning & Weaving Mill Operator
N.A.I.C.S.: 313110
Chandrahas K. Thackersey *(Chm)*

HINDPRAKASH INDUSTRIES LTD.

301 Hindprakash House Plot No 10/6 Phase-I GIDC, Vatva, Ahmedabad, 382445, Gujarat, India
Tel.: (91) 7968127000
Web Site: https://www.hindprakash.in
Year Founded: 1942
543645—(BOM)
Rev.: $12,293,795
Assets: $9,586,428
Liabilities: $4,477,106
Net Worth: $5,109,322
Earnings: $295,558
Emp.: 40
Fiscal Year-end: 03/31/23
Specialty Chemical Product Mfr
N.A.I.C.S.: 325998
Om Prakash Mangal *(Chm)*

HINDUJA GLOBAL SOLUTIONS LTD.

Tower C 1st floor Plot C-21 G Block

HINDUJA GLOBAL SOLUTIONS LTD.

Hinduja Global Solutions Ltd.—(Continued)
Bandra Kurla Complex, Bandra East,
Mumbai, 400 051, India
Tel.: (91) 2261360407
Web Site: https://hgs.cx
532859—(BOM)
Rev.: $685,665,667
Assets: $1,551,237,815
Liabilities: $361,084,515
Net Worth: $1,190,153,301
Earnings: $47,882,071
Emp.: 22,000
Fiscal Year-end: 03/31/23
Business Process Management Services
N.A.I.C.S.: 561499
C. Subramanya *(CEO-MENA & CTO)*

Subsidiaries:

HGS USA (1)
1901 E War Memorial Dr, Peoria, IL 61614
Tel.: (309) 685-5901
Web Site: https://hgs.cx
Sales Range: $350-399.9 Million
Emp.: 1,300
Customer Relationship Management Services
N.A.I.C.S.: 541618
Kathy Hamburger *(Pres)*

Hinduja Global Solutions (UK) Limited (1)
UK Vantage LondonGreat West Road, Brentford, London, TW8 9AG, United Kingdom
Tel.: (44) 203 747 1423
Web Site: http://www.teamhgs.com
Business Process Management Services
N.A.I.C.S.: 561499

Subsidiary (US):

Element Solutions, LLC (2)
651 W Washington Blvd Ste 206, Chicago, IL 60661 (85.63%)
Tel.: (312) 755-1845
Web Site: http://www.hgsdigital.com
Software Publisher
N.A.I.C.S.: 513210

NXTDIGITAL Limited (1)
In Centre 49/50 MIDC 12th Road Andheri East, Mumbai, 400 093, India
Tel.: (91) 2228208585
Web Site: http://nxtdigital.in
Rev.: $137,653,521
Assets: $256,356,241
Liabilities: $226,220,522
Net Worth: $30,135,719
Earnings: ($1,897,582)
Emp.: 878
Fiscal Year-end: 03/31/2021
Computer Software Application Services
N.A.I.C.S.: 611420
Amar Chintopanth *(CFO)*

Subsidiary (Domestic):

Bhima Riddhi Infotainment Private Limited (2)
446/5 E Ward Kailash Tower 3rd Floor Station Road Shahupuri, Kolhapur, 416001, India
Tel.: (91) 2312656977
Web Site: http://www.bripl.in
Cable Television Network Services
N.A.I.C.S.: 516210

IndusInd Media & Communications Limited (2)
IN Centre 49/50 12th Road, MIDC Industrial Area Andheri East, Mumbai, 400093, Maharashtra, India
Tel.: (91) 2228248300
Television Broadcasting Services
N.A.I.C.S.: 516120
Sanjay Kamat *(CEO)*

OneOTT Intertainment Limited (2)
Plot No 49/50 12th Cross Road, MIDC Andheri East, Mumbai, 400093, Maharashtra, India
Tel.: (91) 2262581800
Web Site: http://www.onebroadband.in
Broadband Services
N.A.I.C.S.: 517111

Yugal Kishore Sharma *(CEO)*

Vinsat Digital Private Limited (2)
47-10-6 Plot No 19 & 20 4 th Floor North Block, Sreepada Diamond Towers Near Diamond Park Dwarakanagar, Visakhapatnam, India
Tel.: (91) 891278667
Web Site: http://www.vinsatdigital.com
Multi Channel Transmission Services
N.A.I.C.S.: 517111

Pacific Horizon Limited (1)
St James Ct Ste 308 St Denis St, Port Louis, Mauritius
Tel.: (230) 2116242
Sales Range: $10-24.9 Million
Emp.: 44
Business Management Services
N.A.I.C.S.: 561499
Dennis Seksum *(Mng Dir)*

TekLink International Inc. (2)
4320 Winfield Rd, Ste 215, Warrenville, IL 60555
Tel.: (630) 791-9760
Web Site: http://www.tli-usa.com
Business Consulting Services
N.A.I.C.S.: 561499
Manish Umarwadia *(VP)*

HINDUJA GROUP LTD.

Hinduja House 171 Dr Annie Besant Road, Worli, Mumbai, 400 018, India
Tel.: (91) 22 249 60707
Web Site: http://www.hindujagroup.com
Year Founded: 1914
International Investment Company
N.A.I.C.S.: 523999
Srichand P. Hinduja *(Co-Chm)*

Subsidiaries:

Ashok Leyland Ltd. (1)
No 1 Sardar Patel Road, Guindy, Chennai, 600 032, India
Tel.: (91) 4422206000
Web Site: https://www.ashokleyland.com
Rev.: $3,593,220,540
Assets: $5,951,506,470
Liabilities: $4,778,949,630
Net Worth: $1,172,556,840
Earnings: ($38,963,925)
Emp.: 10,101
Fiscal Year-end: 03/31/2022
Truck, Bus & Other Heavy Vehicle Mfr
N.A.I.C.S.: 336110
Dheeraj G. Hinduja *(Chm)*

Subsidiary (Domestic):

Albonair (India) Private Limited (2)
MCP Industrial Complex Old No 111 New No 49, Sengadu Village Sriperumbudur, 602 002, Kanchipuram, India
Tel.: (91) 44 3719 3000
Automobile Spare Parts Mfr
N.A.I.C.S.: 336390

Subsidiary (Non-US):

Albonair GmbH (2)
Carlo-Schmid-Allee 1, 44263, Dortmund, Germany
Tel.: (49) 231 22240 100
Web Site: http://www.albonair.com
Automobile Spare Parts Mfr
N.A.I.C.S.: 336390
Georg Huthwohl *(Mng Dir)*

Subsidiary (Non-US):

Albonair Automotive Technology Co. Ltd. (3)
East Shanghai Road Caifu Building Room 501, 215400, Taicang, Jiangsu, China
Tel.: (86) 135 6488 7884
Automotive Spare Parts Distr
N.A.I.C.S.: 423120

Subsidiary (Domestic):

Ashok Leland Finance Ltd. (2)
No 1 Sardar Patel Road Guindy, Chennai, 600, India
Tel.: (91) 44 2220 6000
Financial Services
N.A.I.C.S.: 522220

Subsidiary (Non-US):

Ashok Leyland (Nigeria) Limited (2)
Km 33 Lekki /Epe Expressway, Eputu Town, Lagos, Nigeria
Tel.: (234) 8057536447
Automotive Distr
N.A.I.C.S.: 423110
Nujum Riyaz *(Country Mgr)*

Avia Ashok Leyland Motors s.r.o (2)
Beranovych 140, Letnany, 199 03, Prague, Czech Republic
Tel.: (420) 225 141 111
Web Site: http://www.avia.cz
Automobile Mfr & Distr
N.A.I.C.S.: 336110
Petr Znamenacek *(Dir-Production)*

Subsidiary (Non-US):

Avia Ashok Leyland Rus (3)
Avtomobilny proezd 1/1 TPZ Altufievo MKAD 85km, Moscow, 141000, Moskovskaya oblast, Russia
Tel.: (7) 495 987 4713
Automotive Distr
N.A.I.C.S.: 423110

Subsidiary (Domestic):

Gulf Ashley Motors Limited (2)
1st & 2nd Floor New Kalimati Road, Near Howrah Bridge Sakchi, Jamshedpur, 831001, Jharkhand, India
Tel.: (91) 6576002003
Web Site: http://www.gamltrucks.com
Motor Vehicle Distr
N.A.I.C.S.: 423110

Hinduja Foundries Ltd (2)
K H Road Ennore, 600057, Chennai, India
Tel.: (91) 4425752103
Sales Range: $350-399.9 Million
Iron Foundries
N.A.I.C.S.: 331511
Rajan G. R. V. *(Mng Dir)*

Hinduja Leyland Finance Limited (2)
No 27 A Developed Industrial Estate, Guindy, Chennai, 600032, India (61.83%)
Tel.: (91) 44 39252525
Web Site: http://www.hindujaleylandfinance.com
Financial Services
N.A.I.C.S.: 523999

Hinduja Tech Limited (2)
Triton Square 9th floor Unit No C3 to C7 TVK Industrial Estate, Guindy, Chennai, 600032, India
Tel.: (91) 44 3023 1000
Web Site: http://www.hindujatech.com
Software Development Services
N.A.I.C.S.: 541511
Prasan Ramachandra *(Head-Global Ops)*

Subsidiary (Non-US):

Hinduja Tech GmbH (3)
Charles-de-Gaulle-Platz 1 F, 50679, Cologne, Germany
Tel.: (49) 221 933532 0
Software Development Services
N.A.I.C.S.: 541511

Subsidiary (US):

Hinduja Tech, Inc. (3)
39555 Orchard Hill Pl Ste 600, Novi, MI 48375
Tel.: (248) 348-5785
Software Development Services
N.A.I.C.S.: 541511

Holding (Non-US):

Optare Group Ltd. (2)
Hurricane Way South, Sherburn in Elmet, Leeds, LS25 6PT, North Yorkshire, United Kingdom
Tel.: (44) 1977687200
Web Site: http://www.optare.com
Sales Range: $75-99.9 Million
Emp.: 403
Bus & Coach Construction Repair & Service
N.A.I.C.S.: 811198
Abhijit Mukhopadhyay *(Sec)*

Subsidiary (Domestic):

Optare Group Ltd (3)

INTERNATIONAL PUBLIC

Unit 3 Hurricane Way South Sherburn Distribution Park, Leeds, LS25 6PT, West Yorkshire, United Kingdom
Tel.: (44) 84348732
Sales Range: $50-74.9 Million
Emp.: 250
Motor Vehicle Body Mfr
N.A.I.C.S.: 336211

Optare UK Ltd (3)
Lower Philips Rd, Whitebirk Industrial Estate, Blackburn, BB1 5UD, Lancashire, United Kingdom
Tel.: (44) 8458389901
Web Site: http://www.optare.com
Sales Range: $150-199.9 Million
Coach & Bus Mfr
N.A.I.C.S.: 423120

D.A. Stuart S.A. (1)
Cerrito 1320 1 C, C1010ABB, Buenos Aires, Argentina
Tel.: (54) 11 4814 0280
Lubricant Oil Distr
N.A.I.C.S.: 424720

GOCL Corporation Limited (1)
IDL Road Kukatpally, Post Bag No 1, Hyderabad, 500072, Andhra Pradesh, India
Tel.: (91) 4023810671
Web Site: https://www.gulfoilcorp.com
Rev.: $22,166,276
Assets: $78,582,490
Liabilities: $24,645,198
Net Worth: $53,937,293
Earnings: $6,694,451
Emp.: 219
Fiscal Year-end: 03/31/2021
Lubricants & Greases Mfr
N.A.I.C.S.: 324191
Subhas Pramanik *(Mng Dir)*

Division (Domestic):

Gulf Oil Corpn. Ltd. - Lubes Division (2)
In Centre 49/50 MIDC Industrial Area, 12th Road, 400 093, Mumbai, Andheri, India
Tel.: (91) 22 56487777
Lube & Grease Mfr
N.A.I.C.S.: 324191

Gulf Oil International Ltd. (1)
3rd Floor 16 Charles II Street, London, SW1Y 4QU, United Kingdom
Tel.: (44) 20 78392402
Web Site: http://www.gulfoilltd.com
Petroleum Product Distr
N.A.I.C.S.: 424720
Sanjay Gopichand Hinduja *(Chm)*

Subsidiary (Non-US):

GULF OIL Philippines, Inc. (2)
Unit 9A 9th Floor Inoza Tower 40th St, Bonifacio Global City, Taguig, Philippines
Tel.: (63) 28454309
Web Site: http://www.gulfoilphilippines.com
Petroleum Product Mfr & Distr
N.A.I.C.S.: 324191
Alex S. Abao *(Bus Mgr-Mindanao)*

Subsidiary (Domestic):

Gulf Lubricants UK Ltd (2)
302 Bridgewater Place, Birchwood Park, Warrington, WA3 6XG, Cheshire, United Kingdom
Tel.: (44) 845 121 4535
Web Site: http://www.lubricants.gulfoil.co.uk
Petroleum Product Distr
N.A.I.C.S.: 424720

Subsidiary (Non-US):

Gulf Oil Argentina SA (2)
Belisario Roldan 260, La Reja Moreno, Buenos Aires, Argentina
Tel.: (54) 237 463 3331
Web Site: http://www.gulfoil.com.ar
Petroleum Product Mfr
N.A.I.C.S.: 324191

Gulf Oil Middle East Ltd (2)
1301/1302 Al Salemiyah Towers Baniyas Road Clock Tower, PO BOX 5401, Deira, Dubai, United Arab Emirates
Tel.: (971) 4 2223016
Web Site: http://www.gulfoiluae.com
Petroleum Product Mfr & Distr
N.A.I.C.S.: 324191

Mathan Kumar *(Deputy Gen Mgr-Retail Sls)*

Plant (Domestic):

Gulf Oil Middle East Ltd - Jebel Ali Facility (3)
Jebel Ali Free Zone, PO Box 17068, Dubai, United Arab Emirates
Tel.: (971) 4 8870803
Petroleum Product Mfr
N.A.I.C.S.: 324191

Subsidiary (Domestic):

Gulf RAK Oil LLC (3)
PO Box 9667, Maritime City, Ras al Khaimah, United Arab Emirates
Tel.: (971) 7 2668951
Web Site: http://www.gulfoilltd.com
Emp.: 40
Petroleum Product Distr
N.A.I.C.S.: 424720
Venkat Raman *(CEO)*

Subsidiary (Non-US):

Gulf Oil Nederland B.V. (2)
Ampererestraat 5, 3846 AN, Harderwijk, Netherlands
Tel.: (31) 341 439000
Web Site: http://www.gulf.nl
Emp.: 40
Petroleum Product Distr
N.A.I.C.S.: 424720
Yuka Senea *(Mng Dir)*

Oil Trading Poland Sp. z o.o. (3)
ul Mierzynska 42, 71-030, Szczecin, Poland
Tel.: (48) 91 812 96 23
Web Site: http://www.gulf.pl
Petroleum Product Distr
N.A.I.C.S.: 424720

Gulf Oil Lubricants India Limited (1)
IN Centre 49/50 12th Road, MIDC Andheri East, Mumbai, 400093, Maharashtra, India
Tel.: (91) 2266487777
Web Site: https://india.gulfoilltd.com
Rev.: $365,232,504
Assets: $248,373,874
Liabilities: $107,083,448
Net Worth: $141,290,426
Earnings: $27,852,515
Emp.: 592
Fiscal Year-end: 03/31/2023
Oil Distr
N.A.I.C.S.: 811191
Sanjay Gopichand Hinduja *(Chm)*

Hinduja Bank (Switzerland) Ltd (1)
Place de la Fusterie 3 bis, 1204, Geneva, Switzerland
Tel.: (41) 22 906 08 08
Web Site: http://www.hindujabank.com
Financial Investment Services
N.A.I.C.S.: 523999
Jean-Francois Varlet *(Vice Chm)*

Subsidiary (Non-US):

AMAS-Investment and Project Services Ltd. (2)
New Zealand House 80 Haymarket, London, SW1Y 4TE, United Kingdom
Tel.: (44) 207 839 4661
Web Site: http://www.aipsltd.com
Financial Investment Services
N.A.I.C.S.: 523999

Subsidiary (Domestic):

Berafina AG. (2)
Munchensteinerstrasse 43, 4001, Basel, Switzerland
Tel.: (41) 61 225 45 45
Emp.: 4
Financial Investment Services
N.A.I.C.S.: 523999
Reto Tester *(Gen Mgr)*

Subsidiary (Non-US):

Hinduja Bank (Middle East) Ltd. (2)
Dubai International Financial Centre Building GV 10 2nd Floor Unit 1, Dubai, United Arab Emirates
Tel.: (971) 4 436 65 88
Financial Investment Services
N.A.I.C.S.: 523999

Subsidiary (Domestic):

Hinduja Bank (Schweiz) AG. (2)
Pilatusstrasse 35, 6003, Lucerne, Switzerland
Tel.: (41) 41 227 52 52
Financial Investment Services
N.A.I.C.S.: 523999

Subsidiary (Non-US):

Hinduja India Mauritius Holdings Ltd. (2)
St Louis Business Centre Cnr Desroches & St Louis Streets, Port Louis, Mauritius
Tel.: (230) 208 75 75
Emp.: 2
Financial Investment Services
N.A.I.C.S.: 523999
Gaye Ginjlee *(Dir)*

Paterson Securities Pvt Ltd (2)
48 Vanguard House Second Line Beach Parrys, Chennai, 600 001, India
Tel.: (91) 44 2534 2700
Web Site: http://www.paterson.co.in
Securities Brokerage Services
N.A.I.C.S.: 523150
Janakiram Karra *(VP & Head-Fixed Income Grp)*

Subsidiary (Domestic):

Rowena AG. (2)
Grenzstrasse 24, 9430, Basel, Switzerland
Tel.: (41) 71 747 49 59
Web Site: http://www.rowena.ch
Financial Investment Services
N.A.I.C.S.: 523999

Hinduja National Power Corporation Ltd. (1)
Hinduja House 171 Dr Annie Besant Road, Worli, Mumbai, 400018, India
Tel.: (91) 22 24960707
Web Site: http://www.hindujanationalpower.com
Power Generation Services
N.A.I.C.S.: 221118

Houghton (Shanghai) Specialty Industrial Fluids Co. Ltd. (1)
No 188 Jiangtian East Road, Songjiang Industrial Area, Shanghai, China
Tel.: (86) 21 6774 2570
Chemical Products Distr
N.A.I.C.S.: 424690

Houghton Europe BV (1)
Lautamiehentie 3, 02770, Espoo, Finland
Tel.: (358) 40 739 8545
Lubricant Oil Distr
N.A.I.C.S.: 424720

Houghton Kimya Sanayi AS (1)
Kosuyolu Mah Asma Dali Sok No 14, Kadikoy, 34718, Istanbul, Turkiye
Tel.: (90) 216 325 15 15
Lubricant Oil Distr
N.A.I.C.S.: 424720

Houghton Mexico S.A. de C.V. (1)
Efrain Gonzalez Luna 2007 DEPTO19, Col Americana, Guadalajara, 44160, Jalisco, Mexico
Tel.: (52) 333 615 9331
Lubricant Oil Distr
N.A.I.C.S.: 424720

IN Entertainment India Ltd. (1)
49/50 12th Road MIDC, Andheri East, Mumbai, 400 093, India
Tel.: (91) 9819859247
Web Site: http://www.shop24seven.tv
Movie Production Services
N.A.I.C.S.: 512110

IndusInd International Holdings Limited (1)
Level 3 Ebene House Hotel Avenue 33, 72201, Ebene, Mauritius
Tel.: (230) 4655526
Web Site: https://indusindinternational.com
Investment Services
N.A.I.C.S.: 523999

HINDUSTAN ADHESIVES LTD.
B-2/8 Safdarjung Enclave, New Delhi, 110029, India
Tel.: (91) 1122131880
Web Site: https://www.bagla-group.com
514428—(BOM)
Rev.: $30,074,076
Assets: $22,319,565
Liabilities: $16,411,340
Net Worth: $5,908,225
Earnings: $1,194,266
Emp.: 286
Fiscal Year-end: 03/31/21
Adhesive Tape Mfr
N.A.I.C.S.: 322220
S. S. Dua *(Sec)*

HINDUSTAN AERONAUTICS LIMITED
15 1 Cubbon Road, Bengaluru, 560 001, India
Tel.: (91) 8022320701
Web Site: http://www.hal-india.com
Sales Range: $1-4.9 Billion
Aircraft Mfr
N.A.I.C.S.: 336411
K. Naresh Babu *(Mng Dir-Bangalore Complex & Dir-Corp Plng & Mktg)*

HINDUSTAN AGRIGENETICS LIMITED
806 Meghdoot 94 Nehru Place, New Delhi, 110019, India
Tel.: (91) 1126862193
Web Site: https://hindustanagrigenetics.co.in
Year Founded: 1990
519574—(BOM)
Rev.: $17,303
Assets: $475,250
Liabilities: $158,377
Net Worth: $316,873
Earnings: $11,116
Fiscal Year-end: 03/31/14
Tissue Culture Farming Services
N.A.I.C.S.: 111421
Pritam Kapur *(Chm, Mng Dir, CFO & Sec)*

HINDUSTAN BIO SCIENCES LIMITED
H No 8-2-269/S Plot No 31 Sagar Society Rd No 2 Banjara Hills, Hyderabad, 500034, Andhra Pradesh, India
Tel.: (91) 4023555161
Web Site: https://www.hindustanbiosciences.in
532041—(BOM)
Rev.: $111,785
Assets: $398,336
Liabilities: $307,848
Net Worth: $90,488
Earnings: ($4,903)
Emp.: 5
Fiscal Year-end: 03/31/23
Pharmaceuticals Product Mfr
N.A.I.C.S.: 325412
Venkata Rama Mohan Raju Jampana *(Chm, CEO & Mng Dir)*

HINDUSTAN COMPOSITES LIMITED
Peninsula Business Park A Tower 8th Floor 801 Senapati Bapat Marg, Lower Parel, Mumbai, 400 013, India
Tel.: (91) 2266880100
Web Site: https://www.hindcompo.com
HINDCOMPOS—(NSE)
Rev.: $26,040,364
Assets: $125,318,398
Liabilities: $13,797,966
Net Worth: $111,520,432
Earnings: $2,692,271
Emp.: 529
Fiscal Year-end: 03/31/21
Industrial Products & Friction Materials Mfr & Distr
N.A.I.C.S.: 333248
Raghu Mody *(Chm)*

HINDUSTAN CONSTRUCTION CO. LTD
Hincon House LBS Marg Vikhroli W, Mumbai, 400083, India
Tel.: (91) 2225751000
Web Site: https://www.hccindia.com
500185—(BOM)
Rev.: $1,477,183,890
Assets: $1,937,754,000
Liabilities: $2,044,857,360
Net Worth: ($107,103,360)
Earnings: $54,539,940
Emp.: 1,105
Fiscal Year-end: 03/31/22
Construction Company
N.A.I.C.S.: 236210
Ajit Gulabchand *(Chm & Mng Dir)*

Subsidiaries:

Dasve Hospitality Institutes Limited (1)
Information Ctr 80 Event Ctr St Post Mose Dasve, Lavasa, Pune, 412112, Maharashtra, India
Tel.: (91) 2066769300
Web Site: http://www.ecolehotelierelavasa.com
Sales Range: $10-24.9 Million
Emp.: 20
Hospitality Management Educational Services
N.A.I.C.S.: 611310

Lavasa Corporation Limited (1)
Hincon House 247 Park L B S Marg, Vikhroli West, Mumbai, 400 083, Maharashtra, India
Tel.: (91) 2240256000
Web Site: http://www.lavasa.com
Sales Range: $50-74.9 Million
Emp.: 200
Residential Housing
N.A.I.C.S.: 236116
Rajgopal Nogja *(Pres)*

HINDUSTAN COPPER LIMITED
1 Ashutosh Chowdhury Avenue, Kolkata, 700019, India
Tel.: (91) 3322832226
Web Site: https://www.hindustancopper.com
Year Founded: 1967
HINDCOPPER—(NSE)
Rev.: $248,649,069
Assets: $387,363,208
Liabilities: $238,678,822
Net Worth: $148,684,386
Earnings: $15,044,539
Emp.: 1,649
Fiscal Year-end: 03/31/21
Copper Mfr
N.A.I.C.S.: 212230
Chattar Singh Singhi *(Officer-Compliance, Sec & Gen Mgr-Company Affairs)*

HINDUSTAN DORR-OLIVER LTD
Dorr-Oliver House Chakala, Andheri East, Mumbai, 400099, India
Tel.: (91) 2228359400
Web Site: http://www.hdo.in
Year Founded: 1974
Engineeering Services
N.A.I.C.S.: 541330
E. Sudhir Reddy *(Vice Chm)*

HINDUSTAN FOODS LIMITED
Centrium Level II Unit 3 Phoenix Market City 15 LBS Marg, Kurla W, Mumbai, 400070, India
Tel.: (91) 2269801700
Web Site: https://www.hindustanfoodsltd.com

HINDUSTAN FOODS LIMITED

Hindustan Foods Limited—(Continued)
Year Founded: 1988
HNDFDS—(NSE)
Rev.: $355,259,951
Assets: $182,252,684
Liabilities: $131,074,698
Net Worth: $51,177,986
Earnings: $9,707,484
Emp.: 5,500
Fiscal Year-end: 03/31/23
Food Product Mfr & Distr
N.A.I.C.S.: 311230
Shrinivas V. Dempo (Chm)

HINDUSTAN HARDY LIMITED
Plot No C-12 MIDC Area, Ambad Industrial Area, Nashik, 422 010, Maharashtra, India
Tel.: (91) 2532382118
Web Site: https://www.hhardys.com
505893—(BOM)
Rev.: $6,096,732
Assets: $4,159,728
Liabilities: $2,588,641
Net Worth: $1,571,088
Earnings: $434,725
Emp.: 168
Fiscal Year-end: 03/31/21
Automobile Parts Mfr
N.A.I.C.S.: 336390
S. C. Saran (Chm)

Subsidiaries:

XLO India Limited (1)
80 Dhanwatay I Wing Dr Annie Besant Road, Worli, Mumbai, 400018, India
Tel.: (91) 2224937451
Web Site: http://www.xloindia.com
Emp.: 10
Machine Tools Mfr
N.A.I.C.S.: 333517
S. C. Saran (Chm & Mng Dir)

HINDUSTAN MEDIA VENTURES LIMITED
5th Floor Lotus Tower A Block Community Centre New Friends Colony, Kasturba Gandhi Marg, New Delhi, 110001, India
Tel.: (91) 1123704600   In
Web Site: https://www.hmvl.in
Year Founded: 1918
533217—(BOM)
Rev.: $101,946,390
Assets: $298,088,700
Liabilities: $81,078,270
Net Worth: $217,010,430
Earnings: $5,540,535
Emp.: 1,146
Fiscal Year-end: 03/31/22
Newspaper, Magazine & Internet Publisher
N.A.I.C.S.: 513110
Tridib Barat (Officer-Compliance & Sec)

HINDUSTAN MOTORS LIMITED
Birla Building 10th floor Western Side 9/1 R N Mukherjee Road, Kolkata, 700001, India
Tel.: (91) 3330533700
Web Site: https://www.hindmotor.com
500500—(BOM)
Rev.: $1,989,856
Assets: $4,134,298
Liabilities: $5,381,117
Net Worth: ($1,246,818)
Earnings: $2,546,094
Emp.: 292
Fiscal Year-end: 03/31/22
Automobile Mfr
N.A.I.C.S.: 336210
Mahesh Kumar Kejriwal (CFO)

HINDUSTAN OIL EXPLORATION COMPANY LTD
Lakshmi Chambers 192 St Marys Road Alwarpet, Chennai, 600 018, Tamilnadu, India
Tel.: (91) 4466229000
Web Site: https://www.hoec.com
500186—(BOM)
Rev.: $22,821,312
Assets: $208,468,601
Liabilities: $105,667,366
Net Worth: $102,801,235
Earnings: $2,729,140
Emp.: 94
Fiscal Year-end: 03/31/22
Oil & Gas Exploration Services
N.A.I.C.S.: 213112
Ramasamy Jeevanandam (CFO)

Subsidiaries:

HOEC Bardahl India Limited (1)
HOEC House Tandalja Road off Old Padra Rd, Vadodara, 390 020, Gujarat, India
Tel.: (91) 2652333568
Web Site: http://www.hoec.com
Oil & Gas Field Exploration Services
N.A.I.C.S.: 213112

HINDUSTAN ORGANIC CHEMICALS LIMITED
401 402 and 403 4th Floor V Time Square, Plot No 3 Sector 15 CBD Belapur, Mumbai, 400614, India
Tel.: (91) 2227575268
Web Site: https://www.hoclindia.com
Year Founded: 1960
500449—(BOM)
Rev.: $77,268,077
Assets: $178,721,635
Liabilities: $189,018,788
Net Worth: ($10,297,152)
Earnings: ($6,634,758)
Emp.: 435
Fiscal Year-end: 03/31/23
Chemical Products Mfr
N.A.I.C.S.: 325199
Susheela S. Kulkarni (Sec)

Subsidiaries:

Hindustan Fluorocarbons Limited (1)
303 3rd floor Babukhan Estate Bashir Bagh, Hyderabad, 500 001, India
Tel.: (91) 4023297160
Web Site: https://www.hfl.co.in
Rev.: $841,946
Assets: $10,375,324
Liabilities: $20,290,616
Net Worth: ($9,915,292)
Earnings: ($3,389,418)
Fiscal Year-end: 03/31/2021
Organic Chemical Mfr
N.A.I.C.S.: 325199
T. S. Gaikwad (Mng Dir)

HINDUSTAN PHOTO FILMS MANUFACTURING COMPANY LIMITED
Indunagar, Nilgiris, Udhagamandalam, 643 005, Tamilnadu, India
Tel.: (91) 4232443127
Web Site: https://www.hpf-india.com
Year Founded: 1960
524316—(BOM)
Sales Range: $1-9.9 Million
Emp.: 734
Medical Device Mfr
N.A.I.C.S.: 334510
S. Girish Kumar (Chm, Mng Dir & Dir-Fin)

HINDUSTAN TIN WORKS LTD.
426 DLF Tower A Jasola, New Delhi, 110 025, India
Tel.: (91) 1149998888
Web Site: https://www.hindustantin.biz
530315—(BOM)
Rev.: $45,156,922
Assets: $40,481,362
Liabilities: $17,945,002
Net Worth: $22,536,360
Earnings: $1,991,709
Emp.: 465
Fiscal Year-end: 03/31/21
Metal Tank Mfr
N.A.I.C.S.: 332431
Sanjay Bhatia (Mng Dir)

HINDUSTAN WIRES LIMITED
5th floor 3A Shakespeare Sarani, Kolkata, 700071, India
Tel.: (91) 33 22823586   In
Web Site: http://www.hwlgas.com
Year Founded: 1959
Rev.: $1,621,928
Assets: $2,529,434
Liabilities: $336,298
Net Worth: $2,193,135
Earnings: $431,323
Emp.: 11
Fiscal Year-end: 03/31/18
Industrial Gas Mfr
N.A.I.C.S.: 325120
Sita Ram Sharma (CFO)

HINDUSTHAN NATIONAL GLASS & INDUSTRIES LIMITED
2 Red Cross Place, Kolkata, 700001, India
Tel.: (91) 3322543100
Web Site: https://www.hngil.com
HINDNATGLS—(NSE)
Rev.: $289,525,441
Assets: $401,501,987
Liabilities: $506,109,622
Net Worth: ($104,607,635)
Earnings: ($47,573,458)
Emp.: 2,410
Fiscal Year-end: 03/31/22
Glass Container Mfr
N.A.I.C.S.: 327213
Sanjay Somany (Chm & Mng Dir)

Subsidiaries:

Glass Equipment (India) Ltd (1)
National Highway No 10, PO Box No 7, Distt Jhajjar, Bahadurgarh, 124507, Haryana, India
Tel.: (91) 1276 221400
Web Site: http://www.glasseq.com
Emp.: 250
Container Glass Mfr
N.A.I.C.S.: 327213
C. K. Somany (Chm)

HNG Float Glass Limited (1)
Halol GIDC Phase - III, Dist Panchmahal, Halol, 389351, Gujarat, India
Tel.: (91) 3322543100
Web Site: http://www.hngfloat.com
Sales Range: $25-49.9 Million
Emp.: 70
Flat Glass Mfr
N.A.I.C.S.: 327211
Pradeep Tibrewal (Head-Fin & Comml)

Hindusthan National Glass & Industries Ltd. - Bahadurgarh Plant (1)
Delhi, Jhajjar District, Bahadurgarh, 124507, Haryana, India
Tel.: (91) 1276 221400
Web Site: http://www.hngil.com
Sales Range: $125-149.9 Million
Emp.: 500
Container Glass Mfr
N.A.I.C.S.: 327213

Hindusthan National Glass & Industries Ltd. - Rishikesh Plant (1)
PO Virbhadra, Rishikesh, 249202, Uttarakhand, India
Tel.: (91) 135 2470700
Web Site: http://www.hngil.com.in
Container Glass Mfr
N.A.I.C.S.: 327213
Vijaykumar Chitturi (Gen Mgr)

Hindusthan National Glass & Industries Ltd. - Rishra Plant (1)
2 Panchu Gopal Bhaduri Sarani P O Prabhasnagar, Hooghly District, Rishra, 712248,

INTERNATIONAL PUBLIC

West Bengal, India
Tel.: (91) 3326000200
Container Glass Mfr
N.A.I.C.S.: 327213

HINDUSTHAN UDYOG LIMITED
6 Old Post Office Street, Kolkata, 700001, India
Tel.: (91) 3322480941
Web Site: http://www.hindsthanudyog.com
Steel Mfrs
N.A.I.C.S.: 331110
Rajiv Sharma (CEO)

HINDUSTHAN URBAN INFRASTRUCTURE LTD.
Kanchenjunga 7th Floor 18 Barakhamba Road, New Delhi, 110001, India
Tel.: (91) 1123310001
Web Site: https://www.hindusthanurban.com
Year Founded: 1959
539984—(BOM)
Rev.: $71,011,174
Assets: $109,116,396
Liabilities: $60,761,465
Net Worth: $48,354,931
Earnings: ($6,962,173)
Emp.: 340
Fiscal Year-end: 03/31/23
Electronic Components Mfr
N.A.I.C.S.: 334419
Raghavendra Anant Mody (Chm)

Subsidiaries:

Hindusthan Speciality Chemicals Ltd. (1)
Kanchenjunga 7th Floor 18 Barakhamba Road, New Delhi, 110001, India
Tel.: (91) 1123310001
Web Site: https://www.hindusthanspeciality.com
Epoxy Resin Mfr
N.A.I.C.S.: 325211

HINDWARE HOME INNOVATION LIMITED
68 Echelon Inst Area Sector 32, Gurgaon, 122001, Haryana, India
Tel.: (91) 1242889300
Web Site: https://www.hindwarehomes.com
SHIL—(BOM)
Rev.: $244,783,061
Assets: $141,766,307
Liabilities: $96,729,073
Net Worth: $45,037,233
Earnings: $7,486,042
Emp.: 380
Fiscal Year-end: 03/31/21
Consumer Appliance Mfr
N.A.I.C.S.: 335220
Sandip Somany (Chm)

Subsidiaries:

Brilloca Limited (1)
301-302 Park Centra Sector-30 National Highway 8, Gurgaon, Haryana, India
Tel.: (91) 124 477 9200
Web Site: https://www.brilloca.com
Building Materials Distr
N.A.I.C.S.: 444180
Sandip Somany (Mng Dir & Co-Chm)

HING LEE (HK) HOLDINGS LIMITED
Unit 1101 11th Floor Delta House 3 On Yiu Street, Sha Tin, New Territories, China (Hong Kong)
Tel.: (852) 21519600
Web Site: http://www.hingleehk.com.hk
0396—(HKG)
Rev.: $12,799,343
Assets: $28,325,783

Liabilities: $13,187,580
Net Worth: $15,138,203
Earnings: ($3,416,490)
Emp.: 130
Fiscal Year-end: 12/31/22
Holding Company; Furniture Mfr & Retailer
N.A.I.C.S.: 551112
Kai Hing Sung *(Co-Founder, Chm & CEO)*

Subsidiaries:

Shenzhen Ouluo Furniture Company Limited (1)
No 13 Shahe Road Dawan Village Dakang Community Henggang Block, Longgang District, Shenzhen, 518115, China
Tel.: (86) 75584262029
Web Site: http://www.novita.net.cn
Emp.: 400
Furniture Distr
N.A.I.C.S.: 449110

HING MING HOLDINGS LIMITED
Room A4 2/FTsim Sha Tsui Mansion 83 87 Nathan Road, Kowloon, China (Hong Kong)
Tel.: (852) 26592964   Ky
Web Site: https://www.hing-ming.com
Year Founded: 1997
8425—(HKG)
Rev.: $12,524,963
Assets: $22,779,405
Liabilities: $7,803,255
Net Worth: $14,976,150
Earnings: $302,048
Emp.: 37
Fiscal Year-end: 03/31/23
Construction Equipment Rental Services
N.A.I.C.S.: 532412
Hing Keung Tang *(Chm & CEO)*

HINGTEX HOLDINGS LTD.
Unit A6 31/F TML Tower No 3 Hoi Shing Road, Tsuen Wan, New Territories, China (Hong Kong)
Tel.: (852) 23414208   Ky
Web Site:
   http://www.hwtextiles.com.hk
Year Founded: 1981
1968—(HKG)
Rev.: $31,259,940
Assets: $50,288,168
Liabilities: $10,320,488
Net Worth: $39,967,680
Earnings: ($6,370,155)
Emp.: 353
Fiscal Year-end: 12/31/22
Textile Fabric Mfr & Distr
N.A.I.C.S.: 313210
Tsun Hong Tung *(Founder & Chm)*

HIOKI E.E. CORPORATION
81 Koizumi, Ueda, 386-1192, Nagano, Japan
Tel.: (81) 268280555
Web Site: https://www.hioki.com
Year Founded: 1935
6866—(TKS)
Rev.: $277,601,860
Assets: $320,822,500
Liabilities: $57,627,520
Net Worth: $263,194,980
Earnings: $44,872,610
Emp.: 1,048
Fiscal Year-end: 12/31/23
Electrical Measuring Instrument Mfr
N.A.I.C.S.: 334513
Tsutomu Mandai *(Member-Mgmt Bd)*

Subsidiaries:

HIOKI (Shanghai) Sales & Trading Co., Ltd. (1)
Room 4705 Raffles City Office Tower No 268 Xizang Road M, Shanghai, 200001, China
Tel.: (86) 2163910090
Web Site: http://www.hioki.com.cn
Electric Measuring Instruments Distr
N.A.I.C.S.: 423830

HIOKI Engineering Service Corporation (1)
81 Koizumi, Ueda, 386-1192, Nagano, Japan
Tel.: (81) 268280823
Web Site: http://www.hioki.co.jp
Sales Range: $25-49.9 Million
Emp.: 68
Electrical Measuring Instrument Mfr
N.A.I.C.S.: 334515

HIOKI Europe GmbH (1)
Helfmann-Park 2, 65760, Eschborn, Germany
Tel.: (49) 6196765150
Electrical Measuring Instrument Mfr
N.A.I.C.S.: 334519
Hisashi Shimizu *(Mng Dir)*

HIOKI Forest Plaza Corporation (1)
81 Koizumi, Ueda, 386-1192, Nagano, Japan
Tel.: (81) 26 826 8333
Web Site: http://www.hioki.com
Electrical Measuring Instrument Mfr
N.A.I.C.S.: 334515

HIOKI India Engineering Private Limited (1)
415 Bestech Chambers Sushant Lok - 1 B Block, Gurgaon, 122 001, Haryana, India
Tel.: (91) 1244013811
Electrical Measuring Instrument Mfr
N.A.I.C.S.: 334519

HIOKI Korea Co., Ltd. (1)
Room 314 187 Techno 2-ro, Yuseong-gu, Daejeon, 34037, Korea (South)
Tel.: (82) 42 936 1281
Web Site: http://www.hiokikorea.com
Electrical Measuring Instrument Mfr & Distr
N.A.I.C.S.: 334515

HIOKI Singapore Pte. Ltd. (1)
33 Ubi Avenue 3 03-02 Vertex, Singapore, 408868, Singapore
Tel.: (65) 6 634 7677
Web Site: https://www.hioki.com.sg
Emp.: 10
Electrical Measuring Instrument Mfr & Distr
N.A.I.C.S.: 334515

HIOKI Taiwan Co., Ltd. (1)
4F No 900 Jingguo Rd, Luzhu District, Taoyuan, 33858, Taiwan
Tel.: (886) 33467160
Electrical Measuring Instrument Mfr
N.A.I.C.S.: 334515

HIOKI USA Corporation (1)
6600 Chase Oaks Blvd Ste 150, Cranbury, NJ 75023
Tel.: (469) 983-1700
Web Site: http://www.hiokiusa.com
Sales Range: $25-49.9 Million
Emp.: 8
Electrical Measuring Instrument Mfr
N.A.I.C.S.: 334515

HiNSTEC Co., Ltd. (1)
81 Koizumi, Ueda, 386-1192, Nagano, Japan
Tel.: (81) 268281440
Web Site: http://hins.hioki.co.jp
Sales Range: $250-299.9 Million
Emp.: 600
Printed Circuit Boards Whslr
N.A.I.C.S.: 423690

Hind Electronika India Private Limited (1)
Tulsi Chambers 4-5/2 Greater Kailash Road Old Palasia, Indore, 452018, Madhya Pradesh, India
Tel.: (91) 731 402 0081
Web Site: https://www.hindelec.com
Electrical Testing & Measuring Instrument Distr
N.A.I.C.S.: 423610

Hioki (Shanghai) Measurement Technologies Co., Ltd. (1)
Room 4705 Raffles City No 268 Xizang Middle Road, Huangpu District, Shanghai, 200001, China
Electrical Measuring Instrument Mfr
N.A.I.C.S.: 334515

Hioki (Shanghai) Measuring Instruments Co., Ltd. (1)
Room 4703-04 Raffles City Office Tower No 268 Xizang Road M, Shanghai, 200001, China
Tel.: (86) 216 391 0090
Electrical Measuring Instrument Mfr
N.A.I.C.S.: 334515

Hioki (Shanghai) Technology Development Co., Ltd. (1)
Electrical Measuring Instrument Mfr
N.A.I.C.S.: 334515

PT. HIOKI Electric Instrument (1)
Graha MIR 1st Floor Zone C Jl Pemuda 9 Rawamangun, Pulogadung, Jakarta Timur, 13220, Indonesia
Tel.: (62) 2129569853
Electrical Measuring Instrument Mfr
N.A.I.C.S.: 334519

HIOLLE INDUSTRIES S.A.
ZAC Valenciennes Rouvignies, 9 avenue Marc Lefrancq, 59121, Prouvy, France
Tel.: (33) 327475000   FR
Web Site: http://www.hiolle-industries.com
Year Founded: 1976
ALHIO—(EUR)
Sales Range: $75-99.9 Million
Emp.: 800
Construction & Industrial Machinery & Equipment Mfr
N.A.I.C.S.: 333120
Olivier Hiolle *(Member-Mgmt Bd)*

Subsidiaries:

APEGELEC Industries (1)
164 rue de la Chaussee Romaine, BP 205, 02105, Saint-Quentin, Cedex, France
Tel.: (33) 323062425
Web Site: http://www.apegelec.fr
Sales Range: $25-49.9 Million
Emp.: 100
Electricity & Electronics Application Services
N.A.I.C.S.: 334515

Amodiag Environnement (1)
9 Avenue Marc Lefrancq, 59121, Valenciennes, France
Tel.: (33) 3 27 20 11 80
Web Site: http://www.amodiag.com
Sales Range: $25-49.9 Million
Emp.: 40
Engineering & Environmental Services
N.A.I.C.S.: 541330

BMHIOL Industries (1)
Douar Lakloucha Route d, Lissasfa, Casablanca, 20200, Morocco
Tel.: (212) 5 22 65 13 24
Electronics Maintenance Services
N.A.I.C.S.: 811210

Cetam Automatismes (1)
ZA2 Pl des Champs de Colut, 59230, Sars-et-Rosieres, France
Tel.: (33) 327483300
Sales Range: $25-49.9 Million
Emp.: 100
Industrial Control Mfr
N.A.I.C.S.: 335314

Europ Concept (1)
54 Rue Ernest Macarez, 59300, Valenciennes, France
Tel.: (33) 327475000
Industrial Equipment Design & Production Services
N.A.I.C.S.: 333248

Europ Maintenance (1)
33 rue Pasteur, 59243, Quarouble, France
Tel.: (33) 327337478
Industrial & Railway Maintenance
N.A.I.C.S.: 488210

Europ Usinage (1)
Z I du Plouich - Rue du Commerce, BP 135, 59590, Raismes, France
Tel.: (33) 327458200
Web Site: http://www.europusinage.fr
Sales Range: $25-49.9 Million
Emp.: 45
Castings & Mechanical Parts Machining Services
N.A.I.C.S.: 332216

Graff (1)
4 Rue des mesanges, 57290, Fameck, France
Tel.: (33) 382580220
Web Site: http://www.graff-sa.com
Sales Range: $25-49.9 Million
Emp.: 50
Steel Constructions & Boiler Mfr
N.A.I.C.S.: 332410

Hiolle Logistics JSC (1)
Rue Ambroise Croizat, 59125, Trith-Saint-Leger, France
Tel.: (33) 327212425
Web Site: http://www.hiolle-logistique.fr
Logistic Services
N.A.I.C.S.: 488510

Hiolle Technologies SAS (1)
ZI - 2 place des Champs de Colut, 59230, Sars-et-Rosieres, France
Tel.: (33) 327483300
Web Site: http://www.hiolle-technologies.fr
Engineeering Services
N.A.I.C.S.: 541330

Nord Coffrage S.A. (1)
2 rue de l Humanite, 59990, Saultain, France
Tel.: (33) 327470077
Web Site: http://www.nordcoffrage.fr
Sales Range: $25-49.9 Million
Emp.: 12
Formwork & Safety Equipments Rental Services
N.A.I.C.S.: 811310

Ocam JSC (1)
8 Bel Air, Trelivan, 22100, Dinan, France
Tel.: (33) 296395728
Web Site: http://www.ocam.eu
Aeronautical Engineering Services
N.A.I.C.S.: 336412

Rhea Electronique (1)
Rue du Moulin - ZI du Moulin, 59193, Erquinghem-Lys, France
Tel.: (33) 320176969
Web Site: http://www.rhea-electronique.fr
Sales Range: $25-49.9 Million
Emp.: 20
Electronic Specifics Design & Production
N.A.I.C.S.: 334419

SA NTI (1)
33 rue Pasteur, 59243, Quarouble, France
Tel.: (33) 327473894
Industrial Piping & Welding Mfr
N.A.I.C.S.: 238220

SAS Clips Hiolle (1)
9 avenue Marc Lefrancq, ZAC Valenciennes Rouvignies, 59121, Prouvy, France
Tel.: (33) 327475000
Web Site: http://www.hiolle-industries.fr
Solar Photovoltaic Installation & Maintenance Services
N.A.I.C.S.: 333414

SAS Mecatel (1)
Rue universite ZI Technopark, Futura, 62400, Bethune, France
Tel.: (33) 3 21 61 31 61
Web Site: http://www.mecatel.fr
Rotary Tubes Mfr
N.A.I.C.S.: 322219

Team Turbo Machines JSC (1)
Allee Caillemare - Lieu-dit Le Petit Noel, La Trinite-de-Thouberville, 27310, Bernay, France
Tel.: (33) 235182153
Web Site: https://www.teamturbo-machines.fr
Mechanical Machine Maintenance Services
N.A.I.C.S.: 811310

Thermival JSC (1)
Z I du Plouich, BP 133, 59590, Raismes, France
Tel.: (33) 327255820
Web Site: http://www.thermival.fr
Engineeering Services

HIOLLE INDUSTRIES S.A.

Hiolle Industries S.A.—(Continued)
N.A.I.C.S.: 541330

HIP CORPORATION
8-8 Kusunoki-cho, Nishi-ku, Yokohama, 220-0003, Kanagawa, Japan
Tel.: (81) 453281000
Web Site: https://www.hip-pro.co.jp
Year Founded: 1995
2136—(TKS)
Sales Range: $25-49.9 Million
Emp.: 721
Automotive Components Mfr
N.A.I.C.S.: 336110
Yoshitake Tanaka *(Pres)*

HIP-PETROHEMIJA A.D.
Spoljnostarcevacka 82, Pancevo, 26000, Serbia
Tel.: (381) 13307000
Web Site: http://www.hip-petrohemija.com
Sales Range: $350-399.9 Million
Emp.: 2,800
Petroleum & Chemical Products Distr
N.A.I.C.S.: 425120
Sasa Aleksic *(Exec Dir-Function-Supply Chain)*

HIPAGES GROUP HOLDINGS LIMITED
Level 10 255 Pitt Street, Sydney, 2000, NSW, Australia
Tel.: (61) 283961300 AU
Web Site: https://www.hipagesgroup.com.au
Year Founded: 2004
HPG—(ASX)
Rev.: $43,689,770
Assets: $40,565,300
Liabilities: $18,266,284
Net Worth: $22,299,015
Earnings: ($3,353,981)
Fiscal Year-end: 06/30/23
Holding Company
N.A.I.C.S.: 551112
Robert Tolliday *(Chief Revenue Officer & VP)*

Subsidiaries:

Ninety Nine Pty. Ltd. (1)
Level 10 255 Pitt Street, Sydney, 2000, NSW, Australia
Tel.: (61) 1300762862
Web Site: https://tradiecore.com.au
Employment Services
N.A.I.C.S.: 561311

HIPARION DISTRIBUTION SA
B-dul Dimitrie Pompeiu 5D etaj 2 Sector 2, 020335, Bucharest, Romania
Tel.: (40) 372 119 700
Year Founded: 2008
Sales Range: $25-49.9 Million
Emp.: 320
Book Stores, Kiosks & Movie Theaters Operation Services
N.A.I.C.S.: 459210
Dan Vasile *(Mng Dir)*

HIPER GLOBAL LTD.
10 Hamelacha St Park Afek Business Park, Rosh Ha'Ayin, Israel
Tel.: (972) 39109105 IL
Web Site: https://www.hiper-global.com
Year Founded: 1984
HIPR—(TAE)
Rev.: $285,567,000
Assets: $173,049,000
Liabilities: $93,554,000
Net Worth: $79,495,000
Earnings: $14,307,000
Emp.: 270
Fiscal Year-end: 12/31/23

Other Electronic Component Manufacturing
N.A.I.C.S.: 334419

Subsidiaries:

HIPER Global UK Ltd. (1)
Unit 13 Suttons Business Park Suttons Park Avenue, Reading, RG6 1AZ, Berkshire, United Kingdom
Tel.: (44) 1189294990
Web Site: https://hiper-global.co.uk
Hardware Mfr
N.A.I.C.S.: 332510

HIPER Global US Ltd. (1)
1616 Osgood St Ste 1001, North Andover, MA 01845
Tel.: (978) 486-0300
Web Site: https://www.hiper-global.us
Hardware Mfr
N.A.I.C.S.: 332510

HIPERMARC S.A.
Amunategui 178 Piso 6, PO Box 13514, Santiago, Chile
Tel.: (56) 5406047
Web Site: https://www.hipermarcchile.cl
Year Founded: 1961
HIPERMARC—(SGO)
Rev.: $86,609,578
Assets: $174,484,652
Liabilities: $69,098,206
Net Worth: $105,386,446
Earnings: $8,225,082
Emp.: 525
Fiscal Year-end: 12/31/23
Supermarket Operator
N.A.I.C.S.: 445110
Nibaldo Sepulveda Mojer *(CEO & Gen Mgr)*

HIPOL A.D.
Industrijska zona bb, 25250, Odzaci, Serbia
Tel.: (381) 25 464 700
Web Site: http://www.hipol.com
Year Founded: 1983
Gas Production Services
N.A.I.C.S.: 457210

HIPOLIN LIMITED
4th Floor Madhuban Ellisbridge, Ahmedabad, 380 006, India
Tel.: (91) 8155090055
Web Site: https://www.hipolin.com
Year Founded: 1970
530853—(BOM)
Rev.: $2,177,506
Assets: $2,028,109
Liabilities: $347,871
Net Worth: $1,680,239
Earnings: $1,041,127
Emp.: 25
Fiscal Year-end: 03/31/23
Detergent Powder Mfr
N.A.I.C.S.: 325611
Bhupendra Jayantilal Shah *(Chm)*

HIQ INTERNATIONAL AB
Katarinavagen 15 7th Floor, Box 4046, 102 61, Stockholm, Sweden
Tel.: (46) 858890000
Web Site: http://www.hiq.se
Rev.: $200,387,216
Assets: $134,962,610
Liabilities: $47,780,887
Net Worth: $87,181,723
Earnings: $18,894,393
Emp.: 1,560
Fiscal Year-end: 12/31/19
Information Technology & Management Consulting Services
N.A.I.C.S.: 541611
Lars Stugemo *(Pres & CEO)*

Subsidiaries:

HiQ Accelerated Concept Evaluation AB (1)
jarnvagsgatan, 583 30, Linkoping, Ostergotland, Sweden
Tel.: (46) 13210460
Web Site: http://www.hiq.se
Sales Range: $25-49.9 Million
Emp.: 68
Software Development Services
N.A.I.C.S.: 541511
Patrik Holm *(Mng Dir)*

HiQ Approve AB (1)
Gunnarsrovagen 2, PO Box 206, 73224, Arboga, Sweden (100%)
Tel.: (46) 58984500
Web Site: http://www.hiq.com
Sales Range: $25-49.9 Million
Emp.: 100
Custom Computer Programming Services
N.A.I.C.S.: 541511

HiQ Finland OY (1)
Tekniikantie 14, 2150, Espoo, Finland
Tel.: (358) 9 4355 860
Web Site: http://www.hiq.se
Information Technology Consulting Services
N.A.I.C.S.: 541512
Jukka Rautio *(Mng Dir)*

HiQ Goteborg AB (1)
Ostra Hamngatan 24, 41109, Gothenburg, Sweden (100%)
Tel.: (46) 317439100
Web Site: http://www.hiq.se
Sales Range: $75-99.9 Million
Emp.: 300
Custom Computer Programming Services
N.A.I.C.S.: 541511
Jerker Lindsten *(Mng Dir)*

HiQ Karlskrona AB (1)
Drottninggatan 28, 37132, Karlskrona, Sweden (100%)
Tel.: (46) 455617627
Sales Range: $25-49.9 Million
Emp.: 40
Custom Computer Programming Services
N.A.I.C.S.: 541511
Klas Nystrom *(CEO)*

HiQ Kobenhavn A/S (1)
Nyvej 17 B 1, 1851, Frederiksberg, Denmark
Tel.: (45) 45201110
Web Site: http://www.hiq.se
Information Technology Consulting Services
N.A.I.C.S.: 541512

HiQ Malardalen AB (1)
Gunnarsrovagen 2, Box 206, 732 24, Arboga, Sweden
Tel.: (46) 317439100
Web Site: http://www.hiq.se
Emp.: 103
Information Technology Consulting Services
N.A.I.C.S.: 541512

HiQ MobilEyes AB (1)
Katarinavagen 15 7th floor, Box 4046, 102 61, Stockholm, Sweden
Tel.: (46) 8 588 90 000
Web Site: http://www.hiq.se
Emp.: 100
Computer Software Development Services
N.A.I.C.S.: 541511

HiQ Skane AB (1)
Scheelevagen 27, Lund, 22370, Sweden (100%)
Tel.: (46) 5405550
Web Site: http://www.hiq.se
Sales Range: $25-49.9 Million
Emp.: 100
Custom Computer Programming Services
N.A.I.C.S.: 541511
Anna Kleine *(Mng Dir)*

HiQ Softplan Oy (1)
Vaisalantie 6, Espoo, 2130, Finland (100%)
Tel.: (358) 94355860
Web Site: http://www.hiq.fi
Sales Range: $25-49.9 Million
Emp.: 120
Custom Computer Programming Services
N.A.I.C.S.: 541511

HiQ Stockholm AB (1)
PO Box 7421, 10391, Stockholm, Sweden (100%)
Tel.: (46) 858890000
Web Site: http://www.hiq.se

INTERNATIONAL PUBLIC

Sales Range: $25-49.9 Million
Emp.: 100
Custom Computer Programming Services
N.A.I.C.S.: 541511
Magnus Gudehn *(Mng Dir)*

HiQ Wise A/S (1)
Marieluntbek 43, 2730, Herald, Denmark (100%)
Tel.: (45) 45201110
Web Site: http://www.hiq.dk
Sales Range: $25-49.9 Million
Emp.: 20
Other Management Consulting Services
N.A.I.C.S.: 541618

ZAO MobilEyes (1)
8th Tekstilschikov Building 11, 109129, Moscow, Russia
Tel.: (7) 495 987 4397
Web Site: http://www.hiq.ru
Sales Range: $25-49.9 Million
Emp.: 4
Computer Software Development Services
N.A.I.C.S.: 541511

HIRA AUTOMOBILES LIMITED
Rajbaha Raod, Patiala, India
Tel.: (91) 1752300101
Web Site: http://www.hiraautomobiles.com
Year Founded: 1989
Sales Range: $25-49.9 Million
Car Whslr
N.A.I.C.S.: 441110
Rahul Inder Singh Sidhu *(Chm)*

HIRA FERRO ALLOYS LTD.
Plot nos 567 B 568 553 B Urla Industrial Complex, Raipur, 493221, Chhattisgarh, India
Tel.: (91) 7714082450
Web Site: http://www.hiraferroalloys.com
Year Founded: 1990
Rev.: $83,027,900
Assets: $107,432,313
Liabilities: $37,728,934
Net Worth: $69,703,380
Earnings: $15,484,992
Fiscal Year-end: 03/31/22
Ferro Alloy Mfr
N.A.I.C.S.: 331110
Narayan Prasad Agrawal *(Mng Dir)*

HIRA TEXTILE MILLS LIMITED
8-Km Manga Raiwind Road, Raiwind District, Kasur, Pakistan
Tel.: (92) 35392305
Web Site: https://www.hiramills.com.pk
Year Founded: 1991
HIRAT—(KAR)
Rev.: $9,424,128
Assets: $20,749,516
Liabilities: $20,305,275
Net Worth: $444,241
Earnings: ($1,956,398)
Emp.: 826
Fiscal Year-end: 06/30/20
Yarn & Textile Mfr
N.A.I.C.S.: 314120

HIRAGA CO., LTD.
3-20-2 Toshimakita, Nerima-Ku, Tokyo, 176-0012, Japan
Tel.: (81) 339914541
Web Site: https://www.pp-hiraga.co.jp
Year Founded: 1956
7863—(TKS)
Sales Range: Less than $1 Million
Sales Promotion Services
N.A.I.C.S.: 561990
Shintaro Kamide *(Gen Mgr-Finance & Accounting Department-Mgmt)*

HIRAKAWA HEWTECH CORP.
7F Sotetsu Tamachi Bldg 4-17-5 Shiba, Minato-Ku, Tokyo, 108-0014, Japan

Tel.: (81) 334571400
Web Site: https://www.hewtech.co.jp
Year Founded: 1948
5821—(TKS)
Rev.: $193,844,860
Assets: $307,702,110
Liabilities: $59,939,480
Net Worth: $247,762,630
Earnings: $9,544,840
Emp.: 2,212
Fiscal Year-end: 03/31/24
Electrical Wire & Broadcasting Equipment Mfr
N.A.I.C.S.: 335931
Kazuo Sumita *(Chm)*

Subsidiaries:

HEWTECH (BANGKOK) CO., LTD. (1)
54 BB Building 18th Floor Room 1815 Sukhumvit 21 Asoke Road, Khet Wattana, Bangkok, 10110, Thailand
Tel.: (66) 21634722
Electrical Wire Distr
N.A.I.C.S.: 423610

HEWTECH (SHENZHEN) ELECTRONICS CO., LTD. (1)
Block 5 & Block 6 172 Hengpailing Estate Wu Tong Shan Luo Hu District, Shenzhen, 518114, China
Tel.: (86) 75533237178
Electrical Wire Mfr
N.A.I.C.S.: 335931

HEWTECH (THAILAND) CO., LTD. (1)
Rojana Industrial Park 1/41 Moo 5 Tambol Khan Ham Amphur Uthai, Ayutthaya, 13210, Thailand
Tel.: (66) 35330403
Electrical Wire Mfr
N.A.I.C.S.: 335931

HEWTECH HONG KONG LTD. (1)
Unit 15-16 17/F Vanta Industrial Centre No 21-33 Tai Lin Pai Road, Kwai Chung, New Territories, China (Hong Kong)
Tel.: (852) 24251225
Electrical Wire Distr
N.A.I.C.S.: 423610

HEWTECH PHILIPPINES CORP. (1)
Lot C2-9 Carmelray Industrial Park II, Calamba, Laguna, Philippines
Tel.: (63) 495082299
Electrical Wire Mfr
N.A.I.C.S.: 335931

HEWTECH SHANGHAI TRADING CO., LTD. (1)
Rm 1008 Lingyou Bldg No 618 Shangcheng Road Pudong New Area, Shanghai, 200120, China
Tel.: (86) 2158403760
Electrical Wire Distr
N.A.I.C.S.: 423610

HIKAM ELECTRONICA DE MEXICO, S.A.DE C.V. (1)
Las Californias Industrial Park KM 10 5 Carret San Luis RCSon, Mexicali, Baja California, Mexico
Tel.: (52) 6865616551
Testing Equipment Mfr
N.A.I.C.S.: 334515

HIKAM TECNOLOGIA DE SINALOA, S.A.DE C.V. (1)
Km 2 5 Carretera Internacional Zona Industrial Guasave, Sinaloa, Mexico
Tel.: (52) 6878724083
Testing Equipment Mfr
N.A.I.C.S.: 334515

Hewtech (Lianyungang) Electronics Co., Ltd. (1)
No 8 ZhenXing Road, High-tech Industrial Development Zone, Lianyungang, JiangSu, China
Tel.: (86) 51885150321
Electric Equipment Mfr
N.A.I.C.S.: 334419

Hewtech Philippines Electronics Corp. (1)

TECO Industrial Park Ninoy Aquino Highway Bo Bundagul, Mabalacat, 2010, Pampanga, Philippines
Tel.: (63) 459631777
Electric Equipment Mfr
N.A.I.C.S.: 334419

Hikam America, Inc. (1)
3521 Main St Ste 501, Chula Vista, CA 91911
Tel.: (619) 420-0333
Web Site: https://www.hikam.com
Electrical & Electronic Mfr
N.A.I.C.S.: 336320

Hirakawa Hewtech Corp. - Fukushima Factory (1)
1-2 Yanagawa Industrial Park Yanagawa-cho, Date, 960-0719, Fukushima-ken, Japan
Tel.: (81) 245771211
Electrical Wire Mfr
N.A.I.C.S.: 335931

Hirakawa Hewtech Corp. - Koga General R&D Plant (1)
1144 Higashi-ushigaya, Koga, 306-0232, Ibaraki-ken, Japan
Tel.: (81) 280981711
Electrical Wire Mfr
N.A.I.C.S.: 335931

Hirakawa Hewtech Corp. - Monou Factory (1)
107-1 Rai Ushita Monou-cho, Ishinomaki, 986-0305, Miyagi-ken, Japan
Tel.: (81) 225761811
Electrical Wire Mfr
N.A.I.C.S.: 335931

Hirakawa Hewtech Corp. - Niigata Factory (1)
269 Hataya, Nishikan-ku, Niigata, 959-0423, Niigata-ken, Japan
Tel.: (81) 256883035
Electrical Wire Mfr
N.A.I.C.S.: 335931

TAIWAN HEWTECH CORP. (1)
12F-2 No 79 Sec 2 Shuangshi Rd Banqiao Dist, New Taipei City, 22043, Taiwan
Tel.: (886) 282512228
Electrical Wire Distr
N.A.I.C.S.: 423610

HIRAKI CO., LTD.
556 Fukuyoshi Nonaka, Iwaoka-cho Nishi-ku, Kobe, 651-2494, Hyogo, Japan
Tel.: (81) 120028252
Web Site: https://www.hiraki.co.jp
Year Founded: 1978
3059—(TKS)
Rev.: $87,998,930
Assets: $107,498,430
Liabilities: $58,881,880
Net Worth: $48,616,550
Earnings: ($99,150)
Fiscal Year-end: 03/31/24
Mail Order & General Store Services
N.A.I.C.S.: 455219
Eiji Ihara *(Chm, Pres, CEO & COO)*

HIRAMATSU INC.
4-17-3 Ebisu, Shibuya-ku, Tokyo, 150-0013, Japan
Tel.: (81) 357938811
Web Site: https://www.hiramatsu.co.jp
Year Founded: 1982
2764—(TKS)
Rev.: $91,607,990
Assets: $144,573,920
Liabilities: $115,840,250
Net Worth: $28,733,670
Earnings: $1,011,330
Emp.: 703
Fiscal Year-end: 03/31/24
Restaurant Operators
N.A.I.C.S.: 722511
Takaya Jinnai *(Pres)*

HIRAN ORGOCHEM LTD.
908 Ijmima Complex Off Link Road,

Malad West, Mumbai, 400 064, India
Tel.: (91) 22 40144127
Web Site:
http://www.hiranorgochem.com
Sales Range: Less than $1 Million
Emp.: 89
Pharmaceutical Preparation Mfr
N.A.I.C.S.: 325412
Kantilal M. Hiran *(CFO)*

HIRANO TECSEED CO., LTD.
1011 Kawai Kawaicho, Kitakatsuragi-gun, Nara, 636-0051, Japan
Tel.: (81) 745570681
Web Site: https://www.hirano-tec.co.jp
Year Founded: 1935
6245—(TKS)
Rev.: $310,313,060
Assets: $415,960,690
Liabilities: $161,065,870
Net Worth: $254,894,820
Earnings: $16,115,180
Emp.: 413
Fiscal Year-end: 03/31/24
Industrial Machinery Mfr
N.A.I.C.S.: 333248
Kaoru Okada *(Pres)*

HIRATA CORPORATION
3 9 20 Togoshi, Shinagawa, Tokyo, 142-0041, Japan
Tel.: (81) 337861264
Web Site: http://www.hirata.co.jp
Sales Range: $250-299.9 Million
Emp.: 1,000
Semiconductors, Automotive Parts & Industrial Robots Mfg
N.A.I.C.S.: 334413
Katsuyoshi Tachibana *(Sr Exec VP)*

Subsidiaries:

Hirata Automated Machinery (Shanghai) Co., Ltd. (1)
2728 Huan Cheng Xi Road, Feng Xian, Shanghai, 201401, China
Tel.: (86) 21 3365 5610
Web Site: http://www.hirata-cn.com
Industrial Machinery Mfr
N.A.I.C.S.: 333998
Hirata Shojiro *(Chm)*

Hirata Corporation - East Plant (1)
4-5 Iwano Ueki, Kita, Kumamoto, 861-0136, Japan
Tel.: (81) 962733211
Automotive Components Mfr

Hirata Corporation - Kansai Plant (1)
500 Kozutsumi, Yasu, 520-2314, Shiga, Japan
Tel.: (81) 77 587 2266
Automotive Products Mfr
N.A.I.C.S.: 336310

Hirata Corporation - Kanto Plant (1)
10-2 Hiraide Kogyodanchi, Utsunomiya, 321-0905, Tochigi, Japan
Tel.: (81) 28 661 3333
Automotive Products Mfr
N.A.I.C.S.: 336310

Hirata Corporation - Kumamoto Plant (1)
111 Hitotsugi, Ueki Kita, Kumamoto, 861-0198, Japan
Tel.: (81) 96 272 0555
Automotive Products Mfr
N.A.I.C.S.: 336310

Hirata Corporation - Kusuno Plant (1)
1016-6 Kusuno, Kita, Kumamoto, 861-5511, Japan
Tel.: (81) 96 245 1333
Web Site: http://www.hirata.co.jp
Automotive Products Mfr
N.A.I.C.S.: 336310

Hirata Corporation of America (1)
5625 Decatur Blvd, Indianapolis, IN 46241
Tel.: (317) 856-8600
Web Site: http://www.hirata.com

Sales Range: $75-99.9 Million
Emp.: 65
Engineering Services; Conveyors & Conveying Equipment Mfr
N.A.I.C.S.: 541330
Biagio Longo *(Pres)*

Hirata Corporation of Europe Ltd (1)
Grafton Road, Burbage, Marlborough, SN8 3BA, Wiltshire, United Kingdom
Tel.: (44) 1672811555
Sales Range: $1-9.9 Million
Emp.: 17
Industrial Machinery & Elevators & Moving Stairways Mfr
N.A.I.C.S.: 333921

Hirata Engineering (Thailand) Co., Ltd. (1)
11th Floor No 1 MD Tower Soi Bangna-Trad 25 Bangna-Trad Road, Kwaeng Bangna Khet Bangna, Bangkok, 10260, Thailand
Tel.: (66) 2 361 8825
Automotive Products Mfr
N.A.I.C.S.: 336310

Hirata Engineering Europe GmbH (1)
Am Sagewerk 7, 55124, Mainz, Germany
Tel.: (49) 6131 9413 0
Web Site: http://www.uk.hirata.de
Emp.: 50
Automotive Products Mfr
N.A.I.C.S.: 336310
Matthias Schneider *(Mng Dir)*

Hirata Engineering, Inc. (1)
5625 Decatur Blvd, Indianapolis, IN 46241-9509
Tel.: (317) 856-8600
Web Site: http://www.hirata.com
Sales Range: $1-9.9 Million
Emp.: 50
Industrial Machinery & Equipment Whslr
N.A.I.C.S.: 423830
Mitsutaka Hayashi *(VP)*

Subsidiary (Non-US):

Hirata Engineering S.A. de C.V. (2)
Segundo Eje Oriente No. 19029, Local 17, Tijuana, 22500, Baja California, Mexico
Tel.: (52) 6646473886
Web Site: http://www.hirata.com
Industrial Machinery Mfr, Engineering, Installation & Repairing & Maintenance Services
N.A.I.C.S.: 333248

Hirata FA Engineering (M) Sdn. Bhd. (1)
No 6-8 Jalan Mega 1/6 Taman Perindustrian Nusa Cemerlang, 79200, Kuala Lumpur, Johor, Malaysia
Tel.: (60) 7509 5090
Automotive Products Mfr
N.A.I.C.S.: 336310

Hirata Fa Engineering (S) Pte Ltd (1)
51 Benoi Rd Block 8 Ste M-02, Jurong Town, Singapore, 629908, Singapore
Tel.: (65) 68621178
Web Site: http://www.hirata.com
Sales Range: $1-9.9 Million
Emp.: 60
Industrial Machinery Mfr
N.A.I.C.S.: 333248
Yukiharo Yamaguchi *(Mng Dir)*

Hirata Field Engineering Co., Ltd. (1)
54-2 Iwano Uekimachi, Kamoto-gun, Kumamoto, 861 0136, Japan (100%)
Tel.: (81) 9622731335
Web Site: http://www.hirata-fe.com
Industrial Machinery Parts Whslr & Maintenance Services
N.A.I.C.S.: 423830
Michinobu Shuto *(CEO)*

Hirata Field Engineering Co., Ltd. (1)
54-2 Iwano, Ueki Kita, Kumamoto, 861-0136, Japan
Tel.: (81) 96 273 1335
Web Site: http://www.hirata-fe.com
Emp.: 40
Automotive Products Mfr
N.A.I.C.S.: 336310

HIRATA CORPORATION

Hirata Corporation—(Continued)

Satoshi Takamura *(Mgr-Svc)*

Hirata Mechanical Equipment Sales (Shanghai) Co., Ltd. (1)
Room 706 Hongqiao Crystal Business Center No 2 Lane 280 Hongjing Road, Shanghai, 201103, China
Tel.: (86) 21 3471 1110
Web Site: http://www.hirata.com
Automotive Products Mfr
N.A.I.C.S.: 336310

Hirata Software Technology Co., Ltd. (1)
4-5 Iwano, Ueki, Kumamoto, 861 0136, Japan
Tel.: (81) 96 273 3211
Web Site: http://www.hirata.co.jp
Sales Range: $1-9.9 Million
Emp.: 24
Computer Programming Services
N.A.I.C.S.: 541511
Yasunari Hirata *(Pres & CEO)*

KOYA Corp. (1)
1-36 Fukuhara, Koshi, Kumamoto, 861-1116, Japan
Tel.: (81) 96 292 4333
Automotive Products Mfr
N.A.I.C.S.: 336310

Taihei Computer Co., Ltd. (1)
5-4 Myotaiji, Kumamoto, 860 8539, Japan
Tel.: (81) 963454411
Web Site: http://www.tccnet.jp
Sales Range: $1-9.9 Million
Emp.: 54
Custom Computer Programming Services
N.A.I.C.S.: 541511
Yushalo Shelata *(Pres)*

Taihei Technos Co., Ltd. (1)
3-43-11 Takahira, Kita, Kumamoto, 860-0085, Japan
Tel.: (81) 96 300 1010
Web Site: http://www.taiheitechnos.co.jp
Automotive Products Mfr
N.A.I.C.S.: 336310
Masaru Fujimoto *(Pres & CEO)*

Taiwan Hirata Corporation (1)
NO 128 Sec1 Shinhua Rd, Taipei, Taoyuan, Taiwan
Tel.: (886) 3 477 797
Automotive Products Mfr
N.A.I.C.S.: 336310

Trinity Inc. (1)
15th Floor Iidabashi Grand Bloom 2-10-2 Fujimi, Chiyoda, Tokyo, 102-0071, Japan
Tel.: (81) 3 5205 6486
Web Site: http://www.3inc.jp
Automotive Products Mfr
N.A.I.C.S.: 336310

HIRAYAMA HOLDINGS CO., LTD.

6 floor A-PLACE Shinagawa 1-8-40 Kounan, Minato-ku, Tokyo, 108-0075, Japan
Tel.: (81) 357694680
Web Site: https://hirayamastaff.co.jp
Year Founded: 1955
7781—(TKS)
Rev.: $219,516,240
Assets: $76,468,680
Liabilities: $48,690,160
Net Worth: $27,778,520
Earnings: $4,708,540
Emp.: 10,347
Fiscal Year-end: 06/30/24
Consulting, Factory Outsourcing, Temporary Staffing & Job Placement Services
N.A.I.C.S.: 561311
Yoshikazu Hirayama *(Pres)*

Subsidiaries:

Fun To Fun Inc. (1)
5th Floor of the NK Building 2-7-2 Kanda Sudacho, Chiyoda-ku, Tokyo, 101-0041, Japan
Tel.: (81) 352893291
Web Site: http://www.funtofun.co.jp
Paid Employment Agency Services
N.A.I.C.S.: 561311

HIRAYAMA VIETNAM COMPANY LIMITED (1)
No 508 5F Viet Nam Economic Times Building 98 hoang Quoc Viet District, Hanoi, Vietnam
Tel.: (84) 439590247
Human Resource Consulting Services
N.A.I.C.S.: 561311

Heiwa Ironworks Co., Ltd. (1)
39-10 Otsubo Honcho, Shimonoseki, 750-0051, Yamaguchi, Japan
Tel.: (81) 832242321
Human Resources Development Services
N.A.I.C.S.: 561311

Hirayama (Thailand) Co., Ltd. (1)
559 Moo 5, Klongtamru Sub-District Muang District, Chon Buri, 20000, Thailand
Tel.: (66) 33640596
Web Site: http://en.hirayama-thailand.com
Emp.: 2,869
On-Site Improvement Consulting Services
N.A.I.C.S.: 541611
Akio Naito *(Pres)*

Hirayama Co., Ltd. (1)
1-8-40 Konan A-Place Shinagawa 6th Floor, Minato-ku, Tokyo, 108-0075, Japan
Tel.: (81) 357833571
Web Site: http://www.iot-hirayama.com
On-Site Improvement Consulting Services
N.A.I.C.S.: 541611

Hirayama Global Supporter Co., Ltd. (1)
1-84-5 Miyama-cho, Toyota, 471-0849, Aichi Prefecture, Japan
Tel.: (81) 488715171
Web Site: http://www.global-supporter.com
Employment Support Services
N.A.I.C.S.: 561311

Hirayama LACC Co., Ltd. (1)
1-8-40 Konan A-Place Shinagawa 6th Floor, Minato-ku, Tokyo, 108-0075, Japan
Tel.: (81) 298867616
Web Site: http://www.hy-lacc.com
Community Life Support Services
N.A.I.C.S.: 624120

Ohmatsu Services Co., Ltd. (1)
1529-1 Tochihara Odai-cho, Taki, 519-2424, Mie, Japan
Tel.: (81) 598850054
Web Site: http://www.ohmatsuservices.co.jp
Automobile Maintenance Services
N.A.I.C.S.: 811111

Top Engineering Inc. (1)
1-8-40 Kounan Minato-ku, Tokyo, Japan
Tel.: (81) 357819591
Web Site: http://www.topeng.heteml.jp
Human Resource Consulting Services
N.A.I.C.S.: 561311

HIRE INTELLIGENCE INTERNATIONAL LIMITED

110 Jersey Street, Jolimont, 6014, WA, Australia
Tel.: (61) 892841166
Web Site: http://www.hire-intelligence.com.au
Sales Range: $10-24.9 Million
Rental of Computer & Audio Visual Equipment & Rental of Commercial Office Space; Website Development Services
N.A.I.C.S.: 532420
Thomas R. Crage *(Chm, CEO)*

Subsidiaries:

Busby Web Solutions Pty. Ltd. (1)
110 Jersey St, Perth, 6014, WA, Australia
Tel.: (61) 892841800
Web Site: http://www.busbywebsolutions.com
Web Designing Services
N.A.I.C.S.: 513199

HIRE TECHNOLOGIES, INC.

635-333 Bay Street, Toronto, M5H 2R2, ON, Canada
Web Site: https://www.hire.company
HIRE—(TSXV)
Rev.: $9,153,502
Assets: $4,922,644
Liabilities: $1,930,555
Net Worth: $2,992,088
Earnings: ($5,501,349)
Fiscal Year-end: 12/31/19
Information Technology Services
N.A.I.C.S.: 541512
Simon Dealy *(CEO)*

Subsidiaries:

The Headhunters Recruitment, Inc. (1)
Suite 102 11302 119 Street, Edmonton, T5G 2X4, AB, Canada
Tel.: (780) 486-8377
Web Site: http://www.theheadhunters.ca
Recruitment Consulting Services
N.A.I.C.S.: 561311
Danielle Bragge *(Co-Founder & Pres)*

HIREMII LIMITED

Level 1 251 St Georges Terrace, Perth, 6000, WA, Australia
Tel.: (61) 272591501 AU
Web Site: https://www.hiremii.com
Year Founded: 2017
HMI—(ASX)
Rev.: $13,571,106
Assets: $3,854,566
Liabilities: $3,046,093
Net Worth: $808,473
Earnings: ($1,002,581)
Fiscal Year-end: 06/30/23
Recruitment Services
N.A.I.C.S.: 561311

Subsidiaries:

Inverse Group Pty. Ltd. (1)
L1/251 St Georges Terrace, Perth, 6000, WA, Australia
Tel.: (61) 862637731
Web Site: https://inverse-group.com
Designers & Engineers Services
N.A.I.C.S.: 541330

HIROCA HOLDINGS LTD.

Tel.: (86) 76989278888 KY
Web Site: http://www.hirosawa.com.cn
1338—(TAI)
Rev.: $246,976,877
Assets: $335,542,940
Liabilities: $114,156,294
Net Worth: $221,386,646
Earnings: $13,027,018
Emp.: 3,340
Fiscal Year-end: 12/31/19
Holding Company; Automotive Interior & Exterior Parts
N.A.I.C.S.: 551112

Subsidiaries:

ChangShu Mono Hirosawa Automotive Trim Co., Ltd. (1)
Nanxin Road Nanyuan Southeast Development Zone, Changshu, 215542, Jiangsu, China
Tel.: (86) 51281581198
Automobile Component Distr
N.A.I.C.S.: 423120

Dong Guan Hirosawa Automotive Trim Co., Ltd. (1)
Houjie Science and Technology Industrial Park East Road, Houjie Town Industry, Guangdong, 523950, China
Tel.: (86) 76989278888
Automobile Component Distr
N.A.I.C.S.: 423120

DongGuan Taica Hirosawa Technologies Co., Ltd. (1)
First Industrial Zone, Huangang Village Houjie Town, Dongguan, 523950, Guangdong, China
Tel.: (86) 76938836288
Automobile Component Distr
N.A.I.C.S.: 423120

INTERNATIONAL PUBLIC

KaiFeng Hiroyoshi Automotive Trim Co., Ltd. (1)
North of the Middle Section of Longhai 2nd Road, New District, Kaifeng, 475000, Henan, China
Tel.: (86) 37123321000
Automobile Component Distr
N.A.I.C.S.: 423120

WuHan Hiroyoshi Automotive Trim Co., Ltd. (1)
No 516 Weihu Road, Hannan District, Wuhan, 430090, China
Tel.: (86) 2784856999
Automobile Component Distr
N.A.I.C.S.: 423120

HIROGIN HOLDINGS, INC.

1-3-8 Kamiya-cho, Naka-ku, Hiroshima, 730-8691, Japan
Tel.: (81) 822455151
Web Site: https://www.hirogin-hd.co.jp
Year Founded: 2020
7337—(TKS)
Rev.: $1,229,929,310
Assets: $84,544,418,410
Liabilities: $81,006,422,520
Net Worth: $3,537,995,890
Earnings: $125,590
Fiscal Year-end: 03/31/24
Holding Company
N.A.I.C.S.: 551112

Subsidiaries:

Hirogin Area Design Co., Ltd. (1)
1-3-8 Kamiyacho, Naka-ku, Hiroshima, 730-0031, Japan
Tel.: (81) 825043016
Web Site: https://www.hirogin-areadesign.co.jp
Management Consulting Services
N.A.I.C.S.: 541611

Hirogin Capital Partners Co., Ltd. (1)
1-3-8 Kamiyacho, Naka-ku, Hiroshima, 730-0031, Japan
Tel.: (81) 825043762
Web Site: https://www.hicap.co.jp
Investment Fund Services
N.A.I.C.S.: 541690

Hirogin Human Resources Co., Ltd. (1)
1-3-8 Kamiyacho, Naka-ku, Hiroshima, Japan
Tel.: (81) 825043012
Web Site: https://www.hirogin-hr.co.jp
Human Resource Consulting Services
N.A.I.C.S.: 541612

Hirogin IT Solutions Co., Ltd. (1)
1-3-8 Kamiyacho, Naka-ku, Hiroshima, 730-0031, Japan
Tel.: (81) 825043170
Web Site: https://www.hirogin-its.co.jp
Emp.: 473
Information Technology Services
N.A.I.C.S.: 541512

Hirogin Lease Co., Ltd. (1)
1-3-8 Kamiyacho, Naka-ku, Hiroshima, 730-0031, Japan
Tel.: (81) 825453738
Web Site: https://www.hiroginlease.co.jp
Emp.: 103
Asset & Automobile Leasing Services
N.A.I.C.S.: 532112

Hirogin Securities Co., Ltd. (1)
1-3-8 Kamiyacho, Naka-ku, Hiroshima, 730-0031, Japan
Tel.: (81) 822455076
Web Site: https://www.hirogin-sec.co.jp
Investment Securities & Financial Services
N.A.I.C.S.: 525910

HIRON TRADE INVESTMENT & INDUSTRIAL BUILDINGS LTD.

Dereh Ben Tsvi 20, Tel Aviv, 68162, Israel
Tel.: (972) 36825217
Year Founded: 1974
HRON—(TAE)
Rev.: $32,885,481

AND PRIVATE COMPANIES — HIRSCH SERVO AG

Assets: $354,241,464
Liabilities: $82,268,268
Net Worth: $271,973,196
Earnings: $18,784,086
Emp.: 41
Fiscal Year-end: 12/31/23
Other Activities Related to Real Estate
N.A.I.C.S.: 531390

HIRONIC CO., LTD.
19F U-Tower 767 Sinsu-ro Suji-gu, Yongin, 16827, Gyeonggi-do, Korea (South)
Tel.: (82) 315257400
Web Site: http://www.hironic.com
149980—(KRS)
Rev.: $21,144,347
Assets: $51,783,054
Liabilities: $6,761,117
Net Worth: $45,021,937
Earnings: $2,250,333
Emp.: 84
Fiscal Year-end: 12/31/22
Aesthetic Medical Devices Mfr
N.A.I.C.S.: 339112

HIROSE ELECTRIC CO., LTD.
2-6-3 Nakagawa Chuoh, Tsuzuki-ku, Yokohama, 224-8540, Japan
Tel.: (81) 456203526
Web Site: https://www.hirose.com
Year Founded: 1937
6806—(TKS)
Rev.: $1,094,014,490
Assets: $2,666,804,500
Liabilities: $259,620,970
Net Worth: $2,407,183,530
Earnings: $175,032,800
Emp.: 4,654
Fiscal Year-end: 03/31/24
Electrical Equipment, Multipin & Coaxial Connectors, Light Switches
N.A.I.C.S.: 335313
Kazunori Ishii (Pres)

Subsidiaries:

HIROSE ELECTRIC EUROPE B.V (1)
Herikerbergweg 211, 1101 CN, Amsterdam, Netherlands
Tel.: (31) 206557460
Web Site: https://www.hirose.com
Sales Range: $25-49.9 Million
Emp.: 26
Electronic Connector Mfr
N.A.I.C.S.: 334417

HIROSE ELECTRIC HONG KONG CO., LTD. (1)
Room 1001 West Wing Tsim Sha Tsui Centre 66 Mody Road, Tsim Sha Tsui East, Kowloon, China (Hong Kong)
Tel.: (852) 28035338
Electronic Connectors Mfr & Distr
N.A.I.C.S.: 334417

HIROSE ELECTRIC HONG KONG TRADING CO., LTD. (1)
Room 1001 West Wing Tsim Sha Tsui Centre 66 Mody Rd Tsim Sha Tsui East, Kowloon, China (Hong Kong)
Tel.: (852) 28035338
Web Site: http://www.hirose-hongkong.com.hk
Electronic Connectors Mfr & Distr
N.A.I.C.S.: 334417

HIROSE ELECTRIC SINGAPORE PTE.LTD (1)
03 Anson Road 20-01 Springleaf Tower, Singapore, 079909, Singapore
Tel.: (65) 63246113
Web Site: http://www.hirose.com
Sales Range: $25-49.9 Million
Emp.: 20
Electronic Connectors Mfr & Distr
N.A.I.C.S.: 334417
Katsunori Takizawa (Mng Dir)

HIROSE ELECTRIC TAIWAN CO., LTD (1)
103 8 F No 87 Zhengzhou Road, Taipei, Taiwan
Tel.: (886) 2 2555 7377
Web Site: http://www.hirose-taiwan.com.tw
Electronic Connectors Mfr & Distr
N.A.I.C.S.: 334417

HIROSE ELECTRIC TRADING (SHANGHAI) CO., LTD (1)
1601 Henderson Metro No 300 East Nanjing Road, Huang Pu District, Shanghai, 200001, China
Tel.: (86) 21 6391 3355
Web Site: http://www.hirose-china.com.cn
Sales Range: $25-49.9 Million
Emp.: 40
Electronic Connectors Mfr & Distr
N.A.I.C.S.: 334417
Yoshihiro Nakamura (Mgr-China Section)

HST Co, Ltd. (1)
5-23 Osaki 5 Chome, Shinagawa ku, Tokyo, Japan
Tel.: (81) 454724411
Rev.: $384,660,804
Emp.: 100
Current-Carrying Wiring Device Mfr
N.A.I.C.S.: 335931
Tatsuro Nakamura (Pres)

Hirose Electric (U.S.A.), Inc. (1)
2300 Warrenville Rd Ste 150, Downers Grove, IL 60515 (100%)
Tel.: (630) 282-6700
Web Site: http://www.hiroseusa.com
Sales Range: $25-49.9 Million
Emp.: 25
Marketing & Sales of Electrical Equipment
N.A.I.C.S.: 334417

Hirose Electric Co., Ltd., European Branch (1)
(100%)
Tel.: (31) 206557460
Web Site: http://www.hirose.com
Sales Range: $25-49.9 Million
Emp.: 5
Mfr of Electronic Equipment
N.A.I.C.S.: 335999

Hirose Electric Malaysia Sdn Bhd (1)
Lot 720 Jalan Serendah 26/17 Hicom Industrial Estate Section 26, 40000, Shah Alam, Selangor Darul Ehsan, Malaysia
Tel.: (60) 351912839
Web Site: https://www.hirose.com
Sales Range: $200-249.9 Million
Emp.: 615
Electronic Connector Mfr
N.A.I.C.S.: 334417

Hirose Electric UK Ltd. (1)
4 Newton Count Kelvin Drive Knowlhill, Crownhill, Milton Keynes, MK5 8NH, United Kingdom (50%)
Tel.: (44) 1908202050
Web Site: http://www.hirose.com
Sales Range: $25-49.9 Million
Emp.: 9
Electrical Equipment, Multipin & Coaxial Connectors, Light Switches
N.A.I.C.S.: 335313

Hirose Korea Co. Ltd. (1)
429 450 No 2 NA 311 Shihwa Industrial Complex 1261-10, Jeoungwhang Dong, Seoul, Korea (South)
Tel.: (82) 314967000
Web Site: https://www.hirose.co.kr
Sales Range: $100-124.9 Million
Emp.: 450
Electrical Equipment, Multipin & Coaxial Connectors, Light Switches
N.A.I.C.S.: 335313

Hst (Hongkong) Ltd (1)
Room 1003 West Wing Tsim Sha Tsui Centre 66 Mody Road, Kowloon, China (Hong Kong)
Tel.: (852) 25622671
Emp.: 7
Electronic Connectors Mfr & Distr
N.A.I.C.S.: 334417
Yosuke Koizumi (Gen Mgr)

Ichinoseki Hirose Electric Co., Ltd. (1)
14-36 Higashidai, Ichinoseki, 021-0822, Japan
Tel.: (81) 191260500
Electronic Connector Mfr
N.A.I.C.S.: 334417

KORIYAMA HIROSE ELECTRIC CO., LTD (1)
23 Shinagawa-ku 5-chome, Tokyo, 141-8587, Japan
Tel.: (81) 334915300
Web Site: http://www.hirose.co.jp
Electronic Connectors Mfr & Distr
N.A.I.C.S.: 334417

P.T Hirose Electric Indonesia (1)
Kawasan EJIP Plot 3-B 1 Lemahabang, Bekasi, 17550, West Java, Indonesia
Tel.: (62) 218970977
Electronic Connectors Mfr & Distr
N.A.I.C.S.: 334417

Tohoku Hirose Electric Co., Ltd. (1)
21-2 Dai 2-chiwari Akamae, Miyako, 027-0202, Iwate, Japan
Tel.: (81) 193672151
Electrical Equipments Mfr & Sales
N.A.I.C.S.: 334419

HIROSE HOLDINGS & CO.,LTD.
4-1-13 Toyo Central Bldg, Koto-ku, Tokyo, 135-0016, Japan
Tel.: (81) 3 5634 4501
Web Site: http://www.hirose-net.com
Year Founded: 1938
Holding Company
N.A.I.C.S.: 551112
Taichi Hirose (Chm & Pres)

Subsidiaries:

Nippon No-Dig Technology Co., Ltd. (1)
East Square Omori 5th Floor 6-20-14 Minamioi, Shinagawa-ku, Tokyo, 140-0013, Japan
Tel.: (81) 3 5764 2300
Web Site: http://www.no-dig.jp
Pipe Rehabilitation
N.A.I.C.S.: 237110

HIROSE TUSYO, INC.
MG Building 1-3-19 Shinmachi, Nishi-ku, Osaka, 550-0013, Japan
Tel.: (81) 665340708
Web Site: https://www.hirose-fx.co.jp
Year Founded: 2004
7185—(TKS)
Rev.: $70,812,930
Assets: $787,052,700
Liabilities: $671,338,040
Net Worth: $115,714,660
Earnings: $19,334,250
Fiscal Year-end: 03/31/24
Foreign Exchange Trading Services
N.A.I.C.S.: 523160
Yusaku Noichi (Pres)

HIROSHIMA ELECTRIC RAILWAY CO.,LTD.
2-9-29 Higashi Senda-machi, Naka-ku, Hiroshima, 730-8610, Japan
Tel.: (81) 822423521
Web Site: https://www.hiroden.co.jp
9033—(TKS)
Rev.: $201,380,260
Assets: $650,410,780
Liabilities: $375,401,730
Net Worth: $275,009,050
Earnings: $4,336,160
Emp.: 1,625
Fiscal Year-end: 03/31/24
Food Transportation Services
N.A.I.C.S.: 488490
Masao Mukuda (Chm & Pres)

HIROSHIMA GAS CO., LTD.
2-7-1 Minami-machi, Minami-ku, Hiroshima, 734-8555, Japan
Tel.: (81) 822512151
Web Site: https://www.hiroshima-gas.co.jp
Year Founded: 1909
9535—(TKS)
Rev.: $599,328,700
Assets: $909,721,080
Liabilities: $443,636,760
Net Worth: $466,084,320
Earnings: $15,394,690
Emp.: 686
Fiscal Year-end: 03/31/24
Natural Gas Distr
N.A.I.C.S.: 221210
Kensuke Matsufuji (Pres)

Subsidiaries:

Hiroshima Gas Co., Ltd. - Bingo Plant (1)
Tel.: (81) 848606303
Sales Range: $50-74.9 Million
Emp.: 14
Gas Mfr
N.A.I.C.S.: 211120

Hiroshima Gas Living Co., Ltd. (1)
1-30, Minamitakeyacho, Naka-ku, Hiroshima, Japan
Tel.: (81) 822438500
Web Site: http://www.hiroshima-gas.co.jp
Gas Powered Machinery & Equipments Whslr
N.A.I.C.S.: 423830

HIROSHIMA TOYO CARP, K.K.
5-25 Motomachi-cho, Naka-ku, Hiroshima, 730 8508, Japan
Tel.: (81) 82 221 2040   JP
Web Site: http://www.carp.co.jp
Year Founded: 1949
Sales Range: $50-74.9 Million
Emp.: 211
Professional Basketball Team
N.A.I.C.S.: 711211
Kenjiro Nomura (Mgr)

HIRSCH SERVO AG
Glanegg 58, A-9555, Glanegg, Austria
Tel.: (43) 427722110
Web Site: http://www.hirsch-gruppe.com
Year Founded: 1972
Sales Range: $50-74.9 Million
Expandable Polystyrene Mfr
N.A.I.C.S.: 326199
Harald Kogler (CEO & Member-Mgmt Bd)

Subsidiaries:

GGB GmbH (1)
Glanegg 58, 9555, Glanegg, Austria
Tel.: (43) 4277 2211 610
Web Site: http://www.global-green-built.com
Sales Range: $50-74.9 Million
Emp.: 200
Polysterene resins Mfr
N.A.I.C.S.: 325211
Kurt Hirsch (Mng Dir)

HIRSCH Italia S.r.l. (1)
Via XXV Aprile 12, I-22031, Albavilla, CO, Italy
Tel.: (39) 031 6541
Web Site: http://www.hirsch-italia.com
Plastics Product Mfr
N.A.I.C.S.: 326199

HIRSCH Maschinenbau GmbH (1)
Glanegg 58, 9555, Glanegg, Carinthia, Austria
Tel.: (43) 427722110
Web Site: http://www.hirsch-technology.com
Preexpanders, Shape Molding Machines, Blockmolds, Cutting Lines, Automation, Molds, Turn Key Plants, Engineering, EPS, Machinery for EPS, Expandable Polystyrene & Technology
N.A.I.C.S.: 333998

HIRSCH Porozell GmbH (1)
Glanegg 58, 9555, Glanegg, Carinthia, Austria
Tel.: (43) 427722110
Web Site: http://www.hirsch-gruppe.com

HIRSCH SERVO AG

Hirsch Servo AG—(Continued)

Sales Range: $250-299.9 Million
Plastic Materials Mfr
N.A.I.C.S.: 424610
Siegfried Wilding *(Mng Dir)*

HIRSCH Porozell Kft (1)
Ikervari ut 42, H-9600, Sarvar, Hungary
Tel.: (36) 695 520 530
Plastics Product Mfr
N.A.I.C.S.: 326199

HIRSCH Porozell S.r.l. (1)
No 368A, Rascruci village Bontida, 407107, Cluj-Napoca, Romania
Tel.: (40) 264207171
Sales Range: $25-49.9 Million
Emp.: 77
Plastics Product Mfr
N.A.I.C.S.: 424610
Siegfried Wilding *(Mgr)*

HIRSCH Porozell Sp. z o.o. (1)
Ul Bierutowska 55, PL 51317, Wroclaw, Poland
Tel.: (48) 717990953
Web Site: http://www.hirsch-gruppe.com
Sales Range: $25-49.9 Million
Emp.: 15
Plastics Product Mfr
N.A.I.C.S.: 424610

Polyform s.r.o. (1)
Terezie Vansovej 10, Podolinec, 065 03, Presov, Slovakia
Tel.: (421) 524391214
Web Site: http://www.polyform.sk
Polystyrene Product Mfr
N.A.I.C.S.: 326140
Peter Ferencko *(Mgr-Sls Dept)*

Thermozell Entwicklungs- und Vertriebs GmbH (1)
Glanegg 58, A 9555, Glanegg, Carinthia, Austria
Tel.: (43) 427722110
Web Site: http://www.thermozell.com
Sales Range: $50-74.9 Million
Emp.: 200
Plastics Product Mfr
N.A.I.C.S.: 326140
Siegfried Wilding *(Gen Mgr)*

HIRSONDIS
19 Route de Bazancourt, 51110, Isles-sur-Suippe, Marne, France
Tel.: (33) 323583906
Sales Range: $25-49.9 Million
Emp.: 53
Lumber & Building Materials
N.A.I.C.S.: 444180
Bernard Raclot *(Pres)*

HIRTENBERGER HOLDING GMBH
Leobersdorfer Strasse 31 33, 2552, Hirtenberg, Austria
Tel.: (43) 225681184800
Web Site: http://www.hirtenberger.com
Engineeering Services
N.A.I.C.S.: 541330
Markus Haidenbauer *(CEO)*

Subsidiaries:

EMS-PATVAG s.r.o. (1)
Brankovice 350, Brankovice, 683 33, Czech Republic **(100%)**
Tel.: (420) 517302200
Web Site: http://www.emspatvag.com
Systems Engineering
N.A.I.C.S.: 541512
Urs Ulrich Britt *(Mng Dir)*

HISAKA WORKS, LTD.
2-12-7 Sonezaki, Kita-ku, Osaka, 530-0057, Japan
Tel.: (81) 663630006 **JP**
Web Site: https://www.hisaka.co.jp
Year Founded: 1942
6247—(TKS)
Rev.: $225,929,800
Assets: $542,132,370
Liabilities: $143,542,760
Net Worth: $398,589,610
Earnings: $15,996,200
Emp.: 1,011
Fiscal Year-end: 03/31/24
Industrial Equipment & Components Mfr & Whslr
N.A.I.C.S.: 333248
Yoshikazu Takeshita *(Pres)*

Subsidiaries:

Asahi Industry Co., Ltd. (1)
2-9-3 Suehiro-cho, Ome, 198-0025, Tokyo, Japan
Tel.: (81) 428316841
Web Site: https://www.asahiindustry.co.jp
Food Industry Machinery Mfr & Distr
N.A.I.C.S.: 333241
Naofumi Aikawa *(CEO)*

Hisaka (China) Co., Ltd. (1)
No 1 Xiangyuan Road Changshu Southeast Economic Development Zone, Changshu, 215542, Jiangsu, China
Tel.: (86) 51252133000
Web Site: http://www.hisaka-china.com
Industrial Machinery Distr
N.A.I.C.S.: 423830
Darce Qu *(Mgr-Sls)*

Hisaka Korea Co., Ltd. (1)
15th Floor Gwanghwamun Building 149 Sejong-daero, Jongno-gu, Seoul, 03186, Korea (south)
Tel.: (82) 27398861
Industrial Machinery Distr
N.A.I.C.S.: 423830

Hisaka Middle East Co., Ltd (1)
Building No 3861, PO Box 7102, Al Khudhariya Industrial Area, Dammam, 32435, Saudi Arabia
Tel.: (966) 138384700
Heat Exchanger Mfr & Distr
N.A.I.C.S.: 332410

Hisaka Works (China) Co., Ltd. (1)
No 117 Xiangyuan Road, High-tech Industrial Development Zone, Changshu, 215542, Jiangsu, China
Tel.: (86) 5125 213 3000
Web Site: https://www.hisaka-china.com
Industrial Machinery Mfr & Distr
N.A.I.C.S.: 333248

Hisaka Works (Singapore) Pte Ltd. (1)
No 18 Boon Lay Way 02-118 Trade Hub 21, Singapore, 609966, Singapore
Tel.: (65) 68978489
Web Site: https://hisaka-asia.com
Industrial Machinery Distr
N.A.I.C.S.: 423830

Hisaka Works (Thailand) Co., Ltd. (1)
825 Phairojkijja Tower 12th Floor Debaratana Road, Bangna-Nua Bangna, Bangkok, 10260, Thailand
Tel.: (66) 2 744 3287
Web Site: https://www.hisaka-asia.com
Industrial Machinery Distr
N.A.I.C.S.: 423830
Leong Lai Chee *(Mng Dir)*

Hisaka Works, Ltd. - Konoike Plant
2-1-48 Higashi-konoike-cho, Higashi-osaka, 578-0973, Osaka, Japan
Tel.: (81) 729669601
Industrial Machinery Mfr
N.A.I.C.S.: 333248

HisakaWorks S.E.A. Sdn. Bhd. (1)
No 2 Jalan TP 2 Taman Perindustrian SIME UEP, 47600, Subang Jaya, Selangor, Malaysia
Tel.: (60) 38 081 4185
Web Site: https://www.hisaka-asia.com
Heat Exchanger Mfr & Distr
N.A.I.C.S.: 332410

MICROZERO CO., LTD. (1)
Tachikawa Nishikicho Building 7F 1-8-7, Nishikicho, Tachikawa, 190-0022, Tokyo, Japan
Tel.: (81) 425485855
Emp.: 32
Industrial Valve Mfr
N.A.I.C.S.: 332911

NAKAGAWA ENGINEERING CONSULTING (SHANGHAI) CO., LTD. (1)
Flat D 30/F Tower 1 Gateway Plaza No 2601 Xietu Road Xu Hui District, Shanghai, 200030, China
Tel.: (86) 2164263761
Industrial Machinery Distr
N.A.I.C.S.: 423830

PT. HISAKA WORKS INDONESIA (1)
Rukan Grand Aries Niaga Blok G1-1M Jalan Taman Aries, Jakarta, 11620, Barat, Indonesia
Tel.: (62) 2122959806
Web Site: https://hisaka-asia.com
Industrial Machinery Distr
N.A.I.C.S.: 423830

HISAMITSU PHARMACEUTICAL CO., INC.
Tashirodaikan-machi 408, Tosu, 841-0017, Saga, Japan
Tel.: (81) 352931720 **JP**
Web Site: https://www.hisamitsu.co.jp
Year Founded: 1847
4530—(TKS)
Rev.: $1,004,695,540
Assets: $2,331,043,110
Liabilities: $437,431,730
Net Worth: $1,893,611,380
Earnings: $99,040,210
Emp.: 2,759
Fiscal Year-end: 02/29/24
Medical Over-the-Counter Products & Skin Care Products Mfr
N.A.I.C.S.: 325412
Kazuhide Nakatomi *(Pres & CEO)*

Subsidiaries:

CRCC Media Co., Ltd. (1)
1-1 Hyakunenkouen Kurume Research Center Building, Kurume, 839-0864, Fukuoka, Japan
Tel.: (81) 94 237 6411
Web Site: http://www.kumin.ne.jp
Television Broadcasting Services
N.A.I.C.S.: 516120
Minoru Yoshida *(Pres)*

Hisamitsu America, Inc. (1)
3510 Torrance Blvd Ste 301, Torrance, CA 90503 **(100%)**
Tel.: (310) 540-1408
Web Site: http://www.salonpas.us
Sales Range: $50-74.9 Million
Emp.: 6
Drugs & Druggists Whslr
N.A.I.C.S.: 424210

Hisamitsu Farmaceutica do Brasil Ltda. (1)
Rua Vergueiro 2 253-Trend Paulista Offices-Cj 402 a 406 Vila Mariana, Sao Judas, Sao Paulo, 04101-100, Brazil **(100%)**
Tel.: (55) 1155832127
Web Site: https://br.hisamitsu
Sales Range: $25-49.9 Million
Medical Over-the-Counter Products & Skin Care Products Mfr
N.A.I.C.S.: 325412

Hisamitsu UK Ltd. (1)
3 Shortlands, Hammersmith, London, W6 8DA, United Kingdom
Tel.: (44) 2074067410
Web Site: https://uk.hisamitsu
Pain Relief Patch Mfr
N.A.I.C.S.: 325412

Hisamitsu Vietnam Pharmaceutical Co., Ltd. (1)
No 15-2A Street, Bien Hoa Industrial Zone 2, Bien Hoa, Dong Nai, Vietnam
Tel.: (84) 2513836378
Pharmaceuticals Product Mfr
N.A.I.C.S.: 325412

Noven Pharmaceuticals, Inc. (1)
11960 SW 144th St, Miami, FL 33186
Tel.: (305) 253-5099
Web Site: http://www.noven.com

INTERNATIONAL PUBLIC

Sales Range: $100-124.9 Million
Emp.: 610
Transdermal Drug Delivery
N.A.I.C.S.: 325412
John Choi *(CFO, Treas & VP)*

PT. Hisamitsu Pharma Indonesia (1)
Jl HR Moch Mangundiprojo Buduran, Sidoarjo, 61252, Jawa Timur, Indonesia
Tel.: (62) 318941456
Sales Range: $75-99.9 Million
Emp.: 200
Pharmaceutical Products Distr
N.A.I.C.S.: 424210

SAGA Hisamitsu Springs Co., Ltd. (1)
408 Tashiro Daikan-cho, Tosu, Saga, Japan
Tel.: (81) 788555128
Web Site: https://saga-springs.co.jp
Sports Club Services
N.A.I.C.S.: 711211

Saga City-Vision Co., Ltd. (1)
408 Tashiro Daikan-machi, Saga, 841-0017, Tosu, Japan
Tel.: (81) 352931720
Sales Range: $25-49.9 Million
Emp.: 30
Television Broadcasting Services
N.A.I.C.S.: 516120
Hisato Koga *(Pres)*

Taiyo Kaihatsu Co., Ltd. (1)
1-14-3 Owada, Kimitsu, 299-1146, Chiba, Japan
Tel.: (81) 439524734
Commercial Property Development Services
N.A.I.C.S.: 531210

HISAR METAL INDUSTRIES LIMITED
Near Industrial Development Colony Delhi Road, Hisar, 125 005, Haryana, India
Tel.: (91) 1662220067
Web Site: https://www.hisarmetal.com
590018—(BOM)
Rev.: $32,549,271
Assets: $18,646,774
Liabilities: $12,662,941
Net Worth: $5,983,832
Earnings: $1,645,903
Emp.: 285
Fiscal Year-end: 03/31/22
Stainless Steel Strips Mfr
N.A.I.C.S.: 331110
Mahabir Parsad Jindal *(Chm)*

HISAR SPINNING MILLS LIMITED
9th KM Stone Hisar-Bhiwani Road V P O Dabra, Hisar, 125005, India
Tel.: (91) 1662297005
Web Site: https://www.hisarspinningmills.com
Year Founded: 1992
521068—(BOM)
Rev.: $3,975,344
Assets: $2,478,895
Liabilities: $727,067
Net Worth: $1,751,827
Earnings: $200,942
Emp.: 82
Fiscal Year-end: 03/31/21
Yarn Mfr
N.A.I.C.S.: 313110
Anurag Gupta *(Mng Dir)*

HISCOX LTD.
Chesney House 96 Pitts Bay Road, Pembroke, Hamilton, HM 08, Bermuda
Tel.: (441) 2788300
Web Site: https://www.hiscox.com
Year Founded: 1901
HSX—(LSE)
Rev.: $4,483,200,000
Assets: $11,060,500,000
Liabilities: $7,763,800,000
Net Worth: $3,296,700,000

AND PRIVATE COMPANIES

Earnings: $712,000,000
Emp.: 3,000
Fiscal Year-end: 12/31/21
Specialty Insurance Services
N.A.I.C.S.: 524128
Russell Findlay (Grp CMO)

Subsidiaries:

Direct Asia (Thailand) Co., Ltd. (1)
173/21 Asia Centre Building 20/F South Sathorn Rd Thungmahamek, Sathorn, Bangkok, 10120, Thailand
Tel.: (66) 27677777
Web Site: http://www.directasia.co.th
Fire Insurance Services
N.A.I.C.S.: 524128
Tattapat Termjitaree (Head-Mktg)

Direct Asia Insurance (Singapore) Pte Limited (1)
16 Raffles Quay 39-01 Hong Leong Building, Singapore, 048581, Singapore
Tel.: (65) 65321818
Web Site: https://www.directasia.com
General Insurance Services
N.A.I.C.S.: 524210

Hiscox Insurance Company (Guernsey) Limited (1)
Heritage Hall Le Marchant Street, Saint Peter Port, GY1 4EL, Guernsey
Tel.: (44) 1481746500
Ransom Insurance Services
N.A.I.C.S.: 524210

Hiscox Insurance Company Inc. (1)
30 N LaSalle St Ste 1760, Chicago, IL 60602
Web Site: http://www.hiscox.com
General Insurance Services
N.A.I.C.S.: 524210

Hiscox Re Insurance Linked Strategies Ltd. (1)
Chesney House 96 Pitts Bay Road, Hamilton, HM08, Bermuda
Tel.: (441) 2788300
Web Site: https://www.hiscoxils.com
General Insurance Services
N.A.I.C.S.: 524210
Mike Krefta (CEO)

OHB COSMOS International Launch Services GmbH (1)
Manfred-Fuchs-Platz 2-4, 28359, Bremen, Germany
Tel.: (49) 42120208
Web Site: https://www.ohb-cosmos.de
Satellite Mfr
N.A.I.C.S.: 334220

OHB Chile SpA (1)
Calle Limache 3405 Of 94, Vina del Mar, Chile
Tel.: (56) 232027910
Web Site: https://www.ohb-chile.cl
Eletric Power Generation Services
N.A.I.C.S.: 221118

OHB Digital Services GmbH (1)
Konrad-Zuse-Str 8, 28359, Bremen, Germany
Tel.: (49) 421220950
Web Site: https://www.ohb-ds.de
Software Development Services
N.A.I.C.S.: 541511

OHB Digital Solutions GmbH (1)
Karntner Strasse 7b/1, 8020, Graz, Austria
Tel.: (43) 3168909710
Web Site: https://www.ohb-digital.at
Aerospace Component Mfr & Distr
N.A.I.C.S.: 336412

OHB Italia S.p.A. (1)
Via Gallarate 150, 20151, Milan, MI, Italy
Tel.: (39) 02380481
Web Site: https://www.ohb-italia.it
Satellite Communication Services
N.A.I.C.S.: 517410

ORBCOMM Deutschland Satellitenkommunikation AG (1)
Maarstrasse 84, 53227, Bonn, Germany
Tel.: (49) 228926380
Container Transportation Services
N.A.I.C.S.: 484111

HISENSE CO., LTD.

Hisense Tower 17 Donghai Xi Road, Qingdao, 266071, China
Tel.: (86) 532 83878888   CN
Web Site: http://www.hisense.com
Year Founded: 1969
Emp.: 60,000
Holding Company; Consumer Electronics & Appliances Mfr & Whslr
N.A.I.C.S.: 551112
Houjian Zhou (Chm)

Subsidiaries:

Gorenje, d.d. (1)
Partizanska 12, SI-3320, Velenje, Slovenia
Tel.: (386) 38991000
Web Site: http://www.gorenjegroup.com
Rev.: $1,356,261,574
Assets: $1,213,426,223
Liabilities: $933,540,810
Net Worth: $279,885,413
Earnings: ($127,420,494)
Emp.: 11,084
Fiscal Year-end: 12/31/2018
Household Appliance Mfr & Sales
N.A.I.C.S.: 335220
Drago Bahun (Mng Dir)

Subsidiary (Non-US):

ATAG Belgie NV (2)
Keerstraat 1, Industrial Zone Erpe-Mere, 9420, Erpe, East Flanders, Belgium
Tel.: (32) 53806208
Web Site: http://www.atag.be
Household Appliances Mfr & Distr
N.A.I.C.S.: 335220

Subsidiary (Domestic):

ERICo d.o.o. (2)
Koroska cesta 58, SI 3322, Velenje, Slovenia
Tel.: (386) 38981930
Web Site: http://www.erico.si
Sales Range: $50-74.9 Million
Emp.: 53
Energy Development Services
N.A.I.C.S.: 926110
Marko Mavec (Mng Dir)

Subsidiary (Non-US):

Gorenje Austria Handelsgesellschaft mbH (2)
Johann Schorsch Gasse 1, Vienna, A 1140, Austria
Tel.: (43) 1601310
Web Site: http://www.gorenje.at
Sales Range: $25-49.9 Million
Emp.: 40
Household Appliances Mfr & Distr
N.A.I.C.S.: 335220

Gorenje BELUX S.A.R.L. (2)
Hoevestraat 25 A1, Gooik, 1755, Belgium
Tel.: (32) 54569761
Web Site: http://www.gorenje.be
Sales Range: $50-74.9 Million
Emp.: 5
Household Appliance Whslr
N.A.I.C.S.: 423620

Gorenje Budapest Kft (2)
Dulacska utca 1 b, 2045, Torokbalint, Hungary
Tel.: (36) 23511813
Web Site: http://www.gorenje.hu
Sales Range: $25-49.9 Million
Emp.: 26
Household Appliances Mfr
N.A.I.C.S.: 335220

Gorenje Espana S.L. (2)
C Nicaragua 46 3 3, Barcelona, 08029, Spain
Tel.: (34) 93 363 02 17
Web Site: http://www.gorenjespain.com
Household Appliances Mfr & Distr
N.A.I.C.S.: 335220

Gorenje France S.A.S. (2)
85 rue Edouard Vaillant, 92300, Levallois-Perret, France
Tel.: (33) 1 45 19 30 08
Web Site: http://www.gorenje.fr
Household Appliances Mfr & Distr
N.A.I.C.S.: 335220

Subsidiary (Domestic):

Gorenje GTI d.o.o. (2)
Partizanska cesta 12, 3320, Velenje, Slovenia
Tel.: (386) 38992797
Web Site: http://www.toyotavilicarji.si
Sales Range: $150-199.9 Million
Emp.: 4,000
Energy Development Services
N.A.I.C.S.: 926110
Franjo Bobinac (Mng Dir)

Subsidiary (Non-US):

Gorenje Gulf FZE (2)
Warehouse FZS1 AJ05 Blue Shades Area, Jebel Ali Free Zone S, Dubai, 18651, United Arab Emirates
Tel.: (971) 48860858
Web Site: http://www.gorenjegulf.ae
Sales Range: $25-49.9 Million
Emp.: 6
Household Appliances Mfr & Distr
N.A.I.C.S.: 335210

Gorenje Istanbul Ltd. (2)
Fahrettin Kerim Gokay Cad No 5, Altunizade, 34662, Istanbul, Turkiye
Tel.: (90) 2166519000
Web Site: http://www.gorenje.com.tr
Sales Range: $25-49.9 Million
Emp.: 25
Household Appliances Production & Sales Services
N.A.I.C.S.: 335210
Nermin Salman (Gen Mgr)

Gorenje Kazakhstan TOO (2)
Ul Begalina 49, Almaty, 050010, Kazakhstan
Tel.: (7) 7272930307
Web Site: http://www.gorenje.kz
Sales Range: $25-49.9 Million
Emp.: 10
Household Appliances Mfr
N.A.I.C.S.: 335220

Gorenje Korting Italia S.R.L. (2)
Via Trento 1, 34132, Trieste, Italy
Tel.: (39) 0403752111
Web Site: http://www.gorenje.it
Sales Range: $25-49.9 Million
Emp.: 9
Household Appliances Mfr
N.A.I.C.S.: 335220
Mathias Matjaz (Gen Mgr)

Gorenje Kuchen GmbH (2)
Johann-Schorsch-Gasse 1, A 1140, Vienna, Austria
Tel.: (43) 1601310
Web Site: http://www.gorenje.at
Sales Range: $50-74.9 Million
Emp.: 60
Household Appliance Whslr
N.A.I.C.S.: 423620
Sandra Lubej (Mng Dir)

Gorenje Skandinavien A/S (2)
Roskildevej 290, PO Box 2610, Rodovre, 2610, Denmark
Tel.: (45) 36721133
Web Site: http://www.gorenje.dk
Sales Range: $25-49.9 Million
Emp.: 70
Household Appliances Production & Sales Services
N.A.I.C.S.: 335210

Gorenje Skopje d.o.o. (2)
Partisan Units, No 99, 1000, Skopje, North Macedonia
Tel.: (389) 23062323
Web Site: http://www.gorenje.com.mk
Sales Range: $25-49.9 Million
Emp.: 16
Household Appliances Mfr & Distr
N.A.I.C.S.: 335220

Gorenje Slovakia s.r.o. (2)
Hodzovo Namestie 2A, 811 06, Bratislava, Slovakia
Tel.: (421) 269203939
Web Site: http://www.gorenje.sk
Sales Range: $25-49.9 Million
Emp.: 20
Household Appliances Production & Sales Services
N.A.I.C.S.: 335210

Subsidiary (Domestic):

Gorenje Tiki d.o.o. (2)
1 Magistrova Ulica, Ljubljana, Slovenia
Tel.: (386) 15005600
Web Site: http://www.gorenje.com
Sales Range: $1-4.9 Billion
Household Commodities Mfr
N.A.I.C.S.: 332215

Subsidiary (Non-US):

Gorenje Tiki d.o.o. (2)
Golubinacka Bb 22300, Srem, Stara Pazova, Vojvodina, Serbia
Tel.: (381) 2231 67 72
Household Appliances Mfr & Distr
N.A.I.C.S.: 335210

Gorenje Zagreb d.o.o. (2)
STV Ave 26 4, 10000, Zagreb, Croatia
Tel.: (385) 12415000
Web Site: http://www.gorenje.hr
Emp.: 80
Household Appliances Production & Sales Services
N.A.I.C.S.: 335220
Robert Polsak (Mng Dir)

Gorenje aparati za domacinstvo d.o.o. (2)
Milutin Milankovic 7, 11000, Belgrade, Serbia
Tel.: (381) 113534100
Web Site: http://www.gorenje.rs
Household Appliances Mfr & Distr
N.A.I.C.S.: 335220

Gorenje d.o.o. (2)
Milutin Milankovic 7, 11000, Belgrade, Serbia
Tel.: (381) 113534100
Web Site: http://www.gorenje.rs
Household Appliances Mfr & Distr
N.A.I.C.S.: 335220

Subsidiary (Domestic):

INDOP d.o.o. (2)
A Primorska Cesta 6, 3325, Sostanj, Slovenia
Tel.: (386) 38997331
Sales Range: $75-99.9 Million
Emp.: 150
Energy Development Services
N.A.I.C.S.: 926110
Boris Jurkosek (Gen Mgr)

Subsidiary (Non-US):

Kemis BH d.o.o. (2)
Kulina Bana bb, 75300, Lukavac, Bosnia & Herzegovina
Tel.: (387) 35 556 988
Web Site: http://www.kemis.ba
Sales Range: $25-49.9 Million
Emp.: 7
Energy Development Services
N.A.I.C.S.: 541715
Maid Hadzimujic (Mng Dir)

Kemis-Termoclean d.o.o. (2)
Slavonska Avenija, 10000, Zagreb, Croatia
Tel.: (385) 12406303
Web Site: http://www.kemis-termoclean.hr
Sales Range: $50-74.9 Million
Emp.: 57
Energy Development Services
N.A.I.C.S.: 926110

Mora Moravia s r.o. (2)
Nadrazni 50, Hlubocky, Marianske Udoli, 783 66, Czech Republic
Tel.: (420) 585161111
Web Site: http://www.mora.cz
Household Appliance Production & Sale Services
N.A.I.C.S.: 335220

Hisense Kelon Electrical Holdings Co., Ltd. (1)
No 8 Ronggang Road Ronggui Shunde District, Foshan, Guangdong, China
Tel.: (86) 2593 5622
Web Site: http://www.kelon.com
Sales Range: $1-4.9 Billion
Emp.: 33,967
Household Appliances Mfr
N.A.I.C.S.: 335220

HISENSE CO., LTD.

Hisense Co., Ltd.—(Continued)

Joint Venture (Domestic):

Hisense-Whirlpool (Zhejiang) Electric
Appliances Co., Ltd. (2)
North Side of Zhongyang Avenue Changxing, Economic Development Zone,
Hangzhou, 313100, Zhejiang,
China **(50%)**
Tel.: (86) 5726619711
Home Appliance Mfr
N.A.I.C.S.: 335220

Hisense USA Corporation (1)
7310 McGinnis Ferry Rd, Suwanee, GA 30024
Tel.: (678) 318-9060
Web Site: http://www.hisense-usa.com
Consumer Electronics & Appliances Marketer & Distr
N.A.I.C.S.: 423620
Mark Viken *(VP-Mktg)*

Hisense Visual Technology Co.,
Ltd. (1)
No 218 Qianwangang Road, Economic &
Technological Development Zone, Qingdao,
266555, Shandong, China
Tel.: (86) 53283889556
Web Site: http://www.hisense.cn
Rev.: $6,421,632,610
Assets: $5,020,641,283
Liabilities: $2,226,749,040
Net Worth: $2,793,892,243
Earnings: $235,746,847
Emp.: 19,000
Fiscal Year-end: 12/31/2022
Electronics & Electric Home Appliances Mfr & Whslr
N.A.I.C.S.: 423620
Yu Zhitao *(Chm)*

HISTEEL CO., LTD.
8F Hanyoung Bldg 28 Toegye-ro 27-gil, Jung-gu, Seoul,
Chungcheongnam-do, Korea (South)
Tel.: (82) 222732139
Web Site: https://www.histeel.co.kr
Year Founded: 1957
071090—(KRS)
Rev.: $242,689,493
Assets: $224,313,821
Liabilities: $110,066,929
Net Worth: $114,246,892
Earnings: $8,828,781
Emp.: 203
Fiscal Year-end: 12/31/22
Steel Pipe & Tube Mfr
N.A.I.C.S.: 332996
Song Dae Bin *(Gen Mgr)*

Subsidiaries:

JIANGYIN HANIL STEEL CO.,
LTD. (1)
8 Changda-Road Xiagang Development
Area, Jiangyin, Jiangsu, China
Tel.: (86) 510 6031660
Web Site: http://www.hanilsteelchina.com
Steel Pole Mfr
N.A.I.C.S.: 331210

HIT KIT GLOBAL SOLUTIONS LIMITED
55 Tirupati Plaza 1 FloorTirupati
Shoping Centre Premises, Co-op Soc
Ltd Santacruz West S V Road, Mumbai, 400054, Maharashtra, India
Tel.: (91) 2265614984
Web Site: http://www.hitkitglobal.com
532359—(BOM)
Rev.: $51,077
Assets: $1,360,816
Liabilities: $37,659
Net Worth: $1,323,157
Earnings: $1,203
Emp.: 4
Fiscal Year-end: 03/31/21
Vegetable Product Whslr
N.A.I.C.S.: 424480
Kamal Mohanlal Agrawal *(Mng Dir)*

HIT UNION COMPANY LTD.
4 5 26 Ueshio, Tennoji Ku, Osaka,
543 0002, Japan
Tel.: (81) 667731135   JP
Sales Range: $100-124.9 Million
Emp.: 350
Sportswear
N.A.I.C.S.: 424350

Subsidiaries:

Fred Perry Ltd. (1)
14 James St, Covent Garden, London,
WC2E HBU, United Kingdom **(100%)**
Tel.: (44) 2076322800
Web Site: http://www.fredperry.com
Sales Range: $50-74.9 Million
Emp.: 97
Designer & Worldwide Marketer of High-Fashion Sport & Leisure Clothing for Men & Women Mfr
N.A.I.C.S.: 315210
John Flynn *(Mng Dir)*

HIT WELDING INDUSTRY CO., LTD.
No 386 Changhong East Road,
Yaoguan Town Wujin District,
Changzhou, 213102, Jiangsu, China
Tel.: (86) 51988710806
Web Site: https://www.htw.cn
Year Founded: 1997
301137—(CHIN)
Rev.: $222,338,140
Assets: $291,465,605
Liabilities: $102,804,549
Net Worth: $188,661,056
Earnings: $8,167,718
Emp.: 850
Fiscal Year-end: 12/31/23
Welding Product Mfr & Distr
N.A.I.C.S.: 333992
Liansheng Li *(Chm)*

HITACHI ASTEMO, LTD.
Shin-Otemachi Bldg 2-1 Otemachi,
2-chome, Chiyoda-ku, Tokyo, 100-0004, Japan
Tel.: (81) 292766833   JP
Web Site:
  https://www.hitachiastemo.com
Holding Company; Automotive Components Mfr & Distr
N.A.I.C.S.: 551112
Brice Koch *(Pres & CEO)*

Subsidiaries:

Guangzhou Hitachi Unisia Automotive
Parts Co., Ltd. (1)
No 63 Huagang Avenue Xinhua Town,
Huadu District, Guangzhou, 510800,
Guangdong, China
Tel.: (86) 2086876670
Motor Vehicle Parts Mfr
N.A.I.C.S.: 336390

Hitachi Automotive Products (Suzhou)
LTD. (1)
255 Xinglong Street Suzhou Industrial Park,
Suzhou, 215126, China
Tel.: (86) 512 6283 3600
Automotive Engine Control System Mfr
N.A.I.C.S.: 336320

Hitachi Automotive Systems (China)
Ltd. (1)
Rm 2402-2403 Haihan Mansion Linghe M
R, Tianhe Dist, Guangzhou, 570203, China
Tel.: (86) 2085501481
Web Site: http://www.hitachi-automotive.cn
Emp.: 20
Automobile Parts Mfr
N.A.I.C.S.: 336390
Yoichi Okamoto *(Gen Mgr)*

Hitachi Automotive Systems (S) Pte
Ltd. (1)
175A Bencoolen Street 11-11/12 Burlington
Square, Singapore, 189650, Singapore
Tel.: (65) 6738 1193
Web Site: http://www.hitachi-automotive.sg
Emp.: 15

Automobile Parts Distr
N.A.I.C.S.: 423120
Tetsuya Hisatsune *(Mng Dir)*

Hitachi Automotive Systems Americas, Inc. (1)
955 Warwick Rd, Harrodsburg, KY 40330
Tel.: (859) 734-9451
Web Site: http://www.hitachi-automotive.us
Motor Vehicle Components Mfr & Distr
N.A.I.C.S.: 336390
Masaaki Fujisawa *(CEO)*

Branch (Domestic):

Hitachi Automotive Systems Americas, Inc. - Allen Park (2)
17225 Federal Dr Ste 100, Allen Park, MI 48101-3627
Tel.: (313) 336-5310
Web Site: http://www.hitachi-automotive.us
Sales Range: $25-49.9 Million
Emp.: 40
Motor Vehicle Component Whslr
N.A.I.C.S.: 423120

Plant (Domestic):

Hitachi Automotive Systems Americas, Inc. - Berea Plant (2)
301 Mayde Rd Berea Industrial Park, Berea, KY 40403
Tel.: (859) 986-2359
Web Site: http://www.hitachi-automotive.us
Sales Range: $200-249.9 Million
Emp.: 903
Vehicle & Instrumentation Equipment Mfr & Sales
N.A.I.C.S.: 336330

Branch (Domestic):

Hitachi Automotive Systems Americas, Inc. - Farmington Hills (2)
34500 Grand River Ave, Farmington Hills, MI 48335
Tel.: (248) 474-2800
Web Site: http://www.hitachi-automotive.us
Sales Range: $75-99.9 Million
Emp.: 200
Motor Vehicle Component Whslr & Technical Services
N.A.I.C.S.: 423120

Plant (Domestic):

Hitachi Automotive Systems Americas, Inc. - Georgia Plant (2)
1000 Unisia Dr, Monroe, GA 30655
Tel.: (770) 207-0050
Web Site: http://www.hitachi-automotive.us
Sales Range: $50-74.9 Million
Emp.: 175
Motor Vehicle Power Steering & Valve Timing Controls Mfr
N.A.I.C.S.: 336330

Branch (Domestic):

Hitachi Automotive Systems Americas, Inc. - Los Angeles (2)
6200 Gateway Dr, Cypress, CA 90630
Tel.: (949) 471-3500
Web Site: http://www.hitachi-automotive-la.us
Sales Range: $25-49.9 Million
Emp.: 40
Motor Vehicle Component Whslr
N.A.I.C.S.: 423120

Hitachi Automotive Systems Asia,
Ltd. (1)
Industrial Estate 186 Moo 7 Tambol Huasamrong, Gateway City Amphur Plangyao,
Chachoengsao, 24190, Thailand
Tel.: (66) 38 57 5212
Web Site: http://www.hitachi.co.th
Automotive Parts Mfr & Distr
N.A.I.C.S.: 336390

Hitachi Automotive Systems Europe
(France) (1)
18 Rue Grange Dame Ros, BP 134, 78148,
Velizy-Villacoublay, France
Tel.: (33) 134630500
Web Site: http://test.hitachi-eu.com
Automotive Parts Mfr & Distr
N.A.I.C.S.: 336390

INTERNATIONAL PUBLIC

Hitachi Automotive Systems Europe
GmbH (1)
Technopark IV Lohstrasse 28, D-85445,
Schwaig, Germany
Tel.: (49) 8122995820
Web Site: http://www.hitachi-automotive.co.jp
Automotive Systems Mfr & Distr
N.A.I.C.S.: 336390

Branch (Domestic):

Hitachi Automotive Systems Europe
GmbH - Dusseldorf (2)
Am Seestern 18, D-40547, Dusseldorf, Germany
Tel.: (49) 211354008
Sales Range: $25-49.9 Million
Emp.: 9
Mfr & Retailer of Vehicle & Instrumentation
Equipment
N.A.I.C.S.: 336320

Hitachi Automotive Systems Europe
Ltd. (1)
Aspinall Way Middlebrook Business Park,
Horwich, BL6 6JH, Bolton, United Kingdom
Tel.: (44) 1204 46 9879
Emp.: 150
Automotive Parts Mfr & Distr
N.A.I.C.S.: 336390

Hitachi Highly Automotive Products
(Shanghai) Ltd. (1)
Area 2 Qingpu Export Processing Zone No
8228 Beiqing Highway, Shanghai, 201707,
China **(33%)**
Tel.: (86) 2159701234
Automotive Electrical Equipment Mfr
N.A.I.C.S.: 336390

Keihin Corporation (1)
Shinjuku Nomura Bldg 39F 1-26-2 Nishi-Shinjuku, Shinjuku-ku, Tokyo, 163-0539,
Japan
Tel.: (81) 333453411
Web Site: http://www.keihin-corp.co.jp
Rev.: $3,163,933,200
Assets: $2,855,612,340
Liabilities: $833,538,120
Net Worth: $2,022,074,220
Earnings: $161,793,480
Emp.: 22,624
Fiscal Year-end: 03/31/2019
Development, Production & Sales of Automobile Parts, Components & Systems
N.A.I.C.S.: 336390
Tohru Mitsubori *(Mng Officer)*

Subsidiary (Domestic):

Kanazu Mfg. Co., Ltd. (2)
125-3 Aramachi Oyama, Kakuda, 981-1502,
Miyagi, Japan
Tel.: (81) 224632202
Web Site: http://www.keihin-corp.co.jp
Automotive Peripherals Assembly Services
N.A.I.C.S.: 811121

Subsidiary (Non-US):

Keihin (Thailand) Co., Ltd. (2)
298 Moo 13 Tambon Makhuajae Amphur
Muang, Lamphun, 51000, Thailand
Tel.: (66) 53581189
Web Site: http://www.keihin-corp.co.jp
Automotive Carburetor Mfr & Distr
N.A.I.C.S.: 336390

Keihin Asia Bangkok Co., Ltd. (2)
No 591 UBC II Bldg 12th Floor Sukhumbit
Rd North Klongton, Wattana, Bangkok,
10110, Thailand
Tel.: (66) 2 261 0251
Web Site: http://www.keihin-corp.co.jp
Emp.: 70
Motorcycle Parts Distr
N.A.I.C.S.: 423120

Keihin Auto Parts (Philippines)
Corp. (2)
105 Trade Avenue, Laguna Technopark,
Brgy Loma, Binan, Laguna, Philippines
Tel.: (63) 495411840
Sales Range: $50-74.9 Million
Emp.: 107
Auto Parts Mfr
N.A.I.C.S.: 336310

Keihin Auto Parts (Thailand) Co.,
Ltd. (2)

AND PRIVATE COMPANIES

HITACHI ASTEMO, LTD.

Rojana Industrial Park 1/74 Moo 5 Rojana Road Tambol Karnharm, Amphur U-thai, Tambol, 13210, Ayutthaya, Thailand
Tel.: (66) 35330916
Automotive Air Conditioning Units Mfr & Distr
N.A.I.C.S.: 336390

Plant (Domestic):

Keihin Auto Parts (Thailand) Co., Ltd. - 2nd Plant (3)
Rojana Industrial Park 21/9 Moo9 T Karmharm A U-thai, Pranakorn Sri, Tambol, 13210, Ayutthaya, Thailand
Tel.: (66) 35356962
Web Site: http://www.keihin-corp.co.jp
Electronic Control Unit Mfr & Distr
N.A.I.C.S.: 334419

Plant (Domestic):

Keihin Corporation - Kakuda 1st Plant (2)
213 Takabatake-minami Kajika, Kakuda, 981-1581, Miyagi, Japan
Tel.: (81) 224631111
Web Site: http://www.keihin-corp.co.jp
Carburetors Mfr
N.A.I.C.S.: 336310

Keihin Corporation - Kakuda 2nd Plant (2)
3 Miyayachi Sakura, Kakuda, 981-1582, Miyagi, Japan
Tel.: (81) 224633111
Web Site: http://www.keihin-corp.co.jp
Intake Manifolds Mfr
N.A.I.C.S.: 336310

Keihin Corporation - Kakuda 3rd Plant (2)
4-3 Miyayachi Sakura, Kakuda, 981-1583, Miyagi, Japan
Tel.: (81) 224633611
Web Site: http://www.keihin-corp.co.jp
Engine Electronic Control Units Mfr
N.A.I.C.S.: 336320

Keihin Corporation - Marumori Plant (2)
97 Terauchi-mae Marumori-machi, Igu-gun, Miyagi, 981-2112, Japan
Tel.: (81) 224722772
Fuel Injection System Mfr
N.A.I.C.S.: 336310

Keihin Corporation - Sayama Plant (2)
481-1 Hiranoshita Nakashinden, Sayama, 350-1311, Saitama, Japan
Tel.: (81) 429586000
Automotive Air Conditioning Kit Assembling Services
N.A.I.C.S.: 811121

Keihin Corporation - Suzuka Plant (2)
3361-1 Ichigaya Kou-cho, Suzuka, 513-0836, Mie, Japan
Tel.: (81) 593786701
Air Conditioning System Assembling Services
N.A.I.C.S.: 811121

Subsidiary (Domestic):

Keihin Electronics Technology Inc (2)
4F Sendai Aoba-dori Building 3-3-5 Ichibancho, Aoba-ku, Sendai, 980-0811, Miyagi, Japan
Tel.: (81) 227964452
Web Site: http://www.ket-inc.co.jp
Vehicle Control System Software Development Services
N.A.I.C.S.: 541511

Subsidiary (Non-US):

Keihin FIE Pvt Ltd (2)
B-3 Midc Chakan, Mahalunge Village Tal Khed, Pune, 410 501, Maharashtra, India
Tel.: (91) 2135 664300
Web Site: http://www.keihinfie.com
Automobile Carburetors Mfr
N.A.I.C.S.: 336390

Subsidiary (US):

Keihin North America, Inc. (2)

2701 Enterprise Dr, Anderson, IN 46013
Tel.: (765) 298-6030
Web Site: http://www.keihin-na.com
Sales Range: $200-249.9 Million
Emp.: 800
Fuel Injection Devices
N.A.I.C.S.: 336310

Subsidiary (Domestic):

Keihin Aircon North America, Inc. (3)
4400 N Superior Dr, Muncie, IN 47303
Tel.: (765) 213-4915
Web Site: http://www.keihin-na.com
Sales Range: $25-49.9 Million
Emp.: 230
Mfr of Automotive Heating, Ventilating & Air Conditioning Components
N.A.I.C.S.: 333415

Keihin Carolina System Technology, LLC (3)
4047 McNair Rd, Tarboro, NC 27886 (75.1%)
Tel.: (252) 641-6750
Web Site: http://www.keihin-na.com
Sales Range: $75-99.9 Million
Emp.: 460
Engine Control & Electronically Actuated Devices
N.A.I.C.S.: 336390

Keihin IPT Mfg., LLC (3)
400 W New Rd, Greenfield, IN 46140 (75.1%)
Tel.: (317) 462-3015
Web Site: http://www.keihin-na.com
Sales Range: $25-49.9 Million
Emp.: 200
Fuel Injection Parts
N.A.I.C.S.: 336390

Keihin Michigan Manufacturing, LLC (3)
14898 Koehn Rd, Capac, MI 48014
Tel.: (810) 395-3900
Web Site: http://www.keihin-na.com
Sales Range: $125-149.9 Million
Emp.: 300
Automotive Fuel Injection Devices Mfr & Distr
N.A.I.C.S.: 336310

Subsidiary (Non-US):

Keihin Panalfa Ltd. (2)
A-1 & A-2 Sector 81 NOIDA Phase-II, Noida, 201 301, Uttar Pradesh, India
Tel.: (91) 1184568941
Web Site: http://www.keihinfie.com
Automotive Air-Conditioning Unit Mfr
N.A.I.C.S.: 423730

Keihin Sales and Development Europe GmbH (2)
Rote-Kreuz-Strasse 14, 85737, Ismaning, Germany
Tel.: (49) 8992333780
Web Site: http://www.keihin-corp.co.jp
Sales Range: $50-74.9 Million
Emp.: 7
Automobile Parts Distr
N.A.I.C.S.: 423120

Subsidiary (Domestic):

Keihin Sogyo Co., Ltd. (2)
7 Kurouchi Oda, Kakuda, 981-1514, Miyagi, Japan
Tel.: (81) 224620650
Web Site: http://www.keihin-corp.co.jp
Sales Range: $25-49.9 Million
Emp.: 111
Automotive Carburetors Assembling Services
N.A.I.C.S.: 811121

Keihin Valve Corp (2)
1-9-1 Maruyama, Isogo-ku, Yokohama, 235-0011, Kanagawa, Japan
Tel.: (81) 457526391
Web Site: http://www.keihin-valve.co.jp
Emp.: 45
Automatic Valve Mfr
N.A.I.C.S.: 332911
Satoru Kudou (Pres & CEO)

Keihin Watari Co., Ltd. (2)
1-5 Doda Okuma-koya Watari-cho, Watari-gun, Miyagi, 989-2324, Japan

Tel.: (81) 223340451
Web Site: http://www.keihin-corp.co.jp
Sales Range: $100-124.9 Million
Emp.: 400
Automobile Parts Mfr
N.A.I.C.S.: 336390

Nasu Seiki Mfg. Co., Ltd. (2)
818 Kanaga, karasuyamamachi nasu-gun, Tochigi, 321-0632, Japan
Tel.: (81) 287823641
Web Site: http://www.keihin-corp.co.jp
Carburetors Mfr
N.A.I.C.S.: 336310

Subsidiary (Non-US):

P.T. Keihin Indonesia (2)
Kawasan Industri MM2100 Blok JJ-1 Cikarang Barat, Bekasi, 17520, Indonesia
Tel.: (62) 2189981645
Web Site: http://www.keihin-corp.co.jp
Emp.: 1,595
Motorcycle Carburetors Mfr & Distr
N.A.I.C.S.: 423120

Taiwan Keihin Carburetor Co., Ltd. (2)
No 7 7th Road Industrial Park, Shi-Ton District, Taichung, Taiwan
Tel.: (886) 4 2359 1483
Web Site: http://www.keihin-corp.co.jp
Automotive Carburetors Mfr & Distr
N.A.I.C.S.: 336390

Plant (Domestic):

Taiwan Keihin Carburetor Co., Ltd. - Ching-shui Factory (3)
86-20 Shen Ching Road Ching-Shui, Taichung, Taiwan
Tel.: (886) 4 2620 1526
Automotive Carburetors Mfr & Distr
N.A.I.C.S.: 336390

Subsidiary (Non-US):

Zhanjiang Deni Carburetor Co., Ltd (2)
27 Hai Tian Rd Chikan, Zhanjiang, Guangdong, China
Tel.: (86) 759 3320714
Web Site: http://www.dekni.com
Sales Range: $450-499.9 Million
Emp.: 1,500
Automotive Carburetors Mfr & Distr
N.A.I.C.S.: 336390
Liu Tengfei (Gen Mgr)

Showa Corporation (1)
1-14-1 Fujiwara-cho, Gyoda, 361-8506, Saitama, Japan
Tel.: (81) 485541151
Web Site: http://www.showa1.com
Rev.: $2,597,429,520
Assets: $1,905,091,500
Liabilities: $758,693,460
Net Worth: $1,146,398,040
Earnings: $172,611,120
Emp.: 12,615
Fiscal Year-end: 03/31/2019
Automotive Components, Including Power Steering Parts & Shock Absorbers Mfr & Sales
N.A.I.C.S.: 336330
Takeshi Nagao (Mng Officer)

Subsidiary (US):

American Showa, Inc. (2)
707 W Cherry St, Sunbury, OH, 43074
Tel.: (740) 965-1133
Web Site: http://www.amshowa.com
Emp.: 650
Vehicle Shock Absorbers & Hydraulic Power Steering Parts Mfr
N.A.I.C.S.: 336330
Holly Mock (Mgr-HR)

Subsidiary (Non-US):

Chengdu Ningjiang Showa Autoparts Co., Ltd. (2)
Shiling Town Long Quan Yi District, Chengdu, 610106, Sichuan, China
Tel.: (86) 28 8285 8990
Mfr of Shock Absorbers & Electronic Power Steering Systems
N.A.I.C.S.: 336330

Guangzhou Showa Autoparts Co., Ltd. (2)
No 6 Hong Ming Road Eastern Section of Guangzhou, Economic & Technological Development District, Guangzhou, 510760, China
Tel.: (86) 20 8226 8289
Shock Absorbers for 4-Wheeled Vehicles, Hydraulic & Electronic Power Steering Systems Mfr
N.A.I.C.S.: 336330

Subsidiary (Domestic):

HONDA CARS SAITAMA KITA CO., LTD. (2)
479-1 Hirose, Kumagaya, 360-0833, Saitama, Japan
Tel.: (81) 485251412
Web Site: http://www.hondacars-saitamakita.co.jp
Emp.: 193
New & Used Car Dealer
N.A.I.C.S.: 441110

Joint Venture (Non-US):

Munjal Showa Limited (2)
9-11 Maruti Industrial Area Sector-18, Gurgaon, 122015, Haryana, India
Tel.: (91) 1244783000
Web Site: http://www.munjalshowa.net
Rev.: $151,169,234
Assets: $97,189,401
Liabilities: $19,107,955
Net Worth: $78,081,446
Earnings: $3,825,094
Emp.: 2,412
Fiscal Year-end: 03/31/2023
Mfr of Shock Absorbers & Gas Springs for 2- & 4-Wheeled Vehicles
N.A.I.C.S.: 336390
Yogesh Chander Munjal (Chm & Co-Mng Dir)

Subsidiary (Non-US):

P.T. Showa Indonesia Manufacturing (2)
Jababeka Industrial Park Jl Jababeka VI Kav 28-36, Cikarang, Bekasi, 17530, Indonesia (55%)
Tel.: (62) 21 8934855
Web Site: http://www.showa.co.id
Sales Range: $150-199.9 Million
Emp.: 2,550
Motor Vehicle Shock Absorbers & Steering Systems Mfr
N.A.I.C.S.: 336330

PT. SHOWA AUTOPARTS INDONESIA (2)
Kavling No 43 Desa Nagasari Kawasan Industri Terpadu, Kecamatan Serang Baru, Bekasi, 17330, Indonesia
Tel.: (62) 21 36477387
Gear Mfr
N.A.I.C.S.: 336350

SHOWA Deutschland GmbH (2)
Heinrich-Hertz-Strasse 9, 63225, Langen, Germany
Tel.: (49) 1622727101
Auto Parts Whslr
N.A.I.C.S.: 441330

SRT-Taiwan Trading Corporation (2)
No 6-23 Siwei 3rd Rd, Lingya Dist, Kaohsiung, 802, Taiwan
Tel.: (886) 73355180
Two & Four-Wheeled Vehicle Whslr
N.A.I.C.S.: 441227

Shanghai Showa Auto Parts Co., Ltd. (2)
No 1395 Nanle Road Export Industry Zone, Songjiang, Shanghai, 201611, China
Tel.: (86) 21 5774 8158
Mfr of Shock Absorbers & Gas Springs for 4-Wheeled Vehicles
N.A.I.C.S.: 336390

Showa (Guangzhou) Auto Parts R&D Co., Ltd. (2)
No 8 Hong Ming Road, Eastern Section Of Guangzhou Economic And Technological Development, Guangzhou, 510620, China
Tel.: (86) 2032215785
Two-Wheeled Vehicle Mfr
N.A.I.C.S.: 336999

HITACHI ASTEMO, LTD.

Hitachi Astemo, Ltd.—(Continued)

Showa Adominstracao, Servicos E Comercio Ltda (2)
2001 Sala 33 AV Interlagos-Jardim Umuarama, Sao Paulo, 04661-100, SP, Brazil
Tel.: (55) 1156340155
Two-Wheeled Vehicle Mfr
N.A.I.C.S.: 336999

Showa Auto-Parts Vietnam Co., Ltd. (2)
Plot M6 Thang Long Industrial Park, Dong Anh District, Hanoi, Vietnam **(91.6%)**
Tel.: (84) 4 883 5500
Motorcycle & Automobile Shock Absorbers & Power Steering Systems Mfr
N.A.I.C.S.: 336330

Showa Autoparts (Thailand) Co., Ltd. (2)
150/23 Moo 9 T Nongkam, Sriracha, Chon Buri, 20110, Thailand
Tel.: (66) 38 347 031
Web Site: http://www.showa1.com
Hydraulic & Electronic Power Steering Systems Mfr
N.A.I.C.S.: 336330

Showa Autoparts Mexico, S.A. de C.V. (2)
Av Mineral De Penafiel No77, Parque Industrial Santa Fe Iv Puerto Interior, 36275, Guanajuato, Mexico
Tel.: (52) 4727489287
Electronic Power Steering Mfr
N.A.I.C.S.: 336330

Showa Autoparts Wuhan Co., Ltd. (2)
788 Zhushanhu Avenue, Wuhan Economic and Technological Development Zone, Hubei, 430056, China
Tel.: (86) 2784479529
Motor Vehicle Transmission Parts Mfr
N.A.I.C.S.: 336350

Showa Canada Inc. (2)
1 Showa Ct, PO Box 1000, Schomberg, L0G 1T0, ON, Canada
Tel.: (905) 939-0575
Web Site: http://www.showa1.com
Mfr of Propeller Shafts, Hydraulic Power Steering Pumps & Electronic Power Steering Systems
N.A.I.C.S.: 336330

Plant (Domestic):

Showa Corporation - Asaba Plant (2)
2601 Matsubara, Fukuroi, 437 1194, Shizuoka, Japan
Tel.: (81) 538 23 2185
Hydraulic Equipment Mfr
N.A.I.C.S.: 333998

Showa Corporation - Gotemba No.1 Plant (2)
2459-1 Jinba, Gotemba, 412-0047, Shizuoka, Japan
Tel.: (81) 550 80 2500
Web Site: http://www.showa1.com
Electronic Power Steering System Mfr
N.A.I.C.S.: 336330

Showa Corporation - Gotemba No.2 Plant (2)
1-140 Komakado, Gotemba, 412-8511, Shizuoka, Japan
Tel.: (81) 550 87 2500
Electronic Power Steering System Mfr
N.A.I.C.S.: 336330

Showa Corporation - Hadano Plant (2)
97-1 Bodai, Hadano, 259 1302, Kanagawa, Japan
Tel.: (81) 463 75 1414
Gear Mfr
N.A.I.C.S.: 336350

Showa Corporation - Nagoya Plant (2)
2-1 Onomachi, Kasugai, 486 0926, Aichi, Japan
Tel.: (81) 568 31 7101
Motor Vehicle Shaft Mfr
N.A.I.C.S.: 336330

Subsidiary (Non-US):

Showa India Pvt. Ltd. (2)
Plot No 23-32 Sector 58, Faridabad, 121004, Haryana, India
Tel.: (91) 129 429 8000
Electronic Power Steering System Mfr
N.A.I.C.S.: 336330

Showa Industria e Comercio Ltda. (2)
Rua Taguapaca 259 Jurubatuba, Sao Paulo, 04691 170, SP, Brazil
Tel.: (55) 11 5634 0155
Mfr of Shock Absorbers for 2-Wheeled Vehicles
N.A.I.C.S.: 336390

Subsidiary (Domestic):

Showa Kyushu Corporation (2)
1 Toyono-machi Shimogo, Uki, 861-4304, Kumamoto, Japan
Tel.: (81) 964 45 2100
Web Site: http://www.kyushu-showa1.com
Ferrous Sintered Parts & Four Wheeled Vehicle Shock Absorbers Mfr
N.A.I.C.S.: 336390

Subsidiary (Non-US):

Showa Regional Center (Thailand) Co., Ltd. (2)
Amata Nakorn Industrial Estate Phase 8 700/713 Moo 1 Phanthong, Amphur Phanthong, Chon Buri, 20160, Thailand
Tel.: (66) 38 447 491
Research & Development of Shock Absorbers for Motorcycles
N.A.I.C.S.: 336991
Tomoyuki Sutita (Pres)

Subsidiary (Domestic):

Showa Seiko Co., Ltd. (2)
182-2 Hirazawa, Hadano, 257 0015, Kanagawa, Japan
Tel.: (81) 463 80 0441
Precision Parts Machining & Titanium Coating
N.A.I.C.S.: 332710

Subsidiary (Non-US):

Showa UK Ltd. (2)
Aberaman Park Industrial Estate, Aberdare, CF44 6DA, Mid Glamorgan, United Kingdom
Tel.: (44) 1685885800
Electronic Power Steering Mfr
N.A.I.C.S.: 336330

Showa do Brasil Ltda. (2)
Rua Rio Quixito n1376-Distrito Industrial, Manaus, 69075-831, Amazonas, Brazil
Tel.: (55) 9236160500
Two-Wheeled Vehicle Mfr
N.A.I.C.S.: 336999

Showa do Brazil Ltda. (2)
Rua Rio Quixito no 1376 Distrito Industrial, Manaus, 69075 831, Amazonas, Brazil
Tel.: (55) 92 3616 0500
Mfr of Shock Absorbers for 2-Wheeled Vehicles
N.A.I.C.S.: 336390

Summit Showa Manufacturing Co., Ltd. (2)
199/2 M3 Tungsukla, Sriracha, Chon Buri, 20230, Thailand
Tel.: (66) 3849 0448
2- & 4-Wheeled Vehicles Mfr
N.A.I.C.S.: 336110

Tokico (Thailand) Ltd. (1)
398 Moo 6 Nongraweng District Amphur Muang Nakornratchasima, Nakhon Ratchasima, 30000, Thailand **(100%)**
Tel.: (66) 44212050
Web Site: http://www.hitachi.co.th
Sales Range: $150-199.9 Million
Emp.: 870
Mfr & Retailer of Vehicle Equipment
N.A.I.C.S.: 336320

HITACHI CHEMICAL STORAGE BATTERY (THAILAND) PLC.

387 Moo 4 Bangu Industrial Estate Sukhumvit Road Amphoe, Muang District, Samut Prakan, Thailand
Tel.: (66) 2 709 3535   TH
Web Site: http://www.tsbsociety.com
Year Founded: 1986
Rev.: $163,926,039
Assets: $101,600,966
Liabilities: $48,750,190
Net Worth: $52,850,776
Earnings: $4,563,606
Fiscal Year-end: 12/31/19
Battery Mfr & Distr
N.A.I.C.S.: 335910

HITACHI ZOSEN CORPORATION

1-7-89 Nanko Kita, Suminoe-ku, Osaka, 559-8559, Japan
Tel.: (81) 665690001
Web Site:
https://www.hitachizosen.co.jp
Year Founded: 1881
7004—(TKS)
Rev.: $3,674,128,840
Assets: $3,527,049,730
Liabilities: $2,410,316,670
Net Worth: $1,116,733,060
Earnings: $125,583,390
Emp.: 12,148
Fiscal Year-end: 03/31/24
Mfr & Sales of Ships, Steel Structures, Industrial Plants & Machinery & Off-Shore Equipment
N.A.I.C.S.: 336611
Takashi Tanisho (Chm & CEO)

Subsidiaries:

Hitachi Zosen Corporation - Tokyo Office (1)
15th Floor Omori Bellport D-Wing 26-3 Minamioi 6-chome, Shinagawa-ku, Tokyo, 140-0013, Japan **(100%)**
Tel.: (81) 36 404 0800
Web Site: https://www.hitachizosen.co.jp
Sales Range: $75-99.9 Million
Emp.: 400
Business Support Services
N.A.I.C.S.: 561499

Subsidiary (Non-US):

Alam Hzem Sdn. Bhd. (2)
Level 11 Menara TH 1 Sentral Jalan Rakyat, Kuala Lumpur Sentral, 50470, Kuala Lumpur, Malaysia
Tel.: (60) 351923980
Business Consulting Services
N.A.I.C.S.: 541611

Subsidiary (Domestic):

Ataka Asano Co., Ltd. (2)
2-8-7 Kitaueno 6th Floor Sumitomo Real Estate Ueno Building 9, Taito-ku, Tokyo, 110-0014, Japan
Tel.: (81) 358277051
Web Site: http://www.asanoataka.co.jp
Human Waste Treatment Services
N.A.I.C.S.: 562998

Bekkihayami Environment Technology Co., Ltd. (2)
1-7-38-307 Ishigakihigashi, Beppu, 879-0919, Oita, Japan
Tel.: (81) 977676111
Refuse Incineration Services
N.A.I.C.S.: 562213

Casting & Forging Co., Ltd. (2)
2-6-33 Edobori, Nishi-ku, Osaka, 550-0002, Japan
Tel.: (81) 6 6447 5439
Cast & Wrought Products & Canning Products Mfr & Sales
N.A.I.C.S.: 332111

Subsidiary (Non-US):

Dalian Dali Steel Works Co., Ltd. (2)
No 58 Zhongge Street, Ganjingzi, Dalian, 116035, China
Tel.: (86) 41186450137
Web Site: https://en.dali-steelworks.cn

INTERNATIONAL PUBLIC

Emp.: 90
N.A.I.C.S.: 336611

Dalian Datong Machinery Products Co., Ltd. (2)
Rooms 1101-1102 Block B Renmin Road, Zhongshan District, Dalian, Liaoning, China
Tel.: (86) 41182824432
Plastics Product Mfr
N.A.I.C.S.: 326199

Subsidiary (Domestic):

Ecomanage Corporation (2)
6-26-3 Minamioi, Shinagawa-ku, Tokyo, 140-0013, Japan
Tel.: (81) 357535006
Administrative Management Consulting Services
N.A.I.C.S.: 541611

Fujimino Ecowells Corporation (2)
1-2-17 Kamifukuoka, Fujimino, 356-0004, Saitama, Japan
Tel.: (81) 492660267
Refuse Incineration Services
N.A.I.C.S.: 562213

Global Positioning Augmentation Service Corporation (2)
8-17-5 Ginza, Chuo-ku, Tokyo, 104-0016, Japan
Tel.: (81) 362787881
Web Site: http://www.gpas.co.jp
Satellite Telecommunication Services
N.A.I.C.S.: 517410
Hideshi Kozawa (Pres)

Gotenbaoyama Environment Technology Co., Ltd. (2)
862-15 Itazuma, Gotemba, 412-0048, Shizuoka, Japan
Tel.: (81) 550885161
Refuse Incineration Services
N.A.I.C.S.: 562213

Subsidiary (Non-US):

H&F Europe Limited (2)
Unit 12 Bartley Green Business Centre Woodgate Business Park, Birmingham, B32 3DB, United Kingdom
Tel.: (44) 1214211745
Electronic Equipment Distr
N.A.I.C.S.: 423690

H&F Services (Thailand) Co., Ltd. (2)
No 40/14 Bangna Towers C Unit 12C 12th Floor, Moo 12 Bangna-Trad Road km 6 5 Amphur Bangplee, Samut Prakan, Thailand
Tel.: (66) 27519151
Electronic Equipment Distr
N.A.I.C.S.: 423690

Subsidiary (Domestic):

Hitachi Zosen Chugoku Construction Works Co., Ltd. (2)
11-9 Higashigosho-cho, Onomichi, 722-0036, Hiroshima, Japan
Tel.: (81) 848247176
Web Site: http://www.hitachizosen.co.jp
Refuse Incineration Repair Services
N.A.I.C.S.: 562213

Hitachi Zosen Diesel & Engineering Co., Ltd. (2)
1 Ariake Nagasu Machi, Tamana, 869 0113, Kumamoto, Japan **(100%)**
Tel.: (81) 968782155
Web Site: http://www.hitachi.zosen.co.jp
Sales Range: $100-124.9 Million
N.A.I.C.S.: 336611
Ohoks Hiroaki (Mgr)

Subsidiary (Non-US):

Hitachi Zosen Engineering Singapore (Pte.) Ltd. (2)
Unit 23 04 The JTC Summit 7 Jurong, Town Hall Road, Singapore, 609434, Singapore
Tel.: (65) 6316 2771
Shipbuilding
N.A.I.C.S.: 336611

Hitachi Zosen Europe Ltd. (2)
(100%)
Tel.: (44) 2076283891
Web Site: http://www.hitachizosen.co.jp

HITACHI ZOSEN CORPORATION

Sales Range: $25-49.9 Million
Emp.: 50
Ship Building & Repairing
N.A.I.C.S.: 336611

Branch (Non-US):

Hitachi Zosen Europe Ltd. (3)
(100%)
Tel.: (44) 1452724647
Sales Range: $25-49.9 Million
Emp.: 5
N.A.I.C.S.: 336611

Subsidiary (Domestic):

Hitachi Zosen Fukui Corporation (2)
1-8-28 Jiyugaoka, Awara, 919-0695, Fukui, Japan (100%)
Tel.: (81) 77 673 1220
Web Site: https://www.hitachizosen.co.jp
Industrial Machinery Mfr
N.A.I.C.S.: 333248

Hitachi Zosen Handling System Co., Ltd. (2)
14755 Mukaihigashi-cho, Onomichi, 722-0062, Japan
Tel.: (81) 8 4844 1104
Logistics Equipment Mfr
N.A.I.C.S.: 423830

Subsidiary (Non-US):

Hitachi Zosen Inova AG (2)
Hardturmstrasse 127, 8005, Zurich, Switzerland (100%)
Tel.: (41) 44 277 1111
Web Site: https://www.hz-inova.com
Sales Range: $125-149.9 Million
Emp.: 400
Energy-from-Waste Power Plant Construction & Systems Mfr
N.A.I.C.S.: 236210

Branch (Non-US):

Hitachi Zosen Inova AG - Sweden Branch (3)
PO Box 1547, SE-18315, Taby, Sweden
Tel.: (46) 87580350
Web Site: http://www.hz-inova.com
Sales Range: $1-9.9 Million
Environmental Engineering
N.A.I.C.S.: 541330

Subsidiary (Non-US):

Hitachi Zosen Inova Australia Pty Ltd (3)
Level 16 1 Denison, North Sydney, 2060, NSW, Australia
Tel.: (61) 280034110
Energy Waste Plant Services
N.A.I.C.S.: 562211

Hitachi Zosen Inova BioMethan France S.a.r.l. (3)
8 rue Paul Cezanne, 10120, Saint-Germain, France
Tel.: (33) 325453231
Biogas Installation Services
N.A.I.C.S.: 221117

Hitachi Zosen Inova BioMethan GmbH (3)
Ludwig-Elsbett-Strasse 1, 27404, Zeven, Germany
Tel.: (49) 428198760
Biogas Installation Services
N.A.I.C.S.: 221117

Hitachi Zosen Inova Deutschland GmbH (3)
Waltherstrasse 49-51 Gebaude Heizwerk, 51069, Cologne, Germany
Tel.: (49) 22166957610
Biogas Installation Services
N.A.I.C.S.: 221117

Hitachi Zosen Inova Etogas GmbH (3)
Ludwig-Elsbett-Strasse 1, 27404, Zeven, Germany
Tel.: (49) 428198760
Gas Distribution Services
N.A.I.C.S.: 221210

Hitachi Zosen Inova Kraftwerkstechnik GmbH (3)

Delitzscher Chaussee 3, 06188, Landsberg, Germany
Tel.: (49) 34602403815
Energy Waste Plant Services
N.A.I.C.S.: 562211

Hitachi Zosen Inova Slovakia s.r.o. (3)
Ku Bratke 5, 934 05, Levice, Slovakia
Tel.: (421) 363333611
Energy Waste Plant Services
N.A.I.C.S.: 562211

Subsidiary (US):

Hitachi Zosen Inova U.S.A. LLC (3)
10100 Global Way Ste 210, Knoxville, TN 37932 (100%)
Tel.: (865) 777-7400
Web Site: http://www.hz-inova.com
Sales Range: $10-24.9 Million
Emp.: 13
Design & Engineering of Turnkey Hazardous Waste Incineration Plants
N.A.I.C.S.: 541330
Marcus Stango (CEO)

Subsidiary (Non-US):

Hitachi Zosen Inova UK Ltd. (3)
The Hub Fowler Avenue, Farnborough, GU14 7JF, Hampshire, United Kingdom
Tel.: (44) 1252302373
Pipe Mfr & Distr
N.A.I.C.S.: 332996

Schmack Biogas S.r.l. (3)
Via Galileo Galilei 2/E, 39100, Bolzano, Italy (51%)
Tel.: (39) 04711955000
Web Site: https://www.schmack-biogas.it
Biogas Plant Construction Services
N.A.I.C.S.: 237120

Subsidiary (Non-US):

Hitachi Zosen KRB AG (2)
Industriestasse 6, 9470, Buchs, Switzerland
Tel.: (41) 817504500
Web Site: https://www.hz-krb.com
Pipe Mfr & Distr
N.A.I.C.S.: 332996
Marcel van de Wiel (Mgr-Comml)

Hitachi Zosen Services (Malaysia) Sdn. Bhd. (2)
16 3rd Fl Jalan Tengku Ampuan Zabedah D9 D, Section 9, 40100, Shah Alam, Selangor Darul Ehsan, Malaysia (100%)
Tel.: (60) 358806723
Web Site: http://www.hz-fukui.com.my
Sales Range: $25-49.9 Million
Emp.: 4
N.A.I.C.S.: 336611
Kyo Kuno (Gen Mgr)

Subsidiary (US):

Hitachi Zosen U.S.A. Ltd. (2)
One Westchase Ctr 10777 Westheimer Rd Ste 1015, Houston, TX 77042
Tel.: (713) 955-8120
Web Site: http://www.hitachizosen.co.jp
Sales Range: $25-49.9 Million
Emp.: 5
Recycling of Power Generation Products
N.A.I.C.S.: 541910

Subsidiary (Domestic):

Hitachi Zosen Fukui U.S.A., Inc. (3)
2711 Centerville Rd Ste 400, Wilmington, DE 19808
Tel.: (847) 427-8353
Press Machine Equipment Distr
N.A.I.C.S.: 423690

Branch (Domestic):

Hitachi Zosen U.S.A. Ltd. (3)
10777 Westheimer Rd Ste 1075, Houston, TX 77042-2456 (100%)
Tel.: (713) 532-9611
Web Site: http://www.hitachizosen.co.jp.com
Sales Range: $25-49.9 Million
Emp.: 3
Mfr of Components For Power Plant & Gas Plants
N.A.I.C.S.: 541910

Subsidiary (Domestic):

Hitz Holdings U.S.A. Inc. (3)
2711 Centerville Rd Ste 400, Wilmington, DE 19808
Tel.: (713) 955-8120
Financial Services
N.A.I.C.S.: 523999

Kompogas SLO LLC (3)
4300 Old Santa Fe Rd, San Luis Obispo, CA 93401
Tel.: (805) 801-8370
Web Site: https://kompogas-slo.com
Plant Operator
N.A.I.C.S.: 221310

NAC International Inc. (3)
3930 E Jones Bridge Rd, Norcross, GA 30092-2843
Tel.: (770) 447-1144
Web Site: http://www.nacintl.com
Sales Range: $25-49.9 Million
Nuclear Fuel Cycle Management Services
N.A.I.C.S.: 562112
Kent Cole (CEO)

Subsidiary (Non-US):

Hitachi Zosen Vietnam Co., Ltd. (3)
7th Floor HMC Tower 193 Dinh Tien Hoang Street, District 1, Ho Chi Minh City, Vietnam
Tel.: (84) 2838251040
Web Site: https://www.hitachizosen-vn.com
Emp.: 99
CAD Services
N.A.I.C.S.: 541340
Hiroshi Kiyono (Gen Dir)

Hitachi Zosen Yangling Co., Ltd. (2)
Nanbin Road, Yangling Demonstration Zone, Yangling, Shaanxi, China
Tel.: (86) 2987033236
Rubber Mfr
N.A.I.C.S.: 325212

Subsidiary (Domestic):

Hitachi-Zosen Plant Techno-Service Corporation (2)
6-33 Edobori 2-chome, Nishi-ku, Osaka, 550-0001, Japan
Tel.: (81) 662259798
Web Site: http://www.hpt-hitachizosen.co.jp
Sales Range: $25-49.9 Million
Emp.: 20
Industrial Machinery Equipment Mfr
N.A.I.C.S.: 333248

Hitz Environment Service Company Limited (2)
1-1 Minami-machi, Kawasaki-ku, Kawasaki, 210-0015, Kanagawa, Japan
Tel.: (81) 442000022
Energy Waste Plant Services
N.A.I.C.S.: 562211

Hitz Environment Takamatsu Co., Ltd. (2)
11-1 Nakajin-cho, Takamatsu, 760-0056, Kagawa, Japan
Tel.: (81) 878351864
Refuse Incineration Services
N.A.I.C.S.: 562213

Subsidiary (Non-US):

IMEX Co., Ltd. (2)
Tel.: (81) 352917535
Industrial Machinery Mfr
N.A.I.C.S.: 333248

Subsidiary (Domestic):

Ichinomiya Environment Technology Co., Ltd. (2)
53 Miyahigashi Oku-cho, Ichinomiya, 491-0201, Aichi Prefecture, Japan
Tel.: (81) 586476900
Refuse Incineration Services
N.A.I.C.S.: 562213

Jonan Environment Technology Co., Ltd. (2)
18 Uji Orii, Uji, 611-0021, Kyoto, Japan
Tel.: (81) 774946730
Web Site: http://jot.ekankyo21.com
Refuse Incineration Services
N.A.I.C.S.: 562213

Kansai Design Co., Ltd. (2)

2-6-33 Edobori Edobori Fukoku Mutual Life Insurance Co Building 5F 6F, Nishi-ku, Osaka, 550-0002, Japan
Tel.: (81) 664799050
Industrial Machinery Mfr
N.A.I.C.S.: 333248

Kashiwa Environment Technology Co.,Ltd (2)
56-2 Minamimasuo, Kashiwa, 277-0054, Chiba, Japan
Tel.: (81) 471708005
Environmental Consulting Services
N.A.I.C.S.: 541620

Kurashiki Environment Technology Co., Ltd. (2)
124-3-20 Tsurajima Tsurajima-cho, Kurashiki, 712-8012, Okayama, Japan
Tel.: (81) 864471921
Refuse Incineration Services
N.A.I.C.S.: 562213

Logisnext Handling System Corporation (2)
14755 Mukaihigashi-cho, Onomichi, 722-0062, Hiroshima, Japan
Tel.: (81) 848441104
Web Site: https://www.lnhs.jp
Emp.: 92
Transportation Equipment Mfr & Distr
N.A.I.C.S.: 336999

Subsidiary (Non-US):

Long Ho Science Co., Ltd. (2)
2 F No 586 Sec 2 Wenxin Road, Xitun District, Taichung, 407, Taiwan
Tel.: (886) 4 2310 9777
Environmental Consulting Services
N.A.I.C.S.: 541620

Subsidiary (Domestic):

Matsuyama Environment Technology Co., Ltd. (2)
3-525-6 Okaga, Matsuyama, 791-8057, Ehime, Japan
Tel.: (81) 899677015
Refuse Incineration Services
N.A.I.C.S.: 562213

Michinoku Service Co., Ltd. (2)
3-2-21 Chuo, Aoba-Ku, Sendai, 980-0021, Miyagi, Japan
Tel.: (81) 227122920
Water Treatment System Mfr
N.A.I.C.S.: 333310

Murakami Environment Technology Co., Ltd. (2)
3-15 Omachi, Murakami, 958-0842, Niigata, Japan
Tel.: (81) 254602431
Refuse Incineration Services
N.A.I.C.S.: 562213

Nakakitasorachi Environment Technology Co., Ltd. (2)
30-17 Toko, Utashinai, 073-0402, Hokkaido, Japan
Tel.: (81) 125432260
Refuse Incineration Services
N.A.I.C.S.: 562213

Natural Energy Japan Corporation (2)
1-3-7 Mukaihama, Akita, 010-1601, Japan
Tel.: (81) 188669313
Biogas Installation Services
N.A.I.C.S.: 221117

Nichizo Hokkaido Service Corp. (2)
5-1-48 2 Kita4jonishi, Chuo-Ku, Sapporo, 060-0004, Hokkaido, Japan
Tel.: (81) 112321441
Water Treatment System Mfr
N.A.I.C.S.: 333310

Nichizo Kyushu Service Corporation (2)
3-2-1 Hakataekimae Nisseihakataekimae Building, Hakata-ku, Fukuoka, 812-0011, Japan
Tel.: (81) 924516680
Civil Engineering Services
N.A.I.C.S.: 237990

Nichizo Tech Inc. (2)
2-15-26 Tsurumachi, Taisho-ku, Osaka,

HITACHI ZOSEN CORPORATION

Hitachi Zosen Corporation—(Continued)
551-0023, Japan
Tel.: (81) 665557050
Web Site: https://www.nichizotech.co.jp
Refuse Incineration Services
N.A.I.C.S.: 562213

Nippon GPS Data Service Corporation (2)
6-26-3 Minamioi, Shinagawa-ku, Tokyo, 140-0013, Japan
Tel.: (81) 364040145
Computer Control System Services
N.A.I.C.S.: 541512

Nippon Pusnes Co., Ltd. (2)
2-37-4 Nihombashihamacho, Chuo-ku, Tokyo, 103-0007, Japan
Tel.: (81) 336690471
Marine Equipment Mfr & Distr
N.A.I.C.S.: 332999

OCL Corporation (2)
New Nishishinbashi Building 2-11-6 Nishishinbashi, Minato-ku, Tokyo, 105-0003, Japan
Tel.: (81) 335020126
Web Site: http://www.ocl-corp.co.jp
Cask Container Mfr & Maintenance Services
N.A.I.C.S.: 321920

Odate Ecomanage Corporation (2)
49-1 Azamatauemonsawa, Yukisawa, Odate, 017-0021, Akita, Japan
Tel.: (81) 186453900
Water Treatment Equipment Mfr
N.A.I.C.S.: 333310

Ohnami Corporation (2)
6-33 Edobori 2-Chome, Nishi-ku, Osaka, 550-0002, Japan
Tel.: (81) 6 6445 0073
Web Site: http://www.0073.co.jp
Emp.: 257
Warehousing Services
N.A.I.C.S.: 493110

Subsidiary (Non-US):

Osmoflo Engineering Services Pvt. Ltd. (2)
Office 3 3rd floor Solitaire Building ITI Road, Aundh, Pune, 411007, India
Tel.: (91) 2066869500
Waste Treatment Services
N.A.I.C.S.: 221310

Osmoflo Holdings Pty Ltd (2)
382 Diment Road, Burton, Adelaide, 5110, SA, Australia
Tel.: (61) 882829700
Waste Treatment Services
N.A.I.C.S.: 221310

Osmoflo International FZE (2)
Office No LB08109 Jebel Ali Free Zone, PO Box 261077, Dubai, United Arab Emirates
Tel.: (971) 48808584
Waste Treatment Services
N.A.I.C.S.: 221310

Subsidiary (Domestic):

Promotec Corporation (2)
5-3-28 Nishikujo, Konohana-ku, Osaka, 554-0012, Japan
Tel.: (81) 664689771
Steel Structure System Services
N.A.I.C.S.: 238120

SLURRY-21 Co., Ltd (2)
6-26-3 Minamioi Omori Bell Boat Dkan 9f, Shinagawa-ku, Tokyo, 140-0013, Japan
Tel.: (81) 364040136
Sales Range: $25-49.9 Million
Emp.: 7
Ice Making Machinery Mfr & Distr
N.A.I.C.S.: 333248

SN Environment Technology Co., Ltd (2)
Osaka Bay Tower Office 8F 1-2-1 Benten, Minato-ku, Osaka, 552-0007, Japan
Tel.: (81) 665859374
Web Site: https://www.sn-t.co.jp
Sales Range: $25-49.9 Million
Emp.: 234
Environmental Consulting Services
N.A.I.C.S.: 541620

Shimoda Seiji (Pres)

Serachem Co., Ltd. (2)
954-1 Hongo Sera-cho, Sera-gun, Hiroshima, 722-1112, Japan
Tel.: (81) 847220705
Web Site: https://www.serachem.co.jp
Carbon Mfr & Distr
N.A.I.C.S.: 335991

Setozaki Iron Works Co., Ltd. (2)
2-18-6 Takekucho, Shimonoseki, 751-0833, Yamaguchi, Japan
Tel.: (81) 832521311
Web Site: https://www.pusnes.co.jp
Sales Range: $25-49.9 Million
Emp.: 103
Construction Machinery Mfr
N.A.I.C.S.: 333120
Tatsuki Masuda (Pres)

Shikoku Environment Service Co., Ltd. (2)
11-1 Nakajin-cho, Takamatsu, 760-0056, Kagawa, Japan
Tel.: (81) 878351867
Refuse Incineration Services
N.A.I.C.S.: 562213

Toyonaka & Itami Recycle Forest Co., Ltd. (2)
2-2-1 Haradanishimachi, Toyonaka, 561-0806, Osaka, Japan
Tel.: (81) 668421150
Refuse Incineration Services
N.A.I.C.S.: 562213

Tsuyama Ken-iki Environment Technology Co., Ltd. (2)
1834-2 Minamigatanaka, Tsuyama, 709-4616, Okayama, Japan
Tel.: (81) 868578555
Refuse Incineration Services
N.A.I.C.S.: 562213

Ultra Finish Technology Co., Ltd. (2)
1-1-1 Heiseimachi, Yokosuka, 238-0013, Kanagawa, Japan
Tel.: (81) 468285050
Web Site: https://www.uft.co.jp
Emp.: 35
Semiconductor Equipment Mfr
N.A.I.C.S.: 333242
Shinichi Azuma (Pres)

Universal Shipbuilding Corporation (2)
1310 Omiya-cho Saiwai-ku, Kawasaki, 212-8554, Kanagawa, Japan
Tel.: (81) 445432700
Web Site: http://www.u-zosen.co.jp
Ship Building Services
N.A.I.C.S.: 336611

V TEX Corporation (2)
5F Omori Prime Building 6-21-12 Minamioi, Shinagawa-ku, Tokyo, 140-0013, Japan
Tel.: (81) 337654161
Web Site: https://www.vtex.co.jp
Sales Range: $50-74.9 Million
Emp.: 259
Industrial Valve Mfr & Distr
N.A.I.C.S.: 332911
Toshiyuki Ito (Auditor)

Subsidiary (Non-US):

V TEX Korea Co., Ltd. (3)
1107 Gyopo-ri Oseong-myeon, Pyeongtaek, Gyeonggi-do, Korea (South)
Tel.: (82) 316865381
Valve Parts Mfr & Distr
N.A.I.C.S.: 332911

V TEX Shanghai Co., Ltd. (3)
Room 1013 2201 Yan An West Road, Changning, Shanghai, 200336, China
Tel.: (86) 2162950800
Valve Parts Distr
N.A.I.C.S.: 423120

Subsidiary (US):

VTEX America Inc. (3)
2880 Zanker Rd 231, San Jose, CA 95134
Tel.: (408) 432-7277
Valve Parts Distr
N.A.I.C.S.: 423120

Subsidiary (Non-US):

Watersource Pty Ltd (2)
28 Thistlethwaite Street, South Melbourne, 3205, VIC, Australia
Tel.: (61) 419889770
Web Site: http://www.watersourceaustralia.com.au
Waste Treatment Services
N.A.I.C.S.: 221310
Mark Campbell (CEO)

Zhenjiang Zhong Chuan Hitachi Zosen Machinery Co., Ltd (2)
9 Jingjiang Road, Zhenjiang, Jiangsu, China
Tel.: (86) 51185338108
Web Site: http://www.hitachizosen.co.jp
Diesel Engine Parts Mfr & Distr
N.A.I.C.S.: 423840

Zhoushan Nippon Pusnes Ship Machinery Co., Ltd. (2)
Dongsha Industrial Park, Daishan, Zhoushan, Zhejiang, China
Tel.: (86) 5807070001
Marine Deck Machinery Mfr
N.A.I.C.S.: 336611

Subsidiary (Domestic):

ha-na-iro Co., Ltd. (2)
2406 Hayama, Yamada, Hagi, 758-0063, Yamaguchi, Japan
Tel.: (81) 838268716
Refuse Incineration Services
N.A.I.C.S.: 562213

Hitachi Zosen Inova Rus LLC (1)
Leningradskiy Prospect 72 Building 2 Floor 2 Space IV Room 1, Moscow, 125315, Russia
Tel.: (7) 4951396049
Waste Treatment Services
N.A.I.C.S.: 221320

Hitachi Zosen Marine Engine Co., Ltd. (1)
1 Ariake Nagasu-machi, Tamana-gun, Kumamoto, 869-0113, Japan
Tel.: (81) 968782261
Web Site: https://hzme.hitachizosen.co.jp
Emp.: 300
Marine Engine Mfr & Distr
N.A.I.C.S.: 333618

Hitachi Zosen Sus Environment Technology Co., Ltd. (1)
No 9 Songqiu Road, Qingpu District, Shanghai, China
Tel.: (86) 2180268666
Waste Treatment Services
N.A.I.C.S.: 221320

Hitachi Zosen Trading (Shanghai) Co., Ltd. (1)
40th Floor Room No 041A Hang Sang Bank Tower, 1000 Lujiazui Ring Road Pudong New Area, Shanghai, 200120, China
Tel.: (86) 2168872525
Marine Engine Mfr & Distr
N.A.I.C.S.: 333618

Hzf Services (Malaysia) Sdn. Bhd. (1)
A-3A-07 Oasis Square Oasis Damansara No 2 Jalan PJU 1A/7A, Ara Damansara, 47301, Petaling Jaya, Selangor, Malaysia
Tel.: (60) 376202903
Web Site: https://www.hz-fukui.com.my
Industrial Machinery & Equipment Distr
N.A.I.C.S.: 423830

Pt. Hitz Indonesia (1)
Wisma BNI 46 Lt 6 Suite 611 Jl Jendral Sudirman Kav 1, karet Tengsin Tanah Abang, Jakarta Pusat, 10220, Indonesia
Tel.: (62) 215744482
Marine Engine Mfr & Distr
N.A.I.C.S.: 333618

Underground Infrastructure Technologies Corporation (1)
3rd Floor Dojima Plaza Building 1-5-30, Dojima Kita-ku, Osaka, 530-0003, Japan
Tel.: (81) 672220837
Web Site: https://ugitec.co.jp
Civil Engineering Machine Mfr & Distr
N.A.I.C.S.: 333120

HITACHI, LTD.

1-6-6 Marunouchi, Chiyoda-ku, Tokyo, 100-8280, Japan

Tel.: (81) 332581111 JP
Web Site: https://www.hitachi.co.jp
Year Founded: 1910
HIA1—(DEU)
Rev.: $64,306,812,760
Assets: $80,782,687,240
Liabilities: $42,050,711,410
Net Worth: $38,731,975,830
Earnings: $3,899,212,560
Emp.: 268,655
Fiscal Year-end: 03/31/24
Holding Company; Power, Infrastructure, Rail, Urban Planning & Development, Defense, Information Technologies & Telecommunication Systems Mfr & Whslr
N.A.I.C.S.: 551112

Subsidiaries:

Applied Physics Technologies, Inc. (1)
1600 NE Miller St, McMinnville, OR 97128
Tel.: (503) 434-5550
Web Site: http://www.a-p-tech.com
Laboratory Equipment Mfr
N.A.I.C.S.: 334516

Asaka Misono Utility Services Corporation (1)
1509 Miyado, Asaka, 351-0031, Saitama, Japan
Tel.: (81) 484860135
Web Site: http://www.amus-pfi.com
Construction & Engineering Services
N.A.I.C.S.: 541330

Beijing Hitachi Control Systems Co., Ltd. (1)
Tower M7 No 1 Jiuxianqiao East Road, Chaoyang District, Beijing, 100015, China
Tel.: (86) 1064380506
Web Site: http://www.hitachi-bhc.cn
Construction & Engineering Services
N.A.I.C.S.: 541330

Beijing Hitachi Huasun Information Systems Co., Ltd. (1)
Block E 3F Global Trade Center No 36 North Third Ring East Road, Dongcheng District, Beijing, 100013, China
Tel.: (86) 1059575368
Web Site: http://www.bhh.com.cn
Construction & Engineering Services
N.A.I.C.S.: 541330

Cumulus Systems Incorporated (1)
1821 S Bascom Ave Ste 296, Campbell, CA 95008
Tel.: (650) 934-1108
Web Site: https://www.cumulus-systems.com
Computer Software Services
N.A.I.C.S.: 513210
Arun Ramachandran (Co-Founder)

Cumulus Systems Private Limited (1)
502 801 and 802 S R IRIZ Baner-Pashan Link Road, Pashan, Pune, 411021, India
Tel.: (91) 8380063284
Software Services
N.A.I.C.S.: 541511

Dalian Hitachi Machinery & Equipment Co. Ltd. (1)
No 2 Hai North Rd, Ganjingzi District, Dalian, 116032, China
Tel.: (86) 41139523199
Electrical Component Mfr
N.A.I.C.S.: 335999

Eugene Engineering Co. Limited (1)
Block A 11th Floor Fucheng Industrial Building No 1A Yuri Street, Tokwawan Kowloon, Hong Kong, China (Hong Kong)
Tel.: (852) 23653012
Web Site: http://www.eugene.com.hk
Construction & Engineering Services
N.A.I.C.S.: 541330

Flexware Innovation, Inc. (1)
9128 Technology Ln, Fishers, IN 46038
Tel.: (317) 813-5400
Web Site: http://www.flexwareinnovation.com
Rev.: $6,147,093
Emp.: 30

AND PRIVATE COMPANIES — HITACHI, LTD.

Computer System Design Services
N.A.I.C.S.: 541512
Jason Toschlog *(VP-Tech)*

GlobalLogic Inc. (1)
1741 Technology Dr 4th Fl, San Jose, CA 95110
Tel.: (408) 273-8900
Web Site: http://www.globallogic.com
Sales Range: $250-299.9 Million
Emp.: 8,000
Software Publishing & Development Services
N.A.I.C.S.: 513210
Shane Brentham *(VP-Mktg)*

Subsidiary (Domestic):

Method Inc. (2)
585 Howard St Ground Fl, San Francisco, CA 94105
Tel.: (415) 901-6300
Web Site: http://www.method.com
Sales Range: $10-24.9 Million
Emp.: 100
Advertising Agencies
N.A.I.C.S.: 541810
Kevin Farnham *(Founder & CEO)*

Branch (Non-US):

Method London (3)
The Tea Building Studio 7 01 56 Shoreditch High Street, London, E1 6JJ, United Kingdom
Tel.: (44) 2030517935
Web Site: http://www.method.com
Emp.: 34
Design Agency
N.A.I.C.S.: 541810

HMY, Ltd. (1)
1240-5 Hashima-cho, Yasugi, 692-8606, Shimane, Japan
Tel.: (81) 854231716
Web Site: http://www.hitachi-metals-yasugi-seisakusyo.co.jp
Steel Mfrs
N.A.I.C.S.: 331110

HPC Engineering (Thailand) Co., Ltd. (1)
1168/76 Lumpini Tower Building 26FL Rama IV Road Tungmahamek, Sathorn, Bangkok, 10120, Thailand
Tel.: (66) 2 285 6806
Engineeering Services
N.A.I.C.S.: 541330
Koichi Nakamura *(Gen Mgr)*

HPC Venezuela C.A. (1)
UD-502 Arboleda Street, VHPC Building Matanzas Industrial Zone, Puerto Ordaz, 8050, Bolivar State, Venezuela
Tel.: (58) 2869941174
Web Site: https://www.vhpc.com.ve
Emp.: 16
Integrated Engineering Solutions
N.A.I.C.S.: 541330

Hc Queretaro S.A. de C.V. (1)
Circuito El Marques Norte 76 Parque Industrial El Marques, 76246, El Marques, Queretaro, Mexico
Tel.: (52) 4421924900
Automotive Component Mfr & Distr
N.A.I.C.S.: 336390

Hitachi (China) Research & Development Corporation (1)
Room 808 North Building Block C Raycom Information Center, No 2 Ke Xuexue South Road Haidian District, Beijing, China
Tel.: (86) 1082862918
Web Site: http://www.hitachi.com.cn
Automotive Electronic Component Mfr
N.A.I.C.S.: 336320

Hitachi (China), Ltd. (1)
4/F North Tower World Finance Centre Harbour City Canton Road, Tsim Sha Tsui, Kowloon, China (Hong Kong)
Tel.: (852) 27369218
Web Site: http://www.hitachi.com.cn
Industrial Equipment Distr
N.A.I.C.S.: 423830

Hitachi (Hong Kong) Ltd. (1)
18/F Ever Gain Centre 28 On Muk Street, Hong Kong, China (Hong Kong)
Tel.: (852) 21138883

Web Site: http://www.hitachi-homeappliances.com.hk
Electronic Appliance Distr
N.A.I.C.S.: 423620

Hitachi (Shanghai) Trading Co., Ltd. (1)
12th Floor Rui Jin Building No 205 Maoming Road S, Shanghai, 200020, China
Tel.: (86) 21 6472 1002
Sales Range: $75-99.9 Million
Emp.: 20
Industrial Equipment Distr
N.A.I.C.S.: 423830

Hitachi ABB Power Grids AG (1)
Brown Boveri Strasse 5, Zurich, 8050, Switzerland
Tel.: (41) 585850000
Power & Digital Technologies Solutions & Services
N.A.I.C.S.: 541690
Claudio Facchin *(CEO)*

Hitachi Academy Co., Ltd. (1)
Ueno East Tower 18F 16-1 Higashiueno 2-chome, Taito-ku, Tokyo, 110-0015, Japan
Tel.: (81) 362843900
Web Site: http://www.hitachi-ac.co.jp
Professional Skill Development Training Services
N.A.I.C.S.: 611430

Hitachi Aloka Medical, Ltd. (1)
6 22 1 Mure, Mitaka, 181-8622, Japan
Tel.: (81) 422456049
Web Site: http://www.hitachi-aloka.co.jp
Sales Range: $75-99.9 Million
Emp.: 100
Radio & Ultrasonic Diagnostic Equipment, Radiation Measuring Instruments, Nuclear Medical Equipment, Sample Testing & Analysis Equipment & Therapeutic & Surgical Equipment Mfr
N.A.I.C.S.: 334510
Minoru Yoshizum *(Pres)*

Hitachi America, Ltd. (1)
1000 Marino Blvd, Brisbane, CA 94005 (100%)
Tel.: (650) 244-7400
Web Site: http://www.hitachi.us
Sales Range: $50-74.9 Million
Emp.: 100
Holding Company; Regional Managing Office
N.A.I.C.S.: 551112
Hicham Abdessamad *(Chm)*

Subsidiary (Domestic):

AccSys Technology, Inc. (2)
1177 A Quarry Lane, Pleasanton, CA 94566 (100%)
Tel.: (925) 462-6949
Web Site: http://www.accsys.com
Sales Range: $25-49.9 Million
Emp.: 20
Designs & Manufactures Compact Ion Linear Accelerators for Medical & Industrial Applications
N.A.I.C.S.: 335999

Hitachi Capital America Corp. (2)
7808 Creekridge Cir Ste 250, Edina, MN 55439
Tel.: (952) 996-0270
Web Site: http://www.hcavs.com
Vendor Financing & Related Commercial Financial Services
N.A.I.C.S.: 522180
Dave Gnade *(Exec VP-Sls)*

Division (Domestic):

Hitachi Capital America Vendor Services (3)
7808 Creekridge Cir Ste 250, Edina, MN 55439
Web Site: http://www.hcavs.com
Emp.: 200
Vendor Financing & Related Commercial Financial Services
N.A.I.C.S.: 522180
Jim Teal *(Pres)*

Subsidiary (Domestic):

Hitachi Communication Technologies America, Inc. (2)

3617 Parkway Ln, Norcross, GA 30092
Tel.: (770) 446-8820
Web Site: http://www.hitachi-cta.com
Sales Range: $25-49.9 Million
Emp.: 85
Communication Equipment Mfr & Whslr
N.A.I.C.S.: 334290

Division (Domestic):

Hitachi Communication Technologies America, Inc. - HCTA Packet Core Division (3)
2280 Campbell Creek Blvd Ste 325, Richardson, TX 75082
Tel.: (469) 461-5400
Web Site: http://www.hitachi-cta.com
Sales Range: $25-49.9 Million
Emp.: 80
Communication Equipment Mfr
N.A.I.C.S.: 334290
Reg Wilcox *(CEO)*

Subsidiary (Domestic):

Hitachi Computer Products (America), Inc. (2)
1800 E Imhoff Rd, Norman, OK 73071
Tel.: (405) 360-5500
Web Site: http://www.hitachiomd.com
Computer Peripheral Equipment Mfr
N.A.I.C.S.: 334118

Hitachi Consulting Corporation (2)
14643 Dalls Pkwy Ste 800, Dallas, TX 75254 (99.2%)
Tel.: (214) 665-7000
Web Site: http://www.hitachiconsulting.com
Consulting Services
N.A.I.C.S.: 541618
John O'Brien *(Exec VP-Consulting Practice-United Kingdom)*

Subsidiary (Non-US):

Hitachi Consulting (China) Co., Ltd. (3)
202 Wukang road, Shanghai, 200031, China
Tel.: (86) 21 54659911
Web Site: http://www.hitachiconsultingchina.com
Information Technology Consulting Services
N.A.I.C.S.: 541512
Ron Machan *(CEO)*

Hitachi Consulting India Private Limited (3)
3rd Floor Tower VII Magarpatta City SEZ, Magarpatta City Hadapsar, Pune, 411 013, India
Tel.: (91) 2065111001
Web Site: http://www.hitachiconsulting.com
Sales Range: $75-99.9 Million
Emp.: 350
Information Technology Consulting Services
N.A.I.C.S.: 541512

Hitachi Consulting Portugal S.A. (3)
Av Eng Duarte Pacheco Torre 1 - 5 Sala 1 e 2, Lisbon, Portugal
Tel.: (351) 21 122 2100
Emp.: 33
Information Technology Consulting Services
N.A.I.C.S.: 541512
Nargareva Marques *(Gen Mgr)*

Hitachi Consulting Singapore Pte Ltd. (3)
7 Temasek Boulevard 06-02A Suntec Tower One, Singapore, 38987, Singapore
Tel.: (65) 6334 9356
Sales Range: $25-49.9 Million
Emp.: 1
Information Technology Consulting Services
N.A.I.C.S.: 541512

Hitachi Consulting UK Limited (3)
2 More London Riverside, London, SE1 2AP, United Kingdom
Tel.: (44) 20 7947 4500
Web Site: http://www.hitachiconsulting.co.uk
Sales Range: $25-49.9 Million
Emp.: 20
Information Technology Consulting Services
N.A.I.C.S.: 541512

Subsidiary (Domestic):

Hitachi Data Systems Corporation (2)

2845 Lafayette St, Santa Clara, CA 95050 (100%)
Tel.: (408) 970-1000
Web Site: http://www.hds.com
Mainframe Peripheral Products & Storage Devices Service & Distr
N.A.I.C.S.: 423430
Ryuichi Otsuki *(CEO)*

Subsidiary (Non-US):

Hitachi Data Systems (Chile) Limitada (3)
Av Isidora Goyenechea 3120 Piso 11, Las Condes, 7550083, Santiago, Chile
Tel.: (56) 2 353 0000
Web Site: http://www.hds.com
Sales Range: $25-49.9 Million
Emp.: 16
Information Technology Consulting Services
N.A.I.C.S.: 541512
Walter Sunkel *(Reg Mgr)*

Hitachi Data Systems (Polska) Sp. z.o.o. (3)
Al Jana Pawla II 12, 00-124, Warsaw, Poland
Tel.: (48) 22 850 99 00
Sales Range: $25-49.9 Million
Emp.: 12
Information Technology Consulting Services
N.A.I.C.S.: 541512

Hitachi Data Systems (Spain) (3)
Avda Diagonal 605, Barcelona, 8028, Spain
Tel.: (34) 933634100
Web Site: http://www.hds.com
Sales Range: $10-24.9 Million
Emp.: 24
Information Technology Services
N.A.I.C.S.: 541512
Angel Fernandez *(Gen Mgr)*

Hitachi Data Systems A/S (3)
Strandveien 18, 1366, Lysaker, Norway
Tel.: (47) 67518440
Web Site: http://www.hts.com
Information Technology Consulting Services
N.A.I.C.S.: 541512

Hitachi Data Systems A/S (3)
Egebaekvej 98, 2850, Naerum, Denmark
Tel.: (45) 58 10 00
Emp.: 60
Information Technology Consulting Services
N.A.I.C.S.: 541512
David Funk *(Gen Counsel/Corp Sec-Federal Govt Bus)*

Hitachi Data Systems AB (Gothenburg) (3)
Stora Badhusgatan 18-20, Gothenburg, 411 21, Sweden
Tel.: (46) 8 624 64 00
Sales Range: $25-49.9 Million
Emp.: 7
Information Technology Consulting Services
N.A.I.C.S.: 541512
Ann Huynh *(CEO)*

Hitachi Data Systems AG (3)
Richtistrasse 11, 8304, Wallisellen, Switzerland
Tel.: (41) 44 802 64 64
Sales Range: $25-49.9 Million
Emp.: 6
Data Storage Device Mfr
N.A.I.C.S.: 334112
Denise Richard *(Mgr-Mktg)*

Hitachi Data Systems AS (3)
Strandveien 18, 1366, Lysaker, Norway
Tel.: (47) 67518440
Emp.: 20
Electronic Data Processing Services
N.A.I.C.S.: 518210
Rune Sund *(CEO)*

Hitachi Data Systems Australia Pty Ltd (3)
Level 3 82 Waterloo Rd, North Ryde, 2113, NSW, Australia
Tel.: (61) 293253300
Web Site: http://www.hds.com
Sales Range: $25-49.9 Million
Emp.: 90
Computer Products & Services
N.A.I.C.S.: 541512
Phillip Teague *(Dir-Indus & Alliance Solutions-Australia & New Zealand)*

HITACHI, LTD.

Hitachi, Ltd.—(Continued)

Hitachi Data Systems B.V. (3)
Dali Building 3e Verdieping Herikerbergweg 270, Amsterdam, 1101 CT, Netherlands
Tel.: (31) 20650 9000
Web Site: http://www.hds.com
Sales Range: $25-49.9 Million
Emp.: 60
Information Technology Consulting Services
N.A.I.C.S.: 541512
Bastiaan van Amstel *(Sr Mgr-PR-Europe, Middle East & Africa)*

Hitachi Data Systems Belgium NV/SA (3)
Woluwedal 28, Saint-Stevens-Woluwe, 1932, Belgium
Tel.: (32) 26434550
Web Site: http://www.hds.com
Sales Range: $25-49.9 Million
Emp.: 20
Information Technology Consulting Services
N.A.I.C.S.: 541512
Philippe Janssens *(Country Mgr)*

Subsidiary (Domestic):

Hitachi Data Systems Credit Corporation (3)
750 Central Expy, Santa Clara, CA 95050-2638
Tel.: (408) 970-1000
Financial Management Services
N.A.I.C.S.: 523999

Subsidiary (Non-US):

Hitachi Data Systems GmbH (3)
Im Steingrund 10, Buchschlag, 63303, Dreieich, Germany
Tel.: (49) 6103 804 0
Emp.: 80
Information Technology Consulting Services
N.A.I.C.S.: 541512
Bastiaan van Amstel *(Sr Mgr-PR)*

Hitachi Data Systems Inc. (3)
625 President Kennedy Ave Ste 1700, PO Box 1700, Montreal, H3A 1K2, QC, Canada **(100%)**
Tel.: (514) 982-0707
Web Site: http://www.hds.com
Distribution of Mainframe Peripheral Products
N.A.I.C.S.: 449210

Hitachi Data Systems India Pvt. Ltd. (3)
Residency 6th Floor 133/1 Residency Road, Bengaluru, 560 025, Karnataka, India
Tel.: (91) 80 67746000
Web Site: http://www.hds.com
Emp.: 40
Information Technology Consulting Services
N.A.I.C.S.: 541512
Sushma Deshpande *(Mgr-Mktg Comm)*

Hitachi Data Systems Israel Ltd. (3)
27 Maskit, Herzliyya, 46733, Israel
Tel.: (972) 99704500
Data Storage Device Distr
N.A.I.C.S.: 423430

Hitachi Data Systems Italia s.r.l. (3)
Via Tommaso Gulli 39, 20147, Milan, Italy
Tel.: (39) 02 403092 1
Web Site: http://www.hitachi.eu
Sales Range: $10-24.9 Million
Emp.: 50
Information Technology Consulting Services
N.A.I.C.S.: 541512

Hitachi Data Systems Korea Limited (3)
37/F Asem Tower 159 - 1 Samseong-Dong, Gangnam-Gu, Seoul, 135-798, Korea (South)
Tel.: (82) 2 6001 3376
Information Technology Consulting Services
N.A.I.C.S.: 541512

Hitachi Data Systems Limited (3)
4F-C No 167 Hung Kuo Building Tun Hua N Rd, Taipei, 10549, Taiwan
Tel.: (886) 2 27190077
Sales Range: $25-49.9 Million
Emp.: 2
Information Technology Consulting Services
N.A.I.C.S.: 541512

Hitachi Data Systems Ltd. (3)
Sefton Park, Stoke Poges, SL2 4HD, Buckinghamshire, United Kingdom
Tel.: (44) 1753 618000
Web Site: http://www.hds.com
Sales Range: $25-49.9 Million
Emp.: 250
Information Technology Consulting Services
N.A.I.C.S.: 541512

Hitachi Data Systems Ltd. (3)
Suite 3301-06 Shell Tower Times Square, 1 Matheson Street, Causeway Bay, China (Hong Kong)
Tel.: (852) 31897900
Web Site: http://www.hds.com
Emp.: 200
Computer Products & Services
N.A.I.C.S.: 541512
Ryuichi Otsuki *(CEO)*

Hitachi Data Systems Nederland BV (3)
Herikerbergweg 270, Amsterdam-Zuidoost, Amsterdam, 1101 BH, Zuidoost, Netherlands
Tel.: (31) 20 650 9000
Sales Range: $10-24.9 Million
Emp.: 50
Information Technology Consulting Services
N.A.I.C.S.: 541512
Frederik Schroder *(Gen Mgr)*

Hitachi Data Systems Oy (3)
Lars Sonckin Kaari 16, 02600, Espoo, Finland
Tel.: (358) 9 5406 5900
Information Technology Consulting Services
N.A.I.C.S.: 541512

Hitachi Data Systems Pte. Ltd. (3)
300 Beach Road 28-01 Concourse, Singapore, 199555, Singapore
Tel.: (65) 6225 3377
Web Site: http://www.hds.com
Information Technology Consulting Services
N.A.I.C.S.: 541512
Mark Ablett *(Sr VP & Gen Mgr-Asia-Pacific)*

Hitachi Data Systems S.A. (Barcelona) (3)
Avda Diagonal 605, 08028, Barcelona, Spain
Tel.: (34) 933634100
Emp.: 130
Information Technology Services
N.A.I.C.S.: 541512

Hitachi Data Systems S.A.S (3)
Antony Parc 1 2 a 6 Place Du General De Gaulle, 92160, Antony, France
Tel.: (33) 146101400
Sales Range: $25-49.9 Million
Emp.: 50
Information Technology Consulting Services
N.A.I.C.S.: 541512
Emilie Lieblich *(Sr Reg Mgr-Mktg)*

Hitachi Data Systems Sdn Bhd (3)
B-10-1 Level 10 Tower B Menara UOA Bangsar No 5 Jalan Bangsar Utama 1, 59000, Kuala Lumpur, Malaysia
Tel.: (60) 3 2303 3000
Web Site: http://www.hitachi.com.my
Sales Range: $75-99.9 Million
Emp.: 300
Information Technology Consulting Services
N.A.I.C.S.: 541512

Subsidiary (Domestic):

Pentaho Corporation (3)
5950 Hazeltine National Dr, Orlando, FL 32822
Tel.: (407) 812-6736
Web Site: http://www.pentaho.com
Analytics Software Services & Consulting Services
N.A.I.C.S.: 513210
Richard K. Daley *(Co-Founder & Chief Strategy Officer)*

Subsidiary (Non-US):

Pentaho UK (4)
Warnford Court 29 Throgmorton Street, London, EC2N 2AT, United Kingdom
Tel.: (44) 2035744790
Web Site: http://www.pentaho.com
Analytics Software & Consulting Services
N.A.I.C.S.: 513210

Subsidiary (Domestic):

Hitachi Data Systems Holding Corporation (2)
2845 Lafayette St, Santa Clara, CA 95050-2638
Tel.: (408) 970-1000
Web Site: http://www.hds.com
Investment Management Service
N.A.I.C.S.: 523999

Hitachi Electronics Engineering America (2)
3100 N 1st St, San Jose, CA 95134
Tel.: (408) 432-0696
Web Site: http://www.hitachi.com
Sales Range: $25-49.9 Million
Emp.: 20
Electronic Parts & Equipment Merchant Whslr
N.A.I.C.S.: 423690
Akira Suzuki *(Mgr-Sls)*

Hitachi HVB, Inc. (2)
7250 McGinnis Ferry Rd, Suwanee, GA 30024 **(100%)**
Tel.: (770) 495-1755
Web Site: http://hvbi.hitachi.us
Sales Range: $25-49.9 Million
Emp.: 80
Electric Circuit Breaker, Switchgear & Transformer Mfr & Whslr
N.A.I.C.S.: 335313
Dennis McNulty *(VP-Ops)*

Hitachi Healthcare Americas Corporation (2)
1959 Summit Commerce Park, Twinsburg, OH 44087
Tel.: (330) 425-1313
Web Site: http://www.hitachimed.com
Diagnostic Imaging Product Whslr
N.A.I.C.S.: 423450

Subsidiary (Domestic):

Vidistar, LLC (3)
5 Century Dr Ste 230, Greenville, SC 29607
Web Site: http://www.hitachihealthcare.com
Software Publisher
N.A.I.C.S.: 513210
Craig Allan Walker *(Founder & CEO)*

Subsidiary (Domestic):

Hitachi Power Systems America, Ltd. (2)
645 Martinsville Rd, Basking Ridge, NJ 07920
Tel.: (908) 605-2800
Web Site: http://www.mhpowersystems.com
Sales Range: $50-74.9 Million
Emp.: 85
Power Generation Equipment Whslr
N.A.I.C.S.: 423610
William R. Buffa *(Sr VP-Project Ops)*

Hitachi Telecom (USA), Inc. (2)
3617 Pkwy Ln, Norcross, GA 30092-2829
Tel.: (770) 446-8820
Web Site: http://www.hitachi-cta.com
Sales Range: $25-49.9 Million
Emp.: 70
Telecommunications Solutions Mfr & Developer
N.A.I.C.S.: 334210

Hitachi Via Mechanics (USA), Inc. (2)
150C Charcot Ave, San Jose, CA 95131
Tel.: (408) 392-9650
Emp.: 10
Printed Circuit Board Sales & Repair Services
N.A.I.C.S.: 423690
Jenny Tran *(VP-Engrg)*

Hitachi Appliances Techno Service, Ltd. (1)
1-1-1 Higashitaga-cho, Hitachi, 316-8502, Ibaraki, Japan
Tel.: (81) 294332251
Web Site: http://www.hitachi-ap-ts.co.jp
Home Appliance Mfr
N.A.I.C.S.: 335220

Hitachi Architects & Engineers (Shanghai) Co., Ltd. (1)

INTERNATIONAL PUBLIC

Room No 1004 Rui Jin Building 205 Maoming South Road, Shanghai, 200020, China
Tel.: (86) 21 6472 0017
Construction Engineering Services
N.A.I.C.S.: 541330

Hitachi Architects & Engineers Co., Ltd. (1)
3-11-7 Uchikanda, Chiyoda-ku, Tokyo, 101-0047, Japan
Tel.: (81) 367577110
Web Site: http://www.hae.co.jp
Civil Engineering Services
N.A.I.C.S.: 541330
Hirobumi Ito *(Exec Dir)*

Hitachi Asia (M) Sdn Bhd (1)
Suite 17 3 Level 17 Menara IMC No 8 Jalan Sultan Ismail, Letter Box No 5, 50250, Kuala Lumpur, Malaysia
Tel.: (60) 320318751
Web Site: http://www.hitachi.com.my
Emp.: 3,229
Electronic & Industrial Machinery Distr
N.A.I.C.S.: 423690

Subsidiary (Domestic):

Hitachi Sales (M) Sdn Bhd (2)
Lot 12 Jalan Kemajuan, Bangi Industrial Estate, 43650, Bandar Baru Bangi, Selangor Darul Ehsan, Malaysia
Tel.: (60) 3 8911 2600
Web Site: http://www.hitachiconsumer.com.my
Consumer Electronic Appliances Distr
N.A.I.C.S.: 423620
Takahiro Ishii *(Mng Dir)*

Hitachi Asia (Vietnam) Company Limited (1)
Room 8-9-10A 4th Floor The Landmark 5B Ton Duc Thang Street, Ben Nghe Ward District 1, Ho Chi Minh City, Vietnam
Tel.: (84) 2838299725
Web Site: http://www.hitachi.com.vn
Automotive Electronic Component Mfr
N.A.I.C.S.: 336320

Hitachi Asia Ltd. (1)
7 Tampines Grande 08-01 Hitachi Square, Singapore, 528736, Singapore
Tel.: (65) 6 535 2100
Web Site: https://www.hitachi.com.sg
Emp.: 500
Holding Company; Regional Managing Office
N.A.I.C.S.: 551112
Kojin Nakakita *(Chm)*

Subsidiary (Domestic):

Hitachi Aqua-Tech Engineering Pte. Ltd. (2)
40 Changi South Street 1, Singapore, 486764, Singapore
Tel.: (65) 67461688
Web Site: https://www.hitachi-aqt.com
Sales Range: $100-124.9 Million
Emp.: 243
Waste Water Treatment Services
N.A.I.C.S.: 221310

Hitachi Home Electronics Asia (S) Pte. Ltd. (2)
438A Alexandra Road 01-01/02/03, Alexandra Technopark, Singapore, 119967, Singapore **(100%)**
Tel.: (65) 65362520
Web Site: http://www.hitachiconsumer.com.sg
Sales Range: $25-49.9 Million
Emp.: 50
Mfr of Television Sets, Stereo Systems, Cassette Tape Recorders, Compact Disc Players
N.A.I.C.S.: 334310

Hitachi International Treasury Ltd. (2)
7 Tampines Grande 04-04 Hitachi Square, Singapore, 528736, Singapore
Tel.: (65) 62602100
Web Site: http://www.hitachi.com.sg
Emp.: 18
Financial Treasury Operating Services
N.A.I.C.S.: 921130

Hitachi Australia Pty Ltd. (1)
Suite 801 Level 8 123 Epping Road, North

AND PRIVATE COMPANIES

HITACHI, LTD.

Ryde, Sydney, 2113, NSW, Australia
Tel.: (61) 298884100
Web Site: https://www.hitachi.com.au
Emp.: 40
Electronic Components Distr
N.A.I.C.S.: 423690

Hitachi Automotive Systems Chonburi Ltd. (1)
700/357 Moo 6 Tumbol Don Hua Roh, Amphur Muang Chonburi, Chon Buri, 20000, Thailand
Tel.: (66) 3821438994
Web Site: http://www.hitachi-automotive-tc.co.th
Automotive Parts Mfr & Distr
N.A.I.C.S.: 336320

Hitachi Automotive Systems Espelkamp GmbH (1)
Eugen-Gerstenmaier-Str 8, 32339, Espelkamp, Germany
Tel.: (49) 5772567890
Web Site: http://www.hueco.com
Automotive Parts Mfr & Distr
N.A.I.C.S.: 336320
Christian Westerkamp *(Mng Dir)*

Hitachi Automotive Systems Korat, Ltd. (1)
398 Moo 6, Nongraweng District Amphur Muang Nakornratchasima, Nakhon Ratchasima, 30000, Thailand
Tel.: (66) 44212050
Automobile Parts Mfr
N.A.I.C.S.: 336320

Hitachi Automotive Systems Pune (India) Pvt. Ltd. (1)
Survey No 19 Kondhwa Road, Yewalewadi, Pune, 411 048, India
Tel.: (91) 2030455100
Automotive Electronic Component Mfr
N.A.I.C.S.: 336320

Hitachi Brasil Ltda. (1)
Av Paulista 854-11o andar, 01310-913, Sao Paulo, Brazil
Tel.: (55) 11 3284 0922
Web Site: http://www.hitachi.com.br
Sales Range: $25-49.9 Million
Emp.: 22
Electronic Component Mfr & Distr
N.A.I.C.S.: 334419

Subsidiary (Domestic):

Hitachi Kokusai Linear Equipamentos Eletronicos S/A (2)
Avenida Frederico de Paula Cunha 1001 Maristela, Santa Rita do Sapucai, 37540-000, Minas Gerais, Brazil
Tel.: (55) 3534733473
Electronic Component Mfr & Distr
N.A.I.C.S.: 334419

Hitachi Building Systems Business Support Co., Ltd. (1)
1-13-5 Hulic Kudan Building 5th Floor, Kudankita Chiyoda-ku, Tokyo, 102-0073, Japan
Tel.: (81) 362612371
Web Site: http://www.hbs.co.jp
Facility Management Services
N.A.I.C.S.: 561210

Hitachi Building Systems Co., Ltd. (1)
7 Kandamitoshirocho Sumitomofudosankanda Bldg, Chiyoda-Ku, Tokyo, 101-0053, Japan
Tel.: (81) 3 3295 1211
Elevators & Escalator Installation Services & Distr
N.A.I.C.S.: 423830

Hitachi Building Systems Engineering Co., Ltd. (1)
3-27-6 Nihonbashihama-cho Hirata Building, Chuo-ku, Tokyo, 103-0007, Japan
Tel.: (81) 356233251
Web Site: http://www.hitachi-buildingsystems-eng.co.jp
Elevator Installation Services
N.A.I.C.S.: 238290

Hitachi Cable (Johor) Sdn. Bhd. (1)
Plot 40 Kawasan Perindustrian, 81400, Senai, Johor, Malaysia
Tel.: (60) 759943501

Automotive Electronic Component Mfr
N.A.I.C.S.: 336320

Hitachi Cable Philippines Inc. (1)
LIMA Technology Center SEZ, Lipa, 4217, Philippines
Tel.: (63) 439810700
Construction Machinery Product Mfr
N.A.I.C.S.: 332991

Hitachi Canada (1)
5450 Explorer Drive Suite 501, Mississauga, L4W 5N1, ON, Canada
Tel.: (905) 629-9300
Web Site: https://www.hitachi.ca
Electronic Materials, Semiconductors & Automotive Devices Mfr
N.A.I.C.S.: 423690
Howard Shearer *(CEO)*

Division (Domestic):

Hitachi Canada Ltd. - Calgary Power and Industry Division
Suite 460 10655 Southport Road S W, Calgary, T2W 4Y1, AB, Canada
Tel.: (403) 278-1881
Web Site: http://www.psca.mhps.com
Sales Range: $25-49.9 Million
Power Generation System Mfr
N.A.I.C.S.: 335311

Subsidiary (Domestic):

Hitachi ID Systems Holding, Inc (2)
1401 1 St Se Suite 500, Calgary, T2G 2J3, AB, Canada
Tel.: (403) 233-0740
Investment Management Service
N.A.I.C.S.: 523999

Hitachi Computer Products (Europe) S.A.S. (1)
Parc De Limere, 45166, Olivet, France
Tel.: (33) 2 38 69 86 00
Web Site: http://www.hitachi-computerproducts.fr
Sales Range: $50-74.9 Million
Emp.: 180
Computer Storage Device Mfr & Distr
N.A.I.C.S.: 334112

Hitachi Construction Machinery (China) Co., Ltd. (1)
No 98 Gengyun Road, Economic and Technological Development Zone, Hefei, 230601, Anhui, China
Tel.: (86) 55163811065
Construction Machinery Mfr
N.A.I.C.S.: 333120

Hitachi Construction Machinery (Shanghai) Co., Ltd. (1)
65 Taigu Road, Waigaoqiao Free Trade Zone Pudong New Area, Shanghai, 200131, China
Tel.: (86) 2158668686
Web Site: http://www.hitachicm.com.cn
Construction Machinery Mfr
N.A.I.C.S.: 333120

Hitachi Construction Machinery (UK) Limited (1)
Monkton Business Park North, Hebburn, NE31 2JZ, Tyne & Wear, United Kingdom
Tel.: (44) 1914308400
Web Site: http://www.hitachicm.co.uk
Construction Machinery Distr
N.A.I.C.S.: 423810
David Roberts *(CEO)*

Hitachi Construction Machinery Africa Pty. Ltd. (1)
Cnr Paul Smit and Solomon Jefferson Mahlangu Road Boksburg North, Johannesburg, Gauteng, South Africa
Tel.: (27) 118417700
Web Site: http://www.hitachicm.co.za
Construction Machinery Distr
N.A.I.C.S.: 423810
Satoshi Konno *(Pres)*

Hitachi Construction Machinery Co., Ltd. (1)
16-1 Higashiueno 2-chome, Taito-ku, Tokyo, 110-0015, Japan **(50.22%)**
Tel.: (81) 358268100
Web Site: https://hitachicm.com
Rev.: $9,293,184,080
Assets: $12,129,383,050

Liabilities: $6,746,113,120
Net Worth: $5,383,269,930
Earnings: $616,673,340
Emp.: 26,230
Fiscal Year-end: 03/31/2024
Construction Machinery Mfr
N.A.I.C.S.: 333120
Yasushi Ochiai *(CMO, Chief Sls Officer, Exec Officer & Exec VP)*

Subsidiary (Non-US):

Bradken Ltd. (2)
20 McIntosh Drive, Mayfield, 2304, NSW, Australia **(100%)**
Tel.: (61) 249268200
Web Site: http://bradken.com
Ferrous Casting Mfr; Provides Specialist Engineering & Machining Services to the Railway, Mining, Sugar, Petrochemical & Metals Processing Industries
N.A.I.C.S.: 541330
Brad Ward *(Exec Gen Mgr-Mobile Plant)*

Subsidiary (Domestic):

Bradken Holdings Pty Limited (3)
20 Mcintosh Dr, Mayfield West, Mayfield, 2304, NSW, Australia
Tel.: (61) 249412600
Web Site: http://www.bradken.com
Mining Equipment Distr
N.A.I.C.S.: 423810

Bradken Resources Wundowie Foundry Pty. Ltd. (3)
52 Hawke Avenue, PO Box 127, Wundowie, Perth, 6560, WA, Australia
Tel.: (61) 795739282
Web Site: http://www.bradken.com.au
General Iron & Industrial Castings & Wear Resistant Blocks Mfr
N.A.I.C.S.: 331529

Subsidiary (Non-US):

Bradken UK Limited (3)
Belmont House Station Way, Crawley, RH10 1JA, W Sussex, United Kingdom
Tel.: (44) 1142841000
Web Site: http://www.bradken.com
Industrial Machinery Mfr
N.A.I.C.S.: 541330

Subsidiary (US):

Bradken, Inc. (3)
3021 S Wilkeson St, Tacoma, WA 98409-7857
Tel.: (253) 475-4600
Web Site: http://www.bradken.com
Steel Forging Services
N.A.I.C.S.: 332111
Bennett Fors Jr. *(VP-Ops)*

Bradken, Inc. (3)
12200 N Ambassador Dr Ste 647, Kansas City, MO 64163-1244
Tel.: (816) 270-0701
Web Site: http://www.bradken.com
Industrial Machinery Mfr
N.A.I.C.S.: 333248

Bradken, Inc. (3)
400 S 4th St, Atchison, KS 66002
Tel.: (913) 367-2121
Web Site: http://www.bradken.com
Steel, Iron & Non-Ferrous Castings & Forgings
N.A.I.C.S.: 331513

Subsidiary (Domestic):

Bradken-Engineered Products (4)
13040 Foulks Ln, Amite, LA 70422-5738
Tel.: (985) 748-5342
Web Site: http://www.bradken.com
Mfr of Steel Castings
N.A.I.C.S.: 331513

Subsidiary (Non-US):

Bradken-London Ltd. (4)
3040 Osler Street, London, N5V 1V3, ON, Canada
Tel.: (519) 455-5420
Web Site: http://www.bradken.com
Industrial Machine Shop
N.A.I.C.S.: 333310

Subsidiary (Domestic):

Cast Metal Services Pty Limited (3)
275 Toombul Road, Northgate, 4013, QLD, Australia
Tel.: (61) 733264800
Web Site: http://www.castmetal.com.au
Metal Products Mfr
N.A.I.C.S.: 332999
Glenn Pearcy *(Founder)*

Subsidiary (Non-US):

CablePrice (NZ) Ltd. (2)
Wellington Mail Centre 41-51 Bell Road South, PO Box 38 040, Gracefield, 5010, Lower Hutt, Wellington, New Zealand
Tel.: (64) 45684289
Web Site: http://www.cableprice.co.nz
Industrial Machinery & Commercial Vehicle Whslr
N.A.I.C.S.: 423110

Joint Venture (US):

Deere-Hitachi Construction Machinery Corporation (2)
1000 Deere Hitachi Rd, Kernersville, NC 27284
Tel.: (336) 996-8100
Web Site: http://www.deerehitachi.com
Sales Range: $125-149.9 Million
Emp.: 315
Mfr of Hydraulic Excavators & Track Log Loaders; Owned 50% by Hitachi Construction Machinery Co., Ltd. & 50% by Deere & Company
N.A.I.C.S.: 333120

Subsidiary (US):

H-E Parts International LLC (2)
1117 Perimeter Ctr W, Atlanta, GA 30338
Tel.: (678) 443-2142
Web Site: http://www.h-epartsinternational.com
Transportation Equipment & Supplies Merchant Whslr
N.A.I.C.S.: 423860
Steven R. McBrayer *(Pres)*

Subsidiary (Non-US):

HM Plant Ltd. (2)
Monkton Business Park North, Hebburn, NE31 2JZ, Tyne and Wear, United Kingdom
Tel.: (44) 191 430 8400
Web Site: http://www.hmplant.ltd.uk
Sales Range: $25-49.9 Million
Emp.: 80
Escalator Distr
N.A.I.C.S.: 423830

Hitachi Construction Machinery (Europe) N.V. (2)
Sicilieweg 5, 1045 AT, Amsterdam, Netherlands
Tel.: (31) 20 447 6700
Web Site: https://www.hitachicm.eu
Emp.: 500
Construction Machinery Mfr & Distr
N.A.I.C.S.: 333120
Makoto Yamazawa *(Chm-Mgmt Bd & Pres)*

Hitachi Construction Machinery (M) Sdn Bhd (2)
Lot 7 SS13/2 Subang Jaya Industrial Estate, Subang Jaya, 47500, Selangor, Malaysia
Tel.: (60) 3 5568 6000
Construction Machinery Mfr
N.A.I.C.S.: 333120

Hitachi Construction Machinery (Thailand) Co., Ltd. (2)
1858/79 1858/81-82 Interlink Building 17th Floor Debaratna Road, Bangna Tai, Bangkok, 10260, Thailand
Tel.: (66) 23251011
Web Site: http://www.hitachicm.co.th
Sales Range: $25-49.9 Million
Emp.: 251
Distr of Excavators, Wheel Loaders, Backhoe Loaders, Bulldozers, Motor Graders, Vibratory Rollers
N.A.I.C.S.: 333120

Hitachi Construction Machinery Asia and Pacific Pte Ltd. (2)

HITACHI, LTD.

Hitachi, Ltd.—(Continued)

2 Pioneer Walk, Singapore, 627856, Singapore
Tel.: (65) 6265 2377
Sales Range: $25-49.9 Million
Emp.: 100
Construction Machinery Mfr
N.A.I.C.S.: 333120
Simon Poh (Chm)

Hitachi Construction Machinery Australia Pty. Ltd. (2)
3/1 Foundation Pl, Pemulwuy, Sydney, 2145, NSW, Australia
Tel.: (61) 28 863 4800
Web Site: https://www.hitachicm.com.au
Sales Range: $200-249.9 Million
Emp.: 120
Construction & Mining Machinery Distr
N.A.I.C.S.: 423810
David Harvey (Mng Dir)

Hitachi Construction Machinery Eurasia Sales LLC
Bolshoy Savvinsky Lane 12 building 16, 119435, Moscow, Russia
Tel.: (7) 4957037180
Web Site: http://www.hitachicm.ru
Construction Machinery Repair & Maintenance Services & Whslr
N.A.I.C.S.: 423810

Subsidiary (US):

Hitachi Construction Machinery Holding U.S.A Corporation. (2)
1000 Deere Hitachi Rd, Kernersville, NC 27285
Tel.: (336) 992-5740
Investment Management Service
N.A.I.C.S.: 523999

Subsidiary (Non-US):

Hitachi Construction Machinery Middle East Corporation FZE (2)
R/A 12 Street No 12403, PO Box 61052, Jebel Ali Free Zone, Dubai, United Arab Emirates
Tel.: (971) 4 883 3352
Web Site: https://www.hitachicm.ae
Sales Range: $25-49.9 Million
Emp.: 28
Construction & Mining Machinery Distr
N.A.I.C.S.: 423810
Piet Hein Van Bakergem (Gen Mgr)

Hitachi Construction Machinery Mozambique Limited (2)
Av Eduardo Mondlane No 279, C P 205, Tete, Mozambique
Tel.: (258) 843008087
Web Site: http://www.hitachicm.co.za
Construction Machinery Whslr
N.A.I.C.S.: 423830

Hitachi Construction Machinery N.V. (2)
Unit 2 IO Centre Cabot Park Moorend Farm Avenue, Avonmouth, Bristol, BS11 0QL, United Kingdom
Tel.: (44) 788 4113643
Web Site: http://www.hcme.com
Emp.: 2
Construction Machinery Distr
N.A.I.C.S.: 423810
David Roberts (CEO)

Hitachi Construction Machinery Sales and Service France S.A.S. (2)
47-49 Avenue Eduardo Valliant, 92100, Boulogne-Billancourt, France
Tel.: (33) 1 46 20 94 20
Sales Range: $25-49.9 Million
Emp.: 15
Construction Machinery Repair & Maintenance Services
N.A.I.C.S.: 811310

Hitachi Construction Machinery Southern Africa Co., Ltd. (2)
Corner Paul Smit Street & Atlas Road, Boksburg, 1459, Gauteng, South Africa
Tel.: (27) 11 841 7700
Sales Range: $125-149.9 Million
Emp.: 350
Construction & Mining Equipment Distr
N.A.I.C.S.: 423810

Allen Brinkley (Dir)

Hitachi Construction Truck Manufacturing, Ltd. (2)
200 Woodlawn Road West, Guelph, N1H 1B6, ON, Canada
Tel.: (519) 823-2000
Web Site: http://www.hitachigmc.com
Sales Range: $75-99.9 Million
Emp.: 30
Trucks Mfr
N.A.I.C.S.: 336120
Hideo Kitawaki (CEO)

PT. Hitachi Construction Machinery Indonesia (2)
Jl Raya Cibitung KM 48 8 Cibitung, Bekasi, 17520, West Java, Indonesia (82%)
Tel.: (62) 21 890 0515
Web Site: https://www.hitachi-cmid.com
Emp.: 1,006
Excavator Mfr
N.A.I.C.S.: 333120
Fumio Nakajima (Chm)

SCAI S.p.A (2)
Via Don Fulvio Scialba 21, Ospedalicchio, Bastia Umbra, Perugia, Italy
Tel.: (39) 075 801501
Emp.: 150
Construction Machinery Mfr & Distr
N.A.I.C.S.: 333120
Ernesto Scesaee (Mng Dir)

TCM France S.A.S. (2)
35 Rue Roger Salengro, Genas, 69740, France
Tel.: (33) 4 72 23 28 81
Construction Machinery Mfr & Distr
N.A.I.C.S.: 333120

Yungtay-Hitachi Construction Machinery Co., Ltd. (2)
No 11-3 Lane17 Section3 Nansan Road Luchu Hsiang, Taoyuan, Taiwan
Tel.: (886) 33240088
Web Site: https://www.hitachicm.tw
Emp.: 47
Construction Machinery Distr
N.A.I.C.S.: 423810

Hitachi Construction Machinery Japan Co., Ltd. (1)
5-33-25 Benten, Soka, 340-0004, Saitama, Japan
Tel.: (81) 489319306
Web Site: http://japan.hitachi-kenki.co.jp
Construction Machinery Leasing Services
N.A.I.C.S.: 532412

Hitachi Construction Machinery Loaders America Inc. (1)
60 Amljack Blvd, Newnan, GA 30265
Tel.: (404) 760-2500
Web Site: http://www.hitachicm.us
Construction Machinery Mfr
N.A.I.C.S.: 333120

Hitachi Construction Machinery Zambia Co., Ltd. (1)
Plot2350/M Kenneth Kaunda International Airport Road, PO Box 30182, Lusaka, Zambia
Tel.: (260) 211285360
Construction Machinery Mfr & Distr
N.A.I.C.S.: 333120

Hitachi Consulting Asia Pacific Pte. Ltd. (1)
7 Tampines Grande 02-04 Hitachi Square, Singapore, 528736, Singapore
Tel.: (65) 65352100
IT Services
N.A.I.C.S.: 541511

Hitachi Consulting Australia Pty. Ltd. (1)
Tower B Level 6 26 Talavera Road, Macquarie Park, 2113, NSW, Australia
Tel.: (61) 283795000
IT Services
N.A.I.C.S.: 541511

Hitachi Consumer Electronics Co., Ltd. (1)
Shin-Otemachi Bldg 2-1 Otemachi 2-chome, Chiyoda-ku, Tokyo, 100-0004, Japan
Tel.: (81) 3 4232 5000
Web Site: http://www.hitachi-ce.co.jp

Sales Range: $200-249.9 Million
Emp.: 700
Electronic Equipment Mfr & Distr
N.A.I.C.S.: 334419
Shutoku Watanabe (Pres)

Plant (Domestic):

Hitachi Consumer Electronics Co., Ltd. - Yokohama Works (2)
292 Yoshida-cho, Totsuka-ku, Yokohama, 244-0817, Japan
Tel.: (81) 45 866 6152
Household Electronic Appliance Mfr
N.A.I.C.S.: 335220
Watanabe Shutoku (Pres)

Subsidiary (Non-US):

Hitachi Consumer Products (Thailand), Ltd. (2)
610/1 Moo 9 Tambol Nongki, Amphur Kabinburi, Prachin Buri, 25110, Thailand
Tel.: (66) 3 728 4000
Web Site: http://www.hitachi.co.th
Household Appliances Mfr & Distr
N.A.I.C.S.: 335220
Sirukki Sata (Mng Dir)

Hitachi Consumer Marketing (China) Ltd. (1)
23rd Floor Century Center 50 Minzu Road, Siming District, Xiamen, China
Tel.: (86) 5923326688
Web Site: http://www.hitachi-cm.cn
Household Appliances Mfr
N.A.I.C.S.: 335220

Hitachi Critical Facilities Protection Pte. Ltd. (1)
31 Loyang Crescent, Singapore, 509013, Singapore
Tel.: (65) 62141830
Web Site: http://www.hitachi-cfp.com
Engineering Services
N.A.I.C.S.: 541330

Hitachi Digital Host Sdn. Bhd. (1)
Level 2-03 Block B Axis Business Park No 10 Jalan Bersatu 13/4, 46200, Petaling Jaya, Selangor, Malaysia
Tel.: (60) 379569822
Software Consulting Services
N.A.I.C.S.: 541512

Hitachi Digital Media Group Russia (1)
Millenium House 12 Trubnaya Street, Moscow, 103045, Russia
Tel.: (7) 957874023
Web Site: http://www.hitachidigitalmedia.com
Electronic Components Distr
N.A.I.C.S.: 423690

Hitachi Digital Payment Solutions Limited (1)
Level 2 240 Highlevel Road, Colombo, 00600, Sri Lanka
Tel.: (94) 115145415
Web Site: http://www.hitachi-dps.com
Electronic Payment Processing Services
N.A.I.C.S.: 522320

Hitachi Digital Payment Solutions Philippines, Inc. (1)
31D Rufino Pacific Tower V A Rufino Street, Ayala Ave Corner, Makati, 6784, Philippines
Tel.: (63) 28009230
Electronic Payment Processing Services
N.A.I.C.S.: 522320

Hitachi Digital Products China Co., Ltd. (1)
No 98 Dongshan Road, Gushan Town, Fuzhou, 350014, China
Tel.: (86) 59187489089
Electronic Parts Distr
N.A.I.C.S.: 423690

Hitachi Document Printing Co., Ltd. (1)
East 21 Tower 6-3-2 Toyo, Koto-ku, Tokyo, 135-0016, Japan
Tel.: (81) 366668615
Web Site: http://www.hitachi-document.co.jp
Commercial Printing Services
N.A.I.C.S.: 323111

INTERNATIONAL PUBLIC

Hitachi Drives & Automation GmbH (1)
Am Seestern 18, Dusseldorf, 40547, Germany
Tel.: (49) 211 730 621 60
Electronic Products Mfr
N.A.I.C.S.: 334419

Hitachi East Asia Ltd. (1)
8/F Building 20E Phase 3 Hong Kong Science Park, Pak Shek Kok, Hong Kong, New Territories, China (Hong Kong)
Tel.: (852) 27359218
IT Services
N.A.I.C.S.: 541511

Hitachi Electronic Devices (Wujiang) Co., Ltd. (1)
No 1289 Jiangxin East Road Economic Development Zone, Wujiang, 215200, Jiangsu, China
Tel.: (86) 51263439820
Electronic Components Mfr
N.A.I.C.S.: 334419

Hitachi Electronic Products (M) Sdn Bhd (1)
No 12 Jalan Kemajuan, 43650, Bandar Baru Bangi, Selangor, Malaysia
Tel,: (60) 389259230
Web Site: https://www.hepm.hitachi.com.my
Sales Range: $400-449.9 Million
Emp.: 1,513
Optical Data Storage Drive Mfr
N.A.I.C.S.: 334112

Hitachi Elevator (Cambodia) Co., Ltd. (1)
713B Veng Sreng Phum Tropang Thloeung Sangkat Chom Chao, Khan Posenchey, 12405, Phnom Penh, Cambodia
Tel.: (855) 23231229
Web Site: http://www.hitachi-elevator.com.kh
Elevator Mfr & Distr
N.A.I.C.S.: 333921
Sakchai Worrasangasilpa (Mng Dir)

Hitachi Elevator (Chengdu) Co., Ltd. (1)
No 666 Kangsheng Road, High-tech Zone West District, Chengdu, China
Tel.: (86) 2865013333
Elevator Mfr & Distr
N.A.I.C.S.: 333921

Hitachi Elevator (China) Co., Ltd. (1)
62nd Floor Office Building CITIC Plaza 233 Tianhe North Road, Guangzhou, 510613, China
Tel.: (86) 2038700662
Web Site: https://www.hitachi-helc.com
Elevator & Escalator Distr
N.A.I.C.S.: 423830

Subsidiary (Domestic):

Hainan Hitachi Elevator Service Co., Ltd.
3/F Jingmao Building No 15 Huahai Road, Longhua District, Haikou, 570102, China
Tel.: (86) 89866708161
Elevator Repair & Maintenance Services
N.A.I.C.S.: 811310

Subsidiary (Non-US):

Hitachi Elevator Asia Pte. Ltd. (2)
10 Toh Guan Road East, Hitachi Elevator Building, Singapore, 608597, Singapore
Tel.: (65) 6416 1711
Web Site: http://www.hea.hitachi.com.sg
Elevator & Escalator Mfr & Engineering Services
N.A.I.C.S.: 333921

Hitachi Elevator Engineering Company (Hong Kong) Limited (2)
10/F New East Ocean Centre 9 Science Museum Road, Tsimshatsui East, Kowloon, China (Hong Kong)
Tel.: (852) 23117611
Web Site: https://www.hitachi-elev.com.hk
Elevator & Escalator Installation Services
N.A.I.C.S.: 238390

Subsidiary (Domestic):

Hitachi Elevator Motor (Guangzhou) Co., Ltd (2)
No 636-6 Guomao Av S Shilou Town Pa-

nyu, Guangzhou, 511447, Guangdong, China
Tel.: (86) 20 3877 0662
Elevator Mfr
N.A.I.C.S.: 333921

Subsidiary (Non-US):

Hitachi Elevator Philippines Corporation (2)
42 Montreal St, Cubao, Quezon City, 1109, Philippines
Tel.: (63) 2 911 0855
Sales Range: $25-49.9 Million
Emp.: 10
Elevator & Escalator Installation Services
N.A.I.C.S.: 238290

Hitachi Elevator (Guangzhou) Escalator Co., Ltd. (1)
No 1 Kelin Road, Science City Guangzhou High-tech Industrial Development Zone, Guangzhou, 510660, China
Tel.: (86) 2032397999
Elevator Mfr & Distr
N.A.I.C.S.: 333921

Hitachi Elevator Engineering (Malaysia) Sdn. Bhd. (1)
Level 25 Plaza Pengkalan 3rd Mile Jalan Sultan Azlan Shah Jalan Ipo, 51100, Kuala Lumpur, Malaysia
Tel.: (60) 340432166
Web Site: http://www.hitachi-elevator.com.my
Elevator Mfr & Distr
N.A.I.C.S.: 333921
Takayuki Unno (Mng Dir)

Hitachi Elevator Saudi Arabia Limited (1)
8990 King Fahd Unit No 7, Jeddah, 23442-3185, Saudi Arabia
Tel.: (966) 126394047
Web Site: http://www.hitachi-elevator.com.sa
Elevator Mfr & Distr
N.A.I.C.S.: 333921
Hiroshi Nasu (Mng Dir)

Hitachi Elevator Vietnam Co., Ltd. (1)
12 Floor Lim III Tower Building 29A Nguyen Dinh Chieu Street, Da Kao Ward District 1, Ho Chi Minh City, Vietnam
Tel.: (84) 2838244924
Web Site: http://www.hitachi-elevators.com.vn
Elevator Installation Services
N.A.I.C.S.: 238290
Akihito Ando (Gen Dir)

Hitachi Engineering & Services Co., Ltd. (1)
3-2-2 Saiwai-cho, Hitachi, 317-0073, Ibaraki, Japan
Tel.: (81) 294 22 7111
Web Site: http://www.hitachi-hes.com
Engineering Electrical Equipment Mfr & Distr
N.A.I.C.S.: 335999

Hitachi Environmental Technology (Yixing) Co., Ltd. (1)
1st Block Mfg Zone Yuedong Rd Indus Park for Environ Sci & Tech, Yixing, 214205, Jiangsu, China
Tel.: (86) 51087073500
Web Site: http://www.hitachi-yhpt.com.cn
Sales Range: $25-49.9 Million
Emp.: 50
Water Treatment Equipment Mfr & Sales
N.A.I.C.S.: 423830

Hitachi Europe A.B. (GREECE) (1)
1 Delfon & 364 Kifissias Ave, Halandri, 15233, Greece
Tel.: (30) 2106837200
Web Site: http://www.hitachidigitalmedia.com
Sales Range: $25-49.9 Million
Emp.: 17
Household Appliances Mfr & Distr
N.A.I.C.S.: 335220
Apostolos Karydas (Gen Mgr)

Hitachi Europe GmbH (1)
Niederkasseler Lohweg 191, 40547, Dusseldorf, Germany
Tel.: (49) 211 5283 0
Web Site: http://www.hitachi-ds.com
Sales Range: $25-49.9 Million
Emp.: 8
Computer Printer Distr
N.A.I.C.S.: 423430

Division (Domestic):

Hitachi Europe GmbH - Digital Media Group (2)
Niederkasseler Lohweg 191, 40547, Dusseldorf, Germany
Tel.: (49) 21152830
Web Site: http://www.hitachidigitalmedia.com
Electric Appliances Mfr
N.A.I.C.S.: 334220

Hitachi Europe GmbH - European Procurement & Sourcing Group (2)
Am Seestern 18, Dusseldorf, 40547, Germany
Tel.: (49) 211 5283 712
Web Site: http://www.hitachi-eu.com
Sales Range: $25-49.9 Million
Procurement Services
N.A.I.C.S.: 561499

Hitachi Europe Ltd. (1)
Lower Cookham Road, Whitebrook Park, Maidenhead, SL6 8YA, Berkshire, United Kingdom
Tel.: (44) 1628 58 5000
Web Site: http://www.hitachi.eu
Emp.: 400
Holding Company; Regional Managing Office
N.A.I.C.S.: 551112

Division (Domestic):

Hitachi Europe Ltd. - Air Conditioning and Refrigeration Group Division (2)
Whitebrook Park Lower Cookham Road, Maidenhead, SL6 8YA, Berkshire, United Kingdom
Tel.: (44) 1628 58 5000
Air Conditioner & Refrigerator Mfr
N.A.I.C.S.: 333415

Hitachi Europe Ltd. - Digital Media Group Division (2)
Lower Cookham Road, Whitebrook Park, Maidenhead, SL6 8YA, Berkshire, United Kingdom
Tel.: (44) 1628585000
Web Site: http://www.hitachidigitalmedia.com
Electronic Components Mfr
N.A.I.C.S.: 334419

Hitachi Europe Ltd. - Information Systems Group Division (2)
Whitebrook Park Lower Cookham Road, Maidenhead, SL6 8YA, Berkshire, United Kingdom
Tel.: (44) 1628 58 5000
Emp.: 200
Information Technology Consulting Services
N.A.I.C.S.: 541512
Kazuo Abe (Mng Dir)

Hitachi Europe Ltd. - Power Device Division (2)
Lower Cookham Road, Whitebrook Park, Maidenhead, SL6 8YA, Berkshire, United Kingdom
Tel.: (44) 1628585151
Web Site: http://www.pdd.hitachi.eu
Emp.: 250
Semiconductor Mfr
N.A.I.C.S.: 334413

Subsidiary (Domestic):

Hitachi Rail Europe Ltd. (2)
7th Floor 40 Holborn Viaduct, London, EC1N 2PB, United Kingdom
Tel.: (44) 20 7970 2711
Web Site: http://www.hitachi-rail.com
Sales Range: $25-49.9 Million
Emp.: 50
Railway Equipment Mfr
N.A.I.C.S.: 336999
Nick Hughes (Dir-Sls)

Subsidiary (Non-US):

Hitachi Rail STS (3)
Via Paolo Mantovani 3-5, 16151, Genoa, Italy (100%)
Tel.: (39) 0106552111
Web Site: http://www.ansaldo-sts.com
Rev.: $1,630,247,931
Assets: $2,408,232,846
Liabilities: $1,535,001,291
Net Worth: $873,231,555
Earnings: $77,702,782
Emp.: 4,228
Fiscal Year-end: 12/31/2017
Railway & Mass Transit System Engineering Services
N.A.I.C.S.: 488210

Subsidiary (Non-US):

Ansaldo STS France SAS (4)
ZA de Courtaboeuf 1 4 avenue due Canada, BP 243, 91944, Les Ulis, Cedex, France
Tel.: (33) 1 69 29 65 65
Web Site: http://www.ansaldo-sts.com
Emp.: 817
Railway & Mass Transit System Engineering Services
N.A.I.C.S.: 488210
Gilles Pascault (Pres)

Subsidiary (Non-US):

Ansaldo STS Ireland (5)
Mona Valley Industrial Estate, Tralee, V92YT5F, Kerry, Ireland (100%)
Tel.: (353) 667124411
Sales Range: $25-49.9 Million
Emp.: 30
Railway Signaling & Automation Equipment Mfr
N.A.I.C.S.: 488210
Jimmy Laite (Mng Dir)

Ansaldo STS Sweden AB (5)
Solna Strandvag 80, PO Box 6066, Solna, Stockholm, 17106, Sweden
Tel.: (46) 86219500
Web Site: http://www.ansaldo-sts.com
Sales Range: $25-49.9 Million
Emp.: 50
Railway Signaling & Automation Equipment Mfr
N.A.I.C.S.: 488210
Jilles Pascault (Mng Dir)

Subsidiary (US):

Hitachi Rail STS USA (4)
1000 Technology Dr, Pittsburgh, PA 15219-3120
Tel.: (412) 688-2400
Sales Range: $150-199.9 Million
Emp.: 681
Railway Signaling & Automation Equipment Mfr
N.A.I.C.S.: 488210

Subsidiary (Domestic):

The Railway Engineering Company Limited (2)
Manvers House Kingston Road, Bradford-on-Avon, BA15 1AB, Wilts, United Kingdom
Tel.: (44) 1225 860 140
Web Site: http://www.trerail.co.uk
Railway Control Software & Systems Engineering & Technical Consulting Services
N.A.I.C.S.: 335314
Rob Butler (Mng Dir)

Hitachi Europe S.A. (1)
Gran Villa Carles III 86 Planta 5, Edificios Trade-Torre Estate, Barcelona, 08028, Spain
Tel.: (34) 93 409 25 50
Web Site: http://www.hitachi.com
Home Appliance Distr
N.A.I.C.S.: 423620

Hitachi Europe S.r.l. (1)
Via T Gulli 39, 20147, Milan, Italy
Tel.: (39) 02 487861
Air Conditioning Equipment Mfr
N.A.I.C.S.: 333415

Hitachi Financial Equipment System (Shenzhen) Co., Ltd. (1)
No 22 Haoye Road, Xinhe community Fuhai Sub-district Baoan District, Shenzhen, 518103, Guangdong, China
Tel.: (86) 75527661216
Web Site: http://www.hitachi-hfes.com.cn
Emp.: 715
Financial Terminal Equipment Mfr & Distr
N.A.I.C.S.: 334118

Hitachi Foods & Logistics Systems Inc. (1)
6-19-20 Nichirei Higashi Ginza Building Reception is on the 9th Floor, Tsukiji Chuo-ku, Tokyo, 104-0045, Japan
Tel.: (81) 335456264
Web Site: http://www.hitachi-fls.co.jp
Software Services
N.A.I.C.S.: 541511

Hitachi Global Air Power US, LLC (1)
1 Sullair Way, Michigan City, IN 46360
Tel.: (219) 879-5451
Web Site: https://america.sullair.com
Air & Gas Compressor Mfr
N.A.I.C.S.: 333912

Subsidiary (Domestic):

Mountain Air Compressor Inc. (2)
1508 W State St, Bristol, TN 37620-2040
Tel.: (423) 968-4024
Web Site: http://www.mountainaircompressors.com
Industrial Machinery & Equipment Merchant Whslr
N.A.I.C.S.: 423830
Tom White (Pres)

Subsidiary (Non-US):

Sullair Argentina S.A. (2)
Pedro de Lujan 2415, Buenos Aires, Argentina
Tel.: (54) 115 941 4444
Web Site: https://www.sullairargentina.com
Compressor Mfr
N.A.I.C.S.: 333912
Carlos Alberto Rembado (Mgr-Engrg & Works)

Sullair Australia Pty Ltd (2)
7 Bazalgette Cr, Dandenong, 3175, VIC, Australia
Tel.: (61) 1300 266 773
Web Site: http://www.sullair.com.au
Compressors Sales & Services
N.A.I.C.S.: 423830

Sullair Taiwan LLC (2)
3F 1 No 248 Chung Shan Rd Lin Kou District, Taipei, Taiwan
Tel.: (886) 226013500
Web Site: http://www.sullair.com
Compressor Mfr
N.A.I.C.S.: 333912
Thunder Lin (Reg Sls Mgr)

Hitachi Global Life Solutions, Inc. (1)
Hitachi Atago Bldg., 15-12, Nishi Shimbashi 2-chome, Minato-ku, Tokyo, Japan
Tel.: (81) 07035390750
Emp.: 11,300
Home Appliances Mfr
N.A.I.C.S.: 423620

Hitachi Hanbell(Shanghai) Precise Machinery Co., Ltd. (1)
Building No 9 No 8289 TingFeng Rd, Fengjing Area JinShan District, Shanghai, 201501, China
Tel.: (86) 2131756700
Industrial Equipment Mfr & Distr
N.A.I.C.S.: 333248

Hitachi Hi-Rel Power Electronics Pvt. Ltd. (1)
B-62 6th Floor Corporate House Nr Judges Bungalow, Bodakdev, Ahmedabad, 380054, Gujarat, India
Tel.: (91) 7966046200
Web Site: http://www.hitachi-hirel.com
UPS Mfr
N.A.I.C.S.: 335999

Hitachi Hi-System21 Co., Ltd. (1)
Yokohama Landmark Tower 30F 2-2-1, Minatomirai Nishi-ku, Yokohama, 220-8130, Kanagawa, Japan
Tel.: (81) 456502650
Web Site: http://www.hs21.co.jp
Electronic Components Mfr
N.A.I.C.S.: 334419

HITACHI, LTD.

Hitachi, Ltd.—(Continued)

Hitachi High-Tech (Shanghai) Co., Ltd. (1)
21F Hang Seng Bank Tower 1000 Lujiazui Ring Road, Pudong New Area, Shanghai, 200120, China
Tel.: (86) 2161631200
Web Site: http://www.hitachi-hightech.com
Semiconductor Devices Mfr
N.A.I.C.S.: 334413
Yamamoto Yosuke (Chm)

Hitachi High-Tech (Shenzhen) Co., Ltd. (1)
25/F Hangtian Building No 4019 Shennan Avenue, Futian District, Shenzhen, 518048, China
Tel.: (86) 75582029600
Electronic Material Distr
N.A.I.C.S.: 423460
Yamamoto Yosuke (Chm)

Hitachi High-Tech America, Inc. (1)
10 N Martingale Rd Ste 500, Schaumburg, IL 60173-2295
Tel.: (847) 273-4141
Web Site: http://www.hitachi-hightech.com
Semiconductor Equipment Distr
N.A.I.C.S.: 423690
Craig Kerkove (CEO)

Hitachi High-Tech Analytical Science America, Inc. (1)
2 Technology Park Dr 2nd Fl, Westford, MA 01886
Tel.: (978) 850-5580
Analysis Equipment Mfr & Distr
N.A.I.C.S.: 334516

Hitachi High-Tech Analytical Science Finland Oy (1)
Derby Business Park Tarvonsalmenkatu 17, PO Box 85, 02631, Espoo, Finland
Tel.: (358) 9329411
Analysis Equipment Mfr & Distr
N.A.I.C.S.: 334516

Hitachi High-Tech Analytical Science GmbH (1)
Wellesweg 31, 47589, Uedem, Germany
Tel.: (49) 282593830
Analysis Equipment Mfr & Distr
N.A.I.C.S.: 334516

Hitachi High-Tech Analytical Science Limited (1)
Windrush Court Abingdon Business Park, Abingdon, OX14 1SY, United Kingdom
Tel.: (44) 1235977000
Web Site: http://hha.hitachi-hightech.com
Analysis Equipment Mfr
N.A.I.C.S.: 334516

Hitachi High-Tech Analytical Science Shanghai Co., Ltd. (1)
Building 5 Shanghai Laigangxin Bay Technology Innovation Park, No 1601-1609 Lian Road Minhang District, Shanghai, China
Tel.: (86) 4006215191
Analysis Equipment Mfr & Distr
N.A.I.C.S.: 334516

Hitachi High-Tech Corporation (1)
Toranomon Hills Business Tower 1-17-1, Toranomon Minato-ku, Tokyo, 105-6409, Japan
Tel.: (81) 335047111
Web Site: http://www.hitachi-hightech.com
Emp.: 12,276
Semiconductor Devices Mfr
N.A.I.C.S.: 334413
Takashi Iizumi (Pres & CEO)

Subsidiary (US):

NABsys, Inc. (2)
60 Clifford St, Providence, RI 02903
Tel.: (401) 276-9100
Web Site: https://www.nabsys.com
Drugs & Druggists' Sundries Merchant Whslr
N.A.I.C.S.: 424210
Barrett Bready (CEO)

Hitachi High-Tech Diagnostics (Shanghai) Co., Ltd. (1)
21F HSBC Tower 1000 Lujiazui Ring Road, Pudong New Area, Shanghai, China
Tel.: (86) 2161631200

Semiconductor Devices Mfr
N.A.I.C.S.: 334413
Yamamoto Yosuke (Chm)

Hitachi High-Tech Fielding Corporation (1)
Toranomon Hills Business Tower 1-17-1, Toranomon Minato-ku, Tokyo, 105-6410, Japan
Tel.: (81) 353792311
Emp.: 921
Analysis Equipment Distr
N.A.I.C.S.: 423490
Koji Sano (Pres)

Hitachi High-Tech Fine Systems Corporation (1)
1600 Kami, Kamisato, Kodama, 369-0395, Saitama, Japan
Tel.: (81) 495322000
Analysis Equipment Mfr
N.A.I.C.S.: 334516
Joji Honda (Pres)

Hitachi High-Tech Hong Kong Limited (1)
8/F Building 20E Phase 3 Hong Kong Science Park, Pak Shek Kok, Hong Kong, New Territories, China (Hong Kong)
Tel.: (852) 27374700
Electronic Components Mfr
N.A.I.C.S.: 334419

Hitachi High-Tech India Private Limited (1)
209 2nd Floor Time Tower M G Road, Gurgaon, 122 002, Haryana, India
Tel.: (91) 1244217224
Web Site: https://www.hitachi-hightech.com
Emp.: 16
Analysis Equipment Mfr
N.A.I.C.S.: 334516

Hitachi High-Tech Ipc (Malaysia) Sdn. Bhd. (1)
Suite 7 1 Level7 Menara IMC No 8 Jalan Sultan Ismail, Letter Box No 15, 50250, Kuala Lumpur, Malaysia
Tel.: (60) 320788800
Web Site: http://www.hitachi-hightech.com
Analysis Equipment Mfr
N.A.I.C.S.: 334516
Kazunao Homma (Mng Dir)

Hitachi High-Tech Israel, Ltd. (1)
MS Hitachi LC2-3S, PO Box 1000, Kiryat Gat, 82109, Israel
Tel.: (972) 86666342
Analysis Equipment Mfr
N.A.I.C.S.: 334516

Hitachi High-Tech Kyushu Corporation (1)
1892-1 Tegama, Omuta, 836-0004, Fukuoka, Japan
Tel.: (81) 944568520
Web Site: http://www.hitachi-hightech.com
Emp.: 165
Analysis Equipment Mfr
N.A.I.C.S.: 334516

Hitachi High-Tech Manufacturing & Service Corporation (1)
1040 Ichige, Hitachinaka, 312-0033, Ibaraki, Japan
Tel.: (81) 292766340
Analysis Equipment Mfr
N.A.I.C.S.: 334516
Atsushi Takane (Pres)

Hitachi High-Tech Mexico, S.A. de C.V. (1)
Av Paseo de la Reforma No 483 Torre Reforma Piso 21, Col Cuauhtemoc, 06500, Mexico, Mexico
Tel.: (52) 5552805086
Automobile Parts Mfr
N.A.I.C.S.: 336320

Hitachi High-Tech Nexus Corporation (1)
Toranomon Hills Business Tower 1-17-1, Toranomon Minato-ku, Tokyo, 105-6413, Japan
Tel.: (81) 335045011
Petroleum Distr
N.A.I.C.S.: 424720
Hajime Oguma (Pres)

Hitachi High-Tech Rus Limited Liability Company (1)

9 Lesnaya street, 125196, Moscow, Russia
Tel.: (7) 4959339922
Web Site: http://www.hitachi-hightech.com
Analysis Equipment Mfr
N.A.I.C.S.: 334516

Hitachi High-Tech Science America, Inc. (1)
20770 W Nordhoff St Bldg 4, Chatsworth, CA 91311
Tel.: (818) 280-0745
Web Site: http://www.hitachi-hightech.com
Analysis Equipment Mfr
N.A.I.C.S.: 334516
Gregory Rigby (Pres)

Hitachi High-Tech Scientific Solutions (Beijing) Co., Ltd. (1)
Building 7 Tianchangyuan Hongjunying-nanlu, Chaoyang, Beijing, China
Tel.: (86) 1084931958
Analysis Equipment Distr
N.A.I.C.S.: 423490

Hitachi High-Tech Scientific Solutions Co., Ltd. (1)
2601 26/F Tower 1 Ever Gain Plaza 88 Container Port Road, Kwai Chung N T, Hong Kong, China (Hong Kong)
Tel.: (852) 38411200
Analysis Equipment Distr
N.A.I.C.S.: 423490

Hitachi High-Tech Steel Do Brasil Ltda. (1)
Av Celso Ramos 11466 - Area Industrial Sul, Tres Barras, Garuva, 89249-000, Santa Catarina, Brazil
Tel.: (55) 4730330400
Web Site: http://www.hitachi-hightech.com
Analysis Equipment Mfr
N.A.I.C.S.: 334516

Hitachi High-Tech Support Corporation (1)
Toranomon Hills Business Tower 1-17-1, Toranomon Minato-ku, Tokyo, 105-6408, Japan
Tel.: (81) 335047951
Analysis Equipment Mfr
N.A.I.C.S.: 334516
Tsutomu Ogane (Pres)

Hitachi High-Technologies Corporation (1)
24-14 Nishi-Shimbashi 1-chome, Minato-ku, Tokyo, 105-8717, Japan (100%)
Tel.: (81) 335047111
Web Site: http://www.hitachi-hightech.com
Rev.: $6,623,802,240
Assets: $6,037,529,640
Liabilities: $2,180,107,800
Net Worth: $3,857,421,840
Earnings: $441,865,260
Emp.: 11,482
Fiscal Year-end: 03/31/2019
Semiconductor Manufacturing Equipment, Analytical Instrumentation & Other Technological Equipment Mfr, Distr & Maintenance Services
N.A.I.C.S.: 333242
Toshiyuki Ikeda (CTO, Exec Officer-Export Control, Svc Bus & R&D & Sr VP)

Subsidiary (US):

Hitachi High Technologies America, Inc. (2)
10 N Martingale Rd Ste 500, Schaumburg, IL 60173-2295
Tel.: (847) 273-4141
Web Site: http://www.hitachi-hta.com
Sales Range: $25-49.9 Million
Emp.: 60
Semiconductor Manufacturing Equipment, Analytical Instrumentation & Other Technological Equipment Distr & Maintenance Services
N.A.I.C.S.: 423830

Branch (Domestic):

Hitachi High Technologies America, Inc. - Dallas (3)
1375 N 28th Ave, Dallas, TX 75261-2208
Tel.: (972) 615-9000
Web Site: http://www.hitachi-hta.com
Emp.: 250

Semiconductor Manufacturing Equipment, Analytical Instrumentation & Other Technological Equipment Distr & Maintenance Services
N.A.I.C.S.: 423830

Hitachi High Technologies America, Inc. - Pleasanton (3)
5960 Inglewood Dr Ste 200, Pleasanton, CA 94588-3355
Tel.: (925) 218-2800
Web Site: http://www.hitachi-hta.com
Sales Range: $25-49.9 Million
Emp.: 50
Semiconductor Manufacturing Equipment, Analytical Instrumentation & Other Technological Equipment Distr & Maintenance Services
N.A.I.C.S.: 423830
Masahiro Miyazaki (Pres & CEO)

Subsidiary (Non-US):

Hitachi High Technologies Europe GmbH (2)
Europark Fichtenhain A12, 47807, Krefeld, Germany (100%)
Tel.: (49) 215164350
Web Site: http://www.hht-eu.com
Sales Range: $25-49.9 Million
Emp.: 137
N.A.I.C.S.: 333611
Yasukuni Koga (Pres & Mng Dir)

Hitachi High Technologies do Brasil Ltda. (2)
Alameda Santos 415-13 Andar-Cj 132-Ed Maria Santos, Cerqueira Cesar, 1419-000, Sao Paulo, SP, Brazil
Tel.: (55) 11 3253 2511
Web Site: http://www.hitachi-hightech.com
Sales Range: $50-74.9 Million
Emp.: 6
Medical Equipment Distr
N.A.I.C.S.: 423450

Hitachi High-Technologies (S) Pte. Ltd. (2)
7 Tampaines Grande 05-01 Hitachi Square, Singapore, 528736, Singapore
Tel.: (65) 6733 2754
Web Site: http://www.hitachi-hightech.com
Emp.: 65
Electronic Components Mfr
N.A.I.C.S.: 334419
Kunihiko Ukena (Mng Dir)

Hitachi High-Technologies (Thailand) Ltd. (2)
7th Floor Thaniya Building 62 Silom Road, Bang Rak, Bangkok, 10500, Thailand
Tel.: (66) 2 237 4538
Sales Range: $25-49.9 Million
Emp.: 46
Electronic Components Distr
N.A.I.C.S.: 423690

Hitachi High-Technologies Canada Inc. (2)
89 Galaxy Blvd Suite 14, Toronto, M9W 6A4, ON, Canada (100%)
Tel.: (416) 675-5860
Web Site: http://www.hitachi-hightech.com
Sales Range: $25-49.9 Million
Emp.: 15
Semiconductor Manufacturing Equipment, Analytical Instrumentation & Other Technological Equipment Distr & Maintenance Services
N.A.I.C.S.: 423830

Hitachi High-Technologies Hong Kong Ltd. (2)
Rm 1623-23A Landmark North 39 Lung Sum Avenue, Sheung Shui, New Territories, China (Hong Kong)
Tel.: (852) 2737 4700
Sales Range: $25-49.9 Million
Emp.: 10
Electronic Components Distr
N.A.I.C.S.: 423690
Matsumoto Akihiko (Mng Dir)

Hitachi High-Technologies IPC (M) Sdn. Bhd. (2)
29th Floor UBN Tower 10 Jalan P Ramlee, Letter Box No 183, 50250, Kuala Lumpur, Malaysia
Tel.: (60) 3 2078 8800

AND PRIVATE COMPANIES

Sales Range: $25-49.9 Million
Emp.: 20
Industrial Machinery Mfr
N.A.I.C.S.: 333248
Tsutomu Taki *(Mng Dir)*

Hitachi High-Technologies Korea Co., Ltd. (2)
8F Young Poong Bldg 33 Seorin-Dong, Chong Ro-ku, Seoul, 110-752, Korea (South)
Tel.: (82) 2 754 7654
Sales Range: $25-49.9 Million
Emp.: 153
Semiconductor Devices Mfr
N.A.I.C.S.: 334413
Fujitani Takeshi *(Pres)*

Hitachi High-Technologies Taiwan Corporation (2)
Shin Kang Chung Shan Bldg 10F1 44 Sec Chung Shan N Rd, Taipei, 104, Taiwan
Tel.: (886) 225634750
Web Site: http://www.hitachi.com.tw
Emp.: 35
Electronic Component Mfr & Distr
N.A.I.C.S.: 334419

Hitachi Instrument (Dalian) Co., Ltd. (2)
No 15 Xinzhaizi East Street, Ganjinzi-trict, Dalian, Liaoning, China
Tel.: (86) 411 86317716
Analyzing Equipment Mfr
N.A.I.C.S.: 334513
Liu Guocheng *(Chm)*

PT. Hitachi High-Technologies Indonesia (2)
Unit No 315B 15th Floor Sentral Senayan III Jalan Asia Afrika No 8, Gelora Bung Karno - Senayan, Jakarta, 10270, Indonesia
Tel.: (62) 21 2903 9250
Electro Mechanical Equipment Mfr
N.A.I.C.S.: 333248

Hitachi Home Electronics Vietnam Co., Ltd. (1)
4A Floor Vincom Center 72 Le Thanh Ton Str, Dist 1, Ho Chi Minh City, Vietnam
Tel.: (84) 2838237977
Web Site: http://www.hitachi-homeappliances.com
Home Appliance Distr
N.A.I.C.S.: 423620

Hitachi Ibaraki Technical Service Ltd. (1)
1-1-1 Kokubu-cho, Hitachi, 316-0035, Ibaraki, Japan
Tel.: (81) 294385531
Web Site: http://www.hitachi-ibaraki-technicalservice.co.jp
Electrical Equipment Mfr & Distr
N.A.I.C.S.: 335999

Hitachi Ict Business Services, Ltd. (1)
Yokohama Mitsui Building 1-1-2, Takashima Nishi-ku, Yokohama, 220-0011, Kanagawa, Japan
Tel.: (81) 453071043
Web Site: http://www.hitachi-bs.co.jp
Software Services
N.A.I.C.S.: 541511

Hitachi India Pvt. Ltd. (1)
Tower B World Mark 1 Aerocity, New Delhi, 110037, India
Tel.: (91) 11 4060 5252
Web Site: http://www.hitachi.co.in
Sales Range: $25-49.9 Million
Emp.: 70
Home Appliances Mfr & Distr
N.A.I.C.S.: 335220

Subsidiary (Domestic):

Hitachi India Trading Pvt. Ltd. (2)
Units 304-306 3rd Floor ABW Elegance Tower, Jasola District Centre, New Delhi, 110 025, India
Tel.: (91) 11 4060 5252
Web Site: http://www.hitachi.co.in
Sales Range: $50-74.9 Million
Emp.: 70
Semiconductor Device Distr
N.A.I.C.S.: 423690

Hitachi Industrial Equipment (Malaysia) Sdn. Bhd. (1)
Lot 6498 Batu 5 3/4 Lorong Haji Abdul Manan, 42100, Klang, Selangor, Malaysia
Tel.: (60) 332902323
Web Site: http://www.hiem.hitachi.com.my
Industrial Equipment Distr
N.A.I.C.S.: 423830

Hitachi Industrial Equipment (Nanjing) Co., Ltd. (1)
219 Tongtian Road Science Park, Jiangning District, Nanjing, 211100, China
Tel.: (86) 2557929191
Web Site: http://www.hitachi-hinc.cn
Industrial Equipment Mfr & Distr
N.A.I.C.S.: 333248

Hitachi Industrial Equipment (Suzhou) Compressor Co., Ltd. (1)
No 1200 Dongnan Road, Changshu High-Tech Industrial Development Zone, Jiangsu, 215500, China
Tel.: (86) 51252312626
Air Compressor Mfr
N.A.I.C.S.: 333912

Hitachi Industrial Equipment Drive & Solutions Co., Ltd. (1)
3-15-11 Higashinarashino, Narashino, 275-0001, Chiba, Japan
Tel.: (81) 474775300
Web Site: http://www.hitachi-ies-ds.co.jp
Industrial Equipment Distr
N.A.I.C.S.: 423830

Hitachi Industrial Equipment Mexico, S.A. de C.V. (1)
Free Federal Highway Irapuato-Abasolo Km 13 232, El Venado Industrial Park Lot 3 Block 2 Ejido El Venado, 36847, Irapuato, Guanajuato, Mexico
Tel.: (52) 4626357250
Web Site: http://www.hitachi-hiemex.com
Industrial Equipment Mfr & Distr
N.A.I.C.S.: 333248

Hitachi Industrial Equipment Nakajo Engineering Co., Ltd. (1)
46-1 Tomioka, Tainai, 959-2608, Niigata, Japan
Tel.: (81) 254465561
Web Site: http://www.hitachi-ies-ne.co.jp
Industrial Equipment Mfr
N.A.I.C.S.: 333248

Hitachi Industrial Equipment Systems (China) Co., Ltd. (1)
Room 2201 Rui Jin Building 205 Maoming South Road, Huangpu District, Shanghai, 200020, China
Tel.: (86) 2154892378
Web Site: http://www.hitachi-iec.cn
Industrial Equipment Mfr
N.A.I.C.S.: 333248

Hitachi Industrial Equipment Systems (Hong Kong) Co., Ltd. (1)
8th Floor 20E East Science Avenue Phase 3 Hong Kong Science Park, Pak Shek Kok New Territories, Hong Kong, China (Hong Kong)
Tel.: (852) 27359218
Industrial Equipment Mfr
N.A.I.C.S.: 333248

Hitachi Industrial Equipment Systems Co., Ltd. (1)
AKS Bldg 3 Kanda Neribai-cho, Chiyoda-ku, Tokyo, 101-0022, Japan
Tel.: (81) 343456529
Web Site: http://www.hitachi-ies.co.jp
Sales Range: $900-999.9 Million
Emp.: 5,000
Industrial Component Mfr & Distr
N.A.I.C.S.: 333248
Masakazu Aoki *(Chm)*

Division (Domestic):

Hitachi Industrial Equipment Systems Co., Ltd. - Air Compressor System Division (2)
390 Muramatsu, Shimizu, Shizuoka, 424-0926, Japan
Tel.: (81) 54 335 4286
Air Compressor Mfr
N.A.I.C.S.: 333912

Hitachi Industrial Equipment Systems Co., Ltd. - Ebina Division (2)
1007 Kamigoo, Ebina, 243-0434, Kanagawa-ken, Japan
Tel.: (81) 46 232 4811
Air Compressor Mfr
N.A.I.C.S.: 333912

Hitachi Industrial Equipment Systems Co., Ltd. - Narashino Division (2)
1-1 Higashinarashino 7-chome, Narashino, 275-8611, Chiba, Japan
Tel.: (81) 47 477 1111
Industrial Motor & Pump Mfr
N.A.I.C.S.: 333996

Hitachi Industrial Equipment Systems Co., Ltd. - Sagami Division (2)
1116 Ozono, Ayase, 252-1121, Kanagawa-ken, Japan
Tel.: (81) 467700931
Web Site: http://www.hitachi-ies.co.jp
Air Compressor Mfr
N.A.I.C.S.: 333912

Hitachi Industrial Equipment Systems Co., Ltd. - Taga Division (2)
1-1 Higashitaga-cho 1-chome, Hitachi, 316-8502, Ibaraki-ken, Japan
Tel.: (81) 294 36 6111
Web Site: http://www.hitachi-ies.co.jp
Electronic Components Mfr
N.A.I.C.S.: 334419

Subsidiary (Non-US):

Hitachi Industrial Technology (Thailand), Ltd. (2)
610 Moo 9 Kabinburi-Korat Road KM 12, PO Box 48, Nongki Kabinburi, Prachin Buri, 25110, Thailand
Tel.: (66) 3 720 4276
Web Site: https://www.hitachi-hitt.com
Emp.: 700
Electric Motor Mfr
N.A.I.C.S.: 335312
Yukihide Yamada *(Pres)*

Subsidiary (Domestic):

Hitachi KE Systems, Ltd. (2)
7-1-1 Higashi Narashino, Narashino, 275-0001, Chiba, Japan
Tel.: (81) 47 477 3111
Web Site: https://www.hke.jp
Emp.: 450
System Integration Services
N.A.I.C.S.: 541512
Fujiwara Tatsuo *(Pres)*

Subsidiary (Non-US):

Hitachi Qiandian (Hangzhou) Transformer Co., Ltd. (2)
Xingang Village Kanshan Town, Xiaoshan District, Hangzhou, 311243, China
Tel.: (86) 571 8258 8899
Amorphous Transformer Mfr
N.A.I.C.S.: 335311

Unit (Domestic):

Yuji Sugai (2)
46-1 Tomioka, Tainai, 959-2608, Niigata-ken, Japan
Tel.: (81) 254 46 3111
Sales Range: $75-99.9 Million
Emp.: 50
Electric Equipment Mfr
N.A.I.C.S.: 335999
Yuji Sugai *(Chief Procurement Officer)*

Hitachi Industrial Equipment Technology Service, Co., Ltd. (1)
1-2-1 Kinrakuji-cho, Amagasaki, 660-0806, Hyogo, Japan
Tel.: (81) 648681263
Web Site: http://www.hitachi-ies-ts.co.jp
Industrial Equipment Mfr
N.A.I.C.S.: 333248

Hitachi Industrial Products, Ltd. (1)
Sumitomo Fudosan Akihabara First Building 1-5-1, Sotokanda Chiyoda-ku, Tokyo, 101-0021, Japan
Tel.: (81) 362717100
Web Site: http://www.hitachi-ip.com
Electrical Equipment Mfr & Distr
N.A.I.C.S.: 335999
Keizo Kobayashi *(Pres)*

Hitachi Industry & Control Solutions, Ltd. (1)
5-1-26 Omika-cho, Hitachi, 319-1221, Ibaraki, Japan
Tel.: (81) 294536115
Web Site: http://info.hitachi-ics.co.jp
Electrical Equipment Mfr & Distr
N.A.I.C.S.: 335999
Toru Kimura *(Pres)*

Hitachi Information & Control Solutions, Ltd. (1)
5-2-1 Omika-cho, Hitachi, 319-1293, Ibaraki, Japan
Tel.: (81) 294 53 1211
Web Site: http://www.hitachi-ics.co.jp
Sales Range: $700-749.9 Million
Emp.: 2,600
Security System Software Development Services
N.A.I.C.S.: 541511

Hitachi Information Control Systems Europe Ltd. (1)
Solstice House Middleton Drive, Bradford-on-Avon, BA15 1GB, Wiltshire, United Kingdom
Tel.: (44) 1225860140
Web Site: http://www.hitachi-infocon.com
Control System Product Mfr
N.A.I.C.S.: 335314
Tim Gray *(Mng Dir)*

Hitachi Information Engineering, Ltd. (1)
6-13 Hiroshima K Building 7th Floor, Hiroshima, Japan
Tel.: (81) 825412350
Web Site: http://www.hitachi-ife.co.jp
Software Services
N.A.I.C.S.: 541511

Hitachi Information Systems (Shanghai), Ltd (1)
Room 2401 Ruijin Mansion No 205 Maoming South Road, Luwan, Shanghai, 200020, China
Tel.: (86) 21 6473 1244
Information Technology Consulting Services
N.A.I.C.S.: 541512
Murasei Takeshi *(Gen Mgr)*

Hitachi Infrastructure Systems (Asia) Pte. Ltd. (1)
1 Fusionopolis Place 05-10 Galaxis, Singapore, 138522, Singapore
Tel.: (65) 62220665
Construction & Engineering Services
N.A.I.C.S.: 541330

Hitachi Insurance Agency (China) Limited (1)
Room 1808 Ruijin Building No 205 Maoming South Road, Shanghai, 200020, China
Tel.: (86) 2154488677
Web Site: http://www.hitachi-insurance.com.cn
Insurance Services
N.A.I.C.S.: 524210

Hitachi Insurance Services (Hong Kong) Ltd. (1)
8/F Building 20E Phase 3, Hong Kong Science Park Pak Shek Kok, Tai Po, New Territories, China (Hong Kong)
Tel.: (852) 27366611
Web Site: https://www.hitachi.com.hk
Sales Range: $50-74.9 Million
Emp.: 1
General Insurance Services
N.A.I.C.S.: 524210

Hitachi Insurance Services, Ltd. (1)
2-16-1 Ueno East Tower Higashiueno, Taito-ku, Tokyo, 110-0015, Japan
Tel.: (81) 362843456
Web Site: http://www.hitachi-hoken.co.jp
Insurance Services
N.A.I.C.S.: 524210

Hitachi International (Holland) B.V. (1)
Locatellikade 1, 1076 AZ, Amsterdam, Netherlands
Tel.: (31) 206789123
Electronic Components Distr
N.A.I.C.S.: 423690

Hitachi International Treasury (Malaysia) Sdn. Bhd. (1)

HITACHI, LTD.

Hitachi, Ltd.—(Continued)

Suite 17 3 Level 17 Menara IMC No 8 Jalan Sultan Ismail, Letter Box No 5, 50250, Kuala Lumpur, Malaysia
Tel.: (60) 327138751
Cost Management Services
N.A.I.C.S.: 522390

Hitachi Investment Management, Ltd. (1)
AKS Building 3 Kanda, Neribeicho Chiyoda-ku, Tokyo, 101-0022, Japan
Tel.: (81) 345545100
Web Site: http://www.hitachi-im.co.jp
Investment Management Service
N.A.I.C.S.: 523940

Hitachi Kashiwa Reysol Co., Ltd. (1)
1-2-50 Hitachidai, Kashiwa, Chiba, Japan
Tel.: (81) 471622201
Web Site: http://www.reysol.co.jp
Sports Club Services
N.A.I.C.S.: 711211
Takikawa Ryuichiro (Pres)

Hitachi Korea Ltd. (1)
45 Nandaemunro 4ga, Jung-gu, Seoul, 100-743, Korea (South)
Tel.: (82) 2 734 0026
Industrial Machinery Distr
N.A.I.C.S.: 423830

Hitachi Life, Ltd. (1)
1-20-2 Saiwaicho, Hitachi, 317-0073, Ibaraki, Japan
Tel.: (81) 294251269
Web Site: http://www.hitachi-life.co.jp
Sales Range: $200-249.9 Million
Emp.: 662
Real Estate Manangement Services
N.A.I.C.S.: 531390
Kako Shigeru (Pres)

Hitachi Lift India Pvt. Ltd. (1)
Tower-B World Mark 1 Aerocity, New Delhi, 110 037, India
Tel.: (91) 1140605290
Web Site: https://www.hitachi-lift.co.in
Sales Range: $25-49.9 Million
Emp.: 40
Elevator & Escalator Mfr & Distr
N.A.I.C.S.: 333921

Hitachi Management Partner, Corp. (1)
2-29 Kanda Awajicho, Chiyoda-ku, Tokyo, 101-0063, Japan
Tel.: (81) 345412300
Web Site: http://www.hitachi-mp.co.jp
Payroll Management Services
N.A.I.C.S.: 541214

Hitachi Media Electronics Co., Ltd. (1)
Suite 807 Tower 1 Gateway 25 Canton Road, Tsimshatsui, Kowloon, China (Hong Kong)
Tel.: (852) 2111 3992
Picture & Information Device Mfr & Distr
N.A.I.C.S.: 334419

Hitachi Medical (Guangzhou) Co., Ltd. (1)
Unit 812-816 Metro Plaza No 183 Tianhe North Rd, Guangzhou, 510613, China
Tel.: (86) 20 87550788
Medical Equipment Mfr & Distr
N.A.I.C.S.: 334510

Hitachi Medical Systems (S) Pte. Ltd. (1)
7 Tampines Grande Hitachi Square 04-01, Singapore, 528736, Singapore
Tel.: (65) 6602 0110
Web Site: http://www.hitachi-medical.com.sg
Medical Equipment Distr
N.A.I.C.S.: 423450

Hitachi Medical Systems Europe Holding AG (1)
Sumpfstrasse 13, 6312, Steinhausen, Switzerland
Tel.: (41) 41 748 63 33
Web Site: http://www.hitachi-medical-systems.eu
Emp.: 15
Holding Company; Regional Managing Office; Medical Device Mfr & Distr
N.A.I.C.S.: 551112

Masayoshi Takidera (Chm & CEO)

Subsidiary (Non-US):

Hitachi Medical Systems B.V. (2)
Edisonstraat 1a, 2811 EM, Reeuwijk, Netherlands
Tel.: (31) 182 39 77 77
Web Site: http://www.hitachi-medical-systems.nl
Medical Device Distr
N.A.I.C.S.: 423450

Hitachi Medical Systems GmbH (2)
IZ NO-Sud Strasse 2a property M39/II, 2351, Wiener Neudorf, Austria
Tel.: (43) 2236677750
Web Site: http://www.hitachi-medical-systems.de
Medical Device Distr
N.A.I.C.S.: 423450

Hitachi Medical Systems GmbH (2)
Otto-von-Guericke-Ring 3, 65205, Wiesbaden, Germany
Tel.: (49) 6122 7036 0
Web Site: http://www.hitachi-medical-systems.de
Medical Device Distr
N.A.I.C.S.: 423450

Hitachi Medical Systems Kft. (2)
Damjanich u 11-15 Ligetvaros Irodahaz I em 102, 1071, Budapest, Hungary
Tel.: (36) 1 478 0090
Web Site: http://www.hitachi-medical-systems.hu
Sales Range: $50-74.9 Million
Emp.: 6
Medical Device Distr
N.A.I.C.S.: 423450

Hitachi Medical Systems N.V. (2)
Mechelen Noord II Wayenborgstraat 8, 2800, Mechelen, Belgium
Tel.: (32) 15 20 22 55
Web Site: http://www.hitachi-medical-systems.be
Sales Range: $50-74.9 Million
Emp.: 7
Diagnostic Imaging Equipment Distr
N.A.I.C.S.: 423450

Hitachi Medical Systems S.A.S. (2)
39 Avenue Urbain le Verrier, BP 356, 91959, Saint Priest, France
Tel.: (33) 1 69 86 12 34
Medical Equipment Distr
N.A.I.C.S.: 423450

Hitachi Medical Systems S.L. (2)
Edif Alfa III - Local 144 C/Isabel Colbrand 10-12, 28050, Madrid, Spain
Tel.: (34) 91 358 93 50
Sales Range: $25-49.9 Million
Emp.: 29
Medical Device Whslr
N.A.I.C.S.: 423450

Hitachi Medical Systems UK Ltd. (2)
1 Davy Close, Park Farm Industrial Estate, Wellingborough, NN8 6XX, Northamptonshire, United Kingdom
Tel.: (44) 844 800 4294
Web Site: http://www.hitachi-medical-systems.co.uk
Medical Equipment Mfr & Whslr
N.A.I.C.S.: 334510
Stephen Brookes (Mng Dir)

Hitachi Metals (Thailand) Ltd. (1)
1/60 Moo 5 Rojana Industrial Park Tambol Khanharm, Amphur Uthai, Ayutthaya, 13210, Thailand
Tel.: (66) 35330588
Metal Product Mfr & Distr
N.A.I.C.S.: 332999

Hitachi Metals Advanced Machining, Ltd. (1)
13 Kinugaoka, Moka, 321-4367, Tochigi, Japan
Tel.: (81) 285841181
Metal Product Mfr & Distr
N.A.I.C.S.: 332999

Hitachi Metals Korea Co., Ltd. (1)
333 3rd Avenue Jeongwangbon Siheung 3rd Ba 1010, Siheung, 15115, Gyeonggi-do, Korea (South)
Tel.: (82) 313193933

Web Site: http://www.hmk.hitachi-metals.com
Metal Product Mfr & Distr
N.A.I.C.S.: 332999

Hitachi Metals Precision Instruments (Shenzhen) Ltd. (1)
508 Room Bld 2 Sangda Science and Technology Park No 11 Keji Road, Nanshan District, Shenzhen, 518057, Guangdong, China
Tel.: (86) 75586006828
Metal Product Mfr & Distr
N.A.I.C.S.: 332999

Hitachi Metals San Huan Magnetic Materials (Nantong) Co., Ltd. (1)
No 1 Zhongtai Road, Binhai Industrial Park, Qidong, 226236, Jiangsu, China
Tel.: (86) 51380952288
Metal Product Mfr & Distr
N.A.I.C.S.: 332999

Hitachi Metals Taiwan, Ltd. (1)
No 7 & 7-1 WuCyuan 8Th Road, Wugu District, New Taipei City, 24891, Taiwan
Tel.: (886) 222993555
Metal Product Mfr & Distr
N.A.I.C.S.: 332999

Hitachi Metals Trading, Ltd. (1)
Shinagawa Season Terrace Building 2-70 Konan 1-chome, Minato-ku, Tokyo, 108-0075, Japan
Tel.: (81) 367744001
Web Site: http://www.tr.hitachi-metals.com
Emp.: 462
Steel Mfrs
N.A.I.C.S.: 331110
Masaki Mukai (Pres & CEO)

Hitachi Mexico, S.A. de C.V. (1)
Torre Forum Andres Bello 10 Piso 10 Desp 1001-B, Col Chapultepec Polanco, 11560, Mexico, DF, Mexico
Tel.: (52) 55 5282 9040
Web Site: http://www.hitachi-rail.com
Electronic Parts Distr
N.A.I.C.S.: 423690

Hitachi Nico Transmission Co. Ltd. (1)
405-3 Yoshinocho 1-chome, Kita-ku, Saitama, 331-0811, Japan
Tel.: (81) 486526969
Web Site: https://www.hitachi-nico.jp
Emp.: 540
Power Transmission Equipments Mfr & Whslr
N.A.I.C.S.: 423610

Hitachi Operation & Maintenance Egypt S.A.E. (1)
14th Fl Cairo Ctr Bldg 2 Abdul Kader Hamza St Garden City, Cairo, 11111, Egypt
Tel.: (20) 227954864
Sales Range: $25-49.9 Million
Emp.: 5
Air Conditioning System Maintenance Services
N.A.I.C.S.: 811412
Akira Koda (Pres)

Hitachi Payment Services Private Limited (1)
Level - 2 Silicon Towers 23/1-B Velachery Tambaram Main Road, Pallikaranai, Chennai, 600 100, India
Tel.: (91) 4461567600
Web Site: http://www.hitachi-payments.com
Payment Solutions Services
N.A.I.C.S.: 522320
Rustom Irani (CEO & Mng Dir)

Hitachi Plant Construction, Ltd. (1)
World Import Mart Building 1-3 Higashi-Ikebukuro 3-Chome, Toshima-ku, Tokyo, 170-8630, Japan
Tel.: (81) 339881791
Web Site: https://www.hitachi-plant-construction.com
Emp.: 1,517
Power & Industrial Plants Equipment Installation & Construction Services
N.A.I.C.S.: 811310
Yasunori Inada (Pres)

Hitachi Plant Engineering & Construction (Suzhou) Co., Ltd. (1)
10F Jiacheng Building 128 Zhongxin Avenue West, Suzhou Industrial Park, Suzhou, 215021, Jiangsu, China
Tel.: (86) 51262882700
Web Site: http://www.hitachiplant.com.cn
Nuclear Power Plant Construction Services
N.A.I.C.S.: 237130

Hitachi Plant Mechanics Co., Ltd. (1)
794 Higashitoyoi, Kudamatsu, 744-0002, Yamaguchi, Japan
Tel.: (81) 833413080
Web Site: http://www.hitachi-hpm.co.jp
Sales Range: $75-99.9 Million
Emp.: 600
Appliances Recycling & Warehouse Management Services
N.A.I.C.S.: 493190

Hitachi Plant Services Co., Ltd. (1)
Sunshine 60 34F 3-1-1 Higashiikebukuro, Toshima-ku, Tokyo, 170-6034, Japan
Tel.: (81) 363863001
Web Site: http://www.hitachi-hps.co.jp
Home Appliance Mfr & Distr
N.A.I.C.S.: 335220
Kunihiko Okano (Pres)

Hitachi Plant Technologies (Vietnam) Co., Ltd. (1)
10th Floor Richy Building Group 44, Yen Hoa Ward Cau Giay District, Hanoi, Vietnam
Tel.: (84) 2435537100
Semiconductor Component Mfr & Distr
N.A.I.C.S.: 334413

Hitachi Plant Technologies Ltd - CSR Promotion Division (1)
Rise Arena Bldg 5-2 Higashi-Ikebukuro 4-chome, Toshima-ku, Tokyo, 170-8466, Japan
Tel.: (81) 359288064
Sales Range: $350-399.9 Million
Emp.: 2,000
Water Treatment Construction Services
N.A.I.C.S.: 237110

Hitachi Plant Technologies, Ltd. (1)
4th Floor Al Fahim Center 10th & 17th Intersection, PO Box 52392, Al Musaffah Industrial Area, Abu Dhabi, United Arab Emirates
Tel.: (971) 25550856
Emp.: 6
Air Conditioning Equipment Distr
N.A.I.C.S.: 423730
Antonio Mexia (Gen Mgr)

Hitachi Power Solutions Co., Ltd. (1)
3-2-2 Saiwai-cho, Hitachi, 317-0073, Ibaraki, Japan (100%)
Tel.: (81) 29 422 7111
Web Site: https://www.hitachi-power-solutions.com
Emp.: 3,087
Power Plant Piping, Small-Size Steam Turbines Design, Manufacturing & Sales
N.A.I.C.S.: 333611
Kenichiro Nomura (Pres & CEO)

Subsidiary (Non-US):

Horizon Nuclear Power Limited (2)
5210 Valiant Court Gloucester Business Park, Delta Way, Gloucester, GL3 4FE, United Kingdom
Tel.: (44) 845 300 6816
Web Site: http://www.horizonnuclearpower.com
Sales Range: $100-124.9 Million
Emp.: 14
Nuclear Electric Power Generation Services
N.A.I.C.S.: 221113
Alan Raymant (COO)

Hitachi Pump Manufacture (Wuxi) Co., Ltd. (1)
No 116 Hongda Road, Jiguang Electric Industrial Park Hongshan Town New District, Wuxi, China
Tel.: (86) 51080257000
Web Site: http://www.hitachi-pump.com.cn
Pumps Mfr
N.A.I.C.S.: 333914

Hitachi Rail Italy S.p.A (1)
Via Argine 425, 80147, Naples, Italy
Tel.: (39) 081 243 1111
Web Site: http://italy.hitachirail.com
Railway Maintenance Services
N.A.I.C.S.: 488210

AND PRIVATE COMPANIES — HITACHI, LTD.

Maurizio Manfellotto *(Pres & CEO)*

Subsidiary (Non-US):

Hitachi Rail Espana, S.L.U. (2)
San Bernardo 123-5, Madrid, 28015, Spain
Tel.: (34) 917432388
Web Site: http://www.hitachirail.com
Railway Maintenance Services
N.A.I.C.S.: 488210

Hitachi Rail STS Australia Pty Ltd (1)
11 Viola Place, Eagle Farm, Brisbane, 4009, QLD, Australia
Tel.: (61) 738689333
Railroad Rolling Stock Mfr
N.A.I.C.S.: 336510

Hitachi Rail STS Malaysia Sdn. Bhd. (1)
Level 10 Plaza Pengkalan 3rd Mile Jalan Sultan Azlan Shah Jalan Ipoh, 51200, Kuala Lumpur, Malaysia
Tel.: (60) 341458000
Signaling System Mfr
N.A.I.C.S.: 334290

Hitachi Real Estate Partners, Ltd. (1)
3-7-1 Kowa Ichibashi Building, Kanda Nishikicho Chiyoda-ku, Tokyo, 101-0054, Japan
Tel.: (81) 332958981
Web Site: http://www.hitachi-rep.co.jp
Real Estate Services
N.A.I.C.S.: 531210

Hitachi SC, Ltd. (1)
2-16-1 Shinagawa East One Tower, Konan Minato-ku, Tokyo, 108-8205, Japan
Tel.: (81) 357963500
Web Site: http://www.hitachi-sc.co.jp
IT Services
N.A.I.C.S.: 541511

Hitachi Sales (Macau) Ltd. (1)
Av Venceslau de Morais Ed Ind Fu Tai 4-Andar E, Macau, China (Macau)
Tel.: (853) 28719261
Home Appliance Sales & Maintenance Services
N.A.I.C.S.: 423620

Hitachi Sales (Thailand), Ltd. (1)
333 333/1-8 Moo 13 Bangna-Trad Road km7 Bangkaew, Bangplee, Samut Prakan, 10540, Thailand
Tel.: (66) 2335 5455
Web Site: http://www.hitachi-th.com
Sales Range: $50-74.9 Million
Emp.: 100
Electric Household Appliances Distr
N.A.I.C.S.: 423620
Masanori Iwanaga *(Mng Dir)*

Hitachi Sistemas Medicos do Brasil Ltda. (1)
Rua dos Tres Irmaos 201-Vila Progredior, Sao Paulo, 05615-190, Brazil
Tel.: (55) 11 3722 2322
Web Site: http://www.hitachimedica.com.br
Sales Range: $25-49.9 Million
Emp.: 9
Medical Device Distr
N.A.I.C.S.: 423450

Hitachi Soe Electric & Machinery Co., Ltd. (1)
Building No 1 Aung Chan Thar Housing Estate East Shwegondine Rd, Bahan Tsp, Yangon, Myanmar
Tel.: (95) 1546100
Web Site: http://www.hitachi-soeelectric.com
Emp.: 613
Electrical Transformer Mfr & Distr
N.A.I.C.S.: 335311
U. Kyaw Min Htun *(Chm)*

Hitachi Solutions (Thailand) Ltd. (1)
Unit 1-3 15th Floor Silom Complex Building 191 Silom Road, Bangkok, 10500, Thailand
Tel.: (66) 2231 3300
Software Development Services
N.A.I.C.S.: 541511

Hitachi Solutions Asia Pacific Pte. Ltd. (1)
Tower B Level 6 26 Talavera Rd, Macquarie Park, 2113, NSW, Australia
Tel.: (61) 290524944
Software Development Services
N.A.I.C.S.: 541511

Hitachi Solutions Create, Ltd. (1)
4-12-6 Higashi-Shinagawa Shinagawa Seaside Canal Tower, Shinagawa-ku, Tokyo, 140-0002, Japan
Tel.: (81) 357806111
Web Site: http://www.hitachi-solutions-create.co.jp
Software Development Services
N.A.I.C.S.: 541511

Hitachi Solutions East Japan, Ltd. (1)
MetLife Sendai Honcho Bldg 2-16-10 Honcho, Aoba-ku, Sendai, 980-0014, Miyagi Prefecture, Japan
Tel.: (81) 222662181
Web Site: http://www.hitachi-solutions-east.co.jp
Software Development Services
N.A.I.C.S.: 541511
Youichirou Kodama *(Pres & CEO)*

Hitachi Solutions Germany GmbH (1)
Tullnaustrasse 20, 90402, Nuremberg, Germany
Tel.: (49) 911277880
Web Site: http://www.hitachi-solutions.de
Software Development Services
N.A.I.C.S.: 541511

Hitachi Solutions India Private Limited (1)
DLF IT Park 10th Flr Block-5 1/124 Shivaji Garden Nandampakkam Post, Mt Poonamalle Road Manapakkam, Chennai, 600 089, India
Tel.: (91) 4466038383
Software Development Services
N.A.I.C.S.: 541511

Hitachi Solutions Philippines Corporation (1)
12th Floor Marajo Tower 26th St West Cor 4th Ave, Bonifacio Global City, Taguig, 1634, Metro Manila, Philippines
Tel.: (63) 288231672
Software Development Services
N.A.I.C.S.: 541511

Hitachi Solutions Technology, Ltd. (1)
7-1 Midoricho 4th Floor Arbus Tachikawa Takamatsu Station Building, Tachikawa, 190-0014, Tokyo, Japan
Tel.: (81) 425120888
Web Site: http://www.hitachi-solutions-tech.co.jp
Software Development Services
N.A.I.C.S.: 541511

Hitachi Solutions West Japan, Ltd. (1)
3-33 Hatchobori Hiroshima Business Tower 19F, Naka-ku, Hiroshima, 730-0013, Japan
Tel.: (81) 825118011
Web Site: http://www.hitachi-solutions-west.co.jp
Software Development Services
N.A.I.C.S.: 541511

Hitachi Solutions, Ltd. (1)
4-12-7 Higashishinagawa, Shinagawa-ku, Tokyo, 140-0002, Japan (100%)
Tel.: (81) 357802111
Web Site: http://www.hitachi-solutions.co.jp
Sales Range: $1-4.9 Billion
Emp.: 12,610
Information Technology Services & Software Developer
N.A.I.C.S.: 541511
Shigeki Ishihara *(Exec Officer)*

Subsidiary (Non-US):

Hitachi Solutions (China) Co., Ltd. (2)
Room 1701-1708 1719-1721 Beijing Development Building, 5 East Third Ring North Road Chaoyang District, Beijing, 100027, China
Tel.: (86) 1064678383
Web Site: https://www.hitachi-solutions.cn
Emp.: 100
Information Technology Consulting Services
N.A.I.C.S.: 541512

Subsidiary (US):

Hitachi Solutions America, Ltd. (2)
100 Spectrum Center Dr Ste 350, Irvine, CA 92618
Tel.: (650) 615-7600
Web Site: http://us.hitachi-solutions.com
IT Services
N.A.I.C.S.: 541512
Tom Galambos *(Pres & COO)*

Subsidiary (Domestic):

Capax Global, LLC (3)
410 N Michigan Ave, Chicago, IL 60611
Tel.: (973) 401-0660
Web Site: http://www.capaxglobal.com
Sales Range: $25-49.9 Million
Emp.: 1,500
Software Application Development Services
N.A.I.C.S.: 541511
Jerry Hawk *(Founder & CEO)*

Branch (Domestic):

Hitachi Solutions America - Business Solutions Group (3)
25 E Court St Ste 401, Greenville, SC 29601
Tel.: (864) 250-2170
Web Site: http://www.customereffective.com
Sales Range: $10-24.9 Million
Emp.: 40
Customer Interaction Solutions
N.A.I.C.S.: 513210
Scott Millwood *(Sr VP-Worldwide CRM)*

Subsidiary (Non-US):

Hitachi Solutions Europe A.G. (2)
Neues Kranzler Eck Kurfurstendamm 22, 10719, Berlin, Germany
Tel.: (49) 30 8877 2600
Sales Range: $25-49.9 Million
Emp.: 6
Information Technology Consulting Services
N.A.I.C.S.: 541512

Hitachi Solutions Europe Ltd. (2)
11th Floor Tower 42 25 Old Broad Street, London, EC2N 1HQ, United Kingdom
Tel.: (44) 2031985136
Web Site: http://www.hitachisolutions-eu.com
Emp.: 5
Information Technology Consulting Services
N.A.I.C.S.: 541512

Hitachi Solutions Europe S.A.S (2)
7eme Etage 64 rue du Dessous des Berges, 75013, Paris, France
Tel.: (33) 1 53 82 76 00
Sales Range: $25-49.9 Million
Emp.: 6
Information Technology Consulting Services
N.A.I.C.S.: 541512

Hitachi South America, Argentina S.A. (1)
Arenales 1618 6th Floor, Buenos Aires, C1061AAT, Argentina
Tel.: (54) 115811 1561
Web Site: http://www.hitachi.com.ar
Electronic Systems Equipment Mfr
N.A.I.C.S.: 334419
Kazuhiro Ikebe *(Pres)*

Hitachi Storage Battery (Thailand) Co., Ltd. (1)
260 Moo 7 Gateway City Industrial Estate Tambol Huasamrong, Amphur PlangYao, Chachoengsao, 24190, Thailand
Tel.: (66) 38 575 123
Web Site: http://www.hitachi-sbt.co.th
Automotive Lead Acid Battery Mfr & Distr
N.A.I.C.S.: 335910
Hiroki Tsuji *(Pres)*

Hitachi Sunway Data Centre Services Sdn. Bhd. (1)
Level 11 The Pinnacle Persiaran Lagoon, 47500, Bandar Sunway, Selangor, Malaysia
Tel.: (60) 356399911
Software Development Services
N.A.I.C.S.: 541511

Hitachi Sunway Information Systems (Singapore) Pte. Ltd. (1)
140 Paya Lebar Rd 06-02 AZ, Paya Lebar, 409015, Singapore
Tel.: (65) 91053811
Web Site: http://www.hitachisunway-solutions.sg
Software Development Services
N.A.I.C.S.: 541511

Hitachi Sunway Information Systems (Thailand), Ltd. (1)
252/21 Unit E 17th Floor Muang Thai-Phatra Office Tower A, Rachadaphisek Road Huaykwang Subdistrict, Bangkok, 10310, Thailand
Tel.: (66) 822290278
Web Site: http://www.hitachisunway-thailand.co.th
Software Development Services
N.A.I.C.S.: 541511

Hitachi Sunway Information Systems Sdn. Bhd. (1)
Level 11 The Pinnacle Persiaran Lagoon, 47500, Bandar Sunway, Selangor, Malaysia
Tel.: (60) 356399911
Web Site: http://www.hitachi-sunway-is.com
Emp.: 300
Software Development Services
N.A.I.C.S.: 541511
Naofumi Ito *(Chm)*

Hitachi Systems Digital Services (Malaysia) Sdn. Bhd. (1)
Unit 9 2 Level 9 Block A Dataran PHB Saujana Resort Seksyen U2, 40150, Shah Alam, Selangor, Malaysia
Tel.: (60) 358702593
Software Development Services
N.A.I.C.S.: 541511

Hitachi Systems Digital Services (Singapore) Pte. Ltd. (1)
150 Kampong Ampat 05-02 KA Centre, Singapore, 368324, Singapore
Tel.: (65) 68441678
Software Development Services
N.A.I.C.S.: 541511

Hitachi Systems Engineering Services, Ltd. (1)
Yokohama Landmark Tower 32nd Floor 2-2-1, Minatomirai Nishi-ku, Yokohama, 220-8132, Japan
Tel.: (81) 452284141
Web Site: http://www.hitachi-systems-es.co.jp
Software Development Services
N.A.I.C.S.: 541511

Hitachi Systems Field Services, Ltd. (1)
3-5-25 Etchujima I K & T Watanabe Building, Koto-ku, Tokyo, 135-0044, Japan
Tel.: (81) 356212920
Web Site: http://www.hitachi-systems-fs.co.jp
Software Development Services
N.A.I.C.S.: 541511

Hitachi Systems Micro Clinic Pvt. Ltd. (1)
E-44/2 Okhla Industrial Area Ph-II, New Delhi, 110 020, India
Tel.: (91) 1149250700
Web Site: http://www.hitachi-systems-mc.com
Software Development Services
N.A.I.C.S.: 541511
Anuj Gupta *(CEO)*

Hitachi Systems Power Servicies, Ltd. (1)
Seavans Building S 1-2-3, Shibaura Minato-ku, Tokyo, 105-0023, Japan
Tel.: (81) 367571111
Web Site: http://www.hitachi-systems-ps.co.jp
Software Development Services
N.A.I.C.S.: 541511

Hitachi Systems Security Europe SA (1)
Technopole 5, 3960, Sierre, Switzerland
Tel.: (41) 274550022
Cyber Security Services
N.A.I.C.S.: 541519

Hitachi Systems Security Inc. (1)
955 Michele-Bohec Boulevard Suite 244, Blainville, J7C 5J6, QC, Canada
Tel.: (450) 430-8166

HITACHI, LTD.

Hitachi, Ltd.—(Continued)

Web Site: http://www.hitachi-systems-security.com
Cyber Security Services
N.A.I.C.S.: 541519
Akira Kusakabe *(Pres & CEO)*

Hitachi Systems Vietnam Company Limited (1)
Unit 1504 15th Floor IDMC Tower 15 Pham Hung Street, My Dinh 2 Ward Nam Tu Liem District, Hanoi, Vietnam
Tel.: (84) 2439714009
Web Site: http://www.hitachisunway-solutions.vn
Software Services
N.A.I.C.S.: 541511

Hitachi Systems, Ltd. (1)
1-2-1 Osaki, Shinagawa-ku, Tokyo, 141-8672, Japan
Tel.: (81) 35 435 7777
Web Site: https://www.hitachi-systems.com
Emp.: 18,599
Information Technology Services
N.A.I.C.S.: 541513
Kiyoshi Kozuka *(Exec Officer & Exec VP)*

Hitachi T&D Solutions, Inc. (1)
7250 McGinnis Ferry Rd, Suwanee, GA 30024
Tel.: (770) 495-1755
Web Site: http://www.hitachi-tds.com
Electrical Equipment Distr
N.A.I.C.S.: 423610

Hitachi T&D Systems Asia Pte. Ltd. (1)
7 Tampines Grande 03-02 Hitachi Square, Singapore, 528736, Singapore
Tel.: (65) 62201788
Electric Equipment Mfr
N.A.I.C.S.: 335313

Hitachi T&D Systems Saudi Arabia, Ltd. (1)
PO Box 13080, Jeddah, 21493, Saudi Arabia
Tel.: (966) 122637677
Electrical Transformer Mfr & Distr
N.A.I.C.S.: 335311

Hitachi Technologies and Services Ltd. (1)
603 Kandatsucho, Tsuchiura, 300-0013, Ibaraki, Japan
Tel.: (81) 298314158
Web Site: https://www.hitachi-ts.co.jp
Emp.: 474
Air Conditioning System Mfr
N.A.I.C.S.: 333415

Hitachi Terminal Mechatronics, Corp. (1)
1 Ikegami Haruoka-cho, Owariasahi, 488-8501, Aichi, Japan
Tel.: (81) 561 53 6133
Electronic Components Mfr
N.A.I.C.S.: 334419
Teiji Suzuki *(Gen Mgr)*

Hitachi Terminal Solutions (Thailand) Company Limited (1)
18th Floor Ramaland Bldg No 952 Rama IV Road, Bangrak Suriyawongse, Bangkok, 10500, Thailand
Tel.: (66) 20182255
ATM Machine Distr
N.A.I.C.S.: 423420

Hitachi Terminal Solutions India Private Limited (1)
450 Sompura Industrial Area 2nd Stage, Lakshmanpura Village Thyagondlu Hobli Nelamangala, Bengaluru, 562123, India
Tel.: (91) 8067332929
ATM Machine Mfr
N.A.I.C.S.: 334118

Hitachi Terminal Solutions Korea Co., Ltd. (1)
7-6 4-gil Samsung 1-ro, Hwaseong, 18449, Gyeonggi-do, Korea (South)
Tel.: (82) 312118761
Web Site: http://www.hitachi-tsol.co.kr
ATM Machine Mfr & Distr
N.A.I.C.S.: 334118

Hitachi Urban Investment, Ltd. (1)
1-14 Uchikanda 1-Chome, Hitachi Kamakurabashi Building Chiyoda-ku, Tokyo, 101-0047, Japan
Tel.: (81) 33 295 8981
Web Site: http://www.hitachi-urban.co.jp
Real Estate Manangement Services
N.A.I.C.S.: 531390
Tsukasa Hashiguchi *(Pres & CEO)*

Hitachi Urban Support, Ltd. (1)
3-7-1 Kandanishikicho Kowa Ichibashi, Chiyoda-ku, Tokyo, 101-0054, Japan
Tel.: (81) 368803700
Web Site: http://www.hitachi-urban-spt.co.jp
Real Estate Services
N.A.I.C.S.: 531210

Hitachi Vantara (Chile) Limitada (1)
Titanium Building Av Isidora Goyenechea 2800 29th Floor of 2902, Las Condes, Santiago, Chile
Tel.: (56) 23530000
Software Development Services
N.A.I.C.S.: 541511

Hitachi Vantara (China) Co., Ltd. (1)
15th Floor West 2nd Office Building Oriental Economic and Trade City, Oriental Plaza No 1 East Chang'an Street Dongcheng District, Beijing, China
Tel.: (86) 1085003188
Web Site: http://www.hitachivantara.com
Software Development Services
N.A.I.C.S.: 541511

Hitachi Vantara (Ireland) Limited (1)
The Wythe Building 5th Floor 48-50 Cuffe Street, Dublin, D02 CX48, Ireland
Tel.: (353) 873802754
Software Development Services
N.A.I.C.S.: 541511

Hitachi Vantara (Polska) Sp. z o.o. (1)
ul Zlota 59 Skylight 6th Floor, 00-120, Warsaw, Poland
Tel.: (48) 224868510
Software Development Services
N.A.I.C.S.: 541511

Hitachi Vantara A/S (1)
Vedbaek Strandvej 350, 2950, Vedbaek, Denmark
Tel.: (45) 45581000
Software Development Services
N.A.I.C.S.: 541511

Hitachi Vantara A/S (1)
Strandvelen 50 Lysaker, 1366, Oslo, Norway
Tel.: (47) 67518440
Software Development Services
N.A.I.C.S.: 541511

Hitachi Vantara Digital Solutions Japan, K.K. (1)
Hitachi Omori 2nd Bldg 3F Hitachi SSV 6 Chrome 27-18 Minami Of, Shinagawa-ku, Tokyo, 140-8572, Japan
Tel.: (81) 354714745
Software Development Services
N.A.I.C.S.: 541511

Hitachi Vantara GmbH (1)
Im Steingrund 10, 63303, Dreieich, Germany
Tel.: (49) 61038041000
Web Site: http://www.hitachivantara.com
Software Development Services
N.A.I.C.S.: 541511

Hitachi Vantara Israel Ltd. (1)
27 Maskit St, Herzliya, 46733, Israel
Tel.: (972) 99704500
Software Development Services
N.A.I.C.S.: 541511

Hitachi Vantara Kenya Limited (1)
7 ESBC Office Suites Eden Square Westlands Road, Nairobi, Kenya
Tel.: (254) 780991001
Software Development Services
N.A.I.C.S.: 541511

Hitachi Vantara Korea Limited (1)
3901 Trade Tower 511 Yeongdong-daero, Gangnam-gu, Seoul, 06164, Korea (South)
Tel.: (82) 221870999
Software Development Services
N.A.I.C.S.: 541511

Hitachi Vantara LLC (1)
2535 Augustine Dr, Santa Clara, CA 95054
Tel.: (408) 970-1000
Web Site: http://www.hitachivantara.com
Software Development Services
N.A.I.C.S.: 541511
Jun Abe *(Chm)*

Hitachi Vantara Ltd. (1)
33/F Tower 2 Times Square 1 Matheson Street, Causeway Bay, Hong Kong, China (Hong Kong)
Tel.: (852) 31897900
Software Development Services
N.A.I.C.S.: 541511

Hitachi Vantara Nigeria Limited (1)
Suite 205 2nd Floor Mulliner Towers 39 Alfred Rewane Road, Ikoyi, Lagos, Nigeria
Tel.: (234) 9087253353
Software Development Services
N.A.I.C.S.: 541511

Hitachi Vantara OOO (1)
Trubnaya str 12 8th Floor, 107045, Moscow, Russia
Tel.: (7) 4957872793
Software Development Services
N.A.I.C.S.: 541511

Hitachi Vantara Oy (1)
Lars Sonckin kaari 16, 02600, Espoo, Finland
Tel.: (358) 954065900
Software Development Services
N.A.I.C.S.: 541511

Hitachi Vantara S.A. (1)
25 de Mayo 555 Functional Unit No 151 Floor 24 Office B, 1002, Buenos Aires, Argentina
Tel.: (54) 1155508500
Software Development Services
N.A.I.C.S.: 541511

Hitachi de Venezuela, C.A. (1)
castellana principal avenue la castellana Floor 5 office 4, Caracas, 1060, Venezuela
Tel.: (58) 212 2657719
Emp.: 5
Electronic Product Whslr
N.A.I.C.S.: 423690
Florian Winterstein *(Office Mgr)*

Hitachi eBworx Sdn. Bhd. (1)
Level 3A Block B No 10 Jalan Bersatu 13/4, Axis Business Park, 46200, Petaling Jaya, Selangor, Malaysia
Tel.: (60) 379569822
Web Site: http://www.eBworx.com
International Consulting & Technology Solutions in Banking
N.A.I.C.S.: 541512

Subsidiary (Non-US):

Hitachi eBworx (Indo-China) Co. Ltd. (2)
2 Ploenchit Center Ground Floor Unit 1 Sukhumvit Road, Klongtoey, Bangkok, 10110, Thailand
Tel.: (66) 2 305 6601
Digital Commerce Technology Solutions
N.A.I.C.S.: 541512

Hitachi eBworx International Pte. Ltd. (2)
7 Tampines Grande 02-04 Hitachi Square, Singapore, 528736, Singapore
Tel.: (65) 6789 1819
Digital Commerce Technology Solutions
N.A.I.C.S.: 541512

Hitachi eBworx Technology (ChengDu) Co. Ltd. (2)
11F-1108 DongFang XiWang 3 GaoPeng DaDao GaoXinQu, Chengdu, 610041, China
Tel.: (86) 8 6687 6633
Digital Commerce Technology Solutions
N.A.I.C.S.: 541512

PT, Hitachi eBworx Indonesia (2)
Dipo Tower Level 10 Dipo Business Center, Jl Jend Gatot Subroto Kav 51-52, Jakarta, 10260, Indonesia
Tel.: (62) 212 986 6006
Web Site: http://www.hitachi.ebworx.com
Emp.: 35
Digital Commerce Technology Solutions

INTERNATIONAL PUBLIC

N.A.I.C.S.: 541512
Fitrio Pakana *(Country Mgr)*

Hitachi-GE Nuclear Energy, Ltd. (1)
1-1 3-chome, Saiwai-cho, Hitachi, 317-0073, Ibaraki, Japan
Tel.: (81) 294 22 1000
Web Site: http://www.hitachi-hgne.co.jp
Sales Range: $450-499.9 Million
Emp.: 1,600
Water Reactor Equipment Installation Services & Mfr
N.A.I.C.S.: 332410

Hitachi-LG Data Storage (Huizhou) Ltd. (1)
Huifeng Fourth Road 42, Zhongkai Hi-Tech Industry Development Zone, Huizhou, 516006, Guangdong, China
Tel.: (86) 7525755325
Optical Disc Drive Mfr
N.A.I.C.S.: 334112

Hitachi-LG Data Storage Korea, Inc. (1)
LG Gasan Digital Center 189 Gasan Digital 1-ro, Geumcheon-gu, Seoul, 08503, Korea (South)
Tel.: (82) 269454500
Optical Disc Drive Mfr
N.A.I.C.S.: 334112

Hitachi-LG Data Storage, Inc. (1)
22-23 Kaigan 3 Chome, Minato-ku, Tokyo, 108-0022, Japan
Tel.: (81) 354278600
Web Site: http://www.hitachi-lg.com
Optical Disc Drive Mfr
N.A.I.C.S.: 334112
Min Byung Hoon *(Co-Pres & CEO)*

Hitachi-Mycom Maintenance & Solutions Ltda. (1)
Rua Licatem 250 Bloco D - Fazenda Rincao - Polo Industrial, Aruja, 07428-280, Sao Paulo, Brazil
Tel.: (55) 1146543799
Web Site: http://www.hitachi-mycom.com.br
Industrial Equipment Repair & Maintenance Services
N.A.I.C.S.: 811310

Hitachi-Omron Terminal Solutions, Corp. (1)
1-6-3 Osaki, Shinagawa-ku, Tokyo, Japan (100%)
Tel.: (81) 561 53 6132
Web Site: http://www.hitachi-omron-ts.com
Sales Range: $450-499.9 Million
Emp.: 999
Automated Teller Machine Mfr & Distr
N.A.I.C.S.: 334118
Toshiya Hamasaki *(Exec Officer-Operating)*

Subsidiary (Non-US):

Hitachi Terminals Mechatronics Philippines Corporation (2)
Subic Techno Park Boton Area Subic Bay Freeport Zone, Subic, 2222, Philippines
Tel.: (63) 47 252 5236
Automated Teller Machine Component Mfr
N.A.I.C.S.: 334118

Hokenso Sdn. Bhd. (1)
Unit TA-9-2 Level 9 Tower A Plaza 33 No 1 Jalan Kemajuan Seksyen 13, 46200, Petaling Jaya, Selangor, Malaysia
Tel.: (60) 379412188
IT Services
N.A.I.C.S.: 541511

Hokkaido Eco Recycle Systems Co. Ltd. (1)
6-269 Kashiwabara, Tomakomai, 059-1362, Hokkaido, Japan
Tel.: (81) 144539307
Web Site: https://www.go-hers.co.jp
Environmental Services
N.A.I.C.S.: 541620
Ryutaro Fujisawa *(Mgr-Factory)*

Hokkaido Hitachi Systems, Ltd. (1)
9th Floor of Hokuyo Building 3-11 Odori Nishi, Chuo-ku, Sapporo, 060-0042, Japan
Tel.: (81) 112817381
Web Site: http://www.hokkaido-hitachi-systems.co.jp
IT Services
N.A.I.C.S.: 541511

HITACHI, LTD.

Hokuriku Hitachi Co., Ltd. (1)
2-2-7 Toiyamachi, Toyama, 930-0834, Japan
Tel.: (81) 764517741
Web Site: http://www.hitachi-hansya.jp
Electrical Equipment Distr
N.A.I.C.S.: 423610

Hong Kong AIC Limited (1)
Suite 503 5/F Chinachem Golden Plaza 77 Mody Road, Tsim Tsa Tsui, Kowloon, China (Hong Kong)
Tel.: (852) 2739 6225
Web Site: http://www.hitachi.com.hk
Sales Range: $25-49.9 Million
Emp.: 10
Electronic Components Mfr
N.A.I.C.S.: 334419

IE Solution Service Co., Ltd. (1)
1 of 120 Saiwaicho, Inazawa, 492-8221, Aichi Prefecture, Japan
Tel.: (81) 587212111
Web Site: http://www.ie-ss.co.jp
Switchboard Mfr
N.A.I.C.S.: 335313

Ibaraki Technos Ltd. (1)
1-1 Hitaka-cho 5-chome, Hitachi, 319-1414, Ibaraki, Japan
Tel.: (81) 294427155
Metal Product Mfr & Distr
N.A.I.C.S.: 332999

J.R. Automation Technologies, LLC (1)
13365 Tyler St, Holland, MI 49424
Tel.: (616) 399-2168
Web Site: http://www.jrauto.com
Sales Range: $200-249.9 Million
Emp.: 2,000
Automated Industrial Machinery Mfr
N.A.I.C.S.: 333248
Jim Kramer *(VP-Sls)*

Subsidiary (Domestic):

Esys Automation, LLC (2)
1000 Brown Rd, Auburn Hills, MI 48326
Tel.: (248) 754-1900
Consulting & Engineering Services for Auto, Tire & Wheel Mfrs
N.A.I.C.S.: 541330

J.R. Automation - Stevensville (2)
7275 Red Arrow Hwy, Stevensville, MI 49127
Tel.: (269) 465-3263
Web Site: http://www.jrauto.com
Custom Automated Machinery & Mechanical Systems Mfr
N.A.I.C.S.: 333248

Kansai Hitachi Co., Ltd. (1)
Higobashi Shimizu Building 4F 1-3-7 Tosabori, Nishi-ku, Osaka, 550-0001, Japan
Tel.: (81) 642567201
Web Site: http://www.kansaihitachi.co.jp
Electrical Contractor Services
N.A.I.C.S.: 238210

Kanto Hitachi Co., Ltd. (1)
2-7-5 Higashiueno Kyoraku Building Higashiueno II 5th Floor, Taito-ku, Tokyo, 110-0015, Japan
Tel.: (81) 358076380
Web Site: http://www.hitachi-hansya.jp
Electrical Equipment Distr
N.A.I.C.S.: 423610

Keihin De Mexico, S.A. de C.V. (1)
Santiago Poniente 200 Lote 01 Manzana 05, Ciudad Satelite, 78423, San Luis Potosi, Mexico
Tel.: (52) 4442983100
Automobile Parts Mfr
N.A.I.C.S.: 336390

Kyushu Hitachi Systems, Ltd. (1)
Hakataekiminami 2-12-22 Hitachi Systems Kyushu Building, Hakata-ku, Fukuoka, 812-0016, Japan
Tel.: (81) 924349291
Web Site: http://www.kyushu-hitachi-systems.co.jp
IT Services
N.A.I.C.S.: 541511

LG Hitachi Ltd. (1)
LG Mapo Building 155 Mapo-daero, Mapo-gu, Seoul, 04143, Korea (South)
Tel.: (82) 7082903700
Web Site: http://www.lghitachi.co.kr
System Integration Services
N.A.I.C.S.: 541512
Soo-Yeop Kim *(CEO)*

MA micro automation GmbH (1)
Opelstrasse 1, 68789, Sankt Leon-Rot, Germany
Tel.: (49) 622734120
Web Site: https://www.micro-automation.de
Sales Range: $25-49.9 Million
Emp.: 100
Micro-Optic Industrial Automation Technologies Mfr
N.A.I.C.S.: 333248

MHPT Engineering Sdn. Bhd. (1)
Lot 2 5 2 Level 2 PNB Darby Park No 10 Jalan Binjai, Kuala Lumpur, 50450, Malaysia
Tel.: (60) 321635651
Sales Range: $25-49.9 Million
Emp.: 50
Refrigeration Design & Installation Services
N.A.I.C.S.: 423740
Nakamura Daiju *(Mng Dir)*

Mie Hitachi Co., Ltd. (1)
Hinagahigashi Chome No 2 No 6, Yokkaichi, 510-0886, Mie, Japan
Tel.: (81) 593464311
Web Site: http://www.hitachi-hansya.jp
Electrical Equipment Distr
N.A.I.C.S.: 423610

Minmetals Santoku (Ganzhou) Rare Earth Material Co., Ltd. (1)
No 171 Xlangjiang Road, Hongkong Industrial Park North Area, Ganzhou, 341000, jiangxi, China
Tel.: (86) 7978198976
Construction Machinery Product Mfr
N.A.I.C.S.: 333120

Mitsubishi Power, Ltd. (1)
Mitsubishijuko Yokohama Bldg 3-1 Minatomirai 3-chome, Nishi-ku, Yokohama, 220-8401, Kanagawa, Japan
Tel.: (81) 45 200 6100
Web Site: https://power.mhi.com
Boilers, Chemical Plant Equipment & Operational Support Systems Mfr
N.A.I.C.S.: 332410
Yasuo Fujitani *(Sr VP)*

Subsidiary (Non-US):

Babcock-Hitachi (Philippines) Inc. (2)
AG&P Special Economic Zone Barangay San Roque Bauan, Batangas, 4201, Philippines
Tel.: (63) 43 727 1027
Web Site: http://www.bhpi.com.ph
Emp.: 900
Mfr of Boilers, Chemical Plant Equipment & Operational Support Systems
N.A.I.C.S.: 332410
Clara Evelyn Fider *(Mgr-HR)*

Babcock-Hitachi Dongfang Boiler Co., Ltd. (2)
No 4 Bridge Chengnan Road, Jiaxing, 314001, Zhejiang, China
Tel.: (86) 573 8262 5132
Sales Range: $100-124.9 Million
Emp.: 40
Heat Boiler Mfr & Distr
N.A.I.C.S.: 333414

Mitsubishi Hitachi Power Systems Europe GmbH (2)
Schifferstrasse 80, 47059, Duisburg, Germany
Tel.: (49) 20380380
Web Site: http://www.emea.mhps.com
Metalworking Machines Mfr
N.A.I.C.S.: 333519
Rainer Kiechl *(CEO)*

Subsidiary (Non-US):

Mitsubishi Hitachi Power Systems Africa (Pty) Ltd. (3)
Building 30 The Woodlands Office Park 20 Woodlands Drive, Woodmead, 2054, Sandton, South Africa
Tel.: (27) 11 260 4300
Web Site: http://www.za.mhps.com
Eletric Power Generation Services
N.A.I.C.S.: 221111
Kiyoshi Okazoe *(Chm-Mgmt Bd)*

Mitsubishi-Hitachi Metals Machinery, Inc. (1)
Shintamachi Bldg 34-6 Shiba 5-chome, Minato-ku, Tokyo, 108-0014, Japan (34.3%)
Tel.: (81) 3 5765 5231
Web Site: http://www.m-hmm.co.jp
Metal Rolling & Processing Machinery Mfr
N.A.I.C.S.: 333519
Kazunari Haraguchi *(Exec VP)*

Subsidiary (Non-US):

MHPS Plant Services Pty Ltd. (2)
Level 7 19 Lang Parade, PO Box 1559, Milton, 4064, QLD, Australia
Tel.: (61) 738780888
Web Site: http://www.anz.mhps.com
Fabricated Wire Product Mfr
N.A.I.C.S.: 332618

Mitsubishi-Hitachi Metals Machinery (Shanghai), Inc. (2)
Room 1707 Tower A 69 Dongfang Road, Shanghai, 200120, China
Tel.: (86) 21 6859 8835
Web Site: http://www.m-hmm.co.jp
Metal Rolling & Processing Machinery Mfr
N.A.I.C.S.: 333519

Subsidiary (US):

Mitsubishi-Hitachi Metals Machinery USA, Inc. (2)
500 Cherrington Pkwy, Coraopolis, PA 15108-4744
Tel.: (412) 269-6630
Web Site: http://www.m-hmm.com
Metal Rolling & Processing Machinery Mfr & Distr
N.A.I.C.S.: 333519
Kathy Uebelacher *(Office Mgr)*

Subsidiary (Domestic):

MHCG, Inc. (3)
N53 W24900 S Corporate Cir, Sussex, WI 53089
Tel.: (262) 691-0400
Web Site: http://www.gfg-peabody.com
Sales Range: $25-49.9 Million
Metal Roll Coating, Electrostatic Oiling & Coil Coating Equipment Mfr & Distr
N.A.I.C.S.: 333519
Linda Taylor *(Controller)*

Nam Yang Metals Co., Ltd. (1)
20 Nongong-ro 53-gil, Nongong-eup Dalseong-gun, Daegu, Korea (South)
Tel.: (82) 536107530
Web Site: http://www.namyangmetals.co.kr
Automotive Components Mfr
N.A.I.C.S.: 336390
Jae-Ho Seol *(Gen Mgr)*

Nanjing Hitachi Techno. Co., Ltd. (1)
Bldg 1 No 118 Haifuxiang, Nanjing, 210007, China
Tel.: (86) 2584236788
Web Site: http://www.njhitachi.com
Sales Range: $25-49.9 Million
Emp.: 40
Printer Mfr & Whslr
N.A.I.C.S.: 334118

Neomax Engineering Co., Ltd. (1)
2977 Taira, Yoshii Town, Takasaki, 370-2115, Gunma, Japan
Tel.: (81) 273867100
Web Site: http://www.nxe.co.jp
Electrical Motor Mfr & Distr
N.A.I.C.S.: 335312

Neomax Kinki Co., Ltd. (1)
1062 Oyabu, Yabu, 667-0111, Hyogo, Japan
Tel.: (81) 796650126
Metal Product Mfr & Distr
N.A.I.C.S.: 332999

Neomax Kyushuu Co., Ltd. (1)
2738 Osaki, Kitagata-cho, Takeo, 849-2204, Saga, Japan
Tel.: (81) 954364512
Metal Product Mfr & Distr
N.A.I.C.S.: 332999

Nichimoku Sangyou Ltd. (1)
4-1-8 Ayukawa-cho, Hitachi, 316-0036, Ibaraki, Japan
Tel.: (81) 294344151
Web Site: http://www.nichimoku.co.jp
Building Construction Services
N.A.I.C.S.: 236220

Nichiwa Service Ltd. (1)
2-2-10 Higashinarusawa-cho, Hitachi, 316-0034, Ibaraki, Japan
Tel.: (81) 294381121
Web Site: http://www.nichiwa-hitachi.co.jp
Industrial Waste Collection Services
N.A.I.C.S.: 562111

Nichiwa Sougou Setsubi Co., Ltd. (1)
32-22 Higashi-Ikebukuro 2-chome, Toshima-ku, Tokyo, 170-0013, Japan
Tel.: (81) 339890961
Water Treatment Plant Construction Services
N.A.I.C.S.: 237110

Nico Technos Co., Ltd. (1)
405-3 Yoshinocho 1-chome, Kita-ku, Saitama, 331-0811, Japan
Tel.: (81) 486671467
Electrical Equipment Mfr & Distr
N.A.I.C.S.: 335999

Niigata Hitachi Co., Ltd. (1)
752-10 Takeooroshishinmachi, Higashi-ku, Niigata, 950-0867, Japan
Tel.: (81) 252732211
Web Site: http://www.hitachi-hansya.jp
Electrical Equipment Distr
N.A.I.C.S.: 423610

Okinawa Hitachi Co., Ltd. (1)
Aja 230 Address, Naha, 900-0003, Japan
Tel.: (81) 988611045
Web Site: http://www.okinichi.co.jp
Elevator Installation Services
N.A.I.C.S.: 238290

Okinawa Hitachi Network Systems, Ltd. (1)
1-3-31 Naha Shintoshin Media Building, Omoromachi, Naha, 900-0006, Okinawa, Japan
Tel.: (81) 988688420
Web Site: http://www.ohns.co.jp
Software Services
N.A.I.C.S.: 541511

Oxya Consulting Benelux NV (1)
President Kennedy Park 3A, 8500, Kortrijk, Belgium
Tel.: (32) 56234310
Cloud Computing Services
N.A.I.C.S.: 518210

Oxya Corporation (1)
15 Exchange Pl Ste 620, Jersey City, NJ 07302
Tel.: (201) 604-5305
Cloud Computing Services
N.A.I.C.S.: 518210
Sevag Mekhsian *(CTO)*

Oxya UK Limited (1)
2 Venture Road Southampton Science Park, Southampton, SO16 7NP, United Kingdom
Tel.: (44) 2380119830
Cloud Computing Services
N.A.I.C.S.: 518210

PT Hitachi Asia Indonesia (1)
Menara BCA 38th Floor Suite 3804 & 3805 Jl M H Thamrin No 1, 10310, Jakarta, Indonesia
Tel.: (62) 2123586757
Web Site: http://www.hitachi.co.id
Power Transmission & Distribution Services
N.A.I.C.S.: 221122

PT Hitachi Plant Technologies (1)
Menara Bank Danamon Lt 12 Jl Prof Dr Satrio Kav E IV/6 Mega Kuningan, Jakarta, 12950, Indonesia
Tel.: (62) 2157992201
Sales Range: $25-49.9 Million
Emp.: 5
Industrial Plant Erection & Installation Services
N.A.I.C.S.: 237990

PT. Berdiri Matahari Logistik (1)

HITACHI, LTD. — INTERNATIONAL PUBLIC

Hitachi, Ltd.—(Continued)

Graha Mustika Ratu 4th Floor Jl Gatot Subroto Kav 74-75, Jakarta, 12870, Indonesia
Tel.: (62) 21 830 6590
Web Site: http://hts-bml.co.id
Logistics Consulting Servies
N.A.I.C.S.: 541614

PT. Hitachi High-Tech Indonesia (1)
Unit No 315B 15th Floor Sentral Senayan III Jalan Asia Afrika, No 8 Gelora Bung Karno-Senayan, Jakarta Pusat, 10270, Indonesia
Tel.: (62) 2129039250
Web Site: http://www.hitachi-hightech.com
Corporate Services
N.A.I.C.S.: 561410

PT. Hitachi Metals Indonesia (1)
Jl Eropa III Kav N2 Kawasan Industri KIEC Cilegon, 42435, Banten, Indonesia
Tel.: (62) 254393100
Ferrite Magnet Mfr
N.A.I.C.S.: 327110

PT. Hitachi Modern Sales Indonesia (1)
Jl Let Jend S Parman Kav 12 Gd Wisma Slipi Lt 12, 11480, Jakarta, Indonesia
Tel.: (62) 21 5307211
Sales Range: $25-49.9 Million
Emp.: 5
Household Appliance Distr
N.A.I.C.S.: 423620
Masasi Takahashi (Gen Mgr)

PT. Hitachi Plant Technologies Indonesia (1)
Menara Bank Danamon 12th Floor Jl Prof Dr Satrio, Mega Kuningan, Jakarta, 12950, Indonesia
Tel.: (62) 2157992201
Building Facility Services
N.A.I.C.S.: 236220

PT. Hitachi Power Systems Indonesia (1)
EJIP Industrial Park Plot 8E Lemahabang, Cikarang Selatan, Bekasi, 17550, Indonesia
Tel.: (62) 218970350
Gas Circuit Breaker Mfr & Distr
N.A.I.C.S.: 335313

PT. Hitachi Sunway Information Systems Indonesia (1)
Wisma Korindo 4th Floor Jl MT Haryono Kav 62, Pancoran, Jakarta Selatan, 12780, Indonesia
Tel.: (62) 2179186020
Construction & Engineering Services
N.A.I.C.S.: 541330

PT. Hitachi Terminal Solutions Indonesia (1)
Menara BCA 39th Floor Suite 3903 Jl M H Thamrin No 1, 10310, Jakarta, Indonesia
Tel.: (62) 2123586051
ATM Services
N.A.I.C.S.: 522390

PT. Japan AE Power Systems Indonesia (1)
EJIP Industrial Park Plot 8E, Lemahabang, Bekasi, 17550, Indonesia
Tel.: (62) 21 897 0350
Emp.: 40
Power Transmission Equipment Mfr
N.A.I.C.S.: 333613
Patrick Toemen (Gen Mgr)

PT. Sliontec Ekadharma Indonesia (1)
MM2100 Industrial Town Blok OO-1, Cibitung, Bekasi, Indonesia
Tel.: (62) 21 898 1261
Emp.: 119
Adhesive Mfr
N.A.I.C.S.: 325520
Masahiro Saigo (Pres)

Phpc Co. Ltd. Inc. (1)
11th Floor 6788 Ayala Avenue Oledan Square, Makati, 1226, Philippines
Tel.: (63) 28866974
Emp.: 80
Mechanical And Electrical Contracting
N.A.I.C.S.: 238210
Tetsuo Tamura (Pres)

Quality Life Enterprise (India) Pvt. Ltd. (1)
353-357 Sector 29 City Centre, Haryana, Gurgaon, 122001, India
Tel.: (91) 1244604600
Software Services
N.A.I.C.S.: 541511

SCHM Service Co., Ltd. (1)
1858/79 1858/81-82 Interlink Tower 17th Floor Bangna-Trad Rd, Bangna, Bangkok, 10260, Thailand
Tel.: (66) 2325101127
Electrical Machinery Distr
N.A.I.C.S.: 423610

San Technology, Inc. (1)
6210 Marindustry Dr, San Diego, CA 92121
Tel.: (858) 278-7300
Web Site: http://www.santechnology.com
Electric Equipment Mfr
N.A.I.C.S.: 334419
Kuni Yatsugi (CEO)

Sanki Technos Co., Ltd. (1)
2-904-62 Hayama chome, Kudamatsu, 744-0061, Yamaguchi, Japan
Tel.: (81) 833472600
Web Site: http://www.sanki-t.com
Sales Range: $125-149.9 Million
Emp.: 300
Industrial Machinery & Equipment Whslr
N.A.I.C.S.: 423830

Santoku Corporation (1)
4-14-34 Fukaekitamachi, Higashinada-ku, Kobe, 658-0013, Hyogo, Japan
Tel.: (81) 784310531
Web Site: http://www.santoku-corp.co.jp
Rare Earth Mfr
N.A.I.C.S.: 324199
Tatsuhiko Kakuda (CEO)

Seneos GmbH (1)
Josef-Lammerting-Allee 8, 50933, Cologne, Germany
Tel.: (49) 2211792980
Web Site: http://www.seneos.com
Construction & Engineering Services
N.A.I.C.S.: 541330
Guido Renneberg (Mng Dir)

Shanghai Hitachi Metals Cable Materials Co., Ltd. (1)
No 9 C6 No 11 C9 Lane 180 Jinxi Road, Songjiang District, Shanghai, 201613, China
Tel.: (86) 2157837766
Metal Product Mfr & Distr
N.A.I.C.S.: 332999

Shikoku Hitachi Co., Ltd. (1)
chome 1-47, Tokushima, 770-8006, Niihama-cho, Japan
Tel.: (81) 886791010
Web Site: http://www.hitachi-hansya.jp
Electrical Machinery Distr
N.A.I.C.S.: 423610

Shikoku Hitachi Systems, Ltd. (1)
5-31 Chuocho, Takamatsu, 760-0007, Kagawa, Japan
Tel.: (81) 878622929
Web Site: http://www.shikoku-hitachi-systems.co.jp
Software Development Services
N.A.I.C.S.: 541511

Shizuoka Hitachi Co., Ltd. (1)
Hijiriisshiki 84-1, Shizuoka, 422-8007, Japan
Tel.: (81) 542647171
Web Site: http://www.hitachi-hansya.jp
Software Development Services
N.A.I.C.S.: 541511

Siam Hitachi Automotive Products Ltd. (1)
700/357 Moo 6 Amata Nakorn Industrial Park Bangna-Trad Rd Km 57 Don, Hua Roh Amphur Muang Chonburi, Chon Buri, 20000, Thailand
Tel.: (66) 38 21 4390
Web Site: http://www.hitachi.co.th
Sales Range: $200-249.9 Million
Emp.: 580
Automotive Component Mfr & Distr
N.A.I.C.S.: 336390

Siam-Hitachi Elevator Co., Ltd. (1)
30 Soi On-Nuch 55/1, Praves Subdistrict Praves District, Bangkok, 10250, Thailand
Tel.: (66) 2 320 5777
Web Site: https://www.siamhitachi.com
Sales Range: $100-124.9 Million
Emp.: 500
Elevators & Escalators Mfr
N.A.I.C.S.: 333921
Phornthep Phornpraphra (Chm)

Plant (Domestic):

Siam-Hitachi Elevator Co., Ltd. - Chonburi Factory (2)
700/899 Moo 3, Amatanakorn Industrial Estate T Nongkakha A Panthong, Chon Buri, 20160, Thailand
Tel.: (66) 3821231032
Web Site: http://www.siamhitachi.com
Sales Range: $25-49.9 Million
Emp.: 400
Elevator Mfr
N.A.I.C.S.: 333921

Smart Factory & Services Holdings (Thailand) Co., Ltd. (1)
62 Thaniya Bldg 7th Floor 702 Silom Rd, Suriyawong Bangrak, Bangkok, 10500, Thailand
Tel.: (66) 22365338
Software Development Services
N.A.I.C.S.: 541511

Stella Chemifa Singapore Pte. Ltd. (1)
21 Merlimau Pl, Jurong Island, Singapore, 627840, Singapore
Tel.: (65) 63167882
Web Site: http://www.stella-chemifa.co.jp
Sales Range: $25-49.9 Million
Emp.: 50
Semiconductors Sales
N.A.I.C.S.: 334413
Alan Law (Plant Mgr)

Stone Apple Solutions Pte. Ltd. (1)
51 Changi Business Park Central 2 #08-12, Signature, Singapore, 486066, Singapore
Tel.: (65) 6323 5392
Web Site: http://www.hitachi.com.sg
Computer Programming & Development Services
N.A.I.C.S.: 541511

Subsidiary (Non-US):

Stone Apple Consulting Co., Ltd. (2)
1604 Q House Lumpini Building 1 South Sathorn Road, Tungmahamek, Bangkok, 10120, Thailand
Tel.: (66) 26777491
Web Site: http://www.hitachi.co.th
Application Support System & Development Services
N.A.I.C.S.: 541512
Surechet Wong (Sr VP)

Stone Apple Malaysia Sdn Bhd. (2)
21-05 Level 21 G Tower 199 Jalan Tun Razak, Kuala Lumpur, 50400, Malaysia
Tel.: (60) 3 21612075
Computer System Design Services
N.A.I.C.S.: 541512
Rajeev Nair (Sr VP)

Sullair Asia Pte. Ltd. (1)
30 Pioneer Crescent 10-15 West Park Biz-Central, Singapore, 628560, Singapore
Tel.: (65) 63057442
Screw Air Compressor Mfr & Distr
N.A.I.C.S.: 333912

Tadakiko Co., Ltd. (1)
754-14 Suzumi-cho, Funabashi, 274-0052, Chiba, Japan
Tel.: (81) 474900010
Web Site: http://www.tadakiko.co.jp
Hydraulic Equipment Mfr
N.A.I.C.S.: 333996

Taiwan Hitachi Co., Ltd. (1)
63 Nanking East Road Sec 3, Taipei, Taiwan
Tel.: (886) 2 2508 3311
Web Site: http://www.hitachi-ap.com
Air Conditioning Equipment Mfr & Whslr
N.A.I.C.S.: 333415

Tamp Auto Parts Industrial Co., Ltd. (1)
556 Ping-Tung Road, Ping-Che, Taoyuan, Taiwan
Tel.: (886) 34501046
Automobile Mfr & Distr
N.A.I.C.S.: 336110

Tata Hitachi Construction Machinery Company Private Limited (1)
Jubilee Building 45 Museum Road, Bengaluru, 560 025, India
Tel.: (91) 8066953301
Web Site: https://www.tatahitachi.co.in
Construction Services
N.A.I.C.S.: 236220
Girish Wagh (Chm)

Techna Co. Ltd. (1)
88 Zosha, Haramachi, Toyohashi, 441 31, Aichi Ken, Japan (100%)
Tel.: (81) 532412111
Web Site: http://www.techna-jp.com
Sales Range: $50-74.9 Million
Emp.: 150
Mfr of Stereo & Television Cabinets, Furniture
N.A.I.C.S.: 337126

Tohoku Hitachi Co., Ltd. (1)
4-1-25 Ichibancho East 2-chome Square 7th Floor, Aoba-ku, Sendai, 980-0811, Miyagi Prefecture, Japan
Tel.: (81) 222230152
Web Site: http://www.hitachi-hansya.jp
Construction Machinery Distr
N.A.I.C.S.: 423810

Tohoku Rubber Co., Ltd. (1)
1-1-12 Minato, Miyagino-ku, Sendai, 983-0001, Miyagi Prefecture, Japan
Tel.: (81) 223871511
Web Site: http://www.tohoku-rubber.co.jp
Industrial Mold Mfr
N.A.I.C.S.: 333511

Tokyo Eco Recycle Co., Ltd. (1)
2-8-21 Wakasu, Koto-ku, Tokyo, 136-0083, Japan
Tel.: (81) 335226690
Web Site: http://www.tokyo-eco.co.jp
Sales Range: $10-24.9 Million
Emp.: 19
Recycling & Industrial Waste Management Services
N.A.I.C.S.: 562119
Hideaki Kurokawa (Pres)

Tonichi Kyousan Cable, Ltd. (1)
1-1 Aragane, Ishioka, 315-8511, Ibaraki, Japan
Tel.: (81) 299237111
Web Site: http://www.tonichi-kyosan.co.jp
Electrical Wire Mfr
N.A.I.C.S.: 335929

VLC Photonics Sociedad Limitada (1)
Building 9B East entrance Office 0 71, Universidad Politecnica de Valencia access l Camino de Vera s/n, 46022, Valencia, Spain
Tel.: (34) 961337884
Web Site: http://www.vlcphotonics.com
Photonics Mfr
N.A.I.C.S.: 327212

Wenco International Mining Systems Ltd. (1)
100-13777 Commerce Parkway, Richmond, V6V 2X3, BC, Canada
Tel.: (604) 270-8277
Web Site: http://www.wencomine.com
Advanced Technology Services
N.A.I.C.S.: 811210

Yungtay Engineering Co., Ltd. (1)
11F No 99 Fuxing N Rd, Songshan District, Taipei, 105, Taiwan (71.1%)
Tel.: (886) 22 717 2217
Web Site: http://www.yungtay.com.tw
Rev.: $629,917,631
Assets: $920,407,755
Liabilities: $490,123,832
Net Worth: $430,283,923
Earnings: $29,366,734
Fiscal Year-end: 12/31/2021
Escalator Mfr
N.A.I.C.S.: 333921
Tso Ming Hsu (Chm)

Subsidiary (Domestic):

Evest Corporation (2)

Factory 6-1F No 66 Sec 2 Nankan Road
Luchu Hsiang, Taoyuan, Taoyuan, 338, Taiwan
Tel.: (886) 3 311 3811
Web Site: http://www.evest.com.tw
Industrial Automation Equipments Mfr
N.A.I.C.S.: 334513

GIO Automation Technology Co., Ltd. (2)
11F No 99 Fu Hsing North Road, Taipei, 10595, Taiwan
Tel.: (886) 287125977
Web Site: http://www.giotek.com.tw
Emp.: 13
Industrial Automation Equipments Mfr
N.A.I.C.S.: 334513

Subsidiary (Non-US):

Shanghai Yungtay Elevator Equipment Co., Ltd. (2)
No 99 Jiuxin Road Jiuting Town, Songjiang District, Shanghai, 201615, China
Tel.: (86) 2157633888
Web Site: http://www.yungtay.com.cn
Elevators & Escalators Mfr
N.A.I.C.S.: 333921

Shanghai Yungtay Gie Co., Ltd. (2)
Bldg 3 No 180 Yanghebang Rd Jiuting Town High Tech Park, Songjiang, Shanghai, 201600, China
Tel.: (86) 2167696928
Emp.: 300
Electric Machines Mfr
N.A.I.C.S.: 333248
Serela Song *(Gen Mgr)*

Plant (Domestic):

Yungtay Engineering Co., Ltd. - Taoyuan Factory (2)
No 1352 Chunri Rd, Taoyuan Dist, Taoyuan, 330, Taiwan
Tel.: (886) 33254161
Web Site: http://www.yungtay.com.tw
Elevators & Escalators Mfr
N.A.I.C.S.: 333921

HITAY INVESTMENT HOLDINGS A.S.
Eski Buyukdere C Ozcan S No 2 4
Levent, 34416, Istanbul, Turkiye
Tel.: (90) 2123494900
Web Site: http://www.hitay.com
Year Founded: 1980
Emp.: 800
Holding Company; Technology Solutions in Finance, Industry & Logistics
N.A.I.C.S.: 551112
Emin Hitay *(Founder & Chm)*

Subsidiaries:

Exim A.S. (1)
ITU Ayazaga Campus ARI 2 Building B, Blok No 6-1 Maslak, 33469, Istanbul, Turkiye
Tel.: (90) 2123664900
Web Site: http://www.exim.com.tr
Mobile Data Solutions, Services & Systems
N.A.I.C.S.: 513210

Teknoser A.S. (1)
Teknoloji Plaza Eski Buyukdere Cd, Ozcan Sk No 2, 34416 4, Istanbul, Levent, Turkiye
Tel.: (90) 2123393000
Web Site: http://www.teknoser.gen.tr
Field Service, Maintenance & Repair Services for the Information Technology Sector
N.A.I.C.S.: 811210

HITE JINRO CO., LTD.
714 Yeongdong-daero, Gangnam-gu, Seoul, 06075, Korea (South)
Tel.: (82) 232190114
Web Site: https://www.hitejinro.com
Year Founded: 1924
000080—(KRS)
Rev.: $1,915,624,548
Assets: $2,556,747,185
Liabilities: $1,666,238,421
Net Worth: $890,508,764
Earnings: $66,588,071
Emp.: 3,077
Fiscal Year-end: 12/31/22
Alcoholic Beverages Mfr
N.A.I.C.S.: 312140
Mun Deok Park *(Chm & CEO)*

Subsidiaries:

Hite Jinro Co., Ltd. - Cheongju Distillery Factory (1)
51 Jungsam-li 177 Hyeondogongdan-ro Hyeondo-myeon, Seowon-gu, Cheongju, Chungcheongbuk-do, Korea (South)
Tel.: (82) 432701601
Liquor Mfr
N.A.I.C.S.: 312140

Hite Jinro Co., Ltd. - Gangwon Brewery Factory (1)
936 Hahwagae-li 49 Dodun-gil Bukbang-myeon, Hongcheon-gun, Hongcheon, Gangwon-do, Korea (South)
Tel.: (82) 334308100
Liquor Mfr
N.A.I.C.S.: 312140

Hite Jinro Co., Ltd. - Icheon Distillery Factory (1)
28 Muchon-li 13 1707 Jungbudae-ro Bubaleup, Icheon, Gyeonggi-do, Korea (South)
Tel.: (82) 316440998
Liquor Mfr
N.A.I.C.S.: 312140

Hite Jinro Co., Ltd. - Iksan Distillery Factory (1)
126-7 Ma-dong 151 Jungang-ro, Iksan, Jeollabuk-do, Korea (South)
Tel.: (82) 638405111
Liquor Mfr
N.A.I.C.S.: 312140

Hite Jinro Co., Ltd. - Jeonju Brewery Factory (1)
1256 Shinji-li 25-33 Shinjisonggwang-ro Yongjin-eup, Wanju-gun, Jeonbuk, Jeollabuk-do, Korea (South)
Tel.: (82) 632406111
Liquor Mfr
N.A.I.C.S.: 312140

Hite Jinro Co., Ltd. - Masan Brewery Factory (1)
542-3 Guam-dong 8 Seongyeok-ro 3-15, Mansanhoiwon-gu, Changwon, Gyeongsangnam-do, Korea (South)
Tel.: (82) 552508100
Liquor Mfr
N.A.I.C.S.: 312140

HITECH & DEVELOPMENT WIRELESS SWEDEN HOLDING AB
Farogatan 33 Kista Science Tower, 164 51, Kista, Sweden
Tel.: (46) 855118460
Web Site: https://www.hd-wireless.com
HDW.B—(OMX)
Rev.: $1,947,176
Assets: $10,043,522
Liabilities: $2,815,165
Net Worth: $7,228,357
Earnings: ($2,809,061)
Emp.: 30
Fiscal Year-end: 12/31/20
Wireless Communication Equipment Distr
N.A.I.C.S.: 423690

HITECH CORPORATION LTD.
Unit No 201-203 2nd Floor Welspun House Kamla City, Senapati Bapat Marg Lower Parel W, Mumbai, 400013, India
Tel.: (91) 2240016500
Web Site: https://www.hitechgroup.com
Year Founded: 1991
HITECHCORP—(NSE)
Rev.: $80,432,134
Assets: $48,307,541
Liabilities: $18,693,648
Net Worth: $29,613,893
Earnings: $5,104,636
Emp.: 623
Fiscal Year-end: 03/31/22
Plastics Product Mfr
N.A.I.C.S.: 325211
Malav Ashwin Dani *(Mng Dir)*

Subsidiaries:

Clear Plastics Limited (1)
C-130 Solaris 1 Opposite L & T Gate No 6 Saki Vihar Rd, Powai, 400 072, Mumbai, Maharashtra, India
Tel.: (91) 2228574660
Web Site: http://www.hitechplast.co.in
Sales Range: $25-49.9 Million
Emp.: 50
Plastic Mfr
N.A.I.C.S.: 326199

Mipak Polymers Limited (1)
C-130 Solaris 1 Opposite L & T Gate No 6, Powai, Mumbai, 400 072, Maharashtra, India
Tel.: (91) 2240016500
Web Site: http://www.mipak.co.in
Sales Range: $25-49.9 Million
Emp.: 50
Printing Equipment Mfr
N.A.I.C.S.: 333248
Kalpesh Gandhi *(Gen Mgr)*

HITECH GROUP AUSTRALIA LIMITED
Gateway Tower SE3701b Level 37 1 Macquarie Place, Sydney, 2000, NSW, Australia
Tel.: (61) 292411919
Web Site: https://www.hitechaust.com
HIT—(ASX)
Rev.: $42,366,411
Assets: $11,532,602
Liabilities: $5,243,753
Net Worth: $6,288,849
Earnings: $4,027,416
Fiscal Year-end: 06/30/24
Staffing for Information & Communication Technology Sector
N.A.I.C.S.: 561330
Raymond Hazouri *(Founder, Chm & Co-Sec)*

Subsidiaries:

HiTech Group Australia Limited - HiTech Personnel Division (1)
Level 7 9 Young Street, PO Box R182, Sydney, 2000, NSW, Australia
Tel.: (61) 292411919
Web Site: http://www.hitechaust.com
Recruitment & Consulting Services
N.A.I.C.S.: 541612

HITECH STAGES LTD.
145-157 St John Street 2nd Fl, London, EC1V 4PY, United Kingdom
Tel.: (44) 2032952037
Emp.: 4
Stage Production Services
N.A.I.C.S.: 713990
David Rebak *(CEO)*

HITECHPROS S.A.
15-17 bd du General de Gaulle, 92120, Montrouge, France
Tel.: (33) 155580420
Web Site: https://www.hitechpros.com
ALHIT—(EUR)
Sales Range: $10-24.9 Million
Information Technology Services
N.A.I.C.S.: 541512

HITECVISION AS
Jattavagveien 7 Building A, 4068, Stavanger, Norway
Tel.: (47) 5120 2020
Web Site: http://www.hitecvision.com
Year Founded: 1994
Privater Equity Firm
N.A.I.C.S.: 523999
Ole Ertvaag *(Founding Partner & CEO)*

Subsidiaries:

Align AS (1)
Oksenoyveien 10, NO-1366, Lysaker, Norway
Tel.: (47) 815 31 002
Web Site: http://www.align.no
Oil & Gas Industry; Technical Safety & Total Firefighting Solutions
N.A.I.C.S.: 541990
Erik Christensen *(CEO)*

Division (Domestic):

Eureka Pumps AS (2)
Fornebuporten Oksenoyvelen 10, NO-1366, Lysaker, Norway
Tel.: (47) 482 48 920
Web Site: http://www.eureka.no
Oil & Gas & Marine Industry Pump & Generator Mfr & Whslr
N.A.I.C.S.: 333132
Jon Kjetil Jutulstad *(COO)*

Subsidiary (Domestic):

Eureka Pump AS (3)
Snaroyveien 36, 1364, Fornebu, Norway
Tel.: (47) 48248920
Web Site: http://www.eureka.no
Pump & Generator Distr
N.A.I.C.S.: 423830
Oyvind Lund *(Mgr-Modifications & Upgrades)*

Subsidiary (Non-US):

Eureka Pump AS (3)
Suite 11 Level 25 Etiqa Twins Tower 2, 11 Jalan Pinang, Kuala Lumpur, Malaysia
Tel.: (60) 327269911
Web Site: http://www.eureka.no
Pump & Generator Distr
N.A.I.C.S.: 423830
Tom L. Nielsen *(Sls Mgr)*

Subsidiary (Domestic):

Eureka Pumps AS (3)
Litlas 21, NO-5954, Mongstad, Norway
Tel.: (47) 815 31 002
Web Site: http://www.eureka.no
Pump & Generator Distr
N.A.I.C.S.: 423830
Romar Halvorsen *(Mgr-Workshop)*

Eureka Pumps AS - Kristiansund (3)
Dalegat 137, NO-6518, Kristiansund, Norway
Tel.: (47) 913 26 096
Web Site: http://www.eureka.no
Pump & Generator Distr
N.A.I.C.S.: 423830
Jon Kjetil Jutulstad *(Mgr-Svc & Site)*

Eureka Pumps AS - Sorumsand (3)
Industrivegen 22, NO-1920, Sorumsand, Norway
Tel.: (47) 971 70 911
Web Site: http://www.eureka.no
Pumps & Generator Distr
N.A.I.C.S.: 423830
Tommy Aadahl *(Mgr-Assembly & Testing)*

Eureka Pumps AS - Tananger (3)
Energiveien 20, NO-4056, Tananger, Norway
Tel.: (47) 454 86 742
Web Site: http://www.eureka.no
Pump & Generator Distr
N.A.I.C.S.: 423810
Oystein Solberg *(Dir-After Sls Svc)*

Subsidiary (US):

Eureka Pumps Americas, Inc. (3)
8558 Katy Freeway Ste 100, Houston, TX 77024
Tel.: (281) 310-5400
Web Site: http://www.eureka.no
Pump & Generator Distr
N.A.I.C.S.: 423830
Rune Osmundsen *(Pres)*

Subsidiary (Non-US):

Eureka Pumps Korea (3)

HITECVISION AS

HitecVision AS—(Continued)
#1102 Leaders Mark 17, APEC-ro, 612-021, Busan, Korea (South)
Tel.: (82) 1050287520
Web Site: http://www.eureka.no
Pump & Generator Distr
N.A.I.C.S.: 423830
Rune Bjorndal *(Mgr-Site)*

Division (Domestic):

Fire Protection Engineering AS (2)
Kanalarmen 12, N-4033, Stavanger, Norway
Tel.: (47) 51959292
Web Site: http://www.fpe.com
Fire Fighting Systems Whslr
N.A.I.C.S.: 922160
Rolf Thorkildsen *(Mng Dir)*

Origo Solutions AS (2)
Andoyfaret 31, NO-4623, Kristiansand, Norway
Tel.: (47) 42080500
Web Site: http://www.origo-solutions.com
Technical Safety, Control Systems & Fire & Gas Detection Solutions
N.A.I.C.S.: 541420
Jarle Oygarden *(CEO)*

Aquamarine Subsea AS (1)
Jattavagveien 7, 4020, Stavanger, Norway
Tel.: (47) 5120 2020
Web Site: http://www.hitecvision.com
Holding Company; Offshore Drilling & Subsea Support Services
N.A.I.C.S.: 551112
Ola Saetre *(Chm)*

Subsidiary (US):

Aquamarine Subsea Houston, Inc. (2)
8901 Jameel Rd Ste 100, Houston, TX 77040-5090
Tel.: (713) 460-0295
Web Site: http://www.aquamarine.no
Offshore Drilling Services
N.A.I.C.S.: 213111
Tyler Kief *(Mng Dir)*

Subsidiary (Domestic):

Aquamarine Subsea Stavanger AS (2)
Direktor Poulsons Gate 1, 4100, Jorpeland, Norway
Tel.: (47) 5174 3500
Web Site: http://www.aquamarine.no
Industrial Equipment Repair & Maintenance Services
N.A.I.C.S.: 811310
Helge Skjellevik *(Dir-Technical)*

Flux Group AS (1)
Moseidsletta 122, Stavanger, Norway
Tel.: (47) 47882222
Web Site: http://www.fluxgroup.com
Oil & Gas Machinery Mfr & Distr
N.A.I.C.S.: 333132
Adne Grodem *(CEO)*

Subsidiary (Domestic):

Norwegian Piping AS (2)
Idrettsvegen 144, 5353, Straume, Norway
Tel.: (47) 56312300
Web Site: http://www.norwegianpiping.com
Oil & Gas Industry Pipe, Fittings, Flanges & Other Pipe Related Products Mfr & Distr
N.A.I.C.S.: 333132
Gert Christian Strindberg *(Mng Dir)*

Valvision AS (2)
Gamle Forusvei 25, 4031, Stavanger, Norway
Tel.: (47) 47769999
Web Site: http://www.valvision.no
Oil & Gas Industry Valves & Actuators Distr
N.A.I.C.S.: 333132
Leif Gronning *(Mng Dir)*

Subsidiary (Domestic):

Valvision AS (3)
Damsgardsveien 163, 5160, Laksevag, Norway
Tel.: (47) 47769999
Web Site: http://www.valvision.no
Oil & Gas Industry Valves & Actuators Distr

N.A.I.C.S.: 333132
Cicilie Froystein *(Ops Mgr)*

JX Nippon Exploration & Production (U.K.) Limited (1)
8th Floor 199Bishopsgate, London, EC2M 3TY, United Kingdom
Tel.: (44) 2073097650
Sales Range: $50-74.9 Million
Emp.: 40
Oil & Natural Gas Exploration, Development & Extraction
N.A.I.C.S.: 211120
Tim Blackford *(Exec Dir & Gen Mgr)*

Merrick Systems, Inc. (1)
55 Waugh Dr Ste 400, Houston, TX 77007
Tel.: (713) 579-3400
Sales Range: $10-24.9 Million
Software Solutions for the Oil & Gas Industry
N.A.I.C.S.: 513210
Kemal Farid *(Co-Founder & Pres)*

Suretank Group Ltd. (1)
Shamrock Hill Street, Dunleer, County Louth, Ireland
Tel.: (353) 41 686 2022
Web Site: http://www.suretank.com
Emp.: 120
Cargo Container Mfr
N.A.I.C.S.: 332439
John Fitzgerald *(CEO)*

Teresoft AS (1)
Jattavagveien 7, 4020, Stavanger, Norway
Tel.: (47) 91590479
Web Site: http://www.teresoft.no
Drilling & Well Performance Solutions Provider
N.A.I.C.S.: 213112
Toni Fadnes *(CEO)*

HITEJINRO HOLDINGS CO., LTD.

10th floor Hite Jinro Building 14 Seochojungang-ro, Seocho-gu, Seoul, 135-100, Korea (South)
Tel.: (82) 25203103
Web Site: https://www.hitejinroholdings.com
Year Founded: 1924
000140—(KRS)
Rev.: $1,905,440,501
Assets: $3,025,815,740
Liabilities: $2,131,941,475
Net Worth: $893,874,265
Earnings: $55,261,565
Emp.: 14
Fiscal Year-end: 12/31/22
Holding Company
N.A.I.C.S.: 551112
Yin Gyu Kim *(Pres & CEO)*

Subsidiaries:

B&B Korea Corporation (1)
1408-1415 Seonyu-ro 13-gil, Yeongdeungpo-gu, Seoul, 07282, Korea (South)
Tel.: (82) 226026879
Web Site: http://www.bnbkorea.co.kr
Cosmetics Products Mfr
N.A.I.C.S.: 325620
Bong-chun Ham *(CEO)*

HITEK GLOBAL, INC.

Unit 304 No 30 Guanri Road, Siming District, Xiamen, Fujian, China
Tel.: (86) 5925395967 Ky
Year Founded: 2017
HKIT—(NASDAQ)
Rev.: $4,563,731
Assets: $35,428,040
Liabilities: $7,090,454
Net Worth: $28,337,586
Earnings: $1,047,641
Emp.: 48
Fiscal Year-end: 12/31/23
Information Technology Consulting Services
N.A.I.C.S.: 541512
Shenping Yin *(Founder & Chm)*

HITEVISION CO., LTD.

8th-10th Floor Beichen Times Building No 8 Beichen East Road, Chaoyang District, Beijing, 100029, China
Tel.: (86) 1062968869
Web Site: https://www.honghe-tech.com
Year Founded: 2010
002955—(SSE)
Rev.: $638,745,588
Assets: $660,916,152
Liabilities: $152,041,968
Net Worth: $508,874,184
Earnings: $55,612,440
Fiscal Year-end: 12/31/22
Audio Equipment Mfr & Distr
N.A.I.C.S.: 334310
Xiuqing Xing *(Board of Directors & Chm)*

HITGEN INC.

Building 1 Floor 3 No 88 South Keyuan Road, Hi-Tech Zone, Chengdu, Sichuan, China
Tel.: (86) 2885197385 CN
Web Site: https://www.hitgen.com
688222—(SHG)
Rev.: $46,282,860
Assets: $234,326,336
Liabilities: $47,981,475
Net Worth: $186,344,861
Earnings: $3,547,346
Fiscal Year-end: 12/31/22
Bio Technology Services
N.A.I.C.S.: 541714
Jin Li *(Founder)*

HITHINK ROYALFLUSH INFORMATION NETWORK CO., LTD.

No 18 Tongshun Street Yuhang District, Hangzhou, 310023, Zhejiang, China
Tel.: (86) 57188852766
300033—(CHIN)
Rev.: $502,026,049
Assets: $1,386,648,630
Liabilities: $355,718,520
Net Worth: $1,030,930,109
Earnings: $197,537,702
Fiscal Year-end: 12/31/23
Financial Information Support Services
N.A.I.C.S.: 519290

HITI DIGITAL INC.

7F No 2072 Sec 3 Beixin Rd, Xindian Dist, Taipei, 231, Taiwan
Tel.: (886) 229126268
Web Site: https://www.hiti.com
Year Founded: 2001
3494—(TAI)
Rev.: $22,103,632
Assets: $62,671,079
Liabilities: $43,431,079
Net Worth: $19,240,001
Earnings: ($9,074,332)
Emp.: 300
Fiscal Year-end: 12/31/23
Digital Photo Product Mfr & Distr
N.A.I.C.S.: 325992
Kuan Chih Huang *(Exec VP)*

Subsidiaries:

HiTi Digital America, Inc. (1)
675 Brea Canyon Rd Ste 7, Walnut, CA 91789
Web Site: http://www.hiti.com
Emp.: 5
Photo Product Mfr & Distr
N.A.I.C.S.: 323111
Darren Paul *(Mgr-Svc)*

HiTi Digital Europe S.r.l (1)
Via Walter Marcobi 4, 21100, Varese, Italy
Tel.: (39) 03321765314
Web Site: http://www.hiti.com
Emp.: 4

INTERNATIONAL PUBLIC

Photo Product Distr
N.A.I.C.S.: 424120

HiTi Digital Singapore Pte Ltd (1)
5008 Ang Mo Kio Ave 5 04-09 Techplace II, Singapore, 569874, Singapore
Tel.: (65) 64751885
Photo Product Distr
N.A.I.C.S.: 424120

HiTi Digital, Inc. (1)
Pilares 506 Col Del Valle Del Benito Juarez, 03100, Mexico, Mexico
Tel.: (52) 5575874057
Photo Product Distr
N.A.I.C.S.: 424120

Hiti Digital (Suzhou), Inc. (1)
Room 1908 Bank of China Huilong Building No 8 Suzhou Avenue West, Suzhou Industrial Park, Suzhou, Jiangsu, China
Tel.: (86) 512822816882195
Photo Product Distr
N.A.I.C.S.: 424120

HITIM GROUP

4 rue du Radar, 74000, Annecy, France
Tel.: (33) 450679950 FR
Web Site: http://www.hitimgroup.com
Year Founded: 2007
Emp.: 170
Holding Company
N.A.I.C.S.: 551112
Franck Nagy *(Pres)*

Subsidiaries:

GEMMA (1)
4 Rue du Radar, 74000, Annecy, France
Tel.: (33) 450679950
Web Site: http://www.hitimgroup.com
Mfr of Precision Mechanical Components
N.A.I.C.S.: 334419

HITIQ LIMITED

Unit 4/38-42 White Street, South Melbourne, 3205, VIC, Australia
Tel.: (61) 478038567 AU
Web Site: https://www.hitiq.com
Year Founded: 2015
HIQ—(ASX)
Rev.: $1,955,995
Assets: $2,040,368
Liabilities: $2,070,923
Net Worth: ($30,554)
Earnings: ($3,284,414)
Emp.: 42
Fiscal Year-end: 06/30/23
Medical Device Mfr
N.A.I.C.S.: 325412
Damien Hawes *(Chief Comml Officer)*

HITIT HOLDING A.S.

Metin Kasapoglu Cad A Kadam Is Merkezi Blok No 50/9, Antalya, Turkiye
Tel.: (90) 2423116143
Web Site: http://www.hititholding.com.tr
Holding Company
N.A.I.C.S.: 551112
Sait Borekci *(Chm)*

Subsidiaries:

Hitit Ayakkabi Saat Mucevherat Turizm Insaat Petrol San. ve Tic. Ltd.Sti. (1)
Gulabibey Mah Ugur Mumcu Cad No 12, Merkez, Corum, Turkiye
Tel.: (90) 2252505
Footwear Distr
N.A.I.C.S.: 424340

Hitit Gold Kuyumculuk ve Mucevherat San. ve Tic. A.S. (1)
Ozdilek Alsveris Merkezi Dokuma, Antalya, Turkiye
Tel.: (90) 23444656
Diamond & Jewelry Distr
N.A.I.C.S.: 458310
Fatih ChiChek *(Gen Dir)*

Hitit Moda Tasarim Magazaclk Giyim Mucevherat San.Tic.Ltd.Sti. (1)
Metin Kasapoglu Cad A Kadam s Merkezi Blok No 50/9, Antalya, Turkiye
Tel.: (90) 2423116143
Diamond & Jewelry Whslr
N.A.I.C.S.: 458310

Hitit construction company (1)
Gulnur Sok Dalkiran Apt No 11/10 Sahrayicedit Kadikoy, 34740, Istanbul, Turkiye
Tel.: (90) 8757002
Construction Services
N.A.I.C.S.: 236210
Sait Borekci *(Chm)*

HITO COMMUNICATIONS HOLDINGS, INC.
1-9-6 Higashi Ikebukuro, Toshima-Ku, Tokyo, 170-0013, Japan
Tel.: (81) 359521111
Web Site: https://hitocom.co.jp
Year Founded: 2019
4433—(TKS)
Rev.: $364,162,340
Assets: $249,440,660
Liabilities: $133,661,580
Net Worth: $115,779,080
Earnings: ($267,460)
Fiscal Year-end: 08/31/24
Holding Company
N.A.I.C.S.: 551112
Toyoaki Yasui *(Chm, Pres & CEO)*

HITRON SYSTEMS INC.
5953-85 Seodong-daero Samjukmyeon, Anseong, 456-881, Gyeonggi-do, Korea (South)
Tel.: (82) 316709100
Web Site: http://www.hitron.co.kr
Year Founded: 1986
019490—(KRS)
Rev.: $8,257,116
Assets: $12,914,296
Liabilities: $2,958,320
Net Worth: $9,955,976
Earnings: ($5,907,249)
Emp.: 159
Fiscal Year-end: 12/31/22
Security Product Mfr
N.A.I.C.S.: 334290
Young-Duk Choi *(CEO)*

Subsidiaries:

Hitron Systems Inc. - China Factory (1)
No 19 Muqiao Jie Jinfeng Ru, Suzhou, Jiang Su, China
Tel.: (86) 512 6269 7001
Security Product Mfr
N.A.I.C.S.: 334290

HITRON TECHNOLOGIES INC.
No 1-8 Li-Hsin 1st Rd Hsinchu Science Park, Hsinchu, 30078, Taiwan
Tel.: (886) 35786658 CN
Web Site: https://www.hitrontech.com
Year Founded: 1986
2419—(TAI)
Rev.: $307,520,247
Assets: $343,657,203
Liabilities: $146,718,887
Net Worth: $196,938,316
Earnings: $5,357,075
Emp.: 879
Fiscal Year-end: 12/31/23
Communication & Internet Services
N.A.I.C.S.: 513199

Subsidiaries:

Hitron Technologies (SIP) Inc. (1)
No 158 Feng Li Street, Industrial Park, Suzhou, 215000, China
Tel.: (86) 51262653066
Telecommunications Equipment Mfr
N.A.I.C.S.: 334210

Hitron Technologies Americas Inc. (1)
9000 E Nichols Ave Ste 103, Centennial, CO 80112
Tel.: (303) 792-3380
Telecommunications Equipment Mfr
N.A.I.C.S.: 334210

Hitron Technologies Europe Holding B.V. (1)
Kingsfordweg 151, 1043 GR, Amsterdam, Netherlands
Tel.: (31) 204919440
Telecommunications Equipment Mfr
N.A.I.C.S.: 334210

Innoauto Technologies Inc. (1)
7F-2 No 1 Taiyuan 2nd St, Hsinchu County, Zhubei, 302, Taiwan
Tel.: (886) 35601859
Web Site: https://www.innoautotech.com
Electronic Products Mfr
N.A.I.C.S.: 334419

Interactive Digital Technologies Inc. (1)
No 38-1 Wugong 5th Rd, Wugu Dist, New Taipei City, 248, Taiwan
Tel.: (886) 222983456
Telecommunications Equipment Mfr
N.A.I.C.S.: 334210

Jietech Trading (Suzhou) Inc. (1)
Room 1216 West Tower QiuShi Center ZhuZiLin, Futian District, Shenzhen, 518040, China
Tel.: (86) 75583184136
Telecommunications Equipment Mfr
N.A.I.C.S.: 334210

HITTCO TOOLS LIMITED
78 III Phase Peenya Industrial Area, Bengaluru, 560 058, India
Tel.: (91) 8028392265
Web Site: https://www.hittco.in
Year Founded: 1995
531661—(BOM)
Rev.: $844,817
Assets: $1,011,696
Liabilities: $621,816
Net Worth: $389,880
Earnings: $74,239
Fiscal Year-end: 03/31/23
Cutting Tool Mfr
N.A.I.C.S.: 333515
Surendra Bhandari *(Chm & Mng Dir)*

HIVE BLOCKCHAIN TECHNOLOGIES LTD.
Suite 855 - 789 West Pender Street, Vancouver, V6C 1H2, BC, Canada
Tel.: (604) 664-1078
Web Site: https://www.hiveblockchain.com
HIVE—(NASDAQ)
Rev.: $114,465,000
Assets: $307,582,000
Liabilities: $47,890,000
Net Worth: $259,692,000
Earnings: ($51,205,000)
Emp.: 20
Fiscal Year-end: 03/31/24
Software Development Services
N.A.I.C.S.: 541511
Darcy Daubaras *(CFO)*

HIVEST CAPITAL PARTNERS SAS
140 Boulevard Malesherbes, 75017, Paris, France
Tel.: (33) 142890277
Web Site: https://hivestcapital.com
Privater Equity Firm
N.A.I.C.S.: 523940

HIVI ACOUSTICS TECHNOLOGY CO., LTD.
No 13 Sansha Road, Dongyong Town Nansha District, Guangzhou, 511453, China
Tel.: (86) 2084908098
Web Site: https://www.swanspeakers.com
Year Founded: 1991
002888—(SSE)
Rev.: $31,769,712
Assets: $65,599,092
Liabilities: $9,663,732
Net Worth: $55,935,360
Earnings: ($2,054,052)
Fiscal Year-end: 12/31/22
Electronic Product Mfr & Distr
N.A.I.C.S.: 334310

HIWIN MIKROSYSTEM CORP.
No 6 Jingke Central Rd, Precision Machinery Park, Taichung, 408211, Taiwan
Tel.: (886) 423550110
Web Site: https://www.hiwinmikro.tw
Year Founded: 1997
4576—(TAI)
Actuator & Motor Product Mfr
N.A.I.C.S.: 333995
Eric Chuo *(Pres & CEO)*

HIWIN TECHNOLOGIES CORP.
No 7 Jingke Road, Nantun District, Taichung, 408208, Taiwan
Tel.: (886) 423594510
Web Site: https://www.hiwin.tw
Year Founded: 1989
2049—(TAI)
Rev.: $805,545,344
Assets: $1,682,095,165
Liabilities: $533,780,188
Net Worth: $1,148,314,977
Earnings: $59,894,370
Emp.: 4,648
Fiscal Year-end: 12/31/23
Ball Screws, Roller Screws & Linear Guideways Mfr
N.A.I.C.S.: 332991
Eric Y. T. Chuo *(Founder & Co-Chm)*

Subsidiaries:

Eterbright Solar Corporation (1)
No 442-1 Zhonghua Rd, Miaoli County, Toufen, 351, Taiwan
Tel.: (886) 37627668
Web Site: http://www.eterbright.tw
Solar Power Generation Services
N.A.I.C.S.: 221114

HIWIN GmbH (1)
Brucklesbund 1, 77654, Offenburg, Germany
Tel.: (49) 781932780
Web Site: http://www.hiwin.de
Sales Range: $25-49.9 Million
Emp.: 100
Screw & Ball Bearings Mfr
N.A.I.C.S.: 332991

HIWIN JAPAN (1)
3F Sannomiya-Chuo Bldg 4-2-20 Goko-Dori, Chuo-Ku, Kobe, 651-0087, Japan
Tel.: (81) 782625413
Web Site: http://www.hiwin.co.jp
Screws & Engineering Products Mfr
N.A.I.C.S.: 332722

HIWIN S.R.O. (1)
Kastanova 34, CZ 62000, Brno, Czech Republic
Tel.: (420) 548528238
Web Site: http://www.hiwin.cz
Sales Range: $25-49.9 Million
Emp.: 20
Industrial Engineering Products Mfr
N.A.I.C.S.: 541330

HIWIN USA (1)
12455 Jim Dhamer Dr, Huntley, IL 60142
Tel.: (847) 827-2270
Web Site: http://www.hiwin.com
Sales Range: $25-49.9 Million
Emp.: 100
Screws & Engineering Products Mfr
N.A.I.C.S.: 332722
Jo Jo *(Pres)*

Hiwin S.R.L. (1)
ViaPitagora 4, Brugherio, 20861, Milan, Italy
Tel.: (39) 0392876168
Bolt & Screw Mfr
N.A.I.C.S.: 332722

Hiwin Singapore Pte. Ltd. (1)
Blk 203 Woodlands Avenue 9 06-51 Woodlands Spectrum II, Singapore, 738956, Singapore
Tel.: (65) 62570656
Web Site: https://www.hiwin.sg
Bolt & Screw Mfr
N.A.I.C.S.: 332722
Chen Hiwin Taddy *(Mng Dir)*

Luren Precision Co., Ltd. (1)
No 1-1 Li Hsin 1st Rd, Hsinchu Science Park, Hsin-chu, 300-78, Taiwan
Tel.: (886) 35786767
Gear Cutting Tool Mfr
N.A.I.C.S.: 333517

Matrix Machine Tool (Coventry) Limited (1)
Matrix House Herald Avenue, Coventry Business Park, Coventry, CV5 6UB, United Kingdom
Tel.: (44) 2476718886
Web Site: http://www.matrix-machine.com
Tool Mfr
N.A.I.C.S.: 333517

HIYES INTERNATIONAL CO., LTD.
7th Floor No 260 Dunhua North Road, Songshan District, Taipei, 105, Taiwan
Tel.: (886) 227035000 TW
Web Site: https://www.hiyes-group.com.tw
Year Founded: 1985
2348—(TAI)
Rev.: $133,296,868
Assets: $327,533,469
Liabilities: $208,058,925
Net Worth: $119,474,543
Earnings: $50,904,796
Fiscal Year-end: 12/31/20
Real Estate Development
N.A.I.C.S.: 531390
Hsi Wen Huang *(Chm)*

Subsidiaries:

Maxium Technologies (Shanghai) Inc. (1)
15th Floor B5 Huafu Building No 585 Longhua Road West, Xuhui, Shanghai, China
Tel.: (86) 21 6469 7567
Web Site: http://www.maxium.com.cn
Semiconductor Mfr
N.A.I.C.S.: 334413

Subsidiary (Non-US);

UMAX Systems GmbH (2)
Faumaweig 9, 47877, Willich, Germany
Tel.: (49) 215491870
Web Site: http://www.umax.de
Sales Range: $25-49.9 Million
Emp.: 24
Computer Equipment
N.A.I.C.S.: 449210

Subsidiary (US):

UMAX Technologies Inc. (2)
10460 Brockwood Rd, Dallas, TX 75238-1640
Tel.: (214) 739-1915
Web Site: http://www.umax.com
Designer & Distributor of Computer Products
N.A.I.C.S.: 423430

HIZEAERO CO.,LTD.
24 Gongdan 5-ro, Sanam-myun, Sacheon, 52535, Gyeongsangnam-do, Korea (South)
Tel.: (82) 558508800
Web Site: https://www.hizeaero.com
Year Founded: 1999
221840—(KRS)
Rev.: $45,081,435
Assets: $104,942,112
Liabilities: $58,552,694
Net Worth: $46,389,418
Earnings: ($9,445,063)

HIZEAERO CO.,LTD.

HIZEAERO Co.,Ltd.—(Continued)
Emp.: 391
Fiscal Year-end: 12/31/22
Aircraft Part Mfr
N.A.I.C.S.: 336411

HJ SHIPBUILDING & CONSTRUCTION COMPANY, LTD.
233 Taejong ro, Yeongdo gu, Busan, Korea (South)
Tel.: (82) 514103114
Web Site: https://www.hanjinsc.com
Year Founded: 1937
097230—(KRS)
Rev: $1,658,309,991
Assets: $2,217,078,695
Liabilities: $1,955,599,191
Net Worth: $261,479,504
Earnings: ($87,682,673)
Emp.: 2,227
Fiscal Year-end: 12/31/23
Construction & Shipbuilding Services; Commercial Buildings, Hotels, Hospitals & Container Carriers, LNG Carriers, Chemical Tankers & Petroleum Carriers
N.A.I.C.S.: 236220

Subsidiaries:

Hanjin City Gas (1)
711 Sanggye 6 Dong Nowon Gu, Seoul, Korea (South)
Tel.: (82) 29505000
Web Site: http://www.hjcgas.com
Natural Gas Distr
N.A.I.C.S.: 221210

Hanjin Heavy Industries & Construction - Construction Division (1)
103-17 Garwol-dong, Yongsan-gu, Seoul, 140 807, Korea (South)
Tel.: (82) 24508114
Web Site: http://www.hanjinsc.com
Construction of Bridges, Roads, Tunnels, Shipyards, Subways & Railways & Dredging & Harbors & Industrial & Commercial Buildings
N.A.I.C.S.: 237990

Hanjin Heavy Industries & Construction Co., Ltd. - Ulsan Factory (1)
492 Yongjam-dong, Nam-gu, Ulsan, 680-070, Korea (South)
Tel.: (82) 522593114
Ship Building Services
N.A.I.C.S.: 336611

Hanjin Heavy Industries & Construction Co., Ltd. - Yuldo Factory (1)
394 Wonchang-dong, Seo-gu, Incheon, 404-210, Korea (South)
Tel.: (82) 32 580 9114
Ship Building Services
N.A.I.C.S.: 336611

OCI Co., Ltd. - Incheon Plant (1)
595 Hakik-dong, Nam-gu, Incheon, 402-040, Korea (South)
Tel.: (82) 328606114
Sodium Cynate Mfr
N.A.I.C.S.: 325411

HJEMMET MORTENSEN AS
Nydalsveien 12, 0441, Oslo, Norway
Tel.: (47) 22585000
Web Site: http://www.hjemmet.no
Sales Range: $100-124.9 Million
Emp.: 600
Media Company
N.A.I.C.S.: 541840
Lise Hansen (Editor-in-Chief)

Subsidiaries:

Hachette Filipacchi Norge A/S (1)
Hegdehaugsveien 24, PO Box 5134, Majorstua, NO 0302, Oslo, Norway
Tel.: (47) 22609900
Web Site: http://www.elle.no
Sales Range: $1-9.9 Million
Emp.: 25
Magazine Publisher
N.A.I.C.S.: 513120

Signy Fardal (Mng Dir)

HK ACQUISITION CORPORATION
Suites 4310-11 Tower One Times Square 1 Matheson Street, Causeway Bay, China (Hong Kong)
Tel.: (852) 22681800 Ky
Web Site: https://hkacquisition.com
Year Founded: 2022
7841—(HKG)
Rev.: $358,976
Assets: $128,574,324
Liabilities: $152,320,483
Net Worth: ($23,746,159)
Earnings: ($22,323,770)
Fiscal Year-end: 12/31/22
Asset Management Services
N.A.I.C.S.: 523999
Norman Tak Lam Chan (Chm)

HK ASIA HOLDINGS LTD.
Chun Wo Commercial Centre 23 Wing Wo Street 24th Floor, Sheung Wan, China (Hong Kong)
Tel.: (852) 25814050 Ky
Web Site: http://www.hkasiaholdings.com
1723—(HKG)
Rev.: $26,082,420
Assets: $22,828,620
Liabilities: $1,192,253
Net Worth: $21,636,368
Earnings: $502,350
Emp.: 45
Fiscal Year-end: 03/31/23
Telecommunication Product Retailer
N.A.I.C.S.: 423690
Muk Lung Siu (Chm)

HK CO., LTD.
117 Sareupjae gil Yanggam myeon, Hwaseong, Gyeonggi-do, Korea (South)
Tel.: (82) 313502900
Web Site: https://www.hk-global.com
Year Founded: 1990
044780—(KRS)
Rev.: $62,417,412
Assets: $66,127,290
Liabilities: $20,784,415
Net Worth: $45,342,875
Earnings: $3,277,421
Emp.: 127
Fiscal Year-end: 12/31/22
Laser Processing Equipment Mfr
N.A.I.C.S.: 333310
Jay Kay (CEO)

Subsidiaries:

HK America Inc. (1)
1120 N Garfeld St, Lombard, IL 60148
Tel.: (630) 916-0200
Industrial Machinery Mfr
N.A.I.C.S.: 333310

HK ELECTRIC INVESTMENTS LIMITED
Hongkong Electric Centre 44 Kennedy Road, GPO Box 915, Hong Kong, China (Hong Kong)
Tel.: (852) 28433111 Ky
Web Site: https://www.hkelectric.com
Year Founded: 1889
2638—(HKG)
Rev.: $1,376,107,500
Assets: $15,427,755,000
Liabilities: $9,137,797,500
Net Worth: $6,289,957,500
Earnings: $376,635,000
Emp.: 1,690
Fiscal Year-end: 12/31/22
Investment Holding Company
N.A.I.C.S.: 551112
Canning Kin Ning Fok (Chm & Exec Dir)

HK INNO.N CORP.
Pine Avenue Tower A 100 Euljiro, Jung-Gu, Seoul, 04551, Korea (South)
Tel.: (82) 264770000
Web Site: https://www.inno-n.com
Year Founded: 1984
195940—(KRS)
Emp.: 1,679
Pharmaceuticals Product Mfr
N.A.I.C.S.: 325412
Kang Seok Hee (CEO)

HK KOMGRAP AD
Terazije 4, 11000, Belgrade, Serbia
Tel.: (381) 11 362 00 79
Web Site: http://komgrap.com
Year Founded: 1945
Civil Engineering Construction Services
N.A.I.C.S.: 237990
Drasko Pasic (Pres, Member-Exec Bd, Gen Mgr & Exec Dir-Fin Economic Affairs)

HK WUSEJIE GROUP CO. LTD.
149 Zhangbei Road Ailian Village, Longgang District, Shenzhen, 518172, China
Tel.: (86) 75528999790
Web Site: http://www.wusejie.com
Sales Range: $1-9.9 Million
Home Decoration Products Including Wooden Sculptures, Vases & Water-Based Paint Products Mfr & Sales
N.A.I.C.S.: 321999
Zhiming Cai (CEO)

HKC (HOLDINGS) LIMITED
9th Floor Tower 1 South Seas Centre 75 Mody Road Tsimshatsui East, Kowloon, China (Hong Kong)
Tel.: (852) 27310000 BM
Web Site: http://www.hkcholdings.com
Rev.: $133,148,329
Assets: $2,829,270,371
Liabilities: $808,816,067
Net Worth: $2,020,454,304
Earnings: $48,474,775
Emp.: 230
Fiscal Year-end: 12/31/19
Construction & Property Development
N.A.I.C.S.: 236220
Eric Kang Oei (Chm & CEO)

HKC INTERNATIONAL HOLDINGS LIMITED
Block B 14/F Vita Tower 29 Wong Chuk Hang Road, Hong Kong, China (Hong Kong)
Tel.: (852) 2 528 3936 Ky
Web Site: http://www.hkc.com.hk
0248—(HKG)
Rev.: $25,679,402
Assets: $49,098,559
Liabilities: $12,880,717
Net Worth: $36,217,842
Earnings: ($250,608)
Emp.: 92
Fiscal Year-end: 03/31/22
Construction, Engineering & Energy Services
N.A.I.C.S.: 541330
Martin Man Hon Ip (CTO)

Subsidiaries:

Circle Mobile Communications Limited (1)
14/F Block B Vita Tower 29 Wong Chuk Hang Road, Hong Kong, China (Hong Kong)
Tel.: (852) 28611832
Web Site: http://www.hkc.com.hk
Consumer Electronics Retailer
N.A.I.C.S.: 449210

INTERNATIONAL PUBLIC

HKC International (Thailand) Co. Ltd. (1)
496 - 502 Amarin Plaza 10F Ploenchit Road Lumpini, Pathumpawan, Bangkok, 10330, Thailand
Tel.: (66) 23056874
Mobile Phone Distr
N.A.I.C.S.: 423690

HKC Technology (Shanghai) Co. Ltd. (1)
11th Floor East Huai Hai International Building, Baoshan Distrist, Shanghai, 200021, China
Tel.: (86) 2161702233
Web Site: http://www.hkc.com.hk
Telecommunications Equipment Mfr
N.A.I.C.S.: 334210

HKC Technology Limited (1)
14/F Block B Vita Tower 29 Wong Chuk Hang Road, Hong Kong, China (Hong Kong)
Tel.: (852) 22559488
Web Site: http://www.hkc.com.hk
Telecommunications Equipment Mfr
N.A.I.C.S.: 334210

Hong Kong Communications Company Limited (1)
14/F Block B Vita Tower 29 Wong Chuk Hang Road, Hong Kong, China (Hong Kong)
Tel.: (852) 25283936
Web Site: http://www.hkc.com.hk
Sales Range: $75-99.9 Million
Telecommunication Equipment Distr
N.A.I.C.S.: 423690

Singapore Communications Equipment Co. Pte Ltd. (1)
8 Jalan Kilang Timor 03-09 Kewalram House, Singapore, 159305, Singapore
Tel.: (65) 68 800 800
Web Site: http://www.singcomm.com.sg
Sales Range: $25-49.9 Million
Emp.: 20
Communication Equipment Sales
N.A.I.C.S.: 423690
Irene Yeo (Mgr-Fin)

Wavex Technologies Pte. Ltd. (1)
8 Jln Kilang Timor 01-08 Kewalram House, Singapore, 159305, Singapore
Tel.: (65) 63569773
Web Site: http://www.wavex-tech.com
Sales Range: $25-49.9 Million
Emp.: 30
Wireless Products Mfr
N.A.I.C.S.: 333310

HKE HOLDINGS LTD.
10 Admiralty Street 02-47 Northlink Building, Singapore, 757695, Singapore
Tel.: (65) 65551612 Ky
Web Site: http://www.hwakoon.com
Year Founded: 1979
1726—(HKG)
Rev.: $9,961,109
Assets: $25,758,689
Liabilities: $3,487,544
Net Worth: $22,271,146
Earnings: ($10,770,651)
Emp.: 139
Fiscal Year-end: 06/30/23
Medical Equipment Installation Services
N.A.I.C.S.: 811210
Lee Huat Koh (Exec Dir)

Subsidiaries:

Hwa Koon Engineering Pte. Ltd. (1)
10 Admiralty Street No 02-47 Northlink Building, Singapore, 757695, Singapore
Tel.: (65) 65551612
Integrated Design & Building Services
N.A.I.C.S.: 541810
Ryan Ong (Mgr-Bus)

HKFOODS PLC
Lemminkaisenkatu 48, PO Box 50, FI-20521, Turku, Finland
Tel.: (358) 10570100

AND PRIVATE COMPANIES

Web Site: https://www.hkfoods.com
Year Founded: 1913
HKFOODS—(HEL)
Rev.: $1,255,342,111
Assets: $919,166,847
Liabilities: $691,344,701
Net Worth: $227,822,145
Earnings: ($28,491,258)
Emp.: 2,834
Fiscal Year-end: 12/31/23
Meat Product Whslr
N.A.I.C.S.: 424470
Anne Mere *(Exec VP-Bus Unit-Baltics)*

Subsidiaries:

AS HKScan Estonia (1)
Roodevalja kula, Laane-Virumaa, 44207, Rakvere, Estonia
Tel.: (372) 3229221
Food Products Mfr
N.A.I.C.S.: 311999

HKScan Denmark A/S (1)
Agro Food Park 15, 8200, Aarhus, Denmark
Tel.: (45) 9 995 9595
Web Site: https://www.rosepoultry.com
Food Products Mfr
N.A.I.C.S.: 311999

HKScan Finland Oy (1)
Lemminkaisenkatu 48, PO Box 50, 20521, Turku, Finland
Tel.: (358) 10570100
Food Products Mfr
N.A.I.C.S.: 311999
Heidi Karkkainen *(Mgr-Digital Mktg)*

Subsidiary (Domestic):

Lihatukku Harri Tamminen Oy (2)
Itainen Valkoisenlahteentie 21, 01260, Vantaa, Finland
Tel.: (358) 98689000
Web Site: http://www.tamminen.fi
Food Products Mfr
N.A.I.C.S.: 311999

Paimion Teurastamo Oy (2)
Kotkojantie 83, 21530, Paimio, Finland
Tel.: (358) 2 477 2000
Web Site: https://www.paimionteurastamo.fi
Emp.: 40
Food Products Mfr
N.A.I.C.S.: 311999

HKScan Latvia AS (1)
Atlasa iela 7, Riga, LV-1026, Latvia
Tel.: (371) 67368643
Food Products Mfr
N.A.I.C.S.: 311999
Beata Petkevica *(Mgr-HR)*

HKScan Sweden AB (1)
Lindhagensgatan 126, 112 51, Stockholm, Sweden
Tel.: (46) 771510510
Food Products Mfr
N.A.I.C.S.: 311999
Fredrik Sundstrom *(Acct Mgr)*

UAB HKScan Lietuva (1)
Laives pr 3, LT-04215, Vilnius, Lithuania
Tel.: (370) 52490840
Food Products Mfr
N.A.I.C.S.: 311999

HKR INTERNATIONAL LIMITED

23/F China Merchants Tower Shun Tak Centre 168 Connaught Road, Central, China (Hong Kong)
Tel.: (852) 22381188 Ky
Web Site: https://www.hkri.com
Year Founded: 1977
HKR—(HKG)
Rev.: $508,477,854
Assets: $4,919,942,100
Liabilities: $1,488,467,894
Net Worth: $3,431,474,206
Earnings: $145,566,828
Emp.: 1,624
Fiscal Year-end: 03/31/21
Real Estate Development Services
N.A.I.C.S.: 531390

Payson Mou Sing Cha *(Chm)*

Subsidiaries:

Ammed Cancer Center (Central) Limited (1)
Shop B1 G/F 119-120 Connaught Road Central Sheung Wan, Central, China (Hong Kong)
Tel.: (852) 3 607 7600
Web Site: https://www.ammed.com
Health Care Srvices
N.A.I.C.S.: 622110

Health & Care Group Limited (1)
28/F CDW Building 388 Castle Peak Road, Tsuen Wan, NT, China (Hong Kong)
Tel.: (852) 2 666 6661
Web Site: https://www.health-care.com.hk
Health Care Srvices
N.A.I.C.S.: 622110

Humphrey & Partners Medical Services Management Limited (1)
28/F CDW Building 388 Castle Peak Road, Tsuen Wan, China (Hong Kong)
Tel.: (852) 23989852
Web Site: http://www.hpms.com.hk
Medical Devices
N.A.I.C.S.: 621111

Qualigenics Medical Limited (1)
Unit 20-21 6/F Worldwide House 19 Des Voeux Road, Central, China (Hong Kong)
Tel.: (852) 3 607 7800
Web Site: https://www.qualigenics.com
Health Care Srvices
N.A.I.C.S.: 622110

HKS CO., LTD.

2266 Kamiide, Fujinomiya, 418-0192, Shizuoka, Japan
Tel.: (81) 544291111
Web Site: https://www.hks-global.com
Year Founded: 1973
7219—(TKS)
Rev.: $56,004,880
Assets: $82,974,800
Liabilities: $18,796,840
Net Worth: $64,177,960
Earnings: $2,158,340
Emp.: 422
Fiscal Year-end: 08/31/24
Automobile Parts Mfr
N.A.I.C.S.: 336390
Daisuke Mizuguchi *(Pres)*

Subsidiaries:

Boost Controlled Performance Inc. (1)
31203 Schoolcraft, Livonia, MI 48150
Tel.: (734) 744-4467
Web Site: https://boostcontrolledperformance.com
Automobile Parts Distr
N.A.I.C.S.: 423120

Chang Heart Corp. (1)
No 109 Section 1 Guangfu Road, Sanchong District, New Taipei City, Taiwan
Tel.: (886) 285123338
Automobile Parts Mfr
N.A.I.C.S.: 336390

DD Performance Research LLC (1)
4073 FM 3538, Sealy, TX 77474
Tel.: (979) 627-7545
Web Site: https://www.ddperformanceresearch.com
Automotive Repair Services
N.A.I.C.S.: 561621

HKS (Shanghai) Trading Co., Ltd (1)
Floor 1 Building 212 and 213 Lane 3938 Huqingping Highway, Qingpu District, Shanghai, China
Tel.: (86) 2160739590
Web Site: http://www.hks-power.com.cn
Automobile Parts Distr
N.A.I.C.S.: 423120

HKS (Thailand) Co., Ltd. (1)
884 Moo 2 Phraek Sa Mai, Mueang Samutprakan, Samut Prakan, 10280, Thailand
Tel.: (66) 211647004
Automobile Parts Distr
N.A.I.C.S.: 423120

HKS Europe, Ltd. (1)
Unit 4/5 Sawfield House Alconbury Hill, Alconbury Weston, Huntingdon, PE28 4JL, Cambridgeshire, United Kingdom
Tel.: (44) 148 043 1604
Web Site: https://www.hkseurope.com
Automotive Parts Mfr & Distr
N.A.I.C.S.: 336390

HKS Technical Factory Co., Ltd. (1)
5-2-8 Bijyogi, Toda, 335-0031, Saitama, Japan
Tel.: (81) 484210508
Web Site: https://www.hks-tf.co.jp
Automotive Repair Services
N.A.I.C.S.: 811111

N-One Racing Sdn Bhd. (1)
No 8 Lorong SS13/3D, Subang Jaya Industrial Estate, 47500, Subang Jaya, Selangor, Malaysia
Tel.: (60) 356365557
Web Site: https://www.n1racing.net
Motor Vehicle Parts Distr
N.A.I.C.S.: 423140

Performance Wholesale Pty. Ltd. (1)
6 Cronulla Court, Slacks Creek, Brisbane, 4127, QLD, Australia
Tel.: (61) 738081986
Web Site: https://performancewholesale.com.au
Engine Parts Distr
N.A.I.C.S.: 423120

RCTS Autoworx Inc. (1)
526 Cleveland Cres SE, Calgary, T2G 4A9, AB, Canada
Tel.: (403) 259-3106
Web Site: https://rctscanada.com
Automobile Parts Mfr
N.A.I.C.S.: 336390

Real Auto Dynamics Inc. (1)
3574 Lawson Blvd, Oceanside, NY 11572
Tel.: (516) 442-7155
Web Site: https://realautodynamics.com
Automotive Repair Services
N.A.I.C.S.: 561621

Riken Motor Sales Inc. (1)
1020-22 G Masangkay St, Binondo, Manila, 1006, Philippines
Tel.: (63) 22440011
Automobile Parts Distr
N.A.I.C.S.: 423120

ST Hitec Ltd. (1)
20A Sylvia Park Road, Mt Wellington, Auckland, New Zealand
Tel.: (64) 95735575
Automobile Parts Mfr
N.A.I.C.S.: 336390

Sing Hiap Hin Co. (1)
Simpang 21 Unit 27 And 28 Block B, Gadong central gadong bandar seri begawan, BE3180, Negara, Brunei Darussalam
Tel.: (673) 2420142
Automobile Parts Distr
N.A.I.C.S.: 423120

Top Racing Group Ltd. (1)
Flat 6 G/f Sino Ind Plaza No 9 Kai Cheung Road, Kowloon bay, Kowloon, China (Hong Kong)
Tel.: (852) 23111668
Automobile Parts Distr
N.A.I.C.S.: 423120

Tunehouse Pty. Ltd. (1)
11 Chalder Street, Marrickville, 2204, NSW, Australia
Tel.: (61) 295574000
Web Site: https://tunehouse.com.au
Automotive Repair Services
N.A.I.C.S.: 561621

HL CORP

The 3rd Industrial Park Bitou Village Song Gang Town, Baoan District, Shenzhen, 518105, China
Tel.: (86) 75527130185
Web Site: http://www.hlcorp.com
002105—(SSE)
Rev.: $256,210,344
Assets: $269,033,076

HL GLOBAL ENTERPRISES LIMITED

Liabilities: $118,476,540
Net Worth: $150,556,536
Earnings: $26,560,872
Fiscal Year-end: 12/31/22
Sports Apparatus & Fitness Equipment Mfr
N.A.I.C.S.: 339920

Subsidiaries:

HL CORP (HONG KONG) Limited (1)
Room 3 6 Floor Nam Wo Hong Building No 148 Wing Lok Street, Hong Kong, China (Hong Kong)
Tel.: (852) 25593876
Bicycle Parts Mfr & Distr
N.A.I.C.S.: 336991

HL CORP (TAICANG) (1)
San gang Vlg Ludu town, Taicang, 215412, Jiang Su, China
Tel.: (86) 512 81609999
Web Site: http://www.hlcorp.com.cn
Bicycle Parts Mfr & Distr
N.A.I.C.S.: 336991

HL CORP (USA), Inc. (1)
11410 Knott St, Garden Grove, CA 92841
Tel.: (714) 894-1500
Web Site: http://www.hlcorp.com
Sales Range: $25-49.9 Million
Emp.: 7
Sporting & Fitness Equipment Mfr & Distr
N.A.I.C.S.: 339920
Jon Chiang *(Pres)*

HL CORP - Handlebar Division (1)
55 Zhong Huan Road 4th Industrial Park Longhua Town, Baoan District, Shenzhen, 518190, China
Tel.: (86) 755 27749423
Web Site: http://www.hlcorp.com
Sales Range: $800-899.9 Million
Emp.: 2,900
Bicycle Parts Mfr
N.A.I.C.S.: 336991

HL CORP - Medical Equipment Division (1)
3rd Industrial Park, Bitou Village Songgang Town Baoan District, Shenzhen, 518105, China
Tel.: (86) 75527130185
Web Site: http://www.hlcorp.com
Sales Range: $100-124.9 Million
Emp.: 450
Medical Equipment Mfr
N.A.I.C.S.: 339113

HL CORP - Sporting Goods and Fitness Division (1)
The 3rd Industrial Park Bitou Village Songgang Town, Baoan District, Shenzhen, 518105, China
Tel.: (86) 755 2713 0185
Web Site: http://www.hlcorp.cn
Rev.: $63,356,000
Emp.: 70
Sporting & Fitness Equipment Mfr
N.A.I.C.S.: 339920

HL GLOBAL ENTERPRISES LIMITED

10 Anson Road 19-08 International Plaza, Singapore, 079903, Singapore
Tel.: (65) 63249500 SG
Web Site: https://www.hlge.com.sg
Year Founded: 1961
AVX—(SES)
Rev.: $4,445,202
Assets: $60,067,409
Liabilities: $1,710,217
Net Worth: $58,357,192
Earnings: $1,239,870
Emp.: 117
Fiscal Year-end: 12/31/23
Investment Holding Services
N.A.I.C.S.: 551112
Kit Sung Yam *(Gen Mgr-Asset Mgmt-China)*

Subsidiaries:

Equality Hotel Management Sdn. Bhd. (1)

HL GLOBAL ENTERPRISES LIMITED

HL Global Enterprises Limited—(Continued)
Menara Dion 28-01 27 Jalan Sultan Ismail, 50250, Kuala Lumpur, Malaysia
Tel.: (60) 320311133
Web Site: http://www.equatorial.com
Hotel Operator
N.A.I.C.S.: 721110

Equatorial Hotel Management Pte. Ltd. (1)
1 Raffles Place 02-01 One Raffles Place Mall, Singapore, 048616, Singapore
Tel.: (65) 67217155
Hotel Operator
N.A.I.C.S.: 721110

HL SCIENCE CO., LTD.
89 Anyangpangyo-ro, Uiwang, Gyeonggi-do, Korea (South)
Tel.: (82) 314219903
Web Site: https://www.hlscience.com
Year Founded: 2000
239610—(KRS)
Rev.: $40,465,543
Assets: $83,463,083
Liabilities: $3,463,571
Net Worth: $79,999,512
Earnings: $1,173,661
Emp.: 104
Fiscal Year-end: 12/31/22
Healthcare Product Mfr & Distr
N.A.I.C.S.: 325411
Hae-Yeon Lee (CEO)

HL THORNE & CO., LTD.
The Metal Works Union Road, Oldbury, B69 3EX, West Midlands, United Kingdom
Tel.: (44) 1215148000
Web Site: http://www.thorneltd.co.uk
Year Founded: 1955
Sales Range: $75-99.9 Million
Emp.: 20
Metal Product Whslr
N.A.I.C.S.: 423510
Malcolm Thorne (Mng Dir)

Subsidiaries:

Premier Metal Recyclers Ltd (1)
Hainge Road Tividale, PO Box 44, Oldbury, B69 2PA, West Midlands, United Kingdom
Tel.: (44) 1215576155
Web Site:
 http://www.premiermetalrecyclers.co.uk
Nonferrous Metal Recycling Services
N.A.I.C.S.: 331410
Emma Carroll (Deputy Mgr)

HLA CORP., LTD.
Xinqiao Town Jiangyin, Wuxi, 214426, Jiangsu, China
Tel.: (86) 51086121071
600398—(SHG)
Rev.: $2,606,068,605
Assets: $4,597,912,959
Liabilities: $2,559,009,740
Net Worth: $2,038,903,219
Earnings: $302,600,750
Fiscal Year-end: 12/31/22
Apparel Store Operator
N.A.I.C.S.: 458110

HLADNJACA A.D.
Milutina Mandica bb, Cacak, Serbia
Tel.: (381) 32 373 404
Year Founded: 1982
HLCA—(BEL)
Sales Range: Less than $1 Million
Emp.: 34
Refrigerated Warehousing & Storage Services
N.A.I.C.S.: 493120
Miladin Martinovic (Exec Dir)

HLB (THAILAND) LTD.
990 Abdulrahim Place 11th Floor Suite 1101 Rama IV Road Silom, Bangrak, Bangkok, 10500, Thailand
Tel.: (66) 26360354   TH
Web Site: http://www.hlbthai.com
Year Founded: 1999
Emp.: 30
Auditing & Accounting Services
N.A.I.C.S.: 541211
Narumol Sakritchanan (Partner)

HLB AZERBAIJAN LLC
MZ Plaza 5rd Floor Door 56 Ziya Bunyadov Str 1965th estate, AZ1069, Baku, Azerbaijan
Tel.: (994) 125648653
Web Site: http://www.hlbaz.com
Year Founded: 2001
Emp.: 4
Auditing & Accounting Services
N.A.I.C.S.: 541211
Islam Bayramov (Mng Partner)

HLB BIOSTEP CO., LTD.
38 Academy-Ro 79 Beon-Gil, Yeonsu-Gu, Incheon, Korea (South)
Tel.: (82) 328338899
Web Site:
 https://www.hlbbiostep.com
Year Founded: 2012
278650—(KRS)
Rev.: $53,838,240
Assets: $68,278,127
Liabilities: $17,655,747
Net Worth: $50,622,380
Earnings: $7,902,058
Emp.: 147
Fiscal Year-end: 12/31/20
Research & Experimental Development Services
N.A.I.C.S.: 541715
Jeong In-Sung (Co-CEO)

HLB CHILE - CONSULTORES Y AUDITORES DE EMPRESAS LTDA.
Los Militares 5620 Office 1708 Las Condes, Santiago, Chile
Tel.: (56) 223630739
Auditing & Accounting Services
N.A.I.C.S.: 541211

HLB CINNAMON, JANG, WILLOUGHBY & CO.
Metro Tower II Ste 900 4720 Kingsway, Burnaby, V5H 4N2, BC, Canada
Tel.: (604) 435-4317
Web Site: http://www.cjw.com
Year Founded: 1987
Sales Range: $75-99.9 Million
Emp.: 60
Accounting, Tax Planning & Financial Advisory Services
N.A.I.C.S.: 541211
Brian Gardiner (Partner-Governance & Advocacy)

HLB DEUTSCHLAND GMBH
National Secretariat Steinstrasse 27, 40210, Dusseldorf, Germany
Tel.: (49) 2113239193
Web Site: http://www.hlb-deutschland.de
Auditing & Accounting Services
N.A.I.C.S.: 541211

HLB EL SALVADOR, S.A. DE C.V.
75 Avenida Norte N 620 Edificio HLB Col Escalon, San Salvador, El Salvador
Tel.: (503) 22642547
Auditing & Accounting Services
N.A.I.C.S.: 541211

HLB GLOBAL CO LTD
38-13 Dongtan-gil Sabuk-eup, Jongnogu, Jeongseon, 233901, Gangwon-do, Korea (South)
Tel.: (82) 269254450   KR
Web Site: https://www.hlbglobal.co.kr
Year Founded: 1962
003580—(KRS)
Rev.: $34,201,987
Assets: $92,228,824
Liabilities: $40,066,155
Net Worth: $52,162,669
Earnings: ($11,691,576)
Emp.: 43
Fiscal Year-end: 12/31/22
Sea Sand & Molybdenum Mining
N.A.I.C.S.: 212321
Kim Kwang Jae (CEO)

Subsidiaries:

Dandi Bioscience Co., Ltd. (1)
304 Biomedical Science and Technology Building Konkuk Univ 120, Neungdong-ro Gwangjin-gu, Seoul, 05029, Korea (South)
Tel.: (82) 269250379
Web Site: http://www.dandibio.com
Bioscience Development Services
N.A.I.C.S.: 541715

HLB INC.
272-12 Dangwol-ro, Onsan-eup Uljugun, Ulsan, Korea (South)
Tel.: (82) 25611975
Web Site: https://www.hlbkorea.com
Year Founded: 2000
028300—(KRS)
Rev.: $137,835,969
Assets: $741,892,588
Liabilities: $205,776,209
Net Worth: $536,116,379
Earnings: ($59,947,852)
Emp.: 191
Fiscal Year-end: 12/31/22
Boat & Electrical Equipment Mfr
N.A.I.C.S.: 336612
Yang Gon Jin (Board of Directors & Chm)

HLB INNOVATION CO.,LTD.
16 Barangongdan-ro 4-gil Hyangnameup, Haewundae-gu, Hwaseong, Gyeonggi-do, Korea (South)
Tel.: (82) 315223700
Web Site: https://www.psmc.kr
Year Founded: 1978
024850—(KRS)
Rev.: $35,254,654
Assets: $30,834,879
Liabilities: $17,088,898
Net Worth: $13,745,981
Earnings: ($3,500,173)
Emp.: 67
Fiscal Year-end: 03/31/21
Semiconductor & Related Device Mfr
N.A.I.C.S.: 334413
Pyo Chang Min (VP)

HLB INTERNATIONAL LIMITED
21 Ebury Street, London, SW1W 0LD, United Kingdom
Tel.: (44) 2078811100   UK
Web Site: http://www.hlbi.com
Year Founded: 1969
Sales Range: $1-4.9 Billion
Emp.: 27,485
Accounting, Tax Planning & Financial Advisory Services
N.A.I.C.S.: 523940
Marco Donzelli (CEO)

HLB LIFE SCIENCE CO.,LTD.
51-9 Dongtan Advanced Industry 1-ro, Hwaseong, Gyeonggi-do, Korea (South)
Tel.: (82) 226276700
Web Site: https://www.hlb-ls.com
Year Founded: 1998
067630—(KRS)
Rev.: $76,386,585

INTERNATIONAL PUBLIC

Assets: $315,843,215
Liabilities: $134,780,095
Net Worth: $181,063,120
Earnings: ($41,630,793)
Emp.: 88
Fiscal Year-end: 12/31/22
Renewable Energy Consulting Services
N.A.I.C.S.: 541690

Subsidiaries:

Sinwha Advance Co., Ltd. (1)
Room 215 SKY1 Center 10 Seonyuro-gil 9-gil, Yeongdeungpo-gu, Seoul, Korea (South)
Tel.: (82) 28347971
Medical Material Distr
N.A.I.C.S.: 423450

HLB MANN JUDD AUSTRALASIAN ASSOCIATION
Level 5 10 Shelley Street, Sydney, 2000, NSW, Australia
Tel.: (61) 290204000   AU
Web Site: http://www.hlb.com.au
Year Founded: 1981
Sales Range: $75-99.9 Million
Accounting, Tax Preparation, Financial Advisory & Business Consulting Services Association
N.A.I.C.S.: 813910
Tony Fittler (Chm)

Subsidiaries:

HLB Mann Judd (WA) Pty Ltd (1)
Level 4 130 Stirling Street, Perth, 6000, WA, Australia
Tel.: (61) 892277500
Web Site: https://hlb.com.au
Accounting, Tax Preparation, Financial Advisory & Business Consulting Services
N.A.I.C.S.: 541211
Lucio Di Giallonardo (Mng Partner)

HLB PANAGENE CO., LTD.
54 Techno 10-ro, Yuesong-gu, Daejeon, 34027, Korea (South)
Tel.: (82) 428619295
Web Site: https://www.panagene.com
Year Founded: 2001
046210—(KRS)
Rev.: $10,869,365
Assets: $26,594,520
Liabilities: $2,288,869
Net Worth: $24,305,651
Earnings: $1,718,462
Emp.: 73
Fiscal Year-end: 12/31/22
Molecular Diagnostic Product Mfr
N.A.I.C.S.: 621511
Sung Kee Kim (Pres & CEO)

HLB PHARMACEUTICAL CO LTD
778-1Ilpaedong Gyeonggangro, Namyangju, Gyeonggi-do, Korea (South)
Tel.: (82) 315570001
Web Site:
 https://www.hlbpharma.co.kr
Year Founded: 1998
047920—(KRS)
Rev.: $82,438,595
Assets: $109,049,843
Liabilities: $43,142,641
Net Worth: $65,907,202
Earnings: ($9,032,760)
Emp.: 237
Fiscal Year-end: 12/31/22
Pharmaceuticals Product Mfr
N.A.I.C.S.: 325412
Park Jae-Hyeong (CEO)

HLB TECHNOLOGIES (MUMBAI) PRIVATE LIMITED
Suite 51 Bombay Mutual Building Sir Phirozshah Mehta Road, Fort, 400

AND PRIVATE COMPANIES

001, Mumbai, Maharashtra, India
Tel.: (91) 2222336359
Web Site:
http://www.hlbtechnologies.com
Year Founded: 1969
Auditing & Accounting Services
N.A.I.C.S.: 541211
Shivji K. Vikamsey *(Co-Founder)*

HLB THERAPEUTICS CO., LTD.
22nd Floor Parkview Office Tower
248 Jeongjail-ro, Bundang-Gu,
Seongnam, 13554, Gyeonggi-do, Korea (South)
Tel.: (82) 317867800
Web Site:
https://hlbtherapeutics.co.kr
Year Founded: 2000
115450—(KRS)
Rev.: $36,917,397
Assets: $143,922,379
Liabilities: $45,657,755
Net Worth: $98,264,624
Earnings: ($9,283,877)
Emp.: 87
Fiscal Year-end: 12/31/22
Software Development Services
N.A.I.C.S.: 541511
Ki-Hong Ahn *(Pres & CEO)*

HLB UKRAINE LLC
11/11 Gusovskogo Street office 3,
01011, Kiev, Ukraine
Tel.: (380) 445691900 UA
Web Site: http://www.hlb.com.ua
Year Founded: 1994
Auditing & Accounting Services
N.A.I.C.S.: 541211
Valeriy Bondar *(Mng Partner)*

HLD ASSOCIES SA
41-43 rue Saint Dominique, 75007,
Paris, France
Tel.: (33) 180 480 670 FR
Web Site: http://www.groupehld.com
Privater Equity Firm
N.A.I.C.S.: 523999
Jean-Bernard Lafonta *(Co-Founder)*

Subsidiaries:

Rafaut SA (1)
13 Avenue Marcellin Berthelot, 92390, Villeneuve la Garenne, France **(60%)**
Tel.: (33) 147946620
Web Site: http://www.rafaut.fr
Emp.: 140
Aerospace Armaments Interface, Flight Controls & Other Subsystems Designer & Mfr
N.A.I.C.S.: 336413
Jacques Rafaut *(Chm)*

HLE GLASCOAT LIMITED
H-106 G I D C Phase IV, Vithal
Udhyognagar, 388 121, Anand, India
Tel.: (91) 2692236842
Web Site: http://www.glascoat.com
522215—(NSE)
Rev.: $66,669,671
Assets: $51,476,116
Liabilities: $33,074,714
Net Worth: $18,401,401
Earnings: $7,285,142
Emp.: 522
Fiscal Year-end: 03/31/21
Glascoat Heat Exchanger Mfr
N.A.I.C.S.: 332410
Ashley P. Lemos *(Asst Gen Mgr-Mktg)*

Subsidiaries:

H L Equipments Inc. (1)
14701 Interstate 35, Buda, TX 78610
Tel.: (512) 523-8012
Web Site: https://hlequipment.com
Metal Equipment Rental Services
N.A.I.C.S.: 532490

Thaletec GmbH (1)
Steinbachstrasse 3, 06502, Thale, Germany
Tel.: (49) 39477780
Web Site: https://thaletec.com
Emp.: 180
Glass Equipment Mfr & Distr
N.A.I.C.S.: 327211

Thaletec Inc. (1)
5960 Fairview Rd Ste 400, Charlotte, NC 28210
Tel.: (859) 393-9957
Glass Equipment Mfr & Distr
N.A.I.C.S.: 327215

HLM DU COTENTIN
17 Rue Guillaume Fouace, 50100,
Cherbourg, Manche, France
Tel.: (33) 233872121
Web Site: http://www.hlm-du-cotentin.com
Rev.: $26,300,000
Emp.: 37
Apartment Building Operator
N.A.I.C.S.: 531110
Jean Levallois *(Mng Dir)*

HLN RUBBER PRODUCTS PTE. LTD.
Block 16 Kallang Place 01-16/18,
Kallang Basin Industrial Estate, Singapore, 339156, Singapore
Tel.: (65) 6746 1366 SG
Web Site: http://www.hlnrubber.net
Rubber Products Mfr
N.A.I.C.S.: 326291
Leslie Wa *(Mng Dir)*

Subsidiaries:

HLN (Suzhou) Rubber Products Co., Ltd. (1)
No 28 Zhensheng Road, Suzhou Industrial Park, Suzhou, 215126, Jiangsu, China
Tel.: (86) 512 6762 1526
Web Site: http://www.hlnrubber.net
Molded Rubber Goods Mfr
N.A.I.C.S.: 326299

PT HLN Batam (1)
Lot 307/308 Jalan Angsana Batamindo Industrial Park, Muka Kuning, Batam, 29433, Riau Islands, Indonesia
Tel.: (62) 770 612 008
Web Site: http://www.hlnrubber.net
Molded Rubber Goods Mfr
N.A.I.C.S.: 326299
Puji Hastuti *(Mgr-Fin)*

HLS THERAPEUTICS, INC.
10 Carlson Court Suite 701, Etobicoke, M9W 6L2, ON, Canada
Tel.: (647) 495-9000 ON
Web Site:
https://www.hlstherapeutics.com
Year Founded: 2018
74D—(DEU)
Rev.: $63,074,000
Assets: $209,060,000
Liabilities: $111,363,000
Net Worth: $97,697,000
Earnings: ($27,531,000)
Emp.: 91
Fiscal Year-end: 12/31/23
Parts Assembly for the Automotive Industry
N.A.I.C.S.: 336340
William Wells *(Chm)*

Subsidiaries:

Automodular Assemblies, Inc. (1)
200 Montecorte St, Whitby, L1N 9V8, ON, Canada **(100%)**
Tel.: (905) 665-0060
Sales Range: $100-124.9 Million
Emp.: 480
Provider of Parts Assembly for the Automotive Industry
N.A.I.C.S.: 336340

HLT GLOBAL BERHAD
No 6 Jalan Industri Mas 7 Taman
Mas, 47130, Puchong, Selangor
Darul Ehsan, Malaysia
Tel.: (60) 380683616 MY
Web Site:
https://www.hltglobal.com.my
HLT—(KLS)
Rev.: $16,014,856
Assets: $48,722,302
Liabilities: $22,124,455
Net Worth: $26,597,846
Earnings: ($11,329,824)
Fiscal Year-end: 12/31/22
Investment Holding Services
N.A.I.C.S.: 551112
Kok Wah Wong *(Co-Founder & Deputy Chm)*

Subsidiaries:

HL Advance Technologies (M) Sdn. Bhd. (1)
6 Jalan Industri Mas 7 Taman Mas, 47130, Puchong, Selangor, Malaysia
Tel.: (60) 380683616
Web Site: https://www.hladvance.com
Glove Dipping Machine Mfr
N.A.I.C.S.: 333248

HL Rubber Industries Sdn. Bhd. (1)
Lot 10 Kawasan Perindustrian Dioh, 72000, Kuala Pilah, Negeri Sembilan, Malaysia **(100%)**
Tel.: (60) 64811088
Web Site: https://www.hlrubber.com.my
Emp.: 700
Rubber & Plastic Mfr
N.A.I.C.S.: 326220

HLV LTD.
The Leela Mumbai Sahar, Andheri
East, Mumbai, 400 059, Maharashtra,
India
Tel.: (91) 2266911234
Web Site: https://www.hlvltd.com
Year Founded: 1986
HLVLTD—(NSE)
Rev.: $10,417,721
Assets: $76,423,456
Liabilities: $20,151,481
Net Worth: $56,271,975
Earnings: ($5,802,560)
Emp.: 456
Fiscal Year-end: 03/31/22
Hotel & Resort Services
N.A.I.C.S.: 721110
Vivek Nair *(Co-CEO)*

Subsidiaries:

Kovalam Resort Private Limited (1)
The Leela Kovalam, Thiruvananthapuram, 695 527, Kerala, India
Tel.: (91) 47 1305 1234
Web Site: http://www.theleela.com
Emp.: 70
Resort Management Services
N.A.I.C.S.: 721110
Sreejith Kumar *(Mgr-Sls)*

HM INTERNATIONAL HOLDINGS LIMITED
9/F Infinitus Plaza 199 Des Voeux
Road, Central, China (Hong Kong)
Tel.: (852) 21211555 Ky
Web Site: http://www.hetermedia.com
Year Founded: 2016
8416—(HKG)
Rev.: $24,261,465
Assets: $16,982,490
Liabilities: $5,603,370
Net Worth: $11,379,120
Earnings: $910,095
Emp.: 142
Fiscal Year-end: 12/31/22
Business Process Outsourcing Services
N.A.I.C.S.: 561110
Chi Ming Yu *(Chm)*

Subsidiaries:

Talesis Limited (1)
9/F Infinitus Plaza 199 Des Voeux Road, Central, China (Hong Kong)
Tel.: (852) 97939618
Web Site: https://www.talesis.com
Information Technology Services
N.A.I.C.S.: 541511

i.Link Group Limited (1)
Room 901-5 9/F China Insurance Group Building 141 Des Voeux Road, Central, China (Hong Kong)
Tel.: (852) 29021818
Web Site: https://www.ilinkfin.com
Marketing Services
N.A.I.C.S.: 541613

HM INWEST S.A.
Czarnieckiego 4/2, 01-511, Warsaw,
Poland
Tel.: (48) 226163194
Web Site: https://www.grupainwest.pl
Year Founded: 1994
HMI—(WAR)
Rev.: $64,836,636
Assets: $38,454,522
Liabilities: $19,899,390
Net Worth: $18,555,132
Earnings: $7,706,555
Fiscal Year-end: 12/31/23
New Multifamily Housing Construction (except For-Sale Builders)
N.A.I.C.S.: 236116
Piotr Hofman *(CEO)*

HMA AGRO INDUSTRIES LIMITED
18A/5/3 Tajview Crossing Fatehabad
Road, Agra, 282001, Uttar Pradesh,
India
Tel.: (91) 7217018161
Web Site: https://www.hmagroup.co
Year Founded: 2008
HMAAGRO—(NSE)
Rev.: $394,638,229
Assets: $121,073,952
Liabilities: $61,142,128
Net Worth: $59,931,824
Earnings: $14,964,079
Fiscal Year-end: 03/31/23
Food Products Distr
N.A.I.C.S.: 424420
Gulzar Ahmad *(Chm)*

HMC CAPITAL LIMITED
Level 7 1 Macquarie Place, Sydney,
2000, NSW, Australia
Tel.: (61) 1300466326 AU
Web Site:
https://www.hmccapital.com.au
Year Founded: 2017
HMC—(ASX)
Rev.: $44,814,501
Assets: $876,844,233
Liabilities: $94,161,831
Net Worth: $782,682,402
Earnings: $54,334,616
Emp.: 75
Fiscal Year-end: 06/30/23
Investment Management Service
N.A.I.C.S.: 523999
Chris Saxon *(Chm)*

Subsidiaries:

Home Consortium Limited (1)
Level 7 1 Macquarie Place, Sydney, 2000, NSW, Australia
Tel.: (61) 1300466326
Real Estate Manangement Services
N.A.I.C.S.: 531210

HMK AUTOMATION GROUP LIMITED
Kappa House Hatter Street, Congleton, CW12 1QJ, United Kingdom
Tel.: (44) 1260279411 UK
Web Site: http://www.hmk-group.com
Emp.: 40
Engineering Technology Solutions
N.A.I.C.S.: 541330

HMK AUTOMATION GROUP LIMITED

HMK Automation Group Limited—(Continued)
Carl Krajewski (CEO)

HML HOLDINGS PLC
9-11 The Quadrant, Richmond, TW9 1BP, Surrey, United Kingdom
Tel.: (44) 2084398529
Web Site: http://www.hmlgroup.com
Rev.: $35,672,152
Assets: $31,504,691
Liabilities: $11,973,204
Net Worth: $19,531,487
Earnings: $1,752,517
Emp.: 549
Fiscal Year-end: 03/31/19
Holding Company; Property & Estate Management Services
N.A.I.C.S.: 551112
James Alfred Lloyd Howgego (CFO & Sec)

Subsidiaries:

Alexander Bonhill Limited (1)
17 Dominion Street, London, EC2M 2EF, United Kingdom
Tel.: (44) 845 050 2105
Web Site: http://www.alexanderbonhill.co.uk
Emp.: 40
Property Insurance Brokerage Services
N.A.I.C.S.: 524210
Neil Walton (Gen Mgr)

HML Andertons Limited (1)
94 Park Lane, Croydon, CO0 1JP, Surrey, United Kingdom
Tel.: (44) 8451778800
Web Site: http://www.hmlandertons.com
Sales Range: $25-49.9 Million
Emp.: 50
Property & Estate Management Services
N.A.I.C.S.: 531311
Alan Coates (Mng Dir)

HML Shaw Limited (1)
First Fl 9-11 The Quadrant, Richmond, TW9 1BP, Surrey, United Kingdom
Tel.: (44) 2089483211
Web Site: http://www.hmlshaw.com
Sales Range: $25-49.9 Million
Emp.: 40
Property & Estate Management Services
N.A.I.C.S.: 531311
Michael Lee (Mng Dir)

HMM CO., LTD.
108 Yeoui-daero, Yeongdengpo-gu, Seoul, 03127, Korea (South)
Tel.: (82) 237065114   KR
Web Site: https://www.hmm21.com
Year Founded: 1976
011200—(KRS)
Rev.: $6,443,543,223
Assets: $19,722,149,421
Liabilities: $3,277,045,850
Net Worth: $16,445,103,571
Earnings: $1,015,525,641
Emp.: 1,781
Fiscal Year-end: 12/31/23
Marine Cargo Transportation Services, Vessel Chartering, Ship Brokering, Agency Services, Trading & Related Services
N.A.I.C.S.: 483111
Kyung Bae Kim (Chm & CEO)

Subsidiaries:

Hyundai Merchant Marine (America), Inc.
222 W Las Colinas Blvd Ste 700, Irving, TX 75039
Tel.: (972) 501-1100
Sales Range: $150-199.9 Million
Emp.: 400
Marine Freight Transportation Services
N.A.I.C.S.: 488510

Hyundai Merchant Marine (China) Co., Ltd. (1)
33-34th Floor Harbour Ring Plaza No 18 Xi Zhang Middle Road, Shanghai, 200001, China
Tel.: (86) 2161227208
Web Site: http://www.h21.com
Sales Range: $50-74.9 Million
Emp.: 100
Marine Freight Transportation Services
N.A.I.C.S.: 483111

Hyundai Merchant Marine (Europe) Ltd. (1)
4th Floor City Reach, 5 Greenwich View Place, London, E14 9NN, United Kingdom
Tel.: (44) 2074777200
Sales Range: $75-99.9 Million
Emp.: 107
Marine Freight Transportation Services
N.A.I.C.S.: 488510
Soo-Ho Kim (CEO)

Hyundai Merchant Marine (Hong Kong) Ltd. (1)
Suite 1601-6 & 14 Tower 6 The Gateway 9 Canton Road, Tsim Sha Tsui, Kowloon, China (Hong Kong)
Tel.: (852) 25144100
Marine Freight Transportation Services
N.A.I.C.S.: 483111

Hyundai Merchant Marine (Japan) Co., Ltd. (1)
31/F World Trade Center Building 2-4-1 Hamamatsu-cho, Minato-ku, Tokyo, 105 6104, Japan
Tel.: (81) 354254711
Marine Freight Transportation Services
N.A.I.C.S.: 488510

Hyundai Merchant Marine (Singapore) Pte. Ltd. (1)
7 Temasek Boulevard 41-1 Suntec City Tower One, Singapore, 038987, Singapore
Tel.: (65) 63399844
Web Site: http://www.hmm21.com
Sales Range: $50-74.9 Million
Emp.: 95
Marine Freight Transportation Services
N.A.I.C.S.: 483111
David Seong (Mng Dir)

HMS BERGBAU AG
An der Wuhlheide 232, 12459, Berlin, Germany
Tel.: (49) 306566810
Web Site: https://www.hms-ag.com
Year Founded: 1995
HMU—(DEU)
Rev.: $1,430,836,294
Assets: $310,849,792
Liabilities: $268,781,306
Net Worth: $42,068,486
Earnings: $13,798,375
Emp.: 40
Fiscal Year-end: 12/31/23
Coal & Other Energy Products Supplier
N.A.I.C.S.: 423520
Dennis Schwindt (CEO & Member-Mgmt Bd)

Subsidiaries:

HMS Bergbau AG Oil & Gas Division (1)
An der Wuhlheide 232, 12459, Berlin, Germany
Tel.: (49) 306566810
Web Site: http://www.hms-ag.com
Sales Range: $50-74.9 Million
Emp.: 30
Oil & Gas Production Services
N.A.I.C.S.: 213111

HMS Bergbau Africa (Pty.) Ltd. (1)
Workshop 17 138 West Street, Sandowns, Sandton, 2031, South Africa
Tel.: (27) 101403630
Coal Whslr
N.A.I.C.S.: 423520

HMS Bergbau FZCO Dubai LLC (1)
Dubai Silicon Osasis DPP Building A2 101, Dubai, United Arab Emirates
Tel.: (971) 507976934
Raw Material Mfr & Distr
N.A.I.C.S.: 332999

HMS Bergbau Singapore (Pte.) Ltd. (1)
6 Battery Road 03-05, Shenton House, Singapore, 049909, Singapore
Tel.: (65) 62950494
Coal Whslr
N.A.I.C.S.: 423520

HMS Bergbau USA Corp. (1)
1111 Brickell Ave Fl 10, Miami, FL 33131
Tel.: (786) 264-6512
Coal Whslr
N.A.I.C.S.: 423520

PT. HMS Bergbau Indonesia (1)
Menara Rajawali 25th Floor Jl Dr Ide Anak Agung Gde Agung Lot 5 1, Mega Kuningan, Jakarta, 12950, Indonesia
Tel.: (62) 21576457779
Coal Distribution Services
N.A.I.C.S.: 423520
Putri Naomi (Sec)

Silesian Coal International Group of Companies S.A. (1)
z siedziba w Katowicach ul E Imieli 14, 41-605, Swietochlowice, Poland
Tel.: (48) 327710200
Coal Exploration Services
N.A.I.C.S.: 212114

HMS HYDRAULIC MACHINES & SYSTEMS GROUP PLC
7 Chayanova str, 125047, Moscow, Russia
Tel.: (7) 4957306601
Web Site: https://www.grouphms.com
HMSG—(LSE)
Rev.: $769,935,973
Assets: $873,064,852
Liabilities: $688,114,977
Net Worth: $184,949,875
Earnings: $16,716,526
Emp.: 12,419
Fiscal Year-end: 12/31/21
Oil & Gas Pump Mfr
N.A.I.C.S.: 333914
Artem V. Molchanov (CEO & Gen Dir)

Subsidiaries:

Apollo Goessnitz GmbH (1)
Walter-Rabold-Strasse 26, Goessnitz, 04639, Zwickau, Germany
Tel.: (49) 3 449 3770
Web Site: https://www.apollo-goessnitz.de
Pumps Mfr
N.A.I.C.S.: 333914

Bobruisk Machine Building Plant OJSC (1)
Bobruisk Str Karl Marx 235 Mogilev region, Babruysk, 213805, Belarus
Tel.: (375) 225474922
Web Site: http://www.hms-bmbpump.ru
Pump & Pump Equipment Mfr
N.A.I.C.S.: 333914
Demskoi Albina Vyacheslavovna (Deputy Dir-Economics & Fin)

Dimitrovgradkhimmash JSC (1)
st Kuibysheva 256, 433511, Dimitrovgrad, Ulyanovsk, Russia
Tel.: (7) 8423557290
Web Site: http://www.himmash.net
Oil & Gas Equipment Mfr
N.A.I.C.S.: 333132

HMS Livhydromash JSC (1)
231 Mira Street, Livny Town, 303851, Orel, Russia
Tel.: (7) 4867778000
Web Site: http://www.hms-livgidromash.com
Pumps Mfr
N.A.I.C.S.: 333914
Dvoryadkin Anatoly Fedorovich (Mng Dir)

HMS Neftemash JSC (1)
44 Voyennaya Str, 625003, Tyumen, Russia
Tel.: (7) 3452791930
Web Site: http://www.hms-neftemash.ru
Oil & Gas Equipment Mfr
N.A.I.C.S.: 333132
Sergey Nikolaevich (Mng Dir)

Hydromashservice JSC (1)
12 Aviakonstructor Mikoyan Street, 125252, Moscow, Russia
Tel.: (7) 4956648171

INTERNATIONAL PUBLIC

Web Site: http://hms.biz
Pump & Pump Equipment Mfr
N.A.I.C.S.: 333914

Institute Rostovskiy Vodokanalproekt JSC (1)
Per Soborny 17, Rostov-na-Donu, 344002, Russia
Tel.: (7) 8632625612
Web Site: http://www.rvkp.ru
Water Supply Services
N.A.I.C.S.: 237110

Kazankompressormash OJSC (1)
Khalitova Str 1 The Republic of Tatarstan, 420029, Kazan, Russia
Tel.: (7) 8432917979
Web Site: http://www.compressormash.ru
Compressor Mfr
N.A.I.C.S.: 333912
Ilnur Sagdiev (Mng Dir)

Livnynasos JSC (1)
250 Orlovskaya Street, Livny town, 303850, Orel, Russia
Tel.: (7) 4867777615
Web Site: http://www.livnasos.ru
Pumps Mfr
N.A.I.C.S.: 333914

Nasosenergomash Sumy JSC (1)
1 Pryvokzalna Sq, Kiev, 40011, Sumy, Ukraine
Tel.: (380) 542700044
Web Site: http://www.nempump.com
Pump & Pump Equipment Mfr
N.A.I.C.S.: 333914
Nasya Sunday (Mgr-Import)

Nizhnevartovskremservis CJSC (1)
Khanty-Mansiysk Autonomous Okrug Aviatorov St 27, Nizhnevartovsk, 628606, Russia
Tel.: (7) 3466633058
Web Site: https://nv-rs.ru
Pumps Mfr
N.A.I.C.S.: 333914

Sibneftemash JSC (1)
15 km of Tobolskiy Trakt, 625511, Tyumen, Russia
Tel.: (7) 3452535050
Web Site: http://www.sibneftemash.ru
Oil & Gas Equipment Mfr
N.A.I.C.S.: 333132
Osipov Victor Nikolaevich (Mng Dir)

Tomskgazstroy PJSC (1)
St Bolshaya Podgornaya 21, 634009, Tomsk, Russia
Tel.: (7) 3822510622
Oil & Gas Field Construction Services
N.A.I.C.S.: 237120

HMS NETWORKS AB
Stationsgatan 37, 302 50, Halmstad, Sweden
Tel.: (46) 35172900
Web Site: https://www.hms-networks.com
Year Founded: 1988
HMS—(OMX)
Rev.: $179,069,630
Assets: $222,914,051
Liabilities: $73,916,876
Net Worth: $148,997,175
Earnings: $26,908,141
Emp.: 614
Fiscal Year-end: 12/31/20
Industrial Automation Equipment Supplier
N.A.I.C.S.: 423690
Staffan Dahlstrom (CEO)

Subsidiaries:

HMS Industrial Networks AB (1)
Stationsgatan 37, 302 50, Halmstad, Sweden
Tel.: (46) 35172900
Web Site: http://www.hms.se
Sales Range: $25-49.9 Million
Emp.: 200
Industrial Communication Software Development Services
N.A.I.C.S.: 541511

AND PRIVATE COMPANIES

Subsidiary (Non-US):

HMS Industrial Networks ApS (2)
Aarhusgade 130, 2100, Copenhagen, Denmark
Tel.: (45) 35 38 29 00
Remote Management Solutions
N.A.I.C.S.: 334118
Peter Greenfort *(Country Mgr)*

HMS Industrial Networks GmbH (2)
Emmy-Noether-Str 17, 76131, Karlsruhe, Germany
Tel.: (49) 72198 977 7000
Web Site: http://www.hms-networks.com
Emp.: 34
Network Interface Card Mfr
N.A.I.C.S.: 334118

Subsidiary (US):

HMS Industrial Networks Inc. (2)
35 E Wacker Dr Ste 1700, Chicago, IL 60601
Tel.: (312) 829-0601
Network Interface Card Mfr
N.A.I.C.S.: 334118
Katarina Lecander *(Mgr-Quality)*

Subsidiary (Non-US):

HMS Industrial Networks India Private Ltd. (2)
Corporate Plaza Unit 1A and 1B Ground Floor Senapati Bapat Road, Near Chaturshrungi Temple, Pune, 411016, India
Tel.: (91) 202 563 0211
Web Site: http://www.anybus.com
Network Interface Card Mfr
N.A.I.C.S.: 334118
Santosh Tatte *(Country Mgr)*

HMS Industrial Networks K.K. (2)
Tel.: (81) 454785340
Software Products Mfr & Distr
N.A.I.C.S.: 334118
Katsuyoshi Mineji *(Mgr-Sls & Mktg)*

HMS Industrial Networks Ltd (2)
Unit 2 Sovereign Court 1 Sir William Lyons Road, Warwick University Science Park, Coventry, CV4 7EZ, United Kingdom
Tel.: (44) 1926405599
Sales Range: $25-49.9 Million
Emp.: 5
Electronic Components Distr
N.A.I.C.S.: 423690

HMS Industrial Networks S.r.l. (2)
Web Site: http://www.anybus.it
Computer Peripheral Equipment Mfr & Distr
N.A.I.C.S.: 334118

HMS Industrial Networks SAS (2)
4 rue Daniel Schoen, 68200, Mulhouse, France
Tel.: (33) 36 788 0250
Web Site: https://www.anybus.com
Electronic Components Distr
N.A.I.C.S.: 423690

Subsidiary (Domestic):

Intellicom Innovation AB (2)
Linjegatan 3D, 302 50, Halmstad, Sweden
Tel.: (46) 35182170
Web Site: http://www.intellicom.se
Electronic Components Mfr
N.A.I.C.S.: 334419

HMS Industrial Networks Pty. Ltd. (1)
5/15-21 Butler Way, Tullamarine, 3043, VIC, Australia
Tel.: (61) 393388189
Communication Equipment Mfr
N.A.I.C.S.: 334290

Red Lion Controls Inc. (1)
20 Willow Springs Cir, York, PA 17406
Tel.: (717) 767-6511
Web Site: http://www.redlion.net
Sales Range: $50-74.9 Million
Emp.: 200
Electronic Products Mfr
N.A.I.C.S.: 334513

Subsidiary (Domestic):

Sixnet, LLC (2)
331 Ushers Rd, Ballston Lake, NY 12019
Tel.: (518) 877-5173
Web Site: http://www.sixnet.com
Sales Range: $1-9.9 Million
Emp.: 45
Process Automation & Control Instruments Mfr
N.A.I.C.S.: 334513

Unit (Non-US):

Sixnet Wireless Product Group Canada (3)
2425 46th Avenue, Lachine, H8T 3C9, QC, Canada
Tel.: (514) 422-9110
Web Site: http://www.sixnet.com
Sales Range: $1-9.9 Million
Emp.: 10
Wireless Modems Mfr & Software Solutions
N.A.I.C.S.: 541511

Unit (Domestic):

Sixnet Wireless Product Group USA (3)
4645 Laguardia Dr, Saint Louis, MO 63134
Tel.: (314) 426-7781
Wireless Communication Equipment Mfr
N.A.I.C.S.: 334220

HMT (XIAMEN) NEW TECHNICAL MATERIALS CO., LTD.
No 69 Sushan Road, Houxi Town Jimei District, Xiamen, 361024, Fujian, China
Tel.: (86) 5927795189
Web Site: https://www.hmtnew.com
Year Founded: 2002
603306—(SHG)
Rev.: $229,855,734
Assets: $531,313,684
Liabilities: $62,947,750
Net Worth: $468,365,934
Earnings: $27,863,784
Fiscal Year-end: 12/31/22
Industrial Fabric Mfr
N.A.I.C.S.: 314910
Chuquan Quan Zhang *(Chm & Gen Mgr)*

HMT LIMITED
59 Bellary Road, Bengaluru, 560 032, India
Tel.: (91) 8023330333
Web Site: https://www.hmtindia.com
Year Founded: 1953
HMT—(NSE)
Rev.: $14,013,090
Assets: $93,215,850
Liabilities: $736,678,215
Net Worth: ($643,462,365)
Earnings: ($238,875)
Emp.: 101
Fiscal Year-end: 03/31/21
Machine Tools Mfr
N.A.I.C.S.: 333517
S. Girish Kumar *(Chm & Mng Dir)*

Subsidiaries:

Hmt International Limited (1)
HMT Bhavan 59 Bellary Road, Bengaluru, 560 032, India
Tel.: (91) 8023339060
Web Site: http://www.hmti.com
Machine Tools Mfr
N.A.I.C.S.: 333517
Girish Kumar *(Chm & Mng Dir)*

Hmt Machine Tools Limited (1)
59 Bellary Road, Bengaluru, 560 032, Karnataka, India
Tel.: (91) 8023330333
Web Site: https://www.hmtmachinetools.com
Machine Tools Mfr
N.A.I.C.S.: 333517
Mukta Shekhar *(Sec)*

HMVOD LTD.
Unit C 8F D2 Place Two 15 Cheung Shun Street, Kowloon, China (Hong Kong)
Web Site: http://www.hmvod.com
8103—(HKG)
Rev.: $3,059,108
Assets: $2,287,223
Liabilities: $11,459,700
Net Worth: ($9,172,478)
Earnings: ($1,592,730)
Emp.: 33
Fiscal Year-end: 03/31/23
Media Streaming Services
N.A.I.C.S.: 518210
Chi Na Ho *(Exec Dir)*

HNA INNOVATION HAINAN CO., LTD.
4F Orient Mansion No 1500 Century Avenue, Pudong New District, Shanghai, 200122, China
Tel.: (86) 21 68407880
Web Site: http://www.ninedragon.com.cn
600555—(SHG)
Rev.: $1,916,657
Assets: $306,104,387
Liabilities: $177,058,669
Net Worth: $129,045,719
Earnings: ($31,539,811)
Fiscal Year-end: 12/31/20
Tour Management Services
N.A.I.C.S.: 561520

HNA INTERNATIONAL INVESTMENT HOLDINGS LIMITED
Unit 2606A-2608 26/F Island Place Tower 510 Kings Road, North Point, China (Hong Kong)
Tel.: (852) 25581580
Web Site: http://www.hnainterinvest.com
0521—(HKG)
Sales Range: $25-49.9 Million
Emp.: 940
Technical Services
N.A.I.C.S.: 711510
Lap Ngai Lau *(Sec)*

Subsidiaries:

Ever Create Profits Limited (1)
Ste 902 Excellence Mansion No 21-1-6 Ctr, Futian Dist, Shenzhen, 518048, Guangdong, China
Tel.: (86) 75582874936
Sales Range: $25-49.9 Million
Emp.: 20
Set Top Box Mfr
N.A.I.C.S.: 334220

Hop Cheong Technology (International) Limited (1)
Flat 15-18 10F Honour Indus Ctr 6 Sun Yip St, Chai Wan, China (Hong Kong)
Tel.: (852) 28973083
Precision Metals Marketing Services
N.A.I.C.S.: 423830

Hop Cheong Technology Limited (1)
Rm 2142 Tower 2 Admiralty Ctr No 18 Harcout Rd, Chai Wan, China (Hong Kong)
Tel.: (852) 2897 3083
Sales Range: $25-49.9 Million
Emp.: 10
Lathes Mfr
N.A.I.C.S.: 333517

SCT Electronics Limited (1)
Flat No 201 21 F Admiralty Ctr 18 Harcourt Rd, Admiralty, Central, China (Hong Kong)
Tel.: (852) 25581580
Sales Range: $25-49.9 Million
Emp.: 20
Electronic Components Mfr
N.A.I.C.S.: 332993

Shenzhen Tiger Information Technology Development Co., Ltd. (1)
Rm 902 9 F Excellence Bldg Ctr of 21-1-6, Futian Dist, Shenzhen, Guangdong, China
Tel.: (86) 75582874971
Sales Range: $25-49.9 Million
Emp.: 20
Computer Software Sales
N.A.I.C.S.: 423430

HNB ASSURANCE PLC

Shougang Concord Technology Holdings Limited (1)
Unit 2102 31Fl Tower 2 Admiralty Center, 18 Hal Court Road, Central, Admiralty, China (Hong Kong)
Tel.: (852) 25587636
Web Site: http://www.shougan-tech.com.hk
Optoelectronic Component Mfr
N.A.I.C.S.: 334413

Sino Stride Technology Co., Ltd (1)
703-704 7th Fl Shanghai Industry Investment bldg 48-62 Hennessey Rd, Admiralty, Wanchai, China (Hong Kong)
Tel.: (852) 29977565
Web Site: https://www.sinostride.com
Sales Range: $25-49.9 Million
Emp.: 20
Information Technology Solutions
N.A.I.C.S.: 541511
Diana Heng *(Mgr)*

HNA INVESTMENT GROUP CO., LTD.
Floor 16 HNA Office Building No.108 Jianguo Road, Chaoyang District, Beijing, China
Tel.: (86) 10 50960302
Web Site: http://www.hnainvestment.com
Year Founded: 1993
000616—(SSE)
Sales Range: $25-49.9 Million
Investment Management Service
N.A.I.C.S.: 523940
Bo Yu *(Chm)*

HNAC TECHNOLOGY CO., LTD.
No 609 Lusong Road Lugu, Changsha, 410217, Hunan, China
Tel.: (86) 73188906157
Web Site: https://www.hnacglobal.com
Year Founded: 1993
300490—(CHIN)
Rev.: $333,618,169
Assets: $988,742,070
Liabilities: $589,708,076
Net Worth: $399,033,994
Earnings: ($25,328,055)
Fiscal Year-end: 12/31/23
Industrial Project Automation Solution Provider
N.A.I.C.S.: 541512
Huang Wenbao *(Chm)*

Subsidiaries:

Beijing Grant Membrane Separation Equipment Co., Ltd. (1)
Building 2 No 12 Tianzhu West Road, Area A Konggang Industrial Zone Shunyi District, Beijing, 101312, China
Tel.: (86) 1084591818
Web Site: http://www.grantwater.com
Commercial & Service Industry Machinery Mfr
N.A.I.C.S.: 333310

HNB ASSURANCE PLC
Levels 3 and 4 Iceland Business Center No 30 Sri Uttarananda Mawatha, 3, Colombo, 03, Sri Lanka
Tel.: (94) 1301
Web Site: https://www.hnbassurance.com
HASU.N0000—(COL)
Rev.: $52,054,645
Assets: $136,798,229
Liabilities: $110,839,060
Net Worth: $25,959,169
Earnings: $6,093,419
Emp.: 1,307
Fiscal Year-end: 12/31/22
Financial Consulting Services
N.A.I.C.S.: 541611
Deepthi Lokuarachchi *(CEO & Mng Dir)*

HNB ASSURANCE PLC

HNB Assurance PLC—(Continued)

Subsidiaries:

HNB General Insurance Limited (1)
2nd Floor Iceland Business Center No 30
Sri Uttarananda Mawatha, Colombo, Sri Lanka
Tel.: (94) 114676700
Web Site: http://www.hnbgeneral.com
Emp.: 400
General Insurance Services
N.A.I.C.S.: 524210
Rose Cooray (Chm)

HNG CAPITAL SDN BHD

Suite 7A & 8A Menara Northam, 55 Jalan Sultan Ahmad Shah, 10050, Penang, Malaysia
Tel.: (60) 4 2199 888
Web Site: http://www.hngcapital.com
Cable & Wire Mfr
N.A.I.C.S.: 331420
Hui Keat Wong (COO)

HNH INTERNATIONAL LTD.

Level 11 Cyberport 1 100 Cyberport Road, Hong Kong, China (Hong Kong)
Tel.: (852) 27607818
Web Site: http://www.naxos.com
Holding Company; Classical Music Pre-Recorded Tapes & CDs Mfr, Marketer & Sales
N.A.I.C.S.: 551112

Subsidiaries:

Naxos Denmark ApS. (1)
Drejervej 15 5 sal, Nordvest, 2400, Copenhagen, Denmark
Tel.: (45) 86 89 24 28
Musical Instrument Retailer
N.A.I.C.S.: 459140

Naxos Deutchland GmbH (1)
Wienburgstrasse 171a, d-48147, Münster, Germany
Tel.: (49) 251924060
Web Site: http://www.naxos.de
Sales Range: $25-49.9 Million
Emp.: 8
Classical Music CDs Distr
N.A.I.C.S.: 459140
Christof Voll (Mng Dir)

Naxos Deutschland Musik und Video Vertriebs GmbH (1)
Gruber Strasse 70, 85586, Poing, Germany
Tel.: (49) 8121 25007
Web Site: http://www.naxos.de
Musical Instrument Retailer
N.A.I.C.S.: 459140

Naxos Digital Services Limited (1)
Level 11 Cyberport 1, 100 Cyberport Road, Hong Kong, China (Hong Kong) (100%)
Tel.: (852) 27607818
Web Site: http://www.naxos.com
Music-Related Digital Products & Services
N.A.I.C.S.: 334610

Naxos Global Distribution Limited (1)
Level 11 Cyberport 1 100 Cyberport Rd, Hong Kong, China (Hong Kong) (100%)
Tel.: (852) 27607818
Web Site: http://www.naxos.com
Sales Range: $50-74.9 Million
Emp.: 40
Classical Music Distr
N.A.I.C.S.: 459140
Klaus Heymann (Founder)

Naxos Japan Inc (1)
3-82 Kamiubako, Sakae-cho, Toyoake, 470-1162, Aichi, Japan
Tel.: (81) 562972083
Musical Instrument Retailer
N.A.I.C.S.: 459140

Naxos Korea (1)
1110 E-Tech Valley 51-37, Wonhyoro 3-ga Yongsan-gu, Seoul, 140-848, Korea (South)
Tel.: (82) 2 717 1070
Musical Instrument Retailer
N.A.I.C.S.: 459140

Kim Keun-Hye (Bus Mgr-Music Licensing)

Naxos Norway AS (1)
PO Box A, N-1454, Fagerstrand, Norway
Tel.: (47) 66965540
Web Site: http://www.naxos.no
Classical Music Distr
N.A.I.C.S.: 459140

Naxos Rights International Limited (1)
Level 11 Cyberport 1, 100 Cyberport Road, Hong Kong, China (Hong Kong) (100%)
Tel.: (852) 27607818
Web Site: http://www.naxos.com
Sales Range: $25-49.9 Million
Emp.: 50
Music Rights Licensor
N.A.I.C.S.: 512230

Naxos Sweden AB (1)
Kryptongatan 6, 703 74, Orebro, Sweden
Tel.: (46) 19 20 68 60
Web Site: http://www.naxosdirect.se
Musical Instrument Retailer
N.A.I.C.S.: 459140
Mats Byren (Mgr-Mktg)

Naxos of America Inc. (1)
1810 Columbia Ave Ste 28, Franklin, TN 37064-3977
Tel.: (615) 771-9393
Web Site: http://www.naxos.com
Sales Range: $25-49.9 Million
Emp.: 35
Classical Music Distr
N.A.I.C.S.: 334610
Jeff Van Driel (CEO)

Naxos of Canada Ltd. (1)
3510 Pharmacy Ave Unit 3, Scarborough, M1W 2T7, ON, Canada
Tel.: (416) 491-2600
Web Site: http://www.naxoscanada.com
Sales Range: $25-49.9 Million
Emp.: 100
Classical Music Distr
N.A.I.C.S.: 459140

OY Fg-Naxos Ab (1)
Vanha Helsingintie 18 A, 00700, Helsinki, Finland
Tel.: (358) 9 4241 2420
Web Site: http://www.fg-naxos.fi
Musical Instrument Retailer
N.A.I.C.S.: 459140
Silja Nummi (Mgr-Mktg)

HNK MACHINE TOOL CO., LTD.

83-1 Yunoe Industrial Complex-gil, Beopsu-myeon Haman-gun, Gyeongnam, Korea (South)
Tel.: (82) 7070196500
Web Site: https://www.hnkkorea.com
Year Founded: 1960
101680—(KRS)
Rev.: $32,438,221
Assets: $70,754,542
Liabilities: $33,149,857
Net Worth: $37,604,685
Earnings: $394,395
Emp.: 237
Fiscal Year-end: 12/31/22
Machine Tools Mfr
N.A.I.C.S.: 333248
Jongsik Ha (CEO)

Subsidiaries:

Han Kook Steel & Mill Co., Ltd. (1)
1365 Yoohyeon, Gunbuk, Chilseo, Kyeonnam, Korea (South)
Tel.: (82) 55 582 6800
Machine Tools Mfr
N.A.I.C.S.: 333248

The Korea Heavy Machinery Co., Ltd. (1)
477 Jangji, Gunbuk, Chilseo, Kyeong nam, Korea (South)
Machine Tools Mfr
N.A.I.C.S.: 333248

HNT ELECTRONICS CO.,LTD

7F Venture Forum B/D 323 Pangyo-ro Sampyeong-ong, Bundang-gu, Seongnam, 13488, Gyeonggi-do, Korea (South)
Tel.: (82) 317397897
Web Site: http://www.hntelec.com
Year Founded: 2008
176440—(KRS)
Rev.: $2,885,264
Assets: $17,136,157
Liabilities: $6,585,682
Net Worth: $10,550,475
Earnings: ($4,593,937)
Emp.: 19
Fiscal Year-end: 12/31/21
Camera Module Mfr & Distr
N.A.I.C.S.: 333310

Subsidiaries:

HNT (DongGuan) Company Limited (1)
Chashan Industrial Park Chashan Town, Dongguan, 523380, Guangdong, China
Tel.: (86) 76981821666
Camera Module Distr
N.A.I.C.S.: 423410

HNT (Vina) Company Limited (1)
Luong Son Industrial Zone Km 36 National Road 6 Hoa Son ward, Luong, Hoa Binh, Vietnam
Tel.: (84) 2183824700
Camera Module Distr
N.A.I.C.S.: 423410

HO BEE LAND LTD

Tel.: (65) 67040888 SG
Web Site: https://www.hobee.com
Year Founded: 1987
H13—(SES)
Rev.: $336,946,148
Assets: $5,283,634,020
Liabilities: $2,549,365,294
Net Worth: $2,734,268,725
Earnings: ($196,195,562)
Fiscal Year-end: 12/31/23
Property Development Services
N.A.I.C.S.: 237210
Desmond Choon Leng Woon (Exec Dir)

HO CHI MINH CITY INFRASTRUCTURE INVESTMENT JOINT STOCK COMPANY

Floor 12 152 Dien Bien Phu Street 25 Ward, District Binh Thanh, Ho Chi Minh City, Vietnam
Tel.: (84) 836221025
Web Site: https://www.cii.com.vn
Year Founded: 2001
CII—(HOSE)
Rev.: $127,296,052
Assets: $1,367,184,714
Liabilities: $1,016,765,200
Net Worth: $350,419,514
Earnings: $15,242,022
Emp.: 460
Fiscal Year-end: 12/31/23
Financial Investment Services
N.A.I.C.S.: 523999
Vu Hoang Le (Chm)

Subsidiaries:

CII Engineering & Construction JSC (1)
185 Hoa Lan, Ward 2 Phu Nhuan Dist, Ho Chi Minh City, Vietnam
Tel.: (84) 835122712
Web Site: https://www.ciiec.com.vn
Construction Consulting Services
N.A.I.C.S.: 541330

CII Infrastructure Services Co., Ltd. (1)
12th Floor 152 Dien Bien Phu, Ward 25 Binh Thanh, Ho Chi Minh City, Vietnam
Tel.: (84) 2836221025
Web Site: https://cii.com.vn
Investment Services
N.A.I.C.S.: 523999

INTERNATIONAL PUBLIC

HO CHI MINH CITY SECURITIES CORPORATION

Level 2 5 6 7 11&12 AB Tower 76A Le Lai, District 1, Ho Chi Minh City, Vietnam
Tel.: (84) 2838233299
Web Site: https://www.hsc.com.vn
Year Founded: 2003
HCM—(HOSE)
Rev.: $119,610,348
Assets: $737,919,813
Liabilities: $395,461,902
Net Worth: $342,457,911
Earnings: $27,783,585
Emp.: 698
Fiscal Year-end: 12/31/23
Securities Brokerage Services
N.A.I.C.S.: 523150
Do Hung Viet (Chm)

HO HUP CONSTRUCTION COMPANY BERHAD

Level 18 Ho Hup Tower 1 Persiaran Jalil 1 Bandar Bukit Jalil, 57000, Kuala Lumpur, Malaysia
Tel.: (60) 350332788
Web Site:
 https://www.hohupgroup.com.my
Year Founded: 1960
HOHUP—(KLS)
Rev.: $45,088,042
Assets: $322,463,915
Liabilities: $233,638,095
Net Worth: $88,825,820
Earnings: ($7,694,815)
Emp.: 211
Fiscal Year-end: 12/31/22
Construction & Civil Engineering Services
N.A.I.C.S.: 541330
Kit-Leong Wong (CEO)

Subsidiaries:

Ho Hup (Myanmar) E&C Co., Ltd. (1)
No 20 Pale Road Building C, Mya Yeik Nyo Hotel Zone Bahan Township, Yangon, Myanmar
Tel.: (95) 9259582005
Web Site: http://www.hohupmyanmar.com
Engineeering Services
N.A.I.C.S.: 541330

HO TUNG CHEMICAL CORP.

8F No 6 Section 1 Zhongxing Road, Wugu Dist, Taipei, 248, Taiwan
Tel.: (886) 89769268
Web Site:
 https://www.htgroup.com.tw
1714—(TAI)
Rev.: $663,606,044
Assets: $739,109,524
Liabilities: $207,664,762
Net Worth: $531,444,762
Earnings: $28,492,657
Fiscal Year-end: 12/31/23
Chemical Products Distr
N.A.I.C.S.: 424690

HO WAH GENTING BERHAD

Wisma Ho Wah Genting 1st Floor No 35 Jalan Maharajalela, 50150, Kuala Lumpur, Malaysia
Tel.: (60) 321438811
Web Site:
 http://www.hwgenting.com.my
HWGB—(KLS)
Rev.: $53,963,175
Assets: $27,842,751
Liabilities: $9,174,392
Net Worth: $18,668,360
Earnings: $257,143
Emp.: 43
Fiscal Year-end: 12/31/23
Cables & Wires Mfr & Distr
N.A.I.C.S.: 423510
Hui Boon Lim (Pres)

AND PRIVATE COMPANIES

Subsidiaries:

Dviria Nano Tech Sdn. Bhd. (1)
Wisma Ho Wah Genting 1st Floor No 35
Jalan Maharajalela, 50150, Kuala Lumpur,
Malaysia
Tel.: (60) 321438811
Web Site: https://www.dviria.com
Health Care Product Mfr & Distr
N.A.I.C.S.: 325412

HWGB Biotech Sdn. Bhd. (1)
No 35 Jalan Maharajalela, 50150, Kuala
Lumpur, Malaysia
Tel.: (60) 321438811
Web Site: https://hwgbbiotech.com
Health Care Product Mfr & Distr
N.A.I.C.S.: 325412

HWGB EV Sdn. Bhd. (1)
Wisma Ho Wah Genting No 35 Jalan Maharajalela, 50150, Kuala Lumpur, Malaysia
Tel.: (60) 321438811
Web Site: https://www.hwgb.com
Investment Services
N.A.I.C.S.: 523999

Ho Wah Genting Trading Sdn. Bhd. (1)
Wisma Ho Wah Genting 1st Floor No 35
Jalan Maharajalela, 50150, Kuala Lumpur,
Federal Territory, Malaysia
Tel.: (60) 321438811
Web Site: http://www.hwgwirecable.com.my
Sales Range: $25-49.9 Million
Emp.: 50
Wires & Cables Distr
N.A.I.C.S.: 423690

P.T. Ho Wah Genting (1)
Jalan Brigjen Katamso Kawasan Bintang
Industri II Lot 27-30, Tanjung Uncang,
Batam, 29422, Kepulauan Riau, Indonesia
Tel.: (62) 778393009
Web Site: https://www.hw-genting.com
Sales Range: $200-249.9 Million
Emp.: 1,500
Wires & Cables Mfr
N.A.I.C.S.: 335929

HOA AN JOINT STOCK COMPANY

Ap Cau Hang - Xa Hoa An, Bien
Hoa, Dong Nai, Vietnam
Tel.: (84) 613954754
Web Site: http://www.hoaan.com.vn
Year Founded: 1978
DHA—(HOSE)
Rev.: $15,466,398
Assets: $19,326,755
Liabilities: $2,403,114
Net Worth: $16,923,642
Earnings: $3,586,625
Fiscal Year-end: 12/31/23
Mining Services
N.A.I.C.S.: 212321
Trinh Tien Bay *(Exec Dir)*

HOA BINH CONSTRUCTION GROUP JSC

Pax Sky Building 123 Nguyen Dinh
Chieu Street, Vo Thi Sau Ward District 3, Ho Chi Minh City, Vietnam
Tel.: (84) 839325030
Web Site: https://www.hbcg.vn
Year Founded: 1987
HBC—(HOSE)
Rev.: $310,528,396
Assets: $628,294,108
Liabilities: $624,446,811
Net Worth: $3,847,297
Earnings: ($45,951,926)
Emp.: 2,954
Fiscal Year-end: 12/31/23
Construction Services
N.A.I.C.S.: 236210
Viet Hieu Le *(CEO)*

Subsidiaries:

Anh Huy Construction Co., ltd (1)
1700/3C Highway 1A, An Phu Dong Ward
District 12, Ho Chi Minh City, Vietnam
Tel.: (84) 8 37195343

Web Site: http://www.hoabinhaha.com
Sales Range: $25-49.9 Million
Emp.: 100
Aluminium Products Mfr
N.A.I.C.S.: 332999

Anh Viet Mechanical & Aluminum Glass Corporation (1)
1700/3C Quoc lo 1A, Phuong An Phu Dong
Quan 12, Ho Chi Minh City, Vietnam
Tel.: (84) 2873036168
Web Site: http://www.avawindows.vn
Aluminum & Glass Product Mfr
N.A.I.C.S.: 327215

Hoa Binh 479 Joint Stock Company (1)
No 54 Nguyen Du Street, Vinh, Nghe An, Vietnam
Tel.: (84) 2383855478
Web Site: http://www.hb479.vn
Bridge Construction Services
N.A.I.C.S.: 237310

Hoa Binh Architecture Co., Ltd. (1)
235 Vo Thi Sau, Ward Vo Thi Sau District 3, Ho Chi Minh City, Vietnam
Tel.: (84) 915890126
Web Site: https://hbarchitects.vn
Architectural Construction Services
N.A.I.C.S.: 541310

Hoa Binh House JSC (1)
104 Nguyen Du, Ben Nghe Ward District 1, Ho Chi Minh City, Vietnam
Tel.: (84) 839107572
Web Site: https://www.hoabinhhbh.com
Real Estate Manangment Services
N.A.I.C.S.: 531390

Hoa Binh Infrastructure Investment & Construction JSC (1)
Hamlet 7, Nhi Thanh Commune Thu Thua
District, Long An, Vietnam
Tel.: (84) 723613554
Web Site: https://www.hoabinhhbh.com
Build Contractor Services
N.A.I.C.S.: 236220

Hoa Binh Mechanical Electrical (HBE) JSC (1)
235 Vo Thi Sau St, Ward 7 Dist 3, Ho Chi
Minh City, Vietnam
Tel.: (84) 839325030
Mechanical & Electrical Engineering Services
N.A.I.C.S.: 541330

Hoa Binh Paint Co., Ltd. (1)
37/5A Phan Van Hon Street, Tan Thoi Nhat
Ward District 12, Ho Chi Minh City, Vietnam
Tel.: (84) 1800588800
Web Site: https://sonhoabinh.vn
Paint Product Mfr
N.A.I.C.S.: 325510

Hoa Binh Renewable Energy & Investment Joint Stock Company (1)
Room A1 06 03 Goldview Building 346, Ben
Van Don Ward 1 District 4, Ho Chi Minh
City, Vietnam
Tel.: (84) 2862788589
Build Contractor Services
N.A.I.C.S.: 236220

Matec Construction Machinery Co., Ltd. (1)
254 Truong Chinh, Phuong Dong Hung
Thuan Q 12, Ho Chi Minh City, Vietnam
Tel.: (84) 2838833792
Web Site: http://mateo.vn
Construction Equipment Mfr
N.A.I.C.S.: 333120

Moc Hoa Binh Manufacturing & Decorating JSC (1)
4 Pham Ngoc Thach St, Ward 6 District 3, Ho Chi Minh City, Vietnam
Tel.: (84) 2838272622
Build Contractor Services
N.A.I.C.S.: 236220

HOA BINH SECURITIES JOINT STOCK COMPANY

7th-9th Floor 46 - 48 Ba Trieu Street
Hang Bai Quarter, Hoan Kiem, Hanoi, Vietnam
Tel.: (84) 439368866
Web Site: https://www.hbse.com.vn

HBS—(HNX)
Rev.: $1,589,249
Assets: $17,476,587
Liabilities: $175,224
Net Worth: $17,301,363
Earnings: $732,124
Emp.: 32
Fiscal Year-end: 12/31/23
Investment Banking & Securities Brokerage Services
N.A.I.C.S.: 523150
Nguyen Thi Loan *(Chm)*

HOA BINH URBAN ENVIRONMENTAL SERVICES JOINT STOCK COMPANY

Hamlet 1, Da Phuoc Ward Binh
Chanh District, Ho Chi Minh City, Vietnam
Tel.: (84) 2837780645
Organic Fertilizer Mfr
N.A.I.C.S.: 325311

HOA CAM CONCRETE JSC

Zone B6-5 Thuan Yen Industrial Park,
Hoa Thuan Ward, Tam Ky, Quang
Nam, Vietnam
Tel.: (84) 2356335999
HCC—(HNX)
Rev.: $23,350,000
Assets: $13,125,800
Liabilities: $5,046,700
Net Worth: $8,079,100
Earnings: $913,200
Fiscal Year-end: 12/31/23
Building Materials Mfr
N.A.I.C.S.: 327120
Long Van Ngo *(Gen Dir & Member-Mgmt Bd)*

HOA PHAT GROUP JOINT STOCK COMPANY

66 Nguyen Du Nguyen Du Ward, Hai
Ba Trung District, Hanoi, Vietnam
Tel.: (84) 2462848666
Web Site:
https://www.hoaphat.com.vn
Year Founded: 1992
HPG—(HOSE)
Rev.: $4,958,635,543
Assets: $7,736,642,566
Liabilities: $3,499,782,094
Net Worth: $4,236,860,473
Earnings: $280,175,999
Emp.: 29,000
Fiscal Year-end: 12/31/23
Financial Investment Services
N.A.I.C.S.: 523999
Nguyen Thi Thao Nguyen *(Deputy Gen Dir)*

Subsidiaries:

An Thong Mining Investment JSC (1)
415 Tran Phu Street, Tran Phu Ward, Ha
Giang, Vietnam
Tel.: (84) 219 3864 898
Mining Investment Services
N.A.I.C.S.: 213113

Hoa Phat Door JSC (1)
39 Nguyen Dinh Chieu, Hai Ba Trung District, Hanoi, Vietnam
Tel.: (84) 4 6280 9888
Plastic, Wooden & Aluminum Door Mfr
N.A.I.C.S.: 332321

Hoa Phat Dung Quat Steel JSC (1)
Dung Quat Economic Zone, Binh Dong
Commune Binh Son District, Binh Dong,
Quang Ngai, Vietnam
Tel.: (84) 2553609951
Construction Steel Mfr
N.A.I.C.S.: 331221

Hoa Phat Energy JSC (1)
39 Nguyen Dinh Chieu, Hai Ba Trung District, Hanoi, Vietnam
Tel.: (84) 436284440
Electricity Producer & Distr

N.A.I.C.S.: 221122

Hoa Phat Equipment & Accessories Co., Ltd. (1)
243 Giai Phong Street, Dong Da District, Hanoi, Vietnam
Tel.: (84) 43 869 3983
Emp.: 300
Heavy Equipment Mfr & Sales
N.A.I.C.S.: 333248

Hoa Phat Furniture JSC (1)
39 Nguyen Dinh Chieu, Hai Ba Trung District, Hanoi, Vietnam
Tel.: (84) 4 6281 0666
Furniture Mfr & Sales
N.A.I.C.S.: 337127

Hoa Phat Hai Duong Steel JSC (1)
Hiep Son Commune, Kinh Mon District, Hiep Son, Hai Duong, Vietnam
Tel.: (84) 2203535245
Construction Steel Mfr
N.A.I.C.S.: 331221

Hoa Phat Home Appliances JSC (1)
No 39 Nguyen Dinh Chieu Street, Hai Ba
Trung, Hanoi, Vietnam
Tel.: (84) 2462848777
Web Site: https://dienmay.hoaphat.com.vn
Electrical Appliance Mfr
N.A.I.C.S.: 335220

Hoa Phat Metal Producing Co., Ltd. (1)
39 Nguyen Dinh Chieu, Le Dai Hanh Hai
Ba Trung, Hanoi, Vietnam
Tel.: (84) 2436332108
Web Site:
https://chetaokimloai.hoaphat.com.vn
Construction Machinery Mfr
N.A.I.C.S.: 333120

Hoa Phat Mining JSC (1)
39 Nguyen Dinh Chieu Street, Hai Ba Trung
District, Hanoi, Vietnam
Tel.: (84) 4 3944 7357
Coal Mining Services
N.A.I.C.S.: 213113

Hoa Phat Refrigeration Engineering Co., Ltd. (1)
39 Nguyen Dinh Chieu Street, Le Dai Hanh
Ward Hai Ba Trung District, Hanoi, Vietnam
Tel.: (84) 2462848777
Web Site: https://funiki.hoaphat.com
Home Appliances Mfr & Sales
N.A.I.C.S.: 335220

Hoa Phat Steel JSC (1)
39 Nguyen Dien Chieu, Hai Ba Trung District, Hanoi, Vietnam
Tel.: (84) 4 6279 7171
Steel Products Mfr
N.A.I.C.S.: 331110

Hoa Phat Steel One Member Co. Ltd. (1)
39 Nguyen Dinh Chieu Street, Hai Ba Trung
District, Hanoi, Vietnam
Tel.: (84) 4 6279 7096
Steel Investment Services
N.A.I.C.S.: 331512

Hoa Phat Steel Pipe Co., Ltd. (1)
Hoa Phat Building 39 Nguyen Dinh Chieu,
Le Dai Hanh Ward Hai Ba Trung District,
Hanoi, Vietnam
Tel.: (84) 2462797120
Steel Pole Mfr
N.A.I.C.S.: 332996

Hoa Phat Steel Sheet Co., Ltd. (1)
Road E1 zone E, Pho Noi A Industrial Park
Lac Dao Commune Van Lam District, Hung
Yen, Vietnam
Tel.: (84) 243632108
Steel Sheet Product Mfr & Distr
N.A.I.C.S.: 331221

Hoa Phat Trading Co., Ltd. (1)
39 Nguyen Dinh Chieu Street, Le Dai Hanh
Ward Hai Ba TrungDistrict, Hanoi, Vietnam
Tel.: (84) 462821888
Emp.: 15
Steel Products Exporter & Distr
N.A.I.C.S.: 423510

Hoa Phat Urban Development and Construction JSC (1)
39 Nguyen Dinh Chieu, Hai Ba Trung Dis-

HOA PHAT GROUP JOINT STOCK COMPANY

Hoa Phat Group Joint Stock Company—(Continued)
trict, Hanoi, Vietnam
Tel.: (84) 462881234
Web Site: https://www.hoaphat.com.vn
Emp.: 5
Heavy Construction Services
N.A.I.C.S.: 237990

HOA SEN GROUP
No 9 Thong Nhat Boulevard Song Than II Industrial Park Di An Ward, Di An, Binh Duong, Vietnam
Tel.: (84) 939082001
Web Site: https://vietnamsteel.com
Year Founded: 2001
HSG—(HOSE)
Rev.: $3,165,066,100
Assets: $1,736,530,600
Liabilities: $658,514,000
Net Worth: $1,078,016,600
Earnings: $3,000,800
Emp.: 7,584
Fiscal Year-end: 09/30/23
Steel Products Mfr
N.A.I.C.S.: 332999
Phuoc Vu Le (Chm-Mgmt Bd)

Subsidiaries:

Hoa Sen Binhdinh One Member Co., Ltd. (1)
Nhon Hoa Industrial Park, Nhon Hoa Ward, An Nhon, Binh Dinh, Vietnam
Tel.: (84) 2563738991
Rolled Steel Mfr
N.A.I.C.S.: 331221
Ho Thanh Hieu (Chm)

Hoa Sen Building Material One Member Limited Liabilities Company (1)
Phu My 1 Industrial Park, Tan Thanh District, Phu My, Ba Ria-Vung Tau, Vietnam
Tel.: (84) 2543923231
Industrial Steel Mfr
N.A.I.C.S.: 333511
Tran Ngoc Chu (Chm)

Hoa Sen Nghe An One Member Limited Liabilities Company (1)
Lot No 1-8, Dong Hoi Industrial Park Quynh Lap Commune Hoang Mai, Hanoi, Nghe An, Vietnam
Tel.: (84) 2383668112
Rolled Steel Mfr
N.A.I.C.S.: 331221
Nguyen Ngoc Huy (Chm)

Hoa Sen Nhon Hoi - Binh Dinh One Member Limited Liabilities Company (1)
Hoi Son Hamlet, Nhon Hoi Commune, Quy Nhon, Binh Dinh, Vietnam
Tel.: (84) 2562220001
Rolled Steel Mfr
N.A.I.C.S.: 331221

Hoa Sen Plastics Joint Stock Company (1)
Street 2B Phu My I Industrial Park, Phu My Town, Ba Ria, Vung Tau, Vietnam
Tel.: (84) 2543923231
Plastic Pipe Product Mfr & Distr
N.A.I.C.S.: 326122

Hoa Sen Steel Sheet One Member Limited Liabilities Company (1)
No 09 Thong Nhat Boulevard, Song Than 2 Industrial Park Di An Ward, Di An, Binh Duong, Vietnam
Tel.: (84) 6503737200
Rolled Steel Mfr
N.A.I.C.S.: 331221
Tran Ngoc Chu (Chm)

Hoa Sen Yen Bai Building Material Co., Ltd. (1)
Dong Danh Village, Minh Quan Commune Tran Yen, Yen Bai, Vietnam
Tel.: (84) 2162220789
Rolled Steel Mfr
N.A.I.C.S.: 331221
Vu Van Thanh (Chm)

Phu My One Member Limited Liabilities Company (1)
Road 1B, Phu My 1 Industrial Park Tan Thanh District, Phu My, Ba Ria-Vung Tau, Vietnam
Tel.: (84) 2643924790
Rolled Steel Mfr
N.A.I.C.S.: 331221
Cao Quang Sang (Mng Dir)

HOANG ANH GIA LAI JOINT STOCK COMPANY
15 Truong Chinh St, Phu Dong Ward, Pleiku, Tinh Gia Lai, Vietnam
Tel.: (84) 2692225888
Web Site: https://www.hagl.com.vn
HAG—(HOSE)
Rev.: $265,426,756
Assets: $861,214,106
Liabilities: $586,102,342
Net Worth: $275,111,764
Earnings: $73,405,463
Emp.: 1,784
Fiscal Year-end: 12/31/23
Diverse Holding Company; Agriculture & Real Estate
N.A.I.C.S.: 551112
Ho Thi Kim Chi (Deputy Gen Dir)

Subsidiaries:

BAPI Hoang Anh Gia Lai Joint Stock Company (1)
15 Truong Chinh, Phu Dong Ward, Pleiku, Gia Lai, Vietnam
Tel.: (84) 2888898789
Web Site: https://bapi.com.vn
Meat Whslr
N.A.I.C.S.: 424470

HAGL Rubber JSC (1)
The 11th Floor 15 Truong Chinh St, Phu Dong Ward, Pleiku, Gia Lai, Vietnam
Tel.: (84) 592222283
Web Site: https://www.hagl.com.vn
Rubber Plantation Services
N.A.I.C.S.: 115112

HOANG KIM TAY NGUYEN GROUP JOINT STOCK COMPANY
No 18 Le Lai Street, Pleiku, Gia Lai, Vietnam
Tel.: (84) 593824332
Web Site: http://www.gialaictc.com.vn
CTC—(HNX)
Rev.: $3,931,000
Assets: $30,780,300
Liabilities: $18,367,800
Net Worth: $12,412,500
Earnings: ($913,800)
Fiscal Year-end: 12/31/22
Home Management Services
N.A.I.C.S.: 721110

HOANG LONG GROUP JOINT STOCK COMPANY
149 5th floor Nguyen Van Cu Ward 2, District 5, Ho Chi Minh City, Vietnam
Tel.: (84) 0283 9232 400
Web Site: http://www.hoanglonggroup.com
Year Founded: 1999
Tobacco Product Mfr
N.A.I.C.S.: 312230

HOANG PHUC MINERAL TRADING & CONSTRUCTION JSC
Zone 6, Na Sam Ward Van Lang district, Hanoi, Lang Son, Vietnam
Tel.: (84) 936092584
HPM—(HNX)
Construction Materials Whslr
N.A.I.C.S.: 423390
Le Thanh Hong (Chm)

HOANG QUAN CONSULTING - TRADING - SERVICE REAL ESTATE CORPORATION
15 Nguyen Luong Bang, Ward Tan Phu 7 District, Ho Chi Minh City, Vietnam
Tel.: (84) 2836200209
Web Site: https://www.hoangquan.com.vn
Year Founded: 2000
HQC—(HOSE)
Rev.: $12,053,348
Assets: $300,736,722
Liabilities: $120,919,775
Net Worth: $179,816,947
Earnings: $212,510
Emp.: 63
Fiscal Year-end: 12/31/23
Real Estate Development Services
N.A.I.C.S.: 531390
Truong Anh Tuan (Co-Founder & Chm)

Subsidiaries:

Hoang Quan Appraisal Co., Ltd. (1)
121Bis Nguyen Van Troi, Ward 11 Phu Nhuan District, Ho Chi Minh City, Vietnam
Tel.: (84) 934252707
Web Site: https://www.hqa.com.vn
Financial Services
N.A.I.C.S.: 921130

Hoang Quan Binh Thuan Consulting - Trading - Service Real Estate Corporation (1)
No 198 Nguyen Hoi, Phu Trinh Ward, Phan Thiet, Binh Thuan, Vietnam
Tel.: (84) 2523831317
Web Site: https://hoangquanbinhthuan.com.vn
Emp.: 99
Real Estate Services
N.A.I.C.S.: 531210

Hoang Quan Can Tho Investment Real Estate Corporation (1)
27-28 Vo Nguyen Giap Former Quang Trung Street, Phu Thu Ward Cai Rang District, Can Tho, Vietnam
Tel.: (84) 7103917696
Web Site: https://hoangquancantho.com.vn
Emp.: 100
Real Estate Services
N.A.I.C.S.: 531210

HOANGHA JOINT STOCK COMPANY
286 Nguyen Xien, Hanoi, Vietnam
Tel.: (84) 398765768
Web Site: https://hoanghagroup.vn
Year Founded: 2001
HHG—(HNX)
Rev.: $6,147,400
Assets: $20,597,000
Liabilities: $8,651,400
Net Worth: $11,945,600
Earnings: ($4,324,100)
Emp.: 1,000
Fiscal Year-end: 12/31/23
Road Passenger Transportation Services
N.A.I.C.S.: 485999

HOB BIOTECH GROUP CORP., LTD.
C10 Building No 218 Xinghu Road, Suzhou Industrial Park, Suzhou, 215123, Jiangsu, China
Tel.: (86) 51269561996
Web Site: https://www.hob-biotech.com
Year Founded: 2009
688656—(SHG)
Rev.: $44,983,009
Assets: $132,616,027
Liabilities: $23,164,161
Net Worth: $109,451,867
Earnings: $5,847,814
Fiscal Year-end: 12/31/22
Medical Product Mfr & Distr
N.A.I.C.S.: 339112
Li John (Chm & Gen Mgr)

HOB CO., LTD.

INTERNATIONAL PUBLIC

1-14 Kita, Kamikawa-gun, Higashikagura, 071-1544, Hokkaido, Japan
Tel.: (81) 166833555   JP
Web Site: https://www.hob.co.jp
1382—(TKS)
Rev.: $15,668,180
Assets: $6,985,060
Liabilities: $2,201,880
Net Worth: $4,783,180
Earnings: $124,400
Emp.: 56
Fiscal Year-end: 06/30/24
Fruit Whslr; Strawberry Farming; Seed Mfr & Distr
N.A.I.C.S.: 111333
Iwao Takahashi (Chm)

Subsidiaries:

Japan Potato Corporation (1)
Park West Building 8F 4-8-10 Hatchobori, Chuo-ku, Tokyo, 104 0032, Japan
Tel.: (81) 3 5541 5335
Web Site: http://www.japanpotato.co.jp
Sales Range: $1-9.9 Million
Potato Production
N.A.I.C.S.: 111211
Iwao Takahashi (Pres)

HOBART ENTERPRISES LTD
Burleigh Manor Peel Road, Douglas, IM1 5EP, Isle of Man
Tel.: (44) 1624626586
Web Site: http://www.hobartltd.com
Year Founded: 2005
Sales Range: $10-24.9 Million
Emp.: 20
Holding Services
N.A.I.C.S.: 551112
Gaven Westley (Dir-Fin)

Subsidiaries:

AV Pound & Co Ltd (1)
Clyda Business Park, Quartertown, Mallow, Co Cork, Ireland
Tel.: (353) 22 20573
Web Site: http://www.avpound.com
Chemical Products Distr
N.A.I.C.S.: 424690

Anchor Chemicals (Pty) Ltd (1)
20 Sheffield Road, Willowton, Pietermaritzburg, 3200, Kwazulu Natal, South Africa
Tel.: (27) 33 390 8050
Web Site: http://www.anchorchemicals.co.za
Chemical Products Mfr
N.A.I.C.S.: 325998

Carst & Walker (EA) Limited (1)
C&S House Plot No 209/10491 Old Mombasa Road, Embakasi, Nairobi, Kenya
Tel.: (254) 20 2180493
Web Site: http://www.carst.co.ke
Chemical Products Distr
N.A.I.C.S.: 424690

Carst & Walker (PTY) Ltd. (1)
Building 2 5 Sherborne Rd, Johannesburg, 2041, South Africa (100%)
Tel.: (27) 114893600
Web Site: http://www.carst.co.za
Sales Range: $10-24.9 Million
Emp.: 30
Chemicals Mfr
N.A.I.C.S.: 325998
Tanya Smith (Product Mgr-Biosciences)

Carst & Walker Australia (Pty) Ltd (1)
Unit 1 5 Iron Road, Malaga, 6090, WA, Australia
Tel.: (61) 8 9248 9355
Web Site: http://www.carst.com.au
Chemical Products Distr
N.A.I.C.S.: 424690

Chemox Pound Limited (1)
Sussex House The Pines Broad Street, Guildford, GU3 3BH, Surrey, United Kingdom
Tel.: (44) 1483 450660
Web Site: http://www.chemoxpound.com
Chemical Products Distr
N.A.I.C.S.: 424690

AND PRIVATE COMPANIES — HOCHSCHILD MINING PLC

Subsidiary (Domestic):

Capricorn Chemicals Ltd. (2)
Unit 1 e Space North 181 Wisbech Road, Littleport, CB6 1RA, Cambridgeshire, United Kingdom
Tel.: (44) 1353 863 686
Web Site: http://www.capricorn.co.uk
Emp.: 30
Chemical Products Distr
N.A.I.C.S.: 424690
David Barnby (CEO)

HOBART REVENUE MANAGEMENT LIMITED
6th-9th Fl Portland Tower Portland St, Manchester, M1 3LD, Greater Manchester, United Kingdom
Tel.: (44) 1612370495 UK
Web Site: http://www.taxdebts.co.uk
Year Founded: 2003
Financial Advisory Services
N.A.I.C.S.: 523940
Tariq Ali (CEO)

HOBONICHI CO., LTD.
Hobonichi Kanda Building 3-18 Kanda Nishikicho, Chiyoda-Ku, Tokyo, 101-0054, Japan
Tel.: (81) 357701101
Web Site: https://www.hobonichi.co.jp
Year Founded: 1979
3560—(TKS)
Sales Range: Less than $1 Million
Notebook Product Distr
N.A.I.C.S.: 424920
Shigesato Itoi (Pres, CEO & Chief Creative Officer)

HOCHDORF HOLDING AG
Siedereistrasse 9, Postfach 691, 6281, Hochdorf, Switzerland
Tel.: (41) 419146565
Web Site: https://www.hochdorf.com
Year Founded: 2006
HOCN—(SWX)
Rev.: $365,866,415
Assets: $322,930,831
Liabilities: $135,273,355
Net Worth: $187,657,476
Earnings: ($12,135,726)
Emp.: 369
Fiscal Year-end: 12/31/23
Offices of Other Holding Companies
N.A.I.C.S.: 551112
Christoph Hug (Head-Corp Comm)

Subsidiaries:

Bimbosan AG (1)
Siedereistrasse 9, 6280, Hochdorf, Switzerland
Tel.: (41) 32 639 1444
Web Site: https://www.bimbosan.ch
Nutritional Product Mfr
N.A.I.C.S.: 311991

HOCHDORF Holding AG (1)
Siedereistrasse 9, Postfach 691, 6281, Hochdorf, Switzerland
Tel.: (41) 419146565
Web Site: https://www.hochdorf.com
Sales Range: $25-49.9 Million
Emp.: 200
Dairy Products Mfr
N.A.I.C.S.: 311514

HOCHDORF Nutricare Ltd. (1)
Siedereistrasse 9, Postfach 691, 6281, Hochdorf, Switzerland
Tel.: (41) 419146565
Emp.: 200
Infant Health Care Food Mfr & Distr
N.A.I.C.S.: 311999
Janny Vedder (Mgr-Mktg-Nutrition)

HOCHDORF Nutrifood Ltd. (1)
Siedereistrasse 9, Postfach 691, 6281, Hochdorf, Switzerland
Tel.: (41) 41 914 65 65
Web Site: http://www.hochdorf.com

Sales Range: $25-49.9 Million
Emp.: 15
Nutritional Food Mfr
N.A.I.C.S.: 311999

HOCHDORF Swiss Milk Ltd. (1)
Siedereistrasse 9, Postfach 691, 6281, Hochdorf, Switzerland
Tel.: (41) 41 914 65 65
Web Site: http://www.hochdorf.com
Sales Range: $100-124.9 Million
Emp.: 350
Milk Powder Mfr
N.A.I.C.S.: 311514
Werner Schweizer (Mng Dir)

Thur Milch Ring AG (1)
Industriestrasse 26, Sulgen, 8583, Weinfelden, Switzerland
Tel.: (41) 716600404
Web Site: https://www.thurmilch.ch
Nutritional Products Whslr
N.A.I.C.S.: 456191

HOCHENG CORPORATION
1F No 398 Xingshan Road, Neihu District, Taipei, 114, Taiwan
Tel.: (886) 227925511
Web Site: https://www.hcg.com.tw
Year Founded: 1931
1810—(TAI)
Rev.: $159,285,353
Assets: $346,472,697
Liabilities: $126,496,153
Net Worth: $219,976,544
Earnings: $721,966
Emp.: 1,000
Fiscal Year-end: 12/31/23
Glass & Ceramics Mfr
N.A.I.C.S.: 326191
Li-Chien Chiu (Chm)

Subsidiaries:

Hocheng Co., Ltd. (1)
No 115 Luzhi Avenue, Wuzhong Distric, Suzhou, Jiangsu, China
Tel.: (86) 51265010833
Web Site: http://www.hcg.com.cn
Bathroom Fixture Mfr
N.A.I.C.S.: 332999
Scott Chiu (Chm)

Hocheng Philippines Corporation (1)
Lot 2 Blk 4 Phase III, First Cavite Industrial Estate Brgy Langkaan, Dasmarinas, Philippines (100%)
Tel.: (63) 464021310
Web Site: http://www.hcg.com.ph
Sales Range: $200-249.9 Million
Emp.: 750
Enameled Iron & Metal Sanitary Ware Mfr
N.A.I.C.S.: 332999

HOCHIKI CORPORATION
2-10-43 Kamiosaki, Shinagawa-ku, Tokyo, 141-8660, Japan
Tel.: (81) 334444111 JP
Web Site: https://www.hochiki.co.jp
Year Founded: 1918
6745—(TKS)
Rev.: $617,935,850
Assets: $563,390,130
Liabilities: $213,648,420
Net Worth: $349,741,710
Earnings: $37,419,210
Emp.: 2,295
Fiscal Year-end: 03/31/24
Fire Alarms, Fire Extinguishers, Electronic Equipment & Security Devices Mfr, Installation & Sales
N.A.I.C.S.: 334290
Kenji Kanamori (Chm)

Subsidiaries:

Hochiki America Corporation (1)
7051 Vlg Dr Ste 100, Buena Park, CA 90621-2268 (100%)
Tel.: (714) 522-2246
Web Site: https://www.hochikiamerica.com
Sales Range: $75-99.9 Million
Emp.: 140
Mfr of Industrial & Commercial Fire Safety Devices

N.A.I.C.S.: 423610
Peter Holbrook (Mgr-Northwest & Southwest)

Hochiki Asia Pacific Pte. Ltd. (1)
71 UBI Road 1 07-40/41 Oxley Bizhub, Singapore, 408732, Singapore (100%)
Tel.: (65) 68419728
Web Site: http://www.hochikiasiapacific.com
Emp.: 3
Electronic Security System Mfr
N.A.I.C.S.: 334290
Jun Tamura (Pres)

Hochiki Australia Pty Ltd (1)
Block Y Unit 1 Regents Park Estate 391 Park Rd, Regents Park, 2143, NSW, Australia
Tel.: (61) 29 738 5566
Web Site: https://www.hochikiaustralia.com
Fire Detection & Alarm System Mfr
N.A.I.C.S.: 334290

Hochiki Europe (U.K.) Ltd. (1)
Grosvenor Road, Gillingham Business Park, Gillingham, ME8 0SA, Kent, United Kingdom (100%)
Tel.: (44) 1634260133
Web Site: https://www.hochikieurope.com
Sales Range: $50-74.9 Million
Emp.: 80
Fire Prevention Equipment Mfr & Distr
N.A.I.C.S.: 922160

Hochiki Middle East FZE (1)
Office No C-205 HQ Building Dubai Silicon Oasis, PO Box 341415, Dubai, United Arab Emirates
Tel.: (971) 4 372 4130
Fire Detection Equipment Mfr
N.A.I.C.S.: 334290

Hochiki Servicios, S. de R.L. de C.V. (1)
Av Junto Al Rio 24FA Colonia Junto Al Rio Temixco, 62584, Morelos, Mexico
Tel.: (52) 777 326 3855
Fire Detection Equipment Mfr
N.A.I.C.S.: 334290

Hochiki Thailand Co., Ltd. (1)
BB Bldg 10th Floor 1011 54 Sukhumvit 21, Kwaeng Klong Toey Nua Khet Wattana, Bangkok, 10110, Thailand
Tel.: (66) 2 664 4445
Security System Services
N.A.I.C.S.: 561621

Kentec Electronics Ltd. (1)
Units 25-26 Fawkes Avenue Questor, Dartford, DA1 1JQ, United Kingdom
Tel.: (44) 132 222 2121
Web Site: https://kentec.co.uk
Emp.: 2
Electric Equipment Mfr
N.A.I.C.S.: 334419

HOCHLAND SE
Kemptener Str 17, Heimenkirch, 88178, Lindau, Germany
Tel.: (49) 8381 502 0
Web Site: http://www.hochland-group.com
Year Founded: 1927
Emp.: 4,853
Cheese Mfr & Distr
N.A.I.C.S.: 311513
Hansjorg Zelger (Chm-Supervisory Bd)

Subsidiaries:

Bonifaz Kohler GmbH (1)
Gossholz 30 b, 88161, Lindenberg im Allgau, Germany
Tel.: (49) 83815020
Web Site: http://www.bonifaz-kohler.com
Cheese Product Retailer
N.A.I.C.S.: 424430
Volker Brutting (Mng Dir)

E.V.A. GmbH (1)
Alter Feldweg 10, 15366, Hoppegarten, Germany
Tel.: (49) 3342309530
Web Site: http://www.evagmbh.de
Waste Management Services
N.A.I.C.S.: 562998

Franklin Foods, Inc. (1)
2500 N Military Trl Ste 320, Boca Raton, FL 33431
Tel.: (802) 933-4338
Web Site: http://www.franklinfoods.com
Fluid Milk & Dairy Products Mfr
N.A.I.C.S.: 311511
Jon Gutknecht (Pres & CEO)

Fromagerie Henri Hutin S.a.r.l. (1)
Rue du Rattentout, BP 28, 55320, Dieue-sur-Meuse, France
Tel.: (33) 329832323
Web Site: http://www.henri-hutin.com
Cheese Mfr & Distr
N.A.I.C.S.: 311513
Josef Stitzl (Gen Mgr)

Gold Peg International Pty. Ltd. (1)
77 Malcolm Road, Braeside, 3195, VIC, Australia
Tel.: (61) 385312999
Industrial Equipment Distr
N.A.I.C.S.: 423840

Grunland GmbH (1)
Am Sachsenring 2-4, 09337, Hermsdorf, Germany
Tel.: (49) 3723668570
Application Services
N.A.I.C.S.: 541511

Hochland Deutschland GmbH (1)
Kemptener Strasse 17, Heimenkirch, 88178, Lindau, Germany
Tel.: (49) 83815020
Web Site: http://www.hochland.de
Food Production Distr
N.A.I.C.S.: 424490

Hochland Espanola S. A. (1)
C/ Llobatona, 7 Pol Industrial del Centro, 08840, Viladecans, Spain
Tel.: (34) 936370851
Web Site: http://www.hochland.es
Cheese Product Retailer
N.A.I.C.S.: 424430
Juan Carlos Mansilla (Mgr-IT)

Hochland Natec GmbH (1)
Kolpingstrasse 32, Heimenkirch, 88178, Lindau, Germany
Tel.: (49) 8381502400
Web Site: http://www.natec-network.com
Food Production Distr
N.A.I.C.S.: 424490
Horst Fischer (Sls Mgr)

Hochland Romania Srl (1)
Str N Titulescu Nr 3A, 545400, Sighisoara, Mures, Romania
Tel.: (40) 265506200
Web Site: http://www.hochland.ro
Packaging Machinery Mfr
N.A.I.C.S.: 333993

Natec USA LLC (1)
N76 W30500 County Rd, Hartland, WI 53029
Tel.: (262) 457-4071
Web Site: http://www.natec.us.com
Network Services
N.A.I.C.S.: 517810

HOCHSCHILD MINING PLC
17 Cavendish Square, London, W1G 0PH, United Kingdom
Tel.: (44) 2037093260
Web Site: https://www.hochschildmining.com
Year Founded: 1911
HOC—(LSE)
Rev.: $621,827,000
Assets: $1,366,061,000
Liabilities: $559,976,000
Net Worth: $806,085,000
Earnings: $20,426,000
Emp.: 3,352
Fiscal Year-end: 12/31/20
Holding Company; Gold & Silver Exploration
N.A.I.C.S.: 551112
Eduardo Hochschild (Chm)

Subsidiaries:

Amarillo Gold Corporation (1)
82 Richmond St East Suite 201, Toronto,

HOCHSCHILD MINING PLC

Hochschild Mining plc—(Continued)
M5C 1P1, ON, Canada
Tel.: (416) 671-4966
Web Site: http://www.amarillogold.com
Rev.: $39,345
Assets: $72,132,043
Liabilities: $1,567,766
Net Worth: $70,564,277
Earnings: ($3,027,294)
Emp.: 5
Fiscal Year-end: 12/31/2020
Mineral Exploration Services
N.A.I.C.S.: 213114
Hemdat Sawh *(CFO)*

Subsidiary (Non-US):

Amarillo Mineracao do Brasil Limitada (2)
Praca Carlos Chagas 49 - Salas 504 a 506, Bairro Santo Agostinho, Belo Horizonte, 30170-913, Minas Gerais, Brazil
Tel.: (55) 3132615974
Sales Range: $50-74.9 Million
Emp.: 6
Mineral Mining Services
N.A.I.C.S.: 212390

Compania Minera Ares S.A.C. (1)
Calle La Colonia No 180 Urb El Vivero, Santiago de Surco, Lima, Peru
Tel.: (51) 13172000
Web Site: http://www.hochschildmining.com
Emp.: 250
Gold Ore Mining Services
N.A.I.C.S.: 212220

Hochschild Mining (1)
Calle La Colonia No 180 Urb El Vivero, Santiago de Surco, Lima, 33, Peru
Tel.: (51) 1 317 2000
Web Site: https://www.hocplc.com
Sales Range: $450-499.9 Million
Emp.: 887
Gold & Silver Exploration, Mining & Processing
N.A.I.C.S.: 212220

Hochschild Mining Ares (UK) Ltd. (1)
46 Albemarle Street, London, W1S 4JL, United Kingdom
Tel.: (44) 2079072930
Web Site: http://www.hochschildmining.com
Sales Range: $50-74.9 Million
Emp.: 3
Metal Mining Services
N.A.I.C.S.: 212290

Minas Santa Maria de Moris, S.A. de C.V. (1)
5 Km North of Moris, Chihuahua, Mexico
Tel.: (52) 6144199500
Mining Services
N.A.I.C.S.: 212290

Minera Hochschild Mexico, S.A. de C.V. (1)
Boulevard Diaz Ordaz Nro 140 Torre 2 Piso 5, Colonia Santa Maria, Monterrey, 64650, Nuevo Leon, Mexico
Tel.: (52) 8180481000
Web Site: http://www.hocplc.com
Sales Range: $100-124.9 Million
Emp.: 155
Gold Ore Mining Services
N.A.I.C.S.: 212220

Minera MH Chile Ltda. (1)
Alcantara 443 Las Condes, Santiago, 7550281, Chile
Tel.: (56) 2579 7800
Sales Range: $50-74.9 Million
Emp.: 30
Metal Mining Services
N.A.I.C.S.: 213114

Minera Minasnioc S.A.C. (1)
Av Carlos Villaran N 798 Urb, La Victoria, Lima, Peru
Tel.: (51) 14192500
Silver Mining Services
N.A.I.C.S.: 212220

Minera Santa Cruz S.A. (1)
Av Santa Fe 2755 piso 9, C1425BGO, Buenos Aires, CF, Argentina
Tel.: (54) 1141327900
Web Site: https://minerasantacruz.com
Mining Services
N.A.I.C.S.: 212220

HOCK LIAN SENG HOLDINGS LIMITED
80 Marine Parade Road 16-08 Parkway Parade, Singapore, 449269, Singapore
Tel.: (65) 63440555 SG
Web Site: https://www.hlsgroup.com.sg
Year Founded: 1969
J2T—(SES)
Rev.: $105,817,241
Assets: $256,068,127
Liabilities: $80,221,402
Net Worth: $175,846,725
Earnings: $12,157,634
Fiscal Year-end: 12/31/22
Civil Engineering Services
N.A.I.C.S.: 541330
David Tuan Dong Chew *(Deputy CEO)*

Subsidiaries:

Hock Lian Seng Contractors Pte Ltd (1)
80 Marine Parade Road 16-08 Parkway Parade, Singapore, 449269, Singapore
Tel.: (65) 63440555
Sales Range: $25-49.9 Million
Emp.: 100
Construction Engineering Services
N.A.I.C.S.: 541330

Hock Lian Seng Infrastructure Pte Ltd (1)
80 Marine Parade Road 21-08 Parkway Parade, Singapore, 449269, Singapore
Tel.: (65) 63440555
Emp.: 200
Construction Engineering Services
N.A.I.C.S.: 541330

Hock Lian Seng Properties Pte. Ltd. (1)
80 Marine Parade Road 16-08 Parkway Parade, Singapore, Singapore
Tel.: (65) 63440555
Web Site: http://www.hlsgroup.com.sg
Engineeering Services
N.A.I.C.S.: 541330

HOCK SENG LEE BERHAD
No 1 HSL Tower Lorong La Promenade 2 La Promenade, Kuching-Samarahan Expressway, 93450, Kota Samarahan, Sarawak, Malaysia
Tel.: (60) 82332755
Web Site: http://www.hsl.com.my
HSL—(KLS)
Rev.: $133,233,275
Assets: $294,323,477
Liabilities: $85,026,123
Net Worth: $209,297,354
Earnings: $8,127,405
Emp.: 1,200
Fiscal Year-end: 12/31/20
Marine Engineering Services
N.A.I.C.S.: 541330
Augustine Sek Hian Law *(Co-Sec & Gen Mgr-Fin & Admin)*

HOCK SIN LEONG GROUP BERHAD
1-11 Jalan Perdana 10/6 Pandan Perdana, 55300, Kuala Lumpur, Selangor Darul Ehsan, Malaysia
Tel.: (60) 392743288
Sales Range: $10-24.9 Million
Electric & Electronic Appliances Mfr
N.A.I.C.S.: 423620
Ah Lan Lee *(Chm & Mng Dir)*

HOCMON TRADE JOINT STOCK COMPANY
25 Ba Trieu Ward 1 Hoc Mon Town, Hoc Mon, Ho Chi Minh City, Vietnam
Tel.: (84) 838915294
N.A.I.C.S.: 212220
Web Site: https://www.hotraco.com.vn
HTC—(HNX)
Rev.: $104,218,700
Assets: $59,682,300
Liabilities: $28,753,200
Net Worth: $30,929,100
Earnings: $4,616,900
Fiscal Year-end: 12/31/23
Petroleum Product Whslr
N.A.I.C.S.: 424720
Le Van My *(Gen Dir)*

HOD-ASSAF INDUSTRIES LTD.
Kiryat Peleda Complex, PO Box 493, Acre, 24100, Israel
Tel.: (972) 49015000
Web Site: https://www.hodmetal.co.il
Year Founded: 1947
HOD—(TAE)
Rev.: $484,652,569
Assets: $330,197,536
Liabilities: $142,088,960
Net Worth: $188,108,576
Earnings: $7,756,872
Emp.: 1,000
Fiscal Year-end: 12/31/23
Iron & Steel Mills & Ferroalloy Manufacturing
N.A.I.C.S.: 331110

HODEN SEIMITSU KAKO KENKYUSHO CO., LTD.
3-17-6 Shin-Yokohama, Yokohama, 222-8580, Kanagawa, Japan
Tel.: (81) 462478400
Web Site: https://www.hsk.co.jp
6469—(TKS)
Rev.: $86,214,400
Assets: $127,435,660
Liabilities: $76,182,050
Net Worth: $51,253,610
Earnings: $1,637,790
Emp.: 773
Fiscal Year-end: 02/29/24
Dies & Machinery Parts Mfr & Sales
N.A.I.C.S.: 333514
Katsuhiko Futamura *(Chm)*

Subsidiaries:

Kyodo Die-Works (Thailand) Co., Ltd. (1)
60/3 Soi Navanakorn11 Moo 19 Phaholyothin Rd, Klongnueng Klongluang, Pathumthani, 12120, Thailand
Tel.: (66) 252909426
Web Site: https://www.kdt.co.th
Sales Range: $50-74.9 Million
Emp.: 234
Extrusion Dies & Metal Mold Tools Mfr
N.A.I.C.S.: 333514
Itabashi Shigeo *(Pres)*

Tianjin Hexing Mechatronics Technology Co., Ltd. (1)
8 Chenxing Rd, Xiqing Qu, Tianjin, China
Press Parts & Jig Mfr
N.A.I.C.S.: 333514
Bai Zhiqiang *(Pres)*

HODGSON CUSTOM ROLLING INC.
5580 Kalar Rd, Niagara Falls, L2H 3L1, ON, Canada
Tel.: (905) 356-8132
Web Site: http://www.hodgsonrolling.com
Rev.: $11,134,649
Emp.: 45
Fabricated Structural Metal Supplier
N.A.I.C.S.: 423510
Wayne Hodgson *(Pres)*

HODOGAYA CHEMICAL CO., LTD.
Shiodome Sumitomo Bldg 1-9-2 Higashi-Shimbashi, Minato-ku, Tokyo, 105-0021, Japan

INTERNATIONAL PUBLIC

Tel.: (81) 368520300
Web Site: https://www.hodogaya.co.jp
Year Founded: 1916
4112—(TKS)
Rev.: $292,565,210
Assets: $536,447,770
Liabilities: $156,749,540
Net Worth: $379,698,230
Earnings: $16,392,800
Fiscal Year-end: 03/31/24
Chemical Products Mfr
N.A.I.C.S.: 325199
Yuto Matsumoto *(Pres)*

Subsidiaries:

HODOGAYA CHEMICAL KOREA CO., LTD. (1)
206 Orange County 5 Yangcheongsongdae-gil Ochang-eup, Cheongwon-gu, Cheongju, 28118, Chungcheongbuk-do, Korea (South)
Tel.: (82) 432156615
Chemical Products Distr
N.A.I.C.S.: 424690

Hodogaya (Shanghai) Trading Co., Ltd. (1)
Room2608 Shanghai International Trade Center 2201 Yan-an West road, Shanghai, 200336, China
Tel.: (86) 2162956611
Chemical Products Distr
N.A.I.C.S.: 424690

Hodogaya Chemical (U.S.A.), INC. (1)
123 Main St, White Plains, NY 10601
Tel.: (914) 422-0888
Chemical Products Distr
N.A.I.C.S.: 424690

Hodogaya Chemical Co., Ltd. - Koriyama Plant (1)
4-5 Yashima-machi, Koriyama, 963-8802, Fukushima, Japan
Tel.: (81) 249441230
Light Emitting Diode Mfr
N.A.I.C.S.: 334413

Hodogaya Chemical Co., Ltd. - Nanyo Plant (1)
1-1 Fukugawa Minami-machi, Shunan, 746-0042, Yamaguchi, Japan
Tel.: (81) 834613636
Chemical Products Mfr
N.A.I.C.S.: 325998

Hodogaya Chemical Co., Ltd. - Yokohama Plant (1)
7-43 Daikoku-cho, Tsurumi-ku, Yokohama, 230-0053, Kanagawa, Japan
Tel.: (81) 455211321
Chemical Products Mfr
N.A.I.C.S.: 325998

Hodogaya Chemical Europe GmbH (1)
Oststrasse 54, 40211, Dusseldorf, Germany
Tel.: (49) 211 935 0508
Agricultural Chemical Distr
N.A.I.C.S.: 424910

Hodogaya Contract Laboratory Co., Ltd. (1)
45 Miyukigaoka, Tsukuba, 305-0841, Ibaraki, Japan
Tel.: (81) 29 858 6886
Chemicals Mfr
N.A.I.C.S.: 325199

Hodogaya Logistics Co., Ltd. (1)
2-4-1 Yaesu Sumitomo Real Estate Yaesu Building 9th Floor, Chuo-ku, Tokyo, 104-0028, Japan
Tel.: (81) 35 299 8153
Freight Transportation Services
N.A.I.C.S.: 484110

Hodogaya UPL Co., Ltd. (1)
Sumitomo Real Estate Yaesu Building 2-4-1 Yaesu, Chuo-ku, Tokyo, 104-0028, Japan
Tel.: (81) 35 299 8048
Web Site: https://www.hodogaya-upl.com
Agricultural Chemical Mfr & Distr
N.A.I.C.S.: 325320
Hiroshi Nanami *(Pres)*

AND PRIVATE COMPANIES

Katsura Sangyo Co., Ltd. (1)
2-4-1 Yaesu Sumitomo Real Estate Yaesu Building, Chuo-ku, Tokyo, 104-0028, Japan
Tel.: (81) 35 299 8201
Web Site: https://www.katsura-ks.co.jp
Chemical Products Distr
N.A.I.C.S.: 424690

HOE LEONG CORPORATION LTD.
6 Clementi Loop, Singapore, 129814, Singapore
Tel.: (65) 64638666
Web Site: https://www.hoeleong.com
Rev.: $52,938,777
Assets: $53,226,194
Liabilities: $36,493,135
Net Worth: $16,733,059
Earnings: $6,576,941
Fiscal Year-end: 12/31/18
Equipment Mfr
N.A.I.C.S.: 333131
Yap Suat Kam *(Head-Corp Fin)*
Subsidiaries:

Ho Leong Tractors Sdn. Bhd. (1)
7A Jalan 1/57D Off Jalan Segambut, Kuala Lumpur, 51200, Malaysia
Tel.: (60) 362571448
Web Site: http://www.holeongtractors.com
Emp.: 10
Heavy Equipment Spare Parts Mfr
N.A.I.C.S.: 336390
Goh Chu Haw *(Gen Mgr)*

Hoe Leong Machinery (H.K.) Limited (1)
Room 1 Ground Floor Cambridge Plaza 188 San Wan Road, Sheung Shui, New Territories, China (Hong Kong)
Tel.: (852) 26260799
Construction Machinery Distr
N.A.I.C.S.: 423810

Korea Crawler Track Ltd. (1)
455 Cheongdam-ri Jisu-myeon, Jinju, Gyeongsangnam-do, Korea (South)
Tel.: (82) 5575967423
Web Site: http://www.kctrack.co.kr
Track Chain Product Mfr
N.A.I.C.S.: 333613
Hang Lae Cho *(Pres)*

PT. Trackspare (1)
Ji Letjen Mt Haryono 77-A Damai Balikpapan Selatan, Balikpapan, 76114, East Kalimantan, Indonesia
Tel.: (62) 542 875149
Web Site: http://www.trackspare.co.id
Heavy Equipment Spare Parts Distr
N.A.I.C.S.: 423120

Supreme Voyager Pte. Ltd. (1)
6 Clementi Loop, Singapore, 129814, Singapore
Tel.: (65) 64638666
Web Site: http://www.hoeleong.com
Emp.: 40
Vessel Chartering Services
N.A.I.C.S.: 483111
Avril Thng *(Mgr-HR)*

Trackspares (Australia) Pty. Ltd. (1)
295 McDougall St, PO Box 996, Toowoomba, 4350, QLD, Australia
Tel.: (61) 746340900
Web Site: http://www.trackspares.com.au
Sales Range: $50-74.9 Million
Emp.: 10
Heavy Equipment Spare Parts Distr
N.A.I.C.S.: 423120
Greg Temple *(Coord-Sls & Inventory)*

HOECHST PAKISTAN LIMITED
Plot 23 Sector 22 Korangi Industrial Area, Karachi, 74900, Pakistan
Tel.: (92) 2135060221
Web Site: https://hoechst.com.pk
Year Founded: 1970
SAPL—(KAR)
Rev.: $93,384,366
Assets: $49,562,491
Liabilities: $23,226,420
Net Worth: $26,336,071

Earnings: $997,144
Emp.: 1,099
Fiscal Year-end: 12/31/19
Pharmaceuticals Product Mfr
N.A.I.C.S.: 325412
Babar Ali *(Chm)*

HOEDLMAYR INTERNATIONAL AG
Aisting 33, 4311, Schwertberg, Austria
Tel.: (43) 7262660   AT
Web Site: http://www.hoedlmayr.com
Year Founded: 1954
Vehicle Logistics Services
N.A.I.C.S.: 541614
Johannes Hoedlmayr *(CEO)*
Subsidiaries:

HN Autotransport N.V. (1)
Prinsenweg 2, Tongeren, 3700, Belgium
Tel.: (32) 12 390 700
Web Site: http://www.hoedlmayr.at
Emp.: 200
Logistics Management Services
N.A.I.C.S.: 541614
Denis Heusquin *(Mgr-Sls)*

Hodlmayr Logistics Czech Republic a.s. (1)
Nadrazni 350, 25261, Jenec, Czech Republic
Tel.: (420) 2 350 94 826
Sales Range: $25-49.9 Million
Emp.: 160
Logistics Management Services
N.A.I.C.S.: 541614
Eva Kanovska *(Mng Dir)*

Hodlmayr Logistics GmbH (1)
Maggstrasse 30, 8042, Graz, Austria
Tel.: (43) 316 403 639
Emp.: 10
Logistics Management Services
N.A.I.C.S.: 541614
Amina Resch *(Mng Dir)*

Hodlmayr Zastava d.o.o. (1)
Trg Topolivaca Nr 4, 34000, Kragujevac, Serbia
Tel.: (381) 34 323 239
Sales Range: $25-49.9 Million
Emp.: 38
Logistics Management Services
N.A.I.C.S.: 541614

Hoedlmayr-Lazar Romania S.r.l. (1)
Strada Serelor Nr 19, RO-Bascov, Bascov, 117045, Romania
Tel.: (40) 248 207 570
Web Site: http://www.hoedlmayr.com
Sales Range: $25-49.9 Million
Emp.: 120
Logistics Management Services
N.A.I.C.S.: 541614
Michael Geschke *(Mng Dir)*

HOEGH LNG HOLDING LTD.
Drammensveien 134, 0277, Oslo, Norway
Tel.: (47) 9755 7400   BM
Web Site: http://www.hoeghlng.com
Year Founded: 2006
Rev.: $336,137,000
Assets: $2,601,838,000
Liabilities: $1,905,750,000
Net Worth: $696,088,000
Earnings: $8,047,000
Emp.: 759
Fiscal Year-end: 12/31/19
Holding Company; Liquefied Natural Gas Transportation & Services
N.A.I.C.S.: 551112
Morten W. Hoegh *(Chm)*
Subsidiaries:

Hoegh LNG Asia Pte. Ltd. (1)
3 Anson Road 14-04A Springleaf Tower, Singapore, 079909, Singapore
Tel.: (65) 65111950
Port Terminal Services
N.A.I.C.S.: 488310

Hoegh LNG Colombia S.A.S. (1)
Cr 2 11-41 Edificio Grupo Area Of 2001, Bocagrande, Cartagena, Colombia
Tel.: (57) 56925150
Port Terminal Services
N.A.I.C.S.: 488310

Hoegh LNG Egypt LCC. (1)
Trivium Square Building North 90 Street-3rd Sector, 3rd Floor-Office 307A, New Cairo, Cairo, Egypt
Tel.: (20) 1000048709
Port Terminal Services
N.A.I.C.S.: 488310

Hoegh LNG Partners LP (1)
Canon s Court 22 Victoria Street, Hamilton, HM 12, Bermuda
Tel.: (441) 295 6815
Web Site: http://www.hoeghlngpartners.com
Rev.: $141,260,000
Assets: $1,004,008,000
Liabilities: $473,488,000
Net Worth: $530,520,000
Earnings: $59,995,000
Emp.: 697
Fiscal Year-end: 12/31/2021
LNG Storage
N.A.I.C.S.: 493190
John V. Veech *(Chm)*

Leif Hoegh (U.K.) Limited (1)
Uncommon 34-37 Liverpool Street, London, EC2M 7PP, United Kingdom
Tel.: (44) 2073475396
Port Terminal Services
N.A.I.C.S.: 488310

HOEI SANGYO CO., LTD.
Dempocho, Konohana-ku, Osaka, 554-0002, Japan
Tel.: (81) 664609671
Web Site: http://www.hoei-sangyo.co.jp
Year Founded: 1974
Computer Hardware & Software Distr
N.A.I.C.S.: 423430
Masahide Eiraku *(Pres)*

HOEK HOVENIERS B.V.
Loosterweg 39A, 2215 ZG, Voorhout, Netherlands
Tel.: (31) 252210256
Web Site: http://www.hoekhoveniers.nl
Sales Range: $10-24.9 Million
Emp.: 300
Gardening & Landscaping Services
N.A.I.C.S.: 561730
Andre Hoek *(Owner)*
Subsidiaries:

Copijn Utrecht Holding BV (1)
Gagel Degk 4F, PO Box 9177, NL 3506 GD, Utrecht, Netherlands (100%)
Tel.: (31) 302612194
Web Site: http://www.copijn.nl
Project Management Services
N.A.I.C.S.: 541618

HOERBIGER HOLDING AG
Baarerstrasse 18, 6302, Zug, Switzerland
Tel.: (41) 415601000
Web Site: http://www.hoerbiger.com
Sales Range: $25-49.9 Million
Emp.: 35
Holding Company; Automobile Parts Mfr
N.A.I.C.S.: 551112
Martin Komischke *(Pres)*
Subsidiaries:

Deublin Company (1)
2050 Norman Dr, Waukegan, IL 60085-6747
Tel.: (847) 689-8600
Web Site: http://www.deublin.com
Sales Range: $75-99.9 Million
Emp.: 100
Rotating Union Mfr
N.A.I.C.S.: 332996
Donald L. Deubler *(Chm)*

Subsidiary (Non-US):

DEUBLIN Asia Pacific Pte Ltd (2)
51 Goldhill Plaza 11-11/12, Singapore, 308900, Singapore
Tel.: (65) 6259 9225
Sales Range: $10-24.9 Million
Emp.: 3
Rotating Union & Slip Ring Mfr
N.A.I.C.S.: 333248

DEUBLIN Austria GmbH (2)
Trazerberggasse 1/2, 1130, Vienna, Austria
Tel.: (43) 1 8768450
Web Site: http://www.deublin.com
Emp.: 2
Rotary Union Equipment Mfr
N.A.I.C.S.: 334514
Helmut Sasse *(Gen Mgr)*

DEUBLIN Iberica, S.L. (2)
Passeig Lola Anglada 20, Les Fonts, 08228, Terrassa, Spain
Tel.: (34) 932 211 223
Web Site: http://www.deublin.es
Rotating Union & Slip Ring Mfr
N.A.I.C.S.: 333248

DEUBLIN Polska Sp. z o.o (2)
Ul Bierutowska 57-59, 51-317, Wroclaw, Poland
Tel.: (48) 71 352 81 52
Web Site: http://www.deublin.eu
Precision Rotating Connector Mfr
N.A.I.C.S.: 333248

DEUBLIN de Mexico (2)
Norte 79-A No 77, Col Claveria, 02080, Mexico, Mexico
Tel.: (52) 55 5342 0362
Rotating Union & Slip Ring Mfr
N.A.I.C.S.: 335312

Holding (Non-US):

Deublin GmbH (2)
Nassaustrasse 10, D 65719, Hofheim, Wallau, Germany (100%)
Tel.: (49) 612280020
Web Site: http://www.deublin.com
Sales Range: $25-49.9 Million
Emp.: 50
Mfr of Rotating Joints
N.A.I.C.S.: 332919

Deublin Italiana (2)
Via Giovanni, Falcone 36, Milan, 20010, Bareggio, Italy (100%)
Tel.: (39) 0290312711
Sales Range: $25-49.9 Million
Emp.: 50
Sales Office
N.A.I.C.S.: 424120
Mauro Pozzato *(Mgr)*

Deublin Italiana S.r.l. (2)
Via Guido Rossa 9-Loc, Montevegli Comune di Valsamoggia, 40053, Bologna, Italy
Tel.: (39) 051835611
Web Site: http://www.deublin.it
Sales Range: $25-49.9 Million
Emp.: 50
Rotating Joint Mfr
N.A.I.C.S.: 332919
Mauro Pozzato *(Gen Mgr)*

Deublin Japan Ltd. (2)
2-13-1 Minamihanayashiki, Kawanishi, 666-0026, Japan (100%)
Tel.: (81) 727570099
Sales Range: $25-49.9 Million
Emp.: 15
Mfr of Rotating Joints
N.A.I.C.S.: 332919
Takeshi Uemura *(Mgr)*

Deublin Korea Co. Ltd. (2)
Star Tower Building 1003 Sangdaewondong 223-25, Seongnam, 462 738, Korea (South) (100%)
Tel.: (82) 317633311
Web Site: http://www.deublin.co.kr
Sales Range: $25-49.9 Million
Emp.: 11
Mfr of Rotating Joints
N.A.I.C.S.: 332919
Edward Lerner *(Mgr)*

Deublin Ltd. (2)
6 Sopwith Park Royce Close W Portway,

HOERBIGER HOLDING AG

Hoerbiger Holding AG—(Continued)

Andover, SP103TS, Hampshire, United Kingdom **(100%)**
Tel.: (44) 1264333355
Web Site: http://www.deublin.com
Sales Range: $25-49.9 Million
Emp.: 11
Mfr of Rotating Joints
N.A.I.C.S.: 332919
Cenzil Ralph (Mng Dir)

Deublin S.A.R.L. **(2)**
61 bis Avenue de l'Europe ZAC de La Malnoue, 77184, Emerainville-Malnoue, France **(100%)**
Tel.: (33) 164616161
Web Site: http://www.deublin.com
Sales Range: $25-49.9 Million
Emp.: 7
Rotating Joint Mfr
N.A.I.C.S.: 332919

HOERBIGER (Wuxi) Automation Technology Co., Ltd. **(1)**
Science & Technology Business Incubator Anzhen Xidong Park, Xishan EDZ, 214105, Wuxi, China
Tel.: (86) 510 85203468
Hydraulic Equipment Whslr
N.A.I.C.S.: 423830

HOERBIGER Antriebstechnik Holding GmbH **(1)**
Bernbeurener Strasse 13, 86956, Schongau, Germany
Tel.: (49) 8861 2566 2017
Holding Company
N.A.I.C.S.: 551112
Markus Sauter (Head-Test Facility & Testing)

HOERBIGER Australia Pty Ltd. **(1)**
17-19 David Street, Dandenong, 3175, VIC, Australia
Tel.: (61) 3 9797 2444
Web Site: http://www.hoerbiger.com
Emp.: 30
Industrial Valve Mfr
N.A.I.C.S.: 332911
Simon Wood (Mng Dir)

HOERBIGER Automatisierungstechnik GmbH **(1)**
Sudliche Romerstrasse 15, 86972, Altenstadt, Germany
Tel.: (49) 8861 221 0
Pumps Mfr
N.A.I.C.S.: 333914

HOERBIGER Automotive Komfortsysteme GmbH **(1)**
Martina-Horbiger-Strasse 5, 86956, Schongau, Germany
Tel.: (49) 8861 210 34 00
Seat Mfr
N.A.I.C.S.: 336360

HOERBIGER Canada Ltd. **(1)**
Bay 7 2616 - 16th Street N E, Calgary, T2E7J8, AB, Canada
Tel.: (403) 291-3822
Compression Machinery Mfr
N.A.I.C.S.: 333248
Craig Thompson (VP)

HOERBIGER DE CHILE S.A. **(1)**
El Roble 748, Recoleta, Santiago, Chile
Tel.: (56) 2 2622 1123
Compression Machinery Mfr
N.A.I.C.S.: 333248
Jorge Meneses Suzarte (Coord-Ops)

HOERBIGER Drive Technology (Changzhou) Co. Ltd. **(1)**
Building No 7 GDH Industrial Park 16 Chuangye Rd CND, 213000, Changzhou, Jiangsu, China
Tel.: (86) 519 8560 3636
Industrial Machinery Whslr
N.A.I.C.S.: 423830

HOERBIGER France SAS **(1)**
Rue de la Batterie, 67118, Geispolsheim, France
Tel.: (33) 3 88 55 18 55
Industrial Machinery Mfr
N.A.I.C.S.: 333248

HOERBIGER India Private Ltd. **(1)**
Durvankur Bhavan Priyanka Nagari Gat No 2324 Wagholi, 412207, Pune, India
Tel.: (91) 20 3290 2521
Industrial Machinery Whslr
N.A.I.C.S.: 423830

HOERBIGER Micro Fluid GmbH **(1)**
Borsigstrasse 11, 93092, Regensburg, Germany
Tel.: (49) 9401 785 22
Industrial Machinery Mfr
N.A.I.C.S.: 333248
Armin Friedl (Product Mgr)

HOERBIGER Penzberg GmbH **(1)**
Seeshaupter Str 33, 82377, Penzberg, Germany
Tel.: (49) 8856 912 0
Motor Vehicle Parts Mfr
N.A.I.C.S.: 336390

HOERBIGER Service Egypt, LLC **(1)**
20 El Sad El Aly St, Maadi, Cairo, Egypt
Tel.: (20) 2 2358 5870
Industrial Machinery Mfr
N.A.I.C.S.: 333248

HOERBIGER Service GmbH **(1)**
Hanns-Horbiger-Strasse 10, 67133, Maxdorf, Germany
Tel.: (49) 6237 975 60
Industrial Machinery Mfr
N.A.I.C.S.: 333248

HOERBIGER Service Hungaria Kft. **(1)**
Bagoly u 7, 2120, Dunakeszi, Hungary
Tel.: (36) 27 391 379
Web Site: http://www.hoerbiger-hsh.hu
Industrial Machinery Mfr
N.A.I.C.S.: 333248

HOERBIGER Turbomachinery Services B.V.B.A. **(1)**
Zavelstraat 7, 9190, Stekene, Belgium
Tel.: (32) 3 779 64 77
Industrial Machinery Mfr
N.A.I.C.S.: 333248
Johan Tollenaere (Mgr)

HOERBIGER Valves (Changzhou) Co., Ltd. **(1)**
1A-1C Building GDH Industrial Park 16 Chuang Ye Road, Xinbei District, 213033, Changzhou, Jiangsu, China
Tel.: (86) 519 85606638
Industrial Machinery Mfr
N.A.I.C.S.: 333248

HOERBIGER Zandov s.r.o. **(1)**
Sokolovska 2408/222, 19000, Prague, Czech Republic
Tel.: (420) 620 687 954
Industrial Machinery Mfr
N.A.I.C.S.: 333248

HOERBIGER de Argentina S.A. **(1)**
Bejarano 575, Q8302BWK, Neuquen, Argentina
Tel.: (54) 299 445 1515
Compression Machinery Mfr
N.A.I.C.S.: 333248
Jorge Beccalli (Coord-Admin)

HOERBIGER de Colombia LTDA. **(1)**
Carrera 85D 46A 65 Bodega 19 Complejo Logistico San Cayetano, Bogota, Colombia
Tel.: (57) 1 263 0046
Industrial Machinery Whslr
N.A.I.C.S.: 423830
Aladin Huwyler (Coord-HR-Andean Reg)

HOERBIGER del Ecuador, S.A. **(1)**
Calle de Los Arupos E1-203 Uniparque Bodega 4, 170150, Quito, Ecuador
Tel.: (593) 2 3464072
Web Site: http://www.hoerbiger.com
Emp.: 15
Industrial Machinery Whslr
N.A.I.C.S.: 423830
Francisco Alvarez (CEO)

Hoerbiger Corporation of America, Inc.
3350 Gateway Dr, Pompano Beach, FL 33069-4864
Tel.: (954) 974-5700
Web Site: http://www.hoerbiger.com

Sales Range: $50-74.9 Million
Emp.: 200
Compressor Mfr
N.A.I.C.S.: 333912
Hannes Hunschofsky (Pres)

Hoerbiger International Management Services GmbH **(1)**
Franz-Rupp-Strasse 2, D-86956, Schongau, Germany
Tel.: (49) 88612103365
Web Site: http://www.hoerbiger.com
Management Services
N.A.I.C.S.: 541611

Hoerbiger SynchronTechnik GmbH & Co. KG **(1)**
Lembacher Strasse 2, 71720, Oberstenfeld, Germany
Tel.: (49) 70622660
Web Site: http://www.Hoerbiger.com
Sales Range: $100-124.9 Million
Vehicle Parts Mfr
N.A.I.C.S.: 336390
Bernd Eckl (Mgr-Ops)

Hoerbiger-Origa Corp. **(1)**
100 West Lk Dr, Glendale Heights, IL 60139
Tel.: (630) 871-8300
Pneumatic Automation Equipment Solutions
N.A.I.C.S.: 334512

HOFFMANN GREEN CEMENT TECHNOLOGIES SAS

6 rue de la Bretaudiere Chaille under the Ormeaux, Rives-de-l Yon, 85310, La Roche-sur-Yon, France
Tel.: (33) 251460600
Web Site: https://www.ciments-hoffmann.fr
ALHGR—(EUR)
Rev.: $6,668,506
Assets: $106,595,651
Liabilities: $32,597,417
Net Worth: $73,998,234
Earnings: ($8,678,662)
Emp.: 52
Fiscal Year-end: 12/31/23
Cement Product Mfr & Distr
N.A.I.C.S.: 327310
Julien Blanchard (Founder & Chm-Mgmt Bd)

HOFFMANN NEOPAC

Eisenbahnstrasse 71, 3602, Thun, Switzerland
Tel.: (41) 333356363
Web Site: http://www.hoffmann-neopac.com
Sales Range: $75-99.9 Million
Emp.: 1,000
Mfr of Packs & Cans for the Tobacco, Cosmetics & Food Industries & Tubing for the Pharmaceutical, Dental & Cosmetics Industries
N.A.I.C.S.: 332999
Mark Aegler (CEO)

Subsidiaries:

TU-PLAST Tube Producing Ltd. **(1)**
Kishegyesi Ut 265, Debrecen, 4031, Hungary
Tel.: (36) 52314589
Web Site: http://www.tuplast.hu
Sales Range: $25-49.9 Million
Emp.: 90
Plastic Tank Mfr
N.A.I.C.S.: 326199
Nagy Elemer (CEO)

HOFLANDT AUTOMOBILE

28 Route De Borre, BP 227, Hazebrouck, 59524, Lille, France
Tel.: (33) 328429900
Web Site: http://concessions.peugeot.fr
Rev.: $20,600,000
Emp.: 35
New & Used Car Dealers
N.A.I.C.S.: 441110

INTERNATIONAL PUBLIC

Gregory Kaczmarek (Dir)

HOFSETH BIOCARE AS

Keiser Wilhelmsgate 24, N-6003, Alesund, Norway
Tel.: (47) 73102200
Web Site: https://hofsethbiocare.com
HBO—(DEU)
Rev.: $11,125,808
Assets: $37,966,931
Liabilities: $24,293,368
Net Worth: $13,673,564
Earnings: ($12,690,745)
Emp.: 62
Fiscal Year-end: 12/31/22
Fish Protein, Calcium & Oil Products
N.A.I.C.S.: 325414
Bomi Framroze (Chief Scientific Officer)

Subsidiaries:

Nore Nutrition AS **(1)**
Havnegata 11, 6005, Alesund, Norway
Tel.: (47) 45502111
Web Site: http://www.nore-nutrition.no
Calcium Supplement Retailer
N.A.I.C.S.: 456191

HOFTEX GROUP AG

Fabrikzeile 21, D-95028, Hof, Germany
Tel.: (49) 9281490
Web Site: https://www.hoftexgroup.com
Year Founded: 1869
NBH—(MUN)
Rev.: $173,790,705
Assets: $182,608,456
Liabilities: $64,645,104
Net Worth: $117,963,351
Earnings: ($3,938,625)
Emp.: 973
Fiscal Year-end: 12/31/23
Non-Woven Interlining Products, Technical Non-Wovens, Home Decoration, Yarns & Raw Fabrics Mfr
N.A.I.C.S.: 313230
Klaus Steger (CEO)

Subsidiaries:

Eswegee Vliesstoff GmbH **(1)**
Fabrikzeile 21, 95028, Hof, Germany **(100%)**
Tel.: (49) 9281490
Web Site: http://www.hoftexgroup.com
Sales Range: $100-124.9 Million
Emp.: 300
Non-Woven Interfacing Products Mfr
N.A.I.C.S.: 313230
Steni Harald (Mng Dir)

Neutex Home Deco GmbH **(1)**
Kulmbacher Str 82, 95213, Munchberg, Germany
Tel.: (49) 92518710
Web Site: http://www.neutex.com
Decorative Fabric Mfr & Whslr
N.A.I.C.S.: 314999
Joseph Wheeler (Co-CEO)

Resintex Industriale S.r.l. **(1)**
Via Sardegna 18/20, Fizzonasco di, 20090, Pieve Emanuele, MI, Italy
Tel.: (39) 0290724927
Web Site: http://www.resintex.com
Nonwoven Fabric & Composite Mfr
N.A.I.C.S.: 313230
Filippo Boscolo (Mng Dir)

Techtex GmbH Vliestoffe Mittweida **(1)**
Viersener Strasse 18, D 09468, Mittweida, Germany **(100%)**
Tel.: (49) 37279530
Web Site: http://www.textilgruppehof.com
Sales Range: $25-49.9 Million
Emp.: 75
Stitchbonded Non-Wovens Mfr
N.A.I.C.S.: 313230

Tenowo Huzhou New Materials Co., Ltd. **(1)**

555 Huangzhishan Road, Huzhou, 313005, Zhejiang, China
Tel.: (86) 5722582999
Nonwoven Textile Product Mfr
N.A.I.C.S.: 314999
Christian Berndt (Mgr-R&D)

Tenowo Reichenbach GmbH (1)
Am Windrad 5, Heinsdorfergrund, 08468, Reichenbach, Germany
Tel.: (49) 3765386480
Nonwoven Textile Product Mfr
N.A.I.C.S.: 314999

Tenowo de Mexiko S. de R.L. de C.V.
Real de Lomas 1025 Lomas 4a Seccion, 78216, San Luis Potosi, Mexico
Tel.: (52) 14448291874
Nonwoven Textile Product Mfr
N.A.I.C.S.: 314999
Luis Enrique Aguilar (Mgr-Bus Sls)

Tonowo Inc. (1)
1968 Kawai Rd, Lincolnton, NC 28092-5916 (100%)
Tel.: (704) 732-3525
Web Site: http://www.tenowo.com
Sales Range: $25-49.9 Million
Emp.: 70
Non-Woven Interlinings Mfr
N.A.I.C.S.: 314999

HOGAN CHEVROLET BUICK GMC LIMITED
5000 Sheppard Ave East, Scarborough, Toronto, M1S 4L9, ON, Canada
Tel.: (416) 291-5054
Web Site: http://www.hoganchev.com
New & Used Car Dealers
N.A.I.C.S.: 441110

HOGAN LOVELLS INTERNATIONAL LLP
Atlantic House Holborn Viaduct, London, EC1A 2FG, United Kingdom
Tel.: (44) 20 7296 2000 UK
Web Site: http://www.hoganlovells.com
Year Founded: 1899
Law firm
N.A.I.C.S.: 541110
Matthew Johnson (Partner-Perth)

Subsidiaries:

Despacho de Abogados Miembro de Hogan Lovells
Centro San Ignacio Torre Copernico Oficinas TO-P3-04, Av Blandin La Castellana, Caracas, 1060, Venezuela
Tel.: (58) 2122669772
Law firm
N.A.I.C.S.: 541110

Hogan Lovells (Alicante) S.L. & Cia. (1)
Avenida Maisonnave 22, Alicante, 3003, Spain
Tel.: (34) 965138300
Law firm
N.A.I.C.S.: 541110

Hogan Lovells (Luxembourg) LLP (1)
13 rue Edward Steichen, 2540, Luxembourg, Luxembourg
Tel.: (352) 264260
Web Site: http://www.hoganlovells.com
Emp.: 30
Law firm
N.A.I.C.S.: 541110
Gerard Neiens (Partner-Tax)

Hogan Lovells (Middle East) LLP (1)
19th Floor Al Fattan Currency Tower Dubai International Financial Cent, PO Box 506602, Dubai, United Arab Emirates
Tel.: (971) 43779377
Law firm
N.A.I.C.S.: 541110
Cathy Robertson (Office Mgr)

Hogan Lovells (Mongolia) LLP (1)
Suite 401 New Century Plaza Chinggis Avenue-15, Sukhbaatar District 1st Khoroo, Ulaanbaatar, 14253, Mongolia
Tel.: (976) 70128900
Law firm
N.A.I.C.S.: 541110
Christopher Melville (Mng Partner)

Hogan Lovells (Paris) LLP (1)
17 avenue Matignon, CS30027, 75378, Paris, Cedex, France
Tel.: (33) 153674747
Law firm
N.A.I.C.S.: 541110
Sebastien Gros (Partner)

Hogan Lovells (Warszawa) LLP (1)
ul Nowogrodzka 50, Warsaw, 695, Poland
Tel.: (48) 225292900
Law firm
N.A.I.C.S.: 541110
Andrzej Debiec (Partner)

Hogan Lovells BSTL, S.C. (1)
Paseo de los Tamarindos 150-PB, Bosques de las Lomas, Mexico, 5120, DF, Mexico
Tel.: (52) 5550910000
Web Site: http://www.hoganlovells.com
Emp.: 70
Law firm
N.A.I.C.S.: 541110
Eduardo Siqueiros (Partner)

Hogan Lovells CIS LLC (1)
Summit Business Centre 22 Tverskaya Street 9th Floor, Moscow, 125009, Russia
Tel.: (7) 4959333000
Law firm
N.A.I.C.S.: 541110

Hogan Lovells South Africa (1)
22 Fredman Drive, Sandton, Johannesburg, 2196, South Africa
Tel.: (27) 112866900
Web Site: http://www.hoganlovells.com
Emp.: 48
Law firm
N.A.I.C.S.: 541110
Clive Rumsey (Deputy Chm)

Hogan Lovells Studio Legale (1)
Via Santa Maria alla Porta 2, Milan, 20123, Italy
Tel.: (39) 027202521
Web Site: http://www.hoganlovells.com
Law firm
N.A.I.C.S.: 541110
Giovanni Ghirardi (Partner)

Hogan Lovells US LLP (1)
Columbia Sq 555 13th St NW, Washington, DC 20004
Tel.: (202) 637-5600
Web Site: https://www.hoganlovells.com
Emp.: 2,800
Law firm
N.A.I.C.S.: 541110
Ari Q. Fitzgerald (Partner)

HOGANAS AB
Brukfgaton 35, 263 83, Hoganas, Sweden
Tel.: (46) 42338000 SE
Web Site: http://www.hoganas.com
Sales Range: $1-4.9 Billion
Emp.: 1,705
Iron & Non-Ferrous Metal Products Developer & Mfr
N.A.I.C.S.: 332999
Dean Howard (Pres)

Subsidiaries:

Hoganas (China) Ltd (1)
No 5646 Wai Qing Song Road, Qingpu, Shanghai, 201700, China
Tel.: (86) 67001000
Emp.: 90
Iron Powder Mfr
N.A.I.C.S.: 331110

Hoganas Belgium S.A. (1)
Ruelle Gros Pierre 10, 7800, Ath, Hainaut, Belgium
Tel.: (32) 68268989
Web Site: http://www.hoganas.com
Sales Range: $25-49.9 Million
Emp.: 150
Chemical Engineering Services
N.A.I.C.S.: 541330

Hoganas Brasil Ltda. (1)
Av Ricieri Jose Marcatto 110 Vila Suissa, Mogi das Cruzes, 08810 020, Sao Paulo, Brazil
Tel.: (55) 1147937729
Sales Range: $50-74.9 Million
Emp.: 140
Iron Powder Mfr
N.A.I.C.S.: 331492
Adriano Machado (Mng Dir)

Hoganas East Europe LLC (1)
Savushkina St 126 A Office 35H, 197374, Saint Petersburg, Russia
Tel.: (7) 8123342542
Web Site: http://www.hoganas.com
Sales Range: $25-49.9 Million
Emp.: 5
Chemical Engineering Services
N.A.I.C.S.: 541330
Radomir Kononov (Gen Mgr)

Hoganas France S.A.S. (1)
86 Rue Henri Depagneux, BP 30117, 69400, Limas, France
Tel.: (33) 474029750
Web Site: http://www.hoganas.com
Emp.: 6
Chemical Engineering Services
N.A.I.C.S.: 541330
Thierry Calmes (Mgr)

Hoganas GmbH (1)
Moskauer Strasse 25, 40227, Dusseldorf, Germany
Tel.: (49) 211991780
Web Site: http://www.hoganas.com
Sales Range: $25-49.9 Million
Emp.: 16
Chemical Engineering Services
N.A.I.C.S.: 541330
Michael Rehnig (Gen Mgr)

Hoganas Great Britain UK (1)
Munday Works, 55 66 Morley Rd, Tonbridge, TN9 1RP, Kent, United Kingdom (100%)
Tel.: (44) 1732362243
Web Site: http://www.hoganas.com
Sales Range: $25-49.9 Million
Emp.: 26
Water Atomized High Alloy Steel Powders
N.A.I.C.S.: 331513

Hoganas Hamnbyggnads AB (1)
Hoganas Shipping, PO Box 39, 263 21, Hoganas, Skane, Sweden
Tel.: (46) 42342320
Marine Shipping Services
N.A.I.C.S.: 488510

Hoganas Iberica S.A. (1)
C/Basauri street 17 A - Bajo Dcha, 28023, Madrid, Spain
Tel.: (34) 91 708 05 95
Chemical Engineering Services
N.A.I.C.S.: 541330
Ramon Martinez (Gen Mgr)

Hoganas India Ltd (1)
Ganga Commerce 4 North Main Road Koregaon Park, Pune, 411 001, Maharashtra, India
Tel.: (91) 2066030171
Sales Range: $25-49.9 Million
Emp.: 28
Iron Powder & Chemicals Mfr
N.A.I.C.S.: 325998
V. Srinivasan (Mng Dir)

Hoganas Japan K.K. (1)
Akasaka Shasta East Building 2-19 Akasaka 4-Chome, Minato-Ku, Tokyo, Japan
Tel.: (81) 335828280
Sales Range: $25-49.9 Million
Emp.: 18
Chemical Engineering Services
N.A.I.C.S.: 541330

Hoganas Korea Ltd. (1)
3F Yujung B/D 1639-9 Seocho-dong Seocho-gu, 137-880, Seoul, Korea (South)
Tel.: (82) 25114344
Web Site: http://www.hoganas.co.kr
Emp.: 20
Structured Iron Shapes Mfr
N.A.I.C.S.: 331110
Louise Chen (Mgr-Tech Center Asia)

Hoganas Sweden AB (1)
Bruksgatan 35, 263 83, Hoganas, Skane, Sweden
Tel.: (46) 42338000
Chemical Engineering Services
N.A.I.C.S.: 541330
Alderik Danilsom (Gen Mgr)

Hoganas Taiwan Ltd. (1)
Room B No 44 11th Floor Chung Shan North Road Section 2, Taipei, 10448, Taiwan
Tel.: (886) 225431618
Iron Powder Mfr
N.A.I.C.S.: 331110

NAH Financial Services, Inc. (1)
300 Delaware Ave, Wilmington, DE 19801
Tel.: (302) 576-2695
Financial Planning Services
N.A.I.C.S.: 523940

North American Hoganas Holdings, Inc. (1)
111 Hoganas Way, Hollsopple, PA 15935-6416
Tel.: (814) 479-2551
Investment Management Service
N.A.I.C.S.: 523940

Subsidiary (Domestic):

North American Hoganas High Alloys LLC (2)
101 Bridge St, Johnstown, PA 15902-2904
Tel.: (814) 533-7800
Web Site: http://www.hoganas.com
Stainless Steel Powders Mfr
N.A.I.C.S.: 331221

North American Hoganas, Inc. (2)
111 Hoganas Way, Hollsopple, PA 15935-6416 (100%)
Tel.: (814) 479-3500
Web Site: http://www.northamericanhoganas.com
Sales Range: $50-74.9 Million
Emp.: 150
Custom Steel Casting Operations; Ingot & Billet Casting & Scrap Reprocessing
N.A.I.C.S.: 424690
David Milligan (VP-Ops)

North American Hoganas-Pyron Plant (1)
5950 Packard Rd, Niagara Falls, NY 14304 (100%)
Tel.: (716) 285-3451
Web Site: http://www.hoganas.com
Rev: $13,055,762
Emp.: 45
Mfr of Iron Powders
N.A.I.C.S.: 331221

HOGIA AB
Hakenas, 444 28, Stenungsund, Sweden
Tel.: (46) 303 666 00
Web Site: http://www2.hogia.se
Year Founded: 1980
Sales Range: $50-74.9 Million
Emp.: 600
Transportation Software Developer
N.A.I.C.S.: 513210
Bert-Inge Hogsved (Founder)

Subsidiaries:

Hogia Ferry Systems Oy (1)
Cirkelvagen 4, 65100, Vaasa, Finland
Tel.: (358) 63192800
Web Site: http://www.bookit.hogia.fi
Software Development Services
N.A.I.C.S.: 541511
Niclas Blomstrom (Mng Dir)

Hogia Lonn AS (1)
Ostre Akervei 19, PO Box 375, Okern, 0513, Oslo, Norway
Tel.: (47) 23172900
Web Site: http://www.hogia.no
Software Development Services
N.A.I.C.S.: 541511

Hogia Transport Systems Ltd. (1)
St James House 13 Kensington Square, London, W8 5HD, United Kingdom
Tel.: (44) 2077958156
Web Site: http://www.hogia.com
Software Development Services

HOGIA AB

Hogia AB—(Continued)
N.A.I.C.S.: 541511

HOGY MEDICAL CO., LTD.
7-7 Akasaka 2-chome, Minato-ku, Tokyo, 107-8615, Japan
Tel.: (81) 362291300
Web Site: https://www.hogy.co.jp
Year Founded: 1961
3593—(TKS)
Rev.: $258,451,000
Assets: $661,271,010
Liabilities: $92,017,810
Net Worth: $569,253,200
Earnings: $18,534,440
Emp.: 1,408
Fiscal Year-end: 03/31/24
Medical Device Mfr
N.A.I.C.S.: 334510
Susumu Ohashi *(Exec Officer-Sys Admin Dept & Admin Dept)*

Subsidiaries:

HOGY MEDICAL CO. LTD. - Miho Plant No. 1 **(1)**
1873-1 Fusa, Miho-mura, Inashiki, 300-0427, Ibaraki, Japan
Tel.: (81) 298852981
Web Site: http://www.hogy.co.jp
Sales Range: $25-49.9 Million
Emp.: 100
Medical Products Sterilization Services
N.A.I.C.S.: 334510

HOGY MEDICAL Co., Ltd. - Miho Plant No. 2 **(1)**
1776-1 Fusa, Miho-mura, Inashiki, 300-0427, Ibaraki, Japan
Tel.: (81) 298856611
Web Site: http://www.hogy.co.jp
Sales Range: $25-49.9 Million
Emp.: 100
Medical Products Sterilization Services
N.A.I.C.S.: 334510

HOHNER MASCHINENBAU GMBH
Gansacker 19, 78532, Tuttlingen, Germany
Tel.: (49) 746294680
Web Site: http://www.hohner-postpress.com
Year Founded: 1930
Sales Range: $10-24.9 Million
Wire Stitching Machine Mfr
N.A.I.C.S.: 339112
Michelle Nelis *(VP)*

Subsidiaries:

Hohner Maquinaria de Artes Graficas S.L. **(1)**
Via Augusta 59 Despacho 116, 08006, Barcelona, Spain
Tel.: (34) 933682039
Stiching Machinery Distr
N.A.I.C.S.: 423830

Hohner Stitching Products Inc. **(1)**
2521 Technology Dr Ste 206, Elgin, IL 60124
Tel.: (847) 783-0411
Stiching Machinery Distr
N.A.I.C.S.: 423830

Hohner Stitching Technology (Nanjing) Co., Ltd. **(1)**
Qixia Economic Development Zone Runhua Road No 18-1, 210034, Nanjing, China
Tel.: (86) 2583123086
Stiching Machinery Distr
N.A.I.C.S.: 423830

Hohner UK Ltd. **(1)**
Wrest House Wrest Park, Silsoe, MK45 4HS, Bedfordshire, United Kingdom
Tel.: (44) 1525862628
Stiching Machinery Distr
N.A.I.C.S.: 423830

HOI AN TOURIST SERVICE JOINT STOCK COMPANY
10 Tran Hung Dao, Hanoi, Hoi An, Quang Nam, Vietnam
Tel.: (84) 510 3864 733
Web Site: http://www.hoiantourist.com
Hotels & Resorts
N.A.I.C.S.: 721110
Ban Van Nguyen *(Chm)*

HOI TIN UNIVERSAL LIMITED
Rm 607 Shui Hing Ctr 13 Sheung Yuet Rd, Kowloon Bay, Kowloon, China (Hong Kong)
Tel.: (852) 27540363
Sales Range: $25-49.9 Million
Emp.: 15
Leather Product Mfr
N.A.I.C.S.: 316110
Joanne Lai *(Mgr-Mktg)*

HOIST FINANCE AB
Bryggargatan 4, 111 21, Stockholm, Sweden
Tel.: (46) 855517790
Web Site: https://www.hoistfinance.com
HOFI—(OMX)
Rev.: $250,826,566
Assets: $3,043,918,065
Liabilities: $2,505,924,115
Net Worth: $537,993,949
Earnings: $75,023,181
Emp.: 1,304
Fiscal Year-end: 12/31/22
Debt Purchasing & Receivables Management
N.A.I.C.S.: 525990
Ingrid Bonde *(Chm)*

Subsidiaries:

Hoist Finance Craiova S.r.l. **(1)**
Felix Aderca 3, 200413, Craiova, Romania
Tel.: (40) 351419613
Debt Recovery Services
N.A.I.C.S.: 561440

Hoist Finance Spain S.L. **(1)**
Av Manoteras 44 1st Floor, 28050, Madrid, Spain
Web Site: http://www.hoistfinance.es
Financial Services
N.A.I.C.S.: 525990
Monica Moreno *(Mgr-Asset)*

Hoist Hellas S.A **(1)**
44 Zalokosta and Kifissias Avenue, 15233, Chalandri, Greece
Tel.: (30) 2106842776
Web Site: http://www.en.hoistfinance.gr
Loan & Credit Receivable Services
N.A.I.C.S.: 522299

Hoist Hellas S.L.D.S.A. **(1)**
1 Astronafton str, Athens, 15125, Maroussi, Greece
Tel.: (30) 2106842776
Web Site: https://www.hoistfinance.gr
Investment Loan Services
N.A.I.C.S.: 523991

Hoist Italia S.r.l. **(1)**
Via Gino Nais 16, 00136, Rome, Italy
Tel.: (39) 06399501
Web Site: https://www.hoistfinance.it
Financial Services
N.A.I.C.S.: 525990
Veronica Loiacono *(Mgr-Asset)*

Hoist Polska Sp. z o.o. **(1)**
ul Gen Jozefa Bema 2, 50-265, Wroclaw, Poland
Tel.: (48) 717391717
Web Site: https://www.hoistfinance.pl
Debt Management Services
N.A.I.C.S.: 561440
Dorota Swida *(Head-Fin)*

HOIVATILAT OYJ
Lentokatu 2 Pilot Business Park, 90460, Oulu, Finland
Tel.: (358) 207349100
Web Site: http://www.hoivatilat.com
Year Founded: 2009
Real Estate Development Services
N.A.I.C.S.: 531390
Jussi Karjula *(CEO)*

HOJEON LIMITED
Sinhwa building 19 Mapo-daero, Mapo-gu, Seoul, Korea (South)
Tel.: (82) 27066613
Web Site: https://www.hojeon.co.kr
Year Founded: 1985
111110—(KRS)
Rev.: $368,159,675
Assets: $242,447,271
Liabilities: $138,507,083
Net Worth: $103,940,188
Earnings: $20,695,096
Emp.: 160
Fiscal Year-end: 12/31/22
Sport Garment Mfr & Distr
N.A.I.C.S.: 315250
Young-Chul Park *(Chm, Pres & CEO)*

HOJGAARD HOLDING A/S
Knud Hojgaards Vej 7, 2860, Soborg, Denmark
Tel.: (45) 70122400   DK
Web Site: https://www.hojgaard.dk
Year Founded: 2001
Sales Range: $1-9.9 Million
Emp.: 2,587
Holding Company; Building & Construction Services
N.A.I.C.S.: 551112
Soren Bjerre-Nielsen *(Chm)*

Subsidiaries:

Ajos A/S **(1)**
Industriholmen 77, 2650, Hvidovre, Denmark
Tel.: (45) 70256363
Web Site: http://www.ajos.dk
Construction Equipment Rental Services
N.A.I.C.S.: 532412

Bode Byg A/S **(1)**
Yderholmvej 35, 2680, Solrod Strand, Denmark
Tel.: (45) 56167600
Construction Engineering Services
N.A.I.C.S.: 541330

Enemaerke & Petersen A/S **(1)**
Ole Hansens Vej 1, 4100, Ringsted, Denmark
Tel.: (45) 57617272
Web Site: http://www.eogp.dk
Sales Range: $50-74.9 Million
Emp.: 600
Building Maintenance & Restoration Services
N.A.I.C.S.: 238190
Alf Igelso Mortensen *(Mgr-Construction)*

Subsidiary (Domestic):

Ringsted Entreprenorforretning A.p.S. **(2)**
Ole Hansens Vej 1 C/O Klostergarden, 4100, Ringsted, Denmark
Tel.: (45) 57616000
Civil Engineering Services
N.A.I.C.S.: 541330

Hojgaard Industri A/S **(1)**
Klampenborgvej 221 2nd Fll, 2800, Lyngby, Denmark **(100%)**
Tel.: (45) 75922533
Web Site: http://www.hojgaard.dk
Sales Range: $25-49.9 Million
Emp.: 4
Highway & Street Construction
N.A.I.C.S.: 237310

MT Atlantic Inc. **(1)**
1702 Vandenberg Ave, Trenton, NJ 08641-5527
Tel.: (609) 724-1020
Sales Range: $25-49.9 Million
Emp.: 4
Commercial Building Construction Services
N.A.I.C.S.: 327910

MT Hojgaard A/S **(1)**
Knud Hojgaards Vej 9, 2860, Soborg, Denmark

INTERNATIONAL PUBLIC

Tel.: (45) 70122400
Web Site: http://www.mthojgaard.com
Civil Engineering & Construction Services; Joint Venture of Hojgaard Holding A/S (54%) & Monberg & Thorsen A/S (46%)
N.A.I.C.S.: 237310
Jorgen Nicolajsen *(Deputy Chm-Supervisory Bd)*

MT Hojgaard Foroyar P/F **(1)**
Hoydalsvegur 42, PO Box 1349, FO-110, Torshavn, Faroe Islands
Tel.: (298) 31 63 42
Civil Engineering Services
N.A.I.C.S.: 237990

MT Hojgaard Gronland A.p.S. **(1)**
Aqqusinersuaq 9, PO Box 230, 3900, Nuuk, Greenland
Tel.: (299) 311717
Web Site: http://www.mth.dk
Sales Range: $25-49.9 Million
Emp.: 50
Civil Engineering Services
N.A.I.C.S.: 541330

Marius Hansen Facader A/S **(1)**
Blytaekkervej 6, 8800, Viborg, Midtjylland, Denmark
Tel.: (45) 87 38 07 00
Web Site: http://www.mhf.dk
Sales Range: $25-49.9 Million
Emp.: 15
Building Exterior Construction
N.A.I.C.S.: 238190

Yamaha Electronics Marketing Corporation **(1)**
2-17-11 Takanawa Nihonseimeitakanawa Bldg, Minato-Ku, Tokyo, 108-0074, Japan
Tel.: (81) 3 5488 5465
Web Site: http://www.yamaha-elm.co.jp
Electronic Component Distr & Repair Services
N.A.I.C.S.: 423620

HOKKAIDO CHUO BUS CO., LTD.
1-8-6 Ironai, Otaru, 047-8601, Japan
Tel.: (81) 134241111
Web Site: https://www.chuo-bus.co.jp
Year Founded: 1943
9085—(SAP)
Rev.: $269,268,560
Assets: $326,971,040
Liabilities: $81,273,280
Net Worth: $245,697,760
Earnings: ($19,650,400)
Fiscal Year-end: 03/31/22
Public Transportation Services
N.A.I.C.S.: 485999
Nikaido Kyohito *(Pres)*

HOKKAIDO ELECTRIC POWER CO., INC.
2 Higashi 1-chome, Chuo-ku, Sapporo, 060-8677, Hokkaido, Japan
Tel.: (81) 112511111   JP
Web Site: https://www.hepco.co.jp
Year Founded: 1951
9509—(SAP)
Rev.: $5,872,969,937
Assets: $13,831,113,314
Liabilities: $12,125,754,873
Net Worth: $1,705,358,441
Earnings: ($146,633,631)
Emp.: 10,005
Fiscal Year-end: 03/31/23
Electricity Distribution Services
N.A.I.C.S.: 221110
Akihiko Mayumi *(Chm)*

Subsidiaries:

Energy Frontier **(1)**
8-2 E2 S1, Chuo-Ku, Sapporo, Japan
Tel.: (81) 0112515656
Sales Range: $25-49.9 Million
Emp.: 12
Air-conditioning Systems Contracting, Co-generation System Electricity & Thermal Energy Supply Services & ESCO (Energy Conservation Assurance) Service
N.A.I.C.S.: 541330

AND PRIVATE COMPANIES

Hokkai Electrical Construction Co., Inc. (1)
21-8-21 Kikusui 2-jo, Shiroishi-ku, Sapporo, 003-8531, Japan
Tel.: (81) 118119411
Web Site: http://www.hokkaidenki.co.jp
Sales Range: $100-124.9 Million
Emp.: 1,678
Electrical Contractor
N.A.I.C.S.: 238210
Koji Yamasumi (Mng Dir)

Hokkaido Electric Meters Industry (1)
13 2 W17 N5, Chuo-Ku, Sapporo, 0600004, Japan
Tel.: (81) 116213561
Maintenance, Adjustment & Manufacture of Electric Meters
N.A.I.C.S.: 334515

Hokkaido Power Engineering Co., Inc. (1)
Tel.: (81) 112213921
Web Site: http://www.hpec.jp
Sales Range: $550-599.9 Million
Emp.: 1,177
Wholesale of Thermal (Oil-Fired) Electricity; Construction & Repair of Power Plants
N.A.I.C.S.: 221118

Hokkaido Records Management Co., Inc. (1)
Hokuden Kogyo Building 1-1 Kita 1-jo Higashi 3-chome, Chuo-Ku, Sapporo, 060-0031, Japan
Tel.: (81) 112525825
Web Site: https://www.hrm.jp
Emp.: 22
Records & Data Administration
N.A.I.C.S.: 561499
Saito Yasuhiro (Pres)

Hokkaido Telecommunication Network (1)
Tsukamoto Building North 1 Building Kita 1-jo Higashi 2-5-3, Chuo-ku, Sapporo, 060-0031, Hokkaido, Japan (100%)
Tel.: (81) 115905200
Web Site: https://www.hotnet.co.jp
Sales Range: $50-74.9 Million
Emp.: 260
Telecommunications Circuits
N.A.I.C.S.: 517111
Tetsuo Sato (Mng Dir)

Hokuden Associa Co., Inc. (1)
1-1-2 Higashisapporo, Shiroishi-ku, Sapporo, 003-0001, Japan
Tel.: (81) 118161140
Web Site: https://www.hokuden-associa.co.jp
Emp.: 39
Printing & Bookbinding Equipment Mfr
N.A.I.C.S.: 333248

Hokuden Eco-Energy Co., Ltd. (1)
1-14-2 Odorinishi, Chuo-Ku, Sapporo, 060-0042, Hokkaido, Japan
Tel.: (81) 112217745
Sales Range: $125-149.9 Million
Emp.: 13
Electric Power Distribution Services
N.A.I.C.S.: 221122

Hokuden Information Technology (1)
e i Odori Higashi Building 3-4 Odori Higashi, Chuo-ku, Sapporo, 060-0041, Japan
Tel.: (81) 112107717
Web Site: https://www.hokuden-it.co.jp
Sales Range: $100-124.9 Million
Emp.: 416
Planning & Design of Information Networks & Development of Related Software; Data Processing Services
N.A.I.C.S.: 518210
Takaaki Izumi (Pres & Mng Dir)

Hokuden Kogyo (1)
(100%)
Tel.: (81) 112611476
Web Site: http://www.hokudenkogyo.co.jp
Sales Range: $200-249.9 Million
Emp.: 342
Agent of Insurance, Advertising Lease of Buildings & Construction Works
N.A.I.C.S.: 524228

Hokuden Life System (1)

6 E1 N1, Chuo Ku, Sapporo, 060 0031, Japan (100%)
Tel.: (81) 112076611
Web Site: http://www.hols.co.jp
Sales Range: $25-49.9 Million
Emp.: 70
Mfr, Distr & Repair of Electric Appliances; Consultation on Efficient Electricity Usage
N.A.I.C.S.: 335210

Hokuden Service Co., Ltd. (1)
6 Minami 1-jo Higashi 2-chome Odori Bus Center Building 2, Chuo-ku, Sapporo, 060-0051, Japan
Tel.: (81) 118161140
Web Site: https://www.hokuden-service.co.jp
Emp.: 1,208
Electrical Maintenance Services
N.A.I.C.S.: 238210

Hokuden Sogo Sekkei (1)
(100%)
Tel.: (81) 112224420
Web Site: http://www.hokuss.co.jp
Sales Range: $25-49.9 Million
Emp.: 167
Consultation on Civil Engineering, Building, Electricity & Environment
N.A.I.C.S.: 541330

Tomato Coal Center (1)
622 Hama Atsuma, Atsuma-cho, Yufutsu, 059-1742, Hokkaido, Japan
Tel.: (81) 145283121
Web Site: https://www.t-coalcenter.co.jp
Sales Range: $25-49.9 Million
Emp.: 45
Unloading, Storage & Delivery of Coal
N.A.I.C.S.: 324199

HOKKAIDO GAS CO LTD
2-1-1 Higashi Kita 7-Jo, Higashi-ku, Sapporo, 060-0907, Japan
Tel.: (81) 112319511
Web Site: https://www.hokkaido-gas.co.jp
Year Founded: 1911
9534—(TKS)
Rev.: $1,149,379,850
Assets: $1,231,879,260
Liabilities: $709,682,650
Net Worth: $522,196,610
Earnings: $76,854,470
Emp.: 851
Fiscal Year-end: 03/31/24
Gas Mfr & Supplier
N.A.I.C.S.: 221210
Hiroshi Ohtsuki (Pres)

HOKKAN HOLDINGS LIMITED
Nihonbashi Mitsui Tower 13F 2-1-1 Nihonbashimuromachi, Chuo-ku, Tokyo, Japan
Tel.: (81) 332135180
Web Site: https://www.hokkanholdings.co.jp
Year Founded: 1921
5902—(TKS)
Rev.: $601,067,130
Assets: $886,070,500
Liabilities: $483,719,800
Net Worth: $402,350,700
Earnings: $17,972,590
Fiscal Year-end: 03/31/24
Holding Company
N.A.I.C.S.: 551112
Motoki Watanabe (Auditor)

Subsidiaries:

Cosme Science Co., Ltd. (1)
1-2-27 Ukima, Kita-ku, Tokyo, 115-0051, Japan
Tel.: (81) 359487794
Web Site: https://www.cosme-science.co.jp
Cosmetic Mfr & Distr
N.A.I.C.S.: 325620

Os Machinery Corp. (1)
4119-1 Aza-Kurakake Oaza-Akahori, Ouramachi, Oura, Gunma, Japan
Tel.: (81) 276918210
Web Site: https://www.osmachinery.co.jp
Emp.: 122

Industrial Machinery Mfr
N.A.I.C.S.: 333248
Yutaka Osanai (Pres)

PT.Hokkan Deltapack Industri (1)
Axa Tower 42 Floor Suite 6 Jl Prof Dr Satrio Kav 18, Kuningan Setiabudi, Jakarta, 12940, Indonesia
Tel.: (62) 2150101089
Web Site: https://www.deltapack.co.id
Plastic Packaging Mfr
N.A.I.C.S.: 326112

PT.Hokkan Indonesia (1)
Jalan Raya Ciawi Sukabumi Bitung Sari KM 3, Ciawi, Bogor, 16720, Indonesia
Tel.: (62) 2518243555
Web Site: http://www.hokkan.co.id
Beverages Mfr
N.A.I.C.S.: 312112
Makoto Udagawa (Pres)

HOKKO CHEMICAL INDUSTRY CO., LTD.
Sumitomo Fudosan Nihonbashi Building 1-5-4 Nihonbashi-Honcho, chuo-ku, Tokyo, 103-8341, Japan
Tel.: (81) 332795151
Web Site: https://www.hokkochem.co.jp
4992—(TKS)
Rev.: $320,659,430
Assets: $478,426,110
Liabilities: $146,826,810
Net Worth: $331,599,300
Earnings: $26,403,160
Emp.: 628
Fiscal Year-end: 11/30/23
Chemical Products Mfr & Sales
N.A.I.C.S.: 325320
Ken-Ichi Sano (Pres)

Subsidiaries:

HOKKO CHEMICAL INDUSTRY Co., Ltd. - Okayama Factory (1)
402 Muneage, Tamano, 706-0305, Okayama, Japan
Tel.: (81) 863411515
Web Site: http://www.hokkochem.co.jp
Agrochemical Product Mfr
N.A.I.C.S.: 325320

Hokko Sangyo Co., Ltd. (1)
6-1 Imaizumiseibumachi, Chuo-ku, Toyama, 939-8281, Japan
Tel.: (81) 76 491 1235
Web Site: https://www.hokkosangyo.com
Chemical & Allied Product Distr
N.A.I.C.S.: 424690

HOKKOKU CO., LTD.
8F Aoki Bldg 1-3- Kanda Izumi-cho, Chiyoda-ku, Tokyo, 101-0024, Japan
Tel.: (81) 3 5835 3350
Web Site: http://www.hokkoku.net
Year Founded: 1968
Sales Range: $25-49.9 Million
Emp.: 130
Restaurant Operating Services
N.A.I.C.S.: 722511
Tsuguo Nakai (Pres)

HOKKOKU FINANCIAL HOLDINGS, INC.
2-12-6 Hirooka, Ishikawa, 920-8670, Kanazawa, Japan
Tel.: (81) 762631111
Web Site: https://www.hfhd.co.jp
7381—(TKS)
Rev.: $600,445,790
Assets: $38,064,689,720
Liabilities: $36,392,663,780
Net Worth: $1,672,025,940
Earnings: $363,550
Emp.: 2,196
Fiscal Year-end: 03/31/24
Bank Holding Company
N.A.I.C.S.: 551111

Subsidiaries:

COREZO, Ltd. (1)

HOKUETSU CORPORATION

Fukuoka Shogakukan Building 5F No 18 2-4-8 Watanabe-dori, Chuo-ku, Fukuoka, 810-0004, Japan
Tel.: (81) 5053174494
Web Site: https://www.corezo.jp
Information Technology Consulting Services
N.A.I.C.S.: 541690

FD Advisory, Ltd. (1)
2-12-6 Hirooka, Kanazawa, 920-8670, Ishikawa, Japan
Tel.: (81) 762083191
Web Site: https://www.fdalco.co.jp
Investment Advisory Services
N.A.I.C.S.: 541690

Hokkoku General Leasing Co., Ltd. (1)
6F Hokkoku Building 2-2-15 Katamachi, Kanazawa, 920-0981, Japan
Tel.: (81) 762229311
Web Site: https://www.hfhd.co.jp
Credit Card Services
N.A.I.C.S.: 522210

HOKUETSU CORPORATION
3-2-2 Nihonbashi Hongoku-cho, Chuo-ku, Tokyo, 103-0021, Japan
Tel.: (81) 332454500
Web Site: https://www.hokuetsucorp.com
Year Founded: 1907
3865—(TKS)
Rev.: $1,963,540,160
Assets: $2,747,724,120
Liabilities: $1,078,937,080
Net Worth: $1,668,787,040
Earnings: $55,497,560
Emp.: 3,749
Fiscal Year-end: 03/31/24
Paper Products Mfr
N.A.I.C.S.: 322120
Yoshinori Kawashima (Mng Dir)

Subsidiaries:

Alberta-Pacific Forest Industries Inc. (1)
Box 8000, Boyle, T0A 0M0, AB, Canada
Tel.: (780) 525-8002
Web Site: https://www.alpac.ca
Sales Range: $100-124.9 Million
Emp.: 400
Kraft Pulp Mill
N.A.I.C.S.: 322110

BF Co., Ltd. (1)
667-1 Minami Nagai, Tokorozawa, 359-0011, Saitama, Japan
Tel.: (81) 4 2907 3501
Web Site: http://www.b-f.jp
Data Processing Services
N.A.I.C.S.: 518210

Bernard Dumas S.A.S. (1)
2 rue de la Papeterie, PO Box 3, Bergerac, 24100, Creysse, France
Tel.: (33) 553232105
Web Site: https://www.bernard-dumas.fr
Paper Mfr & Distr
N.A.I.C.S.: 322120

Hokuetsu Engineering Co., Ltd. (1)
Hokuetsu Corporation 57 Enoki-cho, Higashi-ku, Niigata, 950-0881, Japan
Tel.: (81) 252734131
Heavy & Civil Engineering Construction
N.A.I.C.S.: 237990

Hokuetsu Forest Co., Ltd. (1)
1529 Aza-Shitadairayamako Oaza-Sakamoto Aizubangemachi Kawanuma-Gun, Fukushima, 969-6586, Japan
Tel.: (81) 242834129
Wood Product Mfr & Distr
N.A.I.C.S.: 321999

Hokuetsu Kishu Paper Co., Ltd. - Osaka Mill (1)
4-20-1 Minami-Suita, Suita City, Osaka, 564-0043, Japan
Tel.: (81) 663853851
Paper Products Mfr
N.A.I.C.S.: 322120

Hokuetsu Kishu Sales Co., Ltd. (1)
Takebashi 3-3 Bldg 3-3 Kandanishiki-cho, Chiyoda-ku, Tokyo, 101-0054, Japan

HOKUETSU CORPORATION

Hokuetsu Corporation—(Continued)
Tel.: (81) 3 6328 0001
Sales Range: $650-699.9 Million
Paper Product Mfr & Distr
N.A.I.C.S.: 322120

Hokuetsu Package Co., Ltd. (1)
Hokuetsu Paper Building 3-2-2 Nihonbashi Honseki-cho, Chuo-ku, Tokyo, 101-0047, Japan
Tel.: (81) 352006060
Web Site: https://www.hokuetsu-pc.co.jp
Sales Range: $25-49.9 Million
Emp.: 75
Die-Cut Paper & Paperboard Supplies Mfr
N.A.I.C.S.: 322230

Hokuetsu Paper Sales Co., Ltd. (1)
3-2-2 Nihonbashi Honseki-cho, Chuo-ku, Tokyo, 103-0021, Japan
Tel.: (81) 363280001
Web Site: https://www.hokuetsu-kami.jp
Tape Distr
N.A.I.C.S.: 424110

Hokuetsu Toyo Fibre Co., Ltd. (1)
888 Ohtsuka, Numazu, 410-0306, Shizuoka, Japan
Web Site: http://www.hokuetsu-toyofibre.jp
Emp.: 120
Paper Mfr & Distr
N.A.I.C.S.: 322120
Masataka Otsuka *(Pres)*

Hokuetsu Trading Corporation (1)
1-4-7 Kaji-machi, Chiyoda-ku, Tokyo, 101-0044, Japan
Tel.: (81) 352946011
Real Estate Agents & Brokers Offices
N.A.I.C.S.: 531210

Jiangmen Xinghui Paper Mill Co., Ltd. (1)
Area A Yinzhou Lake Paper Industry Base, Shuangshui Town Xinhui District, Jiangmen, Guangdong, China
Tel.: (86) 7506407888
Web Site: http://www.xinghuipaper.com
Packaging Paper Mfr & Distr
N.A.I.C.S.: 322220

Techno-Hokuetsu, Ltd. (1)
57 Enoki-cho, Higashi-ku, Niigata, 950-0881, Japan
Tel.: (81) 252752156
Sales Range: $25-49.9 Million
Emp.: 180
Paper & Pulp Mfr
N.A.I.C.S.: 322110
Kazuyasu Imai *(Pres)*

HOKUETSU INDUSTRIES CO., LTD.

Shinjuku SanEi Bldg 8F 1222 Nishi-iShinjuku, Shinjuku-ku, Tokyo, 160-0023, Japan
Tel.: (81) 333487251
Web Site: https://www.airman.co.jp
Year Founded: 1938
6364—(TKS)
Rev.: $343,059,000
Assets: $372,453,670
Liabilities: $124,082,920
Net Worth: $248,370,750
Earnings: $33,697,780
Fiscal Year-end: 03/31/24
Air Compressor Mfr & Distr
N.A.I.C.S.: 333912
Masayoshi Terao *(Pres)*

Subsidiaries:

AIRMAN ASIA SDN. BHD. (1)
Sky Park Office A-8-2 Block A Level 8 One City Jalan USJ 25/1, 47650, Subang Jaya, Selangor, Malaysia
Tel.: (60) 350367228
Web Site: https://airman-asia.com
Compressor Distr
N.A.I.C.S.: 423730
Tony Lim *(Mng Dir)*

AIRMAN USA CORPORATION (1)
42 International Pkwy, Adairsville, GA 30103
Tel.: (678) 800-7070
Web Site: http://www.airman-usa.com

Compressor Distr
N.A.I.C.S.: 423730

AIRMAN-FUSHENG (SHANGHAI) ELECTROMECHANICAL CO., LTD (1)
No 28 Minyi Road, Xinqiao Town Songjiang Dist, Shanghai, 201612, China
Tel.: (86) 4008081938
Web Site: http://www.fs-airman.com
Compressor Distr
N.A.I.C.S.: 423730

Hokuetsu Industries Europe B.V. (1)
Aalsmeerderdijk 156, 1438 AX, Oude Meer, Netherlands
Tel.: (31) 206462636
Web Site: https://www.hokuetsu.eu
Compressor Distr
N.A.I.C.S.: 423730

HOKUETSU METAL CO., LTD.

3-3-1 Zao, Nagaoka, 940-0028, Niigata, Japan
Tel.: (81) 258245111
Web Site: https://www.hokume.co.jp
Year Founded: 1942
5446—(TKS)
Rev.: $210,350,030
Assets: $190,103,600
Liabilities: $77,938,510
Net Worth: $112,165,090
Earnings: $3,086,870
Emp.: 399
Fiscal Year-end: 03/31/24
Iron & Steel Product Mfr & Distr
N.A.I.C.S.: 331110
Katsuyoshi Ohora *(Pres & CEO)*

HOKUHOKU FINANCIAL GROUP, INC.

1-2-26 Tsutsumicho-dori, Toyama, 930-8637, Japan
Tel.: (81) 764237331   JP
Web Site: http://www.hokuhoku-fg.co.jp
Year Founded: 2003
8377—(SAP)
Rev.: $1,241,684,836
Assets: $106,856,293,360
Liabilities: $102,811,285,101
Net Worth: $4,045,008,259
Earnings: $141,625,372
Emp.: 88
Fiscal Year-end: 03/31/23
Financial Investment Services
N.A.I.C.S.: 551111
Eishin Ihori *(Pres)*

Subsidiaries:

Dogin Business Service, Ltd. (1)
1-2-33 3jo Higashisapporo Higashisapporo-dogin Bldg, Shiroishi-Ku, Sapporo, 003-0003, Japan
Tel.: (81) 118151270
Financial Management Services
N.A.I.C.S.: 523999

Dogin Card Co., Ltd. (1)
Tel.: (81) 112411872
Web Site: http://www.dogincard.co.jp
Sales Range: $50-74.9 Million
Emp.: 98
Financial Management Services
N.A.I.C.S.: 523999

Hokkaido Bank, Ltd. (1)
1 Nishi 4-chome Odori, Chuo-ku, Sapporo, 060-8676, Japan **(100%)**
Tel.: (81) 112331093
Web Site: https://www.hokkaidobank.co.jp
Emp.: 2,118
Commericial Banking
N.A.I.C.S.: 522110
Yoshihiro Sekihachi *(Chm)*

Hokugin Business Services Co., Ltd. (1)
1883 Kawahara Hiyodorijima, Toyama, 930-0885, Japan
Tel.: (81) 764421561
Financial Management Services
N.A.I.C.S.: 523999

Hokugin Lease Co., Ltd. (1)
2-21 Aramachi, Toyama, 930-0028, Japan
Tel.: (81) 764254155
Financial Management Services
N.A.I.C.S.: 523999

Hokugin Real Estate Services Co., Ltd. (1)
Hokuriku Ginko Honten Bldg, Toyama, Japan **(100%)**
Tel.: (81) 764237111
Nonresidential Buildings Lessors
N.A.I.C.S.: 531120

Hokugin Software Co., Ltd. (1)
Hokugin Alps Building 1-5-25, Higashida District Town, Toyama, 930-0017, Japan **(100%)**
Tel.: (81) 764333900
Emp.: 138
Custom Computer Programming Services
N.A.I.C.S.: 541511
Takashi Hirase *(Gen Mgr)*

Hokuhoku Tokai Tokyo Securities Co., Ltd. (1)
6th floor Toyama Marunouchi Building 1-8-10, Marunouchi, Toyama, 930-0085, Japan
Tel.: (81) 764718164
Emp.: 135
Financial Services
N.A.I.C.S.: 522220

Hokuriku Card Co., Ltd. (1)
1-2-1 Shintomi-cho Hokuriku Bank Toyama Ekimae Building, Toyama, 930-0002, Japan **(87.39%)**
Tel.: (81) 764313010
Web Site: http://www.hokurikucard.jp
Emp.: 47
Credit Card Operations & Loan Guarantees
N.A.I.C.S.: 522299

Hokuriku Hosho Services Co., Ltd. (1)
1-2-26 Tsutsumichodoori, Toyama, 930-0046, Japan
Tel.: (81) 764932211
Financial Management Services
N.A.I.C.S.: 523999

The Hokkaido Bank, Ltd. (1)
4-1 Odori Nishi, Chuo-ku, Sapporo, 060-8676, Hokkaido, Japan
Tel.: (81) 112331093
Web Site: https://www.hokkaidobank.co.jp
Emp.: 2,118
Banking Services
N.A.I.C.S.: 522110
Masahiro Sasahara *(Pres)*

The Hokuriku Bank, Ltd. (1)
1-226 Tsutsumichodori, Toyama, 930 8637, Japan
Tel.: (81) 764237111
Web Site: http://www.hokugin.co.jp
Emp.: 2,365
Bank
N.A.I.C.S.: 522110

Division (Domestic):

The Hokuriku Bank, Ltd. (2)
Nihonbashi Muramachi 211 Mitsui 2nd Bldg 3rd Fl, Chou ku, Tokyo, 103 0022, Japan
Tel.: (81) 332417771
Web Site: http://www.hokugin.co.jp
Sales Range: $25-49.9 Million
Emp.: 50
Banking & Financial Services
N.A.I.C.S.: 522110
Eishin Ihori *(Pres)*

HOKURIKU COCA-COLA BOTTLING CO., LTD.

3550 Uchijima, Takaoka, 933-0397, Toyama, Japan
Tel.: (81) 766311115   JP
Web Site: http://www.hokuriku.ccbc.co.jp
Year Founded: 1962
Sales Range: $50-74.9 Million
Emp.: 446
Soft Drinks Mfr
N.A.I.C.S.: 312111
Haruhiko Sadakazu *(Pres)*

HOKURIKU ELECTRIC INDUSTRY CO., LTD.

3158 Shimo-Okubo, Toyama, 939-2292, Japan
Tel.: (81) 764671111   JP
Web Site: https://www.hdk.co.jp
Year Founded: 1943
6989—(TKS)
Rev.: $269,760,710
Assets: $275,273,450
Liabilities: $142,372,790
Net Worth: $132,900,660
Earnings: $16,776,180
Emp.: 1,887
Fiscal Year-end: 03/31/24
Film Resistors, IC's, Variable & High-Voltage Resistors, Sensor Components Mfr
N.A.I.C.S.: 334416
Satoshi Tanikawa *(Sr Exec Dir)*

Subsidiaries:

Asahi Denshi Co., Ltd. (1)
15 Sakanoshita, Date, 960-0426, Japan
Tel.: (81) 245842111
Web Site: https://www.asahi-gp.co.jp
Emp.: 218
Electronic Equipment Mfr & Distr
N.A.I.C.S.: 335999

Daiwa Circuit Module Co., Ltd. (1)
597-2 Kuboshima, Kumagaya, 360-0831, Saitama, Japan
Tel.: (81) 485322271
Web Site: http://www.dcm-net.com
Printed Circuit Board Mfr
N.A.I.C.S.: 334412

HDK (Thailand) Co., Ltd. (1)
68 Moo 2 Hi-Tech Industrial Estate T Bhanphao A, Mool Tambol Baanlane, Bangpa-in, 13160, Ayudhaya, Thailand
Tel.: (66) 35350233
Web Site: http://www.hdk.co.jp
Resistors Mfr
N.A.I.C.S.: 334416

HDK America Inc. (1)
200 N NW Hwy Ste 201, Barrington, IL 60010
Tel.: (847) 382-9411
Electronic Components Distr
N.A.I.C.S.: 423690

HDK China Ltd. (1)
Room 701B 7F Eastmark 21 Sheung Yuet Road, Kowloon Bay, Kowloon, China (Hong Kong)
Tel.: (852) 23180997
Electric Component Whslr
N.A.I.C.S.: 423690

HDK Micro Devices Co., Ltd. (1)
Sales Range: $50-74.9 Million
Emp.: 250
Printed Circuit Assemblies Mfr
N.A.I.C.S.: 334418

Han Ryuk Electronics Co., Ltd. (1)
785-4 Wonsi-Dong, Kyungki Do, Ansan, 425 090, Korea (South) **(50%)**
Tel.: (82) 314938811
Web Site: http://www.hanryuk.co.kr
Sales Range: $50-74.9 Million
Emp.: 220
Mfr of Resistors
N.A.I.C.S.: 334416

Hokuden (Malaysia) Sdn. Bhd. (1)
PTB111 244-250 Jalan Tun Mutalib 3, 81440, Bandar Tenggara, 81440, Johor Darul Takzim, Malaysia
Tel.: (60) 78963200
Sales Range: $200-249.9 Million
Emp.: 570
Resistors Mfr
N.A.I.C.S.: 334416
Junichi Izumi *(Mng Dir)*

Hokuriku (Dongguan) Co., Ltd - 2nd Factory (1)
Jiao-She Zone, Dong-Keng Town, Dongguan, Guangdong, China
Tel.: (86) 76983889716
Electronic Components Mfr
N.A.I.C.S.: 334416

Hokuriku (Malaysia), Sdn. Bhd. (1)
Lot 8090 Persiaran Kemajuan Seksyen,
40200, Shah Alam, Selangor Darul Ehsan,
Malaysia **(100%)**
Tel.: (60) 355107020
Web Site: http://www.hdkhms.com.my
Sales Range: $100-124.9 Million
Emp.: 300
Mfr of High Voltage Resistors
N.A.I.C.S.: 334416

Hokuriku (Shanghai) International Trading Co., Ltd. (1)
Unit 17A1 No585 Hua Fu Building Long Hua West Road, Shanghai, 200232, China
Tel.: (86) 2164286448
Sales Range: $25-49.9 Million
Emp.: 20
Electric Component Whslr
N.A.I.C.S.: 423690

Hokuriku (Singapore) Pte., Ltd. (1)
2Jurong East Street 21 02-85 IMM Building, Singapore, 609601, Jurong, Singapore **(100%)**
Tel.: (65) 68611677
Rev.: $82,475,728
Emp.: 34
Printed Hybrid Circuits & Functional Modules Mfr
N.A.I.C.S.: 334412

Hokuriku Electric (Guang Dong) Co., Ltd. - 1st Factory (1)
Jiao-She Zone, Dong-Keng Town, Dongguan, Guangdong, China
Tel.: (86) 76983381868
Electronic Components Mfr
N.A.I.C.S.: 334416

Hokuriku Hong Kong Co., Ltd. (1)
Unit 2-3 9F Fook Hong Industrial Building 19 Sheung Yuet Road, Kowloon Bay, Kowloon, China (Hong Kong)
Tel.: (852) 27558073
Emp.: 4
Electric Component Whslr
N.A.I.C.S.: 423690

Hokuriku International (Thailand) Co., Ltd. (1)
9/217 U M Tower 21st Floor Ramkhamhaeng Road, Suanluang, Bangkok, 10250, Thailand
Tel.: (66) 23693631
Electronic Component Mfr & Distr
N.A.I.C.S.: 334419

Hokuriku Kosan Co., Ltd. (1)
1-1 Tabukuro Mizuhashi City, Toyama, 939-3555, Japan
Tel.: (81) 764791808
Web Site: https://www.h-kousan.co.jp
Sales Range: $50-74.9 Million
Emp.: 6
Residential Real Estate Property Development Services
N.A.I.C.S.: 531210

Hokuriku Seiki Co., Ltd. (1)
Printed Circuit Assemblies Mfr
N.A.I.C.S.: 334418

Hokuriku U.S.A. Ltd. (1)
125 Electronics Blvd SW Ste G, Huntsville, AL 35824-2206 **(50%)**
Tel.: (256) 772-9620
Web Site: http://www.hck.com
Sales Range: $50-74.9 Million
Emp.: 6
Sales & Marketing of Resistors
N.A.I.C.S.: 423690
Makota Hase (Pres & CEO)

Kureha Ceramic Co., Ltd. (1)
163 Takaki nishi, Toyama, 930-0106, Japan
Tel.: (81) 764361500
Sales Range: $25-49.9 Million
Emp.: 28
Ceramic Tile Mfr
N.A.I.C.S.: 327120

MD Tech Phils., Inc. (1)
Main Avenue Corner 3rd Street, Rosario, 4106, Cavite, Philippines
Tel.: (63) 464370628
Sales Range: $200-249.9 Million
Emp.: 700
Resistors Mfr
N.A.I.C.S.: 334416

Hiroyuki Ako (Pres)

Ryohoku Denshi Co., Ltd. (1)
8-5 Harumidai, Toyama, 931-8455, Japan
Tel.: (81) 764387370
Web Site: http://www.ryohoku.co.jp
Printed Circuit Board Mfr
N.A.I.C.S.: 334412

Shanghai HDK Micro Devices Co., Ltd. (1)
No 428 Tian Ying Rd, QingPu Industrial Park, Shanghai, China
Tel.: (86) 2169225228
Electronic Component Mfr & Distr
N.A.I.C.S.: 334419

Taipei Hokuriku Co., Ltd. (1)
5F No 274 Song Chiang Road, Taipei, Taiwan
Tel.: (886) 225222252
Electronic Component Mfr & Distr
N.A.I.C.S.: 334419

Taipei Hokuriku Electric Industry Co., Ltd. (1)
5F No 274 Song Chiang Road, Taipei, 104, Taiwan **(99%)**
Tel.: (886) 225222252
Sales Range: $50-74.9 Million
Emp.: 195
Mfr of Fim Resistors, Variable Resistors & High Voltage Resistors
N.A.I.C.S.: 334416

Tianjin Hokuriku Electric Industry Co., Ltd. (1)
No 77 Bao Yuan Road, Jinnan Economic Development Area Jinnan-Qu, Tianjin, 300000, China
Tel.: (86) 2288519787
Electronic Components Mfr
N.A.I.C.S.: 334416

HOKURIKU ELECTRIC POWER CO.
15-1 Ushijima-cho, Toyama, 930-8686, Japan
Tel.: (81) 120776453
Web Site: https://www.rikuden.co.jp
Year Founded: 1951
9505—(TKS)
Rev.: $5,342,453,180
Assets: $12,264,425,350
Liabilities: $10,099,961,020
Net Worth: $2,164,464,330
Earnings: $375,520,710
Emp.: 3,162
Fiscal Year-end: 03/31/24
Electric Utility Services
N.A.I.C.S.: 221122
Shigeo Takagi (Mng Exec Officer)

Subsidiaries:

Hokuden Information System Service Company, Inc. (1)
3-1 Sakurabashi-dori Toyama Denki Building 2F, Toyama, 930-0004, Japan
Tel.: (81) 764427272
Web Site: https://www.hiss.co.jp
Emp.: 358
Software Services
N.A.I.C.S.: 541511

Hokuden Partner Service Inc. (1)
3rd floor of Hokuden Building 15-1, Ushijima-cho, Toyama, 930-0858, Japan
Tel.: (81) 764334112
Web Site: https://www.ho-partner.co.jp
Emp.: 111
Business Development Services
N.A.I.C.S.: 611430

Hokuriku Telecommunication Network Co., Inc. (1)
1-1-3 Sainen Confidence Kanazawa, Kanazawa, 920-0024, Ishikawa, Japan
Tel.: (81) 762695620
Web Site: http://www.htnet.co.jp
Emp.: 177
Electrical Equipment Mfr & Distr
N.A.I.C.S.: 335999

Nihonkai Concrete Industries Co. (1)
750 Tabata, Toyama, 931-8588, Japan
Tel.: (81) 764378121

Web Site: http://www.nkcon.co.jp
Emp.: 67
Concrete Pile Mfr & Whslr
N.A.I.C.S.: 327120

HOKURIKU ELECTRICAL CONSTRUCTION CO., LTD.
269 Konaka, Toyama, 939-8571, Toyama, Japan
Tel.: (81) 764816092
Web Site: https://www.rikudenko.co.jp
Year Founded: 1944
1930—(TKS)
Rev.: $352,960,780
Assets: $414,770,890
Liabilities: $138,043,240
Net Worth: $276,727,650
Earnings: $14,601,490
Emp.: 1,313
Fiscal Year-end: 03/31/24
Construction Engineering Services
N.A.I.C.S.: 541330
Shigeru Yano (Mng Dir)

HOKURIKU GAS CO., LTD.
1-2-23 Higashiodori, Chuo-ku, Niigata, 950-8748, Japan
Tel.: (81) 252452212
Web Site: https://www.hokurikugas.co.jp
Year Founded: 1913
9537—(TKS)
Rev.: $405,887,050
Assets: $416,648,130
Liabilities: $88,071,640
Net Worth: $328,576,490
Earnings: ($11,626,990)
Emp.: 441
Fiscal Year-end: 03/31/24
Gas Distr
N.A.I.C.S.: 424710
Eiichi Tsurui (Chm)

HOKURYO CO., LTD.
6-15 Chuo 2-jo 3-chome, Sapporo Shiroishi-ku, Hokkaido, 003-0012, Japan
Tel.: (81) 118121131
Web Site: https://www.hokuryo.co.jp
1384—(TKS)
Rev.: $126,420,800
Assets: $137,959,360
Liabilities: $50,345,680
Net Worth: $87,613,680
Earnings: $1,277,760
Emp.: 438
Fiscal Year-end: 03/31/21
Chicken Egg Production & Sales
N.A.I.C.S.: 112310
Daisuke Yoneyama (Pres)

HOKUSHIN CO., LTD.
17-2 Mokuzaicho, Kishiwada, 596-8521, Osaka, Japan
Tel.: (81) 724380141
Web Site: https://www.hokushinmdf.jp
Year Founded: 1931
7897—(TKS)
Rev.: $88,146,080
Assets: $122,723,040
Liabilities: $71,893,360
Net Worth: $50,829,680
Earnings: $1,674,640
Fiscal Year-end: 03/31/21
Wood Products Mfr & Whslr
N.A.I.C.S.: 321219
Hideo Taira (Pres & CEO)

HOKUTO CORPORATION
138-1 Minamibori, Nagano Prefecture, Nagano, 381-0016, Japan
Tel.: (81) 262433111
Web Site: https://www.hokutokinoko.co.jp
Year Founded: 1964

1379—(TKS)
Rev.: $525,005,860
Assets: $684,168,050
Liabilities: $321,781,410
Net Worth: $362,386,640
Earnings: $23,300,250
Emp.: 1,359
Fiscal Year-end: 03/31/24
Mushroom Farming & Sales
N.A.I.C.S.: 111411
Shigeki Komatsu (Dir-Mushroom Cultivation Div)

Subsidiaries:

HOKTO KINOKO COMPANY (1)
2033 Marilyn Ln, San Marcos, CA 92069
Tel.: (760) 744-8453
Emp.: 150
Mushroom Production Services
N.A.I.C.S.: 111411

HOKUTO PRINTING CO., LTD.
67-2 Fukamachi, Kitamachi,, Aizuwakamatsu, 965-0052, Japan
Tel.: (81) 242322366
Web Site: https://aizu-hokuto.com
Year Founded: 1988
Commercial Printing
N.A.I.C.S.: 323111

HOKUYAKU TAKEYAMA HOLDINGS, INC.
1-5 Kita 6-jo Nishi 16-chome, Chuo-Ku, Sapporo, 060-0006, Japan
Tel.: (81) 116331030
Web Site: https://www.hokutake.co.jp
Year Founded: 2006
3055—(SAP)
Rev.: $2,229,245,340
Assets: $1,198,088,010
Liabilities: $714,563,080
Net Worth: $483,524,930
Earnings: $18,734,310
Fiscal Year-end: 03/31/20
Holding Company
N.A.I.C.S.: 551112
Masanobu Manabe (Pres & CEO)

HOKUYU LUCKY CO., LTD.
1-1-1 Hoshioki 1-jo 2-chome, Teine-ku, Sapporo, 006-0851, Hokkaido, Japan
Tel.: (81) 115587000
Web Site: https://www.hokuyu-lucky.co.jp
Year Founded: 1971
27470—(TKS)
Sales Range: Less than $1 Million
Supermarket Operator
N.A.I.C.S.: 445110
Uyu Kiryu (Pres & CEO)

HOLALUZ-CLIDOM SA
Passeig Joan de Borbo 99-10 4th Floor, 08039, Barcelona, Spain
Tel.: (34) 900670707   ES
Web Site: https://www.holaluz.com
Year Founded: 2010
HLZ—(MAD)
Rev.: $678,399,956
Assets: $193,892,933
Liabilities: $180,564,089
Net Worth: $13,328,844
Earnings: ($28,885,151)
Emp.: 423
Fiscal Year-end: 12/31/23
Renewable Energy Distribution Services
N.A.I.C.S.: 221210
Alfonso de Leon (VP)

HOLAND OG SETSKOG SPAREBANK
Tel.: (47) 63857070
Web Site: https://hsbank.no
Year Founded: 1849
HSPG—(OSL)

HOLAND OG SETSKOG SPAREBANK

Holand og Setskog Sparebank—(Continued)

Sales Range: Less than $1 Million
Commercial Banking Services
N.A.I.C.S.: 522110
John Sigurd Bjorknes *(CEO & Mgr-Mng)*

HOLCIM (VENEZUELA) C.A.
Ave Ppl Los Cortijos de Lourdes, VE-1071, Caracas, Los Ruices, Venezuela
Tel.: (58) 2122074000
Sales Range: $200-249.9 Million
Emp.: 568
Cement, Ready-Mixed Concrete & Aggregates Mfr & Marketer
N.A.I.C.S.: 327310
Rafael Corredor *(Mgr-Maintenance)*

HOLCIM LTD.
Grafenauweg 10, 6300, Zug, Switzerland
Tel.: (41) 588585858 CH
Web Site: https://www.holcim.com
Year Founded: 2015
HCMLF—(OTCIQ)
Rev.: $26,207,620,740
Assets: $60,274,583,280
Liabilities: $27,858,762,000
Net Worth: $32,415,821,280
Earnings: $2,267,204,940
Emp.: 67,409
Fiscal Year-end: 12/31/20
Cement, Aggregates & Concrete Mfr
N.A.I.C.S.: 327310
Jamie M. Gentoso *(Pres-Holcim Building Envelope & Head-Solutions & Products Bus Unit-Global)*

Subsidiaries:

Aggregate Industries Holdings Limited (1)
Bardon Hall Copt Road, Markfield, LE67 9PJ, Leics, United Kingdom (100%)
Tel.: (44) 1530 510066
Web Site: http://www.aggregate.com
Holding Company; Construction Aggregates, Asphalt, Ready-Mix Concrete & Precast Concrete Products Mfr
N.A.I.C.S.: 551112
James Roberts *(Dir-Org & HR)*

Subsidiary (US):

Aggregate Industries Management, Inc. (2)
8700 W Bryn Mawr Ave Ste 300, Chicago, IL 20770
Tel.: (773) 372-1000
Web Site: http://www.aggregate-us.com
Aggregate-Based Construction Materials Mfr
N.A.I.C.S.: 327310

Division (Domestic):

Aggregate Industries - Southwest Region (3)
4675 W Teco Ave Ste 140, Las Vegas, NV 89118-4364
Tel.: (702) 281-9696
Web Site: http://www.aggregate-us.com
Aggregates, Asphalt & Ready-Mixed Concrete Mfr
N.A.I.C.S.: 327320

Unit (Domestic):

Lattimore Materials Company, L.P. (4)
15900 Dooley Rd, Addison, TX 75001-4243
Tel.: (972) 221-4646
Web Site: http://www.aggregate-us.com
Ready-Mixed Concrete Products Whslr
N.A.I.C.S.: 423320

Division (Domestic):

Aggregate Industries Mid-Atlantic Region (3)
6401 Golden Triangle Dr Ste 400, Greenbelt, MD 20770-3202
Tel.: (301) 982-1400

Web Site: http://www.aggregate-us.com
Aggregates, Crushed Stone, Sand & Gravel, Asphalt & Ready-Mixed Concrete Whslr
N.A.I.C.S.: 423320

Aggregate Industries Midwest Region (3)
2815 Dodd Rd Ste 101, Eagan, MN 55121
Tel.: (651) 683-8190
Web Site: http://www.aggregate-us.com
Aggregates, Crushed Stone, Sand & Gravel, Asphalt & Ready-Mixed Concrete Whslr
N.A.I.C.S.: 423320

Unit (Domestic):

Meyer Material Company, LLC (4)
7001 West Route 120, McHenry, IL 60050
Tel.: (815) 331-7200
Web Site: http://www.aggregate-us.com
Concrete Products Producer
N.A.I.C.S.: 327320

Division (Domestic):

Aggregate Industries Northeast Region (3)
1715 Broadway, Saugus, MA 01906-4115
Tel.: (781) 941-7200
Web Site: http://www.aggregate-us.com
Aggregates, Crushed Stone, Sand & Gravel, Asphalt & Ready-Mixed Concrete Whslr
N.A.I.C.S.: 423320

Subsidiary (Domestic):

Aggregate Industries UK Limited (2)
Copt Oak Road, Markfield, LE67 9PJ, Leicestershire, United Kingdom
Tel.: (44) 1530816600
Web Site: https://www.aggregate.com
Emp.: 3,700
Aggregates, Crushed Stone, Sand & Gravel, Asphalt & Ready-Mixed Concrete Mfr
N.A.I.C.S.: 324121
John Bowater *(Deputy CEO & CFO)*

Subsidiary (Domestic):

London Concrete Ltd. (3)
London Concrete Transport Avenue Great West Road, Brentford, TW8 9HQ, Middlesex, United Kingdom
Tel.: (44) 2083807300
Web Site: http://www.aggregate.com
Readymix Concrete Mfr
N.A.I.C.S.: 327320

Subsidiary (Domestic):

Charcon Limited (2)
Bardon Hall Copt Oak Road, Markfield, LE67 9PJ, Leics, United Kingdom
Tel.: (44) 1417767881
Web Site: http://www.charcon.com
Construction Materials Whslr
N.A.I.C.S.: 423320
Dave McClelland *(Natl Acct Mgr)*

Subsidiary (Non-US):

Dansk Natursten A/S (2)
Tronholmen 28B, 8960, Randers, Denmark
Tel.: (45) 86448577
Web Site: http://www.dansknatursten.dk
Aggregates, Crushed Stone, Sand & Gravel, Asphalt & Ready-Mixed Concrete Mfr & Whslr
N.A.I.C.S.: 324121
Rene Gosvig *(CEO)*

Subsidiary (Domestic):

Lytag Ltd (2)
Drax Power Station, Selby, YO8 8PH, United Kingdom
Tel.: (44) 1904727922
Web Site: http://www.aggregate.com
Lightweight Aggregates Mfr
N.A.I.C.S.: 327390
Barry Mellor *(Mgr-Comml & Technical)*

Subsidiary (US):

Transit Mix Concrete Co. (2)
444 E Costilla St, Colorado Springs, CO 80903

Tel.: (719) 475-0700
Web Site: http://www.transitmix.com
Construction Materials Mfr
N.A.I.C.S.: 327320
Jerald Schnabel *(Pres)*

Subsidiary (Non-US):

YEOMAN POLAND Sp. z o.o. (2)
ul Wielopole 7B, 80-556, Gdańsk, Poland
Tel.: (48) 728 900 966
Web Site: http://www.yeoman-poland.com.pl
Crushed Stone Distr
N.A.I.C.S.: 423320

Bazian Cement Company Ltd. (1)
Rizgary Neighborhood 412 Building No 70, Sulaymaniyah, Iraq (70%)
Tel.: (964) 7708677000
Web Site: http://www.lafarge-iraq.com
Cement Mfr
N.A.I.C.S.: 327310

Bogaz Endustri ve Madencilik Ltd. (1)
Kalecik Koyu Sahili, Iskele, Larnaca, Cyprus
Tel.: (357) 5338240005
Web Site: http://www.bemltd.com
Cement Mfr
N.A.I.C.S.: 327310

Cement Australia Holdings Pty. Ltd.
18 Station Avenue, Darra, 4076, QLD, Australia
Tel.: (61) 1300236368
Web Site: https://www.cementaustralia.com.au
Cement & Cement Related Products Mfr, Distr & Marketer; Raw Construction Materials Mining
N.A.I.C.S.: 327310
Rob Davies *(CEO & Mng Dir)*

Plant (Domestic):

Cement Australia Holdings Pty Ltd - Bulwer Island Plant (2)
77 Pamela St, Pinkenba, 4008, QLD, Australia
Tel.: (61) 736327813
Web Site: http://www.cementaustralia.com.au
Cement Mfr
N.A.I.C.S.: 327310

Cement Australia Holdings Pty Ltd - Gladstone Plant (2)
Landing Rd, PO Box 285, Gladstone, 4680, QLD, Australia
Tel.: (61) 74 970 1100
Web Site: http://www.cementaustralia.com.au
Cement Mfr
N.A.I.C.S.: 327310

Cement Australia Holdings Pty Ltd - Railton Plant (2)
101 Cement Works Rd, Railton, 7305, TAS, Australia
Tel.: (61) 36 491 0111
Web Site: https://www.cementaustralia.com.au
Construction Material & Cement Mfr & Whslr
N.A.I.C.S.: 327310

Subsidiary (Domestic):

Geocycle Pty. Ltd. (2)
92 Ordish Rd, Dandenong South, Melbourne, 3175, VIC, Australia
Tel.: (61) 130 065 7057
Web Site: https://www.cementaustralia.com.au
Waste Management Services
N.A.I.C.S.: 562920

Colorado River Concrete, LP (1)
8820 Hwy 67, Alvarado, TX 76009
Tel.: (817) 790-8612
Web Site: https://coloradoriverco.com
Asphalt Paving Mixture & Block Mfr
N.A.I.C.S.: 324121

FDT Flachdach Technologie GmbH & Co. KG (1)
Eisenbahnstrasse 6-8, 68199, Mannheim, Germany
Tel.: (49) 6218504100

INTERNATIONAL PUBLIC

Web Site: http://www.fdt.de
Flat Roofing Membrane Mfr
N.A.I.C.S.: 326299
Zeljko Vuksanovic *(CEO)*

Heracles General Cement Company S.A. (1)
19 3 km Leoforos Markopoulou, Paiania, 19002, Athens, Greece (100%)
Tel.: (30) 2102898111
Web Site: http://www.lafarge.gr
Cement & Concrete Aggregates Mfr
N.A.I.C.S.: 327310
Anastasios Manos *(Gen Mgr-Logistics, Exports & IT)*

Hima Cement Ltd. (1)
Mirembe Business Centre 4th Floor Plot 46 Lugogo Bypass, PO Box 7230, Kampala, Uganda (71%)
Tel.: (256) 312213200
Web Site: http://www.lafarge.co.ug
Cement Mfr
N.A.I.C.S.: 327310
Jean-Michel Pons *(CEO)*

Holcibel S.A. (1)
Rue Des Fabriques 2, 7034, Oburg, Belgium (100%)
Tel.: (32) 65358111
Aggregates, Cement & Ready-Mixed Concrete Products Mfr & Distr
N.A.I.C.S.: 327310

Holcim (Australia) Pty., Ltd. (1)
Tower B Level 7 799 Pacific Highway, Chatswood, 2067, NSW, Australia
Tel.: (61) 131188
Web Site: https://www.holcim.com.au
Aggregates, Ready-Mixed Concrete & Concrete Pipe Mfr
N.A.I.C.S.: 327320
George Agriogiannis *(CEO-Australia & New Zealand)*

Subsidiary (Domestic):

Broadway & Frame Premix Concrete Pty Ltd (2)
26-28 Greenaway Street, Bulleen, 3105, VIC, Australia
Tel.: (61) 1300802540
Web Site: http://www.broadwayandframe.com
Construction Materials Mfr & Whslr
N.A.I.C.S.: 327320

Excel Concrete Pty Ltd (2)
1044 Lytton Rd, Murarrie, Brisbane, 4172, QLD, Australia
Tel.: (61) 733311555
Web Site: http://www.excelconcrete.com.au
Readymix Concrete Mfr
N.A.I.C.S.: 327320

Joint Venture (Domestic):

Metromix Pty. Ltd. (2)
Level 4 107 Phillip Street, Parramatta, 2150, NSW, Australia (50%)
Tel.: (61) 29 849 7400
Web Site: https://www.metromix.com.au
Aggregates & Construction Sand Mining & Quarry Operations; Concrete Mfr
N.A.I.C.S.: 212319
John Bailey *(Sls Mgr-Concrete-Sydney)*

Holcim (Azerbaijan) O.J.S.C. (1)
Sahil Settlement Salyan highway, AZ1083, Baku, Azerbaijan
Tel.: (994) 124418888
Web Site: https://www.holcim.az
Emp.: 80,000
Cement & Clinker Mfr
N.A.I.C.S.: 327310
Ali Huseynov *(Mgr-Plant)*

Holcim (Belgique) S.A. (1)
Avenue Robert Schuman 71, 1401, Nivelles, Belgium (100%)
Tel.: (32) 67876601
Web Site: https://www.holcim.be
Concrete, Cement & Aggregates Mfr
N.A.I.C.S.: 327310
Geert De Mets *(Product Mgr-Technical Support-Wallonia & Prefa Flandres)*

Subsidiary (Domestic):

Geocycle S.A. (2)

AND PRIVATE COMPANIES — HOLCIM LTD.

Rue de Courriere 49, 7181, Seneffe, Belgium
Tel.: (32) 64510411
Web Site: http://www.geocycle.com
Industrial Waste Management Services
N.A.I.C.S.: 562998

Holcim (Bulgaria) AD (1)
Beli Izvor, 3040, Vratsa, Bulgaria
Tel.: (359) 92661341
Web Site: https://www.holcim.bg
Cement Mfr
N.A.I.C.S.: 327310
Todor Kostov (CEO)

Holcim (Deutschland) GmbH (1)
Troplowitzstrasse 5, 22529, Hamburg, Germany **(100%)**
Tel.: (49) 40360020
Emp.: 1,800
Cement Mfr
N.A.I.C.S.: 327310
Thorsten Hahn (Chm-Mgmt Bd & CEO)

Plant (Domestic):

Holcim (Deutschland) GmbH - Bremen Grinding Plant (2)
Auf den Delben 35, 28237, Bremen, Germany
Tel.: (49) 4 21 6 43 65 10
Web Site: http://www.holcim.de
Cement Mfr
N.A.I.C.S.: 327310

Holcim (Deutschland) GmbH - Hover Plant (2)
Hannoversche Strasse 28, Hover, Hannover, 31319, Germany
Tel.: (49) 51 32 92 70
Web Site: http://www.holcim.de
Readymix Concrete Mfr
N.A.I.C.S.: 327320

Holcim (Deutschland) GmbH - Lagerdorf Plant (2)
Sandweg 10, 25566, Lagerdorf, Germany
Tel.: (49) 48 28 60 0
Web Site: http://www.holcim.de
Emp.: 300
Cement Mfr
N.A.I.C.S.: 327310
Matthias von der Brelje (Sls Dir-Binder)

Subsidiary (Domestic):

Holcim (Suddeutschland) GmbH (2)
Dormettinger Strasse 27, D-72359, Dotternhausen, Germany **(100%)**
Tel.: (49) 7427790
Web Site: https://www.holcim-sued.de
Concrete, Cement & Aggregate Mfr & Distr
N.A.I.C.S.: 327320
Remo Bernasconi (Chm & Mng Dir)

Plant (Domestic):

Holcim (Suddeutschland) GmbH - Dotternhausen Plant (3)
Dormettinger Str 23, 72359, Dotternhausen, Germany
Tel.: (49) 74 27 79 0
Web Site: http://www.holcim-sued.de
Emp.: 230
Cement Mfr
N.A.I.C.S.: 327310
Dieter Schillo (Plant Mgr)

Subsidiary (Domestic):

Holcim Kies und Beton GmbH (3)
Niederried 5, D-79576, Weil am Rhein, Germany
Tel.: (49) 7621 94 25 0
Web Site: http://www.holcim-sued.de
Construction Materials Whslr
N.A.I.C.S.: 423320

Subsidiary (Domestic):

Holcim Beton und Zuschlagstoffe GmbH (2)
Willy-Brandt-Strasse 69, 20457, Hamburg, Germany
Tel.: (49) 40 3 60 02 0
Web Site: http://www.holcim.de
Emp.: 80
Readymix Concrete Mfr
N.A.I.C.S.: 327320

Holcim (Hrvatska) d.o.o. (1)
Koromacno 7b, 52222, Nedescina, Croatia **(99.9%)**
Tel.: (385) 52876900
Web Site: http://www.holcim.hr
Cement & Construction Aggregate Mfr & Whslr
N.A.I.C.S.: 327310
Virna Viskovic-Agusaj (Chm-Mgmt Bd)

Holcim (Liban) S.A.L. (1)
Mitsulift House 2nd Floor Dbayeh Main Road, PO Box 11-396, Beirut, Lebanon **(52.1%)**
Tel.: (961) 6546000
Web Site: http://www.holcim.com.lb
Cement Producer & Distr
N.A.I.C.S.: 327310
Markus Herbst (CFO)

Holcim (Madagascar) S.A. (1)
1 bis rue Patrice Lumumba Tsaralalana, Tsaralalana, 101, Antananarivo, Madagascar
Tel.: (261) 202229388
Ready-Mix Concrete Product Mfr
N.A.I.C.S.: 327320

Holcim (Malaysia) Sdn. Bhd. (1)
Suite 11 01 Level 11 Johor Bahru City Square 106-108, Jalan Wong Ah Fook, Johor Bahru, 80000, Malaysia **(51%)**
Tel.: (60) 7 251 3411
Web Site: http://www.holcim.com.my
Emp.: 190
Ready Mix Concrete Mfr & Distr
N.A.I.C.S.: 327320
Mahanama Ralapanawa (CEO)

Plant (Domestic):

Holcim (Malaysia) Sdn Bhd - Pasir Gudang Plant (2)
Lot 119 Jalan Pukal 3, 81700, Pasir Gudang, Malaysia
Tel.: (60) 7 2513411
Web Site: http://www.holcim.my
Cement Mfr
N.A.I.C.S.: 327310

Holcim (Nederland) B.V. (1)
IJsseldijk 351, Krimpen aan den IJssel, 2922 BK, Rotterdam, Netherlands
Tel.: (31) 180 54 55 00
Web Site: http://www.holcim.nl
Construction Materials Whslr
N.A.I.C.S.: 423320

Holcim (New Zealand) Ltd. (1)
1/1 Show Place, PO Box 6040, Addington, Christchurch, 8024, New Zealand **(100%)**
Tel.: (64) 33397500
Web Site: https://www.holcim.co.nz
Concrete, Cement & Aggregates Supplier
N.A.I.C.S.: 423320

Holcim (Nicaragua) S.A. (1)
Edificio El Centro 2 1st Floor, Rotonda El Gueguense 700 mts, Managua, Nicaragua
Tel.: (505) 22559255
Web Site: https://www.holcim.com.ni
Cement & Concrete Mfr
N.A.I.C.S.: 327310
Dorisell Blanco (VP & Coord-Sustainable Dev)

Holcim (Philippines) Inc. (1)
7/F Two World Square McKinley Hill Fort Bonifacio, Taguig, 1634, Philippines
Tel.: (63) 285811511
Web Site: http://www.holcim.ph
Rev.: $477,248,928
Assets: $762,800,866
Liabilities: $211,645,075
Net Worth: $551,155,791
Earnings: $16,932,109
Fiscal Year-end: 12/31/2022
Concrete, Cement & Aggregates Mfr & Distr
N.A.I.C.S.: 327310
William C. Sumalinog (Sr VP & Head-Sls)

Holcim (Reunion) S.A. (1)
Z I no 1 rue Armagnac, CS 61087, Le Port, Cedex, Reunion
Tel.: (262) 262 425800
Web Site: http://www.lafargeholcim-io.com
Construction Materials Whslr
N.A.I.C.S.: 423320

Subsidiary (Domestic):

Holcim Precontraint S.A. (2)
Z I n 1 rue Armagnac, 97420, Le Port, Reunion
Tel.: (262) 262 42 5880
Web Site: http://www.holcim.re
Construction Materials Whslr
N.A.I.C.S.: 423320

Holcim (Romania) S.A. (1)
169 A Calea Floreasca Street Building B Floor 7, District 1, 014459, Bucharest, Romania **(99.7%)**
Tel.: (40) 212039100
Web Site: https://www.holcim.ro
Cement & Aggregates Mfr & Supplier
N.A.I.C.S.: 327310
Madalina Craciunescu (Dir-Org & HR)

Plant (Domestic):

Holcim (Romania) S.A. - Alesd Plant (2)
Str Viitorului 2, Alesd, 417022, Romania
Tel.: (40) 259349778
Web Site: http://www.holcim.ro
Cement Mfr
N.A.I.C.S.: 327310

Holcim (Romania) S.A. - Campulung Plant (2)
Comuna Valea Mare Pravat, 117805, Campulung, Romania
Tel.: (40) 248 557 150
Web Site: http://www.holcim.ro
Cement Mfr
N.A.I.C.S.: 327310

Holcim (Romania) S.A. - Turda Grinding Plant (2)
Str Stefan cel Mare 4, 401112, Turda, Romania
Tel.: (40) 264 305 210
Web Site: http://www.holcim.ro
Cement Mfr
N.A.I.C.S.: 327310

Holcim (Schweiz) AG (1)
Hagenholzstrasse 83, 8050, Zurich, Switzerland
Tel.: (41) 588506868
Web Site: https://www.holcim.ch
Emp.: 1,200
Concrete, Cement & Aggregate Mfr & Distr
N.A.I.C.S.: 327320
Nick Traber (CEO)

Plant (Domestic):

Holcim (Schweiz) AG - Siggenthal Plant (2)
Zementweg 1, 5303, Wurenlingen, Switzerland
Tel.: (41) 588505369
Web Site: http://www.holcim.ch
Emp.: 120
Construction Materials Whslr
N.A.I.C.S.: 423320

Holcim (Schweiz) AG - Untervaz Plant (2)
Zementwerk Untervaz, 7204, Untervaz, Switzerland
Tel.: (41) 58 850 32 11
Web Site: http://www.holcim.ch
Emp.: 120
Construction Materials Whslr
N.A.I.C.S.: 423320

Subsidiary (Domestic):

Holcim BF+P SA (2)
Riond Bosson 11, 1110, Morges, Switzerland
Tel.: (41) 588500880
Web Site: http://www.holcim.ch
Concrete, Cement & Aggregate Mfr & Distr
N.A.I.C.S.: 423320

Holcim Kies und Beton AG (2)
Barenzelg 2, 5243, Mulligen, Switzerland
Tel.: (41) 588504511
Web Site: http://www.holcim.ch
Construction Materials Whslr
N.A.I.C.S.: 423320

Holcim (Singapore) Limited (1)
3A International Business Park 07-01/04 Icon IBP Tower A, Singapore, 609935, Singapore **(90.8%)**
Tel.: (65) 66604831
Web Site: http://www.holcim.com.sg

Cement Mfr
N.A.I.C.S.: 327310
Jean-Michel Laye (Dir-Quality & Product Dev)

Holcim (US) Inc. (1)
6211 Ann Arbor Rd, Dundee, MI 48131-0122
Tel.: (734) 529-2411
Web Site: http://www.lafargeholcim.us
Cement Mfr
N.A.I.C.S.: 327310
Toufic Tabbara (Head-North America)

Plant (Domestic):

Holcim (US) Inc. - Ada Plant (2)
14500 County Rd 1550, Ada, OK 74820
Tel.: (580) 332-1512
Web Site: http://www.lafargeholcim.us
Cement Mfr
N.A.I.C.S.: 327310

Holcim (US) Inc. - Artesia Plant (2)
8677 US-45 ALT, Artesia, MS 39736
Tel.: (662) 272-5121
Web Site: http://www.lafargeholcim.us
Cement Mfr
N.A.I.C.S.: 327310

Holcim (US) Inc. - Birmingham Plant (2)
1555 Hartman Industrial Blvd, Birmingham, AL 35221
Tel.: (615) 771-1220
Web Site: http://www.lafargeholcim.us
Cement Mfr
N.A.I.C.S.: 327310

Holcim (US) Inc. - Hagerstown Plant (2)
1260 Security Rd, Hagerstown, MD 21742-0655
Tel.: (301) 739-1150
Web Site: http://www.lafargeholcim.us
Cement Mfr
N.A.I.C.S.: 327310
Fernando Valencia (Plant Mgr)

Holcim (US) Inc. - Holly Hill Plant (2)
200 Safety St Hwy 453, Holly Hill, SC 29059
Tel.: (803) 496-5027
Web Site: http://www.lafargeholcim.us
Cement Mfr
N.A.I.C.S.: 327310

Holcim (US) Inc. - Midlothian Plant (2)
1800 Dove Ln, Midlothian, TX 76065
Tel.: (972) 923-5800
Web Site: http://www.lafargeholcim.us
Cement Mfr
N.A.I.C.S.: 327310

Holcim (US) Inc. - Portland Plant (2)
3500 Hwy 120, Florence, CO 81226
Tel.: (719) 784-6325
Web Site: http://www.lafargeholcim.us
Cement Mfr
N.A.I.C.S.: 327310

Holcim (US) Inc. - Ste. Genevieve Plant (2)
2942 US Hwy 61, Bloomsdale, MO 63627
Tel.: (636) 524-8000
Web Site: http://www.lafargeholcim.us
Cement Mfr; Construction Material Whslr
N.A.I.C.S.: 327310

Holcim (US) Inc. - Theodore Plant (2)
3051 Hamilton Blvd, Theodore, AL 36582
Tel.: (251) 443-6200
Web Site: http://www.lafargeholcim.us
Cement Mfr
N.A.I.C.S.: 327310

Subsidiary (Domestic):

Tezak Heavy Equipment Co., Inc. (2)
205 Tunnel Dr, Canon City, CO 81212-3660
Tel.: (719) 269-1148
Web Site: http://www.tezakheavyequipment.com
Highway, Street & Bridge Construction Services
N.A.I.C.S.: 237310

HOLCIM LTD.

Holcim Ltd.—(Continued)

Daniel E. Tezak (Pres)

Holcim Aggregati Calcestruzzi S.r.l. (1)
Via Volta 1, 22046, Merone, Como, Italy **(100%)**
Tel.: (39) 031616111
Web Site: http://www.holcim.it
Cement Mfr
N.A.I.C.S.: 327310

Holcim Beteiligungs GmbH (1)
Willy-Brandt-Strasse 69, 20457, Hamburg, Germany **(100%)**
Tel.: (49) 40360020
Web Site: http://www.holcim.de
Emp.: 150
Construction Materials Whslr
N.A.I.C.S.: 423320

Holcim Cements (Bangladesh) Ltd. (1)
NinaKabbo Level 7 227/A Bir Uttam Mir Shawkat Sarak, Tejgaon, Dhaka, 1208, Bangladesh **(100%)**
Tel.: (880) 961 0465 246
Web Site: http://www.lafarge-bd.com
Cement Mfr & Distr
N.A.I.C.S.: 327310
Rajesh Kumar Surana (CEO)

Holcim Colombia S.A. (1)
Calle 113 No 7 - 45 12th Floor Tower B Teleport Business Park Building, Bogota, Colombia **(99.8%)**
Tel.: (57) 6016575300
Web Site: https://www.holcim.com.co
Concrete, Cement & Aggregates Mfr & Distr
N.A.I.C.S.: 327310

Holcim Costa Rica S.A. (1)
PO Box 4009, San Jose, Costa Rica **(65.6%)**
Tel.: (506) 2205 2900
Web Site: http://www.holcim.cr
Rev.: $50,595,214
Assets: $175,392,298
Liabilities: $72,772,934
Net Worth: $102,619,364
Earnings: $9,610,525
Fiscal Year-end: 03/31/2017
Cement Mfr
N.A.I.C.S.: 327310

Plant (Domestic):

Holcim (Costa Rica) S.A. - Cartago Plant (2)
5km al sur de los Tribunales de Justicia, Agua Caliente, Cartago, Costa Rica
Tel.: (506) 2550 8000
Web Site: http://www.holcim.cr
Cement Mfr
N.A.I.C.S.: 327310

Holcim El Salvador S.A. de C.V. (1)
Calle Holcim y Av El Espino, Madreselva Antiguo Cuscatlan, La Libertad, El Salvador **(95.4%)**
Tel.: (503) 2505 0000
Web Site: http://www.holcim.com.sv
Emp.: 1,000
Cement Mfr & Distr
N.A.I.C.S.: 327310

Plant (Domestic):

Holcim El Salvador S.A. de C.V. - El Ronco Plant (2)
Caserio El Ronco Canton Tecomapa, Metapan, Santa Ana, El Salvador
Tel.: (503) 2507 8888
Web Site: http://www.holcim.com.sv
Cement Mfr
N.A.I.C.S.: 327310

Holcim El Salvador S.A. de C.V. - Maya Plant (2)
Hacienda La Soledad Canton Tecomapa, Metapan, Santa Ana, El Salvador
Tel.: (503) 25078888
Web Site: http://www.holcim.com.sv
Cement Mfr
N.A.I.C.S.: 327310

Holcim Finance (Luxembourg) S.A. (1)
Rue Louvigny 21, 1946, Luxembourg, Luxembourg **(100%)**
Tel.: (352) 26738842
Financial Management Services
N.A.I.C.S.: 523999

Holcim Group Services Ltd (1)
Grafenauweg 10, 6300, Zug, Switzerland
Tel.: (41) 588585858
Web Site: http://www.lafargeholcim.com
Concrete, Cement & Aggregates Mfr
N.A.I.C.S.: 327332

Holcim Gruppo (Italia) S.p.A. - Ternate Plant (1)
Via A Bongiasca 1364, 21020, Comabbio, Italy
Tel.: (39) 0332 944211
Web Site: http://www.holcim.it
Cement Mfr
N.A.I.C.S.: 327310

Holcim Mexico S.A. de C.V. (1)
Carlos Graef Fernandez No 222 Tower Ii Office 101 Floor 1, Col Santa Fe, 05348, Mexico, Mexico **(100%)**
Tel.: (52) 5557240000
Web Site: http://www.holcim.com.mx
Concrete, Cement & Aggregates Mfr
N.A.I.C.S.: 327310

Holcim Trading S.A. (1)
Tel.: (34) 915750975
Web Site: http://www.holcim.com
Sales Range: $25-49.9 Million
Emp.: 40
Cement & Raw Materials Trading
N.A.I.C.S.: 423390

Subsidiary (US):

Holcim Trading Inc. (2)
2655 LeJeune Rd Ste 606 The Gables International Plaza, Coral Gables, FL 33134
Tel.: (305) 342-9245
Ready-Mix Concrete Product Mfr
N.A.I.C.S.: 327320

Holderfin B.V. (1)
Tel.: (31) 205788000
Holding Company
N.A.I.C.S.: 551112

LAFARGE (MAURITIUS) CEMENT LTD (1)
Chaussee Tromelin, PO Box 479, Port Louis, 230, Mauritius **(58.4%)**
Tel.: (230) 465 2210
Web Site: http://www.lafargeholcim-io.com
Emp.: 250
Cement Mfr
N.A.I.C.S.: 327310
Annie Nankou (Mgr-HR & Comm)

LAFARGE CEMENT d.o.o. (1)
Kolodvorska cesta 5, 1420, Trbovlje, Slovenia **(70%)**
Tel.: (386) 3 56 52 300
Web Site: http://www.lafarge.si
Cement Mfr
N.A.I.C.S.: 327310
Gregor Uranic (Dir-Technical Ops)

LH Trading (Holding) AG (1)
Nuschelerstrasse 45, 8001, Zurich, Switzerland
Tel.: (41) 442256200
Web Site: http://www.lhtrading.com
Holding Company
N.A.I.C.S.: 551112

Subsidiary (Domestic):

LH Trading Ltd (2)
Nuschelerstrasse 45, 8001, Zurich, Switzerland **(100%)**
Tel.: (41) 442256200
Web Site: http://www.lhtrading.com
Trading Services for Cement Industry
N.A.I.C.S.: 561499
Xavier Blondot (CEO)

LH Trading Pte. Ltd. (1)
152 Beach Road 25-01/04 Gateway East, Singapore, 189721, Singapore
Tel.: (65) 62993931
Concrete Product Mfr & Distr
N.A.I.C.S.: 327331
Samar Gurung (Sr Mgr-Trading)

Lafarge Africa Plc. (1)
27B Gerrard Road, Ikoyi, Lagos, Nigeria **(76.3%)**
Tel.: (234) 12713990
Web Site: https://www.lafarge.com.ng
Rev.: $601,795,326
Assets: $1,323,828,475
Liabilities: $385,171,985
Net Worth: $938,656,490
Earnings: $80,497,980
Emp.: 1,379
Fiscal Year-end: 12/31/2020
Holding Company; Cement & Ready-Mix Concrete Mfr; Aggregates Quarrying
N.A.I.C.S.: 551112
Adebode Adefioye (Chm)

Subsidiary (Domestic):

AshakaCem PLC (2)
Ashaka Works, Gombe, Nigeria
Tel.: (234) 80229249412
Web Site: http://www.lafarge.com.ng
Cement Mfr; Coal Mining
N.A.I.C.S.: 327310

Lafarge ReadyMix Nigeria Limited (2)
No 38 Kudirat-Abiola Road Off Adebayo Akande Street, Oregun, Ikeja, Lagos, Nigeria **(100%)**
Tel.: (234) 7088604659
Web Site: http://www.lafarge.com.ng
Cement Mfr
N.A.I.C.S.: 327310

Subsidiary (Non-US):

Lafarge South Africa Holdings (Pty) Ltd. (2)
35 Westfield Road Longmeadow Business Estate Ext 11, Gallo Manor, 2052, South Africa
Tel.: (27) 11 657 0000
Web Site: http://www.lafarge.co.za
Emp.: 2,000
Holding Company; Cement & Ready-Mix Concrete Mfr; Aggregates & Gypsum Quarrying
N.A.I.C.S.: 551112
Alta Theron (Comml Dir & Dir-Interim-Readymix)

Subsidiary (Domestic):

Lafarge Gypsum (Pty) Ltd. (3)
18 Barium Street, Alrode, Alberton, 1451, South Africa
Tel.: (27) 11 389 4500
Gypsum Mining
N.A.I.C.S.: 212390
Jean-Paul Croze (CEO & Mng Dir)

Lafarge Industries South Africa (Pty) Ltd. (3)
35 Westfield Road Longmeadow Business Estate Ext 11, Edenvale, 1609, South Africa
Tel.: (27) 11 657 1000
Web Site: http://www.lafarge.co.za
Cement & Ready-Mix Concrete Mfr
N.A.I.C.S.: 327310

Lafarge Algerie (1)
Tour Geneva 15th and 16th floors Pins Maritimes, Mohammadia, 16058, Algiers, Algeria
Tel.: (213) 21892000
Web Site: http://www.lafarge.dz
Cement Aggregate & Concrete Mfr
N.A.I.C.S.: 327310

Lafarge Beocinska Fabrika Cementa D.O.O. (1)
Trg BFC 1, 21300, Beocin, Serbia **(100%)**
Tel.: (381) 21 87 41 00
Web Site: http://www.lafarge.rs
Cement Mfr
N.A.I.C.S.: 327310
Dimitrije Knjeginjic (Member-Exec Bd)

Lafarge Cement AS (1)
Cizkovice cp 27, 411 12, Cizkovice, Czech Republic **(68%)**
Tel.: (420) 416 577 111
Web Site: http://www.lafarge.cz
Cement Mfr
N.A.I.C.S.: 327310
Milena Hucanova (Mgr-External & Internal Comm)

Lafarge Cement Hungary Ltd. (1)
Kiralyegyhazi Cementgyar 7940, PO Box 54, 7940, Szentlorinckata, Hungary
Tel.: (36) 73500900
Ready-Mix Concrete Product Mfr
N.A.I.C.S.: 327320
Tamas Hoffmann (Gen Mgr)

Lafarge Cement Malawi Ltd. (1)
Makata Heavy Industrial Area MacLeod Road Plot No NY 318, PO Box 523, Blantyre, Malawi **(100%)**
Tel.: (265) 1 871 933
Web Site: http://www.lafarge.mw
Emp.: 400
Cement Mfr
N.A.I.C.S.: 327310
Albert Sigei (CEO)

Lafarge Cement S.A. (1)
ul Warszawska 110, Malogoszcz, 28-366, Kielce, Poland **(100%)**
Tel.: (48) 412487532
Web Site: http://www.lafarge.pl
Emp.: 1,500
Cement Mfr
N.A.I.C.S.: 327310
Xavier Guesnu (Chm-Mgmt Bd)

Lafarge Cement Syria (1)
8th Gate - Yaafour Ru'ya 2 Bldg - 4th Floor, PO Box 31602, Damascus, Syria
Tel.: (963) 11 391 2800
Web Site: http://www.lafargeholcim.com
Cement Mfr
N.A.I.C.S.: 327310

Lafarge Cement Zimbabwe Limited (1)
Manresa Works Arcturus Road, Harare, Zimbabwe **(76.5%)**
Tel.: (263) 86 77 215 000
Web Site: http://www.lafarge.co.zw
Rev.: $2,535,569
Assets: $2,682,238
Liabilities: $1,953,968
Net Worth: $728,270
Earnings: $491,847
Emp.: 800
Fiscal Year-end: 12/31/2019
Cement Mfr
N.A.I.C.S.: 327310
F. Chinhaire (Sec)

Lafarge Ciments Antilles (1)
Pointe des Carrieres, PO Box 863, 97 208, Fort-de-France, Martinique
Tel.: (596) 72 84 84
Web Site: http://www.lafarge-antilles.com
Cement Mfr
N.A.I.C.S.: 327310

Lafarge Gips BV (1)
Oosterhorn 32 34, Farmsum, 9936HD, Delfzijl, Netherlands **(100%)**
Tel.: (31) 596646888
Web Site: http://www.lafargegips.nl
Mfr of Gypsum
N.A.I.C.S.: 327420

Lafarge Kruszywa i Beton Sp. z o.o. (1)
Al Jerozolimskie 142 B, 02-305, Warsaw, Poland **(100%)**
Tel.: (48) 22 324 60 00
Web Site: http://www.lafarge.pl
Cement Mfr
N.A.I.C.S.: 327310

Lafarge Logistique Algerie LLA (1)
Centre Commercial de Bab-Ezzouar Tour n 2 6e etage, Bab-Ezzouar, Algiers, Algeria **(99.5%)**
Tel.: (213) 21 4816 66
Web Site: http://www.lafarge.dz
Building & Construction Material Transportation Services
N.A.I.C.S.: 541614

Lafarge Maroc Holding (1)
6 Route de Mekka Quartier les Cretes, BP 7234, Casablanca, Morocco **(50%)**
Tel.: (212) 522 52 49 72
Holding Company
N.A.I.C.S.: 551112
George Michos (CEO)

Subsidiary (Domestic):

LafargeHolcim Maroc (2)
6 Mecca Boulevard, BP 7234, Les Cretes district, Casablanca, Morocco **(64.76%)**

INTERNATIONAL PUBLIC

AND PRIVATE COMPANIES

Tel.: (212) 522524972
Web Site: https://www.lafargeholcim.ma
Sales Range: Less than $1 Million
Cement Mfr; Stone Quarrying & Construction Materials Distr
N.A.I.C.S.: 327310
Mohammed Amine Cherrat *(Fin Mgr)*

Lafarge North America Inc. (1)
8700 W Bryn Mawr Ave Ste 300, Chicago, IL 60631 **(100%)**
Tel.: (773) 372-1000
Web Site: http://www.lafargeholcim.us
Emp.: 7,000
Holding Company; Cement Mfr
N.A.I.C.S.: 551112
Ian Johnson *(CFO-US ACM & cement)*

Division (Non-US):

Lafarge Canada Inc. (2)
6509 Airport Road, Mississauga, L4V 1S7, ON, Canada **(100%)**
Tel.: (905) 738-7070
Web Site: http://www.lafarge.ca
Emp.: 6,000
Cement Mfr; Concrete & Construction Materials Distr
N.A.I.C.S.: 327310

Lafarge Canada Inc. (2)
6509 Airport Road, Mississauga, L4V 1S7, ON, Canada
Tel.: (905) 738-7070
Web Site: http://www.lafarge.ca
Cement Mfr & Distr
N.A.I.C.S.: 327310
Jan Jenisch *(CEO)*

Branch (Domestic):

Lafarge Dundas Quarry (3)
628 Highway 5, Dundas, L9H 5E2, ON, Canada
Tel.: (905) 538-0639
Web Site: http://www.lafargedundas.com
Stone Quarrying, Road Surfacing Materials & Calcined Dolomite Distr
N.A.I.C.S.: 212311
Peter Sanguineti *(Plant Mgr)*

Unit (Domestic):

Lafarge North America Inc. - Whitehall Cement Plant (2)
5160 Main St, Whitehall, PA 18052-1827
Tel.: (610) 262-7831
Web Site: http://www.lafarge-na.com
Cement Product Mfr
N.A.I.C.S.: 327310

Subsidiary (Domestic):

Lafarge Road Marking (2)
400 Lanidex Plz, Parsippany, NJ 07054-2722
Tel.: (973) 884-0300
Web Site: http://www.lafarge.com
Road Marking Materials & Equipment Mfr
N.A.I.C.S.: 325510

Systech Environmental Corporation (2)
6211 Ann Arbor Rd, Dundee, MI 48131 **(100%)**
Tel.: (937) 643-1240
Web Site: http://www.go2systech.com
Waste Recovery & Management Services
N.A.I.C.S.: 562219
Steve Zimmer *(VP-Fin & Admin)*

Lafarge Zementwerke GmbH (1)
Trabrennstrasse 2A, 1020, Vienna, Austria **(70%)**
Tel.: (43) 1 58 889 0
Web Site: http://www.lafarge.at
Emp.: 250
Cement Mfr & Distr
N.A.I.C.S.: 327310
Gernot Tritthart *(Dir-Sls & Mktg)*

LafargeHolcim Espana S.A. (1)
Avenida de Manoteras 20 Edificio Tokyo 1 Planta, 28050, Madrid, Spain
Tel.: (34) 91 213 3100
Web Site: http://www.lafarge.com.es
Emp.: 700
Cement Mfr & Distr
N.A.I.C.S.: 327310
Isidoro Miranda *(Mng Dir)*

Plant (Domestic):

Holcim (Espana) S.A. - Jerez Plant (2)
Poligono Industrial El Portal 0 S/N, 11408, Jerez de la Frontera, Spain
Tel.: (34) 956 35 86 00
Cement Mfr
N.A.I.C.S.: 327310

LafargeHolcim France SAS (1)
61 rue des Belles Feuilles, BP 40, 75782, Paris, Cedex 16, France
Tel.: (33) 144341111
Cement Mfr
N.A.I.C.S.: 327310
Francois Petry *(CEO & Dir-France - Belgium)*

Subsidiary (Domestic):

Beton Chantiers de Bretagne S.A.S. (2)
5 des Veyettes Zone Industrielle Sud Est, 35063, Rennes, Cedex, France
Tel.: (33) 223303232
Web Site: http://www.lafarge.fr
Concrete Block & Brick Mfr
N.A.I.C.S.: 327331

Granulats Bourgogne Auvergne (2)
Lieu dit Pont de Colonne, Arnay-le-Duc, 21230, Cote-d'Or, France
Tel.: (33) 380900212
Web Site: http://www.lafarge.fr
Cement Mfr
N.A.I.C.S.: 327310

Lafarge Betons - Agence (2)
4 Rue De Charenton, Alfortville, 94140, France
Tel.: (33) 145182400
Web Site: http://www.lafarge.fr
Concrete Mfr
N.A.I.C.S.: 327320

Lafarge Betons centrale BPE QUIMPER (2)
137 avenue du Corniguel, Quimper, 29000, France
Tel.: (33) 2 98 64 65 61
Web Site: http://www.lafarge.fr
Construction Materials Whslr
N.A.I.C.S.: 423320

Lafarge Service Group - R&D Center Lyon (2)
Pole Technologique - 95 rue du Montmurier, 38070, Saint-Quentin-Fallavier, France
Tel.: (33) 47 482 1616
Web Site: http://www.lafargeholcim.com
Construction Materials Research & Development Services
N.A.I.C.S.: 541715

LafargeHolcim Guinee (1)
Usine de la Cimenterie - Sonfonia, BP 3621, Conakry, Guinea
Tel.: (224) 628 68 60 00
Web Site: http://www.lafargeholcim-gn.com
Emp.: 111
Cement Mfr
N.A.I.C.S.: 327310

LafargeHolcim Russia (1)
Silver city Business Center 29 Serebryanicheskaya embankment, 109028, Moscow, Russia
Tel.: (7) 4957457131
Web Site: http://www.lafargeholcim.ru
Emp.: 1,900
Cement Mfr
N.A.I.C.S.: 327310
M. Goncharov *(CEO)*

Plant (Domestic):

Holcim (Rus) CM Ltd. - Shurovo Plant (2)
st Cementnikov 1, Moscow Region, 140414, Kolomna, Russia
Tel.: (7) 4957457131
Web Site: http://www.holcim.ru
Cement Mfr
N.A.I.C.S.: 327310

Holcim (Rus) OOO- Volsk Plant (2)
ul Zemetnikov d 1, Saratovskaya Oblast, 412902, Volsk, Russia
Tel.: (7) 84593 68 101

Web Site: http://www.holcim.ru
Cement Mfr
N.A.I.C.S.: 327310

Marine Cement AG (1)
Nuschelerstrasse 45, 8001, Zurich, Switzerland
Tel.: (41) 417116565
Cement Mfr
N.A.I.C.S.: 327310

Mbeya Cement Company Limited (1)
Oyster Plaza 3rd Floor Plot 1196 Haile Selassie Road, PO Box 46452, Dar es Salaam, Tanzania **(65%)**
Tel.: (255) 222 923 300
Web Site: http://www.lafargeholcim.com
Cement Mfr
N.A.I.C.S.: 327310

Surma Holdings B.V. (1)
Strawinskylaan 3127 8e verdiepin, 1077ZX, Amsterdam, Netherlands
Tel.: (31) 88 560 9950
Holding Company
N.A.I.C.S.: 551112

Holding (Non-US):

LafargeHolcim Bangladesh Limited (2)
NinaKabbo Level 7 227/A Bir Uttam Mir Shawkat Sarak, Tejgaon, Dhaka, 1208, Bangladesh
Tel.: (880) 222281002
Web Site: https://www.lafargeholcim.com.bd
Rev.: $238,199,527
Assets: $343,615,954
Liabilities: $114,007,572
Net Worth: $229,608,382
Earnings: $45,029,379
Emp.: 70,000
Fiscal Year-end: 12/31/2021
Holding Company; Cement Mfr
N.A.I.C.S.: 551112
Narayan Prasad Sharma *(Dir-Ops-LUMPL)*

Tarrant Concrete Company, Inc. (1)
5400 Thelin St, Fort Worth, TX 76115
Tel.: (817) 926-6666
Web Site: http://tarrantconcrete.com
Ready Mixed Concrete
N.A.I.C.S.: 327320
James A. Rainbolt *(Pres)*

Utelite Corp. (1)
6375 West Three Mile Canyon Road, Coalville, UT 84017
Tel.: (801) 467-2800
Rev.: $6,666,666
Emp.: 30
Cut Stone & Stone Product Mfr
N.A.I.C.S.: 327991
Carsten Mortensen *(Pres)*

HOLD KEY ELECTRIC WIRE & CABLE, CO. LTD.

3F No 36-9 Section 1 Fuxing South Road, Zhongshan District, Taipei, 104, Taiwan
Tel.: (886) 223956602
Web Site: https://www.hold-key.com.tw
Year Founded: 1989
1618—(TAI)
Rev.: $146,592,983
Assets: $201,414,983
Liabilities: $36,278,785
Net Worth: $165,136,198
Earnings: $12,649,040
Emp.: 218
Fiscal Year-end: 12/31/23
Electric Cable Mfr & Distr
N.A.I.C.S.: 335921
Biqi Yang *(Chm)*

Subsidiaries:

Hold Key Electric Wire & Cable, Co. Ltd. - Taiwan Factory1 (1)
No 22 Jing-Jiann 5th Rd Kuan Yin Industrial Estate, Taoyuan, Taiwan
Tel.: (886) 34838126
Cable Product Mfr & Distr
N.A.I.C.S.: 331222

Hold Key Electric Wire & Cable, Co. Ltd. - Taiwan Factory2 (1)
No 32 Jing-Jiann 5th Rd Kuan Yin Industrial Estate, Taoyuan, Taiwan
Tel.: (886) 34838126
Cable Product Mfr & Distr
N.A.I.C.S.: 331222

Hold Key Electric Wire & Cable, Co. Ltd. - Taiwan Factory3 (1)
No 16 Jing-Jiann 5th Rd Kuan Yin Industrial Estate, Taoyuan, Taiwan
Tel.: (886) 34838126
Cable Product Mfr & Distr
N.A.I.C.S.: 331222

HOLD ME LTD.

33A Yehoshua Ben Noon St, Tel Aviv, 6274509, Israel
Tel.: (972) 502222755
Year Founded: 2007
HMELF—(OTCIQ)
Rev.: $251,342
Assets: $268,141
Liabilities: $772,917
Net Worth: ($504,777)
Earnings: $53,476
Emp.: 1
Fiscal Year-end: 12/31/23
Software Development Services
N.A.I.C.S.: 541511
Menachem Shalom *(CEO)*

HOLDAL S.A.L.

Gekwaneh, PO Box 11 1332, Beirut, Lebanon
Tel.: (961) 512212
Web Site: http://www.holdal.com.lb
Year Founded: 1947
Sales Range: $125-149.9 Million
Emp.: 350
Import & Distribution of Watches, Pharmaceuticals, Clothing, Personal Care Products & Cosmetics
N.A.I.C.S.: 423990
Raymond Abou Adal *(Pres)*

Subsidiaries:

General Brands s.a.r.l. (1)
Holdal building Mkalles/Dekouaneh Street, Dekwaneh, Lebanon
Tel.: (961) 1 501000
Web Site: http://www.holdal.co.lb
Leather Goods Whslr
N.A.I.C.S.: 424990
Raymong Abou Agal *(CEO)*

INCOMA SAL (1)
Arz Radiators Building Street No 35 Sector No 2, Mkalles, Lebanon
Tel.: (961) 1 684204
Sales Range: $25-49.9 Million
Emp.: 40
Perfume Mfr
N.A.I.C.S.: 325620

HOLDERS TECHNOLOGY PLC

27-28 Eastcastle Street, London, W1W 8DH, United Kingdom
Tel.: (44) 1896759098
Web Site: http://www.holderstechnology.com
Year Founded: 1972
HDT—(AIM)
Rev.: $11,294,873
Assets: $7,152,469
Liabilities: $1,488,061
Net Worth: $5,664,408
Earnings: ($351,649)
Emp.: 53
Fiscal Year-end: 11/30/22
Holding Company; Printed Circuit Board Parts Mfr
N.A.I.C.S.: 551112
Rudi Walter Weinreich *(Chm)*

Subsidiaries:

Holders Components Limited (1)
Monkwood Cottage Whitakers Way, Loughton, IG10 1SQ, United Kingdom

HOLDERS TECHNOLOGY PLC

Holders Technology plc—(Continued)
Tel.: (44) 1896759098
Web Site:
 http://www.holderscomponents.com
Sales Range: $25-49.9 Million
Emp.: 5
Light Emitting Diode Mfr
N.A.I.C.S.: 334419

Holders Technology GmbH (1)
Woogmorgen 12, Kirchheimbolanden, D 67292, Germany
Tel.: (49) 63524040
Web Site: http://www.holderstechnology.com
Electronic Parts Distr
N.A.I.C.S.: 423690

Holders Technology UK Ltd (1)
Block 9 Units 1-4, Tweedbank Industrial Estate, Galashiels, TD1 3RS, United Kingdom
Tel.: (44) 1896758781
Web Site: http://www.holderstechnology.com
Sales Range: $25-49.9 Million
Emp.: 15
Electronic Parts Distr
N.A.I.C.S.: 423690

HOLDING CENTER AD
street No 132 entrance A floor 1 office 3, Sredets district, 1000, Sofia, Bulgaria
Tel.: (359) 884269224
Web Site: https://holding-centre.com
Year Founded: 1998
6C8—(BUL)
Sales Range: Less than $1 Million
Investment Services
N.A.I.C.S.: 523999
Boris Mihailov Nikolov *(Chm)*

HOLDING CO ADMIE (IPTO) SA
89 Dyrrachiou & Kifisou, 104 43, Athens, Greece
Tel.: (30) 2103636936
Web Site:
 https://www.admieholding.gr
Year Founded: 2011
ADMIE—(ATH)
Rev.: $32,040,794
Assets: $820,619,469
Liabilities: $148,932
Net Worth: $820,470,537
Earnings: $31,399,741
Emp.: 1,600
Fiscal Year-end: 12/31/22
Power Transmission Equipment Distr
N.A.I.C.S.: 423610
Panos Iliopoulos *(Vice Chm)*

Subsidiaries:

Independent Power Transmission Operator S.A. (1)
Dyrrachiou 89 and Kafisou, 104 43, Athens, Greece
Tel.: (30) 2105192101
Web Site: http://www.admie.gr
Electric Power Transmission Services
N.A.I.C.S.: 221121

HOLDING COOP-YUG AD
Rakovski St No 99 7th floor office 18, 1000, Sofia, Bulgaria
Tel.: (359) 28510792
Web Site: https://www.coop-yug.eu
HUG—(BUL)
Sales Range: Less than $1 Million
Holding Company
N.A.I.C.S.: 551112
Biser Lazov *(CEO)*

HOLDING FINANCIERE DIMO-TRANS SA
Zac Satolas Green, Pusignan, 69330, France
Tel.: (33) 4 72 93 15 15
Web Site: http://www.dimotrans.com
Emp.: 1,000
Holding Company
N.A.I.C.S.: 551112

Subsidiaries:

FashionPartner Group SAS (1)
15 Boulevard de Beaubourg, BP 20, Croissy-Beaubourg, 77313, Marne-la-Vallee, Cedex 2, France
Tel.: (33) 1 6462 5331
Web Site:
 http://www.fashionpartnergroup.com
Sales Range: $50-74.9 Million
Emp.: 50
Fashion Industry Freight Transportation & Logistics Services
N.A.I.C.S.: 488510
Christophe Cavailles *(Mng Dir)*

HOLDING LE DUFF SA
52 avenue du Canada, CS 90712, 35200, Rennes, France
Tel.: (33) 2 9922 2324 FR
Web Site:
 http://www.en.groupeleduff.com
Sales Range: $1-4.9 Billion
Emp.: 13,400
Holding Company; Branded Coffee Houses & Retail Bakeries Owner, Operator & Franchisor
N.A.I.C.S.: 551112
Louis Le Duff *(Founder & Pres)*

Subsidiaries:

Bridor inc. (1)
3075 de Rouen, Montreal, H1W 3Z2, QC, Canada
Tel.: (450) 641-1265
Web Site: http://www.bridor.com
Bakery Products Mfr
N.A.I.C.S.: 311813

Subsidiary (Non-US):

BRIDOR France (2)
Lieu-dit Olivet ZA Olivet, 35538, Servon, France
Tel.: (33) 2 99 00 11 67
Web Site: http://www.bridordefrance.com
Bakery Products Mfr
N.A.I.C.S.: 311813

Brioche Doree (1)
4 Rue de Grandes Arcades, 67000, Strasbourg, France
Tel.: (33) 3 88 23 23 75
Web Site: http://www.briochedoree.fr
Restaurant Operators
N.A.I.C.S.: 722511
Julie Hauser-Blanner *(Pres)*

Bruegger's Enterprises (1)
159 Bank St PO Box 374, Burlington, VT 05402-0374
Tel.: (802) 660-4020
Web Site: http://www.brueggers.com
Sales Range: $25-49.9 Million
Emp.: 50
Franchisor & Operator of Bakery Cafes
N.A.I.C.S.: 445291
Scott D. Berkman *(Chief Pur Officer)*

Cite Gourmande (1)
Lasserre, 47310, Estillac, France
Tel.: (33) 5 53 48 46 56
Restaurant Operators
N.A.I.C.S.: 722511

FB SOLUTION SAS (1)
Rue Robert Bremond - CS 30045, 93612, Aulnay-sous-Bois, Cedex, France
Tel.: (33) 149384747
Web Site: http://www.fbsolution.fr
Bakery Product Mfr & Distr
N.A.I.C.S.: 311813

Ferme des Loges SARL (1)
Route de Bernay, 27300, Courbepine, France
Tel.: (33) 2 32 46 96 01
Restaurant Operators
N.A.I.C.S.: 722511

Kamps GmbH (1)
Auf dem Mutzer 11, 41366, Schwalmtal, Germany
Tel.: (49) 2163 947 700
Web Site: http://www.kamps.de
Bakery Product Mfr & Distr
N.A.I.C.S.: 311813

Subsidiary (Non-US):

Kamps International (2)
154/155 Tottenham Court Road, London, W1T 7NQ, United Kingdom
Tel.: (44) 20 7383 4333
Web Site: http://www.kamps.co.uk
Bakery Product Mfr & Distr
N.A.I.C.S.: 311813

La Madeleine de Corps, Inc. (1)
12201 Merit Dr Ste 900, Dallas, TX 75251
Tel.: (214) 696-6962
Hotel Operator
N.A.I.C.S.: 721110

Le Duff America, Inc. (1)
2260 Industrial Way, Vineland, NJ 08360
Tel.: (856) 681-8000
Branded Coffee Houses & Retail Bakeries Operator & Franchisor
N.A.I.C.S.: 722515
Claude Bergeron *(Chm)*

Subsidiary (Domestic):

SWH Mimi's Cafe, LLC (2)
18872 MacArthur Blvd Ste 400, Irvine, CA 92612 **(100%)**
Tel.: (714) 544-4826
Web Site: http://www.mimiscafe.com
Holding Company; Restaurants
N.A.I.C.S.: 551112
Phil Costner *(Pres)*

Subsidiary (Domestic):

Mimi's Cafe Kansas, Inc (3)
11885 W 95th St, Overland Park, KS 66214
Tel.: (913) 599-5848
Bakery & Cafe Operator
N.A.I.C.S.: 311812

Mimi's Cafe of Rogers, Inc (3)
2105 Promenade Blvd, Rogers, AR 72758
Tel.: (479) 936-7983
Bakery & Cafe Operator
N.A.I.C.S.: 311812

SWH Frederick Maryland, Inc. (3)
5120 Buckeystown Pike, Frederick, MD 21704
Tel.: (301) 228-2633
Restaurant Operators
N.A.I.C.S.: 722511

SWH Howard Maryland, Inc. (3)
3016 Waldorf Marketplace, Waldorf, MD 20603
Tel.: (301) 396-5885
Restaurant
N.A.I.C.S.: 722511

HOLDING NOV VEK AD
Korab planina 13, 1407, Sofia, Bulgaria
Tel.: (359) 29234716
Web Site:
 https://www.holdingnovvek.com
HNVK—(BUL)
Sales Range: Less than $1 Million
Asset Management Services
N.A.I.C.S.: 523940
Desislava Ivanova Pancheva-Milenova *(Dir-IR)*

HOLDING SVETA SOFIA AD
Bul Bratya Bakston 40, Sofia, Bulgaria
Tel.: (359) 888618102
Web Site: http://www.sveta-sofia.com
4HSA—(BUL)
Sales Range: Less than $1 Million
Investment Bank Services
N.A.I.C.S.: 523150
Dimitar Borisov Raikov *(Member-Mgmt Bd)*

HOLDING VARNA AD-VARNA
Administrative Building Saits Constantine and Helena Resort, 9006, Varna, Bulgaria
Tel.: (359) 52663765
Web Site:
 https://www.holdingvarna.com

INTERNATIONAL PUBLIC

Year Founded: 1996
5V2C—(BUL)
Sales Range: Less than $1 Million
Investment Services
N.A.I.C.S.: 523999
Ivelina Kancheva-Shaban *(Chm-Mgmt Bd & CEO)*

Subsidiaries:

MSAT CABLE JSC (1)
6 Mir Str, 9000, Varna, Bulgaria
Tel.: (359) 52 301001
Web Site: http://www.msatcable.com
Cable Television Operator
N.A.I.C.S.: 516210

REAL FINANCE ASSET MANAGEMENT JSC (1)
24 AS Pushkin Str, 9000, Varna, Bulgaria
Tel.: (359) 52603830
Web Site: http://www.rfasset.eu
Financial Management Services
N.A.I.C.S.: 523999
Marin Marin *(Exec Dir)*

HOLIDAY ENTERTAINMENT CO., LTD.
4th Floor Zhongxiao East Road, Xinyi District, Taipei, 293, Taiwan
Tel.: (886) 227695567
Web Site: http://www.holiday.com.tw
Year Founded: 2002
9943—(TAI)
Rev.: $90,638,637
Assets: $190,649,066
Liabilities: $57,326,398
Net Worth: $133,322,667
Earnings: $24,375,387
Fiscal Year-end: 12/31/22
Audiovisual Equipment Distr
N.A.I.C.S.: 423990
Chiung-Chang Yen *(Chm)*

HOLIDAY FORD SALES (1980) LIMITED
1555 Lansdowne St W, Peterborough, K9J 7m3, ON, Canada
Tel.: (705) 742-5432
Web Site: http://www.holidayford.com
Rev.: $27,292,787
Emp.: 55
New & Used Car Dealers
N.A.I.C.S.: 441110

HOLISTA COLLTECH LIMITED
283 Rokeby Road, Subiaco, 6008, WA, Australia
Tel.: (61) 861413500 AU
Web Site: https://www.holistaco.com
HCT—(ASX)
Rev.: $4,050,752
Assets: $2,282,522
Liabilities: $4,589,012
Net Worth: ($2,306,491)
Earnings: ($3,350,648)
Fiscal Year-end: 12/31/23
Development & Commercialization of Collagen Products
N.A.I.C.S.: 311612
Rajen M. *(Founder, Chm, CEO & Mng Dir)*

Subsidiaries:

Holista Biotech Sdn Bhd (1)
Unit No 1201 1202 & 1209 12th Fl Amcorp Trade Ctr PJ Tower No 18, Persiaran Barat of Jalan Timur, 46200, Petaling Jaya, Selangor Darul Ehsan, Malaysia
Tel.: (60) 379652888
Web Site: http://www.holistaco.com
Sales Range: $50-74.9 Million
Emp.: 60
Bio Pharmaceutical Products Mfr
N.A.I.C.S.: 424210

Total Health Concept Sdn Bhd (1)
Unit 1201 12th Floor Amcorp Trade Centre, PJ Tower No 18 Persiaran Barat, 46050, Petaling Jaya, Selangor, Malaysia
Tel.: (60) 300882700

Web Site: https://thchealthproducts.com
Health Care Products Mfr
N.A.I.C.S.: 311930

Tropical Botanics Sdn Bhd (1)
Unit No 12 01 12 02 & 12 09 12th Fl Amcorp Trade Ctr PJ Tower No 18, Persiaran Barat, 46000, Petaling Jaya, Selangor, Malaysia
Tel.: (60) 379652888
Web Site: http://www.holistaco.com
Sales Range: $25-49.9 Million
Emp.: 60
Sanitizers Mfr
N.A.I.C.S.: 325412
M. Rajen (CEO)

HOLITECH TECHNOLOGY CO., LTD.
No 89 Nanwaihuan Road, Yiyuan County, Zibo, Shandong, China
Tel.: (86) 5332343787
Web Site:
https://www.lianhechem.com.cn
Year Founded: 2015
002217—(SSE)
Rev.: $1,671,919,704
Assets: $3,264,458,652
Liabilities: $2,349,088,560
Net Worth: $915,370,092
Earnings: ($486,595,512)
Emp.: 7,000
Fiscal Year-end: 12/31/22
Chemical Products Mfr
N.A.I.C.S.: 325180
Huang Aiwu (Chm)

HOLLAND COLOURS NV
Halvemaanweg 1, 7323 RW, Apeldoorn, Netherlands
Tel.: (31) 553680700
Web Site:
https://www.hollandcolours.com
HOLCO—(EUR)
Rev.: $120,265,487
Assets: $79,597,453
Liabilities: $16,125,621
Net Worth: $63,471,833
Earnings: $6,333,909
Emp.: 464
Fiscal Year-end: 03/31/23
Coloring Pigment Mfr
N.A.I.C.S.: 325130
Robert Harmsen (Member-Mgmt Bd)

Subsidiaries:

Holland Colours Americas Inc (1)
1501 Progress Dr, Richmond, IN 47374
Tel.: (765) 935-0329
Pigment Mfr
N.A.I.C.S.: 325130

Holland Colours Canada Inc (1)
200 Consumers Rd Suite 303, Toronto, M2J 4R4, ON, Canada
Tel.: (416) 449-4344
Pigment Whslr
N.A.I.C.S.: 424950

Holland Colours China Ltd (1)
Factory Building 7 No 65 Baiyun Road Spark Development Zone, Fengxian District, Shanghai, 201419, China
Tel.: (86) 21 5750 5962
Web Site: http://www.hcacn.com
Emp.: 20
Pigment Mfr & Whslr
N.A.I.C.S.: 325130
Florian Balogh (Gen Mgr)

Holland Colours Europe BV (1)
Halvemaanweg 1, 7323 RW, Apeldoorn, Netherlands
Tel.: (31) 553680700
Web Site: https://www.hollandcolours.com
Additive Mfr & Distr
N.A.I.C.S.: 325998
Coen Vinke (CEO)

Holland Colours Hungaria Kft (1)
Tel.: (36) 56420644
Pigment Mfr
N.A.I.C.S.: 325130
Judit Hajbin (Plant Mgr)

Holland Colours Mexicana SA de CV (1)
Tezozomoc 4 Warehouse 3 Col Hydraulic Resources, 54913, Tultitlan, Edo de Mexico, Mexico
Tel.: (52) 5558943641
Pigment Whslr
N.A.I.C.S.: 424950

Holland Colours UK Ltd (1)
Sabre Court Unit 16/17/18 Valentine Close Gillingham Business Park, Gillingham, ME8 0RW, Kent, United Kingdom
Tel.: (44) 1634388727
Color Pigment Whslr
N.A.I.C.S.: 424950
Mark Burch (Office Mgr)

PT Holland Colours Asia (1)
Jl Berbek Industri II/2, Surabaya Industrial Estate Rungkut, Sidoarjo, 61256, East Java, Indonesia
Tel.: (62) 318493939
Pigment Whslr
N.A.I.C.S.: 424950

HOLLARD INSURANCE COMPANY LTD
22 Oxford Road, Parktown, Johannesburg, South Africa
Tel.: (27) 113515000
Web Site: http://www.hollard.co.za
Year Founded: 1980
Insurance Services
N.A.I.C.S.: 524210
Adi Enthoven (Chm)

Subsidiaries:

Camargue Underwriting Managers (Pty) Limited (1)
15 Eton Road, 2008, Parktown, South Africa
Tel.: (27) 113564842
Web Site: http://www.camargueum.co.za
Sales Range: $50-74.9 Million
Emp.: 8
Direct Property & Casualty Insurance Carriers
N.A.I.C.S.: 524126
Mitch Marefcia (Mng Dir)

HCV Underwriting Managers (Pty) Limited (1)
29 Claribel Rd Morningside, 4001, Durban, South Africa
Tel.: (27) 313121304
Insurance Related Activities
N.A.I.C.S.: 524298

Hollard Botswana (Pty) Ltd (1)
Plot 70667 2nd Floor Building 2 Fairscape Precint Fairgrounds, Gaborone, 9999, Botswana
Tel.: (267) 3958 023
Web Site: http://www.hollard.co.bw
Insurance Services
N.A.I.C.S.: 524210

Hollard Insurance Company of Namibia Limited (1)
Jan Jonker and Thorer Streets Jan Jonker Heights Commercial Suite, Windhoek, Namibia
Tel.: (264) 61 371 300
Web Site: http://www.hollard.com.na
Insurance Services
N.A.I.C.S.: 524210

Hollard Insurance Zambia Limited (1)
Unit 1 The Mount Building Stand No 12522 Thabo Mbeki Road, Lusaka, Zambia
Tel.: (260) 211 255 680
Web Site: http://www.hollard.co.zm
Insurance Services
N.A.I.C.S.: 524210

Hollard Life Assurance Zambia Limited (1)
First Floor South Wing Corporate Park Block 3 Stand No 20849, Alick Nkhata Road, Lusaka, Zambia
Tel.: (260) 211 258 632
Web Site: http://www.hollard.co.zm
Insurance Services
N.A.I.C.S.: 524210

Hollard Life Properties (Pty) Limited (1)
22 Oxford Road Park Town, 2093, Johannesburg, South Africa
Tel.: (27) 113515000
Web Site: http://www.hollard.co.za
Sales Range: $700-749.9 Million
Open-End Investment Funds
N.A.I.C.S.: 525910
Nic Kohler (CEO)

Hollard Mocambique Companhia de Seguros SARL (1)
Av Sociedade de Geografia no 269 Edificio Hollard, Maputo, Mozambique
Tel.: (258) 21 357 700
Web Site: http://www.hollard.co.mz
Insurance Services
N.A.I.C.S.: 524210
Henri Mittermayer (Gen Mgr)

Hollard Specialist Insurance Limited (1)
22 Oxford Road, Parktown, Johannesburg, South Africa (100%)
Tel.: (27) 860000011
Web Site: http://www.hollard.co.za
Comprehensive Motor & Commercial Vehicle Insurance
N.A.I.C.S.: 524128

Subsidiary (Domestic):

Hollard Specialist Life Limited (2)
5 Boeing Road East Elma Park, Edenvale, 1609, South Africa
Tel.: (27) 860734368
Web Site: http://www.hollard.co.za
Fire Insurance Services
N.A.I.C.S.: 524113

Lombard Insurance Company Limited (1)
4th Floor 22 Wellington Road, Parktown, 2193, Johannesburg, South Africa
Tel.: (27) 115510600
Web Site: http://www.lombardins.com
Sales Range: $100-124.9 Million
Emp.: 110
Reinsurance Carrier Services
N.A.I.C.S.: 524130
Miles Japhet (Chm)

The Conservation Corporation SA Limited (1)
Private Bag X27, Benmore, South Africa
Tel.: (27) 118094300
Web Site: http://www.andbeyond.com
Sales Range: $10-24.9 Million
Emp.: 100
Hotels & Motels
N.A.I.C.S.: 721110
Joss Kent (Mng Dir)

HOLLEY HOLDING, LTD.
Holley Technology Park No 181 Wuchang Avenue, Hangzhou, 310023, Yuhang District, China
Tel.: (86) 571 89300088
Web Site: http://www.holley.cn
Year Founded: 1970
Holding Company: Pharmaceuticals, Smart Grid & Energy Technologies Mfr
N.A.I.C.S.: 551112
Xiao QiJing (Pres & CEO)

Subsidiaries:

Holley Group Co., Ltd. (1)
501 Moganshan Rd, Hangzhou, 310005, China
Tel.: (86) 57188900800
Web Site: http://www.holley.cn
Sales Range: $350-399.9 Million
Emp.: 6,500
Holding Company
N.A.I.C.S.: 551112

Subsidiary (Domestic):

Holley Communications Co. Ltd. (2)
No 18 Xidoumen Road, Hangzhou, 310012, China
Tel.: (86) 57188471800
Web Site: http://www.holleycomm.com.cn
Telecommunication Servicesb
N.A.I.C.S.: 517112

Holley Metering Ltd. (2)
No 181 Wuchang Avenue, Yuhang District, Hangzhou, 310023, China
Tel.: (86) 57189300666
Web Site: http://www.holleymeter.com
Sales Range: $1-9.9 Million
Emp.: 3,800
Utility Meters & Systems
N.A.I.C.S.: 334514

HOLLEY HOLLAND LIMITED
Gossard House 5th Floor 7 Savile Row, London, W1S 3PE, United Kingdom
Tel.: (44) 207 125 0351   UK
Web Site:
http://www.holleyholland.com
Year Founded: 2008
Financial Services Industry Business Transformation Consulting Services
N.A.I.C.S.: 541611

Subsidiaries:

IMX Software Group Limited (1)
10 Greycoat Place, Victoria, London, SW1P 1SB, United Kingdom
Tel.: (44) 845 838 2940
Web Site: http://www.imxsoftware.com
Holding Company; Financial Industry Software Developer, Publisher & Whslr
N.A.I.C.S.: 551112
Bill Tickner (Mng Dir)

Subsidiary (Non-US):

IMX Software Group Pty. Ltd. (2)
138 B Thistlethwaite Street, South Melbourne, 3205, VIC, Australia
Tel.: (61) 3 9016 4222
Web Site: http://www.imxsoftware.com
Financial Industry Software Whslr
N.A.I.C.S.: 423430
Trent Hislop (Mgr)

IMX Software South Africa (2)
313 Rivonia Road, Morningside, Sandton, 2057, Gauteng, South Africa
Tel.: (27) 11 706 2930
Web Site: http://www.imxsoftware.co.za
Emp.: 15
Financial Industry Software Developer, Publisher & Whslr
N.A.I.C.S.: 513210
Rob Stansell (Mng Dir)

Subsidiary (Domestic):

IMX Software UK Limited (2)
10 Greycoat Place, Victoria, London, SW1P 1SB, United Kingdom
Tel.: (44) 845 838 2940
Web Site: http://www.imxsoftware.com
Financial Industry Software Developer, Publisher & Whslr
N.A.I.C.S.: 513210
Bill Tickner (Mng Dir)

HOLLY FUTURES CO., LTD.
F9 Hongye Building 50 Zhonghua Road, Nanjing, 210001, China
Tel.: (86) 4008281288   CN
Web Site: http://www.ftol.com.cn
Year Founded: 1995
3678—(HKG)
Rev.: $214,495,634
Assets: $1,471,943,589
Liabilities: $1,213,983,313
Net Worth: $257,960,277
Earnings: $1,738,420
Emp.: 661
Fiscal Year-end: 12/31/22
Investment Brokerage Services
N.A.I.C.S.: 523150
Sharon Wing Han Leung (Co-Sec)

Subsidiaries:

Holly Su Futures (Hongkong) Co., Ltd. (1)
Room 01-02 24F Jubilee Centre 42-46 Gloucester Road, Wanchai, China (Hong Kong)
Tel.: (852) 25296577
Web Site: http://www.ftol.com.hk
Financial Future Services

HOLLY FUTURES CO., LTD.

Holly Futures Co., Ltd.—(Continued)
N.A.I.C.S.: 523160

HOLLYLAND GROUP HOLDINGS LIMITED
31/F Billion Centre Tower A 1 Wang Kwong Road, Kowloon Bay, China (Hong Kong)
Tel.: (852) 3666 5111
Web Site:
http://www.hollylandgroup.com
Year Founded: 1975
Holding Company
N.A.I.C.S.: 551112

Subsidiaries:

Hollyland (China) Electronics Technology Corporation Limited (1)
No 829 Fangshan East 2nd Road, Xiang'an District, Xiamen, 361101, Fujian, China
Tel.: (86) 5925772288
Web Site: http://www.hollyfuse.com
Rev.: $35,522,604
Assets: $82,197,180
Liabilities: $16,067,376
Net Worth: $66,129,804
Earnings: $4,268,160
Emp.: 700
Fiscal Year-end: 12/31/2022
Electron Tube Mfr
N.A.I.C.S.: 334419
Chen Xiu (Chm & Gen Mgr)

Subsidiary (Non-US):

Hollyland Co., Ltd. (2)
31/F Bollion Centre Tower A 1 Wang Kwong Road, Kowloon Bay, China (Hong Kong)
Tel.: (852) 36665111
Electronic Parts & Equipment Distr
N.A.I.C.S.: 423690

HOLLYSYS AUTOMATION TECHNOLOGIES LTD.
No 2 Disheng Middle Road, Beijing Economic-Tech Dvlpmnt Area, Beijing, 100176, China
Tel.: (86) 1058981000 VG
Web Site: https://www.hollysys.com
Year Founded: 2005
HOLI—(NASDAQ)
Rev.: $777,373,000
Assets: $1,684,848,000
Liabilities: $508,615,000
Net Worth: $1,176,233,000
Earnings: $106,931,000
Emp.: 5,042
Fiscal Year-end: 06/30/23
Holding Company; Industrial Automation Mfr
N.A.I.C.S.: 551112
Chit Nim Sung (Deputy CEO)

Subsidiaries:

Hollysys (Asia Pacific) Pte. Limited (1)
200 Pandan Loop 08-01 Pantech 21, Singapore, 128388, Singapore
Tel.: (65) 6777 0950
Web Site: http://www.hollysys.com
Emp.: 50
Automated Control Equipment Distr
N.A.I.C.S.: 423830

Subsidiary (Domestic):

Concord Corporation Pte Ltd (2)
37 Kaki Bukit View Kaki Bukit Tech Park II, Singapore, 415967, Singapore
Tel.: (65) 6748 2221
Web Site: http://www.cepl.com.sg
Emp.: 50
Electrical Engineering Services
N.A.I.C.S.: 238210

HOLLYWOOD BOWL GROUP PLC
Focus 31 West Wing Cleveland Road, Hemel Hempstead, HP2 7BW, Hertfordshire, United Kingdom
Tel.: (44) 7584212632 UK
Web Site:
https://www.hollywoodbowl.com
Year Founded: 2016
BOWL—(LSE)
Rev.: $219,352,428
Assets: $411,158,430
Liabilities: $254,439,306
Net Worth: $156,719,124
Earnings: $42,400,890
Fiscal Year-end: 09/30/22
Ten Pin Bowling Center Operator
N.A.I.C.S.: 713950
Stephen Burns (CEO)

HOLLYWOOD SA
Al Jerozolimskie 6579, 00-697, Warsaw, Poland
Tel.: (48) 242758129
Web Site:
https://www.en.hollywoodsa.pl
HLD—(WAR)
Rev.: $42,398,120
Assets: $61,695,122
Liabilities: $31,731,707
Net Worth: $29,963,415
Earnings: $1,501,778
Fiscal Year-end: 12/31/23
Laundry Services
N.A.I.C.S.: 812320
Adam Andrzej Konieczkowski (Chm)

Subsidiaries:

HTS AMA Sp.z.o.o. (1)
Ul Juraszow 7/19, 60-479, Poznan, Poland
Tel.: (48) 663801794
Web Site: https://www.hts-ama.pl
Laundry Services
N.A.I.C.S.: 812320

HTS Baltica Sp.z.o.o. (1)
ul Rdestowa 65/67, 81-557, Gdynia, Poland
Tel.: (48) 586299090
Web Site: https://www.hts-baltica.pl
Laundry Services
N.A.I.C.S.: 812320

HTS Baxter Sp.z.o.o. (1)
ul Bernardynska 7, 16-080, Tykocin, Poland
Tel.: (48) 856643491
Web Site: https://www.hts-baxter.pl
Laundry Services
N.A.I.C.S.: 812320

HTS Medij Sp.z.o.o. (1)
Ul Kobylinska 12, Pepowo, 63-830, Gostyn, Poland
Tel.: (48) 655727044
Web Site: https://hts-medij.pl
Laundry Services
N.A.I.C.S.: 812320

HTS Stargard Sp.z.o.o. (1)
ul Lotnikow 51, 73-102, Stargard Szczecinski, Poland
Tel.: (48) 915777818
Web Site: https://www.hts-stargard.pl
Laundry Services
N.A.I.C.S.: 812320

HTS Targatz Gmbh (1)
Angermunder Str 9-12, 16227, Eberswalde, Germany
Tel.: (49) 333427920
Web Site: https://pl.hts-targatz.de
Emp.: 100
Laundry Services
N.A.I.C.S.: 812320

Hollywood Rental Sp.z.o.o. (1)
ul Plocka 50a, 09-200, Sierpc, Poland
Tel.: (48) 242750118
Web Site: https://www.hollywoodrental.pl
Laundry Services
N.A.I.C.S.: 812320

Hollywood Textile Service Sp.z.o.o. (1)
ul Bojanowska 2B, 09-200, Sierpc, Poland
Tel.: (48) 242758129
Web Site: https://www.hts-sierpc.pl
Laundry Services
N.A.I.C.S.: 812320

Poltextil Sp.z.o.o. (1)
Al Jerozolimskie 65/79, 00-697, Warsaw, Poland
Tel.: (48) 242316310
Web Site: https://www.poltextil.pl
Laundry Services
N.A.I.C.S.: 812320

Pral Serwis Warszawa Sp.z.o.o. (1)
Al Jerozolimskie 65/79, 00-697, Warsaw, Poland
Tel.: (48) 226305310
Web Site: http://www.pralserwis.pl
Laundry Services
N.A.I.C.S.: 812320

Pralmed Sp.z.o.o. (1)
ul Norbertanska 9, 09-402, Plock, Poland
Tel.: (48) 785024388
Web Site: http://www.pralmed.pl
Laundry Services
N.A.I.C.S.: 812320

HOLM TRAVAROR AB
Almgatan 9, 733 37, Sala, Sweden
Tel.: (46) 224 150 00
Web Site: http://www.holmtravaror.se
Woodworking Supplies Mfr
N.A.I.C.S.: 333243
Bernt Johansson (Owner)

Subsidiaries:

Carstens AB (1)
Kortebovagen 4, PO Box 104, Bankeryd, 56423, Jonkoping, Sweden (100%)
Tel.: (46) 36370480
Web Site: http://www.carstens.se
Sales Range: $1-9.9 Million
Emp.: 15
Construction Materials Whslr
N.A.I.C.S.: 423390
Roger Heikenstrom (Mng Dir)

HOLMARC OPTO-MECHATRONICS LTD.
B 7 H M T Industrial Estate H M T P O, Kalamassery, Kochi, 683503, Kerala, India
Tel.: (91) 4842953780
Web Site: https://www.holmarc.com
Year Founded: 1993
HOLMARC—(NSE)
Rev.: $3,548,823
Assets: $2,017,174
Liabilities: $606,699
Net Worth: $1,410,475
Earnings: $433,066
Emp.: 275
Fiscal Year-end: 03/31/23
Optical Product Mfr
N.A.I.C.S.: 339115
Ishach Sainuddin (CFO)

HOLMBERG GMBH & CO. KG
Ohlauer Str 5-11, 10999, Berlin, Germany
Tel.: (49) 30617800
Web Site: http://www.holmco.de
Year Founded: 1919
Rev.: $14,483,700
Emp.: 120
Electro-Acoustic Equipment Mfr
N.A.I.C.S.: 336413
Lutz-Michael Poppel (Mng Dir)

Subsidiaries:

Holmberg FRANCE SAS (1)
218 Avenue d'Enghien, 95880, Enghien-les-Bains, France
Tel.: (33) 134113861
Electro Acoustic Equipment Mfr
N.A.I.C.S.: 334310

HOLMEN AB
Strandvagen 1, PO Box 5407, SE-114 84, Stockholm, Sweden
Tel.: (46) 86662100
Web Site: https://www.holmen.com
Year Founded: 1873
HOLM—(OMX)
Rev.: $2,584,311,520
Assets: $8,313,770,080
Liabilities: $2,576,986,720

INTERNATIONAL PUBLIC

Net Worth: $5,736,783,360
Earnings: $366,728,320
Emp.: 3,474
Fiscal Year-end: 12/31/21
Production & Sale of Newsprint & Magazine Paper, Wood-Containing Printing Paper, Paperboard & Sawn Timber
N.A.I.C.S.: 113310
Anders Jernhall (CFO & Exec VP)

Subsidiaries:

AS Holmen Mets (1)
Parnu Mnt 105, 11312, Tallinn, Estonia
Tel.: (372) 6652440
Sales Range: $25-49.9 Million
Emp.: 17
Timber Tract Operating Services
N.A.I.C.S.: 113110
Henrick Nomma (Mng Dir)

Holmen B.V. (1)
Paalbergweg 40, Amsterdam, 1105 BV, Netherlands
Tel.: (31) 206559200
Web Site: http://www.iggesund.com
Emp.: 60
Paper Products Mfr
N.A.I.C.S.: 322299

Holmen Data AB (1)
Hornettvagen 1, S 891 80, Ornskoldsvik, Sweden (100%)
Tel.: (46) 66075400
Sales Range: $25-49.9 Million
Emp.: 30
N.A.I.C.S.: 322120

Holmen Energi AB (1)
Tjanstemannagatan 5, 891 80, Ornskoldsvik, Sweden
Tel.: (46) 660377300
Sales Range: $75-99.9 Million
Emp.: 18
Electric Power Generation & Distribution Services
N.A.I.C.S.: 221118
Fredrik Nordqvist (CEO & Head-Wind Power)

Holmen Energi Elnat AB (1)
Strandvagen 1, 114 51, Stockholm, Sweden
Tel.: (46) 86662100
Magazine & Book Publishing Services
N.A.I.C.S.: 513199

Holmen France S.A.S. (1)
10 Avenue de Camberwell, 92330, Sceaux, France
Tel.: (33) 647605366
Magazine & Book Publishing Services
N.A.I.C.S.: 513199

Holmen GmbH (1)
Kajen 6-8, 20459, Hamburg, Germany
Tel.: (49) 4035536016
Sales Range: $25-49.9 Million
Emp.: 20
Printing & Writing Paper Distr
N.A.I.C.S.: 424110

Holmen Paper AB (1)
Vattengranden 2, 60188, Norrkoping, Sweden (100%)
Tel.: (46) 11235000
Web Site: http://www.holmenpaper.com
Sales Range: $25-49.9 Million
Emp.: 100
Production & Sale of Wood Containing Printing Papers; Newsprint, Magazine & Telephone Directory Paper
N.A.I.C.S.: 322120

Subsidiary (Non-US):

Holmen Italia SRL (2)
Via Pola 15, 20124, Milan, Italy (100%)
Tel.: (39) 026697600
Web Site: http://www.holmenpaper.com
Sales Range: $25-49.9 Million
Emp.: 6
Wholesales Paper
N.A.I.C.S.: 424130

Holmen Nederland B.V. (2)
Gedempte Zuiderdiep 22, 9711 HG, Groningen, Netherlands (100%)
Tel.: (31) 503199660
Web Site: http://www.holmenpaper.com

AND PRIVATE COMPANIES

Sales Range: $50-74.9 Million
Emp.: 5
Wholesales Paper
N.A.I.C.S.: 424130

Holmen Paper AG (2)
Sternenstrasse 12, 8002, Zurich, Switzerland **(100%)**
Tel.: (41) 12017888
Web Site: http://www.holmenpaper.com
Sales Range: $25-49.9 Million
Emp.: 3
Wholesales Paper
N.A.I.C.S.: 424130

Holmen Paper Iberica SL (2)
Del Papel 1, Poligono Industrial La Cauntue, 28947, Fuenlabrada, Madrid, Spain **(100%)**
Tel.: (34) 916420603
Web Site: http://www.holmen.es
Sales Range: $50-74.9 Million
Emp.: 200
Wholesales Paper
N.A.I.C.S.: 424130

Holmen Paper Ltd. (2)
95 Aldwych, London, WC2B 4JF, United Kingdom **(100%)**
Tel.: (44) 2072690800
Web Site: http://www.holmenpaper.com
Sales Range: $25-49.9 Million
Emp.: 12
Paper Whslr
N.A.I.C.S.: 424130

Holmen Papiers (2)
Immeuble Atria - 21 Avenue, CS 10144, Edouard Belin, 92566, Rueil-Malmaison, CEDEX, France
Tel.: (33) 64 760 5366
Web Site: http://www.holmenpaper.com
Sales Range: $25-49.9 Million
Emp.: 8
Wholesales Paper
N.A.I.C.S.: 424130

Holmen Paper Madrid S.L. (1)
Parque Industrial La Cantuena C/del Papel 1, Fuenlabrada, 28947, Spain
Tel.: (34) 91 642 06 03
News Printing Paper Mfr
N.A.I.C.S.: 322120

Holmen S.A.S. (2)
31 Rue Du Commandant Cousteau, 26800, Portes-les-Valence, France
Tel.: (33) 475578710
Sales Range: $25-49.9 Million
Emp.: 17
Paper Product Distr
N.A.I.C.S.: 424130

Holmen Skog AB (1)
Horneborgsvagen 6, 891 80, Ornskoldsvik, Sweden **(100%)**
Tel.: (46) 660377400
Web Site: http://www.holmenskog.com
Sales Range: $150-199.9 Million
Emp.: 400
Wood Procurement & Forestry Management Services
N.A.I.C.S.: 321999

Division (Domestic):

Holmen Skog AB-Iggesund (2)
PO Box 15, 825 21, Iggesund, Sweden **(100%)**
Tel.: (46) 65028000
Web Site: http://www.holmenskog.com
Sales Range: $25-49.9 Million
N.A.I.C.S.: 322120

Holmen Skog AB-Lycksele (2)
Vilhelminavagen 3, S 921 35, Lycksele, Sweden **(100%)**
Tel.: (46) 95051700
Web Site: http://www.holmenskog.com
Sales Range: $50-74.9 Million
Emp.: 200
N.A.I.C.S.: 322120

Holmen Skog AB-Ornskoldsvik (2)
Holmen Skog AB, S 891 80, Ornskoldsvik, Sweden **(100%)**
Tel.: (46) 66075400
Web Site: http://www.holmenskog.com
Sales Range: $100-124.9 Million
Emp.: 400
N.A.I.C.S.: 322120

Holmen Skog AB-Robertsfors (2)
Herrvagen 14, PO Box 66, S 915 21, Robertsfors, Sweden **(100%)**
Tel.: (46) 93410500
Web Site: http://www.holmenskog.com
Sales Range: $25-49.9 Million
Emp.: 10
Printing Paper
N.A.I.C.S.: 322120

Holmen Timber AB/Iggesund Sawmill (1)
Norra Kartonggatan, PO Box 45, 825 80, Iggesund, Sweden **(100%)**
Tel.: (46) 6 502 8000
Web Site: http://www.holmentimber.com
Sales Range: $50-74.9 Million
Emp.: 175
Production of Sawn Timber
N.A.I.C.S.: 321113

Subsidiary (Non-US):

Holmen Timber UK (2)
Grain House Mill Court, Great Shelford, Cambridge, CB22 5LD, Cambridgeshire, United Kingdom **(100%)**
Tel.: (44) 1223841831
Web Site: http://www.holmen.com
Emp.: 4
Timber Products Distr
N.A.I.C.S.: 423310

Iggesund Paper Ltd (1)
Ringvagen, PO Box 15, Iggesund, 82580, Sweden **(100%)**
Tel.: (46) 65028000
Web Site: http://www.iggesundpaperboard.com
Sales Range: $200-249.9 Million
Emp.: 800
N.A.I.C.S.: 322120

Iggesund Paperboard AB (1)
Norra Kartonggatan, 825 80, Iggesund, Sweden **(100%)**
Tel.: (46) 65028000
Web Site: http://www.iggesundpaperboard.com
Sales Range: $200-249.9 Million
Emp.: 850
Production & Sale of Paperboard
N.A.I.C.S.: 322130

Unit (Non-US):

Iggesund Paper & Board Service B.V. (2)
Ruimteweg 5, Utrecht, 3542 GW, Netherlands **(100%)**
Tel.: (31) 302410468
Web Site: http://www.home.com
Sales Range: $25-49.9 Million
Emp.: 40
Paperboard Converters
N.A.I.C.S.: 424130

Subsidiary (Domestic):

Iggesund Paper Board (2)
Iggesunds Bruk, Iggesund, 82580, Sweden **(100%)**
Tel.: (46) 65028000
Web Site: http://www.iggesund.com
Sales Range: $25-49.9 Million
Emp.: 900
Pulp & Paper Mills
N.A.I.C.S.: 322110

Unit (Non-US):

Iggesund Paperboard (Workington) Ltd. (2)
Workington Mill, Workington, CA14 1JX, Cumbria, United Kingdom **(100%)**
Tel.: (44) 190 060 1000
Web Site: http://www.iggesundpaperboard.com
Sales Range: $100-124.9 Million
Emp.: 480
Paperboard Mills
N.A.I.C.S.: 322130

Subsidiary (Non-US):

Iggesund Paperboard Asia Pte Ltd (2)
152 Beach Road 25-07/08 Gateway East, Singapore, 189721, Singapore
Tel.: (65) 63928600

Emp.: 6
Fibre Paperboard Mfr
N.A.I.C.S.: 322130
Joan Choo (Dir-Admin)

Unit (Non-US):

Iggesund Paperboard Europe B.V. (2)
Pietersbergweg 295, 1105 BM, Amsterdam, Netherlands **(100%)**
Tel.: (31) 206559200
Web Site: http://www.iggesund.com
Rev.: $20,000,000
Emp.: 80
Wholesales Paper
N.A.I.C.S.: 424130

Subsidiary (US):

Iggesund Paperboard Inc. (2)
1050 Wall St Ste 640, Lyndhurst, NJ 07071 **(100%)**
Tel.: (201) 804-9977
Sales Range: $25-49.9 Million
Emp.: 7
Mfr of Paperboards
N.A.I.C.S.: 424130

Subsidiary (Domestic):

Iggesunds Bruk (2)
Iggesunds Paperboard, Iggesund, 825 80, Sweden **(100%)**
Tel.: (46) 65028000
Web Site: http://www.iggesundspaperboard.se
Sales Range: $200-249.9 Million
Emp.: 800
N.A.I.C.S.: 322120
Daniel Peltonen (Pres)

HOLMES FREIGHT LINES INC.
70 Ward Road, Brampton, L6S 4L5, ON, Canada
Tel.: (905) 458-1155
Web Site: http://www.holmesfreight.net
Year Founded: 1961
Freight & Truck Services
N.A.I.C.S.: 488510
Esly Holmes (Pres)

HOLMES PLACE INTERNATIONAL LTD.
1 Hatidhar, Ra'anana, 4366503, Israel
Tel.: (972) 35722903
Web Site: http://www.holmesplace.com
HLMS—(TAE)
Rev.: $140,493,160
Assets: $349,884,509
Liabilities: $316,325,178
Net Worth: $33,559,331
Earnings: $11,068,656
Fiscal Year-end: 12/31/23
Fitness & Recreational Sports Centers
N.A.I.C.S.: 713940
Allan Fisher (Co-Founder)

HOLOGRAM. INDUSTRIES SA
Parc d activites Gustave Eiffel, 22 avenue de l'Europe, Bussy-Saint-Georges, 77607, France
Tel.: (33) 164763100
Web Site: http://www.hologram-industries.com
Sales Range: $50-74.9 Million
Emp.: 287
Optical Security Solutions for Protection of Documents & Brand Products against Forgery
N.A.I.C.S.: 561621
Hugues Souparis (Founder, Chm & CEO)

Subsidiaries:

Hologram. Industries Research GmbH (1)
Melchior-Huber-St 25, Ottersberg, 85652,

HOLTEK SEMICONDUCTOR INC.

Bremen, Germany
Tel.: (49) 812199250
Web Site: http://www.hi-research.de
Sales Range: $25-49.9 Million
Emp.: 8
Security Devices & Systems Services
N.A.I.C.S.: 561621
Gunther Dausmann (Pres)

HOLOSFIND S.A.
29 rue du Louvre, 75002, Paris, 75002, France
Tel.: (33) 1 7354 7500
Web Site: http://www.referencement.com
Sales Range: $1-9.9 Million
Emp.: 105
Internet Services
N.A.I.C.S.: 517810
Sylvain Bellaiche (Founder & CEO)

HOLSOTHERM GMBH
Rudolf-Caracciola-Str 3, 99625, Kolleda, Germany
Tel.: (49) 363546070
Web Site: http://www.holsotherm.de
Year Founded: 1997
Sales Range: $25-49.9 Million
Emp.: 3
Energy Supply Systems Mfr
N.A.I.C.S.: 237130
Roy Michael (Mng Dir)

HOLTEK SEMICONDUCTOR INC.
No 3 Creation Rd II Science park, Hsinchu, 300, Taiwan
Tel.: (886) 35631999
Web Site: http://www.holtek.com.tw
Year Founded: 1998
6202—(TAI)
Rev.: $84,897,050
Assets: $202,457,202
Liabilities: $68,390,854
Net Worth: $134,066,348
Earnings: $3,748,945
Emp.: 847
Fiscal Year-end: 12/31/23
Semiconductor Equipment Mfr
N.A.I.C.S.: 334413
Chi-Yung Wu (Chm)

Subsidiaries:

Best Modules Corp. (1)
No 3 Creation 2nd Rd Hsinchu Science Park, Hsinchu, 300, Taiwan
Tel.: (886) 36686759
Web Site: https://www.bestmodulescorp.com
Electronic Component Mfr & Distr
N.A.I.C.S.: 334419

Best Solution Technology Inc. (1)
4F-2 No 3-2 YuanQu St Nankang Software Park, Taipei, 115, Taiwan
Tel.: (886) 226558797
Web Site: http://www.bestsolution.com.tw
Electronic Component Mfr & Distr
N.A.I.C.S.: 334419

Holtek Semiconductor (China) Inc. (1)
Room 101 Office Building 10 Xinzhuyuan No 4 Xinzhu Road, Songshan Lake, Dongguan, 523808, China
Tel.: (86) 76938931999
Semiconductor Mfr
N.A.I.C.S.: 334413

Holtek Semiconductor (India) Pvt. Ltd. (1)
The Oriental Towers No 461 2nd Floor 4thSector 17th Cross Rd, HSR Layout, Bengaluru, 560102, Karnataka, India
Tel.: (91) 8043729269
Semiconductor Mfr
N.A.I.C.S.: 334413

Holtek Semiconductor (USA), Inc. (1)
19 Hammond Ste 513, Irvine, CA 92618
Tel.: (949) 273-8988

3453

HOLTEK SEMICONDUCTOR INC.

Holtek Semiconductor Inc.—(Continued)
Semiconductor Mfr
N.A.I.C.S.: 334413

Holtek Semiconductor Inc. (1)
Block A 3/F Tin On Industrial Building 777-779 Cheung Sha Wan Rd, Kowloon, China (Hong Kong)
Tel.: (852) 27458288
Semiconductor Mfr
N.A.I.C.S.: 334413

HOLTER REGELARMATUREN GMBH & CO. KG
Helleforthstrasse 58-60, Schloss Holte-Stukenbrock, 33758, Germany
Tel.: (49) 520789030
Web Site: http://www.hora.de
Year Founded: 1967
Rev.: $41,796,750
Emp.: 290
Valve Mfr
N.A.I.C.S.: 332911
Dieter Dresselhaus *(Pres)*

HOLY STONE ENTERPRISE CO., LTD.
No 62 Sec 2 Huang Shan Rd, Neihu District, Taipei, 11452, Taiwan
Tel.: (886) 226270383
Web Site:
https://www.holystone.com.tw
3026—(TAI)
Rev.: $432,986,674
Assets: $491,656,085
Liabilities: $163,475,189
Net Worth: $328,180,896
Earnings: $21,533,077
Emp.: 1,000
Fiscal Year-end: 12/31/23
Integrated Circuit Board & Graphics Chip Mfr
N.A.I.C.S.: 333248
Subsidiaries:

Holy Stone (Europe) Ltd. (1)
Henderson Business Centre Unit 32 and 33 Ivy Road, Norwich, NR5 8BF, Norfolk, United Kingdom
Tel.: (44) 1603251780
Web Site: http://www.holystoneeurope.com
Sales Range: $50-74.9 Million
Electronic Components Distr
N.A.I.C.S.: 423690

Holy Stone Enterprise Co., Ltd. - Dongguan Plant (1)
Baoshi Industrial Area Jiaoyitang Town, Dongguan, 523723, Guandong, China
Tel.: (86) 76987928002
Web Site: http://www.holystone.com.tw
Electronic Components Mfr
N.A.I.C.S.: 334416

Holy Stone Healthcare Co., Ltd. (1)
4F No 88 Sec 1 Neihu Rd, Neihu Dist, Taipei, 11493, Taiwan
Tel.: (886) 287975966
Web Site: http://www.hshc.com.tw
Sales Range: $150-199.9 Million
Medical Diagnostic Equipment Distr
N.A.I.C.S.: 423450

Holy Stone Holdings Co., Ltd. (1)
Block 7 Kallang Pl 03-04, Singapore, Singapore
Tel.: (65) 132343
Investment Management Service
N.A.I.C.S.: 523940
Eleanor Tan *(Mgr)*

Holy Stone International Trading (Shanghai) Co., Ltd. (1)
16F Metro Bank Plaza 1160 YanAn W Road, Shanghai, 200052, China
Tel.: (86) 2151875266
Sales Range: $50-74.9 Million
Emp.: 80
Electronic Parts Distr
N.A.I.C.S.: 423690

MDT Int'l SA (1)
Rue du 31 Decembre 36, 1207, Geneva, Switzerland
Tel.: (41) 227040545
Web Site: http://www.mdtint.ch
Sales Range: $25-49.9 Million
Medical Devices Mfr & Distr
N.A.I.C.S.: 339113

Martex Co., Ltd. (1)
3rd Floor No 309 Long Jiang Road, Jhongshan District, Taipei, 104, Taiwan
Tel.: (886) 225168997
Sales Range: $25-49.9 Million
Emp.: 19
Electronic Components Distr
N.A.I.C.S.: 423690
Hsing Li Cheng *(Pres)*

OHGA Electronics Co., Ltd. (1)
6th Floor No 119 Jian-Kang Road, Chung Ho, Taipei, 23586, Taiwan
Tel.: (886) 222220949
Web Site: http://www.ohga.com.tw
Sales Range: $25-49.9 Million
Emp.: 90
Lighting Control Products Mfr
N.A.I.C.S.: 334512

HOLZWERKSTOFF HOLDING AG
Bahnhofstrasse 311, 5325, Leibstadt, Switzerland
Tel.: (41) 56 267 60 10
Web Site: http://www.hwh-gruppe.ch
Sales Range: $300-349.9 Million
Emp.: 300
Plywood Distr
N.A.I.C.S.: 423310
George Kuratle *(CEO)*
Subsidiaries:

Kuratle & Jaecker AG (1)
Bahnhofstrasse 311, Leibstadt, 5325, Switzerland
Tel.: (41) 56 267 60 60
Web Site: http://www.holzwerkstoffe.ch
Wood Product Distr
N.A.I.C.S.: 423310
Walter Moser *(CEO)*

Subsidiary (Domestic):

Hiag Handel AG (2)
Wolferstrasse 27, Fullinsdorf, 4414, Basel, Switzerland
Tel.: (41) 562688333
Web Site: http://www.hiag.ch
Wood Product Distr
N.A.I.C.S.: 423310
Walter Moser *(CEO)*

HOMA PUMPENFABRIK GMBH
Industriestrasse 1, 53819, Neunkirchen, Germany
Tel.: (49) 22477020
Web Site: http://www.homa-pumpen.de
Year Founded: 1946
Rev.: $34,485,000
Emp.: 212
Pumps Mfr
N.A.I.C.S.: 333914
Hans Hoffmann *(Founder)*
Subsidiaries:

HOMA Pompen B.V. (1)
Techniekweg 16-18, 4207 HD, Gorinchem, Netherlands
Tel.: (31) 183622212
Web Site: http://www.homapompen.nl
Industrial Machinery Distr
N.A.I.C.S.: 423830

HOME AFRIKA LIMITED
Morningside Office Park 5th Floor Ngong Road, PO Box 6254, 00100, Nairobi, Kenya
Tel.: (254) 202772000
Web Site:
https://www.homeafrika.com
Year Founded: 2008
HAFR—(NAI)
Rev.: $7,416,585
Assets: $34,934,715
Liabilities: $31,065,253
Net Worth: $3,869,461
Earnings: $919,182
Fiscal Year-end: 12/31/13
Real Estate Development Services
N.A.I.C.S.: 531390
Lee Gituto Karuri *(Chm)*

HOME CENTER HOLDINGS CO., LTD.
139-6 Nowonro, Buk-gu, Daegu, Korea (South)
Tel.: (82) 532105140
Web Site: http://www.home-center.co.kr
Year Founded: 1988
060560—(KRS)
Rev.: $331,387,454
Assets: $312,253,786
Liabilities: $152,241,726
Net Worth: $160,012,059
Earnings: $14,409,688
Emp.: 53
Fiscal Year-end: 12/31/22
Construction Material Mfr & Distr
N.A.I.C.S.: 326199
Byung-Youn Park *(Board of Directors & CEO)*

HOME CONCEPT SA
38 boulevard de Vincennes, 94120, Fontenay-sous-Bois, France
Tel.: (33) 556636110
Web Site: http://www.homeconcept.fr
Vinyl Siding Merchant Whslr
N.A.I.C.S.: 423330
Marie-Odile Coiffard *(Chm & CEO)*

HOME CONTROL INTERNATIONAL LIMITED
151 Lorong Chuan 04-03A, New Tech Park, Singapore, 556741, Singapore
Web Site:
https://www.omniremotes.com
Year Founded: 2014
1747—(HKG)
Rev.: $126,560,000
Assets: $80,367,000
Liabilities: $56,063,000
Net Worth: $24,304,000
Earnings: $4,575,000
Emp.: 178
Fiscal Year-end: 12/31/22
Remote Control Product Mfr & Distr
N.A.I.C.S.: 334290
Perrot Alain *(Chm)*

HOME FIRST FINANCE COMPANY INDIA LIMITED
511 Acme Plaza Opposite Sangam Cinema J B Nagar, Andheri East, Mumbai, 400059, India
Tel.: (91) 8880549911
Web Site:
https://www.homefirstindia.com
Year Founded: 2010
543259—(BOM)
Rev.: $108,599,127
Assets: $919,603,913
Liabilities: $671,537,139
Net Worth: $248,066,774
Earnings: $31,161,858
Emp.: 993
Fiscal Year-end: 03/31/23
Housing Finance Services
N.A.I.C.S.: 522310
Jaithirth Rao *(Co-Founder)*

HOME GROUP LIMITED
2 Gosforth Park Way Gosforth Business Park, Newcastle upon Tyne, NE12 8ET, United Kingdom
Tel.: (44) 8451551234
Web Site:
http://www.homegroup.org.uk
Rev.: $466,132,619

INTERNATIONAL PUBLIC

Assets: $3,580,957,438
Liabilities: $2,796,517,801
Net Worth: $784,439,637
Earnings: $56,760,727
Emp.: 2,426
Fiscal Year-end: 03/31/19
Home Developers; House Rental; Elder People Housing & Health Care Services
N.A.I.C.S.: 621610
Mark G. Henderson *(CEO)*
Subsidiaries:

Home Group Developments Limited (1)
2 Salters Lane Gosforth Park Way, NE12 8ET, Newcastle upon Tyne, United Kingdom - England
Tel.: (44) 8451551234
Web Site: http://www.homegroup.org.uk
Sales Range: $50-74.9 Million
Emp.: 10
Real Estate Manangement Services
N.A.I.C.S.: 531390

Home in Scotland Limited (1)
Unit 3 Q Court Quality Street, Davidsons Mains, Edinburgh, EH4 5BP, United Kingdom
Tel.: (44) 131 3365876
Residential Property Leasing Services
N.A.I.C.S.: 531110

Live Smart @ Home Limited (1)
Unit 36 Middleton Road Navigation Point, Hartlepool, TS24 0UJ, United Kingdom
Tel.: (44) 8000283629
Web Site: http://www.livesmarthome.com
Sales Range: $50-74.9 Million
Emp.: 8
Residential Property Leasing Services
N.A.I.C.S.: 531190
Katherine Bolton *(Head-Media)*

Ruislip and Northwood Aged People's Housing Company Limited (1)
Malt House 281 Field Road Eastcote, Ruislip, HA4 9XQ, Middlesex, United Kingdom
Tel.: (44) 20 8868 9000
Sales Range: $50-74.9 Million
Emp.: 100
Old Age Home Leasing Services
N.A.I.C.S.: 531190

HOME HARDWARE STORES LIMITED
34 Henry St W, Saint Jacobs, N0B 2N0, ON, Canada
Tel.: (519) 664-4655
Web Site:
http://www.homehardware.ca
Year Founded: 1906
Sales Range: $1-4.9 Billion
Emp.: 2,000
Hardware, Building Supply & Furniture Stores
N.A.I.C.S.: 444110
Walter Hachborn *(Founder)*
Subsidiaries:

Link With Home Travel Inc. (1)
133 Weber St N, Waterloo, N2J 3G9, ON, Canada
Tel.: (519) 886-8140
Web Site: http://www.ihtravel.on.ca
Sales Range: $25-49.9 Million
Emp.: 7
Travel & Tour Operator
N.A.I.C.S.: 561510
Lynn Gossman *(Mgr)*

HOME INVEST BELGIUM SA
Boulevard De La Woluwe 46/11, B-1200, Brussels, Belgium
Tel.: (32) 27401450
Web Site:
https://www.homeinvestbelgium.be
Year Founded: 1980
H5V0—(DEU)
Rev.: $38,408,213
Assets: $891,718,733
Liabilities: $430,562,976

Net Worth: $461,155,757
Earnings: ($15,764,433)
Emp.: 40
Fiscal Year-end: 12/31/23
Real Estate Investment Services
N.A.I.C.S.: 531390
Lievin Van Overstraeten *(Chm)*

HOME MEAL REPLACEMENT SA
Sant Cugat del Valles, Barcelona, Spain
Tel.: (34) 902150950
HMR—(MAD)
Sales Range: Less than $1 Million
Restaurant Operators
N.A.I.C.S.: 722511
Quirze Salomo Gonzalez *(Founder, Chm & CEO)*

HOME MORTGAGE BANK
Prince's Court Ground Floor, Corners Keate & Pembroke Streets, Port of Spain, Trinidad & Tobago
Tel.: (868) 627 4695 TT
Web Site:
   http://www.homemortgagett.com
Year Founded: 1986
Sales Range: $10-24.9 Million
Secondary Market Mortgage Financing Services
N.A.I.C.S.: 522299
Rawle Ramlogan *(CEO)*

HOME POTTERY PUBLIC COMPANY LIMITED
119 Moo 15 Sopprap Lampang-Tak Road Tambol Sopprab, Amphur, Lampang, 52170, Thailand
Tel.: (66) 54325180
Web Site:
   http://www.homepottery.com
Year Founded: 2001
HPT—(THA)
Rev.: $8,708,548
Assets: $10,953,411
Liabilities: $1,680,582
Net Worth: $9,272,829
Earnings: $689,806
Fiscal Year-end: 12/31/23
China Tableware
N.A.I.C.S.: 327110
Niran Chourkittisopon *(Chm & Mng Dir)*

Subsidiaries:

Central Hospitality Co., Ltd. (1)
417 Bang Na-Trat Road, Bang Na Subdistrict Bang Na District, Bangkok, 10260, Thailand
Tel.: (66) 23992599
Web Site: http://www.chl.co.th
Kitchen Equipment & Appliance Retailer
N.A.I.C.S.: 449210

HOME PRODUCT CENTER PUBLIC COMPANY LIMITED
31 Prachachuen Nonthaburi Road Bang Khen, Mueang Nonthaburi, Nonthaburi, 11000, Thailand
Tel.: (66) 28321000
Web Site: https://www.homepro.co.th
Year Founded: 1995
HMPRO—(THA)
Rev.: $2,125,810,927
Assets: $2,015,643,912
Liabilities: $1,269,532,576
Net Worth: $746,111,336
Earnings: $188,041,705
Emp.: 11,777
Fiscal Year-end: 12/31/23
Buildings, Houses & Residential Facilitites Construction, Improvement, Decoration & Renovation; Home Improvement Retail Store Owner & Operator
N.A.I.C.S.: 236110

Khunawut Thumpornkul *(Mng Dir)*

Subsidiaries:

Home Product Center (Malaysia) Sdn. Bhd. (1)
Suite 17 01 17 05-07 Level 17 Menara Summit, Persiaran Kewajipan USJ 1, 47600, Subang Jaya, Selangor, Malaysia
Tel.: (60) 380635179
Web Site: https://www.homepro.com.my
Interior Design Services
N.A.I.C.S.: 541410

Mega Home Center Company Limited (1)
49 Moo 5 Tambon Khlong Nueng, Amphoe, Khlong Luang, 12120, Pathum Thani, Thailand
Tel.: (66) 25160099
Web Site: http://www.megahome.co.th
Interior Design Services
N.A.I.C.S.: 541410

Mega Home Co., Ltd. (1)
No 155 Keji 5th Rd, Annan District, Tainan City, 70955, Taiwan
Tel.: (886) 63841551
Web Site: https://www.megahome.com.tw
Water Mfr
N.A.I.C.S.: 312112

HOMECAST CO., LTD.
726 Eonju-ro, Gangnam-gu, Seoul, Korea (South)
Tel.: (82) 234008300
Web Site: https://www.homecast.net
Year Founded: 2000
064240—(KRS)
Rev.: $57,910,298
Assets: $77,152,642
Liabilities: $1,829,375
Net Worth: $75,323,267
Earnings: ($573,494)
Emp.: 25
Fiscal Year-end: 12/31/22
Set Top Box Mfr
N.A.I.C.S.: 334220
Young Chul Kwoun *(CEO)*

HOMECO DAILY NEEDS REIT
Level 7 1 Macquarie Place, Sydney, 2000, NSW, Australia
Tel.: (61) 1300466326 AU
Web Site:
   https://www.hmccapital.com.au
Year Founded: 2020
HDN—(ASX)
Rev.: $226,445,850
Assets: $3,146,247,636
Liabilities: $1,140,575,080
Net Worth: $2,005,672,557
Earnings: $66,636,239
Fiscal Year-end: 06/30/23
Property Management Services
N.A.I.C.S.: 531311
Andrew Selim *(Gen Counsel & Sec)*

HOMEEASE INDUSTRIAL CO. LTD.
No 423 Sec 2 Chung Shan Road Shuishang Hsiang, Chiayi, 60852, Taiwan
Tel.: (886) 52688966
Web Site:
   https://www.homeease.com.tw
Year Founded: 1980
Household Product Mfr & Distr
N.A.I.C.S.: 337126

HOMEINNS HOTEL GROUP
No 124 Caobao Road Xuhui District, Shanghai, 200035, China
Tel.: (86) 21 3337 3333 Ky
Web Site: http://www.homeinns.com
Year Founded: 2002
Sales Range: $1-4.9 Billion
Emp.: 25,176
Hotel Owner & Operator
N.A.I.C.S.: 721110

Yi Liu *(Co-Chm)*

HOMELAND INTERACTIVE TECHNOLOGY LTD.
7A Floor Huijin Building 77 Tainan Road, Siming, Xiamen, China
Tel.: (86) 3325599 Ky
Web Site:
   https://www.jiaxianghudong.com
Year Founded: 2009
3798—(HKG)
Rev.: $246,409,365
Assets: $316,642,113
Liabilities: $28,074,601
Net Worth: $288,567,512
Earnings: $60,986,653
Emp.: 652
Fiscal Year-end: 12/31/23
Information Technology Services
N.A.I.C.S.: 541512
Bo Su *(Chief Investment Officer)*

HOMELIFE/BAYVIEW REALTY INC.
505 Highway 7 East Unit 201, Thornhill, L3T 7T1, ON, Canada
Tel.: (905) 889-2200
Web Site:
   http://www.homelifebayview.com
Rev.: $16,925,550
Emp.: 700
Real Estate Services
N.A.I.C.S.: 531390
Steve Schmeiser *(Owner)*

HOMEMAID AB
Kungsgatan 17, 302 46, Halmstad, Sweden
Tel.: (46) 35161550
Web Site: https://homemaid.se
Year Founded: 2000
Building Maintenance Services
N.A.I.C.S.: 561790
Stefan Hogkvist *(CEO)*

HOMENEMA TECHNOLOGY INCORPORATION
10-1F No 1 Songgao Rd, Xinyi, Taipei, Hsien, Taiwan
Tel.: (886) 227099889
Web Site: https://www.leadsungreen.com
Year Founded: 1997
8087—(TPE)
Rev.: $2,202,601
Assets: $12,220,038
Liabilities: $2,265,169
Net Worth: $9,954,869
Earnings: ($205,203)
Fiscal Year-end: 12/31/20
Optical Disc Mfr
N.A.I.C.S.: 334610
Yang Ching-Tang *(Chm & Pres)*

HOMERITZ CORPORATION BERHAD
Lot 8726 Ptd 6023 Batu 8 Kawasan Perindustrian Bukit Bakri, 84200, Muar, Johor, Malaysia
Tel.: (60) 69865000
Web Site:
   https://www.homeritzcorp.com
HOMERIZ—(KLS)
Rev.: $34,421,955
Assets: $64,346,501
Liabilities: $4,806,107
Net Worth: $59,540,394
Earnings: $5,501,348
Emp.: 450
Fiscal Year-end: 08/31/23
Upholstered Household Furniture Mfr
N.A.I.C.S.: 337121
Fen Fatt Chua *(Mng Dir)*

Subsidiaries:

Home Upholstery Industries Sdn. Bhd. (1)
Lot 8726 Ptd 6023 Batu 8, Kawasan Perindustrian Bukit Bakri, 84200, Muar, Johor, Malaysia
Tel.: (60) 69865000
Web Site: http://www.eritz.com.my
Home Product Mfr
N.A.I.C.S.: 325998

HOMERUN RESOURCES INC.
1040 West Georgia Street 14th Floor, PO Box 27, Vancouver, V6E 4H8, BC, Canada
Tel.: (604) 568-1823 BC
Web Site: http://www.envirotekri.com
Year Founded: 1980
ETKH—(OTCIQ)
Copper Exploration Services
N.A.I.C.S.: 212230
Brian Leeners *(CEO)*

HOMES & HOLIDAY AG
Ludwigstrasse 8, 80339, Munich, Germany
Tel.: (49) 89206021106
Web Site: https://www.homes-holiday.com
Year Founded: 2005
HHHA—(MUN)
Rev.: $1,727,244
Assets: $554,424
Liabilities: $394,494
Net Worth: $159,930
Earnings: $223,902
Emp.: 13
Fiscal Year-end: 12/31/22
Real Estate Investment Services
N.A.I.C.S.: 531190
Joachim Semrau *(Founder)*

Subsidiaries:

Porta Mallorquina Real Estate S.L.U. (1)
C / Conquistador 8, 07001, Palma de Mallorca, Spain
Tel.: (34) 971698242
Web Site: https://www.portamallorquina.com
Emp.: 68
Real Estate Consultancy Services
N.A.I.C.S.: 531210

HOMES BY AVI INC.
245 Forge Road SE, Calgary, T2H 0S9, AB, Canada
Tel.: (403) 536-7000
Web Site:
   https://www.homesbyavi.com
Year Founded: 1978
Residential Construction
N.A.I.C.S.: 236115
Avi Amir *(Chm)*

HOMETOGO SE
Pappelallee 78/79, 10437, Berlin, Germany
Tel.: (49) 3020847396 LU
Web Site: https://www.hometogo.com
Year Founded: 2014
HTG—(DEU)
Rev.: $174,868,336
Assets: $349,614,720
Liabilities: $79,680,553
Net Worth: $269,934,168
Earnings: ($30,521,261)
Emp.: 664
Fiscal Year-end: 12/31/23
Vacation Rental Services
N.A.I.C.S.: 531190
Patrick Andra *(CEO)*

Subsidiaries:

Amivac s.a.s (1)
66 Avenue des Champs-Elysees, 75008, Paris, France
Tel.: (33) 187214476
Web Site: https://www.amivac.com

HOMETOGO SE

HomeToGo SE—(Continued)
Vacation Home Rental Services
N.A.I.C.S.: 721199

Atraveo GmbH (1)
Peter-Muller-Str 10, 40468, Dusseldorf, Germany
Tel.: (49) 211668878107
Web Site: https://www.atraveo.de
Vacation Home Rental Services
N.A.I.C.S.: 721199

Casamundo GmbH (1)
Pappelallee 78/79, 10437, Berlin, Germany
Tel.: (49) 40299960902
Web Site: https://www.casamundo.com
Vacation Home Rental Services
N.A.I.C.S.: 721199

E-domizil AG (1)
Binzstrasse 38, 8045, Zurich, Switzerland
Tel.: (41) 444422999
Web Site: https://www.e-domizil.ch
Vacation Home Rental Services
N.A.I.C.S.: 721199

E-domizil GmbH (1)
Taunusstr 21, 60329, Frankfurt am Main, Germany
Tel.: (49) 3022027338
Web Site: https://www.e-domizil.de
Vacation Home Rental Services
N.A.I.C.S.: 721199

Feries S.r.l. (1)
Viale Abruzzi 94, Milan, Italy
Tel.: (39) 0237058202
Web Site: https://www.feries.it
Vacation Home Rental Services
N.A.I.C.S.: 721199

Smoobu GmbH (1)
Pappelallee 78/79, 10437, Berlin, Germany
Tel.: (49) 3025557431
Web Site: https://www.smoobu.com
Information Technology Services
N.A.I.C.S.: 541511

HOMETRACK DATA SYSTEMS LIMITED

The Cooperage 5 Copper Row, London, SE1 2LH, United Kingdom
Tel.: (44) 2037440410
Web Site: http://www.hometrack.com
Year Founded: 1999
Sales Range: $10-24.9 Million
Emp.: 47
Residential Property & Housing Information Services
N.A.I.C.S.: 531311
Charlie Bryant (CEO)

HOMIZY S.P.A.

Viale Umbria 32, Lombardia, 20135, Milan, Italy
Web Site: https://www.homizy.com
HZY—(EUR)
Real Estate Development Services
N.A.I.C.S.: 531190
Alessandro Peveraro (CEO)

HOMOLJE A.D.

Kralja Milana 2, 12000, Zagubica, Serbia
Tel.: (381) 12645059
Web Site:
https://www.homoljead.co.rs
Year Founded: 1947
HMLJ—(BEL)
Rev.: $918,660
Assets: $948,818
Liabilities: $759,713
Net Worth: $189,105
Earnings: $3,011
Fiscal Year-end: 12/31/22
Grocery Store Operator
N.A.I.C.S.: 445110
Sasa Antic (Exec Dir)

HON CORPORATION LTD.

Blk 20 Ang Mo Kio Industrial Park 2A 07-33 AMK Tech Link, Singapore, 567761, Singapore
Tel.: (65) 65113178
Web Site:
http://www.honindustries.com.sg
Rev.: $69,045,809
Assets: $57,102,296
Liabilities: $41,712,708
Net Worth: $15,389,588
Earnings: $8,666,379
Emp.: 255
Fiscal Year-end: 12/31/18
Commercial Building Construction Services
N.A.I.C.S.: 236220
Lien Hwai Ho (CEO & Compliance Officer)

HON HAI PRECISION INDUSTRY CO., LTD.

No 2 Zihyou St, Tucheng Dist, New Taipei City, 236, Taiwan
Tel.: (886) 222683466   TW
Web Site: https://www.foxconn.com
Year Founded: 1974
HNHAF—(OTCIQ)
Rev.: $201,518,072,082
Assets: $128,839,688,288
Liabilities: $73,695,845,053
Net Worth: $55,143,843,235
Earnings: $5,061,950,232
Emp.: 552,341
Fiscal Year-end: 12/31/23
Holding Company; Electronics Components & Systems Mfr & Whslr
N.A.I.C.S.: 551112
Terry Tai-Ming Gou (Founder)

Subsidiaries:

Bang Tai International Logistics Co., Limited (1)
No 10 Siu Hom Estate Ka Lung Road, San Tin New Territories, Yuen Long, China (Hong Kong)
Tel.: (852) 39749189
Web Site: https://www.bangtailogistics.com
Warehouse & Logistic Services
N.A.I.C.S.: 541614

Bharat FIH Limited (1)
Plot No M-2B SIPCOT Industrial Hi-Tech SEZ DTA Area, Sriperumbudur Taluk Park Phase II, Kanchipuram, 602106, Tamil Nadu, India
Tel.: (91) 7893001974
Web Site: https://www.bharatfih.com
Electronic Device Mfr & Distr
N.A.I.C.S.: 335999

Big Innovation Company Ltd. (1)
Foxconn Building, New Taipei City, Taiwan
Tel.: (886) 222683466
Web Site: https://big-inno.com
Electronic Product Mfr & Distr
N.A.I.C.S.: 335999

Dynamic Computing Technology Co., Ltd. (1)
13F No 25 Chenggong 2nd Road, Qianzhen District, Kaohsiung, Taiwan
Tel.: (886) 75369009
Web Site: https://www.dct-cloud.com
Cloud Services
N.A.I.C.S.: 518210

ECMM Services Inc. (1)
8845 Fallbrook Dr, Houston, TX 77064
Tel.: (281) 477-4000
Web Site: https://www.ecmms.com
Electronic Parts Repair & Refurbishment Services
N.A.I.C.S.: 811210

FIH Mexico Industry S.A. de C.V. (1)
Ave Cristobal Colon No 20301 Col Las Aldabas de la I a la IX, 31170, Chihuahua, Chih, Mexico
Tel.: (52) 6142363000
Web Site: https://fih.com.mx
Electronic Device Mfr & Distr
N.A.I.C.S.: 335999

Fenix Industria de Eletronicos Ltda. (1)
Rua Jose Palma Renno 236 Centro, Santa Rita do Sapucai, CEP 37540-000, Brazil
Tel.: (55) 3534733085
Web Site: https://www.fenixindustria.net.br
Electronic Device Mfr & Distr
N.A.I.C.S.: 335999

Foxconn Baja California S.A. de C.V. (1)
Laguna Mainar 5520 Section C El Lago Industrial Park, 22210, Tijuana, Baja California, Mexico
Tel.: (52) 6646277200
Web Site: https://foxconnbc.com
Emp.: 5,000
Electronic Product Mfr & Distr
N.A.I.C.S.: 335999

Foxconn CZ S.r.o. (1)
U Zamecku 27, 532 01, Pardubice, Czech Republic
Tel.: (420) 466056111
Web Site: https://www.foxconn.cz
Emp.: 5,000
Electric Device Mfr
N.A.I.C.S.: 327110

Foxconn Interconnect Technology Limited (1)
66-1 Chungshan Road, Tucheng Dist, Taipei, 23680, Taiwan   (100%)
Tel.: (886) 222680970
Rev.: $4,195,550,000
Assets: $5,093,736,000
Liabilities: $2,656,358,000
Net Worth: $2,437,378,000
Earnings: $129,574,000
Emp.: 66,148
Fiscal Year-end: 12/31/2023
Investment Holding Company
N.A.I.C.S.: 551112

Subsidiary (US):

Belkin International, Inc. (2)
12045 E Waterfront Dr, Playa Vista, CA 90094
Tel.: (310) 898-1100
Web Site: http://www.belkin.com
Connectivity Products Mfr
N.A.I.C.S.: 423430
Chet Pipkin (Founder & CEO)

Subsidiary (Non-US):

Belkin Asia Pacific Limited (3)
Room 2601 26th Floor Harbourside HQ No 8 Lam Chak Street, Kowloon Bay, Kowloon, China (Hong Kong)
Tel.: (852) 30021318
Web Site: https://www.belkin.com
Sales, Service & Technical Support of Connectivity Products for Computers & Consumer Electronics
N.A.I.C.S.: 423430

Belkin BV (3)
Herikerbergweg 106 Plaza Arena-Jupiter, 1101 CM, Amsterdam, Netherlands
Tel.: (31) 9000400790
Web Site: https://www.belkin.nl
Sales, Service & Technical Support of Connectivity Products for Computers & Consumer Electronics
N.A.I.C.S.: 423430

Belkin GmbH (3)
Otto-Hahn-Strasse 20, 85609, Aschheim, Germany
Tel.: (49) 69999915682
Web Site: https://www.belkin.com
Sales, Service & Technical Support of Connectivity Products for Computers & Consumer Electronics
N.A.I.C.S.: 423430

Belkin Limited (3)
Unit 1 Regent Park Booth Drive, Park Farm South, Wellingborough, NN8 6GR, Northamptonshire, United Kingdom
Tel.: (44) 1933770254
Sales, Service & Technical Support of Connectivity Products for Computers & Consumer Electronics
N.A.I.C.S.: 423430

Belkin SAS (3)
130 Rue de Silly, 92100, Boulogne, Billancourt, France
Tel.: (33) 141031440

INTERNATIONAL PUBLIC

Web Site: http://www.belkin.fr
Sales, Service & Technical Support of Connectivity Products for Computers & Consumer Electronics
N.A.I.C.S.: 423430

Belkin Trading (Shanghai) Company Ltd. (3)
Room 1407B No 118 Xinling Rd China Pilot Free-Trade Zone, Xuhui, Shanghai, 200030, China
Tel.: (86) 2161032000
Electronic Equipment Distr
N.A.I.C.S.: 423620

Subsidiary (Domestic):

Linksys (3)
131 Theory Dr, Irvine, CA 92617-3064
Tel.: (949) 270-8500
Web Site: http://www.linksys.com
Rev.: $430,400,000
Emp.: 350
VoIP, Wireless & Ethernet Networking
N.A.I.C.S.: 423690
Tim Thornton (Sr Dir-Eng Svs)

Subsidiary (Domestic):

Pure Networks, Inc. (4)
2901 3rd Ave, Seattle, WA 98121-1042
Tel.: (206) 322-9002
Sales Range: $100-124.9 Million
Developer of Networking Software
N.A.I.C.S.: 513210

Subsidiary (Non-US):

Foxconn Industrial Internet Co., Ltd. (2)
Foxconn Science and Technology Park Donghuan 2nd Road Longhua Street, Longhua Jiedao Longhua District, Shenzhen, 518109, Guangdong, China
Tel.: (86) 75533595881
Web Site: https://www.fii-foxconn.com
Rev.: $71,863,680,892
Assets: $39,899,947,745
Liabilities: $21,741,523,502
Net Worth: $18,158,424,242
Earnings: $2,818,259,309
Emp.: 199,000
Fiscal Year-end: 12/31/2022
Electronic Equipment Mfr & Distr
N.A.I.C.S.: 332216
Junqi Li (Bd of Dirs & Chm)

Foxconn Interconnect Technology Japan Co., Ltd. (2)
3rd Tosho Bldg 6F 3-9-5 Shinyokohama, Kohoku-Ku, Yokohama, 222-0033, Kanagawa, Japan
Tel.: (81) 454715033
Electronics Components & Systems Mfr & Whslr
N.A.I.C.S.: 334417

Foxconn Slovakia, spol. s r.o. (1)
Dolne Hony 29, 949 01, Nitra, Slovakia
Tel.: (421) 376944101
Web Site: https://www.foxconn.sk
Electronic Product Mfr & Distr
N.A.I.C.S.: 335999

Foxconn Technology Co., Ltd. (1)
No 3-2 Chungshan Rd, Tucheng Dist, New Taipei City, 236, Taipei, Taiwan
Tel.: (886) 222680970
Web Site: https://www.foxconntech.com.tw
Rev.: $2,437,395,866
Assets: $4,385,146,373
Liabilities: $946,179,303
Net Worth: $3,438,967,070
Earnings: $141,078,709
Emp.: 7,448
Fiscal Year-end: 12/31/2023
Electronics Components Mfr & Whslr
N.A.I.C.S.: 334419
Chun-Fu Lu (Chm)

Subsidiary (US):

American Industrial Systems, Inc. (2)
1768 McGaw Ave, Irvine, CA 92614
Tel.: (949) 681-7468
Web Site: https://www.aispro.com
Sales Range: $1-9.9 Million
Emp.: 15
Electronic Components Manufacturer

HON HAI PRECISION INDUSTRY CO., LTD.

N.A.I.C.S.: 334419
Santiago Consunji *(Mgr-Mktg)*

Subsidiary (Non-US):

FIH Mobile Limited (2)
8th Floor Peninsula Tower 538 Castle Peak Road Cheung Sha Wan, Kowloon, New Territories, China (Hong Kong) **(70.92%)**
Tel.: (852) 35247877
Web Site: http://www.fihmb.com
Rev: $9,394,319,000
Assets: $5,510,290,000
Liabilities: $3,722,514,000
Net Worth: $1,787,776,000
Earnings: ($72,135,000)
Emp.: 44,055
Fiscal Year-end: 12/31/2022
Telecommunications Equipment
N.A.I.C.S.: 334210
Yu Yang Chih *(Chm-Acting & CEO)*

Subsidiary (Non-US):

Foxconn Oy (3)
Norokatu 5 PL 104, 15101, Lahti, Finland
Tel.: (358) 385050
Sales Range: $25-49.9 Million
Emp.: 90
Precision Moulding Mfr
N.A.I.C.S.: 333511

Subsidiary (US):

Foxconn Corporation (2)
8801 Fallbrook Dr, Houston, TX 77064-4856
Tel.: (281) 668-1668
Web Site: https://www.foxconn.com
Sales Range: $25-49.9 Million
Emp.: 200
Electronic Computer Services
N.A.I.C.S.: 334111
Terry Gou *(Chm)*

Subsidiary (Non-US):

Foxconn Singapore Pte. Ltd. (2)
54 Genting Lane 03-05 Ruby Land Complex 2, Singapore, 349562, Singapore
Tel.: (65) 68439284
Sales Range: $50-74.9 Million
Emp.: 200
Consumer Electronics Distr
N.A.I.C.S.: 423620

Subsidiary (Non-US):

SMART Technologies ULC (3)
Suite 600 214-11 Ave SW, Calgary, T2R 0K1, AB, Canada
Tel.: (403) 245-0333
Web Site: https://www.smarttech.com
Interactive Technology Products Developer & Mfr
N.A.I.C.S.: 334118
John Hui *(Chm-Exec Bd)*

Foxsemicon Integrated Technology Inc. (1)
No 16 kezhong Rd, Zhunan Township, Miao-li, 350401, Hsien, Taiwan
Tel.: (886) 637580088
Web Site: https://www.foxsemicon.com
Rev: $426,807,826
Assets: $633,432,168
Liabilities: $254,013,627
Net Worth: $379,418,541
Earnings: $65,092,643
Emp.: 2,412
Fiscal Year-end: 12/31/2023
Semiconductor Devices Mfr
N.A.I.C.S.: 334413
Young Liu *(Chm)*

Foxtron Vehicle Technologies Co., Ltd. (1)
7F No 26 Baogao Rd, Xindian Dist, New Taipei City, 231029, Taiwan
Tel.: (886) 255906168
Web Site: https://www.foxtronev.com
Automobile Parts Mfr & Distr
N.A.I.C.S.: 336110

Fuchuan Co., Ltd. (1)
Binh Xuyen II Industrial Park, Ba Hien Town, Binh Xuyen, Vinh Phuc, Vietnam
Tel.: (84) 2113888608
Web Site: https://www.binhxuyen2ip.com
Electrical Infrastructure Services
N.A.I.C.S.: 517111

Fushan Technology (Vietnam) Limited Liability Company (1)
8 Road 6 Vsip Bac Ninh Phu Chan, Tu Son, Bac Ninh, Vietnam
Tel.: (84) 2033698899
Web Site: https://fihfushan.vn
Electronic Component & Computer Mfr
N.A.I.C.S.: 334111

Genconn Biotech Co., Ltd. (1)
5F No 54 Sec 1 Jhongsiao E Rd, Zhongzheng Dist, Taipei, 100406, Taiwan
Tel.: (886) 255696099
Web Site: https://www.genconn-biotech.com
Medical Equipment Whslr
N.A.I.C.S.: 423450

Hon Hai Precision Industry Co., Ltd. - Taipei Office (1)
No 32 Ji Hu Rd Nei Hu, 114, Taipei, Taiwan
Tel.: (886) 227996111
Sales Range: $1-4.9 Billion
Emp.: 11,941
Digital Still Camera Mfr
N.A.I.C.S.: 333310

ICana B.V. (1)
Blijde Inkomststraat 22, 3000, Leuven, Belgium
Tel.: (32) 16799260
Wireless Telecommunication Services
N.A.I.C.S.: 517112

ICana Inc. (1)
9920 Pacific Heights Blvd Ste 468, San Diego, CA 92121
Tel.: (619) 859-4529
Wireless Telecommunication Services
N.A.I.C.S.: 517112

Icana Ltd. (1)
5F No 28-2 Baogao Road, Xindian District, New Taipei City, 231, Taiwan
Tel.: (886) 227851339
Web Site: https://www.icana-rf.com
Wireless Telecommunication Services
N.A.I.C.S.: 517112

Ingrasys Technology Inc. (1)
No 1188 Nanqing Rd, Luzhu Dist, Taoyuan, 338009, Taiwan
Tel.: (886) 32718288
Web Site: https://www.ingrasys.com
Electronic Parts Mfr & Distr
N.A.I.C.S.: 336320

Joyspeed Global Cargo China Limited (1)
Unit 601-602 6/F Tower One Magnet Place 77-81 Container Port Road, N T, Kwai Chung, China (Hong Kong)
Tel.: (852) 29509028
Web Site: https://www.joyspeed.com
Transportation & Warehouse Services
N.A.I.C.S.: 236220

Jusda Europe s.r.o. (1)
Holandska 37 IV, 530 02, Pardubice, Czech Republic
Tel.: (420) 466056115
Web Site: https://jusdaeurope.com
Warehouse & Logistic Services
N.A.I.C.S.: 541614

Perobot Co., Ltd. (1)
5th Floor No 586 Ruiguang Road, Neihu District, Taipei, 11492, Taiwan
Tel.: (886) 255816338
Web Site: https://www.perobot.com.tw
Computer Equipment Whslr
N.A.I.C.S.: 423430

Phyn LLC (1)
555 Aviation Blvd Ste 180, El Segundo, CA 90245
Web Site: https://phyn.com
Software Development Services
N.A.I.C.S.: 541511

SMART Technologies (GB) Limited (1)
27-28 Eastcastle Street, London, W1W 8DH, United Kingdom
Tel.: (44) 8081699488
Whiteboard & Touch Panel Mfr
N.A.I.C.S.: 339940

SMART Technologies (Germany) GmbH (1)
Gustav-Heinemann-Ufer 72c, 50968, Cologne, Germany
Tel.: (49) 2218461660
Software Development Services
N.A.I.C.S.: 541511

SMART Technologies (Middle East) FZE (1)
4th Floor Jafza View 19 Jebel Ali, PO Box 263017, Dubai, United Arab Emirates
Tel.: (971) 48857794
Whiteboard & Touch Panel Mfr
N.A.I.C.S.: 339940

SMART Technologies (Seattle) Inc. (1)
2401 4th Ave 3rd Fl, Seattle, WA 98121
Software Development Services
N.A.I.C.S.: 541511

SMART Technologies (Singapore) Private Limited (1)
Blk 9005 Tampines Street 93 04-254 Tampines Ind Park A, Singapore, 528839, Singapore
Tel.: (65) 94594258
Web Site: https://www.smartec.sg
Robot Research & Development Services
N.A.I.C.S.: 541715

SafeDX s.r.o. (1)
K Zizkovu 813/2 9, 190 00, Prague, Czech Republic
Tel.: (420) 296238007
Web Site: https://www.safedx.eu
Information Technology Services
N.A.I.C.S.: 541519

Shanghai Joyspeed Global Cargo Co., Ltd. (1)
Rm 1604-1607 No 440 Zhong Shan Nan Er Rd, Shanghai, 200032, China
Tel.: (86) 2164222741
Transportation & Warehouse Services
N.A.I.C.S.: 236220

Sharp Corporation (1)
1 Takumi-cho, Sakai-ku, Sakai, 590-8522, Osaka, Japan **(60.76%)**
Tel.: (81) 722821221
Web Site: https://www.global.sharp
Rev: $15,347,897,810
Assets: $10,510,111,520
Liabilities: $9,469,538,880
Net Worth: $1,040,572,640
Earnings: ($991,367,800)
Emp.: 42,093
Fiscal Year-end: 03/31/2024
Consumer Audio-Visual, Data & Communication Electronics & Home Appliances Mfr & Whslr
N.A.I.C.S.: 334310
Katsuaki Nomura *(Pres & COO)*

Subsidiary (Domestic):

Dynabook Inc. (2)
NBF Toyosu Garden Front Bldg 8F Toyosu 5-6-15, Koto-Ku, Tokyo, 135-8505, Japan **(100%)**
Tel.: (81) 351443000
Web Site: http://www.dynabook-global.azurewebsites.net
Sales & Maintenance of Computers & Equipment
N.A.I.C.S.: 334118
Kiyofumi Kakudo *(Pres & CEO)*

Subsidiary (US):

Dynabook Americas, Inc. (3)
5241 California Ave Ste 100, Irvine, CA 92617 **(100%)**
Tel.: (949) 583-3000
Web Site: http://us.toshiba.com
Mfr & Sales of Laptop & Desktop Computers, Copiers, Facsimile Machines, Electronic Key Telephones, PBX Systems, Computer Disk Drives, Cellular Mobile Telephones, Laser & Dot Matrix Printers
N.A.I.C.S.: 334111
James Robbins *(Pres & Gen Mgr)*

Subsidiary (Non-US):

Dynabook Europe GmbH (3)
Hammerfelddamm 8, 41460, Neuss, Germany
Tel.: (49) 213115801
Web Site: http://www.toshiba.de
Mfr & Sales of Laptop Computers; Sales of Office Equipment
N.A.I.C.S.: 334118

Subsidiary (Non-US):

Dynabook - UK (4)
Consort House 1 Prince Road, Weybridge, KT13 9TU, Surrey, United Kingdom
Tel.: (44) 932841600
Web Site: http://www.toshiba.co.uk
Sales of Information Systems Office Equipment
N.A.I.C.S.: 449210

Dynabook France (4)
2 Avenue Gambetta, 92400, Paris, France **(100%)**
Tel.: (33) 187156565
Web Site: http://www.toshiba.fr
Information Systems Sales; Office Equipment & Copier Mfr
N.A.I.C.S.: 423420

Subsidiary (Non-US):

Dynabook Singapore Pte. Ltd (3)
20 Pasir Panjang Road #12-25/28 Mapletree Business City, Singapore, 117439, Singapore
Tel.: (65) 62737555
Web Site: http://asia.dynabook.com
Laptops & Accessories Mfr
N.A.I.C.S.: 334310

Subsidiary (Non-US):

P.T. Sharp Electronics Indonesia (2)
Jl Raya Prapen No 305 Kel Sidosermo Kec, Wonocolo, Surabaya, 60238, Jawa Timur, Indonesia
Tel.: (62) 31 847 8010
Web Site: https://id.sharp
Audio-Video Electronics & Household Appliances Mfr
N.A.I.C.S.: 334310

S & O Electronics (Malaysia) Sdn. Bhd. (2)
Lot 202 Bakar Arang Industrial Estate, 8000, Sungai Petani, Kedah, Malaysia
Tel.: (60) 44552196
Consumer Electronics Mfr & Whslr
N.A.I.C.S.: 334310

Subsidiary (Domestic):

Sharp-Roxy Sales & Service Co (M) Sdn. Bhd. (3)
387 & 387A Taman Pringgit Jaya, 75400, Melaka, Malaysia
Tel.: (60) 62836540
Consumer Electronics, Office Equipment & Solar Power Systems Whslr
N.A.I.C.S.: 423620

Subsidiary (Non-US):

Sharp (Phils.) Corporation (2)
Km South Superhighway 23 W Service Rd Alabang, Muntinlupa, Philippines **(100%)**
Tel.: (63) 28427777
Web Site: http://www.sharp.ph
Consumer Electronics & Office Equipment Mfr & Whslr
N.A.I.C.S.: 335220

Sharp (Taiwan) Electronics Corporation (2)
4th Floor No 2 Section 3 Citizen Avenue Zhongzheng Road, Taipei, Taiwan
Tel.: (886) 223412228
Web Site: http://tw.sharp
Holding Company
N.A.I.C.S.: 551112

Sharp Appliances (Thailand) Ltd. (2)
37 Bang Na-Trat Rd Tambon Bang Samak, Amphoe Bang Pakong Chang Wa, Chachoengsao, 24180, Thailand
Tel.: (66) 38538663
Consumer Electronics & Office Equipment Mfr & Whslr
N.A.I.C.S.: 334310

Sharp Business Systems (India) Private Limited (2)
3rd Floor Add India Centre Plot No 9 Sector 125, Noida, 201301, Uttar Pradesh, India
Tel.: (91) 120 335 8888
Web Site: https://in.sharp

HON HAI PRECISION INDUSTRY CO., LTD.

Hon Hai Precision Industry Co., Ltd.—(Continued)
Electronic Components Distr
N.A.I.C.S.: 423690

Branch (Domestic):

Sharp Corporation - Tokyo (2)
Seavans South Building 1-2-3 Shibaura, Minato-ku, Tokyo, 105-0023, Japan (100%)
Tel.: (81) 354468221
Web Site: http://www.sharp-world.com
Executive & Legislative Offices
N.A.I.C.S.: 921140

Subsidiary (Non-US):

Sharp Corporation Mexico, S.A. de C.V. (2)
Jaime Balmes No 8 octavo piso Corporativo Polanco Col, Los Morales Polanco Delegacion Miguel Hidalgo, 11510, Mexico, Mexico
Tel.: (52) 558 000 2600
Web Site: https://sharp.com.mx
Consumer Electronics Distr
N.A.I.C.S.: 423620

Sharp Corporation of Australia Pty. Ltd. (2)
2 Julius Ave, PO Box 84, Macquarie Park, Macquarie Park, 2113, NSW, Australia (100%)
Tel.: (61) 29 830 4844
Web Site: https://www.sharp.net.au
Consumer Electronics & Office Equipment Whslr
N.A.I.C.S.: 423620
Hitoshi Kagawa *(Mng Dir)*

Sharp Corporation of New Zealand Ltd. (2)
59 Hugo Johnston Drive Penrose, Auckland, 1061, New Zealand (100%)
Tel.: (64) 9 920 4165
Web Site: https://www.sharp.net.nz
Consumer Electronics & Office Equipment Whslr
N.A.I.C.S.: 423620

Sharp Electronica Espana S.A. (2)
WTC Almeda Park Placa de la Pau s/n, Edificio-6 Planta-4, 08940, Barcelona, Spain (100%)
Tel.: (34) 935819700
Web Site: http://www.sharp.es
Consumer Electronics Mfr & Whslr; Office Equipment Whslr
N.A.I.C.S.: 334310
Ignacio Fraile *(Gen Mgr-Fin)*

Sharp Electronics (Europe) GmbH (2)
Industriestrasse 180, 50999, Cologne, Germany (100%)
Tel.: (49) 2236323100
Web Site: https://www.sharp.de
Consumer Electronics, Office Equipment & Electronic Components Whslr
N.A.I.C.S.: 423620

Branch (Non-US):

Sharp Electronics (Europe) GmbH (3)
Handelskai 342, 1020, Vienna, Austria (100%)
Tel.: (43) 1727190
Web Site: http://www.sharp.at
Consumer Electronics & Office Equipment Whslr
N.A.I.C.S.: 423620

Subsidiary (Non-US):

Sharp Electronics (Europe) Limited (2)
4 Furzeground Way Stockley Park, Uxbridge, London, UB11 1EZ, Mddx, United Kingdom
Tel.: (44) 208 734 2000
Web Site: https://www.sharp.eu
Liquid Crystal Display Mfr
N.A.I.C.S.: 334419

Sharp Electronics (Malaysia) Sdn. Bhd. (2)
No 76-2 Persiaran Bayan Indah, Sungei Nibong, 11900, Pulau Penang, Malaysia

Tel.: (60) 4 644 3642
Web Site: https://my.sharp
Consumer Electronics Design & Development; Industrial Manufacturing Components & Replacement Parts Whslr
N.A.I.C.S.: 541715

Sharp Electronics (Nordic) AB (2)
Gustavslundsvagen 12 Alvik, Box 14098, 16714, Bromma, Sweden
Tel.: (46) 86343600
Web Site: http://www.sharp.se
Consumer Electronics & Office Equipment Whslr
N.A.I.C.S.: 423620

Sharp Electronics (Schweiz) AG (2)
Moosstrasse 2a, 8803, Ruschlikon, Switzerland (100%)
Tel.: (41) 44 846 6111
Web Site: https://www.sharp.ch
Consumer Electronics & Office Equipment Whslr
N.A.I.C.S.: 423620

Sharp Electronics (Vietnam) Company Limited (2)
3rd Floor Saigon Center No 9 Dinh Tien Hoang, District 1, Ho Chi Minh City, Vietnam
Tel.: (84) 283 910 7499
Web Site: https://vn.sharp
Electronic Components Mfr
N.A.I.C.S.: 334419

Sharp Electronics Benelux B.V. (2)
Papendorpseweg 75, 3528 BJ, Utrecht, Netherlands (100%)
Tel.: (31) 30 635 9500
Web Site: https://www.sharp.nl
Consumer Electronics, Office Equipment & Electronic Components Whslr
N.A.I.C.S.: 423620

Subsidiary (US):

Sharp Electronics Corporation (2)
100 Paragon Dr, Montvale, NJ 07645
Tel.: (201) 529-8200
Web Site: http://www.sharpusa.com
Consumer Audio-Visual, Data & Communication Electronics & Home Appliances Mfr & Whslr
N.A.I.C.S.: 423420
George Grafanakis *(Assoc Dir-Document Hardware)*

Unit (Domestic):

Sharp Business Systems - Washington (3)
11201 SE 8th St Ste 210, Bellevue, WA 98004
Tel.: (425) 885-4755
Web Site: https://www.sharp-sbs.com
Office Equipment & Supplies Distr
N.A.I.C.S.: 423420

Subsidiary (Domestic):

Sharp Business Systems of North Carolina (3)
4404 Stuart Andrew Blvd, Charlotte, NC 28217
Tel.: (704) 523-3333
Web Site: http://www.nc.sharp-sbs.com
Office Equipment & Supplies Distr
N.A.I.C.S.: 423420
Brian Alspector *(Reg Pres-SBS-North Carolina)*

Branch (Non-US):

Sharp Corporation Mexico S.A de C.V. (3)
Jaime Balmes No 8 octavo piso Corporativo Polanco, Col Los Morales Polanco Miguel Hidalgo, 11510, Mexico, Mexico
Tel.: (52) 5580002600
Web Site: https://www.sharp.com.mx
Consumer Electronics Whslr
N.A.I.C.S.: 423620

Branch (Domestic):

Sharp Electronics Corp. - Huntington Beach Office (3)
5901 Bolsa Ave, Huntington Beach, CA 92647
Tel.: (714) 903-4600

Consumer Electronics Marketing, Sales, Warehousing, Distribution, Repair & Maintenance Services
N.A.I.C.S.: 423620

Division (Domestic):

Sharp Imaging and Information Company of America (3)
Sharp Plaza, Mahwah, NJ 07495-1163
Tel.: (800) 237-4277
Web Site: http://www.sharpusa.com
Multifunction Printers & Copiers Mfr
N.A.I.C.S.: 333248
Mike Marusic *(Pres & CEO)*

Subsidiary (Domestic):

ACE Office Solutions Inc. (4)
5-A Dickerson Rd, Hillsborough, NJ 08844
Tel.: (908) 704-0400
Web Site: http://aceofs.com
Electronic Parts & Equipment Merchant Whslr
N.A.I.C.S.: 423690
George Skibinski *(Pres)*

Subsidiary (Domestic):

Ace Copy Systems, Inc. (5)
619 River Dr Ste 230, Elmwood Park, NJ 07407
Tel.: (646) 558-5575
Sales Range: $1-9.9 Million
Emp.: 44
Miscellaneous Store Retailers (except Tobacco Stores)
N.A.I.C.S.: 459999

Division (Domestic):

Sharp Business Systems (4)
100 Paragon Dr, Montvale, NJ 07645
Tel.: (201) 529-8644
Web Site: http://www.sharp-sbs.com
Office Equipment Merchant Whslr
N.A.I.C.S.: 423420
Tim Renegar *(Pres)*

Subsidiary (Domestic):

Saratoga Technologies, Inc. (5)
101 Med Tech Pkwy Ste 307, Johnson City, TN 37604
Tel.: (423) 282-4220
Web Site: http://www.saratogaus.com
Technology Company; Networking, Printing, Communications & Business Services
N.A.I.C.S.: 541512
David Temple *(Pres & CEO)*

Subsidiary (Domestic):

Sharp Laboratories of America, Inc. (3)
17200 SE Mill Plain Blvd Ste 200, Vancouver, WA 98683
Tel.: (360) 834-8600
Web Site: https://www.sharplabs.com
Digital Image Processing Technology & Multimedia Telecommunications Research & Development
N.A.I.C.S.: 541715
Kecia Andersen *(Sr Dir-Fin & Bus Ops)*

Sharp Microelectronics of the Americas (3)
5700 NW Pacific Rim Blvd, Camas, WA 98607
Tel.: (360) 834-8700
Microelectronics Marketer & Whslr
N.A.I.C.S.: 423690

Subsidiary (Non-US):

Sharp Electronics France S.A. (2)
244 route de Seysses, CS 53646, 31036, Toulouse, Cedex, France
Tel.: (33) 82 585 0950
Web Site: https://www.sharp.fr
Consumer Electronics & Office Equipment Whslr
N.A.I.C.S.: 423620
Bruno Humbert *(CEO)*

Sharp Electronics Incorporated of Korea (2)
661-10 Deungchon-Dong, Kangseo-Gu, Seoul, Korea (South)
Tel.: (82) 236606600
Web Site: http://www.sharp-korea.co.kr

INTERNATIONAL PUBLIC

Consumer Electronics & Office Equipment Whslr
N.A.I.C.S.: 423620

Sharp Electronics Russia LLC (2)
2nd Syromyatnichesky lane 1 BC Delta-Plaza, 105120, Moscow, Russia
Tel.: (7) 4957902343
Web Site: https://www.sharp.ru
Electronic Components Mfr
N.A.I.C.S.: 334419

Sharp Electronics of Canada Ltd. (2)
335 Britannia Road East, Mississauga, L4Z 1W9, ON, Canada (100%)
Tel.: (905) 890-2100
Web Site: https://www.sharp.ca
Consumer Electronics & Office Equipment Whslr
N.A.I.C.S.: 423620
Carmine Cinerari *(Pres)*

Subsidiary (Domestic):

Sharp Finance Corporation (2)
5-1-1 Kojimachi Sumitomo Real Estate Kojimachi Garden Tower, Chiyoda-ku, Tokyo, 102-0083, Japan
Tel.: (81) 35 275 2900
Web Site: https://www.sfc.sharp.co.jp
Emp.: 551
Leasing, Real Estate & Insurance Services
N.A.I.C.S.: 523999
Takao Asai *(Pres)*

Subsidiary (Non-US):

Sharp Hong Kong Limited (2)
Level 26 Tower 1 Kawloon Commerce Ctr, 51 Kwai Cheong Rd, Kwai Chung, NT, China (Hong Kong)
Tel.: (852) 24235151
Web Site: http://www.sharp.com.hk
Consumer Electronics, Office Equipment & Electronic Components Whslr
N.A.I.C.S.: 423620

Sharp India Limited (2)
Gat No 686/4 Koregaan Bhima, Taluka Shirur, Pune, 412216, Maharashtra, India
Tel.: (91) 213 725 2453
Web Site: https://www.sharpindialimited.com
Consumer Electronics Mfr & Whslr
N.A.I.C.S.: 334310

Sharp International Finance (U.K.) Plc (2)
4 Furzeground Way Stockley Park, Uxbridge, UB11 1EZ, United Kingdom
Tel.: (44) 20 8734 2099
Financial Management Services
N.A.I.C.S.: 523999

Sharp Korea Corporation Ltd. (2)
418 Chung Cheon Dong Bupyong-ku, Incheon, 418080, Korea (South)
Tel.: (82) 325108000
Office Equipment & Air Conditioners Mfr & Whslr
N.A.I.C.S.: 333310

Sharp Laboratories of Europe Limited (2)
Oxford Science Park, Oxford, OX4 4GB, United Kingdom (100%)
Tel.: (44) 1865747711
Web Site: http://www.sharp.co.uk
Consumer Electronics Research & Development
N.A.I.C.S.: 541715

Sharp Manufacturing France S.A. (2)
12 Rue Louis Courtois de Vicose Building doors, Toulouse, Cedex 1, France
Tel.: (33) 149903400
Web Site: http://www.sharp.fr
Office Equipment Mfr & Whslr
N.A.I.C.S.: 333310

Sharp Manufacturing Poland Sp. z o. o. (2)
Poleczki 33, 02-822, Warsaw, Poland
Tel.: (48) 225458100
Liquid Crystal Display Mfr
N.A.I.C.S.: 334419

Sharp Middle East Free Zone Establishment (2)

AND PRIVATE COMPANIES

Jebel Ali Free Zone, Dubai, United Arab Emirates
Tel.: (971) 4 812 9311
Web Site: https://www.sharpmea.com
Consumer Electronics & Office Equipment Whslr
N.A.I.C.S.: 423620

Subsidiary (Domestic):

Sharp Mie Corporation (2)
2010 Toshima Anou-cho, Tsu, 514-2322, Mie, Japan
Tel.: (81) 592683838
Electronic Component Mfr & Distr
N.A.I.C.S.: 334419

Joint Venture (Domestic):

Sharp NEC Display Solutions, Ltd. (2)
MS Shibaura Bldg 10 F 4 13 23 Shibaura, Minato-ku, Tokyo, 108 0023, Japan (66%)
Tel.: (81) 354465311
Web Site: http://www.nec-display.com
Sales Range: $100-124.9 Million
Emp.: 700
Mfr of Computers; Joint Venture of NEC Corporation (50%) & Mitsubishi Electric Corporation (50%)
N.A.I.C.S.: 334118
Helen Sheldrake (Sls Mgr-Channel)

Subsidiary (US):

Sharp NEC Display Solutions of America, Inc. (3)
500 Park Blvd Ste 1100, Itasca, IL 60143
Tel.: (858) 831-9327
Web Site: http://www.necdisplay.com
Electronic Display Equipment & Projectors Distr
N.A.I.C.S.: 423690
Betsy Larson (VP-Sls-Channel)

Subsidiary (Domestic):

Sharp Niigata Electronics Corporation (2)
1310 Kamihachimai, Niigata, 950-1431, Japan
Tel.: (81) 253723171
Web Site: http://www.sharp.co.jp
Consumer Electronics & Office Equipment Parts & Electronic Components Mfr & Whslr
N.A.I.C.S.: 334419

Subsidiary (Non-US):

Sharp Semiconductor Indonesia (2)
Margakaya West Telukjambe, Karawang, 41361, West Java, Indonesia
Tel.: (62) 218901512
Electronic Components Mfr & Whslr
N.A.I.C.S.: 334413

Sharp Singapore Electronics Corporation Pte. Ltd. (2)
438B Alexandra Road 06-02, Alexandra Technopark, Singapore, 119968, Singapore (100%)
Tel.: (65) 6 419 3388
Web Site: https://sg.sharp
Electronic Components Service Center
N.A.I.C.S.: 423690

Sharp Software Development India Pvt Ltd. (2)
Unit 05 Level 03 Innovator International Tech Park Whitefield Road, ITPL Whitefield Road, Bengaluru, 560 066, India
Tel.: (91) 802 841 0645
Web Site: https://www.sharp.co.in
Software Development Services
N.A.I.C.S.: 541511
Praveen Kanipakam (Pres)

Subsidiary (Domestic):

Sharp Support & Service Corporation (2)
Sharp Makuhari Building 1-9-2 Nakase, Mihama-ku, Chiba, 261-8520, Japan
Tel.: (81) 43 299 8709
Web Site: http://www.sharp-sbs.co.jp
Consumer Electronics Repair & Maintenance Services
N.A.I.C.S.: 811210
Isao Yoneda (Pres)

Subsidiary (Non-US):

Sharp Thai Co., Ltd. (2)
6/10 Pipatanasin Building 19th-20th Floor Soi Patanasin, Naradhiwas Rajanagarindra Road Thungmahamek Sathorn, Bangkok, 10120, Thailand
Tel.: (66) 2 855 8899
Web Site: https://th.sharp
Consumer Electronics, Office Equipment & Solar Power Systems Whslr
N.A.I.C.S.: 423620
Robert Wu (Mng Dir)

Subsidiary (Domestic):

Hifi Orient Thai PLC (3)
83/161-162 Soi Ngamwongwan 47 Chinkhet 2, Thung Song Hong Subdistrict Lak Si District, 10210, Bangkok, Thailand (80%)
Tel.: (66) 29 545 2813
Web Site: http://www.hifithai.co.th
Sales Range: $150-199.9 Million
Emp.: 300
Electronic Parts & Equipment Whslr
N.A.I.C.S.: 423690

Subsidiary (Domestic):

Sharp Trading Corporation (2)
1 Takumi-cho, Sakai-ku, Sakai, 590-8522, Japan
Tel.: (81) 666211221
Web Site: http://www.sharp-world.com
Consumer Electronics, Office Equipment & Electronic Components Importer & Whslr
N.A.I.C.S.: 423620

Sharp Yonago Corporation (2)
650 Ohtsukanoni, Sekishufu, Yonago, 689-3524, Tottori, Japan
Tel.: (81) 859275111
Web Site: http://www.sharp-world.com
Liquid Crystal Displays Developer, Mfr & Whslr
N.A.I.C.S.: 334419

Subsidiary (Non-US):

Sharp-Roxy Sales (Singapore) Pte., Ltd. (2)
2 Leng Kee Rd, Singapore, 159086, Singapore
Tel.: (65) 64195222
Consumer Electronics & Office Equipment Whslr
N.A.I.C.S.: 423620

Sharp Jusda Logistics Corp. (1)
1 Takumi-cho, Sakai-ku, Sakai, 590-8522, Osaka, Japan
Tel.: (81) 722821438
Web Site: https://www.sjlscm.co.jp
Emp.: 267
Marine & Land Transportation Services
N.A.I.C.S.: 541614

Sound Solutions Austria GmbH (1)
Gutheil-Schoder-Gasse 8-12, 1100, Vienna, Austria
Tel.: (43) 1608700
Web Site: https://www.sound-solutions-austria.com
Acoustic Technology Services
N.A.I.C.S.: 541330

Sound Solutions International Co., Ltd. (1)
No 20 Tongji South Road, Beijing Economic and Technology Development Area, Beijing, China
Tel.: (86) 1059090500
Web Site: https://www.sound-solutions.com
Electronic Component & Mechanical Equipment Whslr
N.A.I.C.S.: 423690

Syntrend Creative Park Co., Ltd. (1)
No 2 Sec 3 Civil Blvd, Zhongzheng Dist, New Taipei City, 10058, Taiwan
Tel.: (886) 809093300
Web Site: https://www.syntrend.com.tw
Family Entertainment Streaming Services
N.A.I.C.S.: 512110

Xsemi Corporation (1)
9F-3 No 1 Huanke 1st Road, Hsinchu County, Zhubei, 302047, Taiwan
Tel.: (886) 35558686
Web Site: https://www.xsemi-corporation.com
Electronic Parts Mfr & Distr
N.A.I.C.S.: 336320

HON KWOK LAND INVESTMENT CO., LTD.
23rd Floor Wing On Centre 111 Connaught Road, Sheung Wan, Central, China (Hong Kong)
Tel.: (852) 25237177 HK
Web Site: https://honkwok.com.hk
Year Founded: 1965
0160—(HKG)
Rev.: $142,687,736
Assets: $2,649,058,310
Liabilities: $1,035,117,769
Net Worth: $1,613,940,541
Earnings: $11,835,592
Emp.: 360
Fiscal Year-end: 03/31/22
Holding Company
N.A.I.C.S.: 551112
Xiao-Ping Li (Exec Dir)

HONASA CONSUMER LIMITED
Unit No - 404 4th Floor City Centre Plot No 05 Sector-12 Dwarka, New Delhi, 110075, India
Tel.: (91) 1244071960
Web Site: https://www.honasa.in
Year Founded: 2016
HONASA—(NSE)
Rev.: $171,526,967
Assets: $112,602,557
Liabilities: $36,624,943
Net Worth: $75,977,614
Earnings: ($14,611,387)
Emp.: 993
Fiscal Year-end: 03/31/23
Online Shopping Services
N.A.I.C.S.: 425120

HONBRIDGE HOLDINGS LTD.
Unit 5402 54/F Central Plaza 18 Harbour Road, Wanchai, China (Hong Kong)
Tel.: (852) 28798888 Ky
Web Site: http://www.8137.hk
8137—(HKG)
Sales Range: $1-9.9 Million
Emp.: 522
Lithium Battery Mfr & Distr
N.A.I.C.S.: 335910
Xuechu He (Chm)

HONCO INC.
1190 Chemin Industriel, Saint-Nicolas, J7B1B1, QC, Canada
Tel.: (418) 831-2245
Web Site: http://www.honco.ca
Year Founded: 1974
Rev.: $20,372,500
Emp.: 25
Industrial Building & Warehouse Services
N.A.I.C.S.: 541490
Paul Lacasse (Founder & Pres)

HONDA GABRIEL
7020 boul Henri Bourassa E, Anjou, H1E 7K7, QC, Canada
Tel.: (514) 329-7777
Web Site: http://www.hondagabriel.com
Rev.: $46,689,438
Emp.: 165
New & Used Car Dealers
N.A.I.C.S.: 441110
Cosimo Scarfo (Bus Mgr)

HONDA ILE PERROT
40 Boulevard Don Quichotte, L'Ile Perrot, J7V 6N5, QC, Canada
Tel.: (514) 453-8416
Web Site: http://www.hondaileperrot.com

HONDA MOTOR CO., LTD.

Year Founded: 1979
Sales Range: $10-24.9 Million
New & Used Car Dealers
N.A.I.C.S.: 441110
Simon Castonguay (Mgr-Renewal)

HONDA MOTOR CO., LTD.
2-1-1 Minami-Aoyama, Minato-ku, Tokyo, 107-8556, Japan
Tel.: (81) 334231111 JP
Web Site: https://www.honda.co.jp
Year Founded: 1948
HMC—(NYSE)
Rev.: $134,977,180,574
Assets: $196,723,763,880
Liabilities: $110,791,366,402
Net Worth: $85,932,397,478
Earnings: $7,813,608,648
Emp.: 194,993
Fiscal Year-end: 03/31/24
Motorcycles, All Terrain Vehicles, Automobiles, Portable Generators, Lawn Mowers, Power Tillers & General Purpose Engines Mfr
N.A.I.C.S.: 336110
Yasuhide Mizuno (Mng Exec Officer)

Subsidiaries:

AC Mobil d.o.o. (1)
Baragova 9, 1000, Ljubljana, Slovenia
Tel.: (386) 1 588 3240
Automobile Parts Distr
N.A.I.C.S.: 441330

AS Domzale Moto Center d.o.o. (1)
Blatnica 3a OIC, 1236, Trzin, Slovenia
Tel.: (386) 1 562 3700
Web Site: https://www.ascenter.si
Motor Cycle Distr
N.A.I.C.S.: 423120

Afritool (Pty) Ltd. (1)
Av 25 de Setembro N 2009, 2183, Maputo, Mozambique
Tel.: (258) 2 130 9068
Motor Cycle Distr
N.A.I.C.S.: 423120

Aikitec Co., Ltd. (1)
1-1-1 Sakaehigashi Morioka, Chita-gun, Higashiura, 470-2101, Aichi, Japan
Tel.: (81) 56 282 3270
Web Site: https://www.aikitec.co.jp
Emp.: 523
Automobile Parts Mfr & Distr
N.A.I.C.S.: 336390

American Honda Finance Corp. (1)
1919 Torrance Blvd, Torrance, CA 90501 (100%)
Tel.: (310) 972-2288
Web Site: https://www.hondafinancialservices.com
Rev.: $8,184,000,000
Assets: $68,891,000,000
Liabilities: $49,866,000,000
Net Worth: $19,025,000,000
Earnings: $1,053,000,000
Emp.: 1,350
Fiscal Year-end: 03/31/2023
Financial Services
N.A.I.C.S.: 522291
Paul C. Honda (VP & Asst Sec)

American Honda Motor Co., Inc. (1)
1919 Torrance Blvd, Torrance, CA 90501-2746 (100%)
Tel.: (310) 783-2275
Sales Range: $25-49.9 Million
Emp.: 3,000
Motorcycles, Autos & Power Products Mfr
N.A.I.C.S.: 423110

Subsidiary (Domestic):

Honda International Trading Co. (H.I.T.) (2)
1919 Torrance Blvd, Torrance, CA 90501-2722 (100%)
Tel.: (310) 783-2000
Export Product Purchasing
N.A.I.C.S.: 423120

Honda North America Inc. (2)
1919 Torrance Blvd, Torrance, CA 90501-2722 (100%)

3459

HONDA MOTOR CO., LTD.

Honda Motor Co., Ltd.—(Continued)

Tel.: (310) 783-2000
Web Site: http://www.hondacorporate.com
Coordinating Operations of Subsidiaries in North America
N.A.I.C.S.: 423110
John William Mendel (Exec VP-Acura Auto Sls)

Honda Power Equipment Manufacturing, Inc. (2)
3721 Nc Hwy 119, Swepsonville, NC 27359 (100%)
Tel.: (336) 578-5300
Web Site: http://www.honda.com
Sales Range: $75-99.9 Million
Mfr of Lawn Mowers
N.A.I.C.S.: 333112

Honda of America Manufacturing, Inc. (2)
24000 Honda Pkwy, Marysville, OH 43040 (100%)
Tel.: (937) 642-5000
Web Site: http://www.ohio.honda.com
Mfr of Motorcycles, Automobiles & All-Terrain Vehicles
N.A.I.C.S.: 336110

Asama Coldwater Mfg. (1)
180 Asama Pkwy, Coldwater, MI 49036-1590
Tel.: (517) 279-1090
Web Site: http://www.asamacm.com
Sales Range: $100-124.9 Million
Emp.: 385
Drums Mfr
N.A.I.C.S.: 336390

Asian Honda Motor Co., Ltd. (1)
14 Sarasin Building Surasak Road Silom, BangRak, Bangkok, 10500, Thailand (100%)
Tel.: (66) 38571001
Web Site: https://career.asianhonda.com
Sales Range: $100-124.9 Million
Emp.: 400
Import & Distribution of Honda Products
N.A.I.C.S.: 441227

Subsidiary (Domestic):

Asian Autoparts Co., Ltd. (2)
4/1 Moo 1 Bangna-Trad Road, Bangkok, 10540, Thailand
Tel.: (66) 2337003344
Honda Parts
N.A.I.C.S.: 336991

Honda Lock Thai Co., Ltd. (1)
Amata City Industrial Estate 700/309 Moo 6 Chonburi, Don Hua Lo Subdistrict Mueang Chonburi District, Chon Buri, 20000, Thailand
Tel.: (66) 38214805
Web Site: https://www.minebea-accesssolutions.co.th
Hardware
N.A.I.C.S.: 332510

Atlas Honda Limited (1)
1 Mcleod Road, Lahore, 54000, Pakistan
Tel.: (92) 423 722 5015
Web Site: http://www.atlashonda.com.pk
Rev.: $819,286,499
Assets: $294,494,942
Liabilities: $163,913,310
Net Worth: $130,581,632
Earnings: $34,683,875
Emp.: 2,299
Fiscal Year-end: 03/31/2022
Motorcycle Mfr & Distr; Joint Venture of Atlas Group & Honda Motor Co., Ltd.
N.A.I.C.S.: 336991
Suhail Ahmed (VP-Mktg)

Banco Honda S.A (1)
Rua Dr Jose Aureo Bustamante 377, Santo Amaro, Sao Paulo, 04710-090, Brazil
Tel.: (55) 1121727007
Web Site: https://www.bancohonda.com.br
Automotive Distr
N.A.I.C.S.: 423110

Bangladesh Honda Private Limited (1)
East Tower 10th Floor 111 Bir Uttam C R Dutta Road, Monem Business District Karwanbazar, Dhaka, 1205, Bangladesh

Tel.: (880) 2 963 2273
Web Site: https://www.bdhonda.com
Motorcycle Mfr
N.A.I.C.S.: 336991

Boon Siew Honda Sdn. Bhd. (1)
721 Persiaran Cassia Selatan 1, Kawasan Perindustrian Batu Kawan, 14100, Simpang Empat, Pulau Pinang, Malaysia
Tel.: (60) 4 506 3333
Web Site: https://boonsiewhonda.com.my
Motor Cycle Mfr & Distr
N.A.I.C.S.: 336991

Bukit Batok Driving Centre Ltd. (1)
815 Bukit Batok West Ave 5, Singapore, 659085, Singapore
Tel.: (65) 6 561 1233
Web Site: https://info.bbdc.sg
Driving School Services
N.A.I.C.S.: 611692

C.I.A.P. S.p.A (1)
Via della Concia 10-12, 40023, Castel Guelfo di Bologna, Italy
Tel.: (39) 0542487411
Web Site: http://www.ciapspa.com
Sales Range: $25-49.9 Million
Emp.: 85
Automotive Gear Parts Mfr
N.A.I.C.S.: 336390

Cardington Yutaka Technologies Inc. (1)
575 W Main St, Cardington, OH 43315
Tel.: (419) 864-8777
Web Site: http://www.yutakatech.com
Sales Range: $100-124.9 Million
Emp.: 500
Motor Vehicle Parts & Accessories
N.A.I.C.S.: 336390

Dah Chong Hong Industrial Machinery Co., Ltd. (1)
9/F DCH Building 20 Kai Cheung Road, Kowloon Bay, China (Hong Kong)
Tel.: (852) 2 768 2992
Web Site: https://dch.com.hk
Industrial Machinery Distr
N.A.I.C.S.: 423830

Diesel Electrica Lda. (1)
Av Das FPLM 1690 C P 964 Paragem Sabrina, Maputo, Mozambique
Tel.: (258) 2 146 0094
Web Site: https://www.dieselelectrica.co.mz
Motor Cycle Distr
N.A.I.C.S.: 423120

Dongfeng Honda Automobile Co., Ltd. (1)
No 283 Checheng East Road, Wuhan Economic and Technological Development Zone, Wuhan, 430056, Hubei, China
Tel.: (86) 278 428 6114
Web Site: https://www.dongfeng-honda.com
Automotive Parts Mfr & Distr
N.A.I.C.S.: 336390

E.A.L Man Hin & Sons Ltd. (1)
31 Brabant Street, Port Louis, Mauritius
Tel.: (230) 203 6300
Motor Cycle Distr
N.A.I.C.S.: 423120

EHW (Seychelles) Ltd. (1)
VCS Building Le Chantier, PO Box 1000, Mahe, Victoria, Seychelles
Tel.: (248) 676000
Web Site: https://www.ehw.sc
Motor Cycle Distr
N.A.I.C.S.: 423120

Eastern Nova Co., Ltd. (1)
No 590 Bo Aung Kyaw Road Yangon Pathein Road, 7 Quarter Industrial Zone Hlaingthaya, Yangon, Myanmar
Tel.: (95) 996 114 8888
Automotive Repair Services
N.A.I.C.S.: 811111

Elesys North America Inc. (1)
70 Crestridge Dr Ste 150, Suwanee, GA 30024
Tel.: (770) 904-3400
Web Site: https://www.elesys-na.com
Sales Range: $400-449.9 Million
Emp.: 1,275
Automotive Safety Electronics
N.A.I.C.S.: 336390

Gasan Zammit Motors Co., Ltd. (1)
Mriehel Bypass, Birkirkara, BKR 3000, Malta
Tel.: (356) 2 778 8200
Web Site: https://gasanzammit.com
Automotive Services
N.A.I.C.S.: 811111

Ge Honda Aero Engines LLC (1)
2987 Tucker St, Burlington, NC 27215
Tel.: (513) 552-7820
Web Site: https://www.gehonda.com
Engine Repair Services
N.A.I.C.S.: 811111
Melvyn Heard (Pres)

Hamamatsu Manufacturing Facility (1)
1-13-1 Aoihigashi, Naka Ward, Hamamatsu, 433-8501, Shizuoka, Japan (100%)
Tel.: (81) 534392011
Web Site: https://www.honda.co.jp
Sales Range: $800-899.9 Million
Emp.: 4,500
Mfr of Motorcycles, Power Products & Transmissions
N.A.I.C.S.: 336991
Nitfugu Magsukawa (Mgr)

Hirose Seiko Co., Ltd. (1)
16079-42 Dougasako Sadowarachohigashikaminaka, Miyazaki, 880-0303, Japan
Tel.: (81) 98 530 5806
Web Site: https://www.hondalock.co.jp
Die Mfr
N.A.I.C.S.: 333514
Noboru Takahashi (Pres & CEO)

Honda (Suisse) S.A (1)
10 Rte des Moulihres, 1214, Vernier, Switzerland
Tel.: (41) 229390909
Web Site: http://www.world.honda.com
Sales Range: $25-49.9 Million
Emp.: 60
Automobiles
N.A.I.C.S.: 336110

Honda Access Corporation (1)
8-18-4 Nobidome, Niiza, 352-8589, Saitama, Japan
Tel.: (81) 484772511
Emp.: 709
Automotive Parts Mfr & Distr
N.A.I.C.S.: 336390

Honda Access Europe N.V. (1)
Wijngaardveld 1, 9300, Aalst, Belgium
Tel.: (32) 53725111
Web Site: https://honda-access-europe.com
Sales Range: $25-49.9 Million
Emp.: 54
Automobile Mfr
N.A.I.C.S.: 336110

Honda Aero, Inc. (1)
2987 Tucker St, Burlington, NC 27215 (100%)
Tel.: (513) 552-7820
Web Site: https://www.gehonda.com
Sales Range: $25-49.9 Million
Emp.: 40
Aeronautical Engine Systems Mfr
N.A.I.C.S.: 336412

Honda Aircraft Company, LLC (1)
6430 Ballinger Rd, Greensboro, NC 27410
Tel.: (336) 662-0246
Web Site: https://www.hondajet.com
Aircraft Equipment Mfr & Distr
N.A.I.C.S.: 336413

Honda Airways Co., Ltd. (1)
53-1 Demarushimogo Kawajimamachi, Hiki, 350-0141, Saitama, Japan
Tel.: (81) 492991111
Web Site: http://www.honda-air.com
Emp.: 80
Air Charter Services
N.A.I.C.S.: 488190
Koichi Aonami (Pres & CEO)

Honda Atlas Cars Pakistan Ltd. (1)
43 km Multan Road Manga Mandi, Lahore, Pakistan
Tel.: (92) 423 538 4671
Web Site: https://www.honda.com.pk
Rev.: $670,977,149
Assets: $436,333,528
Liabilities: $312,377,426

INTERNATIONAL PUBLIC

Net Worth: $123,956,102
Earnings: $15,586,516
Emp.: 2,274
Fiscal Year-end: 03/31/2022
Car Mfr; Owned by Honda Motor Co., Ltd. & Atlas Group of Companies
N.A.I.C.S.: 336110
Aamir H. Shirazi (Chm)

Honda Atlas Power Product (Private) Ltd. (1)
F-36 Estate Avenue SITE, Karachi, 75730, Pakistan
Tel.: (92) 2138681446
Web Site: https://www.hondapower.net.pk
Sales Range: $100-124.9 Million
Emp.: 300
Automotive Products
N.A.I.C.S.: 336390

Honda Australia M. & P.E. Pty. Ltd. (1)
1954-1956 Sydney Road, Campbellfield, 3061, VIC, Australia
Tel.: (61) 392701111
Web Site: http://www.hondampe.com.au
Sales Range: $50-74.9 Million
Emp.: 200
Automotive Electrical Equipment Mfr & Distr
N.A.I.C.S.: 336320

Honda Australia Pty., Ltd. (1)
Level 4 6 Gladstone Street, Moonee Ponds, 3039, VIC, Australia (100%)
Tel.: (61) 800804954
Web Site: https://www.honda.com.au
Sales Range: $25-49.9 Million
Emp.: 100
Mfr, Importer & Distributor of Honda Products
N.A.I.C.S.: 441227

Honda Austria G.m.b.H. (1)
Hondastrasse 1, 2351, Wiener Neudorf, South Austria, Austria (100%)
Tel.: (43) 22366900
Web Site: https://www.honda.at
Sales Range: $25-49.9 Million
Emp.: 60
Mfr & Distribution of Honda Products
N.A.I.C.S.: 336110

Honda Auto Body Co., Ltd. (1)
1633-2 Higashi Osawa, Kamiebicho, Yokkaichi, Mie, Japan
Tel.: (81) 59 339 1313
Emp.: 550
Automobile Mfr
N.A.I.C.S.: 336110

Honda Automobile Western Africa Ltd. (1)
Jehovah Shammah Court 376 Ikorodu Road, Maryland, Lagos, Nigeria
Web Site: https://www.honda.com.ng
Automotive Services
N.A.I.C.S.: 811111

Honda Automoveis do Brasil Ltda. (1)
777 Estrada Municipal Velencio Calegari Nova Veneza, Sumare, 13181-903, SP, Brazil (100%)
Tel.: (55) 1938644400
Sales Range: $1-4.9 Billion
Emp.: 12,000
Honda Automobiles & Products Mfr, Importer & Distr
N.A.I.C.S.: 336110

Honda Automoviles Espana S.A. (1)
C/De La Selva 4-Urb Mas Blau, Barcelona, 08820, Spain
Tel.: (34) 933 708 007
Automotive Distr
N.A.I.C.S.: 423110

Honda Bank GmbH (1)
Hanauer Landstrasse 222-226, Hanauerlamdstrasse No-222, 60314, Frankfurt am Main, Germany
Tel.: (49) 6948980
Web Site: https://www.honda-bank.de
Sales Range: $25-49.9 Million
Emp.: 80
Financial Services
N.A.I.C.S.: 561499
Ingo Husemeyer (Mng Dir)

Honda Belgium N.V. (1)

AND PRIVATE COMPANIES — HONDA MOTOR CO., LTD.

Sphere Bus Pk Doornveld 180-184, Zoning 3, B 1731, Zellik, Belgium
Tel.: (32) 26201000
Web Site: http://www.fl.honda.be
Sales Range: $900-999.9 Million
Emp.: 650
Automotive Services
N.A.I.C.S.: 441227

Honda Canada Finance, Inc. (1)
180 Honda Blvd Suite 200, Markham, L6C 0H9, ON, Canada **(100%)**
Tel.: (416) 754-2323
Web Site: http://www.hondafinance.com
Sales Range: $100-124.9 Million
Emp.: 180
Personal Credit Institutions
N.A.I.C.S.: 522291

Honda Canada Inc. (1)
180 Honda Blvd, Markham, L6C 0H9, ON, Canada **(100%)**
Tel.: (905) 888-8110
Web Site: http://www.honda.ca
Sales Range: $1-4.9 Billion
Emp.: 5,000
Automobiles Importer & Distr
N.A.I.C.S.: 423110

Honda Cars Philippines Inc. (1)
105 South Main Avenue Laguna Technnopark, Santa Rosa Laguna, 4026, Philippines
Tel.: (63) 288577200
Web Site: https://www.hondaphil.com
Sales Range: $200-249.9 Million
Emp.: 200
Automobile Mfr
N.A.I.C.S.: 336110

Honda Centre (2010) Pvt. Ltd. (1)
121-123 Harare Road, Harare, Zimbabwe
Tel.: (263) 475 1938
Motor Cycle Distr
N.A.I.C.S.: 423120

Honda Clio Shin Tokyo Co., Ltd. (1)
No 2 26 2 Sibuya Rd, Sasagu-ka, Tokyo, 151-0073, Japan **(100%)**
Tel.: (81) 333757000
Web Site: http://www.clio-shintokyo.co.jp
Sales Range: $250-299.9 Million
Emp.: 150
Sale of Honda Products
N.A.I.C.S.: 441227

Honda Czech Republic Ltd. (1)
Bucharova 2641, Prague, 158 00, Czech Republic
Tel.: (420) 2 57 100 311
Web Site: http://www.honda.cz
Sales Range: $25-49.9 Million
Emp.: 16
Automotive Distr
N.A.I.C.S.: 423110

Honda Del Peru S.A. (1)
Av Republica de Panama 3545, San Isidro, Lima, Peru
Tel.: (51) 12211212
Motorcycle Mfr & Distr
N.A.I.C.S.: 336991

Honda Development & Manufacturing of America, LLC (1)
24000 Honda Pkwy, Marysville, OH 43040
Tel.: (937) 642-5000
Web Site: https://www.ohio.honda.com
Emp.: 9,500
Automobile Parts Mfr
N.A.I.C.S.: 336390

Honda Engineering Asian Co., Ltd. (1)
49 Moo 9 Rojana Industrial Park, Ayutthaya, 13210, Thailand
Tel.: (66) 35226693
Industrial Tools Mfr
N.A.I.C.S.: 333515

Honda Engineering China Co., Ltd. (1)
Lianguang Rd Guangzhou Economic & Technological Development Dist, Guangzhou, Guangdong, China
Tel.: (86) 2032066301
Automobile Parts Mfr
N.A.I.C.S.: 336390

Honda Engineering Europe Ltd. (1)
Highworth Road, Swindon, SN3 4TZ, Wiltsshire, United Kingdom
Tel.: (44) 1793 416527
Web Site: http://www.honda-eng.co.uk
Sales Range: $800-899.9 Million
Emp.: 300
Industrial Tools Mfr
N.A.I.C.S.: 333515

Honda Engineering North America (1)
24000 Honda Pkwy, Marysville, OH 43040-9251
Tel.: (937) 642-5000
Web Site: http://www.ohio.honda.com
Sales Range: $1-4.9 Billion
Emp.: 6,500
Special Dies & Tools
N.A.I.C.S.: 333514

Honda Europe N.V. (1)
Langerbruggestraat 104, Gent, 9000, Belgium **(100%)**
Tel.: (32) 92501211
Web Site: http://www.hondaeurope.be
Sales Range: $750-799.9 Million
Emp.: 600
Import & Distribution of Power Products & Supply of Spare Parts
N.A.I.C.S.: 441330

Subsidiary (Non-US):

Honda Logistic Center Austria G.M.B.H. (2)
Industriestrase 11-13, Guntramsdorf, 2353, Austria
Tel.: (43) 223627727
Web Site: http://www.honda.at
Sales Range: $25-49.9 Million
Emp.: 18
Automotive Parts
N.A.I.C.S.: 336390

Honda Foundry Co., Ltd. (1)
1620 Matoba, Kawagoe, 350-1101, Saitama, Japan
Tel.: (81) 492311521
Web Site: https://www.hondakinzoku.co.jp
Sales Range: $350-399.9 Million
Emp.: 578
Pistons, Engine Suspension Parts, Aluminum Products Casting & Machining Services; Machine Tools, Metallic Molds & Jigs Mfr
N.A.I.C.S.: 336211

Subsidiary (US):

Celina Aluminum Precision Technology Inc. (2)
7059 Staeger Rd, Celina, OH 45822-9395
Tel.: (419) 586-2278
Web Site: https://www.capt-celina.com
Sales Range: $100-124.9 Million
Emp.: 500
Pistons & Piston Rings Mfr
N.A.I.C.S.: 336310

Honda France Manufacturing S.A.S (1)
Pa Industrielles Pole 45 Rue Des Chataigniers, Ormes, 45140, France
Tel.: (33) 238650600
Automotive Power Transmission Equipment Mfr
N.A.I.C.S.: 336350

Honda France S.A.S. (1)
Pariest business park Allee du 1er mai, BP 46, Marne la Vallee, 77312, Croissy-Beaubourg, 02, France **(100%)**
Tel.: (33) 160373000
Web Site: https://www.honda.fr
Sales Range: $50-74.9 Million
Emp.: 140
Import & Distribution, Sales, Marketing & Servicing of Honda Products
N.A.I.C.S.: 336110

Honda Gulf Fze (1)
Jebel Ali, PO Box 61001, Dubai, United Arab Emirates
Tel.: (971) 48815515
Web Site: http://www.honda-eu.com
Sales Range: $25-49.9 Million
Emp.: 55
Automobile Parts & Accessories
N.A.I.C.S.: 336390

Honda Hungary KFT. (1)
Torokbulinti Ut 25/B, PF 96, 2040, Budaors, Hungary
Tel.: (36) 23506406
Web Site: https://www.honda.hu
Automobile & Motorcycle Distr
N.A.I.C.S.: 423110

Honda India Power Products Limited (1)
Plot no 5 Sector 41 Kasna Greater Noida Industrial Development Area, Distt Gautam Budh Nagar, Noida, 201 310, UP, India
Tel.: (91) 1202590100
Web Site: http://www.hondasielpower.com
Rev.: $130,148,655
Assets: $107,967,405
Liabilities: $25,315,290
Net Worth: $82,652,115
Earnings: $6,643,455
Emp.: 782
Fiscal Year-end: 03/31/2021
Portable Generators & Water Pumping Equipment
N.A.I.C.S.: 335312
Vinay Mittal *(Exec Dir)*

Honda Italia Industriale S.p.A. (1)
Via Della Cecchignola 13, 143, Rome, Italy
Tel.: (39) 0800889977
Web Site: https://www.honda.it
Motorcycle Mfr & Distr
N.A.I.C.S.: 336991

Honda Kaihatsu Co., Ltd. (1)
5-39 Hon-cho, Wako, 351-0114, Saitama, Japan
Tel.: (81) 48 452 5800
Web Site: https://www.honda-kaihatsu.co.jp
Emp.: 2,148
Real Estate Services
N.A.I.C.S.: 531390
Tetsuya Tsutsui *(Pres)*

Honda Korea Co., Ltd. (1)
13F Dongil Tower 38 Teheran-ro 114-gil, Gangnam-gu, Seoul, 137-040, Korea (South)
Tel.: (82) 234163300
Web Site: https://www.hondakorea.co.kr
Emp.: 70
Automotive Distr
N.A.I.C.S.: 423110
Woyung Chung *(CEO)*

Honda Logistic Centre (U.K.) Ltd. (1)
Viscount Way South Marston Park, Swindon, SN34TN, United Kingdom
Tel.: (44) 0179383131
Sales Range: $25-49.9 Million
Emp.: 100
Automotive Parts
N.A.I.C.S.: 336390

Honda Logistics Inc. (1)
3-8-1 Shonohayama, Suzuka, 513-0834, Mie Prefecture, Japan
Tel.: (81) 593781161
Web Site: http://www.honda-logistics.co.jp
Emp.: 100
Marine Transportation & Warehousing Services
N.A.I.C.S.: 488390

Honda Malaysia Sdn Bhd (1)
P-3-1 Level 3 Pacific Towers Business Hub Jalan 13/6, PO Box 70 78000 Alor Gajah, Seksyen 13, 46200, Petaling Jaya, Selangor, Malaysia
Tel.: (60) 6591500
Web Site: https://www.honda.com.my
Automobile Mfr
N.A.I.C.S.: 336110

Honda Malmo (1)
Stromgatan 7, Malmo, 212 25, Sweden
Tel.: (46) 40 651 30 77
Web Site: http://www.hondamalmo.se
Emp.: 80
Automotive Sales, Service & Parts
N.A.I.C.S.: 423120
Frederick Enaholo *(Co-Founder)*

Honda Manufacturing of Alabama, LLC (1)
1800 Honda Dr, Lincoln, AL 35096
Tel.: (205) 355-5000
Web Site: https://www.hondaalabama.com
Sales Range: $800-899.9 Million
Emp.: 4,500
Automobile Mfr
N.A.I.C.S.: 336110

Honda Manufacturing of Indiana, LLC (1)
2755 N Michigan Ave, Greensburg, IN 47240-9341
Tel.: (812) 222-6000
Web Site: https://www.indiana.honda.com
Automotive Parts Mfr & Distr
N.A.I.C.S.: 336390

Honda Motor (China) Co., Ltd. (1)
Rm 3901-3903 39/F Times Sq Twr One 1 Matheson St, Causeway Bay, China (Hong Kong)
Tel.: (852) 28828369
Automobile Parts Distr
N.A.I.C.S.: 423120

Honda Motor (China) Investment Co., Ltd. (1)
Rm 301-303 2321 Beijing Fortune Building 5 Dongsanhuan, Beijing, 100004, China
Tel.: (86) 1065909018
Web Site: http://www.acura.com.cn
Automobile Parts Distr
N.A.I.C.S.: 423120

Honda Motor Co., Ltd. (1)
1-10-1 Shinsayama, Sayama, 350 1392, Saitama, Japan **(100%)**
Tel.: (81) 429534111
Web Site: https://global.honda
Sales Range: $100-124.9 Million
Emp.: 500
Technical Research & Development Work to Supply Blueprints to Honda Motor Company Limited
N.A.I.C.S.: 336110

Honda Motor Co., Ltd. (1)
1907 Hirata-Cho, Suzuka, 513 8666, Mie, Japan **(100%)**
Tel.: (81) 593781212
Sales Range: $200-249.9 Million
Emp.: 1,000
Automobiles & Engines Mfr
N.A.I.C.S.: 336110

Honda Motor Co., Ltd. - Hamamatsu Hosoe Factory (1)
5794-1 Kiga Hosoe Cho, Kita-ku, Hamamatsu, Shizuoka, Japan
Tel.: (81) 534392111
Automobile Parts Mfr
N.A.I.C.S.: 336390

Honda Motor Co., Ltd. - Kumamoto Factory (1)
1500 Ozu-machi, Kikuchi-gun, Kumamoto, 869-1293, Japan
Tel.: (81) 962931111
Automobile Mfr
N.A.I.C.S.: 336110

Honda Motor Co., Ltd. - Suzuka Factory (1)
Cert & Reg Div No 1907 Hirata Cho, Suzuka, 513-8666, Mie, Japan
Tel.: (81) 59 378 1212
Web Site: http://www.world.honda.com
Emp.: 7,300
Production of Small-Volume Automobile Models
N.A.I.C.S.: 336110

Honda Motor Europe (North) GmbH (1)
Hanauer Landstrasse 224, PO Box 100644, 63069, Frankfort, Germany **(100%)**
Tel.: (49) 6983090
Web Site: http://www.honda-eu.com
Sales Range: $125-149.9 Million
Emp.: 350
Importer & Distr of Cars, Motorcycles & Power Equipment
N.A.I.C.S.: 441227

Honda Motor Europe Limited (1)
470 London Rd, Slough, SL3 8QY, Berks, United Kingdom **(100%)**
Tel.: (44) 1753590590
Web Site: https://www.honda.co.uk
Sales Range: $200-249.9 Million
Emp.: 700
Import & Distribution of Honda Products
N.A.I.C.S.: 441227

HONDA MOTOR CO., LTD.

Honda Motor Co., Ltd.—(Continued)

Subsidiary (Domestic):

Bristol Honda (2)
Lysander Road, Cribbs Causeway, Bristol, BS10 7UG, United Kingdom **(100%)**
Tel.: (44) 1179012728
Web Site: http://www.bristol-honda.co.uk
Sales Range: $25-49.9 Million
Emp.: 50
Vehicle Motor Retailing
N.A.I.C.S.: 441110

Honda Finance Europe PLC (2)
470 London Road, Slough, SL3 8QY, Berkshire, United Kingdom
Tel.: (44) 1753590010
Sales Range: $150-199.9 Million
Emp.: 500
Automobile Financing
N.A.I.C.S.: 522220

Subsidiary (Non-US):

Honda Motor RUS LLC (2)
Tri Dorozhnaya St Bldg 1, Moscow, 143350, Russia
Tel.: (7) 4957452080
Web Site: http://www.honda.co.ru
Emp.: 15
Automobile & Motorcycle Distr
N.A.I.C.S.: 423110

Subsidiary (Domestic):

Honda Racing Development Ltd. (2)
Boorbrook Buildings Brants Bridge, Bracknell, RG129BQ, Berkshire, United Kingdom
Tel.: (44) 01344386400
Sales Range: $10-24.9 Million
Emp.: 50
Automobiles
N.A.I.C.S.: 811198

Honda Motor Southern Africa (Pty.) Ltd. (1)
111 15th Rd Randjespark, PO Box 7479, Halfway House, 1685, Midrand, South Africa
Tel.: (27) 118479400
Web Site: http://www.honda.co.za
Sales Range: $50-74.9 Million
Emp.: 10
Automobile & Motorcycle Distr
N.A.I.C.S.: 423110

Honda Motor de Argentina S.A. (1)
Avenida Del Libertador 1613, Vicente Lopez, B1638BGC, Argentina
Tel.: (54) 1140094500
Web Site: http://www.honda.com.ar
Automobile & Motorcycle Distr
N.A.I.C.S.: 423110

Honda Motor de Chile S.A. (1)
Av San Ignacio 31, 8720018, Quilicura, Chile
Tel.: (56) 22709800
Sales Range: $50-74.9 Million
Emp.: 7
Automobile & Motorcycle Distr
N.A.I.C.S.: 423110
Eduardo Palma (Gen Mgr)

Honda Motorcycle & Scooter India Pvt. Ltd. (1)
Plot No 1 Sector-03 IMT Manesar, Gurgaon, 122050, Haryana, India
Tel.: (91) 1242290911
Web Site: https://www.honda2wheelersindia.com
Sales Range: $800-899.9 Million
Emp.: 5,000
Motorcycle Mfr
N.A.I.C.S.: 336991
Yadvinder S. Guleria (Dir-Sls & Mktg)

Honda Nederland B.V. (1)
Capronilaan 1, PO Box 75100, 1117 ZR, Schiphol-Rijk, Netherlands **(100%)**
Tel.: (31) 207070081
Web Site: https://www.honda.nl
Sales Range: $25-49.9 Million
Emp.: 50
Import & Distribution of Honda Products in the Netherlands
N.A.I.C.S.: 441227

Honda New Zealand Ltd. (1)
105 Wiri Station Road, PO Box 97-340, Manukau City, Manukau, 2241, New Zealand
Tel.: (64) 92623141
Web Site: http://www.honda.co.nz
Sales Range: $25-49.9 Million
Emp.: 88
Mfr of Automobiles
N.A.I.C.S.: 336110

Honda Parts Mfg. Corp. (1)
101 North Science Avenue Laguna Technopark Phase 2, Binan, 4024, Philippines
Tel.: (63) 495411631
Emp.: 50
Automotive Power Transmission Equipment Mfr
N.A.I.C.S.: 336350
Yoshihiro Yamada (Pres)

Honda Performance Development (1)
25145 Anza Dr, Santa Clarita, CA 91355-1272
Tel.: (661) 294-7300
Web Site: https://hpd.honda.com
Sales Range: $50-74.9 Million
Emp.: 100
Specialized Automotive Engines & Engine Parts
N.A.I.C.S.: 423120
David Salters (Pres)

Honda Philippines Inc. (1)
Lot 34 Phase 1-B Road 3, First Philippine Industrial Park, Batangas, 4232, Tanauan City, Philippines
Tel.: (63) 25816700
Web Site: https://www.hondaph.com
Sales Range: $200-249.9 Million
Emp.: 800
Motorcycle Mfr
N.A.I.C.S.: 336991

Honda Poland Ltd. (1)
Pulawska 381, 02-801, Warsaw, Poland
Tel.: (48) 225457799
Web Site: https://www.honda.pl
Emp.: 50
Automobile & Motorcycle Distr
N.A.I.C.S.: 423110

Honda Power Equipment Sweden A.B. (1)
Langhusgatan 4, PO Box 31002, 20049, Malmo, Sweden
Tel.: (46) 40380700
Web Site: http://www.hondapower.se
Sales Range: $25-49.9 Million
Emp.: 70
Power Equipment
N.A.I.C.S.: 333991
Tatanobu Othiai (Pres)

Honda Precision Parts of Georgia, LLC (1)
550 Honda Pkwy, Tallapoosa, GA 30176-4344
Tel.: (770) 574-3400
Automotive Power Transmission Equipment Mfr
N.A.I.C.S.: 336350

Honda R & D (India) Pvt. Ltd. (1)
Jagatjit Industries Ltd Building, Plot 78 Sector 18, 122001, Gurgaon, Haryana, India
Tel.: (91) 1241094700
Web Site: http://www.hrid.com
Automobile Research & Development
N.A.I.C.S.: 541715

Honda R & D Asia Pacific Co., Ltd. (1)
2/1 Soi 01 Kanchanaphisek 5/5, Tharaeng Bangkhen, Bangkok, 10220, Thailand
Tel.: (66) 25085600
Web Site: https://honda-rd.asia
Automobile Research & Development
N.A.I.C.S.: 541715

Honda R & D Europe (U.K.) Ltd. (1)
Highworth Road, South Marston, SN34TZ, Swindon, United Kingdom
Tel.: (44) 1793417242
Automobile Research & Development
N.A.I.C.S.: 541715

Honda R & D Southeast Asia Co., Ltd. (HRS) (1)
17th Floor United Center Building, 323 Silom Road, Bangkok, 10500, Thailand
Tel.: (66) 23279500
Automobile Research & Development
N.A.I.C.S.: 541715

Honda R&D Americas, Inc. (1)
1900 Harpers Way, Torrance, CA 90501-1528 **(100%)**
Tel.: (310) 781-5500
Web Site: http://www.hra.com
Sales Range: $75-99.9 Million
Emp.: 290
Technical Research & Development Work
N.A.I.C.S.: 541910
James A. Keller (Pres)

Honda R&D Europe (Deutschland) GmbH (1)
Carl-Legien-Strasse 30, 63073, Offenbach, Germany
Tel.: (49) 69890110
Web Site: https://www.honda.de
Automobile Mfr
N.A.I.C.S.: 336110

Honda Research Institute Europe G.M.B.H (1)
Carl-Legien-Strasse 30, 63073, Offenbach, Germany
Tel.: (49) 6989011750
Web Site: https://www.honda-ri.de
Automobile Research & Development
N.A.I.C.S.: 541715

Honda Research Institute Japan Co., Ltd. (1)
8-1 Honcho, Wako, 351-0188, Saitama, Japan
Tel.: (81) 484625219
Web Site: https://www.jp.honda-ri.com
Advanced Technology Research & Development Services
N.A.I.C.S.: 541715

Honda Research Institute USA, Inc. (1)
70 Rio Robles, San Jose, CA 95134
Tel.: (650) 314-0400
Web Site: https://usa.honda-ri.com
Automobile Research & Development
N.A.I.C.S.: 541715

Honda Sales Operations Japan Co., Ltd. (1)
8-1 Honcho, Wako, 351-0188, Saitama, Japan
Tel.: (81) 48 452 0663
Web Site: https://www.honda.co.jp
Automobile Parts Mfr
N.A.I.C.S.: 336390

Honda Siel Cars India Ltd. (1)
Plot No A-1 Sector 40/ 41 Surajpur-Kasna Road, Greater Noida Industrial Devel, Noida, 201 306, Gautam Budh Nagar UP, India
Tel.: (91) 1202341313
Web Site: http://www.hondacarindia.com
Automobile Mfr
N.A.I.C.S.: 336110

Honda Slovakia Spol. S.R.O. (1)
Prievozska 1978/6, 82109, Bratislava, Slovakia
Tel.: (421) 2 3213 1111
Web Site: http://www.honda.sk
Sales Range: $25-49.9 Million
Emp.: 15
Automobile & Motorcycle Distr
N.A.I.C.S.: 423110

Honda South America Ltda. (1)
Rua Dr Jose Aureo Bustamante 377, Santo Amaro, Sao Paulo, 04710-090, Brazil
Tel.: (55) 1155765449
Sales Range: $450-499.9 Million
Emp.: 60
Automotive Parts Mfr & Distr
N.A.I.C.S.: 336390

Honda Taiwan Co., Ltd. (1)
No 337 Daxi Road, Qianjinli, Ping-tung, 90093, Taiwan
Tel.: (886) 87558788
Automotive Distr
N.A.I.C.S.: 423110

Honda Taiwan Motor Co., Ltd. (1)
No 106 Jixian Road, Sanchong District, New Taipei City, 10771, Taiwan
Tel.: (886) 228573999
Web Site: https://moto.honda-taiwan.com.tw
Emp.: 100
Automobile Mfr
N.A.I.C.S.: 336110

Honda Trading Corp. (1)
Akihabara UDX South Wing 18F 4-14-1 Sotokanda, Chiyoda-ku, Tokyo, 101-8622, Japan **(100%)**
Tel.: (81) 352950930
Web Site: https://www.hondatrading.com
Sales Range: $150-199.9 Million
Emp.: 320
Import, Export & Marketing Operations
N.A.I.C.S.: 425120

Subsidiary (Non-US):

Honda Trading (China) Co., Ltd. (2)
2201A R F Center 10 Huaxia Road, Tianhe District, Guangzhou, China
Tel.: (86) 2087322399
Web Site: https://www.hondatrading.com
Sales Range: $25-49.9 Million
Emp.: 100
Automobile Parts Mfr
N.A.I.C.S.: 336390

Honda Trading (Guangzhou) Co., Ltd. (2)
2201A R F Center 10 Huaxia Road, Tianhe District, Guangzhou, China
Tel.: (86) 2087322399
Automotive Parts
N.A.I.C.S.: 336390

Honda Trading (South China) Co., Ltd. (2)
Suite 3201-4 Tower Two Times Square, 1 Matheson Street, Causeway Bay, China (Hong Kong)
Tel.: (852) 28080055
Web Site: https://www.hondatrading.com
Emp.: 5
Automotive Parts
N.A.I.C.S.: 336390

Subsidiary (US):

Honda Trading America Corp. (2)
700 Van Ness Ave MS 300-1-1T, Torrance, CA 90501-1486
Tel.: (310) 781-6605
Sales Range: $1-9.9 Million
Emp.: 38
Automotive Supplies & Parts
N.A.I.C.S.: 423120

Subsidiary (Domestic):

Harmony Agricultural Products in Ohio, LLC (3)
20100 Johnson Rd, Marysville, OH 43040
Tel.: (937) 644-8215
Soybean Production
N.A.I.C.S.: 111110

Subsidiary (Non-US):

Honda Trading Canada, Inc. (3)
4700 Industrial Parkway, Alliston, L9R 1A2, ON, Canada **(100%)**
Tel.: (705) 435-0172
Web Site: https://www.hondatrading.com
Metals Service Centers & Offices
N.A.I.C.S.: 423510

Subsidiary (Non-US):

Honda Trading Asia Co., Ltd. (2)
11/1 8th Floor AIA Sathorn Tower South, Sathorn Road, Yannawa Sathorn, Bangkok, 10120, Pathumwan, Thailand **(94.54%)**
Tel.: (66) 20290080
Web Site: https://www.hondatrading.com
Sales Range: $25-49.9 Million
Emp.: 286
Automobile Parts, Machinery & Materials Distr
N.A.I.C.S.: 423120

Honda Trading Europe Ltd. (2)
First floor Mulberry Kembrey Park, Swindon, SN2 8UY, Wiltshire, United Kingdom - England
Tel.: (44) 1793608100
Web Site: https://www.hondatrading.com
Sales Range: $25-49.9 Million
Emp.: 70
Automotive Parts
N.A.I.C.S.: 336390

AND PRIVATE COMPANIES

HONDA MOTOR CO., LTD.

Honda Trading de Mexico S.A. de C.V. (2)
Carretera a el Castillo No 7250, El Salto Industrial Park, 45680, Jalisco, Mexico
Tel.: (52) 3336880197
Sales Range: $25-49.9 Million
Emp.: 22
Automotive Parts
N.A.I.C.S.: 336390

Honda Trading do Brasil Ltda. (2)
Estrada Municipal Valencio Calegari 777 Nova Veneza, Sumare, Sao Paulo, 13183-091, SP, Brazil
Tel.: (55) 1938645542
Sales Range: $350-399.9 Million
Automotive Parts
N.A.I.C.S.: 336390
Hiromichi Shigano *(Pres)*

P.T. Honda Trading Indonesia (2)
Mid Plaza1 6th Floor Jl Jend Sudirman Kav 10-11, Jakarta, 10220, Indonesia
Tel.: (62) 2157907022
Sales Range: $25-49.9 Million
Emp.: 57
Automotive Parts
N.A.I.C.S.: 336390
Hidenori Yori *(Mgr)*

P.T. Molten Aluminium Producer Indonesia (2)
Kawasan Industri Indotaisei Sektor 1A Blok K-I, Karawang, 41373, Jawa Barat, Indonesia
Tel.: (62) 264350460
Automotive Parts
N.A.I.C.S.: 336390

Honda Transmission Manufacturing of America, Inc. (1)
6964 SR 235 N, Russells Point, OH 43348-9703 **(100%)**
Tel.: (937) 843-5555
Web Site: http://www.htm.honda.com
Sales Range: $200-249.9 Million
Emp.: 1,000
Motor Vehicle Parts & Accessories
N.A.I.C.S.: 336390
Ugyuji Takahashi *(Pres)*

Honda Turkiye A.S. (1)
Aydinevler Mahallesi Sanayi Caddesi No 1, Maltepe, 34854, Istanbul, Kocaeli, Turkiye
Tel.: (90) 2626588383
Web Site: https://www.honda.com.tr
Automobile & Motorcycle Mfr
N.A.I.C.S.: 336110

Honda U-Tec Co., Ltd. (1)
5-39 Honmachi Honda Kaihatsu Wako Building 2F, Chuo-Ku, Wako, 351-0114, Saitama, Japan
Tel.: (81) 484660031
Web Site: https://www.honda-uc.com
Emp.: 176
Used Car Dealers
N.A.I.C.S.: 441120

Honda Uganda Ltd. (1)
Plot 91 Jinja Road Pike House, PO Box 2007, Kampala, Uganda
Tel.: (256) 41 425 0802
Web Site: https://honda.co.ug
Motor Cycle Distr
N.A.I.C.S.: 423120
Andrew Tibeyalirwa *(Mng Dir)*

Honda Vietnam Co., Ltd. (1)
Phuc Thang Ward, Me Linh District, Phuc Yen, Vinh Phuc, Vietnam
Tel.: (84) 2113868888
Web Site: https://www.honda.com.vn
Automobile Mfr & Distr
N.A.I.C.S.: 336110

Honda de Mexico, S.A. de C.V. (1)
Carretera a El Castillo No 7250 Parque Industrial, 45680, El Salto, Jalisco, Mexico **(100%)**
Tel.: (52) 3336880101
Web Site: https://www.honda.mx
Mfr, Importer & Distributor of Honda Products & Spare Parts
N.A.I.C.S.: 441330

Honda of Canada Mfg. (1)
4700 Tottenham Rd, PO Box 5000, Alliston, L9R 1A2, ON, Canada
Tel.: (705) 435-5561
Web Site: http://www.honda.ca
Sales Range: $800-899.9 Million
Emp.: 4,500
Automobile Mfr
N.A.I.C.S.: 336110

Honda of South Carolina Manufacturing (1)
1111 Honda Way, Timmonsville, SC 29161-9421
Tel.: (843) 346-8000
Web Site: http://www.honda.com
Sales Range: $400-449.9 Million
Emp.: 1,450
Motor Vehicles & Car Bodies
N.A.I.C.S.: 336110

Honda of the U.K. Manufacturing Limited (1)
Highworth Road, South Marston, SN34TZ, Swindon, Wiltshire, United Kingdom
Tel.: (44) 1753590010
Sales Range: $800-899.9 Million
Emp.: 3,500
Automobile Mfr
N.A.I.C.S.: 336110

KTH Shelburne Mfg., Inc. (1)
300 Second Line, Shelburne, L9V 3N4, ON, Canada **(100%)**
Tel.: (519) 925-3030
Web Site: https://www.kth.net
Sales Range: $100-124.9 Million
Emp.: 370
Motor Vehicle Parts & Accessories
N.A.I.C.S.: 336390

Kaneta Kogyo Co., Ltd. (1)
3-18-5 Takaoka-higashi, Naka-ku, Hamamatsu, 433-8117, Shizuoka, Japan
Tel.: (81) 53 436 1211
Web Site: https://www.kanetakogyo.co.jp
Shaft Product Mfr
N.A.I.C.S.: 336350
Tomoaki Hirayama *(Pres)*

Kumamoto Manufacturing Facility (1)
1500 Ozu-machi, Kikuchi-gun, Kumamoto, 869 1293, Japan **(100%)**
Tel.: (81) 962931111
Web Site: http://www.kumamotodk.co.jp
Sales Range: $800-899.9 Million
Emp.: 3,000
Motorcycles, Power Products & Engines Mfr
N.A.I.C.S.: 336991

Letzigraben Garage AG (1)
Letzigraben 77, 8003, Zurich, Switzerland
Tel.: (41) 444062222
Web Site: http://www.honda-zuerichletzi.ch
Sales Range: $25-49.9 Million
Emp.: 18
Automotive Repair
N.A.I.C.S.: 811111

Madagascar Automobile SA (1)
BP 350, Rue du Dr Raseta, Antananarivo, 101, Madagascar
Tel.: (261) 20 232 5454
Web Site: https://www.madauto.com
Automotive Services
N.A.I.C.S.: 811111
Stephane Bruno *(Mng Dir)*

Metts Corporation (1)
1620 Matoba, Kawagoe, 350-1101, Saitama, Japan
Tel.: (81) 49 237 5900
Web Site: https://www.metts.co.jp
Automobile Parts Mfr
N.A.I.C.S.: 336110
Akira Kojima *(Pres)*

Mobilityland Corporation (1)
7992 Ino-Cho, Suzuka, 510-0295, Mie, Japan
Tel.: (81) 593781111
Web Site: http://www.mobilityland.co.jp
Amusement Park Operating Services
N.A.I.C.S.: 713110

Montesa Honda Spain (1)
Del Mar Del Nord S N Pl Can Roca, 8130, Santa Perpetua de Mogoda, Barcelona, Spain **(100%)**
Tel.: (34) 935740770
Web Site: http://www.honda.es
Sales Range: $100-124.9 Million
Emp.: 500
Motorcycle Mfr

N.A.I.C.S.: 336991

Monvo Honda Ba Amazonia Ltda. (1)
Dr Jose Aureo Bustamante #377 Santo Amaro, CEP 04710 090, Sao Paulo, Brazil **(100%)**
Tel.: (55) 1155765122
Web Site: http://www.honda.com.br
Sales Range: $400-449.9 Million
Emp.: 1,922
Mfr of Motorcycles & Accessories
N.A.I.C.S.: 336991

Musashi Seimitsu Co., Ltd. (1)
2605-7 Ichibu Nishiki-cho, Kuma-gun, Kumamoto, 868-0302, Japan
Tel.: (81) 96 638 2121
Web Site: https://www.kmusashi.co.jp
Machine Tool Mfr & Distr
N.A.I.C.S.: 333517

NeksVision Co., Ltd. (1)
2-8-15 Yoshinodai, Kawagoe, 350-0833, Saitama, Japan
Tel.: (81) 49 227 6216
Web Site: https://neksvision.co.jp
Emp.: 117
Various Glass Mirror Mfr
N.A.I.C.S.: 327215
Toshiyuki Hosokawa *(Pres & CEO)*

Nissin Kogyo Co., Ltd. (1)
172 Kamisoyagi, Yamato, 242-0029, Kanagawa, Japan **(92.44%)**
Tel.: (81) 462641221
Web Site: https://www.nissin-kogyo.com
Rev.: $1,718,618,580
Assets: $1,861,531,020
Liabilities: $344,760,180
Net Worth: $1,516,770,840
Earnings: $66,536,640
Emp.: 10,325
Fiscal Year-end: 03/31/2019
Motor Vehicle Braking Systems & Parts Mfr
N.A.I.C.S.: 336340
Junya Takei *(Exec Dir)*

Subsidiary (Non-US):

Nissin Brake (Thailand) Co., Ltd. (2)
399 Moo 6 Chokchai-Ratchasima Road Tambol Nongraveang, Amphur Muang, Nakhon Ratchasima, 30000, Thailand
Tel.: (66) 44218375
Motor Vehicle Brake System Mfr
N.A.I.C.S.: 336340

Nissin Brake Do Brasil Ltda (2)
AV Dos Oitis No 534-Distrito Industrial, Bairro Itaim Mirim, Manaus, 69075-842, SP, Brazil
Tel.: (55) 1134144001
Motor Vehicle Brake System Mfr
N.A.I.C.S.: 336340

Nissin Brake Europe, S.L.U (2)
Ciencia 33, 08840, Viladecans, Barcelona, Spain
Tel.: (34) 936472156
Automobile Parts Mfr
N.A.I.C.S.: 336390

Nissin Brake India Pvt. Ltd. (2)
SP-1-34-35 New Industrial Area Phase-III, Neemrana, Alwar, 301705, Rajasthan, India
Tel.: (91) 1494246733
Production & Development of Disc Brakes
N.A.I.C.S.: 336340

Subsidiary (US):

Nissin Brake Ohio, Inc. (2)
1901 Industrial Dr, Findlay, OH 45840
Tel.: (419) 425-6725
Sales Range: $250-299.9 Million
Emp.: 650
Motor Vehicle Brake Systems & Parts Mfr
N.A.I.C.S.: 336340

Subsidiary (Domestic):

Nissin Brake Georgia Inc. (3)
216 Thacker Dr, Rock Spring, GA 30739
Tel.: (706) 764-1239
Sales Range: $50-74.9 Million
Emp.: 310
Motor Vehicle Brake Systems & Parts Mfr
N.A.I.C.S.: 336340
Jin Kobayashi *(Pres)*

Subsidiary (Non-US):

Nissin Brake Philippines Corporation (2)
RBF L-2 Lot 30-B Phase 1B, First Philippines Industrial Park, Tanauan, 4232, Batangas, Philippines
Tel.: (63) 495411335
Motor Vehicle Brake System Mfr
N.A.I.C.S.: 336340

Nissin Brake Realty Philippines Corporation (2)
RBF L-2 Lot 30-B Phase 1B First Philippines Industrial Park, Tanauan, 4232, Batangas, Philippines
Tel.: (63) 49 576 5946
Automotive Brake System Mfr & Distr
N.A.I.C.S.: 336340

Nissin Brake Vietnam Co., Ltd. (2)
Pho Hamlet, Quat Luu Commune Binh Xuyen District, 281359, Quat Luu, Vinh Phuc, Vietnam
Tel.: (84) 2113866400
Motor Vehicle Brake System Mfr
N.A.I.C.S.: 336340

Nissin Brake de Mexico, S.A. de C.V. (2)
Camino de Acceso No 652 Centro Industrial Guanajuato, 36835, Irapuato, Guanajuato, Mexico
Tel.: (52) 4626260308
Automotive Brake System Mfr & Distr
N.A.I.C.S.: 336340
Keiichi Kobayashi *(Mng Dir)*

Plant (Domestic):

Nissin Kogyo Co., Ltd. - Naoetsu Plant (2)
4370 Kamichihara, Joetsu, 942-0035, Niigata, Japan
Tel.: (81) 25 543 1431
Automotive Brake System Mfr
N.A.I.C.S.: 336340

Nissin Kogyo Co., Ltd. - Tobu Plant (2)
801 Kazawa, Tomi, 389-0514, Nagano, Japan
Tel.: (81) 268 62 1191
Automotive Brake System Mfr
N.A.I.C.S.: 336340

Subsidiary (Non-US):

Nissin R&D Asia Co., Ltd (2)
Shinawatra Tower 3 8th Floor 1010 Viphavadi Rangsit Rd, Chatuchak, Bangkok, 10900, Thailand
Tel.: (66) 2 967 7605
Automotive Brake System Mfr & Distr
N.A.I.C.S.: 336340

Nissin R&D Europe, S.L.U. (2)
Ciencia 33, 08840, Viladecans, Spain
Tel.: (34) 902410999
Automotive Brake System Mfr & Distr
N.A.I.C.S.: 336340
Koji Inoue *(Gen Mgr)*

P.T. Chemco Harapan Nusantara (2)
Jl Jababeka Raya Blok F No 19-28, Jababeka Industrial Estate Cikarang Utara, Bekasi, 17530, West Java, Indonesia
Tel.: (62) 218934253
Web Site: https://www.chemco.co.id
Brake System & Aluminum Casting Parts Mfr
N.A.I.C.S.: 336340

Shandong Nissin Industry Co., Ltd. (2)
273 Century Avenue, Rushan, Shandong, China
Tel.: (86) 6316681246
Motor Vehicle Brake System Mfr
N.A.I.C.S.: 336340

Tungaloy Friction Material Vietnam Ltd. (2)
Quat Luu Commune, Binh Xuyen, Vinh Phuc, Vietnam
Tel.: (84) 2113597788
Automobile Parts Mfr
N.A.I.C.S.: 336390

Zhongshan Nissin Industry Co., Ltd. (2)

HONDA MOTOR CO., LTD.

Honda Motor Co., Ltd.—(Continued)
No 37 Jian Ye Road Torch Hi-tech Industrial Development Zone, Zhongshan, Guangdong, China
Tel.: (86) 76085338330
Web Site: http://www.mbz.net.cn
Emp.: 1,093
Motor Vehicle Brake System Mfr
N.A.I.C.S.: 336340
Chen Xian Wei *(Mgr)*

P.T. Honda Precision Parts Manufacturing (1)
Kota Bukit Indah Kawasan Industri Indotaisei Sektor IA Blok S, Kalihurip Clkampek, Karawang, 41373, Jawa Barat, Indonesia
Tel.: (62) 264350380
Web Site: https://www.hppm.co.id
Sales Range: $400-449.9 Million
Emp.: 2,555
Automobile Parts Mfr
N.A.I.C.S.: 336390
Masayuki Ashikawa *(Pres)*

P.T. Honda Prospect Motor (1)
Jl Gaya Motor I Sunter II, Jakarta, 14330, Indonesia
Tel.: (62) 216510403
Web Site: https://www.honda-indonesia.com
Sales Range: $1-4.9 Billion
Emp.: 3,600
Automobile Parts Distr
N.A.I.C.S.: 423120

PSG Co., Ltd. (1)
89-4 Hagadai Hagamachi, Haga-Gun, Tochigi, 321-3325, Japan
Tel.: (81) 28 677 2723
Web Site: http://www.psg.co.jp
Automotive Research & Development Services
N.A.I.C.S.: 541715

PT. Honda Power Products Indonesia (1)
Kawasan Industri Pulogadung Jl Rawa Gelam IV No 14, Cakung, Jakarta, 13260, Timur, Indonesia
Tel.: (62) 2122461158
Web Site: https://www.hondapowerproducts.co.id
Emp.: 6
Water Pump & Generator Distr
N.A.I.C.S.: 423120

Quality Motors Limited (1)
PO Box 235, Dar es Salaam, Tanzania
Tel.: (255) 22 286 1060
Web Site: https://qualitygroup.com
Financial Services
N.A.I.C.S.: 523999

Rainbow Motor School Co., Ltd. (1)
5-27-1 Shimonikura, Wako, 351-0111, Saitama, Japan
Tel.: (81) 484611101
Web Site: https://www.rms.co.jp
Automobile Driving School Operator
N.A.I.C.S.: 611692

SC Honda Trading Romania SRL (1)
Sos Bucuresti Nord no 10 Building O21 floor 9, Global City Business Park, Voluntari, 20337, Ilfov, Romania
Tel.: (40) 317101903
Web Site: https://www.hondatrading.ro
Sales Range: $25-49.9 Million
Emp.: 15
Automobile & Motorcycle Distr
N.A.I.C.S.: 423110
Takashi Kono *(Pres)*

SENA Motors Ltd. (1)
Davit Agmashenebeli Alley N 226, 0131, Tbilisi, Georgia
Tel.: (995) 32 255 1050
Web Site: https://www.senamotors.com.ge
Motor Cycle Mfr & Distr
N.A.I.C.S.: 336991

Sayama Manufacturing Facility (1)
1-10-1 Shinsayama, Saitama, 350 1392, Japan
Tel.: (81) 429534111
Sales Range: $1-4.9 Billion
Emp.: 5,335
Automobile Mfr
N.A.I.C.S.: 336110

Shinnichi Kogyo Co., Ltd. (1)
48 Tenma Hirao-cho, Toyokawa, 442-0863, Aichi, Japan
Tel.: (81) 53 388 4151
Web Site: https://www.shinnichikogyo.co.jp
Steel Products Mfr
N.A.I.C.S.: 331110

Sogo Jimu Service Co., Ltd. (1)
Honda Aoyama Bldg 4F 2-1-1 Minami Aoyama, Minato-ku, Tokyo, 107-8556, Japan
Tel.: (81) 35 412 1519
Web Site: https://www.sjs-net.co.jp
Emp.: 192
Digital Solution Services
N.A.I.C.S.: 541519
Masafumi Asaka *(Pres)*

Sony Honda Mobility Inc. (1)
c/o Honda Motor Company No 1-1 Minami-Aoyama 2-chome, Minato-ku, Tokyo, 107-8556, Japan
Tel.: (81) 334231111 **(50%)**
Web Site: https://www.shm-afeela.com
Electric Motor Vehicle Designer, Developer & Mfr
N.A.I.C.S.: 336110
Yasuhide Mizuno *(Chm & CEO)*

Suzuka Circuitland Co., Ltd. (1)
7992 InoCho, Suzuka, 510-0295, Mie, Japan **(100%)**
Tel.: (81) 593781111
Sales Range: $150-199.9 Million
Emp.: 300
Operation of Amusement Parks & Racing Circuit
N.A.I.C.S.: 713110

Thai Honda Manufacturing Co., Ltd. (1)
2754/1 Soi Sukhumvit 66/1, Sukhumvit Road, 10260, Bangkok, Bangna, Thailand
Tel.: (66) 27447744
Web Site: http://world.honda.com
Sales Range: $800-899.9 Million
Emp.: 2,829
Mfr of Motorcycles & Power Products
N.A.I.C.S.: 336991

TransAfrica Motors Ltd. (1)
Jomvu Miritini Road, Mombasa, Kenya
Tel.: (254) 71 299 9111
Web Site: https://transafricamotors.com
Automotive Services
N.A.I.C.S.: 811111

Tsushima Die-Engineering Corp. (1)
30-1 Azashinden koshizu-cho, Tsushima, 496-0022, Aichi, Japan
Tel.: (81) 56 726 2167
Web Site: https://www.tsushima-die-eng.co.jp
Emp.: 144
Automobile Parts Mfr
N.A.I.C.S.: 336390
Yasushi Miyajima *(Pres)*

Tsuzuki Manufacturing Co., Ltd. (1)
6649-1 Sakaki, Sakaki-machi Hanishina-gun, Nagano, 389-0681, Japan
Tel.: (81) 26 882 2800
Web Site: https://www.tsuzuki-mfg.co.jp
Four & Two Wheeler Vehicle Equipment Mfr
N.A.I.C.S.: 336999
Yuki Kurita *(Pres)*

Ulsan Engineering Co., Ltd. (1)
21-3 Bugok-Dong, Nam-gu, Ulsan, 780820, Korea (South)
Tel.: (82) 522574107
Web Site: https://www.hondatrading.com
Automotive Parts
N.A.I.C.S.: 336390

Yachiyo Industry Co., Ltd. (1)
393 Kashiwabara, Sayama, 3501-335, Japan **(100%)**
Tel.: (81) 429551211
Web Site: http://www.yachiyo-ind.co.jp
Rev.: $1,589,746,400
Assets: $1,386,940,720
Liabilities: $647,398,400
Net Worth: $739,542,320
Earnings: $49,890,720
Emp.: 6,662
Fiscal Year-end: 03/31/2022
Automobile Parts Mfr & Sales
N.A.I.C.S.: 336390

Hiroyuki Kihara *(Sr Operating Officer)*

Subsidiary (US):

AY Manufacturing Ltd. (2)
5200 Crosswind Dr, Columbus, OH 43228
Tel.: (614) 870-8711
Sunroof Mfr
N.A.I.C.S.: 336390

Subsidiary (Domestic):

Goshi Giken Co., Ltd. (2)
1280 Toyooka, Koshi, 861-1115, Kumamoto, Japan
Tel.: (81) 96 248 2431
Web Site: http://www.goshigiken.com
Emp.: 371
Motorcycle Parts Mfr
N.A.I.C.S.: 336991
Ryuichi Nishimura *(Mng Dir)*

Subsidiary (Non-US):

Goshi-Thanglong Auto-Parts Co., Ltd. (3)
No-134 Sai Dong Street 15 Group, Viet Hung Ward Long Bien District, Hanoi, Vietnam
Tel.: (84) 438750859
Emp.: 1,408
Automobile Parts Mfr
N.A.I.C.S.: 336211

Siam Goshi Manufacturing Co., Ltd. (3)
Siam Eastern Industrial Park 60 Moo 3 Mabyangporn Rd Map Yang Phon, A Pluakdaeng, Rayong, 21140, Thailand
Tel.: (66) 388912725
Web Site: https://www.sgm.co.th
Emp.: 1,160
Automobile Parts Mfr
N.A.I.C.S.: 336211
Wanchai Kunanantakul *(Chm)*

Subsidiary (Non-US):

Goshi India Auto Parts Private Ltd. (2)
363-364 Sector-3 IMT Bawal Phase-II, Rewari, 123 501, Haryana, India
Tel.: (91) 1284264061
Web Site: https://goshi-india.com
Motorcycle Parts Mfr
N.A.I.C.S.: 336991

Goshi Philippines, Inc. (2)
108 North Science Avenue, Laguna Technopark Binan, Laguna, Philippines
Tel.: (63) 49 541 2760
Motorcycle Parts Mfr
N.A.I.C.S.: 336991

PT. Yachiyo Trimitra Indonesia (2)
Kawasan Industri Mitra Karawang Jl Mitra Selatan Blok H3-6, Karawang, 41361, West Java, Indonesia
Tel.: (62) 2678634069
Fuel Tank Mfr
N.A.I.C.S.: 336211

Siam Yachiyo Co., Ltd. (2)
304 Industrial Park 214 Moo 7 Tambol Thatoom, Si Maha Phot, 25140, Prachinburi, Thailand
Tel.: (66) 37627501
Web Site: https://www.siamyachiyo.com
Emp.: 420
Plastics Product Mfr
N.A.I.C.S.: 326199

Subsidiary (US):

US Yachiyo, Inc. (2)
1177 Kellogg Pkwy, Marion, OH 43302
Tel.: (740) 375-4687
Fuel Tank Mfr
N.A.I.C.S.: 336211

Subsidiary (Domestic):

Uemura Tec Co., Ltd. (2)
777 Asagirichou-ueminami, Kumagun, Kumamoto, 868-0423, Japan
Tel.: (81) 96604700111
Emp.: 163
Automobile Parts Mfr
N.A.I.C.S.: 336211

YG TECH Co., Ltd. (2)
200 Sekoizumi ohin-cho, Inabe, 511-0252, Mie, Japan
Tel.: (81) 594861010
Sheet Metal Mfr
N.A.I.C.S.: 332322

Subsidiary (Non-US):

Yachiyo Do Brasil Industria E Comercio De Pecas Ltda. (2)
Estrada Municipal Antonio Cavinatto 270 Bairro dos Pereiras, PO Box 345, Limeira, 13480-970, Sao Paulo, Brazil
Tel.: (55) 1934465900
Fuel Tank Mfr
N.A.I.C.S.: 336211

Yachiyo Germany GmbH (2)
Frankfurter Str 3a, 38122, Braunschweig, Germany
Tel.: (49) 5311805240
Automobile Parts Mfr
N.A.I.C.S.: 336211

Yachiyo India Manufacturing Private Ltd. (2)
Spl-1 c, Tapukara Industrial Area Khushkher, Alwar, 301 707, Rajasthan, India
Tel.: (91) 1493667777
Fuel Tank Mfr
N.A.I.C.S.: 336211

Plant (Domestic):

Yachiyo Industry Co., Ltd. - Kashiwabara Plant (2)
370 Kashiwabara, Sayama, 350-1335, Saitama, Japan
Tel.: (81) 429543350
Sunroof Mfr
N.A.I.C.S.: 336390

Yachiyo Industry Co., Ltd. - Suzuka Plant (2)
7764 Ishimaru Kou-cho, Suzuka, 513-0836, Mie, Japan
Tel.: (81) 593781151
Fuel Tank Mfr
N.A.I.C.S.: 336211

Yachiyo Industry Co., Ltd. - Yokkaichi Factory (2)
1633-2 Higashi-ohsawa Kamiebi-cho, Yokkaichi, 512-1201, Mie, Japan
Tel.: (81) 593391313
Car Mfr
N.A.I.C.S.: 336110

Subsidiary (US):

Yachiyo Manufacturing Of America, LLC (2)
565 Beulah Church Rd, Carrollton, GA 30117
Tel.: (678) 390-6300
Fuel Tank Mfr
N.A.I.C.S.: 336211

Subsidiary (Non-US):

Yachiyo Mexico Manufacturing S.A. de C.V. (2)
Av Apaseo el Grande 106 Parques Industriales Amistad Bajio, 38160, Apaseo el Grande, Guanajuato, Mexico
Tel.: (52) 4131586000
Sunroof Mfr
N.A.I.C.S.: 336390

Yachiyo Wuhan Manufacturing Co., Ltd. (2)
786 ZhuShanHu Avenue Wuhan Economic Technological Development Zone, Hubei, China
Tel.: (86) 2784478181
Sunroof Mfr
N.A.I.C.S.: 336390

Yachiyo Zhongshan Manufacturing Co., Ltd. (2)
No 28 Keji Avenue Concentrated-Constructed Area Zhongshan Torch, Hi-Tech Industrial Development Zone, Zhongshan, 528437, Guangdong, China
Tel.: (86) 76085335309
Sunroof Mfr
N.A.I.C.S.: 336390

Subsidiary (US):

Yachiyo of America Inc. (2)

2285 Walcutt Rd, Columbus, OH 43228
Tel.: (614) 876-3220
Sunroof Mfr
N.A.I.C.S.: 336390

Yamada Seisakusho Co., Ltd. (1)
2-1296 Koubayashi-cho, Isesaki, 379-2206, Gunma, Japan
Tel.: (81) 27 040 9111
Web Site: https://www.yamada-s.co.jp
Emp.: 1,560
Automobile Parts Mfr
N.A.I.C.S.: 336390
Sato Masaru *(Pres)*

Yanagawa Seiki Co., Ltd. (1)
1-3-5 Shinsayama Sayama, Saitama, 350-1331, Japan
Tel.: (81) 42 953 5173
Web Site: https://www.yanagawa-seiki.co.jp
Automobile Parts Mfr
N.A.I.C.S.: 336390
Akira Sasahara *(Pres & CEO)*

Yutaka Giken Co., Ltd. (1)
508-1 Yutaka-cho, Higashi-ku Hamamatsu, Shizuoka, 431-3194, Japan (69%)
Tel.: (81) 534334111
Web Site: http://www.yutakagiken.co.jp
Sales Range: $100-124.9 Million
Emp.: 286
Precision Stamping of Parts for Motorcycles, Automobiles & Power Products
N.A.I.C.S.: 336370
Akira Kitajima *(Mng Dir)*

Subsidiary (Non-US):

YS Tech (Thailand) Co., Ltd. (2)
601 Moo 7 Tambol Thatoom, Amphur Srimahaphote, Prachin Buri, 25140, Thailand
Tel.: (66) 3721870813
Web Site: https://www.yst.co.th
Automotive Parts
N.A.I.C.S.: 336390

HONEY BADGER SILVER INC.
145 Wellington Street West Suite 1001, Toronto, M5J 1H8, ON, Canada
Tel.: (416) 364-7029
Web Site:
  https://honeybadgersilver.com
Year Founded: 1992
HBEIF—(OTCQB)
Rev.: $3,411
Assets: $1,909,574
Liabilities: $534,667
Net Worth: $1,374,907
Earnings: ($5,668,853)
Emp.: 3
Fiscal Year-end: 12/31/21
Mineral Exploration Services
N.A.I.C.S.: 213114
Dorian L. Nicol *(CEO)*

HONEY BUN (1982) LTD.
22-26 Retirement Cres, Kingston, 5, Jamaica
Tel.: (876) 9609851
Web Site:
  https://www.honeybunja.com
Year Founded: 1982
HONBUN—(JAM)
Rev.: $22,320,197
Assets: $11,368,725
Liabilities: $2,761,784
Net Worth: $8,606,942
Earnings: $1,517,928
Emp.: 500
Fiscal Year-end: 09/30/23
Bakery Product Distr
N.A.I.C.S.: 424420
Herbert Chong *(Chm)*

HONEY HOPE HONESTY ENTERPRISE CO., LTD.
8F No 316 Neihu Rd Sec 1, Nei-hu District, Taipei, 114, Taiwan
Tel.: (886) 287511779
Web Site:
  https://www.threehhh.com.tw

8043—(TPE)
Rev.: $182,819,936
Assets: $139,996,248
Liabilities: $57,532,939
Net Worth: $82,463,309
Earnings: $4,717,350
Fiscal Year-end: 12/31/22
Capacitor Mfr & Distr
N.A.I.C.S.: 334416
Hsun-Min Lin *(Chm & Pres)*

HONEYS HOLDINGS CO., LTD.
27-1 Shichihonmatsu Hashikuma, Kashima-cho, Iwaki, 971-8141, Fukushima, Japan
Tel.: (81) 246291111
Web Site: https://www.honeys.co.jp
Year Founded: 1978
2792—(TKS)
Rev.: $373,934,310
Assets: $349,265,790
Liabilities: $53,144,400
Net Worth: $296,121,390
Earnings: $32,230,360
Emp.: 6,105
Fiscal Year-end: 05/31/24
Women Cloth & Apparel Mfr
N.A.I.C.S.: 315250
Yoshihisa Ejiri *(Pres)*

HONEYWELL FLOUR MILLS PLC
Flour Mills of Nigeria Plc Golden Penny Place 311 Apapa Rd, Lagos, 102272, Nigeria
Tel.: (234) 2346891000
Web Site:
  https://www.honeywellflour.com
Flour & Livestock Feed Mfr
N.A.I.C.S.: 311119
Yoola Oba Otudeko *(Founder & Chm)*

HONG FOK CORPORATION LIMITED
300 Beach Road No 41-00 The Concourse, Singapore, 199555, Singapore
Tel.: (65) 62928181   SG
Web Site:
  https://www.hongfok.com.sg
Year Founded: 1967
H30—(SES)
Rev.: $83,890,025
Assets: $2,776,058,470
Liabilities: $584,336,135
Net Worth: $2,191,722,335
Earnings: $71,966,977
Emp.: 84
Fiscal Year-end: 12/31/23
Investment Holding Company
N.A.I.C.S.: 551112
Hooi Kheng Cheong *(COO)*

Subsidiaries:

Cocre8 Pte. Ltd. (1)
International Building 360 Orchard Road 08-02, Singapore, 238869, Singapore
Tel.: (65) 119533
Web Site: https://www.cocre8.com.sg
Hospitality Services
N.A.I.C.S.: 721110

Hong Fok Land Pte. Ltd. (1)
300 Beach Rd 41 00 The Concourse, Singapore, 199555, Singapore (100%)
Tel.: (65) 62928181
Web Site: https://www.hongfok.com.sg
Sales Range: $25-49.9 Million
Emp.: 100
Real Estate Developers
N.A.I.C.S.: 237210

Yat Yuen Hong Co., Ltd. (1)
300 Beach Road 41 00 The Concourse, Singapore, 199555, Singapore (100%)
Tel.: (65) 62928181
Web Site: http://www.intl-building.com.sg
Sales Range: $25-49.9 Million
Emp.: 100
Real Estate Developers

N.A.I.C.S.: 237210
C. T. Koh *(Mgr-Fin)*

HONG HA LONG AN JOINT STOCK COMPANY
Hong Gia Long An Industrial Park, My Hanh Nam, Duc Hoa District, Tan An, Long An, Vietnam
Tel.: (84) 723849932
Web Site: http://www.honghala.com
Sales Range: $50-74.9 Million
Emp.: 130
Readymix Concrete Mfr
N.A.I.C.S.: 327320
Tien Van Pham *(Chm)*

HONG HO PRECISION TEXTILES CO., LTD.
No 473 Zhongshan S Rd, Yong-kang Dist, T'ainan, 710, Taiwan
Tel.: (886) 62333133
Web Site: http://www.hongho.com.tw
Year Founded: 1978
1446—(TAI)
Rev.: $18,747,964
Assets: $151,462,534
Liabilities: $101,713,100
Net Worth: $49,749,434
Earnings: $3,595,703
Fiscal Year-end: 12/31/23
Sports Fabrics Mfr
N.A.I.C.S.: 315120
Dagong Huang *(Chm)*

HONG KONG AEROSPACE TECHNOLOGY HOLDINGS LIMITED
6/F St John's Building 33 Garden Road, Central, China (Hong Kong)
Tel.: (852) 28691888   HK
Web Site: http://www.hkatg.com
Year Founded: 2019
Investment Holding Company
N.A.I.C.S.: 551112
Sun Fengquan *(Chm)*

Subsidiaries:

Hong Kong Aerospace Technology Group Limited (1)
6/F St John's Building 33 Garden Road, Central, China (Hong Kong) (70.95%)
Tel.: (852) 28691888
Web Site: http://www.hkatg.com
Rev.: $89,214,653
Assets: $172,320,080
Liabilities: $137,798,248
Net Worth: $34,521,833
Earnings: ($21,662,456)
Emp.: 1,162
Fiscal Year-end: 12/31/2022
Holding Company; Aerospace Technologies & Services
N.A.I.C.S.: 551112
Fujun Ma *(Chm)*

HONG KONG CHAOSHANG GROUP LIMITED
Suite 2202 22/F China Resources Building 26 Harbour Road, Wanchai, China (Hong Kong)
Tel.: (852) 2 598 9868   BM
Web Site: http://www.noblecentury.hk
2322—(HKG)
Rev.: $43,576,280
Assets: $137,718,266
Liabilities: $18,543,971
Net Worth: $119,174,296
Earnings: ($3,024,452)
Emp.: 66
Fiscal Year-end: 03/31/21
Marine Transportation Services
N.A.I.C.S.: 488320
Juhua Zheng *(Chm)*

HONG KONG ECONOMIC TIMES HOLDINGS LTD

6/F Kodak House II 321 Java Road, North Point, China (Hong Kong)
Tel.: (852) 28802888   KY
Web Site: https://www.hketgroup.com
Year Founded: 2005
0423—(HKG)
Rev.: $134,602,883
Assets: $154,560,087
Liabilities: $37,752,962
Net Worth: $116,807,126
Earnings: $4,443,232
Emp.: 1,387
Fiscal Year-end: 03/31/22
Newspaper Publishing
N.A.I.C.S.: 513110
Salome Sau Mei See *(Exec Dir)*

Subsidiaries:

Career Times Online Limited (1)
Unit 1008-9 Kodak House II 321 Java Road, North Point, China (Hong Kong)
Tel.: (852) 21562626
Web Site: http://www.ctgoodjobs.hk
Emp.: 50
Online Recruitment Services
N.A.I.C.S.: 561311

EPRC Limited (1)
RM 1409 Kodak House II 321 Java Road, North Point, China (Hong Kong)
Tel.: (852) 28808699
Web Site: http://www.eprcdm.com
Property Marketing Services
N.A.I.C.S.: 531311

ET Business College Limited (1)
Rm 1111-9 15 F Kodak House II 321 Java Rd, North Point, China (Hong Kong)
Tel.: (852) 28802850
Web Site: http://www.etbc.com.hk
Emp.: 20
Education Services
N.A.I.C.S.: 611710

ET Net Limited (1)
Unit 1505-9 Kodak House II 321 Java Road, North Point, China (Hong Kong)
Tel.: (852) 28807004
Web Site: http://www.etnet.com.hk
Financial Information Services
N.A.I.C.S.: 523940

ET Net News Agency Limited (1)
Rm 1505-9 7 F Kodak House II 321 Java Rd, North Point, China (Hong Kong)
Tel.: (852) 28808600
Web Site: http://www.etnet.com.hk
Sales Range: $350-399.9 Million
Emp.: 1,000
Online Financial Information Services
N.A.I.C.S.: 523940
Siu Por Fung *(Mng Dir)*

ET Trade Limited (1)
Unit 1505-1509 Kodak House II 321 Java Road, North Point, China (Hong Kong)
Tel.: (852) 2880 7090
Web Site: http://www.ettrade.com.hk
Sales Range: $25-49.9 Million
Emp.: 37
Software Development Services
N.A.I.C.S.: 541511

ET Wealth Limited (1)
Unit 1505-1509 Kodak House II 321 Java Road, North Point, China (Hong Kong)
Tel.: (852) 28806460
Web Site: http://www.etwealth.com
Emp.: 10
Wealth Management Software Development Services
N.A.I.C.S.: 541511

ETVision Multimedia Limited (1)
8 F Kodak House II 321 Java Rd, North Point, China (Hong Kong)
Tel.: (852) 2880 2888
Financial Information Video Streaming Services
N.A.I.C.S.: 516210

Health Smart Limited (1)
Room 1407 14th Floor Block 2 Kodak Building, 321 Java Road, North Point, China (Hong Kong)
Tel.: (852) 28800066
Web Site: http://www.healthsmart.com.hk

HONG KONG ECONOMIC TIMES HOLDINGS LTD

Hong Kong Economic Times Holdings Ltd—(Continued)
Sales Range: $10-24.9 Million
Emp.: 20
Health Management & Consultancy Services
N.A.I.C.S.: 621999

Hong Kong Economic Times Limited (1)
8/F Kodak House II 321 Java Road, North Point, China (Hong Kong)
Tel.: (852) 28802888
Web Site: http://www.hket.com
Newspaper Publishing Services
N.A.I.C.S.: 513110

HONG KONG EXCHANGES & CLEARING LIMITED
8/F Two Exchange Square 8 Connaught Place, Central, China (Hong Kong)
Tel.: (852) 25221122
Web Site: http://www.hkexgroup.com
0388—(HKG)
Rev.: $1,973,877,593
Assets: $43,602,821,833
Liabilities: $36,983,270,924
Net Worth: $6,619,550,909
Earnings: $1,531,176,914
Emp.: 2,419
Fiscal Year-end: 12/31/23
Investment Management Service
N.A.I.C.S.: 523210
Richard Leung (CTO-Grp)

Subsidiaries:

HKFE Clearing Corporation Limited (1)
12 Fl One International Finance Ctr, 1 Harbour View St, Central, China (Hong Kong)
Tel.: (852) 25221122
Sales Range: $350-399.9 Million
Emp.: 800
Stock Exchange Services
N.A.I.C.S.: 523210
Charles Xiaojia Li (Chm)

HKSCC Nominees Limited (1)
8/F Two Exchange Square 8 Connaught Place, Central, China (Hong Kong)
Tel.: (852) 2 522 1122
Web Site: https://www.hkex.com.hk
Stock & Future Exchange Services
N.A.I.C.S.: 523210

Hong Kong Futures Exchange Ltd. (1)
12 Fl One International Finance Ctr, 1 Harbour View St, Central, China (Hong Kong) (100%)
Tel.: (852) 25221122
Web Site: http://www.hkex.com.hk
Sales Range: $100-124.9 Million
Emp.: 215
Markets for the Trading of Futures & Options Contracts
N.A.I.C.S.: 523210

Hong Kong Securities Clearing Company Limited (1)
12 Fl One International Finance Ctr, 1 Harbour View St, Central, China (Hong Kong)
Tel.: (852) 25221122
Web Site: http://www.hkex.com.hk
Stock Exchange Services
N.A.I.C.S.: 523210

LME Clear Limited (1)
10 Finsbury Square, London, EC2A1AJ, United Kingdom
Tel.: (44) 2071138888
Metal Product Mfr & Distr
N.A.I.C.S.: 331523

Qianhai Mercantile Exchange Co., Ltd. (1)
Group A Qianhai Shenzhen-Hong Kong Innovation Center No 4008, Menghai Road Qianhai Shenzhen-Hong Kong Cooperation Zone, Shenzhen, 518054, China
Tel.: (86) 75521871100
Web Site: https://www.qme.com
Commodity Trading Platform Operator
N.A.I.C.S.: 423920

The SEHK Options Clearing House Limited (1)
12 Fl One International Finance Ctr, 1 Harbour View St, Central, China (Hong Kong)
Tel.: (852) 25221122
Emp.: 100
Stock Exchange Services
N.A.I.C.S.: 523210
Charles Lee (CEO)

The Stock Exchange of Hong Kong Limited (1)
12 Floor One International Finance Center, 1 Harbour View Street, Central, China (Hong Kong)
Tel.: (852) 25221122
Web Site: http://www.hkex.com.hk
Stock Exchange Services
N.A.I.C.S.: 523210

HONG KONG FINANCE GROUP LIMITED
Unit 3410 34/F Tower II Lippo Centre 89 Queensway Admiralty, Hong Kong, China (Hong Kong)
Tel.: (852) 2 525 3535
Web Site: http://www.hkfinance.com.hk
1273—(HKG)
Rev.: $19,976,680
Assets: $151,819,134
Liabilities: $56,809,886
Net Worth: $95,009,248
Earnings: $9,099,539
Emp.: 43
Fiscal Year-end: 03/31/22
Mortgage Lender
N.A.I.C.S.: 522310
William Kwong Yin Chan (Co-Founder & Chm)

HONG KONG FOOD INVESTMENT HOLDINGS LIMITED
2905-07 29/F Manhattan Place No 23 Wang Tai Road, Kowloon, Kowloon Bay, China (Hong Kong)
Tel.: (852) 21639999
Web Site: https://www.hongkongfood.com.hk
0060—(HKG)
Rev.: $23,620,494
Assets: $88,383,029
Liabilities: $10,354,127
Net Worth: $78,028,902
Earnings: ($2,032,725)
Emp.: 65
Fiscal Year-end: 03/31/22
Holding Company; Frozen Meat, Seafood & Vegetables Trading Services
N.A.I.C.S.: 551112
Siu Wan Tse (Exec Dir)

Subsidiaries:

Miyata Co., Ltd. (1)
950-1 Wanagaya, Matsudo, 270-2232, Chiba, Japan
Tel.: (81) 473691211
Web Site: https://www.miyata-net.co.jp
Confectionery Goods Mfr & Distr
N.A.I.C.S.: 311351
Janzen Tai (CEO)

William Food Company Limited (1)
Four Seas eFood Ctr 2 Hong Ting Rd, Sai Kung, New Territories, China (Hong Kong)
Tel.: (852) 21639999
Web Site: http://www.efood.hk
Frozen Food Whslr
N.A.I.C.S.: 424420

HONG KONG JOHNSON HOLDINGS COMPANY LIMITED
11/F China Aerospace Centre No 143 Hoi Bun Road, Kwun Tong, Kowloon, China (Hong Kong)
Tel.: (852) 25417216
Web Site: http://www.johnsonholdings.com
Year Founded: 1979

1955—(HKG)
Rev.: $290,725,500
Assets: $121,184,160
Liabilities: $46,410,638
Net Worth: $74,773,523
Earnings: $3,895,125
Emp.: 7,400
Fiscal Year-end: 03/31/23
Holding Company
N.A.I.C.S.: 551112
Kam Chiu Cheung (Co-CEO)

Subsidiaries:

Johnson Cleaning Services Company Limited (1)
11th Floor Aerospace Technology Center 143 Hoi Bun Road, Kwun Tong, Kowloon, China (Hong Kong)
Tel.: (852) 25417216
Web Site: http://www.johnson-cleaning.com
Cleaning Service
N.A.I.C.S.: 561720

HONG KONG KAM KEE FOODSTUFFS TRADING CO., LTD.
Workshop C D 9/F Blk 2, Koon Wah Mirror Factory 6th Industrial Building Nos 7-9 Ho Tin Street, Tuen Mun, New Territories, China (Hong Kong)
Tel.: (852) 24071781
Web Site: http://www.hkkamkee.com
Year Founded: 1984
Sales Range: $50-74.9 Million
Emp.: 260
Vegetarian Food Product Mfr
N.A.I.C.S.: 311423

Subsidiaries:

SHAO TONG CHUAN VEGETARIAN FOODS MFG (SG) PTE. LTD., (1)
Blk 171 Kampong Ampat 06-08 Kampong Ampat Industrial Estate, Singapore, 368330, Singapore
Tel.: (65) 62891808
Frozen Food Mfr & Distr
N.A.I.C.S.: 311412

SHAO TONG CHUANG (PHILIPHINE) FOODSTUFFS CO., LTD (1)
85 Sta Catalina St Near Banawest St, Quezon City, Philippines
Tel.: (63) 2 7326845
Frozen Food Mfr & Distr
N.A.I.C.S.: 311412

HONG KONG LAND HOLDINGS LTD.
Jardine House 33-35 Reid Street, Hamilton, HM EX, Bermuda
Tel.: (441) 14412920515 BM
Web Site: http://www.hkland.com
Year Founded: 1889
HKLB—(LSE)
Rev.: $1,844,300,000
Assets: $40,767,900,000
Liabilities: $8,780,600,000
Net Worth: $31,987,300,000
Earnings: ($577,100,000)
Emp.: 2,991
Fiscal Year-end: 12/31/23
Commercial Property Development Services
N.A.I.C.S.: 531210
Ben Keswick (Chm)

Subsidiaries:

Beijing Yee Zhi Real Estate Consultancy Co., Ltd. (1)
Room 1123A 11/F Office Tower 3 Beijing APM No 138 Wangfujing Street, Dongcheng District, Beijing, 100006, China
Tel.: (86) 1065204800
Real Estate Investment Management Services
N.A.I.C.S.: 531390

Central Building Ltd. (1)
31 Hai Ba Trung Street, Hoan Kiem District,

INTERNATIONAL PUBLIC

Hanoi, Vietnam
Tel.: (84) 243825148028
Real Estate Investment Management Services
N.A.I.C.S.: 531390
Cao Ly Anh (Gen Dir)

HKL (Prince's Building) Ltd. (1)
10 Chater Road, Central, China (Hong Kong)
Tel.: (852) 25000555
Web Site: https://www.landmark.hk
Financial Services
N.A.I.C.S.: 541611

HKL (Thai Developments) Limited (1)
Unit B 20th Floor Gaysorn Tower No 127 Rajdamri Road, Lumpini Sub-District Pathumwan District, Bangkok, 10330, Thailand
Tel.: (66) 20330160
Real Estate Investment Management Services
N.A.I.C.S.: 531390

HKL (Vietnam) Consultancy & Management Company Limited (1)
Suite 704 The Metropolitan 235 Dong Khoi, Ben Nghe Ward District 1, Ho Chi Minh City, Vietnam
Tel.: (84) 2838279006
Real Estate Investment Management Services
N.A.I.C.S.: 531390

Hongkong Land (Chengdu) Investment & Development Company Limited (1)
16F Block A Weland Centre No 246 Dongda Road, Jinjiang District, Chengdu, 610065, Sichuan, China
Tel.: (86) 2861556008
Real Estate Investment Management Services
N.A.I.C.S.: 531390

Hongkong Land (Chongqing) Investment & Holding Co. Ltd. (1)
3/F Zone D Neptune Building No 62 Star Light Road, New North Zone, Chongqing, 401147, China
Tel.: (86) 23670330168
Real Estate Investment Management Services
N.A.I.C.S.: 531390

Hongkong Land (Hangzhou) Shengyue Management Co., Ltd. (1)
Unit 3001-1 Building One Ping An Finance Centre No 280 Mingxin Road, Jianggan District, Hangzhou, 310016, Zhejiang, China
Tel.: (86) 57187013930
Real Estate Investment Management Services
N.A.I.C.S.: 531390

Hongkong Land (Nanjing) Puzhi Management Co., Ltd. (1)
Unit B 55/F Nanjing Center No 1 Zhongshan South Road, Qinhuai District, Nanjing, 210001, Jiangsu, China
Tel.: (86) 2583338388
Real Estate Investment Management Services
N.A.I.C.S.: 531390

Hongkong Land (Philippines) Consultancy, Inc. (1)
1803 The Taipan Place F Ortigas Jr Road Ortigas Center, Pasig, 1605, Philippines
Tel.: (63) 26256880
Real Estate Investment Management Services
N.A.I.C.S.: 531390

Hongkong Land (Premium Investments) Limited (1)
Unit 702 7th Floor Exchange Square No 19 and 20 Street 106, Village 2 Sangkat Wat Phnom Khan Daun Penh, Phnom Penh, Cambodia
Tel.: (855) 23992063
Real Estate Investment Management Services
N.A.I.C.S.: 531390

Hongkong Land (Shanghai) Management Company Limited (1)
11/F Tower A LCM No 2389 Zhangyang

AND PRIVATE COMPANIES — HONG LEONG INVESTMENT HOLDINGS PTE. LTD.

Road, Pudong New District, Shanghai, 200135, China
Tel.: (86) 2120200086
Real Estate Investment Management Services
N.A.I.C.S.: 531390

Hongkong Land (Wuhan) Investment & Development Company Limited (1)
Room 1208 CITIC Pacific Mansion No 1627 Zhongshan Avenue, Jiangan District, Wuhan, 430014, Hubei, China
Tel.: (86) 2782891566
Real Estate Investment Management Services
N.A.I.C.S.: 531390

MCL Land (Malaysia) Sdn. Bhd. (1)
Lot G 93A Wangsa Walk Mall Wangsa Avenue 9, Jalan Wangsa Perdana 1 Bandar Wangsa Maju, 53300, Kuala Lumpur, Malaysia
Tel.: (60) 341428888
Real Estate Investment Management Services
N.A.I.C.S.: 531390
Tan Ching Meng *(Gen Mgr)*

PT Hongkong Land Consultancy & Management (1)
World Trade Centre 1 17th Floor Jl Jend Sudirman Kav 29-31, Jakarta, 12920, Indonesia
Tel.: (62) 215211125
Real Estate Investment Management Services
N.A.I.C.S.: 531390

Wangfu Central Real Estate Development Co. Ltd. (1)
No 269 Wangfujing Street, Dongcheng District, Beijing, China
Tel.: (86) 1085648888
Web Site: https://www.wfcentral.cn
Real Estate Investment Management Services
N.A.I.C.S.: 531390
Shirley Lam *(Pres-Comml Property)*

HONG KONG LIFE SCIENCES & TECHNOLOGIES GROUP LIMITED
Unit 2704 27/F West Tower Shun Tak Centre 168-200 Connaught Road, Central, China (Hong Kong)
Tel.: (852) 2549 8033   Ky
Web Site: http://www.hklifesciences.com
Year Founded: 2000
Rev.: $17,939,614
Assets: $42,216,591
Liabilities: $5,218,185
Net Worth: $36,998,406
Earnings: ($10,623,305)
Emp.: 39
Fiscal Year-end: 03/31/18
Holding Company
N.A.I.C.S.: 551112
Zhiqiang Lu *(CEO & Compliance Officer)*

HONG KONG MONETARY AUTHORITY
55th Floor 2 International Finance Centre, 8 Finance Street, Central, China (Hong Kong)
Tel.: (852) 28788196
Web Site: http://www.hkma.gov.hk
Year Founded: 1993
Sales Range: $1-4.9 Billion
Emp.: 590
Banking Services
N.A.I.C.S.: 521110
Stefan Gannon *(Gen Counsel)*

HONG KONG SHANGHAI ALLIANCE HOLDINGS LIMITED
Rooms 1103-05 11th Floor, East Town Building 41 Lockhart Road, Wanchai, China (Hong Kong)
Tel.: (852) 2 528 1238   BM
Web Site: http://www.hkshalliance.com
1001—(HKG)
Rev.: $362,162,942
Assets: $434,433,145
Liabilities: $290,720,017
Net Worth: $143,713,127
Earnings: $8,182,362
Emp.: 235
Fiscal Year-end: 03/31/22
Construction Materials Distr
N.A.I.C.S.: 423610
Andrew Cho Fai Yao *(Chm & CEO)*

Subsidiaries:

VSC Building Products Company Limited (1)
Ground Fl Century Ct 239 Jaffe Rd, Wanchai, China (Hong Kong)
Tel.: (852) 21868280
Web Site: http://www.vlchk.com
Sales Range: $25-49.9 Million
Emp.: 50
Sanitary Ware & Kitchen Cabinet Sales & Installation Services
N.A.I.C.S.: 238220
Patrick Leu *(Mng Dir)*

VSC Plastics Company Limited (1)
Rm 4903-07 Hopewell Ctr 183 Queens Rd E, Wanchai, China (Hong Kong)
Tel.: (852) 25281238
Plastic Resin Whslr
N.A.I.C.S.: 424610

Van Shung Chong Hong Limited (1)
Rm 4903-07 Hopewell Ctr 183 Queens Rd E, Wanchai, China (Hong Kong)
Tel.: (852) 25281238
Steel Product Distr
N.A.I.C.S.: 423510

Vantage Godown Company Limited (1)
Rm 4903 49 F Hopewell Ctr 183 Queens Rd E, Wanchai, China (Hong Kong)
Tel.: (852) 25281238
General Warehousing Services
N.A.I.C.S.: 493110

HONG KONG TECHNOLOGY VENTURE COMPANY LIMITED
HKTV Multimedia and Ecommerce Centre 1 Chun Cheong Street, Tseung Kwan O Industrial Estate, Tseung Kwan O, New Territories, China (Hong Kong)
Tel.: (852) 31456888
Web Site: https://www.hktv.com.hk
Year Founded: 1992
1137—(HKG)
Rev.: $488,076,503
Assets: $461,487,780
Liabilities: $179,866,673
Net Worth: $281,621,108
Earnings: $27,056,010
Emp.: 2,186
Fiscal Year-end: 12/31/22
Telecommunication Servicesb
N.A.I.C.S.: 516120
Alice Nga Lai Wong *(CFO, Grp CFO & Sec)*

Subsidiaries:

City Telecom Inc. (1)
Unit 31 175 West Beaver Creek Road, Richmond Hill, L4B 3M1, ON, Canada   (100%)
Tel.: (416) 502-1838
Web Site: http://www.ctinets.on.ca
Sales Range: $25-49.9 Million
Emp.: 20
Telecommunications Resellers
N.A.I.C.S.: 517121

HKBN Ltd. (1)
19/F Tower1 The Quayside 77 Hoi Bun Road Kwun Tong, Kowloon, China (Hong Kong)   (100%)
Tel.: (852) 731542231
Web Site: https://www.hkbn.net
Rev.: $1,499,542,633
Assets: $2,634,687,100
Liabilities: $1,999,578,875
Net Worth: $635,108,225
Earnings: $71,367,343
Emp.: 4,864
Fiscal Year-end: 08/31/2022
Telecommunications
N.A.I.C.S.: 517810
Elinor Shiu *(Co-Owner & CEO-Residential Solutions)*

Shoalter Automation (UK) Limited (1)
Unit 320 Metroplex Business Park, Quays, Salford, M50 2UE, United Kingdom
Tel.: (44) 1613889818
Web Site: https://www.shoalter-automation.com
Automation Product Distr
N.A.I.C.S.: 423830

HONG KONG TOURISM BOARD
9-11 F Citicorp Centre 18 Whitfield Road, North Point, China (Hong Kong)
Tel.: (852) 28076543
Web Site: http://www.discoverhongkong.com
Year Founded: 1957
Sales Range: $50-74.9 Million
Emp.: 250
Tourism Marketing & Promotion Services
N.A.I.C.S.: 926110
Cynthia Leung *(Gen Mgr-Corp Affairs)*

Subsidiaries:

Hong Kong Tourism Board - New York (1)
115 E 54th St Fl 2, New York, NY 10022
Tel.: (212) 421-3382
Web Site: http://www.discoverhongkong.com
Sales Range: $50-74.9 Million
Emp.: 5
Tourism Marketing & Promotion Services
N.A.I.C.S.: 926110

HONG LAI HUAT GROUP LIMITED
10 Bukit Batok Crescent 1305 The Spire Building, Singapore, 608531, Singapore
Tel.: (65) 68610330
Web Site: https://honglaihuatgroup.com
CTO—(SES)
Rev.: $202,227
Assets: $100,362,796
Liabilities: $16,710,596
Net Worth: $83,652,200
Earnings: ($18,005,756)
Emp.: 127
Fiscal Year-end: 12/31/23
Property Development Services
N.A.I.C.S.: 531311
Helen Campos Thomas *(Sec)*

Subsidiaries:

Almira Development Pte Ltd (1)
82 Playfair Road, Singapore, 368001, Singapore
Tel.: (65) 62898286
Sales Range: $25-49.9 Million
Emp.: 50
Apartment Construction Services
N.A.I.C.S.: 236116

HLH Agri International Pte Ltd (1)
Neo Tiew Lane 2, Singapore, 718813, Singapore
Tel.: (65) 68629717
Agriculture Product Distr
N.A.I.C.S.: 423820

Subsidiary (Domestic):

HLH Agri R&D Pte Ltd (2)
76 Playfair Road, Singapore, 367996, Singapore
Tel.: (65) 68629717
Agricultural Research & Development Services
N.A.I.C.S.: 541715

HLH Global Trading Pte Ltd (2)
10 Bukit Batok Crescent 13-05 The Spire Building, Singapore, 658079, Singapore
Tel.: (65) 68610330
Agricultural Commodities Trading Services
N.A.I.C.S.: 523160

HLH Agriculture (Cambodia) Co., Ltd. (1)
No 315 Preah Ang Duong corner of Preah Monivong St 93 26th Floor, Canadia Tower, Phnom Penh, Cambodia
Tel.: (855) 23995050
Engineeering Services
N.A.I.C.S.: 541330

HLH Development Pte Ltd (1)
1 Gateway Drive 20-12/13 Westgate Tower, Singapore, 608531, Singapore
Tel.: (65) 68610330
Real Estate Development Services
N.A.I.C.S.: 531390

HLHI (Cambodia) Co., Ltd. (1)
No A1 A3 A5 Russian Blvd Sangkat Teuk Thla, Khan Sen Sok, Phnom Penh, Cambodia
Tel.: (855) 23995050
Web Site: https://www.hlhcambodia.com
Residential & Industrial Properties Construction Services
N.A.I.C.S.: 236220

Hong Lai Huat Construction Pte Ltd (1)
82 Playfair Road, Singapore, 368001, Singapore
Tel.: (65) 62898286
Residential Building Construction Services
N.A.I.C.S.: 236115

Lithium Development Pte Ltd (1)
82 Playfair Road, Singapore, 368001, Singapore
Tel.: (65) 62898286
Residential Building Construction Services
N.A.I.C.S.: 236115

PH One Development (Cambodia) Ltd. (1)
No 315 Preah Ang Duong St 110 corner of Preah Monivong St 93, Canadia Tower 26th Floor, Phnom Penh, 12202, Cambodia
Tel.: (855) 23995050
Real Estate Property Development Services
N.A.I.C.S.: 531312

Public Housing Development (Cambodia) Ltd. (1)
Canadia Tower No 315 3rd floor Store 03-01 Preah Ang Duong Street, Sangkat Wat Phnom Khan Daun Penh, Phnom Penh, Cambodia
Tel.: (855) 767689090
Web Site: https://www.camhomes.com
Real Estate Property Development Services
N.A.I.C.S.: 531312

HONG LEONG INVESTMENT HOLDINGS PTE. LTD.
9 Raffles Place 11-00 Republic Plaza, Singapore, 048619, Singapore
Tel.: (65) 68778530
Web Site: http://www.hongleong.com.sg
Year Founded: 1941
Investment Holding Company
N.A.I.C.S.: 551112

Subsidiaries:

Hong Leong Company (Malaysia) Berhad (1)
Level 10 Wisma Hong Leong 18 Jalan Perak, 50450, Kuala Lumpur, Malaysia
Tel.: (60) 321641818
Web Site: http://www.hongleong.com
Sales Range: $1-4.9 Billion
Emp.: 7,116
Holding Company
N.A.I.C.S.: 551112

Subsidiary (Non-US):

Guoco Group Ltd. (2)

HONG LEONG INVESTMENT HOLDINGS PTE. LTD.

Hong Leong Investment Holdings Pte. Ltd.—(Continued)
50th Floor The Center 99 Queens Road Central, Hong Kong, China (Hong Kong) **(77.27%)**
Tel.: (852) 22838833
Web Site: https://www.guoco.com
Rev.: $2,008,688,000
Assets: $16,602,327,000
Liabilities: $7,000,306,000
Net Worth: $9,602,021,000
Earnings: $420,714,000
Emp.: 10,300
Fiscal Year-end: 06/30/2022
Investment Holding Company
N.A.I.C.S.: 551112
Seong Aun Chew *(CFO & Exec Dir)*

Subsidiary (Domestic):

Dao Heng Securities Limited (3)
12th Floor The Center, 99 Queen's Road, Central, China (Hong Kong)
Tel.: (852) 22182818
Web Site: http://www.guococap.com
Sales Range: $50-74.9 Million
Emp.: 70
Investment Services
N.A.I.C.S.: 523150

Subsidiary (Non-US):

GL Limited (3)
1 Wallich Street 15-02 Guoco Tower, Singapore, 078881, Singapore **(100%)**
Tel.: (65) 6438 0002
Web Site: http://www.gl-grp.com
Rev.: $349,300,000
Assets: $1,368,100,000
Liabilities: $294,300,000
Net Worth: $1,073,800,000
Earnings: $50,300,000
Emp.: 1,707
Fiscal Year-end: 06/30/2019
Investment Holding Company
N.A.I.C.S.: 551112
Susan Lim *(Gen Counsel & Sec-Grp)*

Subsidiary (Non-US):

BIL Australia Pty Limited (4)
22 Emerstan Drive, Castle Cove, Sydney, 2069, NSW, Australia
Tel.: (61) 2 9882 1255
Investment Services
N.A.I.C.S.: 523999

Brierley Holdings Limited (4)
144 St Johns Road St Johns, Auckland, New Zealand
Tel.: (64) 21 927700
Investment Services
N.A.I.C.S.: 523999

GLH Hotels Limited (4)
110 Central Street, London, EC1V 8AB, United Kingdom
Tel.: (44) 20 7554 3890
Web Site: http://www.glhhotels.com
Hotel Operator
N.A.I.C.S.: 721110

GLH Hotels Management (UK) Limited (4)
107 Leith Street, Edinburgh, EH1 3SW, United Kingdom
Tel.: (44) 871 376 9016
Hotel Operator
N.A.I.C.S.: 721110
Joey Goei *(Mgr-Design)*

Guoman Hotel Management (UK) Limited (4)
Bath Rd, PO Box 909, Uxbridge, UB8 9FH, United Kingdom **(100%)**
Tel.: (44) 02071380000
Web Site: http://www.guoman.com
Sales Range: $25-49.9 Million
Emp.: 200
Hotels & Motels
N.A.I.C.S.: 721110
Tim Cordon *(Gen Mgr-The Cumberland)*

Subsidiary (US):

Molokai Properties Limited (4)
1003 Bishop St Ste 1170, Honolulu, HI 96813
Tel.: (808) 534-9523
Investment Services

N.A.I.C.S.: 523999
Clay Rumbaoa *(Exec Dir)*

Subsidiary (Non-US):

Tabua Investments Limited (4)
Box PD67 Port Denarau, Nadi, Fiji
Tel.: (679) 675 0251
Investment Services
N.A.I.C.S.: 523999

Thistle Hotels Limited (4)
101 Buckingham Palace Road, London, SW1W 0WA, United Kingdom
Tel.: (44) 871 376 9038
Web Site: http://www.thistlehotels.com
Sales Range: $300-349.9 Million
Emp.: 1,917
Hotel Operator
N.A.I.C.S.: 721110

Subsidiary (Non-US):

GuocoLand (Malaysia) Berhad (3)
Level 10 Wisma Hong Leong, 18 Jalan Perak, 50450, Kuala Lumpur, Malaysia
Tel.: (60) 2 2164 1818
Web Site: http://www.mystorey.com
Property Development Services
N.A.I.C.S.: 531390
Lee Koon Tan *(Mng Dir)*

GuocoLand Limited (3)
1 Wallich Street 31-01 Guoco Tower, Singapore, 078881, Singapore
Tel.: (65) 65356455
Web Site: https://www.guocoland.com.sg
Rev.: $1,144,447,573
Assets: $8,899,459,059
Liabilities: $4,772,045,943
Net Worth: $4,127,413,116
Earnings: $199,213,042
Emp.: 461
Fiscal Year-end: 06/30/2023
Residential & Commercial Real Estate Development & Sales
N.A.I.C.S.: 531390
Moses Kim Poo Lee *(Chm)*

Subsidiary (Non-US):

Chongqing Yuzhong Xinhaojun Real Estate Development Co., Ltd. (4)
3-43 Floor No 28 Minquan Road, Yuzhong District, Chongqing, 400010, China
Tel.: (86) 2386801818
Real Estate Services
N.A.I.C.S.: 531390

Subsidiary (Domestic):

GuocoLand (Singapore) Pte. Ltd. (4)
1 Wallich Street 31-01 Guoco Tower, Singapore, 078881, Singapore
Tel.: (65) 65343132
Property Development Services
N.A.I.C.S.: 531390

Subsidiary (Domestic):

Martin Modern Pte. Ltd. (5)
35 Martin Place, Singapore, Singapore
Tel.: (65) 62710098
Web Site: http://www.martinmodemcondo.com
Residential Property Development Services
N.A.I.C.S.: 531110
Martin Modern *(Sr Dir-Mktg)*

Meyer Mansion Pte. Ltd. (5)
79 Meyer Rd, Singapore, 437906, Singapore
Tel.: (65) 62259000
Web Site: http://www.meyermansion.com.sg
Residential Property Development Services
N.A.I.C.S.: 531110

Midtown Bay Pte. Ltd. (5)
122 Beach Road, Singapore, Singapore
Tel.: (65) 63622058
Web Site: http://www.the-midtown-bay.com
Residential Property Development Services
N.A.I.C.S.: 531110

Sims Urban Oasis Pte. Ltd. (5)
6 Sims Drive, Singapore, 387388, Singapore
Tel.: (65) 62259000
Web Site: http://www.simsurbanoasis.com.sg
Property Development Services

N.A.I.C.S.: 531390
Wallich Residence Pte. Ltd. (5)
3 Wallich Street, Singapore, Singapore
Tel.: (65) 64096339
Web Site: http://www.wallichresidence.com.sg
Real Estate Services
N.A.I.C.S.: 531390

Subsidiary (Non-US):

GuocoLand Binh Duong Property Co., Ltd. (4)
Unit 01-01 Canary Plaza No5 Binh Duong Boulevard, Binh Hoa, Thuan An, Binh Duong, Vietnam
Tel.: (84) 2746262888
Real Estate Services
N.A.I.C.S.: 531390

Subsidiary (Non-US):

HLI-Hume Management Company (3)
Level 9 Wisma Hong Leong, 18 Jalan Perak, Kuala Lumpur, 50450, Malaysia
Tel.: (60) 321642631
Web Site: http://www.hli.com.my
Sales Range: $50-74.9 Million
Emp.: 50
Investment Management Service
N.A.I.C.S.: 523999
Tricia Especkerman *(Dir-HR)*

Subsidiary (Domestic):

Hong Leong Financial Group Berhad (2)
Level 30 Menara Hong Leong No 6 Jalan Damanlela Bukit Damansara, 50490, Kuala Lumpur, Malaysia
Tel.: (60) 320809888
Web Site: https://www.hlfg.com.my
Rev.: $1,707,591,038
Assets: $71,313,121,698
Liabilities: $62,348,898,487
Net Worth: $8,964,223,211
Earnings: $951,763,418
Emp.: 9,361
Fiscal Year-end: 06/30/2023
Financial Investment Services
N.A.I.C.S.: 523999
Leng Chan Quek *(Chm)*

Subsidiary (Domestic):

Hong Leong Assurance Bhd. (3)
Level 3 Tower B PJ City Development 15A Jln 219 Seksyen 51A, 46100, Petaling Jaya, Selangor, Malaysia
Tel.: (60) 376501818
Web Site: http://www.hla.com.my
Rev.: $681,033,129
Assets: $4,970,184,821
Liabilities: $4,534,886,299
Net Worth: $435,298,523
Earnings: $53,754,939
Fiscal Year-end: 06/30/2019
Fire Insurance Services
N.A.I.C.S.: 524298
Guat Lan Loh *(CEO & Mng Dir-Grp)*

Hong Leong Bank Berhad (3)
Level 1 Wisma Hong Leong, 18 Jalan Perak, 50450, Kuala Lumpur, Malaysia
Tel.: (60) 321642828
Web Site: https://www.hlb.com.my
Banking Services
N.A.I.C.S.: 522110
Nisha Ranne Sharma *(Mgr-Talent Acq)*

Hong Leong Capital Berhad (3)
Level 28 Menara Hong Leong No 6 Jalan Damanlela Bukit Damansara, 50490, Kuala Lumpur, Malaysia
Tel.: (60) 320831800
Web Site: https://www.hlcap.com.my
Rev.: $66,147,878
Assets: $1,114,054,757
Liabilities: $920,092,687
Net Worth: $193,962,070
Earnings: $16,466,204
Emp.: 471
Fiscal Year-end: 06/30/2019
Investment Banking Services
N.A.I.C.S.: 523150
Kong Khoon Tan *(Chm)*

Hong Leong Industries Berhad (3)
Level 31 Menara Hong Leong No 6 Jalan

INTERNATIONAL PUBLIC

Damanlela Bukit Damansara, 50490, Kuala Lumpur, Malaysia
Tel.: (60) 320809200
Web Site: https://www.hli.com.my
Rev.: $723,047,619
Assets: $572,018,836
Liabilities: $108,903,492
Net Worth: $463,115,344
Earnings: $83,291,640
Emp.: 2,460
Fiscal Year-end: 06/30/2023
Semiconductor Devices Mfr
N.A.I.C.S.: 333242
Joanne Wei yin Leong *(Co-Sec)*

Subsidiary (Domestic):

Malaysian Pacific Industries Berhad (2)
Level 31 Menara Hong Leong No 6 Jalan Damanlela, Bukit Damansara, 50490, Kuala Lumpur, Malaysia
Tel.: (60) 320809200
Web Site: https://www.mpind.my
Rev.: $432,719,577
Assets: $637,483,810
Liabilities: $137,930,794
Net Worth: $499,553,016
Earnings: $22,888,466
Emp.: 7,617
Fiscal Year-end: 06/30/2023
Semiconductor Devices Mfr
N.A.I.C.S.: 333242
Joanne Wei Yin Leong *(Sec)*

Hong Leong Corporation Holdings Pte. Ltd. (1)
9 Raffles Place 36-00 Republic Plaza, Singapore, 048619, Singapore
Tel.: (65) 64380880
Web Site: http://www.hongleong.com.sg
Sales Range: $1-4.9 Billion
Emp.: 4,000
Holding Company
N.A.I.C.S.: 551112
Lang Beng Kwek *(Chm)*

Holding (Domestic):

City Developments Limited (2)
9 Raffles Place 12-01 Republic Plaza, Singapore, 048619, Singapore
Tel.: (65) 68778228
Web Site: http://www.cdl.com.sg
Rev.: $3,661,445,721
Assets: $17,957,778,436
Liabilities: $10,888,979,622
Net Worth: $7,068,798,814
Earnings: $258,470,545
Emp.: 7,282
Fiscal Year-end: 12/31/2023
Real Estate Investment & Management Services
N.A.I.C.S.: 523999
Leng Beng Kwek *(Chm)*

Holding (Non-US):

Millennium & Copthorne Hotels Limited (3)
Scarsdale Place, Kensington, London, W8 5SY, United Kingdom **(65.2%)**
Tel.: (44) 2078722444
Web Site: http://www.millenniumhotels.co.uk
Sales Range: $1-4.9 Billion
Hotel Operator
N.A.I.C.S.: 721110

Holding (Domestic):

Hong Leong Asia Ltd. (2)
16 Raffles Quay 26-00 Hong Leong Building, Singapore, 048581, Singapore
Tel.: (65) 62208411
Web Site: https://www.hlasia.com.sg
Rev.: $3,091,308,034
Assets: $4,162,675,147
Liabilities: $2,369,552,373
Net Worth: $1,793,122,774
Earnings: $90,956,601
Emp.: 9,581
Fiscal Year-end: 12/31/2023
Holding Company
N.A.I.C.S.: 551112
Joanne Swee Gim Yeo *(Co-Sec)*

Subsidiary (Domestic):

China Yuchai International Limited (3)

16 Raffles Quay 39-01A Hong Leong Building, Singapore, 048581, Singapore
Tel.: (65) 62208411
Web Site: https://www.cyilimited.com
Rev: $2,456,053,742
Assets: $3,698,114,955
Liabilities: $1,884,864,799
Net Worth: $1,813,250,155
Earnings: $51,426,622
Emp.: 8,579
Fiscal Year-end: 12/31/2022
Holding Company; Diesel Engines, Diesel Power Generators & Diesel Engine Parts Mfr & Sales
N.A.I.C.S.: 551112
Ping Yan *(Chm)*

Subsidiary (Non-US):

Guangxi Yuchai Machinery Co. Ltd. (4)
88 Tianqiao Road, Yulin, 537005, Guangxi, China **(76%)**
Tel.: (86) 7753226931
Web Site: http://www.yuchai.com
Sales Range: $25-49.9 Million
Emp.: 60
Diesel Engines, Diesel Power Generators & Diesel Engine Parts Mfr
N.A.I.C.S.: 333618

Subsidiary (Non-US):

Henan Xinfei Electric Co., Ltd. (3)
East Beigandao Road, Xinxiang, 453002, Henan, China
Tel.: (86) 3733381616
Household Appliances Mfr
N.A.I.C.S.: 335220

Shanghai Rex Packaging Co., Ltd. (3)
1500 Bei Song Road, Minhang District, Shanghai, 201111, China
Tel.: (86) 21 640 90460
Web Site: http://www.shanghairex.com
Industrial Packaging Mfr
N.A.I.C.S.: 322220

Tasek Corporation Berhad (3)
6th Floor Office Block Grand Millennium Kuala Lumpur, 160 Jalan Bukit Bintang, 55100, Kuala Lumpur, Malaysia **(100%)**
Tel.: (60) 321446868
Web Site: http://www.tasekcement.com
Sales Range: $125-149.9 Million
Cement Mfr & Distr
N.A.I.C.S.: 325520
Vincent Poh Jin Chow *(Co-Sec)*

Subsidiary (Domestic):

Tasek Concrete Sdn. Bhd. (4)
Lot 1552 Kg Jaya Industrial Area Off Jalan Hospital, 47000, Sungai Buloh, Selangor, Malaysia
Tel.: (60) 361568221
Readymix Concrete Mfr
N.A.I.C.S.: 327320

Plant (Domestic):

Tasek Corporation Berhad - Ipoh Factory (4)
5 Persiaran Tasek Tasek Industrial Estate, 31400, Ipoh, Perak, Malaysia
Tel.: (60) 52911011
Cement Mfr & Distr
N.A.I.C.S.: 327310

Holding (Domestic):

Hong Leong Finance Limited (2)
16 Raffles Quay 01 05 Hong Leong Building, Singapore, 48581, Singapore
Tel.: (65) 64159433
Web Site: https://www.hlf.com.sg
Rev: $53,547,679
Assets: $11,328,952,505
Liabilities: $9,768,488,975
Net Worth: $1,560,463,530
Earnings: $70,721,806
Emp.: 619
Fiscal Year-end: 12/31/2023
Financial Services
N.A.I.C.S.: 522390
Joanne Swee Gim Yeo *(Co-Sec)*

Hong Leong Holdings Ltd. (2)
16 Raffles Quay 25-00, Hong Leong Building, Singapore, 048581, Singapore
Tel.: (65) 62209911
Web Site: http://www.hongleongholdings.com.sg
Sales Range: $25-49.9 Million
Emp.: 100
Holding Company
N.A.I.C.S.: 551112
Leng Beng Kwek *(Chm)*

HONG PHAT CONSTRUCTION INVESTMENT JSC
77-79AA Nguyen Van Cu, An Binh Ward, Ninh Kieu District, Can Tho, Vietnam
Tel.: (84) 710 3895632
Web Site: http://www.hongphatct.com.vn
Real Estate Construction Services
N.A.I.C.S.: 236116
Tien Quang Trinh *(Chm-Mgmt Bd)*

HONG RI DA TECHNOLOGY COMPANY LIMITED
West side of Qingsong Road, Yushan Town, Kunshan, 215300, Jiangsu, China
Tel.: (86) 51257379860
Web Site: https://www.hongrida.com
Year Founded: 2003
301285—(CHIN)
Rev: $83,384,964
Assets: $215,446,608
Liabilities: $60,223,176
Net Worth: $155,223,432
Earnings: $6,924,528
Fiscal Year-end: 12/31/22
Connector Mfr & Distr
N.A.I.C.S.: 334417
Yutian Wang *(Chm & Gen Mgr)*

HONG SENG CONSOLIDATED BERHAD
No 18 Jalan Pemaju U1/15 Section U1 Hicom Glenmarie Industrial Park, 40150, Shah Alam, Selangor Darul Ehsan, Malaysia
Tel.: (60) 355679191   MY
Web Site: http://www.panpages.com
Year Founded: 1989
HONGSENG—(KLS)
Rev: $4,745,405
Assets: $73,200,421
Liabilities: $8,665,251
Net Worth: $64,535,170
Earnings: ($21,222,326)
Emp.: 321
Fiscal Year-end: 03/31/24
Online Advertising Services
N.A.I.C.S.: 551112

Subsidiaries:

CASD Solutions Sdn. Bhd. (1)
D-1-30A Block D Jalan PJU 1A/3A Taipan 2 Damansara, Ara Damansara, Petaling Jaya, Selangor, Malaysia
Tel.: (60) 378428117
Web Site: https://www.case.my
Information Technology Consulting Services
N.A.I.C.S.: 541512

HS Bio Sdn. Bhd. (1)
C-01-3 Block C No 6 Plaza Glomac Jalan SS7/19, Kelana Jaya, 47301, Petaling Jaya, Malaysia
Tel.: (60) 378871666
Web Site: https://www.hsbio.my
Medical & Healthcare Related Product Whslr
N.A.I.C.S.: 423450

Hong Seng Gloves Sdn. Bhd. (1)
Lot 97 Jalan 10 Kawasan Perusahaan Bakar Arang, 08000, Sungai Petani, Kedah, Malaysia
Tel.: (60) 44558322
Web Site: https://www.hongsenggloves.com
Rubber Glove Mfr
N.A.I.C.S.: 326299

Neogenix Laboratoire Sdn. Bhd. (1)
Unit C707 Level 7 Block C Kelana Square 17 Jalan SS7/26, Kelana Jaya, 47301, Petaling Jaya, Selangor, Malaysia
Tel.: (60) 376212154
Web Site: https://www.neogenix.org
Medical Diagnostic & Research Laboratory Services
N.A.I.C.S.: 621511

eMedAsia Sdn. Bhd. (1)
Unit D-2-2 Block D Pacific Place Commercial Centre Jalan PJU 1A/4, Ara Damansara, 47301, Petaling Jaya, Malaysia
Tel.: (60) 173441233
Web Site: https://www.emedasia.com
Pharmaceutical Product Whslr
N.A.I.C.S.: 424210

HONG TAI ELECTRIC INDUSTRIAL CO., LTD.
20F No 65 Sec 2 Dunhua S Rd, Da'an Dist, Taipei, 106, Taiwan
Tel.: (886) 227011000
Web Site: http://www.hong-tai.com.tw
Year Founded: 1968
1612—(TAI)
Rev: $203,807,540
Assets: $277,843,575
Liabilities: $30,845,056
Net Worth: $246,998,519
Earnings: $20,561,528
Fiscal Year-end: 12/31/23
Communication Cable Mfr
N.A.I.C.S.: 331420
Shih-Yi Chen *(Chm)*

Subsidiaries:

Great Team Backend Foundry, Inc. (1)
Building BJingcheng Technology ParkYuyuan Industrial Park, Huangjiang, Dongguan, Guangdong, China
Tel.: (86) 76983635267
Web Site: http://www.gtbf-ltd.com
Integrated Circuits Assembling & Testing Services
N.A.I.C.S.: 561990

Touchtek Corporation (1)
Yokohama Daiichiyuuraku Bldg 2F 3-35 Onoecho, Naka-Ku, Yokohama, 231-0015, Kanagawa, Japan
Tel.: (81) 456506706
Web Site: http://www.touchtek.jp
Touch Panels Mfr & Distr
N.A.I.C.S.: 334118

HONG WEI (ASIA) HOLDINGS COMPANY LIMITED
Unit No 5 10/F Well Tech Centre, No 9 Pat Tat Street San Po Kong, Kowloon, China (Hong Kong)
Tel.: (852) 21173587
Web Site: http://www.hongweiasia.com
8191—(HKG)
Rev: $51,546,593
Assets: $98,569,230
Liabilities: $63,248,415
Net Worth: $35,320,815
Earnings: ($4,434,578)
Emp.: 177
Fiscal Year-end: 12/31/21
Particle Boards Mfr & Distr
N.A.I.C.S.: 322130
Cheung Lok Wong *(Chm & CEO)*

HONG WEI ELECTRICAL INDUSTRY CO., LTD.
No 33 Wuquan 5th Rd New Taipei Industrial Park, Wugu Dist, New Taipei City, 24888, Taiwan
Tel.: (886) 222993348
Web Site: https://www.volbin.com
Year Founded: 1979
4565—(TAI)
Industrial Machinery Maintenance Services
N.A.I.C.S.: 811310
Tan-Cheng Huang *(Chm)*

HONG YI FIBER INDUSTRY CO., LTD.
6F No 66 Tacheng St, Datong District, Taipei, 103, Taiwan
Tel.: (886) 225521191
Web Site: https://www.hongyilon.com.tw
Year Founded: 1968
1452—(TAI)
Rev: $39,218,580
Assets: $94,770,656
Liabilities: $5,365,381
Net Worth: $89,405,275
Earnings: $1,705,811
Emp.: 217
Fiscal Year-end: 12/31/23
Yarn Mfr & Distr
N.A.I.C.S.: 313110
Chen-Jung Shih *(Chm)*

Subsidiaries:

Hong Yi Fiber Industry Co., Ltd. - Yingge Factory (1)
No 609 Yingtao Rd Yingge Township, Taipei, 239, Taiwan
Tel.: (886) 226703525
Textured Polyester Yarn Mfr
N.A.I.C.S.: 313110

Hong Yi International Co., Ltd. (1)
Room A 9/F Hennessy Plaza 164-166 Hennessy Road, Wanchai, China (Hong Kong)
Tel.: (852) 82321050
Web Site: http://en.twhygj.com
Polyester Textured Yarn Mfr
N.A.I.C.S.: 313110

HONGBAOLI GROUP CO., LTD
ShuangGao Road 29, GaoChun District, Nanjing, 211300, China
Tel.: (86) 2557350199
Web Site: https://www.hongbaoli.com
Year Founded: 1994
002165—(SSE)
Rev: $372,845,429
Assets: $687,223,714
Liabilities: $398,903,046
Net Worth: $288,320,668
Earnings: $5,392,231
Emp.: 600
Fiscal Year-end: 12/31/23
Chemical Product Mfr; Polyols, Isopropalamines, High Barrier Films & Cement Admixtures
N.A.I.C.S.: 325998
Jinggong Rui *(Founder & Chm)*

Subsidiaries:

Nanjing Baochun Chemical Industry Co., Ltd. (1)
No 1 C18 1 Nanjing Chemical Indus Park, Nanjing, 210047, China
Tel.: (86) 2558390001
Chemical Products Research & Development Services
N.A.I.C.S.: 541715

Nanjing HBL International Co., Ltd. (1)
158 Fangshui Rd, Luhe, Nanjing, 210047, Jiangsu, China
Tel.: (86) 2558390038
Web Site: http://www.hongbaoli.com
Sales Range: $150-199.9 Million
Chemical Products Research & Development Services
N.A.I.C.S.: 541715
Jillian Zhu *(Mgr-Overseas Sls)*

HONGBO CO., LTD.
21F Block B Hongbo Meiling Guanhai No 26 Nanjiangbin West Avenue, Cangshan District, Fuzhou, 350002, Fujian, China
Tel.: (86) 59188070028
Web Site: https://www.hb-print.com.cn
002229—(SSE)
Rev: $76,607,856
Assets: $344,943,144

HONGBO CO., LTD.

Hongbo Co., Ltd.—(Continued)
Liabilities: $103,243,140
Net Worth: $241,700,004
Earnings: ($10,539,828)
Fiscal Year-end: 12/31/22
Paper Products Mfr
N.A.I.C.S.: 322130
Lijuan You (Vice Chm)

HONGCHANG INTERNATIONAL CO LTD.
No 12-2 Xiantingyashe Haishi Road Dengzhou Street, Penglai, Yantai, 265600, Shandong, China
Tel.: (86) 5355666376   NV
Web Site: https://www.hcfrozen.com
Year Founded: 1987
HCIL—(OTCIQ)
Rev.: $2,675,789
Assets: $50,215,568
Liabilities: $9,727,625
Net Worth: $40,487,943
Earnings: ($378,794)
Fiscal Year-end: 12/31/23
Investment Services
N.A.I.C.S.: 523999

HONGCHENG ENVIRONMENTAL TECHNOLOGY CO., LTD.
Yeyan Road North, Dadongzhuang Village North Shahe Town Laizhou, Yantai, Shandong, China
Tel.: (86) 5352176699   Ky
Web Site: https://www.sdhcgroup.cn
Year Founded: 2011
2265—(HKG)
Rev.: $34,135,341
Assets: $116,100,546
Liabilities: $46,601,886
Net Worth: $69,498,661
Earnings: $12,289,893
Emp.: 195
Fiscal Year-end: 12/31/22
Information Technology Services
N.A.I.C.S.: 541512
Haiyan Sheng (Chief Technical Officer)

HONGDA FINANCIAL HOLDING LIMITED
Room 3618 36/F Two Pacific Place 88 Queensway, Hong Kong, China (Hong Kong)
Tel.: (852) 39189100   Ky
Web Site: http://www.hongdafin.com
Rev.: $84,020,974
Assets: $147,673,555
Liabilities: $145,308,499
Net Worth: $2,365,055
Earnings: ($92,593,112)
Emp.: 42
Fiscal Year-end: 12/31/19
Car Rental Services
N.A.I.C.S.: 532111
Qiu Bin (Chm & CEO)

Subsidiaries:
Perception Digital Technology (Shenzhen) Limited   (1)
3/F No 9 Yuexing 1st Rd Hkust Sz Ier Building South Area Hi-Tech park, Nanshan, Shenzhen, China
Tel.: (86) 75526970883
Electric Equipment Mfr
N.A.I.C.S.: 334419
Jimmy Yan (Sr Engr-Mechanical)

HONGDA HIGH-TECH HOLDING CO., LTD.
No 118 Jianshe Road, Xucun Town, Haining, 314409, Zhejiang, China
Tel.: (86) 57387550882
Web Site: https://www.zjhongda.com.cn
Year Founded: 1985

002144—(SSE)
Rev.: $81,343,548
Assets: $304,015,140
Liabilities: $30,031,560
Net Worth: $273,983,580
Earnings: $11,187,072
Fiscal Year-end: 12/31/22
Fabric Weaving Services
N.A.I.C.S.: 313210
Zheng Wang (Chm)

HONGDA XINGYE CO., LTD.
28th Floor Guangzhou Circle No 1 Guangzhou Circle Rd, Guangzhou, 510385, China
Tel.: (86) 2081802222
Web Site: http://www.002002.cn
002002—(SSE)
Rev.: $677,071,980
Assets: $2,637,633,024
Liabilities: $1,188,491,616
Net Worth: $1,449,141,408
Earnings: $42,121,404
Fiscal Year-end: 12/31/22
Industrial Chemical Product Mfr & Distr
N.A.I.C.S.: 325211
Yifeng Zhou (Chm)

Subsidiaries:
Baotou New Damao Rare Earth Co., Ltd.   (1)
Rare Earth Industrial Park Damao Banner Inner Mongolia, Baotou, 225111, China
Tel.: (86) 4728424902
Plastic Material & Resin Mfr
N.A.I.C.S.: 325211

Guangdong Institute of World Soil Resources   (1)
No 33 Hejing Road, Dongsha Economic Zone Liwan District, Guangzhou, China
Tel.: (86) 2081802222
Soil Preparation Services
N.A.I.C.S.: 115112

Guangdong Plastics Exchange Co., Ltd.   (1)
No 1 Guangzhou Circle Road, Liwan District, Guangzhou, Guangdong, China
Tel.: (86) 2081492222
Plastic Material & Resin Mfr
N.A.I.C.S.: 325211

Inner Mongolia Lianfeng Rare Earth Chemical Institute Co., Ltd.   (1)
Haihua Industrial Park, Hainan District, Wuhai, Inner Mongolia, China
Tel.: (86) 7434338607
Soil Conditioner & Desulfurizer Mfr
N.A.I.C.S.: 325314

Inner Mongolia Menghua Haibowan Power Generation Co., Ltd.   (1)
Lasengmiao Town, Hainan District, Wuhai, Inner Mongolia, China
Tel.: (86) 4734558603
Soil Conditioner & Desulfurizer Mfr
N.A.I.C.S.: 325314

Inner Mongolia Wuhai Chemical Industry Co., Ltd.   (1)
Haihua Industrial Park Inner Mongolia, Hainan District, Wuhai, China
Tel.: (86) 473 4332789
Plastic Material & Resin Mfr
N.A.I.C.S.: 325211

Subsidiary (Domestic):
Inner Mongolia Zhonggu Mining Industry Co., Ltd.   (2)
West Inner Mongolia High-tech Industrial Park Etoke Banner, Ordos, 016034, China
Tel.: (86) 4736116658
Plastic Material & Resin Mfr
N.A.I.C.S.: 325211

Wuhai Guangyu Chemical Metallurgy Co., Ltd.   (2)
Xilaifeng Industrial Park Inner Mongolia, Hainan District, Wuhai, China
Tel.: (86) 4734335616
Plastic Material & Resin Mfr
N.A.I.C.S.: 325211

Inner Mongolia Zhongke Equipment Co., Ltd.   (1)
Haihua Industrial Park, Hainan District, Wuhai, Inner Mongolia, China
Tel.: (86) 4734338575
Soil Conditioner & Desulfurizer Mfr
N.A.I.C.S.: 325314

Jiangsu Golden Material Technology Co., Ltd.   (1)
Shuguang Road, Hangji Town, Yangzhou, 225111, Jiangsu, China
Tel.: (86) 51489883888
Emp.: 450
Plastic Material & Resin Mfr
N.A.I.C.S.: 325211

Western Environmental Protection Co., Ltd.   (1)
Guangzhou Circle No 1 Guangzhou Circle Rd, Liwan District, Guangzhou, China
Tel.: (86) 4734333851
Web Site: https://www.wcep.cn
Soil Conditioner & Desulfurizer Mfr
N.A.I.C.S.: 325314

HONGFA TECHNOLOGY CO LTD
No 564 Donglin Road Jimei North Industrial Zone, Xiamen, 361021, Fujian, China
Tel.: (86) 2783310135
Web Site: http://www.hongfa.com
Year Founded: 1990
600885—(SHG)
Rev.: $1,647,368,110
Assets: $2,245,108,194
Liabilities: $847,744,551
Net Worth: $1,397,363,643
Earnings: $175,128,179
Fiscal Year-end: 12/31/22
Relay Mfr & Distr
N.A.I.C.S.: 335314
Guo Manjin (Chm & Gen Mgr)

Subsidiaries:
Beijing Hongfa Electroacoustic Relay Co., Ltd.   (1)
111Bldg Phase IV Westside Of Liandong U Valley, Tongzhou Dist, Beijing, China
Tel.: (86) 1056495556
Medium & Low Voltage Electrical Appliance Mfr & Distr
N.A.I.C.S.: 335131

Hongfa America, Inc.   (1)
20381 Hermana Cir, Lake Forest, CA 92630
Tel.: (714) 669-2888
Relay & Industrial Control Mfr
N.A.I.C.S.: 335314

Hongfa Electroacoustic (Hongkong) Co., Ltd.   (1)
Rm 1810-12 18/F Shatin Galleria 18-24 Shan Mei St, Fotan, China (Hong Kong)
Tel.: (852) 29477889
Relay & Industrial Control Mfr
N.A.I.C.S.: 335314

Hongfa Europe GmbH   (1)
Marie-Curie-Ring 26, 63477, Maintal, Germany
Tel.: (49) 618143060
Relay & Industrial Control Mfr
N.A.I.C.S.: 335314

Hongfa Italy S.R.L.   (1)
c/o Regus Business Center Via Senigallia 18/2 Torre A, 20161, Milan, Italy
Tel.: (39) 0264672325
Medium & Low Voltage Electrical Appliance Mfr & Distr
N.A.I.C.S.: 335131

Shanghai Hongfa Electroacoustic Co., Ltd.   (1)
No 51 Lane 341 Jiuxin highway, Jiuting Town Songjiang District, Shanghai, China
Tel.: (86) 2137693111
Medium & Low Voltage Electrical Appliance Mfr & Distr
N.A.I.C.S.: 335131

Sichuan Hongfa Relay Co., Ltd.   (1)
12F Hongfa Building no 6 Wuxing 4th Road, Wuhou District, Chengdu, China

INTERNATIONAL PUBLIC

Tel.: (86) 2886627550
Medium & Low Voltage Electrical Appliance Mfr & Distr
N.A.I.C.S.: 335131

The Phillippines Thermopower Climate Control Corporation   (1)
Unit 110 Admiralty Building 1101 Alabang Zapote Road, Madrigal Business Park, Muntinlupa, 1780, Philippines
Tel.: (63) 28175935
Relay & Industrial Control Mfr
N.A.I.C.S.: 335314

Xiamen Hongfa Electroacoustic Science & Technology Co., Ltd.   (1)
3rd Floor No 564 Donglin Road, Xiamen, 361021, China
Tel.: (86) 5926106688
Relay & Industrial Control Mfr
N.A.I.C.S.: 335314

HONGHUA GROUP LTD
99 East Road Information Park, Jinniu District, Chengdu, 610036, Sichuan, China
Tel.: (86) 2868176436   Ky
Web Site: http://www.hh-gltd.com
0196—(HKG)
Rev.: $628,445,002
Assets: $1,730,077,175
Liabilities: $1,281,640,277
Net Worth: $448,436,898
Earnings: ($87,765,584)
Emp.: 2,032
Fiscal Year-end: 12/31/22
Petroleum Drilling & Mining Equipment Researcher, Designer, Mfr & Maintenance Services
N.A.I.C.S.: 333131
Mi Zhang (Vice Chm & Pres)

Subsidiaries:
Egyptian Petroleum HH Rig Manufacturing S.A.E Co.   (1)
19 St No 292 New Maadi, Cairo, Egypt
Tel.: (20) 27036328
Energy Equipment Distr
N.A.I.C.S.: 423830

Gansu Hongteng Oil & Gas Equipment Manufacturing Co., Ltd.   (1)
Wangjiaping East, Longxi, Dingxi, 748112, Gansu, China
Tel.: (86) 932 6628685
Oil & Gas Equipment Mfr
N.A.I.C.S.: 333132

Honghua America, LLC   (1)
5615 W Fuqua Blvd Bldg A Ste 200, Houston, TX 77085
Tel.: (713) 830-9172
Web Site: http://www.honghuaamerica.com
Sales Range: $25-49.9 Million
Emp.: 20
Trading of Drilling Rigs & Related Parts
N.A.I.C.S.: 333132

Honghua Golden Coast Equipment FZE   (1)
PO Box 261868, Jebel Ali, Dubai, United Arab Emirates
Tel.: (971) 48807066
Drilling Equipment Mfr
N.A.I.C.S.: 333131

Honghua International Co., Ltd.   (1)
No 99 East Road Information Park, Jinniu District, Chengdu, 610036, Sichuan, China
Tel.: (86) 2868176436
Drilling Equipment Mfr
N.A.I.C.S.: 333131

Honghua International Sucursal Colombia   (1)
World Trade Center Calle 100 8a-55 of 518, Bogota, Colombia
Tel.: (57) 16423200
Energy Equipment Distr
N.A.I.C.S.: 423830

Honghua International Ukraine Co., Ltd.   (1)
Street M Grushevskogo 28/2 Non-Residential Premises 43, 1021, Kiev, Ukraine

AND PRIVATE COMPANIES

Tel.: (380) 637083023
Energy Equipment Distr
N.A.I.C.S.: 423830

Honghua International de Venezuela, C.A. (1)
Av Francisco de Miranda Torre Mene Grande Piso 9 Oficina 9-4, Los Palos Grandes Chacao, Caracas, Venezuela
Tel.: (58) 2122869883
Energy Equipment Distr
N.A.I.C.S.: 423830

Honghua Sucursal Bolivia (1)
Nro 206 Condominium Aguai Street K Zone, Equipetrol, Santa Cruz, Bolivia
Tel.: (591) 76716670
Energy Equipment Distr
N.A.I.C.S.: 423830

Newco (H.K.) Limited (1)
RM2508 Harcourt House 39 Gloucester Road, Wanchai, China (Hong Kong)
Tel.: (852) 25205533
Drilling Rig Whslr
N.A.I.C.S.: 423840

Sichuan Honghua Electric Co., Ltd. (1)
No 99 East Road Information Park, Jinniu District, Chengdu, 610036, Sichuan, China
Tel.: (86) 2868176683
Drilling Equipment Mfr
N.A.I.C.S.: 333131

Sichuan Honghua Petroleum Equipment Co., Ltd. (1)
South 2 Zhongshan Road, Guanghan, 618300, Sichuan, China
Tel.: (86) 838 608 1123
Web Site: http://www.hhcp.com.cn
Sales Range: $25-49.9 Million
Emp.: 30
Petroleum Product Mfr
N.A.I.C.S.: 333248

HONGLI CLEAN ENERGY TECHNOLOGIES CORP.
North Tiyu Rd, Xinhua District, Pingdingshan, 467000, Henan, China
Tel.: (86) 375 288 2999 FL
Web Site: http://www.cetcchina.net
Year Founded: 1996
Sales Range: $10-24.9 Million
Emp.: 193
Business Services
N.A.I.C.S.: 561499
Jianhua Lv *(Chm, Pres, CEO & Interim CFO)*

Subsidiaries:

icollector.com Technologies, Inc. (1)
114 - 1750 Coast Meridian Road, Coquitlam, V3C 6R8, BC, Canada
Tel.: (604) 941-2221
Web Site: http://www.icollector.com
Sales Range: $50-74.9 Million
Emp.: 120
Online Auction
N.A.I.C.S.: 459510

HONGLI GROUP INC.
No 777 Daiyi Road, Changle, Weifang, 262400, Shandong, China
Tel.: (86) 5362185222 Ky
Year Founded: 2021
HLP—(NASDAQ)
Holding Company
N.A.I.C.S.: 551112
Jie Liu *(CEO & Chm)*

HONGLI ZHIHUI GROUP CO., LTD.
No1 Xianke yi Road, Huadong Town Huadu District, Guangzhou, 510890, China
Tel.: (86) 2086733333
Web Site: https://en.honglitronic.com
Year Founded: 2004
300219—(CHIN)
Rev.: $510,553,368
Assets: $683,993,700
Liabilities: $351,727,272

Net Worth: $332,266,428
Earnings: $25,075,440
Fiscal Year-end: 12/31/22
LED Lamps & Other LED Electronics Mfr
N.A.I.C.S.: 334419
Li Jundong *(Chm & Pres)*

Subsidiaries:

Guangzhou Forda Signal Equipment Co. Ltd. (1)
No 5 Liancheng Road West Side of Dongfeng Ave Auto City, Huadu District, Guangzhou, Guangdong, China
Tel.: (86) 2086733871
Light Mfr & Distr
N.A.I.C.S.: 335139

HONGRUN CONSTRUCTION GROUP CO., LTD.
Hongrun Building No 28 Lane 200 Longcao Road, Shanghai, 200235, China
Tel.: (86) 2164081888
Web Site: https://www.chinahongrun.com
Year Founded: 1994
002062—(SSE)
Rev.: $1,221,322,752
Assets: $2,300,400,648
Liabilities: $1,687,178,376
Net Worth: $613,222,272
Earnings: $51,160,356
Fiscal Year-end: 12/31/22
Road & Bridge Construction Services
N.A.I.C.S.: 237310
Hongfang Zheng *(Chm)*

HONGSHENG HEAT EXCHANGER MANUFACTURING CO.,LTD
8 Liangkang Road Mashan Industry Park, Wuxi, 214092, China
Tel.: (86) 51085998299 CN
Web Site: https://www.hs-exchanger.com
Year Founded: 2000
603090—(SHG)
Rev.: $100,283,522
Assets: $120,921,269
Liabilities: $43,828,247
Net Worth: $77,093,022
Earnings: $7,496,181
Fiscal Year-end: 12/31/22
Heat Exchanger Mfr & Distr
N.A.I.C.S.: 333415
Niu Faqing *(Chm)*

Subsidiaries:

Hangzhou Hongsheng Zhonghong New Energy Co., Ltd. (1)
Room 1715 Shimao Center No 857 Xincheng Road, Binjiang District, Hangzhou, 310053, Zhejiang, China
Tel.: (86) 15858134686
Web Site: http://www.zhnec.com
Aluminum Plate-Fin Heat Exchanger Mfr
N.A.I.C.S.: 332410

Wuxi Guanyun Heat Exchanger Co., Ltd. (1)
No 2 TuanJie Rd, Wuxi, Jiangsu, China
Tel.: (86) 51085990723
Web Site: https://www.guanyuncn.com
Emp.: 300
Aluminum Plate-Fin Heat Exchanger Mfr
N.A.I.C.S.: 332410

HONGTA SECURITIES CO., LTD.
No 155 Beijing Road, Kunming, 650011, Yunnan, China
Tel.: (86) 87163577113
Web Site: http://www.hongtastock.com
Year Founded: 2002
601236—(SHG)
Rev.: $117,398,100

Assets: $6,478,636,793
Liabilities: $3,229,842,316
Net Worth: $3,248,794,477
Earnings: $5,408,924
Fiscal Year-end: 12/31/22
Investment Banking Services
N.A.I.C.S.: 523150
Shishan Li *(Chm & Chm-Supervisory Bd)*

HONGWEI TECHNOLOGIES LIMITED
No2 Factory Xianhou Shuangli Industrial Pk Huli District, Xiamen, Fujian, China
Tel.: (86) 5925783022
Web Site: http://www.hongweikj.com
Sales Range: $50-74.9 Million
Textile Mfr
N.A.I.C.S.: 325220
Jimiao Lin *(Chm & Co-CEO)*

HONGYUAN HARDWARE INDUSTRY & TRADING CO. LTD.
12 Fl At Tower No 180 Electrie Road, North Point, China (Hong Kong)
Tel.: (852) 25668109
Web Site: http://www.fshy-hardware.com
Year Founded: 2000
Rev.: $12,880,000
Emp.: 100
Hardware, Cabinet Pulls & Knobs, Handbag & Craft Accessories Mfr
N.A.I.C.S.: 332510

HONJO CHEMICAL CORPORATION
19 7 Niwajihonmachi 4 Chome, Neyagawa, 572-0076, Osaka, Japan
Tel.: (81) 728272201 JP
Web Site: http://www.honjo-chem.co.jp
Year Founded: 1922
Sales Range: $50-74.9 Million
Emp.: 180
Industrial Chemicals Mfr
N.A.I.C.S.: 325998
Kazuhiko Hirao *(Pres)*

Subsidiaries:

Honjo Chemical (Singapore) Pte Ltd (1)
9A Jurong Pier Road, 619162, Singapore, Singapore
Tel.: (65) 62682055
Sales Range: $25-49.9 Million
Emp.: 20
Industrial Chemicals Mfr
N.A.I.C.S.: 325998

Honjo Chemical Corporation - Naoshima Factory (1)
4092 Naoshima-cho, Kagawa, 761-3110, Japan
Tel.: (81) 87 892 3415
Chemical Products Mfr
N.A.I.C.S.: 325998

HONKARAKENNE OYJ
Tel.: (358) 20575700
Web Site: https://www.honka.com
Year Founded: 1958
HONBS—(HEL)
Rev.: $79,539,175
Assets: $39,472,264
Liabilities: $19,818,692
Net Worth: $19,653,572
Earnings: $2,991,582
Emp.: 191
Fiscal Year-end: 12/31/22
Housing Construction Services
N.A.I.C.S.: 236115
Marko Saarelainen *(Pres & CEO)*

Subsidiaries:

Findrewno Sp. z o.o. (1)
Stronsko 58, Zapolice, 98-161, Zdunska

Wola, Poland
Tel.: (48) 438238307
Web Site: https://www.findrewno.pl
Building Construction Services
N.A.I.C.S.: 236220

Finn Wellness Kft. (1)
Szepvolgyi ut 63/A, 1037, Budapest, Hungary
Tel.: (36) 12504177
Web Site: https://finnwellness.hu
Wellness Care Services
N.A.I.C.S.: 621610

Hel Ved Bolig AS (1)
Bokfinkvegen 7, Porsgrunn, Norway
Tel.: (47) 41609441
Web Site: https://www.helvedbolig.no
Lumber Distr
N.A.I.C.S.: 423310

Honka Finland Houses EOOD (1)
Galabets St 5 Sitnyakovo Blvd 6th Floor Apartment 20, Sofia, Bulgaria
Tel.: (359) 28464290
Web Site: https://honka.com
Building Construction Services
N.A.I.C.S.: 236220

Honka Japan Inc. (1)
i-CAP Building 5F 3-17-2, Takamatsu-cho, Tachikawa, 190-0011, Tokyo, Japan
Tel.: (81) 425484169
Building Materials Distr
N.A.I.C.S.: 423840

Honka Log Home LLC (1)
Central Tower - 606A 8th Horoo Great Chinggis Khaan's Square - 2, Sukhbaatar District, Ulaanbaatar, Mongolia
Tel.: (976) 70110035
Building Construction Services
N.A.I.C.S.: 236220

Lodgico Ltd. (1)
Unit 9 Taw Mill Business Park Howard Avenue, Barnstaple, EX32 8QA, Devon, United Kingdom
Tel.: (44) 1271326343
Web Site: https://www.lodgico.co.uk
Building Construction Services
N.A.I.C.S.: 236220

Primat RD d.o.o. (1)
Zastavnice ul 11/1, Leskovac, Croatia
Tel.: (385) 16593444
Web Site: https://www.primat-rd.hr
Interior Furnishing Product Distr
N.A.I.C.S.: 423220

HONLIV HEALTHCARE MANAGEMENT GROUP COMPANY LIMITED
No 8 Bo Ai Road South, Changyuan County, Henan, China
Tel.: (86) 3738882618 Ky
Web Site: https://www.honlivhp.com
Year Founded: 2004
9906—(HKG)
Rev.: $105,301,146
Assets: $134,125,637
Liabilities: $58,327,149
Net Worth: $75,798,488
Earnings: $5,358,053
Emp.: 1,969
Fiscal Year-end: 12/31/23
Health Care Srvices
N.A.I.C.S.: 621610

HONMA GOLF LIMITED
35F Roppongi Hills Mori Tower 6-10-1 Roppongi Minatoku, PO Box 62, Tokyo, 106-6135, Japan
Tel.: (81) 368641000 Ky
Web Site: http://www.honmagolf.co.jp
Year Founded: 1959
6858—(HKG)
Rev.: $173,259,661
Assets: $281,104,626
Liabilities: $91,660,476
Net Worth: $189,444,149
Earnings: $31,900,407
Emp.: 705
Fiscal Year-end: 03/31/24
Golf Product Mfr & Distr

HONMA GOLF LIMITED

Honma Golf Limited—(Continued)
N.A.I.C.S.: 339920
Jianguo Liu (Pres & Chm)

Subsidiaries:

Honma Golf U.S., Ltd. (1)
1400-B W 240th St, Harbor City, CA 90710
Tel.: (424) 263-4821
Web Site: http://www.honmagolfusa.com
Golf Equipment Mfr & Distr
N.A.I.C.S.: 339920

HONMYUE ENTERPRISE CO., LTD.
No 60 Gongxi 1st Rd Shengang Township, Taipei, 50971, Chang Hwa Hsien, Taiwan
Tel.: (886) 47994888
Web Site: https://fabric.textile-hy.com.tw
Year Founded: 1970
1474—(TAI)
Rev.: $87,829,095
Assets: $123,123,806
Liabilities: $56,634,387
Net Worth: $66,489,418
Earnings: ($1,418,555)
Fiscal Year-end: 12/31/23
Textile Fabric Mfr & Distr
N.A.I.C.S.: 314999

Subsidiaries:

Dongguan Honmyue Textile Limited (1)
Zhu Ping Sha District Wang Niu Dun Town, Dongguan, Guandong, China
Tel.: (86) 76988563858
Textile & Fabric Mfr
N.A.I.C.S.: 313310

Honmyue Enterprise (Zhejiang) Co., Ltd. (1)
No 268 JiaHu Rd XiuZhou Industrial Park, Jiaxing, Zhejiang, China
Tel.: (86) 57382228888
Textile & Fabric Mfr
N.A.I.C.S.: 313310

Jiujiang Deyu Co., Ltd. (1)
North of North Fourth Road East of Chuangye Avenue, Industry New Area Dean County, Jiujiang, Jiangxi, China
Tel.: (86) 7924681888
Industrial Fabric Mfr & Distr
N.A.I.C.S.: 314999

HONSEN ENERGY & RESOURCES INTERNATIONAL LTD.
Room 601-11 Building D Parkview Green Fangcaodi No 9 Dongdaqiao Road, Chaoyang District, Beijing, China
Tel.: (86) 1056907511
Web Site: http://www.honsen-resources.com
Year Founded: 2008
HSEN—(OTCIQ)
Sales Range: Less than $1 Million
Mineral Exploration Services
N.A.I.C.S.: 213114
Xingxing Liu (CFO)

HONSHU CHEMICAL INDUSTRY CO., LTD.
Mercros Bldg 3-9 Nihombashi 3-chome, Chuo-ku, Tokyo, 103-0027, Japan
Tel.: (81) 332721481
Web Site: http://www.honshuchemical.co.jp
Year Founded: 1914
4115—(TKS)
Rev.: $198,227,040
Assets: $302,703,280
Liabilities: $76,404,240
Net Worth: $226,299,040
Earnings: $19,969,840

Emp.: 353
Fiscal Year-end: 03/31/21
Chemical Products Mfr
N.A.I.C.S.: 325199
Hidebumi Kasuga (Mng Exec Officer & Gen Mgr-High Performance Materials Div)

Subsidiaries:

Hi-Bis GmbH (1)
Salegaster Chaussee 1, 06803, Bitterfeld-Wolfen, Germany
Tel.: (49) 3493 75580
Chemical Products Mfr
N.A.I.C.S.: 325998

Honshu Chemical Industry Co., Ltd. - Wakayama Works (1)
5-115 Kozaika 2-chome, Wakayama, 641-0007, Japan
Tel.: (81) 73 422 8171
Chemical Products Mfr
N.A.I.C.S.: 325998

HONTEX INTERNATIONAL HOLDINGS CO., LTD.
Hongkuan Industry Zone Xi Tou, Yang Xia Town, Fuqing, Fujian, China
Tel.: (86) 59185290629
Web Site: http://ir.hontex.cn
Sales Range: $150-199.9 Million
Emp.: 1,900
Chemical Fibre Knitted Fabrics Mfr
N.A.I.C.S.: 313240
Ten-Po Shao (Founder & Chm)

HONWORLD GROUP LIMITED
No 299 Zhongxing Ave, Wuxing District, Huzhou, Zhejiang, China
Tel.: (86) 572 2123225
Web Site: http://www.hzlaohenghe.com
Rev.: $130,960,827
Assets: $569,984,472
Liabilities: $232,129,093
Net Worth: $337,855,379
Earnings: $27,946,571
Emp.: 538
Fiscal Year-end: 12/31/19
Cooking Wine Production & Sales
N.A.I.C.S.: 312130
Chuanli Liu (Controller-Fin)

HONY CAPITAL ACQUISITION CORP.
Suite 06-11 70/F Two International Finance Centre No 8 Finance Street, Central, China (Hong Kong)
Tel.: (852) 3961 9700   Ky
Web Site: http://www.honycapital.com
Year Founded: 2021
HCAA—(NYSE)
Investment Services
N.A.I.C.S.: 523999
John H. Zhao (Chm)

HONYAKU CENTER INC.
OSAKA MIDOUSUJI Bldg 13F 4-1-3 Kyutaro-machi, Chuo-ku, Osaka, 541-0056, Japan
Tel.: (81) 662825010
Web Site: https://www.honyakuctren.com
Year Founded: 1986
2483—(TKS)
Rev.: $74,712,830
Assets: $55,034,860
Liabilities: $13,722,360
Net Worth: $41,312,500
Earnings: $4,699,710
Emp.: 562
Fiscal Year-end: 03/31/24
Translation Services
N.A.I.C.S.: 541930
Ikuo Higashi (Chm)

Subsidiaries:

FIPAS Inc. (1)
7th floor Mita MT Building 3-13-12 Mita, Minato-ku, Tokyo, Japan
Tel.: (81) 363699970
Translation Services
N.A.I.C.S.: 541930
Kenji Kusumi (Pres)

HC Language Solutions, Inc. (1)
4701 Patrick Henry Dr Bldg16 Ste 116, Santa Clara, CA 95054
Tel.: (650) 312-1239
Translation Services
N.A.I.C.S.: 541930

Media Research, Inc. (1)
4F SK Building 4-14-4 Sendagaya, Shibuya-ku, Tokyo, 151-0051, Japan
Tel.: (81) 354146210
Web Site: https://www.mediasoken.jp
Translation Services
N.A.I.C.S.: 541930
Shunichiro Ninomiya (Pres)

HONYE FINANCIAL SERVICES LTD.
89 Nexus Way, Grand Cayman, Camana Bay, KY1-9009, Cayman Islands   Ky
Web Site: https://www.honyefinance.com
Year Founded: 2018
HOME—(LSE)
Assets: $1,569,223
Liabilities: $780,472
Net Worth: $788,751
Earnings: ($1,103,946)
Fiscal Year-end: 07/31/21
Asset Management Services
N.A.I.C.S.: 523999
Wanbao Xu (Founder)

HONYI INTERNATIONA CO., LTD.
4F No 203-1 Gongyuan Rd, Linkou Dist, Taipei, 244, Taiwan
Tel.: (886) 226068111
4530—(TPE)
Rev.: $6,149,329
Assets: $10,707,532
Liabilities: $2,845,762
Net Worth: $7,861,770
Earnings: ($274,333)
Fiscal Year-end: 12/31/22
Electronic Component Mfr & Distr
N.A.I.C.S.: 334419

HONZ PHARMACEUTICAL CO., LTD.
26th Floor Dongshan Plaza No 69 Xianlie Middle Road, Yuexiu District, Guangzhou, China
Tel.: (86) 2087324060
Web Site: https://www.honz.com.cn
300086—(CHIN)
Rev.: $104,168,406
Assets: $305,028,450
Liabilities: $110,933,798
Net Worth: $194,094,652
Earnings: $1,623,986
Fiscal Year-end: 12/31/23
Pharmaceuticals Mfr
N.A.I.C.S.: 325412
Jiangyou Hong (Founder)

HOOPLAH INC.
1655 Dupont St Suite 337, Toronto, M6P 3T1, ON, Canada
Tel.: (416) 783-1157
Web Site: http://www.hooplah.com
Sales Range: $1-9.9 Million
Emp.: 10
Advertising & Marketing Services
N.A.I.C.S.: 541890
Leslie Hartsman (Pres)

HOOSIERS HOLDINGS

INTERNATIONAL PUBLIC

2-2-3 marunouchi, Chiyoda-ku, Tokyo, 100-0005, Japan
Tel.: (81) 332870700   JP
Web Site: https://www.hoosiers.co.jp
Year Founded: 2013
3284—(TKS)
Rev.: $571,222,980
Assets: $1,086,677,390
Liabilities: $776,946,010
Net Worth: $309,731,380
Earnings: $31,767,660
Fiscal Year-end: 03/31/24
Holding Company; Land Subdivision & Condominium Construction
N.A.I.C.S.: 551112
Tetsuya Hirooka (Pres & CEO)

Subsidiaries:

Hoosiers Corporation (1)
10th floor Marunouchi Nakadori Building 2-2-3 Marunouchi, Chiyoda-ku, Tokyo, 100-0005, Japan
Tel.: (81) 332870740
Web Site: https://www.hoosiers.co.jp
Sales Range: $100-124.9 Million
Emp.: 96
Land Subdivision & Condominium Construction
N.A.I.C.S.: 237210
Tsutomu Ikuma (CFO)

Hoosiers Living Service Co., Ltd. (1)
4-3-16 Nihonbashi Muromachi, Chuo-ku, Tokyo, 103-0022, Japan   (100%)
Tel.: (81) 332958222
Residential Property Management
N.A.I.C.S.: 531311

My Home Liner Co., Ltd. (1)
9-1 Kanda Mitoshiro-cho, Chiyoda-ku, Tokyo, 101-0053, Japan   (100%)
Tel.: (81) 332958262
Shuttle Services
N.A.I.C.S.: 485999

HOOTECH INC.
No 1 Liujing Road, Economic & Technological Development Zone, Xuzhou, 221004, Jiangsu, China
Tel.: (86) 51687980258
Web Site: https://www.hootech.com.cn
Year Founded: 2005
301026—(CHIN)
Rev.: $360,724,104
Assets: $238,379,544
Liabilities: $33,714,252
Net Worth: $204,665,292
Earnings: $20,488,572
Fiscal Year-end: 12/31/22
Precious Metal Mfr
N.A.I.C.S.: 331492
Xia Jun (Chm & Gen Mgr)

HOOTSUITE MEDIA, INC.
5 East 8th Avenue, Vancouver, V5T 1R6, BC, Canada
Tel.: (604) 681-4668
Web Site: http://www.hootsuite.com
Year Founded: 2008
Sales Range: $75-99.9 Million
Emp.: 300
Software Applications
N.A.I.C.S.: 513210
Ryan Holmes (Founder & Chm)

HOOVER MECHANICAL PLUMBING & HEATING LTD.
1-3640 61st Avenue SE, Calgary, T2C 2J3, AB, Canada
Tel.: (403) 217-5655
Web Site: https://www.hoovermechanical.com
Year Founded: 1998
Plumbing Contractor
N.A.I.C.S.: 238220
Jonas Deacon (Officer-Safety)

HOP FUNG GROUP HOLDINGS LTD

Workshops E F and H 22nd Floor Superluck Industrial Centre Phase 2, No 57 Sha Tsui Road and Nos 30-38 Tai Chung Road, Tsuen Wan, China (Hong Kong)
Tel.: (852) 24168100   KY
Web Site: https://www.hopfunggroup.com
Year Founded: 1983
2320—(HKG)
Rev.: $54,112,403
Assets: $151,866,398
Liabilities: $29,222,363
Net Worth: $122,644,035
Earnings: ($24,572,438)
Emp.: 360
Fiscal Year-end: 12/31/22
Paper-ware Products Mfr & Sales
N.A.I.C.S.: 322130
Yuen Li Hui *(CFO & Sec)*

Subsidiaries:

Chun Yik (Macao Commercial Offshore) Limited   (1)
Alameda Dr Carlos d'Assumpcao Nos 181-187 Edf Jardim Brilhantismo, 17 Andar G, Macau, China (Macau)
Tel.: (853) 28752517
Web Site: http://www.hopfunggroup.com
Corrugated Packaging Product Distr
N.A.I.C.S.: 424130

Dongguan Chun Yik Paper Ware Factory Limited   (1)
Chun Yik Industrial Building TangLi BiHu Industrial Town FengGang Zhen, Dongguan, GuangDong, China
Tel.: (86) 76987556889
Corrugated Packaging Product Mfr
N.A.I.C.S.: 322211

Green Forest (QingXin) Paper Industrial Limited   (1)
No 28 Industrial Road South TaiHe Zhen, QingXin District, Qingyuan, GuangDong, China
Tel.: (86) 7635383348
Corrugated Packaging Product Mfr & Distr
N.A.I.C.S.: 322211

HOP HING GROUP HOLDINGS LIMITED
Flats E and F 2/F Hop Hing Building 9 Ping Tong Street East, Tong Yan San Tsuen, Yuen Long, New Territories, China (Hong Kong)
Tel.: (852) 2 785 2681
Web Site: http://www.hophing.com
Rev.: $300,912,683
Assets: $258,381,360
Liabilities: $183,517,021
Net Worth: $74,864,339
Earnings: $14,898,141
Emp.: 8,600
Fiscal Year-end: 12/31/19
Oil Blending, Bottling & Packaging
N.A.I.C.S.: 311225
John Gin Chung Seto *(Chm)*

Subsidiaries:

Tianjin Hejia Xingtai Catering Management Company Limited   (1)
Hanhai Culture Bld No 1 of 28th Compound Xiangjun North, Chaoyang District, Beijing, China
Tel.: (86) 1065225588
Edible Oil Distr
N.A.I.C.S.: 424490

HOPE EDUCATION GROUP CO., LTD.
No 2000 West District Avenue High-Tech Zone, Chengdu, 610091, Sichuan, China
Tel.: (86) 286 969 4278   Ky
Web Site: http://www.hopeedu.com
Year Founded: 2005
1765—(HKG)
Rev.: $356,101,713
Assets: $3,044,148,182
Liabilities: $1,848,064,217
Net Worth: $1,196,083,965
Earnings: $92,710,435
Emp.: 10,028
Fiscal Year-end: 08/31/21
Educational Support Services
N.A.I.C.S.: 611710
Changjun Xu *(Chm)*

HOPE LIFE INTERNATIONAL HOLDINGS LIMITED
Flat 1703 17th Floor Wanchai Commercial Centre, Nos 194-204 Johnston Road, Hong Kong, China (Hong Kong)
Tel.: (852) 2 327 9100   Ky
Web Site: http://www.hopelife.hk
Year Founded: 1996
01683—(HKG)
Rev.: $14,598,214
Assets: $33,992,679
Liabilities: $5,285,858
Net Worth: $28,706,821
Earnings: ($1,305,407)
Emp.: 26
Fiscal Year-end: 12/31/20
Holding Company
N.A.I.C.S.: 551112
Huiyong Ren *(Chm)*

HOPE, INC.
MG Yakuin Building 1-14-5 Yakuin, Chuo-Ku, Fukuoka, 810-0022, Japan
Tel.: (81) 927161404
Web Site: https://www.zaigenkakuho.com
6195—(TKS)
Rev.: $16,875,330
Assets: $13,114,240
Liabilities: $6,484,410
Net Worth: $6,629,830
Earnings: $1,725,210
Fiscal Year-end: 03/31/24
Multi Level Marketing Services
N.A.I.C.S.: 541613
Takayasu Tokitsu *(CEO)*

HOPEFLUENT GROUP HOLDINGS LTD
Room 3611 Shun Tak Centre West Tower 200 Connaught Road Central, Hong Kong, China (Hong Kong)
Tel.: (852) 28508233
Web Site: http://www.hopefluent.com
0733—(HKG)
Rev.: $193,399,905
Assets: $389,005,050
Liabilities: $104,165,715
Net Worth: $284,839,335
Earnings: ($95,416,793)
Emp.: 7,300
Fiscal Year-end: 12/31/22
Real Estate Agency
N.A.I.C.S.: 237210
Yat Fung Lo *(Exec Dir)*

Subsidiaries:

Asia Asset Property Group Ltd   (1)
Unit 3611 Shun Tak Ctr 200 Connaught Rd, Central, China (Hong Kong)
Tel.: (852) 28158333
Sales Range: $50-74.9 Million
Emp.: 8
Property Management Services
N.A.I.C.S.: 531312

Asia Asset Property Services (Shanghai) Co., Ltd.   (1)
7F 1319 Yan An West Road Lei Shing International Plaza, Shanghai, China
Tel.: (86) 2162520017
Web Site: http://www.shanghai.asia-asset.com
Sales Range: $50-74.9 Million
Emp.: 50
Residential & Commercial Real Estate Property Management Services
N.A.I.C.S.: 531311
James Huang *(Mgr)*

Hopefluent Properties Limited   (1)
Rm 3411 36 F Shun Tak Ctr W Tower 168-200 Connaught Rd, Central, China (Hong Kong)
Tel.: (852) 28158333
Web Site: http://www.hopefluent.com.hk
Sales Range: $50-74.9 Million
Emp.: 7
Real Estate Property Development Services
N.A.I.C.S.: 531210
Fu Wai Chung *(Mng Dir)*

HOPENING SA
4 rue Bernard Palissy, 92817, Puteaux, Cedex, France
Tel.: (33) 178994646
Web Site: https://www.hopening.fr
Year Founded: 1989
MLHPE—(EUR)
Sales Range: $10-24.9 Million
Financial Support Services
N.A.I.C.S.: 523940
Alexandre Basdereff *(Founder & Chm-Mgmt Bd)*

HOPETECH SDN. BHD.
Bangunan MCOBA 42 Jalan Syed Putra, 50460, Kuala Lumpur, Malaysia
Tel.: (60) 3 2273 8155   MY
Web Site: http://www.hopetech.com.my
Automated Revenue Collection System Services
N.A.I.C.S.: 522320
Mohamed Zafril Zabidin *(CEO & Exec Dir)*

HOPEWELL HOLDINGS LIMITED
64th Floor Hopewell Centre, 183 Queen's Road East, Wanchai, China (Hong Kong)
Tel.: (852) 25284975
Web Site: http://www.hopewellholdings.com
0054—(OTCIQ)
Sales Range: $250-299.9 Million
Emp.: 1,039
Real Estate & Infrastructure Developer
N.A.I.C.S.: 531390
Gordon Y.S. Wu *(Chm)*

Subsidiaries:

Bayern Gourmet Food Company Limited   (1)
11 F Tin Fung Industrial Mansion, 63 Wong Chuk Hang Rd, Aberdeen, China (Hong Kong)
Tel.: (852) 25180860
Web Site: http://www.bgf.com.hk
Sales Range: $25-49.9 Million
Emp.: 75
Seafood Mfr & Sales
N.A.I.C.S.: 311710

Hopewell Centre Management Limited   (1)
Rooms 1801-03 18/F Hopewell Centre 183 Queen s Road East, Wanchai, China (Hong Kong)
Tel.: (852) 25277292
Web Site: http://www.hopewellcentre.com
Property Management Services
N.A.I.C.S.: 531312

Hopewell Construction Company Limited   (1)
Rm 5902-7 59 F Hopewell Ctr, 83 Queens Rd E, Wanchai, China (Hong Kong)
Tel.: (852) 25291929
Construction & Project Management Services
N.A.I.C.S.: 236210

Hopewell Hotels Management Limited   (1)
No 8 Austin Road Tsim Sha Tsui, Tsuen Wan, Kowloon, China (Hong Kong)
Tel.: (852) 23761111
Web Site: http://www.pandahotel.com.hk

Home Management Services
N.A.I.C.S.: 561110
Stephen Yuen *(Deputy Mgr)*

Hopewell Property Management Company Limited   (1)
Rm 1801 18 Fl Hopewell Ctr, 83 Queens Rd E, Wanchai, China (Hong Kong)
Tel.: (852) 25284975
Web Site: http://www.hopewellholdings.com
Construction & Property Management Services
N.A.I.C.S.: 236210

Hopewell Real Estate Agency Limited   (1)
Rooms 1801-03 18/F Hopewell Centre, 183 Queens Road East, Wanchai, China (Hong Kong)
Tel.: (852) 2528 4975
Web Site: http://www.hrea.com.hk
Real Estate Agency Services
N.A.I.C.S.: 531210

International Trademart Company Limited   (1)
Rm 647-671 6F KITEC 1 Trademart Dr, Kowloon Bay, Kowloon, China (Hong Kong)
Tel.: (852) 26202222
Web Site: http://www.kitec.com.hk
Emp.: 100
Property Management Services
N.A.I.C.S.: 531312

Kowloon Panda Hotel Limited   (1)
3 Tsuen Wah Street, Tsuen Wan, China (Hong Kong)
Tel.: (852) 24091111
Web Site: http://www.pandahotel.com.hk
Sales Range: $75-99.9 Million
Emp.: 300
Home Management Services
N.A.I.C.S.: 561110
Stephen Yuen *(Deputy Gen Mgr)*

Kowloonbay International Trade & Exhibition Centre   (1)
1 Trademart Drive, Kowloon Bay, Kowloon, China (Hong Kong)
Tel.: (852) 26202222
Web Site: http://www.kitec.com.hk
Emp.: 100
Business, Concerts, Exhibitions, Conferences, Banqueting & Entertainment Functions
N.A.I.C.S.: 561499
Josephine Lam *(Gen Mgr)*

Panda Place Management Limited   (1)
3 Tsuen Wah St, Tsuen Wan, China (Hong Kong)
Tel.: (852) 31140000
Web Site: http://www.pandaplace.com.hk
Sales Range: $25-49.9 Million
Emp.: 34
Property Management Services
N.A.I.C.S.: 531312
Fanny Mok *(Mgr)*

HOPIUM S.A.
43 rue de Lige, 75008, Paris, France
Tel.: (33) 185736767
Web Site: https://www.hopium.com
Year Founded: 2019
ALHPI—(EUR)
Automobile Parts Mfr
N.A.I.C.S.: 336350
Olivier Lombard *(CEO & Chm)*

HOPKINS CONSTRUCTION (LACOMBE) LTD.
4515 - 48 Avenue, Lacombe, T4L 2C1, AB, Canada
Tel.: (403) 782-4400
Web Site: http://www.hopkins.ab.ca
Year Founded: 1966
Sales Range: $10-24.9 Million
Emp.: 25
Building Construction
N.A.I.C.S.: 423320
Joe Nolan *(VP-Logistics)*

HOPPENSTEDT FIRMENIN INTERNATIONAL PUBLIC

HOPPENSTEDT FIRMENIN—(CONTINUED)

FORMATIONEN GMBH
Havelstrasse 9, 64295, Darmstadt, Germany
Tel.: (49) 61513800
Web Site: http://www.hoppenstedt.de
Sales Range: $10-24.9 Million
Emp.: 100
Business Information Publisher
N.A.I.C.S.: 513140
Ulrich Muller *(Mng Dir)*

HOPPINGS SOFTWOOD PRODUCTS PLC
The Woodyard, Epping, CM16 6TT, Essex, United Kingdom
Tel.: (44) 1992578877
Web Site: http://www.hoppings.co.uk
Year Founded: 1920
Sales Range: $10-24.9 Million
Emp.: 60
Timber Distr & Mfr
N.A.I.C.S.: 321212
David Bryans *(Office Mgr-Sls)*

HOPSCOTCH GROUPE S.A.
23/25 rue Notre-Dame-des-Victoires, 75002, Paris, France
Tel.: (33) 141342000
Web Site: https://www.hopscotchgroupe.com
HOP—(EUR)
Sales Range: $200-249.9 Million
Event Organizing Services
N.A.I.C.S.: 711310
Valerie Bonnement *(Deputy Mng Dir)*

Subsidiaries:

Hopscotch Africa S.A. (1)
40 rue Anatole France, 92594, Levallois-Perret, Cedex, France
Tel.: (33) 141342000
Web Site: http://en.hopscotchafrica.com
Public Relation Agency Services
N.A.I.C.S.: 541820

Hopscotch Europe Ltd. (1)
96 Pembroke Road, Ballsbridge, Dublin, Ireland
Tel.: (353) 16473500
Web Site: http://www.hopscotch.eu
Public Relation Agency Services
N.A.I.C.S.: 541820

Sagarmatha SAS (1)
25 rue Notre-Dame des Victoires, 75002, Paris, France
Tel.: (33) 141341820
Web Site: http://www.sagarmatha.fr
Emp.: 70
Event Communication Agency Services
N.A.I.C.S.: 541810
Sylviane Girardo *(Co-Mng Dir)*

Societe Pour L'Expansion des Ventes des Produits Agricoles et Alimentaires (1)
43-45 Rue De Naples, Paris, 75008, France (66%)
Tel.: (33) 144694000
Web Site: http://www.e-sopexa.com
Sales Range: $75-99.9 Million
Marketing & Communications of French Food & Drink Industry
N.A.I.C.S.: 311412
Alain Ponsard *(Assoc Dir-Bus Dev)*

Subsidiary (Non-US):

Sopexa (Canada) Ltd. (2)
2 St Clair Ave E Ste 800, M4T2T5, Toronto, ON, Canada
Tel.: (416) 921-8400
Web Site: http://www.sopexa.com
Public Relations Agencies
N.A.I.C.S.: 541820

Branch (US):

Sopexa USA (2)
250 Hudson St Ste 703, New York, NY 10013-1437
Tel.: (212) 477-9800

Web Site: http://www.sopexa.com
Rev.: $11,000,000
Emp.: 14
Advertising Agencies
N.A.I.C.S.: 541810
Olivier Moreaux *(Pres-The Americas)*

Sopexa Italia S.A. (1)
Via Aristide De Togni 27, 20123, Milan, Italy
Tel.: (39) 02863741
Marketing & Advertising Services
N.A.I.C.S.: 541810
Matteo Lefebvre *(Mng Dir)*

Sopexa Japon Co., Ltd. (1)
3-12-8 3/4F, Ebisu Shibuya-Ku, Tokyo, 150-0013, Japan
Tel.: (81) 357890081
Marketing & Advertising Services
N.A.I.C.S.: 541810
Loic Brunot *(Mng Dir-Pacific Asia)*

HOPSON DEVELOPMENT HOLDINGS LIMITED
Unit 4903-10 49/F The Center 99 Queen's Road, Central, China (Hong Kong)
Tel.: (852) 25373086   HK
Web Site: https://www.hopson.com.cn
Year Founded: 1992
0754—(HKG)
Rev.: $3,474,631,020
Assets: $38,086,086,128
Liabilities: $25,542,869,963
Net Worth: $12,543,216,165
Earnings: $1,159,381,088
Emp.: 10,482
Fiscal Year-end: 12/31/22
Property Development & Investment Services
N.A.I.C.S.: 523940
Barbara Wai Kun Mok *(Sec)*

HOPU INVESTMENT MANAGEMENT CO., LTD.
Suite 203-205 North Tower Winland Financial Center, 7 Financial Street, Beijing, 100140, China
Tel.: (86) 10 5181 9600   CN
Year Founded: 2007
Privater Equity Firm
N.A.I.C.S.: 523999
Fenglei Fang *(Founder & Chm)*

Subsidiaries:

Ambrx, Inc. (1)
10975 N Torrey Pines Rd, La Jolla, CA 92037
Tel.: (858) 875-2400
Web Site: http://www.ambrx.com
Biopharmaceutical Developer
N.A.I.C.S.: 325412
Feng Tian *(Chm, Pres & CEO)*

HOR KEW CORPORATION LIMITED
66 Kallang Pudding Road 07-01 Hor Kew Business Centre, Singapore, 349324, Singapore
Tel.: (65) 63658322
Web Site: https://www.horkew.com.sg
BBP—(SES)
Rev.: $37,529,559
Assets: $124,592,699
Liabilities: $78,954,008
Net Worth: $45,638,691
Earnings: $250,650
Fiscal Year-end: 12/31/20
Construction Services
N.A.I.C.S.: 236220
Ng Seng Yoong *(Gen Mgr)*

Subsidiaries:

Hor Kew Private Limited (1)
66 Kallang Pudding Road 07-01 Hor Kew Business Center, Singapore, 349324, Singapore
Tel.: (65) 63658322
Web Site: http://www.horkew.com.sg

Emp.: 30
Commercial Building Construction Services
N.A.I.C.S.: 236220

Prefab Technology 3 Pte Ltd (1)
99 Pioneer Road, Singapore, 639580, Singapore
Tel.: (65) 6 863 0608
Web Site: https://www.prefabtech3.com.sg
Emp.: 95
Prefabricated Architectural Metal Components Mfr
N.A.I.C.S.: 332323
Elicia Aw *(Mng Dir)*

Prefab Technology Pte Ltd (1)
66 Sungei Kadut Street 1, Singapore, 729367, Singapore
Tel.: (65) 63683233
Web Site: https://prefabtech.com.sg
Emp.: 200
Rebar Connectors Mfr
N.A.I.C.S.: 331221
Elicia Aw *(Gen Mgr)*

HORAI CO., LTD.
1-8-12 Nihonbashi Horidome-cho, Chuo-Ku, Tokyo, 103-0012, Japan
Tel.: (81) 368108100
Web Site: https://www.horai-kk.co.jp
Year Founded: 1928
9679—(TKS)
Sales Range: $25-49.9 Million
Insurance Services
N.A.I.C.S.: 524298
Toshiyuki Teramoto *(Pres & CEO)*

HORDAGRUPPEN AB
Jarnvagsgatan 24, 330 18, Horda, Sweden
Tel.: (46) 370654600   SE
Web Site: http://www.hordagruppen.com
Year Founded: 1974
Sales Range: $25-49.9 Million
Emp.: 250
Rubber & Plastic Products Mfr
N.A.I.C.S.: 326299
Lars Lejon *(Mng Dir)*

HORDENER HOLZWERK GMBH
Landstrasse 25, 76571, Gaggenau, Germany
Tel.: (49) 722464040
Web Site: http://www.hoerdener-holzwerk.de
Rev.: $33,901,859
Emp.: 60
Wood Product Distr
N.A.I.C.S.: 423310
Gerhard Strobel *(Co-Mng Dir)*

HORIBA LTD
2 Miyanohigashi-cho Kisshoin, Minami-ku, Kyoto, 601-8510, Japan
Tel.: (81) 753138121
Web Site: https://www.horiba.com
6856—(TKS)
Rev.: $2,060,056,220
Assets: $3,183,622,700
Liabilities: $1,171,962,820
Net Worth: $2,011,659,880
Earnings: $285,741,180
Emp.: 8,665
Fiscal Year-end: 12/31/23
Measuring Equipment Mfr & Sales
N.A.I.C.S.: 334513
Atsushi Horiba *(Chm, Chm & CEO/CEO-Grp)*

Subsidiaries:

Abalat S.A. De C.V. (1)
San Marcos No 130 Tlalpan Tlalpan Centro, 14000, Mexico, Mexico
Tel.: (52) 5580001500
Surgical & Medical Instrument Mfr
N.A.I.C.S.: 339112

Acouns Nigeria Ltd. (1)
13 Olori Mojisola Onikoyi Avenue, Banana

Island Ikoyi, Lagos, Nigeria
Tel.: (234) 8037177254
Surgical & Medical Instrument Mfr
N.A.I.C.S.: 334516

Agricultura, Tecnologia, Pasion Atp S.A. (1)
12 Calle 9-11 Zona 1 Edificio Duplex Primer Nivel, Ciudad de Guatemala, 01001, Guatemala, Guatemala
Tel.: (502) 40744807
Environmental Services
N.A.I.C.S.: 541620

Agrocultivo (1)
Monteiro Gomez 126 Centro, Taubate, SP, Brazil
Tel.: (55) 1236221636
Web Site: http://www.agrocultivo.com.br
Farming & Cattle Raising Services
N.A.I.C.S.: 112111

Algam Drugs & Chemicals Co., Ltd. (1)
Block No 7 House No 2 Omak street Alsafa Intersaction, Khartoum, Sudan
Tel.: (249) 183774863
Surgical & Medical Instrument Mfr
N.A.I.C.S.: 339112

All Eights (M) Sdn Bhd (1)
45 Jalan TS 6/10A, Subang Industrial Park, 47600, Subang Jaya, Selangor, Malaysia
Tel.: (60) 356334988
Web Site: http://www.alleights.com.my
Surgical & Medical Instrument Mfr
N.A.I.C.S.: 339112
Heng Chin Lee *(Gen Sls Mgr)*

Alliance Biotech & Analytical Ltd. (1)
04 Ground Floor Road,No 05 Sector 11, Uttara, Dhaka, 1230, Bangladesh
Tel.: (880) 1719346667
Web Site: http://www.alliancebiotech.com
Surgical & Medical Instrument Whslr
N.A.I.C.S.: 339112

Alpax Comercio De Prods. (1)
Rua Serra Da Borborema 40 Barirro Campandario, Diadema, 09930-580, Sao Paulo, Brazil
Tel.: (55) 1140579200
Surgical & Medical Instrument Mfr
N.A.I.C.S.: 339112

Alvog S.A. (1)
Iturbe 1184, Asuncion, Paraguay
Tel.: (595) 21494536
Web Site: http://www.alvog.com.py
Scientific Equipment Mfr
N.A.I.C.S.: 334516

Alvtechnologies Philippines Inc. (1)
Unit 2308 Medical Plaza Ortigas, San Miguel Avenue Ortigas Center, Pasig, 1605, Philippines
Tel.: (63) 286382317
Web Site: http://www.alvtechnologies.com.ph
Analytical Instrument Mfr
N.A.I.C.S.: 334516

Analyt De Centroamerica SA (1)
O Avenida A 9-21 Zona 9, 01009, Guatemala, Guatemala
Tel.: (502) 24141616
Electrical & Electronic Mfr
N.A.I.C.S.: 335999

Analytical Instruments SA (1)
9 Tzavella St, 152 31, Chalandri, Greece
Tel.: (30) 2106748973
Laboratory Services
N.A.I.C.S.: 621511

Annar Diagnostica Import SAS (1)
Calle 49 13-60, 110311, Bogota, Colombia
Tel.: (57) 17447979
Electrical & Electronic Mfr
N.A.I.C.S.: 335999

Arab Medical & Scientific Alliance Co. (1)
Khalil Salem Str Telal El Ali, PO Box 2509, 11953, Amman, Jordan
Tel.: (962) 65528009
Surgical & Medical Instrument Mfr
N.A.I.C.S.: 339112

Arcoa Ghana Ltd. (1)
11 Agostinho Neto RoadAirport Residential

AND PRIVATE COMPANIES — HORIBA LTD

Area, PO Box CT 9678, Accra, Ghana
Tel.: (233) 540122001
Surgical & Medical Instrument Mfr
N.A.I.C.S.: 339112

Ari. Batterjee & Bros Company (1)
Palestine Street Post Box 2 two, 21411, Jeddah, Saudi Arabia
Tel.: (966) 26601021
Electrical & Electronic Mfr
N.A.I.C.S.: 335999

Arquimed S.A. (1)
Arturo Prat 828, Santiago, Chile
Tel.: (56) 226074000
Web Site: http://www.arquimed.cl
Electronic Components Distr
N.A.I.C.S.: 423690

Asesorias Y Representaciones Analiticas S.R.L. (1)
Calle Las Garzas 189 Urb 34, Limatambo, Lima, Peru
Tel.: (51) 12212861
Environmental Services
N.A.I.C.S.: 541620

Avanpro, S.A. (1)
6ta Avenida 2-16 Zona 15 Colonia Trinidad, Guatemala, Guatemala
Tel.: (502) 23657434
Environmental Services
N.A.I.C.S.: 541620

Axon Lab AG (1)
Gewerbezone 1, Polling, 6404, Tirol, Austria
Tel.: (43) 523887766
Surgical & Medical Instrument Mfr
N.A.I.C.S.: 339112

Axon Lab AG (1)
Heinrich-Otto-Strasse 1, 73262, Reichenbach, Germany
Tel.: (49) 715392260
Surgical & Medical Instrument Mfr
N.A.I.C.S.: 339112

Axon Lab B.V. (1)
Oude Bosscheweg 11, 5301 LA, Zaltbommel, Netherlands
Tel.: (31) 880036600
Laboratory Services
N.A.I.C.S.: 621511

Axon Lab D.O.O (1)
Kovinska ulica 4, 10000, Zagreb, Croatia
Tel.: (385) 15807283
Surgical & Medical Instrument Mfr
N.A.I.C.S.: 339112

Axon Lab NV (1)
Jan Emiel Mommaertslaan 20 A, 1831, Diegem, Belgium
Tel.: (32) 23115262
Surgical & Medical Instrument Whslr
N.A.I.C.S.: 423450

Axon Lab Spol. S R.O. (1)
Mladeznicka 1435, 293 01, Mlada Boleslav, Czech Republic
Tel.: (420) 326921318
Surgical & Medical Instrument Mfr
N.A.I.C.S.: 339112

Bcg Publicidad & Agronegocios S.A.C (1)
Calle Alcanfores 1245 18, Miraflores, Peru
Tel.: (51) 995805066
Environmental Services
N.A.I.C.S.: 541620

BeXema GmbH (1)
Otto-von-Guericke-Allee 20, Barleben, D-39179, Magdeburg, Germany
Tel.: (49) 39203964200
Web Site: https://bexema.com
Dynamic Power Electronic Services
N.A.I.C.S.: 532210

Beijing HORIBA METRON Instruments Co., Ltd. (1)
Bei Yuan Road 40, Chaoyang District, Beijing, China
Tel.: (86) 1084929402
Semiconductor Product Distr
N.A.I.C.S.: 423690

Bio-Services Congo Sarl (1)
99 Av des 3 Martyrs Moungali Pointe Noire, Brazzaville, Congo, Republic of

Tel.: (242) 55498286
Surgical & Medical Instrument Mfr
N.A.I.C.S.: 339112

Biomarketing Services (M) Sdn Bhd (1)
No 21 Jalan 4/62A Bandar Menjalara, Kepong, 52200, Kuala Lumpur, Malaysia
Tel.: (60) 362733068
Surgical & Medical Instrument Mfr
N.A.I.C.S.: 339112

Biometric Albania Sh.P.K. (1)
Rruga Vllazen Huta Pallati i Ri Vila Park Shkalla 1/6/23, 1000, Tirana, Albania
Tel.: (355) 4364326
Surgical & Medical Instrument Mfr
N.A.I.C.S.: 339112

Biosigma C.A. (1)
Av Urdaneta Centro Financiero Latino Piso 17 of 8 Distrito Federal, 1011, Caracas, Venezuela
Tel.: (58) 2125630266
Electrical & Electronic Mfr
N.A.I.C.S.: 335999

Biosynergie Sarl (1)
26 BP 953, Abidjan, Cote d'Ivoire
Tel.: (225) 57481844
Surgical & Medical Instrument Mfr
N.A.I.C.S.: 339112

Business International Group LLC (1)
ONEIC Building 1st Floor Bldg No 2785 Way No 3522 Next to IBIS Hotel, Dohat Al Adab Street Al Khuwair South, Muscat, Oman
Tel.: (968) 24399300
Web Site: http://www.bigllcoman.com
Scientific Equipment Mfr
N.A.I.C.S.: 334516

Caribbean Diagnostics Ltd. (1)
Grand Harbor Red Bay, Georgetown, Cayman Islands
Tel.: (345) 3459255069
Web Site: http://www.caribbeandiagnostics.com
Surgical & Medical Instrument Mfr
N.A.I.C.S.: 339112

Casmont Sas (1)
Av Cabildo 661 Piso 1 Dpto 8 1426, Buenos Aires, Argentina
Tel.: (54) 111539545410
Web Site: http://www.casmontsas.com
Surgical & Medical Instrument Whslr
N.A.I.C.S.: 423450

Central Circle Co. (1)
Salmieh 22011 Floor No 69 Al-Hamra Tower, PO Box 1015, Abdel Aziz Hamad Al-Saquer Street AlSharq, Kuwait, Kuwait
Tel.: (965) 1869869214
Surgical & Medical Instrument Mfr
N.A.I.C.S.: 339112

Cientec Instrumentos Cientificos SA (1)
Jose Miguel Claro 815, Providencia, Chile
Tel.: (56) 222350085
Web Site: http://www.cientecinstrumentos.cl
Research & Development Services
N.A.I.C.S.: 541720

Comef Sp. Z O.O. Sp.K. (1)
ul Gdanska 2, 40-719, Katowice, Poland
Tel.: (48) 324283820
Web Site: http://www.comef.com.pl
Laboratory Services
N.A.I.C.S.: 621511

Conceptos E Instrumentos S.A. De C.V. (1)
Creston 212 - 4 Jardines del Pedregal, 01900, Mexico, Mexico
Tel.: (52) 5556527609
Scientific Equipment Mfr
N.A.I.C.S.: 334516

Control Tecnico Y Representaciones Sa De Cv (1)
Ave Lincoln No 3410 Pte Colonia Mitras Norte, Monterrey, 64320, Nuevo Leon, Mexico
Tel.: (52) 8181580600
Environmental Services
N.A.I.C.S.: 541620

Corad Technology Ltd. (1)
1306 Nanyang Plaza 57 Hung To Road, Kwun Tong, China (Hong Kong)
Tel.: (852) 27930330
Electronic Components Distr
N.A.I.C.S.: 423690

Dakila Trading Corporation (1)
613 Calderon Street, Mandaluyong, 1550, Philippines
Tel.: (63) 27247511
Web Site: http://www.dakila.com
Analytical Instrument Mfr
N.A.I.C.S.: 334516

Del Carpio Analisis Y Asesorias Ltda. (1)
Av Sucre 2596, Nunoa, Santiago, Chile
Tel.: (56) 225819500
Web Site: http://www.delcarpio.cl
Engineeering Services
N.A.I.C.S.: 541330

Diagnostic Systems GmbH (1)
234 Lotissement Nassim Lissassfa, Hay Hassani, Casablanca, Morocco
Tel.: (212) 522938182
Scientific Equipment Mfr
N.A.I.C.S.: 334516

Diamedic Import (1)
Av Ormachea 125 esq Calle 6 Obrajes, La Paz, Bolivia
Tel.: (591) 22788493
Surgical & Medical Instrument Mfr
N.A.I.C.S.: 339112

Dias De Sousa S.A. (1)
Rua dos Jasmins 541, 2890-189, Alcochete, Portugal
Tel.: (351) 219533120
Web Site: http://www.dias-de-sousa.pt
Laboratory Equipment Mfr
N.A.I.C.S.: 334516

Diatec Sarl (1)
lotissement pointe d'or n 106 rue des poiriers, Les Abymes, 97139, Abymes, Guadeloupe
Tel.: (590) 841157
Surgical & Medical Instrument Mfr
N.A.I.C.S.: 339112

Dksh Laos Company Limited (1)
3rd Floor Vientiane Center Building Khouvieng Road, Sisattanak District, Vientiane, Lao People's Democratic Republic
Tel.: (856) 21453100
Electrical & Electronic Mfr
N.A.I.C.S.: 335999

Dyn Diagnostics Ltd. (1)
7 Haeshel St Caesarea Industrial Park, PO Box 30637, 38900, Caesarea, Israel
Tel.: (972) 46175300
Surgical & Medical Instrument Mfr
N.A.I.C.S.: 339112

Enol SA (1)
Inocencio Raffo Arrosa 971, 11700, Montevideo, Uruguay
Tel.: (598) 23042666
Electrical & Electronic Mfr
N.A.I.C.S.: 335999

Envirosys Ltd. (1)
10 Lefkados Str, 113 62, Athens, Greece
Tel.: (30) 2108211182
Environmental Services
N.A.I.C.S.: 541620

Eprolab Sa (1)
2A Calle 2-65, Guatemala, Guatemala
Tel.: (502) 22303489
Environmental Services
N.A.I.C.S.: 541620

Equilab, S.A. De C.V. (1)
Calle Constitucion y Condominio Satelite Edificio A Apto No 8, San Salvador, El Salvador
Tel.: (503) 22746336
Environmental Services
N.A.I.C.S.: 541620

Equinlab Sac (1)
Av 28 de Julio Mz V1 Lt 17 Los Olivos, Lima, Peru
Tel.: (51) 16776611
Web Site: http://www.equinlabsac.com
Analytical Instrument Mfr
N.A.I.C.S.: 334516

Equipos Y Laboratorio De Colombia Sas (1)
Carrera 51 6 Sur - 36, Guayabal, Medellin, Antioquia, Colombia
Tel.: (57) 3014765347
Web Site: http://www.equiposylaboratorio.com
Analytical Instrument Mfr
N.A.I.C.S.: 334516

Essar Lab Mate Pvt Ltd (1)
1St Floor Ckikkayelappa Complex Horamavu Agra Main Road, Bengaluru, 560043, India
Tel.: (91) 9746475578
Electrical & Electronic Mfr
N.A.I.C.S.: 335999

Fanda Scientific Fz-LLC (1)
Floor 2 Laboratory Complex, Dubai Science Park, Dubai, United Arab Emirates
Tel.: (971) 44429856
Electrical & Electronic Mfr
N.A.I.C.S.: 335999

Flowen S.A.C (1)
Av de los Condores 699 Oficina 301 Piso 3 Urb La Ensenada, La Molina, Lima, Peru
Tel.: (51) 16546404
Environmental Services
N.A.I.C.S.: 541620

Ganbaro Srl (1)
Calle Jardines del Embajador Esq Sarasota, Edif No 11 Piso 3-C Bella Vista, Santo Domingo, Dominican Republic
Tel.: (809) 5335026
Electrical & Electronic Mfr
N.A.I.C.S.: 335999

H.A. Shar & Sons Ltd. (1)
3rd Floor 109-W Sardar Begum Plaza Jinnah Avenue Blue Area, Islamabad, Pakistan
Tel.: (92) 5123485159
Web Site: http://www.hashah.com
Emp.: 103
Laboratory Services
N.A.I.C.S.: 621511

HORIBA (Austria) GmbH (1)
B-dul Republicii nr 164 Etaj Parter Birourile nr 3 si 4, Judetul Arges, 110177, Pitesti, Romania
Tel.: (40) 348807117
Semiconductor Product Distr
N.A.I.C.S.: 423690

HORIBA (China) Trading Co., Ltd. (1)
Unit D 1F Building A Synnex International Park 1068 West Tianshan Road, Shanghai, 200335, China
Tel.: (86) 2162896060
Analytical & Measuring Instrument Distr
N.A.I.C.S.: 423490
Nakamura Tadao *(Pres)*

HORIBA (Thailand) Limited (1)
46/8 Rungrojthanakul Bld 1st 2nd Floor Ratchadapisek Road, Huai Khwang, Bangkok, 10310, Thailand
Tel.: (66) 28615995
Analytical & Measuring Instrument Distr
N.A.I.C.S.: 423490
Kumpol Jansuwannasorn *(Ops Mgr)*

HORIBA ABX Diagnostics Thailand Ltd. (1)
395 Latya Rd Somdetchaopraya, Klongsan District, Bangkok, 10600, Thailand
Tel.: (66) 28615995
Web Site: http://www.horiba.com
Sales Range: $25-49.9 Million
Emp.: 30
Automotive Testing Equipment Mfr
N.A.I.C.S.: 334519

HORIBA ABX Ltda. (1)
Av das Nacoes Unidas, Sao Paulo, 04795-100, Brazil
Tel.: (55) 1155451500
Emp.: 50
Diagnostic Equipment Mfr
N.A.I.C.S.: 334510

HORIBA ABX S.A.S. (1)
Alfrapark Estrada De Alfragide N 67 Edificio F Piso 0, 2610-008, Amadora, Portugal
Tel.: (351) 214721770

HORIBA LTD

INTERNATIONAL PUBLIC

HORIBA Ltd—(Continued)
Semiconductor Product Distr
N.A.I.C.S.: 423690

HORIBA ABX S.A.S. (1)
Viale Luca Gaurico 209/211, 00143, Rome, Italy
Tel.: (39) 065159221
Semiconductor Product Distr
N.A.I.C.S.: 423690

HORIBA ABX SAS (1)
Calle Apolonio Morales 6, 28036, Madrid, Spain
Tel.: (34) 913533010
Semiconductor Product Distr
N.A.I.C.S.: 423690

HORIBA ABX SAS (1)
Parc Euromedecine Rue du Caducee, PO Box 7290, 34184, Montpellier, Cedex 4, France
Tel.: (33) 467141516
Semiconductor Product Distr
N.A.I.C.S.: 423690

HORIBA ABX Sp. Z o.o. (1)
ul Pulawska 182, 02-670, Warsaw, Poland
Tel.: (48) 226732022
Web Site: http://www.horiba.com
Sales Range: $25-49.9 Million
Emp.: 35
Automotive Testing Equipment Mfr
N.A.I.C.S.: 334519

HORIBA Advanced Techno Co., Ltd. (1)
31 Miyanonishi-cho Kisshoin, Minami-ku, Kyoto, 601-8306, Japan
Tel.: (81) 753217184
Web Site: http://www.horiba-adt.jp
Sales Range: $25-49.9 Million
Emp.: 150
Automotive Testing Equipment Mfr
N.A.I.C.S.: 334519

Plant (Domestic):

HORIBA Advanced Techno Co., Ltd. - Kyoto Factory (2)
2 Miyanohigashi-cho Kisshoin, Minami-ku, Kyoto, 601-8551, Japan
Tel.: (81) 753211215
Web Site: http://www.horiba.com
Semiconductor Mfr
N.A.I.C.S.: 334413

HORIBA Automotive Test Systems Inc. (1)
1115 N Service Road W, Oakville, L6M 1N1, ON, Canada
Tel.: (905) 827-7755
Automotive Equipments Supplier
N.A.I.C.S.: 423120

HORIBA Automotive Test Systems Ltd. (1)
Room 906 World Meridian Venture Centre I, 60-24 Gasan-Dong Geumcheon-Gu, Seoul, 153-78, Korea (South)
Tel.: (82) 25627296
Web Site: http://www.horiba.com
Sales Range: $25-49.9 Million
Emp.: 6
Automotive Testing Equipment Mfr
N.A.I.C.S.: 334519

HORIBA Canada, Inc. (1)
Unit102 5555 North Service Road, Burlington, L7L 5H7, ON, Canada
Tel.: (905) 335-0234
Analytical & Measuring Instrument Distr
N.A.I.C.S.: 423490

HORIBA Europe Automation Division GmbH (1)
Zabergaeustr 3, Neuhausen, 73765, Germany
Tel.: (49) 7158933300
Web Site: http://www.horiba-ats.com
Sales Range: $25-49.9 Million
Emp.: 50
Automotive Testing Equipment Mfr
N.A.I.C.S.: 334519

HORIBA Europe GmbH (1)
Hans Mess Str 6, 61440, Oberursel, Germany
Tel.: (49) 617213960
Web Site: http://www.horiba.com
Sales Range: $25-49.9 Million
Emp.: 80
Automotive Testing Equipment Mfr
N.A.I.C.S.: 334519

Unit (Domestic):

HORIBA Europe GmbH - Leichlingen Facility (2)
Julius-Kronenberg-Strasse 9, 42799, Leichlingen, Germany
Tel.: (49) 217589780
Web Site: http://www.horiba.com
Automotive Testing Equipment Mfr
N.A.I.C.S.: 334519

HORIBA France SARL (1)
12 Av Des Tropiques Hightec Sud, 91955, Les Ulis, France
Tel.: (33) 169299623
Sales Range: $25-49.9 Million
Emp.: 54
Automotive Testing Equipment Mfr
N.A.I.C.S.: 334519

HORIBA FuelCon GmbH (1)
Otto-von-Guericke-Allee 20, 39179, Barleben, Germany
Tel.: (49) 39203964400
Web Site: https://www.horiba-fuelcon.com
Semiconductor Product Distr
N.A.I.C.S.: 423690

HORIBA GmbH (1)
Kaplanstrasse 5, 3430, Tulln, Austria
Tel.: (43) 227265225
Web Site: http://www.horiba.com
Sales Range: $25-49.9 Million
Emp.: 26
Automotive Testing Equipment Mfr
N.A.I.C.S.: 334519

HORIBA India Private Ltd. (1)
Sales Range: $25-49.9 Million
Emp.: 30
Environmental Engineering Services
N.A.I.C.S.: 541330

HORIBA Instruments (Shanghai) Co., Ltd. (1)
No 200 Taitao Rd, Jiading Industrial District, Shanghai, 201814, China
Tel.: (86) 2169522835
Web Site: http://www.horiba.com
Sales Range: $50-74.9 Million
Emp.: 150
Automotive Testing Equipment Mfr
N.A.I.C.S.: 334519

HORIBA Instruments (Singapore) PTE, Ltd. (1)
3 Changi Business Park Vista 01-01, Singapore, 486051, Singapore
Tel.: (65) 67458300
Sales Range: $25-49.9 Million
Emp.: 30
Environmental Engineering Services
N.A.I.C.S.: 541330

HORIBA Instruments Brasil, Ltda. (1)
Rua Presbitero Plinio Alves de Souza, 645 Loteamento Multivias Jardim Ermida II Jundiai, Sao Paulo, 13212-181, Brazil
Tel.: (55) 1129235400
Semiconductor Product Distr
N.A.I.C.S.: 423690

HORIBA Instruments Inc. - Irvine Facility (1)
9755 Research Dr, Irvine, CA 92618
Tel.: (949) 250-4811
Web Site: http://www.horiba.com
Sales Range: $25-49.9 Million
Emp.: 80
Automotive Testing Equipment Mfr
N.A.I.C.S.: 334519

HORIBA Instruments Inc. - Tempe Facility (1)
2520 S Indust Park Dr, Tempe, AZ 85282-1847
Tel.: (480) 967-2283
Web Site: http://www.horiba.com
Automotive Testing Equipment Mfr
N.A.I.C.S.: 334519

HORIBA Instruments Inc. - Troy Facility (1)
2890 John R Rd, Troy, MI 48083
Tel.: (248) 689-9000
Web Site: http://www.horiba.com
Sales Range: $25-49.9 Million
Emp.: 100
Automotive Testing Equipment Mfr
N.A.I.C.S.: 334519
Bill Fostett (Mgr-IT)

HORIBA Instruments Inc.- Ann Arbor Facility (1)
5900 Hines Dr, Ann Arbor, MI 48108
Tel.: (734) 213-6555
Web Site: http://www.horiba.com
Sales Range: $25-49.9 Million
Emp.: 100
Automotive Testing Equipment Mfr
N.A.I.C.S.: 334519
Ken Mitera (Exec VP)

HORIBA Italia SRL (1)
Via Le Luca Gaurico 209, 00143, Rome, Italy
Tel.: (39) 065159221
Analytical & Measuring Instrument Distr
N.A.I.C.S.: 423490

HORIBA Jobin Yvon GmbH (1)
Neuhofstrasse 9, 64625, Bensheim, Germany
Tel.: (49) 89625184750
Semiconductor Product Distr
N.A.I.C.S.: 423690

HORIBA Jobin Yvon GmbH - Raman Division (1)
Neuhofstrasse 9, 64625, Bensheim, Germany
Tel.: (49) 89625184750
Web Site: http://www.horiba.com
Spectroscopy Instruments Mfr
N.A.I.C.S.: 334516

HORIBA Jobin Yvon IBH Ltd. (1)
Tel.: (44) 1412296789
Web Site: http://www.horiba.com
Sales Range: $25-49.9 Million
Emp.: 10
Spectroscopy Instruments Mfr
N.A.I.C.S.: 334516

HORIBA Jobin Yvon Ltd. (1)
2 Dalston Gardens, Stanmore, HA7 1BQ, Middlesex, United Kingdom
Tel.: (44) 2082048142
Web Site: http://www.horiba.com
Sales Range: $25-49.9 Million
Emp.: 26
Spectroscopy Instruments Mfr
N.A.I.C.S.: 334516

HORIBA Jobin Yvon S.A.S. (1)
16 18 Rue du Canal, 91165, Longjumeau, France
Tel.: (33) 164541300
Spectroscopy Instruments Mfr
N.A.I.C.S.: 334516
James Thepot (Pres)

Division (Domestic):

HORIBA Jobin Yvon S.A.S. - Raman Division (2)
231 rue de Lille, 59650, Villeneuve d'Ascq, France
Tel.: (33) 169747200
Web Site: http://www.horiba.com
Spectrometry Instruments Mfr
N.A.I.C.S.: 334516

HORIBA Jobin Yvon S.A.S. - Thin Film Division (2)
5 Auenoe Arago ZI dela Vigne aux Lous, Chilly Mazarin, 91380, Paris, France
Tel.: (33) 169748860
Sales Range: $25-49.9 Million
Emp.: 50
Spectroscopy Instruments Mfr
N.A.I.C.S.: 334516

HORIBA Korea Co., Ltd. - Bucheon Factory (1)
202-501 Bucheon Techno Park 388 Songnae-daero, Wonmi-gu, Bucheon, 420-831, Gyeonggi, Korea (South)
Tel.: (82) 326210100 0104
Web Site: http://www.horiba.com
Sales Range: $25-49.9 Million
Semiconductor Devices Mfr
N.A.I.C.S.: 334413

HORIBA Korea Ltd. (1)
25 94-Gil Iljik-Ro, Manan-gu, Anyang, 13901, Gyeonggi-do, Korea (South)
Tel.: (82) 312967911
Analytical & Measuring Instrument Distr
N.A.I.C.S.: 423490
Selin Hwang (Mgr-Marcom)

HORIBA Ltd - HORIBA Czech Olomouc Factory (1)
Zeleznicni 512/7, Olomouc, 772 00, Czech Republic
Tel.: (420) 588118365
Semiconductor Product Distr
N.A.I.C.S.: 423690

HORIBA MIRA Ltd. (1)
Watling Street, Nuneaton, CV10 0TU, Warwickshire, United Kingdom
Tel.: (44) 2476355000
Web Site: https://www.horiba-mira.com
Emp.: 650
Vehicle Testing Services
N.A.I.C.S.: 811198
George Gillespie (Chm)

HORIBA OOO (1)
Altufievskoe Shosse 13 Building 5, 127106, Moscow, Russia
Tel.: (7) 4952218771
Web Site: http://www.horiba.com
Semiconductor Product Distr
N.A.I.C.S.: 423690

HORIBA STEC Korea Ltd. (1)
110 Suntech-City 513 15 Sangdaewon, Jungwon-ku, Seongnam, 462-120, Kyungki-do, Korea (South)
Tel.: (82) 317772277
Web Site: http://www.horiba.com
Sales Range: $25-49.9 Million
Emp.: 30
Semiconductor Devices Mfr
N.A.I.C.S.: 334413

HORIBA STEC, Co., Ltd. (1)
11 5 Hokodate-cho Kamitoba, Minami-ku, Kyoto, 601-8116, Japan
Tel.: (81) 756932300
Web Site: http://www.horiba-stec.jp
Sales Range: $100-124.9 Million
Emp.: 450
Electric Equipment Mfr
N.A.I.C.S.: 334419
Hideyuki Koishi (Pres)

Plant (Domestic):

HORIBA STEC, Co., Ltd. - Aso Factory (2)
Torikokogyodanchi 358-11 Koumaibata Torikoaza, Nishiharamura-ohaza Aso-gun, Kumamoto, 861-2401, Japan
Tel.: (81) 962792922
Web Site: http://www.horiba.com
Semiconductor Devices Mfr
N.A.I.C.S.: 334413

HORIBA Scientific (1)
20 Knightsbridge Rd, Piscataway, NJ 08854
Tel.: (732) 494-8660
Spectroscopy Instruments Mfr & Supplier
N.A.I.C.S.: 334516
Salvatore Atzeni (VP-Engrg & CTO)

HORIBA Taiwan, Inc. (1)
8F-8 No-38 Taiyuan St, Hsinchu County, Zhubei, 30265, Taiwan
Tel.: (886) 35600606
Analytical & Measuring Instrument Distr
N.A.I.C.S.: 423490

HORIBA Techno Service Co., Ltd. (1)
2 Miyanohigashi-cho Kisshoin, Minami-ku, Kyoto, 601-8305, Japan
Tel.: (81) 753255291
Web Site: http://www.hts.horiba.com
Automotive Testing Equipment Mfr
N.A.I.C.S.: 334519

HORIBA Technology (Suzhou) Co.,Ltd. (1)
No 1 Building No 101 Chenmenjing Rd, Industry Park Taicang, Jiangsu, 215400, China
Tel.: (86) 51233006388
Automotive Parts Mfr & Distr
N.A.I.C.S.: 336390

HORIBA Test Automation Ltd. (1)
Brook Court Whittington Hall Whittington Road, Worcester, WR5 2RX, Worcestershire, United Kingdom
Tel.: (44) 1905359359
Web Site: http://www.horiba.com
Sales Range: $25-49.9 Million
Emp.: 30
Automotive Testing Equipment Mfr
N.A.I.C.S.: 334519

HORIBA Tocadero GmbH (1)
Johann-Hittorf-Str 8, 12489, Berlin, Germany
Tel.: (49) 3063923150
Web Site: https://www.horiba-tocadero.com
Industrial Measurement Product Distr
N.A.I.C.S.: 423690

HORIBA Trading (Shanghai) Co., Ltd. (1)
Unit D 1F Building A Synnex International Park 1068 West Tianshan Road, Shanghai, 200335, China
Tel.: (86) 2162896060
Web Site: http://www.horiba.com
Sales Range: $25-49.9 Million
Emp.: 100
Industrial Analytical Instruments Mfr
N.A.I.C.S.: 333310

HORIBA UK Limited (1)
Kyoto Close Moulton Park, Northampton, NN3 6FL, Northamptonshire, United Kingdom
Tel.: (44) 1604542500
Web Site: http://www.horiba.com
Electronic Components Mfr
N.A.I.C.S.: 334416

HORIBA Vietnam Company Limited (1)
Lot 3 and 4 16 Floor Detech Tower II No 107 Nguyen Phong Sac Street, Dich Vong Hau Ward Cau Giay District, Hanoi, Vietnam
Tel.: (84) 437958552
Semiconductor Product Distr
N.A.I.C.S.: 423690

Hdm Elquitecnica Cia Ltda. (1)
Av Republica de El Salvador N35-182 y Suecia, Edificio Almirante Colon 4to Piso, Quito, Ecuador
Tel.: (593) 22464076
Laboratory Services
N.A.I.C.S.: 621511

Hi-Tech Instruments Sdn Bhd (1)
19 Jalan BP 4/8, Bandar Bukit, 47120, Puchong, Selangor, Malaysia
Tel.: (60) 380612228
Web Site: http://www.htiweb.com
Surgical & Medical Instrument Mfr
N.A.I.C.S.: 339112

Hissab Lasantech Sas (1)
Moroni RP, BP 1540, Moroni, Comoros
Tel.: (269) 7739893
Surgical & Medical Instrument Mfr
N.A.I.C.S.: 339112

Horacio Icaza Y Cia, S.A. (1)
Ave Justo Arosemena y Calle 44 E Apartado, 0816-06679, Panama, Panama
Tel.: (507) 2076300
Surgical & Medical Instrument Mfr
N.A.I.C.S.: 334516

Horiba Europe GmbH (1)
Sydhamnsvagen 55-57, 15138, Sodertalje, Sweden
Tel.: (46) 855080701
Laboratory Equipment Mfr
N.A.I.C.S.: 334516

Horiba Europe GmbH (1)
Kucukbakkalkoy Mah Kayisdagi Cad Flora Residence No 3/2504, Atasehir, 34750, Istanbul, Turkiye
Tel.: (90) 2165721166
Laboratory Equipment Mfr
N.A.I.C.S.: 334516

Horiba Europe GmbH (1)
Science Park 5080, 5692 EA, Son, Netherlands
Tel.: (31) 402900240
Automotive Test System Services
N.A.I.C.S.: 541380

Horiba Precision Instruments (Beijing) Co., Ltd. (1)
Building1 No 3 Xixing Road, Houshayu Town Shun yi District, Beijing, 101318, China
Tel.: (86) 1084929402
Surgical & Medical Instrument Mfr
N.A.I.C.S.: 339112

In Vitro Technologies Pty. Ltd. (1)
7-9 Summit Road, Noble Park, 3174, VIC, Australia
Tel.: (61) 397713716
Electrical & Electronic Mfr
N.A.I.C.S.: 335999

Inscience Sdn Bhd (1)
No 11 Jalan Sungai Merbau N32/N Section 32, Kemuning Greenville, 40460, Shah Alam, Malaysia
Tel.: (60) 355258098
Web Site: http://www.inscience.com.my
Scientific Equipment Whslr
N.A.I.C.S.: 423490

Instrulabq Cia. Ltda. (1)
Rumipamba E1-35 y 10 de Agosto Edificio Vanderbilt Oficina 204, Quito, Ecuador
Tel.: (593) 23520340
Analytical Instrument Mfr
N.A.I.C.S.: 334516

Instrumed Panama, S.A. (1)
El Dorado Edificio Santa Maria Torre B-4, Panama, Panama
Tel.: (507) 8910064
Environmental Services
N.A.I.C.S.: 541620

Inter Business'91 Ltd. (1)
Keshan Str 6, 1527, Sofia, Bulgaria
Tel.: (359) 29446363
Surgical & Medical Instrument Mfr
N.A.I.C.S.: 339112

Inter Science Ltda. (1)
Av Beni Calle Quitachiyu N 76, Santa Cruz de la Sierra, Santa Cruz, Bolivia
Tel.: (591) 33421718
Web Site: http://www.is-bolivia.com
Surgical & Medical Instrument Whslr
N.A.I.C.S.: 423450

Intercovamex, S.A. De C.V. (1)
Nueva China esq Nueva Rusia s/n Rincon del Valle, 62240, Cuernavaca, Mexico
Tel.: (52) 7773114083
Environmental Services
N.A.I.C.S.: 541620

Iss International Scientific Services Co. (1)
73 Emtedad Ramses 2 Nasr City, 11471, Nasr, Cairo, Egypt
Tel.: (20) 1288894762
Laboratory Services
N.A.I.C.S.: 621511

Its Science & Medical Pte. Ltd. (1)
219 Henderson Road 11-02, Henderson Industrial Park, Singapore, 159556, Singapore
Tel.: (65) 62730898
Web Site: http://www.its-sciencemedical.com
Surgical & Medical Instrument Mfr
N.A.I.C.S.: 339112

Ivermedi Ltd. (1)
5a Nodar Bokhua street, 0159, Tbilisi, Georgia
Tel.: (995) 322530560
Surgical & Medical Instrument Mfr
N.A.I.C.S.: 339112

Js Industrial S.A.C. (1)
Av Las Nazarenas 671 Urb, Las Gardenias Surco, Lima, Peru
Tel.: (51) 14151460
Web Site: http://www.jsindustrial.com.pe
Analytical Instrument Mfr
N.A.I.C.S.: 334516

Kaika Sas (1)
Carrera 7 No 69 -53, Bogota, Colombia
Tel.: (57) 13478826
Analytical Instrument Mfr
N.A.I.C.S.: 334516

Kasai Sas (1)
Cra 72a Bis 52 - 28, Bogota, Cundinamarca, Colombia
Tel.: (57) 14161437
Analytical Instrument Mfr
N.A.I.C.S.: 334516

Keis Group (1)
Velania 2/6, 10000, Pristina, Kosovo
Tel.: (383) 38542227
Surgical & Medical Instrument Mfr
N.A.I.C.S.: 339112

Kossodo S.A.C. (1)
Jr Chota 1161, Cercado de Lima, Lima, Peru
Tel.: (51) 16198400
Web Site: http://www.store.kossodo.com
Laboratory Services
N.A.I.C.S.: 621511

Lab Depot S.A. (1)
Avenida Gregorio Escobedo 788 - 101, Lima, Peru
Tel.: (51) 14611357
Web Site: http://www.labdepot-peru.com
Laboratory Services
N.A.I.C.S.: 621511

Lab Science Solution Sdn Bhd (1)
No 27 and 27B Jalan Anggerik Aranda C31/C, Kota Kemuning, 40460, Shah Alam, Selangor, Malaysia
Tel.: (60) 351248299
Web Site: https://www.labsciencesolution.com
Scientific Equipment Whslr
N.A.I.C.S.: 423490
Kevin Law Khoon Huat *(Founder)*

Lab Top Peru S.R.L (1)
Francisco De Toledo 165, 15049, Lima, Peru
Tel.: (51) 12743414
Environmental Services
N.A.I.C.S.: 541620

Labbiotech Ltd. (1)
M Lynkova Str 27-25, 220104, Minsk, Belarus
Tel.: (375) 296238760
Electrical & Electronic Mfr
N.A.I.C.S.: 335999

Labimex Sro (1)
Pocernicka 272/96, Malesice, 108 00, Prague, Czech Republic
Tel.: (420) 241740120
Web Site: http://www.labimexcz.cz
Laboratory Services
N.A.I.C.S.: 621511

Laboratorios Arsal Sa De Cv (1)
Calle Modelo N 512, 1101, San Salvador, El Salvador
Tel.: (503) 22131398
Electrical & Electronic Mfr
N.A.I.C.S.: 335999

Labordiagnosztika Kft. (1)
Mester Utca 9 H-2112, Veresegyhaz, Budapest, Hungary
Tel.: (36) 203263671
Laboratory Services
N.A.I.C.S.: 621511

Laser Spectra Services India Pvt. Ltd. (1)
80/10 First Floor Raj Towers MS Ramaiah Main Rd, Mathikere, Bengaluru, 560 054, India
Tel.: (91) 8023576907
Web Site: http://www.laser-spectra.com
Scientific Equipment Whslr
N.A.I.C.S.: 423490

Leso Industrial Srl (1)
Avenida Jaimes Freyre N 2940, La Paz, Bolivia
Tel.: (591) 22911115
Surgical & Medical Instrument Mfr
N.A.I.C.S.: 339112

MIRA China Ltd. (1)
Unit E B1F Building A No 1068 Tianshan West Road, Synnex International Park, Shanghai, 200335, China
Tel.: (86) 2162206377
Semiconductor Product Distr
N.A.I.C.S.: 423690

Malika Farm LLP (1)
Office 17 221a/4 Raiymbek Avenue, 050016, Almaty, Kazakhstan
Tel.: (7) 7273850532
Laboratory Equipment Mfr
N.A.I.C.S.: 334516

Medicalex Sarl (1)
345 Rue Prince BELL, BP 5023, Douala, Cameroon
Tel.: (237) 233432810
Surgical & Medical Instrument Mfr
N.A.I.C.S.: 339112

Medisell Rwanda Ltd. (1)
KG 622 St Rugando Cell Kimihurura Sector, Gasabo District, Kigali, Rwanda
Tel.: (250) 788316066
Electrical & Electronic Mfr
N.A.I.C.S.: 335999

Medisell UG Ltd. (1)
Plot 560 Kyaggwe Block 120 Gedeya Estate, Mukono, Jinja, Uganda
Tel.: (256) 312311400
Electrical & Electronic Mfr
N.A.I.C.S.: 335999

Meslo Ltd. (1)
40-42 Vyzantiou Street Suite 103, Strovolos, 2064, Nicosia, Cyprus
Tel.: (357) 22666070
Web Site: http://www.meslo.com
Analytical Instrument Mfr
N.A.I.C.S.: 334516

Metron Instruments D.O.O. (1)
Zavrtnica 17, 10000, Zagreb, Croatia
Tel.: (385) 16185687
Web Site: http://www.metron-instruments.com
Surgical & Medical Instrument Mfr
N.A.I.C.S.: 339112

New-Road Agencies Ltd. (1)
11 ha'amal St Afek Business Park, Rosh Haayin, 48092, Caesarea, Israel
Tel.: (972) 39028787
Laboratory Services
N.A.I.C.S.: 621511

Nexus Analytics Sdn Bhd (1)
D12-11-3 Block D12 Pusat Perdagangan Dana 1 Jalan PJU 1A/46, 47301, Petaling Jaya, Selangor, Malaysia
Tel.: (60) 378451111
Web Site: https://www.nexus-analytics.com.my
Scientific Equipment Mfr & Whslr
N.A.I.C.S.: 334516
Nick Grantham *(Mng Dir)*

Nipro Medical Corporation (1)
Costado Este del Polideportivo de Belen, Heredia, Costa Rica
Tel.: (506) 22391246
Surgical & Medical Instrument Mfr
N.A.I.C.S.: 339112

Nipro Medical Corporation (1)
Sucursal Honduras Col 21 de Octubre, Inicio de Anillo Periferico Esquina Opuesta a Tecnica Europea, 11101, Tegucigalpa, Honduras
Tel.: (504) 22368119
Surgical & Medical Instrument Mfr
N.A.I.C.S.: 339112

Norces Equipamiento Cientifico Srl (1)
Santa Fe 2873, Rosario, Argentina
Tel.: (54) 3424555350
Surgical & Medical Instrument Mfr
N.A.I.C.S.: 339112

Normalab France Sas (1)
175 rue Claudie Haignere, BP 221, Valliquerville, 76190, Fecamp, France
Tel.: (33) 232700100
Web Site: http://www.normalab.com
Oil & Energy Distr
N.A.I.C.S.: 424720

OOO Astra - 77 (1)
5th Street Yamskogo Polya 5 blg 1, 1250 40, Moscow, Russia
Tel.: (7) 4959257759
Electrical & Electronic Mfr
N.A.I.C.S.: 335999

Omnipharma S.A.L. (1)
Badaro Str Chaoui and Sioufi Bldg, PO Box 11-7956, 7956, Beirut, Lebanon

HORIBA LTD

HORIBA Ltd—(Continued)
Tel.: (961) 1396704
Surgical & Medical Instrument Mfr
N.A.I.C.S.: 339112

PT HORIBA Indonesia (1)
Jl Jalur Sutera Blok 20A No 16-17, Kel Kunciran Kec Pinang, Tangerang, 15144, Indonesia
Tel.: (62) 2130448525
Semiconductor Product Distr
N.A.I.C.S.: 423690

PT. Besha Analitika (1)
Jl Boulevard Barat Komplek Gading Bukit Indah Blok N No 23, Kelapa Gading, Jakarta Utara, 14240, Indonesia
Tel.: (62) 2145856666
Web Site: http://www.besha-analitika.co.id
Scientific Equipment Whslr
N.A.I.C.S.: 423490

Particular Sciences Ltd. (1)
2 Birch House Rosemount Business Park Ballycoolin Road, Dublin, D11 T327, Ireland
Tel.: (353) 18205395
Web Site: http://www.particular.ie
Scientific Equipment Whslr
N.A.I.C.S.: 423490

Pensalab SA (1)
Rua Minerva 129 - Perdizes Pensalab, Sao Paulo, 05007-030, SP, Brazil
Tel.: (55) 1151808300
Web Site: http://www.pensalab.com.br
Surgical & Medical Instrument Whslr
N.A.I.C.S.: 423450

Pure Lab Tech Ltd. (1)
House-726/4 Flat-306/C Baitul Aman Housing, Adabor Mohammadpur, Dhaka, 1207, Bangladesh
Tel.: (880) 9144992
Surgical & Medical Instrument Mfr
N.A.I.C.S.: 339112

Questron Technologies Corp. (1)
6660 Kennedy Rd 14a, Mississauga, L5T 2M9, ON, Canada
Tel.: (905) 362-1225
Web Site: https://questron.ca
Metal Products Mfr
N.A.I.C.S.: 332312

Radchrom Analitica Ltda. (1)
Rua Divino Salvador 276 Nova, Paulinia, 13140-299, SP, Brazil
Tel.: (55) 1938331300
Web Site: http://www.radchrom.com.br
Electrical & Electronic Mfr
N.A.I.C.S.: 335999

Representaciones Techlab S.A.C (1)
Av Paseo de la Republica 2406, Lince, Lima, Peru
Tel.: (51) 12211333
Web Site: http://www.rptechlab.com
Laboratory Equipment Whslr
N.A.I.C.S.: 423450

S&S Ingenieria S.A.S. (1)
Calle 75C No 71A-37, Bogota, Colombia
Tel.: (57) 13108981
Web Site: http://www.sysingenieria.co
Analytical Instrument Mfr
N.A.I.C.S.: 334516

Samir Trading & Marketing - CJSC (1)
Olaya Main St Khaledia Bldg 4th Floor, PO Box 5519, 11432, Riyadh, Saudi Arabia
Tel.: (966) 14645064
Electrical & Electronic Mfr
N.A.I.C.S.: 335999

Satelit Produtos Para Laboratorios Ltda (1)
R Joao Bim 2387 - Jardim Paulistano, Ribeirao Preto, 14090 340, SP, Brazil
Tel.: (55) 1639670695
Surgical & Medical Instrument Mfr
N.A.I.C.S.: 339112

Scientific Biotech Specialties Inc. (1)
6023 Sacred Heart Cor Kamagong Sts, San Antonio, Makati, 1203, Philippines
Tel.: (63) 288244551
Web Site: http://www.sbsi.com.ph
Analytical Instrument Mfr
N.A.I.C.S.: 334516

Scientific Instruments S.A. De C.V. (1)
Calle los Abetos Pasaje No 1 Casa No 36 Col San Francisco, San Salvador, El Salvador
Tel.: (503) 25273600
Web Site: http://www.scientific.sv
Analytical Instrument Mfr

Selci S.A. De C.V. (1)
Av Isla Raza 2196 Col Jardines de San Jose, 44950, Guadalajara, Jalisco, Mexico
Tel.: (52) 3336632593
Scientific Equipment Mfr
N.A.I.C.S.: 334516

Seppim Caraibes Sa (1)
Lonja del Comercio - 1ero D Habana Vieja La, Havana, Cuba
Tel.: (53) 7801105152
Electrical & Electronic Mfr
N.A.I.C.S.: 335999

Setema Ltd. (1)
PO Box 12882, Addis Ababa, Ethiopia
Tel.: (251) 116478200
Surgical & Medical Instrument Mfr
N.A.I.C.S.: 339112

Shisas Trading Concern Pvt. Ltd. (1)
Durbar Marg Yak and Yeti Plaza Yak and Yeti Entry Road, Kathmandu, Nepal
Tel.: (977) 14233603
Surgical & Medical Instrument Mfr
N.A.I.C.S.: 334516

Sica Medicion Sa De Cv (1)
Andes 98 IV Seccion de Lomas Verdes, 53120, Naucalpan, Mexico
Tel.: (52) 5553447676
Scientific Equipment Mfr
N.A.I.C.S.: 334516

Sigmatech Inc. (1)
Block 136 Lot 1 C Arellano Street, Katarungan Village Daang Hari Brgy Poblacion, Muntinlupa, 1776, Philippines
Tel.: (63) 275015738
Web Site: http://www.sigmatech.com.ph
Laboratory Equipment Mfr
N.A.I.C.S.: 334516

Simed Cia Ltda (1)
Av Amazonas N 37-102 y Naciones Unidas Edif Puerta del Sol Piso 10, Quito, Ecuador
Tel.: (593) 22266930
Electrical & Electronic Mfr
N.A.I.C.S.: 335999

Simed Peru S.A.C. (1)
Av San Borja Sur N 594, San Borja, Lima, Peru
Tel.: (51) 14762296
Electrical & Electronic Mfr
N.A.I.C.S.: 335999

Sistemas Analiticos S.A. (1)
Calle Chituri 230 Barrio Urbari, Santa Cruz, Bolivia
Tel.: (591) 33516298
Surgical & Medical Instrument Mfr
N.A.I.C.S.: 339112

Slem Medical Sarl (1)
Sise au quartier Djambal Barth, BP 5448, N'djamena, Chad
Tel.: (235) 22525034
Surgical & Medical Instrument Mfr
N.A.I.C.S.: 339112

Sma'Lia Medical Group (1)
Palestine Post Office, PO Box 38092, Baghdad, Iraq
Tel.: (964) 65664605
Surgical & Medical Instrument Mfr
N.A.I.C.S.: 339112

Solar Laser Systems JSC (1)
4 Stebeneva Lane, Minsk, 220024, Belarus
Tel.: (375) 173479590
Web Site: http://www.solarlaser.com
Surgical & Medical Instrument Mfr
N.A.I.C.S.: 339112

Soluciones Tecnologicas Avanzadas Ltda. (1)
Roman Diaz 462, Providencia, Santiago, Chile
Tel.: (56) 11981882792
Surgical & Medical Instrument Mfr

N.A.I.C.S.: 339112

Somedib Sarl (1)
Socogim BMCi N 12, BP54, Nouakchott, Mauritania
Tel.: (222) 45254704
Surgical & Medical Instrument Mfr
N.A.I.C.S.: 339112

Specion Sro (1)
Budejovicka 1998/55, 140 00, Prague, Czech Republic
Tel.: (420) 244402091
Web Site: http://www.specion.biz
Laboratory Services
N.A.I.C.S.: 621511

Spectra Research Corporation (1)
3585 Laird Rd Unit 15 16, Mississauga, L5L 5Z8, ON, Canada
Tel.: (905) 890-0555
Web Site: https://www.spectraresearch.com
Electronic Components Distr
N.A.I.C.S.: 423690
Brian Flippance (Pres)

Sumilab S.A. (1)
Casa No 1327 Colonia Alameda Entre 11 y 12 Calle, Esquina de Cooperativa Elga, Tegucigalpa, Honduras
Tel.: (504) 22398730
Electrical & Electronic Mfr
N.A.I.C.S.: 335999

Sumilab, S.A De C.V. (1)
Blvd Enrique Cabrera 2212 Colonia Humaya, 80020, Culiacan, Sinaloa, Mexico
Tel.: (52) 6677509603
Environmental Services
N.A.I.C.S.: 541620

TCA/HORIBA Sistemas de Testes Automotivos Ltda. (1)
Avenida Luigi Papaiz 239 Campanario, Diadema, Sao Paulo, 09931-610, Brazil
Tel.: (55) 1142240200
Semiconductor Product Distr
N.A.I.C.S.: 423690

Tecfresh SAC (1)
Calle Juana Riofrio 197 Of 401, San Miguel, 15087, Lima, Peru
Tel.: (51) 13705481
Environmental Services
N.A.I.C.S.: 541620

Techni-Lab Sarl (1)
482 Avenue Soni Aliber, 10459, Niamey, Niger
Tel.: (227) 20725885
Surgical & Medical Instrument Mfr
N.A.I.C.S.: 334516

Tecnica Del Futuro S.A (1)
Avenida 59A Santa Clara San Jose, Guadalupe, Costa Rica
Tel.: (506) 22455151
Web Site: http://www.tecnicadelfuturo.com
Analytical Instrument Mfr
N.A.I.C.S.: 334516

Triolab Oy (1)
Mustionkatu 2, 20750, Turku, Finland
Tel.: (358) 201226600
Surgical & Medical Instrument Mfr
N.A.I.C.S.: 339112

Tym Medical (1)
villa 2069 Rue L 125 Alignement du Groupe Scolaire Ste Therese, BP 1320, d'Avilla Cocody 2 Plateaux - Ste Cecile 06 06, Abidjan, Cote d'Ivoire
Tel.: (225) 22528871
Electrical & Electronic Mfr
N.A.I.C.S.: 335999

Vansolix S.A (1)
Calle 23 No 116-31 / Floor 5, Puerto Central Industrial Park, Bogota, Colombia
Tel.: (57) 14222300
Web Site: http://www.vansolix.com
Environmental Services
N.A.I.C.S.: 541620

Varnavas Hadjipanayis Limited (1)
226 Giannou Kranidiotti Avenue, Latsia, 2234, Nicosia, Cyprus
Tel.: (357) 22207733
Electrical & Electronic Mfr
N.A.I.C.S.: 335999

Vi Sole Fzc (1)
C3-05/1 Saif Zone, Sharjah, United Arab Emirates
Tel.: (971) 65571772
Web Site: http://www.visole.net
Surgical & Medical Instrument Mfr
N.A.I.C.S.: 339112

Vidrieria Y Reactivos, S.A. De C.V. (1)
Asientos 401 San Jose del Arenal, 20130, Aguascalientes, Mexico
Tel.: (52) 4499135975
Analytical Instrument Mfr
N.A.I.C.S.: 334516

Vitta Scientific - Technical Company (1)
Tbilisi Avenue 129, AZ1122, Baku, Azerbaijan
Tel.: (994) 124971346
Surgical & Medical Instrument Mfr
N.A.I.C.S.: 339112

Wm Argentina Sa (1)
Calle Angel Peluffo 3944, C1202ABB, Buenos Aires, Argentina
Tel.: (54) 1149828500
Electrical & Electronic Mfr
N.A.I.C.S.: 335999

Yalitech Spa (1)
Rio Refugio 9648 Parque de negocios ENEA, Pudahuel, Santiago, Chile
Tel.: (56) 22898822
Surgical & Medical Instrument Mfr
N.A.I.C.S.: 339112

HORII FOODSERVICE CO., LTD.

3-10-17 Jonan Carney Place Mito 4th floor, Mito, 310-0803, Ibaraki, Japan
Tel.: (81) 292335825
Web Site: https://www.horiifood.co.jp
Year Founded: 1983
3077—(TKS)
Sales Range: $5-14.9 Billion
Emp.: 160
Restaurant Operators
N.A.I.C.S.: 722511
Katsumi Horii (Chm)

HORIPRO INC.

1-2-5 Shimo-Meguro, Meguro-ku, Tokyo, 153-8660, Japan
Tel.: (81) 334904601 JP
Web Site: http://www.horipro.co.jp
Year Founded: 1960
Emp.: 292
Media Production; Music, Television & Live Performance Organization
N.A.I.C.S.: 516120
Yoshitaka Hori (Pres & CEO)

HORISONT ENERGI AS

Grenseveien 21, 4313, Sandnes, Norway
Tel.: (47) 51225531
Web Site:
https://www.horisontenergi.no
Year Founded: 2019
HRGI—(OSL)
Rev.: $461,851
Assets: $24,018,464
Liabilities: $6,330,634
Net Worth: $17,687,830
Earnings: ($17,823,296)
Emp.: 36
Fiscal Year-end: 12/31/23
Carbon Product Mfr & Distr
N.A.I.C.S.: 335991
Frode A. Berntsen (Chief Legal Officer)

HORIZAL

174 Route de Lyon, Bourgoine Jallieu, 38307, Domarin, France
Tel.: (33) 474932535
Web Site: http://www.horizal.com
Rev.: $23,000,000
Emp.: 88
Fabricated Structural Metal

N.A.I.C.S.: 332312
Jean-Pierre Delanos *(Pres)*
Subsidiaries:

HORIZONTAL Unip. Lda (1)
Rua Do Paraiso N 51 Apartado N 38, Porto Longo, 2425-622, Redondo, Portugal
Tel.: (351) 244 691 625
Web Site: http://www.horizontal-lda.com
Fabricated Structural Metal Distr
N.A.I.C.S.: 423510

HORIZON CAPITAL LLP
1st Floor Brettenham House, Lancaster Place, London, WC2E 7EN, United Kingdom
Tel.: (44) 20 3436 1415   UK
Web Site: http://www.horizonpe.co.uk
Year Founded: 1999
Privater Equity Firm
N.A.I.C.S.: 523999
Jeremy Hand *(Co-Mng Partner)*
Subsidiaries:

Briefing Media Ltd. (1)
Dean Bradley House, 52 Horseferry Road, London, SW1P 2AF, United Kingdom
Tel.: (44) 207 202 0900
Web Site: http://www.briefingmedia.com
Sales Range: $10-24.9 Million
Emp.: 80
Media Publishing Services
N.A.I.C.S.: 513199
Neil Thackray *(Co-Founder & CEO)*

Carewatch Care Services Ltd. (1)
1 Queen Square, Brighton, BN1 3FD, United Kingdom   **(100%)**
Tel.: (44) 12 7320 8111
Web Site: http://www.carewatch.co.uk
Sales Range: $200-249.9 Million
Women Healthcare Services
N.A.I.C.S.: 621610
Phil Pegler *(CEO)*

Curo Care Limited (1)
First Floor Highbury Crescent Rooms 70 Ronalds Road, London, N5 1XA, United Kingdom
Tel.: (44) 1992 785 460
Web Site: http://www.curocare.co.uk
Residential Care Services
N.A.I.C.S.: 623210

Isotrak Limited (1)
36 Queensbridge Old Bedford Road, Northampton, NN4 7BF, United Kingdom
Tel.: (44) 3301112636
Web Site: http://www.isotrak.com
Fleet Management Software Development Services
N.A.I.C.S.: 541511
Jim Sumner *(Chm)*

Subsidiary (US):

Isotrak, Inc. (2)
3455 Peachtree Rd Ste 500, Atlanta, GA 30326
Tel.: (404) 995-6655
Web Site: http://www.isotrak.com
Application Software Development Services
N.A.I.C.S.: 541511
Gavin Whichello *(Chm)*

Timico Technology Group Limited (1)
Brunel Business Park Jessop Close, Newark, NG24 2AG, Nottinghamshire, United Kingdom
Tel.: (44) 844 871 8100
Web Site: http://www.timico.com
Holding Company; Cloud & Hosting, Managed Networks & Unified Communications Services
N.A.I.C.S.: 551112
Tim P. Radford *(Founder)*

Subsidiary (Domestic):

Power Internet Limited (2)
249 Midsummer Boulevard, Central, Milton Keynes, MK9 1EA, Bucks, United Kingdom
Tel.: (44) 1908605188
Web Site: http://www.powernet.co.uk
Communication Service
N.A.I.C.S.: 517810

Redwood Telecommunications Limited (2)
Brunel Business Park Jessop Close, Newark, NG24 2AG, Notts, United Kingdom
Tel.: (44) 2077381000
Communication Service
N.A.I.C.S.: 517810

Timico Limited (2)
Brunel Business Park Jessop Close, Newark, NG24 2AG, Notts, United Kingdom
Tel.: (44) 8448718100
Cloud & Hosting, Managed Networks & Unified Communications Services
N.A.I.C.S.: 517810
Neil Muller *(CEO)*

Timico Partner Services Limited (2)
Brunel Business Park, Jessop Close, Newark, NG24 2AG, Notts, United Kingdom
Tel.: (44) 844 871 8100
Communication Service
N.A.I.C.S.: 517810

UKDN Waterflow Limited (1)
17 Parkside Lane Parkside Industrial Estate, Leeds, LS11 5TD, United Kingdom
Tel.: (44) 3333442937
Web Site: http://www.ukdnwaterflow.co.uk
Drainage System Installation Services
N.A.I.C.S.: 237110
Steve Shine *(Chm)*

HORIZON CAPITAL LLP
1st Floor Brettenham House Lancaster Place, London, WC2E 7EN, United Kingdom
Tel.: (44) 2034361415
Web Site: http://www.horizonpe.co.uk
Privater Equity Firm
N.A.I.C.S.: 523940
Simon Hitchcock *(Co-Mng Partner)*
Subsidiaries:

Wireless Innovation Ltd. (1)
Unit D2 Churcham Business Park, Gloucester, GL2 8AX, Glos, United Kingdom
Tel.: (44) 1452751940
Web Site: http://www.wireless-innovation.co.uk
Digital Publisher
N.A.I.C.S.: 513199
Phil Rouse *(CEO)*

Subsidiary (US):

Ground Control Systems, Inc. (2)
3100 El Caminoreal, Atascadero, CA 93422
Tel.: (805) 783-4600
Web Site: http://www.groundcontrol.com
Radio & Television Broadcasting & Wireless Communications Equipment Mfr
N.A.I.C.S.: 334220
Jeff Staples *(Pres & CEO)*

HORIZON COPPER CORP.
1440-400 Burrard Street, Vancouver, V6C 3A6, BC, Canada
Tel.: (604) 336-8189   BC
Web Site:
https://www.horizoncopper.com
Year Founded: 2011
HCU—(TSXV)
Rev.: $4,054,000
Assets: $520,245,000
Liabilities: $514,866,000
Net Worth: $5,379,000
Earnings: ($23,682,000)
Emp.: 2
Fiscal Year-end: 12/31/23
Investment Services
N.A.I.C.S.: 523999
Justin Currie *(CEO)*

HORIZON MINERALS LIMITED
Level 2 16 Ord Street, West Perth, 6005, WA, Australia
Tel.: (61) 893869534   AU
Web Site:
https://horizonminerals.com.au
HRZ—(ASX)
Rev.: $4,631,441
Assets: $39,350,362

Liabilities: $8,451,015
Net Worth: $30,899,347
Earnings: ($2,308,692)
Fiscal Year-end: 06/30/24
Mineral Exploration Services
N.A.I.C.S.: 213114
Jonathan Price *(Bd of Dirs & Mng Dir)*
Subsidiaries:

Greenstone Resources Ltd. (1)
Ground Floor 6 Thelma Street, West Perth, 6005, WA, Australia
Tel.: (61) 894813911
Web Site:
https://greenstoneresources.com.au
Rev.: $14,266
Assets: $17,089,107
Liabilities: $487,981
Net Worth: $16,601,126
Earnings: ($1,460,107)
Emp.: 8
Fiscal Year-end: 06/30/2022
Gold Nickel & Cobalt Exploration & Production
N.A.I.C.S.: 331410

HORIZON OIL LIMITED
6 Hope St, Ermington, 2115, NSW, Australia
Tel.: (61) 88773000
Web Site:
https://www.horizonoil.com.au
HZNFF—(OTCQB)
Rev.: $111,465,000
Assets: $205,276,000
Liabilities: $122,033,000
Net Worth: $83,243,000
Earnings: $25,900,000
Emp.: 10
Fiscal Year-end: 06/30/24
Provider of Hydrocarbons
N.A.I.C.S.: 211130
Michael F. Sheridan *(CEO)*

HORIZON PETROLEUM LTD.
920 540 5th Avenue SW, Calgary, T2P 0M2, AB, Canada
Tel.: (403) 619-2957   JE
Web Site: https://www.horizon-petroleum.com
Year Founded: 1987
HPL.H—(TSXV)
Assets: $48,803
Liabilities: $2,454,967
Net Worth: ($2,406,164)
Earnings: ($66,231)
Fiscal Year-end: 08/31/21
Oil & Gas Exploration Services
N.A.I.C.S.: 211120
David A. Winter *(Pres & CEO)*

HORIZONS ALPHAPRO GARTMAN ETF
26 Wellington Street East Suite 700, Toronto, M5E 1S2, ON, Canada
Tel.: (416) 933-5745
Web Site:
http://www.horizonsetfs.com
Year Founded: 2009
Investment Fund Services
N.A.I.C.S.: 525910
Martin Fabregas *(Sr VP)*

HORIZONTAL SOFTWARE SAS
ZAC Euratechnologies 2 rue Hegel, 59160, Lomme, France
Tel.: (33) 366721280
Web Site:
http://www.horizontalsoftware.com
Sales Range: $1-9.9 Million
Human Capital Management Software Development Services
N.A.I.C.S.: 541511
Herve Yahi *(Chm & CEO)*

HORIZONTE MINERALS PLC

1 Knightsbridge Green 5th Floor, London, SW1X 7QA, United Kingdom
Tel.: (44) 2033562901
Web Site:
https://horizonteminerals.com
HZM—(AIM)
Assets: $520,240,938
Liabilities: $220,811,235
Net Worth: $299,429,703
Earnings: ($5,317,302)
Emp.: 146
Fiscal Year-end: 12/31/22
Gold & Other Metal Mining Services
N.A.I.C.S.: 212220
Jeremy John Martin *(CEO)*

HORMANN HOLDING GMBH & CO. KG
Hauptstrasse 45-47, 85614, Kirchseeon, Germany
Tel.: (49) 809156300   De
Web Site: http://www.hoermann-gruppe.de
Year Founded: 1955
Sales Range: $800-899.9 Million
Emp.: 3,500
Investment Holding Company
N.A.I.C.S.: 551112
Johann Schmid-Davis *(CFO)*
Subsidiaries:

AIC Ingenieurgesellschaft fuer Bauplanung Chemnitz GmbH (1)
Bruckenstrasse 8, 09111, Chemnitz, Germany
Tel.: (49) 3716666201
Web Site: http://www.aic-chemnitz.de
Industrial Building Construction Services
N.A.I.C.S.: 236210

Funk Werk Video Systeme GmbH (1)
Thomas-Mann-Strasse 50, 90471, Nuremberg, Germany
Tel.: (49) 911758840
Communication Equipment Mfr
N.A.I.C.S.: 334290
Christian Kaup *(Head-Product Mgmt & Mktg)*

Funkwerk AG (1)
Im Funkwerk 5, D-99625, Kolleda, Germany
Tel.: (49) 36354580
Web Site: https://www.funkwerk.com
Rev.: $172,479,688
Assets: $170,338,180
Liabilities: $71,961,285
Net Worth: $98,376,894
Earnings: $19,107,990
Emp.: 585
Fiscal Year-end: 12/31/2023
Mobile Communication Systems Mfr
N.A.I.C.S.: 334220
Kerstin Schreiber *(Member-Exec Bd)*

Subsidiary (Domestic):

Funkwerk plettac electronic GmbH (2)
Wurzburger Strasse 150, 90766, Furth, Germany
Tel.: (49) 911758840
Web Site: http://www.plettac-electronics.de
Sales Range: $75-99.9 Million
Emp.: 120
Mfr of Mobile Communication Systems
N.A.I.C.S.: 334220

Funkwerk IoT GmbH (1)
Konsul-Smidt-Strasse 8L, 28217, Bremen, Germany
Tel.: (49) 42117667900
Communication Equipment Mfr
N.A.I.C.S.: 334290
Arne Jurgens *(Product Mgr)*

Funkwerk Security Communications GmbH (1)
Windmuhlenbergstr 20-22, 38259, Salzgitter, Germany
Tel.: (49) 534122350
Web Site: http://www.funkwerk-sc.com
Electric Equipment Mfr
N.A.I.C.S.: 334416

HORMANN HOLDING GMBH & CO. KG

Hormann Holding GmbH & Co. KG—(Continued)

Funkwerk Technologies GmbH (1)
Im Funkwerk 9, 99625, Kolleda, Germany
Tel.: (49) 36354133070
Communication Equipment Mfr
N.A.I.C.S.: 334290

Hormann Automationsservice GmbH (1)
Watenstedter Str 6, 38239, Salzgitter, Germany
Tel.: (49) 534189890
Engineeering Services
N.A.I.C.S.: 541330
Gerhard Jacobi (Mng Dir)

Hormann Automotive Bielefeld GmbH (1)
Sudring 90, 33647, Bielefeld, Germany
Tel.: (49) 521404260
Web Site: http://www.bielefeld.hoermann-automotive.com
Welding Machinery Mfr
N.A.I.C.S.: 333992

Hormann Automotive Eislingen GmbH (1)
Hans-Zinser-Strasse 1-3, 73061, Ebersbach, Germany
Tel.: (49) 7163165100
Web Site: http://www.ebersbach.hoermann-automotive.com
Industrial Machinery Mfr
N.A.I.C.S.: 333998
Rudolf Ostwald (Mng Dir)

Hormann Automotive GmbH (1)
Hauptstrasse 45-47Å, 85614, Kirchseeon, Germany
Tel.: (49) 809156300
Web Site: http://www.hoermann-automotive.com
Automotive Vehicle Component Distr
N.A.I.C.S.: 423120
Thomas Vetter (Mng Dir)

Hormann Automotive Gustavsburg GmbH (1)
Ginsheimer Str 2, 65462, Ginsheim, Germany
Tel.: (49) 61345880
Web Site: http://www.gustavsburg.hoermann-automotive.com
Industrial Machinery Mfr
N.A.I.C.S.: 333998

Hormann Automotive Penzberg GmbH (1)
Seeshaupter Strasse 70, 82377, Penzberg, Germany
Tel.: (49) 88568120
Web Site: http://www.penzberg.hoermann-automotive.com
Industrial Machinery Mfr
N.A.I.C.S.: 333998
Sabine Drizisga (Mng Dir)

Hormann Automotive Saarbrucken GmbH (1)
Am Stahlhammer 65, 66121, Saarbrucken, Germany
Tel.: (49) 681819080
Web Site: http://www.saarbruecken.hoermann-automotive.com
Emp.: 100
Industrial Machinery Mfr
N.A.I.C.S.: 333998

Hormann Automotive Slovakia s.r.o. (1)
Partizanska 73, 975 01, Banovce nad Bebravou, Slovakia
Tel.: (421) 383213800
Emp.: 200
Rolled Coil Sheet Mfr
N.A.I.C.S.: 331221
Pavel Roskos (Mng Dir)

Hormann Automotive St. Wendel GmbH (1)
Essener Str 3, 66606, Sankt Wendel, Germany
Tel.: (49) 68518005300
Web Site: http://www.stwendel.hoermann-automotive.com
Emp.: 180

Industrial Machinery Mfr
N.A.I.C.S.: 333998

Hormann Automotive Wackersdorf GmbH (1)
Arthur-B -Modine Str 2, 92442, Wackersdorf, Germany
Tel.: (49) 943174930
Web Site: http://www.wackersdorf.hoermann-automotive.com
Industrial Machinery Mfr
N.A.I.C.S.: 333998
Marcus Schaffranka (Mng Dir)

Hormann Industrieservice GmbH (1)
Burgstadter Strasse 25, 09114, Chemnitz, Germany
Tel.: (49) 37126796310
Web Site: http://www.hoermann-industrieservice.de
Mechanical Engineering Services
N.A.I.C.S.: 541330

Hormann KMT Kommunikations- und Meldetechnik GmbH (1)
Eugen-Muller-Strasse 14, 5020, Salzburg, Austria
Tel.: (43) 6624293720
Web Site: http://www.hoermann-kmt.at
Radio Equipment Rental Services
N.A.I.C.S.: 532490

Hormann Kommunikatinsnetzte GmbH (1)
Hauptstr 45 - 47, 85614, Kirchseeon, Germany
Tel.: (49) 809152173
Web Site: http://www.hoermann-kn.de
Engineering Consulting Services
N.A.I.C.S.: 541330
Johannes Antoni (Mng Dir)

Hormann Logistik GmbH (1)
Gneisenaustrasse 15, 80992, Munich, Germany
Tel.: (49) 891498980
Web Site: http://www.hoermann-logistik.de
Logistics & Warehousing Services
N.A.I.C.S.: 541614
Steffen Dieterich (Mng Dir & Head-Sls)

Hormann Rawema Engineering & Consulting GmbH (1)
Bruckenstrasse 8, 09111, Chemnitz, Germany
Tel.: (49) 3716512379
Web Site: http://www.hoermann-rawema.de
Engineeering Services
N.A.I.C.S.: 541330
Holger Fussel (Mng Dir)

Hormann Vehicle Engineering GmbH (1)
Aue 23-27, 09112, Chemnitz, Germany
Tel.: (49) 37166653100
Web Site: http://www.hoermann-engineering.de
Automotive Vehicle Component Mfr
N.A.I.C.S.: 336390
Upendra Kumar (Engr-Calculation)

Hormann Warnsysteme GmbH (1)
Hauptstrasse 45-47, 85614, Kirchseeon, Germany
Tel.: (49) 80915630300
Web Site: http://www.hoermann-ws.de
Emp.: 110
Commercial & Industrial Equipment Distr
N.A.I.C.S.: 423830
Matthias Mullner (Mng Dir)

Klatt Fordertechnik GmbH (1)
Kostendorferstrasse 7A, Neumarkt am Wallersee, 5202, Salzburg, Austria
Tel.: (43) 6216200200
Web Site: http://www.klatt.at
Container Conveyor Equipment Mfr
N.A.I.C.S.: 333922

MAT Maschinentechnik GmbH (1)
Carl-Zeiss-Weg 7, 38239, Salzgitter, Germany
Tel.: (49) 5341898940
Engineeering Services
N.A.I.C.S.: 541330
Gerhard Jacobi (Mng Dir)

VacuTec Messtechnik GmbH (1)

Dornbluthstrasse 14, 01277, Dresden, Germany
Tel.: (49) 351317240
Web Site: http://www.vacutec-gmbh.de
Healthcare Equipment Mfr & Distr
N.A.I.C.S.: 334510

HORMANN KG VERKAUFSGE-SELLSCHAF

Upheider Weg 94-98, 33803, Steinhagen, Germany
Tel.: (49) 5204 915 0
Web Site: http://www.hoermann.com
Sales Range: $1-4.9 Billion
Emp.: 6,000
Door Mfr
N.A.I.C.S.: 332321
Thomas J. Hormann (Co-Founder)

Subsidiaries:

ALUKON KG (1)
Munchberger Strasse 31, 95176, Konradsreuth, Germany
Tel.: (49) 92 92 950 0
Web Site: http://www.alukon.com
Door Mfr
N.A.I.C.S.: 332321

Berner EazyMatic AG (1)
Mellingerstrasse 19, 5413, Birmenstorf, Switzerland
Tel.: (41) 627940044
Web Site: http://www.eazymatic-torantriebe.ch
Garage Door Drive & Track Mfr
N.A.I.C.S.: 334419

Berner Torantriebe KG (1)
Graf-Bentzel-Str 68, 72108, Rottenburg am Neckar, Germany
Tel.: (49) 7472 9812 0
Web Site: http://www.berner-torantriebe.de
Door Mfr
N.A.I.C.S.: 332321
Frank Kiefer (Mng Dir)

Garador Ltd. (1)
Bunford Lane, Yeovil, BA20 2EJ, United Kingdom
Tel.: (44) 1935 443722
Web Site: http://www.garador.co.uk
Emp.: 120
Garage Door Mfr
N.A.I.C.S.: 332321
Roy Sargant (Mgr-Natl Sls)

HORMANN KAZAKHSTAN LLP (1)
Furmanov Str 65 Office 206, 050004, Almaty, Kazakhstan
Tel.: (7) 727 321 63 17
Web Site: http://www.hormann.kz
Door Mfr
N.A.I.C.S.: 332321

HORMANN MEXICO, S.A. DE C.V (1)
Privada La Puerta 2879 B-14 Colonia Industrial La Pue, 66350, Santa Catarina, Mexico
Tel.: (52) 81 83087481
Web Site: http://www.hormann.com.mx
Door Mfr
N.A.I.C.S.: 332321

HORMANN Serbia (1)
Udarnih desetina 32, 11271, Belgrade, Surcin, Serbia
Tel.: (381) 11 8440 800
Web Site: http://www.hormann.rs
Door Mfr
N.A.I.C.S.: 332321
Igor Albunovic (Exec Mgr-Sls)

Hermann Automation GmbH (1)
Erlenwiese 15, 35794, Mengerskirchen, Germany
Tel.: (49) 647691400
Web Site: http://www.hermann-automation.de
Parking Space Management Services
N.A.I.C.S.: 812930

Hoermann (HK) Limited (1)
Unit 2401 24/F DCH Commercial Centre 25 Westlands Road, Quarry Bay, China (Hong Kong)
Tel.: (852) 2907 9999
Web Site: http://www.hoermann.cn

INTERNATIONAL PUBLIC

Door Mfr
N.A.I.C.S.: 332321
Eddie Kwan (Mgr-Sls)

Hormann (UK) Limited (1)
Gee Road, Coalville, LE67 4JW, Leicestershire, United Kingdom
Tel.: (44) 1530 513000
Web Site: http://www.hormann.co.uk
Emp.: 100
Door Mfr
N.A.I.C.S.: 332321
Paul Eadie (Dir-Fin)

Hormann Alkmaar B.V. (1)
Robbenkoog 20, 1822BB, Alkmaar, Netherlands
Tel.: (31) 72 5624444
Door Mfr
N.A.I.C.S.: 332321

Hormann Baltic, UAB (1)
Budninku k 2 Maisiagalos sen, 14247, Vilnius, Rajonas, Lithuania
Tel.: (370) 69088666
Web Site: http://www.hormann.lt
Door Mfr
N.A.I.C.S.: 332321
Julija Astasova (Mgr-Mktg)

Hormann Beijing Door Production Co. Ltd. (1)
No 13 Zhong He Street BDA, Beijing, 100176, China
Tel.: (86) 10 6788 8371
Web Site: http://www.hoermann.cn
Door Mfr
N.A.I.C.S.: 332321
Dirk Fell (Mng Dir-Asia Pacific)

Hormann Belgium NV/SA (1)
Vrijheidweg 13, 3700, Tongeren, Belgium
Tel.: (32) 12 399 222
Web Site: http://www.hormann.be
Door Mfr
N.A.I.C.S.: 332321

Hormann Brasil Portas Ltda (1)
Rua Artico n 415 Condominio Industrial Granja Viana, 06707 070, Cotia, Brazil
Tel.: (55) 11 3995 4210
Web Site: http://www.hormann.com.br
Door Mfr
N.A.I.C.S.: 332321
Flavio Pinto (Gen Mgr)

Hormann Ceska republika s.r.o. (1)
Stredokluky 315, 252 68, Stredokluky, Czech Republic
Tel.: (420) 233 085 770
Web Site: http://www.hormann.cz
Door Mfr
N.A.I.C.S.: 332321

Hormann Changshu Door Production Co. Ltd. (1)
No 32 Dongzhang Lecheng Road Bixi Street, Changshu, Jiangsu, China
Tel.: (86) 51252158000
Door Mfr
N.A.I.C.S.: 321911

Hormann Danmark AS (1)
Normansvej 6, 8920, Randers, NV Randers, Denmark
Tel.: (45) 86437222
Web Site: http://www.hoermann.dk
Door Mfr
N.A.I.C.S.: 332321

Hormann Doors Malaysia Sdn Bhd (1)
No 22 Jalan Ruang U8/109 Jelutong Prime, Bukit Jelutong, 40150, Shah Alam, Selangor, Malaysia
Tel.: (60) 3 7859 8088
Web Site: http://www.hormann.com.my
Door Mfr
N.A.I.C.S.: 332321
Jason Tan (Gen Mgr)

Hormann Eesti OU (1)
Tule 21, 76505, Saue, Eesti, Estonia
Tel.: (372) 6 105 086
Web Site: http://www.hormann.ee
Door Mfr
N.A.I.C.S.: 332321

Hormann Espana, S.A. (1)
Carretera de Rubi 324 C, 08228, Terrassa, Barcelona, Spain

AND PRIVATE COMPANIES

Tel.: (34) 93 721 69 70
Web Site: http://www.hormann.es
Door Mfr
N.A.I.C.S.: 332321

Hormann Flexon, LLC (1)
Buncher Commerce Park Ave C Bldg 20 A,
Leetsdale, PA 15056
Tel.: (412) 749-0400
Web Site: http://www.hormann-flexon.com
Sales Range: $25-49.9 Million
Emp.: 40
Metal Door Mfr
N.A.I.C.S.: 332321
M. Permigiani *(VP)*

Hormann France S.A. (1)
7 Rue des Salcys Zone Industrielle Gron,
89100, Gron, France
Tel.: (33) 386862500
Web Site: http://www.hormann.fr
Door Mfr
N.A.I.C.S.: 332321

Hormann Hellas Ltd (1)
30 AG Marinas, 19400, Koropi, Greece
Tel.: (30) 210 662 8640
Emp.: 4
Door Mfr
N.A.I.C.S.: 332321
Alexander Parissis *(CEO)*

Hormann Hrvatska d.o.o. (1)
Nova cesta 50, 10000, Zagreb, Croatia
Tel.: (385) 1 3689 800
Web Site: http://www.hormann.hr
Door Mfr
N.A.I.C.S.: 332321
Marina Jovisic *(Product Mgr-Indus Doors)*

Hormann Hungaria Kft. (1)
Leshegy ut 15, 2310, Szigetszentmiklos,
Hungary
Tel.: (36) 24525100
Web Site: http://www.hormann.hu
Door Mfr
N.A.I.C.S.: 332321
Istvan Pataki *(CFO)*

Hormann Italia S.r.l. (1)
Via G Di Vittorio 62, 38015, Lavis, Trentino,
Italy
Tel.: (39) 0461 244444
Web Site: http://www.hormann.it
Door Mfr
N.A.I.C.S.: 332321

Hormann LLC (1)
5050 Baseline Rd, Montgomery, IL 60538
Tel.: (877) 654-6762
Web Site: http://www.hormann.us
Door Mfr
N.A.I.C.S.: 332321
Michael Adam *(Sr Mgr-Pur)*

Hormann Legnica SP. ZO.O (1)
ul Osla 1C, 59-706, Gromadka, Poland
Tel.: (48) 75 784 00 00
Door Mfr
N.A.I.C.S.: 332311

Hormann Maroc SARL (1)
Secteur 6 Bloc G N 10 Rue Kadib Addahab,
10100, Rabat, Morocco
Tel.: (212) 537 717 757
Web Site: http://www.hormann.ma
Door Mfr
N.A.I.C.S.: 332321

Hormann Middle East FZE (1)
Showroom No S3A1SR05, PO Box 262784,
Jebel Ali Freezone South, Dubai, United
Arab Emirates
Tel.: (971) 48 80 76 77
Web Site: http://www.hoermann.ae
Door Mfr
N.A.I.C.S.: 332321
Darius Khanloo *(Mng Dir-Middle East & Africa)*

Hormann Nederland B.V. (1)
Harselaarseweg 90, 3771 MB, Barneveld,
Netherlands
Tel.: (31) 342 429400
Web Site: http://www.hormann.nl
Door Mfr
N.A.I.C.S.: 332321
Peter Stoop *(Mng Dir)*

Hormann Norge AS (1)
Ostre Lohnelier 75, 4640, Sogne, Norway
Tel.: (47) 380 32910
Web Site: http://www.hoermann.no
Door Mfr
N.A.I.C.S.: 332321

Hormann Oensingen AG (1)
Nordringstrasse 14, 4702, Oensingen, Switzerland
Tel.: (41) 623886060
Web Site: http://www.hoermann.ch
Wood Door Mfr
N.A.I.C.S.: 321911
Daniel Friedrich *(Product Mgr)*

Hormann Polska Sp. z o.o. (1)
ul Otwarta 1, 62-052, Komorniki, Poland
Tel.: (48) 61 81 97 300
Web Site: http://www.hormann.pl
Door Mfr
N.A.I.C.S.: 332321

Hormann Portugal, Lda. (1)
Rua Tapada Nova Centro Empresarial
Sintra-Estoril VII - C1, Linho, 2710-297, Sintra, Portugal
Tel.: (351) 21 910 88 30
Web Site: http://www.hormann.pt
Emp.: 15
Door Mfr
N.A.I.C.S.: 332321
Henrique Lehrfeld *(CEO)*

Hormann Romania SRL (1)
Str Complexului Nr 15 Sat, 077040,
Chiajna, Ilfov, Romania
Tel.: (40) 213075430
Web Site: http://www.hormann.ro
Door Mfr
N.A.I.C.S.: 332321

Hormann Schweiz AG (1)
Nordringstrasse 14, Oensingen, 4702, Switzerland
Tel.: (41) 848 463 762
Web Site: http://www.hoermann.ch
Door Mfr
N.A.I.C.S.: 332321
Roland Steiner *(Acct Mgr)*

Hormann Slovenska republika s.r.o. (1)
Pestovatelska 1, 821 04, Bratislava, Slovakia
Tel.: (421) 2 48 20 10 71
Web Site: http://www.hormann.sk
Door Mfr
N.A.I.C.S.: 332321
Jan Bombara *(Mgr-Warehouse)*

Hormann Svenska AB (1)
Skjutbanevagen 10, 703 69, Orebro, Sweden
Tel.: (46) 101900200
Web Site: http://www.hoermann.se
Door Mfr
N.A.I.C.S.: 332321
Per Wetterdahl *(CEO)*

Hormann Tianjin Door Production Co. Ltd. (1)
Floor 8 North of Huaqiao Chuangye Building No10 Jinping Road, Nankai Industrial Park Nankai District, Tianjin, China
Tel.: (86) 88356288
Door Mfr
N.A.I.C.S.: 321911

Hormann Yapi Elemanlari Tic. Ltd. Sti. (1)
Aydinlar Mahallesi Genclik Caddesi No 52/A, Tasdelen Cekmekoy, 34788, Istanbul, Turkiye
Tel.: (90) 216 484 44 61
Web Site: http://www.hoermann.com.tr
Door Mfr
N.A.I.C.S.: 332321

Huga KG (1)
Osnabrucker Landstrasse 139, 33335, Gutersloh, Germany
Tel.: (49) 52419730
Web Site: http://www.huga.de
Wood Door Mfr
N.A.I.C.S.: 321911

IG Doors Ltd. (1)
Lon Gellideg Oakdale Business Park,
Blackwood, NP12 4AE, United Kingdom
Tel.: (44) 1495368200
Web Site: http://www.igdoors.co.uk

Door Mfr
N.A.I.C.S.: 332321

Maviflex SAS (1)
8-14 rue Vaucanson, 69150, Decines-
Charpieu, France
Tel.: (33) 472158888
Web Site: http://www.maviflex.com
Door Mfr
N.A.I.C.S.: 321911
Christophe Gontier *(Sls Mgr)*

Pilomat s.r.l. (1)
Via Zanica 17/P, 24050, Grassobbio, Italy
Tel.: (39) 035297220
Web Site: http://www.pilomat.com
Automatic Bollard Mfr
N.A.I.C.S.: 334512
Alessandra Acerbis *(Dir-Export)*

SC Electronic Service GmbH (1)
Planckstrasse 10, 32052, Herford, Germany
Tel.: (49) 5221122510
Web Site: http://www.sc-electronic.de
Electronic Product Services
N.A.I.C.S.: 811210

Schorghuber Spezialturen KG (1)
Neuhaus 3, Ampfing, 84539, Muhldorf, Germany
Tel.: (49) 86365030
Web Site: http://www.schoerghuber.de
Wood Door Mfr
N.A.I.C.S.: 321911
Matthias Goerres *(Dir-Export)*

Seuster KG (1)
Tietmecker Weg 1, 58513, Ludenscheid, Germany
Tel.: (49) 23519950
Web Site: http://www.seuster.de
Door Mfr
N.A.I.C.S.: 321911

Shakti Hormann Private Limited (1)
No 20 Sripuri Colony, Karkhana, Secunderabad, 500 015, Telangana, India
Tel.: (91) 40 39836800
Web Site: http://www.shaktihormann.com
Door Mfr
N.A.I.C.S.: 332321
N. V. S. Ranga Rao *(Gen Mgr-Mfg Ops)*

TNR Industrial Doors Inc. (1)
200 Fairview Road Unit 2, Barrie, L4N 8X8, ON, Canada
Tel.: (705) 792-9968
Web Site: https://www.tnrdoors.com
Door Mfr
N.A.I.C.S.: 321911

TUBAUTO S.A.S. (1)
7 rue des Salcys, BP 711, Zone Industrielle de Gron, 89107, Sens, France
Tel.: (33) 3 8664 8585
Web Site: http://www.tubauto.fr
Garage Door Mfr
N.A.I.C.S.: 332321

Tortec Brandschutztor GmbH (1)
Imling 10, 4902, Vocklabruck, Austria
Tel.: (43) 7676 6060 0
Web Site: http://www.tortec.at
Emp.: 200
Door Mfr
N.A.I.C.S.: 332321
Martin Biehl *(Mng Dir)*

HORMOZGAN CEMENT CO.
No 37 after Mina Sq Behrooz St Mirdamad Blvd, 1911773183, Tehran, Iran
Tel.: (98) 2122904985
Web Site: https://www.hormozgancement.com
Year Founded: 1936
SHZG—(THE)
Sales Range: Less than $1 Million
Cement Mfr
N.A.I.C.S.: 327310
Mahdi Bashti *(Mng Dir-Acting)*

HORNBACH HOLDING AG & CO. KGAA
Le Quartier Hornbach 19, 67433, Neustadt, Germany
Tel.: (49) 63216780

Web Site: http://www.hornbach-holding.de
Rev.: $4,960,326,281
Assets: $3,195,509,561
Liabilities: $1,443,131,418
Net Worth: $1,752,378,143
Earnings: $114,691,501
Emp.: 16,223
Fiscal Year-end: 02/28/18
Garden & Home Products Sales
N.A.I.C.S.: 333112
Albrecht Hornbach *(Chm-Mgmt Bd)*

Subsidiaries:

Bodenhaus GmbH (1)
In der Windblase 1, 76879, Essingen, Germany
Tel.: (49) 6348604340
Web Site: http://www.bodenhaus.de
Flooring Product Retailer
N.A.I.C.S.: 449121

Etablissements Camille Holtz et Cie S.A. (1)
Rue Du Champ De Mars, 57370, Phalsbourg, Moselle, France
Tel.: (33) 387030310
Home Improvement Services
N.A.I.C.S.: 236118
Blaser Freddy *(Mng Dir)*

HIAG Immobilien Beta GmbH (1)
Hornbachstrasse 13, 76879, Bornheim,
North Rhine-Westphal, Germany
Tel.: (49) 6348 9839 0
Web Site: http://www.hornbach.de
Real Estate Property Management Services
N.A.I.C.S.: 531312

HIAG Immobilien Delta GmbH (1)
Hornbachstr 11, 76879, Bornheim, North
Rhine-Westphal, Germany
Tel.: (49) 63 4860 00
Web Site: http://www.hornbach.de
Real Estate Property Development Services
N.A.I.C.S.: 531210

HORNBACH Baumarkt AG (1)
Hornbachstrasse 11, 76878, Bornheim,
Germany **(76.4%)**
Tel.: (49) 63486000
Web Site: https://www.hornbach.com
Rev.: $6,750,512,669
Assets: $5,016,568,185
Liabilities: $3,251,550,458
Net Worth: $1,765,017,727
Earnings: $232,068,579
Emp.: 18,971
Fiscal Year-end: 02/28/2022
Farm Equipment Distr
N.A.I.C.S.: 423820
Erich Harsch *(Chm-Mgmt Bd & CEO)*

HORNBACH Baustoff Union GmbH (1)
Le Quartier Hornbach 19, Neustadt, 67433,
Rhineland-Palatinate, Germany
Tel.: (49) 63216789000
Web Site: http://www.hornbach-baustoff-union.de
Sales Range: $25-49.9 Million
Emp.: 40
Civil Engineering Services
N.A.I.C.S.: 541330
Albrecht Hornbach *(Mng Dir)*

HORNBACH Centrala SRL (1)
Hornbach Street no 17 - 21, Domnesti Ilfov,
Bucharest, 077090, Romania
Tel.: (40) 212061530
Web Site: http://www.hornbach.ro
Construction Building Material Distr
N.A.I.C.S.: 444180
Roxana Chiribelea Oniga *(Mgr-Pur Electrical & Lighting Dept)*

HORNBACH Immobilien AG (1)
Le Quartier Hornbach 19, 67433, Neustadt,
Rhineland-Palatinate, Germany
Tel.: (49) 63216789394
Real Estate Property Development Services
N.A.I.C.S.: 531390

HR Immobilien Rho GmbH (1)
IZ No Sud Str 3 Obj 64, 2355, Wiener Neudorf, Lower Austria, Austria
Tel.: (43) 2236 31 480
Real Estate Management

HORNBACH HOLDING AG & CO. KGaA

Hornbach Holding AG & Co. KGaA—(Continued)
N.A.I.C.S.: 531390

Hornbach Baumarkt (Schweiz) AG (1)
Schellenrain 9, 6210, Sursee, Switzerland
Tel.: (41) 419296499
Web Site: http://www.hornbach.ch
Construction Building Material Distr
N.A.I.C.S.: 444180

Hornbach Baumarkt CS spol s.r.o. (1)
Chlumecka 2398, 198 98, Prague, Czech Republic
Tel.: (420) 225356000
Web Site: http://www.hornbach.cz
Hardware Paint & Glass Retailer
N.A.I.C.S.: 444180
Marketa Subrtova *(Product Mgr)*

Hornbach Baumarkt Luxemburg SARL (1)
rue du Puits Romain 43, 8070, Bertrange, Luxembourg
Tel.: (352) 3166551
Web Site: http://www.hornbach.lu
Home Improvement Product Retailer
N.A.I.C.S.: 444110

Hornbach Bouwmarkt (Nederland) B.V. (1)
Grootslag 1-5, 3991 RA, Houten, Netherlands
Tel.: (31) 302669898
Web Site: http://www.hornbach.nl
Construction Building Material Distr
N.A.I.C.S.: 444180

Robert Rohlinger GmbH (1)
Gewerbegebiet Klinkenthal 7, 66578, Schiffweiler, Saarland, Germany
Tel.: (49) 682196070
Construction Materials Whslr
N.A.I.C.S.: 423320

Ruhland-Kallenborn & Co. GmbH (1)
Le Quartier-Hornbach 11, 67433, Neustadt, Germany
Tel.: (49) 63216780
Web Site: http://www.hornbach.de
Sales Range: $25-49.9 Million
Emp.: 30
Construction Materials Whslr
N.A.I.C.S.: 423610

Union Bauzentrum Hornbach GmbH (1)
Le Quartier Hornbach 19, 67433, Neustadt, Germany
Tel.: (49) 63216789000
Sales Range: $50-74.9 Million
Emp.: 65
Construction Materials Whslr
N.A.I.C.S.: 423390
Joachim Schoeck *(Mng Dir)*

HORNBY BAY MINERAL EXPLORATION LTD.
217 Queen Street West Suite 401, Toronto, M5V 0R2, ON, Canada
Tel.: (416) 361-2515
Web Site: http://www.hornbybay.com
Year Founded: 1996
FOXG—(TSXV)
Assets: $593,685
Liabilities: $2,046,252
Net Worth: ($1,452,567)
Earnings: ($2,550,240)
Fiscal Year-end: 03/31/23
Mineral Exploration Services
N.A.I.C.S.: 213114
Frederic W. R. Leigh *(Pres & CEO)*

HORNG SHIUE HOLDING CO., LTD.
201611 Chedun Rong Chang Road 100, Songjiang District, Shanghai, China
Tel.: (86) 2157609158
2243—(TAI)
Rev.: $58,754,911
Assets: $109,878,416
Liabilities: $82,435,628
Net Worth: $27,442,788
Earnings: ($4,358,510)
Fiscal Year-end: 12/31/19
Holding Company
N.A.I.C.S.: 551112
Wei-Yuan Lin *(Chm & Pres)*

HORNG TONG ENTERPRISE CO., LTD.
3F-7-8 No 8 Sec 1 Zhongxing Rd, Wugu Dist, New Taipei City, 248, Taiwan
Tel.: (886) 289769168
Web Site:
  https://www.hometom.com.tw
Year Founded: 1998
5271—(TAI)
Electronic Components Mfr
N.A.I.C.S.: 334419
San-Chi Yu *(VP)*

HORRISON RESOURCES INC.
Unit L 16FL MG Tower 133 Hoi Bun Road, Kowloon, 999077, China (Hong Kong)
Tel.: (852) 60194383333
Year Founded: 2000
HRSR—(OTCIQ)
Sales Range: Less than $1 Million
Lubricating Oil Research
N.A.I.C.S.: 324191
Yap Nee Seng *(Chm, Pres & CEO)*

HORSAM AB
Box 603, SE 194 26, Upplands Vasby, Sweden
Tel.: (46) 859000460
Web Site: http://www.licaudio.se
Sales Range: $10-24.9 Million
Emp.: 10
Hospital Equipments Mfr
N.A.I.C.S.: 339113
Kjell Alenius *(Mng Dir)*

HORSESHOE METALS LIMITED
Tel.: (61) 862411844
Web Site:
  https://www.horseshoemetals.com
Assets: $5,235,403
Liabilities: $6,203,426
Net Worth: ($968,023)
Earnings: ($1,893,699)
Emp.: 6
Fiscal Year-end: 12/31/17
Copper & Gold Exploration Services
N.A.I.C.S.: 212230
Carol New *(Co-Sec)*

HORST WELLNESS GMBH & CO. KG
Meerpfad 27-31, 56566, Neuwied, Germany
Tel.: (49) 263186079940
Web Site:
  http://www.duschkabine.com
Holding Company
N.A.I.C.S.: 551112

Subsidiaries:

Breuer GmbH (1)
Industrial Area Block Meerpfad 27-31, 56566, Neuwied, Germany
Tel.: (49) 263186079940
Web Site: http://www.duschkabine.com
Sales Range: $25-49.9 Million
Emp.: 100
Shower Enclosures Mfr
N.A.I.C.S.: 332999

HORTICASH PLANTES
Rue Des Brunelleries, Bouchemaine, Angers, 49080, Maine Et Loire, France
Tel.: (33) 241721172

Web Site: http://www.horticash.com
Year Founded: 1954
Sales Range: $10-24.9 Million
Emp.: 37
Fruit Distr
N.A.I.C.S.: 424480
Gilbert Baudet *(Dir-Admin)*

HORTIFRUT SA
Avenida del Condor 600 Piso 4 Ciudad Empresarial, Huechuraba, Santiago, Chile
Tel.: (56) 24792600
Web Site: http://www.hortifrut.com
Year Founded: 1983
HF—(SGO)
Rev.: $1,016,838,000
Assets: $1,945,271,000
Liabilities: $1,217,478,000
Net Worth: $727,793,000
Earnings: $12,999,000
Emp.: 2,645
Fiscal Year-end: 12/31/23
Fresh Fruit Mfr
N.A.I.C.S.: 311421
Felipe Juillerat Munoz *(Chief Comml Officer)*

HORVIK LIMITED
36 Ayias Elenis Street Galaxias Commercial Centre, 4th floor office/flat 403, 1061, Nicosia, Cyprus
Web Site: http://horviklimited.com
Financial Conglomerates
N.A.I.C.S.: 523999

Subsidiaries:

Trans-Siberian Gold plc (1)
PO Box 278, Saint Neots, PE19 9EA, United Kingdom (51.2%)
Tel.: (44) 1480811871
Web Site: http://www.trans-siberiangold.com
Rev.: $63,108,000
Assets: $117,318,000
Liabilities: $39,078,000
Net Worth: $78,240,000
Earnings: $9,006,000
Emp.: 699
Fiscal Year-end: 12/31/2019
Gold Mining Services
N.A.I.C.S.: 212220
Alexander Dorogov *(CEO)*

Subsidiary (Non-US):

Trans-Siberian Gold Management, LLC (2)
10 Bolshava Tulskaya Street Building 3, Moscow, 115191, Russia
Tel.: (7) 495 232 3777
Web Site: http://www.Transsiberiangold.com
Emp.: 50
Gold Mining Services
N.A.I.C.S.: 212220

HOSA INTERNATIONAL LIMITED
Room 1902 19/F Far East Finance Centre, 16 Harcourt Road, Beijing, China
Tel.: (86) 1059101888
Web Site: http://www.hosa.cn
Rev.: $184,070,980
Assets: $465,040,455
Liabilities: $152,941,174
Net Worth: $312,099,281
Earnings: $37,853,760
Emp.: 1,300
Fiscal Year-end: 12/31/17
Swimwear, Fitness Wear, Sports Underwear & Accessories Mfr
N.A.I.C.S.: 315250
Hongliu Shi *(Chm)*

HOSEN GROUP LTD
267 Pandan Loop, Singapore, 128439, Singapore
Tel.: (65) 65959222
Web Site:
  https://www.hosengroup.com

INTERNATIONAL PUBLIC

5EV—(CAT)
Rev.: $50,970,991
Assets: $39,776,566
Liabilities: $14,444,444
Net Worth: $25,332,121
Earnings: $733,167
Emp.: 173
Fiscal Year-end: 12/31/23
Processed Food Distr
N.A.I.C.S.: 424490
Hai Cheok Lim *(Founder & CEO)*

Subsidiaries:

Hock Seng Food Pte Ltd (1)
267 Pandan Loop, Singapore, 128439, Singapore
Tel.: (65) 6 595 9222
Web Site: https://www.hosen.com.sg
Emp.: 50
Canned Food Distr
N.A.I.C.S.: 424490

Subsidiary (Non-US):

Hock Seng Food (M) Sdn Bhd (2)
No 8 Jalan Kip 3 Taman Perindustrian Kip, 52200, Kuala Lumpur, Malaysia
Tel.: (60) 362733792
Canned Food Distr
N.A.I.C.S.: 424420

HOSHIIRYO-SANKI CO., LTD.
7-11-18 Iriya, Adachi-Ku, Tokyo, 121-0836, Japan
Tel.: (81) 338992101
Web Site: https://www.hosi.co.jp
Year Founded: 1974
7634—(TKS)
Rev.: $123,623,280
Assets: $196,039,360
Liabilities: $55,592,240
Net Worth: $140,447,120
Earnings: $10,715,760
Fiscal Year-end: 03/31/22
Medical Gas Mfr
N.A.I.C.S.: 339113
Yukio Hoshi *(Pres & CEO)*

HOSHINE SILICON INDUSTRY CO., LTD.
No 530 Yashan West Rd Zhapu Town, Pinghu, 315300, Zhejiang, China
Tel.: (86) 57389179027
Web Site:
  http://www.hoshinesilicon.com
Year Founded: 2005
603260—(SHG)
Rev.: $3,680,710,429
Assets: $11,539,660,902
Liabilities: $7,050,431,020
Net Worth: $4,489,229,882
Earnings: $363,152,235
Fiscal Year-end: 12/31/23
Silicon Material Mfr & Distr
N.A.I.C.S.: 325199

Subsidiaries:

Hoshine Silicon (Jiaxing) Industry Co., Ltd. (1)
No 530 Yashan West Rd, Zhapu Town, Pinghu, 314201, Zhejiang, China
Tel.: (86) 57389179027
Silicon Metal Mfr & Distr
N.A.I.C.S.: 331110

Hoshine Silicon (Luzhou) Industry Co., Ltd. (1)
34 Jingang Road Luohan Street, Longmatan District, Luzhou, 646000, Sichuan, China
Tel.: (86) 8302798001
Silicone Products Mfr
N.A.I.C.S.: 334413

Hoshine Silicon (Shanshan) Industry Co., Ltd. (1)
West of Kekeya Road Stone Industrial Park Uygur Autonomous Region, Shanshan County Turpan City Hoshine Industrial Park, Xinjiang, 838200, China

Tel.: (86) 57389179966
Silicone Products Mfr
N.A.I.C.S.: 334413

Xinjiang Eastern Hoshine Silicon Industry Co., Ltd. (1)
West of Kekeya Road Stone Industrial Park, Shanshan County Turpan City Uygur Autonomous Region, Xinjiang, 838200, China
Tel.: (86) 9956288721
Silicone Products Mfr
N.A.I.C.S.: 334413

Xinjiang Jinsong Silicon Industry Co., Ltd. (1)
Wuwu Industrial Park, Xinjiang Uygur Autonomous Region, Karamay, 83320, China
Tel.: (86) 57389179966
Silicone Products Mfr
N.A.I.C.S.: 334413

Xinjiang Middle Hoshine Silicon Industry Co., Ltd. (1)
2979 Helun Street Ganquanbao Economic & Technological Development Zone, Xinjiang Uygur Autonomous Region, Urumqi, 830000, China
Tel.: (86) 9917585205
Silicon Metal Mfr & Distr
N.A.I.C.S.: 331110

Xinjiang Western Hoshine Silicon Industry Co., Ltd. (1)
No11 Weiyi Rd Xinjiang Uygur Autonomous Region, North Industrial Park, Shihezi, 832000, China
Tel.: (86) 9936695628
Silicone Products Mfr
N.A.I.C.S.: 334413

HOSHINO GAKKI CO., LTD.
No 22 3-chome Shumoku-cho, Higashi-ku, Nagoya, 461-8717, Aichi, Japan
Tel.: (81) 529310381
Web Site:
http://www.hoshinogakki.co.jp
Year Founded: 1908
Sales Range: $125-149.9 Million
Emp.: 134
Musical Instrument Mfr & Distr
N.A.I.C.S.: 339992
Yoshihiro Hoshino (Chm)

Subsidiaries:

Guangzhou Hoshino Gakki Mfg. Co., Ltd. (1)
No 26 Junda Road East Section, Guangzhou Economical Technological Development District, Guangzhou, Guangdong, China
Tel.: (86) 2022216001
Web Site: http://www.hoshinogakki.co.jp
Emp.: 146
Percussion Instrument & Accessory Mfr
N.A.I.C.S.: 339992

Guangzhou Hoshino Gakki Trading Co., Ltd. (1)
Sinopec Tower 191 Tiyu West Road, Tianhe District, Guangzhou, 510620, Guangdong, China
Tel.: (86) 20 3892 2251
Emp.: 10
Musical Instrument Distr
N.A.I.C.S.: 423990
Toshitsugu Tanaka (Pres)

Hoshino (USA) Inc. (1)
1726 Winchester Rd, Bensalem, PA 19020
Tel.: (215) 638-8670
Rev.: $77,550,000
Emp.: 100
Musical Instruments & Accessories Whslr
N.A.I.C.S.: 459140
Bill Reim (Pres)

Hoshino Benelux B.V. (1)
J N Wagenaarweg 9, 1422 AK, Uithoorn, Netherlands
Tel.: (31) 297567788
Rev.: $6,187,046
Emp.: 14
Musical Instrument Whslr
N.A.I.C.S.: 459140

Hoshino Gakki Co., Ltd. - Akatsuki Factory (1)
No 3-31 Akatsuki-Cho, Seto, 489-0071, Japan
Tel.: (81) 561 48 4101
Musical Instrument Mfr
N.A.I.C.S.: 339992

Hoshino Gakki Hanbai Co., Ltd. (1)
119 Higashi Nagane-cho, Seto, 489-0871, Japan **(100%)**
Tel.: (81) 561896900
Web Site: http://www.hoshinogakki.co.jp
Sales Range: $10-24.9 Million
Emp.: 23
Domestic Sales of Musical Instruments
N.A.I.C.S.: 459140
Shinichi Kubo (Pres)

HOSHINO RESORTS INC.
6-18 Kyobashi 3-chome, Chuo-ku, Tokyo, 104-0031, Japan
Tel.: (81) 351596338 JP
Web Site:
http://www.hoshinoresorts.com
Year Founded: 1904
Hotel & Resort Investor, Developer & Operator
N.A.I.C.S.: 721110
Yoshiharu Hoshino (CEO)

Subsidiaries:

Hoshino Resorts OMO7 Asahikawa Hotel (1)
9 Rokujo, Asahikawa, 070-0036, Hokkaido, Japan
Tel.: (81) 166 24 2111
Web Site: http://www.omo-hotels.com
Hotel Operator
N.A.I.C.S.: 721110

Hoshino Resorts REIT, Inc. (1)
6-18 Kyobashi 3-chome, Chuo-ku, Tokyo, 104-0031, Japan
Tel.: (81) 351596338
Web Site: http://www.hoshinoresorts-reit.com
Sales Range: Less than $1 Million
Hospitality Real Estate Investment Trust
N.A.I.C.S.: 525990
Kenji Akimoto (Exec Dir)

Subsidiary (Domestic):

Hyatt Regency Osaka (2)
1-13-11 Nanko-kita, Suminoe-ku, Osaka, 559-0034, Japan
Tel.: (81) 6 6612 1234
Hotel Operator
N.A.I.C.S.: 721110

Ishin Hotels Group Co., Ltd. (1)
Hulic Kamiyacho Bldg 10F 4-3-13 Toranomon, Minato-ku, Tokyo, 150-0001, Japan **(50%)**
Tel.: (81) 357337733
Web Site: http://www.ishinhotels.com
Emp.: 222
Holding Company; Hotel Investment, Operation & Asset Management
N.A.I.C.S.: 551112
Kenji Matsuo (VP-Tech Svcs)

Unit (Domestic):

International Garden Hotel Narita (2)
241-1 Yoshikura, Narita, 286-0133, Chiba, Japan
Tel.: (81) 476235522
Sales Range: $25-49.9 Million
Emp.: 60
Hotel Operations
N.A.I.C.S.: 721110
Ikuya Kubo (Gen Mgr)

HOSHIZAKI CORPORATION
3-16 Sakae-cho Minamiyakata, Toyoake, 470-1194, Aichi, Japan
Tel.: (81) 562972111 JP
Web Site: https://www.hoshizaki.co.jp
Year Founded: 1947
6465—(TKS)
Rev.: $2,648,561,670
Assets: $3,299,409,490
Liabilities: $938,886,160
Net Worth: $2,360,523,330
Earnings: $232,800,150
Emp.: 13,271
Fiscal Year-end: 12/31/23
Commercial Refrigeration & Service Industry Equipment Mfr & Whslr
N.A.I.C.S.: 333310
Seishi Sakamoto (Chm & CEO)

Subsidiaries:

Brema Group S.P.A (1)
Via dell industria 10, Villa Cortese, 20035, Milan, Italy
Tel.: (39) 0331434811
Web Site: https://www.bremaice.it
Emp.: 115
Kitchen Equipment Distr
N.A.I.C.S.: 423440

Hoshizaki (Thailand) Limited (1)
9/92 Moo5 Klong Nueng Klong Luang, Pathumthani, 12120, Thailand
Tel.: (66) 2 005 9980
Web Site: https://hoshizaki.co.th
Emp.: 10
Cube Ice Making Machine Mfr
N.A.I.C.S.: 325120

Hoshizaki Chugoku Co., Ltd. (1)
1-13 Dohashi-cho, Naka-ku, Hiroshima, 730-0854, Japan
Tel.: (81) 82 293 9451
Web Site: https://www.hoshizaki-chugoku.co.jp
Cube Ice Making Machine Mfr
N.A.I.C.S.: 325120

Hoshizaki Europe Holdings B.V. (1)
Burgemeester Stramanweg 101, 1101AA, Amsterdam, Netherlands
Tel.: (31) 20 691 8499
Web Site: https://hoshizaki-europe.com
Sales Range: $25-49.9 Million
Emp.: 20
Holding Company
N.A.I.C.S.: 551112

Subsidiary (Non-US):

Gram Commercial A/S (1)
Aage Grams Vej 1, 6500, Vojens, Denmark
Tel.: (45) 73201200
Web Site: http://www.gram-commercial.com
Commercial Refrigerators & Freezers Mfr
N.A.I.C.S.: 423740

Subsidiary (Non-US):

Gram (UK) Ltd. (3)
2 The Technology Centre London Road, Swanley, BR8 7AG, Kent, United Kingdom
Tel.: (44) 1322616900
Web Site: http://www.gram-commercial.com
Sales Range: $25-49.9 Million
Emp.: 15
Commercial Refrigerators & Freezers Distr
N.A.I.C.S.: 423740

Gram Commercial (3)
Box 5157, 217 24, Malmo, Sweden
Tel.: (46) 40 9878 48
Web Site: http://www.gram-commercial.se
Home Appliance Mfr
N.A.I.C.S.: 335220

Gram Commercial BV (3)
Twenteepoort West 62, Postbus 601, 7600 AP, Almelo, Netherlands
Tel.: (31) 546454252
Web Site: http://www.gram.nl
Commercial Refrigerator & Freezer Mfr
N.A.I.C.S.: 423740

Gram Commercial NUF (3)
PO Box 44, 1941, Bjorkelangen, Norway
Tel.: (47) 22 88 17 50
Web Site: http://www.gram.nl
Home Appliance Mfr
N.A.I.C.S.: 335220

Gram Deutschland GmbH (3)
Im Kirchenfelde 1, 31157, Sarstedt, Germany
Tel.: (49) 506660460
Web Site: http://www.gram-commercial.de
Sales Range: $75-99.9 Million
Emp.: 200
Commercial Refrigerator & Freezer Mfr
N.A.I.C.S.: 423740

Subsidiary (Domestic):

Hoshizaki Europe B.V. (2)
Burgemeester Stramanweg 101, Noord-Holland, 1101 AA, Amsterdam, Netherlands
Tel.: (31) 206918499
Web Site: https://www.hoshizaki-europe.com
Sales Range: $25-49.9 Million
Refrigeration & Heating Equipment Mfr
N.A.I.C.S.: 333415

Subsidiary (Non-US):

Hoshizaki Europe Ltd. (2)
Unit B Stafford Park 7, Telford, TF3 3BQ, Shropshire, United Kingdom
Tel.: (44) 1952 291 777
Ice Making Machine Mfr
N.A.I.C.S.: 333248

Hoshizaki Hokkaido K.K. (1)
4-1-8 1jo Kikusui Shiroishi-Ku, Sapporo, Japan
Tel.: (81) 118414433
Industrial Machinery & Equipment Whslr
N.A.I.C.S.: 423830
Toshi Ishikawa (Pres)

Hoshizaki Hokushinetsu K.K. (1)
2-26 Matsushima, Kanazawa, Japan
Tel.: (81) 762402266
Industrial Machinery & Equipment Whslr
N.A.I.C.S.: 423830

Hoshizaki Kanto K.K. (1)
4-37-33 Hakusan, Bunkyo-ku, Tokyo, 112-0001, Japan
Tel.: (81) 33 943 6201
Web Site: https://www.hoshizaki.co.jp
Industrial Machinery Whslr
N.A.I.C.S.: 423830

Hoshizaki Keihan K.K. (1)
Hoshizaki Hommachi Bldg, Osaka, Japan
Tel.: (81) 667625351
Industrial Machinery & Equipment Whslr
N.A.I.C.S.: 423830

Hoshizaki Kitakanto Co Ltd (1)
3-36 Miyahara-cho, Kita-ku, Saitama, 331-0812, Japan
Tel.: (81) 48 660 2311
Web Site: https://www.hoshizaki-kitakanto.co.jp
Emp.: 507
Commercial & Domestic Machinery & Equipment Whslr
N.A.I.C.S.: 423220
Yamazaki Tsukasa (Pres)

Hoshizaki Kitakyu K.K. (1)
3-18-9 Hakataekiminami, Hakata-ku, Fukuoka, 812-0016, Japan
Tel.: (81) 92 471 7396
Web Site: http://www.Hoshizaki.co.jp
Sales Range: $150-199.9 Million
Emp.: 400
Industrial Machinery & Equipment Whslr
N.A.I.C.S.: 423830

Hoshizaki Lancer Pty Ltd. (1)
5 Toogood Avenue, Beverley, Adelaide, 5009, SA, Australia
Tel.: (61) 88 268 1388
Web Site: https://lancerbeverage.com
Sales Range: $25-49.9 Million
Emp.: 60
Automatic Vending Machine Mfr
N.A.I.C.S.: 333310
Joe Thorp (Mng Dir)

Hoshizaki Malaysia Sdn. Bhd. (1)
16 JALAN TP5A Prestij 16 Taman Perindustrian Uep, 47620, Subang Jaya, Selangor, Malaysia
Tel.: (60) 380235823
Web Site: https://hoshizaki.com.my
Kitchen Equipment Mfr
N.A.I.C.S.: 333241

Hoshizaki Nankyu K.K. (1)
4-41-11 Shimoarata, Kagoshima, Japan
Tel.: (81) 998130007
Industrial Machinery & Equipment Whslr
N.A.I.C.S.: 423830

Hoshizaki Okinawa Co Ltd (1)
1-14-32 Akebono, Naha, Japan
Tel.: (81) 988611240
Industrial Machinery & Equipment Whslr

HOSHIZAKI CORPORATION

Hoshizaki Corporation—(Continued)
N.A.I.C.S.: 423830

Hoshizaki Philippines Corporation (1)
Unit No GB-2 G/F Agustin 1 Bldg 28 F Ortigas Center, Pasig, Philippines
Tel.: (63) 288392861
Web Site: https://hoshizaki-sea.com
Kitchen Equipment Mfr
N.A.I.C.S.: 333241

Hoshizaki Shanghai Co., Ltd. (1)
Room 501 Tower 1 Kerry Enterprise Center No 128 Tianmu West Road, Jing'an District, Shanghai, 200070, China
Tel.: (86) 2152288181
Web Site: https://www.hoshizaki.com.cn
Household Refrigerator & Home Freezer Mfr
N.A.I.C.S.: 335220

Hoshizaki Shikoku K.K. (1)
3-3 Konyamachi, Takamatsu, Japan
Tel.: (81) 878622345
Industrial Machinery & Equipment Whslr
N.A.I.C.S.: 423830

Hoshizaki Singapore Pte Ltd. (1)
18 Boon Lay Way 01-102 Tradehub 21, Unit 07-142, Singapore, 609966, Singapore
Tel.: (65) 62252612
Web Site: https://hoshizaki.com.sg
Sales Range: $50-74.9 Million
Emp.: 15
Refrigeration Equipment & Supplies Whslr
N.A.I.C.S.: 423740
June Tay *(Gen Mgr)*

Hoshizaki Suzhou Co., Ltd. (1)
No 15 Qingqiu Street, Industrial Park, Suzhou, Jiangsu, China
Tel.: (86) 51262807850
Web Site: https://www.hoshizaki-suzhou.com.cn
Refrigeration & Heating Equipment Mfr
N.A.I.C.S.: 333415

Hoshizaki Tohoku K.K. (1)
2-38 Showamachi, Aoba-Ku, Sendai, 981-0913, Miyagi, Japan
Tel.: (81) 227289511
Home Appliance Mfr
N.A.I.C.S.: 335220

Hoshizaki Tokai Co., Ltd. (1)
5-21-3 Meieki, Nakamura-ku, Nagoya, 450-0002, Japan
Tel.: (81) 52 563 5581
Web Site: https://www.hoshizaki-tokai.co.jp
Industrial Machinery & Equipment Whslr
N.A.I.C.S.: 423830

Hoshizaki Tokyo K.K. (1)
2-20-32 Takanawa Hoshizaki Takanawa Building 1F, Minato-Ku, Tokyo, 108-0074, Japan
Tel.: (81) 35 791 8001
Web Site: https://www.hoshizaki-tokyo.co.jp
Electrical Appliance Television & Radio Set Whslr
N.A.I.C.S.: 423620

Hoshizaki USA Holdings, Inc. (1)
618 Hwy 74 S, Peachtree City, GA 30269
Web Site: https://www.hoshizakiamerica.com
Holding Company; Commercial Ice Makers, Refrigerators, Freezers & Dishwashing Equipment Mfr & Whslr
N.A.I.C.S.: 551112
Koichi Tsunematsu *(Pres)*

Subsidiary (Domestic):

Hoshizaki America, Inc. (2)
618 Hwy 74 S, Peachtree City, GA 30269
Tel.: (770) 487-2331
Web Site: http://www.hoshizakiamerica.com
Commercial Ice Makers, Refrigerators & Freezers Mfr & Whslr
N.A.I.C.S.: 333310
William C. Anderson *(CFO)*

Jackson WWS, Inc. (2)
6209 N US Hwy 25 E, Gray, KY 40734
Tel.: (606) 523-9795
Web Site: http://www.jacksonwws.com
Emp.: 200
Commercial Dishwashing Equipment Mfr
N.A.I.C.S.: 333310

Lancer Corporation (2)
6655 Lancer Blvd, San Antonio, TX 78219
Tel.: (210) 310-7000
Beverage Dispensing Systems Mfr & Marketer
N.A.I.C.S.: 333241
Scott D. Adams *(Pres-Acting)*

Lancer Europe, S.A. (1)
Mechelsesteenweg 592, 1930, Zaventem, Belgium
Tel.: (32) 27552390
Sales Range: $25-49.9 Million
Emp.: 8
Soft Drinks Mfr
N.A.I.C.S.: 312111
Jaap van Ginneken *(Gen Mgr)*

Lancer International Sales, Inc. (1)
Kashirskoe Shosse 65 1 Office 610, Moscow, 115583, Russia
Tel.: (7) 495 727 4063
Web Site: http://www.lancercorp.com
Emp.: 3
Soft Drink Distr
N.A.I.C.S.: 424490
Vladimir Denkin *(Gen Mgr)*

NESTOR CO., LTD (1)
4-1 Oshimizu Kitasaki-machi, 474-0001, Obu, Japan
Tel.: (81) 562 467560
Home Appliance Mfr
N.A.I.C.S.: 335220

Oztiryakiler Madeni Esya Sanayi ve Ticaret Anonim Sirketi (1)
Cumhuriyet Mah Eski Hadimkoy Yolu Cad No 8 Bagimsiz Bol 1, Buyukcekmece, 34500, Istanbul, Turkiye
Tel.: (90) 2128867800
Web Site: https://oztiryakiler.com.tr
Emp.: 1,600
Kitchen Equipment Mfr
N.A.I.C.S.: 332215

Western Refrigeration Pvt. Ltd. (1)
Office Premises 501 502 503 504 505 5th Floor Ascot Centre Sahar Road, Next to Hotel Hilton Andheri, Mumbai, 400099, India
Tel.: (91) 2267161200
Web Site: https://www.westernequipments.com
Commercial Refrigeration Equipment Mfr
N.A.I.C.S.: 333415
Bhupinder Singh *(Founder & Chm)*

HOSIDEN CORPORATION
4-33 Kitakyuhoji 1-Chome, Yao, 581-0071, Osaka, Japan
Tel.: (81) 729931010
Web Site: https://hosiden.com
Year Founded: 1950
6804—(TKS)
Rev.: $1,446,995,100
Assets: $1,156,802,880
Liabilities: $265,312,180
Net Worth: $891,490,700
Earnings: $76,887,520
Emp.: 580
Fiscal Year-end: 03/31/24
Mfr of Electrical Switches & Liquid Crystal Displays
N.A.I.C.S.: 335931
Kenji Furuhashi *(Pres)*

Subsidiaries:

China Hosiden Co., Ltd. (1)
Hongda Industrial Area, Qiaotou Town, Dongguan, Guangdong, China
Tel.: (86) 76983344134
Connector & Assembled Product Mfr
N.A.I.C.S.: 334417

Hong Kong Hosiden Ltd (1)
Units 01 11/F Perfect Industrial Building 31Tai Yau Street San Po Kong, Kowloon, China (Hong Kong)
Tel.: (852) 23238181
Sales Range: $25-49.9 Million
Emp.: 50
Electronic Products Sales
N.A.I.C.S.: 423690

Hosiden (Shanghai) Co., Ltd. (1)
Room 8B1 Oriental Viking No 333 Xianxia Road, Shanghai, 200336, China
Tel.: (86) 2152081488
Electronic & Electrical Appliance Mfr
N.A.I.C.S.: 335999

Hosiden (Shenzhen) Co., Ltd. (1)
Room 2716 Changping Commercial Building 99 Honghua Road, Futian Free Trade Zone, Shenzhen, 518048, China
Tel.: (86) 75583480955
Web Site: http://www.hosiden.co.jp
Electronic Components Distr
N.A.I.C.S.: 423690

Hosiden (Thailand) Co., Ltd (1)
43 Thai CC Tower 16th Fl Room 163 South Sathorn Rd Kwaeng Yannawa, Khet Sathorn, Bangkok, 10120, Thailand
Tel.: (66) 2 673 9760
Web Site: http://www.hosiden.co.jp
Sales Range: $25-49.9 Million
Emp.: 7
Electronic Components Mfr
N.A.I.C.S.: 334419

Hosiden America Corp (1)
120 E State Pkwy, Schaumburg, IL 60173
Tel.: (847) 885-8870
Electric Equipment Mfr
N.A.I.C.S.: 334419

Hosiden Besson Ltd (1)
12 St Joseph's Trading Estate St Joseph's Close, Hove, BN3 7EZ, East Sussex, United Kingdom
Tel.: (44) 1273860000
Web Site: http://www.hbl.co.uk
Sales Range: $25-49.9 Million
Emp.: 100
Telecommunications Equipment Mfr
N.A.I.C.S.: 334290
Steven Drayton *(Mng Dir)*

Hosiden Corporation (M) Sdn. Bhd (1)
Lot 1 Jalan P/1A Bangi Industrial Estate, 43650, Bandar Baru Bangi, Selangor, Malaysia
Tel.: (60) 389258622
Emp.: 3
Electronic Components Mfr
N.A.I.C.S.: 334417

Hosiden Corporation - China Hosiden LCD Factory (1)
Hongda Industrial Area, Qiaotou Town, Dongguan, 523530, Guangdong, China
Tel.: (86) 76983344134
Web Site: http://www.hosiden.co.jp
Liquid Crystal Display Module Mfr
N.A.I.C.S.: 334419

Hosiden Corporation-Tokyo Factory (1)
1-14-25 Irie, Kanagawa-ku, Yokohama, 221-0014, Japan (100%)
Tel.: (81) 454232201
Web Site: http://www.hosiden.co.jp
Sales Range: $75-99.9 Million
Emp.: 160
Electronics Mfr
N.A.I.C.S.: 334220

Hosiden Electronics (Malaysia) Sdn. Bhd (1)
Lot 1 Jalan P/1A Bangi Industrial Estate, 43650, Bandar Baru Bangi, Selangor, Malaysia
Tel.: (60) 389258622
Emp.: 350
Electronic Components Mfr
N.A.I.C.S.: 334419
Osamu Itoh *(Mng Dir)*

Hosiden Electronics (Shanghai) Co., Ltd (1)
Room 8B1 Oriental Viking No 333 Xianxia Road, Changning District, Shanghai, 200336, China
Tel.: (86) 2152081488
Web Site: http://www.hosiden.com
Emp.: 15
Electronic Components Mfr
N.A.I.C.S.: 334419

Hosiden Electronics (Shenzhen) Co., Ltd. (1)
Room 2716 Changping Commercial Building 99 Honghua Road, Futian Free Trade Zone, Shenzhen, China
Tel.: (86) 75583480955
Electronic & Electrical Appliance Mfr
N.A.I.C.S.: 335999

Hosiden Europe GmbH (1)
Fritz-Vomfelde-Str 8, 40547, Dusseldorf, Germany
Tel.: (49) 211964930
Emp.: 21
Electric Component Whslr
N.A.I.C.S.: 423690
Yoshikazu Fujii *(Gen Mgr)*

Hosiden F.D. Corporation (1)
500 Kita Higashideyanagi Aisyo-cho, Echigun, Shiga, 529-1233, Japan
Tel.: (81) 749373691
Web Site: http://www.hosidenfd.co.jp
Touch Panel Mfr
N.A.I.C.S.: 334419

Hosiden Kyushu Corporation (1)
3024-38 Oaza Nakayama Kurate-cho, Kurate-cho, Kurate, 807-1312, Fukuoka, Japan
Tel.: (81) 949422311
Web Site: https://hosiden-kyushu.com
Emp.: 129
Microphone Product Mfr
N.A.I.C.S.: 334310

Hosiden Plastics Corporation (1)
551 Aza Nakaido Higashide Aisho-cho, Echi-gun, Shiga, 529-1233, Japan
Tel.: (81) 749373661
Plastic Mold Mfr
N.A.I.C.S.: 333511

Hosiden Seiko Corporation (1)
15-1 Enmyo-cho, Kashiwara, 582-0027, Osaka, Japan
Tel.: (81) 729772781
Solenoid & Pin Jack Mfr
N.A.I.C.S.: 332911

Hosiden Service Corporation (1)
123-1 Kyokoji 1-chome, Yao, 581-0874, Osaka, Japan
Tel.: (81) 729438500
Electronic & Electrical Appliance Mfr
N.A.I.C.S.: 335999

Hosiden Singapore Pte Ltd (1)
28 Genting Lane 05-01 Platinum 28, Singapore, 349585, Singapore
Tel.: (65) 62968100
Web Site: http://www.hosiden.co.jp
Sales Range: $25-49.9 Million
Emp.: 10
Electronic Products Mfr
N.A.I.C.S.: 334416

Hosiden Technology (Qingdao) Co., Ltd. (1)
No 16 Xinghui Road Qingdao Jiaozhou Bay Free Trade Zone Hetao, Chengyang, Qingdao, Shagdong, China
Tel.: (86) 53287923588
Electronic & Electrical Appliance Mfr
N.A.I.C.S.: 335999

Hosiden Vietnam (Bac Giang) Co., Ltd. (1)
Lot C1 Quang Chau Industrial Park, Viet Yen Dist, Viet Yen, Bac Giang, Vietnam
Tel.: (84) 2043868948
Web Site: http://www.hosiden.co.jp
Emp.: 6,500
Electronic Products Mfr
N.A.I.C.S.: 334419

Hosiden Wakayama Corporation (1)
454-9 Oaza Habu Aridagawa-cho, Aridagawa-cho, Arida, 643-0025, Wakayama, Japan
Tel.: (81) 737526011
Remote Control Unit & Switch Equipment Mfr
N.A.I.C.S.: 335314

Korea Hosiden Electronics Co., Ltd (1)
No 811 Block 102 Digital Empire II 88 Sinwon-ro, Yeongtong-gu, Suwon, 102-209, Gyeonggi-do, Korea (South)
Tel.: (82) 312167311
Electronic Components Mfr & Sales
N.A.I.C.S.: 334419

Qingdao Hosiden Electronics Co., Ltd. (1)

INTERNATIONAL PUBLIC

AND PRIVATE COMPANIES

Chongqingzhong Road 946, Li Cang District, Qingdao, 266000, Shandong, China
Tel.: (86) 53284813454
Web Site: http://www.hosiden.co.jp
Receiver Units & Microphones Mfr
N.A.I.C.S.: 334419

Taiwan Hosiden Co., Ltd. (1)
3F No 34 Sec 3 Zhongshan N Rd, Zhongshan Dist, Taipei, 10452, Taiwan
Tel.: (886) 225858599
Web Site: http://www.hosiden.co.jp
Electronic Components Distr
N.A.I.C.S.: 423690

HOSKEN CONSOLIDATED INVESTMENTS LIMITED

Suite 801 76 Regent Road, Sea Point, Cape Town, 8005, South Africa
Tel.: (27) 214817560   ZA
Web Site: http://www.hci.co.za
HCI—(JSE)
Rev.: $1,209,293,243
Assets: $2,738,882,065
Liabilities: $1,251,489,824
Net Worth: $1,487,392,241
Earnings: $268,685,347
Fiscal Year-end: 03/31/23
Equity Investment Firm
N.A.I.C.S.: 523999
Kevin Govender *(Dir-Fin)*

Subsidiaries:

Almania Investments (Proprietary) Limited (1)
Block B Longkloof Studios Gardens, Cape Town, Western Cape, South Africa
Tel.: (27) 214262711
Investment Management Service
N.A.I.C.S.: 523999

Fabcos Investment Holding Company (Proprietary) Limited (1)
2nd Floor Fabcos House 81 Pritchard Street, Johannesburg, 2000, Gauteng, South Africa
Tel.: (27) 11 333 3701
Investment Management Service
N.A.I.C.S.: 523999

Gallagher Estate Holdings Limited (1)
64 Wierda Road East, Johannesburg, 2196, Gauteng, South Africa
Tel.: (27) 112663000
Real Estate Investment Services
N.A.I.C.S.: 523999

Golden Arrow Bus Services (Proprietary) Limited (1)
103 Bofors Circle Epping Industria, PO Box 1795, Cape Town, 8000, Western Cape, South Africa
Tel.: (27) 215078800
Web Site: http://www.gabs.co.za
Bus Charter Services
N.A.I.C.S.: 488490
Francois Meyer *(CEO)*

HCI Khusela Coal (Proprietary) Limited (1)
19 Richards Dr Midrand, Johannesburg, 1685, Gauteng, South Africa
Tel.: (27) 114484902
Web Site: http://www.hci.co.za
Coal Mining Services
N.A.I.C.S.: 213113
Russell Jackson *(CEO)*

Hollyberry Props 12 (Proprietary) Limited (1)
Block B Longkloof Studios, Gardens, Cape Town, 8001, Western Cape, South Africa
Tel.: (27) 214262711
Sales Range: $25-49.9 Million
Emp.: 16
Transportation Support Services
N.A.I.C.S.: 488490
Kevin Govender *(Mgr-Fin)*

Johnson Access (Proprietary) Limited (1)
Halfway House, PO Box X121, Midrand, 1685, Gauteng, South Africa
Tel.: (27) 113122118
Web Site: http://www.eazi.co.za

Emp.: 255
Construction Machinery Rental Services
N.A.I.C.S.: 532412
Brett Fleming *(Gen Mgr)*

Limtech Biometric Solutions (Proprietary) Limited (1)
45 Wessel Rd, Rivonia, Johannesburg, 2007, Gauteng, South Africa
Tel.: (27) 100018482
Web Site: http://www.limtech.co.za
Sales Range: $25-49.9 Million
Emp.: 18
Security System Mfr
N.A.I.C.S.: 334419
Chris Snell *(Mng Dir)*

Montauk Energy Capital LLC (1)
680 Andersen Dr Foster Plz Ste 10 5th Fl, Pittsburgh, PA 15220
Tel.: (412) 747-8700
Web Site: http://www.montaukenergy.com
Sales Range: $50-74.9 Million
Emp.: 22
Landfill Methane Gas & Power Generation Services
N.A.I.C.S.: 211120

Sabido Investments (Proprietary) Limited (1)
5 Summit Rd Hyde Park, Johannesburg, 2196, Gauteng, South Africa
Tel.: (27) 115379300
Investment Management Service
N.A.I.C.S.: 523999

Tangney Investments (Proprietary) Limited (1)
Suite 801 76 Regent Road, Cape Town, 8005, South Africa
Tel.: (27) 214262711
Investment Management Service
N.A.I.C.S.: 523999
John Anthony Copelyn *(Gen Mgr)*

Tsogo Investment Holding Company (Pty) Limited (1)
Private Bag X200, Bryanston, 2021, South Africa   **(99.56%)**
Tel.: (27) 114619744
Web Site: http://www.tsogosun.com
Investment Holding Company
N.A.I.C.S.: 551112

Affiliate (Domestic):

Tsogo Sun Limited (2)
Palazzo Towers East Montecasino Boulevard, Fourways, 2055, South Africa   **(47.6%)**
Tel.: (27) 115107700
Web Site: http://www.tsogosun.com
Rev.: $79,351,490
Assets: $962,315,920
Liabilities: $454,684,720
Net Worth: $507,631,200
Earnings: ($67,001,860)
Fiscal Year-end: 03/31/2021
Holding Company; Casino Hotels & Luxury Hotel Resorts Owner & Operator
N.A.I.C.S.: 551112

Subsidiary (Domestic):

Akani Egoli (Pty) Limited (3)
Cnr Northern Parkway and Data Crescen, Private Bag 1998, Ormonde, Johannesburg, 2159, Gauteng, South Africa
Tel.: (27) 11 248 5000
Web Site: https://www.goldreefcity.co.za
Casino Hotel, Theme Park & Theme Park Hotel Operator
N.A.I.C.S.: 721120
Mike Cage *(Gen Mgr)*

Unit (Domestic):

Gold Reef City Theme Park (4)
Cnr Northern Parkway and Data Crescen, Private Bag 1998, Ormonde, Johannesburg, 2159, Gauteng, South Africa
Tel.: (27) 11 248 5000
Web Site: https://www.goldreefcity.co.za
Theme Park & Hotel Operator
N.A.I.C.S.: 713110

Subsidiary (Domestic):

Akani Msunduzi (Pty) Ltd. (3)
45 New England Road, Pietermaritzburg,

3209, Kwazulu-Natal, South Africa
Tel.: (27) 33 395 8000
Web Site: https://www.goldenhorsecasino.co.za
Casino Hotel & Resort Operator
N.A.I.C.S.: 721120

Garden Route Casino (Pty) Ltd. (3)
1 Pinnacle Point Road, Mossel Bay, 6500, South Africa
Tel.: (27) 44 606 7777
Web Site: https://www.gardenroutecasino.co.za
Sales Range: $50-74.9 Million
Emp.: 300
Casino Hotel & Resort Operator
N.A.I.C.S.: 721120

Goldfields Casino & Entertainment Centre (Pty) Ltd. (3)
Goldfields Plaza Cnr Stateway & Buiten Street, PO Box 2700, Welkom, 9460, Free State, South Africa   **(100%)**
Tel.: (27) 573915700
Web Site: http://www.tsogosun.com
Emp.: 500
Casino Hotel & Resort Operator
N.A.I.C.S.: 721120

Hospitality Property Fund Ltd. (3)
The Zone II Loft Offices East Wing, 2nd Floor, Cnr Oxford Road & Tyrwhitt Avenue, Johannesburg, South Africa   **(75%)**
Tel.: (27) 11 994 6300
Web Site: http://www.hpf.co.za
Real Estate Investment Trust
N.A.I.C.S.: 531390
John Copelyn *(Chm)*

Subsidiary (Domestic):

Southern Sun Hotels (Pty) Limited (4)
Palazzo Towers East Cnr William Nicol &, Montecasino Boulevard, Fourways, Johannesburg, 2055, South Africa   **(100%)**
Tel.: (27) 115107500
Web Site: www.southernsun.com
Hotel & Resort Operator
N.A.I.C.S.: 721110
Marcel Nikolaus von Aulock *(CEO)*

Subsidiary (Domestic):

Silverstar Casino (Pty) Ltd. (3)
R28 Muldersdrift, Private Bag X2005, Mogale City, Krugersdorp, 1740, South Africa   **(100%)**
Tel.: (27) 116627300
Web Site: http://www.tsogosun.com
Casino Hotel & Resort Operator
N.A.I.C.S.: 721120
Sanele Ntombela *(Mgr-Mktg)*

Tsogo Sun Emonti (Pty) Ltd. (3)
Corner of Western Avenue and Two Rivers Drive, East London, 5201, Eastern Cape, South Africa   **(80%)**
Tel.: (27) 43 707 7777
Web Site: http://www.hemingways.co.za
Casino Hotel & Resort Operator
N.A.I.C.S.: 721120

Division (Domestic):

Tsogo Sun Gaming (Pty) Limted (3)
Palazzo Towers East Montecasino Boulevard, Fourways, 2055, South Africa
Tel.: (27) 11 510 7700
Web Site: https://www.tsogosungaming.com
Casino Hotel & Resort Operator
N.A.I.C.S.: 721120

Subsidiary (Domestic):

Tsogo Sun KwaZulu-Natal (Pty) Ltd. (3)
Suncoast Boulevard Marine Parade, PO Box 10132, North Beach, Durban, 4056, KwaZulu-Natal, South Africa   **(90%)**
Tel.: (27) 31 328 3000
Web Site: http://www.tsogosun.com
Casino Hotel & Resort Operator
N.A.I.C.S.: 721120
Mike Dowsley *(Exec Dir)*

Subsidiary (Non-US):

West Coast Leisure (Pty) Ltd. (3)   **(70%)**
Tel.: (27) 22 707 6970

HOSOKAWA MICRON CORPORATION

Web Site: https://www.mykonoscasino.co.za
Sales Range: $50-74.9 Million
Emp.: 130
Casino Hotel & Resort Operator
N.A.I.C.S.: 721120
Clive Van Groeningen *(Gen Mgr)*

Yired (Proprietary) Limited (1)
4 Albury Road Dunkeld Crescent, Dunkeld West, Sandton, 2196, Gauteng, South Africa
Tel.: (27) 117720800
Web Site: http://www.yfm.co.za
Radio Broadcasting Services
N.A.I.C.S.: 516210

e.sat tv (Proprietary) Limited (1)
5 Summit Rd, Johannesburg, 2196, Gauteng, South Africa
Tel.: (27) 115379300
Emp.: 508
Television Broadcasting Services
N.A.I.C.S.: 516120
Patrick Conroy *(Gen Mgr)*

e.tv (Proprietary) Limited (1)
4 Stirling Street cnr De Villiers Road and Stirling Street, Zonnebloem, Cape Town, 7925, South Africa
Tel.: (27) 214814500
Web Site: http://www.etv.co.za
Television Broadcasting Services
N.A.I.C.S.: 516120

HOSKING PARTNERS LLP

2 St James Market, London, United Kingdom
Tel.: (44) 20 7004 7850   UK
Web Site: http://www.hoskingpartners.com
Investment Services
N.A.I.C.S.: 523999
Jeremy John Hosking *(Partner)*

HOSOKAWA MICRON CORPORATION

1-9 Shodai-Tachika Hirakata-shi, Osaka, 573 1132, Japan
Tel.: (81) 728552226   JP
Web Site: https://www.hosokawamicron.co.jp
Year Founded: 1916
6277—(TKS)
Rev.: $563,874,790
Assets: $687,935,610
Liabilities: $270,313,340
Net Worth: $417,622,270
Earnings: $42,313,120
Emp.: 1,964
Fiscal Year-end: 09/30/23
Powder & Particle, Blown Film & Confectionery & Bakery Technology Solutions
N.A.I.C.S.: 331492
Hitoshi Kihara *(Sr Exec Dir-Plng & Intl Admin Div)*

Subsidiaries:

HOSOKAWA ALPINE AMERICAN INC. (1)
455 Whitney St, Northborough, MA 01532
Tel.: (508) 655-1123
Web Site: https://www.halpine.com
Emp.: 14
Industrial Machinery Equipment Distr
N.A.I.C.S.: 423830
Dave Nunes *(Pres)*

HOSOKAWA ALPINE JAPAN Co., Ltd. (1)
9 1 Chome Shoudai Tajika, Hirakata, 573-1132, Osaka, Japan
Tel.: (81) 728566750
Blown Film Extrusion Equipment & Parts Distr
N.A.I.C.S.: 423830

HOSOKAWA BEPEX GmbH (1)
Liebigstrasse 8/2, 74211, Leingarten, Germany
Tel.: (49) 7131898669221
Web Site: http://www.bepexhosokawa.com

3485

HOSOKAWA MICRON CORPORATION

Hosokawa Micron Corporation—(Continued)

Sales Range: $75-99.9 Million
Emp.: 170
Food Products Machinery Distr
N.A.I.C.S.: 423830
Wolfgang Pforsich (Mng Dir)

HOSOKAWA DE MEXICO S.A. DE C.V. (1)
Heriberto Frias No 231 Col Narvarte, 03020, Mexico, Mexico
Tel.: (52) 5552863544
Web Site: http://www.hosokawamex.com
Sales Range: $25-49.9 Million
Emp.: 15
Industrial Equipment Distr
N.A.I.C.S.: 423830

HOSOKAWA MICRON (Korea) Ltd (1)
A-303 10 Olympic-ro 35ga-gil, Songpa-gu, Seoul, 05510, Korea (South)
Tel.: (82) 2 420 5691
Web Site:
https://www.hosokawamicron.co.jp
Emp.: 9
Industrial Machinery Distr
N.A.I.C.S.: 423830

HOSOKAWA MICRON (Shanghai) Powder Machinery Co. Ltd (1)
Room 2003-2006 Zhongsheng Financial Center No 2067 Yan'an West Road, Yan An Road West, Shanghai, 200336, China
Tel.: (86) 215 306 8031
Web Site: https://www.hosokawa.com.cn
Sales Range: $25-49.9 Million
Emp.: 20
Industrial Machinery Distr
N.A.I.C.S.: 423830

HOSOKAWA MICRON POWDERS GmbH (1)
Welserstr 9, 51149, Cologne, Germany
Tel.: (49) 2 203 3080
Web Site: https://www.hosokawamicron.de
Sales Range: $25-49.9 Million
Emp.: 50
Chemical Powder Mfr
N.A.I.C.S.: 325180
Christoph Wadenpohl (Mng Dir)

Hosokawa Alpine Aktiengesellschaft & Co. OHG (1)
Peter-Doerfler-Str 13-25, 86199, Augsburg, Germany (100%)
Tel.: (49) 82159060
Web Site: http://www.hosokawa-alpine.de
Emp.: 800
Provider of Blown Film Equipment
N.A.I.C.S.: 333310

Hosokawa Alpine Poland Sp. z o.o. (1)
Pulawska 372, 2819, Warsaw, Poland
Tel.: (48) 577197787
Web Site: https://www.hosokawa-alpine.pl
Plastics Films Mfr
N.A.I.C.S.: 326112

Hosokawa Micron B.V. (1)
Tel.: (31) 31 437 3333
Web Site: https://www.hosokawa-micron-bv.com
Sales Range: $25-49.9 Million
Emp.: 150
Air Pollution Control Equipment
N.A.I.C.S.: 334512

Subsidiary (Non-US):

HOSOKAWA MICRON FRANCE (2)
8/10 Rue du Bois Sauvage, BP 231, 91007, Evry, Cedex, France
Tel.: (33) 16 091 8055
Web Site: https://www.hosokawamicron.fr
Sales Range: $25-49.9 Million
Emp.: 3
Industrial Machinery Equipment Mfr & Distr
N.A.I.C.S.: 333248

Hosokawa Micron GmbH (1)
11 Welserstrasse, PO Box 900749, 51149, Cologne, Germany (100%)
Tel.: (49) 22033080
Web Site: http://www.hosokawamicron.de
Rev.: $35,000,000
Emp.: 53
Air Pollution Control Equipment
N.A.I.C.S.: 334512
Christoph Wadenpohl (Gen Mgr)

Hosokawa Micron India Pvt. Ltd. (1)
2112 13th Main Road, Anna Nagar West, Chennai, Tamil Nadu, India
Tel.: (91) 4426211257
Plastics Films Mfr
N.A.I.C.S.: 326112

Hosokawa Micron International Inc. (1)
10 Chatham Rd, Summit, NJ 07901-1310
Tel.: (908) 277-9300
Web Site: http://www.hmicronpowder.com
Sales Range: $25-49.9 Million
Emp.: 60
Mfr of Specialized Industrial Machinery for Process Applications
N.A.I.C.S.: 333248

Division (Domestic):

Alpine American (2)
455 Whitney St, Northborough, MA 01532 (100%)
Tel.: (508) 655-1123
Web Site: http://www.halpine.com
Emp.: 12
Sales & Service of Plastic Machinery & Equipment
N.A.I.C.S.: 423830
David Nunes (Pres)

Subsidiary (Non-US):

Hosokawa Micron Ltd. (2)
9275 Hwy 48 Ste 202, Markham, L3P 3J3, ON, Canada (100%)
Tel.: (905) 471-5854
Web Site: http://www.hosokawa.ca
Mfr & Designer of Air Pollution Control Equipment
N.A.I.C.S.: 334512

Division (Domestic):

Hosokawa Micron Powder Systems (2)
10 Chatham Rd, Summit, NJ 07901 (100%)
Tel.: (908) 273-6360
Web Site: http://www.hmicronpowder.com
Sales Range: $125-149.9 Million
Emp.: 60
Powder Process, Equipment & Systems Mfr & Engineer
N.A.I.C.S.: 333248

Division (Domestic):

Hosokawa Polymer Systems (3)
63 Fuller Way, Berlin, CT 06037
Tel.: (860) 828-0541
Web Site: http://www.polysys.com
Sales Range: $25-49.9 Million
Emp.: 20
Industrial Equipment Mfr
N.A.I.C.S.: 335999
Douglas Ort (Gen Mgr)

Nano Particle Technology Center (3)
10 Chatham Rd, Summit, NJ 07901
Tel.: (908) 277-9245
Web Site: http://www.hosokawanano.com
Sales Range: $25-49.9 Million
Emp.: 70
Industrial Equipment Mfr
N.A.I.C.S.: 333248

Division (Domestic):

Menardi-Criswell (2)
1 Maxwell Dr, Trenton, SC 29847-2227 (100%)
Tel.: (803) 663-6551
Web Site: http://www.beaconmfg.com
Mfr of Filter Media
N.A.I.C.S.: 314910

Hosokawa Micron Ltd. (1)
Rivington Road, Whitehouse Industrial Estate, Runcorn, WA7 3DS, Cheshire, United Kingdom (100%)
Tel.: (44) 1928755100
Web Site: https://www.hosokawa.co.uk
Emp.: 72
Air Pollution Control Equipment
N.A.I.C.S.: 334512

Hosokawa Solids Chile SpA (1)
Augusto Leguia Nte 100 Of 307, Las Condes, Chile
Tel.: (56) 993583458
Engineeering Services
N.A.I.C.S.: 541330

Hosokawa Solids Mexico S.A. de C.V. (1)
Armando Birlain Shaffler 2001, Centro Sur, 76090, Queretaro, Mexico
Tel.: (52) 4423156483
Engineeering Services
N.A.I.C.S.: 541330

Hosokawa Solids S.L. (1)
Etxepare 6, Gipuzkoa, 20800, Zarautz, Spain
Tel.: (34) 943830600
Engineeering Services
N.A.I.C.S.: 541330

Hosokawa Solids Solutions GmbH (1)
Lechwiesenstr 21, 86899, Landsberg am Lech, Germany
Tel.: (49) 819133590
Emp.: 69
Engineeering Services
N.A.I.C.S.: 541330

MalaysiaHosokawa Micron Malaysia Sdn. Bhd. (1)
109C Jalan SS 21/1A Damansara Utama, 47400, Petaling Jaya, Selangor, Malaysia
Tel.: (60) 377257433
Web Site: https://hosokawa.com.my
Technological Machinery Distr
N.A.I.C.S.: 423840

MexicoHosokawa Micron de Mexico S.A. de C.V. (1)
Heriberto Frias No 231, Col Narvart, 03020, Mexico, Mexico
Tel.: (52) 5552863544
Web Site: https://hosokawamex.com
Toll Processing Services
N.A.I.C.S.: 561990

Solids Components MIGSA S.L. (1)
Erribera Kalea 1, Gipuzkoa, 20749, Aizarnazabal, Spain
Tel.: (34) 943147083
Engineeering Services
N.A.I.C.S.: 541330

Wagner-Hosokawa Micron Ltd (1)
1-9 Shodaida Chika, Hirakata, 573-1132, Osaka, Japan
Tel.: (81) 728566751
Web Site:
https://www.hosokawamicron.co.jp
Powder Coating Equipment Sales
N.A.I.C.S.: 423830

HOSOYA PYRO-ENGINEERING CO., LTD.
1847 Sugao, Akiruno-Shi, Tokyo, 197-0801, Japan
Tel.: (81) 425585111
Web Site: https://www.hosoya-pyro.co.jp
Year Founded: 1951
4274—(TKS)
Sales Range: Less than $1 Million
Pyrotechnic Mfr
N.A.I.C.S.: 325998
Joushi Hosoya (Pres)

HOSPITAL CORPORATION OF CHINA LIMITED
Room 1602 Building B Jinqiu International Building No 6 Zhichun Road, Haidian District, Beijing, 100088, China
Tel.: (86) 1082961882   Ky
Web Site:
http://www.hcclhealthcare.com
Year Founded: 2014
3869—(HKG)
Rev.: $160,470,320
Assets: $341,953,186
Liabilities: $279,695,894
Net Worth: $62,257,291
Earnings: ($74,215,019)
Emp.: 1,422

INTERNATIONAL PUBLIC

Fiscal Year-end: 12/31/22
Health Care Srvices
N.A.I.C.S.: 621491
Wenzuo Lu (Exec Dir)

HOST
1 Bott St, Surrey Hills, Sydney, 2010, NSW, Australia
Tel.: (61) 2 9281 0333
Web Site: http://www.hostsydney.com
Emp.: 101
Advertising Agencies
N.A.I.C.S.: 541810
Anthony Freedman (Founder & Grp CEO)

HOST-PLUS PTY. LIMITED
Level 9 114 William Street, Carlton, Melbourne, 3000, VIC, Australia
Tel.: (61) 396247370
Web Site:
http://www.hostplus.com.au
Year Founded: 1988
Sales Range: $1-4.9 Billion
Emp.: 350
Hospitality Tourism Sport & Recreation Services
N.A.I.C.S.: 721214
David Elia (CEO)

Subsidiaries:

ALE Property Group (1)
Level 10 6 O Connell Street, Sydney, 2000, NSW, Australia (50%)
Tel.: (61) 2 8231 8588
Web Site: http://www.alegroup.com.au
Rev.: $164,113,301
Assets: $1,026,675,445
Liabilities: $457,408,534
Net Worth: $569,266,911
Earnings: $137,279,028
Emp.: 11
Fiscal Year-end: 06/30/2021
Owner of Pubs
N.A.I.C.S.: 531390
Andrew Frederick Osborne Wilkinson (CEO & Mng Dir)

Subsidiary (Domestic):

Australian Leisure & Entertainment Property Management Limited (2)
Level 10 Norwich House 6 O'Connell St, Sydney, 2000, NSW, Australia
Tel.: (61) 282318588
Web Site: http://www.alegroup.com.au
Sales Range: $25-49.9 Million
Emp.: 6
Investment Property Management Services
N.A.I.C.S.: 541618

Australian Leisure & Entertainment Property Trust (2)
Level 10 Norwich House 6 O'Connell St, Sydney, 2000, NSW, Australia
Tel.: (61) 282318588
Web Site: http://www.alegroup.com.au
Sales Range: $25-49.9 Million
Emp.: 6
Investment Property Management Services
N.A.I.C.S.: 541618
Andrew Wilkinson (Mng Dir)

HOSTI INTERNATIONAL GMBH
Max-Eyth-Strasse 18, Pfedelbach, 74629, Germany
Tel.: (49) 794160920
Web Site: http://www.hosti.de
Year Founded: 1949
Rev.: $28,967,400
Emp.: 125
Disposable Tableware Mfr
N.A.I.C.S.: 339999

HOSTMORE PLC
Highdown House Yeoman Way, Worthing, BN99 3HH, West Sussex, United Kingdom
Tel.: (44) 3304605588   UK
Web Site:
https://www.hostmoregroup.com

AND PRIVATE COMPANIES

Year Founded: 2021
MORE—(LSE)
Rev.: $265,732,958
Assets: $320,852,317
Liabilities: $284,787,201
Net Worth: $36,065,116
Earnings: ($132,437,440)
Emp.: 10
Fiscal Year-end: 01/01/23
Restaurant Operators
N.A.I.C.S.: 722511
Alan Clark *(CFO)*

HOSTPAPA, INC.
115 George Street Suite 511, Oakville, ON, Canada
Tel.: (905) 315-3455
Web Site: http://www.hostpapa.com
Web Hosting Services
N.A.I.C.S.: 518210
Paul Stengel *(Head-Tech)*

Subsidiaries:

Data Deposit Box Inc.   (1)
Suite 703 1 Eglinton Avenue East, Toronto, M4P 3A1, ON, Canada
Tel.: (416) 238-7596
Web Site: http://www.datadepositbox.com
Cloud Backup Technology
N.A.I.C.S.: 513210
Siva Cherla *(CFO)*

HOT CHILI LIMITED
First Floor 768 Canning Highway, Applecross, 6153, WA, Australia
Tel.: (61) 893159009
Web Site: https://www.hotchili.net.au
HHLKF—(OTCIQ)
Rev.: $46,328
Assets: $124,120,010
Liabilities: $10,806,889
Net Worth: $113,313,121
Earnings: ($7,389,762)
Fiscal Year-end: 06/30/21
Other Metal Ore Mining
N.A.I.C.S.: 212210
Christian Ervin Easterday *(Mng Dir)*

HOT TELECOMMUNICATION SYSTEMS LTD.
13 Yehushua HaZoref, Beersheba, 84899, Israel
Tel.: (972) 77 7077000
Web Site: http://www.hot.net.il
Sales Range: $1-4.9 Billion
Cable Television, Broadband Internet & Mobile & International Phone Services
N.A.I.C.S.: 517111
Jean-Luc Berrebi *(CFO)*

HOTA INDUSTRIAL MFG. CO., LTD.
No 12 Keya Rd, Daya Dist, Taichung, 42881, Taiwan
Tel.: (886) 425692299
Web Site: https://www.hota.com.tw
Year Founded: 1973
1536—(TAI)
Rev.: $215,809,207
Assets: $730,150,435
Liabilities: $441,001,815
Net Worth: $289,148,620
Earnings: $10,617,188
Emp.: 672
Fiscal Year-end: 12/31/23
Automobile Drive Train Mfr
N.A.I.C.S.: 336390

Subsidiaries:

Amstrong Industry Corporation   (1)
No 12 Keya Rd, Da Ya Hsiang, Taichung, 42881, Taiwan
Tel.: (886) 425692299
Web Site: http://www.amstrong.com.tw
All Terrain Vehicles Distr
N.A.I.C.S.: 441227

Global Technos Ltd.   (1)
906 Hiyamato Building 2-9-15 Higashinakajima, Higashiyodogawa-ku, Osaka, 533-0033, Japan
Tel.: (81) 661952071
Web Site: https://www.gl-t.co.jp
Gear Tools Mfr
N.A.I.C.S.: 333612

HotaTech, Inc.   (1)
15348 E Valley Blvd, City of Industry, CA, 91746
Tel.: (626) 387-5423
Web Site: http://www.hotatech.com
Sales Range: $25-49.9 Million
Emp.: 5
Precision Gears & Shafts Mfr
N.A.I.C.S.: 333612
David Shen *(Pres)*

Kao Fong Machinery Co., Ltd.   (1)
16 Keya Road, Daya District, Taichung, 42881, Taiwan
Tel.: (886) 425662116
Web Site: https://www.kafo.com.tw
Rev.: $64,158,459
Assets: $146,601,445
Liabilities: $89,186,818
Net Worth: $57,414,627
Earnings: $1,456,805
Fiscal Year-end: 12/31/2022
Machine Tools Mfr
N.A.I.C.S.: 333517
Kuo-Jung Shen *(Chm)*

Taiwan Pyrolysis & Energy Regeneration Corp.   (1)
5F 150 Chao Chou Street, Taipei, 10649, Taiwan
Tel.: (886) 223579688
Automobile Parts Mfr
N.A.I.C.S.: 336350
Taniel Lin *(Gen Mgr)*

Wuxi Hota Precision Gear Co., Ltd.   (1)
No 27 Chaqiao East Section Xihu Road, Anzhen Town, Wuxi, 214104, Jiangsu, China
Tel.: (86) 510 88716057
Web Site: http://www.wxhota.com
Sales Range: $50-74.9 Million
Emp.: 220
Transmission Gear & Shaft Mfr & Whslr
N.A.I.C.S.: 336390

HOTAI MOTOR CO., LTD.
Floor 8-14 No 121 Songjiang Road, Taipei, Taiwan
Tel.: (886) 225062121
Web Site:
https://pressroom.hotaimotor.com
Year Founded: 1947
2207—(TAI)
Rev.: $8,738,307,038
Assets: $15,191,831,598
Liabilities: $12,051,464,934
Net Worth: $3,140,366,664
Earnings: $817,006,410
Emp.: 4,101
Fiscal Year-end: 12/31/23
Automotive Distr
N.A.I.C.S.: 423110
Justin Su *(Pres)*

Subsidiaries:

Carmax Co., Ltd.   (1)
320 8F No 121 Sung Chiang Rd, Taipei, Taiwan
Tel.: (886) 3 4522299
Automobile Parts Distr
N.A.I.C.S.: 423120

Subsidiary (Domestic):

Smart Design Technology Co., Ltd.   (2)
20F-8 No 5 Sec 3 New Taipei Blvd, Xinzhuang Dist, New Taipei City, 24250, Taiwan
Tel.: (886) 285227628
Web Site: http://www.smartdesign.com.tw
Transport Navigation System Mfr & Distr
N.A.I.C.S.: 334511

Zurich Insurance (Taiwan) Ltd.   (1)

13/F No 126 Songjiang Rd, Zhongshan Dist, Taipei, 10457, Taiwan
Tel.: (886) 800006808
Web Site: http://www.hotains.com.tw
Insurance Products & Services
N.A.I.C.S.: 524298

HOTBED LIMITED
Lakeside Shirwell Crescent Furzton, Milton Keynes, MK4 1GA, United Kingdom
Tel.: (44) 1908523440
Web Site: http://www.hotbed.uk.com
Sales Range: $25-49.9 Million
Emp.: 30
Privater Equity Firm
N.A.I.C.S.: 523999
Peter Hedges *(Chm)*

HOTEIS OTHON S.A.
995 Our Lady of Copacabana Avenue, Rio de Janeiro, 22060-001, RJ, Brazil
Tel.: (55) 2121250200
Web Site: https://www.othon.com.br
Year Founded: 1943
HOOT4—(BRAZ)
Rev.: $26,414,972
Assets: $91,541,622
Liabilities: $122,860,510
Net Worth: ($31,318,889)
Earnings: $22,552,153
Fiscal Year-end: 12/31/23
Hotel Operator
N.A.I.C.S.: 721110
Fernando Martins Vaz Chabert *(Chm, CEO & Member Exec Bd)*

HOTEL BELA LADA A.D.
Zelena ulica br 2, 21220, Becej, Serbia
Tel.: (381) 21 69 15 608
Year Founded: 1989
Sales Range: Less than $1 Million
Emp.: 21
Home Management Services
N.A.I.C.S.: 721110

HOTEL BOSNA A.D. BANJA LUKA
Kralja Petra I Karadordevica br 97, 78000, Banja Luka, Bosnia & Herzegovina
Tel.: (387) 51215775
Web Site:
https://www.hotelbosna.com
HBSN—(BANJ)
Sales Range: $1-9.9 Million
Emp.: 2,167
Home Management Services
N.A.I.C.S.: 721110
Cedo Milosevic *(Chm-Mgmt Bd)*

HOTEL CLUB ESTIVAL 2002 SA
Hotel Slatina, Neptun, Constanta, Romania
Tel.: (40) 241491073
CLUB—(BUC)
Assets: $2,923,856
Liabilities: $210,560
Net Worth: $2,713,296
Earnings: ($17,259)
Emp.:
Fiscal Year-end: 12/31/23
Accommodation Services
N.A.I.C.S.: 721110

HOTEL DEVELOPERS (LANKA) PLC
Colombo Hilton Echelon Square No 2 Sir Chittampalam A Gardiner Mawath, Colombo, 00200, Sri Lanka
Tel.: (94) 112433435
Web Site:
http://www.hoteldevelopers.lk
Hotel & Restaurant Operator

HOTEL GRAND CENTRAL LIMITED

N.A.I.C.S.: 721110
Shamahil Mohideen *(COO)*

HOTEL FLORA A.S.
Ul 17 Novembra 14, 914 51, Trencianske Teplice, Slovakia
Tel.: (421) 326554555
Web Site: http://www.hotelflora.sk
Hotel & Restaurant Management Services
N.A.I.C.S.: 721110
Miroslav Godal *(Chm-Mgmt Bd)*

HOTEL GOLUBACKI GRAD A.D.
Golubacki Square 4, Golubac, Serbia
Tel.: (381) 12 638 507
Web Site:
http://www.hotelgolubacki.co.rs
Year Founded: 2001
Sales Range: Less than $1 Million
Emp.: 10
Home Management Services
N.A.I.C.S.: 721110

HOTEL GRAND CENTRAL LIMITED
22 Cavenagh Road/Orchard Road, Singapore, 229617, Singapore
Tel.: (65) 67379944   SG
Web Site: https://www.ghihotels.com
Year Founded: 1968
H18—(SES)
Rev.: $114,026,358
Assets: $1,177,917,897
Liabilities: $174,580,020
Net Worth: $1,003,337,877
Earnings: $8,992,653
Emp.: 429
Fiscal Year-end: 12/31/23
Hotel Operator
N.A.I.C.S.: 721110
Eng Teong Tan *(Chm & Mng Dir)*

Subsidiaries:

Hotel Chancellor @ Orchard Pte. Ltd.   (1)
28 Cavenagh Road, Singapore, 229635, Singapore
Tel.: (65) 67088788
Web Site:
https://www.chancellororchard.com.sg
Hotel Services
N.A.I.C.S.: 721110
Wilson Lim *(Mgr)*

Hotel Grand Chancellor (Adelaide) Pty. Limited   (1)
65 Hindley Street, Adelaide, 5000, SA, Australia
Tel.: (61) 882315552
Hotel Services
N.A.I.C.S.: 721110

Hotel Grand Chancellor (Auckland City) Limited   (1)
1 Hobson Street, Auckland, New Zealand
Tel.: (64) 93561000
Hotel Services
N.A.I.C.S.: 721110

Hotel Grand Chancellor (Brisbane) Pty. Limited   (1)
23 Leichhardt St Cnr Wickham Terrace, Brisbane, 4000, QLD, Australia
Tel.: (61) 738314055
Hotel Services
N.A.I.C.S.: 721110

Hotel Grand Chancellor (Hobart) Pty. Limited   (1)
1 Davey Street, Hobart, 7000, TAS, Australia
Tel.: (61) 362354535
Hotel Services
N.A.I.C.S.: 721110

Hotel Grand Chancellor (Launceston) Pty. Limited   (1)
29 Cameron Street, Launceston, 7250, TAS, Australia
Tel.: (61) 363343434

HOTEL GRAND CENTRAL LIMITED

Hotel Grand Central Limited—(Continued)
Hotel Services
N.A.I.C.S.: 721110

Hotel Grand Chancellor (Melbourne) Pty. Limited (1)
131 Lonsdale Street, Melbourne, 3000, VIC, Australia
Tel.: (61) 396564000
Hotel Services
N.A.I.C.S.: 721110

Hotel Grand Chancellor (Palm Cove) Pty. Limited (1)
Coral Coast Drive, Palm Cove, 4879, QLD, Australia
Tel.: (61) 740591234
Hotel Services
N.A.I.C.S.: 721110
Tony Vitinaros *(Mgr-Hotel)*

Hotel Grand Chancellor (Townsville) Pty. Limited (1)
334 Flinders Street, Townsville, 4810, QLD, Australia
Tel.: (61) 747292000
Hotel Services
N.A.I.C.S.: 721110

HOTEL HOLIDAY GARDEN
Rm B 23F No 6 Siwei 3rd Rd, Qianjin Dist, Kaohsiung, 801, Taiwan
Tel.: (886) 72410123
Web Site: http://www.hotelhg.com.tw
Year Founded: 1958
2702—(TAI)
Rev.: $46,866,312
Assets: $271,554,324
Liabilities: $167,318,513
Net Worth: $104,235,811
Earnings: $842,048
Fiscal Year-end: 12/31/23
Home Management Services
N.A.I.C.S.: 721110

HOTEL INTERNATIONAL DE LYON S.A.
70 Quai Charles de Gaulle, 69006, Lyon, France
Tel.: (33) 478175100
Year Founded: 2000
Sales Range: $25-49.9 Million
Emp.: 150
Hotel Operator
N.A.I.C.S.: 721110
Ignacio Rodriguez *(Gen Mgr)*

HOTEL MAJESTIC CANNES SA
10 la Croisette, BP 163, 06400, Cannes, France
Tel.: (33) 492987700
MLHMC—(EUR)
Sales Range: Less than $1 Million
Home Management Services
N.A.I.C.S.: 561110
Charles Richez *(CEO)*

HOTEL MANAGEMENT INTERNATIONAL CO., LTD.
Minatojima-Nakamachi 7-chome 5-1, Chuo-ku, Tokyo, Japan
Tel.: (81) 3 3847 7410   JP
Web Site: http://www.hmi-hotel.co.jp
Year Founded: 1998
Hotel Owner, Developer & Operator
N.A.I.C.S.: 721110
Ryuko Hira *(Pres)*

HOTEL METROPOLE SAM
4 Avenue De La Madone, BP 19, Monte Carlo, Monaco
Tel.: (377) 93151515
Web Site: http://www.metropole.com
Sales Range: $10-24.9 Million
Emp.: 120
Hotel Operator
N.A.I.C.S.: 721110
Lionel Giuriolo *(Dir-HR)*

HOTEL MOSKVA BELGRADE
Terazije 20, 11000, Belgrade, Serbia
Tel.: (381) 113642069
Web Site: http://www.hotelmoskva.rs
Year Founded: 1906
Hotel & Motel Services
N.A.I.C.S.: 721110

HOTEL NARVIK A.D.
Trg Srpskih dobrovoljaca 24, Kikinda, Serbia
Tel.: (381) 230 424 305
Year Founded: 1987
Sales Range: Less than $1 Million
Emp.: 9
Home Management Services
N.A.I.C.S.: 721110
Milija Pavlovic *(CEO)*

HOTEL NEWGRAND CO., LTD.
10 Yamashita-cho, Naka-ku, Yokohama, 231-8520, Kanagawa, Japan
Tel.: (81) 456811841
Web Site: https://www.hotel-newgrand.co.jp
Year Founded: 1927
97200—(TKS)
Hotel Operator
N.A.I.C.S.: 721110
Kenji Hamada *(Pres)*

HOTEL OKURA CO., LTD.
2-10-4 Toranomon, Minato-ku, Tokyo, 105-0001, Japan
Tel.: (81) 335820111   JP
Web Site: http://www.okura.com
Year Founded: 1958
Holding Company; Luxury Hotel & Resort Owner & Operator
N.A.I.C.S.: 721110
Yoshihiko Okura *(Chm)*

Subsidiaries:

Continental Foods Co., Ltd. (1)
14/15F Tokai Hosokaikan 1-14-25 Higashi-sakura, Higashi-Ku, Nagoya, 460-0005, Japan
Tel.: (81) 52 201 3201
Hotel Operator
N.A.I.C.S.: 721110

Hotel Okura Enterprise Co., Ltd. (1)
2-4-11 Higashi-Shinagawa, Shinagawa-ku, Tokyo, 140-0002, Japan
Tel.: (81) 3 5495 7377
Hotel Operator
N.A.I.C.S.: 721110

Hotel Okura Fukuoka (1)
Hakata Riverain 3-2 Shimokawabata-machi, Hakata-ku, Fukuoka, 812-0027, Japan
Tel.: (81) 92 262 1111
Web Site: http://www.okura.com
Luxury Hotel Operator
N.A.I.C.S.: 721110

Hotel Okura Kobe (1)
2-1 Hatoba-cho, Chuo-ku, Kobe, 650-8560, Hyogo, Japan
Tel.: (81) 783330111
Luxury Hotel Operator
N.A.I.C.S.: 721110

Hotel Okura Niigata (1)
53 Kawabata-cho 6-chome, Niigata, 951-8053, Japan
Tel.: (81) 252246111
Web Site: http://www.okura-niigata.com
Sales Range: $25-49.9 Million
Emp.: 200
Luxury Hotel Operator
N.A.I.C.S.: 721110

Hotel Okura Sapporo (1)
Nishi 5-chome Minami 1-Jo, Chuo-ku, Sapporo, 060-0061, Hokkaido, Japan
Tel.: (81) 112212333
Web Site: http://www.sapporo-hotelokura.co.jp
Sales Range: $25-49.9 Million
Emp.: 130
Luxury Hotel Operator
N.A.I.C.S.: 721110

Makoto Miyazaki *(Gen Mgr)*

Hotel Okura Tokyo (1)
2-10-4 Toranomon, Minato-ku, Tokyo, 105-0001, Japan
Tel.: (81) 335820111
Emp.: 1,000
Luxury Hotel Operator
N.A.I.C.S.: 721110
Nasahiro Kiyohara *(Gen Mgr)*

Okura Act City Hotel Hamamatsu (1)
111-2 Itaya-machi, Naka-ku, Hamamatsu, 430-7733, Shizuoka, Japan
Tel.: (81) 534590111
Web Site: http://www.act-okura.co.jp
Emp.: 300
Luxury Hotel Operator
N.A.I.C.S.: 721110
Hajime Harada *(Mng Dir)*

Okura Akademia Park Hotel, Chiba (1)
2-3-9 Kazusakamatari, Kisarazu, Chiba, 292-0818, Japan
Tel.: (81) 438 52 0111
Web Site: http://www.okura.com
Luxury Hotel Operator
N.A.I.C.S.: 721110

Okura Chiba Hotel (1)
1-13-3 Chuo-ko, Chuo-ku, Chiba, 260-0024, Japan
Tel.: (81) 432481111
Emp.: 90
Luxury Hotel Operator
N.A.I.C.S.: 721110
Shoji Takenaka *(Gen Mgr)*

Okura Frontier Hotel Ebina (1)
2-9-50 Chuo, Ebina, 243-0432, Kanagawa, Japan
Tel.: (81) 462354411
Emp.: 100
Luxury Hotel Operator
N.A.I.C.S.: 721110

Okura Frontier Hotel Tsukuba (1)
1-1364-1 Azuma, Tsukuba, Ibaraki, 305-0031, Japan
Tel.: (81) 298521112
Sales Range: $50-74.9 Million
Emp.: 80
Luxury Hotel Operator
N.A.I.C.S.: 721110
Noriyuki Saito *(Mgr)*

Okura Garden Hotel Shanghai (1)
58 Mao Ming Road S, Shanghai, 200020, China
Tel.: (86) 2164151111
Web Site: http://www.gardenhotelshanghai.com
Sales Range: $100-124.9 Million
Emp.: 800
Luxury Hotel & Shopping Plaza
N.A.I.C.S.: 721110

HOTEL PALAS A.D. BANJA LUKA
Kralja Petra I Karadordevica 60, 78 000, Banja Luka, Bosnia & Herzegovina
Tel.: (387) 51223040
Web Site: https://zepterhotelpalace.com
Year Founded: 1933
HPAL—(BANJ)
Sales Range: Less than $1 Million
Emp.: 18
Home Management Services
N.A.I.C.S.: 721110

HOTEL PRAG A.D.
Kraljice Natalije 27, 11000, Belgrade, Serbia
Tel.: (381) 11 321 4444   RS
Web Site: http://www.hotelprag.rs
Year Founded: 1929
Rev.: $1,145,322
Assets: $2,970,896
Liabilities: $95,580
Net Worth: $2,875,315
Earnings: $91,943
Emp.: 49
Fiscal Year-end: 12/31/16

INTERNATIONAL PUBLIC

Home Management Services
N.A.I.C.S.: 721110

HOTEL PRIJEDOR A.D.
Srpskih Velikana 14, 79000, Prijedor, Bosnia & Herzegovina
Tel.: (387) 52231176   BA
Web Site: https://hotel-prijedor.com
Year Founded: 1985
HTLP—(BANJ)
Sales Range: Less than $1 Million
Home Management Services
N.A.I.C.S.: 721110
Danko Galic *(Pres)*

HOTEL PROPERTIES LIMITED
50 Cuscaden Road HPL House 08-01, Singapore, 249724, Singapore
Tel.: (65) 67345250   SG
Web Site: https://www.hotelprop.com.sg
Year Founded: 1980
H15—(SES)
Rev.: $486,344,012
Assets: $3,181,844,276
Liabilities: $1,366,019,086
Net Worth: $1,815,825,190
Earnings: $420,294,630
Emp.: 5,348
Fiscal Year-end: 12/31/23
Investment Holding Services
N.A.I.C.S.: 551112
Arthur Keng Hock Tan *(Chm)*

Subsidiaries:

Concorde Hotel New York Inc. (1)
127 E 55th St, New York, NY 10022
Tel.: (212) 355-2755
Web Site: https://www.concordehotelnewyork.com
Emp.: 45
Investment Holding Services
N.A.I.C.S.: 551112

HPL Hotels & Resorts Pte Ltd (1)
50 Cuscaden Road 05-02 HPL House, Singapore, 249724, Singapore
Tel.: (65) 67352811
Web Site: https://www.hplhotels.com
Home Management Services
N.A.I.C.S.: 721110

Hermill Investments Pte Ltd (1)
583 Orchard Road 05-03 Forum Office Tower, Singapore, 238884, Singapore
Tel.: (65) 67322469
Web Site: https://www.forumtheshoppingmall.com.sg
Investment Holding Services
N.A.I.C.S.: 551112

PT Bali Girikencana (1)
Kawasan Bukit Permai Bali, 80361, Denpasar, Indonesia
Tel.: (62) 361701010
Home Management Services
N.A.I.C.S.: 721110

Seaside Hotel (Thailand) Co. Ltd (1)
429 Moo 9 Pattaya 2nd Road, Bang Lamung, 20150, Thailand
Tel.: (66) 384287559
Web Site: http://www.hardrockhotels.net
Home Management Services
N.A.I.C.S.: 721110

Super Vista Sdn Bhd (1)
No 253 Lubuk Tamang Batu 30, Ringlet, 39200, Malaysia
Tel.: (60) 54956152
Web Site: http://www.lakehouse-cameron.com
Emp.: 25
Home Management Services
N.A.I.C.S.: 721110
Low Lai Fun *(Mgr-Hotel)*

HOTEL PROPERTY INVESTMENTS LIMITED
Suite 2 Level 17 IBM Centre 60 City Rd, Southbank, 3006, VIC, Australia
Tel.: (61) 390381774

Web Site:
https://www.hpitrust.com.au
HPI—(ASX)
Rev.: $54,897,836
Assets: $860,582,929
Liabilities: $338,099,625
Net Worth: $522,483,304
Earnings: $24,035,123
Fiscal Year-end: 06/30/24
Property Investment Services
N.A.I.C.S.: 523999
Raymond Gunston *(Chm)*

HOTEL REGINA PARIS S.A.
2 place des Pyramides, 75001, Paris, France
Tel.: (33) 142609403
Web Site: https://www.regina-hotel.com
Sales Range: $10-24.9 Million
Emp.: 200
Hotel Owner & Operator
N.A.I.C.S.: 721110

HOTEL ROYAL LIMITED
36 Newton Road, Singapore, 307964, Singapore
Tel.: (65) 64260168
Web Site:
https://www.hotelroyal.com.sg
Year Founded: 1991
H12—(SES)
Rev.: $44,186,927
Assets: $626,567,446
Liabilities: $137,776,263
Net Worth: $488,791,184
Earnings: $1,935,166
Emp.: 558
Fiscal Year-end: 12/31/23
Home Management Services
N.A.I.C.S.: 561110
Chou Hock Lee *(CEO)*

Subsidiaries:

Faber Kompleks Sdn. Bhd. (1)
No3 Jln Larut Off Jln Burmah, George Town, 10050, Penang, Malaysia
Tel.: (60) 42267888
Web Site: http://www.hotelroyalpenang.com
Emp.: 150
Home Management Services
N.A.I.C.S.: 721110

Hotel Royal @ Queens (Singapore) Pte Ltd (1)
Hotel Royal Queens 12 Queen Street, Singapore, 188553, Singapore
Tel.: (65) 67259988
Web Site: https://www.royalqueens.com.sg
Home Management Services
N.A.I.C.S.: 721110

Panali Co., Ltd. (1)
9/99 Moo 3 Bophut Koh Samui, Surat Thani, 84320, Thailand
Tel.: (66) 77915555
Hotel Operator
N.A.I.C.S.: 721110

HOTEL SHILLA CO., LTD.
249 Dongho-ro, Jung-gu, Seoul, 04605, Korea (South)
Tel.: (82) 222333131 KR
Web Site: https://www.hotelshilla.net
Year Founded: 1973
008770—(KRS)
Rev.: $3,775,180,694
Assets: $2,253,864,005
Liabilities: $1,839,849,716
Net Worth: $414,014,289
Earnings: ($38,475,980)
Emp.: 2,506
Fiscal Year-end: 12/31/22
Holding Company; Luxury Hotel & Resort Owner & Operator
N.A.I.C.S.: 551112
Boo-Jin Lee *(Board of Directors, Pres & CEO)*

HOTEL SIGIRIYA PLC
Browns Hotels & Resorts No 338 T B Jayah Mawatha, 10, Colombo, Sri Lanka
Tel.: (94) 117930930
Web Site:
https://www.serendibleisure.com
Year Founded: 1971
HSIG—(COL)
Rev.: $817,196
Assets: $3,558,523
Liabilities: $809,308
Net Worth: $2,749,214
Earnings: ($11,983)
Emp.: 131
Fiscal Year-end: 03/31/23
Home Management Services
N.A.I.C.S.: 561110
W. M. De F. Arsakularatne *(Exec Dir)*

HOTELES BESTPRICE S.A.
Avinguda Diagonal 70, 08019, Barcelona, Spain
Tel.: (34) 935991271
Web Site:
https://hotelesbestprice.com
Year Founded: 2013
MLHBP—(EUR)
Hotel Operator
N.A.I.C.S.: 721110
Qscar Sanchez Rodriguez *(Chm & CEO)*

HOTELES CITY EXPRESS, S.A.B. DE C.V.
Juan Salvador Agraz 69 Santa Fe Cuajimalpa, Del Cuajimalpa de Morelos, 05348, Mexico, DF, Mexico
Tel.: (52) 5552498050
Web Site: http://www.cityexpress.com
Year Founded: 2002
HCITY—(MEX)
Rev.: $167,046,084
Assets: $836,253,125
Liabilities: $361,882,655
Net Worth: $474,370,470
Earnings: $3,457,593
Emp.: 4,000
Fiscal Year-end: 12/31/19
Hotel Operator
N.A.I.C.S.: 721110
Carlos Adams Ruelas *(Dir-Franchise Promotion)*

HOTELI BERNARDIN D.D.
St Bernardin Resort Grand Hotel Bernardin Obala 2, 6320, Portoroz, Slovenia
Tel.: (386) 56950000 SI
Web Site: http://www.hoteli-bernardin.si
Year Founded: 1997
Rev.: $21,203,000
Emp.: 100
Hotel Resort Owner & Operator
N.A.I.C.S.: 721110
Mojca Gobina *(Mgr-MICE Dept)*

HOTELI MAESTRAL D.D
Cira Carica 3, 20 000, Dubrovnik, Croatia
Tel.: (385) 20433633
Web Site:
http://www.hotelsindubrovnik.com
Hotel & Restaurant Operator
N.A.I.C.S.: 721110

HOTELI VODICE D.D.
Grgura Ninskog 1, 22211, Sibenik, Croatia
Tel.: (385) 22451451
Web Site: http://www.hotelivodice.hr
Hotel Operator
N.A.I.C.S.: 721110
Andrija Kevic *(Owner)*

HOTELIM SA
11 avenue Myron Herrick, 75008, Paris, France
Tel.: (33) 153580700
Web Site: https://www.hotelim.fr
Year Founded: 1986
MLHOT—(EUR)
Sales Range: Less than $1 Million
Home Management Services
N.A.I.C.S.: 561110

HOTELS ILIDZA D.D. ILIDZA
Hrasnicka Cesta Broj 14, 71000, Sarajevo, Bosnia & Herzegovina
Tel.: (387) 33772000
Web Site: http://www.hoteliilidza.ba
HTILRK2—(SARE)
Rev.: $2,966,707
Assets: $29,050,590
Liabilities: $8,768,090
Net Worth: $20,282,500
Earnings: $185,107
Emp.: 67
Fiscal Year-end: 12/31/21
Hotel Operator
N.A.I.C.S.: 722511

HOTELS MANAGEMENT COMPANY INTERNATIONAL SAOG
Al Khuwair, PO Box 964, 133, Muscat, Oman
Tel.: (968) 24524422
Year Founded: 2002
HMCI—(MUS)
Rev.: $8,570,305
Assets: $32,271,716
Liabilities: $14,185,019
Net Worth: $18,086,696
Earnings: ($4,282,513)
Emp.: 373
Fiscal Year-end: 12/31/21
Home Management Services
N.A.I.C.S.: 561110
Abdullah Humaid Al Maamri *(Vice Chm)*

HOTLAND CO., LTD.
The Park Rex Shintomicho 4th and 5th floors 1-9-6 Shintomi, Chuo-Ku, Tokyo, 104-0041, Japan
Tel.: (81) 335538885
Web Site: https://www.hotland.co.jp
Year Founded: 1991
3196—(TKS)
Rev.: $274,453,900
Assets: $168,125,170
Liabilities: $91,865,130
Net Worth: $76,260,040
Earnings: $7,238,890
Emp.: 300
Fiscal Year-end: 12/31/23
Restaurant Operators
N.A.I.C.S.: 722511
Morio Sase *(Founder, Pres & CEO)*

Subsidiaries:

WAEN International Limited (1)
Room 1805-06 18/F Millennium City Phase II 378 Kwun Tong Road, Kwun Tong, Kowloon, China (Hong Kong)
Tel.: (852) 2 151 0782
Web Site: https://www.waenhk.com
Restaurant Operators
N.A.I.C.S.: 722511

HOTLINE TO HR INC.
1136 Centre Street Suite 124, Thornhill, L4J 3M8, ON, Canada
Tel.: (416) 619-7867 ON
Web Site: http://www.hotlinetohr.com
Year Founded: 2011
Human Resources Management Systems
N.A.I.C.S.: 541512
George Hatzoglou *(CFO)*

HOTMAN CO., LTD.
4-4-17 Nishitaga, Taihaku-ku, Sendai, Miyagi, Japan
Tel.: (81) 222435091
Web Site: https://www.yg-hotman.com
3190—(TKS)
Sales Range: $250-299.9 Million
Emp.: 1,170
Automotive Supply Stores
N.A.I.C.S.: 441330
Nobuyuki Ito *(Pres)*

HOTONDO BUILDING PTY. LTD.
PO Box 354, Moorabbin, 3189, VIC, Australia
Tel.: (61) 395595000
Web Site: http://www.hotondo.com.au
Year Founded: 1979
Residential Building Construction Services
N.A.I.C.S.: 236116
Michael Renwick *(Mng Dir)*

HOTRON PRECISION ELECTRONIC INDUSTRIAL CO. LTD.
No 169 Xing al Rd, Neihu Dist, Taipei, Taiwan
Tel.: (886) 227928558
Web Site: https://www.hotron-ind.com
Year Founded: 1991
3092—(TAI)
Rev.: $105,124,254
Assets: $169,553,294
Liabilities: $105,055,561
Net Worth: $64,497,733
Earnings: $2,055,655
Fiscal Year-end: 12/31/22
Electronic Components Mfr
N.A.I.C.S.: 334419
Li-Jung Chang *(Chm)*

Subsidiaries:

Hotron Precision Electronic (Fuqing) Co., Ltd. (1)
Yuan Hong Investment Zone, Fuzhou, Fujian, China
Tel.: (86) 59185582088
Lightning Cable Mfr
N.A.I.C.S.: 335931

Hotron Precision Electronic (Suzhou) Co., Ltd. (1)
128 Lushan Road, Suzhou New District, Suzhou, Jiangsu, China
Tel.: (86) 51266671188
Lightning Cable Mfr
N.A.I.C.S.: 335931

HOTSPOT INTERNATIONAL, S DE R.L. DE C.V.
Calle Ibsen No 15 despacho 701 Colonia Polanco, C.P. 11560, Mexico, Mexico
Tel.: (52) 5552817081
Web Site:
http://www.hotspotinternational.com
High Speed Internet Access Services
N.A.I.C.S.: 517810
Susana Semblantes *(Co-Founder & & Pres)*

HOTTO LINK INC.
Fujimi Duplexbiz Bldg 5F 1-3-11 Fujimi-cho, Chiyoda-ku, Tokyo, 102-0071, Japan
Tel.: (81) 362616930
Web Site: https://www.hottolink.co.jp
Year Founded: 2000
3680—(TKS)
Rev.: $33,599,510
Assets: $60,194,100
Liabilities: $16,682,770
Net Worth: $43,511,330
Earnings: $1,602,340
Fiscal Year-end: 12/31/23
Social Data & Media Analytics
N.A.I.C.S.: 518210

HOTTO LINK INC.

Hotto Link Inc.—(Continued)
Yuki Uchiyama (Pres & CEO)
Subsidiaries:

Effyis,Inc. (1)
700 Tower Dr Ste 140, Troy, MI 48098
Tel.: (248) 813-8701
Data Processing Services
N.A.I.C.S.: 518210

HOTUNG INVESTMENT HOLDINGS LIMITED
9 Fl 261 Sung Chiang Road, Taipei, 10483, ROC, Taiwan
Tel.: (886) 225006700
Web Site: https://www.hotung.com.tw
Year Founded: 1987
Sales Range: $25-49.9 Million
Emp.: 43
Financial Investment Services
N.A.I.C.S.: 523999
Jennifer Huang Tsui-Hui (Chm, Pres, CEO & Mng Dir)

HOTUSA HOTELS SA
Princesa 58, 08003, Barcelona, Spain
Tel.: (34) 93 268 10 10   ES
Web Site:
    http://www.hotusagroup.com
Year Founded: 1977
Owns & Operates Hotels
N.A.I.C.S.: 721110
Amancio López-Seijas (Chm)

HOUDARD
16 Rue Du President Kennedy, 28110, Luce, Eure Et Loir, France
Tel.: (33) 237912970
Web Site: http://www.houdard.fr
Emp.: 70
Wood Products Mfr
N.A.I.C.S.: 423310
Jean-Marc Baret (Head-Pur)

HOULDER INSURANCE SERVICES LTD.
7th Floor Fountain House 130 Fenchurch Street, London, EC3M 5DJ, United Kingdom
Tel.: (44) 2079803800
Web Site: http://www.houlder.co.uk
General Insurance Services
N.A.I.C.S.: 524210
A. Ma (Mng Dir)

HOULE ELECTRIC LIMITED
5050 North Fraser Way, Burnaby, V5J 0H1, BC, Canada
Tel.: (604) 434-2681
Web Site: https://www.houle.ca
Year Founded: 1944
Rev.: $25,543,969
Emp.: 900
Electrical Contracting Services
N.A.I.C.S.: 238210
Keith Parsonage (Pres)

HOULE RESTAURATION
13 Rue Theodore Monod, 76160, Rouen, Seine Maritime, France
Tel.: (33) 235898909
Web Site: http://www.convivo.fr
Year Founded: 1982
Sales Range: $10-24.9 Million
Emp.: 310
Restaurant
N.A.I.C.S.: 722511

HOUPU CLEAN ENERGY GROUP CO., LTD
No 555 Kanglong Road High-tech West District, Chengdu, Sichuan, China
Tel.: (86) 4000002005
Web Site: https://hqhp.cn

300471—(CHIN)
Rev.: $131,868,488
Assets: $337,130,616
Liabilities: $156,417,686
Net Worth: $180,712,930
Earnings: ($9,887,290)
Fiscal Year-end: 12/31/23
Natural Gas Station Equipment Mfr
N.A.I.C.S.: 333310
Subsidiaries:

Air Liquid Houpu Hydrogen Equipment Co., Ltd. (1)
No 555 Kanglong Road, West Gaoxin District, Chengdu, Sichuan, China
Tel.: (86) 2861547258
Web Site: https://www.alhph2.com
Hydrogen Energy Equipment Mfr
N.A.I.C.S.: 333132

Chengdu Andisoon Measure Co., Ltd. (1)
No 88 West Wulian Road Wulian Industrial Park, SouthWest Hangkonggang Economic Development District Shuangliu County, Chengdu, China
Tel.: (86) 2863165822
Web Site: https://en.andisoon.com
Fluid Meter Mfr
N.A.I.C.S.: 334514

Sichuan Hongda Petroleum & Natural Gas Co., Ltd. (1)
13 of Guangfu Road 8 C Zone Qingyang Industrial ABP, Qingyang District, Chengdu, Sichuan, China
Tel.: (86) 2862325060
Web Site: http://www.schdsy.com
Commercial & Service Industry Machinery Mfr
N.A.I.C.S.: 333310

HOUSE FOODS GROUP INC.
1-5-7 Mikuriya-Sakaemachi, Higashiosaka-city, Osaka, 577-8520, Japan
Tel.: (81) 667881231
Web Site: https://www.housefoods-group.com
Year Founded: 1913
2810—(TKS)
Rev.: $1,980,356,000
Assets: $2,852,882,610
Liabilities: $727,047,120
Net Worth: $2,125,835,490
Earnings: $116,203,800
Emp.: 6,543
Fiscal Year-end: 03/31/24
Holding Company; Food Mfr
N.A.I.C.S.: 551112
Hiroshi Urakami (Pres-Corp Plng Div & Pres-Corp Plng Div)
Subsidiaries:

Asaoka Spice K.K. (1)
6-3 Kioicho, Chiyoda-ku, Tokyo, 102-8560, Japan
Tel.: (81) 352116062
Web Site: https://www.asaokaspice.co.jp
Emp.: 10
Spices Whslr
N.A.I.C.S.: 424490

Delica Chef Corporation (1)
49-2 Kiyohisa-cho, Kuki, 346-0035, Saitama, Japan
Tel.: (81) 480295020
Web Site: https://delica-chef.co.jp
Sales Range: $25-49.9 Million
Emp.: 1,500
Food Mfr
N.A.I.C.S.: 311991

Gaban Co., Ltd. (1)
2-31-1 Shinkawa, Chuo-Ku, Tokyo, 104-0033, Japan
Tel.: (81) 335373020
Web Site: https://www.housegaban.com
Emp.: 393
Cooking Ingredients Mfr & Distr
N.A.I.C.S.: 311423
Seiji Ikoma (Pres)

Gaban Spice Manufacturing (M) Sdn. Bhd. (1)
No 742 Lorong Perindustrian Bukit Minyak 11 MK 13, Taman Perindustrian Bukit Minyak, 14000, Bukit Mertajam, Penang, Malaysia
Tel.: (60) 45072929
Web Site: https://www.gabanspice.com.my
Spice Product Mfr
N.A.I.C.S.: 311942

House Ai-Factory Corporation (1)
Tel.: (81) 667207040
Spice Product Mfr
N.A.I.C.S.: 311942

House Business Partners Corporation (1)
1-5-7 Mikuriyasakaemachi, Higashi, Osaka, Japan
Tel.: (81) 667881238
Accounting & Personnel Services
N.A.I.C.S.: 541219

House Food Analytical Laboratory Inc. (1)
1-4 Takanodai, Yotsukaido, 284-0033, Chiba, Japan
Tel.: (81) 432375676
Web Site: https://www.food-analab.jp
Food Testing Services
N.A.I.C.S.: 541380
Naomi Sasaki (Pres)

House Foods America Corporation (1)
7351 Orangewood Ave, Garden Grove, CA 92841
Tel.: (714) 901-4350
Processed Foods Mfr & Curry Restaurants Operation Services
N.A.I.C.S.: 311612
Subsidiary (Domestic):

El Burrito Mexican Food Products Corp. (2)
14944 Don Julian Rd, City of Industry, CA 91746
Tel.: (626) 369-7828
Web Site: https://www.elburrito.com
Sales Range: $10-24.9 Million
Emp.: 40
Mexican Food Mfr
N.A.I.C.S.: 311421
Grace Roth (Founder)

House Foods China Inc. (1)
Room 1601 Antai Building 107 Zunyi Road, Changning District, Shanghai, 200051, China
Tel.: (86) 2162789990
Emp.: 213
Food Products Mfr
N.A.I.C.S.: 311999

House Foods Corporation (1)
6-3 Kioicho, Chiyoda-ku, Tokyo, 102-8560, Japan
Tel.: (81) 332641231
Emp.: 1,607
Food Products Mfr
N.A.I.C.S.: 311999

House Foods Vietnam Co., Ltd. (1)
Plot 239 Road No 12, Amata Industrial Park, Bien Hoa, Dong Nai, Vietnam
Tel.: (84) 2518877225
Emp.: 60
Packaged Food Mfr
N.A.I.C.S.: 311999
Seiki Nakatani (Gen Dir)

House Logistics Service Corporation (1)
Tel.: (81) 671769297
Web Site: http://www.hls-house.co.jp
Sales Range: $75-99.9 Million
Emp.: 500
Logistic Services
N.A.I.C.S.: 541614

House Osotspa Foods Co., Ltd. (1)
14th Floor No 3 T-One Building 8 Soi Sukhumvit 40, Prakhanong Khlongtoei, Bangkok, 10110, Thailand
Tel.: (66) 228807413
Food & Beverage Product Mfr
N.A.I.C.S.: 311999

House Wellness Foods Corporation (1)
3-20 Founder, Itami, 664-0011, Hyogo, Japan
Tel.: (81) 727781121
Web Site: https://www.house-wf.co.jp
Sales Range: $100-124.9 Million
Emp.: 254
Food & Beverages Mfr
N.A.I.C.S.: 311511

Ichibanya Co., Ltd. (1)
6-12-23 Mitsui, Ichinomiya, 491-8601, Aichi-ken, Japan
Tel.: (81) 586767545
Web Site: https://www.ichibanya.co.jp
Rev.: $390,921,330
Assets: $312,186,880
Liabilities: $89,716,860
Net Worth: $222,470,020
Earnings: $19,036,650
Emp.: 1,175
Fiscal Year-end: 02/29/2024
Full-Service Restaurants
N.A.I.C.S.: 722511
Mamoru Kuzuhara (Pres)

Plant (Domestic):

Ichibanya Co., Ltd. - Saga Plant (2)
308-1 Kokura, Kiyama-cho Miyoki- gun, Saga, 841-0201, Japan
Tel.: (81) 94 292 1330
Web Site: https://www.ichibanya.co.jp
Restaurant Operators
N.A.I.C.S.: 722511

Ichibanya Co., Ltd. - Tochigi Plant (2)
2-2-1 Kobushidai, Yaita, 329-1579, Tochigi, Japan
Tel.: (81) 28 748 3335
Web Site: https://www.ichibanya.co.jp
Restaurant Operators
N.A.I.C.S.: 722511

Ichibanya Hong Kong Limited (1)
Shop 402 4/F Windsor House 311 Gloucester Road, Tsim Sha Tsui, Causeway Bay, China (Hong Kong)
Tel.: (852) 35720460
Web Site: https://www.ichibanya.com.hk
Restaurant Services
N.A.I.C.S.: 722511

Ichibanya USA (1)
2455 Sepulveda Blvd Ste C, Torrance, CA 90501
Tel.: (310) 294-5315
Web Site: https://ichibanyausa.com
Restaurant Services
N.A.I.C.S.: 722511

Malony Co., Ltd. (1)
2-26 Nakanoshimacho, Suita, 564-0035, Osaka, Japan
Tel.: (81) 663812626
Food Products Mfr
N.A.I.C.S.: 311999
Katsuaki Namba (Pres)

PT House & Vox Indonesia (1)
Atria Sudirman 17th Floor Jl Jend Sudirman Kav 33A, Karet Tengsin Tanah Abang, Jakarta Pusat, 10220, Indonesia
Tel.: (62) 215745854
Web Site: https://housejapanesecurry.com
Food Product Mfr & Distr
N.A.I.C.S.: 311999

Shanghai House Curry Coco Ichibanya Restaurant, Inc. (1)
Rm 2003A Aetna Tower 107 Zun Yi Rd, Changning Dist, Shanghai, 200051, China
Tel.: (86) 2162789525
Sales Range: $10-24.9 Million
Emp.: 5
Curry Restaurants Operator
N.A.I.C.S.: 722511

Sun House Foods Corporation (1)
77 Takayacho, Konan, 483-8085, Aichi, Japan
Tel.: (81) 587552141
Web Site: https://www.shouse.jp
Emp.: 342
Food Mfr
N.A.I.C.S.: 311412

Sun Supply Corporation (1)

8 Miyadacho Haibara, Konan, Aichi, Japan
Tel.: (81) 587571780
Processed Meat Product Mfr
N.A.I.C.S.: 311612

Tim Food Co., Ltd. (1)
158 Viphavadee-Rungsit Rd, Dindaeng,
Bangkok, 10400, Thailand
Tel.: (66) 26917886
Web Site: https://www.timfood.co.th
Emp.: 450
Frozen Vegetable & Fruit Mfr
N.A.I.C.S.: 311411

Vox Trading (Thailand) Co., Ltd. (1)
33/66 Wall Street Tower 14F Room 1402
Surawongse Road Suriyawongse, Bangrak,
Bangkok, 10500, Thailand
Tel.: (66) 22374726
Food Product Mfr & Distr
N.A.I.C.S.: 311999

Vox Trading Co., Ltd. (1)
Hatchobori Sankei Bldg 8F 2-7-1 Hatchobori, Chuo-ku, Tokyo, 104-0032, Japan
Tel.: (81) 335555500
Food Products Mfr
N.A.I.C.S.: 311999
Haruki Kawabe *(CEO)*

HOUSE OF HABIB
2nd Floor House of Habib 3 Jinnah
CH Society, Sharea Faisal, Karachi,
75350, Pakistan
Tel.: (92) 2134312030
Web Site: http://www.hoh.net
Year Founded: 1841
Sales Range: $10-24.9 Million
Emp.: 14,000
Holding Company Services
N.A.I.C.S.: 551112
Rafiq Habib *(Chm)*

Subsidiaries:

Agriauto Industries Ltd (1)
5th Floor House of Habib 3 JCHS Block-7/8, Shahra-e-Faisal, Karachi, Pakistan
Tel.: (92) 2134541540
Web Site: https://www.agriauto.com.pk
Rev.: $29,911,509
Assets: $32,843,431
Liabilities: $10,676,529
Net Worth: $22,166,903
Earnings: ($623,376)
Emp.: 698
Fiscal Year-end: 06/30/2023
Automotive Components Mfr
N.A.I.C.S.: 336390
Fahim Kapadia *(CEO)*

Subsidiary (Domestic):

Agriauto Stamping Company (Pvt.)
Ltd. (2)
5th Floor House of Habib 3 JCHS Block-7/8
Shahra-e-Faisal, Karachi, Pakistan
Tel.: (92) 21 34541540
Web Site: http://www.asc.net.pk
Automotive Metal Stamping Parts Mfr
N.A.I.C.S.: 336370
Yutaka Arae *(Chm & CEO)*

AuVitronics Limited (1)
3rd Floor Siddiq Sons Tower Plot 3 Block
7/8 Shahrah-e-Faisal Khi, Jinnah Co-operative Housing Society, Karachi, Pakistan
Tel.: (92) 2134312030
Web Site: http://www.auvitronics.com
Emp.: 900
Audio & Vedio Equipment Mfr
N.A.I.C.S.: 334310
Owais Ul Mustafa *(Chm)*

Unit (Domestic):

AuVitronics Limited - Manufacturing
Unit-1 (2)
A-137 138 153 154 H I T E Hub Distt, Bela,
Balochistan, Pakistan
Tel.: (92) 853 303014
Audio Equipment Mfr
N.A.I.C.S.: 334310

AuVitronics Limited - Manufacturing
Unit-2 (2)
Plot No Sp-6 Nwiz/P-133/C North West Industrial Zone, Port Qasim Authority, Karachi, Sind, Pakistan
Tel.: (92) 34750601
Plastics Product Mfr
N.A.I.C.S.: 326199

Habib METRO Pakistan (Private)
Limited (1)
Mezzanine Floor House of Habib Building 3
Jinnah C H Society, Main Shahra-e-Faisal,
Karachi, Pakistan
Tel.: (92) 213431203044
Web Site: https://habibmetro.pk
Real Estate Development Services
N.A.I.C.S.: 531390
Raza Siddiqui *(Mktg Mgr)*

Indus Motor Company Limited (1)
Plot No N W Z/P-1 Port Qasim Authority,
Karachi, Pakistan
Tel.: (92) 2134721100
Web Site: http://www.toyota-indus.com
Rev.: $1,710,890,881
Assets: $1,328,724,848
Liabilities: $993,316,066
Net Worth: $335,408,782
Earnings: $98,129,476
Emp.: 3,139
Fiscal Year-end: 06/30/2022
Automobile Mfr; Owned by Toyota Motor
Corporation, by Toyota Tsusho Corporation
& by House of Habib
N.A.I.C.S.: 336110
Ali S. Habib *(Founder & Chm)*

Thal Limited (1)
4th Fl House of Habib 3-Jinnah Cooperative
Housing Society Block 7 8, Karachi,
Shahrah-e-Faisal, Pakistan
Tel.: (92) 2134312030
Web Site: https://www.thallimited.com
Rev.: $119,194,533
Assets: $221,576,836
Liabilities: $56,106,501
Net Worth: $165,470,336
Earnings: $17,483,967
Emp.: 4,262
Fiscal Year-end: 06/30/2023
Jute Goods Mfr; Automotive Air Conditioners, Wire Harnesses & Heater Blowers Assembly & Mfr
N.A.I.C.S.: 314994
Saqlain Akthar *(Head-Jute Bus)*

Subsidiary (Domestic):

Makro-Habib Pakistan Ltd. (2)
5-B-3 Gulberg III, 54660, Lahore, Pakistan
Tel.: (92) 42571645155
General Stores
N.A.I.C.S.: 455219

Noble Computer Services (Pvt)
Limited (2)
First Floor House of Habib Jinnah Cooperative Housing Society, Bldg 3 Main Shahrah-e-Faisal, Karachi, 75350, Pakistan
Tel.: (92) 2134325482
Web Site: http://www.noble-computers.com
Emp.: 15
Data Processing Computer Services
N.A.I.C.S.: 518210
Syed Azad Zaidi *(Gen Mgr)*

Pakistan Industrial Aids (Private)
Limited (2)
4th Fl House of Habib Bldg 3-Jinnah C.H.S
Block 7 8, Shahra-e-Faisal, Karachi, Pakistan
Tel.: (92) 215897608
Web Site: http://www.pakial.com
Marketing Services
N.A.I.C.S.: 541613

Thal Engineering (2)
Plot No 1 2 25 26 Korangi Industrial Area,
Karachi, Pakistan
Tel.: (92) 21 3589 6426
Web Site: http://www.thalengg.com
Automobile Parts Mfr
N.A.I.C.S.: 336330

Division (Domestic):

Thal Limited-Laminates Division (2)
4th floor House of Habib 3-Jinnah Co-operative housing society, Block 7/8
Sharae-Faisal, Karachi, 75350, Pakistan
Tel.: (92) 21 345 45195
Web Site: http://www.formite.com.pk
Emp.: 20
Wooden Laminates Mfr
N.A.I.C.S.: 321215
Raza Haider *(Gen Mgr)*

HOUSE OF ROSE CO., LTD.
2-21-7 Akasaka, Minato-ku, Tokyo,
107-8625, Japan
Tel.: (81) 351145825
Web Site:
https://www.houseofrose.co.jp
Year Founded: 1982
7506—(TKS)
Sales Range: $125-149.9 Million
Cosmetic Product Distr & Whslr
N.A.I.C.S.: 456120
Harutoshi Kanno *(Pres)*

HOUSE VIET NAM JOINT STOCK COMPANY
408 Nguyen Thi Minh Khai St Ward
5, District 3, Ho Chi Minh City, Vietnam
Tel.: (84) 8 3818 1888
Sales Range: $1-9.9 Million
Real Estate Development Services
N.A.I.C.S.: 531390
Tran Van Thanh *(Exec Dir)*

HOUSEFREEDOM CO., LTD.
4-1-34 Ao, Matsubara, 580-0043,
Japan
Tel.: (81) 723360503
8996—(FKA)
Rev.: $117,737,840
Assets: $103,488,880
Liabilities: $77,817,520
Net Worth: $25,671,360
Earnings: $5,411,120
Fiscal Year-end: 12/31/20
Home & Office Product Distr
N.A.I.C.S.: 424120
Kenji Ojima *(Pres)*

HOUSING & DEVELOPMENT BANK SAE
26 El Kroum Street - Mohandessin,
Cairo, Egypt
Tel.: (20) 21270600
Web Site: https://www.hdb-egy.com
Year Founded: 1979
HDBK.CA—(EGX)
Rev.: $441,669,808
Assets: $5,059,673,835
Liabilities: $4,357,491,809
Net Worth: $702,182,026
Earnings: $128,645,513
Emp.: 2,453
Fiscal Year-end: 12/31/21
Commercial Banking Services
N.A.I.C.S.: 522110
Hassan Esmaiel Ghanem *(Chm, CEO & Mng Dir)*

HOUSING AND URBAN DEVELOPMENT CORPORATION LIMITED
HUDCO Bhawan Core-7-A India
Habitat Centre Lodhi Road, New
Delhi, 110 003, India
Tel.: (91) 1124649610
Web Site: http://www.hudco.org
Year Founded: 1970
Housing & Urban Development
N.A.I.C.S.: 925110
P. Jayapal *(Sr Exec Dir-Social Housing & Ops)*

HOUSING DEVELOPMENT & INFRASTRUCTURE LIMITED
09-01 HDIL Towers Anant Kanekar
Marg Station Road, Bandra E, Mumbai, 400 051, Maharashtra, India
Tel.: (91) 2267889000
Web Site: https://www.hdil.in
HDIL—(NSE)
Rev.: $57,957,422
Assets: $542,576,894
Liabilities: $848,344,306
Net Worth: ($305,767,412)
Earnings: ($1,906,537,173)
Emp.: 286
Fiscal Year-end: 03/31/20
Real Estate Development & Construction
N.A.I.C.S.: 236115
Sarang Wadhawan *(Vice Chm & Mng Dir)*

Subsidiaries:

Excel Arcade Private Ltd. (1)
9-01 HDIL Towers Anant Kanekar Marg
Bandra East, Mumbai, 400 051, India
Tel.: (91) 22 67888000
Web Site: http://www.hdil.in
Building Construction Services
N.A.I.C.S.: 236220

HOUSING DEVELOPMENT FINANCE BANK OF SRI LANKA
Sir Chittampalam A Gardiner Mawatha, PO Box 2085, 2, Colombo, 2,
Sri Lanka
Tel.: (94) 112356800
Web Site: https://www.hdfc.lk
HDFC.N0000—(COL)
Rev.: $44,722,503
Assets: $209,863,287
Liabilities: $184,757,227
Net Worth: $25,106,060
Earnings: $4,251,438
Emp.: 487
Fiscal Year-end: 12/31/23
Banking Services
N.A.I.C.S.: 522180
W. M. Chandrasena *(Mgr-Valuation)*

HOUSING DEVELOPMENT FINANCE CORPORATION LIMITED
HDFC House H T Parekh Marg 165-166 Backbay Reclamation Churchgate, Mumbai, 400 020, India
Tel.: (91) 2266316000
Web Site: https://www.hdfc.com
Year Founded: 1977
500010—(NSE)
Rev.: $183,439,410
Assets: $1,308,709,118
Liabilities: $1,050,555,806
Net Worth: $258,153,312
Earnings: $33,211,150
Emp.: 4,017
Fiscal Year-end: 03/31/23
Mortgage Banking Services
N.A.I.C.S.: 522110
Deepak S. Parekh *(Chm)*

Subsidiaries:

HDFC Asset Management Company
Limited (1)
Ramon House 3rd Floor HT Parekh Marg
169 Backbay , Reclamation Churchgate,
Mumbai, 400 20, India
Tel.: (91) 2256316300
Web Site: http://www.hdfcfund.com
Financial Management Services
N.A.I.C.S.: 523999
Rahul Baijal *(Sr Mgr-Fund-Equity)*

Unit (Domestic):

HDFC Mutual Fund (2)
165 166 HDFC House 2nd floor Backbay
Reclamation, H T Parekh Marg Churchgate,
Mumbai, 400020, India **(60%)**
Tel.: (91) 2222029111
Financial Investment Services
N.A.I.C.S.: 523999
Krishan Kumar Daga *(Mgr-Arbitrage Fund)*

HDFC Bank Limited (1)
No 11 Neelkanth Kanth IT Corporate Park
Kirol Road, Vidyavihar West, Mumbai,

HOUSING DEVELOPMENT FINANCE CORPORATION LIMITED

Housing Development Finance Corporation Limited—(Continued)

400086, India
Tel.: (91) 9426792001
Web Site: https://www.hdfcbank.com
Rev.: $42,213,985,163
Assets: $528,968,013,512
Liabilities: $434,415,126,457
Net Worth: $94,552,887,055
Earnings: $7,525,111,915
Emp.: 213,527
Fiscal Year-end: 03/31/2024
Banking & Services
N.A.I.C.S.: 522110
Kaizad Bharucha (Exec Dir)

HDFC Capital Advisors Ltd.
Ramon House H T Parekh Marg 169 Backbay Reclamation, Churchgate, Mumbai, 400 020, Maharashtra, India
Tel.: (91) 226 141 3951
Web Site: https://www.hdfcapital.com
Real Estate Private Equity Investment Services
N.A.I.C.S.: 523940
Vipul Roongta (CEO & Mng Dir)

HDFC Credila Financial Services Ltd. (1)
B 301 Citi Point Next to Kohinoor Continental Andheri-Kurla Road, Andheri East, Mumbai, 400 059, Maharashtra, India
Tel.: (91) 225 045 3000
Web Site: https://www.hdfccredila.com
Education Loan Services
N.A.I.C.S.: 522291
Manjeet Bijlani (CFO & Chief IR Officer)

HDFC ERGO General Insurance Company Ltd. (1)
1st Floor HDFC House Backbay Reclamation, H T Parekh Marg Churchgate, Mumbai, 400 020, India
Tel.: (91) 2262346234
Web Site: https://www.hdfcergo.com
Emp.: 800
Insurance Related Activities
N.A.I.C.S.: 524298
Deepak S. Parekh (Chm)

HDFC Sales (1)
4th Floor Wing - A HDFC House BackBay Recl 166 HT Parekh Marg, Churchgate, Mumbai, 400 020, India
Tel.: (91) 2261552400
Web Site: www.hdfcsales.com
Financial Management Solutions
N.A.I.C.S.: 541611
Santosh Nair (CEO)

Subsidiary (Domestic):

HDFC Realty Limited (2)
169 Backbay Reclamation, HT Parekh Marg, Churchgate, Mumbai, 400 020, Maharashtra, India
Tel.: (91) 2266316161
Web Site: http://www.hdfcrealty.com
Sales Range: $800-899.9 Million
Emp.: 1,750
Financial Management & Mortgage Solutions
N.A.I.C.S.: 523999

HDFC Securities Limited (1)
Office Floor 8 i Think Bldg Jolly Board Campus Kanjurmarg East, Mumbai, 400 042, India
Tel.: (91) 2230753400
Web Site: https://www.hdfcsec.com
Securities Investment & Management Services
N.A.I.C.S.: 523150
Dhiraj Relli (CEO)

HDFC Standard Life Insurance Company Ltd. (1)
Trade Star 2nd floor A-Wing Junction of Kondivita & MV Road, Andheri-Kurla Road, Andheri East, Mumbai, 400 059, Maharashtra, India **(61.65%)**
Tel.: (91) 2228220055
Insurance Services
N.A.I.C.S.: 524298
Vibha Padalkar (CEO & Mng Dir)

HDFC Trustee Company Limited (1)
Ramon House 3rd Floor 169 Backbay Reclamation Churchgate, HT Parekh Marg,

Mumbai, 400020, India
Tel.: (91) 60006767
Web Site: http://www.hdfcfund.com
Financial Management & Consulting Services
N.A.I.C.S.: 523999
Anil Kumar Hirjee (Chm)

HOV SERVICES LIMITED
3rd Floor Shard Arcade Pune Satara Road, Bibwewadi, Pune, 411 037, Maharashtra, India
Tel.: (91) 2024221460
Web Site: https://www.hovsltd.com
532761—(BOM)
Rev.: $1,556,291
Assets: $6,179,724
Liabilities: $2,091,412
Net Worth: $4,088,312
Earnings: $293,339
Emp.: 178
Fiscal Year-end: 03/31/22
Holding Company; Business Process Outsourcing Services
N.A.I.C.S.: 551112
Surinder Rametra (Exec Dir)

Subsidiaries:

HOV Environment Solutions Private Limited (1)
3rd Floor Sharda Arcade Pune Satara Road, Bibwewadi, Pune, 411 037, Maharashtra, India
Tel.: (91) 2024221460
Web Site: https://hovenvironment.com
Environmental Services
N.A.I.C.S.: 541620

Meridian Consulting Group, LLC (1)
20 Westport Rd, Wilton, CT 06897
Tel.: (203) 834-0123
Web Site: http://www.meridianconsulting.com
Marketing Consulting Services
N.A.I.C.S.: 541613
Ronald Clark Cogburn (Pres)

HOVDING SVERIGE AB
Grimsbygatan 24, 211 20, Malmo, Sweden
Tel.: (46) 40 23 68 68
Web Site: http://www.hovding.com
HOVD—(OMX)
Rev.: $18,619,642
Assets: $13,942,757
Liabilities: $7,465,192
Net Worth: $6,477,565
Earnings: ($5,402,040)
Emp.: 36
Fiscal Year-end: 12/31/20
Cycle Helmet Mfr
N.A.I.C.S.: 336991
Fredrik Carling (CEO)

HOVE A/S
Herstedostervej 7, 2600, Glostrup, Denmark
Tel.: (45) 70221022
Web Site: https://hove-as.com
Year Founded: 2000
HOVE—(CSE)
Rev.: $27,683,423
Assets: $14,277,041
Liabilities: $3,701,784
Net Worth: $10,575,257
Earnings: $530,096
Emp.: 52
Fiscal Year-end: 12/31/23
Heavy Machinery Mfr
N.A.I.C.S.: 333996
Hans Christian Hansen (Owner)

Subsidiaries:

Hove Americas Inc. (1)
3030 W Hampden Ave, Englewood, CO 80110
Tel.: (720) 682-6181
Industrial Machinery Mfr
N.A.I.C.S.: 333924

Hove Brasil Equipamentos E servicos De Lubrificacao Ltda. (1)
Av Marques de Sao Vicente 230 conjunto 1218 sala 3C, Sao Paulo, 01139-000, Brazil
Tel.: (55) 11999663283
Industrial Machinery Mfr
N.A.I.C.S.: 333924

Hove Lubricants India Private Limited (1)
Gat No/ Survey No 271/4 Bhugaon, Taluka-Mulshi, Pune, 412115, India
Tel.: (91) 7507876137
Industrial Machinery Mfr
N.A.I.C.S.: 333924

HOVID BERHAD
No 121 Jalan Tunku Abdul Rahman, 30010, Ipoh, Perak Darul Ridzuan, Malaysia
Tel.: (60) 55060690 MY
Web Site: http://www.hovid.com
Rev.: $52,822,878
Assets: $88,505,355
Liabilities: $34,454,627
Net Worth: $54,050,728
Earnings: $2,248,144
Fiscal Year-end: 06/30/18
Herbal Tea Mfr
N.A.I.C.S.: 111998
Yuet Seam Ng (Co-Sec)

Subsidiaries:

Hovid Inc. (1)
Unit B 7 Fl Karina Bldg 33 Shaw Blvd, Pasig, 1600, Philippines
Tel.: (63) 26356357
Pharmaceutical Products Distr
N.A.I.C.S.: 424210
David Ho (Mng Dir)

Hovid Limited (1)
World Tech Centre 95 How Ming St, Kwun Tong, Kowloon, China (Hong Kong)
Tel.: (852) 82092638
Sales Range: $25-49.9 Million
Emp.: 15
Pharmaceutical Products Distr
N.A.I.C.S.: 424210
Dennis Chan (Mng Dir)

Hovid Marketing Sdn. Bhd. (1)
64 & 64B Jalan Leong Sin Nam, 30300, Ipoh, Perak Darul Ridzuan, Malaysia
Tel.: (60) 52412028
Web Site: http://www.hovidpure.com
Sales Range: $50-74.9 Million
Emp.: 10
Pharmaceutical Products Distr
N.A.I.C.S.: 424210

Integrated Logistics (H.K.) Limited (1)
Room 1212 12/F Chinachem Golden Plz, Tsimshatsui East, Kowloon, China (Hong Kong)
Tel.: (852) 23698399
Emp.: 5
Logistics Consulting Servies
N.A.I.C.S.: 541614

HOVIONE FARMA CIENCIA S.A.
Sete Casas, 2674-506, Loures, Portugal
Tel.: (351) 219829000 PT
Web Site: http://www.hovione.com
Year Founded: 1959
Sales Range: $50-74.9 Million
Emp.: 600
Development & Synthesis of Active Pharmaceutical Ingredients
N.A.I.C.S.: 325412
Guy Villax (CEO)

Subsidiaries:

Hovione LLC (1)
40 Lake Dr, East Windsor, NJ 08520 **(100%)**
Tel.: (609) 918-2600
Web Site: http://www.hovione.com
Sales Range: $25-49.9 Million
Emp.: 40

INTERNATIONAL PUBLIC

Development & Synthesis of Active Pharmaceutical Ingredients
N.A.I.C.S.: 325412
Guy Villax (CEO)

Hovione Limited (1)
Aubin House 11th Floor, 171-172 Gloucester Road, Wanchai, China (Hong Kong) **(100%)**
Tel.: (852) 28911836
Sales Range: $25-49.9 Million
Emp.: 7
Pharmaceutical Preparation Mfr
N.A.I.C.S.: 325412
Sofia Lee (Mng Dir)

Hovione Limited (1)
Loughbeg, Ringaskiddy, Cork, Ireland
Tel.: (353) 214512856
Pharmaceuticals Product Mfr
N.A.I.C.S.: 325411
Paul Downing (Gen Mgr)

Hovione PharmaScience Ltd. (1)
No 154 Estrada Coronel Nicolau de Mesquita 154, Taipa, China (Macau)
Tel.: (853) 28827544
Sales Range: $50-74.9 Million
Emp.: 125
Pharmaceutical Preparation Mfr
N.A.I.C.S.: 325412
Eddy Leong (Gen Mgr)

Hovione SA (1)
Sete Casas, Loures, 2671 901, Portugal
Tel.: (351) 219829000
Web Site: http://www.hovione.com
Sales Range: $125-149.9 Million
Emp.: 400
Pharmaceutical Preparation Mfr
N.A.I.C.S.: 325412
Diane Villax (Chm)

HOWA BANK LTD.
4-10 Ojinakamachi, Oita, 8708686, Japan
Tel.: (81) 975342611
Financial Consulting Services
N.A.I.C.S.: 541611
Atsushi Gondo (Pres)

HOWA CORPORATION
4-4-18 Kojima Tanokuchi, Kurashiki, Okayama, Japan
Tel.: (81) 86 477 6060
Web Site: http://www.howa-net.co.jp
Year Founded: 1965
Rev.: $33,000,000
Emp.: 250
Dyeing Services
N.A.I.C.S.: 313310
Toyoo Tashiro (Pres)

Subsidiaries:

Kiya Corporation (1)
1-18-6 Nerima-ku, Kitamachi, Tokyo, 179-0081, Japan
Tel.: (81) 339323191
Web Site: http://www.kiyacorp.co.jp
Automotive Component Mfr & Distr
N.A.I.C.S.: 336390
Hiroshi Yokoyama (CEO)

Okayama Beauty Corporation (1)
272 Morisue Setocho, Higashi-ku, Okayama, 709-0874, Japan
Tel.: (81) 869522311
Apparels Mfr
N.A.I.C.S.: 315250

HOWA MACHINERY, LTD.
1900-1 Sukaguchi, Kiyosu, 452-8601, Aichi, Japan
Tel.: (81) 524081111
Web Site: https://www.howa.co.jp
Year Founded: 1907
62030—(TKS)
Rev.: $130,730,059
Assets: $200,125,481
Liabilities: $85,596,276
Net Worth: $114,529,205
Earnings: ($5,768,086)
Emp.: 693
Fiscal Year-end: 03/31/24

AND PRIVATE COMPANIES

Machine Tools Mfr
N.A.I.C.S.: 333517
Takahiro Tsukamoto *(Pres & Mng Dir)*
Subsidiaries:

Chunichi Transportation Co., Ltd. (1)
1900-1 Sukaguchi, Kiyosu, 452-0905, Aichi, Japan
Tel.: (81) 524005251
Web Site: http://www.chunichi-unso.co.jp
Freight Transportation Services
N.A.I.C.S.: 488510

Hoen Co., Ltd. (1)
1900 Sukaguchi, Kiyosu, 452-0905, Aichi, Japan
Tel.: (81) 524091293
Cleaning Service
N.A.I.C.S.: 561720
Katsutoshi Okada *(Pres)*

Howa (Tianjin) Machinery Co., Ltd. (1)
No 28 4th Road Saida, Xiqing Economic Development Area C2 C3 Mould Industrial City, Tianjin, 300385, China
Tel.: (86) 2287204183
Hydraulic Equipment Retailer
N.A.I.C.S.: 423830
Hiromitsu Ishihara *(Chm)*

PT. HowAska Mesin Indonesia (1)
Multiguna Niaga Area Stage II JI Tanjung No 23 Kawasan BIIE, Lippo Cikarang, Bekasi, Jawa Barat, Indonesia
Tel.: (62) 2189900523
Web Site: http://www.howaska.co.id
Machine Tool Repair & Maintenance Services
N.A.I.C.S.: 811310

Securico Co., Ltd. (1)
4075-2 Uruido, Hasuda, 349-0133, Saitama, Japan
Tel.: (81) 487660527
Web Site: http://www.securico.co.jp
Vehicle Equipment Mfr
N.A.I.C.S.: 336320

HOWARD HOTELS LTD.

20 Maurya Complex B-28 Subhash Chowk, Laxmi Nagar, Delhi, 110092, India
Tel.: (91) 5624048600
Web Site: https://www.howardhotelsltd.com
526761—(BOM)
Rev.: $595,222
Assets: $1,871,456
Liabilities: $603,385
Net Worth: $1,268,071
Earnings: ($105,583)
Emp.: 12
Fiscal Year-end: 03/31/22
Home Management Services
N.A.I.C.S.: 721110
Nirankar Nath Mittal *(Chm & Mng Dir)*

HOWCO GROUP PLC

2nd Floor Fountain House 1-3 Woodside Crescent, Glasgow, G3 7UL, United Kingdom
Tel.: (44) 141 353 7800
Web Site: http://www.howcogroup.com
Year Founded: 1982
Emp.: 500
Metal Alloy Supplier & Processor
N.A.I.C.S.: 331110

HOWDEN GROUP HOLDINGS LIMITED

1 Creechurch Place, London, EC3A 5AF, United Kingdom
Tel.: (44) 20 7398 4888
Web Site: http://www.howdenholdings.com
Year Founded: 1994
Sales Range: $150-199.9 Million
Emp.: 1,229
General Insurance Services
N.A.I.C.S.: 524210

David Howden *(CEO)*
Subsidiaries:

Bar-Ziv Ravid Insurance Agency Limited (1)
20 Hamasger, PO Box 36700, Tel Aviv, Israel
Tel.: (972) 36387000
General Insurance Services
N.A.I.C.S.: 524210

Clinical Trials Insurance Services Limited (1)
4 Lloyd s Avenue, London, EC3N 4ED, United Kingdom
Tel.: (44) 2071331243
Web Site: http://www.ctisltd.com
General Insurance Services
N.A.I.C.S.: 524210

Colemont Finland Oy (1)
Malminkaari 9 B 3 floor, 700, Helsinki, Finland
Tel.: (358) 954202400
General Insurance Services
N.A.I.C.S.: 524210

DCR (FI) Limited (1)
140 Leadenhall Street, London, EC3V 4QT, United Kingdom
Tel.: (44) 2073379888
General Insurance Services
N.A.I.C.S.: 524298

DUAL Australia Pty Limited (1)
Level 6 160 Sussex Street, Sydney, 2000, NSW, Australia
Tel.: (61) 292486300
Web Site: http://www.dualaustralia.com.au
General Insurance Services
N.A.I.C.S.: 524210
Leo Abbruzzo *(Mng Dir-ANZ)*

DUAL Commercial LLC (1)
1100 5th Ave S Ste 301, Naples, FL 34102
Tel.: (973) 631-7575
Web Site: http://www.dualcommercial.com
Commercial Property Management Services
N.A.I.C.S.: 531312
Amy Fitzgerald *(Mgr-HR)*

DUAL Corporate Risks Limited (1)
6th Floor Chancery Place 50 Brown Street, Manchester, M2 2JG, United Kingdom
Tel.: (44) 2073379888
Web Site: http://www.dualgroup.com
Commercial Property Management Services
N.A.I.C.S.: 531312
Jim OConnor *(CEO-North America)*

DUAL Deutschland GmbH (1)
Schanzenstrasse 36 / Gebaude 197, 51063, Cologne, Germany
Tel.: (49) 2211680260
Web Site: http://www.dualdeutschland.com
General Insurance Services
N.A.I.C.S.: 524128
Heiner Eickhoff *(Dir-European Dev)*

DUAL Group Americas Inc (1)
505 S Villa Real Dr Ste 211, Anaheim, CA 92807
Tel.: (973) 631-7575
General Insurance Services
N.A.I.C.S.: 524126

DUAL Iberica Riesgos Profesionales S.A. (1)
Alfonso XII 32 - 1a Planta, 28014, Madrid, Spain
Tel.: (34) 913691258
Web Site: http://www.dualiberica.com
General Insurance Services
N.A.I.C.S.: 524126
Isabel Jaraquemada Rodriguez *(Dir-Fin)*

DUAL International Limited (1)
Bankside House 107 Leadenhall Street, London, EC3A 4AF, United Kingdom
Tel.: (44) 2073379888
Web Site: http://www.dualinternational.com
General Insurance Services
N.A.I.C.S.: 524128
Alan Grant *(Deputy Chm-Exec Bd)*

DUAL Italia S.p.A (1)
Via Edmondo De Amicis 51, 20123, Milan, Italy
Tel.: (39) 0272080597
Web Site: http://www.dualitalia.com

HOWDEN GROUP HOLDINGS LIMITED

General Insurance Services
N.A.I.C.S.: 524128
Daniela Rubes *(CFO & Dir-HR)*

DUAL New Zealand Limited (1)
Level 20 191 Queen Street, Auckland, 1010, New Zealand
Tel.: (64) 99730190
Web Site: http://www.dualnewzealand.co.nz
General Insurance Services
N.A.I.C.S.: 524210
Andrew Beaton *(Mng Dir)*

DUAL Specialty Underwriters Inc. (1)
6915 Red Rd Ste 226, Coral Gables, FL 33143
Tel.: (786) 275-3233
Web Site: http://www.dualsu.com
General Insurance Services
N.A.I.C.S.: 524128
Bobby Vernon *(CEO)*

DUAL Underwriting Agency (Hong Kong) Limited (1)
7/F Grand Millennium Plaza 181 Queens Road Central, Hong Kong, China (Hong Kong)
Tel.: (852) 25306804
Web Site: http://www.dualasia.com
General Insurance Services
N.A.I.C.S.: 524128
Jodie Chung *(Gen Mgr)*

DUAL Underwriting Agency (Singapore) Pte. Limited (1)
4 Shenton Way 21-01 SGX Centre 2, Singapore, 068807, Singapore
Tel.: (65) 69080558
Web Site: http://www.dualasia.com
General Insurance Services
N.A.I.C.S.: 524128
Kenneth Tan *(Mgr-Underwriting-Asia)*

Donoria Spolka Akcyjna (1)
ul Wielkie Garbary 7A, 87-100, Torun, Poland
Tel.: (48) 564711010
Web Site: http://www.donoria.pl
General Insurance Services
N.A.I.C.S.: 524210
Dariusz Zajaczkowski *(Chm-Mgmt Bd)*

FP Group Limited (1)
Rm 1708 17/f Kai Tak Coml Bldg 317 - 319 Des Voeux Rd C, Sheung Wan, China (Hong Kong)
Tel.: (852) 28511823
Electronic Component & Peripheral Distr
N.A.I.C.S.: 425120

FP Marine Risks (Australia) Pty Limited (1)
Level 23 111 Pacific Highway, Sydney, 2060, NSW, Australia
Tel.: (61) 282368600
Web Site: http://www.fp-marine.com
General Insurance Services
N.A.I.C.S.: 524128
Andrew Glover *(Mng Dir)*

FP Marine Risks Limited (1)
Room 30 11th Floor North Building Beijing Kerry Centre, Chaoyang, Beijing, 100020, China
Tel.: (86) 1065997927
Web Site: http://www.fp-marine.com
General Insurance Services
N.A.I.C.S.: 524128
Dennis Tang *(Mng Dir)*

FP Reinsurance Brokers Limited (1)
26/F The Centrium 60 Wyndham Street, Central, China (Hong Kong)
Tel.: (852) 25443410
Web Site: http://www.fp-re.com
Reinsurance Services
N.A.I.C.S.: 524130
Philip Bilney *(Exec Dir)*

Haakon AG (1)
Pfeffingerstrasse 41, Basel, 4002, Switzerland
Tel.: (41) 613669191
Web Site: http://www.haakon.ch
Emp.: 15
Reinsurance Services
N.A.I.C.S.: 524130
Eric Mueller *(Exec VP)*

Subsidiary (Non-US):

HAAKON (ASIA) LTD (2)
Suite 17 5 Level 17 Menara IMC 8 Jalan Sultan Ismail, 50250, Kuala Lumpur, Malaysia
Tel.: (60) 3 2031 82 08
Emp.: 4
Reinsurance Services
N.A.I.C.S.: 524130

Hendricks & Co GmbH (1)
Jungfernstieg 1, 20095, Hamburg, Germany
Tel.: (49) 4076794760
Web Site: http://www.hendricks-gruppe.de
General Insurance Services
N.A.I.C.S.: 524128

Howden Broking Group Limited (1)
One Creechurch Place, London, EC3A 5AF, United Kingdom
Tel.: (44) 2076233806
Web Site: http://www.howdengroup.co.uk
Emp.: 10,000
Holding Company; Insurance Brokerage & Consultancy Services
N.A.I.C.S.: 551112
Iain Fox *(Assoc Dir-Employee Benefits)*

Subsidiary (US):

HIG Services US Inc (2)
25 Field St, Babylon, NY 11704
Tel.: (631) 586-8959
Web Site: http://www.higservices.com
Electrical Contracting Services
N.A.I.C.S.: 238210
Andrew V. Culuris *(Founder & CEO)*

Subsidiary (Non-US):

Howden Corretora de Resseguros Ltda (2)
Avenida Luis Carlos Prestes 180 Sala 351, Rio de Janeiro, 22775-055, Brazil
Tel.: (55) 12139580811
General Insurance Services
N.A.I.C.S.: 524210

Howden Forsikringsmegling AS (2)
Karenslyst Alle 2, 0278, Oslo, Norway
Tel.: (47) 40006312
Web Site: http://www.howdengroup.no
General Insurance Services
N.A.I.C.S.: 524128
Anders Kvan *(CEO)*

Subsidiary (Domestic):

Norwegian Insurance Partners AS (3)
Christian Michelsens gate 6B, 5012, Bergen, Norway
Tel.: (47) 5533 6700
Web Site: http://www.nip.no
Emp.: 25
Insurance Brokerage & Consultancy Services
N.A.I.C.S.: 524210
Geir Nygaard *(Founder & CEO)*

Subsidiary (Non-US):

Howden Iberia S.A. (2)
Montalban 7 6 planta, 28014, Madrid, Spain
Tel.: (34) 934880937
Web Site: http://www.howdeniberia.com
General Insurance Services
N.A.I.C.S.: 524210

Howden Insurance & Reinsurance Brokers (Phil.), Inc. (2)
23F Philippine Axa Life Centre Sen Gil Puyat Avenue, Makati, Philippines
Tel.: (63) 28863748
Web Site: http://www.howdengroup.com
Emp.: 50
Reinsurance Services
N.A.I.C.S.: 524130
Augusto L. Toledo *(CEO)*

Howden Insurance Brokers (2002) Limited (2)
Adgar Tower 35 Efal Street, 49511, Petach Tikva, Israel
Tel.: (972) 36270700
Web Site: http://www.howdengroup.com
General Insurance Services
N.A.I.C.S.: 524210
Dafna Perelmutter *(Head-Life Science Dept)*

HOWDEN GROUP HOLDINGS LIMITED

Howden Group Holdings Limited—(Continued)

Howden Insurance Brokers (Bermuda) Limited (2)
Hunter House Lower 4 F Pennos Dr, Saint Georges, GE05, Bermuda
Tel.: (441) 12961848
General Insurance Services
N.A.I.C.S.: 524210

Howden Insurance Brokers (HK) Limited (2)
Room 1001-3 10/F Harcourt House 39 Gloucester Road, Wanchai, China (Hong Kong)
Tel.: (852) 28772238
General Insurance Services
N.A.I.C.S.: 524210

Howden Insurance Brokers (S.) Pte. Limited (2)
61 Robinson Road 07-01 Robinson Centre, Singapore, 68893, Singapore
Tel.: (65) 62581919
Web Site: http://www.howdengroup.com
Emp.: 50
General Insurance Services
N.A.I.C.S.: 524128
Jenny Lim *(Head-Special Risks)*

Howden Insurance Brokers AB (2)
Linnegatan 2, 114 47, Stockholm, Sweden
Tel.: (46) 854567020
Web Site: http://www.howdengroup.com
General Insurance Services
N.A.I.C.S.: 524128
Alan Edwards *(Dir-Reinsurance)*

Howden Insurance Brokers Limited (2)
Dewhurst House Weighbridge, Saint Peter Port, GY1 4ED, Guernsey
Tel.: (44) 1481725536
General Insurance Services
N.A.I.C.S.: 524128

Howden Insurance Brokers Nederland B.V. (2)
1st Floor Parklaan 28, 3016BC, Rotterdam, Netherlands
Tel.: (31) 107200620
General Insurance Services
N.A.I.C.S.: 524210
Martin Besemer *(Dir-Marine)*

Howden Insurance Brokers Oy (2)
Malminkaari 9 B 3rd Floor, 700, Helsinki, Finland
Tel.: (358) 954202400
General Insurance Services
N.A.I.C.S.: 524210

Subsidiary (US):

Howden Insurance Services, Inc (2)
902 Carnegie Ctr Ste 340, Princeton, NJ 08540
Tel.: (609) 917-3166
General Insurance Services
N.A.I.C.S.: 524210

Howden Insurance, LLC (2)
1111 Brickell Ave Ste 2725, Miami, FL 33131
Tel.: (786) 275-3266
General Insurance Services
N.A.I.C.S.: 524210

Subsidiary (Non-US):

Howden Risk Management Consultants Sdn. Bhd. (2)
Unit C-25-03 3 Two Square No 2 Jalan 19/1, 46300, Petaling Jaya, Selangor, Malaysia
Tel.: (60) 379545052
Risk Managemeng Srvices
N.A.I.C.S.: 522320

Howden Sigorta Brokerligi Anonim Sirketi (2)
Sumer Sk Zitas s Merkezi Block C5 No 9 Kozyatagi, Istanbul, Turkiye
Tel.: (90) 2164636300
General Insurance Services
N.A.I.C.S.: 524210

Subsidiary (Domestic):

Howden UK Group Limited (2)
16 Eastcheap, London, EC3M 1BD, United Kingdom **(100%)**
Tel.: (44) 20 7623 3806
Web Site: http://www.howdengroup.co.uk
Holding Company; Insurance & Reinsurance Brokerage & Services
N.A.I.C.S.: 551112
Dominic Collins *(CEO)*

Subsidiary (Domestic):

Howden Employee Benefits Limited (3)
Glamorgan House Cardiff Gate Business Park Greenwood Close, Cardiff, CF23 8RD, United Kingdom
Tel.: (44) 2920731694
General Insurance Services
N.A.I.C.S.: 524298

Howden Insurance Brokers Limited (3)
16 Eastcheap, London, EC3M 1BD, United Kingdom
Tel.: (44) 2076233806
Web Site: http://www.howdengroup.co.uk
Insurance Brokerage Services
N.A.I.C.S.: 524210

Subsidiary (Non-US):

Howden Uruguay Corredores De Reaseguros S.A (2)
Sarandi 675 piso 2 Edificio Pablo Ferrando, Montevideo, 11000, Uruguay
Tel.: (598) 29156868
General Insurance Services
N.A.I.C.S.: 524210

Matrix Insurance & Reinsurance Brokers S.A. (2)
61 Akadimias Street, 106 79, Athens, Greece
Tel.: (30) 2103390354
Web Site: http://www.matrix-brokers.com
Sales Range: $50-74.9 Million
Emp.: 25
Insurance Services
N.A.I.C.S.: 524210
Dimitris Tsesmetzoglou *(CEO)*

Odyssey Insurance, Inc. (1)
14441 Brookhurst St Ste 3, Garden Grove, CA 92843
Tel.: (714) 839-1498
Web Site: http://www.odyins.com
General Insurance Services
N.A.I.C.S.: 524210

PT Howden Insurance Brokers Indonesia (1)
Mayapada Tower 8th Floor Jl Jend Sudirman Kav 28, Jakarta, 12920, Indonesia
Tel.: (62) 2129394900
Web Site: http://www.howdengroup.com
General Insurance Services
N.A.I.C.S.: 524210
Armand Wibisono *(Dir-Mktg)*

Spa Underwriting Services Select Limited (1)
Dowding House Coach and Horses Passage Lower Pantiles, Tunbridge Wells, TN2 5NP, Kent, United Kingdom
Tel.: (44) 1892709622
Web Site: http://www.spa-underwriting.co.uk
General Insurance Services
N.A.I.C.S.: 524210

VK Underwriters LLC (1)
6915 S Red Rd Ste 226, Miami, FL 33143
Tel.: (786) 275-3254
General Insurance Services
N.A.I.C.S.: 524298
Kenia Delgado *(Gen Dir & Dir-Sls)*

HOWDEN JOINERY GROUP PLC

40 Portman Square, London, W1H 6LT, United Kingdom
Tel.: (44) 2075351110
Web Site:
http://www.howdenjoineryplc.com
Year Founded: 1964
HWDN—(OTCIQ)
Rev.: $2,625,571,800
Assets: $2,301,422,940
Liabilities: $1,314,484,200
Net Worth: $986,938,740
Earnings: $423,669,240
Fiscal Year-end: 12/24/22
Mfr of Kitchen Renovation Products
N.A.I.C.S.: 337110
Matthew Ingle *(Founder)*

Subsidiaries:

Howden Joinery Limited (1)
105 Wigmore Street, St James Business Park, London, W1U 1QY, United Kingdom
Tel.: (44) 1604590048
Web Site: http://www.howden.com
Emp.: 12
Lumber Plywood Millwork & Wood Panel Merchant Whslr
N.A.I.C.S.: 423310

Sheridan Fabrications Limited (1)
New Sheridan House Don Pedro Ave, Normanton, West Yorkshire, United Kingdom
Tel.: (44) 1924228377
Web Site: https://www.sheridan-uk.com
Worktops Product Mfr & Distr
N.A.I.C.S.: 337110

HOWKINGTECH INTERNATIONAL HOLDING LIMITED

Building B4 No 9 East Mozhou Road, Jiangning Economic & Technological Development Zone, Nanjing, China
Tel.: (86) 2558097161 Ky
Web Site:
https://www.howkingtech.com
Year Founded: 2012
2440—(HKG)
Rev.: $49,634,524
Assets: $54,954,282
Liabilities: $15,719,652
Net Worth: $39,234,630
Earnings: $4,367,098
Emp.: 75
Fiscal Year-end: 12/31/22
Holding Company
N.A.I.C.S.: 551112
Ping Chen *(Chm)*

HOWTEH TECHNOLOGY CO., LTD.

6F No 25 Tun Hwa S Road Sec 1, Taipei, Taiwan
Tel.: (886) 225708818
Web Site: https://www.howteh.com.tw
Year Founded: 1978
3114—(TPE)
Rev.: $101,429,791
Assets: $91,165,494
Liabilities: $45,478,317
Net Worth: $45,687,178
Earnings: $6,528,437
Emp.: 85
Fiscal Year-end: 12/31/22
Electronic Components Distr
N.A.I.C.S.: 423690
Kuo-Hung Chen *(Chm)*

HOWTELEVISION, INC.

32F Ark Mori Building 1-12-32 Akasaka, Minato-ku, Tokyo, 107-6090, Japan
Tel.: (81) 364272862
Web Site:
https://www.howtelevision.co.jp
7064—(TKS)
Sales Range: $1-9.9 Million
Software Development Services
N.A.I.C.S.: 541511
Yosuke Otonari *(Founder, Pres & CEO)*

HOYA CORPORATION

20F Nittochi Nishishinjuku Building 6-10-1 Nishi-Shinjuku, Shinjuku-ku, Tokyo, 160-8347, Japan
Tel.: (81) 369114811 JP
Web Site: https://www.hoya.com
Year Founded: 1941

INTERNATIONAL PUBLIC

7741—(TKS)
Rev.: $5,040,852,100
Assets: $7,955,948,030
Liabilities: $1,595,382,990
Net Worth: $6,360,565,040
Earnings: $1,198,901,970
Emp.: 35,702
Fiscal Year-end: 03/31/24
Optical Product Mfr
N.A.I.C.S.: 334610
Ryo Hirooka *(CFO & Exec Officer)*

Subsidiaries:

Actio Optical Corp. (1)
4-14-1 Gonokami Lumiere M2f, Hamura, 205-0011, Tokyo, Japan
Tel.: (81) 425701070
Ophthalmic Goods Mfr
N.A.I.C.S.: 339115

EHS Lens Philippines, Inc. (1)
Lat1-A Phase1-B, First Philippines Industrial Park Special Economic Zone, Tanauan, Batangas, Philippines
Tel.: (63) 495431260
Medical Equipment Mfr
N.A.I.C.S.: 339112

HOLT JAPAN Inc. (1)
5th floor Koura Second Building 1-1-8 Kayabacho, Nihonbashi Chūo- ku, Tokyo, 103-0025, Japan
Tel.: (81) 336630811
Web Site: http://www.holt-japan.co.jp
Emp.: 12
Optical Lens Mfr
N.A.I.C.S.: 333310

HOYA HILL OPTICS SOUTH AFRICA (PTY) LTD. (1)
12 Dartfield Road Eastgate Ext 13, Sandton, 2090, South Africa
Tel.: (27) 114441992
Web Site: http://www.hilloptics.co.za
Emp.: 200
Optical & Polarized Lens Distr
N.A.I.C.S.: 423460
Donald Currie *(Mng Dir)*

HOYA Service Corporation (1)
1-29-9 Takadanobaba Hoya Marketing Bldg 10f, Shinjuku, Tokyo, 169-0075, Japan
Tel.: (81) 332327671
Data Processing Services
N.A.I.C.S.: 518210

Hoya Candeo Optronics Corporation (1)
3-5-24 Hikawa-cho, Toda, 335-0027, Saitama, Japan
Tel.: (81) 484476052
Web Site: https://www.hoyacandeo.co.jp
Sales Range: $25-49.9 Million
Emp.: 121
Laser Lens Mfr
N.A.I.C.S.: 333310
Hisao Shirasugi *(Pres)*

Hoya Corporation - Akishima Facility (1)
3-3-1 Musashino, Akishima, 196-8510, Japan
Tel.: (81) 425462511
Optical Instrument Mfr
N.A.I.C.S.: 333310

Hoya Corporation - Miyagi Factory (1)
30-2 Okada Aza-Shimomiyano, Tsukidate, Kurihara, 987-2203, Miyagi, Japan
Tel.: (81) 228 22 5711
Web Site: http://www.hoya.co.jp
Optical Lens Mfr
N.A.I.C.S.: 333310

Hoya Corporation - Ogawa Factory (1)
395 Kakuyama Ogawa-machi, Hiki-gun, Saitama, 355-0316, Japan
Tel.: (81) 493722121
Optical Lens Mfr
N.A.I.C.S.: 333310

Hoya Corporation - PENTAX Lifecare Division (1)
1-1-110 Tsutsujigaoka, Akishima, 196-0012, Japan
Tel.: (81) 425005831

AND PRIVATE COMPANIES — HOYA CORPORATION

Medical Imaging Device Designer, Mfr & Whslr
N.A.I.C.S.: 334510

Unit (Domestic):

Hoya Corporation - PENTAX Lifecare Division, Medical Instrument SBU (2)
3-35-1 Shimorenjaku Mitaka 13th floor, Mitaka, 181-0013, Tokyo, Japan
Tel.: (81) 422 70 3960
Web Site: http://www.pentaxmedical.com
Medical Imaging Device Designer, Mfr & Whslr
N.A.I.C.S.: 334510

Subsidiary (Non-US):

PENTAX Canada Inc. (2)
6715 Millcreek Dr Unit 1, Mississauga, L5N 5V2, ON, Canada
Tel.: (905) 286-5570
Web Site: http://www.pentaxmedical.com
Distr & Marketing of Cameras, Optical, CCTV Lenses, Surveying Instruments, Binoculars & GPS Equipment
N.A.I.C.S.: 333310

PENTAX Europe GmbH (2)
Julius-Vosseler-Strasse 104, 22527, Hamburg, Germany
Tel.: (49) 40561920
Web Site: http://www.pentaxmedical.com
Emp.: 150
Camera & Optical Lens Mfr
N.A.I.C.S.: 333310
Rainer Burkard (Mng Dir)

Subsidiary (Non-US):

SISTEMAS INTEGRALES DE MEDICINA, S.A. (3)
Avenida del Sistema Solar 25 San Fernando de Henares, 28830, Madrid, Spain
Tel.: (34) 913016240
Emp.: 50
Medical Equipment Mfr
N.A.I.C.S.: 339112

Subsidiary (Non-US):

PENTAX France Life Care S.A.S. (2)
112 quai de Bezons, BP 204, 95106, Argenteuil, Cedex, France
Tel.: (33) 130257575
Web Site: http://www.pentaxmedical.com
Camera & Optical Lens Mfr
N.A.I.C.S.: 333310

PENTAX MEDICAL BULGARIA EOOD (2)
ul Vasil Levski 179, Plovdiv, 4003, Bulgaria
Tel.: (359) 32 345 000
Web Site: http://www.pentaxmedical.bg
Emp.: 55
Endoscopy Equipment Repair Services
N.A.I.C.S.: 811210
Stefan Turiyski (Gen Mgr)

PENTAX Medical (Shanghai) Co., Ltd. (2)
Room 701 291 Fumin Road, Shanghai, 200031, China
Tel.: (86) 2161701555
Web Site: http://www.hoya.co.jp
Medical & Surgical Equipment Distr
N.A.I.C.S.: 423450

PENTAX Medical Singapore Pte. Ltd. (2)
438A Alexandra Road 08-06 Alexandra, Singapore, 119967, Singapore
Tel.: (65) 65079266
Web Site: https://www.pentaxmedical.com
Emp.: 20
Surgical & Medical Instrument Mfr
N.A.I.C.S.: 339112

PENTAX Nederland B.V. (2)
Tel.: (31) 885303030
Web Site: http://www.pentaxmedical.com
Camera & Optical Lens Mfr
N.A.I.C.S.: 333310

PENTAX Sintai Holding Co., Ltd. (2)
2/F Continental Electric Bldg 17 Wang Chiu Rd, Kowloon Bay, Kowloon, China (Hong Kong)
Tel.: (852) 35506614
Web Site: http://www.aoci.com.hk
Holding Company
N.A.I.C.S.: 551112
Vivian Ho (Mgr)

Subsidiary (Non-US):

PENTAX Sintai Optical Instrument (Shenzhen) Co., Ltd. (3)
Qiwei Industrial Estate Lisonglang Industrial District Baoan Zone, Gongming Town, Shenzhen, 518106, China
Tel.: (86) 75527165959
Optical Lens Mfr
N.A.I.C.S.: 333310

Subsidiary (Non-US):

PENTAX U.K. Limited (2)
Tel.: (44) 1753792733
Web Site: http://www.pentaxmedical.com
Camera & Opitcal Lens Mfr & Distr
N.A.I.C.S.: 333310

Subsidiary (US):

PENTAX of America, Inc. (2)
3 Paragon Dr, Montvale, NJ 07645-1782
Tel.: (201) 571-2300
Web Site: http://www.pentaxmedical.com
Holding Company
N.A.I.C.S.: 551112

Subsidiary (Domestic):

C2 Therapeutics, Inc. (3)
303 Convention Way Ste 1, Redwood City, CA 94063-1415
Tel.: (650) 521-5304
Web Site: http://www.c2cryoballoon.com
Plastics Bottle Mfr
N.A.I.C.S.: 326160

Division (Domestic):

PENTAX Medical (3)
102 Chestnut Ridge Rd, Montvale, NJ 07645-1856
Tel.: (201) 571-2300
Web Site: http://www.pentaxmedical.com
Sales Range: $50-74.9 Million
Emp.: 150
Medical Imaging & Endoscopy Equipment Mfr
N.A.I.C.S.: 339112
David Woods (Pres-Americas)

Division (Domestic):

KayPentax (4)
3 Paragon Dr, Montvale, NJ 07645
Tel.: (973) 628-6200
Web Site: http://www.kaypentax.com
Sales Range: $25-49.9 Million
Emp.: 50
Medical Imaging & Endoscopy Equipment Mfr
N.A.I.C.S.: 333310
John Crump (Gen Mgr)

Hoya Corporation - Yamagata Factory (1)
4-1 Hinode-cho, Nagai, 993-0012, Yamagata, Japan
Tel.: (81) 238 84 1380
Web Site: http://www.hoya.co.jp
Optical Lens Mfr
N.A.I.C.S.: 333310

Hoya Digital Solutions Corporation (1)
6th Floor Nakano Central Park South 4-10-2 Nakano, Nakano-ku, Tokyo, 164-8545, Japan
Tel.: (81) 359132304
Web Site: http://www.hoyads.co.jp
Medical Device Mfr
N.A.I.C.S.: 334118
Seevali Fernando (Pres & CEO)

Hoya Glass Disk Vietnam II Ltd. (1)
Plot A-9 Thang Long Industrial Park II, Lieu Xa Commune, Yen My, Hung Yen, Vietnam
Tel.: (84) 2439516357
Medical Equipment Mfr
N.A.I.C.S.: 339112

Hoya Glass Disk Vietnam Ltd. (1)
Plot J -3 and 4 Thang Long Industrial Park, Vong La Commune Dong Anh District, Hanoi, Vietnam
Tel.: (84) 2439516357
Medical Equipment Mfr
N.A.I.C.S.: 339112

Hoya Holdings Asia Pacific Pte Ltd. (1)
80 Raffles Place UOB Plaza 1 56-01, 08 03 Cecil Court, Singapore, 048624, Singapore
Tel.: (65) 63291622
Web Site: http://www.hoya.co.jp
Holding Company
N.A.I.C.S.: 551112

Subsidiary (Non-US):

AvanStrate Korea Inc. (2)
Hyeongok Industrial park 84 Hyeongoksandan-ro, Cheongbuk-myeon, Pyeongtaek, 17812, Gyeonggi-do, Korea (South)
Tel.: (82) 316157819
Web Site: https://www.kr-avanstrate.com
Liquid Crystal Display Panel Mfr
N.A.I.C.S.: 334419

AvanStrate Taiwan Inc. (2)
No 8 Industry III Road, Annan, T'ainan, 709, Taiwan
Tel.: (886) 63840225
Web Site: http://www.tw-avanstrate.com
Sales Range: $250-299.9 Million
Emp.: 700
Optical Goods Distr
N.A.I.C.S.: 423460

Daemyung Optical Co., Ltd. (2)
100 Sinilseo-ro 18beon-gil, Daedeok-gu, Daejeon, Korea (South)
Tel.: (82) 429391040
Web Site: https://m.dmo.co.kr
Optical Lens Mfr
N.A.I.C.S.: 333310

HOEV CO., LTD (2)
Plot P2 Thang Long Industrial Park, Vong La commue Dong Anh District, Hanoi, Vietnam
Tel.: (84) 2439590055
Web Site: http://www.hoya.co.jp
Sales Range: $25-49.9 Million
Emp.: 200
Optical Lens Mfr
N.A.I.C.S.: 333310

HOYA ELECTRONICS KOREA CO., LTD. (2)
55 Hyeongoksandan-ro Cheongbuk-myeon, Pyeongtaek, 17812, Gyeonggi, Korea (South)
Tel.: (82) 3 1683 9400
Web Site: http://www.hoya.co.jp
Electronic Components Mfr
N.A.I.C.S.: 334419

HOYA ELECTRONICS MALAYSIA SDN. BHD. (2)
Lot 28 & 29 Phase 1 Jalan Hi-Tech 4 Kulim Hi-Tech Park, 09000, Kulim, Kedah, Malaysia
Tel.: (60) 4 403 3118
Web Site: http://www.hoya.co.jp
Electronic Components Mfr
N.A.I.C.S.: 334419

Subsidiary (Domestic):

HOYA ELECTRONICS SINGAPORE PTE. LTD. (2)
10 Tampines Industrial Crescent, Singapore, 528603, Singapore
Tel.: (65) 62395900
Web Site: http://www.hoya.co.jp
Electronic Components Mfr
N.A.I.C.S.: 334419

Subsidiary (Non-US):

HOYA GLASS DISK (THAILAND) LTD. (2)
Northern Region Industrial Estate 60/26 Moo 4 Tambol Banklang, Amphur Muang, Lamphun, 51000, Thailand
Tel.: (66) 53 581 314
Glass Products Mfr
N.A.I.C.S.: 327215

HOYA GLASS DISK PHILIPPINES, INC. (2)
111 East Main Avenue Special Export Processing Zone Laguna Technopark, Binan, 4024, Laguna, Philippines
Tel.: (63) 49 541 2730
Web Site: http://www.hoya.co.jp
Optical Lens Mfr
N.A.I.C.S.: 333310

HOYA HEALTHCARE (SHANGHAI) CO., LTD. (2)
Room G 12 Zhiyuan Building 768 Xietu Road, Shanghai, 200023, China
Tel.: (86) 21 6305 5050
Web Site: http://www.hoya.co.jp
Emp.: 30
Medical Equipment Mfr & Distr
N.A.I.C.S.: 339112
Taisuke Haiu (Gen Mgr)

Subsidiary (Domestic):

HOYA LENS (S) PTE. LTD. (2)
No 1 Lorong 2 Toa Payoh Braddell House 06-01, Singapore, 319637, Singapore
Tel.: (65) 62210055
Emp.: 3
Optical Lens Mfr
N.A.I.C.S.: 333310

Subsidiary (Non-US):

HOYA LENS AUSTRALIA PTY. LTD. (2)
Tel.: (61) 296981577
Web Site: http://www.hoyalens.com.au
Sales Range: $25-49.9 Million
Emp.: 10
Ophthalmic Lens Mfr & Distr
N.A.I.C.S.: 339115

HOYA LENS GUANGZHOU LTD. (2)
No1 Zhicheng Dong Road Guangzhou Economic Technological, Development District, Guangzhou, 510730, China
Tel.: (86) 2082223999
Optical Lens Mfr
N.A.I.C.S.: 333310
Yasuyuki Nitta (Gen Mgr)

HOYA LENS HONG KONG LTD. (2)
16/F Unison Industrial Centre 27-31 Au Pui Wan Street, Fotan, NT, China (Hong Kong)
Tel.: (852) 25565266
Web Site: http://www.hoya.com.hk
Sales Range: $25-49.9 Million
Emp.: 6
Optical Lens Mfr & Distr
N.A.I.C.S.: 333310

HOYA LENS INDIA PVT.LTD (2)
D28/5 TTC Industrial Area MIDC Turbhe, Navi Mumbai, 400 705, India
Tel.: (91) 2267336733
Web Site: http://www.hoyavisioncare.com
Optical Instrument & Lens Mfr
N.A.I.C.S.: 333310

HOYA LENS KOREA CO., LTD. (2)
3rd Floor of Yunil Building 1443-15 Seocho-Dong, Seocho-gu, Seoul, 137-865, Korea (South)
Tel.: (82) 2 585 1911
Web Site: http://www.hoya.co.kr
Emp.: 14
Optical Lens Mfr
N.A.I.C.S.: 333310

HOYA LENS MANUFACTURING MALAYSIA SDN. BHD. (2)
No 6 Jalan7/32A Off 6 1/2 Miles Jalan Kepong, 52000, Kuala Lumpur, Malaysia
Tel.: (60) 362588977
Optical Lens Mfr
N.A.I.C.S.: 333310

HOYA LENS PHILIPPINES, INC. (2)
10th Floor Sterling Centre cor Ormaza Dela Rosa Sts, Legaspi Village, Makati, 1229, Philippines
Tel.: (63) 2751717376
Sales Range: $25-49.9 Million
Emp.: 30
Optical Lens Mfr
N.A.I.C.S.: 333310

HOYA LENS SHANGHAI LTD. (2)
13F No 99 Wuning Road, Shanghai, 200063, China
Tel.: (86) 2152819663
Optical Lens & Glass Mfr

HOYA CORPORATION

INTERNATIONAL PUBLIC

Hoya Corporation—(Continued)
N.A.I.C.S.: 333310

HOYA LENS TAIWAN LTD. (2)
3F No 146 Songjiang Rd, Zhongshan Dist,
Taipei, 104, Taiwan
Tel.: (886) 225605556
Optical Lens Mfr
N.A.I.C.S.: 333310

HOYA LENS THAILAND LTD. (2)
853 Phaholyothin RD Prachatipat, Thanyaburi, 12130, Patumthani, Thailand
Tel.: (66) 29012021
Optical Lens Mfr & Distr
N.A.I.C.S.: 333310

HOYA LENS VIETNAM LTD. (2)
20 VSIP 2 Street 4 Viet Nam Singapore
Industrial Park 2, Hoa Phu Ward, Thu Dau
Mot, Binh Duong, Vietnam
Tel.: (84) 2743635315
Web Site: http://www.holv.com
Sales Range: $150-199.9 Million
Emp.: 100
Optical Lens Mfr
N.A.I.C.S.: 333310
Gisai Masahiko (Gen Mgr)

Subsidiary (Domestic):

HOYA MEDICAL SINGAPORE PTE. LTD. (2)
455A Jalan Ahmad Ibrahim, Singapore,
639939, Singapore
Tel.: (65) 6862 3673
Web Site: http://www.hoya.co.jp
Sales Range: $50-74.9 Million
Emp.: 250
Optical Goods Mfr & Distr
N.A.I.C.S.: 333310

Subsidiary (Non-US):

HOYA MICROELECTRONICS (SUZHOU) LTD. (2)
Room 801 Xin-Su Building No 1518 Donghuan Road, Suzhou Industrial Park, Suzhou, 215021, Jiangsu, China
Tel.: (86) 51262883928
Web Site: http://www.hoya.co.jp
Microelectronic Software Development Services
N.A.I.C.S.: 541511

HOYA MICROELECTRONICS TAIWAN CO., LTD. (2)
No 36 Kedung 3rd Rd Science-Based industrial Park, Miaoli, Chunan, 350, Taiwan
Tel.: (886) 37580085
Web Site: http://www.hoya.co.jp
Sales Range: $25-49.9 Million
Emp.: 100
Electronic Components Mfr
N.A.I.C.S.: 334419

HOYA OPTICAL (ASIA) CO., LTD (2)
Suite 2211 Tower 1 The Gateway 25 Canton Road, Tsim Sha Tsui, Kowloon, China (Hong Kong)
Tel.: (852) 27236883
Sales Range: $25-49.9 Million
Emp.: 2
Optical Lens Mfr & Distr
N.A.I.C.S.: 333310

HOYA OPTICAL TECHNOLOGY (SUZHOU) LTD. (2)
229 Taishan Road, Suzhou, 215129, Jiangsu, China
Tel.: (86) 512 6665 0752
Web Site: http://www.hoya.co.jp
Optical Glass & Lens Mfr
N.A.I.C.S.: 333310

HOYA OPTICAL TECHNOLOGY (WEIHAI) CO., LTD. (2)
Nanjing Road West Highway 303 South,
Weihai New Industrial District, Weihai,
264211, Shandong, China
Tel.: (86) 6313676110
Emp.: 10
Optical Lens Mfr
N.A.I.C.S.: 333310

HOYA OPTICS (THAILAND) LTD. (2)
Northern Region Industrial Estate 60/31
Moo 4 Tambol Banklang, Amphur Muang,
Lamphun, 51000, Thailand
Tel.: (66) 52039331334
Optical Lens & Glass Mfr
N.A.I.C.S.: 333310

Hoya Opto-Electronics Qingdao Ltd. (2)
No 66 Songhuajiang Road, Qingdao Economic and Technological Development
Zone, Qingdao, Shandong, China
Tel.: (86) 53286760997
Web Site: http://www.hoya.co.jp
Electronic Lens Mfr
N.A.I.C.S.: 333310

ILENS SDN BHD (2)
No 26 Jalan 5/32A Off 6 1/2 Miles, Jalan
Kepong, 52000, Kuala Lumpur, Malaysia
Tel.: (60) 362560031
Web Site: http://www.hoyavisioncare.com
Optical Lens Mfr
N.A.I.C.S.: 333310

Malaysian Hoya Lens Sdn. Bhd. (2)
No 22 Jalan 5/32A Off 6 1/2 Miles Jalan
Kepong, 52000, Kuala Lumpur, Malaysia
Tel.: (60) 362560081
Optical Lens Mfr
N.A.I.C.S.: 333310
Boon Eng Khoo (Gen Mgr)

THAI HOYA LENS LTD. (2)
Payatai Plaza 23rd Floor 128/251-256
Phyathai Road Thung-Phyathai, Rajthavee,
Bangkok, 10400, Thailand
Tel.: (66) 22193972
Web Site: http://www.thaihoyatc.com
Sales Range: $25-49.9 Million
Emp.: 45
Optical Lens Distr
N.A.I.C.S.: 423460

Hoya Holdings N.V. (1)
Radarweg 29-8, 1043 NX, Amsterdam,
Netherlands
Tel.: (31) 207652300
Web Site: http://www.hoya.co.jp
Sales Range: $25-49.9 Million
Emp.: 35
Holding Company
N.A.I.C.S.: 551112
Hans Werquin (Pres & CEO)

Subsidiary (Non-US):

Digital Endoscopy GmbH (2)
Paul-Lenz-Strasse 5, 86316, Friedberg,
Germany
Tel.: (49) 7467 9490 0
Sales Range: $25-49.9 Million
Emp.: 7
Medical Imaging System Mfr
N.A.I.C.S.: 339112
Marc Heinzer (Mng Dir)

Subsidiary (Domestic):

HOYA HOLDINGS (ASIA) B.V. (2)
Amsterdamseweg 29, Uithoorn, 1422 AC,
Netherlands
Tel.: (31) 29 751 4356
Web Site: http://www.hoya.com
Sales Range: $50-74.9 Million
Emp.: 35
Investment Management Service
N.A.I.C.S.: 523999
Grayhans Werquin (Pres & CEO)

Subsidiary (Non-US):

HOYA LENS BELGIUM N.V. (2)
Lieven Gevaertstraat 15, 2950, Kapellen,
Belgium
Tel.: (32) 3 660 01 00
Web Site: http://www.hoya.be
Emp.: 100
Optical Lens Mfr & Distr
N.A.I.C.S.: 333310

HOYA LENS CZ a.s (2)
Antonina Dvoraka 298, 511 01, Turnov,
Czech Republic
Tel.: (420) 488 578 400
Web Site: http://www.hoyavision.cz
Emp.: 25
Optical Lens Mfr
N.A.I.C.S.: 333310

HOYA LENS MANUFACTURING HUNGARY RT (2)
Tel.: (36) 44418200
Web Site: http://www.hoya-mineral.com
Optical Lens & Glass Mfr
N.A.I.C.S.: 333310

HOYA LENS U.K. Limited (2)
Industrial Estate, Wrexham, LL13 9UA,
United Kingdom
Tel.: (44) 8448731110
Web Site: http://www.hoya.co.uk
Sales Range: $50-74.9 Million
Ophthalmic Lenses Mfr & Distr
N.A.I.C.S.: 339115

HOYA Lens Belguim B.V. (2)
Lieven Gevaertstraat 15, Kapellen, 2950,
Belgium
Tel.: (32) 36600100
Web Site: http://www.hoya.be
Sales Range: $25-49.9 Million
Emp.: 80
Optical Lens Sales & Mfr
N.A.I.C.S.: 333310
Hans Werquin (Mng Dir)

HOYA Lens Denmark A/S (2)
Horskaetten 28, 2630, Taastrup, Denmark
Tel.: (45) 43558200
Web Site: http://www.hoyavision.com
Sales Range: $25-49.9 Million
Emp.: 45
Eyeglass Lenses Mfr
N.A.I.C.S.: 333310

HOYA Lens Deutschland GmbH (2)
Krefelder Str 350, 41066, Monchengladbach, Germany
Tel.: (49) 21616520
Web Site: http://www.hoya.de
Sales Range: $75-99.9 Million
Eyeglass Lenses Mfr
N.A.I.C.S.: 333310
Oliver Fischbach (Mng Dir)

HOYA Lens Finland Oy (2)
Tel.: (358) 972884100
Web Site: http://www.hoya.fi
Sales Range: $25-49.9 Million
Emp.: 20
Eyeglass Lens Sales & Mfr
N.A.I.C.S.: 333310

HOYA Lens France S.A. (2)
Tel.: (33) 160377253
Web Site: http://www.hoya.co.jp
Sales Range: $25-49.9 Million
Eyeglass Lens Sales & Mfr
N.A.I.C.S.: 333310

HOYA Lens Hungary Rt (2)
Telek U 3, 1152, Budapest, Hungary
Tel.: (36) 18058510
Web Site: http://www.hoya.hu
Sales Range: $25-49.9 Million
Eyeglass Lens Mfr & Sales
N.A.I.C.S.: 333310

HOYA Lens Iberia S.A. (2)
Avenida 5 de Outubro 293-5, 1600-035,
Lisbon, Portugal
Tel.: (351) 217929696
Web Site: http://www.hoya.pt
Sales Range: $25-49.9 Million
Emp.: 35
Eyeglass Lens Mfr & Sales
N.A.I.C.S.: 333310

HOYA Lens Iberia S.A. (2)
Paseo de Las Flores 23, Coslada, 28823,
Madrid, Spain
Tel.: (34) 916603510
Web Site: http://www.hoya.es
Sales Range: $25-49.9 Million
Eyeglass Lens Mfr & Sales
N.A.I.C.S.: 333310

HOYA Lens Italia S.p.A. (2)
Via Bernardino Zenale 27, Garbagnate
Milanese, 20024, Milan, Italy
Tel.: (39) 02990711
Web Site: http://www.hoya.it
Eyeglass Lens Mfr & Sales
N.A.I.C.S.: 333310

Subsidiary (Domestic):

HOYA Lens Nederland B.V. (2)
Radarweg 29-8, 1043 NX, Amsterdam,
Netherlands
Tel.: (31) 207652300
Web Site: http://www.hoya.nl

Sales Range: $25-49.9 Million
Eyeglass Lens Sales & Mfr
N.A.I.C.S.: 333310

Subsidiary (Non-US):

HOYA Lens Poland Sp. Z.o.o. (2)
ul Pulawska 40a, 05-500, Piaseczno, Poland
Tel.: (48) 225588899
Web Site: http://www.hoya.pl
Eyeglass Lens Mfr & Sales
N.A.I.C.S.: 333310

HOYA Lens Sweden AB (2)
Scheelegatan 15, Box 16125, 200 25,
Malmo, Sweden
Tel.: (46) 406802200
Web Site: http://www.hoya.se
Eyeglass Lens Mfr & Sales
N.A.I.C.S.: 333310
Pontus Widlund (Pres)

HOYA SURGICAL OPTICS GmbH (2)
De-Saint-Exupery-Str 10, 60549, Frankfurt
am Main, Germany
Tel.: (49) 69 6642680
Web Site: http://www.hoyasurgopt.com
Sales Range: $25-49.9 Million
Emp.: 4
Intraocular Lenses Distr
N.A.I.C.S.: 423460
Tom Dunlap (Mng Dir)

Hoya Holdings, Inc. (1)
680 N McCarthy Blvd Ste 120, Milpitas, CA
95035-5120
Tel.: (408) 654-2300
Web Site: http://www.hoya.co.jp
Optical Holding Company
N.A.I.C.S.: 333310

Subsidiary (Non-US):

HOYA LENS CANADA, INC. (2)
3330 Ridgeway Dr 21, Mississauga, L5L
5Z9, ON, Canada
Tel.: (905) 828-3477
Web Site: http://www.hoya.ca
Optical Lens & Instrument Mfr
N.A.I.C.S.: 333310

Plant (Domestic):

HOYA LENS CANADA, INC. - MONTREAL FACILITY (3)
600 Meloche Ave, Dorval, H9P 2P4, QC,
Canada
Tel.: (514) 420-0404
Optical Glass & Lens Mfr
N.A.I.C.S.: 333310

HOYA LENS CANADA, INC. - TORONTO FACILITY (3)
21-3330 Ridgeway Dr, Mississauga, L5L
5Z9, ON, Canada
Tel.: (905) 828-3477
Web Site: http://www.hoya.co.jp
Optical Glass & Lens Mfr
N.A.I.C.S.: 333310

HOYA LENS CANADA, INC. - VANCOUVER FACILITY (3)
6976 Russell Ave Ste 101B, Burnaby, V5J
4R9, BC, Canada
Tel.: (604) 454-9477
Optical Lens Mfr
N.A.I.C.S.: 333310

Subsidiary (Domestic):

Hoya Corporation USA (2)
3285 Scott Blvd, Santa Clara, CA
95054-3014 (100%)
Tel.: (408) 654-2200
Web Site: http://www.hoya.co.jp
Sales Range: $25-49.9 Million
Emp.: 15
Sales of Electro Optics
N.A.I.C.S.: 334511
Andy Wall (Dir-Sls & Mktg)

Subsidiary (Domestic):

HOYA Lens of America Inc. (3)
651 E Corporate Dr, Lewisville, TX 75057-6403
Tel.: (203) 790-0171

AND PRIVATE COMPANIES

HOYA CORPORATION

Sales Range: $50-74.9 Million
Eyeglass Marketing
N.A.I.C.S.: 423460

Subsidiary (Domestic):

HOYA LENS OF CHICAGO,
INC. (4)
3531 Martens St, Franklin Park, IL 60131-2058
Tel.: (847) 678-4700
Web Site: http://www.hoyavision.com
Emp.: 60
Optical Lens & Glass Distr
N.A.I.C.S.: 423460

Division (Domestic):

HOYA Optical Laboratories (3)
3959 Riffin Rd Ste H, San Diego, CA 92123
Tel.: (858) 490-3490
Web Site: http://www.hoyavisioncare.com
Sales Range: $25-49.9 Million
Prescription Lens Laboratory
N.A.I.C.S.: 339115
Barney Dougher (Pres)

Branch (Domestic):

HOYA Optical Laboratories (4)
651 E Corporate Dr, Lewisville, TX 75057-6403
Tel.: (972) 221-4141
Web Site: http://www.hoyaopticallabs.com
Sales Range: $25-49.9 Million
Mfr of Eyeglasses, Provide Products & Services to Optometrists, Ophthalmologists & Opticians
N.A.I.C.S.: 339115

Subsidiary (Domestic):

HOYA SURGICAL OPTICS, INC. (3)
15335 Fairfield Ranch Rd Ste 250, Chino Hills, CA 91709
Tel.: (909) 680-3900
Web Site: http://www.hoyasurgicaloptics.com
Sales Range: $25-49.9 Million
Surgical & Optical Instrument Mfr
N.A.I.C.S.: 339112
John Lassen (CEO)

Plant (Domestic):

HOYA SURGICAL OPTICS, INC. - ATLANTA FACILITY (4)
591-F Thornton Rd, Lithia Springs, GA 30122
Tel.: (770) 944-1800
Web Site: http://www.hoya.co.jp
Sales Range: $25-49.9 Million
Optical Lens & Glass Mfr
N.A.I.C.S.: 333310
Mark Evett (Gen Mgr)

HOYA SURGICAL OPTICS, INC. - CHICAGO FACILITY (4)
3531 Martens St, Franklin Park, IL 60131
Tel.: (847) 678-4700
Web Site: http://www.hoyavision.com
Optical Lens Mfr
N.A.I.C.S.: 333310
Phillip Lest (Gen Mgr)

HOYA SURGICAL OPTICS, INC. - CLEVELAND FACILITY (4)
94 Pelret Industrial Pkwy, Berea, OH 44017
Tel.: (440) 239-0692
Web Site: http://www.hoyavision.com
Optical Lens Mfr
N.A.I.C.S.: 333310

HOYA SURGICAL OPTICS, INC. - DALLAS FACILITY (4)
651 E Corporate Dr, Lewisville, TX 75057
Tel.: (972) 221-4141
Optical Lens Mfr
N.A.I.C.S.: 333310

HOYA SURGICAL OPTICS, INC. - DAYTON FACILITY (4)
1730 Dalton Dr, New Carlisle, OH 45344
Tel.: (937) 849-1000
Web Site: http://www.hoya.co.jp
Sales Range: $25-49.9 Million
Emp.: 20
Optical Lens Mfr
N.A.I.C.S.: 333310

HOYA SURGICAL OPTICS, INC. - EUGENE FACILITY (4)
1370 S Bertelsen Rd, Eugene, OR 97402
Tel.: (541) 683-3898
Web Site: http://www.hoya.co.jp
Optical Lens Mfr
N.A.I.C.S.: 333310

HOYA SURGICAL OPTICS, INC. - HARTFORD FACILITY (4)
580 Nutmeg Rd N, South Windsor, CT 06074
Tel.: (860) 289-5367
Web Site: http://www.hoya.co.jp
Optical Lens Mfr
N.A.I.C.S.: 333310

HOYA SURGICAL OPTICS, INC. - KNOXVILLE FACILITY (4)
1529 Western Ave, Knoxville, TN 37921
Tel.: (865) 524-5448
Web Site: http://www.hoya.co.jp
Optical Lens Mfr
N.A.I.C.S.: 333310

HOYA SURGICAL OPTICS, INC. - LARGO FACILITY (4)
12345-B Starkey Rd Ste E, Largo, FL 33773
Tel.: (727) 531-8964
Web Site: http://www.hoyavision.com
Optical Lens Mfr
N.A.I.C.S.: 333310
Terry Farrell (Mgr)

HOYA SURGICAL OPTICS, INC. - LEWISTON FACILITY (4)
1567 Lisbon St, Lewiston, ME 04240
Tel.: (207) 783-8523
Web Site: http://www.hoya.co.jp
Emp.: 7
Optical Lens Mfr
N.A.I.C.S.: 333310
Buster Waloss (Pres)

HOYA SURGICAL OPTICS, INC. - MODESTO FACILITY (4)
1400 Carpenter Ln, Modesto, CA 95351
Tel.: (209) 579-7739
Web Site: http://www.hoya.co.jp
Emp.: 100
Optical Lens Mfr
N.A.I.C.S.: 333310

HOYA SURGICAL OPTICS, INC. - PORTLAND FACILITY (4)
4500 SE Criterion Ct Ste 200, Milwaukie, OR 97222
Tel.: (503) 233-6211
Optical Lens & Glass Mfr
N.A.I.C.S.: 333310

HOYA SURGICAL OPTICS, INC. - SAN ANTONIO FACILITY (4)
300 W Bitters Ste 103, San Antonio, TX 78213
Tel.: (210) 525-0700
Optical Lens Mfr
N.A.I.C.S.: 333310

HOYA SURGICAL OPTICS, INC. - SAN DIEGO FACILITY (4)
4255 Ruffin Rd, San Diego, CA 92123
Tel.: (858) 309-6050
Web Site: http://www.hoya.co.jp
Optical Lens Mfr
N.A.I.C.S.: 333310
Steve Mazza (Gen Mgr)

HOYA SURGICAL OPTICS, INC. - ST. LOUIS FACILITY (4)
301 Vision Dr, Columbia, IL 62236
Tel.: (618) 281-3344
Web Site: http://www.hoya.co.jp
Sales Range: $25-49.9 Million
Optical Lens & Glass Mfr
N.A.I.C.S.: 333310
Dave Idol (Gen Mgr)

Subsidiary (Domestic):

HOYA VISION CARE North America Inc. (3)
397 Hwy 121 Bypass, Lewisville, TX 75067
Tel.: (972) 221-4141
Web Site: http://www.hoyavision.com
Ophthalmic Lens Mfr & Distr
N.A.I.C.S.: 339115

Subsidiary (Domestic):

HOYA Vision Care Company (4)
397 Hwy 121 Bypass, Lewisville, TX 75067
Tel.: (972) 221-4141
Web Site: http://www.hoyavision.com
Ophthalmic Lens Mfr & Distr
N.A.I.C.S.: 339115

Plant (Domestic):

HOYA Vision Care Company - Seattle Facility (5)
2330 S 78th St, Tacoma, WA 98409-9051
Tel.: (253) 475-7809
Web Site: http://www.hoyavision.com
Sales Range: $25-49.9 Million
Emp.: 100
Wholesale Laboratory for Optometrists, Opticians & Ophthalmologists
N.A.I.C.S.: 339115
Jim Sandige (Mgr-Facility)

Plant (Domestic):

Hoya Corporation - ATLANTA FACILITY (3)
591-F Thornton Rd, Lithia Springs, GA 30122
Tel.: (770) 944-1800
Web Site: http://www.hoya.com
Optical Instrument & Lens Mfr
N.A.I.C.S.: 333310

Hoya Corporation - CLEVELAND FACILITY (3)
94 Pelret Industrial Pkwy, Berea, OH 44017
Tel.: (440) 239-0692
Web Site: http://www.hoya.co.jp
Optical Instrument & Lens Mfr
N.A.I.C.S.: 333310

Hoya Corporation - DALLAS FACILITY (3)
651 E Corporate Dr, Lewisville, TX 75057
Tel.: (972) 221-4141
Web Site: http://www.hoya.co.jp
Optical Lens & Surgical Equipment Mfr
N.A.I.C.S.: 333310

Hoya Corporation - DAYTON FACILITY (3)
1730 Dalton Dr, New Carlisle, OH 45344
Tel.: (937) 849-1000
Web Site: http://www.hoyavision.com
Sales Range: $25-49.9 Million
Optical Instrument & Lens Mfr
N.A.I.C.S.: 333310

Hoya Corporation - EUGENE FACILITY (3)
1370 S Bertelsen Rd, Eugene, OR 97402
Tel.: (541) 683-3898
Web Site: http://www.hoya.co.jp
Optical Instrument & Lens Mfr
N.A.I.C.S.: 333310

Hoya Corporation - HARTFORD FACILITY (3)
580 Nutmeg Rd N, South Windsor, CT 06074
Tel.: (860) 289-5367
Web Site: http://www.hoya.co.jp
Optical Glass & Lens Mfr
N.A.I.C.S.: 333310

Hoya Corporation - KNOXVILLE FACILITY (3)
1529 Western Ave, Knoxville, TN 37921
Tel.: (865) 524-5448
Web Site: http://www.hoya.co.jp
Optical Glass & Lens Mfr
N.A.I.C.S.: 333310

Hoya Corporation - LARGO FACILITY (3)
12345-B Starkey Rd, Largo, FL 33773
Tel.: (727) 531-8964
Web Site: http://www.hoyavision.co.jp
Optical Instrument & Lens Mfr
N.A.I.C.S.: 333310

Hoya Corporation - LEWISTON FACILITY (3)
1567 Lisbon St, Lewiston, ME 04240
Tel.: (207) 783-8523
Web Site: http://www.hoya.com
Emp.: 7
Optical Instrument & Lens Mfr

N.A.I.C.S.: 333310

Hoya Corporation - MODESTO FACILITY (3)
1400 Carpenter Ln, Modesto, CA 95351
Tel.: (209) 579-7739
Web Site: http://www.hoya.co.jp
Sales Range: $25-49.9 Million
Ophthalmic Lens Mfr
N.A.I.C.S.: 333310

Hoya Corporation - NEW ORLEANS FACILITY (3)
5039 Fairfield St, Metairie, LA 70006
Web Site: http://www.hoya.co.jp
Emp.: 6
Optical Glass & Lens Mfr
N.A.I.C.S.: 333310

Hoya Corporation - PORTLAND FACILITY (3)
4500 SE Criterion Ct Ste 200, Milwaukie, OR 97222
Tel.: (503) 233-6211
Web Site: http://www.hoya.co.jp
Sales Range: $25-49.9 Million
Ophthalmic Lens Mfr
N.A.I.C.S.: 333310

Hoya Corporation - SAN ANTONIO FACILITY (3)
300 W Bitters Ste 130, San Antonio, TX 78216
Tel.: (210) 525-0700
Web Site: http://www.hoya.co.jp
Optical Glass & Lens Mfr
N.A.I.C.S.: 333310

Hoya Corporation - SAN DIEGO FACILITY (3)
4255 Ruffin Rd, San Diego, CA 92123
Tel.: (858) 309-6050
Web Site: http://www.hoya.com
Ophthalmic Lens Mfr
N.A.I.C.S.: 339115

Division (Domestic):

Hoya Corporation - USA Optics Division (3)
680 N McCarthy Blvd Ste 120, Milpitas, CA 95035
Tel.: (408) 654-2200
Web Site: http://www.hoyaoptics.com
Optical Glass Products Distr
N.A.I.C.S.: 423460

Subsidiary (Domestic):

Microline Surgical Inc. (3)
50 Dunham Rd Ste 1500, Beverly, MA 01915
Tel.: (978) 922-9810
Web Site: https://www.microlinesurgical.com
Sales Range: $50-74.9 Million
Laparoscopic, Cutting & Dissecting Medical Equipment Mfr
N.A.I.C.S.: 339112
Sharad H. Joshi (Pres & CEO)

NEOSPEECH, INC. (3)
4633 Old Ironsides Dr Ste 200, Santa Clara, CA 95054
Tel.: (408) 914-2710
Web Site: http://www.neospeech.com
Emp.: 10
Speech & Application Software Development Services
N.A.I.C.S.: 541511
Devin Lee (CEO)

Hoya Lamphun Ltd. (1)
Northern Region Industrial Estate 75/2 Moo 4, Tambol Banklang Amphur Muang, Lamphun, 51000, Thailand
Tel.: (66) 53552641
Medical Equipment Mfr
N.A.I.C.S.: 339112

Hoya Laos Co., Ltd. (1)
A-04 Saysettha Development Zone, Nano Village Saysettha District, Vientiane, Lao People's Democratic Republic
Tel.: (856) 21221044
Medical Equipment Mfr
N.A.I.C.S.: 339112

Hoya Lens Manufacturing Hungary Private Co. (1)
Ipari ut 18, 4700, Mateszalka, Hungary

HOYA CORPORATION

Hoya Corporation—(Continued)
Tel.: (36) 44418200
Medical Equipment Mfr
N.A.I.C.S.: 339112

Hoya Lens Russia LLC (1)
Otradnaya Str 2B Building 9 Technopark, Otradnoye, 127273, Moscow, Russia
Tel.: (7) 4992770760
Medical Equipment Mfr
N.A.I.C.S.: 339112

Hoya Medical Device Consulting Co., Ltd. (1)
Room 2603 No 1045 Middle Huaihai Road Huaihai Plaza, Xuhui District, Shanghai, 200031, China
Tel.: (86) 75526031517
Medical Equipment Mfr
N.A.I.C.S.: 339112

Hoya Medical India Pvt. Ltd. (1)
H-9 Block B1 Mohan Co-operative Indl Estate Mathura Road, New Delhi, 110044, India
Tel.: (91) 1148380000
Medical Equipment Mfr
N.A.I.C.S.: 339112

Hoya Memory Disk Technologies Ltd. (1)
Plot A-9 Thang Long Industrial Park II, Lieu Xa Commune, Yen My, Hung Yen, Vietnam
Tel.: (84) 2213974924
Medical Equipment Mfr
N.A.I.C.S.: 339112

Hoya Technosurgical Corporation (1)
YKB Bldg 4-28-4 Yotsuya, Shinjuku-ku, Tokyo, 160-0004, Japan
Web Site:
http://www.hoyatechnosurgical.co.jp
Binocular Loupe Mfr & Distr
N.A.I.C.S.: 333310

Hoya Turkey Optik Lens San. Ve Tic. A.S. (1)
Fatih Mah Yakacik Cad B Blok No 94/1, Sancaktepe, 34885, Istanbul, Türkiye
Tel.: (90) 2165618100
Medical Equipment Mfr
N.A.I.C.S.: 339112

Innovia ST Co., Ltd. (1)
3rd Floor Building D Huayuan Industrial Park No 5 Lanyuan Road, Tianjin, 300384, China
Tel.: (86) 2283718331
Medical Equipment Mfr
N.A.I.C.S.: 339112

Medical Instrument Development (MID) Labs, Inc. (1)
557 McCormick St, San Leandro, CA 94577
Tel.: (510) 357-3952
Web Site: https://www.midlabs.com
Medical Surgical Device Mfr
N.A.I.C.S.: 339112
Harold Jacob *(Pres)*

Microline B.V. (1)
Fortranweg 5, 3821 BK, Amersfoort, Netherlands
Tel.: (31) 337600011
Medical Equipment Mfr
N.A.I.C.S.: 541614

Optotal Hoya Limitada (1)
Rua Gotemburgo No 190 Sao Cristovao Cep, Rio de Janeiro, 20941-080, Brazil
Tel.: (55) 2121028000
Medical Equipment Mfr
N.A.I.C.S.: 339112

PT. Hoya Lens Indonesia (1)
Wisma Lumbini Bldg 3Rd Floor Ji Tomang Raya 53, Jakarta, 11440, Indonesia
Tel.: (62) 215607060
Medical Equipment Mfr
N.A.I.C.S.: 339112

Pentax Italia S.r.l. (1)
Via Dione Cassio 15, 20138, Milan, Italy
Tel.: (39) 025099581
Web Site: http://www.pentaxmedical.com
Electro Medical Mfr
N.A.I.C.S.: 334510

Pentax Medical Rus LLC (1)
Innovation Center Skolkovo Malevicha Str 1, 143026, Moscow, Russia
Tel.: (7) 4952803906
Medical Equipment Mfr
N.A.I.C.S.: 339112

PlasmaBiotics S.A.S. (1)
116 quai de Bezons, 95106, Argenteuil, France
Tel.: (33) 130259676
Medical Equipment Mfr
N.A.I.C.S.: 339112

Vision Care Company (1)
No 1 Lorong 2 Toa Payoh Yellow Pages Building 06-01, Singapore, 319637, Singapore
Tel.: (65) 67339984
Optical Product Mfr
N.A.I.C.S.: 333310

Vision Care Company (1)
399 Interchange Building 22nd Floor Sukhumvit Road, Klongtoey-Nua Wattana, Bangkok, 10110, Thailand
Tel.: (66) 26112720
Medical Equipment Mfr
N.A.I.C.S.: 339112

Wassenburg Medical B.V. (1)
Edisonring 9, 6669 NA, Dodewaard, Netherlands (100%)
Tel.: (31) 488700500
Web Site:
http://www.wassenburgmedical.com
Technical Services
N.A.I.C.S.: 541990

HOYA RESORT HOTEL GROUP

5F-41 No 30-2 Lungquan Road, Wen-Chung Ts'un Beinan Township, Taitung, Hsien, Taiwan
Tel.: (886) 89515005
Web Site:
https://www.hoyaresort.com.tw
2736—(TPE)
Rev.: $18,509,458
Assets: $68,641,091
Liabilities: $31,637,901
Net Worth: $37,003,189
Earnings: $368,977
Fiscal Year-end: 12/31/22
Hotel & Restaurant Operator
N.A.I.C.S.: 721110
Ching-Lang Liu *(Chm)*

HOYER GMBH

Wendenstrasse 414-424, 20537, Hamburg, Germany
Tel.: (49) 40210440
Web Site: http://www.hoyer-group.com
Year Founded: 1946
Rev.: $1,334,653,094
Assets: $933,515,646
Liabilities: $527,058,432
Net Worth: $406,457,214
Emp.: 6,195
Fiscal Year-end: 12/31/18
Liquid Goods Transportation Services
N.A.I.C.S.: 541614
Gerd Peters *(CFO & Member-Exec Bd)*

Subsidiaries:

Aktifsped Uluslararasi Nakliyat ve Tic. Ltd. Sti (1)
Sekerpinar Mahallesi Begonya Sokak No 2 Kaplan Plaza Daire 6, 41420, Cayirova, Kocaeli, Türkiye
Tel.: (90) 26272495800
Logistic Services
N.A.I.C.S.: 488510

Dahm Gaslog GmbH (1)
Industriegebiet Scheid 12, D-56651, Niederzissen, Germany
Tel.: (49) 263680890
Web Site: http://www.dahm-gaslog.de
Chemical & Allied Products Merchant Whslr
N.A.I.C.S.: 424690

G.E.S. Gas Equipment Service GmbH (1)
Wendenstrasse 414-424, Hamburg, 20537, Germany (100%)
Tel.: (49) 402109740
Web Site: http://www.ges-geusa.de
Sales Range: $25-49.9 Million
Emp.: 20
Oil & Gas Field Machinery & Equipment Mfr
N.A.I.C.S.: 333132

G.E.S. Oberhausen GmbH (1)
Pfalzer Str 76, 46145, Oberhausen, Germany
Tel.: (49) 2086281888
Web Site: http://www.lindanau-sahrzeugbau.de
Sales Range: $25-49.9 Million
Emp.: 40
Oil & Gas Field Machinery & Equipment Mfr
N.A.I.C.S.: 333132
Detlef Bergmann *(Gen Mgr)*

Guangzhou HOYER Bulk Transport Co. Ltd. (1)
Room 621 block A Jinhao Zhimao Square No 15 North Guangshen Road, Zengcheng, Guangzhou, 511340, China
Tel.: (86) 2089236165
Logistic Services
N.A.I.C.S.: 488510

HOYER (Svizzera) SA (1)
Via Borromini 20 A, 6850, Mendrisio, Switzerland
Tel.: (41) 91 6407 800
Web Site: http://www.hoyer-group.com
Emp.: 22
Freight Trucking Services
N.A.I.C.S.: 484110
Stephan Koenigs *(Mng Dir)*

HOYER ESPANA, S.A. (1)
Calle Suecia s/n Pol Ind de Constanti 2 Fase, Constanti, 43120, Tarragona, Spain
Tel.: (34) 977 2964 21
Freight Trucking Services
N.A.I.C.S.: 484110
Kurt Weiss *(Area Mgr-Sls)*

HOYER Global Shanghai BV (1)
10/F 01-03 Finance Square 333 Jiu Jiang Road, Shanghai, 200001, China
Tel.: (86) 21 6351 9641
Freight Trucking Services
N.A.I.C.S.: 484110
Sam Fang *(Gen Mgr)*

HOYER Global Transport BV (1)
Oude Maasweg 44-50, 3197 KJ, Botlek, Netherlands
Tel.: (31) 181 691 600
Freight Trucking Services
N.A.I.C.S.: 484110

HOYER Global Transport FZE (1)
Office No 6WB - 847, PO Box 241270, Dubai, United Arab Emirates
Tel.: (971) 4 2146811
Freight Trucking Services
N.A.I.C.S.: 484110
Michel de Kramer *(Mgr-Commi)*

HOYER Luxembourg S.A.R.L. (1)
Zone Industrielle, 8287, Kehlen, Luxembourg
Tel.: (352) 2630 2076
Freight Trucking Services
N.A.I.C.S.: 484110

HOYER Mednarodna Spedicija d.o.o. (1)
Jugova ulica 20, 2342, Ruse, Slovenia
Tel.: (386) 2 6622 024
Freight Trucking Services
N.A.I.C.S.: 484110

HOYER Nederland B.V. (1)
Oude Maasweg 44-50, 3197 KJ, Botlek, Netherlands
Tel.: (31) 10 2953 333
Freight Trucking Services
N.A.I.C.S.: 484110
Sjoerd Reemers *(Key Acct Mgr)*

HOYER Slovenska republika s.r.o. (1)
Chalupkova 9, 819 44, Bratislava, Slovakia
Tel.: (421) 2 45523 554
Freight Trucking Services
N.A.I.C.S.: 484110
Witold Adamczyk *(Mng Dir)*

INTERNATIONAL PUBLIC

HOYER Svenska AB (1)
Ostra Erikbergsgatan 38, 417 63, Gothenburg, Sweden
Tel.: (46) 31 7442 100
Freight Trucking Services
N.A.I.C.S.: 484110
Annette Jonasson *(Mgr-Fin)*

HOYER Ukraine TOV (1)
Office 104 1A Tamozhennaya sqr, 65026, Odessa, Ukraine
Tel.: (380) 48 737 55 99
Freight Trucking Services
N.A.I.C.S.: 484110
Alexey Koval *(Area Mgr-Sls & Mgr-Ops)*

Hoyer Austria Ges. m.b.H. (1)
Internationale Fachspedition, Fabianistr 2-4, Vienna, 1110, Austria (100%)
Tel.: (43) 1760330
Sales Range: $25-49.9 Million
Emp.: 50
Chemical & Allied Products Merchant Whslr
N.A.I.C.S.: 424690
Wolfgang Eidenberger *(Mng Dir)*

Hoyer Baltic Expedition UAB (1)
Plieno gatve 2, 95112, Klaipeda, Lithuania
Tel.: (370) 46404044
Web Site: http://www.hoyer-group.com
Refrigerated Warehousing & Storage
N.A.I.C.S.: 493120

Hoyer Belgie N.V. (1)
Transcontinentaalweg 12 Haven 200, 2030, Antwerp, Belgium (100%)
Tel.: (32) 35405200
Web Site: http://www.hoyer-group.com
Sales Range: $25-49.9 Million
Emp.: 50
Metal Container Mfr
N.A.I.C.S.: 332439
Gerd Bosque *(Gen Mgr)*

Hoyer Bitumen-Logistik GmbH (1)
Luisenweg 40, 20537, Hamburg, Germany
Tel.: (49) 402100960
Logistic Services
N.A.I.C.S.: 488510

Hoyer Bulgaria EOOD (1)
11-13 Tsaritsa Yoanna Sq, 8000, Burgas, Bulgaria (100%)
Tel.: (359) 56843394
Web Site: http://www.hoyerbg.com
Sales Range: $50-74.9 Million
Emp.: 60
Petroleum Bulk Stations & Terminals
N.A.I.C.S.: 424710
Latchezar Anguelov *(Gen Mgr)*

Hoyer Bulk Transport Co. Ltd. Guangzhou (1)
1068 Xin Gang Dong Road Rm 2008 North Tower, Continental Centre, 510335, Guangzhou, PRC, China
Tel.: (86) 2089236165
Web Site: http://www.hoyer-group.com
Transportation of Bulk Goods, Liquids, Silo Products, Chemicals & Foodstuffs
N.A.I.C.S.: 488999
Ricky Zhou *(Gen Mgr)*

Hoyer Danmark A/S (1)
Moellebugtvej 5, 7000, Fredericia, Denmark (100%)
Tel.: (45) 70278900
Web Site: http://www.hoyerdanmark.dk
Sales Range: $25-49.9 Million
Emp.: 50
Support Activities for Road Transportation
N.A.I.C.S.: 488490
Claus Reenberg *(CEO & Mgr-Mktg)*

Hoyer Deepsea Malaysia Sdn. Bhd. (1)
B-03-02 Empire Soho Jalan SS 16/1 SS16, 47500, Subang Jaya, Selangor, Malaysia
Tel.: (60) 356300048
Logistic Services
N.A.I.C.S.: 488510

Hoyer Estonia OU (1)
Peterburi tee 92a, 11415, Tallinn, Estonia
Tel.: (372) 6012978
Logistic Services
N.A.I.C.S.: 488510

Hoyer Finland Oy (1)
Laippatie 3, Helsinki, 811, Finland (100%)

AND PRIVATE COMPANIES

Tel.: (358) 97010250
Web Site: http://www.hoyer-group.com
Sales Range: $25-49.9 Million
Emp.: 10
Support Activities for Road Transportation
N.A.I.C.S.: 488490

Hoyer France S.A. (1)
5 Boulevard du Midi, 76107, Rouen, Cedex, France (100%)
Tel.: (33) 232816310
Sales Range: $25-49.9 Million
Emp.: 15
Support Activities for Road Transportation
N.A.I.C.S.: 488490
Clode Oulsken *(Mgr-Site)*

Hoyer Gaslog GmbH (1)
Wendenstrasse 414-424, 20537, Hamburg, Germany (100%)
Tel.: (49) 4021044377
Sales Range: $25-49.9 Million
Emp.: 8
Support Activities for Road Transportation
N.A.I.C.S.: 488490

Hoyer Global (Brasil) Transportes Ltda. (1)
Rua Haddock Lobo 684-1 Andar, Cerqueira Cesar, Sao Paulo, 01414-000, SP, Brazil
Tel.: (55) 1130675800
Logistic Services
N.A.I.C.S.: 488510
Marta Diogo Fanha *(Reg Mgr)*

Hoyer Global Brazil Ltda (1)
Rua Haddock Lobo 684-3rd Floor, Cerqueira Cesar, 01414-000, Sao Paulo, Brazil
Tel.: (55) 1130675800
Web Site: http://www.hoyer-global.com
Sales Range: $25-49.9 Million
Emp.: 15
Chemical & Allied Products Merchant Whslr
N.A.I.C.S.: 424690
Mark Scapem *(Mgr)*

Hoyer Global Inc. (1)
2100 SPC Park Dr Ste 200, Houston, TX 77058
Tel.: (281) 853-1000
Web Site: http://www.hoyer-global.com
Chemical & Allied Products Merchant Whslr
N.A.I.C.S.: 424690
Ana Flores *(Sr VP-Market & Sls)*

Hoyer Global Singapore Pte Ltd. (1)
10 Hoe Chiang Road, 21-04-05 Keppel Twr, 089315, Singapore, Singapore (100%)
Tel.: (65) 62234073
Web Site: http://www.hoyer-global.com
Support Activities for Road Transportation
N.A.I.C.S.: 488490

Hoyer Hungaria KFT (1)
Bocskai krt 8, 9700, Szombathely, Hungary (100%)
Tel.: (36) 22 575 220
Web Site: http://www.hoyer-group.com
Sales Range: $25-49.9 Million
Emp.: 12
Transportation of Bulk Goods, Liquids & Silo Products, Chemicals, Foodstuffs & Liquid Gases
N.A.I.C.S.: 484110
Norbert Bujna *(Mgr-Sls)*

Hoyer Ireland Ltd. (1)
Corrin Fermoy, Cork, P61FD74, Ireland (100%)
Tel.: (353) 18364698
Web Site: http://www.hoyer-group.com
Sales Range: $25-49.9 Million
Emp.: 5
Support Activities for Road Transportation
N.A.I.C.S.: 488490
Conor Sheehy *(Gen Mgr)*

Hoyer Italia S.R.L. (1)
Via Dogana 2, 21052, Busto Arsizio, Varese, Italy (100%)
Tel.: (39) 0331385511
Sales Range: $50-74.9 Million
Emp.: 8
Natural Gas Liquid Extraction
N.A.I.C.S.: 211130

Hoyer Liquid Drumming B.V. (1)
Zeilmakerijweg 1, 4906 CW, Oosterhout, Netherlands
Tel.: (31) 162478300

Logistic Services
N.A.I.C.S.: 488510
Ramon De Vink *(Mgr-Customer Svcs)*

Hoyer Logistics Australia Pty. Ltd. (1)
102 Dodds Street, Southbank, 3006, VIC, Australia
Tel.: (61) 396116851
Logistic Services
N.A.I.C.S.: 488510

Hoyer Middle East Ltd. (1)
Jubail Industrial 2 Plot 134, Jubail, Saudi Arabia
Tel.: (966) 504580573
Logistic Services
N.A.I.C.S.: 488510

Hoyer Mineralol Logistik GmbH (1)
Luisenweg 40, 20537, Hamburg, Germany (100%)
Tel.: (49) 403009360
Sales Range: $200-249.9 Million
Emp.: 500
Oil & Gas Operations
N.A.I.C.S.: 213112
Volker Schmitz *(Mng Dir)*

Hoyer Polska Sp. z o. o. (1)
ul Glowna 25, PL 05-806, Prague, Komorow, Czech Republic
Tel.: (420) 48 22 7591 444
General Warehousing & Storage
N.A.I.C.S.: 493110

Hoyer Polska Sp.z o.o. (1)
Ul Rozdzienska 41, 40-382, Katowice, Poland
Tel.: (48) 327861800
Web Site: http://www.hoyer.pl
Logistic Services
N.A.I.C.S.: 488510
Christoph Jaehn *(CEO)*

Hoyer Portugal Unipessoal Lda. (1)
Centro de Empresas Maquijig Armazem 1 Sala E7 EN252 Km11 5, Parque Industrial de Carrascas, 2950-402, Palmela, Portugal
Tel.: (351) 265092893
Logistic Services
N.A.I.C.S.: 488510
Rafael Serafim *(Mgr-Ops & Area Sls)*

Hoyer UK Ltd. (1)
517 Leeds Road, Huddersfield, HD2 1YJ, United Kingdom (100%)
Tel.: (44) 1484548221
Web Site: http://www.hoyer.uk.com
Emp.: 1,300
Logistic Services
N.A.I.C.S.: 541614

Hoyer-Odfjell Inc. (1)
16055 Space Center Blvd Ste 500, Houston, TX 77062
Tel.: (713) 740-7400
Sales Range: $25-49.9 Million
Emp.: 40
Freight Transportation Arrangement Services
N.A.I.C.S.: 488510

NWB Nord- und Westdeutsche Bunker GmbH (1)
Koreastrasse 7, 20457, Hamburg, Germany (100%)
Tel.: (49) 40 370 0495 99
Web Site: http://www.nwb-bunker.de
Marine Fuel Distr
N.A.I.C.S.: 424720
Andreas Biniasch *(Mng Dir)*

OOO HOYER RUS (1)
Mitrophanievskoe shosse, 2 bld 1 of 307 310, 198095, Saint Petersburg, Russia
Tel.: (7) 4957451946
Freight Trucking Services
N.A.I.C.S.: 484110
Olga Makeeva *(Area Mgr-Sls Support)*

Scharrer & Andresen GmbH (1)
Wendenstrasse 412, 20537, Hamburg, Germany
Tel.: (49) 402100960
Sales Range: $25-49.9 Million
Emp.: 10
Support Activities for Road Transportation
N.A.I.C.S.: 488490

Shanghai HOYER Sinobulk Transport Co., Ltd. (1)

10/F 01-03 Finance Square 333 Jiu Jiang Road, Shanghai, 200001, China
Tel.: (86) 2163519641
Logistic Services
N.A.I.C.S.: 488510
Ricky Zhou *(Mgr-Bus Dev)*

Wimmer Transportdienst GmbH (1)
Laufenauer Str 6-8, Altenmarkt an der Alz, 83352, Traunstein, Germany
Tel.: (49) 862180050
Web Site: http://www.wimmer-logistik.de
Logistic Services
N.A.I.C.S.: 488510

HOYLU AB
Nordenskioldsgatan 24, 211 19, Malmo, Sweden
Tel.: (46) 40170600
Web Site: https://www.hoylu.com
Year Founded: 2016
HOYLU—(OMX)
Rev.: $4,376,290
Assets: $7,572,123
Liabilities: $8,937,556
Net Worth: ($1,365,433)
Earnings: ($4,558,880)
Emp.: 35
Fiscal Year-end: 12/31/22
Software Development Services
N.A.I.C.S.: 541511
Jakob Leitner *(VP-Product)*

HOYU CO., LTD.
Toku River Tokugawa 1-501, Nagoya, 461-8650, Aichi, Japan
Tel.: (81) 529359556 JP
Web Site: http://www.hoyu.co.jp
Year Founded: 1905
Emp.: 996
Hair Coloring Products, Cosmetics & Medical Supplies Mfr
N.A.I.C.S.: 325620
Mizuno Makio *(Pres)*

Subsidiaries:

Kracie Holdings, Ltd. (1)
20-20 Kaigan 3-chome, Minato-ku, Tokyo, 108-8080, Japan (100%)
Tel.: (81) 354463000
Web Site: http://www.kracie.co.jp
Holding Company; Toiletries, Pharmaceuticals & Food Products Mfr
N.A.I.C.S.: 551112
Akiyoshi Nakajima *(Chm)*

Subsidiary (Domestic):

Kracie Foods, Ltd. (2)
20-20 Kaigan 3-Chome, Minato-ku, Tokyo, 108-8080, Japan
Tel.: (81) 354463291
Web Site: http://www.kracie.co.jp
Sales Range: $100-124.9 Million
Emp.: 500
Food & Beverage Mfr
N.A.I.C.S.: 311999

Subsidiary (Domestic):

Kracie Foods Sales, Ltd. (3)
20-20 Kaigan 3-chome, Minato-ku, Tokyo, 108-8080, Japan
Tel.: (81) 3 5446 3002
Food Product Whslr
N.A.I.C.S.: 311999

Subsidiary (Domestic):

Kracie Home Products, Ltd. (2)
3-20-20 Yokoso Rainbow Tower, Minato-ku, Tokyo, 108-0022, Japan
Tel.: (81) 354463211
Sales Range: $25-49.9 Million
Emp.: 100
Toiletries & Cosmetics Mfr
N.A.I.C.S.: 325620
Yasuya Ishibashi *(Pres)*

Subsidiary (Domestic):

Kracie Home Products Sales Ltd. (3)
3 2 20 Kaigan, Minato Ku, Tokyo, 108 8080, Japan

Tel.: (81) 354463211
Web Site: http://www.kracie.co.jp
Toiletries & Cosmetics Whslr
N.A.I.C.S.: 423990

Tokyo Reine, Ltd. (3)
5 15 18 Ginza Daihachi Kanai Bldg 7 Fl, Chuo Ku, Tokyo, 104 0061, Japan
Tel.: (81) 335454691
Sales Range: $10-24.9 Million
Emp.: 100
Toiletries Mfr
N.A.I.C.S.: 325611

Subsidiary (Domestic):

Kracie Pharma, Ltd. (2)
20-20 Kaigan 3-chome, Minato-ku, Tokyo, 108-8080, Japan
Tel.: (81) 354463300
Web Site: http://www.kracie.co.jp
Sales Range: $25-49.9 Million
Emp.: 50
Pharmaceutical & Medicinal Products Mfr
N.A.I.C.S.: 325412

Joint Venture (Non-US):

HM Science Inc. (3)
Room 719/706 20 Zhichun Road, Haidian District, Beijing, 100088, China
Tel.: (86) 1062362317
Web Site: http://www.hm-science.com
Sales Range: $50-74.9 Million
Emp.: 8
Medicinal Wholesale Trade Agency; Owned by Kracie Holdings, Ltd. & by China National Pharmaceutical Group Corporation (SINOPHARM)
N.A.I.C.S.: 425120

Subsidiary (Domestic):

Kracie Pharmaceutical, Ltd. (3)
Yokoso Rainbow Bldg 6F 20-20 Kaigan 3-chome Minato-ku, Tokyo, 108-8080, Japan
Tel.: (81) 354463002
Web Site: http://www.kracie.co.jp
Sales Range: $25-49.9 Million
Emp.: 15
Production & Sales of Kampo Medicinal Products
N.A.I.C.S.: 325412
Hiroshi Ozawa *(Pres)*

Joint Venture (Non-US):

Qingdao Huazhong Pharmaceuticals Co., Ltd. (3)
202 Chong Qing Nan Road, Qingdao, 266100, Shangdong, China
Tel.: (86) 53284961075
Web Site: http://www.phm-huazhong.com
Traditional Chinese Medicinal Mfr; Owned by Kracie Holdings, Ltd. & by China National Pharmaceutical Group Corporation (SINOPHARM)
N.A.I.C.S.: 325411

HOYUAN GREEN ENERGY CO.,LTD
No 158 Nanhu Middle Road Xuelang Street, Binhu District, Wuxi, 214128, Jiangsu, China
Tel.: (86) 51085390590
Web Site: https://www.hysolar.com
Year Founded: 2002
603185—(SHG)
Rev.: $3,076,084,899
Assets: $2,953,185,029
Liabilities: $1,193,189,414
Net Worth: $1,759,995,615
Earnings: $425,855,818
Fiscal Year-end: 12/31/22
Grinding Machine Mfr
N.A.I.C.S.: 334417
Jianliang Yang *(Chm & Pres)*

HP ADHESIVES LIMITED
G-11 Unique House, Chakala Andheri East, Mumbai, 400099, Maharashtra, India
Tel.: (91) 2268196300
Web Site: https://www.hpadhesives.com

HP ADHESIVES LIMITED

HP Adhesives Limited—(Continued)
Year Founded: 1978
543433—(BOM)
Cement Mfr & Distr
N.A.I.C.S.: 327310
Anjana Motwani (Chm)

HPC AG
Nordlinger Strasse 16, 86655, Harburg, Germany
Tel.: (49) 90809990
Web Site: http://www.hpc.ag
Year Founded: 1948
Emp.: 782
Geotechnical Consulting & Environmental Assessment Services
N.A.I.C.S.: 541620
Manfred Studemann (Chm-Supervisory Bd)

Subsidiaries:

GEYSER HPC, S.A.U. (1)
Iparragirre Hiribidea 80, 48940, Leioa, Spain
Tel.: (34) 944632333
Engineering Consulting Services
N.A.I.C.S.: 541330

HPC Austria GmbH (1)
Schlossplatz 13/1, 2361, Laxenburg, Austria
Tel.: (43) 22367108980
Engineering Consulting Services
N.A.I.C.S.: 541330

HPC Bulgaria EOOD (1)
7 Iskar Str ap 3, 1000, Sofia, Bulgaria
Tel.: (359) 29869350
Engineering Consulting Services
N.A.I.C.S.: 541330

HPC Diering Romania SRL (1)
Bulevardul Ferdinand I 17, 021381, Bucharest, Romania
Tel.: (40) 318241221
Engineering Consulting Services
N.A.I.C.S.: 541330
Bogdan Danulet (Mgr-Ops)

HPC Envirotec S.A. (1)
1 Rue Pierre Marzin, 35230, Paris, France
Tel.: (33) 299131450
Engineering Consulting Services
N.A.I.C.S.: 541330

HPC Italia S.r.l. (1)
Via Francesco Ferrucci 17/A, 20145, Milan, Italy
Tel.: (39) 0245488990
Engineering Consulting Services
N.A.I.C.S.: 541330
Lorenzo Garlati (Project Mgr)

HPC Paseco SP Ltd. (1)
22 Kykladon, 11361, Athens, Greece
Tel.: (30) 2108258200
Engineering Consulting Services
N.A.I.C.S.: 541330

HPC Polska Sp.zo.o. (1)
Ul Solskiego 44, 52416, Wroclaw, Poland
Tel.: (48) 713643031
Engineering Consulting Services
N.A.I.C.S.: 541330

HPC BIOSCIENCES LIMITED
Plot No 22 Pooja Complex Veer Savarkar Block, Shakarpur, New Delhi, 110092, India
Tel.: (91) 1132965576
Web Site: https://www.hpcbiosciences.com
Rev.: $324,053
Assets: $4,864,305
Liabilities: $73,334
Net Worth: $4,790,971
Earnings: $30,638
Fiscal Year-end: 03/31/18
Grain Farming Services
N.A.I.C.S.: 111199
Tarun Chauhan (Exec Dir)

HPC HOLDINGS LIMITED
Block 165 Bukit Merah Central 08-3687, Singapore, 150165, Singapore
Tel.: (65) 62277927
Web Site: http://www.hpc.sg
1742—(HKG)
Rev.: $219,067,636
Assets: $136,347,042
Liabilities: $70,063,622
Net Worth: $66,283,420
Earnings: $2,349,466
Emp.: 1,007
Fiscal Year-end: 10/31/23
Warehouse Construction Services
N.A.I.C.S.: 236220

HPC SYSTEMS, INC.
LOOP-X 8th Floor 3-9-15 Kaigan, Minato-Ku, Tokyo, 108-0022, Japan
Tel.: (81) 354465530
Web Site: https://www.hpc.co.jp
Year Founded: 2006
6597—(TKS)
Rev.: $43,197,900
Assets: $29,638,300
Liabilities: $14,169,160
Net Worth: $15,469,140
Earnings: $1,859,780
Emp.: 121
Fiscal Year-end: 06/30/24
Computer Equipment Mfr & Distr
N.A.I.C.S.: 334118
Teppei Ono (Pres)

HPI AG
Furstenriederstrasse 267, D-81377, Munich, Germany
Tel.: (49) 89800656440 De
Web Site: http://www.hpi-ag.com
Year Founded: 1976
Semiconductors, Electronic Components & Computer Products Distr
N.A.I.C.S.: 423430
Boris Durr (Chm-Supervisory Bd)

Subsidiaries:

3 KV Gmbh (1)
Furstenrieder Strasse 267, 81377, Munich, Germany
Tel.: (49) 89 800 656 0
Web Site: http://www.3kv.de
Sales Range: $25-49.9 Million
Emp.: 15
Information Technology Services
N.A.I.C.S.: 541512

Azego Components AG (1)
Dornacher Str 3a, 85622, Feldkirchen, Bavaria, Germany
Tel.: (49) 89 829 998 0
Web Site: http://www.azego.com
Logistics & Stock Management Services
N.A.I.C.S.: 541614

Subsidiary (Domestic):

HPI Distribution GmbH (2)
Dornacher Str 3a, Feldkirchen, Germany
Tel.: (49) 89 9971 0
Sales Range: $50-74.9 Million
Emp.: 1
Electronic Components Distr
N.A.I.C.S.: 532210

Eastern Dragon Express (H.K.) Ltd. (1)
Unit C 6/F Gemstar Tower 23 Man Lok Street Hunghom, Kowloon, China (Hong Kong)
Tel.: (852) 27120184
Web Site: http://www.ce-global-distribution.com
Sales Range: $25-49.9 Million
Emp.: 40
Electronic Parts & Equipment Whslr
N.A.I.C.S.: 423690

HPI Asia Pacific Ltd. (1)
Room 716 Xinxi Mansion No1403 Minsheng Road, Shanghai, 200135, China
Tel.: (86) 21 3392 6008
Web Site: http://www.hpi-ag.com
Logistics Consulting Servies
N.A.I.C.S.: 541614

HPI Int. Trading & Chemical GmbH (1)
Am Limes-Park 2, 65843, Sulzbach, Germany
Tel.: (49) 69 305 5263
Web Site: http://www.hpi-ag.com
Chemical Products Distr
N.A.I.C.S.: 424690

HPI Logistics GmbH & Co. KG (1)
Am Limes-Park 2, 65843, Sulzbach, Germany
Tel.: (49) 69 305 84780
Web Site: http://www.hpigmbh.com
Logistics Consulting Servies
N.A.I.C.S.: 541614
Bruhard Schnitker (Pres)

HPI Sourcing GmbH & Co. KG (1)
Am Limespark 2, 65843, Sulzbach, Germany
Tel.: (49) 69 3054232
Procurement Services
N.A.I.C.S.: 561499

MRL Mannesmannrohren Logistic GmbH (1)
Am Rosenbaum 29, 40878, Ratingen, Germany
Tel.: (49) 210220710
Logistics Consulting Servies
N.A.I.C.S.: 541614

VCE Europe GmbH (1)
Liebherrstrasse 5, 80538, Munich, Germany
Tel.: (49) 8945224622
Web Site: http://www.virtualchip.com
Internet Based Trading Exchange Connecting Semiconductor Buyers with Sellers
N.A.I.C.S.: 541990

Virtual Chip Exchange, Inc. (1)
Place Du Commerce 330-1 Delecommerce Place, J4W 2Z7, Brossard, QC, Canada
Tel.: (450) 676-2217
Web Site: http://www.virtualchip.com
Sales Range: $50-74.9 Million
Emp.: 10
Electronic Parts & Equipment Whslr
N.A.I.C.S.: 423690

ce Global Sourcing GmbH (1)
Dornacher Strasse 3a, Feldkirchen, 85622, Munich, Germany
Tel.: (49) 89 9971 0
Web Site: http://www.ce-global.de
Sales Range: $25-49.9 Million
Emp.: 38
Electronic Components Distr
N.A.I.C.S.: 423690
Harald Heutink (CEO & Mng Dir)

ce Global Sourcing Taiwan Co Ltd. (1)
Rm 7001 7th Floor No 187 Sec 4, Hsin-Yin Rd-Ta-An Dist, Taipei, Taiwan
Tel.: (886) 227026977
Web Site: http://www.cedistribution.de
Electronic Components Mfr
N.A.I.C.S.: 334419

ce Schweiz AG (1)
Landstrasse 176, 5430, Wattwil, Switzerland (100%)
Tel.: (41) 564371959
Sales Range: $50-74.9 Million
Emp.: 3
Electronic Parts & Equipment Whslr
N.A.I.C.S.: 423690
V. Arny (Mng Dir)

ce UK Ltd. (1)
3rd Floor 11 Waterloo Pl, London, SW1Y4AU, United Kingdom
Tel.: (44) 207839226
Electronic Parts & Equipment Whslr
N.A.I.C.S.: 423690

HPI RESOURCES BERHAD
Lot 15339 HS D 75346 Jalan TS Utama Kawasan Perindustrian Nilai Mini, 71800, Nilai, Negeri Sembilan, Malaysia
Tel.: (60) 67999992
Web Site: http://www.hartapack.com
Sales Range: $100-124.9 Million
Emp.: 2,400
Corrugated Board Mfr

INTERNATIONAL PUBLIC

N.A.I.C.S.: 321999
Chang Kee Soon (Mng Dir)

Subsidiaries:

Cabaran Minda Sdn. Bhd. (1)
Plot 7 Kawasan Perindustrian Parit Raja, 86400, Batu Pahat, Johor, Malaysia
Tel.: (60) 74542788
Web Site: http://www.hartapack.com
Sales Range: $25-49.9 Million
Emp.: 28
General Trucking Services
N.A.I.C.S.: 484121

Cabaran Perspektif Sdn. Bhd. (1)
Plot 7 Kawasan Perindustrian Parit Raja, 86400, Batu Pahat, Johor, Malaysia
Tel.: (60) 74542788
Web Site: http://www.hartapack.com
General Trucking Services
N.A.I.C.S.: 484110

Chiga Light Industries Sdn. Bhd. (1)
Plot 15 Kawasan Perindustrian Parit Raja, Batu Pahat, 86400, Johor, Malaysia
Tel.: (60) 74548333
Web Site: http://www.hartapack.com
Sales Range: $50-74.9 Million
Emp.: 110
Plastics Bag Mfr
N.A.I.C.S.: 322220
Lim Keng Hua (Deputy Gen Mgr)

HPI Resources (Overseas) Sdn. Bhd. (1)
Plot 9 Kawasan Perindustrian Parit Raja, Batu Pahat, 86400, Johor, Malaysia
Tel.: (60) 74548333
Web Site: http://www.hartapack.com
Sales Range: $125-149.9 Million
Emp.: 500
Carton Boxes Mfr
N.A.I.C.S.: 322211
Chan Chor Ngiak (Mng Dir)

Harta Distribution Network Sdn. Bhd. (1)
Plot 7 Kawasan Perindustrian Parit Raja, 86400, Batu Pahat, Johor, Malaysia
Tel.: (60) 74548333
Web Site: http://www.hartapack.com
Emp.: 1
Packaging Product Distr
N.A.I.C.S.: 424990
Chan Chor Ngiak (Mng Dir)

Harta Fleksipak Sdn. Bhd. (1)
Plo 5 Kawasan Perindustrian Parit Raja, 86400, Batu Pahat, Johor, Malaysia
Tel.: (60) 74531333
Emp.: 60
Paper Packaging Product Mfr
N.A.I.C.S.: 322220
Jimmy Keang (Mgr)

Harta Packaging Industries (Cambodia) Limited (1)
National Road No 4 Phum Ang Sangkat Chom Chao, Khan Posenchey, Phnom Penh, Cambodia
Tel.: (855) 17333977
Automotive Components Mfr
N.A.I.C.S.: 336330

Harta Packaging Industries (Malacca) Sdn. Bhd. (1)
PT 3836 & 3837 Taman Tasik Utama Fasa 1, Ayer Keroh, 75450, Melaka, Malaysia
Tel.: (60) 62316666
Sales Range: $25-49.9 Million
Emp.: 1
Paperboard Mfr
N.A.I.C.S.: 322130

Harta Packaging Industries Sdn. Bhd. (1)
Plot 7 Kawasan Perindustrian Parit Raja, Batu Pahat, 86400, Johor, Malaysia
Tel.: (60) 74548333
Web Site: http://www.hartapack.com
Sales Range: $125-149.9 Million
Emp.: 500
Corrugated Boards & Cartons Mfr
N.A.I.C.S.: 322211
Chang Keesoon (Mng Dir)

Subsidiary (Domestic):

Harta Packaging Industries (Perak) Sdn. Bhd. (2)

PT 685 Jln Perusahaan 3, Kawasan Perusahaan, 34200, Parit Buntar, Perak, Malaysia (100%)
Tel.: (60) 57166778
Web Site: http://www.hartapack.com
Corrugated Board Mfr
N.A.I.C.S.: 322211

K.H. Chan Trading Sdn. Bhd. (1)
Plo 7 Kawasan Perindustrian Parit Raja, 86400, Batu Pahat, Johor, Malaysia
Tel.: (60) 74542788
Web Site: http://www.hartapack.com
General Freight Trucking Services
N.A.I.C.S.: 484110

OJI Packaging (Cambodia) Co., Ltd. (1)
Phnom Penh Special Economic Zone National Road No 4 Lot No P1-A2-2, Phumi Kamrieng Sangkat Kantouk Khan Posenchey, Phnom Penh, Cambodia
Tel.: (855) 23888066
Automotive Components Mfr
N.A.I.C.S.: 336330

Ojitex Harta Packaging (Sihanoukville) Limited (1)
Sangkat No 3 Khan Mittapheap, Sihanoukville Port Special Economic Zone, Sihanoukville, Preah Sihanoukville, Cambodia
Tel.: (855) 346363161
Automotive Components Mfr
N.A.I.C.S.: 336330

Trio Paper Mills Sdn. Bhd. (1)
395 Jalan Tasek Simpang Ampat, Seberang Perai Selatan, 14120, Perai, Penang, Malaysia
Tel.: (60) 45887319
Emp.: 112
Paperboard Mfr
N.A.I.C.S.: 322230

HPK A.D.
Draksenic, 79240, Kozarska Dubica, Bosnia & Herzegovina
Tel.: (387) 52443812
HPKD-R-A—(BANJ)
Sales Range: Less than $1 Million
Farm Food Product Mfr
N.A.I.C.S.: 311991

HPL ELECTRIC & POWER LIMITED
Windsor Business Park B-1D Sector 10, Noida, 201 301, Uttar Pradesh, India
Tel.: (91) 1204656300   In
Web Site: https://www.hplindia.com
Year Founded: 1992
HPL—(NSE)
Rev.: $151,762,101
Assets: $203,911,912
Liabilities: $108,552,209
Net Worth: $95,359,703
Earnings: $3,626,749
Emp.: 1,165
Fiscal Year-end: 03/31/23
Electrical Equipment Mfr & Distr
N.A.I.C.S.: 335313
Gautam Seth (Co-Mng Dir)

Subsidiaries:

Himachal Energy Private Limited (1)
VPO Jabli, Tehsil Kasauli Dist, Solan, 173 209, Himachal Pradesh, India
Tel.: (91) 1792277692
Electric Equipment Mfr & Distr
N.A.I.C.S.: 335999

HPMT HOLDING BERHAD
5 Jalan Sungai Kayu Ara 32/39 Taman Berjaya Seksyen 32, 40460, Shah Alam, Selangor Darul Ehsan, Malaysia
Tel.: (60) 358700098   MY
Year Founded: 1978
HPMT—(KLS)
Rev.: $18,780,317
Assets: $35,966,138
Liabilities: $6,980,317
Net Worth: $28,985,820
Earnings: $1,733,757
Emp.: 305
Fiscal Year-end: 12/31/22
Holding Company
N.A.I.C.S.: 551112
Khoo Seng Giap (Mng Dir)

Subsidiaries:

HPMT (Shenzhen) Limited (1)
1223 Kerry Centre 2008 Renminnan Road, Shenzhen, China
Tel.: (86) 75525181722
Cutting Tool Mfr & Distr
N.A.I.C.S.: 333515

HPMT Deutschland GmbH (1)
Vorkamp 6, 23879, Molln, Germany
Tel.: (49) 4542842110
Cutting Tool Mfr & Distr
N.A.I.C.S.: 333515

Herroz Sdn. Bhd. (1)
5 Jalan Sungai Kayu Ara 32/39 Taman Berjaya Seksyen 32, 40460, Shah Alam, Selangor Darul Ehsan, Malaysia
Tel.: (60) 357402838
Web Site: https://www.herroz.com
Cutting Tool Distr
N.A.I.C.S.: 423830

Pentagon Coating Technologies Sdn. Bhd. (1)
Jalan Sungai Kayu Ara 32/39, Taman Perindustrian Berjaya, 40460, Shah Alam, Selangor, Malaysia
Tel.: (60) 2345678900
Web Site: https://pentagonct.com
Metal Coatings Mfr
N.A.I.C.S.: 332812

HPP HOLDINGS BERHAD
37 Jalan TTC 29 Taman Teknologi Cheng, 75250, Melaka, Malaysia
Tel.: (60) 63356485   MY
Web Site: https://www.hppholdings.com
Year Founded: 2018
HPPHB—(KLS)
Rev.: $18,277,756
Assets: $33,514,248
Liabilities: $5,627,023
Net Worth: $27,887,225
Earnings: $2,099,474
Emp.: 330
Fiscal Year-end: 05/31/23
Holding Company
N.A.I.C.S.: 551112
Kok Hon Seng (Mng Dir)

HPQ-SILICON RESOURCES INC.
3000 Rue Omer Lavallee 306, Montreal, H1Y 3R8, QC, Canada
Tel.: (514) 846-3271   Ca
Web Site: https://www.hpqsilicon.com
Year Founded: 1996
HPQ—(TSXV)
Assets: $6,840,985
Liabilities: $5,455,965
Net Worth: $1,385,020
Earnings: ($12,115,328)
Fiscal Year-end: 12/31/23
Gold Exploration Services
N.A.I.C.S.: 212220

HQ AB
Norrlandsgattan 15 Entrance D, 103 71, Stockholm, Sweden
Tel.: (46) 086961700
Web Site: http://www.hqab.se
Sales Range: $125-149.9 Million
Emp.: 301
Security Brokerage Services
N.A.I.C.S.: 523150
Mats Qviberg (Chm)

Subsidiaries:

HQ Direct AB (1)
Hovslagargatan 3, 103 21, Stockholm, Sweden
Tel.: (46) 8 463 85 00
Financial Management Services
N.A.I.C.S.: 541618

HQ GLOBAL EDUCATION INC.
27th Floor BOBO Fortune Center 368 South Furong Road, Changsha, 410007, Hunan, China
Tel.: (86) 73187828601   DE
Web Site: http://www.hq-education.com
HQGE—(OTCIQ)
Sales Range: Less than $1 Million
Emp.: 1,192
Vocational Education & Training Services
N.A.I.C.S.: 611710
Guangwen He (Chm, Pres, CEO & Sec)

HR PATH SAS
Tour Montparnasse 41st Floor 33 Avenue du Maine, 75 015, Paris, France
Tel.: (33) 153 622 214
Web Site: http://www.hr-path.com
Human Resource Consulting Services
N.A.I.C.S.: 541612
Francois Boulet (Founding Partner)

Subsidiaries:

Terra Information Group, Inc (TIG) (1)
896 S Frontenac St Ste 100, Aurora, IL 60504
Tel.: (630) 692-1872
Web Site: http://www.terrainformation.com
Sales Range: $1-9.9 Million
Emp.: 40
SAP Consulting, Training & Support to U.S. & Canadian Companies
N.A.I.C.S.: 611430
Scott Landt (VP-Sls)

Whitaker Taylor, Inc. (1)
1355 Peachtree St NE Ste 2000, Atlanta, GA 30309-3280
Tel.: (310) 684-3044
Web Site: http://www.whitakertaylor.com
Process, Physical Distribution & Logistics Consulting Services
N.A.I.C.S.: 541614
Scott Burton (CEO)

HRAM HOLDING DD
Vilharjeva 29, 1000, Ljubljana, Slovenia
Tel.: (386) 13065566
Web Site: http://www.hram-holding.si
Sales Range: $50-74.9 Million
Investment & Portfolio Management Services
N.A.I.C.S.: 523999

HRB FLORICULTURE LIMITED
A-28 Ram Nagar Shastri Nagar, Jaipur, 302 016, India
Tel.: (91) 1412303098
Web Site: https://www.hrb.co.in
Rev.: $20,057
Assets: $10,984
Liabilities: $33,786
Net Worth: ($22,802)
Earnings: ($107,056)
Fiscal Year-end: 03/31/18
Floriculture Production Services
N.A.I.C.S.: 111422
Krishan Kumar Parwal (Mng Dir)

HRH NEXT SERVICES LIMITED
4-1-976 Abid Road, Hyderabad, 500001, India
Tel.: (91) 4024754338
Web Site: https://www.hrhnext.com
Year Founded: 2007
HRHNEXT—(NSE)
Rev.: $6,211,455
Assets: $3,493,341
Liabilities: $2,227,053
Net Worth: $1,266,287
Earnings: $336,341
Emp.: 284
Fiscal Year-end: 03/31/23
Information Technology Services
N.A.I.C.S.: 541512

HRL HOLDINGS LIMITED
Level 12 145 Eagle Street, Brisbane, 4000, QLD, Australia
Tel.: (61) 731055960
Web Site: http://www.hrlholdings.com
HRL—(ASX)
Rev.: $26,527,796
Assets: $27,739,143
Liabilities: $6,685,008
Net Worth: $21,054,135
Earnings: $1,005,241
Fiscal Year-end: 06/30/21
Exploration & Development of Geothermal Energy
N.A.I.C.S.: 221116
Paul Marshall (Sec)

Subsidiaries:

Morrison Geotechnic Pty Ltd (1)
Unit 1 35 Limestone Street, PO Box 3063, Darra, 4076, QLD, Australia
Tel.: (61) 732790900
Web Site: http://www.morrisongeo.com.au
Emp.: 60
Engineeering Services
N.A.I.C.S.: 541330
Dawn Boughton (Mgr-HR & Accounts)

OCTIEF Pty Ltd (1)
Unit 34/53-57 Link Drive, Yatala, 4207, QLD, Australia
Tel.: (61) 73 386 1164
Web Site: https://www.octief.com.au
Environmental & Occupational Consulting Services
N.A.I.C.S.: 541620

Octfolio Pty Ltd (1)
Level 12 145 Eagle Street, Brisbane, 4000, QLD, Australia
Tel.: (61) 738328835
Web Site: http://www.octfolio.com.au
Software Development Services
N.A.I.C.S.: 541511

HRNETGROUP LIMITED
391A Orchard Road Ngee Ann City Tower A Unit 23-03, Singapore, 238873, Singapore
Tel.: (65) 67307855   SG
Web Site: https://www.hrnetgroup.com
Year Founded: 1992
CHZ—(SES)
Rev.: $438,134,515
Assets: $363,509,808
Liabilities: $65,894,872
Net Worth: $297,614,936
Earnings: $50,033,326
Emp.: 804
Fiscal Year-end: 12/31/23
Investment Holding Company
N.A.I.C.S.: 551114
Peter Sim (Founder & Chm)

Subsidiaries:

Career Personnel Limited (1)
821 Broad St, Augusta, GA 30901
Tel.: (706) 722-1265
Web Site: https://www.careerpersonnel.com
Human Resource Management Services
N.A.I.C.S.: 561320
Louise Aronow (Pres)

PeopleSearch Pte. Ltd. (1)
391A Orchard Road 17-08 Ngee Ann City Tower A, Singapore, 238873, Singapore
Tel.: (65) 67386228
Web Site: http://www.pplesearch.com
Human Resource Consulting Services
N.A.I.C.S.: 541612

HRNETGROUP LIMITED

HRnetGroup Limited—(Continued)
Lorencz Tay Yuh Shiuan *(Mng Dir)*

Recruit Express Pte. Ltd. (1)
391A Orchard Road Ngee Ann City Tower A 12-08, Singapore, 238873, Singapore
Tel.: (65) 67326006
Web Site:
https://www.recruitexpress.com.sg
Human Resource Management Services
N.A.I.C.S.: 561330
Karen Lee *(Mgr-HR)*

RecruitFirst Limited (1)
Suite 1006 Central Plaza 18 Harbour Road Wan Chai, Hong Kong, China (Hong Kong)
Tel.: (852) 39900368
Web Site: http://www.recruitfirst.com.hk
Human Resource Management Services
N.A.I.C.S.: 561330

RecruitFirst Pte. Ltd. (1)
6 Battery Road 17-02, Singapore, 049909, Singapore
Tel.: (65) 62226388
Web Site: http://www.recruitfirst.com.sg
Human Resource Management Services
N.A.I.C.S.: 561330

SearchAsia Consulting Pte. Ltd. (1)
391A Orchard Road 11-03/04 Ngee Ann City Tower A, Singapore, 238873, Singapore
Tel.: (65) 6 735 5885
Web Site: https://www.searchasia.com.sg
Human Resource Management Services
N.A.I.C.S.: 561330
Jerry Tan *(Sr Mgr)*

HRS CO., LTD.

1605 Miwon Bldg 70 Gukjegeumyung-ro, Yeongdeunpo-gu, Seoul, 07333, Korea (South)
Tel.: (82) 27806156
Web Site:
https://www.hrssilicone.com
Year Founded: 1981
036640—(KRS)
Rev.: $66,035,510
Assets: $89,643,975
Liabilities: $7,996,634
Net Worth: $81,647,341
Earnings: $7,695,410
Emp.: 162
Fiscal Year-end: 12/31/22
Silicone Products Mfr
N.A.I.C.S.: 325212
Kim Jin Sung *(CEO)*

Subsidiaries:

HRS Co., Ltd. - Asan Factory (1)
103-15 Sinbong-gil Yeongin-myeon, 31401, Asan, Chungcheongnam-do, Korea (South)
Tel.: (82) 415434003
Silicon Rubber Product Mfr
N.A.I.C.S.: 325212

HRS Co., Ltd. - Pyeongtaek Factory (1)
7 Chupalsandan 2-gil Paengseong-eup, 17998, Pyeongtaek, Gyeonggi-do, Korea (South)
Tel.: (82) 316558822
Silicon Rubber Product Mfr
N.A.I.C.S.: 325212

HRS Co., Ltd. - Suzhou Factory (1)
Plant 1 Science and Technology Park No 777 Kangyuan Road, Suzhou Xiangcheng Economic Development Zone, Suzhou, 215131, China
Tel.: (86) 51269390288
Silicon Rubber Product Mfr
N.A.I.C.S.: 325212

HRVATSKA BANKA ZA OBNOVU I RAZVITAK

Strossmayerov trg 9, 10000, Zagreb, Croatia
Tel.: (385) 14591666
Web Site: http://www.hbor.hr
Sales Range: $150-199.9 Million
Emp.: 270
Banking & Financial Services
N.A.I.C.S.: 522110
Mladen Kober *(Member-Mgmt Bd)*

HRVATSKA ELEKTROPRIVREDA D.D.

Ulica grada Vukovara 37, 10000, Zagreb, Croatia
Tel.: (385) 016322111
Web Site: http://www.hep.hr
Year Founded: 1990
Rev.: $2,340,538,200
Assets: $6,213,842,866
Liabilities: $2,460,955,574
Net Worth: $3,752,887,292
Earnings: $210,171,808
Emp.: 11,011
Fiscal Year-end: 12/31/18
Electricity Production & Transmission Services
N.A.I.C.S.: 221111
Sasa Dujmic *(Member-Mgmt Bd)*

Subsidiaries:

Agencija za posebni otpad d.o.o. (1)
Savska 41/IV, 10000, Zagreb, Croatia
Tel.: (385) 16311999
Web Site: http://www.apo.hr
Sales Range: $25-49.9 Million
Emp.: 20
Environmental Engineering & Consulting Services
N.A.I.C.S.: 541330

HEP ESCO d.o.o. (1)
Ulica grada Vukovara 37, 10000, Zagreb, Croatia
Tel.: (385) 16322923
Web Site: http://www.hepesco.hr
Sales Range: $75-99.9 Million
Emp.: 23
Electric Power Distribution Services
N.A.I.C.S.: 221122
Robert Krklec *(Chm-Supervisory Bd)*

HEP Energija d.o.o. (1)
Dunajska cesta 151, 1000, Ljubljana, Slovenia
Tel.: (386) 12926166
Web Site: https://www.hep-energija.si
Electric Power Distribution Services
N.A.I.C.S.: 221122

HEP Opskrba d.o.o. (1)
Ulica grada Vukovara 37, 10000, Zagreb, Croatia
Tel.: (385) 16323900
Web Site: http://www.hep.hr
Sales Range: $100-124.9 Million
Emp.: 57
Electricity, Heat & Gas Supply Services
N.A.I.C.S.: 221122
Nada Podnar *(Dir-Operational Mktg Dept)*

HEP-NOC Velika (1)
Luke Ibrisimovica 9, Velika, 34 330, Zagreb, Croatia
Tel.: (385) 34313037
Sales Range: $10-24.9 Million
Emp.: 10
Education Training Services
N.A.I.C.S.: 611710

HEP-Obnovljivi izvori energije d.o.o. (1)
Ulica grada Vukovara 37, 10000, Zagreb, Croatia
Tel.: (385) 1 6322 171
Sales Range: $25-49.9 Million
Emp.: 8
Energy Consulting Services
N.A.I.C.S.: 541690

HEP-Odmor i rekreacija d.o.o. (1)
Ulica Grada Vukovara 37, 10000, Zagreb, Croatia
Tel.: (385) 16009024
Electric Power Disribution Systems Mfr
N.A.I.C.S.: 221122

HEP-Operator Distribucijskog Sustava d.o.o. (1)
Ulica grada Vukovara 37, 10000, Zagreb, Croatia
Tel.: (385) 1 63 22 111
Web Site: http://www.hep.hr
Electric Power Transmission Services
N.A.I.C.S.: 221121

HEP-Operator prijenosnog sustava d.o.o. (1)
Kupska 4, 10000, Zagreb, Croatia
Tel.: (385) 14545111
Web Site: http://www.hops.hr
Electric Power Distribution Services
N.A.I.C.S.: 221122
Tomislav Plavsic *(Chm-Mgmt Bd)*

HEP-Plin d.o.o. (1)
Cara Hadrijana 7, Osijek, 31000, Croatia
Tel.: (385) 31244888
Sales Range: $125-149.9 Million
Emp.: 139
Natural Gas Distribution Services
N.A.I.C.S.: 221210
Leo Begovic *(Chm)*

HEP-Proizvodnja d.o.o. (1)
37 Ulica Grada Vukovara, 10000, Zagreb, Croatia
Tel.: (385) 16171084
Electricity & Heat Generation Services
N.A.I.C.S.: 221111
Dubravko Lukacevic *(Asst Dir)*

HEP-Telekomunikacije d.o.o. (1)
Ulica grada Vukovara 37, 10000, Zagreb, Croatia
Tel.: (385) 16322111
Electric Power Distribution Services
N.A.I.C.S.: 221122

HEP-Toplinarstvo d.o.o. (1)
Misevecka 15a, 10000, Zagreb, Croatia
Tel.: (385) 16009602
Web Site: http://www.hep.hr
Sales Range: $250-299.9 Million
Emp.: 355
Heat Production & Distribution
N.A.I.C.S.: 221330
Snjezana Pauk *(Chm-Supervisory Bd)*

HEP-Trgovina d.o.o. (1)
Ulica grada Vukovara 37, 10000, Zagreb, Croatia
Tel.: (385) 16171174
Web Site: http://www.hep.hr
Electric Power Distribution Services
N.A.I.C.S.: 221122

HEP-Upravljanje imovinom d.o.o. (1)
Ulica grada Vukovara 37, 10000, Zagreb, Croatia
Tel.: (385) 13870802
Electric Power Distribution Services
N.A.I.C.S.: 221122

LNG Hrvatska d.o.o. (1)
Slavonska avenija 1B, 10000, Zagreb, Croatia
Tel.: (385) 14094600
Web Site: https://lng.hr
Natural Gas Distribution Services
N.A.I.C.S.: 221210

Plomin Holding d.o.o. (1)
Plomin Luka 50, 52234, Plomin, Croatia
Tel.: (385) 52863347
Sales Range: $75-99.9 Million
Emp.: 3
Electric Power Distribution Services
N.A.I.C.S.: 221122
Marino Roce *(Mng Dir)*

HRVATSKA NORADNA BANKA

Trg Hrvatskih Velikana 3, 10002, Zagreb, Croatia
Tel.: (385) 14564555
Web Site: http://www.hnb.hr
Sales Range: $150-199.9 Million
Emp.: 600
Banking Services
N.A.I.C.S.: 521110
Roman Kos *(Dir-Technical)*

HRVATSKA POSTANSKA BANKA D.D.

Jurisiceva 4, HR-10000, Zagreb, Croatia
Tel.: (385) 14890365   HR
Web Site: https://www.hpb.hr
Year Founded: 1991
HPB—(ZAG)
Rev.: $204,538,394

INTERNATIONAL PUBLIC

Assets: $7,530,355,450
Liabilities: $6,960,119,654
Net Worth: $570,235,795
Earnings: $88,803,386
Emp.: 1,752
Fiscal Year-end: 12/31/23
Investment & Personal Banking Services
N.A.I.C.S.: 523150
Marijana Milicevic *(Chm-Supervisory Bd)*

Subsidiaries:

HPB Invest d.o.o. (1)
Jurisiceva ulica 4, 10000, Zagreb, Croatia
Tel.: (385) 14804516
Web Site: https://www.hpb-invest.hr
Sales Range: $50-74.9 Million
Investment Fund Management Services
N.A.I.C.S.: 523940

HPB Nekretnine d.o.o. (1)
Jurisiceva ulica 4, 10000, Zagreb, Croatia
Tel.: (385) 15553920
Web Site: https://www.hpb-nekretnine.hr
Sales Range: $50-74.9 Million
Real Estate Property Management Services
N.A.I.C.S.: 531210

HPB Stambena stedionica d.d. (1)
Praska 5, 10000, Zagreb, Croatia
Tel.: (385) 15553900
Web Site: http://www.hpb-stedionica.hr
Investment Banking Services
N.A.I.C.S.: 523150

HS AD INC.

LG Mapo Building 155 Mapo-daero, Mapo-gu, Seoul, Korea (South)
Tel.: (82) 27052700
Web Site: https://www.hsad.co.kr
Year Founded: 2004
035000—(KRS)
Rev.: $406,853,657
Assets: $417,856,650
Liabilities: $282,428,820
Net Worth: $135,427,830
Earnings: $13,393,054
Emp.: 83
Fiscal Year-end: 12/31/22
Marketing Consulting Services
N.A.I.C.S.: 541613
Kwang Ryun Song *(CFO)*

Subsidiaries:

Beijing Yuanzhimeng Advertising Co., Ltd (1)
17/F West Tower Shuangzizuo Mansion No 12b Jianguo Menwai Av, Beijing, 100022, China
Tel.: (86) 1058287077
Marketing Consulting Services
N.A.I.C.S.: 541613

GIIR America Inc. (1)
3550 Wilshire Blvd, Los Angeles, CA 90010
Tel.: (213) 251-8822
Marketing Consulting Services
N.A.I.C.S.: 541613

GIIR Communications Pvt. Ltd. (1)
KP Towers 12th Floor Tower D Plot No C-001B Sector-16B, Noida, 201301, Uttar Pradesh, India
Tel.: (91) 1204624900
Advertising Material Services
N.A.I.C.S.: 541870
Hyung June Kim *(Mng Dir)*

GIIR Germany GmbH (1)
Berliner Strasse 93 LG Building, 40880, Ratingen, Germany
Tel.: (49) 21027008210
Marketing Consulting Services
N.A.I.C.S.: 541613

GIIR Group LG (1)
Mapo Bldg 4 9 12 15F 155 Mapo-daero, Mapo-gu, Seoul, Korea (South)
Tel.: (82) 2 705 2600
Communication Consulting Services
N.A.I.C.S.: 541618

LBEST Inc. (1)

63-7 Banpo-dong, Seocho-gu, Seoul, Korea (South)
Tel.: (82) 2 3475 8800
Web Site: http://www.lbest.com
Marketing Consulting Services
N.A.I.C.S.: 541613

HS HOLDINGS CO., LTD.
27F Sumitomo Fudosan Shinjuku Oak Tower 6-8-1 Nishi-Shinjuku, Shinjuku-Ku, Tokyo, 163-6027, Japan
Tel.: (81) 345600398
Web Site: http://www.sawada-holdings.co.jp
Year Founded: 1958
8699—(TKS)
Rev.: $327,836,170
Assets: $652,896,140
Liabilities: $174,226,380
Net Worth: $478,669,760
Earnings: $62,550,430
Fiscal Year-end: 03/31/24
Holding Company
N.A.I.C.S.: 551111
Yasunari Harada *(Pres & CEO)*

Subsidiaries:

iXIT Corporation (1)
Daiwa Azabu Terrace 4F 3-20-1 Minami-azabu, Minato-ku, Tokyo, Japan
Tel.: (81) 366305206
Web Site: https://ixit.co.jp
Content Distribution and Internet Advertising Services
N.A.I.C.S.: 516210

Subsidiary (Non-US):

Index Asia Ltd (2)
496-502 Amarin Tower 18th Floor Room No 4 Ploenchit Road, Lumpini Pathumwan, Bangkok, 10330, Thailand
Tel.: (66) 26271999
Web Site: http://www.indexcorp.co.th
Mobile Content Development Services
N.A.I.C.S.: 541511

HS OPTIMUS HOLDINGS LIMITED
2 kallang Ave CT Hub 07-03, Singapore, 339407, Singapore
Tel.: (65) 67541854 SG
Web Site: https://www.klw.com.sg
Year Founded: 1995
504—(CAT)
Rev.: $8,035,461
Assets: $52,724,044
Liabilities: $6,423,399
Net Worth: $46,300,645
Earnings: ($5,556,700)
Emp.: 1
Fiscal Year-end: 03/31/23
Holding Company
N.A.I.C.S.: 551112
Wong Gloria *(Exec Dir)*

Subsidiaries:

KLW Joinery Pte. Ltd. (1)
2 Kallang Ave CT Hub, Singapore, 339407, Singapore
Tel.: (65) 67541854
Web Site: http://www.klw-joinery.com
Timber & Wooden Door Mfr
N.A.I.C.S.: 321911
Guo Chang Yao *(Asst Project Mgr)*

KLW Wood Products Sdn. Bhd. (1)
PLO 32 34 Taman Perindustrian Simpang Renggam, Simpang Renggam, 86300, Kluang, Johor, Malaysia
Tel.: (60) 77557733
Web Site: https://www.hsowood.com.my
Door Set Related Product Mfr & Distr
N.A.I.C.S.: 321911
Ananthan Muniandy *(Gen Mgr)*

HS VALVE CO., LTD
29 Paldal-ro 2-gil, Seo-gu, Daegu, 703-825, Korea (South)
Tel.: (82) 533535789
Web Site: https://www.hsvalve.com
Year Founded: 1987
039610—(KRS)
Rev.: $65,598,092
Assets: $94,706,188
Liabilities: $32,967,565
Net Worth: $61,738,623
Earnings: $2,285,916
Emp.: 238
Fiscal Year-end: 12/31/22
Ball Valve Mfr
N.A.I.C.S.: 332911

Subsidiaries:

HS VALVE CO., LTD - Factory II (1)
222 Gongdon 8-ro, Jillyang-eup, Gyeongsan, Korea (South), Gyeongsangbuk-do, Korea (South)
Tel.: (82) 53 857 5789
Ball Valve Mfr
N.A.I.C.S.: 332911

HS VALVE CO., LTD - Factory III (1)
138 Damun-ro, Jillyang-eup, Gyeongsan, Gyeongsangbuk-do, Korea (South)
Tel.: (82) 53 854 5780
Web Site: http://www.hsvalve.com
Ball Valve Mfr
N.A.I.C.S.: 332911

HSBC HOLDINGS PLC
8 Canada Square, London, E14 5HQ, United Kingdom
Tel.: (44) 2079918888 UK
Web Site: https://www.hsbc.com
Year Founded: 1865
HSBC—(NYSE)
Rev.: $66,058,000,000
Assets: $3,038,677,000,000
Liabilities: $2,846,067,000,000
Net Worth: $192,610,000,000
Earnings: $22,432,000,000
Emp.: 220,861
Fiscal Year-end: 12/31/23
Bank Holding Company
N.A.I.C.S.: 551111
Peter Tung Shun Wong *(Deputy Chm/CEO-The Hongkong & Shanghai Banking Corporation Ltd)*

Subsidiaries:

Arabian Gulf Investments (Far East) Limited (1)
Room 2606 26th Floor Bank of America Tower, 12 Harcourt Road, Hong Kong, China (Hong Kong) (20%)
Tel.: (852) 2844 1661
Web Site: http://www.rezayat.com
Sales Range: $50-74.9 Million
Emp.: 20
Financial Advisory Services, Equity Trading & Investment & Investment Management Services
N.A.I.C.S.: 523940

BCS Information Systems Private Limited (1)
351 Braddell Road 01-03, Singapore, 579713, Singapore
Tel.: (65) 64246000
Web Site: https://www.nets.com.sg
Finance Company
N.A.I.C.S.: 921130

Banco HSBC S.A. (1)
Av Pres Juscelino Kubitschek 1 909 19th Floor - Torre Norte, Sao Paulo, 04543-907, Brazil
Tel.: (55) 1128022300
Web Site: https://www.business.hsbc.com.br
Banking Services
N.A.I.C.S.: 523150
Alexandre Guiao *(CEO)*

Banco HSBC Salvadoreno, S.A. (1)
Edificio Centro Financiero HSBC Avenida Olimpica 3550, San Salvador, El Salvador
Tel.: (503) 2214 2000
Web Site: http://www.hsbc.com.sv
Commercial Banking Services
N.A.I.C.S.: 522110

Caley Ltd. (1)
3rd Floor Sunley House 4 Bedford Park, Croydon, CR0 2AP, United Kingdom
Tel.: (44) 2082404517
Sales Range: $50-74.9 Million
Emp.: 85
Holding Company; Property & Casualty Insurance Products & Services
N.A.I.C.S.: 551112

Grupo Financiero HSBC, S.A. de C.V. (1)
Ave Paseo de la Reforma 347, Col Cuauhtemoc, Mexico, 06500, DF, Mexico
Tel.: (52) 5557212222
Web Site: http://www.hsbc.com.mx
Sales Range: $1-4.9 Billion
Emp.: 19,200
Bank Holding Company
N.A.I.C.S.: 551111

Subsidiary (Non-US):

HSBC Mexico S.A. (2)
Tel.: (52) 5557212222
Web Site: http://www.hsbc.com.mx
Retail & Commercial Banking
N.A.I.C.S.: 522110

HSBC Algeria (1)
Commercial Banking Services
N.A.I.C.S.: 522110

HSBC Argentina Holdings S.A. (1)
Calle Prov Buenos Aires S/N and Av Enrique Mosconi, Rincon de los Sauces, 8319, Buenos Aires, Argentina
Tel.: (54) 1143443333
Investment Management Service
N.A.I.C.S.: 523940

HSBC Asset Management (India) Private Limited (1)
Tel.: (91) 2266145000
Asset Management Services
N.A.I.C.S.: 523940
Tushar Pradhan *(Chief Investment Officer)*

HSBC BANK (Chile) SA (1)
Avenida Isidora Goyenechea 2800 Piso 23, Santiago, Chile
Web Site: http://www.about.hsbc.cl
Financial Investment Services
N.A.I.C.S.: 523999

HSBC Bank (Uruguay) S.A. (1)
Web Site: http://www.hsbc.com.uy
Commercial Banking Services
N.A.I.C.S.: 522110

HSBC Bank A.S. (1)
Esentepe Mah Buyukdere, Sisli, Istanbul, Turkiye
Tel.: (90) 8502110111
Web Site: http://forms.hsbc.com.tr
Financial Investment Services
N.A.I.C.S.: 523999

HSBC Bank Argentina SA (1)
(100%)
Web Site: http://www.hsbc.com.ar
Sales Range: $350-399.9 Million
Emp.: 1,000
Commericial Banking
N.A.I.C.S.: 522110

HSBC Bank Armenia CJSC (1)
66 Teryan Street, Yerevan, 0009, Armenia
Tel.: (374) 60655000
Web Site: http://www.hsbc.am
Financial Investment Services
N.A.I.C.S.: 523999

HSBC Bank Egypt (SAE) (1)
(94%)
Web Site: http://www.hsbc.com.eg
Commercial Bank & Related Financial Services
N.A.I.C.S.: 522110
Jacques-Emmanuel Blanchet *(CEO & Deputy Chm)*

HSBC Bank Malta P.L.C. (1)
Operations Centre 80 Mill Street, Qormi, QRM 3101, Malta
Tel.: (356) 23803250
Web Site: http://www.about.hsbc.com.mt
Financial Investment Services
N.A.I.C.S.: 523999

HSBC Bank Middle East Limited (1)
PO Box 66, Dubai, United Arab Emirates
Tel.: (971) 42288007

Web Site: http://www.about.hsbc.ae
Rev.: $834,738,319
Assets: $28,514,030,634
Liabilities: $25,195,188,854
Net Worth: $3,318,841,780
Earnings: $386,550,948
Emp.: 246,933
Fiscal Year-end: 12/31/2017
International & Local Banking Services
N.A.I.C.S.: 522110
Martin Tricaud *(CEO & Deputy Chm)*

HSBC Bank Polska S.A. (1)
Rondo ONZ, 00-693, Warsaw, Poland
Tel.: (48) 223540500
Web Site: http://www.hsbc.pl
Commercial Banking Services
N.A.I.C.S.: 522110

HSBC Bank plc (1)
8 Canada Square, London, E14 5HQ, United Kingdom (100%)
Tel.: (44) 2079918888
Web Site: http://www.hsbc.com
Rev.: $6,859,201,440
Assets: $973,964,515,160
Liabilities: $941,357,511,640
Net Worth: $32,607,003,520
Earnings: ($553,949,760)
Emp.: 218,999
Fiscal Year-end: 12/31/2022
Banking, Financial & Related Services
N.A.I.C.S.: 522110

Subsidiary (Domestic):

HSBC Asset Finance (UK) Limited (2)
54 Hagley Road, Birmingham, B16 8TH, United Kingdom
Tel.: (44) 7092813007
Commercial Banking & Financial Management Services
N.A.I.C.S.: 522110

Subsidiary (Non-US):

HSBC Bank (Bahamas) Ltd. (2)
Suite 306 Center of Commerce One Bay Street, PO Box N-4917, Nassau, Bahamas
Tel.: (242) 5022555
Web Site: http://www.hsbc.com
Sales Range: $50-74.9 Million
Emp.: 20
Commercial Bank
N.A.I.C.S.: 522110

HSBC Bank International Limited (2)
HSBC House Esplanade, Saint Helier, JE1 1HS, Jersey
Tel.: (44) 1534616313
Sales Range: $300-349.9 Million
Emp.: 1,000
Financial Services
N.A.I.C.S.: 523150

HSBC Bank UK plc (2)
(100%)
Tel.: (44) 01214553255
Web Site: http://www.hsbc.com
Sales Range: $300-349.9 Million
Emp.: 1,000
Supplier of Personal & Installment Finance, Leasing & Factoring
N.A.I.C.S.: 522299

Subsidiary (Domestic):

Marks & Spencer Financial Services plc (3)
51 Saffron Road, PO Box 10565, Wigston, LE18 9FT, United Kingdom
Tel.: (44) 1244879080
Web Site: https://bank.marksandspencer.com
Insurance & Financial Services
N.A.I.C.S.: 524210
David Lister *(Chm)*

Branch (Non-US):

HSBC Bank plc, Luxembourg Branch (2)
16 boulevard d'Avranches, 1160, Luxembourg, Luxembourg
Tel.: (352) 47 93 31 1
Web Site: http://www.hsbc.lu
Banking Services
N.A.I.C.S.: 522110
Richard Long *(Dir-Asset Mgmt)*

HSBC HOLDINGS PLC

HSBC Holdings plc—(Continued)

Subsidiary (Non-US):

HSBC Corporation (Isle of Man) Limited **(2)**
Tel.: (44) 624684848
Web Site: http://www.hsbc.co.uk
Commericial Banking
N.A.I.C.S.: 522110

Subsidiary (Domestic):

HSBC Equator Bank plc **(2)**
8 Canada Sq, London, E14 5HQ, United Kingdom **(100%)**
Tel.: (44) 2079918888
Web Site: http://www.hsbc.com
Sales Range: $1-4.9 Billion
Emp.: 8,000
Investment Banking
N.A.I.C.S.: 523150

Subsidiary (Non-US):

HSBC Expat **(2)**
HSBC House, Esplanade, Saint Helier, JE1 1HS, Jersey **(100%)**
Web Site: http://www.expat.hsbc.com
Sales Range: $800-899.9 Million
Emp.: 2,115
Banking Services for Local Customers & Expatriates
N.A.I.C.S.: 522110

Subsidiary (Domestic):

HSBC Forfaiting Ltd. **(2)**
4th Floor 10 Lower Thames Street, London, EC3R 6AE, United Kingdom
Tel.: (44) 171 260 5986
Finance Company
N.A.I.C.S.: 921130

HSBC Global Asset Management Limited **(2)**
8 Canada Sq, London, E145HC, United Kingdom **(100%)**
Tel.: (44) 2079918888
Web Site: http://www.assetmanagement.hsbc.com
Holding Company; Global Fund Investment Management
N.A.I.C.S.: 551111

Subsidiary (Non-US):

HSBC Global Asset Management (Canada) Limited **(3)**
3rd Floor 885 West Georgia Street, Vancouver, V6C 3E8, BC, Canada
Web Site: https://www.assetmanagement.hsbc.ca
Financial Investment Services
N.A.I.C.S.: 523999

HSBC Global Asset Management (Deutschland) GmbH **(3)**
Asset Management Services
N.A.I.C.S.: 523940

Subsidiary (Non-US):

HSBC Trinkaus & Burkhardt (International) S.A. **(4)**
8 Rue Lou Hemmer, L 1748, Luxembourg, Luxembourg **(100%)**
Tel.: (352) 4718471
Web Site: http://www.hsbctrinkaus.lu
Sales Range: $75-99.9 Million
Emp.: 150
Private Banking, Portfolio Management for Institutional Investors & Investment Fund Administration Services
N.A.I.C.S.: 522110
Jorg Meier (Member-Exec Bd)

Subsidiary (Domestic):

HSBC Trinkaus Capital Management GmbH **(4)**
Konigsallee 21/23, 40212, Dusseldorf, Germany **(100%)**
Tel.: (49) 2119100
Web Site: http://www.hsbctrinkaus.de
Sales Range: $50-74.9 Million
Emp.: 20
Investment Management
N.A.I.C.S.: 523940

Subsidiary (Non-US):

HSBC Global Asset Management (Japan) K.K. **(3)**
Web Site: http://www.assetmanagement.hsbc.com
Asset Management Services
N.A.I.C.S.: 523940

HSBC Global Asset Management (Malta) Ltd **(3)**
80 Business Banking Centre Mill Street, Qormi, QRM 3101, Malta
Tel.: (356) 23802380
Web Site: https://www.assetmanagement.hsbc.com
Sales Range: $200-249.9 Million
Emp.: 500
Asset Management Services
N.A.I.C.S.: 523940

HSBC Global Asset Management (Oesterreich) GmbH **(3)**
Herrengasse 1-3, 1010, Vienna, Austria
Tel.: (43) 1230606092
Financial Investment Services
N.A.I.C.S.: 523999

HSBC Global Asset Management (Switzerland) AG **(3)**
Gartenstrasse 26, 8002, Zurich, Switzerland
Tel.: (41) 442062600
Web Site: https://www.assetmanagement.hsbc.ch
Financial Investment Services
N.A.I.C.S.: 523999

Subsidiary (Domestic):

HSBC Global Asset Management (UK) Limited **(3)**
8 Canada Square, Canary Wharf, London, E14 5HQ, United Kingdom **(100%)**
Tel.: (44) 2079924127
Emp.: 250
Institutional Asset Management Services for Pension Funds & Other Institutions
N.A.I.C.S.: 531390
Victoria Sharpe (Head-Real Assets)

Subsidiary (US):

HSBC Global Asset Management (USA) Inc. **(3)**
452 5th Ave, New York, NY 10018
Web Site: http://investorfunds.us.hsbc.com
Financial Investment Services
N.A.I.C.S.: 523999

Subsidiary (Domestic):

HSBC Holdings BV **(2)**
8 Canada Square, London, E14 5HQ, United Kingdom **(100%)**
Tel.: (44) 2079918888
Emp.: 70,000
Finance Company
N.A.I.C.S.: 921130

Subsidiary (Non-US):

HSBC International Finance Corporation Limited **(2)**
15-17 King Street, PO Box 14, Saint Helier, JE1 1HS, Channel Islands, Jersey
Tel.: (44) 8456006161
Web Site: http://www.hsbc.co.uk
Sales Range: $300-349.9 Million
Emp.: 600
Commericial Banking
N.A.I.C.S.: 522110

Subsidiary (Domestic):

HSBC Investment Bank plc **(2)**
8 Canada Square, London, E14 5HQ, United Kingdom **(100%)**
Tel.: (44) 79918888
Web Site: http://www.assetsmanagement.hsbc.com
Sales Range: $75-99.9 Million
Emp.: 250
Investment Banking; Coordinates Merchant Banking, Securities & Asset Management Activities of the HSBC Group
N.A.I.C.S.: 522110

HSBC Invoice Finance UK Ltd **(2)**
21 Farncombe Road, Worthing, BN11 2BW, United Kingdom **(100%)**

Tel.: (44) 1903205181
Sales Range: $125-149.9 Million
Emp.: 500
Finance Company
N.A.I.C.S.: 921130
Gordon Harris (Mgr-Sls)

HSBC Life UK Limited **(2)**
8 Canada Sq, London, E14 5HQ, United Kingdom **(100%)**
Sales Range: $1-4.9 Billion
Emp.: 10,000
Life Insurance & Pension Funds
N.A.I.C.S.: 524113

Subsidiary (Non-US):

HSBC Private Bank (Jersey) Limited **(2)**
HSBC Private Bank HSBC International Esplanade, Saint Helier, JE2 1HS, Jersey **(100%)**
Tel.: (44) 1534672000
Web Site: http://www.hsbcprivatebank.com
Sales Range: $75-99.9 Million
Emp.: 160
Holding & Management Company for Private Banking & Trustee Businesses in the Channel Islands
N.A.I.C.S.: 522180

Subsidiary (Domestic):

HSBC International Trustee Limited **(3)**
HSBC House Espoanage, Saint Helier, JE1 1HA, Jersey **(100%)**
Tel.: (44) 1534672400
Web Site: http://www.hsbcpb.com
Sales Range: $75-99.9 Million
Trust Services
N.A.I.C.S.: 523991

Subsidiary (Non-US):

HSBC Private Bank (UK) Ltd **(3)**
8 Canada Sq, London, E14 5HQ, United Kingdom **(100%)**
Sales Range: $75-99.9 Million
Emp.: 250
Provider of Share Holding Services
N.A.I.C.S.: 523910

Subsidiary (Domestic):

HSBC Private Bank Nominees Ltd **(3)**
HSBC house Esplanade, PO Box 88, Saint Helier, JE1 1HS, Jersey **(100%)**
Tel.: (44) 1534672400
Web Site: http://www.hsbcprivatebank.com
Sales Range: $75-99.9 Million
Emp.: 170
Holds Stocks & Shares on Behalf of Clients
N.A.I.C.S.: 523910

Subsidiary (Non-US):

HSBC Trustee (C.I.) Limited **(3)** **(100%)**
Tel.: (44) 1534606500
Web Site: http://www.hsbcprivatebank.com
Sales Range: $75-99.9 Million
Trust Services
N.A.I.C.S.: 523991

Subsidiary (Domestic):

HSBC Trustee (Jersey) Limited **(3)**
1 Grenville Street, Saint Helier, JE4 9F, Jersey **(100%)**
Tel.: (44) 1534672000
Web Site: http://www.hsbcprivatebank.com
Sales Range: $75-99.9 Million
Trust Services
N.A.I.C.S.: 523991

Subsidiary (Non-US):

HSBC Private Bank (Suisse) S.A. **(2)**
9-17 Quai des Bergues, 1201, Geneva, Switzerland **(100%)**
Tel.: (41) 587055555
Sales Range: $600-649.9 Million
Emp.: 1,700
Investment Banking; Global Fund Management Company
N.A.I.C.S.: 523150

INTERNATIONAL PUBLIC

Subsidiary (Domestic):

HSBC Unit Trust Management Limited **(2)**
6 Bevis Marks, London, EC2R 8DU, United Kingdom **(100%)**
Tel.: (44) 2079555050
Web Site: http://www.hsbc.co.uk
Sales Range: $75-99.9 Million
Emp.: 200
Investment Management
N.A.I.C.S.: 523940

Joint Venture (Non-US):

Kelda Group Limited **(2)**
Tel.: (44) 1274600111 **(100%)**
Web Site: https://www.keldagroup.com
Emp.: 3,500
Holding Company; Water, Sewage, Environmental & Land Management Services
N.A.I.C.S.: 551112

Subsidiary (Non-US):

Lion International Management Limited **(2)**
1 Grenville Street, Saint Helier, JE2 4UF, Jersey **(100%)**
Tel.: (44) 1534606500
Sales Range: $75-99.9 Million
Emp.: 160
Trust Services
N.A.I.C.S.: 523991

The Bank of Bermuda Ltd. **(2)**
6 Front Street, Hamilton, HM DX, Bermuda
Tel.: (441) 2954000
Sales Range: $300-349.9 Million
Emp.: 1,000
Commercial Banking, Trust & Fiduciary Services
N.A.I.C.S.: 523991
Philip M. Butterfield (Chm)

Subsidiary (Non-US):

Bank of Bermuda (Cayman) Ltd. **(3)**
Tel.: (345) 9499898
Sales Range: $50-74.9 Million
Emp.: 10
International Banking Services
N.A.I.C.S.: 522110

Bermuda International Finance Ltd. **(3)**
3rd Floor British American Tower, Georgetown, Grand Cayman, Cayman Islands
Tel.: (345) 949 9898
Holding Company; International Banking Services
N.A.I.C.S.: 551111

Subsidiary (Domestic):

Bermuda International Investment Management Ltd. **(3)**
6 Front Street, Hamilton, HM DX, Bermuda
Tel.: (441) 2954000
Sales Range: $50-74.9 Million
Emp.: 32
Financial & Investment Information Services
N.A.I.C.S.: 523991
Philip M. Butterfield (Chm)

Subsidiary (Non-US):

Bermuda Trust (Hong Kong) Ltd. **(3)**
39 F Edinburgh Tower, The Landmark, 15 Queens Road, Central, Hong Kong, China (Hong Kong)
Tel.: (852) 28470100
Sales Range: $150-199.9 Million
Emp.: 500
Trust & Mutual Fund Products & Services
N.A.I.C.S.: 523991

HSBC Institutional Trust Services Singapore Limited **(3)** **(100%)**
Tel.: (65) 65341900
Web Site: http://www.hsbc.com.sg
Sales Range: $75-99.9 Million
Emp.: 135
Trust & Mutual Fund Products & Services
N.A.I.C.S.: 523991

HSBC Ireland **(3)**
1 Grand Canal Square, Grand Canal Harbour, Dublin, D02 P820, Ireland **(100%)**

AND PRIVATE COMPANIES

HSBC HOLDINGS PLC

Tel.: (353) 16356000
Web Site: https://www.business.hsbc.ie
Sales Range: $75-99.9 Million
Emp.: 350
Investment Services
N.A.I.C.S.: 523940
Alan Duffy *(CEO & Head-Banking)*

HSBC Trustee (CI) Limited (3)
Bermuda House, Tutakimoa Road, Rarotonga, Cook Islands
Tel.: (682) 22680
Web Site: http://www.hsbc.com
Sales Range: $50-74.9 Million
Emp.: 10
Holding Company; Trust Services
N.A.I.C.S.: 551112

HSBC Brasil Holding S.A. (1)
Av President Juscelino Kubitschek 1909 / 19th floor - North Tower, Vila Nova Conceicao, Sao Paulo, Brazil
Tel.: (55) 28023250
Financial Investment Services
N.A.I.C.S.: 523999

HSBC Continental Europe S.A. (1)
38 Avenue Kleber, 75116, Paris, France
Tel.: (33) 810246810
Financial Investment Services
N.A.I.C.S.: 523999

HSBC Corporate Banking Switzerland (1)
Commercial Banking Services
N.A.I.C.S.: 522110

HSBC Electronic Data Processing India Private Limited (1)
Plot No 8 Survey No 64, Hyderabad, 500081, India
Tel.: (91) 4039802000
Electronic Data Processing Services
N.A.I.C.S.: 518210

HSBC Finance (Brunei) Berhad (1)
Unit 16 & 17 Sumbangsih Bahagia, Lot B Plot 77, Complex Perindustrian, Bandar Seri Begawan, Beribi, Brunei Darussalam (100%)
Tel.: (673) 2448401
Web Site: http://www.hsbc.com.bn
Sales Range: $50-74.9 Million
Emp.: 50
Hire-Purchase & Leasing Finance; Block Discounting & Mortgage, Bridging & Housing Loans
N.A.I.C.S.: 522310

HSBC Finance Corporation (1)
1421 W Shure Dr Ste 100, Arlington Heights, IL 60004
Tel.: (224) 880-7000
Web Site: http://www.us.hsbc.com
Consumer Lending Services
N.A.I.C.S.: 522291

Subsidiary (Domestic):

Beneficial Finances (2)
926 Main St, East Hartford, CT 06108-2237
Tel.: (860) 289-3371
Web Site: http://www.beneficial.com
Rev.: $4,600,000
Emp.: 4
Mortgage Services
N.A.I.C.S.: 522291

Beneficial Management Inc. (2)
355 E Campus View Blvd, Columbus, OH 43235-5616 (100%)
Tel.: (614) 785-6230
Web Site: http://www.beneficial.com
Rev.: $57,800,000
Emp.: 5
Consumer Finance Companies
N.A.I.C.S.: 522291

Beneficial New Mexico Inc. (2)
500 N Guadalupe St Ste B, Santa Fe, NM 87501
Tel.: (505) 471-4756
Web Site: http://www.beneficial.com
Rev.: $400,000
Emp.: 6
Mortgage Company
N.A.I.C.S.: 522291

Beneficial South Carolina Inc. (2)
1836 Ashley River Rd Ste O, Charleston, SC 29407-4781

Tel.: (843) 571-2310
Web Site: http://www.beneficial.com
Rev.: $10,600,000
Emp.: 7
Federal Savings Institutions
N.A.I.C.S.: 522180

Beneficial Washington Inc. (2)
9750 3rd Ave NE Ste 100, Seattle, WA 98115 (100%)
Tel.: (206) 364-3520
Web Site: http://www.beneficial.com
Sales Range: $50-74.9 Million
Emp.: 5
Consumer Lending Services
N.A.I.C.S.: 522291

Holding (Non-US):

HFC Bank Limited (2)
1 Centenary Square, The Parade, Birmingham, B1 1HQ, United Kingdom (100%)
Tel.: (44) 3700100453
Sales Range: $150-199.9 Million
Emp.: 354
Trust, Loans & Finance Services
N.A.I.C.S.: 921130

Subsidiary (Domestic):

HSBC Insurance Services (2)
200 Somerset Corporate Blvd, Bridgewater, NJ 08807 (100%)
Tel.: (908) 203-2100
Sales Range: $10-24.9 Million
Emp.: 200
Insurance Services
N.A.I.C.S.: 524210

HSBC Mortgage Services (2)
3023 HSBC Way 4th Fl, Fort Mill, SC 29715
Tel.: (803) 835-6432
Web Site: http://www.hsbcmortgageservices.com
Sales Range: $50-74.9 Million
Emp.: 12
Preparing Purchases, Packages & Places Residential Mortgage Portfolios with Institutional Investors
N.A.I.C.S.: 522292
Gary R. Esposito *(CEO & Mng Dir)*

Household Credit Services Inc. (2)
PO Box 81622, Salinas, CA 93912
Tel.: (831) 754-1400
Rev.: $73,642,000
Emp.: 100
Bank Holding Companies
N.A.I.C.S.: 551111

HSBC Financial Services (Cayman) Limited (1)
HSBC House 68 West Bay Road, PO Box 1109, Georgetown, KY1-1102, Grand Cayman, Cayman Islands (100%)
Tel.: (345) 949 7755
Trust Services
N.A.I.C.S.: 523991

HSBC France (1)
103 Ave Des Champs Elysees, 75419, Paris, Cedex, France (99.99%)
Web Site: http://www.hsbc.fr
Sales Range: $1-4.9 Billion
Emp.: 10,466
International Banking
N.A.I.C.S.: 522299

Subsidiary (Non-US):

CCF Representacao E Assessoria S/C Ltda. (2)
Avenida 12 de Octubre 476 y Trevino, PO Box 17, 07 9022, Quito, Ecuador
Tel.: (593) 2 230 713
International Banking
N.A.I.C.S.: 522299

HSBC Germany Holdings GmbH (1)
Konigsalle 21, 40212, Dusseldorf, Germany
Tel.: (49) 211910615
Investment Management Service
N.A.I.C.S.: 523150

Subsidiary (Domestic):

HSBC Trinkaus & Burkhardt AG (2)
Koenigsallee 21 23, E 40212, Dusseldorf, Germany (99.33%)
Tel.: (49) 2119102384

Web Site: http://www.hsbctrinkaus.de
Sales Range: $600-649.9 Million
Emp.: 2,000
Private Banking, Portfolio Management for Institutional Investors & Investment Fund Administration Services
N.A.I.C.S.: 522180
Carola Grafin V. Schmettow *(Chm-Exec Bd)*

HSBC Global Services (UK) Limited (1)
8 Canada Square, London, E14 5HQ, United Kingdom
Tel.: (44) 3456017118
Commercial Banking Services
N.A.I.C.S.: 522110

HSBC Guyerzeller Trust Company SA (1)
Quai Wilson 37, PO Box 2019, Geneva, 1211, Switzerland
Tel.: (41) 58 705 44 45
Trust Management Services
N.A.I.C.S.: 523991

HSBC Institutional Trust Services (Ireland) Limited (1)
1 Grand Canal Square Grand Canal Harbour Street, Dublin, Ireland
Tel.: (353) 16356000
Trust Management Services
N.A.I.C.S.: 523991

HSBC Insurance (Asia) Limited (1)
18/F Tower 1 HSBC Centre,1 Sham Mong Road, Kowloon, China (Hong Kong)
Tel.: (852) 22886688
Insurance Services
N.A.I.C.S.: 524298

HSBC Insurance (Ireland) Limited (1)
1 Grand Canal Square Grand Canal Harbour, Dublin, Ireland
Tel.: (353) 16356000
Insurance Management Services
N.A.I.C.S.: 524298

HSBC Insurance (Singapore) Pte. Limited (1)
10 Marina Boulevard Marina Bay Financial Centre Tower 2 Level 48-01, Singapore, 018983, Singapore
Tel.: (65) 68804888
Web Site: https://www.insurance.hsbc.com.sg
Financial Investment Services
N.A.I.C.S.: 523999

HSBC International Trustee (BVI) Limited (1)
Woodbourne Hall Road Town, PO Box 916, Tortola, Virgin Islands (British)
Tel.: (284) 4945414
Commercial Banking Services
N.A.I.C.S.: 522110

HSBC Life Assurance (Malta) Limited (1)
80 Mill Street, Qormi, QRM 3101, Malta
Tel.: (356) 23808699
Financial Investment Services
N.A.I.C.S.: 523999

HSBC North America Holdings Inc. (1)
452 5th Ave, New York, NY 10018 (100%)
Tel.: (224) 544-2000
Sales Range: $800-899.9 Million
Emp.: 1,200
Holding Company
N.A.I.C.S.: 551112
Kavita Mahtani *(CFO & Sr Exec VP)*

Subsidiary (Domestic):

HSBC USA, Inc. (2)
452 5th Ave, New York, NY 10018
Tel.: (212) 525-5000
Web Site: https://www.us.hsbc.com
Rev.: $3,905,000,000
Assets: $164,655,000,000
Liabilities: $152,542,000,000
Net Worth: $12,113,000,000
Earnings: $548,000,000
Emp.: 2,180
Fiscal Year-end: 12/30/2022
Commercial & International Banking, Mortgage & Deposit Banking, Precious Metals Trading, Futures Trading & Commodities Brokerage Services & Financial & Facility Services

N.A.I.C.S.: 522299
M. Roberts *(Chm, Pres & CEO)*

Subsidiary (Domestic):

HSBC Auto Finance (3)
6602 Convoy Ct, San Diego, CA 92111-1009
Tel.: (858) 492-6200
Sales Range: $150-199.9 Million
Emp.: 500
Automobile Finance Leasing
N.A.I.C.S.: 522220

HSBC Bank USA, N.A. (3)
One HSBC Center, Buffalo, NY 14240
Tel.: (716) 841-7212
Sales Range: $700-749.9 Million
Emp.: 2,200
Commercial & International Banking, Mortgage & Deposit Banking, Precious Metals Trading, Futures Trading & Commodities Brokerage Services & Financial & Facility Services
N.A.I.C.S.: 522299
Kavita Mahtani *(CFO & Sr Exec VP)*

HSBC Capital Markets Corporation (3)
120 Broadway, New York, NY 10005-1141
Tel.: (212) 525-5000
Web Site: http://www.us.hsbc.com
Investment Banking Services
N.A.I.C.S.: 523150

HSBC Private Bank International (3)
1441 Brickell Ave, Miami, FL 33131
Tel.: (305) 539-4700
Web Site: http://www.hsbcprivatebank.com
Sales Range: $75-99.9 Million
Emp.: 143
Commercial Banking Services
N.A.I.C.S.: 522110

HSBC Securities, Inc. (3)
452 5th Ave, New York, NY 10018
Tel.: (212) 525-5000
Web Site: https://www.us.hsbc.com
Sales Range: $50-74.9 Million
Emp.: 30
Dealer in US Government & Federal Agency Securities; Money Market Instruments, Repurchase Agreements, Mortgage-Backed Securities, Strips, Fixed Income Options & Financial Futures
N.A.I.C.S.: 522110
Kapil Seth *(Head-Middle East & North Africa)*

HSBC Private Bank (C.I.) Limited (1)
Web Site: http://www.hsbcprivatebank.com
Commercial Banking Services
N.A.I.C.S.: 522110

HSBC Private Trustee (Hong Kong) Limited (1)
13 and 14 1 Queen's Road, Central, China (Hong Kong)
Tel.: (852) 25336333
Financial Investment Services
N.A.I.C.S.: 523999

HSBC Qianhai Securities Limited (1)
Block 27 A and B Qianhai Enterprise Dream Park No 63 Qianwan Yi Road, Shenzhen-Hong Kong Cooperation Zone, Shenzhen, 518052, China
Tel.: (86) 75588983288
Web Site: http://www.hsbcqh.com.cn
Financial Investment Services
N.A.I.C.S.: 523999

HSBC Reinsurance Ltd (1)
1 Grand Canal Square Grand Canal Harbour, Dublin, Ireland
Tel.: (353) 1 635 6000
Insurance Management Services
N.A.I.C.S.: 524298

HSBC Securities (South Africa) (Pty) Limited (1)
1 Mutual Place 107 Rivonia Road, Sandton, 2196, South Africa
Tel.: (27) 116764200
Web Site: https://www.hsbc.co.za
Financial Security Services
N.A.I.C.S.: 523150

HSBC Securities (Taiwan) Corporation Limited (1)

HSBC HOLDINGS PLC

HSBC Holdings plc—(Continued)

54F No 7 Sec 5 Xinyi Road, Xinyi District, Taipei, 110615, Taiwan
Tel.: (886) 266312899
Financial Investment Services
N.A.I.C.S.: 523999

HSBC Securities Brokers (Asia) Limited (1)
1 Queen's Road, Central, China (Hong Kong)
Tel.: (852) 25211661
Financial Investment Services
N.A.I.C.S.: 523999

HSBC Securities Services (Ireland) Limited (1)
1 Grand Canal Square Grand Canal Harbour, Dublin, D02 P820, Ireland
Tel.: (353) 16356000
Web Site: https://www.hsbc.ie
Emp.: 350
Securities Brokerage Services
N.A.I.C.S.: 523150

HSBC Securities Services (Malta) Ltd (1)
80 Mill Street, Qormi, QRM 3101, Malta
Tel.: (356) 2380 5101
Web Site: http://www.hsbc.com.mt
Securities Brokerage Services
N.A.I.C.S.: 523150

HSBC Securities and Capital Markets (India) Private Limited (1)
Hong Kong Bank Building 52/60 Mahatma Gandhi Road 1st Floor, Mumbai, 400001, India
Tel.: (91) 2222681533
Securities Brokerage Services
N.A.I.C.S.: 523150

HSBC Security Services (Mauritius) Limited (1)
HSBC Centre 6/F 18 CyberCity, Ebene, Mauritius
Tel.: (230) 4030924
Web Site: http://www.hsbc.co.mu
Trust Services
N.A.I.C.S.: 523991

HSBC Service Delivery (Polska) Sp. z o.o. (1)
Kapelanka 42A, 30-347, Krakow, Poland
Tel.: (48) 123993001
Web Site: http://www.about.hsbc.pl
Financial Investment Services
N.A.I.C.S.: 523999

HSBC Transaction Services GmbH (1)
Hansaallee 3, 40549, Dusseldorf, Germany
Tel.: (49) 2119100
Web Site: http://www.hsbc-transactionservices.de
Financial Investment Services
N.A.I.C.S.: 523999

HSBC Trinkaus Investment Managers S.A. (1)
8 Rue Lou Hemmer, 1748, Luxembourg, Luxembourg
Tel.: (352) 47 18 47 9611
Web Site: http://www.hsbctrinkaus.lu
Sales Range: $100-124.9 Million
Emp.: 200
Investment Management Service
N.A.I.C.S.: 523999

HSBC Yatirim Menkul Degerler A.S. (1)
Esentepe Mahallesi Buyukdere Cad No 128, Sisli, Istanbul, Turkiye
Tel.: (90) 2123764000
Financial Investment Services
N.A.I.C.S.: 523999

Hang Seng Bank (China) Limited (1)
34/F 36/F Unit 45-031 45F and 46F Hang Seng Bank Tower, 1000 Lujiazui Ring Road Pudong, Shanghai, 200120, China
Tel.: (86) 2138658888
Web Site: http://www.hangseng.com.cn
Banking Services
N.A.I.C.S.: 522110

Hang Seng Insurance Company Limited (1)
18/F Tower 1 HSBC Centre 1 Sham Mong Road, Kowloon, China (Hong Kong)
Tel.: (852) 22886699
Financial Investment Services
N.A.I.C.S.: 523999

Hang Seng Investment Management Limited (1)
Hang Seng Bank Building 83 Des Voeux Road, Central, China (Hong Kong)
Tel.: (852) 21985890
Web Site: https://www.hangsenginvestment.com
Financial Investment Services
N.A.I.C.S.: 523999

OOO HSBC Bank (RR) (1)
Paveletsky Tower 2 Paveletskaya Square Building 2, 115054, Moscow, Russia
Tel.: (7) 4957211515
Web Site: http://www.hsbc.ru
Commercial Banking Services
N.A.I.C.S.: 522110

Pantelakis Securities S.A. (1)
Ippokratous 3-5, Chalandri, 106 79, Athens, Greece
Tel.: (30) 2106965000
Web Site: https://www.pantelakis.gr
Sales Range: $1-9.9 Million
Brokerage Services
N.A.I.C.S.: 523150
Nikolaos I. Pantelakis *(Chm & CEO)*

The HSBC Savings Bank (1)
Web Site: http://www.hsbc.com.ph
Commercial Banking Services
N.A.I.C.S.: 522110

The Hong Kong and Shanghai Banking Corporation Limited (1)
Level 6 HSBC Main Building 1 Queen's Road, Central, China (Hong Kong) **(100%)**
Tel.: (852) 28221111
Web Site: http://www.hsbc.com.hk
Rev: $14,104,824,150
Liabilities: $920,006,562,000
Net Worth: $96,344,558,700
Earnings: $12,285,503,100
Fiscal Year-end: 12/31/2017
Bank Holding Company; Personal & Commercial Banking & Related Financial Services
N.A.I.C.S.: 551111
Laura May-Lung Cha *(Chm)*

Subsidiary (Non-US):

HSBC (Kuala Lumpur) Nominees Sdn Bhd (2)
2 Leboh Ampang, PO Box 10244, 50100, Kuala Lumpur, Malaysia **(100%)**
Tel.: (60) 320700744
Web Site: http://www.hsbc.com.my
Holds Stocks & Shares on Behalf of Clients
N.A.I.C.S.: 523910

HSBC (Singapore) Ltd. (2)
21 Collyer Quay, Singapore, 049320, Singapore
Tel.: (65) 62169008
Sales Range: $300-349.9 Million
Emp.: 1,000
Corporate Financial Services
N.A.I.C.S.: 522320

Subsidiary (Domestic):

HSBC (Singapore) Nominees Pte. Ltd. (3)
21 Collyer Quay #13-01 HSBC Bldg, Singapore, 049320, Singapore
Tel.: (65) 64722669
Investment Holding Company
N.A.I.C.S.: 551112

Subsidiary (Non-US):

HSBC Global Asset Management (Singapore) Ltd. (3)
Tel.: (65) 66582900
Sales Range: $50-74.9 Million
Emp.: 23
Investment Advisory & Asset Management Services
N.A.I.C.S.: 523940

Subsidiary (Domestic):

HSBC International Trustee (Singapore) Limited (3)
21 Collyer Quay, 09-01 HSBC Building, Singapore, 49320, Singapore **(100%)**
Tel.: (65) 65325050
Web Site: http://www.hsbc.com.sg
Sales Range: $50-74.9 Million
Emp.: 50
Trust Services
N.A.I.C.S.: 523991

Subsidiary (Non-US):

HSBC Trustee (Singapore) Limited (3) **(100%)**
Web Site: http://www.hsbcprivatebank.com
Sales Range: $50-74.9 Million
Emp.: 5
Trust Services
N.A.I.C.S.: 523991

Subsidiary (Non-US):

HSBC Bank (China) Company Limited (2)
Web Site: http://www.hsbc.com.cn
Banking Services
N.A.I.C.S.: 522110

HSBC Bank (Vietnam) Ltd. (2)
The Metropolitan 235 Dong Khoi, District 1, Ho Chi Minh City, Vietnam
Tel.: (84) 2837247247
Web Site: https://www.hsbc.com.vn
International Banking
N.A.I.C.S.: 522299
Khoa Ngo *(Head)*

HSBC Bank Australia Limited (2)
Web Site: http://www.hsbc.com.au
Sales Range: $300-349.9 Million
Emp.: 1,000
Banking Services
N.A.I.C.S.: 522110

HSBC Bank Malaysia Berhad (2)
2 Leboh Ampang, 50100, Kuala Lumpur, Malaysia **(100%)**
Web Site: http://www.hsbc.com.my
Commericial Banking
N.A.I.C.S.: 522110
Krishnan Boon Seng Tan *(Chm)*

Subsidiary (Non-US):

HSBC Amanah Malaysia Berhad (3)
Web Site: http://www.hsbcamanah.com.my
Commercial & Investment Banking Services
N.A.I.C.S.: 522110

Subsidiary (Domestic):

HSBC Booking Securities Asia Ltd. (2)
25th HSBC Bldg 1st Fl, Hong Kong, China (Hong Kong) **(100%)**
Tel.: (852) 25211661
Sales Range: $25-49.9 Million
Emp.: 15
Company Data Information
N.A.I.C.S.: 518210
Steve Wong *(Gen Mgr)*

HSBC Broking Services Asia Ltd (2)
25/F HSBC Main Building 1 Queen's Road, Central, China (Hong Kong) **(100%)**
Tel.: (852) 25211661
Sales Range: $150-199.9 Million
Emp.: 300
Investment Banking & Financial Services
N.A.I.C.S.: 523150

HSBC Corporate Finance Limited (2)
1 Queen's Road, Central, China (Hong Kong) **(100%)**
Tel.: (852) 28418888
Company Reorganizations, Mergers & Acquisitions, Flotations Management & Underwriting & Placing of Securities Issues
N.A.I.C.S.: 541611

HSBC Global Asset Management (Hong Kong) Limited (2)
Level 22 HSBC Main Building 1 Queen's Road, Central, China (Hong Kong) **(100%)**
Tel.: (852) 22841118
Web Site: https://www.assetmanagement.hsbc.com
Investment Advisory & Asset Management Services

INTERNATIONAL PUBLIC

N.A.I.C.S.: 523940

HSBC Hire Purchase & Leasing Ltd. (2)
1 Sham Mong Road, HSBC Ctr Tower 1 Level 10, Kowloon, Hong Kong, China (Hong Kong) **(100%)**
Tel.: (852) 22888777
Mortgage & Investment Company
N.A.I.C.S.: 522310
Katrina Fung *(Mgr-Line)*

Affiliate (Domestic):

Way Chong Finance Limited (3)
18/F Leighton Centre 77 Leighton Road, GPO Box 829, Hong Kong, China (Hong Kong)
Tel.: (852) 2839 6333
Vehicle Hire-Purchase Finance
N.A.I.C.S.: 522220

Subsidiary (Domestic):

HSBC Insurance (Asia-Pacific) Holdings Limited (2)
18 F Tower 1 HSBC Ctr, 1 Sham Mong Rd, Kowloon, China (Hong Kong) **(100%)**
Tel.: (852) 25838000
Web Site: http://www.hsbc.com.hk
Sales Range: $300-349.9 Million
Emp.: 1,000
Property, Liability, Accident, Marine, Motor, Medical & Credit Life Insurance
N.A.I.C.S.: 524126
Carlos Vazquez *(CEO-HSBC Insurance (Singapore) Pte. Ltd)*

Subsidiary (Non-US):

AXA Insurance Pte. Ltd. (3)
8 Shenton Way Unit 27-02 Axa Tower, Singapore, 68811, Singapore
Tel.: (65) 68805500
Web Site: http://www.axalife.com.sg
Sales Range: $100-124.9 Million
Emp.: 120
N.A.I.C.S.: 524128

Joint Venture (Non-US):

Hana HSBC Life Insurance Co., Ltd. (3)
17th Floor Hanabank Building 101-1, Ulchiro 1-ka Chung-ku, Seoul, 100-191, Korea (South)
Tel.: (82) 237097300
Life Insurance Products & Services
N.A.I.C.S.: 524113

Subsidiary (Domestic):

HSBC Investment Bank Asia Limited (2)
Level 15 Hong Kong Bank Bldg, PO Box 8983, 1 Queens Rd, Central, China (Hong Kong) **(100%)**
Tel.: (852) 28221111
Web Site: http://www.hsbc.com.hk
Private Banking
N.A.I.C.S.: 522180

Subsidiary (Non-US):

HSBC Investment Trust (Japan) K.K (2)
HSBC Bldg 3 11 1 Nihonbashi Chuo Ku, Tokyo, 103 0027, Japan **(100%)**
Tel.: (81) 352033980
Web Site: http://www.hsbc.co.jp
Comprehensive Investment; Global Fund Management Company
N.A.I.C.S.: 523940

Subsidiary (Domestic):

HSBC Securities Asia Ltd. (2)
Level 15 Queensway, 1 Queens Road, Central, China (Hong Kong) **(100%)**
Tel.: (852) 28221111
Web Site: http://www.hsbc.com.hk
Investment Banking
N.A.I.C.S.: 522299

Subsidiary (Non-US):

HSBC Securities Japan Limited (2)
HSBC Building 3-11-1 Nihonbashi, Tokyo, 103 0027, Chuo Ku, Japan **(50%)**
Tel.: (81) 352033111
Web Site: https://www.hsbc.co.jp

Sales Range: $300-349.9 Million
Emp.: 700
Investment Banking; Global Fund Management Company
N.A.I.C.S.: 523150

Subsidiary (Domestic):

HSBC Shipping Services Ltd. (2)
Ste 2107 2108, Wan Chai, 108 Gloucester Rd, Hong Kong, China (Hong Kong) (100%)
Tel.: (852) 29237733
Web Site: http://www.hsbc.com.hk
Shipbroking Services, Including New Building Contracting, Second-Hand Sale & Purchase, Dry Cargo & Oil Chartering; Analysis & Assessment of Shipping Projects for New Investors to the Industry
N.A.I.C.S.: 336611

HSBC Trustee (Hong Kong) Limited (2)
Level 13 1 Queens Rd, Central, China (Hong Kong) (100%)
Web Site: http://www.hsbcprivatebank.com
Trust Services
N.A.I.C.S.: 523991

Hang Seng Bank Limited (2)
83 Des Voeux Road, Central, China (Hong Kong) (62.14%)
Web Site: http://www.hangseng.com
Sales Range: $1-4.9 Billion
Emp.: 7,300
Commercial Bank
N.A.I.C.S.: 522210
Raymond Kuo Fung Chien (Chm)

Subsidiary (Non-US):

Hongkong International Trade Finance (Japan) KK (2)
Ginza Daiwa Building 11-1 Ginza 8-chome Chuo-ku, Tokyo, 104, Japan
Tel.: (81) 335718339
Finance Company
N.A.I.C.S.: 921130

PT Bank HSBC Indonesia (2)
World Trade Center 1 Lantai 1 Jl Jendral Sudirman Kav 29 - 31, Jakarta, 12920, Indonesia
Tel.: (62) 1500700
Rev.: $353,500,000
Assets: $7,071,190,000
Liabilities: $6,030,500,000
Net Worth: $1,040,690,000
Earnings: $95,900,000
Emp.: 4,629
Fiscal Year-end: 12/31/2017
Investment Banking Services
N.A.I.C.S.: 523150
Yessika Effendi (Dir-Compliance)

Branch (Non-US):

The Hong Kong & Shanghai Banking Corporation Ltd.-Taiwan (2)
1st Floor No 8 Sect 5 Hsinyie Road, 333 Keelung Rd Sec 1, Taipei, 110, Taiwan (100%)
Tel.: (886) 227230088
Web Site: http://www.hsbc.com.tw
Sales Range: $50-74.9 Million
Emp.: 100
N.A.I.C.S.: 522299

The Hong Kong & Shanghai Banking Corporation Ltd.-Thailand (2)
HSBC Bldg 968 Rama IV Road, Silom Bangrak, 10500, Bangkok, Thailand
Tel.: (66) 2673 7733
Web Site: http://www.hsbc.co.th
Corporate & Investment Banking
N.A.I.C.S.: 523150

HSBC HOLDINGS PLC
8 Canada Square, London, E14 5HQ, United Kingdom
Tel.: (44) 2079918888
Web Site: https://www.hsbc.com
Year Founded: 1865
HSBA—(LSE)
Rev.: $62,611,000,000
Assets: $3,038,677,000,000
Liabilities: $2,846,067,000,000
Net Worth: $192,610,000,000

Earnings: $24,559,000,000
Emp.: 220,861
Fiscal Year-end: 12/31/23
Holding Company
N.A.I.C.S.: 551112
Mark Tucker (Chm)

HSIN BA BA CORPORATION
27F No 6 Minquan 2nd Rd, Qianzhen Dist, Kaohsiung, 80661, Taiwan
Tel.: (886) 75378899
Web Site: https://www.hsinbaba.com.tw
Year Founded: 1967
9906—(TAI)
Rev.: $121,910,947
Assets: $308,399,053
Liabilities: $259,109,314
Net Worth: $49,289,739
Earnings: $17,019,686
Fiscal Year-end: 12/31/23
Construction Engineering Services
N.A.I.C.S.: 237990
Chung-Hui Huang (Chm & Pres)

HSIN CHONG GROUP HOLDINGS LIMITED
Hsin Chong Center 107-109 Wai Yip Street, Kwun Tong, Kowloon, China (Hong Kong)
Tel.: (852) 2579 8238
Web Site: http://www.hsinchong.com
Sales Range: $800-899.9 Million
Holding Company; Construction Services
N.A.I.C.S.: 551112

HSIN KAO GAS CO., LTD.
No 12 Minquan 1st Road Lingya District, Lingya District, Kaohsiung, Taiwan
Tel.: (886) 75315701
Web Site: https://www.hkgas.com.tw
9931—(TAI)
Rev.: $40,161,482
Assets: $199,338,624
Liabilities: $111,425,288
Net Worth: $87,913,336
Earnings: $5,700,906
Fiscal Year-end: 12/31/23
Natural Gas Distribution Services
N.A.I.C.S.: 221210
Chien-Tung Chen (Chm)

HSIN KUANG STEEL CO., LTD.
Floor 25 No 97 Section 4 Chongzhong Road, Sanchong District, New Taipei, Taiwan
Tel.: (886) 229788888
Web Site: https://www.hkssteel.com.tw
Year Founded: 1955
2031—(TAI)
Rev.: $525,683,914
Assets: $927,215,701
Liabilities: $532,717,760
Net Worth: $394,497,941
Earnings: $56,626,441
Fiscal Year-end: 12/31/23
Steel Products Mfr
N.A.I.C.S.: 331221
Ming-Te Su (Chm & Pres)

HSIN SIN TEXTILE CO., LTD.
10F-4 No 289 Changan W Rd, Datong Dist, Taipei, 103, Taiwan
Tel.: (886) 225525757
Web Site: https://www.hsinsin.com.tw
Year Founded: 1980
4406—(TPE)
Rev.: $17,824,469
Assets: $27,092,393
Liabilities: $6,053,372
Net Worth: $21,039,021
Earnings: $643,811
Fiscal Year-end: 12/31/22

Yarn Mfr & Distr
N.A.I.C.S.: 313110
Yingchih Chuang (Founder)

HSIN TAI GAS CO., LTD.
No 221 Section 2 Zhonghua Road, Tucheng District, New Taipei City, Taiwan
Tel.: (886) 280753600
Web Site: https://www.htgas.com.tw
8917—(TPE)
Rev.: $79,293,937
Assets: $170,647,125
Liabilities: $87,982,772
Net Worth: $82,664,353
Earnings: $11,504,581
Emp.: 171
Fiscal Year-end: 12/31/22
Natural Gas Distribution Services
N.A.I.C.S.: 211130
Hung-Wen Chuang (Chm)

HSIN YUNG CHIEN CO., LTD.
No 294 Nangang 3rd Rd, Nantou County, Nant'ou, 54067, Taiwan
Tel.: (886) 492263888
Web Site: http://www.hyc-king.com
Year Founded: 1969
2114—(TAI)
Rev.: $50,955,098
Assets: $124,419,433
Liabilities: $23,415,709
Net Worth: $101,003,724
Earnings: $15,343,372
Emp.: 82
Fiscal Year-end: 12/31/23
Rubber Conveyor Belts Mfr
N.A.I.C.S.: 326220
Chi-Chin Lin (Pres)

Subsidiaries:

Hsin Yung Chien (Tianjin) Co.,Ltd. (1)
Tianjin Ocean Shipping Mansion 3817 No 1 Ocean Square, Hebei District, Tianjin, China
Tel.: (86) 22 24456031
Conveyor Belts Mfr & Sales
N.A.I.C.S.: 326220

Hsin Yung Chien Rubber Co.,Ltd. (1)
Tianjin Ocean Shipping Mansion 3817 No 1 Ocean Square, Hebei District, Tianjin, China
Tel.: (86) 2224456031
Conveyor Belts Mfr & Sales
N.A.I.C.S.: 326220

HSIN-LI CHEMICAL INDUSTRIAL CORP.
No 121 Huazong Rd, Xuejia Dist, Tainan City, 726, Taiwan
Tel.: (886) 67835100
Web Site: https://www.hsinli.com.tw
Year Founded: 1973
4303—(TPE)
Rev.: $10,172,998
Assets: $45,084,670
Liabilities: $19,156,740
Net Worth: $25,927,930
Earnings: ($1,288,122)
Fiscal Year-end: 12/31/22
Chemical Products Mfr
N.A.I.C.S.: 325199
Lin Ching-Lung (Chm & Pres)

HSING TA CEMENT CO., LTD.
7th Floor No 37 Baoqing Road, Zhongzheng District, Taipei, Taiwan
Tel.: (886) 223816731
Web Site: https://www.hsingta.com.tw
1109—(TAI)
Rev.: $204,711,199
Assets: $378,140,867
Liabilities: $51,426,435
Net Worth: $326,714,432
Earnings: $26,409,855
Emp.: 711
Fiscal Year-end: 12/31/23

Cement Mfr
N.A.I.C.S.: 327310
Ta-Kuan Yang (Pres)

HSINJING HOLDING CO., LTD.
3F-1 No 193 Fuxing 2nd Road, Hsinchu, Zhubei, 302, Taiwan
Tel.: (886) 36581956
Web Site: https://www.hsinjing-holding.com.tw
Year Founded: 2008
3713—(TPE)
Rev.: $39,892,130
Assets: $76,534,722
Liabilities: $54,903,636
Net Worth: $21,631,085
Earnings: $2,175,062
Fiscal Year-end: 12/31/22
Holding Company
N.A.I.C.S.: 551112
San-Te Tzu (Chm & CEO)

HSK PARTNERS
92-98 boulevard, Victor Hugo, 92110, Clichy, France
Tel.: (33) 1 47 30 83 00
Web Site: http://www.hsk-partners.com
Year Founded: 1981
Marketing Database & Data Services
N.A.I.C.S.: 518210

HSO GROUP BV
Newtonstraat 27, 3902 HP, Veenendaal, Netherlands
Tel.: (31) 318 509 400
Web Site: http://www.hso.com
Year Founded: 1989
Information Technology & Services
N.A.I.C.S.: 541511
Peter J. Maaten (Founder & CEO)

Subsidiaries:

AKA Enterprise Solutions, Inc. (1)
Empire State Bldg 350 5th Ave Ste 6902, New York, NY 10118
Tel.: (212) 502-3900
Web Site: http://www.akaes.com
Custom Computer Programming Services
N.A.I.C.S.: 541511
Claudia Cruz-Moncada (Product Mgr)

HSS ENGINEERS BERHAD
Block B Plaza Dwitasik No 21 Jalan 5/106 Bandar Sri Permaisuri, 56000, Kuala Lumpur, Malaysia
Tel.: (60) 391730355   MY
Web Site: https://www.hssgroup.com.my
Year Founded: 1988
HSSEB—(KLS)
Rev.: $39,373,913
Assets: $85,438,332
Liabilities: $34,010,307
Net Worth: $51,428,025
Earnings: $3,202,929
Emp.: 860
Fiscal Year-end: 12/31/22
Investment Holding Services
N.A.I.C.S.: 551112
Sharifah Azlina Kamal Pasmah (COO-Grp)

Subsidiaries:

HSS BIM Solutions Private Limited (1)
3rd Floor Ganesh Tower B-1 1st Avenue 100 Ft Road Ashok Nagar, Chennai, 600083, Tamil Nadu, India
Tel.: (91) 4449181100
Web Site: https://www.hssbim.com
Building Information Modeling Services
N.A.I.C.S.: 541310

HSW GMBH
Walterstrasse 7, 86153, Augsburg, Germany
Tel.: (49) 821 56 7155 5   De

HSW GMBH

HSW GmbH—(Continued)

Web Site: http://www.hsw-gmbh.com
Mail Sorting Equipment Mfr & Whslr
N.A.I.C.S.: 335999

HT MEDIA LIMITED
Hindustan Times House 18-20 Kasturba Gandhi Marg, New Delhi, 110 001, India
Tel.: (91) 1166561333
Web Site: https://www.htmedia.in
Year Founded: 1924
532662—(BOM)
Rev.: $229,026,525
Assets: $597,607,920
Liabilities: $258,742,575
Net Worth: $338,865,345
Earnings: $2,592,135
Emp.: 1,553
Fiscal Year-end: 03/31/22
Newspaper & Internet Publisher; Radio Broadcasting
N.A.I.C.S.: 513110
Priyavrat Bhartia *(Exec Dir)*

Subsidiaries:

Firefly e-Ventures Limited (1)
Park Centra Building 7th Floor Sector 30 Delhi-Jaipur Highway, Gurgaon, 122001, India
Tel.: (91) 1243954700
Web Portal Services
N.A.I.C.S.: 519290

HT Music and Entertainment Company Limited (1)
18-20 Kasturba Gandhi Marg, New Delhi, 110001, India
Tel.: (91) 1143104104
Music & Entertainment Event Orgaziners
N.A.I.C.S.: 711310

Mosaic Media Ventures Pvt. Ltd. (1)
HT House Plot no 18-20 Kasturba Gandhi Marg, New Delhi, 110 001, Delhi, India
Tel.: (91) 1166561234
Internet Publishing Services
N.A.I.C.S.: 513199

HTC CORPORATION
No 23 Xinghua Road, Taoyuan Dist, Taoyuan, 330, Taiwan
Tel.: (886) 33753252
Web Site: https://www.htc.com
Year Founded: 1997
HTCCO—(LUX)
Rev.: $144,476,007
Assets: $1,490,673,543
Liabilities: $744,896,142
Net Worth: $745,777,401
Earnings: $(111,048,657)
Emp.: 363
Fiscal Year-end: 12/31/23
Mobile Information & Communications Devices Designer & Mfr
N.A.I.C.S.: 334220
Cher Wang *(Co-Founder & Chm)*

Subsidiaries:

BandRich Inc. (1)
6F-2 No 71 Zhouzi St, Neihu Dist, Taipei, 11493, Taiwan
Tel.: (886) 2 2799 8851
Web Site: http://www.bandrich.com
Sales Range: $25-49.9 Million
Emp.: 100
Wireless Mobile Broadband Routers & Related Equipment Mfr
N.A.I.C.S.: 334118

Communication Global Certification Inc. (1)
14-1 Lane 19, Wen San 3rd St Kueishan Hsiang, Taoyuan, Taiwan
Tel.: (886) 33182525
Web Site: http://www.cgctw.com
Sales Range: $25-49.9 Million
Emp.: 35
Telecommunications Terminal Testing & Certification Services
N.A.I.C.S.: 541380

HTC America, Inc. (1)
13920 SE Eastgate Way Ste 400, Bellevue, WA 98005
Tel.: (425) 679-5318
Web Site: https://www.htc.com
Mobile Information & Communications Devices Designer & Mfr
N.A.I.C.S.: 334220

HTC Europe Co., Ltd. (1)
Salamanca Wellington Street, Hatfield Rd, Slough, SL1 1YP, United Kingdom **(100%)**
Tel.: (44) 1753218960
Web Site: http://www.europe.htc.com
Sales Range: $25-49.9 Million
Emp.: 10
Electronic Components Mfr
N.A.I.C.S.: 334419

High Tech Computer Asia Pacific Pte. Ltd. (1)
260 Orchard Road Suite 07-04 The Heeren Orchard, Singapore, 238855, Singapore
Tel.: (65) 62387788
Holding Company
N.A.I.C.S.: 551112

Subsidiary (Non-US):

HTC Netherlands B.V. (2)
Papendorpseweg 99 Level 4, 3528 BJ, Utrecht, Netherlands
Tel.: (31) 307601606
Wireless & Satellite Communication Component Mfr
N.A.I.C.S.: 334220

High Tech Computer (H.K.) Limited (2)
32/F @Convoy 169 Electric Road, North Point, China (Hong Kong)
Tel.: (852) 31550806
Electronic Parts Whslr
N.A.I.C.S.: 423690

HTC HOLDING A.S.
Dobrovicova 8, 811 09, Bratislava, Slovakia
Tel.: (421) 259334261
Web Site: http://www.htc-investments.com
Year Founded: 1992
Holding Company
N.A.I.C.S.: 551112
Martin Blakovic *(Chm)*

Subsidiaries:

Elektrokarbon a.s. (1)
Tovarnicka 412, 955 22, Topolcany, Slovakia
Tel.: (421) 385354111
Web Site: http://www.elektrokarbon.sk
Sales Range: $10-24.9 Million
Emp.: 311
Carbon Products Mfr
N.A.I.C.S.: 335991

Global Supply, a.s. (1)
Potocna 334, 909 01, Skalica, Slovakia
Tel.: (421) 34 6538 178
Web Site: http://www.globalsuply.com
Ball Bearing Mfr
N.A.I.C.S.: 332991

HTC U.S.A., INC. (1)
1209 86th Ct NW, Bradenton, FL 34209
Tel.: (941) 794-5970
Automotive Spare Parts Distr
N.A.I.C.S.: 423120

HTC-AED, a.s. (1)
Mlynske Nivy 36, 821 09, Bratislava, Slovakia
Tel.: (421) 2 593 342 91
Web Site: http://www.htc-aed.sk
Automobile Spare Parts Mfr
N.A.I.C.S.: 333818

KINEX-EXIM, spol. s r.o. (1)
Nadrazna 33, 90901, Skalica, Slovakia
Tel.: (421) 34 6594 154
Ball Bearing Distr
N.A.I.C.S.: 423540

KINEX-KLF, a.s. (1)
Kukucinova 2346, 024 01, Kysucke Nove Mesto, Slovakia
Tel.: (421) 41 420 1810

Ball Bearing Mfr
N.A.I.C.S.: 332991
Lubomir Galvanek *(Exec Dir)*

SPV68, s.r.o. (1)
Robotnicka 2785, 01701, Povazska Bystrica, Slovakia
Tel.: (421) 424 261 856
Financial Brokerage Services
N.A.I.C.S.: 523150

ZETOR TRACTORS a.s. (1)
Trnkova 111, 628 00, Brno, Czech Republic
Tel.: (420) 533 430 111
Web Site: http://www.zetor.com
Tractor & Spare Parts Mfr & Distr
N.A.I.C.S.: 333111
Martin Blaskovic *(Chm)*

Subsidiary (Non-US):

ZETOR Deutschland, GmbH (2)
Dr Georg-Schafer-Strasse 17, 93437, Furth im Wald, Germany
Tel.: (49) 9973 8046 0
Web Site: http://www.zetor.de
Tractor & Spare Parts Mfr & Distr
N.A.I.C.S.: 333111

ZETOR FRANCE Sarl (2)
2 rue Ampere, 67120, Duttlenheim, France
Tel.: (33) 88 04 59 30
Web Site: http://www.zetor.fr
Tractor & Spare Parts Mfr & Distr
N.A.I.C.S.: 333111

Subsidiary (US):

ZETOR North America, Inc. (2)
5784 Mining Ter, Jacksonville, FL 32257
Tel.: (900) 647-7169
Web Site: http://www.zetorna.com
Tractor & Spare Parts Mfr & Distr
N.A.I.C.S.: 333111
Vladimir Blaskovic *(Pres-Admin)*

Subsidiary (Non-US):

ZETOR Polska, Sp.z o.o. (2)
Inwestorska 3, 62-800, Kalisz, Poland
Tel.: (48) 62 501 44 00
Web Site: http://www.zetor.pl
Tractor & Spare Parts Mfr & Distr
N.A.I.C.S.: 333111

ZETOR UK, Ltd. (2)
Unit B5 Paragon Way Bayton Rd Industrial Estate, Coventry, CV7 9QS, United Kingdom
Tel.: (44) 2476 363382
Web Site: http://www.zetor.co.uk
Tractor & Spare Parts Mfr & Distr
N.A.I.C.S.: 333111
Tibor Liska *(Mng Dir)*

HTC PURENERGY INC.
002 2305 Victoria Ave, Regina, S4P 0S7, SK, Canada
Tel.: (306) 352-6132
Web Site: https://htcextraction.com
Year Founded: 1996
HTC—(DEU)
Sales Range: Less than $1 Million
Emp.: 100
CO2 Capture & Storage Technologies Sales & Marketer for Enhanced Oil Recovery; Hydrogen Production & Bio-Fuel Technologies Developer, Sales & Marketer
N.A.I.C.S.: 213112
Lionel Kambeitz *(Chm & CEO)*

Subsidiaries:

C-Green Carbon Management Solutions Inc. (1)
1560-2002 Victoria Avenue, Regina, S4P 0R7, SK, Canada
Tel.: (306) 790-1782
Web Site: http://www.c-green.ca
Carbon Mfr
N.A.I.C.S.: 325180

Enhanced Hydrocarbon Recovery Inc. (1)
001-2305 Victoria Ave, Regina, S4P 0S7, SK, Canada
Tel.: (306) 352-3448

INTERNATIONAL PUBLIC

Web Site: http://www.hydrocarbonrecovery.com
Oil & Gas Field Development Solutions
N.A.I.C.S.: 213112
Tony Yang *(Dir-Tech Dev & Deployment)*

HTC Hydrogen Technologies Corp. (1)
3 Spring Street, Sydney, 2000, NSW, Australia
Tel.: (61) 412673215
CO2 Capture & Storage Technologies Sales & Marketer for Enhanced Oil Recovery; Hydrogen Production & Bio-Fuel Technologies Developer, Sales & Marketer
N.A.I.C.S.: 213112

Maxx Manufacturing LLC (1)
9105 Zenith Ave, Davenport, IA 52806
Tel.: (563) 332-9453
Oil Field Equipment Distr
N.A.I.C.S.: 423830
Joe Wollner *(CEO)*

SteelBlast Coatings and Painting Inc. (1)
Northgate, Box 26056, Regina, S4R 3C0, SK, Canada
Tel.: (306) 761-2279
Web Site: http://www.steelblast.ca
Protective Coating Product Mfr
N.A.I.C.S.: 325510

HTH HEATECH INC.
8916 44 Street SE, Calgary, T2C 2P6, AB, Canada
Tel.: (403) 279-1990
Web Site: http://www.heatech.ca
Year Founded: 1988
Industrial Product Distr
N.A.I.C.S.: 423840
Robert Fitz *(Pres)*

HTI HIGH TECH INDUSTRIES AG
Gruber & Kaja Strasse 1, A-4502, Sankt Marien, Austria
Tel.: (43) 7229804002800
Web Site: http://www.hti-ag.at
Sales Range: $250-299.9 Million
Emp.: 1,526
Holding Company; Molding & Injection Molding Product Mfr
N.A.I.C.S.: 551112

Subsidiaries:

Gruber & Kaja High Tech Metals GmbH (1)
Gruber & Kaja St 1, A4502, Sankt Marien, Austria
Tel.: (43) 722961141
Web Site: http://www.gruber-kaja.at
Sales Range: $100-124.9 Million
Emp.: 300
Die Casting Mfr
N.A.I.C.S.: 331523
Karlheinz Wintersberger *(CEO & Mng Dir)*

HTM INTERNATIONAL HOLDING LTD.
Chang-An E Rd Sec 2 16 7th Floor-2, Taipei, Taiwan
Tel.: (886) 225677111
Web Site: http://www.hsihou.com
Year Founded: 1989
4924—(TPE)
Rev.: $21,363,818
Assets: $24,070,944
Liabilities: $11,873,339
Net Worth: $12,197,605
Earnings: $1,019,354
Fiscal Year-end: 12/31/22
Holding Company
N.A.I.C.S.: 551112
Foong-Khuan Lew *(Chm)*

HTP FONTANA A.D.
Save Kovacevica 6, Vrnjaacka Banja, Serbia
Tel.: (381) 36 612 564
Web Site: http://www.htpfontana.com

AND PRIVATE COMPANIES

HTP KORCULA D.D.
Year Founded: 1999
Sales Range: Less than $1 Million
Home Management Services
N.A.I.C.S.: 721110

HTP KORCULA D.D.
Setaliste Frana Krsinica 104, Korcula, 20260, Dubrovnik, Croatia
Tel.: (385) 20726306
Web Site: https://htp-korcula.hr
HTPK—(ZAG)
Hotel Services
N.A.I.C.S.: 721199
Ivana Hatvalic Poljak (Pres)

HTP OREBIC D.D.
Setaliste Petra Kresimira IV 11, 20250, Dubrovnik, Croatia
Tel.: (385) 20797678
Web Site: https://htp-orebic.hr
HTPO—(ZAG)
Hotel & Restaurant Operator
N.A.I.C.S.: 721110
Ivana Hatvalic Poljak (Pres)

HTS ENGINEERING LTD.
115 Norfinch Dr, North York, M3N 1W, ON, Canada
Tel.: (516) 747-9477
Web Site: http://www.htseng.com
Rev.: $1,035,000
Emp.: 5
Engineeering Services
N.A.I.C.S.: 541330
Al Walcroft (Dir-Sls)

Subsidiaries:

Oslin Nation Co. (1)
100 E Randol Mill Rd, Arlington, TX 76011
Tel.: (713) 699-3500
Web Site: https://onco-tx.com
Sales Range: $10-24.9 Million
Emp.: 30
Pumps & Pumping Equipment
N.A.I.C.S.: 423720
Angela Brand (Controller)

HTV GMBH
Robert-Bosch-Str 28, Bensheim, 64625, Germany
Tel.: (49) 6251848000
Web Site: http://www.htv-gmbh.de
Year Founded: 1986
Rev.: $23,449,800
Emp.: 200
Electronic Components Testing Services
N.A.I.C.S.: 541380
Edbill Grote (Co-Founder & Co-CEO)

HU AN CABLE HOLDINGS LTD.
Blk 48 Toh Guan Road East, 03 108 Enterprise Hub, Singapore, 608586, Singapore
Tel.: (65) 64389919
Web Site: http://www.huanholdings.com
KI3—(SES)
Sales Range: $1-4.9 Billion
Silo Mfr
N.A.I.C.S.: 333248
Zhi Xiang Dai (Chm & CEO)

Subsidiaries:

Wuxi Hu An Wire and Cable Co., Ltd. (1)
No 6 Donghong Road, Guanlin Town, Yixing, 214251, Jiangsu, China
Tel.: (86) 51087219216
Wire & Cable Mfr
N.A.I.C.S.: 332618

HU LANE ASSOCIATE, INC.
2nd Floor No 1 Lane 342 Fude 1st Road, Xizhi District, New Taipei City, 221, Taiwan
Tel.: (886) 226940551

6279—(TPE)
Rev.: $204,069,318
Assets: $343,063,690
Liabilities: $168,763,124
Net Worth: $174,300,566
Earnings: $31,337,742
Emp.: 852
Fiscal Year-end: 12/31/22
Electronic Components Mfr
N.A.I.C.S.: 334419
Chang Tzu-Hsiung (Chm)

HUA CAPITAL MANAGEMENT CO., LTD.
15F Block A Truth Plaza No 7 Zhichun Road, Haidian District, Beijing, China
Tel.: (86) 10 5994 3900   CN
Web Site: http://www.hua-capital.com
Investment & Asset Management Services
N.A.I.C.S.: 523940
Xisheng Zhang (Pres)

Subsidiaries:

OmniVision Technologies, Inc. (1)
4275 Burton Dr, Santa Clara, CA 95054
Tel.: (408) 567-3000
Web Site: https://www.ovt.com
Sales Range: $1-4.9 Billion
Emp.: 2,176
Image Sensors Mfr
N.A.I.C.S.: 334413
Anson Chan (CFO & VP-Fin)

Subsidiary (Non-US):

OmniVision Technologies (Shanghai) Co., Ltd. (2)
No 88 Shangke Road, Pudong District, Shanghai, 201210, China
Tel.: (86) 216 175 9888
Web Site: http://www.ovt.com
Electronic Parts Whslr
N.A.I.C.S.: 423690

OmniVision Technologies Singapore Pte. Ltd (2)
3A International Business Park 06-07/08 Tower A ICON IBP, 06-07/08 Tower A ICON IBP, Singapore, 609935, Singapore
Tel.: (65) 6 933 1933
Web Site: http://www.ovt.com
Digital Imaging Sensor Chip Mfr
N.A.I.C.S.: 334413

HUA ENG WIRE & CABLE CO., LTD.
170 Chung Cheng 4th Road, Kaohsiung, 80147, Taiwan
Tel.: (886) 72814161
Web Site: http://www.hegroup.com.tw
Year Founded: 1956
Sales Range: $10-24.9 Million
Emp.: 451
Wire & Cable Mfr
N.A.I.C.S.: 332618
Hung Ming Wang (Pres)

Subsidiaries:

Hua Eng Wire & Cable Co. - Kao-Nan Factory (1)
No 30 Kao nan Highway, Jen-Wu, Kaohsiung, Taiwan
Tel.: (886) 73426333
Web Site: http://www.hegroup.com.tw
Cable Product Distr
N.A.I.C.S.: 423510

HUA HAN HEALTH INDUSTRY HOLDINGS LIMITED
Unit 3405 34th Floor China Merchants Tower, Shun Tak Center 168-200 Connaught Road, Central, China (Hong Kong)
Tel.: (852) 28699866
Web Site: http://www.huahanhealth.com.hk
Sales Range: $200-249.9 Million
Emp.: 975

Pharmaceutical Products Mfr & Sales
N.A.I.C.S.: 325412

Subsidiaries:

Hanfang Trading Company Limited (1)
Rm 3405 34 F China Merchants Twr Shun Tak Ctr 168-200 Connaught Rd, Sheung Wan, China (Hong Kong)
Tel.: (852) 28699866
Sales Range: $50-74.9 Million
Emp.: 5
Pharmaceuticals Producut Sales
N.A.I.C.S.: 424210

HUA HONG SEMICONDUCTOR LIMITED
288 halei Road Pudong New Area, Shanghai, 201203, China
Tel.: (86) 2138829909   CN
Web Site: https://www.huahonggrace.com
Year Founded: 2005
1347—(HKG)
Rev.: $2,475,488,000
Assets: $7,055,376,000
Liabilities: $2,919,908,000
Net Worth: $4,135,468,000
Earnings: $406,571,000
Emp.: 6,753
Fiscal Year-end: 12/31/22
Semiconductor Devices Mfr
N.A.I.C.S.: 334413
Zhang Suxin (Chm & Exec Dir)

HUA JUNG COMPONENTS CO., LTD.
1F No 5 Ln 60 Mingui St, Daliao Dist, Kaohsiung, 83146, Taiwan
Tel.: (886) 77015333
Web Site: https://www.hjc.com.tw
Year Founded: 1983
5328—(TPE)
Rev.: $33,123,190
Assets: $75,305,006
Liabilities: $21,900,729
Net Worth: $53,404,277
Earnings: $2,343,745
Emp.: 1,000
Fiscal Year-end: 12/31/22
Electronic Capacitor Mfr
N.A.I.C.S.: 334419
Chi-Ming Han (Sr VP)

Subsidiaries:

Hua Jung Electronics (Guang Dong) Co., Ltd. (1)
No 104 Ke Ji Dong Road, Dongguan, Guangdong, China
Film Capacitor Mfr
N.A.I.C.S.: 334416

Hua Jung Electronics (Shanghai) Co., Ltd. (1)
2rd Floor No 353 Fu Te North Road Pilot Free Trade Zone, Shanghai, China
Tel.: (86) 51257878888
Film Capacitor Mfr
N.A.I.C.S.: 334416

HUA MEDICINE LTD.
No 275 Ai Di Sheng Road, Zhangjiang Hi-Tech Park Pudong, Shanghai, 201203, China
Tel.: (86) 2138101800   Ky
Web Site: http://www.huamedicine.com
Year Founded: 2011
2552—(HKG)
Rev.: $2,470,900
Assets: $157,458,179
Liabilities: $118,205,147
Net Worth: $39,253,032
Earnings: ($28,572,383)
Emp.: 144
Fiscal Year-end: 12/31/22
Pharmaceutical Product Mfr & Distr
N.A.I.C.S.: 325412

HUA NAN FINANCIAL HOLDINGS CO., LTD.

Li Chen (Founder & CEO)

HUA NAN FINANCIAL HOLDINGS CO., LTD.
23 F No 123 Songren Rd, Xinyi Dist, Taipei, 110, Taiwan
Tel.: (886) 23713111
Web Site: https://www.hnfhc.com.tw
Year Founded: 2001
2880—(TAI)
Rev.: $2,743,463,152
Assets: $120,976,824,532
Liabilities: $114,479,237,189
Net Worth: $6,497,587,343
Earnings: $675,934,715
Emp.: 10,855
Fiscal Year-end: 12/31/23
Holding Company
N.A.I.C.S.: 551112
Ming-Cheng Lin (Vice Chm)

Subsidiaries:

Hua Nan Assets Management Co., Ltd. (1)
4/F No 18 Section 1 Chang an East Road, Zhongshan District, Taipei, Taiwan
Web Site: http://www.hnamc.com.tw
Asset Management Services
N.A.I.C.S.: 523940

Hua Nan Commercial Bank, Ltd. (1)
(100%)
Tel.: (886) 223713111
Web Site: http://www.hncb.com.tw
Sales Range: $1-4.9 Billion
Emp.: 7,000
Banking Services
N.A.I.C.S.: 522110
Ming-Cheng Lin (Chm)

Branch (Non-US):

Hua Nan Commercial Bank, Ltd. (2)
Suite 5601-03 56th Fl Central Plaza 18 Harbour Road, Wanchai, Hong Kong, China (Hong Kong)
Tel.: (852) 28240288
Web Site: http://www.hncb.com.tw
Banking Services
N.A.I.C.S.: 522110

Branch (Domestic):

Hua Nan Commercial Bank, Ltd. - Offshore Banking (2)
38 Chung-King South Road Section 1 2nd Floor, Taipei, 100, Taiwan
Tel.: (886) 223821056
Web Site: http://www.hncb.com.tw
Sales Range: $50-74.9 Million
Emp.: 18
Banking Services
N.A.I.C.S.: 522110
Linda Lin (VP & Mgr)

Branch (Non-US):

Hua Nan Commercial Bank, Ltd. - Singapore (2)
80 Robinson Road 14-03, 68898, Singapore, Singapore
Tel.: (65) 63242566
Web Site: http://sg.hncb.com
Banking Services
N.A.I.C.S.: 522110
Chi-Wen Hsu (VP & Deputy Gen Mgr-Singapore Branch & Bank of Taiwan)

Hua Nan Investment Trust Corporation (1)
3f-1 54 Min Sheng E Rd Sec 4, Taipei, Taiwan
Tel.: (886) 227196688
Investment Management Service
N.A.I.C.S.: 523999

Hua Nan Management & Consulting Co., Ltd. (1)
3F 143 Minsheng East Road Sec 2, Taipei, Taiwan (100%)
Tel.: (886) 225000622
Web Site: http://www.hnnc.com.tw
Sales Range: $25-49.9 Million
Emp.: 10
Management & Consulting Services
N.A.I.C.S.: 541611

HUA NAN FINANCIAL HOLDINGS CO., LTD.

Hua Nan Financial Holdings Co., Ltd.—(Continued)
Kevin Yu *(Asst VP)*

Hua Nan Securities Co., Ltd. (1)
5th Floor No 54 Section 4 Minsheng East Road, Songshan District, Taipei, Taiwan (100%)
Tel.: (886) 22955774
Web Site: https://www.entrust.com.tw
Sales Range: $100-124.9 Million
Emp.: 1,454
Securities Brokerage Services
N.A.I.C.S.: 523150

Hua Nan Securities Investment Trust Co., Ltd. (1)
3F-1 54 Minsheng East Road Sec 4, Taipei, Taiwan (100%)
Tel.: (886) 227196688
Web Site: http://www.hnitc.com.tw
Sales Range: $50-74.9 Million
Emp.: 89
Investment Services
N.A.I.C.S.: 523999
Grace Chen *(Head-Fin)*

Hua Nan Venture Capital Co., Ltd. (1)
3F 143 Minsheng East Road Sec 2, Taipei, Taiwan (100%)
Tel.: (886) 223713111
Web Site: http://www.hnfhc.com.tw
Sales Range: $50-74.9 Million
Emp.: 10
Capital Investment Services
N.A.I.C.S.: 523999

South China Insurance Co., Ltd. (1)
5th F1 No 560 Section 4 Zhongxiao E Rd, Taipei, Taiwan (100%)
Tel.: (886) 227588418
Web Site: https://www.south-china.com.tw
Sales Range: $250-299.9 Million
Emp.: 800
Insurance Services
N.A.I.C.S.: 524126

HUA XIA BANK CO., LIMITED
Hua Xia Bank Plaza No 22 Jianguomennei Street, Dongcheng District, Beijing, 100005, China
Tel.: (86) 95577
Web Site: http://www.hxb.com.cn
Year Founded: 1992
600015—(SHG)
Rev.: $13,170,643,200
Assets: $547,583,446,800
Liabilities: $502,189,038,000
Net Worth: $45,394,408,800
Earnings: $3,514,914,000
Emp.: 40,556
Fiscal Year-end: 12/31/22
Banking Services
N.A.I.C.S.: 522110
Yongguang Ren *(VP)*

HUA YANG BERHAD
C-21 Jalan Medan Selayang 1 Medan Selayang, 68100, Batu Caves, Selangor Darul Ehsan, Malaysia
Tel.: (60) 361884488
Web Site: https://www.huayang.com.my
Year Founded: 1978
HUAYANG—(KLS)
Rev.: $25,409,519
Assets: $186,379,174
Liabilities: $85,807,121
Net Worth: $100,572,053
Earnings: $662,935
Emp.: 79
Fiscal Year-end: 03/31/23
Property Development Services
N.A.I.C.S.: 531311
Oi Wah Leong *(Co-Sec)*

Subsidiaries:

Bukit Selim Sdn. Bhd. (1)
123A Jalan Kampar, 30250, Ipoh, Perak, Malaysia
Tel.: (60) 52543812
Residential Property Development Services
N.A.I.C.S.: 236115

Grandeur Park Sdn. Bhd. (1)
No 53 55 Jalan Besi Taman Sri Putri, Skudai, 81300, Johor, Malaysia
Tel.: (60) 75591388
Sales Range: $25-49.9 Million
Emp.: 23
Residential Property Development Services
N.A.I.C.S.: 531210

Pembinaan Hua Yang Sdn. Bhd. (1)
No 123 Jalan Kampar, 30250, Ipoh, Perak, Malaysia
Tel.: (60) 52543812
Web Site: http://www.huayang.com.my
Residential Building Construction Services
N.A.I.C.S.: 236116
Wen Yan Ho *(CEO)*

Prop Park Sendirian Berhad (1)
C-21 Jalan Medan Selayang 1, Medan Selayang, Batu Caves, 68100, Selangor, Malaysia
Tel.: (60) 361884488
Web Site: http://www.huayang.com.my
Sales Range: $25-49.9 Million
Emp.: 38
Real Estate Property Development Services
N.A.I.C.S.: 531312
Ho Wen Yan *(CEO)*

Sunny Mode Sdn. Bhd. (1)
C-21 Jalan Medan Selayang 1, Batu Caves, 68100, Selangor, Malaysia
Tel.: (60) 361884488
Web Site: http://www.huayang.com.my
Sales Range: $25-49.9 Million
Emp.: 35
Residential Property Development Services
N.A.I.C.S.: 531210
Ho Wen Yan *(CEO)*

HUA YIN INTERNATIONAL HOLDINGS LTD.
Room 1305 13th Floor China Resources Building, No 26 Harbour Road, Wanchai, China (Hong Kong)
Tel.: (852) 2 209 2888
Web Site: http://www.huayinternational.com
Year Founded: 1990
0989—(HKG)
Rev.: $17,175,301
Assets: $317,450,201
Liabilities: $310,626,074
Net Worth: $6,824,127
Earnings: ($8,726,842)
Emp.: 235
Fiscal Year-end: 03/31/22
Investment Services
N.A.I.C.S.: 523999
Xintong Cui *(Chm)*

Subsidiaries:

China Motion Holdings Limited (1)
Unit 3101 Level 31 Tower 1 Enterprise Square Five 38 Wang Chiu Road, Kowloon Bay, Hong Kong, China (Hong Kong) (100%)
Tel.: (852) 22092888
Sales Range: $75-99.9 Million
Emp.: 200
Holding Company
N.A.I.C.S.: 551112

Subsidiary (Domestic):

China Motion United Telecom Limited (2)
Unit 3101 Level 31 Tower 1 Enterprise Square Five 38 Wang Chiu Road, Kowloon Bay, Hong Kong, China (Hong Kong) (70%)
Tel.: (852) 22092888
Investment Holding Company
N.A.I.C.S.: 551112

HUA YU LIEN DEVELOPMENT CO., LTD.
11F No 85 Wenlong Rd, Fengshan, Kaohsiung, 830, Taiwan
Tel.: (886) 7801381
Web Site: http://www.huakai.com.tw
Year Founded: 1967
1436—(TAI)
Rev.: $53,252,590
Assets: $492,741,928
Liabilities: $364,031,446
Net Worth: $128,710,483
Earnings: $30,742,665
Emp.: 90
Fiscal Year-end: 12/31/23
Real Estate Lending Services
N.A.I.C.S.: 531190
Chao-Ting Lu *(Chm & Pres)*

HUA YUAN PROPERTY CO., LTD.
Building 11 HuaYuan Enterprise Center No 11 North Beizhan Street, Xicheng District, Beijing, 100044, China
Tel.: (86) 1068036688
Web Site: https://www.hy-online.com
Year Founded: 1983
600743—(SHG)
Rev.: $1,533,776,831
Assets: $6,243,082,041
Liabilities: $5,360,853,144
Net Worth: $882,228,897
Earnings: ($536,568,196)
Emp.: 1,800
Fiscal Year-end: 12/31/22
Real Estate Manangement Services
N.A.I.C.S.: 531390
Li Ran *(Pres & Mng Dir)*

HUAAN SECURITIES CO. LTD
No 1018 Ziyun Road, Binhu New District, Hefei, 230601, Anhui, China
Tel.: (86) 55165161691
Web Site: http://www.hazq.com
Year Founded: 2001
600909—(SHG)
Rev.: $443,530,774
Assets: $10,374,002,079
Liabilities: $7,536,305,991
Net Worth: $2,837,696,088
Earnings: $165,860,024
Fiscal Year-end: 12/31/22
Security Brokerage Services
N.A.I.C.S.: 523150
Hongtao Zhang *(Chm)*

HUABANG TECHNOLOGY HOLDINGS LIMITED
33/F Enterprise Square Three 39 Wang Chiu Road, Kowloon Bay, Kowloon, China (Hong Kong)
Tel.: (852) 23140822
Web Site: https://www.huabangtech.com
Year Founded: 2005
3638—(HKG)
Rev.: $219,594,770
Assets: $66,395,551
Liabilities: $28,385,145
Net Worth: $38,010,406
Earnings: ($30,880,263)
Emp.: 28
Fiscal Year-end: 03/31/22
Holding Company
N.A.I.C.S.: 551112
Kwok Ming Wong *(Mng Dir, Grp CFO, CFO & Sec)*

Subsidiaries:

Huabang Corporate Finance Limited (1)
Unit 1708-13 17/F Nan Fung Tower 88 Connaught Road Central, Hong Kong, China (Hong Kong)
Tel.: (852) 37009588
Financial Services
N.A.I.C.S.: 523940

Huabang Securities Limited (1)
Room 3308 Floor 33 Enterprise Plaza Phase 3 39 Wang Chiu Road, Kowloon Bay, China (Hong Kong)
Tel.: (852) 23899888
Financial Services
N.A.I.C.S.: 523999

HUABAO INTERNATIONAL HOLDINGS LIMITED
Room 3008 Central Plaza 18 Harbour Road, Wanchai, China (Hong Kong)
Tel.: (852) 28778999
Web Site: https://www.hbglobal.com
Year Founded: 1996
0336—(HKG)
Rev.: $537,589,354
Assets: $2,333,310,689
Liabilities: $289,446,394
Net Worth: $2,043,864,295
Earnings: ($126,507,420)
Emp.: 3,875
Fiscal Year-end: 12/31/22
Food Flavors Production & Sale
N.A.I.C.S.: 311942
Chiu Kwok Poon *(Sec)*

Subsidiaries:

Aromascape Development Centre GmbH (1)
Hackelbergstrasse 1, 37603, Neuhaus, Germany
Tel.: (49) 5536960990
Web Site: https://www.aromascape.de
Tobacco Flavour & Fragrances Research & Development Services
N.A.I.C.S.: 312230

F&G (Botswana) (Pty) Limited (1)
Plot 2016/7 Dumela Industrial, Francistown, Botswana
Tel.: (267) 76666260
Web Site: http://fngff.com
Food Mfr & Distr
N.A.I.C.S.: 311999

Guangdong Golden Leaf Technology Development Co., Ltd. (1)
Jinke Road Jinpu Street, Chaoyang District, Shantou, Guangdong, China
Tel.: (86) 75486659000
Web Site: https://www.jinyekj.com
Tobacco Mfr
N.A.I.C.S.: 312230

Guangdong Jiahao Foodstuff Co., Ltd. (1)
Shi Te Industrial Zone, Gangkou Town, Zhongshan, 528447, China
Tel.: (86) 76089872070
Web Site: https://jiahaofoods.globalimporter.net
Food Products Mfr
N.A.I.C.S.: 311999
Zhixiong Chen *(CEO)*

Huabao Flavours & Fragrances (HK) Limited (1)
Rm 4-5 4F Veristrong Indus Ctr Blk A 34-36 Au Pui Wan St, Fotan, Sha Tin, New Territories, China (Hong Kong)
Tel.: (852) 26902565
Web Site: http://www.huabao.com
Sales Range: $25-49.9 Million
Emp.: 12
Food Flavorings Mfr & Sales
N.A.I.C.S.: 325199

Huabao Flavours & Fragrances Co., Ltd. (1)
1299 Yecheng Road, Jiading District, Shanghai, China
Tel.: (86) 2169050000
Web Site: https://en.hbflavor.com
Rev.: $209,109,840
Assets: $1,159,973,893
Liabilities: $123,676,568
Net Worth: $1,036,297,325
Earnings: $53,380,389
Fiscal Year-end: 12/31/2023
Tobacco Flavour & Fragrances Mfr
N.A.I.C.S.: 312230

Xiamen Amber Daily Chemical Technology Co., Ltd. (1)
No 308 Tongan Park, Tongan Industrial Concentration Zone, Xiamen, Fujian, China
Tel.: (86) 5925032591
Web Site: http://www.xmhupo.com
Chemical Product Mfr & Distr

AND PRIVATE COMPANIES

N.A.I.C.S.: 325998

Yancheng City Chunzhu Aroma Co., Ltd. (1)
Qianqiu Town, Sheyang County, Yancheng, Jiangsu, China
Tel.: (86) 51588701580
Web Site: https://www.chunzhuaroma.com
Chemical Product Mfr & Distr.
N.A.I.C.S.: 325998

Yongzhou Shanxiang Flavour Co., Ltd. (1)
No 70 TaoYuan Road West, Lengshuitan District, Yongzhou, Hunan, China
Tel.: (86) 7468227058
Web Site: http://www.samshiang.com
Food Mfr & Distr
N.A.I.C.S.: 311999

Zhaoqing Perfumery Co., Ltd. (1)
Lingshan, Lantang Eastern Suburb, Zhaoqing, 526060, Guangdong, China
Tel.: (86) 7582718598
Web Site: http://www.gdzqperfumery.com.cn
Chemical Products Mfr
N.A.I.C.S.: 325998

HUABO BIOPHARM (SHANGHAI) CO., LTD.
1800 Cailun Road Zhangjiang High Tech Park, Pudong, Shanghai, China
Tel.: (86) 2150799120
Web Site: https://www.huabobio.com
Year Founded: 2011
Pharmaceutical Product Mfr & Distr
N.A.I.C.S.: 325412

HUACHANGDA INTELLIGENT EQUIPMENT GROUP CO., LTD.
No 9 Dongyi Avenue, Shiyan, 442012, Hubei, China
Tel.: (86) 7198767769
Web Site: http://www.hchd.com.cn
Year Founded: 2003
300278—(CHIN)
Rev.: $503,018,100
Assets: $398,121,048
Liabilities: $168,875,928
Net Worth: $229,245,120
Earnings: $14,918,904
Fiscal Year-end: 12/31/22
Automation & Assembly Equipment Mfr
N.A.I.C.S.: 333922
Chen Ze (Chm, Vice Chm, Pres, CEO & Gen Mgr)

HUACHEN PRECISION EQUIPMENT (KUNSHAN) CO., LTD.
No 333 Hengchangjing Road, Zhoushi Town, Kunshan, 215337, Jiangsu, China
Tel.: (86) 51250361922
Web Site: https://www.hiecise.com
Year Founded: 2007
300809—(SSE)
Rev.: $65,934,118
Assets: $286,489,172
Liabilities: $71,032,352
Net Worth: $215,456,820
Earnings: $16,202,579
Emp.: 539
Fiscal Year-end: 12/31/23
Precision Equipment Mfr
N.A.I.C.S.: 332216
Xu Caiying (Sec)

HUACHENG REAL ESTATE SA
51 Shiguang Road, Shanghai, 200433, China
Tel.: (86) 2155785179
Web Site: http://www.huachengrealestate.com
Year Founded: 1995
Sales Range: $25-49.9 Million
Emp.: 260
Real Estate Developers
N.A.I.C.S.: 236116
Feilong Hang (Chm & CEO)

HUADA AUTOMOTIVE TECHNOLOGY CO., LTD.
No 68 Jiangping Road East, Jingjiang, 214500, Jiangsu, China
Tel.: (86) 52384593610
Web Site: http://www.hdqckj.com
Year Founded: 2002
603358—(SHG)
Rev.: $724,830,388
Assets: $897,874,132
Liabilities: $405,517,741
Net Worth: $492,356,391
Earnings: $36,550,079
Fiscal Year-end: 12/31/22
Automotive Parts Mfr & Distr
N.A.I.C.S.: 336390
Jinghong Chen (Chm)

HUADI INTERNATIONAL GROUP CO., LTD.
No 1688 Tianzhong Street, Longwan District, Wenzhou, 325025, Zhejiang, China
Tel.: (86) 57786598888   Ky
Web Site: https://ir.huadi.cc
Year Founded: 2018
HUDI—(NASDAQ)
Rev.: $83,113,259
Assets: $103,010,786
Liabilities: $28,326,976
Net Worth: $74,683,810
Earnings: $3,257,722
Emp.: 362
Fiscal Year-end: 09/30/23
Holding Company
N.A.I.C.S.: 551112
Huisen Wang (CEO)

HUADIAN HEAVY INDUSTRIES CO., LTD.
Block B Building 1 No 6 Auto Museum East Road, Fengtai District, Beijing, 100070, China
Tel.: (86) 1068466145
Web Site: http://www.hhi.com.cn
Year Founded: 1988
601226—(SHG)
Rev.: $1,152,132,284
Assets: $1,584,526,839
Liabilities: $969,631,744
Net Worth: $614,895,096
Earnings: $43,500,118
Fiscal Year-end: 12/31/22
Industrial Machinery Mfr
N.A.I.C.S.: 333248
Wen Duanchao (Chm)

HUADIAN LIAONING ENERGY DEVELOPMENT CO., LTD.
No 2 Yingchun Street, Sujiatun District, Shenyang, 110006, China
Tel.: (86) 2483996040
600396—(SHG)
Rev.: $1,000,929,852
Assets: $2,649,539,955
Liabilities: $2,946,383,940
Net Worth: ($296,843,985)
Earnings: ($283,341,451)
Fiscal Year-end: 12/31/22
Electric Power Generation & Distribution Services
N.A.I.C.S.: 221118
Xue Zhenju (Sec)

HUADIAN POWER INTERNATIONAL CORPORATION LIMITED
No 2 Xuanwumennei Street, Xicheng District, Beijing, 100031, China
Tel.: (86) 1083567888   CN
Web Site: https://www.hdpi.com.cn
Year Founded: 1994
HPIFF—(OTCIQ)
Rev.: $15,031,018,454
Assets: $31,346,034,080
Liabilities: $21,454,959,380

Net Worth: $9,891,074,700
Earnings: $14,013,464
Emp.: 24,755
Fiscal Year-end: 12/31/22
Electricity Distribution Services
N.A.I.C.S.: 221122
Bin Chen (Deputy Gen Mgr)

Subsidiaries:

Hangzhou Huadian Banshan Power Generation Company Limited (1)
No 200 Gongkang Road, Gongshu District, Hangzhou, 310015, Zhejiang, China
Tel.: (86) 57185272234
Eletric Power Generation Services
N.A.I.C.S.: 221118

Hebei Huadian Shijiazhuang Thermal Power Company Limited (1)
No 173 Tiyu North Avenue, Changan District, Shijiazhuang, 050041, Hebei, China
Tel.: (86) 31183726981
Eletric Power Generation Services
N.A.I.C.S.: 221118

HUADONG MEDICINE CO., LTD.
No 866 Mogan Mountain Road, Hangzhou, 311000, China
Tel.: (86) 57189903388
Web Site: https://www.eastchinapharm.com
000963—(SSE)
Rev.: $5,295,128,436
Assets: $4,379,384,880
Liabilities: $1,687,012,704
Net Worth: $2,692,372,176
Earnings: $350,889,084
Fiscal Year-end: 12/31/22
Pharmaceuticals Product Mfr
N.A.I.C.S.: 325412
Lv Liang (Chm)

Subsidiaries:

Sinclair Pharma plc (1)
1st Floor Whitfield Court, 30-32 Whitfield Street, London, W1T 2RQ, United Kingdom
Tel.: (44) 20 7467 6920
Web Site: http://www.sinclairpharma.com
Sales Range: $100-124.9 Million
Emp.: 144
Pharmaceuticals Product Mfr
N.A.I.C.S.: 325412
Alan Olby (CFO)

Unit (Domestic):

Sinclair IS Pharma Manufacturing & Logistics (2)
Office Village Chester Business Park, Chester, CH4 9QZ, United Kingdom
Tel.: (44) 1244625150
Sales Range: $10-24.9 Million
Emp.: 1
Pharmaceuticals Mfr
N.A.I.C.S.: 325412
Ann Hardy (Dir-Global Technical)

Subsidiary (Non-US):

Sinclair Pharma France (2)
44-46 rue de la Bienfaisance, 75008, Paris, France
Tel.: (33) 17 328 3400
Web Site: http://www.sinclairpharma.com
Sales Range: $10-24.9 Million
Emp.: 25
Pharmaceutical Sales
N.A.I.C.S.: 424210

Sinclair Pharma GmbH (2)
Kaiserring 10-16, 68161, Mannheim, Germany
Tel.: (49) 6215 339 8970
Web Site: https://sinclair.com
Pharmaceuticals Producut Sales
N.A.I.C.S.: 424210

Subsidiary (Domestic):

Sinclair Pharmaceuticals Ltd. (2)
1st Floor Whitfield Court 30-32 Whitfield Street, London, W1T 2RQ, United Kingdom
Tel.: (44) 2074676920
Web Site: http://www.sinclairpharma.com

Pharmaceuticals Mfr
N.A.I.C.S.: 325412

HUAFA PROPERTY SERVICES GROUP COMPANY LIMITED
Unit 3605 36/F Cheung Kong Center 2 Queens Road, Central, China (Hong Kong)
Tel.: (852) 34655300
Web Site: http://www.huajinci.com
Year Founded: 2000
0982—(HKG)
Rev.: $250,113,261
Assets: $147,494,035
Liabilities: $112,563,940
Net Worth: $34,930,096
Earnings: $35,249,262
Emp.: 9,193
Fiscal Year-end: 12/31/23
Financial Printing Services
N.A.I.C.S.: 323111
Guangning Li (Chm)

Subsidiaries:

Huajin Financial (International) Holdings Limited (1)
Room 1101 11th Floor Champion Building 3 Garden Road, Central, China (Hong Kong)
Tel.: (852) 31033000
Web Site: https://www.hjfi.hk
Brokerage Services
N.A.I.C.S.: 523150

iOne Financial Press Limited (1)
7/F Wheelock House 20 Pedder Street, Central, China (Hong Kong)
Tel.: (852) 28798787
Web Site: https://www.ione.com.hk
Financial Printing Services
N.A.I.C.S.: 323111

HUAFANG CO., LTD.
No 118 Donghai 1st Road, Binzhou, 256602, Shandong, China
Tel.: (86) 5433288255
Web Site: http://www.hfgf.cn
Year Founded: 1999
600448—(SHG)
Rev.: $489,817,860
Assets: $524,914,772
Liabilities: $346,950,499
Net Worth: $177,964,273
Earnings: ($12,047,457)
Fiscal Year-end: 12/31/22
Textile Products Mfr
N.A.I.C.S.: 313310
Shouxiang Sheng (Chm)

HUAFON CHEMICAL CO., LTD.
No 1788 Development Road Ruian Economic Development Zone Wenzhou, Ruian, 325200, Zhejiang, China
Tel.: (86) 57765150000
Web Site: https://www.spandex.com.cn
Year Founded: 1999
002064—(SSE)
Rev.: $3,634,129,044
Assets: $4,598,769,708
Liabilities: $1,348,876,152
Net Worth: $3,249,893,556
Earnings: $399,293,388
Fiscal Year-end: 12/31/22
Artificial Fiber Product Mfr
N.A.I.C.S.: 325220
Yang Congdeng (Chm)

Subsidiaries:

Huafon Foreign Trade Co., Ltd. (1)
Istanbul Vizyon Park Ofis Plaza Yenibosna, Merkez Mh 29 Ekim Cd A/2 Vizyon 3 Plaza K 5 N 38 Bahcelievler, Istanbul, Turkiye
Tel.: (90) 2127094791
Textile Product Whslr
N.A.I.C.S.: 424310

HUAFON MICROFIBRE (SHANGHAI) CO., LTD.
No 888 Tingwei Road South, Jinshan

HUAFON MICROFIBRE (SHANGHAI) CO., LTD.

Huafon Microfibre (Shanghai) Co., Ltd.—(Continued)
District, Shanghai, 201508, China
Tel.: (86) 2131108666
Web Site:
  https://microfibre.huafeng.com
Year Founded: 2002
300180—(CHIN)
Rev.: $595,173,852
Assets: $1,121,842,332
Liabilities: $453,421,800
Net Worth: $668,420,532
Earnings: ($49,740,912)
Fiscal Year-end: 12/31/22
Ultra Fine Fiber Polyurethane Synthetic Leather Products Mfr
N.A.I.C.S.: 316990
You Feifeng (Chm)

HUAFU FASHION CO., LTD.
59th Floor Tower 1 Chang Fu Jin Mao Building CFC No 5 Shihua Road, Futian, Shenzhen, 518045, China
Tel.: (86) 75583735588
Web Site: https://www.e-huafu.com
Year Founded: 1993
002042—(SSE)
Rev.: $2,030,133,456
Assets: $2,547,417,600
Liabilities: $1,595,693,736
Net Worth: $951,723,864
Earnings: ($49,276,188)
Fiscal Year-end: 12/31/22
Textile Products Mfr
N.A.I.C.S.: 313110
Zheng Zhang (Sec)

HUAGONG TECH COMPANY LIMITED
No 1 6th Rd Science Park Huazhong University of Science & Technology, East Lake High-tech Development Zone, Wuhan, 430223, Hubei, China
Tel.: (86) 2787180126
Web Site: http://www.hgtech.com
Year Founded: 1999
000988—(SSE)
Rev.: $1,686,348,612
Assets: $2,357,696,484
Liabilities: $1,197,541,800
Net Worth: $1,160,154,684
Earnings: $127,213,632
Fiscal Year-end: 12/31/22
Laser Device Mfr
N.A.I.C.S.: 334510
Xinqiang Ma (Chm & Gen Mgr)

HUAHUI EDUCATION GROUP LIMITED
13F Building B1 Wisdom Plaza Qiaoxiang Road, Nanshan District, Shenzhen, 518000, Guangdoang, China
Tel.: (86) 13728708818   NV
Year Founded: 2014
HHEGF—(OTCIQ)
Rev.: $1,371,122
Assets: $2,646,464
Liabilities: $3,098,739
Net Worth: ($452,275)
Earnings: ($12,669)
Emp.: 35
Fiscal Year-end: 12/31/23
Interior Decoration Product Mfr
N.A.I.C.S.: 337212
Junze Zhang (Chm, Pres, CEO, CFO & Sec)

HUAIBEI GREENGOLD INDUSTRY INVESTMENT CO., LTD.
Floor 7 No 18 Suixi North Road West Street Road, Xiangshan District, Huaibei, Anhui, China
Tel.: (86) 5613110109   CN
Web Site: https://www.ljgfjt.com
Year Founded: 2016

2450—(HKG)
Rev.: $62,465,096
Assets: $351,257,213
Liabilities: $268,102,945
Net Worth: $83,154,268
Earnings: $16,095,936
Emp.: 152
Fiscal Year-end: 12/31/22
Investment Management Service
N.A.I.C.S.: 523999
Yinyan Shi (CFO)

HUAIBEI MINING HOLDINGS CO., LTD.
No 276 Renmin Middle Road, Huaibei, 235000, Anhui, China
Tel.: (86) 5614951956
Web Site: https://www.hbkykg.com
600985—(SHG)
Rev.: $10,365,111,927
Assets: $12,252,246,358
Liabilities: $6,401,010,009
Net Worth: $5,851,236,349
Earnings: $876,691,927
Fiscal Year-end: 12/31/23
Coal Mining, Processing & Coal Chemical Products Whslr
N.A.I.C.S.: 212114
Qiu Dan (Sec)

HUAIHE ENERGY (GROUP) CO., LTD.
Commercial & Service Building Group E Juren Village Datong Street, Datong District, Huainan, 232000, Anhui, China
Tel.: (86) 5547628095
Web Site: http://www.wuhuport.com
Year Founded: 2000
600575—(SHG)
Rev.: $3,560,102,568
Assets: $2,561,205,133
Liabilities: $913,219,810
Net Worth: $1,647,985,323
Earnings: $48,718,435
Emp.: 9,000
Fiscal Year-end: 12/31/22
Logistic Services
N.A.I.C.S.: 541614
Zhou Tao (Chm)

HUAIJI DENGYUN AUTOPARTS (HOLDING) CO., LTD.
Dengyunting, Huaicheng Town Huaiji County, Guangdong, 526400, China
Tel.: (86) 7585522482
Web Site:
  https://www.huaijivalve.com
Year Founded: 1971
002715—(SSE)
Rev.: $71,210,880
Assets: $140,517,936
Liabilities: $85,775,976
Net Worth: $54,741,960
Earnings: ($18,535,608)
Emp.: 750
Fiscal Year-end: 12/31/22
Automotive Engine Intake & Exhaust Valves Mfr
N.A.I.C.S.: 332912
Haikun Yang (Chm)

HUAIZHONG HEALTH GROUP, INC.
Tianan Technology Park 13/F Headquarters Center Building 16, 555 Panyu North Ave Panyu District, Guangzhou, 523857, China
Tel.: (86) 2029829356   NV
Web Site:
  http://www.adaiahdistribution.com
Year Founded: 2013
ADAD—(OTCEM)
Assets: $1,250
Liabilities: $80,722
Net Worth: ($79,472)

Earnings: ($29,171)
Fiscal Year-end: 10/31/22
Entertainment Services
N.A.I.C.S.: 512191
Yuantong Wang (Pres, CEO, CFO, Treas & Sec)

HUAJIN INTERNATIONAL HOLDINGS LIMITED
Room 518 Tower A New Mandarin Plaza No 14 Science Museum Road, Tsim Sha Tsui East, Kowloon, China (Hong Kong)
Tel.: (852) 34603221   Ky
Web Site: http://www.huajin-hk.com
Year Founded: 2015
2738—(HKG)
Rev.: $654,764,245
Assets: $392,666,087
Liabilities: $332,948,632
Net Worth: $59,717,455
Earnings: ($23,207,980)
Emp.: 1,170
Fiscal Year-end: 12/31/22
Carbon & Welding Steel Distr
N.A.I.C.S.: 423510
Songqing Xu (Chm)

Subsidiaries:

Jiangmen Huajin Metal Product Company Limited   (1)
Farm Wai, Zhoulang Village Gujing Town Xinhui District, Jiangmen, Guangdong, China
Tel.: (86) 7506538888
Steel Product Mfr & Distr
N.A.I.C.S.: 331210
Songqing Xu (Founder)

HUAKAN INTERNATIONAL MINING INC.
Suite 850 580 Hornby Street, Vancouver, V6C 3B6, BC, Canada
Tel.: (604) 694-2344   BC
Year Founded: 1986
Metal Exploration Services
N.A.I.C.S.: 213114

HUAKANG BIOMEDICAL HOLDINGS CO., LTD.
1-3/F Building D Shenzhen Junxuan 16 Yinkui Road, Kui Xin Community Kui Chong Office Dapeng New District, Shenzhen, China
Tel.: (86) 75532833299   Ky
Web Site: http://www.szhuakang.com
Year Founded: 1992
8622—(HKG)
Rev.: $3,556,332
Assets: $9,322,841
Liabilities: $1,386,871
Net Worth: $7,935,970
Earnings: ($431,730)
Emp.: 82
Fiscal Year-end: 12/31/22
Medical Equipment Mfr & Distr
N.A.I.C.S.: 334510
Shuguang Zhang (Chm)

HUAKE HOLDING BIOLOGY CO., LTD.
Shuhe Road Tangchi Town, Shucheng, Lu'an, 231343, Anhui, China
Tel.: (86) 564 8242 222   Ky
Year Founded: 2019
HUAK—(NASDAQ)
Rev.: $14,636,348
Assets: $21,247,061
Liabilities: $5,526,406
Net Worth: $15,720,655
Earnings: $1,703,903
Emp.: 27
Fiscal Year-end: 09/30/20
Holding Company
N.A.I.C.S.: 551112

INTERNATIONAL PUBLIC

Pingting Wang (CEO)

HUAKU DEVELOPMENT CO., LTD.
7th Floor No 456 Section 4 Xinyi Road, Xinyi Dist, Taipei, Taiwan
Tel.: (886) 227582828
Web Site: https://www.huaku.com.tw
2548—(TAI)
Rev.: $516,857,726
Assets: $1,425,557,061
Liabilities: $745,507,477
Net Worth: $680,049,584
Earnings: $116,810,813
Emp.: 73
Fiscal Year-end: 12/31/23
Building & Construction Materials Mfr
N.A.I.C.S.: 236210
Frank Long Chang Chung (Chm)

HUALAN BIOLOGICAL ENGINEERING INC.
No 1 Hualan Avenue, Xinxiang, 453003, Henan, China
Tel.: (86) 3735056905
Web Site: http://www.hualanbio.com
Year Founded: 1992
002007—(SSE)
Rev.: $634,183,992
Assets: $2,069,632,188
Liabilities: $355,266,756
Net Worth: $1,714,365,432
Earnings: $151,108,308
Fiscal Year-end: 12/31/22
Blood & Vaccine Product Research & Development Services
N.A.I.C.S.: 541715
Ma Chaoyuan (Chm-Supervisory Bd)

HUALAN GROUP CO., LTD.
Nanguo Yiyuan No 1 Yuewan Road, Guangxi Zhuang Autonomous Region Qingxiu District, Nanning, 530029, China
Tel.: (86) 7715775576
Web Site: https://www.gxhl.com
Year Founded: 2012
301027—(CHIN)
Rev.: $118,649,232
Assets: $260,548,704
Liabilities: $125,482,500
Net Worth: $135,066,204
Earnings: $7,671,456
Fiscal Year-end: 12/31/22
Engineeering Services
N.A.I.C.S.: 541330
Xiang Lei (Chm)

HUALE ACOUSTICS CORPORATION
East Room 902 Building 3 East, Saige Sci-Tech Park Futian District, Shenzhen, 518000, Guangdong, China
Tel.: (86) 13723419533   NV
Year Founded: 2014
Assets: $12,000
Liabilities: $71,324
Net Worth: ($59,324)
Earnings: ($49,436)
Fiscal Year-end: 12/31/18
Clothing Embroidery Services
N.A.I.C.S.: 314999
Zhicheng Huang (Pres, CEO, Treas & Sec)

HUALI INDUSTRIAL GROUP COMPANY LIMITED
No 2 Shiji 1st Road, Torch Development Zone, Zhongshan, 528437, Guangdong, China
Tel.: (86) 76028168889
Web Site: https://www.huali-group.com
Year Founded: 2004

AND PRIVATE COMPANIES

300979—(SSE)
Rev.: $2,887,925,508
Assets: $2,402,281,908
Liabilities: $549,643,536
Net Worth: $1,852,638,372
Earnings: $453,214,008
Emp.: 1,500,000
Fiscal Year-end: 12/31/22
Sporting Product Mfr & Distr
N.A.I.C.S.: 339920
Congyuan Zhang *(Chm)*

HUALI INDUSTRIES CO LTD
Song Bai Tang Changping, Huali Industrial District, Dongguan, 523561, Guangdong, China
Tel.: (86) 76983333239
Web Site: https://www.dghuali.com
Year Founded: 1995
603038—(SHG)
Rev.: $108,495,378
Assets: $285,476,106
Liabilities: $94,901,358
Net Worth: $190,574,748
Earnings: $1,496,369
Fiscal Year-end: 12/31/22
Decorative Material Mfr & Distr
N.A.I.C.S.: 337212
Tan Hongyu *(Chm & Pres)*

Subsidiaries:

Guangdong Hongwan Supply Chain Technology Co., Ltd. (1)
Huifu Center No 13 Zongbu 2nd Road, Songshan Lake High Tech Industrial Development Zone, Dongguan, China
Tel.: (86) 76983338072
Sealing Device Mfr
N.A.I.C.S.: 339991

HUAMING POWER EQUIPMENT CO., LTD.
No 977 Tongpu Road, Putuo District, Shanghai, 200333, Shandong, China
Tel.: (86) 53182685200
Web Site: https://www.intl-huaming.com
Year Founded: 1989
002270—(SSE)
Rev.: $240,318,468
Assets: $624,799,656
Liabilities: $156,051,792
Net Worth: $468,747,864
Earnings: $50,465,376
Emp.: 800
Fiscal Year-end: 12/31/22
Metal Processing Machinery Mfr
N.A.I.C.S.: 333998
Xiao Yi *(Chm)*

HUAN HSIN HOLDINGS LTD.
77 Robinson Road 13-00 Robinson 77, Singapore, 068896, Singapore
Tel.: (65) 6500 6400 SG
Web Site: http://www.huanhsin.com
Year Founded: 1980
Rev.: $8,296,321
Assets: $53,800,094
Liabilities: $106,498,853
Net Worth: ($52,698,760)
Earnings: ($8,752,863)
Fiscal Year-end: 12/31/19
Holding Company
N.A.I.C.S.: 551112
Kelly Tock Mui Han *(Sec)*

HUANG HSIANG CONSTRUCTION CORPORATION
8F No 38 Bo ai Rd, Zhongzheng District, Taipei, Taiwan
Tel.: (886) 223882898
Web Site: https://www.hhe.com.tw
2545—(TAI)
Rev.: $155,207,522
Assets: $1,760,388,632
Liabilities: $1,384,894,581
Net Worth: $375,494,050
Earnings: $24,911,540
Fiscal Year-end: 12/31/23
Construction Services
N.A.I.C.S.: 236220
Nian-ji Liao *(Chm)*

HUANGSHAN NOVEL CO., LTD.
No 188 Huizhou East Road, Huizhou District, Huangshan, 245900, Anhui, China
Tel.: (86) 5593518183
Web Site: https://www.en-novel.com
Year Founded: 1992
002014—(SSE)
Rev.: $463,901,256
Assets: $501,614,100
Liabilities: $175,212,180
Net Worth: $326,401,920
Earnings: $50,941,332
Emp.: 1,851
Fiscal Year-end: 12/31/22
Packaging Materials Mfr
N.A.I.C.S.: 322220
Sun Yi *(Chm)*

HUANGSHAN TOURISM DEVELOPMENT CO., LTD.
16-18F Block D Tiandu International Restaurant No 5 Tiandu Avenue, Tunxi District, Huangshan, 245000, Anhui, China
Tel.: (86) 5592586678
Web Site: https://www.huangshan.com.cn
Year Founded: 1996
600054—(SHG)
Rev.: $112,306,620
Assets: $731,252,382
Liabilities: $128,969,853
Net Worth: $602,282,529
Earnings: ($18,528,953)
Emp.: 3,000
Fiscal Year-end: 12/31/22
Tourism & Hotel Services
N.A.I.C.S.: 561520
Wu Chi *(Sr VP)*

Subsidiaries:

Baiyun Hotel, Huangshan Tourism Development Co., Ltd. (1)
In Tianhai scenic area near Haixin Pavilion, Huangshan, China
Tel.: (86) 5592590999
Web Site: https://www.baiyunhotelhuangshan.com
Hotel Operator
N.A.I.C.S.: 721110

Beihai Hotel, Huangshan Tourism Development Co., Ltd. (1)
Beihai Scenic Area of Mount Huangshan Scenic Area, Huangshan, China
Tel.: (86) 5595582555
Home Management Services
N.A.I.C.S.: 721110

Changchun Jingyuetan Skiing Ground Ltd. (1)
Changchun Jingyue Economic Development Zone Jingyuetan Scenic Spot, Tanggu, China
Tel.: (86) 43184529399
Ski Resort Operator
N.A.I.C.S.: 713920

Chongde Lou Hotel Co. (1)
No 1-1 College Road Liyang Town, Tunxi District, Huangshan, China
Tel.: (86) 5592340666
Emp.: 70
Hotel Operator
N.A.I.C.S.: 721110

Huangshan China Overseas Travel Service Management Co., Ltd. (1)
Block A Tiandu Building Tiandu Avenue, Tunxi District, Huangshan, China
Tel.: (86) 5592533820
Transportation Services
N.A.I.C.S.: 561910

Huangshan Huashan Mystery Cave Tourism Development Co., Ltd. (1)
Huashan Mystery Cave Scenic Area of Tunguang Town, Tunxi District, Huangshan, China
Tel.: (86) 5592350275
Tourist Reception Services
N.A.I.C.S.: 561591

Huangshan International Hotel Co., Ltd. (1)
No 31 Huashan Road facing Xin anjiang is close to the old street, Huangshan, China
Tel.: (86) 5592565396
Web Site: https://huangshaninternational.hotel00.com
Home Management Services
N.A.I.C.S.: 561110

Huangshan Procurement and Distribution Center Co. (1)
No 61 Xinan North Road, Tunxi District, Huangshan, Anhui, China
Tel.: (86) 5592532733
Logistic Services
N.A.I.C.S.: 541614

Huangshan Taiping Lake Cultural Tourism Co., Ltd. (1)
Tourist wharf of Taiping Lake, Taipinghu Town Huangshan District, Huangshan, China
Tel.: (86) 5598561515
Transportation Services
N.A.I.C.S.: 561910

Huangshan TumaMart Tourism E-commerce Co., Ltd. (1)
No 32 Yingbin Avenue, Tunxi District, Huangshan, China
Tel.: (86) 5592586505
Transportation Services
N.A.I.C.S.: 561910

Huangshan Xihai Hotel Co., Ltd. (1)
West Sea Scenic Spot under Danxia peak, Huangshan, China
Tel.: (86) 5595588888
Web Site: https://www.xihaihotelhuangshan.com
Hotel Operator
N.A.I.C.S.: 721110

Huangshan Yucheng Crowne Plaza Hotels & Resorts Ltd. (1)
No 1 Huizhou Avenue, Tunxi District, Huangshan, Anhui, China
Tel.: (86) 5592591888
Hotel Operator
N.A.I.C.S.: 721110

Huishangguli Hotel of Huangshan Tourism Development Co., Ltd. (1)
No 14 Xianrendong North Road, Tunxi District, Huangshan, Anhui, China
Tel.: (86) 5592358888
Transportation Services
N.A.I.C.S.: 561910

Scenic Area Development and Management Company (1)
Xiaoyao Pavilion of Mount Huangshan Scenic Area, Huangshan, Anhui, China
Tel.: (86) 5595562939
Environmental Health Services
N.A.I.C.S.: 923120

Shilin Hotel of Huangshan Tourism Development Co., Ltd. (1)
Beihai Scenic Area of Mount Huangshan Scenic Area, Huangshan, Anhui, China
Tel.: (86) 5595584040
Home Management Services
N.A.I.C.S.: 721110

Tangquan Hotel of Huangshan Tourism Development Co., Ltd. (1)
In the Mount Huangshan Scenic Area, Management Committee of Tangkou Town Huangshan District, Huangshan, China
Tel.: (86) 5595583333
Home Management Services
N.A.I.C.S.: 721110

Xuanyuan International Hotel of Huangshan Tourism Development Co., Ltd. (1)
No 1 Xuanyuan Avenue, Huangshan District, Huangshan, Anhui, China
Tel.: (86) 5598508888
Hotel Operator
N.A.I.C.S.: 721110

Yupinglou Hotel of Huangshan Tourism Development Co., Ltd. (1)
Yuping Scenic Area of Mount Huangshan Scenic Area, Huangshan, Anhui, China
Tel.: (86) 5595582288
Home Management Services
N.A.I.C.S.: 721110

HUANGSHI DONGBEI ELECTRICAL APPLIANCE CO., LTD.
No 6 Jinshan Avenue Economic & Technologcl Dvlpmnt Zn, Huangshi, 435000, Hubei, China
Tel.: (86) 714 541 5858
Web Site: http://www.donper.com
900956—(SHG)
Rev.: $660,811,988
Assets: $723,610,092
Liabilities: $486,105,606
Net Worth: $237,504,487
Earnings: $24,347,506
Fiscal Year-end: 12/31/19
Compressor Mfr & Distr
N.A.I.C.S.: 333912

HUANLEJIA FOOD GROUP CO., LTD.
28th 29th 31st and 32nd Floors Huanlejia Building, No 71 Renmin Avenue Middle Development Zone, Zhanjiang, 524026, Guangdong, China
Tel.: (86) 7592268808
Web Site: http://www.gdhlj.com
Year Founded: 2001
300997—(SSE)
Rev.: $224,071,380
Assets: $279,484,452
Liabilities: $91,397,592
Net Worth: $188,086,860
Earnings: $28,557,360
Fiscal Year-end: 12/31/22
Drink Product Mfr & Distr
N.A.I.C.S.: 312111
Xing Li *(Chm & Gen Mgr)*

HUANXI MEDIA GROUP LIMITED
11/F Far East Finance Centre 16 Harcourt Road Admiralty, Hong Kong, China (Hong Kong)
Tel.: (852) 23163900 BM
Web Site: https://www.huanximedia.com
1003—(HKG)
Rev.: $1,737,825
Assets: $281,817,713
Liabilities: $112,442,123
Net Worth: $169,375,590
Earnings: ($28,281,030)
Emp.: 87
Fiscal Year-end: 12/31/22
Holding Company
N.A.I.C.S.: 551112
Ping Dong *(Co/Co-Founder, Chm, Chm & Exec Dir)*

Subsidiaries:

Century 21 Property Agency Limited (1)
140 1/F Paradise Mall 100 Shing Tai Road Heng Fa Chuen, Chai Wan, China (Hong Kong)
Tel.: (852) 25751328
Real Estate Consulting Service
N.A.I.C.S.: 531210

Guangdong Sinofocus Media Limited (1)
Annex Building 14C A Guangdong International Building, 339 Huanshidong Road, Guangzhou, 510098, Guangdong, China
Tel.: (86) 2083312286
Web Site: http://www.sinofocus.com.cn
Advertising Services

HUANXI MEDIA GROUP LIMITED

Huanxi Media Group Limited—(Continued)
N.A.I.C.S.: 541810

HUAPONT LIFE SCIENCES CO., LTD.
No 69 Renhe Xingguang Avenue, Yubei District, Chongqing, 401121, China
Tel.: (86) 2367886900
Web Site: http://www.huapont.com.cn
Year Founded: 2001
002004—(SSE)
Rev.: $1,857,824,748
Assets: $4,215,425,760
Liabilities: $1,891,694,844
Net Worth: $2,323,730,916
Earnings: $60,832,512
Fiscal Year-end: 12/31/22
Pharmaceuticals Product Mfr
N.A.I.C.S.: 325412
Songshan Zhang (Chm & Gen Mgr)

HUAREN PHARMACEUTICAL CO., LTD.
No 197 ZhuzhouRoad, Laoshan District, Qingdao, 266101, Shandong, China
Tel.: (86) 53258070788
Web Site: https://www.huarenmedical.com
Year Founded: 1998
300110—(CHIN)
Rev.: $227,376,396
Assets: $724,817,808
Liabilities: $359,810,100
Net Worth: $365,007,708
Earnings: $25,387,128
Emp.: 3,350
Fiscal Year-end: 12/31/22
Pharmaceuticals Mfr
N.A.I.C.S.: 325412
Xiaodong Yang (Chm & Pres)

HUARONG CHEMICAL CO., LTD.
No 166 Linyang Road, Jiuzuo Town, Pengzhou, 611933, Sichuan, China
Tel.: (86) 2883800329
Web Site: https://www.huarongchem.cn
Year Founded: 2000
301256—(CHIN)
Rev.: $146,672,076
Assets: $345,630,511
Liabilities: $103,316,155
Net Worth: $242,314,355
Earnings: $19,200,390
Fiscal Year-end: 12/31/23
Chemical Product Mfr & Distr
N.A.I.C.S.: 327120
Jun Shao (Chm)

HUARUI ELECTRICAL APPLIANCE CO.,LTD
Jiangshan science and Technology Park, Yinzhou District, Ningbo, 315191, Zhejiang, China
Tel.: (86) 57488098059
Web Site: https://www.china-commutator.com
Year Founded: 1996
300626—(CHIN)
Rev.: $93,779,958
Assets: $134,876,030
Liabilities: $61,385,008
Net Worth: $73,491,023
Earnings: ($12,798,547)
Emp.: 1,500
Fiscal Year-end: 12/31/23
Electrical Appliance Mfr & Distr
N.A.I.C.S.: 335210
Zhang Bo (Pres)

HUARUI INTERNATIONAL NEW MATERIAL LIMITED
No 110 Huancun West Road Huaxi Industrial Park, Huashi Town, Jiangyin, 214421, Jiangsu, China
Tel.: (86) 51080693520   VG
Year Founded: 2019
Emp.: 98
Holding Company
N.A.I.C.S.: 551112
Huhujie Sun (Chm & CEO)

HUASHENG INTERNATIONAL HOLDING LIMITED
Unit 2301-03 23/F Far East Consortium Building 121 Des Voeux Road, Central, China (Hong Kong)
Tel.: (852) 2 169 3699   Ky
Web Site: http://www.newtreeholdings.com
Year Founded: 2010
1323—(HKG)
Rev.: $111,504,242
Assets: $261,217,132
Liabilities: $137,979,966
Net Worth: $123,237,166
Earnings: $4,036,171
Emp.: 221
Fiscal Year-end: 03/31/22
Disposable Product Mfr
N.A.I.C.S.: 326111
Wai Sing Wong (Chm & CEO)

Subsidiaries:

Huizhou Junyang Plastic Co., Ltd.   (1)
Xikeng Industrial Park Huihuan, Huicheng, Huizhou, 516006, China
Tel.: (86) 75 2261 4883
Disposable Product Mfr
N.A.I.C.S.: 326111

Two-Two-Free Limited   (1)
Flat L 12th Floor Macau Finance Centre Rua de Pequim, Macau, China (Macau)
Tel.: (853) 2870 1848
Disposable Products Distr
N.A.I.C.S.: 424130

HUASU HOLDINGS CO., LTD.
No 223 Fujiang Road, Shunqing District, Nanchong, 610041, Sichuan, China
Tel.: (86) 2885365657
000509—(SSE)
Rev.: $124,078,500
Assets: $85,944,456
Liabilities: $54,996,084
Net Worth: $30,948,372
Earnings: ($387,504)
Fiscal Year-end: 12/31/22
Holding Company
N.A.I.C.S.: 551112

HUAT LAI RESOURCES BERHAD
PT 1678 Mukim of Serkam, Merlimau, 77300, Melaka, Malaysia
Tel.: (60) 6 2686 315   MY
Web Site: http://www.huatlai.com
Year Founded: 1994
Holding Company; Egg Production, Poultry Hatchery, Egg Tray & Fertilizer Mfr
N.A.I.C.S.: 551112

Subsidiaries:

HLRB Broiler Farm Sdn. Bhd.   (1)
PT 1678 Mukim of Serkam, Merlimau, 77300, Melaka, Malaysia   (100%)
Tel.: (60) 62686315
Poultry Hatchery & Farming
N.A.I.C.S.: 112340
Yeow-Her Lim (Mng Dir)

HLRB Processing Sdn. Bhd.   (1)
PT 1678 Mukim of Serkam, Merlimau, Melaka, 77300, Malaysia   (100%)
Tel.: (60) 62686315
Egg Production
N.A.I.C.S.: 112310

Yeow Her Lim (Mng Dir)
Huat Lai Paper Products Sdn. Bhd.   (1)
PT 1678 Mukim of Serkam, Merlimau, 77300, Melaka, Malaysia   (100%)
Tel.: (60) 62686315
Egg Tray Mfr
N.A.I.C.S.: 322299

HUATAI SECURITIES CO., LTD.
No 228 Jiangdong Middle Road, Nanjing, 210019, Jiangsu, China
Tel.: (86) 2583389999   CN
Web Site: https://www.htsc.com.cn
Year Founded: 1991
HTSC—(LSE)
Rev.: $5,064,464,070
Assets: $125,374,998,422
Liabilities: $100,145,513,486
Net Worth: $25,229,484,936
Earnings: $1,765,428,736
Emp.: 16,658
Fiscal Year-end: 12/31/23
Financial Investment Services
N.A.I.C.S.: 523999
Xiaoning Jiao (CFO)

Subsidiaries:

China Southern Asset Management Co., Ltd.   (1)
32-42/F Fund Building 5999 Yitian Rd, Futian CBD, Shenzhen, 518048, China
Tel.: (86) 4008898899
Web Site: http://www.southernfund.com
Asset Management Services
N.A.I.C.S.: 523940

Huatai Financial Holdings (Hong Kong) Limited   (1)
Room 4201 5808-12 and 62nd Floor Central Centre 99 Queen'S Road, Central, China (Hong Kong)
Tel.: (852) 3658 6000
Web Site: http://www.htsc.com.hk
Brokerage Services
N.A.I.C.S.: 523160

Huatai Financial USA Inc   (1)
200 W Monroe St, Chicago, IL 60606-5075
Tel.: (312) 750-0640
Futures Brokerage Services
N.A.I.C.S.: 523160

Subsidiary (Domestic):

AssetMark, Inc.   (2)
1655 Grant St 10th Fl, Concord, CA 94520
Web Site: http://www.assetmark.com
Rev.: $20,000,000,000
Investment Management Service
N.A.I.C.S.: 523940
Carrie E. Hansen (COO, Pres-Mutual Funds & Exec VP)

Subsidiary (Domestic):

OBS Financial Services, Inc.   (3)
6330 Levis Commons Blvd, Perrysburg, OH 43551
Tel.: (419) 482-4500
Web Site: http://www.obsfs.com
Investment Advice
N.A.I.C.S.: 523940
John Henry (Pres & CEO)

Huatai Purple Gold Investment Co., Ltd.   (1)
No 180 Hanzhong Road, Nanjing, Jiangsu, China
Tel.: (86) 2583389999
Financial Information Services
N.A.I.C.S.: 522320

Huatai Securities (Shanghai) Asset Management Co., Ltd.   (1)
Floor 21 Poly Plaza Block E 18 Dongfang Road Pudong District, Shanghai, 200120, China
Tel.: (86) 2138476185
Asset Management Services
N.A.I.C.S.: 531390

Huatai Securities (Shanghai) Assets Management Co., Ltd.   (1)
Room 1222 6 Jilong Road Pilot Free Trade Zone, Shanghai, China

INTERNATIONAL PUBLIC

Tel.: (86) 2128972188
Security Asset Management Services
N.A.I.C.S.: 531390

Huatai United Securities Co., Ltd.   (1)
6F Tower A Fortune Capital International Center 22 Fengsheng Hutong, Xicheng District, Beijing, China
Tel.: (86) 1056839300
Web Site: https://www.lhzq.com
Investment Banking Services
N.A.I.C.S.: 523150

HUATIAN HOTEL GROUP CO., LTD.
No 300 Jiefang East Road, Furong District, Changsha, 410001, China
Tel.: (86) 73184442888
Web Site: https://www.huatian-hotel.com
Year Founded: 1995
000428—(SSE)
Rev.: $66,492,036
Assets: $743,545,764
Liabilities: $549,230,760
Net Worth: $194,315,004
Earnings: ($43,622,280)
Fiscal Year-end: 12/31/22
Hotel Operator
N.A.I.C.S.: 721110
Yang Hongwei (Chm)

HUATIONG GLOBAL LIMITED
9 Benoi Crescent, Singapore, 629972, Singapore
Tel.: (65) 63665005
Web Site: https://www.huationg.com.sg
41B—(CAT)
Rev.: $132,235,855
Assets: $213,642,354
Liabilities: $141,111,111
Net Worth: $72,531,243
Earnings: $10,779,368
Emp.: 888
Fiscal Year-end: 12/31/23
Civil Engineering & Construction Equipment Rental Services; Concrete Aggregate Mfr & Distr
N.A.I.C.S.: 237990
Hai Liong Ng (Chm)

HUATU CENDES CO., LTD.
37th Floor Times 1 No 6 Zhiquan Section East Street, Jinjiang District, Chengdu, 610065, China
Tel.: (86) 2886671100
Web Site: https://www.cendes-arch.com
Year Founded: 1999
300492—(CHIN)
Rev.: $34,806,486
Assets: $143,797,441
Liabilities: $114,273,239
Net Worth: $29,524,202
Earnings: ($12,953,791)
Fiscal Year-end: 12/31/23
Architectural Design & Consulting Services
N.A.I.C.S.: 541310

HUAWEI INVESTMENT & HOLDING CO., LTD.
Building 1 Zone B Huawei Base, Bantian Longgang District, Shenzhen, 518129, China
Tel.: (86) 755 28780808
Year Founded: 1987
Rev.: $122,899,002,300
Assets: $122,874,389,100
Liabilities: $80,583,044,400
Net Worth: $42,291,344,700
Earnings: $8,966,073,600
Emp.: 194,000
Fiscal Year-end: 12/31/19
Holding Company
N.A.I.C.S.: 551112

AND PRIVATE COMPANIES

Subsidiaries:

Huawei Technologies Co., Ltd. (1)
Huawei Base Bantian, Longgang District,
Shenzhen, 518129, Guangdong,
China **(100%)**
Tel.: (86) 75528780808
Web Site: http://www.huawei.com
Telecommunications & Related Products
Equipment Mfr
N.A.I.C.S.: 334290
David Shi (Pres-Enterprise Bus Grp-Middle East)

Subsidiary (Non-US):

HexaTier Ltd. (2)
21 Bar Cochva, Bnei Brak, Israel
Tel.: (972) 3 688 8090
Database Security Software
N.A.I.C.S.: 513210
Yaron Ofer (VP-Professional Svcs)

Huawei DEL PER S.A.C. (2)
Av Republica de Panama 3535 Oficina 602,
San Isidro, Lima, Peru
Tel.: (51) 17169888
Web Site: http://www.huawei.com
Telecommunication Equipment Distr
N.A.I.C.S.: 423690
Hector Candela (Mgr-Network Technical Svc Dept)

Huawei Tech Investment Tashkent MChJ (2)
Afrosiab Str 28/14, 100027, Tashkent, Uzbekistan
Tel.: (998) 711500762
Telecommunication Equipment Distr
N.A.I.C.S.: 423690

Huawei Tech. Investment Co., Ltd (2)
3rd floor Zep-Re Place Longonot road, PO Box 66430-00800, Upper Hill, Nairobi, Kenya
Tel.: (254) 202871000
Telecommunication Equipment Distr
N.A.I.C.S.: 423690

Huawei Technologies (Bolivia) S.R.L. (2)
Calacoto 15 St Torre Ketal Building 4 Floor 401, La Paz, Bolivia
Tel.: (591) 22128772
Web Site: http://www.huawei.com
Telecommunication Equipment Distr
N.A.I.C.S.: 423690

Huawei Technologies (UK) Co Ltd (2)
2nd Floor 1 Sheldon Square, Paddington, London, W2 6TT, United Kingdom
Tel.: (44) 207 2667700
Web Site: http://www.huawei.com
Telecommunication Equipment Distr
N.A.I.C.S.: 423690
Philip Candice (Dir-Pub Policy)

Huawei Technologies Co. LTD (2)
3 Floor Mespil Court Mespil Road, Dublin, 4, Ireland
Tel.: (353) 1 2343100
Telecommunication Equipment Distr
N.A.I.C.S.: 423690
Tony Yangxu (CEO)

Huawei Technologies Duesseldorf GmbH (2)
Hansaallee 231, 40549, Dusseldorf, Germany
Tel.: (49) 211 52295 1001
Web Site: http://www.huawei.com
Telecommunication Equipment Distr
N.A.I.C.S.: 423690

Huawei Technologies India Pvt. Ltd. (2)
Survey No 37 Next to EPIP Area, Kundalahalli Whitefield, Bengaluru, 560 037, India
Tel.: (91) 80 49160700
Web Site: http://www.huawei.com
Telecommunication Servicesb
N.A.I.C.S.: 517112
Prameed Paul (Asst Mgr-HR)

Huawei Technologies Phils., INC. (2)
Unit 5302 53/F PB Com Tower Ayala ave cor Rufino, St Salcedo Village, Makati, Philippines
Tel.: (63) 2 8158808
Web Site: http://www.huawei.com
Telecommunication Equipment Distr
N.A.I.C.S.: 423690
Stanley Payte (Dir-Sls)

Huawei Technologies Sweden AB (2)
Plan 3 & 4 Skalholtsgatan 9-11, 164 40, Kista, Sweden
Tel.: (46) 8 12060808
Web Site: http://www.huawei.com
Telecommunication Equipment Distr
N.A.I.C.S.: 423690

Huawei Technologies Tanzania Co., Ltd (2)
17th & 18th Floor Golden Jubilee Towers Ohio Street, PO Box 38264, Dar es Salaam, Tanzania
Tel.: (255) 22 2861971
Telecommunication Equipment Distr
N.A.I.C.S.: 423690
Sylvester Manyara (Sr Mgr-Device Retail)

Huawei Technologies de Mexico, S.A. de C.V. (2)
Avenida Santa Fe No 440 Century Plaza Tower 15th floor Colonia, Cuajimalpa de Morelos Delegation Federal District, 05348, Mexico, Mexico
Tel.: (52) 5585828600
Web Site: http://www.huawei.com
Telecommunication Equipment Distr
N.A.I.C.S.: 423690

Huawei Technologies- (U) Co., Ltd (2)
3rd Floor Rwenzori Towers Plot 6 Nakasero Road, PO Box 25686, Kampala, Uganda
Tel.: (256) 312265690
Telecommunication Equipment Distr
N.A.I.C.S.: 423690

Huawei Telecommunications (India) Company Private Limited (2)
Infinity Think Tank 12th Floor Tower-2 Plot No -A3 Block-GP Sector-V, Saltlake, Kolkata, 700091, India
Tel.: (91) 3344012200
Web Site: http://www.huawei.com
Telecommunication Servicesb
N.A.I.C.S.: 517112

HUAXI HOLDINGS COMPANY LIMITED
Unit 1906-07 19/F Cosco Tower 183 Queen s Road, Central, China (Hong Kong)
Tel.: (852) 21169889 Ky
Web Site:
   http://www.huaxihds.com.hk
Year Founded: 2013
1689—(HKG)
Rev.: $24,803,340
Assets: $73,601,415
Liabilities: $27,540,765
Net Worth: $46,060,650
Earnings: ($6,804,675)
Emp.: 295
Fiscal Year-end: 12/31/22
Holding Company
N.A.I.C.S.: 551112
Andy Yi Sheng Zheng (Founder, Chm, CEO & Gen Mgr)

HUAXI SECURITIES CO., LTD.
Huaxi Securities Building No 198 Tianfu 2nd Street High-tech Zone, Chengdu, 610095, Sichuan, China
Tel.: (86) 95584
Web Site: https://www.hx168.com.cn
Year Founded: 1988
002926—(SSE)
Rev.: $473,931,432
Assets: $13,723,701,264
Liabilities: $10,573,066,296
Net Worth: $3,150,634,968
Earnings: $59,299,344
Fiscal Year-end: 12/31/22
Securities Brokerage Services
N.A.I.C.S.: 523150
Zhou Yi (Chm)

HUAXIA EYE HOSPITAL GROUP CO., LTD.
No 1701 No 999 Wutong West Road, Huli District, Xiamen, 361006, Fujian, China
Tel.: (86) 5922108975
Web Site:
   https://www.huaxiaeye.com
Year Founded: 2004
301267—(CHIN)
Rev.: $453,948,300
Assets: $924,460,992
Liabilities: $204,505,236
Net Worth: $719,955,756
Earnings: $71,855,316
Fiscal Year-end: 12/31/22
Health Care Srvices
N.A.I.C.S.: 621610
Qingcan Su (Chm)

HUAXIA LIFE INSURANCE CO., LTD.
Building 1 Xihai Intl Center 99 Beisanhuan West Road, Beijing, 100086, China
Tel.: (86) 1069630526
Web Site: http://www.hxlife.com
Sales Range: $25-49.9 Billion
Emp.: 500,000
Insurance Services
N.A.I.C.S.: 524210
Ziliang Zhao (CEO)

HUAXIN CEMENT CO., LTD.
Huaxin Building No 426 Gaoxin Avenue, East Lake New Technology Development Zone, Wuhan, 430073, Hubei, China
Tel.: (86) 4001100800
Web Site:
   https://www.huaxincem.com
600801—(SHG)
Rev.: $4,278,041,689
Assets: $9,019,531,353
Liabilities: $4,689,850,810
Net Worth: $4,329,680,542
Earnings: $378,921,137
Emp.: 19,278
Fiscal Year-end: 12/31/22
Cement & Concrete Mfr & Distr
N.A.I.C.S.: 327310
Yunxia Liu (VP)

Subsidiaries:

Chilanga Cement Plc (1)
T2 Chilanga, Lusaka, Zambia
Tel.: (260) 211367600
Web Site: https://chilangacement.co.zm
Building Materials Distr
N.A.I.C.S.: 423390

NPC - CIMPOR (PTY) LIMITED (1)
199 Coedmore Road, PO Box 15245, Bellair, Durban, 4006, South Africa
Tel.: (27) 314504411
Web Site: http://www.npc-eagle.co.za
Sales Range: $150-199.9 Million
Emp.: 500
Cement Concrete Mfr & Distr
N.A.I.C.S.: 423320
Pieter Strauss (Chm)

Oman Cement Company SAOG (1)
PO Box 560, 112, Ruwi, 112,
Oman **(60%)**
Tel.: (968) 24437070
Web Site: https://www.occ.om
Rev.: $177,734,577
Assets: $447,316,756
Liabilities: $51,337,757
Net Worth: $395,978,999
Earnings: $15,591,628
Emp.: 626
Fiscal Year-end: 12/31/2023
Cement Mfr
N.A.I.C.S.: 327310
Abdulla Abbas Ahmed (Chm)

HUAXUN FANGZHOU CO., LTD.

HUAYI BROTHERS MEDIA CORP.
8A Zone A Zhongke Naneng Building No 6 Yuexing Six Road Science Park, Nanshan District, Shenzhen, 518061, Guangdong, China
Tel.: (86) 7552 966 3118
Web Site:
   http://www.huaxunchina.com.cn
Year Founded: 1957
000687—(SSE)
Rev.: $7,154,907
Assets: $153,006,231
Liabilities: $377,972,134
Net Worth: ($224,965,904)
Earnings: ($165,509,699)
Fiscal Year-end: 12/31/20
Chemical Fiber Mfr
N.A.I.C.S.: 327999
Guangsheng Wu (Chm)

HUAYI BROTHERS MEDIA CORP.
9F Tower B Fenglian Plaza No 18 Chaowai Avenue, Chaoyang District, Beijing, 100027, China
Tel.: (86) 1065881012
Web Site:
   http://www.huayimedia.com
Year Founded: 2004
300027—(SSE)
Rev.: $56,487,132
Assets: $736,236,540
Liabilities: $532,837,656
Net Worth: $203,398,884
Earnings: ($137,846,124)
Emp.: 2,047
Fiscal Year-end: 12/31/22
Film & Television Show Production, Talent Agency Operations, Movie Theaters & Movie Theme Parks
N.A.I.C.S.: 512110
Zhonglei Wang (Chm & Gen Mgr)

Subsidiaries:

GDC Technology Limited (1)
Unit 1-7 20th Floor Kodak House II 39 Healthy Street East, North Point, China (Hong Kong)
Tel.: (852) 25079555
Web Site: http://www.gdc-tech.com
Sales Range: $100-124.9 Million
Emp.: 250
Digital Cinema Server Mfr
N.A.I.C.S.: 334220
Man-Nang Chong (Founder, Chm & CEO)

Subsidiary (Non-US):

GDC Digital Cinema Network (Brasil) Ltd (2)
Av Antonio Carlos Comitre 540 SL31, Sorocaba, Sao Paulo, 18047-620, Brazil
Tel.: (55) 1533269301
Digital Equipment Distr
N.A.I.C.S.: 423690

GDC Digital Cinema Network (Mexico) S. de R.L. de C.V. (2)
Av Del Penon 411 Esq Ote 168 Col Moctezuma 2 Seccion, Venustiano Carranza Federal, 01210, Mexico, Mexico
Tel.: (52) 5585266220
Digital Equipment Distr
N.A.I.C.S.: 423690

GDC Digital Cinema Network (Peru), SAC (2)
Calle Rey Bahamonde N 111 Santiago de Surco Lima 33, Lima, Peru
Tel.: (51) 16776708
Digital Equipment Distr
N.A.I.C.S.: 423690

GDC Digital Cinema Network GG (2)
3F Kyobashi-Chuo Bldg 1-14-7 Kyobashi, Chuo-ku, Tokyo, 104-0031, Japan
Tel.: (81) 355243607
Digital Equipment Distr
N.A.I.C.S.: 423690

GDC Digital Cinema Technology Europe, SL (2)
C/ Vallirana 63 Bajos Izq, 08006, Barce-

HUAYI BROTHERS MEDIA CORP.

Huayi Brothers Media Corp.—(Continued)
Iona, Spain
Tel.: (34) 935044466
Digital Equipment Distr
N.A.I.C.S.: 423690

GDC Technology (Beijing) Limited (2)
Rm 609-618 Office Building 20 Xinde Street, Xicheng, Beijing, 100088, China
Tel.: (86) 1062057040
Digital Equipment Distr
N.A.I.C.S.: 423690

GDC Technology (Shenzhen) Limited (2)
Room A701 7/F Languang Technology Building No 7 Xinxi Road, High-Tech Park North Nanshan District, Shenzhen, China
Tel.: (86) 77586086000
Digital Equipment Distr
N.A.I.C.S.: 423690

Subsidiary (US):

GDC Technology (USA) LLC (2)
1016 W Magnolia Blvd, Burbank, CA 91506
Tel.: (818) 972-4370
Digital Equipment Distr
N.A.I.C.S.: 423690
Anthony Foster (Mgr-Product Deployment)

Subsidiary (Non-US):

GDC Technology India Pvt. Ltd. (2)
B-207/208 Everest Chambers Andheri Kurla Road, Marol Andheri, Mumbai, 400 059, India
Tel.: (91) 2240440500
Digital Equipment Distr
N.A.I.C.S.: 423690

GDC Technology Pte Limited (2)
601 Macpherson Road 08-07 Grantral Complex, Singapore, 368242, Singapore
Tel.: (65) 62221082
Digital Equipment Distr
N.A.I.C.S.: 423690
Kevin Tan (Mgr-R&D)

PT GDC Technology Indonesia (2)
Total Building Lantai 4 Suite 0401 Jl Letjen S Parman Kav, 106A Kel Tomang Kec Grogol Petamburan, Jakarta, 11440, Indonesia
Tel.: (62) 2129204691
Digital Equipment Distr
N.A.I.C.S.: 423690

HUAYI ELECTRIC COMPANY LIMITED

No 228 Center Avenue YueQing Economic Development Zone, Yueqing, 325600, Zhejiang, China
Tel.: (86) 57727898877
Web Site: http://www.heag.com
600290—(SHG)
Rev.: $41,628,558
Assets: $503,282,656
Liabilities: $516,685,886
Net Worth: ($13,403,230)
Earnings: ($68,139,813)
Emp.: 1,700
Fiscal Year-end: 12/31/22
Wind Power Generation Equipment Mfr
N.A.I.C.S.: 333611
Menglie Chen (Chm)

HUAYI TENCENT ENTERTAINMENT COMPANY LIMITED

Suite 908 9/F Tower Two Lippo Centre, 89 Queensway, Hong Kong, China (Hong Kong)
Tel.: (852) 36902050
Web Site: http://www.huayitencent.com
0419—(HKG)
Rev.: $215,737,778
Assets: $75,121,215
Liabilities: $30,505,778
Net Worth: $44,615,438
Earnings: ($40,366,245)
Emp.: 306

Fiscal Year-end: 12/31/22
Health Industry, Media & Real Estate Investment Services
N.A.I.C.S.: 523999
Raymond Wai Man Hau (CFO & Sec)

HUAYOU COBALT CO., LTD.

No 79 Wuzhendong Road, Tongxiang, 314500, Zhejiang, China
Tel.: (86) 57388585566
Web Site: https://www.huayou.com
Year Founded: 2002
603799—(SHG)
Rev.: $8,849,943,484
Assets: $15,527,175,585
Liabilities: $10,938,555,674
Net Worth: $4,588,619,911
Earnings: $548,947,250
Fiscal Year-end: 12/31/22
Nonferrous Metal Mining & Smelting Services
N.A.I.C.S.: 212290
Huayou Cobalt (Chm)

Subsidiaries:

Huajin (Hong Kong) Limited (1)
Flat D 12/F Ford Glory Plaza 37-39 Wing-Hong Street, Kowloon, China (Hong Kong)
Tel.: (852) 23723713
Web Site: https://www.huajindp.com
Textile Fabric Mfr & Distr
N.A.I.C.S.: 313310

Quzhou Huayou Cobalt New Material Co., Ltd. (1)
No 18 Nianxin Road High-Tech Zone Phase Ii, Quzhou, 324000, Zhejiang, China
Tel.: (86) 5708059028
Nonferrous Metal Products Mfr
N.A.I.C.S.: 331410

Zhejiang Huayou Cobalt Co., Ltd. (1)
No 18 Wuzhen East Road, Economic Development Zone, Tongxiang, 314500, Zhejiang, China
Tel.: (86) 57388587878
Web Site: http://www.en.huayou.com
Rev.: $9,180,334,450
Assets: $17,379,302,911
Liabilities: $11,185,606,080
Net Worth: $6,193,696,830
Earnings: $623,772,467
Emp.: 29,548
Fiscal Year-end: 12/31/2023
Lithium Battery Mfr
N.A.I.C.S.: 335910
Bryce Lee (Dir-CSR)

HUAYU EXPRESSWAY GROUP LIMITED

Unit 1205 12/F Tower 1 Lippo Centre No 89 Queensway, Hong Kong, China (Hong Kong)
Tel.: (852) 25591210
Web Site: http://www.huayu.com.hk
1823—(HKG)
Rev.: $57,547,994
Assets: $274,615,661
Liabilities: $161,870,249
Net Worth: $112,745,412
Earnings: $12,202,726
Emp.: 451
Fiscal Year-end: 12/31/22
Highway Construction Services
N.A.I.C.S.: 237310
Yeung Nam Chan (Founder & Chm)

HUAZHANG TECHNOLOGY HOLDING LIMITED

1306 Zhenhua Road Wutong Street, Tongxiang, Zhejiang, China
Tel.: (86) 57388588181
Web Site: http://www.hzeg.com
1673—(HKG)
Rev.: $49,619,939
Assets: $159,615,124
Liabilities: $98,934,271
Net Worth: $60,680,853
Earnings: ($56,188,058)

Emp.: 269
Fiscal Year-end: 06/30/22
Industrial Automation System Mfr
N.A.I.C.S.: 335314
Gen Rong Zhu (Chm)

Subsidiaries:

Hangzhou MCN Paper Tech Co., Ltd. (1)
Room 1606 building 26 shuixingge garden, Hangzhou, 310004, Zhejiang, China
Tel.: (86) 5718 509 6526
Web Site: https://www.papermech.com
Head Box Product Mfr
N.A.I.C.S.: 322299

HUAZHONG IN-VEHICLE HOLDINGS COMPANY LIMITED

Unit 19 36th Floor China Merchants Tower Shun Tak Centre, Nos 168-200 Connaught Road, Central, China (Hong Kong)
Tel.: (852) 31506788   Ky
Web Site: http://www.cn-huazhong.com
Year Founded: 1993
6830—(HKG)
Rev.: $270,258,347
Assets: $455,975,536
Liabilities: $255,209,573
Net Worth: $200,765,963
Earnings: $16,518,200
Emp.: 3,144
Fiscal Year-end: 12/31/22
Holding Company
N.A.I.C.S.: 551112
Minfeng Zhou (Chm & CEO)

Subsidiaries:

HZ FBZ Formenbau Zuttlingen GmbH (1)
Wilhelm-Maybach-Strasse 2 Nordstrasse 46 Zuttlingen, 74219, Mockmuhl, Germany
Tel.: (49) 629892680
Web Site: http://www.fbz-formen.com
Plastic Injection Molding Parts Mfr & Distr
N.A.I.C.S.: 326199
Stefan Wendt (Mgr-Design & Dev)

HUB CO., LTD.

7F Akihabara HF Bldg 14-10 3chome Sotokanda, Chiyoda-Ku, Tokyo, 101-0021, Japan
Tel.: (81) 335268682
Web Site: https://www.pub-hub.co.jp
Year Founded: 1998
30300—(TKS)
Sales Range: $100-124.9 Million
Emp.: 317
Pub Chain Operator
N.A.I.C.S.: 713910
Tsuyoshi Ohta (Pres & CEO)

HUB CYBER SECURITY LTD.

Tel.: (972) 37913200
Web Site: https://www.hubsecurity.com
HUBC—(NASDAQ)
Rev.: $42,657,000
Assets: $32,590,000
Liabilities: $83,323,000
Net Worth: ($50,733,000)
Earnings: ($84,606,000)
Emp.: 321
Fiscal Year-end: 12/31/23
Cyber Security Services
N.A.I.C.S.: 561621
Andrey Iaremenko (Founder)

Subsidiaries:

ALD Software Ltd. (1)
Ha-Kharoshet Street 30 Or-Yehuda, Tel Aviv, Israel
Tel.: (972) 37913200
Web Site: https://aldservice.com
Software Publr
N.A.I.C.S.: 513210

INTERNATIONAL PUBLIC

Subsidiary (Non-US):

Beijing Umeone Digital Tec.co., Ltd. (2)
Room 501 Block B of Huirong Mansion 106 LianHuaChi East Rd, Xicheng District, Beijing, 100055, China
Tel.: (86) 1082055848
Logistics Consulting Services
N.A.I.C.S.: 541614

ISD Italia S.R.L. (2)
Via Val Seriana 4, 00141, Rome, Italy
Tel.: (39) 0669221980
Web Site: https://www.isditalia.it
Software Operating Services
N.A.I.C.S.: 541714

SHAMA Technologies (S) Pte Ltd. (2)
1100 Lower Delta Road 03-04B Epl Building, Singapore, 169206, Singapore
Tel.: (65) 67764006
Web Site: https://shamatec.com
Engineering Services
N.A.I.C.S.: 541330

Simweb Inc. (2)
11F No 51 Sec 2 Gongyi Rd, Nantun Dist, Taichung, 40861, Taiwan
Tel.: (886) 423279905
Web Site: https://www.simweb.com.tw
Software Operating Services
N.A.I.C.S.: 541714

Trident Infosol Pvt. Ltd. (2)
Block A Kushal Garden Arcade 1A Peenya Industrial Area Phase II, Bengaluru, 560058, India
Tel.: (91) 8042878787
Web Site: https://tridentinfosol.com
Technology Solution Services
N.A.I.C.S.: 541512

HUB GIRISIM SERMAYESI YATIRIM ORTAKLIGI A.S.

Esentepe Mahallesi Buyukdere Cad No 201, Sisli, 34394, Istanbul, Turkiye
Tel.: (90) 2129630021
Web Site: https://www.hubgsyo.com
Year Founded: 2006
HUBVC—(IST)
Sales Range: Less than $1 Million
Portfolio Management Services
N.A.I.C.S.: 523940
Ersoy Kiraz (Exec Dir)

HUB24 LIMITED

Level 2 7 Macquarie Place, Sydney, 2000, NSW, Australia
Tel.: (61) 1300854994
Web Site: http://www.hub24.com.au
HUB—(ASX)
Rev.: $220,582,932
Assets: $415,821,312
Liabilities: $68,798,077
Net Worth: $347,023,236
Earnings: $31,489,717
Emp.: 893
Fiscal Year-end: 06/30/24
Investment Services
N.A.I.C.S.: 523940
Wendy McIntyre (Gen Counsel & Head-Risk & Compliance)

Subsidiaries:

Agility Applications Pty Ltd (1)
Level 3 518 Brunswick St, Fortitude Valley, Brisbane, 4006, QLD, Australia
Tel.: (61) 731771900
Web Site: http://www.agilityapplications.com
Software Development Services
N.A.I.C.S.: 541511
Eric Klawitter (Head-Dev Svcs)

Class Limited (1)
Level 3 228 Pitt Street, Sydney, 2000, NSW, Australia
Tel.: (61) 1300851057
Web Site: http://www.class.com.au
Rev.: $42,100,608
Assets: $67,128,971
Liabilities: $35,223,287

Net Worth: $31,905,684
Earnings: $2,808,853
Fiscal Year-end: 06/30/2021
Cloud Software Services
N.A.I.C.S.: 561499
Matthew Quinn *(Chm)*

Subsidiary (Domestic):

NowInfinity Pty. Ltd. (2)
Suite 10A - Level 10 Corporate Centre One
2 Corporate Court, Bundall, 4217, QLD,
Australia
Tel.: (61) 1300851057
Web Site: http://www.nowinfinity.com.au
Portfolio Management Services
N.A.I.C.S.: 523940

HUBConnect Pty Ltd (1)
HUB24 Level 2 7 Macquarie Place, GPO
Box 529, Sydney, 2000, NSW, Australia
Tel.: (61) 1300370095
Web Site: https://www.hubconnect.com.au
Software Development Services
N.A.I.C.S.: 541511

Paragem Pty Ltd (1)
Level 7 115 Pitt Street, Sydney, 2000,
NSW, Australia
Tel.: (61) 280366490
Web Site: https://www.paragem.com.au
Financial Advisory Services
N.A.I.C.S.: 523940
Craig Kouimanis *(Gen Mgr-Practice Dev)*

HUBEI BIOCAUSE PHARMACEUTICAL CO., LTD.
No 122 Yangwan Road, Jingmen,
448000, Hubei, China
Tel.: (86) 7242223090
Web Site: https://www.biocause.com
Year Founded: 1995
000627—(SSE)
Pharmaceuticals Mfr
N.A.I.C.S.: 325412
Yiqian Liu *(Chm)*

Subsidiaries:

Wuhan Biocause Pharmaceutical Development Co., Ltd. (1)
4 F 1 Building Hi-Tech Industrial Park
Zhuankou, Wuhan, 430056, Hubei, China
Tel.: (86) 2784222527
Web Site: http://www.whbiocause.com
Pharmaceuticals Product Mfr
N.A.I.C.S.: 325412
Zhou Bo *(Mgr-Export)*

HUBEI BROADCASTING & TELEVISION INFORMATION NETWORK CO., LTD.
Guanggu 4th Road Donghu New
Technology Development Zone, Wuhan, 430074, Hubei, China
Tel.: (86) 2786653990
Web Site: https://www.hrtn.net
Year Founded: 1988
000665—(SSE)
Rev.: $305,452,836
Assets: $1,649,444,472
Liabilities: $800,889,336
Net Worth: $848,555,136
Earnings: ($83,542,212)
Fiscal Year-end: 12/31/22
Television Broadcasting Services
N.A.I.C.S.: 516120
Zeng Wen *(Chm)*

HUBEI CENTURY NETWORK TECHNOLOGY INC
Floor 9-11 Building B7 Financial Port
No 77 Guanggu Avenue, East Lake
New Technology Development Zone,
Wuhan, 430079, China
Tel.: (86) 2786655050
Web Site: https://www.shengtian.com
Year Founded: 2006
300494—(CHIN)
Rev.: $187,216,144
Assets: $280,600,553
Liabilities: $38,984,562
Net Worth: $241,615,991
Earnings: $23,852,652
Fiscal Year-end: 12/31/23
Business Consulting Services
N.A.I.C.S.: 561499
Lai Chunlin *(Chm & CEO)*

HUBEI CHUTIAN SMART COMMUNICATION CO., LTD.
No 9 Longyang Avenue, Hanyang
District, Wuhan, 430050, Hubei,
China
Tel.: (86) 2787576667
600035—(SHG)
Rev.: $409,568,028
Assets: $2,532,797,762
Liabilities: $1,347,648,831
Net Worth: $1,185,148,931
Earnings: $101,459,569
Fiscal Year-end: 12/31/22
Transportation Management Services
N.A.I.C.S.: 488999

HUBEI DINGLONG CO., LTD.
No 1 Dongjing River Road, Wuhan
Economic & Tech Development Zone,
Wuhan, 430057, Hubei, China
Tel.: (86) 27 59881888
Web Site:
http://www.dinglongchem.com
Sales Range: $150-199.9 Million
Inkjet & Cartridge Toner Chemical Mfr
N.A.I.C.S.: 325998
Shuangquan Zhu *(Chm)*

HUBEI DONPER ELECTROMECHANICAL GROUP CO., LTD.
No 6 Jinshan Avenue East Economic
and Technological Development
Zone, Tieshan District, Huangshi,
435000, Hubei, China
Tel.: (86) 7145415858
Web Site: http://www.donper.com
Year Founded: 2002
601956—(SHG)
Rev.: $750,475,009
Assets: $882,162,010
Liabilities: $512,143,749
Net Worth: $370,018,261
Earnings: $19,941,911
Fiscal Year-end: 12/31/22
Refrigeration Equipment Mfr & Distr
N.A.I.C.S.: 333415
Baichang Yang *(Board of Directors & CEO)*

HUBEI DOTI-MICRO TECHNOLOGY CO., LTD.
No 188 South Section of Changban
Road Yuquan Office, Dangyang,
Yichang, 444100, Hubei, China
Tel.: (86) 7173465366
Web Site: https://www.doti-optical.com
Year Founded: 2009
301183—(CHIN)
Rev.: $48,852,874
Assets: $151,376,952
Liabilities: $40,799,457
Net Worth: $110,577,495
Earnings: ($4,519,218)
Emp.: 1,300
Fiscal Year-end: 12/31/23
Optical Goods Mfr & Distr
N.A.I.C.S.: 333310
Denghua Gao *(Chm)*

HUBEI ENERGY GROUP CO., LTD.
No 96 Xudong Avenue, Wuchang
District, Wuhan, 430063, Hubei,
China
Tel.: (86) 2786606100
Web Site: http://www.hbny.com.cn
Year Founded: 1998
000883—(SSE)
Rev.: $2,889,180,684
Assets: $11,158,273,152
Liabilities: $6,002,334,468
Net Worth: $5,155,938,684
Earnings: $163,220,616
Fiscal Year-end: 12/31/22
Electric Power Generation & Distribution Services
N.A.I.C.S.: 221111
He Hongxin *(Chm)*

HUBEI FEILIHUA QUARTZ GLASS CO., LTD.
No 68 Dongfang Avenue, Jingzhou,
434000, Hubei, China
Tel.: (86) 7168304668
Web Site: https://www.feilihua.com
Year Founded: 1966
300395—(CHIN)
Rev.: $294,452,925
Assets: $833,129,581
Liabilities: $199,128,350
Net Worth: $634,001,232
Earnings: $75,727,679
Fiscal Year-end: 12/31/23
Quartz Material Mfr
N.A.I.C.S.: 334419

HUBEI FORBON TECHNOLOGY CO., LTD.
No 288 Shendun 3rd Road East Lake
New Technology Development Zone,
East Lake High tech Development
Zone, Wuhan, 430206, Hubei, China
Tel.: (86) 2787002158
Web Site: http://www.forbon.com
Year Founded: 2007
300387—(CHIN)
Rev.: $98,886,330
Assets: $265,992,477
Liabilities: $76,087,150
Net Worth: $189,905,327
Earnings: $10,600,600
Fiscal Year-end: 12/31/20
Fertilizer Mfr
N.A.I.C.S.: 325312
Renzong Wang *(Chm, CFO & Gen Mgr)*

HUBEI FUXING SCIENCE & TECHNOLOGY CO., LTD.
27F Fuxing International Chamber of
Commerce Building, No 186 Xinhua
Road Jianghan District, Wuhan,
430023, Hubei, China
Tel.: (86) 2785578818
Web Site: http://www.cccme.org.cn
Year Founded: 1993
000926—(SSE)
Rev.: $2,125,981,728
Assets: $5,373,814,212
Liabilities: $3,637,974,600
Net Worth: $1,735,839,612
Earnings: $14,736,384
Emp.: 6,000
Fiscal Year-end: 12/31/22
Real Estate Development Services
N.A.I.C.S.: 531311
Shaoqun Tan *(Chm)*

HUBEI GEOWAY INVESTMENT CO., LTD.
201 Building A No 1 Qianwan 1s,
Shenzhen, 518052, China
Tel.: (86) 75526417750
600462—(SHG)
Rev.: $42,998,890
Assets: $60,789,128
Liabilities: $57,820,244
Net Worth: $2,968,884
Earnings: ($11,267,198)
Fiscal Year-end: 12/31/22
Electronic Component Mfr & Distr
N.A.I.C.S.: 334419
Wen Gen Cui *(Sec & VP)*

HUBEI GOTO BIOPHARM CO., LTD.
33th Floor of Building 1 IFC South
jiangshan Rd Wolong Ave, Fancheng
District, Xiangyang, 441057, Hubei,
China
Tel.: (86) 7103423122
Web Site:
https://www.gotopharm.com
Year Founded: 2006
300966—(SSE)
Rev.: $84,881,628
Assets: $290,392,128
Liabilities: $152,640,072
Net Worth: $137,752,056
Earnings: $5,642,676
Fiscal Year-end: 12/31/22
Pharmaceutical Product Mfr & Distr
N.A.I.C.S.: 325412
Zubin Xi *(Chm & Gen Mgr)*

HUBEI GUANGJI PHARMACEUTICAL CO., LTD.
No 1 Jiangdi Road, Wuxue, 435400,
Hubei, China
Tel.: (86) 7136211112
Web Site:
http://www.guangjipharm.com
Year Founded: 1993
000952—(SSE)
Rev.: $111,988,656
Assets: $346,654,620
Liabilities: $137,204,496
Net Worth: $209,450,124
Earnings: $7,071,948
Emp.: 1,139
Fiscal Year-end: 12/31/22
Pharmaceuticals Product Mfr
N.A.I.C.S.: 325412
Ruan Shu *(Chm)*

HUBEI GUOCHUANG HI-TECH MATERIAL CO., LTD.
No 8 Wudayuan 3rd Road3, Guandong Science & Tech Area, Wuhan,
430074, China
Tel.: (86) 2787617347
Web Site:
https://www.guochuang.com.cn
002377—(SSE)
Rev.: $308,985,300
Assets: $248,426,568
Liabilities: $161,688,852
Net Worth: $86,737,716
Earnings: ($75,611,016)
Emp.: 140
Fiscal Year-end: 12/31/22
High Grade Asphalt, Asphalt Emulsion & Paving Equipment & Services
N.A.I.C.S.: 324121
Wang Xin *(Chm)*

HUBEI HEYUAN GAS CO., LTD.
3F Xinding Building No 33 Wulin
Road, Wujiagang District, Yichang,
443500, Hubei, China
Tel.: (86) 7176074701
Web Site: http://www.hbhy-gas.com
Year Founded: 2003
002971—(SSE)
Rev.: $185,554,044
Assets: $412,745,112
Liabilities: $243,300,564
Net Worth: $169,444,548
Earnings: $10,553,868
Fiscal Year-end: 12/31/22
Oil & Gas Distribution Services
N.A.I.C.S.: 221210
Tao Yang *(Chm & Gen Mgr)*

HUBEI HUARONG HOLDING CO., LTD.
22F Tower B Asia Trade Plaza No
628 Wuluo Road, Wuchang District,
Wuhan, 430070, Hubei, China

HUBEI HUARONG HOLDING CO., LTD.

Hubei Huarong Holding Co., Ltd.—(Continued)
Tel.: (86) 2787654767
600421—(SHG)
Rev.: $17,576,873
Assets: $17,891,635
Liabilities: $11,387,507
Net Worth: $6,504,128
Earnings: ($910,789)
Fiscal Year-end: 12/31/22
Holding Company
N.A.I.C.S.: 551112

HUBEI HUITIAN NEW MATERIALS CO., LTD.
No 1 Guanyu Road, Fancheng District, Xiangyang, 441003, Hubei, China
Tel.: (86) 7103626888
Web Site: https://www.huitian.net.cn
300041—(CHIN)
Rev.: $549,528,979
Assets: $872,608,343
Liabilities: $466,204,345
Net Worth: $406,403,998
Earnings: $42,078,290
Emp.: 1,800
Fiscal Year-end: 12/31/23
Adhesive Mfr
N.A.I.C.S.: 325520

HUBEI JIUZHIYANG INFRARED SYSTEM CO., LTD
No 9 Mingze Street Miaoshan Development Zone, Jiangxia District, Wuhan, 430223, Hubei, China
Tel.: (86) 2759601200
Web Site: https://www.hbjir.com
Year Founded: 2001
300516—(CHIN)
Rev.: $108,412,076
Assets: $245,984,046
Liabilities: $60,565,697
Net Worth: $185,418,349
Earnings: $11,679,930
Fiscal Year-end: 12/31/23
Optoelectronic Parts Mfr & Distr
N.A.I.C.S.: 334413
Guo Liangxian (Chm)

HUBEI JUMPCAN PHARMACEUTICAL CO., LTD.
Baota Bay West Daqing Road, Taixing, 225441, Jiangsu, China
Tel.: (86) 52387606428
Web Site: https://www.jumpcan.com
Year Founded: 1997
600566—(SHG)
Rev.: $1,263,089,927
Assets: $2,103,360,789
Liabilities: $509,466,279
Net Worth: $1,593,894,510
Earnings: $304,773,946
Fiscal Year-end: 12/31/22
Pharmaceutical Product Mfr & Whslr
N.A.I.C.S.: 325412
Cao Longxiang (Chm)

Subsidiaries:

Haiyuan Property Co., Ltd. (1)
Building 11 HuaYuan Enterprise Center No 11 North Beizhan Street, Xicheng District, Beijing, 100044, China
Tel.: (86) 1068036688
Web Site: https://www.hy-online.com
Real Estate Development & Management Services
N.A.I.C.S.: 531390

HUBEI JUNEYAO GREAT HEALTH DAIRY CO., LTD.
31F JuneYao International Plaza No 789 Zhaojiabang Road, Shanghai, 200032, China
Tel.: (86) 2151155807
Web Site: http://www.juneyaodairy.com
Year Founded: 1998
605388—(SHG)
Rev.: $138,449,030
Assets: $335,455,305
Liabilities: $65,086,857
Net Worth: $270,368,448
Earnings: $10,759,035
Fiscal Year-end: 12/31/22
Dairy Products Mfr
N.A.I.C.S.: 333241
Junhao Wang (Chm)

HUBEI KAILE SCIENCE & TECHNOLOGY CO., LTD.
Chengguan Douhudi Town, Gongan County, Hubei, 434300, China
Tel.: (86) 2787250890
Web Site: http://www.cnkaile.com
Year Founded: 1982
600260—(SHG)
Rev.: $1,302,222,184
Assets: $1,926,431,898
Liabilities: $879,115,916
Net Worth: $1,047,315,982
Earnings: $69,519,038
Fiscal Year-end: 12/31/20
Optical Cable & Plastic Tube Mfr
N.A.I.C.S.: 335921
Dixiong Zhu (Chm)

HUBEI KAILONG CHEMICAL GROUP CO., LTD.
20th Quankou Road, Jingmen, 448032, Hubei, China
Tel.: (86) 7242309219
Web Site: https://en.hbklgroup.cn
Year Founded: 1997
002783—(SSE)
Rev.: $478,195,380
Assets: $1,047,813,624
Liabilities: $731,127,384
Net Worth: $316,686,240
Earnings: $18,726,552
Emp.: 4,000
Fiscal Year-end: 12/31/22
Industrial Explosive Mfr & Distr
N.A.I.C.S.: 325920
Shao Xingxiang (Chm & Sec-Party Committee)

HUBEI MAILYARD SHARE CO., LTD.
Meiliya Industrial Park Tuanchengshan Development Zone, Huangshi, 435000, Hubei, China
Tel.: (86) 7146360213
Web Site: https://www.mailyard.com.cn
Year Founded: 1993
600107—(SHG)
Rev.: $60,600,304
Assets: $194,748,686
Liabilities: $102,185,310
Net Worth: $92,563,375
Earnings: ($16,637,021)
Fiscal Year-end: 12/31/22
Men & Women Apparel Mfr & Whslr
N.A.I.C.S.: 315250
Zheng Jiping (Chm)

HUBEI MINKANG PHARMACEUTICAL LTD.
55 Ubi Ave 3 03-01 Mintwell Building, Singapore, 408864, Singapore
Tel.: (65) 67477883 NV
Year Founded: 2006
Sales Range: $10-24.9 Million
Pharmaceuticals Mfr
N.A.I.C.S.: 325412
Tong Tai Lee (Pres, CEO & CFO)

HUBEI SANXIA NEW BUILDING MATERIALS CO., LTD.
No 6 Yide Road, Dangyang, 444105, Hubei, China
Tel.: (86) 7173280108

Web Site: http://www.sxxc.com.cn
Year Founded: 1993
600293—(SHG)
Rev.: $265,199,033
Assets: $516,072,394
Liabilities: $262,275,484
Net Worth: $253,796,910
Earnings: ($41,208,846)
Fiscal Year-end: 12/31/22
Glass Product Mfr & Whslr
N.A.I.C.S.: 327211
Xie Pule (Chm)

HUBEI SHUANGHUAN SCIENCE & TECHNOLOGY STOCK CO., LTD.
No 26 Tuanjie Avenue Dongmafang, Yingcheng City, Xiaogan, 432407, Hubei, China
Tel.: (86) 7123580899
Web Site: http://www.hbshkj.cn
Year Founded: 1993
000707—(SSE)
Rev.: $612,747,720
Assets: $383,553,144
Liabilities: $177,690,240
Net Worth: $205,862,904
Earnings: $122,574,816
Fiscal Year-end: 12/31/22
Chemical Products Mfr
N.A.I.C.S.: 325199
Wanxin Wang (Chm)

HUBEI THREE GORGES TOURISM GROUP CO., LTD.
No 5 Gangyao Road, Wujiagang District, Yichang, 443000, Hubei, China
Tel.: (86) 7176443910
Web Site: https://www.ycjyjt.com
Year Founded: 1935
002627—(SSE)
Rev.: $267,808,788
Assets: $615,328,272
Liabilities: $168,404,184
Net Worth: $446,924,088
Earnings: $609,336
Fiscal Year-end: 12/31/22
Passenger Transportation Services
N.A.I.C.S.: 485999
Wang Jingfu (Chm)

HUBEI W OLF PHOTOELECTRIC TECHNOLOGY CO., LTD.
55 Shenzhen Avenue, Jingzhou Development Zone, Jingzhou, 434000, Hubei, China
Tel.: (86) 7168800009
Web Site: https://www.w-olf.com
Year Founded: 2012
002962—(SSE)
Rev.: $144,530,568
Assets: $282,157,668
Liabilities: $25,121,772
Net Worth: $257,035,896
Earnings: $12,475,944
Fiscal Year-end: 12/31/22
Film Material Mfr
N.A.I.C.S.: 325992
Binbin Liao (Chm & Pres)

Subsidiaries:

Suzhou Wufang Photoelectric Material Co., Ltd. (1)
88 Chang'an Road, Friendship Industrial Zone Songling Town Wujiang City, Suzhou, China
Tel.: (86) 51263636258
Photoelectric Thin Film Component Distr
N.A.I.C.S.: 423410

HUBEI WUCHANGYU CO., LTD.
4F Building 3 East of Middle Section Yanglan Road, Ezhou, 436000, Hubei, China
Tel.: (86) 711 3200330

INTERNATIONAL PUBLIC

600275—(SHG)
Rev.: $3,701,554
Assets: $19,168,103
Liabilities: $12,737,879
Net Worth: $6,430,224
Earnings: ($4,836,840)
Fiscal Year-end: 12/31/20
Agriculture Product Mfr & Distr
N.A.I.C.S.: 311423
Shiqing Gao (Chm)

HUBEI XIANGYUAN NEW MATERIAL TECHNOLOGY, INC.
Hanchuan Economic Development Zone, Huayi Village, Hanchuan, 431600, Hubei, China
Tel.: (86) 7128806405
Web Site: https://www.hbxyxc.com
Year Founded: 2003
300980—(SSE)
Rev.: $52,459,056
Assets: $163,397,520
Liabilities: $29,339,388
Net Worth: $134,058,132
Earnings: $7,955,064
Fiscal Year-end: 12/31/22
Polyolefin Fiber Product Mfr
N.A.I.C.S.: 325220
Zhixiang Wei (Chm)

HUBEI XINGFA CHEMICALS GROUP CO., LTD.
No 58 Gaoyang Avenue, Gufu Town Xingshan County, Yichang, 443000, Hubei, China
Tel.: (86) 7176760091
Web Site: https://www.xingfagroup.com
Year Founded: 1994
600141—(SHG)
Rev.: $4,255,615,779
Assets: $5,842,394,340
Liabilities: $2,846,922,727
Net Worth: $2,995,471,613
Earnings: $821,590,403
Emp.: 11,500
Fiscal Year-end: 12/31/22
Chemical Product Mfr & Whslr
N.A.I.C.S.: 325998
Guo Zhang Li (Chm)

HUBEI YIHUA CHEMICAL INDUSTRY CO., LTD.
No 399 Xiaoting Avenue, Xiaoting District, Yichang, 443000, Hubei, China
Tel.: (86) 1063704082
Web Site: https://www.yihua-chem.com
Year Founded: 1977
000422—(SSE)
Rev.: $2,908,037,808
Assets: $2,761,187,832
Liabilities: $1,805,222,484
Net Worth: $955,965,348
Earnings: $303,880,356
Fiscal Year-end: 12/31/22
Chemical Fertiliser Mfr
N.A.I.C.S.: 325312

HUBEI ZHENHUA CHEMICAL CO., LTD
No 668 Huangshi Road, Xisaishan District, Huangshi, 435001, Hubei, China
Tel.: (86) 7146406387
Web Site: https://en.hbzhenhua.com
Year Founded: 2003
603067—(SHG)
Rev.: $496,145,590
Assets: $558,969,213
Liabilities: $200,067,052
Net Worth: $358,902,161
Earnings: $58,542,546
Emp.: 1,170
Fiscal Year-end: 12/31/22

Chromium Salt Mfr & Distr
N.A.I.C.S.: 325180
Cai Zaihua (Chm)

HUBEI ZHONGYI TECHNOLOGY INC.
No 47 South Mengze Avenue Economic Development Zone, Yunmeng County, Hubei, 432500, China
Tel.: (86) 7124488991
Web Site: https://www.c1cf.com
Year Founded: 2007
301150—(CHIN)
Electronic Component Mfr & Distr
N.A.I.C.S.: 334419
Xiaoxia Wang (Chm & Gen Mgr)

HUBER + SUHNER AG
Degersheimerstrasse 14, 9100, Herisau, Switzerland
Tel.: (41) 713534111   CH
Web Site:
  https://www.hubersuhner.com
Year Founded: 1969
HUBN—(SWX)
Rev.: $1,058,274,945
Assets: $903,528,825
Liabilities: $230,965,632
Net Worth: $672,563,193
Earnings: $93,406,874
Emp.: 4,588
Fiscal Year-end: 12/31/22
Components & Systems for Electrical & Optical Connectivity Developer & Mfr
N.A.I.C.S.: 335921
Urs Kaufmann (Chm)

Subsidiaries:

HUBER+SUHNER (Malaysia) Sdn. Bhd
No 2 Jalan Pensyarah U1/28 Hicom Glenmarie Industrial Park, 40150, Shah Alam, Selangor, Malaysia
Tel.: (60) 350353333
Web Site: http://www.hubersuhner.com.my
Sales Range: $75-99.9 Million
Emp.: 150
Fiber Optic & Coaxial Cable Distr
N.A.I.C.S.: 423610

HUBER+SUHNER (Thailand) Co., Ltd   (1)
896/3 SV City Office Tower 1 4th Floor Rama III Road, Khet Yannawa, Bangkok, 10120, Thailand
Tel.: (66) 26826868
Web Site: http://www.hubersuhner.co.th
Sales Range: $50-74.9 Million
Emp.: 10
Electronic Components Distr
N.A.I.C.S.: 423690

HUBER+SUHNER A/S   (1)
Kirke Vaerlosevej 14, Vaerlose, 3500, Denmark
Tel.: (45) 48 100 500
Web Site: http://www.hubersuhner.dk
Sales Range: $25-49.9 Million
Emp.: 7
Electrical Component Distr
N.A.I.C.S.: 423610
Torsten Magnussen (Mgr-Sls-Nordic Telecom Operators)

HUBER+SUHNER AB   (1)
Knarrarnasgatan 7, Box 1247, 164 28, Kista, Sweden
Tel.: (46) 84475200
Web Site: http://www.hubersuhner.se
Emp.: 10
Electrical Components Suppliers
N.A.I.C.S.: 423610

HUBER+SUHNER America Latina Ltda   (1)
Rodovia Presidente Dutra Km 134 Predio 02, Vila Galvao Cacapava, 12286-160, Sao Paulo, Brazil
Tel.: (55) 1236571000
Web Site: http://www.hubersuhner.com.br
Fiber Optic Cable Distr
N.A.I.C.S.: 423610

HUBER+SUHNER Electronics Private Limited   (1)
Plot 125 Sector 8 IMT Manesar, Gurgaon, 122051, Haryana, India
Tel.: (91) 124 4526100
Web Site: http://www.hubersuhner.co.in
Electrical Component Distr
N.A.I.C.S.: 423610

Huber + Suhner (Australia) Pty. Ltd.   (1)
Unit 6 4 Skyline Pl, PO Box 6201, French's Forest, 2086, NSW, Australia   (100%)
Tel.: (61) 289771200
Web Site: http://www.hubersuhner.com.au
Sales Range: $25-49.9 Million
Emp.: 30
Distr of Antenna Systems; Fiberoptics, Antennas & Lightning Protectors
N.A.I.C.S.: 423690

Huber + Suhner (Hong Kong) Ltd.   (1)
Unit A1 17/F TML Tower, 3 Hoi Shing Road, Tsuen Wan, China (Hong Kong)   (100%)
Tel.: (852) 28666600
Web Site: http://www.hubersuhner.com
Sales Range: $25-49.9 Million
Emp.: 10
Mfr of Cable Assemblies, Cables, Fiberoptics, Antennas, Connectors & Lightning Protectors
N.A.I.C.S.: 334220

Huber + Suhner (Singapore) Pte. Ltd.   (1)
114 Lavender Street 02-67 CT HUB2, Singapore, 338729, Singapore   (100%)
Tel.: (65) 64735500
Web Site: https://www.hubersuhner.com.sg
Sales Range: $25-49.9 Million
Emp.: 22
Distr of Antenna Systems Solutions; Fiberoptics, Antennas, Cable Assemblies, Cables, Connectors & Lightning Protectors
N.A.I.C.S.: 334220

Huber + Suhner (UK) Ltd.   (1)
Telford Road, Bicester, OX26 4LA, Oxfordshire, United Kingdom   (100%)
Tel.: (44) 186 936 4100
Web Site: https://www.hubersuhner.com
Sales Range: $25-49.9 Million
Emp.: 90
Mfr & Sales of Cables, Antennas, Cable Assemblies, Connectors & Lightning Protectors
N.A.I.C.S.: 334220

Huber + Suhner France   (1)
21 E Rue Jacques Cartier, 78960, Voisins-le-Bretonneux, France   (100%)
Tel.: (33) 161372555
Web Site: http://www.hubersuhner.fr
Sales Range: $125-149.9 Million
Emp.: 20
Sales of Fiberoptics, Cables, Antennas, Cable Assemblies, Connectors & Lightning Protectors
N.A.I.C.S.: 423690

Huber + Suhner GmbH   (1)
Mehlberenstrasse 6, PO Box 82024, PO Box 1263, D 82019, Taufkirchen, Germany   (100%)
Tel.: (49) 89612010
Web Site: http://www.hubersuhner.de
Sales Range: $75-99.9 Million
Emp.: 130
Sales of Cables, Antennas, Cable Assemblies, Connectors & Lightning Protectors; Distributor of Antenna Systems Solutions
N.A.I.C.S.: 423690

Huber + Suhner Inc.   (1)
19 Thompson Dr, Essex Junction, VT 05452-3408   (100%)
Tel.: (802) 878-0555
Web Site: http://www.hubersuhnerinc.com
Sales Range: $75-99.9 Million
Emp.: 30
Develops & Manufactures Components & Systems Solutions for Electrical & Optical Transportation of Data & Energy
N.A.I.C.S.: 513210

Huber+Suhner Cube Optics AG   (1)
Eindhoven Avenue 3, 55129, Mainz, Germany

Tel.: (49) 61314995100
Web Site: https://www.cubeoptics.com
Telecommunication Component Mfr
N.A.I.C.S.: 334210
Urs Ryffel (Chm)

OPTICAL CONNECTIVITY LLC   (1)
Ras Al Khor Industrial 3 behind Al Toufiq A2 WH 5, PO Box 75843, Dubai, United Arab Emirates
Tel.: (971) 4 286 3450
Web Site: https://www.oc2me.com
Emp.: 6
Electrical Equipment Mfr & Distr
N.A.I.C.S.: 335999
Micheal Gnoth (Mng Dir)

Polatis Incorporated   (1)
213 Burlington Rd Ste 123, Bedford, MA 01730
Tel.: (781) 275-5080
Web Site: http://www.polatis.com
Business Date Management Support Services
N.A.I.C.S.: 561499
Nick Parsons (Sr VP-Engrg & Tech)

HUBERGROUP DEUTSCHLAND GMBH
Feldkirchener Strasse 15, D-85551, Kirchheim, Germany
Tel.: (49) 89 9003 0
Web Site: http://www.hubergroup.de
Emp.: 900
Holding Company
N.A.I.C.S.: 551112

Subsidiaries:

Hubergroup USA, Inc.   (1)
2850 Festival Dr, Kankakee, IL 60901
Tel.: (815) 929-9293
Web Site: http://www.hubergroup.net
Printing Ink Mfr
N.A.I.C.S.: 325910
Derek McFarland (Pres)

Subsidiary (Domestic):

Hubergroup USA, Inc. - Arlington Heights   (2)
616 E Brook Dr, Arlington Heights, IL 60005
Tel.: (847) 956-6830
Web Site: http://www.hubergroup.net
Sales Range: $10-24.9 Million
Printing Ink Mfr

HUBERT BURDA MEDIA HOLDING KOMMANDITGESELLSCHAFT
Arabellastrasse 23, 81925, Munich, Germany
Tel.: (49) 8992500   De
Web Site: http://www.burda.com
Year Founded: 1908
Sales Range: $1-4.9 Billion
Emp.: 7,116
Holding Company; Multimedia Publisher & Technologies Developer
N.A.I.C.S.: 551112
Hubert Burda (Publr)

Subsidiaries:

BDV Beteiligungen GmbH & Co. KG   (1)
Widenmayerstr 29, Bayern, Munich, 80538, Germany
Tel.: (49) 781 8401
Magazine Publisher
N.A.I.C.S.: 513120

Blue Ocean Entertainment AG   (1)
Seidenstrasse 19, 70174, Stuttgart, Germany
Tel.: (49) 14005020
Web Site: http://www.blue-ocean.de
Publishing Company
N.A.I.C.S.: 513120
Samanta Erdini (Project & Art Dir)

Subsidiary (Non-US):

Heinrich Bauer Ediciones S.L.   (2)
Calle Pedro Teixeira 8 - 5 planta, 28020, Madrid, Spain
Tel.: (34) 91 547 68 00
Web Site: http://www.bauer.es
Newspaper & Magazine Publisher
N.A.I.C.S.: 513110
Frank Simon (Head-IT)

Brand Media Solutions GmbH   (1)
Hubert-Burda-Platz 1, Stadtmitte, 77652, Offenburg, Germany
Tel.: (49) 781 8401
Web Site: http://www.hubert-burda-media.com
Media Advertising Services
N.A.I.C.S.: 541840

Bunte Verlag GmbH   (1)
Arabellastrasse 23, 81925, Munich, Germany   (100%)
Tel.: (49) 8992500
Web Site: http://www.bunte.de
Sales Range: $400-449.9 Million
Emp.: 2,000
Weekly Magazine
N.A.I.C.S.: 513120

Subsidiary (US):

Burda Publications, Inc.   (2)
1270 Avenue Of The Americas Ste 2908, New York, NY 10020-1801
Tel.: (212) 884-4900
Sales Range: $25-49.9 Million
Emp.: 8
Editorial & Publishing; Magazines
N.A.I.C.S.: 551112
Ellem Kiefer (Gen Mgr)

Burda (Thailand) Co., Ltd.   (1)
17th Floor Unit No1702 208 Wireless Rd, Lumpini Pathumwan, Bangkok, 10330, Thailand
Tel.: (66) 2651 5400
Web Site: http://www.burdathailand.com
Magazine Publisher
N.A.I.C.S.: 513120

Burda Communications Sp. z o.o.   (1)
ul Marynarska 15, 2674, Warsaw, Poland
Tel.: (48) 22 360 38 00
Magazine Publisher
N.A.I.C.S.: 513120

Burda Community Network GmbH   (1)
Hubert-Burda-Platz 1, 77652, Offenburg, Germany
Tel.: (49) 781 84 01
Web Site: http://bcn.burda.com
Sales Range: $25-49.9 Million
Media Agency
N.A.I.C.S.: 541890
Michael Fischer (CFO)

Burda Druck Nurnberg GmbH & Co. KG   (1)
Mainstrasse 20, 90451, Nuremberg, Germany
Tel.: (49) 911 5396 0
Web Site: http://www.burda-druck.de
Magazine Publisher Services
N.A.I.C.S.: 513120

Subsidiary (Non-US):

Hollimann S.A.   (2)
Europole de Sarreguemines, 57910, Hambach, France
Tel.: (33) 387989999
Commercial Printing Services
N.A.I.C.S.: 323111

Burda Praha spol. s r.o.   (1)
Premyslovska 2845/43, 130 00, Prague, Czech Republic
Tel.: (420) 221 589 111
Web Site: http://www.burda.cz
Magazine Publisher Services
N.A.I.C.S.: 513120

Burda Service AG   (1)
Aeschengraben 20, 4051, Basel, Switzerland
Tel.: (41) 61 205 61 61
Magazine Publisher
N.A.I.C.S.: 513120

Burda Services GmbH   (1)
Hauptstrasse 130, 77652, Offenburg, Germany

HUBERT BURDA MEDIA HOLDING KOMMANDITGESELLSCHAFT

Hubert Burda Media Holding Kommanditgesellschaft—(Continued)
Tel.: (49) 781 8401
Web Site: http://www.burda-einkauf.de
Media Advertising Services
N.A.I.C.S.: 541840

Burda Singapore Pte. Ltd. (1)
1008 Toa Payoh North 07-11, Singapore, 318996, Singapore
Tel.: (65) 6256 6201
Web Site: http://www.burda.com.sg
Magazine Publisher
N.A.I.C.S.: 513120
Ann Lee *(Dir-Grp Adv)*

Burda Taiwan Co. Ltd. (1)
13F No 394 Keelung Road Section 1, Taipei, 11051, Taiwan
Tel.: (886) 227201900
Web Site: http://www.prestige-taiwan.com
Emp.: 10
Magazine Publisher
N.A.I.C.S.: 513120
Daisy Hu *(Gen Mgr)*

CHIP Holding GmbH (1)
St -Martin- Str 66, 81541, Munich, Germany
Tel.: (49) 89 42625793
Magazine Publisher
N.A.I.C.S.: 513120

Subsidiary (Domestic):

CHIP Communications GmbH (2)
Poccistrasse 11, Munich, 80336, Germany
Tel.: (49) 89 746 42 0
Web Site: http://www.chip-media.de
Magazine Publisher
N.A.I.C.S.: 513120

Cliqz GmbH (1)
Arabellastrasse 23, 81925, Munich, Germany
Tel.: (49) 89 9250 1055
Web Site: http://www.cliqz.com
Emp.: 90
Internet Browser Application Developer
N.A.I.C.S.: 541511
Marc Al-Hames *(Mng Dir)*

Cyberport Services GmbH (1)
Am Brauhaus 5, 01099, Dresden, Germany
Tel.: (49) 351 339560
Web Site: http://www.cyberport.de
Magazine Publisher
N.A.I.C.S.: 513120

Cyberport solutions GmbH (1)
Friedrichstrasse 50-55, 10117, Berlin, Germany
Tel.: (49) 30 692036930
Web Site: http://www.cyberport.de
Online Retailer
N.A.I.C.S.: 449210

FTM Freizeit- und Trendmarketing GmbH & Co. KG (1)
Hoffmannallee 105, 47533, Kleve, Niederrhein, Germany
Tel.: (49) 2821 75300
Magazine Publisher
N.A.I.C.S.: 513120

Fit for Fun Verlag GmbH (1)
Grosse Elbstr 59-63, 22767, Hamburg, Germany
Tel.: (49) 4041310
Web Site: http://www.fitforfun.de
Emp.: 250
Magazine Publisher
N.A.I.C.S.: 513120

Focus Magazin Verlag (1)
Arabellastrasse 23, 81925, Munich, Germany **(100%)**
Tel.: (49) 307544300
Web Site: http://www.focus-magazin.de
Sales Range: $400-449.9 Million
Emp.: 1,200
News Magazine Services
N.A.I.C.S.: 513120
Helmut Markwort *(CEO & Editor-in-Chief)*

Freedreams B.V. (1)
Jonkerbosplein 52, Nijmegen, 6534 AB, Gelderland, Netherlands
Tel.: (31) 627085863
Magazine Publisher
N.A.I.C.S.: 513120

HolidayCheck Group AG (1)
Neumarkter Strasse 61, 81673, Munich, Germany **(73%)**
Tel.: (49) 89357680900
Web Site: https://www.holidaycheckgroup.com
Rev.: $21,931,453
Assets: $164,619,779
Liabilities: $65,901,217
Net Worth: $98,718,562
Earnings: ($89,085,475)
Emp.: 343
Fiscal Year-end: 12/31/2020
Holding Company; Online Travel, Publishing & Subscription Website Developer & Operator
N.A.I.C.S.: 551112
Dirk Altenbeck *(Deputy Chm-Supervisory Bd)*

Subsidiary (Non-US):

HolidayCheck AG (2)
Bahnweg 8, CH 8598, Bottighofen, Switzerland **(80%)**
Tel.: (41) 716869000
Web Site: http://www.holidaycheck.de
Sales Range: $50-74.9 Million
Emp.: 200
Online Travel Rating Services
N.A.I.C.S.: 513199
Christine Eberle *(Dir-Travel Agency)*

Hubert Burda Media Hong Kong Limited (1)
14/F Universal Trade Centre 3 Arbuthnot Road, Central, Hong Kong, China (Hong Kong)
Tel.: (852) 3192 7010
Web Site: http://www.prestigehongkong.com
Emp.: 30
Magazine Publisher
N.A.I.C.S.: 513120
Anne Limchaplain *(Mng Dir)*

INO24 AG (1)
Riedbachstr 5, 74385, Pleidelsheim, Germany
Tel.: (49) 71448080
Web Site: http://www.ino24.de
General Insurance Services
N.A.I.C.S.: 524210

InTime Media Services GmbH (1)
Bajuwarenring 14, 82041, Oberhaching, Germany
Tel.: (49) 89 85 85 3 500
Web Site: http://www.intime-media-services.de
Magazine Publisher
N.A.I.C.S.: 513120

New Work SE (1)
Dammtorstrasse 30, 20354, Hamburg, Germany **(59.2%)**
Tel.: (49) 404191310
Web Site: https://www.new-work.se
Rev.: $357,242,202
Assets: $464,482,293
Liabilities: $294,653,548
Net Worth: $169,828,745
Earnings: $48,646,902
Emp.: 1,712
Fiscal Year-end: 12/31/2021
Business Professional Networking Website & Employment Search Portal
N.A.I.C.S.: 516210
Ingo Chu *(CFO & Member-Exec Bd)*

Subsidiary (Domestic):

XING International Holding GmbH (2)
Gansemarkt 43, 20354, Hamburg, Germany
Tel.: (49) 4041913110
Sales Range: $75-99.9 Million
Emp.: 450
Online Networking Services
N.A.I.C.S.: 541519

Subsidiary (Non-US):

XING Networking Spain, S.L. (2)
Calle Consell De Cent 334 - Piso 6 Pta 1, Barcelona, 08009, Spain
Tel.: (34) 931853900
Magazine Publisher
N.A.I.C.S.: 513120

PaketPLUS Marketing GmbH (1)
Schleiermacherstrasse 14, 10961, Berlin, Germany
Tel.: (49) 30 94 88 79 10
Web Site: http://www.paketplus.de
Packaging Services
N.A.I.C.S.: 561910

STARnetONE GmbH (1)
Friedrichstrasse 148, 10117, Berlin, Germany
Tel.: (49) 030 440378
Web Site: http://www.starnetone.de
Television Broadcasting Services
N.A.I.C.S.: 516120

Valentins GmbH (1)
An der Brucke 24, 64546, Morfelden, Germany
Tel.: (49) 6105 3077133
Flower Retailer
N.A.I.C.S.: 459999

Valiton GmbH (1)
Rosenkavalierplatz 10, 81925, Munich, Germany
Tel.: (49) 89 9250 1226
Web Site: http://www.valiton.com
Information Technology Consulting Services
N.A.I.C.S.: 541512

Verlag Aenne Burda GmbH & Co. KG (1)
Hubert-Burda-Platz 2, 77652, Offenburg, Germany
Tel.: (49) 781846245
Web Site: http://www.burdastyle.de
Clothing Retailer
N.A.I.C.S.: 458110

Verwaltungsgesellschaft MAX Verlag mbH (1)
Milchstr 1, 20148, Hamburg, Germany
Tel.: (49) 4041 310
Web Site: http://www.max.de
Magazine Publisher
N.A.I.C.S.: 513120

computeruniverse GmbH (1)
Gruner Weg 14, Friedberg, 61169, Germany
Tel.: (49) 6031 79100
Web Site: http://www.computeruniverse.net
Online Retailer
N.A.I.C.S.: 449210

daskochrezept.de GmbH (1)
Turmstrasse 5, Wetzlar, 35578, Germany
Tel.: (49) 6441 210220
Web Site: http://www.daskochrezept.de
Online Publishing Services
N.A.I.C.S.: 513199

edelight GmbH (1)
Wilhelmstrasse 4a, Stuttgart, 70182, Germany
Tel.: (49) 711 912 5900
Web Site: http://www.edelight.de
Women's Clothing Retailer
N.A.I.C.S.: 458110

logistik service center s.r.o. (1)
Prazska 422, 47124, Mimon, Czech Republic
Tel.: (420) 273 500 70
Web Site: http://www.lscsro.com
Logistics Consulting Servies
N.A.I.C.S.: 541614

matina GmbH (1)
Herzog-Wilhelm-Strasse 12, 80331, Munich, Germany
Tel.: (49) 89 70809 986
Web Site: http://www.matina-gmbh.de
Dog & Cat Food Distr
N.A.I.C.S.: 424490

tv.gusto GmbH (1)
Arabella St 2381925 Munic, 50672, Cologne, Germany
Tel.: (49) 221277 93 200
Web Site: http://www.tvgusto.com
Television Channels Operator
N.A.I.C.S.: 516120
Frank Horlbeck *(Mgr)*

HUBIFY LIMITED

Suite 1 01 Level 1 65 Epping Road, Macquarie Park, 2113, NSW, Australia
Tel.: (61) 290039573 AU

INTERNATIONAL PUBLIC

Web Site: http://www.unitednetworks.net.au
Year Founded: 2009
HFY—(ASX)
Rev.: $13,168,554
Assets: $8,171,790
Liabilities: $3,232,875
Net Worth: $4,938,916
Earnings: ($3,152,052)
Emp.: 1,000
Fiscal Year-end: 06/30/24
Telecommunication Servicesb
N.A.I.C.S.: 517810
Victor Tsaccounis *(CEO & Dir)*

Subsidiaries:

Hubify Communications Pty Limited (1)
Suite 3 Level 1 6-10 Talavera Rd, Macquarie Park, 2113, NSW, Australia
Tel.: (61) 291346600
Web Site: https://www.hubify.com.au
Cyber Security Services
N.A.I.C.S.: 922190

HUBLINE BERHAD

Wisma Hubline Lease 3815 Lot 10914 Section 64 KTLD, Jalan Datuk Abang Abdul Rahim, 93450, Kuching, Sarawak, Malaysia
Tel.: (60) 82335393
Web Site: http://www.hubline.com
HUBLINE—(KLS)
Rev.: $49,535,121
Assets: $82,694,536
Liabilities: $41,604,285
Net Worth: $41,090,251
Earnings: $1,283,661
Fiscal Year-end: 09/30/23
Shipping Agency Services
N.A.I.C.S.: 488510
Puay Huang Yeo *(Sec)*

Subsidiaries:

Highline Quest Sdn. Bhd. (1)
1st Floor Lot 1458 Jalan Dombeya Lorong 6 Krokop, 98000, Miri, Sarawak, Malaysia
Tel.: (60) 85410069
Ship Owning & Chartering Services
N.A.I.C.S.: 483111

Highline Shipping Sdn. Bhd. (1)
Lot 2F Block 7A-F 2nd F MCLD Jalan Krokop Utama, 98008, Miri, Sarawak, Malaysia
Tel.: (60) 85410069
Dry Bulk Cargo Shipping Services
N.A.I.C.S.: 488320

Hub Marine Pte. Ltd. (1)
No 133 New Bridge Road 23-03/05 Chinatown Point, Singapore, 059413, Singapore
Tel.: (65) 62360737
Web Site: http://www.hubline.com
Freight Forwarding Services
N.A.I.C.S.: 483111

Hub Shipping Sdn. Bhd. (1)
Lease 3815 Lot 10914 Section 64 KTLD Jalan Datuk, Abang Abdul Rahim, 93450, Kuching, Sarawak, Malaysia
Tel.: (60) 82335393
Sales Range: $25-49.9 Million
Emp.: 80
Marine Cargo Handling Services
N.A.I.C.S.: 488320
Ling Li Kuang *(Chm)*

HUBTOWN LIMITED

Hubtown Seasons CTS No 469-A Opp Jain Temple, R K Chemburkar Marg Chembur East, Mumbai, 400071, India
Tel.: (91) 2225265000
Web Site: https://hubtown.co.in
532799—(BOM)
Rev.: $42,595,958
Assets: $604,225,440
Liabilities: $408,664,470
Net Worth: $195,560,970
Earnings: ($16,599,861)

Emp.: 123
Fiscal Year-end: 03/31/21
Real Estate Construction & Development Services
N.A.I.C.S.: 531390
Vyomesh M. Shah *(Mng Dir)*

Subsidiaries:

Gujarat Akruti-TCG Biotech Limited (1)
Akruti Trade Ctr 6th Fl, Marol MIDC Andheri E, Mumbai, 400093, Maharastra, India
Tel.: (91) 2267037400
Web Site: http://www.akrutibiotech.com
Sales Range: $25-49.9 Million
Emp.: 150
Biotechnology Park Promotors & Development Services
N.A.I.C.S.: 541714

Vaishnavi Builders & Developers Private Limited (1)
Akruti Trade Ctr 6th Fl Marol MIDC, Andheri E, Mumbai, 400093, Maharastra, India
Tel.: (91) 2266772301
Real Estate Property Development Services
N.A.I.C.S.: 531311

HUCENTECH CO., LTD.
268 Hagui-ro Gwanyang 2-dong, Dongan-gu, Anyang, Gyeonggi-do, Korea (South)
Tel.: (82) 7078449315
Year Founded: 2015
215090—(KRS)
Rev.: $12,127,884
Assets: $40,628,246
Liabilities: $9,164,074
Net Worth: $31,464,172
Earnings: $11,303,907
Emp.: 98
Fiscal Year-end: 12/31/22
Financial Investment Management Services
N.A.I.C.S.: 523940

HUDACO INDUSTRIES LIMITED
Building 9 Greenstone Hill Office Park Emerald Boulevard, Greenstone Hill, Edenvale, 1609, South Africa
Tel.: (27) 116575000
Web Site: https://www.hudaco.co.za
HDC—(JSE)
Rev.: $484,506,821
Assets: $362,513,099
Liabilities: $172,928,091
Net Worth: $189,585,008
Earnings: $36,454,598
Emp.: 3,635
Fiscal Year-end: 11/30/23
Industrial & Security Products Importer & Distr
N.A.I.C.S.: 423830
Clifford Amoils *(Fin Dir-Grp)*

Subsidiaries:

Ambro Sales (Pty) Ltd. (1)
Cnr Lamp Snapper Rd, Wadeville, Germiston, 1422, South Africa
Tel.: (27) 118244242
Web Site: https://www.ambro.co.za
Sales Range: $25-49.9 Million
Emp.: 35
Metal Cutting Services & Distr
N.A.I.C.S.: 423510

Belting Supply Services (Pty) Ltd (1)
12 Fortune Road, City Deep, Johannesburg, 2136, Gauteng, South Africa (100%)
Tel.: (27) 116105600
Web Site: https://www.belting.co.za
Sales Range: $50-74.9 Million
Emp.: 200
Rubber & Plastics Hoses & Belting Mfr
N.A.I.C.S.: 326220

Elvey Group Ltd (1)
27 Greenstone Place, PO Box 27088, Green Stone Hill Lethabong, Edenvale, 1609, South Africa (100%)
Tel.: (27) 114016700
Web Site: https://www.elveygroup.com
Sales Range: $25-49.9 Million
Emp.: 70
Security System Services
N.A.I.C.S.: 561621

Elvey Security Technologies (Pty) Ltd (1)
27 Greenstone Place Lethabong, Greenstone Hill, 1609, South Africa
Tel.: (27) 114016700
Web Site: https://elvey.co.za
Sales Range: $50-74.9 Million
Emp.: 200
Electrical Apparatus & Equipment Material Whslr
N.A.I.C.S.: 423610
Gary Lowe *(CEO)*

Hudaco Industries Limited - Angus Hawken Division (1)
Hudaco Park, Elandsfontein, 1406, South Africa
Tel.: (27) 14 558 2756
Web Site: http://www.hudaco.co.za
Sales Range: $25-49.9 Million
Emp.: 26
Oil Seal Mfr
N.A.I.C.S.: 339991

Hudaco Industries Limited - Astore Keymak (1)
46 Paul Smit Street Anderbolt, Boksburg, 1459, South Africa
Tel.: (27) 861278673
Web Site: http://astorekeymak.co.za
Thermoplastic Pipe & Fitting Distr
N.A.I.C.S.: 424610
Wayne Masters *(Product Mgr-Industrial & Exports)*

Hudaco Industries Limited - Bauer Geared Motors Division (1)
72 Acacia Road, Primrose, Germiston, 1401, South Africa
Tel.: (27) 118289715
Web Site: https://www.hudacopowertrans.co.za
Sales Range: $25-49.9 Million
Emp.: 4
Geared & Electric Motor Distr
N.A.I.C.S.: 423110

Hudaco Industries Limited - Bearings International Division (1)
Lancaster Commercial Park 12 Merlin Rose Lancaster, Ivy Drives Parkhaven, Boksburg, 1459, South Africa
Tel.: (27) 118990000
Web Site: https://www.bearings.co.za
Emp.: 25
Industrial Bearings Mfr & Distr
N.A.I.C.S.: 333613

Hudaco Industries Limited - Bosworth Division (1)
21 Vereeniging Road, Alrode, 1451, Gauteng, South Africa
Tel.: (27) 118641643
Web Site: https://www.bosworth.co.za
Sales Range: $25-49.9 Million
Emp.: 100
Conveyor Pulleys & Forgings Mfr
N.A.I.C.S.: 332111

Hudaco Industries Pty Ltd. (1)
Emerald Boulevard Greenstone Hill Office Park, Germiston, South Africa
Tel.: (27) 11 878 2600
Web Site: http://www.rutherfordmarine.co.za
Sales Range: $150-199.9 Million
Emp.: 26
Marine Electronic Products Distr
N.A.I.C.S.: 423690

Hudaco Investment Company Limited (1)
4 Walter Place, Durban, 4058, Kwazulu Natal, South Africa
Tel.: (27) 312080101
Investment Management Service
N.A.I.C.S.: 523999

Subsidiary (Domestic):

DD Power Holdings (Pty) Limited (2)
R53 63 Tunney Rd, Germiston, 1401, Gauteng, South Africa
Tel.: (27) 119230600
Emp.: 160
Industrial Equipment Distr
N.A.I.C.S.: 423830
Maurice Pringel *(Mng Dir)*

Subsidiary (Domestic):

DD Power (Pty) Limited (3)
No 5 Tunney Road, Elandsfontein, 1401, Gauteng, South Africa
Tel.: (27) 119230600
Web Site: https://www.deutz.co.za
Emp.: 159
Internal Combustion Engine Mfr
N.A.I.C.S.: 333618

Hudaco Trading Ltd (1)
(100%)
Tel.: (27) 116575000
Web Site: http://www.hudaco.co.za
Emp.: 30
Industrial Machinery & Equipment Whslr
N.A.I.C.S.: 423830

Division (Domestic):

Abes Technoseal (2)
3 Wankel Street Jet Park, Boksburg, 1459, South Africa (100%)
Tel.: (27) 113974070
Web Site: https://www.abes.co.za
Sales Range: $50-74.9 Million
Emp.: 115
Industrial Supplies Whslr
N.A.I.C.S.: 423840

Ernest Lowe (2)
6 Skew Road, Boksburg North, Boksburg, 1460, Gauteng, South Africa (100%)
Tel.: (27) 118986600
Web Site: http://www.elco.co.za
Sales Range: $25-49.9 Million
Emp.: 120
Engineeering Services
N.A.I.C.S.: 541330
Deon Krieger *(Mng Dir)*

Hudaco Transmission (Pty) Ltd (1)
72 Acacia Road Primrose, PO Box 19007, Fishers Hill, Germiston, 1408, South Africa (100%)
Tel.: (27) 118289715
Sales Range: $25-49.9 Million
Emp.: 41
Industrial Machinery & Equipment Whslr
N.A.I.C.S.: 423830

Powermite Africa (Pty) Ltd. (1)
47 Galaxy Ave Linbro Park, Frankenwald, Sandton, 1725, Gauteng, South Africa (100%)
Tel.: (27) 112710000
Web Site: https://www.powermite.co.za
Sales Range: $25-49.9 Million
Emp.: 40
Electrical Equipment & Component Mfr
N.A.I.C.S.: 335999

Division (Domestic):

Powermite Africa (Pty) Ltd. - AMPCO Division (2)
No 1262 Anvil Road Robertville Ext 12, Roodepoort, 1709, South Africa
Tel.: (27) 11 474 9578
Web Site: http://www.ampco.co.za
Sales Range: $25-49.9 Million
Emp.: 7
Industrial Plugs & Sockets Mfr
N.A.I.C.S.: 335931

Valard Bearings Ltd (1)
53 Kelly Road Jet Park, Benoni, 1459, South Africa (100%)
Tel.: (27) 1139734501
Web Site: http://www.valardbearings.com
Emp.: 36
Ball & Roller Bearing Mfr
N.A.I.C.S.: 332991
Alec Scott-Turner *(Mng Dir)*

Varispeed (Pty) Ltd (1)
47 Galaxy Avenue Linbro Business Park, Frankenwald, Sandton, 2090, Gauteng, South Africa (100%)
Tel.: (27) 113125252
Web Site: https://www.varispeed.co.za
Sales Range: $25-49.9 Million
Emp.: 20
Industrial Machinery & Equipment Whslr
N.A.I.C.S.: 423830

HUDBAY MINERALS INC.
25 York Street Suite 800, Toronto, M5J 2V5, ON, Canada
Tel.: (416) 362-8181
Web Site: https://www.hudbayminerals.com
HBM—(NYSE)
Rev.: $1,461,440,000
Assets: $4,325,943,000
Liabilities: $2,754,134,000
Net Worth: $1,571,809,000
Earnings: $70,382,000
Emp.: 2,241
Fiscal Year-end: 12/31/22
Base & Precious Metals Exploration, Development & Mining Services
N.A.I.C.S.: 212290
David Clarry *(VP-Corp Social Responsibility)*

Subsidiaries:

Copper Mountain Mining Corporation (1)
1700 - 700 W Pender Street, Vancouver, V6C 1G8, BC, Canada
Tel.: (604) 682-2992
Web Site: http://www.cumtn.com
Rev.: $267,342,625
Assets: $607,159,581
Liabilities: $334,102,401
Net Worth: $273,057,181
Earnings: $39,320,522
Emp.: 467
Fiscal Year-end: 12/31/2020
Copper Mining Services
N.A.I.C.S.: 212230
Peter Holbek *(VP-Exploration)*

Subsidiary (Domestic):

Similco Mines Ltd (2)
Ste 1700 700 W Pender St, Vancouver, V6C 1G8, BC, Canada
Tel.: (604) 682-2992
Web Site: http://www.cumtn.com
Emp.: 400
Mineral Mining Services
N.A.I.C.S.: 212390

HudBay Marketing and Sales Inc. (1)
25 York Street Suite 800, Toronto, M5J 2V5, ON, Canada
Tel.: (416) 362-8181
Web Site: http://www.hudbayminerals.com
Emp.: 70
Seal Products Distr
N.A.I.C.S.: 423510

HudBay Peru S.A.C. (1)
Calle Amador Merino Reyna No 267 Office 701, San Isidro, Lima, Peru
Tel.: (51) 16122900
Sales Range: $50-74.9 Million
Emp.: 18
Copper Mining
N.A.I.C.S.: 212230

Rockcliff Metals Corporation (1)
82 Richmond Street East, Toronto, M5C 1P1, ON, Canada
Tel.: (416) 644-1752
Web Site: https://www.rockcliffmetals.com
Assets: $618,166
Liabilities: $105,443
Net Worth: $512,724
Earnings: ($1,522,736)
Fiscal Year-end: 03/31/2023
Copper Exploration Services
N.A.I.C.S.: 213114
Omar Gonzalez *(CFO)*

St. Lawrence Zinc Company LLC (1)
408 Sylvia Lk Rd, Gouverneur, NY 13642-3597
Tel.: (315) 287-2500
Lead & Zinc Ore Mining Services
N.A.I.C.S.: 331529

HUDDLESTOCK FINTECH AS
Kanalsletta 2, 4033, Stavanger, Norway
Tel.: (47) 41887412

HUDDLESTOCK FINTECH AS

Huddlestock Fintech AS—(Continued)

Web Site:
https://www.huddlestock.com
Year Founded: 2014
HUDL—(EUR)
Rev.: $2,726,250
Assets: $18,374,355
Liabilities: $5,035,605
Net Worth: $13,338,750
Earnings: ($2,290,110)
Emp.: 30
Fiscal Year-end: 12/31/21
Software Development Services
N.A.I.C.S.: 541511
Gustav Ekeblad (CTO)

HUDDLY AS

Haakon VIIs gate 5, 0161, Oslo, Norway
Tel.: (47) 41215225 NO
Web Site: https://www.huddly.com
Year Founded: 2013
HDLY—(EUR)
Rev.: $39,316,245
Assets: $74,259,766
Liabilities: $22,210,541
Net Worth: $52,049,224
Earnings: ($36,536,923)
Emp.: 87
Fiscal Year-end: 12/31/21
Software Development Services
N.A.I.C.S.: 541511
Stein Ove Eriksen (Chief Product Officer)

HUDLAND REAL ESTATE INVESTMENT AND DEVELOPMENT JSC

12th Floor HUDLAND Tower Block ACC7 Linh Dam Services Complex, Hoang Liet ward Hoang Mai district, Hanoi, Vietnam
Tel.: (84) 436523862
Web Site:
https://www.hudland.com.vn
HLD—(HNX)
Rev.: $3,236,992
Assets: $22,967,225
Liabilities: $5,126,166
Net Worth: $17,841,060
Earnings: $608,853
Fiscal Year-end: 12/31/21
Real Estate Investment & Development
N.A.I.C.S.: 237210

HUDSON BELGIUM SA/NV

Moutstraat 56, 9000, Gent, Belgium
Tel.: (32) 92222695 BE
Employment Solutions Services
N.A.I.C.S.: 561311
Philippe Meysman (COO-Belgium)

Subsidiaries:

Hudson Luxembourg S.A. (1)
15 avenue du Bois, Limpertsberg, L-1251, Luxembourg, Luxembourg (100%)
Tel.: (352) 2697921
Web Site:
http://www.lu.hudsonsolutions.com
Employment Solutions Provider
N.A.I.C.S.: 561311

HUDSON HIGHLAND (APAC) PTY. LIMITED

Level 19 20 Bond St, Sydney, 2000, NSW, Australia
Tel.: (61) 2 8233 2222 AU
Web Site: http://au.hudson.com
Recruitment & Talent Management Services
N.A.I.C.S.: 551112
Mark Steyn (CEO & Mng Dir)

Subsidiaries:

Hudson Global Resources (Australia) Pty Limited (1)
Level 19 20 Bond Street, Sydney, 2000, NSW, Australia (100%)
Tel.: (61) 2 8233 2222
Web Site: http://au.hudson.com
Employment Recruiting Services
N.A.I.C.S.: 561311

Subsidiary (Non-US):

Hudson Global Resources (NZ) Ltd. (2)
Level 12 Crombie Lockwood Tower 191 Queen Street, Auckland, 1010, New Zealand (100%)
Tel.: (64) 99779800
Web Site: http://www.nz.hudson.com
Employment Recruiting Services
N.A.I.C.S.: 561311

Hudson Global Resources Hong Kong Ltd. (1)
Unit 2902-05 29/F Tower Two Times Square, 1 Matheson Street, Causeway Bay, China (Hong Kong) (100%)
Tel.: (852) 25281191
Employment Solutions Provider
N.A.I.C.S.: 561311

Hudson Recruitment Shanghai Limited (1)
No 288 Jiujiang Road Unit 2201-2206 Hongyi International Plaza, No 288 Jiujiang Road, Shanghai, 200001, China (100%)
Tel.: (86) 2123217888
Web Site: http://www.hudson.cn
Employment Solutions Provider
N.A.I.C.S.: 561311

HUDSON INVESTMENT GROUP LIMITED

Level 5 52 Phillip Street, Sydney, 2000, NSW, Australia
Tel.: (61) 292517177
Web Site: https://www.higl.com.au
HGL—(ASX)
Rev.: $1,008,106
Assets: $24,917,240
Liabilities: $9,155,371
Net Worth: $15,761,869
Earnings: $123,970
Emp.: 38
Fiscal Year-end: 12/31/23
Investment Services
N.A.I.C.S.: 213113
John W. Farey (Chm & CEO)

Subsidiaries:

Hudson Marketing Pty Ltd. (1)
2 Kemp Street, Narngulu, Geraldton, 6532, WA, Australia
Tel.: (61) 292517177
Sales Range: $25-49.9 Million
Emp.: 50
Chemical Products Mfr & Marketing Services
N.A.I.C.S.: 325199
Peter Marwood (Mgr)

HUDSON RESOURCES INC.

Suite 1500 701 West Georgia St, Vancouver, V7Y 1C6, BC, Canada
Tel.: (778) 373-2164
Web Site:
https://hudsonresourcesinc.com
Year Founded: 2000
HUDRF—(OTCIQ)
Rev.: $534,569
Assets: $2,571,641
Liabilities: $59,278
Net Worth: $2,512,362
Earnings: $3,293,849
Fiscal Year-end: 03/31/24
Mineral Exploration Services
N.A.I.C.S.: 213114
Jim Cambon (Pres)

HUDSON RESOURCES LIMITED

Hudson House Level 2 131 Macquarie Street, Sydney, 2000, NSW, Australia
Tel.: (61) 2 9251 7177

Web Site:
http://www.hudsonresources.com
Sales Range: $1-9.9 Million
Attapulgite & Diatomite Mining & Sales
N.A.I.C.S.: 212114
Vincent Tan (Exec Dir)

HUDSON RIVER MINERALS LTD.

38 Edmund Seager Drive, Toronto, L4J 4R9, ON, Canada
Tel.: (905) 402-2428 Ca
Year Founded: 2010
Investment Services
N.A.I.C.S.: 523999
Andrew Lindzon (Pres & CEO)

HUESKER SYNTHETIC GMBH

Fabrikstr 13-15, Gescher, 48712, Germany
Tel.: (49) 25427010
Web Site: http://www.huesker.com
Sales Range: $25-49.9 Million
Emp.: 360
Mfr of Geosynthetic Textile Products
N.A.I.C.S.: 314999
Friedrich-Hans Grandin (Mng Dir)

Subsidiaries:

HUESKER Asia Pacific Pte. Ltd. (1)
143 Cecil Street 25-03 GB Building, Singapore, 069542, Singapore
Tel.: (65) 6323 0380
Web Site: http://www.huesker.com
Emp.: 3
Textile Products Distr
N.A.I.C.S.: 424310
Graham Thomson (Mng Dir)

HUESKER Ltd. (1)
3 Quay Business Centre Winwick Quay, Warrington, WA2 8LT, Cheshire, United Kingdom
Tel.: (44) 1925 629 393
Web Site: http://www.huesker.co.uk
Emp.: 4
Textile Products Distr
N.A.I.C.S.: 424310
Graham Horgan (Gen Mgr)

HUESKER Ltda. (1)
R Romualdo Davoli 375 Centro Empresarial Eldorado, San Jose dos Campos, 1238-577, Sao Paulo, Brazil
Tel.: (55) 12 3903 93 00
Web Site: http://www.huesker.com.br
Textile Products Distr
N.A.I.C.S.: 424310

HUESKER OOO (1)
Leningradskoe Chaussee 69 Korp 1, 125445, Moscow, Russia
Tel.: (7) 4952214258
Web Site: http://www.huesker.ru
Textile Products Distr
N.A.I.C.S.: 424310

HUESKER S.A (1)
Pol Industrial Talluntxe II Calle O Nave 8, Noain, 31110, Navarra, Spain
Tel.: (34) 9481 986 06
Web Site: http://www.huesker.es
Textile Products Distr
N.A.I.C.S.: 424310
Hans Grandin (Gen Mgr)

HUESKER SAS (1)
Parc de Manufacture Rue Jacques Coulaux, 67190, Gresswiller, France
Tel.: (33) 3 88 78 26 07
Web Site: http://www.huesker.fr
Textile Products Distr
N.A.I.C.S.: 424310

HUESKER Synthetic B.V. (1)
Het Schild 39 V4, 5275 EB, Den Dungen, Netherlands
Tel.: (31) 88 594 00 50
Textile Products Distr
N.A.I.C.S.: 424310

HUESKER inc. (1)
1419 Gaston St Bldg E, Lincolnton, NC 28092

Tel.: (800) 942-9418
Textile Products Distr
N.A.I.C.S.: 424310

HUESKER s.r.l. (1)
Piazza della Liberta 3, 34132, Trieste, Italy
Tel.: (39) 0403 636 05
Web Site: http://www.huesker.it
Textile Products Distr
N.A.I.C.S.: 424310
Pierpaolo Fantini (Mng Dir)

HUETTENES-ALBERTUS CHEMISCHE WERKE GMBH

Wiesenstrasse 23, 40549, Dusseldorf, Germany
Tel.: (49) 21150870 De
Web Site: http://www.huettenes-albertus.com
Year Founded: 1970
Sales Range: $150-199.9 Million
Emp.: 2,000
Chemicals Mfr
N.A.I.C.S.: 325998
Carsten Kuhlgatz (CEO)

Subsidiaries:

AB Thai Foundry Suppliers Co., Ltd. (1)
2 81 Soi Bangna Trad 25 Bangna Trad Rd, Bangna, 10260, Bangkok, Thailand
Tel.: (66) 23618455
Web Site: http://www.abthai.net
Foundry Raw Material Distr
N.A.I.C.S.: 423510
Panissara Kettong (Mgr-Bus Dev)

Centre West Foundry Supplies Sdn. Bhd. (1)
No 9 Jalan TSB 8, Taman Industri Sungai Buloh, 47000, Petaling Jaya, Kuala Selangor, Malaysia
Tel.: (60) 361576688
Industrial Chemical Whslr
N.A.I.C.S.: 424690

Chemex Foundry Solutions GmbH (1)
Maschstrasse 16, Delligsen, 31073, Holzminden, Germany
Tel.: (49) 518794010
Web Site: http://www.chemex.de
Foundry Raw Material Distr
N.A.I.C.S.: 423510
Karl-Gerhard Klett (Gen Mgr)

EUROKERN Giessereitechnik GmbH (1)
Am Park, 38271, Baddeckenstedt, Germany
Tel.: (49) 5345 9890 0
Web Site: http://www.eurokern.de
Chemical Products Mfr
N.A.I.C.S.: 325998

Gargi Huttenes-Albertus Pvt. Ltd. (1)
2 Mercantile Apartments Dr C Gidwani Road, Chembur, 400074, Mumbai, Maharashtra, India
Tel.: (91) 2225201596
Web Site: http://www.gargi-india.com
Foundry Chemical Product Mfr
N.A.I.C.S.: 325998
Kuldeep Kaushik (Sls Mgr)

HA Foundry Material (Shanghai) Co., Ltd. (1)
No 28 Guinan Road, Litahui Town Songjiang Distric, Shanghai, China
Tel.: (86) 21 5910 1678
Chemical Products Distr
N.A.I.C.S.: 424690

HA France S.A.R.L (1)
Zi of Pont-Brenouille Bp 309, 60870, Pont-Saint-Maxence, France
Tel.: (33) 3 44 70 49 49
Web Site: http://www.huettenes-albertus.fr
Emp.: 50
Chemical Products Mfr
N.A.I.C.S.: 325998

HA International LLC (1)
630 Oakmont Ln, Westmont, IL 60559
Tel.: (630) 575-5700
Web Site: http://www.ha-international.com
Industrial Organic Chemicals
N.A.I.C.S.: 325199

AND PRIVATE COMPANIES / HUGE GROUP LIMITED

Keith McLean *(Pres & CEO)*

HA Italia S.p.A. (1)
Viale della Scienza 78 80, 36100, Vicenza, Italy
Tel.: (39) 0444337444
Web Site: http://www.satef-ha.it
Chemical Product Whslr
N.A.I.C.S.: 424690

HA Kovochem spol s.r.o. (1)
Prazska 900, Mnisek pod Brdy, 252 10, Prague, Czech Republic
Tel.: (420) 318841000
Web Site: http://www.kovochem.cz
Industrial Filter Sleeves Mfr
N.A.I.C.S.: 333413

HA Minerals GmbH (1)
Speditionsinsel 36, 47119, Duisburg, Germany
Tel.: (49) 20357039980
Web Site: http://www.ha-minerals.com
Chemical Products Mfr
N.A.I.C.S.: 325199

HA Romania S.R.L. (1)
Splaiul Unirii Nr 37 Bl M10 Sc 3 Et 6 Apt 93, 030124, Bucharest, Romania
Tel.: (40) 21 320 32 67
Web Site: http://www.huettenes-albertus.ro
Emp.: 4
Chemical Products Mfr
N.A.I.C.S.: 325998

HABRINOL Decin s.r.o. (GmbH) (1)
Tovarni 63, Boletice nad Labem, 407 11, Decin, Czech Republic
Tel.: (420) 412 547 747
Web Site: http://www.habrinol.cz
Chemical Products Mfr
N.A.I.C.S.: 325998
Ladislav Rychtecky *(Co-Mng Dir & Plant Mgr)*

HUETTENES-ALBERTUS CHINA (HONGKONG) CO., LIMITED (1)
Suite 1213 12/F Ocean Centre Harbour City Canton Road, Tsim Sha Tsui, Kowloon, China (Hong Kong)
Tel.: (852) 21 59102226
Chemical Products Distr
N.A.I.C.S.: 424690

Subsidiary (Non-US):

HA Foundry Core (Changchun) Co., Ltd. (2)
No1 Ying Xin Road Dongshan Village Automotive Industry Development Are, Changchun, China
Tel.: (86) 21 59102226
Chemical Products Distr
N.A.I.C.S.: 424690

Huettenes-Albertus Australia Pty. Ltd. (1)
26 Fallon Drive, Dural, 2158, NSW, Australia
Tel.: (61) 2 9651 5966
Web Site: http://www.huettenes-albertus.com.au
Sales Range: $50-74.9 Million
Emp.: 3
Chemical Products Distr
N.A.I.C.S.: 424690
Gary Weber *(Mng Dir)*

Huettenes-Albertus Korea Co., Ltd. (1)
45 Gyeongje ro, Siheung, Gyeonggi, Korea (South)
Tel.: (82) 314991245
Web Site: http://www.hakorea.com
Chemicals Mfr
N.A.I.C.S.: 325199

Huttenes Albertus Belgie N.V. (1)
Bredastraat 29, 3290, Diest, Belgium
Tel.: (32) 2 4791823
Chemical Products Mfr
N.A.I.C.S.: 325998

Huttenes Albertus Nederland B.V. (1)
Einsteinstraat 29a, 3290, Veenendaal, Netherlands
Tel.: (31) 318519171
Chemical Products Mfr
N.A.I.C.S.: 325998

Huttenes-Albertus (UK) Ltd. (1)
Vision Point Vaughan Trading EstateÂ Sedgley Road East, Tipton, DY4 7UJ, West Midlands, United Kingdom
Tel.: (44) 121 270 0834
Web Site: http://www.huttenes-albertus.co.uk
Sales Range: $50-74.9 Million
Emp.: 6
Chemical Product Whslr
N.A.I.C.S.: 424690

Huttenes-Albertus Polska Sp. Z.o.o. (1)
Ul Turystyczna 7, 20-207, Lublin, Poland
Tel.: (48) 817451394
Web Site: http://www.huettenes-albertus.pl
Chemical Product Whslr
N.A.I.C.S.: 424690

Ilarduya Productos de Fundicion (1)
B Boroa S/N Apdo 35, 48340, Amorebieta-Etxano, Biscay, Spain
Tel.: (34) 94 673 08 58
Web Site: http://www.ha-ilarduya.com
Chemical Products Mfr
N.A.I.C.S.: 325998

Metko Huttenes Albertus Kimya Sanayi Ve Ticaret A.S. (1)
Bagdat Cad No 191/A Plaza 215 Kat 4-5 D 9, 34730, Istanbul, Turkiye
Tel.: (90) 216 411 69 11
Web Site: http://www.metkoha.com
Chemical Products Mfr
N.A.I.C.S.: 325998

Okazaki HA Chemicals Co. Ltd. (1)
Okazaki Building No 12-6 Utsubohonmachi 1-Chome, Nishiku, Osaka, 550-0004, Japan
Tel.: (81) 6 6443 8181
Emp.: 20
Chemical Products Distr
N.A.I.C.S.: 424690
Toshiyuki Saiki *(Mgr)*

PT Haltraco Sarana Mulia (1)
Grand Slipi Tower 6th floor Jl Letjen S Parman Kav 22 24, 11480, Jakarta, Indonesia
Tel.: (62) 2129021901
Web Site: http://www.haltraco.com
Foundry Product Distr
N.A.I.C.S.: 423510

Satef Huettenes Albertus S.p.A. (1)
Viale Della Scienza 78/80, Vicenza, 36100, Italy
Tel.: (39) 0444 337444
Chemical Products Mfr
N.A.I.C.S.: 325998

Shanghai HA International Trading Co. Ltd. (1)
Room 808 No 1198 Defu Road, Jiading District, Shanghai, 201801, China
Tel.: (86) 21 60406705
Web Site: http://www.ha-china.com
Sales Range: $25-49.9 Million
Emp.: 30
Chemical Products Distr
N.A.I.C.S.: 424690

Shinmyung HA Ltd. (1)
1Ra-704 Sihwa Industry Complex 1237-4 Jeongwang-Dong, Siheung, 429-848, Gyeonggi-do, Korea (South)
Tel.: (82) 31-432 6236
Chemical Products Distr
N.A.I.C.S.: 424690

Uralchimplast Huttenes-Albertus Ltd. (1)
Severnoe Shosse 21, 622012, Sverdlovskaya, Russia
Tel.: 3435346007
Web Site: http://www.huettenes-albertus.ru
Chemical Products Mfr
N.A.I.C.S.: 325998

HUF HULSBECK & FURST GMBH & CO. KG
Steeger Str 17, 42551, Velbert, Germany
Tel.: (49) 20512720
Web Site: http://www.huf-group.com
Year Founded: 1908
Sales Range: $1-4.9 Billion
Emp.: 7,800
Automotive Mechanical & Electrical Locksets Mfr
N.A.I.C.S.: 336890
Ulrich Hulsbeck *(Co-COO)*

Subsidiaries:

Chongqing Huf Automotive Systems Co., Ltd. (1)
No 6 Jinye Road, Liangjiang New Area Longxing Town, Chongqing, 401135, China
Tel.: (86) 2388958199
Electronic Digital Key & Steering Lockset Mfr
N.A.I.C.S.: 336320

Huf Electronics Dusseldorf GmbH (1)
Oberhausener Strasse 22, 40472, Dusseldorf, Germany
Tel.: (49) 211 90491 6534
Web Site: http://www.huf-group.com
Automotive Mechanical & Electrical Lockset Mfr
N.A.I.C.S.: 336390

Subsidiary (Domestic):

Huf Electronics Bretten GmbH (2)
Gewerbestr 40, Bretten, 75015, Germany
Tel.: (49) 72529700
Emp.: 230
Electric Equipment Mfr
N.A.I.C.S.: 334419
Serge-Patrick Tchuente *(Sr Engr-Software Test)*

Huf Espana s.a. (1)
Poligono Industrial La Guera 6, El Burgo de Osma, 42300, Soria, Spain
Tel.: (34) 975 368100
Emp.: 400
Automotive Parts Mfr & Distr
N.A.I.C.S.: 336390
Jose V. Forner *(Mng Dir)*

Huf India Private Limited (1)
Gat No 304 Nanekarwadi, Tal Khed, Pune, 410501, India
Tel.: (91) 2135 674100
Emp.: 150
Automobile Parts Mfr
N.A.I.C.S.: 336390
Kanchan Bhave *(Head-Maintenance)*

Huf Japan Co., Ltd. (1)
Kitada Building 5F Hamamatsu-Cho 2-1-16, Minato-Ku, Tokyo, 105-0013, Japan
Tel.: (81) 3 5733 5048
Security Device Distr
N.A.I.C.S.: 423710

Huf Korea Limited (1)
321 Keumkang Penterium IT Tower 282 Hagui-ro, Dongan-gu, Anyang, 431-810, Gyeonggi-do, Korea (South)
Tel.: (82) 31 337 5901
New Car Dealers
N.A.I.C.S.: 441110
Huiwon Kim *(Gen Mgr)*

Huf Mexico S. de R.L. de C.V. (1)
Prolongacion Periferico Ecologico 46 San Francisco Ocotlan, Municipio de Coronango, Puebla, 72680, Mexico
Tel.: (52) 222 141 5000
Emp.: 550
Security Device Mfr
N.A.I.C.S.: 327910
Hector Salinas *(Mgr-IT)*

Huf Polska Sp. z.o.o. (1)
Ul Strefowa 6, 43-100, Tychy, Poland
Tel.: (49) 32 7808 500
Emp.: 800
Plastic Molding Mfr
N.A.I.C.S.: 326199
Nikodem Pyka *(Mgr-Tooling & Plastics Tech)*

Huf Portuguesa, Lda. (1)
Municipal Industrial Zone-Adica, 3460-070, Tondela, Portugal
Tel.: (351) 232819100
Electronic Digital Key & Steering Lockset Mfr
N.A.I.C.S.: 336320

Huf Romania S.R.L. (1)
Zona Industriala Nord-Vest Strada IV Nr 7, 310491, Arad, Romania
Tel.: (40) 257 220 110
Web Site: http://www.huf-group.com
Emp.: 400
Door Handle Mfr
N.A.I.C.S.: 332999
Sandor Kiss *(Engr-Software Test)*

Huf Secure Mobile GmbH (1)
Haberstrasse 46, 42551, Velbert, Germany
Tel.: (49) 20512720
Digital Access & Authorization System Services
N.A.I.C.S.: 541512
Mete Koksen *(Head-Quality Svc)*

Huf Tools GmbH (1)
Guterstrasse 17, 42551, Velbert, Germany
Tel.: (49) 2051 2767 0
Web Site: http://www.huf-tools.de
Emp.: 103
Industrial Mold Mfr
N.A.I.C.S.: 333511

Subsidiary (Non-US):

Yantai Huf Tools Co. Ltd. (2)
No 2 Guangzhou Road Building No 9 Development Distriction, 264006, Yantai, Shandong, China
Tel.: (86) 535 695 2358
Security Device Mfr
N.A.I.C.S.: 332510

Huf U.K. Ltd. (1)
Black Country New Road, Tipton, DY4 0PT, West Midlands, United Kingdom
Tel.: (44) 121 521 1300
Emp.: 250
Plastic Molding Mfr
N.A.I.C.S.: 326199
Daniel Keates *(Project Mgr)*

Huf do Brasil Ltda. (1)
Rodovia D Pedro I Km 82 7, Caixa Postal 25, 12954-260, Atibaia, Brazil
Tel.: (55) 11 3402 6020
Security Device Distr
N.A.I.C.S.: 423710
Alessandro Takayama *(Mgr-IT)*

Shanghai Huf Automotive Lock Co., Ltd. (1)
No 396 Yuantai Road Baoshan Urban Industrial Park, Shanghai, 200444, China
Tel.: (86) 21 36161956
Emp.: 500
Automobile Parts Mfr
N.A.I.C.S.: 336390
Jerry Ouyang *(Engr-Supplier Quality)*

Yantai Huf Automotive Lock Co., Ltd. (1)
9 Wuzhi Shan Road Development Zone, Yantai, 264006, Shandong, China
Tel.: (86) 535 6378 608
Emp.: 900
Automobile Parts Mfr
N.A.I.C.S.: 336390
Derek Yu *(Project Engr)*

Subsidiary (Domestic):

Changchun Huf Automotive Lock Co. Ltd. (2)
No 899 Changhong Road Automotive Economic Development Area, Changchun, 130013, Jilin, China
Tel.: (86) 431 85985001
Security Device Distr
N.A.I.C.S.: 423690
Min Hao *(Sec)*

HUGE GROUP LIMITED
1 Melrose Boulevard Melrose Arch, Johannesburg, 2076, South Africa
Tel.: (27) 116036000   ZA
Web Site: https://www.hugegroup.com
HUG—(JSE)
Rev.: $2,068,121
Assets: $108,952,819
Liabilities: $18,326,588
Net Worth: $90,626,232
Earnings: $1,926,478
Emp.: 300
Fiscal Year-end: 02/29/24
Investment Management Service

HUGE GROUP LIMITED

Huge Group Limited—(Continued)
N.A.I.C.S.: 523940
James Charles Herbst *(CEO)*

Subsidiaries:

Huge Connect Proprietary
Limited **(1)**
2nd Floor 267 West Building 267 West Avenue, Centurion, 0157, South Africa
Tel.: (27) 878200220
Web Site: http://www.hugeconnect.co.za
Telecommunication Services
N.A.I.C.S.: 517810
Devante Jacobs *(Mgr-Svc)*

Huge Distribution Proprietary
Limited **(1)**
Unit 10 The Refinery Cnr North Road and George Allen Street wilbart, Edenvale, Johannesburg, South Africa
Tel.: (27) 100106777
Web Site: https://www.hugedistribution.co.za
Telecommunication Distr
N.A.I.C.S.: 423610

Huge Networks Proprietary
Limited **(1)**
Unit 2 22 Rome Road Brackengate Business Park, Brackenfell, 7560, South Africa
Tel.: (27) 107860000
Web Site: http://www.hugenetworks.co.za
Data Services
N.A.I.C.S.: 517810
Lucia Vermaak *(Mgr-HR)*

Huge Telecom Proprietary
Limited **(1)**
First Floor East Wing 146a Kelvin Drive, Woodmead, Johannesburg, 2191, South Africa
Tel.: (27) 116036000
Web Site: http://www.hugetelecom.co.za
Telecommunication Services
N.A.I.C.S.: 517810
Rob Burger *(Mng Dir)*

Pansmart Proprietary Limited **(1)**
Unit 9 Block C Rambo Junxion Corporate Park North Old Pretoria Road, Midrand, Johannesburg, 1682, South Africa
Tel.: (27) 100106777
Web Site: http://www.pansmart.co.za
Communication Service
N.A.I.C.S.: 517810
Louis Fourie *(Mng Dir)*

HUGEL, INC.
61-20 Sinbuk-ro, Sinbuk-eup, 24206, Chuncheon, Gangwon-do, Korea (South)
Tel.: (82) 332553882
Web Site: https://www.hugel-inc.com
Year Founded: 2001
145020—(KRS)
Rev.: $216,044,829
Assets: $805,183,506
Liabilities: $153,651,954
Net Worth: $651,531,552
Earnings: $43,973,510
Emp.: 494
Fiscal Year-end: 12/31/22
Pharmaceuticals Product Mfr
N.A.I.C.S.: 325412
Ji-Hoon Sohn *(CEO)*

HUGHES CASTELL (HONG KONG) LTD.
Room 2101 21/F Singga Commercial Centre 144-151 Connaught Road West, 10 Harcourt Road, Hong Kong, China (Hong Kong)
Tel.: (852) 25201168
Web Site: http://www.hughes-castell.com
Year Founded: 1985
Sales Range: $25-49.9 Million
Emp.: 13
Legal Recruitment Services
N.A.I.C.S.: 561312
Doreen Jaeger-Soong *(Chm & Mng Dir)*

HUHTAMAKI INDIA LIMITED
7th 8th 9th Floor Bellona The Walk, Hiranandani Estate Ghodbunder Road, Thane, 400607, Maharashtra, India
Tel.: (91) 2221735591
Web Site: https://www.huhtamaki.com
509820—(BOM)
Rev.: $359,629,725
Assets: $246,826,125
Liabilities: $149,093,490
Net Worth: $97,732,635
Earnings: ($3,097,185)
Emp.: 3,025
Fiscal Year-end: 12/31/21
Packaging Machinery Mfr
N.A.I.C.S.: 333993
Murali Sivaraman *(Chm)*

Subsidiaries:

Elif Global Packaging S.A.E. **(1)**
Engineering Square Plot No O18-O20, North Extension of Industrial Zones, 6th of October City, Cairo, Egypt
Tel.: (20) 238642188
Packaging Services
N.A.I.C.S.: 561910

Elif Global S.A. **(1)**
Avenue Gratta-Paille 2, C/O Mazars Sa Vaud, 1018, Lausanne, Switzerland
Tel.: (41) 213104949
Packaging Services
N.A.I.C.S.: 561910

Elif Holding Ahonim Sirket **(1)**
Orhangazi Mahallesi 1652 Sokak No 2, Esenyurt, 34538, Istanbul, Turkiye
Tel.: (90) 2126220622
Packaging Services
N.A.I.C.S.: 561910

HUHTAMAKI OYJ
Revontulenkuja 1, 02100, Espoo, Finland
Tel.: (358) 106867000   FI
Web Site: https://www.huhtamaki.com
Year Founded: 1920
HUH1V—(HEL)
Rev.: $4,390,835,176
Assets: $5,578,911,728
Liabilities: $3,617,166,800
Net Worth: $1,961,744,928
Earnings: $248,964,248
Emp.: 19,564
Fiscal Year-end: 12/31/21
Consumer Disposable Tableware & Packaging Products Mfr
N.A.I.C.S.: 322219
Katariina Hietaranta *(Head-Media Rels)*

Subsidiaries:

Arabian Paper Products
Company **(1)**
PO Box 1520, Al Khobar, 31952, Saudi Arabia **(40%)**
Tel.: (966) 38871000
Web Site: http://www.olayangroup.com
Sales Range: $25-49.9 Million
Emp.: 75
Paper Cup Mfr
N.A.I.C.S.: 322219

Elif Holding Anonim Sirketi **(1)**
Orhangazi Mahallesi 1652 Sokak No 2 Esenyurt, 34538, Istanbul, Turkiye
Tel.: (90) 2126220622
Web Site: https://elif.com
Flexible Packaging Services
N.A.I.C.S.: 561910

Huhtamaki (Guangzhou) Limited **(1)**
15 Ganzhu Road GETDD, Yonghe Economy District, Guangzhou, 511356, China
Tel.: (86) 20 32222 883
Web Site: http://foodservice.huhtamaki.cn
Packaging Materials Mfr

N.A.I.C.S.: 322220
Huhtamaki (NZ) Holdings Ltd **(1)**
30 Keeling Road, Henderson, 612, Auckland, New Zealand
Tel.: (64) 9 8370510
Web Site: http://www.huhtamaki.com
Sales Range: $75-99.9 Million
Emp.: 20
Investment Management Service
N.A.I.C.S.: 523999

Unit (Domestic):

Huhtamaki New Zealand Limited -
Flexible Food Packaging Business
Unit **(2)**
31 Bairds Road, Auckland, New Zealand
Tel.: (64) 92768072
Web Site: http://www2.huhtamaki.com
Packaging Paper Products Mfr
N.A.I.C.S.: 322220

Huhtamaki New Zealand Limited -
Molded Fiber Business Unit **(2)**
31 Bairds Road, Otahuhu, Auckland, 2025, New Zealand
Tel.: (64) 9 276 8072
Web Site: http://www.huhtamaki.com
Sales Range: $25-49.9 Million
Emp.: 40
Molded Fiber Tray Mfr
N.A.I.C.S.: 322299

Huhtamaki (Thailand) Limited **(1)**
1/2 Moo 2 Samutsakorn Industrial Estate Rama 2 Road, Ta-Sai Muang, Samut Sakhon, 74000, Thailand
Tel.: (66) 3 440 3000
Web Site: http://www.huhtamaki.co.th
Emp.: 70
Packaging Products Mfr
N.A.I.C.S.: 322220

Plant (Domestic):

Huhtamaki (Thailand) Limited - Plant
1 **(2)**
1/2 M 2 Samutsakorn Industrial Estate Rama 2 Rd, Ta-Sai Muang, Samut Sakhon, 74000, Thailand
Tel.: (66) 34 403 000
Flexible Packaging Products Mfr
N.A.I.C.S.: 322220

Huhtamaki (Thailand) Limited - Plant
2 **(2)**
Samutsakorn Industrial Estate 1/6 Moo 2 Rama 2 Road, Ta-Sai Muang, Samut Sakhon, 74000, Thailand
Tel.: (66) 34 403 000
Packaging Paper Products Mfr
N.A.I.C.S.: 322220

Huhtamaki (Tianjin) Ltd. **(1)**
No 16 Quanhui Road, Wuqing Development District, Tianjin, 301700, Wuqing, China **(100%)**
Tel.: (86) 222 532 2222
Web Site: http://www.huhtamaki.com
Sales Range: $50-74.9 Million
Emp.: 250
Food Packaging Services
N.A.I.C.S.: 327213

Huhtamaki (UK) Ltd. **(1)**
Rowner Rd, Gosport, PO13 OPR, Hampshire, United Kingdom **(100%)**
Tel.: (44) 2392584234
Sales Range: $50-74.9 Million
Emp.: 240
Food Packaging Services
N.A.I.C.S.: 326199

Plant (Domestic):

Huhtamaki (UK) Ltd. **(2)**
1 Pikelaw Pl W Pimbo, Skelmersdale, WN8 9PP, Lancashire, United Kingdom **(100%)**
Tel.: (44) 1695733711
Web Site: http://www.huhtamaki.com
Sales Range: $50-74.9 Million
Emp.: 120
Food Packaging Services
N.A.I.C.S.: 326199

Huhtamaki (Vietnam) Ltd **(1)**
22 VSIP Road No 8 Vietnam-Singapore Industrial Park, Thuan An District, Ho Chi Minh City, Vietnam

INTERNATIONAL PUBLIC

Sales Range: $100-124.9 Million
Emp.: 35
Packaging Paper Products Mfr
N.A.I.C.S.: 322220

Huhtamaki Australia Pty. Ltd. **(1)**
120 Mileham Street, Windsor, 2756, NSW, Australia **(100%)**
Tel.: (61) 245770700
Web Site: http://www.huhtamaki.com
Mfr of Food Packaging & Disposable Dishes
N.A.I.C.S.: 322219

Unit (Domestic):

Huhtamaki Australia Pty Ltd - Flexible
Packaging Sales Unit **(2)**
Level 2 395 Ferntree Gully Road, Mount Waverley, 3149, VIC, Australia
Tel.: (61) 3 951 803 00
Sales Range: $25-49.9 Million
Emp.: 1
Flexible Packaging Materials Mfr
N.A.I.C.S.: 322220
John Kapiniaris *(Dir-Sls)*

Huhtamaki Australia Pty Ltd - Food
Service Business Unit **(2)**
Level 2 3 Rider Blvde, Rhodes, 2138, NSW, Australia
Tel.: (61) 2 457 707 00
Sales Range: $25-49.9 Million
Emp.: 15
Food Packaging Materials Mfr
N.A.I.C.S.: 322220
Brad Kerle *(Gen Mgr)*

Branch (Domestic):

Huhtamaki Australia Pty Ltd. **(2)**
120 Mileham Street, Windsor, 2756, NSW, Australia **(100%)**
Tel.: (61) 180 004 3584
Web Site: http://www.huhtamaki.com
Food Packaging Services
N.A.I.C.S.: 326199

Huhtamaki Australia Pty Ltd. **(2)**
75 Raglan St, PO Box 8263, Preston, 3072, VIC, Australia **(100%)**
Tel.: (61) 394741200
Food Packaging Services
N.A.I.C.S.: 326199

Huhtamaki Ceska Republika A/S **(1)**
Petrovicka 101, Pribyslavice, 675 21, Okrisky, Czech Republic **(100%)**
Tel.: (420) 568894111
Emp.: 200
Food Packaging Services
N.A.I.C.S.: 327213

Huhtamaki Consorcio Mexicana S.A.
de C.V. **(1)**
Avenida 1 No 13, Tultitlan, 54900, Hidalgo, Mexico
Tel.: (52) 5558987000
Plastic Tumbler Mfr
N.A.I.C.S.: 326199

Huhtamaki Egypt **(1)**
2nd Industrial Area Plot 34, PO Box 91, Sadat City, Egypt **(75%)**
Tel.: (20) 48 260 7375
Web Site: https://www.huhtamaki.com
Sales Range: $25-49.9 Million
Emp.: 11
Food Packaging Services
N.A.I.C.S.: 327213

Huhtamaki Estonia Ltd. **(1)**
Adamsoni 2, 10137, Tallinn, Estonia
Tel.: (372) 6691190
Web Site: https://www.huhtamaki.com
Food Packaging Products Mfr
N.A.I.C.S.: 322220

Huhtamaki Finance BV **(1)**
Wegalaan 8, 2132 HE, Hoofddorp, Netherlands **(100%)**
Tel.: (31) 23 567 9988
Web Site: https://www.huhtamaki.com
Sales Range: $50-74.9 Million
Emp.: 10
N.A.I.C.S.: 326199

Huhtamaki Flexible Packaging Germany GmbH & Co. KG
Heinrich Nicolaus Strasse 6, 87671, Rons-

berg, Germany **(100%)**
Tel.: (49) 8306770
Web Site:
https://www.flexibles.huhtamaki.eu
Sales Range: $25-49.9 Million
Emp.: 65
Food Packaging Services
N.A.I.C.S.: 333993

Huhtamaki Flexibles Italy S.r.l. (1)
Corso Genova 18, 15050, Tortona, Italy
Tel.: (39) 013 189 3211
Web Site: http://www.huhtamaki.it
Sales Range: $25-49.9 Million
Emp.: 160
Commercial Packaging Services
N.A.I.C.S.: 561910

Huhtamaki Foodservice (Shanghai) Limited (1)
No 218 East Jiangtian Road, Songjiang District, Shanghai, 201613, China
Tel.: (86) 2161963999
Food Packaging Product Mfr & Distr
N.A.I.C.S.: 322219

Huhtamaki Foodservice (Tianjin) Ltd. (1)
No 16 Quanhui Road, Wuqing Development District, Tianjin, 301700, China
Tel.: (86) 2225322222
Food Product Mfr & Distr
N.A.I.C.S.: 311999

Huhtamaki Foodservice Finland Oy (1)
Polarpakintie, 13300, Hameenlinna, Finland
Tel.: (358) 10 686 7000
Packaging Materials Mfr
N.A.I.C.S.: 322220

Huhtamaki Foodservice France S.A.S. (1)
14 Rue Helle Nice, 28700, Auneau, France
Tel.: (33) 237917740
Emp.: 14
Food Products Packaging Services
N.A.I.C.S.: 561910

Huhtamaki Foodservice Germany GmbH & Co. KG (1)
Bad Bertricher Strasse 6-9, 56859, Alf, Germany **(100%)**
Tel.: (49) 6 542 8020
Web Site: https://www.huhtamaki.com
Sales Range: $125-149.9 Million
Emp.: 450
Paper-Based, Plastic Packaging Products Mfr
N.A.I.C.S.: 322219

Subsidiary (Domestic):

Huhtamaki Alf Zweigniederlassung der Huhtamaki Deutschland GmbH & Co KG (2)
Bad Bertricher Str 6-9, 56859, Alf, Germany
Tel.: (49) 6542 802 0
Packaging Paper Materials Mfr
N.A.I.C.S.: 322220

Huhtamaki Forchheim Zweigniederlassung der Huhtamaki Deutschland GmbH & Co KG (2)
Zweibruckenstrasse 15-25, 91301, Forchheim, Germany
Tel.: (49) 91 918 10
Sales Range: $200-249.9 Million
Emp.: 62
Packaging Paper Products Mfr
N.A.I.C.S.: 322220
D. Anand *(Gen Mgr)*

Huhtamaki Ronsberg - Zweigniederlassung der Huhtamaki Deutschland GmbH & Co KG (2)
Heinrich Nicolaus Strasse 6, Ronsberg Allgau, 87671, Ronsberg, Germany
Tel.: (49) 8306 77 0
Packaging Paper Materials Mfr
N.A.I.C.S.: 322220
Ulf Wienboeker *(Gen Mgr)*

Huhtamaki Foodservice Germany Sales GmbH & Co. KG (1)
Bad Bertricher Strasse 6-9, 56859, Alf, Germany
Tel.: (49) 65428020
Food Product Mfr & Distr

N.A.I.C.S.: 311412

Huhtamaki Foodservice Gliwice Sp. z o.o. (1)
Ul Bojkowska 61A, 44-100, Gliwice, Poland
Tel.: (48) 324169035
Food Packaging Product Mfr & Distr
N.A.I.C.S.: 322219

Huhtamaki Foodservice Poland Sp. z.o.o. (1)
ul Handlowa 20, 41-253, Czeladz, Poland
Tel.: (48) 328885700
Web Site: https://www.huhtamaki.com
Sales Range: $150-199.9 Million
Emp.: 333
Packaging Product Distr
N.A.I.C.S.: 423840

Plant (Domestic):

Huhtamaki Foodservice Poland Sp. z.o.o. - XPS Plant (2)
Budowlana 6 Street, Siemianowice, 41253, Poland
Tel.: (48) 32 888 57 00
Sales Range: $100-124.9 Million
Emp.: 30
Food Packaging Products Mfr
N.A.I.C.S.: 322220
Marcin Gruszczynski *(Gen Mgr)*

Huhtamaki Foodservice Ukraine LLC (1)
Tel.: (380) 442287168
Web Site: http://www.huhtamaki.com
Food Packaging Product Mfr & Distr
N.A.I.C.S.: 322219

Huhtamaki Henderson Ltd. (1) **(100%)**
Tel.: (64) 98370510
Web Site: https://www.huhtamaki.com
Sales Range: $50-74.9 Million
Emp.: 250
Food Packaging & Disposable Dishes Mfr
N.A.I.C.S.: 322219

Unit (Domestic):

Huhtamaki Henderson Limited - Food Service Business Unit (2)
30 Keeling Road, Henderson, Auckland, 0612, New Zealand
Tel.: (64) 98370510
Web Site: https://www.huhtamaki.com
Sales Range: $50-74.9 Million
Emp.: 250
Packaging Paper Products Mfr
N.A.I.C.S.: 322220

Huhtamaki Hong Kong Limited (1)
Units 1709-10 Level 17 Landmark North 39 Lung Sum Avenue, Sheung Shui, New Territories, China (Hong Kong)
Tel.: (852) 2474 3033
Packaging Paper Products Mfr
N.A.I.C.S.: 322220

Branch (Non-US):

Huhtamaki Hong Kong Limited Taiwan Branch Office (2)
12F No 96 Nanking East Road Sec 2, Taipei, Taiwan
Tel.: (886) 225313368
Sales Range: $50-74.9 Million
Emp.: 3
Distribution of Food Packaging & Disposable Dishes
N.A.I.C.S.: 424130

Huhtamaki Hungary Kft (1)
Fehervari Ut 132-144, 1116, Budapest, Hungary
Tel.: (36) 12062906
Sales Range: $50-74.9 Million
Emp.: 6
Packaging Paper Products Distr
N.A.I.C.S.: 424130

Huhtamaki Istanbul Ambalaj Sanayi A.S. (1)
Hadimkoy Yolu Uzeri San Bir Bulvari 3 Bolge 6 Cadde No 46, Buyukcekmece, 34900, Istanbul, Turkiye **(83%)**
Tel.: (90) 2128865011
Web Site: http://www.huhtamaki.tr
Sales Range: $50-74.9 Million
Emp.: 200
Food Packaging Services

N.A.I.C.S.: 327213
Hakam Yayalar *(Gen Mgr)*

Huhtamaki La Rochelle S.A.S. (1)
4 Rue Des Ponts Neufs, 85770, L'Ile-d'Elle, France
Tel.: (33) 251531515
Web Site: https://www.huhtamaki.com
Emp.: 200
Fibber Packaging Mfr
N.A.I.C.S.: 322211

Huhtamaki La Rochelle SNC (1)
4 Rue Des Ponts Neufs, 85770, L'Ile-d'Elle, France
Tel.: (33) 25 153 1515
Web Site: https://www.huhtamaki.com
Sales Range: $50-74.9 Million
Emp.: 200
Food Packaging Services
N.A.I.C.S.: 327213

Huhtamaki Ltd. (1)
66 Ravarnet Rd, Lisburn, BT27 5NB, United Kingdom **(100%)**
Tel.: (44) 2892672116
Sales Range: $25-49.9 Million
Emp.: 9
Food Packaging Services
N.A.I.C.S.: 327213
Corin Goodall *(Mgr-Depot)*

Subsidiary (Domestic):

Huhtamaki (Lisburn) Ltd (2)
66 Ravarnet Road, Lisburn, BT27 5NB, United Kingdom
Tel.: (44) 2892672116
Sales Range: $25-49.9 Million
Emp.: 1
Molded Fiber Tray Distr
N.A.I.C.S.: 424130
Corin Goodall *(Gen Mgr)*

Huhtamaki (Lurgan) Limited (2)
41 Inn Road, Dollingstown, Lurgan, BT66 7JN, Co Armagh, United Kingdom
Tel.: (44) 2838327711
Sales Range: $50-74.9 Million
Emp.: 170
Food Packaging Services
N.A.I.C.S.: 327213

Huhtamaki Malaysia Sdn Bhd (1)
No 1 Jalan Cj 1 4 Cheras Jaya, Balakong, 43200, Selangor Darul Ehsan, Malaysia **(100%)**
Tel.: (60) 390744731
Web Site: http://www.huhtamaki.com
Sales Range: $50-74.9 Million
Emp.: 120
Food Packaging Services
N.A.I.C.S.: 326199

Huhtamaki Mexicana S.A. De C.V. (1)
Av Uno No 13 Parque Industrial Cartagena, 54900, Tultitlan, Estado de Mexico, Mexico **(100%)**
Tel.: (52) 5558987000
Web Site: https://www.huhtamaki.com
Disposable Tableware Mfr
N.A.I.C.S.: 322219

Huhtamaki Moulded Fibre do Brasil Ltda. (1)
BR-376 Km 67 Pavilhao 2, Usina Do Salto, Palmeira, 84130-000, PR, Brazil **(100%)**
Tel.: (55) 413 661 1297
Web Site: http://www.huhtamaki.com
Emp.: 180
Food Packaging Services
N.A.I.C.S.: 326199

Huhtamaki Nederland B.V. (1)
Zuidelijke Industrieweg 3-7, PO Box 5, 8801 JB, Franeker, Netherlands **(100%)**
Tel.: (31) 517399399
Web Site: https://www.huhtamaki.com
Sales Range: $50-74.9 Million
Emp.: 200
Food Packaging Services
N.A.I.C.S.: 327213

Subsidiary (Domestic):

Huhtamaki Molded Fiber Technology B.V. (2)
Poolsterweg 3, 8938 AN, Leeuwarden, Netherlands

Web Site: https://www.huhtamaki.com
Pulp Molding Machinery Distr
N.A.I.C.S.: 423830

Huhtamaki New Zealand Limited (1)
31 Bairds Road, Otahuhu, Auckland, 2025, New Zealand
Tel.: (64) 92768072
Fibber Packaging Mfr
N.A.I.C.S.: 322211

Huhtamaki Norway A/S (1)
Kartverksveien 7, Honefoss, 3511, Norway
Tel.: (47) 32 11 40 00
Web Site: http://www2.huhtamaki.com
Sales Range: $25-49.9 Million
Emp.: 10
Plastic Cup Mfr
N.A.I.C.S.: 326199

Huhtamaki Paper Recycling B.V. (1)
De Hemmen 50, 9206 AG, Drachten, Netherlands **(100%)**
Tel.: (31) 512571100
Sales Range: $25-49.9 Million
Emp.: 30
Food Packaging Services
N.A.I.C.S.: 327213

Subsidiary (Non-US):

LeoCzech spol s.r.o (2)
Hostin u Vojkovic c p 64, Melnik District, 277 44, Hostin u Vojkovic, Czech Republic
Tel.: (420) 608374526
Web Site: https://www.leoczech.cz
Paper Products Mfr
N.A.I.C.S.: 322120
Lenka Jichova *(Mgr)*

Huhtamaki Philippines, Inc. (1)
U-10th Floor Net Lima Centre 5th Avenue Corner 26th Street, Bonifacio Global City, Taguig, 1634, Philippines
Tel.: (63) 286692719
Packaging Product Mfr & Distr
N.A.I.C.S.: 326112

Huhtamaki Protective Packaging B.V. (1)
PO Box 5, 8800 AA, Franeker, Netherlands
Tel.: (31) 517399399
Emp.: 200
Food Packaging Services
N.A.I.C.S.: 327213

Huhtamaki Russia (1)
Zheleznodorozhnaya Ulitsa 1, Ivanteevka, 141281, Moskovskaja Oblast, Russia
Tel.: (7) 4957833731
Web Site:
http://www.foodservice.huhtamaki.ru
Emp.: 400
Food Packaging Services
N.A.I.C.S.: 333993

Huhtamaki Singapore Pte. Ltd. (1)
8 Admiralty Street 07-16 ADMIRAX, Singapore, 757438, Singapore **(100%)**
Tel.: (65) 6 758 7730
Web Site: http://www.huhtamaki.com
Sales Range: $25-49.9 Million
Emp.: 7
Food Packaging Services
N.A.I.C.S.: 326199

Huhtamaki South Africa (Pty) Ltd. (1)
44 Charles Matthew Street, Atlantis, Cape Town, 7349, South Africa **(100%)**
Tel.: (27) 21 577 2257
Web Site: https://www.huhtamaki.com
Sales Range: $25-49.9 Million
Emp.: 60
Food Packaging Services
N.A.I.C.S.: 327213

Plant (Domestic):

Huhtamaki South Africa (Pty) Ltd. (2)
Charles Mathew St, PO Box 1613, Dassenburg, Atlantis, 7350, South Africa **(100%)**
Tel.: (27) 215772257
Sales Range: $25-49.9 Million
Emp.: 80
Food Packaging Services
N.A.I.C.S.: 326199
Nico Nell *(Gen Mgr)*

HUHTAMAKI OYJ

Huhtamaki Oyj—(Continued)

Huhtamaki South Africa (Pty) Ltd. (2)
69 Industry Road, New Era, Springs, 1560, Gauteng, South Africa (100%)
Tel.: (27) 11 730 6300
Web Site: http://www.huhtamaki.com
Sales Range: $50-74.9 Million
Emp.: 250
Food Packaging Services
N.A.I.C.S.: 326199

Huhtamaki Spain S.L. (1)
Ctra Nacional 340 km 955 Polar 1, Pol Ind, 12520, Nules, Castellon, Spain (100%)
Tel.: (34) 964674112
Sales Range: $50-74.9 Million
Emp.: 150
Food Packaging Services
N.A.I.C.S.: 327213

Huhtamaki Svenska AB (1)
Lancashirevagen 32, 810 64, Karlholms Bruk, Sweden
Tel.: (46) 294602400
Web Site: http://www.huhtamaki.com
Sales Range: $25-49.9 Million
Emp.: 70
Food Packaging Services
N.A.I.C.S.: 327213

Huhtamaki Sweden AB (1)
Sjoviksbacken 26, 117 43, Stockholm, Sweden
Tel.: (46) 8 587 409 00
Plastic Cup Mfr
N.A.I.C.S.: 326199

Huhtamaki Tailored Packaging Pty. Ltd. (1)
13 Gibbon Road, Winston Hills, Sydney, 2153, NSW, Australia (100%)
Tel.: (61) 287650444
Web Site: https://www.tailoredpackaging.com.au
Emp.: 130
Food Packaging Product Distr
N.A.I.C.S.: 424130

Huhtamaki Turkey Gida Servisi Ambalaji A.S. (1)
Osmangazi Mah 2647 Sok No 7, Buyukcelemece, 34522, Istanbul, Esenyurt, Turkiye (100%)
Tel.: (90) 2128868190
Web Site: https://www.huhtamaki.com
Sales Range: $75-99.9 Million
Emp.: 48
Mfr of Food Service Disposable Dishes & Food Packaging
N.A.I.C.S.: 424130

Huhtamaki do Brasil Ltda. (1)
BR-376 KM 67 - Pavilhao 2 Usina Do Salto, Palmeira, 84130-000, PR, Brazil (100%)
Tel.: (55) 4232528000
Sales Range: $25-49.9 Million
Emp.: 500
Food Packaging Services
N.A.I.C.S.: 333993

Huhtamaki, Inc. (1)
9201 Packaging Dr, De Soto, KS 66018-8600
Tel.: (913) 583-3025
Sales Range: $50-74.9 Million
Emp.: 100
Food Packaging
N.A.I.C.S.: 551112
Julie Stoetzer (Mgr-Mktg)

Subsidiary (Domestic):

Huhtamaki Consumer Packaging Inc. (2)
9201 Packaging Dr, De Soto, KS 66018
Tel.: (913) 583-3025
Web Site: http://www.huhtamaki.com
Sales Range: $125-149.9 Million
Paper Packaging Systems for Frozen Desserts & Foods Mfr
N.A.I.C.S.: 322219

Plant (Domestic):

Huhtamaki Consumer Packaging (3)
100 State St, Fulton, NY 13069-2518 (100%)
Tel.: (315) 593-5211

Web Site: http://www.us.huhtamaki.com
Packaging of Food Products
N.A.I.C.S.: 322120

Huhtamaki Consumer Packaging (3)
4209 E Noakes St, Los Angeles, CA 90023-4024 (100%)
Tel.: (323) 269-0151
Web Site: http://www.us.huhtamaki.com
Paper & Plastic Containers Mfr
N.A.I.C.S.: 326140

Subsidiary (Domestic):

Huhtamaki, Inc. - Ohio (2)
4000 Commerce Center Dr, Franklin, OH 45005
Tel.: (937) 746-9700
Web Site: https://www.huhtamaki.com
Paperboard Backs Mfr
N.A.I.C.S.: 322212

Pure-Stat Technologies, Inc. (2)
21 Old Farm Rd, Lewiston, ME 04240
Tel.: (207) 786-4790
Web Site: http://www.purestat.com
Rev.: $7,100,000
Emp.: 12
Coated & Laminated Packaging Paper & Plastics Film Mfr
N.A.I.C.S.: 322220

International Paper Foodservice (Shanghai) Co., Ltd. (1)
No 218 East Jiangtian Road, Songjiang District, Shanghai, 201613, China
Tel.: (86) 2161963999
Food Packaging & Paper Cup Mfr
N.A.I.C.S.: 322299

OOO Huhtamaki S.N.G. (1)
Zheleznodorozhnaya Ulitsa 1, 141281, Ivanteevka, Russia
Tel.: (7) 495 741 2520
Web Site: http://www.huhtamaki.ru
Emp.: 50
Packaging Paper Materials Mfr
N.A.I.C.S.: 322220

Rubsteel AB (1)
Verkstadsgatan 8, PO Box 89, S-28400, Perstorp, Sweden
Tel.: (46) 435 34015
Mfr of Complete Machine Lines for Production of Fibre Drums
N.A.I.C.S.: 332439

The Paper Products Ltd. (1)
LBS Marg Majiwade, Thane, 400601, Maharashtra, India (100%)
Tel.: (91) 2221735591
Web Site: http://www.pplpack.com
Sales Range: $200-249.9 Million
Emp.: 700
Provider of Food Packaging Services
N.A.I.C.S.: 333993

HUI LYU ECOLOGICAL TECHNOLOGY GROUPS CO., LTD.
37F Office Building Fangkai Building No 556 Qingnian Road, Jianghan District, Wuhan, 430000, Hubei, China
Tel.: (86) 2783661352
Web Site: https://www.cnhlyl.com
Year Founded: 1990
001267—(SSE)
Rev.: $85,794,228
Assets: $363,095,460
Liabilities: $152,551,620
Net Worth: $210,543,840
Earnings: $8,192,340
Fiscal Year-end: 12/31/22
Engineeering Services
N.A.I.C.S.: 541330
Xiaowei Li (Chm, Vice Chm & Deputy Gen Mgr)

HUI XIAN ASSET MANAGEMENT LIMITED
Unit 303 Cheung Kong Center 2 Queens Road, Central, China (Hong Kong)
Tel.: (852) 21211128

Web Site: https://www.huixianreit.com
Real Estate Investment Trust Services
N.A.I.C.S.: 531190
Tom Ling Fung Cheung (CEO & Exec Dir)

HUI YING FINANCIAL HOLDINGS CORPORATION
Room 2403 Shanghai Mart Tower 2299 West Yan'an Road, Changning District, Shanghai, China
Tel.: (86) 21 23570077 NV
Web Site: http://www.hyjf.com
Year Founded: 2014
Sales Range: $25-49.9 Million
Emp.: 164
Financial Holding Company
N.A.I.C.S.: 551112
Bodang Liu (Chm & CEO)

HUIDA SANITARY WARE CO., LTD.
Huida Ceramic City, Fengnan District, Tangshan, 063307, Hebei, China
Tel.: (86) 3158191721
Web Site: https://www.huidagroup.com
Year Founded: 1982
603385—(SHG)
Rev.: $480,091,229
Assets: $839,761,084
Liabilities: $265,370,166
Net Worth: $574,390,917
Earnings: $18,025,577
Emp.: 8,000
Fiscal Year-end: 12/31/22
Sanitary Product Mfr & Distr
N.A.I.C.S.: 332999
Wang Yanqing (Chm)

HUIFU PAYMENT LIMITED
Building C5 N0 700 Yishan Road, Shanghai, China
Tel.: (86) 2133323999
Web Site: http://www.huifu.com
Year Founded: 2006
Merchant Payment Services
N.A.I.C.S.: 522320
Ye Zhou (Co-Pres & CEO)

Subsidiaries:

China PnR Co., Ltd. (1)
Building C5 Phase 2 No 700 Yishan Road, Putian Information Industrial Park Xuhui District, Shanghai, China
Tel.: (86) 2133323999
Web Site: http://www.chinapnr.com
Payment Processing Services
N.A.I.C.S.: 522320

HUIHENG MEDICAL, INC.
Huiheng Building Gaoxin 7 Street South, Nanshan District, Shenzhen, 518057, Guangdong, China
Tel.: (86) 755 2533 1366 NV
Web Site: http://www.huihengmedical.com
Sales Range: $1-9.9 Million
Emp.: 78
Radiation Oncology Medical Equipment Mfr
N.A.I.C.S.: 339112
Xiaobing Hui (Chm & CEO)

HUIJING HOLDINGS COMPANY LIMITED
Unit 2403-2408 24/F Shui On Centre 6-8 Harbour Road, Wanchai, Hong Kong, China (Hong Kong)
Tel.: (852) 34223968 Ky
Web Site: http://www.huijingholdings.com
Year Founded: 2004
9968—(HKG)
Rev.: $745,424,316

INTERNATIONAL PUBLIC

Assets: $2,131,582,565
Liabilities: $1,534,689,515
Net Worth: $596,893,050
Earnings: $77,275,598
Emp.: 545
Fiscal Year-end: 12/31/21
Holding Company
N.A.I.C.S.: 551112
Zhao Ming Lun (CEO)

HUIKWANG CORP.
259 section 1 Majia Road, Madou, Tainan City, 721010, Taiwan
Tel.: (886) 65702181
Web Site: https://www.huikwang.com
Year Founded: 1965
6508—(TPE)
Rev.: $77,891,943
Assets: $101,892,599
Liabilities: $22,225,307
Net Worth: $79,667,292
Earnings: $9,832,161
Fiscal Year-end: 12/31/22
Agricultural Chemical Product Mfr
N.A.I.C.S.: 325320

Subsidiaries:

HUITEX Limited (1)
500/1 Village 5, Khaokhansong Sub-district Sriracha District, Chon Buri, 20110, Thailand
Tel.: (66) 38190221
Geosynthetics Material Distr
N.A.I.C.S.: 423390

Hui Kwang (Thailand) Co., Ltd. (1)
2922/247 19Floor Charn Issara Tower II New Petchburi Road, Bangkapi Huaykwang, Bangkok, 10320, Thailand
Tel.: (66) 23082566
Agricultural Fertilizer Mfr
N.A.I.C.S.: 325320

Shanghai HKC Ltd. (1)
10F 8 Lane 198 Xinjing Road E, Shanghai, 201100, China
Tel.: (86) 2164148568
Agricultural Fertilizer Mfr
N.A.I.C.S.: 325320

HUILI RESOURCES (GROUP) LIMITED
No 38 Guangchang Bei Road, Uygur Autonomous Region Hami, Xinjiang, China Ky
Web Site: https://www.huili.hk
Year Founded: 2010
1303—(HKG)
Rev.: $308,719,529
Assets: $133,047,104
Liabilities: $45,449,747
Net Worth: $87,597,358
Earnings: $27,681,676
Emp.: 743
Fiscal Year-end: 12/31/22
Coal Mining Services
N.A.I.C.S.: 213113
Yazhou Cui (Chm)

HUIS CLOS SA
35 square Raymond Aron, 76130, Mont-Saint-Aignau, France
Tel.: (33) 2 35 12 11 00
Web Site: http://www.huisclos.fr
Sales Range: $200-249.9 Million
Emp.: 1,730
Polyvinyl Chloride (PVC) & Wooden Building Supplies Mfr & Marketer
N.A.I.C.S.: 423390
Rene Bertin (Chm, Pres & Dir Gen)

HUISEN HOUSEHOLD INTERNATIONAL GROUP LIMITED
Huisen Road Daluo Industrial Park, Longnan Economic Technology Development Zone, Longnan, Jiangxi, China
Tel.: (86) 7973559657 Ky

Web Site:
https://www.jxhmgroup.com
Year Founded: 2005
2127—(HKG)
Rev.: $504,086,176
Assets: $918,572,220
Liabilities: $191,032,759
Net Worth: $727,539,461
Earnings: $28,107,970
Emp.: 3,075
Fiscal Year-end: 12/31/23
Household Furniture Mfr
N.A.I.C.S.: 337122
Ming Zeng (Founder)

HUISHANG BANK CORPORATION LIMITED
Huiyin Building No 1699 Yungu Road, Hefei, Anhui, China
Tel.: (86) 55162667640 CN
Web Site:
https://www.hsbank.com.cn
Year Founded: 2006
3698—(HKG)
Rev.: $8,998,733,108
Assets: $250,075,258,917
Liabilities: $229,759,734,714
Net Worth: $20,315,524,202
Earnings: $2,075,563,525
Emp.: 11,619
Fiscal Year-end: 12/31/23
Commercial Banking Services
N.A.I.C.S.: 522110
Xuemin Wu (Chm)

HUISHENG INTERNATIONAL HOLDINGS LIMITED
Unit 8A 8/F Aubin House 171-172 Gloucester Road, Wanchai, China (Hong Kong)
Tel.: (852) 35778780
Web Site:
http://www.english.hsihl.com
1340—(HKG)
Rev.: $10,241,759
Assets: $91,472,285
Liabilities: $12,711,114
Net Worth: $78,761,171
Earnings: ($1,257,563)
Emp.: 21
Fiscal Year-end: 12/31/22
Pork Products
N.A.I.C.S.: 112210
Chi Ching Chan (Exec Dir)

Subsidiaries:

Deson Japan Co., Ltd. (1)
401 Tensho Shinbashi 5-Chome Building 5-12-11 Shinbashi, Minato-ku, Tokyo, 105-0004, Japan
Tel.: (81) 363815051
Web Site: https://www.deson-japan.com
Underground Resin Pipe Distr
N.A.I.C.S.: 424610

HUITONGDA NETWORK CO., LTD.
Huitongda Building 50 Zhongling Street, Xuanwu District, Nanjing, China
Tel.: (86) 2568727979 CN
Web Site: https://www.htd.cn
Year Founded: 2010
9878—(HKG)
Rev.: $11,413,452,592
Assets: $4,030,525,864
Liabilities: $2,715,861,902
Net Worth: $1,314,663,962
Earnings: $96,546,716
Emp.: 4,508
Fiscal Year-end: 12/31/23
Software Development Services
N.A.I.C.S.: 541511
Jianguo Wang (Chm)

HUIXIN WASTE WATER SOLUTIONS, INC.
99 Jianshe Road 3, Pengjiang District, Jiangmen, 529000, Guangdong, China
Tel.: (86) 7503959988 Ky
Sales Range: $75-99.9 Million
Emp.: 429
Water Purifying Agents & High-Performance Aluminate Calcium (HAC) Powder Mfr & Distr
N.A.I.C.S.: 325998
Mingzhuo Tan (Chm, Pres, CEO, Treas & Sec)

HUIYIN HOLDINGS GROUP LIMITED
Suites 1237 - 1240 12/F Sun Hung Kai Centre 30 Harbour Road, Wanchai, China (Hong Kong)
Tel.: (852) 28682588
Web Site: http://www.vitop.com
Sales Range: $1-9.9 Million
Emp.: 84
Textile Products Mfr
N.A.I.C.S.: 313210
Shun Yee Chan (Exec Dir)

HUIYIN SMART COMMUNITY CO., LTD.
Huiyin International Commercial Building, No 539 Wenchang Zhong Lu, Yangzhou, Jiangsu, China
Tel.: (86) 4001885022 CN
Web Site: http://www.hyjd.com
Year Founded: 1993
Sales Range: $200-249.9 Million
Investment Holding Company
N.A.I.C.S.: 551112
Yuan Li (Chm)

HUIZE HOLDING LIMITED
5/F Building 3-4 Shenzhen Animation Park Yuehai Road Nanhai Avenue, Nanshan District, Shenzhen, 518052, China
Tel.: (86) 75536899088 Ky
Web Site: https://www.huize.com
Year Founded: 2014
HUIZ—(NASDAQ)
Rev.: $177,403,085
Assets: $166,939,761
Liabilities: $114,538,111
Net Worth: $52,401,650
Earnings: ($4,778,160)
Emp.: 1,034
Fiscal Year-end: 12/31/22
Holding Company
N.A.I.C.S.: 551112
Cunjun Ma (Founder, Chm & CEO)

HUIZHONG INSTRUMENTATION CO., LTD.
No 126 West Gaoxin Road High Tech Industrial Zone, Tangshan, 063020, Hebei, China
Tel.: (86) 3153208504
Web Site: https://en.huizhong.co
Year Founded: 1994
300371—(SSE)
Rev.: $71,251,596
Assets: $167,509,836
Liabilities: $27,670,032
Net Worth: $139,839,804
Earnings: $15,240,420
Emp.: 375
Fiscal Year-end: 12/31/22
Ultrasonic Heat Meters, Water Meters, Flow Meters & Related Systems Mfr
N.A.I.C.S.: 334514
Zhang Lixin (Chm)

HUIZHOU CHINA EAGLE ELECTRONIC TECHNOLOGY CO., LTD.
No 6 South Dongsheng Rd Chenjiang St, Zhongkai Hi-tech Zone, Huizhou, Guangdong, China
Tel.: (86) 7525703333
Web Site: https://www.ceepcb.com
Year Founded: 2000
002579—(SSE)
Rev.: $361,037,397
Assets: $896,716,826
Liabilities: $526,136,834
Net Worth: $370,579,992
Earnings: ($18,880,603)
Emp.: 4,500
Fiscal Year-end: 12/31/23
Electronic Components Mfr
N.A.I.C.S.: 334419

HUIZHOU DESAY SV AUTOMOTIVE CO., LTD.
103 Hechang 5th Road West, Zhongkai National Hi-tech Industrial Development Zone, Huizhou, 516025, Guangdong, China
Tel.: (86) 7525995888
Web Site: https://www.desaysv.com
Year Founded: 1986
002920—(SSE)
Rev.: $2,096,580,564
Assets: $1,931,356,440
Liabilities: $1,012,751,532
Net Worth: $918,604,908
Earnings: $166,212,540
Emp.: 4,000
Fiscal Year-end: 12/31/22
Automotive Parts Mfr & Distr
N.A.I.C.S.: 336360
Gao Dapeng (Chm)

Subsidiaries:

Antennentechnik ABB Bad Blankenburg GmbH (1)
In der Buttergrube 3-7, 99428, Weimar, Germany
Tel.: (49) 364347710
Web Site: http://www.attb.de
Vehicle Mfr
N.A.I.C.S.: 336211
Michael Weber (Gen Mgr)

HUIZHOU SPEED WIRELESS TECHNOLOGY CO., LTD.
No SX-01-02 Dongjiang High-Tech Zone, Shangxia District, Huizhou, 516255, Guangdong, China
Tel.: (86) 7522836333
Web Site: https://www.speed-hz.com
Year Founded: 2004
300322—(CHIN)
Rev.: $217,020,492
Assets: $420,380,064
Liabilities: $238,152,096
Net Worth: $182,227,968
Earnings: ($12,160,044)
Emp.: 800
Fiscal Year-end: 12/31/22
Wireless Communication Terminal Antennas Mfr
N.A.I.C.S.: 334220
Kunhua Zhu (Chm)

Subsidiaries:

Huizhou Speed Wireless Technology - San Jose Branch (1)
111 N Market St Ste 300, San Jose, CA 95113
Tel.: (408) 459-0028
Communication Equipment Whslr
N.A.I.C.S.: 423690

Jiangsu A-Kerr Bio-identification Technology Co., Ltd. (1)
568 Fangqiao Road, Caohu Industrial Park Xiangcheng District, Suzhou, 215325, Jiangsu, China
Tel.: (86) 51250362988
Terminal Antenna Mfr & Distr
N.A.I.C.S.: 334220

Speed (Korea) Wireless Technology Co., Ltd. (1)
2F 33 1499 Dukyoungdaero, Yeongtong-gu, Suwon, Gyeonggi, Korea (South)
Tel.: (82) 315481024
Terminal Antenna Mfr & Distr
N.A.I.C.S.: 334220

Speed (Taiwan) Wireless Technology Co., Ltd. (1)
No 46-6 Liufu Road, Luzhu Township, Taoyuan, 338-61, Taiwan
Tel.: (886) 33213353
Terminal Antenna Mfr & Distr
N.A.I.C.S.: 334220

Speed Technology (USA) Co., Ltd. (1)
111 N Market St Ste 300, San Jose, CA 95113
Tel.: (408) 459-0028
Terminal Antenna Mfr & Distr
N.A.I.C.S.: 334220

Suzhou Keyang Photoelectricity Technology Co., Ltd. (1)
No 568 Fangqiao Street Caohu Industrial Park, Xiangcheng District, Suzhou, Jiangsu, China
Tel.: (86) 51268838988
Wireless Communication Equipment Mfr
N.A.I.C.S.: 334220

HULAMIN LIMITED
Moses Mabhida Road, PO Box 74, Pietermaritzburg, 3200, South Africa
Tel.: (27) 333956911
Web Site: https://www.hulamin.com
HLM—(JSE)
Rev.: $751,309,901
Assets: $340,235,528
Liabilities: $147,524,788
Net Worth: $192,710,740
Earnings: $14,802,282
Emp.: 1,866
Fiscal Year-end: 12/31/23
Aluminium Products Mfr
N.A.I.C.S.: 325180
Richard Gordon Jacob (CEO)

Subsidiaries:

Hulamin Operations (Pty) Limited (1)
Mason Mill Mosesmaphida Road, Pietermaritzburg, 3200, Kwazulu-Natal, South Africa
Tel.: (27) 333956911
Web Site: http://www.hulamin.co.za
Sales Range: $400-449.9 Million
Aluminium Products Mfr
N.A.I.C.S.: 331313

Subsidiary (Domestic):

Hulamin Extrusions (Pty) Limited (2)
Corner of Main Olifantsfontein Rd, PO Box 25, Olifantsfontein, 1665, Gauntent, South Africa
Tel.: (27) 112060200
Web Site:
http://www.hulaminextrusions.co.za
Sales Range: $25-49.9 Million
Emp.: 150
Aluminium Products Mfr
N.A.I.C.S.: 331313

Plant (Domestic):

Hulamin Extrusions (Pty) Limited - Cape Town Plant (3)
Hewett Ave Epping 2, PO Box 160, Eppindust, Cape Town, 7764, Western Cape, South Africa
Tel.: (27) 215079100
Web Site: https://www.hulamin.com
Sales Range: $25-49.9 Million
Emp.: 6
Aluminium Products Mfr
N.A.I.C.S.: 331313
Gary van Ster (Mgr-Sls-Western Cape)

Hulamin Extrusions (Pty) Limited - Pietermaritzburg Plant (3)
Moses Mabhida Road, PO Box 74, Pietermaritzburg, 3200, KwaZulu-Natal, South Africa
Tel.: (27) 333956911
Emp.: 2,800
Aluminium Products Mfr
N.A.I.C.S.: 331313

HULAMIN LIMITED

Hulamin Limited—(Continued)
Yugiea Moodley (Mgr-Sls)

Subsidiary (US):

Hulamin North America LLC (2)
1001 Cross Timbers Rd, Flower Mound, TX 75028
Tel.: (972) 874-2600
Extruded Aluminum Products Mfr
N.A.I.C.S.: 331313

Subsidiary (Domestic):

Hulamin Rolled Products (Pty) Limited (2)
Moses Mabhida Road, PO Box 74, Pietermaritzburg, 3200, KwaZulu-Natal, South Africa
Tel.: (27) 333956911
Web Site: http://www.hulaminrolled.co.za
Sales Range: $700-749.9 Million
Aluminium Products Mfr
N.A.I.C.S.: 331313

Hulamin Systems (Pty) Limited (2)
49 Mirabel Corner Mapel Street Pomona Kenton Park, Johannesburg, 1619, Gauteng, South Africa
Tel.: (27) 116263330
Sales Range: $25-49.9 Million
Emp.: 30
Aluminium Products Mfr
N.A.I.C.S.: 331313
Rajesh Harrilall (Mgr-Fin)

HULBEE AG

Bucherstrasse 2, Egnach, 9322, Taegerwilen, Switzerland
Tel.: (41) 716667931
Web Site: http://www.hulbee.com
Year Founded: 2008
Software Publishing Services
N.A.I.C.S.: 513210
Andreas Wiebe (CEO)

HULIC CO., LTD.

7-3 Nihonbashi Odenmacho, Chuo-ku, Tokyo, 103-0011, Japan
Tel.: (81) 356238100
Web Site: https://www.hulic.co.jp
Year Founded: 1931
3003—(TKS)
Rev.: $2,949,342,583
Assets: $16,388,979,187
Liabilities: $11,306,058,804
Net Worth: $5,082,920,383
Earnings: $625,206,475
Emp.: 1,347
Fiscal Year-end: 12/31/23
Real Estate Manangement Services
N.A.I.C.S.: 531390
Saburo Nishiura (Chm)

Subsidiaries:

Hulic Hotel Management Co., Ltd. (1)
2-16-11 Kaminarimon, Taito-ku, Tokyo, 111-0034, Japan
Tel.: (81) 358263877
Emp.: 841
Home Management Services
N.A.I.C.S.: 561110

Hulic Reit Management Co., Ltd. (1)
2-26-9 Hatchobori, Chuo-ku, Tokyo, 104-0032, Japan
Investment Management Service
N.A.I.C.S.: 523940

Nippon View Hotel Co., Ltd. (1)
3-17-1 Nishiasakusa, Taito-ku, Tokyo, 111-0035, Japan (100%)
Tel.: (81) 3 58284429
Web Site: http://www.viewhotels.co.jp
Sales Range: $150-199.9 Million
Emp.: 735
Hotel Operations
N.A.I.C.S.: 721110
Yoshiaki Endo (Pres)

Porte Kanazawa Co., Ltd. (1)
2-15-1 Honmachi, Kanazawa, 920-0853, Ishikawa, Japan
Tel.: (81) 762342222

Web Site: https://porte.co.jp
Real Estate Services
N.A.I.C.S.: 531390

Raysum Co., Ltd. (1)
36th floor Kasumigaseki Common Gate West Wing 3-2-1 Kasumigaseki, Chiyoda-ku, Tokyo, 100-0013, Japan (93.3%)
Tel.: (81) 351578888
Web Site: https://www.raysum.co.jp
Rev.: $662,131,360
Assets: $1,063,318,960
Liabilities: $546,087,520
Net Worth: $517,231,440
Earnings: $64,178,400
Emp.: 203
Fiscal Year-end: 03/31/2022
Real Estate Manangement Services
N.A.I.C.S.: 531390
Tsuyoshi Komachi (Pres)

Subsidiary (Domestic):

Best Medical Co., Ltd. (2)
889-2 Kirigasaku, Noda, 270-0213, Chiba, Japan
Tel.: (81) 471037184
Web Site: https://www.bestmedical.jp
Ophthalmic Equipment Mfr
N.A.I.C.S.: 339115
Steven Yang (Pres)

Sala Azabu Co., Ltd. (2)
3-6-11 Ariake, Koto-ku, Tokyo, 135-0063, Japan
Tel.: (81) 355305555
Web Site: http://www.sala-azabu.co.jp
Furniture Whslr
N.A.I.C.S.: 423210

Wellness Arena Corporation (2)
Grand Maison Daikanyama 601 3-7-10, Ebisu Minami Shibuya-ku, Tokyo, 150-0022, Japan
Tel.: (81) 364128576
Web Site: https://www.warena.net
Spa Services
N.A.I.C.S.: 812199

Riso Kyoiku Co., Ltd. (1)
3-1-40 Mejiro, Toshima-ku, Tokyo, Japan (53.33%)
Tel.: (81) 359962501
Web Site: https://www.riso-kyoikugroup.com
Rev.: $228,404,350
Assets: $128,300,640
Liabilities: $68,149,080
Net Worth: $60,151,560
Earnings: $11,776,490
Emp.: 1,119
Fiscal Year-end: 02/29/2024
Education Services
N.A.I.C.S.: 611110
Masaaki Kume (CFO & VP)

Subsidiary (Domestic):

School TOMAS Co., Ltd. (2)
3-4-14 Tanaka building 3F Mejiro, Toshima-ku, Tokyo, 171-0031, Japan
Tel.: (81) 120372861
Web Site: https://www.school-t.co.jp
Emp.: 221
Exam Preparation Services
N.A.I.C.S.: 611691

Shingakai Co., Ltd. (2)
Hulic Mejiro 5F 3-4-11 Mejiro, Toshima-ku, Tokyo, 171-0031, Japan
Tel.: (81) 335656688
Web Site: http://www.shingakai.co.jp
Emp.: 250
Exam Preparation Services
N.A.I.C.S.: 611691

Simplex Investment Advisors Inc. (1)
Urbannet Nihonbashi 2-chome Bldg 4th Floor 2-1-3 Nihonbashi, Chuo-ku, Tokyo, Japan
Tel.: (81) 332427151
Web Site: http://www.simplexinv.com
Emp.: 25
Real Estate Investment Management Services
N.A.I.C.S.: 531390
Hiroyuki Katsuno (Pres & CEO)

HULISANI LTD.

4th Floor North Tower90 Rivonia Road, Sandton, 2196, South Africa

Tel.: (27) 878062425
Year Founded: 2015
HUL—(JSE)
Rev.: $4,257,006
Assets: $38,051,939
Liabilities: $11,476,286
Net Worth: $26,575,653
Earnings: $911,826
Fiscal Year-end: 02/28/21
Eletric Power Generation Services
N.A.I.C.S.: 221118
Marubini Raphulu (CEO)

HULLERA VASCO LEONESA S.A.

Paseo de la Castellana 126 8 Dcha, Madrid, 28046, Spain
Tel.: (34) 914 42 86 22
Web Site: http://www.sahvl.es
Coal Mining Services
N.A.I.C.S.: 212115
Antonio Jose Del Valle Alonso (Chm & CEO)

HULLERAS DEL NORTE, S.A.

Avenida de Galicia 44, 33005, Oviedo, Spain
Tel.: (34) 985107300
Web Site: http://www.hunosa.es
Year Founded: 1967
Sales Range: $150-199.9 Million
Emp.: 2,700
Coal Mining & Extraction
N.A.I.C.S.: 423520
Maria Teresa Mallada De Castro (Pres)

Subsidiaries:

Sadim Inversiones S.A. (1)
Avenida de Galicia 44, Oviedo, 33005, Asturias, Spain (100%)
Tel.: (34) 985422530
Web Site: http://www.sadiminversiones.es
Sales Range: $50-74.9 Million
Emp.: 6
Miscellaneous Intermediation Services
N.A.I.C.S.: 523910
Gregorio Ravanal (Gen Mgr)

Sociedad Asturiana de Diversificacion Minera S.A. (1)
Jaime Alberti 2, 33900, Asturias, Spain (100%)
Tel.: (34) 985678350
Web Site: http://www.sadim.es
Sales Range: $25-49.9 Million
Emp.: 50
Engineeering Services
N.A.I.C.S.: 541330
Javier Sopena (Mng Dir)

HULLEY & KIRKWOOD CONSULTING ENGINEERS LTD

Watermark Business Park, Govan Road, Glasgow, G51 2SE, United Kingdom
Tel.: (44) 1413325466
Web Site: http://www.hulley.co.uk
Year Founded: 1953
Rev.: $20,978,507
Emp.: 190
Mechanical & Electrical Engineering Services
N.A.I.C.S.: 541330
Tim Crocombe (Dir-Bristol)

HULME SUPERCARS LIMITED

PO Box 97853, Manukau, 2241, New Zealand
Tel.: (64) 92571133
Web Site: http://www.hulmesupercars.com
Sales Range: $25-49.9 Million
Emp.: 10
Motor Vehicles Mfr
N.A.I.C.S.: 336110
James Freemantle (Mng Dir & Coord-Project)

INTERNATIONAL PUBLIC

HULUDAO ZINC INDUSTRY CO., LTD.

No 24 Xinchang Road, Longgang District, Huludao, 125003, Liaoning, China
Tel.: (86) 4292324121
Web Site: http://www.hldxygf.com
Year Founded: 1992
000751—(SSE)
Rev.: $2,619,438,588
Assets: $1,154,315,448
Liabilities: $733,650,372
Net Worth: $420,665,076
Earnings: $9,243,936
Fiscal Year-end: 12/31/22
Non-ferrous Metal Product Smelting Services
N.A.I.C.S.: 331410
En'ruan Yu (Chm)

HUM NETWORK LIMITED

Plot No 10/11 Hassan Ali Street Off I I Chundrigar Road, Karachi, 74000, Pakistan
Tel.: (92) 212628840
Web Site: https://www.humnetwork.tv
HUMNL—(KAR)
Rev.: $34,368,623
Assets: $43,084,585
Liabilities: $19,558,574
Net Worth: $23,526,012
Earnings: ($4,664,704)
Emp.: 903
Fiscal Year-end: 06/30/19
Television Broadcasting Services
N.A.I.C.S.: 516120

Subsidiaries:

Hum World Inc. (1)
29445 Beck Rd Ste A-202-S, Wixom, MI 48393
Tel.: (734) 212-2340
Web Site: http://www.humworld.com
Computer Software Development Services
N.A.I.C.S.: 513210

HUM&C CO., LTD.

29 Wonjeok-Ro 7 Beon-Gil, Seo-Gu, Incheon, Korea (South)
Tel.: (82) 325840789
Year Founded: 2002
263920—(KRS)
Rev.: $17,836,272
Assets: $38,076,977
Liabilities: $3,264,448
Net Worth: $34,812,529
Earnings: ($5,683,536)
Emp.: 95
Fiscal Year-end: 12/31/21
Makeup Product Mfr
N.A.I.C.S.: 325620
Kim Jun-Cheol (CEO)

HUMAN CREATION HOLDINGS, INC.

24th floor Kasumigaseki Common Gate West Wing 3-2-1 Kasumigaseki, Chiyoda-Ku, Tokyo, 100-0013, Japan
Tel.: (81) 351574100
Web Site: https://www.hch-ja.co.jp
Year Founded: 1974
7361—(TKS)
Rev.: $45,985,740
Assets: $21,007,670
Liabilities: $13,485,180
Net Worth: $7,522,490
Earnings: $3,105,420
Emp.: 938
Fiscal Year-end: 09/30/23
Holding Company
N.A.I.C.S.: 551112
Kuniaki Tominaga (Pres)

HUMAN HEALTH HOLDINGS LIMITED

11/F TAL Building 45-53 Austin Road,

Tsim Sha Tsui, Kowloon, China (Hong Kong)
Tel.: (852) 39718266 Ky
Web Site: http://www.humanhealth.com.hk
Year Founded: 1997
1419—(HKG)
Rev.: $144,688,861
Assets: $149,438,034
Liabilities: $53,741,839
Net Worth: $95,696,195
Earnings: $48,407,355
Emp.: 542
Fiscal Year-end: 06/30/22
Health Care Srvices
N.A.I.C.S.: 621491
Kin Ping Chan (Co-Founder, Chm & CEO)

Subsidiaries:

Be Health Specialist Limited (1)
Park Central Shopping Arc Tseung Kwan O, Hong Kong, China (Hong Kong)
Tel.: (852) 34174803
Hospital Speciality Services
N.A.I.C.S.: 622310

Impact Medical Imaging Centre Company Limited (1)
Room 712 7/F Office Tower One Grand Plaza 625 639 Nathan Road, Mong Kok, Kowloon, China (Hong Kong)
Tel.: (852) 23972111
Web Site: https://www.impactmedical.hk
Medical Imaging Services
N.A.I.C.S.: 621512

Laserdontics Limited (1)
1/F Toi Shan Centre 128 Johnston Road, Wanchai, China (Hong Kong)
Tel.: (852) 28329266
Web Site: http://dr-seto.com
Emp.: 9
Dental Care Services
N.A.I.C.S.: 621210
Phyllis Chiu (Mgr-HR)

Seto & Wan Dental Centre Limited (1)
G/F No 82 Tai Wai Road Tai Wai, Sha Tin, New Territories, China (Hong Kong)
Tel.: (852) 26092060
Dental Care Services
N.A.I.C.S.: 621210

HUMAN HOLDINGS CO., LTD.
1F Nishi-Shinjuku Prime Square 7-5-25 Nishi-Shinjuku, Shinjuku-ku, Tokyo, 160-0023, Japan
Tel.: (81) 368468001
Web Site: https://www.athuman.com
Year Founded: 2002
2415—(TKS)
Rev.: $633,601,825
Assets: $338,181,914
Liabilities: $231,588,934
Net Worth: $106,592,980
Earnings: $14,255,378
Emp.: 4,480
Fiscal Year-end: 03/31/24
Management Consulting Services
N.A.I.C.S.: 541618
Koichi Sato (Chm)

Subsidiaries:

Dashing Diva International Co., Ltd. (1)
Nishi-Shinjuku Prime Square 1st Floor 7-5-25 Nishi-Shinjuku, Shinjuku-ku, Tokyo, 160-0023, Japan
Tel.: (81) 366928645
Web Site: https://www.dashingdiva.co.jp
Support Systems for Nail Salons
N.A.I.C.S.: 812113

Human (Shanghai) Commerce Consultants Co., Ltd. (1)
Jing'an Xinshidai Building 12D 188 Wujianglu, Jing'an, Shanghai, 200050, China
Tel.: (86) 21 6136 3959
Recruitment Consulting Services
N.A.I.C.S.: 561311

Human Academy Co., Ltd. (1)
7-8-10 Nishi-Shinjuku, Shinjuku-ku, Tokyo, 160-0023, Japan
Tel.: (81) 120010556
Web Site: https://manabu.athuman.com
Educational Services
N.A.I.C.S.: 611710

Subsidiary (Domestic):

Human Academy High School Co., Ltd. (2)
Nishi-Shinjuku Kimuraya Building 1st Floor 7-5-25 Nishi-Shinjuku, Shinjuku-ku, Tokyo, 160-0023, Japan
Tel.: (81) 3 6846 8001
Web Site: http://www.hchs.ed.jp
Correspondence High School Operator
N.A.I.C.S.: 611710
Tetsuya Takahashi (Pres)

Subsidiary (Non-US):

Human Academy Shanghai Co., Ltd. (2)
Jing'an Xinshidai Building 12D 188 Wujianglu, Jing'an, Shanghai, 200050, China
Tel.: (86) 21 6136 3959
Japanese Language Instruction Services
N.A.I.C.S.: 923110

Human Digicrafts (Thailand) Co., Ltd. (1)
The Trendy office Building 6th Flr Room 601E Soi Sukhumvit 13, Khlong Toei Nuea, Bangkok, 10110, Thailand
Tel.: (66) 21687177
Web Site: http://www.th.athuman.com
Game/Animation School; Japanese Language School
N.A.I.C.S.: 611699
Naoki Niioka (Mng Dir)

Human Digital Consultants Co., Ltd. (1)
6F Ohashi-Gyoen Station Building 1-8-1 Shinjuku, Shinjuku-ku, Tokyo, 160-0022, Japan
Tel.: (81) 35 919 3120
Web Site: https://www.human-dc.com
Digital Marketing Services
N.A.I.C.S.: 541613
Eiji Watanabe (Pres)

Human Global Communications Co., Ltd. (1)
4-4-2 Takadanobaba, Shinjuku-ku, Tokyo, 169-0075, Japan
Tel.: (81) 35 386 9420
Web Site: https://human-gc.jp
English Document Proofreading Services
N.A.I.C.S.: 561410
Takahiro Hattori (Pres)

Human Global Talent Co., Ltd. (1)
Nishi-Shinjuku Prime Square 2nd Floor 7-5-25 Nishi-Shinjuku, Shinjuku-ku, Tokyo, 160-0023, Japan
Tel.: (81) 36 680 6833
Web Site: https://corp.daijob.com
Job Search & Recruitment Services
N.A.I.C.S.: 561311
Tomoki Yokokawa (Pres)

Human International Co., Ltd. (1)
Nishi-Shinjuku Kimuraya Building 1st Floor 7-5-25 Nishi-Shinjuku, Shinjuku-ku, Tokyo, 160-0023, Japan
Tel.: (81) 3 6846 0248
Web Site: http://hi.athuman.com
Internet Employment Information Distr
N.A.I.C.S.: 561311
Naoki Niioka (Pres)

Human Life Care Co., Ltd. (1)
Nishi-Shinjuku Prime Square 1F 7-5-25 Nishi-Shinjuku, Shinjuku-ku, Tokyo, 160-0023, Japan
Tel.: (81) 368460223
Web Site: https://human-lifecare.jp
Emp.: 4
Healthcare Support Services
N.A.I.C.S.: 621610
Nobuhiro Kawakami (Pres)

Human ND Co., Ltd. (1)
Nishi-Shinjuku Kimuraya Building 1st Floor 7-5-25 Nishi-Shinjuku, Shinjuku-ku, Tokyo, 160-0023, Japan
Tel.: (81) 3 6846 0394

Elementary School Management Services
N.A.I.C.S.: 611710
Masato Yamamoto (Pres)

Human Planning Co., Ltd. (1)
Midosuji MID Building 9th Floor 4-3-2 Minami-senba, Chuo-ku, Osaka, 542-0081, Japan
Tel.: (81) 662585311
Web Site: https://hp.athuman.com
Emp.: 58
Athlete Management & Sports Event Promotion Services
N.A.I.C.S.: 711211

Human Resocia Co., Ltd. (1)
1F Nishi-Shinjuku Prime Square 7-5-25 Nishi-Shinjuku, Shinjuku-ku, Tokyo, 160-0023, Japan
Tel.: (81) 368469055
Web Site: https://corporate.resocia.jp
Emp.: 924
Management Consulting, Employment & Outsourcing Services
N.A.I.C.S.: 541618
Kazuo Kuwahara (Pres)

Shanghai Human Resource Co., Ltd. (1)
Room 1406 Guoli Bublibing 1465 West Bejing Road, Jingan, Shanghai, 200050, China
Tel.: (86) 2162668001
Web Site: http://www.athuman.com.cn
Emp.: 3
Recruitment Services
N.A.I.C.S.: 561311

HUMAN METABOLOME TECHNOLOGIES INC.
Tel.: (81) 335512180
Web Site: http://www.humanmetabolome.com
6090—(TKS)
Rev.: $8,365,900
Assets: $16,190,660
Liabilities: $4,086,540
Net Worth: $12,104,120
Earnings: $1,511,460
Emp.: 65
Fiscal Year-end: 06/30/24
Capillary Electrophoresis Mass Spectrometry Based Metabolomics Technologies
N.A.I.C.S.: 339112
Yasuhiro Ohata (Pres & CFO)

Subsidiaries:

Human Metabolome Technologies America, Inc. (1)
24 Denby Rd Ste 217, Boston, MA 02134
Tel.: (617) 987-0554
Biological Product Mfr
N.A.I.C.S.: 325414
Alexander Buko (VP-Bus & Product Dev)

Human Metabolome Technologies Europe B.V. (1)
JH Oortweg 21, 2333 CH, Leiden, Netherlands
Tel.: (31) 713322040
Biological Product Mfr
N.A.I.C.S.: 325414

HUMAN N, INC
Wing Gallery Building 2nd Floor 17-10 Apgujeong-ro 62-gil, Cheongdam-dong Gangnam-gu, Seoul, 06016, Korea (South)
Tel.: (82) 234528449
Web Site: http://www.glosferlabs.com
032860—(KRS)
Rev.: $47,988,438
Assets: $21,732,427
Liabilities: $2,318,286
Net Worth: $19,414,141
Earnings: ($4,300,090)
Emp.: 13
Fiscal Year-end: 12/31/22
Scrap Material Distr
N.A.I.C.S.: 423930

HUMAN SOFT HOLDING K.S.C.C.
4th Floor Dar AlAwadhi Tower Ahmed AlJaber Street, Sharq, Kuwait, 15300, Kuwait
Tel.: (965) 22322588
Web Site: https://www.human-soft.com
HUMANSOFT—(KUW)
Rev.: $274,038,233
Assets: $505,772,924
Liabilities: $71,101,222
Net Worth: $434,671,702
Earnings: $164,675,765
Emp.: 1,000
Fiscal Year-end: 12/31/22
Computer Services
N.A.I.C.S.: 541519
Mayank Hasmukhlal Baxi (CEO)

HUMAN TECHNOLOGY CO., LTD.
7th floor 321 Hwangsaeul-ro, Bundang-gu, Seongnam, 463-875, Gyeonggi-do, Korea (South)
Tel.: (82) 262050505
Web Site: https://www.infomark.co.kr
Year Founded: 2002
175140—(KRS)
Rev.: $27,256,678
Assets: $53,761,345
Liabilities: $22,037,028
Net Worth: $31,724,317
Earnings: ($7,862,544)
Emp.: 69
Fiscal Year-end: 12/31/22
Telecommunication Apparatus Mfr
N.A.I.C.S.: 517810
Hyuk Choi (CEO)

HUMAN XTENSIONS LTD.
4 Meir Ariel St, Netanya, 4250574, Israel
Tel.: (972) 773630300 Il
Web Site: https://human-x.com
Year Founded: 2012
HUMX—(TAE)
Rev.: $1,367,592
Assets: $9,676,751
Liabilities: $2,464,152
Net Worth: $7,212,598
Earnings: ($10,121,564)
Fiscal Year-end: 12/31/23
Custom Computer Programming Services
N.A.I.C.S.: 541511

HUMANA AB
Warfvinges Vag 39 7tr, 112 51, Stockholm, Sweden
Tel.: (46) 859929900 SE
Web Site: https://www.humana.se
Year Founded: 2001
HUM—(OMX)
Rev.: $865,529,611
Assets: $918,448,584
Liabilities: $661,908,642
Net Worth: $256,539,942
Earnings: $19,668,999
Emp.: 12,426
Fiscal Year-end: 12/31/22
Healtcare Services
N.A.I.C.S.: 621391

Subsidiaries:

Assistans pa Gotland AB (1)
Herkulesvagen 9, 621 41, Visby, Sweden
Tel.: (46) 498211095
Web Site: https://assistanspagotland.se
Personal Assistance Services
N.A.I.C.S.: 624229

Cajanuksentienkoti Oy (1)
Cajanuksentie 5A, 90440, Kempele, Finland
Tel.: (358) 504688463
Web Site: https://www.humana.fi
Home Care Services
N.A.I.C.S.: 621610

HUMANA AB

Humana AB—(Continued)

Enigheten Personligassistans AB (1)
Haradsvagen 22, 784 34, Borlange, Sweden
Tel.: (46) 243229622
Web Site: https://enigheten.se
Personal Support Services
N.A.I.C.S.: 812990

Human Care BO AS (1)
Kilengaten 1, 3117, Tonsberg, Norway
Tel.: (47) 90946000
Personal Assistance & Family Care Services
N.A.I.C.S.: 624190

Human Care Holding AS (1)
Kilengaten 1, 3117, Tonsberg, Norway
Tel.: (47) 90946000
Personal Assistance & Family Care Services
N.A.I.C.S.: 624190

Humana Assistans AB (1)
Fabriksgatan 22 5 tr, Box 184, 701 43, Orebro, Sweden
Tel.: (46) 197608600
Personal Assistance & Family Care Services
N.A.I.C.S.: 624190

Humana Danmark ApS (1)
Sydmarken 32 A, 2860, Soborg, Denmark
Tel.: (45) 70701807
Web Site: https://www.humana.dk
Emp.: 70
Personal Assistance Services
N.A.I.C.S.: 624229

Humanan Kallio Oy (1)
Turuntie 21 liikehuoneisto 2, 24220, Salo, Finland
Tel.: (358) 504357070
Personal Assistance & Family Care Services
N.A.I.C.S.: 624190

Jokilaakson Perhekodit Oy (1)
Kytokankaantie 2, 85500, Nivala, Finland
Tel.: (358) 447700337
Web Site: https://www.humana.fi
Home Care Services
N.A.I.C.S.: 621610

Lastensuojeluyksikko Leppalintu Oy (1)
Vuorenmaentie 14, 61800, Kauhajoki, Finland
Tel.: (358) 447507225
Child Protection Services
N.A.I.C.S.: 624410

Lastensuojeluyksikko Pihakoivu Oy (1)
Ojasalonkuja 4, 61400, Ylistaro, Finland
Tel.: (358) 447321848
Personal Assistance & Family Care Services
N.A.I.C.S.: 624190

Luotsimaja Oy (1)
Aatuntie 19, 28600, Pori, Finland
Tel.: (358) 445375900
Home Care Services
N.A.I.C.S.: 621610

Nordic Care AB (1)
Ydrevagen 23, 573 35, Tranas, Sweden
Tel.: (46) 140384060
Web Site: https://www.nonordiccare.se
Wood Furniture Mfr & Distr
N.A.I.C.S.: 337122

Nuorisokoti Valokki Oy (1)
Mantylammintie 6, Jalasjarvi, 61600, Kurikka, Finland
Tel.: (358) 447507225
Child Protection Services
N.A.I.C.S.: 624110

Pirtakoti Oy (1)
Pirkkionkatu 5, 95420, Tornio, Finland
Tel.: (358) 458762984
Health Care Srvices
N.A.I.C.S.: 621610

R.I.K. assistans Aktiebolag (1)
Norra Kyrkogatan 15, 871 32, Harnosand, Sweden
Tel.: (46) 611811010

Web Site: https://www.rikassistans.se
Personal Assistance Services
N.A.I.C.S.: 624229

Solvik Barnevern AS (1)
Torkoppveien 10, 1570, Dilling, Norway
Tel.: (47) 90501184
Web Site: https://solvikbarnevern.no
Foster Care Services
N.A.I.C.S.: 624110

StotteCompagniet ApS (1)
Sydmarken 32 G Soborg, Capital Region, 2860, Gladsaxe, Denmark
Tel.: (45) 70701807
Social Welfare
N.A.I.C.S.: 813319

Wisby Assistans AB (1)
Herkulesvagen 9, 621 41, Visby, Sweden
Tel.: (46) 498211095
Web Site: https://assistanspagotland.se
Emp.: 115
Personal Assistance & Family Care Services
N.A.I.C.S.: 624190

HUMANICA PUBLIC COMPANY LIMITED

2 Soi Rongmuang 5 Rongmuang Rd, Rongmuang Pathumwan, Bangkok, 10330, Thailand
Tel.: (66) 26366999 TH
Web Site: https://www.humanica.com
Year Founded: 2003
HUMAN—(THA)
Rev.: $39,020,206
Assets: $119,667,781
Liabilities: $14,585,739
Net Worth: $105,082,042
Earnings: $8,979,829
Emp.: 1,068
Fiscal Year-end: 12/31/23
Software Development Services
N.A.I.C.S.: 541511
Anotai Adulbhan *(Chm)*

Subsidiaries:

Benix Limited (1)
2 Soi Rong Muang 5 Rong Muang Rd, Rong Muang Pathum Wan, Bangkok, 10330, Thailand
Tel.: (66) 20929222
Web Site: https://www.benix.co.th
Insurance Brokerage Services
N.A.I.C.S.: 524210

Humanica Asia Pte. Ltd. (1)
146 Robinson Road 10-01, Singapore, 068909, Singapore
Tel.: (65) 69142676
Outsourcing Services
N.A.I.C.S.: 541611

Humanica Sdn. Bhd. (1)
5-3-17 Promenade Persiaran Mahsuri, 11950, Bayan Baru, Penang, Malaysia
Tel.: (60) 43717832
Software Development Services
N.A.I.C.S.: 541511

Professional Outsourcing Solutions Limited (1)
No 2 Soi Rongmuang 5 Rongmuang Road, Rongmuang Sub District Pathum Wan District, Bangkok, 10330, Thailand
Tel.: (66) 26464222
Web Site: https://www.pos.co.th
Emp.: 50
Payroll Outsourcing Services
N.A.I.C.S.: 541214

Tiger Soft (1998) Company Limited (1)
7 Vision Business Park Soi 55/8 Ramintra Road, Tharang Subdistrict Bang Khen District, Bangkok, 10230, Thailand
Tel.: (66) 20326060
Web Site: https://www.tigersoft.co.th
Emp.: 150
Software Development Services
N.A.I.C.S.: 541511

HUMANOPTICS AG

Spardorfer Str 150, 91054, Erlangen, Germany
Tel.: (49) 913 150 6650 De
Web Site:
 htttp://www.humanoptics.com
Year Founded: 1999
H9O1—(DEU)
Rev.: $11,982,502
Assets: $10,974,628
Liabilities: $9,518,810
Net Worth: $1,455,818
Earnings: ($2,127,734)
Emp.: 133
Fiscal Year-end: 12/31/19
Biomedical Intraocular Implant Technology Mfr
N.A.I.C.S.: 325414
Diana Bachmann *(CEO)*

Subsidiaries:

Dr. Schmidt Intraocularlinsen GmbH (1)
Westerwaldstr 11-13, Saint Augustin, 53757, Germany
Tel.: (49) 2241257870
Web Site: http://www.humanoptics.com
Sales Range: $25-49.9 Million
Intraocular Lenses Mfr & Sales
N.A.I.C.S.: 333310
Arthur Messner *(CEO)*

HumanOptics Deutschland Verwaltungs GmbH (1)
Spardorfer Str 150, 91054, Erlangen, Germany
Tel.: (49) 9131506650
Web Site: http://www.humanoptics.com
Sales Range: $25-49.9 Million
Emp.: 55
Intraocular Lenses Mfr & Sales
N.A.I.C.S.: 333310
Martha Messner *(CEO)*

HUMANWELL HEALTHCARE (GROUP) CO., LTD.

No 666 Gaoxin Road East Lake High-tech Development Zone, Wuhan, 430075, Hubei, China
Tel.: (86) 2787597232
Web Site:
 https://www.humanwell.com.cn
Year Founded: 1993
600079—(SHG)
Rev.: $3,136,215,804
Assets: $5,057,632,261
Liabilities: $2,538,535,728
Net Worth: $2,519,096,533
Earnings: $348,768,847
Fiscal Year-end: 12/31/22
Pharmaceuticals Product Mfr
N.A.I.C.S.: 325412
Jie Li *(Chm)*

Subsidiaries:

Epic Pharma, LLC (1)
227-15 N Conduit Ave, Laurelton, NY 11413
Tel.: (718) 276-8600
Web Site: https://www.epic-pharma.com
Pharmaceuticals Product Mfr
N.A.I.C.S.: 325412
Anuj Thakur *(Mgr)*

HUMAX HOLDINGS CO., LTD.

Byun 216 Hwangsaeulro Bundanggu Humax Village, Hwangang-gu, Seongnam, 13595, Gyeonggi, Korea (South)
Tel.: (82) 317766114
Web Site:
 https://holdings.humaxdigital.com
Year Founded: 1989
028080—(KRS)
Rev.: $7,958,061
Assets: $145,869,087
Liabilities: $14,170,599
Net Worth: $131,698,488
Earnings: $5,015,662
Emp.: 3
Fiscal Year-end: 12/31/19

INTERNATIONAL PUBLIC

Holding Company
N.A.I.C.S.: 551112
Seong-Min Jung *(CFO)*

Subsidiaries:

HUMAX Co., Ltd. (1)
212-1 Yubang-dong, Cheoin-gu, Yongin, 13595, Gyeonggi-do, Korea (South)
Tel.: (82) 317766114
Web Site: https://www.humaxdigital.com
Rev.: $528,827,519
Assets: $772,803,757
Liabilities: $525,436,923
Net Worth: $247,366,834
Earnings: ($39,180,762)
Emp.: 62
Fiscal Year-end: 12/31/2022
Digital Set-Top Box Mfr
N.A.I.C.S.: 334220
Tae-Hun Kim *(CEO)*

HUMBOLDT ELECTRIC LIMITED

102 Gladstone Cres, Saskatoon, S7P 0C7, SK, Canada
Tel.: (306) 665-6551
Web Site:
 http://www.humboldtelectric.com
Year Founded: 1966
Electrical Contracting Services
N.A.I.C.S.: 238210
Jason Tatlow *(Project Mgr)*

HUME CEMENT INDUSTRIES BERHAD

Level 5 Wisma Hume Block D 15A Jalan 51A/219, 46100, Petaling Jaya, Selangor Darul Ehsan, Malaysia
Tel.: (60) 378669000
Web Site: https://www.humeind.com
HUMEIND—(KLS)
Rev.: $214,662,646
Assets: $251,056,296
Liabilities: $160,297,989
Net Worth: $90,758,307
Earnings: $12,705,608
Emp.: 571
Fiscal Year-end: 06/30/23
Investment Holding Company; Furniture Mfr
N.A.I.C.S.: 551112
Leng San Kwek *(Chm)*

Subsidiaries:

Hume Cement Sdn. Bhd. (1)
Level 5 Wisma Hume Block D 15A Jalan 51A/219, 46100, Petaling Jaya, Selangor Darul Ehsan, Malaysia
Tel.: (60) 378669000
Web Site: https://www.humecement.com.my
Cement Mfr
N.A.I.C.S.: 327390
Kok Choong Low *(Head-Supply Chain)*

Hume Concrete Sdn. Bhd. (1)
Level 5 Wisma Hume Block D 15A Jalan 51A/219, 46100, Petaling Jaya, Selangor Darul Ehsan, Malaysia
Tel.: (60) 378639300
Web Site:
 https://www.humeconcrete.com.my
Concrete Products Mfr
N.A.I.C.S.: 327390
Zolida Mohd Daud *(Head-HR)*

HUMEDIX CO., LTD.

6th Floor HuonsGlobal Bldg A-dong Pangyo I-Square, 17 Changeop-ro Sujeong-gu, Seongnam, 13449, Gyeonggi-do, Korea (South)
Tel.: (82) 7074925600
Web Site: https://www.humedix.com
Year Founded: 2002
200670—(KRS)
Rev.: $94,473,530
Assets: $174,213,578
Liabilities: $67,516,475
Net Worth: $106,697,103
Earnings: $16,224,805
Emp.: 292

AND PRIVATE COMPANIES

Fiscal Year-end: 12/31/22
Pharmaceuticals Mfr
N.A.I.C.S.: 325412
Kim Jin-Hwan (CEO)

HUMM GROUP LIMITED
Tel.: (61) 289052000 AU
HUM—(ASX)
Rev.: $413,531,382
Assets: $3,616,613,388
Liabilities: $3,230,058,702
Net Worth: $386,554,686
Earnings: $4,740,954
Emp.: 570
Fiscal Year-end: 06/30/24
Holding Company; Point-of-Sale Lease & Rental Financing Services
N.A.I.C.S.: 551112
Andrew Abercrombie (Chm)

Subsidiaries:

Certegy Ezi-Pay Pty Ltd (1)
Level 1 97 Pirie Street, Adelaide, 5000, SA, Australia
Tel.: (61) 882322828
Web Site: http://www.certegyezipay.com.au
Retail Payment Services
N.A.I.C.S.: 522320

Fisher & Paykel Finance Limited (1)
31 Highbrook Drive East Tamaki, Private Bag 94013, Auckland, 2241, New Zealand (100%)
Tel.: (64) 95258550
Web Site: http://www.flexicards.co.nz
Financial Services
N.A.I.C.S.: 523999

FlexiGroup (NZ) Ltd (1)
111 Carlton Gore Road, Newmarket, Auckland, 1023, New Zealand
Tel.: (64) 800444827
Web Site: http://flexirent.flexigroup.co.nz
Equipment Leasing Services
N.A.I.C.S.: 532420
Chris Lamers (CEO)

FlexiGroup (New Zealand) Limited (1)
Victoria St West, PO Box 90935, Auckland, 1142, New Zealand
Tel.: (64) 9 525 8550
Web Site: https://nz.flexigroup.co.nz
Financial Services
N.A.I.C.S.: 522110

Flexirent Capital Pty. Ltd. (1)
Level 8 The Forum 201 Pacific Highway, Saint Leonards, 2065, NSW, Australia (100%)
Tel.: (61) 289052000
Sales Range: $200-249.9 Million
Emp.: 400
Point-of-Sale Lease & Rental Financing Services
N.A.I.C.S.: 522220
Marilyn Conyer (CMO)

Subsidiary (Non-US):

Flexirent Capital (New Zealand) Ltd. (2)
120 Albert St, PO Box 90935, Victoria Saint W, Auckland, 1142, New Zealand (100%)
Tel.: (64) 93004494
Sales Range: $25-49.9 Million
Emp.: 30
Point-of-Sale Lease & Rental Financing Services
N.A.I.C.S.: 522220

Flexirent Holdings Pty Limited (1)
Level 8 201 Pacific Highway, Saint Leonards, 2065, NSW, Australia
Tel.: (61) 289052000
Web Site: http://www.flexigroup.com
Sales Range: $100-124.9 Million
Emp.: 250
Investment Management Service
N.A.I.C.S.: 523999

Flexirent Ireland Limited (1)
Level 4 No 5 Custom House Plaza Harbourmaster Place IFSC, Dublin, Ireland
Tel.: (353) 1 840 8627
Web Site: https://www.flexirent.ie
Financial Services
N.A.I.C.S.: 523999

Flexirent SPV No 2 Pty Limited (1)
Level 8 201 Pacific Highway, Saint Leonards, North Shore, 2065, NSW, Australia
Tel.: (61) 289052000
Equipment Leasing Services
N.A.I.C.S.: 532420

Flexirent SPV No 4 Pty Limited (1)
Level 7 179 Elizabeth Street, Sydney, 2000, NSW, Australia
Tel.: (61) 289052000
Web Site: http://www.flexigroup.com.au
Sales Range: $200-249.9 Million
Emp.: 350
Financial Lending Services
N.A.I.C.S.: 522220
Jane Miskell (Grp Head-HR)

Humm Group Limited (1)
3rd Floor 2-4 Wellington Street, Belfast, BT1 6HT, United Kingdom
Tel.: (44) 289 142 2113
Web Site: https://www.shophumm.com
Consumer Finance Solution Services
N.A.I.C.S.: 522291

HUMMING BIRD EDUCATION LTD.
A-95/3 Second Floor Wazirpur Industrial Area, Delhi, 110052, India
Tel.: (91) 1147096144
Web Site: https://www.hummingbird.com
Year Founded: 2010
542592—(BOM)
Rev.: $108,910
Assets: $270,487
Liabilities: $25,015
Net Worth: $245,472
Earnings: ($52,173)
Fiscal Year-end: 03/31/22
Educational Support Services
N.A.I.C.S.: 611710
Mayank Pratap Singh (Chief Compliance Officer & Sec)

Subsidiaries:

SIBIL Education Private Limited (1)
A 95/3 Second Floor, Wazirpur Industrial Area, Delhi, 110052, India
Tel.: (91) 1147096144
Web Site: http://www.sibil.org
Education Services
N.A.I.C.S.: 611710
Savishesh Raj (Chm)

HUMMINGBIRD RESOURCES PLC
26 Mount Row, London, W1K 3SQ, United Kingdom
Tel.: (44) 2074096660 UK
Web Site: https://www.hummingbird.co.uk
Year Founded: 2005
HUM—(AIM)
Rev.: $150,520,000
Assets: $442,400,000
Liabilities: $284,510,000
Net Worth: $157,890,000
Earnings: ($39,990,000)
Fiscal Year-end: 12/31/22
Mineral Exploration Services
N.A.I.C.S.: 212220
Daniel Edward Betts (Founder & Mng Dir)

HUNAN AIHUA GROUP CO., LTD.
East Taohualun Road, Yiyang, 413000, Hunan, China
Tel.: (86) 7376184466
Web Site: https://www.aishi.com
Year Founded: 1985
603989—(SHG)
Rev.: $483,660,352
Assets: $755,988,391
Liabilities: $279,169,437
Net Worth: $476,818,955
Earnings: $62,597,607
Emp.: 5,000
Fiscal Year-end: 12/31/22
Aluminum Electrolytic Capacitor Mfr & Distr
N.A.I.C.S.: 334416
Ai Lihua (Chm)

HUNAN AIRBLUER ENVIRONMENTAL PROTECTION TECHNOLOGY CO., LTD.
Floor 16-19 Building 8 Tiancheng Commercial Plaza, No 979 Section 1 Furong South Road Tianxin District, Changsha, 410205, Hunan, China
Tel.: (86) 73184425216
Web Site: https://www.airbluer.cn
Year Founded: 2013
301259—(CHIN)
Rev.: $66,803,724
Assets: $217,558,224
Liabilities: $89,919,180
Net Worth: $127,639,044
Earnings: $10,391,004
Fiscal Year-end: 12/31/22
Pollution Control Equipment Mfr
N.A.I.C.S.: 334519
Rubo Zhong (Chm)

HUNAN BAILI ENGINEERING SCI & TECH CO.,LTD
No 388 Baling East Road, Yueyang Economic and Technological Development Zone, Yueyang, 414007, Hunan, China
Tel.: (86) 7308501033
Web Site: http://www.blest.com.cn
Year Founded: 1992
603959—(SHG)
Rev.: $452,068,934
Assets: $607,872,737
Liabilities: $507,184,105
Net Worth: $100,688,632
Earnings: $1,205,825
Emp.: 620
Fiscal Year-end: 12/31/22
Engineering Construction Services
N.A.I.C.S.: 541330
Liming Xiao (Vice Chm & Pres)

HUNAN BOYUN NEW MATERIALS CO., LTD.
No 346 Leifeng Avenue, Yuelu District, Changsha, 410205, Hunan, China
Tel.: (86) 73188122999
Web Site: https://www.hnboyun.com.cn
Year Founded: 2001
002297—(SSE)
Rev.: $78,261,768
Assets: $377,108,784
Liabilities: $80,555,904
Net Worth: $296,552,880
Earnings: $3,362,580
Emp.: 580
Fiscal Year-end: 12/31/22
Powder Metallurgy Composite Materials Mfr, Developer & Researcher
N.A.I.C.S.: 332117
Jiqiao Liao (Chm)

HUNAN CHENDIAN INTERNATIONAL DEVELOPMENT CO., LTD.
Wanguo Building Qingnian Avenue, Chenzhou, 423000, Hunan, China
Tel.: (86) 7352339232
Web Site: http://www.chinacdi.com
Year Founded: 2000
600969—(SHG)
Rev.: $563,574,698
Assets: $2,184,744,590
Liabilities: $1,639,743,632
Net Worth: $545,000,957
Earnings: $6,875,500
Emp.: 3,000
Fiscal Year-end: 12/31/22
Electric Power Generation & Distribution
N.A.I.C.S.: 221118
Peishun Fan (Chm & Interim Sec)

HUNAN CHINA SUN PHARMACEUTICAL MACHINERY CO., LTD.
No 9 Panpan Road, Changsha, 410100, Hunan, China
Tel.: (86) 73184030026
Web Site: http://www.chinasun.com.cn
Year Founded: 2002
Rev.: $29,223,390
Assets: $370,599,110
Liabilities: $624,450,050
Net Worth: ($253,850,940)
Earnings: ($362,893,440)
Fiscal Year-end: 12/31/18
Pharmaceutical Machine Mfr
N.A.I.C.S.: 333993
Xianghua Liu (Chm, Pres & Sec-Interim)

HUNAN COPOTE SCIENCE & TECHNOLOGY CO., LTD.
Lugu Base No 2 Yulan Road High-Tech Industrial Development Zone, Changsha, 410205, Hunan, China
Tel.: (86) 73188998688
Web Site: http://www.copote.com
Year Founded: 2000
600476—(SHG)
Rev.: $82,243,849
Assets: $95,324,622
Liabilities: $77,622,429
Net Worth: $17,702,194
Earnings: ($5,529,317)
Fiscal Year-end: 12/31/22
Computer Software Research & Development Services
N.A.I.C.S.: 541715
Zhihong Dong (Chm)

HUNAN CORUN NEW ENERGY CO., LTD.
No 348 Tongzipo West Road, Yuelu District, Changsha, 410205, Hunan, China
Tel.: (86) 71388983638
Web Site: http://www.corun.com
Year Founded: 1998
600478—(SHG)
Rev.: $531,530,841
Assets: $1,119,952,464
Liabilities: $650,024,903
Net Worth: $469,927,561
Earnings: $25,081,674
Emp.: 2,341
Fiscal Year-end: 12/31/22
Battery Mfr
N.A.I.C.S.: 335910
Zhang Judong (Chm)

Subsidiaries:

Changsha Lyrun New material Co., Ltd (1)
No 16 xingsha Avenue changsha Economic & Technical Zone, Changsha, 410100, China
Tel.: (86) 73184016961
Battery Mfr & Distr
N.A.I.C.S.: 335910

Shenzhen National Engineering Research Center of Advanced Energy Storage Material Co., Ltd. (1)
41F China Energy Storage Building No 3099 Keyuan South Road, Nanshan District, Shenzhen, China
Tel.: (86) 75522678989
Web Site: http://www.cesbattery.com
Lithium Battery Mfr
N.A.I.C.S.: 335910

HUNAN CORUN NEW ENERGY CO., LTD.

Hunan Corun New Energy Co., Ltd.—(Continued)

YiYang Corun Battery Co., LTD (1)
No 168 Gaoxing Rd Yiyang High-Tech Industrial Development Zon, Yiyang, 413000, Hunan, China
Tel.: (86) 7376202975
Battery Mfr & Distr
N.A.I.C.S.: 335910

HUNAN CREATOR INFORMATION TECHNOLOGIES CO., LTD.
Kechuang Software Park No 678 Qingshan Road, Yuelu District, Changsha, 410205, Hunan, China
Tel.: (86) 73183757888
Web Site: https://www.chinacreator.com
Year Founded: 1998
300730—(CHIN)
Rev.: $32,957,041
Assets: $132,373,957
Liabilities: $78,687,810
Net Worth: $53,686,147
Earnings: ($22,796,065)
Fiscal Year-end: 12/31/23
Software Development Services
N.A.I.C.S.: 513210

HUNAN DAJIAWEIKANG PHARMACEUTICAL INDUSTRY CO., LTD.
No 30 Fuling Road, Yuelu District, Changsha, 410013, Hunan, China
Tel.: (86) 73184512838
Web Site: https://www.djwk.com.cn
Year Founded: 2002
301126—(CHIN)
Rev.: $549,789,266
Assets: $743,331,730
Liabilities: $492,395,182
Net Worth: $250,936,549
Earnings: $4,830,958
Emp.: 400
Fiscal Year-end: 12/31/23
Pharmaceutical Product Mfr & Distr
N.A.I.C.S.: 325412
Yiqing Wang (Chm)

HUNAN DEVELOPMENT GROUP CO., LTD.
27th Floor Building B Everbright Development Building, No 142 Section 3 Furong Middle Road Tianxin District, Changsha, 410015, Hunan, China
Tel.: (86) 73188789296
Web Site: https://www.hnfzgf.com
Year Founded: 1993
000722—(SSE)
Rev.: $57,846,204
Assets: $470,685,384
Liabilities: $23,999,976
Net Worth: $446,685,408
Earnings: $9,707,256
Fiscal Year-end: 12/31/22
Optic Cable Mfr
N.A.I.C.S.: 335921
Han Zhiguang (Chm)

HUNAN ER-KANG PHARMACEUTICAL CO., LTD.
Liuyang National Economic & Technical Development Zone, Changsha, 410331, Hunan, China
Tel.: (86) 73184659108
Web Site: https://en.hnerkang.com
Year Founded: 2003
300267—(CHIN)
Rev.: $262,623,816
Assets: $822,134,664
Liabilities: $112,961,628
Net Worth: $709,173,036
Earnings: $6,424,704
Fiscal Year-end: 12/31/22
Pharmaceutical Product Mfr & Distr
N.A.I.C.S.: 325412

Handsome Release (Chm)

Subsidiaries:

Hunan Dongting Citric Acid Chemical Co., Limited (1)
2315 Furong Gongguan 459 Furong Road Middle, Changsha, 410007, Hunan, China
Tel.: (86) 73184304988
Emp.: 242
Basic Organic Chemical Mfr
N.A.I.C.S.: 325199

HUNAN FANGSHENG PHARMACEUTICAL CO., LTD.
No 299 Jiayun Road, National High-tech Industrial Development Zone, Changsha, 410205, Hunan, China
Tel.: (86) 73188997188
Web Site: https://www.fangsheng.com.cn
Year Founded: 2002
603998—(SHG)
Rev.: $251,596,926
Assets: $410,269,874
Liabilities: $198,553,848
Net Worth: $211,716,026
Earnings: $40,133,551
Fiscal Year-end: 12/31/22
Pharmaceutical Product Mfr & Distr
N.A.I.C.S.: 325412
Zhou Xiaoli (Chm)

HUNAN FRIENDSHIP & APOLLO COMMERCIAL CO., LTD.
Office Building No 9 Chaoyang Qian Street, Furong District, Changsha, 410001, Hunan, China
Tel.: (86) 73182293541
Web Site: http://www.your-mart.cn
Year Founded: 2004
002277—(SSE)
Rev.: $254,511,504
Assets: $2,082,158,676
Liabilities: $1,116,488,880
Net Worth: $965,669,796
Earnings: $4,641,624
Emp.: 2,487
Fiscal Year-end: 12/31/22
General Merchandise Retailer
N.A.I.C.S.: 455219
Zijing Hu (Chm)

HUNAN GOLD CORPORATION LIMITED
9F Block 1 No 211 Renmin East Road, Economic and Technological Development Zone, Changsha, 410100, Hunan, China
Tel.: (86) 73182290893
Web Site: http://www.hngoldcorp.com
Year Founded: 2000
002155—(SSE)
Rev.: $2,954,132,532
Assets: $1,027,230,984
Liabilities: $198,372,564
Net Worth: $828,858,420
Earnings: $61,405,344
Fiscal Year-end: 12/31/22
Non-ferrous Metal Mining Services
N.A.I.C.S.: 331410
Wen Cui (VP & Deputy Gen Mgr)

HUNAN HAILI CHEMICAL INDUSTRY CO., LTD.
No 251 Section 2 Furong Middle Road, Changsha, 410007, Hunan, China
Tel.: (86) 73185357800
Web Site: https://www.hnhlc.com
Year Founded: 1994
600731—(SHG)
Rev.: $439,467,978
Assets: $551,130,316
Liabilities: $243,177,180
Net Worth: $307,953,135

Earnings: $49,458,610
Fiscal Year-end: 12/31/22
Chemical Product Mfr & Whslr
N.A.I.C.S.: 325320
Xiao Zhiyong (Chm)

Subsidiaries:

Hunan Haili Chemical Industry Stock Co., Ltd. (1)
No 399 Furong Road Central, Changsha, 410007, Hunan, China
Tel.: (86) 73185533493
Emp.: 1,420
Pesticide Chemical Product Mfr
N.A.I.C.S.: 325320

HUNAN HANSEN PHARMACEUTICAL CO., LTD.
No 2688 Yincheng Avenue, Yiyang, 413000, Hunan, China
Tel.: (86) 7376351006
Web Site: https://www.hansenzy.com
Year Founded: 1998
002412—(SSE)
Rev.: $128,614,824
Assets: $321,647,976
Liabilities: $55,712,124
Net Worth: $265,935,852
Earnings: $23,533,848
Fiscal Year-end: 12/31/22
Pharmaceuticals Mfr
N.A.I.C.S.: 325412
Liu Zhengqing (Chm & Pres)

HUNAN HENGGUANG TECHNOLOGY CO., LTD.
No 01 Yanmen, Hongjiang District, Huaihua, 418200, Hunan, China
Tel.: (86) 7457695232
Web Site: https://www.hgkjgf.com
Year Founded: 2008
301118—(CHIN)
Rev.: $151,637,616
Assets: $282,470,760
Liabilities: $74,681,568
Net Worth: $207,789,192
Earnings: $28,290,600
Emp.: 600
Fiscal Year-end: 12/31/22
Chemical Product Mfr & Distr
N.A.I.C.S.: 327120
Lixiang Cao (Chm, Pres & Gen Mgr)

Subsidiaries:

Hunan Hengguang Chemical Co., Ltd. (1)
1 5 kilometers away from Shangni Road, Songmu Economic Development Zone, Hengyang, 421000, Hunan, China
Tel.: (86) 7348227600
Chemical Products Mfr
N.A.I.C.S.: 325998

HUNAN HESHUN PETROLEUM CO., LTD.
Heshun Building No 58 Section 2 Wanjiali Middle Road, Yuhua, Changsha, 410016, Hunan, China
Tel.: (86) 73182224888
Web Site: https://www.hnhsjt.com
Year Founded: 2005
603353—(SHG)
Rev.: $560,763,216
Assets: $326,932,618
Liabilities: $90,186,010
Net Worth: $236,746,608
Earnings: $14,539,459
Fiscal Year-end: 12/31/22
Petroleum Product Distr
N.A.I.C.S.: 424720
Zhong Zhao (Chm & Gen Mgr)

HUNAN HUAKAI CULTURAL AND CREATIVE CO., LTD
Room 2002 Building C Kailin International No 53 Binjiang Road, Yuelu District, Changsha, 410023, Hunan, China
Tel.: (86) 73188652008
Web Site: https://www.huakai.net
Year Founded: 2009
300592—(CHIN)
Rev.: $918,040,666
Assets: $458,624,023
Liabilities: $158,055,405
Net Worth: $300,568,618
Earnings: $46,784,947
Fiscal Year-end: 12/31/23
Art Design Services
N.A.I.C.S.: 541430
Hu Fanjin (Chm & Gen Mgr)

HUNAN HUALIAN CHINA INDUSTRY CO., LTD.
Cigu Avenue, Liling Economic Development Zone, Zhuzhou, 412205, Hunan, China
Tel.: (86) 73123053013
Year Founded: 1994
001216—(SSE)
Rev.: $193,737,960
Assets: $262,914,444
Liabilities: $56,387,448
Net Worth: $206,526,996
Earnings: $23,987,340
Fiscal Year-end: 12/31/22
Ceramic Products Mfr
N.A.I.C.S.: 327110

HUNAN HUAMIN HOLDINGS CO., LTD.
29th Floor IEC Building No 86 Xinjian Lane, Yuhua District, Changsha, 410018, Hunan, China
Tel.: (86) 73189723366
Web Site: http://www.chinahongyu.cn
Year Founded: 1995
300345—(CHIN)
Rev.: $35,278,308
Assets: $186,914,520
Liabilities: $46,285,668
Net Worth: $140,628,852
Earnings: ($4,898,556)
Emp.: 360
Fiscal Year-end: 12/31/22
Wear Resistant Cast Iron Grinding Balls & Grinding Granules Mfr
N.A.I.C.S.: 331511
Ouyang Shaohong (Chm)

HUNAN HUASHENG CO., LTD.
Huasheng Building No 420 Section 3 Furong Middle Road, Changsha, 410015, Hunan, China
Tel.: (86) 73185237818
Web Site: http://www.hunan-huasheng.com
Year Founded: 1998
600156—(SHG)
Rev.: $127,837,106
Assets: $137,018,185
Liabilities: $78,606,829
Net Worth: $58,411,356
Earnings: ($29,267,686)
Emp.: 3,000
Fiscal Year-end: 12/31/22
Textile Product Mfr & Distr
N.A.I.C.S.: 313210
Liu Zhigang (Chm & Gen Mgr)

HUNAN INVESTMENT GROUP CO., LTD.
21F Hunan Investment Building No 447 Wuyi Avenue, Furong District, Changsha, 410005, Hunan, China
Tel.: (86) 73185922066
Web Site: https://www.hntz.com.cn
Year Founded: 1992
000548—(SSE)
Rev.: $58,322,160
Assets: $470,749,968
Liabilities: $209,495,052

Net Worth: $261,254,916
Earnings: $4,908,384
Fiscal Year-end: 12/31/22
Road & Bridge Construction Services
N.A.I.C.S.: 488490
Pi Zhao (Chm)

HUNAN JINGFENG PHARMACEUTICAL CO., LTD.
Shuangchuang Bldg No 661 Taolin Rd Shuanggang Community Zhangmuqiao, Changde Economic & Technological Development Zone, Changsha, 415001, Hunan, China
Tel.: (86) 7367320908
Web Site: http://www.jfzhiyao.com
Year Founded: 1998
000908—(SSE)
Rev.: $118,028,664
Assets: $206,173,188
Liabilities: $176,011,056
Net Worth: $30,162,132
Earnings: ($17,993,664)
Fiscal Year-end: 12/31/22
Pharmaceuticals Mfr
N.A.I.C.S.: 325412
Yang Dong (Pres)

HUNAN JIUDIAN PHARMACEUTICAL CO., LTD.
Bldg A1 Wukuang Lugu Science and Technology Industry Park, No 28 Lutian Road Hi-tech development zone, Changsha, 410205, Hunan, China
Tel.: (86) 73188220222
Web Site: https://www.jiudianph.com
Year Founded: 2001
300705—(CHIN)
Rev.: $379,240,245
Assets: $404,408,492
Liabilities: $126,473,426
Net Worth: $277,935,065
Earnings: $51,869,534
Emp.: 1,200
Fiscal Year-end: 12/31/23
Pharmaceutical Product Mfr & Distr
N.A.I.C.S.: 325412
Zhihong Zhu (Chm)

HUNAN JUNXIN ENVIRONMENTAL PROTECTION CO., LTD.
Office Building, Qiaoyi Town Wangcheng District, Changsha, 410200, Hunan, China
Tel.: (86) 73185608335
Web Site: https://www.junxinep.com
Year Founded: 2011
301109—(SSE)
Rev.: $220,510,836
Assets: $1,372,650,084
Liabilities: $594,894,456
Net Worth: $777,755,628
Earnings: $65,454,480
Fiscal Year-end: 12/31/22
Solid Waste Landfill Services
N.A.I.C.S.: 562212
Daoguo Dai (Chm)

HUNAN KAIMEITE GASES CO., LTD.
West Gate of Baling Petrochemical Fertilizer Division, Qilishan Yueyanglou District, Yueyang, 414003, Hunan, China
Tel.: (86) 7308553359
Web Site: http://www.china-kmt.cn
Year Founded: 1991
002549—(SSE)
Rev.: $119,636,244
Assets: $313,970,904
Liabilities: $140,221,692
Net Worth: $173,749,212
Earnings: $23,239,008
Emp.: 110
Fiscal Year-end: 12/31/22

Carbon Ice, Liquid Carbon Dioxide & Other Industrial Gas Mfr
N.A.I.C.S.: 325120
Enfu Zhu (Chm)

HUNAN LEAD POWER TECHNOLOGY GROUP CO., LTD.
17th Floor Chuangxing Valley Mobile Internet Industrial Park, High-tech Zone Hengzhou Avenue, Hengyang, 421200, Hunan, China
Tel.: (86) 7348813813
Web Site: http://www.dazhichem.com
Year Founded: 2002
300530—(CHIN)
Rev.: $26,793,332
Assets: $235,585,597
Liabilities: $200,721,786
Net Worth: $34,863,812
Earnings: ($29,432,227)
Fiscal Year-end: 12/31/23
Chemical Mfr & Distr
N.A.I.C.S.: 325194
Chen Fenghua (Chm)

HUNAN LICHEN INDUSTRIAL CO., LTD.
No 399 Shetang Road Quantang Street, Changsha, 410100, Hunan, China
Tel.: (86) 73182115109
Web Site: https://www.hnlcwang.com
Year Founded: 1981
001218—(SSE)
Rev.: $447,092,234
Assets: $373,300,934
Liabilities: $78,910,519
Net Worth: $294,390,415
Earnings: $18,675,506
Fiscal Year-end: 12/31/23
Detergent Product Mfr
N.A.I.C.S.: 325611
Qizheng Jia (Chm)

HUNAN MENDALE HOMETEXTILE CO., LTD.
No 168 Guyuan Road, Lugu Industrial Base High-tech Industrial Development Zone, Changsha, 410205, Hunan, China
Tel.: (86) 73182848012
Web Site:
   http://www.mendale.com.cn
Year Founded: 2005
002397—(SSE)
Rev.: $285,405,120
Assets: $388,872,900
Liabilities: $228,506,616
Net Worth: $160,366,284
Earnings: ($62,931,492)
Fiscal Year-end: 12/31/22
Household Textile Product Mfr
N.A.I.C.S.: 314999
Jiang Tianwu (Chm)

HUNAN NEW WELLFUL CO., LTD.
19-20th Floor First Avenue No 2 Wuyi West Road, Furong District, Changsha, 410005, Hunan, China
Tel.: (86) 73184449588
Web Site: https://www.newwf.com
Year Founded: 2001
600975—(SHG)
Rev.: $692,486,412
Assets: $1,415,953,333
Liabilities: $1,007,859,673
Net Worth: $408,093,660
Earnings: ($10,670,217)
Fiscal Year-end: 12/31/22
Pig Breeding & Distribution
N.A.I.C.S.: 112210
Wan Qijian (Chm & Sec-Party)

HUNAN NONFERROUS METALS CORPORATION LTD.
11/F Block A Yousedasha 342 Laodongxi Road, Changsha, Hunan, China
Tel.: (86) 7315385556   CN
Web Site: http://www.hnc2626.com
Emp.: 21,242
Nonferrous Metals Mining & Production Services
N.A.I.C.S.: 331410
He Renchun (Chm)

Subsidiaries:

Abra Mining Limited   (1)
Level 1 34 Colin St, 6005, West Perth, WA, Australia   (100%)
Tel.: (61) 892260200
Web Site: http://www.abramining.com.au
Sales Range: Less than $1 Million
Emp.: 13
Metals Exploration & Development
N.A.I.C.S.: 213114
Mingyan Wang (Mng Dir)

China Tungsten & Hightech Materials Co., Ltd.   (1)
10-12F Zuanshi Building No 288 Zuanshi Road, Hetang District, Zhuzhou, 412000, Hunan, China
Tel.: (86) 73185392435
Web Site:
   http://www.minmetalstungsten.com
Rev.: $1,836,427,788
Assets: $1,639,791,972
Liabilities: $780,229,476
Net Worth: $859,562,496
Earnings: $75,050,820
Fiscal Year-end: 12/31/2022
Cemented Carbide Mfr
N.A.I.C.S.: 327310
Zhongze Li (Chm)

Subsidiary (Domestic):

Zhuzhou Cemented Carbide Cutting Tools Co., Ltd.   (2)
Huanghe Southern Road Tianyuan Zone, Zhuzhou, 412007, Hunan, China
Tel.: (86) 731 2288 9057
Web Site: http://eng.zccct.com
Cutting & Bore Machining Tools Mfr
N.A.I.C.S.: 333515

Subsidiary (Non-US):

HPTec GmbH   (3)
Im Karrer 6, 88214, Ravensburg, Germany
Tel.: (49) 751 7669 0
Web Site: http://www.hptec.de
Cutting Tool Mfr
N.A.I.C.S.: 333515
Heinrch Hoffkecht (Gen Mgr)

ZCC Europe GmbH   (1)
Wanheimer Strasse 59, 40472, Dusseldorf, Germany
Tel.: (49) 211230390
Web Site: http://www.zcc-europe.com
Sales Range: $25-49.9 Million
Emp.: 32
Carbide Products Distr
N.A.I.C.S.: 424690

Zhuzhou Cemented Carbide Group HongKong Co. Ltd.   (1)
Flat E 19/F Block 4 Nan Fung Sun Chuen 38 Greig Road, Quarry Bay, China (Hong Kong)
Tel.: (852) 28151831
Web Site: http://www.chinacarbide.com
Carbide Products Distr
N.A.I.C.S.: 424690
Hu Xiang (Mng Dir)

Zhuzhou Cemented Carbide Works Import & Export Company   (1)
Diamond Road, Hetang District, Zhuzhou, 412000, Hunan, China
Tel.: (86) 731 28261490
Web Site: http://www.chinacarbide.com
Emp.: 60
Carbide Products Mfr
N.A.I.C.S.: 325180
Yuting Mau (Gen Mgr)

Zhuzhou Cemented Carbide Works USA Inc.   (1)
4651 Platt Ln, Ann Arbor, MI 48108
Tel.: (734) 302-0125

Web Site: http://www.chinacarbide.com
Sales Range: $50-74.9 Million
Emp.: 3
Carbide Products Distr
N.A.I.C.S.: 424690
Tina Mitchell (Office Mgr)

HUNAN NUCIEN PHARMACEUTICAL CO., LTD.
Building 1-2 No 196 Kaiyuan Avenue, Huangpu District, Guangzhou, 510100, Guangdong, China
Tel.: (86) 2038952013
Web Site: http://www.nucien.com
Year Founded: 2006
688189—(SHG)
Rev.: $98,115,198
Assets: $274,312,411
Liabilities: $92,301,824
Net Worth: $182,010,587
Earnings: ($11,068,055)
Fiscal Year-end: 12/31/22
Pharmaceutical Product Mfr & Distr
N.A.I.C.S.: 325412
Wenxun Yang (Chm)

HUNAN OIL PUMP CO., LTD.
No 69 Zhen Zheng street, Chengguan, Hengyang, 421400, Hunan, China
Tel.: (86) 7345222517
Web Site: https://www.hnjyb.com
Year Founded: 1949
603319—(SHG)
Rev.: $228,065,746
Assets: $388,496,488
Liabilities: $166,569,647
Net Worth: $221,926,840
Earnings: $23,809,987
Fiscal Year-end: 12/31/22
Pump Mfr & Distr
N.A.I.C.S.: 336310
Zhongqiu Xu (Chm)

Subsidiaries:

HengShan Gear Co., Ltd   (1)
No 408 Hengshan Avenue, Heng Shan county, Hengyang, 421400, Hunan, China
Tel.: (86) 734 581 0238
Web Site: https://www.hsclgs.cn
Pump Gear Reducer Mfr & Distr
N.A.I.C.S.: 333612

Hunan Jiali Machinery Co., Ltd   (1)
Pingtang Road Economic Development Zone, Hengshan County, Hengyang, 421400, Hunan, China
Web Site: https://www.jljxgs.net
Oil Pump Mfr
N.A.I.C.S.: 333914

HUNAN SOKAN NEW MATERIALS CO., LTD.
No 777 Third Ring Road, National Economic Development Zone Ningxiang, Changsha, Hunan, China
Tel.: (86) 73187191777
Web Site: http://www.sokan.com.cn
Year Founded: 2009
688157—(SHG)
Rev.: $70,072,517
Assets: $198,038,637
Liabilities: $20,589,674
Net Worth: $177,448,963
Earnings: $11,548,026
Emp.: 159
Fiscal Year-end: 12/31/22
Chemical Product Mfr & Distr
N.A.I.C.S.: 325520
Yunjian Ling (Chm & Gen Mgr)

HUNAN SUNDY SCIENCE AND TECHNOLOGY CO., LTD
No 558 West Tongzipo Road, Yuelu District, Changsha, 410205, Hunan, China
Tel.: (86) 73188112150
Web Site: https://en.sandegroup.com

HUNAN SUNDY SCIENCE AND TECHNOLOGY CO.,LTD

Hunan Sundy Science and Technology Co.,Ltd—(Continued)
Year Founded: 1993
300515—(CHIN)
Rev.: $65,430,896
Assets: $162,645,692
Liabilities: $57,016,714
Net Worth: $105,628,979
Earnings: $7,568,842
Emp.: 500
Fiscal Year-end: 12/31/23
Coal Analysis Solution Services
N.A.I.C.S.: 213113

HUNAN TIANRUN DIGITAL ENTERTAINMENT & CULTURAL MEDIA CO., LTD.
Floor 6 Xingchang Petrochemical Building Yueyang Avenue, Yueyang, 414000, Hunan, China
Tel.: (86) 07308961178
002113—(SSE)
Rev.: $96,730,666
Assets: $274,400,642
Liabilities: $216,032,228
Net Worth: $58,368,414
Earnings: $42,601,573
Fiscal Year-end: 12/31/20
Holding Company
N.A.I.C.S.: 551112
Jiang Feng *(Chm)*

HUNAN TV & BROADCAST INTERMEDIARY CO., LTD.
East of Liuyang River Bridge, Changsha, 410003, Hunan, China
Tel.: (86) 73184252333
Web Site: http://www.tik.com.cn
Year Founded: 1999
000917—(SSE)
Rev.: $523,086,876
Assets: $2,479,631,076
Liabilities: $887,488,056
Net Worth: $1,592,143,020
Earnings: $29,241,108
Fiscal Year-end: 12/31/22
Television Program Production & Distribution Services
N.A.I.C.S.: 516120
Wang Yanzhong *(Chm)*

HUNAN TYEN MACHINERY CO., LTD.
No 195 Hejiangtao Road, Shigu District, Hengyang, 421005, Hunan, China
Tel.: (86) 7348532012
Web Site: http://www.tyen.com.cn
Year Founded: 1993
900946—(SHG)
Rev.: $46,416,633
Assets: $148,932,094
Liabilities: $42,158,638
Net Worth: $106,773,456
Earnings: ($3,902,994)
Emp.: 1,600
Fiscal Year-end: 12/31/22
Turbocharger Mfr & Distr
N.A.I.C.S.: 336310
Duan Chaoyang *(Chm-Supervisory Bd)*

HUNAN VALIN CABLE CO., LTD.
No 1 Jianshe South Road, Hi-tech Zone, Xiangtan, 411104, Hunan, China
Tel.: (86) 73158590168
Web Site: https://www.hlxl.com
Year Founded: 2003
001208—(SSE)
Rev.: $423,352,332
Assets: $501,431,580
Liabilities: $293,372,820
Net Worth: $208,058,760
Earnings: $15,418,728
Fiscal Year-end: 12/31/22
Wire Product Mfr & Distr
N.A.I.C.S.: 335921
Zhang Zhigang *(Chm)*

HUNAN VALIN STEEL CO., LTD.
Main Tower of Valin Garden No 222 Xiangfu West Road, Tianxin District, Changsha, 410004, China
Tel.: (86) 73189952791
Web Site: http://www.valin.cn
000932—(SSE)
Rev.: $22,771,551,714
Assets: $18,433,281,998
Liabilities: $9,524,691,903
Net Worth: $8,908,590,095
Earnings: $703,169,902
Fiscal Year-end: 12/31/23
Iron & Steel Product Mfr
N.A.I.C.S.: 331110

Subsidiaries:

Valin Tube (1)
No 10 Dasu Xincun No 10 Dasu Xincun, Hengyang, 421001, China
Tel.: (86) 7348373883
Steel Tube & Pipe Mfr
N.A.I.C.S.: 331210

HUNAN XIANGJIA ANIMAL HUSBANDRY CO., LTD.
No 9 Jiashan Road Tiangongshan Residential Committee, Economic Development Zone Shimen County, Changde, 415300, Hunan, China
Tel.: (86) 7365223898
Web Site: http://www.xiangjiamuye.com
Year Founded: 2003
002982—(SSE)
Rev.: $536,749,200
Assets: $531,006,840
Liabilities: $262,685,592
Net Worth: $268,321,248
Earnings: $14,864,148
Fiscal Year-end: 12/31/22
Poultry Processing Product Mfr
N.A.I.C.S.: 311615
Ziwen Yu *(Chm, Vice Chm, Pres & Gen Mgr)*

HUNAN YONKER INVESTMENT GROUP CO., LTD.
18th Floor Hualing Mansion No 111 Furong Middle Road, Second Section, Changsha, Hunan, China
Tel.: (86) 731 8443 3529 CN
Web Site: http://www.yonkergroup.cn
Year Founded: 1998
Investment Holding Company
N.A.I.C.S.: 551112
Zhengjun Liu *(Chm-Yonker Environmental Protection)*

Subsidiaries:

Yonker Environmental Protection Co., Ltd. (1)
Yongqing Industrial Park, Liuyang Economic Development Zone, Changsha, 410330, Hunan, China (60.84%)
Tel.: (86) 73183506688
Web Site: https://www.yonker.com.cn
Rev.: $100,154,340
Assets: $464,679,072
Liabilities: $327,161,484
Net Worth: $137,517,588
Earnings: ($54,339,012)
Emp.: 319
Fiscal Year-end: 12/31/2022
Emission Reduction & Environmental Remediation Services
N.A.I.C.S.: 562910
Wang Feng *(Chm & Gen Mgr)*

Subsidiary (US):

Integrated Science & Technology, Inc. (2)
4940 Cowan Rd, Acworth, GA 30101-5130 (51%)
Tel.: (717) 993-0400
Web Site: http://www.integratedscience.com
Environmental Consulting & Remediation Services
N.A.I.C.S.: 541620
Robert E. Hinchee *(Principal & Engr-Civil & Environmental)*

HUNAN YUJING MACHINERY CO., LTD.
No 01 North Side of Ziyang Avenue Changchun Econmic Development Zone, Yiyang, 413001, Hunan, China
Tel.: (86) 7372218141
Web Site: https://www.hnyj-cn.com
Year Founded: 1998
002943—(SSE)
Rev.: $70,003,181
Assets: $205,961,735
Liabilities: $86,491,641
Net Worth: $119,470,094
Earnings: ($1,037,232)
Emp.: 400
Fiscal Year-end: 12/31/21
Machine Tool Mfr & Distr
N.A.I.C.S.: 333517
Yang Yuhong *(Chm)*

HUNAN YUNENG NEW ENERGY BATTERY MATERIAL CO., LTD.
No 18 Rili Road, Heling Town Yuhu District, Xiangtan, 411202, Hunan, China
Tel.: (86) 73158270060
Web Site: https://www.hunanyuneng.com
Year Founded: 2016
301358—(SSE)
Rev.: $6,007,766,544
Assets: $3,711,393,972
Liabilities: $2,909,083,788
Net Worth: $802,310,184
Earnings: $422,212,284
Fiscal Year-end: 12/31/22
Lithium Battery Mfr
N.A.I.C.S.: 335910
Xinqiao Tan *(Chm)*

HUNAN YUSSEN ENERGY TECHNOLOGY CO., LTD.
9F CNOOC Tower No 426 Mid Petrochemical Way, Dayabay, Huizhou, 516081, Guangdong, China
Tel.: (86) 7525962808
Web Site: https://www.yussen.com.cn
Year Founded: 2009
002986—(SSE)
Rev.: $879,384,168
Assets: $538,963,308
Liabilities: $181,124,424
Net Worth: $357,838,884
Earnings: $60,423,948
Fiscal Year-end: 12/31/22
Energy Distribution Services
N.A.I.C.S.: 221122
Xiannian Hu *(Chm & Gen Mgr)*

HUNAN ZHENGHONG SCIENCE AND TECHNOLOGY DEVELOP CO., LTD.
Room 303 3rd Floor Standardized Factory Building, Yueyang, 414000, Hunan, China
Tel.: (86) 7308828198
Web Site: http://www.chinazhjt.com.ch
Year Founded: 1997
000702—(SSE)
Rev.: $163,017,036
Assets: $111,848,256
Liabilities: $95,386,356
Net Worth: $16,461,900
Earnings: ($16,284,996)
Fiscal Year-end: 12/31/22

INTERNATIONAL PUBLIC

Pig Feedstuff Mfr
N.A.I.C.S.: 311119
Xianwen Liu *(Chm)*

HUNAN ZHONGKE ELECTRIC CO., LTD.
No 168 Economic and Technological Development Zone, Yueyang Road Branch Industrial Park, Yueyang, 414000, Hunan, China
Tel.: (86) 7308688860
Web Site: https://www.cseco.cn
300035—(CHIN)
Rev.: $738,047,700
Assets: $1,609,702,848
Liabilities: $866,296,080
Net Worth: $743,406,768
Earnings: $51,129,468
Emp.: 300
Fiscal Year-end: 12/31/22
Electromagnetic Equipment Mfr
N.A.I.C.S.: 335999

HUNAS HOLDINGS PLC
Tel.: (94) 812476402
Web Site: https://www.hunasfallshotel.com
HUNA—(COL)
Rev.: $3,016,492
Assets: $18,474,865
Liabilities: $10,151,492
Net Worth: $8,323,373
Earnings: ($1,370,970)
Emp.: 74
Fiscal Year-end: 03/31/23
Hotel & Restaurant Operator
N.A.I.C.S.: 721110

HUNDSUN TECHNOLOGIES INC.
11th Floor Hengsheng Building No 3588 Jiangnan Avenue, Binjiang District, Hangzhou, 310053, Zhejiang, China
Tel.: (86) 57128829702 CN
Web Site: http://www.hundsun.com
Year Founded: 1995
600570—(SHG)
Rev.: $912,935,149
Assets: $1,825,842,793
Liabilities: $776,428,441
Net Worth: $1,049,414,352
Earnings: $153,188,811
Emp.: 9,000
Fiscal Year-end: 12/31/22
Financial Software Development Services
N.A.I.C.S.: 541511
Zhenggang Peng *(Chm)*

Subsidiaries:

Hundsun.com Co., Ltd. (1)
West Building of Xinde Center No 200 Connaught Road Central, Sheung Wan, China (Hong Kong)
Tel.: (852) 29123787
Financial Software Services
N.A.I.C.S.: 541611

Japan Hundsun Software Inc. (1)
Floor6 KDX Shinjuku Building 3-2-7 Nishi Shinjuku, Shinjuku-ku, Tokyo, 160-0023, Japan
Tel.: (81) 36 279 4570
Web Site: https://www.hundsun.co.jp
Sales Range: $25-49.9 Million
Emp.: 5
Financial Software Development Services
N.A.I.C.S.: 541511

Shanghai Juyuan Data Co., Ltd. (1)
Floor 7 Building 10 Lujiazhui Software Park No 61 91 E'shan Road, Pudong New District, Shanghai, 200127, China
Tel.: (86) 2160897889
Financial Software Services
N.A.I.C.S.: 541611

HUNEED TECHNOLOGIES

87 Venture-ro, Yeonsu-gu, Incheon, Korea (South)
Tel.: (82) 324576000
Web Site: https://www.huneed.com
Year Founded: 1968
005870—(KRS)
Rev.: $170,635,178
Assets: $233,264,149
Liabilities: $122,557,809
Net Worth: $110,706,340
Earnings: $7,101,695
Emp.: 364
Fiscal Year-end: 12/31/22
Communication Equipment Mfr
N.A.I.C.S.: 334220
Shin Jongseok *(CEO)*

HUNESION CO., LTD.
67 Godeokbizvalley-ro 2ga-gil, Gangdong-gu, Seoul, 05203, Korea (South)
Tel.: (82) 25393961
Web Site: https://www.hunesion.com
Year Founded: 2006
290270—(KRS)
Rev.: $23,334,558
Assets: $32,645,557
Liabilities: $5,086,896
Net Worth: $27,558,661
Earnings: ($3,839,107)
Emp.: 154
Fiscal Year-end: 12/31/22
Software Development Services
N.A.I.C.S.: 541511

HUNG CHING DEVELOPMENT & CONSTRUCTION CO., LTD.
10th Fl 420 Keelung rd Sec 1, Taipei, Taiwan
Tel.: (886) 87803025
Web Site: http://www.asehcc.com.tw
2527—(TAI)
Rev.: $75,717,810
Assets: $915,494,848
Liabilities: $528,803,734
Net Worth: $386,691,113
Earnings: $18,439,746
Emp.: 109
Fiscal Year-end: 12/31/23
Real Estate Lending Services
N.A.I.C.S.: 531190

HUNG CHOU FIBER IND. CO., LTD.
7F No 607 Ruiguang Rd, Neihu Dist, Taipei, 114, Taiwan
Tel.: (886) 226575859
Web Site: https://www.hungchou.tw
Year Founded: 1968
1413—(TAI)
Rev.: $65,620,718
Assets: $76,661,006
Liabilities: $40,846,462
Net Worth: $35,814,545
Earnings: ($4,342,392)
Emp.: 180
Fiscal Year-end: 12/31/23
Textile Mill Operator
N.A.I.C.S.: 314999
Cheng-Tien Chan *(Chm & Gen Mgr)*

HUNG DAO CONTAINER JOINT STOCK COMPANY
62 Nguyen Cuu Van, 17 ward Binh Thanh, Ho Chi Minh City, Vietnam
Tel.: (84) 2838403210
Web Site: http://hungdaocontainer.com.vn
Year Founded: 1994
HDO—(HNX)
Rev.: $360,913
Assets: $401,897
Liabilities: $6,625,566
Net Worth: ($6,223,668)
Earnings: ($7,377,552)
Emp.: 182
Fiscal Year-end: 12/31/19
Metal Container Mfr
N.A.I.C.S.: 332439

HUNG FOOK TONG GROUP HOLDINGS LTD
11 Dai King Street Tai Po Industrial Estate, Tai Po, New Territories, China (Hong Kong)
Tel.: (852) 36512000
Web Site: http://www.hungfookholdings.com
1446—(HKG)
Rev.: $87,556,545
Assets: $96,817,508
Liabilities: $57,472,538
Net Worth: $39,344,970
Earnings: ($245,693)
Emp.: 901
Fiscal Year-end: 12/31/22
Herbal Beverages & Food Products Mfr & Retailer
N.A.I.C.S.: 311999
Po Tat Tse *(Chm)*

HUNG HING PRINTING GROUP LIMITED
Hung Hing Printing Centre 17-19 Dai Hei St Tai Po Industrial Estate, Hong Kong, New Territories, China (Hong Kong)
Tel.: (852) 26648682 HK
Web Site: https://www.hunghingprinting.com
Year Founded: 1950
0450—(HKG)
Rev.: $376,139,280
Assets: $508,106,370
Liabilities: $101,374,995
Net Worth: $406,731,375
Earnings: $6,949,770
Emp.: 6,227
Fiscal Year-end: 12/31/22
Printing & Manufacturing of Paper & Corrugated Packaging Products
N.A.I.C.S.: 323120
Spencer Sung *(Exec Dir-Consumer Product Pkg)*

Subsidiaries:

Beluga Limited (1)
17-19 Dai Hei Street, Tai Po, China (Hong Kong)
Tel.: (852) 26648682
Printing & Packaging Services
N.A.I.C.S.: 561910

Guangdong Rengo Packaging Company Limited (1)
3 Changbao Dong Road Ronggui Huakou Shunde, Foshan, 528306, Guangdong, China
Tel.: (86) 75728801818
Printing & Packaging Product Distr
N.A.I.C.S.: 424110

Hung Hing Off-Set Printing Company, Limited (1)
Hung Hing Printing Centre 17-19 Dai Hei Street, Tai Po Industrial Estate, Tai Po, New Territories, China (Hong Kong)
Tel.: (852) 26648682
Web Site: http://www.hunghingprinting.com
Emp.: 300
Commercial Printing Services
N.A.I.C.S.: 323111

Hung Hing Printing (China) Company Limited (1)
Hung Hing Industrial Park Huaide Industrial Village Fuyong Street, Bao'an District, Shenzhen, 518103, Guangdong, China
Tel.: (86) 7552 739 2288
Web Site: http://www.shop.com.hk
Carton Box Printing Services
N.A.I.C.S.: 323111

Hung Hing Printing (Heshan) Company Limited (1)
No 17 Chao Yang Road, Ya Yao Town, Heshan, 529724, Guangdong, China
Tel.: (86) 7508282288
Printing Paper Mfr
N.A.I.C.S.: 322120

Piguet Graphic & Prints Company Limited (1)
1 F Hung Hing Printing Ctr 17-19 Dai Hei St Tai Po Indus Estate, Tai Po, New Territories, China (Hong Kong)
Tel.: (852) 26648682
Printing Support Services
N.A.I.C.S.: 323120
Cheong Hung Yam *(Mng Dir)*

South Gain Enterprises Limited (1)
Hung Hing Printing Centre 17-19 Dai Hei Street, Tai Po Industrial Estate, Tai Po, New Territories, China (Hong Kong)
Tel.: (852) 26648682
Web Site: http://www.hunghingprinting.com
Sales Range: $125-149.9 Million
Emp.: 350
Paper Cartons Printing & Mfr
N.A.I.C.S.: 322130

Sun Hing Paper Company, Limited (1)
Hung Hing Printing Ctr 17-19 Dai Hei.St Tai Po Indus Estate, Tai Po, New Territories, China (Hong Kong)
Tel.: (852) 26648299
Carton Boxes Whslr
N.A.I.C.S.: 424130
Winky Hong *(Gen Mgr)*

Tai Hing Paper Products Company, Limited (1)
1st Fl Hung Hing Printing Ctr 17-19 Dai Hei St Tai Po Indus Estate, Tai Po, New Territories, China (Hong Kong)
Tel.: (852) 26648982
Web Site: http://www.hunghingprinting.com
Emp.: 300
Corrugated Paper Product Mfr
N.A.I.C.S.: 322211

Zhongshan Hung Hing Printing & Packaging Company Limited (1)
20 Yixian Road, Torch Developing Region, Zhongshan, 528437, Guangdong, China
Tel.: (86) 7608 559 7288
Web Site: http://www.hunghingprinting.com
Printing & Paper Mfr
N.A.I.C.S.: 322212

HUNG LONG MINERAL & BUILDING MATERIALS JSC
An Bien 1 Village Le Loi, Hoanh Bo, Quang Ninh, Vietnam
Tel.: (84) 2033691092
Web Site: http://www.khoangsanhunglong.vn
Year Founded: 2001
Rev.: $9,460
Assets: $4,516,311
Liabilities: $2,685,611
Net Worth: $1,830,701
Earnings: ($41,321)
Fiscal Year-end: 12/31/18
Bricks Mfr
N.A.I.C.S.: 327120
Nguyen Nhat Khanh *(Chm)*

HUNG POO REAL ESTATE DEVELOPMENT CO., LTD.
21F No 71 Ses 2 Dunhua S Rd, Da'an Dist, Taipei, 10682, Taiwan
Tel.: (886) 227552662
Web Site: https://www.hong-pu.com.tw
Year Founded: 1988
2536—(TAI)
Rev.: $105,730,824
Assets: $1,369,593,035
Liabilities: $966,644,785
Net Worth: $402,948,250
Earnings: $7,192,681
Emp.: 31
Fiscal Year-end: 12/31/23
Real Estate Development Services
N.A.I.C.S.: 531390
Jinhua Duan *(Chm & Gen Mgr)*

HUNG SHENG CONSTRUCTION CO., LTD.
14th Floor No 168 Dunhua North Road, Songshan District, Taipei, Taiwan
Tel.: (886) 27199999
Web Site: http://www.hsc.com.tw
Year Founded: 1975
2534—(TAI)
Rev.: $83,492,459
Assets: $1,056,005,585
Liabilities: $575,768,512
Net Worth: $480,237,073
Earnings: $17,033,617
Fiscal Year-end: 12/31/23
Real Estate Development Services
N.A.I.C.S.: 531390
Hsin-Chin Lin *(Chm)*

HUNG THINH INCONS JSC
53 Tran Quoc Thao Street, Vo Thi Sau Ward Ditrict 3, Ho Chi Minh City, Vietnam
Tel.: (84) 2873075888
Web Site: https://www.hungthinhincons.com.vn
HTN—(HNX)
Construction Services
N.A.I.C.S.: 236220
Nguyen Dinh Trung *(Chm)*

HUNG VUONG CORPORATION
144 Chau Van Liem St Ward 11 District 5, Ho Chi Minh City, Tien Giang, Vietnam
Tel.: (84) 2838536052
Web Site: https://www.hungvuongpanga.com
Year Founded: 2003
HVG—(HOSE)
Sales Range: $300-349.9 Million
Emp.: 16,000
Seafood Processor & Distr
N.A.I.C.S.: 311710
Ngoc Minh Duong *(Pres)*

HUNG YEN BOOK PUBLISHING & EDUCATIONAL EQUIPMENT JSC
601 Nguyen Van Linh An Tao Ward, Hanoi, Hung Yen, Vietnam
Tel.: (84) 321 3863 892
Web Site: http://www.sachhungyen.vn
Rev.: $2,671,713
Assets: $2,095,961
Liabilities: $1,427,093
Net Worth: $668,867
Earnings: $26,047
Fiscal Year-end: 12/31/18
Stationery Product Whslr
N.A.I.C.S.: 424120

HUNG-GU OIL CO., LTD.
357-1 dongindong, Jung-Gu, Daegu, Korea (South)
Tel.: (82) 534243395
Web Site: http://www.hunggu.kr
024060—(KRS)
Rev.: $112,532,469
Assets: $72,047,851
Liabilities: $10,621,659
Net Worth: $61,426,192
Earnings: $2,037,939
Emp.: 69
Fiscal Year-end: 12/31/22
Petroleum Product Whslr
N.A.I.C.S.: 424720
Young Sung Kim *(Exec Dir)*

HUNGHAU HOLDINGS
1004A Au Co Str Phu Trung Ward, Tan Phu Dist, Ho Chi Minh City, Vietnam
Tel.: (84) 8 3860 4999
Web Site: http://agri.hunghau.vn

HUNGHAU HOLDINGS

HungHau Holdings—(Continued)
Year Founded: 1976
Frozen Seafood Processing & Packing Services
N.A.I.C.S.: 311710
Tran Van Hau *(Chm)*

HUNT & PALMER PLC.
The Tower Goffs Park Road, Crawley, RH11 8XX, West Sussex, United Kingdom
Tel.: (44) 1293 558000
Web Site:
  http://www.huntandpalmer.com
Year Founded: 1986
Sales Range: $50-74.9 Million
Emp.: 62
Aircraft Charter Services
N.A.I.C.S.: 481211
Jeremy Palmer *(Chm)*

Subsidiaries:

Hunt & Palmer (Pty) Ltd. (1)
PO Box 678, Arundel, 4214, QLD, Australia
Tel.: (61) 755742225
Commercial Aircraft Services
N.A.I.C.S.: 481211

Hunt & Palmer Air Charter India Pvt. Ltd. (1)
319 Level 3 Neo Vikram New Link Rd Andheri West, Mumbai, 400058, India
Tel.: (91) 2265555605
Commercial Aircraft Services
N.A.I.C.S.: 481211

Hunt & Palmer Germany GmbH (1)
Robert-Bosch-Str 2a, Hurth, Germany
Tel.: (49) 22339681330
Commercial Aircraft Services
N.A.I.C.S.: 481211

Hunt & Palmer Hong Kong Ltd. (1)
Unit 2209 22/F Wu Chung House 213 Queens Rd, East Wanchai, Hong Kong, China (Hong Kong)
Tel.: (852) 28933499
Commercial Aircraft Services
N.A.I.C.S.: 481211

HUNT CLUB FORD LINCOLN SALES LIMITED
2496 Bank Street, Ottawa, K1V 0W8, ON, Canada
Tel.: (613) 733-0950
Year Founded: 1984
Rev.: $18,200,000
Emp.: 35
New & Used Car Dealers
N.A.I.C.S.: 441110
Dan McKenna *(Principal)*

HUNT'S TRANSPORT LTD.
168 Majors Path, Saint John's, A1N 4P9, NL, Canada
Tel.: (709) 747-4868
Web Site: https://huntslogistics.com
Rev.: $10,389,464
Emp.: 47
Transportation & Logistics Services
N.A.I.C.S.: 488999
Greer Hunt *(Founder & Pres)*

HUNTER & COMPANY PLC
4575 Narahenpita Road, 5, Colombo, Sri Lanka
Tel.: (94) 112081700
Web Site: https://www.hunters.lk
HUNT—(COL)
Rev.: $19,626,604
Assets: $60,649,331
Liabilities: $18,773,232
Net Worth: $41,876,099
Earnings: $1,531,082
Emp.: 565
Fiscal Year-end: 03/31/23
Domestic Appliances & Garden Equipment Distr
N.A.I.C.S.: 423820
L. Renuka P. Dossa *(Mng Dir)*

Subsidiaries:

Lanka Canneries Limited (1)
Tel.: (94) 112586622
Web Site: http://www.mdfood.lk
Convenience Foods Mfr
N.A.I.C.S.: 311421
Nilhan Ekanayake *(Mgr-Export)*

HUNTER DICKINSON INC.
15th Floor-1040 West Georgia Street, Vancouver, V6E 4H1, BC, Canada
Tel.: (604) 684-6365
Web Site: http://www.hdimining.com
Year Founded: 1985
Mining Operations Management Services
N.A.I.C.S.: 213114
Ronald William Thiessen *(CEO)*

Subsidiaries:

Amarc Resources Ltd. (1)
14th Floor - 1040 West Georgia Street, Vancouver, V6E 4H1, BC, Canada
Tel.: (604) 684-6365
Web Site: https://www.amarcresources.com
Rev.: $5,437
Assets: $7,270,159
Liabilities: $5,920,992
Net Worth: $1,349,167
Earnings: $32,097
Emp.: 7
Fiscal Year-end: 03/31/2024
Mineral Property Acquisition & Exploration Services
N.A.I.C.S.: 213115
Trevor R. Thomas *(Sec)*

Northcliff Resources Ltd. (1)
14th Floor - 1040 West Georgia Street, Vancouver, V6E 4H1, BC, Canada
Tel.: (604) 684-6365
Web Site:
  https://www.northcliffresources.com
Rev.: $21,350
Assets: $25,372,253
Liabilities: $5,139,365
Net Worth: $20,232,888
Earnings: ($1,521,130)
Emp.: 3
Fiscal Year-end: 10/31/2022
Metal Mining
N.A.I.C.S.: 212290
Trevor R. Thomas *(Sec)*

HUNTER GROUP ASA
Dronningen 1, 0287, Oslo, Norway
Tel.: (47) 95772947 NO
Web Site: https://huntergroup.no
Year Founded: 2003
HUNT—(OSL)
Rev.: $1,955,000
Assets: $8,512,000
Liabilities: $317,000
Net Worth: $8,195,000
Earnings: $406,000
Emp.: 3
Fiscal Year-end: 12/31/23
Investment Management Service
N.A.I.C.S.: 523940
Erik A. S. Frydendal *(CEO)*

HUNTER MARITIME ACQUISITION CORP.
Tower A WangXin Building 28 Xiaoyun Rd, Chaoyang District, Beijing, 100027, China
Tel.: (86) 6463080546
Year Founded: 2016
HUNTF—(NASDAQ)
Fintech Company
N.A.I.C.S.: 541990
Huanxiang Li *(Pres)*

HUNTER TECHNOLOGY CORP.
Web Site:
  http://www.huntertechnology.com
Year Founded: 1980
HOC—(OTCIQ)
Assets: $1,275,000

Liabilities: $119,000
Net Worth: $1,156,000
Earnings: ($614,000)
Emp.: 8
Fiscal Year-end: 12/31/19
Oil & Gas Exploration Services
N.A.I.C.S.: 211120
Konstantinos Ghertsos *(CEO)*

HUNTER WEST LEGAL RECRUITMENT LTD.
1055 West Hastings St Suite 300, Vancouver, V6E 2E9, BC, Canada
Tel.: (046) 96188
Web Site: http://www.hunterwest.ca
Recruitment Services
N.A.I.C.S.: 561311
Stephanie Hacksel *(Partner)*

HUNTING PLC
5th Floor 30 Panton Street, London, SW1Y 4AJ, United Kingdom
Tel.: (44) 2073210123
Web Site:
  https://www.huntingplc.com
Year Founded: 1874
HTG—(OTCIQ)
Rev.: $725,800,000
Assets: $1,049,300,000
Liabilities: $203,100,000
Net Worth: $846,200,000
Earnings: ($3,700,000)
Emp.: 2,258
Fiscal Year-end: 12/31/22
Oil & Gas Extraction Equipment Mfr & Distr
N.A.I.C.S.: 333132
Jim Johnson *(CEO)*

Subsidiaries:

Aero Sekur S.p.A. (1)
Via delle Valli 46, PO Box 106, 04011, Aprilia, LT, Italy (100%)
Tel.: (39) 06920161
Auto, Aerospace & Industrial Products
N.A.I.C.S.: 336340

Field Aviation Company Inc. (1)
Unit 125 4300-26 Street NE, Calgary, T1Y 7H7, AB, Canada
Tel.: (403) 516-8200
Web Site: https://www.fieldav.com
Sales Range: $25-49.9 Million
Emp.: 80
Aircraft Modification Services
N.A.I.C.S.: 561990

Huntaven Properties Limited (1)
5 Hanover Square, London, W1S 1 HQ, United Kingdom
Tel.: (44) 2073210123
Property Development Services
N.A.I.C.S.: 531311

Hunting Alpha (EPZ) Limited (1)
Mbarazi Road Near Kencont CFS, PO Box 83344, 80100, Mombasa, Kenya
Tel.: (254) 7308300006
Oil & Gas Machinery Equipment Mfr
N.A.I.C.S.: 333132
Adrian Hart *(Mgr-Ops)*

Hunting Energy De Mexico S. De R.L. De C.V (1)
Avenida Los Olmos 105 Parque Industrial El Sabinal, Apodaca, 66645, Nuevo Leon, Mexico
Tel.: (52) 8181968700
Oil & Gas Machinery Equipment Mfr
N.A.I.C.S.: 333132

Hunting Energy Saudi Arabia LLC (1)
Dammam-Buqayq Highway Building No 7612, PO Box 3104, Dhahran, 34521, Saudi Arabia
Tel.: (966) 569501302
Oil & Gas Machinery Equipment Mfr
N.A.I.C.S.: 333132

Hunting Energy Services (Australia) Pty. Ltd. (1)
Level 25 108 St Georges Terrace, Perth,

INTERNATIONAL PUBLIC

6000, WA, Australia
Tel.: (61) 428877632
Oil & Gas Machinery Equipment Mfr
N.A.I.C.S.: 333132

Hunting Energy Services (Canada) Limited (1)
5550 Skyline Way NE, Calgary, T2E 7Z7, AB, Canada
Tel.: (403) 543-4477
Emp.: 300
Oil Field Exploration Services
N.A.I.C.S.: 211120

Hunting Energy Services (Drilling Tools) Limited (1)
1515-10 St, Nisku, T9E 8C5, AB, Canada
Tel.: (780) 979-6799
Web Site: http://www.hunting-intl.com
Emp.: 12
Oil Field Drilling Services
N.A.I.C.S.: 213111

Hunting Energy Services (International) Limited (1)
Badentoy Avenue Badentoy Industrial Park, Portlethen, Aberdeen, AB12 4YB, United Kingdom
Tel.: (44) 1224787000
Perforating & Logging Equipment Mfr
N.A.I.C.S.: 333132
bruce Ferguson *(Mng Dir)*

Hunting Energy Services (International) Pte Limited (1)
34 Benoi Road, Singapore, 629901, Singapore
Tel.: (65) 68616176
Web Site: http://www.huntingplc.com
Sales Range: $100-124.9 Million
Emp.: 101
Oil & Gas Exploration Services
N.A.I.C.S.: 213112

Hunting Energy Services (Norway) AS (1)
Arabergveieb 6, 4050, Sola, Norway
Tel.: (47) 99629629
Oil & Gas Machinery Equipment Mfr
N.A.I.C.S.: 333132

Hunting Energy Services (South Africa) Pty. Ltd. (1)
18 London Circle Brackengate Business Park, Brackenfell, 7560, Cape Town, South Africa
Tel.: (27) 210036000
Oil & Gas Machinery Equipment Mfr
N.A.I.C.S.: 333132

Hunting Energy Services (UK) Limited (1)
Badentoy Avenue Badentoy Park, Aberdeen, AB12 4YB, Aberdeenshire, United Kingdom
Tel.: (44) 1224787000
Web Site: http://www.hunting-intl.com
Sales Range: $50-74.9 Million
Emp.: 200
Upstream Oil & Gas Equipments Distr
N.A.I.C.S.: 333248

Hunting Energy Services (Well Intervention) Limited (1)
Badentoy Avenue Badentoy Industrial Park, Portlethen, Aberdeen, AB12 4YB, Aberdeenshire, United Kingdom
Tel.: (44) 1224787000
Web Site: http://www.huntingplc.com
Sales Range: $50-74.9 Million
Emp.: 80
Oil Field Services
N.A.I.C.S.: 213111

Hunting Energy Services (Well Intervention) Pte. Ltd. (1)
22 Pioneer Crescent 05-07 West Park Biz Central, Singapore, 628556, Singapore
Tel.: (65) 68630668
Oil & Gas Machinery Equipment Mfr
N.A.I.C.S.: 333132

Hunting Energy Services (Wuxi) Co., Ltd. (1)
Lot No 48 Phase 5 Western of Dong An Road Northern of Yu An Road, Shu Fang Industrial Park New District, Wuxi, 214142, Jiangsu, China
Tel.: (86) 51081190028

Oil & Gas Machinery Equipment Mfr
N.A.I.C.S.: 333132

Hunting Energy Services Inc. (1)
2 Northpoint Dr Ste 400, Houston, TX 77060-3233
Tel.: (281) 442-7382
Web Site: http://www.huntingplc.com
Oil Field Drilling Equipments Distr
N.A.I.C.S.: 423830

Subsidiary (Domestic):

Hunting Energy Services (Drilling Tools) Inc. (2)
1555 View Dr, Casper, WY 82601
Tel.: (307) 265-6550
Web Site: http://www.hunting-intl.com
Sales Range: $25-49.9 Million
Emp.: 60
Drilling Equipment Mfr
N.A.I.C.S.: 333131

Division (Domestic):

Hunting Energy Services - Doffing Div (2)
16825 Northchase Dr, Houston, TX 77060
Tel.: (281) 442-7382
Web Site: http://www.hunting-intl.com
Sales Range: $25-49.9 Million
Emp.: 79
Machine Shops
N.A.I.C.S.: 332710

Hunting Subsea Technologies (2)
1316 Staffordshire Rd, Stafford, TX 77477
Tel.: (281) 499-2583
Web Site: http://www.hunting-intl.com
Couplings Mfr
N.A.I.C.S.: 333613

Hunting Titan (2)
11785 Hwy 152, Pampa, TX 79065
Tel.: (806) 665-3781
Sales Range: $25-49.9 Million
Emp.: 350
Oil Field Machinery & Equipment
N.A.I.C.S.: 333132

Hunting Energy Services L.P. (1)
2 Northpoint Dr Ste 400, Houston, TX 77060-3298 (100%)
Tel.: (281) 442-7382
Web Site: http://www.hunting-intl.com
Sales Range: $75-99.9 Million
Emp.: 75
Distr of Oil Field Tubular Products
N.A.I.C.S.: 213112

Subsidiary (Domestic):

Hunting Company, US Office (2)
2 Northpoint Dr Ste 400, Houston, TX 77060 (100%)
Tel.: (281) 820-3838
Web Site: http://www.hunting-intl.com
Oil Field Services; Distr of Oil Field Tubular Products & Completions Assemblies
N.A.I.C.S.: 213112
Mike Mock *(Gen Mgr-Connection Prods)*

Hunting Energy Services LLC (1)
Building 23 Oilfields Supply Center, PO Box 261929, Jebel Ali, Dubai, United Arab Emirates
Tel.: (971) 48876850
Oil & Gas Machinery Equipment Mfr
N.A.I.C.S.: 333132

Hunting Energy Services Pte. Ltd. (1)
16E Tuas Avenue 1 01-61 JTC Space Tuas, Singapore, 639537, Singapore
Tel.: (65) 69331777
Oil & Gas Machinery Equipment Mfr
N.A.I.C.S.: 333132

Hunting Welltonic LLC (1)
15-05 Jafra View 19 Jebel Ali Free Zone, PO Box 54007, Dubai, United Arab Emirates
Tel.: (971) 48865799
Sales Range: $50-74.9 Million
Emp.: 24
Oil & Gas Engineering Services
N.A.I.C.S.: 213111

Hunting Welltonic Ltd. (1)
Minto Road Altens Industrial Estate, Aberdeen, AB12 3LU, Aberdeenshire, United Kingdom
Tel.: (44) 1224897727
Web Site: http://www.welltonic.co.uk
Sales Range: $50-74.9 Million
Emp.: 15
Oil Field Services
N.A.I.C.S.: 213111

P.T. SMB Industri (1)
Komplex Dragon Industrial Park Blok D Jalan Pattimura, Batam, 29467, Riau Islands, Indonesia
Tel.: (62) 778711930
Web Site: http://www.hunting.pl.uk
Sales Range: $200-249.9 Million
Emp.: 300
Oil & Gas Field Support Services
N.A.I.C.S.: 213112
Soelasno Lasmono *(Mng Dir)*

PT Hunting Energy Asia (1)
Complex Dragon Industrial Park Block D Jl Pattimura Kabil, Batam, 29467, Indonesia
Tel.: (62) 778711927
Oil & Gas Machinery Equipment Mfr
N.A.I.C.S.: 333132

Tenkay Resources Inc. (1)
24 Water Way Ste 700, Woodlands, TX 77380
Tel.: (281) 363-2406
Sales Range: $50-74.9 Million
Emp.: 4
Oil & Gas Field Exploration Services
N.A.I.C.S.: 211120

Welltonic Asia Pte Limited (1)
1 Kaki Bukit Road 1 02-29 Enterprise One, Singapore, Singapore
Tel.: (65) 67427620
Construction Equipment Leasing Services
N.A.I.C.S.: 532412

HUNTINGTON EXPLORATION INC.
82 Richmond Street East Suite 1000, Box 14, Eau Claire Place II, Toronto, M5C 1P1, ON, Canada
Tel.: (587) 351-3538
Web Site: https://angelwingmetals.com
Year Founded: 1995
HEXPF—(OTCIQ)
Rev.: $25,657
Assets: $2,227,334
Liabilities: $150,499
Net Worth: $2,076,835
Earnings: ($2,849,477)
Fiscal Year-end: 12/31/23
Oil & Gas Exploration Services
N.A.I.C.S.: 213112
Christopher Brown *(Interim Pres & Interim CEO)*

HUNTSMAN EXPLORATION INC.
Suite 1680 - 200 Burrard St, Vancouver, V6C 3L6, BC, Canada
Tel.: (604) 678-5308 BC
Web Site: https://www.huntsmanx.com
Year Founded: 2011
BBBMF—(OTCIQ)
Rev.: $4,562
Assets: $8,725,451
Liabilities: $74,064
Net Worth: $8,651,387
Earnings: ($2,077,506)
Fiscal Year-end: 08/31/21
Metal Mining
N.A.I.C.S.: 212290
Peter Dickie *(Pres & CEO)*

HUNYA FOODS CO., LTD.
20F 6 No 86 Section 1 Beixin Road, Xindian, New Taipei, 23147, Taiwan
Tel.: (886) 229180786
Web Site: http://www.hunya.com.tw
Year Founded: 1976
1236—(TAI)
Rev.: $63,113,670
Assets: $125,215,764
Liabilities: $46,362,338
Net Worth: $78,853,426
Earnings: $513,097
Emp.: 714
Fiscal Year-end: 12/31/23
Food Product Mfr & Distr
N.A.I.C.S.: 311999
Yun-Chi Chang *(Chm, Pres & Mgr)*

HUNYVERS SA
19 Rue Jules Noriac, 87000, Limoges, France
Tel.: (33) 587070086
Web Site: https://www.hunyvers.com
Year Founded: 2006
ALHUN—(EUR)
Recreational Vehicle Rental Services
N.A.I.C.S.: 532284
Julien Toumieux *(CEO & Chm)*

HUNZA PROPERTIES BERHAD
No 163E-19-01 & 20-01 Hunza Tower Kelawei Road, 10250, Penang, Malaysia
Tel.: (60) 4 2290 888
Web Site: http://www.hunzagroup.com
Sales Range: $25-49.9 Million
Emp.: 200
Property Development Services
N.A.I.C.S.: 531312
Teng Tong Khor *(Founder)*

Subsidiaries:

Bandar Kepala Batas Sdn. Bhd. (1)
No 8 Persiaran Seksyen 4/14 Bandar Putra Bertam, Seberang Perai Utara, 13200, Kepala Batas, Penang, Malaysia
Tel.: (60) 45757000
Web Site: http://www.mekarsari.com.my
Property Development Services
N.A.I.C.S.: 531312

Hunza Parade Development Sdn. Bhd. (1)
5-4-7/11 Hunza Complex Jalan Gangsa, 11600, Penang, Malaysia
Tel.: (60) 48909184
Property Development Services
N.A.I.C.S.: 236116

Hunza Properties (Gurney) Sdn. Bhd. (1)
No 163E-19-01 and 20-01 Hunza Tower Kelawei Road, 10250, George Town, Penang, Malaysia
Tel.: (60) 42280888
Web Site: http://www.hunzagroup.com
Sales Range: $75-99.9 Million
Emp.: 150
Property Management & Development Services
N.A.I.C.S.: 531312
Lily Tan *(Dir)*

Hunza Properties (Wilayah) Sdn. Bhd. (1)
E-02 Plaza 1 Carat 2 Jalan Kiara, 50480, Kuala Lumpur, Malaysia
Tel.: (60) 322722887
Sales Range: $50-74.9 Million
Emp.: 2
Property Development Services
N.A.I.C.S.: 531312

Hunza Trading Sdn. Bhd. (1)
5-4-8/11 Hunza Complex Jalan Gangsa, 11600, George Town, Penang, Malaysia
Tel.: (60) 46571562
Sales Range: $25-49.9 Million
Emp.: 5
Building Materials Distr
N.A.I.C.S.: 444180

Hunza-Land Corporation Sdn. Bhd. (1)
163 E 19-01 20-01 Hunza Tower Kelawei Road, George Town, 10250, Penang, Malaysia (100%)
Tel.: (60) 46575888
Property Development Services
N.A.I.C.S.: 531312

Masuka Bina Sdn. Bhd. (1)
5-4-8/11 Hunza Complex Jalan Gangsa Island Park, 11600, George Town, Penang, Malaysia
Tel.: (60) 4 229 6354
Sales Range: $50-74.9 Million
Emp.: 14
Property Management Services
N.A.I.C.S.: 531312

HUOBI GLOBAL LTD.
10 Anson Road, Singapore, 079903, Singapore
Web Site: http://www.huobigroup.com
Year Founded: 2013
Cryptocurrency Financial Services Group
N.A.I.C.S.: 522320

HUON FERS SOUDAGE
345 Rue Albert Camus, 59230, Saint-Amand-les-Eaux, Nord, France
Tel.: (33) 327216666
Web Site: http://www.huon.fr
Rev.: $12,500,000
Emp.: 42
N.A.I.C.S.: 423830
Jean-Paul Huon *(Dir-Mktg)*

HUONG VIET REAL ESTATE INVESTMENT JOINT STOCK COMPANY
112 Tran Hung Dao Street, District 5, Ho Chi Minh City, Vietnam
Tel.: (84) 838483721 VN
Roof Tile Mfr & Distr
N.A.I.C.S.: 327120

HUONS GLOBAL CO., LTD.
8th Floor HuonsGlobal Bldg A-dong Pangyo I-Square, 17 Changeop-ro Sujeong-gu, Seongnam, 13449, Gyeonggi-do, Korea (South)
Tel.: (82) 28544700
Web Site: https://www.huons.com
Year Founded: 1965
084110—(KRS)
Rev.: $509,567,739
Assets: $953,464,772
Liabilities: $350,698,191
Net Worth: $602,766,580
Earnings: ($46,214,921)
Emp.: 109
Fiscal Year-end: 12/31/22
Pharmaceuticals Product Mfr
N.A.I.C.S.: 325412
Sooyoung Song *(CEO & Pres-Corp Mgmt)*

HUP BALKAN A.D.
Durmitorska bb, Leskovac, Serbia
Tel.: (381) 16 244 816
Year Founded: 1962
Sales Range: Less than $1 Million
Emp.: 8
Home Management Services
N.A.I.C.S.: 721110

HUP SENG INDUSTRIES BERHAD
3A Mezzanine Floor Jalan Ipoh Kecil, 50350, Kuala Lumpur, Malaysia
Tel.: (60) 340435750
Web Site: https://hsib.com.my
HUPSENG—(KLS)
Rev.: $67,342,716
Assets: $45,044,645
Liabilities: $15,182,052
Net Worth: $29,862,593
Earnings: $5,519,770
Emp.: 1,167
Fiscal Year-end: 12/31/22
Biscuit Mfr
N.A.I.C.S.: 311821
Chiew Siong Kerk *(Vice Chm)*

HUP SENG INDUSTRIES BERHAD

Hup Seng Industries Berhad—(Continued)

Subsidiaries:

Hup Seng Perusahaan Makanan (M) Sdn. Bhd. (1)
14 Jalan Kilang, Kawasan Perindustrian Tongkang Pecah, 83010, Batu Pahat, Johor, Malaysia
Tel.: (60) 74151211
Web Site: https://www.hupseng.com
Cookie & Biscuit Mfr & Whslr
N.A.I.C.S.: 311821

In-Comix Food Industries Sdn. Bhd. (1)
Plo 94 Jalan Cyber 6, Kawasan Perindustrian Senai 3, 81400, Senai, Johor, Malaysia
Tel.: (60) 7 598 2828
Web Site: https://www.in-comix.com
Instant Beverage Product Mfr
N.A.I.C.S.: 311920

HUP SOON GLOBAL CORPORATION LIMITED

47 Scotts Road 04-02 Goldbell Towers, Singapore, 228233, Singapore
Tel.: (65) 67339339
Web Site: http://www.hupsoon.com
Year Founded: 1856
Sales Range: $200-249.9 Million
Emp.: 1,800
Agriculture Tractors Mfr
N.A.I.C.S.: 541715
Timothy Wei Hsien Yong *(Exec Dir)*

Subsidiaries:

Anglo-Thai Co. Ltd. (1)
No 2 Phahonyothin Road Tambol Prachathipat, Amphur Thanyaburi, Pathumthani, 12130, Thailand
Tel.: (66) 21500550
Web Site: http://www.anglo-thai.com
Agriculture Tractors Distr
N.A.I.C.S.: 423820
Komsan Pacharawanich *(Mng Dir)*

Borid Energy (M) Sdn Bhd (1)
No 13 Jalan Jurutera U1/23 Hicom-Glenmarie Industrial Park, 40150, Shah Alam, Selangor, Malaysia
Tel.: (60) 355694618
Web Site: http://www.boridenergy.com
Sales Range: $25-49.9 Million
Emp.: 20
Energy Transmission Products Mfr
N.A.I.C.S.: 335132

Kwikpart Sdn Bhd (1)
No 13 Jalan Jurutera U1/23 Section U1 Hicom, Glenmarie Industrial Park, 40150, Shah Alam, Selangor, Malaysia
Tel.: (60) 355691228
Web Site: http://www.hupsoon.com
Automobile Parts Distr
N.A.I.C.S.: 423120

HUP-ZAGREB INC

Trg Kresimira Cosica 9, 10 000, Zagreb, Croatia
Tel.: (385) 13658333
Web Site: http://www.hupzagreb.com
HUPZ—(ZAG)
Sales Range: Less than $1 Million
Home Management Services
N.A.I.C.S.: 721110
Andelko Leko *(Chm)*

HUPSTEEL LIMITED

116 Neythal Road, Singapore, 628603, Singapore
Tel.: (65) 64192121
Web Site: http://www.hupsteel.com
Rev.: $44,683,125
Assets: $128,269,503
Liabilities: $5,576,415
Net Worth: $122,693,088
Earnings: $3,484,979
Emp.: 154
Fiscal Year-end: 06/30/18
Hardware Product Mfr
N.A.I.C.S.: 332510

Cho Lim Chai *(Mgr-Sls)*

Subsidiaries:

Eastern Win Metals & Machinery Pte Ltd (1)
116 Neythal Rd, Singapore, 628603, Singapore
Tel.: (65) 64192850
Web Site: http://www.easternwin.com
Sales Range: $50-74.9 Million
Emp.: 17
Building Materials & Construction Hardware Distr
N.A.I.C.S.: 423710

Hoe Seng Huat Pte Ltd (1)
116 Neythal Road 3rd Storey, Jurong, 628603, Singapore
Tel.: (65) 62968833
Web Site: http://www.hupsteel.com
Sales Range: $50-74.9 Million
Structured Steel Products Mfr
N.A.I.C.S.: 331110

Hup Seng Huat Land Pte Ltd (1)
155 Gul Circle, Singapore, 629612, Singapore
Tel.: (65) 6897 8741
Real Estate Property Investment Services
N.A.I.C.S.: 531190

Pressure Products Sdn. Bhd. (1)
No 1 Jln Pasaran 23/5, Shah Alam, 300, Selangor, Malaysia
Tel.: (60) 35542 2323
Emp.: 10
Pipe Fitting Mfr
N.A.I.C.S.: 331511
Lin Ktlim *(Gen Mgr)*

HURIX SYSTEMS PVT. LTD.

Unit No 102 1st Floor Multistoried Building Seepz-Sez andheri East, Mumbai, 400 096, India
Tel.: (91) 2267096888
Web Site: http://www.hurix.com
Year Founded: 2001
Sales Range: $25-49.9 Million
Emp.: 150
Training Applications
N.A.I.C.S.: 513210
Subrat Mohanty *(Co-Founder & CEO)*

HURON MOTOR PRODUCTS LTD.

640 Main St S, Exeter, N0M 1S1, ON, Canada
Tel.: (519) 235-0363
Web Site: http://www.hmpexeter.com
Year Founded: 1965
Rev.: $29,039,613
Emp.: 60
New & Used Car Dealers
N.A.I.C.S.: 441110
Bill Vandeworp *(Mgr-New Vehicle Sls)*

HURONIA ALARM & FIRE SECURITY INC.

233 Midland Ave, Midland, L4R 3K1, ON, Canada
Tel.: (705) 526-9311
Web Site: http://www.huroniaalarms.com
Year Founded: 1972
Rev.: $31,786,187
Emp.: 50
Alarms & Security Systems Distr
N.A.I.C.S.: 561621
Glenn Porter *(Mgr-Sls-Custom Audio & Video)*

HURUM CO., LTD.

Daeryung Techno Town III 115 Gasan Digital 2-ro, Geumcheon-gu, Seoul, Korea (South)
Tel.: (82) 15446335
Web Site: http://www.hurumcorp.com
Year Founded: 2005
284420—(KRS)
Sales Range: Less than $1 Million
Biological Product Mfr

N.A.I.C.S.: 325414
Kim Jin Seok *(CEO)*

HURXLEY CORPORATION

3-10 Tsuruno-cho, Kita-ku, Osaka, Japan
Tel.: (81) 663768009
Web Site: https://www.hurxley.co.jp
Year Founded: 1980
7561—(TKS)
Rev.: $309,090,210
Assets: $425,670,780
Liabilities: $266,006,230
Net Worth: $159,664,550
Earnings: $10,582,610
Emp.: 646
Fiscal Year-end: 03/31/24
Bakery Products Mfr
N.A.I.C.S.: 311812
Tatsuya Aoki *(Chm & CEO)*

Subsidiaries:

Asahi L&C Corp. (1)
15-6 Nishimukojima-Cho, Amagasaki, 660-0857, Hyogo, Japan
Tel.: (81) 664305980
Web Site: http://www.asahi-lac.com
Food Products Mfr
N.A.I.C.S.: 311999

Tenpo Ryutsuu Net, Inc. (1)
Tel.: (81) 357776510
Web Site: http://www.trn-g.com
Real Estate Lending Services
N.A.I.C.S.: 531110

Subsidiary (Domestic):

TRN Capital Management, Inc. (2)
1-2-3 Kaigan 20 F Shiba Rikyu Building, Minato-ku, Tokyo, 105-0022, Japan
Tel.: (81) 357776568
Real Estate Brokerage Services
N.A.I.C.S.: 531390

TRN Investment Management, Inc. (2)
2-4-1 World Trade Center Building 32 Floor Hamamatsu-cho, Minato-ku, Tokyo, 105-6132, Japan
Tel.: (81) 357776548
Real Estate Investment Services
N.A.I.C.S.: 531390

HUSCOKE HOLDINGS LIMITED

Room 2301 Floor 23 Tower One Lippo Centre 89 Queensway Admiralty, Hong Kong, China (Hong Kong)
Tel.: (852) 2 861 0704
Web Site: http://www.huscoke.com
Rev.: $206,143,764
Assets: $264,664,310
Liabilities: $188,308,000
Net Worth: $76,356,310
Earnings: $1,888,012
Emp.: 530
Fiscal Year-end: 12/31/19
Coal Washing & Power Generation Services
N.A.I.C.S.: 221111
Baoqi Li *(Exec Dir)*

Subsidiaries:

Castfast Industrial Company Limited (1)
10 F Southeast Indl Bldg 611-619 Castle Peak Rd, Tsuen Wan, Guangdong, China (Hong Kong)
Tel.: (852) 24110913
Web Site: http://www.castfast.com
Plastic Injection Mold Mfr
N.A.I.C.S.: 333248

Huscoke International Group Limited (1)
Rm 4203 42 F Far E Finance Ctr 16 Harcourt Rd, Admiralty, Central, China (Hong Kong)
Tel.: (852) 28610704
Emp.: 10
Coal Mining Support Services

INTERNATIONAL PUBLIC

N.A.I.C.S.: 212114

HUSCOMPAGNIET A/S

Agerovej 31A, Tilst, 8381, Aarhus, Denmark
Tel.: (45) 75645799 DK
Web Site: https://www.huscompagniet.dk
Year Founded: 2010
HUSCO—(CSE)
Rev.: $344,570,329
Assets: $472,322,785
Liabilities: $168,812,490
Net Worth: $303,510,295
Earnings: $2,121,225
Emp.: 393
Fiscal Year-end: 12/31/23
Construction Engineering Services
N.A.I.C.S.: 541330
Jesper Hoybye *(CFO)*

HUSEIN INDUSTRIES LIMITED

HT 8 Landhi Industrial and Trading Estate, Landhi, 75120, Karachi, Pakistan
Tel.: (92) 2150185368
Web Site: http://www.husein.com
HUSI—(PSX)
Rev.: $577,771
Assets: $3,152,924
Liabilities: $3,536,932
Net Worth: $(384,008)
Earnings: $75,788
Emp.: 10
Fiscal Year-end: 06/30/23
Textile Mill
N.A.I.C.S.: 325613
Aziz L. Jamal *(Chm)*

HUSQVARNA AB

Regeringsgatan 28, Box 7454, SE-103 92, Stockholm, Sweden
Tel.: (46) 87389000 SE
Web Site: https://www.husqvarnagroup.com
Year Founded: 1689
HUSQ.B—(OMX)
Rev.: $5,120,401,440
Assets: $5,312,555,360
Liabilities: $3,229,626,400
Net Worth: $2,082,928,960
Earnings: $304,589,600
Emp.: 12,400
Fiscal Year-end: 12/31/20
Chainsaws, Lawn Mowers, Trimmers & Tractors Mfr
N.A.I.C.S.: 333112
Henric Anderson *(Pres & CEO)*

Subsidiaries:

Gardena AG (1)
Hans-Lorenser-Str 40, 89079, Ulm, Germany
Tel.: (49) 731 4900
Web Site: https://www.gardena.com
Sales Range: $500-549.9 Million
Emp.: 2,900
Holding Company; Gardening Products Designer & Producer
N.A.I.C.S.: 551112
Par Astrom *(Pres)*

Affiliate (Non-US):

Agrofix n.v. (2)
Verlengde Hogestraat St, PO Box 2006, Paramaribo, Suriname
Tel.: (597) 472426
Sales Range: $25-49.9 Million
Emp.: 9
Lawn & Gardening Care
N.A.I.C.S.: 333112

Subsidiary (Non-US):

Aguerrebere S.A. (2)
Industriales Importadores, Constituyente 1489, 11200, Montevideo, Uruguay
Tel.: (598) 24096341
Web Site: http://www.aguerrebere.com.uy

HUSQVARNA AB

Sales Range: $25-49.9 Million
Emp.: 25
Mfr of Lawn & Garden Watering Products & Accessories
N.A.I.C.S.: 333112

Coral Co. Ltd. (2)
Altaief salam street block 22 house 501, PO Box 1899, Khartoum, Sudan
Tel.: (249) 120898363
Web Site: http://www.coralcoltd.com
Mfr of Lawn & Garden Watering Products & Accessories
N.A.I.C.S.: 333112

Gardena France S.a.r.l. (2)
ZAC Les Barbanniers Immeuble Exposial 9 11 Allee des Pierres Mayettes, 92635, Gennevilliers, Cedex, France
Tel.: (33) 810007823
Web Site: http://www.gardena.com
Sales Range: $25-49.9 Million
Emp.: 200
Mfr of Lawn & Garden Watering Products & Accessories
N.A.I.C.S.: 333112

Subsidiary (Domestic):

Gardena Manufacturing GmbH (2)
Hans-Lorenser-Str 40, 89079, Ulm, Germany
Tel.: (49) 7314900
Web Site: http://www.gardena.com
Lawn & Garden Equipment Mfr
N.A.I.C.S.: 333112

Subsidiary (Non-US):

Gardena Norden AB (2)
Hojdrodergatan 22, PO Box 9003, 212 39, Malmo, Denmark
Tel.: (45) 70272799
Web Site: http://www.gardena.dk
Sales Range: $75-99.9 Million
Emp.: 300
Mfr of Lawn & Garden Watering Products & Accessories
N.A.I.C.S.: 333112

Gardena Norden AB (2)
PO Box 200, 1541, Vestby, Norway
Tel.: (47) 64834050
Web Site: http://www.gardena.no
Sales Range: $25-49.9 Million
Emp.: 10
Mfr of Lawn & Garden Watering Products & Accessories
N.A.I.C.S.: 333112

Gardena Osterreich GmbH (2)
Industriezeile 36, Linz, 4010, Austria
Tel.: (43) 73277010190
Web Site: http://www.gardena.at
Sales Range: $25-49.9 Million
Emp.: 120
Mfr of Lawn & Garden Watering Products & Accessories
N.A.I.C.S.: 333112
Yohannes Viertlmaur (Mng Dir)

Gardena spol.s.r.o. (2)
Ripska 20, 62700, Brno, Czech Republic
Tel.: (420) 543211049
Web Site: http://www.gardena.com
Mfr of Lawn & Garden Watering Products & Accessories
N.A.I.C.S.: 333112

Husqvarna Magyarorszag Kft (2)
Ezred u 1-3, 1044, Budapest, Hungary
Tel.: (36) 1 251 4161
Web Site: https://www.husqvarna.com
Sales Range: $25-49.9 Million
Emp.: 18
Mfr of Lawn & Garden Watering Products & Accessories
N.A.I.C.S.: 333112

Husqvarna Polska Sp.z.o.o. (2)
ul Wysockiego 15B, 03-371, Warsaw, Poland
Tel.: (48) 22 330 9600
Web Site: https://www.husqvarna.com
Sales Range: $25-49.9 Million
Emp.: 25
Mfr of Lawn & Garden Watering Products & Accessories
N.A.I.C.S.: 333112

Ismail Mohammed Aldanawi Al Sady Garden Equipment Wll (2)
Darrajah Cir, PO Box 67 16, Jeddah, 21452, Saudi Arabia
Tel.: (966) 26607897
Web Site: http://www.gardena.com
Sales Range: $25-49.9 Million
Emp.: 10
Mfr of Lawn & Garden Watering Products & Accessories
N.A.I.C.S.: 333112

M. CASSAB Com. Ind. Ltda (2)
AV das Nacoes Unidas 20 882, Sao Paulo, 04795-000, Brazil
Tel.: (55) 112 162 7788
Web Site: https://www.mcassab.com.br
Sales Range: $75-99.9 Million
Emp.: 500
Mfr of Lawn & Garden Watering Products & Accessories
N.A.I.C.S.: 333112

Husqvarna (India) Products Private Limited (1)
1st Floor Swelect House No 5 Sir PS Sivasamy Salai, Mylapore, Chennai, 600004, Tamil Nadu, India
Tel.: (91) 4449489222
Web Site: https://www.husqvarna.com
Lawn Mower Mfr
N.A.I.C.S.: 333112

Husqvarna Austria GmbH (1)
Industriezeile 36, 4020, Linz, Austria
Tel.: (43) 7327701010
Web Site: https://www.husqvarna.com
Sales Range: $25-49.9 Million
Emp.: 120
Chain Saws, Clearing Saws & Lawn & Garden Equipment Mfr
N.A.I.C.S.: 333112

Husqvarna Belgium SA (1)
Avenue des Artisans 50, 7822, Ath, Belgium
Tel.: (32) 6 825 1362
Web Site: https://www.husqvarnacp.com
Construction Equipment Mfr
N.A.I.C.S.: 333120

Subsidiary (US):

Husqvarna Construction Products North America, Inc. (2)
17400 W 119 St, Olathe, KS 66061 (100%)
Tel.: (913) 928-1000
Web Site: https://www.husqvarnacp.com
Sales Range: $100-124.9 Million
Emp.: 500
Diamond Tools, Equipment & Handheld Power Cutters Mfr
N.A.I.C.S.: 333248
Steve Chamberlin (Pres)

Plant (Domestic):

Husqvarna Construction Products North America, Inc. - Corona (3)
265 Radio Rd, Corona, CA 92879
Tel.: (951) 272-2330
Web Site: http://www.Husqvarnacp.com
Sales Range: $25-49.9 Million
Emp.: 70
Concrete Saw Mfr
N.A.I.C.S.: 333515

Husqvarna Canada Corp. (1)
850 Matheson Blvd W, Mississauga, L5V 0B4, ON, Canada
Tel.: (905) 817-1510
Web Site: http://www.husqvarna.com
Lawn & Garden Equipment Mfr
N.A.I.C.S.: 333112

Husqvarna Colombia S.A. (1)
Cll 18 No 68 D, 31 Industrial Zone Montevideo, Bogota, Colombia
Tel.: (57) 17457331
Farm & Garden Equipment Mfr
N.A.I.C.S.: 333111

Husqvarna Commercial Solutions Austria GmbH (1)
Industriezeile 36, 4020, Linz, Austria
Tel.: (43) 732770101
Outdoor Power Product Mfr & Distr
N.A.I.C.S.: 333112

Husqvarna Commercial Solutions Norge AS (1)
Troskonveien 36, 1708, Sarpsborg, Norway
Tel.: (47) 69600930
Outdoor Power Product Mfr & Distr
N.A.I.C.S.: 333112

Husqvarna Consumer Outdoor Products N.A., Inc. (1)
9335 Harris Corners Pkwy, Charlotte, NC 28269
Tel.: (704) 597-5000
Web Site: http://www.husqvarna.com
Consumer Outdoor Forestry & Garden Care Equipment Mfr & Distr
N.A.I.C.S.: 333112

Plant (Domestic):

Husqvarna Outdoor Products - McRae (2)
Hwy 23 E 263 E Oak St, McRae, GA 31055
Tel.: (229) 868-5641
Sales Range: $350-399.9 Million
Emp.: 1,500
Lawn & Garden Equipment Mfr
N.A.I.C.S.: 333112
Mike Scott (Gen Mgr)

Husqvarna Outdoor Products - Nashville (2)
1 Poulan Dr, Nashville, AR 71852-3106
Tel.: (870) 845-1234
Sales Range: $25-49.9 Million
Emp.: 200
Refrigerator Mfr
N.A.I.C.S.: 335220

Husqvarna Outdoor Products - Orangeburg (2)
172 Old Eloree Rd, Orangeburg, SC 29115
Tel.: (803) 536-3285
Web Site: http://www.husqvarna.com
Sales Range: $350-399.9 Million
Emp.: 2,000
Lawn & Garden Equipment Mfr
N.A.I.C.S.: 333112

Husqvarna Outdoor Products - Swainsboro (2)
561 Electric Dr, Swainsboro, GA 30401-4815
Tel.: (478) 237-9963
Sales Range: $25-49.9 Million
Emp.: 100
Lawn & Garden Mower Parts Mfr
N.A.I.C.S.: 333112
Nona Roberts (Mgr-HR)

Husqvarna Danmark A/S (1)
Lejrvej 19 St, Vaerlose, 3500, Copenhagen, Denmark
Tel.: (45) 70264770
Farm & Garden Equipment Mfr
N.A.I.C.S.: 333111

Husqvarna Deutschland GmbH (1)
Hans-Lorenser-Str 40, 89079, Ulm, Germany
Tel.: (49) 7314902500
Farm & Garden Machinery Distr
N.A.I.C.S.: 423820

Husqvarna Direct AB (1)
Drottninggatan 2, 561 82, Huskvarna, Sweden
Tel.: (46) 87389000
Outdoor Power Product Mfr & Distr
N.A.I.C.S.: 333112

Husqvarna Eesti Osauhing (1)
Valdeku 132, EE-11216, Tallinn, Estonia
Tel.: (372) 6650005
Farm & Garden Equipment Mfr
N.A.I.C.S.: 333111

Husqvarna Finance Ireland Ltd. (1)
Unit 309 Northwest Business Park, Dublin, Ireland
Tel.: (353) 18242600
Farm & Garden Equipment Mfr
N.A.I.C.S.: 333111

Husqvarna Forestry Products NA Inc. (1)
1 Poulan Dr, Nashville, AR 71852
Tel.: (870) 845-1234
Web Site: http://www.husqvarnagroup.com
Emp.: 600
Lawn & Garden Equipment Mfr
N.A.I.C.S.: 333112
Tony Cochran (Branch Mgr)

Husqvarna France SAS (1)
9 11 Allee Des Pierres Mayettes, 92230, Gennevilliers, France
Tel.: (33) 140853000
Farm & Garden Machinery Distr
N.A.I.C.S.: 423830

Husqvarna Holding AB (1)
Drottninggatan 2, 561 82, Huskvarna, 561 31, Sweden
Tel.: (46) 87388077
Sales Range: $700-749.9 Million
Emp.: 170
Investment Management Service
N.A.I.C.S.: 523999

Husqvarna LLC (1)
Leningradskaya Str Estate 39 Bld 6 4th Floor, Khimki, 141400, Russia
Tel.: (7) 495 797 26 73
Sales Range: $25-49.9 Million
Emp.: 60
Lawn & Garden Equipment Mfr
N.A.I.C.S.: 333112

Husqvarna Poland Sp. z o.o. (1)
Ul Burakowska 14, 01-066, Warsaw, Poland
Tel.: (48) 223309600
Outdoor Power Product Mfr & Distr
N.A.I.C.S.: 333112

Husqvarna Professional Products, Inc. (1)
9335 Harris Corners Pkwy Ste 500, Charlotte, NC 28269 (100%)
Tel.: (704) 597-5000
Web Site: http://corporate.husqvarna.com
Sales Range: $100-124.9 Million
Emp.: 350
Commercial Lawn Care & Forestry Equipment Mfr & Retailer
N.A.I.C.S.: 333112

Unit (Domestic):

Husqvarna Turf Care (2)
401 N Commerce St, Beatrice, NE 68310
Tel.: (402) 223-1000
Web Site: http://www.usa.husqvarna.com
Sales Range: $75-99.9 Million
Emp.: 300
Commercial Lawn Care Equipment Mfr
N.A.I.C.S.: 333112

Husqvarna Slovensko s.r.o. (1)
ul capt Sticker 1927 10, 031 01, Liptovsky Mikulas, Slovakia
Tel.: (421) 800199999
Farm & Garden Equipment Mfr
N.A.I.C.S.: 333111

Husqvarna South Africa (Proprietary) Limited (1)
Market Road Extension Mkondeni, Pietermaritzburg, 3201, South Africa
Tel.: (27) 338469700
Farm & Garden Equipment Mfr
N.A.I.C.S.: 333111

Husqvarna UK Ltd. (1)
Preston Rd Aycliffe Industrial Park, Newton Aycliffe, DL5 6UP, Durham, United Kingdom
Tel.: (44) 1325302302
Sales Range: $25-49.9 Million
Emp.: 10
Lawn & Garden Equipment Mfr
N.A.I.C.S.: 333112

Husqvarna Zenoah Co., Ltd (1)
1-9 Minamidai Kawagoe, Saitama, 350-1165, Japan
Tel.: (81) 492431599
Web Site: http://www.zenoah.net
Sales Range: $200-249.9 Million
Emp.: 54
Power Driven Tool Mfr
N.A.I.C.S.: 333991

Outdoor Power Products Husqvarna Kenya Ltd. (1)
38 Lusaka Road, Nairobi, Kenya
Tel.: (254) 727333330
Farm & Garden Equipment Mfr
N.A.I.C.S.: 333111

Oy Husqvarna Commercial Solutions Finland Ab (1)
PL 29, FI-01511, Vantaa, Finland
Tel.: (358) 92472220
Outdoor Power Product Mfr & Distr

HUSQVARNA AB

Husqvarna AB—(Continued)
N.A.I.C.S.: 333112

SIA Husqvarna Latvija (1)
Ulbrock 19a, Riga, LV-1021, Latvia
Tel.: (371) 67520515
Farm & Garden Equipment Mfr
N.A.I.C.S.: 333111
Vladimirs Burcevs (Mgr-Sls)

HUSSOR ERECTA SOC
Zi La Croix D Orbey, Lapoutroie, 68650, Haut Rhin, France
Tel.: (33) 389475737
Web Site: http://www.hussor-erecta.fr
Rev.: $16,300,000
Emp.: 82
Scaffold Mfr
N.A.I.C.S.: 238120
Gilles Husson (Dir)

HUSTEEL CO., LTD.
14F 15F Teheran-ro 512, Gangnam-gu, Seoul, 06179, Korea (South)
Tel.: (82) 28289000
Web Site: https://www.husteel.com
Year Founded: 1967
005010—(KRS)
Rev.: $790,718,299
Assets: $925,288,576
Liabilities: $227,947,176
Net Worth: $697,341,400
Earnings: $174,227,269
Emp.: 548
Fiscal Year-end: 12/31/22
Steel Pole Mfr
N.A.I.C.S.: 331210
Hoon Park (CEO)

Subsidiaries:

HUSTEEL CO., Ltd. - Dangjin Plant (1)
569-1 Bugok-Ri Songak-Myeon, Dangjin, Chungcheongnam-Do, Korea (South)
Tel.: (82) 413508114
Steel Pole Mfr
N.A.I.C.S.: 331210

Husteel USA, Inc. (1)
2222 Greenhouse Rd Ste 500, Houston, TX 77084
Tel.: (281) 497-6784
Web Site: http://www.husteelusa.com
Emp.: 8
Steel Pipe Distr
N.A.I.C.S.: 423510

HUT ADUNA D.D.
Ul V Korpusa 3, 77000, Bihac, Bosnia & Herzegovina
Tel.: (387) 37224107
Web Site: http://www.aduna.ba
Year Founded: 1960
HTADRK1—(SARE)
Rev.: $573,732
Assets: $10,061,604
Liabilities: $930,488
Net Worth: $9,131,117
Earnings: ($232,834)
Emp.: 26
Fiscal Year-end: 12/31/20
Home Management Services
N.A.I.C.S.: 721110

HUTA POKOJ S.A.
Ul Niedurnego 79, 41 709, Ruda Slaska, Poland
Tel.: (48) 327721111
Web Site: http://www.hutapokoj.eu
Year Founded: 1840
Sales Range: $150-199.9 Million
Emp.: 550
Blast Furnace Steel Mfr
N.A.I.C.S.: 324199
Jerzy Meisner (Dir-Trade-Steel Products)

Subsidiaries:

Eurokonstrukcje Sp. z o.o. (1)
Niedurnego 79, 41-709, Ruda Slaska, Poland
Tel.: (48) 327721150
Web Site: http://www.eurokonstrukcje.com.pl
Iron & Steel Mills
N.A.I.C.S.: 331110

Euroserwis Sp. z o.o. (1)
ul Niedurnego 79, 41-709, Ruda Slaska, Poland
Tel.: (48) 327721660
Web Site: http://www.hutapokoj.eu
Iron & Steel Mills
N.A.I.C.S.: 331110

HUTA SZKLA GOSPODARC-ZEGO IRENA S.A.
Ul Szklarska 9, 88 100, Inowroclaw, Poland
Tel.: (48) 523542100
Web Site: http://www.huta-irena.com.pl
Year Founded: 1924
Sales Range: $10-24.9 Million
Emp.: 120
Crystal & Soda Glass Mfr
N.A.I.C.S.: 327212

HUTCHISON MINERALS COMPANY LTD.
3601 Highway 7 Suite 400, Markham, L3R 0M3, ON, Canada
Tel.: (416) 623-8028
Web Site: http://www.hutchisonminerals.com
Nickel & Cobalt Mining Services
N.A.I.C.S.: 212230
Orlando A. dela Cruz (Pres)

HUTCHISON PORT HOLDINGS TRUST
150 Beach Road 17-03 Gateway West, Singapore, 189720, Singapore
Tel.: (65) 62948028
Web Site: https://www.hphtrust.com
NS8U—(SES)
Rev.: $1,361,521,132
Assets: $10,763,702,050
Liabilities: $5,213,546,085
Net Worth: $5,550,155,965
Earnings: $189,654,362
Emp.: 3,291
Fiscal Year-end: 12/31/23
Investment Trust; Port Operator
N.A.I.C.S.: 525990
Canning Kin Ning Fok (Chm)

Subsidiaries:

Yantian International Container Terminals Limited (1)
Yantian Port, Shenzhen, China
Tel.: (86) 7552 529 0888
Web Site: https://www.yict.com.cn
Cargo Handling Services
N.A.I.C.S.: 488320
Patrick Lam (Mng Dir)

HUTTER & SCHRANTZ PMS GES.M.B.H
Grossmarktstrasse 7, 1232, Vienna, Austria
Tel.: (43) 69912650110
Web Site: https://www.hs-pms.com
Year Founded: 1980
Sales Range: $150-199.9 Million
Emp.: 350
Holding Services
N.A.I.C.S.: 551112

Subsidiaries:

H & S Stahlbau AG (1)
Grossmarktstrasse 7, Vienna, 1230, Austria
Tel.: (43) 16174555
Web Site: http://www.hs-stahlbau.at
Steel Construction
N.A.I.C.S.: 238120
Hans Heinz (Mng Dir)

Subsidiary (Non-US):

Claus Queck GmbH (2)
Industriestrasse 13, 52355, Duren, Germany
Tel.: (49) 242159030
Web Site: http://www.stahlbau-queck.de
Sales Range: $25-49.9 Million
Emp.: 150
Building Steel Construction
N.A.I.C.S.: 238120

Subsidiary (Domestic):

stahl + verbundbau GmbH (3)
Im Steingrund 8, 63303, Dreieich, Germany
Tel.: (49) 6103 9862 0
Web Site: http://www.stahlverbundbau.de
Construction Engineering Services
N.A.I.C.S.: 541330

Subsidiary (Domestic):

Haslinger Stahlbau GmbH (2)
Villacher Strasse 20, 9560, Feldkirchen bei Graz, Karnten, Austria
Tel.: (43) 4276 2651 0
Web Site: http://www.haslinger.co.at
Emp.: 300
Construction Engineering Services
N.A.I.C.S.: 541330
Sorger Arno (Gen Mgr)

Subsidiary (Non-US):

Haslinger Acelszerkezetepito Kft (3)
Szechenyi utca 1 Pf 21, 6087, Dunakeszi, Hungary
Tel.: (36) 78 437007
Construction Engineering Services
N.A.I.C.S.: 541330

Haslinger Projekt GmbH (3)
Schandauer Strasse 34, 01309, Dresden, Germany
Tel.: (49) 351 656938 0
Construction Engineering Services
N.A.I.C.S.: 541330

Hutter & Schrantz AG (1)
Grossmarktstrasse 7, A 1230, Vienna, Austria
Tel.: (43) 161745550
Web Site: http://www.hutterschrantz.at
Sales Range: $100-124.9 Million
Emp.: 500
Steel Girders & Other Steel Products Mfr
N.A.I.C.S.: 332312
Hans Heinz (Mng Dir)

Peter Benesch GmbH (1)
Heizwerkstr 2, 1230, Vienna, Austria
Tel.: (43) 1 617455520
Spring Mfr
N.A.I.C.S.: 332613

SK-PRUZINY, spol. s r.o. (1)
Vajanskeho 288, 906 13, Podbrezova, Slovakia
Tel.: (421) 34 6242 690
Web Site: http://www.sk-pruziny.sk
Spring Mfr
N.A.I.C.S.: 332613

Technospring Kft. (1)
hrsz 108/36, 8130, Enying, Hungary
Tel.: (36) 22 372 302
Web Site: http://www.technospring.hu
Emp.: 41
Spring Mfr
N.A.I.C.S.: 332613

HUU LIEN ASIA CORPORATION
KE A2/7 Duong Tran Di Nghia P Tan Tao A, Quan Binh Tan, Ho Chi Minh City, Vietnam
Tel.: (84) 8 3877 0062
Web Site: http://www.huulienachau.com.vn
Sales Range: $125-149.9 Million
Steel Pole Mfr
N.A.I.C.S.: 331210
Tran Xao Co (Chm)

HUU NGHI VINH SINH MINING & MECHANIC JSC
Huu Nghi Apartment Block Thuy Van Industial zone, Viet Tri, Phu Tho, Vietnam
Tel.: (84) 210 2220 350
Web Site: http://www.vinhsinh.vn
Sales Range: $1-9.9 Million
Cement Mfr
N.A.I.C.S.: 327310
Nguyen Thi Yen (Chm)

HUVEPHARMA EOOD
5th Floor 3a Nikolay Haytov Str, 1113, Sofia, Bulgaria
Tel.: (359) 2 862 5331   BG
Web Site: http://www.huvepharma.com
Year Founded: 1954
Pharmaceuticals Product Mfr
N.A.I.C.S.: 325412
Kyril Domuschiev (Pres)

Subsidiaries:

Biovet JSC (1)
3a Nikolay Haytov Str, 1113, Sofia, Bulgaria
Tel.: (359) 2 862 2095
Web Site: http://www.biovet.com
Pharmaceuticals Product Mfr
N.A.I.C.S.: 325412
Kiril Domuschiev (Chm-Supervisory Bd)

Huvepharma NV (1)
Uitbreidingstraat 80, 2600, Antwerp, Belgium
Tel.: (32) 475 377 337
Pharmaceuticals Product Mfr
N.A.I.C.S.: 325412
Lieven Tanghe (Gen Mgr)

Huvepharma, Inc. (1)
525 Westpark Dr, Peachtree City, GA 30269
Tel.: (770) 486-7212
Web Site: http://www.huvepharma.com
Emp.: 30
Pharmaceuticals Product Mfr
N.A.I.C.S.: 325412
Glen Wilkinson (Gen Mgr)

HUVEXEL CO LTD
103 105 Megacenter SK technopark 124 Sagimakgol-ro, Jungwon-gu, Seongnam, Kyunggi-do, Korea (South)
Tel.: (82) 317763690
Web Site: https://www.huvexel.com
Year Founded: 1972
Orthopedic Device Mfr & Distr
N.A.I.C.S.: 339113
Sean K. Her (CEO)

HUVIS CORPORATION
12F 343 Hakdong-ro, Gangnam-gu, 06060, Seoul, 06060, Korea (South)
Tel.: (82) 221894567
Web Site: https://www.huvis.com
Year Founded: 2000
079980—(KRS)
Rev.: $783,663,828
Assets: $608,813,634
Liabilities: $316,378,051
Net Worth: $292,435,584
Earnings: ($61,804,085)
Emp.: 813
Fiscal Year-end: 12/31/22
Polyester & Fiber Product Mfr
N.A.I.C.S.: 325220
Dong You Shin (CEO)

HUVITZ CO., LTD.
38 Burim-ro 170beon-gil, Dongan-gu, Anyang, 14055, Gyeonggi-do, Korea (South)
Tel.: (82) 314289100
Web Site: https://www.huvitz.com
Year Founded: 1998
065510—(KRS)
Rev.: $83,626,996
Assets: $135,921,572
Liabilities: $51,978,036
Net Worth: $83,943,535
Earnings: $12,753,657

Emp.: 225
Fiscal Year-end: 12/31/22
Medical Equipment Mfr
N.A.I.C.S.: 339112
Sun-Jung Kim *(Gen Mgr)*

Subsidiaries:

Shanghai Huvitz Co., Ltd. (1)
Building 2 No 58 Lane 450 Xiaonan Road,
Fengxian, Shanghai, 201401, China
Tel.: (86) 36307061
Web Site: http://www.shhuvitz.com
Optometric Medical Device Mfr
N.A.I.C.S.: 339112

HUXEN CORPORATION
7th Floor No 2 Section 5 Xinyi Road,
Xinyi District, Taipei, Taiwan
Tel.: (886) 23458009
Web Site: https://www.eosasc.com.tw
2433—(TAI)
Rev.: $94,631,116
Assets: $251,302,715
Liabilities: $103,220,474
Net Worth: $148,082,240
Earnings: $16,689,983
Fiscal Year-end: 12/31/23
Office Equipment Distr
N.A.I.C.S.: 423420
Kuo-Hua Weng *(Pres)*

HUXLEY QUAYLE VON BISMARK, INC.
2 Berkeley St Ste 301, Toronto, M5A 4J5, ON, Canada
Tel.: (416) 864-1700
Web Site:
  http://www.huxleyquayle.com
Sales Range: $10-24.9 Million
Emp.: 10
Advertising Agencies
N.A.I.C.S.: 541810
Andy Shortt *(Owner)*

HUY PLC
116 Gloucester Place, London, W1U 6HZ, United Kingdom
Tel.: (44) 2071990129
Sales Range: $1-9.9 Million
Investment Services
N.A.I.C.S.: 523999
Michael Slater *(Sec)*

HUY THANG CONSTRUCTION JSC
14 - 14A Nguyen Xuan Khoat Tan Son Nhi Ward, Tan Phu District, Ho Chi Minh City, Vietnam
Tel.: (84) 838496220
Web Site:
  http://www.huythang.com.vn
Year Founded: 2000
Emp.: 1,000
Civil & Industrial Construction Services
N.A.I.C.S.: 237990
Bay Van Le *(Chm & Gen Mgr)*

HUZUR FAKTORING A.S.
Fulya Mahallesi uyuudere Caddesi Torun Center D Blok 74/A Kat 10, Mecidiyekoy Sisli, 34394, Istanbul, Turkiye
Tel.: (90) 2122134444
Web Site:
  http://www.huzurfaktoring.com
HUZFA—(IST)
Sales Range: Less than $1 Million
Financial Consulting Services
N.A.I.C.S.: 541611

HVC INVESTMENT & TECHNOLOGY JSC
8th Floor Tower C-Ho Guom Plaza 102 Tran Phu, Mo Lao Ward Ha Dong, Hanoi, Vietnam
Tel.: (84) 2435402246
Year Founded: 2011
HVH—(HNX)
Investment Management Service
N.A.I.C.S.: 525990
Do Huy Cuong *(Deputy Gen Dir)*

HVIDBJERG BANK A/S
Oestergade 2, 7790, Thyholm, 7790, Denmark
Tel.: (45) 96955200
Web Site:
  https://www.hvidbjergbank.dk
HVID—(CSE)
Rev.: $15,566,263
Assets: $252,006,193
Liabilities: $220,008,392
Net Worth: $31,997,801
Earnings: $3,641,967
Emp.: 59
Fiscal Year-end: 12/31/22
Banking Services
N.A.I.C.S.: 522110

HWA AG
Benzstrasse 8, D-71563, Affalterbach, Germany
Tel.: (49) 714487170
Web Site: http://www.hwaag.com
Year Founded: 1998
Racing Car Mfr
N.A.I.C.S.: 336110
Ulrich Fritz *(Chm)*

HWA CREATE CORPORATION LTD.
Building 18 Yard 8 Dongbeiwang West Road, Haidian District, Beijing, 100193, China
Tel.: (86) 1082966393
Web Site:
  http://www.hwacreate.com.cn
Year Founded: 2008
300045—(CHIN)
Rev.: $54,068,040
Assets: $319,994,064
Liabilities: $77,339,340
Net Worth: $242,654,724
Earnings: ($15,480,504)
Fiscal Year-end: 12/31/22
Computer Related Electromechanical Emulational, Radio Frequency Emulational Testing Products & Emulational Application Development Services
N.A.I.C.S.: 541512
Gao Xiaoli *(Chm)*

HWA FONG RUBBER INDUSTRY CO., LTD.
No 300 Sec 2 Zhongshan Rd, Dacun Township, Chang-Hua, 515002, Taiwan
Tel.: (886) 48520121
Web Site: https://www.duro.com.tw
Year Founded: 1945
2109—(TAI)
Rev.: $152,859,800
Assets: $259,761,460
Liabilities: $95,238,788
Net Worth: $164,522,673
Earnings: $17,373,131
Emp.: 2,347
Fiscal Year-end: 12/31/23
Tires & Other Rubber Products Mfr
N.A.I.C.S.: 326211

Subsidiaries:

Hwa Fong Rubber (China) Co., Ltd. (1)
No 1 Chang Jiang Road Of Economic Velopment Area, Changshu, Jiangsu, China
Rubber Product Mfr & Distr
N.A.I.C.S.: 326299

Hwa Fong Rubber (Suzhou) Co., Ltd. (1)
1 Xinye Road Changshu Economic Development Zone, Riverside Industrial Park, Suzhou, Jiangsu, China
Tel.: (86) 512 52296377
Rubber Product Mfr & Distr
N.A.I.C.S.: 326299

Hwa Fong Rubber (Thailand) Public Company Limited (1)
317 Moo 6C Soi 4 Bangpoo Industrial Estate, Samut Prakan, 10280, Thailand (82.32%)
Tel.: (66) 27096580
Web Site: http://www.duro.co.th
Sales Range: $50-74.9 Million
Bicycle Tire Tube Mfr
N.A.I.C.S.: 336991
An Jen Hsu *(Mgr-Sls)*

Hwa Fong Rubber (U.S.A.) Inc. (1)
14290 Lochridge Blvd, Covington, GA 30014
Tel.: (770) 788-2060
Web Site: http://www.durotire.com
Rubber Product Mfr & Distr
N.A.I.C.S.: 326299

HWA HONG CORPORATION LIMITED
38 South Bridge Road 04-01, Singapore, 058672, Singapore
Tel.: (65) 65385711   SG
Web Site:
  http://www.hwahongcorp.com
H19—(SES)
Rev.: $7,643,083
Assets: $214,590,478
Liabilities: $74,032,456
Net Worth: $140,558,023
Earnings: $4,368,792
Emp.: 173
Fiscal Year-end: 12/31/21
Investment Holding Company
N.A.I.C.S.: 551112
Mui Eng Ong *(Exec Dir)*

Subsidiaries:

Hwa Hong Edible Oil Industries Pte. Ltd. (1)
38 South Bridge Road 04-01, Singapore, 058672, Singapore
Tel.: (65) 6 538 5711
Web Site: https://www.hwahongcorp.com
Sales Range: $25-49.9 Million
Emp.: 10
Edible Oil Mfr
N.A.I.C.S.: 311225
Eng Loke Ong *(Sr VP-Fund Mgmt)*

Singapore Warehouse Company (Private) Ltd. (1)
400 Orchard Road 11-09/10 Orchard Towers, Singapore, 238875, Singapore
Tel.: (65) 6 734 8355
Web Site: https://www.hwahongcorp.com
Emp.: 4
General Warehousing & Storage Services
N.A.I.C.S.: 493110
Chee Kiew Chen *(Gen Mgr)*

HWA TAI INDUSTRIES BERHAD
No L9 Jalan ML16 ML16 Industrial Park, 43300, Seri Kembangan, Selangor Darul Ehsan, Malaysia
Tel.: (60) 389645600
Web Site: http://www.hwatai.com
HWATAI—(KLS)
Rev.: $16,138,747
Assets: $15,284,364
Liabilities: $11,930,362
Net Worth: $3,354,003
Earnings: ($1,234,708)
Emp.: 4
Fiscal Year-end: 12/31/22
Biscuit Mfr
N.A.I.C.S.: 311821
Jessica Teng Li Chin *(Sec)*

Subsidiaries:

Hwa Tai Distribution Sdn. Bhd. (1)
No L9 Jalan ML16 ML16, Industrial Park Seri Kembangan, 43300, Balakong, Selangor Darul Ehsan, Malaysia
Tel.: (60) 389645600
Web Site: https://www.hwatai.com.my
Sales Range: $25-49.9 Million
Emp.: 18
Biscuits Distr
N.A.I.C.S.: 424490

Hwa Tai Food Industries (Sabah) Sdn.Bhd. (1)
Lot 40 & 41 Phase 1 Lok Kawi Estate, Kinarut, 88848, Kota Kinabalu, Sabah, Malaysia
Tel.: (60) 88750396
Biscuit Mfr
N.A.I.C.S.: 311821

Hwa Tai Industries Berhad - Batu Pahat Factory (1)
No 12 Jalan Jorak Kawasan Perindustrian Tongkang Pecah Darul Takzim, 83010, Batu Pahat, Johor, Malaysia
Tel.: (60) 74151688
Biscuit Mfr
N.A.I.C.S.: 311821

Yinson Power Marine Sdn. Bhd. (1)
No 9 Jalan Selat Kelang Utara Bagan Hylam, 42000, Port Klang, Selangor Darul Ehsan, Malaysia
Tel.: (60) 3 3176 7845
Web Site: http://www.yinson.com.my
Marine Shipping Services
N.A.I.C.S.: 488510

HWA WELL TEXTILES (BD) LTD.
Alamin Icon Center Flat A7 Level 7 House No 57/4, Pragati Sarani Kuril Bishwa Road, Dhaka, 1212, Bangladesh
Tel.: (880) 28412935
Web Site:
  https://www.hwawelltex.com
HWAWELLTEX—(CHT)
Rev.: $18,380,504
Assets: $24,001,466
Liabilities: $4,692,089
Net Worth: $19,309,377
Earnings: $3,032,485
Emp.: 340
Fiscal Year-end: 06/30/23
Textile Products Mfr
N.A.I.C.S.: 314999
Devabrata Saha *(Sec)*

HWACHEON MACHINE TOOL CO., LTD.
123-17 Hanamsandan 4beon-ro, Gwangsan-gu, Gwangju, Korea (South)
Tel.: (82) 629515111
Year Founded: 1977
000850—(KRS)
Rev.: $187,219,876
Assets: $363,583,016
Liabilities: $98,764,145
Net Worth: $264,818,871
Earnings: $28,751,475
Emp.: 322
Fiscal Year-end: 12/31/22
Machine Tools Mfr
N.A.I.C.S.: 333517
Kim Kang-Chul *(Gen Mgr)*

Subsidiaries:

Hwacheon Asia Pacific Pte Ltd (1)
21 Bukit Batok Crescent 08-79 WCEGA Tower, Singapore, 658065, Singapore
Tel.: (65) 85115785
Web Site: https://www.hwacheonasia.com
CNC Machine Tool Mfr
N.A.I.C.S.: 333515
Kwon Seung Gwan *(Chm)*

Hwacheon Machine Tool Vietnam Co., Ltd. (1)
High-Tech Park Training Center Lot E1 - High-Tech Park, Hanoi Highway Hiep Phu Ward District 9 City Thu Duc, Ho Chi Minh City, Vietnam
Tel.: (84) 2862757011

HWACHEON MACHINE TOOL CO., LTD.

Hwacheon Machine Tool Co., Ltd.—(Continued)
Web Site: https://www.hwacheon.vn
CNC Machine Tool Mfr
N.A.I.C.S.: 333515

Hwacheon Machinery America, Inc. (1)
555 Bond St, Lincolnshire, IL 60069
Tel.: (847) 573-0100
CNC Machine Tool Mfr
N.A.I.C.S.: 333515

Hwacheon Machinery Europe GmbH (1)
Josef-Baumann-Str 25, 44805, Bochum, Germany
Tel.: (49) 2349128160
Emp.: 1,500
CNC Machine Tool Mfr
N.A.I.C.S.: 333515
Young Ryual Kwon (Mng Dir)

HWACHEON MACHINERY CO., LTD.
46 Banghae-ro Seocho-gu, Seoul, Korea (South)
Tel.: (82) 25237766
Year Founded: 1975
010660—(KRS)
Rev.: $145,536,677
Assets: $123,814,533
Liabilities: $25,005,952
Net Worth: $98,808,581
Earnings: $2,729,418
Emp.: 282
Fiscal Year-end: 12/31/22
Machine Tools Mfr
N.A.I.C.S.: 333517
Hyong-Yong Kim (Asst VP)

HWACOM SYSTEMS, INC.
12f No 98 Hsin-Tai-Wu Rd Sec 1, Hsi-chih Dist, New Taipei City, Taiwan
Tel.: (886) 226967155
Web Site: https://www.hwacom.com
Year Founded: 1994
6163—(TPE)
Rev.: $190,552,762
Assets: $166,601,757
Liabilities: $95,786,605
Net Worth: $70,815,152
Earnings: $4,317,825
Emp.: 757
Fiscal Year-end: 12/31/22
Telecommunication Services
N.A.I.C.S.: 517112
Gary Chen (Chm & Pres)

HWAIL PHARMACEUTICAL CO.,LTD.
5th floor of Korea Bio Park C-dong 700 Daewang Pangyo-ro, Bundang-gu Sampyeong-dong 694-1, Seongnam, Gyeonggi-do, Korea (South)
Tel.: (82) 316283629
Web Site: https://www.hwail.com
Year Founded: 1974
061250—(KRS)
Rev.: $101,284,458
Assets: $142,352,987
Liabilities: $7,688,217
Net Worth: $134,664,770
Earnings: ($4,852,780)
Emp.: 149
Fiscal Year-end: 12/31/22
Pharmaceuticals Product Mfr
N.A.I.C.S.: 325412

HWAJIN CO., LTD.
206-1 Donam-dong, Yeongcheon, Gyeongbuk, Korea (South)
Tel.: (82) 54 3359655
Web Site: http://www.hwajin-corp.com
Rev.: $71,631,216
Assets: $104,631,863
Liabilities: $56,775,100

Net Worth: $47,856,763
Earnings: ($21,487,576)
Emp.: 273
Fiscal Year-end: 12/31/18
Motor Vehicle Parts Mfr
N.A.I.C.S.: 336390
Han Choon Ki (Pres)

HWANG CAPITAL (MALAYSIA) BERHAD
Level 8 Wisma Sri Pinang 60 Green Hall, Penang, 10200, Malaysia
Tel.: (60) 42636108   MY
Web Site: http://www.hwang.com.my
Year Founded: 1973
Stock Broking & Financial Services
N.A.I.C.S.: 525990
Hui Ling Ooi (Sec)

Subsidiaries:

HDM Capital Sdn Bhd (1)
Level 8 Wisma Sri Pinang 60 Green Hall, 10200, Penang, Malaysia
Tel.: (60) 42636996
Web Site: http://www.hdbs.com.my
Investment Services
N.A.I.C.S.: 523999

HDM Private Equity Sdn. Bhd. (1)
Level 7 Wisma Sri Penang 60 Green Hall, 10200, Penang, Malaysia
Tel.: (60) 42636996
Sales Range: $50-74.9 Million
Emp.: 1
Investment Management Service
N.A.I.C.S.: 523999

HDM Properties Sdn Bhd (1)
Level 8 Wisma Sri Pinang 60 Green Hall, 10200, Penang, Malaysia
Tel.: (60) 42636996
Real Estate Services
N.A.I.C.S.: 531390

HWANG CHANG GENERAL CONTRACTOR CO., LTD.
23rd Floor No 539 Tammei Street, Neihu District, Taipei, 114, Taiwan
Tel.: (886) 227922988
Web Site: https://www.hcgc.com.tw
2543—(TAI)
Rev.: $368,719,826
Assets: $480,907,337
Liabilities: $372,012,642
Net Worth: $108,894,695
Earnings: $19,139,801
Fiscal Year-end: 12/31/23
Civil Engineering & Construction Services
N.A.I.C.S.: 237990
Cheng-Chin Chiang (Chm)

HWANG KUM STEEL & TECHNOLOGY CO., LTD.
25 MTV 1-ro Danwon-gu, Ansan, Gyeonggi, Korea (South)
Tel.: (82) 313638050
Web Site: https://www.hwangkum.com
Year Founded: 1986
032560—(KRS)
Rev.: $255,752,824
Assets: $369,626,989
Liabilities: $83,213,464
Net Worth: $286,413,524
Earnings: $35,471,348
Emp.: 121
Fiscal Year-end: 12/31/22
Steel Product Mfr & Distr
N.A.I.C.S.: 331110

HWANGE COLLIERY COMPANY LIMITED
17 Nelson Mandela Avenue 7th Floor Coal House, Harare, Zimbabwe
Tel.: (263) 4 781985   ZW
Web Site: http://hwangecolliery.co.zw
HCCL—(ZIM)
Sales Range: $50-74.9 Million

Coal Mining Services
N.A.I.C.S.: 213113
Charles Zinyemba (Mng Dir)

HWASEUNG INDUSTRIES CO., LTD.
6th Fl 1079 Jungang-daero, Yeonje-Gu, Busan, Korea (South)
Tel.: (82) 513110081
Web Site: https://www.hsi.co.kr
Year Founded: 1969
006060—(KRS)
Rev.: $1,467,236,953
Assets: $1,364,868,438
Liabilities: $858,917,238
Net Worth: $505,951,200
Earnings: $656,747
Emp.: 39
Fiscal Year-end: 12/31/22
Plastics Films Mfr
N.A.I.C.S.: 326112
Hyun Seokho (Vice Chm & CEO)

Subsidiaries:

BEIJING HECHENG R&A VEHICLE PARTS CO., LTD (1)
14 xinggu Industrial Development Zone, Pinggu, Beijing, China
Tel.: (86) 10 8998 6221
Automotive Rubber Product Mfr
N.A.I.C.S.: 336340

HECHENG VEHICLE PARTS (TAICANG) CO., LTD. (1)
105 Shanghai East Rd, Taicang, Jiangsu, China
Tel.: (86) 512 5356 6596
Automotive Rubber Product Mfr
N.A.I.C.S.: 336340

HS Automotive Alabama Inc. (1)
100 Sonata Dr, Enterprise, AL 36330
Tel.: (334) 348-9516
Automotive Rubber Product Mfr
N.A.I.C.S.: 336340
Pauline Guilford (Mgr-HR)

HS Networks India Pvt Ltd (1)
180 Sector 16, Faridabad, 121001, India
Tel.: (91) 129 4004346
Rubber Products Mfr
N.A.I.C.S.: 326299

HSI AUTOMOTIVES LTD. (1)
Survey No 73 A Block 100 Thandalam Post Mevalurkuppam, Sriperumbudur Taluk Kancheepuram, Chennai, 602105, India
Tel.: (91) 4461103110
Web Site: https://www.hsiauto.com
Power Steering Hose Mfr
N.A.I.C.S.: 336330
Wook Woon Lee (CEO)

HSLS RUBBER INDUSTRIES SDA. BHD. (1)
5Â¼Miles jalan Jelebu, 70100, Seremban, Negeri Sembilan, Malaysia
Tel.: (60) 6 767 9580
Rubber Products Mfr
N.A.I.C.S.: 326299
Young Gyu Lee (Mng Dir)

HWASEUNG (H.K) LTD. (1)
14F Zhong Da Building 38-40 Hai Phong Rd, Tsim Sha Tsui, Kowloon, China (Hong Kong)
Tel.: (852) 2786 2663
Automotive Rubber Product Mfr
N.A.I.C.S.: 336340

HWASEUNG (SHANGHAI) INT'L TRADE CO., LTD. (1)
Rm 901-903 New Town Center No 83 Loushanguan Rd, Shanghai, China
Tel.: (86) 21 6145 3268
Automotive Rubber Product Mfr
N.A.I.C.S.: 336340

HWASEUNG AMERICA CORP. (1)
8503 E Village Ln, Rosemead, CA 91770
Tel.: (626) 572-3833
Shoe Mfr
N.A.I.C.S.: 316210

HWASEUNG Climate Control Industries Co., Ltd. (1)

Tel.: (82) 415381200
Web Site: http://www.hs-cci.com
Shoe Mfr
N.A.I.C.S.: 316210

HWASEUNG ENTERPRISE CO., LTD (1)
8th floor Dong Ik Sung Bong Building 301 Seocho DaeRo, Seocho Gu, Seoul, Korea (South)
Tel.: (82) 25888043
Web Site: https://www.hsenterprise.co.kr
Rev.: $1,268,640,690
Assets: $1,131,962,938
Liabilities: $678,525,664
Net Worth: $453,437,273
Earnings: ($7,673,327)
Emp.: 11
Fiscal Year-end: 12/31/2022
Sports Shoe Mfr & Distr
N.A.I.C.S.: 316210
Ky Lee (CEO)

HWASEUNG EXwill (1)
Tel.: (82) 518603600
Web Site: http://www.hs-exwill.com
Shoe Mfr
N.A.I.C.S.: 316210

HWASEUNG Material Co., Ltd. (1)
147-1 Gyo-dong, Yangsan, Gyeongsangnam-do, Korea (South)
Tel.: (82) 553703331
Web Site: http://www.hscmb.co.kr
Shoe Mfr
N.A.I.C.S.: 316210
Seong-Ryong Heo (Pres & CEO)

HWASEUNG Networks Co., Ltd. (1)
Tel.: (82) 518500100
Web Site: http://www.hsnetw.co.kr
Shoe Mfr
N.A.I.C.S.: 316210

HWASEUNG T&C Co., Ltd. (1)
Eogokgondgan 5-gil, Yangsan, 50591, Gyeongsangnam, Korea (South)
Tel.: (82) 553803600
Web Site: https://www.hstnc.co.kr
Automotive Rubber Product Mfr
N.A.I.C.S.: 336340

Hwaseung Industries Co., Ltd. - DONGGUAN FACTORY (1)
The Second Industrial Complex, Ma Yong Zhen, Dongguan, Guang Dong, China
Tel.: (86) 769 882 7001
Automotive Rubber Product Mfr
N.A.I.C.S.: 336340

HWASEUNG R&A CO., LTD.
61 Chungnyeol-ro, 50592, Yangsan, 50592, Gyeongsangnam-do, Korea (South)
Tel.: (82) 553703331
Web Site: https://www.hsrna.com
013520—(KRS)
Rev.: $1,252,446,975
Assets: $930,002,298
Liabilities: $732,029,886
Net Worth: $197,972,412
Earnings: $12,370,084
Fiscal Year-end: 12/31/22
Automobile Parts Mfr
N.A.I.C.S.: 336390
Kim Hyeong Jin (Pres & CEO)

HWASHIN CO., LTD.
412 Eonha-dong, Yeongcheon, 770-280, Gyeongsangbuk-do, Korea (South)
Tel.: (82) 543305000
Web Site: https://www.hwashin.co.kr
Year Founded: 1975
010690—(KRS)
Rev.: $1,296,438,175
Assets: $770,544,303
Liabilities: $496,829,929
Net Worth: $273,714,374
Earnings: $56,923,151
Emp.: 933
Fiscal Year-end: 12/31/22
Automotive Products Mfr
N.A.I.C.S.: 336110
Seojin Chung (Pres)

AND PRIVATE COMPANIES

Subsidiaries:

Beijing Hwashin Automobile Parts
Co., Ltd. (1)
11 Xinggu Industrial Zone, Pinggu, Beijing,
101200, China
Tel.: (86) 10 6995 2411
Web Site: http://www.hwashin.co.kr
Emp.: 516
Motor Vehicle Parts Mfr
N.A.I.C.S.: 336390
Jong-Sung Kim (VP)

Hwashin America Corp. (1)
661 Montgomery Hwy, Greenville, AL 36037
Tel.: (334) 382-1100
Sales Range: $1-9.9 Million
Emp.: 363
Motor Vehicle Parts Mfr
N.A.I.C.S.: 336498
Kista Hinson (Asst Mgr-HR)

Hwashin Automotive India Pvt.,
Ltd. (1)
Plot F-65A SIPCOT Industrial ParkIrungattu-
kottai, Sriperumbudur, Kanchipuram, 602
105, Tamil Nadu, India
Tel.: (91) 44 47130000
Emp.: 1,078
Motor Vehicle Parts Mfr
N.A.I.C.S.: 336390
Young-Seop Lee (Exec Dir)

Hwashin Brasil Corp. (1)
Emp.: 200
Motor Vehicle Parts Mfr
N.A.I.C.S.: 336390
Kyung-Ho Ru (Mng Dir)

Hwashin Co., Ltd. (1)
412 Eonha-dong, Yeongcheon, 770-280,
Gyeongsangbuk-do, Korea (South)
Tel.: (82) 543305000
Web Site: https://www.hwashin.co.kr
Rev.: $243,861,498
Assets: $123,777,815
Liabilities: $45,814,372
Net Worth: $77,963,443
Earnings: $5,428,124
Emp.: 221
Fiscal Year-end: 12/31/2022
Automobile Parts Mfr
N.A.I.C.S.: 336110
Seojin Chung (Pres)

Hwashin Precision Industry Co.,
Ltd. (1)
193 Donam-dong, Yeongcheon, 770-130,
Gyeongsangbuk-do, Korea (South)
Tel.: (82) 543308200
Automotive Chassis Mfr
N.A.I.C.S.: 336110

HWASHIN TECH CO., LTD.
Road 250 in Dalseogu Dalgubul st 71,
100-30 galsan-dong, dalseo-gu,
Daegu, Korea (South)
Tel.: (82) 535831171
Web Site: http://www.hstech.co.kr
Year Founded: 1985
086250—(KRS)
Rev.: $14,675
Assets: $29,277,273
Liabilities: $15,401,892
Net Worth: $13,875,381
Earnings: ($3,945,928)
Emp.: 8
Fiscal Year-end: 12/31/22
Motor Vehicle Parts Mfr
N.A.I.C.S.: 336370
Jae-Hyung Jung (Chm)

Subsidiaries:

Sae-Hwashin Co., Ltd. (1)
903-7 Shinjang-ri, Ohga-myeon, Yesan,
Chungcheong, Korea (South)
Tel.: (82) 41 3303300
Emp.: 108
Automobile Parts Mfr
N.A.I.C.S.: 336370

HWASUNG INDUSTRIAL CO., LTD.
111 Dongdaegu-ro, Suseong-gu,
Daegu, Korea (South)
Tel.: (82) 537672111
Web Site: https://www.hwasung.com
Year Founded: 1958
002460—(KRS)
Rev.: $495,257,072
Assets: $572,279,978
Liabilities: $298,497,449
Net Worth: $273,782,529
Earnings: $18,644,696
Emp.: 414
Fiscal Year-end: 12/31/22
Building Construction & Engineering
Services
N.A.I.C.S.: 541330
Jin-Yup Choi (Pres & CEO)

HWAXIN ENVIRONMENTAL CO., LTD.
No 3-9 No 4 Jingsheng North 1st St
Zhongguancun Science, Tech Park
Zhongguancun Science & Technology
Park Tongzhou District, Beijing,
101102, China
Tel.: (86) 1080829768
Web Site: https://www.hxepd.com
Year Founded: 2006
301265—(CHIN)
Rev.: $105,611,688
Assets: $318,439,836
Liabilities: $33,600,528
Net Worth: $284,839,308
Earnings: $15,684,084
Fiscal Year-end: 12/31/22
Hazardous Waste Treatment Services
N.A.I.C.S.: 562211
Jun Zhang (Chm)

HWGG ENTERTAINMENT LIMITED
Wisma Ho Wah Genting Ground
Floor No 35 Jalan Maharajalela,
50150, Kuala Lumpur, Malaysia
Tel.: (60) 321482288
Web Site: https://www.hwgg.com.my
Year Founded: 1979
HWGG—(OTCIQ)
Rev.: $5,000
Assets: $9,050,000
Liabilities: $18,019,000
Net Worth: ($8,969,000)
Earnings: ($2,587,000)
Emp.: 2
Fiscal Year-end: 12/31/20
Business Support Services
N.A.I.C.S.: 561499
Pehin Sri Datuk Sri Dato'Lim Hui
Boon (Founder)

HWH INVESTMENTS LIMITED
Unit 3 Ashted Lock, Birmingham, B7
4AZ, United Kingdom
Tel.: (44) 1213593335
Web Site:
http://www.hwhinvestments.co.uk
Year Founded: 1989
Sales Range: Less than $1 Million
Emp.: 10
Investment Holding Company
N.A.I.C.S.: 551112
John G. Harris (Mng Dir)

Subsidiaries:

AB Precision (Poole) Limited (1)
1 Fleets Lane, Poole, BH15 3BZ, Dorset,
United Kingdom
Tel.: (44) 1202665000
Web Site: http://www.abprecision.co.uk
Sales Range: $10-24.9 Million
Emp.: 80
Electromechanical Equipment Designer, Mfr
& Distr
N.A.I.C.S.: 335999
David Brooker (Mgr-Sls-Explosive Ordnance Disposal)

Aeronautical & General Instruments
Limited (1)
Fleets Point Willis Way, Poole, Dorset, United Kingdom
Tel.: (44) 1202685661
Web Site: http://www.agiltd.co.uk
Sales Range: $10-24.9 Million
Emp.: 126
Civil & Defense Instrument Mfr
N.A.I.C.S.: 334511
Geof Beles (Mng Dir)

Division (Domestic):

Metalite Aviation Lighting (2)
Fleets Point Willis Way, Poole, BH15 3SS,
Dorset, United Kingdom
Tel.: (44) 1202689099
Web Site: http://www.metaliteaviation.com
Emp.: 15
Aviation Industry Portable Landing Light
Designer & Mfr
N.A.I.C.S.: 335139
Brian Hunt (Bus Mgr)

Froude Hofmann Ltd. (1)
Blackpole Rd, Worcester, WR3 8YB, United
Kingdom
Tel.: (44) 01905856800
Web Site: http://www.froudehofmann.com
Sales Range: $50-74.9 Million
Dynamometer Mfr
N.A.I.C.S.: 334519

Division (US):

Froude Hofmann, Inc. (2)
41123 Jo Dr, Novi, MI 48375
Tel.: (734) 416-8000
Web Site: http://www.froudehofmann.com
Sales Range: $25-49.9 Million
Emp.: 18
Dynamometer & Engine Test System Mfr
N.A.I.C.S.: 423120
Andy Sadlon (Gen Mgr)

Division (Non-US):

Hofmann Pruftechnik GmbH (2)
Heilswannenweg 50, Elze, 31008,
Hildesheim, Germany
Tel.: (49) 5068462103
Web Site: http://hofmanntesys.com
Dynamometer Mfr
N.A.I.C.S.: 334519

Hoffman Engineering
Corporation (1)
8 Riverbend Dr, Stamford, CT 06907
Tel.: (203) 425-8900
Web Site:
http://www.hoffmanengineering.com
Sales Range: $10-24.9 Million
Aircraft Lighting, Night Vision & Photonic
Test Equipment Designer & Mfr
N.A.I.C.S.: 334516
Andrew Sadlon (Pres)

Horstman Defence Systems
Limited (1)
Locksbrook Road, Bath, BA1 3EX, United
Kingdom
Tel.: (44) 1225423111
Web Site: http://www.horstman.co.uk
Sales Range: $10-24.9 Million
Military Vehicle Supension Systems Designer & Mfr
N.A.I.C.S.: 336330
Paul Barrett (Dir-Fin)

HWP PLANUNGS GMBH
Rotenbergstrasse 8, 70190, Stuttgart,
Germany
Tel.: (49) 71116620
Web Site: http://www.hwp-planung.de
Year Founded: 1970
Sales Range: $10-24.9 Million
Emp.: 1,000
Architectural & Engineering Consulting Services
N.A.I.C.S.: 541310
Norbert Leopold (Mng Dir)

Subsidiaries:

HWP Cairo Planning & Engineering
Consultant Ltd. (1)
26th July Street Building No 159, Zamalek,
11211, Cairo, Egypt
Tel.: (20) 22735485
Engineeering Services

HY-LOK CORPORATION

N.A.I.C.S.: 541330
Nadia Roubin (Office Mgr & Mgr-Admin)

HWP Istanbul Mimarlik Muhendislik
ve Danismanlik Ltd. Sirketi (1)
Valikonagi Caddesi No 74/4 Tesvikiye Mahallesi, Sisli, 34365, Istanbul, Turkiye
Tel.: (90) 2122306558
Web Site: http://www.hwp-istanbul.com.tr
Engineeering Services
N.A.I.C.S.: 541330

HWW WIENBERG WILHELM RECHTSANWALTE PARTNERSCHAFT
Wasastrasse 15, 01219, Dresden,
Germany
Tel.: (49) 351 34085 0
Web Site: http://www.hww.eu
Emp.: 400
Corporate Legal & Insolvency Services
N.A.I.C.S.: 541110
Rudiger Wienberg (Partner)

HY ENERGY GROUP CO., LTD.
No 59 Xishi Street, Zhuji City, Shaoxing, 311800, Zhejiang, China
Tel.: (86) 57587016161
Web Site: http://www.hy600387.com
Year Founded: 1993
600387—(SHG)
Rev.: $925,611,654
Assets: $632,358,132
Liabilities: $165,110,681
Net Worth: $467,247,451
Earnings: $7,868,156
Fiscal Year-end: 12/31/22
Refined Oil Product & Liquefied Gas
Operator
N.A.I.C.S.: 457110
Wang Bin (Chm & Fin Dir)

HY-LOK CORPORATION
97 Noksan Industrial Complex 27-ro,
Gangseo-gu, Busan, Korea (South)
Tel.: (82) 519700800
Web Site: https://www.hy-lok.com
013030—(KRS)
Rev.: $140,246,787
Assets: $315,944,504
Liabilities: $24,387,895
Net Worth: $291,556,609
Earnings: $25,972,555
Emp.: 526
Fiscal Year-end: 12/31/22
Valve Mfr
N.A.I.C.S.: 332911

Subsidiaries:

Hy-Lok Asia Valves & Fittings PTE
Ltd. (1)
62/64 Tech Park Crescent, Singapore,
638079, Singapore
Tel.: (65) 68628811
Web Site: http://www.english.hy-lok.com
Emp.: 40
Valves & Fittings Mfr
N.A.I.C.S.: 332912
Calvin Ong (Mgr)

Hy-Lok Canada Inc. (1)
2407-96 Street, Edmonton, T6N 0A7, AB,
Canada
Tel.: (780) 409-4484
Web Site: http://www.hylok.ca
Sales Range: $25-49.9 Million
Emp.: 10
Semiconductor Equipment Mfr
N.A.I.C.S.: 334413

Hy-Lok China (1)
No 25 Lane 1353 Kangding Road, Jing an
District, Shanghai, 200333, China
Tel.: (86) 2162308533
Sales Range: $25-49.9 Million
Emp.: 20
Semiconductor Equipment Mfr
N.A.I.C.S.: 334413

Hy-Lok Europe B.V. (1)
Buitenvaart 1411, Hoogeveen, 7905SG,

Hy-Lok Corporation—(Continued)
Drenthe, Netherlands
Tel.: (31) 528234084
Web Site: http://www.hy-lok.eu
Sales Range: $25-49.9 Million
Emp.: 5
Semiconductor Equipment Mfr
N.A.I.C.S.: 333242
Erik Nordholt *(Mng Dir)*

Hy-Lok USA (1)
14211 Westfair W Dr, Houston, TX 77041-1137
Tel.: (832) 634-2000
Web Site: https://www.hylokusa.com
Sales Range: $25-49.9 Million
Emp.: 11
Semiconductor Equipment Mfr
N.A.I.C.S.: 333242
Jody Barnes *(Pres)*

Hy-lok Oceania Pty. Ltd. (1)
2B Assembly Drive, Tullamarine, 3043, VIC, Australia
Tel.: (61) 393345700
Web Site: https://www.hylokoceania.com.au
Sales Range: $25-49.9 Million
Emp.: 10
Semiconductor Equipment Mfr
N.A.I.C.S.: 333242

HYAS & CO., INC.
IK Building 5F 24-9 Kamiosaki
2-chome, Shinagawa-ku, Tokyo, 141-0021, Japan
Tel.: (81) 357479800
Web Site: http://www.hyas.co.jp
6192—(TKS)
Rev.: $49,633,300
Assets: $36,749,257
Liabilities: $18,718,203
Net Worth: $18,031,054
Earnings: $2,186,984
Emp.: 257
Fiscal Year-end: 09/30/23
Real Estate Consulting Service
N.A.I.C.S.: 531390
Seiichi Hamamura *(Pres)*

HYBE CO., LTD.
42 Hangang-daero, Yongsan-gu, Seoul, Korea (South)
Tel.: (82) 233340105
Web Site: http://www.hybecorp.com
Year Founded: 2005
352820—(KRS)
Rev.: $1,362,310,085
Assets: $3,735,623,120
Liabilities: $1,489,325,556
Net Worth: $2,246,297,564
Earnings: $36,840,640
Emp.: 618
Fiscal Year-end: 12/31/22
Music Publishers
N.A.I.C.S.: 512230
Si-Hyuk Bang *(Chm)*

HYBIO PHARMACEUTICAL CO., LTD.
No 7 Guansheng 4th Rd Guanlan High-Tech Park, Longhua District, Shenzhen, 518110, Guangdong, China
Tel.: (86) 75526588037
Web Site: https://www.hybio-peptide.com
Year Founded: 1998
300199—(CHIN)
Rev.: $98,886,528
Assets: $507,016,692
Liabilities: $324,926,316
Net Worth: $182,090,376
Earnings: ($52,025,220)
Emp.: 300
Fiscal Year-end: 12/31/22
Pharmaceuticals Mfr
N.A.I.C.S.: 325412
Zeng Shaogui *(Chm)*

HYBRID FINANCIAL SERVICES LIMITED
104 Sterling Centre 1st Floor Opp Divine Child High School, Andheri-Kurla Road Andheri East, Mumbai, 400093, India
Tel.: (91) 2229207802
Web Site: https://hybridfinance.co.in
Year Founded: 1986
HYBRIDFIN—(NSE)
Rev.: $434,662
Assets: $4,498,148
Liabilities: $1,763,431
Net Worth: $2,734,716
Earnings: $60,740
Emp.: 2
Fiscal Year-end: 03/31/23
Financial Investment Services
N.A.I.C.S.: 523999
Chandramouli Krishnamurthy *(Sec)*

Subsidiaries:

Maximus Securities Limited (1)
1st Floor Sterling Center Opp Divine Child High School Andheri, Kurla Road Andheri East, Mumbai, 400 093, India
Tel.: (91) 2261418700
Web Site: https://www.maximussecurities.com
Broking Firm Services
N.A.I.C.S.: 531210

HYBRID KINETIC GROUP LIMITED
Suites 1407-8 14th Floor Great Eagle Centre, 23 Harbour Road, Wanchai, China (Hong Kong)
Tel.: (852) 25309218
Web Site: http://www.hkgroup.com.hk
Sales Range: $1-9.9 Million
Emp.: 183
Automotive Battery Mfr
N.A.I.C.S.: 335910
Yung Yeung *(Chm)*

HYBRID SOFTWARE GROUP PLC
Building 2030, Cambourne Business Park, Cambridge, CB23 6DW, United Kingdom
Tel.: (44) 1954283100
Web Site: https://www.globalgraphics.com
HYSG—(EUR)
Rev.: $50,391,755
Assets: $155,839,629
Liabilities: $36,119,145
Net Worth: $119,720,483
Earnings: $1,402,979
Emp.: 288
Fiscal Year-end: 12/31/22
Digital Printing Solutions
N.A.I.C.S.: 323111
Justin Bailey *(Mng Dir)*

Subsidiaries:

Global Graphics KK (1)
613 AIOS Nagatacho Bldg, 2-17-17 Nagatacho Chiyoda-ku, Tokyo, 100-0014, Japan
Tel.: (81) 362733198
Web Site: https://www.globalgraphics.com
Software Publisher
N.A.I.C.S.: 513210

Global Graphics Software (India) Pvt Ltd (1)
4th Floor O Z Plaza Plot No 2, Survey no 206 Viman Nagar, 411014, Pune, MH, India
Tel.: (91) 2040036885
Web Site: https://www.globalgraphics.com
Sales Range: $25-49.9 Million
Emp.: 40
Software Publisher
N.A.I.C.S.: 513210

Global Graphics Software Inc. (1)
5996 Clark Center Ave, Sarasota, FL 34238
Tel.: (941) 925-1303
Web Site: http://www.globalgraphics.com
Sales Range: $10-24.9 Million
Emp.: 25
Computer Software Development Services
N.A.I.C.S.: 541511

Global Graphics Software Ltd (1)
Building 2030 Cambourne Business Park, Cambourne, Cambridge, CB23 6DW, United Kingdom
Tel.: (44) 1954283100
Graphic Software Development Services
N.A.I.C.S.: 541511

Meteor Inkjet Limited (1)
Harston Mill Royston Road, Cambridge, CB22 7GG, United Kingdom
Tel.: (44) 3458440012
Web Site: https://www.meteorinkjet.com
Software Development Services
N.A.I.C.S.: 541511

RTI Global, Inc. (1)
5996 Clark Ctr Ave, Sarasota, FL 34238
Tel.: (941) 925-1303
Web Site: http://www.rti-rips.com
Emp.: 4
Printing Equipment Distr
N.A.I.C.S.: 423440
Ken Hillier *(Pres)*

Xitron, LLC (1)
4750 Venture Dr Ste 200 A, Ann Arbor, MI 48108
Tel.: (734) 913-8080
Web Site: http://www.xitron.com
Sales Range: $1-9.9 Million
Emp.: 30
Printing Machinery & Equipment Mfr
N.A.I.C.S.: 333248
Sue Wood *(Mgr-Dealer-Europe, Africa & Middle East)*

HYBTRONICS MICROSYSTEMS, S.A.
Oreitiasolo 14, 01006, Vitoria, Spain
Tel.: (34) 945148040
Web Site: http://www.hybtronics.com
Year Founded: 1990
Automotive Ignition Electronic & Sensor Technology Mfr
N.A.I.C.S.: 336390
Santos Martin *(Mng Dir)*

HYDAC INTERNATIONAL GMBH
Industriestrasse, 66280, Sulzbach, Germany
Tel.: (49) 689750901
Web Site: http://www.hydac.com
Sales Range: $550-599.9 Million
Emp.: 4,000
Fluid Technology Product & Services
N.A.I.C.S.: 333996

Subsidiaries:

Aerofluid Co., Ltd. (1)
169/4 169/5 Moo 1 Rangsit-Nakornnayok Rd, Lamlookka, Thanyaburi, 12130, Patumthanee, Thailand
Tel.: (66) 25772999
Hydraulic Equipment Mfr & Whslr
N.A.I.C.S.: 333995

Brammertz Ingenieros S.A. (1)
Av Jose Pardo 182 Of 902 Miraflores, Lima, 15074, Peru
Tel.: (51) 12084600
Web Site: http://www.brammertz.com
Hydraulic Equipment Mfr & Distr
N.A.I.C.S.: 335910

Delta-P Technologies Ltd. (1)
38 Amfipoleos Str, 11855, Athens, Greece
Tel.: (30) 2103410181
Hydraulic Equipment Mfr & Whslr
N.A.I.C.S.: 333995

EEM Tecnologias de Accionamiento y Control, S.A. (1)
17 Avenida 19-70 Zona 10 Torino Building Level 10 Office 1011, Guatemala, Guatemala
Tel.: (502) 22036862
Hydraulic Equipment Mfr & Whslr
N.A.I.C.S.: 333995

ETS Ingenieria SAS (1)
Calle 96 A No 61-36, Bogota, Colombia
Tel.: (57) 7713154
Web Site: http://www.etsingenieria.com
Integrated Technology Services
N.A.I.C.S.: 541519

El-Masry Industrial Services LLC (1)
3 Africa St 9th District Nasr City, Cairo, 11471, Egypt
Tel.: (20) 224701111
Hydraulic Equipment Mfr & Whslr
N.A.I.C.S.: 333995

Friederich-Hydrotech S.a.r.l. (1)
16 Route d'Esch, Schifflange, 3835, Luxembourg, Luxembourg
Tel.: (352) 5452441
Web Site: http://www.hydrotech.lu
Hydraulic Equipment Mfr & Whslr
N.A.I.C.S.: 333995

German-Gulf Enterprises Ltd. (1)
No 7 Al Khan Road Behind Safeer Mall, PB No 5937, Industrial Area, Sharjah, United Arab Emirates
Tel.: (971) 65314161
Web Site: http://www.germangulf.com
Emp.: 500
Construction & Hydraulic Machinery Mfr
N.A.I.C.S.: 333120
Mark Johnson *(Gen Mgr)*

HYDAC (India) Pvt. Ltd. (1)
A-58 TTC Industrial Area MIDC, Mahape, Navi Mumbai, 400 701, India
Tel.: (91) 22 41 11 88 88
Hydraulic Components Mfr
N.A.I.C.S.: 333998
Ashok Tare *(VP)*

HYDAC A/S (1)
Havretoften 5, 5550, Langeskov, Denmark
Tel.: (45) 702 702 99
Web Site: http://www.hydac.dk
Hydraulic Component Distr
N.A.I.C.S.: 423840

HYDAC ACCESSORIES GMBH (1)
Hirschbachstr 2, 66280, Sulzbach, Germany
Tel.: (49) 6897 509 01
Industrial Equipment Distr
N.A.I.C.S.: 423830

HYDAC AG (1)
Zona Industriale 3 Via Sceresa, 6805, Mezzovico-Vira, Switzerland
Tel.: (41) 91 935 57 09
Web Site: http://www.hydac.ch
Hydraulic Component Distr
N.A.I.C.S.: 423830

HYDAC AS (1)
Berghagan 4, 1405, Langhus, Norway
Tel.: (47) 64 85 86 00
Web Site: http://www.hydac.no
Emp.: 35
Hydraulic Components Mfr
N.A.I.C.S.: 333998
Petter Holten *(Mng Dir)*

HYDAC B.V. (1)
Vossenbeemd 109, 5705 CL, Helmond, Netherlands
Tel.: (31) 4 92 59 74 70
Web Site: http://www.hydac.com
Hydraulic Component Distr
N.A.I.C.S.: 423830

HYDAC Belarus (1)
Timirjazeva 65a biura 504-505, 220035, Minsk, Belarus
Tel.: (375) 17 209 01 32
Web Site: http://www.hydac.com.by
Hydraulic Component Distr
N.A.I.C.S.: 423830

HYDAC Corporation (1)
14 Federal Road, Welland, L3B 3P2, ON, Canada
Tel.: (905) 714-9322
Web Site: http://www.hydac.ca
Emp.: 40
Hydraulic Components Mfr
N.A.I.C.S.: 333998
Craig Goodwin *(Gen Mgr)*

HYDAC EOOD (1)
Business Center Iskar-Yug Munchen Str 14, 1592, Sofia, Bulgaria

HYDAC INTERNATIONAL GMBH

Tel.: (359) 2 970 60 00
Web Site: http://www.hydac.bg
Hydraulic Components Mfr
N.A.I.C.S.: 333998

HYDAC Electronic GmbH (1)
Hauptstrasse 27, 66128, Saarbrucken, Germany
Tel.: (49) 6897 509 01
Hydraulic Components Mfr
N.A.I.C.S.: 333998

HYDAC Electronic, s.r.o. (1)
Krasna Horka 290, 027 44, Tvrdosin, Slovakia
Tel.: (421) 43 5321310
Hydraulic Components Mfr
N.A.I.C.S.: 333998

HYDAC Engineering AG (1)
Allmendstr 11, 6312, Steinhausen, Switzerland
Tel.: (41) 41 747 03 20
Web Site: http://www.hydac.ch
Hydraulic Components Mfr
N.A.I.C.S.: 333998

HYDAC Fluidteknik AB (1)
Domnarvsgatan 29, PO Box 8250, 16308, Spanga, Sweden
Tel.: (46) 8 445 29 70
Web Site: http://www.hydac.com
Hydraulic Component Distr
N.A.I.C.S.: 423830
Lars Forslid *(CFO)*

HYDAC Hidraulika es Szurestschnika Kft. (1)
Jasz u 152/A, 1131, Budapest, Hungary
Tel.: (36) 1 3 59 93 59
Hydraulic Component Distr
N.A.I.C.S.: 423830

HYDAC Hydraulik Ges.m.b.H. (1)
Industriestrasse 3, 4066, Pasching, Austria
Tel.: (43) 72 29 6 18 11 0
Web Site: http://www.hydac.at
Hydraulic Components Mfr
N.A.I.C.S.: 333998

HYDAC International SA de CV (1)
Pirul 212, Los Reyes Ixtacala, 54090, Tlalnepantla, Mexico
Tel.: (52) 555 565 85 11
Hydraulic Components Mfr
N.A.I.C.S.: 333998

HYDAC Korea Co. Ltd. (1)
6th Floor Wonwook Bldg 768-12 Bangbae, Seocho, Seoul, 137-829, Korea (South)
Tel.: (82) 2 591 09 31
Web Site: http://www.hydac.com
Emp.: 70
Hydraulic Components Mfr
N.A.I.C.S.: 333998
John Kim *(Mng Dir)*

HYDAC Ltd. (1)
108A Penrose Road, Mount Wellington, Auckland, New Zealand
Tel.: (64) 9 271 4120
Web Site: http://www.hydac.co.nz
Hydraulic Pumps Mfr
N.A.I.C.S.: 333996
Dimitrios Konstantopoulos *(Gen Mgr)*

HYDAC Ltd. Sti. (1)
Namik Kemal Mahallesi Adile Nasit Bulvari 174 Sok No 9, Esenyurt, 34550, Istanbul, Turkiye
Tel.: (90) 212 428 25 25
Web Site: http://www.hydac.com.tr
Hydraulic Component Distr
N.A.I.C.S.: 423830

HYDAC Pty. Ltd. (1)
109 -111 Dohertys Road, PO Box 224, Altona, 3025, VIC, Australia
Tel.: (61) 3 9272 8900
Web Site: http://www.hydac.com.au
Hydraulic Pumps Mfr
N.A.I.C.S.: 333996
Mark le Roux *(Mgr-Natl Dev)*

HYDAC S.a.r.l. (1)
Technopole Forbach Sud, BP 30260, 57604, Forbach, France
Tel.: (33) 3 87 29 26 00
Web Site: http://www.hydac.fr
Hydraulic Component Distr
N.A.I.C.S.: 423830

HYDAC S.p.A. (1)
Via Archimede 76, Agrate Brianza, 20041, Milan, Italy
Tel.: (39) 039 64 22 11
Web Site: http://www.hydac.it
Hydraulic Component Distr
N.A.I.C.S.: 423830
Lucio Sergio Barelli *(Product Mgr)*

HYDAC Sp. z o.o. (1)
ul Reymonta 17, 43-190, Mikolow, Poland
Tel.: (48) 32 326 29 00
Web Site: http://www.hydac.com.pl
Hydraulic Component Distr
N.A.I.C.S.: 423830

HYDAC Technology (Hongkong) Ltd. (1)
Room 602 6/F Silvercord Tower 1 30 Canton Road, Tsim Sha Tsui, Kowloon, China (Hong Kong)
Tel.: (852) 23 69 35 68
Hydraulic Components Mfr
N.A.I.C.S.: 333998

HYDAC Technology (Shanghai) Ltd. (1)
271 Luchun Road Shanghai Minhang, Economic & Technological, Shanghai, 200245, China
Tel.: (86) 21 64 63 35 10
Web Site: http://www.hydac.com.cn
Fluid Control Equipment Distr
N.A.I.C.S.: 423830

HYDAC Technology Ltd. (1)
No 6 Shuyi Road, South District, Taichung, 40241, Taiwan
Tel.: (886) 4 2260 2278
Hydraulic Components Mfr
N.A.I.C.S.: 333998

HYDAC Technology Pte. Ltd. (1)
2A Second Chin Bee Road, Singapore, 618781, Singapore
Tel.: (65) 6741 74 58
Web Site: http://www.hydac.com.sg
Fluid Control Equipment Distr
N.A.I.C.S.: 423830
Frederick Chin *(Mgr-Sls)*

HYDAC Technology Pty Ltd (1)
165 Van der Bijl Street, Edenvale, 1614, Johannesburg, South Africa
Tel.: (27) 11 723 90 80
Web Site: http://www.hydac.co.za
Hydraulic Components Mfr
N.A.I.C.S.: 333998
Heijboer Walter *(Mng Dir)*

HYDAC Technology SL (1)
Pol Ind Pla de la Bruguera Apdo Correos 162 Solsones 54, Castellar del Valles, 08211, Barcelona, Spain
Tel.: (34) 93 747 36 09
Hydraulic Component Distr
N.A.I.C.S.: 423830
Oswaldo Cabrera Orta *(Dir-Sls)*

HYDAC Technology Sdn. Bhd. (1)
Lot 830 Kawasan Per Industrian Kampung Jaya, Jalan Kusta, 47000, Sungai Buloh, Malaysia
Tel.: (60) 3 5567 0250
Web Site: http://www.hydac.com.my
Emp.: 20
Fluid Control Equipment Distr
N.A.I.C.S.: 423830
Derek Chin *(Gen Mgr)*

HYDAC Tecnologia Chile Ltda (1)
Las Araucarias 9080 - 9110 Parque Industrial Las Araucarias, Quilicura, 8720041, Santiago, Chile
Tel.: (56) 2 5846754
Hydraulic Components Mfr
N.A.I.C.S.: 333998

HYDAC Tecnologia Ltda (1)
Estrada Fukutaro Yida 225, Sao Bernardo do Campo, 09852-060, Brazil
Tel.: (55) 11 4393 6600
Web Site: http://www.hydac.com.br
Hydraulic Components Mfr
N.A.I.C.S.: 333998

HYDAC Tecnologia, Unipessoal, Lda. (1)
Castelo da Maia Business Center Rua Manuel Assuncao Falcao 501, 4475-041, Maia, Portugal
Tel.: (351) 223160364
Hydraulic Equipment Mfr & Whslr
N.A.I.C.S.: 333995

HYDAC Ukraine (1)
ul Novokonstantinovskaya 9 Korpus 13 2 Etage, 04080, Kiev, Ukraine
Tel.: (380) 44 495 33 96
Web Site: http://www.hydac.com.ua
Hydraulic Component Distr
N.A.I.C.S.: 423830

HYDAC d.o.o. (1)
Zagrebska cesta 20, 2000, Maribor, Slovenia
Tel.: (386) 2 460 15 20
Web Site: http://www.hydac.si
Hydraulic Components Mfr
N.A.I.C.S.: 333998

HYDAC s.r.o. (1)
Gorkeho 4, 03601, Martin, Slovakia
Tel.: (421) 43 4135893
Web Site: http://www.hydac.sk
Hydraulic Components Mfr
N.A.I.C.S.: 333998

Hydac Co., Ltd. (1)
Daiwa Hatchobori Ekimae Bldg 2F 3-25-7 Hatchobori, Chuo-ku, Tokyo, 104-0032, Japan
Tel.: (81) 335373620
Hydraulic Equipment Mfr & Whslr
N.A.I.C.S.: 333995

Hydac Cooling GmbH (1)
Postfach 1251, Industrial Area, 66280, Sulzbach, Germany
Tel.: (49) 689750901
Fluid Air Cooler Mfr
N.A.I.C.S.: 333415

Hydac Drive Center GmbH (1)
Kiesgrable 13, 89129, Langenau, Germany
Tel.: (49) 7345933600
Hydraulic Equipment Mfr & Whslr
N.A.I.C.S.: 333995

Hydac Filtertechnik GmbH (1)
Industriegebiet, 66280, Sulzbach, Germany
Tel.: (49) 6897 509 01
Hydraulic Components Mfr
N.A.I.C.S.: 333998
John Duchowski *(Dir-Tech Dev)*

Hydac Fluidtechnik GmbH (1)
Justus-von-Liebig-Strasse, 66280, Sulzbach, Germany
Tel.: (49) 689750901
Fluid Coupling Mfr
N.A.I.C.S.: 332912

Hydac Oy (1)
Kisallintie 5, 01730, Vantaa, Finland
Tel.: (358) 10 773 7100
Web Site: http://www.hydac.fi
Hydraulic Component Distr
N.A.I.C.S.: 423830
Mikko Seppala *(Mgr-Production)*

Hydac Process Technology GmbH (1)
Industriegebiet Grube Konig, Am Wrangelfloz 1, 66538, Neunkirchen, Germany (100%)
Tel.: (49) 689750901
Web Site: http://www.hydac.com
Fluid Technology Product & Services
N.A.I.C.S.: 333996

Hydac Software GmbH (1)
Zum Kiesberg 16, 14979, Grossbeeren, Germany
Tel.: (49) 3370133894450
Hydraulic Product Mfr
N.A.I.C.S.: 334519

Hydac Systems & Services GmbH (1)
Friedrichsthaler Str 15, 66540, Neunkirchen, Germany
Tel.: (49) 689750901
Hydraulic Equipment Mfr & Whslr
N.A.I.C.S.: 333995

Hydac Technology Argentina S.rl. (1)
Av Belgrano 2729, Don Torcuato, B1611DVG, Buenos Aires, Argentina
Tel.: (54) 11 4727 1155
Hydraulic Components Mfr
N.A.I.C.S.: 333998

Hydac Technology GmbH (1)
Postfach 12 51, Industrial Area, 66280, Sulzbach, Germany
Tel.: (49) 689750901
Hydraulic Equipment Mfr & Whslr
N.A.I.C.S.: 333995

Hydac Technology Limited (1)
De Havilland Way Windrush Park, Witney, OX29 OYG, Oxfordshire, United Kingdom
Tel.: (44) 1993 866366
Web Site: http://www.hydac.com
Emp.: 120
Hydraulic Component Distr
N.A.I.C.S.: 423830
Darren Wait *(Mng Dir & Mgr-Sls)*

Hydac Technology Pte. Ltd. (1)
E-Town Building Mezzanine Floor Executive office Room 7 364, Cong Hoa Street Tan Binh District, Ho Chi Minh City, Vietnam
Tel.: (84) 88120545215
Hydraulic Equipment Mfr & Whslr
N.A.I.C.S.: 333995

Hydac d.o.o. (1)
Oreskoviceva 6c, 10000, Zagreb, Croatia
Tel.: (385) 14854270
Hydraulic Equipment Mfr & Whslr
N.A.I.C.S.: 333995

Hydac n.v. (1)
Overhaemlaan 33, 3700, Tongeren, Belgium
Tel.: (32) 12 260 400
Hydraulic Components Mfr
N.A.I.C.S.: 333998

Hydac spol. s r.o. (1)
Canadian 794, 39111, Plana, Czech Republic
Tel.: (420) 381201711
Hydraulic Equipment Mfr & Whslr
N.A.I.C.S.: 333995

Hydrosaar GmbH (1)
Hirschbachstrasse 7, 66280, Sulzbach, Germany
Tel.: (49) 68975099700
Hydraulic Equipment Mfr & Whslr
N.A.I.C.S.: 333995

Hyser C.A. (1)
Hidraulica y Servicios Los Pinos C C Tecina-Location 2 Zona Industrial, UD-304 Manzana Industrial Park 14-Parcela 06 Pto Ordaz Edo, Ciudad Guayana, 8050, Bolivar, Venezuela
Tel.: (58) 2869948581
Hydraulic Equipment Mfr & Whslr
N.A.I.C.S.: 333995

OOO HYDAC International (1)
st Smolnaya 14 9th floor room I room 13, 125493, Moscow, Russia
Tel.: (7) 4959808001
Web Site: http://www.hydac.com.ru
Hydraulic Component Distr
N.A.I.C.S.: 423830

PT. Hydac Technology Indonesia (1)
komplek pergudangan T8 No 27 29 Alam Sutera, Serpong, Tangerang, 15325, Selatan Banten, Indonesia
Tel.: (62) 2129211671
Web Site: http://www.hydac.co.id
Hydraulic Equipment Mfr & Whslr
N.A.I.C.S.: 333995

S.C. HYDAC SRL (1)
Soseaua Vestului nr 12 etaj 2, 100298, Ploiesti, Prahova, Romania
Tel.: (40) 244 575 778
Web Site: http://www.hydac.ro
Emp.: 15
Hydraulic Component Distr
N.A.I.C.S.: 423830
Daniela Enescu *(Gen Mgr)*

Saudi Gulf Hydraulics Co., Ltd. (1)
Road 190, PO Box 307, 2nd Industrial City 2, 11383, Riyadh, Saudi Arabia
Tel.: (966) 112651616
Web Site: http://www.saudigulfhydraulics.com
Hydraulic Equipment Mfr & Whslr
N.A.I.C.S.: 333995
Mohammed Ali *(Gen Mgr)*

Hydac International GmbH—(Continued)

HYDE'S DISTRIBUTION
6868 Kinsmen Court, Niagara Falls,
L2H 0Y5, ON, Canada
Web Site:
http://www.hydesdistribution.com
Year Founded: 2016
Miscellaneous Product Distr
N.A.I.C.S.: 423990
Gary Hyde (Pres)

Subsidiaries:

Zippo Canada Sales, LLC (1)
6868 Kinsman Ct, Niagara Falls, L2E 6V9,
ON, Canada
Tel.: (905) 358-3674
Web Site: http://www.zippo.ca
Sales Range: $25-49.9 Million
Emp.: 30
Mfr of Cigarette Lighters & Writing Instruments
N.A.I.C.S.: 339999
Don Grigor (Gen Mgr & Mgr-Adv)

HYDERABAD STOCK EXCHANGE LIMITED
6-3-654 Somajiguda, Hyderabad, 500
082, India
Tel.: (91) 4023371701
Web Site: http://www.hseindia.org
Stock Exchange Services
N.A.I.C.S.: 523210
B. R. Baskar Reddy (CEO)

HYDRACO INDUSTRIES INC.
2111 9th Ave SW, Medicine Hat, T1A
8M9, AB, Canada
Tel.: (403) 526-2244
Web Site: http://www.hydraco.com
Year Founded: 1985
Sales Range: $10-24.9 Million
Industrial Products Repair & Services
N.A.I.C.S.: 811198
Tim Galbraith (Gen Mgr)

HYDRACT A/S
Nybovej 34, 7500, Holstebro, Denmark
Tel.: (45) 61851000
Web Site: https://www.hydract.com
Year Founded: 2008
HYDRCT—(CSE)
Rev.: $949,137
Assets: $6,871,992
Liabilities: $2,616,421
Net Worth: $4,255,571
Earnings: ($1,990,079)
Emp.: 10
Fiscal Year-end: 12/31/23
Food Products Mfr
N.A.I.C.S.: 311813
Morten Lindberg (CFO)

HYDRATEC INDUSTRIES NV
Spoetnik 20, 3824 MG, Amersfoort,
Netherlands
Tel.: (31) 334697325
Web Site: https://www.hydratec.nl
Year Founded: 1919
HYDRA—(EUR)
Rev.: $305,699,331
Assets: $259,355,709
Liabilities: $166,447,226
Net Worth: $92,908,483
Earnings: $17,073,171
Emp.: 1,374
Fiscal Year-end: 12/31/22
Plastic Component Mfr & Distr
N.A.I.C.S.: 325211
Bart F. Aangenendt (CEO & Member-Exec Bd)

Subsidiaries:

Helvoet Rubber & Plastic Technologies BV (1)
Centaurusweg 146, 5015 TA, Tilburg, Netherlands

Tel.: (31) 135478600
Emp.: 800
Precision Component Mfr & Distr
N.A.I.C.S.: 333248
Herman Koks (Acct Mgr-Health Tech)

Subsidiary (Non-US):

Helvoet Rubber & Plastic Technologies NV (2)
Anton Philipsweg 4, 3920, Lommel, Belgium
Tel.: (32) 11548811
Precision Component Mfr & Distr
N.A.I.C.S.: 333248
Eric Germeys (Sr Acct Mgr)

Lan Handling Technologies BV (1)
Nieuwe Atelierstraat 9, Berkel-Enschot,
5056 DZ, Tilburg, Netherlands
Tel.: (31) 135322525
Web Site: https://www.lanhandling.com
Handling Product Mfr
N.A.I.C.S.: 332313

Plant (Domestic):

Lan Handling Technologies BV - Halfweg Factory (2)
Haarlemmerstraatweg 153 - 157, 1165 MK,
Halfweg, Netherlands
Tel.: (31) 20 407 2040
Web Site: https://www.lanhandling.com
Handling Product Mfr
N.A.I.C.S.: 332313
Wouter De Lange (Dir-Ops)

Pas Reform Hatchery Technologies BV (1)
Bovendorpsstraat 11, Zeddam, 7038 CH,
Montferland, Netherlands
Tel.: (31) 314659111
Web Site: http://www.pasreform.com
Poultry Hatchery Equipment Mfr
N.A.I.C.S.: 333111
Harm Langen (CEO)

Timmerije B.V. (1)
Schoolweg 29, 7161 PK, Neede, Netherlands
Tel.: (31) 545283800
Web Site: https://www.timmerije.nl
Injection Mould Component Mfr
N.A.I.C.S.: 333248
Pim Peeters (Controller)

HYDRAULIC ELEMENTS & SYSTEMS PLC
1 Pirin Str, 8600, Yambol, Bulgaria
Tel.: (359) 46661464
Web Site: https://www.hes.bg
Year Founded: 1968
HES—(BUL)
Sales Range: Less than $1 Million
Hydraulic Cylinder Mfr
N.A.I.C.S.: 339999

HYDRAULIC SPECIALISTS AUSTRALIA PTY. LTD.
9 National Drive, Hallam, 3803, VIC,
Australia
Tel.: (61) 397965433 AU
Web Site: http://www.hsaus.com.au
Year Founded: 1987
Sales Range: $10-24.9 Million
Hydraulic Equipment Mfr
N.A.I.C.S.: 333996
Tony Cheers (Mng Dir)

HYDRIX LIMITED
30-32 Compark Circuit, Mulgrave,
3170, VIC, Australia
Tel.: (61) 395508100 AU
Web Site: https://www.hydrix.com
Year Founded: 2002
HYD—(ASX)
Rev.: $7,155,629
Assets: $5,758,863
Liabilities: $7,999,177
Net Worth: ($2,240,313)
Earnings: ($6,382,780)
Emp.: 60
Fiscal Year-end: 06/30/24

Information Management Software Solutions
N.A.I.C.S.: 513210
Peter Lewis (Exec VP-Corp Dev)

HYDRO EXPLOITATION SA
Rue de l'Industrie 10, CP 750, 1951,
Sion, Switzerland
Tel.: (41) 273284411
Web Site: https://hydro.ch
Year Founded: 2002
MLHYE—(EUR)
Sales Range: $75-99.9 Million
Emp.: 500
Power Generation & Distribution Services
N.A.I.C.S.: 221111
P. Klopfenstein (Mgr)

HYDRO LITHIUM INC
744-27 moonhyung-ri, Gwangju,
464894, Gyonggi-do, Korea (South)
Tel.: (82) 314664822
Web Site: http://www.korease.co.kr
Year Founded: 1995
101670—(KRS)
Rev.: $8,805,840
Assets: $107,744,865
Liabilities: $65,415,051
Net Worth: $42,329,813
Earnings: ($2,600,843)
Emp.: 49
Fiscal Year-end: 12/31/22
Construction Materials Mfr
N.A.I.C.S.: 332999

HYDRO MOBILE INC.
125 de LIndustrie, L'Assomption,
J5W 2T9, QC, Canada
Tel.: (450) 589-8100
Web Site: http://www.hydro-mobile.com
Rev.: $14,345,917
Emp.: 110
Hydraulic Product Design & Mfr
N.A.I.C.S.: 333996
Vincent Dequoy (Pres)

HYDRO ONE LIMITED
483 Bay Street South Tower 8th
Floor, Toronto, M5G 2P5, ON,
Canada
Tel.: (416) 345-5000 Ca
Web Site: https://www.hydroone.com
Year Founded: 2015
H—(TSX)
Rev.: $5,651,973,000
Assets: $23,768,013,240
Liabilities: $15,197,353,560
Net Worth: $8,570,659,680
Earnings: $761,158,440
Emp.: 6,300
Fiscal Year-end: 12/31/21
Holding Company
N.A.I.C.S.: 551112
Mark Poweska (Pres & CEO)

Subsidiaries:

Hydro One Inc. (1)
483 Bay Street South Tower 8th Floor, Toronto, M5G 2P5, ON, Canada
Tel.: (416) 345-5000
Web Site: http://www.hydroone.com
Rev.: $7,493,276,800
Assets: $43,905,876,800
Liabilities: $27,735,326,400
Net Worth: $16,170,550,400
Earnings: $1,477,982,400
Emp.: 6,900
Fiscal Year-end: 12/31/2023
Electricity Transmission & Distribution; Telecommunications & Energy Services
N.A.I.C.S.: 221122
Chris Lopez (CFO & Exec VP)

Subsidiary (Domestic):

Alectra Utilities Corporation (2)
55 John Street North, Hamilton, L8R 3M8,
ON, Canada
Tel.: (905) 522-6611
Web Site: http://www.alectrautilities.com
Hydro Electric Power Generation & Distr
N.A.I.C.S.: 221111

Subsidiary (Domestic):

Alectra Inc. (3)
2185 Derry Road West, Mississauga, L5N
7A6, ON, Canada
Tel.: (905) 273-7425
Web Site: http://alectrautilities.com
Electricity Utility & Distr
N.A.I.C.S.: 221122

Enersource Technologies (3)
3240 Mavis Rd, Mississauga, L5C 3K1, ON,
Canada
Tel.: (905) 803-6467
Sales Range: $75-99.9 Million
Energy Solutions
N.A.I.C.S.: 221122

Subsidiary (Domestic):

Hydro One Networks, Inc. (2)
483 Bay St 10th Fl, Toronto, M5G 2P5, ON,
Canada (100%)
Tel.: (416) 345-5000
Web Site: http://www.hydroonenetwork.com
Sales Range: $1-4.9 Billion
Emp.: 1,500
Electricity Transmission & Distribution
N.A.I.C.S.: 221122

Hydro One Remote Communities Inc. (2)
680 Beaverhall Place, Thunder Bay, P7E
6G9, ON, Canada
Tel.: (807) 474-2837
Electricity Generation Services
N.A.I.C.S.: 237990

Hydro One Telecom Inc. (2)
65 Kelfield Street, Toronto, M9W 5A3, ON,
Canada
Tel.: (416) 345-6820
Web Site: http://www.hydroonetelecom.com
Broadband Telecommunication Services
N.A.I.C.S.: 517111
Mukul Sarin (VP-Fin, Regulatory, and Carrier Svcs)

HYDRO OTTAWA HOLDING INC.
2711 Hunt Club Road, PO Box 8700,
Ottawa, K1G 3S4, ON, Canada
Tel.: (613) 738-6400 ON
Web Site:
http://www.hydroottawa.com
Year Founded: 2000
Rev.: $901,754,225
Assets: $1,654,819,256
Liabilities: $1,278,312,759
Net Worth: $376,506,498
Earnings: $24,887,135
Emp.: 716
Fiscal Year-end: 12/31/19
Holding Company; Electric Power Generation & Distribution Services
N.A.I.C.S.: 551112
Bryce Conrad (Pres & CEO)

Subsidiaries:

Energy Ottawa Inc. (1)
2711 Hunt Club Road, PO Box 8700, Ottawa, K1G 3S4, ON, Canada (100%)
Tel.: (613) 225-0418
Web Site: http://portagepower.com
Sales Range: $75-99.9 Million
Emp.: 55
Hydroelectric Power Generation
N.A.I.C.S.: 221111

Hydro Ottawa Limited (1)
2711 Hunt Club Road, PO Box 8700, Ottawa, K1G 3S4, ON, Canada (100%)
Tel.: (613) 738-6400
Web Site: https://www.hydroottawa.com
Sales Range: $500-549.9 Million
Emp.: 545
Electricity Distr
N.A.I.C.S.: 221122

HYDRO POWER JOINT STOCK COMPANY
Nha Den Hamlet, Ea Po Commune, Cu Jut, DakNong, Vietnam
Tel.: (84) 5013684888
Web Site: https://www.pc3hp.com.vn
DRL—(HOSE)
Rev.: $4,343,469
Assets: $5,535,344
Liabilities: $701,677
Net Worth: $4,833,666
Earnings: $2,390,836
Fiscal Year-end: 12/31/23
Eletric Power Generation Services
N.A.I.C.S.: 221111

HYDRO-QUEBEC
75 Boulevard Rene-Levesque Ouest, Montreal, H2Z 1A4, QC, Canada
Tel.: (514) 289-2211
Web Site: http://www.hydroquebec.com
Year Founded: 1944
Rev.: $10,729,430,040
Assets: $60,119,550,120
Liabilities: $43,706,682,600
Net Worth: $16,412,867,520
Earnings: $2,236,796,520
Emp.: 16,977
Fiscal Year-end: 12/31/19
Public Utility; Energy Supplier
N.A.I.C.S.: 221111
Jean-Hugues Lafleur *(CFO & Exec VP)*

Subsidiaries:

HQ Energy Services (U.S.) Inc. (1)
225 Asylum St, Hartford, CT 06103
Tel.: (860) 241-4024
Electric Power Generation Services
N.A.I.C.S.: 221118

HYDRO-QUEBEC INDUSTECH INC (1)
1000 Sherbrooke Street West 16th Floor, Montreal, H3A 3G4, QC, Canada
Tel.: (514) 289-6800
Electric Motor Mfr
N.A.I.C.S.: 335312

Subsidiary (Domestic):

TM4 INC. (2)
135 J-A Bombardier Bureau 25, Boucherville, J4B 8P1, QC, Canada
Tel.: (450) 645-1444
Web Site: http://www.tm4.com
Electric & Hybrid Drivetrain Mfr
N.A.I.C.S.: 335312

Hydro-Quebec International (1)
Jean-Lesage bldg 75 Rene-Levesque Blvd W, Montreal, H2Z 1A4, QC, Canada (100%)
Tel.: (514) 385-7252
N.A.I.C.S.: 221310

Societe d'energie de la Baie James (1)
800 boul de Maisonneuve Est ste 1100, Montreal, H2L 4L8, QC, Canada (100%)
Tel.: (514) 286-2020
Web Site: http://www.hydroquebec.com
Sales Range: $25-49.9 Million
Emp.: 100
Services for Engineering & Construction Projects in the Energy Industry
N.A.I.C.S.: 541330

HYDROCARBON DYNAMICS LIMITED
Level 6 412 Collins Street, Melbourne, 3000, VIC, Australia
Tel.: (61) 396422899
Web Site: https://www.hcdinvestor.com
HCD—(ASX)
Rev.: $236,383
Assets: $2,493,991
Liabilities: $116,302
Net Worth: $2,377,689
Earnings: ($1,127,018)
Fiscal Year-end: 12/31/22
Crude Petroleum Extraction Services
N.A.I.C.S.: 211120
Nicholas Castellano *(Exec Dir)*

HYDRODEC GROUP PLC
76 Brook Street, London, W1K 5EE, United Kingdom
Tel.: (44) 1292 471444 UK
Web Site: http://www.hydrodec.com
Rev.: $15,016,000
Assets: $41,366,000
Liabilities: $16,793,000
Net Worth: $24,573,000
Earnings: ($13,681,000)
Emp.: 34
Fiscal Year-end: 12/31/18
Holding Company; Petroleum & Chemical Process Technology Developer, Mfr, Distr & Services
N.A.I.C.S.: 551112
Christopher John Ellis *(CEO)*

Subsidiaries:

Hydrodec Australia Pty. Ltd. (1)
Level 20 Tower A The Zenith 821 Pacific Highway, Chatswood, 2067, NSW, Australia (100%)
Tel.: (61) 263825387
Web Site: http://www.hydrodec.com
Sales Range: $25-49.9 Million
Emp.: 50
Petroleum & Chemical Process Technology Developer, Mfr, Distr & Services
N.A.I.C.S.: 333248

Hydrodec Development Corporation Pty Limited (1)
90 Old Temora Road, Young, 2594, NSW, Australia
Tel.: (61) 263825387
Web Site: http://www.hydrodec.com.au
Oil Refining Services
N.A.I.C.S.: 213112

Hydrodec North American Holdings Inc (1)
2021 Steinway Blvd SE, Canton, OH 44707
Tel.: (330) 454-8202
Web Site: http://www.hydrodec.com
Emp.: 35
Petroleum Refineries Services
N.A.I.C.S.: 324110

Subsidiary (Domestic):

Hydrodec North America LLP (2)
2021 Steinway Blvd SE, Canton, OH 44707
Tel.: (330) 454-8202
Web Site: http://www.hydrodec.com
Oil Treatment Services
N.A.I.C.S.: 562219

HYDROELECTRICITY INVESTMENT & DEVELOPMENT COMPANY LTD.
4th Floor Nagarik Lagani Kosh Bhawan New Baneshwor, Kathmandu, Nepal
Tel.: (977) 14595016
Web Site: https://www.hidcl.org.np
Year Founded: 1911
HIDCL—(NEP)
Rev.: $9,758,188
Assets: $150,630,924
Liabilities: $13,819,530
Net Worth: $136,811,394
Earnings: $5,828,593
Fiscal Year-end: 07/15/21
Hydroelectric Power Generation Services
N.A.I.C.S.: 221111
Dinesh Kumar Ghimire *(Chm & Sec)*

HYDROGEN GROUP PLC
30 Eastcheap, London, EC3M 1HD, United Kingdom
Tel.: (44) 207 002 0000
Web Site: http://www.hydrogengroup.com
Rev.: $159,070,848
Assets: $50,312,976
Liabilities: $19,569,072
Net Worth: $30,743,904
Earnings: $1,705,080
Emp.: 345
Fiscal Year-end: 12/31/19
Executive Recuiting Services
N.A.I.C.S.: 541612
Ian Temple *(Founder & CEO)*

Subsidiaries:

Argyll Scott Hong Kong Ltd. (1)
Unit 1005 10/F World-Wide House 19 Des Voeux Road, Central, China (Hong Kong)
Tel.: (852) 36955180
Web Site: http://www.argyllscott.com.hk
Staffing & Recruiting Services
N.A.I.C.S.: 561311

Argyll Scott International (Singapore) Ltd. (1)
Unit 03-118 We Work City House 36 Robinson Road, Singapore, 068877, Singapore
Tel.: (65) 67978365
Web Site: http://www.argyllscott.sg
Staffing & Recruiting Services
N.A.I.C.S.: 561311
Tom Swain *(Mng Dir)*

Argyll Scott Malaysia Sdn Bhd (1)
Level 9 Menara Binjai, 50450, Kuala Lumpur, Malaysia
Tel.: (60) 321749000
Web Site: http://www.argyllscott.my
Staffing & Recruiting Services
N.A.I.C.S.: 561311
Tristan Bullworthy *(COO)*

Argyll Scott Recruitment (Thailand) Ltd. (1)
No 188 Spring Tower 11th Floor Unit 101 Phayathai Road, Thung Phaya Thai Subdistrict Ratchathewi District, Bangkok, 10400, Thailand
Tel.: (66) 21072560
Web Site: http://www.argyllscott.co.th
Staffing & Recruiting Services
N.A.I.C.S.: 561311
Chris Russell *(Mng Dir)*

Hydrogen Group Pty. Limited (1)
Level 2 383 George Street, Sydney, 2000, NSW, Australia
Tel.: (61) 291617118
Staffing & Recruiting Services
N.A.I.C.S.: 561311

Hydrogen Group Sdn. Bhd. (1)
Level 9-04 Menara Binjai No 2 Jalan Binjai, Kuala Lumpur, 50450, Malaysia
Tel.: (60) 321749000
Staffing & Recruiting Services
N.A.I.C.S.: 561311

Hydrogen International Limited (1)
Pountney Hill Ho 6, Laurence Pountney Hill, London, EC4R 0BL, United Kingdom
Tel.: (44) 2079291800
Sales Range: $25-49.9 Million
Emp.: 250
Labor Recruitment Services
N.A.I.C.S.: 561311
Tim Smeaton *(CEO)*

Hydrogen UK Limited (1)
Pountney Hill House, 6 Laurence Pountney Hill, London, EC4R 0BL, United Kingdom
Tel.: (44) 2078454200
Web Site: http://www.hydrogengroup.eu
Sales Range: $75-99.9 Million
Labour Recruitment & Personnel Services
N.A.I.C.S.: 561311

HYDROGEN REFUELING SOLUTIONS SA
ZAC of Saut du Moine, Champ-sur-Drac, 38560, Grenoble, France
Tel.: (33) 476140778
Web Site: https://www.hydrogen-refueling-solutions.fr
Year Founded: 2004
ALHRS—(EUR)
Hydrogen Fuel Mfr
N.A.I.C.S.: 325120
Hassen Rachedi *(Chm)*

HYDROGEN UTOPIA INTERNATIONAL PLC
c/o Laytons LLP 3rd Floor Pinners Hall 105-108 Old Broad Street, London, EC2N 1ER, United Kingdom
Tel.: (44) 2038118770 UK
Web Site: https://www.hydrogenutopia.eu
Year Founded: 2020
HUI—(LSE)
Assets: $5,091,439
Liabilities: $856,747
Net Worth: $4,234,692
Earnings: ($1,883,733)
Emp.: 7
Fiscal Year-end: 12/31/22
Waste Management Services
N.A.I.C.S.: 562998
Aleksandra Binkowska *(Founder)*

HYDROGENE DE FRANCE SA
35 rue Jean Duvert, Lormont, 33290, Blanquefort, France
Tel.: (33) 335567711111 FR
Web Site: https://www.hdf-energy.com
Year Founded: 2012
HDF—(EUR)
Renewable Energy Services
N.A.I.C.S.: 221210
Anne Jallet-Auguste *(Sec)*

HYDROGENONE CAPITAL GROWTH PLC
6th Floor 125 London Wall, London, EC2Y 5AS, United Kingdom UK
Web Site: https://www.hydrogenonecapital.com
Year Founded: 2021
HGEN—(LSE)
Rev.: $4,134,057
Assets: $158,427,165
Liabilities: $193,133
Net Worth: $158,234,032
Earnings: $1,961,626
Fiscal Year-end: 12/31/22
Asset Management Services
N.A.I.C.S.: 523999
Simon Hogan *(Chm)*

HYDROGENPRO A.S.
Hydrovegen 55, 3936, Porsgrunn, Norway
Tel.: (47) 99079500 NO
Web Site: https://www.hydrogen-pro.com
Year Founded: 2013
HYPRO—(OSL)
Rev.: $5,210,974
Assets: $52,943,285
Liabilities: $12,501,940
Net Worth: $40,441,345
Earnings: ($8,296,601)
Emp.: 144
Fiscal Year-end: 12/31/22
Electric Power Distribution Services
N.A.I.C.S.: 221111

HYDROGRAPH CLEAN POWER INC.
1 King Street W Suite 4800 118, Toronto, M5H 1A1, ON, Canada
Tel.: (604) 220-3120 BC
Web Site: https://www.hydrograph.com
Year Founded: 2017
HG—(CNSX)
Rev.: $5,099
Assets: $7,938,735
Liabilities: $452,348
Net Worth: $7,486,387
Earnings: ($2,982,512)
Fiscal Year-end: 09/30/22
Eletric Power Generation Services
N.A.I.C.S.: 221115
Bob Wowk *(CFO)*

HYDROKIT

HydroGraph Clean Power Inc.—(Continued)

HYDROKIT
19 rue du Bocage La Ribotiere,
85170, Le Poire-sur-Vie, France
Tel.: (33) 251344528
Web Site: http://www.hydrokit.com
Year Founded: 1980
Sales Range: $10-24.9 Million
Emp.: 120
Industrial Machinery & Vehicle Mfr
N.A.I.C.S.: 336320
Claude Bonnaud *(Pres)*

Subsidiaries:

Hydrokit UK LTD (1)
Units 12 & 13 Yew Tree Courtyard, Earl Soham, Woodbridge, IP137SG, Suffolk, United Kingdom
Tel.: (44) 1728684800
Industrial Machinery & Equipment Distr
N.A.I.C.S.: 423830
Dave Freeman *(Mgr-Sls)*

Rau Serta Hydraulik GmbH (1)
Heimenwiesen 60, 73230, Kirchheim, Germany
Tel.: (49) 7021 7377 0
Web Site: http://www.rauserta-hydraulik.de
Industrial Machinery & Equipment Distr
N.A.I.C.S.: 423830

HYDROMELIORACIE AS
ul SNP c 3, Kalna nad Hronom, 935 32, Levice, Slovakia
Tel.: (421) 366312709 Sk
Year Founded: 1992
1HML01AE—(BRA)
Sales Range: Less than $1 Million
Financial Banking Services
N.A.I.C.S.: 522110

HYDROMET CORPORATION LIMITED
201 Five Islands Road, Unanderra, Sydney, 2526, NSW, Australia
Tel.: (61) 242472100
Web Site:
  http://www.hydromet.com.au
Sales Range: $25-49.9 Million
Emp.: 50
Recycling & Waste Disposal Technologies & Services; Chemical Mfr & Sales
N.A.I.C.S.: 562998
Jeremy Perera *(Gen Mgr)*

Subsidiaries:

Hydromet Corporation Pty Limited - Southern, NSW (1)
201 Five Islands Road, PO Box 42, Unanderra, 2526, NSW, Australia
Tel.: (61) 242711822
Web Site: http://www.hydromet.com.au
Sales Range: $10-24.9 Million
Emp.: 35
Collecting & Recycling Contaminant Metal Wastes from Smelters & Industrial Manufacturers
N.A.I.C.S.: 562219
Jeremy Perera *(Gen Mgr)*

Hydromet Operations Limited (1)
3 Five Islands Road, Unanderra, 2526, NSW, Australia
Tel.: (61) 242711092
Waste Treatment & Disposal Services
N.A.I.C.S.: 562211

Minmet Operations Pty Limited (1)
25 School Dr, Tomago, 2322, NSW, Australia
Tel.: (61) 242711822
Sales Range: $25-49.9 Million
Emp.: 3
Waste Treatment & Disposal Services
N.A.I.C.S.: 562219
Jeremy Perera *(Dir)*

HYDROTECH COMPANY LTD.
68-3 Seongseo- Ro Galsan-Dong, Dalsu-Gu, Daegu, Korea (South)

Tel.: (82) 535938468 KR
Web Site: http://www.hydrotech.kr
Year Founded: 2003
Gear Pump Mfr
N.A.I.C.S.: 333996
Park Su-Chul *(Pres)*

HYDROTEK PUBLIC COMPANY LIMITED
1TP and T Tower 14th Floor Soi Vibhavadee-Rangsit 19, Chatuchak, Bangkok, 10900, Thailand
Tel.: (66) 29361661
Web Site: https://www.hydrotek.co.th
Year Founded: 1982
HYDRO—(THA)
Rev.: $2,245,379
Assets: $10,800,360
Liabilities: $10,203,566
Net Worth: $596,794
Earnings: ($2,093,499)
Emp.: 34
Fiscal Year-end: 12/31/23
Environmental & Waste Management Services
N.A.I.C.S.: 562998
Somprasong Panjalak *(Chm)*

Subsidiaries:

SUT Global Company Limited (1)
128/200 Phayathai Plaza Building 30th J Village No 6 Phayathai r, Thung Phayathai Ratcha Thewi, Bangkok, Thailand
Tel.: (66) 2 129 3303
Web Site: https://www.sutglobal.co.th
Engineeering Services
N.A.I.C.S.: 541330

HYDSOFT TECHNOLOGY CO., LTD.
33rd Floor Building 2 EFC Cangqian street, Yuhang District, Hangzhou, 311100, Zhejiang, China
Tel.: (86) 57186505079
Web Site: https://www.hydsoft.com
Year Founded: 2009
301316—(CHIN)
Rev.: $166,218,156
Assets: $183,213,576
Liabilities: $44,002,764
Net Worth: $139,210,812
Earnings: $12,546,144
Fiscal Year-end: 12/31/22
Information Technology Services
N.A.I.C.S.: 541512
Bin Liu *(COO)*

HYDUKE ENERGY SERVICES INC.
110 3903-75 Avenue, Leduc, T9E 0K3, AB, Canada
Tel.: (780) 955-0355 AB
Web Site: http://www.hyduke.com
Rev.: $17,709,788
Assets: $8,753,435
Liabilities: $9,868,405
Net Worth: ($1,114,971)
Earnings: ($7,426,091)
Emp.: 34
Fiscal Year-end: 12/31/18
Oil Field Equipment & Supplies Mfr, Repair, Sales & Services
N.A.I.C.S.: 333132
Patrick F. Ross *(Pres & CEO)*

Subsidiaries:

Canwest Crane & Equipment Ltd. (1)
9305 - 27 Avenue, Edmonton, T6N 1C9, AB, Canada
Tel.: (780) 463-8688
Sales Range: $25-49.9 Million
Emp.: 28
Truck-Mounted Equipment Sales & Service
N.A.I.C.S.: 423850

Hyduke Building Solutions (1)
2107 6th Street, Nisku, T9E 7X5, AB, Canada
Tel.: (780) 955-0360
Sales Range: $10-24.9 Million
Emp.: 50
Oilfield Service Equipment Welding & Fabrication Services
N.A.I.C.S.: 213112

Hyduke Drilling Solutions Inc (1)
2107 6th St, Nisku, T9E 7X8, AB, Canada
Tel.: (780) 955-0360
Web Site: http://www.hyduke.com
Drilling Equipment Mfr.
N.A.I.C.S.: 333132

Hyduke Energy Services Inc. - Big Rig Sandblasting, Painting and Repair Division (1)
8224 Sparrow Cres, Leduc, T9E 8B7, AB, Canada
Tel.: (780) 986-8683
Sales Range: $25-49.9 Million
Emp.: 4
Automotive Painting & Repair Services
N.A.I.C.S.: 811121
Bob Belseth *(Gen Mgr)*

Hyduke Energy Services Inc. - Hyduke Design & Engineering Division (1)
609 - 21 Ave, Nisku, T9E 7X9, AB, Canada
Tel.: (780) 955-0355
Sales Range: $25-49.9 Million
Emp.: 30
Oil Field Machinery Mfr
N.A.I.C.S.: 333132

Hyduke Energy Services Inc. - Hyduke Mechanical & Machining Division (1)
2311-8th St, Nisku, T9E 7Z3, AB, Canada
Tel.: (780) 955-9559
Industrial Machinery Mfr
N.A.I.C.S.: 333248

Hyduke Machining Solutions Inc. (1)
2915 15 Street Northeast, Calgary, T2E 7L8, AB, Canada
Tel.: (403) 250-5322
Web Site: http://www.hyduke.com
Sales Range: $25-49.9 Million
Emp.: 40
Mfr & Fabrication Services
N.A.I.C.S.: 332999

T&T Inspections & Engineering Ltd. (1)
609 - 21 Avenue, Nisku, T9E 7X9, AB, Canada
Tel.: (780) 955-9688
Web Site: http://www.ttinspections.com
Sales Range: $25-49.9 Million
Emp.: 12
Oil Rig Asset Inspection & Certification Services
N.A.I.C.S.: 561499

HYFLUX LTD
Hyflux Innovation Centre 80 Bendemeer Road, Singapore, 339949, Singapore
Tel.: (65) 62140777 SG
Web Site: http://www.hyflux.com
Year Founded: 2000
600—(SES)
Sales Range: $250-299.9 Million
Emp.: 2,500
Water Recycling Services
N.A.I.C.S.: 325998
Suat Wah Lim *(CFO & Grp Exec VP)*

Subsidiaries:

Eflux Singapore Pte Ltd (1)
202 Kallang Bahru Hyflux Building, Singapore, 339339, Singapore
Tel.: (65) 62140777
Waste Management Services
N.A.I.C.S.: 562920

Hydrochem (S) Pte Ltd (1)
202 Kallang Bahru Hyflux Building, Singapore, 339339, Singapore
Tel.: (65) 6214 0777
Water Treatment Equipment Mfr
N.A.I.C.S.: 333310

INTERNATIONAL PUBLIC

Hydrochem Engineering (S) Pte Ltd (1)
202 Kallang Bahru Hyflux Building, Singapore, 339339, Singapore
Tel.: (65) 62140777
Water Desalination Plant Construction Services
N.A.I.C.S.: 237110

Hydrochem Engineering (Shanghai) Co., Ltd. (1)
No 99 Juli Road Zhangjiang High-Tech Park, Pudong New District, Shanghai, 201203, China
Tel.: (86) 2150803082
Water Desalination Plant Construction Services
N.A.I.C.S.: 237110

Hyflux (Malaysia) Sdn Bhd (1)
Unit A5 1 Level 5 Block A Bangunan Pan Global No 1A Jalan Tandang, 46050, Petaling Jaya, Selangor, Malaysia
Tel.: (60) 377857085
Water Treatment Equipment Mfr
N.A.I.C.S.: 333310

Hyflux Consumer Products Pte. Ltd. (1)
Hyflux Bldg 202 Kallang Bahru, Singapore, 339339, Singapore
Tel.: (65) 62140777
Web Site: http://www.hyfluxconsumer.com
Water Treatment Equipment Mfr
N.A.I.C.S.: 333310

Hyflux Engineering (India) Pvt Ltd (1)
Unit 7A & 7B Doshi Towers 156 Poonamallee High Road, Kilpauk, Chennai, 600010, Tamil Nadu, India
Tel.: (91) 4445428888
Water Treatment Equipment Mfr
N.A.I.C.S.: 333310

Hyflux Lifestyle Products (India) Pvt Ltd (1)
2nd Floor Hari Krupa 71/1 McNicholas Road, Chennai, 600 031, Chetput, India
Tel.: (91) 4442867101
Water Purification Equipment Mfr
N.A.I.C.S.: 333310

Hyflux Membrane Manufacturing (S) Pte.Ltd (1)
80 Bendemeer Road Hyflux Innovation Centre, Singapore, 339949, Singapore
Tel.: (65) 6214 0777
Web Site: http://www.hyfluxmembranes.com
Water Treatment Equipment Mfr
N.A.I.C.S.: 333310

Hyflux NewSpring Construction Engineering (Shanghai) Co., Ltd (1)
No 99 Juli Road Zhangjiang High Tech Park, Pudong New District, Shanghai, 201203, China
Tel.: (86) 2150805118
Web Site: http://www.hyflux.com
Construction Engineering Services
N.A.I.C.S.: 541330

Hyflux Water Trust Management Pte Ltd (1)
Hyflux Innovation Centre 80 Bendemeer Rd, Singapore, 339949, Singapore
Tel.: (65) 6214 0777
Web Site: http://www.hyfluxwatertrust.com
Trust Management Services
N.A.I.C.S.: 525920

Kunshan Eco Water Systems Co., Ltd (1)
483 San Xiang Road Kunshan Economic & Technical Development Zone, Kunshan, 215335, Jiangsu, China
Tel.: (86) 257026555
Water Treatment Equipment Mfr
N.A.I.C.S.: 333310

Tianjin Dagang NewSpring Co. (1)
No 1999 Tianjin Manifold Road South, Dagang District, Tianjin, 300161, China
Tel.: (86) 22 23398585
Water Desalination Plant Construction Services
N.A.I.C.S.: 237110

AND PRIVATE COMPANIES

HYFUSIN GROUP HOLDINGS LTD.
2nd Floor Aberdeen Marina Tower 8 Shum Wan Road, Aberdeen, China (Hong Kong)
Tel.: (852) 25690312   Ky
Web Site: http://hyfusingroup.com
8512—(HKG)
Rev.: $105,137,144
Assets: $62,295,147
Liabilities: $19,672,803
Net Worth: $42,622,344
Earnings: $13,697,289
Emp.: 1,400
Fiscal Year-end: 12/31/21
Decorative Product Mfr & Distr
N.A.I.C.S.: 339999
Wai Chit Wong *(Chm & Compliance Officer)*

HYGEIA HEALTHCARE HOLDINGS COMPANY LIMITED
Suites 702-707 Enterprise Square No 228 Meiyuan Road, Jing'an District, Shanghai, China   Ky
Web Site: https://www.hygeia-group.com.cn
Year Founded: 2009
6078—(HKG)
Rev.: $564,449,490
Assets: $1,486,287,522
Liabilities: $620,249,363
Net Worth: $866,038,159
Earnings: $94,836,619
Emp.: 8,238
Fiscal Year-end: 12/31/23
Health Care Srvices
N.A.I.C.S.: 621610
Yiwen Zhu *(Vice Chm)*

HYGGE INTEGRATED BRANDS CORP.
1 Yonge Street Unit 1801, Toronto, M5E 1W7, ON, Canada
Tel.: (416) 214-3656   NV
Web Site: http://www.myhyggehound.com
Year Founded: 2018
Rev.: $1,989
Assets: $21,797
Liabilities: $68,417
Net Worth: ($46,620)
Earnings: ($32,546)
Emp.: 1
Fiscal Year-end: 05/31/20
Pet Care Product Distr
N.A.I.C.S.: 459910
Elena Krioukova *(Chm, Pres, CEO, CFO, Principal Acctg Officer, Treas & Sec)*

HYGIANIS SPA
18 Rue Hamdani Lahcen Coop Mohamed Boudiaf Sidi Yahia, 16405, Algiers, Algeria
Tel.: (213) 21436034   DG
Web Site: https://hygianis-dz.com
Year Founded: 2003
Hygiene Products Distr
N.A.I.C.S.: 322291

Subsidiaries:

Can Hygiene SPA   (1)
Haouch Sbaat Nord Zone Industrielle Lot 83B Voie H, PO Box 36, Rouiba, 16012, Algiers, Algeria
Tel.: (213) 23864130
Disposable Baby Diaper Mfr
N.A.I.C.S.: 322291

HYGIEIA GROUP LIMITED
6 Tagore Drive B1-02, Singapore, 787623, Singapore
Tel.: (65) 62504328   Ky
Web Site: https://www.hygieiagroup.com
Year Founded: 1991
1650—(HKG)
Rev.: $50,396,122
Assets: $33,685,526
Liabilities: $10,892,221
Net Worth: $22,793,305
Earnings: $359,767
Emp.: 2,464
Fiscal Year-end: 12/31/23
Holding Company
N.A.I.C.S.: 551112
Eng Kui Toh *(Founder & Chm)*

Subsidiaries:

Eng Leng Thailand Co., Ltd.   (1)
90/103 Village No 15, Bangkaew Subdistrict Bangplee District, Samut Prakan, 10540, Thailand
Tel.: (66) 20494328
Web Site: https://www.englengthailand.com
Cleaning Service
N.A.I.C.S.: 561720

Titan Facilities Management Pte. Ltd.   (1)
6 Tagore Drive B1-03, Singapore, 787623, Singapore
Tel.: (65) 64593420
Web Site: http://www.titanfmpl.com
Cleaning Service
N.A.I.C.S.: 561720
Alan Toh *(CEO)*

HYGON INFORMATION TECHNOLOGY CO. LTD.
Floor 4-5 Tower C Qianfang Building Building 27, No 8 Dongbei Wangxi Road Haiding District, Beijing, China
Tel.: (86) 01082826550   CN
Web Site: https://www.hygon.cn
Year Founded: 2014
688041—(SHG)
Rev.: $832,410,141
Assets: $3,171,043,974
Liabilities: $357,558,097
Net Worth: $2,813,485,877
Earnings: $174,897,347
Fiscal Year-end: 03/31/24
Processors, Accelerators & Other Computing Chip Products Research & Development
N.A.I.C.S.: 334118
Meng Xiantang *(Chm)*

HYGROVEST LIMITED   AU
HGV—(ASX)
Rev.: $800,620
Assets: $14,620,835
Liabilities: $1,790,211
Net Worth: $12,830,624
Earnings: ($87,474)
Fiscal Year-end: 06/30/24
Cannabis Investment Holding Company
N.A.I.C.S.: 551112
Jim Hallam *(CFO & Sec)*

Subsidiaries:

Delivra Health Brands Inc.   (1)
Suite 404 999 Canada Place, Vancouver, V6C 3E2, BC, Canada   **(59.96%)**
Tel.: (604) 449-9280
Web Site: https://www.delivrahealthbrands.com
Rev.: $9,048,937
Assets: $7,348,515
Liabilities: $3,551,441
Net Worth: $3,797,074
Earnings: $640,400
Emp.: 22
Fiscal Year-end: 06/30/2024
Holding Company; Cannabis Cultivation & Products Distr
N.A.I.C.S.: 551112
Frank Holler *(Chm)*

Subsidiary (Domestic):

Delivra Corp.   (2)
347 Grays Road, Hamilton, L8E 2Z1, ON, Canada
Tel.: (905) 561-5014
Web Site: http://www.delivracorp.com
Rev.: $3,703,489
Assets: $2,432,184
Liabilities: $2,534,985
Net Worth: ($102,801)
Earnings: ($1,999,558)
Fiscal Year-end: 12/31/2018
Investment Services
N.A.I.C.S.: 523999
Joseph Gabriele *(Chm, CEO & Chief Science Officer)*

Subsidiary (US):

Sarpes Beverages, LLC   (2)
20185 NE16 Pl 2nd Fl, Miami, FL 33179
Tel.: (305) 792-7900
Web Site: http://www.drinkdreamwater.com
Specialty Sleep Aid Bottled Water Mfr & Whslr
N.A.I.C.S.: 312112
Andrew Garven *(VP-Mktg)*

Subsidiary (Non-US):

Satipharm AG   (2)
Riedstrasse 7, 6330, Cham, Switzerland
Tel.: (41) 1223790034
Web Site: http://www.satipharm.com
Cannabis-Based Medicinal Products Mfr
N.A.I.C.S.: 325411
Stanislav Sologubov *(CEO)*

Subsidiary (Domestic):

United Greeneries Ltd.   (2)
5250 Mission Rd, Duncan, V9L 6V2, BC, Canada
Tel.: (236) 889-8271
Web Site: https://www.unitedgreeneries.ca
Cannabis Cultivator & Distr
N.A.I.C.S.: 111998
Daniela Vaschi *(CEO)*

HYLANDS INTERNATIONAL HOLDINGS INC.
1701 Union Plaza 20 ChaoWai Avenue, ChaoYang District, Beijing, 100020, China
Tel.: (86) 01065884188   BC
Web Site: http://www.neweramineralsinc.com
Year Founded: 2007
NEM—(TSXV)
Sales Range: Less than $1 Million
Metal Mining
N.A.I.C.S.: 212290
Tian Xiang Sun *(Chm & CEO)*

HYLINK DIGITAL SOLUTION CO., LTD.
15th Floor Building E No 6 Gongyuan West Street, Dongcheng District, Beijing, 100005, China
Tel.: (86) 1085135025
Web Site: http://www.hylinkad.com
Year Founded: 1994
603825—(SHG)
Rev.: $1,194,004,099
Assets: $881,686,391
Liabilities: $664,387,191
Net Worth: $217,299,200
Earnings: ($90,782,121)
Emp.: 3,400
Fiscal Year-end: 12/31/22
Digital Agency Services
N.A.I.C.S.: 541870
Feng Kangjie *(Chm)*

HYLORIS PHARMACEUTICALS SA
Boulevard Patience et Beaujonc N 3/1, 4000, Liege, Belgium
Tel.: (32) 43460207   BE
Web Site: https://www.hyloris.com
Year Founded: 2012
HYL—(EUR)
Rev.: $3,624,536
Assets: $75,983,839
Liabilities: $8,375,369
Net Worth: $67,608,471
Earnings: ($13,228,145)
Emp.: 37
Fiscal Year-end: 12/31/22
Pharmaceutical Product Mfr & Distr
N.A.I.C.S.: 325412
Jean Luc Vandebroek *(CFO)*

HYLTON GROUP LTD.
Everoak Est Bromyard, Worcester, WR2 5HW, United Kingdom
Tel.: (44) 1905 748282
Web Site: http://www.hylton.co.uk
Sales Range: $25-49.9 Million
Emp.: 170
Car Dealership Owner & Operator
N.A.I.C.S.: 441110
Louise Bourne *(Mgr-Mktg)*

Subsidiaries:

Hylton Cheltenham   (1)
MacKenzie Way Manor Road, Cheltenham, GL51 9TX, United Kingdom   **(100%)**
Tel.: (44) 1242222400
Sales Range: $25-49.9 Million
Emp.: 30
New & Used Automotive Sales & Services
N.A.I.C.S.: 441110

Hylton of Worcester   (1)
Everoak Est Bromyard Rd, Worcester, WR2 5HW, United Kingdom   **(100%)**
Tel.: (44) 905748282
Web Site: http://www.Hylton.com
Sales Range: $25-49.9 Million
Emp.: 50
Vehicle Motor Retailing
N.A.I.C.S.: 441110

HYMETAL CONSTRUCTION PRODUCTS CO., LTD.
155 Shuhui Road, Songjiang District, Shanghai, China
Tel.: (86) 21 51870366
Web Site: http://www.hymetal.com.cn
Building Components Mfr
N.A.I.C.S.: 444180

HYMSON LASER TECHNOLOGY GROUP CO LTD
Building B Comron Science and Technology Park Guansheng 5th Road, Longhua District, Shenzhen, Guangdong, China
Tel.: (86) 75528197985
Web Site: https://global.hymson.com
Year Founded: 2008
688559—(SHG)
Rev.: $576,400,336
Assets: $1,245,276,494
Liabilities: $959,038,887
Net Worth: $286,237,608
Earnings: $53,408,357
Fiscal Year-end: 12/31/22
Automation Equipment Mfr
N.A.I.C.S.: 334512
Shengyu Zhao *(Chm & Gen Mgr)*

Subsidiaries:

Anshan Hymson Science & Technology Co., Ltd.   (1)
No 1 Section A Anshan High-tech Zone, Laser Industrial Park, Liaoning, China
Tel.: (86) 4125294008
Water Equipment Mfr
N.A.I.C.S.: 334510

Guangzhou Hymson Laser Co., Ltd.   (1)
103 No 2 Shiling Rd, Dongchong Town, Nansha District, Guangzhou, Guangdong, China
Tel.: (86) 2039004644
Water Equipment Mfr
N.A.I.C.S.: 334510

Hymson (Jiangmen) Laser Intelligent Equipments Co., Ltd.   (1)
No 18 Jintong 8th Road, Pengjiang District, Jiangmen, Guangdong, China
Tel.: (86) 4008043288
Web Site: https://www.hymsonlaser.net
Water Equipment Mfr

HYMSON LASER TECHNOLOGY GROUP CO LTD

Hymson Laser Technology Group Co Ltd—(Continued)
N.A.I.C.S.: 334510

Hymson Laser Intelligent Equipments (Jiangsu) Co., Ltd. (1)
No 66 Jintan Rd, Jintan District, Changzhou, Jiangsu, China
Tel.: (86) 51982990888
Water Equipment Mfr
N.A.I.C.S.: 334510

HYNAR WATER GROUP CO., LTD.

Floor 19 Block B Building 6 Shenzhen International Innovation Valley, Xili Community Dashi Dashi 1st Road Xili Street Nanshan District, Shenzhen, 518052, Guangdong, China
Tel.: (86) 75526969307
Web Site: http://www.hainawater.com
Year Founded: 2001
300961—(SSE)
Rev: $69,858,828
Assets: $359,775,000
Liabilities: $211,477,500
Net Worth: $148,297,500
Earnings: ($171,288)
Fiscal Year-end: 12/31/22
Water Supply Services
N.A.I.C.S.: 221310
Haibo Li (Chm & Gen Mgr)

HYNION AS

Sandviksveien 17, 1363, Hovik, Norway
Tel.: (47) 22448000   NO
Web Site: https://www.hynion.com
Year Founded: 2019
HYN—(OSL)
Rev: $427,832
Assets: $3,304,911
Liabilities: $911,796
Net Worth: $2,393,116
Earnings: ($2,976,176)
Emp.: 6
Fiscal Year-end: 12/31/23
Hydrogen Fuel Mfr
N.A.I.C.S.: 325120
Lars Amnell (Chm)

HYOKI KAIUN KAISHA LTD.

3-6-1 Minatojima, Chuo-ku, Kobe, 650-0045, Hyogo, Japan
Tel.: (81) 789402351
Web Site: https://www.hyoki.co.jp
Year Founded: 1942
9362—(TKS)
Rev: $138,821,850
Assets: $96,594,700
Liabilities: $66,394,700
Net Worth: $30,200,000
Earnings: $3,337,100
Fiscal Year-end: 03/31/23
Marine Freight Transportation Services
N.A.I.C.S.: 483111
Yoji Ohigashi (Pres)

HYON AS

Stromso Torg 4, 3044, Drammen, Norway
Tel.: (47) 98259775
Web Site: https://www.knox-energy.com
Year Founded: 2017
HYON—(EUR)
Rev: $47,901
Assets: $3,166,252
Liabilities: $409,316
Net Worth: $2,756,937
Earnings: ($2,423)
Emp.: 9
Fiscal Year-end: 12/31/22
Hydrogen Fuel Mfr
N.A.I.C.S.: 325120
Harald Bjorn Hansen (COO)

HYOSUNG ADVANCED MATERIALS CO., LTD.

119 Mapo-daero Gongdeok-dong, Mapo-gu, Seoul, 04144, Korea (South)
Tel.: (82) 27076114
Web Site: https://www.hyosungmaterials.com
Year Founded: 2018
298050—(KRS)
Rev: $2,946,332,957
Assets: $2,250,925,238
Liabilities: $1,637,664,628
Net Worth: $613,260,610
Earnings: $96,135,845
Emp.: 951
Fiscal Year-end: 12/31/22
Automotive Carpet Mfr
N.A.I.C.S.: 314110

Subsidiaries:

Hyosung Goodsprings, Inc. (1)
119 Mapo-daero, Mapo-gu, Seoul, Korea (South)
Tel.: (82) 232798240
Web Site: http://www.hsgoodsprings.com
Pumps Mfr
N.A.I.C.S.: 333914
Abhijeet Kadam (Engr-Design)

Hyosung Tns Inc. (1)
119 Mapo-daero Gongdeok-dong, Mapo-gu, Seoul, 04144, Korea (South)
Tel.: (82) 27076114
Web Site: http://www.hyosungmaterials.com
Yarn Mfr
N.A.I.C.S.: 313110
Jungmo Hwang (CEO)

HYOSUNG CAPITAL CO., LTD.

21 22nd Floor Merits Tower 825-2 Yeoksam-Dong, Kangnam-gu, Seoul, 135-280, Korea (South)
Tel.: (82) 2 2018 0700
Web Site: http://www.hyosung-capital.co.kr
Year Founded: 1997
Financial Factoring Services
N.A.I.C.S.: 522299
Kim Yong-Deok (CEO)

HYOSUNG CORPORATION

119 Mapo-daero, Mapo-gu, Seoul, 4144, Korea (South)
Tel.: (82) 27077114
Web Site: https://www.hyosung.com
Year Founded: 1962
004800—(KRS)
Rev: $2,852,722,676
Assets: $4,040,007,381
Liabilities: $1,817,774,734
Net Worth: $2,222,232,646
Earnings: $19,027,114
Emp.: 655
Fiscal Year-end: 12/31/22
Synthetic Fiber Products, Specialty Chemicals, Packing Materials & Industrial Machinery Mfr & Developer
N.A.I.C.S.: 313110
Hyun-Joon Cho (Chm)

Subsidiaries:

Beijing Computer Technology Co., Ltd. (1)
No 202 Lizezhongyuan, Wangzing, Beijing, 100102, Chaoyang, China
Tel.: (86) 64392551
Sales Range: $25-49.9 Million
Emp.: 20
N.A.I.C.S.: 315210

Beijing Hyosung Container Co., Ltd. (1)
26 Yong Chang North St BDA, Beijing, 100176, China (100%)
Tel.: (86) 1067885551
Web Site: http://www.hyosung.com
N.A.I.C.S.: 315210

Forza Motors Korea Corporation (1)
456 Dosan-daero, Gangnam-gu, Seoul, 06062, Korea (South)
Tel.: (82) 234330808
Web Site: https://www.seoul.ferraridealers.com
New & Used Car Dealer
N.A.I.C.S.: 441110
In Su Jo (CEO)

Galaxia Device Co., Ltd. (1)
Gosaekdong 967, Gwonseongu, Suwon, Kyungkido, Korea (South)
Tel.: (82) 31 548 9800
Web Site: http://www.galaxiadevice.com
Electronic Component Mfr & Distr
N.A.I.C.S.: 334419

Galaxia Electronics Co., Ltd. (1)
50 Omokcheon-ro 132beon-gil, Gwonseon-gu, Suwon, 16642, Gyeonggi-do, Korea (South)
Tel.: (82) 3180608976
Web Site: https://eng.galaxialed.com
Light Emitting Diode Particle Mfr
N.A.I.C.S.: 334413

Hyosung (America), Inc. (1)
5 Penn Plz Ste 2347, New York, NY 10001
Tel.: (212) 896-3967
Web Site: www.hyosung.com
Sales Range: $25-49.9 Million
Emp.: 15
Mfr & Developer of Synthetic Fiber Products
N.A.I.C.S.: 424990
Scott Hackl (Exec VP-Sls-North America)

Hyosung (H.K.) Ltd. (1)
1918 19 Fl Mirama Tower 132 Naphan Rd, Tsim Tsa Tsui, China (Hong Kong) (100%)
Tel.: (852) 28456778
Web Site: http://www.hyosung.com
Sales Range: $25-49.9 Million
Emp.: 20
N.A.I.C.S.: 315210
C. Park Sun (Mng Dir)

Hyosung Chemicals (Jiaxing) Co., Ltd. (1)
Sales Range: $25-49.9 Million
Emp.: 100
Chemical Products Mfr
N.A.I.C.S.: 325199

Hyosung Chemicals Gumi Plant I (1)
108 3 Gongdan2-ro, 39404, Gumi, Gyeongbuk, Korea (South)
Tel.: (82) 544709171
Web Site: http://www.hyosungchemical.com
Sales Range: $15-24.9 Billion
Emp.: 80,000
Mfr of PET Films
N.A.I.C.S.: 322220

Hyosung Computer Performance Unit (1)
52 Cheongdam-dong, Gangnam-gu, Seoul, 137 100, Korea (South) (100%)
Tel.: (82) 25100200
Sales Range: $200-249.9 Million
Emp.: 800
N.A.I.C.S.: 315210

Hyosung Construction Performance Unit (1)
9 Myeongdai-ro Seocho-gu, Seoul, 137-850, Korea (South) (100%)
Tel.: (82) 2 707 6114
Web Site: http://www.hyosungtown.co.kr
Sales Range: $100-124.9 Million
Emp.: 400
Residential, Commercial, Engineering, Redevelopment Services
N.A.I.C.S.: 236220
S.R. Cho (Chm)

Hyosung Corporation - Anyang Plant (1)
74 Simindaero, Dongan-gu, 14080, Anyang, Gyeonggi, Korea (South)
Tel.: (82) 31 428 1000
Web Site: http://www.hyosung.com
Textile Products Mfr
N.A.I.C.S.: 314999

Hyosung Corporation - Daegu Plant (1)
45 55-gil Seongseogongdan-ro, Dalseo-gu, 42701, Daegu, Korea (South)
Tel.: (82) 53 589 7084
Web Site: http://www.hyosung.com

INTERNATIONAL PUBLIC

Fiber Textile Products Mfr
N.A.I.C.S.: 314999

Hyosung Corporation - Daejeon Plant (1)
49-1 Munpyeong-dong Daedeok, Daejeon, 306-220, Korea (South)
Tel.: (82) 42 932 6187
Web Site: http://www.hyosung.com
Textile Fiber Products Mfr
N.A.I.C.S.: 314999
Yong-Tae Kim (Mgr)

Hyosung Corporation - Gwanghyewon Plant (1)
313 Jukhyeon-ri Gwanghyewon-myeon, Jincheon, Chungcheongbuk-do, Korea (South)
Tel.: (82) 43 530 1600
Packaging Materials Mfr
N.A.I.C.S.: 322220

Hyosung Corporation - Icheon Plant (1)
188-2 Namjeong-ri Sindun-myeon, Icheon, 467-842, Gyeonggi, Korea (South)
Tel.: (82) 31 634 0669
Web Site: http://www.hyosung.com
Textile Fiber Products Mfr
N.A.I.C.S.: 314999

Hyosung Corporation - Jincheon Plant (1)
274-3 Mundeok-ri Munbaek-myeon, Jincheon, 365-862, Chungbuk, Korea (South)
Tel.: (82) 43 530 7715
Web Site: http://www.hyosung.com
Textile Fiber Products Mfr
N.A.I.C.S.: 314999

Hyosung Corporation - Jochiwon Plant (1)
518 Yeongi-ri Nam-myeon, Yeongi, 339-828, Chungnam, Korea (South)
Tel.: (82) 97266105
Industrial Equipment Mfr
N.A.I.C.S.: 333248

Hyosung Corporation - Kwanghaewon Plant (1)
313 Jukhyeon-Ri Kwanghaewon-Myeon, Jincheon, Korea (South)
Tel.: (82) 43 530 1600
Textile Fiber Products Mfr
N.A.I.C.S.: 314999

Hyosung Corporation - Ulsan Plant (1)
30 Nabdoro, Nam-gu, 44781, Ulsan, Korea (South)
Tel.: (82) 52 278 7000
Web Site: http://www.hyosung.com
Textile Fiber Products Mfr
N.A.I.C.S.: 314999

Hyosung Corporation - Yangsan Plant (1)
872-1 Bukjeong-dong, Yangsan, 626-110, Gyeongnam, Korea (South)
Tel.: (82) 55 387 7165
Web Site: http://www.hyosung.com
Textile Fiber Products Mfr
N.A.I.C.S.: 314999

Hyosung Corporation - Yongyeon Plant 1 (1)
186 Seongam-dong, Nam-gu, Ulsan, 680-140, Korea (South)
Tel.: (82) 52 279 2014
Web Site: http://www.hyosung.com
Textile Fiber Products Mfr
N.A.I.C.S.: 314999

Hyosung Corporation - Yongyeon Plant 3 (1)
529 Yongyeon-dong, Nam-gu, Ulsan, 680150, Korea (South)
Tel.: (82) 52 279 0408
Textile Fiber Products Mfr
N.A.I.C.S.: 314999

Hyosung Corporation Bangkok (1)
Rm 1404 14th Fl Pacific Phase 1 142 Sukhumvit Rd, Bangkok, Thailand (100%)
Tel.: (66) 26532031
Web Site: http://www.hyosung.co.kr
Sales Range: $25-49.9 Million
Emp.: 4
N.A.I.C.S.: 315210

Hyosung Corporation Beijing (1)
Room No 501 5F Scitech Tower No 22 Jian

HYOSUNG CORPORATION

AND PRIVATE COMPANIES

Guo Men Wai Street, Beijing, 100004, China **(100%)**
Tel.: (86) 10 6512 9692
Web Site: http://www.hyosung.com
Sales Range: $25-49.9 Million
Emp.: 30
Clothing Mfr
N.A.I.C.S.: 315210
Mon Koihyok *(Mgr-Sls)*

Hyosung Corporation Dubai (1)
Office No 804 Green Tower Riggat Al Buteen Street, PO Box 15287, Deira, Dubai, United Arab Emirates **(100%)**
Tel.: (971) 42218483
Sales Range: $25-49.9 Million
Emp.: 11
N.A.I.C.S.: 315210
S K Sohn *(Gen Mgr)*

Hyosung Corporation Education Center (1)
183 Hogye Dong Dongan gu, 431 080, Anyang, Gyeonggi, Korea (South)
Tel.: (82) 314281250
Sales Range: $25-49.9 Million
Emp.: 12
Mfr & Developer of Synthetic Fiber Products
N.A.I.C.S.: 315250

Hyosung Corporation Guangzhou (1)
Unit 818 South Tower World Trade Center Complex, 371 375 Huanshidong Lu, Guangzhou, 510095, China **(100%)**
Tel.: (86) 2087787988
Web Site: http://www.hyosung.co.kr
Sales Range: $25-49.9 Million
N.A.I.C.S.: 315210

Hyosung Corporation Ho Chi Minh (1)
Floor 7 Room 06 Vincom Center B 72 Le Thanh Ton, Ben Nghe ward District 1, Ho Chi Minh City, Vietnam
Tel.: (84) 88251617
Web Site: http://www.hyosung.co.kr
Sales Range: $25-49.9 Million
Emp.: 5
N.A.I.C.S.: 315210

Hyosung Corporation Istanbul (1)
Buyukdere Caddesi Noramin Is Merkezi NO 237 Kat 3, Daire 301 Maslak, Istanbul, Turkiye **(100%)**
Tel.: (90) 2122841601
Web Site: http://www.hyosung.co.kr
Sales Range: $25-49.9 Million
Emp.: 8
N.A.I.C.S.: 315210

Hyosung Corporation Kaohsiung (1)
7F 6 No 251 Min Chuan First Rd, Kaohsiung, 800, Taiwan **(40%)**
Tel.: (886) 72262021
Sales Range: $25-49.9 Million
Emp.: 4
N.A.I.C.S.: 315210

Hyosung Corporation Kuala Lumpur (1)
Suite 23-01 Level 23 Wisma Goldhill No 67 Jalan Raja Chulan, 50200, Kuala Lumpur, Malaysia **(100%)**
Tel.: (60) 320312416
Web Site: http://www.hyosung.com
Sales Range: $25-49.9 Million
Emp.: 5
N.A.I.C.S.: 315210
Liching Hoh *(Mgr-Sls)*

Hyosung Corporation Manila (1)
11/F Unit 1112 Ayala Tower 1 Ayala Triangle Ayala Avenue, Makati, Philippines
Tel.: (63) 28486204
Web Site: http://www.hyosung.co.kr
Sales Range: $25-49.9 Million
Emp.: 5
N.A.I.C.S.: 315210
Yong Wan Kim *(Gen Mgr)*

Hyosung Corporation Mexico (1)
Paseo de Tamarindos 90 Torre 1 Piso10 Col Bosques de las Lomas, Mexico, 05120, Mexico **(100%)**
Tel.: (52) 5552502790
Web Site: http://www.hyosung.co.jp
Sales Range: $25-49.9 Million
Emp.: 7
Mfr & Developer of Synthetic Fiber Products
N.A.I.C.S.: 315250

Hyosung Corporation Moscow (1)
D105 Park Place Leninsky Prospect 113/1, Moscow, Russia **(100%)**
Tel.: (7) 4959565142
Web Site: http://www.hyosung.ru
Sales Range: $25-49.9 Million
Emp.: 10
N.A.I.C.S.: 315210

Hyosung Corporation Panama (1)
International Business Center Piso 8, Ave Manuel Espinosa Bantista Bella Vista Apdo, 0819-06390, Panama, Panama **(100%)**
Tel.: (507) 2148968
Web Site: http://www.hyosung.co.kr
Sales Range: $25-49.9 Million
Emp.: 4
Mfr & Developer of Synthetic Fiber Products
N.A.I.C.S.: 325220

Hyosung Corporation Shanghai (1)
Rm 1115 Shangai International Trading Ctr No 2200, Yan An Xi Rd, Shanghai, 200336, China **(100%)**
Tel.: (86) 2162090123
Web Site: http://www.hyosung.com
Sales Range: $25-49.9 Million
Emp.: 30
N.A.I.C.S.: 315210

Hyosung Corporation Taipei (1)
1714 17/F International Trade Building No 333 Sec1 Keelung Road, Taipei, 110, Taiwan **(100%)**
Tel.: (886) 227584636
Web Site: http://www.hyosung.com.tw
Sales Range: $25-49.9 Million
Emp.: 13
N.A.I.C.S.: 315210
D. Kang *(Branch Mgr)*

Hyosung Corporation Tehran Liaison Office (1)
Apt 7&9 Building 9 4th Street, Ahmad Ghassir Ave, Tehran, Iran
Tel.: (98) 212058381
Web Site: http://www.hyosung.co.jp
N.A.I.C.S.: 315210

Hyosung Do Brasil (1)
Av Eng Luis Carlos Berrini 1297 Conj 142, Brooklin Edificio Sudameris, Sao Paulo, Brazil **(100%)**
Tel.: (55) 1151854200
Web Site: http://www.hyosung.com
Sales Range: $25-49.9 Million
Emp.: 30
Mfr & Developer of Synthetic Fiber Products
N.A.I.C.S.: 325220
Hyun Ho Tong *(Mgr)*

Hyosung EBARA Engineering Co., Ltd.
7th Floor Bangbae Building 1006-2 Bangbae-Dong, Soecho-Gu, Seoul, Korea (South)
Tel.: (82) 57485060
Web Site: http://www.heec.co.kr
Sales Range: $50-74.9 Million
Emp.: 230
Water Treatment Plant Construction Services
N.A.I.C.S.: 237110

Hyosung Ebara Co., Ltd. (1)
(67%)
Sales Range: $25-49.9 Million
Emp.: 40
Mfr & Sales of Pumps; Joint Venture of Ebara Corporation & Hyosung Corporation
N.A.I.C.S.: 333914

Hyosung Ebara Environmental Engineering Co. Ltd. (1)
183 Hoge Dong Dongan Gu, Kyunggi, 430 080, Anyang, Korea (South) **(100%)**
Tel.: (82) 27075872
Web Site: http://www.heec.co.kr
Sales Range: $50-74.9 Million
Emp.: 200
N.A.I.C.S.: 315210

Hyosung Europe S.R.L. (1)
Via Del Tecchione 34, 20098, San Giuliano Milanese, Italy
Tel.: (39) 029886251
Electronic Components Mfr
N.A.I.C.S.: 334419

Hyosung Holdings USA, Inc. (1)
15801 Brixham Hill Ave Ste 575, Charlotte, NC 28277
Tel.: (704) 790-6100
Holding Company; Tire Cord Fabric Mills Operator
N.A.I.C.S.: 551112
Kei Ho Lee *(Pres)*

Subsidiary (Domestic):

HICO America Sales & Technology, Inc. (2)
3 Penn Ctr W Ste 300, Pittsburgh, PA 15276-0101
Tel.: (412) 787-1170
Web Site: https://www.hicoamerica.com
Sales Range: $25-49.9 Million
Emp.: 30
Power Transformer Mfr & Distr
N.A.I.C.S.: 335311
Henry Paik *(Pres)*

Hyosung USA, Inc. (2)
15801 Brixham Hill Ave Ste 575, Charlotte, NC 28277
Tel.: (704) 790-6100
Web Site: http://www.hyosungusa.com
Tire Cord Fabric Mills Operator
N.A.I.C.S.: 314994
Kei Ho Lee *(Pres)*

Plant (Domestic):

Hyosung USA, Inc. - Decatur Plant (3)
500 19th Ave SE, Decatur, AL 35601
Tel.: (256) 353-7461
Web Site: http://www.hyosungusa.com
Emp.: 40
Tire Cord Fabric Mfr
N.A.I.C.S.: 314994
John Gorman *(Plant Mgr)*

Branch (Domestic):

Hyosung USA, Inc. - Los Angeles Office (3)
910 Columbia St, Brea, CA 92821
Tel.: (714) 989-8900
Web Site: http://www.hyosungusa.com
Emp.: 20
Tire Cord Fabric Whslr
N.A.I.C.S.: 424990

Subsidiary (Domestic):

Nautilus Hyosung America, Inc. (2)
6641 N Beltline Rd Ste 100, Irving, TX 75063
Tel.: (972) 350-7600
Web Site: http://www.nhatm.com
Sales Range: $50-74.9 Million
Emp.: 80
Automatic Teller Machine Distr
N.A.I.C.S.: 423420
Joe Militello *(VP-Engrg)*

Hyosung Industrial PG (1)
450 Gongdeok Dong Mapo-gu, Seoul, Korea (South)
Tel.: (82) 27077000
Web Site: http://www.hyosungetara.co.kr
Sales Range: $1-4.9 Billion
Emp.: 3,588
Transformers, Electric Motors, Pumps, Circuit Breakers & Gear Reducers Mfr & Exporter
N.A.I.C.S.: 334416

Hyosung Information Systems Co., Ltd. (1)
(100%)
Tel.: (82) 25100300
Web Site: http://www.his21.co.kr
Sales Range: $25-49.9 Million
Emp.: 100
N.A.I.C.S.: 315210

Hyosung International (HK) Ltd. (1)
Suite 3510 Tower 6 The Gateway 9 Canton Road, Kowloon, China (Hong Kong)
Tel.: (852) 28456778
Emp.: 20
Electronic Components Mfr
N.A.I.C.S.: 334419
Yong-Tae Kim *(Mng Dir)*

Hyosung International Trade (Jiaxing) Co., Ltd. (1)
Textile & Fiber Products Mfr

N.A.I.C.S.: 313310

Hyosung Japan (1)
SVAX TT Bldg 6F 11-15 3-Chome Toranomon, Minato Ku, Tokyo, Japan
Tel.: (81) 334321005
Web Site: http://www.hyosung.com
Fabrics Mfr
N.A.I.C.S.: 313310

Branch (Domestic):

Hyosung Japan Osaka (2)
Sun Mullion NBF Tower 2-6-12 Minamihonmachi, Chuo Ku, Osaka, Japan
Tel.: (81) 6 6253 3500
Web Site: http://www.hyosung.co.jp
Sales Range: $25-49.9 Million
Fabrics Mfr
N.A.I.C.S.: 315250
Toshiyuki Hasegawa *(Pres)*

Hyosung Luxembourg S.A. (1)
6 Rue de L'Industrie, 7737, Colmar-Berg, Luxembourg
Tel.: (352) 26817 601
Web Site: http://www.hyosunglux.com
Sales Range: $25-49.9 Million
Emp.: 200
Textile Products Mfr
N.A.I.C.S.: 314999

Hyosung Media Co., Ltd. (1)
630 Kupo-dong,, 730-400, Kumi, Kyungbuk, Korea (South)
Tel.: (82) 5464672114
N.A.I.C.S.: 315210

Hyosung R&DB Labs (1)
74 Simin-daero, Dongan-gu, 14080, Anyang, Gyunggi-do, Korea (South)
Tel.: (82) 31 428 1000
Web Site: http://www.research.hyosung.co.kr
Research & Development of Synthetic Fiber Products
N.A.I.C.S.: 325220

Hyosung Singapore Pte. Ltd. (1)
5 Temasek Boulevard 08-03 Suntec Tower Five, Singapore, 038985, Singapore **(100%)**
Tel.: (65) 63372079
Web Site: http://www.hyosung.co.kr
Sales Range: $25-49.9 Million
Emp.: 6
N.A.I.C.S.: 315210
Y. S. Jung *(Gen Mgr)*

Hyosung Spandex (Guangdong) Co., Ltd. (1)
Textile Products Mfr
N.A.I.C.S.: 314999

Hyosung Spandex (Jiaxing) Co., Ltd. (1)
Spandex Fiber Mfr
N.A.I.C.S.: 325220

Hyosung Steel Cord (Qingdao) Co., Ltd. (1)
No 15 Huanghe West Road, Qingdao Economic and Development Zone, Qingdao, Shandong, China
Tel.: (86) 53286839020
Steel Cord Mfr & Distr
N.A.I.C.S.: 331222

Hyosung Taegu Business Center (1)
103 6 Dongsan Dong Chung Gu, Daegu, 700 310, Korea (South) **(100%)**
Tel.: (82) 534269800
Mfr & Developer of Synthetic Fiber Products
N.A.I.C.S.: 313320

Hyosung Technical Research Institute (1)
450 Gongdeok-Dong Mapo-Gu, 121720, Seoul, Korea (South) **(100%)**
Tel.: (82) 27075800
Web Site: http://www.hyosung.com
Mfr & Developer of Synthetic Fiber Products
N.A.I.C.S.: 325220
Paul Lee *(Mgr-Mktg)*

Hyosung Trading Performance Group (1)
235 Banpo-daero Banpo-dong, Seocho-gu, Seoul, Korea (South) **(100%)**
Tel.: (82) 27077114
Web Site: http://www.trade.hyosung.com

3551

HYOSUNG CORPORATION

Hyosung Corporation—(Continued)
Sales Range: $10-24.9 Million
Emp.: 45
Provider of Trading Services
N.A.I.C.S.: 561990

Hyosung Trans-World Co., Ltd. (1)
3F A Block 92 Mapo-daero, Mapo-Gu
Dohwa-dong Hyosung Harrington Square,
04168, Seoul, Korea (South)
Tel.: (82) 27078709
Web Site:
  http://www.hyosungtransworld.com
Sales Range: $25-49.9 Million
Emp.: 5
Freight Forwarding Services
N.A.I.C.S.: 488510
Song Sung Jin *(CEO)*

Hyosung Wire Luxembourg S.A. (1)
6 Rue De l'industrie, 7759, Rost, Luxembourg
Tel.: (352) 26818
Sales Range: $100-124.9 Million
Emp.: 300
Fiber Wire Mfr
N.A.I.C.S.: 332618

**Hysoung Investment &
Development** (1)
450 Kongduk Dong, Mapo Gu, Seoul,
121020, Korea (South) **(100%)**
Tel.: (82) 27077000
Web Site: http://www.hyosung.com
Real Estate Lessor
N.A.I.C.S.: 531190

KIS-BANK Inc. (1)
Tel.: (82) 220261502
Web Site: http://www.kisbank.co.kr
Commercial Banking Services
N.A.I.C.S.: 522110

Myanmar Hyosung Co., Ltd. (1)
Condo F Rm-304 Kaba Aye Villa Residence
Mayangone Township, Yangon, Myanmar
Tel.: (95) 1660927
Web Site: http://www.hyosung.co.kr
N.A.I.C.S.: 315210

Nautilus Hyosung, Ltd. (1)
52 Cheongdam Dong, Kangnam Gu, Seoul,
135 100, Korea (South) **(100%)**
Tel.: (82) 25100200
Web Site: http://www.nautilus.hyosung.com
Sales Range: $200-249.9 Million
Emp.: 800
Data Systems for Transportation Co.
N.A.I.C.S.: 517810
Hyun Sik Sohn *(CEO)*

Sumiden Hyosung Steel Cord (Thailand) Co., Ltd. (1)
54 Sukhumvit 21 Road Asoke, Wattana,
Bangkok, 10110, Thailand
Tel.: (66) 22607092
Automotive Steel Tire Cord Mfr & Distr
N.A.I.C.S.: 336390

Zhangjiagang Xiao-sha Coil Service Co., Ltd. (1)
North of Yangjiang Rd, Jinfeng Town,
Zhangjiagang, Jiangsu, China
Sales Range: $25-49.9 Million
Emp.: 70
Rolled Steel Mfr
N.A.I.C.S.: 331221

HYOSUNG HEAVY INDUSTRIES CORP.
119 Mapo-daero, Mapo-gu, Seoul,
04144, Korea (South)
Tel.: (82) 27076000
Web Site:
  https://www.hyosungindustries.com
Year Founded: 1962
Engineering & Contrustruction Services
N.A.I.C.S.: 237990
Takeshi Yokota *(CEO)*

Subsidiaries:

Mitsubishi Electric Power Products, Inc. (1)
Thorn Hill Industrial Pk 530 Keystone Dr,
Warrendale, PA 15086
Tel.: (724) 772-2555
Web Site: http://www.meppi.com
Sales Range: $75-99.9 Million
Emp.: 430
Provides High Voltage Power Circuit Breakers & Gas Insulates Substations for the
Electric Utility Industry
N.A.I.C.S.: 335313
Tricia Breeger *(Pres & CEO)*

Subsidiary (Domestic):

Computer Protection Technology, Inc. (2)
1537 Simpson Way, Escondido, CA 92029
Tel.: (760) 745-8562
Web Site: http://www.cptups.com
Sales Range: $1-9.9 Million
Emp.: 24
Electrical Contractor
N.A.I.C.S.: 238210
June Murphy *(VP & Sec)*

Division (Domestic):

**Diamond Vision Systems
Division** (2)
530 Keystone Dr, Warrendale, PA 15086
Tel.: (724) 772-2555
Web Site: http://www.meppi.com
Sales Range: $25-49.9 Million
Emp.: 40
Mfr of Full-Color Outdoor Video Display Systems
N.A.I.C.S.: 423990

Subsidiary (Domestic):

Mitsubishi Wireless Communications, Inc. (2)
5665 Plaza Dr, Cypress, CA 90630-0007
Web Site: http://www.mitsubishiwireless.com
Distr of Digital Wireless Telephones
N.A.I.C.S.: 423690

HYOSUNG ITX CO., LTD.
15th floor 57 Seonyu dong 2 ro,
Yeongdeungpo-gu, Seoul, Korea
(South)
Tel.: (82) 221028400
Web Site:
  https://www.hyosungitx.com
Year Founded: 1997
094280—(KRS)
Rev.: $392,141,498
Assets: $135,619,971
Liabilities: $85,190,828
Net Worth: $50,429,143
Earnings: $11,444,723
Emp.: 8,201
Fiscal Year-end: 12/31/22
Business Outsourcing Services
N.A.I.C.S.: 561439
Kyeong Hwan Nam *(CEO)*

Subsidiaries:

Galaxia Moneytree Co. Ltd. (1)
15F Suseo Bldg 715, Suseo-dong
Gangnam-gu, Seoul, 06349, Korea (South)
Tel.: (82) 215660123
Web Site:
  https://www.galaxiamoneytree.co.kr
Financial Payment Services
N.A.I.C.S.: 522320

HYOSUNG ONB CO, LTD
46 Yuseong-daero 1596beon-gil,
Yuseong-gu, Daejeon, Korea (South)
Tel.: (82) 426247613
Web Site: https://www.hsonb.com
Year Founded: 1984
097870—(KRS)
Rev.: $31,304,011
Assets: $77,848,845
Liabilities: $10,807,584
Net Worth: $67,041,260
Earnings: $3,524,794
Emp.: 81
Fiscal Year-end: 06/30/22
Organic Fertilizer Mfr
N.A.I.C.S.: 325314
Tai Hurn Park *(Chm & CEO)*

Subsidiaries:

**Hyosung ONB Co, Ltd - Asan
Factory** (1)
1785 Oncheon-daero, Asan, Chungcheong,
Korea (South)
Tel.: (82) 415458116
Organic Fertilizer Mfr
N.A.I.C.S.: 325314

**Hyosung ONB Co, Ltd - Cheongdo
Factory** (1)
49-17 Maejeonsinchon-gil, Cheongdo-gun,
Maejon, North Gyeongsang, Korea (South)
Tel.: (82) 543711728
Organic Fertilizer Mfr
N.A.I.C.S.: 325314

**Hyosung ONB Co, Ltd - Euisung
Factory** (1)
40-17 Yongyeon 1-gil, Euisung,
Gyeongsangbuk-do, Korea (South)
Tel.: (82) 548337613
Organic Fertilizer Mfr
N.A.I.C.S.: 325314

**Hyosung ONB Co, Ltd - Hampyeong
Factory** (1)
85-23 Jukjeong-ri, Hakgyo, Jeonnam, Korea
(South)
Tel.: (82) 61 323 4088
Organic Fertilizer Mfr
N.A.I.C.S.: 325314

**Hyosung ONB Co, Ltd - Sri Lanka
Factory** (1)
Welihena South, Kochchikade, Colombo,
Sri Lanka
Tel.: (94) 312276111
Organic Fertilizer Mfr
N.A.I.C.S.: 325314

HYOSUNG TNC CO. LTD.
119 Mapo-daero, Mapo-gu, Seoul,
04144, Korea (South)
Tel.: (82) 27077114
Web Site: https://www.hyosung.com
298020—(KRS)
Rev.: $6,813,053,653
Assets: $3,313,347,433
Liabilities: $2,150,940,787
Net Worth: $1,162,406,646
Earnings: $8,890,570
Emp.: 1,497
Fiscal Year-end: 12/31/22
Textile Products Mfr
N.A.I.C.S.: 314999
Yong-seup Kim *(CEO)*

Subsidiaries:

**Hyosung Brasil Industria E Comercio
De Fibras Ltda.** (1)
BR 101 Km 69, Bairro Rainha, Araquari,
89245-000, Santa Catarina, Brazil
Tel.: (55) 4730259600
Fabric Product Mfr & Distr
N.A.I.C.S.: 313310

Hyosung Dong Nai Co., Ltd. (1)
N3 street, Nhon Trach 5 Industrial Zone,
Nhon Trach, Dong Nai, Vietnam
Tel.: (84) 2519811500
Tire Cord Fabric Mfr
N.A.I.C.S.: 314994

Hyosung India Pvt. Ltd. (1)
Plot No 1 Sector 11 Auric City, Auric City
Shendra, Aurangabad, 431007, Maharashtra, India
Tel.: (91) 1244012255
Fabric Product Mfr & Distr
N.A.I.C.S.: 313310

**Hyosung Mexico City S.A. de
C.V.** (1)
Paseo de Tamarindos 90 Torre 1 Piso 10,
Col Bosques de las Lomas, 5120, Mexico,
Mexico
Tel.: (52) 5552502790
Fabric Product Mfr & Distr
N.A.I.C.S.: 313310

**Hyosung New Material & HighTech
(Quzhou) Co., Ltd.** (1)
No 10 Xiaoxing Road National high and
New Technology Development Zone, Qu-
zhou, ZheJiang, China
Tel.: (86) 5708051100
Fabric Product Mfr & Distr
N.A.I.C.S.: 313310

**Hyosung Spandex (Quzhou) Co.,
Ltd.** (1)
No 8 Xiaoxing Road National high and New
Technology Development Zone, Quzhou,
ZheJiang, China
Tel.: (86) 5708051100
Fabric Product Mfr & Distr
N.A.I.C.S.: 313310

**Hyosung Spandex (Zhuhai) Co.,
Ltd.** (1)
Air Port Road, Haicheng Industrial Area
Sanzao Jinwan, Zhuhai, Guangdong, China
Tel.: (86) 7567785800
Fabric Product Mfr & Distr
N.A.I.C.S.: 313310

**Hyosung TNC (Taiwan)
Corporation** (1)
1714 17/F International Trade Building No
333 Sec1 Keelung Road, Taipei, 110, Taiwan
Tel.: (886) 227584636
Fabric Product Mfr & Distr
N.A.I.C.S.: 313310

Some Sevit Corporation (1)
2085-14 Olympic-daero, Seocho-gu Banpo-
dong, Seoul, Korea (South)
Tel.: (82) 15663433
Web Site: https://www.somesevit.com
Restaurant Services
N.A.I.C.S.: 722511
Yeon-ho Kim *(Mgr)*

HYPCO
19 Cours du Prince Imperial, 20090,
Ajaccio, Corse, France
Tel.: (33) 8 99 697397
Rev.: $15,100,000
Emp.: 55
Grocery Stores
N.A.I.C.S.: 445110
Pascal Taliercio *(Dir)*

HYPEBEAST LIMITED
10/F KC100 100 Kwai Cheong Road,
Kwai Chung, New Territories, China
(Hong Kong)
Tel.: (852) 35639035 Ky
Web Site: http://www.hypebeast.ltd
0150—(HKG)
Rev.: $86,959,864
Assets: $75,012,833
Liabilities: $28,419,711
Net Worth: $46,593,122
Earnings: $9,103,924
Emp.: 363
Fiscal Year-end: 03/31/21
Marketing Communication Services
N.A.I.C.S.: 541810
Kevin Pak Wing Ma *(Chm & CEO)*

HYPEFACTORS A/S
Kronprinsessegade 8B 4, 1306, Copenhagen, Denmark
Tel.: (45) 31152424
Web Site:
  https://www.hypefactors.com
Year Founded: 2015
HYPE—(NASDAQ)
Rev.: $1,346,640
Assets: $2,610,901
Liabilities: $2,811,202
Net Worth: ($200,301)
Earnings: ($793,731)
Emp.: 13
Fiscal Year-end: 12/31/22
Software Development Services
N.A.I.C.S.: 541511
Casper Janns *(CEO)*

HYPER CORPORATION
15F Cykan Holdings Tower 637
Eonju-ro, Gangnam-gu, Seoul,
08502, Korea (South)
Tel.: (82) 25459277

AND PRIVATE COMPANIES

Web Site: https://www.hyper-corp.com
Year Founded: 1999
065650—(KRS)
Rev.: $34,737,356
Assets: $42,762,301
Liabilities: $18,915,492
Net Worth: $23,846,809
Earnings: ($9,223,037)
Emp.: 53
Fiscal Year-end: 12/31/22
Interactive Voice Service Provider
N.A.I.C.S.: 561421
Sangseok Lee *(CEO)*

HYPER INC.
New ESR Bldg 2-9-6 Nihombashi Horidome-cho, Chuo-Ku, Tokyo, 103-0012, Japan
Tel.: (81) 368558180
Web Site: https://www.hyperpc.co.jp
Year Founded: 1990
3054—(TKS)
Rev.: $80,804,730
Assets: $51,622,290
Liabilities: $32,004,260
Net Worth: $19,618,030
Earnings: $553,020
Emp.: 193
Fiscal Year-end: 12/31/23
Computer Peripheral Equipment Distr
N.A.I.C.S.: 423430

HYPERA PHARMA S.A.
Avenida Magalhaes de Castro 4800 Tower 24TH floor, Cidade Jardim Continental Tower Building, Sao Paulo, 05676-120, Brazil
Tel.: (55) 136274206 **BR**
Web Site: https://www.hyperapharma.com.br
Year Founded: 2001
HYPE3—(BRAZ)
Rev.: $1,414,822,365
Assets: $4,381,178,447
Liabilities: $2,322,246,233
Net Worth: $2,058,932,213
Earnings: $295,152,564
Emp.: 10,000
Fiscal Year-end: 12/31/23
Pharmaceutical, Personal Care & Other Consumer Goods Developer, Mfr & Whslr
N.A.I.C.S.: 325412
Breno Toledo Pires de Oliveira *(CEO)*

Subsidiaries:

Mabesa do Brasil Ltda (1)
Av Cap Arcilio Rizzi 93 Cezar de Souza, 08820-130, Mogi das Cruzes, Sao Paulo, Brazil
Tel.: (55) 11 3474 5200
Web Site: http://www.mabesa.com.br
Diapers Mfr & Distr
N.A.I.C.S.: 315250

York S.A (1)
Rua Sao Felipe 737, Tatuape, Sao Paulo, 03085-9002, Brazil
Tel.: (55) 11 2090 6241
Personal Care Product Mfr
N.A.I.C.S.: 325412

HYPERBLOCK, INC.
140 Yonge Street Suite 209, Toronto, M5C 1X6, ON, Canada
HYBOF—(OTCIQ)
Sales Range: Less than $1 Million
Software Development Services
N.A.I.C.S.: 541511

HYPERCHARGE NETWORKS CORP.
208-1075 W 1st St, North Vancouver, V7P 3T4, BC, Canada **BC**
Web Site: https://www.hypercharge.com
Year Founded: 2018
HCNWF—(OTCQB)
Rev.: $361,227
Assets: $6,939,902
Liabilities: $998,729
Net Worth: $5,941,173
Earnings: ($7,192,520)
Emp.: 16
Fiscal Year-end: 08/31/22
Electric Equipment Mfr
N.A.I.C.S.: 335999
David Bibby *(CEO)*

HYPERION ASSET MANAGEMENT LIMITED
Level 19 307 Queen Street, Brisbane, 4000, QLD, Australia
Tel.: (61) 730203700
Web Site: http://www.hyperion.com.au
Year Founded: 1997
Sales Range: $25-49.9 Million
Emp.: 17
Asset Management Services
N.A.I.C.S.: 523940
Mark Arnold *(Chief Investment Officer)*

HYPERION S.A.
ul Podwale 3 lok 18, 00-252, Warsaw, Poland
Tel.: (48) 22 254 54 23
Web Site: http://www.hyperion.pl
Sales Range: $1-9.9 Million
Television Broadcasting Services
N.A.I.C.S.: 516120
Piotr Chodzen *(Chm-Supervisory Bd)*

HYPERSOFT TECHNOLOGIES LIMITED
Plot No 28 Goyal Society Moti Valley, Tirmulgherry, Secunderabad, 500 015, Andhra Pradesh, India
Tel.: (91) 4027744754
Web Site: https://www.hypersoftindia.net
539724—(BOM)
Rev.: $152,198
Assets: $519,260
Liabilities: $65,220
Net Worth: $454,040
Earnings: $1,338
Emp.: 11
Fiscal Year-end: 03/31/22
Information Technology Services
N.A.I.C.S.: 541512
Feroz Russi Bhote *(Mng Dir)*

HYPERVIEW INC.
590 - 1122 Mainland Street, Vancouver, V6B 5L1, BC, Canada
Web Site: https://www.hyperviewhq.com
Technology Services
N.A.I.C.S.: 541990
Jad Jebara *(Pres & CEO)*

HYPEX BIO EXPLOSIVES TECHNOLOGY AB
Marbackagatan 11 Hus K 1 Tr, 12343, Farsta, Sweden
Tel.: (46) 86839100
Web Site: https://www.hypexbio.com
Year Founded: 2020
Explosive Product Mfr
N.A.I.C.S.: 325920

HYPHENS PHARMA INTERNATIONAL LIMITED
16 Tai Seng Street Level 4, Singapore, 534138, Singapore
Tel.: (65) 63388551 **SG**
Web Site: https://www.hyphensgroup.com
Year Founded: 1998
1J5—(SES)
Rev.: $129,209,271
Assets: $91,467,848
Liabilities: $41,583,731
Net Worth: $49,884,117
Earnings: $6,498,523
Emp.: 440
Fiscal Year-end: 12/31/23
Pharmaceutical Product Mfr & Distr
N.A.I.C.S.: 325412
See Wah Lim *(Chm & CEO)*

Subsidiaries:

DocMed Technology, Pte. Ltd. (1)
16 Tai Seng St Level 4, Singapore, 534138, Singapore
Tel.: (65) 63388551
Web Site: https://www.docmedtech.com
Pharmaceutical Products Distr
N.A.I.C.S.: 424210

Hyphens Pharma Philippines, Inc. (1)
16th Floor Unit 1606 Orient Square Bldg F Ortigas Jr Road, Ortigas Centre Pasig city, Manila, Philippines
Tel.: (63) 27063386
Medical Product Distr
N.A.I.C.S.: 423450

Hyphens Pharma Pte. Ltd. (1)
16 Tai Seng Street Level 4, Singapore, 534138, Singapore
Tel.: (65) 63388551
Web Site: https://www.hyphens.com.sg
Pharmaceutical Product Whslr
N.A.I.C.S.: 424210
Stella Ang *(Head-Regulatory Affairs)*

Hyphens Pharma Sdn. Bhd. (1)
L1-10 and L1-11 PJ Mid Town Jalan Kemajuan Seksyen 13, 46200, Petaling Jaya, Selangor, Malaysia
Tel.: (60) 379316188
Medical Product Distr
N.A.I.C.S.: 423450
Francis Ang *(Head-Country)*

Ocean Health Pte. Ltd. (1)
16 Tai Seng St Level 4, Singapore, 534138, Singapore
Tel.: (65) 62886810
Web Site: https://www.oceanhealth.com
Health Supplement Services
N.A.I.C.S.: 456191

Pan-Malayan Pharmaceuticals Pte Ltd (1)
16 Tai Seng Street Level 4, Singapore, 534138, Singapore
Tel.: (65) 62965751
Web Site: https://www.panmalayan.com.sg
Medical Product Distr
N.A.I.C.S.: 423450

HYPO REAL ESTATE HOLDING AG
Freisinger Str 5, Unterschleissheim, 85716, Germany
Tel.: (49) 8928800
Web Site: http://www.hyporealestate.com
Year Founded: 2003
Sales Range: $5-14.9 Billion
Emp.: 1,419
Holding Company Real Estate & Financial Services
N.A.I.C.S.: 551112
Wolfgang Groth *(Mng Dir)*

Subsidiaries:

Deutsche Pfandbriefbank AG (1)
Parkring 28, 85748, Garching, Germany (100%)
Tel.: (49) 8928800
Web Site: https://www.pfandbriefbank.com
Assets: $56,168,217,210
Liabilities: $52,453,694,660
Net Worth: $3,714,522,550
Earnings: $100,452,170
Emp.: 848
Fiscal Year-end: 12/31/2023
Real Estate Banking Services
N.A.I.C.S.: 522292

Unit (Domestic):

Deutsche Pfandbriefbank - Central & Eastern Europe (2)
Freistringer Strasse 5, 85716, Unterschleissheim, Germany
Tel.: (49) 8928800
Web Site: http://www.pfandbriefbank.com
Sales Range: $350-399.9 Million
Emp.: 700
Banking Services
N.A.I.C.S.: 522110

Branch (Non-US):

Deutsche Pfandbriefbank - London (2)
30 St Mary Axe 21st Fl, London, EC3A 8BF, United Kingdom
Tel.: (44) 2077437743
Web Site: http://www.pfandbriefbank.com
Sales Range: $100-124.9 Million
Emp.: 140
Banking Services
N.A.I.C.S.: 522110

Deutsche Pfandbriefbank - Madrid (2)
Monte Esquinza n 30 4 Derecha, 28010, Madrid, Spain
Tel.: (34) 913493200
Web Site: http://www.pfandbriefbank.com
Sales Range: $50-74.9 Million
Emp.: 14
Banking Services
N.A.I.C.S.: 522110
Luis Chapa *(Mgr)*

Deutsche Pfandbriefbank - Milan (2)
Via Brera 3, I-20121, Milan, Italy
Tel.: (39) 0236576800
Banking Services
N.A.I.C.S.: 522110

Deutsche Pfandbriefbank - Paris (2)
11 Rue Saint Georges, 75009, Paris, France
Tel.: (33) 153057400
Web Site: http://www.pfandbriefbank.com
Sales Range: $50-74.9 Million
Emp.: 54
Banking Services
N.A.I.C.S.: 522110

Branch (Domestic):

Deutsche Pfandbriefbank AG - Eschborn (2)
Ludwig-Erhard-Strasse 14, 65760, Eschborn, Germany
Tel.: (49) 619699900
Sales Range: $125-149.9 Million
Emp.: 100
Public Sector Financing, Global Funding, Treasury & Property Finance
N.A.I.C.S.: 921130

Frappant Altona GmbH (1)
Prinzregentenstr 56, 85716, Unterschleissheim, Germany
Tel.: (49) 89288018000
Real Estate Manngement Services
N.A.I.C.S.: 531390

Hypo Pfandbrief Bank International S.A. (1)
8 Rue Jean Monnet, 2099, Luxembourg, Luxembourg
Tel.: (352) 26414700
Web Site: http://www.hpbi.lu
Sales Range: $50-74.9 Million
Emp.: 17
Public Sector Financial Management
N.A.I.C.S.: 921130

Hypo Public Finance Bank (1)
19th Fl 30th St Mary Axe, EC3A 8BF, London, United Kingdom - England
Tel.: (44) 2077437712
Public Sector Financial Management
N.A.I.C.S.: 921130

Hypo Real Estate Capital Hong Kong Corporation Limited (1)
Suites 3007 3008 1 International Finance Centre, No 1 Harbour View Street, Hong Kong, China (Hong Kong)
Tel.: (852) 3413 8356
Web Site: http://www.hyporealestate.com
Real Estate Banking
N.A.I.C.S.: 522110

Hypo Real Estate Capital India Corporation Private Limited (1)

HYPO REAL ESTATE HOLDING AG

Hypo Real Estate Holding AG—(Continued)
401 Cee Jay House Drive Annie Besant Road, Mumbai, 400 018, Worli, India
Tel.: (91) 2224999900
Web Site: http://www.hypointernational.com
Sales Range: $75-99.9 Million
Emp.: 70
Real Estate Banking
N.A.I.C.S.: 522110

Hypo Real Estate Capital Japan Corporation (1)
Otemachi 1st Sq W Tower 10F 1-5-1 Otemachi, Chiyoda-Ku, Tokyo, 100-0004, Japan
Tel.: (81) 352885860
Sales Range: $50-74.9 Million
Emp.: 20
Real Estate Banking
N.A.I.C.S.: 522110
Uehara Takehiko (Gen Mgr)

Hypo Real Estate Capital Singapore Corporation Private Limited (1)
9 Raffles Place #17-20 Republic Plaza, Singapore, Singapore
Tel.: (65) 63726812
Sales Range: $75-99.9 Million
Emp.: 2
Real Estate Banking
N.A.I.C.S.: 522110

Ragnarok Vermogensverwaltung AG & Co. KG (1)
Prinzregentenstr 56, 80538, Munich, Germany
Tel.: (49) 89288018000
Real Estate Managements Services
N.A.I.C.S.: 531390

HYPOPORT SE
Heidestrabe 8, 10179, Berlin, Germany
Tel.: (49) 30420860
Web Site: https://www.hypoport.com
Year Founded: 1999
HYQ—(MUN)
Rev: $397,271,774
Assets: $690,768,730
Liabilities: $316,998,348
Net Worth: $373,770,382
Earnings: $22,231,942
Emp.: 2,209
Fiscal Year-end: 12/31/23
Financial Support Services
N.A.I.C.S.: 523940
Ronald Slabke (Founder, Chm-Mgmt Bd & CEO)

HYPOTHEKARBANK LENZBURG AG
Bahnhofstrasse 2, 5600, Lenzburg, 5600, Switzerland
Tel.: (41) 628851111
Web Site: https://www.hbl.ch
Year Founded: 1868
HBLN—(SWX)
Sales Range: Less than $1 Million
Commercial Banking Services
N.A.I.C.S.: 522110
Marianne Wildi (Board of Directors, Chm-Mgmt Bd & CEO)

HYPROP INVESTMENTS LIMITED
2nd Floor Cradock Heights 21 Cradock Avenue, Rosebank, 2196, South Africa
Tel.: (27) 114470090
Web Site: https://www.hyprop.co.za
HYP—(JSE)
Rev.: $212,929,659
Assets: $2,543,363,109
Liabilities: $1,126,216,252
Net Worth: $1,417,146,857
Earnings: $91,712,924
Emp.: 292
Fiscal Year-end: 06/30/22
Investment Management Service
N.A.I.C.S.: 523999

Brett Till (CFO & CFO)

Subsidiaries:

Canal Walk Shopping Centre (1)
Century Boulevard, Century City, Cape Town, 7441, South Africa
Tel.: (27) 215299600
Web Site: http://www.canalwalk.co.za
Sales Range: $50-74.9 Million
Emp.: 60
Shopping Center
N.A.I.C.S.: 531120
Camilla Lor (Reg Mgr-Mktg)

Hyde Park Shopping Centre (1)
Jan Smuts Avenue, Hyde Park, Sandton, 2124, South Africa
Tel.: (27) 113254340
Web Site: http://www.hydeparkshopping.co.za
Sales Range: $25-49.9 Million
Emp.: 70
Shopping Center
N.A.I.C.S.: 455110
Brett Meyers (Mgr-Facilities)

The Glen Shopping Centre (1)
Cnr Orpen and Letaba Streets, Oakdene, Johannesburg, 2190, South Africa
Tel.: (27) 114359252
Web Site: http://www.theglenshopping.co.za
Sales Range: $25-49.9 Million
Emp.: 20
Shopping Center
N.A.I.C.S.: 455110
Glen Maboe (Gen Mgr)

HYRICAN INFORMATIONSSYSTEME AG
Kalkplatz 5, Kindelbruck, Sommerda, Germany
Tel.: (49) 363755130
Web Site: https://www.hyrican.de
HYI—(BER)
Sales Range: Less than $1 Million
Computer Equipment Mfr & Distr
N.A.I.C.S.: 334111
Michael Lehmann (Chm-Mgmt Bd & CEO)

HYSAN DEVELOPMENT COMPANY LIMITED
50/F Lee Garden One 33 Hysan Avenue, Causeway Bay, China (Hong Kong)
Tel.: (852) 28955777
Web Site: https://www.hysan.com.hk
0014—(HKG)
Rev.: $441,150,000
Assets: $15,193,537,500
Liabilities: $4,558,635,000
Net Worth: $10,634,902,500
Earnings: ($120,997,500)
Emp.: 486
Fiscal Year-end: 12/31/22
Property Investment, Development & Management Services
N.A.I.C.S.: 523940
Irene Yun Lien Lee (Chm)

Subsidiaries:

Admore Investments Limited (1)
49th Floor Manulife Plaza The Lee Gardens, Causeway Bay, China (Hong Kong) (100%)
Tel.: (852) 28955777
Web Site: http://www.hysandevelopment.com
Sales Range: $150-199.9 Million
Emp.: 500
Holding Company; Real Estate Investments
N.A.I.C.S.: 551112

Bamboo Grove Recreational Services Limited (1)
Kennedy Rd No 74286, Wanchai, China (Hong Kong)
Tel.: (852) 28335621
Real Estate Property Lessors
N.A.I.C.S.: 531190

Barrowgate Limited (1)
49th Floor Manulife Plaza The Lee Gardens, 33 Hysan Avenue, Causeway Bay, China (Hong Kong)
Tel.: (852) 28955777
Web Site: http://www.hysandevelopment.com
Sales Range: $150-199.9 Million
Emp.: 500
Holding Company; Real Estate Investments
N.A.I.C.S.: 551112

Gearup Investments Limited (1)
49/f The Lee Gardens Manulife Plz 33 Hysan Ave, Causeway Bay, China (Hong Kong)
Tel.: (852) 28955777
Web Site: http://www.hysan.com
Sales Range: $150-199.9 Million
Emp.: 300
Property Management Services
N.A.I.C.S.: 531312

Golden Capital Investment Limited (1)
33 Hysan Ave 49th Fl The Lee Gardens, Causeway Bay, China (Hong Kong) (100%)
Tel.: (852) 28955777
Web Site: http://www.hysandevelopment.com
Sales Range: $150-199.9 Million
Emp.: 400
Real Estate Property Lessors
N.A.I.C.S.: 551112

Hysan Leasing Company Limited (1)
50th Floor Lee Garden One 33 Hysan Avenue, Causeway Bay, China (Hong Kong) (100%)
Tel.: (852) 28955777
Web Site: http://www.hysandevelopment.com
Sales Range: $150-199.9 Million
Emp.: 500
Real Estate Property Lessors
N.A.I.C.S.: 531190

Hysan Property Management Limited (1)
50th floor The Lee Gardens 1 33 Hysan Avenue, Causeway Bay, China (Hong Kong) (100%)
Tel.: (852) 29727000
Web Site: http://www.hysandevelopment.com
Sales Range: $150-199.9 Million
Emp.: 500
Real Estate Property Lessors
N.A.I.C.S.: 531190

Kwong Wan Realty Limited (1)
49th Floor Manulife Plaza The Lee Gardens, Causeway Bay, China (Hong Kong) (100%)
Tel.: (852) 28955777
Web Site: http://www.hysandevelopment.com
Sales Range: $100-124.9 Million
Emp.: 400
Land Subdivision & Developers
N.A.I.C.S.: 237210

Lee Theatre Realty Limited (1)
49th Floor Manulife Plaza The Lee Gardens, Causeway Bay, China (Hong Kong) (100%)
Tel.: (852) 28955777
Web Site: http://www.hysandevelopment.com
Sales Range: $150-199.9 Million
Emp.: 500
Real Estate Property Lessors
N.A.I.C.S.: 531190

Minsal Limited (1)
49th Floor Manulife Plaza The Lee Gardens, Causeway Bay, China (Hong Kong) (100%)
Tel.: (852) 28955777
Web Site: http://www.hysan.com.hk
Sales Range: $150-199.9 Million
Emp.: 500
Holding Company
N.A.I.C.S.: 551112

Mondsee Limited (1)
49th Floor Manulife Plaza The Lee Gardens, Causeway Bay, China (Hong Kong) (100%)
Tel.: (852) 28955777

INTERNATIONAL PUBLIC

Web Site: http://www.hysandevelopment.com
Sales Range: $100-124.9 Million
Emp.: 500
Land Subdivision & Developers
N.A.I.C.S.: 237210

Silver Nicety Company Limited (1)
49th Floor Manulife Plaza The Lee Gardens, Causeway Bay, China (Hong Kong)
Tel.: (852) 28955777
Web Site: http://www.hysandevelopment.com
Sales Range: $150-199.9 Million
Emp.: 500
Real Estate Property Lessors
N.A.I.C.S.: 531190

HYSONIC CO., LTD.
508 RIT Center Gyeonggi Techno Park Sa 3-dong, Sangnok-Gu, Ansan, 426-901, Gyeonggi-do, Korea (South)
Tel.: (82) 80400500
Web Site: http://www.hysonic.com
Year Founded: 2001
106080—(KRS)
Rev.: $13,294,291
Assets: $14,709,908
Liabilities: $2,383,606
Net Worth: $12,326,302
Earnings: $623,764
Emp.: 24
Fiscal Year-end: 12/31/22
Electro-optical Application Device Mfr
N.A.I.C.S.: 334419
Chanjong Kim (CEO)

Subsidiaries:

HYSONIC Philippines Inc. (1)
Lot 3 Carmelray Industrial Park II Brgy, Tulo, Calamba, 7210, Laguna, Philippines
Tel.: (63) 495450232
Actuator System Mfr
N.A.I.C.S.: 333995

HYTERA COMMUNICATIONS CORPORATION LIMITED
Hytera Tower Hi Tech Industrial Park North 9108 No Beihuan Road, Nanshan District, Shenzhen, 518057, China
Tel.: (86) 75586137081 CN
Web Site: https://www.hytera.com
Year Founded: 1993
002583—(SSE)
Rev.: $793,655,928
Assets: $1,615,943,628
Liabilities: $722,755,332
Net Worth: $893,188,296
Earnings: $57,210,192
Emp.: 2,240
Fiscal Year-end: 12/31/22
Wireless Communication Equipment Mfr & Distr
N.A.I.C.S.: 334220
Qingzhou Chen (Founder & Chm)

Subsidiaries:

HYT America, Inc. (1)
3315 Commerce Pkwy, Miramar, FL, 33025
Tel.: (954) 846-1011
Web Site: http://www.hytera.us
Communication Equipment Mfr & Distr
N.A.I.C.S.: 334290

HYT Telecomunication (UK) Co., Ltd. (1)
Hytera House 939 Yeovil Road, Slough, SL1 4NH, Berkshire, United Kingdom
Tel.: (44) 1753826120
Sales Range: $50-74.9 Million
Emp.: 1
Telecommunication Equipment Distr
N.A.I.C.S.: 423690
Andrew Yuan (Gen Mgr)

Hytera Communications (Australia) Pty Ltd (1)
53 Brandl St, Eight Mile Plains, 4113, QLD, Australia
Web Site: http://hytera.com.au
Professional Services

AND PRIVATE COMPANIES

N.A.I.C.S.: 541990

Hytera Communications (Canada) Inc. (1)
Tel.: (905) 305-7545
Web Site: http://www.hytera.ca
Radio Terminal Mfr & Distr
N.A.I.C.S.: 334220

Hytera Communications (Hong Kong) Company Limited (1)
Unit Nos 303-304 3/F Hi-Tech Center 9 Choi Yuen Road, Sheung Shui, New Territories, China (Hong Kong)
Tel.: (852) 23474055
Radio Terminal Mfr & Whslr
N.A.I.C.S.: 334220

Hytera Communications (UK) Co., Ltd. (1)
939 Yeovil Road, Slough, SL1 4NH, Berkshire, United Kingdom
Tel.: (44) 1753826120
Two-Way Radio Mfr
N.A.I.C.S.: 334220

Hytera Communications FZCO (1)
Tel.: (971) 44313969
Web Site: http://hytera.ae
Two-Way Radio Mfr
N.A.I.C.S.: 334220

Hytera Comunicacoes do Brasil Ltda. (1)
Rua George Ohm 230 11th floor tower B, Cidade Moncoes, Sao Paulo, 04576-020, Brazil
Tel.: (55) 1131926600
Web Site: https://www.hytera.com.br
Telecommunication Equipment Distr
N.A.I.C.S.: 423690

Hytera Mobilfunk GmbH (1)
Fritz-Hahne-Strasse 7, 31848, Bad Munder am Deister, Germany
Tel.: (49) 50429980
Web Site: https://hmf-smart-solutions.de
Wireless Telecom Equipment Mfr
N.A.I.C.S.: 334290
Matthias Klausing (CEO)

Hytera US Inc. (1)
8 Whatney Ste 200, Irvine, CA 92618
Tel.: (949) 238-4000
Web Site: http://www.hytera.us
Radio Terminal Mfr & Distr
N.A.I.C.S.: 334220

Norsat International Inc. (1)
110 4020 Viking Way, Richmond, V6V 2L4, BC, Canada
Tel.: (604) 821-2800
Web Site: http://www.norsat.com
Satellite & Microwave Products Mfr
N.A.I.C.S.: 334419
Amiee Chan (Pres & CEO)

Sepura plc (1)
9000 Cambridge Research Park Beach Drive, Waterbeach, Cambridge, CB25 9TL, United Kingdom
Tel.: (44) 1223876000
Web Site: https://www.sepura.com
Terrestrial Trunked Radio (TETRA) Terminals Developer
N.A.I.C.S.: 335931
Duncan Crouch (Dir-Ops)

Subsidiary (Non-US):

Sepura Deutschland GmbH (2)
Parkring 31, 85748, Garching, Germany
Tel.: (49) 8961465700
Radio Communication Devices Mfr
N.A.I.C.S.: 334220

Sinclair Technologies Inc. (1)
85 Mary St, Aurora, L4G 6X5, ON, Canada
Tel.: (905) 727-0165
Professional Communication Services
N.A.I.C.S.: 517810

Teltronic S.A.U. (1)
Poligono Malpica C/F Oeste, 50016, Zaragoza, Spain
Tel.: (34) 976465656
Web Site: https://www.teltronic.es
Telecommunication Servicesb
N.A.I.C.S.: 517121
Juan Ferro (CEO)

HYULIM A-TECH CO. LTD

364 Gain-ri Sannae-myeon, Gangnam-gu, Miryang, Kyungsangnam-do, Korea (South)
Tel.: (82) 7050572779
Web Site: http://www.idual.co.kr
Year Founded: 1993
078590—(KRS)
Rev.: $33,394,232
Assets: $33,765,125
Liabilities: $7,153,094
Net Worth: $26,612,031
Earnings: $7,465,839
Emp.: 90
Fiscal Year-end: 12/31/22
Automobile Parts Mfr
N.A.I.C.S.: 336110
Cho Ian Hwe (CEO)

HYULIM NETWORKS CO., LTD.

185-44 Geumgok-ro, Hwaseong, 445-811, Gyeonggi-do, Korea (South)
Tel.: (82) 318318800
Web Site:
  https://www.hyulimnetworks.com
Year Founded: 1997
192410—(KRS)
Rev.: $16,133,776
Assets: $53,785,215
Liabilities: $9,043,398
Net Worth: $44,741,817
Earnings: ($14,834,673)
Emp.: 88
Fiscal Year-end: 12/31/22
Mobile Communication Antenna Mfr
N.A.I.C.S.: 334290

Subsidiaries:

Gamma Nu Theta Inc. (1)
151 N Kraemer Blvd Ste 205, Placentia, CA 92870
Tel.: (714) 646-9911
Antenna Mfr
N.A.I.C.S.: 334220

HYUN WOO INDUSTRIAL CO., LTD

51 Geomdan-ro, Seo-gu, Incheon, Korea (South)
Tel.: (82) 328766105
Web Site:
  https://www.hyunwoopcb.com
Year Founded: 1987
092300—(KRS)
Rev.: $160,968,614
Assets: $155,347,034
Liabilities: $84,599,809
Net Worth: $70,747,226
Earnings: $3,573,412
Emp.: 365
Fiscal Year-end: 12/31/22
Printed Circuit Board Mfr
N.A.I.C.S.: 334412

HYUNDAI ABLE 1ST SPECIAL PURPOSE ACQUISITION COMPANY

52 Gukjegeumyung-ro, Yeongdeungpo-gu, Seoul, Korea (South)
Tel.: (82) 261141039
Year Founded: 2014
Assets: $9,819,848
Liabilities: $1,122,754
Net Worth: $8,697,094
Earnings: $1,160
Financial Investment Management Services
N.A.I.C.S.: 523940

HYUNDAI ADM BIO INC

711 Royal Building 19 Saemunan-ro 5-gil, Jongno-Gu, Seoul, 03173, Korea (South)
Tel.: (82) 27301457
Web Site:
  https://www.admkorea.co.kr
Year Founded: 2003

187660—(KRS)
Emp.: 111
Clinical Operation Service
N.A.I.C.S.: 622110
Seokmin Yoon (Founder)

Subsidiaries:

Smart Research Corp. (1)
1st Floor - 1sd Floor - No 7 68 Street, Tan Phong Ward - District 7, Ho Chi Minh City, 700000, Vietnam
Tel.: (84) 283 838 5472
Web Site:
  https://www.smartresearch.com.vn
Scientific Research Support Services
N.A.I.C.S.: 541715

HYUNDAI BIOLAND CO., LTD.

22 Osongsaengmyeong 2-ro osong-eup, Heungdeok-gu, Cheonan, Chungcheongbuk-do, Korea (South)
Tel.: (82) 432496720
Web Site:
  https://www.hyundaibioland.co.kr
Year Founded: 1995
052260—(KRS)
Rev.: $94,577,686
Assets: $158,924,613
Liabilities: $43,602,792
Net Worth: $115,321,821
Earnings: ($10,751,268)
Emp.: 330
Fiscal Year-end: 12/31/21
Pharmaceutical Preparation Mfr
N.A.I.C.S.: 325412
O. H. Young Kun (CFO)

Subsidiaries:

Bioland co., ltd - Ansan Plant (1)
152 Manhae-Ro, Daewon-Gu Kyunggi, Ansan, 425-839, Korea (South)
Tel.: (82) 31 8085 7500
Pharmaceuticals Product Mfr
N.A.I.C.S.: 325412

Bioland co., ltd - Ochang Plant (1)
162 Gwahaksanup 3-Rio, Chungbuk, Ochang, 363-885, Cheongwon-Gun, Korea (South)
Tel.: (82) 43 240 8600
Pharmaceutical Preparation Mfr
N.A.I.C.S.: 325412

Bioland co., ltd - Osong Plant (1)
22 Osongsaeng 2-Ro, Cheongwon-Gun, Osong, 393-951, Chungbuk, Korea (South)
Tel.: (82) 43 249 6700
Pharmaceuticals Product Mfr
N.A.I.C.S.: 325412

HYUNDAI BIOSCIENCE CO., LTD.

3F 150 Bugahyeon-ro, Seodaemun-gu, Seoul, 03759, Korea (South)
Tel.: (82) 15443194
Web Site:
  https://www.hyundaibioscience.com
Year Founded: 2000
048410—(KRS)
Rev.: $6,022,160
Assets: $51,639,664
Liabilities: $6,973,121
Net Worth: $44,666,543
Earnings: ($12,124,174)
Emp.: 71
Fiscal Year-end: 12/31/22
Liquid Crystal Display Mfr & Distr
N.A.I.C.S.: 334419
O. H. Sang-Gi (CEO)

HYUNDAI CORPORATION

25 Yulgok-ro 2-gil, Jongno-gu, Seoul, 3143, Korea (South)
Tel.: (82) 23901114
Web Site:
  https://www.hyundaicorp.com
Year Founded: 1976
011760—(KRS)
Rev.: $4,699,385,032
Assets: $1,404,608,482

HYUNDAI DEPARTMENT STORE CO., LTD.

Liabilities: $1,069,740,667
Net Worth: $334,867,814
Earnings: $60,374,465
Emp.: 263
Fiscal Year-end: 12/31/22
General Trading Services
N.A.I.C.S.: 425120
Monghyuck Chung (Chm & CEO)

Subsidiaries:

Hyundai Corporation (Cambodia) Co., Ltd. (1)
Office 306 PPCB HO Bldg 217 Preah Nordom Bld, Sangkat Khan Chamkarmon, Phnom Penh, Cambodia
Tel.: (855) 16888646
Trading & Investment Services
N.A.I.C.S.: 523999

Hyundai Corporation (Shanghai) Co., Ltd. (1)
1701 Shanghai International Trade Center 2201 Yan-An Road West, Shanghai, 200336, China
Tel.: (86) 2162754703
Steel Product Distr
N.A.I.C.S.: 423510

Hyundai Corporation Europe GmbH (1)
Am Kronberger Hang 2A, 65824, Schwalbach, Germany
Tel.: (49) 619690080
Sales Range: $50-74.9 Million
Emp.: 6
Computer & Computer Peripheral Equipment & Software Merchant Whslr
N.A.I.C.S.: 423430

Hyundai Corporation Holdings Co., Ltd. (1)
25 Yulgok-ro 2-gil, Jongno-gu, Seoul, 13143, Korea (South)
Tel.: (82) 23901568
Web Site:
  https://www.hyundaicorpholdings.com
Rev.: $126,053,214
Assets: $227,129,843
Liabilities: $55,186,604
Net Worth: $171,943,239
Earnings: $25,777,400
Emp.: 74
Fiscal Year-end: 12/31/2022
Household Appliance Distr
N.A.I.C.S.: 423620
Monghyuck Chung (Co-CEO)

Hyundai One Asia Pte. Ltd. (1)
9 Temasek Boulevard 26-01 Suntec Tower Two, Singapore, 038989, Singapore
Tel.: (65) 63378880
Marine Engine Spare Parts Whslr
N.A.I.C.S.: 423860

PT Hyundai Inti Develop (1)
3rd Fl Menera Pacifik JL MH Thamrin, Lippo Cikarang, Bekasi, 17550, Jawa Barat, Indonesia
Tel.: (62) 218972378
Real Estate Development Services
N.A.I.C.S.: 531390

HYUNDAI DEPARTMENT STORE CO., LTD.

12 Teheran-ro 98-gil, Gangnam-gu, Seoul, Korea (South)
Tel.: (82) 25492233
Web Site: http://www.ehyundai.com
Year Founded: 1971
069960—(KRS)
Rev.: $3,845,832,823
Assets: $9,257,114,485
Liabilities: $4,373,448,407
Net Worth: $4,883,666,079
Earnings: $110,509,891
Emp.: 2,961
Fiscal Year-end: 12/31/22
Department Store Owner & Operator; E-Business; Tourism; Hotel Owner & Operator; Garment Mfr; Expressway Service Area; Catering Services; Food Distr
N.A.I.C.S.: 455110
Jiyoung Jung (Pres)

HYUNDAI DEPARTMENT STORE CO., LTD.

Hyundai Department Store Co., Ltd.—(Continued)

Subsidiaries:

Hyundai Futurenet Co., Ltd (1)
19 Banpo-daero, Seocho-gu, Seoul, 06710, Korea (South)
Tel.: (82) 234502233
Web Site: https://www.hyundaifuturenet.com
Rev.: $118,281,551
Assets: $702,001,699
Liabilities: $53,893,752
Net Worth: $648,107,947
Earnings: ($4,129,297)
Emp.: 56
Fiscal Year-end: 12/31/2022
Broadcasting Services
N.A.I.C.S.: 516120
Sung-Il Kim (CEO)

Hyundai Home Shopping Network Corporation (1)
454-2 Cheonho-dong, Gangdong-gu, Seoul, Korea (South)
Tel.: (82) 221432000
Web Site: http://www.hyundaihmall.com
Rev.: $1,611,979,025
Assets: $2,133,815,470
Liabilities: $631,462,411
Net Worth: $1,502,353,059
Earnings: $66,209,141
Emp.: 1,048
Fiscal Year-end: 12/31/2022
Online Shopping Services
N.A.I.C.S.: 423940
Dong-Yoon Lim (Mng Dir)

Hyundai L&C Co., Ltd. (1)
7-8 Floor Center 1 Building 5-gil Euljiro, Jung-gu, Seoul, 04539, Korea (South)
Tel.: (82) 729 8272
Web Site: http://www.hlcc.co.kr
Flooring, Windows, Home Door, PVC Compounds, Films, Sheets, GMT, EPP, Upholstery, SMC, Conpanel, Hanex & Decor Sheets Mfr
N.A.I.C.S.: 326199

Hyundai Livart Co., Ltd. (1)
201 Apgujeong-ro, Gangnam-gu, Seoul, Korea (South)
Tel.: (82) 234808000
Furniture Designer, Mfr & Whslr
N.A.I.C.S.: 423210

Subsidiary (Non-US):

Hyundai H&S Co., Ltd. (2)
Tel.: (82) 230142500
Web Site: http://www.hyundaihns.com
Food Mfr & Whslr
N.A.I.C.S.: 311999
Kim Whaeung (Pres)

HYUNDAI ELECTRIC & ENERGY SYSTEMS CO., LTD.

477 Bundang Suseo-ro, Bundang-gu, Seongnam, Gyeonggi-do, Korea (South)
Tel.: (82) 24799180
Web Site: https://www.hd-hyundaielectric.com
Year Founded: 2017
267260—(KRS)
Rev.: $1,614,151,107
Assets: $1,867,668,141
Liabilities: $1,230,161,614
Net Worth: $637,506,527
Earnings: $124,267,801
Emp.: 2,084
Fiscal Year-end: 12/31/22
Electric Equipment Mfr
N.A.I.C.S.: 335313
Seok Cho (Chm, Pres & CEO)

Subsidiaries:

Hyundai Heavy Industries Co., Ltd. (1)
41 Rojen Blvd, 1271, Sofia, Bulgaria
Tel.: (359) 28033312
Web Site: https://www.hhi-co.bg
Electric Equipment Mfr
N.A.I.C.S.: 335313

Hyundai Power Transformers USA Inc. (1)
215 Folmar Pkwy, Montgomery, AL 36105
Tel.: (334) 481-2000
Web Site: http://www.hhiamerica.com
Transmission Power Supply Mfr
N.A.I.C.S.: 335311

HYUNDAI ENGINEERING & CONSTRUCTION CO., LTD.

Hyundai Bldg 75 Yulgok-ro, Jongno-gu, Seoul, 03058, Korea (South)
Tel.: (82) 27461114
Web Site: https://en.hdec.kr
Year Founded: 1947
000720—(KRS)
Rev.: $16,620
Assets: $18,066
Liabilities: $9,391
Net Worth: $8,675
Earnings: $510
Emp.: 6,324
Fiscal Year-end: 12/31/21
Construction Engineering Services
N.A.I.C.S.: 541330

Subsidiaries:

Hyundai Engineering & Steel Industries Co., Ltd. (1)
18-9 Cheonheung 8-gil, Seonggeo-eup Seobuk-gu, Cheonan, Chungcheongnam-do, Korea (South)
Tel.: (82) 415297200
Sales Range: $75-99.9 Million
Emp.: 450
Engineering & Steel Services
N.A.I.C.S.: 541330

Hyundai Engineering Co., Ltd. (1)
75 Yulgok-Ro Jongno-gu, Seoul, 110-920, Korea (South)
Web Site: http://www.hec.co.kr
Rev.: $5,848,860,000
Assets: $5,437,780,000
Liabilities: $2,426,060,000
Net Worth: $3,011,720,000
Earnings: $257,140,000
Emp.: 5,611
Fiscal Year-end: 12/31/2019
Engineeering Services
N.A.I.C.S.: 541330

HYUNDAI EVERDIGM CORP

49 Buyeong-gil Jincheon-eup, Jincheon, 365-802, Chungcheongbuk-do, Korea (South)
Tel.: (82) 435303300
Web Site: http://www.everdigm.com
Year Founded: 1994
041440—(KRS)
Rev.: $287,195,477
Assets: $224,230,017
Liabilities: $86,991,721
Net Worth: $137,238,295
Earnings: $8,216,976
Emp.: 573
Fiscal Year-end: 12/31/22
Construction Machinery Mfr
N.A.I.C.S.: 333120
Jun-Hyuck Kwon (Mgr-Team)

Subsidiaries:

Everdigm America Inc. (1)
655 W Lytell St, Metter, GA 30439
Tel.: (912) 685-5099
Web Site: http://www.everdigm-america.com
Concrete Pump Mfr
N.A.I.C.S.: 333914
Carlos Ahn (Mng Dir)

Everdigm Heavy Equipment & Machinery Trading LLC
Room No 408 Suntech Tower Dubai Silicon Oasis, PO Box 282925, Dubai, United Arab Emirates
Tel.: (971) 43307637
Construction Machinery Mfr
N.A.I.C.S.: 333120

Everdigm Mongolia LLC
1st Khoroo Solar Road -91 Sandrohd 7th Floor, Sukhbaatar District, Ulaanbaatar, Mongolia
Tel.: (976) 70123300

Web Site: http://www.everdigm.mn
Building Construction Services
N.A.I.C.S.: 236220

Hyundai Everdigm America Inc. (1)
69 Newnan S Industrial Dr, Newnan, GA 30263
Tel.: (770) 683-5099
Construction Machinery Mfr
N.A.I.C.S.: 333120

HYUNDAI EZWEL CO.,LTD

23 Chungjeong-ro, Part of the 8th floor 9th & 10th floors Seodaemun-gu, Seoul, Korea (South)
Tel.: (82) 221316000
Web Site: http://www.ezwel.com
Year Founded: 2003
090850—(KRS)
Rev.: $86,257,095
Assets: $154,850,748
Liabilities: $84,282,908
Net Worth: $70,567,840
Earnings: $11,633,563
Emp.: 283
Fiscal Year-end: 12/31/22
Welfare Programs, Benefit Package Programs & Government Support Businesses Software Publisher
N.A.I.C.S.: 513210
Park Sung-Su (Mng Dir)

HYUNDAI GF HOLDINGS CO., LTD.

Gyungido Yonginsi Sujigu Moon in Ro 30 Dong Chun Dong, Yongin, 16827, Gyeonggi-do, Korea (South)
Tel.: (82) 315252233
Web Site: https://www.hyundaigreenfood.com
Year Founded: 1968
005440—(KRS)
Rev.: $2,686,931,676
Assets: $2,551,255,091
Liabilities: $731,171,575
Net Worth: $1,820,083,516
Earnings: $47,124,082
Emp.: 5,629
Fiscal Year-end: 12/31/19
Food Distr
N.A.I.C.S.: 722310
Hong Jin Park (CEO)

Subsidiaries:

Hyundai Dream Tour Co., Ltd. (1)
23 Chungjeong-ro, Seodaemun-gu, Seoul, Korea (South)
Tel.: (82) 27232233
Web Site: https://www.hyundaidreamtour.co.kr
Tour Operating Services
N.A.I.C.S.: 561520

HYUNDAI GLOVIS CO., LTD.

83-21 Wangsimni-ro, Seongdong-gu, Seoul, Korea (South)
Tel.: (82) 261919114
Web Site: https://www.glovis.net
Year Founded: 2011
086280—(KRS)
Rev.: $19,063,281,894
Assets: $10,929,605,202
Liabilities: $5,152,009,474
Net Worth: $5,777,595,728
Earnings: $787,623,246
Emp.: 11,193
Fiscal Year-end: 12/31/23
Logistic Services
N.A.I.C.S.: 541614
Jung Hoon Kim (Chm, Pres & CEO)

Subsidiaries:

Adampol Czech Republic Corporation (1)
Tel.: (420) 558408173
Web Site: http://adampol.cz
Cargo Transportation Services
N.A.I.C.S.: 488490

INTERNATIONAL PUBLIC

Adampol S.A. Corporation (1)
ul Uslugowa 3, 15-521, Bialystok, Poland
Tel.: (48) 857407660
Web Site: http://www.adampolsa.com.pl
Emp.: 1,300
Cargo Transportation Services
N.A.I.C.S.: 488490
Krzysztof Dakowicz (CEO)

Adampol Slovakia Corporation (1)
KMS Factory Vehicle Processing Centre (VPC) Sv Jana Nepomuckeho 1282/1, 013 01 Teplicka nad Vahom, Slovakia
Tel.: (421) 415157300
Cargo Transportation Services
N.A.I.C.S.: 488490

Beijing GLOVIS Warehousing & Transportation Co., Ltd.
9-2 Nanfaxin Sector Shun Ping Rd Shunyi Fhunjie Bldg 605, Beijing Konggang Logistics Base Shunyi, Beijing, 101316, China
Tel.: (86) 10 8453 8560
Web Site: http://www.china.glovis.net
Transportation Services
N.A.I.C.S.: 483211

Europe Corporation (1)
Kaiserleipromenade 5, 63067, Offenbach, Germany
Tel.: (49) 69273166700
Web Site: http://www.glovis.eu
Emp.: 98
Logistic Services
N.A.I.C.S.: 541614
Chan Jul Park (Mng Dir)

GLOVIS America Inc. (1)
17305 Von Karman Ave, Irvine, CA 92614
Tel.: (714) 435-2960
Web Site: http://www.america.glovis.net
Emp.: 86
Transportation Services
N.A.I.C.S.: 483211

GLOVIS Australia Pty. Ltd. (1)
394 Lane Cove Rd, Macquarie, 2113, NSW, Australia
Tel.: (61) 2 8873 6099
Web Site: http://www.hyundaiglovis.com.au
Transportation Services
N.A.I.C.S.: 483211

GLOVIS Brazil Logistica Ltda. (1)
Transportation Services
N.A.I.C.S.: 483211

GLOVIS Canada Inc. (1)
4 Robert Speck Parkway Ste 370, Mississauga, L4Z 1S1, ON, Canada
Tel.: (905) 361-1642
Transportation Services
N.A.I.C.S.: 483211

GLOVIS Czech Republic s.r.o. (1)
Tel.: (420) 558408124
Web Site: http://www.glovis.cz
Emp.: 600
Transportation Services
N.A.I.C.S.: 483211

GLOVIS Europe GmbH (1)
Kia Motors Bldg 6F, Theodor-Heuss-Allee 11, Frankfurt, D60486, Germany
Tel.: (49) 69 850 928 607
Transportation Services
N.A.I.C.S.: 483211

GLOVIS Georgia, LLC (1)
6101 Sorrento Rd, West Point, GA 31833
Tel.: (706) 902-7200
Web Site: https://georgia.glovis.net
Transportation Services
N.A.I.C.S.: 483211

GLOVIS Holdings Mongol (1)
#703 Bluesky Tower Enkh taivni urgun choloo 1-r khoroo, Sukhbaatar Distr, Ulaanbaatar, Mongolia
Tel.: (976) 7011 0922
Transportation Services
N.A.I.C.S.: 483211

GLOVIS India Pvt. Ltd. (1)
Old No 109 New No 50, Mannur Village Sriperumbuthur Talik, Kanchipuram, 602 105, Tamilnadu, India
Tel.: (91) 447118659
Web Site: https://www.glovis.co.in
Transportation Services
N.A.I.C.S.: 483211

AND PRIVATE COMPANIES

GLOVIS Russia, LLC (1)
126 Savushkina str, Atlantic City, 197374,
Saint Petersburg, Russia
Tel.: (7) 8124180800
Web Site: http://www.russia.glovis.net
Transportation Services
N.A.I.C.S.: 483211

GLOVIS Slovakia s.r.o. (1)
Sv Jana Nepomuckeho 1282/1, 013 01,
Teplicka nad Vahom, Slovakia
Tel.: (421) 415157117
Web Site: https://www.glovis.sk
Transportation Services
N.A.I.C.S.: 483211

GLOVIS Turkey Lojistik Tic. San. ve Tic. Ltd. Sti. (1)
No 83 Hayriye Is Merkezi K:1 D:2 Kozyatagi Istanbul Turkey, Hayriye Is Merkezi K1 D2 Kozyatag, Istanbul, 34742, Türkiye
Tel.: (90) 216 380 0701
Transportation Services
N.A.I.C.S.: 483211

Global Auto Processing Services (1)
567 W. ChannAutel Islands Blvd Ste 213,
Port Hueneme, CA 93041
Tel.: (805) 382-9601
Transportation Services
N.A.I.C.S.: 483211

Global Auto Processing Services Georgia LLC (1)
2000 Webb Rd, West Point, GA 31833
Tel.: (706) 902-7300
Transportation Services
N.A.I.C.S.: 483211

Global Auto Processing Services, LLC (1)
250 Hyundai Blvd, Montgomery, AL 36105
Tel.: (334) 286-0600
Transportation Services
N.A.I.C.S.: 483211

Global Logistics New Jersey, LLC (1)
275 Veterans Blvd, Rutherford, NJ 07070
Tel.: (201) 549-8777
Transportation Services
N.A.I.C.S.: 483211

Glovis Alabama, LLC (1)
300 Hyundai Blvd, Montgomery, AL 36105
Tel.: (334) 387-4200
Web Site: http://alabama.glovis.net
Sales Range: $1-9.9 Million
Logistic Services
N.A.I.C.S.: 541614
J. J. Lee (Principal)

Glovis Chennai Corporation (1)
Old No 109 New No - 50, Mannur Village Sriperumbudur, Chennai, 602105, Tamilnadu, India
Tel.: (91) 4467148679
Web Site: http://www.glovis.co.in
Logistic Services
N.A.I.C.S.: 541614

Russia Corporation (1)
126 Savushkina str 18 Floor Atlantic City Business Center, Saint Petersburg, Russia
Tel.: (7) 8124180800
Web Site: http://russia.glovis.net
Logistic Services
N.A.I.C.S.: 541614

Tianjin GLOVIS Automotive Parts Co., Ltd. (1)
No.129 Jiyun#3 Road Container Logistic Center, Beijiang Harbor Area, Beijing, China
Tel.: (86) 22 2560 1500
Transportation Services
N.A.I.C.S.: 483211

Turkey Corporation (1)
Tel.: (90) 2163800701
Web Site: http://www.glovis.com.tr
Logistic Services
N.A.I.C.S.: 541614

HYUNDAI GROUP
194 Yulgok-ro, Jongro-gu, Seoul, 110-754, Korea (South)
Tel.: (82) 237827783
Web Site:
http://www.hyundaigroup.com
Year Founded: 1947
Holding Company
Jeong-Eun Hyun (Chm & CEO)

Subsidiaries:

Hyundai Asan Corporation (1)
Hyundai Group Building 1-7 Yeonji-dong, Jongro-gu, Seoul, 110-754, Korea (South)
Tel.: (82) 2 3669 3000
Web Site: http://www.hdasan.com
Emp.: 285
Civil Engineering Services
N.A.I.C.S.: 541330
Kun Shik Cho (Pres & CEO)

Hyundai Elevator Co., Ltd. (1)
2091 Gyeongchung-daero Bubal-eup, In-cheon, 17336, Gyeonggi-do, Korea (South)
Tel.: (82) 316445114
Web Site: http://www.hyundaielevator.co.kr
Rev.: $1,633,173,945
Assets: $2,312,099,306
Liabilities: $1,417,200,503
Net Worth: $894,898,802
Earnings: $60,004,285
Emp.: 2,735
Fiscal Year-end: 12/31/2022
Elevators, Escalators, Auto Parking Systems, Material Handling Systems, Platforms & Screen Doors Mfr, Installation, Sales & Services
N.A.I.C.S.: 333921
Cho Jae-Cheon (CEO)

Subsidiary (Non-US):

HD global (hk) Engineering Services Ltd. (Hong Kong) (2)
11F Cnt House 120 Johnston Road, Wan-chai, China (Hong Kong)
Tel.: (852) 63259038
Marine Engineering Services
N.A.I.C.S.: 541330
S. C. Kim (Mgr)

HD-global (hk) Engineering Services Ltd. - Shenzhen (2)
Worl Finance Ctr Tower B 1020 4003 Rd Lo Wu, Shenzhen, 518001, Guangdong, China
Tel.: (86) 75525855903
Web Site: http://www.bip.163.com
Emp.: 20
Marine Engineering Services
N.A.I.C.S.: 541330
S. C. Kim (Mgr)

Hyco Industrial Sales Corp. (2)
81 Kapiligan Corner Bayani St Brgy Dona Imelda, Bayani St Dona Imelda Quezon, Quezon City, Philippines (100%)
Tel.: (63) 27160905
Web Site:
http://www.hyundaielevator.com.ph
Sales Range: $25-49.9 Million.
Emp.: 50
Industrial Machinery & Equipment Whslr
N.A.I.C.S.: 423830
Sergio C. Yu (Pres)

Representative Office (US):

Hyundai Elevator Co., Ltd. (2)
879 W 190th St Ste 580, Gardena, CA 90248
Tel.: (310) 538-4770
Escalator & Elevator Installer, Sales & Services
N.A.I.C.S.: 333921

Subsidiary (Non-US):

PT. Superhelindo Jaya (2)
JL KH Moch Mansyur No 19B Duri Pulo Gambir, 10140, Jakarta, Indonesia
Tel.: (62) 216318444
Sales Range: $50-74.9 Million
Emp.: 100
Elevator Distr
N.A.I.C.S.: 423830

Shanghai Hyundai Elevator Manufacturing Co., Ltd. (2)
No 182 Zhenxi Nanlu Liantang Zhen, Qingpu-Qu, Shanghai, 201716, China
Tel.: (86) 2159813981
Web Site:
http://www.hyundaielevator.com.cn
Elevators & Escalators Distr
N.A.I.C.S.: 423830

HYUNDAI HEAVY INDUSTRIES CO., LTD.
1000 Bangeojin Ring Road, Dong-gu, Ulsan, Korea (South)
Tel.: (82) 522022114
Web Site: https://www.hhi.co.kr
Year Founded: 1972
009540—(KRS)
Rev.: $15,807,049,548
Assets: $23,931,956,849
Liabilities: $14,750,282,241
Net Worth: $9,181,674,608
Earnings: $107,574,102
Emp.: 1,189
Fiscal Year-end: 12/31/23
Ship Building Mfr
N.A.I.C.S.: 336611
In-soo Chun (COO & Sr Exec VP-Indus Plant & Engrg Div)

Subsidiaries:

Hyundai Construction Equipment Industrial Co., Ltd. (1)
1000 Bangeojinsunhwan-doro, Dong-gu, Ulsan, 682-792, Korea (South)
Tel.: (82) 52 202 7722
Web Site: http://www.hyundai-ce.com
Construction Equipment Mfr & Whslr
N.A.I.C.S.: 333120
Ki Young Kong (COO)

Subsidiary (Domestic):

Hyundai Construction Equipment Service Co., Ltd. (2)
1 Cheonha-dong, Dong-gu, Ulsan, Korea (South)
Tel.: (82) 522027977
Web Site: http://www.hyundai-ce.com
Construction Equipment Sales & Services
N.A.I.C.S.: 423810

Subsidiary (US):

Hyundai Construction Equipment U.S.A., Inc. (2)
955 Estes Ave, Elk Grove Village, IL 60007
Tel.: (847) 437-3333
Sales Range: $25-49.9 Million
Emp.: 40
Construction Machinery Mfr
N.A.I.C.S.: 333120
David Lynes (Mgr-Sls-Great Lakes)

Hyundai Financial Leasing Co., Ltd. (1)
Room 3301 China Merchants Tower 161 East Lu Jia Zui Road, Shanghai, 200120, China
Tel.: (86) 2120332000
Ship Building Services
N.A.I.C.S.: 336611

Hyundai Heavy Industries France SAS (1)
17 Rue Beffroy, 92200, Neuilly-sur-Seine, France
Tel.: (33) 146371761
Ship Building Services
N.A.I.C.S.: 336611

Hyundai Khorol Agro Ltd. (1)
Primorye Office 203 5A Pushkin Str, Primor-sky Krai, Ussuriysk, Russia
Tel.: (7) 4234269635
Ship Building Services
N.A.I.C.S.: 336611

Hyundai Mipo Dockyard Co., Ltd. (1)
100 Bangeojinsunhwandoro, Dong-gu, Ul-san, 682 712, Kyongnam Do, Korea (South)
Tel.: (82) 522503038
Web Site: https://www.hd-hmd.com
Rev.: $3,128,458,342
Assets: $3,802,321,278
Liabilities: $2,241,437,866
Net Worth: $1,560,883,413
Earnings: $107,625,829)
Emp.: 3,546
Fiscal Year-end: 12/31/2023
Ship Building, Ship Repair & Conversion, Including General Hull Repair, Damage Repair, Machinery Repair
N.A.I.C.S.: 336611

Hyundai Shipbuilding (1)
1 Jeonha-dong, Dong-gu, Ulsan, 682-792, Korea (South)
Tel.: (82) 522023001
Shipbuilding
N.A.I.C.S.: 336611

Korea Shipbuilding & Offshore Engineering Co., Ltd. (1)
Calle 50 Torre Global Bank Piso 16 Oficina 1610, Panama, Panama
Tel.: (507) 2778711
Web Site: https://www.hdksoe.co.kr
Rev.: $16,334,189,675
Assets: $24,730,049,797
Liabilities: $15,242,180,848
Net Worth: $9,487,868,949
Earnings: $111,161,528
Emp.: 1,189
Fiscal Year-end: 12/31/2023
Ship Building Mfr
N.A.I.C.S.: 336611

HYUNDAI HT CO., LTD
107 Yeouidaebang-ro, Yeongdeungpo-gu, Seoul, Korea (South)
Tel.: (82) 222409114
Web Site:
https://www.hyundaitel.co.kr
Year Founded: 1998
039010—(KRS)
Rev.: $80,490,700
Assets: $90,023,289
Liabilities: $20,265,086
Net Worth: $69,758,202
Earnings: $1,529,220
Emp.: 199
Fiscal Year-end: 12/31/22
Home Automation Services
N.A.I.C.S.: 238210
Oh Hyeuk Kweon (Exec Dir)

HYUNDAI INDUSTRIAL CO., LTD.
28 Maegoksaneop 5-gil, Buk-gu, Ul-san, Korea (South)
Tel.: (82) 522761900
Web Site: https://www.hdi21.co.kr
Year Founded: 1978
170030—(KRS)
Rev.: $213,606,051
Assets: $158,383,291
Liabilities: $53,690,074
Net Worth: $104,693,218
Earnings: $8,745,431
Emp.: 178
Fiscal Year-end: 12/31/22
Automotive Seat Mfr
N.A.I.C.S.: 336360
Hyun-Suk Kang (CEO)

Subsidiaries:

Hyundai Industrial Co., Ltd. - Asan Plant (1)
313 Seobunam-ro Seonjang-myun, Cheong-nam, Asan, Korea (South)
Tel.: (82) 415436411
Emp.: 22
Automobile Parts Mfr
N.A.I.C.S.: 336390

Hyundai Industrial Co., Ltd. - Beijing Plant (1)
Cangshang Cun Beiwu zhen, Shunyi District, Beijing, China
Tel.: (86) 1061450377
Emp.: 48
Automobile Parts Mfr
N.A.I.C.S.: 336390

HYUNDAI MARINE & FIRE INSURANCE CO., LTD.
163 Sejong-daero, Jongno-gu, Seoul, 03183, Korea (South)
Tel.: (82) 15885656
Web Site: https://www.hi.co.kr
Year Founded: 1955
001450—(KRS)
Rev.: $9,973,011,313
Assets: $32,724,185,680

HYUNDAI MARINE & FIRE INSURANCE CO., LTD.

Hyundai Marine & Fire Insurance Co.,
Ltd.—(Continued)
Liabilities: $28,229,587,847
Net Worth: $4,494,597,833
Earnings: $451,159,098
Emp.: 4,231
Fiscal Year-end: 12/31/23
Investment Management Service
N.A.I.C.S.: 523999
Mong-Yoon Chung (Chm)

Subsidiaries:

Hyundai Insurance (China) Company
Ltd. (1)
Room No 508 Hyundai Motor Tower 38 Xiaoyun Road, Chaoyang District, Beijing,
China
Tel.: (86) 108 442 8100
Insurance Services
N.A.I.C.S.: 524210

Hyundai Insurance Brokers Pte.
Ltd. (1)
20 Collyer Quay 20-05, Singapore, 049319,
Singapore
Tel.: (65) 6 812 7360
Web Site: https://www.hib.com.sg
Insurance Services
N.A.I.C.S.: 524210
Chin Kwang Tan (CEO)

Hyundai Investment (America)
Ltd. (1)
300 Sylvan Ave Ste 101, Englewood Cliffs,
NJ 07632-2525
Tel.: (201) 871-8881
Investment Management Service
N.A.I.C.S.: 523940

Hyundai Investments Co., Ltd. (1)
14F Kyobo Securities Bldg 26 4 Yeouido
Dong, Youngdeungpo Gu, Seoul, 150 737,
Korea (South)
Tel.: (82) 262767083
Web Site: http://www.hdfund.co.kr
Sales Range: $25-49.9 Million
Emp.: 40
Asset Management Services
N.A.I.C.S.: 541618

Hyundai U.K Underwriting Ltd. (1)
7F 37-39 Lime Street, London, EC3M 7AY,
United Kingdom
Tel.: (44) 207 929 3822
Insurance Services
N.A.I.C.S.: 524210

HYUNDAI MOBIS CO., LTD.

203 Teheran-ro, Gangnam-gu, Seoul,
06141, Korea (South)
Tel.: (82) 220185114 KR
Web Site: https://www.mobis.co.kr
Year Founded: 1977
012330—(KRS)
Rev.: $39,812,126,731
Assets: $42,496,937,366
Liabilities: $13,498,483,622
Net Worth: $28,998,453,744
Earnings: $1,906,189,818
Emp.: 10,243
Fiscal Year-end: 12/31/22
Automobile Mfr
N.A.I.C.S.: 336110

Subsidiaries:

Beijing Hyundai Mobis Automotive
Parts Co., Ltd. (1)
59 Shuanghe Rd, Shunyi District, Beijing,
101300, China
Tel.: (86) 17728
Automotive Components Mfr
N.A.I.C.S.: 336390

Hyundai IHL Co., Ltd. (1)
215 Munsangongdan-gil, Oedong-eup,
Gyeongju, Gyeongsangbuk-do, Korea
(South)
Tel.: (82) 547707700
Automotive Components Mfr
N.A.I.C.S.: 336390
Chun Yong Duk (CEO)

Hyundai MOBIS Co., Ltd.- Anyang
Factory (1)
337-53 Bakdal-ro, Manan-gu, Anyang,
Gyeonggi-do, Korea (South)
Tel.: (82) 419507682
Automotive Components Mfr
N.A.I.C.S.: 336390

Hyundai MOBIS Co., Ltd. - Asan
Factory (1)
40 Tojeong-ro, Yeongin-myeon, Asan, 336-820, Chungcheongnam-do, Korea (South)
Tel.: (82) 415382500
Automotive Components Mfr
N.A.I.C.S.: 336390

Hyundai MOBIS Co., Ltd. -
Changwon Factory (1)
87 Seongsanpaechong-ro, Seongsan-gu,
Changwon, Gyeongsangnam-do, Korea
(South)
Tel.: (82) 552683200
Automotive Components Mfr
N.A.I.C.S.: 336390

Hyundai MOBIS Co., Ltd. - Cheonan
IP Factory (1)
105 2gongdan 2-ro, Sebuk-gu, Cheonan,
330-200, Chungcheongnam-do, Korea
(South)
Tel.: (82) 416205800
Automotive Components Mfr
N.A.I.C.S.: 336390

Hyundai MOBIS Co., Ltd. - Chungju
Factory (1)
47 Giupdosi 1-ro, Daesowon-myeon, Chungju, 380-871, Chungcheongbuk-do, Korea
(South)
Tel.: (82) 437209000
Automotive Components Mfr
N.A.I.C.S.: 336390

Hyundai MOBIS Co., Ltd. - Gimcheon
Factory (1)
258-45 Gongdan-ro, Gimcheon, 740-180,
Gyeongsangbuk-do, Korea (South)
Tel.: (82) 544204306
Automotive Components Mfr
N.A.I.C.S.: 336390

Hyundai MOBIS Co., Ltd. - Gwangju
Factory (1)
45 Jingoksandanjungang-ro, Gwangsan-gu,
Gwangju, 506-253, Korea (South)
Tel.: (82) 629498200
Automotive Components Mfr
N.A.I.C.S.: 336390

Hyundai MOBIS Co., Ltd. - Ihwa
Factory (1)
707 Namyangmoo-ro, Ujeong-eup,
Hwaseong, 445-954, Gyeonggi-do, Korea
(South)
Tel.: (82) 313586090
Automotive Components Mfr
N.A.I.C.S.: 336390

Hyundai MOBIS Co., Ltd. - Jincheon
Factory (1)
95 Sayang 2-gil, Munbaek-myeon Jincheon-gun, Jincheon, Chungcheongbuk-do, Korea
(South)
Tel.: (82) 435399114
Automotive Components Mfr
N.A.I.C.S.: 336390

Hyundai MOBIS Co., Ltd. - Poseung
Factory (1)
16 Poseunggongdan-ro 118beon-gil,
Poseung-eup, Pyeongtaek, 451-821,
Gyeonggi-do, Korea (South)
Tel.: (82) 316821741
Automotive Components Mfr
N.A.I.C.S.: 336390

Hyundai MOBIS Co., Ltd. - Seosan
Factory (1)
140 Eumam-ro, Eumam-myeon, Seosan,
356-840, Chungcheongnam-do, Korea
(South)
Tel.: (82) 416607300
Automotive Components Mfr
N.A.I.C.S.: 336390

Hyundai MOBIS Co., Ltd. - Yeompodong Factory (1)
706 Yeompo-ro, Buk-gu, Ulsan, 683-711,
Korea (South)
Tel.: (82) 522157095
Automotive Components Mfr

N.A.I.C.S.: 336390

Hyundai Motor (Shanghai) Co.,
Ltd. (1)
No 1011 Jiujing ro Songjiang Hi-Tech Park
No 1800 Husong Rdjiu Ting, Shanghai,
201615, China
Automotive Components Mfr
N.A.I.C.S.: 336390

Jiangsu Mobis Automotive Parts Co.,
Ltd. (1)
Automotive Components Mfr
N.A.I.C.S.: 336390

Mobis Alabama, LLC (1)
1395 Mitchell Young Rd, Montgomery, AL
36108
Tel.: (334) 387-4800
Automotive Components Mfr
N.A.I.C.S.: 336390

Mobis Automotive Czech s.r.o. (1)
Nosovice 171, 739 51, Dobrany, Czech
Republic
Tel.: (420) 720653527
Automotive Components Mfr
N.A.I.C.S.: 336390

Mobis Georgia LLC (1)
7001 KIA Pkwy, West Point, GA 31833
Tel.: (706) 902-7000
Automotive Components Mfr
N.A.I.C.S.: 336390

Mobis India, Ltd. (1)
Plot No G-1, Sipcot Industrial Park Irungattukottai Sriperumbudur Taluk, Kanchipuram,
602 105, Tamil Nadu, India
Tel.: (91) 4467101000
Automotive Components Mfr
N.A.I.C.S.: 336390

Mobis North America, LLC (1)
3900 Stickney Ave, Toledo, OH 43608
Automotive Components Mfr
N.A.I.C.S.: 336390

Mobis Parts America, LLC (1)
10550 Talbert Ave 4th Fl, Fountain Valley,
CA 92708
Tel.: (949) 468-1544
Automotive Components Mfr
N.A.I.C.S.: 336390

Mobis Parts Australia Pty. Ltd. (1)
77 Peter Brock Drive, Sydney, Eastern
Creek, 2766, NSW, Australia
Tel.: (61) 288228777
Automotive Components Mfr
N.A.I.C.S.: 336390

Mobis Parts Canada Corporation (1)
10 Mobis Drive, Markham, L6C 0Y3, ON,
Canada
Tel.: (905) 927-3350
Automotive Components Mfr
N.A.I.C.S.: 336390

Mobis Parts Europe B.V. (1)
Bosstraat 52, 3560, Lummen,
Belgium (100%)
Tel.: (32) 13619400
Web Site: http://www.mobis.co.kr
Sales Range: $25-49.9 Million
Emp.: 40
Automotive Parts & Accessories
N.A.I.C.S.: 336390
Jaap Kohne (Gen Mgr)

Mobis Parts Miami, LLC (1)
13200 NW 17th St, Miami, FL 33182
Tel.: (786) 515-1101
Automotive Components Mfr
N.A.I.C.S.: 336390

Mobis Parts Middle East FZE (1)
Jebel Ali Free Zone, PO Box 17337, Dubai,
United Arab Emirates
Tel.: (971) 48832228
Automotive Components Mfr
N.A.I.C.S.: 336390

Mobis Slovakia s.r.o. (1)
Automotive Components Mfr
N.A.I.C.S.: 336390

Tianjin Mobis Automotive Parts Co.,
Ltd. (1)
No 12 West of Donting Road South of No 9
Avenue Teda, Tianjin, China
Tel.: (86) 11494

INTERNATIONAL PUBLIC

Automotive Components Mfr
N.A.I.C.S.: 336390

Wuxi Mobis Automotive Parts Co.,
Ltd. (1)
Tel.: (86) 51088553600
Automotive Components Mfr
N.A.I.C.S.: 336390

HYUNDAI MOTOR COMPANY

12 Heolleung-ro, Seocho-gu, Seoul,
06797, Korea (South)
Tel.: (82) 234641114 KR
Web Site: https://www.hyundai.com
Year Founded: 1967
HYUP2—(LUX)
Rev.: $108,202
Assets: $215,231
Liabilities: $139,224
Net Worth: $76,007
Earnings: $4,547
Emp.: 71,982
Fiscal Year-end: 12/31/21
Automobile Parts Mfr
N.A.I.C.S.: 336110
Albert Biermann (Co-Pres & Dir-R&D
Div)

Subsidiaries:

Autoever Systems Europe
GmbH (1)
Kaiserleistrasse 8A, 63067, Offenbach, Germany
Tel.: (49) 69271472999
Emp.: 265
Automotive Information Technology Consulting Services
N.A.I.C.S.: 541512

Beijing Mobis Transmission Co.,
Ltd. (1)
2 Jiachuang Rd Opto-Mechatronics Industrial Base, Tongzhou District, Beijing,
101111, China
Tel.: (86) 1051652212
Mobile Transmission Equipment Mfr
N.A.I.C.S.: 333613

Boston Dynamics Inc. (1)
78 4th Ave, Waltham, MA
02451-7507 (80%)
Tel.: (617) 868-5600
Web Site: http://www.bostondynamics.com
Advanced Mobile Manipulation Robots Developer
N.A.I.C.S.: 333998
Robert Playter (CEO)

Dymos Czech Republic s.r.o (1)
Tel.: (420) 558409014
Automobile Parts Mfr
N.A.I.C.S.: 336390

G-Marine Service Co., Ltd. (1)
13th 14th 15th Floor Meritz Tower 331
Jungang-daero, Dong-gu, Busan, 48792,
Korea (South)
Tel.: (82) 513309300
Web Site: https://en.gmarineservice.com
Marine Cargo Services
N.A.I.C.S.: 488320
Hwang Chang-Kuk (CEO)

Hysco Steel India, Ltd. (1)
49 Sengadu Village Sriperumbudur, Manavala Nagar Via Kancheepuram District,
Chennai, 602 002, Tamilnadu, India
Tel.: (91) 4427670009
Steel Service Center & Distr
N.A.I.C.S.: 423510

Hyundai Architects & Engineers Associates Co., Ltd. (1)
4F Hyundai Bldg 75 Yulgok-ro, Seoul,
03058, Korea (South)
Tel.: (82) 2 746 6500
Web Site:
https://www.hyundaimotorgroup.com
Emp.: 381
Architectural Services
N.A.I.C.S.: 541310
Lee Young Chul (CEO)

Hyundai Assan Otomotiv Sanayi Ve
Ticaret A.S. (1)
Aydinevler Mah Sanayi Cad No 32 Ic Kapi

AND PRIVATE COMPANIES

HYUNDAI MOTOR COMPANY

No 20 Maltepe, 34742, Istanbul, Turkiye
Tel.: (90) 2165716363
Web Site: https://www.hyundai.com
Automobile Whslr
N.A.I.C.S.: 423110

Hyundai BNG Steel Co., Ltd. (1)
124 Jeokhyeon-ro, Seongsan-gu, Changwon, 51707, Gyeongsangnam-do, Korea (South)
Tel.: (82) 552684142
Web Site: https://www.bngsteel.com
Rev: $982,647,538
Assets: $657,966,226
Liabilities: $255,423,483
Net Worth: $402,542,744
Earnings: $19,982,331
Emp.: 511
Fiscal Year-end: 12/31/2022
Steel Products Mfr
N.A.I.C.S.: 331221
Chung Il Sun (CEO)

Hyundai Capital Corporation (1)
14 Sejong-daero, Jung-gu, Seoul, 07237, Korea (South)
Tel.: (82) 15882114
Financial Services
N.A.I.C.S.: 523999
Ted Chung (CEO & Vice Chm)

Hyundai Capital Europe GmbH (1)
Friedrich Ebert facility 35-37, 60327, Frankfurt am Main, Germany
Tel.: (49) 69920383000
Web Site: https://www.hyundaicapitalbank.eu
Financial Management Services
N.A.I.C.S.: 523999

Hyundai Capital Services, Inc. (1)
14 Sejong-daero, Jung-gu, Seoul, 07237, Korea (South) **(59.68%)**
Tel.: (82) 15882114
Web Site: https://ir.hyundaicapital.com
Rev: $3,774,626,078
Assets: $30,673,751,949
Liabilities: $25,998,500,509
Net Worth: $4,675,251,440
Earnings: $356,206,318
Fiscal Year-end: 12/31/2023
Financial Lending Services
N.A.I.C.S.: 522220
Hyung-Jin David Chung (Pres & CEO)

Joint Venture (Non-US):

Hyundai Capital Bank Europe GmbH (1)
Friedrich-Ebert-Anlage 35-37, 60327, Frankfurt am Main, Germany
Tel.: (49) 6992 038 3000
Web Site: https://www.hyundaicapitalbank.eu
Private Banking Services
N.A.I.C.S.: 523150
Martin Liehr (Mng Dir)

Subsidiary (Domestic):

Allane SE (3)
Dr -Carl-von-Linde-Str 2, 82049, Pullach, Germany **(92.07%)**
Tel.: (49) 897080810
Web Site: https://allane-mobility-group.com
Rev: $918,355,048
Assets: $1,591,307,744
Liabilities: $1,329,078,504
Net Worth: $262,229,240
Earnings: $2,702,128
Emp.: 693
Fiscal Year-end: 12/31/2020
Auto Leasing Services
N.A.I.C.S.: 532112
Michael Martin Ruhl (Chm-Mgmt Bd & CEO)

Subsidiary (Non-US):

Sixt Mobility Consulting AG (4)
Grossmattstr 9, 8902, Urdorf, Switzerland
Tel.: (41) 848111144
Automobile Parts Distr
N.A.I.C.S.: 423120

Subsidiary (Domestic):

Sixt Mobility Consulting GmbH (4)
Zugspitzstr 1, 82049, Pullach, Germany
Tel.: (49) 89744440

Web Site: http://www.mobility-consulting.com
Automobile Parts Distr
N.A.I.C.S.: 423120

Subsidiary (Non-US):

Sixt Mobility Consulting S.a.R.L. (4)
1 rue Francois Jacob, 92500, Rueil-Malmaison, France
Tel.: (33) 182732646
Automobile Parts Distr
N.A.I.C.S.: 423120

Hyundai Card Co., Ltd. (1)
3 Uisadang-daero, Yeongdeungpo-gu, Seoul, 07237, Korea (South)
Tel.: (82) 230159411
Credit Card Processing Services
N.A.I.C.S.: 522320
Ted Chung (CEO)

Hyundai Commercial Inc. (1)
3 Gukhoe-daero 66-gil, Yeongdeungpo-gu, Seoul, Korea (South)
Tel.: (82) 15775200
Financial Services
N.A.I.C.S.: 523999

Hyundai Farm Land & Development Company (1)
533 Cheonsuman-ro, Buseok-myeon, Seosan, Chungcheongnam, Korea (South)
Tel.: (82) 416618800
Farm Management Services
N.A.I.C.S.: 115116

Hyundai HYSCO Rus LLC (1)
Bld 20 lit A Levashovskoe motorway Sestroretsk, Kurortniy District, Saint Petersburg, 197706, Russia
Tel.: (7) 8124180100
Sales Range: $25-49.9 Million
Emp.: 50
Automotive Steel Parts Distr
N.A.I.C.S.: 423120
Park Chong-Keun (Gen Dir)

Hyundai KEFICO Corporation (1)
102 Gosan-ro, Gunpo, 15849, Gyeonggi-do, Korea (South) **(100%)**
Tel.: (82) 314509015
Web Site: https://www.hyundai-kefico.com
Emp.: 3,700
Automotive Electronic Management System Mfr
N.A.I.C.S.: 336110
ChangSeob Bang (CEO)

Hyundai Mnsoft, Inc. (1)
Hyundai Motor Bldg 74 Wonhyoro, Yongsan-gu, Seoul, Korea (South)
Tel.: (82) 23 483 8500
Web Site: https://update.hyundai-mnsoft.com
Automobile Parts Mfr
N.A.I.C.S.: 336390

Hyundai Motor America (1)
10550 Talbert Ave, Fountain Valley, CA 92708-6031
Tel.: (714) 965-3000
Web Site: https://www.hyundaiusa.com
Sales Range: $300-349.9 Million
Automotive Distr
N.A.I.C.S.: 423110
Jose Antonio Munoz Barcelo (Pres & CEO)

Subsidiary (Domestic):

Hyundai America Technical Center, Inc. (2)
5075 Venture Dr, Ann Arbor, MI 48108-9561
Tel.: (734) 747-6600
Automobile Mfr
N.A.I.C.S.: 336110
Christopher Giler (Engr-EMS)

Division (Non-US):

Hyundai Auto Canada (2)
75 Frontenac Drive, Markham, L3R 6H2, ON, Canada **(100%)**
Tel.: (905) 477-0202
Web Site: http://www.hyundaicanada.com
Sales Range: $50-74.9 Million
Passenger Vehicles Whslr & Distr Through Authorized Hyundai Dealers
N.A.I.C.S.: 423120

Subsidiary (Domestic):

Hyundai Capital America, inc. (2)
3161 Michelson Dr Ste 1900, Irvine, CA 92612
Tel.: (949) 468-4000
Web Site: http://www.hyundaicapitalamerica.com
Sales Range: $300-349.9 Million
Emp.: 1,700
Automotive Financial Leasing Services
N.A.I.C.S.: 522220
Marcelo Brutti (Pres & CEO)

Hyundai Motor Detroit (2)
5075 Venture Dr, Ann Arbor, MI 48108-9561
Tel.: (734) 747-6600
N.A.I.C.S.: 336110

Hyundai Motor Manufacturing Alabama, LLC (2)
700 Hyundai Blvd, Montgomery, AL 36105
Tel.: (334) 387-8000
Web Site: https://www.hmmausa.com
Sales Range: $350-399.9 Million
Automobile Mfr
N.A.I.C.S.: 336110
Robert Burns (VP-HR & Admin)

Hyundai Translead, Inc. (2)
8880 Rio San Diego Dr Ste 600, San Diego, CA 92108
Tel.: (619) 574-1500
Web Site: http://www.hyundaitranslead.com
Sales Range: $25-49.9 Million
Van Trailer & Domestic Container Mfr
N.A.I.C.S.: 336214
Kenny Lee (CEO)

Hyundai Motor Company Italy S.r.l. (1)
Via Giovanni Bensi 11, 20152, Milan, Italy
Tel.: (39) 0800352127
Web Site: https://www.hyundai.com
Automobile Whslr
N.A.I.C.S.: 423110

Hyundai Motor Espana, S.L.U. (1)
Calle Quintanapalla 2 Edificio Nectar, 28050, Madrid, Spain
Tel.: (34) 900622110
Web Site: https://www.hyundai.com
New Car Dealers
N.A.I.C.S.: 441110
Leopoldo Satrustegui (Mng Dir)

Hyundai Motor Europe GmbH (1)
Kaiserleipromenade 5, 63067, Offenbach, Germany
Tel.: (49) 69271472100
Web Site: https://www.hyundai.com
Sales Range: $100-124.9 Million
Emp.: 300
New Car Dealers
N.A.I.C.S.: 441110

Hyundai Motor Group (China) Ltd. (1)
Hyundai Motor Tower 25th Floor No 38 Xiaoyun Road, Chaoyang District, Beijing, 100027, China
Tel.: (86) 1084539666
Automobile Parts Mfr
N.A.I.C.S.: 336390
Tao Hung Tan (CEO)

Subsidiary (Non-US):

Hyundai Autoever Corp. (2)
510 Teheran-ro, Gangnam-gu, Seoul, 06179, Korea (South)
Tel.: (82) 262966000
Web Site: https://www.hyundai-autoever.com
Rev: $2,112,707,638
Assets: $2,009,107,663
Liabilities: $865,985,569
Net Worth: $1,143,122,093
Earnings: $87,375,514
Emp.: 4,138
Fiscal Year-end: 12/31/2022
Information Technology Services
N.A.I.C.S.: 541512
Kim Yun-Goo (Pres & CEO)

Hyundai Motor India Ltd. (1)
Unit No 602 - 605 6th Floor Elegance Tower Plot No -8, Jasola, New Delhi, 110 025, India **(100%)**

Tel.: (91) 1166445000
Sales Range: $50-74.9 Million
Emp.: 160
Mfr, Distr & Marketer of Automobiles
N.A.I.C.S.: 336110
Tarun Garg (COO)

Hyundai Motor Japan Co. (1)
12F Akasaka 1-chome Center BLDG 11-30 Akasaka 1-chome, Minato-ku, Tokyo, 107-0052, Japan
Tel.: (81) 362343550
Web Site: http://www.hyundai-motor.co.jp
Automobile Whslr
N.A.I.C.S.: 423110

Hyundai Motor Japan R&D Center Inc. (1)
3-2-2 Nishinohara, Inzai, 270-1334, Chiba, Japan
Tel.: (81) 476 47 6332
Automotive Research & Development Services
N.A.I.C.S.: 541715

Hyundai Motor Norway AS (1)
Alf Bjerckes vei 8, 0582, Oslo, Norway
Tel.: (47) 22706010
Web Site: https://www.hyundai.com
Sales Range: $25-49.9 Million
Automobile Whslr
N.A.I.C.S.: 423110

Hyundai Motor Poland Sp. z.o.o (1)
ul Woloska 24 6th floor, 02-675, Warsaw, Poland
Tel.: (48) 226451700
Web Site: https://www.hyundai.com
New Car Dealers
N.A.I.C.S.: 441110

Hyundai Motor Tokyo (1)
8 Fl Yurakucho Denki Bldg Kitakan 1-7-1 Yuraku-Cho, Chiyoda-Ku, Tokyo, 100 0051, Japan **(100%)**
Tel.: (81) 351570126
Sales Range: $25-49.9 Million
Emp.: 50
N.A.I.C.S.: 336110

Hyundai Motor U.K. Ltd (1)
728 London Road, High Wycombe, HP11 1HE, Bucks, United Kingdom
Tel.: (44) 1494428600
Web Site: https://www.hyundai.com
Sales Range: $25-49.9 Million
Emp.: 80
N.A.I.C.S.: 336110
Robin Hayles (Mgr-Sustainable Fuel Dev)

Hyundai Mseat Co., Ltd. (1)
231 Seobubuk-ro, Sinchang-myeon, Asan, 356-705, South Chungcheong, Korea (South)
Tel.: (82) 415400700
Web Site: https://www.hyundai-mseat.com
Emp.: 498
Car Seat Mfr
N.A.I.C.S.: 336360
Cho Won-Jang (CEO)

Hyundai Partecs Inc. (1)
29 Mujang-gil, Jigok-myeon, Seosan, Chungcheongnam-do, Korea (South)
Tel.: (82) 416600114
Motor Vehicle Parts Mfr
N.A.I.C.S.: 336390
Won Jong Hoon (Pres)

Hyundai Rotem Company (1)
37 Cheoldobakmulgwan-ro, Uiwang, Gyeonggi-do, Korea (South)
Tel.: (82) 3180908114
Web Site: https://www.hyundai-rotem.co.kr
Rev: $2,426,284,553
Assets: $3,699,908,124
Liabilities: $2,555,950,180
Net Worth: $1,143,957,944
Earnings: $149,207,772
Emp.: 3,591
Fiscal Year-end: 12/31/2022
Rolling Stock Mfr
N.A.I.C.S.: 336510
Yong-Bae Lee (Chm & CEO)

Subsidiary (Non-US):

Eurotem DEMIRYOLU ARACLARI SAN. VE TIC A.S. (2)
Ahi Evran Cad Polaris Plaza No 21 K 18 D 73 Maslak, Sisli, Istanbul, Turkiye

HYUNDAI MOTOR COMPANY

Hyundai Motor Company—(Continued)
Tel.: (90) 2122769786
Rolling Stock Mfr
N.A.I.C.S.: 336510

Plant (Domestic):

Hyundai Rotem Company - Changwon Plant (2)
85 Daewon-Dong, Uichang-gu, Changwon, Kyungsangnam-do, Korea (South)
Tel.: (82) 55 273 1341
Rolling Stock Mfr
N.A.I.C.S.: 336510

Hyundai Rotem Company - Dangjin Plant (2)
315 Godae-li Songak-myeon, Dangjin, 343-820, Chungnam, Korea (South)
Tel.: (82) 41 680 0600
Automobile Parts Mfr
N.A.I.C.S.: 336390

Subsidiary (US):

Rotem USA Corporation (2)
2400 Weccacoe Ave, Philadelphia, PA 19148
Tel.: (215) 227-6836
Sales Range: $25-49.9 Million
Emp.: 30
Railroad Equipment Mfr
N.A.I.C.S.: 336510
H. Kim (Pres)

Hyundai Transys (1)
105 Sindang 1-ro 703-2 Galhyeon-ri, Seongyeon-myeon, Seosan, 31930, Chungcheongnam-do, Korea (South)
Tel.: (82) 416617061
Sales Range: $1-4.9 Billion
Automotive & Other Vehicle Parts Mfr
N.A.I.C.S.: 336390

Hyundai WIA Automotive Engine (Shandong) Company (1)
No 188 Shanghai Rd, Donggang Dist, Rizhao, 276826, Shandong, China
Tel.: (86) 6332299064
Automotive Engine Mfr
N.A.I.C.S.: 336310

Hyundai WIA Corporation (1)
153 Jeongdong-ro, Seongsan-gu, Changwon, 641110, Gyeongnam, Korea (South)
Tel.: (82) 552809114
Web Site: https://www.hyundai-wia.com
Rev.: $6,295,239,938
Assets: $5,788,127,917
Liabilities: $2,924,417,600
Net Worth: $2,863,710,317
Earnings: $33,350,694
Emp.: 2,954
Fiscal Year-end: 12/31/2022
Automobile Parts Mfr
N.A.I.C.S.: 336390
Jae-Wook Jung (Pres, CEO & Exec Dir)

Plant (Domestic):

Hyundai WIA Corporation - Ulsan Plant 2 (1)
35 Songdo-gil, Buk-gu, Ulsan, 683-360, Korea (South)
Tel.: (82) 52 219 1300
Automobile Parts Mfr
N.A.I.C.S.: 336390

Subsidiary (US):

Hyundai-Wia Machine America Corp. (2)
450 Commerce Blvd, Carlstadt, NJ 07072
Tel.: (201) 987-7298
Web Site: http://www.hyundai-wiamachine.com
Industrial Machinery Mfr
N.A.I.C.S.: 333248

Hyundai-Wia India PVT LTD (1)
No 6 Papparambakkam Village, Thiruvallur, Chennai, 602025, Tamilnadu, India
Tel.: (91) 4427672016
Sales Range: $50-74.9 Million
Emp.: 250
Automobile Parts Mfr
N.A.I.C.S.: 336390

Jeonbuk Hyundai Motors FC Co., Ltd. (1)
763-1 Banwol-Dong, Deokjin-Gu, Chonju, 561370, Chollabuk-Do, Korea (South)
Tel.: (82) 632731763
Football Club Management Services
N.A.I.C.S.: 711211

HYUNDAI MOTOR SECURITIES CO. LTD.
25-3 Youido-dong, Yeoungdeungpo-gu, Seoul, Korea (South)
Tel.: (82) 237872114
Web Site: http://www.hmcib.com
Year Founded: 1955
001500—(KRS)
Rev.: $1,174,381,277
Assets: $8,599,124,777
Liabilities: $7,650,680,129
Net Worth: $948,444,647
Earnings: $39,718,536
Emp.: 892
Fiscal Year-end: 12/31/23
Financial Services
N.A.I.C.S.: 523999
Byung Chul Choi (Pres & CEO)

HYUNDAI MOVEX CO., LTD.
194 Yulgok-Ro, Jongno-Gu, Seoul, Korea (South)
Tel.: (82) 220726000
Web Site: https://www.hyundaimovex.com
Year Founded: 2019
319400—(KRS)
Sales Range: Less than $1 Million
Emp.: 350
General Purpose Machinery Mfr
N.A.I.C.S.: 333998
Ki-Bong Hyun (CEO)

HYUNDAI OILBANK CO., LTD.
Yonsei Bldg 20F 10 Tongil-ro, Jung-gu, Seoul, 04527, Korea (South)
Tel.: (82) 220043000
Web Site: http://www.oilbank.co.kr
Year Founded: 1964
Rev.: $18,160,485,812
Assets: $11,056,041,016
Liabilities: $6,376,270,753
Net Worth: $4,679,770,262
Earnings: $269,110,009
Fiscal Year-end: 12/31/19
Petroleum Refining & Marketing Service Petrochemical Mfr
N.A.I.C.S.: 324110
Dal Ho Kang (CEO)

Subsidiaries:

Hyundai Oilbank Co., Ltd. - DAESAN Refinery Plant (1)
182 Pyeongsin 2-ro, Daesan-eup, Seosan, Chungcheongnam-do, Korea (South)
Tel.: (82) 416605114
Petroleum Refinery Services
N.A.I.C.S.: 324110

Hyundai Oilbank Singapore Pte Ltd. (1)
7 Temasek Blvd Unit 29-01 Suntec Tower One, Singapore, 038987, Singapore
Tel.: (65) 63321400
Web Site: http://www.oilbank.co.sr
Sales Range: $50-74.9 Million
Emp.: 5
Petroleum Refining & Marketing Services; Petrochemical Mfr
N.A.I.C.S.: 324110

HYUNDAI PHARM CO., LTD.
55 Jandari-gil Pungse-myeon Dongnam-gu, Cheonan, Chungcheongnam-do, Korea (South)
Tel.: (82) 415705114   KR
Web Site: http://www.hyundaipharm.co.kr
Year Founded: 1965
004310—(KRS)
Rev.: $113,883,032

Assets: $126,811,599
Liabilities: $66,222,902
Net Worth: $60,588,697
Earnings: ($115,208)
Emp.: 382
Fiscal Year-end: 11/30/22
Pharmaceutical & Beverage Mfr
N.A.I.C.S.: 325412
Han Gu Lee (Chm & CEO)

HYUNDAI PHARMACEUTICAL CO., LTD.
Hyundai Pharm bldg Bongeunsa-ro 135, Gangnam-gu, Seoul, 06121, Chungcheong, Korea (South)
Tel.: (82) 415705114
Web Site: https://www.hyundaipharm.co.kr
Year Founded: 1965
004310—(KRS)
Rev.: $128,618,533
Assets: $150,748,823
Liabilities: $71,076,525
Net Worth: $79,672,299
Earnings: ($2,919,322)
Emp.: 364
Fiscal Year-end: 11/30/21
Pharmaceuticals Product Mfr
N.A.I.C.S.: 325412
Lee Sang Joon (CEO)

HYUNDAI STEEL COMPANY
63 Jungbongdae-ro, Dong-gu, Incheon, Korea (South)
Tel.: (82) 327602114   KR
Web Site: https://www.hyundai-steel.com
Year Founded: 1953
004020—(KRS)
Rev.: $19,235,159,105
Assets: $26,141,087,786
Liabilities: $11,670,235,591
Net Worth: $14,470,852,195
Earnings: $328,803,246
Emp.: 11,833
Fiscal Year-end: 12/31/23
Iron & Steel Product Mfr
N.A.I.C.S.: 331221
An Tong-il (Pres & CEO)

Subsidiaries:

Green Air Co., Ltd. (1)
315 Godae-ri Songak-myeon, Dangjin, 343823, Korea (South) (51%)
Tel.: (82) 4 1680 7580
Emp.: 40
Industrial Gas Mfr & Whslr
N.A.I.C.S.: 325120
Kae Kwan Choi (Mgr)

Hyundai Beijing Steel Process Co., Ltd. (China) (1)
NO 63 Shuanghe Street, Shuny, Beijing, 101300, China
Tel.: (86) 1089401525
Steel Service Center & Distr
N.A.I.C.S.: 423510

Hyundai Special Steel Co., Ltd. (1)
10F 308 Gangnam-Daero, Gangnam-gu, Seoul, Korea (South)
Tel.: (82) 261918555
Web Site: http://www.en.hyundai-specialsteel.com
Steel Mfrs
N.A.I.C.S.: 331221

Hyundai Steel America, Inc. (1)
200 Team Member Ln, Greenville, AL 36037 (100%)
Tel.: (334) 382-9100
Web Site: https://www.hyundai-steel.us
Steel Service Center & Whslr
N.A.I.C.S.: 423510

Hyundai Steel Chongqing Co., Ltd. (1)
No 2 Zhiyuan Road Longjun Avenue, Longxing Town Yubei, Chongqing, 401135, China
Tel.: (86) 2363422386
Steel Mfrs

INTERNATIONAL PUBLIC

N.A.I.C.S.: 331221

Hyundai Steel Company - Ulsan Plant (1)
706 Yeompo-ro, Buk-gu, Ulsan, Korea (South)
Tel.: (82) 522800114
Steel Mfrs
N.A.I.C.S.: 331221

Hyundai Steel Company - Yesan Plant (1)
131 Sandan 1-gil Sapgyo-eup, Yesan, Chungcheongnam, Korea (South)
Tel.: (82) 413304500
Steel Mfrs
N.A.I.C.S.: 331221

Hyundai Steel Czech s.r.o (1)
Hyundai 333/5, 739 51, Nosovice, Czech Republic
Tel.: (420) 558419303
Web Site: https://www.hyundai-steel.cz
Steel Mfrs
N.A.I.C.S.: 331221

Hyundai Steel India Private, Ltd. (1)
49 Sengadu Village, Sriperumbudur - Manavala Nagar Via, Kanchipuram, 602 002, India
Web Site: http://www.hyundai-steel.co.in
Emp.: 110
Steel Mfrs
N.A.I.C.S.: 331221

Subsidiary (Domestic):

Hyundai Steel Pipe India Private, Ltd. (2)
49 Sengadu Village Sriperumbudur-Manavala Nagar Sriperumbudur Taluk, Kanchipuram, India
Tel.: (91) 4427670002
Steel Mfrs
N.A.I.C.S.: 331221

Hyundai Steel Industry & Trade Brazil LLC (1)
Avenida Hyundai 1505 Agua Santa-Piracicaba, Sao Paulo, Brazil
Tel.: (55) 1934305803
Steel Mfrs
N.A.I.C.S.: 331221

Hyundai Steel Investment (China) Co., Ltd. (1)
17th TEDA MSD-G2 Bldg No 57 2nd Avenue TEDA, Tianjin, 300457, China
Tel.: (86) 18622797847
Steel Mfrs
N.A.I.C.S.: 331221

Hyundai Steel Jiangsu Process Co., Ltd. (1)
No 51 Huangshan South Road Economic Developement Zone, Yancheng, 22007, Jiangsu, China
Tel.: (86) 5158140020
Steel Mfrs
N.A.I.C.S.: 331221

Hyundai Steel Mexico S de R. L. de C. V. (1)
Carretera Pesqueria-Ramones KM 13-15 interior 15 pesqueria Nuevo, 66650, Leon, Mexico
Tel.: (52) 8188525810
Steel Mfrs
N.A.I.C.S.: 331221

Hyundai Steel Rus LLC (1)
20 Levashovskoe highway, Sestroretsk, 197701, Saint Petersburg, Russia
Tel.: (7) 8124180907
Web Site: http://en.hyundai-steel.ru
Steel Pole Mfr
N.A.I.C.S.: 331110

Hyundai Steel Slovakia s.r.o. (1)
Mobis ullica 417/1A, Gbelany, 013 02, Zilina, Slovakia
Tel.: (421) 415157700
Web Site: https://hyundai-steel.sk
Steel Products Fabrication Services
N.A.I.C.S.: 423510

Hyundai Steel Suzhou Process Co., Ltd. (1)
No 26 Zijing Road Economic Technological Development Zone, South Area, Zhangjia-

gang, Jiangsu, China
Tel.: (86) 51288837001
Steel Mfrs
N.A.I.C.S.: 331221

Hyundai Steel TR Automotive Steel Parts Co., Ltd. (1)
Ataturk Mah Kocaeli Asim Kibar OSB 4 Cad No 2 Alikahya, Izmit, Kocaeli, Turkiye
Tel.: (90) 2623102016
Steel Mfrs
N.A.I.C.S.: 331221

Hyundai Steel Tianjin Co., Ltd. (1)
No 65 Bibo East Street, Hangu District, Tianjin, 300480, China
Tel.: (86) 2267161861
Steel Mfrs
N.A.I.C.S.: 331221

Hyundai Steel USA, Inc. (1)
16200 Park Row Ste 270, Houston, TX 77084
Tel.: (281) 578-5325
Web Site: http://www.hyundai-steel.com
Steel Pipe Distr
N.A.I.C.S.: 423510

Qingdao Hyundai Machinery Co., Ltd. (1)
North of NO 8 Rd East of zhuzhou Rd, Jiaozhouwan Industry Park, Qingdao, 266300, Shandong, China
Tel.: (86) 53287273900
Steel Mfrs
N.A.I.C.S.: 331221

HYUNDAI WEST-ISLAND
1625 boul Hymus, Dorval, H9P 1J5, QC, Canada
Tel.: (514) 683-5702
Web Site: http://www.hyundaiwestisland.com
New & Used Car Dealer
N.A.I.C.S.: 441110
Christin Dubreuil (Pres)

HYUNGJI ELITE INC.
10F Business Building 49 Harmony-ro 177beon-gil, Yeonsu-gu, Incheon, Korea (South)
Tel.: (82) 324548431
Web Site: https://www.hyungji-elite.com
Year Founded: 1969
093240—(KRS)
Rev.: $72,754,203
Assets: $96,347,319
Liabilities: $42,503,702
Net Worth: $53,843,617
Earnings: $1,538,101
Emp.: 131
Fiscal Year-end: 06/30/23
Apparels Mfr
N.A.I.C.S.: 315990
Choi Byoung-Oh (CEO)

HYUNGJI INNOVATION AND CREATIVE COMPANY LIMITED
49 Harmony-ro 177beon-gil, Yeonsu-gu, Incheon, Korea (South)
Tel.: (82) 261194900
Web Site: http://www.woosunginc.com
Year Founded: 1976
011080—(KRS)
Rev.: $54,070,230
Assets: $46,070,358
Liabilities: $23,774,860
Net Worth: $22,295,498
Earnings: ($501,763)
Emp.: 70
Fiscal Year-end: 12/31/22
Men's Apparel Mfr & Distr
N.A.I.C.S.: 315250
Ham Jong Hyuk (Gen Mgr)

HYUNGKUK F&B CO.,LTD
23-24F 60 Mabang-ro, Seocho-gu, Seoul, 06775, Korea (South)
Tel.: (82) 257224456

Web Site: https://www.hyungkuk.com
Year Founded: 2008
189980—(KRS)
Rev.: $74,591,952
Assets: $161,487,924
Liabilities: $90,213,769
Net Worth: $71,274,155
Earnings: $9,124,109
Emp.: 154
Fiscal Year-end: 12/31/22
Non-Alcoholic Beverage Mfr
N.A.I.C.S.: 722515
Kwon Soon Seok (Deputy Gen Mgr)

HYUNION HOLDING CO., LTD.
No 1626 Qingwei Road, Jimo District, Qingdao, 266200, Shandong, China
Tel.: (86) 53289066166
Web Site: http://www.haili.com.cn
Year Founded: 2004
002537—(SSE)
Sales Range: $350-399.9 Million
Metal Products Mfr
N.A.I.C.S.: 332999
Liu Guoping (Chm & Pres)

HYUPJIN CO., LTD.
16 MTV28-ro, Siheung, 27650, Gyeonggi-do, Korea (South)
Tel.: (82) 314329023   KR
Web Site: https://www.hjfm.co.kr
Year Founded: 2001
138360—(KRS)
Rev.: $11,469,772
Assets: $39,979,516
Liabilities: $9,756,281
Net Worth: $30,223,235
Earnings: ($4,649,802)
Emp.: 44
Fiscal Year-end: 12/31/22
Phytochemical Material Mfr & Distr
N.A.I.C.S.: 325411

HYVISION SYSTEM INC.
527 Duncheon-daero, Jungwon-gu, Seongnam, 13216, Gyeonggi-do, Korea (South)
Tel.: (82) 317351573
Web Site: https://www.hyvision.co.kr
Year Founded: 2002
126700—(KRS)
Rev.: $151,619,014
Assets: $237,286,091
Liabilities: $66,146,178
Net Worth: $171,139,913
Earnings: $18,431,518
Emp.: 333
Fiscal Year-end: 12/31/22
Measuring & Controlling Device Mfr
N.A.I.C.S.: 334519
Doowon Choi (CEO)

Subsidiaries:

Cubicon Inc. (1)
Web Site: http://www.3dcubicon.com
Electric Device Mfr
N.A.I.C.S.: 334419

HyVision Technology Inc. (1)
Tel.: (86) 76926267682
Automatic Test & Measurement Equipment Mfr
N.A.I.C.S.: 334519

HyVision Vina Company Limited (1)
Que Vo Industry Park Inside MY A Company Hamlet, Que Vo Dist, Phuong Lieu, Bac Ninh, Vietnam
Tel.: (84) 2223903046
Automatic Test & Measurement Equipment Mfr
N.A.I.C.S.: 334519

HYWEB TECHNOLOGY CO., LTD.
5F -6 No 8 Taiyuan 1st St, Hsin-Chu, Zhubei, 302, Taiwan
Tel.: (886) 35601296

5212—(TPE)
Rev.: $30,515,368
Assets: $27,295,657
Liabilities: $11,211,425
Net Worth: $16,084,232
Earnings: $3,104,399
Fiscal Year-end: 12/31/22
Credit Card Payment Services
N.A.I.C.S.: 522210
Yang-Juh Lai (Chm & CEO)

HYWIN HOLDINGS LTD.
F3 8 Yincheng Mid Road, Pudong New District, Shanghai, 200120, China
Tel.: (86) 2180133992   Ky
Web Site: http://ir.hywinwealth.com
Year Founded: 2006
HYW—(NASDAQ)
Rev.: $293,682,683
Assets: $333,238,277
Liabilities: $162,986,148
Net Worth: $170,252,129
Earnings: $18,235,292
Emp.: 2,905
Fiscal Year-end: 06/30/23
Holding Company
N.A.I.C.S.: 551112
Huichuan Zhou (VP-Strategic Projects)

HZ HRVATSKE ZELJEZNICE HOLDING D.O.O.
Antuna Mihanovica 12, 10000, Zagreb, Croatia
Tel.: (385) 14577111   HR
Web Site: http://www.hznet.hr
Sales Range: $1-4.9 Billion
Emp.: 15,000
Holding Company; Passenger & Freight Railroads Operator
N.A.I.C.S.: 551112
Marijan Klaric (Member-Mgmt Bd)

Subsidiaries:

AGIT - Agencija za integralni transport d.o.o. (1)
Heinzelova 51, 10000, Zagreb, Croatia
Tel.: (385) 12350800
Web Site: http://www.agit.hr
Sales Range: $75-99.9 Million
Emp.: 15
Railroad Freight Transportation Arrangement Services
N.A.I.C.S.: 488510

HZPC HOLLAND B.V.
Edisonweg 5, Joure, 8501 XG, Netherlands
Tel.: (31) 513 48 98 88
Web Site: http://www.hzpc.nl
Rev.: $392,281,359
Assets: $144,881,888
Liabilities: $84,913,385
Net Worth: $59,968,503
Earnings: $10,474,051
Fiscal Year-end: 06/30/19
Seed Potato Production Services
N.A.I.C.S.: 111211

Subsidiaries:

Bonna Terra B.V. (1)
Edisonweg 5, 8501 XG, Joure, Netherlands
Tel.: (31) 513489888
Web Site: http://www.en.bonnaterra.nl
Organic Chemical Distr
N.A.I.C.S.: 424690

HZPC America Latina S.A. (1)
Cnel E Arias 1691 Piso 9 C, C1429DWA, Buenos Aires, Argentina
Tel.: (54) 1147029099
Seed Potato Distr
N.A.I.C.S.: 424450

HZPC Deutschland GmbH (1)
Hasslau 2, 49406, Eydelstedt, Germany
Tel.: (49) 5442804225
Seed Potato Distr
N.A.I.C.S.: 424450

HZPC France SAS (1)
Avenue Industrielle, 59931, La Chapelle-d'Armentieres, France
Tel.: (33) 320358513
Web Site: http://www.hzpc.fr
Potato Production
N.A.I.C.S.: 111211
Pierre Huchette (Dir Gen)

HZPC Kantaperuna Oy (1)
Leppiojantie 11, 91800, Tyrnava, Finland
Tel.: (358) 85617812
Seed Potato Distr
N.A.I.C.S.: 424450

HZPC Patatas Espana S.L. (1)
Avenida Santa Apolonia 39, 46901, Torrente, Spain
Tel.: (34) 961589551
Seed Potato Mfr
N.A.I.C.S.: 111211

HZPC Polska Sp. z.o.o (1)
Ul Baltycka 6, 61-960, Poznan, Poland
Tel.: (48) 618483886
Web Site: http://www.hzpc.pl
Seed Potato Distr
N.A.I.C.S.: 424450

HZPC Portugal Lda (1)
Urbanizacao quinta de Sao Mateus Lote3d Loja17, 3060-209, Cantanhede, Portugal
Tel.: (351) 231024020
Seed Potato Distr
N.A.I.C.S.: 424450

HZPC Sverige AB (1)
Bolshedens Industrivag 28 2 tr, 427 50, Billdal, Sweden
Tel.: (46) 31224020
Web Site: http://www.hzpc-kantaperuna.com
Seed Potato Distr
N.A.I.C.S.: 424450

HZPC UK Ltd (1)
2 Wharf Road, Crowle, DN17 4HS, North Lincolnshire, United Kingdom
Tel.: (44) 1724710033
Seed Potato Distr
N.A.I.C.S.: 424450

Stet Holland B.V. (1)
Produktieweg 2a, 8304 AV, Emmeloord, Netherlands
Tel.: (31) 527630063
Web Site: http://www.stet.nl
Seed Potato Mfr
N.A.I.C.S.: 111211
Peter Ton (Gen Mgr)

ZOS. B.V. (1)
Postbus 1003, 8300 BA, Emmeloord, Netherlands
Tel.: (31) 527 69 73 31
Web Site: http://www.zos.nl
Organic Chemical Distr
N.A.I.C.S.: 424690

I & E CONSULTANTS
32 rue de Trevise, 75423, Paris, France
Tel.: (33) 1 56 03 12 12
Year Founded: 1962
Rev.: $14,910,279
Emp.: 150
Public Relations Agency
N.A.I.C.S.: 541820
Jean-Pierre Beaudoin (Mng Dir)

I GRANDI VIAGGI S.P.A.
Via della Moscova 36, 20121, Milan, Italy
Tel.: (39) 02290461
Web Site: https://www.igrandiviaggi.it
Year Founded: 1932
IGV—(ITA)
Sales Range: $100-124.9 Million
Tour & Resort Operator
N.A.I.C.S.: 561599
Luigi Mario Clementi (Chm)

I J MCGILL TRANSPORT LTD
Broadmead Lane, Keynsham, Bristol, BS31 1ST, United Kingdom
Tel.: (44) 1179861777

I J MCGILL TRANSPORT LTD

I J McGill Transport Ltd—(Continued)
Web Site:
http://www.ijmcgilltransport.com
Year Founded: 1979
Sales Range: $10-24.9 Million
Emp.: 200
Transportation Services
N.A.I.C.S.: 488999
Ian McGill *(Owner & Mng Dir)*

I JIANG INDUSTRIAL CO., LTD.
4 Hsing Kung Rd Lun Chiao Village, Pitou Township, Chang-Hua, 523, Taiwan
Tel.: (886) 48926130
Web Site: https://www.i-jang.com
Year Founded: 1987
8342—(TPE)
Metal Furniture & Display Rack Mfr
N.A.I.C.S.: 337215

I M QUARRIES LIMITED
1 Commonwealth Lane 09-28 One-Commonwealth, Singapore, 149544, Singapore
Tel.: (65) 64625123 SG
Web Site:
https://www.imquarries.com
Year Founded: 2011
IM1—(NSXA)
Assets: $1,038,100
Liabilities: $697,880
Net Worth: $340,220
Earnings: ($584,407)
Fiscal Year-end: 03/31/23
Mineral Mining & Exploration Services
N.A.I.C.S.: 212390
Rebecca Lin *(VP-Grp-Regulatory & Compliance)*

I SYNERGY GROUP LIMITED
Tel.: (61) 289991199
Web Site: https://www.i-synergygroup.com
Year Founded: 2008
IS3—(ASX)
Rev.: $710,721
Assets: $380,211
Liabilities: $1,989,662
Net Worth: ($1,609,451)
Earnings: ($615,666)
Fiscal Year-end: 12/31/23
Marketing & Advertising Services
N.A.I.C.S.: 541613
Lawrence Teo *(Founder, Exec Chm, Chm & Mng Dir)*
Subsidiaries:
Ocean Nexus Sdn. Bhd. (1)
C-2-3A Pacific Place Jalan PJU 1A/4, Ara Damansara, 47301, Petaling Jaya, Selangor, Malaysia
Tel.: (60) 376258836
Web Site: http://www.oceannexus.my
Emp.: 13
Software Services
N.A.I.C.S.: 541511

PT Inovatif Sinergi International (1)
Kantor Taman E3 3 Unit A2 Jl DR Ide Anak Agung Gde Agung, Lot 8 6-8 7/E 3 3 Kawasan Mega Kuningan Kuningan Timur Setiabudi, Jakarta Selatan, 12950, Indonesia
Tel.: (62) 2157942020
Marketing & Advertising Services
N.A.I.C.S.: 541890

I SYNERGY HOLDINGS BERHAD
1-1 Jalan Tasik Utama 4 Medan Niaga Tasik Damai, Lake Fields Sg Besi, Kuala Lumpur, Malaysia
Tel.: (60) 3 9054 8355
Web Site: http://www.i-s.com.my
Marketing Services
N.A.I.C.S.: 541613

Will Ong *(Chief Bus Officer)*

I T K INTERNATIONALES TRANSPORT-KONTOR GMBH
Nordbeckenstr 10 13, 76189, Karlsruhe, Germany
Tel.: (49) 721559010
Web Site: http://www.itklogistics.com
Year Founded: 1925
Sales Range: $25-49.9 Million
Logistic Services
N.A.I.C.S.: 541614
Ursula Cantrup Korporal *(Mng Dir)*

I YUAN PRECISION INDUSTRIAL CO., LTD.
No 24 Dinghu Rd, Guishan Dist, Taoyuan, 333, Taiwan
Tel.: (886) 33973868
Web Site: https://www.tiy-motor.com
2235—(TPE)
Rev.: $22,606,072
Assets: $67,026,483
Liabilities: $24,621,174
Net Worth: $42,405,309
Earnings: $5,149,986
Fiscal Year-end: 12/31/22
Automobile Parts Mfr & Distr
N.A.I.C.S.: 336390
Chieh-Shih Wu *(Chm & Pres)*

I&C TECHNOLOGY CO., LTD.
I&C Building 24 Pangyo-ro 255 beon-gil Bundang-gu, Seongnam-si, Seoul, 13486, Gyeonggi-do, Korea (South)
Tel.: (82) 316963300
Web Site: http://www.inctech.co.kr
Year Founded: 1996
052860—(KRS)
Rev.: $30,208,062
Assets: $50,159,571
Liabilities: $16,164,393
Net Worth: $33,995,178
Earnings: $789,493
Emp.: 93
Fiscal Year-end: 12/31/22
Semiconductor Product Mfr & Sales
N.A.I.C.S.: 334413
Chang-Il Park *(CEO)*

I&I GROUP PUBLIC COMPANY LIMITED
475 Siripinyo Building 18 Fl Si Ayutthaya Rd, Thanon Phaya Thai Ratchathewi, Bangkok, 10400, Thailand
Tel.: (66) 22483746 TH
Web Site: https://www.ii.co.th
Year Founded: 1991
IIG—(THA)
Rev.: $27,692,379
Assets: $44,760,340
Liabilities: $27,366,304
Net Worth: $17,394,035
Earnings: ($9,150,515)
Fiscal Year-end: 12/31/23
Information Technology Services
N.A.I.C.S.: 541512
Somchai Mekasuvanroj *(Vice Chm & CEO)*

I&M GROUP PLC
IM Tower Kenyatta Avenue, PO Box 30238, 00100, Nairobi, Kenya
Tel.: (254) 203221000
Web Site:
https://www.imbankgroup.com
I&M—(NAI)
Rev.: $265,662,424
Assets: $3,083,542,792
Liabilities: $2,488,310,740
Net Worth: $595,232,052
Earnings: $100,822,392
Emp.: 1,330
Fiscal Year-end: 12/31/19
Holding Company

N.A.I.C.S.: 551112
Sarit S. Raja Shah *(Exec Dir)*
Subsidiaries:

I&M Burbidge Capital Limited (1)
1 Park Avenue First Parklands Ave, Westlands, Nairobi, Kenya
Tel.: (254) 719088160
Web Site:
https://www.imburbidgecapital.com
Financial Advisory Services
N.A.I.C.S.: 523940
Ferdinand Okoth *(Head-Corp Fin Technical)*

I'ANSON BROTHERS LTD
The Mill Thorpe Road, Masham, Ripon, HG4 4JB, North Yorkshire, United Kingdom
Tel.: (44) 1765689332
Web Site: http://www.ianson.co.uk
Year Founded: 1900
Rev.: $46,519,171
Emp.: 70
Animal Feedstuffs Mfr
N.A.I.C.S.: 311119
Will I'Anson *(Dir-Sls)*

I'LL INC.
Front Osaka Tower B 34th floor 3-1 Ofukacho, Kita-ku, Osaka, 530-0011, Japan
Tel.: (81) 647981170
Web Site: https://www.ill.co.jp
3854—(TKS)
Rev.: $108,899,760
Assets: $88,031,660
Liabilities: $27,822,060
Net Worth: $60,209,600
Earnings: $17,957,140
Emp.: 938
Fiscal Year-end: 07/31/24
Communication Product Mfr
N.A.I.C.S.: 334290

I'ROM GROUP CO., LTD.
Iidabashi Grand Bloom 2-10-2 Fujimi, Chiyoda-ku, Tokyo, 102-0071, Japan
Tel.: (81) 332643148
Web Site:
https://www.iromgroup.co.jp
Year Founded: 1997
2372—(TKS)
Rev.: $117,261,400
Assets: $245,548,280
Liabilities: $161,125,360
Net Worth: $84,422,920
Earnings: $9,353,150
Emp.: 824
Fiscal Year-end: 03/31/24
Holding Company
N.A.I.C.S.: 551112
Toyotaka Mori *(Founder, Pres & CEO)*
Subsidiaries:

Cmax Clinical Research Pty Ltd (1)
Ground Floor 21-24 North Terrace, Adelaide, 5000, SA, Australia
Tel.: (61) 870887900
Healthcare Services
N.A.I.C.S.: 621610

Cmax Japan Co., Ltd. (1)
2-10-2 Fujimi Grand Bloom, Chiyoda-ku Iidabashi, Tokyo, 102-0071, Japan
Tel.: (81) 352101668
Healthcare Services
N.A.I.C.S.: 621610

I'rom Co., Ltd. (1)
2-10-2 Fujimi Grand Bloom 5F/6F, Chiyoda-ku Iidabashi, Tokyo, 102-0071, Japan
Tel.: (81) 332643345
Web Site: http://www.irom.co.jp
Healthcare Services
N.A.I.C.S.: 621610

I'rom Cs Co., Ltd. (1)
11th Floor Acros Fukuoka 1-1-1 Tenjin, Chuo-ku, Fukuoka, 810-0001, Japan

Tel.: (81) 927380500
Web Site: http://www.irom-cs.co.jp
Healthcare Services
N.A.I.C.S.: 621610

I'rom Ec Co., Ltd. (1)
2-10-2 Fujimi Grand Bloom, Chiyoda-ku, Tokyo, 102-0071, Japan
Tel.: (81) 332343300
Web Site: http://www.ethic.co.jp
Healthcare Services
N.A.I.C.S.: 621610

I'rom Na Co., Ltd. (1)
2-5 Kita Gojo Nishi JR Tower Office Plaza Sapporo 12F, Chuo-ku, Sapporo, 060-0005, Hokkaido, Japan
Tel.: (81) 112426200
Web Site: http://www.irom-na.co.jp
Healthcare Services
N.A.I.C.S.: 621610

I'rom Pm Co., Ltd. (1)
2-10-2 Fujimi Grand Bloom, Chiyoda-ku Iidabashi, Tokyo, 102-0071, Japan
Tel.: (81) 52156408
Web Site: http://www.irom-pm.co.jp
Real Estate Lending Services
N.A.I.C.S.: 531110

I-BERHAD
i-Gallery Persiaran Multimedia I-City, 40000, Shah Alam, Selangor, Malaysia
Tel.: (60) 355218800
Web Site: https://www.i-bhd.com
Year Founded: 1967
IBHD—(KLS)
Rev.: $19,852,965
Assets: $471,951,810
Liabilities: $189,296,168
Net Worth: $282,655,643
Earnings: $104,940
Emp.: 250
Fiscal Year-end: 12/31/21
Property Development & Investment Services
N.A.I.C.S.: 531312
Kim Hong Lim *(Chm)*

I-CHIUN PRECISION INDUSTRY CO., LTD.
17 Wu-Gung-Wu Rd, Shin-Chuang District, New Taipei City, 24890, Taiwan
Tel.: (886) 222990001
Web Site: https://www.i-chiun.com.tw
Year Founded: 1977
2486—(TAI)
Rev.: $165,757,409
Assets: $254,985,798
Liabilities: $111,645,210
Net Worth: $143,340,588
Earnings: $6,504,725
Emp.: 1,610
Fiscal Year-end: 12/31/23
Electric Equipment Mfr
N.A.I.C.S.: 334419
Subsidiaries:

I-Chiun Precision Electric (Nanjing) Co., Ltd. (1)
No 68-6 Suyuan Avenue Nanjing City Export Manufacture Zone South, Nanjing, China
Tel.: (86) 2552728288
Optoelectronic Lead Frame Mfr
N.A.I.C.S.: 334413

I-Chiun Precision Electric Industry (China) Co., Ltd. (1)
No 2 Songnan East Road Qiandeng Township, Kunshan, Jiangsu, China
Tel.: (86) 51257408111
Optoelectronic Lead Frame Mfr
N.A.I.C.S.: 334413

I-Chiun Precision Industry Co., Ltd. (1)
17 Wu-Gung-Wu Rd Shin-Chuang District, New Taipei City, 24890, Taiwan
Tel.: (886) 222990001
Optoelectronic Lead Frame Mfr

AND PRIVATE COMPANIES

N.A.I.C.S.: 334413

I-Chiun Precision Industry Co., Ltd. - Nanjing Plant (1)
No 68-6 Suyuan Avenue Nanjing City Export Manufacture Zone South, Nanjing, China
Tel.: (86) 2552728288
Optoelectronic Lead Frame Mfr
N.A.I.C.S.: 334413

I-Zou Hi-Tech (Szn) Co., Ltd. (1)
Industrial Park Jiangbian Songgang Township, Baoan District, Shenzhen, Guangdong, China
Tel.: (86) 75527074999
Optoelectronic Lead Frame Mfr
N.A.I.C.S.: 334413

I-COMPONENTS CO., LTD.
903 Kins Tower 25-1 Jeongja-dong, Bundang-gu, Seongnam, 463-847, Gyeonggi-do, Korea (South)
Tel.: (82) 316535990
Web Site: http://www.i-components.co.kr
Year Founded: 2000
059100—(KRS)
Rev.: $27,079,507
Assets: $43,117,409
Liabilities: $16,309,623
Net Worth: $26,807,786
Earnings: $2,492,429
Emp.: 106
Fiscal Year-end: 12/31/22
Optical Plastic Film Mfr
N.A.I.C.S.: 326112
Gi Ho Lee *(Mng Dir)*

I-CONTROL HOLDINGS LIMITED
Unit A & B 12/F MG Tower 133 Hoi Bun Road Kwun Tong, Kowloon, China (Hong Kong)
Tel.: (852) 2 590 0299 Ky
Web Site: http://www.i-controlholdings.com
Year Founded: 2001
1402—(HKG)
Rev.: $22,113,363
Assets: $31,444,808
Liabilities: $8,861,958
Net Worth: $22,582,850
Earnings: $862,231
Emp.: 85
Fiscal Year-end: 03/31/22
Information Technology;Video Conferencing Services
N.A.I.C.S.: 561499
Sai Wong Tong *(Co-Founder)*

Subsidiaries:

Eduserve International Limited (1)
Unit L 12/F MG Tower 133 Hoi Bun Road, Kwun Tong, Kowloon, China (Hong Kong)
Tel.: (852) 37608100
Professional Audio Visual System Integration Services
N.A.I.C.S.: 238210
Alan Tong *(Exec Dir)*

I-FACTORY CO., LTD.
2359 Jungbu-daero Yangji-myeon, Cheoin-gu, Yongin, Korea (South)
Tel.: (82) 31 330 3000
Web Site: http://www.i-factory21.com
Year Founded: 1994
Sales Range: $25-49.9 Million
Emp.: 140
Semiconductor Equipment Mfr & Sales
N.A.I.C.S.: 334413
Dae-Young Hur *(CEO)*

I-FREEK MOBILE INC.
10th floor Gyoen Sky Building 1-11 Shinjuku 2-chome, Shinjuku-ku, Tokyo, Japan
Tel.: (81) 924715211
Web Site: https://www.i-freek.co.jp
Year Founded: 2001
3845—(TKS)
Rev.: $16,994,310
Assets: $8,500,460
Liabilities: $4,058,540
Net Worth: $4,441,920
Earnings: ($654,390)
Emp.: 569
Fiscal Year-end: 03/31/24
Mobile Content Providing Services
N.A.I.C.S.: 541990
Ayami Uehara *(Pres)*

I-HWA INDUSTRIAL CO., LTD.
12th Floor No 392 Section 1 Neihu Road, Taipei, 114, Taiwan
Tel.: (886) 287978100
Web Site: http://www.ihwa.com.tw
Year Founded: 1999
1456—(TAI)
Rev.: $55,099,740
Assets: $390,650,562
Liabilities: $340,535,845
Net Worth: $50,114,717
Earnings: $166,258
Emp.: 1,200
Fiscal Year-end: 12/31/23
Worsted Fabrics & Weaving Mills
N.A.I.C.S.: 313210
Wencheng Huang *(Pres)*

Subsidiaries:

I-Hwa Industrial Co., Ltd. - Textile Division (1)
7F No 26 Section 3 Nanking East Road, Taipei, 104, Taiwan
Tel.: (886) 225068000
Yarn Spinning & Cotton Fabrics Mfr
N.A.I.C.S.: 313110

I-MAB
Suite 802 West Tower OmniVision 88 Shangke Road, Pudong District, Shanghai, 201210, China
Tel.: (86) 2160578000 Ky
Year Founded: 2016
IMAB—(NASDAQ)
Rev.: $4,122,575
Assets: $624,126,215
Liabilities: $178,300,129
Net Worth: $445,826,085
Earnings: ($384,146,038)
Emp.: 318
Fiscal Year-end: 12/31/22
Holding Company
N.A.I.C.S.: 551112
Joan Huaqiong Shen *(CEO)*

I-MOBILE CO., LTD.
8F Kepco Real Estate Shibuya Building 26-20 Shibuya 3-chome, Shibuya-ku, Tokyo, 150-0002, Japan
Tel.: (81) 354595250 JP
Web Site: https://www.i-mobile.co.jp
Year Founded: 2007
6535—(TKS)
Rev.: $116,531,700
Assets: $152,315,360
Liabilities: $55,078,100
Net Worth: $97,237,260
Earnings: $15,052,400
Emp.: 219
Fiscal Year-end: 07/31/24
Online Advertising Services
N.A.I.C.S.: 541810
Tetsuya Noguchi *(Pres & CEO)*

I-NE CO., LTD.
4-1-2 Midosuji Daibiru 8th floor, Minami-Kubouji-cho, Osaka, 541-0058, Japan
Tel.: (81) 664430881
Web Site: https://www.i-ne.co.jp
Year Founded: 2007
4933—(TKS)
Rev.: $295,248,870
Assets: $162,417,720
Liabilities: $60,810,930
Net Worth: $101,606,790
Earnings: $28,033,860
Emp.: 322
Fiscal Year-end: 12/31/23
Cosmetic Product Mfr & Distr
N.A.I.C.S.: 325620
Yohei Onishi *(Pres & CEO)*

I-NET CORPORATION
13F Yokohama Symphostage West Tower 5-1-2 Minatomirai, Nishi-Ku, Yokohama, 220-0012, Kanagawa, Japan
Tel.: (81) 456820800
Web Site: https://www.inet.co.jp
Year Founded: 1971
9600—(TKS)
Rev.: $249,613,430
Assets: $248,582,270
Liabilities: $115,741,100
Net Worth: $132,841,170
Earnings: $14,522,170
Emp.: 1,774
Fiscal Year-end: 03/31/24
Information Technology & Business Process Outsourcing Services
N.A.I.C.S.: 541512
Hiroshi Wanibuchi *(Sr Mng Exec Officer)*

Subsidiaries:

I-NET DATA SERVICE CORP. (1)
644-12 Maioka-cho, Totsuka-ku, Yokohama, 244-0813, Kanagawa, Japan
Tel.: (81) 458205897
Emp.: 31
Software Development Services
N.A.I.C.S.: 541511
Masato Ikeda *(Pres)*

IST-Software Co., Ltd. (1)
13F Nissei Aroma Square 5-37-1 Kamata, Ota-ku, Tokyo, 144-8721, Japan
Tel.: (81) 354807211
Emp.: 514
Software Development Services
N.A.I.C.S.: 541511

I-NEXUS GLOBAL PLC
27-28 Eastcastle Street, London, W1W 8DH, United Kingdom
Tel.: (44) 8456070061 UK
Web Site: https://i-nexus.com
Year Founded: 2018
INX—(AIM)
Rev.: $4,245,324
Assets: $2,779,163
Liabilities: $5,520,408
Net Worth: ($2,741,245)
Earnings: ($1,182,417)
Emp.: 39
Fiscal Year-end: 09/30/22
Custom Computer Programming Services
N.A.I.C.S.: 541511
Simon Crowther *(CEO)*

Subsidiaries:

i-nexus (America) Inc. (1)
245 1st St Ste 1800, Cambridge, MA 02142-1292
Software Development Services
N.A.I.C.S.: 541511

I-O DATA DEVICE, INC.
3-10 Sakurada-machi, Kanazawa, 920-8512, Ishikawa, Japan
Tel.: (81) 762603377
Web Site: http://www.iodata.com
Year Founded: 1976
69160—(TKS)
Rev.: $548,207,440
Assets: $414,197,520
Liabilities: $132,964,480
Net Worth: $281,233,040
Earnings: $13,358,400
Emp.: 540
Fiscal Year-end: 06/30/21
Electronic Equipment Mfr & Distr
N.A.I.C.S.: 334419
Akio Hosono *(Chm)*

Subsidiaries:

TAIWAN I-O DATA DEVICE, INC. (1)
14F-1 No 11 Sec 1 Zhongshan N Rd, Taipei, 10441, Taiwan
Tel.: (886) 225231399
Electronic Equipment Distr
N.A.I.C.S.: 423690

I-ON DIGITAL CORP.
15 Tehran-ro 10-gil, Gangam-gu, Seoul, 06234, Korea (South)
Tel.: (82) 234301200 DE
Web Site: http://www.i-on.net
Year Founded: 2013
IONI—(OTCQB)
Rev.: $10,471,502
Assets: $13,160,227
Liabilities: $3,864,246
Net Worth: $9,295,981
Earnings: $1,620,448
Emp.: 127
Fiscal Year-end: 12/31/20
Software Developer; Data Management & Digital Marketing
N.A.I.C.S.: 518210
Rod Smith *(Sec)*

I-PEX INC.
12-4 Negoro Momoyama-cho, Fushimi-ku, Kyoto, 612-8024, Japan
Tel.: (81) 454727111
Web Site: https://www.i-pex.com
Year Founded: 1963
6640—(TKS)
Rev.: $418,409,260
Assets: $649,465,270
Liabilities: $235,501,440
Net Worth: $413,963,830
Earnings: ($8,997,210)
Emp.: 5,928
Fiscal Year-end: 12/31/23
Electronic Components Semiconductor & Industrial Mold Mfr
N.A.I.C.S.: 334419
Takaharu Tsuchiyama *(Pres & Exec Dir-Sls Unit)*

Subsidiaries:

DJ Precision Co., Ltd. (1)
863 Mitsusawa, Ogori, 838-0106, Fukuoka, Japan
Tel.: (81) 942752521
Electronic Components Mfr
N.A.I.C.S.: 334419

DONG GUAN DAI-ICHI SEIKO MOLD & PLASTICS CO., LTD. (1)
305 Zhen An West Road Shang Jiao Area, Chang An Town, Dongguan, 523878, Guangdong, China
Tel.: (86) 76958358671
Web Site: http://www.daiichi-seiko.co.jp
Emp.: 300
Injection Molded Plastic Products Mfr
N.A.I.C.S.: 326199

Dai-Ichi Seiko America, Inc. (1)
41700 Gardenbrook Rd Ste 133, Novi, MI 48375
Tel.: (248) 308-2706
Electronic Components Mfr
N.A.I.C.S.: 334419

Dai-Ichi Seiko I-Pex Co., Ltd. (1)
7F-5 No 700 Jung-Jeng Rd, Jung-He Dist, New Taipei City, 235, Taiwan
Tel.: (886) 282279288
Electronic Components Mfr
N.A.I.C.S.: 334419

Dai-ichi Seiko Co., Ltd. - Johor Bahru Factory (1)
No 85 Jalan Tampoi Darul Takzim, 81200, Johor Bahru, Johor, Malaysia
Tel.: (60) 72366851
Electronic Components Mfr

I-PEX INC.

I-PEX Inc.—(Continued)
N.A.I.C.S.: 334419

Dai-ichi Seiko Co., Ltd. - Ogori Plant (1)
863 Mitsusawa, Ogori, 838-0106, Fukuoka, Japan
Tel.: (81) 94 275 5115
Web Site: http://www.daiichi-seiko.co.jp
Electronic Connector Mfr
N.A.I.C.S.: 334417

Dai-ichi Seiko Co., Ltd. - Onojo Plant (1)
6-1-8 Mikasagawa, Onojo, 816-0912, Fukuoka, Japan
Tel.: (81) 92 503 0551
Electronic Connector Mfr
N.A.I.C.S.: 334417

Dai-ichi Seiko Co., Ltd. - Tachiarai Plant (1)
2455-1 Takata Chikuzen-machi, Asakura, 838-0814, Fukuoka, Japan
Tel.: (81) 946 24 0300
Electronic Connector Mfr
N.A.I.C.S.: 334417

Dai-ichi Seiko Co., Ltd. - YAMANASHI PLANT (1)
1816-1 Shotokuji, Yamanashi, 405-0032, Japan
Tel.: (81) 553 23 0450
Electronic Connector Mfr
N.A.I.C.S.: 334417

Daiichi Seiko (M) Sdn. Bhd. (1)
No 1 Jalan Teknologi Perintis 2, Taman Teknologi Nusajaya, 79200, Iskandar Puteri, Johor, Malaysia
Tel.: (60) 75225888
Electronic Components Mfr
N.A.I.C.S.: 334419

I-PEX Co., Ltd (1)
Machida ST BLDG 1-33-10 Morino, Machida, 194-0022, Tokyo, Japan
Tel.: (81) 42 729 1781
Web Site: http://www.i-pex.com
Sales Range: $50-74.9 Million
Emp.: 248
Electronic Components Mfr
N.A.I.C.S.: 334419

I-PEX Global Operations, Inc. (1)
Room 303 Toyopla 3-59, Toyosaki, Tomigusuku, 901-0225, Okinawa, Japan
Tel.: (81) 988946803
Electronic Components Mfr
N.A.I.C.S.: 334419

I-PEX Singapore Pte. Ltd. (1)
55 Yishun Industrial Park A, Singapore, 768728, Singapore
Tel.: (65) 63330662
Electronic Equipment Distr
N.A.I.C.S.: 423690

I-Pex (Shanghai) Co., Ltd. (1)
20F Tong Quan Tower No 678 Gubei Road, Chang Ning District, Shanghai, 200336, China
Tel.: (86) 2152081611
Electronic Components Mfr
N.A.I.C.S.: 334419

I-Pex Electronics (H.K.) Ltd. (1)
Unit10-11 16/F Metropole Square 2 On Yiu Street, Sha Tin, China (Hong Kong)
Tel.: (852) 27358077
Electronic Components Mfr
N.A.I.C.S.: 334419

I-Pex Europe SARL (1)
17 Rue de l Etang, BP 54298, Tremblay En France, 95958, Charles de Gaulle, Cedex, France
Electronic Components Mfr
N.A.I.C.S.: 334419

I-Pex Korea Co., Ltd. (1)
4F IK Bldg 101 Hyoryeong-ro, Seocho-gu, Seoul, 06687, Korea (South)
Tel.: (82) 269594504
Electronic Components Mfr
N.A.I.C.S.: 334419

LAGUNA DAI-ICHI, INC. (1)
103 North Science Avenue Laguna Tecnopark SEPZ, Binan, 4024, Laguna, Philippines
Tel.: (63) 49 541 2860
Electronic Connector Mfr
N.A.I.C.S.: 334417

MDI SDN. BHD. (1)
85 Jalan Tampoi, 81200, Johor Bahru, Malaysia
Tel.: (60) 7 236 6851
Web Site: http://www.daiichi-seiko.co.jp
Emp.: 900
Injection Molded Plastic Products Mfr
N.A.I.C.S.: 326199

Matsue Dai-ichi Seiko Co., Ltd (1)
12 Hokuryo-cho, Matsue, 690-0816, Shimane, Japan
Tel.: (81) 852 60 5710
Electronic Components Mfr
N.A.I.C.S.: 334419

PT. PERTAMA PRECISION BINTAN (1)
Lot SD26/27 Bintan Industrial Estate Lobam, Pulau Bintan, Tanjunguban, 29152, Riau, Indonesia
Tel.: (62) 770 696 668
Emp.: 827
Injection Molded Plastic Products Mfr
N.A.I.C.S.: 326199
Affendy Bin Saidi (Dir)

Rendell Sales Company Limited (1)
3621 W Devon Ave, Chicago, IL 60659
Tel.: (773) 539-1820
Web Site: https://www.rendellsales.com
Electronic Components Distr
N.A.I.C.S.: 423690

SINGAPORE DAI-ICHI PTE. LTD. - WOODLANDS PLANT (1)
Block 2 Woodlands Sector 1 01-24 Woodlands Spectrum 1, Singapore, 738068, Singapore
Tel.: (65) 6753 8558
Injection Molded Plastic Products Mfr
N.A.I.C.S.: 326199

Shanghai Dai-Ichi Seiko Mould & Plastics Co., Ltd. (1)
100 Baiyun Road, Minhang, Shanghai, 200245, China
Tel.: (86) 2164303470
Electronic Components Mfr
N.A.I.C.S.: 334419
Plant (Domestic):

Shanghai Dai-Ichi Seiko Mould & Plastics Co., Ltd. - Minhang Plant (2)
169 Bei Dou Road, Minhang, Shanghai, 200245, China
Tel.: (86) 2164636616
Electronic Components Mfr
N.A.I.C.S.: 334419

Shanghai Dai-Ichi Seiko Mould & Plastics Co., Ltd. - Shanghai Plant 1 (1)
100 Baiyun Road Minhang SMEDZ, Shanghai, 200245, China
Tel.: (86) 21 6430 3470
Web Site: http://www.daiichi-seiko.co.jp
Injection Molded Plastic Products Mfr
N.A.I.C.S.: 326199

Shanghai Dai-Ichi Seiko Mould & Plastics Co., Ltd. - Shanghai Plant 2 (1)
169 Bei Dou Road Minhang SMEDZ, Shanghai, 200245, China
Tel.: (86) 21 6463 6616
Web Site: http://www.daiichi-seiko.co.jp
Injection Molded Plastic Products Mfr
N.A.I.C.S.: 326199

Singapore Dai-Ichi Pte. Ltd. (1)
55 Yishun Industrial Park A, Singapore, 768728, Singapore
Tel.: (65) 67556667
Electronic Components Mfr
N.A.I.C.S.: 334419

THAI DAI-ICHI SEIKO CO., LTD - Thai Plant (1)
700/390 Moo 6 Tambol Donhuaroh, Amphur Muangchonburi, Chon Buri, 20000, Thailand
Tel.: (66) 3846 8316

Web Site: http://www.daiichi-seiko.co.jp
Electronic Connector Mfr
N.A.I.C.S.: 334417

Techno Dai-ichi Co., Ltd (1)
12-4 Negoro Momoyama-chō, Fushimi-ku, Kyoto, 612-8024, Japan
Tel.: (81) 75 602 2191
Sales Range: $25-49.9 Million
Emp.: 13
Injection Molding Machine Mfr
N.A.I.C.S.: 333248
Ogata Kenji (Pres)

Touchstone Precision, Inc. (1)
239 Technology Pkwy, Auburn, AL 36830-0500
Tel.: (334) 887-6688
Electronic Components Mfr
N.A.I.C.S.: 334419

VIETNAM DAI-ICHI SEIKO CO., LTD. - Vietnam Plant (1)
41 Tu Do Avenue Viet Nam Singapore Industrial Park, Thuan An, Binh Duong, Vietnam
Tel.: (84) 2743767744
Web Site: http://www.daiichi-seiko.co.jp
Emp.: 100
Electronic Connector Mfr
N.A.I.C.S.: 334417

Vietnam Dai-Ichi Seiko Co., Ltd. (1)
41 Tu Do Avenue, Viet Nam Singapore Industrial Park, Thuan An, Binh Duong, Vietnam
Tel.: (84) 2743767744
Electronic Components Mfr
N.A.I.C.S.: 334419

I-POWER SOLUTIONS INDIA LTD.

New No 17 Old No 7/4 Vaigai Street Besant Nagar, Chennai, 600 090, India
Tel.: (91) 4424910871
Web Site: https://www.ipwrs.com
512405—(BOM)
Rev.: $9,444
Assets: $524,124
Liabilities: $13,321
Net Worth: $510,803
Earnings: ($28,064)
Fiscal Year-end: 03/31/23
Software Development Services
N.A.I.C.S.: 541511
Venugopalan Parandhaman (Chm & Mng Dir)

I-REMIT, INC.

26/F Discovery Centre 25 ADB Avenue Ortigas Center, Pasig, Metro Manila, Philippines
Tel.: (63) 27069999
Web Site: https://iremitx.com
Year Founded: 2001
I—(PHI)
Rev.: $11,329,057
Assets: $54,389,819
Liabilities: $29,969,055
Net Worth: $24,420,764
Earnings: ($2,476,676)
Emp.: 261
Fiscal Year-end: 12/31/21
Remittance Services
N.A.I.C.S.: 522320
Elizabeth G. Yao (Exec VP)

Subsidiaries:

I-Remit New Zealand Limited (1)
903A 2nd Floor Fountain Lane North Botany Town Centre, East Auckland, 2013, Auckland, New Zealand
Tel.: (64) 92772181
Web Site: http://www.myiremit.com
Sales Range: $50-74.9 Million
Emp.: 7
Money Remittance Services
N.A.I.C.S.: 522320

IREMIT EUROPE Remittance Consulting AG (1)

INTERNATIONAL PUBLIC

Mariahilferstrasse 142, Vienna, 1150, Austria
Tel.: (43) 15131666
Financial Payment Services
N.A.I.C.S.: 522320

IRemit Global Remittance Limited (1)
1st Floor Orchard House 167-169 High Street, Kensington, London, W8 6SH, United Kingdom
Tel.: (44) 2079383388
Money Transmission Services
N.A.I.C.S.: 522390

International Remittance (Canada) Ltd. (1)
8132 Park Rd, Richmond, V6Y 1T1, BC, Canada
Tel.: (604) 284-5141
Foreign Currency Exchange Services
N.A.I.C.S.: 523160

Lucky Star Management Limited (1)
Rm 223 2/f World Wide Plaza, 19 Des Voeux Road, Central, China (Hong Kong)
Tel.: (852) 24901028
Web Site: http://www.myiremit.com
Emp.: 10
Financial Payment Services
N.A.I.C.S.: 522320

Worldwide Exchange Pty. Ltd. (1)
Suite 1 16 Main Street, Blacktown, 2148, NSW, Australia
Tel.: (61) 2 9621 6373
Web Site: http://www.myiremit.com
Sales Range: $50-74.9 Million
Emp.: 11
Money Remittance Services
N.A.I.C.S.: 522390

I-SENS INC.

43 Banpo-daero 28-gil Seocho-gu, Seoul, 06646, Korea (South)
Tel.: (82) 7070939609
Web Site: http://www.i-sens.com
Year Founded: 2000
099190—(KRS)
Rev.: $203,130,080
Assets: $344,820,328
Liabilities: $111,072,360
Net Worth: $233,747,967
Earnings: $12,377,861
Emp.: 845
Fiscal Year-end: 12/31/22
Medicinal Product Mfr
N.A.I.C.S.: 339112

Subsidiaries:

Agamatrix, Inc. (1)
7C Raymond Ave, Salem, NH 03079
Tel.: (603) 328-6000
Web Site: http://www.agamatrix.com
Research & Development in the Physical, Engineering & Life Sciences
N.A.I.C.S.: 541715
Bill McGrail (VP-R&D)

i-SENS Inc. - Songdo Factory (1)
13-35 Songdo-dong, Yeonsu-gu, Incheon, Korea (South)
Tel.: (82) 33 850 0900
Medical Device Mfr
N.A.I.C.S.: 339112

i-SENS Inc. - Wonju Factory (1)
1642-9 Donghwa-ri, Munmak-eup, Wonju, Gangwon-do, Korea (South)
Tel.: (82) 33 903 0700
Medical Device Mfr
N.A.I.C.S.: 339112

i-SENS USA Inc. (1)
10050 Medlock Bridge Rd Ste 100, Duluth, GA 30097
Tel.: (678) 417-5990
Medical Device Distr
N.A.I.C.S.: 423450

I-SHENG ELECTRIC WIRE & CABLE CO,, LTD.

No 50 Dinghu Road Dahuali, Guishan Dist, Taoyuan, 333, Taiwan
Tel.: (886) 33282391

Web Site: https://www.isheng.com.tw
6115—(TAI)
Rev.: $206,973,438
Assets: $273,849,527
Liabilities: $105,816,668
Net Worth: $168,032,859
Earnings: $16,992,511
Fiscal Year-end: 12/31/23
Power Cords Mfr
N.A.I.C.S.: 335999

Subsidiaries:

I-SHENG JAPAN CO., LTD. (1)
1847-1 Nakagawa Hosoecyou, Kita-Ku, Hamamatsu, Japan
Tel.: (81) 431 1304
Electric Equipment Mfr
N.A.I.C.S.: 335999

I-Sheng Electric Wire & Cable Co., Ltd. - I-Sheng Manufacturing (Song Gang) Factory (1)
Tang Xia Yong Road Songgang Town, Baoan District, Shenzhen, 518105, Guangdong, China
Tel.: (86) 75527140088
Electric Equipment Mfr
N.A.I.C.S.: 334417

I-Sheng Electronics (Kunshan) Co., Ltd. (1)
No 888 Tai Shan Road Kunshan Development Zone, Kunshan, Jiang Su, China
Tel.: (86) 512 5738 6890
Electric Equipment Mfr
N.A.I.C.S.: 334419

I. KLOUKINAS - I. LAPPAS CONSTRUCTION & COMMERCE S.A.
2 Omirou Str, Tavros, 17778, Athens, Greece
Tel.: (30) 2104821186
Web Site: https://www.klmate.gr
Year Founded: 1986
KLM—(ATH)
Sales Range: $75-99.9 Million
Emp.: 618
Civil Engineering & Contracting Services
N.A.I.C.S.: 541330
Anthodesmi-Maria Benetatou (Mgr-Fin)

Subsidiaries:

KLSLV D.O.O (1)
Smartinska Cesta 152, 1000, Ljubljana, Slovenia
Tel.: (386) 51364534
Sales Range: $50-74.9 Million
Emp.: 7
Toy Retailer
N.A.I.C.S.: 423920
Renata Mum (Mgr-Store)

I.A GROUP CORPORATION
545 5 Shinano-cho Totsuka-ku, Yokohama, 244-0801, Kanagawa, Japan
Tel.: (81) 458217500   JP
Web Site: http://www.ia-group.co.jp
Year Founded: 1980
7509—(TKS)
Rev.: $235,739,040
Assets: $183,625,800
Liabilities: $86,670,320
Net Worth: $96,955,480
Earnings: $8,870,620
Emp.: 1,057
Fiscal Year-end: 03/31/24
Automotive Distr
N.A.I.C.S.: 423110
Noriyuki Furukawa (Pres)

I.A. HEDIN BIL AB
Krokslatts Parkgata 2, Box 2114, SE-431 02, Molndal, Sweden
Tel.: (46) 31 790 00 00
Web Site: http://www.hedinbil.se
Car Dealership; Automobile Accessories Sales & Installation Services

N.A.I.C.S.: 441110
Jan Litborn (Chm)

I.A.M.U. S.A.
38 Gh Baritiu, 515400, Blaj, Romania
Tel.: (40) 258711907
Web Site: https://www.iamu.ro
IAMU—(BUC)
Rev.: $30,287,933
Assets: $22,088,713
Liabilities: $7,897,930
Net Worth: $14,190,783
Earnings: $1,832,824
Emp.: 615
Fiscal Year-end: 12/31/22
Machine Tools Mfr
N.A.I.C.S.: 333517
Gligor Cimpean (Gen Mgr)

I.C.T.C. HOLDINGS CORPORATION
720 Eaton Way, Delta, V3M 6J9, BC, Canada
Tel.: (604) 522-6543
Web Site: http://www.hero.ca
Year Founded: 1969
Precision Paint Dispensing & Mixing Equipment Mfr
N.A.I.C.S.: 333998
Steve Balmer (Pres & COO)

Subsidiaries:

HERO Europe S.r.l. (1)
Via Bricco 1, 12040, Salmour, Italy
Tel.: (39) 0172 654866
Painting Equipment Mfr
N.A.I.C.S.: 333998

HERO LATIN AMERICA SISTEMAS TINTOMETRICOS LTDA (1)
Av Dom Pedro I 953 - Vila Conceicao, Diadema, 09991-000, Sao Paulo, Brazil
Tel.: (55) 11 4308 1755
Painting Equipment Mfr
N.A.I.C.S.: 333998

HERO Products India Pvt. Ltd. (1)
P1 & P2 Shree Rajlaxmi Hi-Tech Textile Park, Sonale Village Taluka Bhiwandi, Thane, 421 302, Maharashtra, India
Tel.: (91) 2522 304600
Painting Equipment Mfr
N.A.I.C.S.: 333998

Italtinto S.r.l. (1)
Via Zibido 3, Zibido San Giacomo, 20080, Milan, Italy
Tel.: (39) 0290005234
Web Site: http://www.italtinto.com
Automatic & Manual Tinting & Dispensing Equipment
N.A.I.C.S.: 325130

Subsidiary (Non-US):

Italtinto Equipments Pvt. Limited (2)
Bldg No S5/2422 Vrundavan Complex Sonale Village Off, Mumbai Nasik Highway Taluka, Bhiwandi, 421302, India
Tel.: (91) 9821507298
Web Site: http://www.italtinto.com
Automatic Colorant Machinery & Gyro Mixer Mfr
N.A.I.C.S.: 333998

I.CENTURY HOLDING LIMITED
Unit 212-215 2/F Elite Industrial Centre No 883 Cheung Sha Wan Road, Lai Chi Kok, Kowloon, China (Hong Kong)
Tel.: (852) 2 744 1438   Ky
Web Site:
http://www.icenturyholding.com
8507—(HKG)
Rev.: $12,189,771
Assets: $8,367,578
Liabilities: $5,867,558
Net Worth: $2,500,019
Earnings: ($2,152,805)
Emp.: 54
Fiscal Year-end: 03/31/21
Apparel Accessory Mfr

N.A.I.C.S.: 315990
Wilson Kwok Hung Leung (Chm, CEO & Compliance Officer)

I.CERAM
1 rue Columbia, 87068, Limoges, France
Tel.: (33) 555691212
Web Site: https://www.iceram.fr
ALICR—(EUR)
Sales Range: $1-9.9 Million
Orthopedic Implants Mfr
N.A.I.C.S.: 339112
Andre Kerisit (Pres & CEO)

I.M.A. INDUSTRIA MACCHINE AUTOMATICHE S.P.A.
Via Emilia 428-442, 40064, Ozzano dell'Emilia, Bo, Italy
Tel.: (39) 0516514111   IT
Web Site: http://www.ima.it
Year Founded: 1961
Rev.: $1,716,109,346
Assets: $1,898,500,387
Liabilities: $1,417,040,287
Net Worth: $481,460,100
Earnings: $142,508,227
Emp.: 5,456
Fiscal Year-end: 12/31/18
Mfr of Packaging Machinery
N.A.I.C.S.: 333993
Alberto Vacchi (Chm & CEO)

Subsidiaries:

CO.MA.DI.S. S.p.A (1)
Via Piemonte 34, 20030, Senago, 20030, MI, Italy   (100%)
Tel.: (39) 0299010284
Industrial Machinery & Equipment Whslr
N.A.I.C.S.: 423830

Ciemme S.r.l. (1)
Via Padre Meroni 10 B, Albavilla, Como, Italy
Tel.: (39) 031631623
Web Site: http://www.ciemme-packaging.com
Emp.: 40
Mechanical Contractor Services
N.A.I.C.S.: 238220

Digidoc S.r.l. (1)
Via Emilia 428-442, 40064, Ozzano dell'Emilia, Bologna, Italy
Tel.: (39) 0516514111
Web Site: http://www.digidoc.net
Industrial Machinery Mfr
N.A.I.C.S.: 333248

Eurotekna S.r.l. (1)
Via Borgazzi 2, 20122, Milan, Italy
Tel.: (39) 0258324110
Web Site: http://www.eurotekna.eu
Machine Tools Mfr
N.A.I.C.S.: 333515

G.S. Coating Technologies S.r.l. (1)
Via Friuli 38/40, Osteria Grande, 40060, Bologna, Italy
Tel.: (39) 0516958305
Web Site: http://www.gscoating.com
Industrial Machinery Mfr
N.A.I.C.S.: 333248

GIMA S.p.A. (1)
Via Kennedy 17, 40069, Zola Predosa, BO, Italy   (73.5%)
Tel.: (39) 0516169711
Web Site: http://www.gima.com
Packaging Machinery Mfr
N.A.I.C.S.: 333993

Subsidiary (Non-US):

IMA Automation Malaysia Sdn. Bhd. (2)
Plot 96 IV Solok Bayan Lepas, Bayan Lepas Industrial Park, 11900, Penang, Malaysia   (76%)
Tel.: (60) 4627 2233
Web Site: http://www.ima-industries.com
Medical Device Mfr
N.A.I.C.S.: 334510

Subsidiary (US):

IMA Automation USA, Inc. (2)
4608 Interstate Blvd, Loves Park, IL 61111   (100%)
Tel.: (815) 885-8800
Medical Assemly Machines Mfr
N.A.I.C.S.: 339112

Subsidiary (Non-US):

IMA Medtech Switzerland SA (2)
Allee Du Quartz 12, 2301, La Chaux-de-Fonds, Switzerland   (100%)
Tel.: (41) 329257111
Medical Assemly Machines Mfr
N.A.I.C.S.: 339112
Rene Ronchetti (CEO)

Hassia Packaging Pvt. Ltd. (1)
768/3 Sanaswadi, Taluka Shirur District, Pune, 412207, India
Tel.: (91) 2137667788
Web Site: http://www.hassiaindia.in
Packaging Machinery Mfr
N.A.I.C.S.: 333993

IMA Est Verpackungssysteme Handelsgesellschaft Gm.bH. (1)
Friedlgasse 12-1, Vienna, 1190, Austria
Tel.: (43) 13690636
Web Site: http://www.ima.it
Sales Range: $50-74.9 Million
Emp.: 2
Industrial Machinery & Equipment Whslr
N.A.I.C.S.: 423830

IMA Germany GmbH (1)
Scarletallee 11, Koln, 50735, Cologne, Germany   (100%)
Tel.: (49) 2217174500
Web Site: http://www.ima.it
Sales Range: $25-49.9 Million
Emp.: 30
Industrial Machinery & Equipment Whslr
N.A.I.C.S.: 423830

IMA Kilian Verwaltungs GmbH (1)
Scarletallee 11, Koln, 50735, Cologne, Germany   (100%)
Tel.: (49) 2217174500
Web Site: http://www.ima.it
Sales Range: $25-49.9 Million
Emp.: 30
Management Consulting Services
N.A.I.C.S.: 541618

IMA Life (Beijing) Pharmaceutical Systems Co. Ltd. (1)
No 3 JianAn Street BDA Yizhuang, Beijing, 100176, China
Tel.: (86) 59623866899
Pharmaceutical Process Equipment Mfr
N.A.I.C.S.: 325412

IMA Life North America Inc. (1)
2175 Military Rd, Tonawanda, NY 14150
Tel.: (716) 695-6354
Pharmaceutical Process Equipment Mfr
N.A.I.C.S.: 325412

IMA Life The Netherlands B.V. (1)
De Leest 3, 5107 RC, Dongen, Netherlands
Tel.: (31) 162383500
Pharmaceutical Process Equipment Mfr
N.A.I.C.S.: 325412

IMA North America Inc. (1)
4608 Interstate Blvd, Loves Park, IL 61111   (100%)
Tel.: (815) 885-8860
Web Site: http://www.imanorthamerica.com
Sales Range: $25-49.9 Million
Emp.: 75
Commercial & Industrial Machinery & Equipment Repair & Maintenance
N.A.I.C.S.: 811310

IMA Pacific Co. Ltd. (1)
All Seasons Place 18 F M Thai Tower 87 Wireless Road, Khwaeng Lumpini Khet Pathumwan, 10330, Bangkok, 10330, Thailand   (99.99%)
Tel.: (66) 26540780
Web Site: http://www.ima.it
Sales Range: $25-49.9 Million
Emp.: 7
Industrial Machinery Mfr
N.A.I.C.S.: 333248

I.M.A. INDUSTRIA MACCHINE AUTOMATICHE S.P.A.

I.M.A. Industria Macchine Automatiche S.p.A.—(Continued)

IMA Packaging & Processing Equipment Co., Ltd. (1)
No 3 JianAn Street BDA (Yi Zhuang), No 8 Beisihuan Zhong Road, Beijing, 100176, China **(100%)**
Tel.: (86) 1084986663
Web Site: http://www.ima-china.com
Sales Range: $25-49.9 Million
Emp.: 10
Packaging Machinery Mfr
N.A.I.C.S.: 333993

IMA UK Ltd. (1)
3 Arden Rd, Arden Forest Indus Est, Alcester, B49 6HN, United Kingdom **(100%)**
Tel.: (44) 1789767330
Web Site: http://www.ima.it
Sales Range: $50-74.9 Million
Emp.: 60
Industrial Machinery & Equipment Whslr
N.A.I.C.S.: 423830

IMA-PG India Pvt. Ltd. (1)
Plot No R-677 MIDC T T C Indl Area Thane Belapur Road, Rabale Navi, Mumbai, 400 701, India
Tel.: (91) 2267179000
Industrial Machinery Mfr
N.A.I.C.S.: 333248

Ilapak (Beijing) Packaging Machinery Co. Ltd. (1)
No 3 JianAn Street BDA Yizhuang, Beijing, China
Tel.: (86) 1067890232
Packaging Machinery Mfr
N.A.I.C.S.: 333993

Ilapak International SA (1)
PO Box 756, Grancia, 6916, Lugano, Switzerland
Tel.: (41) 919605900
Packaging Machinery Mfr
N.A.I.C.S.: 333993

Petroncini Impianti S.p.A. (1)
Via del Fantino 2/A, 44047, Sant'Agostino, Ferrara, Italy
Tel.: (39) 0532350076
Web Site: http://www.petroncini.com
Coffee Install Processing Plant Mfr
N.A.I.C.S.: 311920

Pharmasiena Service S.r.l. (1)
Via Benedetto Zalaffi 1/3 Zona Industriale Renaccio, 53100, Siena, Italy
Tel.: (39) 0577247720
Industrial Machinery Mfr
N.A.I.C.S.: 333248

Precision Gears Ltd. (1)
Plot No R 677 T T C Indl Area Off Thane Belapur Road, Rabale, Navi Mumbai, 400701, India **(100%)**
Tel.: (91) 2267179000
Web Site: http://www.precisiongears-ima.com
Sales Range: $50-74.9 Million
Emp.: 250
Industrial Machinery Mfr
N.A.I.C.S.: 333248

Spreafico Automation S.r.l. (1)
Via Enrico Fermi 9, Calolziocorte, 23801, Lecco, Italy
Tel.: (39) 0341240311
Web Site: http://www.spreafico-srl.com
Packaging Machinery Mfr
N.A.I.C.S.: 333993

Teknoweb Converting S.r.l. (1)
Via dei Salici n 7 Cremona, 26020, Palazzo Pignano, Italy
Tel.: (39) 0373951311
Web Site: http://www.teknowebconverting.com
Tissue Packaging Machinery Mfr
N.A.I.C.S.: 333993

Teknoweb N.A. LLC (1)
506b Plantation Park Dr, Loganville, GA 30052
Tel.: (770) 466-1890
Web Site: http://www.hotmelttech.com
Tissue Packaging Machinery Co. Ltd.
N.A.I.C.S.: 333993

Tissue Machinery Company S.p.A. (1)
Via I Maggio 3/Z I Poggio Piccolo, 40023, Castel Guelfo di Bologna, Italy
Tel.: (39) 0542676891
Web Site: http://www.tmcspa.com
Tissue Packaging Machinery Mfr
N.A.I.C.S.: 333993

Subsidiary (Domestic):

Asset Management Service S.r.l. (2)
Via I Maggio 3 Z I Poggio Piccolo, 40023, Castel Guelfo di Bologna, Italy
Tel.: (39) 0542367411
Web Site: http://www.ams-service.it
Industrial Machinery Parts Whslr
N.A.I.C.S.: 423810

Subsidiary (US):

TMC North America Inc. (2)
3116 N Pointer Rd, Appleton, WI 54911-8602
Tel.: (920) 830-9723
Web Site: http://www.tmcna.com
Tissue Packaging Machinery Mfr
N.A.I.C.S.: 333993

I.M.D. INTERNATIONAL MEDICAL DEVICES S.P.A.
Via E Fermi 26, 24050, Grassobbio, Bergamo, Italy
Tel.: (39) 0356594811
Web Site: https://www.imdgroup.it
Year Founded: 1998
IMD—(EUR)
Medical Device Mfr
N.A.I.C.S.: 339112
Aniello Aliberti *(Pres)*

I.M.G. 2 S.R.L.
Piazza della Repubblica 2, 23880, Milan, Casatenovo, Italy
Tel.: (39) 09208395
Web Site: http://www.img2.it
Year Founded: 2009
Management Waste Disposal
N.A.I.C.S.: 562998

Subsidiaries:

Esposito Servizi Ecologici Srl (1)
Via Maestri del Lavoro, Gorle, 6, Bergamo, Italy
Tel.: (39) 035510898
Web Site: http://www.gruppoesposito.it
Waste Collection Services
N.A.I.C.S.: 562112
Ezio Esposito *(Owner & Pres)*

I.M.P. GROUP INTERNATIONAL INC.
2651 Joseph Howe Drive, Halifax, B3L 4T1, NS, Canada
Tel.: (902) 453-2400
Web Site: http://www.impgroup.com
Year Founded: 1967
Sales Range: $250-299.9 Million
Emp.: 3,500
Holding Company Hotel Marine & Medical Distr
N.A.I.C.S.: 551112
Stephen K. Plummer *(CEO)*

Subsidiaries:

CanJet Airlines Ltd. (1)
PO Box 980, Enfield, B2T 1R6, NS, Canada
Tel.: (800) 809-7777
Web Site: http://www.canjet.com
Nonscheduled Passenger Air Transportation Services
N.A.I.C.S.: 481211

I.M.P. Aerospace Division (1)
579 Barnes Rd, PO Box 970, Enfield, B2T 1L5, NS, Canada
Tel.: (902) 873-2250
Web Site: https://www.impaerospace.com
Sales Range: $200-249.9 Million
Emp.: 1,100
Aerospace Services
N.A.I.C.S.: 336413

I.M.P. Group International Inc. - IMP Aerospace & Defence Unit (1)
PO Box 970, Enfield, B2T 1L5, NS, Canada
Tel.: (902) 873-2250
Aerospace Engineering Services
N.A.I.C.S.: 541330

I.M.P. Group International Inc. - Pacific Avionics & Instruments Division (1)
4200 Cowley Crescent Vancouver International Airport, Richmond, V7B 1B8, BC, Canada
Tel.: (604) 278-2105
Web Site: http://www.pacificavionics.com
Aircraft Parts Distr
N.A.I.C.S.: 423860
Gordon Bott *(VP, Gen Mgr & Dir-Maintenance)*

IMP Solutions Inc. (1)
2651 Joseph Howe Drive Suite 202, Halifax, B3L 4G5, NS, Canada
Tel.: (902) 482-1600
Web Site: http://www.impsolutions.com
Information Technology Consulting Services
N.A.I.C.S.: 541512
Joe Adams *(Dir-Aerospace Dev & Support)*

I2 CAPITAL PARTNERS SGR SPA
Foro Buonaparte 44, 20121, Milan, Italy
Tel.: (39) 02 85 979 1
Web Site: http://www.i2capital.it
Privater Equity Firm
N.A.I.C.S.: 523999
Vincenzo Manes *(Chm)*

I2 DEVELOPMENT SA
Ul Iaciarska 4B, Wroclaw, 50-104, Poland
Tel.: (48) 717978892
I2D—(WAR)
Sales Range: Less than $1 Million
Real Estate Manangement Services
N.A.I.C.S.: 531390
Marcin Misztal *(Chm-Mgmt Bd)*

I2 ENTERPRISE PUBLIC COMPANY LIMITED
104 Soi Nakniwat 6 Nakniwat Road, Latphrao, Bangkok, 10230, Thailand
Tel.: (66) 20440134
Web Site:
https://www.i2enterprise.com
Year Founded: 2006
I2—(THA)
Rev.: $41,683,740
Assets: $59,590,998
Liabilities: $41,536,511
Net Worth: $18,054,487
Earnings: $2,491,393
Emp.: 40
Fiscal Year-end: 12/31/23
Information Technology Services
N.A.I.C.S.: 541512

I2S SA
28-30 rue Jean Perrin, 33608, Pessac, Cedex, France
Tel.: (33) 557266900   FR
Web Site: https://www.i2s-corp.com
Year Founded: 1979
ALI2S—(EUR)
Sales Range: $10-24.9 Million
Emp.: 59
Electronic Equipment Mfr & Distr
N.A.I.C.S.: 334419
Jean-Louis Blouin *(Co-Founder & Mng Dir)*

Subsidiaries:

Kirtas Technologies, Inc. (1)
749 Phillips Rd, Victor, NY 14564
Tel.: (585) 924-2420
Web Site: http://www.kirtas.com
Book Digitization Services
N.A.I.C.S.: 561990
Robb Richardson *(CEO)*

I2S Linescan Imaging Inc. (1)
5 Lia Fail Way, Cos Cob, CT 06807-2200
Tel.: (203) 298-0741
Web Site: http://www.i2s-linescan.com
Electronic Equipment Mfr & Distr
N.A.I.C.S.: 423690

I3 ENERGY PLC
Westpoint House Prospect Road Arnhall Business Park, Westhill, AB32 6FJ, United Kingdom
Tel.: (44) 1224945980   UK
Web Site: https://www.i3.energy
Year Founded: 2014
ITE—(TSX)
Rev.: $263,110,326
Assets: $445,862,156
Liabilities: $237,902,045
Net Worth: $207,960,111
Earnings: $52,955,062
Emp.: 56
Fiscal Year-end: 12/31/22
Oil & Gas Exploration Services
N.A.I.C.S.: 213111
Majid Shafiq *(CEO)*

Subsidiaries:

I3 Energy Canada Limited (1)
500 207 - 9th Avenue SW, Calgary, T2P 1K3, AB, Canada
Tel.: (403) 410-6790
Natural Gas & Natural Gas Liquid Mfr
N.A.I.C.S.: 325120

Toscana Energy Income Corporation (1)
46th floor Bankers Hall West Tower 888 3rd St SW, Calgary, T2P 5C5, AB, Canada
Tel.: (403) 410-6790
Web Site: http://toscanaenergy.ca
Rev.: $12,062,828
Assets: $43,500,921
Liabilities: $42,976,010
Net Worth: $524,911
Earnings: ($3,165,208)
Emp.: 5
Fiscal Year-end: 12/31/2019
Energy Asset Mutual Fund
N.A.I.C.S.: 525910
Joseph S. Durante *(Chm)*

I3 INTERACTIVE, INC.
810 789 West Pender Street, Vancouver, V6C 1H2, BC, Canada
Tel.: (647) 477-2382
Web Site:
https://www.i3company.com
Year Founded: 2007
BETS—(CNSX)
Rev.: $285,297
Assets: $4,625,083
Liabilities: $1,852,653
Net Worth: $2,772,430
Earnings: ($24,380,808)
Fiscal Year-end: 12/31/20
Mineral Exploration Services
N.A.I.C.S.: 213114
Greg Ball *(CFO)*

I3 INTERNATIONAL INC.
780 Birchmount Rd Unit 16, Scarborough, M1K 5H4, ON, Canada
Tel.: (416) 261-2266
Web Site:
http://www.i3international.com
Year Founded: 1990
Sales Range: $10-24.9 Million
Emp.: 50
Digital Video Technologies Designer, Mfr & Supplier
N.A.I.C.S.: 334310
Grace Baba *(VP)*

I3 SYSTEMS, INC.
4th Floor Daiichi Myojo Building Tenjin 4-1-37, Chuo-ku, Fukuoka, 810-0001, Japan
Tel.: (81) 925524358

Web Site: https://www.i3-systems.com
Year Founded: 2001
4495—(TKS)
Rev.: $18,342,780
Assets: $22,447,980
Liabilities: $6,406,600
Net Worth: $16,041,380
Earnings: $2,879,860
Fiscal Year-end: 06/30/24
Application Development Services
N.A.I.C.S.: 541511
Tsutomu Sasaki *(Pres & CEO)*

I3SYSTEM INC.
69 Techno 5-ro, Yuseong-gu, Daejeon, 34014, Korea (South)
Tel.: (82) 7077842500
Web Site: https://www.i3system.com
Year Founded: 1998
214430—(KRS)
Rev.: $64,309,569
Assets: $86,921,035
Liabilities: $26,588,536
Net Worth: $60,332,498
Earnings: $4,742,505
Emp.: 444
Fiscal Year-end: 12/31/22
Thermal Imaging Detector & X-Ray Detector Mfr
N.A.I.C.S.: 339999
Han Chung *(CEO)*

I4VENTURES SP. Z O.O.
Bobrowicka 1, 00-728, Warsaw, Poland
Tel.: (48) 223737001 PL
Web Site: http://www.i4ventures.com
Year Founded: 1989
Long Term Investment Company
N.A.I.C.S.: 525910
Boguslaw Bartczak *(Partner & VP-Mgmt Bd)*

Subsidiaries:

NOMI S.A. **(1)**
Ul Witosa 76, 25-561, Kielce, Poland **(75%)**
Tel.: (48) 413635500
Web Site: http://www.nomi.com.pl
Home Center Operator
N.A.I.C.S.: 444110
Marc Ferrentino *(Founder)*

IA FINANCIAL CORPORATION INC.
1080 Grande Allee Quest Terminus Quebec branch, CP 1907, Quebec, G1K 7M3, QC, Canada
Tel.: (418) 684-5000
Web Site: https://ia.ca
Year Founded: 2018
1OD—(DEU)
Rev.: $4,240,230,479
Assets: $69,325,552,190
Liabilities: $64,126,468,198
Net Worth: $5,199,083,992
Earnings: $568,072,690
Emp.: 9,400
Fiscal Year-end: 12/31/23
Financial Investment Services
N.A.I.C.S.: 551112
Jacques Martin *(Chm)*

Subsidiaries:

Industrial Alliance Insurance and Financial Services Inc. **(1)**
1080 Grande Allee West Station Terminus, PO Box 1907, Station Terminus, Quebec, G1K 7M3, QC, Canada
Tel.: (418) 684-5000
Web Site: https://www.ia.ca
Sales Range: $5-14.9 Billion
Life & Health Insurance & Financial Services
N.A.I.C.S.: 524113
Francois Blais *(COO-iA Auto & Home Insurance)*

Subsidiary (Domestic):

Corporation Financiere L'Excellence Ltee (CFE) **(2)**
1080 Grande Allee, Quebec, G1S 1C7, QC, Canada
Tel.: (418) 684-5275
Management Consulting Services
N.A.I.C.S.: 541611
Martin Nicoletti *(Pres)*

Subsidiary (US):

Dealers Assurance Company **(2)**
15920 Addison Rd, Addison, TX 75001
Web Site: https://www.dealersassurance.com
Property & Casualty Insurance Services
N.A.I.C.S.: 524126

Subsidiary (Domestic):

FundEX Investments Inc. **(2)**
400 Applewood Crescent 3rd Floor, Vaughan, L4K 0C3, ON, Canada **(83.5%)**
Tel.: (905) 305-1651
Web Site: http://www.fundex.com
Sales Range: $100-124.9 Million
Emp.: 80
Mutual Fund Dealer
N.A.I.C.S.: 525190
Robert Corbett *(VP-Sls & Bus Dev)*

HollisWealth Advisory Services Inc. **(2)**
26 Wellington St E Suite 700, Toronto, M5E 1S2, ON, Canada
Tel.: (416) 350-3250
Web Site: http://www.holliswealth.com
Wealth Management Services
N.A.I.C.S.: 523940

Subsidiary (US):

IA American Life Insurance Company **(2)**
17550 N Perimeter Dr Ste 210, Scottsdale, AZ 85255
Tel.: (480) 473-5550
Web Site: https://www.iaamerican-waco.com
Emp.: 15
Life & Health Insurance
N.A.I.C.S.: 524113
Michael L. Stickney *(Pres)*

Subsidiary (Domestic):

American-Amicable Holdings, Inc. **(3)**
425 Austin Ave, Waco, TX 76701
Tel.: (254) 297-2776
Web Site: http://www.americanamicable.com
Holding Company; Life Insurance Services
N.A.I.C.S.: 551112
S. Lanny Peavy *(Pres & CEO)*

Subsidiary (Domestic):

American-Amicable Life Insurance Company of Texas **(4)**
425 Austin Ave, Waco, TX 76701-2147
Tel.: (254) 297-2777
Web Site: http://www.americanamicable.com
Sales Range: $75-99.9 Million
Emp.: 111
Fire Insurance Services
N.A.I.C.S.: 524113

Pioneer American Insurance Company **(4)**
425 Austin Ave, Waco, TX 76701
Tel.: (254) 297-2776
Web Site: http://www.pioneeramerican.com
Sales Range: $75-99.9 Million
Emp.: 120
Insurance Services
N.A.I.C.S.: 524113

Pioneer Security Life Insurance Company **(4)**
425 Austin Ave, Waco, TX 76701-2147
Tel.: (254) 297-2778
Web Site: https://www.pioneeramerican.com
Sales Range: $75-99.9 Million
Emp.: 118
Insurance Services
N.A.I.C.S.: 524113

Subsidiary (Domestic):

IA Clarington Investments Inc. **(2)**
522 University Avenue Suite 700, Toronto, M5G 1Y7, ON, Canada **(100%)**
Tel.: (416) 860-9880
Web Site: https://www.iaclarington.com
Sales Range: $350-399.9 Million
Emp.: 1,000
Mutual Fund Brokerage
N.A.I.C.S.: 524210
Eric Frape *(Sr VP-Product & Investments)*

Industrial Alliance Auto & Home Insurance **(2)**
925 Grande Allee West Suite 230, Quebec, G1S 1C1, QC, Canada
Tel.: (418) 650-4600
Web Site: http://www.industriellealianceauto.com
Sales Range: $200-249.9 Million
Emp.: 650
Auto & Home Insurance Products
N.A.I.C.S.: 524126

Industrial Alliance Pacific General Insurance Corporation **(2)**
925 Grande Allee West, Quebec, G1S 1C7, QC, Canada
Tel.: (418) 684-5000
Banking Services
N.A.I.C.S.: 522110

Industrial Alliance Pacific Insurance and Financial Services Inc. **(2)**
2165 Broadway W, PO Box 5900, Vancouver, V6B 5H6, BC, Canada
Tel.: (604) 737-3802
Web Site: http://www.ia.ca
Sales Range: $100-124.9 Million
Emp.: 25
Insurance & Financial Management Services
N.A.I.C.S.: 524298

Industrial Alliance Pacific Life Insurance Company **(2)**
2165 W Broadway, Vancouver, V6B 5H6, BC, Canada **(100%)**
Tel.: (604) 734-1667
Web Site: http://www.iapacific.com
Sales Range: $400-449.9 Million
Emp.: 300
Life Insurance
N.A.I.C.S.: 524113

Industrial Alliance Securities Inc. **(2)**
2200 McGill College Avenue Suite 350, Montreal, H3A 3P8, QC, Canada **(100%)**
Tel.: (514) 499-1066
Web Site: http://www.iasecurities.ca
Sales Range: $50-74.9 Million
Emp.: 9
Securities Brokerage Firm
N.A.I.C.S.: 523150

Industrial Alliance Trust Inc. **(2)**
9150 Leduc Boulevard Suite 601, Brossard, J4Y 0E3, QC, Canada
Web Site: https://www.iatrust.ca
Banking Services
N.A.I.C.S.: 522110

Investia Financial Services Inc. **(2)**
6700 Pierre-Bertrand Blvd Suite 300, Quebec, G2J 0B4, QC, Canada **(100%)**
Tel.: (418) 684-5548
Web Site: https://www.investia.ca
Sales Range: $50-74.9 Million
Emp.: 80
Financial Products & Services
N.A.I.C.S.: 523999

Subsidiary (Domestic):

National Financial Insurance Agency Inc. **(3)**
300-6700 Pierre Bertrand Blvd, Quebec, G2J 0B4, QC, Canada
Tel.: (418) 623-4330
Web Site: http://www.nfiai.ca
General Insurance Services
N.A.I.C.S.: 524210

Subsidiary (Domestic):

Jovian Capital Corporation **(2)**
26 Wellington Street East Suite 920, Toronto, M5E 1S2, ON, Canada
Tel.: (416) 933-5750
Web Site: http://www.joviancapital.com
Sales Range: $125-149.9 Million
Emp.: 600
Financial & Investment Services
N.A.I.C.S.: 523999
Mark L. Arthur *(Pres)*

Subsidiary (Domestic):

DeltaOne Capital Partners Corp. **(3)**
Suite 700 Bow Valley Square 2, 205 5th Avenue Southwest, Calgary, T2P 2V7, AB, Canada **(50.1%)**
Tel.: (403) 264-9875
Asset Management Services
N.A.I.C.S.: 523150

Hahn Investment Stewards & Company Inc. **(3)**
214-1634 Harvey Ave, Kelowna, V1Y 6G2, BC, Canada
Tel.: (250) 861-6562
Web Site: http://www.hahninvest.com
Portfolio Management Services
N.A.I.C.S.: 523940
James Garcelon *(Pres)*

Jovian Asset Management Inc. **(3)**
26 Wellington St E Ste 920, Toronto, M5E 1S2, ON, Canada
Tel.: (416) 933-5756
Asset Management Services
N.A.I.C.S.: 523940

Leon Frazer & Associates Inc. **(3)**
26 Wellington Street East Suite 800, Toronto, M5E 1S2, ON, Canada **(100%)**
Tel.: (416) 864-1120
Web Site: https://www.leonfrazer.com
Sales Range: $50-74.9 Million
Emp.: 40
Investment Advice & Services
N.A.I.C.S.: 523940
Mark Arthur *(CEO)*

MGI Insurance Brokerage Inc. **(3)**
340 50th Ave S E, Calgary, T2G 2B1, AB, Canada
Tel.: (519) 886-9957
Insurance Brokerage Services
N.A.I.C.S.: 524210

MGI Securities Inc. **(3)**
26 Wellington Street East Suite 900, Toronto, M5E 1S2, ON, Canada
Tel.: (416) 864-6477
Web Site: http://www.mgisecurities.com
Emp.: 50
Investment Services & Securities Dealer
N.A.I.C.S.: 523150
Crawford Gordon *(Mng Dir-Retail)*

Mission Hills Capital Partners Inc **(3)**
26 Wellington St E Ste 920, Toronto, M1E 1S2, ON, Canada
Tel.: (416) 933-5760
Web Site: http://www.missionhillscapital.com
Investment Management Service
N.A.I.C.S.: 523999
Lyle Stein *(Chief Investment Officer)*

T.E. Financial Consultants Ltd. **(3)**
26 Wellington St East Suite 800, Toronto, M5E 1S2, ON, Canada
Tel.: (416) 366-1451
Web Site: http://www.tewealth.com
Sales Range: $50-74.9 Million
Emp.: 50
Financial, Investment, Tax & Estate Planning Services
N.A.I.C.S.: 523999

T.E. Investment Counsel Inc. **(3)**
26 Wellington St East Suite 800, Toronto, M5E 1S2, ON, Canada
Tel.: (416) 366-1451
Web Site: http://www.tewealth.com
Sales Range: $50-74.9 Million
Emp.: 50
Investment Management Service
N.A.I.C.S.: 523940
Steven Belchetz *(Sr VP-Bus Dev & Client Relationships-Natl)*

Subsidiary (Domestic):

Prysm General Insurance Inc. **(2)**
801 Grande Allee West Suite 300, Quebec, G1X 1A1, QC, Canada
Web Site: https://www.prysmassurances.ca
Banking Services

IA FINANCIAL CORPORATION INC.

iA Financial Corporation Inc.—(Continued)
N.A.I.C.S.: 522110

Solicour Inc. (2)
Place Val Des Arbres, Laval, H7G 4R8, QC, Canada
Tel.: (450) 669-9454
Sales Range: $50-74.9 Million
Emp.: 7
Securities Brokerage Services
N.A.I.C.S.: 523150

Subsidiary (US):

Southwest Reinsure, Inc. (2)
2400 Louisiana Blvd NE Bldg 4 Ste 100, Albuquerque, NM 87110
Tel.: (505) 881-2244
Web Site: http://www.southwestre.com
Banking Services
N.A.I.C.S.: 522110
Kristen Gruber (Pres)

Subsidiary (Domestic):

The Excellence Life Insurance Company (2)
1611 Cremazie Blvd East Suite 900, Montreal, H2M 2P2, QC, Canada
Tel.: (514) 327-0020
Web Site: http://www.excellence.qc.ca
Health Insurance Services
N.A.I.C.S.: 524114

iA Auto Finance Inc. (2)
PO Box 61040, Oakville, L6J 7P5, ON, Canada
Tel.: (905) 815-9510
Web Site: https://iaautofinance.ca
Banking Services
N.A.I.C.S.: 522110

Innovative Aftermarket Systems L.P. (1)
10800 Pecan Park Blvd Ste 410, Austin, TX 78750
Tel.: (512) 421-8001
Web Site: http://www.iasdirect.com
Insurance Underwriting Services
N.A.I.C.S.: 524298
Stephanie Carrasquillo (Dir-Mktg)

Subsidiary (Domestic):

First Dealer Resources, Inc. (2)
14000 Quail Springs Pkwy, Oklahoma City, OK 73134
Tel.: (405) 844-9066
Web Site: http://www.firstdealer.net
Sales Range: $1-9.9 Million
Emp.: 25
Aftermarket Financial Products Mfr
N.A.I.C.S.: 541611
Frank Klaus (Founder & CEO)

Lubrico Warranty Inc. (1)
2124 Jetstream Road, London, ON, Canada
Web Site: https://www.lubrico.com
Car Warranty Services
N.A.I.C.S.: 524128

Vericity, Inc. (1)
1350E Touhy Ste 205 W, Des Plaines, IL 60018
Tel.: (312) 379-2397
Web Site: https://www.vericity.com
Rev.: $163,912,000
Assets: $770,078,000
Liabilities: $658,735,000
Net Worth: $111,343,000
Earnings: ($20,460,000)
Emp.: 417
Fiscal Year-end: 12/31/2022
Holding Company
N.A.I.C.S.: 551112
Eric Rahe (Chm)

iA Private Wealth (USA) Inc. (1)
26 Wellington St E Suite 700, Toronto, ON, Canada
Web Site: https://www.iaprivatewealthusa.com
Wealth Management Services
N.A.I.C.S.: 522180

iA Private Wealth Inc. (1)
2200 McGill College Avenue Suite 350, Montreal, QC, Canada
Tel.: (514) 499-1066

Web Site: https://www.iaprivatewealth.ca
Wealth Management Services
N.A.I.C.S.: 522180

IA INC.
5-23 22-gil Songpa-daero, Songpa-gu, Seoul, Korea (South)
Tel.: (82) 30151300
Web Site: https://www.ia-inc.kr
Year Founded: 1993
038880—(KRS)
Rev.: $56,922,686
Assets: $127,042,691
Liabilities: $40,893,906
Net Worth: $86,148,785
Earnings: ($805,791)
Emp.: 36
Fiscal Year-end: 12/31/22
Semiconductor Mfr
N.A.I.C.S.: 334413
Dong-Jin Kim (Chm & CEO)

Subsidiaries:

TRinno Technology Co., Ltd. (1)
5-23 22-gil Songpa-daero Munjeong-dong, Songpa-gu, Seoul, 05805, Korea (South)
Tel.: (82) 64833782
Web Site: https://www.trinnotech.com
Power Semiconductor Mfr
N.A.I.C.S.: 334413
Yun Chong Man (CEO)

iA Powertron Co., Ltd. (1)
26 Bupyeong 329beon-gil, Bupyeong-gu, Incheon, Korea (South)
Tel.: (82) 325104979
Power Semiconductor Mfr
N.A.I.C.S.: 334413
Choi Chan-Ho (CEO)

IAB HOLDINGS LIMITED
10/9 Hunter Street, Sydney, 2000, NSW, Australia
Tel.: (61) 300783526
Rev.: $78,924,710
Assets: $22,857,430
Liabilities: $21,959,867
Net Worth: $897,564
Earnings: $10,666,176
Fiscal Year-end: 06/30/18
Telecommunication Servicesb
N.A.I.C.S.: 517810
Damian Kay (CEO & Mng Dir)

IAG GLASS COMPANY LIMITED
3 Hungerford Street, Kolkata, 7000 017, India
Tel.: (91) 33 2290 1940
Web Site: http://www.iagcompany.in
Sales Range: $10-24.9 Million
Glass Products Mfr
N.A.I.C.S.: 327215
Vijay Joshi (Exec Dir)

IAI CORPORATION
577-1 Obane, Shimizu-ku, Shizuoka, 424-0103, Japan
Tel.: (81) 543645105
Web Site: http://www.iai-robot.co.jp
Year Founded: 1976
Emp.: 827
Small Industrial Robots Designer, Mfr & Distr
N.A.I.C.S.: 333248
Toru Ishida (Pres)

Subsidiaries:

IA KOREA CORP (1)
4F Seyoung Bldg 1228-1 Gaepo-Dong, Gangnam-Gu, Seoul, 135-964, Korea (South)
Tel.: (82) 2 578 3523
Web Site: http://www.iakorea.co.kr
Industrial Machinery Mfr & Distr
N.A.I.C.S.: 333248

IAI (Shanghai) Co., Ltd. (1)
Shanghai Jiahua Business Center A8-303

808 Hongqiao Rd, Shanghai, 200030, China
Tel.: (86) 21 6448 4753
Web Site: http://www.iai-robot.com
Industrial Machinery Mfr & Distr
N.A.I.C.S.: 333998

IAI America, Inc. (1)
2690 W 237th St, Torrance, CA 90505
Tel.: (310) 891-6015
Web Site: http://www.intelligentactuator.com
Rev.: $13,500,545
Emp.: 15
Small Industrial Parts & Systems Distr
N.A.I.C.S.: 423830
Toru Ishida (Pres)

IAI Industrieroboter GmbH (1)
Ober der Roth 4, 65824, Schwalbach am Taunus, Germany
Tel.: (49) 6196 8895 0
Web Site: http://www.iai-gmbh.de
Emp.: 15
Industrial Machinery Distr
N.A.I.C.S.: 423830
Satoshi Kazama (Mgr-Sls Engrg)

IAI Robot (Thailand) Co., Ltd. (1)
825 PhairojKijja Tower 12th Floor Bangna-Trad RD, Bangna, Bangkok, 10260, Thailand
Tel.: (66) 2 361 4457
Industrial Machinery Mfr & Distr
N.A.I.C.S.: 333998

IAI HOLDING A/S
Industrivej 12 20, 5550, Langeskov, Denmark
Tel.: (45) 63 38 22 22
Web Site: http://www.iai.dk
Year Founded: 1967
Emp.: 600
Processed Steel Product Mfr
N.A.I.C.S.: 331221

Subsidiaries:

Andresen Towers A/S (1)
Lindholm Havnevej 33, 5800, Nyborg, Denmark
Tel.: (45) 63 38 22 22
Web Site: http://www.andresen-towers.com
Steel Products Mfr
N.A.I.C.S.: 331110
Bjorn Thorsen (Mng Dir)

Europrofil Norge AS (1)
Naustvegen 12, Aursnes, 6230, Sykkylven, Norway
Tel.: (47) 70 24 64 00
Construction Materials Distr
N.A.I.C.S.: 423390

Ib Andresen Industri A/S (1)
Industrivej 12-20, 5550, Langeskov, Denmark
Tel.: (45) 63382222
Web Site: http://www.iai.dk
Processed Steel Product Mfr
N.A.I.C.S.: 331221
Bjorn Thorsen (Pres & CEO)

Subsidiary (Non-US):

Europrofil AB (2)
Pershyttans Industriomrade, Box 147, 713 23, Nora, Sweden
Tel.: (46) 58781880
Web Site: http://www.europrofil.se
Sales Range: $25-49.9 Million
Steel Products Mfr
N.A.I.C.S.: 331221

Plant (Domestic):

Ib Andresen Industri A/S-Fredericia (2)
Vejlbyvej 31, 7000, Fredericia, Denmark (100%)
Tel.: (45) 76201900
Web Site: http://www.iai.dk
Emp.: 30
Processed Steel Product Mfr
N.A.I.C.S.: 331221
Pierre Rasmussen (Mng Dir)

Ib Andresen Industry (Thailand) Co. Ltd (1)

INTERNATIONAL PUBLIC

239 Moo 3 Laemchabang Industrial Estate Zone 1, T Tungsukha, Si Racha, 20230, Chon Buri, Thailand
Tel.: (66) 38 495212 3
Web Site: http://www.iai.co.th
Steel Products Mfr
N.A.I.C.S.: 331221
Bjorn Hansen (CEO)

IAMBA ARAD S.A.
Str 6 Vinatori 51-53, Arad, Romania
Tel.: (40) 728988048
FERO—(BUC)
Rev.: $640,105
Assets: $4,467,201
Liabilities: $202,070
Net Worth: $4,265,131
Earnings: $318,437
Emp.: 1
Fiscal Year-end: 12/31/23
Lock & Hinge Product Mfr
N.A.I.C.S.: 332510

IAMGOLD CORPORATION
150 King Street West Suite 2200, PO Box 153, Toronto, M5H 1J9, ON, Canada
Tel.: (416) 360-4710 Ca
Web Site: https://www.iamgold.com
Year Founded: 1990
IAG—(NYSE)
Rev.: $958,800,000
Assets: $4,425,100,000
Liabilities: $2,218,300,000
Net Worth: $2,206,800,000
Earnings: ($52,800,000)
Emp.: 5,065
Fiscal Year-end: 12/31/22
Gold Exploration & Mining
N.A.I.C.S.: 212220
Carol T. Banducci (CFO & Exec VP)

Subsidiaries:

EURO Ressources S.A. (1)
23 rue du Roule, 75001, Paris, France (100%)
Tel.: (33) 4506777056
Web Site: http://www.goldroyalties.com
Rev.: $23,914,310
Assets: $41,926,398
Liabilities: $1,632,851
Net Worth: $40,293,546
Earnings: $12,242,607
Fiscal Year-end: 12/31/2022
Gold Mining Services
N.A.I.C.S.: 212220
Tidiane Barry (Dir Gen)

IAMGOLD Essakane S.A. (1)
Secteur 13 rue 13 16 porte 72, 09 BP 11, Ouagadougou, Burkina Faso
Tel.: (226) 25428700
Web Site: https://www.iamgoldessakane.com
Emp.: 2,500
Gold Ore Mining Services
N.A.I.C.S.: 212210

OMAI Gold Mines Limited (1)
176 D Middle St Cummingsburg, PO Box 12249, Georgetown, Guyana
Tel.: (592) 2266463
Web Site: http://www.psc.org.gy
Sales Range: $50-74.9 Million
Emp.: 20
Gold Mining
N.A.I.C.S.: 212220
Renaud Adams (Chm)

Rosebel Gold Mines N.V. (1)
President da Costalaan 2, Paramaribo, Suriname
Tel.: (597) 422741
Web Site: https://www.rosebelgoldmines.sr
Gold Mining Services
N.A.I.C.S.: 212220

Sociedad Minera Cambior Peru SA (1)
AV Jose Casimiro Ulloa 312, Urban San Antonio Miraflores, Lima, 18, Peru
Tel.: (51) 14448282

AND PRIVATE COMPANIES

Sales Range: $50-74.9 Million
Emp.: 20
N.A.I.C.S.: 212220

Vanstar Mining Resources Inc. (1)
410 rue Saint-Nicolas Suite 236, Montreal, H2Y 2P5, QC, Canada
Tel.: (514) 907-9016
Web Site: https://www.vanstarmining.com
Rev.: $3,710,057
Assets: $5,817,550
Liabilities: $582,454
Net Worth: $5,235,096
Earnings: ($3,406,794)
Fiscal Year-end: 12/31/2020
Metal Mining Services
N.A.I.C.S.: 212290
Martin Nicoletti (CFO)

IAN MACLEOD DISTILLERS & CO. LTD.
Russell House Dunnet Way, Broxbourne, EH52 5BU, United Kingdom
Tel.: (44) 1506852205
Web Site:
   http://www.ianmacleod.com
Year Founded: 1936
Sales Range: $10-24.9 Million
Emp.: 20
Distilled & Blended Liquor Mfr
N.A.I.C.S.: 312130
Leonard J. Russell (Founder & Mng Dir)

Subsidiaries:

Ian Macleod Distillers Ltd. (1)
Russell House, Dunnet Way, Broxbourne, EH52 5BU, United Kingdom
Tel.: (44) 1506852205
Web Site: http://www.ianmacleod.com
Emp.: 50
Producer of Scotch Whiskey
N.A.I.C.S.: 312130
Leonard Russell (Mng Dir)

IAN MOSEY LTD
Village Farm Main Street, Gilling East, York, YO62 4JH, United Kingdom
Tel.: (44) 1439 788300
Web Site:
   http://www.ianmoseyltd.com
Year Founded: 1977
Sales Range: $50-74.9 Million
Pig, Sheep & Cattle Farming; Animal Feed Distr
N.A.I.C.S.: 112210
Ian Mosey (Mng Dir)

IANTE INVESTMENTS SOCIMI, S.A.
57th Serrano St 2nd floor, 28006, Madrid, Spain
Web Site: https://www.iante.es
Year Founded: 2017
MLINT—(EUR)
Rev.: $7,745,032
Assets: $296,857,989
Liabilities: $319,217,618
Net Worth: ($22,359,629)
Earnings: ($14,486,849)
Emp.: 18
Fiscal Year-end: 12/31/21
Investment Management Service
N.A.I.C.S.: 523999
Kevin Jeremiah Cahill (Chm)

IAR SA
No 34 Hermann Oberth Street, Ghimbav, 507075, Brasov, Romania
Tel.: (40) 268475269
Web Site: https://www.iar.ro
IARV—(BUC)
Rev.: $97,031,282
Assets: $132,453,546
Liabilities: $79,217,113
Net Worth: $53,236,432
Earnings: $5,181,991
Emp.: 369

Fiscal Year-end: 12/31/23
Aircraft & Spacecraft Maintenance Services
N.A.I.C.S.: 336411
Neculai Banea (Gen Dir)

IAR SYSTEMS GROUP AB
Strandbodgatan 1, 753 23, Uppsala, Sweden
Tel.: (46) 18167800
Web Site: http://www.iar.com
Year Founded: 1999
IAR—(OMX)
Rev.: $39,328,632
Assets: $86,375,004
Liabilities: $23,921,249
Net Worth: $62,453,754
Earnings: $5,413,658
Emp.: 209
Fiscal Year-end: 12/31/22
Distr of Software & IT Products
N.A.I.C.S.: 513210
Ann Zetterberg (CFO)

Subsidiaries:

IAR Systems AB (1)
Strandbodgatan 1 A, 753 23, Uppsala, Sweden
Tel.: (46) 18167800
Web Site: https://www.iar.se
Sales Range: $10-24,9 Million
Emp.: 100
Software Producer for Programming Microprocessors in Embedded Systems
N.A.I.C.S.: 423430

Subsidiary (Non-US):

IAR Systems AG (2)
Werner-Eckert-Strasse 9, 81829, Munich, Germany
Tel.: (49) 898898900
Web Site: http://www.iar.com
Embedded Systems Software Producer
N.A.I.C.S.: 423430

IAR Systems K.K. (2)
C-5 Bldg 5F 1-21-5 Kandasuda-cho, Chiyoda-ku, Tokyo, 101-0041, Japan
Tel.: (81) 352984800
Emp.: 8
Embedded Systems Software Producer
N.A.I.C.S.: 423430

IAR Systems Ltd. (2)
Spencer House, 3 Spencer Parade, Northampton, NN1 5AA, United Kingdom
Tel.: (44) 1604250440
Web Site: http://www.iar.com
Embedded Systems Software Producer
N.A.I.C.S.: 423430

Subsidiary (US):

IAR Systems Software Inc. (2)
Century Plaza 1065 E Hillsdale Blvd, Foster City, CA 94404
Tel.: (650) 287-4250
Web Site: http://www.iar.com
Sales Range: $1-9.9 Million
Emp.: 10
Embedded Systems Software Producer
N.A.I.C.S.: 423430

IAR Systems Software Inc. (2)
2 Mount Royal Ave Ste 420, Marlborough, MA 01752
Tel.: (508) 281-6680
Embedded Systems Software Producer
N.A.I.C.S.: 423430

Signum Systems Corp. (2)
1211 Flynn Rd 104, Camarillo, CA 93012
Tel.: (805) 523-9774
Web Site: http://www.signum.com
Instrument Mfr for Measuring & Testing Electricity & Electrical Signals
N.A.I.C.S.: 334515

IAR Systems GmbH (1)
Hanns-Schwindt-Strasse 11, 81829, Munich, Germany
Tel.: (49) 898898900
Software Development Services
N.A.I.C.S.: 541511

IARGENTO HI TECH ASSETS LP
88 Agripas Street, Jerusalem, Israel
Tel.: (972) 25853159
Web Site: https://www.iargento.com
Year Founded: 1995
IARG—(TAE)
Assets: $11,025,832
Liabilities: $74,320
Net Worth: $10,951,512
Earnings: ($1,930,377)
Fiscal Year-end: 12/31/23
Investment Management Service
N.A.I.C.S.: 523940
Shai Hod (CEO)

IASON SA
Str Avram Iancu 40-42, Brasov, Romania
Tel.: (40) 26 847 1849
Sales Range: $1-9.9 Million
Emp.: 153
Knitted Apparel Mfr
N.A.I.C.S.: 315120

IB MAROC
Lotissement La Colline Lot n 11 - Sidi Maarouf, 20270, Casablanca, Morocco
Tel.: (212) 522436304
Web Site: http://www.ib-maroc.com
Year Founded: 1997
IBC—(CAS)
Sales Range: $1-9.9 Million
Software & Computer Services
N.A.I.C.S.: 541519
Bernard Decorps (CEO & Mng Dir)

IB SECURITIES JOINT STOCK COMPANY
Floor 22 No 52 Le Dai Hanh Street, Le Dai Hanh Ward Hai Ba Trung District, Hanoi, Vietnam
Tel.: (84) 2444568888
Web Site: https://www.ibsc.vn
Year Founded: 2007
Rev.: $18,094,259
Assets: $61,211,389
Liabilities: $17,038,620
Net Worth: $44,172,769
Earnings: $8,662,234
Fiscal Year-end: 12/31/18
Securities Brokerage Services
N.A.I.C.S.: 523150
Thai Hoang Long (Chm)

IBAR A.D.
Ibarska 4, Raska, Serbia
Tel.: (381) 36 736 153
Year Founded: 1954
Sales Range: Less than $1 Million
Emp.: 10
Grocery Store Operator
N.A.I.C.S.: 445110

IBASE SOLUTION CO., LTD
24F No 93 Sec 1 Xintai 5th Rd, Xizhi Dist, New Taipei City, 221416, Taiwan
Tel.: (886) 277535888
Web Site:
   https://www.ibasesolution.com
Year Founded: 2011
6441—(TPE)
Rev.: $14,653,159
Assets: $57,074,196
Liabilities: $24,519,463
Net Worth: $32,554,732
Earnings: ($32,517)
Fiscal Year-end: 12/31/22
Peripheral Equipment Distr
N.A.I.C.S.: 423430
Lain-Bin Liao (Chm)

IBASE TECHNOLOGY PTE. LTD.
No 19 Kallang Ave 04-15, Singapore, Singapore
Tel.: (65) 6557 2516 SG
Web Site: http://www.ibase.com.sg
Information Technology Services
N.A.I.C.S.: 519290
Ernest Ong (CEO)

Subsidiaries:

IBase Technology International Pte. Ltd. (1)
No 19 Kallang Ave 04-15, Singapore, 119963, Singapore (65%)
Tel.: (65) 6557 2516
Information Technology Products & Services
N.A.I.C.S.: 541519

IBB AMSTERDAM BV
Klaprozenweg 75E, 1033 NN, Amsterdam, Netherlands
Tel.: (31) 20 3428080
Web Site:
   http://www.ibbamsterdam.com
Year Founded: 1993
Sales Range: $50-74.9 Million
Emp.: 200
Watches & Jewelry Distr
N.A.I.C.S.: 423940

Subsidiaries:

IBB Dublin Ltd (1)
Unit 1 01 First Floor Office Southgate Dublin Road, Co Louth, Drogheda, Ireland
Tel.: (353) 41 9818080
Web Site: http://www.ibbdublin.com
Jewellery Distr
N.A.I.C.S.: 424990
Dennis Hicks (Brand Mgr-CASIO, GUESS Jewellery & GUESS Watches)

IBB Paris SARL (1)
6 Boulevard de la Liberation, 93284, Saint Denis, France
Tel.: (33) 148139595
Jewellery Distr
N.A.I.C.S.: 424990
Christophe Devaux (Gen Mgr)

Internationnal Bullion & Metal Brokers (1)
Urbaparc I Batiment F 6 Boulevard De La Liberation, 93200, Saint Denis, France
Tel.: (33) 148130540
Sales Range: $75-99.9 Million
Emp.: 121
Durable Goods
N.A.I.C.S.: 423990

IBC SOLAR AG
Am Hochgericht 10, 96231, Bad Staffelstein, Germany
Tel.: (49) 957392240
Web Site: http://www.ibc-solar.de
Sales Range: $650-699.9 Million
Emp.: 200
Solar Power Equipment Distr
N.A.I.C.S.: 423690
Udo Moehrstedt (CEO)

Subsidiaries:

IBC SOLAR A.E. (1)
Panos Biazzos 29 Paradeisou & Zagoras str, Marousi, 15125, Athens, Greece
Tel.: (30) 210 6828163
Web Site: http://www.ibc-solar.gr
Solar Equipment Mfr & Distr
N.A.I.C.S.: 333414

IBC SOLAR AUSTRIA GmbH (1)
Thomas Alva Edison-Strasse 2, 7000, Eisenstadt, Austria
Tel.: (43) 2682 704 8230
Web Site: http://www.ibc-solar.at
Solar Equipment Mfr & Distr
N.A.I.C.S.: 333414
Andrea Anteri (Gen Mgr)

IBC SOLAR B.V. (1)
Hoeverveldweg 7, 3600, Schinnen, Netherlands
Tel.: (31) 46 4 42 47 47
Web Site: http://www.ibc-solar.nl
Solar Equipment Mfr & Distr

3569

IBC SOLAR AG

IBC Solar AG—(Continued)
N.A.I.C.S.: 333414
Jack Peter (CEO)

IBC SOLAR Projects Private Limited (1)
614 B-Wing 215 Atrium Andheri-Kurla Road, Andheri, 400 069, Mumbai, India
Tel.: (91) 22 30771 490
Web Site: http://www.ibc-solar.in
Solar Equipment Mfr & Distr
N.A.I.C.S.: 333414
Reinhard Ling (Mng Dir)

IBC SOLAR Srl (1)
Via Nazionale 20, Buttrio, 33042, Udine, Italy
Tel.: (39) 0432 683058
Web Site: http://www.ibc-solar.it
Solar Equipment Mfr & Distr
N.A.I.C.S.: 333414

IBC Solar Teknik SDN BHD (1)
B112 1st floor Block B Kelana Square No 17 - Jalan SS 7/26, Kelana Jaya, 47301, Petaling Jaya, Selangor Darul Ehsan, Malaysia
Tel.: (60) 3 7803 3328
Web Site: http://www.ibc-solar.my
Solar Equipment Mfr & Distr
N.A.I.C.S.: 333414
Faish Azim Yahaya (Sr Project Mgr-On-Grid)

IBERDROLA, S.A.
Plaza Euskadi n 5, 48009, Bilbao, Biscaia, Spain
Tel.: (34) 917843232 ES
Web Site: https://www.iberdrola.com
Year Founded: 1901
IBE—(VAL)
Rev.: $40,805,355,653
Assets: $137,036,155,059
Liabilities: $84,184,737,512
Net Worth: $52,851,417,547
Earnings: $3,814,591,436
Emp.: 35,374
Fiscal Year-end: 12/31/19
Energy Production & Distribution, Natural Gas Distribution & Residential Construction
N.A.I.C.S.: 221112
Santiago Martinez Garrido (Dir-Corp Legal Svcs)

Subsidiaries:

Adicora Servicios de Ingenieria, S.L. (1)
Calle Eladio Lopez Vilches 18 1 B, 28033, Madrid, Spain
Tel.: (34) 917660706
Web Site: http://www.adicora.es
Sales Range: $25-49.9 Million
Emp.: 3
Electrical Engineering Services
N.A.I.C.S.: 541330

Ailes Marine, S.A.S. (1)
Tour Ariane - 5 Place de la Pyramide, CS 20209, La Defense, 92088, Paris, Cedex, France
Tel.: (33) 147041443
Web Site: https://ailes-marines.bzh
Wind Electric Power Services
N.A.I.C.S.: 221115

Amara Brasil, Ltda. (1)
Av Prof Magalhaes Neto 1856 Ed TK Tower Sala 1006, Pituba, 41810-012, Salvador, Bahia, Brazil
Tel.: (55) 71 3273 7887
Web Site: http://www.amarabrasil.com.br
Sales Range: $150-199.9 Million
Emp.: 60
Logistics Consulting Servies
N.A.I.C.S.: 541614
Santiago Gonzalez (Gen Dir)

Anselmo Leon Distribucion, S.L. (1)
C / Mino 14, Laguna De Duero, 47140, Valladolid, Spain
Tel.: (34) 983457327
Web Site: https://www.anselmoleon.com
Electric Power Distribution Services
N.A.I.C.S.: 221122

Atlantic Renewable Energy Corporation (1)
PO Box 313, Clifton, VA 20124
Tel.: (703) 830-8477
Web Site: https://www.atlanticrenewableenergy.com
Electric Power Distribution Services
N.A.I.C.S.: 221122

Avangrid, Inc. (1)
180 Marsh Hill Rd, Orange, CT 06477
(81.5%)
Tel.: (207) 629-1190
Web Site: https://www.avangrid.com
Rev.: $8,309,000,000
Assets: $43,989,000,000
Liabilities: $23,313,000,000
Net Worth: $20,676,000,000
Earnings: $786,000,000
Emp.: 7,999
Fiscal Year-end: 12/31/2023
Utility Holding Company
N.A.I.C.S.: 221122
Pedro Azagra Blazquez (CEO)

Subsidiary (Domestic):

Avangrid Renewables, LLC (2)
2701 NW Vaughn St Ste 300, Portland, OR 97210
Tel.: (503) 796-7000
Web Site: http://www.avangridrenewables.com
Alternate Power Development
N.A.I.C.S.: 221118
Barrett Stambler (VP-Renewable Origination)

Blue Creek Wind Farm, LLC (2)
1125 NW Couch St Ste 700, Portland, OR 97209-4129
Tel.: (503) 796-7000
Eletric Power Generation Services
N.A.I.C.S.: 221118

CNE Energy Services Group, LLC (2)
855 Main St, Bridgeport, CT 06604
Tel.: (203) 382-8111
Natural Gas Distribution Services
N.A.I.C.S.: 221210

Central Maine Power Company (2)
83 Edison Dr, Augusta, ME 04336
Tel.: (207) 623-3521
Sales Range: $1-4.9 Billion
Emp.: 1,200
Electric Utility
N.A.I.C.S.: 221122
Douglas Herling (Pres & CEO)

Branch (Domestic):

Central Maine Power Company (3)
24 Gordon Dr, Rockland, ME 04841-2137
Tel.: (207) 594-1090
Web Site: http://www.cmpco.com
Sales Range: $75-99.9 Million
Emp.: 55
Electronic Services
N.A.I.C.S.: 221118

Central Maine Power Company (3)
280 Bath Rd, Brunswick, ME 04011-2619
Tel.: (207) 729-1195
Web Site: http://www.cmpco.com
Sales Range: $75-99.9 Million
Emp.: 54
Electric Power Distribution
N.A.I.C.S.: 221122
Jayme Holland (Mgr-Programs & Projects)

Subsidiary (Domestic):

Maine Electric Power Co., Inc. (3)
83 Edison Dr, Augusta, ME 04336
Web Site: http://www.cmpco.com
Rev.: $20,623,757
Owns Transmission Line
N.A.I.C.S.: 221118

Subsidiary (Domestic):

Copper Crossing Solar, LLC (2)
1125 NW Couch St Ste 700, Portland, OR 97209-4129
Tel.: (503) 796-7000
Web Site: http://www.avangrid.com
Emp.: 200
Solar Electric Power Generation Services
N.A.I.C.S.: 221118

Dry Lake Wind Power II, LLC (2)
1125 NW Couch St Ste 700, Portland, OR 97209
Tel.: (503) 796-7000
Wind Electric Power Generation Services
N.A.I.C.S.: 221118

E.O. Resources, LLC (2)
20329 State Hwy 249 Ste 500, Houston, TX 77070
Tel.: (281) 374-3050
Natural Gas Distribution Services
N.A.I.C.S.: 221210

Elk River Wind Farm, LLC (2)
14980 Se 190th St, Latham, KS 67072-9059
Tel.: (620) 965-2289
Wind Electric Power Generation Services
N.A.I.C.S.: 221118
Ryan Orban (Mgr-Site)

Elm Creek Wind II, LLC (2)
1125 NW Couch St Ste 700, Portland, OR 97209-4129
Tel.: (503) 478-6305
Eletric Power Generation Services
N.A.I.C.S.: 221118

Enstor Inc. (2)
10375 Richmond Ave Ste 1900, Houston, TX 77042
Tel.: (281) 374-3050
Web Site: http://www.enstorinc.com
Sales Range: $25-49.9 Million
Emp.: 30
Natural Gas Storage Services
N.A.I.C.S.: 486210
John McStravick (Gen Counsel, Sec & VP)

Enstor Operating Company, LLC (2)
20329 State Hwy 249 Ste 500, Houston, TX 77070-4129
Tel.: (281) 374-3050
Emp.: 80
Natural Gas Transmission Services
N.A.I.C.S.: 486210
Daryl Gee (CEO)

Enstor Waha Storage and Transportation L.P. (2)
20329 State Hwy 249 Ste 500, Houston, TX 77070
Tel.: (281) 374-3050
Web Site: http://www.enstor.com
Emp.: 80
Natural Gas Distr
N.A.I.C.S.: 221210
Tracy Schuring (Office Mgr)

Ergytech Inc. (2)
2400 Augusta Dr Ste 310, Houston, TX 77057
Tel.: (713) 953-0300
Electric Power Distribution Services
N.A.I.C.S.: 221122

Groton Wind, LLC (2)
1125 NW Couch St Ste 700, Portland, OR 97209-4129
Tel.: (503) 796-7000
Wind Electric Power Generation Services
N.A.I.C.S.: 221118

Hardscrabble Wind Power, LLC (2)
1125 NW Couch St Ste 700, Portland, OR 97209-4129
Tel.: (503) 478-6305
Wind Electric Power Generation Services
N.A.I.C.S.: 221118

Hay Canyon Wind, LLC (2)
66781 Fairview Rd, Moro, OR 97039
Tel.: (503) 796-6943
Wind Electric Power Generation Services
N.A.I.C.S.: 221118

Iberdrola Energy Service, LLC (2)
20329 State Hwy 249 Ste 500, Houston, TX 77070
Tel.: (281) 379-7400
Web Site: http://www.iberdrolaens.com
Eletric Power Generation Services
N.A.I.C.S.: 221118
Jim Artley (VP-Gas Trading)

Iberdrola USA Enterprises, Inc. (2)
52 Farm View Dr, New Gloucester, ME 04260
Tel.: (207) 688-6300
Natural Gas Distribution Services

INTERNATIONAL PUBLIC

N.A.I.C.S.: 221210

Plant (Domestic):

Iberdrola USA, Inc. (2)
23 E Main St, Gowanda, NY 14070-1207
Tel.: (716) 532-3148
Sales Range: $75-99.9 Million
Emp.: 8
Electronic Services
N.A.I.C.S.: 221118

Iberdrola USA, Inc. (2)
1798 W Sullivan St, Olean, NY 14760-1942
Tel.: (800) 572-1111
Sales Range: $75-99.9 Million
Emp.: 10
Liquefied Petroleum Gas Delivered To Customers Premises
N.A.I.C.S.: 221118

Iberdrola USA, Inc. (2)
601 113th St NW Ste 720 S, Washington, DC 20005-2615
Tel.: (202) 783-5521
Sales Range: $75-99.9 Million
Emp.: 1
Electronic Services
N.A.I.C.S.: 221118

Iberdrola USA, Inc. (2)
Styles Rd, Penn Yan, NY 14527
Tel.: (315) 536-2324
Sales Range: $75-99.9 Million
Emp.: 12
Electronic Services
N.A.I.C.S.: 221118

Iberdrola USA, Inc. (2)
Weirk Ave, Liberty, NY 12754
Tel.: (845) 292-2434
Web Site: http://www.nyseg.com
Sales Range: $125-149.9 Million
Emp.: 146
Electric & Other Services Combined
N.A.I.C.S.: 221118

Iberdrola USA, Inc. (2)
50 Ossian St, Dansville, NY 14437-1029
Tel.: (585) 335-9058
Sales Range: $75-99.9 Million
Emp.: 30
Electronic Services
N.A.I.C.S.: 221122

Iberdrola USA, Inc. (2)
31 Dardess Dr, Chatham, NY 12037-1438
Tel.: (518) 392-2972
Sales Range: $75-99.9 Million
Emp.: 66
Electric & Other Services Combined
N.A.I.C.S.: 221118

Joint Venture (Domestic):

Iroquois Gas Transmission System, LP (2)
1 Corporate Dr Ste 600, Shelton, CT 06484-6209 (4.87%)
Tel.: (203) 925-7200
Web Site: http://www.iroquois.com
Sales Range: $25-49.9 Million
Emp.: 109
Natural Gas Pipelines
N.A.I.C.S.: 486210
Jeffrey A. Bruner (Pres)

Subsidiary (Domestic):

Klamath Energy, LLC (2)
1125 NW Couch St Ste 700, Portland, OR 97209
Tel.: (503) 796-6927
Eletric Power Generation Services
N.A.I.C.S.: 221118

Maine Natural Gas (2)
9 Industrial Pkwy, Brunswick, ME 04011
Tel.: (207) 729-0420
Web Site: https://www.mainenaturalgas.com
Sales Range: $50-74.9 Million
Emp.: 18
Provider of Natural Gas
N.A.I.C.S.: 221210

New Hampshire Gas Corporation (2)
32 Central Sq, Keene, NH 03431
Tel.: (603) 352-1230
Natural Gas Distribution Services
N.A.I.C.S.: 221210

AND PRIVATE COMPANIES — IBERDROLA, S.A.

New Harvest Wind Project, LLC (2)
1125 NW Couch St Ste 700, Portland, OR 97209
Tel.: (503) 796-7001
Wind Electric Power Generation Services
N.A.I.C.S.: 221118

New York State Electric & Gas Corporation (2)
6544 Lincoln Ave, Lockport, NY 14094-6108
Tel.: (716) 438-9803
Web Site: http://www.nyseg.com
Sales Range: $25-49.9 Million
Emp.: 45
Provider of Electric & Gas Services
N.A.I.C.S.: 926130
Mark V. Dolan *(Sec & Deputy Gen Counsel)*

Subsidiary (Domestic):

New York State Electric & Gas Corp. (3)
18 Link Dr, Binghamton, NY 13902-5224
Tel.: (607) 762-7200
Web Site: http://www.nyseg.com
Transmission & Distribution Of Gas And Electricity
N.A.I.C.S.: 221122
Mark V. Dolan *(Sec & Deputy Gen Counsel)*

New York State Electric & Gas Corp. (3)
4125 State Route 22, Plattsburgh, NY 12901-5619
Tel.: (518) 566-9846
Web Site: http://www.nyseg.com
Electric & Other Services Combined
N.A.I.C.S.: 221122

New York State Electric & Gas Corp. (3)
6 Warner Rd, Clifton Park, NY 12065
Tel.: (518) 664-9534
Web Site: http://www.nyseg.com
Sales Range: $100-124.9 Million
Electric & Other Items
N.A.I.C.S.: 221122

New York State Electric & Gas Corp. (3)
1 Electric Pkwy, Horseheads, NY 14845
Tel.: (607) 796-4675
Web Site: http://www.nyseg.com
Provider of Electrical & Gas Services
N.A.I.C.S.: 221122

New York State Electric & Gas Corp. (3)
1387 Dryden Rd, Ithaca, NY 14850
Tel.: (607) 347-4131
Web Site: http://www.nyseg.com
Distr of Electric Power
N.A.I.C.S.: 221112

New York State Electric & Gas Corp. (3)
3768 State Route 14, Watkins Glen, NY 14891-9715
Tel.: (607) 535-8827
Web Site: http://www.nyseg.com
Sales Range: $75-99.9 Million
Emp.: 7
Natural Gas Compressor Station Construction
N.A.I.C.S.: 221118

Subsidiary (Domestic):

Pebble Springs Wind LLC (2)
1125 NW Couch St Ste 700, Portland, OR 97209-4129
Tel.: (503) 796-7000
Wind Electric Power Generation Services
N.A.I.C.S.: 221118

Rochester Gas & Electric Corporation (2)
180 S Clinton Ave, Rochester, NY 14604
Tel.: (585) 771-4999
Web Site: https://www.rge.com
Rev.: $885,960,000
Assets: $2,846,268,000
Liabilities: $2,113,869,000
Net Worth: $732,399,000
Earnings: $83,222,000
Emp.: 1,078
Fiscal Year-end: 12/31/2012
Electric & Gas Utility Services
N.A.I.C.S.: 221118

Joseph J. Syta *(Treas, VP & Controller)*

TEN Transmission Company (2)
60 Columbus Blvd, Hartford, CT 06103
Tel.: (860) 548-7350
Web Site: http://www.hartfordsteam.com
Emp.: 50
Natural Gas Distribution Services
N.A.I.C.S.: 221210

The Hartford Steam Company (2)
60 Columbus Blvd, Hartford, CT 06103-2805
Tel.: (860) 548-7350
Web Site: http://www.hartfordsteam.com
Emp.: 50
Heat Power Generation Services
N.A.I.C.S.: 221330

Tule Wind LLC (2)
1125 NW Couch St Ste 700, Portland, OR 97209
Tel.: (503) 796-7001
Web Site: http://www.iberdrolarenewables.us
Wind Electric Power Generation Services
N.A.I.C.S.: 221118

Twin Buttes Wind, LLC (2)
1195 NW Couch St Ste 700, Portland, OR 97209
Tel.: (503) 796-7001
Eletric Power Generation Services
N.A.I.C.S.: 221118

UIL Holdings Corporation (2)
157 Church St, New Haven, CT 06510
Tel.: (203) 499-2000
Web Site: http://www.uinet.com
Holding Company; Owner of Electricity & Energy Related Services
N.A.I.C.S.: 221112
Linda L. Randell *(Gen Counsel & Sr VP)*

Subsidiary (Domestic):

Connecticut Natural Gas Corporation (3)
76 Meadow St, East Hartford, CT 06108 (100%)
Tel.: (860) 524-8361
Web Site: https://www.cngcorp.com
Natural Gas Sales & Distr
N.A.I.C.S.: 486210
William Reis *(VP-Admin Svcs)*

The Berkshire Gas Company (3)
115 Cheshire Rd, Pittsfield, MA 01201
Tel.: (413) 442-1511
Web Site: https://www.berkshiregas.com
Natural Gas Distr
N.A.I.C.S.: 221210
Christopher C. Farrell *(Mgr-Comm & Govt Rels)*

The Southern Connecticut Gas Company (3)
60 Marsh Hill Rd, Orange, CT 06477 (100%)
Tel.: (866) 268-2887
Web Site: http://www.soconngas.com
Natural Gas Distr
N.A.I.C.S.: 221210
Robert M. Allessio *(Pres & CEO)*

The United Illuminating Company (3)
180 Marsh Hill Rd, Orange, CT 06477
Tel.: (203) 499-2000
Energy Services
N.A.I.C.S.: 221122
Susan Allen *(Treas & VP-IR)*

Bidelek Sareak, A.I.E. (1)
Avenida San Adrian 48, Bilbao, 48003, Spain
Tel.: (34) 944035600
Sales Range: $75-99.9 Million
Emp.: 10
Eletric Power Generation Services
N.A.I.C.S.: 221118

Central Nuclear de Trillo (1)
Apartado Correos 2, Trillo, 19450, Guadalajara, Spain (49%)
Tel.: (34) 949 81 7900
Web Site: http://www.cnat.es
Nuclear Energy Operations
N.A.I.C.S.: 221113

Electrica Conquense, S.A. (1)
Calle Parque de San Julian n 5 1st floor, Cuenca, 16001, Madrid, Spain (54%)
Tel.: (34) 900233423
Web Site: https://www.electricaconquense.es
Sales Range: Less than $1 Million
Emp.: 3,000
Electric Power Distr
N.A.I.C.S.: 221122

Electricidad de La Paz, S.A. (1)
Avenida Illimani I973, Casilla, La Paz, 10511, Bolivia
Tel.: (591) 2 222 2200
Web Site: http://www.electropaz.com.bo
Eletric Power Generation Services
N.A.I.C.S.: 221118

Elektro Electricidade e Servicos, S.A. (1)
Rua Ary Antenor de Souza 321 Jardim Nova America, Campinas, 13053-024, Sao Paulo, Brazil
Tel.: (55) 19 2122 1009
Web Site: http://www.elektro.com.br
Electric Power Distribution Services
N.A.I.C.S.: 221122
Marcio Henrique Fernandes *(CEO)*

Empresa de Luz y Fuerza Electrica de Oruro, S.A. (1)
Calle Catacora y 12 de Octubre S/N, Oruro, Bolivia
Tel.: (591) 2 5252233
Sales Range: $100-124.9 Million
Emp.: 97
Electric Power Generation & Distribution Services
N.A.I.C.S.: 221118

Energyworks Aranda, S.L. (1)
Calle Veinte de Febrero 8, Valladolid, 47001, Spain
Tel.: (34) 947503189
Electric Power Generation Services
N.A.I.C.S.: 221118

Energyworks Carballo, S.L. (1)
Carretera Ac 552 Km 34 5, Carballo, 15100, Spain
Tel.: (34) 981703697
Web Site: http://www.iberdrola.es
Eletric Power Generation Services
N.A.I.C.S.: 221118
Tomas Lopez Curros *(Plant Mgr)*

Energyworks Cartagena, S.L. (1)
Ctra Alhama de Murcia Km 13, Cartagena, 30390, Spain
Tel.: (34) 968878406
Sales Range: $75-99.9 Million
Emp.: 2
Natural Gas Distribution Services
N.A.I.C.S.: 221210
Carlos Gonzalez Costa *(Gen Mgr)*

Energyworks Fonz, S.L. (1)
Calle Rabal De Abajo S/N, Fonz, 22422, Spain
Tel.: (34) 974417936
Electric Power Generation Services
N.A.I.C.S.: 221118

Energyworks Monzon, S.L. (1)
Calle Paules, 22400, Monzon, Spain
Tel.: (34) 917842438
Eletric Power Generation Services
N.A.I.C.S.: 221118

Energyworks San Millan, S.L. (1)
Camino De Pobladora Pol Ind Uno Finca 44, San Millan de los Caballeros, 24237, Spain
Tel.: (34) 987686006
Production & Distribution of Electric Energy
N.A.I.C.S.: 221118

Energyworks Venezuela, S.A. (1)
Av Domingo Olavarria Cruce Con Calle Norte-Sur, Zona Industrial Municipal Sur, Valencia, 2003, Carabobo, Venezuela
Tel.: (58) 241838 9074
Electric Power Generation Services
N.A.I.C.S.: 221118

Energyworks Villarrobledo, S.L. (1)
Avda Reyes Catolicos 135, Villarrobledo, 02600, Spain
Tel.: (34) 944702034
Electric Power Generation Services
N.A.I.C.S.: 221118

Eolica Dobrogea (Schweiz) I, GmbH. (1)
Bahnhofstrasse 3, Pfaffikon, 8808, Switzerland
Tel.: (41) 44 261 07 07
Eletric Power Generation Services
N.A.I.C.S.: 221118

Grupo Iberdrola Mexico, S.A. de C.V. (1)
Boulevard Manuel Avila Camacho 24 Piso 19 Edif Torre del Bosque Col, Chapultepec, Mexico, 11000, Mexico
Tel.: (52) 55 85034600
Eletric Power Generation Services
N.A.I.C.S.: 221118

Subsidiary (Domestic):

Amergy Mexicana, S.A. de C.V. (2)
Calzada del Valle 110 ote PB Col de Valle, San Pedro, Garza Garcia, 66220, Nuevo Leon, Mexico
Tel.: (52) 81 81534646
Web Site: http://amara.com.mx
Emp.: 80
Eletric Power Generation Services
N.A.I.C.S.: 221114

Enermon S.A. de C.V. (2)
Melchor Ocampo No 193 Tc Veronica Anzures, Miguel Hidalgo, Mexico, 11300, Mexico
Tel.: (52) 55 9150 2100
Electric Power Generation Services
N.A.I.C.S.: 221118

Enertek, S.A. de C.V. (2)
Innortek Sade Cv Carretera Tampico Mante KM 17 5, Altamira, 89600, Tamaulipas, Mexico
Tel.: (52) 8332241900
Sales Range: $50-74.9 Million
Emp.: 30
Electric Power Transmission Services
N.A.I.C.S.: 221121

Iberdrola Mexico, S.A. de C.V. (2)
Calle Montes Urales 540 Colonia Lomas de Chapultepec, Edificio Torre Del Bosque Colonia Lomas De Chapultepec, 11000, Mexico, Mexico
Tel.: (52) 5585034600
Web Site: https://www.iberdrolamexico.com
Electric Power Generation Services
N.A.I.C.S.: 221118

Subsidiary (Domestic):

Iberdrola Energia Altamira, S.A. de C.V. (3)
Km 10 3 Blvd De Los Rios, Altamira, 89600, Mexico
Tel.: (52) 8332604600
Electric Power Generation Services
N.A.I.C.S.: 221118

Subsidiary (Domestic):

Iberdrola Energia Altamira de Servicios, S.A. de C.V. (4)
Bulevar Manuel Aguila Camacho 24 - Piso 19 Edificio Torre del Bosque, PO Box 11000, Colonia Lomas de Chapultepec, 162606, Mexico, Mexico
Tel.: (52) 5585034600
Web Site: http://www.iberdrola.com
Sales Range: $50-74.9 Million
Emp.: 150
Eletric Power Generation Services
N.A.I.C.S.: 221118

Subsidiary (Domestic):

Iberdrola Energia La Laguna, S.A. de C.V. (3)
Circuito Industrial Durango No 4300, Gomez Palacio, 35140, Mexico
Tel.: (52) 8717051600
Eletric Power Generation Services
N.A.I.C.S.: 221118

Iberdrola Energia Monterrey, S.A. de C.V. (3)
Km 12 2 Carr A Dulces Nombres, Pesqueria, 66650, Mexico
Tel.: (52) 8181534600
Web Site: http://www.iberdrola.com
Emp.: 60
Eletric Power Generation Services

IBERDROLA, S.A.

INTERNATIONAL PUBLIC

Iberdrola, S.A.—(Continued)
N.A.I.C.S.: 221118
Arnoldo Rico (Gen Mgr)

Subsidiary (Domestic):

Iberdrola Servicios Monterrey, S.A. de C.V. (4)
Blvd Manuel Avila Camacho No 24 Piso 19, Lomas de Chapultepec Seccion M, Mexico, 11000, Mexico
Tel.: (52) 5585034600
Emp.: 50
Electric Power Transmission Services
N.A.I.C.S.: 221121
Ricardo Antunano (Office Mgr)

Subsidiary (Domestic):

Iberdrola Energia del Golfo, S.A. de C.V. (3)
Blvd De Los Rios Km 11 2, Altamira, 89600, Mexico
Tel.: (52) 8332604600
Electric Power Generation Services
N.A.I.C.S.: 221118

Iberdrola Ingenieria y Construccion Mexico, S.A. de C.V. (3)
Melchor Ocampo 193 Torre C Privanza Piso 11 Despacho C, Veronica Anzures, 11300, Mexico, Mexico
Tel.: (52) 5552552022
Web Site: http://www.iberdrola.es
Electric Power Generation Services
N.A.I.C.S.: 221118

Subsidiary (Domestic):

Servicios Operacion Eoloelectrica de Mexico, S.A. de C.V. (2)
Blvd Manuel Avila Camacho 24 Piso 19 Lomas de Chapultepec, Seccion Miguel Hidalgo, Mexico, 11000, Mexico
Tel.: (52) 5585034600
Sales Range: $50-74.9 Million
Emp.: 5
Electric Power Distribution Services
N.A.I.C.S.: 221122

Hidroelectrica Iberica, S.L. (1)
Plaza Euskadi, 48009, Bilbao, Spain
Tel.: (34) 944151411
Web Site: http://www.iberdrola.es
Electric Power Generation Services
N.A.I.C.S.: 221118

IBERDROLA Energias Renovaveis S.A. (1)
Edificio Tivoli Forum Avendia da Liberdadae 180-A 7 Planta, 1250-146, Lisbon, Portugal
Tel.: (351) 21 350 2750
Web Site: http://www.iberdrola.es
Emp.: 3
Eletric Power Generation Services
N.A.I.C.S.: 221118

Iberdrola Clientes Portugal, Unipessoal (1)
Av D Joao II Edificio Meridiano 30 Piso 3, 1990-092, Lisbon, Portugal
Tel.: (351) 211163614
Web Site: https://www.iberdrola.pt
Electric Power Distribution Services
N.A.I.C.S.: 221122

Iberdrola Clienti Italia, S.R.L. (1)
Piazzale dell'Industria 40, 00144, Rome, RM, Italy
Tel.: (39) 0800690960
Web Site: https://www.iberdrola.it
Wind Electric Power Services
N.A.I.C.S.: 221115

Iberdrola Cogeneracion, S.L.U. (1)
Rodriguez Arias 15-6, Bilbao, 48008, Spain
Tel.: (34) 944702034
Electric Power Generation Services
N.A.I.C.S.: 221118

Iberdrola Consultoria e Servicos do Brasil, Ltd. (1)
R Lauro MULler 116, Botafogo, Brazil
Tel.: (55) 21 3820 1501
Eletric Power Generation Services
N.A.I.C.S.: 221118

Iberdrola Distribucion Electrica, S.A.U. (1)
Plaza Euskadi number 5, 48009, Bilbao, Spain (100%)
Tel.: (34) 944151411
Web Site: http://www.iberdrola.com
Sales Range: $1-4.9 Billion
Emp.: 2,000
Distr of Electricity
N.A.I.C.S.: 221122

Iberdrola Distribucion de Gas, S.A.U. (1)
Calle Menorca 19, Valencia, 46023, Spain
Tel.: (34) 963510722
Sales Range: $250-299.9 Million
Emp.: 30
Electric Power Distribution Services
N.A.I.C.S.: 221122

Iberdrola Diversificacion, S.A.U. (1)
Tomas Redondo 1, 28033, Madrid, Spain (100%)
Tel.: (34) 915776500
Web Site: http://www.iberdrola.com
Sales Range: $75-99.9 Million
Emp.: 200
Holding Company
N.A.I.C.S.: 551112
Jose Sainz Armada (CFO)

Iberdrola Energia Solar Puertollano, S.A. (1)
Calle Berna 1, Toledo, 45003, Spain
Tel.: (34) 925 25 08 63
Solar Power Generation Services
N.A.I.C.S.: 221118

Iberdrola Energia do Brasil, Ltda. (1)
Lauro Muller 116/1101-1102, Botafogo, 22290-160, Rio de Janeiro, Brazil
Tel.: (55) 21 3820 1500
Hydroelectric Power Generation Services
N.A.I.C.S.: 221111

Subsidiary (Domestic):

Elektro Redes S.A. (2)
Rua Ary Antenor de Souza, Jd Nova America, Campinas, 13053-024, SP, Brazil
Tel.: (55) 21221487
Web Site: http://www.elektro.com.br
Sales Range: Less than $1 Million
Eletric Power Generation Services
N.A.I.C.S.: 221118
Simone Aparecida Borsato Simao (CFO, Officer-Controlling & IR & Member-Exec Bd)

Iberdrola Energia, S.A.U. (1)
Tomas Redondo 1, 28033, Madrid, Spain (100%)
Tel.: (34) 915776500
Web Site: http://www.iberdrola.com
Sales Range: $250-299.9 Million
Emp.: 1,000
Holding Company
N.A.I.C.S.: 551112

Iberdrola Energias Renovables, S.A.U. (1)
Tomas Redondo 1, 28033, Madrid, Spain (100%)
Tel.: (34) 915776500
Web Site: http://www.iberdrolarenovablesenergia.es
Sales Range: $125-149.9 Million
Emp.: 200
Provider of Renewable Energy
N.A.I.C.S.: 221122
Javier Garcia de Fuentes Churruca (Sec)

Iberdrola Energias Renovaveis do Brasil, S.A. (1)
Luis Carlos Crestes 180 2FL, 22290-160, Rio de Janeiro, Brazil
Tel.: (55) 21 3820 1500
Wind Electric Power Generation Services
N.A.I.C.S.: 221118
Mario Saez (Pres)

Iberdrola Energie France, S.A.S. (1)
Tour Ariane 5 Place de la Pyramide, La Defense, 92088, Paris, Cedex, France
Tel.: (33) 187105742
Web Site: https://www.iberdrola.fr
Solar Electric Power Services
N.A.I.C.S.: 221114

Iberdrola Engineering and Construction Bulgaria (1)
113 Evlogi Georgiev Blvd Ground Floor Apartment n 3, 1504, Sofia, Bulgaria
Tel.: (359) 2 846 53 93
Web Site: http://www.iberdrola.es
Sales Range: $25-49.9 Million
Emp.: 4
Construction Engineering Services
N.A.I.C.S.: 541330

Iberdrola Engineering and Construction Poland, Sp. z. o. o. (1)
Filiale Latvija Al Niepodleglosci 69, 02-626, Warsaw, Poland
Tel.: (48) 22 322 72 00
Construction Engineering Services
N.A.I.C.S.: 541330

Iberdrola Engineering and Construction UK, Ltd. (1)
1 Atlantic Quay Robertson Street, Glasgow, G2 8SP, United Kingdom
Tel.: (44) 141 248 8200
Construction Engineering Services
N.A.I.C.S.: 541330

Iberdrola Espana, S.A.U. (1)
Edificio Aqua 19 Planta 13, Menorca, 46023, Valencia, Spain
Tel.: (34) 96 351 0722
Wind Electric Power Services
N.A.I.C.S.: 221115

Iberdrola Financiacion, S.A. (1)
Plaza Euskadi Edif Torre Iberdrola 5, Bilbao, 48009, Spain
Tel.: (34) 944151411
Financial Management Services
N.A.I.C.S.: 523999

Iberdrola Generacion, S.A.U. (1)
Plaza Euskadi 5, 48009, Bilbao, Spain (100%)
Tel.: (34) 944354349
Web Site: http://www.iberdrolageneracionespana.es
Sales Range: $1-4.9 Billion
Emp.: 2,000
Generator of Electricity
N.A.I.C.S.: 221122
Aitor Moso Raigoso (Chm)

Iberdrola Ingenieria de Explotacion, S.A.U. (1)
Ribera De Axpe 5, Erandio, 48950, Vizcaya, Spain
Tel.: (34) 944151411
Web Site: http://www.iberdrola.com
Eletric Power Generation Services
N.A.I.C.S.: 221118

Iberdrola Ingenieria y Construccion, S.A. (1)
Avda de Manoteras 20 Edificios D 3 planta B, 28050, Madrid, Spain (100%)
Tel.: (34) 913833180
Web Site: http://www.iberinco.es
Sales Range: $150-199.9 Million
Emp.: 600
Provider of Engineering & Consultancy Services
N.A.I.C.S.: 541330

Iberdrola Inmobiliaria, S.A. (1)
C/ Alcala 265, 28027, Madrid, Spain
Tel.: (34) 914059760
Web Site: https://www.iberdrolainmobiliaria.com
Real Estate Services
N.A.I.C.S.: 531210

Iberdrola International, B.V. (1)
Rapanburgarstraat 179D, 1011VM, Amsterdam, Netherlands
Tel.: (31) 205792124
Electric Power Generation Services
N.A.I.C.S.: 221118

Iberdrola Ireland, Ltd. (1)
Fitzwilliam House 4 Upper Pembroke Street, PO Box 13051, Dublin, D02 VN24, Ireland
Tel.: (353) 1800300370
Web Site: http://www.iberdrola.ie
Electric Power Distribution Services
N.A.I.C.S.: 221122

Iberdrola Magyarorszag Mernoki es Epito Korlatolf (1)
Vaci Ut 33, 1134, Budapest, Hungary
Tel.: (36) 12353010
Electric Power Generation Services
N.A.I.C.S.: 221118

Iberdrola QSTP, LLC (1)
PO Box 210000, Doha, Qatar
Tel.: (974) 44547070
Web Site: https://www.qstp.org.qa
Scientific & Technical Services
N.A.I.C.S.: 541990
Ahmed Al Said (Dir)

Iberdrola Redes, S.A.U. (1)
Avda San Adrian 48, 48003, Bilbao, Spain (100%)
Tel.: (34) 900171171
Web Site: http://www.iberdrola.com
Sales Range: $1-4.9 Billion
Emp.: 2,000
Distr of Electricity
N.A.I.C.S.: 221122
Ignacio Sanchez Galan (Pres)

Iberdrola Renewables Romania, S.R.L. (1)
Strada Polona n 95-99 3 floor, 010507, Bucharest, Romania
Tel.: (40) 312292224
Wind Electric Power Services
N.A.I.C.S.: 221115

Iberdrola Renovables Andalucia, S.A. (1)
Calle Inca Garcilaso S/N Ed Expo, Seville, Spain
Tel.: (34) 954467940
Eletric Power Generation Services
N.A.I.C.S.: 221118

Iberdrola Renovables Aragon, S.A. (1)
Plaza Antonio Beltran Martinez 1 -planta 7 D, Zaragoza, 50002, Spain
Tel.: (34) 976207080
Sales Range: $75-99.9 Million
Emp.: 25
Wind Electric Power Generation Services
N.A.I.C.S.: 221118
Ignacio Sanchez Galan (Chm & CEO)

Iberdrola Renovables Castilla La Mancha, S.A.U. (1)
Tomas Redondo 1, Madrid, 28033, Spain
Tel.: (34) 925229801
Eletric Power Generation Services
N.A.I.C.S.: 221118

Iberdrola Renovables Castilla y Leon, S.A. (1)
Paseo Zorrilla 34 - Entreplanta, Valladolid, 47006, Spain
Tel.: (34) 983453100
Wind Electric Power Generation Services
N.A.I.C.S.: 221118

Iberdrola Renovables France, S.A.S. (1)
Oficina Central 40 Rue de la Boetie, 75008, Paris, France
Tel.: (33) 14 704 0714
Wind Electric Power Services
N.A.I.C.S.: 221115

Iberdrola Renovables La Rioja, S.A. (1)
Carretera Lagurdia Km 93, Logrono, 26009, Spain
Tel.: (34) 941223304
Eletric Power Generation Services
N.A.I.C.S.: 221118

Iberdrola Renovables Magyarorszag Megujulo (1)
Eiffel Office Building B 5th Floor Terez Krt 55-57, 1062, Budapest, Hungary
Tel.: (36) 1 815 6341
Eletric Power Generation Services
N.A.I.C.S.: 221118

Iberdrola Renovables Magyarorszag, KFT. (1)
Eiffel Square Office Building Terez krt 55, Building A 4th Floor, 1062, Budapest, Hungary
Tel.: (36) 18156341
Wind Electric Power Services
N.A.I.C.S.: 221115

Iberdrola Renovables de Valencia, S.A.U. (1)
Calle Menorca Numero 19, Valencia, 46023, Spain
Tel.: (34) 96 388 45 88

AND PRIVATE COMPANIES — IBERDROLA, S.A.

Electric Power Generation Services
N.A.I.C.S.: 221118

Iberdrola Servicios Energeticos, S.A.U. (1)
Plaza Euskadi 5, Bilbao, 48009, Spain
Tel.: (34) 944151411
Web Site: http://www.iberdrola.com
Electric Power Generation Services
N.A.I.C.S.: 221118

Iberdrola Sistemas, S.A.U. (1)
Tomas Redondo 1, 28033, Madrid, Spain (100%)
Tel.: (34) 915776500
Web Site: http://www.iberdrola.com
Sales Range: $25-49.9 Million
Emp.: 200
Provider of Computer & Communications Related Activities & Services
N.A.I.C.S.: 541512
Jose Sainz Armada *(CFO)*

Ingenieria, Estudios y Construcciones, S.A. (1)
Alameda de Urquijo 28-6, 48010, Bilbao, Spain
Tel.: (34) 944 70 19 11
Web Site: http://www.inecosa.com
Sales Range: $25-49.9 Million
Emp.: 60
Construction Engineering Services
N.A.I.C.S.: 541330

Investigacion y Desarrollo de Equipos Avanzados, S.A.U. (1)
Calle Tomas Redondo 1, 28033, Madrid, Spain
Tel.: (34) 917 40 72 40
Sales Range: $25-49.9 Million
Emp.: 10
Electrical Equipment Installation Services
N.A.I.C.S.: 238210
Luis del Olmo *(Gen Mgr)*

Korinthos Power S.A. (1)
12A Irodou Attikou St, Maroussi, Athens, 151 24, Greece (70%)
Tel.: (30) 2108094038
Energy Production & Distribution Services
N.A.I.C.S.: 221112

Minicentrales Del Tajo, S.A. (1)
Calle Tomas Redondo 1, Madrid, Spain
Tel.: (34) 915640682
Eletric Power Generation Services
N.A.I.C.S.: 221118

Montague Solar, LLC (1)
2001 Park Ridge Dr, Urbana, IL 61802
Tel.: (217) 722-0429
Web Site: https://www.montaguesolar.com
Electric Power Distribution Services
N.A.I.C.S.: 221122

NECEC Transmission, LLC (1)
1 City Ctr Fl 5, Portland, ME 04101
Web Site:
https://www.necleanenergyconnect.org
Hydroelectric Power Generation Services
N.A.I.C.S.: 221111
Thorn Dickinson *(Pres & CEO)*

Navidul Cogeneracion, S.A. (1)
Av Europa 24 Parque Empresarial La, 28100, Madrid, Spain
Tel.: (34) 925777100
Real Estate Manangement Services
N.A.I.C.S.: 531390

Neoenergia S.A. (1)
Praia Do Flamengo 78-4th Floor, 22210030, Rio de Janeiro, Brazil
Tel.: (55) 2132359800
Web Site: http://www.neoenergia.com
Rev.: $7,926,744,038
Assets: $17,717,237,333
Liabilities: $12,340,858,791
Net Worth: $5,376,378,542
Earnings: $809,245,434
Emp.: 15,138
Fiscal Year-end: 12/31/2023
Electric Power Generation & Distribution Services
N.A.I.C.S.: 221118

Subsidiary (Domestic):

Afluente Transmissao de Energia Eletrica S.A. (2)
Praia Do Flamengo 78 - 1 Floor, Flamengo, Rio de Janeiro, 22210-904, RJ, Brazil
Tel.: (55) 32359828
Web Site: http://www.afluentet.com.br
Sales Range: $10-24.9 Million
Electric Power Distribution Services
N.A.I.C.S.: 221122
Renato de Almeida Rocha *(Dir-Investor Relations)*

Companhia Energetica de Pernambuco - Celpe (2)
Av Joao de Barros 111 - Sala 705, 50050902, Recife, PE, Brazil
Tel.: (55) 8132175118
Web Site: http://www.celpe.com.br
Rev.: $1,746,110,248
Assets: $2,832,560,528
Liabilities: $2,506,955,171
Net Worth: $325,605,357
Earnings: $1,236,476
Emp.: 1,676
Fiscal Year-end: 12/31/2023
Electric Power Generation & Distribution Services
N.A.I.C.S.: 221117
Erik Da Costa Breyer *(Dir-IR)*

Companhia Energetica do Rio Grande do Norte - Cosern (2)
R Mermoz 150, 59025250, Natal, 59025250, RN, Brazil (85%)
Tel.: (55) 8432156105
Web Site: https://www.neoenergia.com
Rev.: $646,752,812
Assets: $1,011,959,001
Liabilities: $735,596,412
Net Worth: $276,362,589
Earnings: $104,931,979
Emp.: 755
Fiscal Year-end: 12/31/2023
Electric Power Generation & Distribution Services
N.A.I.C.S.: 221118
Erik Da Costa Breyer *(Dir-IR)*

Subsidiary (Non-US):

Companhia de Eletricidade do Estado da Bahia (2) (89%)
Tel.: (55) 32359800
Web Site: http://www.coelba.com.br
Sales Range: Less than $1 Million
Electric Power Distribution Services
N.A.I.C.S.: 221122
Luiz Antonio Ciarlini *(CEO)*

Subsidiary (Domestic):

Termopernambuco S.A. (2)
Pr Do Flamengo 78 Andar 7, Rio de Janeiro, 22210-901, Brazil
Tel.: (55) 81 3527 6500
Web Site: http://www.termope.com.br
Eletric Power Generation Services
N.A.I.C.S.: 221111
David Benavent Del Prado *(CEO)*

PPC Renewables Rokas, S.A. (1)
3 Kapodistriou Str, Agia Paraskevi, Markopoulon, 15343, Greece
Tel.: (30) 211 211 8000
Electric Power Generation Services
N.A.I.C.S.: 221118

Rokas Construction, S.A. (1)
3 Rizareiou Str, 15233, Halandri, Greece
Tel.: (30) 2108774100
Web Site: http://www.rokasconstructions.gr
Industrial Equipment Mfr
N.A.I.C.S.: 333248

Subsidiary (Domestic):

C. Rokas Industrial Commercial Company, S.A. (2)
Tripolis Industrial Zone, Tripoli, 22100, Greece
Tel.: (30) 2710237863
Eletric Power Generation Services
N.A.I.C.S.: 221118

Rokas Aeoliki Evia, S.A. (2)
3 Rizariou Street, Halandri, 15233, Greece
Tel.: (30) 2108774100
Electric Power Generation Services
N.A.I.C.S.: 221118

Rokas Aeoliki Komito, S.A. (2)
3 Rizariou Street, Halandri, 15233, Greece
Tel.: (30) 2108774100
Electric Power Generation Services
N.A.I.C.S.: 221118

Rokas Aeoliki Kriti, S.A. (2)
3 Rizariou Street, Halandri, 15233, Greece
Tel.: (30) 2108774100
Web Site: http://www.rokasgroup.gr
Emp.: 7
Eletric Power Generation Services
N.A.I.C.S.: 221118

Rokas Aeoliki Thraki II, S.A. (2)
3 Rizariou Street, Halandri, 15233, Greece
Tel.: (30) 2108774100
Web Site: http://www.iberdrola.gr
Eletric Power Generation Services
N.A.I.C.S.: 221118

Rokas Aeoliki Thraki III, S.A. (2)
3 Rizariou Street, Halandri, 15233, Greece
Tel.: (30) 2108774100
Eletric Power Generation Services
N.A.I.C.S.: 221118

Rokas Aeoliki Thraki, S.A. (2)
3 Rizariou Street, Halandri, 15233, Greece
Tel.: (30) 2108774100
Web Site: http://www.iberdrola.gr
Emp.: 5
Electric Power Generation Services
N.A.I.C.S.: 221118

Rokas Aeoliki Zarakes, S.A. (2)
3 Rizariou Street, Halandri, 15233, Greece
Tel.: (30) 2108774100
Web Site: http://www.rokasconstructions.gr
Sales Range: $75-99.9 Million
Emp.: 80
Electric Power Generation Services
N.A.I.C.S.: 221118

Rokas Aeoliki, S.A. (2)
3 Rizariou Street, Halandri, 152 33, Greece
Tel.: (30) 2108774100
Web Site: http://www.rokas.com
Electric Power Generation Services
N.A.I.C.S.: 221118

SMW, Ltd. (1)
Unit 6 Damery Works, Berkeley, GL13 9JR, Lanarkshire, United Kingdom
Tel.: (44) 1454261617
Web Site: https://www.smwltd.com
Sales Range: $75-99.9 Million
Emp.: 70
Wind Electric Power Generation Services
N.A.I.C.S.: 221118
Dylan Hughes *(Gen Mgr)*

Scottish Power plc (1)
320 St Vincent Street, Glasgow, G2 5AD, United Kingdom
Tel.: (44) 1416146903
Web Site: https://www.scottishpower.com
Sales Range: $1-4.9 Billion
Emp.: 16,142
Electricity, Water & Waste Services
N.A.I.C.S.: 221122
Ignacio Sanchez Galan *(Chm)*

Subsidiary (Domestic):

CRE Energy Ltd (2)
3rd Fl Bldg 7 Vantage Point Business Vlg, Mitcheldean, GL17 0DD, Gloucestershire, United Kingdom
Tel.: (44) 1594546334
Electric Utility Company
N.A.I.C.S.: 221122

Core Utility Solutions Ltd (2)
4th Fl E Wing Chadwick House, Warrington, WA3 6AE, Cheshire, United Kingdom
Tel.: (44) 8707771153
Web Site:
http://www.coreutilitysolutions.com
Sales Range: $100-124.9 Million
Emp.: 200
Electric Services Company
N.A.I.C.S.: 221122

Subsidiary (Non-US):

Iberdrola Canada Energy Services, Ltd. (2)
208-5 Richard Way SW, Calgary, T3E 7M8, AB, Canada
Tel.: (403) 206-3160
Web Site:
http://www.iberdrolarenewables.us
Thermal Electric Power Generation Services
N.A.I.C.S.: 221118
Annette Sturgill *(Dir-Credit Risk)*

Subsidiary (Domestic):

SP Dataserve, Ltd. (2)
1 Atlantic Quay, Glasgow, G2 8SP, United Kingdom
Tel.: (44) 1415659000
Web Site: http://www.dataserve-uk.com
Data Collection & Aggregation Services
N.A.I.C.S.: 518210

SP Distribution, Ltd. (2)
1 Atlantic Quay, Glasgow, G2 8SP, Lanarkshire, United Kingdom
Tel.: (44) 1698413000
Electric Power Distribution Services
N.A.I.C.S.: 221122

Joint Venture (Domestic):

ScotAsh Limited (2)
Longannet Power Station, Kincardine, FK104AA, Scotland, United Kingdom
Tel.: (44) 1259730110
Web Site:
http://www.scotash.com.server116.net
Recycled Pulverized Fuel Ash Construction Products Mfr
N.A.I.C.S.: 327120
Chris Bennett *(Mgr-Sls & Quality)*

Subsidiary (Domestic):

Scottish Power Renewable Energy, Ltd. (2)
Arnott House 12-16 Bridge Street, Belfast, BT1 1LS, United Kingdom
Tel.: (44) 141 568 2242
Eletric Power Generation Services
N.A.I.C.S.: 221118

Scottish Power Renewable UK, Ltd. (2)
ScottishPower House 320 St Vincent St, Glasgow, G2 5AD, United Kingdom
Tel.: (44) 1416140000
Web Site:
http://www.scottishpowerrenewables.com
Sales Range: $100-124.9 Million
Emp.: 116
Eletric Power Generation Services
N.A.I.C.S.: 221118

Scottish Power UK Group, Ltd. (2)
1 Atlantic Quay, Glasgow, G2 8SP, United Kingdom
Tel.: (44) 1412488200
Electric Power Generation Services
N.A.I.C.S.: 221118

Scottish Power UK Holdings, Ltd. (2)
1 Atlantic Quay, Glasgow, G2 8SP, United Kingdom
Tel.: (44) 1412 488 200
Web Site: http://www.scottispower.com
Investment Management Service
N.A.I.C.S.: 523999

ScottishPower Energy Management, Ltd. (2)
1 Atlantic Quay Robertson Street, Glasgow, G2 8SP, United Kingdom
Tel.: (44) 1412488200
Eletric Power Generation Services
N.A.I.C.S.: 221118

ScottishPower Energy Retail Ltd (2)
Dealain House, Napier Road Wardpark North, Cumbernauld, G68 0DF, Glasgow, United Kingdom
Tel.: (44) 8452721212
Web Site: http://www.scottishpower.com
Gas & Electricity Whslr
N.A.I.C.S.: 221122

Subsidiary (US):

ScottishPower Group Holdings Company (2)
1125 NW Couch St Ste 700, Portland, OR 97209
Tel.: (503) 796-7000

IBERDROLA, S.A.

Iberdrola, S.A.—(Continued)

Sales Range: $350-399.9 Million
Holding Company
N.A.I.C.S.: 551112
Ralph Currey (Pres)

Subsidiary (Domestic):

ScottishPower Financial Services, Inc. (3)
1125 NW Couch St Ste 700, Portland, OR 97209
Tel.: (503) 796-7000
Sales Range: $75-99.9 Million
Emp.: 100
Holding Company
N.A.I.C.S.: 551112
Ralph Currey (Pres)

Subsidiary (Domestic):

ScottishPower NA 1, Ltd. (2)
1 Atlantic Quay Robertson Street, Glasgow, G2 8SP, United Kingdom
Tel.: (44) 141 568 2000
Eletric Power Generation Services
N.A.I.C.S.: 221118

ScottishPower Overseas Holdings, Ltd. (2)
1 Atlantic Quay Robertson Street, Glasgow, G2 8SP, United Kingdom
Tel.: (44) 1412488200
Web Site: http://www.scottishpower.co.uk
Investment Management Service
N.A.I.C.S.: 523999
Keith Anderson (Gen Mgr)

ScottishPower SP EnergyNetworks (2)
Lister Drive, PO Box 290, Liverpool, L13 7HJ, Tuebrook, United Kingdom
Tel.: (44) 8452700783
Sales Range: $150-199.9 Million
Emp.: 400
Asset Management Services
N.A.I.C.S.: 531390

Sistemas Energeticos Chandrexa, S.A. (1)
Calle Circunvalacion 17, Orense, Spain
Tel.: (34) 981535920
Electric Power Distribution Services
N.A.I.C.S.: 221122

Sistemas Energeticos La Gomera, S.A.U (1)
Avenida Europa 18, Madrid, 28108, Spain
Tel.: (34) 916576461
Web Site: http://www.acciona.es
Sales Range: $250-299.9 Million
Emp.: 30
Solar Electric Power Generation Services
N.A.I.C.S.: 221118

Sistemas Energeticos Los Lirios, S.A.U. (1)
Avda Padre Garcia Tejero 9, Seville, 41012, Spain
Tel.: (34) 981703697
Eletric Power Generation Services
N.A.I.C.S.: 221118

Sistemas Energeticos Mas Garullo, S.A. (1)
Calle Antonio Beltran Martinez 1 7 D Centro Emp, 50002, Zaragoza, Spain
Tel.: (34) 976148038
Electric Power Generation Services
N.A.I.C.S.: 221118

Sociedad Gestora Parques Eolicos Andalucia, S.A. (1)
C/ Sierra de Sialda 4 T-1 Bajo Dcha, 29016, Malaga, Spain
Tel.: (34) 952122458
Eletric Power Generation Services
N.A.I.C.S.: 221118

Tarragona Power, S.L. (1)
National Rd 340 Km 1143 la Canomza, Tarragona, 43110, Spain
Tel.: (34) 977554080
Sales Range: $50-74.9 Million
Emp.: 4
Heat Power Generation Services
N.A.I.C.S.: 221330
Joaquin Lloret (Gen Mgr)

Torre Iberdrola, A.I.E. (1)
Plaza Euskadi 5, 48009, Bilbao, Spain
Tel.: (34) 944354349
Web Site: https://www.torreiberdrola.es
Office Space Leasing Services
N.A.I.C.S.: 531120

IBERFRANCE

Case N1 Marche Internat St Charles, 66000, Perpignan, Pyrenees Orientales, France
Tel.: (33) 468544255
Web Site: http://iberfrance.fr
Rev.: $21,800,000
Emp.: 15
Fresh Fruits & Vegetables
N.A.I.C.S.: 424480
Henri Ribes (Pres)

Subsidiaries:

Iberfrance Poland (1)
Ui Swierkowa nr 15, 64-320, Niepruszewo, Poland
Tel.: (48) 61 222 33 32
Fruit & Vegetable Whslr
N.A.I.C.S.: 424480

IBERIA INDUSTRY CAPITAL GROUP SARL

51 Route de Thionville, 2611, Luxembourg, Luxembourg
Tel.: (352) 26 33 75 650
Web Site:
http://www.iberiaindustrycapital.com
Industrial Holding & Investment Firm
N.A.I.C.S.: 551112
Jan Pyttel (Mng Partner)

Subsidiaries:

RailMaint GmbH (1)
Karl-Marx-Strasse 39, 04509, Delitzsch, Germany
Tel.: (49) 34202 970 0
Web Site: http://www.railmaint.com
Emp.: 750
Rolling Stock Repair & Maintenance Service Distr
N.A.I.C.S.: 488210
Robert Lehmann (Mng Dir)

IBERPAPEL GESTION SA

Avenida Sancho El Sabio 2 - 1, San Sebastian, 20010, Guipuzcoa, Spain
Tel.: (34) 915640720
Web Site: https://www.iberpapel.es
IBG—(MAD)
Rev.: $187,778,244
Assets: $488,768,282
Liabilities: $168,338,890
Net Worth: $320,429,392
Earnings: $5,207,738
Emp.: 297
Fiscal Year-end: 12/31/20
Paper Mfr
N.A.I.C.S.: 322120
Inigo Echevarria Canales (Chm)

Subsidiaries:

Copaimex, S.A. (1)
Avda Sancho El Sabio 2-1, 20010, San Sebastian, Gipuzkoa, Spain
Tel.: (34) 943462600
Paper Whslr
N.A.I.C.S.: 424110

Distribuidora Papelera, S.A. (1)
Calle de Velazquez 105, 28006, Madrid, Spain
Tel.: (34) 915648716
Paper Whslr
N.A.I.C.S.: 424110
Franci Fortin Alvarez (Dir-Comml)

Iberbarna Papel, S.A. (1)
Calle Bogatell 43-49, 08930, Sant Adria de Besos, Barcelona, Spain
Tel.: (34) 93 462 04 47
Paper Whslr
N.A.I.C.S.: 424110

Ibereucaliptos, S.A.U. (1)
C/Real 14 La Palma del Condado, 21700, Huelva, Spain
Tel.: (34) 959402285
Paper Mfr
N.A.I.C.S.: 322291

Iberpapel Argentina, S.A. (1)
C General Urquiza 137, E3280DJB, Colon, Entre Rios, Argentina
Tel.: (54) 3447421751
Sales Range: $25-49.9 Million
Emp.: 55
Timber Logging Services
N.A.I.C.S.: 113110
Jorge Campos Gil (Gen Mgr)

Iberpapel On Line, S.L.U. (1)
Avda Sancho El Sabio 2 1, Gipuzkoa, 20010, San Sebastian, Spain
Tel.: (34) 943462600
Paper Mfr
N.A.I.C.S.: 322291

Papelera Guipuzcoana de Zicunaga, S.A. (1)
B Zicunaga S N, 20120, Hernani, Gipuzkoa, Spain
Tel.: (34) 943551100
Web Site: http://www.iberpapel.com
Sales Range: $150-199.9 Million
Emp.: 250
Paper Mfr & Whslr
N.A.I.C.S.: 322120

Samakil, S.A. (1)
Camino Bajo de la Petiza 4675, 12800, Montevideo, Uruguay
Tel.: (598) 29030138
Sales Range: $25-49.9 Million
Emp.: 13
Lumber Product Whslr
N.A.I.C.S.: 423990

Zicuimex France, S.A.R.L (1)
Rue de l'industrie Centre d'entreprises des Joncaux Bidasoa n 7, 64700, Hendaye, Pyrenees-Atlantiques, France
Tel.: (33) 5 59 20 3893
Web Site: http://www.iberpapel.es
Paper Whslr
N.A.I.C.S.: 424110

Zicupap, S.A. (1)
Avda Sancho El Sabio 2 - 1, 20010, San Sebastian, Gipuzkoa, Spain
Tel.: (34) 943462600
Web Site: http://www.iberpapel.es
Paper Whslr
N.A.I.C.S.: 424110

IBERSOL S.G.P.S., S.A.

Edificio Peninsula Praca do Bom Sucesso 105 a 159- 9, 4150-146, Porto, Portugal
Tel.: (351) 226089700
Web Site: https://www.ibersol.pt
Year Founded: 1989
IBS—(EUR)
Rev.: $380,532,468
Assets: $704,340,588
Liabilities: $290,252,999
Net Worth: $414,087,589
Earnings: $154,520,245
Emp.: 7,379
Fiscal Year-end: 12/31/22
Restaurant Operators
N.A.I.C.S.: 722511

Subsidiaries:

Jose Silva Carvalho Catering, S.A. (1)
Rua Professor Fernando da Fonseca, Lisboa, 1501-806, Lisbon, Portugal
Tel.: (351) 707503305
Web Site:
https://www.silvacarvalhocatering.com
Event Planner Services
N.A.I.C.S.: 561920

IBF FINANCIAL HOLDINGS CO., LTD.

4F 167 Sec 2 Nanjing E Rd, Taipei, 104, Taiwan
Tel.: (886) 225154567

INTERNATIONAL PUBLIC

Web Site: http://www.waterland-fin.com.tw
2889—(TAI)
Rev.: $194,618,620
Assets: $11,900,990,525
Liabilities: $10,305,366,529
Net Worth: $1,595,623,995
Earnings: $81,330,027
Emp.: 1,579
Fiscal Year-end: 12/31/23
Investment Banking Services
N.A.I.C.S.: 523150

Subsidiaries:

IBF Securities Co., Ltd. (1)
15F No 188 Sec 5 Nanjing E Rd, Taipei, 105, Taiwan
Tel.: (886) 227421303
Securities Brokerage Services
N.A.I.C.S.: 525910

IBF Venture Capital Co., Ltd. (1)
5F No 188 Sec 5 Nanjing E Rd, Taipei, 105, Taiwan
Tel.: (886) 225288077
Securities Brokerage Services
N.A.I.C.S.: 525910

International Bills Finance Corp. (1)
8-10F No 128 Lequn 3rd Rd, Zhongshan Dist, Taipei, 104, Taiwan
Tel.: (886) 225181688
Securities Brokerage Services
N.A.I.C.S.: 525910

Waterland Venture Capital Co., Ltd. (1)
5F No 188 Sec 5 Nanjing East Road, Taipei, 10571, Taiwan
Tel.: (886) 225288077
Venture Capital Services
N.A.I.C.S.: 523910

IBI GROUP HOLDINGS LIMITED

3/F Bangkok Bank Building 18 Bonham Strand West, Hong Kong, China (Hong Kong)
Tel.: (852) 2 511 9933
Web Site: http://www.ibi.com.hk
Year Founded: 1997
1547—(HKG)
Rev.: $52,558,189
Assets: $40,976,817
Liabilities: $19,350,611
Net Worth: $21,626,206
Earnings: $3,412,424
Emp.: 98
Fiscal Year-end: 03/31/22
Building Construction Services
N.A.I.C.S.: 236116
Neil David Howard (Chm & CEO)

Subsidiaries:

IBI Macau Limited (1)
20/F AIA Tower 251A-301 Avenida Comercial De Macau, Macau, China (Macau)
Tel.: (853) 28715960
Web Site: http://www.ibimacau.com
Renovation Contracting Services
N.A.I.C.S.: 236220
Neil David Howard (Mng Dir)

IBI INVESTMENT HOUSE LTD.

Ahad Ha'am St Migdal Shalom floor 26 9, Tel Aviv, Israel
Tel.: (972) 35193444
Web Site: https://www.ibi.co.il
Year Founded: 1971
IBI—(TAE)
Rev.: $221,728,688
Assets: $350,493,433
Liabilities: $148,936,039
Net Worth: $201,557,394
Earnings: $52,233,733
Emp.: 200
Fiscal Year-end: 12/31/23
Miscellaneous Financial Investment Activities
N.A.I.C.S.: 523999
David Lubetzky (CEO)

IBIDEN CO., LTD.

IBIDEN CO., LTD.
2-1 Kanda-cho, Ogaki, 503-8604,
Gifu, Japan
Tel.: (81) 584813111   JP
Web Site: https://www.ibiden.co.jp
Year Founded: 1912
4062—(NGO)
Rev.: $2,448,046,886
Assets: $7,466,083,142
Liabilities: $4,150,610,004
Net Worth: $3,315,473,138
Earnings: $209,778,600
Emp.: 11,375
Fiscal Year-end: 03/31/24
Electronic Circuits, Printed Circuit
Boards, Special Carbon-Based Building Materials, Electric Furnaces &
Synthetic Products Mfr & Sales
N.A.I.C.S.: 334418
Takeshi Aoki *(Chm, Pres & CEO)*

Subsidiaries:

IBIDEN Asia Holdings Pte. Ltd. (1)
60 Paya Lebar Road 11-54 Paya Lebar
Square, Singapore, 409051, Singapore
Tel.: (65) 62960096
Financial Services
N.A.I.C.S.: 523999

IBIDEN Canada Inc. (1)
60 Renfrew Dr 320, Markham, L3R 0E1,
ON, Canada
Tel.: (905) 604-3103
Sales Range: $50-74.9 Million
Emp.: 3
Electronic Substrates Distr
N.A.I.C.S.: 423690

IBIDEN Ceram GmbH (1)
Gamserstrasse 38, 8523, Frauental an der
Lassnitz, Austria
Tel.: (43) 346220000
Web Site: http://www.ibiden-ceram.com
Ceramic Products Mfr
N.A.I.C.S.: 327110
Christian Kogl *(CEO)*

IBIDEN Deutschland GmbH (1)
Loeffelstrase 44, 70597, Stuttgart, Germany
Tel.: (49) 711 4691 8600
Ceramic Product Distr
N.A.I.C.S.: 423320

IBIDEN Electronics Malaysia SDN.
BHD. (1)
No 1049 Jalan Perindustrian Bukit Minyak
8, Kawsan Perindustrian Bukit Minyak,
14100, Simpang Empat, Penang, Malaysia
Tel.: (60) 45049999
Electronic Substrate Mfr
N.A.I.C.S.: 334419

IBIDEN Electronics Technology
(Shanghai) Co., Ltd. (1)
Room 712-717 Qiye Guanchang No 228
Mei Yuan Road, Shanghai, China
Tel.: (86) 21 6381 2277
Printed Wiring Board Mfr
N.A.I.C.S.: 334412

IBIDEN Fine Ceramics (Suzhou) Co.,
Ltd. (1)
No 500 Xinjing East Road, Tang City Yangshe Town Zhangjiagang City, Suzhou, Jiangsu, China
Tel.: (86) 51258586880
Automobile Parts Mfr
N.A.I.C.S.: 336390

IBIDEN France S.A.S. (1)
19 Rue du General Foy, 75008, Paris,
France
Tel.: (33) 1 4401 7097
Emp.: 10
Ceramic Product Distr
N.A.I.C.S.: 423320
Thierry Ozoux *(Mgr-Sls)*

IBIDEN Graphite Korea Co., Ltd. (1)
41 75 South Road Yeongil Indestrial Complex, Heunghae-eup Buk-gu, Pohang,
37948, Gyeongsangbuk, Korea (South)
Tel.: (82) 542713000
Graphite Specialty Product Mfr
N.A.I.C.S.: 335991

IBIDEN Industries Co., (1)
1-197 Uchiwara, Ogaki, 503-0936, Gifu,
Japan
Tel.: (81) 58 489 0777
Web Site: http://www.ibidensangyo.co.jp
Petroleum Product Whslr
N.A.I.C.S.: 424720

IBIDEN Jushi Co., Ltd. (1)
360 Shirotori Ikedacho, Ibi-Gun, Ogaki,
503-2413, Gifu, Japan
Tel.: (81) 585452405
Foam Resin Products Mfr
N.A.I.C.S.: 325211

IBIDEN Korea Co., Ltd. (1)
1314 HiBrand Bldg Maeheon-ro 16-gil,
Seocho-Gu, Seoul, 06771, Korea (South)
Tel.: (82) 221553400
Sales Range: $25-49.9 Million
Emp.: 2
Electronic Substrates Distr
N.A.I.C.S.: 423690

IBIDEN Mexico, S.A. de C.V. (1)
Villa de Reyes, 79526, San Luis Potosi,
Mexico
Tel.: (52) 4448348430
Ceramic Products Mfr
N.A.I.C.S.: 327110

IBIDEN Philippines Landholding,
Inc. (1)
Road 1 First Philippine Industrial Park Brgy
Sta Anastacia Sto Tomas, Batangas, Philippines
Tel.: (63) 43 405 5250
Web Site: http://www.ibiden.com.ph
Electronic Components Mfr
N.A.I.C.S.: 334419
Katsumi Mabuchi *(Pres)*

IBIDEN U.S.A. Corp. (1)
710 Lakeway Dr Ste 185, Sunnyvale, CA
94085-4048
Tel.: (408) 991-9801
Electronic Equipment & Component Distr
N.A.I.C.S.: 423690

Ibiden Bussan Co., Ltd. (1)
339 Arisato, Motosu, 501-0415, Gifu, Japan
Tel.: (81) 58 324 1151
Web Site: https://www.ibiden-bussan.co.jp
Emp.: 186
Agricultural & Marine Products Whslr
N.A.I.C.S.: 424460

Ibiden Career Techno Corp. (1)
300 Aoyanagi-cho, Ogaki, 503-8503, Gifu,
Japan
Tel.: (81) 58 489 7435
Web Site: http://www.e-ccc.jp
Business Support Services
N.A.I.C.S.: 561499

Ibiden Chemicals Co., Ltd. (1)
300 Aoyanagi-cho, Ogaki, 503-8503, Gifu,
Japan
Tel.: (81) 58 489 7491
Web Site: https://www.ibichemi.co.jp
Sales Range: $25-49.9 Million
Emp.: 40
Chemical & Allied Products Merchant Whslr
N.A.I.C.S.: 424690

Ibiden Circuits of America Corp. (1)
1701 Golf Rd Ste 1-1108, Rolling Meadows,
IL 60008-4244
Tel.: (847) 608-4800
Web Site: http://www.ibidenusa.com
Bare Printed Circuit Board Mfr
N.A.I.C.S.: 334412

Ibiden Co., Ltd. - Aoyanagi Plant (1)
300 Aoyanagi-cho, Ogaki, 503-8503, Gifu,
Japan
Tel.: (81) 58 489 3312
Web Site: https://www.ibiden.com
Graphite & Electronic Products Mfr
N.A.I.C.S.: 335991

Ibiden Co., Ltd. - Gama Plant (1)
3-200 Gama-cho, Ogaki, 503-8559, Gifu,
Japan
Tel.: (81) 584 81 4472
Ceramic Fiber & Integrated Circuit Package
Mfr
N.A.I.C.S.: 334418
Tatsuya Sato *(Gen Mgr)*

Ibiden Co., Ltd. - Godo Plant (1)
1120-1 Suemori Goudo-cho, Anbachi-gun,
Gifu, 503-2321, Japan
Tel.: (81) 58 428 1150
Web Site: https://www.ibiden.com
Integrated Circuit Package Mfr
N.A.I.C.S.: 334418

Ibiden Co., Ltd. - Kinuura Plant (1)
5-1-7 Shinden-cho, Takahama, 444-1301,
Aichi, Japan
Tel.: (81) 566 53 4111
Graphite & Foamed Resin Products Mfr
N.A.I.C.S.: 335991

Ibiden Co., Ltd. - Ogaki Central
Plant (1)
100-1 Kasanui-cho, Ogaki, 503-0027, Gifu,
Japan
Tel.: (81) 58 483 8620
Web Site: https://www.ibiden.com
Integrated Circuit Package Mfr
N.A.I.C.S.: 334418

Ibiden Co., Ltd. - Ogaki Plant (1)
905 Kido-cho, Ogaki, 503-0973, Gifu, Japan
Tel.: (81) 58 481 3102
Web Site: http://www.ibiden.com
Integrated Circuit Packaging Mfr
N.A.I.C.S.: 334412
Koji Kawashima *(Sr Mng Officer)*

Ibiden Co., Ltd. - Ogaki-Kita
Plant (1)
1-1 Kitagata Ibigawa-cho, Ibi-gun, Gifu,
501-0695, Japan
Tel.: (81) 585 22 1111
Graphite & Fine Ceramic Products Mfr
N.A.I.C.S.: 327120

Ibiden DPF France S.A.S. (1)
55 rue Aristide Briand, 92300, Levallois-
Perret, France
Tel.: (33) 14 737 4011
Web Site: http://www.ibiden.fr
Sales Range: $50-74.9 Million
Emp.: 250
Vitreous China Fine Earthenware & Other
Pottery Product Mfr
N.A.I.C.S.: 327110

Ibiden Electronics (Beijing) Co.,
Ltd. (1)
15 Rongchang East Street BDA, Beijing,
100176, China
Tel.: (86) 106 788 2288
Web Site: http://www.ibiden.co.jp
Bare Printed Circuit Board Mfr
N.A.I.C.S.: 334412

Ibiden Electronics (Shanghai) Co.,
Ltd. (1)
1/FA Building 73 No 17 Hancheng Road,
Waigaoqiao Free Trade Zone Pudong,
Shanghai, 200131, China
Tel.: (86) 215 046 5200
Web Site: https://www.ibiden.com
Business Support Services
N.A.I.C.S.: 561499

Ibiden Electronics Industries Co.,
Ltd. (1)
300 Aoyanagi-cho, Ogaki, 503-8503, Gifu,
Japan
Tel.: (81) 584893312
Web Site: http://www.ibiden.co.jp
Manufacture & Inspection of Electronic Substrates
N.A.I.C.S.: 334419

Ibiden Engineering Co., Ltd. (1)
1122 Kidocho, Ogaki, 503-0973, Gifu, Japan
Tel.: (81) 58 475 2301
Web Site: https://www.ibieng.co.jp
Sales Range: $50-74.9 Million
Emp.: 315
Building Equipment & Other Machinery Installation Contractors
N.A.I.C.S.: 238220
Kazuo Hasegawa *(Pres)*

Ibiden Europe B.V. (1)
Polarisavenue 85f, 2132 JH, Hoofddorp,
Netherlands
Tel.: (31) 235543180
Web Site: http://www.ibedian.com
Sales Range: $50-74.9 Million
Emp.: 12
Construction Materials Whslr
N.A.I.C.S.: 423390
Hiroshi Kawai *(Gen Mgr)*

Branch (Non-US):

Ibiden Finland (2)
Kaisaniemenkatu 1BA 72, 00100, Helsinki,
Finland
Tel.: (358) 9 6812 620
Web Site: http://www.ibiden.com
IC Packaging, Printed Wiring Boards, Ceramic Fibers & Substrate Holding Mats
N.A.I.C.S.: 334417

Ibiden European Holdings B.V. (1)
Polarisavenue 85f, 2132 JH, Hoofddorp,
Netherlands
Tel.: (31) 23 554 3180
Web Site: http://www.ibiden.co.jp
Sales Range: $50-74.9 Million
Emp.: 12
Holding Company
N.A.I.C.S.: 551112
Hiroyuki Tsuji *(Mng Dir)*

Subsidiary (Non-US):

CERAM Liegenschaftsverwaltung
GmbH (2)
Gamserstrasse 38, 8523, Frauental an der
Lassnitz, Austria (50%)
Tel.: (43) 346220000
Sales Range: $25-49.9 Million
Emp.: 50
Ceramic Honeycomb Material Mfr
N.A.I.C.S.: 327120

IBIDEN Porzellanfabrik Frauenthal
GmbH (2)
Gamserstrasse 38, 8253, Frauental an der
Lassnitz, Austria
Tel.: (43) 346220000
Web Site: http://www.ceram-ibiden.com
Sales Range: $100-124.9 Million
Ceramic Honeycomb Material Mfr
N.A.I.C.S.: 327120
Karl Fuhrer *(Mng Dir)*

Subsidiary (US):

IBIDEN CERAM Environmental
Inc. (3)
7304 W 130th St Ste 140, Overland Park,
KS 66213 (100%)
Tel.: (913) 239-9896
Sales Range: $25-49.9 Million
Emp.: 7
Ceramic Honeycomb Material Mfr
N.A.I.C.S.: 327120
John Cochran *(Pres)*

Ibiden Graphite Co., Ltd. (1)
300 Aoyanagi-cho, Ogaki, 503-8503,
Japan
Tel.: (81) 584896425
Web Site: http://ibiden-graphite.co.jp
Carbon & Graphite Product Mfr
N.A.I.C.S.: 335991

Ibiden Greentec Co., Ltd. (1)
3-55 Gama-cho, Ogaki, 503-0021, Gifu,
Japan
Tel.: (81) 58 481 6111
Web Site: https://www.ibiden-greentec.co.jp
Emp.: 350
Heavy & Civil Engineering Construction
N.A.I.C.S.: 237990

Ibiden Hungary Kft. (1)
2336 Dunavarsany Ipari Park Neumann
Janos u 1, 2336, Dunavarsany, Hungary
Tel.: (36) 2 450 1300
Web Site: http://www.ibiden.hu
Sales Range: $450-499.9 Million
Emp.: 2,650
Vitreous China Fine Earthenware & Pottery
Product Mfr
N.A.I.C.S.: 327110

Ibiden International, Inc. (1)
1701 Golf Rd Ste 1-1108, Rolling Meadows,
IL 60008-4244
Tel.: (847) 608-4800
Holding Company
N.A.I.C.S.: 551112

Ibiden Philippines, Inc. (1)
Road 1, First Philippine Industrial Park Brgy
Sta Anastacia, Santo Tomas, Batangas,
Philippines
Tel.: (63) 434055250
Web Site: http://www.ibiden.com.ph
IC Package Substrates Mfr

IBIDEN CO., LTD.

Ibiden Co., Ltd.—(Continued)
N.A.I.C.S.: 334413
Katsumi Mabuchi (Pres)

Ibiden Singapore Pte. Ltd. (1)
60 Paya Lebar Road 11-54 Paya Lebar Square, Singapore, 409051, Singapore
Tel.: (65) 6 296 0096
Web Site: http://www.Ibiden.com
Sales Range: $25-49.9 Million
Emp.: 8
Bare Printed Circuit Board Mfr
N.A.I.C.S.: 334412

Ibiden Taiwan Co., Ltd. (1)
8F-5 No 366 Bo'ai 2nd Rd, Zuoying Dist, Kaohsiung, 81358, Taiwan
Tel.: (886) 7 550 8599
Web Site: http://www.ibiden.co.jp
Sales Range: $50-74.9 Million
Emp.: 5
Electronic Parts & Equipment Merchant Whslr
N.A.I.C.S.: 423690

Ibiden U.S.A. R&D Inc. (1)
970 Knox St Ste A, Torrance, CA 90502
Tel.: (310) 768-0519
Web Site: http://www.ibiden.co.jp
Scientific & Technical Consulting Services
N.A.I.C.S.: 541690

Ibiken Co., Ltd. (1)
1-60 Gama-cho, Ogaki, 503-0013, Gifu, Japan
Tel.: (81) 584743355
Sales Range: $25-49.9 Million
Emp.: 52
Architectural Services
N.A.I.C.S.: 541310

Ibitech Co., Ltd. (1)
300 Aoyanagi-cho, Ogaki, 503-8503, Gifu, Japan
Tel.: (81) 584896212
Web Site: http://www.ibitech.co.jp
Computer Related Services
N.A.I.C.S.: 541519

L.G. Graphite S.r.l. (1)
Via C Battisti 53, 26842, Caselle Landi, LO, Italy
Tel.: (39) 037769021
Web Site: https://www.lggraphite.com
Graphite Mfr
N.A.I.C.S.: 335991

Micro-Mech Inc. (1)
33 Tpke Rd, Ipswich, MA 01938-1048
Tel.: (978) 356-2966
Web Site: https://www.ibiden.com
Mfr of Graphite
N.A.I.C.S.: 332710

Tak Co., Ltd. (1)
4-35-12 Kono, Ogaki, 503-0803, Gifu, Japan
Tel.: (81) 58 475 6501
Web Site: https://www.taknet.co.jp
Sales Range: $75-99.9 Million
Emp.: 360
Business Support Services
N.A.I.C.S.: 561499
Koichi Takashima (Pres)

IBISWORLD PTY LTD
Level 3 1 Collins St, Melbourne, 3000, VIC, Australia
Tel.: (61) 396553881
Web Site: http://www.ibisworld.com.au
Year Founded: 1971
Market Research Services
N.A.I.C.S.: 541910
Justin Ruthven (Chm)

Subsidiaries:

IBISWorld Inc. (1)
401 Wilshire Blvd Ste 200, Santa Monica, CA 90401
Tel.: (800) 330-3772
Web Site: https://www.ibisworld.com
Market Research
N.A.I.C.S.: 541910

IBISWorld Ltd (1)
2nd Floor North 11-19 Artillery Row, London, SW1P 1RT, United Kingdom
Tel.: (44) 20 7222 9898
Web Site: http://www.ibisworld.co.uk
Emp.: 31
Market Research
N.A.I.C.S.: 541910
Harvey Jones (Head-Mktg-Global)

IBJ INC.
12F Shinjuku First West 1-23-7 Nishi-shinjuku, Shinjuku-ku, Tokyo, 160-0023, Japan
Tel.: (81) 8070270983
Web Site: https://www.ibj-gl.com
6071—(TKS)
Rev.: $125,131,410
Assets: $128,470,800
Liabilities: $71,587,730
Net Worth: $56,883,070
Earnings: $11,549,610
Emp.: 1,230
Fiscal Year-end: 12/31/23
Marriage Matching Services
N.A.I.C.S.: 812990
Tetsuhiro Nakamoto (COO)

Subsidiaries:

Kamome Co., Ltd. (1)
Sumitomo Seimei Nishi-Shimbashi Bldg 1-10-2 Nishi-Shimbashi Minato-Ku, Tokyo, 105-0003, Japan
Tel.: (81) 3 3506 0761
Web Site: http://www.kamometour.jp
Travel Ticket Booking Services
N.A.I.C.S.: 561510
Eiju Abe (Pres & CEO)

Subsidiary (Non-US):

ARS DREAM PNG LTD. (2)
-, PO Box 5244, Boroko, Papua New Guinea
Tel.: (675) 3252050
Travel Ticket Booking Services
N.A.I.C.S.: 561510

ARS DREAM TRAVEL & TOURS CORP. (2)
Suite 1701 Metropolitan Tower 1746 A Mabini St Malate, Manila, Philippines
Tel.: (63) 25235689
Web Site: http://www.arsdreamph.com
Travel Ticket Booking Services
N.A.I.C.S.: 561510

Zwei Co., Ltd. (1)
Chen Ginza 5 Floor Cross 5-chrome Ginza, Chuo-ku, Tokyo, 104-0061, Japan (100%)
Tel.: (81) 03 68580281
Web Site: http://www.zwei.com
Sales Range: $25-49.9 Million
Matrimonial Services
N.A.I.C.S.: 812990
Takeshi Aoni (Pres & CEO)

IBKIMYOUNG CO., LTD.
4th & 5th Floors 279 Gangnam-Daero, Seocho-Gu, Seoul, Korea (South)
Tel.: (82) 7040145137
Year Founded: 2019
339950—(KRS)
Rev.: $73,087,095
Assets: $68,939,127
Liabilities: $35,079,693
Net Worth: $33,859,435
Earnings: $3,686,386
Emp.: 194
Fiscal Year-end: 12/31/21
Education Services
N.A.I.C.S.: 611710
Jae-Kwang Song (CFO)

IBKS NO. 14 SPECIAL PURPOSE ACQUISITION CO., LTD.
11 Gukjegeumyung-ro 6-gil, Yeongdeungpo-gu, Seoul, Korea (South)
Tel.: (82) 2 6915 5797
Investment Services
N.A.I.C.S.: 523999
Dong Heon Lee (CEO)

IBL HEALTHCARE LIMITED
One IBL Centre 2nd floor plot No 1 Block 7 and 8 DMCHS, Cooperative Housing Society Tipu Sultan Road off Shahra-e-Faisal, Karachi, Pakistan
Tel.: (92) 2135652420
Web Site: https://www.iblhc.com
Year Founded: 1997
IBLHL—(PSX)
Rev.: $14,490,293
Assets: $12,784,547
Liabilities: $5,204,160
Net Worth: $7,580,387
Earnings: $1,111,496
Emp.: 311
Fiscal Year-end: 06/30/23
Healthcare Product Distr
N.A.I.C.S.: 456191
Mufti Islam (CEO)

Subsidiaries:

IBL Unisys Limited (1)
2nd Floor One IBL Center Plot No 1 Block 7 and 8 DMCHS, hahrah-e-Faisal Rd, Karachi, 75400, Pakistan
Tel.: (92) 213 242 3216
Web Site: https://www.ibl-unisys.com
Information Technology Services
N.A.I.C.S.: 541511

IBNSINA PHARMA CO.
Industrial Zone 1, PO Box 91, Obour, Egypt
Tel.: (20) 244891102
Web Site: https://www.ibnsina-pharma.com
Year Founded: 2001
IBNP.CA—(EGX)
Rev.: $715,961,700
Assets: $391,199,316
Liabilities: $360,638,645
Net Worth: $30,560,671
Earnings: $4,497,730
Emp.: 5,500
Fiscal Year-end: 12/31/23
Pharmaceutical Products Distr
N.A.I.C.S.: 424210
Omar Abdel-Gawad (Co-CEO)

IBO TECHNOLOGY COMPANY LIMITED
23/F Sunshine Plaza 358 Lockhart Road, Wanchai, China (Hong Kong)
Tel.: (852) 2 308 1266 Ky
Web Site: http://www.ibotech.hk
Year Founded: 2000
2708—(HKG)
Rev.: $85,847,393
Assets: $145,052,793
Liabilities: $87,136,043
Net Worth: $57,916,751
Earnings: $4,216,646)
Emp.: 226
Fiscal Year-end: 03/31/21
Electronic Product Mfr & Distr
N.A.I.C.S.: 334419
Tse Ming Lai (Chm)

IBOCO
7 Place Copernic, Courcouronnes, 91080, Essonne, France
Tel.: (33) 160917272
Rev.: $17,100,000
Emp.: 38
N.A.I.C.S.: 423610
Patrick Pichon (Dir)

IBOKIN CO., LTD.
379 Masajo Ibogawacho, Tatsuno, 671-1621, Japan
Tel.: (81) 791723531
Web Site: https://www.ibokin.co.jp
5699—(TKS)
Rev.: $61,399,400
Assets: $40,763,690
Liabilities: $12,159,350
Net Worth: $28,544,340

INTERNATIONAL PUBLIC

Earnings: $2,807,640
Emp.: 160
Fiscal Year-end: 12/31/23
Waste Management Services
N.A.I.C.S.: 562111

IBRACO BERHAD
No 6 The NorthBank Off Kuching-Samarahan Expressway, 93350, Kuching, Sarawak, Malaysia
Tel.: (60) 82361111 MY
Web Site: https://www.ibraco.com
Year Founded: 1974
IBRACO—(KLS)
Rev.: $85,300,542
Assets: $206,467,370
Liabilities: $100,268,234
Net Worth: $106,199,135
Earnings: $9,870,849
Emp.: 190
Fiscal Year-end: 12/31/23
Investment Holding Services
N.A.I.C.S.: 551112
Chiaw Han Chew (Mng Dir)

IBRAHIM FIBRES LIMITED
15 - Club Road, Faisalabad, 38000, Pakistan
Tel.: (92) 412617836
Web Site: https://www.igcpk.com
Year Founded: 1986
IBFL—(KAR)
Rev.: $475,588,483
Assets: $384,631,693
Liabilities: $101,209,477
Net Worth: $283,422,216
Earnings: $7,169,176
Emp.: 4,021
Fiscal Year-end: 06/30/19
Textile Mfr
N.A.I.C.S.: 313310
Mukhtar Ahmad (Chm)

Subsidiaries:

Allied Bank Limited (1)
3 Tipu Block Main Boulevard New Garden Town, Lahore, 54000, Pakistan (100%)
Tel.: (92) 4235880043
Web Site: https://www.abl.com
Rev.: $343,011,878
Assets: $9,552,989,360
Liabilities: $8,798,146,952
Net Worth: $754,842,408
Earnings: $93,307,634
Emp.: 11,665
Fiscal Year-end: 12/31/2019
Commericial Banking
N.A.I.C.S.: 522110
Mohammad Naeem Mukhtar (Chm)

Ibrahim Leasing Ltd. (1)
Ibrahim Centre 1-A Ahmed Block, New Garden Town, Lahore, Pakistan
Tel.: (92) 42586915144
Sales Range: $100-124.9 Million
Finance Leasing & Services
N.A.I.C.S.: 523999

IBS GROUP HOLDING LTD.
9-b Dmitrovskoe Shosse, Moscow, 127434, Russia
Tel.: (7) 495 967 8080 IM
Web Site: http://www.ibsgr.com
Year Founded: 1992
Sales Range: $900-999.9 Million
Emp.: 10,085
Holding Company; Software Developer & Other Computer Related Services
N.A.I.C.S.: 551112
Anatoly Mikhailovich Karachinsky (Co-Founder & Pres)

IBS SOFTWARE PRIVATE LIMITED
5th Floor NILA Technopark Campus, Trivandrum, 695 581, India
Tel.: (91) 4716614200 In
Web Site: http://www.ibsplc.com

AND PRIVATE COMPANIES

Year Founded: 1997
Travel Tourism & Logistics Tracking Software Development Services
N.A.I.C.S.: 513210
V. K. Mathews *(Founder & Chm)*

Subsidiaries:

AD OPT Technologies Inc. (1)
5250 Boul DEcarie 5th Fl, Montreal, H3X 2H9, QC, Canada
Tel.: (514) 345-0580
Web Site: http://www.ad-opt.com
Developer & Vendor of Advanced Workforce Management Software
N.A.I.C.S.: 334610

IBS Software Services Americas, Inc. (1)
900 Cir 75 Pkwy Ste 550, Atlanta, GA 30339
Tel.: (678) 391-6080
Web Site: http://www.ibsplc.com
Sales Range: $25-49.9 Million
Emp.: 15
Travel & Logistics Software Mfr
N.A.I.C.S.: 513210

Subsidiary (Domestic):

IBS Technics, Inc. (2)
100 Burtt Rd Ste 226, Andover, MA 01810-5915
Tel.: (978) 570-1600
Sales Range: $25-49.9 Million
Airline Operations Management Software Mfr
N.A.I.C.S.: 513210
David R.A. Steadman *(CEO)*

IBSP PLC
5 Krapivny pereulok, Saint Petersburg, Russia
Tel.: (7) 812 327 11 07
Web Site: http://www.ibsp.ru
Year Founded: 1989
Banking Services
N.A.I.C.S.: 522110

IBSTOCK PLC
Leicester Rd, Ibstock, LE67 6HS, Leicestershire, United Kingdom
Tel.: (44) 1530261999   UK
Web Site: https://www.ibstock.co.uk
Year Founded: 2015
IBST—(LSE)
Rev.: $647,419,843
Assets: $962,865,438
Liabilities: $437,481,697
Net Worth: $525,383,741
Earnings: $109,669,275
Emp.: 2,293
Fiscal Year-end: 12/31/22
Holding Company; Clay & Concrete Brick & Other Construction Products Mfr & Whslr
N.A.I.C.S.: 551112
Jonathan C. Nicholls *(Chm)*

Subsidiaries:

Anderton Concrete Products Ltd. (1)
Units 1 and 2 Cosgrove Business Park, Soot Hill Anderton, Northwich, CW9 6AA, Cheshire, United Kingdom
Tel.: (44) 3332343434
Web Site: https://www.andertonconcrete.co.uk
Precast Concrete Product Mfr & Distr
N.A.I.C.S.: 327390

Coltman Precast Concrete Limited (1)
London Road Canwell, Sutton Coldfield, B75 5SX, West Midlands, United Kingdom
Tel.: (44) 1543480482
Web Site: https://www.coltman.co.uk
Construction Services
N.A.I.C.S.: 532412

Ibstock Group Limited (1)
Leicester Road, Ibstock, LE67 6HS, Leicestershire, United Kingdom
Tel.: (44) 1530261999
Web Site: http://www.ibstock.com

Emp.: 200
Holding Company
N.A.I.C.S.: 551112

Subsidiary (Domestic):

Forticrete Ltd (2)
Boss Avenue Grovebury Road, Leighton Buzzard, LU7 4SD, Bedfordshire, United Kingdom
Tel.: (44) 1525244900
Web Site: http://www.forticrete.co.uk
Concrete Bricks & Roof Tiles Mfr
N.A.I.C.S.: 327331

Ibstock Brick Limited (2)
Leicester Road, Ibstock, LE67 6HS, Leicestershire, United Kingdom
Tel.: (44) 153 026 1999
Web Site: https://www.ibstockbrick.co.uk
Building Products & Materials Mfr
N.A.I.C.S.: 327331
Mihailo Simeunovich *(Head-Design & Technical Svcs)*

Subsidiary (Domestic):

Kevington Building Products Limited (3)
Hamsey Road, Sharpthorne, RH19 4PB, United Kingdom
Tel.: (44) 1342718899
Web Site: http://www.kevington.com
Building Product & Material Mfr
N.A.I.C.S.: 327331
Iain Durrant *(Dir-Ops)*

Subsidiary (Domestic):

Supreme Concrete Limited (2)
Coppingford Hall Coppingford Road Sawtry, Huntingdon, PE28 5GP, United Kingdom
Tel.: (44) 1487833300
Web Site: http://www.supremeconcrete.co.uk
Building Materials Mfr
N.A.I.C.S.: 326199
Lisa Mackett *(Area Mgr-Sls)*

Longley Concrete Ltd. (1)
Ravensthorpe Road, Thornhill Lees, Dewsbury, WF12 9EF, West Yorkshire, United Kingdom
Tel.: (44) 1924464283
Web Site: https://www.longley.uk.com
Precast Concrete Block Product Mfr & Distr
N.A.I.C.S.: 327331

IBU-TEC ADVANCED MATERIALS AG
Hainweg 9-11, 99425, Weimar, Germany
Tel.: (49) 364386490
Web Site: https://www.ibu-tec.de
Year Founded: 1885
IBU—(BER)
Rev.: $56,943,529
Assets: $83,733,704
Liabilities: $21,132,049
Net Worth: $62,601,655
Earnings: ($2,703,680)
Emp.: 211
Fiscal Year-end: 12/31/23
Inorganic Chemical Mfr
N.A.I.C.S.: 325199
Jens Thomas Thau *(Vice Chm-Supervisory Bd)*

Subsidiaries:

BNT Chemicals GmbH (1)
PC-Strasse 1, 06749, Bitterfeld-Wolfen, Germany
Tel.: (49) 349331630
Web Site: http://www.bnt-chemicals.de
Organometallic Compound Mfr
N.A.I.C.S.: 325199
Arndt Schlosser *(Mng Dir)*

Chemiepark Bitterfeld-Wolfen GmbH (1)
OT Bitterfeld Zorbiger Strasse 22, 06749, Bitterfeld-Wolfen, Germany
Tel.: (49) 349351550
Web Site: http://www.chemiepark.de
Chemicals Mfr
N.A.I.C.S.: 325998

IBUYNEW GROUP LIMITED
Suite 2302 Level 23 100 Miller Street, North Sydney, 2000, NSW, Australia
Tel.: (61) 1300 123463
Web Site: http://www.ibuynew.com.au
Investment Services
N.A.I.C.S.: 523999
Adir Shiffman *(Chm-Disruptive Investments)*

IBYKUS AG
Herman Hollerith Strasse 1, 99099, Erfurt, Germany
Tel.: (49) 36144100   De
Web Site: http://www.ibykus.de
Year Founded: 1990
Rev.: $14,681,284
Emp.: 140
IT Services
N.A.I.C.S.: 541511
Helmut C. Henkel *(Member-Mgmt Bd)*

IC CO., LTD.
7F Shinagawa Intercity Building C 2-15-3 Konan, Minato-ku, Tokyo, 108-6207, Japan
Tel.: (81) 343358188   JP
Web Site: https://www.ic-net.co.jp
Year Founded: 1978
4769—(TKS)
Rev.: $64,658,400
Assets: $56,445,600
Liabilities: $14,504,640
Net Worth: $41,940,960
Earnings: $2,672,640
Fiscal Year-end: 09/30/24
Software Development Services
N.A.I.C.S.: 541512
Shohei Misawa *(Sr Exec VP)*

IC CONSULT GROUP GMBH
Leopoldstrabe 252b, Munich, 80807, Bayern, Germany
Tel.: (49) 2016161620
Web Site: http://www.ic-consult.com
Year Founded: 1997
Consultancy, Systems Integrator & Managed Services
N.A.I.C.S.: 541611
Ulli Rottmuller *(Head-Mktg)*

Subsidiaries:

ICSynergy International, LLC (1)
5601 Democracy Dr, Plano, TX 75024
Tel.: (214) 764-7644
Web Site: http://www.icsynergy.com
Custom Computer Programming Services
N.A.I.C.S.: 541511
Martin Gee *(CTO)*

IC IMMOBILIEN HOLDING AG
Hanauer Landstrasse 293, 60314, Frankfurt am Main, Germany
Tel.: (49) 89552270
Web Site: http://www.ic-group.de
Sales Range: $10-24.9 Million
Emp.: 280
Real Estate Services
N.A.I.C.S.: 531390
Markus Reinert *(Chm-Exec Bd & CEO)*

Subsidiaries:

IC Fonds GmbH (1)
Ohmstr 4, 85716, Unterschleissheim, Bavaria, Germany
Tel.: (49) 89552270
Web Site: http://www.ic-group.de
Fund Management Services
N.A.I.C.S.: 523940

IC PLUS CORP.
10F No 47 Ln 2 Sec 2 Guangfu Rd, East Dist, Hsinchu, 30071, Taiwan
Tel.: (886) 35750275
Web Site: https://www.icplus.com.tw
Year Founded: 1997

8040—(TPE)
Rev.: $40,727,042
Assets: $37,169,528
Liabilities: $9,649,126
Net Worth: $27,520,401
Earnings: $4,692,712
Emp.: 150
Fiscal Year-end: 12/31/22
Transceiver Product Distr
N.A.I.C.S.: 423690
Lo Jui-Hsiang *(Chm)*

IC ZERICH CAPITAL MANAGEMENT JSC
Vsevolozhsky Per 2 Building 2, Moscow, 119034, Russia
Tel.: (7) 4957370580
Web Site: http://www.zerich.com
Sales Range: Less than $1 Million
Investment & Asset Management Services
N.A.I.C.S.: 523940

ICA GRUPPEN AB
Kolonnvagen 20, 16971, Solna, Sweden
Tel.: (46) 856150000   SE
Web Site: https://www.icagruppen.se
Year Founded: 1917
ICA—(OMX)
Rev.: $12,761,714,762
Assets: $11,401,088,351
Liabilities: $10,019,388,013
Net Worth: $1,381,700,338
Earnings: $421,478,547
Emp.: 23,877
Fiscal Year-end: 12/31/22
Holding Company
N.A.I.C.S.: 551112
Claes-Goran Sylven *(Chm)*

Subsidiaries:

Apotek Hjartat AB (1)
Kolonnvagen 20, 169 71, Solna, Sweden
Tel.: (46) 771405405
Web Site: https://www.apotekhjartat.se
Sales Range: $1-4.9 Billion
Emp.: 3,000
Pharmacy Store Operator
N.A.I.C.S.: 456110
Camilla As Fritz *(Head-HR)*

Hemtex AB (1)
Stora Brogatan 11, Box 495, 503 30, Boras, Sweden
Tel.: (46) 3 322 6677
Web Site: https://www.hemtex.se
Home Furnishing Product Distr
N.A.I.C.S.: 423220

ICA Banken AB (1)
Box 4075, 169 04, Solna, Sweden
Tel.: (46) 33474790
Web Site: https://www.icabanken.se
Emp.: 444
Vegetable & Dairy Product Distr
N.A.I.C.S.: 424480

ICA Fastigheter AB (1)
Ingenjor Baaths gata 11, PO Box 50008, 721 84, Vasteras, Sweden
Tel.: (46) 21193000
Web Site: https://www.icafastigheter.se
Sales Range: $50-74.9 Million
Emp.: 40
Commercial Real Estate Acquisition, Development & Leasing Services
N.A.I.C.S.: 531390

ICA Handlarnas AB (1)
Kolonnvagen 20, 169 70, Solna, Sweden (60%)
Tel.: (46) 85 615 0000
Web Site: https://www.icahandlarna.se
Sales Range: $125-149.9 Million
Emp.: 500
Grocery Stores, Convenience Stores, Pharmacies & Discount Department Stores Owner & Operator
N.A.I.C.S.: 457110

ICA Sverige AB (1)
Kolonnvagen 20, 169 70, Solna, Sweden

ICA GRUPPEN AB

ICA Gruppen AB—(Continued)
Tel.: (46) 856150000
Web Site: https://www.ica.se
Sales Range: $200-249.9 Million
Emp.: 700
Supermarket & Convenience Stores Developer & Operator
N.A.I.C.S.: 445110

ICANDY INTERACTIVE LIMITED
Level 4 91 William Street, Melbourne, 3000, VIC, Australia
Tel.: (61) 86115353
Web Site: https://www.icandy.io
ICI—(ASX)
Rev.: $17,781,764
Assets: $50,471,449
Liabilities: $6,400,219
Net Worth: $44,071,229
Earnings: ($9,661,588)
Emp.: 700
Fiscal Year-end: 12/31/23
Investment Holding Company
N.A.I.C.S.: 523999
Desmond Lee (COO)

ICAP TOTAN SECURITIES CO., LTD.
8 Fl Totan Muromachi Bldg 4-4-10 Nihonbashi-Muromachi, Chuo-ku, Tokyo, 103-0022, Japan
Tel.: (81) 352008300   JP
Year Founded: 1997
Sales Range: $50-74.9 Million
Emp.: 25
Equity Derivatives Brokerage & Dealing Services
N.A.I.C.S.: 523150

ICAPE HOLDING S.A.
33 Avenue du General Leclerc Fontenay-aux-Roses, 92260, Paris, France
Tel.: (33) 15818391
Web Site: https://www.icape-group.com
Year Founded: 1999
ALICA—(EUR)
Rev.: $198,190,750
Assets: $166,511,756
Liabilities: $131,533,282
Net Worth: $34,978,474
Earnings: $4,669,390
Emp.: 572
Fiscal Year-end: 12/31/23
Electronics Mfr
N.A.I.C.S.: 334412
Arnaud Le Coguic (CFO)

Subsidiaries:

Nujay Technologies Inc.   (1)
26170 Enterprise Way Ste 300, Lake Forest, CA 92630-8414
Tel.: (949) 215-8555
Web Site: http://www.nujaytech.com
Electronic Parts & Equipment Merchant Whslr
N.A.I.C.S.: 423690
Jahanvi Solanki (Coord-Pur, Supply Chain & Customer Svc)

ICAPITAL.BIZ BERHAD
12th Floor Menara Symphony No 5 Jalan Prof Khoo Kay Kim Seksyen 13, 46200, Petaling Jaya, Selangor, Malaysia
Tel.: (60) 378904800   MY
Web Site: http://www.icapital.my
ICAP—(KLS)
Rev.: $2,392,579
Assets: $100,883,120
Liabilities: $115,004
Net Worth: $100,768,116
Earnings: $369,621
Fiscal Year-end: 05/31/23
Financial Services
N.A.I.C.S.: 523999
Yit Chan Tai (Co-Sec)

Subsidiaries:

Capital Dynamics Asset Management Sdn. Bhd.   (1)
16 01B Plaza First Nationwide 161 Jalan Tun H S Lee, 50000, Kuala Lumpur, Malaysia
Tel.: (60) 320702106
Web Site: http://www.cdam.biz
Asset Management Services
N.A.I.C.S.: 541611
Tan Teng Boo (Mng Dir)

TMF Administrative Services Malaysia Sdn. Bhd.   (1)
10th Floor Menara Hap Seng No 1 and 3 Jalan P Ramlee, 50250, Kuala Lumpur, Malaysia
Tel.: (60) 323824288
Financial Services
N.A.I.C.S.: 523999

ICAR
Saint Julien Gameux, 42406, Saint-Chamond, Cedex, France
Tel.: (33) 477314242
Web Site: http://www.icar-stcham.peugeout.fr
Rev.: $24,400,000
Emp.: 78
New & Used Car Dealers
N.A.I.C.S.: 441110
John Masson (Mgr-DP)

ICARES MEDICUS, INC.
4th Floor No 16 Section 2 Shengyi Road, Hsinchu, 30261, Zhubei, Taiwan
Tel.: (886) 36579530
Web Site: https://www.icaresmedicus.com
6612—(TPE)
Rev.: $16,003,908
Assets: $32,623,925
Liabilities: $3,303,224
Net Worth: $29,320,702
Earnings: $3,451,584
Fiscal Year-end: 12/31/22
Healtcare Services
N.A.I.C.S.: 621610
I-Hung Le (Chm)

ICB FINANCIAL GROUP HOLDINGS AG
Schulhausstrasse 1, 8834, Schindellegi, Switzerland
Tel.: (41) 44 687 4550   CH
Web Site: http://www.icbbankinggroup.com
Year Founded: 2003
Sales Range: $125-149.9 Million
Emp.: 3,300
Commercial Banking Services
N.A.I.C.S.: 522110
Michael Robert Hanlon (Chm)

Subsidiaries:

ICB Global Management Sdn. Bhd.   (1)
No 3 Jalan Sri Hartamas 7 Taman Sri Hartamas, 50480, Kuala Lumpur, Malaysia
Tel.: (60) 3 6201 6051
Sales Range: $10-24.9 Million
Emp.: 3
Business Management Services
N.A.I.C.S.: 561499
George Koshy (Mng Dir)

ICB Islamic Bank Limited   (1)
TK Bhaban 15th floor 13 Kazi Nazrul Islam Avenue Kawran Bazar, Dhaka, 1215, Bangladesh   (50.1%)
Tel.: (880) 255012061
Web Site: https://www.icbislamic-bd.com
Rev.: $3,388,633
Assets: $134,363,179
Liabilities: $274,190,388
Net Worth: ($139,827,208)
Earnings: ($4,579,875)
Emp.: 456
Fiscal Year-end: 12/31/2021
Commercial Banking Services
N.A.I.C.S.: 522110
Mohammad Nasir Ali (Chm)

International Commercial Bank (Mozambique), S.A.   (1)
25 de Setembro Avenue 1915 1st Floor, Maputo, Mozambique
Tel.: (258) 21 311 111
Web Site: http://www.icbank-mz.com
Sales Range: $50-74.9 Million
Emp.: 7
Commercial Banking Services
N.A.I.C.S.: 522110
Nuno Alvarez (Gen Mgr)

International Commercial Bank Lao Ltd   (1)
127/07 Hatsady Road Chanthaboury, Hatsady Tai Village, Vientiane, Lao People's Democratic Republic
Tel.: (856) 21 250388
Web Site: http://www.icb-lao.com
Commercial Banking Services
N.A.I.C.S.: 522110
Pritesh Bakrania (Sr Mgr-IT & Corp Svcs)

International Commercial Bank Limited   (1)
Stansfield House Plot BC 92-93 Haile Selassie road, PO Box 437, Blantyre, Malawi
Tel.: (265) 1832444
Web Site: http://www.icb-malawi.com
Commercial Banking Services
N.A.I.C.S.: 522110

International Commercial Bank SH.A.   (1)
Street Murat Toptani Eurocol Center, Tirana, 1001, Albania
Tel.: (355) 4 2256 254
Web Site: http://www.icbank-albania.com
Commercial Banking Services
N.A.I.C.S.: 522110
Gideon Van Den Broek (CEO)

International Commercial Bank Zambia Ltd   (1)
Plot 4302 Corner of Great North & Washama Road, PO Box 32678, Villa Elizabetha, Lusaka, Zambia
Tel.: (260) 211 368700
Web Site: http://www.icb-zambia.com
Sales Range: $50-74.9 Million
Emp.: 40
Commercial Banking Services
N.A.I.C.S.: 522110
Lalit Tewari (CEO)

ICBC TURKEY BANK A.S.
Maslak Mah Dereboyu / 2 Caddesi No 13, Sariyer, 34398, Istanbul, Turkiye
Tel.: (90) 2123355335
Web Site: https://www.icbc.com.tr
Year Founded: 1986
ICBCT—(IST)
Rev.: $129,994,811
Assets: $1,913,932,449
Liabilities: $1,817,030,872
Net Worth: $96,901,577
Earnings: $43,266,266
Emp.: 756
Fiscal Year-end: 12/31/22
Banking Services
N.A.I.C.S.: 522110
Xiangyang Gao (Chm)

Subsidiaries:

ICBC Turkey Yatirim Menkul Degerler A.S.   (1)
Dereboyu /2 Caddesi No 13, Maslak, 34398, Istanbul, Turkiye
Tel.: (90) 2122762727
Web Site: https://www.icbcyatirim.com.tr
Financial Services
N.A.I.C.S.: 523999

Subsidiary (Domestic):

ICBC Portfoy Yonetimi A.S.   (2)
Abdulhak Hamit Cad No 25, Beyoglu, 34437, Istanbul, Turkiye
Tel.: (90) 2122506151

INTERNATIONAL PUBLIC

Web Site: http://www.icbcportfoy.com.tr
Financial Investment Services
N.A.I.C.S.: 523999
I. Alper Koc (Gen Mgr)

ICC BIG CONSTRUCTION INVESTMENT JOINT STOCK COMPANY
Cotana Group Building Lot CC5A Linh Dam Peninsula, Hoang Liet Ward Hoang Mai District, Hanoi, Vietnam
Tel.: (84) 2435635165   VN
Year Founded: 2009
Construction Services
N.A.I.C.S.: 236220

ICCREA HOLDING S.P.A.
Via Lucrezia Romana 41/47, 00178, Rome, Italy
Tel.: (39) 06 7207 1   IT
Web Site:
    http://www.gruppobancarioiccrea.it
Year Founded: 1995
Sales Range: $750-799.9 Million
Emp.: 2,418
Bank Holding Company
N.A.I.C.S.: 551111
Giulio Magagni (Chm)

Subsidiaries:

BCC Assicurazioni S.p.A.   (1)
Maciachini Business Park - MAC 1 Via Benigno Crespi 19, 20159, Milan, Italy   (51%)
Tel.: (39) 02466275
Web Site: https://www.bccassicurazioni.com
General Insurance Products & Services
N.A.I.C.S.: 524126

BCC Vita S.p.A.   (1)
    (30%)
Tel.: (39) 02466275
Web Site: http://www.bccvita.it
Life Insurance Products & Services
N.A.I.C.S.: 524113

Banca per lo Sviluppo della Cooperazione di Credito S.p.A.   (1)
Piazza Beata Vergine del Carmelo 4/5, 00144, Rome, Italy
Tel.: (39) 065262231
Web Site: https://www.bancasviluppo.bcc.it
Commercial Banking Services
N.A.I.C.S.: 522110
Cornaglia Ernesto (Vice Chm)

Bcc Factoring SpA   (1)
Via Giuseppe Revere 14, 20123, Milan, Italy
Tel.: (39) 023343401
Web Site: http://www.bccfactoring.it
Financial Advisory Services
N.A.I.C.S.: 523940
Ignazio Parrinello (Chm)

Bcc Lease SpA   (1)
Via Carlo Esterle 9, 20132, Milan, Italy
Tel.: (39) 0228141288
Web Site: http://www.bcclease.it
Financial Lending Services
N.A.I.C.S.: 522220

Bcc Risparmio & Previdenza SGrpA   (1)
Via Carlo Esterle 9/11, 20132, Milan, Italy
Tel.: (39) 02430281
Web Site:
    http://www.bccrisparmioeprevidenza.it
Asset Management Services
N.A.I.C.S.: 531390
Claudio Corsi (Chm)

Bcc Sistemi Informatici SpA   (1)
Via Rivoltana 95, 20096, Pioltello, Milan, Italy
Tel.: (39) 02753981
Web Site: http://www.bccsi.bcc.it
Information Technology Consulting Services
N.A.I.C.S.: 541512
Francesco Liberati (Chm)

Iccrea Banca S.p.A.   (1)
Via Lucrezia Romana 41-47, 00178, Rome, Italy

Tel.: (39) 06 7207 1
Web Site: http://www.iccreabanca.it
Commericial Banking
N.A.I.C.S.: 522110
Francesco Carri *(Chm)*

ICD CO., LTD.
274 Manse-ro Daedeok-Myeon, Anseong, 456-833, Gyeonggi-do, Korea (South)
Tel.: (82) 316783333
Web Site: https://www.icd.co.kr
040910—(KRS)
Rev.: $115,774,743
Assets: $155,317,779
Liabilities: $37,778,071
Net Worth: $117,539,708
Earnings: ($4,156,606)
Emp.: 325
Fiscal Year-end: 12/31/22
Plasma Digital Display Equipment
N.A.I.C.S.: 334419

ICDS LIMITED
Syndicate House, Upendranagar, Manipal, 576 104, India
Tel.: (91) 8202701500
Web Site: https://www.icdslimited.com
Year Founded: 1971
ICDSLTD—(NSE)
Rev.: $203,180
Assets: $3,632,142
Liabilities: $190,458
Net Worth: $3,441,684
Earnings: $796,559
Emp.: 16
Fiscal Year-end: 03/31/22
Financial Services
N.A.I.C.S.: 523150
T. Mohandas Pai *(Chm)*

ICE CONCEPT S.A.
Pl des Hauts-Sarts Avenue Deuxieme 31, 4040, Herstal, Liege, Belgium
Tel.: (32) 42481242
Web Site: http://www.iceconcept.be
ICE—(EUR)
Sales Range: $1-9.9 Million
Emp.: 15
Refrigerated Vehicles Sales & Rental Services
N.A.I.C.S.: 423110
Olivier Zonderman *(CEO)*

ICE FISH FARM AS
Fiskeldi austfjaroa hf Nesbala 122, Seltjamarnes, 170, Reykjavik, Iceland
Tel.: (354) 8960426
Web Site: https://www.icefishfarm.is
Year Founded: 2020
IFISH—(EUR)
Rev.: $37,663,331
Assets: $199,905,373
Liabilities: $69,056,092
Net Worth: $130,849,281
Earnings: $2,327,499
Emp.: 51
Fiscal Year-end: 12/31/21
Finfish Farming Services
N.A.I.C.S.: 112511
Asle Ronning *(Chm)*

ICE MAKE REFRIGERATION LTD.
226 Dantali Industrial Estate On Gota-Vadsar Road Near Ahmedabad City, At Dantali Ta Kalol Dist, Gandhinagar, 382721, Gujarat, India
Tel.: (91) 9879107881
Web Site: https://www.icemakeindia.com
Year Founded: 1993
ICEMAKE—(NSE)
Rev.: $37,566,789
Assets: $19,066,423
Liabilities: $9,339,692
Net Worth: $9,726,731
Earnings: $2,493,999
Emp.: 300
Fiscal Year-end: 03/31/23
Commercial Refrigerator Distr
N.A.I.C.S.: 423740
Chandrakant Patel *(Chm & Mng Dir)*

Subsidiaries:

Bharat Refrigerations Private Limited (1)
B-20 1st Main Road, Ambattur Industrial Estate, Chennai, 600058, India
Tel.: (91) 9791175004
Web Site: https://www.bharatref.in
Refrigerator Equipment Mfr
N.A.I.C.S.: 333415

ICE RIVER SPRINGS WATER COMPANY INC.
485387 30 Sideroad, Shelburne, L9V 3N5, ON, Canada
Tel.: (519) 925-2929
Web Site: http://www.iceriversprings.ca
Sales Range: $25-49.9 Million
Emp.: 45
Spring Water
N.A.I.C.S.: 312112
Jamie Gott *(Pres & CEO)*

ICECO INC.
1212 Shinbashi-cho, Izumi-Ku, Yokohama, 245-0009, Kanagawa, Japan
Tel.: (81) 458111302
Web Site: https://www.iceco.co.jp
Year Founded: 1952
7698—(TKS)
Emp.: 1,209
Dairy Product Mfr & Distr
N.A.I.C.S.: 311514

ICECURE MEDICAL LTD.
7 Ha Eshel St, PO Box 316, 3079504, Caesarea, 3079504, Israel
Tel.: (972) 46020333
Web Site: https://www.icecure-medical.com
Year Founded: 2006
ICCM—(NASDAQ)
Rev.: $3,229,000
Assets: $16,410,000
Liabilities: $4,247,000
Net Worth: $12,163,000
Earnings: ($14,652,000)
Emp.: 71
Fiscal Year-end: 12/31/23
Medical Device Mfr & Distr
N.A.I.C.S.: 334510
Ron Mayron *(Chm)*

Subsidiaries:

IceCure Medical Inc. (1)
41-18 Christine Ct, Fair Lawn, NJ 07410
Tel.: (646) 844-3066
Health Care Srvices
N.A.I.C.S.: 621999
Eyal Shamir *(CEO)*

ICELAND FOODS LTD.
Second Avenue, Deeside Industrial Park, Deeside, CH5 2NW, Flintshire, United Kingdom
Tel.: (44) 1244830100   UK
Web Site: http://www.iceland.co.uk
Year Founded: 1970
Grocery Stores Owner & Operator
N.A.I.C.S.: 445110
Tarsem Dhaliwal *(CEO)*

ICELAND SEAFOOD ICELAND
Kollunarklettsvegur 2, 104, Reykjavik, Iceland
Tel.: (354) 5508000
Web Site: https://www.icelandseafood.is
Seafood Distr
N.A.I.C.S.: 424460
Bjarni Benediktsson *(Mng Dir)*

ICELANDAIR GROUP HF.
Reykjavik Airport, 102, Reykjavik, Iceland
Tel.: (354) 5050300
Web Site: https://www.icelandairgroup.com
ICEAIR—(ICE)
Rev.: $1,523,569,000
Assets: $1,527,676,000
Liabilities: $1,239,329,000
Net Worth: $288,347,000
Earnings: $11,169,000
Emp.: 3,542
Fiscal Year-end: 12/31/23
Air Transportation & Airport Services
N.A.I.C.S.: 481111
Ulfar Steindorsson *(Chm)*

Subsidiaries:

CAE Icelandair Flight Training ehf. (1)
Flugvellir 1, 221, Hafnarfjordur, Iceland
Tel.: (354) 5050550247
Web Site: https://www.training.is
Airline Pilot Training Services
N.A.I.C.S.: 611512

IGS ehf. (1)
Keflavik International Airport, Reykjavik, Iceland
Tel.: (354) 4250200
Web Site: http://www.igs.is
Aircraft Handling Services
N.A.I.C.S.: 488119
Gunnar Olsen *(Mng Dir)*

Loftleioir - Icelandic ehf. (1)
Reykjavik Airport, 102, Reykjavik, Iceland
Tel.: (354) 5050333
Web Site: https://www.loftleidir.com
Airline Services
N.A.I.C.S.: 481111
Arni Hermannsson *(Mng Dir)*

ICENI GOLD LIMITED
Level 2 41-43 Ord Street, West Perth, 6005, WA, Australia
Tel.: (61) 864584200   AU
Web Site: https://www.icenigold.com.au
Year Founded: 2020
ICL—(ASX)
Rev.: $14,987
Assets: $20,937,262
Liabilities: $1,845,310
Net Worth: $19,091,952
Earnings: ($1,008,777)
Fiscal Year-end: 06/30/22
Gold Exploration Services
N.A.I.C.S.: 212220
Brian Rodan *(Chm)*

ICESOFT TECHNOLOGIES, INC.
Suite 340 600 Crowfoot Cres NW, Calgary, T3G 0B4, AB, Canada
Tel.: (403) 663-3322
Web Site: https://www.icesoft.com
Year Founded: 2001
ISFT—(CNSX)
Rev.: $1,332,686
Assets: $161,997
Liabilities: $2,279,265
Net Worth: ($2,117,268)
Earnings: ($521,765)
Emp.: 8
Fiscal Year-end: 12/31/23
Software Development Services
N.A.I.C.S.: 541511
David L. Gordon *(CFO)*

ICETANA LIMITED
Level 36 152 St Georges Terrace, Perth, 6000, WA, Australia
Tel.: (61) 862822811   AU
Web Site: https://www.icetana.ai
Year Founded: 2009
ICE—(ASX)
Rev.: $1,137,585
Assets: $1,560,685
Liabilities: $1,288,499
Net Worth: $272,186
Earnings: ($1,385,515)
Fiscal Year-end: 06/30/23
Software Development Services
N.A.I.C.S.: 541511
Matthew Macfarlane *(Mng Dir)*

ICF KURSMAKLER AG
Kaiserstrasse 1, Frankfurt am Main, 60311, Germany
Tel.: (49) 69928770
Web Site: http://www.icfgroup.de
Year Founded: 1997
Sales Range: $25-49.9 Million
Emp.: 70
Banking Services
N.A.I.C.S.: 522299
Bernd Gegenheimer *(Chm-Mgmt Bd)*

Subsidiaries:

ICF Systems AG (1)
Kaiserstrasse 1, Frankfurt am Main, 60311, Germany
Tel.: (49) 6929925600
Web Site: http://www.icfsystems.de
Sales Range: $25-49.9 Million
Emp.: 40
Computer Services
N.A.I.C.S.: 541519
Michael Krug *(Gen Mgr)*

Novis Software GmbH (1)
Morgensonne 9, Braunichswalde, 07580, Seelingstadt, Germany
Tel.: (49) 366082000
Web Site: http://www.novis-software.de
Sales Range: $25-49.9 Million
Emp.: 30
Computer Services
N.A.I.C.S.: 541519
Peter Janich *(Mng Dir)*

ICG-LONGBOW SENIOR SECURED UK PROP DEBT INV LTD.
Procession House 55 Ludgate Hill, London, EC4M 7JW, United Kingdom
Tel.: (44) 2035452000
Web Site: https://www.icg-longbow-ssup.com
Year Founded: 1989
LBOW—(LSE)
Rev.: $8,756,715
Assets: $94,215,990
Liabilities: $1,047,915
Net Worth: $93,168,075
Earnings: $2,360,820
Fiscal Year-end: 01/31/23
Investment Management Service
N.A.I.C.S.: 523940

ICHEMCO S.R.L.
Via 11 Setembre 5, Cuggiono, 20012, Milan, Italy
Tel.: (39) 0297243100   IT
Web Site: http://www.ichemco.it
Year Founded: 1979
Sales Range: $25-49.9 Million
Emp.: 20
Chemical Products Producer & Marketer
N.A.I.C.S.: 325998
Ezio Curioni *(Pres)*

ICHIA TECHNOLOGIES INC.
268 Hwa-Ya 2nd Rd, Hwa-Ya Technology Park Gueishan, Taoyuan, Taiwan
Tel.: (886) 33973345
Web Site: https://www.ichia.com
Year Founded: 1983
2402—(TAI)
Rev.: $279,976,902
Assets: $330,840,074

ICHIA TECHNOLOGIES INC.

Ichia Technologies Inc.—(Continued)

Liabilities: $127,872,947
Net Worth: $202,967,127
Earnings: $15,215,049
Emp.: 4,000
Fiscal Year-end: 12/31/23
Rubber Keypads Mfr
N.A.I.C.S.: 334118
Eric Tseng (Gen Mgr-BU)

Subsidiaries:

Ichia Rubber Ind. (M) Sdn. Bhd. (1)
No 977A Solok Perusahaan 3 Prai Ind Estate, 13600, Perai, Penang, Malaysia
Tel.: (60) 43903900
Emp.: 200
Handset Keypads Mfr
N.A.I.C.S.: 326291

ICHIGO ASSET MANAGEMENT, LTD.
Hiroo Tower Bldg 8F N 1-1-31 Hiroo
Shibuyo-Ku, Tokyo, 150 0012, Japan
Tel.: (81) 332301515
Web Site: http://www.ichigoasset.com
Investment Management Service
N.A.I.C.S.: 523940
Scott Callon (CEO & Partner)

Subsidiaries:

JAPAN OFFICE ADVISORS, Inc. (1)
COI Nanpeidai Bldg 1-10 Nanpeidai-cho,
Shibuya-ku, Tokyo, 150-0036,
Japan (100%)
Tel.: (81) 364161284
Sales Range: $50-74.9 Million
Emp.: 25
Real Estate Investment Management Services
N.A.I.C.S.: 523940

ICHIGO GREEN INFRASTRUCTURE INVESTMENT CORPORATION
Marunouchi Park Building 20F 2-6-1
Marunouchi, Chiyoda-ku, Tokyo, 100-6920, Japan
Tel.: (81) 335024863
Web Site: https://www.ichigo-green.co.jp
Year Founded: 2016
9282—(TKS)
Rev.: $10,487,631
Assets: $93,285,889
Liabilities: $53,268,343
Net Worth: $40,017,546
Earnings: $2,045,965
Fiscal Year-end: 06/30/22
Real Estate Investment Trust Services
N.A.I.C.S.: 531120
Nanako Ito (Exec Dir)

ICHIGO HOTEL REIT INVESTMENT CORPORATION
Marunouchi Park Building 20F 2-6-1
Marunouchi, Chiyoda-ku, Tokyo, 100-6920, Japan
Tel.: (81) 344855232
Web Site: https://www.ichigo-hotel.co.jp
Year Founded: 2015
34630—(TKS)
Sales Range: $1-4.9 Billion
Real Estate Related Services
N.A.I.C.S.: 531390
Osamu Miyashita (Exec Dir)

ICHIGO OFFICE REIT INVESTMENT CORPORATION
Marunouchi Park Building 20F 2-6-1
Marunouchi, Chiyoda-ku, Tokyo, 100-6920, Japan
Tel.: (81) 335024886
Web Site: https://www.ichigo-office.co.jp
Year Founded: 2005

8975—(TKS)
Sales Range: $25-49.9 Million
Real Estate Investment Services
N.A.I.C.S.: 523999
Takafumi Kagayama (Exec Dir)

ICHIGO, INC.
Marunouchi Park Building 20F 2-6-1
Marunouchi, Chiyoda-ku, Tokyo, 100-6920, Japan
Tel.: (81) 335024800
Web Site: https://www.ichigo.gr.jp
Year Founded: 2000
2337—(TKS)
Rev.: $586,676,230
Assets: $2,602,136,350
Liabilities: $1,777,704,060
Net Worth: $824,432,290
Earnings: $85,845,720
Fiscal Year-end: 02/29/24
Real Estate Manangement Services
N.A.I.C.S.: 531210
Scott Callon (Chm)

Subsidiaries:

Ichigo ECO Energy Co., Ltd. (1)
The Imperial Hotel Tower 1-1-1 Uchisaiwa-icho, Chiyoda-ku, Tokyo, 100-0011, Japan
Tel.: (81) 335024884
Web Site: https://www.ichigo.gr.jp
Real Estate Development Services
N.A.I.C.S.: 531210

Ichigo Estate Co., Ltd. (1)
The Imperial Hotel Tower 1-1-1 Uchisaiwa-icho, Chiyoda-ku, Tokyo, 100-0011, Japan
Tel.: (81) 335025625
Web Site: https://www.ichigo.gr.jp
Real Estate Development Services
N.A.I.C.S.: 531210

Ichigo Investment Advisors Co., Ltd. (1)
The Imperial Hotel Tower 1-1-1 Uchisaiwa-icho, Chiyoda-ku, Tokyo, 100-0011, Japan
Tel.: (81) 335024886
Web Site: https://www.ichigo.gr.jp
Real Estate Development Services
N.A.I.C.S.: 531210

Ichigo Land Shinchiku Co., Ltd. (1)
1-1-1 Uchisaiwaicho, Chiyoda-ku, Tokyo, 100-0011, Japan
Tel.: (81) 335024904
Real Estate Development Services
N.A.I.C.S.: 531210

Ichigo Marche Co., Ltd. (1)
30 Matsudo Shinden, Matsudo, 270-2241, Chiba, Japan
Tel.: (81) 473632222
Web Site: https://www.matsudo-nanbuichiba.com
Property Management Services
N.A.I.C.S.: 531210

Ichigo Owners Co., Ltd. (1)
The Imperial Hotel Tower 1-1-1 Uchisaiwa-icho, Chiyoda-ku, Tokyo, 100-0011, Japan
Tel.: (81) 335024904
Web Site: https://www.ichigo.gr.jp
Real Estate Development Services
N.A.I.C.S.: 531210

Ichigo Real Estate Services Fukuoka Co., Ltd. (1)
3-14-36 Haruyoshi, Chuo-ku, Fukuoka, 810-0003, Fukuoka, Japan
Tel.: (81) 927392065
Real Estate Development Services
N.A.I.C.S.: 531210

ICHIHIRO CO., LTD.
4-1-6 Hatchonishi, Imabari, 794-0832, Ehime, Japan
Tel.: (81) 898 23 6126 JP
Web Site: http://www.ichihiro.co.jp
Year Founded: 1974
Emp.: 220
Towels Mfr
N.A.I.C.S.: 458110
Yasuyuki Ochi (Pres & CEO)

Subsidiaries:

T.KAWABE & CO., LTD. (1)
4-16-3 Yotsuya, Shinjuku-Ku, Tokyo, 160-8403, Japan (55%)
Tel.: (81) 333527123
Web Site: https://www.kawabe.co.jp
Rev.: $86,379,480
Assets: $83,913,950
Liabilities: $38,556,130
Net Worth: $45,357,820
Earnings: $1,758,260
Emp.: 145
Fiscal Year-end: 03/31/2024
Clothing Goods Whslr
N.A.I.C.S.: 458110

ICHIKAWA CO. LTD.
14-15 Hongo 2-Chome, Bunkyo-ku, Tokyo, 113-8442, Japan
Tel.: (81) 338161111
Web Site: https://www.ik-felt.co.jp
Year Founded: 1949
3513—(TKS)
Rev.: $89,915,830
Assets: $193,289,620
Liabilities: $52,133,070
Net Worth: $141,156,550
Earnings: $6,728,980
Emp.: 687
Fiscal Year-end: 03/31/24
Paper Making Equipment
N.A.I.C.S.: 811310
Masataka Ushio (Pres)

Subsidiaries:

Ichikawa China Co., LTD. (1)
Rm 1101 Guoli Bldg 1465, Beijing Xi Rd Jing An Qu, Shanghai, 200040, China
Tel.: (86) 2152120109
Felt Mfr & Technical Services
N.A.I.C.S.: 324122

Ichikawa Europa GmbH (1)
Friedrich-Ebert-Str 1, 40210, Dusseldorf, Germany
Tel.: (49) 2111719595
Web Site: http://www.ik-felt.co.jp
Sales Range: $25-49.9 Million
Emp.: 6
Industrial Felts Distr
N.A.I.C.S.: 313210

ICHIKEN CO., LTD.
Hamamatsucho Bldg 6F 1-1-1
Shibaura, Minato-ku, Tokyo, 105-0023, Japan
Tel.: (81) 359315610
Web Site: https://www.ichiken.co.jp
Year Founded: 1930
1847—(TKS)
Sales Range: $500-549.9 Million
Construction & Real Estate Services
N.A.I.C.S.: 541330
Minoru Yoshida (Mng Officer)

ICHIKURA CO., LTD.
699-1 Taisei-cho, Kita-ku, Saitama, 331-0815, Japan
Tel.: (81) 486776151
Web Site: https://www.ichikura.jp
Year Founded: 1991
6186—(TKS)
Rev.: $135,035,690
Assets: $132,907,270
Liabilities: $102,957,360
Net Worth: $29,949,910
Earnings: $4,157,690
Emp.: 726
Fiscal Year-end: 03/31/24
Wedding Clothing & Accessories
N.A.I.C.S.: 532281
Yoshihiko Kawabata (Founder, Pres & CEO)

ICHIMASA KAMABOKO CO., LTD.
7-77 Tsushimaya, Higashi-ward, Niigata, 950-8735, Japan
Tel.: (81) 252707111

INTERNATIONAL PUBLIC

Web Site: https://www.ichimasa.co.jp
Year Founded: 1965
2904—(TKS)
Rev.: $214,509,140
Assets: $195,258,240
Liabilities: $105,043,360
Net Worth: $90,214,880
Earnings: $5,952,540
Emp.: 714
Fiscal Year-end: 06/30/24
Seafood Product Mfr & Whslr
N.A.I.C.S.: 311941
Masahiko Takizawa (Exec Officer & VP)

Subsidiaries:

P.T. KML Ichimasa Foods (1)
JI KIG Selatan IV Kav C9 Kawasan Industri, Gresik, Indonesia
Tel.: (62) 313976349
Web Site: https://www.kmlichimasa.com
Emp.: 400
Food Product Mfr & Distr
N.A.I.C.S.: 311421

ICHINEN HOLDINGS CO., LTD.
4-10-6 Nishinakajima, Yodogawa-ku, Osaka, 532-8567, Japan
Tel.: (81) 663091816
Web Site: https://www.ichinenhd.co.jp
Year Founded: 1963
9619—(TKS)
Rev.: $913,852,330
Assets: $1,339,225,660
Liabilities: $935,969,390
Net Worth: $403,256,270
Earnings: $80,992,330
Emp.: 2,031
Fiscal Year-end: 03/31/24
Holding Company
N.A.I.C.S.: 551112
Masashi Kuroda (Pres & CEO)

Subsidiaries:

ICHINEN AUTOS (N.Z.) LTD (1)
57 Maurice Road, Penrose, Auckland, 1061, New Zealand
Tel.: (64) 95800050
Motor Vehicle Distr
N.A.I.C.S.: 423110

ICHINEN JIKCO CO., LTD. (1)
9F East Wing Sumitomo Fudosan Mita Twin Bldg 4-2-8 Shibaura, Minato-ku, Tokyo, 108-0023, Japan
Tel.: (81) 36 311 6231
Web Site: https://www.jikco.co.jp
Gas Densitometer Mfr & Distr
N.A.I.C.S.: 334516
Eizo Haimoto (Pres & CEO)

Subsidiary (Domestic):

ICHINEN JIKCO POLYMER CO., LTD. (2)
2667 Shiraishi Misato-Cho, Kodama-Gun, Saitama, Japan
Tel.: (81) 495751488
Gas Densitometer Mfr
N.A.I.C.S.: 334516

ICHINEN JIKCO TEC CO., LTD. (2)
339-1 Kamieguro Meiwamachi, Oura-Gun, Gunma, Japan
Tel.: (81) 276701410
Gas Densitometer Mfr
N.A.I.C.S.: 334516

KYOUEI Co., LTD. (1)
1-56 Midorigaokamachi, Takayama, Japan
Tel.: (81) 577336067
Web Site: http://www.ichinenhd.co.jp
Machine Tools Mfr
N.A.I.C.S.: 333517

Ohtori Corporation (1)
Shinjuku Gyoen Side Building 8F 1-36-14 Shinjuku, Shinjuku-ku, Tokyo, 160-0022, Japan
Tel.: (81) 3 5312 6681
Web Site: http://www.ohtori-gp.co.jp
Sales Range: $25-49.9 Million
Emp.: 21

AND PRIVATE COMPANIES

Holding Company; Textiles, Parking, Business Contracting & Factoring Services
N.A.I.C.S.: 551112

ICHIROKUDO CO., LTD.
1-8-9 Yaesu Chuo-ku, Tokyo, 103-0028, Japan
Tel.: (81) 3 35106116 — JP
Web Site: http://www.ichirokudo.com
Year Founded: 1995
Sales Range: $75-99.9 Million
Restaurant Owner & Operator
N.A.I.C.S.: 722511
Hirokazu Yuhara *(CEO)*

ICHISHIN HOLDINGS CO., LTD.
GE Edison Building 3-11 Yahata 2-chome, Ichikawa, 272-8518, Chiba, Japan
Tel.: (81) 473352888
Web Site: https://ir.ichishin.co.jp
Year Founded: 1979
4645—(TKS)
Rev.: $127,254,730
Assets: $92,236,282
Liabilities: $72,844,612
Net Worth: $19,391,670
Earnings: $2,573,739
Fiscal Year-end: 02/29/24
Holding Company
N.A.I.C.S.: 551111
Toshihiro Shimoya *(Pres)*

Subsidiaries:

Edo Cultural Center Co., Ltd. (1)
7-10-9 Akasaka, Minato-ku, Tokyo, 107-0052, Japan
Tel.: (81) 335890202
Web Site: https://www.edocul.com
Language Training Services
N.A.I.C.S.: 611630

Japan Laim Co., Ltd. (1)
4-2-8 Hongo, Bunkyo-ku, Tokyo, 113-0033, Japan
Tel.: (81) 358409980
Web Site: https://www.japanlaim.co.jp
Emp.: 43
Video Production & Distribution Services
N.A.I.C.S.: 512110

ICHITAN GROUP PUBLIC COMPANY LIMITED
No 8 T-One Building 42nd-44th Floor Soi Sukhumvit 40, Phra Khanong Sub-District Khlong Toei District, Bangkok, 10110, Thailand
Tel.: (66) 20231111
Web Site: https://www.ichitangroup.com
Year Founded: 2010
ICHI—(THA)
Rev.: $236,018,370
Assets: $210,333,569
Liabilities: $39,808,371
Net Worth: $170,525,198
Earnings: $32,123,437
Emp.: 379
Fiscal Year-end: 12/31/23
Tea Mfr
N.A.I.C.S.: 311920
Jinda Sognrod *(Sec)*

ICHIYOSHI SECURITIES CO., LTD.
Tokyo Shoken Kaikan Bldg 4th 5th & 6th Floors 1-5-8 Nihonbashi, Kayabacho Chuo-ku, Tokyo, 103-0025, Japan
Tel.: (81) 343464500 — JP
Web Site: https://www.ichiyoshi.co.jp
Year Founded: 1944
8624—(TKS)
Rev.: $124,512,570
Assets: $308,336,670
Liabilities: $116,593,790
Net Worth: $191,742,880
Earnings: $12,750,690

Emp.: 872
Fiscal Year-end: 03/31/24
Banking & Security Services
N.A.I.C.S.: 523150
Masaki Yano *(Sr Operating Officer)*

Subsidiaries:

Ichiyoshi Asset Management Co., Ltd. (1)
1-5-8 Nihonbashi Kayabacho, Chuo-Ku, Tokyo, 103-0025, Japan **(95.1%)**
Tel.: (81) 366706711
Web Site: https://www.ichiyoshiam.jp
Sales Range: $50-74.9 Million
Emp.: 13
Investment Advice
N.A.I.C.S.: 523940
Tomonori Soeda *(Pres)*

Ichiyoshi Business Service Co., Ltd. (1)
2-14-4 Hatchobori Yabuhara Building 9th Floor, Chuo-ku, Tokyo, 104-0032, Japan
Tel.: (81) 35 541 5131
Web Site: https://www.ichiyoshi-bs.co.jp
Emp.: 42
Real Estate Services
N.A.I.C.S.: 531390

Ichiyoshi Research Institute Inc (1)
1-5-8 Nihonbashikayaba-cho, Chuo-ku, Tokyo, 103-0025, Japan **(85%)**
Tel.: (81) 342123480
Web Site: https://www.ichiyoshi-research.co.jp
Information Services
N.A.I.C.S.: 519290
Nobuhisa Yamanaka *(Pres)*

ICICI BANK LIMITED
ICICI Bank Towers Bandra-Kurla Complex, Mumbai, 400051, Maharashtra, India
Tel.: (91) 18001080
Web Site: https://www.icicibank.com
Year Founded: 1955
IBN—(NYSE)
Rev.: $28,300,191,774
Assets: $283,443,828,402
Liabilities: $251,067,798,631
Net Worth: $32,376,029,771
Earnings: $13,176,075,868
Emp.: 187,765
Fiscal Year-end: 03/31/24
Commercial Banking & Services
N.A.I.C.S.: 522110
Rakesh Jha *(CFO)*

Subsidiaries:

ICICI Bank Canada Ltd. (1)
Don Valley Business Park 150 Ferrand Drive Suite 1200, Toronto, M3C 3E5, ON, Canada
Web Site: http://www.icicibank.ca
Commercial Banking Services
N.A.I.C.S.: 522110
Hemang Thanavala *(CFO & Head-Ops)*

ICICI Bank UK PLC (1)
One Thomas More Square, PO Box 68921, London, E1W 1YN, United Kingdom
Tel.: (44) 2034785319
Web Site: https://www.icicibank.co.uk
Commercial Banking Services
N.A.I.C.S.: 522110
Loknath Mishra *(CEO & Mng Dir)*

ICICI Home Finance Company Limited (1)
ICICI Bank Towers Bandra - Kurla Complex, Mumbai, 400 051, India
Tel.: (91) 2226531414
Web Site: https://www.icicihfc.com
Financial Mortgage Services
N.A.I.C.S.: 522310

ICICI Lombard General Insurance Co. Ltd. (1)
Ground floor- Interface 11 Sixth floor- Interface 16, Office no 601 602 New linking Road Malad, Mumbai, 400064, India **(65%)**
Tel.: (91) 8655222666
Web Site: http://www.icicilombard.com

Insurance Services
N.A.I.C.S.: 524210
Bhargav Dasgupta *(CEO & Mng Dir)*

ICICI Prudential Asset Management Company Limited (1)
One BKC 13th Floor Bandra Kurla Complex, Mumbai, 400 051, Bandra, India
Tel.: (91) 2226525000
Web Site: https://www.icicipruamc.com
Sales Range: $100-124.9 Million
Emp.: 140
Financial Services
N.A.I.C.S.: 523999
Sankaran Naren *(Chief Investment Officer)*

ICICI Prudential Life Insurance Company Ltd. (1)
ICICI PruLife Towers 1089 Appasaheb Marathe Marg, Prabhadevi, Mumbai, 400025, India
Tel.: (91) 40391600
Web Site: https://www.iciciprulife.com
Life Insurance Services; Joint Venture Between ICICI Bank Limited & Prudential Plc
N.A.I.C.S.: 524113
Puneet Nanda *(Deputy Mng Dir)*

ICICI Securities Limited (1)
ICICI Venture House Appasaheb Marathe Marg, Prabhadevi, Mumbai, 400 025, India **(74.85%)**
Tel.: (91) 2268077100
Web Site: https://www.icicisecurities.com
Sales Range: $125-149.9 Million
Emp.: 200
N.A.I.C.S.: 523910
Ajay Saraf *(Exec Dir)*

Subsidiary (US):

ICICI Securities Inc. (2)
275 Madison Ave Ste 1417, New York, NY 10016
Tel.: (212) 388-0677
Securities Brokerage Services
N.A.I.C.S.: 523150

ICICI Venture Funds Management Company Limited (1)
ICICI Venture House Ground Floor Appasaheb Marathe Marg, Prabhadevi, Mumbai, 400 025, India **(100%)**
Tel.: (91) 2266555050
Web Site: https://www.iciciventure.com
Sales Range: $50-74.9 Million
Emp.: 16
Investment Company
N.A.I.C.S.: 523940

ICL FINCORP LIMITED
VKK Building Main Road Irinjalakuda, Thissur, Kerala, India
Tel.: (91) 480 2828071
Web Site: http://www.iclfincorp.com
Year Founded: 1991
Financial Services
N.A.I.C.S.: 523999
K. G. Anikumar *(Chm & Mng Dir)*

Subsidiaries:

Salem Erode Investments Limited (1)
1st Fl V K K Building Main Road, Irinjalakunda Thrissur, Kerala, 680121, India **(74.27%)**
Tel.: (91) 3324752834
Web Site: https://www.salemerode.com
Financial Planning Services
N.A.I.C.S.: 523940
K G Anilkumar *(Mng Dir)*

ICL ORGANIC DAIRY PRODUCTS LIMITED
A-105 3Rd Floor Sector-63 Gautam Buddha Nagar, Noida, 201301, Uttar Pradesh, India
Tel.: (91) 1204319744
542935—(BOM)
Dairy Product Mfr & Distr
N.A.I.C.S.: 333241
Roop Kishore Gola *(Exec Dir)*

ICLICK INTERACTIVE ASIA GROUP LIMITED

ICM LIMITED

15/F Prosperity Millennia Plaza 663 Kings Road, Quarry Bay, China (Hong Kong)
Tel.: (852) 37009000 — Ky
Web Site: https://www.i-click.com
Year Founded: 2010
ICLK—(NASDAQ)
Rev.: $307,702,000
Assets: $507,734,000
Liabilities: $216,145,000
Net Worth: $291,589,000
Earnings: ($13,631,000)
Emp.: 1,192
Fiscal Year-end: 12/31/21
Online Marketing Services
N.A.I.C.S.: 459999
Sammy Wing Hong Hsieh *(Co-Founder)*

Subsidiaries:

iClick Interactive (Singapore) Pte. Ltd. (1)
Unit 1306 Level 13 16 Collyer Quay, Singapore, 049318, Singapore
Tel.: (65) 88929379
Online Marketing Services
N.A.I.C.S.: 541810

ICM LIMITED
1st Floor Bermuda Commercial Bank Bldg 19 Par-la-Ville Road, PO Box HM1748, Hamilton, HM GX, Bermuda
Tel.: (441) 2992897 — BM
Web Site: http://www.icm.bm
Holding Company; Investment Management Services
N.A.I.C.S.: 551112
Charles Jillings *(Exec Dir)*

Subsidiaries:

ICM Capital Research Limited (1)
12 James s Terrace, Malahide, Dublin, Ireland
Tel.: (353) 18168582
Financial Consulting Services
N.A.I.C.S.: 523940

ICM Corporate Services (Pty) Ltd (1)
Postnet Suite 122, Private Bag X3, Plumstead, 7801, Cape Town, South Africa
Tel.: (27) 217614154
Financial Consulting Services
N.A.I.C.S.: 523940
Werner Van Kets *(Mng Dir)*

ICM Investment Management Limited (1)
PO Box 208, Epsom, KT18 7YF, Surrey, United Kingdom
Tel.: (44) 1372 271 486
Investment Management Service
N.A.I.C.S.: 523940
Charles Jillings *(CEO)*

ICM Investment Research Limited (1)
PO Box 208, Epsom, KT18 7YF, Surrey, United Kingdom
Tel.: (44) 1372 271 486
Investment Research & Advisory Services
N.A.I.C.S.: 523940
Charles Jillings *(CEO)*

ICM NZ Limited (1)
Level 10 45 Johnston Street, PO Box 25437, Wellington, 6146, New Zealand
Tel.: (64) 49017600
Financial Consulting Services
N.A.I.C.S.: 523940
Dugald Morrison *(Gen Mgr)*

ICM Research Pte Ltd (1)
Tanglin, PO Box 147, Singapore, 912405, Singapore
Tel.: (65) 64663038
Financial Consulting Services
N.A.I.C.S.: 523940

UIL Limited (1)
Clarendon House 2 Church Street, Hamilton, HM 11, United Kingdom
Tel.: (44) 1372271486

ICM LIMITED

ICM Limited—(Continued)

Web Site: http://www.uil.limited
Rev.: $15,453,741
Assets: $304,098,837
Liabilities: $130,267,947
Net Worth: $173,830,889
Earnings: ($31,616,532)
Fiscal Year-end: 06/30/2024
Closed-End Investment Fund
N.A.I.C.S.: 525990
Peter Burrows (Chm)

Affiliate (Non-US):

Somers Limited (2)
34 Bermudiana Road, Hamilton, HM 11, Bermuda (49.75%)
Tel.: (441) 2992897
Web Site: http://www.somers.limited
Rev.: $2,654,239
Assets: $422,156,318
Liabilities: $84,729,927
Net Worth: $337,426,391
Earnings: ($210,262,540)
Emp.: 450
Fiscal Year-end: 09/30/2022
Investment Holding Company
N.A.I.C.S.: 551112
Warren McLeland (Chm)

Subsidiary (Domestic):

Bermuda Commercial Bank Ltd. (3)
34 Bermudiana Road, Hamilton, HM 11, Bermuda
Tel.: (441) 295 5678
Web Site: http://www.bcb.bm
Rev.: $15,399,891
Assets: $460,464,488
Liabilities: $362,955,451
Net Worth: $97,509,037
Earnings: ($8,312,630)
Fiscal Year-end: 09/30/2019
Banking Services
N.A.I.C.S.: 522110
David Morgan (Deputy Chm)

Subsidiary (Non-US):

Thorn Group Limited (3)
Level 1 62 Hume Hwy, Chullora, 2190, NSW, Australia
Tel.: (61) 291015000
Web Site: http://www.thorn.com.au
Rev.: $79,786,429
Assets: $221,237,363
Liabilities: $148,346,643
Net Worth: $72,890,719
Earnings: $6,432,931
Fiscal Year-end: 03/31/2021
Electrical Equipment Rental Services
N.A.I.C.S.: 423620
Pete Lirantzis (CEO)

Subsidiary (Domestic):

Thorn Equipment Finance Pty Ltd (4)
Level 1 62 Hume Highway, Chullora, 2190, NSW, Australia
Tel.: (61) 1800623611
Equipment Finance Leasing Services
N.A.I.C.S.: 522220
Andrew Arnold (Mgr-Bus Dev)

Votraint No 1537 Pty Ltd (4)
L 2 577 Little Bourke St, Melbourne, 3000, VIC, Australia
Tel.: (61) 3 8643 5500
Web Site: http://www.ncml.com.au
Emp.: 60
Fund Management Consulting Services
N.A.I.C.S.: 541611
James Marshall (Gen Mgr)

Subsidiary (Non-US):

Waverton Investment Management Limited (3)
16 Babmaes St London, London, SW1Y6AH, United Kingdom (62.5%)
Tel.: (44) 2074847484
Web Site: https://www.waverton.co.uk
Sales Range: $25-49.9 Million
Emp.: 100
Investment Management Service
N.A.I.C.S.: 523940
Stephen Browne (Head-Mktg)

Westhouse Holdings plc (3)

Heron Tower 110 Bishopsgate, London, EC2N 4AY, United Kingdom (63.05%)
Tel.: (44) 207601 6100
Web Site: http://www.westhousesecurities.com
Sales Range: $1-9.9 Million
Emp.: 50
Holding Company; Financial Advisory, Securities Brokerage & Dealing Services
N.A.I.C.S.: 551112

Subsidiary (Domestic):

Westhouse Securities Limited (4)
One Angel Court, London, EC2R 7HJ, United Kingdom
Tel.: (44) 20 7601 6100
Web Site: http://www.westhousesecurities.com
Financial Advisory, Securities Brokerage & Dealing Services
N.A.I.C.S.: 523150
Micheal Harrison (Head-Secondary Trading)

Subsidiary (Non-US):

Zeta Resources Limited (2)
34 Bermudiana Road, Hamilton, HM 11, Bermuda (100%)
Tel.: (441) 295567
Web Site: http://www.zetaresources.limited
Rev.: $21,490
Assets: $151,244,240
Liabilities: $4,479,031
Net Worth: $146,765,209
Earnings: ($4,344,791)
Fiscal Year-end: 06/30/2023
Closed-End Investment Fund
N.A.I.C.S.: 525990

Holding (Non-US):

Horizon Gold Limited (3)
Unit 8 47 Havelock Street, West Perth, 6005, WA, Australia (72%)
Tel.: (61) 863316092
Web Site: https://www.horizongold.com.au
Rev.: $104,202
Assets: $32,156,228
Liabilities: $8,811,951
Net Worth: $23,344,277
Earnings: ($373,135)
Emp.: 1
Fiscal Year-end: 06/30/2022
Support Activities for Nonmetallic Minerals (except Fuels) Mining
N.A.I.C.S.: 213115
Leigh Ryan (Mng Dir)

Kumarina Resources Limited (3)
Level 2 907 Canning Highway, Mount Pleasant, 6153, WA, Australia
Tel.: (61) 8 9364 7577
Web Site: http://www.kumarina.com
Copper & Gold Mining
N.A.I.C.S.: 212230

Utilico Emerging Markets Trust plc (1)
The Cottage Ridge Court The Ridge, Epsom, KT18 7EP, Surrey, United Kingdom
Tel.: (44) 1372271486
Web Site: http://www.uemtrust.co.uk
Rev.: $89,024,236
Assets: $667,790,963
Liabilities: $7,688,715
Net Worth: $660,102,248
Earnings: $73,076,243
Fiscal Year-end: 03/31/2024
Closed-End Investment Trust
N.A.I.C.S.: 525990
John Leonard Rennocks (Chm)

Subsidiary (Domestic):

Utilico Emerging Markets Limited (2)
c/o ICM Investment Management Ltd, PO Box 208, Epsom, KT18 7YF, Surrey, United Kingdom (100%)
Tel.: (44) 1372271486
Rev.: $54,551,667
Assets: $795,381,791
Liabilities: $13,214,630
Net Worth: $782,167,160
Earnings: $40,418,286
Fiscal Year-end: 03/31/2018
Closed-End Investment Fund
N.A.I.C.S.: 525990
Alastair Moreton (Sec)

ICMA RETIREMENT CORPORATION

Str Industrilor 3-5 S3 Bucharest, Bucharest, Romania
Tel.: (40) 212529292
Heating Radiator & Boiler Mfr
N.A.I.C.S.: 333414
Mircea Popa (Pres)

ICMA S.A.

Str Matei Voievod No 29 Room 1 Floor 4, District 2, Bucharest, Romania
Tel.: (40) 741450001
ICMA—(BUC)
Rev.: $62,160
Assets: $784,492
Liabilities: $9,462
Net Worth: $775,029
Earnings: $691
Emp.: 2
Fiscal Year-end: 12/31/23
Heating Machinery Mfr
N.A.I.C.S.: 333414
Mircea Popa (Pres, Gen Mgr & Dir Gen)

ICO GROUP LIMITED

Unit A 25/F TG Place 10 Shing Yip Street, Kwun Tong, Kowloon, China (Hong Kong)
Tel.: (852) 2 891 5397
Web Site: http://www.ico.com.hk
Year Founded: 1992
1460—(HKG)
Rev.: $91,891,801
Assets: $100,275,501
Liabilities: $28,727,715
Net Worth: $71,547,786
Earnings: $2,439,528
Emp.: 264
Fiscal Year-end: 03/31/22
Information Technology Consulting Services
N.A.I.C.S.: 541690
Roy Cheong Yuen Lee (CEO)

Subsidiaries:

ICO Limited (1)
Unit A 25/F TG Place 10 Shing Yip Street, Kwun Tong, Kowloon, China (Hong Kong)
Tel.: (852) 28915397
Software Development Services
N.A.I.C.S.: 541511

ICOLLEGE LIMITED

205 North Quay, Adelaide, 4000, QLD, Australia
Tel.: (61) 32296000
Web Site: http://www.icollege.edu.au
NXD—(ASX)
Rev.: $74,363,648
Assets: $89,666,132
Liabilities: $66,546,474
Net Worth: $23,119,658
Earnings: ($20,854,033)
Fiscal Year-end: 06/30/24
Vocational Education & Training Solutions
N.A.I.C.S.: 611710
Simon Tollhurst (Chm)

Subsidiaries:

RedHill Education Limited (1)
Level 2 7 Kelly Street, Ultimo, 2007, NSW, Australia
Tel.: (61) 2 8355 3820
Web Site: http://www.redhilleducation.com
Edcuational Services
N.A.I.C.S.: 923110

Subsidiary (Domestic):

Academy of Information Technology Pty Ltd (2)
Level 2 7 Kelly Street, Ultimo, 2007, NSW, Australia
Tel.: (61) 292118399
Web Site: http://www.ait.edu.au

INTERNATIONAL PUBLIC

Education Services
N.A.I.C.S.: 611310

Go Study Australia Pty Limited (2)
249 Bondi Rd, Bondi Junction, 2026, NSW, Australia
Tel.: (61) 469812476
Web Site: http://www.gostudy.com.au
Education Services
N.A.I.C.S.: 611310

Greenwich English College Pty Ltd (2)
Level 2 396 Pitt Street Enter Via Goulburn Street, Sydney, 2000, NSW, Australia
Tel.: (61) 292642223
Web Site: http://www.greenwichcollege.edu.au
Education Services
N.A.I.C.S.: 611310

International School of Colour & Design Pty Ltd (2)
Level 2 7 Kelly Street, Ultimo, 2007, NSW, Australia
Tel.: (61) 283553838
Web Site: http://www.iscd.edu.au
Education Services
N.A.I.C.S.: 611310

ICOM INCORPORATED

1-1-32 Kamiminami, Hirano-ku, Osaka, 547-0003, Japan
Tel.: (81) 667935301
Web Site: https://www.icom.co.jp
6820—(TKS)
Rev.: $245,343,370
Assets: $483,580,990
Liabilities: $49,006,540
Net Worth: $434,574,450
Earnings: $22,877,210
Emp.: 1,034
Fiscal Year-end: 03/31/24
Wireless Communication Equipment Mfr
N.A.I.C.S.: 334220
Tokuzo Inoue (Chm)

Subsidiaries:

Asia Icom Inc. (1)
6F No 68 Sec 1 Cheng-Teh Road, Taipei, Taiwan
Tel.: (886) 225591899
Web Site: http://www.asia-icom.com
Radio Equipments Mfr
N.A.I.C.S.: 334220

Icom (Australia) Pty. Ltd. (1)
Unit1 103 Garden Road, Clayton, 3168, VIC, Australia
Tel.: (61) 395497500
Web Site: https://www.icom-australia.com
Sales Range: $25-49.9 Million
Emp.: 22
Radio Equipments Mfr
N.A.I.C.S.: 334220
Takashi Aoki (Mng Dir)

Icom (Europe) GmbH (1)
Auf der Krautweide 24, 65812, Bad Soden am Taunus, Germany
Tel.: (49) 6196766850
Web Site: http://www.icomeurope.com
Sales Range: $25-49.9 Million
Emp.: 13
Communication Equipment Mfr
N.A.I.C.S.: 334220

Icom (UK) Ltd. (1)
Blacksole House The Boulevard Altira Park, Herne Bay, CT6 6GZ, Kent, United Kingdom
Tel.: (44) 1227741741
Web Site: https://www.icomuk.co.uk
Sales Range: $25-49.9 Million
Emp.: 30
Radio Communication Equipments Mfr & Distr
N.A.I.C.S.: 334220
Dave Stockley (Founder & Chm)

Icom America License Holding LLC (1)
2380 116th Ave NE, Bellevue, WA 98004
Tel.: (425) 454-8155
Web Site: http://www.icomamerica.com

AND PRIVATE COMPANIES

Sales Range: $25-49.9 Million
Emp.: 100
Radio Communication Equipment Mfr
N.A.I.C.S.: 334220
Holly Loutsis *(Mgr-HR)*

Icom America, Inc. (1)
12421 Willows Rd NE, Kirkland, WA 98034
Tel.: (425) 454-8155
Sales Range: $50-74.9 Million
Emp.: 100
Radio Communications Equipment Distr
N.A.I.C.S.: 423690

Icom France S.A.S. (1)
1 rue Brindejonc des Moulinais ZAC de la plaine, BP 45804, 31505, Toulouse, Cedex 5, France
Tel.: (33) 561360303
Web Site: https://www.icom-france.com
Sales Range: $25-49.9 Million
Emp.: 40
Radio Communication Equipments Mfr & Sales
N.A.I.C.S.: 334220

Icom Information Products Inc. (1)
3-8-15 Nipponbashi, Naniwa-ku, Osaka, 556-0005, Japan
Tel.: (81) 667930331
Radio Communication Equipment Mfr
N.A.I.C.S.: 334220
Tsutomu Fukui *(Pres)*

Icom New Zealand (1)
39 c Renee Dr, Auckland, 2022, New Zealand
Tel.: (64) 92744062
Web Site: http://www.icom.co.nz
Sales Range: $50-74.9 Million
Emp.: 8
Radio Communication Equipment Distr
N.A.I.C.S.: 423620
Sharon Dawson *(Mng Dir)*

Icom Spain, S.L. (1)
Carretera de Rubi 88 Bajos A, 08174, Sant Cugat del Valles, Barcelona, Spain
Tel.: (34) 935902670
Web Site: http://www.icomspain.com
Radio Communication Equipments Distr
N.A.I.C.S.: 334220

Wakayama Icom Inc. (1)
1866-1 Tokuda Aridagawa-cho, Arita-gun, Wakayama, 643-0801, Japan
Tel.: (81) 737526600
Web Site: https://www.icom.co.jp
Wireless Communication Equipment Mfr
N.A.I.C.S.: 334220

ICOMM TELE LIMITED
ICOMM House Plot No 31 Phase-I Kamalapuri Colony Srinagar Colony, Banjara Hills, Hyderabad, 500 073, Andhra Pradesh, India
Tel.: (91) 4023552222
Web Site: http://www.icommtele.com
Year Founded: 1989
Sales Range: $350-399.9 Million
Emp.: 2,000
Telecommunications Equipment Mfr
N.A.I.C.S.: 334220
Sumanth Paturu *(Mng Dir)*

Subsidiaries:

ICOMM International Lanka (Pvt) Ltd (1)
4/99L Thalakotuwa Gardens Polhengoda, Colombo, Sri Lanka
Tel.: (94) 7734 02480
Telecommunications Equipment Mfr
N.A.I.C.S.: 334220

ICOMM Tele Limited - Towers Unit (1)
47/60 Nagaram Road Kesara Road, Hyderabad, Andhra Pradesh, India
Tel.: (91) 40 2712 8566
Emp.: 265
Telecommunications Equipment Mfr
N.A.I.C.S.: 334220

ICOMM Tele Limited - Turnkey Services Division (1)
Trendset Towers Road 2 Banjara Hills, Hyderabad, 500 034, Andhra Pradesh, India

Tel.: (91) 40 2355 2222
Telecommunications Equipment Mfr
N.A.I.C.S.: 334220

ICON ANALYTICAL EQUIPMENT PVT. LTD.
301 Landmark 554 Dr G M Bhosale Marg, Worli, Mumbai, 400018, India
Tel.: (91) 2243451600   In
Web Site: http://www.iconanalytical.com
Year Founded: 1999
Analytical Laboratory Instrument Mfr
N.A.I.C.S.: 334516

ICON AVIATION SA
Av Jurandir 856, Planalto Paulista, Sao Paulo, 04072-000, Brazil
Tel.: (55) 1150706000
Web Site: http://www.iconaviation.com.br
Aviation Services
N.A.I.C.S.: 488119

Subsidiaries:

Morro Vermelho Taxi Aereo Ltda. (1)
Rua Joao Carlos Mallet 180 Hangar Morro Vermelho, Aeroporto de Congonhas, 04072-040, Sao Paulo, Brazil
Tel.: (55) 11 5591 1700
Web Site: http://www.mvta.com.br
Air Charter Services
N.A.I.C.S.: 481211

ICON COMMUNICATIONS CJSC
26/4 Saryan Street, Yerevan, Armenia
Tel.: (374) 10 59 09 00
Web Site: http://www.icon.am
Broadband Internet Service Solutions
N.A.I.C.S.: 517810
Raffi Kassarjian *(CEO)*

ICON CULTURE GLOBAL COMPANY LIMITED
29/F Kingold Century No 62 Jinsui Road, Zhujiang New Town Tianhe, Guangzhou, 510623, Guangdong, China
Tel.: (86) 2066235299   Ky
Web Site: http://www.iconspace.com
Year Founded: 2009
8500—(HKG)
Rev.: $9,683,248
Assets: $19,805,105
Liabilities: $9,632,984
Net Worth: $10,172,120
Earnings: ($5,582,304)
Emp.: 59
Fiscal Year-end: 12/31/22
Advertising & Marketing Services
N.A.I.C.S.: 541850
Eric Tse To Chow *(Founder & Chm)*

ICON ENERGY LIMITED
Tel.: (61) 407200200
Web Site: https://www.iconenergy.com
ICN—(ASX)
Rev.: $109,990
Assets: $982,410
Liabilities: $3,727,861
Net Worth: ($2,745,451)
Earnings: ($771,945)
Emp.: 15
Fiscal Year-end: 06/30/24
Exploration & Development Of Oil & Gas
N.A.I.C.S.: 213112
Raymond Swinburn James *(Mng Dir)*

ICON FASHION HOLDING AG
Limmatquai 94, 8001, Zurich, Switzerland
Tel.: (41) 442654303
Web Site: http://www.iconfashion.ch

Women's, Men's & Children's Clothing Mfr & Distr
N.A.I.C.S.: 315250
Juergen Schnappinger *(Chm-Mgmt Bd)*

ICON FINE WINE & SPIRITS LTD.
100-1152 Mainland Street, Vancouver, V6B 4X2, BC, Canada
Tel.: (604) 685-8693
Web Site: http://www.iconwineandspirits.com
Wine & Spirits Marketing Agency
N.A.I.C.S.: 541613
Jay Garnett *(Pres & CEO)*

Subsidiaries:

Free House Wine & Spirits Ltd. (1)
2818 Main St, Vancouver, V5T 0C1, BC, Canada
Tel.: (604) 269-9040
Web Site: http://www.freehousewine.com
Wine & Spirits Supplier
N.A.I.C.S.: 424820
Ted Latimer *(Pres)*

ICON GROUP LTD.
Wallstrabe 14a, 10179, Berlin, Germany
Tel.: (49) 30886633100
Web Site: https://www.icongroup.com
Year Founded: 2015
ICON—(TAE)
Rev.: $398,976,372
Assets: $155,912,416
Liabilities: $89,076,114
Net Worth: $66,836,302
Earnings: $9,043,238
Fiscal Year-end: 12/31/23
Custom Computer Programming Services
N.A.I.C.S.: 541511

ICON INFRASTRUCTURE LLP
1st Floor Pollen House 10-12 Cork Street, London, W1S 3NP, United Kingdom
Tel.: (44) 2072929670
Web Site: http://www.iconinfrastructure.com
Infrastructure Investment Services
N.A.I.C.S.: 523999
Paul Malan *(Chm & Sr Partner)*

Subsidiaries:

Capstone Infrastructure Corporation (1)
155 Wellington Street West Suite 2930, Toronto, M5V 3H1, ON, Canada   (100%)
Tel.: (416) 649-1300
Web Site: https://www.capstoneinfrastructure.com
Rev.: $180,485,007
Assets: $1,245,063,754
Liabilities: $909,320,790
Net Worth: $335,742,965
Earnings: ($22,043,463)
Fiscal Year-end: 12/31/2023
Infrastructure Investment Holding Company
N.A.I.C.S.: 551112
Aileen Gien *(Gen Counsel & Sec)*

Subsidiary (Domestic):

Cardinal Power of Canada, L.P. (2)
170 Henry Street, PO Box 70, Cardinal, K0E 1E0, ON, Canada
Tel.: (613) 657-1400
Power Generation Services
N.A.I.C.S.: 221118

Whitecourt Power Limited Partnership (2)
Highway 43 3km northwest of Whitecourtt, PO Box 1888, Whitecourt, T7S 1P6, AB, Canada
Tel.: (780) 778-3334
Web Site: http://www.capstoneinfra.com
Biomass Power Generation Services
N.A.I.C.S.: 221117

ICON PLC

Leonard Sanche *(Plant Mgr)*

Firmus Energy Ltd (1)
A4-A5 Fergusons Way Kilbegs Rd, Antrim, BT41 4LZ, United Kingdom
Tel.: (44) 3300249000
Web Site: http://www.firmusenergy.co.uk
Natural & Liquified Petroleum Gas Distr
N.A.I.C.S.: 221210
Michael Scott *(Mng Dir)*

Service Terminal Rotterdam B.V. (1)
Torontostraat 20 Port number 4540, Botlek, 3197 KN, Rotterdam, Netherlands
Tel.: (31) 181291100
Web Site: http://www.serviceterminal.com
Freight Transportation Services
N.A.I.C.S.: 488510

ICON INTERNATIONAL COMMUNICATIONS PTY. LTD.
Ground Fl 439-441 Kent St, Sydney, 2000, NSW, Australia
Tel.: (61) 2 8235 7600   AU
Web Site: http://www.iconinternational.com.au
Advetising Agency
N.A.I.C.S.: 541810
Phil Burford *(Co-Founder & CEO)*

Subsidiaries:

PT ICON International Communications Indonesia (1)
Jalan Cililin IV No 43A, Kebayoran Baru, Jakarta, 12170, Selatan, Indonesia
Tel.: (62) 21 739 2790
Web Site: http://www.iconinternational.co.id
Advetising Agency
N.A.I.C.S.: 541810

ICON PLC
South County Business Park, Leopardstown, Dublin, 18, Ireland
Tel.: (353) 12912000   NY
Web Site: http://www.iconplc.com
Year Founded: 1990
ICLR—(NASDAQ)
Rev.: $8,120,176,000
Assets: $16,989,863,000
Liabilities: $7,749,120,000
Net Worth: $9,240,743,000
Earnings: $612,335,000
Emp.: 41,100
Fiscal Year-end: 12/31/23
Contract Pharmaceutical Research & Development Services
N.A.I.C.S.: 541715
Ronan Lambe *(Co-Founder)*

Subsidiaries:

Accellacare Espana S.L. (1)
Marques de la Valdavia 103, Alcpbendas, 28100, Madrid, Spain
Tel.: (34) 651691682
Clinical Research Services
N.A.I.C.S.: 541715

Accellacare South Africa (Pty.) Ltd. (1)
Newgate Center 104 Jeppe St, Newton, Johannesburg, South Africa
Tel.: (27) 114920336
Clinical Research Services
N.A.I.C.S.: 541715

Accellacare US Inc. (1)
1901 S Hawthorne Rd Ste 306, Winston Salem, NC 27103
Tel.: (336) 768-8062
Clinical Research Services
N.A.I.C.S.: 541715

Accellacare of Bristol, LLC (1)
1958 W State St, Bristol, TN 37620
Tel.: (423) 989-3105
Clinical Research Services
N.A.I.C.S.: 541715

Accellacare of Charleston, LLC (1)
180 Wingo Way Ste 203, Mount Pleasant, SC 29464
Tel.: (843) 849-1880
Clinical Research Services
N.A.I.C.S.: 541715

ICON PLC

Accellacare of Charlotte, LLC (1)
3541 Randolph Rd Ste 101W, Charlotte, NC 28211
Tel.: (704) 527-6672
Clinical Research Services
N.A.I.C.S.: 541715

Accellacare of Hickory, LLC (1)
221 13th Ave Pl NW Ste 201, Hickory, NC 28601
Tel.: (828) 345-5060
Clinical Research Services
N.A.I.C.S.: 541715

Accellacare of Raleigh, LLC (1)
3521 Haworth Dr Ste 100, Raleigh, NC 27609
Tel.: (919) 783-4895
Clinical Research Services
N.A.I.C.S.: 541715

Accellacare of Rocky Mount, LLC (1)
901 N Winstead Ave Ste 280, Rocky Mount, NC 27804
Tel.: (252) 937-0484
Clinical Research Services
N.A.I.C.S.: 541715

Accellacare of Salisbury, LLC (1)
410 Mocksville Ave, Salisbury, NC 28144
Tel.: (704) 647-9913
Clinical Research Services
N.A.I.C.S.: 541715

Accellacare of Wilmington, LLC (1)
1907 Tradd Ct, Wilmington, NC 28401
Tel.: (910) 799-5500
Clinical Research Services
N.A.I.C.S.: 541715

Accellacare of Winston-Salem, LLC (1)
1901 S Hawthorne Rd Ste 306, Winston Salem, NC 27103
Tel.: (336) 608-3500
Web Site: https://www.accellacare.com
Clinical Research Services
N.A.I.C.S.: 541715

Accellecare Espana S.L. (1)
Marques de la Valdavia 103, Alcobendas, 28100, Madrid, Spain
Tel.: (34) 651691682
Clinical Research Services
N.A.I.C.S.: 541715

Accellacare South Africa (Pty) Ltd. (1)
Building 29 2nd Floor Highlands Estate-Woodlands Office Park, Woodmead, Johannesburg, 2191, South Africa
Tel.: (27) 793753903
Web Site: https://www.accellacare.co.za
Clinical Research Services
N.A.I.C.S.: 541715

Accellecare of Raleigh, LLC (1)
3521 Haworth Dr Ste 100, Raleigh, NC 27609
Tel.: (919) 783-4895
Clinical Research Services
N.A.I.C.S.: 541715

Accellecare of Wilmington, LLC (1)
1907 Tradd Ct, Wilmington, NC 28401
Tel.: (910) 799-5500
Clinical Research Services
N.A.I.C.S.: 541715

Aptiv Solutions, Inc. (1)
1925 Isaac Newton Sq Ste 100, Reston, VA 20190
Tel.: (703) 483-6400
Web Site: http://www.aptivsolutions.com
Sales Range: $75-99.9 Million
Emp.: 750
Clinical Research Services
N.A.I.C.S.: 541715

Subsidiary (Non-US):

Aptiv International Ltd. (2)
4 Hatnufa Street, POB 2626, Kiryat Arieh, 49125, Petah Tiqwa, Israel
Tel.: (972) 39200100
Cancer, Cardiovascular Diseases, Vaccines & Central Nervous System Clinical Developer
N.A.I.C.S.: 325412

Aptiv International Ltd. (2)
3 Tealgate Charnham Park, Hungerford, RG17 0YT, Berkshire, United Kingdom
Tel.: (44) 01488686486
Web Site: http://www.aptivsolutions.com
Clinical Research Services
N.A.I.C.S.: 325412

Aptiv International bv (2)
Smederijstraat 2, 4814 DB, Breda, Netherlands
Tel.: (31) 765317997
Sales Range: $25-49.9 Million
Emp.: 10
Clinical Research Services
N.A.I.C.S.: 541715

Aptiv International sarl (2)
Le Platon Rue Jean Sapidus, Parc D'innovation d'Illkirch, 67400, Illkirch-Graffenstaden, France
Tel.: (33) 369085000
Web Site: http://www.aptivsolutions.com
Sales Range: $25-49.9 Million
Emp.: 15
Clinical Research Services
N.A.I.C.S.: 541715

Aptiv International sp. z o.o. (2)
Al Jerozolimskie 176, 02486, Warsaw, Poland
Tel.: (48) 225944470
Web Site: http://www.aptivsolutions.com
Sales Range: $25-49.9 Million
Emp.: 10
Clinical Research Services
N.A.I.C.S.: 541715

Unit (Domestic):

Aptiv Solutions, Inc. - Maryland (2)
18310 Montgomery Village Ave Ste 620, Gaithersburg, MD 20879
Tel.: (301) 208-9100
Clinical Research Services
N.A.I.C.S.: 541715

Subsidiary (Non-US):

Niphix KK (2)
21-7 Nihonbashi Kabuto-cho, Chuo-ku, Tokyo, 103-0026, Japan
Tel.: (81) 356511411
Web Site: http://www.niphix.co.jp
Clinical Research Services
N.A.I.C.S.: 541715

CRS (Beijing) Clinical Research Co., Limited (1)
Floor 1-3 No 3 Building No 8 Hongda North Road, Hongda Industrial Park Yizhhuang Development Zone Daxing District, Beijing, 100176, China
Tel.: (86) 1089045100
Clinical Research Services
N.A.I.C.S.: 541715

Clinical Research Management, Inc. (1)
1265 Ridge Rd, Hinckley, OH 44233
Tel.: (330) 278-2343
Web Site: http://www.clinicalrm.com
Biotechnology & Medical Research Services
N.A.I.C.S.: 541714
Victoria Tifft (Founder)

DOCS Global Inc. (1)
2100 10 Brooke Pkwy, North Wales, PA 19454
Tel.: (215) 616-3000
Web Site: http://www.docsglobal.com
Human Resource Consulting Services
N.A.I.C.S.: 541612

DOCS International BV (1)
Handelsweg 53, Amstelveen, Amsterdam, 1181 ZA, Netherlands
Tel.: (31) 20 715 0000
Web Site: http://www.docsglobal.com
Sales Range: $75-99.9 Million
Emp.: 50
Clinical Research Staffing Services
N.A.I.C.S.: 561320

DOCS International Belgium N.V. (1)
Interleuvenlaan 62, 3001, Heverlee, Belgium
Tel.: (32) 16394732
Clinical Research Services
N.A.I.C.S.: 325412

DOCS International Poland Sp. z o.o. (1)
Grojecka 5, 02-019, Warsaw, Poland
Tel.: (48) 224453000
Clinical Research Services
N.A.I.C.S.: 541715

DOCS International Sweden AB (1)
Klarabergsviadukten 90 Hus B, 111 64, Stockholm, Sweden
Tel.: (46) 851484700
Clinical Research Services
N.A.I.C.S.: 541715

Firecrest Clinical Ltd. (1)
Clive House National Technology Park, Castletroy, Limerick, Ireland
Tel.: (353) 61266700
Sales Range: $10-24.9 Million
Emp.: 120
Clinical Research Services
N.A.I.C.S.: 621111

ICON Ankara Klinik Arastirma Dis Ticaret Anonim Sirketi (1)
Capitol Vista Eskisehir Yolu 2176 Cadde No 9, Sogutozu, 06510, Ankara, Turkiye
Tel.: (90) 2129093340
Clinical Research Services
N.A.I.C.S.: 541715

ICON Central Laboratories Inc. (1)
123 Smith St, Farmingdale, NY 11735
Tel.: (631) 777-8833
Emp.: 250
Research & Development in the Physical Engineering & Life Sciences
N.A.I.C.S.: 541511

ICON Clinical Investments, LLC (1)
731 Arbor Way Ste 100, Blue Bell, PA 19422
Tel.: (215) 616-3000
Investment Management Service
N.A.I.C.S.: 523940

ICON Clinical Research (New Zealand) Limited (1)
C/-Regus AIG Building Plaza Level 41 Shortland Street, Auckland, 1010, New Zealand
Tel.: (64) 93639630
Clinical Research Services
N.A.I.C.S.: 541715

ICON Clinical Research (Rus) LLC (1)
24 D Smolnaya Str 5th Floor, 125445, Moscow, Russia
Tel.: (7) 4992723200
Clinical Research Services
N.A.I.C.S.: 541715

ICON Clinical Research (Switzerland) GmbH (1)
Clarahuus Centre Teichgasslein 9, 4058, Basel, Switzerland
Tel.: (41) 6156402222
Clinical Research Services
N.A.I.C.S.: 541715

ICON Clinical Research (Thailand) Limited (1)
1 Empire Tower 24th Floor Unit 2408 South Sathorn Road, Yannawa Sathorn, Bangkok, 10120, Thailand
Tel.: (66) 26972600
Clinical Research Services
N.A.I.C.S.: 541715

ICON Clinical Research Austria GmbH (1)
Pyrkergasse 10/6, A 1190, Vienna, Austria
Tel.: (43) 136700880
Clinical Research Services
N.A.I.C.S.: 541715

ICON Clinical Research EOOD (1)
3rd Floor Em Building 17 Henrik Ibsen Region Reg, Lozenets, 1407, Sofia, Bulgaria
Tel.: (359) 24931700
Clinical Research Services
N.A.I.C.S.: 541715

ICON Clinical Research Limited (1)
South County Business Park, Leopardstown, Dublin, 18, Ireland
Tel.: (353) 1 291 2000
Web Site: http://www.iconplc.com
Sales Range: $100-124.9 Million
Emp.: 65
Clinical Research Services
N.A.I.C.S.: 621111

Subsidiary (Non-US):

ICON Clinical Research (2)
Gewerbestrasse 24, CH-4123, Allschwil, Switzerland
Tel.: (41) 614871400
Sales Range: $10-24.9 Million
Emp.: 50
Clinical Research Services
N.A.I.C.S.: 325412

ICON Clinical Research (2)
18th Floor Capital Tower 142 Teheran-ro, Gangnam-gu, Seoul, 06236, Korea (South)
Tel.: (82) 25205200
Clinical Research Services
N.A.I.C.S.: 621111

ICON Clinical Research (Beijing) Co. Limited (2)
Floor 1-3 No 3 Building Hongda Industrial Park No 8 Hongda North Road, Yizhuang Development Zone Daxing District, Beijing, 100176, China
Tel.: (86) 1085295100
Sales Range: $10-24.9 Million
Emp.: 4
Clinical Research Services
N.A.I.C.S.: 621111
Bin Xie Yan (Gen Mgr)

ICON Clinical Research (Canada) Inc. (2)
7405 Transcanada Hwy Suite 222, Saint Laurent, H4T 1Z2, QC, Canada
Tel.: (514) 332-0700
Clinical Research Services
N.A.I.C.S.: 541715

ICON Clinical Research (UK) Limited (2)
Concept House 6 Stoneycroft Rise, Chandlers Ford, SO53 3LD, United Kingdom
Tel.: (44) 2380688500
Web Site: http://www.iconplc.com
Sales Range: $25-49.9 Million
Emp.: 120
Research & Development in the Physical Engineering & Life Sciences
N.A.I.C.S.: 541715

ICON Clinical Research Espana S.L (2)
Torre Diagonal Mar C/ Josep Pla N 2 Planta 11 Mod A1, 08019, Barcelona, Spain
Tel.: (34) 932408100
Sales Range: $25-49.9 Million
Research & Development in the Physical Engineering & Life Sciences
N.A.I.C.S.: 541715

ICON Clinical Research GmbH (2)
Heinrich-Hertz-Strasse 26, 63225, Langen, Germany
Tel.: (49) 61039040
Web Site: http://www.iconplc.com
Research & Development in the Physical Engineering & Life Sciences
N.A.I.C.S.: 541715

Subsidiary (US):

ICON Clinical Research Inc (2)
456 Montgomery St Ste 2200, San Francisco, CA 94104
Tel.: (415) 371-2100
Web Site: http://www.iconclinical.com
Sales Range: $25-49.9 Million
Emp.: 40
Research & Development in the Physical Engineering & Life Sciences
N.A.I.C.S.: 541715

Subsidiary (Non-US):

ICON Clinical Research India Private Limited (2)
Tel.: (91) 4443902800
Web Site: http://www.icon.com
Sales Range: $75-99.9 Million
Emp.: 500
Research & Development in the Physical Engineering & Life Sciences
N.A.I.C.S.: 541715

ICON PLC

ICON Clinical Research Israel Limited (2)
6 Habaal Shem Tov St N Industrial Area
Lod 7128, 71289, Lod, Israel (100%)
Tel.: (972) 89152111
Web Site: http://www.iconplc.com
Sales Range: $25-49.9 Million
Research & Development in the Physical Engineering & Life Sciences
N.A.I.C.S.: 541715

ICON Clinical Research LLC (2)
24 Polyova Str 4th floor Business Center, 03056, Kiev, Ukraine
Tel.: (380) 445835600
Sales Range: $10-24.9 Million
Emp.: 42
Clinical Research Services
N.A.I.C.S.: 621111

ICON Clinical Research Pte Ltd (2)
30 Loyang Way 02/12, Loyang Industrial Estate, Singapore, 508769, Singapore (100%)
Tel.: (65) 68962538
Sales Range: $25-49.9 Million
Emp.: 50
Research & Development in the Physical Engineering & Life Sciences
N.A.I.C.S.: 541715

ICON Clinical Research Pty Limited (2)
Suite 201 Level 2 2-4 Lyon Park Road, North Ryde, 2113, NSW, Australia (100%)
Tel.: (61) 298593900
Sales Range: $25-49.9 Million
Emp.: 60
Research & Development in the Physical Engineering & Life Sciences
N.A.I.C.S.: 541715

ICON Clinical Research Russia OOO (2)
Meridian Commercial Tower 6th Floor, Ulitza Smolnaya 24-D, 125445, Moscow, Russia (100%)
Tel.: (7) 4955404124
Web Site: http://www.iconclinical.com
Research & Development in the Physical Engineering & Life Sciences
N.A.I.C.S.: 541715

ICON Clinical Research S.A. (2)
Av Fondo de la Legua 936 2nd floor, B1640EDO, Buenos Aires, Argentina
Tel.: (54) 1140062222
Research & Development in the Physical Engineering & Life Sciences
N.A.I.C.S.: 541715
Pabao Hanner *(Gen Mgr)*

ICON Clinical Research S.R.O (2)
Tel.: (420) 272124000
Web Site: http://www.iconplc.com
Sales Range: $25-49.9 Million
Clinical Research Services
N.A.I.C.S.: 541715

ICON Clinical Research SARL (2)
Le Capitole Building 55 avenue des Champs Pierreux, 92000, Nanterre, France
Tel.: (33) 146296500
Sales Range: $25-49.9 Million
Research & Development in the Physical Engineering & Life Sciences
N.A.I.C.S.: 541715

ICON Clinical Research Mexico, S.A. de C.V. (1)
Av Barranca del Muerto 329, Col San Jose Insurgentes, 03900, Mexico, Mexico
Tel.: (52) 5559994660
Clinical Research Services
N.A.I.C.S.: 541715

ICON Clinical Research Peru S.A. (1)
Av Paseo de la Republica 5895 Oficina 606, Lima, Peru
Tel.: (51) 12025600
Clinical Research Services
N.A.I.C.S.: 541715

ICON Clinical Research S.R.L. (1)
Sky Tower Building 246C Calea Floreasca, 014476, Bucharest, Romania
Tel.: (40) 214011400
Clinical Research Services
N.A.I.C.S.: 541715

ICON Clinical Research Services Philippines, Inc. (1)
24F The Salcedo Towers 169 H V Dela Costa St, Salcedo Village, Makati, 1227, Philippines
Tel.: (63) 282305700
Clinical Research Services
N.A.I.C.S.: 541715

ICON Clinical Research Slovakia, s.r.o. (1)
Regus 4D Prievozska street Apollo Business Centre II, 821 09, Bratislava, Slovakia
Tel.: (421) 232343300
Clinical Research Services
N.A.I.C.S.: 541715

ICON Clinical Research Taiwan Limited (1)
2F No 96 Sec 1 Chien Kou North Road, Taipei, 10489, Taiwan
Tel.: (886) 277066300
Clinical Research Services
N.A.I.C.S.: 541715

ICON Clinical Research d.o.o. (1)
38-40 Vladimira Popovica Street, 11070, Belgrade, Serbia
Tel.: (381) 117156921
Clinical Research Services
N.A.I.C.S.: 541715

ICON Contracting Solutions Holdings B.V. (1)
Boeing Avenue 62-68 4th Floor, 1119 PE, Schiphol-Rijk, Netherlands
Tel.: (31) 206558900
Clinical Research Services
N.A.I.C.S.: 541715

ICON Development Solutions Limited (1)
Skelton House Manchester Science Park, Manchester, M15 6SH, United Kingdom
Tel.: (44) 161 2266525
Web Site: http://www.iconplc.com
Clinical Research & Development Services
N.A.I.C.S.: 541715

ICON Early Phase Services, LLC (1)
8307 Gault Ln, San Antonio, TX 78209
Tel.: (210) 225-5437
Clinical Research Services
N.A.I.C.S.: 541715
Cassandra C. Key *(Sr Dir-Medical)*

ICON Japan K.K. (1)
6th/7th Floor Sumitomo ShinToranomon Bldg 4-3-9 Toranomon, Minato-ku, Tokyo, 105-0001, Japan
Tel.: (81) 345304200
Research & Development in the Physical Engineering & Life Sciences
N.A.I.C.S.: 541715

ICON Klinikai Kutato Korlatolt Felelossegu Tarsasag (1)
13 Rottenbiller Street FMC Building 2nd Floor, 1077, Budapest, Hungary
Tel.: (36) 14628602
Clinical Research Services
N.A.I.C.S.: 541715

ICON Laboratory Services, Inc. (1)
123 Smith St, Farmingdale, NY 11735
Tel.: (631) 777-8833
Clinical Research Services
N.A.I.C.S.: 541715

ICON Life Sciences Canada Inc. (1)
Unit 400 3455 North Service Road, Burlington, L7N 3G2, ON, Canada
Tel.: (905) 689-3980
Clinical Research Services
N.A.I.C.S.: 541715

Mapi Life Sciences Singapore Pte. Ltd. (1)
Block 30 Loyang Way 02-12 Loyang Industrial Estate, Singapore, Singapore
Tel.: (65) 68958270
Clinical Research Services
N.A.I.C.S.: 541715

MedPass International SAS (1)
95 bis boulevard Pereire, 75017, Paris, France
Tel.: (33) 142128330
Web Site: http://www.medpass.org
Clinical Research & Development Services

N.A.I.C.S.: 541715
Sarah Sorrel *(Dir-Editorial)*

PRA Development Center KK (1)
H Building-11th and 12th Floors Osaka Center Building and 12th Floor, Osaka Midosuji Building 1-3 Kyutaro-machi 4-Chome Chuo-ku, Osaka, Japan
Tel.: (81) 645602001
Clinical Research Services
N.A.I.C.S.: 541715

PRA Health Sciences, Inc. (1)
4130 ParkLake Ave Ste 400, Raleigh, NC 27612
Tel.: (919) 786-8200
Web Site: http://www.prahs.com
Rev.: $3,183,365,000
Assets: $4,178,501,000
Liabilities: $2,699,316,000
Net Worth: $1,479,185,000
Earnings: $197,043,000
Emp.: 18,100
Fiscal Year-end: 12/31/2020
Health Related Contract Research Services
N.A.I.C.S.: 325412
Samir Shah *(Pres-Strategic Solutions & Regulatory Affairs-Global & Exec VP)*

Division (Domestic):

CRI Lifetree (2)
16000 Horizon Way Ste 100, Mount Laurel, NJ 08054
Tel.: (856) 533-5020
Web Site: http://www.crilifetree.com
Sales Range: $1-9.9 Million
Emp.: 250
Inpatient & Outpatient Clinical Research Services
N.A.I.C.S.: 622210

Subsidiary (Domestic):

Nextrials, Inc. (2)
2010 Crow Canyon Pl Ste 410, San Ramon, CA 94583 (100%)
Tel.: (925) 355-3000
Web Site: https://www.nextrials.com
Emp.: 50
Research Software Solutions
N.A.I.C.S.: 541720

PRA International Inc. (2)
4130 ParkLake Ave Ste 400, Raleigh, NC 27612
Tel.: (919) 786-8200
Web Site: http://www.prainternational.com
Sales Range: $350-399.9 Million
Emp.: 5,300
Clinical Drug Development
N.A.I.C.S.: 541715

Branch (Domestic):

PRA International Inc. (3)
4105 Lewis & Clark Dr, Charlottesville, VA 22911
Tel.: (434) 951-3000
Sales Range: $25-49.9 Million
Emp.: 300
Clinical Drug Development
N.A.I.C.S.: 541715
Joe Murray *(Assoc Dir-Biostatistics)*

Division (Domestic):

ReSearch Pharmaceutical Services, Inc. (3)
520 Virginia Dr, Fort Washington, PA 19034
Tel.: (215) 540-0700
Web Site: http://www.rpsweb.com
Sales Range: $250-299.9 Million
Emp.: 5,000
Clinical Research Services
N.A.I.C.S.: 541715
Harris Koffer *(Pres)*

Subsidiary (Non-US):

RPS Beijing, Inc (4)
Room 2308 2318 23F Tower B Gemdale Plaza No 91 Jianguo Road, Chaoyang, Beijing, 100022, China
Tel.: (86) 10 6561 0216
Clinical Research Services
N.A.I.C.S.: 541715

RPS Chile Ltda. (4)
Avda Vitacura 2670 15th Floor, Las Condes, 7550098, Chile

Tel.: (56) 2 820 4310
Web Site: http://www.prahs.com
Clinical Research Services
N.A.I.C.S.: 541715

RPS Colombia Ltda. (4)
Torre Cusezar Calle 116 7 15 Oficina 1002, Bogota, 110111, Colombia
Tel.: (57) 1 6577777
Web Site: http://www.rps.com
Emp.: 75
Clinical Research Services
N.A.I.C.S.: 541715

RPS Research France, S.A.S. (4)
60 rue Carnot, F 92100, Paris, France
Tel.: (33) 1 46 99 94 50
Clinical Research Services
N.A.I.C.S.: 541715

RPS Research Iberica, S.L.U. (4)
Via Augusta 21 23 plantas 5 y 6, 08006, Barcelona, Spain
Tel.: (34) 93 215 80 08
Emp.: 120
Clinical Research Services
N.A.I.C.S.: 541715

RPS Research S.A. (4)
Juana Manso 205 Piso 7, C1107CBE, Buenos Aires, Argentina
Tel.: (54) 11 4138 4777
Clinical Research Services
N.A.I.C.S.: 541715

RPS Research Servicios, S, de RL de CV (4)
Paseo de la Reforma 222 Torre I Piso 8 B, Colonia Juarez Del Cuauhtemoc, CP 06600, Mexico, Mexico
Tel.: (52) 55 5141 4777
Clinical Research Services
N.A.I.C.S.: 541715

RPS do Brasil Servicos de Pesquisa Ltda. (4)
Tel.: (55) 1135274777
Web Site: http://www.rpsweb.com
Clinical Research Services
N.A.I.C.S.: 541715

Subsidiary (Domestic):

Parallel 6, Inc. (2)
1455 Frazee Rd #900, San Diego, CA 92108
Tel.: (619) 452-1750
Web Site: http://www.parallel6.com
Software Publishers; Mobile Enrollment & Engagement Solutions (for Clinical Research, Health & Public Sector Organizations)
N.A.I.C.S.: 513210

Symphony Health Solutions Corporation (2)
731 Arbor Way Ste 100, Blue Bell, PA 19422
Tel.: (215) 444-8700
Web Site: http://symphonyhealth.prahs.com
Data, Applications, Analytics & Consulting Services for Pharmaceutical Market
N.A.I.C.S.: 519290
Jeff Cottle *(VP-HR)*

PRA International Operations B.V. (1)
Martini Hospital Van Swietenlaan 6, 9728 NZ, Groningen, Netherlands
Tel.: (31) 504022222
Clinical Research Services
N.A.I.C.S.: 541715

PRA Pharmaceutical S A (Proprietary) Limited (1)
Block 29 Second Floor The Highlands Estate The Woodlands, Woodlands Drive Woodmead, Johannesburg, South Africa
Tel.: (27) 112311900
Clinical Research Services
N.A.I.C.S.: 541715

Pharmaceutical Research Associates Israel Ltd. (1)
Hod Towers 4 Haharash Street Building E 13th Floor, PO Box 7335, Hod Hasharon, Israel
Tel.: (972) 97909704
Clinical Research Services
N.A.I.C.S.: 541715

ICON PLC

ICON plc—(Continued)

Pharmaceutical Research Associates Ltda. (1)
Avenida Ibirapuera 2332 - Torre II - 4o Andar, Moema, Sao Paulo, Brazil
Tel.: (55) 1135255710
Clinical Research Services
N.A.I.C.S.: 541715

Pharmaceutical Research Associates Romania S.R.L. (1)
Sky Tower Building 246C Calea Floreasca, 014476, Bucharest, Romania
Tel.: (40) 214011400
Clinical Research Services
N.A.I.C.S.: 541715

Pharmaceutical Research Associates Taiwan, Inc. (1)
5th and 6th Floor Aurora International Building No 2 Sec 5 Xinyi Road, Xinyi District, Taipei, Taiwan
Tel.: (886) 277066327
Clinical Research Services
N.A.I.C.S.: 541715

Pra Turkey Saglik Arastirma Ve Gelistirme Limited Sirketi (1)
Kisikli Caddesi No 28 K 1-2, Altunizade, 34662, Istanbul, Turkiye
Tel.: (90) 2162663434
Clinical Research Services
N.A.I.C.S.: 541715

PriceSpective LLC (1)
460 Norristown Rd Ste 350, Blue Bell, PA 19422
Tel.: (610) 828-6780
Web Site: http://www.pricespective.com
Sales Range: $10-24.9 Million
Emp.: 25
Medical Therapy Imaging Services
N.A.I.C.S.: 621512

RPS Latvia SIA (1)
Regus Business Garden 2nd Floor Maldugunu Iela 4, Marupe, Latvia
Tel.: (371) 67869130
Clinical Research Services
N.A.I.C.S.: 541715

RPS Research (Thailand) Co., Ltd. (1)
1 Empire Tower 24th Floor Unit 2408 South Sathorn Road, Yannawa Sathorn, Bangkok, Thailand
Tel.: (66) 26972600
Clinical Research Services
N.A.I.C.S.: 541715

RPS Spain S.L. (1)
Avda Europa 19 - Edif 1 - 1 Planta, Pozuelo de Alarcon, 28224, Madrid, Spain
Tel.: (34) 917081110
Clinical Research Services
N.A.I.C.S.: 541715

Symphony Clinical Research Sp. z o.o. (1)
Potokowa 26, 80-283, Gdansk, Poland
Tel.: (48) 585008881
Clinical Research Services
N.A.I.C.S.: 541715

ICON POLYMER GROUP, LTD.
Victoria Works Thrumpton Lane, Retford, DN22 6HH, Notts, United Kingdom
Tel.: (44) 1777714300
Web Site: http://www.iconpolymer.com
Sales Range: $50-74.9 Million
Emp.: 260
Mfr of Fabricated Rubber Products
N.A.I.C.S.: 314910
Tim Pryce (Mng Dir)

ICONIC MINERALS LTD.
303 - 595 Howe Street, Vancouver, V6C 2T5, BC, Canada
Tel.: (604) 336-8614 BC
Web Site: https://www.iconicminerals.com
Year Founded: 1979
YQG—(DEU)
Rev.: $160,500
Assets: $3,180,624
Liabilities: $1,037,460
Net Worth: $2,143,164
Earnings: $13,113,600
Fiscal Year-end: 08/31/23
Gold & Silver Mining & Exploration Services
N.A.I.C.S.: 212220
Richard R. Kern (Pres & CEO)

ICONIC SPORTS ACQUISITION CORP.
190 Elgin Avenue, Georgetown, KY1-9008, Cayman Islands
Tel.: (345) 270393702 Ky
Web Site: https://www.iconicsportsacq.com
Year Founded: 2021
ICNC—(NYSE)
Rev.: $20,438,289
Assets: $359,472,960
Liabilities: $375,463,069
Net Worth: ($15,990,109)
Earnings: $18,512,854
Emp.: 4
Fiscal Year-end: 12/31/22
Investment Services
N.A.I.C.S.: 523999
Fausto Zanetton (CEO, CFO & Principal Acctg Officer)

ICONIC WORLDWIDE BHD
No 1-2 Jalan Icon City Icon City, 14000, Bukit Mertajam, Penang, Malaysia
Tel.: (60) 43903699
Web Site: https://www.iconicworldwide.com.my
Year Founded: 1969
ICONIC—(KLS)
Rev.: $18,378,413
Assets: $63,957,672
Liabilities: $26,668,360
Net Worth: $37,289,312
Earnings: ($5,217,566)
Fiscal Year-end: 03/31/23
Travel Services
N.A.I.C.S.: 561520
Zainurin Karman (Chm)

ICONOVO AB
Ideongatan 3A-B, Medicon Village, 223 70, Lund, Sweden
Tel.: (46) 462756777
Web Site: https://www.iconovo.se
Year Founded: 2013
ICO—(OMX)
Rev.: $1,603,492
Assets: $11,358,379
Liabilities: $2,995,308
Net Worth: $8,363,071
Earnings: ($4,510,757)
Emp.: 30
Fiscal Year-end: 12/31/22
Medical Device Mfr
N.A.I.C.S.: 339112
Mats Johansson (Chm)

ICONTRONIC SDN. BHD.
No 12 Lorong Usahajaya 1 Kawasan Perindustrian Usahajaya, Permatang Tinggi, 14000, Bukit Mertajam, Penang, Malaysia
Tel.: (60) 45885336
Year Founded: 2003
Industrial Electronic Automation Control Systems Mfr
N.A.I.C.S.: 334513
Pheow Leng Goh (Mgr)

ICORR PROPERTIES INTERNATIONAL
700 Richmond Street Suite 100, London, N6A 5C7, ON, Canada
Tel.: (519) 432-1888
Web Site: http://www.icorr.com
Sales Range: $1-9.9 Million
Emp.: 12
Commercial Real Estate Property Management, Leasing, Facilities Management & Financial Services
N.A.I.C.S.: 531312
Norton P. Wolf (Chm)

ICOTTON SIA
Ziemelu iela 19, Liepaja, Latvia
Tel.: (371) 63488522
Web Site: http://www.icotton.eu
Year Founded: 2012
Emp.: 200
Hygienic & Cosmetic Good Mfr
N.A.I.C.S.: 325620
Sergejs Binkovskis (Exec Dir)

Subsidiaries:

Harper Hygienics S.A. (1)
Jerozolimskie Avenue 96 Equator 2 13 P, 00-807, Warsaw, Poland (66%)
Tel.: (48) 257598400
Web Site: https://www.harperhygienics.com
Rev.: $119,333,943
Assets: $66,886,763
Liabilities: $51,085,493
Net Worth: $15,801,270
Earnings: $1,217,302
Emp.: 500
Fiscal Year-end: 12/31/2023
Cosmetics & Hygiene Products Mfr
N.A.I.C.S.: 325620
Robert Neymann (Chm-Mgmt Bd)

ICP LTD.
6 Temasek Boulevard 23-01 Suntec Tower Four, Singapore, 038986, Singapore
Tel.: (65) 62214665 SG
5I4—(CAT)
Rev.: $7,398,296
Assets: $41,608,744
Liabilities: $16,844,016
Net Worth: $24,764,728
Earnings: $796,591
Emp.: 195
Fiscal Year-end: 06/30/23
Investment Management Service
N.A.I.C.S.: 523999
Aw Ming-Yao Marcus (Exec Dir)

ICPEI HOLDINGS INC.
2680 Matheson Blvd East Suite 300, Mississauga, L4W 0A5, ON, Canada
Tel.: (905) 214-7880
Web Site: http://www.echeloninsurance.ca
EFH—(TSX)
Rev.: $33,785,109
Assets: $64,046,046
Liabilities: $45,401,184
Net Worth: $18,644,862
Earnings: ($758,812)
Emp.: 255
Fiscal Year-end: 12/31/20
Insurance Services
N.A.I.C.S.: 524126
Serge Lavoie (Pres & CEO)

Subsidiaries:

EGI Insurance Managers Inc. (1)
2680 Matheson Blvd E Ste 300, Mississauga, L4W 0A5, ON, Canada
Tel.: (905) 214-7880
Web Site: http://www.echelon-insurance.ca
Sales Range: $50-74.9 Million
Emp.: 18
Insurance Agencies
N.A.I.C.S.: 524210
Zahir Moosa (Bus Mgr-Comm)

ICPROA SA
Str 13 Decembrie Nr 96, Brasov, Romania
Tel.: (40) 268 545675
Sales Range: Less than $1 Million

Emp.: 4
Technical Consulting Services
N.A.I.C.S.: 541690

ICPV SA
Calea Aurel Vlaicu 29-31, Arad, Romania
Tel.: (40) 257202361
Sales Range: $1-9.9 Million
Emp.: 38
Engineering & Related Consulting Services
N.A.I.C.S.: 541690

ICRAFT CO., LTD.
8 Teheran-ro 44-gil, Gangnam-gu, Seoul, Korea (South)
Tel.: (82) 25410474
Web Site: https://www.icraft21.com
Year Founded: 2000
052460—(KRS)
Rev.: $86,593,020
Assets: $68,567,258
Liabilities: $43,024,630
Net Worth: $25,542,629
Earnings: $247,860
Emp.: 179
Fiscal Year-end: 12/31/22
Information Technology Services
N.A.I.C.S.: 541512
Woo-Jin Park (Co-CEO)

ICSA (INDIA) LTD.
Plot No 1091 Khanamet Madhapur, Cyberabad, Hyderabad, 500 081, Andhra Pradesh, India
Tel.: (91) 4023114923
Web Site: https://www.icsa-india.com
ICSA—(NSE)
Sales Range: $1-9.9 Million
Emp.: 1,101
Software Development Services
N.A.I.C.S.: 541511
G. Bala Reddy (Chm & Mng Dir)

ICSGLOBAL LIMITED
C/-TCAP Suite 303 20 Bond Street, Sydney, 2000, NSW, Australia
Tel.: (61) 2 8073 7888
Web Site: http://icsglobal.com.au
Rev.: $4,002,096
Assets: $5,616,854
Liabilities: $1,316,647
Net Worth: $4,300,207
Earnings: $709,280
Emp.: 19
Fiscal Year-end: 06/30/19
Medical Banking, E Health Services & Medical Billing Services
N.A.I.C.S.: 541219
Kevin Barry (Chm)

Subsidiaries:

ICSGlobal Limited - Cybrand (1)
201 Level 26 Kent St, Sydney, 2000, NSW, Australia
Tel.: (61) 2 9247 2111
Sales Range: $25-49.9 Million
Emp.: 10
Management Consulting Services
N.A.I.C.S.: 541611

Thelma Pty Ltd. (1)
Suite 302 Level 3 53 Berry St, North Sydney, 2060, NSW, Australia
Tel.: (61) 291998000
Web Site: http://www.thelma.com.au
Sales Range: $50-74.9 Million
Emp.: 10
Medical Banking Services
N.A.I.C.S.: 926150

ICSH S.A
DN 68B FN, 331130, Hunedoara, 331130, Romania
Tel.: (40) 354881335
Web Site: https://www.icsh.ro
Sales Range: $1-9.9 Million
Emp.: 208

AND PRIVATE COMPANIES

Commercial & Residential Building Construction Services
N.A.I.C.S.: 236220
Victor Leu *(Gen Mgr)*

ICTA AB
Tel.: (46) 102122000
Web Site: https://intellecta.se
Advertising Communications Services
N.A.I.C.S.: 541890
Agnes Hebert *(Project Mgr-Strategic)*

Subsidiaries:

FFW (1)
Enigheden Rentemestervej 2b, 2400, Copenhagen, Denmark
Tel.: (45) 39 16 27 00
Web Site: http://www.ffwagency.com
Emp.: 400
Digital Solutions Agency
N.A.I.C.S.: 541890
Michael Koefoed Steensborg Drejer *(CEO-Global)*

Subsidiary (US):

FFW (2)
116 Village Blvd Suite 303, Princeton, NJ 08540 (80%)
Tel.: (732) 792-6566
Web Site: http://www.ffwagency.com
Sales Range: $1-9.9 Million
Emp.: 100
Digital Solutions Agency
N.A.I.C.S.: 541890
Michael Koefoed Steensborg Drejer *(CEO-Global)*

ICTS INTERNATIONAL, N.V.
Walaardt Sacrestraat 425-5, 1117 BM, Schiphol, Netherlands
Tel.: (31) 203471077 NI
Web Site: https://www.ictsintl.com
Year Founded: 1982
ICTSF—(OTCQB)
Rev.: $324,934,000
Assets: $195,880,000
Liabilities: $111,234,000
Net Worth: $84,646,000
Earnings: $34,807,000
Emp.: 6,290
Fiscal Year-end: 12/31/21
Security Services Including Risk Analysis, Passport & Visa Inspection & Cargo Screening
N.A.I.C.S.: 541990
Menachem J. Atzmon *(Chm-Supervisory Bd)*

Subsidiaries:

AU10TIX B.V. (1)
Biesbosch 225, 1181 JC, Amstelveen, Netherlands (100%)
Tel.: (31) 203471077
Web Site: http://www.au10tix.com
Sales Range: $10-24.9 Million
Emp.: 40
Security & Identity Protection Technology Products & Services
N.A.I.C.S.: 561621

Huntleigh Corporation (1)
10701 Lambert International Blvd, Saint Louis, MO 63145
Tel.: (314) 562-7423
Web Site: http://www.huntleighusa.com
Sales Range: $1-4.9 Billion
Security Screening & Security Guard Services
N.A.I.C.S.: 561621

I-SEC International Security B.V. (1)
Walaardt Sacrestraat 425-4, 1117 BM, Schiphol, Netherlands (100%)
Tel.: (31) 207163410
Web Site: https://www.i-sec.com
Sales Range: $25-49.9 Million
Airport Security Management Services
N.A.I.C.S.: 561612
Mart Vergouwen *(CEO & Mng Dir)*

I-SEC International Security B.V. (1)
Walaardt Sacrestraat 425-4, Schiphol, 1117 BM, Netherlands

Tel.: (31) 207163410
Web Site: http://www.i-sec.com
Sales Range: $25-49.9 Million
Aviation Security Services
N.A.I.C.S.: 561612
Nimrod Sternefeld *(Chief Comml Officer)*

I-SEC Italia Services s.r.l. (1)
Malpensa Airport Terminal 1 Floor 1, 21010, Ferno, VA, Italy
Tel.: (39) 0274867321
Web Site: https://it.i-sec.com
Emp.: 80
Aviation Security Services
N.A.I.C.S.: 488190
Barbara Sarfatti *(Country Mgr)*

ICTS Technologies USA, Inc. (1)
1 Rockefeller Plz Ste 2412, New York, NY 10020
Tel.: (212) 218-1850
Security Management Services
N.A.I.C.S.: 561612

ICURE PHARMACEUTICAL, INC.
SamSung Icure Tower Bongeunsa-ro 104-gil, Gangnam-gu, Seoul, 10, Korea (South)
Tel.: (82) 269596909
Web Site: https://www.icure.co.kr
Year Founded: 2000
175250—(KRS)
Rev.: $45,534,574
Assets: $171,900,461
Liabilities: $101,444,932
Net Worth: $70,455,529
Earnings: ($32,634,737)
Emp.: 201
Fiscal Year-end: 12/31/22
Pharmaceutical Product Mfr & Distr
N.A.I.C.S.: 325414
Young Seok Lee *(Dir)*

ICZOOM GROUP INC.
Room 3801 Building A Sunhope eM-ETRO No 7018 Cai Tian Road, Futian District, Shenzhen, 518000, China
Tel.: (86) 75588603072 Ky
Web Site: https://ir.iczoomex.com
Year Founded: 2015
IZM—(NASDAQ)
Rev.: $177,933,890
Assets: $39,975,042
Liabilities: $24,594,328
Net Worth: $15,380,714
Earnings: ($2,272,297)
Emp.: 96
Fiscal Year-end: 06/30/24
Holding Company
N.A.I.C.S.: 551112
Lei Xia *(Co-Founder, Chm, CEO & CFO)*

ID BUSINESS SOLUTIONS LTD.
2 Occam Court Surrey Research Park, Guildford, GU2 7QB, United Kingdom
Tel.: (44) 1483595000
Web Site: http://www.idbs.com
Year Founded: 1989
Rev.: $38,360,934
Emp.: 154
Information Technology Services
N.A.I.C.S.: 518210
Neil Kipling *(Chm & CEO)*

ID HOLDINGS CORPORATION
Banchokaikan 12-1 Goban-cho, Chiyoda-ku, Tokyo, 102-0076, Japan
Tel.: (81) 332643571
Year Founded: 1969
4709—(TKS)
Rev.: $216,014,800
Assets: $132,603,210
Liabilities: $53,217,110
Net Worth: $79,386,100

Earnings: $11,745,970
Fiscal Year-end: 03/31/24
Computer Facilities Management Services
N.A.I.C.S.: 541513
Masaki Funakoshi *(Chm, Pres & CEO-Grp)*

Subsidiaries:

INFORMATION DEVELOPMENT AMERICA INC. (1)
245 First St Ste 1800, Cambridge, MA 02142
Tel.: (617) 264-0981
Web Site: http://www.idnet-us.com
Recruitment & Training Services
N.A.I.C.S.: 541612
Masaki Funakoshi *(Pres)*

INFORMATION DEVELOPMENT SINGAPORE PTE. LTD. (1)
138 Robinson Road 24-03 Oxley Tower, Singapore, 068906, Singapore
Tel.: (65) 63362203
Web Site: https://www.idnet-sg.com
Software Development Services
N.A.I.C.S.: 541511
Fan Na *(Mng Dir)*

INFORMATION DEVELOPMENT Wuhan Co., Ltd. (1)
2-11-6 8 Xiongzhuang Road, D ShuGuangXingCheng East Lake High-tech Development Zone, Wuhan, 430073, Hubei, China
Tel.: (86) 2782666620
Web Site: http://www.idwuhan.com
Software Development Services
N.A.I.C.S.: 541511
Masaki Funakoshi *(Pres)*

K.K. PURAIDO (1)
Banchokaikan 12-1 Goban-cho, Chiyoda-ku, Tokyo, 102-0076, Japan
Tel.: (81) 3 3239 5431
Web Site: http://www.naska.co.jp
Emp.: 26
Information System Consulting Services
N.A.I.C.S.: 541512
Akira Tahara *(Pres)*

ID INFO BUSINESS SERVICES LTD.
104 Mahinder Chambers Opp Dukes Factory W T Patil Marg, Chembur, Mumbai, 400057, Maharashtra, India
Tel.: (91) 2225216700
Web Site: http://www.idinfo.in
Year Founded: 1940
Rev.: $9,291
Assets: $93,674
Liabilities: $449,757
Net Worth: ($356,083)
Earnings: ($7,786)
Fiscal Year-end: 03/31/19
Paperboard Mfr
N.A.I.C.S.: 322120
K. K. Khan *(Chief Compliance Officer)*

ID KOMMUNIKATION AB
Beijerskajen 12, SE 211 19, Malmo, Sweden
Tel.: (46) 406906300
Web Site: http://www.idkommunikation.com
Year Founded: 1968
Sales Range: $10-24.9 Million
Emp.: 33
Consumer Marketing, Industrial
N.A.I.C.S.: 541810
Ulf Petterson *(Dir-Art/Designer)*

ID LOGISTICS SAS
410 route du Moulin de Losques, CS 70132, 84304, Cavaillon, France
Tel.: (33) 432529600
Web Site: http://www.id-logistics.com
IDL—(EUR)
Sales Range: Less than $1 Million
Emp.: 18,500

ID LOGISTICS SAS

Logistic Services
N.A.I.C.S.: 541614
Eric Hemar *(Chm & CEO)*

Subsidiaries:

CEPL Holding SAS (1)
Z I Les Longs Reages 28 rue Moulin Trubert, 28700, Beville-le-Comte, France
Tel.: (33) 2 37 91 76 00
Web Site: http://www.cepl.fr
Logistics Consulting Servies
N.A.I.C.S.: 541614

Subsidiary (Non-US):

CEPL Michelstadt GmbH (2)
Reuboldstrasse 13, 63 937, Weilbach, Germany
Tel.: (49) 9373 2068 113
Web Site: http://www.cepl.com
Logistics Consulting Servies
N.A.I.C.S.: 541614

Groupe Logistics Idl S.A.U. (1)
C / Federico Mompou 5 Edif 1 6th Floor, 28050, Madrid, Spain
Tel.: (34) 918783800
Logistics & Supply Chain Services
N.A.I.C.S.: 541614

ID Do Brasil Logistica Ltda (1)
Alameda Mamore 503 - 4 Andar, Alphaville, Barueri, 06454-040, Brazil
Tel.: (55) 1138092600
Logistics & Supply Chain Services
N.A.I.C.S.: 541614

ID Logistics Benelux B.V. (1)
Dongenseweg 200, 5047 SH, Tilburg, Netherlands
Tel.: (31) 135157515
Logistics & Supply Chain Services
N.A.I.C.S.: 541614

ID Logistics Espana (1)
Doctor Sevro Ochoa 51 2F, 28108, Alcobendas, Madrid, Spain
Tel.: (34) 915980511
Web Site: http://www.id-logistics.com
Emp.: 1,300
Logistics Consulting Servies
N.A.I.C.S.: 541614
Javier Echenique *(CEO)*

ID Logistics Polska S.A. (1)
Al Rozdzienskiego 91, 40-203, Katowice, Poland
Tel.: (48) 324115312
Logistics & Supply Chain Services
N.A.I.C.S.: 541614

ID Logistics Rus OOO (1)
8 Marta Street Building 1 Construction 12 Business Center Trio, 127083, Moscow, Russia
Tel.: (7) 4952283839
Web Site: http://www.id-logistics.com
Logistics & Supply Chain Services
N.A.I.C.S.: 541614

ID Logistics Taiwan Co., Ltd. (1)
No 36 Section 2 Changxing Road, Luzhu District, Taoyuan, 338, Taiwan
Tel.: (886) 33127166
Logistics & Supply Chain Services
N.A.I.C.S.: 541614

ID Logistics US, Inc. (1)
2007 Gandy Blvd N 1210, Saint Petersburg, FL 33702
Tel.: (813) 514-2580
Logistics & Supply Chain Services
N.A.I.C.S.: 541614

ID Supply Chain S.A. (1)
Cuyo 3532 Martinez, B1640GJF, Buenos Aires, Argentina
Tel.: (54) 1132202973
Logistics & Supply Chain Services
N.A.I.C.S.: 541614

Jagged Peak, Inc. (1)
7650 Courtney Campbell Causeway Ste 1200, Tampa, FL 33607
Tel.: (813) 637-6900
Web Site: http://www.jaggedpeak.com
E-Business Software
N.A.I.C.S.: 513210
Paul Demirdjian *(Pres & CEO)*

ID LOGISTICS SAS

ID Logistics SAS—(Continued)

PT Inti Dinamika ID Logitama
Indonesia (1)
Palma One Building Jl HR Rasuna Said
X-2/4, Setiabudi, South Jakarta, 12950, Jakarta, Indonesia
Tel.: (62) 212521002
Logistics & Supply Chain Services
N.A.I.C.S.: 541614

IDB DEVELOPMENT CORPORATION LTD.
3 Azrieli Center 44th Floor, Tel Aviv, 67023, Israel
Tel.: (972) 36075666
Web Site: http://www.idb.co.il
Year Founded: 1981
Sales Range: $1-9.9 Million
Emp.: 37
Investment Holding Company
N.A.I.C.S.: 551112
Sholem Lapidot *(CEO)*

Subsidiaries:

Astoria Energy LLC (1)
1710 Steinway St, Astoria, NY 11105
Tel.: (718) 274-7700
Web Site: http://www.astoriaenergy.com
Fossil Fuel Power Generation
N.A.I.C.S.: 221112
Chuck McCall *(CEO)*

Clal Insurance Enterprises Holdings
Ltd. (1)
Menachem Begin 48 Way, Tel Aviv, 66180, Israel **(56%)**
Tel.: (972) 36387575
Web Site: http://www.clalbit.co.il
Rev.: $5,819,641,017
Assets: $44,362,290,548
Liabilities: $42,016,430,779
Net Worth: $2,345,859,769
Earnings: $59,649,694
Emp.: 5,700
Fiscal Year-end: 12/31/2023
Holding Company
N.A.I.C.S.: 551112
Elite Caspi *(Exec VP & Head-Non-Life Insurance Div)*

Subsidiary (Domestic):

Clal Credit & Financing Ltd. (2)
48 Menachem Begin Road, Tel Aviv, 66180, Israel **(100%)**
Tel.: (972) 3942 0440
Commercial & Consumer Credit Activities
N.A.I.C.S.: 522299

Subsidiary (Domestic):

Clal Factoring Ltd. (3)
37 Menachem Begin Road, Tel Aviv, 65220, Israel **(100%)**
Tel.: (972) 37613600
Web Site: http://cde.clalbit.co.il
Sales Range: $25-49.9 Million
Emp.: 25
Commercial Factoring Services
N.A.I.C.S.: 522299

Clal Financing Consumer Credit
Ltd. (3)
48 Menachem Begin Road, Tel Aviv, 66180, Israel **(100%)**
Tel.: (972) 39420440
Web Site: http://cde.clalbit.co.il
Retail Non-Banking Lending & Credit Management Services
N.A.I.C.S.: 522291

Unit (Domestic):

Clal Mortgages (3)
48 Menachem Begin Road, Tel Aviv, 66180, Israel
Tel.: (972) 36251000
Non-Banking Mortgage Credit Services
N.A.I.C.S.: 522292
Yuval Harari *(CEO)*

Subsidiary (Domestic):

Clal Finance Ltd. (2)
Robinstein House 37 Menahem Begin
Road, Tel Aviv, 65220, Israel **(81.6%)**

Tel.: (972) 35653501
Web Site: http://www.clalfinance.com
Sales Range: $25-49.9 Million
Emp.: 375
Investment Banking, Portfolio Management & Other Investment Transaction Services
N.A.I.C.S.: 523150

Division (Domestic):

Clal Insurance Company Ltd. (2)
48 Menachem Begin Road, Tel Aviv, 66180, Israel
Tel.: (972) 39420440
Web Site: http://www.clalbit.co.il
Non-Life Insurance & Pension Products & Services
N.A.I.C.S.: 524126

Subsidiary (Domestic):

Canaf-Clal Finance Management
Ltd. (3)
Menhame Begin 48 st, Tel Aviv,
Israel **(100%)**
Tel.: (972) 39420440
Insurance Investment Services
N.A.I.C.S.: 523999

Clal Credit Insurance Ltd. (3)
Raoul Wallenberg 36, Tel Aviv, 6136902, Israel **(80%)**
Tel.: (972) 36276333
Web Site: http://www.cde.clalbit.co.il
Credit Insurance Products & Services
N.A.I.C.S.: 524126
Shlomi Sarid *(CEO)*

Clal Health Insurance Company
Ltd. (3)
Raul Valnberg 36, Tel Aviv, 6136902, Israel **(100%)**
Tel.: (972) 3 638 8400
Health Insurance Products & Services
N.A.I.C.S.: 524114

Discount Investment Corp. Ltd. (1)
114 Igal Alon Street 27th Floor, Tel Aviv, 6702301, Israel **(68%)**
Tel.: (972) 36075666
Web Site: https://www.dic.co.il
Rev.: $328,222,125
Assets: $8,134,548,844
Liabilities: $6,122,945,062
Net Worth: $2,011,603,781
Earnings: ($257,494,125)
Emp.: 5,000
Fiscal Year-end: 12/31/2023
Offices of Other Holding Companies
N.A.I.C.S.: 551112
Aaron Kaufman *(Gen Counsel & VP)*

Affiliate (Domestic):

Cellcom Israel Ltd. (2)
10 Hagavish Street, Netanya, 4250708, Israel **(45.17%)**
Tel.: (972) 529990052
Web Site: http://www.cellcom.co.il
Rev.: $1,215,079,440
Assets: $1,828,973,600
Liabilities: $1,203,751,960
Net Worth: $625,221,640
Earnings: $37,021,520
Emp.: 2,954
Fiscal Year-end: 12/31/2023
Telephone Communication Services
N.A.I.C.S.: 517121
Amos Maor *(VP-Sls & Svcs)*

Subsidiary (Domestic):

Golan Telecom Ltd. (3)
PO Box 2058, 61020, Tel Aviv,
Israel **(90%)**
Tel.: (972) 5 8555 5858
Web Site: http://www.golantelecom.co.il
Mobile Telecommunications Carrier
N.A.I.C.S.: 517112
Shai Amsalem *(CFO)*

Subsidiary (Domestic):

Iscar Blades Ltd. (2)
Industrial Zone, PO Box 330, Nahariyya, 22102, Israel **(100%)**
Tel.: (972) 49878888
Sales Range: $150-199.9 Million
Emp.: 700
Mfr of Turbine Vanes & Blade for Jet Engines

N.A.I.C.S.: 336412

Koor Industries Ltd. (2)
Azrieli Center Triangle Tower 43rd Floor, Tel Aviv, 67023, Israel
Tel.: (972) 36075111
Sales Range: $150-199.9 Million
Emp.: 11
Investment Holding Company
N.A.I.C.S.: 551112
Raanan Cohen *(CEO)*

Maxima Air Separation Center
Ltd. (2)
10 Haogen, 7 Abba Hillel Road, Ashdod, 77141-01, Israel
Tel.: (972) 3 7534 222
Web Site: http://www.maxima.co.il
Sales Range: $10-24.9 Million
Emp.: 100
Atmospheric & Semiconductor Process Gases, Services & Systems
N.A.I.C.S.: 221210
Ishai Hammer *(Mng Dir)*

Property and Building Corp. Ltd. (2)
114 Yigal Alon St, Tel Aviv, 6744320, Israel **(68%)**
Tel.: (972) 36075666
Web Site: https://www.pbc.co.il
Rev.: $304,185,656
Assets: $6,051,940,781
Liabilities: $4,385,688,562
Net Worth: $1,666,252,219
Earnings: ($109,959,937)
Emp.: 400
Fiscal Year-end: 12/31/2023
Other Activities Related to Real Estate
N.A.I.C.S.: 531390
Eli Elefant *(CEO-Real Estate-USA)*

Subsidiary (Domestic):

Gav-Yam Lands Corp. Ltd (3)
Matam Tower 1 9 Andrei Sakharov Street, PO Box 15041, Haifa, 31905, Israel
Tel.: (972) 46644200
Web Site: https://www.gav-yam.co.il
Rev.: $193,819,207
Assets: $3,981,809,013
Liabilities: $2,588,335,774
Net Worth: $1,393,473,239
Earnings: $252,132,748
Emp.: 70
Fiscal Year-end: 12/31/2022
Industrial, Commercial & Residential Real Estate Management & Construction Services
N.A.I.C.S.: 531312
Mark Zack *(CFO)*

Property & Buildings Commercial
Centers, Ltd. (3)
Electra International Tower St No 98 Yigal Alon, Tel Aviv, 64239, Israel
Tel.: (972) 35672777
Web Site: http://www.pbc.co.il
Sales Range: $25-49.9 Million
Emp.: 20
Commercial Properties
N.A.I.C.S.: 531312
Segi Eitam *(Gen Mgr)*

IDB Tourism (2009) Ltd. (1)
Ben Yehuda St No 23 Bet Israel Bldg, PO Box 26444, Tel Aviv, 63806, Israel **(100%)**
Tel.: (972) 35115525
Web Site: http://www.idb.co.il
Travel & Tourism Holding Company
N.A.I.C.S.: 551112

Israel Credit Cards Ltd. (2)
13 Tefutzot Israel St, 53583, Givatayim, Israel
Tel.: (972) 35723489
Web Site: http://www.cal-intl.com
N.A.I.C.S.: 522299

Subsidiary (Domestic):

Diners Club Israel Ltd. (2)
13 Tefutzot Israel St, Givatayim, 53583, Israel **(100%)**
Tel.: (972) 35726767
Credit Card Services
N.A.I.C.S.: 522299

Israel Discount Bank Ltd. (1)
1 Discount Street, Rishon LeZion, 7574602, Israel
Tel.: (972) 39439111

INTERNATIONAL PUBLIC

Web Site: https://www.discountbank.co.il
Rev.: $7,008,839,000
Assets: $107,294,615,259
Liabilities: $99,367,170,978
Net Worth: $7,927,444,282
Earnings: $1,136,597,798
Emp.: 8,404
Fiscal Year-end: 12/31/2023
Commercial Banking Services
N.A.I.C.S.: 522110
Asaf Pasternak *(Exec VP & Head-Fin Markets Div)*

Subsidiary (US):

Israel Discount Bank of New
York (2)
511 5th Ave, New York, NY
10017-4903 **(100%)**
Tel.: (212) 551-8500
Web Site: http://www.idbny.com
Rev.: $150,321,104
Emp.: 500
International Banking
N.A.I.C.S.: 522110
Lissa Baum *(Chief Lending Officer & Exec VP)*

Subsidiary (Domestic):

Mercantile Discount Bank Ltd (2)
103 Allenby Street, PO Box 1292, Tel Aviv, 61012, Israel
Tel.: (972) 35647429
Web Site: http://www.discountbank.co.il
Commericial Banking
N.A.I.C.S.: 522110
Zion Becker *(Head-Fin Div)*

IDBI HOMEFINANCE LTD.
4th Floor Shreenath Plaza F C Road, Shivajinagar, Pune, 411 004, India
Tel.: (91) 2025533121
Financial Support Services
N.A.I.C.S.: 523940
Asit Jivani *(CFO)*

IDEA CONSULTANTS, INC.
3-15-1 Komazawa, Setagaya-ku, Tokyo, 154-8585, Japan
Tel.: (81) 345447600
Web Site: https://www.ideacon.co.jp
Year Founded: 1953
9768—(TKS)
Rev.: $160,928,820
Assets: $244,633,360
Liabilities: $56,478,940
Net Worth: $188,154,420
Earnings: $14,102,010
Emp.: 1,013
Fiscal Year-end: 12/31/23
Environmental Consulting Services
N.A.I.C.S.: 541620
Hideo Tabata *(Chm)*

IDEA SPA
Via Verdi 3, Ossona, Italy
Tel.: (39) 0290380189
Cane Sugar Refining
N.A.I.C.S.:

IDEAFORGE TECHNOLOGY LIMITED
EL-146 TTC Industrial Area Electronic Zone MIDC Mahape, Navi Mumbai, 400710, Maharashtra, India
Tel.: (91) 8447612778
Web Site:
https://www.ideaforgetech.com
Year Founded: 2007
IDEAFORGE—(NSE)
Rev.: $23,803,922
Assets: $59,137,116
Liabilities: $19,780,931
Net Worth: $39,356,185
Earnings: $3,876,946
Fiscal Year-end: 03/31/23
Aircraft Product Mfr
N.A.I.C.S.: 336411
Ashish Bhat *(VP)*

IDEAL CAPITAL BERHAD

Tel.: (60) 46416888
Web Site:
   https://www.idealcapital.com.my
Year Founded: 2017
9687—(KLS)
Rev.: $88,740,965
Assets: $247,959,571
Liabilities: $100,271,549
Net Worth: $147,688,021
Earnings: $7,075,810
Fiscal Year-end: 12/31/22
Heavy Machinery Equipment Distr
N.A.I.C.S.: 423810
Ooi Kee Liang (Chm)

Subsidiaries:

I Homes Properties Sdn. Bhd. (1)
5th Floor 1st Avenue Penang 182 Jalan Magazine, 10300, Penang, Malaysia
Tel.: (60) 42611121
Web Site: https://www.1st-avenuepenang.com.my
Mall Operator
N.A.I.C.S.: 531312

Viral Shield Life Science Sdn. Bhd. (1)
Suite E-12-16 Block E Plaza Mont Kiara, 2 Jalan Kiara Mont Kiara, 50480, Kuala Lumpur, Malaysia
Tel.: (60) 194773818
Web Site: https://viralshield.asia
Sanitization Product Mfr
N.A.I.C.S.: 325612

IDEAL GROUP S.A.
25 Kreontos, 10442, Athens, Greece
Tel.: (30) 2105193500
Web Site: http://idealgroup.gr
INTEK—(ATH)
Rev.: $283,337,013
Assets: $884,255,437
Liabilities: $720,583,950
Net Worth: $163,671,487
Earnings: $18,645,546
Emp.: 1,725
Fiscal Year-end: 12/31/23
Real Estate Development Services
N.A.I.C.S.: 531390
Savvas Asimiadis (CFO)

Subsidiaries:

Adacom S.A. (1)
Kreontos St 25, 104 42, Athens, Greece
Tel.: (30) 2105193740
Financial Institution Operator
N.A.I.C.S.: 522320
Constantina Theodorou (Sls Mgr)

BYTE COMPUTER SA (1)
98 Kallirrois and Trivoli str, 117 41, Athens, Greece
Tel.: (30) 2109002000
Web Site: https://www.byte.gr
Rev.: $52,156,427
Assets: $44,042,870
Liabilities: $21,844,872
Net Worth: $22,197,998
Earnings: $3,927,147
Emp.: 198
Fiscal Year-end: 12/31/2022
Information Technology Consulting Services
N.A.I.C.S.: 541512
Spyridogeorgis Vyzantios (CEO & Exec Dir)

Subsidiary (Non-US):

BYTE Bulgaria Ltd. (2)
Quarter Mladost 3 51 Aleksandar Malinov blv, Entry 3 Floor 6 App 7, Sofia, 1712, Bulgaria
Tel.: (359) 2 872 9313
Web Site: http://www.bytebulgaria.com
Emp.: 3
Computer Consulting Services
N.A.I.C.S.: 541519
Kostas Fotinoulos (Gen Mgr)

BYTE IT Srl (2)
Calea Dorobanti nr 42 sector 1, Bucharest, Romania
Tel.: (40) 21 2023604
Web Site: http://www.byteromania.com
Computer Consulting Services

N.A.I.C.S.: 541519

IDEAL JACOBS (XIAMEN) CORPORATION
No 506 Tongsheng Road Tongan Industrial Zone, Xiamen, 361100, China
Tel.: (86) 5925064000
Web Site:
   http://www.idealjacobs.com.cn
Year Founded: 2005
Industrial Label & Nameplate Mfr
N.A.I.C.S.: 332999

IDEAL ROOFING COMPANY LTD.
1418 Michael Street, Ottawa, K1B 3R2, ON, Canada
Tel.: (613) 746-3206
Web Site:
   http://www.idealroofing.com
Year Founded: 1929
Rev.: $79,215,653
Emp.: 225
Metal Roofing Products Mfr
N.A.I.C.S.: 332322
Rene Laplante (Pres & CEO)

IDEAL SPINNING MILLS LTD
1088 Jail Road, Faisalabad, Pakistan
Tel.: (92) 412632301
Web Site: https://www.idealsm.com
IDSM—(PSX)
Rev.: $24,678,309
Assets: $13,234,660
Liabilities: $10,342,306
Net Worth: $2,892,354
Earnings: ($1,993,269)
Emp.: 1,232
Fiscal Year-end: 06/30/23
Spinning Mill Operator
N.A.I.C.S.: 314999
Amjad Saeed (CEO)

Subsidiaries:

Ideal Rice Industries (Pvt) Ltd. (1)
1088/2 Jail Road, Faisalabad, 38000, Pakistan
Tel.: (92) 414689251
Web Site: http://www.idealrice.com
Flour Product Mfr
N.A.I.C.S.: 311211

IDEAL UNITED BINTANG BERHAD
71-5 Ideal The One Jalan Mahsuri Bayan Lepas, Penang, 11950, Malaysia
Tel.: (60) 4641 6888   MY
Web Site: http://www.idealubb.cc
Rev.: $163,080,320
Assets: $155,718,881
Liabilities: $69,185,932
Net Worth: $86,532,949
Earnings: $26,434,441
Fiscal Year-end: 12/31/18
Holding Company; Heavy Construction Machinery Distr
N.A.I.C.S.: 551112

Subsidiaries:

United Bintang Machinery Sdn. Bhd. (1)
Lot 999 Jalan Batu Arang, Rawang, 48000, Selangor, Malaysia
Tel.: (60) 360926633
Web Site: http://www.unitedbintang.com.my
Sales Range: $25-49.9 Million
Emp.: 24
Used Construction Machinery Distr
N.A.I.C.S.: 423810

IDEAL WELDERS LTD.
660 Caldew Street Annacis Island, Delta, V3M 5S2, BC, Canada
Tel.: (604) 525-5558
Web Site:
   https://www.idealwelders.com
Rev.: $12,085,348

Emp.: 85
Pipes Mfr
N.A.I.C.S.: 332996
Jim Longo (Founder & Pres)

IDEALIST GAYRIMENKUL YATIRIM ORTAKLIGI A.S.
Hanim Seti Sok No 38, Kisikli Mah Uskudar, Istanbul, Turkiye
Tel.: (90) 2164438290
Web Site:
   https://www.idealistgyo.com
Year Founded: 2007
IDGYO—(IST)
Real Estate Investment Services
N.A.I.C.S.: 531390

IDEATION TRAINING PTY LTD.
PO Box 130, Goodna, 4300, QLD, Australia
Tel.: (61) 410858822
Professional Training Services
N.A.I.C.S.: 611430

IDEC CORPORATION
2-6-64 Nishimiyahara, Yodogawa-ku, Osaka, 532-0004, Japan
Tel.: (81) 120992336
Web Site: https://www.idec.com
Year Founded: 1947
6652—(TKS)
Rev.: $480,619,710
Assets: $708,182,180
Liabilities: $271,882,520
Net Worth: $436,299,660
Earnings: $29,130,270
Fiscal Year-end: 03/31/24
Control Devices Mfr & Whslr
N.A.I.C.S.: 335314
Toshi K. Funaki (Chm & CEO)

Subsidiaries:

APEM S.A. (1)
55 avenue Edouard Herriot, BP1, 82303, Caussade, Cedex, France
Tel.: (33) 563931498
Web Site: https://www.apem.com
Switch, Keyboard & Integrated Assemblies Mfr & Distr
N.A.I.C.S.: 334419
Joel Becquet (Dir-Fin)

Subsidiary (Non-US):

APEM AB (2)
Torshamnsgatan 39, S-164 40, Kista, Sweden
Tel.: (46) 86263800
Web Site: http://www.apem.se
Electronic Parts & Equipment Whslr
N.A.I.C.S.: 423690
Stefan Steiner (Mng Dir & Sls Mgr)

APEM Benelux NV/SA (2)
Belgicastraat 7/1, 1930, Zaventem, Belgium
Tel.: (32) 27250500
Web Site: http://www.apem.be
Electronic Parts & Equipment Whslr
N.A.I.C.S.: 423690

APEM Components Ltd. (2)
Drakes Drive, Long Crendon, Aylesbury, HP18 9BA, Buckinghamshire, United Kingdom
Tel.: (44) 1844202400
Web Site: https://www.apem.com
Emp.: 300
Electrical Equipment & Components Distr
N.A.I.C.S.: 423690

APEM GmbH (2)
Gewerbehof Giesing Paulsdorfferstrasse 34 2 OG, D-81549, Munich, Germany
Tel.: (49) 894599110
Web Site: http://www.apem.de
Electronic Parts & Equipment Whslr
N.A.I.C.S.: 423690
Michael Schulze (Mng Dir)

APEM Italia S.r.l. (2)
Via Marconi 147G, 12030, Marene, CN, Italy
Tel.: (39) 0172743170
Web Site: http://www.apem.it

Electronic Components & Equipment Distr
N.A.I.C.S.: 423690

Subsidiary (US):

APEM, Inc. (2)
63 Neck Rd, Haverhill, MA 01835
Tel.: (978) 372-1602
Web Site: http://www.apem.com
Electronic Components Mfr & Distr
N.A.I.C.S.: 334419

Subsidiary (Non-US):

MEC A/S (2)
Industriparken 23, 2750, Ballerup, Denmark
Tel.: (45) 44973366
Web Site: http://www.mec.dk
Electronic Switches Components Mfr
N.A.I.C.S.: 334419
Dan Larsen (Mng Dir)

Conet Taiwan Co., Ltd. (1)
36-4 Nanjing W Rd Zhongshan District, Taipei, Taiwan
Tel.: (886) 225583383
Control Device Mfr
N.A.I.C.S.: 335314

IDEC (Beijing) Corporation (1)
Room310 Tower B The Grand Pacific Building 8A Guanghua Road, Chaoyang District, Beijing, 100026, China
Tel.: (86) 1065816131
Control Device Distr
N.A.I.C.S.: 423610

IDEC (Shanghai) Corporation (1)
Room 701-702 Chong Hing Finance Center No 288 Nanjing Road West, Shanghai, 200003, China
Tel.: (86) 2161351515
Control Device Distr
N.A.I.C.S.: 423610
Hiroto Matsui (Gen Mgr)

IDEC (Shenzhen) Corporation (1)
Unit AB-3B2 Tian Xiang Building Tian'an Cyber Park Fu Tian District, Shenzhen, 518040, Guang Dong, China
Tel.: (86) 75583562977
Control Device Distr
N.A.I.C.S.: 423610

IDEC Australia Pty. Ltd. (1)
Unit 17 104 Ferntree Gully Road, Oakleigh, 3166, VIC, Australia
Tel.: (61) 385235900
Control Device Distr
N.A.I.C.S.: 423610

IDEC Canada Ltd. (1)
5800 Ambler Drive Suite 210, Mississauga, L4W 4J4, ON, Canada
Tel.: (905) 890-8561
Control Device Distr
N.A.I.C.S.: 423610
Marianne Lenchak Popadiuk (Mgr-Acct)

IDEC Corporation (1)
1175 Elko Dr, Sunnyvale, CA 94089-2209
Tel.: (408) 747-0550
Web Site: https://us.idec.com
Control Device Distr
N.A.I.C.S.: 423610
William H. Rastetter (Founder & CEO)

IDEC Corporation - Fukusaki Plant (1)
860-2 Haio Saiji Fukusaki-cho, Kanzaki, Hyogo, Japan
Tel.: (81) 790226556
Control Device Mfr
N.A.I.C.S.: 335314

IDEC Corporation - Kyoto Plant (1)
20 Ohari Kotari, Nagaokakyo, Kyoto, Japan
Tel.: (81) 759517121
Control Device Mfr
N.A.I.C.S.: 335314

IDEC Corporation - Takino Plant (1)
355-18 Kawadaka, Kato, 679-0221, Hyogo, Japan
Tel.: (81) 795485700
Control Device Mfr
N.A.I.C.S.: 335314

IDEC Corporation - Tsukuba Plant (1)
1-9 Koyodai, Ryugasaki, Ibaragi, Japan

IDEC CORPORATION

IDEC Corporation—(Continued)
Tel.: (81) 297628211
Control Device Mfr
N.A.I.C.S.: 335314

IDEC Engineering Service Corporation (1)
2-1114 Uedaminami, Tenpaku-ku, Nagoya, 468-0053, Aichi, Japan
Tel.: (81) 528008110
Web Site: http://www.idec-eng.com
Control Device Distr
N.A.I.C.S.: 423610

IDEC IZUMI (H.K.) Co., Ltd. (1)
Unit G H 26/F MG Tower No 133 Hoi Bun Road, Kwun Tong, Kowloon, China (Hong Kong)
Tel.: (852) 28038989
Control Device Distr
N.A.I.C.S.: 423610

IDEC IZUMI Asia Pte. Ltd. (1)
08 Kallang Avenue Tower 1 Unit 13-09, Singapore, 339509, Singapore
Tel.: (65) 67461155
Web Site: https://apac.idec.com
Control Device Distr
N.A.I.C.S.: 423610

IDEC IZUMI Suzhou Co., Ltd. (1)
20 Zhuyuan Road Suzhou New District, Suzhou, 215011, China
Tel.: (86) 51268087788
Control Device Mfr
N.A.I.C.S.: 335314

IDEC IZUMI Taiwan Corporation (1)
87 Shui Kuan Rd Chu Hou Vill, Kaohsiung, 81465, Taiwan
Tel.: (886) 73713151
Control Device Mfr
N.A.I.C.S.: 335314

IDEC Logistics Service Corporation (1)
7-31 Nishi-Miyahara 1-chome Yodogawa-ku, Osaka, Japan
Tel.: (81) 663982501
Logistics Consulting Servies
N.A.I.C.S.: 541614

IDEC Taiwan Corporation (1)
Rm B 2F No 18 Sec 4 Nanjing E Rd, Songshan Dist, New Taipei City, 10553, Taiwan
Tel.: (886) 225776938
Control Device Distr
N.A.I.C.S.: 423610

TAICANG CONET ELECTRONICS CO., LTD. (1)
Room No 1206 Home Inn 5 Shanghai East Road, Taicang, Jiangsu, China
Tel.: (86) 51282786867
Control Device Mfr
N.A.I.C.S.: 335314

IDEMITSU KOSAN CO., LTD.
1-2-1 Otemachi, Chiyoda-ku, Tokyo, 100 8321, Japan
Tel.: (81) 120132015   JP
Web Site: https://www.idemitsu.com
Year Founded: 1911
5019—(TKS)
Rev.: $57,633,918,610
Assets: $33,131,269,950
Liabilities: $21,150,440,040
Net Worth: $11,980,829,910
Earnings: $1,510,503,980
Emp.: 14,000
Fiscal Year-end: 03/31/24
Refined Petroleum Mfr & Distr
N.A.I.C.S.: 324110
Atsuhiko Hirano *(Mng Exec Officer)*

Subsidiaries:

Apollo (Thailand) Co., Ltd. (1)
Amata City Industrial Estate Chonburi Phase 6 700/623 Village No 4, Ban Kao Subdistrict Phan Thong District, Bangkok, 20160, Chonburi, Thailand
Tel.: (66) 38456900
Web Site: https://www.apollothai.com
Oil Refining
N.A.I.C.S.: 324110

Apolloretailing Co., Ltd. (1)
2 Auedfune 3-Dam, Chuo-Ku, Tokyo, 104-0041, Japan
Tel.: (81) 335518711
Automobile Parts Distr
N.A.I.C.S.: 423120

Astomos Energy Corporation (1)
Sapia Tower 24F 1-7-12 Marunouchi, Chiyodaku, Tokyo, 100-0005, Japan (51%)
Tel.: (81) 5038160730
Web Site: https://www.astomos.com
Sales Range: $5-14.9 Billion
Emp.: 349
Import & Sales of Liquified Petroleum Gas; Owned 51% by Idemitsu Kosan Co., Ltd. & 49% by Mitsubishi Corporation
Osamu Masuda *(Mng Dir)*

Central Energy K.K. (1)
764 1 Tamuracho, Kagawa, Japan
Tel.: (81) 877222277
Oil Products Sales
N.A.I.C.S.: 457210

DSM Idemitsu Corp. Ltd. (1)
1 1 Anegacaki Kaigan, Chiba, 299 0111, Japan
Tel.: (81) 436601860
Sales Range: $25-49.9 Million
Emp.: 35
Mfr of Polyethylene; Joint Venture of Royal DSM N.V. (50%) & Idemitsu Kosan Co., Ltd. (50%)
N.A.I.C.S.: 325211

Dalian Idemitsu Chinaoil Co., Ltd. (1)
33 26 1 Dalian Industrial Park Economic And Development Zone, Dalian, Liaoning, China
Tel.: (86) 4117610808
Web Site: http://www.idemitsu.co.jp
Oil Refining
N.A.I.C.S.: 324110

Enessance Holdings Co., Ltd. (1)
Floor 12 No 2-20 Kaigan 1-chome, Minato-ku, Tokyo, 105-0022, Japan
Tel.: (81) 354045231
Web Site: https://www.enessance.co.jp
Emp.: 1,689
Liquefied Gas & Automation Equipment Distr
N.A.I.C.S.: 424720

Ensham Resources Pty. Ltd. (1)
Level 9 175 Eagle Street, Brisbane, 4000, QLD, Australia
Tel.: (61) 732225600
Petroleum Refineries Services
N.A.I.C.S.: 541330

Formosa Idemitsu Petrochemical Corporation (1)
Rm 391 7F 201 Tung Hwa N Road, Songshan District, Taipei, 10508, Taiwan
Tel.: (886) 227122211
Petrochemical Mfr
N.A.I.C.S.: 325110

Freedom Fuels Australia Pty. Ltd. (1)
Unit 5/16 Theodore St, Eagle Farm, 4009, QLD, Australia
Tel.: (61) 732685077
Web Site: http://www.freedomfuels.com.au
Petroleum Refineries Services
N.A.I.C.S.: 541330

Genex Co., Ltd. (1)
3-1 Mizue-cho, Kawasaki-ku, Kawasaki, 210-0866, Japan
Tel.: (81) 4 4280 0604
Emp.: 26
Eletric Power Generation Services
N.A.I.C.S.: 221118
KET Awashima *(Pres)*

Global OLED Technology LLC (1)
107 Carpenter Dr Ste 225, Sterling, VA 20164
Tel.: (703) 870-3282
Web Site: https://www.globaloledtech.com
Professional, Scientific & Technical Services
N.A.I.C.S.: 541990

Gyxis Corporation (1)
12F Mita-Belljú Building 5-36-7 Shiba, Minato-ku, Tokyo, 108-0014, Japan
Tel.: (81) 354845308
Petroleum Refineries Services
N.A.I.C.S.: 541330
Fumiaki Nokura *(Pres)*

Heiwa Kisen Kaisha, Ltd. (1)
7th Floor Kasumigaseki Building 2-5 Kasumigaseki 3-chome, Chiyoda-ku, Tokyo, 100-6007, Japan
Tel.: (81) 367473198
Web Site: http://www.heiwa-kisen.co.jp
Emp.: 99
Depot Operation & Shipping Brokerage Services
N.A.I.C.S.: 813910

Idemitsu Apollo Corporation (1)
1831 16th St, Sacramento, CA 95811-6606
Tel.: (916) 443-0890
Web Site: http://www.idemitsu.com
Sales Range: $50-74.9 Million
Emp.: 3
Oil Refining
N.A.I.C.S.: 324110

Idemitsu Australia Resources Pty. Ltd. (1)
Level 9/175 Eagle Street, PO Box 301, Brisbane, 4000, QLD, Australia (100%)
Tel.: (61) 732225600
Web Site: https://www.idemitsu.com.au
Sales Range: $50-74.9 Million
Emp.: 13,000
Coal Mining
N.A.I.C.S.: 212115

Subsidiary (Domestic):

Boggabri Coal Pty Limited (2)
Leard Forest Road, PO Box 12, Boggabri, 2382, NSW, Australia (100%)
Tel.: (61) 267434775
Web Site: https://www.idemitsu.com.au
Sales Range: $75-99.9 Million
Coal Mining
N.A.I.C.S.: 212114

Muswellbrook Coal Company Limited (2)
Muscle Creek Road, PO Box 123, Muswellbrook, 2333, NSW, Australia (100%)
Tel.: (61) 265422300
Web Site: https://www.idemitsu.com.au
Sales Range: $75-99.9 Million
Emp.: 150
Coal Mining
N.A.I.C.S.: 212114

Idemitsu Canada Resources Ltd. (1)
630202 6th Ave SW, Calgary, T2P2R9, AB, Canada
Tel.: (403) 264-9590
Uranium Ore Mining Services
N.A.I.C.S.: 212290

Idemitsu Chemicals (Hong Kong) Co., Ltd. (1)
3012 30/F The Gateway Tower 6 9 Canton Road, Tsim Sha Tsui, Hong Kong, China (Hong Kong)
Tel.: (852) 28023626
Web Site: http://www.idemitsu.jp
Sales Range: $50-74.9 Million
Emp.: 1
Petrochemical Whslr
N.A.I.C.S.: 424690
Yasuyuki Kanehara *(Mng Dir)*

Idemitsu Chemicals (M) Sdn. Bhd. (1)
PLO408 Jalan Pekeliling, 81700, Pasir Gudang, Johor, Malaysia
Tel.: (60) 72525009
Emp.: 10
Chemical Products Mfr & Distr
N.A.I.C.S.: 325998
N. G. Wendy *(Mng Dir)*

Idemitsu Chemicals (Shanghai) Co., Ltd. (1)
HuaiHai Plaza Rm 3806A HuaiHai Zhong Rd 1045, Shanghai, 200031, China
Tel.: (86) 2154652255
Petroleum Refineries Services
N.A.I.C.S.: 541330

Idemitsu Chemicals Europe PLC (1)

INTERNATIONAL PUBLIC

Immermannstrasse 40, 40210, Dusseldorf, Germany
Tel.: (49) 211 17734 0
Web Site: http://www.idemitsu-chemicals.de
Sales Range: $50-74.9 Million
Emp.: 7
Petrochemical Distr
N.A.I.C.S.: 424720

Idemitsu Chemicals Southeast Asia Pte. Ltd. (1)
3 Killiney Road 04-03 Winsland House I, Singapore, 239519, Singapore
Tel.: (65) 67353393
Web Site: http://www.idemitsu.co.jp
Sales Range: $50-74.9 Million
Emp.: 5
Petrochemical Mfr & Distr
N.A.I.C.S.: 325110
Harald Sturm *(Mng Dir)*

Idemitsu Chemicals Taiwan Corp. (1)
7F- 5 No 89 Songren Road, Xinyi District, Taipei, 110413, Taiwan
Tel.: (886) 227773291
Petroleum Refineries Services
N.A.I.C.S.: 541330

Idemitsu Chemicals U.S.A. Corporation (1)
3000 Town Ctr Ste 2820, Southfield, MI 48075
Tel.: (248) 355-9590
Web Site: http://www.xarecsps.com
Emp.: 5
Petrochemical Product Mfr & Distr
N.A.I.C.S.: 325110
Yuichi Kurimoto *(Pres)*

Idemitsu Clean Energy (Yantai) Co., Ltd. (1)
8 Zhuji West Road Zhifu, Yantai, 264014, Shandong, China
Tel.: (86) 535 681 2507
Web Site: https://www.idemitsu.com
Sales Range: $50-74.9 Million
Emp.: 5
Coal Mining Services
N.A.I.C.S.: 213113
Taka Maesu *(Mgr)*

Idemitsu Coal Marketing Australia Pty. Ltd. (1)
Level 9 175 Eagle Street, Brisbane, 4000, QLD, Australia
Tel.: (61) 732225600
Petroleum Refineries Services
N.A.I.C.S.: 541330

Idemitsu Electronic Materials (China) Co., Ltd. (1)
8-20 KeXin Road, Chengdu High-Tech West District, Sichuan, 611731, China
Tel.: (86) 2862402230
Petroleum Refineries Services
N.A.I.C.S.: 541330

Idemitsu Electronic Materials (Shanghai) Co., Ltd. (1)
1205 Building I Arch Shanghai 523 Loushanguan Road, Changning District, Shanghai, 200051, China
Tel.: (86) 2164225723
Petroleum Refineries Services
N.A.I.C.S.: 541330

Idemitsu Electronic Materials Korea Co., Ltd. (1)
15 Dangdong 2-ro, Munsan-eup, Paju, 10816, Gyeonggi-do, Korea (South)
Tel.: (82) 319549676
Web Site: https://www.idemitsu.com
Emp.: 80
Petroleum Refineries Services
N.A.I.C.S.: 541330

Idemitsu Energy Consulting (Beijing) Co., Ltd. (1)
C613B Lufthansa Center Office Building 50 Liangmaqiao Road, Chaoyang District, Beijing, 100125, China
Tel.: (86) 1064651061
Coal Mining Services
N.A.I.C.S.: 213113

Idemitsu Engineering Co., Ltd. (1)
World Business Garden Malibu East 34th floor 2-6-1 Nakase, Mihama-ku, Chiba, 261-

IDEMITSU KOSAN CO., LTD.

7134, Japan
Tel.: (81) 432966940
Web Site: https://www.idemitsu.com
Sales Range: $150-199.9 Million
Emp.: 380
Construction Engineering Services
N.A.I.C.S.: 237990

Idemitsu Engineering Vietnam Co., Ltd. (1)
7F Centre Point Building 106 Nguyen Van Troi St, Ward 8 Phu Nhuan Dis, Ho Chi Minh City, Vietnam
Tel.: (84) 2838226984
Petroleum Refineries Services
N.A.I.C.S.: 541330

Idemitsu Fine Composites Co., Ltd. (1)
5F TIXTOWER UENO 4-8-1 Higashiueno, Taito-ku, Tokyo, 110-0015, Japan
Tel.: (81) 358300530
Petroleum Refineries Services
N.A.I.C.S.: 541330

Idemitsu Gas Production (Vietnam) Co., Ltd. (1)
28th Floor Vietcombank Tower 5 Me Linh Square, Ben Nghe Ward District 1, Ho Chi Minh City, Vietnam
Tel.: (84) 2838278640
Petroleum Refineries Services
N.A.I.C.S.: 541330

Idemitsu International (Asia) Pte. Ltd. (1)
3 Killiney Road 04-03 Winsland House I, Singapore, 239519, Singapore (100%)
Tel.: (65) 67353393
Web Site: https://www.idemitsu.com
Sales Range: $25-49.9 Million
Emp.: 20
Purchase & Distribution of Crude Oil & Petroleum Products
N.A.I.C.S.: 424720

Idemitsu Lube (China) Co., Ltd. (1)
SongHong Road 207-C-6-AD, Shanghai, 200335, China
Tel.: (86) 2154660066
Emp.: 128
Petroleum Products Mfr & Distr
N.A.I.C.S.: 324199
Tatsuya Suzuki *(CEO)*

Idemitsu Lube (Malaysia) Sdn. Bhd. (1)
Lot 14 Block B Jalan Teknologi Taman Sains Selangor 1, Kota Damansara PJU 5, 47810, Petaling Jaya, Selangor, Malaysia
Tel.: (60) 361579529
Web Site: https://idemitsu-ilm.com.my
Petroleum Refineries Services
N.A.I.C.S.: 541330

Idemitsu Lube (Singapore) Pte.Ltd. (1)
37 Pandan Road, Singapore, 609280, Singapore
Tel.: (65) 6268 5888
Web Site: http://www.idemitsu-ils.com.sg
Sales Range: $25-49.9 Million
Emp.: 53
Lubricants & Petroleum Products Refinery Services & Distr
N.A.I.C.S.: 324110
Philip Hurley *(Mng Dir)*

Idemitsu Lube Asia Pacific Pte. Ltd. (1)
31 International Business Park Creative Resource 05-03/04, Singapore, 609921, Singapore
Tel.: (65) 66970550
Petroleum Refineries Services
N.A.I.C.S.: 541330

Idemitsu Lube Europe GmbH (1)
Immermannstrasse 40, 40210, Dusseldorf, Germany
Tel.: (49) 2111754370
Petroleum Lubricant Distr
N.A.I.C.S.: 424720

Idemitsu Lube India Pvt Ltd (1)
304 3rd Floor Eros Corporate Tower Nehru Place, New Delhi, 110019, India
Tel.: (91) 1166794200
Web Site: http://ilindia.idemitsu.com
Sales Range: $25-49.9 Million
Emp.: 2
Petroleum Product Distr
N.A.I.C.S.: 424720
Kohei Ueda *(Mng Dir)*

Idemitsu Lube Middle East & Africa FZE (1)
Dubai Airport Free Zone Bldg 4WB-642, PO Box 293514, Dubai, United Arab Emirates
Tel.: (971) 42602960
Sales Range: $50-74.9 Million
Emp.: 9
Lubricant & Grease Whslr
N.A.I.C.S.: 424720
Yoshinori Nagaoka *(Mng Dir)*

Idemitsu Lube Pakistan (Private) Limited (1)
Emerald Tower 11th Floor Office 1103 Clifton Block-5, Karachi, 74000, Pakistan
Tel.: (92) 2135188111
Petroleum Refineries Services
N.A.I.C.S.: 541330

Idemitsu Lube South America Ltda. (1)
Alameda Santos 745 conj 61, Sao Paulo, 01419-001, SP, Brazil
Tel.: (55) 1131461800
Web Site: http://www.idemitsu.com
Sales Range: $25-49.9 Million
Emp.: 3
Petroleum Products Mfr & Distr
N.A.I.C.S.: 324199
Shinichi Yochida *(CEO)*

Idemitsu Lube Vietnam Co., Ltd. (1)
Land lot CN52E Dinh Vu IZ, Dong Hai 2 Ward Hai An Dist, Haiphong, Vietnam
Tel.: (84) 2253246508
Petroleum Refineries Services
N.A.I.C.S.: 541330

Idemitsu Lubricants (Thailand) Co., Ltd. (1)
Amata City Industrial Estate No7/467 Moo6, T Mabyangporn A Pluakdaeng, Rayong, 21140, Thailand
Tel.: (66) 38018333
Petroleum Refineries Services
N.A.I.C.S.: 541330

Idemitsu Lubricants America Corporation (1)
701 Port Rd, Jeffersonville, IN 47130-8425
Tel.: (812) 284-3300
Web Site: http://www.ilacorp.com
Sales Range: $50-74.9 Million
Engine Oil & Petroleum Lubricant Mfr
N.A.I.C.S.: 324199
Noriaki Ito *(Pres)*

Idemitsu Lubricants Mexico S.A. de C.V. (1)
L07-B Conjunto Miyana Av, Ejercito Nacional 769 Esquina Moliere Col Granada Miguel Hidalgo, 11520, Mexico, Mexico
Tel.: (52) 5562742248
Petroleum Refineries Services
N.A.I.C.S.: 541330

Idemitsu Lubricants Philippines Inc. (1)
Unit 3 24th Floor Excuadra Tower 1 Jade Drive, Ortigas Business Center, Pasig, 1500, Philippines
Tel.: (63) 282828535
Web Site: http://ilp.idemitsu.ph
Petroleum Refineries Services
N.A.I.C.S.: 541330

Idemitsu Lubricants RUS LLC (1)
Millennium House Trubnaya St 12, 107045, Moscow, Russia
Tel.: (7) 4957757318
Web Site: http://www.idemitsu.ru
Sales Range: $25-49.9 Million
Emp.: 16
Petroleum Products Mfr & Distr
N.A.I.C.S.: 324199

Idemitsu OLED Materials Europe AG (1)
Mattenstrasse 22, PO Box 2548, 4058, Basel, Switzerland
Tel.: (41) 615537150
Web Site: http://idemitsu.ch
Petroleum Refineries Services

Idemitsu Oil & Gas Co., Ltd. (1)
No 2-5 Toranomon 2-chome Kyodo Tsushin Kaikan Bldg, Minato-ku, Tokyo, 105-0001, Japan
Tel.: (81) 3 5575 0340
Web Site: http://www.iog-idemitsu.co.jp
Sales Range: $50-74.9 Million
Emp.: 50
Oil & Gas Exploration Services
N.A.I.C.S.: 213112
Kosuke Tsuji *(Pres)*

Idemitsu Petrochemical Co., Ltd. (1)
1-1 Marunouchi 3-chome, Chiyoda-ku, Tokyo, 1008321, Japan (100%)
Tel.: (81) 33213360
Web Site: http://www.idemitsu.co.jp
Sales Range: $125-149.9 Million
Emp.: 500
Petrochemical Products Mfr
N.A.I.C.S.: 325110

Joint Venture (Domestic):

BASF Idemitsu Co., Ltd. (2)
OVOL Nihonbashi Building 3F 3-4-4 Nihonbashi Muromachi, Chuo-ku, Tokyo, 103-0022, Japan
Tel.: (81) 352902400
Web Site: http://www.basf.com
Emp.: 1,138
Chemical Product Mfr; Owned 50% by BASF Aktiengellschaft & 50% by Idemitsu Petrochemical Co., Ltd.
N.A.I.C.S.: 325998

Idemitsu Petroleum Norge AS (1)
Lysaker Torg 25, 1366, Lysaker, Norway
Tel.: (47) 23 25 05 00
Web Site: http://www.idemitsu.no
Sales Range: $50-74.9 Million
Emp.: 50
Crude Oil & Natural Gas Exploration Services
N.A.I.C.S.: 211120

Idemitsu SM (Malaysia) Sdn. Bhd. (1)
PLO408 Jalan Pekeliling, 81700, Pasir Gudang, Johor, Malaysia
Tel.: (60) 72525350
Petrochemical Mfr & Distr
N.A.I.C.S.: 325110

Idemitsu Tanker Co., Ltd. (1)
16F Jinbocho Mitsui Building 105 Kanda-Jimbocho 1-Chome, Chiyoda-ku, Tokyo, 101-0051, Japan (100%)
Tel.: (81) 368605300
Web Site: http://www.idemitsu.com
Sales Range: $125-149.9 Million
Emp.: 149
Marine Transportation of Crude Oil & Petroleum Products
N.A.I.C.S.: 213112

Idemitsu Technofine Co., Ltd. (1)
Kokusai Fashion Center Bldg 6-1Yokoami 1-chome, Sumida-ku, Tokyo, 130 0015, Japan (100%)
Tel.: (81) 3 3829 0934
Web Site: http://www.idemitsu.co.jp
Sales Range: $25-49.9 Million
Emp.: 37
Mfr of Materials Produced with Natural-Artificial-Composite & Polymerization Technologies
N.A.I.C.S.: 325998

Idemitsu Unitech Co., Ltd. (1)
NMF Shiba Bldg 6F 2-3 Shiba 4 -Chome, Minato-ku, Tokyo, 108-0014, Japan (100%)
Tel.: (81) 368658858
Web Site: http://www.idemitsu.com
Sales Range: $350-399.9 Million
Emp.: 446
Research & Development, Production & Distribution of Synthetic Plastic Processed Products
N.A.I.C.S.: 326199

Plant (Domestic):

Idemitsu Unitech Co., Ltd. - Chiba Plant (2)
417-1 Sakuda Kujukuri-machi, Sambu-gun, Chiba, 283-0101, Japan
Tel.: (81) 475 76 7956
Web Site: http://www.idemitsu.com
Processed Synthetic Plastic Products Mfr
N.A.I.C.S.: 325211

Idemitsu Unitech Co., Ltd. - Engineering Material Plant (2)
1059-1 Aza-Ushibitsu Fuke-cho, Kameyama, 519-0166, Mie, Japan
Tel.: (81) 595 82 6588
Web Site: http://www.idemitsu.com
Synthetic Plastic Products Mfr
N.A.I.C.S.: 326199

Idemitsu Unitech Co., Ltd. - Hyogo Plant (2)
841-3 Ko Sirahama-cho, Himeji, 672-8023, Hyogo, Japan
Tel.: (81) 792 45 3811
Web Site: http://www.idemitsu.com
Processed Synthetic Plastic Products Mfr
N.A.I.C.S.: 325211

Idemitsu Unitech Co., Ltd. - Syizuoka Plant (2)
215-2 Kazurayama, Susono, 410-1103, Shizuoka, Japan
Tel.: (81) 55 997 3451
Web Site: http://www.idemitsu.com
Emp.: 8
Processed Synthetic Plastic Products Mfr
N.A.I.C.S.: 325211
Shigeru Oyama *(Mgr-Factory)*

K.K. Marushin (1)
Web Site: http://www.kk-marushin.com
Oil Product Sales
N.A.I.C.S.: 213112

K.K. Rising Sun (1)
2-3-2 Daiba Frontier Building 20th floor, Daiba Minato-ku, Tokyo, 135-8074, Japan
Tel.: (81) 355316800
Web Site: http://www.rising-sun.co.jp
Emp.: 111
Oil & Automobile Parts Sales Services
N.A.I.C.S.: 441330

K.K. Shinyo Sekiyu (1)
1-7-5 Kanayamacho Sumitomo Seimei Kanayama No 2 Bldg 9f, Atsuta-Ku, Nagoya, 456-0002, Aichi, Japan
Tel.: (81) 526816511
Web Site: http://www.shinyo-sekiyu.co.jp
Petroleum Product Distr
N.A.I.C.S.: 424720

Kuo Horng Co., Ltd. (1)
11th Floor No 69 Section 1 Jianguo North Road, Taipei, 10489, Taiwan
Tel.: (886) 225076711
Web Site: https://www.idemitsu.com.tw
Sales Range: $25-49.9 Million
Emp.: 25
Oil Refining
N.A.I.C.S.: 324110

Lion Idemitsu Composites Co., Ltd (1)
5F TIXTOWER UENO 4-8-1 Higashiueno, Taito-ku, Tokyo, 110-0015, Japan (50%)
Tel.: (81) 358300530
Web Site: https://www.idemitsu.com
Production & Sales of Special Composite Plastics
N.A.I.C.S.: 325211
Yasuyuki Kanehara *(Pres)*

Subsidiary (Non-US):

Lion Idemitsu Composites (Hong Kong) Limited (2)
Unit No 1509 15/F The Metropolis Tower 10 Metropolis Drive, Hung Hom, Kowloon, China (Hong Kong)
Tel.: (852) 25301000
Toilet Preparation Mfr
N.A.I.C.S.: 325620

Lion Idemitsu Composites (India) Private Limited (2)
No 503 5th Floor Suncity Business Tower Golf Course Road Sector 54, Gurgaon, Haryana, India
Tel.: (91) 1244233965
Toilet Preparation Mfr
N.A.I.C.S.: 325620

Lion Idemitsu Composites (Shanghai) Co., Ltd. (2)

IDEMITSU KOSAN CO., LTD.

Idemitsu Kosan Co., Ltd.—(Continued)

Room 3806B Huaihai Plaza NO 1045 Huaihai Zhong Road, Xuhui District, Shanghai, 200031, China
Tel.: (86) 2154655055
Toilet Preparation Mfr
N.A.I.C.S.: 325620

Lion Idemitsu Composites (Thailand) Co., Ltd. (2)
571 RSU Tower 8 Floor Room 803 Sukhumvit Road Klongton Nua, Wattana, Bangkok, 10110, Thailand
Tel.: (66) 22596095
Toilet Preparation Mfr
N.A.I.C.S.: 325620

Nakagawa Oil Co., Ltd (1)
8-29 Yubacho, Nishinomiya, 662-0964, Hyogo, Japan
Tel.: (81) 798228657
Petroleum Product Distr
N.A.I.C.S.: 424720

Nippon Grease Co., Ltd. (1)
4-11-28 Minami-Senba, Chuo-ku, Osaka, 542-0081, Japan
Tel.: (81) 662825411
Web Site: http://www.nippon-grease.co.jp
Sales Range: $50-74.9 Million
Emp.: 174
Grease & Lubricant Sales
N.A.I.C.S.: 324191
Atsushi Abo (Pres)

On Site Power Co., Ltd. (1)
2-3-2 Daiba Daiba Frontier Bldg, Minato-Ku, Tokyo, 135-0091, Japan
Tel.: (81) 3 5531 5784
Web Site: http://www.onsitepwr.co.jp
Emp.: 5
Heating Systems Distr
N.A.I.C.S.: 423730

P.T. Idemitsu Lube Indonesia (1)
Block CK No 03 Kota Deltamas, Desa Pasirranji Kawasan GIIC Central Cikarang District Kab, Bekasi, West Java, Indonesia
Tel.: (62) 2189977630
Petroleum Refineries Services
N.A.I.C.S.: 541330

P.T. Idemitsu Lube Techno Indonesia (1)
Jl Permata Raya Lot BB-4A, Kawasan Industri KIIC, Karawang, 41361, West Java, Indonesia
Tel.: (62) 2189114768
Web Site: http://ilti.idemitsu.com
Petroleum Refineries Services
N.A.I.C.S.: 541330

PT. Idemitsu Energy Indonesia (1)
The Plaza Office Tower 21st Floor, Jalan MH Thamrin Kav 28-30, Jakarta, 10350, Indonesia
Tel.: (62) 2129921919
Petroleum Refineries Services
N.A.I.C.S.: 541330

Petrochemicals (Malaysia) Sdn. Bhd. (1)
PLO 408 409 Off Jalan Pekeliling Pasir, Gudang Industrial Estate, 81700, Pasir Gudang, Johor, Malaysia
Tel.: (60) 72596300
Web Site: https://www.idemitsu-ps.com.my
Sales Range: $75-99.9 Million
Emp.: 200
Petrochemical Mfr & Distr
N.A.I.C.S.: 325110

Plaloc Asia (Thailand) Co., Ltd. (1)
700/736 Moo 1 T Panthong, A Panthong, Chon Buri, 20160, Thailand
Tel.: (66) 38185576
Emp.: 60
Petroleum Refineries Services
N.A.I.C.S.: 541330

Prime Polymer Co., Ltd. (1)
Shiodome City Center 19th floor 1-5-2 Higashi-Shimbashi, Minato-ku, Tokyo, 105-7122, Japan
Tel.: (81) 36 253 4500
Web Site: https://www.primepolymer.co.jp
Emp.: 684
Polyolefin Mfr & Sales; Owned 65% by Mitsui Chemicals, Inc. & 35% by Idemitsu Kosan Co., Ltd.

N.A.I.C.S.: 325110

Kensuke Fujimoto (Pres & Gen Mgr-Plng & Admin Div)

Red and Yellow Co., Ltd (1)
13F Fukoku Seimei Building 2-2-2 Uchisaiwaicho, Chiyoda-ku, Tokyo, 100-0011, Japan
Tel.: (81) 368127783
Web Site: http://www.rednyellow.co.jp
Lubricant Import & Distr
N.A.I.C.S.: 424720

Rekisei Kagaku K.K. (1)
580-14 Nagaura, Sodegaura, 299-0265, Chiba, Japan
Tel.: (81) 438624320
Asphalt Paving Mixtures & Blocks Mfr
N.A.I.C.S.: 324121

SDS Biotech KKS (1)
1-5 Higashi-Nihombashi 1-chome, Chuo-ku, Tokyo, 103-0004, Japan (100%)
Tel.: (81) 358255511
Web Site: http://www.sdsbio.co.jp
Sales Range: $125-149.9 Million
Emp.: 494
Agricultural Chemical Mfr
N.A.I.C.S.: 325320
Kenichi Komatsubara (Mng Dir)

SHELL JAPAN TRADING LTD. (1)
Daiba Frontier Bldg 2-3-2 Daiba, Minato-Ku, Tokyo, 135-0091, Japan
Tel.: (81) 355315696
Web Site: http://www.showa-shell.co.jp
Oil Lubricants Distr
N.A.I.C.S.: 424720

Shanghai Idemitsu Lube Trading Co., Ltd (1)
SongHong Road 207-C-6-AD, ChangNing District, Shanghai, 200335, China
Tel.: (86) 2154660066
Petroleum Refineries Services
N.A.I.C.S.: 541330

Shoseki Engineering & Construction Co., Ltd. (1)
2-3-2 Daiba Daiba Frontier Bldg 16f, Minato, Tokyo, 135-8074, Japan
Tel.: (81) 355315610
Web Site: http://www.shoseki-eng.co.jp
Emp.: 100
Plant Construction Engineering Services
N.A.I.C.S.: 237990

Shoseki Kako K.K. (1)
Sales Range: $600-649.9 Million
Emp.: 96
Building Materials Mfr
N.A.I.C.S.: 444180

Showa Shell Business & IT Solutions Limited (1)
Technopia Ohi 1-7-8 Minami-ohi, Shinagawa, Tokyo, Japan
Tel.: (81) 3 5493 4300
Oil Lubricants Distr
N.A.I.C.S.: 424720

Showa Shell Sempaku K.K. (1)
Daiba Frontier Bldg, 2 3 2 Daiba Minato ku, Tokyo, 135-8075, Japan
Tel.: (81) 355315811
Emp.: 9
Oil Product Distr
N.A.I.C.S.: 213112

Showa Yokkaichi Sekiyu Co., Ltd. (1)
Tel.: (81) 593475511
Web Site: http://www.showa-yokkaichi.co.jp
Sales Range: $125-149.9 Million
Emp.: 551
Petroleum & Petroleum Products Mfr
N.A.I.C.S.: 324199

Solar Frontier K.K. (1)
Teigeki Building 3-1-1 Marunouchi, Chiyoda-ku, Tokyo, 100-0005, Japan
Tel.: (81) 120558983
Web Site: https://www.solar-frontier.com
Sales Range: $50-74.9 Million
Emp.: 100
Solar Power Panels Distr
N.A.I.C.S.: 423610

TOA Oil Co., Ltd. (1)
3-1 Mizue-cho, Kawasaki-ku, Kawasaki, 210-0866, Japan (100%)

Tel.: (81) 442800600
Web Site: http://www.toaoil.co.jp
Rev.: $258,910,960
Assets: $856,196,000
Liabilities: $565,641,120
Net Worth: $290,554,880
Earnings: $20,599,040
Emp.: 500
Fiscal Year-end: 03/31/2022
Oil Refinery Services
N.A.I.C.S.: 324110

Subsidiary (Domestic):

NIIGATA JOINT OIL STOCKPILING Co., Ltd (2)
1-1-176 Higashi Minato Seiro-cho, Kitakanbara-gun, Niigata, 957-0101, Japan
Tel.: (81) 25 256 2311
Oil Refinery Services
N.A.I.C.S.: 324110

OHGISHIMA OIL TERMINAL Co., Ltd (2)
1-2 Ohgishima, Tsurumi-ku, Yokohama, 230-0055, Japan
Tel.: (81) 44 276 0406
Oil Refinery Services
N.A.I.C.S.: 324110

Tokyo Shell Pack K.K. (1)
5-26-27 Kitami, Setagaya-ku, Tokyo, 157-0067, Japan
Tel.: (81) 334171211
Web Site: https://www.tokyo-shellpack.net
Oil Product Distr
N.A.I.C.S.: 424720

Wakamatsu Gas K.K. (1)
4-16 Sengokucho, Aizuwakamatsu, 965-0817, Fukushima, Japan
Tel.: (81) 242281311
Web Site: https://www.wakagas.co.jp
Emp.: 196
Oil Products Mfr & Distr
N.A.I.C.S.: 213112

IDENTA CORP.

Bethlehem Road 120, 93420, Jerusalem, Israel
Tel.: (972) 25872220
Web Site: https://www.identa-corp.com
Year Founded: 2002
IDTA—(OTCQB)
Rev.: $1,051,590
Assets: $1,529,275
Liabilities: $1,013,159
Net Worth: $516,116
Earnings: $14,644
Emp.: 15
Fiscal Year-end: 12/31/23
Illicit Drugs, Drug Precursors, Explosives & Bullet-Holes Testing Kit Mfr
N.A.I.C.S.: 339999
Richard Naimer (Chm)

IDENTITII LIMITED

C/- Boardroom Pty Limited Level 8 210 George Street, Sydney, 2000, NSW, Australia
Tel.: (61) 288060438 AU
Web Site: https://www.identitii.com
Year Founded: 2014
ID8—(ASX)
Rev.: $1,733,149
Assets: $2,056,404
Liabilities: $1,268,651
Net Worth: $787,753
Earnings: ($2,366,130)
Fiscal Year-end: 06/30/24
Financial Technology Services
N.A.I.C.S.: 518210
Elissa Hansen (Sec)

IDENTITY HEALTHCARE LTD.

29 Yad Harutzim St Building 9 Poleg Industrial Zone, PO Box 8249, Netanya, 4250437, Israel
Tel.: (972) 98354848
Web Site:
https://www.identimedical.com

IDNT—(TAE)
Rev.: $2,724,906
Assets: $4,155,686
Liabilities: $1,254,270
Net Worth: $2,901,415
Earnings: ($1,837,482)
Fiscal Year-end: 06/30/23
Health Care Srvices
N.A.I.C.S.: 622110
Shlomo Matityaho (Chm & CEO)

IDEON S.A.

Ul Paderewskiego 32 C, 40-282, Katowice, Poland
Tel.: (48) 32 7829700
Natural Gas Distribution Services
N.A.I.C.S.: 221210
Ireneusz Krol (Chm-Mgmt Bd)

IDEX BIOMETRICS ASA

Dronning Eufemias gate 16, 0191, Oslo, Norway
Tel.: (47) 67839119
Web Site:
https://www.idexbiometrics.com
IDBA—(NASDAQ)
Rev.: $4,091,000
Assets: $29,016,000
Liabilities: $6,175,000
Net Worth: $22,841,000
Earnings: ($32,662,000)
Emp.: 85
Fiscal Year-end: 12/31/22
Fingerprint Recognition, Authentication & Verification Technology
N.A.I.C.S.: 561621
Morten Opstad (Chm)

Subsidiaries:

IDEX America Inc. (1)
187 Ballardvale St Ste A 260, Wilmington, MA 01887
Tel.: (339) 215-8020
Fingerprint Technology Services
N.A.I.C.S.: 561611

IDEX Biometrics America Inc. (1)
187 Ballardvale St Ste A260, Wilmington, MA 01887
Tel.: (339) 215-8020
Biometric Technology Services
N.A.I.C.S.: 561611

IDEX Biometrics UK Ltd. (1)
Abbey House 282 Farnborough Road, Farnborough, GU14 7NA, United Kingdom
Tel.: (44) 1276534630
Health Equipment Mfr
N.A.I.C.S.: 339112

IDFC FIRST BANK LIMITED

C-61 G Block Bandra-Kurla Complex, Bandra East, Mumbai, 400051, Maharashtra, India
Tel.: (91) 2271325500
Web Site: https://www.idfcbank.com
Year Founded: 2015
IDFCFIRSTB—(NSE)
Rev.: $3,260,606,810
Assets: $28,761,111,576
Liabilities: $25,662,070,643
Net Worth: $3,099,040,933
Earnings: $297,935,304
Emp.: 35,352
Fiscal Year-end: 03/31/23
Banking Services
N.A.I.C.S.: 522110
Rajiv Lall (Founder)

Subsidiaries:

Capital First Ltd. (1)
One Indiabulls Centre Tower 2A and 2B 10th Floor Senapati Bapat Marg, Lower Parel W, Mumbai, 400 013, India
Tel.: (91) 2240423400
Web Site: http://www.capfirst.com
Rev.: $593,154,311
Assets: $4,071,673,659
Liabilities: $3,664,380,669
Net Worth: $407,292,990

AND PRIVATE COMPANIES — IDG CAPITAL

Earnings: $50,950,395
Emp.: 2,590
Fiscal Year-end: 03/31/2018
Investment Advisory, Retail Financial, Wholesale Credit & Treasury Services
N.A.I.C.S.: 523940
V. Vaidyanathan *(Founder & Chm)*

Subsidiary (Domestic):

Capital First Securities Limited (2)
Technopolis Knowledge Park A Wing 4th Fl 401-407 Mahakali Caves Road, Andheri, Mumbai, 400093, India
Tel.: (91) 22 6197 9100
Web Site: http://www.capitalfirstdirect.com
Emp.: 200
Financial Management Services
N.A.I.C.S.: 523940

IDFC LIMITED

906/907 9th Floor Embassy Centre Jamnalal Bajaj Road, Nariman Point, Mumbai, 400021, India
Tel.: (91) 2222821549
Web Site: https://www.idfc.com
Year Founded: 1997
IDFC—(NSE)
Rev.: $13,352,430
Assets: $1,250,899,650
Liabilities: $32,413,290
Net Worth: $1,218,486,360
Earnings: $8,778,315
Emp.: 6
Fiscal Year-end: 03/31/22
Financial Intermediation for Infrastructure Projects & Services
N.A.I.C.S.: 523999
Mahendra N. Shah *(Mng Dir)*

Subsidiaries:

IDFC AMC Trustee Company Limited (1)
39/3993b2 Vantage Point Ravipuram, Ernakulam, Kochi, 682015, Kerala, India
Tel.: (91) 4842358639
Investment Banking Services
N.A.I.C.S.: 523150

IDFC Capital Limited (1)
Naman Chambers C 32 G Block Bandra Kurla Complex, Bandra East, Mumbai, 400051, Maharashtra, India
Tel.: (91) 2266222000
Web Site: http://www.idfc.com
Sales Range: $700-749.9 Million
Emp.: 2,000
Investment Banking Services
N.A.I.C.S.: 523150
Sandeep Gupta *(Mng Dir-Corp Fin Div)*

IDFC Investment Advisors Limited (1)
6th Floor One Indiabulls Center Jupiter Mills Compound 841, Mumbai, 400013, Maharashtra, India
Tel.: (91) 2266289999
Web Site: http://www.idfcia.com
Sales Range: $50-74.9 Million
Emp.: 80
Investment Management Service
N.A.I.C.S.: 523999
Kulpin Parekh *(CEO)*

IDFC Pension Fund Management Company Limited (1)
6th Floor One India Bulls Centre 841 Jupiter Mills Compound, Senapati Bapat Marg, Mumbai, 400013, India
Tel.: (91) 22 66289999
Web Site: http://www.idfcpf.com
Sales Range: $25-49.9 Million
Emp.: 80
Fund Management Services
N.A.I.C.S.: 541618

IDFC Private Equity (IDFC PE) (1)
201 Naman Chambers C 32 G Block 6th FL Bandra Kurla Complex, Bandra East, Mumbai, 400 051, India (100%)
Tel.: (91) 2242222000
Web Site: http://www.idfcpe.com
Rev.: $1,300,000,000
Private Equity Investments
N.A.I.C.S.: 523999

IDFC Project Equity Company Limited (1)
The Capital Court 2nd Floor, Olof Palme Marg Munirka, Delhi, 110 067, India (100%)
Tel.: (91) 1143311000
Web Site: http://www.idfcprojectequity.com
Sales Range: $50-74.9 Million
Emp.: 30
Equity Investment Projects
N.A.I.C.S.: 523999

IDFC Project Finance (1)
No 39 5th Cross 8th Main RMV Extension, Sadashiv Nagar, 560 080, Bengaluru, India (100%)
Tel.: (91) 8023613014
Web Site: http://www.ideck.net
Sales Range: $50-74.9 Million
Emp.: 42
Investment Project Financing
N.A.I.C.S.: 523999

IDFC Projects Limited (1)
2nd Floor The Capital Court Olof Palme Marg, Munirka, New Delhi, 110067, India
Tel.: (91) 11 433 11000
Web Site: http://www.idfcprojects.com
Asset Management Services
N.A.I.C.S.: 541618

IDFC SECURITIES LIMITED

One Indiabulls Centre Senapati Bapat, Marg Elphinstone Road West 6th Floor, Mumbai, 400051, Maharashtra, India
Tel.: (91) 22 4222 2000
Holding Company
N.A.I.C.S.: 551112
Vikram Limaye *(Chm)*

IDG CAPITAL

6 Floor Tower A COFCO Plaza 8 Jianguomennei Ave, Beijing, 100005, China
Tel.: (86) 1085901800
Web Site: http://www.idgcapital.com
Year Founded: 1993
Private Equity Services
N.A.I.C.S.: 523999
Hugo Shong *(Co-Chm)*

Subsidiaries:

International Data Group, Inc. (1)
140 Kendrick St Blg B, Needham, MA 01701
Tel.: (508) 879-0700
Web Site: http://www.idg.com
Holding Company; Technology Industry Trade Journal, Internet & Mobile Application Publisher, Marketer & Convention Organizer
N.A.I.C.S.: 551112
Mohamad S. Ali *(CEO)*

Subsidiary (Domestic):

IDG Enterprise (2)
140 Kendrick St Bldg B, Needham, MA 02494
Tel.: (508) 879-0700
Web Site: https://www.idg.com
Publishing Services
N.A.I.C.S.: 513120
Genevieve Juillard *(CEO)*

Subsidiary (Non-US):

CW Fachverlag GmbH (3)
Sandleitengasse 15-17 Stiege 1 1st floor TOP 19, 1160, Vienna, Austria
Tel.: (43) 650 3347035
Web Site: http://www.computerwelt.at
IT & Telecommunications
N.A.I.C.S.: 519290

Subsidiary (Domestic):

Computerworld, Inc. (3)
265 Worthington St, Springfield, MA 01603
Tel.: (508) 875-5000
Web Site: http://www.computerworld.com
Magazine Publisher
N.A.I.C.S.: 513120

Connell Communications Inc. (3)
360 Fee Fee Rd, Maryland Heights, MO 63043
Tel.: (314) 298-8727
Web Site: http://www.connellcom.com
Provider of Publishing Services
N.A.I.C.S.: 513120

Subsidiary (Non-US):

IDC Asean (3)
The Pinnacle Suite 7-03 Level 7 Persiaran Lagoon Bandar Sunway, Subang Jaya, Subang Jaya, 47500, Malaysia
Tel.: (60) 37663 2288
Web Site: http://www.idc.com
Provider of Business Information & Data
N.A.I.C.S.: 561499

IDC Asia & Pacific (3)
Unit 801A, Tower B Manulife Finance Centre, 223-231 Wai Yip Street, Kwun Tong, Kowloon, China (Hong Kong)
Tel.: (852) 25303831
Web Site: http://www.idc.com
Telecommunications Products & Services
N.A.I.C.S.: 517810

IDC Asia Pacific (Singapore) (3)
Fuji Xerox Tower 80 Anson Road 38th Floor, Singapore, 079907, Singapore
Tel.: (65) 62260330
Web Site: http://www.idc.com
Publisher
N.A.I.C.S.: 513120
Eva Au *(Mng Dir)*

IDC Australia (3)
11/160-166 Sussex Street, North Sydney, 2000, NSW, Australia
Tel.: (61) 2 9925 2298
Web Site: http://www.idc.com
Information Technology Services
N.A.I.C.S.: 519290

IDC Benelux (3)
Suikersilo Oost 1, 1165 MS, Halfweg, Netherlands
Tel.: (31) 20 333 0650
Web Site: http://www.idcbenelux.com
Publishing
N.A.I.C.S.: 513120
Martin Canning *(Grp VP-Consulting)*

IDC Brazil (3)
Av Eng Luiz Carlos Berrini 1645 - 8andar, 04571-000, Sao Paulo, Brazil
Tel.: (55) 1155083400
Web Site: http://www.idc.com
International Fund to Assist Entrepreneurs with Business Expansion
N.A.I.C.S.: 523150
Denis Arcieri *(Country Mgr)*

IDC Central Europe GmbH (3)
Karntner Ring 5-7, A 1090, Vienna, Austria
Tel.: (43) 2051160 1103
Web Site: http://www.idc.com
Computer Newspapers, Magazines & Books
N.A.I.C.S.: 513120

IDC Central Europe GmbH (3)
Hanauer Landstr 182 D, Frankfurt, 60314, Germany
Tel.: (49) 69905020
Web Site: http://www.idc.com
Market Analysis, Intelligence & Tactical Support to Users in IT & Telecommunications
N.A.I.C.S.: 517810
Wafa Moussavi-Amin *(Mng Dir-Northern Europe & Grp VP)*

IDC China (3)
Room 901 Tower E Global Trade Center 36 North 3rd Ring Road, Beijing, 100013, China
Tel.: (86) 10 5889 1666
Web Site: http://www.idc.com
Provider of Business Information & Data
N.A.I.C.S.: 561499
Xi Wang *(Mgr-Res)*

IDC Columbia (3)
Carrera 13 A 89 38 Nippon Ctr Oficina 627, Bogota, Colombia
Tel.: (57) 16914356
Web Site: http://www.idccolombia.com.co
Market Analysis, Intelligence & Tactical Support to Users in IT & Telecommunications
N.A.I.C.S.: 517810
Carlos Villate *(Partner-Consulting)*

IDC France (3)
13 rue Paul Valery, 75116, Paris, Cedex, France
Tel.: (33) 156262666
Web Site: http://www.idc.fr
Publishing
N.A.I.C.S.: 513120
Helen Fily *(Sls Dir)*

IDC India Ltd. (3)
Unit no.221-223 Vipul Plaza 2nd Floor Sector 54 Golf Course Road, Gurgaon, 122002, India
Tel.: (91) 124 476 2300
Web Site: http://www.idc.com
Provider of Business Information & Data
N.A.I.C.S.: 561499

IDC Israel (3)
11 Tuval St - 5th Floor, Ramat Gan, 5252226, Israel
Tel.: (972) 36871727
Web Site: http://www.idc.com
IT Consulting Services
N.A.I.C.S.: 541618
Gideon Lopez *(Country Mgr)*

IDC Italy (3)
Viale Monza 14, 20127, Milan, Italy
Tel.: (39) 02284571
Web Site: http://www.idcitalia.com
Market Analysis, Intelligence & Tactical Support to Users in IT & Telecommunications
N.A.I.C.S.: 517810
Barbara Cambieri *(Mng Dir & Grp VP)*

IDC Japan Co., Ltd. (3)
1 13 5 Kudankita Chiyoda, Tokyo, 102-0073, Japan
Tel.: (81) 335564760
Web Site: http://www.idc.com
Market Analysis, Intelligence & Tactical Support to Users in IT & Telecommunications
N.A.I.C.S.: 517810
Masato Takeuchi *(Pres & CEO)*

IDC Korea Ltd. (3)
Suite 406 Trade Tower 511 Yeongdongdaero, Gangnam-gu, Seoul, 06164, Korea (South)
Tel.: (82) 25514380
Web Site: http://www.idc.com
Business Information & Data Services
N.A.I.C.S.: 561499

Subsidiary (Domestic):

IDC Latin America (3)
4090 NW 97 Ave Ste 350, Miami, FL 33178-6204
Tel.: (305) 351-3020
Web Site: http://www.idc.com
Internet Connectivity Services
N.A.I.C.S.: 517810
Eric Prothero *(Sr VP-Worldwide Tracker Res & Corp Dev)*

Subsidiary (Non-US):

IDC Mexico (3)
Manuel Avila Camacho 32 - 1102 piso 11, Col Lomas de Chapultepec, Mexico, 11000, Distrito Federal, Mexico
Tel.: (52) 5550101400
Web Site: http://www.idc.com
Market Analysis, Intelligence & Tactical Support to Users in IT & Telecommunications
N.A.I.C.S.: 517810

IDC Nordic (Denmark) A/S (3)
Predgate 23 A, K 1260, Copenhagen, Denmark
Tel.: (45) 39162222
Web Site: http://www.nordic.idc.com
Sales Range: $10-24.9 Million
Emp.: 16
Provider of Business Information & Data
N.A.I.C.S.: 561499
Johnny Cederlund *(Mgr-Global Acct)*

IDC Nordic (Sweden) (3)
Magnus Ladulasgatan 65, 106 78, Stockholm, Sweden
Tel.: (46) 8 444 15 90
Web Site: http://www.nordic.idc.com
Provider of Business Information & Data
N.A.I.C.S.: 561499
Jan Larsen *(VP-EMEA)*

IDC Philippines (3)

IDG CAPITAL

IDG Capital—(Continued)

Unit 1803 Trade and Financial Tower 7th Avenue corner 32nd Street, Bonifacio Global City, Taguig, 1201, Philippines
Tel.: (63) 24787260
Web Site: http://www.idc.com
Provider of Business Information & Data
N.A.I.C.S.: 561499

IDC Polska (3)
Godara 9, Warsaw, 02 626, Poland
Tel.: (48) 225484050
Web Site: http://www.idc.com
Business Information & Data
N.A.I.C.S.: 561499

IDC Portugal (3)
Centro Empresarial Torres de Lisboa Rua Tomas da Fonseca Torre G, Lisbon, 1600-209, Portugal
Tel.: (351) 21 723 06 22
Web Site: http://www.idc.pt
Information Technology Services
N.A.I.C.S.: 519290

Subsidiary (Domestic):

IDC Research, Inc. (3)
5 Speen St, Framingham, MA 01701-4674
Tel.: (508) 872-8200
Web Site: http://www.idc.com
Market Intelligence, Advisory & Marketing Event Organizing Services
N.A.I.C.S.: 561499
Leif Eriksen *(VP-Res-Future of Ops)*

Subsidiary (Non-US):

IDC Russia (3)
Timiryazevskaya Street 1 Building 5, Moscow, 127422, Russia
Tel.: (7) 495 9 747 747
Web Site: http://www.idc.com
Market Analysis, Intelligence & Tactical Support to Users in IT & Telecommunications
N.A.I.C.S.: 517810
Robert Farish *(VP-IDC Russia & CIS)*

IDC Spain (3)
C/Serrano 41 - 3A planta, Madrid, 28001, Spain
Tel.: (34) 917872150
Web Site: http://www.idcspain.com
International Fund to Assist Entrepreneurs with Business Expansion
N.A.I.C.S.: 523150
Jorge Gil *(Gen Mgr)*

IDC Taiwan (3)
E-1 4F No 89 Sungren Rd, Xinyi District, Taipei, 110, Taiwan
Tel.: (886) 287580800
Web Site: http://www.idc.com
Provider of Business Information & Data
N.A.I.C.S.: 561499

IDC Turkey (3)
Nispetiye Mahallesi Cahit Aybar Sokak Zincirlikuyu Harp Akademileri, 4 Daire 74 Besiktas, 34340, Istanbul, Turkiye
Tel.: (90) 2123560282
Web Site: http://www.idc.com
Provider of Business Information
N.A.I.C.S.: 513120
Nevin Cizmeciogullari *(Country Dir)*

IDC UK Ltd. (3)
5th floor Ealing Cross 85 Uxbridge Road, London, W5 5TH, United Kingdom
Tel.: (44) 2089877100
Web Site: http://www.uk.idc.com
IT Consulting Services
N.A.I.C.S.: 541618
Dan Timberlake *(Mng Dir-UK & Ireland)*

IDC Venezuela (3)
Lomas de La Trinidad Calle del Sauce Quinta El Sauce No 1, Caracas, 1080, Venezuela
Tel.: (58) 212 945 2314
Web Site: http://www.idc.com
Market Analysis, Intelligence & Tactical Support to Users in IT & Telecommunications
N.A.I.C.S.: 513120

IDG Business Verlag GmbH (3)
YonelSeinengir Strasse 26, Munich, 80807, Germany
Tel.: (49) 89 360 86 0
Web Site: http://www.idg.de

Magazine Publisher
N.A.I.C.S.: 513120

IDG China Co., Ltd. (3)
Room 901m Tower E Global Trade Center 36 North 3rd Ring Road, 100013, Beijing, China
Tel.: (86) 10 5889 1666
Web Site: http://www.idc.com
Magazine Publisher
N.A.I.C.S.: 513120
Xi Wang *(Mgr-Res)*

IDG Communications Italia Srl (3)
S.S. Del Sempione 28, 20017, Milan, Italy
Tel.: (39) 02 4997 7209
Web Site: http://www.fieramilano.it
Market Analysis, Intelligence & Tactical Support to Users in IT & Telecommunications
N.A.I.C.S.: 517810

IDG Communications Media AG (3)
Lyonel-Feininger-Strasse 26, 80807, Munich, Germany
Tel.: (49) 89 360 86 0
Web Site: http://www.idg.de
Marketing Consulting Services
N.A.I.C.S.: 541910
Kevin Krull *(Chm)*

IDG Communications Media AG (3)
Lyonel-Feininger-Str 26, Munich, 80807, Germany
Tel.: (49) 89360860
Web Site: http://www.idg.de
Computer Magazine Publisher
N.A.I.C.S.: 513120
Kevin Krull *(Chm)*

IDG Communications Norge AS (3)
PO Box 171 City Center, 0102, Oslo, Norway
Tel.: (47) 22053000
Publishing Services
N.A.I.C.S.: 513120
Morten Hansen *(CEO)*

IDG Communications Pty. Ltd. (3)
Level 10 15 Blue St, Sydney, 2060, NSW, Australia
Tel.: (61) 294395133
Web Site: http://www.idg.com.au
Media & Research Pubishing Services
N.A.I.C.S.: 513120
Barbara Simon *(Pres)*

IDG Communications Publishing Group SRL (3)
8 10 Maresal Averescu Fl 7 Rm 705 715, Bucharest, 71316, Romania
Tel.: (40) 212242621
N.A.I.C.S.: 513120
Gineta Rosca *(Mgr-Sls)*

IDG Communications UK, Ltd. (3)
101 Euston Road, London, NW1 2RA, United Kingdom
Tel.: (44) 20 7756 2800
Web Site: http://www.idg.co.uk
Magazine Publisher
N.A.I.C.S.: 513120
Kit Gould *(Pres-B2C)*

IDG Communications, S.A.U. (3)
Velazquez 105 Floor 5, 28006, Madrid, Spain
Tel.: (34) 913496600
Web Site: http://www.idg.es
Market Analysis, Intelligence & Tactical Support to Users in IT & Telecommunications
N.A.I.C.S.: 513120

IDG Computerworld do Brazil (3)
Avenida Chedid Jafet 222 Via Olimpia, Sao Paulo, Brazil
Tel.: (55) 11 3823 6600
Magazine Publisher
N.A.I.C.S.: 513120

IDG Czech Republic, a.s. (3)
Seydlerova 2451, Prague, 158 00, Czech Republic
Tel.: (420) 775 210 150
Web Site: http://www.idg.com
Newspaper & Magazines Publisher
N.A.I.C.S.: 513120
Jana Pelikanova *(Mng Dir)*

IDG Denmark A/S (3)
Horkaer 18, 2730, Herlev, Denmark
Tel.: (45) 77300300

Market Analysis, Intelligence & Tactical Support to Users in IT & Telecommunications
N.A.I.C.S.: 517810

IDG Entertainment Media GmbH (3)
Lyonel-Feininger-Str 26, Munich, 80807, Germany
Tel.: (49) 89 360 86 0
Magazine Publisher
N.A.I.C.S.: 513120

IDG Entertainment Verlag GmbH (3)
Lyonel Feininger Street 26, Munich, 80807, Germany
Tel.: (49) 89360860
Web Site: http://www.idg.de
International Fund to Assist Entrepreneurs with Business Expansion
N.A.I.C.S.: 523150

IDG Global Solutions (3)
Lionel Feininger Strasse 26, Munich, D 80807, Germany
Tel.: (49) 89 360 86 0
Web Site: http://www.idg.com
International Fund to Assist Entrepreneurs with Business Expansion
N.A.I.C.S.: 523150

IDG Global Solutions APAC (3)
80 Anson Road #31-05 Fuji Xerox Tower, Singapore, 077907, Singapore
Tel.: (65) 98337294
Web Site: http://www.idg.com
International Fund to Assist Entrepreneurs with Business Expansion
N.A.I.C.S.: 523150

IDG Japan, Inc. (3)
4-3-12 Toranomon, Minato-ku, Tokyo, 105-8308, Japan
Tel.: (81) 358003111
Web Site: http://www.idg.co.jp
Magazine Publisher
N.A.I.C.S.: 513120

IDG Magazines Norge AS (3)
PO Box 171 City Center, 0102, Oslo, Norway
Tel.: (47) 2205 3000
Web Site: http://www.cw.no
Magazine Publisher
N.A.I.C.S.: 513120
Morten Hansen *(Mng Dir)*

IDG Media Private Limited (3)
35/2 Langford Rd Cross Bheemanna Garde, Sampangi Rama Nagara, Bengaluru, 560025, India
Tel.: (91) 96063 93030
Web Site: http://www.idg.com
Magazine Publisher
N.A.I.C.S.: 513120

IDG Netherlands (3)
Joop Geesinkweg 701 51, 1114 AB, Amsterdam, Netherlands
Tel.: (31) 207585955
Web Site: http://www.idg.nl
Publisher of News & Business Information
N.A.I.C.S.: 513120

IDG Poland S.A. (3)
Twarda 18 Spektrum Tower, Warsaw, 2092, Poland
Tel.: (48) 223217800
Web Site: http://www.idg.com.pl
Market Analysis, Intelligence & Tactical Support to Users in IT & Telecommunications
N.A.I.C.S.: 513120
Marcin Tyborowski *(Dir-Sls)*

IDG Sweden AB (3)
Magnus Ladulasgatan 65, Stockholm, 106 78, Sweden
Tel.: (46) 84536000
Web Site: http://www.idgsverige.se
Marketing Publisher
N.A.I.C.S.: 513120

IDG Taiwan (3)
19F NO15-1 Sec 1 Hang Chou S Road, Taipei, Taiwan
Tel.: (886) 2 23214335
Magazine Publisher
N.A.I.C.S.: 513120

International Data Corporation (Canada) Ltd (3)
33 Yonge Street Suite 902, Toronto, M5E 1G4, ON, Canada

INTERNATIONAL PUBLIC

Tel.: (416) 369-0033
Web Site: http://www.idc.com
Market Research on Information Technology Industry
N.A.I.C.S.: 541910
Lars Goransson *(Mng Dir)*

Inviarco SAS (3)
Carrera 90 No 154A 75 Piso 4, Bogota, DC, Colombia
Tel.: (57) 1 686 2462
Web Site: http://www.computerworld.co
Computer Magazine Publisher
N.A.I.C.S.: 513120

Media Trans Asia Limited (3)
Ocean Tower 2 No 75-8 Suksumbit Rd, Suksumbit Soi 19 Wattana Dist, Bangkok, 10110, Thailand
Tel.: (66) 22042370
Web Site: http://www.mediatransasia.com
Market Analysis, Intelligence & Tactical Support to Users in IT & Telecommunications
N.A.I.C.S.: 513120

Mediateam Ltd. (3)
55 Spruce Avenue Stillorgan Industrial Estate Sandyford, Leopardstown, Dublin, Ireland
Tel.: (353) 1 294 7777
Web Site: http://www.mediateam.ie
Technology Magazine Publisher
N.A.I.C.S.: 513120
Paul Byrne *(Dir-Sls)*

Subsidiary (Domestic):

Network World, Inc. (3)
5 Speen St, Framingham, MA 01701
Tel.: (508) 875-5000
Web Site: http://www.networkworld.com
Publisher of Computer Magazines
N.A.I.C.S.: 513120

Subsidiary (Non-US):

PT Prima Infosarana Media (3)
Gramedia Majalah Building Unit I 3th Floor, Jl Panjang No 8A Kebon Jeruk, Jakarta, 11530, Indonesia
Tel.: (62) 215330150
Web Site: http://www.infokomputer.com
IT Magazine Publisher
N.A.I.C.S.: 513120
Dahlan Dahi *(Grp Dir)*

Subsidiary (Domestic):

IDG World Expo Corporation (2)
492 Old Connecticut Path Ste 420, Framingham, MA 01701
Tel.: (508) 879-6700
Web Site: http://www.idgworldexpo.com
Organizes Trade Shows
N.A.I.C.S.: 561920

MEMSIC, Inc. (2)
1 Tech Dr Ste 325, Andover, MA 01810
Tel.: (978) 738-0900
Web Site: http://www.memsic.com
Semiconductor Sensor & System Solutions Based on Integrated Micro Electro-Mechanical Systems (MEMS), Technology & Mixed Signal Circuit Design
N.A.I.C.S.: 334413

IDH DEVELOPMENT SA

Herbu Janina 5 room U03 1st floor, 02-972, Warsaw, Poland
Tel.: (48) 221120754
Web Site: https://idhsa.pl
Year Founded: 1995
700—(DEU)
Construction Services
N.A.I.C.S.: 236220
Dariusz Lesniak Paduch *(Pres)*

IDI SCA

23-25 Avenue Franklin Delano Roosevelt, 75008, Paris, France
Tel.: (33) 155278000 FR
Web Site: https://www.idi.fr
Year Founded: 1970
IDIP—(EUR)
Sales Range: $50-74.9 Million
Emp.: 13

Holding Company; Private Equity & Investment Management Services
N.A.I.C.S.: 551112
Christian Langlois-Meurinne (CEO)

Subsidiaries:

IDI Asset Management SA (1)
18 Avenue Matignon, 75008, Paris, France (49.9%)
Tel.: (33) 155278000
Sales Range: $25-49.9 Million
Emp.: 16
Asset Management Services
N.A.I.C.S.: 523940
Bernard Meheut (Chm)

IDI Emerging Markets S.A. (1)
11 rue Sainte Zithe, Luxembourg, 2763, Luxembourg
Tel.: (352) 27489695
Web Site: http://www.idi-em.com
Sales Range: $50-74.9 Million
Emp.: 4
Privater Equity Firm
N.A.I.C.S.: 523999
Peter Bieliczky (Co-Mng Dir)

IDICO INVESTMENT CONSULTANT JSC
No 100 Nguyen Gia Tri, Ward 25 Binh Thanh District, Ho Chi Minh City, Vietnam
Tel.: (84) 838995588
INC—(HNX)
Rev.: $2,466,700
Assets: $3,708,900
Liabilities: $1,271,100
Net Worth: $2,437,800
Earnings: $201,600
Fiscal Year-end: 12/31/23
Consultancy Services
N.A.I.C.S.: 541690
Nguyen Ngoc Khanh (Member-Mgmt Bd)

IDIS CO., LTD.
IDIS Tower 344 Pangyo-ro, Bundang-gu, Seongnam, 13493, Gyeonggi-do, Korea (South)
Tel.: (82) 317235035
Web Site: https://www.idisglobal.com
Year Founded: 1997
143160—(KRS)
Rev.: $207,031,207
Assets: $253,491,143
Liabilities: $56,762,828
Net Worth: $196,728,315
Earnings: $10,959,119
Emp.: 416
Fiscal Year-end: 12/31/22
Audio & Video Equipment Mfr
N.A.I.C.S.: 334310
Yeong Dal Kim (Pres & CEO)

Subsidiaries:

Costar Technologies Inc. (1)
101 Wrangler Dr Ste 201, Coppell, TX 75019-4657
Tel.: (469) 635-6800
Web Site: http://www.costartechnologies.com
Rev.: $60,367,000
Assets: $40,326,000
Liabilities: $31,878,000
Net Worth: $8,448,000
Earnings: ($8,971,000)
Fiscal Year-end: 12/31/2020
Security System Services
N.A.I.C.S.: 561621
Sally A. Washlow (Chm)

Subsidiary (Domestic):

Arecont Vision LLC (2)
425 E Colorado St 7th Fl, Glendale, CA 91205
Tel.: (818) 937-0700
Web Site: http://www.arecontvision.com
High-Performance Megapixel Cameras Mfr for Professional Surveillance & Security Applications
N.A.I.C.S.: 561621

Michael Kaplinsky (Co-Founder & CEO)

IDIS America Co., Ltd. (1)
801 Hammond St Ste 200, Coppell, TX 75019
Tel.: (469) 444-6538
Network Camera Mfr
N.A.I.C.S.: 333310

IDIS Benelux BV (1)
De Slof 9, 5107 RH, Dongen, Netherlands
Tel.: (31) 162387247
Network Camera Mfr
N.A.I.C.S.: 333310

IDIS Europe Limited (1)
1000 Great West Road, Brentford, TW8 9HH, Middlesex, United Kingdom
Tel.: (44) 2036575678
Network Camera Mfr
N.A.I.C.S.: 333310

IDIS HOLDINGS CO., LTD.
8-10 Techno 3-ro, Yuseong-gu, Daejeon, Korea (South)
Tel.: (82) 429339677
Web Site: https://www.idisholdings.co.kr
Year Founded: 1997
054800—(KRS)
Rev.: $670,397,325
Assets: $836,055,619
Liabilities: $262,080,005
Net Worth: $573,975,613
Earnings: $68,572,077
Emp.: 16
Fiscal Year-end: 12/31/22
Holding Company
N.A.I.C.S.: 551112
Kim Young-Dal (CEO)

IDJ VIETNAM INVESTMENT JOINT STOCK COMPANY
3rd Floor Grand Plaza Shopping Center, No 117 Tran Duy Hung Trung Hoa Ward, Hanoi, Vietnam
Tel.: (84) 435558999
Web Site: https://www.idjf.vn
Year Founded: 2007
IDJ—(HNX)
Rev.: $35,516,213
Assets: $192,982,613
Liabilities: $108,369,431
Net Worth: $84,613,182
Earnings: $4,507,651
Emp.: 134
Fiscal Year-end: 12/31/23
International Financial Investment & Enterprise Development Services
N.A.I.C.S.: 523999
Khanh Cong Han (Chm-Mgmt Bd)

IDLC FINANCE PLC.
Bay's Galleria 1st Floor 57 Gulshan Avenue, Dhaka, 1212, Bangladesh
Tel.: (880) 28834990
Web Site: https://www.idlc.com
IDLC—(CHT)
Rev.: $102,422,339
Assets: $1,351,680,556
Liabilities: $1,186,492,080
Net Worth: $165,188,476
Earnings: $17,463,541
Emp.: 30
Fiscal Year-end: 12/31/22
Financial Services
N.A.I.C.S.: 522291
M. Jamal Uddin (Deputy Mng Dir & Head-Bus)

Subsidiaries:

IDLC Finance Limited - MERCHANT BANKING DIVISON (1)
36 Dilkusha Commercial Area 13th Floor, Dhaka, 1000, Bangladesh
Tel.: (880) 29571842
Web Site: http://www.idlc.com
Portfolio Fund Management Services
N.A.I.C.S.: 523940

IDLC Securities Limited (1)
DR Tower 4th Floor Bir Protik Gazi Golam Dastagir Road Purana Paltan, Dhaka, 1000, Bangladesh
Tel.: (880) 9609994352
Web Site: https://securities.idlc.com
Securities Brokerage Services
N.A.I.C.S.: 523150
Khalilur Rahman (Chm)

IDM S.A.
Stefan Okrzeja 1A, 03-715, Warsaw, Poland
Tel.: (48) 532400199
Web Site: https://www.idmsa.pl
Year Founded: 2005
IDM—(WAR)
Rev.: $145,221
Assets: $763,869
Liabilities: $962,237
Net Worth: ($198,368)
Earnings: ($344,522)
Fiscal Year-end: 04/30/23
Asset Management Services
N.A.I.C.S.: 523940
Grzegorz Leszczynski (Chm-Mgmt Bd & Pres)

IDNNT SA
Via Maestri Comacini 4, 6830, Chiasso, Switzerland
Web Site: https://www.idntt.ch
Year Founded: 2010
IDNTT—(EUR)
Advertising Media Services
N.A.I.C.S.: 541840
Christian Traviglia (Founder, Chm & Pres)

IDNOW GMBH
Auenstrasse 100, 80469, Munich, Germany
Tel.: (49) 89 413 24 600
Web Site: http://www.idnow.io
Identification Systerm Services
N.A.I.C.S.: 513210
Andreas Bodczek (CEO)

IDOM, INC.
JP Tower 26F 2-7-2 Marunouchi, Chiyoda-ku, Tokyo, 100-7026, Japan
Tel.: (81) 352085503
Web Site: https://www.idom-inc.com
Year Founded: 1994
7599—(TKS)
Rev.: $2,976,750,680
Assets: $1,304,779,790
Liabilities: $808,976,090
Net Worth: $495,803,700
Earnings: $81,123,780
Emp.: 3,132
Fiscal Year-end: 02/29/24
Used Car Sales
N.A.I.C.S.: 441120

IDOMOO LTD.
5 Hatidhar St, Ra'anana, 4366507, Israel
Tel.: (972) 772033227
Web Site: https://www.idomoo.com
IDMO—(TAE)
Rev.: $16,752,000
Assets: $7,456,000
Liabilities: $11,526,000
Net Worth: ($4,070,000)
Earnings: ($6,849,000)
Fiscal Year-end: 06/30/23
Digital Video Stream Services
N.A.I.C.S.: 512110
Assaf Fogel (Co-Founder & VP-R&D)

IDORSIA LTD.
Hegenheimermattweg 91, 4123, Allschwil, Switzerland
Tel.: (41) 588440000 CH
Web Site: https://www.idorsia.com
Year Founded: 2017

IDIA—(SWX)
Rev.: $107,651,885
Assets: $1,002,416,851
Liabilities: $1,735,186,253
Net Worth: ($732,769,401)
Earnings: ($917,844,789)
Emp.: 1,300
Fiscal Year-end: 12/31/22
Holding Company; Biopharmaceutical Research, Development & Manufacturing Services
N.A.I.C.S.: 551112
Jean-Paul Clozel (CEO)

Subsidiaries:

Idorsia Pharmaceuticals Japan Ltd. (1)
9th Floor of Otemachi Financial City Grand Cube 1-9-2, Otemachi Chiyoda-ku, Tokyo, 100-0004, Japan
Tel.: (81) 35 204 1320
Web Site: https://www.idorsia.jp
Pharmaceutical R&D Services
N.A.I.C.S.: 541715

Idorsia Pharmaceuticals Ltd. (1)
Hegenheimermattweg 91, 4123, Allschwil, Switzerland
Tel.: (41) 588440000
Web Site: https://www.idorsia.com
Emp.: 650
Biopharmaceutical Research, Development & Manufacturing Services
N.A.I.C.S.: 541713
Jean-Paul Clozel (CEO)

IDOX PLC
Kendleshire Lodge Down Road, Winterbourne Down, Bristol, BS36 1AU, United Kingdom
Tel.: (44) 3330111200
Web Site: https://www.idoxgroup.com
IDOX—(AIM)
Rev.: $89,859,340
Assets: $176,540,258
Liabilities: $85,008,207
Net Worth: $91,532,052
Earnings: $6,848,340
Emp.: 595
Fiscal Year-end: 10/31/22
Information & Knowledge Management Services
N.A.I.C.S.: 541512
David Meaden (CEO)

Subsidiaries:

IDOX PLC - Software Division (1)
2nd Floor Chancery Exchange 10 Furnival St, London, EC4A 1AB, United Kingdom
Tel.: (44) 8703337101
Sales Range: $25-49.9 Million
Emp.: 100
Software Solutions & Information Services
N.A.I.C.S.: 541511

IDOX Software Limited (1)
Unit 5 Woking 8 Forsyth Road, Woking, GU21 5SB, Surrey, United Kingdom
Tel.: (44) 8703337101
Web Site: https://www.idoxgroup.com
Sales Range: $25-49.9 Million
Emp.: 50
Software Development Services
N.A.I.C.S.: 541511

Idox Belgium NV (1)
Pegasuslaan 5, 1831, Diegem, Belgium
Tel.: (32) 27136300
Information & Knowledge Management Services
N.A.I.C.S.: 541512

Idox France SARL (1)
75 Avenue Parmentier, 75544, Paris, Cedex 11, France
Tel.: (33) 299276000
Information & Knowledge Management Services
N.A.I.C.S.: 541512

Idox Germany GmbH (1)
Hauptstr 65, 12159, Berlin, Germany
Tel.: (49) 308419140

IDOX PLC

IDOX PLC—(Continued)

Web Site:
http://www.compliance.idoxgroup.com
Consulting Management Services
N.A.I.C.S.: 541618

Rippleffect Studio Limited (1)
20 Chapel St, Liverpool, L3 9AG, United Kingdom
Tel.: (44) 8458038381
Web Site: http://www.rippleffect.com
Digital Marketing Services
N.A.I.C.S.: 541613
Kirstie Buchanan *(Dir-Sls & Mktg)*

digital spirit GmbH (1)
Hauptstrasse 65, 12159, Berlin, Germany
Tel.: (49) 308419140
Web Site: http://www.digital-spirit.de
Corporate Training & Education Programs Developer
N.A.I.C.S.: 611430

j4b Software & Publishing Limited (1)
First Fl Alderley House Alderley Rd, Wilmslow, SK9 1AT, Cheshire, United Kingdom
Tel.: (44) 1625628007
Web Site: http://www.j4b.com
Sales Range: $25-49.9 Million
Emp.: 30
Information & Technology Solutions
N.A.I.C.S.: 541512

IDP CORP., LTD.

601 50 Digital-Ro 33-Gil, Guro-Gu, Seoul, 08377, Korea (South)
Tel.: (82) 260993700
Web Site: https://www.idp-corp.com
Year Founded: 2005
332370—(KRS)
Rev: $33,066,574
Assets: $44,245,480
Liabilities: $5,284,126
Net Worth: $38,961,354
Earnings: $7,923,487
Emp.: 45
Fiscal Year-end: 12/31/22
Computer & Peripheral Equipment Mfr
N.A.I.C.S.: 334118
Brian Roh *(CEO)*

Subsidiaries:

IDP Americas, Inc. (1)
1485 S County Trl Unit 306, East Greenwich, RI 02818
Tel.: (401) 400-7111
Identity Card Printer Machine Mfr
N.A.I.C.S.: 333248
Brian Roh *(CEO)*

IDP EDUCATION AUSTRALIA LIMITED

Level 10 697 Collins St, Docklands, 3008, VIC, Australia
Tel.: (61) 396124400
Web Site: https://www.idp.com
IEL—(ASX)
Rev: $6,078,438,879
Assets: $746,871,285
Liabilities: $397,972,877
Net Worth: $348,898,408
Earnings: $8,794,980
Emp.: 4,709
Fiscal Year-end: 06/30/22
Study Abroad & Teaching English Abroad
N.A.I.C.S.: 611710
Andrew Barkla *(CEO & Mng Dir)*

IDRA S.R.L.

Via dei Metalli 2, Travagliato, 25039, Brescia, Italy
Tel.: (39) 03020111
Web Site: http://www.idracasting.com
Year Founded: 1945
Sales Range: $75-99.9 Million
Emp.: 400

Pressure Die-Casting Machines for Working with Non-Ferrous Metals Mfr, Marketer & Retailer
N.A.I.C.S.: 333517
Riccardo Ferrario *(Gen Mgr)*

Subsidiaries:

Idra China Ltd (1)
Room 1011 Qilu Building 836 Dongfang Road, Pudong, Shanghai, 200122, China
Tel.: (86) 2168751216
Web Site: http://www.idracasting.com
Sales & Service of Die-Casting Machines
N.A.I.C.S.: 423830

Idra Limited (1)
Unit 7 Apollo Park Lichfield Rd Industrial Estate, Apollo, Tamworth, B79 7TA, Staffordshire, United Kingdom **(100%)**
Tel.: (44) 01827311654
Web Site: http://www.idracasting.com
Metal Castings
N.A.I.C.S.: 333517

Idra North America (1)
1619 Rank Pwy, Kokomo, IN 46901 **(100%)**
Tel.: (765) 459-0085
Web Site: http://www.idracasting.com
Sales Range: $25-49.9 Million
Emp.: 5
Metal Castings
N.A.I.C.S.: 333517
Michael Groves *(Gen Mgr)*

Idra Pressen GmbH (1)
Eisenbahnstrasse 6, 73630, Remshalden, Germany
Tel.: (49) 715170080
Web Site: http://www.idragroup.com
Sales & Services of Die Casting Machinery
N.A.I.C.S.: 423830
Jorg Muller *(Gen Mgr)*

IDREAM FILM INFRASTRUCTURE COMPANY LIMITED

2nd Floor Trade View Building Oasis Complex, Kamala Mills Gate No 4 Pandurang Budhkar Marg Lower Parel, Mumbai, 400 013, India
Tel.: (91) 2267400900
Web Site:
https://www.idreamfilminfra.com
504375—(BOM)
Assets: $719
Liabilities: $500,701
Net Worth: ($499,982)
Earnings: ($31,041)
Fiscal Year-end: 03/31/23
Motion Picture & Video Production Services
N.A.I.C.S.: 512110
Rupesh Kodere *(CFO)*

IDREAMSKY TECHNOLOGY LIMITED

16/F A3 Building Kexing Science Park 15 Keyuan Road North, Nanshan District, Shenzhen, 518057, Guangdong, China
Tel.: (86) 755 8668 5111 Ky
Web Site: http://www.idreamsky.com
Year Founded: 2012
Sales Range: $200-249.9 Million
Emp.: 613
Mobile Game Publisher
N.A.I.C.S.: 513210
Michael Xiangyu Chen *(Chm & CEO)*

IDREES TEXTILE MILLS LIMITED

6-C Ismail Centre 1st Floor Central Commercial Area, Bahadurabad, Karachi, Pakistan
Tel.: (92) 2134940026 PK
Web Site:
https://www.idreestextile.com
Year Founded: 1990
IDRT—(PSX)
Rev: $15,151,407
Assets: $22,021,216

Liabilities: $12,857,757
Net Worth: $9,163,489
Earnings: ($38,821)
Emp.: 768
Fiscal Year-end: 06/30/23
Apparel Garment Mfr
N.A.I.C.S.: 315990
S. Muhammad Idrees Allawala *(Chm)*

Subsidiaries:

ORA Home LLC (1)
1215 Livingston Ave Ste 4 N, New Brunswick, NJ 08902
Tel.: (213) 642-1213
Web Site: https://www.orahome.us
Label Towel Mfr
N.A.I.C.S.: 314120

IDS SA

20 rue Joseph Serlin, BP 1076, 69001, Lyon, France
Tel.: (33) 380905252
Web Site: https://www.idsplc.com
Year Founded: 1994
MLIDS—(EUR)
Sales Range: $1-9.9 Million
Computer System Design Services
N.A.I.C.S.: 541512

IDSUD SA

3 place du General de Gaulle, 13001, Marseille, France
Tel.: (33) 491130900
Web Site: https://www.idsud.com
ALIDS—(EUR)
Sales Range: $1-9.9 Million
Emp.: 100
Financial Services
N.A.I.C.S.: 525990
Jeremie Luciani *(Chm-Exec Bd & CFO)*

IDT AUSTRALIA LIMITED

45 Wadhurst Drive, Boronia, 3155, VIC, Australia
Tel.: (61) 398018888
Web Site: https://en.idtaus.com.au
IDT—(ASX)
Rev: $9,429,086
Assets: $20,947,516
Liabilities: $5,295,139
Net Worth: $15,652,377
Earnings: ($3,614,450)
Emp.: 50
Fiscal Year-end: 06/30/24
Pharmaceutical Manufacturing Company
N.A.I.C.S.: 236210
David Sparling *(CEO & Co-Sec)*

IDT INTERNATIONAL LIMITED

Block C 9/F Kaiser Estate Phase 1 41 Man Yue Street, Hunghom, Kowloon, China (Hong Kong)
Tel.: (852) 27647873 BM
Web Site: http://www.idthk.com
Year Founded: 1977
0167—(HKG)
Rev: $2,180,250
Assets: $10,365,750
Liabilities: $49,329,750
Net Worth: ($38,964,000)
Earnings: ($10,735,500)
Emp.: 353
Fiscal Year-end: 12/31/21
Electronics Mfr & Marketer
N.A.I.C.S.: 334111
Yongning Zhu *(CEO)*

Subsidiaries:

IDT (Japan) Limited (1)
Yuemu Building 8th Floor, 1-14-5 Higashi Ueno Taito-Ku, Tokyo, 110-0015, Japan
Tel.: (81) 338373791
Web Site: http://www.oregonscientific.com
Sales Range: $25-49.9 Million
Emp.: 4
Business Support Services

INTERNATIONAL PUBLIC

N.A.I.C.S.: 561499

IDT Communication Technology Limited (1)
Block C 9th Fl Kaiser Estate Phase 1 41 Man Yue St, Hunghom, Hung Hom, China (Hong Kong)
Tel.: (852) 27647873
Electronic Parts & Equipment Whslr
N.A.I.C.S.: 423690
Raymond Chan *(Chm)*

IDT Data System Limited (1)
9th Fl Kaiser Estate Phase 1 Blk C, 41 Man Yue Street Hunghom, Kowloon, China (Hong Kong)
Tel.: (852) 27647873
Web Site: http://www.idthk.com
Electronic Parts & Equipment Whslr
N.A.I.C.S.: 423690

IDT Electronic Products Limited (1)
9th Floor Kaiser Est Ph 1 Blk C, Hung Hom, Kowloon, China (Hong Kong)
Tel.: (852) 27647873
Toy & Hobby Goods & Supplies Whslr
N.A.I.C.S.: 423920

IDT Sonicvision Limited (1)
9th Floor Kaiser Estate Phase 1 Blk C 41 Man Yue Street, Hunghom, Kowloon, China (Hong Kong)
Tel.: (852) 27647873
Web Site: http://www.idthk.com
Electronic Parts & Equipment Whslr
N.A.I.C.S.: 423690

IDT Technology Limited (1)
9th Floor Kaiser Est Ph 1 Blk C, Hung Hom, Kowloon, China (Hong Kong)
Tel.: (852) 27647873
Electronic Parts & Equipment Whslr
N.A.I.C.S.: 423690

Integrated Display Technology Limited (1)
9th Fl Kaiser Est Ph 1 Blk C, Hung Hom, Kowloon, China (Hong Kong)
Tel.: (852) 27647873
Web Site: http://www.idtha.com
Waste Management Services
N.A.I.C.S.: 562998

Ming Win Electronics Limited (1)
9th Floor Kaiser Estate Phase 1 Blk C 41 Man Yue Street, Hunghom, Kowloon, China (Hong Kong)
Tel.: (852) 27647873
Toy & Hobby Goods & Supplies Whslr
N.A.I.C.S.: 423920

Oregon Scientific Global Distribution Limited (1)
41 Man Yue Street Block C 9/F Kaiser Estate Phase 1, Hung Hom, Kowloon, China (Hong Kong)
Tel.: (852) 2 764 7873
Web Site: http://www.idthk.com
Electronic Parts & Equipment Whslr
N.A.I.C.S.: 423690

Subsidiary (Non-US):

Oregon Scientific (Deutschland) GmbH (2)
Siemensstrasse 3, 63263, Neu-Isenburg, Germany **(100%)**
Tel.: (49) 61027985388
Web Site:
http://www.de.oregonscientific.com
Warm Air Heating & Air-Conditioning Equipment & Supplies Whslr
N.A.I.C.S.: 423730

Oregon Scientific (U.K.) Limited (2)
One St Peter's Road, Gardner Road, Maidenhead, SL6 7QU, Berkshire, United Kingdom **(100%)**
Tel.: (44) 1628879675
Web Site: http://www.oregonscientific.co.uk
Sales Range: $25-49.9 Million
Emp.: 20
Electronic Parts & Equipment Whslr
N.A.I.C.S.: 423690

Oregon Scientific Australia Pty Limited (2)
6 Beaumont Road, Mount Kuring-Gai, 2080, NSW, Australia **(100%)**
Tel.: (61) 294570000

Web Site: http://oregonshop.com.au
Sales Range: $25-49.9 Million
Emp.: 10
Electronic Parts & Equipment Whslr
N.A.I.C.S.: 423690
Shibleey Moidy *(Mgr-Ops)*

Oregon Scientific Brasil Ltda (2)
Av Ibirapuera 2 907 - cj 1602 Bourbon Convention - Ed Comercial State, Moema, Sao Paulo, 04029-200, SP, Brazil
Tel.: (55) 1151039800
Web Site:
http://www.oregonscientific.com.br
Emp.: 6
Electrical Appliance Television & Radio Set Whslr
N.A.I.C.S.: 423620

Oregon Scientific Enterprise (Shanghai) Limited (2)
98 Liu He Road Harbor Huangpu Ring Center 18th Floor, Shanghai, 200001, China
Tel.: (86) 2163507072
Web Site: http://www.oregonscientific.com
Jewelry Watch Precious Stone & Precious Metal Whslr
N.A.I.C.S.: 423940

Oregon Scientific France S.A.R.L. (2)
Parispace 9 rue de la Sabliere, 92230, Gennevilliers, France **(100%)**
Tel.: (33) 157677994
Web Site: http://www.oregonscientific.fr
Sales Range: $25-49.9 Million
Emp.: 8
Electrical Appliance Television & Radio Set Whslr
N.A.I.C.S.: 423620

Subsidiary (Domestic):

Oregon Scientific Hong Kong Limited (2)
Unit 1 5/F Yen Shing Centre 64 Hoi Yuen Road, Kwun Tong, Kowloon, China (Hong Kong)
Tel.: (852) 23031889
Web Site: http://www.oregonscientific.com
Retail Stores
N.A.I.C.S.: 459999

Subsidiary (Non-US):

Oregon Scientific Iberica, S.A. (2)
Calle zurbano 45 piso primer, Madrid, 28010, Spain
Tel.: (34) 916503795
Web Site: http://www.oregonscientific.es
Electrical Appliance Television & Radio Set Whslr
N.A.I.C.S.: 423620

Oregon Scientific Italia Spa (2)
Centro Direzionale Colleoni, Palazzo Taurus 2 Viale Colleoni 3, 20864, Agrate Brianza, Italy
Tel.: (39) 039656181
Web Site: http://www.oregonscientific.it
Sales Range: $25-49.9 Million
Emp.: 50
Electronic Parts & Equipment Whslr
N.A.I.C.S.: 423690

Oregon Scientific South East Asia Pte Limited (2)
250 North Bridge Road, Singapore, Singapore
Tel.: (65) 65351226
Medical Dental & Hospital Equipment & Supplies Whslr
N.A.I.C.S.: 423450

Oregon Scientific Trading (Beijing) Co., Ltd. (2)
RM 1902 Building 10 Jianwai SOHO 39 East 3rd Road, Chao Yang District, Beijing, 100022, China
Tel.: (86) 1058699065
Web Site: http://www.ouxiya.com.cn
Sales Range: $25-49.9 Million
Emp.: 50
General Merchandise Whslr
N.A.I.C.S.: 455219

Subsidiary (US):

Oregon Scientific, Inc. (2)
19861 SW 95th Ave, Tualatin, OR 97062

Tel.: (503) 783-5100
Web Site: http://www.oregonscientific.com
Retailer of Electronic Consumer Products
N.A.I.C.S.: 423620

Super Win Electronics Limited (1)
9th Floor Kaiser Est Ph 1 Blk C, Hung Hom, Kowloon, China (Hong Kong)
Tel.: (852) 27647873
Web Site: http://www.superwin.com
Sales Range: $25-49.9 Million
Emp.: 25
Plastics Product Mfr
N.A.I.C.S.: 326199

IDVERDE UK LTD.
Landscapes House 3 Rye Hill Office Park, Birmingham Road Allesley, Coventry, CV5 9AB, United Kingdom
Tel.: (44) 2476405660
Web Site: http://www.idverde.co.uk
Year Founded: 1919
Outdoor Facilities Management Services
N.A.I.C.S.: 541320
Nick Temple-Heald *(Chm)*

Subsidiaries:

TCLandscapes Ltd. (1)
Pitsford Road Chapel Brampton, Carlisle, NN6 8BE, Northants, United Kingdom
Tel.: (44) 1604 821 843
Web Site: http://www.tclandscapes.co.uk
Landscape Services
N.A.I.C.S.: 541320
Jonathan Clive Highley *(Mng Dir)*

IE LIMITED
6 Bongeunsa-ro 86-gil 7F, Gangnam-gu, Seoul, Korea (South)
Tel.: (82) 2 556 7115
Web Site: http://ieholdings.com
Year Founded: 1984
023400—(KRS)
Sales Range: $10-24.9 Million
Venture Investment; Marketing Platform Influencer; Game Development
N.A.I.C.S.: 523999
Sung Won Choi *(CEO)*

IEC EDUCATION LTD.
E-578 First Floor Greater Kailash, New Delhi, 110048, India
Tel.: (91) 1141052893
Web Site: https://www.iecgroup.in
Rev.: $140
Assets: $5,598,612
Liabilities: $430,888
Net Worth: $5,167,725
Earnings: ($133,240)
Emp.: 100
Fiscal Year-end: 03/31/18
Educational Support Services
N.A.I.C.S.: 611710
Navin Gupta *(Mng Dir)*

IEI INTEGRATION CORP.
No 29 ZhongXing Rd, Xizhi Dist, New Taipei City, 221, Taiwan
Tel.: (886) 286916798
Web Site: https://www.ieiworld.com
3022—(TAI)
Rev.: $248,979,454
Assets: $468,370,792
Liabilities: $138,120,829
Net Worth: $330,249,963
Earnings: $45,199,514
Emp.: 219
Fiscal Year-end: 12/31/23
Computer Peripheral Equipment Mfr
N.A.I.C.S.: 334118

Subsidiaries:

Armorlink SH Corp. (1)
No 515 Shenfu Road XinZhuang Industrial Development Zone, Minhang, Shanghai, 201108, China
Tel.: (86) 2154429000
Web Site: http://www.armorlink.com.cn
Electronic Components Mfr

N.A.I.C.S.: 334419

IEI Technology USA Corp. (1)
138 University Pkwy, Pomona, CA 91768-4300
Tel.: (909) 595-2819
Web Site: http://www.ieiworld.com
Emp.: 30
Stationery & Office Supplies Merchant Whslr
N.A.I.C.S.: 334118
William Chang *(Exec VP)*

IEMR RESOURCES INC.
1300-1500 West Georgia Street, Vancouver, V6G 2Z6, BC, Canada
Tel.: (778) 375-3223 BC
Web Site: http://www.iemr-resources.com
Year Founded: 2008
IRI—(TSXV)
Rev.: $81
Assets: $2,425,596
Liabilities: $20,415
Net Worth: $2,405,181
Earnings: ($42,438)
Emp.: 3
Fiscal Year-end: 10/31/22
Investment Services
N.A.I.C.S.: 523999
Charles Yuen *(Interim CEO, CFO & Sec)*

IENERGIZER LIMITED
Mont Crevelt House Bulwer Avenue, Saint Sampson's, GY2 4LH, Guernsey
Tel.: (44) 1481242233 GY
Web Site: http://www.ienergizer.com
IBPO—(AIM)
Rev.: $265,225,244
Assets: $273,931,809
Liabilities: $215,363,063
Net Worth: $58,568,746
Earnings: $74,537,715
Emp.: 22,000
Fiscal Year-end: 03/31/22
Business Process Outsourcing Services
N.A.I.C.S.: 561499
Anil Aggarwal *(CEO)*

Subsidiaries:

Aptara, Inc. (1)
2901 Telestar Ct Ste 522, Falls Church, VA 22042-4536
Tel.: (703) 352-0001
Web Site: https://www.aptaracorp.com
Sales Range: $1-4.9 Billion
Emp.: 3,700
Digital Publishing Solutions
N.A.I.C.S.: 323111
Samir Kakar *(Pres)*

IEP INVEST SA
Noorderlaan 139, BE-2030, Antwerp, Belgium
Tel.: (32) 32349413
Web Site: https://www.iepinvest.be
Year Founded: 1982
IEP—(EUR)
Sales Range: $10-24.9 Million
Emp.: 1,885
Holding Company
N.A.I.C.S.: 551112
Guido Segers *(Chm)*

Subsidiaries:

Diringer S.A. (1)
3 rue Hilti ZI, Munster, France
Tel.: (33) 389779090
Wholesale Industrial Machinery
N.A.I.C.S.: 423830

Punch Graphix UK Ltd. (1)
Unit 1C Harwood Rd Northminster Business Park, Upper Poppleton, York, YO26 6QU, United Kingdom
Tel.: (44) 1904520555
Web Site: http://www.punchgraphix.com

Wholesale Industrial Machinery
N.A.I.C.S.: 423830
Wim Maes *(CEO)*

Punch PlastX Evergem NV (1)
Jacques Parijslaan 6, Evergem, 9940, Belgium
Tel.: (32) 92576311
Electronic Components Mfr
N.A.I.C.S.: 334513

Punch PlastX sro (1)
Vlarska 28, 917 01, Trnava, Slovakia
Tel.: (421) 335909100
Electronic Component
N.A.I.C.S.: 334513

Punch Powerglide Strasbourg SAS (1)
81 Rue De La Rochelle, PO Box 33, 67026, Strasbourg, Cedex, France **(100%)**
Tel.: (33) 388558855
Sales Range: $200-249.9 Million
Emp.: 1,200
Automatic Transmission Mfr
N.A.I.C.S.: 336350
Arnaud Bailo *(Pres)*

Punch Technix NV (1)
Kromme Spieringweg 289b, Vlaardingen, Netherlands
Tel.: (31) 23 558 9050
Wholesale Industrial Machinery
N.A.I.C.S.: 423830

Punch sro (1)
Vavrecka 311, 02901, Svit, Slovakia
Tel.: (421) 435515111
Electronic Components Mfr
N.A.I.C.S.: 334513

Wevada NV (1)
Bootweg 4, 8940, Wervik, Belgium
Tel.: (32) 56239411
Web Site:
http://www.punchinternational.com
Electronic Components Mfr
N.A.I.C.S.: 334513

IERVOLINO & LADY BACARDI ENTERTAINMENT S.P.A.
Via Barberini 29, Lazio, 00187, Rome, Italy
Tel.: (39) 0694368100
Web Site: https://www.ilbegroup.it
Year Founded: 2011
ALIE—(EUR)
Rev.: $181,481,804
Assets: $218,028,809
Liabilities: $110,574,443
Net Worth: $107,454,366
Earnings: $25,482,311
Emp.: 12
Fiscal Year-end: 12/31/21
Entertainment Industry Services
N.A.I.C.S.: 711410
Flavio Marziali *(CFO)*

Subsidiaries:

SoBe Sport S.R.L. (1)
Via Boccaccio 29, 20123, Milan, Italy
Tel.: (39) 0236765199
Web Site: https://www.sobesport.com
Online & Offline Advertising Services
N.A.I.C.S.: 541810

Wepost S.R.L. (1)
Via Albalonga 44, 00183, Rome, Italy
Tel.: (39) 0640067282
Web Site: https://www.wepostlab.com
Film & Video Production Services
N.A.I.C.S.: 512120

IES HOLDINGS LTD.
33 Montefiore St, Tel Aviv, 6520102, Israel
Tel.: (972) 37133222
Web Site: https://www.ies.com
Year Founded: 1987
IES—(TAE)
Rev.: $14,356,403
Assets: $500,653,950
Liabilities: $85,351,290
Net Worth: $415,302,660
Earnings: $18,155,822

IES HOLDINGS LTD.

IES Holdings Ltd.—(Continued)
Emp.: 5
Fiscal Year-end: 12/31/23
Offices of Other Holding Companies
N.A.I.C.S.: 551112
Chaym Geyer *(Chm)*

IESA PTY LTD
26 Len Shield Street, Paget, 4740, QLD, Australia
Tel.: (61) 7 4952 6826   AU
Year Founded: 1995
Environmental Services
N.A.I.C.S.: 541620

Subsidiaries:

IESA Inc. (1)
Edificio Millenium Avenida Vitacura 2939 Piso 10, Las Condes, Santiago, 7550011, Chile
Tel.: (56) 2 2431 5313
Environmental Services
N.A.I.C.S.: 541620

IESA Inc. (1)
Edificio Bancafe Carrera 7a 71-21 Torre B, Piso 13 Oficina, Bogota, 1301, Colombia
Tel.: (57) 1 325 1210
Environmental Services
N.A.I.C.S.: 541620

IETG LTD.
Cross Green Way Cross Green Industrial Estate, Leeds, LS9 0SE, United Kingdom
Tel.: (44) 8450179333   UK
Web Site: http://www.ietg.co.uk
Water & Waste Water Multi Disciplinary Support Services
N.A.I.C.S.: 541620
Ian Edwards *(Mng Dir)*

IEX GROUP N.V.
Beursplein 5, 1012 JW, Amsterdam, Netherlands
Tel.: (31) 204352170
Web Site: https://www.iexgroup.nl
Year Founded: 1999
IEX—(EUR)
Sales Range: $1-9.9 Million
Online Investment Management Services
N.A.I.C.S.: 523940
Peter van Sommeren *(CEO)*

Subsidiaries:

Trilab Advanced Solutions B.V. (1)
Laan Van Zuid Hoorn 60, 2289 DE, Rijswijk, Netherlands
Tel.: (31) 703457381
Web Site: http://www.trilab.com
Website Development Services
N.A.I.C.S.: 541511

IFA HOTEL & TOURISTIK AG
Duesseldorfer Strasse 50, Duisburg, 47051, Germany
Tel.: (49) 203992760
Year Founded: 1982
IFA—(DEU)
Rev.: $85,781,276
Assets: $742,355,194
Liabilities: $235,618,544
Net Worth: $506,736,650
Earnings: ($26,316,710)
Emp.: 1,719
Fiscal Year-end: 12/31/19
Tourism Service Provider
N.A.I.C.S.: 561520

IFABRIC CORP.
525 Denison Street Unit 1, Markham, L3R 1B8, ON, Canada
Tel.: (905) 752-0566   AB
Web Site: https://www.ifabriccorp.com
Year Founded: 2007

IFABF—(OTCQX)
Rev.: $21,444,342
Assets: $19,568,024
Liabilities: $3,937,400
Net Worth: $15,630,624
Earnings: ($1,593,175)
Fiscal Year-end: 12/31/23
Women's Intimate Apparel
N.A.I.C.S.: 315250
Hylton Karon *(Pres & CEO)*

Subsidiaries:

CG Intimates Inc. (1)
304 Hudson St Fl 8, New York, NY 10013-1015
Tel.: (905) 752-0566
Apparel Whslr
N.A.I.C.S.: 424350

IFAD AUTOS LTD.
Sonartori Tower 8th-18th Floor 12 Biponon Commercial Area, Sonargaon Road, Dhaka, Bangladesh
Tel.: (880) 16598
Web Site: https://www.ifadautos.com
Year Founded: 1988
IFADAUTOS—(CHT)
Rev.: $82,434,575
Assets: $371,729,884
Liabilities: $279,881,487
Net Worth: $91,848,398
Earnings: ($1,402,477)
Emp.: 1,171
Fiscal Year-end: 06/30/23
Transport Vehicle Mfr
N.A.I.C.S.: 336320
Iftekhar Ahmed Tipu *(Chm)*

IFAMIYSC CO., LTD.
122 Dongnam-ro, Songpa-gu, Seoul, 05804, Korea (South)
Tel.: (82) 25404112
Web Site: https://www.ifamily.co.kr
Year Founded: 2000
114840—(KRS)
Emp.: 126
Makeup Product Mfr
N.A.I.C.S.: 325620
Taewook Kim *(Co-CEO)*

IFAST CORPORATION LIMITED
10 Collyer Quay 26-01 Ocean Financial Centre, Singapore, 049315, Singapore
Tel.: (65) 65358033
Web Site: https://www.ifastcorp.com
Year Founded: 2000
AIY—(SES)
Rev.: $163,226,338
Assets: $169,756,020
Liabilities: $73,395,268
Net Worth: $96,360,752
Earnings: $22,955,781
Emp.: 1,097
Fiscal Year-end: 12/31/21
Internet-Based Investment Products
N.A.I.C.S.: 525990
Chung Chun Lim *(Co-Founder, Chm & CEO)*

Subsidiaries:

iFAST Capital Sdn. Bhd. (1)
Level 29 Menara AIA Sentral No 30 Jalan Sultan Ismail, 50250, Kuala Lumpur, Malaysia
Tel.: (60) 32 149 0567
Web Site: https://www.fsmone.com.my
Fund Management Services
N.A.I.C.S.: 523940

iFAST Financial (HK) Limited (1)
Two Exchange Square Suite 1303 13/F 8 Connaught Pl, Central, China (Hong Kong)
Tel.: (852) 3 766 4399
Web Site: https://secure.ifastfinancial.com.hk
Asset Management Services
N.A.I.C.S.: 523940

iFAST Financial Limited (1)
Room 1704 17th Floor Block A Aerospace Science and Technology Plaza, Haide 3rd Road Nanshan, Shenzhen, China
Tel.: (86) 400 684 0500
Web Site: https://www.ifastps.com.cn
Fund Management Services
N.A.I.C.S.: 523940
Dawn Zhu *(Supvr-Fin)*

iFAST Financial Pte. Ltd. (1)
10 Collyer Quay 26-01 Ocean Financial Centre Building, Singapore, 049315, Singapore
Tel.: (65) 65572000
Investment Management Service
N.A.I.C.S.: 523940

iFAST Platform Services (HK) Limited (1)
Suite 1303 Two Exchange Square 8 Connaught Place, Central, China (Hong Kong)
Tel.: (852) 37664334
Investment Advisory Services
N.A.I.C.S.: 523940

IFB AGRO INDUSTRIES LIMITED
Plot No Ind-5 Sector-1 East Kolkata Township, Kolkata, 700107, West Bengal, India
Tel.: (91) 3339849675
Web Site: https://www.ifbagro.in
507438—(BOM)
Rev.: $216,549,060
Assets: $86,268,000
Liabilities: $11,410,035
Net Worth: $74,857,965
Earnings: $6,706,245
Emp.: 421
Fiscal Year-end: 03/31/23
Beverage Distr
N.A.I.C.S.: 424820
Bikram Nag *(Chm)*

IFB INDUSTRIES LIMITED
14 Taratolla Road, Kolkata, 700 088, India
Tel.: (91) 3330489299
Web Site: https://www.ifbindustries.com
505726—(BOM)
Rev.: $468,668,655
Assets: $277,157,790
Liabilities: $188,670,300
Net Worth: $88,487,490
Earnings: ($6,573,840)
Emp.: 2,640
Fiscal Year-end: 03/31/22
Engineering Products Mfr
N.A.I.C.S.: 339999
Bijon Nag *(Co-Chm)*

Subsidiaries:

IFB Automotive Private Limited (1)
16 Visveswariah Industrial Estate 1st Main Road Off Whitefield Road, Mahadevpura, Bengaluru, 560 048, Karnataka, India
Tel.: (91) 8039884450
Web Site: http://www.ifbautomotive.com
Automotive Components Mfr
N.A.I.C.S.: 336390

Thai Automotive & Appliances Ltd. (1)
7/247 Moo 6 Mapyangporn, Amata City Industrial Estate Pluakdaeng, Rayong, 21140, Thailand
Tel.: (66) 386508578
Web Site: https://taal.co.th
Household Appliances Mfr
N.A.I.C.S.: 335220

IFC SOLID CJSC
32A Horoshevskoe highway, 125284, Moscow, Russia
Tel.: (7) 4952287010
Web Site: http://www.solid-ifc.ru
Sales Range: Less than $1 Million
Investment Banking Services
N.A.I.C.S.: 523150

INTERNATIONAL PUBLIC

Vladimir V. Semernin *(Chm)*

IFCA MSC BERHAD
Wisma IFCA No 19 Jalan PJU 1/42A Dataran Prima, 47301, Petaling Jaya, Selangor Darul Ehsan, Malaysia
Tel.: (60) 378053838   MY
Web Site: https://www.ifca.asia
Year Founded: 1987
IFCAMSC—(KLS)
Rev.: $15,973,745
Assets: $31,497,314
Liabilities: $6,630,510
Net Worth: $24,866,804
Earnings: ($888,251)
Emp.: 532
Fiscal Year-end: 12/31/22
Software Solutions Services
N.A.I.C.S.: 541511
Keang Cheun Yong *(Founder & Chm)*

Subsidiaries:

IFCA (Guangzhou) Technology Company Limited (1)
Room 512 5th Floor Building Of Tiancheng Square No 342-360, Long Kou Dong Road, Guangzhou, 510030, China
Tel.: (86) 2061246118
Business Software Development Services
N.A.I.C.S.: 541511

Subsidiary (Domestic):

IFCA (Wuhan) Technology Company Limited (2)
Donghu New Technology Development Guandong Road 2-2 Room No 803-812, Block B Optical Valley International Plaza, Wuhan, 430074, China
Tel.: (86) 876388288
Business Software Development Services
N.A.I.C.S.: 541511

IFCA Consulting (Sabah) Sdn Bhd (1)
Shop 23 Lot 24 1st Floor Block C Damai Plaza, 88300, Kota Kinabalu, Sabah, Malaysia
Tel.: (60) 88268189
Business Software Development Services
N.A.I.C.S.: 541511

IFCA Consulting (Sarawak) Sdn Bhd (1)
Fortuneland Business Centre Lot 2471-1 Block Kcld Jalan Rock, 93260, Kuching, Malaysia
Tel.: (60) 82418006
Business Software Development Services
N.A.I.C.S.: 541511

IFCA Consulting Private Limited (1)
75 Bukit Timah Road 03-08/09 Boon Siew Building, Singapore, 229833, Singapore
Tel.: (65) 63390755
Web Site: http://www.ifca.com.my
Business Software Development Services
N.A.I.C.S.: 541511
Tiaw Leong Lim *(Gen Mgr)*

IFCA Software (Guangzhou) Co., Ltd. (1)
8th Floor Building A Longwei Plaza No 130 Longkou Middle Road, Tianhe District, Guangzhou, 510635, China
Tel.: (86) 4009006321
Custom Computer Programming Services
N.A.I.C.S.: 541511

IFCA Systems (JB) Sdn Bhd (1)
31 Jalan Permas 10/7 Taman Permas Jaya, 81750, Johor Bahru, Malaysia
Tel.: (60) 73862268
Business Software Development Services
N.A.I.C.S.: 541511
Stanley Wong *(Mgr-Bus Unit)*

IFCA Systems (Penang) Sdn Bhd (1)
441-2-5 Pulau Tikus Plaza Jalan Burma, 10350, Penang, Malaysia
Tel.: (60) 42267525
Web Site: http://www.myifca.com
Emp.: 13
Business Software Development Services
N.A.I.C.S.: 541511

AND PRIVATE COMPANIES

Viva Liang *(Mgr-Bus Dev)*

Jingyou Information Technology (Shanghai) Co., Ltd (1)
Room 513 Building D No 877 Aite Road, Jiading District, Shanghai, 200436, China (100%)
Tel.: (86) 2152907262
Web Site: https://www.goldengui.com
Business Software Development Services
N.A.I.C.S.: 541511

PT IFCA Property365 Indonesia (1)
Jl Sultan Agung No 58 A-B, Jakarta Selatan, 12970, Indonesia
Tel.: (62) 218282455
Business Software Development Services
N.A.I.C.S.: 541511

PT IFCA Property365 Indonesia (1)
Jl Sultan Agung No 58 A-B, Jakarta Selatan, 12970, Indonesia
Tel.: (62) 218282455
Custom Computer Programming Services
N.A.I.C.S.: 541511

IFCI LIMITED
IFCI Tower 61 Nehru Place, New Delhi, 110 019, India
Tel.: (91) 1141792800
Web Site: https://www.ifciltd.com
500106—(BOM)
Rev.: $217,807,590
Assets: $2,114,023,275
Liabilities: $1,424,075,835
Net Worth: $689,947,440
Earnings: ($240,403,800)
Emp.: 170
Fiscal Year-end: 03/31/22
Investment Management
N.A.I.C.S.: 523940
Rupa Sarkar *(Officer-Compliance, Sec & Gen Mgr)*

Subsidiaries:

IFCI Factors Ltd (1)
IFCI Tower 61 Nehru Place, New Delhi, 110 019, India
Web Site: http://www.ifcifactors.com
Sales Range: $50-74.9 Million
Emp.: 60
Export Factoring Services
N.A.I.C.S.: 522299
Bikash Kanti Roy *(Mng Dir)*

IFCI Financial Services Ltd (1)
142 Mahatma Gandhi Road, Nungambakkam, Chennai, 600 034, Tamil Nadu, India
Tel.: (91) 4428306600
Web Site: https://www.ifinltd.in
Emp.: 90
Investment Banking Services
N.A.I.C.S.: 523150
K. V. Rao *(Mng Dir)*

IFCI Venture Capital Funds Ltd (1)
IFCI Tower 16th Floor 61 Nehru Place, New Delhi, 110 019, India
Tel.: (91) 1141732509
Web Site: https://www.ifciventure.com
Sales Range: $200-249.9 Million
Emp.: 300
Financial Advisory Services
N.A.I.C.S.: 523940
Indu Gupta *(CFO)*

IFE ELEVATORS CO., LTD
Jinlong Road, Qingxi Town, Dongguan, 523652, Guangdong, China
Tel.: (86) 76982078888
Web Site: https://www.ife-elevator.com
Year Founded: 1998
002774—(SSE)
Rev.: $206,674,416
Assets: $284,951,628
Liabilities: $116,004,096
Net Worth: $168,947,532
Earnings: $10,610,028
Emp.: 1,700
Fiscal Year-end: 12/31/22
Elevator Mfr & Distr
N.A.I.C.S.: 333921
Luo Aiwen *(Chm)*

IFIC BANK PLC
IFIC Tower 61 Purana Paltan, Dhaka, 1000, Bangladesh
Tel.: (880) 9666716250
Web Site: https://www.ificbank.com.bd
IFIC—(CHT)
Rev.: $142,050,731
Assets: $4,292,146,497
Liabilities: $3,985,578,823
Net Worth: $306,567,674
Earnings: $31,399,846
Emp.: 4,977
Fiscal Year-end: 12/31/22
Corporate & Retail Banking Services
N.A.I.C.S.: 522180
Salman F. Rahman *(Chm)*

Subsidiaries:

IFIC Money Transfer (UK) Limited (1)
18 Brick Ln, London, E1 6RF, United Kingdom
Tel.: (44) 2072479670
Web Site: http://www.ificuk.co.uk
Financial Banking Services
N.A.I.C.S.: 522110
Jalal Ahmed *(Chm)*

IFIRMA S.A.
Grabiszynska 241B, 53-234, Wroclaw, Poland
Tel.: (48) 717694300
Web Site: https://www.power.com.pl
Year Founded: 1997
IFI—(WAR)
Rev.: $13,026,931
Assets: $5,772,612
Liabilities: $2,507,368
Net Worth: $3,265,244
Earnings: $2,033,791
Fiscal Year-end: 12/31/23
Information Technology Services
N.A.I.C.S.: 519290
Wojciech Narczynski *(Pres & CEO)*

IFL ENTERPRISES LTD.
412 4th Floor Shilp Zaveri Samruddhi SOC Nr Shyamal Cross Road, Satellite, Ahmedabad, 380015, India
Tel.: (91) 7990080239
Web Site: https://www.iflenterprises.com
Year Founded: 2009
540377—(BOM)
Rev.: $201,258
Assets: $878,229
Liabilities: $4,603
Net Worth: $873,626
Earnings: ($16,767)
Emp.: 3
Fiscal Year-end: 03/31/21
Textile Products Mfr
N.A.I.C.S.: 313310
Ashok Kumar Bansal *(Chm)*

IFL PROMOTERS LIMITED
A-66 2nd Floor Guru Nanak Pura Vikas Marg Laxmi Nagar, Delhi, 110092, India
Tel.: (91) 11 47315500
Year Founded: 1992
Rev.: $111,565
Assets: $3,965,201
Liabilities: $2,141,974
Net Worth: $1,823,227
Earnings: $1,914
Fiscal Year-end: 03/31/18
Financial Services
N.A.I.C.S.: 523999
Pawan Kumar Bhatt *(CFO & Compliance Officer)*

IFLAG CO., LTD.
2-4-1 Shibakoen, Minato-Ku, Tokyo, 105-0011, Japan
Tel.: (81) 3 64306622
Web Site: http://www.iflag.co.jp
Year Founded: 1997
Sales Range: $50-74.9 Million
Information Technology Consulting Services
N.A.I.C.S.: 541512
Hiroyuki Gonen *(Chm & Pres)*

IFLYTEK CO., LTD.
No 666 Wangjiang West Road, High-Tech Development Zone, Hefei, 230088, Anhui, China
Tel.: (86) 55165331880
Web Site: http://www.iflytek.com
002230—(SSE)
Rev.: $2,720,747,840
Assets: $5,238,026,556
Liabilities: $2,782,882,338
Net Worth: $2,455,144,218
Earnings: $91,010,315
Emp.: 2,982
Fiscal Year-end: 12/31/23
Software Development Services
N.A.I.C.S.: 541511
Qing Feng Liu *(Founder, Chm & Pres)*

IFM IMMOBILIEN AG
Karl-Ludwig-Strasse 2, 69117, Heidelberg, Germany
Tel.: (49) 62 21 434 06 0
Web Site: http://www.ifm.ag
Sales Range: $10-24.9 Million
Emp.: 8
Commercial Real Estate Property Developer & Manager
N.A.I.C.S.: 531312
Volker de Boer *(Chm-Mgmt Bd & CEO)*

IFM INVESTMENTS LIMITED
19A2 Hanwei Plaza No 7 Guanghua Road, Chaoyang District, Beijing, 100004, China
Tel.: (86) 10 65617788
Web Site: http://www.century21cn.com
Year Founded: 2000
Sales Range: $75-99.9 Million
Emp.: 3,102
Real Estate Brokerage & Other Real Estate Services
N.A.I.C.S.: 531210

Subsidiaries:

Shanghai Anshijie Real Estate Consultant Co., Ltd (1)
Rm 308 No 1318 Shangnan Rd, Pudong New Area, Shanghai, 200000, China
Tel.: (86) 2151692228
Investment Holding Services
N.A.I.C.S.: 551112

IFMA SA
Calea Giulesti nr 8D sect.6, Bucharest, 060274, Romania
Tel.: (40) 0213120701
Web Site: http://www.mpifma.ro
SOMB—(BUC)
Rev.: $9,760,339
Assets: $4,352,290
Liabilities: $3,496,675
Net Worth: $855,615
Earnings: $710,322
Emp.: 145
Fiscal Year-end: 12/31/20
Lifting & Handling Equipment Mfr
N.A.I.C.S.: 333248
Bogdan Barbalata *(Fin Dir)*

IFOLOR AG
Sonnenwiesenstrasse 2, 8280, Kreuzlingen, Switzerland
Tel.: (41) 716865454
Web Site: http://www.ifolor.ch
Year Founded: 1978
Sales Range: $25-49.9 Million
Emp.: 200
Photofinishing Mail Orders
N.A.I.C.S.: 812921
Philipp Schwarz *(CEO)*

Subsidiaries:

Dialab Oy (1)
Tyopajakatu 10 B, 580, Helsinki, Finland
Tel.: (358) 925300100
Web Site: http://www.dialab.com
Sales Range: $25-49.9 Million
Emp.: 10
Professional Photography Labs
N.A.I.C.S.: 812921

Ifolor GmbH (1)
Leutragraben 1, 07743, Jena, Germany
Tel.: (49) 36415733450
Web Site: http://www.ifolor.de
Sales Range: $25-49.9 Million
Photofinishing
N.A.I.C.S.: 812921

Ifolor Oy (1)
Posliinitehtaankatu 1, Kerava, 4260, Finland
Tel.: (358) 9348400
Web Site: http://www.ifolora.fi
Sales Range: $10-24.9 Million
Emp.: 80
Photofinishing
N.A.I.C.S.: 812921

StarFoto BV (1)
Hallenstraat 3, Bladel, 5531 AB, Netherlands
Tel.: (31) 497386869
Web Site: http://www.starfoto.nl
Sales Range: $25-49.9 Million
Emp.: 16
Professional Photography Labs
N.A.I.C.S.: 812921

IFP ENERGIES NOUVELLES
1 & 4 avenue de Bois-Preau, 92852, Rueil-Malmaison, Cedex, France
Tel.: (33) 147526000
Web Site: https://www.ifpenergiesnouvelles.fr
Year Founded: 1944
Emp.: 1,660
Energy Transportation & Environment Research & Training Services
N.A.I.C.S.: 541715
Jean-Jacques Lacour *(Dir-Strategy)*

Subsidiaries:

IFP Energies Nouvelles - Lyon Site (1)
Rond Point de l'echangeur de, PO Box 3, Solaize, 69360, Lyon, France
Tel.: (33) 437702000
Web Site: http://www.ifpenergiesnouvelles.com
Emp.: 800
Energy, Transportation & Environment Research & Training Services
N.A.I.C.S.: 541715

IFS CAPITAL LIMITED
10 Eunos Road 8 09-04 Singapore Post Centre, Singapore, 408600, Singapore
Tel.: (65) 62707711
Web Site: https://www.ifscapital.com.sg
Year Founded: 1987
I49—(SES)
Rev.: $16,941,792
Assets: $295,211,171
Liabilities: $147,965,584
Net Worth: $147,245,587
Earnings: $3,600,724
Emp.: 94
Fiscal Year-end: 12/31/22
Holding Company; Investment & Finance Services
N.A.I.C.S.: 551112
Ley Yen Tan *(CEO-IFS Capital Thailand Public Company Limited)*

Subsidiaries:

ECICS Limited (1)

IFS CAPITAL LIMITED

IFS Capital Limited—(Continued)
10 Eunos Road 8 09-04A Singapore Post Centre, Singapore, 408600, Singapore **(100%)**
Tel.: (65) 6 206 5588
Web Site: https://www.ecics.com.sg
Emp.: 50
Credit Insurance, Bonds & Guarantees Products & Services
N.A.I.C.S.: 524126

IFS Capital (Malaysia) Sdn. Bhd. **(1)**
2nd Floor Menara Atlan 161B Jalan Ampang, 50450, Kuala Lumpur, Malaysia
Tel.: (60) 32 161 7080
Web Site: https://www.ifscapital.com.my
Financial Services
N.A.I.C.S.: 523999

IFS Capital Assets Pte. Ltd. **(1)**
09 04 Singapore Post Centre, Singapore, 408600, Singapore **(100%)**
Tel.: (65) 6270 7711
Web Site: http://www.ifscapital.com.sg
Emp.: 80
Investment & Finance Services
N.A.I.C.S.: 525990
Phyllis Yin Wah Chiu *(Asst Gen Mgr-Credit Risk Mgmt)*

IFS Capital Holdings (Thailand) Limited **(1)**
20th Floor Lumpini Tower 1168/55 Rama IV Road, Tungmahamek Sathorn, Bangkok, 10120, Thailand
Tel.: (66) 2285 6326
Holding Company
N.A.I.C.S.: 551112

Holding (Domestic):

IFS Capital (Thailand) PCL **(2)**
20th Floor Lumpini Tower Building 116855 Rama IV Road, Thung Maha Mek Subdistrict, Bangkok, 10120, Thailand **(36.64%)**
Tel.: (66) 22856326
Web Site: https://www.ifscapthai.com
Rev.: $12,591,948
Assets: $111,456,558
Liabilities: $59,735,919
Net Worth: $51,720,639
Earnings: $4,624,165
Emp.: 89
Fiscal Year-end: 12/31/2023
Investment & Finance Services
N.A.I.C.S.: 525990
Ley Yen Tan *(CEO)*

IFS Ventures Private Limited **(1)**
10 Eunos Road 8 09-04A Singapore Post Centre, Singapore, 408600, Singapore
Tel.: (65) 62707711
Commercial Finance Services
N.A.I.C.S.: 522291

Lendingpot Private Limited **(1)**
10 Eunos Road 8 09-04A Singapore Post Centre, Singapore, 408600, Singapore
Tel.: (65) 63030918
Web Site: http://www.lendingpot.sg
Commercial Finance Services
N.A.I.C.S.: 522291
Randy Sim *(CEO)*

PT. IFS Capital Indonesia **(1)**
ANZ Tower 10th Floor Jl Jend Sudirman Kav 33A, Jakarta, 10220, Indonesia
Tel.: (62) 21 57901090
Web Site: http://www.ifscapital.co.id
Emp.: 30
Financial Services
N.A.I.C.S.: 523999

IFUJI SANGYO CO., LTD.
2-1-29 Tohara Higashi, Kasuyamachi, Kasuya, 811-2318, Fukuoka, Japan
Tel.: (81) 929384561
Web Site: https://ifuji.co.jp
Year Founded: 1972
2924—(TKS)
Rev.: $161,964,830
Assets: $96,743,960
Liabilities: $32,673,230
Net Worth: $64,070,730
Earnings: $10,556,170
Emp.: 122
Fiscal Year-end: 03/31/24
Egg Production & Products; Seasonings Mfr
N.A.I.C.S.: 112310
Munenori Fujii *(Pres & CEO)*

IG DESIGN GROUP PLC
Howard House Howard Way, Interchange Park, Newport Pagnell, MK16 9PX, United Kingdom
Tel.: (44) 1525887310
Web Site:
https://www.thedesigngroup.com
Year Founded: 1979
IGR—(AIM)
Rev.: $800,051,000
Assets: $661,343,000
Liabilities: $291,856,000
Net Worth: $369,487,000
Earnings: $37,119,000
Emp.: 2,766
Fiscal Year-end: 03/31/24
Greeting Cards & Wraping Paper Designer & Mfr
N.A.I.C.S.: 513191
Anders Hedlund *(Founder)*

Subsidiaries:

Alligator Books Limited **(1)**
2nd Floor 314 Regents Park Road, London, N3 2JX, United Kingdom
Tel.: (44) 2083716622
Web Site: https://www.alligatorbooks.co.uk
Sales Range: $25-49.9 Million
Emp.: 15
Children Book Publishing Services
N.A.I.C.S.: 513130
Andrew H. Rabin *(Co-Founder, Mng Dir & Dir-Publ & Sls)*

Anchor International BV **(1)**
Voltastraat 12, 3281 NG, Numansdorp, Netherlands
Tel.: (31) 186 610555
Web Site: http://www.anchorinternational.eu
Sales Range: $25-49.9 Million
Emp.: 20
Stationery Products & Greeting Cards Distr
N.A.I.C.S.: 424120

Anker International PLC **(1)**
Howard House Howard Way, Interchange Park Newport Pagne, Hertford, MK16 9PX, United Kingdom
Tel.: (44) 1908618811
Web Site: http://www.theankergroup.com
Sales Range: $50-74.9 Million
Emp.: 200
Stationery Stores
N.A.I.C.S.: 459410

Hoomark Artex Sp. z o.o **(1)**
Jedrzychowice 116a, 59-900, Zgorzelec, Poland
Tel.: (48) 757756235
Web Site: http://www.artex.zgorzelec.pl
Emp.: 20
Gift Wrapping Paper Mfr & Distr
N.A.I.C.S.: 322220
Aleksander Kanculis *(Dir-Sls)*

Hoomark B.V. **(1)**
Industrieweg 62, Hoogeveen, 7902, Netherlands
Tel.: (31) 528 22 51 51
Web Site: http://www.hoomark.nl
Sales Range: $75-99.9 Million
Emp.: 130
Gift Wrappers Mfr & Distr
N.A.I.C.S.: 322220
Andreas Steinhoff *(Mgr-Sls-Germany)*

Hoomark Gift-Wrap Partners BV **(1)**
Industrieweg 62, 7903, Hoogeveen, Netherlands **(100%)**
Tel.: (31) 528225151
Web Site: http://www.hoomark.com
Sales Range: $25-49.9 Million
Emp.: 100
Coated & Laminated Packaging Paper & Plastics Film Mfr
N.A.I.C.S.: 322220
Joost Bogers *(Mng Dir)*

IG Design Group Americas, Inc. **(1)**
5555 Glenridge Connector Ste 300, Atlanta, GA 30342
Tel.: (912) 884-9727
Web Site: http://igdesigngroup-americas.com
Greeting Cards Whslr
N.A.I.C.S.: 424120

Subsidiary (Domestic):

CSS Industries, Inc. **(2)**
450 Plymouth Rd Ste 300, Plymouth Meeting, PA 19462
Tel.: (610) 729-3959
Web Site: http://www.cssindustries.com
Rev.: $382,263,000
Assets: $285,595,000
Liabilities: $95,664,000
Net Worth: $189,931,000
Earnings: ($53,545,000)
Emp.: 2,000
Fiscal Year-end: 03/31/2019
Holding Company; Seasonal Consumer Products
N.A.I.C.S.: 513191
Denise M. Andahazy *(VP-HR)*

Subsidiary (Domestic):

Berwick Offray, LLC **(3)**
PO Box 428, Berwick, PA 18603 **(100%)**
Tel.: (570) 752-5934
Web Site:
http://www.berwickoffraywholesale.com
Sales Range: $25-49.9 Million
Emp.: 200
Gift Wrap, Ribbons & Bows Mfr
N.A.I.C.S.: 326112

Subsidiary (Domestic):

Hollywood Ribbon Industries Inc. **(4)**
9000 Rochester Ave, Rancho Cucamonga, CA 91730-5522
Tel.: (323) 266-0670
Web Site: http://www.hollywoodribbon.com
Ribbon Mfr
N.A.I.C.S.: 313220
Vicki Butcher *(Mgr-Sls)*

Subsidiary (Domestic):

C.R. Gibson, LLC **(3)**
402 BNA Dr Bldg 100 Ste 600, Nashville, TN 37217
Tel.: (615) 724-2900
Web Site: http://www.crgibson.com
Sales Range: $50-74.9 Million
Emp.: 350
Stationery Items, Gift Books & Photo Albums
N.A.I.C.S.: 459410

Subsidiary (Non-US):

India Trimmings Private Limited **(3)**
6/636 Pilliappampalayam Telungupalayam, Annur, Coimbatore, 641653, India
Tel.: (91) 9894665181
Web Site: http://indtrim.com
Trimming Mfr
N.A.I.C.S.: 316990

Subsidiary (Domestic):

Lion Ribbon Company, LLC **(3)**
240 Peachtree St NW Ste 18C-10, Atlanta, GA 30303
Tel.: (404) 525-7927
Web Site: http://www.lionribbon.com
Emp.: 1
Ribbon Mfr & Importer
N.A.I.C.S.: 313220
Michael Sims *(Mgr)*

Subsidiary (Non-US):

McCall Pattern Company Limited **(3)**
38 New Lane, Havant, PO9 2ND, United Kingdom
Tel.: (44) 3448801263
Web Site: http://www.sewdirect.com
Sewing Product Distr
N.A.I.C.S.: 424350

Subsidiary (Domestic):

Paper Magic Group, Inc. **(3)**
54 Glenmaura National Blvd Ste 200, Moosic, PA 18507
Tel.: (570) 961-3863

INTERNATIONAL PUBLIC

Greeting Cards, Gift Tags, Decor, Valentine & Educational Products Mfr
N.A.I.C.S.: 513191

Philadelphia Industries, Inc. **(3)**
1105 N Market St, Wilmington, DE 19801
Tel.: (302) 427-8204
Investment Management Service
N.A.I.C.S.: 523940
Liz Bochner *(Mgr)*

Simplicity Creative Corp. **(3)**
2015 W Front St, Revesby, PA 18603
Tel.: (570) 752-5934
Decorative Product Mfr & Distr
N.A.I.C.S.: 322220

Subsidiary (Non-US):

Simplicity Pty Limited **(3)**
25 Violet Street, Revesby, NSW, Australia
Tel.: (61) 297745855
Web Site: http://www.simp.com.au
Trimming Mfr
N.A.I.C.S.: 316990

Subsidiary (Domestic):

The McCall Pattern Company, Inc. **(3)**
120 Broadway Fl 34, New York, NY 10271
Tel.: (800) 782-0323
Web Site: http://www.mccall.com
Sewing Product Distr
N.A.I.C.S.: 424350

Subsidiary (Domestic):

Impact Innovations, Inc. **(2)**
223 1st Ave NE, Clara City, MN 56222
Tel.: (320) 847-1210
Commercial Printing
N.A.I.C.S.: 323111
Jane Hagert *(CMO-Sls & VP-Mktg)*

IG Design Group BV **(1)**
Industrieweg 62, 7903 AK, Hoogeveen, Netherlands
Tel.: (31) 528225151
Web Site: http://www.igdesigngroup.nl
Gift Wrap Material Mfr
N.A.I.C.S.: 322220

International Greetings (UK) Limited **(1)**
Penallta Industrial Estate Ystrad Mynach, Hengoed, CF82 7SS, United Kingdom
Tel.: (44) 1443 814 917
Web Site:
http://www.internationalgreetings.co.uk
Emp.: 450
Gift Wrappers & Greeting Cards Distr
N.A.I.C.S.: 424120
Lance Burn *(Mng Dir)*

International Greetings Asia Limited **(1)**
20/F Times Media Centre No 133 Wanchai Road, Hong Kong, China (Hong Kong) **(100%)**
Tel.: (852) 21146912
Web Site:
http://www.internationalgreetings.co.uk
Sales Range: $25-49.9 Million
Emp.: 20
Gift Novelty & Souvenir Stores
N.A.I.C.S.: 459420
Lance Burn *(Mng Dir)*

Polaris Plastics Limited **(1)**
Howard House Howard Way Interchange Park, Newport Pagnell, MK16 9PX, Bucks, United Kingdom
Tel.: (44) 1908 618 811
Web Site: http://www.polarisplastics.co.uk
Sales Range: $25-49.9 Million
Emp.: 10
Plastics Product Mfr
N.A.I.C.S.: 326199
David Garcia *(Chm)*

Scoop Designs Ltd **(1)**
Belgrave House Frobisher Wi Hatefield Business Park, AL10 9TQ, Hertford, United Kingdom - England **(100%)**
Tel.: (44) 1707630630
Sales Range: $25-49.9 Million
Emp.: 70
Gift Novelty & Souvenir Stores
N.A.I.C.S.: 459420

AND PRIVATE COMPANIES — IGB BERHAD

Shenzhen Gift Intenational Greetings Company Ltd (1)
Fuyuan Yi Road Fuyong Street, No 1 - 2 Zone 2 Dejin Industry, Shenzhen, China (100%)
Tel.: (86) 75529707000
Web Site: http://www.thedesigngroup.com
Greeting Cards & Wrapping Paper Designer & Mfr
N.A.I.C.S.: 513191
Henry Lim *(Mng Dir)*

IG GROUP HOLDINGS PLC
Cannon Bridge House 25 Dowgate Hill, London, EC4R 2YA, United Kingdom
Tel.: (44) 2078960011 UK
Web Site: https://www.iggroup.com
IGG—(OTCIQ)
Rev.: $1,171,712,360
Assets: $2,346,275,932
Liabilities: $807,571,856
Net Worth: $1,538,704,076
Earnings: $504,936,068
Emp.: 2,026
Fiscal Year-end: 05/31/21
Offices of Other Holding Companies
N.A.I.C.S.: 551112
Bridget Messer *(Chief Comml Officer)*

Subsidiaries:

Brightpool Limited (1)
Cedars Oasis Building 9th Floor, Office 902 169-171 Arch Makarios III Avenue, 3027, Limassol, Cyprus
Tel.: (357) 2 555 2530
Web Site: https://www.brightpool-markets.com
Marketing Services
N.A.I.C.S.: 541613

FXOnline Japan Co., Ltd. (1)
Halifax Onarimon Bldg 8F, 3 24 10 Nishi Shinbashi, Minato ku, Tokyo, 105 0003, Japan
Tel.: (81) 33431 5777
Sales Range: $10-24.9 Million
Emp.: 30
Internet-Based Foreign Exchange Trading Services
N.A.I.C.S.: 523210

IG Asia Pte Limited (1)
9 Battery Road 01-02 MYP Centre, Singapore, 049910, Singapore
Tel.: (65) 6 390 5133
Web Site: https://www.ig.com
Market Leading Services
N.A.I.C.S.: 541613

IG Bank S.A. (1)
42 Rue du Rhone, 1204, Geneva, Switzerland
Tel.: (41) 58 810 7740
Web Site: https://www.ig.com
Market Leading Services
N.A.I.C.S.: 541613

IG Index plc (1)
Cannonbridge House 25 Dowgatehill, London, EC4R R2YA, United Kingdom (100%)
Tel.: (44) 2078960011
Web Site: http://www.igindex.co.uk
Sales Range: $400-449.9 Million
Emp.: 900
Spread Betting & Fixed-Odds Bookmaking Services
N.A.I.C.S.: 523999

IG Limited (1)
Tower 2 Level 27 Al Fattan Currency House DIFC, Dubai, United Arab Emirates
Tel.: (971) 4 559 2108
Web Site: https://www.ig.com
Market Leading Services
N.A.I.C.S.: 541613

IG Securities Limited (1)
Izumi Garden Tower 26F 1-6-1 Roppongi, Minato-ku, Tokyo, 106-6026, Japan
Tel.: (81) 34 520 8500
Web Site: https://www.ig.com
Market Leading Services
N.A.I.C.S.: 541613

IG US Holdings Inc. (1)
200 W Jackson Blvd Ste 1450, Chicago, IL 60606
Tel.: (312) 981-0499
Web Site: https://www.ig.com
Market Leading Services
N.A.I.C.S.: 541613

Nadex, Inc. (1)
311 S Wacker Dr Ste 2675, Chicago, IL 60606
Tel.: (312) 884-0100
Web Site: http://www.nadex.com
Emp.: 40
Retail Marketing Services
N.A.I.C.S.: 523210
Jacob Mulaikal *(CFO)*

Raydius GmbH (1)
Westhafen Tower Westhafenplatz 1, 60327, Frankfurt am Main, Germany
Tel.: (49) 6942 729 9114
Web Site: https://www.raydius.de
Foreign Exchange Services
N.A.I.C.S.: 523160
Nicos Demetriades *(Mng Dir)*

Spectrum MTF Operator GmbH (1)
Westhafen Tower Westhafenplatz 1, 60327, Frankfurt am Main, Germany
Tel.: (49) 6942 729 9180
Web Site: https://www.spectrum-markets.com
Market Leading Services
N.A.I.C.S.: 541613
Nicky H. S. Maan *(CEO & Mng Dir)*

IG PETROCHEMICALS LTD.
401-404 Raheja Centre Free Press Journal Marg, 214 Nariman Point, Mumbai, 400 021, India
Tel.: (91) 2230286100
Web Site: https://www.igpetro.com
Year Founded: 1988
IGPL—(NSE)
Rev.: $284,668,209
Assets: $238,824,711
Liabilities: $90,764,546
Net Worth: $148,060,164
Earnings: $23,981,500
Emp.: 498
Fiscal Year-end: 03/31/23
Petrochemical Mfr
N.A.I.C.S.: 325110
Nikunj Dhanuka *(CEO & Mng Dir)*

IG PORT, INC.
2-1-9 Nakamachi, Musashino, Tokyo, 180-0006, Japan
Tel.: (81) 422530257
Web Site: https://www.igport.co.jp
Year Founded: 1987
3791—(TKS)
Rev.: $78,269,010
Assets: $92,546,610
Liabilities: $44,174,630
Net Worth: $48,371,980
Earnings: $7,654,380
Emp.: 600
Fiscal Year-end: 05/31/24
Game Video Production Services
N.A.I.C.S.: 512110

IGARASHI MOTORS INDIA LIMITED
Plots B-12 to B-15 Phase II Mepz-Sez Tambaram, Chennai, 600 045, Tamil Nadu, India
Tel.: (91) 4442298199
Web Site: https://www.igarashimotors.com
IGARASHI—(NSE)
Rev.: $80,508,724
Assets: $88,018,640
Liabilities: $34,747,204
Net Worth: $53,271,436
Earnings: $634,809
Emp.: 669
Fiscal Year-end: 03/31/23
Automobile Parts Mfr
N.A.I.C.S.: 336110
R. Chandrasekaran *(Mng Dir)*

Subsidiaries:

Igarashi Electric Works (Zhuhai) Ltd. (1)
South Langshan Road, Fine Chemistry And Industry Zone Gaoloang Port Economic District, Zhuhai, China
Tel.: (86) 7567232331
Motor Vehicle Parts Mfr
N.A.I.C.S.: 336390

Igarashi Motoren GmbH (1)
Steinbacher Strasse 47-51, Burgthann, 90559, Nuremberg, Germany
Tel.: (49) 9188940520
Motor Vehicle Parts Mfr
N.A.I.C.S.: 336390

Yat Yue Industrial Co. (HK) Ltd. (1)
Unit 1 7/Floor Sun Hing Industrial Building 46Wong Chuk Hang Rd, Aberdeen, China (Hong Kong)
Tel.: (852) 25538278
Motor Vehicle Parts Mfr
N.A.I.C.S.: 336390

IGB BERHAD
Level 32 The Gardens South Tower, Mid Valley City Lingkaran Syed Putra, 59200, Kuala Lumpur, Malaysia
Tel.: (60) 322898989 MY
Web Site: https://www.igbbhd.com
Year Founded: 1964
5606—(KLS)
Rev.: $273,284,656
Assets: $1,889,827,725
Liabilities: $1,044,083,598
Net Worth: $845,744,127
Earnings: $69,415,026
Emp.: 100
Fiscal Year-end: 12/31/22
Pharmaceuticals Mfr
N.A.I.C.S.: 456110
Robert Chung Meng Tan *(CEO-Grp)*

Subsidiaries:

GTower Sdn. Bhd. (1)
199 Jalan Tun Razak, 50400, Kuala Lumpur, Malaysia (80%)
Tel.: (60) 321681919
Web Site: http://www.gtower.com.my
Sales Range: $100-124.9 Million
Emp.: 20
Commercial Property Management & Leasing Services
N.A.I.C.S.: 531312
Lei Cheng Tan *(Chm)*

Goldis Water Sdn Bhd (1)
Suite 28-03 Level 28 G-Tower 199 Jalan Tun Razak, 50400, Kuala Lumpur, Malaysia
Tel.: (60) 321631111
Sales Range: $50-74.9 Million
Emp.: 25
Investment Management Service
N.A.I.C.S.: 523999
Goh Chu Lang *(Dir-HR)*

IGB Corporation Berhad (1)
Level 32 The Gardens South Tower Mid Valley City Lingkaran Syed Putra, 59200, Kuala Lumpur, Malaysia (100%)
Tel.: (60) 322898989
Web Site: http://www.igbcorp.com
Rev.: $347,612,758
Assets: $1,896,720,518
Liabilities: $982,547,024
Net Worth: $914,173,493
Earnings: $109,037,006
Emp.: 2,105
Fiscal Year-end: 12/31/2023
Property Development & Investment Services
N.A.I.C.S.: 531311
Tina Lai Yin Chan *(Sec)*

Subsidiary (Domestic):

Cititel Hotel Management Sdn. Bhd. (2)
The Gardens Lingkaran Syed Putra, Mid Valley City, 59200, Kuala Lumpur, Malaysia (60%)
Tel.: (60) 320811188
Web Site: https://www.chm-hotels.com
Emp.: 10
Home Management Services
N.A.I.C.S.: 721110
Cristy Yeo *(Dir-HR)*

Ensignia Construction Sdn. Bhd. (2)
Level 29 The Gardens South Tower Mid Valley City Lingkaran Syed Putra, 59200, Kuala Lumpur, Federal Territory, Malaysia (100%)
Tel.: (60) 329389900
Commercial Building Construction Services
N.A.I.C.S.: 236220

Kondoservis Sdn. Bhd. (2)
Level 29 The Gardens South Tower Mid Valley City Lingkaran Fyed Putra, Lingkaran Syed Putra, 59200, Kuala Lumpur, Malaysia (100%)
Tel.: (60) 3 2282 3232
Emp.: 26
Condominium Management Services
N.A.I.C.S.: 531312
Tham Siew Pang *(Dir)*

MVEC Exhibition and Event Services Sdn. Bhd. (2)
Level 31 The Gardens South Tower Lingkaran Syed Putra, Mid Valley City, 59200, Kuala Lumpur, Malaysia (100%)
Tel.: (60) 322898688
Web Site: https://www.mvec.com.my
Exhibition & Event Hall Rental Services
N.A.I.C.S.: 531120

Tan & Tan Developments Berhad (2)
Level 29 The Gardens South Tower, Mid Valley City, 59200, Kuala Lumpur, Malaysia (100%)
Tel.: (60) 322898999
Web Site: https://www.tantan.com
Property Development Services
N.A.I.C.S.: 531311

IGB Digital Sdn. Bhd. (1)
Level 32 The Gardens South Tower, Mid Valley City Lingkaran Syed Putra, 59200, Kuala Lumpur, Malaysia
Tel.: (60) 322898386
Web Site: https://igbdigital.com.my
Software Development Services
N.A.I.C.S.: 541511

IGB International School Sdn. Bhd. (1)
Jalan Sierramas Utama Sierramas, 47000, Sungai Buloh, Selangor, Malaysia
Tel.: (60) 361454688
Web Site: https://www.igbis.edu.my
Professional School Services
N.A.I.C.S.: 611310

Kondoservis Management Sdn. Bhd. (1)
Level 29 The Gardens South Tower Mid Valley City Lingkaran Syed Putra, 59200, Kuala Lumpur, Malaysia
Tel.: (60) 322823232
Web Site: https://www.kondoservis.com
Information Technology Services
N.A.I.C.S.: 541519

Macro Lynx Sdn. Bhd. (1)
Suite 14 03 GTower 199 Jalan Tun Razak, 50400, Kuala Lumpur, Malaysia (100%)
Tel.: (60) 321632177
Web Site: http://www.macrolynx.com
Sales Range: $25-49.9 Million
Emp.: 40
Wireless Technology Services
N.A.I.C.S.: 517112
Sabrina Chor *(Mgr-Customer Svc)*

OM3 Fish (Asia) Sdn Bhd (1)
No 169 Jalan Maharajalela, 50150, Kuala Lumpur, Malaysia
Tel.: (60) 321441896
Web Site: http://www.om3fish.com
Sales Range: $25-49.9 Million
Emp.: 10
Animal Aquaculture Services
N.A.I.C.S.: 112519
Tony Chow *(COO)*

ReU Living Sdn. Bhd. (1)
Micasa All Suites Hotel 368B Jln Tun Razak Taman U Thant, 50400, Kuala Lumpur, Malaysia
Tel.: (60) 103800938
Web Site: https://reuliving.com
Assisted Living & Care Services

IGB BERHAD

IGB Berhad—(Continued)
N.A.I.C.S.: 623110

The Gardens Theatre Sdn. Bhd. (1)
Level 5 The Gardens North Tower
Lingkaran Syed Putra, Mid Valley City,
59200, Kuala Lumpur, Malaysia
Tel.: (60) 32280730
Web Site:
https://www.gardenstheatre.com.my
Boutique & Specialty Retailer
N.A.I.C.S.: 455219

IGB REAL ESTATE INVESTMENT TRUST
Level 32 The Gardens South Tower
Mid Valley City Lingkaran Syed Putra,
59200, Kuala Lumpur, Malaysia
Tel.: (60) 322898989   MY
Web Site: https://www.igbreit.com
Year Founded: 2012
5227—(KLS)
Rev.: $117,758,519
Assets: $1,125,399,365
Liabilities: $306,186,243
Net Worth: $819,213,122
Earnings: $83,844,233
Fiscal Year-end: 12/31/22
Investment Management Service
N.A.I.C.S.: 523940
Antony Patrick Barragry (CEO)

IGC INDUSTRIES LIMITED
Premises No 23 Impax Lohia Square
4th Floor, Ganggadhar Babu Lane
Office No 4B, Kolkata, 700012, West
Bengal, India
Tel.: (91) 3346021453
539449—(BOM)
Rev.: $5,405
Assets: $2,074,759
Liabilities: $1,899,138
Net Worth: $175,621
Earnings: ($47,529)
Fiscal Year-end: 03/31/22
Commercial Trading Services
N.A.I.C.S.: 425120
Prachi Rajesh Marwah (CFO)

IGD SIIQ S.P.A
Via Trattati Comunitari Europei 1957-
2007 13, 40127, Bologna, Italy
Tel.: (39) 051509111
Web Site: https://www.gruppoigd.it
IGD—(ITA)
Rev.: $14,812,217
Assets: $2,385,901,144
Liabilities: $1,175,238,506
Net Worth: $1,210,662,638
Earnings: ($24,082,668)
Emp.: 157
Fiscal Year-end: 12/31/22
Real Estate Development Services
N.A.I.C.S.: 531110
Claudio Albertini (CEO)

Subsidiaries:

Winmarkt Management S.R.L. (1)
B-Dul Decebal 25-29 Olympia Tower Etaj
10 Sector 3, 030964, Bucharest, Romania
Tel.: (40) 214084700
Web Site: https://www.winmarkt.ro
Grocery Product Services
N.A.I.C.S.: 445110

IGEA PHARMA N.V.
Siriusdreef 17-27, 2132 WT, Hoofddorp, Netherlands
Tel.: (31) 235689494   NI
Web Site: http://www.igeapharma.nl
Year Founded: 2017
IGPH—(SWX)
Rev.: $2,374
Assets: $23,959
Liabilities: $282,970
Net Worth: ($259,011)
Earnings: ($12,711,094)
Emp.: 2

Fiscal Year-end: 12/31/22
Biomedical Research & Development Services
N.A.I.C.S.: 541715
Vincenzo Moccia (CEO & CFO-Interim)

IGEAMED SPA
Via Francesco Benaglia 13, 00153, Rome, Italy
Tel.: (39) 06669911
Web Site: https://www.igeamedspa.it
Year Founded: 1979
MED—(EUR)
Health Care Srvices
N.A.I.C.S.: 621610
Michele Casciani (Pres)

IGG INC.
80 Pasir Panjang Road 18-84 Mapletree Business City, Singapore, 117372, Singapore
Tel.: (65) 34695132   Ky
Web Site: https://www.igg.com
Year Founded: 2006
0799—(HKG)
Rev.: $674,122,916
Assets: $473,332,537
Liabilities: $123,238,050
Net Worth: $350,094,487
Earnings: $9,351,981
Emp.: 1,976
Fiscal Year-end: 12/31/23
Software Development Services
N.A.I.C.S.: 513210
Cai Zongjian (Co-Founder, Chm & CEO)

IGI HOLDINGS LIMITED
7th Floor The Forum Suite 701-713
G-20 Block 9, Khayaban-e-Jami Clifton, Karachi, 75600, Pakistan
Tel.: (92) 42111308308
Web Site:
https://www.igiholdings.com.pk
IGIHL—(PSX)
Rev.: $62,125,842
Assets: $415,898,102
Liabilities: $180,915,302
Net Worth: $234,982,800
Earnings: $13,892,620
Emp.: 359
Fiscal Year-end: 12/31/23
Investment Holding Company; General & Life Insurance Products & Services
N.A.I.C.S.: 551112

Subsidiaries:

GI General Insurance Limited (1)
7th Floor The Forum Suite 701-713 G-20
Block 9, Khayaban-e-Jami Clifton, Karachi, Pakistan
Tel.: (92) 21111308308
Web Site: https://igiinsurance.com.pk
Insurance Services
N.A.I.C.S.: 524298

IGI Life Insurance Limited (1)
7th Floor The Forum Suit No 701-703, G-20
Kahayan-e-Jami Block 9 Clifton, Karachi,
75600, Pakistan (69.68%)
Tel.: (92) 2135360040
Web Site: https://www.igilife.com.pk
Rev.: $31,007,679
Assets: $129,727,998
Liabilities: $115,297,806
Net Worth: $14,430,192
Earnings: ($1,138,064)
Emp.: 211
Fiscal Year-end: 12/31/2019
Fire Insurance Services
N.A.I.C.S.: 524113
Hyder Ali (CEO)

IGI PRUDENTIAL INSURANCE LIMITED
Narayanchaur Naxal, Kathmandu, Nepal

Tel.: (977) 16600179353
Web Site: https://igiprudential.com
Year Founded: 2001
IGI—(NEP)
Rev.: $17,878,827
Assets: $80,853,158
Liabilities: $43,773,561
Net Worth: $37,079,598
Earnings: $1,284,567
Fiscal Year-end: 07/16/23
Insurance Services
N.A.I.C.S.: 524298
Yugesh Bhakta Bade Shrestha (CEO)

IGIS NEPTUNE BARCELONA HOLDCO SOCIMI, S.A.
Calle Principe de Vergara 112 4 floor, 28002, Madrid, Spain   ES
Web Site: https://www.igisnbhs.com
Year Founded: 2019
MLABC—(EUR)
Rev.: $8,294,657
Assets: $163,676,702
Liabilities: $105,676,209
Net Worth: $58,000,493
Earnings: ($3,373,029)
Fiscal Year-end: 12/31/21
Real Estate Investment Services
N.A.I.C.S.: 531190
Cristina Ferrer Sama (Sec)

IGIS RESIDENCE REIT CO., LTD.
14th floor Sewoo Building 115 Yeoui Park-ro, Yeongdeungpo-Gu, Seoul, Korea (South)
Tel.: (82) 269593100
Web Site:
https://www.igisresidencereit.com
Year Founded: 2020
350520—(KRS)
Rev.: $50,927,948
Assets: $271,396,450
Liabilities: $87,434,479
Net Worth: $183,961,971
Earnings: $48,117,114
Fiscal Year-end: 12/31/22
Real Estate Services
N.A.I.C.S.: 531210
Lee Sangcheon (Gen Mgr)

IGIS VALUE PLUS REIT CO., LTD.
14th floor Sewoo Building 115 Yeoui Parkro, Yeongdeungpo-Gu, Seoul, Korea (South)
Tel.: (82) 269593100
Web Site:
https://www.igisvaluereit.com
Year Founded: 2019
334890—(KRS)
Real Estate Services
N.A.I.C.S.: 531210
Dong-Soo Shin (Mgr-Team)

IGLOO CORPORATION
6 Floor 7 Jeongui-ro 8-gil, Songpa-gu, Seoul, 05836, Korea (South)
Tel.: (82) 234528814
Web Site: https://www.igloo.co.kr
Year Founded: 1999
067920—(KRS)
Rev.: $79,005,621
Assets: $69,821,424
Liabilities: $15,572,750
Net Worth: $54,248,674
Earnings: $5,794,928
Emp.: 656
Fiscal Year-end: 12/31/22
Computer Security Products
N.A.I.C.S.: 513210
Deuk-Choon Lee (CEO)

IGLUE, INC.
Soroksariut 94-96, 1095, Budapest, Hungary

Tel.: (36) 1 4566061   NV
Web Site: http://www.iglue.com
Year Founded: 2000
Emp.: 1
Online Application Development Services
N.A.I.C.S.: 541511

IGM DRINA AD
Pantelinska 102, 76300, Bijeljina, Bosnia & Herzegovina
Tel.: (387) 55258486
DRIN-R-A—(BANJ)
Sales Range: Less than $1 Million
Clay Building Material Mfr
N.A.I.C.S.: 327120

IGMAN D.D. KONJIC
Donje Polje 42, 88400, Konjic, Bosnia & Herzegovina
Tel.: (387) 3 672 6276
Web Site: http://www.igman.co.ba
IGKCRK3—(SARE)
Rev.: $69,527,558
Assets: $101,790,480
Liabilities: $26,049,821
Net Worth: $75,740,659
Earnings: $3,174,270
Emp.: 1,363
Fiscal Year-end: 12/31/20
Weapons & Ammunition Mfr
N.A.I.C.S.: 332993
Miroslav Sain (Exec Mgr-Quality Control)

IGNIS LTD
Ebisu Business Tower 12th floor
1-19-19 Ebisu, Shibuya-ku, Tokyo,
150-0013, Japan
Tel.: (81) 364086820
Web Site: http://www.1923.co.jp
3689—(TKS)
Rev.: $51,086,070
Assets: $36,276,520
Liabilities: $15,497,300
Net Worth: $20,779,220
Earnings: ($5,786,270)
Emp.: 215
Fiscal Year-end: 09/30/19
Smartphone Applications
N.A.I.C.S.: 513210
Takaaki Suzuki (CTO)

IGNITE LIMITED
Level 32 200 George Street, Sydney, 2000, NSW, Australia
Tel.: (61) 1300481179   AU
Web Site: https://www.igniteco.com
Year Founded: 1997
IGN—(ASX)
Rev.: $64,528,579
Assets: $8,728,632
Liabilities: $3,611,111
Net Worth: $5,117,521
Earnings: $411,325
Emp.: 44
Fiscal Year-end: 06/30/24
Employment Services
N.A.I.C.S.: 561311
Julian Sallabank (CEO)

Subsidiaries:

Candle IT & T Recruitment Limited (1)
L14 333 Colin St, Melbourne, 3000, Vic, Australia
Tel.: (61) 398328000
Web Site: http://www.candlerecruit.com
Sales Range: $10-24.9 Million
Emp.: 30
Recruitment Services
N.A.I.C.S.: 561311
Rob Fortescue (Gen Mgr)

Candle IT & T Recruitment Pty Limited (1)
Level 9 1 York St, Sydney, 2000, NSW, Australia

Tel.: (61) 292508100
Sales Range: $75-99.9 Million
IT Recruitment Services
N.A.I.C.S.: 561311

Lloyd Morgan China Limited (1)
Room 517-520 Office 1 China World Trade Center, 1 Jian Guo Men Wai Avenue Chaoyang District, Beijing, 10002, China
Tel.: (86) 18600525188
Web Site: http://www.lloydmorgan.com
Sales Range: $10-24.9 Million
Emp.: 30
Employment Services
N.A.I.C.S.: 561311
Christian Buttrose *(Mng Dir)*

Lloyd Morgan Hong Kong Limited (1)
2403 A World Trade Ctr 24th Fl 280 Gloucester Rd, Causeway Bay, China (Hong Kong)
Tel.: (852) 28955282
Web Site: http://www.lloydmorgan.com
Sales Range: $10-24.9 Million
Emp.: 30
Employment Services
N.A.I.C.S.: 561311

Lloyd Morgan International Pty Limited (1)
Level 14 333 Collins St, Melbourne, 3000, VIC, Australia
Tel.: (61) 396835200
Web Site: http://www.clarius.com
Sales Range: $25-49.9 Million
Emp.: 60
Employment Services
N.A.I.C.S.: 561311
Goeff Moles *(Gen Mgr)*

The One Umbrella Pty Limited (1)
Level 9 1 York St, Sydney, 2000, NSW, Australia
Tel.: (61) 292630000
Web Site: http://www.oneumbrella.com.au
Sales Range: $25-49.9 Million
Emp.: 8
Employment Services
N.A.I.C.S.: 561311
Catherine Hill *(Gen Mgr)*

IGO LIMITED
Suite 4 Level 5 South Shore Centre 85 South Perth Esplanade, South Perth, 6151, WA, Australia
Tel.: (61) 892388300   AU
Web Site: https://www.igo.com.au
IGO—(ASX)
Rev.: $691,716,332
Assets: $3,712,343,788
Liabilities: $1,080,327,900
Net Worth: $2,632,015,888
Earnings: $253,532,271
Emp.: 244
Fiscal Year-end: 06/30/22
Precious & Semi-Precious Metals Exploration, Development & Mining
N.A.I.C.S.: 212290
Scott Steinkrug *(CFO)*

Subsidiaries:

Western Areas Limited (1)
Level 2 2 Kings Park Road, West Perth, 6005, Australia
Tel.: (61) 893347777
Web Site: http://www.westernareas.com.au
Rev.: $197,043,381
Assets: $618,241,010
Liabilities: $131,377,067
Net Worth: $486,863,943
Earnings: ($5,907,325)
Emp.: 24
Fiscal Year-end: 06/30/2021
Nickel Mine Development & Explorer
N.A.I.C.S.: 212230
Daniel Lougher *(CEO)*

IGORIA TRADE SA
Ul Pulawska 111A/109, 02-707, Warsaw, Poland
Tel.: (48) 221015880
Web Site: https://www.igoriatrade.com
Year Founded: 2011
Electronic Payment Process Services
N.A.I.C.S.: 522320
Wojciech Kulinski *(CEO)*

IGP ADVANTAG AG
Friedrichstrasse 185, 10117, Berlin, Germany
Tel.: (49) 3021015100
Web Site: https://www.igp-advantag.ag
Year Founded: 2009
A62—(MUN)
Rev.: $60,250,962
Assets: $77,598,036
Liabilities: $45,697,332
Net Worth: $31,900,704
Earnings: ($2,985,360)
Emp.: 380
Fiscal Year-end: 12/31/22
Real Estate Manangement Services
N.A.I.C.S.: 531190

Subsidiaries:

Auximio AG (1)
Glockengasse 5, 47608, Geldern, Germany
Tel.: (49) 28313959370
Web Site: https://www.auximio.de
Corporate Financial Services
N.A.I.C.S.: 522220

IGS CAPITAL GROUP LTD.
E-702 Block E Pusat Dagangan Phileo Damansara 1 No 9 Jalan 16-11, 46350, Kuala Selangor, Selangor, Malaysia
Tel.: (60) 377726616   HK
IGSC—(OTCIQ)
Sales Range: Less than $1 Million
Industrial Waste Recycling Services
N.A.I.C.S.: 562111

IGUA SANEAMENTO SA
R Gomes de Carvalho 1510 - 1 Floor - Cj 12, 4547005, Sao Paulo, Brazil
Tel.: (55) 1121990249
Web Site: http://www.cabambiental.com.br
IGSN3—(BRAZ)
Rev.: $419,004,654
Assets: $2,165,687,184
Liabilities: $1,688,126,732
Net Worth: $477,560,453
Earnings: ($68,225,092)
Fiscal Year-end: 12/31/23
Sewage Treatment Services
N.A.I.C.S.: 221320
Eduardo Carlos Torzecki *(CFO, Chief Admin Officer & Dir-IR)*

Subsidiaries:

Aguas de Andradina S.A. (1)
Rua Doutor Orensy Rodrigues da Silva 1062, Andradina, Sao Paulo, 16901-016, Brazil
Tel.: (55) 8007750195
Web Site: http://www.aguasdeandradina.com.br
Water Supply System Design & Construction Services
N.A.I.C.S.: 237110

Aguas de Castilho S.A. (1)
Avenida Presidente Getulio Vargas 20, Castilho, Sao Paulo, Brazil
Tel.: (55) 8007703195
Water Supply System Design & Construction Services
N.A.I.C.S.: 237110

CAB Aguas de Paranagua S.A. (1)
Rua Vieira Dos Santos 333, Campo Grande, 83203-050, Parana, Brazil
Tel.: (55) 4134223322
Web Site: http://www.cabaguasdeparanagua.com.br
Water Supply System Design & Construction Services
N.A.I.C.S.: 237110

CAB Canarana Ltda. (1)
R Redentora 78 Centro, Canarana, 78640-000, Mato Grosso, Brazil
Tel.: (55) 6634781414
Water Supply System Design & Construction Services
N.A.I.C.S.: 237110

CAB Colider Ltda. (1)
Av Presidente Dutra 1391 Colider, Mato Grosso, Brazil
Tel.: (55) 6635414528
Water Supply System Design & Construction Services
N.A.I.C.S.: 237110

CAB Comodoro Ltda. (1)
R Acacias 3621, Comodoro, 78310-000, Mato Grosso, Brazil
Tel.: (55) 6536237485
Water Supply System Design & Construction Services
N.A.I.C.S.: 237110

CAB Guaratingueta S.A. (1)
Rua Dr Neir Augusto Ortiz Pereira 1209, Guaratingueta, 12505-020, Sao Paulo, Brazil
Tel.: (55) 1221318200
Water Supply System Design & Construction Services
N.A.I.C.S.: 237110

CAB MT Participacoes Ltda. (1)
Av Goncalo Antunes de Barros 3196 - Sala 01 Carumbe, Cuiaba, 78050-667, Mato Grosso, Brazil
Tel.: (55) 6533185813
Water Supply System Design & Construction Services
N.A.I.C.S.: 237110

CAB Piquete S.A. (1)
Estr Da Tabuleta S/N, Piquete, Sao Paulo, Brazil
Tel.: (55) 1231563913
Water Supply System Design & Construction Services
N.A.I.C.S.: 237110

Mirassol S/A Saneamento de Mirassol (1)
0195 Rua Joao Caetano Mendonca de Almeida 2005, Mirassol, Sao Paulo, 15130-000, Brazil
Tel.: (55) 1732539199
Web Site: http://www.sanessol.com.br
Water Supply System Design & Construction Services
N.A.I.C.S.: 237110

IGUATEMI S.A.
R Angelina Maffei Vita 200 - 9 Andar, 1489900, Sao Paulo, Brazil
Tel.: (55) 1130487344
Web Site: https://iguatemi.com.br
Year Founded: 1946
IGTI3—(BRAZ)
Holding Companies
N.A.I.C.S.: 551112

Subsidiaries:

Iguatemi Empresa de Shopping Centers S.A. (1)
Rua Angelina Maffei Vita 200 - 9 Floor Jardim Paulistano, Sao Paulo, 0145-070, Brazil
Tel.: (55) 1131377000
Web Site: https://iguatemi.com.br
Shopping Malls & Real Estate Services
N.A.I.C.S.: 236220

IHAG HOLDING AG
Bleicherweg 18, 8002, Zurich, Switzerland
Tel.: (41) 44 205 14 14
Web Site: http://www.ihagholding.ch
Holding Company
N.A.I.C.S.: 551112
Gratian Anda *(Chm & CEO)*

Subsidiaries:

AdNovum Informatik AG (1)
Roentgenstrasse 22, 8005, Zurich, Switzerland
Tel.: (41) 442726111
Web Site: http://www.adnovum.ch
Emp.: 370
Software Development Services
N.A.I.C.S.: 541511
Chris Tanner *(CEO)*

IHARA SCIENCE CORPORATION
11-3 Takanawa 3-chome, Minato-ku, Tokyo, 108-0074, Japan
Tel.: (81) 367216981
Web Site: http://www.ihara-sc.co.jp
Year Founded: 1941
5999—(TKS)
Rev.: $199,475,760
Assets: $267,458,400
Liabilities: $52,765,680
Net Worth: $214,692,720
Earnings: $32,060,160
Emp.: 500
Fiscal Year-end: 03/31/22
Metal Valve & Pipe Fitting Mfr
N.A.I.C.S.: 332919
Tokuo Nakano *(Chm)*

Subsidiaries:

IHARA SCIENCE CORPORATION - Gifu Plant (1)
10424 Arama Tsukechi-cho, Nakatsugawa, 508-0351, Gifu, Japan
Tel.: (81) 57 382 4125
Web Site: https://www.ihara-sc.co.jp
Piping Product Mfr
N.A.I.C.S.: 326122

IHARA SCIENCE CORPORATION - Shizuoka Plant (1)
Shimoshiraiwa, Izu, 410-2501, Shizuoka, Japan
Tel.: (81) 558 83 2811
Piping Product Mfr
N.A.I.C.S.: 326122

Yamagata-Ihara Corporation (1)
5600-3 Higashineko Oaza, Higashine, 999-3701, Yamagata, Japan
Tel.: (81) 237 43 5501
Piping Product Mfr
N.A.I.C.S.: 326122

IHC MERWEDE HOLDING B.V.
Molendijk 94, Molandegk 94, 3361 EP, Sliedrecht, Netherlands
Tel.: (31) 880155000
Web Site: https://www.royalihc.com
Year Founded: 1943
Sales Range: $350-399.9 Million
Emp.: 3,000
Designs, Builds & Supplies Capital Goods & Services For the Dredging Industry
N.A.I.C.S.: 212321

Subsidiaries:

IHC Hydrohammer BV (1)
Smitweg 6, 2961 AW, Kinderdijk, Netherlands   (100%)
Tel.: (31) 786910302
Web Site: http://www.ihchydrohammer.com
Sales Range: $25-49.9 Million
Emp.: 100
Produces Hydraulic Hammers
N.A.I.C.S.: 333120

IHDATHIAT CO-ORDINATES
PO Box 925239, Jabal Amman, Amman, 11190, Jordan
Tel.: (962) 65508900
IHCO—(AMM)
Rev.: $4,788
Assets: $4,666,882
Liabilities: $158,773
Net Worth: $4,508,109
Earnings: ($181,577)
Emp.: 4
Fiscal Year-end: 12/31/20
Real Estate Development Services
N.A.I.C.S.: 531390
Omar Alanati *(Gen Mgr)*

IHI CORPORATION
Toyosu IHI Bldg 1-1 Toyosu 3-chome,

IHI CORPORATION

IHI Corporation—(Continued)
Koto-ku, Tokyo, 135-8710, Japan
Tel.: (81) 362047800   JP
Web Site: https://www.ihi.co.jp
Year Founded: 1853
IHICY—(OTCIQ)
Rev.: $9,700,579,800
Assets: $13,923,881,880
Liabilities: $10,652,562,210
Net Worth: $3,271,319,670
Earnings: $319,387,650
Emp.: 28,486
Fiscal Year-end: 03/31/23
Industrial Machinery & Power Plant Mfr
N.A.I.C.S.: 333310
Tamotsu Saito *(Chm)*

Subsidiaries:

Alpha Automotive Technologies LLC (1)
23 Avtozavodskaya, 115280, Moscow, Russia
Tel.: (7) 4957831745
Industrial Machinery Mfr
N.A.I.C.S.: 333248

Central Conveyor Co., Ltd. (1)
3-2 Nobatsutsuka Noba, Koda-cho Nadagun, Nagoya, 444-0128, Aichi, Japan
Tel.: (81) 564623113
Web Site: http://www.centralcv.co.jp
Conveyor & Conveying Equipment Mfr
N.A.I.C.S.: 333922

Changchun Fawer-Ihi Turbo Co., Ltd. (1)
No 3377 Yangpu Street, Economical and Technological Development Zone, Changchun, 130033, China
Tel.: (86) 43185089998
Industrial Machinery Mfr
N.A.I.C.S.: 333248

Contratistas Ihi E&C Mexico, S.A.de C.V. (1)
Av Paseo de la Reforma 295 Piso 8 Col, 06500, Cuauhtemoc, Mexico
Tel.: (52) 5552805200
Industrial Machinery Mfr
N.A.I.C.S.: 333248

Felguera-IHI S.A. (1)
Via de los Poblados 7, Las Rozas, 28232, Madrid, Spain
Tel.: (34) 916402051
Sales Range: $25-49.9 Million
Emp.: 200
Engineering Services
N.A.I.C.S.: 541330
Pedro Floriano *(Mng Dir-Mining & Handling)*

Hauzer Techno Coating B.V. (1)
Van Heemskerckweg 22, 5928 LL, Venlo, Netherlands
Tel.: (31) 77 355 97 77
Web Site: http://www.hauzertechnocoating.com
Sales Range: $25-49.9 Million
Emp.: 100
Physical Vapour Deposition Coating Services
N.A.I.C.S.: 332812
Jeroen Landsbergen *(CEO)*

I&H Engineering Co., Ltd. (1)
Plot No 3 Kalakone Village, Myaungdagar Steel Industrial Zone Hmawbi Township, Yangon, Myanmar
Tel.: (95) 1395526
Industrial Machinery Mfr
N.A.I.C.S.: 333248

IHI (HK) Ltd. (1)
Room 2203 22/F Causeway Bay Plaza 2 463-483 Lockhart Road, Causeway Bay, China (Hong Kong) (100%)
Tel.: (852) 2 522 4093
Web Site: https://www.ihi.co.jp
Sales Range: $25-49.9 Million
Emp.: 9
Engineering, Construction & Agriculture Equipment Mfr
N.A.I.C.S.: 541330

IHI Aerospace Co., Ltd. (1)
Toyosu IHI Bldg 1-1 Toyosu 3-chome, Koto-ku, Tokyo, 135-0061, Japan
Tel.: (81) 362048000
Web Site: http://www.ihi.co.jp
Sales Range: $25-49.9 Million
Emp.: 1,000
Design, Manufacture & Sales of Space Equipment & Defense Machinery
N.A.I.C.S.: 927110

IHI Charging Systems International GmbH (1)
Wolff-Knippenberg-Strasse 2, Amt Wachsenburg, 99334, Ichtershausen, Germany
Tel.: (49) 36 285 8130
Web Site: https://www.ihi-csi.de
Industrial Machinery Mfr
N.A.I.C.S.: 333248

IHI Charging Systems International S.p.A. (1)
Via Regina 25, 23870, Cernusco Lombardone, Lecco, Italy (100%)
Tel.: (39) 0399993811
Sales Range: $50-74.9 Million
Emp.: 178
Construction of Turbo Chargers
N.A.I.C.S.: 335999

IHI E&C International Corporation (1)
West Memorial Pl II 15377 Memorial Dr Ste 300, Houston, TX 77079
Tel.: (713) 270-3100
Web Site: https://ihi-ec.com
Engineering Services
N.A.I.C.S.: 541330
Chris Celano *(Pres)*

IHI Engineering Australia Pty. Ltd. (1)
Suite 32 02 L32 100 Miller Street, North Sydney, 2060, NSW, Australia (100%)
Tel.: (61) 29 923 9300
Web Site: https://www.ihi.com.au
Sales Range: $25-49.9 Million
Emp.: 15
Mfr of Aircraft Parts & Components
N.A.I.C.S.: 336412

IHI Europe Ltd. (1)
2nd Floor America House 2 America Square, London, EC3N 2LU, United Kingdom (100%)
Tel.: (44) 207 481 8180
Web Site: https://www.ihieuro.co.uk
Sales Range: $25-49.9 Million
Emp.: 15
Aircraft Engine & Engine Parts Manufacturing
N.A.I.C.S.: 336412

IHI Inc. (1)
1251 Avenue of the Americas 7th Fl Ste 750, New York, NY 10020 (100%)
Tel.: (212) 599-8100
Web Site: https://www.ihiincus.com
Sales Range: $50-74.9 Million
Emp.: 887
Sales of Ships & Industrial Machinery
N.A.I.C.S.: 423990

Subsidiary (Domestic):

Compact Excavator Sales, LLC (2)
400 Production Ct, Elizabethtown, KY 42701
Tel.: (270) 737-1447
Web Site: https://katoces.com
Sales Range: $25-49.9 Million
Emp.: 22
Construction Equipment Sales & Rental Services
N.A.I.C.S.: 423810
Michael Smith *(Co-Owner)*

IHI Press Technology America, Inc. (2)
46850 Magellan Dr Ste 150, Novi, MI 48377
Tel.: (248) 295-9240
Web Site: http://www.ihi.co.jp
Magazine Publishing Services
N.A.I.C.S.: 513120

IHI Southwest Technologies Inc. (2)
6766 Culebra Rd, San Antonio, TX 78238
Tel.: (210) 256-4100
Web Site: http://www.ihiswt.com
Sales Range: $10-24.9 Million
Engineering Services
N.A.I.C.S.: 541330

Steve J. Todd *(Pres)*

Subsidiary (Domestic):

Nitrocision, LLC (3)
6766 Culebra Rd, San Antonio, TX 78238-4700 (100%)
Tel.: (210) 256-4100
Web Site: http://www.nitrocision.com
Ultra-High Pressure Liquid Nitrogen Injection Systems Equipment Mfr & Distr
N.A.I.C.S.: 333998

Subsidiary (Domestic):

IHI Turbo America Co. (2)
1598 IL-16, Shelbyville, IL 62565
Tel.: (217) 774-9571
Web Site: https://www.ihi-turbo.com
Sales Range: $25-49.9 Million
Emp.: 150
Mfr & Sales of Turbo Chargers
N.A.I.C.S.: 336390

IHI Infrastructure Asia Co., Ltd. (1)
Plot CN4 2A Dinh Vu Industrial Zone Dinh Vu - Cat Hai Economic Zone, Dong Hai 2 Ward Hai An District, Haiphong, Vietnam
Tel.: (84) 2258830112
Web Site: http://www.ihi.co.jp
Sales Range: $25-49.9 Million
Emp.: 200
Bridge Construction Engineering Services
N.A.I.C.S.: 237310

IHI Inspection & Instrumentation Co., Ltd. (1)
6-25-3 Minami Oi, Shinagawaku, Tokyo, 140-0013, Japan
Tel.: (81) 364046033
Web Site: http://www.iic-hq.co.jp
Sales Range: $100-124.9 Million
Emp.: 450
Non-Destructive Inspection Services & Manufacturing of Related Devices
N.A.I.C.S.: 333248

IHI Logistics System Technology Shanghai Co., Ltd. (1)
Room 021 24F HSBC Tower No 1000 Lujiazui Ring Road, Pudong New Area, Shanghai, 200120, China
Tel.: (86) 21 6841 2886
Web Site: http://www.ihi.co.jp
Sales Range: $25-49.9 Million
Emp.: 15
Logistics Consulting Servies
N.A.I.C.S.: 541614
Moriwaki Ichiro *(Gen Mgr)*

IHI Metaltech Co., Ltd. (1)
Da Vinci 510 Building 2nd Floor 5-10-5 Shimbashi, Minato-ku, Tokyo, 105-0004, Japan (100%)
Tel.: (81) 334328398
Web Site: http://www.i-webspace.com
Sales Range: $25-49.9 Million
Emp.: 91
Engineering & Sales of Rolling Mill Equipment for Steel & Non-Ferrous Metals, Continuous Caster, Process Line & Control Equipment
N.A.I.C.S.: 333248
Shinji Dairen *(Pres & CEO)*

IHI Oxyfuel Australia Pty.Ltd. (1)
Suite 2201 Level 22 111 Pacific Highway, North Sydney, Sydney, 2060, NSW, Australia
Tel.: (61) 2 9923 9300
Sales Range: $25-49.9 Million
Emp.: 33
Aircraft Part Mfr
N.A.I.C.S.: 336412
Tom Yoshida *(Gen Mgr)*

IHI Philippines, Inc. (1)
Unit 703-705 One Corporate Center Dona Julia Vargas corner, Meralco Avenue Ortigas Center, Pasig, 1605, Metro Manila, Philippines (100%)
Tel.: (63) 2 631 0986
Web Site: https://ihi.com.ph
Engineeering Services
N.A.I.C.S.: 541330
Akiyoshi Hara *(Pres)*

IHI Power System Malaysia Sdn. Bhd. (1)
19th Floor UBN Tower 10 Jalan P Ramlee, 50250, Kuala Lumpur, Malaysia
Tel.: (60) 3 2026 2688
Sales Range: $25-49.9 Million
Emp.: 2
Energy Engineering Services
N.A.I.C.S.: 541330
Yoshimitsu Tsumita *(Mng Dir)*

IHI Transport Machinery Co., Ltd. (1)
St Luke Tower Akashi-cho 8-1, Chuo-ku, Tokyo, 104-0044, Japan
Tel.: (81) 355505321
Web Site: http://www.iuk.co.jp
Emp.: 1,577
Engineering, Manufacturing & Maintenance for Materials Handling Equipment & Parking Systems
N.A.I.C.S.: 333248
Yutaka Yoshida *(Pres)*

IHI do Brasil Representacoes Ltda. (1)
Av Paulista 726 9 Andar CJ 901 - Bela Vista, Sao Paulo, 01310-910, Brazil
Tel.: (55) 1132512593
Web Site: http://www.ihiincom
Engine Equipment Mfr
N.A.I.C.S.: 333618
Osami Imai *(CEO)*

INC Engineering Co., Ltd. (1)
15-18 Hyakunincho 1-chome, Shinjuku-ku, Tokyo, 169-0073, Japan (100%)
Tel.: (81) 333603223
Web Site: http://www.ihi.co.jp
Sales Range: $50-74.9 Million
Emp.: 146
Consulting, Engineering & Construction of Noise & Vibration Suppressing Equipment
N.A.I.C.S.: 333248
Tetsuo Watai *(Pres)*

Ihi (Shanghai) Management Co., Ltd. (1)
24th Floor Hang Seng Bank Building 1000 Lujiazui Ring Road, Shanghai, 200120, China
Tel.: (86) 216 841 1717
Web Site: https://www.ihi-china.cn
Emp.: 34
Industrial Machinery Mfr
N.A.I.C.S.: 333248

Ihi Asia Pacific (Thailand) Co., Ltd. (1)
11th and 12th Floor Ramaland Building 952 Rama IV Road Suriyawongse, Bangrak, 10500, Bangkok, Thailand
Tel.: (66) 22363490
Industrial Machinery Mfr
N.A.I.C.S.: 333248
Shotaro Tabata *(Mng Dir)*

Ihi Asia Pacific Pte. Ltd. (1)
77 Robinson Road 14-03 Robinson 77, Singapore, 068896, Singapore
Tel.: (65) 65156609
Industrial Machinery Mfr
N.A.I.C.S.: 333248

Ihi Canada Projects Inc. (1)
1200 Waterfront Centre 200 Burrard Street, PO Box 48600, Vancouver, V7X 1T2, BC, Canada
Tel.: (713) 270-3100
Industrial Machinery Mfr
N.A.I.C.S.: 333248

Ihi Construction Materials Co., Ltd. (1)
2-10-14 Ryogoku, Sumida-ku, Tokyo, 130-0026, Japan
Tel.: (81) 36 271 7211
Web Site: https://www.ikk.co.jp
Emp.: 205
Concrete Material Mfr
N.A.I.C.S.: 327390

Ihi Construction Service Co., Ltd. (1)
East Net Building 7-1-1 Toyo, Koto-ku, Tokyo, 135-0016, Japan
Tel.: (81) 336992790
Engineering Services
N.A.I.C.S.: 541330

Ihi Dalgakiran Makina Sanayi Ve Ticaret A.S. (1)
Cerkesli OSB Mahallesi IMES 1 Kisim 6 Cadde No 3 Dilovasi, Kocaeli, Turkiye

AND PRIVATE COMPANIES

Tel.: (90) 2625021070
Industrial Machinery Mfr
N.A.I.C.S.: 333248

Ihi Fuso Engineering Co., Ltd. (1)
Ojima Building 7-22-18 Ojima, Koto-ku, Tokyo, 136-0072, Japan
Tel.: (81) 35 626 5611
Web Site: https://www.fuso-e.co.jp
Emp.: 133
Engineeering Services
N.A.I.C.S.: 541330

Ihi Infrastructure Systems Co., Ltd. (1)
3 Ohamanishi-machi, Sakai-ku, Sakai, 590-0977, Osaka, Japan
Tel.: (81) 722230981
Emp.: 878
Engineering Services
N.A.I.C.S.: 541330
Susumu Ishihara *(Pres)*

Ihi Jet Service Co., Ltd. (1)
Street address 3975-18 Haijima-cho, Akishima, 196-8686, Tokyo, Japan
Tel.: (81) 425008300
Aircraft Engine & Equipment Mfr
N.A.I.C.S.: 333611

Ihi Logistics & Machinery Corporation (1)
3-1-1 Toyosu, Koto-ku, Tokyo, 135-0061, Japan
Tel.: (81) 362048181
Engineeering Services
N.A.I.C.S.: 541330
Shunji Kasa *(Pres)*

Ihi Master Metal Co., Ltd. (1)
5292 Aion, Aioi-shi, Hyogo, 678-0041, Japan
Tel.: (81) 791242563
Metal Products Mfr
N.A.I.C.S.: 332312
Mitsuharu Sugeta *(Pres)*

Ihi Packaged Boiler Co., Ltd. (1)
2-8-19 Fukagawa Sakura Building 5th Floor, Koto-ku, Tokyo, 135-0033, Japan
Tel.: (81) 35 245 3131
Web Site: https://www.ibk-ihi.co.jp
Emp.: 180
Engineering Services
N.A.I.C.S.: 541330

Ihi Plant Services Corporation (1)
Toyosu IHI Bldg 1-1 Toyosu 3-chome, Koto-ku, Tokyo, 135-0061, Japan
Tel.: (81) 36 204 8300
Web Site: https://www.ipc-ihi.co.jp
Emp.: 702
Engineeering Services
N.A.I.C.S.: 541330
Koji Takeda *(Pres)*

Ihi Power Generation Corp. (1)
1251 Ave of the Americas 7th Fl Ste 750, New York, NY 10020
Tel.: (212) 599-8116
Industrial Machinery Mfr
N.A.I.C.S.: 333248

Ihi Power System (Thailand) Co., Ltd. (1)
23/34 Sorachai Building 15th Floor Soi Sukhumvit 63, Sukhumvit Road North Klongton Wattana, Bangkok, 10110, Thailand
Tel.: (66) 23816435
Industrial Machinery Mfr
N.A.I.C.S.: 333248

Ihi Power Systems Co., Ltd. (1)
14-5 Sotokanda 2-Chome, Chiyoda-ku, Tokyo, 101-0021, Japan
Tel.: (81) 343661200
Diesel Engine Mfr & Whslr
N.A.I.C.S.: 333618
Koji Yahagi *(Pres)*

Ihi Scube Co., Ltd. (1)
3-1-1 Toyosu Toyosu IHI Building, Koto-ku, Tokyo, 135-0061, Japan
Tel.: (81) 36 204 8031
Web Site: https://www.iscube.co.jp
Emp.: 519
Engineeering Services
N.A.I.C.S.: 541330

Ihi Solid Biomass Malaysia Sdn. Bhd. (1)
19th Floor UBN Tower 10 Jalan P Ramlee, 50250, Kuala Lumpur, Malaysia
Tel.: (60) 320721255
Industrial Machinery Mfr
N.A.I.C.S.: 333248

Ihi System Technology Taiwan Co., Ltd. (1)
7F No 168 Song Jiang Rd, Taipei, 104, Taiwan
Tel.: (886) 225711191
Industrial Machinery Mfr
N.A.I.C.S.: 333248

Ihi Taiwan Corporation (1)
Room 1202 Chia Hsin Bldg No 96 Sec 2 Chung Shan N Road, Taipei, 10449, Taiwan
Tel.: (886) 225425520
Industrial Machinery Mfr
N.A.I.C.S.: 333248

Ihi Terrasun Solutions Inc. (1)
100 N Riverside Plz Ste 2200, Chicago, IL 60606
Tel.: (312) 878-8532
Industrial Machinery Mfr
N.A.I.C.S.: 333248

Ihi Turbo (Thailand) Co., Ltd. (1)
Amata Nakorn Industrial Estate700/487 Moo 2, Tumbol Bankao Amphure Phanthong, Chon Buri, 20160, Thailand
Tel.: (66) 3845405356
Industrial Machinery Mfr
N.A.I.C.S.: 333248

Ihi Turbo Korea Co., Ltd. (1)
Rm 507 Building-B Woorim Lion's Valley 168 Gasan Digital 1-ro, Geumcheon-gu, Seoul, Korea (South)
Tel.: (82) 2732299697
Industrial Machinery Mfr
N.A.I.C.S.: 333248

Ihi Vtn GmbH (1)
Rusbergstr 75, 58456, Witten, Germany
Tel.: (49) 23 249 3420
Web Site: https://www.ihi-vtn.com
Industrial Machinery Mfr
N.A.I.C.S.: 333248
Georg Niessen *(Co-CEO)*

Ihi-Icr, LLC. (1)
330 W Industrial Ct, Villa Rica, GA 30180
Tel.: (770) 456-4148
Web Site: https://ihi-icr.com
Engineeering Services
N.A.I.C.S.: 541330
Kaz Sato *(Pres)*

Ihi-Sullair Compression Technology (Suzhou) Co., Ltd. (1)
No 262 Changyang Street, Suzhou Industrial Park, Suzhou, 215024, Jiangsu, China
Tel.: (86) 5128 518 8500
Web Site: https://www.ihi-sullair.cn
Industrial Machinery Mfr
N.A.I.C.S.: 333248

IonBond AG (1)
Division CVD Industriestrasse 211, 4600, Olten, Switzerland
Tel.: (41) 62 553 4200
Web Site: https://www.ionbond.com
Emp.: 65
Coatings & Coating Equipment
N.A.I.C.S.: 325510
Antonio Santana *(Head-Medical Segment)*

Subsidiary (Non-US):

IonBond (Malaysia) Sdn. Bhd. (2)
No 5 Block B Jalan Sungai Kayu Ara 32-39, Taman Berjaya Seksyen 32, Shah Alam, 40460, Selangor, Malaysia
Tel.: (60) 166612727
Web Site: http://www.ionbond.com
Sales Range: $25-49.9 Million
Emp.: 15
Paint & Coating Mfr
N.A.I.C.S.: 325510
Yokeheng Lum *(Gen Mgr)*

IonBond Ag - Nuremberg (2)
Allersberger Strasse 185, 90461, Nuremberg, Germany
Tel.: (49) 9114780365
Web Site: http://www.ionbond.com
Electroplating Plating Polishing Anodizing & Coloring
N.A.I.C.S.: 332813

IonBond Austria GmbH (2)
High-Tech-Park 25, 8605, Kapfenberg, Austria
Tel.: (43) 38623363710
Web Site: http://www.tce.at
Emp.: 20
Electroplating Plating Polishing Anodizing & Coloring
N.A.I.C.S.: 332813
Gerald Kogler *(Mng Dir)*

IonBond Consett (2)
No 1 Industrial Estate Medomsley Rd Unit 36, Consett, Durham, DH8 6TS, United Kingdom
Tel.: (44) 1207500823
Sales Range: $25-49.9 Million
Emp.: 35
Metal Coating
N.A.I.C.S.: 332812

IonBond CzechCoating CzechCoating s.r.o. (2)
Dolni Becva 20, 75655, Dolni Becva, Czech Republic
Tel.: (420) 571647360
Paint & Coating Mfr
N.A.I.C.S.: 325510

IonBond Czechia, S.r.o. (2)
CTPark Humpolec 1574, 396 01, Humpolec, Czech Republic
Tel.: (420) 565381439
Web Site: http://www.ionbond.com
Sales Range: $25-49.9 Million
Emp.: 30
Paint & Coating Mfr
N.A.I.C.S.: 325510

IonBond ICC Paris Innovative Coating Co. (2)
75 rue Robert-Schuman, FR-77350, Le Mee-sur-Seine, France
Tel.: (33) 164830125
Sales Range: $25-49.9 Million
Emp.: 40
Paint & Coating Mfr
N.A.I.C.S.: 325510

IonBond Italia Srl (2)
V le delle industrie 91, Cambiago, 20040, Milan, Italy
Tel.: (39) 0396082093
Web Site: http://www.ionbond.com
Emp.: 25
Heavy & Civil Engineering Construction
N.A.I.C.S.: 237990

Subsidiary (US):

IonBond LLC (2)
1823 E Whitcomb, Madison Heights, MI 48071-1413
Tel.: (248) 398-9100
Web Site: http://www.ionbond.com
Sales Range: $25-49.9 Million
Emp.: 50
Coating Equipment
N.A.I.C.S.: 325510

Subsidiary (Non-US):

IonBond Mexico - Tecate (2)
Carretera Libre Tecate-Mexicali km 127, 21505, Tecate, Baja California, Mexico (100%)
Tel.: (52) 6656550750
Web Site: https://www.ionbond.com
Sales Range: $25-49.9 Million
Emp.: 22
Metal Heat Treatment & Coating
N.A.I.C.S.: 332811

IonBond Mulhouse (2)
ZA La Savonnerie 22 rue de la Savonnerie, Lutterbach, 68460, France
Tel.: (33) 389534478
Web Site: http://www.ionbond.com
Emp.: 4
Paint & Coating Mfr
N.A.I.C.S.: 325510
Philippe Brucker *(Gen Mgr)*

IonBond Netherlands B.V. (2)
Van Heemskerckweg 30, Venlo, 5928LL, Netherlands (100%)
Tel.: (31) 774656565
Sales Range: $25-49.9 Million
Emp.: 60

IHI CORPORATION

Electroplating Plating Polishing Anodizing & Coloring
N.A.I.C.S.: 332813
Gerrit J. van der Kolk *(CTO)*

IonBond Sweden AB (2)
Vastra Svedengatan 2F, 582 73, Linkoping, Sweden (100%)
Tel.: (46) 13253303
Web Site: http://www.ionbond.se
Sales Range: $25-49.9 Million
Emp.: 20
Electroplating Plating Polishing Anodizing & Coloring
N.A.I.C.S.: 332813

IonBond Tinkap Istanbul Tinkap Vakum Plazma Tek. Ltd. (2)
Sti imes San Si C Blok 307 Bldg 3, Duduliu/Istanbul, Istanbul, 34776, Turkiye
Tel.: (90) 2163131233
Web Site: http://www.ionbond-tinkap.com
Sales Range: $25-49.9 Million
Emp.: 4
Paint & Coating Mfr
N.A.I.C.S.: 325510
Gerry Vanderkolk *(Gen Mgr)*

Ishi Power Sdn Bhd (1)
19th Floor UBN Tower 10 Jalan P Ramlee, 50250, Kuala Lumpur, Malaysia
Tel.: (60) 320707088
Industrial Machinery Mfr
N.A.I.C.S.: 333248

Ishikawajima SCE (Xiamen) Construction Machinery Co., Ltd. (1)
No. 38 Huanzhu Road North Industrial Area, Jimei District, Xiamen, 361021, China
Tel.: (86) 592 6292222
Web Site: http://www.ihi-kenki.co.jp
Construction Machinery Mfr & Distr
N.A.I.C.S.: 333120

Ishikawajima-Harima Sul-America Ltda. (1)
Av Presidente Antonio Carlos 607-Sobreloja-Centro, Rio de Janeiro, CEP 20020-010, RJ, Brazil
Tel.: (55) 21 2533 6671
Ship Machinery & Equipment Mfr
N.A.I.C.S.: 333998

Japan Jurong Engineering Co., Ltd. (1)
Toranomon Takagi Building 5F 7-2 Nishi-Shimbashi 1-chome, Minato-ku, Tokyo, 105-0003, Japan
Tel.: (81) 362573819
Web Site: http://www.jjel.co.jp
Engineeering Services
N.A.I.C.S.: 541330
Masao Akamatsu *(CEO & Mng Dir)*

Japan Marine United Corporation (1)
Yokohama Blue Avenue Building 4-4-2 Minatomirai, Nishi-ku, Yokohama, 220-0012, Japan (45.9%)
Tel.: (81) 452647200
Web Site: https://www.jmuc.co.jp
Emp.: 6,000
Ships & Patrol Vessels Mfr
N.A.I.C.S.: 336611
Kotaro Chiba *(Pres & CEO)*

Subsidiary (Non-US):

IMBV B.V. (2)
De Linie 3 - I, 2905 AX, Capelle aan den IJssel, Netherlands
Tel.: (31) 104116406
Web Site: https://www.imbvrotterdam.com
Sales Range: $25-49.9 Million
Emp.: 17
Technical & Navigation Services to Ships
N.A.I.C.S.: 488330
Y. Okita *(Mng Dir)*

IMCS Marine (Shanghai) Co., Ltd. (2)
Room No 706-707 Information Tower No 1403 Minsheng Road, Pudong New Area, Shanghai, 200135, China
Tel.: (86) 2163518029
Web Site: http://www.ihi-imcs.cn
Sales Range: $25-49.9 Million
Emp.: 41
Consulting & Engineering for Shipbuilding, Ship Repair & Supply of Marine Equipment
N.A.I.C.S.: 336611

IHI CORPORATION

IHI Corporation—(Continued)
Wang Kegui *(Mng Dir)*

IMES Pte. Ltd. (2)
27 Tanjong Kling Road, Singapore, 628052, Singapore
Tel.: (65) 62687360
Web Site: http://www.imes.com.sg
Sales Range: $25-49.9 Million
Emp.: 60
Marine Engineering
N.A.I.C.S.: 541330
Nakashima Tomohiro *(Mng Dir)*

Jiangsu Ihi Fengdong Vacuum Technology Co., Ltd. (1)
No 333 Nanxiang West Road, Economic Development Zone Dafeng District, Dafeng, Jiangsu, China
Tel.: (86) 5158 352 0966
Web Site: https://www.ihi-fengdong.cn
Industrial Machinery Mfr
N.A.I.C.S.: 333248

Jim Technology Corporation (1)
10th Floor Cube Kawasaki Building 1-14 Nisshin-cho, Kawasaki-ku, Kawasaki, 210-0024, Kanagawa, Japan
Tel.: (81) 44 201 8263
Web Site: https://www.jimt.co.jp
Tunnel Construction Equipment Mfr
N.A.I.C.S.: 333120

Jurong Engineering Limited (1)
25 Tanjong Kling Road, Singapore, 628050, Singapore
Tel.: (65) 6 265 3222
Web Site: https://www.jel.com.sg
Sales Range: $400-449.9 Million
Emp.: 300
Engineeering Services
N.A.I.C.S.: 541330
Bob Tan Beng Hai *(Chm)*

Meisei Electric Co., Ltd. (1)
2223 Naganumamachi, Isesaki, 372-8585, Gunma, Japan (100%)
Tel.: (81) 270321111
Web Site: http://www.meisei.co.jp
Rev.: $60,276,180
Assets: $93,861,600
Liabilities: $42,935,340
Net Worth: $50,926,260
Earnings: $2,319,360
Emp.: 347
Fiscal Year-end: 03/31/2019
Communication Equipment Mfr & Whslr
N.A.I.C.S.: 334290
Takehisa Irisawa *(Auditor)*

New Metal Engineering, LLC (1)
4259 E 49th St, Cleveland, OH 44125
Tel.: (216) 883-3220
Industrial Machinery Mfr
N.A.I.C.S.: 333248

Nico Precision Co., Inc. (1)
1095-1 Kawakubo Minamiuonuma, Niigata, 949-6603, Japan
Tel.: (81) 25 772 3121
Web Site: https://www.nico-precision.com
Emp.: 165
Fuel Injection Equipment Mfr & Whslr
N.A.I.C.S.: 336310

Niigata Power Systems (Singapore) Pte. Ltd. (1)
31 Bukit Batok Crescent 01-33 The Splendour, Singapore, 658070, Singapore
Tel.: (65) 68991500
Industrial Machinery Mfr
N.A.I.C.S.: 333248

Niigata Power Systems Co., Ltd. (1)
9-7 Yaesu 2-chome, Tokyo, 104-0028, Chuo-ku, Japan
Tel.: (81) 362142800
Web Site: http://www.niigata-power.com
Sales Range: $200-249.9 Million
Emp.: 1,000
Diesel, Gas & Dual Fuel Engines, Fuel Injection Equipment & Power Generators Mfr
N.A.I.C.S.: 336310
Ichiro Hashimoto *(COO)*

Subsidiary (Non-US):

Niigata Power Systems (Europe) B.V. (2)

Beursplein 37, 3011 AA, Rotterdam, Netherlands
Tel.: (31) 10 405 3085
Emp.: 4
Marine Diesel Engines Mfr
N.A.I.C.S.: 333618
Y. Kino *(Mng Dir)*

Niigata Power Systems Philippines, Inc. (2)
2nd Floor BJ Marthel Building No 5 Ascie Avanue Km 16, West Service Road, Paranaque, 1700, Philippines
Tel.: (63) 2 822 3678
Emp.: 10
Engine Equipment Repair & Maintenance Services
N.A.I.C.S.: 811310

Niigata Power Sytems (Shanghai) Co., Ltd. (1)
RM902 Orient International Plaza Part C No 85 Loushanguan Road, Shanghai, 200336, China
Tel.: (86) 2162787681
Industrial Machinery Mfr
N.A.I.C.S.: 333248

Niigata Trsnsys Co., Ltd. (1)
1-12-1 Yurakucho, Chiyoda-ku, Tokyo, 100-0006, Japan
Tel.: (81) 352935061
Web Site: http://www.niigata-transys.com
Industrial Vehicle Mfr & Whslr
N.A.I.C.S.: 333924
Takefumi Ishizuka *(Pres)*

PRIMUS Processamento de Tubos S.A. (1)
Rua Campo Grande 3760 Campo Grande, Rio de Janeiro, 23063-000, Brazil
Tel.: (55) 21 3461 4700
Web Site: http://www.protubo.com.br
Sales Range: $25-49.9 Million
Emp.: 100
Pipe & Pipe Fitting Mfr
N.A.I.C.S.: 332996
Nelson Hashimoto *(Pres)*

PT Cilegon Fabricators (1)
Jl Raya Bojonegara Salira Argawana Pulo Ampel, Serang, 42454, Banten, Indonesia
Tel.: (62) 254 575 0068
Web Site: https://www.cilegonfab.co.id
Sales Range: $250-299.9 Million
Emp.: 1,400
Steel Fabrication Services & Distr
N.A.I.C.S.: 423510
Masakazu Nagayoshi *(Pres)*

PT. IHI Transport Machinery Indonesia (1)
19th Floor UBN Tower 10 Jalan P Ramlee, 50250, Kuala Lumpur, Malaysia
Tel.: (60) 320728899
Industrial Machinery Mfr
N.A.I.C.S.: 333248

PT. IHI Transport Machinery Indonesia (1)
14th Floor Wisma Keiai Building Jl Jend Sudirman Kav 3, Jakarta, Indonesia
Tel.: (62) 215724290
Industrial Machinery Mfr
N.A.I.C.S.: 333248

Paul Wurth Ihi Co., Ltd. (1)
Toyosu Center Bldg 9F 3-3 Toyosu 3-chome, Koto-ku, Tokyo, 135-6009, Japan
Tel.: (81) 366304786
Industrial Vehicle Whslr
N.A.I.C.S.: 423110

Shanghai Star Modern Agriculture Equipment Co., Ltd. (1)
1300 Huaning Road, Minhang, Shanghai, China
Tel.: (86) 2164625848
Industrial Machinery Mfr
N.A.I.C.S.: 333248

Steinmuller Engineering GmbH (1)
Fabrikstrasse 5, 51643, Gummersbach, Germany (100%)
Tel.: (49) 2261 78950 0
Web Site: http://www.steinmueller.com
Sales Range: $25-49.9 Million
Emp.: 100
Environmental Consulting Services
N.A.I.C.S.: 541620

Hans-Ulrich Thierbach *(Member-Mgmt Bd)*
Takashima Giken Co., Ltd. (1)
15-1-1 Ii, Awara, 919-0614, Fukui, Japan
Tel.: (81) 77 674 0880
Web Site: https://www.takashima-giken.co.jp
Industrial Machinery Mfr
N.A.I.C.S.: 333248

Voith Ihi Paper Technology Co., Ltd. (1)
River-City M-Square 2-1-6 Tsukuda, Chuo-ku, Tokyo, 104-0051, Japan
Tel.: (81) 36 221 3100
Web Site: https://www.voithihi.com
Paper Mfr
N.A.I.C.S.: 322120
Tetsuhiko Nogami *(Pres)*

Wuxi IHI Turbo Co., Ltd. (1)
Meiyu Road 110, Wuxi National Hi-Tech Industrial Development Zone, Wuxi, 214000, Jiangsu, China
Tel.: (86) 510 85216911
Web Site: http://www.witihi.com
Vehicle Engine Equipment Mfr
N.A.I.C.S.: 336320

IHLAS EV ALETLERI IMALAT SANAYI VE TICARET A.S.
Mermerciler Sanayi Sitesi 7'nci Cadde No 12, Beylikduzu, 34524, Istanbul, Turkiye
Tel.: (90) 2128753562
Web Site:
    https://www.ihlasevaletleri.com.tr
Year Founded: 1975
IHEVA—(IST)
Rev.: $71,239,616
Assets: $48,877,901
Liabilities: $14,156,387
Net Worth: $34,721,513
Earnings: ($7,111,499)
Fiscal Year-end: 12/31/23
Household Appliances Mfr
N.A.I.C.S.: 335220
Sedat Kurucan *(Chm, Vice Chm & Gen Mgr)*

IHLAS HOLDING A.S.
Merkez Mahallesi 29 Ekim Caddesi Ihlas Plaza No 11 B/21, Yenibosna, 34197, Istanbul, Turkiye
Tel.: (90) 2124542000
Web Site: https://www.ihlas.com.tr
Year Founded: 1993
IHLAS—(IST)
Rev.: $104,862,679
Assets: $262,817,623
Liabilities: $100,446,845
Net Worth: $162,370,778
Earnings: $29,131,741
Emp.: 2,517
Fiscal Year-end: 12/31/22
Holding Company
N.A.I.C.S.: 551112
Ahmet Mucahid Oren *(Chm)*

Subsidiaries:

Ihlas Gayrimenkul Proje Gelistirme ve Ticaret A.S. (1)
Merkez Mah 29 Ekim Cad Ihlas Plaza No 11-A/11, Yenibosna-Bahcelievler, 34197, Istanbul, Turkiye
Tel.: (90) 2124542700
Web Site: https://www.ihlasgayrimenkul.com
Rev.: $17,688,161
Assets: $41,188,074
Liabilities: $7,336,716
Net Worth: $33,851,358
Earnings: $4,137,192
Fiscal Year-end: 12/31/2022
Metal Mining Services
N.A.I.C.S.: 212290
Sedat Kurucan *(Chm)*

Ihlas Gazetecilik A.S. (1)
Merkez Street 29 Ekim Road Ihlas Plaza No 11 A/41, Yenibosna Bahcelievler, 34197, Istanbul, Turkiye
Tel.: (90) 2124543000
Web Site:
    https://www.ihlasgazetecilik.com.tr

INTERNATIONAL PUBLIC

Newspaper Publishing Services
N.A.I.C.S.: 513110
Ismail Kapan *(Chm & Editor-in-Chief)*

Ihlas Girisim Sermayesi Yatirim Ortakligi A.S. (1)
Yenibosna Merkez Mah 29 Ekim Cad No 11B Ic Kapi No 21, Bahcelievler, 34197, Istanbul, Turkiye
Tel.: (90) 2124542165
Web Site: https://www.ihlasgirisim.com
Venture Capital Investment Services
N.A.I.C.S.: 523910

Ihlas Haber Ajansi A.S (1)
29 Ekim Cad Ihlas Plaza No 11 A/21, Yenibosna, 34197, Istanbul, Turkiye
Tel.: (90) 2124543333
Web Site: http://www.iha.com.tr
Sales Range: $50-74.9 Million
News Reporting Services
N.A.I.C.S.: 516210

Ihlas Motor A.S. (1)
29 Ekim Caddesi No 23, Yenibosna, 34197, Istanbul, Turkiye
Tel.: (90) 2124542300
Web Site: http://www.ihlasmotor.com.tr
Cars & Trucks Mfr
N.A.I.C.S.: 333120

Ihlas Net A.S (1)
Ihlas Medya Center, Yenibosna, 34530, Istanbul, Turkiye
Tel.: (90) 2124542600
Web Site: https://www.ihlas.net.tr
Sales Range: $25-49.9 Million
Internet Service Provider
N.A.I.C.S.: 517810

Ihlas Pazarlama A.S (1)
Merkez Mahallesi 29 Ekim Caddesi Ihlas Plaza No 11 B/11, Yenibosna Bahcelievler, 34197, Istanbul, Turkiye
Tel.: (90) 4444949
Web Site: http://ihlaspazarlama.com.tr
Household Appliances Online Retailer
N.A.I.C.S.: 449210

Ihlas Yapi Turizm ve Saglik A.S. (1)
29 Ekim Street No 11, Yenibosna - Bahcelievler, 34197, Istanbul, Turkiye
Tel.: (90) 2124544550
Web Site: https://www.ihlasyapi.com.tr
Building Construction Services
N.A.I.C.S.: 541330

Kuzuluk Kaplica Insaat Turizm Saglik ve Petrol Urunleri Tic. A.S (1)
Orta Mahalle Caddesi No 352 Akyazi, Sakarya, Turkiye
Tel.: (90) 2644210020
Web Site: https://otel.ihlaskuzuluk.com
Home Management Services
N.A.I.C.S.: 541618

Pastas Comarrico S.A.S (1)
Cl 39 51-58 Via 40 Atlantic, Barranquilla, Colombia
Tel.: (57) 5 3704275
Pasta Foods Mfr
N.A.I.C.S.: 311824

Sifa Yemek ve Gida Uretim Tesisleri Tic. A.S. (1)
Cobancesme Mah Fatih Cad 1 Bahcelievler, 34196, Istanbul, Turkiye
Tel.: (90) 2125032500
Web Site: https://www.sifayemek.com.tr
Food Production Services
N.A.I.C.S.: 722310

Voli Fuar Hizmetleri A.S. (1)
Evren Mah Bahar Cad Polat Is Merkezi B Blok No 6-1/41, Gunesli-Bagcilar, 34212, Istanbul, Turkiye
Tel.: (90) 212 604 50 50
Web Site: http://voli.com.tr
Trade Fair Management Services
N.A.I.C.S.: 561920

IHLAS YAYIN HOLDING A.S.
Merkez Mahallesi 29 Ekim Caddesi Ihlas Plaza No 11 B/31Yenibosna, Bahcelievler, 34197, Istanbul, Turkiye
Tel.: (90) 2124542422
Web Site:
    https://www.ihlasyayinholding.com.tr
Year Founded: 2003

AND PRIVATE COMPANIES

IHYAY—(IST)
Rev.: $60,030,320
Assets: $114,583,358
Liabilities: $38,390,832
Net Worth: $76,192,526
Earnings: ($29,789,867)
Fiscal Year-end: 12/31/23
Holding Company
N.A.I.C.S.: 551112
Ahmet Mucahid Oren *(Chm)*

IHO-AGRO INTERNATIONAL, INC.
4th Floor Section D Jinhao Pioneering Park, Guanlan Dafu Industrial Zone, Shenzhen, Guangdong, China
Tel.: (86) 755 2973 7673 NV
Web Site: http://www.ihoagro.com
Year Founded: 2014
All-Natural Mineral Based Fertilizers Distr
N.A.I.C.S.: 325312
Yingying Zhou *(CEO)*

IHQ, INC.
501-8 Gangseo-ro, Gangseo-gu, Seoul, Korea (South)
Tel.: (82) 260056000
Web Site: http://www.sidushq.com
Year Founded: 1962
003560—(KRS)
Rev.: $3,180,275
Assets: $188,927,539
Liabilities: $121,832,753
Net Worth: $67,094,786
Earnings: ($78,595,957)
Emp.: 200
Fiscal Year-end: 12/31/22
Broadcasting Video & Motion Picture Services
N.A.I.C.S.: 512110
Kim Hyeonchang *(Dir)*

IHS HOLDING LIMITED
1 Cathedral Piazza 123 Victoria Street, London, SW1E 5BP, United Kingdom
Tel.: (44) 2081061600 Ky
Web Site: https://www.ihstowers.com
Year Founded: 2012
IHS—(NYSE)
Rev.: $1,961,299,000
Assets: $6,320,865,000
Liabilities: $4,962,217,000
Net Worth: $1,358,648,000
Earnings: ($470,397,000)
Emp.: 2,786
Fiscal Year-end: 12/31/22
Offices of Other Holding Companies
N.A.I.C.S.: 551112
Sam Darwish *(Chm & CEO)*

IHS NIGERIA PLC
Plot 934 Idejo Street Off Adeola Odeku, Victoria Island, Lagos, 101241, Nigeria
Tel.: (234) 7000777777
Web Site: http://www.ihstowers.com
Year Founded: 2001
Communication Service
N.A.I.C.S.: 334290
Mohamad Darwish *(CEO & Sr VP)*

IHUMAN INC.
Floor 8 Building 2 No 1 Wangjing East Road, Chaoyang District, Beijing, 100102, China
Tel.: (86) 1057806606 Ky
Web Site: https://www.ihuman.com
Year Founded: 2019
IH—(NYSE)
Rev.: $150,991,060
Assets: $204,290,061
Liabilities: $86,402,320
Net Worth: $117,887,741
Earnings: $16,825,369
Emp.: 770
Fiscal Year-end: 12/31/22
Holding Company
N.A.I.C.S.: 551112
Michael Yufeng Chi *(Founder & Chm)*

IHUNT TECHNOLOGY IMPORT-EXPORT S.A.
Str Marin Mehedinteanu No 1F, Prahova, Ploiesti, Romania
Tel.: (40) 219951
Web Site: https://www.ihunt.ro
HUNT—(BUC)
Rev.: $9,537,412
Assets: $8,908,139
Liabilities: $4,591,301
Net Worth: $4,316,838
Earnings: ($298,021)
Emp.: 19
Fiscal Year-end: 12/31/23
Online Shopping Site Operator
N.A.I.C.S.: 455219
Cezar Catalin Stroe *(Pres & Gen Mgr)*

IID INC.
Harmony Tower 17F Honcho 1-32-2, Nakano-ku, Tokyo, 164-0012, Japan
Tel.: (81) 366342232
Web Site: https://www.iid.co.jp
Year Founded: 2000
6038—(TKS)
Rev.: $38,097,500
Assets: $38,993,180
Liabilities: $12,458,660
Net Worth: $26,534,520
Earnings: $1,013,860
Emp.: 236
Fiscal Year-end: 06/30/24
Market Research
N.A.I.C.S.: 541910
Hiroshi Miyakawa *(Pres & CEO)*

Subsidiaries:

Interface in Design, Inc. (1)
21171 S Western Ave Ste 2707, Torrance, CA 90501
Tel.: (310) 212-7555
Web Site: http://www.iid-usa.com
Marketing Research Service
N.A.I.C.S.: 541910

IIDA GROUP HOLDINGS CO., LTD.
1-2-11 Nishikubo, Musashino City, Tokyo, 180-0013, Japan
Tel.: (81) 422608888 JP
Web Site: https://www.ighd.co.jp
Year Founded: 2013
3291—(TKS)
Rev.: $9,512,979,800
Assets: $11,971,893,190
Liabilities: $5,545,129,000
Net Worth: $6,426,764,190
Earnings: $245,918,440
Emp.: 13,366
Fiscal Year-end: 03/31/24
Holding Company
N.A.I.C.S.: 551112
Yoichi Nishikawa *(Pres)*

Subsidiaries:

Arnest One Corporation (1)
3-2-22 Kitahara-cho, Nishi-Tokyo, 188-0003, Tokyo, Japan
Tel.: (81) 424616444
Sales Range: $100-124.9 Million
Emp.: 1,689
Construction Engineering Services
N.A.I.C.S.: 541330
Shigeyuki Matsubayashi *(Pres)*

Subsidiary (Domestic):

Aone Plus Co., Ltd. (2)
1-2-2 Nishiharacho, Nishi-Tokyo, Tokyo, Japan
Tel.: (81) 424518240
Housing Construction Services
N.A.I.C.S.: 236115

First Plus, Inc. (1)
1-6-22 Nishikubo IGHD Annex 8F, Musashino, 180-0013, Tokyo, Japan
Tel.: (81) 422603350
Web Site: http://www.first-plus.co.jp
Housing Equipment Mfr & Distr
N.A.I.C.S.: 333248

First Wood Co., Ltd. (1)
126-1 Kawashiri-cho No 40, Fukui, 910-3136, Japan
Tel.: (81) 776880015
Web Site: https://www.1stwood.jp
Housing Construction Services
N.A.I.C.S.: 236115

Hajime Construction Co., Ltd. (1)
Tokyu Building East Building No 5 2-25-5 Minami-Ikebukuro, Toshima-ku, Tokyo, 171-0022, Japan
Tel.: (81) 359281700
Web Site: https://www.hajime-kensetsu.co.jp
Sales Range: $1-4.9 Billion
Emp.: 810
Residential Real Estate Development, Housing Construction & Brokerage Services
N.A.I.C.S.: 236117
Tadayoshi Horiguchi *(CEO)*

Subsidiary (Domestic):

Jutakujohokan Co., Ltd. (2)
2-8-8 Fujimi, Chuo-ku, Sagamihara, Kanagawa, Japan
Tel.: (81) 427047333
Housing Construction Services
N.A.I.C.S.: 236115

Jutakujohokan Financial Service Co., Ltd. (2)
2-8-8 Fujimi, Chuo-ku, Sagamihara, Kanagawa, Japan
Tel.: (81) 120975622
Housing Construction Services
N.A.I.C.S.: 236115

Living Corporation, Inc. (2)
4-2-12 Shibuya, Shibuya-ku, Tokyo, Japan
Tel.: (81) 363000919
Housing Construction Services
N.A.I.C.S.: 236115

Home Trade Center Co., Ltd. (1)
1-3-14 Sakai, Musashino, Tokyo, Japan
Tel.: (81) 367397520
Housing Construction Services
N.A.I.C.S.: 236115

ID Home Co., Ltd. (1)
3-46-25 Takadanobaba, Shinjuku-ku, Tokyo, 169-0075, Japan
Tel.: (81) 353376988
Web Site: https://www.idhome.co.jp
Sales Range: $750-799.9 Million
Emp.: 749
Residential Real Estate Acquisition, Development, Construction & Brokerage Services
N.A.I.C.S.: 531390
Hisarin Kinya *(Pres)*

Subsidiary (Domestic):

Sun Plaza Home Co., Ltd. (2)
7-56-17 Hibaru, Minami-ku, Fukuoka, Japan
Tel.: (81) 924043331
Housing Construction Services
N.A.I.C.S.: 236115

IG Windows Co., Ltd. (1)
1-6-22 Nishikubo 7th Floor, Musashino, 180-0013, Tokyo, Japan
Tel.: (81) 422568280
Web Site: https://www.igw.co.jp
Emp.: 170
Double Glazing Mfr & Distr
N.A.I.C.S.: 327215

Iida Home Max Co., Ltd. (1)
2-2-2 Sakai, Musashino, 180-0022, Tokyo, Japan
Tel.: (81) 422368848
Web Site: https://www.iidasangyo.co.jp
Emp.: 1,189
Residential Real Estate Investment, Development, Construction, Brokerage & Leasing Services
N.A.I.C.S.: 531390
Kazuhiko Mori *(Chm)*

Iida Sangyo Co., Ltd. (1)
2-2-2 Sakai, Musashino, Tokyo, Japan
Tel.: (81) 422368848
Web Site: https://www.iidasangyo.co.jp
Emp.: 1,403
Housing Construction Services
N.A.I.C.S.: 236115
Kazuhiko Mori *(Chm)*

Tact Home Co., Ltd. (1)
3-6-19 Higashifushimi, Nishi-Tokyo, 202-0021, Tokyo, Japan
Tel.: (81) 424648788
Web Site: https://www.tacthome.co.jp
Emp.: 922
Residential Real Estate Acquisition, Development, Construction, Brokerage & Leasing Services
N.A.I.C.S.: 531390
Shigeho Yamamoto *(Chm)*

Subsidiary (Domestic):

Solidone Co., Ltd. (2)
3-8-13 Higashifushimi Graphare Building 3F, Nishi-Tokyo, 202-0021, Tokyo, Japan
Tel.: (81) 424521588
Web Site: https://solidone.co.jp
Single & Multi-Family Housing Development & Construction
N.A.I.C.S.: 236117
Hironobu Arima *(Pres)*

T-Around Co., Ltd. (2)
Grapher Re Building 2F 3-8-13 Higashifushimi, Nishi-Tokyo, 202-0021, Japan
Tel.: (81) 424521808
Web Site: https://www.t-around.co.jp
Residential Real Estate Agency & Homeowner's Insurance Brokerage Services
N.A.I.C.S.: 531210
Takeshi Ebato *(Pres & CEO)*

Touei Housing Corporation (1)
4-26-3 Shibakubo-cho, Nishi-Tokyo, 188-0014, Tokyo, Japan
Tel.: (81) 120281082
Emp.: 773
Residential Real Estate Development, Housing Construction & Brokerage Services
N.A.I.C.S.: 236117
Hiroshi Nishino *(Pres)*

Subsidiary (Domestic):

Touei Fujiyoshi Construction Corporation (2)
69-1 Matsuhidai, Matsudo, 270-2214, Chiba, Japan
Tel.: (81) 473941081
Web Site: http://www.toueifujiyoshi.co.jp
Housing Construction Services
N.A.I.C.S.: 236115

Touei Home Service Corporation (2)
1-4-7 Hanakoganei, Kodaira, 187-0002, Tokyo, Japan
Tel.: (81) 120881706
Web Site: https://www.touei-home.co.jp
Emp.: 136
Housing Construction Services
N.A.I.C.S.: 236115

IINO KAIUN KAISHA LTD.
2F Iino Building Uchisaiwaich 2-1-1, Chiyoda-ku, Tokyo, 100-0011, Japan
Tel.: (81) 362733069 JP
Web Site: https://www.iino.co.jp
Year Founded: 1899
9119—(TKS)
Rev.: $911,849,500
Assets: $1,938,237,080
Liabilities: $1,064,884,220
Net Worth: $873,352,860
Earnings: $130,514,450
Emp.: 680
Fiscal Year-end: 03/31/24
Shipping & Real Estate Services
N.A.I.C.S.: 483111
Tomoshige Jingu *(Bd of Dirs & Mng Exec Officer/Mng Exec Officer-Fin & Acctg Dept)*

Subsidiaries:

Godo Marine Industry Co., Ltd. (1)
1-8-9 Minamicho Sumiyoshi, Higashinada-

IINO KAIUN KAISHA LTD.

Iino Kaiun Kaisha Ltd.—(Continued)
ku, Kobe, 658-0041, Hyogo, Japan
Tel.: (81) 788513161
Web Site: http://www.iino.co.jp
Sales Range: $25-49.9 Million
Emp.: 7
Shipping Services
N.A.I.C.S.: 488390

Godo Senpaku Kogyo Co., Ltd. (1)
1-8-9 Minamicho Sumiyoshi, Higashinada-ku, Kobe, 658-0041, Hyogo, Japan
Tel.: (81) 78 851 3161
Web Site: http://www.iino.co.jp
Sales Range: $25-49.9 Million
Emp.: 8
Ship Building & Repairing Services
N.A.I.C.S.: 336611

Subsidiary (Non-US):

Iino Shipping Asia Pte. Ltd. (2)
168 Robinson Road 13th Fl No 2 Capital Tower, Singapore, 68912, Singapore
Tel.: (65) 62740570
Web Site: http://www.iinochem.com
Sales Range: $25-49.9 Million
Ship Management Services
N.A.I.C.S.: 488390
Grece Goh *(Mgr-HR)*

Iino Building Technology Co., Ltd. (1)
IINO Building 2-1-1, Uchisaiwaicho, Chiyoda-ku, Tokyo, 100-0011, Japan
Tel.: (81) 36 273 3448
Web Site: http://www.iino.co.jp
Real Estate Management Services
N.A.I.C.S.: 531390

Iino Business Service co., Ltd. (1)
NS Toranomon Building Nishi Shimbashi 1-6-15, Minato-ku, Tokyo, 105-0003, Japan
Tel.: (81) 36 273 3274
Web Site: http://www.iino.co.jp
General Insurance Services
N.A.I.C.S.: 524210

Iino Enterprise Co., Ltd. (1)
1-6-15 Nishi-Shimbashi NS Toranomon Building 5th floor, Minato-ku, Tokyo, 105-0003, Japan
Tel.: (81) 36 273 3442
Web Site: https://www.ariakesouko.com
Conference Hall Leasing & Warehousing Services
N.A.I.C.S.: 531120

Iino Gas Transport Co., Ltd. (1)
4th fl Boueki Building 123-1 Higashimachi, Chuo-ku, Kobe, 650-0031, Hyogo, Japan (100%)
Tel.: (81) 78 321 8611
Web Site: https://www.iino.co.jp
Marine Cargo Handling Services
N.A.I.C.S.: 488320

Iino Management Data Processing Co., Ltd. (1)
IINO Building 2-1-1, Uchisaiwaicho, Chiyoda-ku, Tokyo, 100-0011, Japan
Tel.: (81) 33 506 3172
Web Site: http://www.iino.co.jp
Accounting & Data Processing Services
N.A.I.C.S.: 541219

Iino Marine Service Co., Ltd. (1)
Iino Building Uchisaiwaicho 2-1-1, Chiyoda-ku, Tokyo, 100-0011, Japan
Tel.: (81) 36 273 3317
Web Site: https://www.iino.co.jp
Sales Range: $25-49.9 Million
Emp.: 60
Marine Staff Recruitment Services
N.A.I.C.S.: 561311

Iino Media Pro Co., Ltd. (1)
4-5 Hiroo 3-Chome, Shibuya-ku, Tokyo, 150-0012, Japan
Tel.: (81) 35 467 7415
Web Site: https://www.iinomediapro.com
Sales Range: $25-49.9 Million
Emp.: 82
Commercial Photography
N.A.I.C.S.: 541922
Wataru Chomei *(Pres)*

Iino Singapore Pte. Ltd. (1)
168 Robinson Road 13-02 Capital Tower, Singapore, 068912, Singapore
Tel.: (65) 6 274 0570
Web Site: http://www.iino.co.jp
Sales Range: $25-49.9 Million
Emp.: 20
Shipping Services
N.A.I.C.S.: 483111

Iino UK Ltd. (1)
6th floor 125 Old Broad Street, London, EC2N 1AR, United Kingdom
Tel.: (44) 203 968 5320
Web Site: http://www.iino.co.jp
Sales Range: $25-49.9 Million
Emp.: 2
Shipping Services
N.A.I.C.S.: 483111

Taiho Marine Co., Ltd. (1)
4-2-7 Ariake, Koto-ku, Tokyo, 135-0063, Japan
Tel.: (81) 33 529 5521
Web Site: http://www.iino.co.jp
Warehousing & Ship Leasing Services
N.A.I.C.S.: 493110

IIVARI MONONEN OY

Rantakatu 25 C, 80100, Joensuu, Finland
Tel.: (358) 20 7330500
Web Site: http://www.iivarimononen.fi
Year Founded: 1945
Emp.: 150
Telecommunication Network Services
N.A.I.C.S.: 517112
Ari Mononen *(CEO)*

Subsidiaries:

ScanPole Oy (1)
Rantakatu 25 C, 80100, Joensuu, Finland
Tel.: (358) 207 330 500
Web Site: http://www.scanpole.com
Wood Pole Mfr
N.A.I.C.S.: 321999

Subsidiary (Non-US):

Burt Boulton & Haywood Ltd. (2)
Alexandra Dock, Newport, NP20 2WA, United Kingdom
Tel.: (44) 1633 235800
Web Site: http://www.bbhpreservingwood.co.uk
Wood Product Distr
N.A.I.C.S.: 423310
Ari Mononen *(Gen Mgr)*

IJM CORPORATION BERHAD

Wisma IJM Jalan Yong Shook Lin, 46050, Petaling Jaya, Selangor Darul Ehsan, Malaysia
Tel.: (60) 379858288
Web Site: https://www.ijm.com
Year Founded: 1983
IJM—(KLS)
Rev.: $1,091,222,550
Assets: $5,200,481,880
Liabilities: $2,363,950,215
Net Worth: $2,836,531,665
Earnings: $219,087,990
Emp.: 2,878
Fiscal Year-end: 03/31/22
Construction Services
N.A.I.C.S.: 236220
Cyrus Eruch Daruwalla *(Head-Country-Indian Ops)*

Subsidiaries:

Akrab Perkasa Sdn Bhd (1)
2nd Floor Wisma Ijm, Jalan Yong Shook Lin, 46050, Petaling Jaya, Selangor, Malaysia (48%)
Tel.: (60) 379858288
Web Site: http://www.ijm.com
Oil & Gas Operations
N.A.I.C.S.: 213112

Ampas Maju Sdn Bhd (1)
2nd Floor Wisma Ijm, Jalan Yong Shook Lin, 46050, Petaling Jaya, Selangor, Malaysia (48%)
Tel.: (60) 379858288
Web Site: http://www.ijm.com
Sales Range: $150-199.9 Million
Emp.: 300
Farm Product Raw Material Merchant Whslr
N.A.I.C.S.: 424590

Azam Ekuiti Sdn Bhd (1)
2nd Fl Wisma Ijm, Jalan Yong Shook Lin, 46050, Petaling Jaya, Selangor, Malaysia (66%)
Tel.: (60) 379858288
Web Site: http://www.ijm.com
Sales Range: $1-4.9 Billion
Emp.: 4,000
Crushed & Broken Stone Mining & Quarrying
N.A.I.C.S.: 212319

BW Yee Seng Hardware Trading Sdn. Bhd. (1)
1571 Jalan Serunai Kawasan Perindustrian Valdor Sungai Jawi, Seberang Prai Selatan, 14200, Penang, Pulau, Malaysia (20%)
Tel.: (60) 45859999
Web Site: https://www.bwysgroup.com
Emp.: 200
Mfr of Scaffolding Assemblies, Metal Roofing & Multi-Truss, Total Storage Solutions & Steel Pipes & Plates
N.A.I.C.S.: 332510

Berakan Maju Sdn Bhd (1)
Wisma Ijm Plantations Jalan Utara Batu 6, Lot 1 Jalan Bandar Utama, Sandakan, 90000, Selangor, Malaysia (100%)
Tel.: (60) 89667721
Web Site: http://www.ijm.com
Oilseed Processing
N.A.I.C.S.: 311224

CIDB Inventures Sdn Bhd (1)
Level 22 Menara Datoonn Pwtc No 45 Jalan Tun Ismail, 50450, Kuala Lumpur, Malaysia (36%)
Tel.: (60) 340428880
Sales Range: $25-49.9 Million
Emp.: 12
Holding Company
N.A.I.C.S.: 551112

Cofreth (M) Sdn Bhd (1)
No 39 Jalan USJ Sentral 3 USJ Sentral Persiaran Subang 1, 47600, Subang Jaya, Selangor, Malaysia (25%)
Tel.: (60) 380238878
Web Site: https://www.cofreth.com.my
Management Consulting Services
N.A.I.C.S.: 541618
Ong Ching Loon *(Mng Dir)*

Commerce House Sdn Bhd (1)
2nd Floor Wisma IJM Jalan Yong Shook Lin, 46050, Petaling Jaya, Selangor Darul Ehsan, Malaysia
Tel.: (60) 379858288
Web Site: https://www.ijm.com
Construction Materials Distr
N.A.I.C.S.: 423390
Yoke Kian Ng *(Sec)*

Damansara Rock Products Sdn Bhd (1)
2nd Fl Wisma Ijm, Jalan Yong Shook Lin, 46050, Petaling Jaya, Selangor, Malaysia (66%)
Tel.: (60) 379858288
Crushed & Broken Granite Mining & Quarrying
N.A.I.C.S.: 212313

Desa Talisai Sdn Bhd (1)
2nd Floor Wisma Ijm, Jalan Yong Shook Lin, 46050, Petaling Jaya, Selangor, Malaysia (48%)
Tel.: (60) 379858288
Oilseed & Grain Combination Farming
N.A.I.C.S.: 111191
Krishnan Tan Boon Seng *(Chm)*

Durabon Sdn Bhd (1)
2nd Floor Wisma IJM, PO Box 1, Jalan Yong Shook Lin, 46050, Petaling Jaya, Selangor Darul Ehsan, Malaysia (66%)
Tel.: (60) 379858288
Sales Range: $50-74.9 Million
Emp.: 200
Structural Steel Erection Contractors
N.A.I.C.S.: 238120

Dynasive Enterprise Sdn Bhd (1)
2nd Floor Wisma Ijm, Jalan Yong Shook Lin, 46050, Petaling Jaya, Selangor, Malaysia (48%)
Tel.: (60) 379858288
Sales Range: $700-749.9 Million
Emp.: 1,200
Financial Investment Activities
N.A.I.C.S.: 523999
Krishnan Tan Boon Seng *(Mng Dir)*

Expedient Resources Sdn Bhd (1)
No 15 & 17 Jalan Tembaga, Kawasan Perusahaan Banting, 42700, Kelang, Selangor, Malaysia (66%)
Tel.: (60) 331813388
Web Site: http://www.tradenex.com
Rubber Products Mfr
N.A.I.C.S.: 326299

Hexacon Construction Pte Limited (1)
432 Balestier Road Public Mansion 02-432, Singapore, 329813, Singapore (46%)
Tel.: (65) 62519388
Web Site: http://www.hexacon.com.sg
Heavy & Civil Engineering Construction
N.A.I.C.S.: 237990
Pang Hoe Sang *(Mng Dir)*

ICP Marketing Sdn Bhd (1)
2nd Floor Wisma IJM, Jalan Yong Shook Lin, 46050, Petaling Jaya, Selangor Darul Ehsan, Malaysia (66%)
Tel.: (60) 379858288
Concrete Products Mfr
N.A.I.C.S.: 327390
Krishnan Tan Boon Seng *(Mng Dir)*

IJM (India) Infrastructure Limited (1)
H No 3-71/NR Plot No 71 Kavuri Hills Phase-II, Madhapur, Hyderabad, 500 033, AP, India (97%)
Tel.: (91) 4023114661
Web Site: https://www.ijmindia.com
Construction Materials Whslr
N.A.I.C.S.: 423390

IJM Building Systems Sdn Bhd (1)
2nd Floor Wisma IJM Jalan Yong Shook Lin, 46050, Petaling Jaya, Selangor Darul Ehsan, Malaysia (100%)
Tel.: (60) 379571580
New Single-Family Housing Construction
N.A.I.C.S.: 236115

IJM Construction (Middle East) Limited Liability Company (1)
Flat 101 Building U05 International City, PO Box 36634, Dubai, United Arab Emirates
Tel.: (971) 48742377
Sales Range: $25-49.9 Million
Emp.: 3
Construction Engineering Services
N.A.I.C.S.: 541330

IJM Construction Sdn Bhd (1)
2nd Floor Wisma IJM Jalan Yong Shook Lin, 46050, Petaling Jaya, Selangor Darul Ehsan, Malaysia (100%)
Tel.: (60) 379858288
Web Site: https://www.ijm.com
Engineeering Services
N.A.I.C.S.: 541330
Tan Gim Foo *(Chm)*

IJM Edible Oils Sdn Bhd (1)
Wisma Ijm Plantations, Sandakan, Malaysia (48%)
Tel.: (60) 89616776
Farm Product Raw Material Merchant Whslr
N.A.I.C.S.: 424590
Vela Than *(Mng Dir)*

IJM Land Berhad (1)
Ground Floor Wisma IJM Jalan Yong Shook Lin, 46050, Petaling Jaya, Selangor, Malaysia (100%)
Tel.: (60) 379858288
Web Site: https://www.ijmland.com
Sales Range: $600-649.9 Million
Emp.: 580
Industrial Building Constructor & Mfr
N.A.I.C.S.: 236210
Tony Ling Thou Lung *(CEO)*

Subsidiary (Domestic):

IJM Properties Sdn Bhd (2)
9th Floor Wisma Penang Garden 42 Jalan Sultan Ahmad Shah, Penang, 10050, Malaysia

AND PRIVATE COMPANIES

Tel.: (60) 4 226 3492
Web Site: http://www.ijmproperties.com
Property Management Services
N.A.I.C.S.: 531311

IJM Management Services Sdn Bhd (1)
2nd Floor Wisma IJM Jalan Yong Shook Lin, Gelugor, 46050, Petaling Jaya, Selangor Darul Ehsan, Malaysia **(100%)**
Tel.: (60) 42961222
Web Site: http://www.ijmland.com
Sales Range: $25-49.9 Million
Emp.: 128
Management Consulting Services
N.A.I.C.S.: 541618

IJM Overseas Ventures Sdn Bhd (1)
2nd Floor Wisma Ijm, Jalan Yong Shook Lin, 46050, Petaling Jaya, Selangor, Malaysia **(100%)**
Tel.: (60) 379858288
Web Site: http://www.ijm.com
Real Estate Investment Trust
N.A.I.C.S.: 525990
Krishnan Tan Boon Seng (Chm)

Ikatan Flora Sdn Bhd (1)
2nd Fl Wisma IJM, PO Box 504, Jalan Yong Shook Lin, 46050, Petaling Jaya, Selangor Darul Ehsan, Malaysia
Tel.: (60) 379858288
Property Development Services
N.A.I.C.S.: 531390
Yoke Kian Ng (Co-Sec)

Industrial Concrete Products Berhad (1)
Wisma IJM Annexe Jalan Yong Shook Lin, 46050, Petaling Jaya, Selangor, Malaysia **(66%)**
Tel.: (60) 379558888
Web Site: https://www.icpb.com.my
Concrete Products Mfr
N.A.I.C.S.: 327390

Subsidiary (Non-US):

ICP Jiangmen Co. Ltd. (2)
No 6 Sihang Avenue Gujing Town, Xinhui District, Jiangmen, 529145, China
Tel.: (86) 7508269008
Concrete Pile Mfr & Distr
N.A.I.C.S.: 327390

Jalinan Masyhur Sdn Bhd (1)
2nd Floor Wisma Ijm, Jalan Yong Shook Lin, 46050, Petaling Jaya, Selangor Darul Ehsan, Malaysia **(100%)**
Tel.: (60) 379858288
Direct Property & Casualty Insurance Carriers
N.A.I.C.S.: 524126

Jelutong Development Sdn Bhd (1)
2nd Floor Wisma Ijm, Jalan Yong Shook Lin, 46050, Petaling Jaya, Selangor, Malaysia **(80%)**
Tel.: (60) 379858288
Heavy & Civil Engineering Construction
N.A.I.C.S.: 237990

Kemena Industries Sdn Bhd (1)
Sub Lot 56 1st Floor Tanjung Bt Commercial, Centre Jln Tanjung Batu, 97007, Bintulu, Sarawak, Malaysia **(55%)**
Tel.: (60) 86333524
Sales Range: $25-49.9 Million
Emp.: 60
Concrete Products Mfr
N.A.I.C.S.: 327390
Kiang Chee Hiw (Gen Mgr)

Kuang Rock Products Sdn Bhd (1)
2nd Floor Wisma IJM Jalan Yong Shook Lin, Jalan Yong Shook Lin, 46050, Petaling Jaya, Selangor Darul Ehsan, Malaysia **(66%)**
Tel.: (60) 379858288
Web Site: https://www.ijm.com
Emp.: 3
Crushed & Broken Granite Mining & Quarrying
N.A.I.C.S.: 212313

Kuantan Port Consortium Sdn Bhd (1)
Wisma KPC KM25 Tanjung Gelang, PO Box 199, 25720, Kuantan, Pahang Darul Makmur, Malaysia

Tel.: (60) 95863888
Port Operation Services
N.A.I.C.S.: 488310

Kuching Riverine Resort Management Sdn Bhd (1)
2nd Floor Wisma IJM Jalan Yong Shook Lin, 46050, Petaling Jaya, Selangor Darul Ehsan, Malaysia
Tel.: (60) 82421651
Property Management Services
N.A.I.C.S.: 531312
Yoke Kian Ng (Sec)

Kulim Mewah Sdn Bhd (1)
2nd Floor Wisma Ijm, Jalan Yong Shook Lin, 46050, Petaling Jaya, Selangor, Malaysia **(48%)**
Tel.: (60) 379858288
Web Site: http://www.ijm.com
Farm Product Raw Material Merchant Whslr
N.A.I.C.S.: 424590
Krishnan Tan Boon Seng (Mng Dir)

Minat Teguh Sdn Bhd (1)
2nd Floor Wisma Ijm, Jalan Yong Shook Lin, 46050, Petaling Jaya, Selangor, Malaysia **(48%)**
Tel.: (60) 379858288
Web Site: http://www.ijm.com
Emp.: 1,000
Financial Investment Activities
N.A.I.C.S.: 523999
Soam-Heng Choon (Mng Dir)

Nekadsatu Jaya Sdn Bhd (1)
2nd Floor Wisma Ijm, Jalan Yong Shook Lin, Petaling Jaya, 46050, Selangor, Malaysia **(50%)**
Tel.: (60) 379858288
Web Site: http://www.ijm.com
Construction Materials Whslr
N.A.I.C.S.: 423390

Nilai Cipta Sdn Bhd (1)
2nd Floor Wisma Ijm, Jalan Yong Shook Lin, 46050, Petaling Jaya, Selangor, Malaysia **(100%)**
Tel.: (60) 379858288
Building Equipment & Machinery Installation Contractors
N.A.I.C.S.: 238220

Scaffold Master Sdn Bhd (1)
2nd Floor Wisma IJM Jalan Yong Shook Lin, Seksyen 52, 46050, Petaling Jaya, Selangor Darul Ehsan, Malaysia **(66%)**
Tel.: (60) 379571580
Sales Range: $25-49.9 Million
Emp.: 30
Iron & Steel Mills
N.A.I.C.S.: 331110

Seremban Two Holdings Sdn Bhd (1)
2nd Floor Wisma IJM Jalan Yong Shook Lin, 46050, Petaling Jaya, Selangor Darul Ehsan, Malaysia
Tel.: (60) 67619188
Sales Range: $50-74.9 Million
Emp.: 90
Investment Management Service
N.A.I.C.S.: 523999

Sijas Plantations Sdn Bhd (1)
2nd Floor Wisma Ijm, Jalan Yong Shook Lin, 46050, Petaling Jaya, Selangor, Malaysia **(48%)**
Tel.: (60) 379858288
Web Site: http://www.ijm.com
Farm Product Raw Material Merchant Whslr
N.A.I.C.S.: 424590
Krishnan Tan Boon Seng (Deputy Chm)

Strong Mixed Concrete Sdn Bhd (1)
Tel.: (60) 379562862
Ready Mix Concrete Mfr & Distr
N.A.I.C.S.: 327320

THB-IJM Joint Venture Sdn Bhd (1)
2nd Floor Wisma Ijm, Jalan Yong Shook Lin, 46050, Petaling Jaya, Selangor, Malaysia **(49%)**
Tel.: (60) 379858288
Sales Range: $25-49.9 Million
Emp.: 30
Construction Materials Whslr
N.A.I.C.S.: 423390

IK HOLDINGS CO., LTD.

5th floor of KDX Nagoya Station Building 3-26-8 Meieki, Nakamura-ku, Nagoya, 450-0002, Aichi, Japan
Tel.: (81) 528563101
Web Site: https://www.ai-kei.co.jp
Year Founded: 1990
2722—(NGO)
Rev.: $93,683,951
Assets: $44,854,648
Liabilities: $31,835,851
Net Worth: $13,018,797
Earnings: ($3,062,656)
Emp.: 282
Fiscal Year-end: 05/31/23
Food Product & Goods Distr
N.A.I.C.S.: 424420
Hiroshi Iida (Chm & CEO)

IK INVESTMENT PARTNERS LIMITED

1-11 John Adam Street, London, WC2N 6HT, United Kingdom
Tel.: (44) 2073044300 UK
Web Site: http://www.ikinvest.com
Year Founded: 1989
Private Equity Firm & Investment Management Services
N.A.I.C.S.: 523999
Christopher Masek (CEO)

Subsidiaries:

Debitor-Inkasso GmbH (1)
Markttwiete 2, 23611, Bad Schwartau, Germany
Tel.: (49) 451 2009 399
Web Site: http://www.debitor.de
Debt Collection Services
N.A.I.C.S.: 561440

Doedijns Group International B.V. (1)
Coenecoop 103-105, Waddinxveen, 2740AD, Netherlands
Tel.: (31) 182302888
Web Site: http://www.dgi-company.com
Sales Range: $125-149.9 Million
Emp.: 465
Holding Company; Motor Vehicle & Industrial Components Mfr
N.A.I.C.S.: 551112
Juul Ijzermans (CEO)

Subsidiary (Domestic):

Doedijns Automotive B.V. (2)
Edisonweg 11, 3208KB, Spijkenisse, Netherlands
Tel.: (31) 181601222
Web Site: http://www.doedijns.com
Sales Range: $50-74.9 Million
Emp.: 10
Automobile Parts Mfr
N.A.I.C.S.: 423120

Doedijns Controls B.V. (2)
Australieweg 10, 9407 TE, Assen, Netherlands
Tel.: (31) 592405070
Sales Range: $50-74.9 Million
Emp.: 250
Instrument Relay & Control Components Mfr
N.A.I.C.S.: 335314
Ijzernans Jules (CEO)

Doedijns Hydraulics B.V. (2)
Coenecoop 103-105, 2741 PH, Waddinxveen, Netherlands
Tel.: (31) 182302888
Web Site: http://www.doedijns.com
Emp.: 200
Hydraulic Components Mfr
N.A.I.C.S.: 332912
Dirk Smulders (Mng Dir)

Doedijns Pneumatics B.V. (2)
Lange Linden 32, Katwijk, 5431LG, Netherlands
Tel.: (31) 485337100
Web Site: http://www.doedijns.nl
Pneumatic Engineering
N.A.I.C.S.: 332912

Domia Group SA (1)
7 rue de la Baume, 75008, Paris, France

Tel.: (33) 1 7301 1300
Web Site: http://www.acadomia.fr
Tutoring Services
N.A.I.C.S.: 611691
Maxime Aiach (Pres)

Elektrokoppar AB (1)
Elektro Gatan 20, PO Box 914, Helsingborg, 25109, Sweden
Tel.: (46) 42195300
Web Site: http://www.elektrokoppar.se
Sales Range: $50-74.9 Million
Mfr of Wire & Strip Conductors Made of Copper & Aluminum
N.A.I.C.S.: 335931
Leis Olson (Gen Mgr)

IK Investment Partners AB (1)
Norrlandsgatan 15 7th FL, Stockholm, 11434, Sweden
Tel.: (46) 86789500
Web Site: http://www.ikinvest.com
Private Equity Investment Services
N.A.I.C.S.: 523999
Detlef Dinsel (Mng Partner)

IK Investment Partners GmbH (1)
Neuer Wall 80, Hamburg, 20354, Germany **(100%)**
Tel.: (49) 403698850
Web Site: http://www.ikinvestment.com
Sales Range: $100-124.9 Million
Emp.: 5
N.A.I.C.S.: 532210
Detlef Dinsel (Mng Partner & Head-Investment Committee)

Medica Group PLC (1)
Sixth Floor One Priory Square, Hastings, TN34 1EA, East Sussex, United Kingdom
Tel.: (44) 3333111222
Web Site: http://www.medicagroup.co.uk
Sales Range: $50-74.9 Million
Emp.: 100
Medical Specialty Services
N.A.I.C.S.: 622310
Richard Jones (CFO)

Subsidiary (Non-US):

Global Diagnostics Ireland Limited (2)
1st Floor North Block Rockfield Medical Campus, Dundrum Balally, Dublin, D16 W7W3, Ireland
Tel.: (353) 1800456225
Web Site: https://www.medica.ie
Emp.: 190
Diabetic Retinopathy Screening Services
N.A.I.C.S.: 621498

Subsidiary (US):

Medica US, Inc. (2)
401 Carlson Pkwy, Minnetonka, MN 55305
Tel.: (952) 992-2900
Web Site: https://www.medica.com
Health Insurance Services
N.A.I.C.S.: 524114

RadMD Inc. (2)
1100 E Hector St Ste 320, Conshohocken, PA 19428
Tel.: (484) 284-6994
Web Site: https://www.radmdimaging.com
Imaging Core Labs Services
N.A.I.C.S.: 621512

Netel AB (1)
Fagelviksvagen 9 7 tr, 145 84, Stockholm, Sweden
Tel.: (46) 8 444 74 00
Web Site: http://www.netel.se
Communications Infrastructure Construction Services
N.A.I.C.S.: 237130
David Wirsen (Operations Officer)

Subsidiary (Non-US):

Netel AS (2)
Ostre Aker vei 22, 0581, Oslo, Norway
Tel.: (47) 47774000
Web Site: http://www.netel.se
Communications Infrastructure Construction Services
N.A.I.C.S.: 237130
Edward Olastuen (CEO & Country Mgr)

Ondal Medical Systems GmbH (1)
Wellastrasse 6, Hunfeld, 36088, Germany

IK INVESTMENT PARTNERS LIMITED

IK Investment Partners Limited—(Continued)
Tel.: (49) 6652 81 0
Web Site: http://www.ondal.de
Developer, Designer & Mfr of Carrying Systems, Sauna Systems & Isolation & Fixation Bundles for Wires & Cables for Medical Equipment
N.A.I.C.S.: 332999
Andreas Muhlenbeck (Mng Dir)

Subsidiary (US):

Ondal Medical Systems of America, Inc. (2)
540 Eastpark Ct Ste A, Sandston, VA 23150
Tel.: (804) 532-1440
Web Site: http://www.ondal.de
Sales Range: $25-49.9 Million
Developer, Designer & Mfr of Carrying Systems, Sauna Systems & Isolation & Fixation Bundles for Wires & Cables for Medical Equipment
N.A.I.C.S.: 332999
Richard Davenport (Mgr-Fin)

TeleComputing Sweden AB (1)
Knarrarnasgatan 7, Kista Entre, 164 40, Kista, Sweden
Tel.: (46) 855610920
Emp.: 900
Financial Investment Services
N.A.I.C.S.: 523940
Tomas Rinda (Mgr-Bus Unit)

Veritas Petroleum Services (1)
Torweien 1, 1383, Asker, Norway
Tel.: (47) 9922 8217
Web Site: http://www.v-p-s.com
Sales Range: $1-4.9 Billion
Fuel Testing Services
N.A.I.C.S.: 541380
Eirik Andreassen (CEO)

IK PARTNERS
1-11 John Adam St, London, WC2N 6HT, United Kingdom
Tel.: (44) 207 304 4300
Web Site: https://ikpartners.com
Year Founded: 1989
Emp.: 185
Private Equity
N.A.I.C.S.: 523940
Syed Abdal (Accountant-London)

IK SEMICON CO., LTD.
8FL Hanssem SangAm 179 Seongam-ro, Mapo-gu, Seoul, 121-912, Korea (South)
Tel.: (82) 231527090
Web Site: https://www.iksemi.com
Year Founded: 2000
Semiconductor Mfr
N.A.I.C.S.: 334413

IKANG HEALTHCARE GROUP, INC.
B-6F Shimao Tower 92A Jianguo Road, Chaoyang District, Beijing, 100022, China
Tel.: (86) 10 5320 6688   Ky
Web Site: http://www.ikanggroup.com
Rev.: $563,932,000
Assets: $865,155,000
Liabilities: $485,330,000
Net Worth: $379,825,000
Earnings: ($17,309,000)
Emp.: 15,918
Fiscal Year-end: 03/31/18
Healthcare Treatment Centers
N.A.I.C.S.: 622110
Lee Ligang Zhang (Founder, Chm & CEO)

Subsidiaries:

MediFast (Hong Kong) Limited (1)
1/F Bonaventure House 91 Leighton Road Causeway Bay, Hong Kong, China (Hong Kong)
Tel.: (852) 22728222
Health Care Srvices
N.A.I.C.S.: 621491

IKARBUS A.D.
Autoput 24, Zemun, 11080, Belgrade, Serbia
Tel.: (381) 11 314 92 29
Web Site: http://www.ikarbus.rs
Year Founded: 1991
Sales Range: $10-24.9 Million
Motor Vehicles Mfr
N.A.I.C.S.: 336120
Aleksandar Vicentic (Gen Mgr)

IKD CO., LTD.
No 588 Jin Shan Road Jiangbei Investment Pioneering Park, Ningbo, 315033, China
Tel.: (86) 57487562111
Web Site: https://en.ikd-sales.com
Year Founded: 2003
600933—(SHG)
Rev.: $598,839,864
Assets: $1,393,370,920
Liabilities: $605,081,824
Net Worth: $788,289,096
Earnings: $91,055,058
Emp.: 360
Fiscal Year-end: 12/31/22
Aluminum Alloy Product Mfr & Distr
N.A.I.C.S.: 331314
Zhang Jiancheng (Chm & Gen Mgr)

Subsidiaries:

Ikd Faeza S.A. de C.V. (1)
Av. Rio San Lorenzo 2294 Fracc A Mz K Lote 2 Parque Tecno Industrial, Casro del Rio Irapuato, 36615, Guanajuato, Mexico
Tel.: (52) 4626937035
Aluminium Die Casting Products Mfr
N.A.I.C.S.: 331524

IKEGAMI TSUSHINKI CO., LTD.
5-6-16 Ikegami, Ohta-ku, Tokyo, 146-8567, Japan
Tel.: (81) 357001111   JP
Web Site: http://www.ikegami.co.jp
Year Founded: 1946
Sales Range: $25-49.9 Million
Emp.: 914
Broadcast, Security, Medical & Inspection Equipment Mfr & Distr
N.A.I.C.S.: 334220
Yosuke Kiyomori (Pres)

Subsidiaries:

Ikegami Electronics (Europe) GmbH (1)
Ikegami Strasse 1, West Street, D 41460, Neuss, Dorset, Germany (100%)
Tel.: (49) 21311230
Web Site: http://www.ikegami.de
Rev.: $50,175,044
Emp.: 25
Radio & Television Broadcasting & Communications Equipment
N.A.I.C.S.: 334220
Bernd Kowollik (Mgr-Fin)

Ikegami Electronics (U.S.A.), Inc. (1)
37 Brook Ave, Maywood, NJ 07607
Tel.: (201) 368-9171
Web Site: http://www.ikegami.com
Sales Range: $25-49.9 Million
Emp.: 25
Sales of Broadcast Equipment & CCTV Cameras & Monitors
N.A.I.C.S.: 423690
Sofia Ko (CFO)

Ikegami Electronics Asia Psific Pte. LTD. (1)
1 Tampines Central 5 3-3 Cpf Tampines Building, Singapore, 529508, Singapore
Tel.: (65) 62608820
Television Broadcasting Equipment Distr
N.A.I.C.S.: 423690
Toshifumi Mouri (Mgr-Sls Mktg)

Ikegami Tsushinki Co., Ltd.-Overseas Sales Division (1)
5 6 16 Ikegami, Ohta Ku, Tokyo, 146 8567, Japan (100%)
Tel.: (81) 357004111

Sales Range: $25-49.9 Million
Emp.: 30
Radio & Television Broadcasting & Communications Equipment
N.A.I.C.S.: 334220
Fumio Yamaguchi (Mgr-Sls)

TECHNO IKEGAMI CO., LTD (1)
4-13-15 Shiohama, Kawasaki-ku, Kawasaki, 210-8533, Kanagawa, Japan
Tel.: (81) 442705471
Web Site: http://www.techno-ikegami.co.jp
Television Broadcasting Equipment Mfr
N.A.I.C.S.: 334220

IKEGPS GROUP LIMITED
Level 7 186 Willis Street, Wellington, 6011, New Zealand
Tel.: (64) 43828064   NZ
Web Site: https://www.ikegps.com
Year Founded: 2006
IKE—(ASX)
Rev.: $18,414,474
Assets: $25,881,579
Liabilities: $5,585,526
Net Worth: $20,296,053
Earnings: ($4,717,105)
Emp.: 8
Fiscal Year-end: 03/31/23
Measurement System Mfr
N.A.I.C.S.: 334519
Richard Christie (Chm)

Subsidiaries:

ikeGPS Inc. (1)
329 Interlocken Pkwy Ste 120, Broomfield, CO 80021
Tel.: (303) 222-3218
Software Development Services
N.A.I.C.S.: 541511

IKEJA HOTEL PLC
84 Opebi Road, Ikeja, Lagos, Nigeria
Tel.: (234) 012701060
Web Site: https://ikejahotelplc.com
Year Founded: 1972
IKEJAHOTEL—(NIGE)
Rev.: $9,546,309
Assets: $22,105,090
Liabilities: $16,344,194
Net Worth: $5,760,896
Earnings: ($2,915,488)
Emp.: 201
Fiscal Year-end: 12/31/22
Restaurant Operating Services
N.A.I.C.S.: 722511
Anthony Idigbe (Chm)

Subsidiaries:

Tourist Company of Nigeria Plc. (1)
6-8 Ahmadu Bello Way Victoria Island, Lagos, Nigeria
Tel.: (234) 14480887
Web Site: https://www.tcn.com.ng
Rev.: $10,045,065
Assets: $91,372,925
Liabilities: $60,696,277
Net Worth: $30,676,648
Earnings: ($3,314,120)
Emp.: 346
Fiscal Year-end: 12/31/2019
Casino Resort Operator
N.A.I.C.S.: 721120
Anthony Idigbe (Chm & Chm)

IKESHITA SEKKEI CO. LTD.
1-17-18 Asagaya Minami, Suginami-ku, Tokyo, 166-0004, Japan
Tel.: (81) 353788111
Web Site: http://www.ikeshita-sekkei.com
Architectural Design & Construction Management Services
N.A.I.C.S.: 541310

Subsidiaries:

Soh Mechanical & Electrical Engineers Corporation (1)
7th Floor 5th TOC Building 7-21-1 Nishi Gotanda, Shinagawa-ku, Tokyo, 141-0031, Japan

INTERNATIONAL PUBLIC

Tel.: (81) 363039271
Web Site: http://www.sohmec.com
Facility Management Services
N.A.I.C.S.: 541613

IKF FINANCE LIMITED
Plot no's - 30/A Survey no – 83/1 11th Floor My Home Twitza, APIIC Hyderabad Knowledge City Raidurg Village Serilingampally Mandal, Hyderabad, 500 081, India
Tel.: (91) 4069268899   In
Web Site: http://www.ikffinance.com
Year Founded: 1991
Rev.: $37,086,641
Assets: $283,112,957
Liabilities: $226,299,473
Net Worth: $56,813,484
Earnings: $6,979,259
Emp.: 690
Fiscal Year-end: 03/31/22
Mortgage Loan Brokerage Services
N.A.I.C.S.: 522310
V. G. K. Prasad (Mng Dir)

IKF S.P.A.
Viale Tunisia 41, 20124, Milan, Italy
Tel.: (39) 02 4953 4200
Web Site: http://www.ikf-holding.com
Sales Range: $25-49.9 Million
Investment Holding Company
N.A.I.C.S.: 551112
Andrea Maria Gritti (CEO)

IKF TECHNOLOGIES LIMITED
3rd Floor Plot No J-1/12 Block-EP & GP Sector-V, Salt Lake, Kolkata, 700 091, India
Tel.: (91) 33 2357 2610
Web Site: http://www.ikf-technologies.com
Year Founded: 2000
Rev.: $6,408,588
Assets: $37,671,849
Liabilities: $16,150,486
Net Worth: $21,521,363
Earnings: $39,834
Emp.: 5,500
Fiscal Year-end: 03/31/18
Business Process Outsourcing Services
N.A.I.C.S.: 561499
Sunil Kumar Goyal (Chm)

IKIGAI VENTURES LTD.
Level 3 Plaza House Elizabeth Avenue, PO Box 119, Saint Peter Port, GY1 2HU, Guernsey
Tel.: (44) 1481211000   GY
Web Site: https://www.ikigaiventuresltd.com
Year Founded: 2021
IKIV—(LSE)
Rev.: $17,670
Assets: $1,483,023
Liabilities: $49,136
Net Worth: $1,433,888
Earnings: ($797,639)
Fiscal Year-end: 06/30/23
Investment Management Service
N.A.I.C.S.: 523999
Nicholas Harris Bryan-Brown (CEO)

IKIO LIGHTING LIMITED
D-234 Sec-63, Noida, 201305, Uttar Pradesh, India
Tel.: (91) 1205084101   In
Web Site: https://www.ikio.in
Year Founded: 2016
IKIO—(NSE)
Rev.: $43,866,158
Assets: $37,688,473
Liabilities: $20,458,560
Net Worth: $17,229,913
Earnings: $6,064,606
Emp.: 762
Fiscal Year-end: 03/31/23

Lighting Product Mfr
N.A.I.C.S.: 335139
Hardeep Singh *(Chm)*

IKK HOLDINGS INC
722-5 Shintencho Imari, Saga, 848-0041, Japan
Tel.: (81) 5035391122
Web Site: https://www.ikk-grp.jp
Year Founded: 1995
2198—(TKS)
Rev.: $155,909,100
Assets: $141,885,080
Liabilities: $70,630,580
Net Worth: $71,254,500
Earnings: $9,500,600
Emp.: 999
Fiscal Year-end: 10/31/23
Wedding & Funeral Services
N.A.I.C.S.: 812990
Katsushi Kaneko *(Chm & CEO)*

Subsidiaries:

PT International Kansha Kandou Indonesia (1)
Menara Mandiri 9th Floor Jl Jenderal Sudirman Kav 54 - 55, Jakarta Selatan, 12190, Indonesia
Tel.: (62) 215266211
Web Site: https://ikkwedding.co.id
Wedding Planning Services
N.A.I.C.S.: 812990

IKKA DINING PROJECT CO., LTD.
Itoshin Building 3rd Floor 2-5-6 Yawata, Ichikawa, 272-0021, Japan
Tel.: (81) 473025115
Web Site: http://www.ikkadining.co.jp
9266—(TKS)
Sales Range: Less than $1 Million
Dining Services
N.A.I.C.S.: 722511
Taro Takenaga *(Pres & CEO)*

IKM GRUPPEN AS
Ljosheimvegen 14, 4051, Sola, Norway
Tel.: (47) 51 64 90 00
Web Site: http://www.ikm.com
Sales Range: $700-749.9 Million
Emp.: 2,450
Holding Company
N.A.I.C.S.: 551112
Stale Kyllingstad *(Chm, CEO & Dir-Subsea, Completion & Commissioning)*

Subsidiaries:

IKM Acona AS (1)
Luramyrveien 12, 4313, Sandnes, Norway
Tel.: (47) 52977600
Web Site: https://www.acona.com
Business Consulting Services
N.A.I.C.S.: 541611

IKM Alfa Solution AS (1)
Osterskogen 60, 4879, Grimstad, Norway
Tel.: (47) 37091920
Web Site: https://www.alfasolution.no
Transportation Equipment Distr
N.A.I.C.S.: 423860
Rune Johansen *(Mng Dir)*

IKM Consultants A/S (1)
Ljosheimvegen 12, Sola, 4051, Norway
Tel.: (47) 51695100
Web Site: http://ikmconsultants.com
Engineering & Project Administration Consulting Services
N.A.I.C.S.: 541690
Einar Refsnes *(CEO)*

IKM Consultants UK Ltd. (1)
Ljosheimvegen 12, 4051, Sola, Norway
Tel.: (47) 47977200
Web Site: https://www.ikm.com
Consultancy Services
N.A.I.C.S.: 541611
Anne Ferkingstad *(Acct Mgr)*

IKM DSC Engineering AS (1)
Dolasletta 3, 3408, Tranby, Norway
Tel.: (47) 32226580
Engineeering Services
N.A.I.C.S.: 541330
Jon Robertsen *(Mgr-Technical)*

IKM HVAC AS (1)
Langflatveien 3, 4017, Stavanger, Norway
Tel.: (47) 90032045
Oil & Gas Distr
N.A.I.C.S.: 423830
Kenneth Abrahamsen *(Mng Dir)*

IKM HVAC Production Sp. z.o.o. (1)
Ljosheimvegen 12, 4051, Sola, Norway
Tel.: (47) 91118288
Web Site: https://www.ikm.com
Heating & Air Conditioning Equipment Distr
N.A.I.C.S.: 423730
Bjorn Tovslid *(Gen Mgr)*

IKM Haaland AS (1)
Skogateigen 28, 4362, Vigrestad, Norway
Tel.: (47) 51 79 20 00
Sheet Metal Mfr
N.A.I.C.S.: 332322
Morten Saedberg *(Gen Mgr)*

Subsidiary (Domestic):

IKM Industrigravoren AS (2)
Fabrikkveien 6, PO Box 55, 4362, Rogaland, Norway
Tel.: (47) 51641330
Engineeering Services
N.A.I.C.S.: 541330
Sigval Bryne *(Gen Mgr)*

IKM Hydraulic Services AS (1)
Risavika Havnering 224, 4056, Tananger, Norway
Tel.: (47) 21641407
Hydraulic Pumps Mfr
N.A.I.C.S.: 333996
Erik Svanes *(Gen Mgr)*

IKM Inspection AS (1)
Holmejordet 21A, PB 68, 3291, Stavern, Norway
Tel.: (47) 33132450
Inspection Services
N.A.I.C.S.: 541350
Tor Skaatan *(Gen Mgr)*

IKM Invest AS (1)
Skagen 27 4etg, 4006, Stavanger, Norway
Tel.: (47) 51641380
Web Site: http://www.ikm-invest.no
Real Estate Investment Services
N.A.I.C.S.: 531210
Ole Rettedal *(CEO)*

IKM Kran & Lofteteknikk AS (1)
Tankbatveien 1, 4056, Tananger, Norway
Tel.: (47) 51648100
Oil & Ship Building Services
N.A.I.C.S.: 336611
Erik Johannessen *(Gen Mgr)*

IKM Laboratorium AS (1)
NorSea Base Bygg 53, 4056, Tananger, Norway (91%)
Tel.: (47) 51 71 95 00
Web Site: http://www.ikm.com
Calibration & Equipment Rental for Oil & Gas Industry
N.A.I.C.S.: 532490
Hans Jakob Mellgren *(Gen Mgr)*

Subsidiary (Domestic):

IKM Elektro AS (2)
Skvadronveien 24, 4050, Sola, Norway
Tel.: (47) 51 81 17 30
Web Site: http://www.ikm.com
Subsea Technology & Topside Electrical Applications for Oil, Gas & Energy Sector
N.A.I.C.S.: 213112
Oystein Stjern *(Gen Mgr & Mktg Mgr)*

IKM Instrutek AS (2)
Elveveien 28, 3262, Larvik, Norway
Tel.: (47) 33 16 57 00
Web Site: http://www.ikm.com
Measuring Instrument Process Instrumentation Condition Monitoring & Calibration Services
N.A.I.C.S.: 334513
Trond Jacobsen *(CEO)*

Subsidiary (Non-US):

IKM Measurement Services Australia Pty. Ltd. (2)
33 Kewdale Road, Welshpool, 6106, WA, Australia
Tel.: (61) 8 9452 6100
Web Site: http://www.ikm.com
Emp.: 6
Supplier of Production Technology, Test Instruments & Rental Services to Marine, Oil & Gas & Resources Industry
N.A.I.C.S.: 213112
Stuart Taylor *(Gen Mgr)*

IKM Measurement Services Ltd. (2)
Unit B4 Airport Industrial Park Howe Moss Drive, Kirkhill Industrial Estate Dyce, Aberdeen, AB21 0GL, Scotland, United Kingdom
Tel.: (44) 1224 793262
Web Site: http://www.ikm.com
Emp.: 12
Supplier of Calibration, Measurement & Rental Services to Marine, Oil & Gas & Resources Industry
N.A.I.C.S.: 213112
Gary Thomson *(Mng Dir)*

Subsidiary (Domestic):

IKM Norwegian Technology Solutions AS (2)
Gamle Forusvei 25, 4031, Stavanger, Norway (67%)
Tel.: (47) 51 64 13 00
Web Site: http://www.ikm.com
Instrumentation Services for Offshore Industry
N.A.I.C.S.: 213112
Morten Molven *(Gen Mgr)*

IKM Maskinering AS (1)
Breivikveien 17, 4120, Stavanger, Norway
Tel.: (47) 51754444
Engineeering Services
N.A.I.C.S.: 541330
Torger Salte *(Mng Dir)*

IKM Mekaniske AS (1)
Sandviksveien 30, 4016, Stavanger, Norway
Tel.: (47) 51 82 56 00
Web Site: http://www.ikm.com
Fabrication of Stainless Materials, Fabrication for Installation & Contracting Services for Oil & Gas Industry
N.A.I.C.S.: 332999
Per Morten Helland *(Gen Mgr)*

IKM Mekaniske Kristiansund AS (1)
Dalegata 137, 6518, Kristiansund, Norway
Tel.: (47) 70 33 14 00
Web Site: http://www.ikm.com
Construction, Modification & Repair Contracts for Ships & Offshore Market
N.A.I.C.S.: 336611
Per Willy Pettersen *(Gen Mgr)*

IKM Mooring Services AS (1)
Skvadronveien 27, 4050, Sola, Norway
Tel.: (47) 97502480
Web Site: https://www.ikm.com
Shipping Mooring Services
N.A.I.C.S.: 713930
Trond Egil Watland *(Mgr-Marketing-Sales)*

IKM Ocean Design AS (1)
Vassbotnen 1, 4313, Sandnes, Norway
Tel.: (47) 51212100
Engineeering Services
N.A.I.C.S.: 541330
Peder Hoas *(Gen Mgr)*

IKM Operations AS (1)
Ljosheimvegen 12, 4051, Sola, Norway
Tel.: (47) 51641360
Web Site: https://www.ikm.com
Shipping Machinery Distr
N.A.I.C.S.: 423860
Anstein Laedre *(Mgr)*

IKM Production Technology AS (1)
35J-2-9 KLSC Jalan Wangsa Delima 5, Wangsa Maju, 53300, Kuala Lumpur, Malaysia
Tel.: (60) 96506909
Oil & Gas Distr
N.A.I.C.S.: 423830
Mustaffa Kamal *(Gen Mgr)*

IKM Production Technology UK Ltd. (1)
Peregrine Road, Westhill, AB32 6JL, Aberdeenshire, United Kingdom
Tel.: (44) 1224725599
Drilling Machines Mfr
N.A.I.C.S.: 333132

IKM Promech AS (1)
Kanalvegen 2, 4033, Stavanger, Norway
Tel.: (47) 90832733
Drilling Machines Mfr
N.A.I.C.S.: 333132

IKM Rada AS (1)
Spaces Media City Bergen Lars Hilles gate 30, 5008, Bergen, Norway
Tel.: (47) 92023726
Web Site: https://www.radanorge.no
Recruitment & Consultancy Services
N.A.I.C.S.: 541612

IKM Rontgenkontrollen AS (1)
Evjelokka 7, Rolvsoy, 1661, Fredrikstad, Ostfold, Norway
Tel.: (47) 69361950
Engineeering Services
N.A.I.C.S.: 541330

IKM SolidTech AS (1)
Omagata 114 B, 6517, Kristiansund, Norway
Tel.: (47) 99212630
Web Site: https://www.ikm.no
Crane & Loose Lifting Equipment Distr
N.A.I.C.S.: 423830
Frode Tolcsiner *(CEO)*

IKM Stainless Technology AS (1)
Bjorhaugsletta 9, 4365, Rogaland, Norway
Tel.: (47) 51791720
Oil & Gas Distr
N.A.I.C.S.: 423830

IKM Subsea AS (1)
Nordlysveien 7, 4340, Bryne, Norway
Tel.: (47) 96200210
Web Site: https://www.ikm.com
Drilling Machinery Distr
N.A.I.C.S.: 423830
Oystein Stjern *(Mng Dir)*

IKM Subsea Brasil LTDA (1)
Rua Lauro Muller 116, Botafogo, Rio de Janeiro, 2401, RJ, Brazil
Tel.: (55) 279999296890
Drilling Machinery Distr
N.A.I.C.S.: 423830
Ben Pollard *(CEO)*

IKM Subsea Malaysia Sdn. Bhd (1)
Jalan Wangsa Delima 5, Wangsa Maju, 53300, Kuala Lumpur, Malaysia
Tel.: (60) 96506949
Industrial Component Distr
N.A.I.C.S.: 423830
Mustaffa Kamal *(Mng Dir)*

IKM Subsea Middle East FZE (1)
Unit 29-03 29th Floor Reef Tower, Cluster O Jumeirah Lakes Towers, Dubai, United Arab Emirates
Tel.: (971) 44487560
Drilling Machinery Distr
N.A.I.C.S.: 423830
Thina Suppaiyan *(Country Mgr)*

IKM Subsea Motor Solutions AS (1)
Nordlysvegen 7, 4340, Bryne, Norway
Tel.: (47) 91520130
Subsea Motor Distr
N.A.I.C.S.: 423860
Tove Bergsholm Lia *(Gen Mgr)*

IKM Subsea Singapore Pte Ltd (1)
22 Pandan Road 1st Floor, Singapore, 609274, Singapore
Tel.: (65) 65928597
Industrial Component Distr
N.A.I.C.S.: 423830
Mahesh Govindan *(Mgr-Bus Dev)*

IKM Subsea UK Ltd (1)
Peregrine Road, Westhill, AB32 6JL, United Kingdom
Tel.: (44) 1224725599
Industrial Component Mfr
N.A.I.C.S.: 334513
Gary Thomson *(Mng Dir)*

IKM Tech Team Solutions AS (1)
Tankbatvegen 1, 4056, Tananger, Norway
Tel.: (47) 51648100
Lifting Equipment Distr
N.A.I.C.S.: 423860

IKM GRUPPEN AS

IKM Gruppen AS—(Continued)
Kato Ovestad *(Project Mgr)*

IKM Technique AS (1)
Torneroseveien 12, 4315, Sandnes, Norway
Tel.: (47) 51800520
Engineeering Services
N.A.I.C.S.: 541330
Jostein H. Reinsnos *(Gen Mgr)*

IKM Testing AS (1)
Ljosheimvegen 14, 4051, Sola, Norway
Tel.: (47) 51 64 90 00
Web Site: http://www.ikm.com
Emp.: 850
Mechanical Completion/Commissioning Onshore & Offshore Industry Services
N.A.I.C.S.: 213112
Pal Orke *(Dir-Mktg)*

Subsidiary (Non-US):

IKM Testing Asia Pte. Ltd. (2)
117 Defu Lane 10, Singapore, 539229, Singapore **(100%)**
Tel.: (65) 6777 8803
Web Site: http://www.ikm.com
Emp.: 30
Commissioning, Inspection, Testing & Cleaning Services for Onshore (Refinery & Shipbuilding) & Offshore Industries
N.A.I.C.S.: 213112
William Tan *(Country Mgr)*

Subsidiary (Non-US):

IKM Testing (Thailand) Co. Ltd. (3)
72/2 Moo 3 Ban Chang Sub-District Banchang District, Rayong, 21130, Thailand
Tel.: (66) 38601 996
Web Site: http://www.ikm.com
Industrial Cleaning, Inspection & Commissioning Services for Onshore & Offshore Industries
N.A.I.C.S.: 213112
William Tan *(Country Mgr)*

PT IKM Indonesia (3)
Puri Industrial Park 2000 Jl Engku Putri Block C No 10A, Batam, 29453, Indonesia
Tel.: (62) 778 469211
Industrial Cleaning, Inspection & Commissioning Services for Onshore & Offshore Industries
N.A.I.C.S.: 213112
William Tan *(Country Mgr)*

Subsidiary (Non-US):

IKM Testing Australia Pty. Ltd. (2)
33 Kewdale Road, Welshpool, 6106, WA, Australia
Tel.: (61) 420 988 146
Industrial Cleaning, Inspection & Commissioning Services for Onshore & Offshore Industries
N.A.I.C.S.: 213112
Keith Noble *(Country Mgr)*

IKM Testing Brasil Ltda (2)
Rua Araujo Porto Alegre 70 Sala 1206, Centro, Rio de Janeiro, 20030 015, RJ, Brazil
Tel.: (55) 21 2217 4001
Web Site: http://www.ikm.com
Industrial Cleaning, Inspection & Commissioning Services for Onshore & Offshore Industries
N.A.I.C.S.: 213112
Andre Franca *(Bus Mgr)*

IKM Testing Canada Ltd (2)
40 St Annes Crescent, Paradise, Saint John's, A1L 1K1, NL, Canada **(100%)**
Tel.: (709) 782-5051
Web Site: http://www.ikm.com
Supplier for Industrial Cleaning, Inspection & Commissioning Services for Onshore & Offshore Industries
N.A.I.C.S.: 213112

IKM Testing Poland Sp. z.o.o (2)
Ul Trzy Lipy 3, 80 172, Gdansk, Poland
Tel.: (48) 731 857 555
Industrial Cleaning, Inspection & Commissioning Services for Onshore & Offshore Industries
N.A.I.C.S.: 213112
Slawomir Rosa *(Supvr)*

IKM Testing UK Limited (2)
Unit 42 Colbourne Crescent, Nelson Park Industrial Estate, Cramlington, NE23 1WB, Northumberland, United Kingdom
Tel.: (44) 1670 70 7265
Web Site: http://www.ikm.com
Industrial Cleaning, Inspection & Commissioning Services for Onshore & Offshore Industries
N.A.I.C.S.: 213112
Tony Perkin *(Mng Dir)*

IKM Testing Kazaksthan
Atambaeva Street 12/A, Atyrau, Kazakhstan
Tel.: (7) 122251538
Oil & Gas Field Services
N.A.I.C.S.: 213112

IKM Testing Korea LLC (1)
1124-6 Dalsan-ri Joenggwan-meyon, Busan, Gijang-gun, Korea (South)
Tel.: (82) 7041689060
Inspection Services
N.A.I.C.S.: 541350
Ki Sang You *(Country Mgr)*

IKM Testing Malaysia Sdn. Bhd
No 6 Jalan P8 Perdana 8 Kawasan Perindustrian, Kampung Baru Balakong, 43300, Seri Kembangan, Selangor, Malaysia
Tel.: (60) 389644911
Oil & Gas Distr
N.A.I.C.S.: 423830
William Tan *(Country Mgr)*

IKM Testing Mexico S de RL de CV (1)
Calle 50-B Num 19, Colonia Burocrata, 24160, Ciudad del Carmen, Campeche, Mexico
Tel.: (52) 9382860215
Oil & Gas Distr
N.A.I.C.S.: 423830
Jose Luis Aragon Trujillo *(Gen Mgr)*

IKM WellDrone Technology AS (1)
Naeringsveien A, 4323, Sandnes, Norway
Tel.: (47) 40027626
Electro Mechanical Tool Mfr
N.A.I.C.S.: 333517
Jostein Kallevik *(CTO)*

Sigma Inspection AS (1)
Finnestadveien 38, Stavanger, Norway
Tel.: (47) 51839200
Lifting Equipment Distr
N.A.I.C.S.: 423860
Ivar Djuve *(Mng Dir)*

Smaken av Grimstad AS (1)
Bergemoveien 42, 4886, Grimstad, Norway
Tel.: (47) 37258383
Web Site: http://www.smakenavgrimstad.no
Food Products Mfr
N.A.I.C.S.: 311919
Oivind Moen *(Dir-Comml)*

Stavanger Mekaniske AS (1)
Notberget 1 Bygg 47, 4029, Stavanger, Norway
Tel.: (47) 51825600
Web Site: https//stavangermekaniske.no
Engineeering Services
N.A.I.C.S.: 541330

Uniteam Holding AS (1)
Gneisveien 8, PO Box 44, Skedsmokorset, 2021, Oslo, Norway
Tel.: (47) 63879070
Web Site: http://www.uniteam.com
Holding Company
N.A.I.C.S.: 551112
Kjell Ivar Myrvang *(CEO)*

IKO ENTERPRISES LTD.

1600-42nd Ave SE, Calgary, T2G 5B5, AB, Canada
Tel.: (403) 265-6022
Web Site: http://www.ikogroup.com
Year Founded: 1951
Emp.: 3,500
Holding Company
N.A.I.C.S.: 551112

Subsidiaries:

Blair Rubber Company (1)
5020 Panther Pkwy, Seville, OH 44273
Tel.: (330) 769-5583

Web Site: http://www.blairrubber.com
Rubber Tank Lining Distr
N.A.I.C.S.: 423840

CanRoof Corporation Inc. (1)
309 Rutherford Road South, Brampton, L6W 3R4, ON, Canada
Tel.: (905) 874-1010
Web Site: http://www.canroof.com
Roof Shingle Mfr
N.A.I.C.S.: 324122

Hyload, Inc. (1)
9976 Rittman Road, Wadsworth, OH 44281
Tel.: (330) 334-5022
Web Site: http://www.hyload.com
Rev.: $6,666,666
Emp.: 25
Synthetic Rubber Mfr
N.A.I.C.S.: 325212

IKO Industries Ltd. (1)
1600-42nd Ave SE, Calgary, T2G 5B5, AB, Canada
Tel.: (403) 265-6022
Roof Shingle Mfr
N.A.I.C.S.: 324122

IKO Manufacturing Inc. (1)
120 Hay Rd, Wilmington, DE 19809-3509
Tel.: (302) 764-3100
Web Site: http://www.ikogroup.com
Sales Range: $25-49.9 Million
Emp.: 152
Mfr of Building Materials
N.A.I.C.S.: 423330
Roy Baumer *(Gen Mgr)*

IKO Midwest Inc. (1)
235 W South Tec Dr, Kankakee, IL 60901
Tel.: (815) 936-9600
Roof Shingle Mfr
N.A.I.C.S.: 324122

IKO PLC (1)
Appley Lane North Appley Bridge, Wigan, WN6 9AB, United Kingdom
Tel.: (44) 844 412 7224
Web Site: http://www.ikogroup.co.uk
Emp.: 200
Roof Shingle Mfr
N.A.I.C.S.: 324122
Andy Williamson *(Mng Dir)*

IKO Production Inc. (1)
120 Hay Rd, Wilmington, DE 19809-3509
Tel.: (302) 764-3100
Web Site: http://www.iko.com
Sales Range: $10-24.9 Million
Emp.: 100
Provider of Building Materials
N.A.I.C.S.: 324122
Ron Healey *(Controller)*

Sun Gro Horticulture Distribution, Inc. (1)
770 Silver St, Agawam, MA 01001-0790
Tel.: (413) 786-4343
Web Site: http://www.sungro.com
Sales Range: $75-99.9 Million
Emp.: 240
Agricultural Products Supplier
N.A.I.C.S.: 424910
Tom King *(VP-Ops & Admin)*

Subsidiary (Non-US):

Sun Gro Horticulture, Inc. (2)
52130 Range Road 65, Seba Beach, T0E 2B0, AB, Canada
Tel.: (780) 797-3019
Web Site: http://www.sungro.com
Horticultural Products Distr
N.A.I.C.S.: 424910

IKON COMMUNICATIONS

Level 11, 65 York St, Ikon House, Sydney, NSW 2000, Australia
Tel.: (61) 1 2 9290 7500
Emp.: 150
Brand Development & Integration, Digital/Interactive, Entertainment, Environmental, Media Planning, Mobile Marketing, Production, Trade & Consumer Magazines
N.A.I.C.S.: 541810
Simon White *(Founder)*

INTERNATIONAL PUBLIC

IKON SCIENCE LIMITED
The Causeway Teddington, London, TW11 0JR, United Kingdom
Tel.: (44) 208 943 1122
Web Site: http://www.ikonscience.com
Year Founded: 2001
GeoPrediction Software Systems & Development Services
N.A.I.C.S.: 541512
Martyn Millwood Hargrave *(Founder & Chm)*

IKTINOS HELLAS SA
7 Likovrissis Str, Metamorfossis, 14452, Athens, Greece
Tel.: (30) 2102826825
Web Site: https://www.iktinos.gr
Year Founded: 1974
IKTIN—(ATH)
Rev.: $35,442,854
Assets: $131,551,633
Liabilities: $78,283,295
Net Worth: $53,268,337
Earnings: ($349,888)
Emp.: 392
Fiscal Year-end: 12/31/22
Marble Product Mfr
N.A.I.C.S.: 327991
Evangelos Chaidas *(Founder)*

Subsidiaries:

Iktinos Marmaron S.A. (1)
Kifissias 112, Maroussi, 15125, Athens, Greece
Tel.: (30) 2108056276
Web Site: http://www.ikt-marmaron.com
Construction Marble Product Distr
N.A.I.C.S.: 423320

IKUYO CO., LTD.
3019 Kamiechi, Atsugi, 243-0801, Kanagawa, Japan
Tel.: (81) 462851800
Web Site: https://www.ikuyo194.co.jp
Year Founded: 1947
7273—(TKS)
Rev.: $114,690,110
Assets: $102,329,410
Liabilities: $62,378,570
Net Worth: $39,950,840
Earnings: $3,225,680
Emp.: 229
Fiscal Year-end: 03/31/24
Automobile Part Mfr & Distr
N.A.I.C.S.: 336360
Xiupeng Li *(Chm)*

IKWEZI MINING LIMITED
Clarendon House 2 Church Street, Hamilton, HM 11, Bermuda
Tel.: (441) 893210771   BM
Web Site: http://www.ikwezimining.com
Year Founded: 2011
IKW—(ASX)
Rev.: $13,835,264
Assets: $24,638,471
Liabilities: $7,425,408
Net Worth: $17,213,064
Earnings: ($1,153,858)
Fiscal Year-end: 06/30/21
Coal Mining Services
N.A.I.C.S.: 213113
David Pile *(Chm)*

IL JEONG INDUSTRIAL CO., LTD
21 Sanseong-ro, Danwon-gu, Ansan, 425-866, Gyeonggi-do, Korea (South)
Tel.: (82) 314930031
Web Site: https://www.iljeong.co.kr
Year Founded: 1973
008500—(KRS)
Rev.: $23,866,681
Assets: $24,727,185
Liabilities: $21,389,871

Net Worth: $3,337,315
Earnings: ($6,545,502)
Emp.: 88
Fiscal Year-end: 12/31/22
Fabric Product Mfr & Whslr
N.A.I.C.S.: 313210
Dong-Soo Koh *(Pres & CEO)*

Subsidiaries:

Suzhou il jeong co., ltd (1)
Shaxi industrial development zone, Taicang, Jiansu, China
Tel.: (86) 51253229991
Fabric Product Distr
N.A.I.C.S.: 424310

IL SCIENCE CO., LTD.

5 Saemal-ro 5-gil, Songpa-gu, Seoul, Gyeonggi-do, Korea (South)
Tel.: (82) 220398039
Web Site: https://www.ilscience.co.kr
Year Founded: 2008
307180—(KRS)
Rev.: $44,744,008
Assets: $67,031,360
Liabilities: $52,850,287
Net Worth: $14,181,073
Earnings: ($7,061,671)
Emp.: 58
Fiscal Year-end: 12/31/21
Lighting Equipment Mfr
N.A.I.C.S.: 335139
Song Seonggeun *(CEO)*

IL SEUNG CO., LTD.

31 Noksan Industrial Complex 165 ro 14beon gil, Gangseo-Gu, Busan, Korea (South)
Tel.: (82) 518314110
Web Site: https://www.ilseung.co.kr
Year Founded: 1988
333430—(KRS)
Oil Purifier Mfr
N.A.I.C.S.: 324110
Son Jiik *(CEO)*

IL SOLE 24 ORE SPA

Viale Sarca 223, 20126, Milan, Italy
Tel.: (39) 0230221
Web Site: https://du.ilsole24ore.com
Year Founded: 1999
S24—(ITA)
Rev.: $237,408,102
Assets: $277,092,394
Liabilities: $251,043,162
Net Worth: $26,049,233
Earnings: $8,495,419
Emp.: 731
Fiscal Year-end: 12/31/23
Book Publishers
N.A.I.C.S.: 513130
Edoardo Garrone *(Chm)*

IL&FS ENGINEERING & CONSTRUCTION COMPANY LTD.

8-2-120/113 1st Floor B Block Sanali Info Park, Road No 2 Banjara Hills, Hyderabad, 500 033, India
Tel.: (91) 4040409333
Web Site: https://www.ilfsengg.com
IL&FSENGG—(NSE)
Rev.: $51,689,820
Assets: $261,555,840
Liabilities: $668,623,410
Net Worth: ($407,067,570)
Earnings: ($52,706,745)
Emp.: 264
Fiscal Year-end: 03/31/22
Infrastructure Development, Construction & Project Management Services
N.A.I.C.S.: 237990
Khan K. R. *(CEO)*

ILAM CEMENT CO.

No 5 Anoushirvani St Taqavi St Ferdowsi Ave, Tehran, Iran
Tel.: (98) 2166341471
Web Site: http://www.ilamcement.com
Year Founded: 1989
SEIL—(THE)
Sales Range: Less than $1 Million
Emp.: 563
Cement Mfr
N.A.I.C.S.: 327310

ILAPAK S.A.

Almolino 49, PO Box 756, 6916, Lugano, Switzerland
Tel.: (41) 919605900
Web Site: http://www.ilapak.com
Year Founded: 1970
Sales Range: $75-99.9 Million
Emp.: 400
Packaging Machinery Mfr
N.A.I.C.S.: 333310
Claudio Sala *(Dir-Fin)*

Subsidiaries:

Delta Systems & Automation Inc. (1)
535 W Dyke Rd, Rogers, AR 72758
Tel.: (479) 631-2210
Web Site: http://www.delta-systems-inc.com
Sales Range: $10-24.9 Million
Emp.: 100
Automation Control Systems Mfr
N.A.I.C.S.: 334513
Liam Buckley *(Dir-Sls)*

ILAPAK (Langfang) PACKAGING MACHINERY CO.,LTD
No8 Xiangyun Road No.3 Workshop Export Processing Zone, Langfang Development Zone, Langfang, China
Tel.: (86) 316 5910164
Packaging Machinery Mfr
N.A.I.C.S.: 333310

ILAPAK ASIA (1)
C-09-04 Plaza Mont Kiara No 2 Jalan Kiara, Mont Kiara, 50480, Kuala Lumpur, Malaysia
Tel.: (60) 12 32 31 270
Packaging Machinery Mfr
N.A.I.C.S.: 333310

ILAPAK FRANCE S.A. (1)
Rue Lech Walesa ZI Pariest, F-77437, Marne-la-Vallee, France
Tel.: (33) 1 60 06 82 82
Packaging Machinery Mfr
N.A.I.C.S.: 333310

ILAPAK HUNGARY (1)
Mako u14, H-9400, Sopron, Hungary
Tel.: (36) 99 510829
Packaging Machinery Mfr
N.A.I.C.S.: 333310

ILAPAK ISRAEL Ltd. (1)
Bareket St 9, PO Box 3555, Ganei Cesarea Industrial Park, 38900, Caesarea, Israel
Tel.: (972) 4 6272111
Web Site: http://www.ilapakisrael.co.il
Packaging Machinery Distr
N.A.I.C.S.: 423830
Guy Loewenstein *(Country Mgr)*

ILAPAK ITALIA S.p.A. (1)
Via Luciano Lama 11-13, 52045, Arezzo, Italy
Tel.: (39) 0575 649751
Packaging Machinery Mfr
N.A.I.C.S.: 333310

ILAPAK ITALIA S.p.A. - FillDose Division (1)
Via Luciano Lama 11-13, 52045, Foiano della Chiana, Italy
Tel.: (39) 0575 649751
Packaging Machinery Mfr
N.A.I.C.S.: 333993

ILAPAK Inc. (1)
105 Pheasant Run, Newtown, PA 18940
Tel.: (215) 579-2900
Web Site: http://www.ilapak.com
Emp.: 36
Packaging Machinery Mfr
N.A.I.C.S.: 333310
Edward Young *(CEO)*

ILAPAK Ltd (1)
Chalfont House Silverdale Road, Hayes, UB3 3BN, United Kingdom
Tel.: (44) 20 8797 2000
Packaging Machinery Mfr
N.A.I.C.S.: 333310

ILAPAK SNG (1)
Ordjonikidze Street 12 Office 308, 119071, Moscow, Russia
Tel.: (7) 4952341992
Packaging Machinery Mfr
N.A.I.C.S.: 333310

ILAPAK Sp. z o.o. (1)
ul. Tyniecka 233, 30 376, Krakow, Poland
Tel.: (48) 12 266 20 75
Packaging Machinery Mfr
N.A.I.C.S.: 333310

ILAPAK Verpackungsmaschinen GmbH (1)
Rheinische Str 16, 42781, Haan, Germany
Tel.: (49) 2129 7033
Web Site: http://www.ilapak.com
Emp.: 20
Packaging Machinery Mfr
N.A.I.C.S.: 333310
Manfred Scheid *(Gen Mgr)*

ILAPAK do BRASIL LTDA (1)
Alameda Juari 560, 06460-090, Sao Paulo, Brazil
Tel.: (55) 11 4195 3425
Packaging Machinery Mfr
N.A.I.C.S.: 333310

LAPAK ISRAEL Ltd (1)
Bareket St 9, 38900, Caesarea, Israel
Tel.: (972) 44 6272111
Packaging Machinery Mfr
N.A.I.C.S.: 333310

ILB GROUP BERHAD

No 12 Jalan PJU 5/1 Kota Damansara, M-1F-1 M-1F-2 & M-1F-3 Pusat Perdagangan Kota Damansara, 47810, Petaling Jaya, Selangor Darul Ehsan, Malaysia
Tel.: (60) 361503353   MY
Web Site: https://www.ilb.com.my
Year Founded: 1973
NHB—(KLS)
Rev.: $10,052,424
Assets: $57,249,398
Liabilities: $6,396,477
Net Worth: $50,852,921
Earnings: $113,496
Emp.: 36
Fiscal Year-end: 12/31/23
Warehousing & Logistics Services
N.A.I.C.S.: 541614
Tuan Sem Tee *(CEO)*

Subsidiaries:

Integrated Forwarding & Shipping Berhad (1)
No 21 Jalan Firma 2 Kawasan Perindustrian Nusa 1, 81100, Johor Bahru, Johor Darul Takzim, Malaysia
Tel.: (60) 73518995
Web Site: http://www.ilb.com.my
Sales Range: $25-49.9 Million
Emp.: 50
Freight Forwarding & Shipping Services
N.A.I.C.S.: 488510

Integrated Freight Services Sdn. Bhd. (1)
2503 Tingkat Perusahaan Lima Kawasan Perindustrian, Kawasan Perindustrian Prai, 13600, Prai, Penang, Malaysia
Tel.: (60) 43988988
Web Site: http://www.integrated.my
Sales Range: $25-49.9 Million
Emp.: 80
Freight Forwarding Services
N.A.I.C.S.: 488510

Integrated Shun Hing Logistics (Lingang) Co. Ltd. (1)
No 30 Taohua West Road, Shenzhen, 518038, Guangdong, China
Tel.: (86) 75583485868
Logistics & Warehousing Services
N.A.I.C.S.: 493110
Jasper Tai *(Gen Mgr)*

Integrated Shun Hing Logistics (Shanghai) Ltd. (1)
No 80 FuTe Road North Wai Gao Qiao Free Trade Zone, Pudong, Shanghai, 518038, China
Tel.: (86) 2158682778
Warehousing & Logistics Management Services
N.A.I.C.S.: 493110

Integrated Shun Hing Logistics (Shenzhen) Co. Ltd. (1)
7Fl No 30 Taohua Rd, Futian Free Trade Zone, Shenzhen, 518038, Guangdong, China
Tel.: (86) 75583485868
Web Site: http://www.ish.com.cn
Sales Range: $150-199.5 Million
Emp.: 1,000
Warehousing & Logistics Management Services
N.A.I.C.S.: 493110

ILCC CO., LTD

2-7-15 Ichigaya tamachi, Shinjuku-ku, Tokyo, 162-0843, Japan
Tel.: (81) 355623661   JP
Web Site: http://www.ilcc.com
Year Founded: 1976
Rev.: $300,000,000
Emp.: 20
N.A.I.C.S.: 541820
Keiko Miyakawa *(Pres)*

ILDONG HOLDINGS CO., LTD.

2 Baumoe-ro 27-gil, Seocho-gu, Seoul, 137-733, Korea (South)
Tel.: (82) 25263114
Web Site: https://www.ildongholdings.com
Year Founded: 1941
Investment Holding Company
N.A.I.C.S.: 551112
Park Dae-Chang *(CEO)*

ILDONG PHARMACEUTICAL CO., LTD.

2 Baumoe-Ro 27-Gil, Seocho-Gu, 137733, Seoul, 137733, Korea (South)
Tel.: (82) 25263114   KR
Web Site: https://www.ildong.com
Year Founded: 1941
249420—(KRS)
Rev.: $489,127,014
Assets: $503,006,434
Liabilities: $350,968,444
Net Worth: $152,037,990
Earnings: ($108,595,656)
Emp.: 1,451
Fiscal Year-end: 12/31/22
Pharmaceuticals Product Mfr
N.A.I.C.S.: 325412
Paul Yun Woongsup *(CEO)*

Subsidiaries:

Ildong Pharmaceutical Co., Ltd. - Cheongju Plant (1)
70-38 Songjeong-dong, Heungduk-gu, Chongju, 360-290, Korea (South)
Tel.: (82) 43 267 7631
Web Site: http://www.ildong.com
Pharmaceuticals Product Mfr
N.A.I.C.S.: 325412

Uni Communications Inc (1)
60 Yangjae-Dong, Seochu-Gu, Seoul, 137-733, Korea (South)
Tel.: (82) 2 526 3660
Advertising Agencies
N.A.I.C.S.: 541810

ILEX MEDICAL LTD.

7 Hatnufa St, PO Box 3156, Kiriat Arie Industrial Park, Petah Tikva, 4951025, Israel
Tel.: (972) 39385501
Web Site: https://www.ilexmedical.com
Year Founded: 1977

ILEX MEDICAL LTD.

Ilex Medical Ltd.—(Continued)
ILX—(TAE)
Rev.: $252,396,833
Assets: $275,503,227
Liabilities: $106,448,945
Net Worth: $169,054,281
Earnings: $13,796,303
Emp.: 100
Fiscal Year-end: 09/30/23
Medical Equipment Services
N.A.I.C.S.: 456199
Moshe Benshaul (Chm)

Subsidiaries:

Ilex Biotech Ltd. (1)
7 Hatnufa St, POB 10249, Kiriat Arie Industrial Park, Petah Tikva, 4900202, Israel
Tel.: (972) 39385501
Medical Equipment Distr
N.A.I.C.S.: 423450

Ilex South Africa (Pty) Ltd. (1)
19 Polo Crescent Woodmead Office Park, PO Box 5673, Rivonia, 2128, Gauteng, South Africa
Tel.: (27) 118044004
Ivy Product Distr
N.A.I.C.S.: 423450
J. C. Stoltz (CEO)

ILFA FEINSTLEITERTECHNIK GMBH

Lohweg 3, Hannover, 30559, Germany
Tel.: (49) 511959550
Web Site: http://www.ilfa.de
Year Founded: 1979
Sales Range: $10-24.9 Million
Emp.: 174
Industrial Product Distr
N.A.I.C.S.: 423830
Walter Sullau (Member-Mgmt Bd)

ILFORD IMAGING SWITZERLAND GMBH

Route De L Ancienne Papdrerie, 1723, Marly, Switzerland
Tel.: (41) 264357111
Web Site: http://www.ilford.com
Year Founded: 1996
Sales Range: $75-99.9 Million
Emp.: 400
Photographic Paper & Chemicals Mfr
N.A.I.C.S.: 333310
David Jones (Mng Dir)

Subsidiaries:

Lumiere Imaging France SAS (1)
Tour Switzerland 1 Blvd Vivier Merle, 69443, Lyon, France
Tel.: (33) 426298564
Photo Imagery Services
N.A.I.C.S.: 325992

Tecco GmbH (1)
Buchholzstrasse 79, 51469, Bergisch Gladbach, Germany
Tel.: (49) 220229240
Web Site: http://www.tecco.de
Rev.: $19,630,309
Emp.: 55
Paper Printing Machine Mfr
N.A.I.C.S.: 333243

ILIAD S.A.

16 rue de la Ville-L Eveque, 75008, Paris, France
Tel.: (33) 173502000   FR
Web Site: https://www.iliad.fr
Year Founded: 1999
ILD—(EUR)
Rev.: $9,973,019,642
Assets: $28,415,713,361
Liabilities: $23,237,642,996
Net Worth: $5,178,070,365
Earnings: $343,190,158
Emp.: 17,700
Fiscal Year-end: 12/31/23
Telecommunication Servicesb
N.A.I.C.S.: 517112
Nicolas Jaeger (CFO)

Subsidiaries:

FREE SAS (1)
8 rue de la Ville, l'Eveque, 75008, Paris, France
Tel.: (33) 178569560
Web Site: http://www.free.fr
Sales Range: $800-899.9 Million
Emp.: 4,000
Dial-up & Broadband Internet Access
N.A.I.C.S.: 517810

PROTELCO SAS (1)
str Ecaterina Teodoroiu nr 43D, Prahova, 105600, Campina, Romania
Tel.: (40) 244 37 56 89
Web Site: http://www.protelco.ro
Emp.: 18
Architectural & Engineering Services
N.A.I.C.S.: 541310

Play Communications S.A. (1)
4/6 rue du Fort Bourbon, 1249, Luxembourg, Luxembourg (96.7%)
Tel.: (352) 286848124
Web Site:
   http://www.playcommunications.com
Rev.: $1,850,815,096
Assets: $2,335,757,672
Liabilities: $2,251,192,393
Net Worth: $84,565,279
Earnings: $227,882,003
Fiscal Year-end: 12/31/2019
Holding Company
N.A.I.C.S.: 551112
Ioannis Karagiannis (Chm)

Subsidiary (Non-US):

P4 Sp. z o.o. (2)
ul Wynalazek 1, 02-677, Warsaw, Poland
Tel.: (48) 790500500
Web Site: http://www.play.pl
Telecommunication Servicesb
N.A.I.C.S.: 517810

Subsidiary (Domestic):

3GNS Sp. z o.o. (3)
Marszalkowska Street 80 lok 164, 00-517, Warsaw, Poland
Tel.: (48) 223905240
Web Site: http://www.3gns.pl
Telecommunication Network Services
N.A.I.C.S.: 517810

Virgin Mobile Polska Sp. z o.o (3)
ul Wynalazek 1, 02-677, Warsaw, Poland
Tel.: (48) 799555222
Web Site: http://www.virginmobile.pl
Telecommunication Servicesb
N.A.I.C.S.: 517810

ILIKA PLC

Unit 10a The Quadrangle Abbey Park Industrial Estate, Romsey, SO51 9DL, Hampshire, United Kingdom
Tel.: (44) 2380111400
Web Site: https://www.ilika.com
IKA—(AIM)
Rev.: $655,600
Assets: $44,489,016
Liabilities: $3,264,888
Net Worth: $41,224,128
Earnings: ($9,348,856)
Fiscal Year-end: 04/30/22
Materials for Energy & Electronics Applications Developer & Researcher
N.A.I.C.S.: 541715
Graeme Purdy (CEO)

Subsidiaries:

Ilika Technologies Limited (1)
Kenneth Dibben House Enterprise Road, University of Southampton Science Park, Southampton, SO16 7NS, Hampshire, United Kingdom
Tel.: (44) 2380111400
Web Site: http://www.ilika.com
Emp.: 28
Biotechnology Research & Development Services
N.A.I.C.S.: 541714
Elaine Moore (Mgr-Admin)

ILIM TIMBER INDASTRI OOO

Sinopskaja Nabereschnaja 22 A, 191167, Saint Petersburg, Russia
Tel.: (7) 8123327227
Web Site: http://www.ilimtimber.com
Year Founded: 2007
Timber Production
N.A.I.C.S.: 113110
Boris Zingarevich (Founder & Chm)

Subsidiaries:

Ilim Timber Europe GmbH (1)
Franz-Kollmann-Str 5, 86899, Landsberg am Lech, Germany
Tel.: (49) 819194710
Lumber Distr
N.A.I.C.S.: 423990

ILIRIJA D.D.

Tina Ujevica 7, Biograd na Moru, 23210, Dalmatia, Croatia
Tel.: (385) 23383165
Web Site: https://ilirijabiograd.com
Year Founded: 1957
ILRA—(ZAG)
Rev.: $30,961,263,941
Assets: $78,993,476
Liabilities: $20,361,986
Net Worth: $58,631,490
Earnings: $3,620,190
Emp.: 312
Fiscal Year-end: 12/31/23
Hotels (except Casino Hotels) & Motels
N.A.I.C.S.: 721110

ILJI TECHNOLOGY CO., LTD.

50 Gongdan 4-ro Jillyang-eup, Gyeongsan, Gyeongsangbuk-do, Korea (South)
Tel.: (82) 538568080
Web Site: https://www.iljitech.co.kr
Year Founded: 1986
019540—(KRS)
Rev.: $175,753,840
Assets: $292,488,648
Liabilities: $221,025,789
Net Worth: $71,462,859
Earnings: ($6,975,474)
Emp.: 416
Fiscal Year-end: 12/31/22
Automobile Parts Mfr
N.A.I.C.S.: 336390
Bon Il Koo (CEO)

ILJIN DIAMOND CO LTD

6F 15 Magokjungang 14-ro, Gangseo-gu, Seoul, Korea (South)
Tel.: (82) 237778400
Web Site:
   https://www.iljindiamond.co.kr
081000—(KRS)
Rev.: $143,303,836
Assets: $459,667,435
Liabilities: $54,718,111
Net Worth: $404,949,324
Earnings: $2,958,623
Emp.: 258
Fiscal Year-end: 12/31/22
Industrial Diamonds Mfr
N.A.I.C.S.: 423840
Jung-Chul Byeon (CEO)

Subsidiaries:

Iljin Diamond Co Ltd - Ansan Plant (1)
15 Jinheung-ro 10beon-gil, Danwon-gu, Ansan, Gyeonggi, Korea (South)
Tel.: (82) 316895100
Industrial Diamond Mfr
N.A.I.C.S.: 333514

Iljin Diamond Co Ltd - Eumseong Plant (1)
157 Daegeum-ro Daeso-myeon, Eumseong, Chungcheongbuk, Korea (South)
Tel.: (82) 438794800
Industrial Diamond Mfr

INTERNATIONAL PUBLIC

N.A.I.C.S.: 333514

ILJIN DISPLAY CO., LTD.

18 Chenogbuksandan-ro 99 Beno-gil, Cheongbuk, Pyeongtaek, 17792, Gyeonggi-do, Korea (South)
Tel.: (82) 316800114
Web Site: https://www.iljindisplay.com
Year Founded: 1994
020760—(KRS)
Rev.: $95,374,795
Assets: $89,971,839
Liabilities: $67,782,019
Net Worth: $22,189,820
Earnings: ($2,502,769)
Emp.: 399
Fiscal Year-end: 12/31/22
Semiconductor Devices Mfr
N.A.I.C.S.: 334413
Woo-Jong Lee (Pres & CEO)

Subsidiaries:

ALPINION Medical Systems Co., Ltd. (1)
77 Heungan-daero 81beon-gil, Dongan-gu, Anyang, Korea (South)
Tel.: (82) 2 3282 0900
Web Site: http://www.alpinion.com
Medical Equipment Mfr
N.A.I.C.S.: 334510
Ko Sukbin (CEO)

Subsidiary (Non-US):

ALPINION GuangZhou Medical Systems Co., Ltd. (2)
1302 Victory Plaza No 103 Tiyu West Road, Tianhe, Guangzhou, China
Tel.: (86) 20 3867 8286
Web Site: http://www.alpinion.com.cn
Medical Equipment Distr
N.A.I.C.S.: 423450

ALPINION MEDICAL Deutschland GmbH (2)
Lilienthalstrasse 17a, 85399, Hallbergmoos, Germany
Tel.: (49) 8119982860
Web Site: https://www.alpinion.de
Emp.: 20
Medical Equipment Distr
N.A.I.C.S.: 423450

Subsidiary (US):

Alpinion Usa, Inc. (2)
21312 30th Dr SE Ste 100, Bothell, WA 98021
Tel.: (425) 949-4900
Web Site: http://www.alpinionusa.com
Medical Equipment Distr
N.A.I.C.S.: 423450

ILJIN Electric Co., Ltd. (1)

905-17 Mannyeon-ro, Hwaseong, Gyeonggi-do, Korea (South)
Tel.: (82) 31 220 0500
Web Site: http://www.iljinelectric.com
Electrical Transformer Mfr
N.A.I.C.S.: 334416
Jungsuk Huh (Co-CEO)

ILJIN Semiconductor Co., Ltd. (1)

10-81 Songdo-Dong, Yeonsu-gu, Incheon, 406-840, Korea (South)
Tel.: (82) 327146604
Web Site: http://www.iljinsemicon.co.kr
Semiconductor Devices Mfr
N.A.I.C.S.: 334413
H. Chris Kim (CEO)

ILJIN Steel Corporation (1)

446-1 Gwaerang-ri, Jungnam-myeon, Hwaseong, Gyeonggi-do, Korea (South)
Tel.: (82) 31 220 6900
Web Site: http://www.iljinsteel.com
Steel Tube Mfr
N.A.I.C.S.: 331210
Cha Jong-min (Mgr-Section)

ILJIN HOLDINGS CO., LTD.

Iljin Building 45 Mapo-daero, Mapo-gu, Seoul, Korea (South)
Tel.: (82) 27079114
Web Site: https://www.iljin.co.kr

AND PRIVATE COMPANIES

Year Founded: 1968
015860—(KRS)
Rev.: $1,099,792,318
Assets: $1,216,549,836
Liabilities: $520,200,585
Net Worth: $696,349,251
Earnings: $22,006,409
Emp.: 12
Fiscal Year-end: 12/31/22
Holding Company
N.A.I.C.S.: 551112
Chin Kyu Huh *(Chm)*

ILJIN HYSOLUS CO., LTD.
97-46 Wanjusandan 5-ro, Wanju-gun, Bongdong-eup, Jeollabuk-do, Korea (South)
Tel.: (82) 632631700
Web Site: https://hysolus.co.kr
Year Founded: 1999
271940—(KRS)
Rev.: $83,664,994
Assets: $262,701,681
Liabilities: $21,312,290
Net Worth: $241,389,391
Earnings: $5,402,245
Emp.: 199
Fiscal Year-end: 12/31/22
Hydrogen Mfr
N.A.I.C.S.: 325120
Sung Mo Yang *(Pres & CEO)*

ILJIN POWER CO., LTD.
42 Sanam-no Onsan-eup, Ulju-gun, Ulsan, Korea (South)
Tel.: (82) 522375330
Web Site: http://www.ijeng.com
Year Founded: 1989
094820—(KRS)
Rev.: $150,343,882
Assets: $146,167,149
Liabilities: $49,962,561
Net Worth: $96,204,588
Earnings: $12,023,043
Emp.: 618
Fiscal Year-end: 12/31/22
General Purpose Machinery Mfr
N.A.I.C.S.: 333998
Sang-eop Lee *(Co-CEO)*

Subsidiaries:

ILJINENERGY CO., LTD. - Plant 2 (1)
294-1 Mangyang-ri Onyang, Ulsan, Ulju, Korea (South)
Tel.: (82) 52 240 3700
General Purpose Machinery Mfr
N.A.I.C.S.: 333998

ILKKA YHTYMAE OYJ
Koulukatu 10, PO Box 60, 60100, Seinajoki, Finland
Tel.: (358) 62477100
Web Site: https://www.ilkka-yhtyma.fi
Year Founded: 1906
ILK2S—(HEL)
Rev.: $62,389,381
Assets: $201,295,057
Liabilities: $34,135,549
Net Worth: $167,159,508
Earnings: $777,034
Emp.: 533
Fiscal Year-end: 12/31/22
Newspaper Publisher & Printer
N.A.I.C.S.: 513110
Timo Jaakko Antero Aukia *(Chm)*

Subsidiaries:

I print Oy (1)
Teollisuustie 24 PL 21, Seinajoki, 60101, Finland
Tel.: (358) 62477750
Web Site: http://www.iprint.fi
Sales Range: $25-49.9 Million
Emp.: 80
Digital Printing Services
N.A.I.C.S.: 323111
Seppo Lahti *(Mng Dir)*

Pohjanmaan Lahisanomat Oy (1)
Koulukatu 10 A, 60100, Seinajoki, Finland
Tel.: (358) 64186555
Web Site: http://www.alkka.si
Sales Range: $125-149.9 Million
Digital Printing Services
N.A.I.C.S.: 323111

Sanomalehti Ilkka Oy (1)
Koulukatu 10, PO Box 60, 60100, Seinajoki, Finland
Tel.: (358) 62477830
Web Site: http://www.ilkka.fi
Digital Printing Services
N.A.I.C.S.: 323111
Matti Korkiatua *(Mng Dir)*

Vaasa Oy (1)
Hietasaarenkatu 19, 65100, Vaasa, Finland
Tel.: (358) 63 24 91 11
Sales Range: $50-74.9 Million
Emp.: 104
Digital Printing Services
N.A.I.C.S.: 323111

ILLA S.P.A.
Via Ghisolfi e Guareschi 17, Noceto, 43015, Parma, Italy
Tel.: (39) 0521667511
Web Site: http://www.illa.it
Year Founded: 1946
Cookware Product Mfr
N.A.I.C.S.: 332215
Giuseppe Brioni *(Chm)*

ILLBRUCK GMBH
Burscheider Strasse 454, 51381, Leverkusen, Germany
Tel.: (49) 21713910   De
Web Site: http://www.illbruck.com
Sales Range: $100-124.9 Million
Emp.: 900
Architectural & Building Services
N.A.I.C.S.: 541310

Subsidiaries:

Illbruck Foam Tec (1)
2601 49th Ave N, Minneapolis, MN 55430-2142
Tel.: (612) 521-3555
Web Site: http://www.illbruck.com
Sales Range: $75-99.9 Million
Emp.: 115
Mfr of Insulation Products
N.A.I.C.S.: 326150
Rob Huebsch *(Pres)*

ILLE ROUSSILLON
3 avenue Cote Vermeille, 66300, Thuir, France
Tel.: (33) 468530426
Web Site: http://www.ille-roussillon.com
Sales Range: $25-49.9 Million
Emp.: 50
Fresh Fruits & Vegetables
N.A.I.C.S.: 424480
Julien Battle *(Pres)*

ILLIG MASCHINENBAU GMBH & CO. KG
Robert-Bosch-Strasse 10, 74081, Heilbronn, Germany
Tel.: (49) 71315050
Web Site: http://www.illig.de
Year Founded: 1946
Sales Range: $75-99.9 Million
Thermoforming & Packaging Machinery Tools Mfr
N.A.I.C.S.: 333517
Wolfgang Illig *(Co-Mng Dir)*

ILLIMITY BANK S.P.A.
Via Soperga 9, 20124, Milan, Italy
Tel.: (39) 0282849000
Web Site: https://www.illimity.com
ILTY—(ITA)
Rev.: $438,559,444
Assets: $8,013,077,604
Liabilities: $6,957,660,891

Net Worth: $1,055,416,713
Earnings: $114,597,638
Emp.: 921
Fiscal Year-end: 12/31/23
Mortgage Banking Services
N.A.I.C.S.: 522292
Rosalba Casiraghi *(Chm)*

Subsidiaries:

illimity SGR S.p.A. (1)
Via Soperga 9, 20124, Milan, Italy
Tel.: (39) 0282849000
Web Site: https://www.illimitysgr.com
Financial Investment Services
N.A.I.C.S.: 523999
Paola Tondelli *(Head-Investment Area)*

ILLUMIN HOLDINGS INC.
70 University Ave Suite 1200, Toronto, M5J 2M4, ON, Canada
Tel.: (416) 218-9888   Ca
Web Site: https://illumin.com
Year Founded: 2011
K3S0—(DEU)
Rev.: $95,385,248
Assets: $88,269,752
Liabilities: $27,333,079
Net Worth: $60,936,674
Earnings: ($8,296,503)
Emp.: 243
Fiscal Year-end: 12/31/23
Investment Services
N.A.I.C.S.: 523999
Elliot Muchnik *(CFO)*

ILLUMINATOR INVESTMENT COMPANY LIMITED
10 Murray Street, Hamilton, 2303, NSW, Australia
Tel.: (61) 249202877
Web Site: https://www.illuminator.com.au
Year Founded: 2003
Rev.: $37,574
Assets: $1,483,200
Liabilities: $466,821
Net Worth: $1,016,379
Earnings: ($44,038)
Fiscal Year-end: 06/30/19
Investment Services
N.A.I.C.S.: 523999
Steven Shane Pritchard *(Chm)*

ILLYCAFFE S.P.A.
Via Flavia 110, 34147, Trieste, Italy
Tel.: (39) 0403890111   IT
Web Site: http://www.illy.com
Year Founded: 1933
Sales Range: $300-349.9 Million
Emp.: 700
Coffee & Tea Mfr
N.A.I.C.S.: 311920
Andrea Illy *(Chm)*

Subsidiaries:

ILLYCAFFE' SUD AMERICA COM. IMP. EXP. LTD. (1)
Rua Bela Cintra 1870, Jardim, Paulista, 01415-002, Sao Paulo, Brazil
Tel.: (55) 11 23623888
Web Site: http://www.illycaffe.com
Coffee & Tea Distr
N.A.I.C.S.: 424490
Juliana Solari *(Gen Mgr)*

Illycaffe Shanghai Co. Ltd. (1)
7 D Silver Tower Jiu An Plaza 258 Tong Ren Road, Shanghai, 200040, China
Tel.: (86) 21 6279 1979
Coffee & Tea Distr
N.A.I.C.S.: 424490

illy espresso Canada (1)
1260 Lakeshore Road East Suite 213, Mississauga, ON, Canada
Tel.: (800) 665-4559
Coffee & Tea Distr
N.A.I.C.S.: 424490

illycaffe France Belux Sarl (1)

ILMVAC GMBH

19 Rue du Quatre Septembre, 75002, Paris, France
Tel.: (33) 145220010
Web Site: http://www.illy.com
Sales Range: $25-49.9 Million
Emp.: 50
General Merchandise Stores
N.A.I.C.S.: 455219

illycaffe France SAS (1)
19 rue du Quatre Septembre, 75002, Paris, France
Tel.: (33) 1 45 220 010
Coffee & Tea Distr
N.A.I.C.S.: 424490

illycaffe Korea Co. Ltd. (1)
Dongwon Building 2F Samseong-dong 143-28, Gangnam-gu Yangcheon-Ku, Seoul, Korea (South)
Tel.: (82) 2 2606 1282
Coffee & Tea Distr
N.A.I.C.S.: 424490

illycaffe Nederland B.V. (1)
Mijlweg 12, 's-Gravendeel, 3295KH, Netherlands (100%)
Tel.: (31) 786738888
Web Site: http://www.illy.com
Sales Range: $25-49.9 Million
Emp.: 45
General Merchandise Stores
N.A.I.C.S.: 455219
Gert Korteweg *(Mng Dir)*

illycaffe North America Inc. (1)
800 Westchester Ave Ste S440, Rye Brook, NY 10573
Tel.: (914) 253-4500
Web Site: http://www.housewares.org
General Merchandise Stores
N.A.I.C.S.: 455219
Christine Moncrief *(Mgr-Events Mktg)*

illycaffe S.p.A. Niederlassung Deutschland (1)
Staffelseestrasse 4, Munich, 81477, Germany
Tel.: (49) 898189440
Web Site: http://www.illy.com
Sales Range: $25-49.9 Million
Emp.: 40
Sales & Distribution of Specialty Coffee Products
N.A.I.C.S.: 311920
Andrea Zappalorto *(Mng Dir)*

illycaffe Shanghai Co. Ltd. (1)
7 D Silver Tower Jiu An Plaza, 258 Tong Ren Road, Shanghai, 200040, China (100%)
Tel.: (86) 2162791979
Web Site: http://www.illy.com
Sales Range: $25-49.9 Million
Emp.: 30
General Merchandise Stores
N.A.I.C.S.: 455219

ILLYRIA (PTY) LTD.
33 Nickson Street, Surrey Hills, Sydney, Australia
Tel.: (61) 2 9690 4611   AU
Web Site: http://www.illyria.com.au
Privater Equity Firm
N.A.I.C.S.: 523999
Lachlan Keith Murdoch *(Owner, Exec Chm & CEO)*

ILMARINEN MUTUAL PENSION INSURANCE COMPANY
Porkkalankatu 1, 00018, Helsinki, Finland
Tel.: (358) 10 284 2011   FI
Web Site: http://www.ilmarinen.fi
Year Founded: 1961
Pension Insurance & Fund Management Services
N.A.I.C.S.: 524292
Mikko Helander *(Chm)*

ILMVAC GMBH
Am Vogelherd 20, 98693, Ilmenau, Germany
Tel.: (49) 36776040
Web Site: http://www.ilmvac.de

ILMVAC GMBH

Ilmvac GmbH—(Continued)
Year Founded: 1947
Rev.: $19,196,846
Emp.: 89
Laboratory Apparatus Mfr
N.A.I.C.S.: 334516
Friedrich Geyer *(Founder)*

ILOODA CO., LTD.
9F 25 Deokcheon-ro 152beon-gil, Manan-gu, Anyang, 16200, Gyeonggi-do, Korea (South)
Tel.: (82) 312784660
Web Site: http://www.sg.ilooda.com
Year Founded: 2006
164060—(KRS)
Rev.: $35,499,208
Assets: $60,236,864
Liabilities: $26,212,410
Net Worth: $34,024,454
Earnings: $6,043,048
Emp.: 104
Fiscal Year-end: 12/31/22
Surgical Equipment Mfr
N.A.I.C.S.: 339112
Jin-Hyun Lee *(Mgr-Personal Info)*

ILP FUNDS
30 rue Marie Adelaide, 2128, Luxembourg, Luxembourg
Tel.: (352) 27029681
Web Site: http://www.ilpfunds.com
Sales Range: $25-49.9 Million
Emp.: 11
Private Equity Investment Services
N.A.I.C.S.: 523999
Adrien Coulombel *(Gen Mgr)*

ILPRA SPA
Via Mattei 21/23, 27036, Mortara, PV, Italy
Tel.: (39) 03842905
Web Site: https://www.ilpra.com
ILP—(ITA)
Rev.: $68,482,664
Assets: $103,213,107
Liabilities: $71,179,751
Net Worth: $32,033,357
Earnings: $7,108,777
Emp.: 324
Fiscal Year-end: 12/31/23
Packaging Machinery Mfr
N.A.I.C.S.: 333993
Vittorio Vecchio *(CFO)*

Subsidiaries:

Ilpra Benelux BV (1)
Hermesweg 19, 3771 ND, Barneveld, Netherlands
Tel.: (31) 342404730
Web Site: http://www.ilpra.nl
Packaging Machinery Mfr
N.A.I.C.S.: 333993

Ilpra Deutschland GmbH (1)
Boschstrasse 16, 47533, Kleve, Germany
Tel.: (49) 28218944820
Packaging Machinery Mfr
N.A.I.C.S.: 333993

Ilpra Hong Kong Ltd. (1)
5/F Concord Commercial Building 157 Kings Rd, North Point, China (Hong Kong)
Tel.: (852) 68886033
Packaging Machinery Mfr
N.A.I.C.S.: 333993

Ilpra Systems Espana SL (1)
C/Batista I Roca 31 - 35 Pol Ind Pla d en Boet, 08302, Mataro, Barcelona, Spain
Tel.: (34) 937573462
Web Site: http://www.ilpra.es
Packaging Machinery Mfr
N.A.I.C.S.: 333993

Ilpra Systems UK Ltd. (1)
Units 5 7 and 13 RO24 Avro Gate Broadmoor Road, South Marston Business Park, Swindon, SN3 4AG, Wiltshire, United Kingdom (71.84%)
Tel.: (44) 1793832020

Web Site: http://www.ilpra.co.uk
Emp.: 200
Packaging Machinery Mfr
N.A.I.C.S.: 333993

ILS LABORATORIES SCANDINAVIA A/S
Gydevang 22A, 3450, Allerod, Denmark
Tel.: (45) 4814 1850 DK
Web Site: http://www.ilsdk.dk
Year Founded: 1992
Sales Range: $10-24.9 Million
Emp.: 20
Laboratory Equipment & Supplies Distr
N.A.I.C.S.: 423450
Kim Saksager *(CEO)*

ILSHIN SPINNING CO., LTD.
11 Eunhaeng-ro, Yeongdeungpo-gu, Seoul, 07237, Korea (South)
Tel.: (82) 237740114
Web Site: https://www.ilshin.co.kr
Year Founded: 1951
003200—(KRS)
Rev.: $454,876,075
Assets: $902,564,171
Liabilities: $208,852,686
Net Worth: $693,711,485
Earnings: $87,648,997
Emp.: 546
Fiscal Year-end: 12/31/22
Yarn Mfr & Sales
N.A.I.C.S.: 313110
Ho Choi *(Gen Mgr-Dyed Yarn & Fabric Sls)*

Subsidiaries:

BSK Corporation (1)
32-35 Myeong-dong-2-ga, Jung-gu, Seoul, Korea (South)
Tel.: (82) 2 759 0700
Web Site: http://www.ilshin.co.kr
Sales Range: $75-99.9 Million
Emp.: 250
Cosmetic Product Distr
N.A.I.C.S.: 424210
Park Jong Ho *(Pres)*

Ilshin Investment Co., Ltd. (1)
11 Eunhaeng-ro, Yeongdeungpo-gu, Seoul, 150872, Korea (South)
Tel.: (82) 27676400
Web Site: http://www.iic.co.kr
Sales Range: $50-74.9 Million
Emp.: 15
Investment Management Service
N.A.I.C.S.: 523940

Shindong Corporation (1)
Sales Range: $25-49.9 Million
Emp.: 5
Clothing Apparel Mfr & Distr
N.A.I.C.S.: 315250
Hoon Lee Jong *(Pres)*

Subsidiary (Domestic):

Shindong Wine Co., Ltd. (2)
Shindong Building 150 Hannam-daero, Yongsan-gu, Seoul, Korea (South)
Tel.: (82) 27944531
Web Site: https://www.shindongwine.com
Sales Range: $25-49.9 Million
Wine Distr
N.A.I.C.S.: 424820
Kiman Hong *(CEO)*

ILSHIN STONE CO., LTD
19 Seongnae-ro, Gangdong-gu, Seoul, Korea (South)
Tel.: (82) 24879009
Web Site: https://www.ilshinstone.co.kr
Year Founded: 1971
007110—(KRS)
Rev.: $105,593,650
Assets: $89,100,752
Liabilities: $46,741,323
Net Worth: $42,359,429
Earnings: $1,800,597

Emp.: 104
Fiscal Year-end: 12/31/22
Stone Mining Services
N.A.I.C.S.: 212311
Hak-Sun Kim *(CEO)*

ILSHINBIOBASE CO., LTD.
84 Samyuksa-ro 548beon-gil, Dongducheon, Gyeonggi-do, Korea (South)
Tel.: (82) 7043543951
Web Site: https://www.1sbb.com
Year Founded: 1994
068330—(KRS)
Rev.: $15,672,392
Assets: $44,831,989
Liabilities: $3,552,648
Net Worth: $41,279,341
Earnings: $2,926,146
Emp.: 45
Fiscal Year-end: 12/31/22
Industrial Refrigeration Equipment Mfr
N.A.I.C.S.: 333415
Sung Dae Hong *(CEO)*

ILSHINWELLS CO., LTD.
Hanbeol Building 3th floor 25-1 Dongmak-ro, Mapo-gu, Seoul, Korea (South)
Tel.: (82) 23335511
Web Site: https://www.ise.co.kr
Year Founded: 1972
Industrial Material Mfr
N.A.I.C.S.: 331222

ILSUNG CONSTRUCTION CO., LTD.
4 and 5th floor 21 Gukhoe-daero 62-gil, Yeondeungpo-gu, Seoul, Korea (South)
Tel.: (82) 232716000
Web Site: https://www.ilsungconst.co.kr
Year Founded: 1978
013360—(KRS)
Rev.: $354,815,438
Assets: $317,002,632
Liabilities: $224,589,449
Net Worth: $92,413,183
Earnings: $5,542,662
Emp.: 495
Fiscal Year-end: 12/31/22
Construction Engineering Services
N.A.I.C.S.: 541330
Pilsang Yoo *(CEO)*

ILSUNG PHARMACEUTICALS CO., LTD
10th floor Gwacheon Smart K A Tower, 20 Gwacheon-daero 7-gil, Gwacheon, Gyeonggi-do, Korea (South)
Tel.: (82) 232718800
Web Site: https://www.ilsungis.com
Year Founded: 1954
003120—(KRS)
Rev.: $46,977,098
Assets: $379,220,215
Liabilities: $37,470,166
Net Worth: $341,750,049
Earnings: $80,719,994
Emp.: 223
Fiscal Year-end: 12/31/22
Pharmaceutical Product Mfr & Whslr
N.A.I.C.S.: 325412
S. K. Yoon *(Vice Chm & CEO)*

ILUKA RESOURCES LIMITED
Tel.: (61) 893604700 AU
Web Site: https://www.iluka.com
Year Founded: 1954
ILU—(ASX)
Rev.: $1,075,703,880
Assets: $2,004,001,680
Liabilities: $739,033,200
Net Worth: $1,264,968,480

INTERNATIONAL PUBLIC

Earnings: $390,212,200
Emp.: 950
Fiscal Year-end: 12/31/22
Mineral Sands Exploration, Mining & Marketing Services
N.A.I.C.S.: 212290
Matthew Blackwell *(Head-Major Projects & Mktg)*

Subsidiaries:

Iluka Resources Inc. (1)
12472 St Johns Church Rd, Stony Creek, VA 23882
Tel.: (434) 348-4300
Mineral Sand Product Distr
N.A.I.C.S.: 423520

Iluka Trading (Shanghai) Co., Ltd. (1)
Unit 2601 26th Floor Westgate Mall 1038 Nanjing West Road, Jing'an District, Shanghai, 200041, China
Tel.: (86) 2162532266112
Mineral Sand Product Distr
N.A.I.C.S.: 423520

Sierra Rutile Limited (1)
30 Siaka Stevens Street 2nd Floor Access Bank Building, Freetown, Sierra Leone (100%)
Tel.: (232) 76801416
Web Site: http://www.sierra-rutile.com
Sales Range: $100-124.9 Million
Emp.: 1,400
Titanium Exploration & Mining Services
N.A.I.C.S.: 212290
Derek Folmer *(CMO)*

ILUSTRATO PICTURES INTERNATIONAL INC.
Suite 220 2 Old Brompton Road, South Kensington, London, SW7 3DQ, United Kingdom
Tel.: (44) 2075437720 NV
Web Site: https://ilus-group.com
Year Founded: 2010
ILUS—(OTCIQ)
Rev.: $78,344,131
Assets: $251,417,462
Liabilities: $195,300,330
Net Worth: $56,117,132
Earnings: $4,559,375
Emp.: 1,805
Fiscal Year-end: 12/31/22
Theatrical Film Producer
N.A.I.C.S.: 512110
John-Paul Backwell *(Mng Dir)*

Subsidiaries:

Bull Head Products Inc. (1)
387 Thorngrove Pike, Kodak, TN 37764
Tel.: (865) 932-5100
Web Site: https://bullheadproducts.com
Tray Truck Bed Mfr
N.A.I.C.S.: 337127

E-Raptor Technologies Inc. (1)
2900 N Loop W Ste 900, Houston, TX 77092
Tel.: (713) 880-8902
Web Site: https://raptortech.com
Software Development Services
N.A.I.C.S.: 541511

Emergency Response Technologies, Inc. (1)
26 Broadway Ste 934, New York, NY 10004
Tel.: (917) 522-3202
Web Site: https://ert-international.com
Security System Services
N.A.I.C.S.: 561621

FB Fire Technologies Ltd. (1)
Matrix Dinnington Business Centre Nobel Way, Dinnington, Sheffield, S25 3QB, United Kingdom
Tel.: (44) 1909547070
Web Site: https://firebuggroup.com
Fire Rescue Services
N.A.I.C.S.: 922160

Georgia Fire-Rescue Supply (1)
602 Water Tank Rd, Canton, GA 30115-6210

Tel.: (229) 254-1972
Web Site: http://www.georgiafirerescue.net
Durable Goods Merchant Whslr
N.A.I.C.S.: 423990
Barbara J. Whidby (Owner)

QUALITY INDUSTRIAL CORP. (1)
315 Montgomery St, San Francisco, CA 94104 (77.4%)
Web Site: https://qualityindustrialcorp.com
Rev.: $65,603,673
Assets: $200,692,193
Liabilities: $173,814,801
Net Worth: $26,877,392
Earnings: $6,773,268
Emp.: 1,355
Fiscal Year-end: 12/31/2022
Oil & Gas Field Machinery & Equipment Manufacturing
N.A.I.C.S.: 333132
John-Paul Backwell (CEO)

The Vehicle Converters LLC (1)
Aweer Warehouses Opp The Automarket Al Aweer, Dubai, United Arab Emirates
Tel.: (971) 43207572
Web Site: https://tvc-international.com
Truck Transportation Services
N.A.I.C.S.: 811111

ILWOUL GML CO.,LTD
48 Jeonpa-ro Manan-gu, Anyang, Gyeonggi-do, Korea (South)
Tel.: (82) 314440202
Web Site: http://www.u-tech.co.kr
Year Founded: 2006
178780—(KRS)
Rev.: $10,064,786
Assets: $9,178,318
Liabilities: $4,333,239
Net Worth: $4,845,078
Earnings: ($3,128,695)
Emp.: 44
Fiscal Year-end: 12/31/22
Electronic Components Mfr
N.A.I.C.S.: 334419
Lee Su Hong (Gen Mgr)

ILYANG PHARMACEUTICAL CO., LTD.
110 Hagal-ro, Giheung-gu, Yongin, 17096, Gyeonggi-do, Korea (South)
Tel.: (82) 312817851
Web Site: https://www.ilyang.co.kr
Year Founded: 1946
007570—(KRS)
Rev.: $294,382,900
Assets: $382,108,077
Liabilities: $158,255,986
Net Worth: $223,852,090
Earnings: $14,755,498
Emp.: 655
Fiscal Year-end: 12/31/22
Pharmaceutical Product Mfr & Distr
N.A.I.C.S.: 325412
Do-oen Chung (Chm)

ILYDA SA
29 Adrianeiou N Psychiko, 115 25, Athens, Greece
Tel.: (30) 2106705000
Web Site: https://www.ilyda.com
Year Founded: 1992
ILYDA—(ATH)
Sales Range: Less than $1 Million
Emp.: 38
Software Development Services
N.A.I.C.S.: 541511
Vasilios Apostolou Anifantakis (Chm & CEO)

ILYUSHIN FINANCE CO.
Michurinskii Prospekt Olimpiiskaia Derevnia 1-1, 119602, Moscow, Russia
Tel.: (7) 4957109960
Web Site: http://www.ifc-leasing.com
Year Founded: 1999
Sales Range: $25-49.9 Million
Emp.: 80

Aircraft Sales & Leasing Services
N.A.I.C.S.: 532411
Alexander Ivanovich Rubtsov (Dir Gen)

IM CANNABIS CORP.
1 Adelaide St E, Toronto, M5C 2V9, ON, Canada
Tel.: (416) 256-4202   BC
Web Site: https://www.imcannabis.com
IMCC—(NASDAQ)
Rev.: $42,505,184
Assets: $47,465,621
Liabilities: $28,849,704
Net Worth: $18,615,917
Earnings: ($149,650,946)
Emp.: 153
Fiscal Year-end: 12/31/22
Premium Cannabis Distr
N.A.I.C.S.: 325411
Marc Lustig (Exec Chm)

Subsidiaries:

MYM Nutraceuticals Inc. (1)
Suite 250 - 1095 W Pender Street, Vancouver, V6E 2M6, BC, Canada
Tel.: (778) 522-2261
Web Site: http://www.mym.ca
Botanical Products Producer
N.A.I.C.S.: 325411
Mark Forster (CFO)

Trichome Financial Corp. (1)
150 King St West Suite 200, Toronto, M5H 3T9, ON, Canada
Tel.: (416) 998-2900
Rev.: $967,694
Assets: $22,136,829
Liabilities: $1,027,822
Net Worth: $21,109,007
Earnings: ($4,433,610)
Fiscal Year-end: 12/31/2019
Financial Consulting Services
N.A.I.C.S.: 541611

IM CO., LTD.
58-1 Giheung-ro, Giheung-gu, Yongin, 445-170, Gyeonggi-do, Korea (South)
Tel.: (82) 312313114   KR
Web Site: http://www.im2006.com
Year Founded: 2006
101390—(KRS)
Rev.: $90,030,185
Assets: $55,625,712
Liabilities: $24,287,707
Net Worth: $31,338,004
Earnings: ($4,730,088)
Emp.: 52
Fiscal Year-end: 12/31/22
Optical Electronic Equipment Mfr & Distr
N.A.I.C.S.: 333310
Koo Bon Kyong (Exec Dir)

Subsidiaries:

Dongguan IM Digital Electronics Co. Ltd (1)
Baiye Ind Zone, Liaobu, Dongguan, 523413, Guangdong, China
Tel.: (86) 769 8303 8000
Electronic Equipment Distr
N.A.I.C.S.: 423690

IM (HK) Co., Ltd. (1)
Room 502-3 5/F Nan Fung Tower 173 Des Voeuk Road, Central, China (Hong Kong)
Tel.: (852) 755 8351 0834
Electronic Equipment Distr
N.A.I.C.S.: 423690

Xiangtan IM Digital Electronics Co. Ltd (1)
No 18 Dazhongxi Road Jiuhua Economical Industrial Park, Xiangtan, Hunan, China
Tel.: (86) 73286980
Electronic Equipment Distr
N.A.I.C.S.: 423690

IM RAKOVICA U RESTRUK-

TURIRANJU A.D.
Patrijarha Dimitrija 7-13, Rakovica, 11090, Belgrade, Serbia
Tel.: (381) 11 3564 013
Web Site: http://www.imr-rakovica.com
Year Founded: 1927
Sales Range: $1-9.9 Million
Tractor Mfr
N.A.I.C.S.: 333924

IM TECH INC
274-43 LG-ro Wollong-myeon, Paju, Gyeonggi-do, Korea (South)
Tel.: (82) 3180712581
Web Site: https://www.im-tech.com
226350—(KRS)
Rev.: $9,395,440
Assets: $12,328,644
Liabilities: $12,453,019
Net Worth: ($124,375)
Earnings: ($2,023,775)
Emp.: 86
Fiscal Year-end: 12/31/22
Electronic Equipment Mfr & Distr
N.A.I.C.S.: 334220
Sang-Bum Lee (CEO)

IM+ CAPITALS LIMITED
72 Ground Floor World Trade Center Babar Road, Connaught Place, New Delhi, 110001, India
Tel.: (91) 9810266747
Web Site: https://www.imcapitals.com
Year Founded: 1991
511628—(BOM)
Rev.: $400,728
Assets: $9,538,102
Liabilities: $855,829
Net Worth: $8,682,273
Earnings: $131,819
Emp.: 4
Fiscal Year-end: 03/31/22
Financial Support Services
N.A.I.C.S.: 523999
Jyoti Gupta (CFO)

IMAFLEX INC.
5710 Notre Dame West, Montreal, H4C 1V2, QC, Canada
Tel.: (514) 935-5710
Web Site: https://www.imaflex.com
Year Founded: 1994
IFX—(TSXV)
Rev.: $70,673,902
Assets: $59,238,610
Liabilities: $17,059,125
Net Worth: $42,179,485
Earnings: $384,191
Emp.: 264
Fiscal Year-end: 12/31/23
Polyethylene Films Mfr
N.A.I.C.S.: 326111
Joseph Abbandonato (Chm, Pres & CEO)

Subsidiaries:

Imaflex USA Inc. (1)
1200 Unity St, Thomasville, NC 27360-3220
Tel.: (336) 474-1190
Sales Range: $25-49.9 Million
Emp.: 70
Plastic Packaging Materials Mfr
N.A.I.C.S.: 322220
Joe Abbandonato (Gen Mgr)

IMAGE CHAIN GROUP LIMITED, INC.
No 6 6-1 6-2 Jalan BS 10/6 Taman Bukit Serdang 43300, 43350, Seri Kembangan, Selangor, Malaysia
Tel.: (60) 85231882700   NV
Year Founded: 2013
ICGL—(OTCIQ)
Rev.: $301,290
Assets: $24,205
Liabilities: $739,279

Net Worth: ($715,074)
Earnings: ($4,082)
Fiscal Year-end: 12/31/21
Television Program Production Services
N.A.I.C.S.: 512110

IMAGE INFORMATION INC.
Inuzuka Building 1F 2-4-11 Sarugaku-cho Kanda, Chiyoda-Ku, Tokyo, 101-0064, Japan
Tel.: (81) 352177811
Web Site: https://www.image-inf.co.jp
Year Founded: 1975
3803—(TKS)
Rev.: $3,483,470
Assets: $4,144,470
Liabilities: $1,923,510
Net Worth: $2,220,960
Earnings: ($132,200)
Fiscal Year-end: 03/31/24
Information Technology Services
N.A.I.C.S.: 519290
Takuji Tainaga (Pres & CEO)

IMAGE PAKISTAN LIMITED
F/538 S I T E, Karachi, 75700, Pakistan
Tel.: (92) 2132582613   PK
Web Site: https://imagepakistan.net
Year Founded: 1992
IMAGE—(PSX)
Rev.: $9,699,992
Assets: $13,018,932
Liabilities: $3,800,003
Net Worth: $9,218,929
Earnings: $1,038,373
Emp.: 878
Fiscal Year-end: 06/30/23
Polyester Yarn Mfr
N.A.I.C.S.: 313110
Asad Ahmad (CEO)

IMAGE POWER S.A.
ul Wybrzeze Kosciuszkowskie 21 lok U1, 00-390, Warsaw, Poland
Tel.: (48) 663936116
Web Site: https://www.imagepower.pl
Year Founded: 2012
IPW—(WAR)
Software Development Services
N.A.I.C.S.: 541511
Marcin Zalenski (Chm)

IMAGE RESOURCES NL
Level 2 1 Walker Avenue, West Perth, 6005, WA, Australia
Tel.: (61) 894852410
Web Site: https://www.imageres.com.au
I5R—(DEU)
Rev.: $114,518,101
Assets: $134,240,340
Liabilities: $56,667,223
Net Worth: $77,573,117
Earnings: $10,126,157
Emp.: 2
Fiscal Year-end: 12/31/22
Support Activities for Nonmetallic Minerals (except Fuels) Mining
N.A.I.C.S.: 213115
George Sakalidis (Head-Exploration)

IMAGE SCAN HOLDINGS PLC
16 & 18 Hayhill Industrial Estate Sileby Road, Barrow Upon Soar, Loughborough, LE12 8LD, Leicestershire, United Kingdom
Tel.: (44) 1509817400
Web Site: https://www.3dx-ray.com
IGE—(AIM)
Rev.: $2,264,400
Assets: $2,739,924
Liabilities: $1,166,166
Net Worth: $1,573,758
Earnings: ($305,694)
Fiscal Year-end: 09/30/22

IMAGE SCAN HOLDINGS PLC

Image Scan Holdings plc—(Continued)
Three-Dimensional Imaging Technology
N.A.I.C.S.: 518210
Vincent James Deery *(Dir-Sls & Mktg)*

Subsidiaries:

3DX-RAY Ltd. (1)
16 18 Hayhill Industrial Estate Sileby Road, Barrow upon Soar, Loughborough, LE12 8LD, Leicestershire, United Kingdom
Tel.: (44) 1509817400
Web Site: https://www.3dx-ray.com
Sales Range: $25-49.9 Million
Emp.: 15
X Ray Inspection Services
N.A.I.C.S.: 541380

Todd Research Limited (1)
Unit 9C Trafalgar Way, Bar Hill, Cambridge, CB23 8SQ, United Kingdom
Tel.: (44) 1480832202
Web Site: https://www.toddresearch.co.uk
X Ray & Security Equipments Mfr & Sales
N.A.I.C.S.: 334510

IMAGE SYSTEMS AB

Snickaregatan 40, 582 26, Linkoping, Sweden
Tel.: (46) 13200100
Web Site: https://www.imagesystemsgroup.se
IS—(OMX)
Rev.: $16,877,874
Assets: $18,235,972
Liabilities: $6,724,924
Net Worth: $11,511,047
Earnings: $805,492
Emp.: 72
Fiscal Year-end: 12/31/22
Image Processing Equipment Mfr
N.A.I.C.S.: 333310
Thomas Wernhoff *(Chm)*

Subsidiaries:

Digital Vision Systems Inc (1)
6464 Sunset Blvd Ste 830, Hollywood, CA 90028
Tel.: (818) 769-8111
Emp.: 2
Image Processing Equipment Mfr
N.A.I.C.S.: 333310
Robin Melhuish *(Dir-Sls-Americas)*

Digital Vision Systems Ltd. (1)
21 Poplar Business Park 10 Prestons Road, London, E14 9RL, United Kingdom
Tel.: (44) 3330148148
Web Site: http://www.digitalvision.world
Emp.: 16
Image Processing Equipment Mfr
N.A.I.C.S.: 333310

Image Systems Nordic AB (1)
Snickaregatan 40, 582 26, Linkoping, Sweden
Tel.: (46) 13200100
Web Site: https://imagesystems.se
Software Development Services
N.A.I.C.S.: 541511

RemaSawco AB (1)
Snickaregatan 40, 582 26, Linkoping, Sweden
Tel.: (46) 15555950
Web Site: https://remasawco.com
Emp.: 100
Sawmill Equipment Mfr
N.A.I.C.S.: 333243

Subsidiary (Domestic):

RemaControl Sweden AB (2)
Pilgatan 21, 721 30, Vasteras, Sweden
Tel.: (46) 21812100
Web Site: http://www.rema.se
Sales Range: $1-9.9 Million
Emp.: 26
Sawmill Electrical Equipment
N.A.I.C.S.: 333243

RemaSawco AS (1)
Gaupevegen 8, 2211, Kongsvinger, Norway
Tel.: (47) 62946630

Measuring Instrument Mfr & Distr
N.A.I.C.S.: 334513

IMAGELINX PLC

Julias Way Station Park, Lowmoor Road, Sutton in Ashfield, NG17 7RB, Notts, United Kingdom
Tel.: (44) 1623689500 UK
Web Site: http://www.imagelinx.co.uk
Sales Range: $10-24.9 Million
Emp.: 132
Holding Company; Packaging Graphics Solutions
N.A.I.C.S.: 551112
Alistair Rae *(CEO)*

Subsidiaries:

imagelinx Milton Keynes Ltd (1)
34/36 Tanners Drive, Blakelands, Milton Keynes, MK14 5BW, Buckinghamshire, United Kingdom
Tel.: (44) 1908283700
Graphic Design Services
N.A.I.C.S.: 541430

imagelinx Scotland Ltd (1)
4 Cairn Court, Nerston East Kilbride, Glasgow, G74 4NB, United Kingdom
Tel.: (44) 1355575300
Graphic Design Services
N.A.I.C.S.: 541430

imagelinx USA inc (1)
33 Upton Dr Ste 2, Wilmington, MA 01887
Tel.: (978) 657-8666
Graphic Design Services
N.A.I.C.S.: 541430

IMAGEONE CO., LTD.

6F Osaki New City3 1-6-3, Osaki Shinagawa, Tokyo, 141-0032, Japan
Tel.: (81) 357192180
Web Site: https://www.imageone.co.jp
Year Founded: 1984
2667—(TKS)
Sales Range: Less than $1 Million
Emp.: 53
Medical Imaging Services
N.A.I.C.S.: 621512
Satoshi Arai *(Pres & CEO)*

IMAGESAT INTERNATIONAL (ISI) LTD.

6 Yoni Netanyahu St, Or Yehuda, 6037604, Israel
Tel.: (972) 37960600 IL
Web Site: https://www.imagesatintl.com
Year Founded: 1997
ISI—(TAE)
Rev.: $43,913,000
Assets: $269,893,000
Liabilities: $102,632,000
Net Worth: $167,261,000
Earnings: $4,673,000
Fiscal Year-end: 12/31/23
Aerospace Equipment Mfr
N.A.I.C.S.: 335991

Subsidiaries:

Discount Capital Ltd. (1)
22 Rothschild Blvd 18th Floor, Tel Aviv, 6688218, Israel
Tel.: (972) 37100102
Web Site: https://www.dcapital.co.il
Investment Banking Services
N.A.I.C.S.: 523150

IMAGI INTERNATIONAL HOLDINGS LTD.

Room 2205-09 22nd Floor China United Centre 28 Marble Road, North Point, China (Hong Kong)
Tel.: (852) 36793988 BM
Web Site: http://www.imagi.hk
Year Founded: 2000
0585—(OTCIQ)
Rev.: $4,134,930

Assets: $194,845,353
Liabilities: $129,756,892
Net Worth: $65,088,461
Earnings: ($20,505,921)
Emp.: 37
Fiscal Year-end: 12/31/19
Animated Films Production & Distribution Services
N.A.I.C.S.: 512110
Osman Bin Kitchell *(Chm-Acting)*

Subsidiaries:

John & Wong Securities Company Limited (1)
9/F Malahon Ctr, Central, China (Hong Kong)
Tel.: (852) 25224488
Security Brokerage Services
N.A.I.C.S.: 523150

IMAGICA CORP.

1-1-8 Nishi-Gotanda Shinagawa-ku, Tokyo, Japan
Tel.: (81) 332807530 JP
Web Site: http://www.imagica.com
Sales Range: $125-149.9 Million
Emp.: 800
Motion Picture Services
N.A.I.C.S.: 512199
Fumio Nagase *(Pres & CEO)*

Subsidiaries:

IMAGICA Corp. of America (1)
1840 Century Park E, Los Angeles, CA 90067
Tel.: (310) 277-1790
Web Site: http://www.imagica-la.com
Rev.: $5,000,000
Emp.: 5
Film Production Services
N.A.I.C.S.: 423410

IMAGICA GROUP INC.

1-14-2 Kaigan, Minato-ku, Tokyo, 105-0022, Japan
Tel.: (81) 367415750
Web Site: https://www.imagicagroup.co.jp
Year Founded: 1935
6879—(TKS)
Rev.: $658,911,240
Assets: $520,167,340
Liabilities: $256,388,680
Net Worth: $263,778,660
Earnings: $15,685,530
Emp.: 4,202
Fiscal Year-end: 03/31/24
Video Technology Services
N.A.I.C.S.: 512110
Fumio Nagase *(Chm)*

Subsidiaries:

Cosmo Space Co., Ltd. (1)
5-6 Yonbancho 3rd Floor Yonbancho Building No 1, Chiyoda-ku, Tokyo, 102-0081, Japan
Tel.: (81) 332637210
Web Site: https://www.cosmospace.co.jp
Emp.: 319
Media Services
N.A.I.C.S.: 541840

Cosmo Space Of America Co., ltd. (1)
8800 Venice Blvd Ph401, Los Angeles, CA 90034
Tel.: (310) 287-2645
Web Site: https://www.cosmospaceusa.com
Emp.: 5
Television Broadcasting Services
N.A.I.C.S.: 516120

IMAGICA KADOKAWA EDITORIAL Co., LTD. (1)
1-8-19 Fujimi Chiyoda-Ku, Tokyo, 102-0071, Japan
Tel.: (81) 332388447
Web Site: http://www.iket.co.jp
Magazine Book Editing Services
N.A.I.C.S.: 561410

INTERNATIONAL PUBLIC

IMAGICA TV Corp. (1)
Shiroyama Trust Tower 4-3-1 Toranomon Minato-ku, Tokyo, 105-6026, Japan
Tel.: (81) 367020240
Web Site: http://www.imagicatv.jp
Emp.: 67
Broadcasting Services
N.A.I.C.S.: 516120
Akira Ito *(Pres & CEO)*

IMAGICA Total Service Corp. (1)
2-8-3 Higashigotanda Shinagawa-ku, Tokyo, 141-0022, Japan
Tel.: (81) 332807518
Web Site: http://www.imagicatos.jp
Civil Engineering Services
N.A.I.C.S.: 541330

IPmotion Inc. (1)
6th Floor Hamamatsucho Rise Square 1-3-3 Shibaura, Minato-ku, Tokyo, 105-0023, Japan
Tel.: (81) 345314330
Web Site: https://www.ipmotion.jp
Emp.: 43
Software Development Services
N.A.I.C.S.: 541511

Imagica Alobase Co., Ltd. (1)
1-10-8 Shibuya Dogenzaka Tokyu Building 8F, Dogenzaka Shibuya-ku, Tokyo, Japan
Tel.: (81) 368923550
Web Site: https://www.alobase.co.jp
Emp.: 73
Software Development Services
N.A.I.C.S.: 541511

Imagica Digital Scape Co., Ltd. (1)
Shibuya Dogenzaka Tokyu Building 8F 1-10-8, Dogenzaka Shibuya-ku, Tokyo, 150-0043, Japan
Tel.: (81) 354596236
Web Site: https://corp.dsp.co.jp
Emp.: 238
Media Services
N.A.I.C.S.: 541840
Atsushi Shinohara *(CEO)*

Imagica Lab. Inc. (1)
3-13-6 Higashishinagawa, Shinagawa-ku, Tokyo, 140-0002, Japan
Tel.: (81) 334581728
Web Site: https://www.imagicalab.co.jp
TV Commercial Services
N.A.I.C.S.: 541810
Kiyosh Sano *(Pres & CEO)*

Imagica Live Corp. (1)
3-3-6 Kudanminami, Chiyoda-ku, Tokyo, 102-0074, Japan
Tel.: (81) 335112585
Web Site: https://www.imagicalive.com
Media Services
N.A.I.C.S.: 541840
Yukihiro Fujikawa *(Pres & CEO)*

OLM Digital, Inc. (1)
Mikami Bldg 8F 1-18-10 Wakabayashi, Setagaya-ku, Tokyo, 154-0023, Japan
Tel.: (81) 354335588
Web Site: https://www.olm.co.jp
Emp.: 136
Animation Technology Services
N.A.I.C.S.: 512110
Toshiaki Okuno *(Pres & CEO)*

P.I.C.S. Co., Ltd. (1)
Saishin Building 3-9-19 Ebisu minami, Shibuya-ku, Tokyo, 150-0022, Japan
Tel.: (81) 337918855
Web Site: https://www.pics.tokyo
Video Production Services
N.A.I.C.S.: 512110

Photron Europe Limited (1)
The Barn Bottom Road, West Wycombe, High Wycombe, HP14 4BS, Bucks, United Kingdom
Tel.: (44) 1494481011
Video Equipment Mfr & Distr
N.A.I.C.S.: 334310

Photron Limited (1)
21F Jinbocho Mitsui Bldg 1-105, Chiyoda-ku Kanda Jimbocho, Tokyo, 101-0051, Japan
Tel.: (81) 335186271
Video Equipment Mfr & Distr
N.A.I.C.S.: 334310

Photron M&E Solutions Inc. (1)

AND PRIVATE COMPANIES

21F Jimbocho Mitsui Building 1-105,
Chiyoda-ku Kanda Jimbocho, Tokyo, 101-
0051, Japan
Tel.: (81) 335186282
Web Site:
    https://www.photronmandesolutions.co.jp
Emp.: 35
Network Outsourcing Service
N.A.I.C.S.: 541613
Yagi Hidetada *(Pres)*

Photron USA, Inc. (1)
9520 Padgett St Ste 110, San Diego, CA
92126
Tel.: (858) 684-3555
Web Site: https://www.photron.com
High Speed Camera Product Mfr & Distr
N.A.I.C.S.: 333310
Hidy Osato *(Mgr)*

ROBOT COMMUNICATIONS INC. (1)
8F 7-16-21 Ginza, Chuou-Ku, Tokyo, 104-
0061, Japan
Tel.: (81) 368667177
Web Site: https://www.robot.co.jp
Television Production Services
N.A.I.C.S.: 512110

SDI Media A/S (1)
Dortheavej 4 Nordvest, 2400, Copenhagen,
Denmark
Tel.: (45) 38320320
Sound Dubbing Services
N.A.I.C.S.: 512191
Mads Eggert *(Mgr-Studio)*

SDI Media Group, Inc. (1)
6060 Center Dr Ste 100, Los Angeles, CA
90045
Tel.: (310) 388-8800
Web Site: http://www.sdimedia.com
Sound Dubbing Services
N.A.I.C.S.: 512191
Mark Howorth *(CEO)*

SDI Media Holdings Germany GmbH (1)
Rheingaustr 29, 12161, Berlin, Germany
Tel.: (49) 307908330
Sound Dubbing Services
N.A.I.C.S.: 512191

SDI Media Ltd. (1)
32 Galena Road, London, W6 0LT, United
Kingdom
Tel.: (44) 2082377900
Sound Dubbing Services
N.A.I.C.S.: 512191

SDI Media Sweden AB (1)
Greta Garbos vag 13 4tr, Solna, Sweden
Tel.: (46) 852203000
Sound Dubbing Services
N.A.I.C.S.: 512191
Cathrine Wyreson *(Mgr-Ops)*

Shonan Hi-Tech Planning Co., Ltd. (1)
1-27-6 Hon-Atsugi Maibiru, Asahimachi, At-
sugi, 243-0014, Kanagawa, Japan
Tel.: (81) 462806812
Web Site: http://www.sh-k.com
Human Resource Consulting Services
N.A.I.C.S.: 541612

Shufunotomo Infos Co., Ltd. (1)
3-3-3 Kanda Ogawamachi HF Kanda
Ogawamachi Building 2F / 8F, Chiyoda-ku,
Tokyo, 101-0052, Japan
Tel.: (81) 362737850
Web Site: http://www.st-infos.co.jp
Book Publishers
N.A.I.C.S.: 513130

Weather Map Co., Ltd. (1)
The Hexagon 5F 5-4-7, Akasaka Minato-ku,
Tokyo, 107-0052, Japan
Tel.: (81) 332241785
Web Site: http://www.weathermap.co.jp
Weather Forecasting Services
N.A.I.C.S.: 541990

i-Chips Technology Inc. (1)
1-2-6 Shioe Amagasaki, Hyogo, 661-0976,
Japan
Tel.: (81) 664927277
Web Site: https://www.i-chips.co.jp
Semiconductor Devices Mfr
N.A.I.C.S.: 334413

Akihiro Yanai *(Pres)*

IMAGICAAWORLD ENTERTAINMENT LTD.
30/31 Sangdewadi Khopoli Pali Road,
Taluka-Khalapur, Khopoli, 410203,
Maharashtra, India
Tel.: (91) 2262552929
Web Site:
    https://www.imagicaaworld.com
IMAGICAA—(NSE)
Rev.: $6,342,090
Assets: $127,570,457
Liabilities: $211,954,456
Net Worth: ($84,384,000)
Earnings: ($36,669,592)
Emp.: 600
Fiscal Year-end: 03/31/21
Amusement Park Owner & Operator
N.A.I.C.S.: 713110
Manmohan Shetty *(Chm)*

IMAGIN MEDICAL INC.
Suite 600 890 West Pender Street,
Vancouver, V6C 1J9, BC, Canada BC
Web Site:
    https://www.imaginmedical.com
Year Founded: 1987
IMEXF—(OTCQB)
Rev.: $53,494
Assets: $1,908,947
Liabilities: $292,616
Net Worth: $1,616,332
Earnings: ($3,410,921)
Emp.: 4
Fiscal Year-end: 09/30/19
Investment Services
N.A.I.C.S.: 523999
James Hutchens *(Pres & CEO)*

IMAGINE LITHIUM INC.
1240-789 W Pender St, Vancouver,
V6C 1H2, BC, Canada
Tel.: (604) 683-3995 BC
Web Site: https://imaginelithium.com
Year Founded: 2004
A3DDVZ—(DEU)
Assets: $10,175,013
Liabilities: $198,534
Net Worth: $9,976,479
Earnings: ($389,476)
Fiscal Year-end: 01/31/22
Mining Company; Lithium Exploration
N.A.I.C.S.: 213114
John Parker Masters *(CFO & Sec)*

IMAGINEAR INC.
250 - 750 Pender St, Vancouver,
V6C 2T7, BC, Canada
Tel.: (818) 850-2490 BC
Web Site: https://imaginear.com
Year Founded: 2011
IPNFF—(OTCQB)
Rev.: $213,126
Assets: $3,386,377
Liabilities: $375,306
Net Worth: $3,011,072
Earnings: $4,775,859
Fiscal Year-end: 08/31/21
Motion Picture Production
N.A.I.C.S.: 512110
Alen Paul Silverrstieen *(Chm, Pres & CEO)*

IMAGINEER CO., LTD.
2-7-1 Nishi-Shinjuku Shinjuku Daiichi
Life Building 15th floor, Shinjuku-Ku,
Tokyo, Japan
Tel.: (81) 333438911
Web Site:
    https://www.imagineer.co.jp
Year Founded: 1977
4644—(TKS)
Rev.: $39,395,600
Assets: $88,911,110
Liabilities: $9,320,100

Net Worth: $79,591,010
Earnings: $2,749,760
Emp.: 128
Fiscal Year-end: 03/31/24
Software Development Services
N.A.I.C.S.: 513210
Kazunori Sumioka *(Pres & CEO)*

IMAGING DYNAMICS COMPANY LTD.
130 3510-29th Street NE, Calgary,
T1Y 7E5, AB, Canada
Tel.: (403) 251-9939
Web Site:
    https://www.imagingdynamics.com
Year Founded: 1995
IDL—(TSXV)
Rev.: $198,171
Assets: $322,663
Liabilities: $2,022,975
Net Worth: ($1,700,311)
Earnings: ($542,702)
Emp.: 13
Fiscal Year-end: 12/31/21
Medical Technology Services; Digital
Radiography Equipment Mfr
N.A.I.C.S.: 339112
Paul Lin *(CEO-Interim)*

Subsidiaries:

IDC USA, Inc. (1)
933 Western Dr, Indianapolis, IN 46242-
0428
Tel.: (317) 244-9200
Web Site: http://www.idc-usa.com
Industrial Equipment Mfr
N.A.I.C.S.: 333248
Todd T. Carroll *(VP)*

IMAGION BIOSYSTEMS LIMITED
Level 4 100 Albert Road, South Melbourne, 3205, VIC, Australia
Tel.: (61) 5052431058 AU
Web Site:
    https://www.imagionbiosystems.com
Year Founded: 1996
IBX—(ASX)
Rev.: $3,385,830
Assets: $3,123,939
Liabilities: $5,704,167
Net Worth: ($2,580,228)
Earnings: ($84,966,062)
Fiscal Year-end: 12/31/23
Medical Research & Development
Services
N.A.I.C.S.: 541713
Jovanka Naumoska *(Sec)*

IMAGIS CO., LTD.
3F-301 Gyeonggi R&DB Center 105
Gwanggyo-ro, Yeongtong-Gu, Suwon,
443-766, Gyeonggi-Do, Korea
(South)
Tel.: (82) 318885280
Web Site: https://imagis.co.kr
Year Founded: 2004
115610—(KRS)
Rev.: $16,810,398
Assets: $12,710,639
Liabilities: $4,647,934
Net Worth: $8,062,705
Earnings: $1,385,528
Emp.: 50
Fiscal Year-end: 12/31/22
Semiconductor Product Mfr
N.A.I.C.S.: 334413
Jeong-cheol Kim *(Pres & CEO)*

IMAGO GROUP
Ramon Marti Alsina 2 4 6, 08911,
Badalona, Spain
Tel.: (34) 933412100
Web Site:
    http://www.imagoscreens.com
Large LED Signs Mfr
N.A.I.C.S.: 339950

IMARKETING SOLUTIONS GROUP INC.

Juan Carlos Rovira *(Pres)*

Subsidiaries:

IMAGO North America (1)
240 Arlington Ave E, Saint Paul, MN 55117
Tel.: (651) 488-8600
Web Site: http://www.imagoscreens.com
Sales Range: $25-49.9 Million
Emp.: 50
Electronic Traffic Sign Mfr
N.A.I.C.S.: 339950
Jeff Nicholson *(Pres & CEO)*

IMAKO A.D.
Kralja Alfonsa Xiii 21, 78000, Banja
Luka, Bosnia & Herzegovina
Tel.: (387) 51224110
Year Founded: 1982
IMAK-RA—(BANJ)
Rev.: $335,306
Assets: $5,066,664
Liabilities: $695,616
Net Worth: $4,371,048
Earnings: $822
Emp.: 3
Fiscal Year-end: 12/31/12
Farm Product Whslr
N.A.I.C.S.: 424590
Ljubomir Klincov *(Chm-Mgmt Bd)*

IMAM BUTTON INDUSTRIES LTD.
Lilypond Center Level-F 16 3 RK Mission Road, Dhaka, 1203, Bangladesh
Tel.: (880) 1886343916
Web Site:
    https://www.imambutton.com
Year Founded: 1996
IMAMBUTTON—(DHA)
Sales Range: Less than $1 Million
Clothing Button Mfr
N.A.I.C.S.: 339993

IMAQLIQ SERVICE LTD.
Obvodny Canal 93 A, Saint Petersburg, 191119, Russia
Tel.: (7) 812 416 75 55
Web Site: http://www.imaqliq.com
Sales Range: $10-24.9 Million
Emp.: 30
Importer & Distributor of General
DataComm Products
N.A.I.C.S.: 517111

IMAREX ASA
Hieronymus Heyerdahls Gate 1,
0160, Oslo, Norway
Tel.: (47) 23 00 31 60
Web Site:
    http://www.imarexgroup.com
Sales Range: $100-124.9 Million
Emp.: 93
Derivatives Exchange Operator
N.A.I.C.S.: 523210
Christian Due *(Chm)*

Subsidiaries:

IMAREX, Inc. (1)
363 N Sam Houston Pkwy E, Houston, TX
77060
Tel.: (281) 445-5151
Sales Range: $50-74.9 Million
Emp.: 7
Derivatives Exchange Services
N.A.I.C.S.: 523210

IMARKETING SOLUTIONS GROUP INC.
8000 Jane Street Tower A Suite 401,
Concord, L4K 5B8, ON, Canada
Tel.: (416) 921-6595
Web Site:
    http://www.imarketingsolutions.com
Year Founded: 1998
IMR—(TSXV)
Sales Range: $75-99.9 Million

IMARKETING SOLUTIONS GROUP INC.

iMarketing Solutions Group Inc.—(Continued)
Fund-Raising, Membership Development & Special Events Services to Community & Non-Profit Service Organizations
N.A.I.C.S.: 561499
Andrew Langhorne (CEO)

Subsidiaries:

Xentel Inc. (1)
5159 S University Dr, Davie, FL 33328
Tel.: (954) 522-5200
Web Site: http://www.xentel.com
Sales Range: $25-49.9 Million
Emp.: 4
Telemarketers
N.A.I.C.S.: 561421
David A. Winograd (Pres)

IMARKETKOREA, INC.
16th Floor Samseong-dong Building
512 Samseong-ro, Gangnam-gu,
Seoul, Korea (South)
Tel.: (82) 237085678   KR
Web Site:
  https://www.imarketkorea.com
Year Founded: 2000
122900—(KRS)
Rev.: $2,752,129,992
Assets: $939,540,237
Liabilities: $624,936,768
Net Worth: $314,603,469
Earnings: $22,321,946
Emp.: 422
Fiscal Year-end: 12/31/22
Electronic Marketplace & Business Consulting Services
N.A.I.C.S.: 425120

Subsidiaries:

IMarketEurope Kft. (1)
Radnoti Miklos utca 9 fszt 2, 1137, Budapest, Hungary
Tel.: (36) 202889696
Web Site: https://www.imemall.u
Marketing Consulting Services
N.A.I.C.S.: 541613

IMASA S.A.
C/ Palacio Valdes 1 3, Asturias,
33002, Oviedo, Asturias, Spain
Tel.: (34) 985227366
Web Site: http://www.imasa.com
Sales Range: $25-49.9 Million
Emp.: 115
Heavy Construction & Engineering Services
N.A.I.C.S.: 237310

Subsidiaries:

Industrial Mecanica Agricola S. A. (1)
Edificio Malaga Modulo No A15 Plz Espana, PO Box 2658, Managua, Nicaragua   (100%)
Tel.: (505) 266 0489
Sales Range: $50-74.9 Million
Emp.: 6
Specialty Chemical Products Importer
N.A.I.C.S.: 424690

IMASEN ELECTRIC INDUSTRIAL CO., LTD.
1 Aza Kakihata, Aichi, Inuyama, 484-8507, Japan
Tel.: (81) 568671211
Web Site: https://www.imasen.co.jp
Year Founded: 1939
7266—(NGO)
Rev.: $658,936,056
Assets: $536,379,103
Liabilities: $197,634,566
Net Worth: $338,744,537
Earnings: ($66,072)
Emp.: 1,231
Fiscal Year-end: 03/31/24
Automobile Parts Mfr & Sls
N.A.I.C.S.: 336360

Takashi Adachi (Chm)

Subsidiaries:

CMICRO Corporation (1)
269-1 Hayashi-cho, Takamatsu, 761-0301, Kagawa, Japan
Tel.: (81) 878698310
Computer Peripheral Equipment Mfr
N.A.I.C.S.: 334118
Mitsuru Saiki (Mng Dir)

Gifu Tokoden Co., Ltd. (1)
1023 Ize Hachiya-cho, Minokamo, 505-0005, Gifu, Japan
Tel.: (81) 574257906
Cable Mfr & Distr
N.A.I.C.S.: 331491

Guangzhou Imasen Electric Industrial Co., Ltd. (1)
Huaqiao Science & Technology Industrial Park Huashan Town, Huadu, Guangzhou, Guangdong, China
Tel.: (86) 2086946883
Automobile Parts Mfr & Distr
N.A.I.C.S.: 336360

Imasen Bucyrus Technology Inc. (1)
260 Crossroads Blvd, Bucyrus, OH 44820
Tel.: (419) 563-9590
Automobile Parts Mfr & Distr
N.A.I.C.S.: 336360

Imasen Electric & Machinery Co., Ltd. (1)
10F-6 No 33 Sec2 Chen Kuo N Road, Taipei, Taiwan
Tel.: (886) 2 25079251
Automobile Parts Mfr & Distr
N.A.I.C.S.: 336360

Imasen Engineering Corporation (1)
3-1-8 Techno Plaza, Kakamigahara, 509-0109, Gifu, Japan
Tel.: (81) 583792714
Web Site: https://www.imasengiken.co.jp
Emp.: 41
Electrical Equipment Mfr & Distr
N.A.I.C.S.: 335999

Imasen Manufacturing (Thailand) Co., Ltd. (1)
Hi-Tech Industrial Estate Bang Pa-In, Ayutthaya, 13160, Thailand
Tel.: (66) 3 531 4245
Automobile Parts Mfr & Distr
N.A.I.C.S.: 336360

Imasen Philippine Manufacturing Corporation (1)
101 East Main Ave Laguna Technopark, Binan, Laguna, Philippines
Tel.: (63) 495411480
Automobile Parts Mfr & Distr
N.A.I.C.S.: 336360

Toyo Koku Denshi Co., Ltd. (1)
63-1 Kakibata, Inuyama, 484-0901, Aichi, Japan
Tel.: (81) 568672160
Web Site: https://tokoden.co.jp
Emp.: 152
Cable Mfr
N.A.I.C.S.: 331491

IMASPRO CORPORATION BERHAD
Unit 30-01 Level 30 Tower A Vertical Business Suite Avenue 3, Bangsar South No 8 Jalan Kerinchi, 59200, Kuala Lumpur, Malaysia
Tel.: (60) 327839191
Web Site: https://www.imaspro.com
IMASPRO—(KLS)
Rev.: $10,611,850
Assets: $29,212,511
Liabilities: $2,744,435
Net Worth: $26,468,076
Earnings: $328,987
Fiscal Year-end: 06/30/23
Pesticides & Agrochemicals Mfr
N.A.I.C.S.: 325320
Chin Hen Tong (Mng Dir)

Subsidiaries:

Imaspro Resources Sdn. Bhd. (1)
37 Jalan Batai Laut 5 Kawasan 16 Taman Intan, 41300, Kelang, Selangor, Malaysia
Tel.: (60) 333431633
Sales Range: $50-74.9 Million
Emp.: 80
Agrochemicals Mfr & Distr
N.A.I.C.S.: 424910
Chin Hen Tong (Gen Mgr)

Mosfly International Sdn. Bhd. (1)
33 Jalan 5 Kawasan 16 Taman Intan, 41300, Klang, Selangor, Malaysia
Tel.: (60) 333431633
Web Site: https://www.mosfly.com.my
Insecticides Mfr
N.A.I.C.S.: 325320

IMAX CORPORATION
2525 Speakman Dr, Mississauga, L5K 1B1, ON, Canada
Tel.: (905) 403-6500   Ca
Web Site: https://www.imax.com
Year Founded: 1967
IMAX—(NYSE)
Rev.: $300,805,000
Assets: $821,154,000
Liabilities: $492,108,000
Net Worth: $329,046,000
Earnings: ($22,800,000)
Emp.: 779
Fiscal Year-end: 12/31/22
Designer, Mfr, Retailer & Lessor of Large Format Motion Picture Projection Systems, Film & Equipment
N.A.I.C.S.: 333310
Robert D. Lister (Chief Legal Officer & Sr Exec VP)

Subsidiaries:

David Keighley Productions 70MM Inc. (1)
12582 Millennium, Los Angeles, CA 90094   (100%)
Tel.: (310) 255-5537
Sales Range: $25-49.9 Million
Emp.: 120
Provider of Motion Picture Services
N.A.I.C.S.: 512199
David Keighley (Pres)

IMAX (Shanghai) Multimedia Technology Co., Ltd. (1)
7F Verdant Place No 128 West Nanjing Rd, Huangpu District, Shanghai, 200003, China
Tel.: (86) 2123157000
Web Site: http://www.imax.cn
Movie Theatre Operator
N.A.I.C.S.: 512131

IMAX China Holding, Inc. (1)
7F Verdant Place 128 West Nanjing Road, Huangpu, Shanghai, 200003, China   (71.63%)
Tel.: (86) 2123157000
Web Site: http://www.imax.cn
Rev.: $73,330,000
Assets: $326,403,000
Liabilities: $93,331,000
Net Worth: $233,072,000
Earnings: $10,758,000
Emp.: 99
Fiscal Year-end: 12/31/2022
Holding Company
N.A.I.C.S.: 551112
Edwin Tan (CEO)

IMAX VR, LLC (1)
157 S Fairfax, Los Angeles, CA 90036
Tel.: (323) 452-4081
Web Site: http://imaxvr.imax.com
Photographic Equipment Mfr
N.A.I.C.S.: 333310

IMAXSHIFT, LLC (1)
127 Plymouth St, Brooklyn, NY 11201
Tel.: (718) 858-1200
Web Site: http://www.imaxshift.com
Physical Fitness Studio Operator
N.A.I.C.S.: 713940

Imax Corporation (1)
2111 Pkwy Ofc Cir, Birmingham, AL 35244   (100%)
Tel.: (205) 733-0500
Mfr of Motion Picture Theater Equipment & Parts

INTERNATIONAL PUBLIC

N.A.I.C.S.: 621999

IMBC CO., LTD.
10F MBC Media Center 255 Seongam-ro, Mapo-gu, Seoul, Korea (South)
Tel.: (82) 221051100
Web Site: http://www.imbc.com
Year Founded: 2000
052220—(KRS)
Rev.: $36,401,942
Assets: $53,762,168
Liabilities: $9,450,390
Net Worth: $44,311,778
Earnings: $1,280,424
Emp.: 99
Fiscal Year-end: 12/31/22
Television Broadcasting Services
N.A.I.C.S.: 516120

IMC
119 Lobanovsky Valeriya Avenue, DemievSky Business Center, 3039, Kiev, Ukraine
Tel.: (380) 674474551   LU
Web Site:
  https://www.imcagro.com.ua
IMC—(WAR)
Rev.: $114,034,000
Assets: $326,499,000
Liabilities: $176,184,000
Net Worth: $150,315,000
Earnings: ($1,121,000)
Emp.: 1,680
Fiscal Year-end: 12/31/22
Milk, Corn, Wheat, Sunflower, Soybean & Potatoes Producer
N.A.I.C.S.: 112120
Oleksandr Petrov (Chm)

IMC EXPLORATION GROUP PLC
70 Ballybough Road, Ballybough, Dublin, 3, Ireland
Tel.: (353) 872819215
Web Site:
  https://www.imcexploration.com
IMC—(LSE)
Assets: $810,814
Liabilities: $1,032,318
Net Worth: ($221,504)
Earnings: ($350,655)
Fiscal Year-end: 06/30/23
Rail Freight Services
N.A.I.C.S.: 488210
Eamon O'Brien (Chm)

IMC INTERNATIONAL MARKETMAKERS COMBINATION B.V.
Amstelveenseweg 500, 1081 KL, Amsterdam, Netherlands
Tel.: (31) 207988400   NI
Web Site: http://www.imc.nl
Year Founded: 1989
Emp.: 1,000
Holding Company; Market-Making & Alternative Investment Management Services
N.A.I.C.S.: 551112
Rob Defares (Co-CEO & Member-Mgmt Bd)

Subsidiaries:

IMC Asset Management B.V. (1)
WTC D-Tower 11th Floor Strawinskylaan 361, 1077 XX, Amsterdam, Netherlands
Tel.: (31) 20 305 0600
Web Site: http://www.imc.nl
Emp.: 120
Alternative Investment Management Services
N.A.I.C.S.: 523940
Ingeborg Schepers (COO)

IMC Trading B.V. (1)
WTC D-Tower 3rd Floor Strawinskylaan 377, 1077 XX, Amsterdam, Netherlands

AND PRIVATE COMPANIES

Tel.: (31) 20 798 8400
Web Site: http://www.imc.nl
Emp.: 150
Securities & Commodities Dealing Services
N.A.I.C.S.: 522320
Rob Defares (Co-CEO)

IMC PAN ASIA ALLIANCE PTE. LTD.
9 Temasek Boulevard 06-02A Suntec Tower Two, Singapore, 038989, Singapore
Tel.: (65) 63362233   SG
Web Site: http://www.imcgroup.info
Sales Range: $1-4.9 Billion
Emp.: 9,000
Holding Company
N.A.I.C.S.: 551112
Frank Wen King Tsao (Founder & Sr Chm)

Subsidiaries:

Aurora Tankers USA Inc.   (1)
6060 Richmond Ave Ste 260, Houston, TX 77057
Tel.: (713) 789-2402
Freight Forwarding & Shipping Services
N.A.I.C.S.: 488510

IMC Industrial Pte. Ltd.   (1)
5 Temasek Boulevard 12-01 Suntec City Tower Five, Singapore, 038985, Singapore
Tel.: (65) 63362233
Web Site: http://www.imcgroup.info
Holding Company; Shipping, Logistics & Marine Engineering Services
N.A.I.C.S.: 551112
Tai Sook Yee (Exec Dir-AITIA Institute)

IMC Investments Pte. Ltd.   (1)
7 Temasek Boulevard Level 37 Suntec Tower One, Singapore, 038987, Singapore
Tel.: (65) 6411 9800
Web Site: http://www.imcgroup.info
Direct Investment & Fund Management Services
N.A.I.C.S.: 523999
Michael Chye (Mng Dir)

IMC Resources (Australia) Pty Ltd   (1)
Citibank House Level 2 37 St Georges Terrace, Perth, 6000, WA, Australia
Tel.: (61) 894228800
Coal Mining Services
N.A.I.C.S.: 213113

IMC Resources (China) Ltd   (1)
1705-08 17th Floor St Georges Building 2 Ice House Street, Central, China (Hong Kong)
Tel.: (852) 28201100
Coal Mining Services
N.A.I.C.S.: 213113

IMC Shipping (China) Company Limited   (1)
8/F A Mansion 291 Fu Min Road, Xuhui, Shanghai, 200031, China
Tel.: (86) 2161711888
Freight Forwarding & Shipping Services
N.A.I.C.S.: 488510
Bingchen Liu (Project Mgr)

IMC Shipping Services Co. Pte. Ltd.   (1)
100 Beach Road 21-06 Shaw Tower, Singapore, 189702, Singapore
Tel.: (65) 65172400
Freight Forwarding & Shipping Services
N.A.I.C.S.: 488510

MSI International (Thailand) Ltd.   (1)
Vanissa Building 5th floor Suite 5A-1 29 Soi Chidlom, Ploenchit Road Lumping Pathum Wan, Bangkok, 10330, Thailand
Tel.: (66) 265039656
Ship Management Services
N.A.I.C.S.: 488510

MSI Ship Management (Qingdao) Co. Ltd.   (1)
Room 2101 Sunshine Tower 61 Central Hong Kong Road, Qingdao, 266071, China
Tel.: (86) 53266773966
Ship Management Services
N.A.I.C.S.: 488510

MSI Ship Management Pte. Ltd.   (1)
2/F T M Kalaw Centre 667A T M Kalaw Avenue, Ermita, Manila, 1000, Philippines
Tel.: (63) 25361108
Ship Management Services
N.A.I.C.S.: 488510

PT. Pelita Samudera Shipping   (1)
Menara Citicon 19th Floor Jl Letjen S Parman Kav 72, Jakarta, 11410, Indonesia
Tel.: (62) 2129308801
Web Site: http://www.ptpss.co.id
Freight Forwarding & Logistics Consulting Services
N.A.I.C.S.: 488510
Iskhandar Shah Mohamed (Head-Ops)

United Thai Shipping Corp Limited   (1)
498/1 Taiban Road Tambon Paknam, Mueang Samut Prakan, Samut Prakan, 10270, Thailand
Tel.: (66) 27556888
Ship Management Services
N.A.I.C.S.: 488510
Amornrat Su-Archawarat (Mgr-Corp Plng & Risk Mgmt)

Unithai Shipyard and Engineering Limited   (1)
48 Moo 3 Tambon Tungsukhla, Si Racha, 20230, Chonburi, Thailand
Tel.: (66) 38407000
Ship Management Services
N.A.I.C.S.: 488510

IMCAP PARTNERS AG
Lavaterstrasse 45, 8002, Zurich, Switzerland
Tel.: (41) 76 323 7558   CH
Web Site: http://www.imcap-partners.com
Private Equity Firm
N.A.I.C.S.: 523999
Leif Lupp (Mng Partner)

Subsidiaries:

Sematell GmbH   (1)
Neugrabenweg 1, 66123, Saarbrucken, Germany
Tel.: (49) 681 857 670
Web Site: http://www.sematell.com
Emp.: 40
Business Intelligence & Customer Interaction Management Software & Services
N.A.I.C.S.: 513210
Thomas Dreikasus (CEO)

IMCD N.V.
Wilhelminaplein 32, 3072 DE, Rotterdam, Netherlands
Tel.: (31) 102908684   NI
Web Site: https://www.imcdgroup.com
Year Founded: 2001
IMCD—(EUR)
Rev.: $4,219,311,460
Assets: $4,017,030,158
Liabilities: $2,222,136,721
Net Worth: $1,794,893,437
Earnings: $254,535,545
Emp.: 3,740
Fiscal Year-end: 12/31/21
Holding Company; Specialty Chemicals, Food & Pharmaceutical Ingredients Mfr, Marketer, Whslr & Distr
N.A.I.C.S.: 551112
Piet Van Der Slikke (CEO & Member-Mgmt Bd)

Subsidiaries:

Andes Chemical Corporation   (1)
11125 NW 29 St, Miami, FL 33172
Tel.: (305) 591-5601
Web Site: https://andeschem.com
Petrochemical Mfr
N.A.I.C.S.: 325110
Cristina Espinosa (Sec)

DCS Pharma AG   (1)
Immengasse 9, 4001, Basel, Switzerland
Tel.: (41) 417660490
Web Site: http://www.dcspharma.com

Pharmaceuticals Distr
N.A.I.C.S.: 424210

Gopharma S.r.l.   (1)
Via Carlo Alberto Dalla Chiesa 3, 20068, Peschiera Borromeo, Italy
Tel.: (39) 0255305855
Web Site: http://gopharma-srl.lookchem.com
Pharmaceuticals Distr
N.A.I.C.S.: 424210

IMCD Brasil Comercio e Industria de Produtos Quimicos Ltda.   (1)
Rua Arquiteto Olavo Redig de Campos 105 25th Floor, Edificio EZ Towers - Torre B Chacara Santo Antonio 04711-905, Sao Paulo, 04711-130, Brazil
Tel.: (55) 1143606400
Specialty Chemicals Distr
N.A.I.C.S.: 424690
Nicolas Kaufmann (Mng Dir)

IMCD Canada Limited   (1)
99 Summerlea Road, Brampton, L6T 4V2, ON, Canada
Specialty Chemicals Distr
N.A.I.C.S.: 424690
Mike Staley (Mng Dir)

IMCD Egypt LLC   (1)
Business Park 13C01 Business Capital C01 Ground Floor, Cairo Festival City, New Cairo, Egypt
Tel.: (20) 261115630
Specialty Chemicals Distr
N.A.I.C.S.: 424690
Rafik Adel (Mng Dir)

IMCD Group B.V.   (1)
Wilhelminaplein 32, 3072 DE, Rotterdam, Netherlands
Tel.: (31) 102908684
Web Site: https://www.imcdgroup.com
Emp.: 800
Holding Company
N.A.I.C.S.: 551112

Subsidiary (Non-US):

IMCD (Shanghai) Trading Co. Ltd.   (2)
2505 K Wah Centre 1010 Huai Hai Road M, Shanghai, 200031, China
Tel.: (86) 21 5403 3300
Logistics Management Consulting Services
N.A.I.C.S.: 541614
Eugen Rothermel (Country Mgr)

IMCD (Thailand) Co., Ltd.   (2)
1858/99-100 Interlink Tower 22nd floor Debaratna Rd, Bangna Tai Bangna, Bangkok, 10260, Thailand
Tel.: (66) 20268929
Sales Range: $25-49.9 Million
Emp.: 6
Chemical Products Distr
N.A.I.C.S.: 424690

IMCD Algeria   (2)
Bureau de Liaison 5 rue du Bassin, El-Achour, Algiers, 16140, Algeria
Tel.: (213) 551 6398 04
Logistics Management Consulting Services
N.A.I.C.S.: 541614

IMCD Asia Pte. Ltd.   (2)
Orchard Gateway Emerald 218 Orchard Road 06-01/02, Singapore, 238851, Singapore
Tel.: (65) 69705782
Sales Range: $25-49.9 Million
Emp.: 3
Food Ingredient Distr
N.A.I.C.S.: 424490

IMCD Australia Limited   (2)
Level 1 352 Wellington Road, PO Box 689, Mulgrave, 3170, VIC, Australia
Tel.: (61) 38 544 3100
Web Site: http://www.imcd.com.au
Sales Range: $25-49.9 Million
Emp.: 45
Specialty Chemicals & Food Ingredients Marketing, Sales & Distribution Services
N.A.I.C.S.: 424690

IMCD Baltics UAB   (2)
Ukmerges g 120-1, 08105, Vilnius, Lithuania
Tel.: (370) 52363660
Web Site: https://www.imcdgroup.com

Sales Range: $25-49.9 Million
Emp.: 5
Food Ingredient Distr
N.A.I.C.S.: 424690

Subsidiary (Domestic):

IMCD Benelux B.V.   (2)
Wilhelminaplein 32, 3072 DE, Rotterdam, Netherlands
Tel.: (31) 882918600
Web Site: https://www.imcd.nl
Sales Range: $25-49.9 Million
Emp.: 150
Specialty Chemicals, Food & Pharmaceutical Ingredients Marketing, Sales & Distribution Services
N.A.I.C.S.: 424690

Branch (Domestic):

IMCD Benelux BV   (3)
Dali building 1st floor Herikerbergweg 240, 1101 CT, Amsterdam, Netherlands
Tel.: (31) 882918600
Web Site: http://www.jandekker.com
Sales Range: $10-24.9 Million
Emp.: 45
Food Ingredients Supplier
N.A.I.C.S.: 311999

Subsidiary (Non-US):

IMCD Benelux N.V.   (2)
Zenith Business Park Zandvoortstraat 49, Blarenberglaan 21, 2800, Mechelen, Belgium
Tel.: (32) 15294950
Web Site: https://www.imcdgroup.com
Sales Range: $25-49.9 Million
Emp.: 43
Specialty Chemicals, Food & Pharmaceutical Ingredients Marketing, Sales & Distribution Services
N.A.I.C.S.: 424690
Wim de Coster (Mng Dir)

IMCD Czech Republic a.s.   (2)
Belohorska 260/39, 169 00, Prague, Czech Republic
Tel.: (420) 23 331 1736
Web Site: http://www.imcd.cz
Specialty Chemicals & Food Ingredients Marketing, Sales & Distribution Services
N.A.I.C.S.: 424690

IMCD Deutschland GmbH & Co. KG   (2)
Konrad-Adenauer-Ufer 41-45, 50668, Cologne, Germany
Tel.: (49) 22177650
Web Site: https://www.imcd.de
Sales Range: $25-49.9 Million
Emp.: 270
Specialty Chemicals & Food Ingredients Marketing, Sales & Distribution Services
N.A.I.C.S.: 424690
Ulla Sterlau (Asst Mgr-HR)

IMCD Espana especialidades Quimicas, S.A.   (2)
Carrer del Marroc 33 Planta 11, 08018, Barcelona, Spain
Tel.: (34) 932413858
Web Site: https://www.imcd.es
Sales Range: $25-49.9 Million
Emp.: 100
Specialty Chemicals & Food Ingredients Marketing, Sales & Distribution Services
N.A.I.C.S.: 424690
Jose R. Alcover (Country Mgr)

Subsidiary (Non-US):

IMCD Maroc S.A.R.L.   (3)
Lotissement no 67, BP 4041, Zone Industrielle Sud Ouest, Mohammedia, Morocco
Tel.: (212) 2 331 6267
Web Site: http://www.imcd.ma
Sales Range: $25-49.9 Million
Emp.: 10
Specialty Chemicals & Food Ingredients Marketing, Sales & Distribution Services
N.A.I.C.S.: 424690

IMCD Portugal Produtos Quimicos, Lda.   (3)
Via Lidador - Church 210 2nd Floor - Room 8, Vila Nova da Telha, 4470-411, Maia, Portugal

IMCD N.V.

INTERNATIONAL PUBLIC

IMCD N.V.—(Continued)
Tel.: (351) 229410684
Web Site: http://www.imcd.pt
Sales Range: $25-49.9 Million
Emp.: 12
Specialty Chemicals & Food Ingredients Marketing, Sales & Distribution Services
N.A.I.C.S.: 424690

Subsidiary (Non-US):

IMCD France S.A.S. (2)
266 avenue du President Wilson, 93457, La Plaine Saint-Denis, Cedex, France
Tel.: (33) 149333131
Web Site: http://www.imcdgroup.com
Emp.: 200
Specialty Chemicals & Food Ingredients Marketing, Sales & Distribution Services
N.A.I.C.S.: 424690

IMCD India (2)
24th The Ruby 29 Senapati Bapat Marg, Dadar West, Mumbai, 400028, India
Tel.: (91) 2261460900
Web Site: http://www.imcd.in
Sales Range: $25-49.9 Million
Emp.: 35
Food Ingredient Distr
N.A.I.C.S.: 424490

IMCD Ireland Ltd (2)
Office 109a-Unit 3013 Lake Drive CityWest Business Campus, Dublin, 24, Ireland
Tel.: (353) 14693153
Logistics Management Consulting Services
N.A.I.C.S.: 541614
Paul Hanbury *(Country Mgr)*

IMCD Italia S.p.A. (2)
Centro Leoni-Edificio A Via Giovanni Spadolini 5, 20141, Milan, Italy
Tel.: (39) 02557091
Sales Range: $50-74.9 Million
Emp.: 50
Specialty Chemicals, Food & Pharmaceutical Ingredients Marketing, Sales & Distribution Services
N.A.I.C.S.: 424690
Gabriele Bonomi *(Country Mgr)*

IMCD Malaysia Sdn Bhd (2)
B-28-1, The Ascent Paradigm No 1 Jalan SS 7/26A, Kelana Jaya, 47301, Petaling Jaya, Selangor Darul Ehsan, Malaysia
Tel.: (60) 327156200
Web Site: http://www.imcd.com.my
Sales Range: $25-49.9 Million
Emp.: 20
Personal Care Product Distr
N.A.I.C.S.: 424210
Eng Hoi Koh *(Mng Dir)*

IMCD New Zealand Ltd. (2)
Ground Floor 459 Great South Road, Penrose, Auckland, 1061, New Zealand
Tel.: (64) 95820250
Web Site: https://www.imcdgroup.com
Sales Range: $25-49.9 Million
Emp.: 12
Food Ingredient Distr
N.A.I.C.S.: 424490

IMCD Polska SP. Z.o.o. (2)
Ul Domaniewska 32, 02-672, Warsaw, Poland
Tel.: (48) 222236700
Sales Range: $25-49.9 Million
Emp.: 50
Industrial Chemicals Mfr
N.A.I.C.S.: 325998

IMCD South Africa (Pty) Ltd (2)
275 Oak Avenue, PO Box 1378, Bassonia, Randburg, 2125, South Africa
Tel.: (27) 115704260
Web Site: http://www.imcd.co.za
Sales Range: $25-49.9 Million
Emp.: 100
Specialty Chemicals & Food Ingredients Marketing, Sales & Distribution Services
N.A.I.C.S.: 424690

IMCD South East Europe GmbH (2)
Wienerbergstrasse 11/Turm B/17 OG, 1100, Vienna, Austria
Tel.: (43) 18651202
Web Site: http://www.imcd.at
Specialty Chemicals, Food & Pharmaceutical Ingredients Marketing, Sales & Distribution Services

N.A.I.C.S.: 424690

IMCD Sweden AB (2)
Hyllie Boulevard 53, 215 37, Malmo, Sweden
Tel.: (46) 40167500
Web Site: https://www.imcd.se
Sales Range: $150-199.9 Million
Emp.: 110
Specialty Chemicals, Food & Pharmaceutical Ingredients Marketing, Sales & Distribution Services
N.A.I.C.S.: 424690
Sami Valkama *(Country Mgr)*

Subsidiary (Non-US):

IMCD Danmark A/S (3)
Sturups Plads 1 Plan 6, 3000, Helsingor, Denmark
Tel.: (45) 49250580
Web Site: https://www.imcd.dk
Sales Range: $25-49.9 Million
Emp.: 10
Specialty Chemicals & Food Ingredients Marketing, Sales & Distribution Services
N.A.I.C.S.: 424690

IMCD Finland Oy (3)
Keilaranta 15, 02150, Espoo, Finland
Tel.: (358) 92515160
Web Site: https://www.imcd.fi
Sales Range: $25-49.9 Million
Emp.: 9
Specialty Chemicals & Food Ingredients Marketing, Sales & Distribution Services
N.A.I.C.S.: 424690

IMCD Norway AS (3)
Innspurten 1b, PO Box 3437, Bjolsen, 0663, Oslo, Norway
Tel.: (47) 23005200
Web Site: https://www.imcd.no
Sales Range: $25-49.9 Million
Emp.: 30
Specialty Chemicals, Food & Pharmaceutical Ingredients Marketing, Sales & Distribution Services
N.A.I.C.S.: 424690

Subsidiary (Non-US):

IMCD Switzerland AG (2)
Hufgasse 10, CH-8008, Zurich, Switzerland
Tel.: (41) 432448000
Food Ingredient Distr
N.A.I.C.S.: 424490

IMCD TiCARET PAZARLAMA VE DANISMANLIK LiMiTED SiRKETi (2)
Icerenkoy Mah Umut Sk Quick Tower No 10-12 Kat 20/85, Atasehir, 34752, Istanbul, Turkiye
Tel.: (90) 2164254800
Web Site: https://www.imcd.com.tr
Food Ingredient Distr
N.A.I.C.S.: 424490

IMCD UK Ltd. (2)
5th Floor Times House Throwley Way, Sutton, SM1 4AF, Surrey, United Kingdom
Tel.: (44) 2087707090
Web Site: https://www.imcd.co.uk
Sales Range: $25-49.9 Million
Emp.: 80
Specialty Chemicals, Food & Pharmaceutical Ingredients Marketing, Sales & Distribution Services
N.A.I.C.S.: 424690

Subsidiary (US):

IMCD US (2)
14725 Detroit Ave Ste 300, Lakewood, OH 44107-4124
Tel.: (216) 228-8900
Web Site: http://www.imcdgroup.com
Emp.: 90
Specialty Chemicals Distr
N.A.I.C.S.: 424690
John Mastrantoni *(Country Mgr)*

Subsidiary (Non-US):

Indchem International
A-Wing 3rd Floor 3/20 3/6 Tardeo AC Market Bldg Tardeo, Mumbai, 400034, Maharashtra, India
Tel.: (91) 222 351 0937

Web Site: https://www.indcheminternational.com
Emp.: 5
Pharmaceutical Preparation Mfr & Distr
N.A.I.C.S.: 325412

PT Alam Subur Tirta Kencana (2)
Jalan Daan Mogot KM 12, Jakarta, 11740, Indonesia
Tel.: (62) 21 619 2265
Food Ingredients & Beverage Distr
N.A.I.C.S.: 424420

PT IMCD Indonesia (2)
Blugreen-Boutique Office Tower C-D, 3rd Floor Jl Lingkar Luar Barat Kav 88, Jakarta, 11740, Puri Kembangan, Indonesia
Tel.: (62) 2129527355
Food Ingredient Distr
N.A.I.C.S.: 424490

IMCD Kenya Ltd. (1)
C S House Old Mombasa Road, PO Box 61639, City Square, 00200, Nairobi, Kenya
Tel.: (254) 200612310189
Specialty Chemicals Distr
N.A.I.C.S.: 424690
Ryan Harrison *(Country Mgr)*

IMCD Mexico S.A. de C.V. (1)
Mariano Escobedo 476 Piso 17 Oficina 1701 Anzures, Miguel Hidalgo, 11590, Mexico, Mexico
Tel.: (52) 5552033722
Specialty Chemicals Distr
N.A.I.C.S.: 424690
Miguel Ruisenor *(Mng Dir)*

IMCD Middle East ZFCO (1)
Jafza One BCW Office 1183 Jebel Ali Free Zone, Dubai, United Arab Emirates
Tel.: (971) 48170245
Specialty Chemicals Distr
N.A.I.C.S.: 424690
Manuel Baumann *(Mng Dir)*

IMCD Philippines Corporation (1)
9th Floor Wilcon IT Hub 2251 Chino Roces Ave, Makati, 1231, Philippines
Tel.: (63) 288930789
Specialty Chemicals Distr
N.A.I.C.S.: 424690
Nancy C. Soyangco *(Mng Dir)*

IMCD Plastics (Shanghai) Co., Ltd. (1)
Unit 2301 K Wah Centre 1010 Huaihai Road, Shanghai, 200031, China
Tel.: (86) 2154033300
Specialty Chemicals Distr
N.A.I.C.S.: 424690
Andreas Igerl *(Mng Dir)*

IMCD Rus LLC (1)
Professora Popova st 37 lit Shch Office 512, 197022, Saint Petersburg, Russia
Tel.: (7) 8123329241
Specialty Chemicals Distr
N.A.I.C.S.: 424690
Johann Milchram *(Mng Dir)*

IMCD Singapore Pte. Ltd. (1)
218 Orchard Road 06-01/02, Singapore, 238851, Singapore
Tel.: (65) 69705782
Specialty Chemicals Distr
N.A.I.C.S.: 424690
Eugen Rothermel *(Mng Dir)*

IMCD Tunisia S.a.r.l. (1)
40 Rue Jerissa Zone industrielle Saint Gobain, 2014, Megrine, Tunisia
Tel.: (216) 71433611
Specialty Chemicals Distr
N.A.I.C.S.: 424690
Jose Alcover *(Mng Dir)*

IMCD Ukraine LLC (1)
Shovkovychna 42-44 str 3 floor, 01004, Kiev, Ukraine
Tel.: (380) 444901212
Specialty Chemicals Distr
N.A.I.C.S.: 424690
Johann Milchram *(Mng Dir)*

IMCD Vietnam Company Ltd. (1)
Unit 12-01 12th Floor Pearl 5 Tower No 5 Le Quy Don Street, Vo Thi Sau Ward District 3, Ho Chi Minh City, Vietnam
Tel.: (84) 2873002537
Specialty Chemicals Distr

N.A.I.C.S.: 424690
Nguyen Thi Minh Tram *(Country Mgr)*

Nutri Granulations, Inc. (1)
16024 Phoebe Ave, La Mirada, CA 90638
Tel.: (714) 994-7855
Web Site: http://www.nutrigranulations.com
Rev: $6,666,666
Emp.: 18
Pharmaceutical Preparation Mfr
N.A.I.C.S.: 325412
Mike Garcia *(Mgr-Production)*

Oy Kokko-Fiber AB (1)
Kosilankatu 3, 67100, Kokkola, Finland
Tel.: (358) 68311709
Web Site: http://www.kokko-fiber.fi
Fiber Reinforced Plastic Distr
N.A.I.C.S.: 424610
Stefan Brannkarr *(Bus Mgr)*

Signet Excipients Private Ltd. (1)
A-801 Crescenzo C/38-39 G Block Bandra Kurla Complex, Mumbai, 400051, Maharashtra, India (100%)
Tel.: (91) 2261462725
Web Site: https://www.signetexcipients.com
Pharmaceuticals Distr
N.A.I.C.S.: 424210
Sung Park *(CEO)*

VELOX GmbH
Brandstwiete 1, 20457, Hamburg, Germany
Tel.: (49) 40 369 688 0
Web Site: http://www.velox.com
Plastic & Rubber Raw Material Mfr
N.A.I.C.S.: 326299
Bernard Goursaud *(Co-Founder & Mng Dir)*

Subsidiary (Non-US):

VELOX CMS s.r.o (2)
Belohorska 39, 169 00, Prague, Czech Republic
Tel.: (420) 233311736
Chemical Products Distr
N.A.I.C.S.: 424690

Subsidiary (Domestic):

VELOX Composites GmbH i.G. (2)
An den Kolonaten 11, 26160, Bad Zwischenahn, Germany
Tel.: (49) 44869388648
Chemical Products Distr
N.A.I.C.S.: 424690

Subsidiary (Non-US):

VELOX Dis Tic.Ltd.Sti. (2)
19 Mayis Mahallesi Ataturk Caddesi Yamac Sokak Seref Yazgan Is Merkezi, No 1 Kat 3 Daire 11 Kadikoy, 34736, Istanbul, Turkiye
Tel.: (90) 2163492445
Chemical Products Distr
N.A.I.C.S.: 424690

VELOX FRANCE S.A.S. (2)
70 Rue d'Hautpoul, 75019, Paris, France
Tel.: (33) 180058850
Chemical Products Distr
N.A.I.C.S.: 424690

VELOX Italia S.r.l. (2)
Via B Luini 2, 21100, Varese, Italy
Tel.: (39) 0332238744
Chemical Products Distr
N.A.I.C.S.: 424690

VELOX Oy (2)
Porkkalankatu 7 A, 00180, Helsinki, Finland
Tel.: (358) 405201179
Chemical Products Distr
N.A.I.C.S.: 424690

VELOX Poland Sp. z o.o. (2)
Ul Trojpole 7, 61-693, Poznan, Poland
Tel.: (48) 616610435
Chemical Products Distr
N.A.I.C.S.: 424690

VELOX Specialities AB (2)
Aminogatan 34, 431 53, Molndal, Sweden
Tel.: (46) 317464440
Chemical Products Distr
N.A.I.C.S.: 424690

VELOX Specialities AB (2)
Storengveien 8, 1358, Baerum, Norway
Tel.: (47) 67102200
Chemical Products Distr
N.A.I.C.S.: 424690

AND PRIVATE COMPANIES

VELOX Trading S.L.U. (2)
Edificio Forum SCV Ctra De Sant Cugat a Rubi Km 1 n 40-50 Oficina 6 2a, Sant Cugat del Valles, 8173, Barcelona, Spain
Tel.: (34) 935901178
Chemical Products Distr
N.A.I.C.S.: 424690

VELOX U.K. Ltd (2)
57 London Road GB, High Wycombe, HP11 1BS, Buckinghamshire, United Kingdom
Tel.: (44) 1442825455
Chemical Products Distr
N.A.I.C.S.: 424690

Whawon Pharm Co., Ltd. (1)
3rd Floor Dae-kwan Bldg Yangjae-dong 190, Gangnam-daero Seocho-gu, Seoul, Korea (South)
Tel.: (82) 25731858
Web Site: http://www.whawon.co.kr
Pharmaceuticals Distr
N.A.I.C.S.: 424210

IMCO INDUSTRIES LTD.
8 Hata'Asiya St, Nesher, Israel
Tel.: (972) 48213322
Web Site: https://www.imco-ind.com
IMCO—(TAE)
Rev.: $72,207,581
Assets: $62,253,132
Liabilities: $36,284,095
Net Worth: $25,969,036
Earnings: $1,682,392
Fiscal Year-end: 06/30/23
Military Equipment Mfr
N.A.I.C.S.: 336992
Yermiahu Koren *(Chm)*

Subsidiaries:

Nir-Or Israel Ltd. (1)
13 Amal Street Afek Industrial Park, Rosh Ha'Ayin, Israel
Tel.: (972) 39155222
Web Site: https://www.nir-or.com
Electronic Equipment & Systems Mfr
N.A.I.C.S.: 336320

IMD INTERNATIONAL
23 Chemin de Bellerive, PO Box 915, 1001, Lausanne, Switzerland
Tel.: (41) 216180111
Web Site: http://www.imd.ch
Year Founded: 1946
Sales Range: $25-49.9 Million
Emp.: 300
Business Education Services
N.A.I.C.S.: 611410
Vito Angelillo *(Gen Dir)*

IMDEX LIMITED
216 Balcatta Road, Balcatta, 6021, WA, Australia
Tel.: (61) 894454010 AU
Web Site: https://www.imdexlimited.com
Year Founded: 1980
IMD—(ASX)
Rev.: $297,331,730
Assets: $524,935,895
Liabilities: $143,474,225
Net Worth: $381,461,670
Earnings: $21,633,948
Emp.: 816
Fiscal Year-end: 06/30/24
Drilling Products & Services; Minerals Processing
N.A.I.C.S.: 213111
Bernard William Ridgeway *(Mng Dir)*

Subsidiaries:

AMC Chile S.A. (1)
El Juncal 091 Parque Industrial Portezuelo, Quilicura, Santiago, Chile
Tel.: (56) 25899300
Drilling Fluids & Chemicals Whslr
N.A.I.C.S.: 424690

AMC North America Ltd (1)
7053 Hwy 101 E 70 C Mount Joy St N Ste 510, Timmins, P4N 4V7, ON, Canada
Tel.: (705) 235-2169
Web Site: http://www.imdexlimited.com
Sales Range: $50-74.9 Million
Emp.: 10
Drilling Fluids Distr
N.A.I.C.S.: 424690

Australian Mud Company Pty Ltd. (1)
216 Balcatta Road, Balcatta, 6021, WA, Australia (100%)
Tel.: (61) 894454000
Web Site: https://www.amcmud.com
Sales Range: $10-24.9 Million
Emp.: 120
Drilling Fluids & Chemicals Supplier
N.A.I.C.S.: 213111
Paul Evans *(CEO)*

Subsidiary (Non-US):

Suay Energy Services LLP (2)
Office 100/1 30 Saina street Almaty Build 3 micro 17, 130000, Aktau, Mangystau, Kazakhstan
Tel.: (7) 7475184305
Web Site: http://www.suayenergy.com
Drilling Fluids Mfr & Distr
N.A.I.C.S.: 213111

DHS Oil International Pty Ltd (1)
PO Box 268, Abu Dhabi, United Arab Emirates (30%)
Tel.: (971) 48153817
Web Site: http://www.vesinternational.com
Oil & Gas Surveying & Other Support Services
N.A.I.C.S.: 213112

Subsidiary (US):

Gyro Technologies, Inc. (2)
3400 CR 48, Robstown, TX 78380
Tel.: (361) 767-0602
Sales Range: $1-9.9 Million
Emp.: 20
Oil & Gas Directional Surveying Services
N.A.I.C.S.: 213112
Keith Havelka *(Gen Mgr)*

Drillhole Surveying Instruments (Pty) Ltd (1)
31 Basalt St, Alrode, Germiston, 1454, Gauteng, South Africa
Tel.: (27) 117920452
Web Site: http://www.incmub.com
Sales Range: $25-49.9 Million
Emp.: 17
Drilling Fluids Mfr & Sales
N.A.I.C.S.: 325998
Justin Moyes *(Mgr)*

Flexit Australia Pty Ltd (1)
216 Balcatta Road, Balcatta, Perth, 6021, WA, Australia
Tel.: (61) 894454030
Web Site: http://www.flexit.se
Sales Range: $25-49.9 Million
Emp.: 150
Drilling Equipments Mfr & Repair Services
N.A.I.C.S.: 333132
Paul Nielsen *(Gen Mgr)*

Imdex Technology Germany GmbH (1)
Bahnhofstr 6, 79359, Riegel, Baden-Württemberg, Germany
Tel.: (49) 7642902417
Geological Research & Development Services
N.A.I.C.S.: 541715

Imdex Technology UK Ltd (1)
3 Hyde Clo The Street, Lewes, BN7 3PA, East Sussex, United Kingdom
Tel.: (44) 1273483800
Sales Range: $50-74.9 Million
Emp.: 6
Drilling Fluids Mfr & Sales
N.A.I.C.S.: 325998

Reflex Instrument North America Ltd. (1)
7053 Highway 101 East Porcupine, Timmins, P0N 1C0, ON, Canada
Tel.: (705) 235-2169
Web Site: http://www.reflexnow.com
Sales Range: $25-49.9 Million
Emp.: 17
Survey & Core Orientation Instruments Distr
N.A.I.C.S.: 423990
Sergio Jimenez *(VP)*

Reflex Instruments Asia Pacific Pty Ltd (1)
216 Balcatta Road, Balcatta, 6021, WA, Australia
Tel.: (61) 894454020
Web Site: http://www.imdexlimited.com
Sales Range: $50-74.9 Million
Emp.: 165
Drilling Fluids Distr
N.A.I.C.S.: 424690
Sean Migulfe *(Gen Mgr)*

Reflex Instruments Europe Ltd (1)
Unit 4/5 Upper Stalls Iford, Lewes, BN7 3EJ, East Sussex, United Kingdom
Tel.: (44) 1273483700
Web Site: http://www.reflexnow.com
Sales Range: $50-74.9 Million
Emp.: 6
Industrial Equipment Distr
N.A.I.C.S.: 423810
Christian Van Der Put *(Mgr)*

Samchem Drilling Fluids & Chemicals (Pty) Ltd (1)
Corner Boron Vasa Street, Alrode Ext 7, Alberton, 1454, South Africa (100%)
Tel.: (27) 0119085595
Web Site: http://www.amcmud.com
Sales Range: $1-9.9 Million
Emp.: 55
Drilling Fluids & Chemicals Supplier & Stocker
N.A.I.C.S.: 213111
Justin Moyes *(Gen Mgr)*

IME YOUNYI CO., LTD.
272 Mosi-ri Jiksan-eup, Seobuk-gu, Cheonan, 331-814, Chungcheongnam-do, Korea (South)
Tel.: (82) 416201500
Web Site: http://www.younyi.co.kr
Year Founded: 2003
090740—(KRS)
Rev.: $170,886,282
Assets: $86,796,001
Liabilities: $41,200,852
Net Worth: $45,595,149
Earnings: $24,118,598
Emp.: 50
Fiscal Year-end: 12/31/21
Electronic Components Mfr
N.A.I.C.S.: 334419
Pyeong-jik Cho *(CEO)*

Subsidiaries:

Younyi Electronics (Suzhou) Co., Ltd. (1)
No 8 Dongjing Industrial Square No 8 Dongfu Rd Suzhou Industrial Park, Suzhou, Jiangsu, China
Tel.: (86) 51262653995
Web Site: http://www.imdexlimited.com
Light Emitting Diode Products Distr
N.A.I.C.S.: 423690

Younyi Electronics (Tianjin) Co., Ltd. (1)
TianJin Xiqing Development Zone Saida International City Block A5, Tianjin, China
Tel.: (86) 2258335201
Light Emitting Diode Product Mfr
N.A.I.C.S.: 334413

Younyi Information & Communication Co., Ltd. - The Second Factory (1)
192 Mundeok-ri Seonggeo-eup Seobuk-gu, Cheonan, 330-832, Chungcheongnam-do, Korea (South)
Tel.: (82) 415896200
Light Emitting Diode Product Mfr
N.A.I.C.S.: 334413

IMEC SERVICES LIMITED
501/B Mahakosh House 7/5 South Tukoganj, Nath Mandir Road, Indore, 452 001, Madhya Pradesh, India
Tel.: (91) 7314017509
Web Site:
https://www.imecservices.in
Year Founded: 1987

513295—(BOM)
Rev.: $772,756
Assets: $345,888
Liabilities: $149,707
Net Worth: $196,180
Earnings: $3,897
Emp.: 15
Fiscal Year-end: 03/31/24
Rolled Steel Coils Mfr
N.A.I.C.S.: 334416
Arvind Mishra *(CEO)*

Subsidiaries:

RSAL Steel Private Limited (1)
301 The Horizon 11/5 South Tukoganj Nath Mandir Road, Indore, 452 001, India
Tel.: (91) 7314017577
Web Site: http://www.rsalsteel.com
Steel Products Mfr
N.A.I.C.S.: 331210
Arvind Mishra *(CEO)*

IMEIK TECHNOLOGY DEVELOPMENT CO., LTD.
21F Block C Shi Mao Building A 92 Jian Guo Road, Chao Yang District, Beijing, 102200, China
Tel.: (86) 1085809026
Web Site: https://www.imeik.com
Year Founded: 2004
300896—(SSE)
Rev.: $272,213,136
Assets: $878,700,420
Liabilities: $43,912,908
Net Worth: $834,787,512
Earnings: $177,403,824
Fiscal Year-end: 12/31/22
Pharmaceutical Product Mfr & Distr
N.A.I.C.S.: 325412
Jun Jian *(Chm)*

IMER INTERNATIONAL S.P.A.
Via Salceto 53-55, 53036, Poggibonsi, Siena, Italy
Tel.: (39) 057797341 IT
Web Site: http://www.imergroup.com
Year Founded: 1962
Emp.: 600
Construction & Conveying Equipment Mfr & Distr
N.A.I.C.S.: 333120
Silvano Bencini *(Founder)*

Subsidiaries:

IHIMER S.p.A. (1)
Localita Cusona, 53037, San Gimignano, SI, Italy
Tel.: (39) 057795121
Web Site: http://www.ihimer.com
Sales Range: $25-49.9 Million
Emp.: 54
Construction Machinery Mfr
N.A.I.C.S.: 333120
Igino Elefante *(Dir-Sls & Mktg)*

IMER France (1)
18 Rue de l Industrie, BP 34, ZI Les Speyres, 38450, Vif, France
Tel.: (33) 4 7672 5269
Web Site: http://www.imer.fr
Construction Machinery Whslr
N.A.I.C.S.: 423810
Nicolas Fossa *(Mgr-Publication)*

IMER USA, Inc. (1)
221 Westhampton Pl, Capitol Heights, MD 20743
Tel.: (301) 336-3700
Web Site: http://www.imerusa.com
Sales Range: $1-9.9 Million
Emp.: 15
Construction Machinery & Equipment Whslr
N.A.I.C.S.: 423810
Mace T. Coleman Jr. *(Pres)*

Le Officine Riunite - Udine S.p.A. (1)
Via Santa Caterina 35, Basaldella, 33030, Campoformido, UD, Italy
Tel.: (39) 0432563911
Web Site: http://www.oru.it

IMER INTERNATIONAL S.P.A.

IMER International S.p.A.—(Continued)
Sales Range: $50-74.9 Million
Emp.: 250
Concrete Construction Machinery Mfr
N.A.I.C.S.: 333120
Paolo Salvadori (Pres & CEO)

IMERI JOINT STOCK COMPANY
119 Lado Asiatini Str, Kutaisi, 384600, Georgia
Tel.: (995) 3312 07 08
Web Site: http://www.imeri.ge
Apparel Product Mfr
N.A.I.C.S.: 315250

IMETAL RESOURCES INC.
800 West Pender Street Suite 550, Vancouver, V6C 2V6, BC, Canada
Tel.: (604) 484-3031
Web Site: https://www.imetalresources.ca
A7VA—(DEU)
Assets: $4,281,101
Liabilities: $501,458
Net Worth: $3,779,643
Earnings: ($1,672,579)
Fiscal Year-end: 03/31/24
Mineral Exploration Services
N.A.I.C.S.: 213114
Mark M. Fedikow (Dir-Qualified Person & VP-Exploration)

IMEXHS LIMITED
122 O Riordan Street, Mascot, 2020, NSW, Australia
Tel.: (61) 290300040
Web Site: https://www.imexhs.com.au
IME—(ASX)
Rev.: $13,397,618
Assets: $15,430,334
Liabilities: $4,543,049
Net Worth: $10,887,286
Earnings: ($2,855,623)
Emp.: 250
Fiscal Year-end: 12/31/23
Software Development Services
N.A.I.C.S.: 513210
German Arango (Co-Founder & CEO)

Subsidiaries:
Imaging Experts & Healthcare Services S.A.S. (1)
Calle 92 11-51 Of 202 Edificio Chico 9211 Ofc 202, Bogota, Colombia
Tel.: (57) 13164890
Software Development Services
N.A.I.C.S.: 541511

IMEXPHARM CORPORATION
No 4 30/4 Street Ward 1, Cao Lanh, Dong Thap, Vietnam
Tel.: (84) 2773851941
Web Site: https://www.imexpharm.com
Year Founded: 2001
IMP—(HOSE)
Rev.: $87,091,436
Assets: $98,575,744
Liabilities: $12,691,092
Net Worth: $85,884,652
Earnings: $12,341,707
Emp.: 1,405
Fiscal Year-end: 12/31/23
Pharmaceuticals Product Mfr
N.A.I.C.S.: 325412
Thi Dao Tran (Vice Chm, Gen Dir & Member-Exec Bd)

IMF BENTHAM LIMITED
Level 18 68 Pitt Street, Sydney, 2000, NSW, Australia
Tel.: (61) 2 8223 3567
Web Site: http://www.imf.com.au
Rev.: $4,032,263
Assets: $498,542,896
Liabilities: $136,035,096
Net Worth: $362,507,800
Earnings: ($25,419,997)
Emp.: 101
Fiscal Year-end: 06/30/19
Funding Services for Litigation
N.A.I.C.S.: 561499
Tania Sulan (Chief Investment Officer)

Subsidiaries:
Omni Bridgeway Holding B.V. (1)
Schiphol Boulevard 121, Amsterdam, 1118 BG, Schiphol, Netherlands
Tel.: (31) 703384343
Web Site: http://www.omnibridgeway.com
Sales Range: $25-49.9 Million
Emp.: 25
Litigation & Legal Disputes Services
N.A.I.C.S.: 541199
Michiel Jenniskens (Controller)

Subsidiary (US):

Americas Insurance Co (2)
400 Poydras St Ste 1150, New Orleans, LA 70130-3245
Tel.: (504) 528-9555
Web Site: http://www.omniwhittington.com
Sales Range: $50-74.9 Million
Emp.: 6
Insurance Services
N.A.I.C.S.: 524126

Subsidiary (Non-US):

Omni Bridgeway Emerging Markets Limited (2)
Audrey House 3rd Floor 16 Ely Place, London, EC1N 6SN, United Kingdom
Tel.: (44) 20 7743 0900
Fund Management Services
N.A.I.C.S.: 523940

ROLAND ProzessFinanz AG (2)
Deutz-Kalker Strasse 46, 50679, Cologne, Germany
Tel.: (49) 221 8277 3000
Web Site: http://www.roland-prozessfinanz.de
Litigation Funding Services
N.A.I.C.S.: 541199

IMGT CO., LTD.
408 Healthcare Innovation Park 172 Dolma-ro, Bundang-gu, Seongnam, 13605, Korea (South)
Tel.: (82) 319947077
Web Site: https://www.imgt.co.kr
Year Founded: 2010
456570—(KRS)
Healthcare Technology Services
N.A.I.C.S.: 541511
Jong Hak Lee (CEO)

IMI CO., LTD.
3-3-12 Ryutsu-danchi, Koshigaya, 343-0824, Saitama, Japan
Tel.: (81) 48 988 4411
Web Site: http://www.imimed.co.jp
Year Founded: 1974
Sales Range: $100-124.9 Million
Emp.: 260
Professional Equipment Whslr
N.A.I.C.S.: 423490
Kazumasa Tsumuga (CEO)

IMI PLC
Lakeside Solihull Parkway Birmingham Business Park, Birmingham, B37 7XZ, United Kingdom
Tel.: (44) 1217173700   UK
Web Site: https://www.imiplc.com
Year Founded: 1862
IMIAF—(OTCIQ)
Rev.: $2,775,530,834
Assets: $3,122,345,798
Liabilities: $1,820,273,000
Net Worth: $1,302,072,798
Earnings: $299,924,165
Emp.: 10,771
Fiscal Year-end: 12/31/23

Holding Company; Industrial & Fluid Systems Engineering & Components Mfr
N.A.I.C.S.: 551112
Jackie Hu (Mng Dir-Critical Engrg)

Subsidiaries:

Adaptas Solutions, LLC (1)
Palmer Industrial Park 9 2nd St, Palmer, MA 01069
Tel.: (413) 284-9975
Web Site: https://www.adaptas.com
Laboratory Supplies Mfr
N.A.I.C.S.: 334516
Laura Ray (Sr VP)

Subsidiary (Domestic):

Scientific Instrument Services, Inc. (2)
1027 Old York Rd, Ringoes, NJ 08551-1054
Tel.: (908) 788-5550
Web Site: http://www.sisweb.com
Analytical Laboratory Instrument Mfr & Distr
N.A.I.C.S.: 334516

Division (Domestic):

Scientific Instrument Manufacturing (3)
42 Appletree Ln, Pipersville, PA 18947
Tel.: (908) 788-5550
Web Site: http://www.scientificmachining.com
Analytical Laboratory Instrument Mfr
N.A.I.C.S.: 334516

Aero Dynamiek BV (1)
Havenstraat 9, Postbus 173, 3860 AD, Nijkerk, Netherlands
Tel.: (31) 33 245 9064
Web Site: https://www.aero-dynamiek.nl
Air Conditioning & Ventilation Equipment Mfr
N.A.I.C.S.: 333415

Asterm SAS (1)
3 Rue du Pont des Halles, 94150, Rungis, France
Tel.: (33) 15 634 7020
Web Site: https://www.asterm.com
Indoor Climate System Installation Services
N.A.I.C.S.: 238220

Bimba Manufacturing Company, Inc. (1)
25150 S Governors Hwy, University Park, IL 60484
Tel.: (708) 534-8544
Web Site: http://www.bimba.com
Hydraulic & Pneumatic Fluid Power Cylinders Mfr
N.A.I.C.S.: 333995

Subsidiary (Domestic):

Acro Associates, Inc. (2)
1990 Olivera Rd Ste A, Concord, CA 94520
Tel.: (925) 676-8828
Web Site: http://www.acroassociates.com
Other Metal Valve & Pipe Fitting Mfr
N.A.I.C.S.: 332919

Subsidiary (Non-US):

Acro Associates Europe (3)
Aquamarijnstraat 97, Hengelo, 7554 NN, Netherlands
Tel.: (31) 74 8200 345
Web Site: http://www.acroassociates.com
Fluid Control Systems
N.A.I.C.S.: 333996

Subsidiary (Domestic):

Pneumadyne, Inc. (2)
14425 23rd Ave N, Plymouth, MN 55447-4706
Tel.: (763) 559-0177
Web Site: https://www.pneumadyne.com
Pneumatic Components Mfr
N.A.I.C.S.: 333248

TRD Manufacturing, Inc. (2)
10914 N 2nd St, Machesney Park, IL 61115-1400
Tel.: (815) 654-7775
Aluminum Cylinder Mfr
N.A.I.C.S.: 331315

INTERNATIONAL PUBLIC

Vaccon Co., Inc. (2)
9 Industrial Park Rd, Medway, MA 02053
Tel.: (508) 359-7200
Web Site: http://www.vaccon.com
Surgical & Medical Instrument Mfr
N.A.I.C.S.: 339112

Bopp & Reuther Valves GmbH (1)
Carl-Reuther-Strasse 1, 68305, Mannheim, Germany
Tel.: (49) 621762200
Web Site: http://www.bursr.com
Valve Mfr
N.A.I.C.S.: 332911

Buschjost GmbH (1)
Detmolder Strasse 256, 32545, Bad Oeynhausen, Germany
Tel.: (49) 57317910
Web Site: http://www.buschjost.com
Magnetic Valve Mfr
N.A.I.C.S.: 332911
Torsten Bredthauer (Mgr-Mktg)

Cannon Solutions (1)
15100 Business Pkwy, Rosemount, MN 55068 (100%)
Tel.: (651) 322-6300
Web Site: http://www.cannonequipment.com
Sales Range: $125-149.9 Million
Emp.: 274
Mfr & Distributor of Carts; Mobile Packaging & Handling Equipment
N.A.I.C.S.: 337126

Subsidiary (Domestic):

Cannon Equipment Company (2)
324 Washington St W, Cannon Falls, MN 55009 (100%)
Tel.: (507) 263-6400
Web Site: https://www.cannonequipment.com
Sales Range: $50-74.9 Million
Emp.: 150
Design, Engineering & Manufacturing of POP Displays & Material Handling Systems
N.A.I.C.S.: 337126

DCI Marketing Inc (2)
2727 West Good Hope Rd, Milwaukee, WI 53209 (100%)
Tel.: (414) 228-7000
Web Site: https://www.dcimarketing.com
Sales Range: $25-49.9 Million
Emp.: 200
Signs & Advertising Specialties
N.A.I.C.S.: 561990

Cash Acme, Inc. (1)
2400 7th Ave SW, Cullman, AL 35055-0295
Tel.: (256) 775-8200
Web Site: https://www.cashacme.com
Rev.: $26,000,000
Emp.: 135
Mfr of Automatic Valves
N.A.I.C.S.: 332911

Control Components, Inc. (1)
22591 Avenida Empresa, Rancho Santa Margarita, CA 92688-2003
Tel.: (949) 858-1877
Web Site: http://www.ccivalve.com
Sales Range: $50-74.9 Million
Emp.: 200
High-technology, Severe Service Control Valves For Power & Process Industries
N.A.I.C.S.: 332911

Subsidiary (Non-US):

CCI AG (2)
Fabrikstrasse 10, 8370, Sirnach, Switzerland
Tel.: (41) 522649500
Industrial Valve & Control System Mfr
N.A.I.C.S.: 332911
Gregg Smith (Gen Mgr)

CCI Czech Republic sro (2)
Tel.: (420) 517540020
Emp.: 35
Oil & Gas Exploration Services
N.A.I.C.S.: 213112

CCI KK (2)
6-2-2 Takatsukadai, Nishi-Ku, Kobe, 651-2271, Hyogo, Japan
Tel.: (81) 789915910
Web Site: http://www.ccijapan.co.jp
Industrial Equipment Mfr

AND PRIVATE COMPANIES IMI PLC

N.A.I.C.S.: 333248

CCI Ltd (2)
81-21 Ongjeong-ri Tongjin-eup, 415-865, Gimpo, Gyeonggi, Korea (South)
Tel.: (82) 31 980 9812
Web Site: http://www.ccivalve.co.kr
Sales Range: $25-49.9 Million
Emp.: 196
Industrial Valve Mfr
N.A.I.C.S.: 332919

CCI Valve Technology AB (2)
Industrigatan 7, Box 603, 661 29, Saffle, Sweden
Tel.: (46) 533689600
Sales Range: $50-74.9 Million
Emp.: 20
Industrial Valve & Control System Mfr
N.A.I.C.S.: 332911

CCI Valve Technology GmbH (2)
Lembockgasse 63/1, 1230, Vienna, 1230, Austria
Tel.: (43) 18692740
Web Site: http://www.imi-critical.com
Sales Range: $25-49.9 Million
Emp.: 100
Industrial Valve & Control System Mfr
N.A.I.C.S.: 332911

Control Components India Pty Ltd (2)
Ground 1st & 2nd Floor Tower 4 SJR i park Plot 13 14 & 15, EPIP Zone Phase 1 Whitefield Road, Bengaluru, 560066, India
Tel.: (91) 8040303583
Emp.: 35
Valve & Control Component Mfr
N.A.I.C.S.: 332919

Shanghai CCI Power Control Equipment Co Ltd (2)
229C 2F No 11 Lane 465 Tengyue Road, Yangpu District, Shanghai, 200090, China
Tel.: (86) 2165205577
Sales Range: $50-74.9 Million
Emp.: 110
Industrial Power Control Equipment Mfr
N.A.I.C.S.: 334519
Taylor Qian *(Gen Mgr)*

Flow Design Inc (1)
8908 Governors Row, Dallas, TX 75247
Tel.: (214) 631-0011
Web Site: https://www.imiflowdesign.com
Emp.: 60
Industrial Valve & Control Machinery Mfr
N.A.I.C.S.: 332911

Fluid Automation Systems GmbH (1)
Stuttgarter Str 120, 70736, Fellbach, Germany
Tel.: (49) 711167860
Web Site: https://www.fluid-automation.de
Emp.: 6
Industrial Automation System Mfr
N.A.I.C.S.: 333248

Fluid Automation Systems SA (1)
Route de l'Etraz 126, CP 256, Versoix, 1290, Geneva, Switzerland
Tel.: (41) 22 775 1000
Web Site: http://www.fas.ch
Emp.: 70
Fluid Automation System Mfr
N.A.I.C.S.: 333248

Fluid Automation Systems Technologies SA (1)
126 Route De L'etraz, Palezieux, Oron, 1290, Switzerland
Tel.: (41) 219077971
Web Site: http://www.imi.com
Industrial Automation System Mfr
N.A.I.C.S.: 333248

Herion Systemtechnik GmbH (1)
Untere Talstrasse 65, 71263, Weil der Stadt, Germany
Tel.: (49) 703330180
Web Site: http://www.herion-systemtechnik.de
Sales Range: $25-49.9 Million
Emp.: 50
Hydraulic Components Mfr
N.A.I.C.S.: 333120

IMI Aero-Dynamiek BVBA (1)
Antwerpsesteenweg 124, 2630, Aartselaar, Belgium
Tel.: (32) 3 843 2550
Web Site: http://www.aero-dynamiek.be
Engineering Services
N.A.I.C.S.: 488119

IMI CCI South Africa (Pty) Ltd. (1)
38 Industrial Crescent ext 25, Witbank, South Africa
Tel.: (27) 136973305
Security Valve & Loader Mfr
N.A.I.C.S.: 332911
Tracy Cantin *(Area Mgr)*

IMI Components Ltd (1)
Lakeside Solihull Parkway Birmingham Business Park, Birmingham, B37 7XZ, West Midlands, United Kingdom
Tel.: (44) 1213445800
Web Site: http://www.imicomponents.com
Ammunition Mfr
N.A.I.C.S.: 332993

IMI Hydronic Engineering (Spain) SAU (1)
C/Foronda 4 Planta Segunda A, 28034, Madrid, Spain
Tel.: (34) 916401295
Hydronic Engineering Product Mfr
N.A.I.C.S.: 326299
Jose J. Vilchez *(Mgr-Technical)*

IMI Hydronic Engineering A/S (1)
Borupvang 2D 1 tv, 2750, Ballerup, Denmark
Tel.: (45) 44570999
Web Site: https://www.imi-hydronic.com
Hydronic Engineering Product Mfr
N.A.I.C.S.: 326299

IMI Hydronic Engineering AB (1)
Falkopingsvagen 2, 524 42, Ljung, Sweden
Tel.: (46) 51354000
Web Site: https://www.imi-hydronic.com
Hydronic Engineering Product Mfr
N.A.I.C.S.: 326299

IMI Hydronic Engineering AS (1)
Glynitveien 7, 1400, Ski, Norway
Tel.: (47) 64911610
Web Site: https://www.imi-hydronic.com
Hydronic Engineering Product Mfr
N.A.I.C.S.: 326299

IMI Hydronic Engineering BV (1)
Klipperaak 101, 2411 ND, Bodegraven, Netherlands
Tel.: (31) 172492041
Web Site: https://www.imi-hydronic.com
Hydronic Engineering Product Mfr
N.A.I.C.S.: 326299
David Molevelt *(Acct Mgr)*

IMI Hydronic Engineering Deutschland GmbH (1)
Vollinghauser Weg, 59597, Erwitte, Germany
Tel.: (49) 29438910
Hydronic Engineering Product Mfr
N.A.I.C.S.: 326299

IMI Hydronic Engineering FZE (1)
Jafza One-Tower A Office 1307-10, PO Box 262611, Jafza, Dubai, United Arab Emirates
Tel.: (971) 48073111
Hydronic Engineering Product Mfr
N.A.I.C.S.: 326299
Biren Patel *(Mng Dir)*

IMI Hydronic Engineering France S.A. (1)
Paris Nord II - 13 Rue De La Perdrix Roissy Charles De Gaulle, BP 84004, 95931, Tremblay-en-France, Cedex, France
Tel.: (33) 158020820
Web Site: https://www.imi-hydronic.com
Hydronic Engineering Product Mfr
N.A.I.C.S.: 326299

IMI Hydronic Engineering GesmbH (1)
Industriestrasse 9 Object 5, PO Box 45, 2353, Guntramsdorf, Austria
Tel.: (43) 2236230000
Web Site: https://www.imi-hydronic.com
Hydronic Engineering Product Mfr
N.A.I.C.S.: 326299

IMI Hydronic Engineering Inc. (1)
8908 Governors Row, Dallas, TX 75247
Tel.: (214) 631-0011
Hydronic Engineering Product Mfr

IMI Hydronic Engineering International SA (1)
Route de Crassier 19, 1262, Eysins, Switzerland
Tel.: (41) 229909898
Hydronic Engineering Product Mfr
N.A.I.C.S.: 326299

IMI Hydronic Engineering Limited (1)
Hat House 3rd Floor 32 Guildford Street, Luton, LU1 2NR, Bedfordshire, United Kingdom
Tel.: (44) 1582866377
Web Site: https://www.imi-hydronic.com
Hydronic Engineering Product Mfr
N.A.I.C.S.: 326299
Mark Pardy *(Mgr-Specification)*

IMI Hydronic Engineering Ltda. (1)
Av Fagundes Filho 134-Cj 43, Vila Monte Alegre, Sao Paulo, 04304-010, Brazil
Tel.: (55) 1155890638
Hydronic Engineering Product Mfr
N.A.I.C.S.: 326299

IMI Hydronic Engineering NV (1)
Fountain Business Park C Van Kerckhovenstraat 110 Gebouw 3, 2880, Bornem, Belgium
Tel.: (32) 36403380
Hydronic Engineering Product Mfr
N.A.I.C.S.: 326299

IMI Hydronic Engineering OY (1)
Robert Huberin tie 7, 1510, Vantaa, Finland
Tel.: (358) 207401600
Hydronic Engineering Product Mfr
N.A.I.C.S.: 326299
Mikko Lattila *(Reg Mgr-Technical)*

IMI Hydronic Engineering S.A. (1)
9 Rue Des 3 Cantons, 8399, Windhof, Luxembourg
Tel.: (352) 2626151
Hydronic Engineering Product Mfr
N.A.I.C.S.: 326299

IMI Hydronic Engineering S.R.L. (1)
Via Roma 108, 20051, Cassina de' Pecchi, MI, Italy
Tel.: (39) 0283550690
Hydronic Engineering Product Mfr
N.A.I.C.S.: 326299

IMI Hydronic Engineering Switzerland AG (1)
Muhlerainstrasse 26, 4414, Fullinsdorf, Switzerland
Tel.: (41) 619062626
Hydronic Engineering Product Mfr
N.A.I.C.S.: 326299
Michel Wenger *(Head-Sls)*

IMI Indoor Climate Trading (Shanghai) Co Ltd (1)
9F UC Tower No 500 Fu Shan Road, Pudong, Shanghai, 200122, China
Tel.: (86) 21 6163 6555
Web Site: http://www.tourandersson.com
Industrial Machinery Whslr
N.A.I.C.S.: 423830

IMI International Co Srl (1)
Str Aristide Pascal 36 Sector 3, 31445, Bucharest, Romania
Tel.: (40) 212560141
Hydronic Engineering Product Mfr
N.A.I.C.S.: 326299
Nica Gabriela *(Mgr-Fin)*

IMI International Kft (1)
Kunigunda Utja 60, PF 108, HU-1037, Budapest, Hungary
Tel.: (36) 12849000
Web Site: http://www.norgren.hu
Sales Range: $25-49.9 Million
Emp.: 13
Industrial Valve Mfr
N.A.I.C.S.: 332911

IMI International LLC (1)
Leninskaya Sloboda Str 19 2, 115280, Moscow, Russia
Tel.: (7) 495 223 4878
Web Site: http://www.stiactuation.com
Room Temperature Control Services
N.A.I.C.S.: 238210

IMI International d.o.o. (1)
Slavonska Avenija 17, 10040, Zagreb, Croatia
Tel.: (385) 12371102
Hydronic Engineering Product Mfr
N.A.I.C.S.: 326299

IMI International s.r.o. (1)
Evropska 852, 664 42, Modrice, Czech Republic
Tel.: (420) 565533602
Hydronic Engineering Product Mfr
N.A.I.C.S.: 326299

IMI International sp zoo (1)
Olewin 50A, 32-300, Olkusz, Poland
Tel.: (48) 327588200
Web Site: https://www.imi-hydronic.com
Emp.: 300
Industrial Machinery Mfr
N.A.I.C.S.: 333248
Grzegorz Gonet *(Gen Mgr)*

IMI Kynoch Ltd (1)
Lakeside Solihull Parkway Birmingham Business Park, Birmingham, B37 7XZ, West Midlands, United Kingdom
Tel.: (44) 1217173700
Emp.: 130
Fluid Control System Mfr
N.A.I.C.S.: 332912

IMI Manufacturing de Mexico SA de CV (1)
Brecha No E-99 Lote A 12 Parque Industria, Reynosa, 88780, Mexico
Tel.: (52) 8999218100
Measuring & Dispensing Pump Mfr
N.A.I.C.S.: 333914

IMI Norgren (1)
5400 S Delaware St, Littleton, CO 80120
Tel.: (937) 833-4033
Web Site: http://www.usa.norgren.com
Sales Range: $10-24.9 Million
Emp.: 152
Pneumatic & Fluid Control Products Mfr
N.A.I.C.S.: 334519

IMI Norgren Herion Pvt. Limited (1)
A-62 Sector 63, Noida, 201301, Uttar Pradesh, India
Tel.: (91) 1204089500
Precision Engineering Product Mfr
N.A.I.C.S.: 332721
Sona Gaur *(Mgr-HR)*

IMI Norgren Los Angeles (1)
1308 S Allec St, Anaheim, CA 92805
Tel.: (714) 239-2966
Web Site: http://www.norgren.com
Pneumatic Products Distr
N.A.I.C.S.: 332912

IMI Norgren Ltd (1)
3-5 Walls Road, PO Box 12-893, Penrose, Auckland, 1061, New Zealand
Tel.: (64) 9 579 0189
Web Site: http://www.norgren.com
Sales Range: $25-49.9 Million
Emp.: 30
Industrial Fluid Control Machinery Mfr
N.A.I.C.S.: 332912

IMI Norgren Oy (1)
Robert Huberin tie 7, 01510, Vantaa, Finland
Tel.: (358) 9 571 2140
Web Site: http://www.imi-precision.com
Industrial Machinery Mfr
N.A.I.C.S.: 333248

IMI Norgren SA (1)
Colcm 390 2 Edificio Tecno, 08223, Terrassa, Spain
Tel.: (34) 937489800
Web Site: https://www.norgren.com
Industrial Machinery Mfr
N.A.I.C.S.: 333248

IMI Overseas Investments Ltd (1)
Lakeside Solihull Parkway Birmingham Business Park, Birmingham, B37 7XZ, West Midlands, United Kingdom
Tel.: (44) 1217173700
Investment Management Service
N.A.I.C.S.: 523999

IMI Property Investments Ltd (1)
Lakeside Solihull Parkway Birmingham Business Park, Birmingham, B37 7XZ, West Midlands, United Kingdom

IMI PLC

IMI plc—(Continued)
Tel.: (44) 1217173700
Emp.: 60
Property Management Services
N.A.I.C.S.: 531312

IMI Scott Ltd (1)
Dallimore Road Roundthorn Industrial Estate, Wythenshawe, Manchester, M23 9WJ, United Kingdom
Tel.: (44) 161 998 5533
Web Site: http://www.imiscott.co.uk
Electrical Coil & Wire Mfr
N.A.I.C.S.: 334416

IMI Webber Ltd (1)
Blenheim Way Fradley Park, Easton, Lichfield, WS13 8SY, Staffordshire, United Kingdom
Tel.: (44) 1179555511
Web Site: http://www.imiwebber.com
Sales Range: $50-74.9 Million
Emp.: 150
Solenoid Valve Mfr
N.A.I.C.S.: 332912
Andy Matthews *(Gen Mgr)*

ISI Norgren, Inc. (1)
44831 Groesbeck Hwy, Clinton Township, MI 48036
Tel.: (586) 463-3000
Web Site: http://www.norgren.com
Sales Range: $125-149.9 Million
Emp.: 400
Mfr of Automated Systems, Parts, Clamps & Fluid Power Products
N.A.I.C.S.: 339999

Subsidiary (Domestic):

Norgren (2)
72 Spring Ln, Farmington, CT 06032
Tel.: (860) 677-0272
Rev.: $20,000,000
Emp.: 130
Solenoid Valves
N.A.I.C.S.: 332912

Norgren, Inc. (2)
5400 S Delaware St, Littleton, CO 80120
Tel.: (303) 794-2611
Web Site: https://www.norgren.com
Compressed Air Filters, Regulators, Lubricators, Rodless Cylinders, Dryers & Mufflers Mfr
N.A.I.C.S.: 332912
William J. Wolsky *(Deputy Pres)*

Kloehn Inc (1)
10000 Banburry Cross Dr, Las Vegas, NV 89144
Tel.: (702) 243-7727
Web Site: http://www.kloehn.com
Fluid Control System Mfr
N.A.I.C.S.: 332912
Christy Rowley *(Mgr-HR)*

MCF Controls Inc. (1)
1110 N Post Oak Rd Ste 345, Houston, TX 77055-7246
Tel.: (713) 686-3923
Sales of Industrial Ball Valves
N.A.I.C.S.: 332919

MI Hydronic Engineering Hydraulic Systems Ltd. (1)
Atasehir Bulvari Ata Carsi Kat 4 59, Atasehir, Istanbul, 34750, Turkiye
Tel.: (90) 216 469 48 18
Web Site: http://www.imi-hydronic.com
Thermostatic Control Equipment Mfr
N.A.I.C.S.: 334512
Oktay Akyol *(Dir-Sls)*

Norgren A/S (1)
Borupvang World Trade Center Ballerup 3 8, 2750, Ballerup, Denmark
Tel.: (45) 44500800
Web Site: https://www.norgren.com
Motion & Fluid Control Mfr & Distr
N.A.I.C.S.: 332912

Norgren AG (1)
Fabrikstrasse 10, Sirnach, 8370, Munchwilen, Switzerland
Tel.: (41) 719732800
Web Site: https://www.norgren.com
Fluid Control System Mfr
N.A.I.C.S.: 332912

Norgren AS (1)
Glynitveien 7, 1400, Ski, Norway
Tel.: (47) 22908080
Web Site: https://www.norgren.com
Industrial Equipment Distr
N.A.I.C.S.: 423830

Norgren Automation Solutions LLC (1)
1325 Woodland Dr, Saline, MI 48176
Tel.: (734) 429-4989
Precision Engineering Product Mfr
N.A.I.C.S.: 332721

Norgren BV (1)
Versterkerstraat 6, 1322 AP, Almere, Netherlands
Tel.: (31) 365486828
Web Site: https://www.norgren.com
Industrial Machinery Mfr
N.A.I.C.S.: 333248

Norgren European Logistics Company Ltd (1)
Blenheim Way Fradley Park Unit 7, Lichfield, WS13 8SY, Staffordshire, United Kingdom
Tel.: (44) 1543 265000
Emp.: 500
Logistics Consulting Servies
N.A.I.C.S.: 541614
Niel Williams *(Dir-Plant)*

Norgren Finland OY (1)
Robert Huberin Tie 7, 01510, Vantaa, Finland
Tel.: (358) 95712140
Precision Engineering Product Mfr
N.A.I.C.S.: 332721

Norgren GesmbH (1)
Industriezentrum NO - Sud Strasse 2a Objekt M39/I, 2355, Wiener Neudorf, Austria
Tel.: (43) 2236635200
Web Site: https://www.norgren.com
Industrial Control Equipment Mfr & Distr
N.A.I.C.S.: 334519

Norgren GmbH (1)
Bruckstrasse 93, Postfach 11 20, 46519, Alpen, Germany
Tel.: (49) 2802490
Web Site: https://www.norgren.com
Pneumatic Equipment Mfr
N.A.I.C.S.: 332912

Norgren Limited (1)
15A Vestey Drive, PO Box 12893, Penrose, Auckland, 1060, New Zealand
Tel.: (64) 800763862
Precision Engineering Product Mfr
N.A.I.C.S.: 332721
Duncan Gilmore *(Mgr-Sls)*

Norgren Ltd (1)
6/F Benson Tower 74 Hung To Road, Kwun Tong, China (Hong Kong)
Tel.: (852) 2 498 0705
Web Site: https://www.norgren.com
Sales Range: $25-49.9 Million
Emp.: 10
Fluid Control System Mfr
N.A.I.C.S.: 334519

Norgren Ltd (1)
Blenheim Way Fradley Park, Lichfield, WS13 8SY, Staffordshire, United Kingdom
Tel.: (44) 154 326 5000
Web Site: https://www.norgren.com
Emp.: 300
Fluid Control System Mfr
N.A.I.C.S.: 332912

Norgren Ltda (1)
Av Engineer Alberto de Zagottis 696-B, Sao Paulo, 04675-085, Brazil
Tel.: (55) 1156984000
Web Site: https://www.norgren.com
Pneumatic Tool Mfr
N.A.I.C.S.: 332912
Ricardo Rodrigues *(Pres)*

Norgren Manufacturing (Suzhou) Co., Ltd. (1)
No 975 Xinzi Road Wujiang Economic & Technological Development Zone, Minhang District, Suzhou, 215200, Jiangsu, China
Tel.: (86) 4006768030
Fluid Control Component Mfr
N.A.I.C.S.: 332912

Norgren Manufacturing Co Ltd (1)
Building 3 No 1885 Duhui Road, Minhang Dist, Shanghai, 201108, China
Tel.: (86) 2124161800
Industrial Machinery Mfr
N.A.I.C.S.: 333248

Norgren Manufacturing de Mexico SA de CV (1)
Av De la Montana 120 Parque Industrial Queretaro, 76220, Santiago de Queretaro, Queretaro, Mexico
Tel.: (52) 4422295000
Industrial Machinery Mfr
N.A.I.C.S.: 333248

Norgren NV (1)
Fr Walravensstraat 84, Beersel, 1651, Lot, Belgium
Tel.: (32) 23334411
Web Site: https://www.norgren.com
Emp.: 47
Industrial Machinery Mfr
N.A.I.C.S.: 333248

Norgren Pte Ltd (1)
Jtc Space Tuas 16B Tuas Ave 1 03-40, Singapore, 639534, Singapore
Tel.: (65) 68621811
Web Site: https://www.norgren.com
Sales Range: $25-49.9 Million
Emp.: 50
Industrial Machinery Mfr
N.A.I.C.S.: 333248

Norgren Pty Ltd (1)
33 South Corporate Ave, Rowville, 3178, VIC, Australia
Tel.: (61) 39 213 0800
Web Site: https://www.norgren.com
Sales Range: $25-49.9 Million
Emp.: 90
Fluid Power Cylinder Mfr
N.A.I.C.S.: 333995

Norgren SAS (1)
1 rue de Lamirault, 77090, Collegien, France
Tel.: (33) 160049595
Web Site: https://www.norgren.com
Industrial Fluid Control Machinery Mfr
N.A.I.C.S.: 333248

Norgren SpA (1)
Via Roma 108 Cap, 20051, Milan, Monza And Brianza, Italy
Tel.: (39) 03960631
Fluid Control Machinery Mfr
N.A.I.C.S.: 332912

Norgren Sweden AB (1)
Ventilgatan 6, PO Box 14001, 200 24, Malmo, Sweden
Tel.: (46) 40595100
Web Site: https://www.norgren.com
Sales Range: $25-49.9 Million
Emp.: 3
Fluid Control System Mfr
N.A.I.C.S.: 332912

Norgren Taiwan Co. Limited (1)
3F No 540 Sec 1 Minsheng N Rd, Gulshan Dist, Taoyuan, 333, Taiwan
Tel.: (886) 32128813
Precision Engineering Product Mfr
N.A.I.C.S.: 332721

Orton srl (1)
Via Dei Bazachi 50, 29121, Piacenza, Italy
Tel.: (39) 0523762511
Web Site: https://www.ortonvalve.com
Industrial Valve Mfr
N.A.I.C.S.: 332911
Stefano Nucci *(Mgr-Sls)*

PBM, Inc. (1)
1070 Sandy Hill Rd, Irwin, PA 15642
Tel.: (724) 863-0550
Web Site: http://www.pbmvalve.com
Industrial Valve Mfr
N.A.I.C.S.: 332911
Matthew Cullen *(Dir-Life Sciences-Global & Reg Mgr)*

Remosa S.R.L. (1)
VI Strada Ovest - Macchiareddu, Uta, 09068, Cagliari, Italy
Tel.: (39) 07020201
Web Site: https://www.remosa-valves.com
Emp.: 223
Valve Mfr

INTERNATIONAL PUBLIC

N.A.I.C.S.: 332911
Cristian Argiolas *(Mgr-R&D)*

STI S.R.L. (1)
Via Dei Caravaggi 15, Levate, 24040, Bergamo, Italy
Tel.: (39) 03529282
Web Site: https://www.stiactuation.com
Valve Mfr
N.A.I.C.S.: 332911

Stainless Steel Fasteners Ltd (1)
Broombank Road, Chesterfield, S41 9QJ, United Kingdom
Tel.: (44) 1246 451818
Web Site: http://www.ssfast.co.uk
Sales Range: $25-49.9 Million
Emp.: 80
Steel Fastener Products Mfr
N.A.I.C.S.: 339993

TA Heimeier GmbH (1)
Vollinghauser Weg, Erwitte, 59597, Germany
Tel.: (49) 2943 891 0
Web Site: http://www.taheimeier.de
Sales Range: $100-124.9 Million
Emp.: 400
Value & Control System Mfr
N.A.I.C.S.: 332911
Claus Biernoth *(Mng Dir)*

TA Hydronics AS (1)
Glynitveien 7, 1400, Ski, Norway
Tel.: (47) 64 91 16 10
Web Site: http://www.tahydronics.com
Sales Range: $25-49.9 Million
Emp.: 9
Measuring Instrument & Valve Mfr
N.A.I.C.S.: 332911
Ove Hjelleset *(Dir-Admin)*

TA Regulator d.o.o (1)
Orliska Ulica 13, 8250, Brezice, Slovenia
Tel.: (386) 74966100
Web Site: https://www.imi-hydronic.com
Sales Range: $25-49.9 Million
Emp.: 59
Hydraulic Equipment Mfr
N.A.I.C.S.: 333996

Thompson Valves Ltd (1)
17 Balena Close Creekmoor, Poole, BH17 7EF, Dorset, United Kingdom
Tel.: (44) 1202697521
Web Site: http://www.thompson-valves.com
Sales Range: $50-74.9 Million
Emp.: 161
Industrial Valve Mfr
N.A.I.C.S.: 332911
Dave Whitfield *(Dir-Bus Excellence)*

Tour & Andersson A/S (1)
Lsykaer 9, 2730, Herlev, Denmark
Tel.: (45) 44 570999
Web Site: http://www.imi-hydronic.com
Industrial Machinery Mfr
N.A.I.C.S.: 333248

Tour & Andersson NV/SA (1)
Boomsesteenweg 28, 2627, Schelle, Belgium
Tel.: (32) 3 640 33 80
Web Site: http://www.tourandersson.be
Sales Range: $25-49.9 Million
Emp.: 15
Industrial Machinery Distr
N.A.I.C.S.: 423830
Rudy Ballegeer *(Dir-Sls)*

Tour & Andersson Oy (1)
Robert Huberin Tie 7, 01510, Vantaa, Finland
Tel.: (358) 207 401 600
Web Site: http://www.tour-andersson-oy.rakentajalle.fi
Plumbing & Heating Equipment Whslr
N.A.I.C.S.: 423720

Tour & Andersson SA (1)
Paris Nord II - 13 rue de la Perdrix Batiment Les Flamants 8 - Hall E, BP 82054, Tremblay en France, 95931, Charles de Gaulle, France
Tel.: (33) 1 58 02 08 20
Web Site: https://www.tahydronics.com
Industrial Machinery Mfr
N.A.I.C.S.: 333248

Tour & Andersson SA (1)
Complejo Europa Empresarial C/Playa de

Liencres 2, Las Rozas, 28230, Madrid, Spain
Tel.: (34) 91 640 12 95
Industrial Machinery Mfr & Distr
N.A.I.C.S.: 333248

Truflo International plc (1)
Lakeside Solihull Parkway Birmingham Business Park, Birmingham, B37 7XZ, West Midlands, United Kingdom
Tel.: (44) 1217173700
Web Site: http://www.truflointernational.com
Sales Range: $125-149.9 Million
Emp.: 70
Valves & Flow Control Equipment Mfr & Distr
N.A.I.C.S.: 332912

Truflo Marine Ltd (1)
2 Priory Road Aston, Birmingham, B6 7LG, United Kingdom
Tel.: (44) 1213274789
Web Site: http://www.truflomarine.com
Industrial Valve Mfr & Distr
N.A.I.C.S.: 332919

Truflo Rona S.R.L. (1)
Via Grilli 2/A, San Nicolo di Rottofreno, 29010, Belluno, Italy
Tel.: (39) 0523766111
Security Valve & Loader Mfr
N.A.I.C.S.: 332911

Z & J High Temperature Equipment (Shanghai) Co., Ltd. (1)
No 2 Workshop 819 Yinchunh Road, Minhang District, Shanghai, 201109, China
Tel.: (86) 216497780
Valve Mfr
N.A.I.C.S.: 332911

Z&J Technologies GmbH (1)
Bertramsweg 6, 52355, Duren, Germany (90%)
Tel.: (49) 24216910
Web Site: https://www.zjtechnologies.de
Sales Range: $150-199.9 Million
Emp.: 300
Industrial Valve Mfr
N.A.I.C.S.: 332911

Subsidiary (Domestic):

Th. Jansen-Armaturen GmbH (2)
Blucherstrasse 47, 66386, Saint Ingbert, Germany
Tel.: (49) 68945930
Web Site: http://www.thj-a.de
Sales Range: $10-24.9 Million
Emp.: 120
Pipe Systems Products for Water, Gas & Industrial Applications Including Pumps & Valves
N.A.I.C.S.: 486990

Subsidiary (US):

Zimmermann & Jansen, Inc. (2)
4525 Kennedy Commerce Dr, Houston, TX 77032
Tel.: (281) 446-8000
Web Site: http://www.zjinc.com
Sales Range: $25-49.9 Million
Emp.: 100
Industrial Valve Mfr
N.A.I.C.S.: 332911
Nick Andryuk (Pres)

Subsidiary (Non-US):

Zimmermann & Jansen, S.A. (Pty.) Ltd. (2)
11 Michelin Street, PO Box 1335, Vanderbijlpark, 1900, South Africa
Tel.: (27) 169860159
Web Site: http://www.zjtechnologies.de
Sales Range: $25-49.9 Million
Emp.: 80
Industrial Valve Mfr
N.A.I.C.S.: 332911

IMI SOFTWARE LTD.
Kautilya 6-3-652, Somajiguda, Hyderabad, 500 082, India
Tel.: (91) 4023310233
Web Site: http://www.imisoft.com
Sales Range: $25-49.9 Million
Emp.: 130
Software Technology & Professional Services
N.A.I.C.S.: 541511
Aluri R. Vishwanath (Founder & Chm)

IMING CORP.
Langham Place Office Tower Suite 2512 8 Argyle St, Mong Kok, China (Hong Kong)
Tel.: (852) 36193974
Year Founded: 1983
IMNG—(OTCIQ)
Sales Range: Less than $1 Million
Broadcasting Services
N.A.I.C.S.: 516210

IMINING TECHNOLOGIES INC.
580 Hornby Street Suite 750, Vancouver, V6C 3B6, BC, Canada
Tel.: (604) 602-4935 BC
Web Site: https://www.imining.com
Year Founded: 2007
IMIN—(DEU)
Assets: $12,882,292
Liabilities: $197,449
Net Worth: $12,684,843
Earnings: ($1,866,061)
Emp.: 35
Fiscal Year-end: 05/31/21
Data Mining Services
N.A.I.C.S.: 518210
Robert Eadie (Pres & CEO)

IMJACK PLC
57 Cardigan Lane, Leeds, LS4 2LE, United Kingdom
Tel.: (44) 8708368700
Sales Range: Less than $1 Million
Emp.: 25
Secure Instant Messaging Software Developer
N.A.I.C.S.: 513210
Jeffrey C. Morris (Interim CEO)

IMM INVESTMENT CORP
5F Gangnam Finance Center 152 Teheran-ro, Gangnam-gu, Seoul, 06236, Korea (South)
Tel.: (82) 2 2112 1777
Web Site: http://imm.co.kr
Investment Services
N.A.I.C.S.: 523999

IMMATICS N.V.
Paul-Ehrlich-Str 15 - 19, 72076, Tubingen, Germany
Tel.: (49) 707153970 NI
Web Site: https://www.immatics.com
Year Founded: 2000
4A3—(DEU)
Rev.: $59,608,980
Assets: $562,929,545
Liabilities: $314,470,486
Net Worth: $248,459,060
Earnings: ($107,064,351)
Emp.: 343
Fiscal Year-end: 12/31/23
Biotechnology Research & Development Services
N.A.I.C.S.: 541714
Arnd Christ (CFO)

Subsidiaries:

Immatics Biotechnologies GmbH (1)
Machtlfinger Str 11, 81379, Munich, Germany
Tel.: (49) 895404150
Pharmaceuticals Mfr
N.A.I.C.S.: 325412

Immatics US, Inc. (1)
2201 W Holcombe Blvd Ste 205, Houston, TX 77430
Tel.: (346) 204-5400
Pharmaceuticals Mfr
N.A.I.C.S.: 325412

IMMEDIA GROUP PLC
7-9 The Broadway, Newbury, RG14 1AS, Berkshire, United Kingdom
Tel.: (44) 8456301635
Web Site: https://avcimmedia.com
Year Founded: 2000
Rev.: $5,947,813
Assets: $2,501,577
Liabilities: $2,224,435
Net Worth: $277,143
Earnings: $197,649
Emp.: 33
Fiscal Year-end: 12/31/18
In-Store Radio Stations Operator
N.A.I.C.S.: 516210
Bruno Brookes (Founder)

Subsidiaries:

Immedia Broadcasting Trustees Limited (1)
79 Broadway, Newbury, RG141AS, Berkshire, United Kingdom
Tel.: (44) 8456348488
Web Site: http://www.immediaplc.com
Sales Range: $50-74.9 Million
Trust Management Services
N.A.I.C.S.: 523991

IMMERSION GAMES SA
Ciszewskiego 15 Street, 02-777, Warsaw, Poland
Tel.: (48) 505029821
Web Site: https://www.immersion.games
Year Founded: 2014
IMGP—(WAR)
Software Development Services
N.A.I.C.S.: 541511
Bartosz Roslonski (Pres)

IMMERSION SA
3 rue Raymond Lavigne, 33100, Bordeaux, France
Tel.: (33) 557541700
Web Site: https://www.immersion.fr
Year Founded: 1994
ALIMR—(EUR)
Sales Range: $1-9.9 Million
Emp.: 45
High End Display System Mfr
N.A.I.C.S.: 334513
Christophe Chartier (Founder & Pres)

IMMI AD
ul Iliensko shose 10 p k 107, District of Nadezhda, 1220, Sofia, 1220, Bulgaria
Tel.: (359) 29382857
IMMI—(BUL)
Sales Range: Less than $1 Million
Metal Cutting & Metal Machine Mfr
N.A.I.C.S.: 333517

IMMO MECHELEN CITY CENTER S.A.
Avenue du Port 2, 1080, Brussels, Belgium
MCC—(EUR)
Real Estate Investment Services
N.A.I.C.S.: 531190
Kim Mario Jos (Chm)

IMMO MOURY SCA
BTE 71 Rue des Anglais 6A, Ans, 4430, Liege, Belgium
Tel.: (32) 42210310
Web Site: https://www.immomoury.com
Year Founded: 2007
IMMOU—(EUR)
Sales Range: $1-9.9 Million
Real Estate Investment Services
N.A.I.C.S.: 525990
Sonia Laschet (CFO & Fin Dir)

IMMO-BEAULIEU NV
Havenlaan 2, 1080, Brussels, Belgium
Tel.: (32) 24295930
BEAB—(EUR)
Sales Range: $1-9.9 Million
Investment Management Service
N.A.I.C.S.: 523940
Hubert de Peuter (CEO)

IMMOBEL SA
Rue de la Regence 58, 1000, Brussels, Belgium
Tel.: (32) 24225311 BE
Web Site: https://www.immobel.be
Year Founded: 1863
IMMO—(EUR)
Rev.: $263,193,395
Assets: $1,886,495,791
Liabilities: $1,267,954,889
Net Worth: $618,540,902
Earnings: $11,572,415
Emp.: 200
Fiscal Year-end: 12/31/22
Real Estate Investment Trust; Commercial Real Estate Development & Property Management
N.A.I.C.S.: 525990
Adel Yahia (Chm & Mng Dir)

Subsidiaries:

ALLFIN NV-SA (1)
Rue de la regence 58, 1000, Brussels, Belgium
Tel.: (32) 24225311
Web Site: http://www.allfin.be
Real Estate Development Services
N.A.I.C.S.: 531190

Compagnie Immobiliere de Lotissements (Lotinvest) (1)
BoulevardAnspach1, 1000, Brussels, Belgium
Tel.: (32) 24225311
Web Site: https://www.immobelgroup.com
Sales Range: $50-74.9 Million
Emp.: 10
Real Estate Rental Services
N.A.I.C.S.: 531190

Compagnie Immobiliere de Participations Financieres (1)
Ave Jean Dubrucq 175, Saint-Jean, 1080, Molenbeek, Belgium
Tel.: (32) 92 356570
Real Estate Financial Services
N.A.I.C.S.: 522292

Compagnie Immobiliere de Wallonie (CIW) (1)
Rue de Le Rejence No 58, 1000, Brussels, Belgium
Tel.: (32) 24225311
Web Site: http://www.immobel.be
Sales Range: $25-49.9 Million
Real Estate Agencies
N.A.I.C.S.: 531210

Immobilien Vennootschap van Vlaanderen (Investimmo) (1)
Regentschapsstraat 58, 1000, Brussels, Belgium
Tel.: (32) 24225311
Sales Range: $25-49.9 Million
Real Estate Agencies
N.A.I.C.S.: 531210
Alexander Hodac (Mng Dir)

Immobiliere Deka (1)
Rue de la Regence No 58, 1000, Brussels, Belgium
Tel.: (32) 24225311
Sales Range: $25-49.9 Million
Emp.: 35
Real Estate Agencies
N.A.I.C.S.: 531210
Gaetan Piret (CEO)

Progex (1)
175 Ave Jean Dubrucq, 1080, Molenbeek, Belgium
Tel.: (32) 24225311
Web Site: http://www.immobel.be
Sales Range: $25-49.9 Million
Real Estate Agencies
N.A.I.C.S.: 531210

Projectontwikkelingsmaatschappij Immo (1)

IMMOBEL SA

Immobel SA—(Continued)

Regentschapsstraat 58, 1000, Brussels, Belgium
Tel.: (32) 24226311
Real Estate Agencies
N.A.I.C.S.: 531210

IMMOBILIERE DISTRI-LAND NV
Havenlaan 12, BE-1080, Brussels, Belgium
Tel.: (32) 24291548
DISL—(EUR)
Sales Range: $1-9.9 Million
Real Estate Investment Services
N.A.I.C.S.: 531210
Kim Creten *(Chm & CEO)*

IMMOBILIERE HOTELIERE SA
48 rue de la Bienfaisance, 75008, Paris, France
Tel.: (33) 142997400
Web Site: http://www.ihgroupe.fr
Real Estate Support Services
N.A.I.C.S.: 531390
Nicolas Schlumberger *(Chm & CEO)*

IMMOBILIERE PARISIENNE DE LA PERLE ET DES PIERRES PRECIEUSES SA
48 avenue Victor Hugo, 75116, Paris, France
Tel.: (33) 145230892
Holding Company
N.A.I.C.S.: 551112
Francois Gontier *(Chm & CEO)*

IMMOFINANZ AG
Wienerbergstrasse 9, 1100, Vienna, Austria
Tel.: (43) 188090
Web Site: https://www.immofinanz.com
Year Founded: 1990
IIA—(WAR)
Rev.: $802,468,264
Assets: $10,652,298,268
Liabilities: $5,615,225,743
Net Worth: $5,037,072,525
Earnings: ($253,296,170)
Emp.: 174
Fiscal Year-end: 12/31/23
Nonresidential Property Managers
N.A.I.C.S.: 531312
Stefan Schoenauer *(CFO & Member-Exec Bd)*

Subsidiaries:

Center Invest Kft. (1)
Nagy Lajos Kiraly utja 10, 1148, Budapest, Hungary
Tel.: (36) 613432975
Web Site: https://www.centerinvest.eu
Real Estate Management Services
N.A.I.C.S.: 531320

Central Bud Sp. z o. o (1)
Grojecka 5, Warsaw, 02-019, Poland
Tel.: (48) 224605189
Real Estate Manangement Services
N.A.I.C.S.: 531390

Expo Business Park S.R.L. (1)
54A Comandor Aviator Popisteanu, District 1, 012095, Bucharest, Romania
Tel.: (40) 213176060
Web Site: https://expobusinesspark.ro
Parks & Sports Facilities Services
N.A.I.C.S.: 711310

Frescura Investments B.V (1)
Leliegracht 10, Amsterdam, 1015 DE, Netherlands
Tel.: (31) 205216344
Real Estate Manangement Services
N.A.I.C.S.: 531390

Grand Centar d.o.o (1)
2 Hektoroviceva, Zagreb, 10000, Croatia
Tel.: (385) 14882555
Real Estate Manangement Services

N.A.I.C.S.: 531390

IMMOFINANZ Deutschland GmbH (1)
Von-Werth-Strasse 1, 50670, Cologne, Germany
Tel.: (49) 221922850
Commercial Real Estate Services
N.A.I.C.S.: 531210

IMMOFINANZ Services Czech Republic, s.r.o (1)
Jugoslavska 620, Prague, Czech Republic
Tel.: (420) 224007740
Real Estate Manangement Services
N.A.I.C.S.: 531390

IMMOFINANZ Services Hungary Kft (1)
Arboc u 6, 1133, Budapest, Hungary
Tel.: (36) 12360435
Real Estate Manangement Services
N.A.I.C.S.: 531390

IMMOFINANZ Services Poland Sp. z o.o (1)
Europejski 1 sq, 00-844, Warsaw, Poland
Tel.: (48) 222563400
Web Site: http://www.immofinanz.com
Real Estate Manangement Services
N.A.I.C.S.: 531390

IMMOFINANZ Services Slovak Republic, s.r.o (1)
Vajnorska 100/B, 831 04, Bratislava, Slovakia
Tel.: (421) 249203911
Web Site: http://www.immofinanz.com
Real Estate Manangement Services
N.A.I.C.S.: 531390

Immoeast AG (1)
Wienerbergstrasse 11, 1100, Vienna, Austria (54%)
Tel.: (43) 188090
Web Site: http://www.immoeast.com
Sales Range: $250-299.9 Million
Emp.: 16
Investment Property Services
N.A.I.C.S.: 531312
Stefan Schoenauer *(CFO & Member-Exec Bd)*

Subsidiary (Non-US):

ELCO Sp. z o.o. (2)
Hetmanska 30, 60-252, Poznan, Poland
Tel.: (48) 618665581
Holding Company
N.A.I.C.S.: 551112

IMMOEAST Netherlands II B.V (2)
Leliegracht 10, Amsterdam, 1015 DE, Netherlands
Tel.: (31) 205216341
Real Estate Manangement Services
N.A.I.C.S.: 531390

IMV Hungaria Kft (2)
Becsi Ut 3-5, Budapest, Hungary
Tel.: (36) 13528542
Sales Range: $25-49.9 Million
Real Estate Property Lessors
N.A.I.C.S.: 531190

Subsidiary (Domestic):

Immoeast Acquisition & Management GmbH (2)
Bankgasse 2, Vienna, Austria
Tel.: (43) 15328760
Real Estate Property Lessors
N.A.I.C.S.: 531190

Immoeast GmbH (2)
Bankgasse 2, 1010, Vienna, Austria
Tel.: (43) 15320639
Holding Company
N.A.I.C.S.: 551112

Subsidiary (Non-US):

Iride S.A. (2)
9-9a Dimitrie Pompei Bld, Sector 2, Bucharest, Romania
Tel.: (40) 212421524
Real Estate Investment Trust
N.A.I.C.S.: 525990

Polus a.s. (2)
Vajnorska 100, Okres Bratislava III, 83104,

Bratislava, Slovakia
Tel.: (421) 249102030
Web Site: http://www.poluscitycenter.sk
Sales Range: $25-49.9 Million
Emp.: 22
Holding Company
N.A.I.C.S.: 551112

Silesia Residential Project Sp. z o.o. (2)
Chorzowska 109 A 40-101, Katowice, 40-101, Poland
Tel.: (48) 326050058
Web Site: http://www.debowetarasy.com
Sales Range: $25-49.9 Million
Emp.: 5
Residential Buildings & Dwellings Lessors
N.A.I.C.S.: 531110
Janus Orlsinski *(Mng Dir)*

Szepvolgyi Business Park Kft. (2)
Szepvolgyi ut 35-37, 1037, Budapest, Hungary
Tel.: (36) 14368800
Web Site: http://www.szepvolgyibp.hu
Real Estate Agency
N.A.I.C.S.: 531210

LLC Real Estate Investment Management (1)
Presnenskaya nab Nr 10 C, Moscow, 123317, Russia
Tel.: (7) 4955807000
Web Site: http://www.immofinanz.com
Emp.: 97
Real Estate Manangement Services
N.A.I.C.S.: 531390

OOO Krona Design (1)
11 Prospekt Novoyasenevski, Moscow, 117588, Russia
Tel.: (7) 4953801690
Real Estate Manangement Services
N.A.I.C.S.: 531390

Ocean Atlantic DORCOL d.o.o. (1)
Mike Alasa 34, Belgrade, 11001, Serbia
Tel.: (381) 653226107
Web Site: http://www.oceanatlantic.com
Real Estate Manangement Services
N.A.I.C.S.: 531390

Perlagonia 1 Holding GmbH (1)
Wienerbergstrasse 11, Vienna, 1100, Austria
Tel.: (43) 571110
Web Site: http://www.immofinanz.com
Real Estate Manangement Services
N.A.I.C.S.: 531390

Rheinische Lagerhaus GmbH (1)
Akazienallee 65, Mulheim an der Ruhr, 45478, Germany
Tel.: (49) 208469230
Real Estate Manangement Services
N.A.I.C.S.: 531390

Subsidiary (Domestic):

Deutsche Lagerhaus Beteiligungs GmbH u. Co KG (2)
Akazienallee 65, Mulheim an der Ruhr, 45478, Germany
Tel.: (49) 208469230
Real Estate Manangement Services
N.A.I.C.S.: 531390

Deutsche Lagerhaus GmbH u. Co KG (2)
Akazienallee 65-71, 45478, Mulheim an der Ruhr, Germany
Tel.: (49) 208 469 23 0
Web Site: http://www.deutschelagerhaus.de
Sales Range: $25-49.9 Million
Emp.: 15
Real Estate Manangement Services
N.A.I.C.S.: 531390

Deutsche Lagerhaus Poing GmbH u. Co KG (2)
Akazienallee 65, Mulheim an der Ruhr, 45478, Germany
Tel.: (49) 208469230
Real Estate Manangement Services
N.A.I.C.S.: 531390

Deutsche Lagerhaus neunzehnte Objekt GmbH & Co KG (2)
Akazienallee 65, Mulheim an der Ruhr, 45478, Germany

INTERNATIONAL PUBLIC

Tel.: (49) 208469230
Real Estate Manangement Services
N.A.I.C.S.: 531390

RHEIN-INVEST GmbH (2)
Akazienallee 65, Mulheim an der Ruhr, 45478, Germany
Tel.: (49) 208469230
Real Estate Management Services
N.A.I.C.S.: 531390

Valette Finance B.V (1)
Leliegracht 10, Amsterdam, 1015 DE, Netherlands
Tel.: (31) 205216344
Real Estate Manangement Services
N.A.I.C.S.: 531390

IMMSI S.P.A.
P zza Vilfredo Pareto 3, 46100, Mantua, Italy
Tel.: (39) 03762541
Web Site: https://www.immsi.it
IMS—(ITA)
Rev.: $1,691,000,300
Assets: $2,613,578,037
Liabilities: $2,169,017,797
Net Worth: $444,560,240
Earnings: $19,413,561
Emp.: 385
Fiscal Year-end: 12/31/20
Diversified Real Estate Services
N.A.I.C.S.: 531390
Roberto Colaninno *(Chm)*

Subsidiaries:

Intermarine S.p.A. (1)
Via Alta 100, 19038, Sarzana, SP, Italy
Tel.: (39) 0187 6171
Web Site: https://www.intermarine.it
Ship Construction Services
N.A.I.C.S.: 811310
Livio Corghi *(CEO)*

Is Molas S.p.A. (1)
Loc Is Molas, Pula, 09010, Cagliari, Sardinia, Italy
Tel.: (39) 070 924 1006
Web Site: https://www.ismolas.it
Hotel Services
N.A.I.C.S.: 721110

Piaggio & C. SpA (1)
Viale Rinaldo Piaggio 25, 56025, Pontedera, PI, Italy (56%)
Tel.: (39) 0587272111
Web Site: https://www.piaggiogroup.com
Rev.: $2,252,798,403
Assets: $2,114,015,757
Liabilities: $1,663,108,137
Net Worth: $450,907,619
Earnings: $91,613,425
Emp.: 5,650
Fiscal Year-end: 12/31/2022
Motorized Two-Wheeled Vehicles Mfr
N.A.I.C.S.: 336991
Roberto Colaninno *(Chm & CEO)*

Subsidiary (Domestic):

Aprilia SpA (2)
Via Galilei Galileo 1, Noale, 30033, Venice, Italy
Tel.: (39) 0415829111
Web Site: http://www.aprilia.com
Sales Range: $350-399.9 Million
Emp.: 1,200
Motorcycles & Scooters Mfr
N.A.I.C.S.: 336991

Subsidiary (US):

Piaggio Group Americas, Inc. (3)
257 Park Ave S 4th Fl, New York, NY 10010
Tel.: (212) 380-4400
Web Site: http://www.motoguzzi-us.com
Sales Range: $25-49.9 Million
Emp.: 60
Motorcycle Importer & Distr
N.A.I.C.S.: 441227
Alessandro Zappia *(Mgr-Trade Mktg)*

Subsidiary (US):

Piaggio USA, Inc. (2)
257 Pk Ave South 4th Fl, New York, NY 10010

Tel.: (212) 380-4400
Web Site: http://www.piaggiousa.com
Sales Range: $25-49.9 Million
Emp.: 45
Scooters & Accessories Distr
N.A.I.C.S.: 336991

Piaggio Deutschland GmbH (1)
Reisholzer Werftstrasse 40, 40589, Dusseldorf, Germany
Tel.: (49) 21 117 5220
Web Site: https://www.de.piaggio.com
Automobile Parts Mfr
N.A.I.C.S.: 336390

Piaggio Vehicles Private Limited (1)
Sky one 8th Floor Sno 210 Final Plot No 72, Town Planning Scheme Yerwada No 1 Kalyani Nagar, Pune, 411006, Maharashtra, India
Tel.: (91) 206 749 2800
Web Site: https://piaggio-cv.co.in
Vehicle Mfr.
N.A.I.C.S.: 336110
Diego Graffi *(CEO & Mng Dir)*

IMMUNO-BIOLOGICAL LABORATORIES CO., LTD.
1091-1 Naka Aza-Higashida, Fujioka, 375-0005, Gunma, Japan
Tel.: (81) 274222889
Web Site: https://www.ibl-japan.co.jp
Year Founded: 1982
4570—(TKS)
Rev.: $5,393,760
Assets: $10,694,980
Liabilities: $2,333,330
Net Worth: $8,361,650
Earnings: $1,229,460
Emp.: 57
Fiscal Year-end: 03/31/24
Medical & Biological Research & Development Services
N.A.I.C.S.: 541715
Tsutomu Seito *(Pres)*

Subsidiaries:

Skylight Biotech, Inc. (1)
100-4 Sunada Iijima-aza, Chiyoda-ku, Akita, 011-0911, Japan
Tel.: (81) 188805060
Web Site: http://www.skylight-biotech.com
Research & Development Services
N.A.I.C.S.: 541715
Tsutomu Seito *(Chm)*

IMMUNOCORE HOLDINGS PLC
92 Park Drive Milton Park, Abingdon, OX14 4RY, Oxfordshire, United Kingdom
Tel.: (44) 1235438600 UK
Web Site:
  https://www.immunocore.com
Year Founded: 2021
IMCR—(NASDAQ)
Rev.: $195,154,600
Assets: $591,311,499
Liabilities: $212,838,903
Net Worth: $378,472,596
Earnings: ($55,970,649)
Emp.: 408
Fiscal Year-end: 12/31/22
Holding Company
N.A.I.C.S.: 551112
Bahija Jallal *(CEO)*

Subsidiaries:

Immunocore Commercial LLC (1)
6 Tower Bridge Ste 200 181 Washington St, Conshohocken, PA 19428
Tel.: (484) 534-5261
Biotechnology Research Services
N.A.I.C.S.: 541714

IMMUNODIAGNOSTIC SYSTEMS HOLDINGS PLC
10 Didcot Way Boldon Business Park, Boldon, NE35 9PD, Tyne and Wear, United Kingdom

Tel.: (44) 1915190660
Web Site: http://www.idsplc.com
IDH—(LSE)
Rev.: $48,873,767
Assets: $83,652,529
Liabilities: $13,471,916
Net Worth: $70,180,613
Earnings: $1,010,140
Emp.: 283
Fiscal Year-end: 03/31/19
Medical Diagnostic Products Distributor & Mfr
N.A.I.C.S.: 334510
Burkhard Wittek *(Chm)*

Subsidiaries:

Immunodiagnostic Systems Limited (1)
10 Didcot Way, Boldon Business Park, Boldon, NE35 9PD, Tyne and Wear, United Kingdom
Tel.: (44) 1915190660
Web Site: http://www.idsltd.com
Sales Range: $25-49.9 Million
Emp.: 100
Medical Diagnostic Equipments Mfr & Distr
N.A.I.C.S.: 334510

Subsidiary (Non-US):

IDS GmbH (2)
Mainzer Landstrasse 49, 60329, Frankfurt am Main, Hesse, Germany
Tel.: (49) 6930855025
Sales Range: $25-49.9 Million
Emp.: 10
Diagnostic Test Kits Distr
N.A.I.C.S.: 423450
Rudolf Schemer *(Mng Dir)*

Immunodiagnostic Systems France SAS (2)
42 Rue Stephane Mazeau, Pouilly-en-Auxois, 21320, Dijon, France
Tel.: (33) 390907307
Web Site: http://www.idsplc.com
Sales Range: $25-49.9 Million
Diagnostic Test Kits Distr
N.A.I.C.S.: 423450

Subsidiary (US):

Immunodiagnostic Systems, Inc. (2)
948 Clopper Rd, Gaithersburg, MD 20878
Tel.: (480) 278-8333
Web Site: http://www.idsplc.com
Sales Range: $1-9.9 Million
Emp.: 20
Diagnostic Equipment Distr
N.A.I.C.S.: 423450

Immunodiagnostic Systems Nordic A/S (1)
Marielundvej 30 2 Sal, 2730, Herlev, Denmark
Tel.: (45) 44840091
Web Site: http://www.idsnordic.com
Sales Range: $50-74.9 Million
Emp.: 3
Diagnostic Test Kits Distr
N.A.I.C.S.: 423450

IMMUNOPRECISE ANTIBODIES LTD.
3204-4464 Markham Street, Victoria, V8Z 7X8, BC, Canada
Tel.: (250) 483-0308
Web Site:
  https://www.immunoprecise.com
Year Founded: 1983
IPA—(NASDAQ)
Rev.: $18,111,842
Assets: $44,314,102
Liabilities: $19,256,113
Net Worth: $25,057,989
Earnings: ($20,076,088)
Emp.: 72
Fiscal Year-end: 04/30/24
Pharmaceutical Services
N.A.I.C.S.: 325412
Teri Otto *(Gen Mgr)*

IMMUNOTEC INC.
300 Joseph Carrier, Vaudreuil-Dorion, J7V 5V5, QC, Canada
Tel.: (450) 424-9992
Web Site: http://www.immunotec.com
Year Founded: 1996
Pharmaceuticals Product Mfr
N.A.I.C.S.: 325412

Subsidiaries:

Immunotec Medical Corp. (1)
300 Joseph-Carrier St, Vaudreuil-Dorion, J7V 5V5, QC, Canada
Tel.: (450) 424-9992
Web Site: http://www.immunotec.com
Health Care Products Mfr
N.A.I.C.S.: 325412

IMMUNOTECH BIOPHARM LTD.
8th Floor Building 1 No 1 Kangding Street, Beijing Economic & Technological Development Zone, Beijing, 100176, China
Tel.: (86) 1088400295 Ky
Web Site: https://www.eaal.net
Year Founded: 2006
6978—(HKG)
Rev.: $1,460,318
Assets: $117,174,900
Liabilities: $93,513,790
Net Worth: $23,661,110
Earnings: ($46,449,795)
Emp.: 197
Fiscal Year-end: 12/31/23
Biotechnology Research & Development Services
N.A.I.C.S.: 541714
Jian Zhang *(Sr VP)*

IMMUNOVIA AB
Medicon Village Scheelevagen 2, 223 63, Lund, Sweden
Tel.: (46) 462756000
Web Site:
  https://investor.immunovia.com
Year Founded: 2007
IMMNOV—(OMX)
Rev.: $112,769
Assets: $28,153,737
Liabilities: $5,318,685
Net Worth: $22,835,052
Earnings: ($15,743,816)
Emp.: 64
Fiscal Year-end: 12/31/22
Biotechnology Research & Development Services
N.A.I.C.S.: 541714
Carl Borrebaeck *(Chm)*

Subsidiaries:

Immunovia GmbH (1)
Hahnstr 70, 60528, Frankfurt, Germany
Tel.: (49) 69667780028
Healtcare Services
N.A.I.C.S.: 621999

IMMUPHARMA PLC
One Bartholomew Close, London, EC1A 7BL, United Kingdom
Tel.: (44) 2072062650
Web Site:
  https://www.immupharma.org
IMM—(AIM)
Rev.: $36,083
Assets: $5,017,295
Liabilities: $1,832,017
Net Worth: $3,185,278
Earnings: ($4,806,149)
Emp.: 13
Fiscal Year-end: 12/31/22
Pharmaceutical Development Services
N.A.I.C.S.: 325412
Dimitri F. Dimitriou *(Co-CEO & Co-Founder)*

Subsidiaries:

ImmuPharma France S.A. (1)
5 Rue du Rhone, F-68100, Mulhouse, Paris, France
Tel.: (33) 389661322
Web Site: https://www.immupharma.org
Sales Range: $25-49.9 Million
Emp.: 5
Pharmaceutical Research & Development Services
N.A.I.C.S.: 325412

IMMURON LIMITED
Building 10 25-37 Chapman Street, Melbourne, 3131, VIC, Australia
Tel.: (61) 388924854 AU
Web Site:
  https://www.immuron.com.au
Year Founded: 1994
IMC—(ASX)
Rev.: $3,273,815
Assets: $10,383,259
Liabilities: $1,896,718
Net Worth: $8,486,541
Earnings: ($4,632,049)
Emp.: 7
Fiscal Year-end: 06/30/24
Biotechnology Research & Development Services
N.A.I.C.S.: 541715
Phillip Allen Hains *(CFO & Sec)*

IMMUTEP LIMITED
Level 32 Suite 3207 Australia Square 264 George Street, Sydney, 2000, NSW, Australia
Tel.: (61) 283157003 AU
Web Site: https://www.immutep.com
Year Founded: 1987
IMM—(ASX)
Assets: $134,601,549
Liabilities: $8,051,241
Net Worth: $126,550,308
Earnings: ($28,523,387)
Emp.: 44
Fiscal Year-end: 06/30/24
Immunotherapeutic Products Mfr
N.A.I.C.S.: 541715
Marc Voigt *(CEO & CFO)*

IMO PRECISION CONTROLS LTD
1000 North Circular Road Staples Corner, London, NW2 7JP, United Kingdom
Tel.: (44) 2084526444
Web Site: http://www.imopc.com
Year Founded: 1972
Rev.: $21,447,454
Emp.: 74
Electronic Components Mfr
N.A.I.C.S.: 334419
Maurice Hatter *(Founder)*

Subsidiaries:

IMO Canada (1)
Suite 608 1B-701 Rossland Road East, Whitby, L1N 9K3, ON, Canada
Tel.: (905) 799-9237
Electronic Components Distr
N.A.I.C.S.: 423690

IMO Jeambrun Automation SAS (1)
30 rue de Rocroy, 94100, Saint Maur-des-Fosses, France
Tel.: (33) 145132781
Web Site: http://www.imojeambrun.fr
Electronic Components Distr
N.A.I.C.S.: 423690

IMO Pacific Pty Ltd (1)
1/34 Fallon Road, Landsdale, Perth, WA, Australia
Tel.: (61) 893025246
Web Site: http://www.imopacific.com.au
Electronic Components Distr
N.A.I.C.S.: 423690
David Gent *(Mng Dir)*

IMO Russia (1)

IMO PRECISION CONTROLS LTD

IMO Precision Controls Ltd—(Continued)

Unit 4063 9 Zemlyanoy Val, Moscow, 105064, Russia
Tel.: (7) 4959679322
Electronic Components Distr
N.A.I.C.S.: 423690

IMO South Africa (Pty) Ltd (1)
G16 Centurion Business Park Montague Gardens, Cape Town, 7441, South Africa
Tel.: (27) 215511787
Web Site: http://www.imopc.co.za
Electronic Components Distr
N.A.I.C.S.: 423690

IMOBILIARIA CONSTRUTORA GRAO-PARA, S.A.

Edificio Espaco Chiado rua da Misericordia 12 - 20, Office 19 - 5th floor, 1200-273, Lisbon, Portugal
Tel.: (351) 210121000
Web Site: https://www.graopara.pt
Year Founded: 1960
GPA—(EUR)
Sales Range: Less than $1 Million
Real Estate Manangement Services
N.A.I.C.S.: 531390

IMOS A.D.

Veljka Paunovica 21, Nis, Serbia
Tel.: (381) 22 712 930
Web Site: http://www.imos.rs
Year Founded: 1993
IMOS—(BEL)
Sales Range: Less than $1 Million
Emp.: 18
Commodity Contracts Dealing Services
N.A.I.C.S.: 523160
Zoran Obradovic (Exec Dir)

IMP POWERS LTD

Unit No 21a Film Centre Building 2nd Floor, 68 Tardeo Road Near AC Market, Mumbai, 400034, Maharashtra, India
Tel.: (91) 2223539180
Web Site: https://www.imp-powers.com
INDLMETER—(NSE)
Rev.: $9,109,999
Assets: $26,498,851
Liabilities: $49,941,415
Net Worth: ($23,442,564)
Earnings: $4,458,163
Emp.: 1,000
Fiscal Year-end: 03/31/22
Electrical Measuring Instruments, Testing Equipments & Power Transformers Mfr
N.A.I.C.S.: 335311
Ramdas Trimbak RajGuroo (Chm)

Subsidiaries:

IMP Powers Ltd. - Unit 1 (1)
Survey No 263/3/2/2 Village Sayli Umerkuin Road, Dadra & Nagar Haveli, Silvassa, 396230, India
Tel.: (91) 260 2630810
Web Site: http://www.imp-powers.com
Sales Range: $25-49.9 Million
Emp.: 30
Transformer Mfr
N.A.I.C.S.: 335311

IMPACT DEVELOPER & CONTRACTOR S.A.

Greenfield Baneasa, 31 -41 Padurea Mogosoaia Road District 1, Bucharest, Romania
Tel.: (40) 212307570
Web Site: https://www.impactsa.ro
Year Founded: 1991
IMP—(BUC)
Rev.: $36,861,289
Assets: $318,267,135
Liabilities: $120,719,285
Net Worth: $197,547,850
Earnings: $6,266,012
Emp.: 55
Fiscal Year-end: 12/31/23
Building Construction & Real Estate Services
N.A.I.C.S.: 531311
Iuliana Mihaela Urda (Chm)

Subsidiaries:

Actual Invest House SRL (1)
Drumul Padurea Neagra 34 Bloc Bl04A Parter Ap 1, 44 31 53 N 26 6 9 E 304 grade N-V sector 1, Bucharest, Romania
Tel.: (40) 729100975
Web Site: http://www.nord-rezidential.ro
Financial Investment Services
N.A.I.C.S.: 523999

IMPACT GROWTH REAL ESTATE INVESTMENT TRUST

10th Fl Bangkok Land Building 47/569 - 576 Popular 3 Road, Banmai Sub-district Pakkred District, Nonthaburi, 11120, Thailand
Tel.: (66) 28335579
Web Site: https://www.impactgrowthreit.com
Year Founded: 1999
IMPACT—(THA)
Rev.: $48,933,785
Assets: $566,567,193
Liabilities: $118,312,867
Net Worth: $448,254,326
Earnings: $26,167,754
Fiscal Year-end: 03/31/23
Real Estate Investment Trust Services
N.A.I.C.S.: 531190
Phichai Namsirikul (Chm)

IMPACT HEALTHCARE REIT PLC

The Scalpel 18th Floor 52 Lime Street, London, EC3M 7AF, United Kingdom
Tel.: (44) 2074090181
Web Site: https://www.impactreit.uk
IHR—(LSE)
Rev.: $49,418,293
Assets: $698,540,151
Liabilities: $163,267,188
Net Worth: $535,272,964
Earnings: $43,403,593
Fiscal Year-end: 12/31/21
Other Activities Related to Real Estate
N.A.I.C.S.: 531390
Mahesh Patel (Mng Partner)

IMPACT HOLDINGS (UK) PLC

7500 Daresbury Park, Daresbury, WA4 4BS, United Kingdom
Tel.: (44) 1928 793 550
Web Site: http://www.impactholdings.net
Sales Range: $1-9.9 Million
Emp.: 40
Loan Administration & IT Support Services
N.A.I.C.S.: 541511
Stuart Burn (Dir-Ops)

Subsidiaries:

Impact Bridging Solutions Limited (1)
Manchester Intl Office Ctr, Styal Road, Manchester, M22 5WB, United Kingdom
Tel.: (44) 8456521840
Web Site: http://www.impactbridging.com
Short Term Loan Providers
N.A.I.C.S.: 522291

Impact Funding (UK) Limited (1)
Manchester Intl Office Center, Styal Road, Manchester, M22 5HQ, United Kingdom
Tel.: (44) 1614379499
Web Site: http://www.impactholdings.net
Short Term Funding Solutions
N.A.I.C.S.: 522299

IMPACT INSURANCE BROKERS, INC.

1600 Steeles Avenue West Suite 214, Concord, L4K 4M2, ON, Canada
Tel.: (905) 660-6170
Web Site: http://www.impactinsurance.com
Insurance Products & Financial Services
N.A.I.C.S.: 524210
Howard Wasser (Pres)

IMPACT INVESTMENT GROUP PTY. LTD.

11 Prices Street, Saint Kilda, 3182, VIC, Australia
Tel.: (61) 3 8534 8060 AU
Web Site: http://www.impact-group.com.au
Property & Facility Asset Invesment & Portfolio Management Services
N.A.I.C.S.: 531390
Danny Almagor (Chm & CEO)

IMPACT MINERALS LIMITED

9 Richardson Street, West Perth, 6005, WA, Australia
Tel.: (61) 864546666 AU
Web Site: https://www.impactminerals.com.au
IPT—(ASX)
Rev.: $374,394
Assets: $10,607,481
Liabilities: $601,805
Net Worth: $10,005,676
Earnings: ($4,508,926)
Fiscal Year-end: 06/30/24
Uranium, Nickel, Platinum & Gold Mining
N.A.I.C.S.: 212220
Michael G. Jones (Mng Dir)

Subsidiaries:

Endeavour Minerals Pty Ltd (1)
42 Evelyn Avenue, Turramurra, 2074, NSW, Australia
Tel.: (61) 291447384
Mining Exploration Services
N.A.I.C.S.: 213114

IMPACT SILVER CORP.

Suite 303 543 Granville Street, Vancouver, V6C 1X8, BC, Canada
Tel.: (604) 664-7707 BC
Web Site: https://www.impactsilver.com
Year Founded: 2006
IPT—(DEU)
Rev.: $12,067,510
Assets: $50,820,355
Liabilities: $5,143,442
Net Worth: $45,676,912
Earnings: ($2,336,402)
Fiscal Year-end: 12/31/22
Silver Exploration & Mining
N.A.I.C.S.: 212220
Frederick W. Davidson (Pres & CEO)

Subsidiaries:

Minera Aguila Plateada S.A. de C.V. (1)
Jaime Balmes No 11 Torre D Piso 3 Miguel Hidalgo, Mexico, 11510, Mexico
Tel.: (52) 5555862559
Web Site: http://www.energold.com
Sales Range: $200-249.9 Million
Emp.: 30
Metal Mining Services
N.A.I.C.S.: 212220
Edgar Dominguez (Controller)

Minera El Porvenir de Zacualpan S.A. de C.V. (1)
Jaime Balmes No 11 Torre D Piso 3 Los Morales Polanco Miguel Hidalgo, Mexico, 11510, Mexico
Tel.: (52) 5555862559
Web Site: http://www.energold.com
Emp.: 20

INTERNATIONAL PUBLIC

Silver Ore Mining Services
N.A.I.C.S.: 212220
Beatriz Sanchez (Office Mgr)

IMPALA PLATINUM HOLDINGS LIMITED

2 Fricker Road, Illovo, 2196, South Africa
Tel.: (27) 117319000 ZA
Web Site: https://www.implats.co.za
IMPUF—(OTCIQ)
Rev.: $5,629,231,403
Assets: $8,945,278,256
Liabilities: $2,289,367,230
Net Worth: $6,655,911,026
Earnings: $326,260,311
Emp.: 70,000
Fiscal Year-end: 06/30/23
Platinum, Nickel, Copper & Cobalt Mining, Refining & Marketing
N.A.I.C.S.: 212230
Mandla Sizwe Vulindlela Gantsho (Chm)

Subsidiaries:

Impala Canada Ltd. (1)
69 Yonge Street Suite 700, Toronto, M5E 1K3, ON, Canada
Tel.: (416) 360-7590
Web Site: https://www.nap.com
Assets: $496,000,799
Liabilities: $93,087,190
Net Worth: $402,913,609
Earnings: $87,370,024
Emp.: 604
Palladium & Other Precious Metal Ore Exploration & Mining
N.A.I.C.S.: 212290
Timothy Hill (CEO)

Subsidiary (Domestic):

Lac des Iles Mines Ltd. (2)
PO Box 10547, Thunder Bay, P7B 6T9, ON, Canada
Tel.: (807) 448-2000
Palladium & Other Precious Metal Ore Mining
N.A.I.C.S.: 212290

Impala Platinum Japan Limited (1)
Uchisaiwaicho Daibiru Room No 702 3-3 Uchisaiwaicho 1-Chome, Chiyoda-Ku, Tokyo, 1000011, Japan (100%)
Tel.: (81) 335040712
Sales Range: $50-74.9 Million
Emp.: 5
Metal Ore Mining
N.A.I.C.S.: 212290

Impala Platinum Limited (1)
2 Fricker Road, Illovo, 2196, South Africa (100%)
Tel.: (27) 117319000
Sales Range: $50-74.9 Million
Emp.: 40
Metal Ore Mining
N.A.I.C.S.: 212290

Impala Refining Services Limited (1)
2 Fricker Road, Illovo, 2196, South Africa (100%)
Tel.: (27) 117319000
Web Site: https://www.implats.co.za
Sales Range: $750-799.9 Million
Emp.: 70,000
Metal Ore Mining
N.A.I.C.S.: 212290

Royal Bafokeng Platinum Limited (1)
The Pivot No 1 Monte Casino Boulevard Block C Floor 4 Fourways, PO Box 2283, Johannesburg, 2055, South Africa
Tel.: (27) 105904510
Web Site: https://www.bafokengplatinum.co.za
Rev.: $912,876,462
Assets: $2,179,566,412
Liabilities: $827,472,971
Net Worth: $1,352,093,441
Earnings: $240,783,670
Emp.: 5,623
Fiscal Year-end: 12/31/2020
Metal Mining Services
N.A.I.C.S.: 212290
Neil Carr (COO)

AND PRIVATE COMPANIES

Zimbabwe Platinum Mines (Pvt) Limited (1)
1st Floor South Block Borrowdale Office Park Borrowdale Road, PO Box 6380, Harare, Zimbabwe
Tel.: (263) 24288687885
Web Site: https://www.zimplats.com
Platinum Mfr
N.A.I.C.S.: 332999
Fholisani Sydney Mufamadi *(Chm)*

Zimplats Holdings Limited (1)
1st and 2nd Floors Elizabeth House, Les Ruettes Brayes, Saint Peter Port, GY1 1EW, Channel Islands, Guernsey **(87%)**
Tel.: (44) 1481737217
Web Site: https://www.zimplats.com
Rev.: $962,290,000
Assets: $2,472,759,000
Liabilities: $592,531,000
Net Worth: $1,880,228,000
Earnings: $205,466,000
Emp.: 3,732
Fiscal Year-end: 06/30/2023
Platinum Mining Services
N.A.I.C.S.: 212290
Charles Mugwambi *(Gen Mgr-Comml)*

IMPALA SAS
4 rue Euler, 75008, Paris, France
Tel.: (33) 1 81 69 25 80
Web Site: http://www.impala-sas.com
Privater Equity Firm
N.A.I.C.S.: 523999
Jacques Veyrat *(Pres)*

Subsidiaries:

Ales Groupe SA (1)
99 Rue du Faubourg Saint-Honore, 75008, Paris, France
Tel.: (33) 153939900
Web Site: http://www.alesgroupe.com
Perfume, Hair & Skin Care Products Mfr & Distr
N.A.I.C.S.: 325620
Romain Ales *(Chm-Supervisory Bd)*

Subsidiary (Non-US):

ALES GROUPE Cosmetic Deutschland GmbH (2)
Hanauer Landstrasse 135-137, Frankfurt am Main, 60314, Germany
Tel.: (49) 69 96 88 50 0
Web Site: http://www.alesgroupe.com
Emp.: 20
Cosmetic Product Whslr
N.A.I.C.S.: 424210
Stephanie Maurer *(Gen Mgr)*

ALES GROUPE ESPANA S.L. (2)
Paseo de la Habana 1 28036, 28006, Madrid, Spain
Tel.: (34) 917814750
Web Site: http://www.alesgroupe.com
Sales Range: $50-74.9 Million
Emp.: 9
Cosmetic Product Whslr
N.A.I.C.S.: 424210

ALES GROUPE ITALIA S.p.A (2)
Largo Donegani 2, 20121, Milan, Italy
Tel.: (39) 022906671
Web Site: http://www.alesgroupe.it
Cosmetic Product Whslr
N.A.I.C.S.: 424210
Phileppo Manucce *(Mgr)*

Ales Group Cosmetic Gmbh (2)
Hanauerlandstrasse 1352137, Frankfurt, 60528, Germany **(99.96%)**
Tel.: (49) 699688500
Web Site: http://www.alesgroupe.com
Emp.: 30
All Other Miscellaneous Store Retailers
N.A.I.C.S.: 459999
Stephanie Maurer *(Mgr)*

Subsidiary (US):

Ales Group Inc (2)
1350 Ave of the Americas, New York, NY 10019 **(79.97%)**
Tel.: (212) 265-5625
Sales Range: $25-49.9 Million
Emp.: 45
Cosmetics Beauty Supplies & Perfume Stores
N.A.I.C.S.: 456120

Subsidiary (Non-US):

Ales Group Uk Ltd (2)
115 Southwark Bridge Rd, London, SE1 0AX, United Kingdom **(99.96%)**
Tel.: (44) 2076201771
Web Site: http://www.phyto.com
Sales Range: $25-49.9 Million
Emp.: 13
Cosmetics Beauty Supplies & Perfume Stores
N.A.I.C.S.: 456120

Ales Groupe Benelux Sprl (2)
Rue Victor Allard 45, 1180, Brussels, Belgium **(99.7%)**
Tel.: (32) 23337272
Web Site: http://www.alesgroupe.com
Sales Range: $25-49.9 Million
Emp.: 10
Cosmetics Beauty Supplies & Perfume Stores
N.A.I.C.S.: 456120

Ales Groupe Canada Inc (2)
980 Sainte Catherine W Ste 6, Montreal, H3B 1E5, QC, Canada
Tel.: (514) 932-3636
Sales Range: $50-74.9 Million
Emp.: 8
Cosmetic Product Whslr
N.A.I.C.S.: 424210

Subsidiary (Domestic):

Ales Groupe Industries (2)
99 R Du Faubourg Saint Honore, 95870, Paris, France **(100%)**
Tel.: (33) 153939900
Sales Range: $25-49.9 Million
Emp.: 90
Cosmetics Beauty Supplies & Perfume Stores
N.A.I.C.S.: 456120
Patrick Ales *(Pres)*

Subsidiary (Non-US):

Ales Groupe Polska Sp. z o.o. (2)
Ulica Nowoursynowska 95, Warsaw, 2797, Poland **(100%)**
Tel.: (48) 226496190
Web Site: http://www.lierac.com.pl
Sales Range: $25-49.9 Million
Emp.: 10
Cosmetics Beauty Supplies & Perfume Stores
N.A.I.C.S.: 456120

Ales Groupe Portugal Lda (2)
Rua do Campo Alegre N 830 8 Andar Sala 37, 4150-171, Porto, Portugal
Tel.: (351) 220110030
Web Site: http://www.alesgroupe.pt
Sales Range: $25-49.9 Million
Emp.: 30
Cosmetic Product Distr
N.A.I.C.S.: 456120

Subsidiary (Domestic):

Lab. Lierac SA (2)
35 Avenue F Delano Roosevelt, 75008, Paris, France **(99.95%)**
Tel.: (33) 153939905
Web Site: http://www.lierac.fr
Sales Range: $50-74.9 Million
Emp.: 200
Cosmetics Beauty Supplies & Perfume Stores
N.A.I.C.S.: 456120

Laboratoires PHYTOSOLBA (2)
99 rue du Faubourg Saint-Honore, 75008, Paris, France **(99.96%)**
Tel.: (33) 153939906
Web Site: http://www.alesgroupe.com
Cosmetic Laboratories
N.A.I.C.S.: 541380

Parfums Caron (2)
90 R Du Faubourg Saint Honore, 75008, Paris, France **(99.99%)**
Tel.: (33) 142682568
Web Site: http://www.parfumscaron.com
Cosmetics Beauty Supplies & Perfume Stores
N.A.I.C.S.: 456120
Garance Doin *(Gen Mgr)*

IMPAX ASSET MANAGEMENT GROUP PLC
Seventh Floor 30 Panton Street, London, SW1Y 4AJ, United Kingdom
Tel.: (44) 2039123000 UK
Web Site: https://www.impaxam.com
Year Founded: 1994
IPX—(AIM)
Rev.: $194,229,992
Assets: $234,009,831
Liabilities: $83,951,901
Net Worth: $150,057,930
Earnings: $54,641,441
Emp.: 195
Fiscal Year-end: 09/30/21
Holding Company; Environmental Investment & Asset Management Services
N.A.I.C.S.: 551112
Ian R. Simm *(CEO & Founder)*

Subsidiaries:

Impax Asset Management Ireland Limited (1)
The Lennox Building Richmond Street South, Dublin, D02 FK02, Ireland
Tel.: (353) 1 592 1413
Fund Management Services
N.A.I.C.S.: 523940

Impax New Energy Investors (GP) Limited (1)
Norfolk House 31 St James s Square, London, SW1Y 4JR, United Kingdom
Tel.: (44) 2074341122
Emp.: 50
Investment Management Service
N.A.I.C.S.: 523999

IMPAX ENVIRONMENTAL MARKET PLC
7th Floor 30 Panton Street, London, SW1Y 4AJ, United Kingdom
Tel.: (44) 2039123000 UK
Web Site: https://impaxenvironmental.co.uk
Year Founded: 2002
IEM—(LSE)
Sales Range: $10-24.9 Million
Investment Management Service
N.A.I.C.S.: 523940
John Scott *(Chm)*

IMPEDIMED LIMITED
Unit 1 50 Parker Court, Pinkenba, 4008, QLD, Australia
Tel.: (61) 738603700
Web Site: https://www.impedimed.com
IPD—(ASX)
Rev.: $8,095,564
Assets: $44,974,587
Liabilities: $5,865,184
Net Worth: $39,109,402
Earnings: ($15,227,260)
Emp.: 73
Fiscal Year-end: 06/30/22
Medical Device Mfr
N.A.I.C.S.: 339112
Catherine Kingsford *(Sr VP-Medical Affairs)*

Subsidiaries:

ImpediMed Inc. (1)
5900 Pasteur Ct Ste 125, Carlsbad, CA 92008
Tel.: (760) 585-2100
Web Site: https://www.impedimed.com
Sales Range: $25-49.9 Million
Emp.: 20
Medical Device Mfr
N.A.I.C.S.: 339112

Xitron Technologies, Inc. (1)
7507 Convoy Ct, San Diego, CA 92111
Tel.: (858) 530-8099
Web Site: http://www.xitrontech.com
Power Testing Analyzer Mfr
N.A.I.C.S.: 334515

IMPEL S.A.
ul Slezna 118, 53-111, Wroclaw, Poland
Tel.: (48) 717110000
Web Site: http://www.impel.pl
Year Founded: 1990
Rev.: $11,161,022
Assets: $77,485,637
Liabilities: $19,366,696
Net Worth: $58,118,941
Earnings: $2,272,140
Emp.: 20,887
Fiscal Year-end: 12/31/18
Diversified Holding Company; Cleaning, Security, Catering, Facility Management, Human Resources, Medical, Clothing & Industrial Cleaning Services
N.A.I.C.S.: 551112

Subsidiaries:

Asekuracja Cash Handling sp. z.o.o. (1)
Ul M.Kasprzaka 7, Warsaw, 01-211, Poland
Tel.: (48) 71 711 00 00
Financial Software Development Services
N.A.I.C.S.: 541511
Krzysztof Kaszuba *(Chm-Mgmt Bd)*

Black Oak Security Sp. z o.o. (1)
Slezna 118, 53-111, Wroclaw, Poland **(100%)**
Tel.: (48) 717809190
Armored Car Services
N.A.I.C.S.: 561613

Brokers Union sp. z.o.o. (1)
Ul Slezna 112B U8, 53-111, Wroclaw, Poland
Tel.: (48) 71 781 82 98
Web Site: http://www.brokersunion.pl
Insurance Brokerage Services
N.A.I.C.S.: 524210

DC System Sp. z. o.o. (1)
Ul Marsa 56a, 04-242, Warsaw, Poland **(100%)**
Tel.: (48) 224604495
Web Site: http://www.dcpremium.pl
Sales Range: $25-49.9 Million
Emp.: 100
Commercial Laundry Drycleaning & Pressing Machine Mfr
N.A.I.C.S.: 333310
Lukasz Onysyk *(Officer-Data Protection)*

GP Bis Sp. z. o.o. (1)
Al Stanow Zjednoczonych 61, 04-028, Warsaw, Poland **(99.38%)**
Tel.: (48) 225162240
Web Site: http://www.gpbis.pl
Real Estate Agency
N.A.I.C.S.: 531210

Impel Accounting sp. z.o.o. (1)
Ul Teczowa 13, 53-601, Wroclaw, Poland
Tel.: (48) 71 711 00 00
Accounting Services
N.A.I.C.S.: 541219

Impel Airport Partner sp. z.o.o. (1)
Ul Slezna 118, Wroclaw, 53-111, Poland
Tel.: (48) 71 711 00 00
Web Site: http://www.impel.pl
Airport Ground Handling Services
N.A.I.C.S.: 488119

Impel Cash Handling Sp. z. o.o. (1)
ul M Kasprzaka 7, 01-211, Warsaw, Poland **(100%)**
Tel.: (48) 0717110000
Web Site: http://www.impel.pl
Financial Transactions Processing Reserve & Clearinghouse Activities
N.A.I.C.S.: 522320

Impel Catering Sp. z. o.o. (1)
ul Slezna 118, 53 111, Wroclaw, Poland
Tel.: (48) 717110000
Web Site: http://www.impel.pl
Catering & Meal Preparation
N.A.I.C.S.: 722320

Impel Cleaning sp. z. o.o. (1)
Slezna 118, 53-111, Wroclaw, Poland
Tel.: (48) 71 711 00 00
Industrial Cleaning Services

IMPEL S.A.

Impel S.A.—(Continued)
N.A.I.C.S.: 561720
Bogdan Dzik *(Chm-Mgmt Bd)*

Impel Food Hygiene sp. z o.o. (1)
Ul Marsa 56, 04-242, Warsaw, Poland
Tel.: (48) 71 711 00 00
Janitorial Services
N.A.I.C.S.: 561720
Dariusz Witkowski *(Chm-Mgmt Bd)*

Impel HR Service sp. z o.o. (1)
Ul Ruska 3/4, 50-079, Wroclaw, Poland
Tel.: (48) 71 711 00 00
Payroll & Personal Services
N.A.I.C.S.: 541214
Grzegorz Tyszka *(Chm-Mgmt Bd)*

Impel IT sp. z o.o. (1)
Ul Slezna 118, 53111, Wroclaw, Poland
Tel.: (48) 71 711 00 00
Security Software Development Services
N.A.I.C.S.: 541511
Wojciech Knapik *(Chm-Mgmt Bd)*

Impel Perfekta Sp. z o.o. (1)
ul Magazynowa 4, Bielany Wroclawski, 55-040, Kobierzyce, Poland (50%)
Tel.: (48) 717110000
Web Site: http://www.impel.pl
Commercial Laundry Drycleaning & Pressing Machine Mfr
N.A.I.C.S.: 333310
Wojciech Kiestrzyn *(Dir-Dev)*

Impel Real Estate Sp. z o.o. (1)
Slezna 118, 53-111, Wroclaw, Poland (100%)
Tel.: (48) 717809500
Activities Related to Real Estate
N.A.I.C.S.: 531390

Impel Rental Sp. z o.o. (1)
ul Slezna 118, 53-111, Wroclaw, Poland (100%)
Tel.: (48) 717110000
Consumer Goods Rental
N.A.I.C.S.: 532289
Grzegorz Dzik *(CEO)*

Subsidiary (Domestic):

Agrobud BHP S.A. (2)
Ul Swierczewskiego 5, Ruszow, 59-950, Poland
Tel.: (48) 75 77 14 318
Web Site: http://www.agrobudbhp.pl
Sales Range: $25-49.9 Million
Emp.: 15
Protective Fabrics Mfr & Distr
N.A.I.C.S.: 313220
Leszek Szubala *(Mng Dir)*

Impel Logistics sp. z o.o. (2)
Ul Slezna 118, 53-111, Wroclaw, Poland
Tel.: (48) 71 711 00 00
Logistics Consulting Servies
N.A.I.C.S.: 541614
Marek Piekarowicz *(Chm-Mgmt Bd)*

Impel SA-Wroclaw (1)
ul Slezna 118, 53-111, Wroclaw, Poland (100%)
Tel.: (48) 717110000
Web Site: http://www.impel.pl
Real Estate Property Lessors
N.A.I.C.S.: 531190

Impel Security Polska Sp. z o.o. (1)
Ul Slezna 118, 53-011, Wroclaw, Poland (100%)
Tel.: (48) 510201849
Web Site: http://www.impelsecurity.pl
Sales Range: $25-49.9 Million
Emp.: 300
Armored Car Services
N.A.I.C.S.: 561613

Impel Security Provider Sp. z o.o. (1)
Slezna 118, 53-111, Wroclaw, Poland (100%)
Tel.: (48) 717809605
Business Support Services
N.A.I.C.S.: 561499

Impel Security Technologies Sp. z o.o. (1)
ul Slezna 18, 53-111, Wroclaw, Poland (100%)

Tel.: (48) 717809191
Security System Services
N.A.I.C.S.: 561621

Impel Serviks SIA (1)
Skanstes iela 50C, 1013, Riga, Latvia
Tel.: (371) 67372729
Web Site: http://www.serviks.lv
Sales Range: $150-199.9 Million
Emp.: 700
Cleaning Service
N.A.I.C.S.: 561720

Krakpol sp. z o.o. (1)
ul Kulawki 2, 32-566, Alwernia, Poland
Tel.: (48) 71 711 00 00
Laundry Services
N.A.I.C.S.: 812320
Arkadiusz Szargut *(Chm-Mgmt Bd)*

North Ochrona Sp. z o.o. (1)
Marynarki Polskiej 177, 80-958, Gdansk, Poland (100%)
Tel.: (48) 583096431
Web Site: http://www.ochrona.pl
Sales Range: $10-24.9 Million
Emp.: 50
Security System Services
N.A.I.C.S.: 561621

Nutit A.S. (1)
Evropska 178, Vokovice, Prague, Czech Republic
Tel.: (420) 737467661
Web Site: http://www.nutit.cz
Financial Services
N.A.I.C.S.: 523999
Wojciech Swiatkowski *(Pres)*

OPM sp. z o.o. (1)
Ul Marsa 56 A, 04-242, Warsaw, Poland
Tel.: (48) 22 460 45 45
Web Site: http://www.impel.pl
Property Management Software Development Services
N.A.I.C.S.: 541511
Marek Biegasiewicz *(Chm-Mgmt Bd)*

Pi Sp.zo.o. (1)
Ofiar Oswiecimskich 41-43, 50-950, Wroclaw, Poland (75%)
Tel.: (48) 713446222
Management Consulting Services
N.A.I.C.S.: 541618

SaneChem Service Sp. z o.o. (1)
Berlinga 8, Lomianki, 05092, Warsaw, Poland (100%)
Tel.: (48) 227143080
Web Site: http://www.sanechem.com.pl
Exterminating & Pest Control Services
N.A.I.C.S.: 561710

Sanpro Job Service sp. z o.o. (1)
ul Ruska 3/4, 50-079, Wroclaw, Poland
Tel.: (48) 71 711 00 00
Web Site: http://www.impel.pl
Temporary Help Service
N.A.I.C.S.: 561320

Subsidiary (Domestic):

Sanpro - APT sp. z o.o. (2)
ul Ruska 3/4, 50-079, Wroclaw, Poland
Tel.: (48) 71 711 00 00
Temporary Help Service
N.A.I.C.S.: 561320
Grzegorz Tyszka *(Chm-Mgmt Bd)*

Serviks Riga SIA (1)
Skanstes iela 50C, 1013, Riga, Latvia (66.99%)
Tel.: (371) 67372729
Web Site: http://www.impel.lv
Sales Range: $150-199.9 Million
Emp.: 700
Cleaning Service Company
N.A.I.C.S.: 811210
Ivars Garancs *(Member-Mgmt Bd)*

TeleBT Sp.zo.o. (1)
ul Zaporoska 27/14, 53-519, Warsaw, Poland (80%)
Tel.: (48) 7171503344
Web Site: http://www.telebt.pl
Sales Range: $25-49.9 Million
Emp.: 10
Other Telecommunications
N.A.I.C.S.: 517810

Wena Floor System Sp. z o.o. (1)

Ul Slezna 118, 53-111, Wroclaw, Poland (80%)
Tel.: (48) 583021713
Sales Range: $25-49.9 Million
Emp.: 14
Floor Laying & Other Floor Contractors
N.A.I.C.S.: 238330

IMPELUS LIMITED
Level 23 100 William Street, Sydney, 2011, NSW, Australia
Tel.: (61) 293603385
Web Site: http://www.impelus.com
Rev.: $8,490,951
Assets: $8,976,215
Liabilities: $6,159,642
Net Worth: $2,816,573
Earnings: ($7,536,945)
Fiscal Year-end: 06/30/19
Mobile Phone Applications Developer
N.A.I.C.S.: 517112
Neil Wiles *(CEO & Mng Dir)*

Subsidiaries:

MobileActive Limited - Mobile Embrace Division (1)
Level 23 100 William Street, E Sydney, Sydney, 2010, NSW, Australia
Tel.: (61) 293808071
Web Site: http://www.mobileembrace.com
Sales Range: $25-49.9 Million
Emp.: 55
Cellular Phone Content Development & Marketing Services
N.A.I.C.S.: 517112
Chris Thorpe *(CEO)*

IMPERA CAPITAL SA
Plac Europejski 1, 00-844, Warsaw, Poland
Tel.: (48) 223988270
Web Site: https://www.imperioasi.pl
Year Founded: 1997
IMP—(WAR)
Sales Range: Less than $1 Million
Investment Services
N.A.I.C.S.: 523999
Adam Wojacki *(Member-Mgmt Bd)*

IMPERIAL AUTO INDUSTRIES LTD.
Opp Railway Goods Shed, Faridabad, 121 001, Haryana, India
Tel.: (91) 129 2412311
Web Site: http://www.impauto.com
Sales Range: $150-199.9 Million
Emp.: 3,000
Fluid Transmission Equipment Mfr
N.A.I.C.S.: 332912
Jagjit Singh *(Chm)*

Subsidiaries:

Tokai Imperial Rubber India Private Limited (1)
45 Milestone VPO Prithla Delhi-Mathura Road, Palwal, 121 102, Haryana, India
Tel.: (91) 1275262102
Motor Vehicle Hose Mfr
N.A.I.C.S.: 326220

IMPERIAL BRANDS PLC
121 Winterstoke Road, Bristol, BS3 2LL, United Kingdom
Tel.: (44) 1179636636 UK
Web Site: https://www.imperialbrandsplc.com
Year Founded: 1901
IMBBF—(OTCQX)
Rev.: $40,993,436,001
Assets: $37,226,710,427
Liabilities: $28,842,464,024
Net Worth: $8,384,246,402
Earnings: $3,100,227,215
Emp.: 25,200
Fiscal Year-end: 09/30/23
Tobacco Products Mfr & Distr
N.A.I.C.S.: 312230
Simon Evans *(Mgr-Grp Media Rels)*

INTERNATIONAL PUBLIC

Subsidiaries:

Altadis, S.A.U. (1)
Calle Comandante Azcarraga 5, 28016, Madrid, Spain
Tel.: (34) 913609000
Emp.: 350
Tobacco Product Mfr & Distr
N.A.I.C.S.: 312230
Rocio Ingelmo *(Dir-Corp & Legal Affairs)*

Subsidiary (Non-US):

Altadis Distribution France S.A.S. (2)
143 Boulevard Romain Rolland, 75014, Paris, France
Tel.: (33) 1 58 35 61 50
Tobacco Products Whslr
N.A.I.C.S.: 424940

Altadis Middle East Fzco. (2)
Office No Lb 16507, PO Box 261718, Jebel Ali, Dubai, United Arab Emirates
Tel.: (971) 48816235
Web Site: http://www.imperialtobacco.com
Sales Range: $25-49.9 Million
Emp.: 6
Tobacco Product Distr
N.A.I.C.S.: 424940

Balkan Star (2)
22 Pobeda Strasse, 150040, Yaroslavl, Russia
Tel.: (7) 0951184545
Cigarette Production
N.A.I.C.S.: 312230

Affiliate (Domestic):

CITA Tabacos de Canarias, S.A. (2)
1 Juan Ravina Mendez St, 38005, Santa Cruz de Tenerife, Spain
Tel.: (34) 922219022
Cigarette & Cigar Manufacturing & Marketing
N.A.I.C.S.: 312230

Subsidiary (Domestic):

Compania de Distribucion Integral Logista Holdings, S.A.U. (2)
C/ Trigo 39, Poligono Industrial Polvoranca, CP 28914, Leganes, Spain (72.72%)
Tel.: (34) 914819800
Web Site: https://www.logista.com
Rev.: $12,252,344,845
Assets: $8,223,327,962
Liabilities: $7,617,644,346
Net Worth: $605,683,616
Earnings: $212,848,314
Emp.: 4,912
Fiscal Year-end: 09/30/2022
Holding Company; Cigarettes & Other Tobacco Products Distr & Logistics Services
N.A.I.C.S.: 551112
Gregorio Maranon y Bertran de Lis *(Chm)*

Subsidiary (Domestic):

Compania de Distribucion Integral Logista, S.A. (3)
C / Trigo 39, Poligono Industrial Polvoranca, 28914, Leganes, Madrid, Spain
Tel.: (34) 91 481 9800
Web Site: https://www.logista.com
Sales Range: $5-14.9 Billion
Emp.: 2,000
Cigarettes & Other Tobacco Products Distr & Logistics Services
N.A.I.C.S.: 424940

Subsidiary (Non-US):

Logista Italia S.p.A. (4)
Via Valadier 37, 00193, Rome, Italy
Tel.: (39) 06 974 4201
Web Site: https://www.logista.it
Cigarettes & Other Tobacco Products Distr
N.A.I.C.S.: 424940

Subsidiary (Non-US):

Corporacion Habanos, S.A. (2)
Calle 3ra no 2006 e/ 20 y 22, Miramar Ciudad de la Habana, Havana, Cuba
Tel.: (53) 7339509
Web Site: http://www.habanos.com
Cigarette Production
N.A.I.C.S.: 312230

AND PRIVATE COMPANIES

IMPERIAL BRANDS PLC

MacoTab (2)
RN 193, 20600, Bastia Furiani, France
Tel.: (33) 495301615
Web Site: http://www.altadis.com
Sales Range: $10-24.9 Million
Emp.: 50
Cigarette Production
N.A.I.C.S.: 312230

Metavideotex (2)
Parc d'activite de la Breche, Rue Olof Palme Batiment Euclid, 94000, Creteil, France
Tel.: (33) 149806900
STRATOR Terminals Development
N.A.I.C.S.: 312230

PBC (2)
Cavite Export Processing Zone, Cavite, 4106, Philippines
Tel.: (63) 464371629
Cigarette Wrapper & Bobbin Production
N.A.I.C.S.: 312230
Harbier Plantada *(Mng Dir)*

Subsidiary (Domestic):

Servicio de Venta Automatica S.A. (S.V.A.) (2)
Volta, 28906, Madrid, Getase, Spain
Tel.: (34) 913797800
Web Site: http://www.serventa.es
Sales Range: $50-74.9 Million
Emp.: 150
Vending Machine Distribution
N.A.I.C.S.: 423440

Subsidiary (Non-US):

Sitar Group
Zl n 2 BP 256, 97457, Saint-Pierre, CEDEX, France
Tel.: (33) 262357400
Production & Logistics of Cigarettes
N.A.I.C.S.: 312230

Casa de Montecristo Inc. (1)
5900 N Andrews Ave Ste 600, Fort Lauderdale, FL 33309
Web Site:
  http://www.casademontecristo.com
Cigar Product Retailer
N.A.I.C.S.: 459991

Casa de Montecristo TN LLC (1)
600 9th Ave S Ste 130, Nashville, TN 37203
Tel.: (615) 800-3397
Web Site:
  https://www.casademontecristo.com
Cigar Product Distr
N.A.I.C.S.: 424940

Casa de Montecristo TX LLC (1)
3801 N Capital of Texas Hwy, Austin, TX 78746
Tel.: (737) 529-8466
Web Site:
  https://www.casademontecristo.com
Cigar Product Distr
N.A.I.C.S.: 424940

Commonwealth-Altadis, Inc. (1)
5900 N Andrews Ave Ste 1000, Fort Lauderdale, FL 33309
Tel.: (954) 772-9000
Web Site:
  http://www.commonwealthaltadis.com
Holding Company; Cigarette & Other Tobacco Products Mfr & Distr
N.A.I.C.S.: 551112
Kevin E. Freudenthal *(Pres & CEO)*

Subsidiary (Domestic):

Altadis U.S.A. Inc. (2)
5900 N Andrews Ave Ste 600, Fort Lauderdale, FL 33309
Tel.: (954) 772-9000
Web Site: https://www.altadisusa.com
Emp.: 5,000
Cigars, Pipe Tobaccos, Cigarette Rolling Tobaccos & Smoking Accessories Mfr
N.A.I.C.S.: 312230
James Colucci *(Exec VP-Sls & Mktg)*

Commonwealth Brands, Inc. (2)
900 Church St, Bowling Green, KY 42101
Tel.: (270) 781-9100
Web Site: http://www.joinusagold.com

Sales Range: $300-349.9 Million
Emp.: 720
Cigarettes Mfr & Distr
N.A.I.C.S.: 312230

Congar International Corp. (1)
Ave Barcelo Carr 14 KM 72 2 Frente Reparto Montellano, Cayey, PR 00737
Tel.: (787) 738-2106
Web Site: http://www.congaronlinepr.com
Cigar Product Mfr
N.A.I.C.S.: 312230

Ets. L. Lacroix Fils N.V (1)
Sint-Bavostraat 66, Wilrijk, 2610, Antwerp, Belgium
Tel.: (32) 38210900
Web Site: http://www.imptobnet.com
Sales Range: $100-124.9 Million
Emp.: 27
Tobacco Products Mfr & Distr
N.A.I.C.S.: 312230
Zijlstra Bart *(Gen Mgr)*

Fontem Ventures B.V. (1)
Radarweg 60, 1043 NT, Amsterdam, Netherlands
Tel.: (31) 850027200
Web Site: http://www.fontemventures.com
Electronic Vapor Product Mfr
N.A.I.C.S.: 312230
Christiaan Brommersma *(Partner-Bus & Fin)*

ITG Brands, LLC (1)
714 Green Valley Rd, Greensboro, NC 27408-7018
Tel.: (336) 335-6669
Cigarette & Other Tobacco Products Mfr, Research & Development
N.A.I.C.S.: 312230
Adam Britner *(CFO & Exec VP-Fin & Plng)*

Imperial Tobacco (Asia) Pte Ltd (1)
80 Robinson Road 02-00, Singapore, 068898, Singapore (100%)
Tel.: (65) 63118388
Web Site: http://www.imperial-tobacco.com
Sales Range: $100-124.9 Million
Emp.: 30
Marketing & Sales of Cigarettes
N.A.I.C.S.: 424990

Imperial Tobacco (Efka) GmbH & Co KG (1)
Industriestr 6, 78647, Trossingen, Germany
Tel.: (49) 7425280
Web Site: http://www.efk.de
Emp.: 200
Tobacco Product Mfr
N.A.I.C.S.: 312230

Imperial Tobacco Australia Ltd (1)
John Player Special House Level 4 4-8 Inglewood Place, Norwest, Sydney, 2153, NSW, Australia
Tel.: (61) 29 881 0888
Web Site: http://www.imperialbrandsplc.com
Sales Range: $25-49.9 Million
Emp.: 250
Cigarette Manufacturing
N.A.I.C.S.: 312230

Imperial Tobacco Belgium (1)
Schalienhoevedreef 20 H, 2800, Machelen, Belgium (100%)
Tel.: (32) 15299911
Web Site:
  https://www.imperialbrandsplc.com
Sales Range: $50-74.9 Million
Emp.: 100
Distribution of Cigarettes
N.A.I.C.S.: 424940
Bart Alkemade *(Gen Mgr)*

Imperial Tobacco CR, s.r.o. (1)
Tel.: (420) 296541111
Sales Range: $50-74.9 Million
Emp.: 150
Cigarette Mfr
N.A.I.C.S.: 312230

Imperial Tobacco Finance PLC (1)
Upton Road, PO Box 244, Bristol, BS99 7UJ, United Kingdom
Tel.: (44) 1179636636
Financial Transaction Processing Services
N.A.I.C.S.: 522320

Imperial Tobacco Finland OY (1)
PO Box 718, 20101, Turku, Finland

Tel.: (358) 25118200
Sales Range: $25-49.9 Million
Emp.: 40
Cigarette Production, Marketing & Sales
N.A.I.C.S.: 312230

Imperial Tobacco France S.A. (1)
43-45 Avenue de Clichy, 75017, Paris, France
Tel.: (33) 1 56 026 666
Web Site: http://www.imperial-tobacco.com
Sales Range: $25-49.9 Million
Emp.: 133
Chewing & Smoking Tobacco Products Mfr
N.A.I.C.S.: 312230

Subsidiary (Domestic):

Tobaccor S.A. (2)
122 Avenue Charles de Gaulle, BP 25, Suresnes Cedex, 92200, Neuilly-sur-Seine, France
Tel.: (33) 141384500
Web Site: http://www.imperial-tobacco.com
Cigarette Mfr & Distr
N.A.I.C.S.: 312230

Imperial Tobacco Hellas S.A. (1)
300 Klisthenous Str, Gerakas Attikis, 15344, Athens, Greece (100%)
Tel.: (30) 2106615055
Web Site: https://www.imperial-tobacco.gr
Marketing & Sales of Cigarettes
N.A.I.C.S.: 459991

Imperial Tobacco International Ltd. (1)
Lenton Industrial Est Thane Rd, West PDO, Nottingham, NG7 5PL, United Kingdom (100%)
Tel.: (44) 159242888
Web Site: http://www.imperial-tobacco.com
Sales Range: $25-49.9 Million
Emp.: 100
Export Division of Imperial Tobacco Limited
N.A.I.C.S.: 312230

Imperial Tobacco Italy S.r.l. (1)
Via Luca Passi 22, 53 Palazzina B, 00166, Rome, Italy (50%)
Tel.: (39) 06614111
Web Site: http://www.imperial-tobacco.com
Cigarettes Marketing & Sales
N.A.I.C.S.: 424940

Imperial Tobacco Limited (1)
121 Winterstoke Road, Bristol, BS3 2LL, United Kingdom
Tel.: (44) 117 963 6636
Web Site: http://www.imperial-trade.co.uk
Sales Range: $25-49.9 Million
Emp.: 250
Cigarette Manufacturing
N.A.I.C.S.: 312230
Lindsay Mennell Keating *(Head-Corp & Legal Affairs-UK & Ireland)*

Division (Domestic):

Imperial Tobacco Ltd. - Northern Trading Division (2)
Unit 35 Technology Ctr Scottish Enterprise Technology Park, East Kilbride, G75 0QZ, United Kingdom
Tel.: (44) 1355813130
Web Site: http://www.imperialtobacco.com
Sales Range: $25-49.9 Million
Emp.: 100
Cigarettes, Cigars, Tobacco (Chewing/Smoking) & Snuff
N.A.I.C.S.: 312230

Imperial Tobacco Magyarorszag Dohanyforgalmazo Kft (1)
Vaci ut 141, PO Box 73, 1138, Budapest, Hungary
Tel.: (36) 61 412 8200
Web Site: https://www.imptob.hu
Manufacture & Sale of Cigarettes & Tobacco Products
N.A.I.C.S.: 312230

Imperial Tobacco Mullingar (1)
Tobacco Factory Dublin Rd, Mullingar, Westmeath, Ireland
Tel.: (353) 449348691
Sales Range: $25-49.9 Million
Emp.: 95
Tobacco Products Mfr & Distr
N.A.I.C.S.: 312230

Imperial Tobacco Netherlands (1)
Hoevestean 22, 4903 SC, Oosterhout, Netherlands
Tel.: (31) 162468888
Web Site: http://www.imperial-tobacco.com
Sales Range: $50-74.9 Million
Emp.: 100
Sales & Marketing of Cigarettes
N.A.I.C.S.: 424940

Imperial Tobacco New Zealand Limited (1)
Tel.: (64) 45871500
Web Site: http://www.imperialtobacco.com
Sales Range: $25-49.9 Million
Emp.: 100
Cigarette Manufacturing
N.A.I.C.S.: 312230

Imperial Tobacco Norway A.S. (1)
Ryensvingen 2-4, Oslo, 680, Norway
Tel.: (47) 23243800
Sales Range: $25-49.9 Million
Emp.: 5
Tobacco Products Whslr
N.A.I.C.S.: 424940

Imperial Tobacco Polska Manufacturing SA (1)
Ul Tytoniowa 2/6, 26-600, Radom, Poland
Tel.: (48) 3611000
Tobacco Product Mfr
N.A.I.C.S.: 312230

Imperial Tobacco Polska S.A. (1)
Jankowice ul Przemyslowa 1, 62-080, Tarnowo Podgorne, Poland (100%)
Tel.: (48) 618165000
Sales Range: $150-199.9 Million
Emp.: 900
Cigarette Mfr
N.A.I.C.S.: 312230

Imperial Tobacco Portugal SSPLC (1)
144 7 DT Avenida da Liberdade, 1990-077, Lisbon, Portugal
Tel.: (351) 218988190
Web Site: http://www.imperial-tobacco.pt
Tobacco Product Mfr & Retailer
N.A.I.C.S.: 312230

Imperial Tobacco Production Ukraine CJSC (1) (99.9%)
Web Site: https://www.imperial-tobacco.com.ua
Cigarette Mfr
N.A.I.C.S.: 312230

Imperial Tobacco Sigara ve Tutunculuk Sanayi ve Ticaret A.S. (1)
Manisa Organize Sanayi Bolgesi 3 Kisim No 11, 45030, Manisa, Turkiye
Tel.: (90) 236 226 3500
Web Site:
  https://www.imperialtobacco.com.tr
Sales Range: $25-49.9 Million
Emp.: 30
Cigarette Manufacturing
N.A.I.C.S.: 312230

Imperial Tobacco Slovakia (1)
Galvaniho 7/A, 82453, Bratislava, Slovakia (100%)
Tel.: (421) 258232111
Emp.: 75
Cigarettes, Cigars & Pipe Tobacco Mfr
N.A.I.C.S.: 312230

Imperial Tobacco TKS a.d. (1)
ul 11 Oktomvri 125, PO Box 37, 1000, Skopje, North Macedonia
Tel.: (389) 23204544
Web Site: http://www.imperial-tobacco.com
Tobacco Products Mfr & Distr
N.A.I.C.S.: 312230

Imperial Tobacco Taiwan Co. Limited (1)
6F1-2 No 2 Sec 3 Minsheng E road, Zhongshen District, Taipei, 10434, Taiwan
Tel.: (886) 225068996
Web Site: http://www.imperial-tobacco.com
Emp.: 100
Tobacco Products Whslr
N.A.I.C.S.: 424940
Wayne Merrett *(Pres)*

Imperial Tobacco Tutun Urunleri Satis ve Pazarlama A.S. (1)

IMPERIAL BRANDS PLC

INTERNATIONAL PUBLIC

Imperial Brands PLC—(Continued)

Manisa Organize Sanayi Bolgesi 3 Kisim
No 11, Sisli, 45030, Manisa, Turkiye
Tel.: (90) 2362263500
Sales Range: $25-49.9 Million
Emp.: 25
Tobacco Product Mfr
N.A.I.C.S.: 312230

Imperial Tobacco Ukraine (1)
street Academician Zabolotny 35, 03026,
Kiev, Ukraine
Tel.: (380) 442012999
Emp.: 480
Tobacco Products Mfr & Distr
N.A.I.C.S.: 312230

JR Cigars.com, Inc. (1)
2589 Eric Ln, Burlington, NC 27215
Web Site: https://www.jrcigars.com
Tobacco Products Retailer
N.A.I.C.S.: 459991

Nerudia Limited (1)
Wellington House Physics Road, Speke,
Liverpool, L24 9HP, United Kingdom
Tel.: (44) 1519098500
Web Site: http://www.nerudia.com
Nicotine Product Mfr
N.A.I.C.S.: 312230
Molly McGuinness (Engr-Mechanical Dev)

OOO Imperial Tobacco Volga
LLC (1)
7 Tomskaya Ul, Volgograd, 400048, Russia
Tel.: (7) 8442532300
Tobacco Product Mfr
N.A.I.C.S.: 312230
Alexey Kozhanov (Gen Mgr)

Philippine Bobbin Corporation (1)
Phase II Export Processing Zone, Rosario,
4106, Cavite, Philippines
Tel.: (63) 46 437 1629
Sales Range: $150-199.9 Million
Emp.: 800
Cigarette Mfr
N.A.I.C.S.: 312230
Carlos Baez (Gen Mgr)

Real Club de Golf la Herreria
S.A. (1)
Carretera de Robledo de Chavela s/n, San
Lorenzo de El Escorial, 28200, Madrid,
Spain
Tel.: (34) 918905111
Web Site:
http://www.golfmadridlaherreria.com
Golf Course Management Services
N.A.I.C.S.: 713910

Reemtsma Cigarettenfabriken
GmbH (1)
Behringstrasse 122A, 22763, Hamburg,
Germany (90.01%)
Tel.: (49) 4082200
Sales Range: $150-199.9 Million
Emp.: 800
Mfr of Cigarette & Fine Cut Tobacco
N.A.I.C.S.: 312230

Subsidiary (Non-US):

Altadis S.A. (2)
Calle Comandante Azcarraga 5, Edificios
7-8 Plantas 3 y 4, 28016, Madrid, Spain
Sales & Marketing of Tobacco Products
N.A.I.C.S.: 459991

Imperial Tobacco Sales & Marketing
LLC (2)
Degtyarnij Pereulok 4 1, Moscow, 125009,
Russia (100%)
Tel.: (7) 495937200
Web Site: http://www.imperial-tobacco.com
Cigarette Sales & Marketing
N.A.I.C.S.: 312230

Reemtsma International China
Ltd. (2)
1201 Kerry Centre 683 King's Road, 25
Canton Rd Tsim Sha Tsui, Hong Kong,
China (Hong Kong) (100%)
Tel.: (852) 23696962
Web Site: http://www.imperial-tobacco.com
Sales Range: $25-49.9 Million
Emp.: 100
Cigarette Sales
N.A.I.C.S.: 424990

Reemtsma Kiev Tyutyunova
Fabrika (2)
ul Academica Zabolotnogo 35, 03026, Kiev,
Ukraine (65%)
Tel.: (380) 442019999
Web Site: http://www.reemtsma.com
Marketing & Sales of Cigarettes
N.A.I.C.S.: 459991

Tobacna Ljubljana d.o.o. (2)
Cesta 24 junija 90, Crnuce, 1231, Ljubljana,
Slovenia
Tel.: (386) 14777100
Web Site: https://tobacna.si
Sales Range: $25-49.9 Million
Emp.: 200
Cigarette Mfr
N.A.I.C.S.: 312230
Pia Barboric Jurjasevic (Mng Dir)

Santa Clara Inc. (1)
2589 Eric Ln, Burlington, NC 27215
Web Site: https://www.santaclaracigars.com
Tobacco Product Distr
N.A.I.C.S.: 424940

Skruf Snus AB (1)
Tulegatan 15, 113 53, Stockholm, Sweden
Tel.: (46) 87892200
Emp.: 300
Cigarette Products Mfr & Whslr
N.A.I.C.S.: 312230

Tobacna 3DVA, Trgovsko Podjetje,
d.o.o. (1)
Cesta 24 junija 90, Crnuce, 1231, Ljubljana,
Slovenia
Tel.: (386) 14777319
Web Site: http://www.trafika3dva.si
Tobacco Products Retailer
N.A.I.C.S.: 459991

Tobacna Grosist d.o.o. (1)
Cesta 24 junija 90, Crnuce, 1231, Ljubljana,
Slovenia
Tel.: (386) 14777100
Web Site: https://www.tobacna-grosist.si
Tobacco Product Distr & Retailer
N.A.I.C.S.: 424940
Pia Barboric Jurjasevic (Mng Dir)

Tutunski Kombinat AD Prilep (1)
St Prilepski Braniteli 85, 7500, Prilep, Makedonija, North Macedonia
Tel.: (389) 48510101
Web Site: https://www.tkprilep.com.mk
Rev.: $17,181,489
Assets: $22,116,926
Liabilities: $21,058,068
Net Worth: $1,058,858
Earnings: $708,313
Fiscal Year-end: 12/31/2019
Tobacco Distr
N.A.I.C.S.: 424940

Van Nelle Tabak Nederland B.V. (1)
Slachtedijk 28a, Postbus 31, 8501 ZA,
Joure, Netherlands
Tel.: (31) 513413966
Web Site: http://www.imperial-tobacco.com
Sales Range: $150-199.9 Million
Emp.: 300
Tobacco & Tobacco Products Whslr
N.A.I.C.S.: 424940

Van Nelle Tobacco International Holdings B.V. (1)
Slachtedijk 28a, 8501 ZA, Joure, Netherlands
Tel.: (31) 162468888
Web Site: http://www.imperial-tobacco.com
Sales Range: $75-99.9 Million
Emp.: 200
Holding Company: Tobacco Products
N.A.I.C.S.: 551112

Subsidiary (Non-US):

John Player & Sons Ltd (2)
21 Beckett Way Pk W Bus Pk, Dublin, Ireland
Tel.: (353) 12434800
Sales Range: $50-74.9 Million
Emp.: 60
Non-Durable Goods Whslr
N.A.I.C.S.: 424990
Peter Lassche (Gen Mgr)

ZAO Balkanskaya Zvezda (1)
Ul Pobedy 22, Yaroslavl, 150040, Russia
Tel.: (7) 4852 72 03 05
Tobacco Product Mfr
N.A.I.C.S.: 312230

IMPERIAL CAPITAL GROUP LTD.

200 King St W Ste 1701, PO Box 57,
Toronto, M5H 3T4, ON, Canada
Tel.: (416) 362-3658
Web Site:
http://www.imperialcap.com
Year Founded: 1989
Sales Range: $10-24.9 Million
Emp.: 23
Investment Capital Firm
N.A.I.C.S.: 523999
Jeffrey L. Rosenthal (Co-Founder & Mng Partner)

Subsidiaries:

AIM Health Group Inc. (1)
19 Allstate Pkwy Ste 100, Markham, L3R
5A4, ON, Canada
Tel.: (905) 475-3353
Web Site: http://www.aimhealthgroup.com
Sales Range: $50-74.9 Million
Health Care Services
N.A.I.C.S.: 621111
Gregory J. Van Staveren (CFO)

Subsidiary (Domestic):

CPM Health Centres Inc. (2)
6400 Mill Creek Drive, Mississauga, L5N
3E7, ON, Canada
Tel.: (905) 858-1368
Web Site: http://www.cpm-centres.com
Sales Range: $10-24.9 Million
Chronic Pain Management Services
N.A.I.C.S.: 622110

Med-Emerg International Inc. (2)
6400 Millcreek Dr Ste 9, Mississauga, L5N
3E7, ON, Canada
Tel.: (905) 858-1368
Web Site: http://www.med-emerg.com
Sales Range: $10-24.9 Million
Healthcare Staffing Services & Community Clinics Operator
N.A.I.C.S.: 561311

Petra Pet, Inc. (1)
5801 Westside Ave, North Bergen, NJ
07047
Tel.: (201) 854-6157
Web Site: http://www.beefeaters.com
Sales Range: $1-9.9 Million
Pet Food Distr & Whslr
N.A.I.C.S.: 424490
Dean Triandafellos (Pres)

Subsidiary (Domestic):

Nutri-Vet, LLC (2)
549 N Dupont Ave, Boise, ID 83713
Tel.: (208) 377-1938
Web Site: http://www.nutri-vet.com
Emp.: 12
Veterinary Product Mfr
N.A.I.C.S.: 325412
Steve Twohig (VP-Sls)

IMPERIAL COFFEE & SERVICES, INC.

12 Kodiak Crescent, Toronto, M3J
3G5, ON, Canada
Tel.: (416) 638-7404
Web Site:
http://www.imperialcoffee.com
Year Founded: 1974
Rev.: $11,286,000
Emp.: 150
Coffee Beans, Vending Machines & Water Systems Distr
N.A.I.C.S.: 311920
Nick Kammer (VP-Ops)

IMPERIAL EQUITIES INC.

2151 Rice Howard Place 10060 Jasper Avenue, Edmonton, T5J 3R8, AB,
Canada
Tel.: (780) 424-7227
Web Site:
https://www.imperialequities.com
Year Founded: 1998
IEI—(TSXV)
Rev.: $14,903,545
Assets: $199,376,793
Liabilities: $114,858,432
Net Worth: $84,518,361
Earnings: $5,144,552
Emp.: 14
Fiscal Year-end: 09/30/23
Real Estate Manangement Services
N.A.I.C.S.: 531390
Sine Chadi (Founder, Pres & CEO)

Subsidiaries:

Imperial Distributors Canada Inc (1)
16504 121A Ave, Edmonton, T5V 1J9, AB,
Canada
Tel.: (780) 453-1701
Web Site: http://www.imperialdistributors.ca
Pharmaceutical Products Distr
N.A.I.C.S.: 424210
Paul Fu (Pres)

Imperial Equities Inc. - Pharmaceutical Division (1)
Ste 100 18207 105 Ave NW, Edmonton,
T5S 2L5, AB, Canada
Tel.: (780) 484-2287
Web Site: http://www.imperialdistributors.ca
Emp.: 15
Pharmaceuticals Product Mfr
N.A.I.C.S.: 325412
Matthew Staric (Mgr-Ops)

Imperial Equities Inc. - Real Estate
Division (1)
2151 Scotia Place 10060 Jasper Avenue,
Edmonton, T5J 3R8, AB, Canada
Tel.: (780) 424-7227
Web Site: http://www.imperialequities.com
Real Estate Manangement Services
N.A.I.C.S.: 531390

IMPERIAL GARDEN & RESORT, INC.

106 Zhouzi Street 4th Floor 4E,
Rouhu District, Taipei, 11493, Taiwan
Tel.: (886) 2 2658 2927
Year Founded: 2015
Emp.: 85
Golf Resort Management Services
N.A.I.C.S.: 713910
Fun-Ming Lo (Chm & CEO)

IMPERIAL GINSENG PRODUCTS LTD.

1030 West Georgia Street, Box
49256, Vancouver, V6E 2Y3, BC,
Canada
Tel.: (236) 479-0909
Web Site:
https://www.imperialginseng.com
Year Founded: 1989
IGP—(OTCIQ)
Rev.: $5,726,541
Assets: $23,499,530
Liabilities: $5,875,700
Net Worth: $17,623,830
Earnings: ($3,630,052)
Fiscal Year-end: 06/30/19
Ginseng Products Mfr
N.A.I.C.S.: 325414
Stephen P. McCoach (Chm, CEO & Sec)

Subsidiaries:

Canadian Imperial Ginseng Ontario
Ltd. (1)
245715 Milldale Road RR 1, Otterville, N0J
1R0, ON, Canada
Tel.: (519) 879-9861
Web Site: http://www.imperialginseng.com
Sales Range: $25-49.9 Million
Emp.: 50
Ginseng Products Mfr
N.A.I.C.S.: 325414

Imperial Ginseng Distributors
Ltd. (1)

AND PRIVATE COMPANIES

1274 McGill Road, Kamloops, V2C 6N6,
BC, Canada
Tel.: (250) 851-8656
Ginseng Products Distr
N.A.I.C.S.: 424210

IMPERIAL HOTEL, LTD.
1-1-1 Uchisaiwaicho, Chiyoda-ku, Tokyo, 100-8558, Japan
Tel.: (81) 335041111
Web Site:
https://www.imperialhotel.co.jp
Year Founded: 1890
9708—(TKS)
Rev.: $423,712,960
Assets: $597,672,240
Liabilities: $210,472,240
Net Worth: $387,200,000
Earnings: $18,885,680
Fiscal Year-end: 03/31/23
Hotel Operator
N.A.I.C.S.: 721110
Masahiro Kohda (Mng Exec Officer)

IMPERIAL INNOVATIONS GROUP PLC
52 Princes Gate Exhibition Road,
London, SW7 2PG, United Kingdom
Tel.: (44) 203 053 8850
Web Site:
http://www.imperialinnovations.co.uk
IVO—(LSE)
Sales Range: $1-9.9 Million
Emp.: 64
Commercialization & Consulting Services
N.A.I.C.S.: 541611
Brian Graves (Dir-Bus Dev)

IMPERIAL METALS CORPORATION
580 Hornby Street Suite 200, Vancouver, V6C 3B6, BC, Canada
Tel.: (604) 669-8959   BC
Web Site:
https://www.imperialmetals.com
III—(OTCIQ)
Rev.: $104,505,567
Assets: $928,050,837
Liabilities: $331,096,099
Net Worth: $596,954,739
Earnings: ($20,394,040)
Emp.: 49
Fiscal Year-end: 12/31/21
Copper & Gold Mining Services
N.A.I.C.S.: 212230
Pierre Lebel (Chm)

Subsidiaries:

Huckleberry Mines Ltd.   (1)
1030-999 W Hastings St, Vancouver, V6C 2W2, BC, Canada
Tel.: (604) 685-8299
Sales Range: $100-124.9 Million
Emp.: 250
Metal Mining Services
N.A.I.C.S.: 213114

Mount Polley Mining Corporation   (1)
200 - 580 Hornby St, Vancouver, V6C 3B6, BC, Canada
Tel.: (604) 669-8959
Web Site: http://www.imperialmetals.com
Sales Range: $50-74.9 Million
Emp.: 30
Metal Mining Services
N.A.I.C.S.: 213114

Red Chris Development Company Ltd. (1)
200 - 580 Hornby St, Vancouver, V6C 3B6, BC, Canada   (30%)
Tel.: (604) 669-8959
Web Site: http://www.imperialmetals.com
Sales Range: $50-74.9 Million
Emp.: 30
Metal Exploration Services
N.A.I.C.S.: 213114

Sterling Gold Mining Corporation   (1)
PO Box 549, Beatty, NV 80093

Tel.: (866) 608-4381
Gold Mining Services
N.A.I.C.S.: 212220
Charles Stevens (Gen Mgr)

IMPERIAL MINING GROUP LTD.
410 Saint-Nicolas Street Suite 236,
Montreal, H2Y 2P5, QC, Canada
Tel.: (514) 907-9016
Web Site:
https://www.imperialmgp.com
IMPNF—(OTCQB)
Rev.: $18,649
Assets: $6,033,992
Liabilities: $318,064
Net Worth: $5,715,928
Earnings: ($2,742,386)
Fiscal Year-end: 08/31/21
Metal Exploration Services
N.A.I.C.S.: 213114
Pierre Neatby (Pres & CEO)

IMPERIAL MUSIC & MEDIA PLC
1 Bacon Lane, Hayling Island, South Hayling, PO11 0DN, Hampshire, United Kingdom
Tel.: (44) 2392 463000
Web Site:
http://www.imperialplc.co.uk
Entertainment Industry Investment Services
N.A.I.C.S.: 523999
Philip McCool (Exec Dir)

IMPERIAL PACIFIC INTERNATIONAL HOLDINGS LIMITED
Suites 7001 7002 and 7014-7016 70/F Two International Finance Centre, No. 8 Finance Street, Central, China (Hong Kong)
Tel.: (852) 28271177
1076—(HKG)
Rev.: $120,360
Assets: $494,152,005
Liabilities: $1,559,050,365
Net Worth: ($1,064,898,360)
Earnings: ($137,396,168)
Emp.: 385
Fiscal Year-end: 12/31/21
Frozen Foods
N.A.I.C.S.: 311412
Li Jie Cui (Chm)

IMPERIAL PACIFIC LIMITED
Suite 212 Level 2 111 Harrington Street, The Rocks, Sydney, 2000, NSW, Australia
Tel.: (61) 292479315
Web Site:
http://www.imperialpacific.com.au
IPC—(ASX)
Rev.: $495,700
Assets: $7,557,368
Liabilities: $1,157,969
Net Worth: $6,399,399
Earnings: $256,910
Fiscal Year-end: 06/30/24
Investment Services
N.A.I.C.S.: 523999
Peter E. J. Murray (Chm, Chm & CEO)

IMPERIAL RESOURCES INC.
82-J 4th Street, New Manila, Quezon City, Philippines
Tel.: (63) 87216994
Web Site:
https://www.imperialresources.ph
Year Founded: 1969
IMP—(PHI)
Rev.: $776,470
Assets: $17,210,164
Liabilities: $1,357,256
Net Worth: $15,852,909
Earnings: $341,828

Emp.: 8
Fiscal Year-end: 12/31/23
Oil Exploration Services
N.A.I.C.S.: 213112
Desiderio L. Laperal (CFO, Treas & VP)

IMPERIO ARGO GROUP S.A.
Mavrokordatou Str 11-13, 185 38, Piraeus, Greece
Tel.: (30) 210 4583800
Emp.: 264
Freight Forwarding Services
N.A.I.C.S.: 488510
Likoudi Dimitra (IR Officer)

IMPERIUM CROWN LIMITED
1 Commonwealth Lane 06-20 One Commonwealth, Singapore, 149544, Singapore
Tel.: (65) 62500925
Web Site: https://www.imperium-crown.com
Year Founded: 1995
5HT—(SES)
Rev.: $1,399,714
Assets: $17,009,474
Liabilities: $12,675,946
Net Worth: $4,333,528
Earnings: ($57,887,325)
Fiscal Year-end: 06/30/22
Investment Holding Services
N.A.I.C.S.: 551112
Bowen Sun (Chm)

Subsidiaries:

Clements and Street Ltd   (1)
12 Broad Ground Rd, Lakeside, Redditch, B98 8YP, Worcestershire, United Kingdom
Tel.: (44) 1527513890
Web Site:
http://www.clementsandstreet.com
Exhibition Contractors
N.A.I.C.S.: 238390
Paul Simson (Dir-Comml & Mktg)

IMPERIUM FINANCIAL GROUP LIMITED
2603 26/F One Harbour Square 181 Hoi Bun Road, Kwun Tong, Kowloon, China (Hong Kong)
Tel.: (852) 21678029   Ky
Web Site: http://www.sun8029.com
Year Founded: 2000
8029—(HKG)
Rev.: $6,925,065
Assets: $44,314,304
Liabilities: $35,457,634
Net Worth: $8,856,670
Earnings: ($13,692,904)
Emp.: 43
Fiscal Year-end: 03/31/22
Investment Holding Company
N.A.I.C.S.: 551112
Ting Kong Cheng (Chm)

Subsidiaries:

Sun Finance Company Limited   (1)
Room 1101A 11th Floor Ginza Plaza 565-567 Nathan Road, Mong Kok, Kowloon, China (Hong Kong)
Tel.: (852) 25222111
Web Site: http://www.sunfinance.com.hk
Loan Lending Services
N.A.I.C.S.: 522291

Sun International Securities Limited (1)
Room 2603A 26th Floor One Harbour Square 181 Hoi Bun Road, Kwun Tong, Kowloon, China (Hong Kong)
Tel.: (852) 35858988
Web Site: https://www.imperiumhk.com
Securities Brokerage Services
N.A.I.C.S.: 523150
Miranda Heung (Officer-Compliance)

Sun Stud Pty. Limited   (1)
56 Mount Eliza Rd, Riddells Creek, Melbourne, 3434, VIC, Australia

Tel.: (61) 354285168
Web Site: http://www.sunstud.com.au
Stallion Production Services
N.A.I.C.S.: 112920
David Grant (Mgr-Ops)

IMPERIUM TECHNOLOGY GROUP LIMITED
Room 2408 24/F China Merchants Tower, Shun Tak Centre 168-200 Connaught Road, Central, China (Hong Kong)
Tel.: (852) 36283281
Web Site: http://www.776.hk
0776—(HKG)
Rev.: $16,970,396
Assets: $31,418,789
Liabilities: $47,778,584
Net Worth: ($16,350,795)
Earnings: ($22,994,793)
Emp.: 226
Fiscal Year-end: 12/31/22
Investment Services
N.A.I.C.S.: 523999
Ting Kong Cheng (Chm)

IMPERO A/S
Klamsagervej 27, Abyhoj, 8230, Aarhus, Denmark
Tel.: (45) 70225364
Web Site: https://www.impero.com
Year Founded: 2013
IMPERO—(CSE)
Rev.: $3,993,286
Assets: $5,009,333
Liabilities: $2,837,609
Net Worth: $2,171,724
Earnings: ($1,873,218)
Emp.: 34
Fiscal Year-end: 12/31/23
Software Development Services
N.A.I.C.S.: 541511
Morten Lehmann Nielsen (CFO)

IMPEX ELECTRO LLC
Building 5 Office 12A, 6 Barklaya Street, Moscow, 121087, Russia
Tel.: (7) 495 543 73 00
Cable Conductor Products Mfr
N.A.I.C.S.: 332999

Subsidiaries:

Nexans Russia   (1)
4th Floor Business Centre Pokrovsky 47A Pokrovka Str, Moscow, 105062, Russia
Tel.: (7) 495 775 82 40
Web Site: http://www.nexans.ru
Cable & Power Accessories Mfr
N.A.I.C.S.: 335921

Plant (Domestic):

Nexans Russia - Uglich Factory   (2)
Kamyshevskoye Road 10, Uglich, 152616, Yaroslavl, Russia
Tel.: (7) 485 329 13 00
Sales Range: $25-49.9 Million
Emp.: 20
Fabricated Wire Product Mfr
N.A.I.C.S.: 332618
Frederick Vincent (Pres)

IMPEX FERRO TECH LIMITED
132A S P Mukherjee Road, Kolkata, 700 026, India
Tel.: (91) 3340168000
Web Site:
https://www.impexferrotech.com
Year Founded: 1995
Rev.: $14,354,125
Assets: $31,379,304
Liabilities: $59,174,383
Net Worth: ($27,795,079)
Earnings: ($2,401,419)
Emp.: 294
Fiscal Year-end: 03/31/19
Manganese Mfr
N.A.I.C.S.: 212290

Impex Ferro Tech Limited—(Continued)

Suresh Kumar Patni (Chm & Mng Dir)

IMPIANA HOTELS & RESORTS MANAGEMENT SDN BHD
21st Floor Menara KH Jalan Sultan Ismail, 50250, Kuala Lumpur, Malaysia
Tel.: (60) 321416233
Web Site: https://www.impiana.com.my
MAGMA—(KLS)
Rev.: $3,147,211
Assets: $30,605,986
Liabilities: $53,376,700
Net Worth: $22,770,715
Earnings: ($2,851,514)
Emp.: 83
Fiscal Year-end: 12/31/23
Drinking Water Processor
N.A.I.C.S.: 312112

IMPIANTI S.P.A.
Via della Valle 46/a, Carate Brianza, 20841, Monza, Italy
Web Site: https://www.lubenda.com
Year Founded: 1992
MPT—(EUR)
Information Technology Services
N.A.I.C.S.: 541512
Lucrezia Toscana (CFO)

IMPLANET SA
Technopole Bordeaux Montesquieu Allee Francois Magendie, 33650, Martillac, France
Tel.: (33) 557995555
Web Site: https://www.implanet.com
ALIMP—(EUR)
Sales Range: $1-9.9 Million
Emp.: 33
Medical Implants & Devices Mfr
N.A.I.C.S.: 339112
Ludovic Lastennet (CEO)

IMPLENIA AG
Thurgauerstrasse 101A, CH-8152, Opfikon, Switzerland
Tel.: (41) 584747474 CH
Web Site: https://www.implenia.com
Year Founded: 1872
IMPN—(SWX)
Rev.: $4,273,721,197
Assets: $3,453,222,026
Liabilities: $2,768,916,104
Net Worth: $684,305,922
Earnings: $168,477,538
Emp.: 9,056
Fiscal Year-end: 12/31/23
Offices of Other Holding Companies
N.A.I.C.S.: 551112
Rene Kotacka (Head-Civil Engrg-Div)

Subsidiaries:

Building Construction Logistics GmbH (1)
Am Prime Parc 1, 65479, Raunheim, Germany
Tel.: (49) 61428737700
Web Site: https://bcl-baulogistik.com
Logistics Management Services
N.A.I.C.S.: 541614

Graviere de La Claie-aux-Moines S.A. (1)
Chemin de Geffry 2, 1073, Savigny, Switzerland
Tel.: (41) 21 784 8430
Web Site: https://www.gcm.ch
Concrete Products Mfr
N.A.I.C.S.: 327231

Implenia Bau AG (1)
Obere Grundlistrasse, 6055, Alpnach, Switzerland
Tel.: (41) 670 04 24
Construction Engineering Services
N.A.I.C.S.: 541330

Implenia Bau AG - Tunnel + TU Division (1)
Bahnhofstrasse 24, CH-5001, Aarau, Switzerland
Tel.: (41) 628320400
Web Site: http://www.implenia-bau.com
Sales Range: $125-149.9 Million
Subterranean Construction, Tunnelling & Railway Engineering Contractor
N.A.I.C.S.: 237990

Implenia Construction GmbH (1)
Durener Strasse 403, 50858, Cologne, Germany
Tel.: (49) 22116809113
Construction Services
N.A.I.C.S.: 236220

Implenia Fassadentechnik GmbH (1)
Suderstrasse 32, 20097, Hamburg, Germany
Tel.: (49) 407139020
Real Estate Services
N.A.I.C.S.: 531390

Implenia France SA (1)
Savoie Technolac Parc Ouragan - Bat A 20 Rue du Lac Majeur, 73370, Le Bourget du Lac, France
Tel.: (33) 458020132
Web Site: https://implenia.com
Real Estate Services
N.A.I.C.S.: 531390

Implenia Global Solutions AG (1)
Husacherstrasse 3, CH-8304, Wallisellen, Switzerland (100%)
Tel.: (41) 432333990
Web Site: http://www.implenia-globalsolutions.com
Sales Range: $1-9.9 Million
Civil & Commercial Construction, Engineering & Real Estate Services
N.A.I.C.S.: 237310

Implenia Holding GmbH (1)
Gewerbestr 1, Rummingen, 79595, Baden-Wurttemberg, Germany
Tel.: (49) 762140500
Financial Investment Management Services
N.A.I.C.S.: 523999
Otmar Manner (Mgr)

Implenia Management AG (1)
Industriestrasse 24, 8305, Dietlikon, Switzerland
Tel.: (41) 44 805 45 43
Real Estate Development Services
N.A.I.C.S.: 531390

Implenia Norge AS (1)
Tel.: (47) 22507300
Web Site: https://implenia.com
Real Estate Services
N.A.I.C.S.: 531390

Implenia Osterreich GmbH (1)
Innsbrucker Bundesstrasse 67, 5020, Salzburg, Austria
Tel.: (43) 662216621
Web Site: https://implenia.com
Real Estate Services
N.A.I.C.S.: 531390

Implenia Real Estate Division (1)
Industriestrasse 24, CH-8305, Dietikon, Switzerland (100%)
Tel.: (41) 448054411
Real Estate Investment Management, Development, Facility Engineering, Construction & Building Automation Contracting Services
N.A.I.C.S.: 531390

Subsidiary (Domestic):

Implenia Generalunternehmung AG (2)
Industriestrasse 24, CH-8305, Dietikon, Switzerland (100%)
Tel.: (41) 44 805 4411
Commercial, Institutional, Industrial & Residential Construction & Renovation Contracting Services
N.A.I.C.S.: 238990

Implenia Immobilien AG (2)
Industriestrasse 24, 8305, Dietikon, Switzerland
Tel.: (41) 448054200
Real Estate Project Development Services

N.A.I.C.S.: 236220

Implenia Switzerland Ltd. (2)
Thurgauerstrasse 101A, Glattpark, 8152, Opfikon, Switzerland (100%)
Tel.: (41) 584747474
Web Site: https://www.implenia.com
Sales Range: $25-49.9 Million
Emp.: 60
Commercial, Institutional & Industrial Facility Planning & Technical Consulting Services
N.A.I.C.S.: 541690

Implenia Schalungsbau GmbH (1)
Industriestrasse 21, 67240, Bobenheim-Roxheim, Germany
Tel.: (49) 623999820
Real Estate Services
N.A.I.C.S.: 531390

Implenia Spezialtiefbau GmbH (1)
Robert-Bosch-Strasse 25, 63225, Langen, Germany
Tel.: (49) 610398811345
Real Estate Services
N.A.I.C.S.: 531390

Reprojet AG (1)
Bettnaustrasse 9a, 8854, Siebnen, Switzerland
Tel.: (41) 584747760
Web Site: https://www.reprojet.ch
Emp.: 45
Construction Engineering Services
N.A.I.C.S.: 541330
Urs Metzger (Gen Mgr)

Sisag SA (1)
Aniaman 13eme etage Plateau, Williamsville, Abidjan, Cote d'Ivoire
Tel.: (225) 777103118
Web Site: https://sisagci.com
Construction Services
N.A.I.C.S.: 236220

Wincasa AG (1)
Theaterstr 17, 8400, Winterthur, Switzerland
Tel.: (41) 584557777
Web Site: https://www.wincasa.ch
Sales Range: $350-399.9 Million
Emp.: 670
Real Estate Investment, Development, Property Management & Brokerage Services
N.A.I.C.S.: 531390

IMPLICO GMBH
Weidestrasse 120 b, 22083, Hamburg, Germany
Tel.: (49) 40 27 09 360
Web Site: http://www.implico.com
Year Founded: 1983
Emp.: 200
Custom Computer Programming Services
N.A.I.C.S.: 541511

Subsidiaries:

Implico (M) Sdn Bhd (1)
20.05 Level 20 Wisma Goldhill, 67 Jalan Raja Chulan, 50200, Kuala Lumpur, Malaysia
Tel.: (60) 3 2070 4600
Web Site: http://www.en.implico.com
Emp.: 9
Custom Computer Programming Services
N.A.I.C.S.: 541511
Nordin Salleh (Mng Dir)

Implico AG (1)
Schlosslifeld 7, 2504, Biel, Switzerland
Tel.: (41) 32 344 40 52
Custom Computer Programming Services
N.A.I.C.S.: 541511

Implico Consulting S.R.L. (1)
Str Valea Oltului Nr 73-75 Parter, Camera Nr 5 Sector 6, Bucharest, 061971, Romania
Tel.: (40) 7370 966 80
Custom Computer Programming Services
N.A.I.C.S.: 541511

Implico, Inc. (1)
600 W. Germantown Pike Ste 400, Plymouth Meeting, PA 19462
Tel.: (215) 468-0210
Web Site: http://www.implico.com

Sales Range: $10-24.9 Million
Emp.: 10
Custom Computer Programming Services
N.A.I.C.S.: 541511
John Roche (Pres)

IMPLIX SP. Z O.O.
Arkonska 6, 80-387, Gdansk, Poland
Tel.: (48) 58 668 31 30
Web Site: http://www.implix.com
Sales Range: $25-49.9 Million
Emp.: 100
Email Marketing Services & Software
N.A.I.C.S.: 541613
Simon Grabowski (CEO)

IMPOL D.D.
Partizanska 38, 2310, Slovenska Bistrica, Slovenia
Tel.: (386) 28453100
Web Site: http://www.impol.com
Year Founded: 1825
Sales Range: $200-249.9 Million
Emp.: 980
Aluminum Producer
N.A.I.C.S.: 331318
Jernej Cokl (Chm)

Subsidiaries:

Alcad, d.o.o. (1)
Partizanska 38, 2310, Slovenska Bistrica, Slovenia
Tel.: (386) 28187413
Web Site: http://www.alcad.si
Aluminum Production & Distr
N.A.I.C.S.: 331315

Impol Aluminum Corporation (1)
155 Erie Blvd, Schenectady, NY 12305-2235
Tel.: (518) 393-2135
Web Site: http://www.impolaluminum.com
Aluminum Distr
N.A.I.C.S.: 423510

Impol Montal, d.o.o. (1)
38 Partizanska, 2310, Slovenska Bistrica, Slovenia
Tel.: (386) 62811201
Web Site: http://www.impol.com
Aluminum Production
N.A.I.C.S.: 331318

Impol Seval, a.d. (1)
BB Prvomajska, Sevojno, 31205, Serbia
Tel.: (381) 31591107
Web Site: http://www.seval.rs
Sales Range: $200-249.9 Million
Emp.: 605
Aluminum Production & Distr
N.A.I.C.S.: 331318
Ninko Tesic (Gen Mgr)

Subsidiary (Domestic):

Impol Seval Final, d. o. o. (2)
Prvomajska bb, 31205, Sevojno, Serbia
Tel.: (381) 31 591 113
Financial Services
N.A.I.C.S.: 541219
Djordje Pjevic (Mgr)

Impol Seval President, d. o. o. (2)
Naselje Kamalj bb, 31 315, Zlatibor, Serbia
Tel.: (381) 31 841386
Web Site: http://www.hotel-president.biz
Hotel Operator
N.A.I.C.S.: 721110

Impol Seval Tehnika, d. o. o. (2)
Banjickih Zrtava Bb, 31000, Uzice, Serbia
Tel.: (381) 31 564 012
Aluminium Products Mfr
N.A.I.C.S.: 331318
Milan Djokovic (Mgr)

Impol Stanovanja, d.o.o. (1)
38 Partizanska, Slovenska Bistrica, 2310, Slovenia
Tel.: (386) 28453100
Web Site: http://www.impol.com
Emp.: 2,000
Aluminum Production & Distr
N.A.I.C.S.: 331315
Jernej Cokel (CEO)

Stampal SB, d.o.o. (1)

AND PRIVATE COMPANIES | **IMPROVE MEDICAL INSTRUMENTS CO., LTD**

38 Partizanska, 2310, Slovenska Bistrica, Slovenia
Tel.: (386) 28187268
Web Site: http://www.stampal-sb.si
Aluminum Production & Distr
N.A.I.C.S.: 331318

Unidel, d.o.o. (1)
Kraigherjeva ulica 37, 2310, Slovenska Bistrica, Slovenia
Tel.: (386) 28055230
Web Site: http://www.unidel.si
Sales Range: $25-49.9 Million
Emp.: 42
Aluminum Production & Distr
N.A.I.C.S.: 331315

IMPORT TOOL CORP. LTD.
5533 48 Street, Edmonton, T6B 3R1, AB, Canada
Tel.: (780) 434-6406
Web Site: https://www.importtool.com
Year Founded: 1952
Rev.: $18,258,440
Emp.: 70
Oil Field Equipment Mfr, Sales & Services
N.A.I.C.S.: 333132
Robert Mcleod (Pres)

IMPRESA SGPS S.A.
242 2770-022 Paco de Arcos, 1200-787, Lisbon, Portugal
Tel.: (351) 213929780
Web Site: https://www.impresa.pt
IPR—(EUR)
Rev.: $199,923,157
Assets: $420,483,309
Liabilities: $249,930,987
Net Worth: $170,552,321
Earnings: $1,226,061
Emp.: 925
Fiscal Year-end: 12/31/22
Television Broadcasting; Newspaper & Magazine Publisher
N.A.I.C.S.: 516120
Francisco Jose Pereira Pinto de Balsemao (Chm)
Subsidiaries:
Edimpresa-Editora Lda. (1)
Rua Calvet de Magalhaes 242, Paco de Arcos, 2770-022, Lisbon, Portugal (100%)
Tel.: (351) 214698000
Web Site: http://www.edimpresa.pt
Sales Range: $100-124.9 Million
Emp.: 500
Publishing
N.A.I.C.S.: 513120
Ana Marta Heleno (Dir-Mktg)

Hearst Edimpresa - Editora de Publicacoes, Lda. (1)
Rua Calvet De Magalhaes 242 Paco De Arcos, Oeiras, 2770 022, Portugal
Tel.: (351) 214698700
Television Broadcasting Services
N.A.I.C.S.: 516120

Impresa Media Solutions - Sociedade Unipessoal, Lda. (1)
Rua Calvet de Magalhaes 242, Paco De Arcos, Oeiras, 2770-022, Portugal
Tel.: (351) 214179550
Web Hosting Services
N.A.I.C.S.: 518210

Impresa Publishing S.A. (1)
Edificio Sao Francisco de Sales Rua Calvet de Magalhaes n 242, Paco De Arcos, 2770-022, Oeiras, Portugal
Tel.: (351) 21 469 80 00
Web Site: http://www.impresa.pt
Sales Range: $25-49.9 Million
Emp.: 9
Periodical & Newspaper Publishing
N.A.I.C.S.: 513120
Diego Cortez (Gen Mgr)

Infoportugal Sistemas de Informacao e Conteudos S.A. (1)
Rua Conselheiro Costa Braga 502, 4450-102, Matosinhos, Portugal (100%)
Tel.: (351) 220437110

Web Site: https://www.infoportugal.pt
Geographic Information Systems, Content Development, Software Development & Consulting Services
N.A.I.C.S.: 513210

Office Share - Gestao de Imoveis e Servicos, Lda (1)
Rua Calvet de Magalhaes 242, Paco De Arcos, Lisbon, 2770-022, Portugal (100%)
Tel.: (351) 214544000
Web Site: http://www.expresso.pt
Sales Range: $100-124.9 Million
Emp.: 600
Real Estate & Facilities Management Services
N.A.I.C.S.: 531390
Henrique Santos (Mng Dir)

Olhares.com - Fotografia Online, S.A. (1)
Rua Conselheiro Costa Braga n 502, 4450-102, Matosinhos, Portugal (100%)
Tel.: (351) 22 043 7036
Web Site: http://olhares.sapo.pt
Online Photography Courses
N.A.I.C.S.: 541921
Bernardo Dias Pinheiro (Comml Dir-Digital)

SIC - Sociedade Independente de Comunicacao, S.A. (1)
Estrada Outurela 119 Carnaxide, Carnaxide, 2794-052, Lisbon, Portugal
Tel.: (351) 214179400
Web Site: http://www.sic.pt
Television Broadcasting Services
N.A.I.C.S.: 516120

SIC Filmes, Lda (1)
Estrada Da Outorela 119, Carnaxide, 2799 526, Oeiras, Portugal
Tel.: (351) 214179550
Web Site: http://www.sic.pt
Sales Range: $100-124.9 Million
Emp.: 500
Motion Picture Production Services
N.A.I.C.S.: 512191

Solo - Investimentos em Comunicacao, SGPS, S.A. (1)
Rua De Ribeiro Sanches 65, Lisbon, 1200-787, Portugal
Tel.: (351) 213929780
Sales Range: $400-449.9 Million
Web Hosting Services
N.A.I.C.S.: 518210
Jose Freire (Dir-IR)

IMPRESS HOLDINGS INC.
Jinbo-cho mitsui Bldg 1-105 Kanda jinbo-cho, Chiyoda-ku, Tokyo, 101-0051, Japan
Tel.: (81) 368375000
Web Site: https://www.impressholdings.com
Year Founded: 1992
9479—(TKS)
Rev.: $95,620,260
Assets: $96,142,450
Liabilities: $40,611,840
Net Worth: $55,530,610
Earnings: ($6,847,960)
Emp.: 43
Fiscal Year-end: 03/31/24
Holding Company
N.A.I.C.S.: 551112
Daisuke Matsumoto (Pres)
Subsidiaries:
Impress Group Singapore Pte. Ltd. (1)
80 Robinson Road 08-01, Singapore, 068898, Singapore
Tel.: (65) 62212950
Advertising Services
N.A.I.C.S.: 541810
Shinya Kurata (Pres)

Impress Technology (Beijing) Co., Ltd. (1)
Room 1011 I Tower Blue Castel International Center, No 3 West Dawang Road Chaoyang District, Beijing, 100026, China
Tel.: (86) 1065820031
Web Site: http://www.impresstech.com.cn

Information Technology Services
N.A.I.C.S.: 541512
Shinya Kurata (Pres)

Kindai Kagaku Sha Co., Ltd. (1)
2-7-15 Ichigayatamachi Shinjyuku-Ku, Tokyo, 162-0843, Japan
Tel.: (81) 332606161
Web Site: http://www.kindaikagaku.co.jp
Books Publishing Services
N.A.I.C.S.: 513130
Toru Koyama (Pres)

Rittor Music, Inc. (1)
Web Site: http://www.rittor-music.co.jp
Books Publishing Services
N.A.I.C.S.: 513130

IMPRESSIONS PRESSES DE BRETAGNE
Z I Sud Est Rue Des Charmilles, 35510, Saint Etienne, France
Tel.: (33) 299265500
Web Site: http://www.pressesdebretagne.com
Rev.: $24,100,000
Emp.: 86
Commercial Printing
N.A.I.C.S.: 323111
Dov Kayat (Mgr)

IMPRIMERIE BILLET S.A.S.
6 rue de Romery, BP 3, 51480, Damery, France
Tel.: (33) 3 2658 4011
Web Site: http://www.imprimerie-billet.fr
Sales Range: $10-24.9 Million
Emp.: 88
Commercial Printing Services
N.A.I.C.S.: 323111
Arnold Deregnaucourt (Dir Gen)

IMPRIMERIE CHIRAT SA
744 route de Sainte Colombe, 42540, Saint-Just-la-Pendue, France
Tel.: (33) 477632544
Web Site: https://www.imprimerie-chirat.fr
MLIMP—(EUR)
Sales Range: $25-49.9 Million
Books Publishing Services
N.A.I.C.S.: 513130
Jacques Chirat (Chm & CEO)

IMPRIMERIE HENRI DRIDE
Z I Des Chanoux 49 Rue Des Freres Lumiere, 93330, Neuilly-sur-Marne, Seine Saint Denis, France
Tel.: (33) 143098888
Web Site: http://www.dride.com
Rev.: $22,200,000
Emp.: 85
Commercial Printing
N.A.I.C.S.: 323111
Michel Dride (Mng Dir)

IMPRIMERIE LEBONFON INC.
1051 Rue De lEccho, PO Box 40, Val d'Or, J9P 4N9, QC, Canada
Tel.: (819) 825-8888
Web Site: http://www.lebonfon.com
Sales Range: $10-24.9 Million
Emp.: 135
Comic Book Publishing
N.A.I.C.S.: 513110
Alain Roberge (Pres & Gen Mgr)

IMPRIMERIE LEFRANCQ & CIE
ZI La Ramee, BP 9, 49440, Cande, France
Tel.: (33) 241947050
Web Site: http://www.lefrancq.com
Sales Range: $10-24.9 Million
Emp.: 71
Food, Pharmaceutical & Cosmetics Industries Printing & Packaging Services

N.A.I.C.S.: 323111
Eric Lefrancq (CEO)

IMPRIMERIE RAULT SA
Le Bois Brouchard, BP 4, 36140, Gap, Aigurande, France
Tel.: (33) 254063200
Web Site: http://www.imprimerierault.fr
Rev.: $20,500,000
Emp.: 49
Commercial Printing
N.A.I.C.S.: 323111
Alexandre Desrieux (Mgr-Repairs)

IMPRIMERIE SAVOY OFFSET
Zae Les Glaisins 4 Rue Des Bouvieres, 74940, Annecy, Haute Savoie, France
Tel.: (33) 450640004
Web Site: http://www.savoyoffset.com
Sales Range: $10-24.9 Million
Emp.: 17
Printing Services
N.A.I.C.S.: 323111

IMPRIMERIE TONNELLIER
Parcd'Activite Charles Tellier Rue Des Dragons, BP 91, Conde-sur-Noireau, 14110, Calvados, France
Tel.: (33) 231591212
Rev.: $20,700,000
Emp.: 151
Commercial Printing
N.A.I.C.S.: 323111
Beno T. Duquesne (Pres)

IMPRO PRECISION INDUSTRIES LIMITED
Unit 1008 Shui On Centre 6-8 Harbour Road, Wanchai, China (Hong Kong)
Tel.: (852) 25728628
Web Site: http://www.improprecision.com
Year Founded: 1998
1286—(HKG)
Rev.: $555,225,653
Assets: $989,775,360
Liabilities: $429,030,743
Net Worth: $560,744,618
Earnings: $74,304,450
Emp.: 7,762
Fiscal Year-end: 12/31/22
Agricultural Product Mfr & Distr
N.A.I.C.S.: 325320
Ruibo Lu (Chm & CEO)
Subsidiaries:
BFG Feinguss Niederrhein GmbH (1)
Am Wehrhahn 8, 40211, Dusseldorf, Germany
Tel.: (49) 284117980
Web Site: https://www.bfg-feinguss.de
Precision Casting Mfr
N.A.I.C.S.: 331512

Cengiz Makina Sanayi ve Ticaret Anonim Sirketi (1)
TOSB Otomotiv OSB Mah 3 Cadde No 22/2, Cayirova, 41420, Kocaeli, Turkiye
Tel.: (90) 2626581220
Emp.: 810
High Precision Component Mfr
N.A.I.C.S.: 332721

IMPROVE MEDICAL INSTRUMENTS CO., LTD
No 102 Kaiyuan Avenue, Guangzhou Economic & Technological Development District, Guangzhou, 510530, Guangdong, China
Tel.: (86) 2032312610
Web Site: https://www.improve-med.com
Year Founded: 1996

IMPROVE MEDICAL INSTRUMENTS CO., LTD

Improve Medical Instruments Co., Ltd—(Continued)
300030—(CHIN)
Rev.: $99,792,108
Assets: $218,768,472
Liabilities: $103,554,828
Net Worth: $115,213,644
Earnings: ($27,841,320)
Emp.: 571
Fiscal Year-end: 12/31/22
Medical & Surgical Instrument Mfr
N.A.I.C.S.: 339112
Deng Guanhua *(Chm & Gen Mgr)*

Subsidiaries:

GIMDX, Inc (1)
2440 Grand Ave Ste A, Vista, CA 92081
Tel.: (760) 201-8878
Medical Instrument Distr
N.A.I.C.S.: 423490

Guangzhou Rida Medical Instruments Co., Ltd (1)
No 48 Chenjiaci Road Science Park, Liwan District, Guangzhou, China
Tel.: (86) 2081370132
Medical Instrument Distr
N.A.I.C.S.: 423490

IMPULSE (QINGDAO) HEALTH TECH CO., LTD.
369 Huashan Er Road, Qingdao, 266200, Shandong, China
Tel.: (86) 53283951531
Web Site: https://www.impulsehealthtech.com
Year Founded: 1991
002899—(SSE)
Rev.: $115,787,880
Assets: $285,004,980
Liabilities: $122,122,728
Net Worth: $162,882,252
Earnings: $9,218,664
Fiscal Year-end: 12/31/22
Fitness Equipment Mfr & Distr
N.A.I.C.S.: 333991
Liu Hongtao *(Chm & Gen Mgr)*

IMPULSE FITNESS SOLUTIONS, S.A.
Juan Florez street number 8 1st Floo, 15004, A Coruna, Spain
Tel.: (34) 7862955224 ES
Web Site: https://www.impulsebodyfitness.com
Year Founded: 2016
MLIFS—(EUR)
Rev.: $343,828
Assets: $4,663,874
Liabilities: $1,308,571
Net Worth: $3,355,302
Earnings: ($41,300)
Fiscal Year-end: 12/31/21
Fitness Club Operator
N.A.I.C.S.: 713940
Esteban Hernandez *(CTO)*

IMPULSORA DEL DESARROLLO Y EL EMPLEO EN AMERICA LATINA S.A. DE C.V.
Avenida de las Palmas numero 781 piso 1 Lomas de Chapultepec Seccion, 11000, Mexico, Mexico
Tel.: (52) 5511031300
Web Site: http://www.ideal.com.mx
4GO—(DEU)
Transportation Terminal Construction & Maintenance Services
N.A.I.C.S.: 488999
Alejandro Aboumrad Aboumrad Gonzalez *(CEO)*

IMS GROUP HOLDINGS LTD.
Unit 1201 Block C Seaview Estate No 8 Watson Road, Hong Kong, China (Hong Kong)
Tel.: (852) 3 183 4888 Ky
Web Site: http://www.imsgroupholdings.com
Year Founded: 1998
8136—(HKG)
Rev.: $7,177,479
Assets: $11,987,917
Liabilities: $2,441,720
Net Worth: $9,546,197
Earnings: $700,232
Emp.: 65
Fiscal Year-end: 03/31/21
Electric Lighting Product Mfr & Distr
N.A.I.C.S.: 335139
Andrew Yat Ming Tam *(Co-Founder, Chm & CEO)*

IMS MAXIMS PLC
Saxon Court 502 Avebury Boulevard, Milton Keynes, MK9 3GD, United Kingdom
Tel.: (44) 2036686999
Web Site: http://www.imsmaxims.com
Year Founded: 1986
Sales Range: $1-9.9 Million
Emp.: 54
Computer Software Developer
N.A.I.C.S.: 334610
Terry Fossey *(Dir-Tech)*

Subsidiaries:

Integrated Medical Solutions Limited (1)
Sandy Mount Sta Rd Woburn Sands, Milton Keynes, MK17 8RR, Buckinghamshire, United Kingdom
Tel.: (44) 1908588800
Clinical Software Development Services
N.A.I.C.S.: 541511

Irish Medical Systems (Computers) Limited (1)
Clara Hs Glenageary Pk Co, Dublin, Dun Laoghaire, Ireland
Tel.: (353) 12840555
Web Site: http://www.imsmaxims.com
Emp.: 20
Medical Software Services
N.A.I.C.S.: 513210
Shane Tickell *(CEO)*

IMS S.A.
Pulawska 366, 02-819, Warsaw, Poland
Tel.: (48) 228706776
Web Site: https://www.imssensory.com
Year Founded: 2000
IMS—(WAR)
Rev.: $15,501,181
Assets: $13,809,087
Liabilities: $8,582,968
Net Worth: $5,226,118
Earnings: $2,471,241
Fiscal Year-end: 12/31/19
Advertising & Marketing Services
N.A.I.C.S.: 541810
Wieslaw Rozlucki *(Chm-Supervisory Bd)*

IMSTALCON JSC
Area Zhetysu 71 B, Almaty, Kazakhstan
Tel.: (7) 7273768935
Web Site: http://www.imstalcon.kz
Sales Range: $200-249.9 Million
Emp.: 9,000
Construction Engineering Services
N.A.I.C.S.: 541330

IMT CO., LTD.
8F 306 Sinwon-ro, Yeongtong-gu, Suwon, 16675, Gyeonggi-do, Korea (South)
Tel.: (82) 3180473400
Web Site: https://www.imt-c.co.kr
Year Founded: 2000
451220—(KRS)
Semiconductor Devices Mfr
N.A.I.C.S.: 334413

Jae-Sung Choi *(CEO)*

IMTEL KOMUNIKACIJE A.D.
Boulevard Mihaila Pupina 165b, 11070, Belgrade, Serbia
Tel.: (381) 112129317
Web Site: https://www.insimtel.com
Year Founded: 2006
IMKM—(BEL)
Rev.: $462,345
Assets: $1,133,578
Liabilities: $115,916
Net Worth: $1,017,662
Earnings: $8,117
Emp.: 20
Fiscal Year-end: 12/31/22
Telecommunication Equipment Mfr & Distr
N.A.I.C.S.: 334220
Vladimir Smiljakovic *(CEO & Gen Mgr)*

IMTEL RTV A.D.
Bulevar Mihaila Pupina 165b, Belgrade, Serbia
Tel.: (381) 11 311 4560
Year Founded: 2006
Sales Range: $1-9.9 Million
Technical Science Research & Development Services
N.A.I.C.S.: 541990

IMUGENE LIMITED
Suite 1201 Level 12 4-6 Bligh Street, Sydney, 2000, NSW, Australia
Tel.: (61) 398245254 AU
Web Site: https://www.imugene.com
IMU—(ASX)
Rev.: $3,318,664
Assets: $101,093,627
Liabilities: $22,131,016
Net Worth: $78,962,611
Earnings: ($99,946,941)
Fiscal Year-end: 06/30/24
Pharmaceutical Product Mfr & Distr
N.A.I.C.S.: 325412
Phillip Allen Hains *(Co-Sec)*

IMURA CO., LTD.
Namba SkyO 18th floor 1-60 Namba 5-chome, Chuō-ku, Osaka, 542-0076, Japan
Tel.: (81) 665866121
Web Site: https://www.imura.co.jp
Year Founded: 1950
3955—(TKS)
Rev.: $147,961,210
Assets: $145,742,040
Liabilities: $30,728,060
Net Worth: $115,013,980
Earnings: $6,735,500
Emp.: 664
Fiscal Year-end: 01/31/24
Envelope Product Mfr & Distr
N.A.I.C.S.: 322230
Morihiro Imura *(Chm)*

IMURAYA GROUP CO., LTD.
7-1-1 Takajaya, Tsu, 514-8530, Mie, Japan
Tel.: (81) 592342131
Web Site: https://www.imuraya-group.com
Year Founded: 1947
2209—(TKS)
Rev.: $318,747,420
Assets: $251,774,900
Liabilities: $112,931,850
Net Worth: $138,843,050
Earnings: $12,757,300
Emp.: 944
Fiscal Year-end: 03/31/24
Confectionery Product Mfr & Distr
N.A.I.C.S.: 311351
Takeo Asada *(CEO, CMO & Chm)*

INTERNATIONAL PUBLIC

Subsidiaries:

IMURAYA USA, INC. (1)
2502 Barranca Pkwy, Irvine, CA 92606
Tel.: (949) 251-9205
Web Site: https://www.imuraya-usa.com
Confectionary Product Mfr
N.A.I.C.S.: 311340

Imuraya foods Co., Ltd. (1)
1 of 24 Jibu Nakahara-cho, Toyohashi, 441-3106, Aichi, Japan
Tel.: (81) 532411191
Emp.: 238
Raw Material Mfr
N.A.I.C.S.: 311942

IMV CORPORATION
2-6-10 Takeshima, Nishiyodogawa-ku, Osaka, 5550011, Japan
Tel.: (81) 664782565
Web Site: https://we-are-imv.com
Year Founded: 1957
7760—(TKS)
Rev.: $98,324,120
Assets: $122,557,740
Liabilities: $57,024,870
Net Worth: $65,532,870
Earnings: $7,983,340
Emp.: 412
Fiscal Year-end: 09/30/23
Measuring & Control Instrument Mfr
N.A.I.C.S.: 334515
Shigeo Kojima *(Chm & CEO)*

Subsidiaries:

ABC MTS Inc. (1)
5th Floor Cheongwoo Building 22 Heungan-daero, Gunpo, Gyeonggi, Korea (South)
Tel.: (82) 314560667
Web Site: https://www.abcmts.co.kr
Electrical Equipment Mfr & Distr
N.A.I.C.S.: 335999

Euroc Test Equipment (GuangDong) Co., Ltd. (1)
1601-1604 Room A Block Dongling Plaza No 242 Fenghuangbeiheng Road, AutoCity Avenue Yongning Street Xintang, Guangzhou, China
Tel.: (86) 2032146200
Automotive Equipment Measurement & Testing Services
N.A.I.C.S.: 541380

IMV (THAILAND) CO., LTD. (1)
Amata City Chonburi Industrial Estate Phase9 700/907 Moo 5 Tambol, Nhongkakha Amphur Phanthong, Chon Buri, 20160, Thailand
Tel.: (66) 3 821 2226
Web Site: https://www.imv.co.th
Laboratory Testing Services
N.A.I.C.S.: 541380

IMV EUROPE LIMITED (1)
Suite 10 Devonshire Business Centre Works Road, Letchworth, SG6 1GJ, Hertfordshire, United Kingdom
Tel.: (44) 1462488210
Electronic Equipment Mfr & Maintenance Services
N.A.I.C.S.: 334419

Keiseiking Enterprises, Ltd. (1)
9F-3 No 92 Section 1 Nanjing East Road, Taipei, Taiwan
Tel.: (886) 225515570
Web Site: https://www.keiseiking.com
Precision Testing Instrument Distr
N.A.I.C.S.: 423490

Moritani America Inc. (1)
300 Park Blvd Ste 320, Itasca, IL 60143
Tel.: (630) 250-9898
Web Site: https://www.moritaniusa.com
Emp.: 9
Industrial Machine & Equipment Distr
N.A.I.C.S.: 423830

IMV INC.
130 Eileen Stubbs Avenue Suite 19, Dartmouth, B3B 2C4, NS, Canada
Tel.: (902) 492-1819 Ca
Web Site: https://www.imv-inc.com

Year Founded: 2007
IMV—(NASDAQ)
Rev.: $329,000
Assets: $31,348,000
Liabilities: $37,950,000
Net Worth: ($6,602,000)
Earnings: ($37,991,000)
Emp.: 63
Fiscal Year-end: 12/31/22
Biotechnology Research Services
N.A.I.C.S.: 541714
Pierre Labbe (CFO)

IMVEST S.P.A.
Via Calabria 56, Rome, Italy
Tel.: (39) 066876006
Web Site: http://www.imvest.it
YIV—(ITA)
Sales Range: Less than $1 Million
Real Estate Development Services
N.A.I.C.S.: 531390
Raffaele Israilovici (CEO)

IMW IMMOBILIEN SE
Hausvogteiplatz 11a, 10117, Berlin, Germany
Tel.: (49) 3025461200
Web Site: http://www.imw-se.eu
Year Founded: 1813
Sales Range: $10-24.9 Million
Emp.: 50
Real Estate Manangement Services
N.A.I.C.S.: 531390
Roland Pohlmann (CFO & Member-Exec Bd)

IN CONSTRUCTION HOLDINGS LIMITED
26/F Park Avenue Tower 5 Moreton Terrace, Causeway Bay, China (Hong Kong)
Tel.: (852) 2 576 0802
Web Site: http://www.inconstruction.hk
1500—(HKG)
Rev.: $59,620,489
Assets: $53,687,022
Liabilities: $13,101,659
Net Worth: $40,585,363
Earnings: $8,021,524
Emp.: 51
Fiscal Year-end: 03/31/22
Foundation, Demolition, Site Formation & Ground Investigation Field Works
N.A.I.C.S.: 238110
Pak Man Lau (Chm, CEO & Gen Mgr)

IN PHASE INTERNATIONAL LTD.
DB House Rani Drive, Nottingham, NG5 1RF, United Kingdom
Tel.: (44) 115 975 8600
Web Site: http://ww.ipitrade.com
Gadget Dist
N.A.I.C.S.: 449210
Steve Digva (CEO)

Subsidiaries:

Performance Products Limited (1)
Cleaver House Sarus Court Stuart Road, Manor Park, Runcorn, WA7 1UL, United Kingdom
Tel.: (44) 3331212252
Web Site: http://www.snooperneo.co.uk
Broadcast, Navigation & Wireless Communications Equipment Mfr
N.A.I.C.S.: 423690
Mark Close (Mng Dir)

IN TECHNICAL PRODUCTIONS HOLDINGS LIMITED
Unit D2 5/F Hoi Bun Industrial Building 6 Wing Yip Street Kwun Tong, Kowloon, China (Hong Kong)
Tel.: (852) 35952636 Ky

Web Site: http://www.intechproductions.com
Year Founded: 2009
8446—(HKG)
Rev.: $2,594,301
Assets: $11,150,773
Liabilities: $5,293,504
Net Worth: $5,857,270
Earnings: ($3,112,184)
Emp.: 86
Fiscal Year-end: 05/31/22
visual Design Services
N.A.I.C.S.: 541490
Dennis Ho ting Yeung (Founder, Chm, CEO & Officer-Compliance)

IN THE F CO.,LTD.
21 Teheran-ro 104-gil, Gangnam-gu Daechi-dong, Seoul, 06174, Korea (South)
Tel.: (82) 234569000
Web Site: https://www.inthef.co.kr
Year Founded: 1980
014990—(KRS)
Rev.: $103,800,459
Assets: $91,844,543
Liabilities: $62,741,431
Net Worth: $29,103,113
Earnings: ($7,803,890)
Emp.: 183
Fiscal Year-end: 12/31/22
Apparels Mfr
N.A.I.C.S.: 315990
Soo-Geun Son (CEO)

IN THE STYLE GROUP PLC
Unit 5 Olympic Court, Salford, M50 2QP, United Kingdom   UK
Web Site: https://www.inthestyle.com
Year Founded: 2013
ITS—(AIM)
Rev.: $77,820,437
Assets: $25,485,762
Liabilities: $10,937,792
Net Worth: $14,547,970
Earnings: ($1,804,410)
Emp.: 175
Fiscal Year-end: 03/31/22
Ecommerce Retailer
N.A.I.C.S.: 459999

IN WIN DEVELOPMENT INC.
No 57 Lane 350 Nanshang Road, Guishan Dist, Taoyuan, 333014, Taiwan
Tel.: (886) 33229898
Web Site: https://www.in-win.com
Year Founded: 1985
6117—(TAI)
Rev.: $77,466,723
Assets: $119,410,081
Liabilities: $79,537,915
Net Worth: $39,872,166
Earnings: $2,889,467
Emp.: 785
Fiscal Year-end: 12/31/23
Computer Peripherals Mfr
N.A.I.C.S.: 334118

Subsidiaries:

In Win Development (N.L.) B.V. (1)
Geyssendorfferweg 47, 3088 GJ, Rotterdam, South Holland, Netherlands
Tel.: (31) 107 505 700
Computer Casing Mfr
N.A.I.C.S.: 332510

In Win Development (U.S.A.) Inc. (1)
188 Brea Canyon Rd, City of Industry, CA 91789-3086
Tel.: (909) 348-0588
Sales Range: $25-49.9 Million
Emp.: 20
Computer Chassis Mfr
N.A.I.C.S.: 334112

In Win Development (UK) Ltd. (1)
Stirling House Breasy Place 9 Burroughs Gardens, Hendon, London, NW4 4AU, United Kingdom
Tel.: (44) 2083591155
Web Site: http://www.in-win.com
Sales Range: $25-49.9 Million
Emp.: 4
Computer Peripheral Equipment Mfr
N.A.I.C.S.: 334118

Inwinstack Inc. (1)
25F No 285 Sec 2 Wenhua Rd, Banqiao Dist, New Taipei City, 220503, Taiwan
Tel.: (886) 277382858
Web Site: https://www.inwinstack.com
Software Development Services
N.A.I.C.S.: 541511

IN'TECH MEDICAL SAS
158 rue de l'Eglise, BP15, 62180, Rang-du-Fliers, France
Tel.: (33) 3 21 896 000
Web Site: http://www.intech-medical.com
Medical Equipment Mfr
N.A.I.C.S.: 339112
Laurent Provost (Pres & CEO)

Subsidiaries:

Bradshaw Medical, Inc. (1)
10325 58th Pl, Kenosha, WI 53144
Tel.: (262) 925-1374
Web Site: http://www.intech-medical.com
Miscellaneous Ambulatory Health Care Services
N.A.I.C.S.: 621999

In'Tech Medical INC (1)
1407 Union Ave Ste 1204, Memphis, TN 38104
Tel.: (901) 375-1109
Web Site: http://www.intech-medical.com
Medical Equipment Mfr
N.A.I.C.S.: 339112

INA GROUP LTD OY
Pyhajarvenkatu 5 2nd Fl, 33200, Tampere, Finland
Tel.: (358) 3 2173111
Web Site: http://www.ina.fi
Sales Range: $100-124.9 Million
Emp.: 250
Enterprise & E-Government Services
N.A.I.C.S.: 561499
Pia Pursiainen (CEO)

Subsidiaries:

Midas Touch Oy (1)
Tekniikantie 14 Innopoli 2, 02150, Espoo, Finland
Tel.: (358) 303 9891
Web Site: http://www.midastouch.fi
Sales Range: $25-49.9 Million
Emp.: 170
Communication & Telemarketing Services
N.A.I.C.S.: 561422
Janne Savonen (Dir-Sls & Production)

INA-HOLDING SCHAEFFLER GMBH & CO. KG
Industriestrasse 1-3, 91074, Herzogenaurach, Germany
Tel.: (49) 9132820   De
Web Site: http://www.schaeffler.com
Year Founded: 1946
Sales Range: $5-14.9 Billion
Emp.: 65,000
Holding Company
N.A.I.C.S.: 551112
Georg F. W. Schaeffler (Co-Owner)

Subsidiaries:

CBF Europe GmbH (1)
Mettmanner Str 79, 42115, Wuppertal, Germany
Tel.: (49) 2022930
Industrial Machinery Mfr
N.A.I.C.S.: 333248

Egon von Ruville GmbH (1)
Billbrookdeich 112, PO Box 74 02 27, 22113, Hamburg, Germany
Tel.: (49) 40733440

Web Site: http://www.ruville.com
Industrial Machinery Mfr
N.A.I.C.S.: 333248

Elmotec Statomat GmbH (1)
Max Planck-Strasse 20-24, 61184, Karben, Germany
Tel.: (49) 60394880
Web Site: http://www.elmotec-statomat.eu
Machinery Products Mfr
N.A.I.C.S.: 333248

FAG Industrial Services GmbH (1)
Kaiserstrasse 100, 52134, Herzogenrath, Germany
Tel.: (49) 240791490
Industrial Machinery Mfr
N.A.I.C.S.: 333248

GURAS Beteiligungs GmbH & Co. Vermietungs-KG (1)
Emil-Riedl-Weg 6, 82049, Pullach, Germany
Tel.: (49) 8951200
Industrial Machinery Mfr
N.A.I.C.S.: 333248

Gesellschaft fur Arbeitsmedizin und Umweltschutz mbH - AMUS (1)
Berliner Str 134, 66424, Homburg, Germany
Tel.: (49) 68417012499
Industrial Machinery Mfr
N.A.I.C.S.: 333248

IFT Ingenieurgesellschaft fur Triebwerks-Technik mbH (1)
Sachsenweg 7, 38678, Clausthal-Zellerfeld, Germany
Tel.: (49) 532393990
Industrial Machinery Mfr
N.A.I.C.S.: 333248
Christopher Lehme (Gen Mgr)

LuK Unna GmbH & Co. KG (1)
Alfred-Nobel-Strasse 9, 59423, Unna, Germany
Tel.: (49) 23038830
Industrial Machinery Mfr
N.A.I.C.S.: 333248

Schaeffler Aerospace (Singapore) Pte. Ltd. (1)
18 Tai Seng Street 09-07 and 09-08, Singapore, Singapore
Tel.: (65) 65408600
Machinery Products Mfr
N.A.I.C.S.: 333248

Schaeffler Aerospace Canada Inc. (1)
151 Wright Blvd Plant 2, Stratford, N4Z 1H3, ON, Canada
Tel.: (519) 276-6518
Machinery Products Mfr
N.A.I.C.S.: 333248

Schaeffler Aerospace Germany GmbH & Co. KG (1)
Georg-Schafer-Str30, 97421, Schweinfurt, Germany
Tel.: (49) 9721913372
Machinery Products Mfr
N.A.I.C.S.: 333248

Schaeffler Automotive Aftermarket GmbH&Co. KG (1)
Paul-Ehrlich-Strasse 21, 63225, Langen, Germany
Tel.: (49) 61037530
Web Site: http://www.schaeffler-aftermarket.com
Industrial Machinery Mfr
N.A.I.C.S.: 333248
Vjekoslav Mestrovic (Dir-Matl Mgmt & Central Sls & Svc)

Schaeffler Automotive Aftermarket Services Consulting (Shanghai) Co. (1)
No1 Antuo Road, Jiading, Shanghai, China
Tel.: (86) 2139576702
Machinery Products Mfr
N.A.I.C.S.: 333248

Schaeffler Elfershausen AG & Co. KG (1)
August-Ullrich-Str 36 -38, 97725, Elfershausen, Bayern, Germany
Tel.: (49) 97046080
Industrial Machinery Mfr

INA-HOLDING SCHAEFFLER GMBH & CO. KG

INA-Holding Schaeffler GmbH & Co. KG—(Continued)
N.A.I.C.S.: 333248

Schaeffler Engineering GmbH (1)
Gewerbestrasse 14, 58791, Werdohl, Germany
Tel.: (49) 23928090
Web Site: http://www.schaeffler-engineering.com
Industrial Machinery Mfr
N.A.I.C.S.: 333248
Rolf Laufs (CEO)

Schaeffler Industrial Drives AG & Co. KG (1)
Mittelbergstrasse 2, 98527, Suhl, Germany
Tel.: (49) 368175740
Machinery Products Mfr
N.A.I.C.S.: 333248

Schaeffler Monitoring Services GmbH (1)
Kaiserstrasse 100, 52134, Herzogenrath, Germany
Tel.: (49) 540791490
Machinery Products Mfr
N.A.I.C.S.: 333248

Schaeffler Paravan Technologie GmbH & Co. KG (1)
Industriestrasse 1-3, 91074, Herzogenaurach, Germany
Tel.: (49) 9132814519
Web Site: http://www.schaeffler-paravan.de
Vehicle Product Services
N.A.I.C.S.: 423120
Roland Arnold (CEO)

Schaeffler Romania S.R.L. (1)
Aleea Schaeffler Nr 3, Cristian, Brasov, 507055, Romania
Tel.: (40) 268505000
Machinery Products Mfr
N.A.I.C.S.: 333248

Schaeffler Rus OOO (1)
44-y Inzhenerny proezd 11, 432072, Ulyanovsk, Russia
Tel.: (7) 8422273325
Machinery Products Mfr
N.A.I.C.S.: 333248

Schaeffler Schweiz GmbH (1)
Sternenstrasse 2, 8590, Romanshorn, Switzerland
Tel.: (41) 715566655
Machinery Products Mfr
N.A.I.C.S.: 333248

Schaeffler Transmision, S. de R.L. de C.V. (1)
Av Resurreccion Norte No 12, Fraccionamiento Industrial Resurreccion, 72920, Puebla, Mexico
Tel.: (52) 2222299200
Machinery Products Mfr
N.A.I.C.S.: 333248

Schaeffler Turkey Endustri ve Otomotiv Ticaret Limited Sirketi (1)
Saray Mah Omer Faik Atakan Cad Yilmaz Plaza No 3, Umraniye, Istanbul, 34768, Turkiye
Tel.: (90) 2122792741
Machinery Products Mfr
N.A.I.C.S.: 333248

Schaeffler Verwaltung Zwei GmbH (1)
Industriestrasse 1-3, 91074, Herzogenaurach, Germany
Tel.: (49) 9132 82 0
Emp.: 8,000
Holding Company
N.A.I.C.S.: 551112

Subsidiary (Non-US):

FAG Aerospace (Singapore) Pte. Ltd. (2)
151 Lorong Chuan 06-01 New Tech Park Lobby A, Singapore, 556741, Singapore
Tel.: (65) 65408600
Automotive Components Mfr
N.A.I.C.S.: 333612
Klaus Rosenfeld (CEO)

FAG Aerospace Inc. (2)
151 Wright Boulevard Plant 2, Stratford, N4Z 1H3, ON, Canada
Tel.: (519) 271-3231
Industrial Machinery Distr
N.A.I.C.S.: 423830

Subsidiary (US):

FAG Bearings LLC (2)
200 Park Ave, Danbury, CT 06813-2449
Tel.: (203) 744-2211
Automotive Components Mfr
N.A.I.C.S.: 333612
Klaus Rosenfeld (CEO & CFO)

Subsidiary (Non-US):

FAG Magyarorszag Ipari Kft. (2)
Hatar ut 1 D ep, 4031, Debrecen, Hungary
Tel.: (36) 52581700
Automotive Components Mfr
N.A.I.C.S.: 333612

FAG Roller Bearings Private Ltd. (2)
Nariman Bhavan 8th Floor 227 Backbay Reclamation Nariman Point, Mumbai, 400 021, India
Tel.: (91) 2266814444
Automotive Component Mfr & Distr
N.A.I.C.S.: 333612
Rajendra Anandpara (Mng Dir)

Hydrel Gmbh (2)
Badstrasse 14, 8590, Romanshorn, Switzerland
Tel.: (41) 714666666
Web Site: http://www.hydrel.ch
Industrial Machinery Distr
N.A.I.C.S.: 423830

Subsidiary (Domestic):

INA - Drives & Mechatronics AG & Co. KG (2)
Mittelbergstr 2, 98527, Suhl, Germany
Tel.: (49) 36 81 75 74 0
Web Site: http://www.schaeffler.com
Industrial Machinery Mfr
N.A.I.C.S.: 333248

Subsidiary (Non-US):

INA Bearing (Pty) Ltd. (2)
58-64 Burman Road Deal Party Estate, 6012, Port Elizabeth, South Africa
Tel.: (27) 41 407 5000
Automotive Components Mfr
N.A.I.C.S.: 333612
Myburgh Marshal (Gen Mgr)

INA Bearings India Private Limited (2)
Plot No A-3 Talegaon Industrial Floriculture Park Ambi, Navalakha Umbre Maval, Pune, 410 507, India
Tel.: (91) 20 30614100
Automotive Component Mfr & Distr
N.A.I.C.S.: 333612
Dharmesh Arora (Mng Dir)

INA Lanskroun, s.r.o. (2)
Dvorakova 328, 563 01, Lanskroun, Czech Republic
Tel.: (420) 465355111
Emp.: 800
Industrial Machinery Distr
N.A.I.C.S.: 423830
Jan Golan (Dir)

INA Rolamentos Lda. (2)
Rua Daciano Baptista Marques 181-Torre C-2 Canidelo, Vila Nova de Gaia, 4400-617, Portugal
Tel.: (351) 225 320 800
Automotive Components Mfr
N.A.I.C.S.: 333612

INA Skalica spol. s r.o. (2)
Ulica Dr G Schaefflera 1, 90901, Skalica, Slovakia
Tel.: (421) 346961111
Automobile Component Distr
N.A.I.C.S.: 423120

LuK (UK) Limited (2)
Waleswood Road Wales Bar, Sheffield, S26 5PN, United Kingdom
Tel.: (44) 1909510500
Web Site: http://www.luk.co.uk
Industrial Machinery Distr
N.A.I.C.S.: 423830
Klaus Rosenfeld (CEO & CFO)

Subsidiary (US):

LuK Clutch Systems, LLC (2)
3401 Old Airport Rd, Wooster, OH 44691
Tel.: (330) 264-4383
Automotive Component Mfr & Distr
N.A.I.C.S.: 333612

Subsidiary (Non-US):

LuK India Private Limited (2)
Royakottah Road, Hosur, 635 109, India
Tel.: (91) 4344222313
Automotive Component Mfr & Distr
N.A.I.C.S.: 333612
Dharmesh Arora (Mng Dir)

LuK Puebla, S. de R.L. de C.V. (2)
Av Resurreccion Norte No 12 Fraccionamiento Industrial Resurreccion, 72920, Puebla, Mexico
Tel.: (52) 2222299211
Automotive Component Mfr & Distr
N.A.I.C.S.: 333612

LuK Savaria Kft. (2)
Zanati ut 31, 9700, Szombathely, Hungary
Tel.: (36) 94588119
Automotive Components Mfr
N.A.I.C.S.: 423830

Subsidiary (US):

LuK-Aftermarket Services, LLC (2)
5370 Wegman Dr, Valley City, OH 44280-9700
Tel.: (800) 274-5001
Automobile Component Distr
N.A.I.C.S.: 423120
Klaus Rosenfeld (CEO & CFO)

Subsidiary (Non-US):

Radine B.V. (2)
Energieweg 15, 3771 NA, Barneveld, Netherlands
Tel.: (31) 342403230
Automotive Component Mfr & Distr
N.A.I.C.S.: 333612
Remco Van Dijk (Mgr-Production)

Rodamientos FAG S.A. de C.V (2)
Henry Ford 141 Col Bondojito Deleg Gustavo A Madero, 7850, Mexico, Mexico
Tel.: (52) 5550626085
Automotive Components Mfr
N.A.I.C.S.: 333612

SC Schaeffler Romania S.R.L. (2)
Aleea Schaeffler Nr 3, 507055, Brasov, Romania
Tel.: (40) 268504816
Automotive Components Mfr
N.A.I.C.S.: 333612

Schaeffler (China) Co., Ltd. (2)
No 1 Antuo Road Anting, Jiading, Shanghai, 201804, China
Tel.: (86) 21 3957 6500
Industrial Machinery Distr
N.A.I.C.S.: 423830

Schaeffler (Ningxia) Co., Ltd. (2)
Wenchang South Rd 86, xixia, Yinchuan, 750021, China
Tel.: (86) 9512072333
Industrial Machinery Distr
N.A.I.C.S.: 423830

Schaeffler (Thailand) Co., Ltd. (2)
388 Exchange Tower 31st 34th Floor Unit 3103 3403-3404 Sukhumvit Road, Klongtoey, Bangkok, 10110, Thailand
Tel.: (66) 26970000
Automobile Component Distr
N.A.I.C.S.: 423120

Subsidiary (Domestic):

Schaeffler AG (2)
Industriestrasse 1-3, 91074, Herzogenaurach, Germany (83.3%)
Tel.: (49) 9132820
Web Site: https://www.schaeffler.com
Rev: $12,600,000,000
Assets: $13,207,000,000
Liabilities: $11,462,000,000
Net Worth: $1,745,000,000
Earnings: ($424,000,000)
Emp.: 83,297
Fiscal Year-end: 12/31/2020

INTERNATIONAL PUBLIC

Holding Company; Automotive & Industrial Products Mfr & Whslr
N.A.I.C.S.: 551112
Stefan Spindler (Member-Mgmt Bd)

Subsidiary (Domestic):

Compact Dynamics GmbH (3)
Moosstrasse 9, 82319, Starnberg, Germany
Tel.: (49) 815190430
Web Site: http://www.compact-dynamics.de
Electrical & Electronic Mfr
N.A.I.C.S.: 335999

Subsidiary (Non-US):

Schaeffler (Xiangtan) Co., Ltd. (3)
West Baishi Road 6, Xiangtan, 411201, Hunan, China
Tel.: (86) 73155292999
Motor Vehicle Parts Mfr
N.A.I.C.S.: 336390

Subsidiary (Domestic):

Schaeffler Bio-Hybrid GmbH (3)
Rollnerstrasse 110a, 90408, Nuremberg, Germany
Tel.: (49) 91191947700
Web Site: http://www.biohybrid.com
Automobile Mfr
N.A.I.C.S.: 336110

Subsidiary (Non-US):

Schaeffler Global Services Europe Sp. z o.o. (3)
Plac Nowy Targ 28, 50-141, Wroclaw, Poland
Tel.: (48) 538248344
Motor Vehicle Parts Mfr
N.A.I.C.S.: 336390

Schaeffler Kysuce, Spol. s r.o. (3)
Ulica Dr G Schaefflera 1, 02401, Kysucke Nove Mesto, Slovakia
Tel.: (421) 414205110
Web Site: http://www.schaeffler.sk
Automobile Mfr
N.A.I.C.S.: 336110

Schaeffler Production CZ s.r.o. (3)
Prumyslova 2295/26, 56802, Svitavy, Czech Republic
Tel.: (420) 465837101
Motor Vehicle Parts Mfr
N.A.I.C.S.: 336390

Schaeffler Savaria Kft. (3)
Zanati ut 31, 9700, Szombathely, Hungary
Tel.: (36) 94588100
Motor Vehicle Parts Mfr
N.A.I.C.S.: 336390

Schaeffler Skalica spol. s r.o. (3)
Street Dr G Schaefflera 1, 90901, Skalica, Slovakia
Tel.: (421) 346961111
Motor Vehicle Parts Mfr
N.A.I.C.S.: 336390

Subsidiary (Domestic):

Schaeffler Technologies GmbH & Co. KG (3)
Industriestrasse 1-3, 91074, Herzogenaurach, Germany
Tel.: (49) 9132 82 0
Web Site: http://www.schaeffler.com
Automotive & Industrial Products Mfr & Whslr
N.A.I.C.S.: 332991
Dirk Spindler (Member-Mgmt Bd-Indus R&D)

Subsidiary (Domestic):

LuK GmbH & Co. oHG (4)
Industriestr 3, 77815, Buhl, Germany
Tel.: (49) 72239410
Web Site: http://www.luk.de
Emp.: 8,000
Drive-Train Components Mfr
N.A.I.C.S.: 336350
Gabriele Veith (Mgr-Corp Commun)

Subsidiary (US):

LuK USA LLC (5)
3401 Old Airport Rd, Wooster, OH 44691
Tel.: (330) 264-4383
Web Site: http://www.schaeffler.us

AND PRIVATE COMPANIES — INA-HOLDING SCHAEFFLER GMBH & CO. KG

Sales Range: $150-199.9 Million
Emp.: 1,700
Automotive Start-Up System Mfr
N.A.I.C.S.: 336350
Scott Heldreth *(Engr-Customer Quality)*

Subsidiary (Non-US):

Schaeffler (Singapore) Pte. Ltd. (4)
151 Lorong Chuan #06-01, New Tech Park Lobby A, Singapore, 556741,
Singapore **(100%)**
Tel.: (65) 6540 8600
Web Site: http://www.schaeffler.sg
Roller Bearing Mfr
N.A.I.C.S.: 332991
Michel Berger *(Mng Dir)*

Schaeffler (UK) Ltd. (4)
Forge Lane, Minworth, Sutton Coldfield, B76 1AP, United Kingdom **(100%)**
Tel.: (44) 121 313 5870
Web Site: http://www.schaeffler.co.uk
Provider of Services of Automotive, Power Transmission, Materials Handling, Machine Tool, Textile Machinery, Power Tools & Office Machines
N.A.I.C.S.: 336350
Philip Elson *(Ops Mgr)*

Schaeffler Australia Pty. Ltd. (4)
Level 1 Building 8 Forest Central Business Park, 49 French's Forest Road, French's Forest, 2086, NSW, Australia **(100%)**
Tel.: (61) 289771000
Web Site: http://www.schaeffler.com.au
Precision Rolling Bearing for the Automotive Mechanical Engineering & Aerospace Industry Mfr
N.A.I.C.S.: 332991
David Nevin *(Gen Mgr)*

Subsidiary (Domestic):

Schaeffler Friction Products GmbH (4)
Industriestrasse 7, 54497, Morbach, Germany
Tel.: (49) 6533780
Web Site: http://www.schaeffler-friction.de
Mfr of Clutch Facings, Brake Linings & Automatic Transmission Friction Elements
N.A.I.C.S.: 336350
Lars Haufschild *(Mng Dir)*

Subsidiary (US):

Schaeffler Group USA Inc (4)
308 Springhill Farm Rd, Fort Mill, SC 29715-9784
Tel.: (803) 548-8500
Web Site: http://www.schaeffler.com
Roller Bearings & Part Mfr
N.A.I.C.S.: 332991
Bruce Warmbold *(CEO)*

Unit (Non-US):

Schaeffler Canada Inc. - Automotive Unit (5)
801 Ontario Street Plant 1, Stratford, N5A 6T2, ON, Canada
Tel.: (519) 271-3200
Web Site: http://www.schaeffler.ca
Sales Range: $150-199.9 Million
Emp.: 400
Automotive Bearing Mfr
N.A.I.C.S.: 332991

Subsidiary (Domestic):

The Barden Corp. (5)
200 Park Ave, Danbury, CT 06813-2449
Tel.: (203) 744-2211
Web Site: http://www.bardenbearings.com
Sales Range: $50-74.9 Million
Emp.: 480
Mfr of High Precision Bearings & Components
N.A.I.C.S.: 332991
Ed Silva *(Coord-Facilities)*

Division (Non-US):

The Barden Corporation (UK) Ltd. (6)
Plymbridge Road, Estover, Plymouth, PL6 7LH, United Kingdom **(100%)**
Tel.: (44) 752735555
Web Site: http://www.bardenbearings.co.uk
Sales Range: $75-99.9 Million
Emp.: 360
Mfr of High Precision Bearings & Components
N.A.I.C.S.: 332991

Division (Domestic):

Winsted Precision Ball Co. (6)
159 Colebrook River Rd, Winsted, CT 06098
Tel.: (860) 379-7558
Web Site: http://www.winball.com
Sales Range: $25-49.9 Million
Emp.: 70
Mfr of Precision Balls
N.A.I.C.S.: 332991

Subsidiary (Non-US):

Schaeffler Italia S.r.l. (4)
Via Dr Georg Schaeffler 7, Momo, 28015, Novara, NO, Italy **(100%)**
Tel.: (39) 0321 929 211
Web Site: http://www.schaeffler.it
Mfr of Roller Bearings
N.A.I.C.S.: 332991

Schaeffler Japan Co., Ltd. (4)
LIVMO Rising Building 3-19-1, Shinyokohama, Kohoku-ku, Yokohama, 222-0033, Japan
Tel.: (81) 45 476 5900
Web Site: http://www.schaeffler.jp
Industrial Machinery
N.A.I.C.S.: 423830

Subsidiary (Domestic):

Vitesco Technologies Group AG (3)
Siemensstrasse 12, 93055, Regensburg, Germany **(79.82%)**
Tel.: (49) 94120310
Web Site:
https://www.vitesco-technologies.com
Rev.: $10,192,294,957
Assets: $8,370,791,479
Liabilities: $5,223,313,832
Net Worth: $3,147,477,647
Earnings: ($106,413,511)
Emp.: 35,528
Fiscal Year-end: 12/31/2023
Automotive Engine System & Powertrain Component Developer & Mfr
N.A.I.C.S.: 336310

Plant (Domestic):

Continental Automotive GmbH (4)
Schorndorfer Strasse 91, 93426, Roding, Germany
Tel.: (49) 9461914407
Web Site: http://www.continental-corporation.com
Sales Range: $200-249.9 Million
Emp.: 600
Automotive Engine Pump Mfr
N.A.I.C.S.: 333618

Subsidiary (Domestic):

Continental Mechatronic Germany GmbH & Co. KG (4)
Auer Strasse 19, 09366, Stollberg, Germany
Tel.: (49) 372965490
Sales Range: $50-74.9 Million
Emp.: 200
Automotive Actuator & Fuel Supply Component Mfr
N.A.I.C.S.: 336390

Emitec Gesellschaft fur Emissionstechnologie mbH (4)
Hauptstrasse 128, 53797, Lohmar, Germany **(50%)**
Tel.: (49) 22461090
Web Site: http://www.emitec.com
Sales Range: $200-249.9 Million
Emp.: 900
Automotive Catalytic Converter Developer & Mfr
N.A.I.C.S.: 336390

Subsidiary (Non-US):

Emitec Japan K.K. (5)
Cedar Shibaura 4 F 3-13-16 Shibaura, Minato-ku, Tokyo, 108-0023, Japan
Tel.: (81) 354186066
Web Site: http://www.emitec.com
Automotive Catalytic Converter Component Developer & Mfr
N.A.I.C.S.: 441227

Emitec Korea Inc. (5)
Room 901 Baek Young Building 630 19 Sinsa Dong, Gangnam gu, Seoul, 135 895, Korea (South)
Tel.: (82) 251794913
Web Site: http://www.emitec.com
Sales Range: $25-49.9 Million
Emp.: 3
Automotive Catalytic Converter Component Developer & Mfr
N.A.I.C.S.: 336390

Subsidiary (Non-US):

Schaeffler Ansan Corporation (2)
603-2 Block 179 Seonggok-ro, Danwongu, Ansan, 425-020, Gyeonggi, Korea (South)
Tel.: (82) 314906911
Automotive Component Mfr & Distr
N.A.I.C.S.: 333612

Schaeffler Argentina S.R.L. (2)
Alvarez Jonte 1938 1416 Ciudad Autonoma de, Buenos Aires, Argentina
Tel.: (54) 1140161500
Industrial Machinery Distr
N.A.I.C.S.: 423830

Schaeffler Austria Gmbh (2)
Ferdinand Polzl-Strasse 2, 2560, Berndorf, Austria
Tel.: (43) 2672 202 0
Web Site: http://www.schaeffler.at
Industrial Machinery Distr
N.A.I.C.S.: 423830

Schaeffler Automotive Aftermarket (UK) Limited (2)
Holme Lacy Rd Rotherwas, Hereford, HR2 6BQ, United Kingdom
Tel.: (44) 1432264264
Industrial Machinery Distr
N.A.I.C.S.: 423830

Schaeffler Automotive Aftermarket Mexico, S. de R.L. de C.V. (2)
Av Henry Ford 145 Col Bondojito, 7850, Mexico, Mexico
Tel.: (52) 5550626010
Automotive Component Assembling & Testing Services
N.A.I.C.S.: 336110
Thomas Kerkhoff *(Dir-Sls)*

Schaeffler Bearings (Malaysia) Sdn. Bhd. (2)
5-2 Wisma Fiamma No 20 Jalan 7A/62A Bandar, Menjalara, 52200, Kuala Lumpur, Malaysia
Tel.: (60) 3 6275 0620
Automotive Components Mfr
N.A.I.C.S.: 333612
Soo Kuan Ong Sr. *(Mgr-Fin)*

Schaeffler Bearings Indonesia, PT (2)
Lippo Kuningan 19th Floor Unit A & F Jl HR Rasuna Said Kav B - 12, Jakarta, 12920, Indonesia
Tel.: (62) 2129110280
Automotive Components Mfr
N.A.I.C.S.: 423830
Sifera Siwi *(Mgr-Supply chain)*

Schaeffler Belgium SPRL (2)
Avenue du Commerce 38, 1420, Braine-l'Alleud, Belgium
Tel.: (32) 23891389
Industrial Machinery Distr
N.A.I.C.S.: 423830

Schaeffler Brasil Ltda. (2)
Av Independencia 3500-A Bairro Eden, Sorocaba, 18087-101, Sao Paulo, Brazil
Tel.: (55) 1533351500
Industrial Machinery Distr
N.A.I.C.S.: 423830

Schaeffler Bulgaria OOD (2)
bulevard Knyaz Aleksandar Dondukov 62, 1504, Sofia, Bulgaria
Tel.: (359) 29463900
Industrial Machinery Distr
N.A.I.C.S.: 423830
Mihail Krachniak *(Gen Mgr)*

Schaeffler CZ s.r.o. (2)
Prubezna 74a, 100 00, Prague, Czech Republic
Tel.: (420) 267298111
Industrial Machinery Distr
N.A.I.C.S.: 423830
Petr Hromir *(Fin Mgr)*

Schaeffler Chain Drive Systems SAS (2)
1000 rue Louis Breguet CS 20 099, Calais, France
Tel.: (33) 321466826
Industrial Machinery Distr
N.A.I.C.S.: 423830

Schaeffler Chile Rodamientos Ltda. (2)
Hernando de Aguirre 268 of 201, Providencia, Santiago, Chile
Tel.: (56) 24775000
Industrial Machinery Distr
N.A.I.C.S.: 423830

Schaeffler Colombia Ltda. (2)
Cr10 97 A-13 Trr A Of 209, Bogota, Colombia
Tel.: (57) 16211999
Industrial Machinery Distr
N.A.I.C.S.: 423830

Schaeffler Danmark Aps (2)
Jens Baggesens Vej 90P, PO Box 1139, 8200, Arhus, Denmark
Tel.: (45) 70154444
Web Site: http://www.schaeffler.dk
Emp.: 20
Industrial Machinery Distr
N.A.I.C.S.: 423830
Steffen Fabrin *(Mgr-District)*

Schaeffler Finland Oy (2)
Lautamiehentie 3, 02770, Espoo, Finland
Tel.: (358) 207366204
Web Site: http://www.schaeffler.fi
Industrial Machinery Distr
N.A.I.C.S.: 423830

Schaeffler France SAS (2)
93 route de Bitche, PO Box 30186, 67506, Haguenau, France
Tel.: (33) 388634040
Industrial Machinery Distr
N.A.I.C.S.: 423830

Schaeffler Friction Products (Suzhou) Co., Ltd. (2)
No 36 Daoan Road Xuguan Industry Park, Suzhou, 215151, Jiangsu, China
Tel.: (86) 51268088908
Industrial Machinery Mfr
N.A.I.C.S.: 333248

Schaeffler Hong Kong Company Limited (2)
Unit 3404-5 34/Floor Tower One Lippo Center 89 Queensway, Hong Kong, China (Hong Kong)
Tel.: (852) 23712680
Industrial Machinery Distr
N.A.I.C.S.: 423830
Zhang Yilin *(Pres & CEO)*

Schaeffler Hrvatska d.o.o. (2)
Ogrizoviceva 28b, 10000, Zagreb, Croatia
Tel.: (385) 13701943
Industrial Machinery Distr
N.A.I.C.S.: 423830

Schaeffler Iberia, S.L.U. (2)
Divisao Industria C/ Foment 2 Pol Pont Reixat, 08960, Barcelona, Spain
Tel.: (34) 93 480 34 10
Web Site: http://www.schaeffler.es
Industrial Machinery Distr
N.A.I.C.S.: 423830
Ferran Perez Ayats *(Mgr-Technical)*

Schaeffler Israel Ltd. (2)
5 Ha Karmel St, 20692, Yokneam, Israel
Tel.: (972) 48114146
Automotive Components Mfr
N.A.I.C.S.: 423830

Schaeffler Korea Corporation (2)
452-9 Nae-dong, Changwon, 641-050, Gyeongsangnam, Korea (South)
Tel.: (82) 55 280 8611
Automotive Components Mfr
N.A.I.C.S.: 333612

Schaeffler Magyarorszag Ipari Kft. (2)

INA-HOLDING SCHAEFFLER GMBH & CO. KG

INA-Holding Schaeffler GmbH & Co. KG—(Continued)

Retkoz u 5, 1118, Budapest, Hungary
Tel.: (36) 14813050
Automotive Components Mfr
N.A.I.C.S.: 423830

Schaeffler Manufacturing (Thailand) Co., Ltd. (2)
19/10 Sukhumvit Road Tambol Nuenpra Amphur, Muang, Rayong, 21150, Thailand
Tel.: (66) 38694540
Automotive Components Mfr
N.A.I.C.S.: 333612
Jindong Tao *(Mgr-Pur)*

Schaeffler Manufacturing Rus OOO (2)
Ul Ryleev 41, 432071, Ulyanovsk, Russia
Tel.: (7) 8422273325
Automotive Components Mfr
N.A.I.C.S.: 333612

Schaeffler Mexico, S. de R.L. de C.V. (2)
Av Rio San Lorenzo No 888 Parque Tecnoindustrial Castro del Rio, 36815, Irapuato, Mexico
Tel.: (52) 4621661100
Automobile Parts Mfr & Distr
N.A.I.C.S.: 423120

Schaeffler Nederland B.V. (2)
Gildeweg 31, 3771 NB, Barneveld, Netherlands
Tel.: (31) 342403000
Automotive Component Mfr & Distr
N.A.I.C.S.: 333612

Schaeffler Norge AS (2)
Grenseveien 107B, 0663, Oslo, Norway
Tel.: (47) 23249330
Automotive Components Mfr
N.A.I.C.S.: 333612

Schaeffler Philippines Inc. (2)
5th Floor Optima Building 221 Salcedo Street, Legaspi, 1229, Makati, Philippines
Tel.: (63) 27593583
Automotive Components Mfr
N.A.I.C.S.: 333612

Schaeffler Polska Sp. z.o.o. (2)
Budynek E ul Szyszkowa 35/37, 02-285, Warsaw, Poland
Tel.: (48) 228784120
Automotive Components Mfr
N.A.I.C.S.: 333612

Schaeffler Portugal S.A. (2)
Rua Estrada do Lavradio 25, 2500-294, Caldas da Rainha, Portugal
Tel.: (351) 262837000
Automotive Components Mfr
N.A.I.C.S.: 333612
Mario Cunha *(Mng Dir)*

Schaeffler Rulmanlari Ticaret Ltd. Sti. (2)
Omer Faik Atakan cad Saray Mah Yilmaz Plaza No 3, 34768, Istanbul, Turkiye
Tel.: (90) 2122792741
Automotive Components Mfr
N.A.I.C.S.: 333612

Schaeffler Russland GmbH (2)
Leningradsky Prospekt 47 Bau 3 Business Center Avion, 125167, Moscow, Russia
Tel.: (7) 495 73776 60
Automobile Component Distr
N.A.I.C.S.: 423120
Maxim Shakhov *(CEO)*

Schaeffler Slovenija d.o.o. (2)
Glavni trg 17/b, 2000, Maribor, Slovenia
Tel.: (386) 22282070
Automobile Component Distr
N.A.I.C.S.: 423120

Schaeffler South Africa (Pty.) Ltd. (2)
1 End Street Ext Corner Heidelberg Road, 2000, Johannesburg, South Africa
Tel.: (27) 112253000
Automotive Components Mfr
N.A.I.C.S.: 333612

Schaeffler Sverige AB (2)
Charles gata 10, 195 61, Arlandastad, Sweden
Tel.: (46) 859510900

Automobile Component Distr
N.A.I.C.S.: 423120

Schaeffler Taiwan Co., Ltd. (2)
23F No 76 Sec 2 Dunhua S Rd Da an Dist, Taipei, 106, Taiwan
Tel.: (886) 277301911
Automotive Components Mfr
N.A.I.C.S.: 333612
Klaus Rosenfeld *(CEO & CFO)*

Schaeffler Ukraine GmbH (2)
Zhylyanskaya Str 75 5 Stock Businesscenter, 1032, Kiev, Ukraine
Tel.: (380) 445201380
Automobile Component Distr
N.A.I.C.S.: 423120

Schaeffler Venezuela, C.A. (2)
Urbanizacion San Jose de Tarbes Torre BOD Piso 14 Oficina 14-1, Valencia, Venezuela
Tel.: (58) 241 825 9250
Automobile Component Distr
N.A.I.C.S.: 423120

Schaeffler Vietnam Co., Ltd. (2)
3B Road Amata Industrial Zone, Bien Hoa, Dong Nai, Vietnam
Tel.: (84) 61 3936622
Automotive Components Mfr
N.A.I.C.S.: 333612
Klaus Rosenfeld *(CEO & CFO)*

Statomat Special Machines (India) Pvt. Ltd. (1)
Plot No R-719 M I D C Rabale, TTC Undustrial Area, Navi Mumbai, India
Tel.: (91) 2261386500
Machinery Products Mfr
N.A.I.C.S.: 333248

Xtronic GmbH (1)
Herrenberger Strasse 56, 71034, Boblingen, Germany
Tel.: (49) 703120947
Web Site: http://www.xtronic.de
Automobile Product Distr
N.A.I.C.S.: 423120

INA-INDUSTRIJA NAFTE, D.D.

Avenija Veceslava Holjevca 10 PP 555, 10002, Zagreb, Croatia
Tel.: (385) 15566365
Web Site: https://www.ina.hr
INA—(ZAG)
Rev.: $5,034,470,100
Assets: $3,388,146,300
Liabilities: $1,694,569,800
Net Worth: $1,693,576,500
Earnings: ($17,595,600)
Emp.: 8,056
Fiscal Year-end: 12/31/22
Oil & Natural Gas Exploration, Refining & Distribution
N.A.I.C.S.: 213111
Jozsef Simola *(Member-Mgmt Bd)*

Subsidiaries:

Adriagas S.r.l. (1)
Milano Piazza del Duomo 17 2nd Fl, 20123, Milan, Italy **(100%)**
Tel.: (39) 0272094718
Web Site: http://www.ina.hr
Sales Range: $50-74.9 Million
Emp.: 1
Oil & Gas Operations
N.A.I.C.S.: 213112

CROSCO Integrated Drilling & Well Services Co., Ltd. (1)
Lovinciceva ulica 6B, 10000, Zagreb, Croatia **(100%)**
Tel.: (385) 13652332
Web Site: https://www.crosco.com
Sales Range: $250-299.9 Million
Oil & Natural Gas Drilling Services
N.A.I.C.S.: 213111

Subsidiary (Non-US):

CROSCO INTERNATIONAL Ltd. (2)
Mlinska 5, Lendava, 9220, Maribor, Slovenia **(100%)**
Tel.: (386) 2 57 72 240
Web Site: http://www.crosco.com
Crude Petroleum & Natural Gas Extraction

N.A.I.C.S.: 211120
Joint Venture (Domestic):

CorteCros d.o.o. (2)
Nova Ves 57, 10000, Zagreb, Croatia **(60%)**
Tel.: (385) 14669280
Web Site: https://www.cortecros.com
Anti-Corrosion & Spill Containment Systems Mfr; Owned by INA-Industrija nafte, d.d. & Cortec Corporation
N.A.I.C.S.: 332812

Subsidiary (Non-US):

Crosco B.V. (2)
Prins Bernhardplein 200, 1097 JB, Amsterdam, Netherlands
Tel.: (31) 205214777
Offshore Drilling Services
N.A.I.C.S.: 213111

Subsidiary (Domestic):

Crosco Naftni Servisi d.o.o. (2)
Lovinciceva ulica 6B, 10000, Zagreb, Croatia **(100%)**
Tel.: (385) 13652332
Web Site: https://crosco.com
Petroleum Lubricating Oil & Grease Mfr
N.A.I.C.S.: 324191

Subsidiary (Non-US):

Rotary Drilling Company Limited (2)
Erzsebet ter 22, POB 351, 8800, Nagykanizsa, Hungary
Tel.: (36) 203156321
Web Site: http://www.rotarydrilling.hu
Sales Range: $350-399.9 Million
Oil & Natural Gas Well Drilling & Maintenance Servcies
N.A.I.C.S.: 213111

Croplin d.o.o. (1)
Josipa Marohnica 1, 10000, Zagreb, Croatia **(100%)**
Tel.: (385) 12225640
Web Site: http://www.croplin.hr
Emp.: 2
Basic Inorganic Chemical Mfr
N.A.I.C.S.: 325180

ED INA d.o.o. (1)
Subiceva 29, 10000, Zagreb, Croatia **(50%)**
Tel.: (385) 14552474
Sales Range: $50-74.9 Million
Emp.: 20
Research, Development & Hydrocarbon Production
N.A.I.C.S.: 213112

Energopetrol d.d. (1)
Azize Sacirbegovic 4b, 71000, Sarajevo, Bosnia & Herzegovina **(67%)**
Tel.: (387) 3 372 3989
Web Site: http://www.energopetrol.ba
Rev.: $80,028,364
Assets: $40,737,395
Liabilities: $32,108,153
Net Worth: $8,629,241
Earnings: $1,289,127
Fiscal Year-end: 12/31/2020
Fuel Distr
N.A.I.C.S.: 457210

Eni Croatia BV (1)
Strawinskylaan 1725, Amsterdam, 1077 XX, Netherlands
Tel.: (31) 205707100
Oil & Gas Exploration Services
N.A.I.C.S.: 213112

Affiliate (Non-US):

INAgip d.o.o. (2)
Subiceva 29, 10000, Zagreb, Croatia **(50%)**
Tel.: (385) 14592737
Sales Range: $50-74.9 Million
Emp.: 60
Crude Petroleum & Natural Gas Exploration & Production
N.A.I.C.S.: 211120

FPC Ltd. (1)
Marlborough House, 30-32 Yarm Road, Stockton-on-Tees, United Kingdom **(100%)**

INTERNATIONAL PUBLIC

Tel.: (44) 1642618990
Basic Inorganic Chemical Mfr
N.A.I.C.S.: 325180

Hayan Petroleum Company (1)
Dummar - Terraces - Island 13 - Block 2 Rafaat Tahtawi St, Damascus, Syria **(50%)**
Tel.: (963) 1131907110
Web Site: http://www.hpc.com.sy
Oil Exploration, Development & Production
N.A.I.C.S.: 211120

Holdina d.o.o. (1)
Azize Sacirbegovic 4b, 71000, Sarajevo, Bosnia & Herzegovina **(100%)**
Tel.: (387) 33723900
Web Site: http://www.holdina.ba
Emp.: 500
Crude Petroleum & Natural Gas Extraction
N.A.I.C.S.: 211120

Hostin d.o.o. (1)
Barciceva 9, 10000, Zagreb, Croatia
Tel.: (385) 14592210
Web Site: http://www.hostin.hr
Sales Range: $50-74.9 Million
Crude Petroleum & Natural Gas Extraction
N.A.I.C.S.: 211120

INA Bh d.d. (1)
Azize Sacirbegovic 4b, 71000, Sarajevo, Bosnia & Herzegovina **(100%)**
Tel.: (387) 33 72 39 11
Web Site: http://www.ina.hr
Crude Petroleum & Natural Gas Extraction
N.A.I.C.S.: 211120

INA Crna Gora d.o.o. (1)
Ul Jovana Popovica Lipovca br 24 Blok IX, Podgorica, Montenegro **(100%)**
Tel.: (382) 20268253
Web Site: http://www.inacg.me
Natural Gas Liquid Extraction
N.A.I.C.S.: 211130

INA Hungary Kft. (1)
Aldas utca 5, Budapest, Hungary **(100%)**
Tel.: (36) 12027194
Petroleum & Petroleum Products Merchant Whslr
N.A.I.C.S.: 424720

INA Kosovo d.o.o. (1)
Devet Jugovica Bardosh, 38000, Pristina, Kosovo, Serbia
Tel.: (381) 38 515 811
Oil & Gas Exploration Services
N.A.I.C.S.: 213112

INA MAZIVA d.o.o. (1)
Radnicka cesta 175, 10000, Zagreb, Croatia **(100%)**
Tel.: (385) 12412000
Web Site: https://www.ina-maziva.hr
Emp.: 141
Oil & Gas Field Machinery & Equipment Mfr
N.A.I.C.S.: 333132

INA d.o.o. (1)
Partizanske Vode 6, Belgrade, Serbia **(100%)**
Tel.: (381) 113975664
Crude Petroleum & Natural Gas Extraction
N.A.I.C.S.: 211120

INA-Osijek - Petrol d.d. (1)
Ina Osijek Petrol Gunduliceva 5, 31000, Osijek, Croatia
Tel.: (385) 31250670
Web Site: http://www.osijek-petrol.hr
Sales Range: $25-49.9 Million
Emp.: 100
Petroleum Lubricating Oil & Grease Mfr
N.A.I.C.S.: 324191

ITR d.o.o. (1)
Subiceva 29, 10000, Zagreb, Croatia **(100%)**
Tel.: (385) 14592691
Web Site: http://www.ina.hr
Sales Range: $25-49.9 Million
Emp.: 50
Passenger Car Leasing
N.A.I.C.S.: 532112

Inter INA Ltd. (1)
112 Jermyn St, London, SW1Y 6LS, United Kingdom **(100%)**
Tel.: (44) 2079250125
Sales Range: $25-49.9 Million
Emp.: 10
Oil & Gas Field Machinery & Equipment Mfr

Interina Holding Ltd. (1)
112 Jermyn St, London, SW1Y6LS, United Kingdom (100%)
Tel.: (44) 2079250125
Sales Range: $25-49.9 Million
Emp.: 7
Pipeline Transportation Petroleum Products
N.A.I.C.S.: 486910

Interina d.o.o. (1)
Ul Azize Sacirbegovic 4 B, 71000, Sarajevo, Bosnia & Herzegovina (100%)
Tel.: (387) 36333512
Crude Petroleum & Natural Gas Extraction
N.A.I.C.S.: 211120

SOL-INA d.o.o. (1)
Stjepana i Antuna Radica 17, Sisak, 44000, Zagreb, Croatia (37.2%)
Tel.: (385) 44534852
Sales Range: $25-49.9 Million
Emp.: 6
Industrial Gas Production
N.A.I.C.S.: 325120

STSI-Integrirani Tehnicki Servisi d.o.o. (1)
Lovinciceva 4, 10000, Zagreb, Croatia (100%)
Tel.: (385) 12381122
Web Site: https://www.stsi.hr
Sales Range: $50-74.9 Million
Oil & Gas Operations
N.A.I.C.S.: 213112

INABA DENKI SANGYO CO., LTD.
4-11-14 Itachibori, Nishi-ku, Osaka, 550-0012, Japan
Tel.: (81) 643911781
Web Site: https://www.inaba.co.jp
Year Founded: 1938
9934—(TKS)
Rev.: $2,282,889,090
Assets: $1,737,180,710
Liabilities: $664,582,620
Net Worth: $1,072,598,090
Earnings: $103,268,030
Emp.: 2,574
Fiscal Year-end: 03/31/24
Electrical Equipment Whslr
N.A.I.C.S.: 423610
Yoshihiro Moriya (Chm)

Subsidiaries:

ITF Co., Ltd. (1)
Tel.: (82) 326211213
Electronic Components Mfr
N.A.I.C.S.: 334419

PATLITE Corporation (1)
4-1-3 Kutaro-cho, Chuo-ku, Osaka, 541-0056, Japan
Tel.: (81) 677118950
Electronic Components Mfr
N.A.I.C.S.: 335311
Hisato Takano (Pres & CEO)

Subsidiary (Non-US):

PATLITE Europe GmbH (2)
Graf-Landsberg-Str 3-5, 41460, Neuss, Germany
Tel.: (49) 21311255730
Web Site: https://www.patlite.eu
Electronic Components Mfr
N.A.I.C.S.: 335311
Udo Will (Mng Dir)

PATLITE KOREA CO., LTD. (2)
A2603 Daesung D-POLIS 606 Seobusaet-gil, Geumcheon-gu, Seoul, 08504, Korea (South)
Tel.: (82) 25236636
Web Site: https://www.patlite.co.kr
Electronic Components Mfr
N.A.I.C.S.: 335311
Atsushi Kuwahara (Pres)

PATLITE(CHINA) Corporation (2)
Room 706-707 Baohua Internation Plaza No 555 Guangzhong West Road, Jing an District, Shanghai, 200072, China
Tel.: (86) 216 630 8969
Web Site: https://www.patlite.cn
Electronic Components Mfr
N.A.I.C.S.: 335311

PATLITE(SINGAPORE) PTE LTD (2)
No 2 Leng Kee Road 05-01 Thye Hong Centre, Singapore, 159086, Singapore
Tel.: (65) 62261111
Web Site: https://www.patlite.com
Electronic Components Mfr
N.A.I.C.S.: 335311
Nobuyuki Onishi (Mng Dir)

PT.PATLITE INDONESIA (2)
Lot 321 Batamindo Industrial Park Jalan Beringin Mukakuning, Batam, 29433, Indonesia
Tel.: (62) 77 061 1123
Web Site: https://www.patlite.com
Electronic Components Mfr
N.A.I.C.S.: 335311

Subsidiary (US):

Patlite USA Corp. (2)
20130 S Western Ave, Torrance, CA 90501
Tel.: (310) 328-3222
Electrical Equipment & Component Mfr
N.A.I.C.S.: 335999

INABA SEISAKUSHO CO., LTD.
5-25 Yaguchi 2-Chome, Ohta-ku, Tokyo, 146-8543, Japan
Tel.: (81) 337595201
Web Site: https://www.inaba-ss.co.jp
Year Founded: 1950
3421—(TKS)
Rev.: $263,815,080
Assets: $376,571,240
Liabilities: $105,565,840
Net Worth: $271,005,400
Earnings: $15,183,020
Emp.: 588
Fiscal Year-end: 07/31/24
Office Furniture Mfr & Whslr
N.A.I.C.S.: 337214

INABATA & CO. LTD.
1-15-14 Minami-semba, Chuo-ku, Osaka, 542-8558, Japan
Tel.: (81) 662676051
Web Site: https://www.inabata.co.jp
Year Founded: 1890
8098—(TKS)
Rev.: $5,063,405,420
Assets: $2,824,585,200
Liabilities: $1,457,941,260
Net Worth: $1,366,643,940
Earnings: $132,200,000
Emp.: 4,631
Fiscal Year-end: 03/31/24
Information Technology, Electronics, Chemicals, Plastics, Housing Materials & Food Enterprise Solutions
N.A.I.C.S.: 425120
Katsutaro Inabata (Pres)

Subsidiaries:

Aikei Farms Shakotan Co., Ltd. (1)
604-1 Osawa Bikuni-cho Shakotan-cho, Shakotan-gun, Hokkaido, 046-0201, Japan
Tel.: (81) 135235150
Agricultural Product Mfr
N.A.I.C.S.: 333111

Aikei Farms Yoichi Co., Ltd. (1)
2041-15 Sakae-machi Yoichi-cho, Youichi-gun, Hokkaido, 046-0003, Japan
Tel.: (81) 135235150
Agricultural Product Mfr
N.A.I.C.S.: 333111

Apple Film Co., Ltd. (1)
475 Moo4 Bangpoo Industrial Estate Sukhumvit Road, Praeksa Subdistrict Muangsamutprakarn District, Bangkok, 10280, Samutprakarn, Thailand
Tel.: (66) 232408023
Web Site: http://www.apple-film.com
Emp.: 250
Coated & Laminated Packaging Paper & Plastics Film Mfr
N.A.I.C.S.: 322220

Apple Film Da Nang Co., Ltd. (1)
Road No 1 14 Hoa Cam Industrial Zone, Hoa Tho Tay Ward Cam Le District, Da Nang, Vietnam
Tel.: (84) 2363783000
Web Site: http://www.apple-film.com
Plastics Bag Mfr
N.A.I.C.S.: 326111

DNI Group, LLC (1)
9 Commercial Blvd Ste 210, Novato, CA 94949
Tel.: (415) 382-9999
Web Site: http://www.dnigroup.com
Seafood Product Mfr
N.A.I.C.S.: 311710

Daiwa Foods Co., Ltd. (1)
2136-8 Mure Mure-cho, Takamatsu, Kagawa, Japan
Tel.: (81) 87 845 6117
Marine Food Products Distr
N.A.I.C.S.: 424460

Dongguan Inabata Engineering Plastics Co., Ltd. (1)
Shilong Information Industrial Park Xi-Hu, Shilong, Dongguan, 523325, Guangdong, China
Tel.: (86) 769 8618 8280
Web Site: http://www.inabata.co.jp
Resin Compounding Services
N.A.I.C.S.: 325991

Guangzhou Inabata Trading Co., Ltd. (1)
Room 4116B B Tower China Shine Plaza No 3-15 Linhexi Road, Tianhe District, Guangzhou, 510610, Guangdong, China
Tel.: (86) 2085271379
Web Site: http://www.inabata.co.jp
Specialty Chemicals & Electronic Materials Distr
N.A.I.C.S.: 424690

Hi-Tech Rubber Products Co., Ltd. (1)
Saha Ratana Nakorn Industrial Estate 103/9-10 Moo 4 Bangprakru, Nakonluang, Ayutthaya, 13260, Thailand
Tel.: (66) 35364087
Rubber Products Mfr
N.A.I.C.S.: 326291

I & P Co. Ltd. (1)
53-1 Furukawa Inaba, Osaki, 989-6135, Miyagi, Japan
Tel.: (81) 229237887
Web Site: http://www.inabata.co.jp
Sales Range: $25-49.9 Million
Emp.: 75
Plastics Films Mfr
N.A.I.C.S.: 326121

IK Lease & Insurance Co., Ltd. (1)
1-15-14 Minamisemba, 542-8558, Osaka, Japan
Tel.: (81) 662676371
Web Site: http://www.inabata.co.jp
Commercial & Industrial Machinery & Equipment Rental & Leasing
N.A.I.C.S.: 532490

IK Plastic Compound Mexico, S.A. de C.V. (1)
Mina De Guadalupe No 462 Parque Industrial Santa Fe IV Puerto Interior, Silao, 36275, Guanajuato, Mexico
Tel.: (52) 4721039700
Resin Mfr
N.A.I.C.S.: 325991

IK Plastic Compound Phils. Inc. (1)
Lot 4 & 5 Block 2 Phase 7 Laguna Technopark, Special Export Processing Zone, Binan, 4024, Laguna, Philippines
Tel.: (63) 495406881
Web Site: http://www.ikpc-ph.com.ph
Plastic Coloring Compound Mfr
N.A.I.C.S.: 325211

IKA Logistics, Inc. (1)
1790 N Lee Trevino Dr Suite 304, El Paso, TX 79936
Tel.: (915) 790-2565
Web Site: http://www.inabata.co.jp
Sales Range: $25-49.9 Million
Emp.: 4
General Warehousing & Storage
N.A.I.C.S.: 493110

Ikkoen Co., Ltd. (1)
3-7-15 Ishizu-cho, Sakai-ku, Sakai, 590-0814, Osaka, Japan
Tel.: (81) 722440501
Web Site: https://www.ikkoen.com
Emp.: 91
Marine Products Distr
N.A.I.C.S.: 424460

Inabata America Corporation (1)
1270 Ave of the Americas Ste 602, New York, NY 10020
Tel.: (212) 586-7764
Web Site: https://us.inabata.com
Sales Range: $50-74.9 Million
Emp.: 3
Farm Product Raw Material Whslr
N.A.I.C.S.: 424590

Inabata Brazil Import & Export Ltd. (1)
Alameda Santos 455 Conjunto 411/412, Sao Paulo, 01419-000, SP, Brazil
Tel.: (55) 1135785985
Synthetic Resin Electronic Material Mfr
N.A.I.C.S.: 325211

Inabata Europe GmbH (1)
Am Seestern 4, 40547, Dusseldorf, Germany
Tel.: (49) 21195776100
Plastic Material & Resin Mfr
N.A.I.C.S.: 325211

Inabata Europe S.A. (1)
326 Avenue Louise Bte 18, 1050, Brussels, Belgium
Tel.: (32) 26404995
Web Site: http://www.inabata.be
Sales Range: $50-74.9 Million
Emp.: 7
Chemical & Allied Products Merchant Whslr
N.A.I.C.S.: 424690

Inabata Fine Tech Co., Ltd. (1)
8th floor Sakaisuji Inabata Building 1-15-14 Minamisenba, Chuo-ku, Osaka, 542-0081, Japan
Tel.: (81) 5036844250
Web Site: https://www.ik-ft.com
Emp.: 81
Chemical & Allied Products Merchant Whslr
N.A.I.C.S.: 424690
Jiro Hiraki (Pres & CEO)

Inabata France S.A.S. (1)
6-8 Rue du 4 Septembre, 92130, Issy-les-Moulineaux, France
Tel.: (33) 160491710
Web Site: https://inabata.fr
Chemical & Allied Products Whslr
N.A.I.C.S.: 424690

Inabata India Private Ltd. (1)
319 Time Tower Sector-28 Main MG Road, Gurgaon, 122002, Haryana, India
Tel.: (91) 1244372101
Synthetic Resin Electronic Material Mfr & Distr
N.A.I.C.S.: 325211

Inabata Industry & Trade (Dalian F.T.Z.) Co., Ltd. (1)
No ID-31 Dalian Free Trade Zone, Dalian, Liaoning, China
Tel.: (86) 41187324831
Specialty Chemicals Distr
N.A.I.C.S.: 424690

Inabata Korea & Co., Ltd. (1)
414 Gold Tower 14-2 Pangyoyeok-ro 192beon-gil, Bundang-gu, Seongnam, 013-524, Korea (South)
Tel.: (82) 220528550
Emp.: 9
Electronic Components Distr
N.A.I.C.S.: 423690
Hiroki Sakurai (Pres)

Inabata Malaysia Sdn. Bhd. (1)
25th Floor Ubn Tower 10 Jalan P Ramlee, PO Box 83, 50250, Kuala Lumpur, Malaysia
Tel.: (60) 320788588
Plastic Material & Resin Mfr
N.A.I.C.S.: 325211

Inabata Mexico, S.A. de C.V. (1)
Armando Birlaing 2001 Corporativo 1 Piso 4 Oficina B, Centro Sur, 76090, Queretaro, Mexico

INABATA & CO. LTD.

Inabata & Co. Ltd.—(Continued)
Tel.: (52) 4422293102
Plastic Material & Resin Mfr
N.A.I.C.S.: 325211

Inabata Nanodax Co., Ltd. (1)
2-8-2 Nihonbashi-honcho, Chuo-ku, Tokyo, 103-8448, Japan
Tel.: (81) 5036844021
Plastic Compound Mfr & Distr
N.A.I.C.S.: 325211

Inabata Optech Co., Ltd. (1)
A-210 RandD Building Kanagawa Science Park 3-2-1 Sakado, Takatsu-ku, Kawasaki, 213-0012, Kanagawa, Japan
Tel.: (81) 447125920
Optical Semiconductor Device Mfr & Distr
N.A.I.C.S.: 334413
Tetsuro Yano *(Pres)*

Inabata Philippines, Inc. (1)
CCMC Compound 3 Lot 4 5 Block 2 Phase 7A, Laguna Technopark Inc - SEZ, Binan, 4024, Laguna, Philippines
Tel.: (63) 495406930
Web Site: http://www.inabata.co.jp
Sales Range: $25-49.9 Million
Emp.: 15
Synthetic Resin Whslr
N.A.I.C.S.: 424690

Inabata Sangyo (H.K.) Ltd. (1)
Unit 2513-2515 25/F Mira Place Tower A 132 Nathan Road, Tsim Sha Tsui, Kowloon, China (Hong Kong)
Tel.: (852) 25213669
Sales Range: $25-49.9 Million
Emp.: 40
Plastics Materials & Basic Forms & Shapes Whslr
N.A.I.C.S.: 424610

Inabata Singapore (Pte.) Ltd. (1)
6 Temasek Boulevard 17-05 Suntec Tower Four, No 18-00 Lippo Centre, Singapore, 038986, Singapore
Tel.: (65) 62200796
Web Site: http://www.inabata.co.jp
Sales Range: $25-49.9 Million
Emp.: 34
Plastics Materials & Basic Forms & Shapes Whslr
N.A.I.C.S.: 424610

Inabata Singapore (Pte.) Ltd. (1)
Barbaros Mah Halk Cad No 8/A Unit312 Palladium Ofis ve Residence, Binasi Kat 2 Atasehir, 34746, Istanbul, Turkiye
Tel.: (90) 2166636059
Synthetic Resin Electronic Material Mfr & Distr
N.A.I.C.S.: 325211

Inabata Thai Co., Ltd. (1)
191 Silom Complex Bldg 14th Fl Silom Rd Silom, Bangrak, Bangkok, 10500, Thailand
Tel.: (66) 26253200
Web Site: http://www.inabata.co.jp
Sales Range: $50-74.9 Million
Emp.: 90
Plastics Materials & Basic Forms & Shapes Whslr
N.A.I.C.S.: 424610

Inabata Thai Co., Ltd. (1)
Room 206 Building E 2nd Floor Sabal Street Yuzana Highway Complex, Between Han Thar Waddy Rd and Nar Nat Taw Rd Ward 6 Kamayut Township, Yangon, Myanmar
Tel.: (95) 1534494
Plastic Material & Resin Mfr
N.A.I.C.S.: 325211

Inabata UK Limited (1)
Office 17 Battlefield Enterprise Park Stafford Drive, Shrewsbury, SY1 3FE, Shropshire, United Kingdom
Tel.: (44) 1952608456
Web Site: http://www.inabata.co.jp
Sales Range: $25-49.9 Million
Emp.: 7
Electrical Equipment & Component Mfr
N.A.I.C.S.: 335999

Inabata Vietnam Co., Ltd. (1)
Unit 902B Sun Red River Building 23 Phan Chu Trinh St, Phan Chu Trinh Ward Hoan Kiem District, Hanoi, Vietnam

Tel.: (84) 2437725119
Web Site: http://www.inabata.vn
Emp.: 66
Synthetic Resin Electronic Material Mfr & Distr
N.A.I.C.S.: 325211
Kazuyuki Oguchi *(Gen Dir)*

Kansai Kobunshi Co., Ltd. (1)
113-1 Yokotacho, Yamatokoriyama, Nara, 639-1115, Japan
Tel.: (81) 743590781
Coated & Laminated Packaging Paper & Plastics Film Mfr
N.A.I.C.S.: 322220

Langfang Zhongben Package Co., Ltd. (1)
Hui Yuan Road Economy Technology Exploitation Section, Langfang, Hebei, China
Tel.: (86) 316 6088452
Packaging Plastic Film Mfr
N.A.I.C.S.: 322220

Maruishi Chemical Trading Co., Ltd. (1)
2-1-1 Edobori, Nishi-ku, Osaka, 550-0002, Japan
Tel.: (81) 664435644
Web Site: https://www.maruishi-chem.co.jp
Emp.: 98
Chemical Engineering Product Mfr
N.A.I.C.S.: 325998
Yoshiya Oda *(Pres)*

Musashino Fine Glass Co., Ltd. (1)
617-3 Shimoakasaka, Kawagoe, 350-1155, Saitama, Japan
Tel.: (81) 492663988
Web Site: http://www.mfg.jp
Sales Range: $25-49.9 Million
Emp.: 16
Glass & Glazing Contractors
N.A.I.C.S.: 238150
Shigehiko Morimoto *(Pres)*

N. I. C Co., Ltd. (1)
4-14-11 Hosoda, Katsushika-ku, Tokyo, 124-0021, Japan
Tel.: (81) 336506511
Web Site: https://www.nickk.co.jp
Emp.: 40
Coated & Laminated Packaging Paper & Plastics Film Mfr
N.A.I.C.S.: 322220

Nihon B.F. & Co., Ltd. (1)
3-2-7 Ningyocho, Nihonbashi Chuo-ku, Tokyo, 103-0013, Japan
Tel.: (81) 336396580
Web Site: http://www.inabata.co.jp
Sales Range: $25-49.9 Million
Emp.: 6
Food Supplement Stores
N.A.I.C.S.: 456191
Ito Takashiro *(Gen Mgr)*

Nobel NC Company Limited (1)
24 Rama 1 Road Rongmuang, Pathumwan, Bangkok, 10330, Thailand
Tel.: (66) 26138923
Web Site: http://www.nobelnc.com
Nitrocellulose Mfr
N.A.I.C.S.: 325211

Subsidiary (Non-US):

Nobel NC Europe Ltd. (1)
Elliott House Kilwinning Rd, Irvine, KA12 8TG, Ayrshire, United Kingdom
Tel.: (44) 1294315243
Sales Range: $25-49.9 Million
Emp.: 9
Nitrocellulose Sales
N.A.I.C.S.: 424950
Don Beck *(Mng Dir)*

Ordiy Co., Ltd. (1)
10F Midosuji Honmachi Urban Building 3-5-12 Kitakyuhojimachi, Chuo-ku, Osaka, 541-0057, Japan
Tel.: (81) 662411375
Web Site: http://www.ordiy.com
Coated & Laminated Packaging Paper & Plastics Film Mfr
N.A.I.C.S.: 322220

PT. IK Precision Indonesia (1)
Jl Jababeka XVII-F SFB Blok U23C Kawasan Industri, Cikarang, Bekasi, 17530, Indonesia

Tel.: (62) 2189106602
Web Site: http://www.inabata.co.jp
Synthetic Resin Mfr
N.A.I.C.S.: 325211

PT. Inabata Creation Indonesia (1)
Jl Serui Block AE5 Kawasan Industri MM2100 Desa Jatiwangi Kecamatan, Cikarang Barat Kabupaten, Bekasi, 17845, Indonesia
Tel.: (62) 2150116020
Plastic Material & Resin Mfr
N.A.I.C.S.: 325211

PT. Inabata Indonesia (1)
Summitmas 1 11th Floor Jl Jend Sudirman 61-62, 12190, Jakarta, Indonesia
Tel.: (62) 212521514
Web Site: http://www.inabata.com
Sales Range: $25-49.9 Million
Emp.: 50
Plastics Materials & Basic Forms & Shapes Whslr
N.A.I.C.S.: 424610
Ohashi Motoo *(Mng Dir)*

PT. S-IK Indonesia (1)
Ejip Industrial Park Plot 4L, Sukaresmi Cikarang Selatan, Bekasi, 17530, Jawa Barat, Indonesia
Tel.: (62) 218970432
Web Site: http://www.s-ik.com
Sales Range: $50-74.9 Million
Emp.: 230
Plastic Resin Mfr
N.A.I.C.S.: 325211

Pharmasynthese S.A.S. (1)
57 Rue Gravetel, Saint-Pierre-Les-Elbeuf, 76320, Rouen, France
Tel.: (33) 232969780
Web Site: http://www.pharmasynthese.fr
Sales Range: $25-49.9 Million
Emp.: 50
Pharmaceutical Preparation Mfr
N.A.I.C.S.: 325412

S&I Consultants Co., Ltd. (1)
477 Moo4 Bangpoo Industrial Estate Sukhumvit Road, Samut Prakan, 10280, Thailand
Tel.: (66) 27093556
Tax & Accounting Management Consulting Services
N.A.I.C.S.: 541990

SENKA (Thailand) Co., Ltd. (1)
652 Moo 2 Bangpoo Industrial Estate, Bang Pu Mai Subdistrict Mueang District, Samut Prakan, 10280, Thailand
Tel.: (66) 27093556
Web Site: https://www.senka-thailand.com
Textile Auxiliary Chemicals Mfr & Distr
N.A.I.C.S.: 325998

SIK (Thailand) Ltd. (1)
477 Moo 4 Bangpoo Industrial Estate Soi1 Sukhumvit Road, Tambon Praksa Amphur Muang, Samut Prakan, 10280, Thailand
Tel.: (66) 27093556
Web Site: https://www.sik-t.com
Sales Range: $50-74.9 Million
Emp.: 308
Plastics Material & Resin Mfr
N.A.I.C.S.: 325211
Kazuhiro Takagi *(Mgr-Factory)*

SIK Color (M) Sdn. Bhd. (1)
No 97 Jalan Sawit Baru 6 Taman Perindustrian Sawit Baru, 81030, Kulai, Johor, Malaysia
Tel.: (60) 76523306
Web Site: https://www.sikm.com.my
Plastic Material & Resin Mfr
N.A.I.C.S.: 325211
Aotani Hisashi *(Mng Dir)*

SIK Vietnam Co., Ltd. (1)
Land Plot A7-8 Japan-Haiphong Industrial Zone, AnHung Commune Anduong District, Haiphong, 0313, Vietnam
Tel.: (84) 2253618660
Web Site: https://sikv.com.vn
Plastic Resin Mfr
N.A.I.C.S.: 325211

Sanyo - IK Color (DG) Ltd. (1)
Wen Quan Lu Shi Long Zhen, Xi Hu Industrial District, Dongguan, Guang Dong, China
Tel.: (86) 76986111088
Resin Compounding Services

INTERNATIONAL PUBLIC

N.A.I.C.S.: 325991

Sanyo-IK Color (H.K.) Ltd. (1)
Tel.: (852) 25015885
Web Site: http://www.inabata.co.jp
Sales Range: $25-49.9 Million
Emp.: 40
Plastics Material & Resin Mfr
N.A.I.C.S.: 325211

Plant (Non-US):

Sanyo - IK Color (H.K.) Ltd. - Dong Guan Plant (2)
Tel.: (86) 769 8611 1088
Web Site: http://www.inabata.co.jp
Compounding Resin Mfr
N.A.I.C.S.: 325991

Sanyo-IK Color (Pte.) Ltd. (1)
8 Boon Lee Way Unit 07-06 Treadup 21, 629964, Singapore, Singapore
Tel.: (65) 62650288
Web Site: http://www.sikm.com.my
Sales Range: $25-49.9 Million
Emp.: 4
Inorganic Dye & Pigment Mfr
N.A.I.C.S.: 325130

Shanghai Inabata Fine Chemical Co., Ltd. (1)
No 358 Jinou Road No 2 Industrial Park, Jinshan, Shanghai, 201512, China
Tel.: (86) 2137285170
Specialty Chemicals Mfr
N.A.I.C.S.: 325998

Shanghai Inabata Trading Co., Ltd. (1)
43rd Floor Hang Seng Bank Tower, 1000 Lujiazui Ring Rd Pudong, Shanghai, 200120, China
Tel.: (86) 2168411780
Plastics Material & Resin Mfr
N.A.I.C.S.: 325211

Shinano Electronics Co., Ltd. (1)
3967-29 Minamin Nishihara, Aata Nagano Matsumoto, Nagano, 3911242, Japan
Tel.: (81) 263401111
Web Site: http://www.synax.co.jp
Instruments & Related Products Mfr
N.A.I.C.S.: 334513
Vincent So *(Pres & CEO)*

Taiwan Inabata Sangyo Co., Ltd. (1)
2F No 178 Sec 2 Gongdao Wu Rd Nan Shan Hi-Tech Building, Sector 2, Hsinchu, 30070, Taiwan
Tel.: (886) 35713300
Web Site: http://www.inabata.com
Electronic Parts & Equipment Merchant Whslr
N.A.I.C.S.: 423690

Taiyo Plastics Co., Ltd. (1)
553 Kamihirano, Hasuda, 349-0136, Saitama, Japan
Tel.: (81) 487668411
Web Site: https://www.taiyo-pla.co.jp
Emp.: 75
Plastics Packaging Film & Sheet Mfr
N.A.I.C.S.: 326112
Masao Togashi *(Pres)*

The Shredder Company, LLC (1)
7380 Doniphan Dr, Canutillo, TX 79835
Tel.: (915) 877-3814
Web Site: http://www.theshredderco.com
Industrial Machinery & Equipment Whslr
N.A.I.C.S.: 423830
Scott Newell Jr. *(CEO)*

Tianjin Inabata Trading Co., Ltd. (1)
Unit 807 Tianjin International Building 75 Nanjing Road, Tianjin, China
Tel.: (86) 2223118270
Emp.: 4
Chemical Engineering Product Mfr & Distr
N.A.I.C.S.: 325998
Osamu Nishimura *(Pres)*

INAGEYA CO., LTD.

1-1 Sakaemachi 6-chome, Tachikawa, 190-8517, Tokyo, Japan
Tel.: (81) 425375111
Web Site: https://www.inageya.co.jp
Year Founded: 1948

8182—(TKS)
Rev.: $1,728,422,460
Assets: $676,335,200
Liabilities: $306,069,440
Net Worth: $370,265,760
Earnings: $3,285,170
Fiscal Year-end: 03/31/24
Supermarket Operator
N.A.I.C.S.: 445110

INALWAYS CORP.
No 61 Wuquan Rd, Wugu Dist, New Taipei City, 248, Taiwan
Tel.: (886) 222991185
Web Site: https://www.inalways.com.cn
Year Founded: 1978
5398—(TPE)
Rev.: $8,052,622
Assets: $19,032,892
Liabilities: $2,164,056
Net Worth: $16,868,837
Earnings: ($212,332)
Fiscal Year-end: 12/31/22
Electric Equipment Mfr
N.A.I.C.S.: 335999
Shih Miao-Ju (VP)

Subsidiaries:

Inalways Electronics (Dongguan) Co., Ltd. (1)
Hubin North Rd, Tielukeng Village Qishi Town, Dongguan, 523758, Guangdong, China
Tel.: (86) 76986916111
Electronic Components Mfr
N.A.I.C.S.: 334419

Inalways Electronics Inc. (1)
No 61 Wuquan Rd, Wugu Dist, New Taipei City, 248, Taiwan
Tel.: (886) 222991185
Electronic Components Mfr
N.A.I.C.S.: 334419

Salecom Electronics Co., Ltd. (1)
1F No 61 Wu-Chyuan Road, Wugu District, New Taipei City, 24886, Taiwan
Tel.: (886) 222996622
Web Site: http://www.salecom.com
Switch Mfr
N.A.I.C.S.: 335313

INANI MARBLES & INDUSTRIES LTD.
Araji No 1312 Udaipur- Bhilwara Highway, Near Mataji Ki Pandoli, Chittaurgarh, 312001, India
Tel.: (91) 1472240111
Web Site: https://www.inanimarbles.com
Year Founded: 1987
531129—(BOM)
Rev.: $11,483,704
Assets: $14,154,354
Liabilities: $7,178,358
Net Worth: $6,975,996
Earnings: $444,048
Emp.: 156
Fiscal Year-end: 03/31/22
Granite & Marble Mfr & Distr
N.A.I.C.S.: 212313
Mahesh Kumar Inani (Exec Dir)

INANI SECURITIES LTD.
Office No 1408 14th Floor Naman Midtown B-Wing, Senapati Bapat Marg Next To Indiabull Finance Centre Elphistone, Mumbai, 400013, India
Tel.: (91) 2243486000
Web Site: https://www.inanisec.in
Year Founded: 1994
531672—(BOM)
Rev.: $352,801
Assets: $2,878,645
Liabilities: $578,258
Net Worth: $2,300,388
Earnings: $53,899

Fiscal Year-end: 03/31/21
Textile Products Distr
N.A.I.C.S.: 314999
Ramakanth Inani (CFO)

INAPA - INVESTIMENTOS, PARTICIPACOES E GESTAO, SA
Rua das Cerejeiras 5-11 Vale Flores - S Pedro de Penaferrim, 2710-632, Sintra, Portugal
Tel.: (351) 213823007
Web Site: https://www.inapa.pt
Year Founded: 1965
INA—(EUR)
Rev.: $1,263,776,048
Assets: $882,777,413
Liabilities: $695,212,215
Net Worth: $187,565,198
Earnings: ($18,756,520)
Emp.: 1,709
Fiscal Year-end: 12/31/20
Investment Management Service
N.A.I.C.S.: 523940
Diogo Bastos Mendes Rezende (Chm & CEO)

Subsidiaries:

Complott Papier Union, GmbH (1)
Industriestrasse 27, 40822, Mettmann, Germany
Tel.: (49) 21 04 17 56 0
Web Site: http://www.complottpapierunion.de
Printing Equipment Distr
N.A.I.C.S.: 423610

Da Hora Artigos de Embalagem, Lda. (1)
Urbanizacao Minhoteira Lote 3, Moreira, 4470-623, Maia, Portugal
Tel.: (351) 229 410 187
Packaging Services
N.A.I.C.S.: 561910

Edicoes Inapa, Lda. (1)
Rua das Cerejeiras no 5-11 Vale Flores, 2710-632, Sintra, Portugal
Tel.: (351) 213823007
Web Site: https://www.edicoes-inapa.pt
Book Editing & Publishing Services
N.A.I.C.S.: 513130

HTL Verpackung, GmbH (1)
Werner-von-Siemens-Strasse 4-6, 21629, Neu Wulmstorf, Germany
Tel.: (49) 40 700 405 0
Web Site: http://www.inapa-packing.de
Packaging Services
N.A.I.C.S.: 561910

Hennessen & Potthoff, GmbH (1)
Tempelsweg 22, 47918, Tonisvorst, Germany
Tel.: (49) 21 51 99 808 0
Web Site: http://www.hennessen-potthoff.de
Packaging Services
N.A.I.C.S.: 561910

Inapa Angola Distribuicao de Papel, SA (1)
Estrada de Catete Km 25 Polo Industrial de Viana, Viana, Luanda, Angola
Tel.: (244) 926302333
Paper Product Distr
N.A.I.C.S.: 424110

Inapa Belgique, SA (1)
Vaucampslaan 30, 1654, Huizingen, Belgium
Tel.: (32) 23632811
Web Site: https://www.inapa.be
Office Supplies Whslr
N.A.I.C.S.: 424120
Chris Luyten (Officer-Country & Mgr)

Subsidiary (Non-US):

Inapa Luxembourg, SA (2)
ZARE Ouest, PO Box 87, 3901, Mondercange, Luxembourg
Tel.: (352) 31 85 08
Web Site: http://www.inapa.pt
Emp.: 1
Office Supplies Whslr

N.A.I.C.S.: 424120
Chris Luyten (CEO)

Inapa Deutschland, GmbH (1)
Osterbekstrasse 90a, 22083, Hamburg, Germany
Tel.: (49) 40411750
Web Site: https://www.inapa.de
Logistics Consulting Servies
N.A.I.C.S.: 541614

Inapa Espana Distribuicion de Papel, SA (1)
Calle Delco no 1-3 Pol Ind Ciudad del Automovil, 28914, Leganes, Madrid, Spain
Tel.: (34) 902301010
Web Site: http://www.inapa.es
Paper Product Distr
N.A.I.C.S.: 424110

Inapa France, SA (1)
11 Rue de la Nacelle Villabe, 91813, Corbeil-Essonnes, Cedex, France
Tel.: (33) 160899091
Web Site: https://www.inapa.fr
Emp.: 280
Paper Product Distr
N.A.I.C.S.: 424110

Inapa Packaging, Lda. (1)
Rua Goncalves Zarco 3386, Do Bispo, 4455-822, Santa Cruz, Portugal
Tel.: (351) 229440033
Web Site: https://www.inapapackaging.pt
Packaging Products Mfr
N.A.I.C.S.: 326112

Inapa Portugal Distribuicao de Papel, SA (1)
Rua das Cerejeiras no 5-11, 2710-632, Sintra, Portugal
Tel.: (351) 219239544
Web Site: https://www.inapaportugal.pt
Paper Product Distr
N.A.I.C.S.: 424110

Inapa Suisse, SA (1)
Route de la Venoge 3, 1026, Echandens, Switzerland
Tel.: (41) 21 632 52 52
Web Site: http://www.inapa.ch
Paper Product Whslr
N.A.I.C.S.: 424110
Bernard Warpelin (Key Acct Mgr)

Korda Kagit Pazarlama ve Ticaret Anonim irketi (1)
Kasap soka Konak Azer Ishani No 12 Kat 3, Esentepe, 34394, Istanbul, Turkiye
Tel.: (90) 2122740140
Web Site: http://www.korda.com.tr
Tape Distr
N.A.I.C.S.: 424110
Murat Taylan (Sls Dir)

Papier Union GmbH (1)
Osterbekstrasse 90 a, Hamburg, Germany
Tel.: (49) 40411750
Paper Mfr
N.A.I.C.S.: 322299
Martin Tewes (Mng Dir)

Subsidiary (Domestic):

Papyrus Deutschland GmbH & Co. KG (2)
Gehrnstrasse 7-11, Ettlingen, 76275, Germany
Tel.: (49) 7243730
Web Site: http://www.papyrus.com
Paper, Office Supplies & Industrial Packaging Whslr; Envelope Mfr
N.A.I.C.S.: 424110

Semaq Emballages, SA (1)
Bordeaux Fret - Z I de Bruges rue de Strasbourg, 33521, Bruges, Cedex, France
Tel.: (33) 5 56 69 40 40
Web Site: http://www.semaq.fr
Packaging Services
N.A.I.C.S.: 561910

INARI AMERTRON BERHAD
D-07-3 Plaza Kelana Jaya Jalan SS7/13A, Kelana Jaya, 47301, Petaling Jaya, Selangor Darul Ehsan, Malaysia
Tel.: (60) 378760169

Web Site: https://www.inari-amertron.com
INARI—(KLS)
Rev.: $286,561,481
Assets: $627,884,021
Liabilities: $76,381,799
Net Worth: $551,502,222
Earnings: $68,788,360
Emp.: 5,677
Fiscal Year-end: 06/30/23
Semiconductor Mfr
N.A.I.C.S.: 334413
Kean Cheong Lau (CEO)

Subsidiaries:

Amertron Technology (Kunshan) Co. Ltd. (1)
No 8 Xin Zhu Road, Kunshan Comprehensive Bonded Zones, Kunshan, 215300, Jiangsu, China
Tel.: (86) 51257366835
Optoelectronic Device Mfr
N.A.I.C.S.: 334413

Inari Berhad - PLANT 8 (1)
Plot 255 Phase 3 Bayan Lepas Free Industrial Zone, 11900, Bayan Lepas, Pulau Pinang, Malaysia
Tel.: (60) 4 645 6618
Web Site: http://www.inariberhad.com
Electronic Components Mfr
N.A.I.C.S.: 334419

Inari Integrated Systems Sdn. Bhd. (1)
Plot 201 Phase 3 Bayan Lepas FTZ, Lebuh Kampung Jawa, 11900, Bayan Lepas, Pulau Pinang, Malaysia
Tel.: (60) 46806806
Communication Chip Mfr
N.A.I.C.S.: 334413

Inari Semiconductor Labs Sdn. Bhd. (1)
Plot 98 Hala Kampung Jawa Satu, Non-Free Industrial Zone, 11900, Bayan Lepas, Pulau Pinang, Malaysia
Tel.: (60) 46806618
Semiconductor Mfr
N.A.I.C.S.: 334413

INBAR GROUP FINANCE LTD
Magdali HaArbea 30 HaArbea Street, Tel Aviv, 67137, Israel
Tel.: (972) 37914455 II
Web Site: https://www.inbar-group.com
Year Founded: 1980
INBR—(TAE)
Assets: $21,286,146
Liabilities: $17,171,135
Net Worth: $4,115,011
Earnings: ($5,298,713)
Fiscal Year-end: 12/31/20
Financial Services
N.A.I.C.S.: 523999
Moshe Shmueli (VP-Risk Mgmt)

INBIOGEN CO., LTD
7F 803 Seolleung-ro, Gangnam-gu, Seoul, Gyeonggi-do, Korea (South)
Tel.: (82) 269787183
Web Site: http://www.btone.com
Year Founded: 2008
101140—(KRS)
Rev.: $8,746,662
Assets: $108,771,989
Liabilities: $28,685,661
Net Worth: $80,086,327
Earnings: ($91,800,089)
Emp.: 37
Fiscal Year-end: 12/31/22
Shoe Mfr & Distr
N.A.I.C.S.: 316210
No Yong Hyun (CFO)

INBIT CORP.
L9-02 Level 9 Brem Mall Jalan Jambu Mawar, Off Jalan Kepong, 52000, Kuala Lumpur, Malaysia
Tel.: (60) 362570088 NV

Inbit Corp.—(Continued)

Web Site: http://www.inbit-corp.com
Year Founded: 2014
INBT—(OTCBB)
Assets: $40,458
Liabilities: $237,453
Net Worth: ($196,995)
Earnings: ($70,668)
Fiscal Year-end: 12/31/19
Investment Holding Services
N.A.I.C.S.: 551110
Chee Hong Tan (Chm, CEO & Sec)

INBODY CO., LTD.
625 Eonju-ro, Gangnam-gu, Seoul, 06106, Korea (South)
Tel.: (82) 25013939   KR
Web Site: https://www.inbody.com
Year Founded: 1996
041830—(KRS)
Rev.: $122,722,895
Assets: $186,124,306
Liabilities: $20,422,091
Net Worth: $165,702,215
Earnings: $25,936,515
Emp.: 296
Fiscal Year-end: 12/31/22
Medical Equipment Mfr
N.A.I.C.S.: 334510
Ki-Chul Cha (Founder & CEO)

Subsidiaries:

InBody Europe B.V.   (1)
Gyroscoopweg 122, 1042 AZ, Amsterdam, Netherlands
Tel.: (31) 202386080
Web Site: https://www.nl.inbody.com
Medical Instrument Mfr
N.A.I.C.S.: 339112

InBody Japan Inc.   (1)
Tani Building 1-28-6 Kameido, Koto-ku, Tokyo, 136-0071, Japan
Tel.: (81) 358755780
Web Site: http://www.inbody.co.jp
Height Meter Mfr
N.A.I.C.S.: 334515

Inbody India Pvt Ltd   (1)
GA-03 Ground Floor Art Guild House Phoenix Market City LBS Marg, Kurla, Mumbai, 400070, India
Tel.: (91) 7506191294
Web Site: https://www.inbody.in
Body Composition Analyzer Machine Mfr
N.A.I.C.S.: 334519

INC S.A.
ul Abpa A Baraniaka 6, 61-131, Poznan, Poland
Tel.: (48) 618518677
Web Site: https://www.incsa.pl
Year Founded: 1995
INC—(WAR)
Rev.: $1,874,746
Assets: $7,848,831
Liabilities: $1,495,427
Net Worth: $6,353,404
Earnings: ($2,336,382)
Fiscal Year-end: 12/31/23
Investment Services
N.A.I.C.S.: 523999
Piotr Bialowas (Head-Capital Markets)

INCA MINERALS LTD.
Unit 1/16 Nicholson Road, Subiaco, 6008, WA, Australia
Tel.: (61) 862634738
Web Site: https://www.incaminerals.com.au
ICG—(ASX)
Rev.: $94,252
Assets: $7,074,518
Liabilities: $207,998
Net Worth: $6,866,520
Earnings: ($1,167,552)
Emp.: 2
Fiscal Year-end: 06/30/24

Copper, Nickel, Lead & Zinc Mining
N.A.I.C.S.: 212230
Ross Brown (Mng Dir)

INCA ONE GOLD CORP.
850-1140 West Pender, Vancouver, V6E 4G1, BC, Canada
Tel.: (604) 568-4877   BC
Web Site: https://www.incaone.com
Year Founded: 2005
SU92—(DEU)
Rev.: $40,227,202
Assets: $20,937,930
Liabilities: $24,846,009
Net Worth: ($3,908,079)
Earnings: ($5,704,519)
Fiscal Year-end: 04/30/23
Mineral Exploration Services
N.A.I.C.S.: 213114
Edward Kelly (Pres & CEO)

INCAM AG
Lange Hecke 75, 41564, Kaarst, Germany
Tel.: (49) 213140660
Web Site: http://www.incam.de
Sales Range: $25-49.9 Million
Emp.: 23
Dealers & Security Brokers
N.A.I.C.S.: 523150
Harmut Bergmann (Chm)

INCANNEX HEALTHCARE LIMITED
Level 23 Rialto South Tower 525 Collins Street, Melbourne, 3000, VIC, Australia
Tel.: (61) 425703805
Web Site: https://www.incannex.com
IXHL—(NASDAQ)
Rev.: $11,612,000
Assets: $17,047,000
Liabilities: $5,830,000
Net Worth: $11,217,000
Earnings: ($18,459,000)
Emp.: 9
Fiscal Year-end: 06/30/24
Miscellaneous Financial Investment Activities
N.A.I.C.S.: 523999
Joel Latham (CEO & Mng Dir)

INCAP LTD.
1-58 Nidamanur, Vijayawada, 521104, Andhra Pradesh, India
Tel.: (91) 8662842479
Web Site: http://www.incaplimited.com
517370—(BOM)
Rev.: $3,322,065
Assets: $4,005,472
Liabilities: $1,845,288
Net Worth: $2,160,185
Earnings: $109,542
Emp.: 174
Fiscal Year-end: 03/31/22
Capacitor Mfr
N.A.I.C.S.: 334419
Challagulla Bhagavantha Rao (Chm)

INCAP OYJ
Bulevardi 21, 00180, Helsinki, Finland
Tel.: (358) 4521723   FI
Web Site: https://www.incapcorp.com
ICP1V—(HEL)
Rev.: $284,656,810
Assets: $181,659,832
Liabilities: $87,308,439
Net Worth: $94,351,392
Earnings: $29,780,919
Emp.: 741
Fiscal Year-end: 12/31/22
Electronic & Electrical Equipment Mfr
N.A.I.C.S.: 334419
Ville Vuori (Chm)

Subsidiaries:

Incap Electronics Estonia OU   (1)
Tel.: (372) 4521723
Sales Range: $50-74.9 Million
Emp.: 15
Electronic Components Mfr
N.A.I.C.S.: 334419

Plant (Domestic):

Incap Electronics Estonia OU - Kuressaare Factory   (2)
Tehnika 9, 93815, Kuressaare, Estonia
Tel.: (372) 452 1723
Web Site: http://www.incap.fi
Sales Range: $25-49.9 Million
Electromechanical Products Mfr
N.A.I.C.S.: 334419

Incap Oyj - Helsinki Factory   (1)
Bulevardi 21 Entrance Albertinkatu 25A, 00180, Helsinki, Finland
Tel.: (358) 372 452 1723
Web Site: https://www.incapcorp.com
Sales Range: $50-74.9 Million
Emp.: 200
Electromechanic Products Mfr
N.A.I.C.S.: 334514

INCAR FINANCIAL SERVICE CO LTD
27 Seongsui-ro 7-gil Seongdong-gu, Seoul, Korea (South)
Tel.: (82) 221928900
Software Development Services
N.A.I.C.S.: 513210
Choi Byeong-Chae (CEO)

INCEKARALAR A.S.
1404 Sok No 16 N Akar Mah, Balgat, 06520, Ankara, Turkiye
Tel.: (90) 3122952525
Web Site: http://www.incekara.com.tr
Year Founded: 1951
Emp.: 150
Medical Instruments Developer & Mfr
N.A.I.C.S.: 334516
Fusun Yigit (Mgr-Mktg)

Subsidiaries:

Incekara Teknik Cihazlar Endustri Ve Ticaret A.S.   (1)
Nasuh Akar Mahallesi No 16-25, Sokak 1404, Ankara, 06520, Turkiye
Tel.: (90) 3122952525
Web Site: http://www.incekara.com.tr
Sales Range: $25-49.9 Million
Emp.: 90
Medical & Hospital Equipment Mfr
N.A.I.C.S.: 339112

INCENTIAPAY LIMITED
Level 6 Suite 7 3 Spring Street, Sydney, 2000, NSW, Australia
Tel.: (61) 282565300
Web Site: https://www.incentiapay.com
INP—(ASX)
Rev.: $11,095,056
Assets: $2,789,589
Liabilities: $22,343,093
Net Worth: ($19,553,504)
Earnings: ($5,101,916)
Emp.: 60
Fiscal Year-end: 06/30/24
Investment Services
N.A.I.C.S.: 523999
Toby Ellis (Exec Gen Mgr-Corporate Sales)

INCEPTUM ENTERPRISES LIMITED
B-10 Near Muskan Restaurant Keshav chowk, Panchshe Naveen Shahdara, New Delhi, 110032, India
Tel.: (91) 1165912003   In
Year Founded: 1990
Rev.: $140,978
Assets: $776,309

Liabilities: $518,924
Net Worth: $257,385
Earnings: ($4,109)
Fiscal Year-end: 03/31/18
Commodity Contracts Dealing Services
N.A.I.C.S.: 523160
Vinay Prakash (Compliance Officer)

INCH KENNETH KAJANG RUBBER PUBLIC LIMITED COMPANY
2 Semple Street, Midlothian, Edinburgh, EH3 8BL, United Kingdom
Tel.: (44) 3333202220   UK
Web Site: http://www.ikkr.com.my
Year Founded: 1894
INCKEN—(KLS)
Rev.: $4,448,254
Assets: $142,973,122
Liabilities: $19,471,746
Net Worth: $123,501,376
Earnings: ($2,238,095)
Emp.: 192
Fiscal Year-end: 12/31/22
Investment Holding Company: Rubber Tree & Oil Palm Plantations, Real Estate & Tourism Operations
N.A.I.C.S.: 551112
Hussain Ahmad Abdul Kader (COO-Grp)

Subsidiaries:

Inch Kenneth Kajang Rubber PLC - Malaysia Principal Office   (1)
26th Floor Menara Promet, Sultan Ismail, 50250, Kuala Lumpur, Malaysia
Tel.: (60) 32 144 4446
Web Site: https://www.ikkr.com.my
Executive & Administrative Office
N.A.I.C.S.: 921140
Hussain Ahmad Abdul Kader (COO)

Subsidiary (Domestic):

Inch Kenneth Development (M) Sdn. Bhd.   (2)
Menara Promet Jalan Sultan Ismail 22nd Fl, Kuala Lumpur, 50250, Malaysia
Tel.: (60) 321444446
Web Site: http://www.ikkr.com
Real Estate & Investment Management Services
N.A.I.C.S.: 523999
Hussain Ahmad Abdul Kader (COO)

Perhentian Island Resort Sdn. Bhd.   (2)
Pulau Perhentian Besar, Jalan Sultan Ismail, 22200, Terengganu, Malaysia (100%)
Tel.: (60) 321448530
Web Site: https://www.perhentianislandresort.net
Sales Range: $10-24.9 Million
Emp.: 6
Resort Operating Services
N.A.I.C.S.: 721110
Ryan Samsung (Gen Mgr)

Motel Desa Sdn Bhd   (1)
Bukit Pak Apil, 20300, Kuala Terengganu, Terengganu, Malaysia
Tel.: (60) 96223033
Rubber Products Mfr
N.A.I.C.S.: 326299

INCHCAPE PLC
22a St Jamess Square, London, SW1Y 5LP, United Kingdom
Tel.: (44) 2075460022   UK
Web Site: https://www.inchcape.com
Year Founded: 1800
IHCPF—(OTCIQ)
Rev.: $9,795,837,150
Assets: $8,387,776,650
Liabilities: $6,500,325,150
Net Worth: $1,887,451,500
Earnings: $339,669,000
Fiscal Year-end: 12/31/22
New Car Dealers
N.A.I.C.S.: 441110

AND PRIVATE COMPANIES

George Ashford *(CEO-APAC)*

Subsidiaries:

Atkins Kroll (Saipan) Inc. (1)
Chalan Monsignor Guerrero Susupe, Saipan, MP 96950
Tel.: (670) 234-5911
Web Site: https://www.aksaipan.com
Car Retailer
N.A.I.C.S.: 441110

Atkins Kroll Inc. (1)
443 S Marine Corps Dr, Tamuning, GU 96913-3802
Tel.: (671) 649-6410
Web Site: https://www.akguam.com
Sales Range: $50-74.9 Million
Emp.: 250
Dealers of Cars
N.A.I.C.S.: 441227
Daena Mansapit *(Mgr-Customer Rels)*

AutoNexus Pty. Ltd. (1)
Level 2 4 Burbank Place, Baulkham Hills, 2153, NSW, Australia
Tel.: (61) 180 065 0134
Web Site: https://www.autonexus.com.au
Car Retailer & Mfr
N.A.I.C.S.: 441110
Darren Bowler *(Mng Dir)*

Borneo Motors (Singapore) Pte Ltd (1)
33 Leng Kee Road, Singapore, 159102, Singapore
Tel.: (65) 67493288
Web Site: http://www.borneomotors.com.sg
New Car Dealers
N.A.I.C.S.: 441110

Cooper Teesside BMW (1)
Concorde Way Preston Farm, Industrial Estate, Stockton-on-Tees, TS18 3RB, Cleveland, United Kingdom
Tel.: (44) 1642032157
Web Site:
http://www.cooperteessidebmw.co.uk
Sales Range: $25-49.9 Million
Emp.: 100
BMW Motor Retailing
N.A.I.C.S.: 441110

Crown Motors Ltd (1)
11/F Block B Manulife Financial Centre 223-231 Wai Yip Street, Kwun Tong, Kowloon, China (Hong Kong) **(100%)**
Tel.: (852) 2 562 2226
Web Site: https://www.crown-motors.com
Sales Range: $50-74.9 Million
Emp.: 160
Motor Vehicle Dealers
N.A.I.C.S.: 441110

Distribuidora Automatriz Argentina SA (1)
Balbastro 650, Don Torcuato, Buenos Aires, Argentina
Tel.: (54) 810 555 3200
Web Site: https://www.suzuki.com.ar
Car Retailer
N.A.I.C.S.: 441110

European Motor Holdings Ltd. (1)
Suite 3 Building 8 Croxley Green Business Park, Hatters Lane, Watford, WD18 8PY, United Kingdom
Tel.: (44) 1923 22 11 44
Web Site: http://www.emhplc.com
Car Dealership Operator
N.A.I.C.S.: 441110

Inchcape Argentina SA (1)
Balbastro 650 Don Torcuato, Buenos Aires, Argentina
Tel.: (54) 8105558410
Web Site: http://www.inchcape.com.ar
Car Retailer
N.A.I.C.S.: 441110

Inchcape Australia Limited (1)
4 Burbank Place, PO Box 8313, Baulkham Hills, 2153, NSW, Australia
Tel.: (61) 28 892 9199
Web Site: https://www.inchcape.com.au
Sales Range: $400-449.9 Million
Emp.: 1,200
Automobile Dealership
N.A.I.C.S.: 441110

Inchcape Finance plc (1)
30-35 Pall Mall, London, SW1Y 5LP, United Kingdom
Tel.: (44) 20 7546 0022
Web Site: http://www.inchcape.co.uk
Emp.: 60
Automobile Financing Services
N.A.I.C.S.: 522220

Inchcape Fleet Solutions Limited (1)
Haven House Compass Road, Portsmouth, PO6 4RP, Hampshire, United Kingdom
Tel.: (44) 8701914444
Web Site: http://www.ifs.inchcape.co.uk
Sales Range: $75-99.9 Million
Emp.: 175
Fleet Management Services
N.A.I.C.S.: 532112
Matthew Rumble *(Mng Dir)*

Inchcape International Holdings Limited (1)
22A St James's Square, Westminster, London, SW1Y 5LP, United Kingdom
Tel.: (44) 2075460022
Investment Management Service
N.A.I.C.S.: 523999

Inchcape Latam Peru SA (1)
Jiron Morro Solar 812 Surco, Lima, Peru
Tel.: (51) 16303000
Web Site: http://www.inchcape.com.pe
Car Retailer
N.A.I.C.S.: 441110

Inchcape Management Services Ltd. (1)
22A St James Sq, London, SW1Y 5LP, United Kingdom **(100%)**
Tel.: (44) 75460022
Web Site: http://www.inchcape.co
Management Services
N.A.I.C.S.: 541611

Inchcape Motors Finland OY (1)
Laivalahdenkatu 8, 00880, Helsinki, Finland
Tel.: (358) 20 770 4300
Web Site: https://www.inchcape.fi
Sales Range: $25-49.9 Million
Emp.: 100
Car Dealer
N.A.I.C.S.: 441110

Inchcape Park Lane Ltd. (1)
Unit 9 Alton Business Centre Omega Park, Alton, GU34 2YU, United Kingdom
Tel.: (44) 1420544300
Car Retailer
N.A.I.C.S.: 441110
Roland Dane *(Mng Dir)*

Inchcape Retail Limited (1)
Inchcape House Langford Lane, Kidlington, OX5 1HT, Oxford, United Kingdom
Tel.: (44) 8451255900
Web Site: http://www.inchcaperetail.co.uk
Emp.: 30
New Car Dealers
N.A.I.C.S.: 441110

NBT (Brunei) Sdn. Bhd. (1)
Km 4 Jalan Gadong, 4119, Bandar Seri Begawan, Brunei Darussalam
Tel.: (673) 243 3777
Web Site: https://toyota.com.bn
Car Retailer
N.A.I.C.S.: 441110
Genalyn Seneres *(Mgr-Svc)*

Subaru (Australia) Pty Limited (1)
Level 3/4 Burbank Place, Baulkham Hills, 2153, NSW, Australia
Tel.: (61) 298289111
Web Site: http://www.subaru.com.au
Sales Range: $25-49.9 Million
Emp.: 100
Car Dealer
N.A.I.C.S.: 441110

Toyota Balkans EOOD (1)
163 Tsarigradsko Shosse Blvd, Sofia, 1784, Bulgaria
Tel.: (359) 7 007 0044
Web Site: https://www.toyota.bg
Car Retailer
N.A.I.C.S.: 441110
Nina Mihaylova *(Mgr-HR)*

Toyota Belgium NV/SA (1)
Leuvensesteenweg 369, 1932, Zaventem, Belgium
Tel.: (32) 2 386 7211
Web Site: https://nl.toyota.be
Car Dealer
N.A.I.C.S.: 441110
Bertrand Mallet *(CEO)*

Toyota Hellas SA (1)
Ethnikis Antistaseos 48, 152 31, Chalandri, Greece
Tel.: (30) 2102808555
Web Site: https://www.toyota.gr
Car Import & Distr
N.A.I.C.S.: 423110

Yat Fung Motors Ltd. (1)
No 223-225 Av Do Dr Rodrigo Rodrigues 8/F Nam Kwong Building Apt B-C, Macau, China (Macau)
Tel.: (853) 2 856 1668
Web Site: https://www.yatfung-motors.com
Car Retailer
N.A.I.C.S.: 441110

INCHCAPE SHIPPING SERVICES LTD.
Units 5-8 Fleming Road Chafford Hundred Lakeside Business Village, Grays, RM16 6EW, United Kingdom
Tel.: (44) 1375 484900
Web Site: http://www.iss-shipping.com
Year Founded: 1847
Sales Range: $50-74.9 Million
Emp.: 3,800
Marine Logistics Services
N.A.I.C.S.: 541614
Simon Tory *(Sec)*

INCHEON CITY GAS CO., LTD.
178-24 Gajwa 1-dong, Seo-gu, Incheon, Korea (South)
Tel.: (82) 16000002
Web Site: http://www.icgas.co.kr
Year Founded: 1983
034590—(KRS)
Rev.: $558,751,406
Assets: $324,551,127
Liabilities: $171,151,373
Net Worth: $153,399,754
Earnings: $9,345,329
Emp.: 197
Fiscal Year-end: 12/31/22
Natural Gas Distribution Services
N.A.I.C.S.: 221210
Lee Sang Kyu *(Dir)*

INCITEC PIVOT LIMITED
Level 8 28 Freshwater Place, Southbank, 3006, VIC, Australia
Tel.: (61) 386954400
Web Site:
https://www.incitecpivot.com.au
ICPVF—(OTCIQ)
Rev.: $3,357,367,961
Assets: $7,194,983,814
Liabilities: $3,081,616,180
Net Worth: $4,113,367,634
Earnings: $114,238,929
Emp.: 5,000
Fiscal Year-end: 09/30/21
Nitrogenous Fertilizer Manufacturing
N.A.I.C.S.: 325311
Brian G. Kruger *(Chm)*

Subsidiaries:

Castonguay Blasting Limited (1)
640 Garson Coniston Road Garson, PO Box 2725, Sudbury, P3L 1V9, ON, Canada
Tel.: (705) 693-3887
Web Site: https://www.castonguay.ca
Sales Range: $50-74.9 Million
Emp.:
Oil Drilling & Blasting Services
N.A.I.C.S.: 213111

Castonguay G.P. (1)
640 Garson Coniston Road, Garson, P3L 1Z9, ON, Canada
Tel.: (705) 693-3887
Web Site: http://www.castonguay.ca

INCITEC PIVOT LIMITED

Sales Range: $50-74.9 Million
Emp.: 25
Drilling & Blasting Services
N.A.I.C.S.: 213114
Jason Murphy *(Gen Mgr)*

Dyno Nobel Explosivos Chile Limitada (1)
Ebro 2740 Office 201-202, Santiago, Chile
Tel.: (56) 2 231 4558
Web Site: http://www.dynonobel.com
Emp.: 70
Explosives Mfr
N.A.I.C.S.: 325920

Dyno Nobel Holdings USA, Inc. (1)
2795 E Cottonwood Pkwy 500, Salt Lake City, UT 84121-5695
Tel.: (801) 364-4800
Web Site: http://www.dynonobel.com
Emp.: 100
Investment Management Service
N.A.I.C.S.: 523999
Amanda Groendyke *(Dir-HR)*

Dyno Nobel Moranbah Pty Ltd (1)
282 Paringa Rd Gibson Island, Murarrie, 4172, QLD, Australia
Tel.: (61) 730263900
Explosives Mfr
N.A.I.C.S.: 325920

Dyno Nobel Moura Pty Limited (1)
PO Box 295, Moura, 4718, QLD, Australia
Tel.: (61) 749972072
Explosives Mfr
N.A.I.C.S.: 325920

Dyno Nobel, Inc. (1)
2795 E Cottonwood Pkwy Ste 500, Salt Lake City, UT 84121
Tel.: (801) 364-4800
Web Site: http://www.dynonobel.com
Sales Range: $1-4.9 Billion
Emp.: 170
Commercial Explosive Mfr
N.A.I.C.S.: 325920

Subsidiary (Domestic):

DNX Drilling Inc. (2)
2650 Decker Lake Blvd, Salt Lake City, UT 84119 **(100%)**
Tel.: (801) 450-2564
Water Well Drilling Contractor
N.A.I.C.S.: 237110

Affiliate (Non-US):

Denesoline Western Explosives Inc. (2)
111 Nahanni Drive, X1A2P4, Yellowknife, NT, Canada **(49%)**
Tel.: (867) 766-5170
Explosives Mfr
N.A.I.C.S.: 325920

Joint Venture (Non-US):

DetNet South Africa (Pty) Ltd. (2)
Block 1B Founders Hill Office Park Centenary Way, PO Box 10, Centenary Way, Modderfontein, 1645, South Africa **(50%)**
Tel.: (27) 11 657 7600
Web Site: https://www.detnet.com
Sales Range: $25-49.9 Million
Emp.: 90
Explosives Mfr
N.A.I.C.S.: 325920
Gys Landman *(CEO)*

Subsidiary (Non-US):

Dyno Nobel Asia Pacific Limited (2)
L 20 111 Pacific Highway, Sydney, 2060, NWS, Australia **(100%)**
Tel.: (61) 299689000
Web Site: http://www.dynonobel.com
Sales Range: $75-99.9 Million
Emp.: 120
Metal Mining Services
N.A.I.C.S.: 213114

Dyno Nobel Canada, Inc. (2)
350 Dupont Rd, North Bay, P1B 8K2, ON, Canada **(100%)**
Tel.: (705) 472-1300
Web Site: http://www.dynonobel.com
Sales Range: $25-49.9 Million
Emp.: 20
Commercial Explosive Mfr

INCITEC PIVOT LIMITED

Incitec Pivot Limited—(Continued)
N.A.I.C.S.: 325920

Dyno Nobel Nitrogen, Inc. (2)
1301 Brock Chem, Maitland, K0E 1P0, ON, Canada
Tel.: (613) 348-3681
Web Site: http://www.dynonobel.com
Sales Range: $25-49.9 Million
Emp.: 10
Explosives Mfr
N.A.I.C.S.: 325920

Subsidiary (Domestic):

Dyno Nobel Transportation Inc. (2)
6440 S Millrock Dr Ste 150, Salt Lake City, UT 84121-5695
Tel.: (801) 364-4800
Emp.: 140
General Freight Trucking, Long-Distance, Truckload
N.A.I.C.S.: 484121

Affiliate (Domestic):

Midland Powder Company (2)
4 NW 2nd St, Evansville, IN 47708 (50%)
Tel.: (812) 402-4070
Sales Range: $25-49.9 Million
Emp.: 80
Chemical & Allied Products Merchant Whslr
N.A.I.C.S.: 325920
Andy Koors (Dir-HR & Asst Controller)

Affiliate (Non-US):

Newfoundland Hard-Rok Inc. (2)
41 Beclin Road, Mount Pearl, A1N 0A4, NL, Canada
Tel.: (709) 754-4900
Web Site: http://www.hardrok.ca
Sales Range: $25-49.9 Million
Emp.: 8
Explosives Mfr & Supplier
N.A.I.C.S.: 325920

Subsidiary (Non-US):

Polar Explosives Ltd. (2)
Unit 130 160 Quarry Blvd SE, Calgary, T2Z 3G3, AB, Canada
Tel.: (403) 236-7980
Web Site: http://www.dynonobel.com
Sales Range: $25-49.9 Million
Emp.: 20
Explosives & Related Products Supplier
N.A.I.C.S.: 325920

Joint Venture (Non-US):

Queensland Nitrates Management Pty Ltd (2)
4 Three Chain Rd, Moura, 4718, QLD, Australia (50%)
Tel.: (61) 749975100
Chemicals & Fertilizers Mfr
N.A.I.C.S.: 325311

Queensland Nitrates Pty Ltd. (2)
4 Three Chain Rd, Moura, 4718, QLD, Australia (50%)
Tel.: (61) 749975100
Sales Range: $25-49.9 Million
Emp.: 88
Nitrogenous Fertilizer Mfr
N.A.I.C.S.: 325311
David Armstrong (Gen Mgr)

Subsidiary (Domestic):

The Ensign-Bickford Aerospace & Defense Company (2)
640 Hopmeadow St, Simsbury, CT 06070-2429
Tel.: (860) 843-2289
Web Site: https://www.ebad.com
Sales Range: $200-249.9 Million
Explosives Mfr
N.A.I.C.S.: 325920

Subsidiary (Domestic):

AFB International, Inc. (3)
3 Research Park Dr, Saint Charles, MO 63304
Tel.: (636) 634-4100
Web Site: https://www.afbinternational.com

Sales Range: $25-49.9 Million
Emp.: 120
Pet Food Flavor Mfr
N.A.I.C.S.: 311930

Ensign-Bickford Realty Corporation (3)
125 Powder Forest Dr 3rd Fl, Simsbury, CT 06070-0711
Tel.: (860) 843-2001
Web Site: http://www.ensign-bickfordrealty.com
Sales Range: $50-74.9 Million
Emp.: 9
Real Estate Services
N.A.I.C.S.: 531120

Goex International Inc. (3)
423 W Vaughn Rd, Cleburne, TX 76033-5068
Tel.: (817) 641-2261
Sales Range: $50-74.9 Million
Emp.: 85
Supplier Of Chemicals & Allied Products
N.A.I.C.S.: 424690

Affiliate (Domestic):

Western Explosives Systems Company (2)
3135 S Richmond St, Salt Lake City, UT 84106
Tel.: (801) 484-6557
Web Site: http://www.wescoexplosives.com
Sales Range: $50-74.9 Million
Emp.: 12
Explosives Distr & Blasting Services
N.A.I.C.S.: 325920
Thomas Fredrick Sr. (Founder)

Incitec Pivot Explosives Holdings Pty Limited (1)
Level 8 28 Freshwater Place, Southbank, 3006, VIC, Australia
Tel.: (61) 386954400
Web Site: http://www.incitecpivot.com.au
Emp.: 150
Industrial Chemicals & Fertilizer Distr
N.A.I.C.S.: 424690

Incitec Pivot Fertilizers Limited (1)
Level 8 28 Freshwater Place, Southbank, 3006, VIC, Australia
Tel.: (61) 38 695 4400
Web Site: https://www.incitecpivotfertilisers.com.au
Sales Range: $1-4.9 Billion
Fertilizer Mfr
N.A.I.C.S.: 325311

Incitec Pivot Finance Australia Pty Ltd (1)
Level 8 28 Freshwater Place, Southbank, 3006, VIC, Australia
Tel.: (61) 386954400
Emp.: 150
Financial Management Services
N.A.I.C.S.: 523999
James Fazzino (CEO)

Incitec Pivot US Holdings Pty Ltd (1)
Level 8 28 Freshwater Place, Southbank, 3006, VIC, Australia
Tel.: (61) 386954400
Web Site: http://www.incitecpivot.com.au
Emp.: 20
Specialty Chemicals Mfr
N.A.I.C.S.: 325180

Nitromak DNX Kimya Sanayii A.S. (1)
Via Flat Is ve Yasam Merkezi Bestepeler Mah Nergis Sok No 7/2, Kat 1 Ofis No 52 Sogutozu Yenimahalle, 06510, Ankara, Turkiye
Tel.: (90) 3122017700
Web Site: https://www.nitromak.com
Commercial Explosive Mfr
N.A.I.C.S.: 325920
Burak Gonen (Gen Mgr)

PT DNX Indonesia (1)
Gedung Plaza Park View 1st Floor 27 Jl Taman Kemang 2, Jakarta, 12730, Indonesia
Tel.: (62) 2171794791
Commercial Explosives Distr
N.A.I.C.S.: 424690

Quantum Fertilisers Limited (1)

2302A Great Eagle Centre 23 Harbour Road, Wanchai, China (Hong Kong)
Tel.: (852) 31052682
Web Site: http://www.quantumfertilisers.com
Agricultural Fertilizer Mfr
N.A.I.C.S.: 325320

SC Romnitro Explosives Srl. (1)
No 16 Nicolae Balcescu Ave Entr B 6th Floor Apt 7, 1st District, Bucharest, 010052, Romania
Tel.: (40) 21 313 36 95
Web Site: http://www.romnitro.ro
Sales Range: $25-49.9 Million
Emp.: 18
Explosives Mfr
N.A.I.C.S.: 325920

Southern Cross International Pty Ltd. (1)
PO Box 6018, Kincumber, 2251, NSW, Australia
Tel.: (61) 245776633
Web Site: http://www.sthnxi.com
Emp.: 150
Farm Product Distr
N.A.I.C.S.: 424910

Tradestar Corporation (1)
1590 S Gladiola St, Salt Lake City, UT 84104
Tel.: (801) 568-2000
Mining Industry Equipment Mfr
N.A.I.C.S.: 333131

INCITY IMMOBILIEN AG

Lilienthalstrabe 2, 12529, Schonefeld, Germany
Tel.: (49) 3040364770
Web Site: https://www.incity.ag
Year Founded: 2005
IC8—(DUS)
Rev.: $39,283,402
Assets: $170,623,786
Liabilities: $86,229,225
Net Worth: $84,394,561
Earnings: ($6,475,286)
Emp.: 15
Fiscal Year-end: 12/31/23
Real Estate Services
N.A.I.C.S.: 531390

INCKA

85 Avenue Pierre Grenier, 92100, Boulogne-Billancourt, Hauts De Seine, France
Tel.: (33) 158171220
Web Site: http://www.incka.com
Rev.: $20,300,000
Emp.: 143
Management Consulting Services
N.A.I.C.S.: 541611
Claude Xufre (Mng Dir, Mng Dir & Chm)

INCLAM SA

Limonero 22, 28020, Madrid, Spain
Tel.: (34) 915749107
Web Site: http://www.inclam.com
INC—(MAD)
Sales Range: Less than $1 Million
Engineeering Services
N.A.I.C.S.: 541330
Alfonso Andres Picazo (Founder & Chm)

INCLARITY PLC

8 Fulton Rd Olympic Office Centre 7th Fl, London, HA9 0NU, United Kingdom
Tel.: (44) 8456980800
Web Site: http://www.inclarity.co.uk
Year Founded: 1991
Sales Range: $25-49.9 Million
Telecommunication Servicesb
N.A.I.C.S.: 517810
Nilesh Pandyah (CFO)

INCLUSIO SA

Herrmann-Debrouxlaan 40, Oudergem, 1160, Brussels, Belgium

INTERNATIONAL PUBLIC

Tel.: (32) 26757882 BE
Web Site: https://www.inclusio.be
Year Founded: 2011
INCLU—(EUR)
Real Estate Investment Services
N.A.I.C.S.: 531190
Andre Bosmans (Chm)

INCLUSIVE, INC.

Kamiyacho Trust Tower 4-1-1 Toranomon, Minato-Ku, Tokyo, 105-0001, Japan
Tel.: (81) 364272020
Web Site: https://www.inclusive.co.jp
Year Founded: 2007
7078—(TKS)
Rev.: $35,422,990
Assets: $35,550,440
Liabilities: $12,539,170
Net Worth: $22,520,270
Earnings: $2,075,540
Fiscal Year-end: 03/31/24
Media Advertising Services
N.A.I.C.S.: 541840
Makoto Fujita (Founder & Pres)

INCOAX NETWORKS AB

Utmarksvagen 4, 802 91, Gavle, Sweden
Tel.: (46) 264209042
Web Site: https://www.incoax.com
Year Founded: 2009
INCOAX—(OMX)
Rev.: $7,385,739
Assets: $10,764,518
Liabilities: $3,306,632
Net Worth: $7,457,886
Earnings: ($1,583,694)
Emp.: 29
Fiscal Year-end: 12/31/23
Fiber Optic Cable Mfr
N.A.I.C.S.: 335921
Helge Tiainen (Chief Sls Officer)

INCOME

18 Nawa st, PO Box 2210, Cairo, 12211, Egypt
Tel.: (20) 237626004
Web Site: http://www.income-igi.com
Year Founded: 1973
Sales Range: $125-149.9 Million
Emp.: 390
Investment Holding Company
N.A.I.C.S.: 551112
Mohamed Sheta (Chm)

INCOME ASSET MANAGEMENT GROUP LIMITED

Level 20 215 Adelaide Street, Brisbane, 4000, QLD, Australia
Tel.: (61) 1300784132 AU
Web Site: https://incomeam.com
Year Founded: 1986
IAM—(ASX)
Rev.: $9,360,236
Assets: $6,248,544
Liabilities: $9,772,298
Net Worth: ($3,523,754)
Earnings: ($9,662,636)
Emp.: 54
Fiscal Year-end: 06/30/24
Financial Investment Services
N.A.I.C.S.: 523999
John Nantes (Chm)

Subsidiaries:

Australian Adventure Tourism Group Limited (1)
366 Shute Harbour Road, PO Box 313, Airlie Beach, 4802, QLD, Australia
Tel.: (61) 749641111
Web Site: https://www.aatgroup.com.au
Rev.: $2,408,244
Assets: $7,872,959
Liabilities: $618,703
Net Worth: $7,254,256
Earnings: $1,395,359
Fiscal Year-end: 06/30/2018

AND PRIVATE COMPANIES

INDENA S.P.A.

Property Ownership & Management Services
N.A.I.C.S.: 531312
Jerome Jones *(Sec)*

INCON CO., LTD.
4th floor 1 Guin-ro, Dongan-gu, Anyang, Gyeonggi-do, Korea (South)
Tel.: (82) 314558600
Web Site: https://www.incon.kr
Year Founded: 2000
083640—(KRS)
Rev.: $42,422,086
Assets: $98,390,418
Liabilities: $16,020,206
Net Worth: $82,370,212
Earnings: $2,722,866
Emp.: 81
Fiscal Year-end: 12/31/22
Electronic Security Device Mfr.
N.A.I.C.S.: 561621
Jongjin Park *(CEO)*

INCON ENGINEERS LIMITED
B-6/3 I D A Uppal, Hyderabad, 500 039, India
Tel.: (91) 4027203943
Web Site: https://www.incon.in
Year Founded: 1970
019098—(KOL)
Rev.: $184,326
Assets: $162,190
Liabilities: $40,838
Net Worth: $121,351
Earnings: ($893)
Emp.: 6
Fiscal Year-end: 03/31/22
Industrial Machinery Mfr & Distr
N.A.I.C.S.: 333248
Sreedhar Chowdhury *(Mng Dir)*

INCORDEX CORP.
6 Rosemary Way, Nuneaton, CV10 7ST, United Kingdom
Tel.: (44) 2039911252   NV
Year Founded: 2020
ICDX—(OTCIQ)
Rev.: $31,079
Assets: $22,288
Liabilities: $32,004
Net Worth: ($9,716)
Earnings: ($11,682)
Fiscal Year-end: 06/30/24
Online Handwritten Letter Services
N.A.I.C.S.: 517810
Iurii Abramovici *(Chm, Pres, CEO, Treas & Sec)*

INCREDIBLE HOLDINGS LTD.
Harvest Woodlands 280 Woodlands Industrial Park E5 10-50, Singapore, 757322, Singapore
Tel.: (65) 62689565   SG
Web Site: https://Incredible.sg
Year Founded: 1999
43J—(SES)
Rev.: $7,285,762
Assets: $18,493,829
Liabilities: $14,560,639
Net Worth: $3,933,190
Earnings: ($3,069,361)
Emp.: 2
Fiscal Year-end: 12/31/22
Dry Film Photoresist Distr
N.A.I.C.S.: 424610
Christian Yau Heilesen Kwok-Leun *(Exec Dir)*

INCREDIBLE INDUSTRIES LIMITED
Lansdowne Towers 2/1A Sarat Bose Road, Kolkata, 700020, West Bengal, India
Tel.: (91) 3366384700
Web Site: https://www.incredibleindustries.com
538365—(BOM)
Rev.: $89,811,418
Assets: $25,361,718
Liabilities: $10,014,223
Net Worth: $15,347,495
Earnings: $594,765
Emp.: 209
Fiscal Year-end: 03/31/23
Metal Products Mfr
N.A.I.C.S.: 331110
Rama Shankar Gupta *(Mng Dir)*

INCROSS CO., LTD.
3F 5F 8F 9F Kyungdong B/D 1926 Nambusunwhan-ro, Gwanak-gu, Seoul, 08793, Korea (South)
Tel.: (82) 234752800
Web Site: https://www.incross.com
Year Founded: 2007
216050—(KRS)
Rev.: $40,887,269
Assets: $181,700,499
Liabilities: $100,431,767
Net Worth: $81,268,731
Earnings: $11,818,433
Emp.: 298
Fiscal Year-end: 12/31/22
Mobile Advertising Services
N.A.I.C.S.: 541850
Won Junghwan *(Mng Dir)*

IND BANK HOUSING LTD
480 Anna Salai Nandanam, Chennai, 600 035, India
Tel.: (91) 4424329235
Web Site: https://www.indbankhousing.com
523465—(BOM)
Rev.: $49,593
Assets: $1,437,529
Liabilities: $17,706,872
Net Worth: ($16,269,343)
Earnings: ($25,758)
Emp.: 1
Fiscal Year-end: 03/31/21
Banking Services
N.A.I.C.S.: 521110
Rajaraman A. *(Mng Dir)*

IND RENEWABLE ENERGY LIMITED
503 Western Edge II Western Express High Way, Borivali East, Mumbai, 400066, Maharashtra, India
Tel.: (91) 2228702070
Web Site: https://www.indrenewable.com
Year Founded: 2011
536709—(BOM)
Rev.: $7,630
Assets: $456,006
Liabilities: $20,161
Net Worth: $435,845
Earnings: ($11,821)
Emp.: 1
Fiscal Year-end: 03/31/22
Solar Power Generato
N.A.I.C.S.: 221114
Kalpesh Kantilal Sanghavi *(CFO & Compliance Officer)*

IND-AGIV COMMERCE LTD.
301-B Kanara Business Center Andheri Ghatkoper Link Road, Near Laxmi Nagar Ghatkoper East, Mumbai, 400075, India
Tel.: (91) 2225003493
Web Site: http://www.agivavit.com
517077—(BOM)
Rev.: $1,358,506
Assets: $2,328,212
Liabilities: $2,158,616
Net Worth: $169,595
Earnings: $8,505
Fiscal Year-end: 03/31/22
Broadcasting Equipment Distr
N.A.I.C.S.: 423690

Vashdev B. Rupani *(Chm)*

IND-SWIFT LABORATORIES LIMITED
SCO 850 NAC Shivalik Enclave Manimajra, Chandigarh, 160101, India
Tel.: (91) 1725061850
Web Site: https://www.indswiftlabs.com
Year Founded: 1995
INDSWFTLAB—(NSE)
Rev.: $124,766,719
Assets: $248,218,261
Liabilities: $165,851,923
Net Worth: $82,366,339
Earnings: ($429,593)
Emp.: 1,531
Fiscal Year-end: 03/31/21
Active Pharmaceutical Ingredients Mfr
N.A.I.C.S.: 325412
N. R. Munjal *(Chm & Co-Mng Dir)*

Subsidiaries:

Ind Swift Laboratories Inc.   (1)
3500 S Dupont Hwy, Dover, DE 19901
Tel.: (908) 421-1234
Pharmaceuticals Product Mfr
N.A.I.C.S.: 325412

IND-SWIFT LTD.
781 Industrial Area - Phase II, Chandigarh, 160002, India
Tel.: (91) 1724680800
Web Site: https://www.indswiftltd.com
524652—(NSE)
Rev.: $50,693,903
Assets: $77,838,343
Liabilities: $162,329,537
Net Worth: ($84,491,194)
Earnings: $3,121,719
Emp.: 1,200
Fiscal Year-end: 03/31/23
Pharmaceuticals Mfr
N.A.I.C.S.: 325412
Vikrant Rai Mehta *(Co-Mng Dir)*

INDAG RUBBER LTD.
11 Khemka House Community Centre, New Delhi, 110017, India
Tel.: (91) 1126963172
Web Site: https://www.indagrubber.com
509162—(BOM)
Rev.: $34,431,197
Assets: $34,275,082
Liabilities: $5,362,648
Net Worth: $28,912,434
Earnings: $1,806,796
Emp.: 327
Fiscal Year-end: 03/31/23
Rubber Products Mfr
N.A.I.C.S.: 326299
Nand Khemka *(Chm & Mng Dir)*

INDAMIN COMPANY
Zarathustra Ghaffari Street Alley No 20, PO Box 1991-3885, Tehran, 13861 43311, Iran
Tel.: (98) 21 4419670
Year Founded: 1970
INDM—(THE)
Sales Range: Less than $1 Million
Motor Vehicle Parts Mfr
N.A.I.C.S.: 336390

INDEGENE LIFESYSTEMS PVT. LTD.
Aspen Block G4 3rd Floor Manyata Embassy Business Park Outer Ring Road, Nagawara, Bengaluru, 560 045, India
Tel.: (91) 8046447777
Web Site: http://www.indegene.com
Medical, Marketing, Training, Intelligence & Analytics Services
N.A.I.C.S.: 621999
Rajesh Nair *(Pres)*

Subsidiaries:

Indegene Encima, Inc.   (1)
1 Innovation Way Ste 400, Newark, DE 19711
Tel.: (888) 508-5688
Web Site: http://www.encimagroup.com
Business Intelligence, Digital & CRM Analytics & Strategy Services
N.A.I.C.S.: 541613
Shouvanik Chatterjee *(COO)*

MEDSN, INC   (1)
4727 Wilshire Blvd, Los Angeles, CA 90010
Tel.: (310) 899-9000
Web Site: http://www.medsn.com
Medical Devices
N.A.I.C.S.: 621491

Wincere, Inc.   (1)
2700 Augustine Dr Ste 261, Santa Clara, CA 95054-2911
Tel.: (916) 201-7381
Web Site: http://www.wincere.com
Scientific & Technical Consulting Services
N.A.I.C.S.: 541690
Harry Singh *(Mgr-Talent Acq)*

INDEKS BILGISAYAR SISTEMLERI MUHENDISLIK SANAYI VE TICARET A.S.
Ayazaga Mahallesi Mimar Sinan Sokak No 21 Seba Office Boulevard, D Blok Kat 1 Bolum Saryer, 34485, Istanbul, Turkiye
Tel.: (90) 2123312121
Web Site: https://www.index.com.tr
Year Founded: 1989
INDES—(IST)
Rev.: $1,774,825,075
Assets: $942,501,854
Liabilities: $794,330,285
Net Worth: $148,171,568
Earnings: $54,639,803
Emp.: 325
Fiscal Year-end: 12/31/21
Computer Peripheral Whslr
N.A.I.C.S.: 423430
Nevres Erol Bilecik *(Chm)*

Subsidiaries:

Artim Bilisim Cozum ve Dagitim A.S.   (1)
No 21 Seba Office Boulevard D Block Floor 1 Section No 7 Ayazaga, Mahallesi Mimar Sinan Street Sariyer, 34485, Istanbul, Turkiye
Tel.: (90) 2123312222
Web Site: http://www.artimbilisim.com
Electronic Equipment Distr
N.A.I.C.S.: 423690

Teklos Teknoloji Lojistik Hizmetleri A.S.   (1)
Web Site: http://www.teklos.com.tr
Logistic Services
N.A.I.C.S.: 541614

INDEL B S.P.A.
Via Sarsinate 27, Sant'Agata Feltria, 47866, Rimini, Italy
Tel.: (39) 0541848711
Web Site: http://www.indelb.com
Year Founded: 1967
Mobile Refrigerators Stores & Mfr
N.A.I.C.S.: 423740

INDENA S.P.A.
Viale Ortles 12, 20139, Milan, Italy
Tel.: (39) 02574961   IT
Web Site: http://www.indena.com
Sales Range: $150-199.9 Million
Emp.: 800
Plant Extract Processor for Use in Cosmetics, Pharmaceuticals & Health Foods
N.A.I.C.S.: 325412
Daniele Giavini *(Mng Dir)*

Subsidiaries:

Bernett S.r.l.   (1)

INDENA S.P.A.

Indena S.p.A.—(Continued)

Via Robbio - S S Dei Cairoli Km 53, 27030, Palestro, Pavia, Italy
Tel.: (39) 0384 683020
Sales Range: $25-49.9 Million
Emp.: 40
Production of Plant Extracts
N.A.I.C.S.: 325411

Indena Biotechnology Co. Ltd. (1)
Unit 03 16/F Cross Tower 318 Fu Zhou Road, Shanghai, 200001, China
Tel.: (86) 2122815900
Healthcare Product Distr
N.A.I.C.S.: 424210
Zhang Bin *(Gen Mgr)*

Indena Brasil Ltda (1)
Rua Bandeira Paulista 600, 04532-001, Sao Paulo, Brazil
Tel.: (55) 1127690624
Healthcare Product Distr
N.A.I.C.S.: 424210
Alessio Tagliaferri *(Gen Mgr)*

Indena France S.A.S. (1)
23 Rue de Madrid, 75008, Paris, France
Tel.: (33) 145229128
Sales Range: $250-299.9 Million
Chemical & Allied Products Merchant Whslr
N.A.I.C.S.: 424690
Louis Joussrault *(Mgr)*

Indena India Pvt. Ltd (1)
353 13th Main Sector A, Yelahanka New Town, 560064, Bengaluru, India (100%)
Tel.: (91) 80285672478
Web Site: http://www.indena.com
Sales Range: $25-49.9 Million
Emp.: 100
Medicinal Crops Grown Under Cover
N.A.I.C.S.: 325411

Indena Japan Co. Ltd (1)
KDDI Bldg 21st Fl 1- 8-1, Otemachi Chiyoda-Ku, Tokyo, 100-0004, Japan (100%)
Tel.: (81) 332439924
Web Site: http://www.indena.com
Sales Range: $25-49.9 Million
Emp.: 2
Chemicals Mfr
N.A.I.C.S.: 325180
Kawea Susumu *(Mng Dir)*

Indena USA Inc (1)
601 Union St Ste330, Seattle, WA 98101 (100%)
Tel.: (206) 340-6140
Sales Range: $25-49.9 Million
Emp.: 5
Pharmaceutical Preparation Mfr
N.A.I.C.S.: 325412
Greg Ris *(VP-Sls)*

INDEPENDENCE GOLD CORP.

625 Howe Street Suite 580, Vancouver, V6C 2T6, BC, Canada
Tel.: (604) 687-3959 **BC**
Web Site: https://www.ingold.ca
Year Founded: 2011
IEGCF—(OTCQB)
Rev.: $2,247
Assets: $5,487,115
Liabilities: $616,250
Net Worth: $4,870,865
Earnings: ($6,998,319)
Fiscal Year-end: 12/31/21
Gold Mining
N.A.I.C.S.: 212220
Randy C. Turner *(Pres & CEO)*

Subsidiaries:

Golden Pavilion Resources Ltd. (1)
650 Georgia St E Suite 1410, Vancouver, V6A 2A1, BC, Canada
Tel.: (604) 687-3959
Silver Mining Services
N.A.I.C.S.: 212220

INDEPENDENT DIGITAL NEWS & MEDIA LIMITED

2 Derry Street, London, W8 5HF, United Kingdom
Tel.: (44) 20 7005 2000 **UK**
Web Site: http://www.independent.co.uk
Year Founded: 2010
Newspaper Publishers
N.A.I.C.S.: 513110
Christian Broughton *(Mng Dir)*

INDEPENDENT INVESTMENT TRUST PLC

17 Dublin Street, Edinburgh, EH1 3PG, United Kingdom
Tel.: (44) 131 558 9434 **UK**
Web Site: http://www.independenttrust.co.uk
IIT—(LSE)
Rev.: $57,579,547
Assets: $442,871,971
Liabilities: $118,122
Net Worth: $442,753,850
Earnings: $56,468,933
Emp.: 2
Fiscal Year-end: 11/30/21
Investment Management Service
N.A.I.C.S.: 523940
Douglas McDougall *(Chm)*

INDEPENDENT NEWS & MEDIA (SOUTH AFRICA) (PTY) LIMITED

6th Floor The Star Building 47 Sauer Street, Johannesburg, 2001, South Africa
Tel.: (27) 11 633 2994
Web Site: http://www.iol.co.za
Newspaper Publishing Services
N.A.I.C.S.: 513110
Iqbal Surve *(Chm)*

INDEPENDENT PETROLEUM GROUP COMPANY S.A.K.

AREA 1A 7 STREETBUILDING NO 18 4th RING ROAD JABRIYA, PO Box 24027, Safat, 13101, Kuwait, 13101, Kuwait
Tel.: (965) 22276222
Web Site: https://www.ipg.com.kw
IPG—(KUW)
Rev.: $5,349,666,873
Assets: $1,426,880,952
Liabilities: $1,101,677,013
Net Worth: $325,203,939
Earnings: $24,882,187
Emp.: 168
Fiscal Year-end: 12/31/22
Crude Oil Marketing Services
N.A.I.C.S.: 424720
Mohammed Abdul Hamid Mohammed Al-Qasim *(Mng Dir-Mktg)*

Subsidiaries:

D&K Holdings L.L.C. (1)
Burj Al-Salam Building Office No C804 and C805 Trade Centre First, PO Box 124317, Dubai, United Arab Emirates
Tel.: (971) 43135000
Petroleum Product Distr
N.A.I.C.S.: 424720
Ajay Sharma *(Superintendent-Technical)*

Independent Petroleum Group (Asia) Pte. Limited (1)
6 Tesmasek Boulevard 30-01B, Suntec Tower Four, Singapore, 038986, Singapore
Tel.: (65) 62506637
Petroleum Product Distr
N.A.I.C.S.: 424720

Independent Petroleum Group (Southern Africa) (Pty) Limited (1)
Unit GS07 Rostra House The Forum North Bank Lane, Century City, 7441, Cape Town, South Africa
Tel.: (27) 215519730
Petroleum Product Distr
N.A.I.C.S.: 424720

Independent Petroleum Group Kenya Limited (1)
6th Floor Muthangari Drive Westlands Sarit Centre, PO Box 2232-00606, Nairobi, Kenya
Tel.: (254) 111045000
Crude Oil & Petroleum Distr
N.A.I.C.S.: 424720

Independent Petroleum Group SA (1)
24 Jaber Ben Hayane Street Dan Hel Building Block A 4th Floor, Office No 74, 20000, Casablanca, Morocco
Tel.: (212) 522490213
Crude Oil & Petroleum Distr
N.A.I.C.S.: 424720

Independent Petroleum Group of Kuwait Limited (1)
112 Jermyn Street, London, SW1Y 6LS, United Kingdom
Tel.: (44) 2079250505
Petroleum Product Distr
N.A.I.C.S.: 424720
Faiz Makkar *(Head-Risk Mgmt)*

INDEPENDENT TANKERS CORPORATION LIMITED

Par-la-Ville Place 14 Par-la-Ville Road, PO Box 1593, Hamilton, HM 08, Bermuda
Tel.: (441) 2950182
Web Site: http://www.itcl.bm
Year Founded: 2008
ITKSF—(OTCIQ)
Sales Range: Less than $1 Million
Oil & Gas Exploration Services
N.A.I.C.S.: 213112
Inger Marie Klemp *(Exec Dir)*

INDEPENDENTA S.A.

Str Stefan Cel Mare Nr 152-154, Sibiu, Romania
Tel.: (40) 269505000
Web Site: https://www.independentasa.ro
Year Founded: 1868
INTA—(BUC)
Rev.: $1,913,685
Assets: $8,572,993
Liabilities: $380,359
Net Worth: $8,192,635
Earnings: $439,884
Emp.: 31
Fiscal Year-end: 12/31/23
Tool Mfr
N.A.I.C.S.: 332216

INDEQUITY GROUP LIMITED

1st Floor Cascade House Constantia Office Park, Cnr 14th and Hendrik Potgieter Road Constantia Kloof, Roodepoort, 1709, South Africa
Tel.: (27) 114750816
Web Site: http://www.indequity.com
Year Founded: 1996
IDQ—(JSE)
Rev.: $4,735,810
Assets: $4,545,848
Liabilities: $868,944
Net Worth: $3,676,904
Earnings: $777,555
Emp.: 20
Fiscal Year-end: 09/30/19
Insurance Management Services
N.A.I.C.S.: 524210
Lourens Janse Van Rensburg *(CEO)*

INDERGIRI FINANCE LIMITED

Unit No 806 B Wing 8th Floor Kanakia Wall Street Andheri Kurla Road, Chakala Andheri East, Mumbai, 400093, MH, India
Tel.: (91) 8655618551
Web Site: https://www.indergiri.com
Year Founded: 1995
531505—(BOM)
Rev.: $94,585
Assets: $629,906
Liabilities: $31,087
Net Worth: $598,819

INTERNATIONAL PUBLIC

Earnings: $1,161
Fiscal Year-end: 03/31/23
Financial Services
N.A.I.C.S.: 523999
Laxmi Narayan Sharma *(Mng Dir & CFO)*

INDESA HOLDINGS CORP.

Banco General Tower 8th Floor Aquilino de la Guardia Street, PO Box 0823-01731, 5 B South Avenue, Panama, Panama
Tel.: (507) 3005560
Web Site: https://www.indesa.com.pa
Year Founded: 1968
INDH—(PAN)
Sales Range: $1-9.9 Million
Financial Services
N.A.I.C.S.: 523999
Luis A. Navarro *(Vice Chm & Mng Partner)*

Subsidiaries:

Indesa Capital, Inc. (1)
Torre Banco General 8th Floor Calle Aquilino de la Guardia Marbella, PO Box 0823, 01731, Panama, Panama
Tel.: (507) 300 5560
Web Site: http://www.indesa.com.pa
Financial Services
N.A.I.C.S.: 523999
Luis A. Navarro *(Vice Chm & Mng Partner)*

INDESIGN GROUP

Plaza Vapor 9 C - Pol Les Guixeres, 08915, Badalona, Spain
Tel.: (34) 934 655 504
Web Site: http://www.indesign.es
Year Founded: 2006
Sales Range: $10-24.9 Million
Emp.: 150
Marketing Consultancy Services
N.A.I.C.S.: 541613
Massimo Scattarreggia *(Co-Founder, CEO & Sr Partner)*

INDEX BROOK LIMITED

301B Island way Dolphin Estate Ikoyi, Lagos, Nigeria
Tel.: (234) 1 462 4044 **NG**
Web Site: http://www.indexbrook.com
Year Founded: 1989
Sales Range: $1-9.9 Million
Emp.: 100
Technical Oil & Gas Support Services
N.A.I.C.S.: 213112
Kofo Fasanmi *(Mgr-Bus Dev)*

Subsidiaries:

Index Brook Limited (1)
No 7 Senchi Loop Airport Residential Area, Accra, Ghana (100%)
Tel.: (233) 302 797 423
Web Site: http://www.indexbrook.com
Technical Oil & Gas Support Services
N.A.I.C.S.: 211120
Emmanuel Ijekhuemen *(Gen Mgr)*

INDEX INTERNATIONAL GROUP

Grev Turegatan 18, SE- 103 95, Stockholm, Sweden
Tel.: (46) 851803000
Web Site: https://indexinvest.com
Emp.: 100
Investment Services
N.A.I.C.S.: 523999

Subsidiaries:

Index Investment Group (1)
1000 N US Hwy One Ste 902, Jupiter, FL 33477
Tel.: (561) 571-0360
Web Site: https://indexinvest.com
Investment Services
N.A.I.C.S.: 523999

INDEX INTERNATIONAL

GROUP PUBLIC COMPANY LIMITED
1/814 Village No 17 Soi Amporn Phahonyothin Road, Khu Khot Subdistrict Lam Luk Ka District, Pathumthani, 12130, Thailand
Tel.: (66) 25323623   TH
Web Site: https://www.index.co.th
Year Founded: 1983
IND—(THA)
Rev.: $22,201,153
Assets: $21,317,791
Liabilities: $9,298,680
Net Worth: $12,019,111
Earnings: $390,105
Emp.: 195
Fiscal Year-end: 12/31/23
Engineeering Services
N.A.I.C.S.: 541330
Chainarong Na Lamphun *(CEO)*

INDEX LIVING MALL PUBLIC COMPANY LIMITED
147 Soi Rama 2 Soi 50 Rama 2 Road, Samaedam Bangkhunthien, Bangkok, 10150, Thailand
Tel.: (66) 28986420   TH
Web Site:
  https://www.indexlivingmall.com
Year Founded: 2002
ILM—(THA)
Rev.: $274,877,839
Assets: $359,775,601
Liabilities: $185,250,604
Net Worth: $174,524,997
Earnings: $21,095,487
Emp.: 3,743
Fiscal Year-end: 12/31/23
Home Furnishings Retailer
N.A.I.C.S.: 449129
Pisith Patamasatayasonthi *(CEO)*

Subsidiaries:

Index Interfurn Company Limited   (1)
18/2 Moo 4 Soi Sap Maha Chok Rama 2 Road, Nadi Subdistrict, Mueang Samut Sakhon, 74000, Samut Sakhon, Thailand
Tel.: (66) 3483341322
Web Site: http://www.index-interfurn.com
Furniture Mfr
N.A.I.C.S.: 337121

The Walk Company Limited   (1)
No 147 Soi Rama 2 Soi 50 Rama 2 Road, Samae Dam Subdistrict Bang Khun Thian District, Bangkok, 10150, Thailand
Tel.: (66) 289864205
Shopping Center Rental Services
N.A.I.C.S.: 531120

INDEX VENTURES SA
Rue de Jargonnant 2, 1207, Geneva, Switzerland
Tel.: (41) 227370000   CH
Web Site:
  http://www.indexventures.com
Year Founded: 1996
Sales Range: $25-49.9 Million
Emp.: 38
Private Equity & Venture Capital Firm
N.A.I.C.S.: 523999
Neil Rimer *(Co-Founder & Partner)*

INDEX-WERKE GMBH & CO. KG
Plochinger Strasse 92, 73730, Esslingen, Germany
Tel.: (49) 71131910
Web Site: http://www.index-werke.de
Year Founded: 1914
Sales Range: $400-449.9 Million
Emp.: 2,270
Natural Gas Mfr
N.A.I.C.S.: 333517
Dirk Prust *(Member-Exec Bd)*

Subsidiaries:

INDEX Corporation   (1)
14700 N Pointe Blvd, Noblesville, IN 46060
Tel.: (317) 770-6300
Web Site: http://www.index-usa.com
Sales Range: $75-99.9 Million
Emp.: 200
Sales & Service of Machine Tools
N.A.I.C.S.: 423830

INDEX DALIAN MACHINE TOOL LTD.   (1)
19 Changxing Road, Dalian, 116600, China
Tel.: (86) 411 8761 9788
Machine Tool Distr
N.A.I.C.S.: 423830

INDEX Machine Tools (Taicang) Co., Ltd.   (1)
1-1-4 Fada Road Banqiao, Chengxiang Town, Taicang, 215413, Jiangsu, China
Tel.: (86) 1065900959
Web Site: http://www.index-traub.cn
CNC Turning Machine Tool Mfr
N.A.I.C.S.: 333517

INDEX RUS   (1)
Lesnaya street 66 Office 3, 445011, Togliatti, Samarskaya, Russia
Tel.: (7) 8482691600
Web Site: http://ru.index-traub.com
CNC Turning Machine Tool Mfr
N.A.I.C.S.: 333517

INDEX Slovakia s.r.o.   (1)
Vinohradok 5359, Malacky, 90101, Slovakia
Tel.: (421) 342861000
Web Site: http://www.sk.index-traub.com
CNC Turning Machine Tool Mfr
N.A.I.C.S.: 333517
Michal Oborny *(Founder)*

INDEX Trading (Shanghai) Co., Ltd.   (1)
South Commercial Building Rm 1004 No 18 Gu Fang Rd, Shanghai, 201102, China
Tel.: (86) 2154176637
Machine Tool Distr
N.A.I.C.S.: 423830
Rainer Kehder *(Gen Mgr)*

INDEX Werkzeugmaschinen Schweiz AG   (1)
Av des paquiers 16, 2072, Saint-Blaise, Switzerland
Tel.: (41) 327569600
Web Site: http://www.index-traub.ch
CNC Turning Machine Tool Mfr
N.A.I.C.S.: 333517

INDEX-France s.a.r.l.   (1)
Avenue du Quebec / ZA de Courtaboeuf, 91941, Les Ulis, Cedex, France
Tel.: (33) 1 69187676
Machine Tool Distr
N.A.I.C.S.: 423830

INDEX-TRAUB AB   (1)
Hernepellontie 27, 00710, Helsinki, Finland
Tel.: (358) 108432001
Web Site: http://www.index-traub.fi
CNC Turning Machine Tool Mfr
N.A.I.C.S.: 333517

INDEX-TRAUB Denmark   (1)
Havretoften 1, 5550, Langeskov, Denmark
Tel.: (45) 65993401
Web Site: http://www.index-traub.dk
Machine Tool Distr
N.A.I.C.S.: 423830

INDEX-Tornos Automaticos Industria e Comercio Ltda.   (1)
Rua Joaquim Machado 250, 18087-280, Sorocaba, Sao Paulo, Brazil
Tel.: (55) 1521026017
Web Site: http://www.br.index-traub.com
CNC Turning Machine Tool Mfr
N.A.I.C.S.: 333517
Glauco Sbrana *(Coord-Industrial)*

Index-Traub AB   (1)
Fagerstagatan 2, Box 8308, SE-163 08, Spanga, Sweden   (100%)
Tel.: (46) 711 31910
Web Site: http://www.index-werke.de
Sales & Service in Sweden & Finland
N.A.I.C.S.: 333517

TRAUB Drehmaschinin GmbH   (1)
Hauffstrasse 4, PO Box 1180, D 73262, Reichenbach, Fils, Germany   (100%)
Tel.: (49) 7001535020
Web Site: http://www.traub.de
Sales Range: $400-449.9 Million
Emp.: 1,600
Mfr of Mill Turning Centers & Flexible Manufacturing Systems
N.A.I.C.S.: 333517

Thelle Teknologi AS   (1)
Liadammen 23 Vesteroy, 1684, Oslo, Norway
Tel.: (47) 93080550
Web Site: http://www.index-traub.no
CNC Turning Machine Tool Mfr
N.A.I.C.S.: 333517

Tornos Automaticos Ind. E Com. Ltda.   (1)
Rua Joaquim Machado 250 Bl 4, Caixa Postal 563, CEP 18087 280, Sorocaba, SP, Brazil   (100%)
Tel.: (55) 152356017
Web Site: http://www.index.com.br
Sales Range: $50-74.9 Million
Emp.: 130
Mfr of Turning Automatics & CNC Turning Centers
N.A.I.C.S.: 333517

INDIA CAPITAL GROWTH FUND LIMITED
1 Royal Plaza Royal Avenue, Saint Peter Port, GY1 2HL, Guernsey
Tel.: (44) 2070689870
Web Site:
  https://www.indiacapitalgrowth.com
Year Founded: 2005
IGC—(LSE)
Rev.: $5,746,024
Assets: $171,408,735
Liabilities: $771,270
Net Worth: $170,637,465
Earnings: $4,762,686
Fiscal Year-end: 12/31/22
Investment Fund Services
N.A.I.C.S.: 525990
Elisabeth Scott *(Chm)*

INDIA FINSEC LIMITED
D-16 First Floor Prashant Vihar Sector 14, Rohini, New Delhi, 110085, India
Tel.: (91) 8595010101
Web Site: https://www.indiafinsec.in
Year Founded: 1994
535667—(BOM)
Rev.: $3,321,242
Assets: $24,606,057
Liabilities: $12,957,998
Net Worth: $11,648,059
Earnings: $551,472
Emp.: 4
Fiscal Year-end: 03/31/22
Financing & Loan Services
N.A.I.C.S.: 522220
Gopal Bansal *(Chm & Mng Dir)*

INDIA GELATINE & CHEMICALS LTD.
77/78/79 Mittal Chambers 228 Nariman Point, Mumbai, 400 021, India
Tel.: (91) 2222020341
Web Site:
  https://www.indiagelatine.com
Year Founded: 1973
531253—(BOM)
Rev.: $28,439,816
Assets: $24,563,666
Liabilities: $5,944,398
Net Worth: $18,619,269
Earnings: $3,262,268
Emp.: 102
Fiscal Year-end: 03/31/23
Gelatin Mfr
N.A.I.C.S.: 325998
Viren Chandrasinh Mirani *(Chm & Mng Dir)*

INDIA GLYCOLS LIMITED
A-1 Industrial Area Bazpur Road, Udham Singh Nagar, Kashipur, 244 713, Uttarakhand, India
Tel.: (91) 5947269000
Web Site:
  https://www.indiaglycols.com
Year Founded: 1983
500201—(BOM)
Rev.: $742,933,027
Assets: $562,276,356
Liabilities: $402,772,952
Net Worth: $159,503,403
Earnings: $17,964,369
Emp.: 1,330
Fiscal Year-end: 03/31/21
Industrial Gas Mfr
N.A.I.C.S.: 325120
U. S. Bhartia *(Chm & Mng Dir)*

Subsidiaries:

IGL Chem International Pte Ltd.   (1)
101 Cecil Street 17-02 Tong Eng Building, Singapore, 069533, Singapore
Tel.: (65) 64109720
Paper Mfr
N.A.I.C.S.: 322120

IGL Chem International USA LLC   (1)
10701 Corporate Dr Ste 142, Stafford, TX 77477
Tel.: (281) 295-1673
Paper Mfr
N.A.I.C.S.: 322120

INDIA GREEN REALITY LIMITED
308 Iscon mall Above Star Bazar Satellite, Ahmedabad, 380 015, India
Tel.: (91) 7948008787
Web Site:
  https://www.indiagreenreality.com
Year Founded: 2009
Rev.: $930,040
Assets: $23,272,708
Liabilities: $19,419,027
Net Worth: $3,853,681
Earnings: $4,905
Emp.: 45
Fiscal Year-end: 03/31/19
Real Estate Manangement Services
N.A.I.C.S.: 541320
Vinodkumar Mahasukhlal Thaker *(Co-Founder & Mng Dir)*

INDIA GRID TRUST
Unit No 101 First Floor Windsor Village Kolekalyan Off Cst Road, Vidyanagari Marg Kalina Santacruz East, Mumbai, 400098, India
Tel.: (91) 7208493885
Web Site: https://www.indigrid.co.in
Year Founded: 2016
INDIGRID—(NSE)
Rev.: $310,461,197
Assets: $2,669,535,278
Liabilities: $1,919,074,112
Net Worth: $750,461,166
Earnings: $46,857,038
Fiscal Year-end: 03/31/22
Electric Power Transmission Services
N.A.I.C.S.: 221122
Jyoti Kumar Agarwal *(Co-CFO)*

Subsidiaries:

Bhopal Dhule Transmission Company Limited   (1)
Unit No 101 First Floor Windsor Village KoleKalyan off CST Road, Vidyanagari Marg Kalina Santacruz East, Mumbai, 400 098, Maharashtra, India
Tel.: (91) 7028493885
Web Site: https://www.bdtcl.com
Electricity Transmission Services
N.A.I.C.S.: 221121

INDIA HOME LOAN LIMITED
504-504A Nirmal Ecstasy 5th Floor, Jatashankar Dossa Road Mulund, Mumbai, 400080, India

INDIA HOME LOAN LIMITED

India Home Loan Limited—(Continued)
Tel.: (91) 2225683353
Web Site:
https://www.indiahomeloan.co.in
Year Founded: 1990
530979—(BOM)
Rev.: $3,165,217
Assets: $18,997,879
Liabilities: $12,908,805
Net Worth: $6,089,074
Earnings: $82,651
Emp.: 68
Fiscal Year-end: 03/31/23
Mortgage Lending Services
N.A.I.C.S.: 522292
Mahesh Narshibhai Pujara *(Mng Dir)*

INDIA INFRASPACE LIMITED
701 Sarap Building Opp Navjeevan Press Ashram Road, Ahmedabad, 380 014, Gujarat, India
Tel.: (91) 7927544003
Web Site:
http://www.indiainfraspace.com
531343—(BOM)
Rev.: $220,416
Assets: $1,903,095
Liabilities: $1,944,679
Net Worth: ($41,583)
Earnings: ($187,205)
Emp.: 2
Fiscal Year-end: 03/31/21
Construction & Infrastructure Development Services
N.A.I.C.S.: 531390
Pradip Babulal Shah *(Mng Dir)*

INDIA INFRASTRUCTURE FINANCE COMPANY LIMITED
5th Floor Block 2 Plate A B NBCC Tower, East Kidwai Nagar, New Delhi, 110 023, India
Tel.: (91) 1124662777
Web Site: https://iifcl.in
Year Founded: 2006
Rev.: $652,019,973
Assets: $9,426,666,604
Liabilities: $7,900,902,405
Net Worth: $1,525,764,199
Earnings: $87,245,668
Fiscal Year-end: 03/31/22
Economic Development Administration
N.A.I.C.S.: 926110
S. B. Nayar *(Chm & Mng Dir)*

Subsidiaries:

IIFCL Asset Management Company Ltd (1)
3rd Floor Amba Deep Building 14 Kasturba Gandhi Marg, New Delhi, 110 001, India
Tel.: (91) 1123731331
Financial Consulting Services
N.A.I.C.S.: 523940
S. B. Nayar *(Chm)*

IIFCL Projects Ltd. (1)
5th Floor Plate - A NBCC Tower Block -2, Kidwai Nagar East, New Delhi, 110023, India
Tel.: (91) 1123445100
Web Site: http://www.iifclprojects.com
Civil Engineering & Construction Services
N.A.I.C.S.: 237990
Paritosh Garga *(Gen Mgr)*

India Infrastructure Finance Company (UK) Limited (1)
Third Floor 72 King William Street, London, EC4N 7HR, United Kingdom **(100%)**
Tel.: (44) 207776 8950
Web Site: http://www.iifc.org.uk
Financial Services
N.A.I.C.S.: 522320
Naresh Goyal *(Mng Dir)*

INDIA INFRASTRUCTURE TRUST
Unit 1 4th Floor Godrej Bkc Bandra Kurla Complex, Mumbai, 400051, India
Tel.: (91) 2266000700
Web Site:
http://www.indinfratrust.com
Year Founded: 2018
542543—(BOM)
Rev.: $339,740,568
Assets: $1,808,174,316
Liabilities: $993,876,360
Net Worth: $814,297,956
Earnings: $66,184,896
Fiscal Year-end: 03/31/23
Investment Services
N.A.I.C.S.: 523150
Pratik Desai *(Compliance Officer)*

INDIA LEASE DEVELOPMENT LTD.
4/17-B Asaf Ali Road, New Delhi, 110 002, India
Tel.: (91) 1141520070
Web Site: http://www.indialease.com
500202—(BOM)
Rev.: $456,087
Assets: $1,511,164
Liabilities: $52,334
Net Worth: $1,458,830
Earnings: ($18,782)
Emp.: 5
Fiscal Year-end: 03/31/22
Financial Lending Services
N.A.I.C.S.: 523999
Rohit Madan *(CFO, Compliance Officer, Sec & Mgr)*

INDIA MOTOR PARTS & ACCESSORIES LTD
Sundaram Tower III Floor 46 Whites Road, Royapettah, Chennai, 600 014, India
Tel.: (91) 4428591433
Web Site: https://www.impal.net
590065—(BOM)
Rev.: $90,222,405
Assets: $186,811,170
Liabilities: $18,252,780
Net Worth: $168,558,390
Earnings: $8,308,755
Emp.: 826
Fiscal Year-end: 03/31/22
Automobile Spare Parts & Accessories Distr
N.A.I.C.S.: 332510
N. Krishnan *(Mng Dir)*

INDIA NIPPON ELECTRICALS LIMITED
No 11 and 13 Patullos Road, Chennai, 600 002, Tamil Nadu, India
Tel.: (91) 4428460063
Web Site:
https://www.indianippon.com
Year Founded: 1984
INDNIPPON—(NSE)
Rev.: $67,894,691
Assets: $80,941,947
Liabilities: $19,382,768
Net Worth: $61,559,180
Earnings: $5,409,891
Emp.: 549
Fiscal Year-end: 03/31/21
Electronic Ignition Systems Mfr
N.A.I.C.S.: 334419
Arvind Balaji *(Mng Dir)*

INDIA PESTICIDES LIMITED
Swarup Cold Storage Compound Water Works Road Aishbagh, Lucknow, 226004, Uttar Pradesh, India
Tel.: (91) 5222653602
Web Site:
https://www.indiapesticidesltd.com
Year Founded: 1984
IPL—(NSE)
Rev.: $122,599,932
Assets: $12,569,835
Liabilities: $2,016,337
Net Worth: $10,553,498
Earnings: $1,955,158
Emp.: 680
Fiscal Year-end: 03/31/23
Agricultural Chemical Mfr
N.A.I.C.S.: 325320
Rajendra Singh Sharma *(Exec Dir)*

INDIA POWER CORPORATION LIMITED
Plot No X1 2&3 Block-EP Sector-V, Salt Lake City, Kolkata, 700 091, India
Tel.: (91) 3366094300
Web Site:
https://www.indiapower.com
Year Founded: 1919
DPSCLTD—(NSE)
Rev.: $77,930,064
Assets: $242,169,402
Liabilities: $121,581,536
Net Worth: $120,587,866
Earnings: $1,898,687
Emp.: 396
Fiscal Year-end: 03/31/23
Power Generation, Transmission & Trading
N.A.I.C.S.: 221118
Somesh Dasgupta *(Pres)*

INDIA RADIATORS LIMITED
No 88 Mount Road, Guindy, Chennai, 600032, Tamilnadu, India
Tel.: (91) 4440432208
Web Site:
http://www.indiaradiators.com
Year Founded: 1949
Automotive Components Mfr
N.A.I.C.S.: 336390
Rita Chandrasekar *(Chm)*

INDIA SHELTER FINANCE CORPORATION LIMITED
6th Floor Plot No 15 Sector 44 Institutional Area, Gurgaon, 122002, Haryana, India
Tel.: (91) 18005728888
Web Site: https://www.indiashelter.in
Year Founded: 1998
544044—(BOM)
Rev.: $70,844,988
Assets: $520,625,423
Liabilities: $370,273,587
Net Worth: $150,351,836
Earnings: $18,827,463
Emp.: 2,700
Fiscal Year-end: 03/31/23
Financial Investment Services
N.A.I.C.S.: 523910

INDIA STEEL WORKS LTD.
304 A-wing Naman Midtown Near India Bull Finance Centre, Senapati Bapat Marg Elphinstone Road W, Mumbai, 400 013, India
Tel.: (91) 2262304304
Web Site: https://www.indiasteel.in
513361—(BOM)
Rev.: $4,474,129
Assets: $59,699,613
Liabilities: $48,013,329
Net Worth: $11,686,284
Earnings: ($6,918,421)
Emp.: 150
Fiscal Year-end: 03/31/22
Stainless Steel Bright Bars Mfr
N.A.I.C.S.: 331513
Sudhirkumar H. Gupta *(Mng Dir)*

INDIA SUGARS & REFINERIES LIMITED
Chitwadgi, Hospet, Bellary, 583 211, Karnataka, India
Tel.: (91) 8394 228845

INTERNATIONAL PUBLIC

Web Site:
http://www.indiasugars.com
Year Founded: 1933
Sales Range: $10-24.9 Million
Sugar Product Mfr & Whslr
N.A.I.C.S.: 311314
Siddharth R. Morarka *(Co-Mng Dir)*

INDIA TOURISM DEVELOPMENT CORPORATION LTD
Scope Complex Core 8 6th Floor 7, Lodhi Road, New Delhi, 110003, Delhi, India
Tel.: (91) 1124360303
Web Site:
https://www.theashokgroup.com
Year Founded: 1965
ITDC—(NSE)
Rev.: $26,456,471
Assets: $74,953,024
Liabilities: $37,065,319
Net Worth: $37,887,704
Earnings: ($5,047,743)
Emp.: 663
Fiscal Year-end: 03/31/21
Tourism Development
N.A.I.C.S.: 926110
V. K. Jain *(Sec)*

Subsidiaries:

India Tourism Development Corporation Ltd - Catering Units (1)
Daawat Khana, Red Fort Complex, New Delhi, 110006, India
Tel.: (91) 1123281802
Sales Range: $10-24.9 Million
Emp.: 25
Catering Services
N.A.I.C.S.: 722320

INDIA VALUE FUND ADVISORS PVT LTD.
Suite F9C Grand Hyatt Plaza Santacruz East, Mumbai, 400 055, India
Tel.: (91) 2266954888
Web Site: http://www.ivfa.com
Sales Range: $25-49.9 Million
Emp.: 35
Privater Equity Firm
N.A.I.C.S.: 523999
Vishal Nevatia *(Mng Partner)*

Subsidiaries:

Atria Convergence Technologies Private Limited (1)
Indian Express Building No 1 2nd Floor Queen's Road, Bengaluru, 560 010, Karnataka, India
Tel.: (91) 8042840099
Internet Service Provider
N.A.I.C.S.: 517111
C.S. Sunder Raju *(Mng Dir)*

RDC Concrete (India) Pvt. Limited (1)
IIIrd Floor Vinmar House Plot No A/41 MIDC Road No 2, Opp Marol Bus Depot Andheri, Mumbai, 400 093, Maharashtra, India
Tel.: (91) 22 6789 6789
Web Site: www.rdcconcrete.com
Readymix Concrete Mfr
N.A.I.C.S.: 327320
Suresh Kumar *(Mgr-Info Sys & Network Security)*

Plant (Domestic):

RDC Concrete (India) Pvt Ltd Ahmedabad Plant (2)
Survey No 806/12 Kothari Char Rastab Santej-Ahmedabad Road, Santej Kalol Ghandhinagar, Ahmedabad, 382 721, Gujarat, India
Tel.: (91) 9099063709
Readymix Concrete Mfr
N.A.I.C.S.: 327320

RDC Concrete (India) Pvt Ltd Bengaluru Plant (2)
37B Doddanekkundi Industrial Area 1st Phase Whitefield Road, Bengaluru, 560

048, India
Tel.: (91) 9739993573
Readymix Concrete Mfr
N.A.I.C.S.: 327320

RDC Concrete (India) Pvt Ltd Chennai Plant (2)
Plot No 2 / 129 S No 55 / 4d1 Avdi Road, Senneerkuppam Poonamallee Taluk Thiruvallur District, Chennai, 600 056, India
Tel.: (91) 4426802041
Readymix Concrete Mfr
N.A.I.C.S.: 327320

RDC Concrete (India) Pvt Ltd Coimbatore Plant (2)
63 S Fno 256 & 258 Kanampalayam Trichy Road, Sulur Taluk, Coimbatore, 641 402, India
Tel.: (91) 4222680824
Readymix Concrete Mfr
N.A.I.C.S.: 327320

RDC Concrete (India) Pvt Ltd Gurgaon Plant (2)
Behrampur Road, Khandsa, Gurgaon, 122 001, India
Tel.: (91) 9911521302
Readymix Concrete Mfr
N.A.I.C.S.: 327320

RDC Concrete (India) Pvt Ltd Hyderabad Plant (2)
Plot No 8/A Survey No 334 to 337 IDA Bachupally, Rangareddy, Hyderabad, 500090, India
Tel.: (91) 9948028999
Readymix Concrete Mfr
N.A.I.C.S.: 327320

RDC Concrete (India) Pvt Ltd Jaipur Plant (2)
Plot No 41 A 1 Industrial area Jhotwara, Jaipur, 301 012, Rajasthan, India
Tel.: (91) 9672223333
Readymix Concrete Mfr
N.A.I.C.S.: 327320

RDC Concrete (India) Pvt Ltd Kerala Plant (2)
Plot No VI / 58 & 59 Industrial Development Area, Edayar Muppathadom PO, Cochin, 683 110, Kerala, India
Tel.: (91) 4842550530
Readymix Concrete Mfr
N.A.I.C.S.: 327320

RDC Concrete (India) Pvt Ltd Kerala Plant (2)
Plot No 191 / 1P & 8P, Mundoor PO, Thrissur, 680 541, Kerala, India
Tel.: (91) 4872211212
Readymix Concrete Mfr
N.A.I.C.S.: 327320

RDC Concrete (India) Pvt Ltd Kolkata Plant (2)
Block DH Plot no 01 Street 316 New Town, Rajarhat, Kolkata, 700 156, West Bengal, India
Tel.: (91) 3364508331
Readymix Concrete Mfr
N.A.I.C.S.: 327320

RDC Concrete (India) Pvt Ltd Mangalore Plant (2)
Plot No 27 Baikampadi Industrial area Opp to Mungaru Bus Stop, Baikampadi P O, Mangalore, 575 011, Karnataka, India
Tel.: (91) 8242400900
Readymix Concrete Mfr
N.A.I.C.S.: 327320

RDC Concrete (India) Pvt Ltd Mumbai Plant (2)
Plot No102/22/105 Basni Gavli Wada Penkarpada Street Mahajanwadi, Near Dahiser Check Naka Mira Road, Thane, 401104, Maharashtra, India
Tel.: (91) 9920722209
Readymix Concrete Mfr
N.A.I.C.S.: 327320

RDC Concrete (India) Pvt Ltd Pune Plant (2)
Ramtekdi Industrial Estate Survey No 107 Plot No 5 Hissa No 2B, Hadapsar, Pune, 411 013, Maharashtra, India
Tel.: (91) 9766624099

Readymix Concrete Mfr
N.A.I.C.S.: 327320

RDC Concrete (India) Pvt Ltd Visakapattanam Plant (2)
Plot No 98C Block D Auto Nagar, Visakhapatnam, 500 012, Andhra Pradesh, India
Tel.: (91) 8912702759
Readymix Concrete Mfr
N.A.I.C.S.: 327320

INDIABULLS GROUP
1A Hamilton House 1st Floor, Connaught Place, New Delhi, 110 001, India
Tel.: (91) 11 3047 6100
Web Site: http://www.indiabulls.com
Year Founded: 1999
Holding Company
N.A.I.C.S.: 551112
Sameer Gehlaut (Founder & Chm)

Subsidiaries:

Indiabulls Housing Finance Ltd. (1)
Indiabulls House Indiabulls Finance Centre Tower 1 17th Floor, Senapati Bapat Marg Elphinstone Road, Mumbai, 400 013, Maharashtra, India
Tel.: (91) 2261891000
Web Site:
 http://www.indiabullshomeloans.com
Rev.: $1,369,111,380
Assets: $12,726,969,255
Liabilities: $10,524,697,365
Net Worth: $2,202,271,890
Earnings: $164,017,035
Emp.: 3,480
Fiscal Year-end: 03/31/2021
Real Estate Credit & Mortgage Investment Services
N.A.I.C.S.: 522292
Gagan Banga (Vice Chm, CEO & Mng Dir)

Subsidiary (Domestic):

Indiabulls Infrastructure Credit Limited (2)
825/1 Street No 2 A, Dehradun, 248001, India
Tel.: (91) 9761230212
Financial Services
N.A.I.C.S.: 522291

Indiabulls Trustee Company Limited (2)
M - 62 & 63 1st Floor Connaught Place, New Delhi, 110 001, India
Tel.: (91) 11 3025 2900
Financial Services
N.A.I.C.S.: 522291

Indiabulls Real Estate Limited (1)
Indiabulls House 448-451 Udyog Vihar Phase-V, Gurgaon, 122 016, India
Tel.: (91) 1246682850
Web Site:
 http://www.indiabullsrealestate.com
Rev.: $77,749,535
Assets: $780,220,610
Liabilities: $340,515,557
Net Worth: $439,705,054
Earnings: ($72,848,151)
Emp.: 6
Fiscal Year-end: 03/31/2023
Real Estate Manangement Services
N.A.I.C.S.: 531390
Narendra Gehlaut (Vice Chm)

Indiabulls Securities Limited (1)
Indiabulls House Indiabulls Finance Centre, Senapati Bapat Marg, Elphinstone Road, Mumbai, 400 013, India
Tel.: (91) 22 3044 5894
Web Site: http://www.indiabulls.com
Investment Services
N.A.I.C.S.: 523999
Divyesh Shah (CEO)

INDIAMART INTERMESH LIMITED
6th Floor Tower 2 Assotech Business Cresterra Plot No 22 Sector 135, Noida, 201305, Uttar Pradesh, India
Tel.: (91) 1206777777

Web Site:
 https://www.corporate.indiamart.com
Year Founded: 1999
542726—(BOM)
Rev.: $159,148,763
Assets: $470,191,995
Liabilities: $189,207,837
Net Worth: $280,984,158
Earnings: $38,742,386
Emp.: 4,583
Fiscal Year-end: 03/31/23
Online Shopping Operator
N.A.I.C.S.: 518210
Amarinder Singh Dhaliwal (Chief Product Officer)

Subsidiaries:

Tolexo Online Private Limited (1)
1st Floor 29-Daryagang Netaji Subash Marg, New Delhi, 110002, India
Tel.: (91) 1149995600
Ecommerce Services
N.A.I.C.S.: 423690

INDIAN ACRYLICS LIMITED.
SCO 49-50 Sector 26 Madhya Marg, Chandigarh, 160019, India
Tel.: (91) 1722793112
Web Site:
 https://www.indianacrylics.com
514165—(BOM)
Rev.: $72,850,118
Assets: $78,482,927
Liabilities: $58,214,738
Net Worth: $20,268,189
Earnings: $857,261
Emp.: 2,873
Fiscal Year-end: 03/31/21
Dry Spun Acrylic Fiber Mfr
N.A.I.C.S.: 325220
Rajinder Kumar Garg (Mng Dir)

Subsidiaries:

Indlon Chemicals Ltd (1)
SCO 49-50 Sector 26 Madhya Marg, Chandigarh, 160 019, India
Tel.: (91) 17 2279 3117
Web Site: http://www.indianacrylics.com
Sales Range: $200-249.9 Million
Emp.: 700
Acrylic Fiber Mfr
N.A.I.C.S.: 325220

INDIAN BANK
254-260 Avvai Shanmugam Salai, PB No 5555, Royapettah, Chennai, 600 014, India
Tel.: (91) 4428134300
Web Site: https://www.indianbank.in
Year Founded: 1907
532814—(BOM)
Rev.: $6,329,315,988
Assets: $85,526,527,187
Liabilities: $85,377,202,806
Net Worth: $149,324,381
Earnings: $796,604,520
Emp.: 41,699
Fiscal Year-end: 03/31/23
Commercial Banking & Off-shore Banking Services
N.A.I.C.S.: 522110
Nagarajan M (Gen Mgr-RBD / FI)

Subsidiaries:

Indbank Merchant Banking Services Ltd. (1)
1st Floor Khiviraj Complex I No 480 Anna Salai, Nandanam, Chennai, 600035, India (64.84%)
Tel.: (91) 4424313094
Web Site: https://www.indbankonline.com
Rev.: $2,657,871
Assets: $11,491,393
Liabilities: $2,717,036
Net Worth: $8,774,357
Earnings: $553,374
Emp.: 92
Fiscal Year-end: 03/31/2021

Merchant Banking, Securities Brokerage & Investment Advisory Services
N.A.I.C.S.: 523150
Sesha Sai (Pres)

INDIAN BRIGHT STEEL COMPANY LIMITED
Aurum Platz B N Cross Lane, Pandita Ramabai Marg, Mumbai, 400 007, Maharashtra, India
Tel.: (91) 2261919700
Web Site:
 http://www.indianbrightsteel.com
504731—(BOM)
Rev.: $1,918
Assets: $19,795
Liabilities: $10,623
Net Worth: $9,172
Earnings: ($10,863)
Emp.: 1
Fiscal Year-end: 03/31/23
Steel Products Mfr
N.A.I.C.S.: 331210
Manubhai Kalidas Parekh (Chm)

INDIAN ENERGY EXCHANGE LIMITED
First Floor Unit No 1 14a Avanta Business Centre, Southern Park D-2 District Centre Saket, New Delhi, 110017, India
Tel.: (91) 1143004000
Web Site: https://www.iexindia.com
Year Founded: 2007
540750—(BOM)
Rev.: $66,120,846
Assets: $231,530,263
Liabilities: $135,514,811
Net Worth: $96,015,451
Earnings: $42,128,787
Emp.: 159
Fiscal Year-end: 03/31/22
Electric Power Distribution Services
N.A.I.C.S.: 221122
Satyanarayan Goel (Co-CEO & Co-Mng Dir)

INDIAN EXTRACTION LTD.
247 Park Lal Bahadur Shastri Marg, Vikhroli West, Mumbai, 400083, Maharashtra, India
Tel.: (91) 7940026095
Web Site: https://www.ielindia.in
Year Founded: 1956
524614—(BOM)
Rev.: $1,325,377
Assets: $423,952
Liabilities: $308,045
Net Worth: $115,907
Earnings: $283,707
Emp.: 2
Fiscal Year-end: 03/31/23
Oil & Gas Mfr
N.A.I.C.S.: 333132
Shantilal Bhogilal Jhaveri (Chm)

INDIAN EXTRACTIONS LIMITED
Pandit Nehru Marg, Jamnagar, 361 002, India
Tel.: (91) 288 2757422
Web Site:
 http://www.nanavatigroup.com
Year Founded: 1956
Rev.: $227,043
Assets: $979,203
Liabilities: $609,973
Net Worth: $369,230
Earnings: ($10,658)
Emp.: 2
Fiscal Year-end: 03/31/18
Deoiled Cake Distr
N.A.I.C.S.: 424990
Priyam Shantilal Jhaveri (Chm)

INDIAN FARMERS FERTILISER

INDIAN FARMERS FERTILISER

INDIAN FARMERS FERTILISER —(CONTINUED)

COOPERATIVE LIMITED
IFFCO Sadan C-1 District Centre Saket Place, New Delhi, 110017, India
Tel.: (91) 11 4259 2626
Web Site: http://www.iffco.in
Year Founded: 1967
Sales Range: $1-4.9 Billion
Fertilizer Mfr & Sales Cooperatives; Insurance & Telecom Services
N.A.I.C.S.: 325311
Udai Shanker Awasthi *(CEO & Mng Dir)*

Subsidiaries:

IFFCO-Tokio General Insurance Co., Ltd. (1)
IFFCO Tower Plot No 3 Sector 29, Gurgaon, 122001, Haryana, India (74%)
Tel.: (91) 124 428 5499
Web Site: https://www.iffcotokio.co.in
Emp.: 4,238
Insurance Services
N.A.I.C.S.: 524210
K. Srinivasa Gowda *(Chm)*

INDIAN HUME PIPE COMPANY LTD.
Construction House 5 Walchand Hirachand Marg, Ballard Estate, Mumbai, 400 001, India
Tel.: (91) 2240748181
Web Site: https://www.indianhumepipe.com
INDIANHUME—(NSE)
Rev.: $208,175,604
Assets: $269,360,009
Liabilities: $180,605,402
Net Worth: $88,754,607
Earnings: $7,888,349
Emp.: 1,472
Fiscal Year-end: 03/31/22
Pipeline Installation & Mfr
N.A.I.C.S.: 327332
S. M. Mandke *(Compliance Officer & Sec)*

INDIAN INFOTECH & SOFTWARE LIMITED
Office No 1101st floorGolden Chambers Pre Co-op Soc LtdNew Link Road, Andheri West, Mumbai, 400053, India
Tel.: (91) 49601435
Web Site: https://www.indianinfotechltd.com
Year Founded: 1982
509051—(BOM)
Rev.: $5,620,874
Assets: $31,371,536
Liabilities: $124,680
Net Worth: $31,246,856
Earnings: ($1,550,273)
Emp.: 10
Fiscal Year-end: 03/31/21
Software Development Services
N.A.I.C.S.: 541511
Kamal Nayan Sharma *(Mng Dir)*

INDIAN METALS & FERRO ALLOYS LIMITED
IMFA Building, Bhubaneswar, 751 010, Odisha, India
Tel.: (91) 6742580100
Web Site: http://www.imfa.in
Year Founded: 1961
IMFA—(NSE)
Rev.: $258,532,365
Assets: $346,897,005
Liabilities: $173,228,055
Net Worth: $173,668,950
Earnings: $22,792,770
Emp.: 2,165
Fiscal Year-end: 03/31/21
Ferro Alloy Mfr
N.A.I.C.S.: 331110

Subhrakant Panda *(CEO & Mng Dir)*

INDIAN OIL CORPORATION LIMITED
3079/3 Sadiq Nagar J B Tito Marg, New Delhi, 110 049, India
Tel.: (91) 18002333555
Web Site: https://www.iocl.com
Year Founded: 1959
530965—(BOM)
Rev.: $100,984,482,690
Assets: $56,050,292,025
Liabilities: $37,605,504,300
Net Worth: $18,444,787,725
Earnings: $3,511,680,900
Emp.: 31,254
Fiscal Year-end: 03/31/22
Refined Petroleum Mfr & Distr
N.A.I.C.S.: 324110
Sanjiv Singh *(Chm)*

Subsidiaries:

Chennai Petroleum Corporation Limited (1)
New No 536 Anna Salai Teynampet, Chennai, 600 018, India (100%)
Tel.: (91) 4424349833
Web Site: https://cpcl.co.in
Sales Range: $450-499.9 Million
Emp.: 2,000
Petroleum Refining
N.A.I.C.S.: 324110
Sanjiv Singh *(Chm)*

Indian Oil Corporation Limited - Guwahati Refinery Division (1)
Noonmati, Guwahati, 781020, Assam, India
Tel.: (91) 3612597017
Sales Range: $25-49.9 Million
Emp.: 60
Petroleum Refining Services
N.A.I.C.S.: 324110

Indian Oil Corporation Limited - IBP Division (1)
09th Floor BD Eastern Zone IBP House 34A Nirmal Chandra Street, Kolkata, 700013, West Bengal, India
Tel.: (91) 3322150049
Web Site: http://www.indianoil.in
Sales Range: $25-49.9 Million
Emp.: 25
Petroleum Refining Services
N.A.I.C.S.: 324110
Indrajit Bose *(Exec Dir-Retail Sls)*

IndianOil (Mauritius) Limited (1)
Mer Rouge, Port Louis, Mauritius (100%)
Tel.: (230) 2172710
Web Site: https://ioml.mu
Sales Range: $10-24.9 Million
Emp.: 30
Bulk Storage Terminal
N.A.I.C.S.: 493190

IndianOil Middle East FZE (1)
Lobby 12114, PO Box 261338, Jebel Ali Free Zone, Dubai, United Arab Emirates
Tel.: (971) 48871397
Sales Range: $50-74.9 Million
Emp.: 10
Petroleum Products Marketing
N.A.I.C.S.: 424720

Lanka IOC PLC (1)
Level 20 West Tower World Trade Center Echelon Square, 01, Colombo, Sri Lanka (100%)
Tel.: (94) 112475720
Petroleum Products Marketing
N.A.I.C.S.: 424720
Ranjan Kumar Mohapatra *(Chm)*

INDIAN OVERSEAS BANK
762/763 IOB Anna Salai, Chennai, 600 002, India
Tel.: (91) 4428889352
Web Site: https://www.iob.in
Year Founded: 1937
IOB—(NSE)
Rev.: $3,210,946,612
Assets: $42,785,911,896
Liabilities: $39,390,332,491
Net Worth: $3,395,579,405

Earnings: ($2,171,203,207)
Emp.: 22,052
Fiscal Year-end: 03/31/23
Banking Services
N.A.I.C.S.: 522110
Ajay Kumar Srivastava *(Exec Dir)*

Subsidiaries:

Indian Overseas Bank (1)
IOB Building 64 Cecil Street, Singapore, 049711, Singapore
Tel.: (65) 63724402
Web Site: https://www.iob.in
Sales Range: $50-74.9 Million
Emp.: 59
Banking Services
N.A.I.C.S.: 522110

INDIAN RAILWAY CATERING & TOURISM CORPORATION LIMITED
B-148 11th Floor Statesman House Barakhamba Road, New Delhi, 110001, India
Tel.: (91) 7556610661
Web Site: http://www.irctc.co.in
542830—(BOM)
Rev.: $439,050,824
Assets: $610,126,347
Liabilities: $312,973,407
Net Worth: $297,152,940
Earnings: $120,602,014
Emp.: 1,356
Fiscal Year-end: 03/31/23
Travel Arrangement & Reservation Services
N.A.I.C.S.: 561599
Ajit Kumar *(Exec Dir)*

INDIAN RAILWAY CATERING & TOURISM CORPORATION LTD.
B-148 11th Floor Statesman House Barakhamba Road, New Delhi, 110001, India
Tel.: (91) 1123327746
Web Site: https://www.irctc.co.in
Year Founded: 1999
IRCTC—(NSE)
Rev.: $439,050,824
Assets: $610,126,347
Liabilities: $312,973,407
Net Worth: $297,152,940
Earnings: $120,602,014
Emp.: 1,356
Fiscal Year-end: 03/31/23
Railway Services
N.A.I.C.S.: 482111
Suman Kalra *(Sec & Compliance Officer)*

INDIAN RAILWAY FINANCE CORPORATION LTD.
UG Floor East Tower NBCC Place Bhisham Pitamah Marg Lodhi Rd, Pragati Vihar, New Delhi, 110003, India
Tel.: (91) 1124361480
Web Site: https://irfc.co.in
IRFC—(NSE)
Rev.: $2,869,447,635
Assets: $53,951,228,823
Liabilities: $49,035,895,210
Net Worth: $4,915,333,613
Earnings: $759,788,142
Emp.: 41
Fiscal Year-end: 03/31/23
Financial Investment Services
N.A.I.C.S.: 523999
A. Samantaray *(Gen Mgr-Fin)*

INDIAN RESTAURANTS GROUP PLC
Suite 201 Temple Chambers 3-7 Temple Avenue, London, EC4Y 0DT, United Kingdom
Tel.: (44) 2076592247

INTERNATIONAL PUBLIC

Web Site: http://www.indianrestaurants.com
Sales Range: $1-9.9 Million
Emp.: 77
Restaurant Owner & Operator
N.A.I.C.S.: 722511

Subsidiaries:

Chandan Ltd. (1)
156 Shaftesbury Ave, London, WC2H 8HL, United Kingdom
Tel.: (44) 2078368635
Restaurants Operating & Management Services
N.A.I.C.S.: 722511

INDIAN SUCROSE LIMITED
G T Road, Hoshiarpur, Mukerian, 144 211, Punjab, India
Tel.: (91) 9115110651
Web Site: https://www.muksug.in
500319—(BOM)
Rev.: $61,435,661
Assets: $68,893,065
Liabilities: $48,181,920
Net Worth: $20,711,145
Earnings: $5,087,901
Emp.: 337
Fiscal Year-end: 03/31/22
Sugar Mfr
N.A.I.C.S.: 311314
Kunal Yadav *(Chm & Mng Dir)*

INDIAN TERRAIN FASHIONS LIMITED
No 208 Velachery Tambaram Road Narayanapuram Pallikaranai, Chennai, 600100, India
Tel.: (91) 4442279100
Web Site: https://www.indianterrain.com
Year Founded: 2009
533329—(BOM)
Rev.: $60,704,994
Assets: $65,494,874
Liabilities: $40,131,887
Net Worth: $25,362,988
Earnings: $850,069
Emp.: 302
Fiscal Year-end: 03/31/23
Jean Apparel Mfr
N.A.I.C.S.: 315250
Vidyuth Venkatesh Rajagopal *(Co-Mng Dir)*

INDIAN TONERS & DEVELOPERS LTD.
1223 DLF Tower B Jasola, New Delhi, 110 025, India
Tel.: (91) 1145017000
Web Site: https://www.indiantoners.com
523586—(BOM)
Rev.: $21,705,411
Assets: $28,829,305
Liabilities: $3,131,911
Net Worth: $25,697,394
Earnings: $3,591,902
Emp.: 227
Fiscal Year-end: 03/31/23
Printer Toner Mfr
N.A.I.C.S.: 333248
Sushil Jain *(Chm, CEO & Mng Dir)*

Subsidiaries:

ITDL Imagetec Limited (1)
D-11 Phase-II Eldeco-Sidcul Industrial Park, Udham Singh Nagar, Sitarganj, 262405, Uttarakhand, India
Tel.: (91) 9758345100
Copier Whslr
N.A.I.C.S.: 423420

Inter Imaging Pte. Ltd. (1)
17 Kim Keat Road 10-01 Regal Court, Singapore, 328837, Singapore
Tel.: (65) 62999691

AND PRIVATE COMPANIES

Sales Range: $50-74.9 Million
Emp.: 3
Copier Whslr
N.A.I.C.S.: 423420

INDIANA RESOURCES LIMITED
Suite 3 339 Cambridge Street, Wembley, 6014, WA, Australia
Tel.: (61) 862411870
Web Site:
https://indianaresources.com.au
IDA—(ASX)
Rev.: $146,234
Assets: $5,455,395
Liabilities: $615,652
Net Worth: $4,839,744
Earnings: ($2,787,126)
Emp.: 20
Fiscal Year-end: 06/30/24
Gold Mining Services
N.A.I.C.S.: 212220
Heavenlight Kavishe *(Mgr)*

Subsidiaries:

IMX UK Limited (1)
Typhoon Business Centre Oakcroft Road, Surrey, Chessington, United Kingdom
Tel.: (44) 2037932572
Web Site: https://www.imx.co.uk
International Postal Services
N.A.I.C.S.: 541860

Marvel Gold Limited (1)
Level 1 Emerald House 1202 Hay Street, West Perth, 6005, WA, Australia
Tel.: (61) 892004960
Web Site: https://marvelgold.com.au
Graphite Exploration Services
N.A.I.C.S.: 213115
Chris Knee *(CFO)*

INDIANIVESH LTD.
1703 17th Floor Lodha Supremus Senapati Bapat Marg Lower Parel, Mumbai, 400013, India
Tel.: (91) 2262406240
Web Site: https://www.indianivesh.in
501700—(BOM)
Rev.: $1,206,771
Assets: $12,501,268
Liabilities: $17,111,919
Net Worth: ($4,610,651)
Earnings: ($531,135)
Emp.: 2
Fiscal Year-end: 03/31/22
Investment Banking & Consulting Businesses Services
N.A.I.C.S.: 523150
Rajesh Nuwal *(Mng Dir & CFO)*

Subsidiaries:

IndiaNivesh Securities Pvt. Ltd. (1)
601 & 602 Sukh Sagar N S Patkar Marg, Grigaum Chowpatty, Mumbai, 400007, Maharastra, India
Tel.: (91) 2266188800
Web Site: http://www.indianivesh.in
Sales Range: $50-74.9 Million
Financial Services
N.A.I.C.S.: 523940
Dinesh Nuwal *(CEO)*

INDICO RESOURCES LIMITED
507- 837 West Hastings Street, Vancouver, V6C 3N6, BC, Canada
Tel.: (604) 691-7462   BM
Web Site:
http://www.indicoresources.com
Year Founded: 2002
Assets: $5,009
Liabilities: $4,334,398
Net Worth: ($4,329,389)
Earnings: ($382,383)
Emp.: 2
Fiscal Year-end: 05/31/18
Mineral Exploration & Development Services
N.A.I.C.S.: 212220

Scott M. Ross *(CFO)*

INDIES PHARMA JAMAICA LTD.
Unit-5 Montego Bay Trade Centre Howard Cooke Blvd, Montego Bay, Jamaica
Tel.: (876) 8765780281
Web Site:
https://www.indiespharma.com
Year Founded: 2003
INDIES—(JAM)
Rev.: $6,847,373
Assets: $12,240,055
Liabilities: $6,619,199
Net Worth: $5,620,856
Earnings: $1,387,935
Emp.: 71
Fiscal Year-end: 10/31/23
Pharmaceutical Products Distr
N.A.I.C.S.: 424210
Guna S. Muppuri *(Founder, Pres & CEO)*

INDIFRA LIMITED
9 Krishna Villa Nr Aamrakunj Society Karamsad V V Nagar Road, Anand, 388325, Gujarat, India
Tel.: (91) 8888845001
Web Site: https://www.indifra.com
Year Founded: 2009
INDIFRA—(NSE)
Rev.: $1,324,001
Assets: $525,463
Liabilities: $439,871
Net Worth: $85,591
Earnings: $48,407
Emp.: 11
Fiscal Year-end: 03/31/22
Natural Gas Distribution Services
N.A.I.C.S.: 221210

INDIGO CAPITAL LLP
33 St James Square, London, SW1Y 4JS, United Kingdom
Tel.: (44) 20 7397 1530   UK
Web Site: http://www.indigo-capital.com
Privater Equity Firm
N.A.I.C.S.: 523999
Richard Collins *(Co-Founder & Mng Partner)*

Subsidiaries:

Indigo Capital France SAS (1)
69 rue la Boetie, 75008, Paris, France
Tel.: (33) 1 56 88 17 50
Web Site: http://www.indigo-capital.fr
Emp.: 8
Privater Equity Firm
N.A.I.C.S.: 523999
Monique Deloire *(Mng Partner)*

Joint Venture (Domestic):

Ubiqus SAS (2)
1 avenue du General de Gaulle, 92074, Paris, Cedex, La Defense, France
Tel.: (33) 1 44 14 15 16
Web Site: http://www.ubiqus.fr
Language Translation Services
N.A.I.C.S.: 541930
Joanne Bove *(CEO)*

Subsidiary (US):

The Language Works, Inc. (3)
1123 Broadway Ste 201, New York, NY 10010
Tel.: (212) 447-6060
Web Site: http://www.languageworks.com
Translation & Interpretation Services
N.A.I.C.S.: 541930
Kevin Rees *(Pres)*

Ubiqus Reporting, Inc. (3)
22 Cortlandt St Ste 802, New York, NY 10007
Tel.: (212) 346-6666
Web Site: http://www.ubiqus.com

Court Reporting & Stenotype Services; Language Translation Services
N.A.I.C.S.: 561492
Joanne Bove *(CEO)*

Subsidiary (Non-US):

Ubiqus UK Limited (3)
61 Southwark Street, London, SE1 0HL, United Kingdom
Tel.: (44) 207 269 0370
Language Translation Services
N.A.I.C.S.: 541930

INDIGO EXPLORATION INC.
1100-1199 W Hastings Street, Vancouver, V6E 3T5, BC, Canada
Tel.: (604) 340-7711   BC
Web Site:
https://www.indigoexploration.com
Year Founded: 2008
INEN—(DEU)
Assets: $741,717
Liabilities: $152,532
Net Worth: $589,185
Earnings: ($886,082)
Emp.: 4
Fiscal Year-end: 09/30/23
Metal Mining Services
N.A.I.C.S.: 212290
Paul S. Cowley *(Pres & CEO)*

INDIGO GROUP S.A.S.
Tour Voltaire 1 place des Degres, La Defense, 92800, Puteaux, France
Tel.: (33) 149031500   FR
Web Site: http://www.group-indigo.com
Rev.: $777,966,742
Assets: $4,163,863,452
Liabilities: $3,530,582,622
Net Worth: $633,280,830
Earnings: $4,367,454
Emp.: 8,497
Fiscal Year-end: 12/31/19
Holding Company; Parking Facilities Operator
N.A.I.C.S.: 551112
Serge Clemente *(Chm-Exec Bd & Pres)*

Subsidiaries:

Aparcamientos Triana SA (1)
C/Rafael Cabrera n 7 de Gran Canaria, 35002, Las Palmas, Spain
Tel.: (34) 928372135
Web Site: http://www.parkingtriana.com
Parking Solution Services
N.A.I.C.S.: 812930

Cagnes Sur Mer Stationnement SA (1)
Place de l'Hotel de Ville, 06800, Cagnes-sur-Mer, France
Tel.: (33) 493221900
Web Site: http://www.cagnes-sur-mer.fr
Garage & Parking Lot Services
N.A.I.C.S.: 812930

Indigo Infra Belgium N.V. (1)
Bijenstraat 21, Sint-Denijs-Westrem, 9051, Gent, Belgium
Tel.: (32) 440502536
Web Site: http://www.vincipark.be
Motor Vehicle Parking Management Solutions
N.A.I.C.S.: 812930

Indigo Infra CGST S.A. (1)
61 avenue Jules Quentin, 92000, Nanterre, France
Tel.: (33) 1 41 91 45 00
Motor Vehicle Parking Management Solutions
N.A.I.C.S.: 812930

Indigo Infra Espana S.A. (1)
CL Orense n 68, 28020, Madrid, Spain
Tel.: (34) 902230270
Web Site: http://www.vincipark.es
Motor Vehicle Parking Management Solutions
N.A.I.C.S.: 812930

Indigo Infra Neuilly SAS (1)
Face au 94 Avenue du Roule, 92200, Neuilly-sur-Seine, France
Tel.: (33) 147476387
Garage & Parking Lot Services
N.A.I.C.S.: 812930

Indigo Infra Noisy-le-grand SA (1)
12 Bis Avenue Emile Cossonneau, 93160, Noisy-le-Grand, France
Tel.: (33) 143046638
Garage & Parking Lot Services
N.A.I.C.S.: 812930

Indigo Infra Russie (1)
Moscow Area Khimki Sheremetyevo Airport Terminal C, 141 400, Moscow, Russia
Tel.: (7) 495 229 3470
Web Site: http://www.parkindigo.com
Motor Vehicle Parking Management Solutions
N.A.I.C.S.: 812930
Alexander Petroz *(Mgr)*

Indigo Park Canada Inc. (1)
1 place Ville-Marie Bureau 2131, Montreal, H3B 2C6, QC, Canada
Tel.: (514) 874-1208
Web Site: http://www.vincipark.ca
Emp.: 1,500
Motor Vehicle Parking Management Solutions
N.A.I.C.S.: 812930
Louis Jacob *(Exec VP)*

Indigo Park Luxembourg S.A. (1)
83 Rue de Strasbourg, 2561, Luxembourg, Luxembourg
Tel.: (352) 48 13 36
Web Site: http://lu.parkindigo.com
Sales Range: $25-49.9 Million
Motor Vehicle Parking Management Solutions
N.A.I.C.S.: 812930

Indigo Park S.A. (1)
Ile de France Building - Building A 4 place de la Pyramide, La Defense, 92800, Puteaux, France
Tel.: (33) 1 49 03 15 00
Web Site: http://www.parkindigo.com
Sales Range: $800-899.9 Million
Emp.: 14,000
Motor Vehicle Parking Management Solutions
N.A.I.C.S.: 812930
Benjamin Voron *(Dir-Comm)*

Marseille Etienne D'orves Stationnement SA (1)
Rue de la Republique, 13002, Marseille, France
Tel.: (33) 491313935
Garage & Parking Lot Services
N.A.I.C.S.: 812930

Northern Valet Inc. (1)
69 Yonge St Suite 300, Toronto, M5E 1K3, ON, Canada
Tel.: (416) 615-2493
Web Site: https://www.northernvalet.com
Parking Lot Management Services
N.A.I.C.S.: 812930
Matthew Hiez *(Area Mgr)*

Parking 4040 (1)
Rue Elisa Dumonceau 26, 4040, Herstal, Belgium (97%)
Tel.: (32) 25408200
Parking Lot Management Services
N.A.I.C.S.: 812930

Parking Gare De Lausanne SA (1)
Rue du Simplon 32, 1006, Lausanne, Switzerland
Tel.: (41) 216176744
Garage & Parking Lot Services
N.A.I.C.S.: 812930

Parking Partners NV (1)
Dienstweg Havengeul 12a, 8620, Nieuwpoort, Belgium
Tel.: (32) 58240479
Web Site: http://www.parkingpartners.be
Garage & Parking Lot Services
N.A.I.C.S.: 812930

Saint-maur Stationnement SAS (1)
Place Charles de Gaulle, 94100, Saint-Maur, France
Tel.: (33) 145116565

INDIGO GROUP S.A.S.

Indigo Group S.A.S.—(Continued)
Web Site: http://www.saint-maur.com
Garage & Parking Lot Services
N.A.I.C.S.: 812930

INDIGO PAINTS LIMITED
Street 5 Pallod Farms Ii, Baner,
Pune, 411045, India
Tel.: (91) 2066814300
Web Site:
  https://www.indigopaints.com
Year Founded: 2000
543258—(BOM)
Rev.: $125,152,482
Assets: $125,564,371
Liabilities: $36,858,699
Net Worth: $88,705,672
Earnings: $11,472,552
Emp.: 708
Fiscal Year-end: 03/31/22
Paints Mfr
N.A.I.C.S.: 325510
Sujoy Bose *(Sec)*

INDIGO PROPERTIES AUSTRALIA LIMITED
Level 3 18 Richardson Street, West
Perth, 6005, WA, Australia
Tel.: (61) 300 792 995   AU
Sales Range: $1-9.9 Million
Investment Management Service
N.A.I.C.S.: 523940
Stephen Mackay *(Mng Dir)*

INDIGO STAR HOLDINGS LIMITED
5 Upper Aljunied Link 03-08 Quartz
Industrial Building, Singapore,
367903, Singapore
Tel.: (65) 62876998   Ky
Web Site: https://indigostar.sg
Year Founded: 1996
8373—(HKG)
Rev.: $33,566,614
Assets: $25,697,947
Liabilities: $14,800,424
Net Worth: $10,897,523
Earnings: $756,646
Emp.: 880
Fiscal Year-end: 12/31/23
Steel Reinforcing Services
N.A.I.C.S.: 238120
Cheng Seng Goh *(Founder, Chm & CEO)*

Subsidiaries:

Interno Engineering (1996) Pte.
Ltd.   (1)
5 Upper Aljunied Link 03-08 Quartz Industrial Building, Singapore, 367903, Singapore
Tel.: (65) 62876998
Civil Engineering Services
N.A.I.C.S.: 541330

INDINFRAVIT TRUST
5th Floor SKCL - Tech Square Lazer
St South Phase, SIDCO Industrial
Estate Guindy, Chennai, 600 032,
Tamil Nadu, India
Tel.: (91) 4443986000
Web Site: http://www.indinfravit.com
541300—(BOM)
Rev.: $222,013,114
Assets: $2,168,380,087
Liabilities: $1,398,440,098
Net Worth: $769,939,989
Earnings: ($64,171,380)
Fiscal Year-end: 03/31/21
Investment Management Service
N.A.I.C.S.: 525990
Ganesh Ramachandran *(Officer-Compliance)*

INDITRADE CAPITAL LIMITED
Second Floor M E S Building Kaloor,
Ernakulam, Kochi, 682 017, Kerala,
India
Tel.: (91) 4846714800   In
Web Site: https://www.inditrade.com
Year Founded: 1994
532745—(BOM)
Rev.: $27,430,235
Assets: $89,545,065
Liabilities: $60,278,905
Net Worth: $29,266,160
Earnings: $522,358
Emp.: 1
Fiscal Year-end: 03/31/22
Financial Holding Company; Securities & Commodities Brokerage & Trading Services
N.A.I.C.S.: 551112
Naveen Kumar Jain *(CFO)*

Subsidiaries:

Inditrade Derivatives & Commodities Limited   (1)
Towter II Rambhavan Complex, Kodialbail, Mangalore, 575001, Karnataka, India
Tel.: (91) 8242449502
Sales Range: $50-74.9 Million
Emp.: 7
Derivatives & Commodities Broker & Dealer
N.A.I.C.S.: 523160
K. J. Samson *(Mng Dir)*

JRG Fincorp Limited   (1)
JRG House Ashoka Rd, Kaloor, Kochi, 682 017, Kerala, India
Tel.: (91) 4842796297
Web Site: http://www.jrgfincorp.com
Financial Services
N.A.I.C.S.: 522320

INDIVER S.A.
Teatinos 280 Piso 15, PO Box 983,
Santiago, Chile
Tel.: (56) 2232025010
Web Site: http://www.indiver.cl
Investment Management Service
N.A.I.C.S.: 523940
Julio Guzman Herrera *(CEO)*

INDIVIDUAL RESTAURANT CO. LTD.
Ridgefield House 4th Floor 14 John
Dalton Street, Manchester, M2 6JR,
United Kingdom
Tel.: (44) 1618395511
Web Site:
  http://individualrestaurants.com
Year Founded: 2000
Restaurant Operators
N.A.I.C.S.: 722511

INDIVIOR PLC
234 Bath Road, Slough, SL1 4EE,
Berkshire, United Kingdom
Tel.: (44) 1753427900   UK
Web Site: https://www.indivior.com
Year Founded: 2014
INDV—(NASDAQ)
Rev.: $901,000,000
Assets: $1,769,000,000
Liabilities: $1,718,000,000
Net Worth: $51,000,000
Earnings: ($53,000,000)
Emp.: 953
Fiscal Year-end: 12/31/22
Pharmaceuticals Mfr
N.A.I.C.S.: 325412
Graham Hetherington *(Chm)*

Subsidiaries:

Opiant Pharmaceuticals, Inc.   (1)
233 Wilshire Blvd Ste 280, Santa Monica, CA 90401
Tel.: (310) 598-5410
Web Site: http://www.opiant.com
Rev.: $47,785,478
Assets: $70,427,798
Liabilities: $23,587,990
Net Worth: $46,839,808
Earnings: $3,008,790
Emp.: 30
Fiscal Year-end: 12/31/2021
Pharmaceutical Researcher, Developer & Mfr
N.A.I.C.S.: 325412

INDO AMINES LTD
Plot No-W-44 Phase-II MIDC Dombivli East, Thane, 421203, Maharashtra, India
Tel.: (91) 2512871354
Web Site:
  https://www.indoaminesltd.com
524648—(BOM)
Rev.: $74,882,426
Assets: $61,853,706
Liabilities: $39,678,953
Net Worth: $22,174,753
Earnings: $5,124,633
Emp.: 458
Fiscal Year-end: 03/31/21
Mfr of Chemicals
N.A.I.C.S.: 325199
Bharati Vijay Palkar *(Exec Dir)*

INDO BORAX & CHEMICALS LTD.
302 Link Rose Linking Road, Santacruz West, Mumbai, 400 054, India
Tel.: (91) 2226489142
Web Site: https://www.indoborax.com
INDOBORAX—(NSE)
Rev.: $27,846,664
Assets: $33,008,273
Liabilities: $2,428,344
Net Worth: $30,579,929
Earnings: $6,078,053
Emp.: 98
Fiscal Year-end: 03/31/23
Specialty Chemicals Mfr
N.A.I.C.S.: 325998
Sajal Jain *(Mng Dir & CFO)*

INDO COTSPIN LIMITED
Delhi Mile Stone 78 K M G T Road N
H-1 Village Jhattipur, Po Box 3, Post
Office Samalkha, Panipat, 132 103,
Haryana, India
Tel.: (91) 1804001287
Web Site:
  https://www.indocotspin.com
Year Founded: 1955
538838—(BOM)
Rev.: $1,889,869
Assets: $1,304,298
Liabilities: $412,880
Net Worth: $891,418
Earnings: $18,908
Emp.: 12
Fiscal Year-end: 03/31/22
Textile Product Mfr & Distr
N.A.I.C.S.: 314110
Bal Kishan Aggarwal *(Chm & Mng Dir)*

INDO COUNT INDUSTRIES LTD.
301 Arcadia 3rd Floor Nariman Point,
Mumbai, 400021, Maharashtra, India
Tel.: (91) 2243419500
Web Site: https://www.indocount.com
521016—(BOM)
Rev.: $415,366,770
Assets: $417,650,415
Liabilities: $172,946,865
Net Worth: $244,703,550
Earnings: $37,780,470
Emp.: 3,000
Fiscal Year-end: 03/31/23
Yarn Mfr
N.A.I.C.S.: 339999
Kamal Mitra *(Dir-Works)*

Subsidiaries:

Indo Count Global Inc.   (1)
295 Fifth Ave Ste 621, New York, NY 10016
Tel.: (646) 416-7000
Clothes Mfr

INTERNATIONAL PUBLIC

N.A.I.C.S.: 315250

Indo Count UK Limited   (1)
Ground Floor of Unit 2 The Stables Wilmslow Road, Didsbury, Manchester, M20 5PG, United Kingdom
Tel.: (91) 1617110670
Clothes Mfr
N.A.I.C.S.: 315250

Pranavaditya Spinning Mills Limited   (1)
Office No 2 Plot No 266 Village Alte Kumbhoj Road Taluka Hatkanangale, Kolhapur, 416109, Maharashtra, India
Tel.: (91) 230 246 3100
Web Site: http://www.pranavaditya.com
Rev.: $541,004
Assets: $4,826,394
Liabilities: $1,453,957
Net Worth: $3,372,437
Earnings: $98,608
Emp.: 27
Fiscal Year-end: 03/31/2022
Textile Product Mfr & Whslr
N.A.I.C.S.: 313110
Amruta Avasare *(Officer-Compliance & Sec)*

INDO CREDIT CAPITAL LIMITED
304 Kaling B/h Bata Show Room Nr
Mt Carmel School Ashram Road,
Ahmedabad, 380009, Gujarat, India
Tel.: (91) 7926580366
Web Site:
  https://www.indocreditcapital.com
Year Founded: 1993
526887—(BOM)
Rev.: $6,300
Assets: $845,891
Liabilities: $4,743
Net Worth: $841,148
Earnings: ($13,362)
Emp.: 3
Fiscal Year-end: 03/31/21
Investment Management Service
N.A.I.C.S.: 523999
Ramkaran Mangachand Saini *(Exec Dir)*

INDO EURO INDCHEM LIMITED
78/C The Dawn Building 1st Floor 7th
Golibar Road, Santacruz East, Mumbai, 400 055, India
Tel.: (91) 2226135626
Web Site:
  https://www.indoeuroindchem.com
Year Founded: 1990
524458—(BOM)
Rev.: $1,097,728
Assets: $2,328,449
Liabilities: $1,007,657
Net Worth: $1,320,791
Earnings: $9,173
Emp.: 1
Fiscal Year-end: 03/31/21
Specialty Chemical Mfr & Distr
N.A.I.C.S.: 325180
Vardhman Chhaganlal Shah *(Chm, Mng Dir & Compliance Officer)*

INDO GLOBAL EXCHANGES PTE LTD
Menara Standard Chartered Jl Prof
Dr Satrio, 30th Floor, Jakarta,
KAV146, Indonesia
Tel.: (62) 2125555600   NV
Web Site: http://www.igex.com
Year Founded: 2008
IGEX—(OTCIQ)
Assets: $1,087,000
Liabilities: $541,000
Net Worth: $546,000
Earnings: ($707,000)
Emp.: 1
Fiscal Year-end: 07/31/23
Online Global Trading Platform
N.A.I.C.S.: 516210
Jason Black *(Pres & CEO)*

AND PRIVATE COMPANIES

INDORAMA CORPORATION PTE. LTD.

INDO GULF INDUSTRIES LTD.
4237/11 Narendra Bhawan 1 2nd Floor Ansari Road, Daryaganj, Delhi, 110002, India
Tel.: (91) 1126533689
506945—(BOM)
Rev.: $9,823,373
Assets: $2,913,714
Liabilities: $3,571,568
Net Worth: ($657,854)
Earnings: $58,106
Emp.: 4
Fiscal Year-end: 03/31/21
Explosives Mfr
N.A.I.C.S.: 325920
Rajesh Jain *(Mng Dir)*

INDO INTERNACIONAL S.A.
Alcalde Barnils 72, 08174, Sant Cugat del Valles, Spain
Tel.: (34) 93 298 26 00   ES
Web Site: http://www.indo.es
Year Founded: 1937
Ophthalmic Equipment & Lenses Mfr
N.A.I.C.S.: 339115
Jose Ignacio Gonzalez Freixa *(Chm)*

Subsidiaries:

Indo Maroc, S.A   (1)
Z I Allee1 lot 5 Z I Route de Tetouan, Tangiers, Morocco
Tel.: (212) 39350042
Optical Product Mfr
N.A.I.C.S.: 339115

Indo Optical S.L.   (1)
Alcalde Barnils 72, Sant Cugat del Valles, Barcelona, Spain
Tel.: (34) 932982600
Optical Product Mfr
N.A.I.C.S.: 339115

Sedosa Portugal, S.A.   (1)
Av D Antonio Correia de Sa 82 B/C0, 2709-503, Sintra, Portugal
Tel.: (351) 219609030
Optical Product Mfr
N.A.I.C.S.: 339115

INDO PACIFIC PROJECTS LTD.
1st Floor B Poonam Chambers Byramji Town, Chhindwara Road, Nagpur, 440013, India
Tel.: (91) 0712 6611216   In
Year Founded: 1982
Rev.: $537,863
Assets: $19,179,256
Liabilities: $14,196,073
Net Worth: $4,983,183
Earnings: ($112,670)
Fiscal Year-end: 03/31/18
Software Development Services
N.A.I.C.S.: 541511
Nandkumar Khattumal Harchandani *(Chm & Mng Dir)*

INDO RAMA SYNTHETICS (INDIA) LTD.
Plot No 53 & 54 Phase-IV, Gurgaon, 122015, Haryana, India
Tel.: (91) 1244997000
Web Site: https://www.indoramaindia.com
Year Founded: 1986
INDORAMA—(NSE)
Rev.: $552,061,965
Assets: $287,395,290
Liabilities: $205,466,625
Net Worth: $81,928,665
Earnings: $36,726,690
Emp.: 1,462
Fiscal Year-end: 03/31/22
Polyester Mfr
N.A.I.C.S.: 325220
Om Prakash Lohia *(Chm & Mng Dir)*

Subsidiaries:

Indorama Yarns Private Limited   (1)

A 31 MIDC Industrial Area, Butibori, Nagpur, 441122, Maharashtra, India
Tel.: (91) 7104663000
Polyester Product Mfr
N.A.I.C.S.: 325220

INDO THAI SECURITIES LTD
Capital Tower 2nd Floor Plot Nos 169A-171 PU 4 Scheme No-54, Indore, 452 010, Madhya Pradesh, India
Tel.: (91) 7314255800
Web Site: https://www.indothai.co.in
Year Founded: 1995
533676—(BOM)
Rev.: $3,146,926
Assets: $10,730,292
Liabilities: $3,177,597
Net Worth: $7,552,695
Earnings: $1,387,290
Emp.: 49
Fiscal Year-end: 03/31/21
Investment Banking & Securities Dealing
N.A.I.C.S.: 523150
Parasmal Doshi *(Chm & Co-CFO)*

Subsidiaries:

Femto Green Hydrogen Limited   (1)
1105A B Wing Kanakia Wall Street M V Road Chakala Andheri East, Mumbai, 400093, India
Tel.: (91) 8169306358
Web Site:
    https://www.femtogreenhydrogen.com
Green Energy Services
N.A.I.C.S.: 541350

INDO US BIO-TECH LTD.
309 Shanti Mall Satadhar Cross Road Sola Road, Ahmedabad, 380 061, Gujarat, India
Tel.: (91) 7927491807
Web Site:
    https://www.indousagriseeds.com
Year Founded: 2004
541304—(BOM)
Rev.: $6,857,945
Assets: $7,591,639
Liabilities: $2,335,348
Net Worth: $5,256,291
Earnings: $691,134
Emp.: 883
Fiscal Year-end: 03/31/22
Chemical Research & Development Services
N.A.I.C.S.: 541715
Jagdish Ajudiya *(Chm)*

INDO-BANGLA PHARMACEUTICALS LTD.
Plot 183 7th floor Road 04 Block B Ahmed Akbar Sobhan Road, Bashundhara R/A Baridhara, Dhaka, 1229, Bangladesh
Tel.: (880) 9678777995
Web Site: https://www.indo-banglapharma.com
Year Founded: 1954
IBP—(CHT)
Rev.: $3,415,877
Assets: $17,110,006
Liabilities: $2,316,407
Net Worth: $14,793,598
Earnings: $76,686
Fiscal Year-end: 06/30/23
Pharmaceuticals Product Mfr
N.A.I.C.S.: 325412

INDO-CITY INFOTECH LTD.
A6 Mittal Estate Bldg N0 2 Andheri - Kurla Road Andheri E, Mumbai, 400059, India
Tel.: (91) 2228505903
Web Site: https://www.indocity.co
532100—(BOM)
Rev.: $2,470,254
Assets: $1,699,835

Liabilities: $26,972
Net Worth: $1,672,862
Earnings: ($16,790)
Fiscal Year-end: 03/31/23
Software Development Services
N.A.I.C.S.: 541511
Aneel Jain *(Chm & Mng Dir)*

INDO-GLOBAL ENTERPRISES LIMITED
Block D904 Richmond Grand NrTorrent Power SS 100 Ft Rd, Makarba, Ahmedabad, 380051, Gujarat, India
Tel.: (91) 7926586152
Web Site: http://www.indoglobalinc.in
539433—(BOM)
Assets: $1,091,396
Liabilities: $126,498
Net Worth: $964,897
Earnings: ($56,985)
Fiscal Year-end: 03/31/20
Health Care Srvices
N.A.I.C.S.: 621610
Rupesh Bhaidas Mehta *(Chm)*

INDO-NATIONAL LIMITED
No 609 Lakshmi Bhavan 4th Floor, Mount Road, Chennai, 600006, Tamil Nadu, India
Tel.: (91) 4428272711
Web Site: https://www.nippo.in
Year Founded: 1972
504058—(BOM)
Rev.: $80,390,815
Assets: $69,810,004
Liabilities: $32,179,138
Net Worth: $37,630,866
Earnings: $1,752,564
Emp.: 509
Fiscal Year-end: 03/31/22
Cell Battery Mfr
N.A.I.C.S.: 335910
P. Dwaraknath Reddy *(CEO & Co-Mng Dir)*

Subsidiaries:

Kineco Kaman Composites India Private Limited   (1)
Plot No 60 Pilerne Industrial Estate, Pilerne Bardez, Goa, 403511, India
Tel.: (91) 8326648888
Web Site:
    https://www.kinecokamanindia.com
Composite Structural Part Mfr
N.A.I.C.S.: 332312
Shekhar Ravindra Sardessai *(Chm & Mng Dir)*

INDOCO REMEDIES LTD
Indoco House 166 CST Road Santacruz East, Mumbai, 400 098, India
Tel.: (91) 2262871000
Web Site: https://www.indoco.com
532612—(BOM)
Rev.: $228,084,675
Assets: $226,344,300
Liabilities: $85,988,175
Net Worth: $140,356,125
Earnings: $19,417,125
Emp.: 6,000
Fiscal Year-end: 03/31/23
Pharmaceutical Ingredients Mfr & Marketing
N.A.I.C.S.: 325412
Aditi Kare Panandikar *(Co-Mng Dir)*

Subsidiaries:

Xtend Industrial Designers & Engineers Private Limited   (1)
R and D Centre R-92/93 MIDC Thane - Belapur Road, TTC Industrial Area Rabale, Navi Mumbai, 400 701, India
Tel.: (91) 222 769 3300
Web Site: https://www.xidel.in
Construction Management Services
N.A.I.C.S.: 236220
Johnson Dias *(Gen Mgr)*

INDOKEM LIMITED
Khatau House Plot No 410/411 Mogul Lane, Mahim, Mumbai, 400016, India
Tel.: (91) 61236767
Web Site: https://www.indokem.co.in
Year Founded: 1945
504092—(BOM)
Rev.: $13,750,140
Assets: $9,725,088
Liabilities: $5,468,544
Net Worth: $4,256,544
Earnings: $37,572
Emp.: 122
Fiscal Year-end: 03/31/23
Dye Mfr
N.A.I.C.S.: 325130
Mahendra K. Khatau *(Chm & Mng Dir)*

INDONESIA ENERGY CORPORATION LIMITED
DEA Tower I 11th Floor Suite 1103, Jl Mega Kuningan Barat Kav E4 3 No1-2, Jakarta, 12950, Indonesia
Tel.: (62) 215768888   Ky
Web Site: https://www.indo-energy.com
Year Founded: 2018
INDO—(NYSEAMEX)
Rev.: $4,097,403
Assets: $20,574,328
Liabilities: $3,250,319
Net Worth: $17,324,009
Earnings: ($3,122,592)
Emp.: 30
Fiscal Year-end: 12/31/22
Holding Company
N.A.I.C.S.: 551112
Frank C. Ingriselli *(Pres)*

INDOOR & OUTDOOR COMMUNICATION HOLDING SA
Avenue Louise 143, BE-1050, Brussels, Belgium
Tel.: (32) 47181320
Web Site: http://iocgroup.eu
MLIOC—(EUR)
Sales Range: Less than $1 Million
Digital Marketing Services
N.A.I.C.S.: 541850
Alexander Rhea *(CEO)*

INDOOR MEDIA
47 The Lynch, Riverside House, Uxbridge, UB8 2TQ, United Kingdom
Tel.: (44) 2071250007
Web Site:
    http://www.indoormedia.co.uk
Sales Range: $10-24.9 Million
Emp.: 20
Business-To-Business, Financial, Health Care, Recruitment, Sports Marketing, Technical Advertising
N.A.I.C.S.: 541810
Murly Tiwari *(Owner)*

INDORAMA CORPORATION PTE. LTD.
143 Cecil Street 14-00 GB Building, Singapore, 069542, Singapore
Tel.: (65) 62221347   SG
Web Site: http://www.indorama.com
Holding Company; Chemicals & Synthesized Products Mfr & Whslr
N.A.I.C.S.: 551112
Sri Prakash Lohia *(Founder & Chm)*

Subsidiaries:

Indorama India Pvt. Ltd.   (1)
PO Durgachak, Purba East Midinipur, Haldia, 721 602, West Bengal, India
Tel.: (91) 3224 251 001
Web Site: http://www.inviya.com
Phosphatic Fertilizer Mfr
N.A.I.C.S.: 325312

Indorama Industries Limited   (1)

INDORAMA CORPORATION PTE. LTD.

Indorama Corporation Pte. Ltd.—(Continued)
Tower B 2nd Floor DLF IT Park, Chandigarh, 160101, India
Tel.: (91) 172 4919 400
Web Site: http://www.indorama.com
Spandex Filament Yarn Mfr
N.A.I.C.S.: 325220

PT. Indo-Rama Synthetics Tbk (1)
Graha Irama 17th Floor Jl H R Rasuna Said Blok X-1 Kav 1-2, Jakarta, 12950, Indonesia
Tel.: (62) 215261555
Web Site: https://www.indorama.co.id
Rev.: $785,598,037
Assets: $821,100,204
Liabilities: $405,935,865
Net Worth: $415,164,339
Earnings: ($40,810,864)
Emp.: 6,972
Fiscal Year-end: 12/31/2023
Polyester Filament Yarns, Spun Yarns, PET Resins, Polyester Staple Fibers & Polyester Filament Fabrics Mfr & Marketer
N.A.I.C.S.: 313110
Vishnu Swaroop Baldwa (Chm & Sec)

Subsidiary (Non-US):

ISIN Lanka Pvt. Ltd. (2)
Rahula Mawatha Off Minuwangoda Road, Andiambalama, Colombo, Sri Lanka (100%)
Tel.: (94) 112253700
Web Site: http://www.indorama.co.id
Spun Yarn Mfr
N.A.I.C.S.: 313110

Indorama Iplik Sanayi Ve Ticaret A.S. (2)
AS Caglayan Sitesi C Blok Ebululah Caddesi, No 22 D 1 Akatlar, 34335, Istanbul, Turkiye (100%)
Tel.: (90) 2123510844
Web Site: http://www.indorama.co.id
Sales Range: $50-74.9 Million
Emp.: 6
Mfr & Marketing of Polyester Filament Yarns, Spun Yarns, PET Resins, Polyester Staple Fibers & Polyester Filament Fabrics
N.A.I.C.S.: 424590
Sandeep Sharma (Mgr-Mktg)

Plant (Domestic):

Indorama Iplik Sanayi Ve Ticaret A.S. (3)
Vakiflar Koyu Ulas Mevkii, Corlu, 59800, Tekirday, Turkiye
Tel.: (90) 2826556586
Web Site: http://www.indorama.com
Emp.: 300
Polyester Yarn Mfr
N.A.I.C.S.: 313110
M. Ashokan (Gen Mgr)

Plant (Domestic):

PT. Indorama Synthetics - Bandung Plant (2)
Jl Batujajar Km 5 5 Desa Giri Asih, Padalarang, Bandung, 40561, Jawa Barat, Indonesia
Tel.: (62) 226866610
Polyester Fiber Mfr
N.A.I.C.S.: 325220

PT. Indorama Synthetics - Purwakarta Plant (2)
Kembang Kuning Ubrug, Post Box 7, Jatiluhur, Purwakarta, Jatiluhur, Indonesia
Tel.: (62) 264202311
Textile Raw Materials Mfr
N.A.I.C.S.: 314999

PT. Medisafe Technologies (1)
Jl S Parman No 23, Medan, 20153, Indonesia
Tel.: (62) 617941463
Web Site: http://www.medisafe-tech.com
Mfr of Latex & Synthetic Exam Gloves
N.A.I.C.S.: 339113

INDORAMA VENTURES PUBLIC COMPANY LIMITED
75/102 Ocean Tower 2 37th Floor Sukhumvit Soi 19, Bangkok, 10110, Thailand
Tel.: (66) 26616661
Web Site: https://www.indoramaventures.com
Year Founded: 2009
INDOY—(OTCIQ)
Rev.: $15,954,846,799
Assets: $17,227,114,677
Liabilities: $12,028,961,269
Net Worth: $5,198,153,408
Earnings: ($318,582,011)
Emp.: 26,093
Fiscal Year-end: 12/31/23
Chemical Products Mfr
N.A.I.C.S.: 551112
Prakash Lohia (Chm)

Subsidiaries:

Auriga Polymers Inc. (1)
4235 S Stream Blvd, Charlotte, NC 28217
Petrochemical Mfr & Distr
N.A.I.C.S.: 325110

Autofil Worldwide Limited (1)
Sherwood Park, Annesley, Nottingham, NG15 0RS, United Kingdom
Tel.: (44) 1623426100
Web Site: http://www.autofil.co.uk
Polyester Yarn Mfr & Distr
N.A.I.C.S.: 313110
Michael Heck (Co-Founder)

Avgol Industries 1953 Ltd. (1)
9 Shimshon St Lexus House 7th floor, Petah Tikva, 4952707, Israel
Tel.: (972) 39061555
Web Site: https://www.avgol.com
Rev.: $318,067,000
Assets: $441,638,000
Liabilities: $242,625,000
Net Worth: $199,013,000
Earnings: $3,989,000
Emp.: 24,000
Fiscal Year-end: 12/31/2023
Nonwoven Fabric Product Mfr
N.A.I.C.S.: 313230
Gilad Frenkel (VP-Sls & Mktg-Europe & Asia)

Beverage Plastics Ltd. (1)
Silverwood Business Park 70 Silverwood Road, Lurgan Armagh, Craigavon, BT66 6LN, United Kingdom
Tel.: (44) 2838311800
Petrochemical Mfr & Distr
N.A.I.C.S.: 325110

Bevpak (Nigeria) Limited (1)
Km3 Ibadan-Lagos Expressway Sanyo, Ibadan, Oyo, Nigeria
Tel.: (234) 8067800580
Web Site: http://www.bevpaknigeria.com
Plastics Bottle Mfr
N.A.I.C.S.: 326160
Syd Carter (CEO)

CEPSA Chimie Montreal, S.E.C. (1)
10200 rue Sherbrooke Est, Montreal, H1B 1B4, QC, Canada
Tel.: (514) 645-7887
Web Site: http://www.cepsa.com
Chemical Products Mfr
N.A.I.C.S.: 325998

FiberVisions A/S (1)
Engdraget 22, 6800, Varde, Denmark
Tel.: (45) 79942200
Fiber Mfr
N.A.I.C.S.: 325220

FiberVisions Corporation (1)
3700 Crestwood Pkwy Ste 900, Duluth, GA 30096
Tel.: (678) 578-7240
Web Site: http://www.fibervisions.com
Fiber Mfr
N.A.I.C.S.: 325220
Tom Zaiser (CEO & CMO)

Subsidiary (Domestic):

Fibervisions Manufacturing Company (2)
7101 Alcovy Rd, Covington, GA 30014
Tel.: (770) 786-7011
Polyolefin Staple Fiber Mfr
N.A.I.C.S.: 325220
Stephen Wood (CEO)

Fibervisions Products, Inc. (1)
1885 Olympic Dr, Athens, GA 30601
Tel.: (706) 357-5100
Petrochemical Mfr & Distr
N.A.I.C.S.: 325110

Filatura Tollegno 1900 S.r.l. (1)
Via Roma 9, Tollegno, 13818, Biella, Italy
Tel.: (39) 0152429200
Web Site: https://www.tollegno1900.it
Merino Wool Yarn & Fabric Mfr
N.A.I.C.S.: 313310

Glanzstoff Industries AG (1)
Rue Schwärzenhof, BP 11, L-8401, Steinfort, Luxembourg
Tel.: (352) 399 881 1
Web Site: http://www.glanzstoff.com
Holding Company
N.A.I.C.S.: 551112
Arnaud Closson (Mng Dir)

Subsidiary (Non-US):

Glanzstoff Bohemia s.r.o. (2)
Terezinska 60, 41002, Lovosice, Czech Republic
Tel.: (420) 416 575 120
Web Site: http://www.glanzstoff.com
Textile Viscose Filament Yarns Mfr
N.A.I.C.S.: 313110

Glanzstoff Industries (Qingdao) Co., Ltd. (2)
No 1735 Maoshan Road, Huangdao district, Qingdao, 266500, China
Tel.: (86) 53280987237
Petrochemical Mfr & Distr
N.A.I.C.S.: 325110

Glanzstoff Longlaville S.A.S. (1)
Pole Europeen de Developpement 9087 rue Ernest Hemingway, 54810, Longlaville, France
Tel.: (33) 382448000
Petrochemical Mfr & Distr
N.A.I.C.S.: 325110

Guangdong IVL PET Polymer Co. Ltd. (1)
No 1 Meihua Road, Shuikou Town, Kaiping, Guangdong, China
Tel.: (86) 7502209680
Petrochemical Mfr & Distr
N.A.I.C.S.: 325110

Indorama Netherlands B.V. (1)
Markweg 201 Europoort, 3198 NB, Rotterdam, Netherlands
Tel.: (31) 181 285 400
Web Site: http://www.indoramaventures.com
Holding Company; Investment Services
N.A.I.C.S.: 551112

Indorama PET (Nigeria) Ltd. (1)
East West Expressway Eleme, Port Harcourt, Rivers, Nigeria
Tel.: (234) 7054006059
Packaging Services
N.A.I.C.S.: 561910

Indorama Polymers Public Company Limited (1)
75 102 Ocean Tower 2 37th Floor, Soi Sukhumvit 19, Bangkok, 10110, Thailand
Tel.: (66) 26616661
Web Site: http://www.indoramaventures.com
Sales Range: $1-4.9 Billion
Emp.: 550
PET Polymers Mfr
N.A.I.C.S.: 326199

Subsidiary (US):

Alphapet Inc. (2)
1301 Finley Island Rd, Decatur, AL 35601
Tel.: (256) 308-1180
Web Site: http://www.indorama.net
Petrochemical Products Mfr
N.A.I.C.S.: 325110

StarPet Inc. (2)
801 Pineview Rd, Asheboro, NC 27203
Tel.: (336) 672-0101
Web Site: http://www.indoramaventures.com
Sales Range: $25-49.9 Million
Emp.: 100
PET Polymers Mfr
N.A.I.C.S.: 326199

INTERNATIONAL PUBLIC

Subsidiary (Non-US):

UAB Orion Global Pet (2)
Metalo g 16, 94102, Klaipeda, Lithuania
Tel.: (370) 46300749
Web Site: http://ogp.lt
Sales Range: $25-49.9 Million
Emp.: 120
PET Polymers Mfr
N.A.I.C.S.: 326199

Indorama Ventures Adana PET Sanayi Anonim Sirketi (1)
Sarihamzali Mahallesi Turhan Cemal Beriker Blv No559/3A, Seyhan, Adana, Turkiye
Tel.: (90) 3224410253
Petrochemical Mfr & Distr
N.A.I.C.S.: 325110

Indorama Ventures Corlu PET Sanayi Anonim Sirketi (1)
Karamehmet Mah Avrupa Serbest Bolgesi 3 Sok No 2, Ergene, Tekirdag, 59860, Turkiye
Tel.: (90) 2826911100
Petrochemical Mfr & Distr
N.A.I.C.S.: 325110

Indorama Ventures Europe B.V. (1)
Markweg 201 Europoort, PO Box 8005, 3198 NB, Rotterdam, Netherlands
Tel.: (31) 181285400
Petrochemical Mfr & Distr
N.A.I.C.S.: 325110

Indorama Ventures Fibras Brasil Ltda. (1)
Rodovia BR 101 Sul N 2426, Cabo de Santo Agostinho, 54505-000, Pernambuco, Brazil
Tel.: (55) 8121198201
Petrochemical Mfr & Distr
N.A.I.C.S.: 325110

Indorama Ventures Oxides Ankleshwar Private Limited (1)
Plot 321 Panoli GIDC Tal Ankleshwar, Dist Bharuch, Gujarat, 394116, India
Tel.: (91) 2646660700
Emp.: 200
Petrochemical Mfr & Distr
N.A.I.C.S.: 325110

Indorama Ventures PTA Montreal L.P. (1)
10200 Sherbrooke East, East Montreal, QC, Canada
Tel.: (514) 645-7887
Petrochemical & Fibber Distr
N.A.I.C.S.: 424690

Indorama Ventures Packaging (Ghana) Ltd. (1)
Plot 234 Meridian Road Community 2, PO Box PMB 350, Tema Harbour, Tema, Ghana
Tel.: (233) 266082249
Petrochemical Mfr & Distr
N.A.I.C.S.: 325110

Indorama Ventures Packaging (Mynamar) Ltd. (1)
Lot No A11-1, Thilawa Special Economic Zone A, Yangon, Myanmar
Tel.: (95) 1230902225
Petrochemical Mfr & Distr
N.A.I.C.S.: 325110

Indorama Ventures Packaging (Nigeria) Ltd. (1)
East West Expressway Eleme, Port Harcourt, Rivers, Nigeria
Tel.: (234) 8052501268
Plastics Bottle Mfr
N.A.I.C.S.: 326160

Indorama Ventures Poland Sp.z.o.o. (1)
ul Krzywa Gora 19, 87-805, Wloclawek, Poland
Tel.: (48) 544166400
Petrochemical Mfr & Distr
N.A.I.C.S.: 325110

Indorama Ventures Polimeros S.A. (1)
Complexo Industrial Portuario De Suape, Ipojuca, Pernambuco, Brazil
Tel.: (55) 8133118600
Petrochemical Mfr & Distr

AND PRIVATE COMPANIES

N.A.I.C.S.: 325110

Indorama Ventures Polymers Mexico, S.de R.L. de C.V. (1)
Access IV No 202, Benito Juarez Industrial Zone, 76120, Queretaro, Mexico
Tel.: (52) 4422112701
Plastics Bottle Mfr
N.A.I.C.S.: 326160

Indorama Ventures Portugal PTA (1)
Zona Industrial e Logistica de Sines Sector Norte Zona 2, Monte Feio, 7520-064, Sines, Portugal
Tel.: (351) 269189000
Web Site: http://www.indoramaventures.com
Purified Terephthalic Acid Mfr
N.A.I.C.S.: 325199

Indorama Ventures Portugal PTA-Unipessoal, LDA. (1)
Zona Industrial e Logistica de Sines, Sector Norte Zona 2 Lote 2E1 Monte Feio, 7520-064, Sines, Portugal
Tel.: (351) 269189000
Petrochemical Mfr & Distr
N.A.I.C.S.: 325110

Indorama Ventures Quimica S.L.U. (1)
Poligono Industrial Guadarranque S/N, PO Box No 54, 11360, San Roque, Cadiz, Spain
Tel.: (34) 95 667 1000
Polyethylene Terephthalate Mfr
N.A.I.C.S.: 325211

Indorama Ventures Sustainable Solutions LLC (1)
1764 Wilkinson St, Athens, AL 35611
Tel.: (256) 232-3543
Plastic Bottle Distr
N.A.I.C.S.: 423930

Subsidiary (Domestic):

Indorama Ventures Sustainable Solutions Fontana, Inc. (2)
11591 Etiwanda Ave, Fontana, CA 92337
Tel.: (951) 332-4660
Petrochemical Mfr & Distr
N.A.I.C.S.: 325110

Indorama Ventures Xylenes & PTA, LLC (1)
1401 Finley Is Rd, Decatur, AL 35601
Tel.: (256) 340-5200
Web Site: http://www.indoramaventures.com
Industrial Organic Chemicals Mfr
N.A.I.C.S.: 325199

PHP Fibers GmbH (1)
Industrie Center, Obernburg, 63784, Miltenberg, Germany
Tel.: (49) 6022812260
Web Site: http://www.php-fibers.com
Fiber Mfr
N.A.I.C.S.: 325220
Klaus Holz (Chm)

PHP Fibers Inc. (1)
300 Serrano Way, Scottsboro, AL 35769
Tel.: (256) 218-4000
Sales Range: $1-9.9 Million
Emp.: 76
Petrochemical Mfr & Distr
N.A.I.C.S.: 325110

PT. Indorama Petrochemicals (1)
Graha Irama 16th Floor Jalan H R Rasuna Said Blok X-1, Kav 1-2 Kuningan Timur Setiabudi, Jakarta Selatan, Indonesia
Tel.: (62) 215261155
Petrochemical Mfr & Distr
N.A.I.C.S.: 325110

PT. Indorama Polychem Indonesia (1)
JL Desa Kembang Kuning, Kecamatan Jatiluhur, Purwakarta, Jawa Barat, Indonesia
Tel.: (62) 264207727
Petrochemical Mfr & Distr
N.A.I.C.S.: 325110

PT. Indorama Polyester Industries Indonesia (1)
Jl Surya Lertari Kav 1-16A Kawasan Industri Surya Cipta, Ciampel, Karawang, 41361, Indonesia
Tel.: (62) 267440501

Polyester Filament Mfr
N.A.I.C.S.: 325220

PT. Indorama Polypet Indonesia (1)
JL Raya Anyar Km 121 Kel Kepuh Kec, Ciwanden, Banten, Indonesia
Tel.: (62) 254602300
Petrochemical Mfr & Distr
N.A.I.C.S.: 325110

PT.Indorama Ventures Indonesia (1)
Desa Cihuni RT/RW 002/004, Cihuni Pagedangan, Tangerang, 15820, Banten, Indonesia
Tel.: (62) 215371111
Packaging Services
N.A.I.C.S.: 561910

Performance Fibers Operations Mexico, S. de R.L. de C.V. (1)
Av de la Luz No 77 Zona Industrial Benito Juarez, 76120, Queretaro, Mexico
Tel.: (52) 442 211 3000
Web Site: http://www.indoramaventures.com
Industrial Nylon Mfr
N.A.I.C.S.: 325212

Petform (Thailand) Ltd. (1)
72 Moo 11 Khaosamorkorn Amphur Tahwung, Lopburi, 15180, Thailand
Tel.: (66) 34891634
Petrochemical Mfr & Distr
N.A.I.C.S.: 325110

Schoeller GmbH & Co KG (1)
Spinnereistrasse 10, 6971, Hard, Austria
Tel.: (43) 55746090
Web Site: http://www.schoeller-wool.com
Clothe & Fabric Mfr
N.A.I.C.S.: 313310

Schoeller Kresice s.r.o. (1)
Prazska 98, Kresice, 411 48, Usti nad Labem, Czech Republic
Tel.: (420) 416716111
Web Site: http://www.schoeller-wool.com
Wool & Yarn Mfr
N.A.I.C.S.: 313110

Sinterama Asia Limited (1)
Unit 1804 Zheng Da Cube Edifice 58 Chang Liu Road, Pudong New Area, Shanghai, 200135, China
Tel.: (86) 2168544232
Petrochemical Mfr & Distr
N.A.I.C.S.: 325110

Sinterama Bulgaria Eood (1)
KV Industrialen, 8900, Nova Zagora, Bulgaria
Tel.: (359) 44612800
Fabrics Mfr
N.A.I.C.S.: 313310

Sinterama S.p.A. (1)
via Gramsci 5, Sandigliano, 13876, Biella, Italy
Tel.: (39) 0152495111
Web Site: http://www.sinterama.com
Clothe & Fabric Mfr
N.A.I.C.S.: 313310

Sinterama Yarns (Dongguan) Co., Ltd. (1)
Unit 1804 Zheng Da Cube Edifice 58 Chang Liu Road, Pudong New Area, Shanghai, 200 135, China
Tel.: (86) 2168544232
Web Site: http://www.sinteramaasia.com
Yarn Mfr
N.A.I.C.S.: 313110

Sinterama do Brasil Ltda. (1)
Av Alberto Vieira Romao 1650, Distrito Industrial Alfenas, Gerais, 37135-516, Brazil
Tel.: (55) 3532991992
Web Site: http://www.sinteramadobrasil.com
Clothe & Fabric Mfr
N.A.I.C.S.: 313310

UTT de Mexico Technical Textiles, S.A. de C.V. (1)
Circuito Esteban de Antunano N 12 MANZANA 3, Parque Industrial Ciudad Textil Huejotzingo, 74160, Puebla, Mexico
Tel.: (52) 2224543660
Fabrics Mfr
N.A.I.C.S.: 313310

Wellman France Recyclage S.A.S. (1)

Zone Industrielle de Regret, 55100, Verdun, France
Tel.: (33) 971002000
Petrochemical Mfr & Distr
N.A.I.C.S.: 325110

Wellman International Limited (1)
Mullagh, Kells, A82 NN93, County Meath, Ireland
Tel.: (353) 469280200
Web Site: http://www.wellman-intl.com
Sales Range: $150-199.9 Million
Emp.: 260
Polyester & Nylon Staple Fibers; Plastic Waste Processing Services
N.A.I.C.S.: 325220

Wellman Neufchateau Recyclage S.A. (1)
100 Chemin de Grety, Rebeuville, 88300, Neufchateau, France
Tel.: (33) 329061180
Petrochemical Mfr & Distr
N.A.I.C.S.: 325110

Winnsboro Fibers LLC (1)
199 Maple St, Winnsboro, SC 29180
Tel.: (803) 815-2901
Petrochemical Mfr & Distr
N.A.I.C.S.: 325110

INDOSOLAR LIMITED
C-12 Friends Colony (East), New Delhi, 110065, India
Tel.: (91) 1126841375
Web Site: http://www.indosolar.co.in
Year Founded: 2008
533257—(BOM)
Sales Range: Less than $1 Million
Emp.: 269
Crystalline Silicon SPV Cell Mfr
N.A.I.C.S.: 334413
Anand Kumar Agarwal (CFO)

INDOSTAR CAPITAL FINANCE LIMITED
Silver Utopia Third Floor Unit No 301-A Opposite P & G Plaza, Cardinal Gracious Road Chakala Andheri E, Mumbai, 400099, India
Tel.: (91) 2250799503
Web Site:
https://www.indostarcapital.com
INDOSTAR—(NSE)
Rev.: $160,290,626
Assets: $1,318,791,324
Liabilities: $918,971,808
Net Worth: $399,819,516
Earnings: ($100,533,929)
Emp.: 2,613
Fiscal Year-end: 03/31/22
Financial Support Services
N.A.I.C.S.: 541611
Dhanpal Jhaver (Chm)

INDOWIND ENERGY LTD
Kothari Buildings 4th Floor 114 M G Road, Nungambakkam, Chennai, 600034, TN, India
Tel.: (91) 4428331956
Web Site: https://indowind.co.in
532894—(BOM)
Rev.: $3,684,886
Assets: $39,284,468
Liabilities: $7,753,391
Net Worth: $31,531,077
Earnings: $17,390
Emp.: 63
Fiscal Year-end: 03/31/22
Wind Farms Development & Green Power Generation
N.A.I.C.S.: 221118
Bala Venckat Kutti (Chm)

INDOWORTH HOLDING LIMITED
Rawdon Chambers 11A Sarojini Naidu Sarani, 4th Floor Unit 4B, Kolkata, 700 017, India
Tel.: (91) 3340061301

Web Site:
http://www.uniworthsecurities.com
512408—(BOM)
Rev.: $35,489
Assets: $1,795,552
Liabilities: $1,581,800
Net Worth: $213,752
Earnings: ($2,290)
Fiscal Year-end: 03/31/23
Investment Management Service
N.A.I.C.S.: 523940
Ramchandra Pyarelal Mehta (CFO)

INDRA INDUSTRIES LTD.
406 Airen Heights Opp Orbit Mall AB Road, Scheme No 54, Indore, 452 010, Madhya Pradesh, India
Tel.: (91) 7314989811
Web Site: https://indraindustries.in
539175—(BOM)
Rev.: $397,554
Assets: $2,336,059
Liabilities: $3,095,882
Net Worth: ($759,823)
Earnings: ($117,835)
Emp.: 5
Fiscal Year-end: 03/31/23
Fertilizer Mfr
N.A.I.C.S.: 325314
Virendra Jain (Mng Dir)

INDRA SISTEMAS, S.A.
Avenida de Bruselas 35 Alcobendas, 28108, Madrid, Spain
Tel.: (34) 914805002
Web Site:
https://www.indracompany.com
Year Founded: 1993
IDR—(VAL)
Rev.: $4,794,206,867
Assets: $5,213,147,147
Liabilities: $3,959,180,926
Net Worth: $1,253,966,222
Earnings: $230,374,214
Emp.: 58,000
Fiscal Year-end: 12/31/23
Information Technology Services
N.A.I.C.S.: 541511
Alberto Terol (Vice Chm)

Subsidiaries:

AC-B air Traffic Control & Business Systems GmbH (1)
Hauptstr 30, 88677, Markdorf, Germany
Tel.: (49) 754450950
Web Site: http://www.ac-b.de
Software Services
N.A.I.C.S.: 541511

Advance Control Systems, Inc. (1)
2540 E Franklin Rd, Meridian, ID 83642
Tel.: (208) 362-5858
Web Site: http://www.advancedcontrol.com
Engineeering Services
N.A.I.C.S.: 541330
Deanne Landreth (Founder, Pres & Principal)

Advanced Control Systems, Inc. (1)
2755 Northwoods Pkwy, Norcross, GA 30071
Tel.: (770) 446-8854
Web Site: http://www.acspower.com
Emp.: 120
Electricty Transmission & Generation Control Systems Mfr & Whslr
N.A.I.C.S.: 334515
Kevin Sullivan (CEO)

Avitech GmbH (1)
Bahnhofplatz 3, 88045, Friedrichshafen, Germany
Tel.: (49) 75412820
Web Site: https://indra-avitech.aero
Sales Range: $25-49.9 Million
Emp.: 50
Aviation Software Development & Sales
N.A.I.C.S.: 513210
Ulrich Lais (Member-Exec Bd & Dir-Ops)

Avitech s.r.o. (1)
Prievozska 4D, Bratislava, 82109, Slovakia

INDRA SISTEMAS, S.A.

Indra Sistemas, S.A.—(Continued)
Tel.: (421) 255642801
Web Site: http://www.avitech-ag.com
Sales Range: $25-49.9 Million
Emp.: 55
Aviation Software Development Services
N.A.I.C.S.: 541511
Branislav Klco *(Mng Dir)*

BMB Gestion Documental Canarias S.L. (1)
Calle Tomas Miller No 47-49 Plot 1 Las Palmas De Gran Canari, 35007, Las Palmas, Spain
Tel.: (34) 928221231
Sales Range: $25-49.9 Million
Emp.: 6
Document Processing Services
N.A.I.C.S.: 561410

Baltik IT (1)
Strelnieku iela 6-2, Riga, LV-1010, Latvia
Tel.: (371) 63422230
Web Site: https://www.baltikit.lv
Business Management Services
N.A.I.C.S.: 541611
Anatolijs Glasmans *(Mng Dir)*

COM S.A. (1)
Av Javier Prado Oeste No 1661 2nd Floor, San Isidro, Lima, Peru
Tel.: (51) 1 421 2264
Web Site: http://www.comsa.com.pe
Computer Software Consulting Services
N.A.I.C.S.: 541512

Elecnor Deimos (1)
Ronda Poniente de 19, Tres Cantos, 28760, Madrid, Spain
Tel.: (34) 91 806 34 50
Web Site: http://www.elecnor-deimos.com
Emp.: 200
Engineering Solutions & Technology Services
N.A.I.C.S.: 541330

Elektrica Soluziona S.A. (Romania) (1)
Iancu De Hunedoara 54 B Fl 5, Bucharest, 11745, Romania
Tel.: (40) 212332485
Web Site: http://www.elektricasoluziona.ro
Sales Range: $25-49.9 Million
Emp.: 26
Business Management Software Development Services
N.A.I.C.S.: 541511
Dan Hurezran *(Mng Dir)*

Europraxis Atlante S.L. (1)
Calle Caravel la La Nina 12 Plot 3, 08017, Barcelona, Spain
Tel.: (34) 932064343
Web Site: http://www.europraxis.com
Strategy & Management Consulting Services
N.A.I.C.S.: 541611

Subsidiary (Domestic):

Advanced Logistics Group S.A. (2)
Tanger 98 3rd Floor A, 08018, Barcelona, Spain
Tel.: (34) 934304016
Sales Range: $25-49.9 Million
Emp.: 120
Logistics & Distribution Services
N.A.I.C.S.: 541614
Joan Rojas *(Mng Dir)*

Tourism & Leisure Advisory Service S.L. (2)
Carabela La Nina 12 3 Planta, 08017, Barcelona, Spain
Tel.: (34) 932064343
Web Site: http://www.tladvisors.com
Tourism & Leisure Consulting Services
N.A.I.C.S.: 561520

Europraxis Consulting S.R.L. (1)
Via Fatebenefratelli 26, 20121, Milan, Italy
Tel.: (39) 023057551
Web Site: http://www.europaxis.com
Sales Range: $25-49.9 Million
Emp.: 15
Business Consulting Services
N.A.I.C.S.: 541611
Guillermo Sagnier Guimon *(Pres)*

Indra ATM, S.L. (1)
Ctra de Loeches 9, Torrejon de Ardoz, 28850, Madrid, Spain (51%)
Tel.: (34) 91 626 81 97
Web Site: http://www.indra.es
Sales Range: $25-49.9 Million
Emp.: 30
Research, Design, Manufacture, Sale & Maintenance of Electronic & IT Equipment & Systems for Air Traffic Control
N.A.I.C.S.: 334511

Indra Australia Pty Limited (1)
Unit 21 38-46 South Street, Rydalmere, 2116, NSW, Australia
Tel.: (61) 298988700
Web Site: http://www.indracompany.com
Sales Range: $25-49.9 Million
Emp.: 45
Navigation Equipments Mfr & Distr
N.A.I.C.S.: 334511

Indra BMB S.L. (1)
Anbel Segura No 7, Alcobendas, 28108, Madrid, Spain
Tel.: (34) 915948700
Business Process Outsourcing Services
N.A.I.C.S.: 561410

Subsidiary (Domestic):

Indra BMB Servicios Digitales S.A. (2)
Calle Tanger 98 Edif Interface, 08018, Barcelona, Spain
Tel.: (34) 934630807
Document Processing Services
N.A.I.C.S.: 561410

Indra Bahrain Consultancy SPC (1)
Road n 3621 Block 436, Seef District, Manama, Bahrain
Tel.: (973) 17116977
IT Services
N.A.I.C.S.: 541511

Indra Beijing Information Technology Systems Co.Ltd. (1)
17 West Dawang Road Building 3 Room 202A, Chaoyang District, Beijing, 100600, China
Tel.: (86) 1065906455
Emp.: 40
Administrative Management Consulting Services
N.A.I.C.S.: 541611

Indra Brasil, Ltda. (1)
2200 Alexandre Dumas Street, 04717-004, Sao Paulo, Brazil
Tel.: (55) 1151863000
Web Site: http://www.indracompany.com.br
Sales Range: $25-49.9 Million
Emp.: 150
Enterprise Management Software Development Services
N.A.I.C.S.: 541511

Indra Business Consulting, S.L.U. (1)
Calle Tanger 98, 08018, Barcelona, Spain
Tel.: (34) 934632312
Logistics & Transportation Consulting Services
N.A.I.C.S.: 541614

Indra Colombia Ltda. (1)
No 13-11 96 Street, Bogota, Colombia
Tel.: (57) 914805002
Web Site: http://www.indracompany.com
Emp.: 2,000
Traffic Management Software Development Services
N.A.I.C.S.: 541511

Indra Czech Republic S.R.O. (1)
Pobrezni 620/3, 18600, Prague, Czech Republic
Tel.: (420) 246085700
IT Services
N.A.I.C.S.: 541511

Indra EMAC, S.A. (1)
Paseo de la Habana 141, 28036, Madrid, Spain (65.01%)
Tel.: (34) 913 591 728
Sales Range: $25-49.9 Million
Emp.: 7
Maintenance, Supply, Training & Engineering of Systems for Use in Air Defence & Other Related Areas

N.A.I.C.S.: 541330

Indra EWS, S.A. (1)
Joaquin Rodrigo 11, Aranjuez, 28300, Madrid, Spain (51%)
Tel.: (34) 918948800
Web Site: http://www.indra.es
Sales Range: $200-249.9 Million
Emp.: 650
Development, Manufacture, Sale & Maintenance of Electronic, Optical Electronic & IT Equipment & Systems
N.A.I.C.S.: 334118

Indra Eslovakia, A.S. (1)
Mlynske Nivy 10, 821 09, Bratislava, Slovakia
Tel.: (421) 258229111
Sales Range: $25-49.9 Million
Emp.: 80
Business Management Software Development Services
N.A.I.C.S.: 541511

Indra Espacio, S.A. (1)
Mar Egeo 4 Pol Ind 1, 28830, San Fernando de Henares, Madrid, Spain
Tel.: (34) 916269000
Sales Range: $1-4.9 Billion
Emp.: 6,000
Research, Design, Manufacture & Maintenance of Engineering Projects for Electronic & IT Systems, Telematics & Telecommunications
N.A.I.C.S.: 517112

Indra France S.A.S. (1)
35 Avenue Raymond Aron, 92160, Antony, Hauts-de-Seine, France
Tel.: (33) 141870520
Sales Range: $25-49.9 Million
Emp.: 15
Business Management Software Development Services
N.A.I.C.S.: 541511

Indra Hungary L.L.C. (1)
Bem Ter 18 C Atomki Building, 4026, Debrecen, Hajdu-Bihar, Hungary
Tel.: (36) 52 415 458
Sales Range: $25-49.9 Million
Emp.: 8
Business Management Software Development Services
N.A.I.C.S.: 541511

Indra L.L.C (1)
Knowledge Oasis Muscat Building KOM 4 GF Muscat, PO Box 895, Azaiba, 130, Muscat, Oman
Tel.: (968) 24499879
IT Services
N.A.I.C.S.: 541511

Indra Limited (Kenya) (1)
Laxcon House 6 Floor Parklands Limuru Road, PO Box 32443, Nairobi, 600, Kenya
Tel.: (254) 203655500
Web Site: http://www.indra.es
Sales Range: $25-49.9 Million
Emp.: 30
Air Traffic Control Services
N.A.I.C.S.: 488111

Indra Ltda (1)
Laxcon House Limuru Road 6th Floor, Nairobi, Kenya
Tel.: (254) 2036555000
IT Services
N.A.I.C.S.: 541511

Indra Panama, S.A. (1)
Main Ave the Rotunda Business Park East Tower 4th Floor, Costa del Este, 0843-02525, Panama, Panama
Tel.: (507) 3784200
Sales Range: $25-49.9 Million
Emp.: 160
Traffic Management Software Development Services
N.A.I.C.S.: 541511

Indra Philippines, Inc. (1)
11-12th Floors Tower 1 Rockwell Business Center Ortigas Avenue, Pasig, 1600, Philippines
Tel.: (63) 26203888
Web Site: http://www.indracompany.com
Sales Range: $75-99.9 Million
Emp.: 500
Information Technology Consulting Services

INTERNATIONAL PUBLIC

N.A.I.C.S.: 541512

Indra Sistemas Chile S.A. (1)
Del Valle 765 Piso 3, Huechuraba, Santiago, Chile
Tel.: (56) 28103600
Enterprise Management Software Development Services
N.A.I.C.S.: 541511

Indra Sistemas De Seguridad, S.A. (1)
Carrer de Roc Boronat 133, Barcelona, Spain (100%)
Tel.: (34) 934005800
Sales Range: $75-99.9 Million
Emp.: 300
Design, Development, Manufacture & Maintenance of Security Equipment & Systems
N.A.I.C.S.: 561621

Indra Sistemas India Private Ltd. (1)
EROS CORPORATE TOWER Nehru Place 14th Floor, New Delhi, 110 019, India
Tel.: (91) 1146189900
Sales Range: $25-49.9 Million
Emp.: 22
Business Consulting Services
N.A.I.C.S.: 541611

Indra Sistemas Magreb S.A.R.L. (1)
Technopolis Batiment B4, Sala, 11100, El Jadida, Morocco
Tel.: (212) 538 014 200
Business Management Software Development Services
N.A.I.C.S.: 541511

Indra Sistemas Mexico S.A. de C.V. (1)
National Army Avenue No 843-B, Miguel Hidalgo, 11520, Mexico, Mexico
Tel.: (52) 5591261100
Business Software Development Services
N.A.I.C.S.: 541511

Indra Sistemas Portugal S.A. (1)
Estrada Seminario 4 Alfrapark Edificio C Piso 2, 2610 171, Amadora, Portugal
Tel.: (351) 214724600
Enterprise Management Software Development Services
N.A.I.C.S.: 541511

Indra Sistemas de Comunicaciones Seguras S.L. (1)
Av de Bruselas 35, Alcobendas, 28108, Madrid, Spain
Tel.: (34) 914807208
Internet & Telecommunication Services
N.A.I.C.S.: 517810

Indra Sisteme S.R.L. (1)
Stefan cel Mare 202, MD-2004, Chisinau, Moldova
Tel.: (373) 22838364
IT Services
N.A.I.C.S.: 541511

Indra Slovakia, A.S. (1)
Mlynske Nivy 10, 82109, Bratislava, Slovakia
Tel.: (421) 258229111
IT Services
N.A.I.C.S.: 541511

Indra Software Labs S.L.U. (1)
Avenida de Bruselas 35, 28108, Alcobendas, Madrid, Spain
Tel.: (34) 914805002
Web Site: http://www.indracompany.com
Software Development Services
N.A.I.C.S.: 541511

Indra Technology Solutions Malasya Sdn. Bhd. (1)
Level 3A IKHLAS Point Tower 11 Avenue 5, 59200, Kuala Lumpur, Malaysia
Tel.: (60) 322409360
IT Services
N.A.I.C.S.: 541511

Indra USA Inc. (1)
800 Brickell Ave Ste 1270, Miami, FL 33131-2971
Tel.: (305) 373-7749
Web Site: http://www.indracompany.com
Sales Range: $25-49.9 Million
Emp.: 40
Defence Software Development Services
N.A.I.C.S.: 541511

AND PRIVATE COMPANIES

Indra Ucrania L.L.C. (1)
4 Muzuiny Lane, 01001, Kiev, Ukraine
Tel.: (380) 445920262
Sales Range: $25-49.9 Million
Emp.: 2
Enterprise Management Software Development Services
N.A.I.C.S.: 541511

Inmize Capital S.L. (1)
Avenida de Bruselas 33-35, Alcobendas, 28108, Madrid, Spain
Tel.: (34) 914807208
Venture Capital Financing Services
N.A.I.C.S.: 523910

Inmize Sistemas S.L. (1)
C/ Mar Egeo 4 Polígono Industrial 1, 28830, San Fernando de Henares, Madrid, Spain
Tel.: (34) 916268746
Sales Range: $25-49.9 Million
Emp.: 20
Missile System Controlling Software Development Services
N.A.I.C.S.: 541511

Intos S.A.U. (1)
Mallorca 221.7 2, 08008, Barcelona, Spain
Tel.: (34) 93 451 95 65
Financial Software Development Services
N.A.I.C.S.: 541511

Metradis S.L. (1)
Paseo del club deportivo 1 Parque Empresarial La Finca, Bloque 4 Planta 1, 28223, Pozuelo de Alarcon, Madrid, Spain
Tel.: (34) 914 806 796
Web Site: http://www.metradis.es
Enterprise Management Software Development Services
N.A.I.C.S.: 541511

Morpheus Aiolos, S.L. (1)
Wells House 80 Upper Street, London, N1 0NU, United Kingdom
Tel.: (44) 2038688713
Web Site: http://www.afterbanks.com
Software Services
N.A.I.C.S.: 541511

PT Indra Indonesia (1)
The Executive Center Level 11 One Pacific Place, Jakarta, 12190, Indonesia
Tel.: (62) 2129859666
IT Services
N.A.I.C.S.: 541511

Paradigma Digital, S.L. (1)
Via de las Dos Castillas 33 - Atica 2, Pozuelo de Alarcon, 28224, Madrid, Spain
Tel.: (34) 913525942
Web Site: https://www.paradigmadigital.com
Emp.: 600
Software Services
N.A.I.C.S.: 541511

Park Air Systems Limited (1)
Northfields Market Deeping, Peterborough, PE6 8UE, United Kingdom
Tel.: (44) 1778345434
Web Site: http://www.parkairsystems.com
Sales Range: $25-49.9 Million
Emp.: 150
Airspace Communication, Navigation & Surveillance
N.A.I.C.S.: 334511

Prointec S.A. (1)
Avda Castilla N 2 Japan Building, 28830, Madrid, Spain
Tel.: (34) 916272400
Web Site: https://www.prointec.es
Sales Range: $75-99.9 Million
Emp.: 500
Engineering Consulting Services
N.A.I.C.S.: 541330

Subsidiary (Non-US):

Consis Proiect SRL (2)
Sos Iancului nr 31 etaj 2 - 5 sector 2, 021725, Bucharest, Romania
Tel.: (40) 215391131
Civil Engineering Services
N.A.I.C.S.: 541330

Subsidiary (Domestic):

GICSA-Goymar Ingenieros Consultores S.L. (2)
Avenida Burgos 12, 28036, Madrid, Spain

Tel.: (34) 914298085
Web Site: http://www.linux13.dns-servicios.com
Sales Range: $25-49.9 Million
Emp.: 16
Construction Engineering Services
N.A.I.C.S.: 541330

Geoprin S.A. (2)
Calle Pino 44 B, 41016, Seville, Spain
Tel.: (34) 954514612
Mechanical Engineering Services
N.A.I.C.S.: 541330

Procinsa Energias Renovables, S.L. (2)
Parque Tecnologico de Asturias Parcela 28, 33428, Llanera, Asturias, Spain
Tel.: (34) 985257344
Web Site: http://www.isastur.com
Civil Engineering & Consultancy Services
N.A.I.C.S.: 541330

Prointec Extremadura S.L. (2)
Calle Jose Luis Cotallo 1 Bajo 6, 10001, Caceres, Spain
Tel.: (34) 927 21 68 87
Engineering Consulting Services
N.A.I.C.S.: 541330

Subsidiary (Non-US):

Prointec Panama, S.A. (2)
Costa del Este Business Park Torre Telefonica Torre Este Piso No 4, Panama, Panama
Tel.: (507) 3784266
Civil Engineering Services
N.A.I.C.S.: 541330

Subsidiary (US):

Prointec USA LLC (2)
9001 Airport Fwy Ste 600, North Richland Hills, TX 76180
Tel.: (817) 605-8912
Civil Engineering Services
N.A.I.C.S.: 541330

Sistemas informaticos Abiertos, S.A. (1)
Avda de Bruselas 35, Alcobendas, 28108, Madrid, Spain
Tel.: (34) 913077997
Web Site: https://www.sia.es
Emp.: 1,200
Cyber Security Services
N.A.I.C.S.: 541519

Softfobia, S.R.L. (1)
Via San Tommaso D'Aquino 18/A, Cagliari, Italy
Tel.: (39) 0702087115
Web Site: http://www.softfobia.com
Emp.: 50
Software Services
N.A.I.C.S.: 541511

Unclick Srl (1)
Via Falzarego 9, Cagliari, Italy
Tel.: (39) 0702087115
Web Site: https://www.unclick.eu
Software Services
N.A.I.C.S.: 541511

INDRAPRASTHA GAS LIMITED
Plot No 4 Community Centre, Sector 9 RK Puram, New Delhi, 110022, India
Tel.: (91) 1146074607   In
Web Site: https://www.iglonline.net
Year Founded: 1998
532514—(BOM)
Rev.: $2,157,509,445
Assets: $1,722,711,900
Liabilities: $640,097,640
Net Worth: $1,082,614,260
Earnings: $223,812,225
Emp.: 707
Fiscal Year-end: 03/31/23
Natural Gas Distribution
N.A.I.C.S.: 221210
S. K. Jain *(Officer-Compliance & Sec)*

INDRAPRASTHA MEDICAL CORPORATION LIMITED

Sarita Vihar Delhi Mathura Road, New Delhi, 110 076, India
Tel.: (91) 1126925858
Web Site: http://www.delhi.apollohospitals.com
Year Founded: 1988
INDRAMEDCO—(NSE)
Rev.: $83,819,190
Assets: $58,961,994
Liabilities: $21,730,800
Net Worth: $37,231,194
Earnings: $317,909
Emp.: 3,500
Fiscal Year-end: 03/31/21
Hospital Management Services
N.A.I.C.S.: 622110
Chander Prakash Tyagi *(CFO)*

INDRAYANI BIOTECH LIMITED
Module 32 33 Block-1 SIDCO Electronics Complex, Thiru Vi Ka Industrial Estate Guindy, Chennai, 600 032, Tamil Nadu, India
Tel.: (91) 4424463751   In
Web Site: https://www.indrayani.com
526445—(BOM)
Rev.: $2,914,736
Assets: $5,467,497
Liabilities: $2,726,524
Net Worth: $2,740,973
Earnings: ($1,530,767)
Emp.: 621
Fiscal Year-end: 03/31/21
Agricultural Product Mfr
N.A.I.C.S.: 325320

INDSIL HYDRO POWER AND MANGANESE LTD.
INDSIL HOUSE T V Samy Road West, R S Puram, Coimbatore, 641002, India
Tel.: (91) 4224522922
Web Site: https://www.indsil.com
522165—(BOM)
Rev.: $30,098,195
Assets: $39,368,716
Liabilities: $19,758,894
Net Worth: $19,609,822
Earnings: $13,045,906
Emp.: 217
Fiscal Year-end: 03/31/22
Power Generation Services & Carbon Silico Manganese Mfr
N.A.I.C.S.: 221118
Vinod Narasiman *(Mng Dir)*

Subsidiaries:

Sree Mahalakshmi Smelters Private Limited (1)
Merakamudidam Mandalam, Garbham, Vizianagaram, 535 102, Andhra Pradesh, India
Tel.: (91) 8952 288333
Emp.: 300
Ferro Alloy Smelting Services
N.A.I.C.S.: 331314
Uppu Srinivas *(Mgr)*

INDSOYA LTD.
1111A Raheja Chambers, 213 Nariman Point, Mumbai, 400021, India
Tel.: (91) 2222852796
Web Site: https://www.indsoya.com
Year Founded: 1980
503639—(BOM)
Rev.: $298,061
Assets: $145,050
Liabilities: $1,988
Net Worth: $143,063
Earnings: $7,628
Emp.: 1
Fiscal Year-end: 03/31/22
Soya Bean Extraction Services
N.A.I.C.S.: 111110
Sarita Mansingka *(Chm & Mng Dir)*

INDTACT GMBH

INDUS COAL LIMITED

Friedrich-Bergius-Ring 15, 97076, Wurzburg, Germany
Tel.: (49) 93129997330
Web Site: https://www.indtact.de
Electronic Products Mfr
N.A.I.C.S.: 334417

INDUCT AS
Cort Adelers gate 17, NO-0254, Oslo, Norway
Tel.: (47) 41580000
Web Site: https://www.web.induct.net
Year Founded: 2007
INDUCT-ME—(OSL)
Sales Range: Less than $1 Million
Computer Network Design
N.A.I.C.S.: 541512
Karl Kristian Mydske *(COO)*

INDUCTION HEALTHCARE GROUP PLC
30 Crown Place Earl Street, London, EC2A 4ES, United Kingdom
Tel.: (44) 3339398091   UK
Web Site: https://www.inductionhealthcare.com
Year Founded: 2018
INHC—(AIM)
Rev.: $15,999,351
Assets: $47,606,887
Liabilities: $17,436,114
Net Worth: $30,170,773
Earnings: ($21,586,209)
Emp.: 83
Fiscal Year-end: 03/31/23
Healthcare Software Development Services
N.A.I.C.S.: 541511
Hugo Stephenson *(Co-CEO)*

INDUCTO STEEL LTD.
156 Maker Chambers VI, 220 Jamnalal Bajaj Marg Nariman Point, Mumbai, 400 021, Maharashtra, India
Tel.: (91) 2222043211
532001—(BOM)
Rev.: $421,881
Assets: $6,135,238
Liabilities: $647,966
Net Worth: $5,487,273
Earnings: ($189,544)
Emp.: 2
Fiscal Year-end: 03/31/21
Boat Yard Mfr
N.A.I.C.S.: 336612
Rajeev Shantisarup Reniwal *(Chm & Mng Dir)*

INDUKERN, S.A.
Parc Empresarial Mas Blau II, Alta Ribagorza 6-8, Barcelona, 08820, Spain
Tel.: (34) 93 506 91 00
Web Site: http://www.indukern.com
Year Founded: 1962
Emp.: 500
Holding Company
N.A.I.C.S.: 551112
Jose Diaz-Varela Somoza *(Pres)*

Subsidiaries:

Granard Pharmaceutical (1)
2317 Hwy 34, Manasquan, NJ 08736
Tel.: (732) 292-2661
Web Site: http://www.granardrx.com
Rev.: $1,098,000
Emp.: 6
Teleproduction & Other Postproduction Services
N.A.I.C.S.: 512191
Stephen Flood *(Owner)*

INDUS COAL LIMITED
Level 3 18 Richardson Street, West Perth, 6005, WA, Australia
Tel.: (61) 300532786

INDUS COAL LIMITED

Indus Coal Limited—(Continued)
Web Site:
http://www.induscoal.com.au
Sales Range: Less than $1 Million
Coal Mining
N.A.I.C.S.: 212115
Vinay Hariani *(Chm)*

Subsidiaries:

Indus Coal Singapore Pte Ltd (1)
33 Ubi Avenue 3 07 12 Vertex, Singapore, 408868, Singapore
Tel.: (65) 6509 4494
Coal Mining Services
N.A.I.C.S.: 212115

PT Mukomuko Baratama Sajahtera (1)
Menara BCA 39th Floor Suite 3902, Jl M H Thamrin No 1, Jakarta, 10310, Indonesia
Tel.: (62) 21 2358 7555
Emp.: 22
Coal Mining Services
N.A.I.C.S.: 212115
Rajeev Kumar *(Gen Mgr)*

INDUS DYEING & MANUFACTURING COMPANY LTD.

508 5th Floor Beaumont Plaza Beaumont Road Civil Lines Qtrs, Karachi, 75530, Pakistan
Tel.: (92) 21111404404
Web Site: https://www.indus-group.com
Year Founded: 1955
IDYM—(KAR)
Rev.: $253,975,110
Assets: $219,913,822
Liabilities: $108,305,095
Net Worth: $111,608,727
Earnings: $16,740,148
Emp.: 2,668
Fiscal Year-end: 06/30/19
Textile Products Mfr
N.A.I.C.S.: 314999
Shahzad Ahmed *(CEO)*

INDUS ENERGY NL

Unit 17 Level 2 100 Railway Road, PO Box 8129, Subiaco, 6008, WA, Australia
Tel.: (61) 8 9380 9920
Web Site:
http://www.indusenergy.com.au
Sales Range: Less than $1 Million
Oil & Gas Exploration
N.A.I.C.S.: 211120
Jonathan Whyte *(Sec)*

INDUS FILA LIMITED

#107 Industrial Suburb 2nd Stage, Yeshwantpur, Bengaluru, 560 022, India
Tel.: (91) 80 41369 700
Sales Range: $100-124.9 Million
Textile Processing Services
N.A.I.C.S.: 313310
Nitin N. Mandhana *(Vice Chm & Mng Dir)*

INDUS FINANCE LIMITED

Kothari Buildings 4th Floor 114 MG Road, Chennai, 600 034, India
Tel.: (91) 4428331310
Web Site: http://www.indusfinance.in
Year Founded: 1992
531841—(BOM)
Rev.: $126,495
Assets: $4,415,939
Liabilities: $1,422,958
Net Worth: $2,992,981
Earnings: $(461,493)
Emp.: 8
Fiscal Year-end: 03/31/22
Financial Services
N.A.I.C.S.: 523999
K. V. Bala *(Chm)*

INDUS GAS LIMITED

1st Floor Tudor House, Le Bordage, Saint Peter Port, GY1 1DB, Guernsey
Tel.: (44) 1481 721500 GY
Web Site: http://www.indusgas.com
Year Founded: 2008
Rev.: $60,605,486
Assets: $948,157,576
Liabilities: $747,792,274
Net Worth: $200,365,302
Earnings: $37,486,671
Fiscal Year-end: 03/31/19
Oil & Gas Exploration Services
N.A.I.C.S.: 213112
Ajay Kalsi *(Founder & CEO)*

INDUS HOLDING AG

Kolner Strasse 32, D-51429, Bergisch Gladbach, Germany
Tel.: (49) 220440000
Web Site: https://www.indus.de
INH—(MUN)
Rev.: $1,989,648,404
Assets: $2,129,122,379
Liabilities: $1,336,609,951
Net Worth: $792,512,428
Earnings: $62,688,777
Emp.: 8,929
Fiscal Year-end: 12/31/23
Investment Management
N.A.I.C.S.: 523940
Johannes Schmidt *(Chm-Mgmt Bd)*

Subsidiaries:

ASS End of Arm Tooling, Inc. (1)
1324 Goldsmith, Plymouth, MI 48170
Tel.: (734) 542-4398
Web Site: https://www.eoat.net
Automation Component Mfr
N.A.I.C.S.: 334512

ASS Maschinenbau GmbH (1)
Klef 2, 51491, Overath, Germany
Tel.: (49) 2206905470
Web Site: https://www.ass-automation.com
Emp.: 100
Robotic Hand Systems Mfr
N.A.I.C.S.: 334511

AURORA Konrad G. Schulz GmbH & Co. KG (1)
Joachim-Schulz-Str 4, 69427, Mudau, Germany
Tel.: (49) 628492020
Web Site: https://www.aurora-eos.com
Emp.: 300
Vehicles Heating & Ventilation & Air Conditioning Systems Sales
N.A.I.C.S.: 238220
Hannes Wolf *(Co-CEO)*

AURORA North America LLC (1)
4311 Patterson Ave SE, Grand Rapids, MI 49512
Tel.: (616) 698-8545
Heating & Air Conditioning System Mfr
N.A.I.C.S.: 333415
Joseph Hamilton *(Pres & CEO)*

Ancotech AG (1)
Industriestrasse 3, 8157, Dielsdorf, Switzerland
Tel.: (41) 448547222
Web Site: https://www.ancotech.ch
Stainless Steel Distr
N.A.I.C.S.: 423510

Subsidiary (Non-US):

Ancotech GmbH (2)
Am Westhover Berg 30, 51149, Cologne, Germany
Tel.: (49) 2203599280
Web Site: http://www.ancotech.de
Special Reinforcement Distr
N.A.I.C.S.: 423510

Anneliese KOSTER GmbH & Co. KG (1)
Spreeler Weg 32, Nordrhein-Westfalen, 58256, Ennepetal, Germany
Tel.: (49) 233383060
Web Site:
http://www.bolzenschweisstechnik.de
Sales Range: $25-49.9 Million
Emp.: 65
Stud Welding Machines Mfr
N.A.I.C.S.: 333992

Aurora Isi Araclari San. ve Tic. Ltd. Sti (1)
BOSB Mermerciler San Sitesi 8 Caddesi No 12/B, Beylikduzu, 34526, Istanbul, Turkiye
Tel.: (90) 2128769410
Heating & Air Conditioning System Mfr
N.A.I.C.S.: 333415

BETEK Bergbau- und Hartmetalltechnik Karl-Heinz Simon GmbH & Co. KG (1)
Sülgener Strasse 19-23, Baden-Wurttemberg, 78733, Aichhalden, Germany
Tel.: (49) 74225650
Web Site: http://www.betek.de
Sales Range: $50-74.9 Million
Emp.: 180
Tungsten Carbide Tools Mfr
N.A.I.C.S.: 331492
Anne-Christine Jahnke *(Mgr-Mktg)*

BETOMAX Kunststoff- und Metallwarenfabrik GmbH & Co. KG (1)
Dyckhofstrasse 1, 41460, Neuss, Nordrhein-Westfalen, Germany
Tel.: (49) 213127970
Web Site: https://www.betomax.de
Sales Range: $50-74.9 Million
Emp.: 80
Concrete Building Construction Materials Whslr
N.A.I.C.S.: 423320

BILSTEIN & SIEKERMANN GmbH + Co. KG (1)
Industriestrasse 1, 54576, Hillesheim, Germany
Tel.: (49) 65932108
Web Site: http://www.bsh-vs.com
Sales Range: $25-49.9 Million
Emp.: 90
Screws & Cold Extrusion Presses Mfr
N.A.I.C.S.: 332722

Bacher AG (1)
Kagenstrasse 14, 4153, Reinach, Switzerland
Tel.: (41) 617153535
Web Site: http://www.bacherag.ch
Interior Design Services
N.A.I.C.S.: 541410
Semir Korac *(COO)*

Betek GmbH & Co. KG (1)
Sulgener Strasse 21-23, 78733, Aichhalden, Germany
Tel.: (49) 74225650
Web Site: https://www.betek.de
Emp.: 400
Investment Management Service
N.A.I.C.S.: 523940

Subsidiary (Non-US):

Betek Tools Taicang Ltd. (2)
Building 12 No 188 East Guangzhou Rd, Taicang, 215413, Jiangsu, China
Tel.: (86) 51253679789
Wear Tool & Carbide Tool Mfr
N.A.I.C.S.: 333515
Hao Zhang *(Gen Mgr)*

Subsidiary (US):

Betek Tools, Inc. (2)
8107 R Arrowridge Blvd, Charlotte, NC 28273
Tel.: (980) 498-2523
Wear Tool & Carbide Tool Mfr
N.A.I.C.S.: 333515
Joseph J. Redman *(VP-Mining Div)*

Betomax Systems GmbH & Co. KG (1)
Dyckhofstrasse 1, 41460, Neuss, Germany
Tel.: (49) 213127970
Web Site: https://www.betomax.com
Concrete Construction Mfr
N.A.I.C.S.: 327320

Bilstein & Siekermann Cold Forming (Taicang) Co., Ltd. (1)
Building 6 No 188 East Guangzhou Rd, Taicang, 215413, Jiangsu, China
Tel.: (86) 51253679774
Cold Pressed Parts & Screw Plug Mfr
N.A.I.C.S.: 335931

Budde Fordertechnik GmbH (1)
Kollerbreite 12, 33699, Bielefeld, Germany
Tel.: (49) 521924650
Web Site: http://www.budde.de
Logistic Services
N.A.I.C.S.: 541614

Eltherm GmbH (1)
Ernst-Heinkel-Strasse 6-10, 57299, Burbach, Germany
Tel.: (49) 273644130
Web Site: http://www.eltherm.com
Emp.: 265
Electrical Heat Tracing System Mfr
N.A.I.C.S.: 333414

Subsidiary (Non-US):

Eltherm (Shanghai) Co., Ltd. (2)
Rm18-07 XinJian Mansion No 488 YaoHua Road, Pudong, Shanghai, 200126, China
Tel.: (86) 2120286188
Heating Cable & Hose Mfr
N.A.I.C.S.: 333414

Eltherm Asia-Pacific Pte. Ltd. (2)
60 Macpherson Road 08-11 Siemens Centre Blk 1, Singapore, 348615, Singapore
Tel.: (65) 66349100
Heating Cable & Hose Mfr
N.A.I.C.S.: 333414

Eltherm Canada Inc. (2)
1155 Appleby Line Unit E7, Burlington, L7L 5H9, ON, Canada
Tel.: (289) 812-6631
Heating Cable & Hose Mfr
N.A.I.C.S.: 333414

Eltherm Italy Srl (2)
Via Carlo Mariani 1, Cernusco sul Naviglio, 20063, Milan, Italy
Tel.: (39) 0235984650
Heating Cable & Hose Mfr
N.A.I.C.S.: 333414

Eltherm Kazakhstan (2)
Kabanbay Batyr Avenue 6/1 Business Centre Kaskad Office 21/4, Nur-Sultan, 010000, Kazakhstan
Tel.: (7) 7172792755
Heating Cable & Hose Mfr
N.A.I.C.S.: 333414

Eltherm Kazakhstan (2)
Kabanbay Batyr Avenue 6/1 Business Centre Kaskad Office, 21/4 Nur-Sultan, 010000, Astana, Kazakhstan
Tel.: (7) 7172792755
Heating Cable & Hose Mfr
N.A.I.C.S.: 333414

Eltherm North Africa SARL (2)
11 rue El Wahda Res Iman Ali Appt 2, 20000, Casablanca, Morocco
Tel.: (212) 15152406051
Heating Cable & Hose Mfr
N.A.I.C.S.: 333414

Eltherm Rus Limited Liability Company (2)
21V Shkolnaya Street Room 1 Moscow Region, Bolshevo District, 141060, Korolev, Russia
Tel.: (7) 9067700811
Heating Cable & Hose Mfr
N.A.I.C.S.: 333414

Eltherm Schweiz AG (2)
Untere Steig 11, 8462, Rheinau, Switzerland
Tel.: (41) 523194286
Heating Cable & Hose Mfr
N.A.I.C.S.: 333414

Eltherm South Africa (Pty) Ltd. (2)
Upper Graystone Office Park 150 Linden Rd, Sandton, South Africa
Tel.: (27) 113266475
Heating Cable & Hose Mfr
N.A.I.C.S.: 333414

Eltherm Spain, S.L.U. (2)
Avd Mas d en Serra N 114 Local 7 Les Roquetes, 08812, Barcelona, Spain
Tel.: (34) 938141984
Heating Cable & Hose Mfr
N.A.I.C.S.: 333414

AND PRIVATE COMPANIES

INDUS HOLDING AG

Eltherm UK Ltd. (2)
Unit 7 Kingfisher Court Hambridge Road,
Newbury, RG14 5SJ, United Kingdom
Tel.: (44) 1635255280
Heating Cable & Hose Mfr
N.A.I.C.S.: 333414

FS-BF GmbH & Co. KG (1)
Hahnenseifener Strasse 15, Hahn, 51580,
Reichshof, Germany
Tel.: (49) 229791030
Web Site: https://www.fsbf.com
Construction Materials Whslr
N.A.I.C.S.: 423320

GSR Ventiltechnik GmbH & Co.
KG (1)
Im Meisenfeld 1, Nordrhein-Westfalen,
32602, Vlotho, Germany
Tel.: (49) 52287790
Web Site: https://www.ventiltechnik.de
Sales Range: $50-74.9 Million
Emp.: 150
Automated Mechanical Valves Mfr
N.A.I.C.S.: 332911

H. Heitz Furnierkantenwerk GmbH &
Co. KG (1)
Maschweg 27, 49324, Melle, Germany
Tel.: (49) 54229680
Web Site: https://www.h-heitz.de
Wood Veneer Edge Mfr
N.A.I.C.S.: 321211
Ralf Diekmann *(Mgr-Technical)*

HAKAMA AG (1)
Hauptstrasse 50, 4112, Battwil,
Switzerland (60%)
Tel.: (41) 61 735 45 45
Web Site: http://www.hakama.ch
Developer, Designer & Mfr of Individual
Housings & Structural Components in Steel
Sheet, Stainless Steel, Aluminum & Other
Non-Precious Metals
N.A.I.C.S.: 331110

HAUFF-TECHNIK GmbH & Co.
KG (1)
Robert-Bosch-Strasse 9, Hermaringen,
89568, Stuttgart, Germany
Tel.: (49) 732213330
Web Site: https://www.hauff-technik.de
Emp.: 450
Pipes & Ducts Mfr
N.A.I.C.S.: 322220
Michael Seibold *(Gen Mgr)*

HELD Systems GmbH (1)
Marie-Curie-Str 9, 63128, Dietzenbach,
Germany
Tel.: (49) 610466480
Web Site: https://held-systems.com
Electric Equipment Mfr
N.A.I.C.S.: 334419

HORN GmbH & Co. KG (1)
Tel.: (49) 46186960
Web Site: http://www.tecalemet.de
Sales Range: $50-74.9 Million
Emp.: 120
Fuel Dispensing Systems Mfr
N.A.I.C.S.: 333914

Heavac B.V. (1)
Gulberg 10, Nuenen, 5674 TE, Netherlands
Tel.: (31) 402092100
Bus Product Mfr
N.A.I.C.S.: 336211

Heiber Schroder GmbH (1)
Feldheider Str 52, 40699, Erkrath, Germany
Tel.: (49) 210493760
Web Site: https://heiber-schroeder.com
Emp.: 70
Packaging Products Mfr
N.A.I.C.S.: 326112

Helmut RUBSAMEN GmbH & Co.
KG (1)
Carl-Goerdeler-Allee 6, 56470, Bad Marienberg, Germany
Tel.: (49) 266198510
Web Site: https://www.helmut-ruebsamen.de
Precision Tool Mfr
N.A.I.C.S.: 332216

Horngroup Holding GmbH & Co.
KG (1)
Munketoft 42, 24937, Flensburg, Germany
Tel.: (49) 46186960

Web Site: http://www.tecalemit.de
Measuring & Dispensing Equipment Mfr
N.A.I.C.S.: 333914
Torsten H. Kutschinski *(Mng Dir)*

IEF-Werner GmbH (1)
Wendelhofstr 6, 78120, Furtwangen, Germany
Tel.: (49) 77239250
Web Site: https://www.ief-werner.de
Emp.: 160
Modular Component Mfr
N.A.I.C.S.: 334419

Subsidiary (Non-US):

IEF-Werner (Taiwan) Limited (2)
No 12 RongHua 3rd Road TW- 112, Taipei,
Taiwan
Tel.: (886) 228220460
Modular Component Mfr
N.A.I.C.S.: 332311

IMECO Einwegprodukte GmbH & Co.
KG Vliesstoffvertrieb (1)
Boschstrasse 5, 63768, Hosbach, Germany
Tel.: (49) 602133380
Web Site: http://www.imeco.de
Nonwoven Product Mfr
N.A.I.C.S.: 313230

IMECO GmbH & Co. KG (1)
Am Sagewerk 10, 63773, Goldbach, Germany
Tel.: (49) 602133380
Web Site: https://www.imeco.de
Emp.: 165
Nonwoven Product Mfr
N.A.I.C.S.: 313230

IPETRONIK GmbH & Co. KG (1)
Im Rollfeld 28, 76532, Baden-Baden, Germany
Tel.: (49) 722199220
Web Site: https://www.ipetronik.com
Sales Range: $25-49.9 Million
Emp.: 100
Measurement Devices Mfr
N.A.I.C.S.: 334513

Subsidiary (Domestic):

CAETEC GmbH (2)
Industriestrasse 1, 82140, Olching,
Germany (100%)
Tel.: (49) 8142 501 360
Web Site: http://www.caetec.com
Mobile Measurement Technology Developer
& Mfr
N.A.I.C.S.: 334513

Ipetronik Eichstatt GmbH (1)
Industriestrasse 10, 85072, Eichstaett, Germany
Tel.: (49) 842193740
DAQ Software & Test Bench Services
N.A.I.C.S.: 541511

Ipetronik Inc. (1)
24445 Northwestern Hwy Ste 114, Southfield, MI 48075
Tel.: (248) 728-4555
DAQ Software & Test Bench Services
N.A.I.C.S.: 541511

Ipetronik India Private Limited (1)
No 20 6th Floor Unit No 603 Brigade Rubix
Building, Watch Factory Road HMT Main
Road Yeshwanthpur, Bengaluru, 560022,
India
Tel.: (91) 8029724480
DAQ Software & Test Bench Services
N.A.I.C.S.: 541511

KIEBACK GmbH & Co. KG (1)
Kiebitzheide 2-4, 49084, Osnabruck, Lower
Saxony, Germany
Tel.: (49) 541957060
Web Site: http://www.kieback.de
Emp.: 90
Moulds & Prototypes Mfr
N.A.I.C.S.: 333511

Karl SIMON GmbH & Co. KG (1)
Sulgener Strasse 19-23, 78733, Aichhalden,
Baden-Wurttemberg, Germany
Tel.: (49) 7422565123
Web Site: http://www.simon.de
Sales Range: $25-49.9 Million
Emp.: 70
Metallic Components Mfr

N.A.I.C.S.: 325130

Knur Maschinenbau GmbH (1)
Gewerbepark B7, Worth an der Donau,
93086, Regensburg, Germany
Tel.: (49) 9482802190
Web Site: https://www.knur-mb.de
Emp.: 30
Automotive Machinery Mfr
N.A.I.C.S.: 333248
Reinhold Ziewers *(Mng Dir)*

Konrad SCHAFER GmbH (1)
Brueckenstrasse 4-6, 49090, Osnabruck,
Lower Saxony, Germany
Tel.: (49) 541910560
Web Site: http://www.konrad-schaefer.de
Sales Range: $25-49.9 Million
Emp.: 400
Automobile Models Designing Services
N.A.I.C.S.: 339999
Jorg Kieback *(Gen Mgr)*

Koster & Co. GmbH (1)
Spreeler Weg 32, 58256, Ennepetal, Germany
Tel.: (49) 233383060
Web Site: https://www.koeco.net
Welding Machine & Welding Gun Mfr
N.A.I.C.S.: 333992
Harald Schulz *(CEO)*

Koster CZ s.r.o. (1)
Nadrazni 235, Zacler, 542 01, Hradec Kralove, Czech Republic
Tel.: (49) 499776165
Welding Machine & Welding Gun Mfr
N.A.I.C.S.: 333992

M&P International Mess-und Rechnertechnik GmbH (1)
Thumithistrasse 2, 30519, Hannover, Germany
Tel.: (49) 511856030
Web Site: http://www.mpihome.com
Vibration Testing & Dynamic Signal Analysis
Equipment Mfr
N.A.I.C.S.: 334519

M. Braun-Inertgas-Systeme
GmbH (1)
Dieselstrasse 31, 85748, Garching, Germany
Tel.: (49) 89326690
Web Site: https://www.mbraun.de
Emp.: 150
Glovebox Equipment Mfr
N.A.I.C.S.: 334516

Subsidiary (US):

M. Braun Incorporated (2)
14 Marin Way, Stratham, NH 03885-2578
Tel.: (603) 773-9333
Web Site: http://www.mbraunusa.com
Emp.: 60
Glovebox Systems & Gas Purification
Equipment Mfr
N.A.I.C.S.: 333413
Chris Chausse *(Pres & CEO)*

Subsidiary (Non-US):

M. Braun Inertgas Systems (Shanghai) Co. Ltd. (2)
Bld 1 No 145 Jintang Road, Tangzhen Pudong, Shanghai, 201201, China
Tel.: (86) 2150320257
Web Site: https://www.mbraunchina.com
Sales Range: $25-49.9 Million
Emp.: 40
Glovebox & Gas Purification Equipments
Sales
N.A.I.C.S.: 423830
Michael Zhou *(Mng Dir)*

M. Braun UK Ltd. (2)
Mansfield Business Centre Ashfield Avenue,
Mansfield, NG18 2AE, Nottinghamshire,
United Kingdom
Tel.: (49) 1623404329
Web Site: http://www.mbraun.co.uk
Sales Range: $25-49.9 Million
Emp.: 3
Glovebox Systems & Gas Purification
Equipment Mfr
N.A.I.C.S.: 333413
Paul Bane *(Pres & CEO)*

Mecalab-M. Braun AG (2)

Industriestr 22, CH 9301, Wittenbach, Switzerland
Tel.: (41) 712921099
Web Site: http://www.mecalab.com
Sales Range: $25-49.9 Million
Emp.: 5
Glove Box System Mfr
N.A.I.C.S.: 334516

MEWESTA Hydraulik GmbH & Co.
KG (1)
Dottinger Strasse 67 Industriegebiet, 72525,
Munsingen, Germany
Tel.: (49) 738193010
Web Site: https://www.mewesta.de
Sales Range: $25-49.9 Million
Emp.: 50
Hydraulic Valves & Control Units Mfr
N.A.I.C.S.: 332912

MIGUA Fugensysteme GmbH & Co.
KG (1)
Tel.: (49) 20587740
Web Site: http://www.migua.com
Sales Range: $25-49.9 Million
Emp.: 60
Mechanical Expansion Joints Mfr
N.A.I.C.S.: 332312

MIKROP AG (1)
Industriestrasse 22, 9301, Wittenbach, Switzerland
Tel.: (41) 712921080
Web Site: https://www.mikrop.ch
Sales Range: $25-49.9 Million
Emp.: 70
Optical Systems Mfr
N.A.I.C.S.: 326199

Maschinenfabrik BERNER GmbH &
Co. KG (1)
Industriestrasse 7, 97653, Bischofsheim,
Germany
Tel.: (49) 977291000
Web Site: http://www.berner-nes.de
Sales Range: $25-49.9 Million
Emp.: 75
Industrial Process Control Machines Mfr
N.A.I.C.S.: 334519

Mesutronic Geratebau GmbH (1)
Hackenfeld 13, 94259, Kirchberg, Germany
Tel.: (49) 992794100
Web Site: https://www.mesutronic.de
Metal Detector Distr
N.A.I.C.S.: 423830

NISTERHAMMER Maschinenbau
GmbH & Co. KG (1)
Hammerstr 34, 57645, Nister, Germany
Tel.: (49) 266295150
Web Site: http://www.nisterhammer.de
Sales Range: $25-49.9 Million
Emp.: 70
Cleaning Equipment Mfr & Whslr
N.A.I.C.S.: 333131
Carsten Schauhoff *(Gen Mgr)*

Nea International bv (1)
PO Box 305, 6199 ZN, Maastricht,
Netherlands (100%)
Tel.: (31) 434079220
Web Site: http://www.push.eu
Orthopaedic Brace Mfr
N.A.I.C.S.: 339112

OBUK Hausturfullungen GmbH & Co.
KG (1)
Am Landhagen 96-98, 59302, Oelde, Germany
Tel.: (49) 25229170
Web Site: http://www.obuk.de
Sales Range: $50-74.9 Million
Emp.: 110
Entrance Door Panels Mfr
N.A.I.C.S.: 332321

OFA Bamberg GmbH (1)
Laubanger 20, 96052, Bamberg, Germany
Web Site: http://www.ofa.de
Sales Range: $100-124.9 Million
Emp.: 350
Medical Stockings & Bandages Mfr
N.A.I.C.S.: 339113

OOO Koster RUS (1)
Shluzovaya nab 8/1, 115114, Moscow, Russia
Tel.: (7) 4996782021
Welding Machine & Welding Gun Mfr

INDUS HOLDING AG

INDUS Holding AG—(Continued)
N.A.I.C.S.: 333992

PLANETROLL GmbH & Co. KG (1)
Brunnenbergstrasse 11-13, 89597,
Munderkingen, Germany
Tel.: (49) 739395180
Web Site: https://www.planetroll.de
Sales Range: $25-49.9 Million
Emp.: 40
Mechanical Power Transmission Products Whslr
N.A.I.C.S.: 423840

Peiseler GmbH & Co. KG (1)
Morsbachtalstrasse 1 and 3, 42855, Remscheid, Germany
Tel.: (49) 21919130
Web Site: https://www.peiseler.de
Emp.: 200
Rotary Tilt Table Mfr
N.A.I.C.S.: 337126

Subsidiary (US):

Peiseler LLC (2)
601 Crosby St NW, Grand Rapids, MI 49504
Tel.: (616) 235-8460
Heating & Air Conditioning System Mfr
N.A.I.C.S.: 333415

REBOPLASTIC GmbH & Co. KG (1)
Industriestr 7, 32689, Kalletal, Germany
Tel.: (49) 573391010
Web Site: http://www.reboplastic.de
Plastic Parts Mfr & Distr
N.A.I.C.S.: 325211

REMKO GmbH & Co. KG (1)
Im Seelenkamp 12, 32791, Lage, Germany
Tel.: (49) 52326060
Web Site: https://www.remko.de
Construction Services
N.A.I.C.S.: 236220

REMKO GmbH & Co. KG Klima- und Warmetechnik (1)
Im Seelenkamp 12, Lippe, 32791, Lage, Germany
Tel.: (49) 52326060
Web Site: http://www.remko.de
Emp.: 100
Air Conditioner & Heating Systems Mfr
N.A.I.C.S.: 333415

Subsidiary (Domestic):

Krone Kalte+Klima Vertriebs-GmbH (2)
Fabrikstrasse 39, 33659, Bielefeld, Germany
Tel.: (49) 5218006990
Web Site: http://www.krone-klima.de
Air Conditioner Mfr
N.A.I.C.S.: 333415

Raguse Gesellschaft Fur Medizinische Produkte Mbh (1)
Sudfeld 6 Herbern, 59387, Ascheberg, Germany
Tel.: (49) 259993910
Web Site: https://www.raguse.de
Emp.: 66
Medical Device Mfr
N.A.I.C.S.: 339112

Rolko Kohlgruber GmbH (1)
Industriestr 14-16, Borgholzhausen, 33829, Gutersloh, Germany
Tel.: (49) 542594020
Web Site: http://www.rolko-en.com
Wheelchair Accessories Mfr & Distr
N.A.I.C.S.: 339113

Subsidiary (Non-US):

Rolko Nederland bv (2)
Package Boat 51, 3991 CH, Houten, Netherlands
Tel.: (31) 302567890
Rehabilitation Equipment Distr
N.A.I.C.S.: 423450

Rolko Scandinavia ApS (2)
Suensonsvej 2, 8600, Silkeborg, Denmark
Tel.: (45) 87201888
Rehabilitation Equipment Distr
N.A.I.C.S.: 423450

S.M.A.Metalltechnik GmbH & Co. KG (1)
Karl-Ferdinand-Braun-Strasse 9, 71522, Backnang, Baden-Wurttemberg, Germany
Tel.: (49) 719132500
Web Site: http://www.sma-metalltechnik.de
Sales Range: $100-124.9 Million
Emp.: 480
Automotive Pipes Mfr
N.A.I.C.S.: 336390

SCHUSTER Klima Luftung GmbH & Co. KG (1)
Balthasar Schaller Str 2, 86316, Friedberg, Germany
Tel.: (49) 821 2 46 750
Web Site: http://www.klima-schuster.de
Emp.: 69
Air Conditioning Systems Design & Installation Services
N.A.I.C.S.: 238220

SELZER Automotiva do Brasil Ltda. (1)
Rua Francisco Foga 550 Distrito Industrial, Vinhedo, 13280-000, Sao Paulo, Brazil
Tel.: (55) 1938267900
Emp.: 50
Transmission & Brake Component Mfr
N.A.I.C.S.: 336390
Lutz Henkel (Mng Dir)

SELZER Automotive RO SRL (1)
Borsului Street Number 34, 410605, Oradea, Romania
Tel.: (40) 2775810
Gearbox Component Mfr
N.A.I.C.S.: 333612

SELZER Automotive Systems Co., Ltd. (1)
No 329 Jujin Road, Thang Pu Town, Kunshan, 215321, Jiangsu, China
Tel.: (86) 51236851111
Gearshift Dome Mfr
N.A.I.C.S.: 333612

SEMET Maschinenbau GmbH & Co. KG (1)
Daimlerstr 13, Meimsheim, 74336, Brackenheim, Baden-Wurttemberg, Germany
Tel.: (49) 713598800
Web Site: http://www.semet-gmbh.de
Sales Range: $25-49.9 Million
Emp.: 30
Industrial Transport & Handling Systems Mfr
N.A.I.C.S.: 333922

SIKU GmbH (1)
Stockenstrasse 5, 6221, Rickenbach, Zurich, Switzerland
Tel.: (41) 419302570
Web Site: http://www.simon.de
Plastic Molding Parts Mfr
N.A.I.C.S.: 333248

SITEK-Spikes GmbH & Co. KG (1)
Sulgener Strasse 19-23, 78733, Aichhalden, Germany
Tel.: (49) 74225650
Web Site: https://www.betek.de
Tyre Studs Mfr
N.A.I.C.S.: 332322

TSN Turmbau Steffens & Nolle GmbH (1)
Meeraner Strasse 21, 12681, Berlin, Germany
Tel.: (49) 30747020
Web Site: https://www.turmbau.de
Sales Range: $25-49.9 Million
Emp.: 50
Communication Tower Construction Services
N.A.I.C.S.: 237130
Steffen Traue (Mng Dir)

VULKAN INOX GmbH (1)
Gottwaldstr 21, 45525, Hattingen, Germany
Tel.: (49) 232456160
Web Site: https://www.vulkan-inox.de
Sales Range: $25-49.9 Million
Emp.: 50
Stainless Steel Balls Mfr
N.A.I.C.S.: 331513

Subsidiary (Non-US):

Blastmaster Pty. Ltd. (2)
1-3 Bruce Ave, PO Box 1144, Marleston, Adelaide, 5033, SA, Australia
Tel.: (61) 882922000
Web Site: http://www.blastmaster.com.au
Sales Range: $25-49.9 Million
Emp.: 40
Steel Abrasives Distr
N.A.I.C.S.: 423840

Cym Materiales S.A. (2)
Brig Estanislao Lopez N 6, S2108AIB, Santa Fe, Argentina
Tel.: (54) 341 490 1100
Web Site: http://www.cymmateriales.com.ar
Sales Range: $25-49.9 Million
Emp.: 65
Steel Abrasives Distr
N.A.I.C.S.: 423840

In & Out ST Co., Ltd. (2)
Rm 405 Junwon Bldg 1635-6 Seocho 1-Dong, Seocho-Gu, Seoul, 137-879, Korea (South)
Tel.: (82) 25221023
Emp.: 5
Steel Abrasives Distr
N.A.I.C.S.: 423840

Kinsei Matec Co., Ltd. (2)
No 2-3-7 Hiranochima, Chuo-ku, Osaka, 541-0046, Japan
Tel.: (81) 662211291
Web Site: http://www.kinseimatec.co.jp
Silica Sands Mfr
N.A.I.C.S.: 327120
Takeshita Gentaro (Pres)

Metalltechnik (UK) Ltd (2)
YEW Tree Meadow Maple Rd Clows Top, Kidderminster, DY14 9HX, Shropshire, United Kingdom
Tel.: (44) 1299832100
Sales Range: $25-49.9 Million
Emp.: 6
Steel Abrasives Distr
N.A.I.C.S.: 423840
John Albert Moore (Mng Dir)

Metimpex Sp. z o.o. (2)
Ul Gromadzka 101, 30-719, Krakow, Poland
Tel.: (48) 122668071
Web Site: http://www.metimpex.com.pl
Sales Range: $25-49.9 Million
Emp.: 13
Steel Abrasives Distr
N.A.I.C.S.: 423840

Sirikul Engineering Ltd. Part. (2)
55/11 Village No 3 Suksawat Road 70 Yaek 13, Bang Khru, Phra Pradaeng, 10130, Samutprakarn, Thailand
Tel.: (66) 24626787
Web Site: http://www.sirikul.com
Steel Abrasives Sales
N.A.I.C.S.: 423840

Sonnimax A/S (2)
Nyvang 3, 5500, Middelfart, Denmark
Tel.: (45) 64401122
Web Site: https://www.sonnimax.com
Emp.: 18
Shotblasting Machines & Equipments Distr
N.A.I.C.S.: 423830
Erik Pandrup (Mgr)

Syntech Distributors Ltd. (2)
12A Saunders Pl, PO Box 19341, Avondale, 1026, Auckland, New Zealand
Tel.: (64) 98202121
Web Site: http://www.syntechnz.com
Steel Abrasives Distr
N.A.I.C.S.: 423840

WEIGAND Bau GmbH (1)
Herbstadter Strasse 17, 97631, Konigshofen im Grabfeld, Germany
Tel.: (49) 976191000
Web Site: https://www.weigandbau.de
Sales Range: $50-74.9 Million
Emp.: 150
Drilling & Underground Cable Laying Services
N.A.I.C.S.: 237130

WEINISCH GmbH & Co. KG (1)
Gewerbepark 9-15, Oberviechtach, 92526, Schwandorf, Germany
Tel.: (49) 967192120
Web Site: https://www.weinisch.de
Powder Coating Mfr
N.A.I.C.S.: 325510

INTERNATIONAL PUBLIC

WIESAUPLAST Kunststoff und Formenbau GmbH & Co. KG (1)
Am Industriepark 1, 95676, Wiesau, Germany
Tel.: (49) 9634880
Web Site: http://www.wiesauplast.de
Sales Range: $125-149.9 Million
Emp.: 350
Automotive Plastic Mold Mfr
N.A.I.C.S.: 325211

Wiesauplast Deutschland GmbH & Co. KG (1)
Am Industriepark 1, 95676, Wiesau, Germany
Tel.: (49) 9634880
Web Site: http://www.wiesauplast.de
Investment Management Service
N.A.I.C.S.: 523940

Subsidiary (Domestic):

Mid-Tronic Wiesauplast GmbH (2)
Max-Planck-Weg 7, 95676, Wiesau, Germany
Tel.: (49) 963488820
Plastic Injection Molding Mfr
N.A.I.C.S.: 326199

Subsidiary (Non-US):

Wiesauplast De Mexico S. De R.L. De C.V (2)
AV Santa Fe No 15 Parque Industrial Opcion, Guanajuato, San Jose Iturbide, 37980, Mexico
Tel.: (52) 4191090402
Plastic Injection Molding Mfr
N.A.I.C.S.: 326199

Subsidiary (US):

Wiesauplast USA LLC (2)
26200 Town Center Dr Ste 145, Detroit, MI 48375
Tel.: (248) 531-6411
Plastic Injection Molding Mfr
N.A.I.C.S.: 326199

in-situ Gmbh (1)
Muhlweg 2C, 82054, Sauerlach, Germany
Tel.: (49) 8104909600
Web Site: http://www.in-situ.de
Camera System Mfr
N.A.I.C.S.: 333310

INDUS PETROCHEM LIMITED

1501-A Universal Majestic PL
Lokhande Marg, Chembur, Mumbai, 400088, India
Tel.: (91) 22 6516 3911   In
Industrial Inorganic Chemical Mfr
N.A.I.C.S.: 325180

Subsidiaries:

Sunshield Chemicals Ltd. (1)
1501-A Universal Majestic P L Lokhande Marg, Opp RBK International School Chembur West, Mumbai, 400043, Maharashtra, India **(62.36%)**
Tel.: (91) 2225550126
Web Site: https://sunshieldchemicals.com
Rev: $29,563,719
Assets: $21,248,067
Liabilities: $13,335,016
Net Worth: $7,913,051
Earnings: $1,637,923
Emp.: 170
Fiscal Year-end: 03/31/2023
Chemical Products Mfr & Distr
N.A.I.C.S.: 325998
Manoj Khullar (Mng Dir)

INDUSIND BANK LTD.

2401 Gen Thimmayya Road, Pune, 411 001, India
Tel.: (91) 2026343201   In
Web Site: https://www.indusind.com
Year Founded: 1994
IDUSB—(LUX)
Rev.: $5,339,522,019
Assets: $54,889,281,698
Liabilities: $48,340,313,590
Net Worth: $6,548,968,107
Earnings: $3,154,830,286
Emp.: 38,179

AND PRIVATE COMPANIES

INDUSTRIA DE DISENO TEXTIL, S.A.

Fiscal Year-end: 03/31/23
Financial Investment Services
N.A.I.C.S.: 523999
Haresh K. Gajwani *(Sec)*

Subsidiaries:

Bharat Financial Inclusion
Limited (1)
3rd Floor My Home Tycoon Block A, 6-3-1192 Kundanbagh Begumpet, Hyderabad, 500 016, Telangana, India
Tel.: (91) 4044526000
Web Site: https://www.bfil.co.in
Rev.: $327,070,950
Assets: $1,794,175,873
Liabilities: $1,327,570,302
Net Worth: $466,605,571
Earnings: $70,872,413
Emp.: 15,465
Fiscal Year-end: 03/31/2018
Microfinance Lending Services
N.A.I.C.S.: 522310
Rajendra Patil *(Officer-Compliance, Sec & Sr Exec VP-Legal)*

INDUSTRI BETON AS
Hovergardevej 15, Olstrup Middle Jutland, Ringkobing, 6950, Denmark
Tel.: (45) 97 34 60 24
Web Site: http://www.industribeton.dk
Year Founded: 2002
Concrete Material Mfr
N.A.I.C.S.: 327390
Soren Bank Sorensen *(Mgr)*

Subsidiaries:

Perstrup Beton Industri A/S (1)
Krindelen 4-6 Pederstrup, 8560, Kolind, 8560, Denmark **(100%)**
Tel.: (45) 87748500
Web Site: http: www.industribeton.dk
Mfr of Concrete Furnishings for Farm Buildings & Concrete Tanks for Water Storage & Fertilizer
N.A.I.C.S.: 327390

INDUSTRIA AUTOMOTRIZ, S.A. DE C.V.
Avenida Universidad 1011 Norte Centro De La Ciudad, 66400, San Nicolas, Nuevo Leon, Mexico
Tel.: (52) 18183769797
Year Founded: 1957
IASASA—(MEX)
Sales Range: Less than $1 Million
Automobile Assembly Parts Mfr
N.A.I.C.S.: 336110
Gregorio Ramirez Jauregui *(Chm & CEO)*

INDUSTRIA DE DISENO TEXTIL, S.A.
Edificio Inditex Avda de la Diputacion s/n, 15143, La Coruna, Spain
Tel.: (34) 981185400
Web Site: https://www.inditex.com
Year Founded: 1963
ITX—(MAD)
Rev.: $38,794,517,591
Assets: $35,328,081,157
Liabilities: $15,176,991,150
Net Worth: $20,151,090,006
Earnings: $5,822,361,321
Emp.: 161,281
Fiscal Year-end: 01/31/24
Clothing Product Mfr
N.A.I.C.S.: 315250
Amancio Ortega Gaona *(Founder)*

Subsidiaries:

BCN Disenos, S.A. de C.V (1)
Centro Comercial No 2251, Naucalpan, 53100, Mexico
Tel.: (52) 5553438173
Fashion Apparels Retailer
N.A.I.C.S.: 458110

BSKE, Gmbh (1)
Monckebergstrasse 11, 20095, Hamburg, Germany

Tel.: (49) 4030962220
Web Site: http://www.bershka.com
Clothing Apparel & Accessories Retailer
N.A.I.C.S.: 458110

Bershka BSK Espana S.A. (1)
Poligono Inditex Ctra Tordera Palafolls PK 06, 08490, Tordera, Barcelona, Spain
Tel.: (34) 937667698
Web Site: http://www.bershka.com
Sales Range: $1-4.9 Billion
Family Clothing Stores
N.A.I.C.S.: 458110
Oscar Perez Marcote *(Mgr)*

Subsidiary (Non-US):

Bershka Belgique S.A. (2)
Rue du Marais 49-53, PO Box 53, 1000, Brussels, Belgium
Tel.: (32) 22210260
Web Site: http://www.bershka.com
Emp.: 20
Retail Clothing Stores
N.A.I.C.S.: 458110
Smerels Flrncoes *(Dir Gen)*

Bershka Ceska Republica S.R.O. (2)
Rybna 682/14, 11000, Prague, Czech Republic
Tel.: (420) 224239873
Clothing Whslr
N.A.I.C.S.: 424350

Bershka Deutschland B.V. & CO. KG (2)
Monckebergstrasse 10, 20095, Hamburg, Germany
Tel.: (49) 4030962222
Web Site: http://www.bershka.com
Fashion Apparel & Leather Goods Retailer
N.A.I.C.S.: 458110
Matthias Alipass *(Gen Mgr)*

Subsidiary (Domestic):

Bershka Diseno, S.L. (2)
Poligono Inditex Ctra, Palafolls PK 0 6, 08490, Tordera, Barcelona, Spain
Tel.: (34) 937667698
Fashion Apparels Retailer
N.A.I.C.S.: 458110

Subsidiary (Non-US):

Bershka France, S.A.R.L. (2)
80 Av des Terroirs de France - 6 Immeuble, Garonne, 75012, Paris, France
Tel.: (33) 155788888
Fashion Apparels Retailer
N.A.I.C.S.: 458110

Bershka Hellas, S.A. (2)
Scadiou 59, Athens, 10551, Greece
Tel.: (30) 2103243101
Web Site: http://www.bershka.com
Fashion Apparels Retailer
N.A.I.C.S.: 458110
Ilias Malamas *(Gen Mgr)*

Bershka Hong Kong Limited (2)
Suite 3402-05 Tower 2 The Gateway 25 Canton Road, Tsim Tsa Tsui, China (Hong Kong)
Tel.: (852) 29563322
Sales Range: $25-49.9 Million
Emp.: 50
Fashion Apparels Retailer
N.A.I.C.S.: 458110

Bershka Ireland Ltd. (2)
Block 5 5th Floor Harcourt Centre Harcourt Road, Dublin, Munster, Ireland
Tel.: (353) 14161024
Sales Range: $25-49.9 Million
Emp.: 20
Clothing Accessories Stores
N.A.I.C.S.: 458110
Aisling Campbell *(Gen Mgr)*

Bershka Italia S.R.L. (2)
Largo Corsia Dei Servi 3, 20122, Milan, Italy
Tel.: (39) 028180081
Apparel Stores
N.A.I.C.S.: 458110

Bershka Japan, Ltd. (2)
Fujiwara Building 6F 1-10-11 Ebisu-nishi, Shibuya-Ku, Tokyo, 150-0021, Japan

Tel.: (81) 364158061
Web Site: http://www.bershka.com
Fashion Apparel Mfr & Distr
N.A.I.C.S.: 458110

Bershka Korea, Ltd. (2)
20th Fl World Trade Center 159-1 Samsung-dong, Kangnam-ku, Seoul, 135-729, Korea (South)
Tel.: (82) 234139800
Sales Range: $25-49.9 Million
Emp.: 70
Fashion Apparels Retailer
N.A.I.C.S.: 458110

Subsidiary (Domestic):

Bershka Logistica, S.A. (2)
Deputacion Pg Ind Sabon Ed Inditex S/N, 15142, Arteixo, Spain
Tel.: (34) 937667698
Freight Forwarding Services
N.A.I.C.S.: 488510

Subsidiary (Non-US):

Bershka Magyaroszag Kft. (2)
Vaxi Utca 6 Kristof Ter 2, Budapest, 1052, Hungary
Tel.: (36) 13270200
Web Site: http://www.bershka.com
Emp.: 10
Fashion Apparels Retailer
N.A.I.C.S.: 458110
Roland Retfalvi *(Pres)*

Bershka Nederland B.V. (2)
Nieuwezijds Voorbugwal 305, 1012 RM, Amsterdam, Netherlands
Tel.: (31) 205305660
Sales Range: $25-49.9 Million
Emp.: 8
Women Apparel Sales
N.A.I.C.S.: 458110
Natale Can Timmeren *(Mgr)*

Bershka Osterreich Clothing GmbH (2)
Shopping City Seiersberg, 8055, Seiersberg, Styria, Austria
Tel.: (43) 316241440
Web Site: http://www.bershka.com
Sales Range: $25-49.9 Million
Emp.: 15
Clothing Accessories Stores
N.A.I.C.S.: 458110

Bershka Polska Sp Z O.O. (2)
Varso Tower Ul Chmielna 69, 00-801, Warsaw, Poland
Tel.: (48) 225965150
Fashion Apparels Retailer
N.A.I.C.S.: 458110

Bershka Suisse S.A.R.L. (2)
Rue Louie-daffry 6, 1700, Fribourg, Switzerland
Tel.: (41) 263501660
Sales Range: $25-49.9 Million
Emp.: 11
Footwear Mfr
N.A.I.C.S.: 316210

Bershka Bulgaria, Ltd. (1)
115 K Tsarigradsko Shose Blvd - Office Building B, Office 1 1 2nd Office 1 1, 1784, Sofia, Bulgaria
Tel.: (359) 28057105
Fashion Apparels Retailer
N.A.I.C.S.: 458110

Bershka Cis, Ltd. (1)
6 Gasheka Street 6 -Building 1 - 11th floor, 125047, Moscow, Russia
Tel.: (7) 4956431355
Web Site: http://www.bershka.com
Clothing Apparel & Accessories Retailer
N.A.I.C.S.: 458110

Bershka Commercial (Shanghai) Co. Ltd. (1)
21F ShengGao International Building - 137 XianXia Road, Shanghai, 200051, China
Tel.: (86) 2161611900
Web Site: http://www.bershka.com
Clothing Apparel & Accessories Retailer
N.A.I.C.S.: 458110

Bershka Giyim Ithalat Ihracat Ve Tic. Ltd. (1)
MM Plaza Nispetiye Mahallesi Aytar Cad

Baslik Sokak No 3 Kat 4, Levent Besiktas, Istanbul, Turkiye
Tel.: (90) 2123868101
Clothing Apparel & Accessories Retailer
N.A.I.C.S.: 458110

Bershka Mexico, S.A. de C.V. (1)
C/ Poniente 146 No 730 Colonia Industrial Vallejo Deleg, Azcapotzalco, 02300, Mexico, Mexico
Tel.: (52) 5550782000
Clothing Apparel & Accessories Retailer
N.A.I.C.S.: 458110

Bershka Portugal Conf. Soc. Unip. SA (1)
Av Fontes Pereira de Melo 49 2 izquierda, 1050-120, Lisbon, Portugal
Tel.: (351) 213183900
Clothing Apparel & Accessories Retailer
N.A.I.C.S.: 458110

Bershka Serbia, D.O.O. (1)
Milentija Popovica 7u, 11070, Belgrade, Serbia
Tel.: (381) 112011800
Web Site: http://www.bershka.com
Clothing Apparel & Accessories Retailer
N.A.I.C.S.: 458110

Bershka Slovakia, S.R.O. (1)
Einsteinova 18, 851 01, Bratislava, Slovakia
Tel.: (421) 36780243
Web Site: http://www.bershka.com
Clothing Apparel & Accessories Retailer
N.A.I.C.S.: 458110

Bershka U.K., Ltd. (1)
Lumina House 89 New Bond Street, London, W1S 1DA, United Kingdom
Tel.: (44) 2078514300
Web Site: http://www.bershka.com
Clothing Apparel & Accessories Retailer
N.A.I.C.S.: 458110

Choolet S.A. (1)
Avenida Deputacion LGO Industrials, Arteixo, La Coruna, 15142, Spain
Tel.: (34) 981185438
Emp.: 100
Men Clothing Stores
N.A.I.C.S.: 315210

Comditel S.A. (1)
Avda Disputacion S N, Arteixo, La Coruna, 15142, Spain
Tel.: (34) 934677046
Textiles Goods Whslr
N.A.I.C.S.: 314999

Confecciones Fios, S.A. (1)
Sabon Industrial Estate Avenue Of The Council s/n Edificio Inditex, Arteixo, 15142, La Coruna, Spain
Tel.: (34) 981185407
Fashion Apparels Mfr
N.A.I.C.S.: 314999

Denllo S.A. (1)
Avda Deputacion Ed Inditex Pg Indust Sabon, Arteixo, 15142, La Coruna, Spain
Tel.: (34) 981185312
Textile Products Mfr
N.A.I.C.S.: 314999

G. Zara Home Uruguay, S.A. (1)
Luis Alberto Herrera 1290 - Local 400, 11300, Montevideo, Uruguay
Tel.: (598) 26289017
Clothing Apparel & Accessories Retailer
N.A.I.C.S.: 458110

G.Zara Uruguay, S.A. (1)
Luis Alberto Herrera 1290 - Local 400, 11300, Montevideo, Uruguay
Tel.: (598) 26289017
Cloth Retail Sales Services
N.A.I.C.S.: 458110

Glencare S.A. (1)
Av de la Diputacion Edificio Inditex, Arteixo, La Coruna, 15142, Spain
Tel.: (34) 981185392
Web Site: http://www.inditex.com
Sales Range: $25-49.9 Million
Emp.: 100
Textile Designing Services
N.A.I.C.S.: 541490
Misael Miguel *(Mng Dir)*

Goa Invest S.A. (1)

3665

INDUSTRIA DE DISENO TEXTIL, S.A.

Industria de Diseno Textil, S.A.—(Continued)

Plg Sabon Arteixo Av Diputacion S N Ed Inditex, Arteixo, La Coruna, 15142, Spain
Tel.: (34) 981185400
Property Management Services
N.A.I.C.S.: 531312

Grupo Massimo Dutti S.A. (1)
Avda de la Diputacion Edificio Inditex, Palafolls KM 06, 15143, Arteixo, Spain
Tel.: (34) 937667699
Sales Range: $1-4.9 Billion.
Emp.: 500
Women's Clothing Store
N.A.I.C.S.: 458110

Subsidiary (Non-US):

MD Benelux, N.V. (2)
Zuidzandstraat 41, 8000, Brugge, Belgium
Tel.: (32) 50344038
Sales Range: $25-49.9 Million
Emp.: 11
Fashion Apparels Retailer
N.A.I.C.S.: 458110

Massimo Dutti Danmark A/S (2)
Klosterstraede 1, 1157, Copenhagen, Denmark
Tel.: (45) 80250589
Web Site: https://www.massimodutti.com
Fashion Apparel Distr
N.A.I.C.S.: 424310

Massimo Dutti Deutschland Gmbh (2)
Monckebergstr 7, 20095, Hamburg, Germany
Tel.: (49) 4032004999
Web Site: http://www.inditext.com
Emp.: 90
Clothing Accessories Stores
N.A.I.C.S.: 458110
Matthias Alipass *(Mgr)*

Subsidiary (Domestic):

Massimo Dutti Diseno, S.L (2)
Avda de la Diputacion, Edificio Inditex, 15143, Arteixo, Spain
Tel.: (34) 937667699
Fashion Apparels Retailer
N.A.I.C.S.: 458110

Subsidiary (Non-US):

Massimo Dutti France S.A.R.L. (2)
24 rue Royale, 75009, Paris, France
Tel.: (33) 800916597
Web Site: https://static.massimodutti.net
Women's Apparel Stores
N.A.I.C.S.: 458110

Massimo Dutti Giyim Ithalat Ih.Ve Tic. Ltd (2)
Kule 2 K 21 Is Kuleleri, Istanbul, Turkiye
Tel.: (90) 2122840422
Fashion Apparels Retailer
N.A.I.C.S.: 458110

Massimo Dutti Hellas S.A (2)
59 Stadiou St, 10564, Athens, Greece
Tel.: (30) 2103243101
Web Site: http://www.massimodutti.com
Clothing Accessories Stores
N.A.I.C.S.: 458110
Ilias Malamas *(Gen Mgr)*

Massimo Dutti Hong Kong Ltd (2)
Room 1 8-12 Tower 2 34/F The Gateway Harbour City, 25 Canton Road TSIMSHA TSUI, Kowloon, China (Hong Kong)
Tel.: (852) 29560322
Web Site: https://www.massimodutti.com
Sales Range: $25-49.9 Million
Emp.: 25
Apparel Retailing & Sales
N.A.I.C.S.: 315990

Massimo Dutti Ireland Ltd. (2)
Fifth Floor Block 5 Harcourt Centre Harcourt Road, Sandyford Rd, Dublin, 2, Ireland
Tel.: (353) 800553426
Web Site: https://www.massimodutti.com
Sales Range: $25-49.9 Million
Emp.: 23
Broadwoven Cotton Fabric Mills
N.A.I.C.S.: 313210
Rocio Moreno *(Mgr)*

Subsidiary (Domestic):

Massimo Dutti Logistica S.A. (2)
Av Virgen De Monstserrat S/N, Tordera, 8490, Spain
Tel.: (34) 937667699
Sales Range: $1-4.9 Billion
Cargo Handling Services
N.A.I.C.S.: 488999
Rejes Umberto *(Mgr-Logistics)*

Subsidiary (Non-US):

Massimo Dutti Mexico S.A. de C.V. (2)
Poniente 146 No 730, Indust Vallejo, 06600, Cuauhtemoc, Colima, Mexico
Tel.: (52) 5550782000
Shoe Mfr
N.A.I.C.S.: 316210

Massimo Dutti Nederland, B.V. (2)
Nieuwezijds Voorburgwal 305, 1012 RM, Amsterdam, Netherlands
Tel.: (31) 8000234183
Web Site: https://www.massimodutti.com
Fashion Apparel Distr
N.A.I.C.S.: 424310

Massimo Dutti Norge AS. (2)
Bogstadveien 23, 0355, Oslo, Norway
Tel.: (47) 22598900
Web Site: http://www.massimodutti.com
Men Apparel Retailing & Sales
N.A.I.C.S.: 458110

Massimo Dutti Polska Sp z.o.o. (2)
Mysia 5, Warsaw, 00496, Poland
Tel.: (48) 225965150
Web Site: http://www.massimodutti.com
Sales Range: $25-49.9 Million
Emp.: 85
Apparel Sales
N.A.I.C.S.: 458110
Mariusz Leszczynski *(Gen Mgr)*

Massimo Dutti Portugal - Comercio e Industria Textil, S.A. (2)
Avenida Fontes Pereira de Melo 49 2 Esq, Lisbon, 1050-120, Portugal
Tel.: (351) 213183900
Fashion Apparels Retailer
N.A.I.C.S.: 458110

Massimo Dutti Ro, Srl (2)
201 Barbu Vacarescu street office no 1 9th Floor sector 2, Bucharest, 30602, Romania
Tel.: (40) 800420888
Web Site: https://www.massimodutti.com
Emp.: 15
Fashion Apparels Retailer
N.A.I.C.S.: 458110
Paul Cuza *(Gen Mgr)*

Massimo Dutti Sverige AB (2)
Vasagatan 11 7th Fl, 111 20, Stockholm, Uppland, Sweden
Tel.: (46) 854522900
Web Site: http://www.inditex.com
Sales Range: $25-49.9 Million
Emp.: 21
Women Apparel Sales
N.A.I.C.S.: 458110
Phileppa Henerdal *(Gen Mgr)*

Massimo Dutti UK Ltd (2)
156 Regent St, London, W1B 5LB, United Kingdom
Tel.: (44) 2078511280
Men Apparel Sales
N.A.I.C.S.: 315210

Subsidiary (US):

Massimo Dutti USA, Ltd. (2)
689 5th Ave Frnt 1, New York, NY 10022
Tel.: (212) 371-2417
Web Site: http://www.massimodutti.com
Fashion Apparel Distr
N.A.I.C.S.: 458110
Caisey Ashley *(Gen Mgr)*

Subsidiary (Non-US):

Massimo Dutti Ukraine, Llc (2)
Sportyvna sqr 1-A tower A 15th floor, 01001, Kiev, Ukraine
Tel.: (380) 443932990
Web Site: https://www.massimodutti.com
Fashion Apparels Retailer
N.A.I.C.S.: 458110

Gruputerque Portugal Confeccoes e Acessorios Lda. (1)
Avenida Fontes Pereira de Melo 49 2 N Esq, 1050-120, Lisbon, Portugal
Tel.: (351) 217159592
Sales Range: $125-149.9 Million
Emp.: 500
Fashion Apparels Retailer
N.A.I.C.S.: 458110
Pablo Isla *(CEO)*

Hampton S.A. (1)
Avda Diputacion Plgo Indust Sabon, Arteixo, 15142, La Coruna, Spain
Tel.: (34) 981185331
Womens Wear Mfr
N.A.I.C.S.: 315250

ITX Merken, B.V. (1)
Nieuwezijdsvoorburgwal 307, Amsterdam, 1012RM, Netherlands
Tel.: (31) 205309650
Fashion Apparels Retailer
N.A.I.C.S.: 458110

ITX Trading S.A. (1)
Rue Louis d'affry 6, 1700, Fribourg, Switzerland
Tel.: (41) 263092400
Web Site: http://www.inditex.com
Sales Range: $25-49.9 Million
Emp.: 15
Clothing Accessories Stores
N.A.I.C.S.: 458110
Sein Pettenhofer *(Mgr)*

Indiput Diseno, S.L. (1)
Well Industrial Poligono Rio S/N Sector 2, Naron, 15570, La Coruna, Spain
Tel.: (34) 981334800
Emp.: 250
Fashion Apparels Retailer
N.A.I.C.S.: 458110

Indiput, S.L. (1)
Industrial Rio Pozo Sector 2 Par 2, Naron, 15570, La Coruna, Spain
Tel.: (34) 981334800
Web Site: http://www.inditex.com
Sales Range: $100-124.9 Million
Emp.: 500
Textile Products Mfr
N.A.I.C.S.: 314999
Ivan Pampin *(Gen Mgr)*

Inditex Logistica, S.A. (1)
Avenue Deputation S/N, Arteixo, 15143, Spain
Tel.: (34) 981185400
Sales Range: $300-349.9 Million
Emp.: 1,500
Travel Arrangement Services
N.A.I.C.S.: 561599

Invercarpro, S.A. (1)
Pg Sabon Ind Provincial Av Ed Inditex, 15142, Arteixo, La Coruna, Spain
Tel.: (34) 981185420
Fashion Apparels Retailer
N.A.I.C.S.: 458110

Kiddy's Class Espana, S.A. (1)
Avenida Deputacion Pol Industrial Sabon S/N Edif Inditex, Arteixo, 15142, La Coruna, Spain
Tel.: (34) 981185400
Fashion Apparels Retailer
N.A.I.C.S.: 458110

Kommanditgesellschaft ZARA Deutschland B.V. & Co. (1)
Monckebergstr 10, 20095, Hamburg, Germany
Tel.: (49) 4030309827
Fashion Apparels Retailer
N.A.I.C.S.: 458110

Lefties Espana, S.A. (1)
Av Of The Delegation Edificio Inditex, Arteixo, La Coruna, Spain
Tel.: (34) 981185420
Fashion Apparels Retailer
N.A.I.C.S.: 458110

Massimo Dutti Korea, Ltd. (1)
33rd Fl 511 Yeongdong-daero, Gangnam-gu, Seoul, Korea (South)
Tel.: (82) 805006446
Web Site: https://www.massimodutti.com
Cloth Retail Sales Services

INTERNATIONAL PUBLIC

N.A.I.C.S.: 458110

Massimo Dutti Magyarorxzag Kft. (1)
Rakoczi UT 1-3 6 Floor, 1088, Budapest, Hungary
Tel.: (36) 680982540
Web Site: https://www.massimodutti.com
Cloth Retail Sales Services
N.A.I.C.S.: 458110

Massimo Dutti Slovakia, S.R.O. (1)
Einsteinova 18, 851 01, Bratislava, Slovakia
Tel.: (421) 260201080
Web Site: https://www.massimodutti.com
Clothing Apparel & Accessories Retailer
N.A.I.C.S.: 458110

Nikole S.A. (1)
Poligono Indust Sabon-Ed Inditex Avda Diputacion, Arteixo, La Coruna, 15142, Spain
Tel.: (34) 981185400
Apparels & Accessories Stores
N.A.I.C.S.: 458110

Oysho Ceska Republica, SRO (1)
Roztylska 19, 148 00, Prague, Czech Republic
Tel.: (420) 272075561
Web Site: http://www.oysho.com
Cloth Retail Sales Services
N.A.I.C.S.: 458110

Oysho Espana S.A. (1)
Camino de Tordera a Palafolls S/N, 08490, Tordera, Barcelona, Spain
Tel.: (34) 937667500
Web Site: http://www.oysho.com
Sales Range: $400-449.9 Million
Women's Apparel Stores
N.A.I.C.S.: 458110
Carmen Sevillaho Chaves *(Mgr)*

Subsidiary (Non-US):

Oysho CIS Ltd. (2)
Gasheka Bldg No 6 Fl 11 & 12th, Moscow, 125047, Russia
Tel.: (7) 4956431355
Sales Range: $25-49.9 Million
Emp.: 25
Textile Designing Services
N.A.I.C.S.: 313310

Oysho France, S.A.R.L. (2)
22 Rue Bergere, 75 009, Paris, France
Tel.: (33) 149120319
Perfume & Cosmetics Mfr
N.A.I.C.S.: 456120

Oysho Giyim Ithalat Ihracat Ve Ticaret Ltd (2)
Kule 2 K 21 Is Kuleleri, Istanbul, Turkiye
Tel.: (90) 2122840422
Women Apparel Distr
N.A.I.C.S.: 424350

Oysho Hellas S.A. (2)
Stadiou 59, Athens, 10551, Greece
Tel.: (30) 2103243101
Web Site: http://www.oysho.com
Footwear Mfr
N.A.I.C.S.: 316210
Ilias Malamas *(Mng Dir)*

Oysho Italia, S.R.L. (2)
Largo Corsia dei Servi 3, 20121, Milan, Italy
Tel.: (39) 0354596324
Women Apparel Distr
N.A.I.C.S.: 458110

Subsidiary (Domestic):

Oysho Logistica, S.A. (2)
Pg Ind Sabon Av Diputacion Ed Inditex, Arteixo, La Coruna, 15142, Spain
Tel.: (34) 981 18 54 20
Logistics Consulting Servies
N.A.I.C.S.: 541614

Subsidiary (Non-US):

Oysho MAGYARORSZAG, KFT (2)
Kristof Ter 2, Budapest, 1052, Hungary
Tel.: (36) 1 3270 200
Web Site: http://www.oysho.com
Emp.: 20
Women's Apparel Retailer
N.A.I.C.S.: 458110
Roland Retfalvi *(Gen Mgr)*

Oysho Mexico, S.A. de C.V. (2)

AND PRIVATE COMPANIES

INDUSTRIA DE DISENO TEXTIL, S.A.

5 De Febrero S/N, Queretaro, 76175, Mexico
Tel.: (52) 4422157205
Women's Apparel Retailer
N.A.I.C.S.: 458110

Oysho Polska Sp zo.o. (2)
5 Mysia, Warsaw, 00-496, Poland
Tel.: (48) 225965150
Web Site: http://www.oysho.com
Emp.: 80
Leather Clothing Mfr
N.A.I.C.S.: 316990
Mariusz Leszczynski *(Gen Mgr)*

Oysho Portugal Conf. Lda. (2)
Avenida Fontes Pereira de Melo n 49 2 Esq, 1050-120, Lisbon, Portugal
Tel.: (351) 213183900
Retail Clothing Stores
N.A.I.C.S.: 458110

Oysho Ro, Srl (2)
201 Barbu Vacarescu street office no 1 9th Floor sector 2, Bucharest, Romania
Tel.: (40) 317309272
Women Apparel Distr
N.A.I.C.S.: 424350

Oysho Serbia, D.O.O. (2)
Kneza Mihaila 11-15, Belgrade, 11102, Serbia
Tel.: (381) 112023400
Web Site: http://www.oysho.com
Emp.: 14
Women's Apparel Retailer
N.A.I.C.S.: 458110
Paulino Moreno de Leon *(Country Mgr)*

P&B Gmbh (1)
Breitscheider Weg 38, 40885, Ratingen, Germany
Tel.: (49) 2102893118
Web Site: https://www.pundbgmbh.de
Projector & Photo Printing System Repair Services
N.A.I.C.S.: 811210

Plataforma Europa S.A. (1)
C Turiaso 11 Pol Plz, 50197, Zaragoza, Spain
Tel.: (34) 976539200
Web Site: http://www.inditex.com
Sales Range: $75-99.9 Million
Emp.: 1,200
Logistics & Distribution Services
N.A.I.C.S.: 541614
Roger Navasa *(Gen Mgr)*

Plataforma Logistica Meco S.A. (1)
Poligono Indust Sabon Av Diputacion Ed Inditex, Arteixo, 15142, La Coruna, Spain
Tel.: (34) 8873500
Children Underwear Mfr
N.A.I.C.S.: 458110

Pull & Bear Bulgaria, Ltd. (1)
Totleben Boulevard 55, 1606, Sofia, Bulgaria
Tel.: (359) 928057105
Clothing Apparel & Accessories Retailer
N.A.I.C.S.: 458110

Pull & Bear Deutschland BV& Co. (1)
Monckebergstrasse 11, 20095, Hamburg, Germany
Tel.: (49) 4030962222
Clothing Apparel & Accessories Retailer
N.A.I.C.S.: 458110

Pull & Bear Espana, S.A. (1)
Poligono Industrial Rio do Pozo Av Gonzalo Navarro 37-43, Naron, 15573, La Coruna, Spain
Tel.: (34) 981334900
Web Site: http://www.pullandbear.com
Sales Range: $1-4.9 Billion
Emp.: 200
Fashion Apparels Retailer
N.A.I.C.S.: 458110
Jose Pablo del Bado Rivas *(Mgr)*

Subsidiary (Non-US):

Pull & Bear Belgique, S.A. (2)
Rue aux Laines 68-72, 1000, Brussels, Belgium
Tel.: (32) 22210261
Men & Women Apparel Distr
N.A.I.C.S.: 458110

Pablo Danglade *(Mng Dir)*

Pull & Bear Ceska Republika S.R.O. (2)
Rybna 682/14, 110 00, Prague, 1, Czech Republic
Tel.: (420) 224239873
Clothing Accessories Stores
N.A.I.C.S.: 458110

Pull & Bear Mexico S.A. de C.V. (2)
Ave Channel of Tezontle Col Alfonso Ortiz Tirado Delegation, Iztapalapa, 09020, Mexico, Mexico
Tel.: (52) 5591290294
Web Site: https://www.pullandbear.com
Clothing Whslr
N.A.I.C.S.: 458110

Pull & Bear Nederland, B.V. (2)
Nieuwezijds Voorbugwal 305, 1012RM, Amsterdam, Netherlands
Tel.: (31) 205305660
Women Apparel Distr
N.A.I.C.S.: 424350

Pull & Bear Osterreich Clothing, Gmbh (2)
Karntner Strasse 11 / Top 6, 1010, Vienna, Austria
Tel.: (43) 151279140
Apparel Retailer
N.A.I.C.S.: 458110

Pull & Bear Polska Sp zo.o (2)
5 Pawia, 31 154, Krakow, Poland
Tel.: (48) 126287823
Web Site: http://www.pullandbear.com
Sales Range: $25-49.9 Million
Emp.: 14
Clothing Accessories Stores
N.A.I.C.S.: 458110
Michael Sulaka *(Mgr)*

Pull & Bear Portugal Conf. Lda (2)
Avenida Fontes Pereira de Melo 49, 1050-120, Lisbon, Portugal
Tel.: (351) 213183900
Web Site: http://www.bearpull.com
Clothing Accessories Stores
N.A.I.C.S.: 458110

Pull & Bear Slovakia, S.R.O. (2)
Einsteinova 18, Petrzalka, 851 01, Bratislava, Slovakia
Tel.: (421) 262410857
Women Apparel Distr
N.A.I.C.S.: 424350

Pull & Bear France, S.A.R.L. (2)
Immeuble Garonne Av des Terroirs de France 80, 75012, Paris, France
Tel.: (33) 155788888
Cloth Retail Sales Services
N.A.I.C.S.: 458110

Pull & Bear Giyim Ith. Ihrac.Ve Tic. Ltd. (1)
MM Plaza Nispetiye Mahallesi Baslik Sokak No 3 Kat 4, Levent Besiktas, Istanbul, Turkiye
Tel.: (90) 2123868101
Cloth Retail Sales Services
N.A.I.C.S.: 458110

Pull & Bear Hellas, S.A. (1)
Stadiou 59, 10551, Athens, Greece
Tel.: (30) 2103243101
Cloth Retail Sales Services
N.A.I.C.S.: 458110

Pull & Bear Hong Kong Ltd. (1)
Suite 3401-5 Tower 2 - The Gateway Canton Road 25, Tsim Sha Tsui, Kowloon, China (Hong Kong)
Tel.: (852) 37180000
Clothing Apparel & Accessories Retailer
N.A.I.C.S.: 458110

Pull & Bear Ireland, Ltd. (1)
Fifth Floor Block 5 Harcourt Centre Harcourt Road, Dublin, Ireland
Tel.: (353) 2078514300
Cloth Retail Sales Services
N.A.I.C.S.: 458110

Pull & Bear Italia, S.R.L. (1)
Largo Corsia dei Servi 3, 20122, Milan, Italy
Tel.: (39) 028180081
Cloth Retail Sales Services
N.A.I.C.S.: 458110

Pull & Bear Korea, Ltd. (1)
17th Fl Lotte Shopping Bldg, Sogong-dong Joong gu, Seoul, 6538, Korea (South)
Tel.: (82) 2234139800
Clothing Apparel & Accessories Retailer
N.A.I.C.S.: 458110

Pull & Bear Magyarorszag Kft. (1)
Kristof Ter 2 - Vaci Utca 6, 1053, Budapest, Hungary
Tel.: (36) 13270200
Cloth Retail Sales Services
N.A.I.C.S.: 458110

Pull & Bear Ro, Srl (1)
Corneliu Coposu Boulevard Sector 3 2A, 30605, Bucharest, Romania
Tel.: (40) 317309272
Clothing Apparel & Accessories Retailer
N.A.I.C.S.: 458110

Pull & Bear Suisse, SARL (1)
Rue Louis d Affry 6, 1700, Fribourg, Switzerland
Tel.: (41) 263501660
Clothing Apparel & Accessories Retailer
N.A.I.C.S.: 458110

Pull & Bear Sverige, AB (1)
Sverige AB Klara Norra Kyrkogata 29, 111 22, Stockholm, Sweden
Tel.: (46) 854522900
Clothing Apparel & Accessories Retailer
N.A.I.C.S.: 458110

Pull & Bear Uk Limited (1)
Lumina House 89 New Bond Street, London, W1S 1DA, United Kingdom
Tel.: (44) 2078514300
Cloth Retail Sales Services
N.A.I.C.S.: 458110

Pull & Bear Ukraine, LLC (1)
Business Center GULLIVER Sportyvna square 1A tower A 15 floor, 01001, Kiev, Ukraine
Tel.: (380) 444958801
Clothing Apparel & Accessories Retailer
N.A.I.C.S.: 458110

Samlor S.A. (1)
Pg Idn Sabon Av Diputacion Ed Inditex S N, Arteixo, 15142, La Coruna, Spain
Tel.: (34) 981185420
Textile Designing Services
N.A.I.C.S.: 541490

Stear S.A. (1)
Avda Deputacion Lgo Indust Sabon Plgo, Arteixo, 15142, La Coruna, Spain
Tel.: (34) 981185400
Textile Designing Services
N.A.I.C.S.: 541490

Stradivarius Espana, S.A (1)
Industrial Berenguer Ii, 08650, Sallent, Spain
Tel.: (34) 938378000
Sales Range: $1-4.9 Billion
Supermarket Operator
N.A.I.C.S.: 445110
Jordi Triquell Valls *(Mgr)*

Subsidiary (Non-US):

Stradivarius BH, D.O.O. (2)
Kardinala Stipinca bb Mepas Mall, Mostar, 88000, Bosnia & Herzegovina
Tel.: (387) 33 943391
Clothing Accessories Retailer
N.A.I.C.S.: 458110

Stradivarius CIS Ltd. (2)
Gasheka St 6, Moscow, 146025, Russia
Tel.: (7) 4956431355
Clothing Accessories Stores
N.A.I.C.S.: 458110

Stradivarius Ceska Republika, s.r.o (2)
Plzenska 8, Prague, Czech Republic
Tel.: (420) 251643800
Sales Range: $25-49.9 Million
Emp.: 12
Clothing Accessories Retailer
N.A.I.C.S.: 458110
Vaclava Velkoska *(Gen Mgr)*

Stradivarius Commercial Shangai CO, LTD (2)
Yu Fashion Garden 168 Fangbang Rd, Huangpu District, 200010, Shanghai, China
Tel.: (86) 2161363923
Fashion Apparels Retailer
N.A.I.C.S.: 458110

Subsidiary (Domestic):

Stradivarius Diseno, S.L. (2)
Pol Industrial renger no 2, 08016, Sallent, La Coruna, Spain
Tel.: (34) 938378000
Web Site: http://www.stradivarius.com
Emp.: 300
Fashion Apparels Retailer
N.A.I.C.S.: 458110
Gordi Criqwell *(Gen Mgr)*

Subsidiary (Non-US):

Stradivarius France S.A.R.L. (2)
Route Nationale 352, 59320, Englos, France
Tel.: (33) 320005000
Clothing Accessories Stores
N.A.I.C.S.: 458110

Stradivarius Hellas, S.A. (2)
Seaview 59, Athens, 10551, Greece
Tel.: (30) 2103243101
Web Site: http://www.stradivarius.com
Fashion Apparels Retailer
N.A.I.C.S.: 458110

Stradivarius Hong Kong, LTD (2)
Olympian City 2-58 Hoi Fai Road West, Kowloon, China (Hong Kong)
Tel.: (852) 27404606
Apparel Retailer
N.A.I.C.S.: 458110

Stradivarius Ireland Limited (2)
Upper Abbey Street 125, D01 W3X5, Dublin, Ireland
Tel.: (353) 18788058
Sales Range: $25-49.9 Million
Emp.: 12
Clothing Accessories Retailer
N.A.I.C.S.: 458110

Subsidiary (Domestic):

Stradivarius Logistica S.A. (2)
Boligon Indust Berenguer, 08650, Sellent, Barcelona, Spain
Tel.: (34) 938378000
Web Site: http://www.stradivarius.es
Nightwear Dresses Mfr
N.A.I.C.S.: 315210
Jordi Triquill *(Gen Mgr)*

Subsidiary (Non-US):

Stradivarius Magyaroszag Kft. (2)
Vorosmarty ter 3, Budapest, 1051, Hungary
Tel.: (36) 14110382
Women's Apparel Retailer
N.A.I.C.S.: 458110

Stradivarius Polska Sp zo.o (2)
Mysia 5, 00496, Warsaw, Poland
Tel.: (48) 225965150
Web Site: http://www.indtex.com
Sales Range: $25-49.9 Million
Emp.: 17
Women Apparel Sales
N.A.I.C.S.: 458110

Stradivarius Portugal, Conf. Unip. Lda. (2)
Avenida Fontes Pereira De Melo 49 2 Esq, Lisbon, 1050-120, Portugal
Tel.: (351) 213183900
Family Clothing Retailer
N.A.I.C.S.: 458110

Stradivarius Slovakia, S.R.O. (2)
Einsteinova 18, 851 01, Bratislava, Slovakia
Tel.: (421) 262410930
Sales Range: $25-49.9 Million
Emp.: 15
Women Apparel Mfr
N.A.I.C.S.: 315250

Stradivarius Nederland, B.V. (1)
Kalverstraat 42, 1012 PE, Amsterdam, Netherlands
Tel.: (31) 205286444
Clothing Apparel & Accessories Retailer
N.A.I.C.S.: 458110

Trisko S.A. (1)
Poligono Sabon Parcela 79B, Arteixo, La

INDUSTRIA DE DISENO TEXTIL, S.A.

Industria de Diseno Textil, S.A.—(Continued)
Coruna, 15142, Spain
Tel.: (34) 981185404
Sales Range: $25-49.9 Million
Emp.: 50
Textile Design Services
N.A.I.C.S.: 541490
Gerardo Arias *(Mgr)*

UTC Benelux, N.V. (1)
Lippenslaan 343, 8300, Knokke-Heist, Belgium
Tel.: (32) 50605816
Apparel & Accessory Retailer
N.A.I.C.S.: 458110

Uterque Espana, S.A. (1)
Avenida Deputacion Ed Inditex, Arteixo, La Coruna, Galicia, Spain
Tel.: (34) 981185400
Sales Range: $75-99.9 Million
Men Apparel Retailer
N.A.I.C.S.: 458110
Aose Luis Rodrieugues *(Mgr)*

Subsidiary (Non-US):

Uterque Cis, LTD (2)
Naberezhnaya Presnenskaya 10, 123317, Moscow, Russia
Tel.: (7) 495 6431355
Fashion Apparels Retailer
N.A.I.C.S.: 458110

Subsidiary (Domestic):

Uterque Diseno, S.L. (2)
Avenida Deputacion S/N - Edif Inditex, Arteixo, 15142, La Coruna, Spain
Tel.: (34) 981185400
Fashion Apparels Retailer
N.A.I.C.S.: 458110

Subsidiary (Non-US):

Uterque Giyim Limited (2)
Is Kuleleri K 21 Kule 2, Istanbul, Turkiye
Tel.: (90) 2122840422
Fashion Apparels Retailer
N.A.I.C.S.: 458110

Subsidiary (Domestic):

Uterque Logistica, S.A. (2)
Avenida Deputacion S/N - Ed Inditex, Arteixo, 15142, La Coruna, Spain
Tel.: (34) 981185400
Web Site: http://www.inditex.com
Logistics Consulting Services
N.A.I.C.S.: 541614

Uterque S.A. (2)
Avenida Portal de L Angel 15, 08002, Barcelona, Spain
Tel.: (34) 933186004
Web Site: http://www.uterque.com
Sales Range: $25-49.9 Million
Emp.: 11
Clothing Accessories Stores
N.A.I.C.S.: 458110

Z-Fashion Finland Oy (1)
Aleksanterinkatu 52, 00100, Helsinki, Finland
Tel.: (358) 9 121 6600
Sales Range: $75-99.9 Million
Emp.: 180
Fashion Apparels Retailer
N.A.I.C.S.: 424350

Zara Brasil, Ltda. (1)
Alameda Xingu 350 24 andar, Alphaville Industrial, Barueri, 06455-030, Sao Paulo, Brazil
Tel.: (55) 1121011900
Web Site: http://www.zara.com
Cloth Retail Sales Services
N.A.I.C.S.: 458110

Zara Espana, S.A. (1)
Avenida de la Diputacion s/n, Arteixo, La Coruna, 15142, Spain
Tel.: (34) 981185400
Web Site: http://www.inditex.com
Sales Range: $5-14.9 Billion
Apparel Sales
N.A.I.C.S.: 315250
Carlos Mato Lopez *(Mgr)*

Subsidiary (Non-US):

Za Clothing Ireland Ltd. (2)
5th floor Hainault House 69-71 St Stephens Green, Dublin, Leinster, Ireland
Tel.: (353) 12910700
Clothing Accessories Stores
N.A.I.C.S.: 458110

Za Giyim Ithalat Ihracat Ve Ticaret Ltd. (2)
Zencirlibaglar Mevkii Sadik Ahmet Bulvari 3811 Ada 4, Alisveris Merkezi Seyhan, Adana, Turkiye
Tel.: (90) 322 271 01 31
Family Apparel Retailer
N.A.I.C.S.: 458110

Zara Argentina S.A. (2)
Constituyentes y Soldi, Partido de Malvinas, 1667, Tortuguitas, Buenos Aires, Argentina
Tel.: (54) 2320555100
Textile Designing Services
N.A.I.C.S.: 541490

Zara Asia, Ltd. (2)
Suite 3402-05 - Tower 2 - The Gateway 25 Canton Road, Tsim Sha Tsui, Kowloon, China (Hong Kong)
Tel.: (852) 29563322
Apparel Mfr & Whslr
N.A.I.C.S.: 315990

Zara Belgique S.A. (2)
Rue des Cendres 22, 1000, Brussels, Belgium
Tel.: (32) 22210260
Web Site: http://www.inditex.be
Sales Range: $150-199.9 Million
Emp.: 900
Textile Designing Services
N.A.I.C.S.: 541490
Florence Deboosere *(Mgr-Comml)*

Zara Bucuresti, Srl (2)
Globalworth Tower etajul 9 Str Barbu Vacarescu 201 sector 2, 020276, Bucharest, Romania
Tel.: (40) 317309272
Emp.: 1,800
Family Apparel Retailer
N.A.I.C.S.: 458110
Paul Cuza *(Gen Mgr)*

Zara Canada Inc. (2)
1200 Ave McGill College, Montreal, H3B 4G7, QC, Canada
Tel.: (514) 868-1516
Web Site: http://www.zara.ca
Sales Range: $25-49.9 Million
Emp.: 25
Men Apparel Sales
N.A.I.C.S.: 458110
Alexis Drouault *(CFO)*

Zara Ceska Republika S.R.O. (2)
Na Prikope 15/583, Stare Mesto, 110 00, Prague, Czech Republic
Tel.: (420) 800050332
Sales Range: $25-49.9 Million
Emp.: 60
Women Apparel Designs & Sales
N.A.I.C.S.: 458110
Roland Revsalvi *(Gen Mgr)*

Zara Chile S.A. (2)
Calle Cerro Colorado, Las Condes, 5040, Santiago, Chile
Tel.: (56) 24329092
Web Site: http://www.zara.com
Sales Range: $25-49.9 Million
Emp.: 25
Textile Designing Services
N.A.I.C.S.: 541490
Cesar Pattarone *(Mgr)*

Zara Commercial (Shanghai), Co Ltd. (2)
Longemont Yes Tower 31 Floor, 200051, Shanghai, China
Tel.: (86) 2161611922
Sales Range: $75-99.9 Million
Emp.: 300
Men's Apparel Distr
N.A.I.C.S.: 458110

Zara Denmark A/S (2)
Klosterstraede 1, 1157, Copenhagen, Denmark
Tel.: (45) 33690499
Web Site: https://www.zara.com
Family Apparel Distr
N.A.I.C.S.: 458110

Zara Deutschland Gmbh (2)
Monckebergstr 10, Hamburg, 20095, Germany
Tel.: (49) 403096220
Web Site: http://www.zara.com
Sales Range: $25-49.9 Million
Emp.: 80
Clothing Accessories Stores
N.A.I.C.S.: 458110
Matthias Alipass *(Gen Mgr)*

Subsidiary (Domestic):

Zara Diseno, S.L. (2)
Avenida Deputacion Edif Inditex, Arteixo, 15142, La Coruna, Spain
Tel.: (34) 981185400
Web Site: http://www.inditex.com
Emp.: 155
Supermarket Operator
N.A.I.C.S.: 445110
Pablo Isla *(Gen Mgr)*

Subsidiary (Non-US):

Zara Hellas, S.A. (2)
59 Stadiou Str, 10551, Athens, Greece
Tel.: (30) 2103243101
Web Site: http://www.zara.com
Fashion Apparel Distr
N.A.I.C.S.: 424310

Zara Holding B.V. (2)
Nieuwezijds Voorburgwal 307, 1012 RM, Amsterdam, North Holland, Netherlands
Tel.: (31) 205309650
Web Site: http://www.initex.com
Sales Range: $50-74.9 Million
Emp.: 10
Investment Holding Services
N.A.I.C.S.: 523999
Jose De Lacolinar *(Pres)*

Zara Italia, S.R.L (2)
Largo Corsia dei Servi 3, 20122, Milan, Italy
Tel.: (39) 028180081
Web Site: https://www.zara.com
Family Apparel & Accessory Retailer
N.A.I.C.S.: 458110

Zara Japan Corp. (2)
Fujiwara Building 6F 1-10-11 Ebisu-nishi, Shibuya-ku, Tokyo, 150-0021, Japan
Tel.: (81) 364158061
Fashion Apparels Retailer
N.A.I.C.S.: 458110

Subsidiary (Domestic):

Zara Logistica S.A. (2)
Avda Diputacion Pol Ind Sabon, Arteixo, 15142, La Coruna, Spain
Tel.: (34) 981185409
General Warehousing & Storage Services
N.A.I.C.S.: 493110

Subsidiary (Non-US):

Zara Luxembourg S.A. (2)
Boulevard F W Raiffeisen 25, 2411, Luxembourg, Luxembourg
Tel.: (352) 3222210260
Web Site: https://www.zara.com
Sales Range: $25-49.9 Million
Emp.: 35
Women Apparel Sales
N.A.I.C.S.: 458110

Zara Magyarorszag, KFT. (2)
Rakoczi ut 1-3, 1088, Budapest, Hungary
Tel.: (36) 13270200
Web Site: https://www.zara.com
Family Clothing Retailer
N.A.I.C.S.: 458110
Alfonso Vazquez Bergantinos *(Mng Dir)*

Zara Monaco SAM (2)
6 Square Beaumarchais - immeuble sun tower, 98000, Monaco, Monaco
Tel.: (377) 97974080
Web Site: https://www.zara.com
Clothing Accessories Stores
N.A.I.C.S.: 458110

Zara Nederland B.V. (2)
Nieuwezijds Voorburgwal 305, 1012 RM, Amsterdam, Netherlands
Tel.: (31) 205305660
Web Site: https://www.zara.com

INTERNATIONAL PUBLIC

Sales Range: $10-24.9 Million
Emp.: 40
Textile Designing Services
N.A.I.C.S.: 541490

Zara Norge, AS (2)
Bogstadveien 12, Oslo, 0355, Norway
Tel.: (47) 28199650
Fashion Apparel Distr
N.A.I.C.S.: 424310

Zara Osterreich Clothing GmbH (2)
Stock-im-Eisen-Platz 4, Vienna, 1010, Austria
Tel.: (43) 15339812
Women Apparel Sales
N.A.I.C.S.: 458110

Zara Polska, Sp. Z.o.o. (2)
Ul Mysia 5, Warsaw, 00-496, Poland
Tel.: (48) 22 596 5174
Web Site: http://www.zara.com
Sales Range: $150-199.9 Million
Emp.: 1,000
Apparel Store Operator
N.A.I.C.S.: 458110
Alberto Vara Garcia *(Pres & CEO)*

Zara Portugal Confeccoes Lda. (2)
Av Fontes Pereira de Melo 49 2 izquierda, 1050-120, Lisbon, Portugal
Tel.: (351) 213183900
Web Site: https://www.zara.com
Textile Designing Services
N.A.I.C.S.: 541490

Zara Retail Korea Ltd. (2)
20th Fl World Trade Center 159-1 Samsung-dong, Kangnam-ku, Seoul, 135-729, Korea (South)
Tel.: (82) 234139800
Web Site: https://www.zara.com
Sales Range: $25-49.9 Million
Emp.: 38
Fashion Retailing Services
N.A.I.C.S.: 459999

Zara Suisse S.A.R.L. (2)
Rue Louis d'Affry 6, 1700, Fribourg, Switzerland
Tel.: (41) 263501660
Web Site: https://www.zara.com
Sales Range: $150-199.9 Million
Emp.: 600
Footwear Mfr
N.A.I.C.S.: 316210

Zara Sverige AB (2)
Klara Norra Kyrkogata 29, 111 22, Stockholm, Uppland, Sweden
Tel.: (46) 854522900
Web Site: https://www.zara.com
Apparel Sales
N.A.I.C.S.: 458110

Zara Taiwan, B.V. (2)
Suite 3 Floor 9 Number 88 Tunhua North Road, Taipei, 105, Taiwan
Tel.: (886) 227782111
Web Site: https://www.zara.com
Sales Range: $75-99.9 Million
Emp.: 500
Apparel Retailer
N.A.I.C.S.: 458110
Debbie Lu *(Country Mgr)*

Zara UK Ltd. (2)
Lumina House 89 New Bond Street, Soho, London, W1S 1DA, United Kingdom
Tel.: (44) 2078514300
Web Site: https://www.zara.com
Textile Designing Services
N.A.I.C.S.: 541490

Subsidiary (US):

Zara USA, Inc. (2)
500 5th Ave Ste 400, New York, NY 10110
Tel.: (212) 355-1415
Web Site: https://www.zara.com
Sales Range: $10-24.9 Million
Emp.: 35
Textile Designing Services
N.A.I.C.S.: 541490
Nina Kartveli *(Mgr-Man's Store)*

Subsidiary (Non-US):

Zara Ukraine LLC (2)
Bogdana Khmelnytskogo 19-21 A Business Ctr Leanordo 3, Kiev, 1030, Ukraine

AND PRIVATE COMPANIES

Tel.: (380) 444958801
Web Site: http://www.zara.com
Sales Range: $25-49.9 Million
Emp.: 20
Clothing Accessories Stores
N.A.I.C.S.: 458110
Sergey Drobyshev *(Gen Mgr)*

Zara, S.A. (2)
Constituyentes y Soldi - Tortuguitas - Partido de Malvinas, 1667, Buenos Aires, Argentina
Tel.: (54) 2320555100
Fashion Apparel Distr
N.A.I.C.S.: 424310

Zara Fashion (Shanghai) Co., Ltd. (1)
B1 B2 GF 1F and 2F No592-600 East Nanjing Road, Shanghai, China
Tel.: (86) 4008216002
Web Site: http://www.zara.cn
Cloth Retail Sales Services
N.A.I.C.S.: 458110

Zara France, S.A.R.L. (1)
80 Av des Terroirs de France - 6 Immeuble Garonne, 75012, Paris, France
Tel.: (33) 155788888
Cloth Retail Sales Services
N.A.I.C.S.: 458110

Zara Home Australia Pty. Ltd. (1)
75 Castlereagh Level 6 Suite 6 02, Sydney, 2000, NSW, Australia
Tel.: (61) 293767600
Clothing Apparel & Accessories Retailer
N.A.I.C.S.: 458110

Zara Home Brasil Produtos para o Lar, Ltda. (1)
Alameda Xingu 350 24 Andar Alphaville Industrial, Barueri, Sao Paulo, 06455-030, Brazil
Tel.: (55) 1121011900
Clothing Apparel & Accessories Retailer
N.A.I.C.S.: 458110

Zara Home Canada, Inc. (1)
1200 McGill College Av - Suite 1550, Montreal, H3B 4G7, QC, Canada
Tel.: (514) 868-1516
Clothing Apparel & Accessories Retailer
N.A.I.C.S.: 458110

Zara Home Ceska Republika, SRO (1)
Rybna 682/14, 11000, Prague, Czech Republic
Tel.: (420) 224239873
Clothing Apparel & Accessories Retailer
N.A.I.C.S.: 458110

Zara Home Chile SPA (1)
Cerro Colorado - 50-30 Off 502, Santiago, Chile
Tel.: (56) 2224329092
Clothing Apparel & Accessories Retailer
N.A.I.C.S.: 458110

Zara Home Espana S.A. (1)
Avda de la Diputacion Edificio Inditex, Arteixo, 15143, La Coruna, Spain
Tel.: (34) 900900314
Web Site: https://www.zarahome.com
Sales Range: $400-449.9 Million
Sportswear Mfr
N.A.I.C.S.: 339920

Subsidiary (Non-US):

Zara Home Belgique S.A. (2)
Zuidzandstraat 27, 8000, Brugge, West Flanders, Belgium
Tel.: (32) 50444580
Web Site: http://www.zarahome.com
Sales Range: $25-49.9 Million
Emp.: 6
Interior Designing Services
N.A.I.C.S.: 541410
Danielle Lemmens *(Gen Mgr)*

Zara Home CIS Ltd. (2)
Presnenskaya Embankment Building No 10 Block C, Moscow, 123317, Russia
Tel.: (7) 495 6431315
Web Site: http://www.zara.ru
Sales Range: $25-49.9 Million
Emp.: 200
Clothing Accessories Stores
N.A.I.C.S.: 458110

Subsidiary (Domestic):

Zara Home Diseno, S.L. (2)
Avenida Deputacion Ed Inditex, Arteixo, 15142, La Coruna, Spain
Tel.: (34) 981185400
Supermarket Operator
N.A.I.C.S.: 445110

Subsidiary (Non-US):

Zara Home Francia, S.A.R.L. (2)
22 Rue Bergere, 75009, Paris, France
Tel.: (33) 805980034
Web Site: https://www.zarahome.com
Furniture Distr
N.A.I.C.S.: 449110

Zara Home Giyim Ithalat Ihracat Ve Ticaret Ltd. (2)
Eskibaglar Mh Universite Cd Espark Avm No 21/GF062, 34330, Eskisehir, Turkiye
Tel.: (90) 2122840422
Sales Range: $25-49.9 Million
Emp.: 100
Fashion Apparels Retailer
N.A.I.C.S.: 458110

Zara Home Hellas, S.A. (2)
33-37 Athinas, Athens, Greece
Tel.: (30) 80033152382
Family Clothing Distr
N.A.I.C.S.: 458110

Zara Home Italia S.R.L. (2)
590 Italy Ave, Sesto San Giovanni, 20099, Milan, Italy
Tel.: (39) 0224860258
Sportswear Mfr
N.A.I.C.S.: 339920

Subsidiary (Domestic):

Zara Home Logistica, S.A. (2)
Avenida Deputacion S/N - Pg Ind Sabon Edf Inditex, Arteixo, 15142, Spain
Tel.: (34) 981185400
Fashion Apparel Distr
N.A.I.C.S.: 424310

Subsidiary (Non-US):

Zara Home Mexico, S.A. de C.V. (2)
Poniente 146 No 730 Col Industrial Vallejo Azcapotzalco, 02300, Mexico, Mexico
Tel.: (52) 8000830986
Women Apparel Distr
N.A.I.C.S.: 458110

Zara Home Nederland B.V. (2)
Kalver Straat 6672, 1012 PG, Amsterdam, North Holland, Netherlands
Tel.: (31) 8000201115
Web Site: https://www.zarahome.com
Women Apparel Retailing & Sales
N.A.I.C.S.: 458110
D. C. Zerghmans *(Mng Dir)*

Zara Home Polska, Sp zo.o (2)
Ul Mysia 5, Warsaw, 00-496, Poland
Tel.: (48) 225965150
Fashion Apparel Distr
N.A.I.C.S.: 458110
Mariusz Leszczynski *(Gen Mgr)*

Zara Home U.K., Ltd. (2)
89 New Bond Street, London, W1S 1DA, United Kingdom
Tel.: (44) 2078514300
Sales Range: $25-49.9 Million
Emp.: 60
Home Furnishings Stores
N.A.I.C.S.: 449129

Zara Home Hong Kong Ltd. (1)
Suite 3402-05 - Tower 2 - The Gateway 25 Canton Road, Tsim Sha Tsui, Kowloon, China (Hong Kong)
Tel.: (852) 29563322
Clothing Apparel & Accessories Retailer
N.A.I.C.S.: 458110

Zara Home Ireland Limited (1)
5th Floor Hainault House 69/71 St Stephens Green, Dublin, Ireland
Tel.: (353) 14070714
Clothing Apparel & Accessories Retailer
N.A.I.C.S.: 458110

Zara Home Korea Limited (1)
20th Fl World Trade Center 159-1, Samsung-dong Kangnam-ku, 135-729, Seoul, Korea (South)
Tel.: (82) 234139800
Clothing Apparel & Accessories Retailer
N.A.I.C.S.: 458110

Zara Home Magyarorszag KFT (1)
Rakoczi Ut 1-3, 1088, Budapest, Hungary
Tel.: (36) 13270200
Clothing Apparel & Accessories Retailer
N.A.I.C.S.: 458110

Zara Home Osterreich Clothing Gmbh (1)
Karntnerstrasse 11 / Top 6, 1010, Vienna, Austria
Tel.: (43) 1512791400
Clothing Apparel & Accessories Retailer
N.A.I.C.S.: 458110

Zara Home SRB D.O.O. (1)
Knez Mihailova 11 - 15 7 Floor, 11000, Belgrade, Serbia
Tel.: (381) 112023400
Clothing Apparel & Accessories Retailer
N.A.I.C.S.: 458110

Zara Home Ukraine, LLC (1)
Chervonoarmyiskaya Str 77, 03150, Kiev, Ukraine
Tel.: (380) 444958801
Clothing Apparel & Accessories Retailer
N.A.I.C.S.: 458110

Zara Immobiliare Italia SRL (1)
Via G Garibaldi 10, Padenghe sul Garda, 41122, Brescia, Italy
Tel.: (39) 0309907374
Web Site: https://www.zaraimmobiliare.it
Real Estate Services
N.A.I.C.S.: 531210

Zara Mexico, S.A. de C.V. (1)
C/ Poniente 146 No 730 - Colonia Industrial Vallejo, Deleg Azcapotzalco, 02300, Mexico, Mexico
Tel.: (52) 5550782000
Cloth Retail Sales Services
N.A.I.C.S.: 458110

Zintura S.A. (1)
Avda Diputacion Pg Ind Sabon Ed Inditex S N, Arteixo, 15142, La Coruna, Spain
Tel.: (34) 981185391
Textile Designing Services
N.A.I.C.S.: 541490

INDUSTRIAL & COMMERCIAL BANK OF CHINA LIMITED

No 55 Fuxingmennei Street, Xicheng District, Beijing, 100140, China
Tel.: (86) 1066108608   CN
Web Site: https://www.icbc-ltd.com
Year Founded: 1984
1398—(SHG)
Rev.: $167,385,142,410
Net Worth: $445,766,793,150
Earnings: $48,672,518,850
Emp.: 439,787
Fiscal Year-end: 12/31/20
Banking Services
N.A.I.C.S.: 522110
Shu Gu *(Vice Chm & Pres)*

Subsidiaries:

Chongqing Bishan ICBC Rural Bank Co., Ltd (1)
No 1 Aokang Avenue, Bishan County, Chongqing, 402760, China
Tel.: (86) 2385297704
Commercial Banking Services
N.A.I.C.S.: 522110

ICBC (London) PLC (1)
81 King william St, London, EC4N 7BG, United Kingdom
Tel.: (44) 2073978888
Web Site: http://www.icbclondon.com
Sales Range: $50-74.9 Million
Emp.: 50
Banking Services
N.A.I.C.S.: 523150
Zeng Qing Hui *(Head-Banking)*

ICBC (Macau) Capital Limited (1)
17/F Macau Landmark No 555 Avenida da Amizade, Macau, China (Macau)
Tel.: (853) 83982363
Commercial Banking Services
N.A.I.C.S.: 522110

ICBC (Macau) Pension Fund Management Company Limited (1)
11/F Macau Landmark No 555 Avenida da Amizade, Macau, China (Macau)
Tel.: (853) 83982362
Commercial Banking Services
N.A.I.C.S.: 522110

ICBC Austria Bank GmbH (1)
Kolingasse 4, 1090, Vienna, Austria
Tel.: (43) 19395588
Web Site: http://www.icbc-at.com
Banking Services
N.A.I.C.S.: 522110
Yanni Li *(CEO)*

ICBC Credit Suisse Asset Management Co., Ltd (1)
Bank of Beijing Building 17 C Financial Street, Xicheng District, Beijing, 100140, China   (80%)
Tel.: (86) 1066583333
Web Site: http://www.icbccs.com.cn
Commercial Banking Services
N.A.I.C.S.: 522110
Elvin Yu *(Head-Intl Sls & Client Relationships)*

ICBC Financial Asset Investment Co., Limited (1)
19-20/F Tower B Yang Zi S and T Innovation Center, Phase I Jiangbei New Area No 211 Pubin Road, Nanjing, 211800, Jiangsu, China
Tel.: (86) 2558172219
Commercial Banking Services
N.A.I.C.S.: 522110

ICBC Financial Leasing Co., Ltd. (1)
E5AB Finance Street No 20 Plaza East Road Economic Development Zone, Tianjin, 300457, China
Tel.: (86) 22 66283766
Commercial Banking Services
N.A.I.C.S.: 522110

ICBC International Holdings Limited (1)
37/F ICBC Tower 3 Garden Road, Central, China (Hong Kong)
Tel.: (852) 2 683 3888
Web Site: https://www.icbci.com.hk
Sales Range: $50-74.9 Million
Emp.: 100
Investment Banking Services
N.A.I.C.S.: 523150
Huang Mingxiang *(CEO)*

ICBC Peru Bank S.A. (1)
Calle Las orquideas 585 Of 501, San Isidro, Lima, Peru
Tel.: (51) 16316800
Web Site: http://www.pe.icbc.com.cn
Banking Services
N.A.I.C.S.: 522110

ICBC Standard Bank PLC (1)
20 Gresham Street, London, EC2V 7JE, United Kingdom   (60%)
Tel.: (44) 2031455000
Web Site: https://www.icbcstandardbank.com
Rev.: $524,700,000
Assets: $23,247,100,000
Liabilities: $21,376,200,000
Net Worth: $1,870,900,000
Earnings: $187,100,000
Emp.: 844
Fiscal Year-end: 12/31/2023
Investment Bank
N.A.I.C.S.: 523150

ICBC Wealth Management Co., Ltd. (1)
COCP Fortune Center No 96 Taipingqiao Avenue, Xicheng District, Beijing, 100032, China
Tel.: (86) 1066076588
Banking Services
N.A.I.C.S.: 522110

ICBC-AXA Assurance Co., Ltd. (1)
19/F Mirae Asset Tower No 166 Lujiazui Ring Road, Pudong New Area, Shanghai, 200120, China
Tel.: (86) 2158792288

INDUSTRIAL & COMMERCIAL BANK OF CHINA LIMITED — INTERNATIONAL PUBLIC

Industrial & Commercial Bank of China Limited—(Continued)
Banking Services
N.A.I.C.S.: 522110

ICBC-AXA Life Assurance (1)
Unit E 18th and 19th Floor No 166 Lujiazui Ring Road, Shanghai, 200120, Pudong, China
Tel.: (86) 215 879 2288
Web Site: https://www.icbc-axa.com
Medical Insurance Services
N.A.I.C.S.: 524114

ICBC-AXA-Minmetals Assurance Co., Ltd. (1)
12/F China Merchants Tower 161 Lu Jai Zui Road, Pudong New District, Shanghai, 200120, China (60%)
Tel.: (86) 2158792288
Web Site: http://www.icbc-axa.com
Sales Range: $10-24.9 Million
Insurance Services in Life, Education, Retirement, Health & Wealth Management
N.A.I.C.S.: 524113

Industrial & Commercial Bank of China (Asia) Limited (1)
33/F ICBC Tower 3 Garden Road, Central, Central, China (Hong Kong)
Tel.: (852) 3 510 8888
Web Site: https://www.icbcasia.com
Commercial Banking Services
N.A.I.C.S.: 522110
Gao Ming (Chm)

Subsidiary (Domestic):

ICBC Asset Management (Global) Company Limited (2)
Room 2507-10 25/F Industrial and Commercial Bank of China Tower, Central, China (Hong Kong)
Tel.: (852) 3 510 0800
Web Site: https://www.icbcamg.com
Commercial Banking Services
N.A.I.C.S.: 522110

Industrial & Commercial Bank of China (Brasil) S.A. (1)
Av Brigadeiro Faria Lima 3477 Bloco B 6 andar Itaim Bibi, Sao Paulo, 04538-133, Brazil
Tel.: (55) 23956600
Web Site: https://br.icbc.com.cn
Commercial Banking Services
N.A.I.C.S.: 522110
Liang Zhu (Head & Dir-Corp Banking)

Industrial & Commercial Bank of China (Canada) Limited (1)
Bay Adelaide Centre West Tower Suite 3710 333 Bay Street, Toronto, M5H 2R2, ON, Canada
Tel.: (416) 366-5588
Web Site: https://www.icbc.ca
Commercial Banking Services
N.A.I.C.S.: 522110

Industrial & Commercial Bank of China (Europe) S.A. (1)
32 Boulevard Royal, 2449, Luxembourg, 2449, Luxembourg
Tel.: (352) 26866621
Emp.: 351
Commercial Banking Services
N.A.I.C.S.: 522110
Sylvain Spiquel (Chief Compliance Officer)

Industrial & Commercial Bank of China (Macau) Limited (1)
18th Floor ICBC Tower Macau Landmark 555 Avenida da Amizade, Macau, China (Macau)
Tel.: (853) 2 855 5222
Web Site: http://www.icbc-ltd.com
Commercial Banking Services
N.A.I.C.S.: 522110

Industrial & Commercial Bank of China (Malaysia) Berhad (1)
Level 10 Menara Maxis, 50088, Kuala Lumpur, Malaysia
Tel.: (60) 323013399
Web Site: https://malaysia.icbc.com.cn
Sales Range: $50-74.9 Million
Emp.: 50
Commercial Banking Services
N.A.I.C.S.: 522110

Huiman Yi (Chm)

Industrial & Commercial Bank of China (Middle East) Limited (1)
Difc gate village 1 5th floor, PO Box 506664, Dubai, 506856, United Arab Emirates
Tel.: (971) 47031111
Web Site: http://www.icbcme.ae
Emp.: 65
Commercial Banking Services
N.A.I.C.S.: 522110
Zhou Xiaovong (Gen Mgr)

Industrial & Commercial Bank of China (New Zealand) Limited (1)
Level 11 188 Quay Street, Auckland, New Zealand
Tel.: (64) 9 374 7288
Web Site: https://nz.icbc.com.cn
Commercial Banking Services
N.A.I.C.S.: 522110

Industrial & Commercial Bank of China (Thai) Public Company Limited (1)
L 11-13 Fl Emporium Tower, 622 Sukhumvit Rd Khlong Ton Klong Toei, Bangkok, 10110, Thailand (97.24%)
Tel.: (66) 26295588
Web Site: http://www.icbcthai.com
Rev.: $297,495,733
Assets: $8,372,575,322
Liabilities: $7,308,249,401
Net Worth: $1,064,325,920
Earnings: $71,342,467
Fiscal Year-end: 12/31/2019
Banking Services
N.A.I.C.S.: 522110
Yang Liu (Sr Exec VP-Branch Banking & IT Grp)

Subsidiary (Domestic):

BBL Asset Management Co., Ltd. (2)
175 Sathorn City Tower 26th Floor Room No 2601 South Sathorn Road, Bangkok, 10120, Thailand
Tel.: (66) 26746488
Web Site: https://www.bblam.co.th
Sales Range: $50-74.9 Million
Emp.: 60
Insurance Funds
N.A.I.C.S.: 525190

R.M. Property Co., Ltd. (2)
152-60 Moo 1 Petchakasem Road, Bang Khae Bang Phai, 10160, Bangkok, Thailand
Tel.: (66) 28041981
Real Estate Agents & Brokers
N.A.I.C.S.: 531210

Industrial & Commercial Bank of China (USA) NA (1)
202 Canal St, New York, NY 10013 (80%)
Tel.: (212) 238-8208
Web Site: https://www.icbc-us.com
Emp.: 25
Banking Services
N.A.I.C.S.: 522110
Mui Ming (Branch Mgr)

Branch (Domestic):

Industrial & Commercial Bank of China (USA) NA (2)
388 E Valley Blvd Ste 118, Alhambra, CA 91801-4713
Tel.: (626) 300-8888
Web Site: http://www.icbc-us.com
Sales Range: $25-49.9 Million
Emp.: 42
Commercial Banking Services
N.A.I.C.S.: 522110
Daisy Tung (Sr VP & Sr Bus Mgr)

Industrial & Commercial Bank of China (USA) NA - Brooklyn Branch (2)
5714 8th Ave, Brooklyn, NY 11220
Tel.: (718) 210-0508
Commercial Banking Services
N.A.I.C.S.: 522110

Industrial & Commercial Bank of China (USA) NA - Flushing Branch (2)
39-02 Main St, Flushing, NY 11354
Tel.: (347) 905-9772
Commercial Banking Services
N.A.I.C.S.: 522110

Industrial & Commercial Bank of China (USA) NA - Hacienda Heights Branch (2)
17180 Colima Rd, Hacienda Heights, CA 91745
Tel.: (626) 965-3938
Commercial Banking Services
N.A.I.C.S.: 522110

Industrial & Commercial Bank of China (USA) NA - Noriega Branch (2)
1250 Noriega St, San Francisco, CA 94122
Tel.: (415) 665-8877
Commercial Banking Services
N.A.I.C.S.: 522110

Industrial & Commercial Bank of China (USA) NA - Oakland Branch (2)
401 9th St, Oakland, CA 94607
Tel.: (510) 208-2140
Commercial Banking Services
N.A.I.C.S.: 522110

Industrial & Commercial Bank of China (USA) NA - San Gabriel Branch (2)
168 W Valley Blvd, San Gabriel, CA 91776
Tel.: (626) 656-0880
Commercial Banking Services
N.A.I.C.S.: 522110

Industrial & Commercial Bank of China (USA) NA - South San Francisco Branch (2)
235 Grand Ave Ste 101, South San Francisco, CA 94080
Tel.: (650) 872-9700
Commercial Banking Services
N.A.I.C.S.: 522110

Industrial & Commercial Bank of China (USA) NA - Temple City Branch (2)
5773 Rosemead Blvd, Temple City, CA 91780
Tel.: (626) 656-8888
Commercial Banking Services
N.A.I.C.S.: 522110
Jason He (Mgr)

Industrial & Commercial Bank of China (USA) NA - Torrance Branch (2)
23133 Hawthorne Blvd Ste 100, Torrance, CA 90505
Tel.: (310) 803-7388
Commercial Banking Services
N.A.I.C.S.: 522110

Subsidiary (Domestic):

Industrial & Commercial Bank of China Financial Services LLC (2)
1633 Broadway 28th Fl, New York, NY 10019
Tel.: (212) 993-7300
Web Site: https://www.icbcfs.com
Commercial Banking Services
N.A.I.C.S.: 522110

Industrial & Commercial Bank of China Almaty JSC (1)
110 Furmanov Ave, Almaty, 50000, Kazakhstan
Tel.: (7) 7272596391
Sales Range: $50-74.9 Million
Emp.: 40
Financial Services
N.A.I.C.S.: 522320

Industrial & Commercial Bank of China Luxembourg S.A. (1)
32 Boulevard Royal, Luxembourg, 2449, Luxembourg
Tel.: (352) 26 86 6621
Web Site: http://www.icbc.com
Sales Range: $50-74.9 Million
Emp.: 85
Commercial Banking Services
N.A.I.C.S.: 522110
Ming Gao (CEO)

Industrial & Commercial Bank of China Mexico S.A. (1)
Paseo de la Reforma 250 Torre B Piso 18 Col Juaez Del Cuauhtemoc, 6600, Mexico, 6600, Mexico
Tel.: (52) 5541253388
Web Site: https://www.icbc.com.mx
Commercial Banking Services
N.A.I.C.S.: 522110

Industrial and Commercial Bank of China (Argentina) S.A. (1)
Boulevard Cecilia Grierson 355 Dique IV 11th Floor, Puerto Madero, Buenos Aires, C1107CBP, Argentina (100%)
Tel.: (54) 1148202021
Commercial Banking Services
N.A.I.C.S.: 522110

PT. Bank ICBC Indonesia (1)
ICBC Tower 32nd Floor Jalan M H Thamrin No 81, Jakarta, 10310, Indonesia
Tel.: (62) 212 355 6000
Web Site: https://www.icbc.co.id
Commercial Banking Services
N.A.I.C.S.: 522110

Seng Heng Development Company Limited (1)
17/F ICBC Tower Macau Landmark 555 Avenida da Amizade, Macau, China (Macau)
Tel.: (853) 83987178
Commercial Banking Services
N.A.I.C.S.: 522110

ZAO Industrial and Commercial Bank of China (MOSCOW) (1)
Serebryanicheskaya Naberejnaya Street build 29, First Fl Room 46-1, 109028, Moscow, Russia
Tel.: (7) 4952873099
Banking Services
N.A.I.C.S.: 523150

Zhejiang Pinghu ICBC Rural Bank Co., Ltd. (1)
No 258 Chengnan West Road, Pinghu, Zhejiang, China
Tel.: (86) 5738 513 9616
Web Site: http://www.icbc-ltd.com
Sales Range: $50-74.9 Million
Emp.: 30
Commercial Banking Services
N.A.I.C.S.: 522110

INDUSTRIAL & GENERAL INSURANCE PLC
IGI House No 2 Agoro Odiyan Street off Adeola Odeku Street, Victoria Island, Lagos, Nigeria
Tel.: (234) 12918853
Web Site: http://www.iginigeria.com
Year Founded: 1992
Sales Range: $10-24.9 Million
Emp.: 400
Insurance Services
N.A.I.C.S.: 524298
Yakubu Gowon (Chm)

Subsidiaries:

Global Trust Savings & Loans Limited (1)
Plot 740 Adeola Hopewell Street, Victoria Island, Lagos, Nigeria
Tel.: (234) 1 6215041
Web Site: http://www.globaltrustsavings.com
Commercial Banking Services
N.A.I.C.S.: 522110
Rotimi Fashola (Chm)

IGI Gamstar Insurance Company (1)
79 Daniel Golddard Street, PO Box 1276, Banjul, Gambia
Tel.: (220) 4226021
Insurance Services
N.A.I.C.S.: 524113

IGI Life Assurance Company Ltd (1)
Block 1 Design Resource Estate 4th Circular Road Near Togo Embassy, Accra, Ghana
Tel.: (233) 21 762121
Insurance Services
N.A.I.C.S.: 524113

IGI Pension Fund Managers Limited (1)
8 Adeola Odeku, Victoria Island, Lagos, Nigeria
Tel.: (234) 1 6213143
Web Site: http://www.igipfm.com
Pension Fund Administration Services
N.A.I.C.S.: 525110
Apostle Hayford I. Alile (Chm)

International Health Management Services Ltd. (1)
No 2 Joseph Street Off Broad Street, Lagos, Nigeria
Tel.: (234) 7041446622
Web Site: http://www.ihmsnigeria.com
Health Insurance Services
N.A.I.C.S.: 524114
T. A. J. Ogunbiyi (Chm)

National Insurance Corporation (1)
Plot 3 Pilkington Road, PO Box 7134, Kampala, Uganda (60%)
Tel.: (256) 417119900
Web Site: http://www.nic.co.ug
Sales Range: $1-9.9 Million
Emp.: 88
Insurance Services
N.A.I.C.S.: 524298

SONARWA s.a. (1)
2417 Boulevard de la Revolution, G P 1035, Kigali, Rwanda
Tel.: (250) 572101 3
Insurance Services
N.A.I.C.S.: 524113

INDUSTRIAL & INFRASTRUCTURE FUND INVESTMENT CORPORATION
2-7-3 Marunochi, Chiyoda-Ku, Tokyo, 100-6420, Japan
Tel.: (81) 352937090
Web Site: https://www.iif-reit.com
Year Founded: 2007
3249—(TKS)
Sales Range: Less than $1 Million
Investment Management Service
N.A.I.C.S.: 525990
Kumi Honda (Exec Dir)

INDUSTRIAL ASPHALTS (CEYLON) PLC
345D Negombo Road, Peliyagoda, Wattala, Sri Lanka
Tel.: (94) 11289845
Web Site: https://www.iac.lk
Year Founded: 1964
ASPH.N0000—(COL)
Rev.: $183,186
Assets: $4,826,631
Liabilities: $281,240
Net Worth: $4,545,391
Earnings: $491,954
Emp.: 4
Fiscal Year-end: 03/31/23
Coal Product Mfr & Distr
N.A.I.C.S.: 333120

INDUSTRIAL BANK CO., LTD.
No 398 Jiangbin Middle Avenue, Taijiang District, Fuzhou, 350014, Fujian, China
Tel.: (86) 59187839338
Web Site: https://www.cib.com.cn
Year Founded: 1988
601166—(SHG)
Rev.: $29,191,266,061
Assets: $1,406,502,824,546
Liabilities: $1,294,667,562,029
Net Worth: $111,835,262,517
Earnings: $10,677,337,173
Emp.: 61,633
Fiscal Year-end: 12/31/23
Commercial Banking Services
N.A.I.C.S.: 522110
Xiongpeng Sun (VP)

Subsidiaries:

CIB Fund Management Co., Ltd. (1)
25th Floor Xinhe Plaza No 137 Wusi Road, Gulou District, Fuzhou, 350001, Fujian, China
Tel.: (86) 2122211888
Web Site: http://www.cib-fund.com.cn
Fund Management Services
N.A.I.C.S.: 523940

China Industrial Asset Management Co., Ltd. (1)
35th Floor Times Financial Center No 68 Yincheng Middle Road, Pudong New Area, Shanghai, 200120, China
Tel.: (86) 2138601822
Web Site: http://www.ciitam.com
Financial Services
N.A.I.C.S.: 541611

China Industrial International Trust Limited (1)
Floor 23-26 Xinhe Plaza No 137 Wusi Road, Gulou District, Fuzhou, 350003, Fujian, China
Tel.: (86) 59188263888
Web Site: https://www.ciit.com.cn
Financial Services
N.A.I.C.S.: 541611

Industrial Bank Financial Leasing Co., Ltd. (1)
1st Floor Building D Comprehensive Service Office Building Chuangye Rd, Nangang Industrial Zone Tianjin Economic & Technological Dev Zone, Tianjin, 300457, China
Tel.: (86) 226 312 5018
Web Site: https://www.cib-leasing.com.cn
Financial Lending Services
N.A.I.C.S.: 522220

Industrial Consumer Finance Co., Ltd. (1)
17th Floor Industrial Bank Building No 213 Fengze Street, Fengze District, Quanzhou, Fujian, China
Tel.: (86) 4001095561
Web Site: https://www.ksdao.com
Financial Services
N.A.I.C.S.: 522291

Industrial Futures Co., Ltd. (1)
11th Floor Donghang Building No 796 Zhongshan East Road, Jiangdong District, Ningbo, 315040, Zhejiang, China
Web Site: https://www.cifutures.com.cn
Banking Services
N.A.I.C.S.: 522110

INDUSTRIAL BANK OF KOREA
79 Eulji-ro, Jung-gu, Seoul, Korea (South)
Tel.: (82) 318888000   KR
Web Site: https://www.ibk.co.kr
Year Founded: 1961
024110—(KRS)
Rev.: $8,160,132,360
Assets: $273,575,492,680
Liabilities: $253,987,576,260
Net Worth: $19,587,916,420
Earnings: $1,388,264,460
Emp.: 13,256
Fiscal Year-end: 12/31/19
Financial Investment Services
N.A.I.C.S.: 523999
Byeong-Seong Jeon (Chief Compliance Officer)

Subsidiaries:

IBK Asset Management Co., Ltd. (1)
11th Fl Kbiz New Bldg Yeouido-dong, Eunhaeng-ro, Seoul, 150-740, Korea (South) (100%)
Tel.: (82) 27278800
Web Site: http://www.ibkasset.com
Sales Range: $50-74.9 Million
Emp.: 49
Investment Management Service
N.A.I.C.S.: 523940

IBK Capital Corporation (1)
Dry Building 702-22 Yeoksam-dong, Gangnam-Gu 6-8 Floors, Seoul, 135-080, Korea (South)
Tel.: (82) 25319300
Web Site: http://www.ibkcapital.co.kr
Venture Capital Investment Services
N.A.I.C.S.: 523999

IBK China Ltd. (1)
Fl 30 31 The Exchange 2 189 Nanjing Road, Tianjin, China
Tel.: (86) 2258853500
Banking Services
N.A.I.C.S.: 522110

IBK Insurance Co., Ltd. (1)
19th floor HSBC Building 25 Bongraedong 1-ga, Jung-gu, Seoul, Korea (South)
Tel.: (82) 25671234
Web Site: http://www.ibki.co.kr
Pension Insurance Services
N.A.I.C.S.: 524210
Kim Sung-Hun (Mgr-Bus Plng)

IBK Securities Co., Ltd. (1)
Samdeok Bldg 11 Gukjegeumyung-ro 6-gil, Yeongdeungpo-gu, Seoul, Korea (South)
Tel.: (82) 269155000
Web Site: http://www.ibks.com
Emp.: 710
Financial Investment Services
N.A.I.C.S.: 523150

IBK Systems Co., Ltd. (1)
New Seoul Building 11F 12F 13F 141-7 Toegye-ro, Jung-gu, Seoul, Korea (South)
Tel.: (82) 234076600
Web Site: http://www.ibksystem.co.kr
Banking Services
N.A.I.C.S.: 522110

PT Bank Agris Tbk (1)
Wisma GKBI Suite UG-01 Jl Jend Sudirman No 28, Jakarta, 10210, Pusat, Indonesia
Tel.: (62) 21 57908888
Web Site: http://www.bankagris.co.id
Banking Services
N.A.I.C.S.: 522110
Leng Ho Sia (Chm)

PT Bank IBK Indonesia Tbk (1)
Wisma GKBI Suites-UG01 Jl Jend Sudirman No 28, Jakarta Pusat, Indonesia
Tel.: (62) 2157908888
Web Site: http://ibs.ibk.co.id
Banking Services
N.A.I.C.S.: 522110
Park Ju Yong (Pres)

INDUSTRIAL CAPITAL HOLDING AD-SOFIA
Bacho Kiro St 8, 1000, Sofia, Bulgaria
Tel.: (359) 29802648
Web Site: https://www.hika-bg.com
Year Founded: 1996
HIKA—(BUL)
Sales Range: Less than $1 Million
Financial Services
N.A.I.C.S.: 523999
Milko Angelov Angelov (CEO)

Subsidiaries:

SILOMA JSC (1)
22 Industrialna zona Str, 7500, Silistra, Bulgaria
Tel.: (359) 86 820 020
Web Site: http://www.siloma-bg.com
Emp.: 182
Machine Tool Mfr & Whslr
N.A.I.C.S.: 333517

INDUSTRIAL COMMERCIAL EQUIPMENT MANUFACTURING LTD.
51 Aikins Street, Winnipeg, R2W 4E3, MB, Canada
Tel.: (204) 586-8565
Web Site: http://www.ice-ww.com
Year Founded: 1987
Rev.: $33,389,888
Emp.: 200
Heating, Ventilation & Air-Conditioning Mfr
N.A.I.C.S.: 333415
Nichole Clancy (Owner)

INDUSTRIAL CREDIT COMPANY AFRICA HOLDINGS LIMITED
2nd Floor East Wing, 11 Alice Lane, Sandton, 2057, South Africa
Tel.: (27) 11 6841444
Sales Range: $1-9.9 Million
Emp.: 22
Financing & Operating Leasing of Commercial Equipment & Vehicles
N.A.I.C.S.: 522220
Johan Mostert (Dir-Fin)

INDUSTRIAL DEVELOPMENT AND RENOVATION ORGANIZATION OF IRAN
Vali e Asr Buliding Vali Asr St Jam e Jam Ave, PO Box 19395-1855, Tehran, Iran
Tel.: (98) 2122044101
Web Site: http://www.idro.ir
Year Founded: 1967
TOSA—(THE)
Sales Range: Less than $1 Million
Industrial Development Services
N.A.I.C.S.: 333248
M. A. Azizmohammadi (Dir-Industrial Renovation & Reg Dev)

INDUSTRIAL DEVELOPMENT COMPANY SAL
Tellet Al Assafir INDEVCO Building, Ajaltoun Keserwan, PO Box 11-2354, Beirut, Lebanon
Tel.: (961) 9230130
Web Site: https://www.indevcogroup.com
Emp.: 100
Building Products, Packaging & Container Mfr
N.A.I.C.S.: 322219

Subsidiaries:

INDEVCO North America, Inc. (1)
10351 Verdon Rd, Doswell, VA 23047
Tel.: (804) 876-9176
Web Site: https://indevconorthamerica.com
Building Products & Packaging Products Mfr
N.A.I.C.S.: 322219

Subsidiary (Domestic):

Perma R Products Inc. (2)
106 Perma R Rd, Johnson City, TN 37604
Tel.: (423) 929-8007
Web Site: http://www.sipsproducts.com
Rev.: $11,000,000
Emp.: 35
Insulating Board, Hard Pressed
N.A.I.C.S.: 321219

INDUSTRIAL DEVELOPMENT CORPORATION OF SOUTH AFRICA, LTD.
19 Fredman Drive Sandown, PO Box 784055, Sandton, 2146, South Africa
Tel.: (27) 11 269 3000
Web Site: http://www.idc.co.za
Year Founded: 1940
Rev.: $1,239,909,300
Assets: $10,011,142,610
Liabilities: $3,413,315,920
Net Worth: $6,597,826,690
Earnings: $49,845,600
Emp.: 846
Fiscal Year-end: 03/31/19
Industrial Investment & Development Services
N.A.I.C.S.: 523999
Busisiwe Mabuza (Chm)

Subsidiaries:

Crossley Holdings (1)
2096 Old South Coast Road, Reunion, Durban, South Africa
Tel.: (27) 31 910 6500
Web Site: http://www.crossleysa.com
Emp.: 200
Carpet Mfr
N.A.I.C.S.: 326150
Lyndon Jacobs (Mgr-HR & Training)

INDUSTRIAL DEVELOPMENT CORPORATION OF SOUTH AFRICA, LTD.

Industrial Development Corporation of South Africa, Ltd.—(Continued)

Foskor (Pty) Limited (1)
Block G Riverview Office Park Janadel Road, Midrand, South Africa (59%)
Tel.: (27) 11 347 0600
Web Site: http://www.foskor.co.za
Sales Range: $400-449.9 Million
Emp.: 1,945
Newspaper Publishers
N.A.I.C.S.: 513110
J. R. Barton (Chm)

Prilla 2000 (Pty) Ltd (1)
227 Bhambatha Rd, PO Box 376, Allandale, 3201, Pietermaritzburg, Kwazulu-Natal, South Africa
Tel.: (27) 33 397 7800
Web Site: http://www.prilla.co.za
Emp.: 290
Yarn Mfr & Whslr
N.A.I.C.S.: 313110

Scaw Metals Ltd. (1)
Lower Germiston Road, Heriotdale, Johannesburg, 2022, South Africa (74%)
Tel.: (27) 116200000
Web Site: http://www.scaw.co.za
Sales Range: $200-249.9 Million
Mfr of Rolled & Forged Steel Products
N.A.I.C.S.: 331221
Markus Hannemann (CEO)

Sheraton Textiles (Pty) Ltd (1)
Sheraton House De Waal Road, Diep River, Cape Town, 7800, South Africa
Tel.: (27) 21 707 5555
Pillow Cover Mfr
N.A.I.C.S.: 313210

Small Enterprise Finance Agency (SOC) Ltd. (1)
Block D 13 Candela Street Highveld Extension 73, Bylsbridge Office Park, Centurion, 0157, South Africa (100%)
Tel.: (27) 127489600
Web Site: http://www.sefa.org.za
Sales Range: $10-24.9 Million
Small Business Financing Services
N.A.I.C.S.: 522310
Hlonela Lupuwana-Pemba (Chm)

South African Fibre Yarn Rugs (Pty) Limited (1)
16 Van Eck Avenue, Hammarsdale, 3700, South Africa
Tel.: (27) 31 736 7100
Yarn Mfr & Whslr
N.A.I.C.S.: 313110

Sustainable Fibre Solutions (PTY) LTD (1)
1004 Wilde Perde Vlei, PO Box 330, Winterton, 3340, Kwazulu-Natal, South Africa
Tel.: (27) 36 488 1430
Web Site: http://www.kenaf.co.za
Food Products Mfr
N.A.I.C.S.: 311991
Edwin Warden (Mgr-Production)

Thelo Rolling Stock Leasing (1)
First Floor Building 3 Inanda Greens Business Park, 54 Wierda Road West, Johannesburg, Gauteng, South Africa
Tel.: (27) 11 290 2300
Web Site: http://www.thelorollingstock.com
Financial Management Services
N.A.I.C.S.: 541611
Para Naidoo (COO)

INDUSTRIAL ELECTRONICS PTE. LTD.

50 Macpherson Road Amazana Building 05-01, Singapore, 348471, Singapore
Tel.: (65) 67446873
Web Site: http://www.ie-pl.com
Year Founded: 1986
Sales Range: $25-49.9 Million
Emp.: 2
Electronic Display Products Mfr
N.A.I.C.S.: 334513

INDUSTRIAL ENGINEERING COMPANY FOR CONSTRUCTION & DEVELOPMENT

ICON Industrial Zone Wadi Houf, Helwan, Egypt
Tel.: (20) 223671327
Web Site: https://www.iconegypt.com
Year Founded: 1977
ENGC.CA—(EGX)
Sales Range: Less than $1 Million
Engineeering Services
N.A.I.C.S.: 541330
Arafat Sakr (Chm)

INDUSTRIAL FUND AD-SOFIA

Kalina Malina street 8 floor 1, 1202, Sofia, Bulgaria
Tel.: (359) 29500656
Web Site: https://www.indf-bg.com
INDF—(BUL)
Sales Range: Less than $1 Million
Financial Services
N.A.I.C.S.: 523999

INDUSTRIAL GROWTH PLATFORM, INC.

Gran Tokyo South Tower 17F 1-9-2 Marunouchi, Chiyoda-ku, Tokyo, 100-6617, Japan
Tel.: (81) 3 4562 1111
Web Site: http://www.igpi.co.jp
Sales Range: $100-124.9 Million
Emp.: 3,500
Corporate Consulting Services
N.A.I.C.S.: 561499
Tetsuya Hishida (Mng Dir & Partner)

Subsidiaries:

IGPI (Shanghai) Limited (1)
Room N309 Apollo Building 1440 Yan an Road, Shanghai, 200040, China
Tel.: (86) 2161331818
Management Consulting Services
N.A.I.C.S.: 541618

Industrial Growth Platform Pte. Ltd. (1)
30 Cecil Street Prudential Tower Level 26, Singapore, 49712, Singapore
Tel.: (65) 66378834
Management Consulting Services
N.A.I.C.S.: 541618

Michinori Holdings, Inc. (1)
Gran Tokyo South Tower 17F 1-9-2 Marunouchi, Chiyoda-ku, Tokyo, 100-6617, Japan
Tel.: (81) 3 4562 1520
Web Site: http://www.michinori.co.jp
Holding Company; Public Transportation Systems Operator
N.A.I.C.S.: 551112
Jun Matsumoto (CEO)

Subsidiary (Domestic):

Shonan Monorail Co., Ltd. (2)
18 Tokiwa, Kamakura, 248-0022, Kanagawa, Japan (92%)
Tel.: (81) 467 45 3181
Web Site: http://www.shonan-monorail.co.jp
Sales Range: $10-24.9 Million
Emp.: 105
Monorail Operator
N.A.I.C.S.: 487110

INDUSTRIAL HOLDING BULGARIA AD

79 Knyaginya Maria Luiza Blvd 3th floor, 1142, Sofia, Bulgaria
Tel.: (359) 29807101
Web Site: https://www.bulgariaholding.com
4ID—(BUL)
Rev.: $83,900,784
Assets: $232,697,826
Liabilities: $22,330,869
Net Worth: $210,366,957
Earnings: $12,994,151
Emp.: 1,063
Fiscal Year-end: 12/31/22
Investment Services
N.A.I.C.S.: 523999

Elena Petkova Kirtcheva (Chm-Supervisory Bd)

Subsidiaries:

Agro pari AD (1)
5 Lachezar Stanchev str Sopharma Business Towers, Tower B flour 14, 1756, Sofia, Bulgaria
Tel.: (359) 2 44 79 240
Web Site: http://www.agropari.bg
Agricultural Land Rental & Leasing Services
N.A.I.C.S.: 531190
Georgi Georgiev (Exec Dir)

Bulgarian Register of Shipping AD (1)
South Industrial Zone Administrative building of Bulyard, Shipbuilding Industry EAD, 9000, Varna, Bulgaria
Tel.: (359) 52681510
Ship Building & Maintenance Services
N.A.I.C.S.: 336611
Dimitar Notak (Exec Dir)

IHB Metal Castings EAD (1)
8 Iliyansko Shose Str, 1220, Sofia, Bulgaria
Tel.: (359) 28364402
Web Site: https://www.ihbmetalcastings.com
Cast Iron Mfr
N.A.I.C.S.: 331511

IHB Shipdesign AD (1)
South Industrial Zone Administrative Building Bulport, 9000, Varna, Bulgaria
Tel.: (359) 52949939
Web Site: https://ihbshipdesign.com
Shipbuilding & Marine Engineering Services
N.A.I.C.S.: 541330

IHB Shipping Co EAD (1)
Southern Industrial Zone, 9000, Varna, Bulgaria
Tel.: (359) 52912965
Web Site: https://www.ihbshipping.com
Shipbuilding Repair & Maintenance Services
N.A.I.C.S.: 811310

KLVK AD (1)
37A Fridtjof Nansen str, 1142, Sofia, Bulgaria
Tel.: (359) 29807101
Marine Transportation Services
N.A.I.C.S.: 541990

KRZ Port - Bourgas AD (1)
Tel.: (359) 56849006
Web Site: https://www.krzport-bourgas.com
Marine Cargo Handling Services
N.A.I.C.S.: 488320

Maritime Holding AD (1)
79 Knyaginya Maria Luiza Blvd 4th floor, 1202, Sofia, Bulgaria
Tel.: (359) 29807101
Marine Transportation Services
N.A.I.C.S.: 541990

ZMM Bulgaria Holding AD (1)
79 Knyaginya Maria Luiza Blvd fl 4, 1202, Sofia, Bulgaria
Tel.: (359) 29810753
Web Site: https://zmmbulgaria.com
Metal Cutting Equipment Mfr
N.A.I.C.S.: 333517
Daneta Zheleva (Chm)

Subsidiary (Domestic):

IHB Electric AD (2)
41 Rojen Blvd, Sofia, 1271, Bulgaria
Tel.: (359) 2 936 0753
Web Site: http://www.ihbelectric.com
Electric Motor Mfr
N.A.I.C.S.: 335312

ZMM Nova Zagora AD (2)
55 Industrial, 8900, Nova Zagora, Bulgaria
Tel.: (359) 45763056
Web Site: https://www.en.zmmnz.com
Metal Cutting Equipment Mfr
N.A.I.C.S.: 333517

ZMM Sliven AD (2)
16 Bansko shosse Str, 8800, Sliven, Bulgaria
Tel.: (359) 44662108
Web Site: https://www.zmmsliven.com
Emp.: 400
Metal Cutting Equipment Mfr

INTERNATIONAL PUBLIC

N.A.I.C.S.: 333517
Georgi Valkov (CEO)

INDUSTRIAL INVESTMENT TRUST LIMITED

Office No 101A B wing The Capital GBlock Plot No C70, Bandra Kurla Complex, Mumbai, 400 001, India
Tel.: (91) 2243250100
Web Site: https://www.iitlgroup.com
IITL—(NSE)
Rev.: $1,665,307
Assets: $47,694,372
Liabilities: $4,782,833
Net Worth: $42,911,539
Earnings: $4,840,248
Emp.: 12
Fiscal Year-end: 03/31/22
Investment Management Service
N.A.I.C.S.: 523999
Bidhubhusan Samal (Chm)

Subsidiaries:

IIT Insurance Broking and Risk Management Private Limited (1)
Office No 101A B wing The Capital G-Block Plot No C-70, Bandra Kurla Complex, Mumbai, 400051, Bandra East, India
Tel.: (91) 2243250100
Web Site: https://iitlgroup.com
Sales Range: $50-74.9 Million
Emp.: 16
General Insurance Services
N.A.I.C.S.: 524298
B. Samal (Chm)

IIT Investrust Limited (1)
Office No 101A B wing The Capital G-Block Plot No C-70, Bandra Kurla Complex, Mumbai, 400051, Bandra East, India
Tel.: (91) 2222626844
Investment Management Service
N.A.I.C.S.: 523940

IITL PROJECTS LIMITED (1)
Office No 101A B wing The Capital G Block Plot No C 70, Bandra Kurla Complex Bandra, Mumbai, 400051, India
Tel.: (91) 2243250100
Web Site: https://www.iitlprojects.com
Rev.: $178,478
Assets: $3,280,189
Liabilities: $9,969,285
Net Worth: ($6,689,096)
Earnings: ($358,745)
Emp.: 1
Fiscal Year-end: 03/31/2023
Real Estate Development Services
N.A.I.C.S.: 531390
Kamlesh Kumar Agrawal (CFO)

INDUSTRIAL INVESTORS LLC

17-19 Prechistenskaya Embankment, Moscow, 119034, Russia
Tel.: (7) 495 980 6454 RU
Web Site: http://www.industrial-investors.com
Year Founded: 2000
Investment Management Service
N.A.I.C.S.: 523940
Sergei V. Generalov (Pres)

INDUSTRIAL MINERALS LTD.

38/460 Stirling Highway, Peppermint Grove, Perth, 6011, WA, Australia
Tel.: (61) 862706316 AU
Web Site: https://www.industmin.com
Year Founded: 2021
IND—(ASX)
Rev.: $641
Assets: $3,289,704
Liabilities: $319,435
Net Worth: $2,970,270
Earnings: ($948,234)
Fiscal Year-end: 06/30/22
Mineral Exploration Services
N.A.I.C.S.: 212390

INDUSTRIAL SAVINGS BANK JSC

19/7 Planetnaya Street, Moscow, 125167, Russia
Tel.: (7) 4952138890
Web Site: http://www.isbank.ru
Sales Range: Less than $1 Million
Securities Brokerage Services
N.A.I.C.S.: 523150
Gerald Kowalski *(Chm)*

INDUSTRIAL SECURITIES CO., LTD.
No 268 Hudong Road, Fuzhou, 350003, Fujian, China
Tel.: (86) 59138507869
Web Site: http://www.xyzq.com.cn
Year Founded: 2000
601377—(SHG)
Rev.: $1,496,613,175
Assets: $34,518,645,397
Liabilities: $26,538,665,086
Net Worth: $7,979,980,311
Earnings: $370,245,442
Fiscal Year-end: 12/31/22
Security Brokerage & Investment Management Services
N.A.I.C.S.: 523150
Zhihui Liu *(Pres)*

INDUSTRIAL TECHNICAL HOLDINGS CORPORATION
Huanxiu Street Office Shuanglong Industrial Park, Jimo, Qingdao, 266201, China
Tel.: (86) 5328 965 7397   VG
Web Site: http://www.ithc.online
Year Founded: 2018
Rev.: $6,631,309
Assets: $3,851,430
Liabilities: $3,121,358
Net Worth: $730,072
Earnings: ($738,465)
Emp.: 136
Fiscal Year-end: 12/31/21
Holding Company
N.A.I.C.S.: 551112
Andreas Spiegler *(Chm, Pres & CEO)*

INDUSTRIAL UNION OF DONBASS CORPORATION
Shorsa Str 48, 83050, Donetsk, Ukraine
Tel.: (380) 623814002
Web Site: http://www.isd.com.ua
Year Founded: 1995
Sales Range: $1-4.9 Billion
Emp.: 600
Holding Company; Steel Production; Ferrous Metallurgy Equipment; Engineering Services; Telecommunications; Tourism; Agriculture
N.A.I.C.S.: 551112
Sergey A. Taruta *(Pres-Metallurg)*

Subsidiaries:

ISD Dunaferr Zrt.   (1)
Vasmu ter 1-3, Dunaujvaros, 2400, Hungary
Tel.: (36) 25 584 000
Web Site: http://www.dunaferr.hu
Steel Product Distr
N.A.I.C.S.: 423510
Leonid Frumkin *(Chm)*

ISD Huta Czestochowa Sp. z o.o.   (1)
Ul Kucelinska 22, 42-207, Czestochowa, Poland
Tel.: (48) 34323126163
Web Site: http://www.hutaczestochowa.pl
Steel Product Mfr & Distr
N.A.I.C.S.: 331110

Industrial Union of Donbass Corporation - Alchevsk Coking Plant   (1)
1 Krasnye Partizany Street, Alchevsk, 94223, Ukraine
Tel.: (380) 64 427 62 86
Coke Mfr
N.A.I.C.S.: 331110

JSC Dneproptrovsk Tube Works   (1)
31 Mayakovsky Str, 49068, Dnepropetrovsk, Ukraine
Tel.: (380) 562596131
Web Site: http://aodtz.ptcor.net
Tube Mfr
N.A.I.C.S.: 331210

OJSC Alchevsk Iron & Steel Works   (1)
Schmidt 4, 94202, Alchevsk, Lugansk, Ukraine
Tel.: (380) 644273125
Iron & Steel Mfr
N.A.I.C.S.: 331110

OJSC Dneprovsky Iron & Steel Integrated Works   (1)
Kirov Str 18B, 51902, Dnepropetrovsk, Ukraine
Tel.: (380) 569232237
Web Site: http://www.dmkd.dp.ua
Iron & Steel Mfr
N.A.I.C.S.: 331110

INDUSTRIALBANK PJSC
Vulytsya Kostenka 11, 50000, Dnipropetrovsk, Ukraine
Tel.: (380) 800503535
Web Site: http://www.industrialbank.ua
Year Founded: 1990
INDB—(UKR)
Sales Range: $25-49.9 Million
Banking Services
N.A.I.C.S.: 522110
Gerald Kowalski *(Chm)*

INDUSTRIAS ALEN S.A. DE C.V.
Blvd Diaz Ordaz No 1000 Col Los Trevino, Santa Catarina, 66150, Nuevo Leon, Mexico
Tel.: (52) 81221000
Web Site: http://www.grupoalen.com
Year Founded: 1949
Sales Range: $150-199.9 Million
Emp.: 1,000
Holding Company Household Cleaner Mfr
N.A.I.C.S.: 551112
Alfonso E. Garcia *(CEO)*

Subsidiaries:

AlEn USA, LLC   (1)
9326 Baythorne Dr, Houston, TX 77041
Tel.: (800) 615-3191
Web Site: http://www.alenamericas.com
Floor Cleaner & Laundry Product Mfr
N.A.I.C.S.: 325611

Alen Americas Inc.   (1)
14825 NW Fwy Ste 500, Houston, TX 77040
Tel.: (832) 484-1508
Web Site: http://www.alen.com
Sales Range: $25-49.9 Million
Emp.: 35
Household Cleaning Products Mfr & Distr
N.A.I.C.S.: 424690
Erwin Salazar *(Mgr-Mktg)*

Subsidiary (Domestic):

White Cap, Inc.   (2)
9326 Bay Thorne Dr, Houston, TX 77041
Tel.: (609) 267-8990
Sales Range: $25-49.9 Million
Emp.: 3
Mfr & Sales of Disinfectants & Cleaners
N.A.I.C.S.: 541618

Subsidiary (Domestic):

Pine-O-Pine LP   (3)
14825 NW Freeway Ste 500, Houston, TX 77040
Tel.: (832) 484-1508
Web Site: http://www.alenamericas.com
Sales Range: $25-49.9 Million
Mfr of Cleaning Agents
N.A.I.C.S.: 325612
Jesus Camacho *(Gen Mgr)*

INDUSTRIAS BACHOCO S.A.B. DE C.V.
Avenida Tecnologico 401 Ciudad Industrial, 38010, Celaya, Guanajuato, Mexico
Tel.: (52) 4616183555   MX
Web Site: http://www.bachoco.com.mx
Year Founded: 1980
IBA—(NYSE)
Rev.: $5,537,950
Assets: $4,712,893
Liabilities: $1,463,691
Net Worth: $3,249,202
Earnings: $264,845
Fiscal Year-end: 12/31/23
Poultry, Swine & Feed Producer
N.A.I.C.S.: 311615
Ernesto Salmon Castelo *(Dir-Ops)*

Subsidiaries:

Bachoco Aguascalientes   (1)
Jose Maria Guzman 204, Aguascalientes, Mexico
Tel.: (52) 4499712300
Web Site: http://www.bachoco.mx
Poultry, Swine & Feed Mfr
N.A.I.C.S.: 311615

Bachoco Celaya   (1)
Norte 11 esquina poniente 4, Celaya, 38010, Guanajuato, Mexico
Tel.: (52) 4616188800
Poultry, Swine & Feed Mfr
N.A.I.C.S.: 311615

Bachoco Chinameca   (1)
Carretera Transistmica Km 7.5 Elvira, Hernandez de Ochoa, Veracruz, Mexico
Tel.: (52) 922 261 0012
Web Site: http://www.bachoco.com
Poultry, Swine & Feed Mfr & Sales
N.A.I.C.S.: 311615

Bachoco Cuautla   (1)
Tacambaro 6, Lazaro Cardenas, Cuautla, Mexico
Tel.: (52) 735 398 4616
Poultry, Swine & Feed Mfr
N.A.I.C.S.: 311615

Bachoco Culiacan   (1)
Carretera a Recursos Km 2.5, Culiacan, Sinaloa, Mexico
Tel.: (52) 667 714 1044
Poultry, Swine & Feed Mfr
N.A.I.C.S.: 311615

Bachoco Gomez Palacio   (1)
Valle del Guadiana 433, Parque Industrial Lagunero, Gomez Palacio, Durango, Mexico
Tel.: (52) 871 719 9821
Web Site: http://bachoco.com.mx
Poultry, Swine & Feed Mfr
N.A.I.C.S.: 311615

Bachoco Hermosillo   (1)
Carretera la Colorada km 35, Hermosillo, Sonora, Mexico
Tel.: (52) 6622610615
Poultry, Swine & Feed Mfr
N.A.I.C.S.: 311615

Bachoco Lagos de Moreno   (1)
Castilla 45, Loma Bonita Lagos de Moreno, Jalisco, Mexico
Tel.: (52) 4747419220
Poultry, Swine & Feed Mfr
N.A.I.C.S.: 311615

Bachoco Merida   (1)
Av Pirncipal s/n por Jose Maria Castro Tejero, Ciudad Industrial, Merida, Yucatan, Mexico
Tel.: (52) 1 999 930 4400
Web Site: http://bachoco.com.mx
Poultry, Swine & Feed Mfr
N.A.I.C.S.: 311615

Bachoco Mexico   (1)
Planta Minatitlan 1 Electra Tlanepantla Edo de Mexico, Mexico, Mexico
Tel.: (52) 1 55 5366 8000
Web Site: http://bachoco.com.mx
Poultry, Swine & Feed Mfr
N.A.I.C.S.: 311615

Bachoco Monterrey   (1)
Av Acueducto Mina Monterrey, S/n Col Provileon, Escobedo, Nuevo Leon, Mexico
Tel.: (52) 8183528692
Poultry, Swine & Feed Mfr
N.A.I.C.S.: 311615

Bachoco Puebla   (1)
Diagonal Defensores de la Republica 866, Col Adolfo Lopez Mateos, Puebla, Mexico
Tel.: (52) 2222205290
Sales Range: $25-49.9 Million
Emp.: 55
Poultry, Swine & Feed Mfr
N.A.I.C.S.: 311615

Bachoco Saltillo   (1)
Carretera Saltillo-Monterrey Km 20, Ramos Arizpe, Saltillo, Mexico
Tel.: (52) 844 7900 000
Poultry, Swine & Feed Mfr
N.A.I.C.S.: 311615

Bachoco Tecamachalco   (1)
9 Oriente esquina Sur, Tecamachalco, Puebla, Mexico
Tel.: (52) 2494223500
Poultry, Swine & Feed Mfr
N.A.I.C.S.: 311615

Bachoco Vercruz   (1)
Calle Mango 19, Central de Avastos, Veracruz, Mexico
Tel.: (52) 2299220634
Poultry, Swine & Feed Mfr
N.A.I.C.S.: 311615

Bachoco, S.A. de C.V.   (1)
Av Tecnologico No 401, Celaya, Mexico   (100%)
Tel.: (52) 4616183500
Web Site: http://www.bacho.com.mx
Sales Range: $25-49.9 Million
Emp.: 250
Perishable Prepared Food Mfr
N.A.I.C.S.: 311991

Campi Alimentos, S.A. de C.V.   (1)
Av Tecnologico No 401 Cd Industrial, 38010, Celaya, Mexico   (99.99%)
Tel.: (52) 1 800 55 22674
Web Site: http://www.campialimentos.com
Animal Feed Products Mfr & Distr
N.A.I.C.S.: 311119

O.K. Industries Inc.   (1)
4601 N 6th St, Fort Smith, AR 72904
Tel.: (479) 783-4186
Web Site: http://www.tenderbird.com
Sales Range: $600-649.9 Million
Emp.: 4,200
Poultry Products Mfr & Distr
N.A.I.C.S.: 311615

Subsidiary (Domestic):

O.K. Farms, Inc.   (2)
4601 N 6th St, Fort Smith, AR 72904-2208
Tel.: (479) 783-4186
Web Site: http://www.okfoods.com
Provider of Poultry & Poultry Products
N.A.I.C.S.: 112320

O.K. Foods, Inc.   (2)
4601 N 6th St, Fort Smith, AR 72904-2208   (100%)
Tel.: (479) 783-4186
Web Site: http://www.okfoods.com
Emp.: 1,000
Provider of Poultry & Poultry Products
N.A.I.C.S.: 311615

Subsidiary (Domestic):

Albertville Quality Foods, Inc.   (3)
130 Quality Dr, Albertville, AL 35950
Tel.: (256) 840-9923
Web Site: http://www.albertvillequalityfoods.com
Chicken Tenderloin & Associated Products Mfr
N.A.I.C.S.: 311615
Eric Tucker *(Pres)*

Operadora de Servicios de Personal, S.A. de C.V.   (1)
Av Tecnologico No 401 Ciudad Industrial, Celaya, 38010, Guanajuato, Mexico
Tel.: (52) 4616183500
Poultry Products Whslr
N.A.I.C.S.: 424440

INDUSTRIAS BACHOCO S.A.B. DE C.V.

Industrias Bachoco S.A.B. de C.V.—(Continued)

Pecuarius Laboratorios, S.A. de C.V. (1)
Carretera Obregon-Bacum Km1, Ciudad Obregon, Sonora, Mexico
Tel.: (52) 644 414 65 00
Pharmaceuticals Product Mfr
N.A.I.C.S.: 325412

Sepetec, S. A. de C.V. (1)
Av Tecnologico No 401, Celaya, Mexico (100%)
Tel.: (52) 4616183500
Sales Range: $25-49.9 Million
Emp.: 250
Perishable Prepared Food Mfr
N.A.I.C.S.: 311991

INDUSTRIAS CH, S.A.B. DE C.V.

Agustin Melgar No 23, Ninos Heroes, 54030, Tlalnepantla, Mexico
Tel.: (52) 5511651000
Web Site: https://www.industriasch.com.mx
Year Founded: 1938
ICH—(MEX)
Rev.: $2,748,764
Assets: $4,451,951
Liabilities: $907,143
Net Worth: $3,544,808
Earnings: $226,214
Emp.: 5,228
Fiscal Year-end: 12/31/23
Holding Company; Metal Production
N.A.I.C.S.: 551112
Rufino Vigil Gonzalez *(Chm & CEO)*

Subsidiaries:

Grupo Simec, S.A.B. de C.V. (1)
Calzada Lazaro Cardenas 601 Colonia La Nogalera, 4444, Guadalajara, Jalisco, Mexico (84%)
Tel.: (52) 3337706700
Web Site: https://www.gsimec.com.mx
Rev.: $2,423,948,353
Assets: $3,935,164,836
Liabilities: $1,000,597,951
Net Worth: $2,934,566,885
Earnings: $251,833,217
Emp.: 4,260
Fiscal Year-end: 12/31/2023
Structural Steel Products Mfr
N.A.I.C.S.: 332312
Luis Garcia Limon *(CEO)*

Subsidiary (Domestic):

Compania Siderurgica de Guadalajara S.A. de C.V. (2)
Lazaro Cardenas 601, Col La Nogalera, 44440, Guadalajara, Jalisco, Mexico
Tel.: (52) 1 33 1057 5757
Steel Production
N.A.I.C.S.: 331110

Procarsa, S.A. de C.V. (1)
Prolongacion Francisco I Madero Zona Industrial, Cd Frontera Coahuila, CP 25680, Monclova, Mexico (99.9%)
Tel.: (52) 55 1165 1000
Web Site: http://www.industriasch.com.mx
Tube & Pipe Producer
N.A.I.C.S.: 331210

Pytsa Industrial de Mexico, S.A. de C.V. (1)
Calle 2 No 10 Fraccionamiento Ecatepec de Morelos, Rustica Xalostoc, 55340, Mexico, Mexico
Tel.: (52) 56990700
Web Site: http://www.pytsa.mx
Steel Pole Mfr
N.A.I.C.S.: 331210

Sigosa S.A. De C.V. (1)
Prolongacion Av Uniones 100 Fracc Industrial del Norte, 87340, Matamoros, Tamaulipas, Mexico
Tel.: (52) 8681501900
Web Site: http://sigosa.com.mx
Steel Product Mfr & Distr
N.A.I.C.S.: 331110

Tuberias Procarsa S.A. de C.V. (1)
Prolongacion Sur Francisco I Madero, Cd Frontera, 25680, Coahuila, Mexico
Tel.: (52) 8666362266
Web Site: http://www.procarsa.mx
Carbon Steel Pipe Mfr
N.A.I.C.S.: 331210

INDUSTRIAS ELECTRO QUIMICAS SA

Tel.: (51) 16144300
Web Site: https://www.ieqsa.com.pe
Year Founded: 1922
IEQSAI1—(LIM)
Sales Range: Less than $1 Million
Zinc Alloy Product Mfr
N.A.I.C.S.: 331529

INDUSTRIAS ESTRA SA

Calle 30 No 55 - 72, Medellin, Colombia
Tel.: (57) 6046044100
Web Site: https://www.estrasoluciones.com
Year Founded: 1953
ESTRA—(COLO)
Sales Range: Less than $1 Million
Plastic Container Mfr
N.A.I.C.S.: 326160
Juan Fernando Gomez *(Pres)*

INDUSTRIAS ROMI S.A.

Rodovia SP 304 Km 141 5, Santa Barbara d'Oeste, 13459057, SP, Brazil
Tel.: (55) 1934559000 BR
Web Site: https://www.romi.com
Year Founded: 1930
ROMI3—(BRAZ)
Rev.: $244,739,655
Assets: $455,088,643
Liabilities: $221,497,457
Net Worth: $233,591,186
Earnings: $32,822,216
Emp.: 1,964
Fiscal Year-end: 12/31/23
Machine Tools Mfr
N.A.I.C.S.: 333517
Carlos Guimaraes Chiti *(Vice Chm)*

Subsidiaries:

BURKHARDT+WEBER Fertigungssysteme GmbH (1)
Burkhardt Weber-Strasse 57, 72760, Reutlingen, Germany
Tel.: (49) 7121 315 0
Web Site: http://www.burkhardt-weber.de
Emp.: 250
Machine Tool Mfr & Distr
N.A.I.C.S.: 333517
Olaf Furtmeier *(CEO)*

Burkhardt + Weber / Romi (Shanghai) Co., Ltd. (1)
Room 502B Bldg 10 Lane 198 Zhangheng Road, Zhangjiang High-Tech Zone, Shanghai, 201204, China
Tel.: (86) 2161005568
Industrial Machinery Whslr
N.A.I.C.S.: 423830

Burkhardt + Weber LLC (1)
1845 Airport Exchange Blvd Ste 180, Erlanger, KY 41018
Tel.: (859) 308-6625
Machine Tools Mfr
N.A.I.C.S.: 333517

Romi Europa GmbH (1)
Burkhardt Weber Strasse 57, 72760, Reutlingen, Germany
Tel.: (49) 7121315604
Web Site: http://www.romi-europa.de
Machine Tool Whslr
N.A.I.C.S.: 423830

Romi France SAS (1)
240 rue Ferdinand Perrier, Geneva park, 69800, Saint-Priest-en-Jarez, France
Tel.: (33) 437256070
Web Site: http://www.romifrance.fr
Industrial Equipment Whsr
N.A.I.C.S.: 423830

Romi Italia S.r.l. (1)
Corso Re Umberto 1, 10121, Turin, Italy
Tel.: (39) 0523778956
Web Site: http://www.romiitalia.it
Industrial Machinery Mfr
N.A.I.C.S.: 333310
Fabio Matteo Salmeri *(Gen Mgr)*

Romi Machine Tools, Ltd. (1)
1845 Airport Exchange Blvd Ste 180, Erlanger, KY 41018
Tel.: (859) 647-7566
Web Site: http://www.romiusa.com
Machine Tool Mfr & Distr
N.A.I.C.S.: 333517
Americo Emilio *(Founder)*

Romi Machines UK Ltd. (1)
Leigh Road Swift Valley Industrial Estate, Rugby, CV21 1DS, United Kingdom
Tel.: (44) 1788544221
Web Site: http://www.romiuk.com
Industrial Machinery Mfr
N.A.I.C.S.: 333310
Eduardo Paiva *(Gen Mgr)*

Romi Maquinas Espana S.A. (1)
Comadran 15 Nave B1 Can Salvatella Industrial Estate, Barbera del Valles, 08210, Barcelona, Spain
Tel.: (34) 937194926
Web Site: http://www.romi.es
Machine Maintenance Services
N.A.I.C.S.: 811310

INDUSTRIE CHIMICHE FORESTALI S.P.A.

Via Fratelli Kennedy 75 Marcallo con Casone, 20010, Milan, Italy
Tel.: (39) 02972141 IT
Web Site: https://www.icf.forestali.it
Year Founded: 1918
ICF—(ITA)
Commercial Adhesive & High-Tech Fabric Products Mfr & Marketer
N.A.I.C.S.: 325520
Guido Cami *(CEO)*

INDUSTRIE DE NORA S.P.A

Via Bistolfi 35, 20134, Milan, Italy
Tel.: (39) 02 21291 IT
Web Site: http://www.denora.com
Year Founded: 1923
Sales Range: $300-349.9 Million
Emp.: 1,200
Holding Company; Electromechanical Products Mfr & Services
N.A.I.C.S.: 551112
Paolo Dellacha *(CEO)*

Subsidiaries:

De Nora Deutschland GmbH (1)
Industriestrasse 17, 63517, Rodenbach, Germany
Tel.: (49) 61845980
Electronic Chemical Distr
N.A.I.C.S.: 424690
Francesco L'Abbate *(Mgr-Fin & Control)*

De Nora Elettrodi (Suzhou) Co. Ltd (1)
113 Longtan Road - Suzhou Industrial Park, 215126, Suzhou, Jiangsu, China
Tel.: (86) 51262831001
Electronic Chemical Distr
N.A.I.C.S.: 424690
Hideto Shimizu *(Mgr-Section)*

De Nora India Limited (1)
Plot Nos 184 185 189 Kundaim Industrial Estate, Kundaim, Goa, 403 115, India
Tel.: (91) 8326731100
Web Site: http://www.india.denora.com
Rev.: $7,148,396
Assets: $10,866,661
Liabilities: $1,724,449
Net Worth: $9,142,211
Earnings: $770,639
Emp.: 56
Fiscal Year-end: 03/31/2021
Electrolytic Products Mfr
N.A.I.C.S.: 334419
Jyoti Bandodkar *(Officer-Compliance & Sec)*

INTERNATIONAL PUBLIC

De Nora Permelec Techno Service Ltd. (1)
2023-15 Endo, Kanagawa, Fujisawa, 252-0816, Japan
Tel.: (81) 466878857
Web Site: http://www.permelec.co.jp
Emp.: 70
Metal Product Mfr & Distr
N.A.I.C.S.: 333517
Danilo Parini *(Pres)*

De Nora Tech, Inc. (1)
7590 Discovery Ln, Painesville, OH 44077-9190
Tel.: (440) 710-5300
Web Site: http://www.denora.com
Electrode Mfr & Coating Services
N.A.I.C.S.: 334513
Paolo Dellacha *(CEO)*

De Nora Water Technologies Texas, LLC (1)
1110 Industrial Blvd, Sugar Land, TX 77478
Tel.: (281) 240-6770
Electronic Chemical Distr
N.A.I.C.S.: 424690
Brian Riedel *(Mgr-Comml)*

De Nora Water Technologies UK Services Ltd (1)
Arley Drive Birch Coppice Business Park, Tamworth, Warwickshire, United Kingdom
Tel.: (44) 1827266000
Web Site: http://www.denora.com
Electronic Chemical Distr
N.A.I.C.S.: 424690

De Nora Water Technologies, Inc. (1)
3000 Advance Ln, Colmar, PA 18915-9727
Tel.: (215) 997-4000
Web Site: http://www.denora.com
Water & Waste Water Treatment Solutions
N.A.I.C.S.: 562219

De Nora do Brasil LTDA (1)
Avenida Jerome Case No 1959 18087 - Eden, Sorocaba, Sao Paulo, Brazil
Tel.: (55) 1521014450
Electronic Chemical Distr
N.A.I.C.S.: 424690

MIOX Corporation (1)
5601 Balloon Fiesta Pkwy N, Albuquerque, NM 87113
Tel.: (505) 343-0090
Web Site: http://www.miox.com
Sales Range: $1-9.9 Million
Emp.: 51
Water Purification Machinery Mfr
N.A.I.C.S.: 333310
Justin Sanchez *(CTO & VP-Engrg)*

INDUSTRIE ZIGNAGO SANTA MARGHERITA SPA

Via Ita Marzotto 8, Fossalta Di Portogruaro, 30025, Venice, Italy
Tel.: (39) 035996711
Web Site: http://www.zignago.com
Year Founded: 1940
Sales Range: $300-349.9 Million
Emp.: 1,684
Holding Company
N.A.I.C.S.: 551112

Subsidiaries:

Cantine Torresella Srl (1)
Via Ita Marzotto 8, Villanova di Portogruaro, 30025, Venice, Italy (100%)
Tel.: (39) 0421246111
Web Site: http://www.santamargherita.com
Beer Wine & Liquor Stores
N.A.I.C.S.: 445320

New High Glass Inc (1)
12713 SW 125th Ave, Miami, FL 33186
Tel.: (305) 232-0840
Web Site: http://www.newhigh.com
Sales Range: $25-49.9 Million
Emp.: 30
Glass Bottle Mfr
N.A.I.C.S.: 541611
Enrico Raccah *(Gen Mgr)*

Vetri Special SpA (1)
Via Manci 5, Trento, 38122, Italy (43%)
Tel.: (39) 0461270111

AND PRIVATE COMPANIES

Web Site: http://www.vetrispeciali.com
Sales Range: $125-149.9 Million
Emp.: 500
Glass Container Mfr
N.A.I.C.S.: 327213

INDUSTRIE-CONTACT AG
Bahrenfelder Marktplatz 7, 22761,
Hamburg, Germany
Tel.: (49) 40 899 666 0   De
Web Site: http://www.ic-gruppe.com
Year Founded: 1979
Advetising Agency
N.A.I.C.S.: 541810
Uwe Schmidt *(Co-Owner & Co-CEO)*

INDUSTRIE-ELECTRONIC GMBH & CO. KG
Carl Jacob Kolb Weg 1, 97877,
Wertheim, Germany
Tel.: (49) 93428710
Web Site: http://www.industronic.com
Year Founded: 1964
Rev.: $26,203,524
Emp.: 109
Industrial Communication Systems Mfr
N.A.I.C.S.: 517810
Wolfgang Stallmeyer *(Pres)*

Subsidiaries:

INDUSTRONIC Industrie-Electronic Equipment Co. Ltd.   (1)
Carl-Jacob-Kolb-Weg 1, 97877, Wertheim, Germany
Tel.: (49) 93428710
Web Site: http://www.industronic.com
Security System Services
N.A.I.C.S.: 561621

INDUSTRONIC, Inc.   (1)
1011 US Hwy 22 W Ste 301, Bridgewater, NJ 08807
Tel.: (908) 393-5960
Security System Services
N.A.I.C.S.: 561621

INDUSTRIEBANK LIOF N.V.
Boschstraat 76, Maastricht, 6211 AX,
Limburg, Netherlands
Tel.: (31) 433280280
Web Site: http://www.liof.nl
Sales Range: $25-49.9 Million
Emp.: 50
Bank Holding Company
N.A.I.C.S.: 551111
Armand Thomassen *(CFO)*

INDUSTRIEHOF SCHEREN- BOSTEL HEINRICH RODEN- BOSTEL GMBH
Im Winkel 5, Wedemark, 30900, Germany
Tel.: (49) 513060720
Web Site: http://www.industriehof.com
Rev.: $23,936,519
Emp.: 50
Agricultural Machinery Parts Distr
N.A.I.C.S.: 423820
Heinrich-Wilhelm Rodenbostel *(Mng Dir)*

INDUSTRIELLE DE CON- TROLE ET D EQUIPEMENT
11 rue Marcel Sembat, 94146, Alfortville, Cedex, France
Tel.: (33) 141797600
Web Site: http://www.icegroupe.com
Sales Range: $25-49.9 Million
Emp.: 1,000
Electronic Services
N.A.I.C.S.: 238210
Pierre Fustier *(Chm-Exec Bd)*

Subsidiaries:

CEE Italiana Srl   (1)
Via Verga 11, 20863, Concorezzo, Monza and Brianza, Italy
Tel.: (39) 039 647401
Web Site: http://www.ceeitaliana.com
Electrical Equipment Mfr & Distr
N.A.I.C.S.: 335314

CEE Relays Ltd.   (1)
87C Whitby Road, Slough, SL1 3DR, United Kingdom
Tel.: (44) 1753 576477
Web Site: http://www.ceerelays.co.uk
Relay & Industrial Control Mfr
N.A.I.C.S.: 335314

COMPELMA S.A.S.   (1)
Z A des GODETS 33 rue des Petits Ruisseaux, 91370, Verrieres-le-Buisson, France
Tel.: (33) 1 69 75 21 21
Web Site: http://www.compelma.com
Electronic Components Mfr
N.A.I.C.S.: 334419

Continental de Equipos Electricos SA   (1)
Europa Empresarial - Edificio Londres C/Playa de Liencres 2, Las Rozas, 28230, Madrid, Spain
Tel.: (34) 9 16 40 04 11
Electrical Equipment Distr
N.A.I.C.S.: 423610

EC2E   (1)
ZAC du pont des rayons 4 boulevard Napoleon 1er, 95290, L'Isle-Adam, France
Tel.: (33) 1 83 02 02 02
Web Site: http://www.electrocablage.fr
Electronic Product Distr
N.A.I.C.S.: 423690
Didier Martineau *(Pres)*

Mediane Ingenierie   (1)
Immeuble Calliope 121 rue Jean BART, 31670, Labege, France
Tel.: (33) 5 61 52 90 22
Web Site: http://www.medianeingenierie.com
Relay Mfr
N.A.I.C.S.: 335314

Mediane Systeme S.a.   (1)
Le Parc du Saint-Laurent 54 route de Sartrouville, Le Pecq, 78232, Paris, Cedex, France
Tel.: (33) 1 30 15 95 00
Web Site: http://www.medianesysteme.com
Industrial Technology Consulting Services
N.A.I.C.S.: 541512

STILOG I.S.T.   (1)
Le Capitole 55 avenue des champs pierreux, 92022, Nanterre, Cedex, France
Tel.: (33) 1 47 29 99 69
Web Site: http://www.stilog.com
Software Development Services
N.A.I.C.S.: 541511

SocieteTechnique d'Ingenierie et de Cooperation   (1)
La Boursidiere Quercy, 92357, Le Plessis-Robinson, Cedex, France
Tel.: (33) 1 46 30 28 90
Broadcasting Services
N.A.I.C.S.: 516210

INDUSTRIELLE NALE REEMP- LOIS AUTOMOBILES
80 rue Condorcet CS 30112 38096
VILLEFONTAINE Cedex, 38307,
Bourgoin-Jallieu, Isere, France
Tel.: (33) 474273400
Web Site: http://www.indra.fr
Rev.: $15,000,000
Emp.: 240
Automobile Deconstruction
N.A.I.C.S.: 423930
Nadine Desroches *(Mgr-IT)*

INDUSTRIJA BRUSNIH ALATA A.D., ADA
Krajiska 27A, 24430, Ada, 24430,
Serbia
Tel.: (381) 611854911
Web Site: https://www.ibaada.co.rs
Year Founded: 1991
IBAA—(BEL)
Sales Range: Less than $1 Million

Grinding & Cutting Tool Mfr
N.A.I.C.S.: 333515
Marija Djorovic *(Dir)*

INDUSTRIJA NAMESTAJA BAJMOK A.D.
ul Strosmajerova 14, 24210, Bajmok,
Serbia
Tel.: (381) 24 762 568
Web Site: http://www.inbajmok.com
Year Founded: 1987
INBB—(BEL)
Sales Range: Less than $1 Million
Emp.: 13
Furniture Mfr
N.A.I.C.S.: 337211
Derd Klinocki *(Exec Dir)*

INDUSTRONICS BERHAD
No 9 Jalan Taming 3 Taman Tanming
Jaya, Off Jalan Balakong, 43300,
Seri Kembangan, Selangor Darul Ehsan, Malaysia
Tel.: (60) 389613024   MY
Web Site: http://www.industronics.com.my
ITRONIC—(KLS)
Rev.: $11,706,360
Assets: $18,560,110
Liabilities: $10,179,847
Net Worth: $8,380,263
Earnings: ($1,633,215)
Fiscal Year-end: 06/30/23
Electronics Products & Communication Technology System Mfr
N.A.I.C.S.: 238210
Amy Wing Yee Liu *(Exec Dir)*

Subsidiaries:

Ademco (Malaysia) Sdn. Bhd.   (1)
No 60 Jalan Manis Tiga Taman Segar Cheras, Kuala Lumpur, 56100, Federal Territory, Malaysia
Tel.: (60) 391331313
Sales Range: $10-24.9 Million
Emp.: 30
Fire Detection & Security Solutions
N.A.I.C.S.: 561621

Industronics Manufacturing Sdn. Bhd.   (1)
No 6 Jalan Perusahaan Utama Tmn Industri Selesa Jaya Darul Ehsan, 43300, Balakong, Selangor, Malaysia
Tel.: (60) 389622032
Electronics Mfr
N.A.I.C.S.: 334419

INDUSTRY SUPER HOLDINGS PTY. LTD.
Level 39 Casselden 2 Lonsdale
Street, 2 Lonsdale Street, Melbourne,
3000, VIC, Australia
Tel.: (61) 396574321   AU
Web Site: http://www.industrysuper.com
Year Founded: 2006
Emp.: 358
Holding Company Services
N.A.I.C.S.: 551112

Subsidiaries:

Industry Fund Services Pty. Limited   (1)
Casselden Place Level 31, 2 Lonsdale Street, Melbourne, 3000, VIC, Australia   **(100%)**
Tel.: (61) 396574321
Web Site: http://www.ifs.net.au
Sales Range: $125-149.9 Million
Emp.: 250
Fund Management & Financial Consulting Services
N.A.I.C.S.: 524292

Subsidiary (Domestic):

IFM Investors Pty. Ltd.   (2)
Level 29 Casselden Place 2 Lonsdale

INDUSTRY SUPER HOLDINGS PTY. LTD.

Street, Melbourne, 3000, VIC,
Australia   **(100%)**
Tel.: (61) 3 8672 5300
Web Site: http://www.ifminvestors.com
Emp.: 110
Investment Management Service
N.A.I.C.S.: 523940
Brett Himbury *(CEO)*

Subsidiary (Non-US):

Aleatica, S.A.B. de C.V.   (3)
Boulevard Manuel Avila Camacho N 5 Torre A Piso 12 Lomas De Sotelo, De Juarez Mex, 53390, Naucalpan, Mexico **(63.64%)**
Tel.: (52) 5550039552
Web Site: http://www.ohlmexico.com.mx
Rev.: $839,859,604
Assets: $6,478,462,362
Liabilities: $3,313,788,753
Net Worth: $3,164,673,609
Earnings: $63,046,729
Emp.: 2,032
Fiscal Year-end: 12/31/2023
Roadway, Bridge & Tunnel Engineering & Construction Services
N.A.I.C.S.: 237310
Juan Luis Osuna Gomez *(Chm)*

Subsidiary (Domestic):

Autopista Urbana Norte, S.A. de C.V.   (4)
Avda Paseo de la Reforma n 222 piso 25, Ciudad Juarez, 06600, Mexico
Tel.: (52) 55 52 555250
Road Construction Services
N.A.I.C.S.: 237990

Concesionaria Mexiquense, S.A. de C.V.   (4)
Avda Paseo de la Reforma n 222- piso 25 Col Juarez Delegacion Cuauhtem, 06600, Mexico, Mexico
Tel.: (52) 55 52 555250
Web Site: http://www.conmex.com.mx
Concession & Road Construction Services
N.A.I.C.S.: 237990

Constructora Mayaluum, S.A. de C.V.   (4)
Carretera Federal- Chetumal Puerto Juarez Km 298, Playa del Carmen, 77710, Quintana Roo, Mexico
Tel.: (52) 984 873 4920
Property Development Services
N.A.I.C.S.: 531390

Constructora de Proyectos Viales de Mexico, S.A. de C.V.   (4)
Av Chapultepec 481 Juarez, 06600, Mexico, Mexico
Tel.: (52) 5552031312
Construction Engineering Services
N.A.I.C.S.: 237990

Gastronomica Santa Fe, S.A. de C.V   (4)
Paseo de la Reforma 222-25 piso 23, Juarez Delegacion Cuauhtemoc, 06600, Mexico, Mexico
Tel.: (52) 55 5955 7384
Web Site: http://www.ohldesarrollos.com
Shopping Center Rental Services
N.A.I.C.S.: 531120

Sociedad de Servicios Paseo de San Francisco, S.A. de C.V.   (4)
Arroyo Xonaca 1006, 72000, Puebla, Mexico
Tel.: (52) 22 22 46 53 81
Real Estate Development Services
N.A.I.C.S.: 531390

Joint Venture (Non-US):

Anglian Water Group Limited   (3)
Lancaster House Lancaster Way Ermine Business Park, Huntingdon, PE29 6XU, Cambs, United Kingdom   **(19.8%)**
Tel.: (44) 1480323000
Web Site: https://www.awg.com
Sales Range: $1-4.9 Billion
Emp.: 5,967
Holding Company; Water Supply, Sewerage & Property Development Services
N.A.I.C.S.: 551112
Stephen Billingham *(Chm)*

Subsidiary (Domestic):

AWG Property Limited   (4)

INDUSTRY SUPER HOLDINGS PTY. LTD.

Industry Super Holdings Pty. Ltd.—(Continued)
47 Melville Street, Edinburgh, EH4 7HL, United Kingdom
Tel.: (44) 01313431000
Web Site: http://www.awgproperty.co.uk
Sales Range: $50-74.9 Million
Emp.: 30
Commercial & Residential Property Investment & Development
N.A.I.C.S.: 531390
Tony Donnelly *(Chm)*

Anglian Water Services Limited (4)
Lancaster House Lancaster Way Ermine Business Park, Huntingdon, PE29 6XU, Cambridgeshire, United Kingdom
Tel.: (44) 3457919155
Web Site: https://www.anglianwater.co.uk
Rev.: $1,719,141,394
Assets: $14,320,002,386
Liabilities: $12,272,438,616
Net Worth: $2,047,563,770
Earnings: ($41,623,856)
Emp.: 4,764
Fiscal Year-end: 03/31/2019
Water Supply Distribution & Sewerage Services
N.A.I.C.S.: 221310
Peter Simpson *(CEO & Member-Mgmt Bd)*

Holding (US):

Buckeye Partners, L.P. (3)
One Greenway Plz Ste 600, Houston, TX 77046
Tel.: (832) 615-8600
Web Site: http://www.buckeye.com
Rev.: $4,108,275,000
Assets: $9,355,550,000
Liabilities: $5,224,380,000
Net Worth: $4,131,170,000
Earnings: ($59,038,000)
Emp.: 1,600
Fiscal Year-end: 12/31/2018
Refined Petroleum Products
N.A.I.C.S.: 486910
Daniel J. Driscoll *(Sr Mgr-Pur)*

Subsidiary (Non-US):

Bahamas Oil Refining Company International Limited (4)
West Sunrise Highway Grand Bahama, PO Box 42435, Freeport, Bahamas
Tel.: (242) 3502100
Petroleum Bulk Stations & Fuel Blending Services
N.A.I.C.S.: 424710
Khalid A. Muslih *(Pres-Intl Pipelines & Terminals Bus Unit)*

Subsidiary (Domestic):

Buckeye GP LLC (4)
100 Matonsford Rd 5 Radnor Corporate Ctr Ste 500, Radnor, PA 19087
Tel.: (610) 254-4600
Petroleum Pipeline Transportation Services
N.A.I.C.S.: 486910
Clark C. Smith *(Chm, Pres & CEO)*

Farm & Home Oil Company (4)
3115 State Rd, Telford, PA 18969-1076
Tel.: (215) 257-0131
Web Site: http://www.fhoil.com
Sales Range: $700-749.9 Million
Emp.: 198
Energy & Petroleum Supplier
N.A.I.C.S.: 424720
Jim Boyd *(Sec & VP-Fin)*

Gulf Coast Pipe Line, L.P. (4)
1301 Dickinson Ave, Dickinson, TX 77539
Tel.: (832) 340-7692
Web Site: http://www.gulfcoastpipelineservices.com
Petroleum Pipeline Transportation Services
N.A.I.C.S.: 486910

Joint Venture (Non-US):

Vitol Tank Terminals International B.V. (4)
KP van der Mandelelaan 130, PO Box 1546, Rotterdam, 3062 MB, Netherlands
Tel.: (31) 104987200
Web Site: http://www.vtti.com
Holding Company; Storage Terminals Operator
N.A.I.C.S.: 493190

Rob Nijst *(CEO)*

Subsidiary (Non-US):

Antwerp Terminal & Processing Company N.V. (5)
Beliweg 22 Haven 279, B-2030, Antwerp, Belgium
Tel.: (32) 3 303 1600
Oil Bulk Terminal & Refinery
N.A.I.C.S.: 424710
Pascal Demaeijer *(Gen Mgr)*

Holding (US):

ITR Concession Company LLC (3)
52551 Ash Rd, Granger, IN 46530
Tel.: (547) 674-8836
Web Site: http://www.ezpassin.com
Road Transportation Support Services
N.A.I.C.S.: 488999
Ken Daley *(CEO)*

Subsidiary (Non-US):

OHL Concesiones, S.L. (3)
Torre Espacio Paseo de la Castellana 259D, 28046, Madrid, 28046, Spain
Tel.: (34) 913484100
Sales Range: $100-124.9 Million
Emp.: 500
Civil Engineering Services
N.A.I.C.S.: 237990

Subsidiary (Domestic):

ALEATICA Labs, S.A. (4)
Paseo de la Castellana 259C Torre Cristal Planta 16, 28046, Madrid, Spain
Tel.: (34) 91 348 9300
Web Site: http://www.aleaticalabs.com
Research & Development in the Physical, Engineering & Life Sciences
N.A.I.C.S.: 541715

Subsidiary (Non-US):

Autopark, S.A. (4)
Av Brigadeiro Faria Lima 2894, Jardim Paulistano, 01451-938, Sao Paulo, Brazil
Tel.: (55) 1130791775
Web Site: http://www.ohuartelain.com
Civil Engineering Services
N.A.I.C.S.: 237990

Autopista Fernao Dias, S.A. (4)
Av Brigadeiro Faria Lima 2894, Jardim Paulistano, CEP 01451-938, Sao Paulo, Brazil
Tel.: (55) 35 3425 8233
Civil Engineering Services
N.A.I.C.S.: 237990

Autopista Fluminense, S.A. (4)
Av Brigadeiro Faria Lima 2895, Jardim Paulistano, CEP 01451-938, Sao Paulo, Brazil
Tel.: (55) 2127348888
Civil Engineering Services
N.A.I.C.S.: 237990

Subsidiary (Domestic):

Autovia de Aragon Tramo 1, S.A. (4)
Rotonda Aristoteles n 1, 28806, Alcala de Henares, Madrid, Spain
Tel.: (34) 918773418
Web Site: http://www.autoviadearagon.com
Civil Engineering Services
N.A.I.C.S.: 237990

Subsidiary (Non-US):

Autovias, S.A. (4)
Bairro Jardim Hiqyeu Clube Rodovia Anhanguera km 312 2 Pista Norte, 14079-000, Ribeirao Preto, Brazil
Tel.: (55) 1621024200
Web Site: http://www.autovias.com.br
Sales Range: $50-74.9 Million
Emp.: 150
Civil Engineering Services
N.A.I.C.S.: 237990
David Biaz *(Pres)*

Subsidiary (Domestic):

Cercanias Mostoles Navalcarnero, S.A. (4)
Ave Europa 2 Edificio Alcor Plaza B Planta 0 Ala Oeste, 28922, Madrid, Alcorcon, Spain
Tel.: (34) 916890664

Civil Engineering Services
N.A.I.C.S.: 237990

Marina Urola, S.A. (4)
Barrio Santiago s/n Edificio Capitania, Puerto Deportivo, 20750, Zumaya, Gaipuzcoa, Spain
Tel.: (34) 943860938
Emp.: 10
Civil Engineering Services
N.A.I.C.S.: 237990
Jon Irigoien *(Mng Dir)*

Metro Ligero Oeste, S.A. (4)
Edgar Neville 9 Ciudad de la Imagen, Pozuelo de Alarcon, 28223, Madrid, Spain
Tel.: (34) 915031600
Web Site: http://www.metroligero-oeste.es
Sales Range: $50-74.9 Million
Emp.: 200
Civil Engineering Services
N.A.I.C.S.: 237990

Nautic Tarragona, S.A. (4)
Port Esportiu local Capitania s/n, 43004, Tarragona, Spain
Tel.: (34) 977213100
Web Site: http://www.ohlconcesiones.es
Civil Engineering Services
N.A.I.C.S.: 237990

Nova Darsena Esportiva de Bara, S.A. (4)
Plaza Mediterraneo s/n Apartado de Correos N 50, Roda de Bara, 43883, Tarragona, Spain
Tel.: (34) 977138169
Civil Engineering Services
N.A.I.C.S.: 237990

Subsidiary (Non-US):

OHL Concesiones Argentina, S.A. (4)
Avenida De Mayo 1437, Buenos Aires, Argentina
Tel.: (34) 1150323159
Infrastructure Concession Services
N.A.I.C.S.: 488999

OHL Concesiones Chile, S.A. (4)
Edificios Alto el Plomo Torre Norte-Cerro El Plomo 5855 Piso 16, Oficinas 1607-1608, Las Condes, 7561160, Santiago, Chile
Tel.: (56) 2 2871 8500
Web Site: http://www.ohlconcesiones.cl
Transport Infrastructure Construction, Maintenance & Operator
N.A.I.C.S.: 237990

Subsidiary (US):

OHL Infrastructure, Inc. (4)
Austin Ctr 701 Brazos St Ste 320, Austin, TX 78701
Tel.: (512) 860-3850
Sales Range: $25-49.9 Million
Emp.: 75
Civil Engineering Services
N.A.I.C.S.: 237990

Subsidiary (Domestic):

Port Torredembarra, S.A. (4)
Edificio Capitania, 43830, Tarragona, Torredembarra, Spain
Tel.: (34) 977643234
Web Site: http://www.port-torredembarra.es
Civil Engineering Services
N.A.I.C.S.: 237990

Subsidiary (Non-US):

Sociedad Concesionaria Autopista Los Andes, S.A. (4)
Monjitas 392 piso 17, Edificio El Comercio, 8320113, Santiago, Chile
Tel.: (56) 27 142300
Civil Engineering Services
N.A.I.C.S.: 237990

Sociedad Concesionaria Autopista Los Libertadores, S.A. (4)
Monjitas 392 piso 6, Edificio El comercio, 8320113, Santiago, Chile
Tel.: (56) 27142350
Civil Engineering Services
N.A.I.C.S.: 237990

Sociedad Concesionaria Autopista del Sol, S.A. (4)

INTERNATIONAL PUBLIC

Monjitas 392 piso 6, Edificio El Comercio, 8320113, Santiago, Chile
Tel.: (56) 27142350
Civil Engineering Services
N.A.I.C.S.: 237990

Terminal Cerros de Valparaiso, S.A. (4)
Avenida Errazuriz 755 Piso 7 Oficina 708, Valparaiso, Chile
Tel.: (56) 32 3142400
Web Site: http://www.tcval.cl
Port Terminal Management Services
N.A.I.C.S.: 488310

Subsidiary (Domestic):

Terminales Maritimas del Sureste, S.A. (4)
Puerto de Alicante - Prolongacion Sur Muelle 23, Frente Al Muelle n 17 s/n, 03008, Alicante, Spain
Tel.: (34) 965984923
Web Site: http://www.tmsalc.com
Sales Range: $25-49.9 Million
Emp.: 27
Civil Engineering Services
N.A.I.C.S.: 237990

Subsidiary (Non-US):

Vianorte, S.A. (4)
Rodivia Attilo Balbo km 327 5 Zona Rural, CEP 14173-000, Sertaozinho, SP, Brazil
Tel.: (55) 1636011122
Web Site: http://www.vianorte.com.br
Management, Operation & Maintenance of Government Highway Concessions
N.A.I.C.S.: 921190

Joint Venture (US):

Switch, Inc. (3)
7135 S Decatur Blvd, Las Vegas, NV 89118
Tel.: (702) 444-4111
Web Site: http://www.switch.com
Rev.: $592,045,000
Assets: $2,918,618,000
Liabilities: $2,299,977,000
Net Worth: $618,641,000
Earnings: $5,412,000
Emp.: 829
Fiscal Year-end: 12/31/2021
Internet Service Provider
N.A.I.C.S.: 517121
Rob Roy *(Founder, Chm & CEO)*

Subsidiary (Domestic):

Data Foundry, Inc. (4)
2700 Via Fortuna Ste 500, Austin, TX 78746
Tel.: (512) 684-9000
Web Site: http://www.datafoundry.com
Sales Range: $1-9.9 Million
Emp.: 105
Internet Service Provider
N.A.I.C.S.: 517810
Edward Henigin *(CTO)*

InNEVation, LLC (4)
6795 S Edmond St 3rd Fl, Las Vegas, NV 89118
Tel.: (702) 444-1111
Web Site: http://www.innevation.com
Internet Publishing & Broadcasting Services
N.A.I.C.S.: 516210

Members Equity Bank Limited (1)
Level 28 360 Elizabeth St, Melbourne, 3000, VIC, Australia
Tel.: (61) 396056000 **(100%)**
Web Site: http://www.membersequity.com.au
Sales Range: $100-124.9 Million
Emp.: 600
Savings, Loans & Commercial Banking Services
N.A.I.C.S.: 522180

INDUTRADE AB

Raseborgsgatan 9, 164 74, Kista, Sweden
Tel.: (46) 87030300
Web Site: https://www.indutrade.com
Year Founded: 1978
INDT—(OMX)
Rev.: $2,530,369,871
Assets: $2,703,269,737

AND PRIVATE COMPANIES — INDUTRADE AB

Liabilities: $1,506,926,297
Net Worth: $1,196,343,439
Earnings: $251,107,552
Emp.: 9,128
Fiscal Year-end: 12/31/22
Industrial Component & Equipment Mfr
N.A.I.C.S.: 333248
Bengt David Harry Kjell (Vice Chm)

Subsidiaries:

A/S Industek (1)
Parnu mnt139E, Tallinn, 11317, Estonia
Tel.: (372) 666 2800
Web Site: https://www.industek.ee
Emp.: 5
Utility Equipment Importer
N.A.I.C.S.: 333414
Madi Mardson (Gen Mgr)

AB Carlsson & Moller (1)
Garnisonsgatan 45, PO Box 22161, 254 66, Helsingborg, Sweden
Tel.: (46) 4 225 3800
Web Site: https://www.c-m.se
Emp.: 50
Provider of Business Technology Services
N.A.I.C.S.: 561499
Michael Andersson (CEO)

AD MediCal AB (1)
Ragnar Thorngrensgata 8, 431 45, Gothenburg, Sweden
Tel.: (46) 3 149 5999
Web Site: https://www.ad-medical.se
Medical Device Mfr
N.A.I.C.S.: 339112

ALH Systems Limited (1)
1 Kingdom Avenue, Northacre Industrial Park, Westbury, BA13 4WE, Wiltshire, United Kingdom
Tel.: (44) 137 385 8234
Web Site: https://www.alh-systems.co.uk
Polymer & Mechanical Product Mfr
N.A.I.C.S.: 326291
David Lyes (Mng Dir)

ALPHR Technology Europe SRL (1)
Calea Zimandului Nr 30 Hala 2, 310216, Arad, Romania
Tel.: (40) 357800444
Industrial Automation Equipments Mfr
N.A.I.C.S.: 334512
Florin Radu Cordos (Mng Dir)

ALPHR Technology Ltd. (1)
Amor Way Dunhams Lane, West Haddon, Letchworth, SG6 1UG, Hertfordshire, United Kingdom
Tel.: (44) 146 267 5838
Web Site: https://www.alphrtechnology.com
Industrial Automation Equipments Mfr
N.A.I.C.S.: 334512
Paul Bridgwater (Dir-Sls)

APG Europe B.V. (1)
Johan Enschedeweg 21, 1422 DR, Uithoorn, Netherlands
Tel.: (31) 29 751 4620
Web Site: https://www.apg-pharma.com
Packaging Material Product Whslr
N.A.I.C.S.: 424130
Marco Benard (Acct Mgr)

ATB Automation NV (1)
Vermogenweg 109, 3641 SR, Mijdrecht, Netherlands
Tel.: (31) 29 728 5821
Web Site: https://www.atbautomation.eu
Industrial Equipment Whsr
N.A.I.C.S.: 423830
Olaf Van de Ven (Mng Dir)

Abelko Innovation AB (1)
Gjuterigatan 9, 553 18, Jonkoping, Sweden
Tel.: (46) 92 045 0608
Web Site: https://www.abelko.se
Electrical & Electronic Mfr
N.A.I.C.S.: 335999

Acti-Chem A/S (1)
Bogeskovvej 16, 3490, Kvistgaard, Denmark
Tel.: (45) 56144444
Web Site: https://acti-chem.dk
Water Treatment Chemical Mfr
N.A.I.C.S.: 325998

Acumo AB (1)
Soderby Gards Vag 11A, Uttran, 147 60, Tumba, Sweden
Tel.: (46) 85 577 3030
Web Site: https://www.acumo.se
Industrial Equipment Whsr
N.A.I.C.S.: 423830
Mikael Tornberg (CEO)

Adaero Precision Components Ltd. (1)
Down End Lords Meadow Ind Est Crediton, Devon, EX17 1HN, United Kingdom
Tel.: (44) 136 377 5744
Web Site: https://www.adaero.co.uk
Precision Product Mfr
N.A.I.C.S.: 332721
Sam Charlton (Ops Mgr)

Akamex Oy (1)
Heinamaentie 6, 40250, Jyvaskyla, Finland
Tel.: (358) 29006230
Web Site: http://www.akamex.fi
Sales Range: $75-99.9 Million
Emp.: 28
N.A.I.C.S.: 522299
Martie Eskelanen (Gen Mgr)

Alcatraz Interlocks B.V. (1)
Stedenbaan 6, 5121 DP, Rijen, Netherlands
Tel.: (31) 76 514 7172
Web Site: https://www.alcatrazinterlocks.com
Machine Part Mfr
N.A.I.C.S.: 332710
Rob Kouvelt (Mng Dir)

Alnab Armatur AB (1)
Ogardesvagen 4B, 433 30, Partille, Sweden
Tel.: (46) 3 144 9450
Web Site: https://www.alnab.se
Emp.: 36
Provider of Business Technology Services
N.A.I.C.S.: 561499
Jan-Erik Larsson (CEO)

Aluflex System AB (1)
Lilla Garnisonsgatan 34, 254 67, Helsingborg, Sweden
Tel.: (46) 42 38 02 30
Web Site: http://www.aluflex.se
Emp.: 30
Building Systems Distr
N.A.I.C.S.: 423390
Fredrik Jonsson (Gen Mgr)

Aluflex System AS (1)
Industrivegen 23B, 2069, Jessheim, Norway
Tel.: (47) 6 394 4920
Web Site: https://www.aluflex.no
Machine Part Mfr
N.A.I.C.S.: 332710

Armaturen Aichhorn GmbH (1)
Gewerbepark 1, 4631, Krenglbach, Austria
Tel.: (43) 7249461660
Web Site: https://www.armaturen-aichhorn.at
Valves Mfr & Distr
N.A.I.C.S.: 332911

Ateco Tobler AG (1)
Quellmattstrasse 79, 5035, Unterentfelden, Switzerland
Tel.: (41) 62 723 2241
Web Site: https://www.ateco.ch
Metals Mfr
N.A.I.C.S.: 332813

Autoroll UK Ltd. (1)
Pinewood Business Park Wilden Road, Washington, NE38 8QB, Tyne & Wear, United Kingdom
Tel.: (44) 1914155888
Web Site: https://www.auto-roll.com
Garage Door Mfr & Distr
N.A.I.C.S.: 332321

Avintos AG (1)
Weidenweg 17, 4310, Rheinfelden, Switzerland
Tel.: (41) 61 836 1530
Web Site: https://www.avintos.ch
Consulting & Training Services
N.A.I.C.S.: 541612
Jerome Chabloz (Mng Dir)

BL Products AB (1)
Fabriksgatan 9, 602 23, Norrkoping, Sweden
Tel.: (46) 1 113 5262
Web Site: https://www.bl-products.se
Packaging Services
N.A.I.C.S.: 561910

Bailey Morris Limited (1)
Little End Road Industrial Estate, Eaton Socon, Saint Neots, PE19 8GE, Cambridgeshire, United Kingdom
Tel.: (44) 148 021 6250
Web Site: https://www.baileymorris.co.uk
Propeller Shaft Equipment Mfr & Distr
N.A.I.C.S.: 333613
Jamie Woodbridge (Head-Sls)

Beck Sensortechnik GmbH (1)
Ferdinand-Steinbeis-Str 4, 71144, Steinenbronn, Germany
Tel.: (49) 715752870
Web Site: https://www.beck-sensors.com
Electric Equipment Mfr
N.A.I.C.S.: 334419

Beldam Crossley Limited (1)
Units A and B Lostock Industrial Estate Lostock Lane, Bolton, BL6 4BL, United Kingdom
Tel.: (44) 120 467 5700
Web Site: https://www.beldamcrossley.co.uk
Sensor Product Mfr
N.A.I.C.S.: 334513
Gareth Holt (Dir-Sls)

Bemmgtsson Maskin (1)
Klangfargatan 25 27, PO Box 325, 42652, Gothenburg, Sweden
Tel.: (46) 313382700
Sales Range: $1-9.9 Million
Importer of Pneumatic & Power Tools
N.A.I.C.S.: 423830

Bengtssons Maskin AB (1)
Foretagsvagen 14, Box 501, Arlov, 232 37, Malmo, Sweden
Tel.: (46) 40 680 7300
Web Site: https://www.bengtssons-maskin.se
Sales Range: $10-24.9 Million
Emp.: 27
Provider of Business Technology Services
N.A.I.C.S.: 561499
Paul Pullen (CEO)

Biameditek Sp. Z o. o. (1)
Ul Elewatorska 58, 15-620, Bialystok, Poland
Tel.: (48) 85 664 5200
Web Site: https://www.biameditek.pl
Medical Device Mfr
N.A.I.C.S.: 339112

Birmingham Specialities Ltd. (1)
Lincoln Works Moor Lane, Witton, Birmingham, B6 7HE, United Kingdom
Tel.: (44) 121 356 5026
Web Site: https://www.bhamspec.co.uk
Machinery Mfr
N.A.I.C.S.: 333248
Steve Page (Mgr-Quality)

Bramming Plast-Industri A/S (1)
Vardevej 9, Bramming, 6740, Esbjerg, Denmark
Tel.: (45) 79571050
Web Site: https://bpi.dk
Carousel Molding Mfr
N.A.I.C.S.: 333511

C&M Plast AB (1)
Garnisonsgatan 45, Helsingborg, 254 66, Sweden
Tel.: (46) 42 25 38 00
Plastics Product Mfr
N.A.I.C.S.: 326199

CaTec B.V. (1)
Turfschipper 114, 2292 JB, Wateringen, Netherlands
Tel.: (31) 174272330
Web Site: https://www.catec.nl
Measuring Instruments Mfr
N.A.I.C.S.: 334513

Carlsson & Moller AB (1)
Garnisonsgatan 45, Box 22161, 250 23, Helsingborg, Sweden
Tel.: (46) 42 25 38 00
Plastics Product Mfr
N.A.I.C.S.: 326199

Cepro International BV (1)
Provincienbaan 16, 5121 DL, Rijen, Netherlands
Tel.: (31) 16 122 6472
Web Site: https://www.cepro.eu
Metal Products Mfr
N.A.I.C.S.: 332313
Luuk Mulkens (Mng Dir)

Colly Company AB (1)
Raseborgsgatan 9, Box 6042, 164 06, Kista, Sweden
Tel.: (46) 8 703 0100
Web Site: https://www.colly.se
Sales Range: $25-49.9 Million
Emp.: 100
Provider of Business Technology Services
N.A.I.C.S.: 561499

Colly Components AB (1)
Raseborgsgatan 9, 164 74, Kista, Sweden
Tel.: (46) 8 703 0100
Web Site: https://www.collycomponents.se
Emp.: 100
Provider of Business Technology Services
N.A.I.C.S.: 561499

Colly Components AS (1)
Tollbugata 105, 3041, Drammen, Norway
Tel.: (47) 32890010
Fastener & Battery Tool Mfr
N.A.I.C.S.: 332722
Tom Opsahl (Mgr-Sls)

Colly Components OY (1)
Tiilenlyojankuja 9 B, 01720, Vantaa, Finland
Tel.: (358) 447555772
Mounting Accessory & Component Mfr
N.A.I.C.S.: 332994

Colly Filtreringsteknik AB (1)
Raseborgsgatan 9, Box 81, 164 94, Kista, Sweden
Tel.: (46) 8 703 0100
Web Site: https://www.collyfiltreringsteknik.se
Sales Range: $10-24.9 Million
Emp.: 30
Provider of Business Technology Services
N.A.I.C.S.: 561499
Patrick Olsenlung (Mng Dir)

Colly Flowtech AB (1)
Sodra Vasteravsvagen 6, 734 51, Kolback, Sweden
Tel.: (46) 2 204 5530
Web Site: https://www.collyflowtech.se
Stainless Steel Mfr & Distr
N.A.I.C.S.: 331110

Colly Verkstadsteknik AB (1)
Raseborgsgatan 9, Box 6042, 164 06, Kista, Sweden
Tel.: (46) 8 703 0100
Web Site: https://www.collyverkstadsteknik.se
Machinery Mfr
N.A.I.C.S.: 333248
Par Joelsson (CEO)

Combilent A/S (1)
Ryttermarken 5, 3520, Farum, Denmark
Tel.: (45) 4 816 9200
Web Site: https://www.combilent.com
Mobile Communication Product Mfr
N.A.I.C.S.: 334220
Claus Dall-Hansen (Co-Founder, CEO & COO)

Conroy Medical AB (1)
Valhallavagen 1, 194 63, Upplands Vasby, Sweden
Tel.: (46) 85 942 0250
Web Site: https://conroymedical.com
Medical Equipment Mfr
N.A.I.C.S.: 339112
Per Jansson (Founder & Sr VP)

Corona Control AB (1)
Vallenvagen 5, Stora Hoga, 444 60, Hoganas, Sweden
Tel.: (46) 30 379 8150
Web Site: https://www.corona-control.se
Machinery Mfr
N.A.I.C.S.: 333248

Corrosion Resistant Products Ltd. (1)
Todmorden Road, Littleborough, OL15 9EG, United Kingdom
Tel.: (44) 170 675 6400
Web Site: https://www.crp.co.uk

INDUTRADE AB

Indutrade AB—(Continued)
Lined Piping Product Mfr & Whslr
N.A.I.C.S.: 332996
Phil Brown *(Office Mgr-Sls)*

Crysberg A/S (1)
Oldenvej 6, 3490, Kvistgaard, Denmark
Tel.: (45) 4 913 8303
Web Site: https://www.crysberg.dk
Electrical & Electronic Mfr
N.A.I.C.S.: 335999
Niels Klagenberg *(CEO)*

Damalini AB (1)
Alfagatan 6, 431 49, Molndal, Sweden
Tel.: (46) 31 708 63 00
Web Site: http://www.damalini.se
Sales Range: $25-49.9 Million
Emp.: 4
Laser Based Measurement System Mfr
N.A.I.C.S.: 334513
Eilif Johansen *(Area Mgr-Sls)*

Dasa Control Systems AB (1)
Hammerdalsvagen 3, 352 46, Vaxjo, Sweden
Tel.: (46) 47 077 0950
Web Site: https://www.dasa.se
Machinery Mfr
N.A.I.C.S.: 333248
Hakan Lavin *(Mgr-Sls & Mktg)*

Datum Electronics Ltd. (1)
Castle Street, Isle of Wight, East Cowes, PO32 6EZ, United Kingdom
Tel.: (44) 198 328 2834
Web Site: https://datum-electronics.com
Electronics Mfr
N.A.I.C.S.: 334419
Malcolm Habens *(Mng Dir)*

Diatomj A/S (1)
Avedoreholmen 84, 2650, Hvidovre, Denmark
Tel.: (45) 3 677 3600
Web Site: https://www.diatom.dk
Emp.: 20
Adhesives, Lubricants, Silicones, Dispensing Equipment, Seals & Gaskets, Tools & Fasteners Mfr
N.A.I.C.S.: 333414
Allan Orland *(CEO)*

EDECO Tools AB (1)
Grasdalsgatan 9, Box 2119, 650 02, Karlstad, Sweden
Tel.: (46) 5 455 8000
Web Site: https://www.edeco.se
Sales Range: $1-9.9 Million
Emp.: 20
Industrial Tools
N.A.I.C.S.: 333515
Anders Hoogh *(CEO)*

EIE AB (1)
PO Box 7, 124 21, Bandhagen, Sweden
Tel.: (46) 87278800
Web Site: http://www.eie.se
Industrial Equipment Whslr
N.A.I.C.S.: 423830

EIE Maskin AS (1)
Tvetenveien 164, 0671, Oslo, Norway
Tel.: (47) 9 079 0897
Web Site: https://www.eiemaskin.no
Machine Part Mfr
N.A.I.C.S.: 332710

EPE-Goldman BV (1)
Admiraal Trompstraat 4, 3115 HH, Schiedam, Netherlands
Tel.: (31) 10 426 9999
Web Site: https://www.epg.eu
Pipe Component Whslr
N.A.I.C.S.: 423830
Harry Reichwein *(Acct Mgr)*

ES Hydagent AB (1)
Kontaktvagen 5, 901 33, Umea, Sweden
Tel.: (46) 9 014 1450
Web Site: https://www.eshydagent.se
Machine Part Mfr
N.A.I.C.S.: 332710

ESI Technologies Ltd. (1)
North Esk Business Park Dunkettle, Cork, T45 NW94, Ireland
Tel.: (353) 214510900
Web Site: http://www.esi.ie
Process Equipment Distr

N.A.I.C.S.: 423730
Brian Fahy *(Dir-Sls)*

Subsidiary (Non-US):

ESI Process UK Limited (2)
Unit 1 Lakeside House Lakeside Park, Cwmbran, NP44 3XS, Torfaen, United Kingdom
Tel.: (44) 1633877505
Pumps Mfr
N.A.I.C.S.: 333996

ESI Technologies B.V. (2)
Ambachtsweg 12A, 2641 KS, Pijnacker, Netherlands
Tel.: (31) 850499770
Pumps Mfr
N.A.I.C.S.: 333996

ETP Transmission AB (1)
Tel.: (46) 1 324 7100
Web Site: https://www.etp.se
Sales Range: $25-49.9 Million
Emp.: 55
Provider of Hydraulic Sleeves & Shocks
N.A.I.C.S.: 333414

Easy-Laser AB (1)
Alfagatan 6, 431 49, Molndal, Sweden
Tel.: (46) 31 708 6300
Web Site: https://www.easylaser.com
Measurement Equipment Mfr
N.A.I.C.S.: 334515
Anders Edenhammar *(Mng Dir)*

Eco Analytics AG (1)
Weidenweg 17, 4310, Rheinfelden, Switzerland
Tel.: (41) 61 827 9400
Web Site: https://www.ecoanalytics.ch
Gas Mfr
N.A.I.C.S.: 325120

Eie Maskin AB (1)
Skebokvarnsvagen 370, 12450, Bandhagen, Sweden
Tel.: (46) 87278800
Web Site: https://www.eiemaskin.se
Sales Range: $25-49.9 Million
Emp.: 21
Automotive Transportation Component Distr
N.A.I.C.S.: 423120
Anders Lundkvist *(Mng Dir)*

Ellard Limited (1)
Ellard House Floats Road, Manchester, M23 9WB, United Kingdom
Tel.: (44) 161 945 4561
Web Site: https://www.ellard.co.uk
Electric Door & Shutter Drive Mfr
N.A.I.C.S.: 335999
David Lewis *(CEO)*

Elma Instruments A/S (1)
Ryttermarken 2, 3520, Farum, Denmark
Tel.: (45) 7 022 1000
Web Site: https://www.elma.dk
Electrical & Electronic Mfr
N.A.I.C.S.: 335999

Euroflon Tekniska Produkter AB (1)
Drakvagen 6, 591 32, Motala, Sweden
Tel.: (46) 141234430
Web Site: http://www.euroflon.se
Hose Whslr
N.A.I.C.S.: 423840

Farber & Schmid AG (1)
Lerzenstrasse 19 A, 8953, Dietikon, Switzerland
Tel.: (41) 433224040
Web Site: http://www.faerber-schmid.ch
Water Treatment Chemical Product Mfr
N.A.I.C.S.: 325180
Horst Farber *(Co-Founder, Mng Dir & Head-Engrg Div)*

Subsidiary (Non-US):

Farber & Schmid GmbH (2)
Asangstrasse 132, 70329, Stuttgart, Germany
Tel.: (49) 742943599330
Environmental Services
N.A.I.C.S.: 541620

Fergin Sverige AB (1)
Dynamovagen 7A, 591 61, Motala, Sweden
Tel.: (46) 1 415 0025
Web Site: https://www.fergin.se

Lighting Contractor Services
N.A.I.C.S.: 238210

Filterteknik A/S (1)
Korskildeeng 2, 2670, Greve, Denmark
Tel.: (45) 5 613 1072
Web Site: https://www.filterteknik.dk
Filter & Equipment Mfr
N.A.I.C.S.: 333413

Filterteknik Sverige AB (1)
Dagvindgatan 2, 652 21, Karlstad, Sweden
Tel.: (46) 54 690900
Sales Range: $25-49.9 Million
Emp.: 20
Filtration Products Distr
N.A.I.C.S.: 423830
Per-Arne Forsman *(Pres)*

Filtration Ltd. (1)
303B Dean Road, Avonmouth, BS11 8AT, United Kingdom
Tel.: (44) 117 982 2206
Web Site: https://www.filtrationltd.wordpress.com
Industrial Equipment Whsr
N.A.I.C.S.: 423830
Derek Campion *(Mng Dir)*

Finisterra AS (1)
Garver Ytteborgsvei 83, 977, Oslo, Norway
Tel.: (47) 22104270
Web Site: http://www.finisterra.no
Industrial Equipment Whsr
N.A.I.C.S.: 423830

Finkova Oy (1)
Sinikellontie 10B, 01300, Vantaa, Finland
Tel.: (358) 10 229 1570
Web Site: https://www.finkova.fi
Measuring & Precision Instrument Whslr
N.A.I.C.S.: 423830
Anssi Lahti *(Mng Dir)*

Firentis AG (1)
Weidenweg 16, 4310, Rheinfelden, Switzerland
Tel.: (41) 61 836 1818
Web Site: https://www.firentis.ch
Fire Protection Equipment Whslr
N.A.I.C.S.: 423850

Flintec Group AB (1)
Kopmangatan 1B, 72215, Vasteras, Sweden
Tel.: (46) 21 120 155
Web Site: http://www.flintec.com
Sales Range: $200-249.9 Million
Emp.: 100
Precision Electronic Component Mfr
N.A.I.C.S.: 334419

Subsidiary (Non-US):

Beijing Flintec Electronics and Technology Ltd Co. (2)
Room B601 Hui Zhong Li, Chao Yang District, Beijing, 100101, China
Tel.: (86) 10 84 990 020
Sales Range: $25-49.9 Million
Emp.: 15
Electronic Components Distr
N.A.I.C.S.: 423690

Flintec France (2)
50 rue de Verdun, 57130, Ars-sur-Moselle, France
Tel.: (33) 38 731 3620
Web Site: http://www.flintec.com
Electronic Components Distr
N.A.I.C.S.: 423690

Flintec GmbH (2)
Bemannsbruch 9, 74909, Meckesheim, Germany
Tel.: (49) 6226 9240 00
Sales Range: $25-49.9 Million
Emp.: 35
Electronic Components Distr
N.A.I.C.S.: 423690
Jens Achenbach *(Mng Dir)*

Subsidiary (US):

Flintec Inc. (2)
18 Kane Industrial Dr, Hudson, MA 01749
Tel.: (978) 562-7800
Web Site: https://www.flintec.com
Sales Range: $25-49.9 Million
Emp.: 20
Electronic Components Distr

N.A.I.C.S.: 423690

Subsidiary (Non-US):

Flintec Italy (2)
Viale Monte Santo 1/3, 20124, Milan, MI, Italy
Tel.: (39) 039 245 5666
Web Site: http://www.flintec.com
Electronic Components Distr
N.A.I.C.S.: 423690

Flintec UK Ltd (2)
W4/5 Capital Point Capital Business Park Wentloog Avenue, Cardiff, CF3 2PW, United Kingdom
Tel.: (44) 2920 797959
Sales Range: $25-49.9 Million
Emp.: 18
Electronic Components Distr
N.A.I.C.S.: 423690
Gareth Roberts *(Gen Mgr)*

Flowtec Industrietechnik GmbH (1)
Stattegger Strasse 179, 8046, Graz, Austria
Tel.: (43) 316 697 0690
Web Site: https://www.flowtec.at
Valve Product Mfr
N.A.I.C.S.: 332911
Albert Igler *(Gen Mgr)*

Fluid Controls Limited (1)
50 Easter Park Benyon Road, Aldermaston, RG7 2PQ, Berkshire, United Kingdom
Tel.: (44) 118 970 2060
Web Site: https://www.fluidcontrols.co.uk
Fitting & Pressure Regulator Whslr
N.A.I.C.S.: 423930

G A Lindberg ChemTech AB (1)
Raseborgsgatan 9, 164 74, Kista, Sweden
Tel.: (46) 87030200
Web Site: http://www.galindberg.se
Adhesive & Lubricant Mfr
N.A.I.C.S.: 325520
Stefan Pettersson *(CEO)*

G A Lindberg ProcessTeknik AB (1)
Raseborgsgatan 9, Postbox 6044, 164 06, Kista, Sweden
Tel.: (46) 8 703 0200
Web Site: https://www.galindbergprocessteknik.se
Metal Processing Product Distr
N.A.I.C.S.: 423510

G A Lindberg SealTech AB (1)
PO Box 6044, 164 06, Kista, Sweden
Tel.: (46) 87030200
Web Site: http://www.sealtech.se
Emp.: 6
Inflatable Seal & Gasket Mfr
N.A.I.C.S.: 339991

GA Lindberg AB (1)
Tel.: (46) 8 703 0200
Web Site: https://www.galindberg.se
Sales Range: $25-49.9 Million
Emp.: 35
Supplier of Advanced Products & Service for Bonding, Sealing, Lubrication, Gasketing, Dispensing & Industrial Fluids
N.A.I.C.S.: 333414

GEFA Processtechnik GmbH (1)
Germaniastrasse 28, 44379, Dortmund, Germany
Tel.: (49) 23 161 0090
Web Site: https://www.gefa.com
Sales Range: $25-49.9 Million
Emp.: 100
Industrial Valve Mfr
N.A.I.C.S.: 332911

GPA Flowsystem AB (1)
Brovagen 5, 266 75, Hjarnarp, Sweden
Tel.: (46) 43 144 5800
Web Site: https://www.gpa.se
Flow Technology Equipment Distr
N.A.I.C.S.: 423490

GPA Flowsystem AS (1)
Regnbueveien 9, 1405, Langhus, Norway
Tel.: (47) 6 485 6800
Web Site: https://www.gpa.no
Valve & Pipe System Distr
N.A.I.C.S.: 423840

GPA Plast A/S (1)
Paul Bergsoes Vej 8, 2600, Glostrup, Denmark

Tel.: (45) 43860300
Web Site: http://www.gpa.dk
Sales Range: $25-49.9 Million
Emp.: 6
Flow Technique System Services
N.A.I.C.S.: 334513

GPA Plast AB (1)
Brovagen 5, 26697, Hjarnarp, Sweden
Tel.: (46) 431445800
Web Site: http://www.gpa.se
Sales Range: $25-49.9 Million
Emp.: 45
Flow Technique System Solutions
N.A.I.C.S.: 335314

Gaveco AB (1)
PO Box 2103, Trollbacken, 135 02, Tyreso, Sweden
Tel.: (46) 87420000
Web Site: http://www.gaveco.se
Pressure Gas Equipment Mfr
N.A.I.C.S.: 333912

Gedevelop AB (1)
Florettgatan 27A, Helsingborg, 254 67, Sweden
Tel.: (46) 42 38 66 70
Web Site: http://www.gedevelop.com
Industrial Measuring Instrument Mfr
N.A.I.C.S.: 334513

Gelins-KGK AB (1)
Goteborgsvagen 1, Box 207, 532 37, Skara, Sweden
Tel.: (46) 5 111 3130
Web Site: https://www.gelins-kgk.se
Industrial Equipment Whsr
N.A.I.C.S.: 423830
Johan Nyholm *(Mgr-Pur)*

Geotrim Oy (1)
Perintokuja 6, 01510, Vantaa, Finland
Tel.: (358) 20 751 0600
Web Site: https://www.geotrim.fi
Electrical Equipment Whslr
N.A.I.C.S.: 423610

Granzow A/S (1)
Ejby Industrivej 26, 2600, Glostrup, Denmark
Tel.: (45) 4 320 2600
Web Site: https://www.granzow.dk
Sales Range: $75-99.9 Million
Emp.: 35
Air & Gas Compressor Mfr
N.A.I.C.S.: 333912

Gustaf Fagerberg A/S (1)
Kornmarksvej 8-10, 2605, Brondby, Denmark
Tel.: (45) 4 329 0200
Web Site: https://www.fagerberg.dk
Industrial Equipment Whsr
N.A.I.C.S.: 423830

Gustaf Fagerberg Holding AB (1)
Klangfargsgatan 25-27, PO Box 12105, Gothenburg, Sweden
Tel.: (46) 31693700
Web Site: http://www.fagerberg.se
Investment Management Service
N.A.I.C.S.: 523999

HITMA BV (1)
Anton Philipsweg 1, 1422 AL, Uithoorn, Netherlands
Tel.: (31) 29 751 4614
Web Site: https://www.hitma.nl
Sales Range: $25-49.9 Million
Emp.: 80
Provider of Equipment & Services of Filtration & Separations Systems
N.A.I.C.S.: 333414

HITMA UltraPure B.V (1)
Anton Philipsweg 1, 1422 AL, Uithoorn, Netherlands
Tel.: (31) 297 514 714
Web Site: http://www.hitma-ultrapure.nl
Plastic Pipe Fitting Mfr
N.A.I.C.S.: 326122
J. Tangenberg *(Gen Mgr)*

HP Valves B.V (1)
Haaksbergerstraat 55, 7554 PA, Hengelo, Netherlands
Tel.: (31) 747820000
Web Site: https://www.hpvalves.com
Sales Range: $50-74.9 Million
Emp.: 120
Medium & High Pressure Valve Distr

N.A.I.C.S.: 423830
Rolf Koop *(Mgr-Sls & Europe South-East)*

Hydnet AB (1)
EA Rosengrens Gata 29, 421 31, Vastra Frolunda, Sweden
Tel.: (46) 3 149 9490
Web Site: https://www.hydnet.se
Machinery Mfr
N.A.I.C.S.: 333248

IFTG Sverige AB (1)
Metallvagen 2, 435 33, Molnlycke, Sweden
Tel.: (46) 31 710 3990
Web Site: https://www.iftg.se
Emp.: 4,000
Valve Equipment Mfr
N.A.I.C.S.: 332911

Induflow (1)
Agerhatten 16 A 8, 5220, Odense, Denmark
Tel.: (45) 6 310 0036
Web Site: https://www.induflow.dk
Luminaire Product Distr
N.A.I.C.S.: 423690

Industri Belos AB (1)
Axel Johanssons gata 4-6, 754 50, Uppsala, Sweden
Tel.: (46) 1 867 6780
Web Site: https://www.belos.se
Sales Range: $25-49.9 Million
Emp.: 10
Provider of Business Technology Services
N.A.I.C.S.: 561499

Industri Verktoy AS (1)
Hardangervegen 72, 5224, Nesttun, Norway
Tel.: (47) 5 511 2727
Web Site: https://www.industri-verktoy.no
Construction Equipment Whslr
N.A.I.C.S.: 423810

Indutrade Benelux B.V. (1)
Anton Philipsweg 1, PO Box 175, 1420 AD, Uithoorn, Netherlands
Tel.: (31) 29 751 4750
Web Site: https://www.indutradebenelux.com
Sales Range: $50-74.9 Million
Emp.: 4
Investment Management Service
N.A.I.C.S.: 523999
Leo van Diemen *(Controller-Fin)*

Subsidiary (Domestic):

Aluglas B.V (2)
Johan Enschedeweg 21, 1422 DR, Uithoorn, Netherlands
Tel.: (31) 29 751 4429
Web Site: http://www.aluglas.nl
Sales Range: $10-24.9 Million
Pharmaceutical & Cosmetics Packaging Services
N.A.I.C.S.: 561910

Ammertech B.V (2)
Grasbeemd 21, 5705 DE, Helmond, Netherlands
Tel.: (31) 49 259 4300
Web Site: https://www.ammertech.nl
Sales Range: $25-49.9 Million
Power Transmission Equipment Distr
N.A.I.C.S.: 423830

Douwes International B.V (2)
Weteringweg 8, 2641 KM, Pijnacker, Netherlands
Tel.: (31) 15 361 5200
Sales Range: $25-49.9 Million
Emp.: 3
Machine Tools Mfr
N.A.I.C.S.: 333517

Gimex technische keramiek B.V. (2)
Grasbeemd 21, 5705 DE, Helmond, Netherlands
Tel.: (31) 34 557 4255
Web Site: https://www.gimex.nl
Ceramic Products Mfr
N.A.I.C.S.: 327120

HITMA Filtratie B.V. (2)
Anton Philipsweg 1, 1422 AL, Uithoorn, Netherlands
Tel.: (31) 297 514715
Web Site: http://www.hitma-filtratie.nl
Sales Range: $25-49.9 Million
Air Filtration Equipment Mfr
N.A.I.C.S.: 333413

HITMA Instrumentatie B.V. (2)
Anton Philipsweg 1, Uithoorn, 1422 Al, Netherlands
Tel.: (31) 297 514 833
Web Site: http://www.hitma-instrumentatie.nl
Electronic Components Mfr
N.A.I.C.S.: 334419

Subsidiary (Non-US):

HITMA Instrumentatie B.V. (2)
Brusselstraat 51, 2018, Antwerp, Belgium
Tel.: (32) 2 387 2864
Emp.: 8
Industrial Measuring Instrument Mfr
N.A.I.C.S.: 334513
Kees Veen *(Gen Mgr)*

Subsidiary (Domestic):

HITMA Process B.V. (2)
Anton Philipsweg 1, 1422 AL, Uithoorn, Netherlands
Tel.: (31) 297514614
Web Site: http://www.hitma-process.nl
Sales Range: $25-49.9 Million
Emp.: 10
Industrial Valve Distr
N.A.I.C.S.: 423830

Subsidiary (Non-US):

Hanwel Belgie N.V. (2)
Industriezone TTS - Zone B Winninglaan 15, 9140, Temse, Belgium
Tel.: (32) 3 711 0353
Web Site: https://www.hanwel.be
Emp.: 7
Industrial Pipe & Valve Mfr
N.A.I.C.S.: 332996

Subsidiary (Domestic):

Hanwel Nederland B.V. (2)
Jan Tinbergenstraat 209, 7559 SP, Hengelo, Netherlands
Tel.: (31) 74 265 0000
Web Site: https://www.hanwel.com
Sales Range: $25-49.9 Million
Emp.: 12
Industrial Pipe Distr
N.A.I.C.S.: 423830

Indutrade Oy (1)
Tiilenlyojankuja 9 B, 01720, Vantaa, Finland
Tel.: (358) 2 900 6100
Web Site: https://www.indutrade.com
Sales Range: $100-124.9 Million
Emp.: 60
Industrial Components & Equipment Sales
N.A.I.C.S.: 423830

Ingenjorsfirman GA Lindberg AB (1)
Raseborgsgstan 9, 164 74, Kista, Sweden
Tel.: (46) 8 7030200
Sales Range: $50-74.9 Million
Emp.: 3
Industrial Machinery Mfr
N.A.I.C.S.: 333248
Stefan Pettersson *(CEO)*

Ingenjorsfirman Geotech AB (1)
Datavagen 53, 436 32, Askim, Sweden
Tel.: (46) 31289920
Web Site: https://geotech.eu
Probes & Rigs Mfr
N.A.I.C.S.: 333132

Inovatools Eckerle & Ertel GmbH (1)
Im Huttental 3-6, 85125, Kinding, Germany
Tel.: (49) 84 678 4000
Web Site: https://www.inovatools.eu
Metal Cutting Tool Mfr
N.A.I.C.S.: 333517
Georg Eckerle *(Mng Dir)*

Subsidiary (Non-US):

Inovatools Austria GmbH (2)
Schenkendorfgasse 47, Vienna, 1210, Austria
Tel.: (43) 121235880
Tool Mfr
N.A.I.C.S.: 333517
Memo Ildirar *(Mng Dir)*

Inovatools Italy SRL (2)
Via Malavolti 45/a, 41122, Modena, Italy
Tel.: (39) 059250930
Tool Mfr
N.A.I.C.S.: 333517

Inovatools Portugal Lda (2)
Rua da Industria Metalurgica 593 Cumeiras Embra, 2430-528, Marinha Grande, Portugal
Tel.: (351) 244566731
Tool Mfr
N.A.I.C.S.: 333517

Inovatools Spain S.L. (2)
C/Miquel Servet 37 nau 13 Pol Ind Bufalvent, 08243, Manresa, Spain
Tel.: (34) 938745639
Tool Mfr
N.A.I.C.S.: 333517

Subsidiary (US):

Inovatools USA LLC (2)
PO Box 387, Hartland, MI 48353
Tel.: (810) 991-4716
Tool Mfr
N.A.I.C.S.: 333517

International Plastic Systems Ltd (1)
Seaham Grange Industrial Estate, Seaham, SR7 0PT, Durham, United Kingdom
Tel.: (44) 191 521 3111
Web Site: https://www.ipsflowsystems.com
Emp.: 4
Industrial Plastic Piping System Distr
N.A.I.C.S.: 423840

Iris Hjalpmedel AB (1)
Sandsborgsvagen 52, 122 33, Enskede, Sweden
Tel.: (46) 839 9400
Web Site: https://www.irishjalpmedel.se
Medical Device Whslr
N.A.I.C.S.: 423450

Irvine Spring Company Ltd. (1)
6 Kyle Rd, Irvine Industrial Estate, Irvine, KA12 8JS, United Kingdom
Tel.: (44) 129 427 9396
Web Site: https://www.irvinesprings.com
Spring Mfr
N.A.I.C.S.: 332613
Neil Matthews *(Mng Dir)*

Item Profiili Oy (1)
Lyhtykuja 6, 00750, Helsinki, Finland
Tel.: (358) 9 854 5650
Web Site: https://www.itemprofiili.fi
Machine Part Mfr
N.A.I.C.S.: 332710

KA Olsson & Gems AB (1)
Sallarangsgatan 3, 431 37, Molndal, Sweden
Tel.: (46) 31 746 4900
Web Site: https://www.kao.nu
Various Goods Whslr
N.A.I.C.S.: 423840

Kabetex Kullager & Transmission AB (1)
Lyddevagen 33, Box 67, 511 58, Kinna, Sweden
Tel.: (46) 32 020 9880
Web Site: https://www.kabetex.se
Sales Range: $50-74.9 Million
Emp.: 9
Industrial Gas Distr
N.A.I.C.S.: 423840
Lars Henning *(CEO)*

Key Valve Technologies Ltd. (1)
13 Gongdan 2-Daero 139beon-Gil, Siheung, Gyeonggi, Korea (South)
Tel.: (82) 31 363 0700
Web Site: https://www.keyvalve.com
Valve Product Mfr
N.A.I.C.S.: 332911

Kiinnike-Kolmio Oy (1)
Hautalankatu 19C, 33560, Tampere, Finland
Tel.: (358) 3 258 2400
Web Site: https://www.kiinnikekolmio.fi
Sales Range: $25-49.9 Million
Emp.: 20
Importer of Building Supplies & Tools
N.A.I.C.S.: 444180
Markku Moisio *(Dir-Sls)*

Kin Pompentechniek B.V. (1)
Stedenbaan 6, 5121 DP, Rijen, Netherlands
Tel.: (31) 16 124 4250
Web Site: https://www.kinpompentechniek.nl
Pump Whslr
N.A.I.C.S.: 423830

INDUTRADE AB

Indutrade AB—(Continued)

Klokkerholm Karosseridele A/S (1)
Klovervej 6, 9320, Hjallerup, Denmark
Tel.: (45) 9 828 4444
Web Site: https://www.klokkerholm.com
Automobile Parts Distr
N.A.I.C.S.: 423140
Thomas Sloth *(Mgr-Logistic)*

Kontram Oy (1)
Tuupakantie 32 a, PO Box 741, 01741, Vantaa, Finland
Tel.: (358) 98 866 4500
Web Site: https://www.kontram.fi
Industrial Equipment Whsr
N.A.I.C.S.: 423830

Kontrollautomatik Svenska AB (1)
Mekanikervagen 13, 146 33, Tullinge, Sweden
Tel.: (46) 87788700
Web Site: http://www.kontrollautomatik.se
Sensor Product Mfr
N.A.I.C.S.: 334513

Kramer AG (1)
Grindelstrasse 23, 8303, Bassersdorf, Switzerland
Tel.: (41) 44 838 4466
Web Site: https://www.kraemerag.ch
Pharmaceutical Machine Mfr
N.A.I.C.S.: 333993

Subsidiary (Non-US):

Kraemer Pharmaceutical (Shanghai) Equipment Co., Ltd. (2)
Room 705 Block D No 80 Caobao Rd, Xuhui District, Shanghai, 200235, China
Tel.: (86) 2164703920
Machinery Mfr
N.A.I.C.S.: 333248

Subsidiary (US):

Kraemer US, LLC (2)
240 W Crescent Ave, Allendale, NJ 07401
Tel.: (201) 962-8200
Machinery Mfr
N.A.I.C.S.: 333248

LYMA Kemiteknik AB (1)
Virvelvagen 1, 232 36, Arlov, Sweden
Tel.: (46) 4 043 8800
Web Site: https://www.lyma.se
Emp.: 12
Chemical Equipment Retailer
N.A.I.C.S.: 423820
Magnus Gustavson *(CEO)*

Labkotec Oy (1)
Myllyhaantie 6, 33960, Pirkkala, Finland
Tel.: (358) 2 900 6260
Web Site: https://www.labkotec.fi
Measurement Equipment Mfr
N.A.I.C.S.: 334515

Leiderdorp Instruments BV (1)
Achthovenerweg 19, 2351 AX, Leiderdorp, Netherlands
Tel.: (31) 71 541 5514
Web Site: https://www.leiderdorpinstruments.nl
Industrial Equipment Whsr
N.A.I.C.S.: 423830

Lekang Filter AS (1)
Gamle Hobolvei 11, 1550, Holen, Norway
Tel.: (47) 6 498 2000
Web Site: https://www.lekangfilter.no
Filter & Equipment Mfr
N.A.I.C.S.: 333413

Lekang Maskin AS (1)
Gamle Hobolvei 11, 1550, Holen, Norway
Tel.: (47) 64 98 20 00
Web Site: http://www.lekang.com
Sales Range: $25-49.9 Million
Emp.: 26
Offshore Industries Filtration System Distr
N.A.I.C.S.: 423840
Egil Lekang *(Dir-Bus Dev)*

Liljegrens Maskinverktyg AB (1)
Hardgatan 23B, 432 32, Varberg, Sweden
Tel.: (46) 34 027 2400
Web Site: https://www.liljegrens.com
Trading Services
N.A.I.C.S.: 523100

LinearModul A/S (1)
Sivlandvaenget 13B, 5260, Odense, Denmark
Tel.: (45) 6 591 7210
Web Site: https://www.linearmodul.dk
Machine Part Mfr
N.A.I.C.S.: 332710

Lining Components Oy (1)
Tillyojankuja 9 B, 01720, Vantaa, Finland
Tel.: (358) 29006170
Web Site: http://www.liningcomponents.fi
Sales Range: $1-9.9 Million
Emp.: 75
Components & Conveyor Solutions Mfr
N.A.I.C.S.: 333922

MW Instruments B.V. (1)
Antennestraat 26, 1322 AB, Almere, Netherlands
Tel.: (31) 36 535 0651
Web Site: https://www.mw-instruments.nl
Industrial Equipment Whsr
N.A.I.C.S.: 423830

MWS Ventilservice AB (1)
Vadstenavagen 28, 591 37, Motala, Sweden
Tel.: (46) 14 121 3100
Web Site: https://www.mws.se
Telecommunication Servicesb
N.A.I.C.S.: 517810

MaxxVision GmbH (1)
Sigmaringer Strasse 121, 70567, Stuttgart, Germany
Tel.: (49) 711 997 9963
Web Site: https://www.maxxvision.com
Audio Visual Equipment Whslr
N.A.I.C.S.: 423690
Christian Scheidt *(Acct Mgr)*

MeHow Medical Ireland Ltd. (1)
Bray Business Park Southern Cross Rd, Wicklow, Bray, A98W8P3, Ireland
Tel.: (353) 19066071
Web Site: https://www.mehow.ie
Medical Device Equipment Mfr
N.A.I.C.S.: 339113

Medexa Diagnostisk Service AB (1)
Krossverksgatan 11B, 216 16, Limhamn, Sweden
Tel.: (46) 4 016 0020
Web Site: https://www.medexa.se
Medical Device Mfr
N.A.I.C.S.: 339112

Meson AB (1)
Kullsgardvagen 27, 312 34, Laholm, Sweden
Tel.: (46) 4 302 9500
Web Site: https://www.mesongroup.com
Sales Range: $50-74.9 Million
Emp.: 50
Valve & Fitting Mfr
N.A.I.C.S.: 332919
Anders Ruth *(CEO)*

Subsidiary (Non-US):

Wilhelm Sander Fertigung GmbH (2)
Zum Panrepel 41, 28307, Bremen, Germany
Tel.: (49) 4214860313
Web Site: http://www.sander-marine.com
Sales Range: $25-49.9 Million
Emp.: 30
Valve Mfr
N.A.I.C.S.: 332911

Milltech Precision Engineering Ltd. (1)
Liberamus House Witchcraft Way, Rackheath Industrial Estate, Norwich, NR13 6GA, Norfolk, United Kingdom
Tel.: (44) 160 372 1337
Web Site: https://www.milltechgroup.co.uk
Emp.: 60
Machinery Mfr
N.A.I.C.S.: 333248
Paul Lebbon *(Mng Dir)*

Modul Plastic Oy (1)
Linjatie 4, 28430, Pori, Finland
Tel.: (358) 29006250
Plastic Equipment Installation Services
N.A.I.C.S.: 238390
Jarmo Katajisto *(Reg Mgr)*

NRG Automation Ltd. (1)
Ellard House Floats Road, Rounthorn Industrial Estate, Wythenshawe, M23 9WB, United Kingdom
Tel.: (44) 1514248900
Web Site: http://www.nrgautomation.co.uk
Door Control Distr
N.A.I.C.S.: 423610

NTi Audio AG (1)
Im alten Riet 102, 9494, Schaan, Liechtenstein
Tel.: (423) 2396060
Web Site: https://www.nti-audio.com
Measuring Instrument Mfr & Distr
N.A.I.C.S.: 334513

Natgraph Ltd. (1)
Dabell Avenue, Blenheim Industrial Estate, Nottingham, NG6 8WA, United Kingdom
Tel.: (44) 115 979 5800
Web Site: https://www.natgraph.co.uk
Machinery Mfr
N.A.I.C.S.: 333248
Geoff Bowley *(Mgr-Production)*

Nolek AB (1)
Hantverkarvagen 11, 145 63, Norsborg, Sweden
Tel.: (46) 85 319 4200
Web Site: https://www.nolek.com
Leak Testing Product Mfr
N.A.I.C.S.: 334519

Subsidiary (Non-US):

Nolek (Beijing) Technology Co., Ltd. (2)
Room 910 HongYu Building No 7 XuwYuan Road, Haidian District, Beijing, 1000083, China
Tel.: (86) 1051313670
Leak Testing Product Mfr
N.A.I.C.S.: 334519

Nolek A/S (2)
Birkedam 10 V, 6000, Kolding, Denmark
Tel.: (45) 72206630
Leak Testing Product Mfr
N.A.I.C.S.: 334519

Nolek Central Europe Kft. (2)
Rev ut 16/A, 2310, Szigetszentmiklos, Hungary
Tel.: (36) 24540545
Leak Testing Product Mfr
N.A.I.C.S.: 334519

Nolek Sdn. Bhd. (2)
1127 Jalan Perindustrian Bukit Minyak 8, Taman Perindustrian Bukit Minyak Simpang Ampat, 14100, Pulau Penang, Malaysia
Tel.: (60) 45040788
Leak Testing Product Mfr
N.A.I.C.S.: 334519

Subsidiary (US):

Nolek, Inc. (2)
4 Commerce Way Unit C, Carver, MA 02330
Tel.: (781) 585-5606
Leak Testing Product Mfr
N.A.I.C.S.: 334519

Norsecraft Tec AS (1)
Skuiveien 43, 1339, Voyenenga, Norway
Tel.: (47) 6 717 7580
Web Site: https://www.norsecrafttec.no
Emp.: 18
Construction Equipment Services
N.A.I.C.S.: 532412

Norske Geotech AS (1)
Sturparksvagen 10, 451 55, Uddevalla, Sweden
Tel.: (46) 5 222 3435
Web Site: https://www.norskegeotech.no
Machinery Mfr
N.A.I.C.S.: 333248

Novisol AG (1)
Weidenweg 15, 4310, Rheinfelden, Switzerland
Tel.: (41) 618361616
Construction Services
N.A.I.C.S.: 236220

Subsidiary (Non-US):

Novisol GmbH (2)
Niederlassung Hannover Borsigring 24, 31319, Sehnde, Germany
Tel.: (49) 51387087902
Construction Services
N.A.I.C.S.: 236220

INTERNATIONAL PUBLIC

Oscar Medtec AB (1)
Arntorpsgatan 24, 442 45, Kungalv, Sweden
Tel.: (46) 30317050
Web Site: https://www.oscarmedtec.se
Medical Equipment Mfr
N.A.I.C.S.: 339112

Oy Colly Company AB (1)
Tiilenlyojankuja 9 B, 01720, Vantaa, Finland
Tel.: (358) 29006150
Web Site: http://www.colly.fi
Sales Range: $10-24.9 Million
Emp.: 25
Importers of High Quality Technical Goods
N.A.I.C.S.: 541990

Oy Lining AB (1)
Tiilenlyojankuja 9 B, 01720, Vantaa, Finland
Tel.: (358) 2 900 6160
Web Site: https://www.lining.fi
Sales Range: $10-24.9 Million
Emp.: 40
Technical solution for clean & sewage line & plant Services
N.A.I.C.S.: 522299

Oy Maantera AB (1)
Keinumaenkuja 2, PO Box 2, 01510, Vantaa, Finland
Tel.: (358) 2 900 6130
Web Site: https://www.maantera.fi
Sales Range: $1-9.9 Million
Emp.: 19
Machine Tools Mfr
N.A.I.C.S.: 333517

Oy Teollisuusapu Ab (1)
Kirkniementie 6, Kirkniemi, 08800, Finland
Tel.: (358) 19340231
Web Site: http://www.teollisuusapu.fi
Sales Range: $100-124.9 Million
Emp.: 10
Sales Financing
N.A.I.C.S.: 522299

PMH International AB (1)
Ekenasgatan 6, 271 39, Ystad, Sweden
Tel.: (46) 20212999
Web Site: https://www.pmh-hallen.com
Storage Hall Services
N.A.I.C.S.: 531130

PRP-Plastic Oy (1)
Moreenikatu 2A, 04600, Mantsala, Finland
Tel.: (358) 29006250
Plastic Equipment Mfr
N.A.I.C.S.: 333248
Juha Raiha *(CEO)*

Palmstiernas Svenska AB (1)
Aspstigen 122, 663 91, Hammaro, Sweden
Tel.: (46) 54 52 14 70
Industrial Supplies Distr
N.A.I.C.S.: 423840

Pentronic AB (1)
Bergsliden 1, 593 96, Vastervik, Sweden
Tel.: (46) 49 025 8500
Web Site: https://www.pentronic.se
Sales Range: $25-49.9 Million
Emp.: 100
Industrial Temperature Sensor Mfr
N.A.I.C.S.: 334513
Jan Halling *(Controller & Mgr-HR)*

Pipe Equipment Specialists Limited (1)
66 Dukesway, Teesside Industrial Estate Thornaby, Stockton-on-Tees, TS17 9LT, United Kingdom
Tel.: (44) 164 276 9789
Web Site: https://www.pipe-equipment.co.uk
Pipe Equipment Mfr
N.A.I.C.S.: 332999
Steven Law *(Gen Mgr)*

Plooijer Zaandam B.V. (1)
Tel.: (31) 75 635 0800
Web Site: https://www.plooijer.nl
Mining & Metal Mfr
N.A.I.C.S.: 332312
Frank Kalf *(Owner & CEO)*

Precision Products Ltd (1)
Unit 1 Cobnar Wood Close, Chesterfield

AND PRIVATE COMPANIES — INDUTRADE AB

Trading Estate, Chesterfield, S41 9RQ, United Kingdom
Tel.: (44) 124 626 1621
Web Site: https://www.ppuk.com
Emp.: 70
Piston Rings Mfr
N.A.I.C.S.: 336310

Precision UK Ltd. (1)
Technology Building Pepper Road, Hazel Grove, Stockport, SK7 5BW, United Kingdom
Tel.: (44) 161 487 2822
Web Site: https://www.precisionuk.co.uk
Gas Pipeline Equipment Mfr & Whslr
N.A.I.C.S.: 333248

Primed Fysio och Rehab AB (1)
Arntorpsgatan 24, 442 45, Kungalv, Sweden
Tel.: (46) 30317050
Web Site: https://primed.se
Medical Equipment Distr
N.A.I.C.S.: 423450

Pro-Flex AS (1)
Janaflaten 39 Godvik, 5179, Bergen, Norway
Tel.: (47) 5 551 3330
Web Site: https://www.pro-flex.no
Hoses & Fitting Product Mfr
N.A.I.C.S.: 332912

Processpumpar AB (1)
Ostra Vagngatan 8B, 702 27, Orebro, Sweden
Tel.: (46) 1 922 3800
Web Site: https://www.ppab.se
Pumps Mfr
N.A.I.C.S.: 333914
Martin Andersson *(Mgr-Technical Sls)*

Processpumparab I Motala AB (1)
Ostra Vagngatan 8B, 702 27, Orebro, Sweden
Tel.: (46) 19223800
Web Site: http://www.ppab.se
Emp.: 20
Technical solution for clean & sewage line & plant Services
N.A.I.C.S.: 522299

Prodia AB (1)
Vellinge Esex 669, 235 91, Vellinge, Sweden
Tel.: (46) 406850088
Web Site: https://www.prodia.se
Drug Testing Laboratory Services
N.A.I.C.S.: 541380

Professional Parts Sweden AB (1)
Fagelviksvagen 9B, 145 53, Norsborg, Sweden
Tel.: (46) 85 562 0030
Web Site: https://www.proparts.se
Machinery Equipment Whslr
N.A.I.C.S.: 423830

QbiQ B.V.
Hoorn 234, 2404 HK, Alphen aan den Rijn, Netherlands
Tel.: (31) 88 501 0500
Web Site: https://www.qbiq.nl
Building Materials Distr
N.A.I.C.S.: 444180
Kim Zandbergen *(CEO)*

RA Howarth Engineering Ltd. (1)
Earl Road Rackheath Industrial Estate Rackheath, Norwich, NR13 6NT, Norfolk, United Kingdom
Tel.: (44) 1603721155
Web Site: http://www.howarthengineering.com
Machinery Mfr
N.A.I.C.S.: 333248

RS Technics BV (1)
Noordhoek 15, 9301 ZG, Roden, Netherlands
Tel.: (31) 50 501 3745
Web Site: https://www.rstechnics.nl
Temperature Sensor Mfr
N.A.I.C.S.: 334512
Richard Van Leeuwen *(Mgr-Sls)*

Relekta AS (1)
Innspurten 1 A, 0663, Oslo, Norway
Tel.: (47) 2 266 0400
Web Site: https://www.relekta.no
Cleaning Product Mfr

N.A.I.C.S.: 325612

Robota AB (1)
Ritarslingan 9, 187 66, Taby, Sweden
Tel.: (46) 8 630 08 90
Sales Range: $25-49.9 Million
Emp.: 23
Pump & Pump Accessories Distr
N.A.I.C.S.: 423830
Lars Ruden *(Gen Mgr)*

Rostfria VA-System i Storfors AB (1)
ndustrivagen 7, 68233, Filipstad, Sweden
Tel.: (46) 55062030
Web Site: http://www.rostfria.com
Pipes Mfr
N.A.I.C.S.: 332996

Rostfria VA-System i Storfors AB (1)
Tallbacksgatan 12, 688 30, Storfors, Sweden
Tel.: (46) 55062030
Web Site: http://www.rostfria.com
Pipes Mfr
N.A.I.C.S.: 332996

Rubin Medical AB (1)
Krossverksgatan 7B, 216 16, Limhamn, Sweden
Tel.: (46) 4 015 5480
Web Site: https://www.rubinmedical.se
Medical Device Mfr
N.A.I.C.S.: 339112

SIA Indutek LV (1)
Piedrujas iela 7 k-4, Riga, 1073, Latvia
Tel.: (371) 6 780 4949
Web Site: https://www.indutek.lv
Sales Range: $25-49.9 Million
Emp.: 23
Provider of Ventilation, Air Conditioning, Water Supply & Sewage Supplies & Service
N.A.I.C.S.: 333415

STRIHL Scandinavia AB (1)
Magasinsgatan 6B, 434 37, Kungsbacka, Sweden
Tel.: (46) 30 056 9980
Web Site: https://www.strihl.se
Lighting Mfr
N.A.I.C.S.: 335139
Glenn Winberg *(Mgr-Sls)*

Saniflex AB (1)
Agavagen 58, 181 55, Lidingo, Sweden
Tel.: (46) 84 002 6060
Web Site: https://www.saniflex.se
Sales Range: $50-74.9 Million
Emp.: 4
Hose & Pipe Component Distr
N.A.I.C.S.: 423840
Claes Palmgren *(CEO)*

Scanmaskin Sverige AB (1)
Heljesvagen 10, 437 36, Lindome, Sweden
Tel.: (46) 3 199 4970
Web Site: https://www.scanmaskin.com
Emp.: 29
Machinery Mfr
N.A.I.C.S.: 333248
Paulo Bergstrand *(Mng Dir)*

Subsidiary (Non-US):

Scanmaskin Danmark ApS (2)
Torvegade 22, DK-7330, Brande, Denmark
Tel.: (45) 97180058
Machinery Mfr
N.A.I.C.S.: 333248

Scanmaskin Finland Oy (2)
Raudoittajantie 3 A, 06450, Porvoo, Finland
Tel.: (358) 102924700
Machinery Mfr
N.A.I.C.S.: 333248

Scanmaskin Middle East FZE (2)
DSO-HQ-F1-102-4 F Block Dubai Silicon Oasis Head Quarters, Dubai, United Arab Emirates
Tel.: (971) 565312558
Machinery Mfr
N.A.I.C.S.: 333248

Scanmaskin Norge AS (2)
Maridalsveien 91, 0461, Oslo, Norway
Tel.: (47) 63876000
Machinery Mfr
N.A.I.C.S.: 333248

Subsidiary (US):

Scanmaskin USA Inc. (2)

18868 72nd Ave S, Kent, WA 98032
Tel.: (425) 209-0147
Machinery Mfr
N.A.I.C.S.: 333248

Senmatic A/S (1)
Industrivej 8, 5471, Sonderso, Denmark
Tel.: (45) 6 489 2211
Web Site: https://www.senmatic.com
Emp.: 90
Sensor Product Mfr
N.A.I.C.S.: 334513
Anders Gottschalk Nystrup *(Dir-Sls)*

Sensor Partners BV (1)
James Wattlaan 15, 5151 DP, Drunen, Netherlands
Tel.: (31) 416378239
Industrial Equipment Whsr
N.A.I.C.S.: 423830
Hans Giezenberg *(Mng Dir)*

Subsidiary (Non-US):

Sensor Partners BVBA (2)
Z 1 Researchpark 310, 1731, Zellik, Belgium
Tel.: (32) 24649690
Industrial Equipment Whsr
N.A.I.C.S.: 423830

Sepab Fordonsprodukter AB (1)
Bergkallavagen 31 B, 192 79, Sollentuna, Sweden
Tel.: (46) 86269500
Web Site: https://www.sepab.se
Cabling & Electronic Mfr
N.A.I.C.S.: 335929
Mikael Goffhe *(Mgr-Quality Environmental)*

Sigum Fagerberg AS (1)
Billingstadsletta 19 B, 1396, Billingstad, Norway
Tel.: (47) 4 150 1100
Web Site: https://www.sigumfagerberg.no
Valve Equipment Distr
N.A.I.C.S.: 423830

Spinova AB (1)
Sagverksgatan 13, Box 150, 385 22, Torsas, Sweden
Tel.: (46) 4 864 1200
Web Site: https://www.spinova.se
Emp.: 5
Industrial Spring Mfr
N.A.I.C.S.: 332613
Anders Knutsson *(Mng Dir)*

Stabalux GmbH (1)
Fraunhoferstrasse 8, 53121, Bonn, Germany
Tel.: (49) 2289090430
Web Site: https://www.stabalux.com
Steel Products Mfr
N.A.I.C.S.: 331110

Stalprofil AB (1)
Karrastrandvagen 126, 451 76, Uddevalla, Sweden
Tel.: (46) 52 264 6870
Web Site: https://www.stalprofil.se
Steel Mfrs
N.A.I.C.S.: 331221

Stalprofil PK AB (1)
Vastra Gotaland Parkgatan 10, Vargarda, 447 31, Sweden
Tel.: (46) 32262 50 60
Pipe Fitting Mfr
N.A.I.C.S.: 326122

Starke Arvid AB (1)
Lyckasvagen 3, Ljungskile, 459 30, Vastra Gotaland, Sweden
Tel.: (46) 5 222 2000
Web Site: https://starkearvid.com
Metal Product Distr
N.A.I.C.S.: 423510

Stockholms Geomekaniska AB (1)
Fagerstagatan 51, 163 53, Spanga, Sweden
Tel.: (46) 8 744 0500
Web Site: https://www.geomek.se
Machinery Mfr
N.A.I.C.S.: 333248

Sunflower Medical Ltd. (1)
17 Roydsdale Way Euroway Trading Estate, Bradford, BD4 6SE, United Kingdom
Tel.: (44) 1274684004

Health Care Furniture Mfr
N.A.I.C.S.: 337127
Carron Wood *(Mgr-Export)*

Svenska Geotech AB (1)
Stureparksvagen 10, 451 55, Uddevalla, Sweden
Tel.: (46) 5 222 3435
Web Site: https://www.svenskageotech.se
Fibertex Product Whslr
N.A.I.C.S.: 424450

TX RX Systems Inc. (1)
8625 Industrial Pkwy, Angola, NY 14006
Tel.: (716) 549-4700
Intercommunication Systems, Electric
N.A.I.C.S.: 334290
Anthony J. DelGobbo *(Mgr-Project Field Svcs)*

Tebra Messen Industrie B.V. (1)
Edisonstraat 14, 7903 AN, Hoogeveen, Netherlands
Tel.: (31) 528272898
Web Site: https://www.tebra.nl
Sharpening & Knife Mfr
N.A.I.C.S.: 333517

Tecalemit Flow Oy (1)
Tiilitie 6 A, 01720, Vantaa, Finland
Tel.: (358) 2 900 6280
Web Site: https://www.tecalemitflow.fi
Machinery Mfr
N.A.I.C.S.: 333248
Petri Puumalainen *(Mng Dir)*

TechnoSkruv i Varnamo AB (1)
Bangardsgatan 14, Box 627, 331 35, Varnamo, Sweden
Tel.: (46) 37 069 5510
Web Site: https://www.technoskruv.se
Sales Range: $25-49.9 Million
Emp.: 17
Mechanical Component Distr
N.A.I.C.S.: 423830

The Micro Spring & Presswork Company Ltd. (1)
Elizabeth Way, Enfield Industrial Estate, Redditch, B97 6BL, Worcestershire, United Kingdom
Tel.: (44) 15 276 9121
Web Site: https://www.microspring.co.uk
Spring Whslr
N.A.I.C.S.: 424490
Anne Calleia-Cutts *(Dir-Fin)*

Thermo Electric Instrumentation B.V. (1)
Coenecoop 71-73, Waddinxveen, 2740, Netherlands
Tel.: (31) 857607300
Web Site: http://www.thermo-electric.nl
Temperature Measuring & Control Equipment Mfr
N.A.I.C.S.: 334519

Topflight AB (1)
Metallgatan 19B, PO Box 1124, 262 22, Angelholm, Sweden
Tel.: (46) 43 144 9330
Web Site: https://www.topflight.se
Label Mfr
N.A.I.C.S.: 323117
Thomas Carlsson *(CFO)*

Tradinco Instrumenten-Apparaten B.V. (1)
Radonstraat 250, 2718 TB, Zoetermeer, Netherlands
Tel.: (31) 79 203 3130
Web Site: https://www.tradinco.com
Calibration Equipment Mfr & Distr
N.A.I.C.S.: 334515
Oscar Man *(Dir-Sls)*

Trelawny SPT Limited (1)
Trelawny House 13 Highdown Road, Sydenham Industrial Estate, Leamington Spa, CV31 1XT, Warwickshire, United Kingdom
Tel.: (44) 192 688 3781
Web Site: https://www.trelawnyspt.com
Marine Product Mfr
N.A.I.C.S.: 336611
Adam Dickinson *(Mng Dir)*

Tribotec AB (1)
Metallvagen 2, 435 33, Molnlycke, Sweden
Tel.: (46) 3 188 7880

INDUTRADE AB

Indutrade AB—(Continued)
Web Site: https://www.tribotec.se
Automotive & Mechanical Supplies Distr
N.A.I.C.S.: 423120
Peter Lindgren (CFO)

Tubeworkx B.V. (1)
Twente Noord 96 Business Park, 7602 KS, Almelo, Netherlands
Tel.: (31) 54 657 6955
Web Site: https://www.tubeworkx.com
Metals Mfr
N.A.I.C.S.: 332313
Arjan Klaassen (Mng Dir)

Turenfabrik Safenwil AG (1)
Kanalstrasse 14, Safenwil, 5745, Zofingen, Switzerland
Tel.: (41) 56 622 1777
Web Site: https://www.tuerenfabrik.ch
Building Materials Mfr
N.A.I.C.S.: 327120

UAB Industek (1)
Dariaus ir Gireno str 177, LT-02189, Vilnius, Lithuania
Tel.: (370) 270 0225
Web Site: https://www.industek.lt
Sales Range: $25-49.9 Million
Emp.: 12
Provider of Flow Technology & Air Conditioning Supplies & Service
N.A.I.C.S.: 333415
Vaidas Ragaisis (Mng Dir)

Uniska AG (1)
Schliessa 6, 9495, Triesen, Liechtenstein
Tel.: (423) 392 4191
Web Site: https://www.uniska.ch
Interior Fitting Contractor Services
N.A.I.C.S.: 541410

Vacuum Engineering Services Ltd. (1)
St Modwen Road, Manchester, M32 0ZE, United Kingdom
Tel.: (44) 161 866 8860
Web Site: https://www.vac-eng.com
Machinery Mfr
N.A.I.C.S.: 333248
Richard Hodgkinson (Mgr-Bus Dev-Europe & Asia)

Ventim AB (1)
Tel.: (46) 48 042 9100
Web Site: https://www.ventim.se
Emp.: 38
N.A.I.C.S.: 522299
Thony Lundell (Mng Dir)

Verplas Limited (1)
Unit 7 Verwood Industrial Estate, Blackhill Verwood, Dorset, BH31 6HA, United Kingdom
Tel.: (44) 120 282 5898
Web Site: https://www.verplas.co.uk
Ventilation Duct Mfr
N.A.I.C.S.: 333415

Vipmek Oy (1)
Hankasuontetie 3 A, FI 00390, Helsinki, Finland
Tel.: (358) 947625800
Web Site: http://www.vipmek.fi
Sales Range: $1-9.9 Million
Emp.: 13
N.A.I.C.S.: 522299

Weldability Sif Limited (1)
The Orbital Centre Icknield Way, Letchworth, SG6 1ET, Hertfordshire, United Kingdom
Tel.: (44) 146 248 2200
Web Site: https://www.weldability-sif.com
Welding Whslr
N.A.I.C.S.: 423840
Gareth Hawkins (Mng Dir)

Wennerstrom Ljuskontroll AB (1)
Jan Inghes Torg 34, 120 71, Stockholm, Sweden
Tel.: (46) 1 529 1000
Web Site: https://www.wlk.eu
Emp.: 21
Electrical & Electronic Mfr
N.A.I.C.S.: 335999
Fredrik Persson (Acct Mgr)

Winab Vikvaggar AB (1)
Ekerovagen 110, 178 52, Ekero, Sweden
Tel.: (46) 85 602 1100
Web Site: https://www.winab.se
Building Materials Whslr
N.A.I.C.S.: 444180
Jan Hjorth (Mgr-Production)

YTM-Industrial Oy (1)
Tiilenlyojankuja 9 B, 01720, Vantaa, Finland
Tel.: (358) 2 900 6230
Web Site: https://www.ytm.fi
Sales Range: $75-99.9 Million
Emp.: 75
Mechanical & Industrial Engineering Services
N.A.I.C.S.: 522299

Subsidiary (Domestic):

Pinteco Oy (2)
Petikontie 20, 1720, Vantaa, Finland
Tel.: (358) 29006210
Web Site: https://www.pinteco.fi
Sales Range: $1-9.9 Million
Emp.: 15
N.A.I.C.S.: 522299

Young Black IS Ltd. (1)
Thistle House Radway Road Britannia Business Park, Swindon, SN3 4ND, Wiltshire, United Kingdom
Tel.: (44) 1793838400
Web Site: http://www.youngblack.co.uk
Tool Mfr
N.A.I.C.S.: 333517

ZAO Indutek STP (1)
st Tsvetochnaya 16 BC Osipoff 1st floor, 196084, Saint Petersburg, Russia
Tel.: (7) 812 326 9500
Web Site: https://www.indutek.ru
Sales Range: $25-49.9 Million
Emp.: 15
Provider of Equipment for Conveyer Belts
N.A.I.C.S.: 333922

Zijtveld Grijpers B.V. (1)
De Boomgaard 1, 1243 HV, 's-Graveland, Netherlands
Tel.: (31) 35 656 3359
Web Site: https://www.zijtveld-grijpers.nl
Emp.: 528
Construction Machinery Mfr
N.A.I.C.S.: 333248
Mariandel Van Der Sluijs-Hage (Office Mgr)

INDVR BRANDS INC.
350 7 Avenue SW Suite 3400, C/O Fasken Martineau DuMoulin LLP, Calgary, T2P 3N9, AB, Canada
Tel.: (403) 803-2799
Web Site: http://www.indvr-brands.com
Year Founded: 2007
INDVR—(CNSX)
Rev.: $903,927
Assets: $7,444,927
Liabilities: $5,990,648
Net Worth: $1,454,279
Earnings: ($5,659,697)
Fiscal Year-end: 01/31/21
Investment Services
N.A.I.C.S.: 523999
Jordan Shapiro (VP-Bus Dev)

INDYGOTECH MINERALS SA
Ul Swietokrzyska 30/lok 63, 00-549, Warsaw, Poland
Tel.: (48) 226291247
Web Site: http://www.indygotechminerals.com
Year Founded: 2008
IDG—(WAR)
Sales Range: $1-9.9 Million
Venture Capital Services
N.A.I.C.S.: 523999
Dariusz Janus (Chm-Mgmt Bd & CEO)

INEEDHITS.COM PTY LTD.
Level 1 229 Stirling Hwy, Claremont, 6010, WA, Australia
Tel.: (61) 8 93338222
Web Site: http://www.ineedhits.com
Year Founded: 1996
Sales Range: $1-9.9 Million
Emp.: 30
Search Engine Marketing
N.A.I.C.S.: 541613
Clay Cook (CEO)

INEO MIDI PYRENEES LANGUEDOC ROUSSILLON
52 Rue Jacques Rabinet, 31100, Toulouse, Haute Garonne, France
Tel.: (33) 561503300
Rev.: $41,600,000
Emp.: 205
N.A.I.C.S.: 238210
Bernard Moreau (Mgr-Computers Dept)

INEOS LIMITED
3 Avenue des Uttins, 1180, Rolle, Switzerland
Tel.: (41) 216277040   IM
Year Founded: 2016
Emp.: 100
Investment Holding Company
N.A.I.C.S.: 551112
James A. Ratcliffe (Chm)

Subsidiaries:

INEOS AG (1)
3 Avenue des Uttins, 1180, Rolle, Switzerland
Tel.: (41) 216277040
Holding Company
N.A.I.C.S.: 551112

Subsidiary (Domestic):

INEOS Group AG (2)
3 Avenue des Uttins, 1180, Rolle, Switzerland
Tel.: (41) 21 627 7040
Web Site: http://www.ineos.com
Sales Range: $25-49.9 Billion
Emp.: 19,000
Petrochemicals, Specialty Chemicals & Oil Products Mfr
N.A.I.C.S.: 325110
Jim Ratcliffe (Chm)

Subsidiary (Non-US):

Hess (Denmark) ApS (3)
Ostergade 26 B, DK-1100, Copenhagen, Denmark
Tel.: (45) 33301233
Natural Gas Distr
N.A.I.C.S.: 324110

Subsidiary (US):

INEOS ABS Corporation (3)
356 Three Rivers Pkwy, Addyston, OH 45001
Tel.: (513) 467-2479
Web Site: http://www.lustran-polymers.com
Thermoplastic Resin Product Mfr
N.A.I.C.S.: 326199

INEOS Americas LLC (3)
7770 Rangeline Rd, Theodore, AL 36582
Tel.: (251) 443-3000
Chemical Products Mfr
N.A.I.C.S.: 325199
Marc Hill (Mgr-Pur Logistic)

Subsidiary (Non-US):

INEOS Bamble AS (3)
Asdalstrand 291, 3960, Stathelle, Norway
Tel.: (47) 35577000
Emp.: 130
Petrochemical Products Mfr
N.A.I.C.S.: 324110

Subsidiary (US):

INEOS Bio USA, LLC (3)
3030 Warrenville Rd Ste 650, Lisle, IL 60532
Tel.: (630) 857-7146
Petrochemical Products Mfr
N.A.I.C.S.: 324110

Subsidiary (Non-US):

INEOS Cologne GmbH (3)

INTERNATIONAL PUBLIC

Alte Strasse 201, Cologne, 50769, Germany
Tel.: (49) 22135550
Web Site: http://www.ineoskoeln.de
Petrochemical, Ethylene Oxide & Glycols, Ethanol Polyethylene, Propylene Oxide & Butadiene Mfr
N.A.I.C.S.: 325110
Tom Crotty (CEO)

INEOS Feluy sprl (3)
Parc Industriel Nord Zone C, Feluy, 7181, Belgium
Tel.: (32) 67875211
Petrochemical Products Mfr
N.A.I.C.S.: 324110
Claude Moreau (Mgr-IT)

INEOS Group Limited (3)
Hawkslease Chapel Lane, Lyndhurst, SO43 7FG, Hants, United Kingdom
Tel.: (44) 2380287067
Web Site: http://www.ineos.com
Sales Range: $25-49.9 Billion
Holding Company; Petrochemicals, Specialty Chemicals & Oil Products Mfr
N.A.I.C.S.: 551112
James A. Ratcliffe (Chm & CEO)

Subsidiary (Domestic):

INEOS ChlorVinyls Limited (4)
Runcorn Site HQ S Parade, PO Box 9, Runcorn, WA7 4JE, Cheshire, United Kingdom
Tel.: (44) 1928561111
Web Site: http://www.ineos.com
Sales Range: $1-4.9 Billion
Emp.: 3,350
Chlorine, Chlorine Derivatives & Polyvinyl Chloride Mfr
N.A.I.C.S.: 325180
Andrew Currie (Chm)

Subsidiary (Non-US):

INEOS Manufacturing Belgium NV (3)
Scheldelaan 482, Antwerp, 2040, Belgium
Tel.: (32) 32103511
Petrochemical Product Distr
N.A.I.C.S.: 424910
Christine Goris (Mgr-HR)

INEOS Manufacturing France SAS (3)
Rue Ernest Solvay, 57430, Sarralbe, France
Tel.: (33) 387977000
Petrochemical Products Mfr
N.A.I.C.S.: 324110

INEOS Manufacturing Italia SpA (3)
Via Plave 6, 57013, Rosignano Marittimo, Italy
Industrial Chemical Mfr & Distr
N.A.I.C.S.: 325211
Elena Leonildi (Mgr-Mfg)

INEOS NV (3)
Haven 1053 Nieuwe Weg 1, Zwijndrecht, 2070, Belgium
Tel.: (32) 32509111
Petrochemical Product Distr
N.A.I.C.S.: 424910

Subsidiary (US):

INEOS Nitriles (3)
2600 S Shore Blvd Ste 250, League City, TX 77573
Tel.: (281) 535-6600
Web Site: http://www.ineosnitriles.com
Sales Range: $1-4.9 Billion
Emp.: 370
Acrylonitrile, Acetonitrile, Hydrogen Cyanide, Acetone Cyanohydrin & Other Specialty Nitriles Mfr
N.A.I.C.S.: 325998
Rob Nevin (CEO)

Plant (Domestic):

INEOS Nitriles (4)
1900 Ft Amanda Rd, Lima, OH 45804-1827
Tel.: (419) 226-1200
Web Site: http://www.ineosnitriles.com
Sales Range: $50-74.9 Million
Emp.: 150
Acrylonitrile, Acetonitrile & Hydrogen Cyanide Mfr

N.A.I.C.S.: 325998
Marcy Boone *(Dir-Site)*

INEOS Nitriles - Green Lake Site (4)
13050 State Hwy 185 N, Port Lavaca, TX 77979
Tel.: (361) 552-7543
Web Site: http://www.ineosnitriles.com
Sales Range: $50-74.9 Million
Emp.: 200
Acrylonitrile, Acetonitrile, Acetone Cyanohydrin & Other Specialty Nitriles Mfr
N.A.I.C.S.: 325998

Subsidiary (US):

INEOS Olefins & Polymers USA (3)
Marina View 2600 S Shore Blvd, League City, TX 77573
Tel.: (281) 535-6600
Web Site: http://www.innovene.com
Sales Range: $1-4.9 Billion
Emp.: 300
Mfr of Olefins, Polyethylene & Polypropylene
N.A.I.C.S.: 325110
Brian Young *(Coord-IT Site)*

Subsidiary (Non-US):

INEOS Phenol Belgium N.V. (3)
Geslecht 1 Haven 1930, Doel, 9130, Belgium
Tel.: (32) 37301211
Web Site: http://www.ineosphenol.com
Petrochemical Product Distr
N.A.I.C.S.: 424910

INEOS Phenol GmbH & Co. KG (3)
Dechenstrasse 3, D-45966, Gladbeck, Germany
Tel.: (49) 2043 958 304
Web Site: http://www.ineosphenol.com
Sales Range: $1-4.9 Billion
Emp.: 300
Mfr of Phenol & Acetone Products
N.A.I.C.S.: 325998
Dietmar Schlug *(Dir-HR)*

Subsidiary (Non-US):

INEOS Phenol (4)
Haven 1930 Geslecht 1, Doel, 45966, Belgium
Tel.: (32) 37301211
Web Site: http://www.ineosphenol.com
Sales Range: $50-74.9 Million
Emp.: 175
Mfr of Phenol & Acetone
N.A.I.C.S.: 325998

Mitsui Phenols Singapore Pte Ltd. (4)
3 HarbourFront Place 10-01 HarbourFront Tower 2, Singapore, 099254, Singapore
Tel.: (65) 65340537
Emp.: 200
Chemical Products Mfr & Distr
N.A.I.C.S.: 325998
Masaaki Higashi *(Mng Dir)*

Subsidiary (Non-US):

INEOS Styrenics Netherlands B.V. (3)
Lijndonk 25, 4825 BG, Breda, Netherlands
Tel.: (31) 765790000
Petrochemical Products Mfr
N.A.I.C.S.: 324110
Steven Floris *(Mgr-Pur)*

INEOS Styrenics Ribecourt SAS (3)
704 Rue Pierre et Marie Curie, BP 5002, 60771, Ribecourt-Dreslincourt, Cedex, France
Tel.: (33) 344757000
Petrochemical Products Mfr
N.A.I.C.S.: 324110

INEOS Styrenics Wingles SAS (3)
Avenue de la Verrerie, BP NO 62, 62410, Wingles, France
Tel.: (33) 321 77 3200
Petrochemical Products Mfr
N.A.I.C.S.: 324110

INEOS Vinyls Belgium SA/NV (3)
De Kampelaar 7, Hoogstraten, 2320, Belgium
Tel.: (32) 33140889
Petrochemical Product Distr

N.A.I.C.S.: 424910

Ineos Oxide Ltd. (3)
Hawkslease House Chapel Lane, Lyndhurst, Southampton, SO43 7FG, United Kingdom
Tel.: (44) 2380287067
Petrochemical Products Mfr
N.A.I.C.S.: 324110

Joint Venture (Non-US):

Lotte INEOS Chemical Co., Ltd. (3)
8F West Center 26 Eulji ro 5 gil, Jung gu, Seoul, 1320-10, Korea (South) (51%)
Tel.: (82) 522781100
Web Site: http://www.lotteineos.com
Sales Range: Less than $1 Million
Acetic Acid, Vinyl Acetate Monomer & Other Specialty Fine Chemicals Mfr
N.A.I.C.S.: 325998
Young Joon Kim *(CEO)*

Subsidiary (Non-US):

Styrolution Group GmbH (3)
Erlenstrasse 2, 60325, Frankfurt am Main, Germany
Tel.: (49) 69 509550 1200
Web Site: http://www.styrolution.com
Sales Range: $5-14.9 Billion
Emp.: 340
Holding Company; Styrene Products Mfr
N.A.I.C.S.: 551112
Kevin McQuade *(CEO)*

Subsidiary (Non-US):

Styrolution (Thailand) Co., Ltd. (4)
No 4/2 I-8 Road, Map Ta Phut A Muang, Rayong, 21150, Thailand
Tel.: (66) 38910700
Web Site: http://www.styrolution.com
Thermoplastic Resin Product Mfr
N.A.I.C.S.: 325211

Subsidiary (US):

Styrolution America LLC (4)
25846 SW Frontage Rd, Channahon, IL 60410
Tel.: (815) 423-5541
Web Site: http://www.styrolution.com
Sales Range: $200-249.9 Million
Emp.: 700
Styrene & Styrenic Polymer Mfr
N.A.I.C.S.: 326140
Alexander Gluck *(Pres)*

Plant (Domestic):

Styrolution America LLC (5)
950 Worcester St, Indian Orchard, MA 01551
Tel.: (413) 781-1441
Web Site: http://www.styrolution.com
Sales Range: $25-49.9 Million
Emp.: 70
Styrene & Styrenic Polymers Mfr
N.A.I.C.S.: 325211

Styrolution America LLC (5)
1609 Biddle Ave, Wyandotte, MI 48192
Tel.: (734) 324-5608
Web Site: http://www.styrolution.com
Styrenic Products Mfr
N.A.I.C.S.: 326199

Subsidiary (Domestic):

Styrolution GmbH (4)
Carl-Bosch-Strasse 38, Ludwigshafen, 67063, Germany
Tel.: (49) 621600
Web Site: http://www.basf.com
Styrene Products Mfr
N.A.I.C.S.: 326199

Subsidiary (Non-US):

Styrolution India Pvt. Ltd. (4)
1st Floor VIBGYOR Tower Plot No C-62 G Block, Bandra Kurla Complex, 400 018, Mumbai, India
Tel.: (91) 2256618000
Web Site: http://www.styrolution.com
Polystyrene Mfr
N.A.I.C.S.: 326140

Subsidiary (Domestic):

INEOS Styrolution India Limited (5)
6th Floor ABS Towers Old Padra Road, Vadodara, 390 007, India
Tel.: (91) 2652303201
Web Site: http://www.styrolutionabsindia.com
Sales Range: $300-349.9 Million
Thermoplastic Resin Product Mfr
N.A.I.C.S.: 325211
Sanjiv Vasudeva *(CEO & Mng Dir)*

Subsidiary (Non-US):

Styrolution International S.A. (4)
Rue des Uttins 3, 1180, Rolle, Switzerland
Tel.: (41) 21 627 7040
Web Site: http://www.styrolution.com
Styrene & Styrenic Polymer Mfr
N.A.I.C.S.: 326140
Rob Buntinx *(Pres-EMEA)*

Subsidiary (Domestic):

Styrolution Koln GmbH (4)
Alte Strasse 201, 50769, Cologne, Germany
Tel.: (49) 22135550
Web Site: http://www.styrolution.com
Sales Range: $1-4.9 Billion
Thermoplastic Resin Mfr
N.A.I.C.S.: 325211
Gerd Franken *(CEO)*

INEPAR S.A INDUSTRIA E CONSTRUCOES
Al Dos Jurupis 455 - 10 Floor, 4088001, Sao Paulo, Brazil
Tel.: (55) 1150544000
Web Site: http://www.inepar.com.br
Year Founded: 1953
INEP3—(BRAZ)
Rev.: $1,158,900
Assets: $208,542,030
Liabilities: $409,583,658
Net Worth: ($201,041,628)
Earnings: $85,344,378
Emp.: 11,910
Fiscal Year-end: 12/31/23
Industrial Building Construction Services
N.A.I.C.S.: 236210
Cesar Romeu Fiedler *(CEO)*

INERTIA STEEL LIMITED
422 Tulsiani Chamber Nariman Point, Mumbai, 400 021, India
Tel.: (91) 22 22832381
Web Site: http://www.inertiasteel.com
Year Founded: 1984
Sales Range: Less than $1 Million
Iron & Steel Product Whslr
N.A.I.C.S.: 423510
H. G. Joshi *(Compliance Officer)*

INES CORPORATION
1-38-11 Nihonbashi Kakigara-cho, Chuo-ku, Tokyo, 103-0014, Japan
Tel.: (81) 367754401   JP
Web Site: https://www.ines.co.jp
Year Founded: 1964
9742—(TKS)
Rev.: $268,081,770
Assets: $359,762,470
Liabilities: $109,970,570
Net Worth: $249,791,900
Earnings: $11,864,950
Emp.: 1,383
Fiscal Year-end: 03/31/24
Information Network System Services
N.A.I.C.S.: 541512
Koichi Yoshimura *(Pres & CEO)*

Subsidiaries:

ISS Corporation (1)
3-2-1 Sakado, Takatsu-ku, Kawasaki, 213-0012, Kanagawa, Japan (100%)
Tel.: (81) 44 812 1175
Web Site: http://www.k-iss.co.jp
Network Systems Services
N.A.I.C.S.: 517810
Kenshiro Sasaki *(Pres)*

KDS, Inc. (1)
4-7-15 Kudanminami, Chiyoda-ku, Tokyo, 102-0074, Japan (100%)
Tel.: (81) 332306677
Web Site: http://www.kds-net.co.jp
Data Entry & Temporary Staffing
N.A.I.C.S.: 518210

Security & Knowledge Support Service, Inc. (1)
549-6 Shinano-cho, Totsuka-ku, Yokohama, 244-0801, Kanagawa, Japan (100%)
Tel.: (81) 458268600
Web Site: http://www.skss.jp
Network Systems Services
N.A.I.C.S.: 517810

INESA INTELLIGENT TECH INC.
9th10th Floor Building B6 No 180 Yizhou Road, Xuhui District, Shanghai, 200233, China
Tel.: (86) 2162980202
Web Site: http://www.inesa-e.com
Year Founded: 1987
600602—(SHG)
Rev.: $636,608,840
Assets: $1,013,375,849
Liabilities: $349,281,785
Net Worth: $664,094,064
Earnings: $25,384,657
Emp.: 2,232
Fiscal Year-end: 12/31/22
Electronic Components Mfr
N.A.I.C.S.: 334419
Huang Jin Gang *(Chm)*

INEST, INC.
8F Takase Building Annex 1-25-9 Higashi-Ikebukuro, Toshima-ku, Tokyo, 170-0013, Japan
Tel.: (81) 368923864
Web Site: https://www.inest-inc.co.jp
Year Founded: 1996
3390—(TKS)
Rev.: $64,139,680
Assets: $65,988,560
Liabilities: $42,417,760
Net Worth: $23,570,800
Earnings: ($561,440)
Fiscal Year-end: 03/31/22
Process Outsourcing Services
N.A.I.C.S.: 541614
Mari Koizumi *(Pres & CEO)*

INETVIDEO.COM
6800A Trans Canada Hwy, Pointe-Claire, H9R 5L4, QC, Canada
Web Site: http://www.inetvideo.ca
Year Founded: 1999
Sales Range: $10-24.9 Million
Emp.: 60
Video Game, Movie & Music Online Retail
N.A.I.C.S.: 512120
Richard Brotto *(Owner)*

Subsidiaries:

iNetVideo.com (1)
334 Cornelia St Ste 292, Plattsburgh, NY 12901 (100%)
Web Site: http://www.inetvideo.com
Sales Range: $10-24.9 Million
Emp.: 52
Retails Video Games & Music CDs & DVDs Online
N.A.I.C.S.: 512120

INEX BAKAR AD
Svetog Save 57, 19250, Majdanpek, Serbia
Tel.: (381) 30581016
Web Site:
https://www.inexbakarad.co.rs
Year Founded: 1999
INXB—(BEL)
Rev.: $596,081
Assets: $948,388
Liabilities: $681,045
Net Worth: $267,342

INEX BAKAR AD

Inex Bakar AD—(Continued)
Earnings: $1,931
Fiscal Year-end: 12/31/23
Grocery Store Operator
N.A.I.C.S.: 445110
Ranko Sekaric (Exec Dir)

INEX BUDUCNOST A.D.
Kralja Aleksandra 20, Pozega, Serbia
Tel.: (381) 31811113
Year Founded: 1946
INBU—(BEL)
Sales Range: Less than $1 Million
Emp.: 10
Grocery Store Operator
N.A.I.C.S.: 445110
Milka Jankovic (Exec Dir)

INEX DIVCIBARE A.D.
Karadordeva 26, Kosjeric, Serbia
Tel.: (381) 31781114
Web Site: http://www.inex.rs
Year Founded: 2003
INXD—(BEL)
Sales Range: Less than $1 Million
Emp.: 1
Grocery Store Operator
N.A.I.C.S.: 445110
Vera Nikolic (Head-Sls-Market-Center)

INEX DRIM AD
Kej Boris Kidric 51, 6330, Struga, North Macedonia
Tel.: (389) 46785800
Web Site: https://www.drim.com.mk
Year Founded: 1977
Home Management Services
N.A.I.C.S.: 721110

INEX LORIS A.D.
Dostitejeva 21, Belgrade, Serbia
Tel.: (381) 11 3286 577
Year Founded: 1947
INLO—(BEL)
Sales Range: Less than $1 Million
Emp.: 5
Grocery Store Operator
N.A.I.C.S.: 445110
Snezana Bogosavljevic-Sokic (Dir)

INEX RADULASKA A.D.
Gucevska bb, 11000, Belgrade, Serbia
Tel.: (381) 11 2651 483
Web Site: http://www.inexradulaska.rs
Year Founded: 1946
Sales Range: Less than $1 Million
Emp.: 2
Office Furniture Mfr
N.A.I.C.S.: 337211

INEX-UZOR A.D.
Vojvode Misica 15, Negotin, Serbia
Tel.: (381) 19542134
Year Founded: 1998
INUZN—(BEL)
Sales Range: $1-9.9 Million
Emp.: 140
Grocery Store Operator
N.A.I.C.S.: 445110
Ivan Mladenovic (Gen Mgr)

INFAC CORPORATION
450 Baekjegobun-ro, Songpa-gu, Seoul, 05641, Korea (South)
Tel.: (82) 234323333
Web Site: http://www.infac.co.kr
Year Founded: 1969
023810—(KRS)
Rev.: $392,888,455
Assets: $315,362,930
Liabilities: $209,773,958
Net Worth: $105,588,972
Earnings: $12,983,572

Emp.: 373
Fiscal Year-end: 12/31/22
Automotive Part Mfr & Whslr
N.A.I.C.S.: 334220
Do Sungwon (Sr Dir)

Subsidiaries:

INFAC Cable (1)
1819 Jingsung-ro, Geumwang-eup, Geumwang, 27624, Choongcheonbuk-go, Korea (South)
Tel.: (82) 43 535 5011
Automobile Cable Mfr
N.A.I.C.S.: 336320

INFAC Corporation - Cheonan Plant (1)
47 2 Industrial Complex 6-gil, Seobuk-gu, Cheonan, Choongcheognam-do, Korea (South)
Tel.: (82) 41 621 6191
Automobile Cable Mfr
N.A.I.C.S.: 336320

INFAC Elecs Co., Ltd. (1)
(65%)
Automobile Antenna Mfr
N.A.I.C.S.: 334220

INFAC Horn Systems Co., Ltd. (1)
7 Yongwon1-gil Sungnam-myun, Dongnam-gu, Cheonan, Choongcheognam-do, Korea (South)
Tel.: (82) 41 553 6262
Automobile Spare Parts Mfr
N.A.I.C.S.: 336390

INFAC India Pvt Ltd. (1)
No 113 Ellaiamman Koil Street, Keel Padappai Village Sriperumbudur Taluk, Kanchipuram, 601 301, India
Automobile Cable Mfr
N.A.I.C.S.: 336320

INFAC North America Inc. (1)
1 INFAC Dr, Campbellsville, KY 42718
Tel.: (270) 789-1040
Automobile Cable Mfr
N.A.I.C.S.: 336320
Brian Bland (Gen Mgr)

INFAI GMBH
Gottfried-Hagen-Str 60-62, 51105, Cologne, Germany
Tel.: (49) 221880443
Web Site: http://www.infai.com
Year Founded: 1989
Sales Range: $10-24.9 Million
Pharmaceutical & Diagnostic Products Mfr
N.A.I.C.S.: 325412
Sitke Aygen (Founder, Pres & Head-R&D)

Subsidiaries:

INFAI France SARL (1)
Eurocentre Tertiaire 50 Avenue d'Alsace, 68025, Colmar, Cedex, France
Tel.: (33) 389204382
Web Site: http://www.infai.fr
Pharmaceutical Products Distr
N.A.I.C.S.: 424210

INFAI TR GmbH (1)
Necatibey Caddesi Balikcioglu ishani No 4/171, Sihhiye Cankaya, Ankara, Turkiye
Tel.: (90) 3122304974
Web Site: http://www.infai.com.tr
Pharmaceutical Products Distr
N.A.I.C.S.: 424210

INFAI UK Ltd (1)
Innovation Centre University Science Park University Road, Heslington, York, YO1 5DG, United Kingdom
Tel.: (44) 1904435228
Web Site: http://www.infai.co.uk
Pharmaceutical Products Distr
N.A.I.C.S.: 424210
Sitke Aygen (Founder)

Infai Ch GmbH (1)
Bahnhofstrasse 29, 9470, Buchs, Switzerland
Tel.: (41) 817556380
Pharmaceutical Products Distr

N.A.I.C.S.: 424210

INFANT BACTERIAL THERAPEUTICS AB
Bryggargatan 10, 111 21, Stockholm, 111 21, Sweden
Tel.: (46) 762193738
Web Site: https://www.ibtherapeutics.com
Year Founded: 2013
IBT.B—(OMX)
Rev.: $7,644
Assets: $34,877,400
Liabilities: $4,584,351
Net Worth: $30,293,050
Earnings: ($12,217,127)
Emp.: 8
Fiscal Year-end: 12/31/23
Pharmaceuticals Product Mfr
N.A.I.C.S.: 325412
Staffan Stromberg (CEO)

INFARCO SA
Travesia de Roncesvalle n 1 Poligono de Olloki, 31699, Navarra, Spain
Tel.: (34) 948 00 50 05
Web Site: http://www.infarco.com
Year Founded: 1964
Pharmaceuticals Product Mfr
N.A.I.C.S.: 325412

Subsidiaries:

Orliman SL (1)
C/ Ausias March No 3 Pol Ind La Pobla L'Eliana Apdo de Correos 49, La Pobla de Vallbona, 46185, Valencia, Spain
Tel.: (34) 962725704
Web Site: http://www.orliman.com
Sales Range: $25-49.9 Million
Emp.: 84
Orthopedic Braces & Supports Mfr
N.A.I.C.S.: 339112
Ignacio Mansergas (Founder)

INFAS HOLDING AG
KurtSchumacherStrabe 24, 53113, Bonn, Germany
Tel.: (49) 22833607239
Web Site: https://www.infas-holding.de
Year Founded: 1959
IFS—(DEU)
Rev.: $54,640,622
Assets: $70,925,966
Liabilities: $59,130,153
Net Worth: $11,795,813
Earnings: ($64,753)
Emp.: 336
Fiscal Year-end: 12/31/23
Social Research Services
N.A.I.C.S.: 541910
Menno Smid (CEO)

INFECTIOUS MEDIA LTD.
3-7 Herbal Hill, London, EC1R 5EJ, United Kingdom
Tel.: (44) 20 7775 5606
Web Site: http://www.infectiousmedia.com
Year Founded: 2008
Sales Range: $10-24.9 Million
Emp.: 70
Digital Marketing Services
N.A.I.C.S.: 541613

INFIBEAM AVENUES LIMITED
28th Floor GIFT Two Building Block No 56 Road-5C Zone-5, GIFT CITY Gandhinagar Taluka and District, Gandhinagar, 382 355, Gujarat, India
Tel.: (91) 7967772200
Web Site: https://www.ia.ooo
539807—(BOM)
Rev.: $177,986,718
Assets: $526,117,683
Liabilities: $122,780,385

INTERNATIONAL PUBLIC

Net Worth: $403,337,298
Earnings: $11,418,225
Emp.: 647
Fiscal Year-end: 03/31/22
Internet & E-commerce Company; Digital Payment Services
N.A.I.C.S.: 518210
Vishal A. Mehta (Mng Dir)

Subsidiaries:

Avenues World FZ-LLC (1)
Building 17 Level 2 Office 253 Opp DIC Metro Station seaside, PO Box 500416, Dubai Internet City, Dubai, United Arab Emirates
Tel.: (971) 45531029
Web Services
N.A.I.C.S.: 518210

DRC Systems India Private Limited (1)
24th Floor GIFT Two Building Block No 56 Road - 5C Zone - 5, GIFT CITY Gandhinagar Taluka & District, Gandhinagar, 382 355, Gujarat, India
Tel.: (91) 7967772222
Web Site: http://www.drcsystems.com
Consultancy Services
N.A.I.C.S.: 541618
Hiten Barchha (Mng Dir)

INFICON HOLDING AG
Hintergasse 15 B, CH-7310, Bad Ragaz, Switzerland
Tel.: (41) 813004980   CH
Web Site: https://www.inficon.com
IFCN—(SWX)
Rev.: $397,801,000
Assets: $305,182,000
Liabilities: $82,296,000
Net Worth: $222,886,000
Earnings: $49,299,000
Emp.: 1,220
Fiscal Year-end: 12/31/20
Vacuum Instruments to Monitor, Analyze & Control Production Processes for Semiconductor Industry
N.A.I.C.S.: 334513
Lukas Winkler (Pres & CEO)

Subsidiaries:

INFICON Aaland Ab. (1)
Godbyvagen 1A, 22100, Mariehamn, Finland (100%)
Tel.: (358) 1817250
Web Site: http://www.inficon.com
Sales Range: $25-49.9 Million
Emp.: 20
General Purpose Machinery Mfr
N.A.I.C.S.: 333998

INFICON Inc. (1)
2 Technology Pl, East Syracuse, NY 13057-9714
Tel.: (315) 434-1100
Sales Range: $50-74.9 Million
Emp.: 250
General Purpose Machinery Mfr
N.A.I.C.S.: 333998

Subsidiary (Domestic):

INFICON EDC, Inc. (2)
9075 Cody St, Overland Park, KS 66214-1731
Tel.: (913) 888-1750
Web Site: http://www.electrodynamics.com
Sales Range: $25-49.9 Million
Emp.: 65
Mfr of Quartz Crystals & Oscillators
N.A.I.C.S.: 334419
Tim Abbott (Pres)

Instrutech, Inc. (2)
1475 S Fordham St, Longmont, CO 80503 (100%)
Tel.: (303) 651-0551
Web Site: https://www.instrutechinc.com
Vacuum Gauges & Control Instrumentation Products Mfr
N.A.I.C.S.: 334412
Jerry Howard (Pres)

Photovac (2)
300 2nd Ave, Waltham, MA 02451

Tel.: (781) 290-0777
Web Site: http://www.photovac.com
Rev.: $1,500,000
Emp.: 13
Analytical Laboratory Instrument Mfr
N.A.I.C.S.: 334516

INFICON InstruTech LLC (1)
1475 S Fordham St, Longmont, CO 80503
Tel.: (303) 651-0551
Vacuum Measurement Device Mfr
N.A.I.C.S.: 334513

INFICON Pte. Ltd. (1)
3A International Business Park Tower B 06-13 ICON IBP, Singapore, 609935, Singapore
Tel.: (65) 68906250
Web Site: http://www.inficon.com
Sales Range: $25-49.9 Million
Emp.: 9
Commercial & Service Industry Machinery Mfr
N.A.I.C.S.: 333310

INFICON S.a.r.l. (1)
7 Av du Quebec, 91140, Villebon-sur-Yvette, France (100%)
Tel.: (33) 160137695
Sales Range: $50-74.9 Million
Emp.: 4
Industrial Machinery & Equipment Whslr
N.A.I.C.S.: 423830

INFIELD MINERALS CORP.
1600 609 Granville Street, Vancouver, V7Y 1C3, BC, Canada
Tel.: (604) 220-4691
Web Site:
 https://www.infieldminerals.com
INFD—(TSXV)
Assets: $1,466,899
Liabilities: $88,514
Net Worth: $1,378,385
Earnings: ($209,785)
Fiscal Year-end: 12/31/23
Gold & Silver Mining
N.A.I.C.S.: 212220
Scott Edwin Ackerman *(Chm)*

INFIFRESH FOODS PVT. LTD.
1st Floor, Uday Mansion, No 86, Koramangala Industrial Layout, Koramangala, Bengaluru,, Karnataka, 560095, India
Tel.: (91) 7406882224
Web Site: https://www.captainfresh.in
Emp.: 100
Fish & Seafood Markets
N.A.I.C.S.: 445250
Utham Gowda *(CEO)*

INFIGEN ENERGY LIMITED
Level 17 56 Pitt Street, Sydney, 2000, NSW, Australia
Tel.: (61) 280319900 AU
Web Site:
 http://www.infigenenergy.com
IFN—(ASX)
Rev.: $187,645,818
Assets: $898,194,074
Liabilities: $488,004,442
Net Worth: $410,189,632
Earnings: $28,755,369
Emp.: 67
Fiscal Year-end: 06/30/19
Renewable Energy Wind Farms Investment Trust
N.A.I.C.S.: 525990
David Richardson *(Sec & Gen Mgr-Corp Governance)*
Subsidiaries:

Aragonne Wind LLC (1)
1837 Muniz Rd, Santa Rosa, NM 88345
Tel.: (575) 472-0826
Power Generation Services
N.A.I.C.S.: 221118

Crescent Ridge LLC (1)
6250 1475 East St, Tiskilwa, IL 61368-9305
Tel.: (815) 646-4312

Emp.: 2
Eletric Power Generation Services
N.A.I.C.S.: 221118
Scott Jensen *(Mgr)*

Infigen Energy RE Limited (1)
Level 22 56 Pitt St, Sydney, 2000, NSW, Australia
Tel.: (61) 280319900
Web Site: http://www.infigenenergy.com
Sales Range: $50-74.9 Million
Emp.: 60
Eletric Power Generation Services
N.A.I.C.S.: 221118

Kumeyaay Wind LLC (1)
40002 Tusil Rd, Boulevard, CA 91905-9748
Tel.: (619) 766-9200
Web Site: http://www.infigen-us.com
Sales Range: $75-99.9 Million
Emp.: 8
Eletric Power Generation Services
N.A.I.C.S.: 221118
Duane Yee *(Gen Mgr)*

Windfarm Seehausen GmbH (1)
Herzog-Heinrich-Strasse 9, 80336, Munich, Germany
Tel.: (49) 441 92540 0
Eletric Power Generation Services
N.A.I.C.S.: 221118

Windpark Eifel GmbH & Co. KG (1)
Herzog Heinrich Str 9, Munich, 80336, Germany
Tel.: (49) 89 38393274
Sales Range: $75-99.9 Million
Emp.: 1
Eletric Power Generation Services
N.A.I.C.S.: 221118

INFIMER LTD.
6 Hashomer St, Avihail, Netanya, 4291000, Israel
Tel.: (972) 737000266
Web Site: https://infimer-ltd.spinframe.com
Year Founded: 2013
INFR.M—(TAE)
Assets: $38,679
Liabilities: $3,396,878
Net Worth: ($3,358,199)
Earnings: ($589,584)
Fiscal Year-end: 12/31/23
Solid Waste Landfill
N.A.I.C.S.: 562212
Batya Many *(CFO)*

INFINEON TECHNOLOGIES AG
Am Campeon 1-15, 85579, Neubiberg, Germany
Tel.: (49) 892340 De
Web Site: https://www.infineon.com
Year Founded: 1999
IFX—(DEU)
Rev.: $17,600,906,540
Assets: $30,691,776,387
Liabilities: $12,297,647,313
Net Worth: $18,394,129,074
Earnings: $3,387,653,788
Emp.: 58,600
Fiscal Year-end: 09/30/23
Semiconductor Mfr
N.A.I.C.S.: 334413
Sven Schneider *(CFO & Member-Mgmt Bd)*
Subsidiaries:

Cypress Semiconductor Corporation (1)
12121 Scripps Summit Dr Ste 300, San Diego, CA 92131
Tel.: (408) 943-2600
Web Site: http://www.cypress.com
Rev.: $2,205,314,000
Assets: $3,556,114,000
Liabilities: $1,455,859,000
Net Worth: $2,100,255,000
Earnings: $40,428,000
Emp.: 5,871
Fiscal Year-end: 12/29/2019

Integrated Circuits, Static RAMs, Programmable Logic, Data Communications Chips, Universal Serial Business Microcontrollers & Timing Chips Mfr
N.A.I.C.S.: 334413
Thurman John Rodgers *(Founder)*

Subsidiary (Non-US):

AgigA Tech (Chengdu) LLC (2)
Room 27-30 8F E1 Tianfu Software Park No 1268 Tianfu Avenue, Chengdu, 610041, China
Tel.: (86) 2885331775
Computer Hardware Accessory Mfr
N.A.I.C.S.: 332510

Subsidiary (Domestic):

AgigA Tech, Inc. (2)
12230 World Trade Dr Ste 200, San Diego, CA 92128
Tel.: (858) 375-4530
Web Site: http://www.agigatech.com
Computer Storage Device Mfr
N.A.I.C.S.: 334112
Jeff Chang *(VP & Gen Mgr)*

Cypress International, LLC (2)
1201 E Abingdon Dr Ste 400, Alexandria, VA 22314
Tel.: (703) 549-5880
Web Site: https://www.cypressintl.com
Business Development Consulting Services
N.A.I.C.S.: 541611
David D Halverson *(Chm & CEO)*

Subsidiary (Non-US):

Cypress Semiconductor (Shanghai) Trading Co., Ltd. (2)
Building 50 No 1387 ZhangDong Road, Capital of Leader Zhangjiang Semiconductor Industry Park, Shanghai, 201203, China
Tel.: (86) 2161622600
Web Site:
 http://www.cypresssemiconductor.com
Sales Range: $25-49.9 Million
Emp.: 200
Semiconductor Mfr & Distr
N.A.I.C.S.: 334413

Cypress Semiconductor AB (2)
Stora Marknadsvagen 15, Taby C Ing S, 183 34, Taby, Sweden
Tel.: (46) 86380100
Web Site: http://www.cypress.com
Sales Range: $1-9.9 Million
Emp.: 1
Semiconductor Mfr & Distr
N.A.I.C.S.: 334413

Cypress Semiconductor GmbH (2)
Pittlerstrasse 47, 63225, Langen, Germany
Tel.: (49) 810620087
Sales Range: $10-24.9 Million
Emp.: 1
Semiconductor Product Mfr
N.A.I.C.S.: 334413

Cypress Semiconductor International (Hong Kong) Limited (2)
Unit 706-707 7/F Bio-Informati No 2 Science Park West Ave, Sha Tin, NT, China (Hong Kong)
Tel.: (852) 24202568
Web Site: http://www.cypress.com
Sales Range: $100-124.9 Million
Emp.: 12
Semiconductor Mfr & Distr
N.A.I.C.S.: 334413

Cypress Semiconductor K.K. Japan (2)
Harmony Tower Bldg 17th Fl 1-3 Nishi-shimbashi 1-chome, 1-32-2 Honcho Nakano-ku, Tokyo, 164 0012, Japan
Tel.: (81) 353711921
Web Site: http://www.cypress.com
Sales Range: $100-124.9 Million
Emp.: 37
Semiconductor Mfr & Distr
N.A.I.C.S.: 334413

Cypress Semiconductor Korea (2)
No 93 Baekhyun-ro, Bundang-gu, Seongnam, 13595, Kyunggi-do, Korea (South)
Tel.: (82) 234600235
Web Site: http://www.cypress.com

Sales Range: $100-124.9 Million
Semiconductor Mfr & Distr
N.A.I.C.S.: 334413

Cypress Semiconductor Limited (2)
Parsonage Road, Takeley, Bishop's Stortford, CM22 6PU, Hertfordshire, United Kingdom
Tel.: (44) 61035099201
Web Site: http://www.cypress.com
Sales Range: $10-24.9 Million
Emp.: 20
Semiconductor Mfr & Distr
N.A.I.C.S.: 334413

Cypress Semiconductor SARL (2)
6 Ave des &es Bat B, ZA de Courtboeuf, Les Ulis, 91952, France
Tel.: (33) 169298894
Web Site: http://www.cypress.com
Sales Range: $10-24.9 Million
Emp.: 3
Semiconductor Mfr & Distr
N.A.I.C.S.: 334413

Cypress Semiconductor Singapore Pte. Ltd. (2)
8 Kallang Sector, Singapore, 349253, Singapore
Tel.: (65) 63511140
Web Site: http://www.cypress.com
Sales Range: $1-9.9 Million
Emp.: 10
Semiconductor Distr
N.A.I.C.S.: 423690

Cypress Semiconductor Technology India Pvt. Ltd. (2)
65/2 Bagmane Tech Park Block C Bagmane Laurel C V Raman Nagar, Bengaluru, 560 093, Karnataka, India
Tel.: (91) 8067073999
Web Site: http://www.cypress.com
Sales Range: $100-124.9 Million
Emp.: 550
Semiconductor Mfr & Distr
N.A.I.C.S.: 334413

Subsidiary (Domestic):

Deca Technologies Inc. (2)
7855 S River Pkwy Ste 205, Tempe, AZ 85284
Tel.: (480) 345-9895
Web Site: https://thinkdeca.com
Sales Range: $10-24.9 Million
Emp.: 8
Semiconductor Product Mfr
N.A.I.C.S.: 334413
Garry Pycroft *(VP-Sls & Mktg)*

Spansion LLC (2)
915 DeGuigne Dr, Sunnyvale, CA 94085
Tel.: (408) 962-2500
Sales Range: $25-49.9 Million
Emp.: 98
Flash Memory For Electronic Devices Mfr
N.A.I.C.S.: 334419

Hitex GmbH (1)
Greschbachstr 12, 76229, Karlsruhe, Germany (100%)
Tel.: (49) 72196280
Web Site: https://www.hitex.com
Software Consulting Services
N.A.I.C.S.: 541512
Jorg Stender *(Mng Dir)*

Subsidiary (Non-US):

Hitex (UK) Limited (2)
Millburn Hill Road University of Warwick Science Park, Coventry, CV4 7HS, United Kingdom
Tel.: (44) 2476692066
Web Site: https://www.hitex.co.uk
Sales Range: $25-49.9 Million
Software Development Services
N.A.I.C.S.: 541511
Michael Beach *(Gen Mgr)*

Representative Office (US):

Hitools Inc. (2)
2070 Business Ctr Dr Ste 210, Irvine, CA 92612
Tel.: (949) 863-0320
Web Site: http://www.hitex.com
Software Tool Distr
N.A.I.C.S.: 423430

INFINEON TECHNOLOGIES AG

Infineon Technologies AG—(Continued)

Infineon Integrated Circuit (Beijing) Co., Ltd. (1)
18/F Tower B Zhao Lin Plaza No 19 Ronghua Middle Road, Beijing Economic-Technological Development Area, Beijing, 100176, China
Tel.: (86) 1087125888
Emp.: 80
Integrated Circuit Board Mfr
N.A.I.C.S.: 334412
Qunxin Lai *(Gen Mgr)*

Infineon Technologies (Advanced Logic) Sdn. Bhd. (1)
Batu Berendam, 75914, Melaka, Malaysia **(100%)**
Tel.: (60) 62325266
Sales Range: $800-899.9 Million
Emp.: 5,000
Mfr of Semiconductors & Related Devices
N.A.I.C.S.: 334413

Infineon Technologies (Integrated Circuit) Sdn. Bhd. (1)
Suite 21.02 21St Fl Menara MPPJ Jln Tengah, 75350, Melaka, Malaysia **(100%)**
Tel.: (60) 3 7955 5855
Mfr of Semiconductors & Related Devices
N.A.I.C.S.: 334413

Infineon Technologies (Kulim) Sdn. Bhd. (1)
Lot 10 & 11 Jalan High-Tech 7 Industrial Zone Phase II, Kulim Hi-Tech Park, 09000, Kulim, Kedah, Malaysia
Tel.: (60) 4278888
Semiconductor Devices Mfr
N.A.I.C.S.: 334413

Infineon Technologies (Malaysia) Sdn Bhd
(100%)
Tel.: (60) 62325266
Web Site: http://www.infineon.com
Semiconductor Test Facility
N.A.I.C.S.: 334515

Infineon Technologies (Wuxi) Co., Ltd. (1)
No 8 Xing Chuang san Lu, Singapore Industrial Park, Wuxi, 214028, Jiangsu, China
Tel.: (86) 51081060300
Electronic Component Mfr & Distr
N.A.I.C.S.: 334419
Peiliang Yu *(Mgr-Quality)*

Infineon Technologies AG - Duisburg (1)
Voelklinger Strasse 2, 40219, Duisburg, Germany
Tel.: (49) 2037298711
Web Site: http://www.infineon.com
Mfr of Semiconductors
N.A.I.C.S.: 334413

Infineon Technologies AG - Warstein (1)
Max Planck Strasse 5, D 59581, Warstein, Germany
Tel.: (49) 29027641148
Web Site: http://www.infineon.com
Sales Range: $25-49.9 Million
Emp.: 100
Mfr of Electronic Components
N.A.I.C.S.: 334419

Infineon Technologies Americas Corp. (1)
640 N McCarthy Blvd, Milpitas, CA 95035 **(100%)**
Tel.: (408) 503-2791
Sales Range: $900-999.9 Million
Emp.: 2,800
Semiconductor Mfr
N.A.I.C.S.: 334413

Subsidiary (Domestic):

Infineon Technologies Industrial Power, Inc. (2)
1050 Rte 22, Lebanon, NJ 08833
Tel.: (908) 236-5600
Electronic Components Distr
N.A.I.C.S.: 423690

Infineon Technologies Asia Pacific Pte. Ltd. (1)
8 Kallang Sector, Singapore, 349282, Singapore
Tel.: (65) 68763070
Web Site: http://www.infineon.com
Sales Range: $400-449.9 Million
Emp.: 2,000
Mfr of Semiconductors
N.A.I.C.S.: 334413

Infineon Technologies Australia Pty. Ltd. (1)
Suite 4 Level 1 29 Railway Road, Blackburn, Melbourne, 3130, VIC, Australia
Tel.: (61) 388780188
Sales Range: $25-49.9 Million
Emp.: 9
Semiconductor Devices Mfr
N.A.I.C.S.: 334413
Mark Walsh *(Mng Dir)*

Infineon Technologies Austria AG (1)
Siemensstrasse 2, 9500, Villach, Austria **(100%)**
Tel.: (43) 517772808
Semiconductor Mfr
N.A.I.C.S.: 334413

Subsidiary (Domestic):

DICE Danube Integrated Circuit Engineering GmbH & Co. KG (2)
Donaufeldstrasse 5, 4040, Linz, Austria
Tel.: (43) 5177715151
Integrated Circuit Board Mfr
N.A.I.C.S.: 334412
Christian Gamsjaeger *(Mgr-Radar Product Dev)*

Infineon Technologies Austria Pensionskasse AG
Siemensstrasse 2, 9500, Villach, Austria
Tel.: (43) 51777
Web Site: http://www.infineon.com
Microchip Mfr
N.A.I.C.S.: 334413

Infineon Technologies Batam P.T. (1)
Lot 317 Jalan Beringin, Muka Kuning Batamindo Industrial Park, Batam, 29433, Indonesia
Tel.: (62) 770612103
Semiconductor Devices Mfr
N.A.I.C.S.: 334413

Infineon Technologies Bipolar GmbH & Co. KG (1)
Max-Planck-Strasse 5, 59581, Warstein, Germany
Tel.: (49) 290298990
Web Site: https://www.ifbip-shop.com
Sales Range: $550-599.9 Million
Emp.: 600
Electric Power Generation & Distribution Services
N.A.I.C.S.: 221118
Martin Obertrifter *(CFO)*

Subsidiary (Domestic):

Infineon Technologies Bipolar Verwaltungs GmbH (2)
Max-Planck-Str 5, 59581, Warstein, 59581, Germany
Tel.: (49) 29027640
Semiconductor Devices Mfr
N.A.I.C.S.: 334413

Infineon Technologies Cegled Kft. (1)
Ipartelepi Ut 3, 2760, Cegled, Hungary
Tel.: (36) 53510710
Web Site: http://www.infineon.com
Electronic Components Mfr
N.A.I.C.S.: 334419

Infineon Technologies Center of Competence (Shanghai) Co., Ltd. (1)
No 4 Lane 55 Chuanhe Road Zhang Jiang Hi-Tech Park, Pudong, Shanghai, 201203, China
Tel.: (86) 2161019000
Electric Equipment Mfr
N.A.I.C.S.: 335999

Infineon Technologies China Co., Ltd. (1)
Room 4108 41F WanDa Center No 96 Linjiang Avenue, Wuchang District, Wuhan, 430060, Hubie, China
Tel.: (86) 4001200951

Electronic Components Distr
N.A.I.C.S.: 423690

Infineon Technologies Dresden GmbH & Co. KG (1)
Konigsbrucker Strasse 180, 01099, Dresden, Germany **(100%)**
Tel.: (49) 892304
Web Site: http://www.infineon.com
Researcher, Developer & Producer of Microelectronic Chips
N.A.I.C.S.: 334413

Infineon Technologies Fabrico de Semicondutores (Portugal) S.A. (1)
Avenida Primeiro de Maio 801, Vila do Conde, Portugal **(100%)**
Tel.: (351) 252246000
Sales Range: $200-249.9 Million
Emp.: 580
Semiconductor Mfr
N.A.I.C.S.: 334413
Thomas Lorenz *(Dir-Sls)*

Infineon Technologies France S.A.S. (1)
Burolines 2 2ter Rue Marcel Doret, 93527, Blagnac, France
Tel.: (33) 148097200
Web Site: http://www.infineon.com
Semiconductor Mfr
N.A.I.C.S.: 334413

Infineon Technologies Holding B.V (1)
WTC Rotterdam Beursplein 37, 3011 AA, Rotterdam, Netherlands
Tel.: (31) 102176800
Rev.: $18,003,090,851
Assets: $31,393,089,749
Liabilities: $12,578,651,067
Net Worth: $18,814,438,682
Earnings: $3,462,854,620
Emp.: 58,590
Fiscal Year-end: 12/31/2023
Mfr of Semiconductors
N.A.I.C.S.: 334413

Infineon Technologies Hong Kong Ltd. (1)
Units 803-810 8th Floor Building 16W Phase Three, Hong Kong Science Park Pak Shek Kok, Hong Kong, China (Hong Kong) **(100%)**
Tel.: (852) 28320500
Web Site: http://www.infineon.com
Sales Range: $25-49.9 Million
Emp.: 30
Mfr of Semiconductors
N.A.I.C.S.: 334413

Infineon Technologies IT-Services GmbH (1)
Lakeside B05, 9020, Klagenfurt, Austria
Tel.: (43) 517770
Information Technology Consulting Services
N.A.I.C.S.: 541512

Infineon Technologies Iberia S.L.U. (1)
Avenida de Burgos 17 - 5th Floor Left Complejo Triada Edif A, Madrid, Spain
Tel.: (34) 917682226
Web Site: http://www.infineon.com
Sales Range: $25-49.9 Million
Emp.: 12
Electronic Components Distr
N.A.I.C.S.: 423690

Infineon Technologies India Pvt. Ltd. (1)
11 Mahatma Gandhi Road, Whitefield, Bengaluru, 560008, India
Tel.: (91) 8025261102
Web Site: http://www.infineon.com
Mfr of Semiconductors
N.A.I.C.S.: 334413

Infineon Technologies Investment B.V. (1)
Westblaak 32, Rotterdam, 3012 KM, Netherlands
Tel.: (31) 102176811
Web Site: http://www.infineon.com
Sales Range: $50-74.9 Million
Emp.: 5
Investment Management Service
N.A.I.C.S.: 523999

Infineon Technologies Ireland Ltd. (1)

INTERNATIONAL PUBLIC

13-14 New Market The Liberties, New St, Dublin, D08 KD91, Ireland **(100%)**
Tel.: (353) 17999500
Web Site: http://www.infineon.com
Sales Range: $25-49.9 Million
Emp.: 35
Mfr of Semiconductors
N.A.I.C.S.: 334413

Infineon Technologies Italia S.r.l (1)
48 Via dei Valtorta, 20128, Milan, Italy
Tel.: (39) 02252041
Web Site: http://www.infineon.com
Sales Range: $25-49.9 Million
Emp.: 20
Semiconductors Sales
N.A.I.C.S.: 334413

Infineon Technologies Japan K.K. (1)
NBF Shibuya Garden Front 3-25-18 Shibuya, Shibuya-ku, Tokyo, 141 0032, Japan **(100%)**
Tel.: (81) 357457100
Web Site: http://www.infineon.com
Sales Range: $50-74.9 Million
Emp.: 200
Mfr of Semiconductors
N.A.I.C.S.: 334413

Infineon Technologies Korea Co., Ltd. (1)
1st 11-13th FL Glass Tower 534 Teheran-ro, Gangnam-gu, Seoul, 135-910, Korea (South)
Tel.: (82) 234600900
Web Site: http://www.infineon.com
Sales Range: $50-74.9 Million
Emp.: 100
Semiconductors Sales
N.A.I.C.S.: 334413
Nadine Kim *(Sls Mgr)*

Infineon Technologies Nordic A/S (1)
Horkaer 16, 2730, Herlev, Denmark **(100%)**
Tel.: (45) 44507700
Web Site: http://www.infineon.com
Sales Range: $25-49.9 Million
Emp.: 100
Mfr of Semiconductors
N.A.I.C.S.: 334413

Infineon Technologies Nordic AB (1)
Isafjordsgaten 30B, Box 1297, 164 29, Kista, Stockholm, Sweden
Tel.: (46) 87575000
Web Site: https://www.infineon.com
Sales Range: $25-49.9 Million
Emp.: 33
Semiconductor Device Distr
N.A.I.C.S.: 423690

Infineon Technologies Nordic OY (1)
Stella Luna Park/Stella Luna Lars Sonckin Kaari 14, PO Box 276, 02600, Espoo, Finland **(100%)**
Tel.: (358) 106808400
Web Site: http://www.infineon.com
Sales Range: $25-49.9 Million
Emp.: 7
Mfr of Semiconductors
N.A.I.C.S.: 334413

Infineon Technologies RUS LLC (1)
Leninskiy Prospect 113/1, 117198, Moscow, Russia
Tel.: (7) 495 9565195
Sales Range: $50-74.9 Million
Emp.: 3
Semiconductor Device Distr
N.A.I.C.S.: 423690
Ilia Zverev *(Gen Dir)*

Infineon Technologies Romania & Co. Societate in Comandita (1)
Bd Dimitrie Pompeiu 6 Novo Parc complex, building A 1st floor B C D G F & 1st floor Sector 2, 020337, Bucharest, Romania
Tel.: (40) 318607701
Electronic Component Mfr & Distr
N.A.I.C.S.: 334419

Infineon Technologies SC 300 GmbH & Co. KG (1)
Konigsbrucker Strasse 150, 1099, Dresden, Germany **(100%)**
Tel.: (49) 3518861557
Web Site: http://www.infineon.com

Sales Range: $400-449.9 Million
Emp.: 1,100
Mfr of Semiconductors & Related Devices
N.A.I.C.S.: 334413

Infineon Technologies South America Ltda. (1)
250 Rua Elvira Ferraz - Suite 104, Vila Olimpia, Sao Paulo, 04552-040, Brazil (100%)
Tel.: (55) 1130469230
Web Site: http://www.infineon.com
Sales Range: $25-49.9 Million
Emp.: 8
Mfr of Semiconductors
N.A.I.C.S.: 334413

Infineon Technologies Sweden AB (1)
Isafjordsgatan 30 B, 164 29, Kista, Sweden
Tel.: (46) 87575000
Web Site: http://www.infineon.com
Sales Range: $25-49.9 Million
Emp.: 25
Semiconductors Sales
N.A.I.C.S.: 334413

Infineon Technologies Taiwan Company Ltd. (1)
17F No 335 Ruiguang Rd, Neihu Dist, Taipei, 115, Taiwan (100%)
Tel.: (886) 226557500
Web Site: http://www.infineon.com
Sales Range: $25-49.9 Million
Emp.: 86
Mfr of Semiconductors
N.A.I.C.S.: 334413

Infineon Technologies UK Ltd. (1)
Infineon House Great Western Court Hunts Ground Road, Stoke Gifford, BS34 8HP, United Kingdom (100%)
Tel.: (44) 1179528823
Web Site: http://www.infineon.co.uk
Sales Range: $25-49.9 Million
Emp.: 100
Semiconductors Research & Development & Sales
N.A.I.C.S.: 334413

Kompetenzzentrum Automobil- und Industrieelektronik GmbH (1)
Technologiepark Villach Europastrasse 8, 9524, Villach, Austria
Tel.: (43) 5177719900
Web Site: https://www.k-ai.at
Automotive & Industrial Component Research Services
N.A.I.C.S.: 541715

Molstanda Vermietungsgesellschaft mbH (1)
Tel.: (49) 8923426655
Semiconductor Device Rental Services
N.A.I.C.S.: 532490

INFINITE COMPUTER SOLUTIONS (INDIA) LTD.
157 EPIP Zone Phase 2 Kundalahalli Whitefield, Bengaluru, 560066, India
Tel.: (91) 8041930000
Web Site: http://www.infinite.com
Rev.: $435,716,877
Assets: $299,023,055
Liabilities: $145,799,378
Net Worth: $153,223,677
Earnings: $17,380,364
Emp.: 2,271
Fiscal Year-end: 03/31/18
Application Management Outsourcing, Packaged Application Services, Independent Validation & Verification, Product Development & Support, Managed Platform & Product Engineering Services
N.A.I.C.S.: 541512
Sanjay Govil (Founder & Chm)

Subsidiaries:

Infinite Computer Solutions Inc. (1)
15201 Diamondback Dr Ste 125, Rockville, MD 20850
Tel.: (301) 355-7722
Sales Range: $25-49.9 Million
Emp.: 15

Infrastructure Management Software Development Services
N.A.I.C.S.: 541511

Subsidiary (Non-US):

India Comnet International Pvt Ltd (2)
Unit 21 Block 3 SDF Bldg Phase 1 MEPZ, Chennai, 600045, Tamil Nadu, India
Tel.: (91) 4422621232
Web Site: http://www.indiacomnet.com
Infrastructure Software Development Services
N.A.I.C.S.: 541511

Infinite Computer Solutions Ltd (1)
Northumberland House 11 The Pavement Popes Lane, Ealing, London, W5 4NG, United Kingdom
Tel.: (44) 20 8832 7455
Sales Range: $25-49.9 Million
Emp.: 10
Infrastructure Management Software Development Services
N.A.I.C.S.: 541511

Infinite Computer Solutions Pte. Ltd. (1)
20 Changi South Avenue 2, Singapore, 486547, Singapore
Tel.: (65) 62211611
Web Site: http://www.infinite.com
Sales Range: $25-49.9 Million
Emp.: 280
Infrastructure Management Software Development Services
N.A.I.C.S.: 541511
Ritesh Ailawadi (Mgr-HR & Fin)

Infinite Data Systems Pvt. Ltd. (1)
157 2nd Floor EPIP Zone Phase II Kundalahalli, Whitefield, Bengaluru, 560066, Karnataka, India
Tel.: (91) 8041930000
Infrastructure Software Development Services
N.A.I.C.S.: 541511

Infinite Infosoft Services Pvt. Ltd. (1)
Building No 6 Tower C 12th Floor Sector 24 & 25A, DLF Cyber City Phase III, Gurgaon, 122002, India
Tel.: (91) 1244785633
Infrastructure Management Software Development Services
N.A.I.C.S.: 541511

INFINITI SOLUTIONS LTD.
122 Middle Rd Midlink Plaza 04 01, 06-09 Honeywell Building, Singapore, 188973, Singapore
Tel.: (65) 63360082
Web Site:
http://www.infinitisolutions.com
Year Founded: 2001
Sales Range: $50-74.9 Million
Emp.: 1,570
Semiconductor Test & Assembly Services
N.A.I.C.S.: 334413
Inderjit Singh (Pres & CEO)

Subsidiaries:

Infiniti Solutions USA (1)
3910 N 1st St, San Jose, CA 95134
Tel.: (408) 923-7300
Electronic Circuits Mfr
N.A.I.C.S.: 334416

INFINITT BRASIL IMPORTADORA
Av Paulista 807 cj 2315, Bela Vista, Sao Paulo, Brazil
Tel.: (55) 1132510565   BR
Health Care Srvices
N.A.I.C.S.: 621610

INFINITT HEALTHCARE CO., LTD.
12F Daerung Post Tower III 27 Digital-ro 34 Street, Guro-gu, Seoul, 152-746, Korea (South)
Tel.: (82) 221941600

Web Site: https://www.infinitt.com
Year Founded: 2002
071200—(KRS)
Rev.: $67,715,620
Assets: $114,672,708
Liabilities: $26,592,669
Net Worth: $88,080,040
Earnings: $100,913
Emp.: 313
Fiscal Year-end: 12/31/22
Medical Imaging & Information Technology Services
N.A.I.C.S.: 519290
Choi Jae Min (Deputy Head-Dept)

Subsidiaries:

INFINITT China (1)
Room 709 Huaxingkejidasha No 477 Wensan Road, Xihu Dist, Hangzhou, 310013, China
Tel.: (86) 21 5489 2670
Web Site: http://www.infinitt.net
Sales Range: $10-24.9 Million
Emp.: 40
Health Care Srvices
N.A.I.C.S.: 621999

INFINITT Europe GmbH (1)
Gaugrafenstr 34, 60489, Frankfurt am Main, Germany
Tel.: (49) 69583000200
Web Site: https://infinitteurope.com
Healthcare Software Consulting Services
N.A.I.C.S.: 541512

INFINITT Japan Co., Ltd. (1)
6th floor Uenonomori First Building 2-14-27 Ueno, Taito-ku, Tokyo, 110-0005, Japan
Tel.: (81) 368060279
Web Site: http://www.infinitt.co.jp
Medical Equipment Mfr & Computer Software Distr
N.A.I.C.S.: 334510
Xiao Zhao (CEO)

INFINITT North America Inc. (1)
Hillcrest Professional Plz 755 Memorial Pkwy Ste 304, Phillipsburg, NJ 08865
Tel.: (908) 387-6960
Web Site: http://www.infinittna.com
Sales Range: $25-49.9 Million
Emp.: 35
Healthcare Information Technology Services
N.A.I.C.S.: 519290
David O. Smarro (Pres & CEO)

INFINITT MEA DMCC
Unit No 804 JBC 4 Tower Cluster N Jumeirah Lake Towers, Dubai, United Arab Emirates
Tel.: (971) 44356977   AE
Health Care Srvices
N.A.I.C.S.: 621610

INFINITT SE ASIA SDN BHD
A1-3A-3A and A1-3A-6 Arcoris No 10 Jalan Kiara, Mont Kiara, 50480, Kuala Lumpur, Malaysia
Tel.: (60) 332777180   MY
Health Care Srvices
N.A.I.C.S.: 621610

INFINITT UK LTD.
Indigo 10 Mulberry Business Park Fishponds Road, Wokingham, RG41 2GY, Berkshire, United Kingdom
Tel.: (44) 1189778569   UK
Health Care Srvices
N.A.I.C.S.: 621610

INFINITUM COPPER CORP.
Tel.: (403) 265-8820   Ca
Year Founded: 2003
BSH—(TSXV)
Rev.: $42,113
Assets: $249,430
Liabilities: $1,489,179
Net Worth: ($1,239,749)
Earnings: ($905,514)
Fiscal Year-end: 12/31/19
Oil & Gas Exploration Services

N.A.I.C.S.: 211120
Peter Ho (CEO)

INFINITY (INTL) TRAVEL HOLDINGS INC.
Room 16 10/F New Commerce Centre No 19 On Sum Street Shatin, New Territories, Hong Kong, China (Hong Kong)
Tel.: (852) 3955 0197   NV
Web Site:
http://www.infinitytravelholdings.com
Year Founded: 2014
Emp.: 3
Tour Operator
N.A.I.C.S.: 561520
Ta-Chih Kuo (Pres & Treas)

INFINITY BIO-ENERGY LTD.
Rua Joaquim Floriano 413, 04534-011, Sao Paulo, Brazil
Tel.: (55) 1125259900   BM
Web Site:
http://www.infinitybio.com.br
Year Founded: 2006
Sales Range: $125-149.9 Million
Emp.: 3,861
Ethanol & Other Biofuels Producer & Distr
N.A.I.C.S.: 325414
Sergio Thompon-Flores (CEO)

Subsidiaries:

Alcana Destilaria de Alcool de Nanuque S/A (1)
Estr Nanuque Pedro Canario S N Km 09, Governador Valadares, Brazil
Tel.: (55) 3336219200
Sugarcane Products Mfr
N.A.I.C.S.: 111930

Cridasa - Cristal Destilaria Autonoma de Alcool S/A (1)
Est Cristal - Mountain s n, Vitoria, Espirito Santo, Brazil
Tel.: (55) 2737645111
Sugarcane Products Mfr
N.A.I.C.S.: 111930

Disa Destilaria Itaunas S/A (1)
Br 101 Km 39 Conceicao da Barra, Vitoria, 29960 000, Espirito Santo, Brazil
Tel.: (55) 2737620100
Sugar Products Mfr
N.A.I.C.S.: 311313

INFINITY DEVELOPMENT HOLDINGS COMPANY LIMITED
Rua de Pequim No 202A-246 Macau Finance Centre 16 Andar A-D, Macau, China (Macau)
Tel.: (853) 28701717   Ky
Web Site:
http://www.infinitydevelopment.com
Year Founded: 1987
0640—(HKG)
Rev.: $70,160,993
Assets: $76,331,396
Liabilities: $21,852,952
Net Worth: $54,478,443
Earnings: $7,225,202
Emp.: 333
Fiscal Year-end: 09/30/20
Adhesive Mfr
N.A.I.C.S.: 325520
Un Ieong (Chm & CEO)

INFINITY EQUITY
3 Azrieli Center Triangle Tower 42nd Floor, Tel Aviv, 67023, Israel
Tel.: (972) 3 607 5456
Web Site: http://www.infinity-equity.com
Year Founded: 1993
Emp.: 80
Privater Equity Firm
N.A.I.C.S.: 523999

INFINITY EQUITY

Infinity Equity—(Continued)

Amir Gal-Or *(Co-Founder & Mng Partner)*

INFINITY HOLDING GROUP
7th Floor 42 Hotel Street CyberCity, 72201, Ebene, Mauritius
Tel.: (230) 404 3900
Web Site:
https://www.infinitygroup.mu
Emp.: 100
Holding Company
N.A.I.C.S.: 551112

INFINITY LITHIUM CORPORATION LIMITED
Unit 32 Level 3 22 Railway Road, Subiaco, 6008, WA, Austria
Tel.: (43) 861465325   AU
Web Site:
https://www.infinitylithium.com
INF—(ASX)
Rev.: $292,756
Assets: $18,244,116
Liabilities: $325,357
Net Worth: $17,918,759
Earnings: ($2,551,998)
Fiscal Year-end: 06/30/23
Metal Mining Services
N.A.I.C.S.: 212290
David Valls *(Executives)*

Subsidiaries:

Extremadura Mining S.L.   (1)
Avenida de Espana 18, Caceres, Spain
Tel.: (34) 927208134
Lithium Hydroxide Mfr
N.A.I.C.S.: 325180
David Valls *(Mgr-Technical)*

INFINITY LOGISTICS & TRANSPORT VENTURES LIMITED
Infinity House No 2 Jalan Kasuarina 8/KS07 Bandar Botanic, Selangor, 41200, Klang, Malaysia
Tel.: (60) 333252926   Ky
Web Site: http://www.infinity.com.my
Year Founded: 2003
1442—(HKG)
Rev.: $80,780,366
Assets: $142,400,088
Liabilities: $68,461,254
Net Worth: $73,938,834
Earnings: $4,000,653
Emp.: 908
Fiscal Year-end: 12/31/23
Logistic Services
N.A.I.C.S.: 541614
Chan Kong Yew *(Chm & CEO)*

Subsidiaries:

Infinity Bulk Logistics Sdn. Bhd.   (1)
Lot 54 Jalan Sungai Pinang 5/7/KS11 Taman Perindustrian Pulau Indah 2, Taman Perindustrian Pulau Indah 2 Pelabuhan Klang, 42920, Port Klang, Selangor, Malaysia
Tel.: (60) 331012926
Web Site: https://www.iblflexitank.com
Logistic Services
N.A.I.C.S.: 541614

INFINITY SDC LIMITED
22a St James Square, London, SW1Y 4JH, United Kingdom
Tel.: (44) 20 7661 8190
Web Site: http://www.infinitysdc.com
Year Founded: 2006
Sales Range: $25-49.9 Million
Emp.: 67
Computer Data Storage Services
N.A.I.C.S.: 518210
Stuart Sutton *(CEO)*

INFINITY TRUST MORTGAGE BANK PLC

No 11 Kaura Namoda StreetOff Faskari Crescent Area 3, Garki, Abuja, Nigeria
Tel.: (234) 9087121713
Web Site:
https://www.infinitytrustbank.com
Year Founded: 2002
INFINITY—(NIGE)
Rev.: $1,551,805
Assets: $12,416,041
Liabilities: $7,119,052
Net Worth: $5,296,989
Earnings: $468,899
Emp.: 93
Fiscal Year-end: 12/31/22
Investment Management Service
N.A.I.C.S.: 525990
Okwa Ene Iyana *(Chm)*

INFITECH VENTURES INC.
20 Lyall Avenue, Toronto, M4E 1V9, ON, Canada
Tel.: (416) 691-4068   NV
Web Site:
http://www.infitechventures.com
Year Founded: 2000
Assets: $511
Liabilities: $391,828
Net Worth: ($391,317)
Earnings: ($95,162)
Emp.: 1
Fiscal Year-end: 07/31/18
Wax & Resin Compounds for Clean Technology
N.A.I.C.S.: 325211
Paul G. Daly *(Pres, CEO, Treas & Sec)*

INFLAME APPLIANCES LTD.
Khasra no 40/ 14-15-16-17/1 Block-Raipur Rani NH-73, Panchkula, 134202, Haryana, India
Tel.: (91) 1795246820
Web Site:
https://www.inflameindia.com
541083—(BOM)
Rev.: $5,422,030
Assets: $5,317,302
Liabilities: $3,364,486
Net Worth: $1,952,817
Earnings: ($224,823)
Emp.: 119
Fiscal Year-end: 03/31/22
Gas Stove Mfr
N.A.I.C.S.: 335220
Aditya Kaushik *(Chm & Mng Dir)*

INFLARX N.V.
Winzerlaer Str 2, 07745, Jena, Germany
Tel.: (49) 3641508180   NL
Web Site: https://www.inflarx.de
Year Founded: 2017
IFRX—(NASDAQ)
Rev.: $68,087
Assets: $129,730,792
Liabilities: $19,023,119
Net Worth: $110,707,673
Earnings: ($46,047,409)
Emp.: 66
Fiscal Year-end: 12/31/23
Biopharmaceutical Research & Development Services
N.A.I.C.S.: 541714
Nicolas Fulpius *(Co-Founder)*

Subsidiaries:

InflaRx GmbH   (1)
Winzerlaer Str 2, 07745, Jena, Germany
Tel.: (49) 3641508180
Web Site: https://www.inflarx.de
Rev.: $248,180
Assets: $31,576,585
Liabilities: $59,057,136
Net Worth: ($27,480,551)
Earnings: ($9,562,406)
Emp.: 17
Fiscal Year-end: 12/31/2016

Pharmaceuticals Product Mfr
N.A.I.C.S.: 325412
Nicolas Fulpius *(Co-Founder & Chm)*

INFLECTION MANAGEMENT CORPORATION LIMITED
3 Afentrikas Street Office 102-3, 6018, Larnaca, Cyprus
Tel.: (357) 2 425 4554
Investment Holding Company
N.A.I.C.S.: 551112
Christina Theodosiadou *(Dir)*

Subsidiaries:

Superglass Insulation Ltd.   (1)
Thistle Industrial Estate Kerse Road, Stirling, FK7 7QQ, Scotland, United Kingdom
Tel.: (44) 1786 451 170
Web Site: http://www.superglass.co.uk
Sales Range: $25-49.9 Million
Thermal & Acoustic Mineral Wool Products Mfr
N.A.I.C.S.: 327993
Mark Atherton *(Chief Production Officer & Head-Ops)*

INFLECTION RESOURCES LTD.
12101130 West Pender Street Vancouver BC V6E 4A4, Vancouver, V6E 4A4, BC, Canada
Tel.: (604) 681-9100
Web Site:
https://www.inflectionresources.com
AUCUF—(OTCQB)
Rev.: $20,892
Assets: $9,113,677
Liabilities: $865,907
Net Worth: $8,247,771
Earnings: ($1,081,159)
Emp.: 10
Fiscal Year-end: 09/30/23
Mineral Exploration Services
N.A.I.C.S.: 213115
Wendell Zerb *(Chm)*

INFLEXION PRIVATE EQUITY PARTNERS LLP
47 Queen Anne Street, London, W1G 9JG, United Kingdom
Tel.: (44) 2074879888   UK
Web Site: http://www.inflexion.com
Year Founded: 1999
Private Equity
N.A.I.C.S.: 523940
John Hartz *(Mng Partner)*

Subsidiaries:

ANS Group Limited   (1)
Synergy House Manchester Science Park, Manchester, M15 6SY, United Kingdom
Tel.: (44) 161 227 1002
Web Site: http://www.ansgroup.co.uk
Sales Range: $50-74.9 Million
Emp.: 270
Computer System Design Services
N.A.I.C.S.: 541512
Scott Fletcher *(Founder & Chm)*

ATCORE Technology Ltd.   (1)
353 Buckingham Avenue, Slough, SL1 4PF, Berks, United Kingdom
Tel.: (44) 1753804000
Web Site: http://www.atcoretec.com
Travel Reservation & e-Commerce Services
N.A.I.C.S.: 518210
Mike Wright *(Comml Dir)*

Asperity Employee Benefits Ltd.   (1)
90 Westbourne Grove, London, W2 5RT, United Kingdom
Tel.: (44) 20 7229 0349
Web Site: http://www.asperity.co.uk
Sales Range: $125-149.9 Million
Emp.: 80
Employee Benefit Administration Services
N.A.I.C.S.: 561499

Subsidiary (US):

Asperity Employee Benefits Inc.   (2)

INTERNATIONAL PUBLIC

8 E 41st St 6th Fl, New York, NY 10017
Tel.: (212) 659-0587
Web Site: http://www.asperity.com
Employee Benefit Administration Services
N.A.I.C.S.: 561499

Subsidiary (Non-US):

Asperity Employee Benefits Ltd.   (2)
27 Northumberland Road Ballsbridge, Dublin, Ireland
Tel.: (353) 12542881
Web Site: http://www.asperity.ie
Employee Benefit Administration Services
N.A.I.C.S.: 561499

Asperity Employee Benefits Pty. Ltd.   (2)
Suite 301 Level 3 15 Lime Street, Sydney, 2000, NSW, Australia
Tel.: (61) 2 9112 0100
Web Site: http://www.rewardgateway.com
Emp.: 200
Employee Benefit Administration Services
N.A.I.C.S.: 561499
Tracy Mellor *(Mng Dir)*

Avantus Aerospace Limited   (1)
7A/B Millington Road, Hayes, UB3 4AZ, Mddx, United Kingdom
Tel.: (44) 208 571 0055
Web Site: https://avantusaerospace.com
Holding Company; Aerospace Shim Mfr
N.A.I.C.S.: 551112
Brian Williams *(CEO)*

Subsidiary (Domestic):

Attewell Limited   (2)
7A/B Millington Road, Hayes, UB3 4AZ, Middlesex, United Kingdom
Tel.: (44) 2085710055
Web Site: http://www.shimtechgroup.com
Laminated Sheet Materials, Shims & Fabricated Metal Product Mfr
N.A.I.C.S.: 332999

Subsidiary (US):

Bolsan Company, Inc.   (2)
163 Linnwood Rd, Eighty Four, PA 15330
Tel.: (724) 225-0446
Web Site: http://www.shimtechgroup.com
Laminated Sheet Materials, Shims & Fabricated Metal Product Mfr
N.A.I.C.S.: 332999

California Screw Products Corp.   (2)
14957 Gwenchris Ct, Paramount, CA 90723
Tel.: (562) 633-6626
Web Site: http://www.calscrew.net
Sales Range: $1-9.9 Million
Emp.: 41
Hardware Mfr
N.A.I.C.S.: 332510
Larry Valeriano *(Pres & CEO)*

Fastener Innovation Technology, Inc.   (2)
19300 S Susana Rd, Compton, CA 90221
Tel.: (310) 538-1111
Web Site: http://www.fitfastener.com
Aerospace Fastener Mfr
N.A.I.C.S.: 339993
Anna Stayer *(Exec VP)*

Fastener Technology Corp.   (2)
7415 Fulton Ave, North Hollywood, CA 91605
Tel.: (818) 764-6467
Web Site: http://www.ftc-usa.com
Fasteners, Buttons, Needles, And Pins
N.A.I.C.S.: 339993
Tom Boat *(CFO)*

Lamsco West, Inc.   (2)
29101 The Old Rd, Santa Clarita, CA 91355
Tel.: (661) 295-8620
Web Site: http://www.shimtechgroup.com
Laminated Plastics Plate Sheet & Shape Mfr
N.A.I.C.S.: 326130

Subsidiary (Domestic):

Pillar Seals & Gaskets Limited   (2)
15 & 16 Hazelwood Close, Worthing, BN14 8NP, West Sussex, United Kingdom
Tel.: (44) 1903207101
Web Site: http://www.shimtechgroup.com
Gasket Packing & Sealing Device Mfr

AND PRIVATE COMPANIES

N.A.I.C.S.: 339991

DWF Group Plc (1)
1 Scott Place 2 Hardman Street, Manchester, M3 3AA, United Kingdom
Tel.: (44) 3333202220
Web Site: http://dwfgroup.com
Law firm
N.A.I.C.S.: 541110
Graham Dickinson *(Partner)*

Subsidiary (Domestic):

15Squared Limited (2)
150 Minories, London, EC3N 1LS, United Kingdom
Tel.: (44) 8451300112
Web Site: http://www.claimbase.com
Software Development Services
N.A.I.C.S.: 541511
Oszkar Olah *(CTO)*

DWF Pension Trustees Limited (2)
5 Saint Paul's Square Old Hall Street, Liverpool, L3 9AE, Merseyside, United Kingdom
Tel.: (44) 1519073000
Web Site: http://www.dwf.law
Pension Fund Management Services
N.A.I.C.S.: 523940
Andrew Leaitherland *(Mgr)*

Subsidiary (Non-US):

Whitelaw Twining Law Corp. (2)
2400 - 200 Granville St, Vancouver, V6C 1S4, BC, Canada
Tel.: (604) 682-5466
Web Site: http://www.whitelawtwining.com
Emp.: 21
Law firm
N.A.I.C.S.: 541110
Eva M. Christopher *(Atty)*

FDM Group Ltd. (1)
Cottons Centre Cottons Lane, London, SE1 2QG, London, United Kingdom
Tel.: (44) 2030568240
Web Site: http://www.fdmgroup.com
Sales Range: $50-74.9 Million
IT Services
N.A.I.C.S.: 541512
Rod Flavell *(CEO)*

Subsidiary (Non-US):

FDM Group GmbH (2)
Beethovenstrasse 4, 60325, Frankfurt am Main, Germany
Tel.: (49) 697560050
IT Services
N.A.I.C.S.: 541512

Subsidiary (US):

FDM Group Inc. (2)
14 Wall St, New York, NY 10005
Tel.: (347) 329-3255
Web Site: http://www.fdminc.com
IT Services
N.A.I.C.S.: 541512
Matthew Jones *(Acct Mgr)*

Subsidiary (Non-US):

FDM Group SA (2)
283 Route D Arlon, L 8011, Strassen, Luxembourg
Tel.: (352) 26 31 441
IT Services
N.A.I.C.S.: 541512

Lintbells Limited (1)
West Barn Fairclough Hall Farm Halls Green, Weston, SG4 7DP, United Kingdom
Tel.: (44) 1462416866
Web Site: https://www.lintbells.com
Pet Supplements & Food Mfr
N.A.I.C.S.: 459910
Fiona Hope *(CEO)*

Subsidiary (US):

Handicapped Pets, Inc. (2)
105 Route 101A Ste 18, Amherst, NH 03031
Tel.: (603) 577-8854
Web Site: https://www.handicappedpets.com
Pet & Pet Supplies Stores
N.A.I.C.S.: 459910
Mark C. Robinson *(Founder & CEO)*

Mycom Group Ltd. (1)
4th Floor Thames Central, 90 Hatfield Road, Slough, SL1 1QE, United Kingdom
Tel.: (44) 1753 213740
Web Site: http://www.mycom-int.com
Communication Service
N.A.I.C.S.: 517112
Siamak Sarbaz *(Founder, Chm & CEO)*

Subsidiary (US):

Mycom North America Inc (2)
1080 Holcomb Bridge Rd Bldg 200 Ste 350, Roswell, GA 30076
Tel.: (770) 776-0000
Web Site: http://www.mycom-networks.com
Computer System Design Services
N.A.I.C.S.: 541512
David Winters *(CFO)*

Branch (Domestic):

Mycom North America Inc. - Orlando (3)
1629 Prime Ct 800, Orlando, FL 32809
Tel.: (407) 470-1077
Computer System Design Services
N.A.I.C.S.: 541512

Subsidiary (Domestic):

Mycom Software (2)
4th Floor Thames Central, 90 Hatfield Road, Slough, SL1 1QE, United Kingdom
Tel.: (44) 1753 213 740
Web Site: http://www.mycom-osi.com
Software Publisher
N.A.I.C.S.: 513210
Payam Taaghol *(CEO)*

Subsidiary (Non-US):

OSI India Private Limited (3)
MM Tower Plot No 8 & 9 Udyog Vihar Phase IV, Gurgaon, 122016, India
Tel.: (91) 1244758600
Management Software Developer & Publisher
N.A.I.C.S.: 513210

OSI Singapore Private Limited (3)
Block 86, Marine Parade Central, 04-303, Singapore, Singapore
Tel.: (65) 63424600
Management Software Developer & Publisher
N.A.I.C.S.: 513210
Nicholas Brown *(VP-Asia)*

Subsidiary (US):

Objective Systems Integrators, Inc. (3)
35 Iron Point Circle Ste 250, Folsom, CA 95630
Tel.: (946) 467-1500
Web Site: http://www.osi.com
Emp.: 100
Management Software Developer & Publisher
N.A.I.C.S.: 513210
Bob Franzetta *(CFO)*

Rosemont Pharmaceuticals Ltd. (1)
Rosemont House Yorkdale Industrial Park, Braithwaite Street, Leeds, LS11 9XE, United Kingdom
Tel.: (44) 1132441400
Web Site: http://www.rosemontpharma.com
Emp.: 200
Liquid Pharmaceutical Products Mfr
N.A.I.C.S.: 325412
Howard Taylor *(CEO)*

SteriPack Group Ltd. (1)
National Science Park Dublin Road, Mullingar, Westmeath, Ireland
Tel.: (353) 57 9331888
Web Site: http://www.steripackgroup.com
Sales Range: $50-74.9 Million
Emp.: 250
Contract Products Mfr
N.A.I.C.S.: 339999
Gary Leonard *(Grp Dir-Technical)*

Subsidiary (US):

HS Design, Inc. (2)
906 Mt Kemle, Morristown, NJ 07960
Tel.: (908) 883-4849
Web Site: http://www.hs-design.com

Research & Development in the Physical, Engineering & Life Sciences
N.A.I.C.S.: 541715
Tor Alden *(Pres)*

Halleck-Willard, Inc. (2)
7097 Colorado Blvd, Frederick, CO 80530
Tel.: (303) 833-3223
Web Site: http://www.hwimfg.com
Rev.: $2,333,333
Emp.: 10
Software Reproducing Services
N.A.I.C.S.: 334610
Michael Halleck *(Pres)*

Subsidiary (Non-US):

SteriPack Asia Sdn Bhd (2)
Lot 119992 Jalan Canang Emas 8 Telok Gong Industrial Estate, 42000, Klang, Selangor, Malaysia
Tel.: (60) 331673596
Contract Products Mfr
N.A.I.C.S.: 339999
Enda Keena *(Mgr-R&D)*

SteriPack Medical Poland Sp. z o.o. (2)
Leg ul Japonska 1, 55-220, Jelcz-Laskowice, Poland
Tel.: (48) 713818199
Contract Products Mfr
N.A.I.C.S.: 339999

Subsidiary (US):

SteriPack USA LLC (2)
4255 S Pipkin Rd, Lakeland, FL 33811
Tel.: (863) 648-2333
Contract Products Mfr
N.A.I.C.S.: 339999
David Moore *(Mgr-Bus Dev)*

Virgin Experience Days Ltd. (1)
Stamford House Boston Drive, Bourne End, SL8 5YS, Buckinghamshire, United Kingdom
Tel.: (44) 3445040844
Web Site: http://www.virginexperiencedays.co.uk
Travel Voucher & Rewards Program Services
N.A.I.C.S.: 561599
Paul O'Brien *(Mng Dir)*

Unit (Domestic):

Acorne plc - Exhilaration (2)
Stamford House Boston Drive, Bourne End, SL8 5YS, Bucks, United Kingdom
Tel.: (44) 3445040600
Web Site: http://www.virginexperiencedays.co.uk
Travel Incentive Program Services
N.A.I.C.S.: 561599

Subsidiary (US):

Cloud 9 Living, Inc. (2)
11101 W 120th Ave Ste 150, Broomfield, CO 80021
Tel.: (303) 443-8777
Web Site: http://www.cloud9living.com
Sales Range: $1-9.9 Million
Emp.: 9
Sales Incentives & Customer Loyalty Services
N.A.I.C.S.: 541618
John Augst *(Co-Founder & Pres)*

INFO EDGE INDIA LTD
B - 8 Sector - 132, Noida, 201304, India
Tel.: (91) 1204841100
Web Site: https://www.infoedge.in
NAUKRI—(BOM)
Rev.: $182,296,533
Assets: $457,302,026
Liabilities: $94,626,362
Net Worth: $362,675,665
Earnings: $84,921,767
Emp.: 4,243
Fiscal Year-end: 03/31/19
Online Recruitment, Matrimonial, Real Estate & Educational Services
N.A.I.C.S.: 561311
Hitesh Oberoi *(CEO & Mng Dir)*

INFOBANK CORPORATION

Subsidiaries:

Aisle Network Private Limited (1)
Unit No N - 801 & 802 8th Floor North Block Manipal Centre 47, Dickenson Road Bangalore, Bengaluru, KA, India
Tel.: (91) 8861471128
Web Site: https://www.aisle.co
Information Technology Services
N.A.I.C.S.: 541512

Allcheckdeals India Pvt. Ltd. (1)
E-2 Sector 1, 201301, Noida, Uttar Pradesh, India
Tel.: (91) 9999998663
Web Site: http://www.allcheckdeals.com
Real Estate Manangement Services
N.A.I.C.S.: 531390

Naukri Internet Services Private Limited (1)
B-77 B-56 Sector 5, 201301, Noida, Uttar Pradesh, India
Tel.: (91) 1204041700
Web Site: http://www.naukri.com
Employment & Recruitment Services
N.A.I.C.S.: 561311
Pawan Goyal *(Chief Bus Officer)*

INFO YATIRIM MENKUL DEGERLER A.S.
Barbaros Mah Ihlamur Bl No 3 Agaoglu My Newwork Inside Door No 188, Atasehir, Istanbul, Turkiye
Tel.: (90) 2127003501   TR
Web Site: http://www.infoyatirim.com
Year Founded: 1994
INFO.IYF—(IST)
Sales Range: Less than $1 Million
Securities Brokerage Services
N.A.I.C.S.: 523150
Vahit Vardar *(Chm & Gen Mgr)*

INFO-TECH RESEARCH GROUP
602 Queens Ave, London, N6B 1Y8, ON, Canada
Tel.: (519) 432-3550
Web Site: http://www.infotech.com
Year Founded: 1997
Sales Range: $25-49.9 Million
Emp.: 350
IT Research & Advice Publisher
N.A.I.C.S.: 513199
Joel McLean *(Founder & Chm)*

INFO-TEK CORPORATION
No 12 Shijian Road, Hsin-Chu Industrial, Hsin-chu, Taiwan
Tel.: (886) 35979999
Web Site: https://www.psaitc.com
8183—(TPE)
Rev.: $218,432,413
Assets: $208,949,631
Liabilities: $100,536,050
Net Worth: $108,413,580
Earnings: $17,762,483
Emp.: 1,382
Fiscal Year-end: 12/31/23
Software Development Services
N.A.I.C.S.: 541511

INFOBANK CORPORATION
12th floor Building A Youth Space 1 660 Daewangpangyo-ro, Bundang-gu, Seongnam, 13494, Gyeonggi-do, Korea (South)
Tel.: (82) 316281500
Web Site: https://www.infobank.net
Year Founded: 1995
039290—(KRS)
Rev.: $107,513,818
Assets: $68,367,434
Liabilities: $19,053,303
Net Worth: $49,314,131
Earnings: $1,107,185
Emp.: 161
Fiscal Year-end: 12/31/22
Mobile Software Development Services

INFOBANK CORPORATION

Infobank Corporation—(Continued)
N.A.I.C.S.: 541511
Junho Jang (Co-Pres)

INFOBEANS TECHNOLOGIES LIMITED
Crystal IT Park Bhavarkua Road, Indore, 452001, Madhya Pradesh, India
Tel.: (91) 7317162000 In
Web Site: https://www.infobeans.com
Year Founded: 2000
INFOBEAN—(NSE)
Rev.: $39,445,770
Assets: $56,534,205
Liabilities: $25,065,495
Net Worth: $31,468,710
Earnings: $7,512,960
Emp.: 1,400
Fiscal Year-end: 03/31/22
Custom Software Development Services
N.A.I.C.S.: 541511
Siddharth Sethi (Co-Founder & Mng Dir)

Subsidiaries:
InfoBeans Inc. (1)
4115 Blackhawk Plz Cir Ste 100, Danville, CA 94506
Web Site: http://www.infobeans.com
Information Technology & Software Services
N.A.I.C.S.: 541511

INFOBIP LTD.
35-38 New Bridge St 5th Floor, London, EC4V 6BW, United Kingdom - England
Tel.: (44) 2078374180
Web Site: https://www.infobip.com
Year Founded: 2006
IT Services & Consulting
N.A.I.C.S.: 561990
Silvio Kutic (CEO)

Subsidiaries:
OpenMarket, Inc. (1)
300 Elliott Ave W Ste 200, Seattle, WA 98119
Tel.: (877) 277-2801
Web Site: https://www.openmarket.com
Cloud Communications
N.A.I.C.S.: 518210

Subsidiary (Domestic):
Peerless Network, Inc. (2)
433 W Van Buren St Ste 410, 60606, Chicago, IL
Tel.: (312) 506-0920
Web Site: http://www.peerlessnetwork.com
Call Termination Services
N.A.I.C.S.: 517810
John Barnicle (Pres & CEO)

INFOBIRD CO., LTD.
Room 12A05 Tower A Boya International Center, Building 2 No 1 Lizezhongyi Road Chaoyang District, Beijing, 100102, China
Tel.: (86) 4007072008 Ky
Web Site: https://www.infobird.com
Year Founded: 2020
IFBD—(NASDAQ)
Rev.: $5,505,734
Assets: $16,634,271
Liabilities: $10,132,589
Net Worth: $6,501,682
Earnings: ($15,266,979)
Emp.: 213
Fiscal Year-end: 12/31/22
Holding Company
N.A.I.C.S.: 551112
Hsiaochien Tseng (Exec VP)

INFOCLIP SA
20 rue de La Michodiere, 75002, Paris, France
Tel.: (33) 143181920
Web Site: https://www.infoclip.com
Year Founded: 1989
MLIFC—(EUR)
Sales Range: $1-9.9 Million
Emp.: 20
IT Services
N.A.I.C.S.: 541511
Laurent Azoulay (Chm & CEO)

INFOCORP COMPUTER SOLUTIONS LTD.
80 Tiverton Ct Ste 203, Markham, L3R 0G4, ON, Canada
Tel.: (905) 477-2854 Ca
Web Site:
    https://www.infocorpnow.com
Year Founded: 1984
Sales Range: $10-24.9 Million
Emp.: 18
Revenue Management Solutions
N.A.I.C.S.: 541512
Govin Misir (Chm & Pres)

INFODEMA S.A.
Av Espada 1000-Cerro Colorado 5240, PO Box 9218, Valdivia, Santiago, Chile
Tel.: (56) 63278000
Web Site: http://www.infodema.cl
Year Founded: 1942
INFODEMA—(SGO)
Sales Range: Less than $1 Million
Plywood Board Mfr
N.A.I.C.S.: 321211
Marling Moya Domke (CEO)

INFOLINE TEC GROUP BERHAD
53-3 Jalan PJU 5/20e Kota Damansara, 47810, Petaling Jaya, Selangor, Malaysia
Tel.: (60) 361480890
Web Site: https://www.infolinetec.com
Year Founded: 2013
INFOTEC—(KLS)
Rev.: $15,657,162
Assets: $17,041,141
Liabilities: $4,543,970
Net Worth: $12,497,170
Earnings: $3,993,252
Fiscal Year-end: 12/31/23
Information Technology Services
N.A.I.C.S.: 541512
Say Tsui Rebecca Kong (Co-Sec)

INFOLLION RESEARCH SERVICES LIMITED
3rd Floor Tower B Unitech Cyberpark Sector 39, Gurgaon, 122003, Haryana, India
Tel.: (91) 1244406555
Web Site: https://infollion.com
Year Founded: 2009
INFOLLION—(NSE)
Rev.: $4,680,872
Assets: $2,188,436
Liabilities: $465,520
Net Worth: $1,722,917
Earnings: $581,040
Fiscal Year-end: 03/31/23
Investment Management Service
N.A.I.C.S.: 523999
Abhay Sangal (VP)

INFOLOG SOLUTIONS
13 Avenue De La Porte D Italie, 75013, Paris, France
Tel.: (33) 153616500
Web Site: http://www.infolog-solutions.com
Year Founded: 2001
Rev.: $17,300,000
Emp.: 138
Software Development Services
N.A.I.C.S.: 541511
Bernard Sauvage (Mgr-Sls)

INFOMART CORPORATION
13th Floor Shiodome Shibarikyu Building 1-2-3 Kaigan, Minato-ku, Tokyo, 105-0022, Japan
Tel.: (81) 357761147
Web Site: https://corp.infomart.co.jp
Year Founded: 1998
2492—(TKS)
Rev.: $94,743,670
Assets: $96,026,960
Liabilities: $20,631,900
Net Worth: $75,395,060
Earnings: $2,112,820
Emp.: 680
Fiscal Year-end: 12/31/23
Electronic Commerce Services
N.A.I.C.S.: 425120
Osamu Nagao (Pres & CEO)

Subsidiaries:
Infomart International Corporation (1)
Room 301 3rd Floor Sun Hung Kai Centre 30 Harbour Road, Wanchai, China (Hong Kong)
Tel.: (852) 2802 1092
Web Site:
    http://www.infomartinternational.com
Electronic Commerce Services
N.A.I.C.S.: 425120
Naotake Fujita (VP)

INFOMEDIA LTD
3 Minna Cl, Belrose, 2085, NSW, Australia
Tel.: (61) 294541500
Web Site:
    http://www.infomedia.com.au
IFM—(ASX)
Rev.: $94,265,491
Assets: $121,572,516
Liabilities: $31,583,867
Net Worth: $89,988,648
Earnings: $8,468,884
Emp.: 300
Fiscal Year-end: 06/30/24
Supplier of Electronic Parts Catalogue & Service Quoting Systems
N.A.I.C.S.: 424120
Bart Vogel (Chm & Mng Dir)

Subsidiaries:
IFM Americas Inc. (1)
Plymouth Exec Park 14500 Sheldon Rd Ste 100, Plymouth, MI 48170-2698
Tel.: (248) 381-8850
Web Site: https://www.infomedia.com.au
Sales Range: $25-49.9 Million
Emp.: 24
Electronic Parts Catalogues Distr
N.A.I.C.S.: 513140

Subsidiary (Domestic):
SimplePart, LLC (2)
84 Walton St NW Ste 400, Atlanta, GA 30303
Tel.: (404) 620-9764
Web Site: http://www.simplepart.com
Software Design & Development Services
N.A.I.C.S.: 541511
Sarah Atchley (Project Mgr)

IFM Deutschland GmbH (1)
Oskar-Schindler-Street 9, 50769, Cologne, Germany
Tel.: (49) 16095205919
Micro Cat Electronic & Data Services
N.A.I.C.S.: 518210

IFM Europe Ltd (1)
Second Floor Suite B Terrington House 13-15 Hills Road, Great Abington, Cambridge, CB2 1NL, Cambridgeshire, United Kingdom
Tel.: (44) 1253335501
Web Site: http://www.ifmeurope.com
Sales Range: $25-49.9 Million
Emp.: 7
Electronic Parts Catalogues Development & Distr
N.A.I.C.S.: 513199

INTERNATIONAL PUBLIC

INFOMEDIA PRESS LTD.
1st floor Empire Complex, 414 Senapati Bapat Marg Lower Parel, Mumbai, 400 013, India
Tel.: (91) 2240019000
Web Site:
    https://www.infomediapress.in
INFOMEDIA—(NSE)
Assets: $1,146,407
Liabilities: $7,280,448
Net Worth: ($6,134,041)
Earnings: ($419,061)
Fiscal Year-end: 03/31/23
Business Directories & Magazine Publisher
N.A.I.C.S.: 323111
Tasneem Cementwala (Sec)

INFOMINA BERHAD
BO3-C-12-1 Menara 3A No 3 Jalan Bangsar, KL Eco City, 59200, Kuala Lumpur, Malaysia
Tel.: (60) 322017188
Web Site: https://www.infomina.co
Year Founded: 2007
INFOM—(KLS)
Rev.: $47,652,931
Assets: $55,574,195
Liabilities: $25,316,916
Net Worth: $30,257,279
Earnings: $6,994,935
Emp.: 207
Fiscal Year-end: 05/31/24
Information Technology Services
N.A.I.C.S.: 541512

INFONET INC.
Otemachi First Square West Tower 2F 1-5-1 Otemachi, Chiyoda-ku, Tokyo, 100-0004, Japan
Tel.: (81) 352217591
Web Site: https://www.e-infonet.jp
Year Founded: 2002
4444—(TKS)
Rev.: $11,679,870
Assets: $10,754,470
Liabilities: $3,886,680
Net Worth: $6,867,790
Earnings: $654,390
Emp.: 137
Fiscal Year-end: 03/31/24
Website Construction CMS & System Development Cloud Services
N.A.I.C.S.: 518210
Makoto Kishimoto (Pres & CEO)

Subsidiaries:
iact Corporation (1)
NBF Higashi Ginza Square Bldg Tsukiji 1-13-14, Chuo-Ku, Tokyo, 104-0045, Japan
Tel.: (81) 368255611
Web Site: http://www.iact.co.jp
Information Technology Consulting Services
N.A.I.C.S.: 541512
Takayoshi Kasai (Pres & Dir)

INFOPIA CO., LTD.
132 Anyangcheondong-ro, Dongan-gu, Anyang, Gyeonggi, Korea (South)
Tel.: (82) 31 460 0300
Web Site: http://www.infopia21.com
Year Founded: 1996
Sales Range: $50-74.9 Million
Emp.: 300
Medical Equipment Mfr
N.A.I.C.S.: 334510
Dong Hyun Lee (CEO)

INFOPLUS TECHNOLOGIES LIMITED
6 Capital Business Park Manor Way, Borehamwood, WD6 1GW, United Kingdom
Tel.: (44) 8452573936
Web Site: http://www.infoplusltd.co.uk
Sales Range: $25-49.9 Million
Emp.: 15

AND PRIVATE COMPANIES

Information Technology Services
N.A.I.C.S.: 541512
Srikanth Settipalli *(Mgr)*

Subsidiaries:

Infoplus Technologies B.V (1)
Weena 290, NJ City, 3012, Rotterdam, Netherlands
Tel.: (31) 10 282 1234
Information Technology Consulting Services
N.A.I.C.S.: 541512

Infoplus Technologies SPRL (1)
Gulledelle 96 6th floor, 1200, Brussels, Belgium
Tel.: (32) 277 11907
Information Technology Consulting Services
N.A.I.C.S.: 541512

INFORE ENVIRONMENT TECHNOLOGY GROUP CO., LTD.

1818 Renmin West Road Dongguan Street, Shangyu District, Shaoxing, 528300, Zhejiang, China
Tel.: (86) 57582530802
Web Site: https://www.sz-gf.com.cn
000967—(SSE)
Rev.: $1,720,740,996
Assets: $4,109,689,116
Liabilities: $1,619,356,752
Net Worth: $2,490,332,364
Earnings: $58,798,116
Emp.: 10,000
Fiscal Year-end: 12/31/22
Holding Company
N.A.I.C.S.: 551112

INFORICH INC.

Jingumae 6-31-15 A-6A, Shibuya-Ku, Tokyo, 150-0001, Japan
Tel.: (81) 345009212
Web Site: https://www.inforich.net
Year Founded: 2015
9338—(TKS)
Rev.: $54,458,290
Assets: $62,058,770
Liabilities: $40,214,480
Net Worth: $21,844,290
Earnings: $4,048,390
Fiscal Year-end: 12/31/23
Software Development Services
N.A.I.C.S.: 541511

INFORM P. LYKOS S.A.

5th km Varis Koropiou Ave, 19400, Koropi, Greece
Tel.: (30) 2106697500
Web Site: http://www.austriacard.com
LYK—(ATH)
Rev.: $92,094,429
Assets: $94,837,454
Liabilities: $51,799,977
Net Worth: $43,037,477
Earnings: $563,849
Emp.: 508
Fiscal Year-end: 12/31/21
Commercial Printing & Information Services
N.A.I.C.S.: 323111
Panagiotis I. Spyropoulos *(Vice Chm & CEO)*

Subsidiaries:

Austria Card GmbH (1)
Lamezanstrasse 4-8, 1230, Vienna, Austria
Tel.: (43) 1610650
Web Site: http://www.austriacard.at
Sales Range: $125-149.9 Million
Emp.: 300
Smartcard Mfr
N.A.I.C.S.: 326199

Austria Card Polska Sp.z.o.o. (1)
53 Emilii Plater St 10th floor, 00-113, Warsaw, Poland
Tel.: (48) 225286777
Web Site: https://www.austriacard.at

Sales Range: $50-74.9 Million
Emp.: 10
Mobile Communication Support Services
N.A.I.C.S.: 424990

Compaper Converting S.A. (1)
Celulozei 6, Constanta, 900175, Romania
Tel.: (40) 744170977
Digital Printing Services
N.A.I.C.S.: 323111

Inform Lykos S.A. (1)
Odaii Nr 347-363, 021689, Bucharest, Romania
Tel.: (40) 213503420
Web Site: http://www.lykos.co
Sales Range: $125-149.9 Million
Emp.: 300
Commercial Printing Services
N.A.I.C.S.: 323111

Lykos Paperless Solutions S.A. (1)
7th Km Varis-koropiou Avenue, Koropi, 19400, Greece
Tel.: (30) 2106697500
Sales Range: $50-74.9 Million
Emp.: 4
Electronic Bill Presentation & Payment Services
N.A.I.C.S.: 522320
Nikolaos Lykos *(Chm)*

INFORMA PLC

5 Howick Place, London, SW1P 1WG, United Kingdom
Tel.: (44) 2080520400 UK
Web Site: https://www.informa.com
Year Founded: 1998
IFJPY—(OTCIQ)
Rev.: $4,031,344,786
Assets: $14,565,470,146
Liabilities: $5,484,833,155
Net Worth: $9,080,636,991
Earnings: $584,807,886
Emp.: 12,295
Fiscal Year-end: 12/31/23
Holding Company; Books, Journals, Directories & Online Media Publisher & Trade Shows Organizer
N.A.I.C.S.: 551112
Rupert Hopley *(Gen Counsel & Sec)*

Subsidiaries:

AMA Research Limited (1)
Eagle Tower Montpellier Drive, Cheltenham, GL50 1TA, United Kingdom
Tel.: (44) 1242235724
Web Site: http://www.amaresearch.co.uk
Market Research Services
N.A.I.C.S.: 541910

APLF Limited (1)
1701-1705 China Resources Building 26 Harbour Road, Wanchai, China (Hong Kong)
Tel.: (852) 2 827 6211
Web Site: https://www.aplf.com
Trade Exhibition Services
N.A.I.C.S.: 561920

Agra Ceas Consulting Limited (1)
The Brand Building Briar Close Wye, Canterbury, TN25 5HB, Kent, United Kingdom
Tel.: (44) 1233812181
Web Site: http://www.ceasc.co
Consulting Services
N.A.I.C.S.: 541618
Edward Oliver *(Mng Dir)*

Ascential plc (1)
The Prow 1 Wilder Walk, London, W1B 5AP, United Kingdom
Tel.: (44) 207 516 5000
Web Site: http://www.ascential.com
Information Services
N.A.I.C.S.: 519290
Duncan Painter *(CEO)*

Subsidiary (Domestic):

Glenigan Limited (2)
80 Holdenhurst Rd, Bournemouth, BH8 8AQ, Dorset, United Kingdom
Tel.: (44) 8000608698
Web Site: https://www.glenigan.com
Sales Range: $25-49.9 Million
Emp.: 100

Sales Leads & Contract Information Magazines & Directories
N.A.I.C.S.: 513120

Warc Ltd. (2)
33 Kingsway, London, WC2B 6UF, United Kingdom
Tel.: (44) 20 7467 8100
Web Site: http://www.warc.com
Business Intelligence Services; Advertising & Marketing Periodical Publisher
N.A.I.C.S.: 561499
Eva Kasten *(Pres-Americas)*

Subsidiary (US):

Warc Americas (3)
229 W 43rd St 7th Fl, New York, NY 10036
Tel.: (212) 201-2800
Web Site: http://www.warc.com
Business Intelligence Services; Advertising & Marketing Periodical Publisher
N.A.I.C.S.: 561499
Elizabeth Kennedy *(Head-Sls)*

Subsidiary (Non-US):

Warc Asia (3)
OUE Downtown 1 44 03 6 Shenton Way, Singapore, 068809, Singapore
Tel.: (65) 3157 6200
Business Intelligence Services; Advertising & Marketing Periodical Publisher
N.A.I.C.S.: 561499
Ed Pank *(Mng Dir)*

Bangkok Exhibition Services Ltd. (1)
18th Floor Ari Hills Building 428 Phahonyothin Road Soi 10, Samen Nai Phaya Thai District, Bangkok, Thailand
Tel.: (66) 20360500
Pharmaceutical Preparation Mfr
N.A.I.C.S.: 325412

CBI Research Inc. (1)
70 Blanchard Rd, Burlington, MA 01803
Tel.: (339) 298-2100
Web Site: http://www.cbinet.com
Medical Affair & Event Services
N.A.I.C.S.: 561920
Timothy Berry *(Project Mgr-Customer Experience)*

China International Exhibitions Limited (1)
8/F Urban Development International Tower No 355 Hong Qiao Road, Xuhui District, Shanghai, 200030, China
Tel.: (86) 2133392152
Trade Exhibition Services
N.A.I.C.S.: 561920

Clinerion AG (1)
Elisabethenanlage 11, 4051, Basel, Switzerland
Tel.: (41) 618656060
Web Site: https://www.clinerion.com
Data Processing Services
N.A.I.C.S.: 518210

Clinerion Turkey Teknoloji Arastirma Limited Sirketi (1)
Uphill Towers A-87 Bati, Atasehir, Istanbul, Turkiye
Tel.: (90) 2166880086
Data Processing Services
N.A.I.C.S.: 518210

Cogent OA Limited (1)
2 3 and 4 Park Square Milton Park, Abingdon, OX14 4RN, Oxfordshire, United Kingdom
Tel.: (44) 2070176000
Web Site: http://www.cogentoa.com
Educational Research Services
N.A.I.C.S.: 611710
Emma Greenwood *(Dir-Editorial)*

EBD GmbH (1)
Baarerstrasse 139, 6300, Zug, Switzerland
Tel.: (41) 435003545
Events Services
N.A.I.C.S.: 561920
Katharina Schropp *(Mng Dir)*

EBD Group GmbH (1)
Kaufingerstr 24, 80331, Munich, Germany
Tel.: (49) 89231217290
Web Site: https://www.ebdgroup.com
Events Services
N.A.I.C.S.: 561920

Sanne Dech *(Sr Mgr-Exhibits)*

Futurum Media Limited (1)
12 John Prince's Street, London, W1G 0JR, United Kingdom
Tel.: (44) 2038666356
Web Site: https://www.futurum-media.com
Conference & Exhibition Services
N.A.I.C.S.: 561920
Daniel Pitchford *(Comml Dir)*

Guangzhou Informa Yi Fan Exhibitions Co., Ltd. (1)
Room 202 Yin Yan Building No 25-27 Yan Ling Road, Tian He District, Guangzhou, China
Tel.: (86) 2088521856
Web Site: https://www.ihe-china.com
Exhibition Organizing Services
N.A.I.C.S.: 561920

Informa Connect Limited (1)
240 Blackfriars Road, London, SE1 8BF, United Kingdom
Tel.: (44) 79009340781
Event & Meeting Planning Services
N.A.I.C.S.: 561920

Informa Economics FNP Consultoria Ltda. (1)
Avenida Paulista 726 - 17 andar - Bela Vista, Sao Paulo, 01310-100, SP, Brazil
Tel.: (55) 1145041414
Web Site: http://www.informaecon-fnp.com
Consulting Services
N.A.I.C.S.: 541618

Informa Group plc (1)
Informa House 30-32 Mortimer Street, London, W1W 7RE, United Kingdom
Tel.: (44) 20 7017 5000
Holding Company
N.A.I.C.S.: 551112
Steven Carter *(Mng Dir)*

Subsidiary (Domestic):

Agra Informa Ltd. (2)
80 Calverley Rd, Tunbridge Wells, TN1 2UN, Kent, United Kingdom (100%)
Tel.: (44) 2070177499
Web Site: http://www.agra-net.com
Sales Range: $25-49.9 Million
Emp.: 85
Commodities Information Journal Publisher
N.A.I.C.S.: 513130

Subsidiary (Non-US):

Euroforum BV (2)
Emmasingel 29-17, Postbus 845, 5600 AV, Eindhoven, Netherlands
Tel.: (31) 40 297 4977
Web Site: https://www.euroforum.nl
Emp.: 80
Meeting & Conference Management Services
N.A.I.C.S.: 561492

Euroforum Deutschland (Holding) GmbH (2)
Prinzenallee 3, 40549, Dusseldorf, Germany
Tel.: (49) 21196863000
Web Site: http://www.euroforum.de
Sales Range: $200-249.9 Million
Emp.: 30
Investment Management Service
N.A.I.C.S.: 523999

IBC Asia (S) Pte Limited (2)
103 Penang Road 04-01 Visioncrest Commercial, Singapore, 238467, Singapore
Tel.: (65) 69896610
Web Site:
  https://www.informaconnect.com.sg
Books Publishing Services
N.A.I.C.S.: 513130

Subsidiary (Domestic):

IIR Exhibitions Limited (2)
29 Bressenden Place 5th Floor, London, SW1E 5EW, United Kingdom
Tel.: (44) 20 70177108
Exhibition Management Services
N.A.I.C.S.: 711310

Subsidiary (Non-US):

IIR Hungary Limited (2)

INFORMA PLC

Informa plc—(Continued)

Rozsafa Utca 13-17, 1134, Budapest, Hungary
Tel.: (36) 4198627
Web Site: http://www.iir-hungary.hu
Marketing Research Service
N.A.I.C.S.: 541910

Group (Domestic):

Informa Business Information (2)
Christchurch Court 10-15 Newgate Street,
London, EC1A 7AZ, United Kingdom
Tel.: (44) 207 017 5000
Web Site:
   http://www.informabusinessinfo.com
Business Information Services
N.A.I.C.S.: 519290
Giles Catron (COO)

Subsidiary (Domestic):

Datamonitor (3)
Christchurch Court 10-15 Newgate Street,
EC1A 7AZ, United Kingdom
Tel.: (44) 2076757000
Web Site: https://www.datamonitor.com
Sales Range: $125-149.9 Million
Emp.: 1,500
Analysis & In-Depth Business Forecasts
N.A.I.C.S.: 519290
Shahid Qazi (Dir-Global Accts)

Subsidiary (Domestic):

Business Insights Ltd. (4)
119 Faringdon Road, London, EC1R 3DA,
United Kingdom
Tel.: (44) 207 551 9888
Web Site: http://www.business-insights.com
Sales Range: $100-124.9 Million
Emp.: 400
Industry Analysis Research & Reporting
Services
N.A.I.C.S.: 513199

Subsidiary (Non-US):

Butler Direct Ltd. (4)
37-43 Prostact Straight, HU2 8PX, Hull,
United Kingdom - England
Tel.: (44) 1482586149
Web Site: http://www.butlergroup.com
Sales Range: $25-49.9 Million
Emp.: 50
Information Technology Research & Industry Analysis
N.A.I.C.S.: 519290

Subsidiary (Domestic):

Butler Research Ltd. (4)
Europa Ho 3rd Fl, Hull, United Kingdom
Tel.: (44) 1482586149
Other Management Consulting Services
N.A.I.C.S.: 541618

Subsidiary (US):

Datamonitor, Inc. (4)
52 Vanderbilt Ave 11th Fl, New York, NY 10017
Tel.: (212) 686-7400
Web Site: http://www.datamonitor.com
Sales Range: $25-49.9 Million
Emp.: 20
Business Information & Market Analysis Services
N.A.I.C.S.: 519290
Cynthia Jesus (Office Mgr)

Subsidiary (Domestic):

Life Science Analytics Inc. (5)
800 James Ave, Scranton, PA 18510
Tel.: (570) 504-1800
Web Site:
   http://www.lifescienceanalytics.com
Sales Range: $25-49.9 Million
Research & Development in the Physical
Engineering & Life Sciences
N.A.I.C.S.: 541715

Subsidiary (Non-US):

Excellence Data Research Pvt. Ltd (4)
Plot No 17 Software Layout Unit VB IT
Park, Veega Block 8th Floor Madhapur,
500081, Hyderabad, India

Tel.: (91) 4066729500
Web Site: http://www.datamonitor.com
Sales Range: $100-124.9 Million
Emp.: 500
Company & Industry Research & Analysis
N.A.I.C.S.: 519290
Rahul Bhatia (CEO)

MarketLine International Ltd. (4)
119 Farringdon Road, EC1R 3DA, London,
United Kingdom - England
Tel.: (44) 2075519565
Web Site: http://www.marketlineinfo.com
Sales Range: $50-74.9 Million
Emp.: 200
Product, Industry & Business Reporting & Analysis
N.A.I.C.S.: 513199

Subsidiary (Domestic):

eBenchmarkers Ltd. (4)
Blue Fin Building 110 Southwark Street,
London, SE1 0SU, United Kingdom
Tel.: (44) 207 551 9034
Web Site: http://www.ebenchmarkers.com
Sales Range: $100-124.9 Million
Emp.: 35
Financial Services Research & Analysis
N.A.I.C.S.: 519290
Felix Moore (Mng Dir)

Subsidiary (US):

Informa Business Information, Inc. (3)
52 Vanderbilt Ave, New York, NY 10017
Tel.: (212) 520-2777
Web Site:
   http://www.informabusinessinfo.com
Emp.: 50
Business Information Services
N.A.I.C.S.: 519290
Stephan Carter (Pres)

Group (Domestic):

Informa Business Information, Inc. - Pharma & MedTech Business Intelligence (4)
52 Vanderbilt Ave 11th Fl, New York, NY 10017
Tel.: (908) 748-1221
Web Site: http://www.pharmamedtechbi.com
Emp.: 100
Healthcare & Pharmaceutical Industry Business Intelligence Publisher
N.A.I.C.S.: 513120
Phil Jarvis (Pres & Mng Dir-Publ)

Branch (Domestic):

Informa Business Information, Inc. - Pharma & MedTech Business Intelligence, Rockville Editorial Office (5)
5635 Fishers Lane Ste 6000, Rockville, MD 20852
Tel.: (240) 221-4500
Web Site: http://www.pharmamedtechbi.com
Healthcare & Pharmaceutical Industry Business Intelligence Publisher
N.A.I.C.S.: 513120
M. Nielsen Hobbs (Editor-The Pink Sheet)

Subsidiary (Domestic):

Sagient Research Systems, Inc. (4)
3655 Nobel Dr Ste 600, San Diego, CA 92122
Tel.: (858) 623-1600
Web Site: https://www.sagientresearch.com
Financial Research & Data Publisher
N.A.I.C.S.: 519290
Roger Lowe (Controller)

Subsidiary (Domestic):

Informa Global Markets (Europe) Limited (2)
14th Floor 240 Blackfriars, London, SE1 8BF, United Kingdom
Tel.: (44) 2070175402
Web Site: https://www.informagm.com
Sales Range: $50-74.9 Million
Emp.: 60
Financial Management Services
N.A.I.C.S.: 523999

Subsidiary (Non-US):

Informa Healthcare AB (2)

Kungsbroplan 3A 1st Floor, PO Box 3255,
103 65, Stockholm, Sweden
Tel.: (46) 84408044
Books Publishing Services
N.A.I.C.S.: 513130

Informa Switzerland Limited (2)
Gubelstrasse 11, 6300, Zug, Switzerland
Tel.: (41) 41 444 1344
Web Site: http://www.informa.com
Emp.: 7
Holding Company
N.A.I.C.S.: 551112

Subsidiary (Domestic):

Informa Finance GmbH (3)
Gubelstrasse 11, 6300, Zug, Switzerland
Tel.: (41) 414441344
Corporate Financial Services
N.A.I.C.S.: 522299

Informa IP GmbH (3)
Daarerstrassse 139, 6300, Zug, Switzerland
Tel.: (41) 414441344
Web Site: https://www.informa.com
Emp.: 10
Intellectual Property Management Services
N.A.I.C.S.: 533110
Claudia Tutas (Gen Mgr)

Subsidiary (US):

Informa USA Inc. (2)
1 Research Dr Ste 400A, Westborough, MA 01581
Tel.: (508) 616-6600
Web Site: https://www.informa.com
Magazine Publishing Services
N.A.I.C.S.: 513120

Subsidiary (Domestic):

BioTechniques (3)
52 Vanderbilt Ave 11th Fl, New York, NY 10017
Tel.: (212) 520-2777
Web Site: http://www.biotechniques.com
Medical Journal Publisher
N.A.I.C.S.: 513120

Informa Financial Information, Inc. (3)
1 Research Dr Ste 400A, Westborough, MA 01581
Tel.: (508) 616-6600
Web Site: http://www.imoneynet.com
Financial Information & Analysis Provider
N.A.I.C.S.: 513120
Kenneth B. Bohlin (Pres & CEO)

Informa Investment Solutions, Inc. (3)
4 Gannett Dr, White Plains, NY 10604
Tel.: (914) 640-0200
Web Site: http://www.informais.com
Software Developer
N.A.I.C.S.: 541618
Lac Vuong (Co-Mng Dir)

Informa Media, Inc. (3)
605 Third Ave, New York, NY 10158
Tel.: (212) 520-2700
Web Site: http://www.informa.com
Trade Publications, Websites, Trade Shows
& Other Proprietary Business Information
Media Products & Services
N.A.I.C.S.: 513199

Unit (Domestic):

Delta Farm Press, Inc. (4)
14920 US Hwy 61, Clarksdale, MS 38614
Tel.: (662) 624-8503
Newspaper Publishers
N.A.I.C.S.: 513110

Nutrition Business Journal (4)
5541 Central Ave Ste 150, Boulder, CO 80301
Tel.: (303) 939-8440
Web Site: https://www.newhope.com
Nutrition Magazine
N.A.I.C.S.: 513120

Supermarket News (4)
1166 Avenue of the Americas 10th Fl, New York, NY 10036
Tel.: (800) 944-4676
Web Site:
   https://www.supermarketnews.com

INTERNATIONAL PUBLIC

Trade & Newspaper Publications
N.A.I.C.S.: 513120
Leigh Anne Zinsmeister (Mng Editor)

Subsidiary (Domestic):

Institute for International Research, Inc. (3)
708 3rd Ave 4th Fl, New York, NY 10017
Tel.: (212) 661-3500
Web Site: http://www.iirusa.com
Emp.: 80
Business Information, Seminars & Conventions
N.A.I.C.S.: 611699
Kim Rivielle (Mng Dir-Mktg & Strategy)

Subsidiary (Non-US):

IIR Holdings Ltd. (4)
Level 20 Sheikh Rashid Tower Dubai World
Trade Centre, PO Box 21743, Dubai,
United Arab Emirates
Tel.: (971) 43352437
Web Site: http://www.informa-nea.com
Seminars, Conferences & Exhibitions
N.A.I.C.S.: 561499
Timothy Hawes (Dir-Sls)

Subsidiary (Domestic):

Light Reading LLC (3)
PO Box 1953, New York, NY 10156
Tel.: (212) 925-0020
Web Site: http://www.lightreading.com
Emp.: 200
Online Telecommunications Trade Publisher
N.A.I.C.S.: 513120
Stephen Saunders (Founder)

Robbins-Gioia Inc. (3)
11 Canal Ctr Plz, Alexandria, VA 22314-1595
Tel.: (703) 548-7006
Web Site: http://www.robbinsgioia.com
Management Consulting Services
N.A.I.C.S.: 541611
Christopher Samulski (Dir-Ops, Defense & Intelligence)

Subsidiary (Non-US):

Institute for International Research (IIR) BV (2)
Kabelweg 37 5e etage, 1014 BA, Amsterdam, Netherlands
Tel.: (31) 205805400
Web Site: http://www.iir.nl
Sales Range: $10-24.9 Million
Emp.: 30
Business Conferences & Training Services
N.A.I.C.S.: 561499
Ermelinda Vermeulen (Mng Dir)

Subsidiary (Domestic):

Martin Dunitz Ltd. (2)
The Livery House 7-9, Pratt Street, London,
NW1 0AE, United Kingdom
Tel.: (44) 20 7482 2202
Web Site: http://www.dunitz.co.uk
Sales Range: $25-49.9 Million
Emp.: 35
Medical Books & Journals Publisher
N.A.I.C.S.: 513130

Ovum Limited (2)
Christchurch Court 10-15 Newgate Street,
London, EC1A 7AZ, United Kingdom
Tel.: (44) 207 017 4994
Web Site: http://www.ovum.com
Holding Company; Telecommunications,
Information Technology & Media Business
Intelligence Publisher
N.A.I.C.S.: 551112

Subsidiary (Domestic):

Informa UK Limited (3)
240 Blackfriars, London, SE18BF, United Kingdom
Tel.: (44) 2070174555
Web Site: https://www.informatandm.com
Sales Range: $800-899.9 Million
Emp.: 4,000
Wireless & Mobile Technological Issues Reports Publisher
N.A.I.C.S.: 513130

Branch (Domestic):

Informa UK Limited - Baskerville (4)

AND PRIVATE COMPANIES — INFORMA PLC

Sheepen Pl, Colchester, CO3 3LP, Essex,
United Kingdom
Tel.: (44) 2070175537
Web Site: http://www.informa.com
Emp.: 250
Business Information Directories Publisher
N.A.I.C.S.: 513140
Emma Blaney (Dir-HR)

Subsidiary (Non-US):

Ovum Australia (3)
459 Little Collins Street Level 5, Melbourne,
3000, VIC, Australia
Tel.: (61) 396016720
Web Site: http://www.ovum.com
Software, Telecoms & IT Support Services
N.A.I.C.S.: 561499

Ovum Hong Kong (3)
23rd Floor China Online Centre, 333 Lockhart Road, Wanchai, China (Hong Kong)
Tel.: (852) 39667222
Sales Range: $25-49.9 Million
Emp.: 15
Software, Telecoms & IT Support Services
N.A.I.C.S.: 561499

Ovum Korea Limited (3)
3rd Floor Call center Susongtong, Jongno-Gu, Seoul, 110-727, Korea (South)
Tel.: (82) 232103966
Web Site: http://www.ovumkc.com
Sales Range: $25-49.9 Million
Emp.: 20
Software, Telecoms & IT Support Services
N.A.I.C.S.: 561499

Subsidiary (US):

Ovum, Inc. (3)
265 Franklin St, Boston, MA 02110
Tel.: (617) 523-1294
Web Site: https://www.ovum.com
Sales Range: $25-49.9 Million
Emp.: 65
IT & Telecom Consulting Services
N.A.I.C.S.: 541618

Subsidiary (Non-US):

Ovum-RHK (3)
14-24-1006 Ogawa-cho, Kawasaki-ku, Kawasaki, 210-0023, Kanagawa, Japan
Tel.: (81) 44 244 8461
Software, Telecoms & IT Support Services
N.A.I.C.S.: 561499

Branch (Domestic):

Ovum-RHK (4)
Taihei bldg 6th fl 3-6-23 Nyshigotanda,
Shinagawa-ku, Tokyo, 141-0031, Japan
Tel.: (81) 334925699
Web Site: http://www.ovum.com
Sales Range: $25-49.9 Million
Emp.: 200
Software, Telecoms & IT Support Services
N.A.I.C.S.: 561499
Takashi Kimura (Dir-Sls)

Subsidiary (Domestic):

Psychology Press (2)
27 Church Rd, Hove, BN3 2FA, E Sussex,
United Kingdom (100%)
Tel.: (44) 1273207411
Web Site: http://www.psypress.co.uk
Sales Range: $25-49.9 Million
Emp.: 30
Psychology Books & Journals Publisher
N.A.I.C.S.: 513130

Subsidiary (Non-US):

SAM Monaco Yacht Show (2)
7 rue Suffren-Reymond - Le Suffren, 98000,
Monaco, MC, Monaco
Tel.: (377) 93104170
Web Site:
https://www.monacoyachtshow.com
Logistics Consulting Servies
N.A.I.C.S.: 541614
Gaeelle Tallarida (Mng Dir)

Subsidiary (Domestic):

Taylor & Francis Group Limited (2)
2 & 4 Park Square Milton Park, Abingdon,
OX14 4RN, Oxford, United Kingdom
Tel.: (44) 2080520500

Web Site: https://www.taylorandfrancis.com
Books Publishing Services
N.A.I.C.S.: 513130
Leon Heward-Mills (Mng Dir-Researcher Svcs)

Subsidiary (Domestic):

SM 2016 Ltd. (3)
Park House 116 Park Street, London, W1K 6AF, United Kingdom
Tel.: (44) 845 034 4610
Resources Publishing Services
N.A.I.C.S.: 513199
Katrina Hulme-Cross (Sr Editor)

Subsidiary (US):

Taylor & Francis Group LLC (3)
2385 NW Executive Ctr Dr Ste 320, Boca Raton, FL 33431
Tel.: (561) 994-0555
Web Site: https://www.tandf.com
Sales Range: $50-74.9 Million
Emp.: 200
Books Publishing Services
N.A.I.C.S.: 513130

Subsidiary (Domestic):

Taylor & Francis Limited (3)
2 and 4 Park Square, Milton Park, Abingdon, OX14 4RN, Oxon, United
Kingdom (100%)
Tel.: (44) 2070176000
Web Site: https://www.taylorandfrancis.com
Sales Range: $200-249.9 Million
Emp.: 600
Educational Book Publisher
N.A.I.C.S.: 513130
Alex Robinson (Mgr-Mktg)

Subsidiary (Domestic):

UCL Press (2)
11 New Fetter Lane, London, EC4P 4EE,
United Kingdom
Tel.: (44) 1715839855
Web Site: http://www.tandf.co.uk
Sales Range: $25-49.9 Million
Emp.: 15
Geography, Planning, Environment, History & Sociology Book Publisher
N.A.I.C.S.: 513130

Informa Markets B.V. (1)
13th and 15th Floor de Entree 73 Toren A,
1101 BH, Amsterdam, Netherlands
Tel.: (31) 202455350
Event & Meeting Planning Services
N.A.I.C.S.: 561920

Informa Markets BN Co., Ltd. (1)
8/F Woodo Building 214 Manguro,
Jungnang-Gu, Seoul, Korea (South)
Tel.: (82) 267155400
Dental Care Services
N.A.I.C.S.: 621210

Informa Markets Japan Co. Ltd. (1)
Kanda 91 Bldg, 1-8-3 Kaji-cho Chiyoda-ku,
Tokyo, 101-0044, Japan
Tel.: (81) 352961011
Event & Meeting Planning Services
N.A.I.C.S.: 561920

Informa Markets Limited (1)
240 Blackfriars Road, London, SE1 8BF,
United Kingdom
Tel.: (44) 2079215000
Web Site: https://www.informamarkets.com
Event & Meeting Planning Services
N.A.I.C.S.: 561920

Informa Markets Ltda. (1)
Birmann 21 Avenida Doutora Ruth Cardoso
7221 - 22 Andar, Pinheiros, Sao Paulo,
05425-902, SP, Brazil
Tel.: (55) 1146320200
Event & Meeting Planning Services
N.A.I.C.S.: 561920

Informa Markets Malaysia Sdn Bhd (1)
Suite 5-01 Level 5 Sunway Visio Tower
Lingkaran SV Sunway Velocity, 55100,
Kuala Lumpur, Malaysia
Tel.: (60) 397712688
Event & Meeting Planning Services
N.A.I.C.S.: 561920

Informa Tianyi Exhibitions (Chengdu) Co., Ltd. (1)
No 1022 Western Federal Building No 19
on Renmin South Road, Chengdu, China
Tel.: (86) 2867936034
Exhibition & Event Services
N.A.I.C.S.: 561920

Novantas, Inc. (1)
485 Lexington Ave, New York, NY 10017,
Tel.: (212) 953-4444
Web Site: http://www.novantas.com
Management Consulting Services
N.A.I.C.S.: 541611
David G. Kaytes (Co-CEO)

PT Pamerindo Indonesia (1)
Menara Jamsostek Menara Utara Lantai 12
Unit TA-12-04, Jl Jendral Gatot Subroto No
38, Jakarta, 12710, Indonesia
Tel.: (62) 21 252 5320
Web Site: https://www.pamerindo.com
Trade Exhibition Services
N.A.I.C.S.: 561920

PT UBM Pameran Niaga Indonesia (1)
3/F Aquarius Building Jalan Sultan Iskandar
Muda No 7 Pondok Indah, Jakarta, 12240,
Indonesia
Tel.: (62) 2129305959
Trade Exhibition Services
N.A.I.C.S.: 561920

Pharma Intelligence U.K. Limited (1)
Suite 1 3rd Floor 11 - 12 St James's
Square, London, SW1Y 4LB, United Kingdom
Tel.: (44) 2080520700
Web Site:
  https://pharmaintelligence.informa.com
Pharmaceutical Mfr & Distr
N.A.I.C.S.: 325412

Shanghai IMsinoexpo Digital Services Co., Ltd. (1)
7/8F Urban Development International
Tower No 355 HongQiao Road, Shanghai,
200030, China
Tel.: (86) 2164371178
Show & Online Platform Services
N.A.I.C.S.: 561920

Shanghai UBM Showstar Exhibition Co Limited (1)
9/F Ciros Plaza No 388 West Nanjing
Road, Shanghai, 200003, China
Tel.: (86) 2161577288
Web Site: http://www.ubmshowstar.com
Trade Exhibition Services
N.A.I.C.S.: 561920
Grant Chen (Mng Dir)

Shanghai UBM Sinoexpo International Exhibitions Company Limited (1)
6-8/F Xian Dai Mansion 218 Xiang Yang
Road S, Shanghai, 200031, China
Tel.: (86) 2164371178
Trade Exhibition Services
N.A.I.C.S.: 561920

Shenzhen UBM Herong Exhibition Company (1)
Room 607 East Block Coastal Building
Haide 3rd Road, Nanshan District, Shanghai, 518054, Guangdong, China
Tel.: (86) 75586290901
Web Site: https://www.ubmherong.com
Emp.: 1,300
Trade Exhibition Services
N.A.I.C.S.: 561920
Kara Wei (Mgr-Sls)

Skipta, LLC (1)
319 Newburyport Tpke Ste 104, Rowley,
MA 01969
Tel.: (571) 919-2876
Web Site: http://www.skipta.com
Online Medical Community & Communication Services
N.A.I.C.S.: 621999
Theodore Search (Founder & CEO)

Southern Convention Services, Inc. (1)
10446 County Line Rd, Madison, AL 35756
Tel.: (256) 461-8815
Web Site: https://www.scsworx.com

Marketing Services
N.A.I.C.S.: 541613

Spotlight Financial, Inc. (1)
30501 Agoura Rd 2nd Fl, Agoura Hills, CA
91301
Web Site: http://www.bank-trends.com
Financial Bank Services
N.A.I.C.S.: 522110

Taylor & Francis (S) Pte. Ltd. (1)
103 Penang Road 04-01 Visioncrest Commercial, Singapore, 238467, Singapore
Tel.: (65) 69896600
Scholarly Journal & Textbook Publisher
N.A.I.C.S.: 513130

Trimtabs Investment Research, Inc. (1)
101 2nd St Ste 350, San Francisco, CA
94105
Tel.: (628) 220-2068
Web Site: http://www.trimtabs.com
Investment Advisory Services
N.A.I.C.S.: 523940
David Santschi (CEO)

UBM China (Hangzhou) Company Limited (1)
11th Floor No 2 Building Mansion Commerce Plaza 69 Wenzhou Road, Hangzhou,
310015, China
Tel.: (86) 57126895000
Trade Exhibition Services
N.A.I.C.S.: 561920

UBM China (Shanghai) Co., Limited (1)
9/F Ciros Plaza No 388 West Nanjing
Road, Shanghai, 200003, China
Tel.: (86) 2161577288
Trade Exhibition Services
N.A.I.C.S.: 561920

UBM Exhibitions Philippines, Inc. (1)
Unit I Mezzanine Floor Fly Ace Corporate
Center 13 Coral Way, Central Business
Park Metro Manila, Pasay, 1300, Philippines
Tel.: (63) 285517803
Trade Exhibition Services
N.A.I.C.S.: 561920

UBM Rotaforte Ullararasi Fuarcolik (1)
Molla Fenari Mah Bab-i Ali Cad No 9/301
Cagaloglu, Fatih, 34120, Istanbul, Turkiye
Tel.: (90) 2125190719
Web Site:
  http://www.march.istanbuljewelryshow.com
Jewelry Show & Exhibition Services
N.A.I.C.S.: 561920

UBM Trust Company Limited (1)
Rm 1806-1807 Fu Li Tian He Business
Mansion, No 4 Hua Ting Rd Lin He Dong
Rd Tian He District, Guangzhou, 510610,
China
Tel.: (86) 2038106161
Web Site: http://www.ubmtrust.com
Trade Exhibition Services
N.A.I.C.S.: 561920

UBM plc (1)
240 Blackfriars Road, London, SE1 8BF,
United Kingdom
Tel.: (44) 2079215000
Web Site: http://www.ubm.com
Rev.: $1,353,032,448
Assets: $3,308,042,240
Liabilities: $1,622,586,624
Net Worth: $1,685,455,616
Earnings: $243,246,336
Emp.: 3,933
Fiscal Year-end: 12/31/2017
Holding Company; Newspaper & Magazine
Publishing; Electronic News Distribution;
Trade Show & Exhibition Management
N.A.I.C.S.: 551112

Subsidiary (Non-US):

CNW Group Ltd. (2)
RBC WaterPark Place 88 Queens Quay
West Suite 3000, Toronto, M5J 0B8, ON,
Canada (100%)
Tel.: (416) 863-9350
Web Site: https://www.newswire.ca
Sales Range: $50-74.9 Million
Emp.: 250
News Publisher

INFORMA PLC

Informa plc—(Continued)
N.A.I.C.S.: 516210

Societe d'Editions Scientifiques et Culturelles SA (2)
21 Rue Camille Desmoulins, 92130, Issy-les-Moulineaux, France
Tel.: (33) 173281868
Newspaper Publishing Services
N.A.I.C.S.: 513110

Subsidiary (Domestic):

UBM (UK) Limited (2)
Ludgate House 240 Blackfriars Road, London, SE1 8VR, United Kingdom
Tel.: (44) 2079215000
Web Site: http://www.ubminformation.com
Business Media Services
N.A.I.C.S.: 541840

Subsidiary (Non-US):

UBM Asia Ltd. (2)
17th Fl China Resources Bldg, Wan Chai, Hong Kong, China (Hong Kong) (100%)
Tel.: (852) 28276211
Web Site: http://www.cmpasia.com
Sales Range: $250-299.9 Million
Emp.: 650
Business Media Services; Organizer of Trade Fairs
N.A.I.C.S.: 513120
Jime Essink (Pres)

Subsidiary (Non-US):

UBM Asia (Thailand) Co., Ltd. (3)
428 Ari Hills Building 18th Floor Phahonyothin Road Samsen Nai, Phaya Thai, Bangkok, 10400, Thailand
Tel.: (66) 2 036 0500
Web Site: http://www.ubmthailand.com
Business Media Information Services
N.A.I.C.S.: 513120

UBM China (Guangzhou) Co. Ltd. (3)
Room 1159-1164 China Hotel Office Tower, Liu Hua Lu, Guangzhou, 510015, China
Tel.: (86) 208 666 0158
Web Site: http://www.ubmkorea.com
Business Media Information Services
N.A.I.C.S.: 513120

UBM India Pvt. Ltd (3)
1st Floor North Wing S 14 Solitaire Corporate Park, Chakala Andheri East, Mumbai, 400093, India
Tel.: (91) 226 172 7000
Web Site: https://imp-jewellers.com
Sales Range: $50-74.9 Million
Emp.: 120
Business Media Services
N.A.I.C.S.: 513120

UBM Japan Co., Ltd. (3)
Kanda 91 Building 2F 1-8-3 Kaji-cho, Chiyoda-ku, Tokyo, 101 0044, Japan
Tel.: (81) 352961020
Web Site: http://www.ubmjapan.com
Sales Range: $25-49.9 Million
Emp.: 15
Business Media Information Services
N.A.I.C.S.: 513120
Christopher Eve (Pres)

UBM Korea Corporation (3)
8/F Woodo Building 214 Mangu-ro, Jungnang-gu, Seoul, 02121, Korea (South)
Tel.: (82) 26 715 5400
Web Site: http://www.ubmkorea.com
Sales Range: $25-49.9 Million
Emp.: 12
Business Media Information Services
N.A.I.C.S.: 513120

UBM Medica Asia Pte Limited (3)
3 Lim Teck Kim Road 10-01 Singapore Technology Building, Singapore, 88934, Singapore
Tel.: (65) 6223 3788
Media Publishing Services
N.A.I.C.S.: 541840

Subsidiary (US):

UBM LLC (2)
600 Community Dr, Manhasset, NY 11030-3847 (100%)

Tel.: (516) 562-5000
Web Site: http://www.ubm.com
Sales Range: $750-799.9 Million
Emp.: 3,376
High-Tech Publishing, Marketing & Information Services
N.A.I.C.S.: 541618

Subsidiary (Domestic):

Advanstar Communications Inc. (3)
2901 28th St Ste 100, Santa Monica, CA 90405
Tel.: (310) 445-4200
Web Site: http://ubmadvanstar.com
Trade & Business Journal Publisher & Trade Show Organizer
N.A.I.C.S.: 561920

Subsidiary (Domestic):

UBM Life Sciences Veterinary Group (4)
485 Rte 1 S Bldg F Ste 210, Iselin, NJ 08830
Tel.: (732) 596-0276
Web Site: http://www.ubmlifesciences.com
Veterinary Medicine & Journals Publisher
N.A.I.C.S.: 513120
Christie McFall (Mng Dir)

Subsidiary (Domestic):

Content Marketing Institute (3)
17040 Amber Dr, Cleveland, OH 44111
Tel.: (216) 941-5842
Web Site: http://www.contentmarketinginstitute.com
Emp.: 28
Marketing Consulting Services
N.A.I.C.S.: 541613
Joe Pulizzi (Founder)

Continuing Medical Education LLC (3)
806 Plaza Three, Jersey City, NJ 07311-1112
Tel.: (949) 250-1008
Rev.: $2,300,000
Emp.: 75
Provider of Continuing Medical Education
N.A.I.C.S.: 561990
Su Barnwell (Dir-Program Mgmt)

Makalot Group USA (3)
1515 Broadway, New York, NY 10036-8901
Tel.: (212) 869-1300
Clothing Mfr
N.A.I.C.S.: 424350

Unit (Domestic):

UBM Canon (3)
2901 28th St Ste 100, Santa Monica, CA 90405
Tel.: (310) 445-4200
Web Site: http://www.ubmcanon.com
Sales Range: $100-124.9 Million
Emp.: 150
Business-to-Business Marketing Services
N.A.I.C.S.: 541810

UBM Tech (3)
303 2nd St S Tower Ste 900, San Francisco, CA 94107
Tel.: (415) 947-6000
Web Site: http://www.tech.ubm.com
Emp.: 260
Marketing Services & Business Information
N.A.I.C.S.: 541613
Marco Pardi (Pres-Bus Tech Events Grp)

Subsidiary (Non-US):

UBMi B.V. (2)
De Entree 73 Toren A, Amsterdam, 1101 BH, Netherlands
Tel.: (31) 204099544
Sales Range: $25-49.9 Million
Emp.: 60
Business Consulting Services
N.A.I.C.S.: 541611

Winsight LLC (1)
300 S Riverside Plz Ste 1600, Chicago, IL 60606
Tel.: (312) 876-0004
Web Site: http://www.winsightmedia.com
Sales Range: $25-49.9 Million
Emp.: 50

Magazines, Periodicals & Online Media Publishers
N.A.I.C.S.: 513120
Lynda Hislop (Sr VP-Meetings & Events)

Subsidiary (Domestic):

Technomic Inc. (2)
300 S Riverside Plz Ste 1600, Chicago, IL 60606
Tel.: (312) 876-0004
Web Site: http://www.technomic.com
Food Service Management Consulting Services
N.A.I.C.S.: 541611
Bernadette Noone (VP)

Yachting Promotions, Inc. (1)
1115 NE 9th Ave, Fort Lauderdale, FL 33304-2110
Tel.: (954) 764-7642
Web Site:
https://www.showmanagement.com
Boating Trade Show Organizer
N.A.I.C.S.: 561920

INFORMA SA
Avda de La Industria 32, 28108, Alcobendas, Madrid, Spain
Tel.: (34) 916617119
Web Site: http://www.informa.es
Year Founded: 1998
Sales Range: $25-49.9 Million
Emp.: 226
On-Line Credit & Financial Information Compiler & Publisher
N.A.I.C.S.: 513199
Juan Maria Senz (Mng Dir)

Subsidiaries:

CTI Tecnologia y Gestion, S.A. (1)
Calle de la Industria 32, 28011, Madrid, Spain
Tel.: (34) 902 11 58 54
Web Site: http://www.ctisa.es
Information Technology & Credit Management Services
N.A.I.C.S.: 541512

DBK, S.A. (1)
Av Industria 32, Alcobendas, 28108, Madrid, Spain
Tel.: (34) 902176076
Web Site: http://www.dbk.es
Industry Analysis & Scientific Research Services
N.A.I.C.S.: 541690

Informa DB Ltd. (1)
Rua Barata Salgueiro 28 3rd Fl, 1250 044, Lisbon, Portugal
Tel.: (351) 213500300
Web Site: http://www.informadb.pt
Sales Range: $50-74.9 Million
Emp.: 130
Business Information Services
N.A.I.C.S.: 519290
Trissa Menezaoes (Mgr)

INFORMASCOPE
Prof Dr Ahmet Taner Kislali Mahallesi 2830 Cadde No 18, Cayyolu, 06810, Ankara, Turkiye
Tel.: (90) 3124467792
Web Site:
https://www.informascope.com
Information Technology Services
N.A.I.C.S.: 541512

INFORMATICS EDUCATION LTD
7 Temasek Boulevard 12-07 Suntec Tower One, Singapore, 038987, Singapore
Tel.: (65) 96984237 SG
Web Site:
http://www.informaticseducation.com
Year Founded: 1983
BOU—(SES)
Rev.: $5,517,321
Assets: $2,753,376
Liabilities: $3,999,831
Net Worth: ($1,246,455)

INTERNATIONAL PUBLIC

Earnings: ($1,161,899)
Emp.: 115
Fiscal Year-end: 06/30/21
Education Services
N.A.I.C.S.: 611710

Subsidiaries:

Informatics Academy Pte. Ltd. (1)
45 Middle Rd, Singapore, 188954, Singapore
Tel.: (65) 6580 4555
Educational Support Services
N.A.I.C.S.: 611710

Informatics Education (HK) Ltd. (1)
5th Floor Hechy Tower 9 Chatham Road South, Tsim Tsa Tsui, Kowloon, China (Hong Kong)
Tel.: (852) 35566000
Web Site: http://www.informatics.edu.hk
Educational Support Services
N.A.I.C.S.: 611699

Informatics Global Campus Pte Ltd (1)
12 Science Centre Road Informatics Campus, Singapore, 609080, Singapore
Tel.: (65) 9362 9292
Web Site:
http://www.informaticsglobalcampus.com
Information Technology Educational Services
N.A.I.C.S.: 611110

NCC Education (Beijing) Consulting Co., Ltd. (1)
LG2-T1 Tower C COFCO Plaza No 8 Jianguomennei Avenue, Dongcheng District, Beijing, 100005, China
Tel.: (86) 1065204030
Education Management Services
N.A.I.C.S.: 923110

NCC Education (M) Sdn Bhd (1)
Unit No C-7-4 Wisma Goshen Plaza Pantai No 5 Persiaran Pantai Baru, 59200, Kuala Lumpur, Malaysia
Tel.: (60) 322846200
Web Site: http://www.nccedu.com
Sales Range: $10-24.9 Million
Educational Support Services
N.A.I.C.S.: 611710

NCC Education Limited (1)
The Towers Towers Business Park Wilmslow Road, Didsbury, Manchester, M20 2EZ, Greater Manchester, United Kingdom
Tel.: (44) 1614386200
Web Site: http://www.nccedu.com
Educational Support Services
N.A.I.C.S.: 611710
Peter Ford (Dir)

Singapore Informatics Computer Institute (Pvt) Ltd (1)
249 R A De Mel Mawatha, Colombo, 00300, Western Province, Sri Lanka
Tel.: (94) 112699898
Web Site: http://www.singaporeinformatics.lk
Emp.: 15
Educational Support Services
N.A.I.C.S.: 611691

INFORMATICS SERVICES CORPORATION
No 4 Shangarf Mirdamad Blvd, Tehran, 15496 34511, Iran
Tel.: (98) 21 29982803
Web Site: http://www.isc.co.ir
Year Founded: 1993
INFO1—(THE)
Sales Range: Less than $1 Million
Emp.: 1,991
Software Development Services
N.A.I.C.S.: 541511

INFORMATIKA A.D.
Jevrejska 32, 11000, Belgrade, Serbia
Tel.: (381) 113215273
Web Site:
https://www.informatika.com
Year Founded: 1976

AND PRIVATE COMPANIES

INFM—(BEL)
Rev.: $73,467,563
Assets: $32,705,963
Liabilities: $19,859,063
Net Worth: $12,846,900
Earnings: $1,155,724
Emp.: 171
Fiscal Year-end: 12/31/23
Computer & Peripheral Equipment Mfr
N.A.I.C.S.: 334118
Slavoljub Kacarevic (Acting Mng Dir & Member-Exec Bd)

INFORMATION & COMMUNICATION NETWORKS PCL
D K J Building 5th Floor No 393 Sukhonthasawat Road, Latphrao, Bangkok, 10230, Thailand
Tel.: (66) 25530755
Web Site: https://www.icn.co.th
Year Founded: 2007
ICN—(THA)
Rev.: $54,302,952
Assets: $61,775,457
Liabilities: $35,616,965
Net Worth: $26,158,492
Earnings: $5,103,595
Emp.: 339
Fiscal Year-end: 12/31/23
Telecommunication Servicesb
N.A.I.C.S.: 517512
Monchai Manepairoj (Board of Directors & CEO)

INFORMATION & NETWORKING TECHNOLOGY JOINT STOCK COMPANY
Infonet Building 33 Vu Ngoc Phan Lang Ha Str, Dong Da District, Hanoi, Vietnam
Tel.: (84) 2437730793
Web Site: https://www.infonet.com.vn
Year Founded: 2003
Rev.: $19,479,837
Assets: $11,980,119
Liabilities: $6,751,851
Net Worth: $5,228,268
Earnings: $320,424
Fiscal Year-end: 12/31/15
Information Technology Consulting Services
N.A.I.C.S.: 541512
Tran Thanh Hai (Chm)

INFORMATION PLANNING CO., LTD.
2-3-13 Azuchi-cho Osaka International Building 28th floor, Chuo-ku, Osaka, 541-0052, Japan
Tel.: (81) 662658530
Web Site:
  https://www.jyohokikaku.co.jp
Year Founded: 1986
3712—(TKS)
Rev.: $25,013,520
Assets: $47,666,070
Liabilities: $8,699,430
Net Worth: $38,966,640
Earnings: $6,834,760
Emp.: 125
Fiscal Year-end: 09/30/23
Business Support Services
N.A.I.C.S.: 541513
Hitoshi Matsuoka (Pres)

INFORMATION SECURITY ONE (CHINA) LTD.
Unit 1208 Tower W3 Oriental Plaza No 1 East Changan Ave Dongcheng, Beijing, 100738, China
Tel.: (86) 1085181101
Web Site: http://bj.is-one.net
Sales Range: $1-9.9 Million
Integrated Network Security Solutions & Services
N.A.I.C.S.: 517810

INFORMATION SERVICES CORPORATION
300-10 Research Drive, Regina, S4S 7J7, SK, Canada
Tel.: (306) 787-8179 SK
Web Site: https://company.isc.ca
Year Founded: 2000
5IS—(DEU)
Rev.: $161,988,342
Assets: $404,988,224
Liabilities: $277,539,825
Net Worth: $127,448,398
Earnings: $18,911,980
Emp.: 545
Fiscal Year-end: 12/31/23
Saskatchewan Land Registry, Personal Property Registry, Survey Plan Registry & Geomatics Services
N.A.I.C.S.: 531390
Jeff Stusek (Pres & CEO)
Subsidiaries:
AVS Systems Inc. (1)
1325 Polson Drive Suite 201, Vernon, V1T 8H2, BC, Canada
Tel.: (250) 558-0726
Web Site: http://www.avssystems.ca
Financial Data Processing Services
N.A.I.C.S.: 522320

Alliance Online Ltd. (1)
201 Portage Ave 18th Floor, Winnipeg, R3B 3K6, MB, Canada
Tel.: (204) 926-8875
Web Site: https://www.allianceonline.ca
Public Data Management Services
N.A.I.C.S.: 541910

ESC Corporate Services Ltd. (1)
445 King Street West 4th Floor, Toronto, M5V 1K4, ON, Canada
Tel.: (416) 595-7177
Web Site: http://www.eservicecorp.ca
Corporate Legal Services
N.A.I.C.S.: 541199
Clare Colledge (Pres)

INFORMATION SERVICES NETWORK LIMITED
52 New Eskaton Road TMC Building 4th Floor, Dhaka, 1000, Bangladesh
Tel.: (880) 28322785
Web Site: http://www.bangla.net
ISNLTD—(CHT)
Rev.: $1,204,043
Assets: $1,340,906
Liabilities: $1,027,822
Net Worth: $313,084
Earnings: ($1,070,548)
Fiscal Year-end: 06/30/21
Internet Services
N.A.I.C.S.: 517810
Sayeed Hossain Chowdhury (Chm)

INFORMED TECHNOLOGIES INDIA LIMITED
20th Floor Nirmal Building Nariman Point, Mumbai, 400021, India
Tel.: (91) 2222023055
Web Site: https://www.informed-tech.com
Year Founded: 1946
504810—(BOM)
Rev.: $396,732
Assets: $2,073,317
Liabilities: $172,898
Net Worth: $1,900,418
Earnings: ($53,955)
Emp.: 24
Fiscal Year-end: 03/31/23
Business Process Outsourcing Services
N.A.I.C.S.: 561439
Suelve Gautam Khandelwal (Exec Dir)

INFORMER GROUP S.A.
Autokrat Nikolaou and Suggrou, 17671, Athens, Greece
Tel.: (30) 2109009200
Web Site: http://www.informer.gr
Sales Range: $1-9.9 Million
Emp.: 126
Computer Software Development & Distr
N.A.I.C.S.: 541511
Subsidiaries:
Artemis Information Management S.A. (1)
1 rue Bender, 1229, Luxembourg, Luxembourg
Tel.: (352) 45 91 45 1
Web Site: http://www.artemis.lu
Information Technology Consulting Services
N.A.I.C.S.: 541512
Fraschini Giorgio (Bus Mgr)

INFORTREND TECHNOLOGY INC.
8F No 102 Sec 3 Zhongshan Rd, Jhonghe District, New Taipei City, 23544, Taiwan
Tel.: (886) 222260126
Web Site: https://www.infortrend.com
2495—(TAI)
Rev.: $45,487,882
Assets: $216,794,949
Liabilities: $78,896,625
Net Worth: $137,898,324
Earnings: $7,895,811
Emp.: 435
Fiscal Year-end: 12/31/23
Data Storage Solutions
N.A.I.C.S.: 334112
Subsidiaries:
Infortrend Corporation (1)
435 Lakeside Dr, Sunnyvale, CA 94085
Tel.: (408) 988-5088
Emp.: 20
Network Storage Devices Mfr & Distr
N.A.I.C.S.: 334112

Infortrend Deutschland GmbH (1)
Wappenhalle Business Center Konrad-Zuse-Platz 8, 81829, Munich, Bavaria, Germany
Tel.: (49) 89207042650
Networking Products Mfr & Distr
N.A.I.C.S.: 334210

Infortrend Europe Ltd. (1)
57 Tempus Business Centre Kingsclere Road, Basingstoke, RG21 6XG, Hants, United Kingdom
Tel.: (44) 1256305220
Web Site: http://www.infortrend.com
Sales Range: $25-49.9 Million
Emp.: 20
Networked Storage Products Mfr
N.A.I.C.S.: 423430

Infortrend Japan, Inc. (1)
6F Okayasu Bldg 1-7-14 Shibaura, Minato-ku, Tokyo, 105-0023, Japan
Tel.: (81) 357306551
Networking Products Distr
N.A.I.C.S.: 423430

Infortrend Technology, Ltd. (1)
Room 1804 Block C Ocean International Center, Dis Chaoyang, Beijing, China
Tel.: (86) 1063106168
Web Site: https://www.infortrend.com.cn
Networking Products Distr
N.A.I.C.S.: 423430

INFOSERVE GROUP PLC
South Side Aviation Leeds Bradford International Airport, Leeds, LS19 7UG, West Yorkshire, United Kingdom
Tel.: (44) 845 36 77 400
Web Site:
  http://www.infoservegroup.com
Year Founded: 2006
Rev.: $168,082
Liabilities: $126,902
Net Worth: ($126,902)
Emp.: 85
Fiscal Year-end: 03/31/19
Online Search Services
N.A.I.C.S.: 541810
Derek I. J. Oliver (Founder & CEO)
Subsidiaries:
Infoserve Limited (1)
S Side Aviation Leeds Bradford Intl Airport, Leeds, LS19 7UG, West Yorkshire, United Kingdom
Tel.: (44) 8453677500
Web Site: http://www.infoserve.com
Sales Range: $50-74.9 Million
Online Business Directory & Search Services
N.A.I.C.S.: 519290
Derek Oliver (Dir-Ops)

INFOSMART GROUP LIMITED
41D 6F phase 2 Wah Lok Industry Centre No 31-35 Shan Mei Street, Fo Tan, Sha Tin, New Territories, China (Hong Kong)
Tel.: (852) 2637 0497 HK
Web Site:
  http://www.infosmartgp.com
Aluminum Die Cast Alloy Mfr
N.A.I.C.S.: 331314

INFOSYS LIMITED
Plot No 44/97 A 3rd cross Electronic City Hosur Road, Bengaluru, 560 100, Karnataka, India
Tel.: (91) 8028520261 In
Web Site: https://www.infosys.com
Year Founded: 1981
INFY—(NYSE)
Rev.: $18,562,000,000
Assets: $16,523,000,000
Liabilities: $5,918,000,000
Net Worth: $10,605,000,000
Earnings: $3,169,000,000
Emp.: 317,240
Fiscal Year-end: 03/31/24
IT Infrastructure Services & Business Solutions Developer
N.A.I.C.S.: 541511
Nandan M. Nilekani (Co-Founder)
Subsidiaries:
Danske IT & Support services India Private Limited (1)
7th and 8th Floor Campus 5B Plot B RMZ Ecoworld SEZ Campus, Outer Ring Road Devarabeesanahalli, Bengaluru, 560103, India
Tel.: (91) 8046771000
Web Site: http://www.danskeit.co.in
Emp.: 1,500
Investment Banking Services
N.A.I.C.S.: 523150
Deval Shah (Mng Dir)

Fluido Denmark A/S (1)
Strandveien 125, 2900, Hellerup, Denmark
Tel.: (45) 89884235
Sales Force Consulting Services
N.A.I.C.S.: 541613

Fluido Norway A/S (1)
Tollbugata 8, 0152, Oslo, Norway
Tel.: (47) 23960763
Sales Force Consulting Services
N.A.I.C.S.: 541613

Fluido Oy (1)
Keilaranta 1, 02150, Espoo, Finland
Tel.: (358) 67812121
Web Site: http://www.fluidogroup.com
Sales Force Consulting Services
N.A.I.C.S.: 541613
Kai Makela (CEO)

Fluido Slovakia s.r.o (1)
Lazovna 62, 97401, Banska Bystrica, Slovakia
Tel.: (421) 484180256
Sales Force Consulting Services
N.A.I.C.S.: 541613

Fluido Sweden AB (1)

INFOSYS LIMITED

Infosys Limited—(Continued)
Drottninggatan 71D, 111 36, Stockholm, Sweden
Tel.: (46) 812458830
Sales Force Consulting Services
N.A.I.C.S.: 541613

HIPUS Co., Ltd. (1)
Shin-Otemachi Building 2-2-1 Otemachi, Chiyoda-ku, Tokyo, 100-0004, Japan
Tel.: (81) 332314570
Web Site: http://www.hipus.com
Business Consulting Services
N.A.I.C.S.: 541611
Shinichiro Nagagata (CEO)

Infosys BPM Limited (1)
Plot no 26/3 26/4 26/6, Electronics City Hosur Road, Bengaluru, 560 100, India **(99.98%)**
Tel.: (91) 8028522405
Sales Range: $25-49.9 Million
Emp.: 20,000
Business Process Outsourcing
N.A.I.C.S.: 561499
Anantha Radhakrishnan (CEO & Mng Dir)

Subsidiary (US):

Infosys McCamish Systems LLC (2)
3225 Cumberland Blvd Ste 700, Atlanta, GA 30339
Tel.: (770) 690-1500
Web Site: https://www.infosysbpm.com
Software Services
N.A.I.C.S.: 541511
Richard E. Magner (CEO & Mng Dir)

Subsidiary (Non-US):

Infosys Poland Sp. z o.o. (2)
ul Pomorska 106 A, 91-402, Lodz, Poland
Tel.: (48) 422781500
Software Services
N.A.I.C.S.: 541511

Infosys Consulting Holding AG (1)
Obstgartenstrasse 27, 8302, Kloten, Switzerland
Tel.: (41) 444341100
IT Services
N.A.I.C.S.: 541511

Infosys Consulting Pte. Ltd. (1)
Suntec Office Level 43 Unit 02 Suntec Tower 2 9 Temasek Blvd, Singapore, 038989, Singapore
Tel.: (65) 65728400
IT Services
N.A.I.C.S.: 541511

Infosys Consulting SAS (1)
Tour Opus 12 4th Floor 77 Esplanade du General de Gaulle, La Defense 9, 92914, Paris, France
Tel.: (33) 156391200
IT Services
N.A.I.C.S.: 541511

Infosys Consulting, Inc. (1)
6100 Tennyson Pkwy Ste 200, Plano, TX 75024 **(100%)**
Tel.: (469) 229-9400
Sales Range: $1-9.9 Million
Emp.: 304
Business Consulting Services
N.A.I.C.S.: 541618

Infosys Management Consulting Pty. Limited (1)
Level 3 100 Arthur Street, North Sydney, 2060, NSW, Australia
Tel.: (61) 289121500
IT Services
N.A.I.C.S.: 541511

Infosys Middle East FZ LLC (1)
22nd Floor Aurora Tower, PO Box No 502292, Dubai Internet City, Dubai, United Arab Emirates
Tel.: (971) 44330100
IT Services
N.A.I.C.S.: 541511

Infosys Nova Holdings LLC (1)
2400 N Glenville Dr Ste C150, Richardson, TX 75082
Tel.: (214) 306-2100
IT Services
N.A.I.C.S.: 541511

Infosys Public Services, Inc. (1)
700 King Farm Blvd Ste 200, Rockville, MD 20850
Tel.: (301) 354-8600
Web Site: https://www.infosyspublicservices.com
Information Technology Consulting Services
N.A.I.C.S.: 541511
Eric Paternoster (Co-Pres & CEO)

Infosys South Africa (Pty.) Ltd (1)
Johannesburg West Towers 2nd Floor Maude Street, Sandton, Johannesburg, 2195, South Africa
Tel.: (27) 873633610
IT Services
N.A.I.C.S.: 541511

Infosys Technologies (Australia) Pty. Limited (1)
Level 4 697 Collins Street, Docklands, 3008, VIC, Australia **(100%)**
Tel.: (61) 398602000
Sales Range: $50-74.9 Million
Emp.: 306
Computer Systems Design
N.A.I.C.S.: 541512
Asheesh Mehra (Head-Sls-BPO & APAC & Asst VP)

Infosys Technologies (China) Co. Ltd. (1)
12F fangtianxia building No 82Yueda lane, Binjiang District, Hangzhou, 310052, China **(100%)**
Tel.: (86) 57187930031
Sales Range: $1-9.9 Million
Emp.: 1,053
Computer Programming Services
N.A.I.C.S.: 541511

Infosys Technologies (Shanghai) Co. Limited (1)
No 506 Ziyue Road, Minhang District, Shanghai, China
Tel.: (86) 2158843000
Software Services
N.A.I.C.S.: 541511

Infosys Technologies (Sweden) AB (1)
Karlavagen 108 lift 3 9th floor, 115 26, Stockholm, Sweden **(100%)**
Tel.: (46) 84631112
Business Consulting & Custom Information Technology Services
N.A.I.C.S.: 541618

Infosys Technologies S. de R. L. de C. V. (1)
Corporativo Santa Maria No 130 Boulevard Diaz Ordaz 18th Floor Col, 4piso Col, Santa Maria, 64650, Monterrey, Nuevo Leon, Mexico **(100%)**
Tel.: (52) 8188509300
Sales Range: Less than $1 Million
Emp.: 221
Business Consulting & Information Technology Services
N.A.I.C.S.: 541618

Infy Consulting B.V. (1)
World Trade Center I Tower 7th Floor Strawinskylaan, 1077 XX, Amsterdam, Netherlands
Tel.: (31) 207965500
IT Services
N.A.I.C.S.: 541511

Lodestone Management Consultants AG (1)
Obstgartenstrasse 27 Kloten, Postfach 201, Kloten, 8808, Zurich, Switzerland
Tel.: (41) 444341100
Web Site: http://www.lodestonemc.com
Sales Range: $250-299.9 Million
Emp.: 800
Business Management Consulting Services
N.A.I.C.S.: 541611
Peter Odman (Partner & Member-Exec Bd)

Outbox Systems, Inc. (1)
10 W Broadway Ste 500, Salt Lake City, UT 84101
Web Site: https://www.simplus.com
Financial Solutions Provider
N.A.I.C.S.: 522990
Ryan Westwood (Co-Founder & CEO)

Subsidiary (Domestic):

CRM manager, LLC (2)

5 Great Vly Pkwy, Malvern, PA 19355
Tel.: (610) 889-2050
Software Publisher
N.A.I.C.S.: 513210

Panaya Inc. (1)
Continental Plaza 411 Hackensack Ave, Hackensack, NJ 07601
Tel.: (201) 273-7287
Software Services
N.A.I.C.S.: 541511

Panaya Ltd. (1)
6 HaHarash St, Hod Hasharon, 4524079, Israel
Tel.: (972) 97618000
Web Site: https://www.panaya.com
Software Services
N.A.I.C.S.: 541511
David Binny (CEO)

Simplus Australia Pty. Ltd. (1)
Level 7 151 Castlereagh Street, Sydney, 2000, NSW, Australia
Tel.: (61) 292999001
Sales Force Consulting Services
N.A.I.C.S.: 541613

Stater Belgium N.V. / S.A. (1)
Rue de la Chancellerie 17A, 1000, Brussels, Belgium
Tel.: (32) 28891430
IT Services
N.A.I.C.S.: 541511

Stater N.V. (1)
Podium 1, Postbus 2686, 3800 GE, Amersfoort, Netherlands **(75%)**
Tel.: (31) 334509300
Web Site: https://stater.nl
Emp.: 1,400
Mortgage Services
N.A.I.C.S.: 522310
Erwin Dreuning (CEO)

Subsidiary (Domestic):

HypoCasso B.V. (2)
Podium 1, 3826 PA, Amersfoort, Netherlands
Tel.: (31) 334509583
Web Site: http://corporate.hypocasso.nl
Mortgage Consulting Services
N.A.I.C.S.: 522310

WongDoody Holding Company, Inc. (1)
1011 Western Ave Ste 900, Seattle, WA 98104
Tel.: (206) 624-5325
Web Site: http://www.wongdoody.com
Advetising Agency
N.A.I.C.S.: 541810
Tracy Wong (Founder & Chm)

Branch (Domestic):

WongDoody - Culver (2)
8500 Steller Dr Ste 5, Culver City, CA 90232
Tel.: (310) 280-7800
Advetising Agency
N.A.I.C.S.: 541810
Ben Wiener (CEO)

INFOTEL SA

Le Valmy 6/8/18 avenue Leon Gaumont, 75020, Paris, Cedex, France
Tel.: (33) 148973838
Web Site: https://www.infotel.com
Year Founded: 1979
INF—(EUR)
Rev.: $324,215,411
Assets: $279,968,703
Liabilities: $155,751,133
Net Worth: $124,217,570
Earnings: $22,935,463
Emp.: 1,869
Fiscal Year-end: 12/31/22
Management Software Solutions & IT Consulting Services
N.A.I.C.S.: 513210
Bernard Connes-Lafforet (Founder, Chm & CEO)

Subsidiaries:

Collaboractif Portail Services SARL (1)

INTERNATIONAL PUBLIC

22 avenue Rene Cassin, 69009, Lyon, France
Tel.: (33) 478354533
Web Site: http://www.collaboractif.fr
Web Portal Services
N.A.I.C.S.: 519290

Infotel Business Consulting SAS (1)
13 rue Madeleine Michelis, 92205, Neuilly-sur-Seine, France
Tel.: (33) 155621920
Web Site: http://www.consulting.infotel.com
Management Consulting Services
N.A.I.C.S.: 541611

Infotel Corporation (1)
PO Box 7730, Saint Petersburg, FL 33743-7730
Tel.: (727) 343-5958
Web Site: https://infotelcorp.com
Sales Range: $25-49.9 Million
HelpDesk & Software Services
N.A.I.C.S.: 334610

Infotel GmbH (1)
Walter-Kolb-Str 9-11, Frankfurt am Main, D 60594, Germany
Tel.: (49) 6996 21 76 59
Web Site: http://www.infotel.com
Software Training Services
N.A.I.C.S.: 611710

Insoft Infotel Software GmbH (1)
Sternstr 9-11, 40479, Dusseldorf, Germany
Tel.: (49) 2114403166
Web Site: https://www.insoft-infotel.com
Software Development Services
N.A.I.C.S.: 541511
Bernard Lafforet (Chm & CEO)

INFOTMIC CO., LTD.

3F No 2 Building No 111 Xiangke Road, Changning District, Shanghai, 201204, China
Tel.: (86) 21588553066
Web Site: https://www.infotm.com
Year Founded: 1993
000670—(SSE)
Rev.: $438,637,680
Assets: $277,629,768
Liabilities: $228,807,072
Net Worth: $48,822,696
Earnings: $2,091,960
Emp.: 200
Fiscal Year-end: 12/31/22
Real Estate Property Development Services
N.A.I.C.S.: 531390
Shi Haoliang (Chm)

Subsidiaries:

Shanghai InfoTM Microelectronics Co., LTD. (1)
Room 512 R and D Buiding Tsinghua Hi-Tech Park, Nanshan District, Shenzhen, 518057, China
Tel.: (86) 75582718600
Computer Peripheral Equipment Mfr
N.A.I.C.S.: 334118

INFOTRACK PTY LTD.

Level 8 135 King Street, Sydney, 2000, NSW, Australia
Tel.: (61) 2 8203 7600
Web Site: http://www.infotrack.com.au
Year Founded: 2012
Online Searching & Information Services
N.A.I.C.S.: 519290
John Ahern (CEO)

Subsidiaries:

One Legal, LLC (1)
1400 N McDowell Blvd, Petaluma, CA 94954
Tel.: (213) 617-1212
Web Site: http://www.onelegal.com
Law firm
N.A.I.C.S.: 541199
Robert Battaglia (Founder)

INFOVINE CO., LTD.

Mapo-daero 144 5F Taeyeong Bldg 252 - 5, Gongdeok-dong Mapo-gu, Seoul, 04212, Korea (South)
Tel.: (82) 237753366
Web Site: https://www.infovine.co.kr
Year Founded: 2000
115300—(KRS)
Rev.: $16,034,679
Assets: $84,526,432
Liabilities: $6,276,186
Net Worth: $78,250,247
Earnings: $4,610,390
Emp.: 72
Fiscal Year-end: 12/31/22
Electronic Payment Services
N.A.I.C.S.: 522320
Kwon Seung Jun *(CEO)*

INFOVISION OPTOELECTRONICS KUNSHN CO., LTD.
No 1 Longteng Road, Kunshan Development Zone, Kunshan, 215300, Jiangsu, China
Tel.: (86) 51257278888
Web Site: http://www.ivo.com.cn
Year Founded: 2005
688055—(SHG)
Rev.: $590,629,385
Assets: $965,359,498
Liabilities: $290,896,585
Net Worth: $674,462,913
Earnings: $35,330,116
Emp.: 3,000
Fiscal Year-end: 12/31/22
Electronic Product Mfr & Distr
N.A.I.C.S.: 334419
Yuan Tao *(Chm & Gen Mgr)*

INFRA HOLDING PLC
38 Maistor Aleksi Rilets Str, 1618, Sofia, Bulgaria
Tel.: (359) 28952410
Web Site: https://www.infraholding.bg
Year Founded: 2007
INFH—(BUL)
Sales Range: Less than $1 Million
Highway Construction Services
N.A.I.C.S.: 237310
Anton Bozhkov *(Chm)*

INFRA INDUSTRIES LTD.
Survey No 46 Plot No 5 Pen Khopoli Road Village Arav P O Ransai, Dist Raigad, Mumbai, 402 107, India
Tel.: (91) 2267929912
Web Site: https://www.infra.co.in
Year Founded: 1991
530777—(BOM)
Sales Range: Less than $1 Million
Emp.: 27
Plastic Storage Tank Mfr
N.A.I.C.S.: 326199
Mukesh Bhupendra Ambani *(Mng Dir)*

INFRAAVEST LIMITED
20 Sin Ming Lane 03-52/53 Midview City, Singapore, 573968, Singapore
Tel.: (65) 6836 5521 HK
Web Site: http://www.infraavest.com
Year Founded: 1992
Emp.: 20
Oil & Gas Industry Equity Investment Firm
N.A.I.C.S.: 523999
Brian Chang *(Founder)*
Subsidiaries:

Fauji Oil Terminal & Distribution Company Limited (1)
Port Bin Qasim, PO Box 9101 PQA, Karachi, 75020, Pakistan (44%)
Tel.: (92) 21 3472 0003
Web Site: http://www.fotco.pk
Petroleum Bulk Terminal Operator & Distr
N.A.I.C.S.: 424710
Shujahat Hussain *(Asst Mgr-Ops & Technical Svcs)*

INFRABEL NV
Marcel Broodthaersplein 2, 1060, Brussels, Belgium
Tel.: (32) 25252211
Web Site: http://www.infrabel.be
Year Founded: 2005
Railway Transportation Services
N.A.I.C.S.: 488210
Luc Lallemand *(CEO)*

INFRACOM GROUP AB
Gamlestadsvagen 1, 415 11, Gothenburg, Sweden
Tel.: (46) 105220000
Web Site: https://infracomgroup.se
8HG—(DEU)
Web Hosting Services
N.A.I.C.S.: 518210
Bo Kjellberg *(CEO)*

INFRAHARTA HOLDINGS BERHAD
B-3-9 3rd Floor Block B Megan Avenue II No 12, Jalan Yap Kwan Seng, 50450, Kuala Lumpur, Malaysia
Tel.: (60) 362011120 MY
Web Site: https://www.infraharta.com
Year Founded: 2007
VERTICE—(KLS)
Rev.: $1,997,880
Assets: $24,706,828
Liabilities: $7,259,300
Net Worth: $17,447,528
Earnings: ($9,237,711)
Emp.: 1,206
Fiscal Year-end: 03/31/22
Women's Clothing Mfr & Retailer
N.A.I.C.S.: 315250
Khim Soon Seow *(Exec Deputy Chm)*
Subsidiaries:

Greenview Pavilion Sdn. Bhd. (1)
No 38 Jalan Bayu Tinggi 2/ks 6 Batu Unjur, 41200, Klang, Selangor, Malaysia
Tel.: (60) 43838988
Web Site: https://www.greenviewpavilion.com.my
Condominium & Factories Services
N.A.I.C.S.: 531312

Infraharta Bina Sdn. Bhd. (1)
Unit 9-2 Level 9 Wisma Miramas 1 Jalan 2/109E Taman Desa, 58100, Kuala Lumpur, Malaysia
Tel.: (60) 379721331
Web Site: https://www.infraharta.com
Civil Engineering Services
N.A.I.C.S.: 541330

INFRANODE HOLDING AB
Kungsgatan 32, SE-11535, Stockholm, Sweden
Tel.: (46) 852523900 SE
Web Site: http://infranode.se
Year Founded: 2013
Investment Management Service
N.A.I.C.S.: 523999
Christian Doglia *(CEO & Partner)*
Subsidiaries:

Oslofjord Varme AS (1)
Brynsveien 2, 1338, Sandvika, Norway (42.5%)
Tel.: (47) 67804960
Web Site: http://www.oslofjordvarme.no
Sales Range: $75-99.9 Million
Emp.: 14
District Heating & Cooling Services
N.A.I.C.S.: 221330

INFRASET PUBLIC COMPANY LIMITED
165/37-39 Ram Intra Road, Anusawari Subdistrict, Bangkok, 10220, Thailand
Tel.: (66) 20927444 TH
Web Site: https://www.infraset.co.th
Year Founded: 2006

INSET—(THA)
Rev.: $48,398,285
Assets: $55,103,320
Liabilities: $14,934,127
Net Worth: $40,169,193
Earnings: $3,186,474
Emp.: 109
Fiscal Year-end: 12/31/23
Information Technology Services
N.A.I.C.S.: 541512
Metha Chotiapisitkul *(Deputy Mng Dir-Gen Mgmt)*

INFRASTRUCTURE DEVELOPMENT AND CONSTRUCTION CORPORATION
G1 Building South Thanh Xuan, Thanh Xuan District, Hanoi, Vietnam
Tel.: (84) 48542365
Web Site: http://www.licogi.com.vn
Sales Range: $1-4.9 Billion
Emp.: 8,000
Heavy & Civil Engineering Construction Services
N.A.I.C.S.: 237990
Quang Hong Ngo *(Chm)*
Subsidiaries:

Dong Anh Investment, Construction and Building Material Joint Stock Company (1)
Group 8 Dong Anh District, Hanoi, Vietnam
Tel.: (84) 04 38832504
Web Site: http://www.domatco.vn
Construction Materials Distr
N.A.I.C.S.: 327910

LICOGI construction and foundation engineering Joint Stock Company No.20 (1)
61E De La Thanh Ba Dinh, Hanoi, Vietnam
Tel.: (84) 04 37754676
Engineeering Services
N.A.I.C.S.: 327910

Licogi 13 Joint Stock Company (1)
4th FloorLICOGI13 TOWER164 Khuat Duy TienNhan Chinh Ward, Thanh Xuan District, Hanoi, Vietnam
Tel.: (84) 38544623
Web Site: https://www.licogi13.com.vn
Rev.: $296,617,100
Assets: $647,036,000
Liabilities: $516,379,200
Net Worth: $130,656,800
Earnings: $758,300
Emp.: 390
Fiscal Year-end: 12/31/2022
Heavy & Civil Construction Services
N.A.I.C.S.: 237990

Licogi 16.6 Joint Stock Company (1)
4th Floor 34 Company Building 164 Khuat Duy Tien Street, Nhan Chinh Ward Thanh Xuan, Hanoi, Vietnam
Tel.: (84) 2422250718
Web Site: http://www.licogi166.vn
Rev.: $3,161,141
Assets: $13,142,005
Liabilities: $9,751,054
Net Worth: $3,390,951
Earnings: $10,252
Emp.: 450
Fiscal Year-end: 12/31/2020
Heavy Construction Services
N.A.I.C.S.: 237990
Vu Quoc Su *(Chm)*

INFRASTRUCTURE INDIA PLC
55 Athol Street, Douglas, IM1 1LA, Isle of Man
Tel.: (44) 1624681250 IM
Web Site: https://www.iiplc.com
IIP—(AIM)
Rev.: $265,085
Assets: $125,568,038
Liabilities: $359,000,252
Net Worth: ($233,432,214)
Earnings: ($74,784,145)
Emp.: 320
Fiscal Year-end: 03/31/23
Investment Services

N.A.I.C.S.: 523999
Philip Scales *(Sec)*
Subsidiaries:

Indian Energy Limited (1)
528 Laxmi Mall Building 5 Laxmi Industrial Estate, Anheri West, Mumbai, 400053, India
Tel.: (91) 2242086666
Web Site: http://www.indianenergy.in
Wind Power
N.A.I.C.S.: 221118
Shantanu Bagchi *(COO)*

INFRASTRUCTURE LEASING & FINANCIAL SERVICES LIMITED
The IL FS Financial Centre Plot C22 G Block Bandra Kurla Complex, Post Box No 8145, Bandra East, Mumbai, 400 051, India
Tel.: (91) 2226533333
Web Site: http://www.ilfsindia.com
Rev.: $118,118,150
Assets: $594,811,585
Liabilities: $3,023,313,098
Net Worth: ($2,428,501,514)
Earnings: ($3,232,812,755)
Emp.: 116
Fiscal Year-end: 03/31/19
Equipment Leasing & Other Financing Services
N.A.I.C.S.: 532490
Maharudra M. Wagle *(CFO-Grp)*
Subsidiaries:

Andra Pradesh Expressway Limited (1)
First Floor 2-19-10-9/7 Balaji Nagar Near Lakshmi, Stantanpuram, Kurnool, 518 006, India
Tel.: (91) 8518 254880
Road Construction Services
N.A.I.C.S.: 237310
Mallikarjun Reddy *(Office Mgr)*

Area De Servicio Coiros SL (1)
Calle San Severo 18, 28042, Madrid, Spain
Tel.: (34) 913 294 477
Eletric Power Generation Services
N.A.I.C.S.: 221118

Baleshwar Kharagpur Expressway Limited (1)
Plot No 125 Hijli co-operative society Prem Bazar, Paschim Medinipur, 721 306, Kharagpur, West Bengal, India
Tel.: (91) 3222 278008
Highway Construction Services
N.A.I.C.S.: 237310
Narayan Nayak *(Office Mgr)*

Control 7, S.A (1)
Calle E Parcela 59-61 Nave 9, 50057, Zaragoza, Spain
Tel.: (34) 976 571 227
Web Site: http://www.control7.es
Waste Water Disposal Services
N.A.I.C.S.: 221320

Critical Paradigm Gestlat BPO Pvt Limited (1)
Survey No 51/1 Ward No 192 Via Chikka Begur Gate Lakshmi Layout, Bommanahalli, Bengaluru, 560068, Karnataka, India
Tel.: (91) 80 4128 0442
Web Site: http://www.cpgindia.in
Emp.: 40
Customer Care Services
N.A.I.C.S.: 561422
Shivaram Prasad *(Mgr-Ops)*

Elsamex Brasil LTDA (1)
Rua Caramuru 417, Sao Paulo, Brazil
Tel.: (55) 11 55848404
Highway Construction Services
N.A.I.C.S.: 237310

Elsamex India Pvt Limited (1)
306 Aggarwal Mall Plot No - 3 Sector - 5, Dwarka, 110075, New Delhi, India
Tel.: (91) 11 46154600
Web Site: http://www.elsamexindia.com
Highway Construction Services
N.A.I.C.S.: 237310

INFRASTRUCTURE LEASING & FINANCIAL SERVICES LIMITED

Infrastructure Leasing & Financial Services Limited—(Continued)

Elsamex Portugal S.A (1)
Rua Quinta das Romeiras Ed Eduardo Viana N 104 5 Andar, Miraflores, 1495-236, Alges, Portugal
Tel.: (351) 219 108 880
Web Site: http://www.elsamex.pt
Highway Construction Services
N.A.I.C.S.: 237310

Futureage Infrastructure India Limited (1)
3rd Floor A1 Crescent Krishna Metropolis Rukminipuri ECIL-Post, Hyderabad, 500062, Andhra Pradesh, India
Tel.: (91) 98 49 021934
Web Site: http://www.futureage.in
Emp.: 22
Parking Garage Construction Services
N.A.I.C.S.: 236220
Mosalikanti Kameswara Rao (Founder & Mng Dir)

Goodearth Shipbuilding Pvt Limited (1)
5th Floor Tower 2 TVH Beliciaa Towers No 94 MRC Nagar, Chennai, 600 028, India
Tel.: (91) 44 43033444
Web Site: http://www.archeangroup.com
Ship Building Services
N.A.I.C.S.: 336611
Balakrishna K. (Gen Mgr)

IL&FS Energy Development Company Limited (1)
Core 4B 4th Floor India Habitat Centre Lodhi Road, New Delhi, 110003, India
Tel.: (91) 11 2468 2060
Power Plant Construction Services
N.A.I.C.S.: 237130

IL&FS Financial Services Limited (1)
3rd Floor D Quadrant IL&FS Financial Centre, Plot No C-22 G Block, Bandra Kurla Complex, Bandra, 400051, Mumbai, India **(100%)**
Tel.: (91) 22 2659 3560
Web Site: http://www.ilfsfin.com
Sales Range: $200-249.9 Million
Emp.: 180
Investment Banking & Corporate Advisory Services
N.A.I.C.S.: 523150
Asesh Jyoti Dutta (COO-Bus Dev)

Subsidiary (Non-US):

IL&FS Global Financial Services (HK) Limited (1)
Suites 706-07 7th Floor Citibank Tower 3 Garden Road, Central, China (Hong Kong)
Tel.: (852) 3976 6666
Investment Advisory Services
N.A.I.C.S.: 523940

IL&FS Global Financial Services (ME) Limited (2)
Office No 402 & 403 Tower 1 Currency House, PO Box 482084, Dubai, United Arab Emirates
Tel.: (971) 4 427 9707
Web Site: http://www.ilfsifin.com
Emp.: 6
Investment Advisory Services
N.A.I.C.S.: 523940

IL&FS Global Financial Services (UK) Limited (2)
40 Queen Street, London, EC4R 1DD, United Kingdom
Tel.: (44) 20 7651 4900
Web Site: http://www.ilfsifin.com
Emp.: 5
Investment Advisory Services
N.A.I.C.S.: 523940

IL&FS Investment Advisor LLC (1)
IFS Court Twenty Eight Cybercity, Ebene, Mauritius
Tel.: (230) 467 3000
Investment Advisory Services
N.A.I.C.S.: 523940

IL&FS Investment Managers Limited (1)
The IL FS Financial Centre 1st Floor Plot No C 22 G Block, Bandra Kurla Complex Bandra East, Mumbai, 400 051, India
Tel.: (91) 2226533333
Web Site: https://www.iimlindia.com
Rev.: $8,002,299
Assets: $34,095,434
Liabilities: $3,611,872
Net Worth: $30,483,562
Earnings: $1,307,110
Emp.: 25
Fiscal Year-end: 03/31/2021
Privater Equity Firm
N.A.I.C.S.: 523999
Susim Mukul Datta (Chm)

IL&FS Rail Limited (1)
2nd Floor Ambience Corporate Tower Ambience Island National Highway 8, Gurgaon, 122 001, Haryana, India
Tel.: (91) 124 4716300
Web Site: http://www.ilfsrail.com
Emp.: 49
Railway Construction Services
N.A.I.C.S.: 237990
Keshav Mishra (Mgr)

IL&FS Securities Services Limited (1)
IL&FS House Plot No 14 Raheja Vihar Chandivali Andheri E, Mumbai, 400 072, India **(81.24%)**
Tel.: (91) 22 42493000
Web Site: http://www.ilfsdp.com
Investment Banking Services
N.A.I.C.S.: 523150
Girish Palshikar (Sr VP)

IL&FS Transportation Networks Limited (1)
The IL&FS Financial Centre Plot C22 G Block Bandra Kurla Complex, Bandra East, Mumbai, 400 051, Maharashtra, India
Tel.: (91) 2226533333
Web Site: http://www.itnlindia.com
Rev.: $31,725,330
Assets: $408,702,840
Liabilities: $2,437,051,890
Net Worth: $(2,028,349,050)
Earnings: $(132,807,675)
Emp.: 101
Fiscal Year-end: 03/31/2020
Road Construction Services
N.A.I.C.S.: 237310
Krishna Ghag (Officer-Compliance, Sec & VP)

Subsidiary (Domestic):

Chhattisgarh Highway Development Company Limited (2)
House no 705 Sector-2 Avanti Vihar Infront of White House, Near Khushi Vihar Telibandha, Raipur, 492 006, India
Tel.: (91) 771 4268373
Highway Construction Services
N.A.I.C.S.: 237310

Moradabad Bareily Expressway Limited (2)
Block-A Incampus Drive in 24 Hotel & Resto Opposite Circuit House, Delhi Road, Moradabad, 244 001, India
Tel.: (91) 591 2480044
Highway Construction Services
N.A.I.C.S.: 237310

North Karnataka Expressway Limited (2)
Plot No 798 Sector No V Double Rd Shrinagarmalmaruti Extn, Belgaum, 590016, India
Tel.: (91) 831 2458280
Highway Construction Services
N.A.I.C.S.: 237310

Pune Sholapur Road Development Company Limited (2)
Crossroads Commercial Complex Unit No 101-105 New Pune Naka Pune Road, Sholapur, 413 002, India
Tel.: (91) 217 2623201
Highway Construction Services
N.A.I.C.S.: 237310

Vansh Nimay Infraprojects Limited (2)
Block No 301-304 3rd Floor N I T Complex Near Cinemax Sitabuldi, Nagpur, 440 012, India
Tel.: (91) 712 6639909
Highway Construction Services
N.A.I.C.S.: 237310

Ajay Dhawangale (Mng Dir)

West Gujarat Expressway Limited (2)
2nd Floor Surya Complex 150 feet ring road, Rajkot, 380 005, India
Tel.: (91) 281 2573180
Highway Construction Services
N.A.I.C.S.: 237310

IL&FS Urban Infrastructure Mangaers Limited (1)
Karumuttu Centre 498 3rd Floor South Wing Anna Salai, Chennai, 600035, India
Tel.: (91) 44 2431 3535
Web Site: http://www.iuiml.com
Asset Management Services
N.A.I.C.S.: 525920
Manoj Borkar (CFO)

IL&FS Water Limited (1)
A4-A6 Navin's Presidium 103 Nelson Manickam Road Aminjikarai, Chennai, 600029, India
Tel.: (91) 44 4344 3345
Web Site: http://www.ilfswater.com
Waste Water Treatment Services
N.A.I.C.S.: 221320
Pradeep Puri (Chm)

Intevial-Gaesto Integral Rodoviaria S.A. (1)
Avenida do Brasil 43 5 Dt, 1700-062, Lisbon, Portugal
Tel.: (351) 21 413 7600
Highway Construction Services
N.A.I.C.S.: 237310

Mantenimiento Y Conservacion De Vialidades, S.A. DE C.V (1)
Av Prolongacin Tecnolgico No 950-B Oficina 4-E, Col San Pablo Edificio Corporativo blanco, 76130, Queretaro, Mexico
Tel.: (52) 442 135 4800
Web Site: http://www.macovi.com.mx
Highway Infrastructure Development Services
N.A.I.C.S.: 237310

Road Infrastructure Development Company of Rajasthan Limited (1)
1st Floor LIC Jeevan Nidhi Building Ambedkar Circle Bhawani Singh Road, Jaipur, 302 005, Rajasthan, India
Tel.: (91) 141 274 7001
Web Site: http://www.ridcor.in
Emp.: 70
Highway Construction Services
N.A.I.C.S.: 237310
Vijay Pandharinath Kini (CFO)

Tamil Nadu Water Investment Company Limited (1)
Polyhose Towers 1st Floor No 86 Mount Road Guindy, Chennai, 600 032, India
Tel.: (91) 44 2235 1870
Web Site: http://www.twic.co.in
Waste Water Treatment Services
N.A.I.C.S.: 221320
Harmander Singh (Chm)

INFRATEC GMBH
Gostritzer Str 61-63, 01217, Dresden, Germany
Tel.: (49) 3518718635
Web Site: http://www.infratec.de
Year Founded: 1991
Rev.: $12,138,720
Emp.: 130
Sensor Device Mfr
N.A.I.C.S.: 334419
Matthias Krauss (Mng Dir)

Subsidiaries:

InfraTec Infrared LLC (1)
5048 Tennyson Pkwy Ste 250, Plano, TX 75024
Tel.: (877) 797-6748
Web Site: http://www.infratec-infrared.com
Sensor Mfr
N.A.I.C.S.: 334413
Matthias Krauss (Mng Dir)

InfraTec Infrared Ltd. (1)
Dunston Innovation Centre Dunston Road, Chesterfield, S41 8NG, United Kingdom
Tel.: (44) 1246267562

INTERNATIONAL PUBLIC

Web Site: http://www.infratec.co.uk
Sensor Mfr
N.A.I.C.S.: 334413
Matthias Krauss (Mng Dir)

INFRATIL LIMITED
5 Market Lane, PO Box 320, Wellington, 6140, New Zealand
Tel.: (64) 44733663
Web Site: https://www.infratil.com
IFT—(NZX)
Rev.: $761,421,000
Assets: $6,857,246,800
Liabilities: $3,917,112,000
Net Worth: $2,940,134,800
Earnings: $(11,504,000)
Emp.: 128
Fiscal Year-end: 03/31/21
Holding Company; Energy, Airports & Public Transportation
N.A.I.C.S.: 551112
Marko Bogoievski (CEO)

Subsidiaries:

Cityline (NZ) Limited (1)
2-12 Allen Street Level 1 Te Aro, Wellington, 6011, New Zealand
Tel.: (64) 48024100
Public Utility Association
N.A.I.C.S.: 813910

Manawa Energy Limited (1)
Building 108 Durham Street, Private Bag 12055, Tauranga Mail Centre, Tauranga, 3110, New Zealand **(51%)**
Tel.: (64) 75729800
Web Site: https://www.mercury.co.nz
Rev.: $261,234,450
Assets: $1,258,596,292
Liabilities: $499,667,464
Net Worth: $758,928,828
Earnings: $60,549,043
Emp.: 238
Fiscal Year-end: 03/31/2023
Energy Distr
N.A.I.C.S.: 221122
Peter Calderwood (Gen Mgr-Strategy & Growth)

New Zealand Bus Finance Limited (1)
2-12 Allen Street, PO Box 14 070, Wellington, 6011, New Zealand
Tel.: (64) 48024100
Web Site: http://www.nzbus.co.nz
Sales Range: $25-49.9 Million
Emp.: 1,300
Automobile Leasing Services
N.A.I.C.S.: 532112

Transportation Auckland Corporation Limited (1)
2-12 Allen Street Level 1 Te Aro, Wellington, 6421, New Zealand
Tel.: (64) 48024100
Public Transportation Services
N.A.I.C.S.: 488999

Vodafone New Zealand Ltd. (1)
No 20 Via Back Harbour Ave, PO Box 92161, Auckland, 1142, New Zealand
Tel.: (64) 93552000
Web Site: http://www.vodafone.co.nz
Sales Range: $1-4.9 Billion
Emp.: 3,000
Cellular Communications Network Operator
N.A.I.C.S.: 517112
Tony Baird (Dir-Wholesale & Infrastructure)

Wellington City Transport Limited (1)
Kilbirnie Depot 45 Onepu Road, Wellington, 6022, New Zealand
Tel.: (64) 43878700
Web Site: http://www.nzbus.co.nz
Sales Range: $125-149.9 Million
Emp.: 300
Public Transportation Services
N.A.I.C.S.: 488999
Richard Graham (Reg Mgr)

Wellington International Airport Limited (1)
28 Stewart Duff Drive, PO Box 14175, Rongotai, Wellington, 6022, New Zealand
Tel.: (64) 43855100

Web Site:
https://www.wellingtonairport.co.nz
Emp.: 94
Airport Services
N.A.I.C.S.: 488119
Ayolt Wiertsema (Gen Mgr-Aeronautical Ops)

INFRAVIA CAPITAL PARTNERS SAS
22 rue Vernier, 75017, Paris, France
Tel.: (33) 1 40 68 17 17
Web Site: http://infraviacapital.com
Year Founded: 2008
Investment Company
N.A.I.C.S.: 523999
Vincent Levita (Founder & CEO)

Subsidiaries:

SAVE S.p.A. (1)
Viale G Galilei 30/1, 30173, Tessera, VE, Italy
Tel.: (39) 0412606111
Web Site: http://www.grupposave.it
Sales Range: $200-249.9 Million
Emp.: 1,064
Investment Holding Company; Airport Management Services
N.A.I.C.S.: 551112
Monica Scarpa (Mng Dir)

Subsidiary (Domestic):

Aer Tre S.p.a. (2)
Viale Noalese 63/E, 31100, Treviso, Italy (80%)
Tel.: (39) 0422315111
Web Site: http://www.trevisoairport.it
Airport Management Services
N.A.I.C.S.: 488119
Adriano Andreon (Mgr-Safety)

Affiliate (Domestic):

Airest S.r.l. (2)
Via Fratelli Bandiera 7 Gaggio di Marcon, 30020, Venice, Italy (50%)
Tel.: (39) 0412603966
Web Site: http://www.airest.com
Food & Beverage Retailer
N.A.I.C.S.: 445298

Subsidiary (Non-US):

Airest Catering D.O.O. (3)
Zg Brnik 130a, Brnik Aerodrom, 4210, Ljubljana, Slovenia
Tel.: (386) 51600581
Web Site: http://www.airest.com
Sales Range: $10-24.9 Million
Emp.: 60
Airline Catering Services
N.A.I.C.S.: 722310
Johannes Hecht (Mng Dir)

Airest Gastronomy & Retail GmbH (3)
Office Park 1, Vienna, 1300, Austria
Tel.: (43) 1700731101
Web Site: http://www.airest.com
Emp.: 250
Catering Services
N.A.I.C.S.: 722320
Lopert Hyenz (Mng Dir)

Airest Russia O.O.O. (3)
5 Korp 1 Per Novokirochny, Moscow, 105005, Russia
Tel.: (7) 8423561202
Web Site: http://www.airest-russia.ru
Food & Beverage Mfr
N.A.I.C.S.: 311999

Shanghai Airest Catering Company Ltd. (3)
768 Xietu Road 17th Floor, Luwan Dist, Shanghai, 200023, China
Tel.: (86) 2153827381
Web Site: http://www.airest.net
Sales Range: $10-24.9 Million
Emp.: 80
Airline Catering Services
N.A.I.C.S.: 722310
Radek Turecek (Mgr)

Subsidiary (Domestic):

Very Italian Food (V.I.F.) S.r.l. (3)
Via Pontina Vecchia Km 31 8, Pomezia, 40, Roma, Italy
Tel.: (39) 0691629372
Food & Beverage Products Mfr
N.A.I.C.S.: 311999

Subsidiary (Domestic):

Marco Polo Park S.r.l. (2)
Viale Galileo Galilei 5, 30173, Venice, Italy (100%)
Tel.: (39) 0412603060
Web Site: http://www.marcopolopark.it
Sales Range: $25-49.9 Million
Emp.: 10
Airport Parking Lot Management Services
N.A.I.C.S.: 812930

N-Aitec S.r.l. (2)
Via dei Da Prata 14, Treviso, 31100, Italy
Tel.: (39) 0422422903
Web Site: http://www.n-aitec.com
Sales Range: $25-49.9 Million
Emp.: 13
Application Software Development Services
N.A.I.C.S.: 541511
Alberto Torresan (Acct Mgr)

Save Engineering S.p.A. (2)
Viale Galileo Galilei 68, Tessera, 30173, Venice, Italy (100%)
Tel.: (39) 0412606111
Sales Range: $25-49.9 Million
Emp.: 8
Airport Engineering & Construction Management Services
N.A.I.C.S.: 541330

INFRONEER HOLDINGS, INC.
2-10-2 Fujimi, Chiyoda-ku, Chiyoda-ku, Tokyo, 102-0071, Japan
Tel.: (81) 363808253
Web Site: https://www.infroneer.com
5076—(TKS)
Rev.: $5,243,475,040
Assets: $9,323,781,770
Liabilities: $6,553,048,240
Net Worth: $2,770,733,530
Earnings: $215,294,310
Emp.: 7,149
Fiscal Year-end: 03/31/24
Construction Equipment Services & Mfg.
N.A.I.C.S.: 333120

Subsidiaries:

Japan Wind Development Co., Ltd. (1)
6th Floor Bussan Building Annex 1-1-15 Nishi-shimbashi, Minato-ku, Tokyo, 105-0003, Japan
Tel.: (81) 3 3519 7250
Web Site: http://www.jwd.co.jp
Emp.: 134
Wind Power Generation Services
N.A.I.C.S.: 221115
Yasuhiro Inagawa (Chm)

INFRONT ASA
Munkedamsveien 45, 0250, Oslo, Norway
Tel.: (47) 2331 0000 NO
Web Site:
http://www.infrontfinance.com
Year Founded: 1998
Financial Information & Data Processing Services
N.A.I.C.S.: 518210
Kristian Nesbak (Founder & CEO)

Subsidiaries:

Spafid Connect S.p.A (1)
Foro Buonaparte 10, 20121, Milan, Italy
Tel.: (39) 02806871
Web Site: http://www.spafid.it
Asset Management Services
N.A.I.C.S.: 523940

TDN Finans AS (1)
Fjordalleen 16, 0250, Oslo, Norway
Tel.: (47) 93256206
Web Site: http://infrontfinance.com
Newspapers
N.A.I.C.S.: 513110

Thomas Frantsvold (Editor-in-Chief)

vwd Vereinigte Wirtschaftsdienste GmbH (1)
Mainzer Landstrasse 178-190, 60327, Frankfurt am Main, Germany
Tel.: (49) 69 507010
Web Site: http://www.vwd.com
Software Development Services
N.A.I.C.S.: 541511

Subsidiary (Domestic):

EDG AG (2)
Mainzer Landstrasse 178-190, 60327, Frankfurt am Main, Germany (100%)
Tel.: (49) 69 50701 570
Web Site: http://www.derivatives-group.com
Emp.: 16
Investment Management Service
N.A.I.C.S.: 523940
Bjoern Doehrer (Chm-Supervisory Bd)

Subsidiary (Domestic):

vwd academy AG (3)
Mainzer Landstrasse 178-190, 60327, Frankfurt am Main, Germany
Tel.: (49) 69 50701 570
Web Site: http://www.ed-academy.com
Investment Management Service
N.A.I.C.S.: 523940
Bjorn Dohrer (Mng Dir & Member-Mgmt Bd)

Subsidiary (Domestic):

Lenz + Partner AG (2)
Bronnerstrasse 7, 44141, Dortmund, Germany
Tel.: (49) 231 91533 00
Web Site: http://www.lp-software.de
Sales Range: $25-49.9 Million
Emp.: 25
Trading Software Development Services
N.A.I.C.S.: 541511
Dirk Albrecht (CEO)

Subsidiary (Non-US):

vwd PortfolioNet Service AG (2)
Hardturmstrasse 125, Zurich, 8005, Switzerland
Tel.: (41) 43 4444 777
Web Site: http://www.portfolionet.ch
Sales Range: $50-74.9 Million
Emp.: 32
Multi-Bank Portfolio Management Services
N.A.I.C.S.: 523940
Ivo Bieri (Mng Dir)

Subsidiary (Domestic):

vwd Transaction Solutions AG (2)
Tilsiter Strasse 1, 60487, Frankfurt am Main, Germany
Tel.: (49) 69 597991 0
Web Site: http://www.transactionsolutions.de
Sales Range: $25-49.9 Million
Emp.: 8
Trading Software Development Services
N.A.I.C.S.: 541511

Subsidiary (Non-US):

vwd group Italia S.r.L. (2)
Via Carlo Pisacane 1, 20016, Pero, Italy
Tel.: (39) 02 87330 252
Web Site: http://www.vwd-italia.com
Sales Range: $50-74.9 Million
Emp.: 35
Fund Management Services
N.A.I.C.S.: 523940

vwd information solutions AG (2)
Hardturmstrasse 125, 8021, Zurich, Switzerland
Tel.: (41) 43 4444 999
Web Site: http://www.vwd.com
Sales Range: $25-49.9 Million
Emp.: 12
Financial Software Publisher
N.A.I.C.S.: 513210
Ivo Bieri (CEO)

INFUND HOLDING CO., LTD.
Sanzao Technology Industrial Park, Sanzao Town Jinwan District, Zhuhai, 523073, Guangdong, China
Tel.: (86) 76922088897
Web Site: http://www.ronsen.com.cn

Year Founded: 1985
002141—(SSE)
Rev.: $124,359,300
Assets: $188,603,532
Liabilities: $17,465,760
Net Worth: $171,137,772
Earnings: $32,614,920
Fiscal Year-end: 12/31/22
Enameled Wire Mfr
N.A.I.C.S.: 335929
Han Taozi (Chm)

ING GROEP N.V.
Bijlmerdreef 106, 1102 CT, Amsterdam, Netherlands
Tel.: (31) 205764190
Web Site: https://www.ing.com
Year Founded: 1991
ING—(NYSE)
Rev.: $56,549,751,781
Assets: $1,057,952,730,412
Liabilities: $997,918,195,554
Net Worth: $60,034,534,859
Earnings: $4,720,483,488
Emp.: 59,434
Fiscal Year-end: 12/31/23
Financial Investment Services
N.A.I.C.S.: 551112
Ljiljana Cortan (Chief Risk Officer)

Subsidiaries:

Blue Sky Financial Group (1)
218 Main St, Sturgeon Falls, P2B 1P2, ON, Canada (100%)
Tel.: (705) 753-0520
Web Site:
http://www.blueskyfinancialgroup.com
Rev.: $351,050
Emp.: 11
Insurance Agents Brokers & Service
N.A.I.C.S.: 524298
Chantal Erudel Salardeau (Pres)

Guernsey International Fund Managers Limited (1)
(100%)
Sales Range: $100-124.9 Million
Emp.: 180
Fund Management
N.A.I.C.S.: 524292

ING Administradora de Fondos de Inversiones S.A. (1)
Suecia 211 Piso 12 Providencia, Santiago, Chile (100%)
Tel.: (56) 23300600
Web Site: http://www.ing.cl
Sales Range: $50-74.9 Million
Emp.: 32
Pension Funds & Investment Management
N.A.I.C.S.: 525110

ING Asia Pacific Ltd. (1)
1 International Financial Ctr 1 Harbour View St, Central, China (Hong Kong) (100%)
Tel.: (852) 25256618
Sales Range: $50-74.9 Million
Emp.: 100
Regional Management Center for Insurance Operations
N.A.I.C.S.: 524298

ING Australia Ltd. (1)
60 Margaret Street, PO Box 3938, Sydney, 2000, NSW, Australia (100%)
Tel.: (61) 290284077
Web Site: https://www.ing.com.au
Sales Range: $1-4.9 Billion
Emp.: 2,700
Fund Manager & Life Insurance Carrier
N.A.I.C.S.: 524113

Subsidiary (Domestic):

Oasis Asset Management Ltd. (2)
Level 14 346 Kent Str, Sydney, 2000, NSW, Australia (76%)
Tel.: (61) 299563700
Web Site: http://www.oasisasset.com.au
Sales Range: $25-49.9 Million
Emp.: 20
Financial Services & Software Consultancy
N.A.I.C.S.: 561499

Subsidiary (Non-US):

RetireInvest Pty Limited (2)

ING GROEP N.V.

ING Groep N.V.—(Continued)
Web Site: http://www.retireinvest.com.au
Sales Range: $25-49.9 Million
Emp.: 45
Financial Planning Services
N.A.I.C.S.: 523999

ING Bank N.V. (1)
Web Site: http://www.ing.nl
Retail Banking, Lending & Investment Management Services
N.A.I.C.S.: 522110
Erwin Maspolim *(Head-Network-South East Asia & Country Mgr)*

Subsidiary (Non-US):

Bank Mendes Gans NV (2)
(100%)
Tel.: (31) 205235311
Web Site: http://www.mendesgans.com
Sales Range: $100-124.9 Million
Emp.: 170
Portfolio Management
N.A.I.C.S.: 523940

ING Bank (Australia) Limited (2)
Level 28 60 Margaret Street, Sydney, 2000, NSW, Australia (100%)
Web Site: http://www.ing.com.au
Rev.: $1,570,993,480
Assets: $45,458,250,460
Liabilities: $42,313,450,620
Net Worth: $3,144,799,840
Earnings: $281,991,220
Emp.: 1,262
Fiscal Year-end: 12/31/2018
Financial Services
N.A.I.C.S.: 522110
Michael Anthony Witts *(Treas)*

ING Bank (Eurasia) ZAO (2)
36 Krasnoproletarskaya Street Bldg 36, 127473, Moscow, Russia (100%)
Tel.: (7) 4957555400
Web Site: http://www.ing.ru
Sales Range: $150-199.9 Million
Emp.: 400
Commercial Bank
N.A.I.C.S.: 522110

ING Bank A.S. (2)
Resitpasa Mahallesi Eski Buyukdere Caddesi No 8, 34467, Sariyer, Turkiye
Tel.: (90) 212 335 10 00
Web Site: http://www.ingbank.com.tr
Commercial Banking Services
N.A.I.C.S.: 522110

Subsidiary (Domestic):

ING Menkul Degerler A.S. (3)
Resitpasa Mahallesi Eski Buyukdere Caddesi No 8 Kat 11, 34467, Sariyer, Istanbul, Turkiye
Tel.: (90) 2123351000
Web Site: http://www.ingmenkul.com.tr
Securities Brokerage Services
N.A.I.C.S.: 523150

ING Portfoy Yonetimi A.S. (3)
Resitpasa Mahallesi Eski Buyukdere Caddesi No 8 Kat 9, 34467, Sariyer, Istanbul, Turkiye (100%)
Tel.: (90) 212 365 4600
Web Site: http://www.ingportfoy.com.tr
Asset Management Services
N.A.I.C.S.: 523940

Subsidiary (Non-US):

ING Bank Luxembourg SA (2)
26 place de la Gare, 1616, Luxembourg, Luxembourg (100%)
Tel.: (352) 44991
Sales Range: $300-349.9 Million
Emp.: 800
Private Banking & Asset Management Services
N.A.I.C.S.: 522180

ING Bank Magyarorszag Rt (2)
Dozsa Gyorgy ut 84 b, H-1068, Budapest, Hungary
Tel.: (36) 12679263
Web Site: http://www.ing.hu
Sales Range: $350-399.9 Million
Emp.: 633
Commercial Bank
N.A.I.C.S.: 522110

Representative Office (Non-US):

ING Bank N.V. - London Representative Office (2)
60 London Wall, London, EC2M 5TQ, United Kingdom
Tel.: (44) 2077671000
Web Site: http://www.ingcb.com
Regional Managing Office
N.A.I.C.S.: 551114

Subsidiary (Non-US):

ING Bank Slaski S.A. (2)
Ul Sokolska 34, 40-086, Katowice, Poland
Tel.: (48) 228204416
Rev.: $1,233,182,550
Assets: $36,118,104,018
Liabilities: $32,737,478,442
Net Worth: $3,380,625,576
Earnings: $402,156,522
Emp.: 7,979
Fiscal Year-end: 12/31/2017
Commercial Banking Services
N.A.I.C.S.: 522110
Malgorzata Kolakowska *(Deputy Chm-Supervisory Bd)*

ING Belgie N.V. (2)
Avenue Marnix 24, 1000, Brussels, Belgium
Tel.: (32) 25472111
Commercial Banking Services
N.A.I.C.S.: 522110

Subsidiary (Domestic):

ING Commercial Finance B.V. (2)
Runnenburg 30, PO Box 3030, 3980 DJ, Bunnik, Netherlands
Tel.: (31) 30 659 31 93
Web Site: http://www.ingcommercialbanking.com
Sales Range: $75-99.9 Million
Emp.: 144
Commercial Banking Services
N.A.I.C.S.: 522110

Subsidiary (Domestic):

ING Lease (Nederland) B.V. (3)
Bijlmerplein 888, 1102 MG, Amsterdam, Netherlands
Tel.: (31) 205769644
Web Site: http://www.inglease.nl
Personal & Commercial Lending Services
N.A.I.C.S.: 522291

Subsidiary (Domestic):

ING Corporate Investments B.V. (2)
Bijlmerplein 888 Amp F 02 041, Amsterdam, 1102 MG, North Holland, Netherlands
Tel.: (31) 205639111
Investment Management Service
N.A.I.C.S.: 523999

Subsidiary (US):

ING Financial Holdings Corporation (2)
1325 Avenue of the Americas, New York, NY 10019
Tel.: (646) 424-6000
Financial Management Services
N.A.I.C.S.: 523999

Subsidiary (Domestic):

ING Real Estate B.V. (2)
Bijlmerplein 888, Amsterdam, 1102 MG, Netherlands
Tel.: (31) 703418418
Web Site: http://www.ingrealestate.com
Sales Range: $1-4.9 Billion
Emp.: 2,700
Real Estate Manangement Services
N.A.I.C.S.: 531390

Subsidiary (Non-US):

ING Real Estate Development Italy S.R.L. (3)
Corso Magenta 85, I-20123, Milan, Italy
Tel.: (39) 024805721
Web Site: http://www.ingrealestate.it
Real Estate Investment & Development Services
N.A.I.C.S.: 531390

Subsidiary (Domestic):

ING Vastgoed Belegging B.V. (3)
Schenkkade 65, 2595 AS, Hague, Netherlands
Tel.: (31) 703418418
Financial Management Services
N.A.I.C.S.: 523999

Subsidiary (Non-US):

Record Bank N.V. (2)
Avenue Henri Matisse 16, Evere, 1140, Brussels, Belgium
Tel.: (32) 2 728 98 88
Web Site: http://www.recordbank.be
Commercial Banking Services
N.A.I.C.S.: 522110

WestlandUtrecht Bank N.V. (2)
Web Site: http://www.westlandutrechtbank.nl
Sales Range: $300-349.9 Million
Emp.: 600
Investment Management Service
N.A.I.C.S.: 523999

ING Belgium SA/NV (1)
Ave Marnix 24, 1000, Brussels, Belgium
Tel.: (32) 25472111
Web Site: http://www.ing.be
Rev.: $6,071,146,180
Assets: $181,856,521,416
Liabilities: $169,654,654,686
Net Worth: $12,201,866,730
Earnings: $885,186,198
Emp.: 8,231
Fiscal Year-end: 12/31/2017
Banking
N.A.I.C.S.: 522299
Eric Boyer de la Giroday *(Chm)*

Affiliate (Domestic):

Bank Card Company (2)
Rue Albert 2nd No 9, B 1210, Brussels, Belgium
Tel.: (32) 22058111
Sales Range: $50-74.9 Million
Emp.: 60
Credit Cards
N.A.I.C.S.: 522210

Affiliate (Non-US):

Banque Commerciale du Burundi S.A.R.L. (2)
Sales Range: $150-199.9 Million
Emp.: 258
Commercial Bank
N.A.I.C.S.: 522110
Genevieve Buzungu *(CFO)*

Subsidiary (Non-US):

ING Dublin (2)
Block 4 Dundrum Town Centre Sandyford Road, Dublin, 16, Ireland
Tel.: (353) 16384000
Sales Range: $50-74.9 Million
Emp.: 22
Banking
N.A.I.C.S.: 522299

Subsidiary (Domestic):

ING Lease Belgium N.V (2)
155 Colonel Bourg St, 1140, Brussels, Belgium
Tel.: (32) 27396411
Web Site: http://www.inglease.be
Sales Range: $75-99.9 Million
Emp.: 130
Real Estate & Equipment Leasing
N.A.I.C.S.: 531110

Subsidiary (Non-US):

ING Luxembourg S.A. (2)
26 place de la Gare, L-1616, Luxembourg, Luxembourg
Tel.: (352) 35244991
Web Site: https://www.ing.lu
Rev.: $762,975,905
Assets: $18,163,695,093
Liabilities: $16,744,278,839
Net Worth: $1,419,416,254
Earnings: $290,153,664
Emp.: 996
Fiscal Year-end: 12/31/2023

INTERNATIONAL PUBLIC

Domestic Retail, Corporate, Institutional & Private Banking, Equity & Financial Markets & Mutual Fund Investment Management
N.A.I.C.S.: 522110
Peter Vandekerckhove *(Chm)*

ING Commercial Banking (1)
Pisos 3/4 Bosque de Alisos 45B Bosques de las Lomas, 05120, Mexico, DF, Mexico
Tel.: (52) 55 5258 2000
Web Site: http://www.ingcb.com
Commercial Banking & Insurance Services
N.A.I.C.S.: 522110

ING Financial Services LLC (1)
Tel.: (646) 424-6000
Web Site: http://www.ingcb.com
Sales Range: $350-399.9 Million
Emp.: 550
Investment Banking
N.A.I.C.S.: 523999
Gerald Walker *(CEO)*

Subsidiary (Domestic):

ING Capital LLC (2)
1325 Ave of the Americas, New York, NY 10019
Tel.: (646) 424-6000
Sales Range: $10-24.9 Million
Emp.: 10
Financial Services
N.A.I.C.S.: 541618
Anne van Rielas *(Head--Sustainable Fin-Americas)*

ING Insurance International (1)
Tower 1 Landmark Bldg Rm 1508, Beijing, 100004, China (100%)
Tel.: (86) 1065907568
Web Site: http://www.ing.com.hk
Sales Range: $50-74.9 Million
Emp.: 2
Insurance Carrier
N.A.I.C.S.: 524210

ING Lease (Eurasia) LLC (1)
Krasnoproletarskaya street 36, 127473, Moscow, Russia
Tel.: (7) 4957555400
Web Site: http://www.ingwb.com
Commercial Bank
N.A.I.C.S.: 522110

ING Securities (Andean Pact) (1)
Financial Markets, Carrera 9 No. 76-49, Pisos 7-8, Bogota, Colombia
Tel.: (57) 013120241
Securities Brokerage
N.A.I.C.S.: 523150

ING Trust (Hong Kong) (1)
Rm 1&2 10th Fl Man Yee Bldg 58 des Rd, Central, China (Hong Kong) (100%)
Tel.: (852) 28463955
Web Site: http://www.ing-trust.com
Sales Range: $50-74.9 Million
Emp.: 12
Financial Trust & Management Services
N.A.I.C.S.: 523991

ING Trust Company (Jersey) Ltd. (1)
3 Fl Forum House Grenville St, Saint Helier, JE2 4UF, Jersey
Tel.: (44) 1534880888
Web Site: http://www.ing.je
Sales Range: $50-74.9 Million
Emp.: 11
Trust Company
N.A.I.C.S.: 523991

ING-DiBa AG (1)
Theodor-Heuss-Allee 2, 60486, Frankfurt, am Main, Germany
Tel.: (49) 692722266807
Banking Services
N.A.I.C.S.: 522110

Interhyp AG (1)
Domagkstr 34, Bavaria, 80807, Munich, Germany (100%)
Tel.: (49) 89203070
Web Site: https://www.interhyp-gruppe.de
Sales Range: $125-149.9 Million
Emp.: 595
Residential Mortgage Brokerage Services
N.A.I.C.S.: 522310
Marcus Wolsdorf *(Co-Founder)*

PJSC ING Bank (1)
30-A Spas ka Str, Kiev, 04070, Ukraine

Tel.: (380) 442303030
Web Site: http://www.ingbankukraine.com
Banking Services
N.A.I.C.S.: 522110
Roman Vysotskiy (Head-Financial Markets Sls)

Payvision Canada Services Ltd. (1)
1315 Pickering Pkwy Suite 300, Pickering, L1V 7G5, ON, Canada
Tel.: (289) 830-8953
Financial Services
N.A.I.C.S.: 523999

Security Life of Denver International Limited (1)
Continental Building Second Floor 25 Church Street, Hamilton, Bermuda
Tel.: (441) 295 82 70
Fire Insurance Services
N.A.I.C.S.: 524113

South Western Insurance Group Limited (1)
21 Four Seasons Place Suite 105, Toronto, M9B 6J8, ON, Canada (100%)
Web Site: http://www.swgins.com
Sales Range: $50-74.9 Million
Emp.: 16
Insurance Agents Brokers & Service
N.A.I.C.S.: 524298

Uta Finanz und Leasing (1)
Am Glockenturm 1, 63814, Aschaffenburg, Germany (70%)
Tel.: (49) 602179440
Web Site: http://www.uta-leasing.de
Sales Range: $50-74.9 Million
Emp.: 2
Lessor of Goods
N.A.I.C.S.: 532289

INGDAN, INC.
11F Microsoft Comtech Tower No 55 Gaoxin South 9th Road, Nanshan District, Shenzhen, 518057, China
Tel.: (86) 4008830393
Web Site: http://www.cogobuy.com
0400—(HKG)
Rev.: $1,338,786,868
Assets: $1,362,615,556
Liabilities: $737,364,935
Net Worth: $625,250,621
Earnings: $63,519,768
Emp.: 549
Fiscal Year-end: 12/31/22
Electronic Component Internet Retailer
N.A.I.C.S.: 423690
Jeffrey Jingwei Kang (Founder, Chm & CEO)

Subsidiaries:

Risingnovas (HK) Limited (1)
5th Floor Block A Goodman Kwai Chung Logistics Center 585-609, Castle Peak Road, Kwai Chung, New Territories, China (Hong Kong)
Tel.: (852) 35680135
Web Site: http://www.risingnovas.com
Electronic Communication Product Mfr & Whslr
N.A.I.C.S.: 334111

INGENIA COMMUNITIES GROUP
Level 3 88 Cumberland Street, The Rocks, Sydney, 2000, NSW, Australia
Tel.: (61) 1300132946 AU
Web Site:
  https://www.ingeniacommunity.com
INA—(ASX)
Rev.: $26,137,445
Assets: $1,155,891,635
Liabilities: $422,578,731
Net Worth: $733,312,903
Earnings: $25,456,739
Emp.: 1,300
Fiscal Year-end: 06/30/23
Senior Living Property Management Services
N.A.I.C.S.: 531311
Simon Owen (CEO & Mng Dir)

Subsidiaries:

Eighth Gate Capital Management Pty Ltd (1)
PO Box 3304, West End, 4101, QLD, Australia
Tel.: (61) 738710517
Web Site: http://www.eighthgate.com.au
Investment Management Service
N.A.I.C.S.: 523940

INGENIC SEMICONDUCTOR CO., LTD.
Junzheng Building Building 14 East District No 10 Xibeiwang East Road, Haidian Dist, Beijing, 100193, China
Tel.: (86) 1056345000
Web Site: https://www.ingenic.com.cn
Year Founded: 2005
300223—(CHIN)
Rev.: $759,826,548
Assets: $1,744,026,336
Liabilities: $163,259,928
Net Worth: $1,580,766,408
Earnings: $110,809,296
Emp.: 160
Fiscal Year-end: 12/31/22
Semiconductor Mfr
N.A.I.C.S.: 334413

INGENICS AG
Schillerstrasse 1 15, 89077, Ulm, Germany
Tel.: (49) 731936800
Web Site: http://www.ingenics.com
Year Founded: 1979
Rev.: $24,139,500
Emp.: 580
Industrial Engineering Consulting Services
N.A.I.C.S.: 541618
Andreas Hoberg (Chief Sls Officer)

Subsidiaries:

Ingenics Consulting (Shanghai) Co., Ltd. (1)
Shanghai Stock Exchange Building Unit S2007 528 Pudong Rd, Pudong, 200120, Shanghai, China
Tel.: (86) 2158889060
Web Site: http://www.ingenics.cn
Logistics Consulting Servies
N.A.I.C.S.: 541614
Evan Zeng (Sr Project Engr)

Ingenics Corporation (1)
3443 Pelham Rd Ste 400, Greenville, SC 29615
Tel.: (678) 528-7042
Logistics Consulting Servies
N.A.I.C.S.: 541614
Johannes Zettl (Project Mgr)

Ingenics S.A. de C.V. (1)
Calle 39 Poniente 3515 5 Stock Triangulo Las Animas Col Las Animas, 72400, Puebla, Mexico
Tel.: (52) 2221414883
Logistics Consulting Servies
N.A.I.C.S.: 541614
Joerg Baetzel (Mng Dir)

Ingenics SAS (1)
75 Boulevard Haussmann, 75008, Paris, France
Tel.: (33) 142685026
Web Site: http://www.ingenics.fr
Business Communications Services
N.A.I.C.S.: 541611
Alexandre Zisa (Mgr-Competitive Engr)

Ingenics s.r.o. (1)
Office Park Nove Butovice Building A Bucharova 1281/2, Prague, Czech Republic
Tel.: (420) 721767122
Logistics Consulting Servies
N.A.I.C.S.: 541614
Thomas Limpert (Gen Mgr)

INGENIERIAS Y BIOGAS, S.L.
Calle Donoso Cortes 7, 33204, Gijon, Spain
Tel.: (34) 985175950 ES

Web Site: http://www.inbiogas.es
Biogas Plant Equipment Design & Mfr
N.A.I.C.S.: 541330
Adrian Beyebach (Dir Gen)

INGENIEROS ASESORES, S.A.
Parque Tecnologico de Asturias Parc 47, Llanera, 33428, Asturias, Spain
Tel.: (34) 985 98 00 50
Web Site:
  http://www.ingenierosasesores.com
Year Founded: 1985
Sales Range: $10-24.9 Million
Emp.: 100
Consulting Engineer Services
N.A.I.C.S.: 541330
Luis Hernandez (Mng Dir)

INGENIEUR GUDANG BERHAD
Ground Floor No 3 Jalan TP 2, Taman Perindustrian UEP, 47600, Subang Jaya, Selangor, Malaysia
Tel.: (60) 78662303
Web Site:
  https://www.ingenieur.com.my
Year Founded: 1978
INGENIEU—(KLS)
Rev.: $4,429,351
Assets: $52,678,853
Liabilities: $16,542,158
Net Worth: $36,136,695
Earnings: $3,904,712
Emp.: 320
Fiscal Year-end: 11/30/23
Steel Processor & Mfr
N.A.I.C.S.: 331110
Thomas Chee Fong Liang (Chm)

Subsidiaries:

Superinox Pipe Industry Sdn. Bhd. (1)
No 1564 Mk Malaysia Kannada 12 Perai Jalannafari Vldor Indsrl Estate, Prai Industrial Estate IV, 13600, Sungai Jawi, Penang, Malaysia
Tel.: (60) 45021155
Web Site: http://wwwsuperinoxtubes.com
Emp.: 100
Stainless Steel Wire Mfr
N.A.I.C.S.: 332996
Kevin Fiah (Mng Dir)

Tatt Giap Hardware Sdn. Bhd. (1)
1068 Jalan Bagan Lalang, 13400, Butterworth, Penang, Malaysia
Tel.: (60) 43310066
Sales Range: $25-49.9 Million
Emp.: 39
Stainless Steel Stockist & Distr
N.A.I.C.S.: 423510

INGENIOR IVAR PETTERSEN AS
Bjornstjerne Bjornsons Gate 110, PO Box 166, Drammen, 3044, Buskerud, Norway
Tel.: (47) 32212121
Web Site: http://www.pettersen.no
Year Founded: 1927
Sales Range: $10-24.9 Million
Emp.: 100
Electrical System Engineering & Installation Services
N.A.I.C.S.: 541330
Geir Ivar Pettersen (Owner)

INGENIOUS ENE-CARBON NEW MATERIALS CO., LTD.
No 109 Qingnian Avenue, Shenhe District, Shenyang, 110014, Liaoning, China
Tel.: (86) 24 22903598
Web Site: http://www.enecarbon-materials.com
Rev.: $370,406,991
Assets: $504,195,368
Liabilities: $356,503,391

Net Worth: $147,691,978
Earnings: $9,891,850
Fiscal Year-end: 12/31/17
Carbon & Graphite Product Mfr
N.A.I.C.S.: 335991
Yixin Chen (VP & Controller)

INGENIOUS MEDIA LIMITED
15 Golden Square, London, W1F 9JG, United Kingdom
Tel.: (44) 2073194000
Web Site:
  http://www.theingeniousgroup.co.uk
Year Founded: 1998
Media & Entertainment, Infrastructure & Real Estate Consulting Services
N.A.I.C.S.: 523999
Patrick McKenna (Founder)

INGENTA PLC
Suite 2 John Smith Drive Parkway Court Whichford House, Oxford, OX4 2JY, United Kingdom
Tel.: (44) 1865397800 UK
Web Site: https://www.ingenta.com
Year Founded: 2007
ING—(AIM)
Rev.: $13,787,348
Assets: $11,763,167
Liabilities: $4,557,591
Net Worth: $7,205,576
Earnings: $2,928,061
Emp.: 71
Fiscal Year-end: 12/31/23
Holding Company; Publishing Software & Related Technology Services
N.A.I.C.S.: 551112
Martyn C. Rose (Chm)

Subsidiaries:

VISTA International Ltd (1)
8100 alec issigonis way, Oxford business Pk North, Oxford, OX4 2HU, United Kingdom
Tel.: (44) 1865397800
Sales Range: $75-99.9 Million
Emp.: 120
Holding Company
N.A.I.C.S.: 551112

Subsidiary (US):

Publishers Communication Group, Inc. (2)
38 Chauncy St Ste 1002, Boston, MA 02111 (100%)
Tel.: (617) 497-6514
Web Site: https://www.pcgplus.com
Sales Range: $25-49.9 Million
Emp.: 20
Marketing Consulting Services for Publisher
N.A.I.C.S.: 541613

Branch (Non-US):

Publishers Communication Group, Inc. - Oxford Office (3)
8100 Alec Issigonis Way, Oxford Business Park North, Oxford, OX4 2HU, United Kingdom
Tel.: (44) 1865 397 800
Web Site: http://www.pcgplus.com
Marketing Consulting for Publishing
N.A.I.C.S.: 541613

Subsidiary (Domestic):

Publishing Technology (Europe) Limited (2)
8100 Alec Issigonis Way, Oxford, OX4 2HU, United Kingdom
Tel.: (44) 1865397800
Sales Range: $25-49.9 Million
Emp.: 60
Publishing Software & Related Technology Services
N.A.I.C.S.: 513210
John Simons (Mgr)

Subsidiary (US):

Publishing Technology, Inc. (2)
80 Cottontale Ln 2nd Fl, Somerset, NJ 08873

INGENTA PLC

Ingenta plc—(Continued)
Tel.: (732) 563-9292
Sales Range: $25-49.9 Million
Emp.: 50
Publishing Software & Related Technology Services
N.A.I.C.S.: 513210

Vista Computer Services LLC (1)
317 George St Ste 320, New Brunswick, NJ 08901
Tel.: (732) 563-9292
Sales Range: $25-49.9 Million
Emp.: 30
Computer Sales & Maintenance Services
N.A.I.C.S.: 423430

INGENUITY PROPERTY INVESTMENTS LIMITED
Suite 102 1st Floor Intaba 25 Protea Road, Claremont, Cape Town, 7708, South Africa
Tel.: (27) 216745170
Web Site: http://www.ingenuityproperty.com
Rev.: $37,826,288
Assets: $320,553,723
Liabilities: $191,103,034
Net Worth: $129,450,689
Earnings: $12,064,979
Emp.: 5
Fiscal Year-end: 08/31/18
Investment Management Service
N.A.I.C.S.: 523940
John Bielich (Exec Dir)

INGERSOLL PAPER BOX CO LIMITED
327 King Street West, Ingersoll, N5C 2K9, ON, Canada
Tel.: (519) 485-1830
Web Site: http://www.ipb.on.ca
Year Founded: 1922
Sales Range: $10-24.9 Million
Paper Bag Mfr
N.A.I.C.S.: 322212
David Skinner (Pres)

INGERSOLL RAND (INDIA) LIMITED
First Floor Subramanya Arcade No 12/1 Bannerghatta Road, Bengaluru, 560029, India
Tel.: (91) 8046855100
Web Site: https://www.irco.com
Year Founded: 1921
INGERRAND—(NSE)
Rev.: $125,985,883
Assets: $117,106,121
Liabilities: $41,773,627
Net Worth: $75,332,494
Earnings: $15,034,697
Emp.: 536
Fiscal Year-end: 03/31/22
Industrial Machinery Distr
N.A.I.C.S.: 423830
Mary Betsch (VP-Sustainbility)

INGERSOLL TILLAGE GROUP, INC.
460 Sherman Ave N, Hamilton, L8L 8J6, ON, Canada
Tel.: (905) 667-6549
Web Site: http://www.ingersolltillage.com
Farm Machinery & Equipment Mfr
N.A.I.C.S.: 333111
Steven L. Garrette (Pres & CEO)

Subsidiaries:

Corporacion Patricio Echeverria, S.A. (1)
Urola 10, 20230, Guipuzcoa, Legazpi, Spain
Tel.: (34) 943739000
Web Site: http://www.bellota.com

Sales Range: $250-299.9 Million
Emp.: 1,300
Holding Company
N.A.I.C.S.: 551112
Enrique Mir Sagardia (Gen Mgr)

Subsidiary (US):

Bellota Agrisolutions & Tools USA, LLC (2)
1421 11th St W, Milan, IL 61264-2262
Tel.: (309) 787-2491
Web Site: http://www.bellota.com
Agricultural Tool Mfr
N.A.I.C.S.: 332216

Subsidiary (Non-US):

Bellota Brasil, Ltda. (2)
Rodovia BR470 Km 73 5 No 3500, PO Box 248, Indaial, 89130004, SC, Brazil (100%)
Tel.: (55) 47 3301 8000
Web Site: http://www.bellota.com
Sales Range: $10-24.9 Million
Emp.: 300
Garden & Agricultural Machinery & Hand Tools Mfr
N.A.I.C.S.: 423820

Bellota Colombia, S.A. (2)
Parque Ind Juanchito Terraza 8, 1120, Manizales, Caladas, Colombia (100%)
Tel.: (57) 68748585
Web Site: http://www.bellota.com
Sales Range: $150-199.9 Million
Emp.: 300
Garden & Agricultural Machinery & Tools Mfr
N.A.I.C.S.: 423820

Subsidiary (Domestic):

Bellota Herramientas S.L.U. (2)
Urola 10, 20230, Legazpi, Guipuzcoa, Spain
Tel.: (34) 943739000
Web Site: http://www.bellota.com
Gardening & Agricultural Tools Mfr
N.A.I.C.S.: 423820

Subsidiary (Non-US):

Bellota Mexico, S.A. de C.V. (2)
Prolo Av 16 Esq n 400 Km 1, Fortin, Veracruz, 94470, Mexico (100%)
Tel.: (52) 2717170207
Web Site: http://www.bellota.com
Sales Range: $1-9.9 Million
Emp.: 300
Garden & Agricultural Machinery & Tools Mfr
N.A.I.C.S.: 423820

Subsidiary (US):

Corona Clipper, Inc. (2)
22440 Temescal Canyon Rd, Corona, CA 92883 (100%)
Tel.: (951) 737-6515
Web Site: http://www.coronatoolsusa.com
Sales Range: $50-74.9 Million
Emp.: 185
Gardening Tools Mfr
N.A.I.C.S.: 333111
Al Schulten (Controller)

Subsidiary (Domestic):

Rozalma Agrisolutions, S.L.U. (2)
Pol Argixao n 62 Apdo 55, 20700, Zumarraga, Guipuzcoa, Spain
Tel.: (34) 943 720 158
Web Site: http://www.bellota.com
Agricultural Tool Mfr
N.A.I.C.S.: 333111

Subsidiary (Non-US):

Solbjerg Staalvarefabrik A/S (2)
Industriomradet 107, 8732, Hovedgard, Denmark (100%)
Tel.: (45) 75662022
Web Site: http://www.bellota.com
Emp.: 5
Garden & Agricultural Machinery & Tools Mfr
N.A.I.C.S.: 423820
Eric Madsen (Mgr-Sls)

INGEVEC S.A.
Calle Cerro El Plomo 5680 Piso 14, Santiago, Chile
Tel.: (56) 6743800
Web Site: http://www.ingevec.cl
INGEVEC—(SGO)
Sales Range: Less than $1 Million
Construction Engineering Services
N.A.I.C.S.: 541330
Rodrigo Gonzalez Yutronic (CEO & Gen Mgr)

INGHAMS GROUP LIMITED
Level 4 1 Julius Avenue, North Ryde, 2113, NSW, Australia
Tel.: (61) 298264444 AU
Web Site: https://www.inghams.com.au
Year Founded: 1918
ING—(ASX)
Rev.: $2,126,889,240
Assets: $1,564,848,000
Liabilities: $1,421,664,408
Net Worth: $143,183,592
Earnings: $66,180,030
Emp.: 8,000
Fiscal Year-end: 06/29/24
Restaurant Operators
N.A.I.C.S.: 722511
Peter Bush (Chm)

Subsidiaries:

Ingham Enterprises Pty Limited (1)
203-209 Northumberland St, Liverpool, 2170, NSW, Australia
Tel.: (61) 296028744
Poultry Product Mfr
N.A.I.C.S.: 311615
Mick Mc'mahon (CEO)

The Free Ranger Pty. Limited (1)
1 Julius Ave, North Ryde, NSW, Australia
Tel.: (61) 1800841311
Web Site: https://www.thefreerangerchicken.com.au
Chicken Hatchery Services
N.A.I.C.S.: 112340

INGO MAURER GMBH
Kaiserstrasse 47, 80801, Munich, Germany
Tel.: (49) 8938160691
Web Site: http://www.ingo-maurer.com
Rev.: $14,817,299
Emp.: 50
Light Mfr
N.A.I.C.S.: 335139
Ingo Maurer (Mng Dir)

Subsidiaries:

Ingo Maurer LLC (1)
89 Grand Str, New York, NY 10013
Tel.: (212) 965-8817
Lighting Product Distr
N.A.I.C.S.: 423220

INGOSSTRAKH INSURANCE COMPANY
GSP-7 ul Pyatniskaya d 12 str 2, Moscow, 117997, Russia
Tel.: (7) 4959565555
Web Site: http://www.ingos.ru
Year Founded: 1947
Mortgage Insurance Services
N.A.I.C.S.: 524126
Mikhail Yuryevich Volkov (Chm-Mgmt Bd & Pres)

Subsidiaries:

Bank SOYUZ (JSC) (1)
27 b 1 Sushchovskaya street, 127030, Moscow, Russia
Tel.: (7) 4957295555
Web Site: http://banksoyuz.ru
Commercial Banking Services
N.A.I.C.S.: 522110
Panarin Oleg Stanislavovich (Chm-Mgmt Bd)

INTERNATIONAL PUBLIC

Ingosstrakh - Investments Asset Management, JSC (1)
12 build 2 Pyatnitskaya ul, 115035, Moscow, Russia
Tel.: (7) 4957204898
Web Site: http://www.ingosinvest.ru
Asset Management Services
N.A.I.C.S.: 531390
Vladimir Krekoten (Gen Mgr)

INGOT METAL COMPANY LIMITED
111 Fenmar Dr, Weston, M9L 1M3, ON, Canada
Tel.: (416) 749-1372 Ca
Web Site: http://www.ingot.ca
Iron & Metal Mfr
N.A.I.C.S.: 332812

INGRA D.D.
Alexandera un Humboldta 4b, 10000, Zagreb, Croatia
Tel.: (385) 16102555
Web Site: https://www.ingra.hr
Year Founded: 1955
INGR—(ZAG)
Sales Range: $25-49.9 Million
Construction Engineering Services
N.A.I.C.S.: 236116
Mladen Markoc (Deputy Pres)

INGRAM D.D.
Industrijska bb, Srebrenik, Tuzla, Bosnia & Herzegovina
Tel.: (387) 35645911
Web Site: http://www.ingram.ba
INGMRK2—(SARE)
Rev.: $12,366,829
Assets: $28,776,422
Liabilities: $7,450,725
Net Worth: $21,325,698
Earnings: $1,428,790
Emp.: 177
Fiscal Year-end: 12/31/20
Stone Mining & Quarrying Services
N.A.I.C.S.: 212311

INGRAM MOTOR GROUP LIMITED
2 Wheatpark Place Heathfield Road, Ayr, KA8 9RT, United Kingdom
Tel.: (44) 1292269522
Web Site: http://www.ingramvolkswagen.co.uk
Sales Range: $25-49.9 Million
Emp.: 89
New & Used Car Dealers
N.A.I.C.S.: 441110
Alex Ingram (Founder)

INGRESS CORPORATION BERHAD
Lot 2778 5th Floor Jalan Damansara Sungai Penchala, Kuala Lumpur, 60000, Malaysia
Tel.: (60) 377255565 MY
Web Site: http://www.ingresscorp.com.my
Year Founded: 1991
Sales Range: $250-299.9 Million
Emp.: 2,121
Automotive Components Mfr
N.A.I.C.S.: 336350
Rameli Musa (Vice Chm)

Subsidiaries:

Fine Components (Thailand) Co., Ltd. (1)
600 Moo 4 Tambol Makhamkhu, Amphur Nikhompattana, Rayong, 21180, Thailand
Tel.: (66) 38029235
Web Site: https://www.finecomp.co.th
Sales Range: $50-74.9 Million
Emp.: 130
Industrial Precision Tools Mfr & Distr
N.A.I.C.S.: 333517

Ingress Auto Sdn. Bhd. (1)

AND PRIVATE COMPANIES
INISSION AB

2779 Jalan Damansara Sungai Penchala, 60000, Kuala Lumpur, Federal Territory, Malaysia
Tel.: (60) 377212288
Web Site: http://www.ingressauto.com.my
Sales Range: $25-49.9 Million
Emp.: 90
New Car Dealers
N.A.I.C.S.: 441110
Mohamed Amin Ariff *(Principal)*

Ingress Autoventures Co., Ltd. (1)
64/6 Moo 4 Pluakdaeng, Rayong, 21140, Thailand
Tel.: (66) 389549425
Web Site: http://www.ingress.co.th
Automotive Components Mfr
N.A.I.C.S.: 336330

Plant (Domestic):

Ingress Autoventures Co., Ltd. - Rayong Plant (2)
64/6 Moo 4 Pluakdaeng, Rayong, 21140, Thailand
Tel.: (66) 38 954942
Web Site: http://www.ingresscorp.com.my
Automotive Components Mfr
N.A.I.C.S.: 336330

Ingress Engineering Sdn. Bhd. (Nilai Plant) (1)
PT 2475-2476 Kawasan Perindustrian Nilai, PO Box 45, 71807, Nilai, Negeri Sembilan, Malaysia
Tel.: (60) 67995599
Sales Range: $125-149.9 Million
Emp.: 300
Extruded Plastic Molded Products Mfr
N.A.I.C.S.: 326199

Ingress Katayama Technology Centre Sdn. Bhd. (1)
Lot 9 Jalan P/7 Seksyen 13, PO Box 9, Kawasan Perindustrian Bangi, 43650, Bandar Baru Bangi, Selangor Darul Ehsan, Malaysia
Tel.: (60) 389264806
Automotive Component Mfr & Distr
N.A.I.C.S.: 336390

Ingress Motors Centre Sdn. Bhd. (1)
Bandar Bukit, 47100, Puchong, Selangor, Malaysia
Tel.: (60) 380660264
Web Site: https://ingressmotors.com
Car Dealer
N.A.I.C.S.: 441110
Ali Hashemi *(Mgr)*

Ingress Precision Sdn. Bhd. (1)
PT 2475-2476 Kawasan Perindustrian Nilai, PO Box 45, 71807, Nilai, Negeri Sembilan, Malaysia
Tel.: (60) 67995599
Web Site: https://www.ingresscorp.com.my
Sales Range: $100-124.9 Million
Emp.: 300
Automotive Doors Sash Mfr
N.A.I.C.S.: 332321

Ingress Swede Automobile Sdn. Bhd. (1)
No 10 Jalan PJU 7/3 Mutiara Damansara, 47800, Petaling Jaya, Selangor, Malaysia
Tel.: (60) 377330555
Web Site: https://volvo.ingress-swede.com.my
Car Dealer
N.A.I.C.S.: 441110

Ingress Technologies Sdn. Bhd. (1)
Lot 11 Jalan Jasmine 4 Kawasan Perindustrian Bukit Beruntung TST 29, 48009, Rawang, Selangor Darul Ehsan, Malaysia
Tel.: (60) 360283003
Sales Range: $100-124.9 Million
Emp.: 350
Automotive Exterior Component Mfr
N.A.I.C.S.: 336370

Multi Discovery Sdn. Bhd. (1)
Lot 2778 5th Floor Jalan Damansara Wilayah Persekutuan, Sungai Penchala, Kuala Lumpur, 60000, Federal Territory, Malaysia
Tel.: (60) 377255565
Web Site: http://www.ingresscorp.com.my
Sales Range: $25-49.9 Million
Emp.: 45
Electrical Engineering Services
N.A.I.C.S.: 541330

P.T. Ingress Malindo Ventures (1)
JL Industri Selatan 6A Block GG-7A/B Kawasan Industrial, Jababeka II Cikarang Selatan, Bekasi, 17530, West Java, Indonesia
Tel.: (62) 2189834330
Web Site: https://www.ingresscorp.com.my
Sales Range: $75-99.9 Million
Emp.: 127
Moldings & Sash Mfr
N.A.I.C.S.: 326199

Ramusa Engineering Sdn. Bhd. (1)
4th Floor Bangunan Ingress Auto 2779 Jalan Damansara, Sungai Penchal, 60000, Kuala Lumpur, Federal Territory, Malaysia
Tel.: (60) 377225767
Sales Range: $25-49.9 Million
Emp.: 60
Electrical Engineering Services
N.A.I.C.S.: 541330
Hanati Halim *(CEO)*

INGRESS INDUSTRIAL (THAILAND) PUBLIC COMPANY LIMITED
No 9/141 UM Tower Floor 14th Unite A 1 Ramkhamhaeng Road, Suanluang, Bangkok, 10250, Thailand
Tel.: (66) 2719964446 TH
Web Site: https://www.ingress.co.th
Year Founded: 2014
INGRS—(THA)
Rev.: $194,040,055
Assets: $189,071,797
Liabilities: $140,330,165
Net Worth: $48,741,631
Earnings: $1,127,401
Emp.: 2,700
Fiscal Year-end: 01/31/24
Automotive Components Mfr
N.A.I.C.S.: 336330
Nuthavuth Chatlertpipat *(Chm)*

Subsidiaries:

Ingress AOI Technologies Sdn. Bhd. (1)
Lot 40481 Seksyen 20 Mukim Bandar, Hulu Selangor, 48200, Serendah, Selangor, Malaysia
Tel.: (60) 360283003
Automotive Component Mfr & Distr
N.A.I.C.S.: 336390

Ingress Industrial (Malaysia) Sdn. Bhd. (1)
Lot 2778 5th Floor Jalan Damansara, Sungai Penchala, 60000, Kuala Lumpur, Malaysia
Tel.: (60) 377255565
Investment Holding Services
N.A.I.C.S.: 551112

PT Ingress Technologies Indonesia (1)
Jl Industri Selatan 6A Block GG 7A/B, Kawasan Industri Jababeka II Selatan, Bekasi, 17530, Indonesia
Tel.: (62) 2189834330
Automotive Component Mfr & Distr
N.A.I.C.S.: 336390

INHALERX LIMITED
Level 16 414 La Trobe Street, Melbourne, 3000, VIC, Australia
Tel.: (61) 391910135
Web Site: http://www.lifespot-health.com
Year Founded: 2016
IRX—(ASX)
Rev.: $16,556
Assets: $1,507,494
Liabilities: $237,210
Net Worth: $1,270,283
Earnings: ($1,286,498)
Fiscal Year-end: 12/31/22
Diagnostic Equipment Mfr
N.A.I.C.S.: 334510
Sean Williams *(Chm)*

Subsidiaries:

BodyTel GmbH (1)
Hufelandstr 14, 34537, Bad Wildungen, Germany
Tel.: (49) 5621967760
Web Site: http://bodytel.com
Medical Application Development Services
N.A.I.C.S.: 513210
Stefan Schraps *(Mng Dir)*

INHWA PRECISION CO., LTD.
Charyong-ro 14beon-gill 55, Uichang-gu, Changwon, Gyeongnam, Korea (South)
Tel.: (82) 552990954
Web Site: http://www.ihpre.co.kr
Year Founded: 1999
101930—(KRS)
Rev.: $113,814,884
Assets: $261,333,552
Liabilities: $130,674,637
Net Worth: $130,658,915
Earnings: ($8,261,377)
Emp.: 69
Fiscal Year-end: 12/31/22
Engine Component Mfr
N.A.I.C.S.: 333618
Lee Jae Goo *(Dir)*

INICIJAL A.D.
Knez Mihailova 35, Belgrade, Serbia
Tel.: (381) 11 2630 335
Year Founded: 1991
INCL—(BEL)
Sales Range: Less than $1 Million
Books Publishing Services
N.A.I.C.S.: 513130
Milena Petakovic *(Exec Dir)*

ININ GROUP AS
Henrik Ibsens gate 100, 255, Oslo, Norway
Tel.: (47) 41621300 NO
Web Site: https://www.inin.no
Year Founded: 2013
ININ—(EUR)
Rev.: $1,524,672
Assets: $38,781,105
Liabilities: $5,239,381
Net Worth: $33,541,724
Earnings: ($12,373,691)
Emp.: 136
Fiscal Year-end: 12/31/21
Information Technology Services
N.A.I.C.S.: 541512
Leif Christian Salomonsen *(Chm)*

Subsidiaries:

Jobbreiser AS (1)
PO Box 474, The Business Center, 1411, Kolbotn, Norway
Tel.: (47) 22120145
Web Site: https://www.connectin.no
Business Support Services
N.A.I.C.S.: 561499

Konvei Kompetansesenter AS (1)
Rosenholmveien 25, 1414, Trollasen, Norway
Tel.: (47) 22120142
Web Site: https://www.konvei.no
Management Consultancy Services
N.A.I.C.S.: 541611

Nordic Infrastructure Group AS (1)
Rosenholmveien 25, 1414, Trollasen, Norway
Tel.: (47) 22120147
Web Site: https://www.nigroup.no
Holding Company Services
N.A.I.C.S.: 551112

Rail Production AS (1)
Rosenholmveien 25, 1414, Trollasen, Norway
Tel.: (47) 22120143
Web Site: https://www.railpro.no
Railway Construction Services
N.A.I.C.S.: 237990

INISSION AB
Bruttovagen 3, 175 43, Jarfalla, Sweden
Tel.: (46) 8 564 406 50
Web Site: http://www.inission.com
INISS.B—(OMX)
Rev.: $129,287,603
Assets: $63,797,787
Liabilities: $30,983,904
Net Worth: $32,813,883
Earnings: $3,320,576
Emp.: 541
Fiscal Year-end: 12/31/20
Electronics Manufacturing Services
N.A.I.C.S.: 334419
Fredrik Berghel *(Co-Founder)*

Subsidiaries:

Enedo Finland Oy (1)
Martinkylantie 43, 01720, Vantaa, Finland
Tel.: (358) 9478466
Dc Power System Mfr
N.A.I.C.S.: 335311

Enedo Inc. (1)
80 Orville Dr Ste 100, Bohemia, NY 11716
Tel.: (631) 542-2003
Dc Power System Mfr
N.A.I.C.S.: 335311

Enedo Plc (1)
Quartetto Business Park Linnoitustie 4B, 02600, Espoo, Finland (80.43%)
Tel.: (358) 9478466
Web Site: http://www.efore.com
Rev.: $59,935,740
Assets: $52,259,765
Liabilities: $41,518,433
Net Worth: $10,741,332
Earnings: ($8,952,444)
Emp.: 406
Fiscal Year-end: 12/31/2018
Electronic Components Mfr
N.A.I.C.S.: 334419

Subsidiary (Non-US):

Efore (Suzhou) Automotive Technology Co., Ltd. (2)
Building 21 A And B No 428 Xinglong Street Suzhou Industrial Park, Suzhou, 215126, China
Tel.: (86) 51267671500
Electronic Components Mfr
N.A.I.C.S.: 334419

Efore (Suzhou) Electronics Co., Ltd. (2)
Unit 301 Building 11 No 50 Weixin Road, Suzhou Industrial Park, Suzhou, 215122, China
Tel.: (86) 51267671500
Electronic Components Mfr
N.A.I.C.S.: 334419

Efore AB (2)
Manskarsvagen 10B, 141 75, Kungens Kurva, Sweden
Tel.: (46) 768 714 600
Electronic Components Mfr
N.A.I.C.S.: 334419

Enedo S.p.A. (1)
Via Ancona 59, 60027, Osimo, AN, Italy
Tel.: (39) 0717214611
Electric Power Distr
N.A.I.C.S.: 423610

Enedo Sarl (1)
36 Rue 8601 ZI, 2035, Charguia, Tunisia
Tel.: (216) 71770386
Dc Power System Mfr
N.A.I.C.S.: 335311

Inission Malmo AB (1)
Jagersrovagen 204, 213 77, Malmo, Sweden
Tel.: (46) 406500200
Electronic Components Mfr
N.A.I.C.S.: 334419

Inission Munkfors AB (1)
Stalvagen 4, 684 92, Munkfors, Sweden
Tel.: (46) 563540540
Electric Equipment Mfr
N.A.I.C.S.: 334419

Inission Stockholm AB (1)
Bruttovagen 3, 175 43, Jarfalla, Sweden
Tel.: (46) 856440650
Electric Equipment Mfr
N.A.I.C.S.: 334419

INISSION AB

Inission AB—(Continued)

Inission Tallinn OU (1)
Sostramae 8, 13 816, Tallinn, Estonia
Tel.: (372) 6064420
Electronic Product Mfr & Distr
N.A.I.C.S.: 334111

Inission Vasteras AB (1)
Metallverksgatan 8, 721 30, Vasteras, Sweden
Tel.: (46) 21802500
Electronic Components Mfr
N.A.I.C.S.: 334419

Montronic AB (1)
Fabriksgatan 24, 280 10, Sosdala, Sweden
Tel.: (46) 45161525
Web Site: http://www.montronic.com
Electric Equipment Mfr
N.A.I.C.S.: 334419
Stig Leander (Mng Dir)

Sweco Elektronik AB (1)
Metallverksgatan 8, 721 30, Vasteras, Sweden
Tel.: (46) 21 80 25 00
Web Site: http://www.swecoelektronik.se
Sales Range: $25-49.9 Million
Emp.: 40
Electronic Components Mfr
N.A.I.C.S.: 334419
Mikael Helin (CEO)

INIT AG

Kopenicker Str 9, 10997, Berlin, Germany
Tel.: (49) 30970060
Web Site: http://www.init.de
Year Founded: 1995
Rev.: $12,525,389
Emp.: 146
Telecommunication Servicesb
N.A.I.C.S.: 517810
Dirk Stocksmeier (CEO)

Subsidiaries:

Init India (1)
German Centre Industry & Trade Unit No 17 Level 14 Building No 9, DLF Cyber City Phase III, Gurgaon, 122 002, Haryana, India
Tel.: (91) 1244636030
Web Site: http://www.init.co.in
Information Technology Consulting Services
N.A.I.C.S.: 541512
Roman Radtke (Branch Mgr)

Init Middle East (1)
Abu Dhabi Mall East Tower Office No E103, PO Box 109551, Abu Dhabi, United Arab Emirates
Tel.: (971) 26445560100
Web Site: http://www.init.ae
Software Development Services
N.A.I.C.S.: 541511
Matthias Topfer (Mgr-Sls)

init Europe (1)
Square Ambiorix 13, 1000, Brussels, Belgium
Tel.: (32) 27917002
Web Site: http://www.init.eu
Information Technology Consulting Services
N.A.I.C.S.: 541512
Harald Felling (Chief Sls Officer)

INIT INNOVATION IN TRAFFIC SYSTEMS SE

Kaeppelstrasse 4-10, 76131, Karlsruhe, Germany
Tel.: (49) 72161000
Web Site: https://www.initse.com
IXX—(MUN)
Rev.: $232,695,796
Assets: $287,536,058
Liabilities: $154,895,038
Net Worth: $132,641,019
Earnings: $16,756,747
Emp.: 1,140
Fiscal Year-end: 12/31/23
Hardware & Software Installation
N.A.I.C.S.: 541715
Gottfried Greschner (CEO & Member-Mgmt Bd)

Subsidiaries:

CarMedialab Corp. (1)
1450 2nd St, Santa Monica, CA 90401
Tel.: (424) 645-5195
Information Technology Services
N.A.I.C.S.: 513210

CarMedialab GmbH (1)
Zeiloch 6a, Bruchsal, 76646, Baden-Wurttemberg, Germany
Tel.: (49) 7251386250
Web Site: http://www.carmedialab.de
Sales Range: $25-49.9 Million
Emp.: 5
Motor Vehicle Telematic & Telephonic Embedded System Development Services
N.A.I.C.S.: 336360
Heiko Bauer (Mng Dir)

DResearch Fahrzeugelektronik GmbH (1)
Tor 2 Aufgang R R03 020 Wolfener Strasse 36, 12681, Berlin, Germany
Tel.: (49) 305159320
Web Site: https://www.dresearch-fe.de
Automotive Electronic Mfr
N.A.I.C.S.: 336320

Derovis GmbH (1)
Tor 2 Aufgang R R03 020 Wolfener Strasse 36, 12681, Berlin, Germany
Tel.: (49) 30515932100
Web Site: https://www.derovis.de
Consulting Services
N.A.I.C.S.: 541618

Dilax Intelcom GmbH (1)
Alt-Moabit 96b, 10559, Berlin, Germany
Tel.: (49) 3077309240
Web Site: http://www.dilax.com
Sensor Product Mfr
N.A.I.C.S.: 334519
Thorsten Kies (CEO)

HanseCom Public Transport Ticketing Solutions GmbH (1)
Amsinckstrasse 34, 20097, Hamburg, Germany
Tel.: (49) 15209073406
Web Site: http://www.hansecom.com
Emp.: 55
Public Transportation Services
N.A.I.C.S.: 485999
Martin Timmann (Mng Dir)

INIT Innovations in Transportation (Eastern Canada) Inc. (1)
1 Place du Commerce Ste 405 ile-des-Soeurs, Montreal, H3E 1A2, QC, Canada
Tel.: (514) 766-2836
Web Site: http://www.initag.com
Sales Range: $75-99.9 Million
Emp.: 3
Passenger Ticketing & Electronic Fare Collecting Services
N.A.I.C.S.: 522320

INIT Innovations in Transportation (Western Canada) Inc. (1)
22 Adelaide Street West Suite 3400, Toronto, M5H 4E3, ON, Canada
Tel.: (757) 413-9100
Public Transportation Services
N.A.I.C.S.: 485999
Roland Staib (Pres)

INIT Innovations in Transportation Inc. (1)
424 Network Station, Chesapeake, VA 23320
Tel.: (757) 413-9100
Public Transportation Services
N.A.I.C.S.: 485999
Matthias Herkert (Mgr-IT)

INIT Innovations in Transportation Ltd. (1)
Price House 37 Stoney Street The Lace Market, Nottingham, NG1 1LS, United Kingdom
Tel.: (44) 8708904648
Public Transportation Services
N.A.I.C.S.: 485999
Jens Mullak (Mng Dir)

INIT Innovations in Transportations Ltd. (1)
Block K Unit 1B Maynooth Business Campus, Maynooth, W23 TF98, Co Kildare, Ireland
Tel.: (353) 19041713
Sensor Component Mfr
N.A.I.C.S.: 334419

INIT Innovative Informatikanwendungen in Transport-, Verkehrs- und Leitsystemen GmbH (1)
Adolph-Menzel-Strasse 60, 04425, Taucha, Saxony, Germany
Tel.: (49) 3429830746
Web Site: http://www.init-ka.de
Telematic Software Development & Consulting Services
N.A.I.C.S.: 541511

INIT Mobility Software Solutions GmbH (1)
Kaeppelstrasse 4-10, 76131, Karlsruhe, Germany
Tel.: (49) 72161000
Web Site: https://www.initmss.com
Emp.: 80
Software Product Services
N.A.I.C.S.: 541511

INIT PTY LTD (1)
Level 5 Toowong Tower 9 Sherwood Rd, Toowong, 4066, QLD, Australia
Tel.: (61) 733108818
Sales Range: $25-49.9 Million
Emp.: 2
Transport System Management Services
N.A.I.C.S.: 541614

Init Innovation in Traffic Systems FZE (1)
Dubai Airport Free Zone Ofc 6EB 244, PO Box 54280, Dubai, United Arab Emirates
Tel.: (971) 47017286
Traffic Management Software Development Services
N.A.I.C.S.: 541511

Iris intelligent sensing SASU (1)
26 Avenue Jean Kuntzmann, 38330, Montbonnot-Saint-Martin, France
Tel.: (33) 673690406
Sensor Component Mfr
N.A.I.C.S.: 334511

Iris-Gmbh Infrared & Intelligent Sensors (1)
Ostendstrasse 1-14, 12459, Berlin, Germany
Tel.: (49) 305858140
Web Site: http://www.iris-sensing.com
Sensor Component Mfr
N.A.I.C.S.: 327910
Marc-Oliver Brammann (Gen Mgr)

Subsidiary (US):

Iris - Infrared & Intelligent Sensores NA, Inc. (2)
34 Peachtree St Nw Ste 2610, Atlanta, GA 30303
Tel.: (678) 927-9313
Sensor Component Mfr
N.A.I.C.S.: 334419

Subsidiary (Non-US):

Iris Asia-Pacific Pty. Ltd. (2)
Level 5 121 Exhibition Street, Melbourne, 3000, VIC, Australia
Tel.: (61) 414957019
Sensor Component Mfr
N.A.I.C.S.: 334419

Mattersoft Oy (1)
Hameenkatu 13 b, 33100, Tampere, Finland
Tel.: (358) 103225000
Public Transportation Services
N.A.I.C.S.: 485999

Mattorsoft Oy (1)
Hameenkatu 13 b, 33100, Tampere, Finland
Tel.: (358) 103225000
Software & Information Services
N.A.I.C.S.: 423430

TOA Total Quality Assembly LLC (1)
424 Network Sta, Chesapeake, VA 23320
Tel.: (757) 413-9100
Web Site: https://www.tqallc.com
Cable Harnesses & Connectors Mfr
N.A.I.C.S.: 334417

initperdis GmbH (1)
Am Stadtrand 56, 22047, Hamburg, Germany
Tel.: (49) 406965060
Public Transportation Services
N.A.I.C.S.: 485999
Ulrich Schmidt (Mng Dir)

initplan GmbH (1)
Kaeppelstrasse 4-6, 76131, Karlsruhe, Baden-Wurttemberg, Germany
Tel.: (49) 72161000
Web Site: http://www.initag.com
Sales Range: $75-99.9 Million
Emp.: 300
Transport Planning Software Development Services
N.A.I.C.S.: 541511

inola GmbH (1)
Schardinger Strasse 1, Pasching b, 4061, Linz, Austria
Tel.: (43) 720370588
Web Site: https://www.inola.at
Software Development Services
N.A.I.C.S.: 513210
Markus Fochler (Mgr-Bus Dev)

INITIATOR PHARMA A/S

Lyngsiesvej 18, Abyhoj, 8230, Aarhus, Denmark
Tel.: (45) 61260035
Web Site: http://www.initiatorpharma.com
Assets: $1,714,671
Liabilities: $229,362
Net Worth: $1,485,308
Earnings: ($1,242,454)
Emp.: 1
Fiscal Year-end: 12/31/19
Pharmaceuticals Product Mfr
N.A.I.C.S.: 325412
Claus Elsborg (CEO)

INIZIATIVE BRESCIANE S.P.A.

Piazza Vittoria n 19, 25043, Breno, Brescia, Italy
Tel.: (39) 0364320012
Web Site: https://www.iniziativebrescianespa.it
IB—(ITA)
Sales Range: Less than $1 Million
Hydro-Electric Power Plants Operator & Mfr
N.A.I.C.S.: 221111
Battista Albertani (Chm & CEO)

INJAZZAT REAL ESTATE DEVELOPMENT COMPANY K.S.C.C.

Kuwait Sharq Arabian Gulf Street Ahmad Tower Floor 20-19, PO Box 970, Safat, Kuwait, 13010, Kuwait
Tel.: (965) 22275200
Web Site: https://injazzat.com
Year Founded: 1998
INJAZZAT—(KUW)
Rev.: $26,852,592
Assets: $345,982,434
Liabilities: $156,949,127
Net Worth: $189,033,306
Earnings: $9,546,414
Emp.: 35
Fiscal Year-end: 12/31/22
Real Estate Investment & Management Services
N.A.I.C.S.: 531390
Mohammad Ibrahim Al-Farhan (CEO)

INKEL CORPORATION

3-8 Cheongcheon-Dong, Bupyeong-gu, Incheon, 403-853, Korea (South)
Tel.: (82) 32 650 6000
Web Site: http://www.inkel.co.kr
Year Founded: 1980
Sales Range: $10-24.9 Million
Emp.: 20
Mfr & Retailer of Electronics & Digital Components
N.A.I.C.S.: 334419

AND PRIVATE COMPANIES

H. S. Jeon *(Co-Pres)*
Subsidiaries:

Dongguan Inkel Electronics Co Ltd (1)
Shang qiao Industrial Road No 36, Dongcheng District, Dongguan, 523111, Guangdong, China
Tel.: (86) 769 8898 4000
Telecommunication Servicesb
N.A.I.C.S.: 517810

INKEL Corporation - Bu-Pyeong Factory (1)
93 Cheongjung-ro, Bupyong-Gu, Incheon, 403-853, Korea (South)
Tel.: (82) 82 32 650 6000
Telecommunication Servicesb
N.A.I.C.S.: 517810

Inkel Vietnam Co Ltd (1)
Plot 26 Quang Minh Industrial Park Quang Minh Town, Me Linh District, Hanoi, Vietnam
Tel.: (84) 44 3525 9663
Telecommunication Servicesb
N.A.I.C.S.: 517810

Sherwood America Inc. (1)
14730 Beach Blvd #102, La Mirada, CA 90638
Tel.: (714) 739-2000
Web Site: http://www.sherwoodamerica.com
Mfr & Retailer of Home & Car Audios & Communication Systems
N.A.I.C.S.: 423620
Charles Park *(Gen Mgr)*

INKEVERSE GROUP LIMITED
31/F Tower Two Times Square 1 Matheson Street, Causeway Bay, China (Hong Kong)
Tel.: (852) 31506788
Web Site: http://www.inke.com
Year Founded: 2015
3700—(HKG)
Rev.: $887,232,668
Assets: $654,350,206
Liabilities: $113,467,349
Net Worth: $540,882,857
Earnings: ($23,651,644)
Emp.: 1,531
Fiscal Year-end: 12/31/22
Media Streaming Services
N.A.I.C.S.: 518210
Yousheng Feng *(Co-Founder, Chm & CEO)*

INKON LIFE TECHNOLOGY CO., LTD.
17th Floor Yingkang Yisheng Building No 1 Haier Road, Laoshan District, Qingdao, 266103, Shandong, China
Tel.: (86) 53255776787
Web Site: http://www.starway.com.cn
Year Founded: 1998
300143—(CHIN)
Rev.: $162,337,500
Assets: $284,711,544
Liabilities: $99,757,008
Net Worth: $184,954,536
Earnings: ($83,667,168)
Fiscal Year-end: 12/31/22
Mushroom Production
N.A.I.C.S.: 111411
Tan Lixia *(Chm)*
Subsidiaries:

Guangdong Starway Bio-technology Co.,Ltd (1)
No 83 Jiaoping Avenue, Tangxia Town, Dongguan, 523722, Guangdong, China
Tel.: (86) 76987916623
Mushroom Mfr & Distr
N.A.I.C.S.: 111411

Starway Bio-Technology Co., Ltd. - Qingxi I Factory (1)
No 9 Hong Menshan Chang Shantou Industrial Zone, Dongguan, Guangdong, China
Tel.: (86) 76982773773
Mushrooms Mfr

Starway Bio-Technology Co., Ltd. - Shaoguan Factory (1)
Quijiang City Economic & Development Zone, Qujiang, Shaoguan, Guangdong, China
Tel.: (86) 7516481038
Web Site: http://www.starway.com.cn
Mushroom Farming Services
N.A.I.C.S.: 111411

INKTEC CO., LTD.
98-12 Neungan-ro, Danwon-gu, Ansan, 15426, Gyeonggi-do, Korea (South)
Tel.: (82) 314940001
Web Site: https://www.inktec.com
Year Founded: 1992
049550—(KRS)
Rev.: $47,199,178
Assets: $85,868,015
Liabilities: $32,179,887
Net Worth: $53,688,128
Earnings: $3,039,244
Emp.: 203
Fiscal Year-end: 12/31/22
Printer Accessories Mfr
N.A.I.C.S.: 325910
Kwang-Choon Chung *(CEO)*
Subsidiaries:

InkTec (Zhuhai) Trading Co., Ltd. (1)
No 709 HongFeng B/D No306 Jinji Road, QianShan, Zhuhai, 519070, Guangdong, China
Tel.: (86) 7563320660
Printing Ink Distr
N.A.I.C.S.: 424120

InkTec America Corp. (1)
223 W Dyer Rd, Santa Ana, CA 92707
Tel.: (714) 545-0117
Printing Ink Distr
N.A.I.C.S.: 424120
Kwang Hyun Lee *(Pres)*

INKY
36 Aigyptou Avenue, Larnaca, 6030, Cyprus
Tel.: (357) 25057246
Web Site: http://www.inky.live
Year Founded: 2018
Rev.: $1,000
Assets: $125,851
Liabilities: $122,250
Net Worth: $3,601
Earnings: ($66,442)
Emp.: 1
Fiscal Year-end: 11/30/22
Application Software Development Services
N.A.I.C.S.: 541511
Ioanna Kallidou *(Pres, CEO, CFO, Chief Acctg Officer, Treas & Sec)*

INLAND AUTO CENTRE LTD
11600 8th Street, Dawson Creek, V1G 4R7, BC, Canada
Tel.: (250) 782-5507
Web Site: http://www.inlandauto.dealers.ca
Rev.: $14,373,255
Emp.: 30
New & Used Car Dealers
N.A.I.C.S.: 441110
Dan Brennan *(Pres)*

INLAND HOMES PLC
Burnham Yard London End, Beaconsfield, HP2 2JH, Bucks, United Kingdom
Tel.: (44) 1494762450
Web Site: http://www.inlandhomes.co.uk
INL—(AIM)
Rev.: $246,697,724
Assets: $567,255,416
Liabilities: $318,792,656
Net Worth: $248,462,760
Earnings: $13,034,112
Emp.: 149
Fiscal Year-end: 09/30/21
Housing Construction Services
N.A.I.C.S.: 236116
Simon Bennett *(Chm)*
Subsidiaries:

Inland Homes Limited (1)
Decimal Place Chiltern Avenue, Amersham, HP6 5FG, Bucks, United Kingdom
Tel.: (44) 1494762450
Web Site: http://www.inlandhomes.co.uk
Real Estate Property Development Services
N.A.I.C.S.: 531210
Stephen Wicks *(CEO)*

Subsidiary (Domestic):

Inland ZDP PLC (2)
Burnham Yard London End, Beaconsfield, HP9 2JH, Buckinghamshire, United Kingdom
Tel.: (44) 1494762450
Web Site: http://www.inlandhomesplc.com
Rev.: $246,697,724
Assets: $567,255,416
Liabilities: $318,792,656
Net Worth: $248,462,760
Earnings: $13,034,112
Emp.: 149
Fiscal Year-end: 09/30/2021
Property Management Services
N.A.I.C.S.: 531311
Terry Royden *(Chm)*

INLAND PRINTERS LIMITED
800 8th Floor Sangita Ellipse Sahakar Road, Vile Parle East, Mumbai, 400 057, India
Tel.: (91) 22 40482500
Web Site: http://www.inlandprinters.in
Assets: $1,794
Liabilities: $59,500
Net Worth: ($57,706)
Earnings: ($8,990)
Fiscal Year-end: 03/31/19
Commercial Printing Services
N.A.I.C.S.: 323111
Bhavesh Patel *(Officer-Compliance)*

INLES D.D.
Kolodvorska ulica 22, 1310, Ribnica, Slovenia
Tel.: (386) 18377100
Web Site: http://www.inles.si
Sales Range: $25-49.9 Million
Emp.: 540
Wood, Aluminum & Vinyl Windows Mfr
N.A.I.C.S.: 321911
Subsidiaries:

INLES RAZSTAVNO PRODAJNI SALON RIBNICA (1)
Kolodvorska ulica 22, 1310, Ribnica, Slovenia
Tel.: (386) 1 8377 308
Web Site: http://www.inles.si
Wood Window & Door Mfr
N.A.I.C.S.: 321911

Inles CENTER MOZE d.o.o. (1)
Markljeva Ulica 2, 8000, Novo Mesto, Slovenia
Tel.: (386) 7 308 1173
Wooden Window Installation Services & Distr
N.A.I.C.S.: 238390

Inles Komerc d.o.o. (1)
Dubrovacka 115, 34300, Pozega, Croatia
Tel.: (385) 34248843
Sales Range: $25-49.9 Million
Emp.: 2
Windows & Doors Mfr
N.A.I.C.S.: 238350

Inles USA, LLC (1)
21092 Bake Pkwy Ste 104, Lake Forest, CA 92630
Tel.: (949) 215-6091
Web Site: http://www.inles-usa.com
Wood & Aluminium Window Distr

INLES KOMERC A.D.

N.A.I.C.S.: 423310

Inles Vinkovci d.o.o. (1)
Bana Jelacica 101, 32100, Vinkovci, Croatia
Tel.: (385) 32331088
Web Site: http://www.vinkovci.com.hr
Windows & Doors Mfr
N.A.I.C.S.: 238350

Inles d.d. - Lili Rus (1)
Kolodvorska 22, 1310, Ribnica, Slovenia
Tel.: (386) 18377167
Web Site: http://www.inles.si
Sales Range: $125-149.9 Million
Emp.: 500
Windows & Doors Mfr
N.A.I.C.S.: 321911
Andrea Mate *(Gen Mgr)*

Kosec TIM d.o.o. (1)
Tbilisijska 57b, 1000, Ljubljana, Slovenia
Tel.: (386) 1 2561 756
Web Site: http://www.kosec-trade.si
Windows & Doors Mfr
N.A.I.C.S.: 238350

Kosec Tim d.o.o. (1)
Perovo 26, 1241, Kamnik, Slovenia
Tel.: (386) 18310508
Web Site: http://www.kosec-trade.si
Sales Range: $25-49.9 Million
Emp.: 9
Windows & Doors Mfr
N.A.I.C.S.: 238350

Lesco GmbH & Company KG (1)
Isarholz Ausstellungs & Schulungszentrum Neumarkter St 23, 81673, Munich, Germany
Tel.: (49) 8957833100
Web Site: http://www.isarholz.de
Sales Range: $25-49.9 Million
Emp.: 4
Windows & Doors Mfr
N.A.I.C.S.: 321911

Plastles d.o.o. (1)
Breze 18, 1310, Ribnica, Slovenia
Tel.: (386) 18363433
Windows & Doors Mfr
N.A.I.C.S.: 238350

Produkt Invest d.o.o. (1)
Dujmovaca b b, 21000, Split, Croatia
Tel.: (385) 21544890
Web Site: http://www.produkt-invest.hr
Engineering & Design Services
N.A.I.C.S.: 541310

Sitolor d.o.o. (1)
Pavla Radica b b, 35000, Slavonski Brod, Croatia
Tel.: (385) 35405407
Web Site: http://www.sitolor.hr
Sales Range: $25-49.9 Million
Emp.: 60
Windows & Doors Mfr
N.A.I.C.S.: 238350

T.I.P. Engineering d.o.o. (1)
IX Korpusa 80 Solkan, 5000, Nova Gorica, Slovenia
Tel.: (386) 53005498
Web Site: http://www.oprematip.com
Sales Range: $25-49.9 Million
Emp.: 1
Windows & Doors Mfr
N.A.I.C.S.: 238350
Ivan Vogrich *(Gen Mgr)*

Ventana Design S.L. (1)
Carretera Cabo la Nao/Pla 170 Local 18a, 03730, Valencia, Javeo, Spain
Tel.: (34) 965 66 3666
Web Site: http://www.ventanadesignsl.es
Engineering Design Services
N.A.I.C.S.: 541310

Zgonec d.o.o. (1)
Mlaka 37A, 1218, Komenda, Slovenia
Tel.: (386) 18342140
Web Site: http://www.zgonec.si
Sales Range: $25-49.9 Million
Emp.: 8
Windows & Doors Mfr
N.A.I.C.S.: 238350
Janice Garnett *(Gen Mgr)*

INLES KOMERC A.D.

INLES KOMERC A.D.

Inles Komerc a.d.—(Continued)
Jirecekova 5b, Novi Sad, Serbia
Tel.: (381) 214770564
Year Founded: 1999
INLS—(BEL)
Sales Range: Less than $1 Million
Emp.: 9
Hardware Product Retailer
N.A.I.C.S.: 444140
Aleksandra Rulj *(Exec Dir)*

INLY MEDIA CO., LTD.
No 1 Room 635 138 Changhua Road, Haidian, 100020, China
Tel.: (86) 1087521979
603598—(SHG)
Rev.: $608,376,001
Assets: $194,363,414
Liabilities: $173,941,406
Net Worth: $20,422,008
Earnings: ($14,042,176)
Fiscal Year-end: 12/31/22
Advertising Agency Services
N.A.I.C.S.: 541810
Yanji Luo *(Chm & Pres)*

INMA GULF DEVELOPMENT & CONSTRUCTION L.L.C.
Rashidiya Industrial Area 17 Umm Ramool, PO Box 4560, Dubai, United Arab Emirates
Tel.: (971) 42857272
Web Site: http://www.inmagulf.ae
Year Founded: 1972
Sales Range: $25-49.9 Million
Emp.: 100
Construction & Industrial equipment Mfr
N.A.I.C.S.: 333120
Samir A. Aweidah *(Dir)*

Subsidiaries:

INMA Co. QATAR L.L.C. (1)
Al Thuraiya Souq Office No 5 Salwa Rd, PO Box 9238, Doha, Qatar
Tel.: (974) 44430088
Web Site: http://www.inmagulf.com
Emp.: 10
Construction Machinery Distr
N.A.I.C.S.: 423810
Antonie Azar *(Gen Mgr)*

INMAX HOLDING CO., LTD.
7F No 3 Sec 5 Nanjing E Rd, Songshan Dist, New Taipei City, 105409, Taiwan
Tel.: (886) 277097667
1591—(TPE)
Rev.: $21,322,546
Assets: $19,637,839
Liabilities: $3,900,134
Net Worth: $15,737,704
Earnings: $2,687,115
Fiscal Year-end: 12/31/22
Design Fastener Mfr
N.A.I.C.S.: 332722
Chiang Wen-Chou *(Chm & Pres)*

INMED PHARMACEUTICALS INC.
1445 885 West Georgia St, Vancouver, V6C 3E8, BC, Canada
Tel.: (604) 669-7207
Web Site:
https://www.inmedpharma.com
Year Founded: 1981
INM—(NASDAQ)
Rev.: $4,597,730
Assets: $11,822,782
Liabilities: $2,616,673
Net Worth: $9,206,109
Earnings: ($7,675,550)
Emp.: 13
Fiscal Year-end: 06/30/24
Biopharmaceutical Mfr
N.A.I.C.S.: 325412
Eric A. Adams *(Pres & CEO)*

INMEDIA PUBLIC RELATIONS INC
126 York Street Suite 310, Ottawa, K1N 5T5, ON, Canada
Tel.: (613) 234-7227
Web Site: http://www.inmedia.com
Public Relations
N.A.I.C.S.: 541820
Francis Moran *(Founder & Mng Partner)*

Subsidiaries:

inmedia Public Relations - Glasgow (1)
3/1 131 Ingram St, Glasgow, G1 1DJ, Scotland, United Kingdom
Tel.: (44) 141 404 6478
Public Relations
N.A.I.C.S.: 541820

inmedia Public Relations Inc - Bedford (1)
1202 Avalon Dr, Bedford, MA 01730
Tel.: (781) 538-5245
Public Relations
N.A.I.C.S.: 541820

INMOBI PTE LTD.
7th Floor Block Delta B Block Embassy Tech Square Kadubeesanahalli, Village Outer Ring Road, Bengaluru, 560 103, India
Tel.: (91) 8065834445
Web Site: http://www.inmobi.com
Year Founded: 2007
Emp.: 700
Mobile Advertising Services
N.A.I.C.S.: 541890
Naveen Tewari *(Co-Founder & CEO)*

Subsidiaries:

Quantcast Corporation (1)
201 3rd St, San Francisco, CA 94103-3153
Tel.: (415) 738-4755
Web Site: http://www.quantcast.com
Emp.: 201
Online Advertising Services
N.A.I.C.S.: 541810
Konrad Feldman *(Founder & CEO)*

INMOBILIARIA CLUB DE CAMPO S.A.
Burgos 176 Ofcina 7, PO Box 2446, Las Condes, Santiago, Chile
Tel.: (56) 2070662
Real Estate Development Services
N.A.I.C.S.: 531390

INMOBILIARIA COLONIAL SOCIMI SA
Avenida Diagonal 532, 08006, Barcelona, Spain
Tel.: (34) 934047900
Web Site:
https://www.inmocolonial.com
COL—(MAD)
Rev.: $427,510,763
Assets: $13,063,911,030
Liabilities: $6,498,945,801
Net Worth: $6,564,965,229
Earnings: ($1,299,897,340)
Emp.: 234
Fiscal Year-end: 12/31/23
Holding Company; Real Estate Services
N.A.I.C.S.: 551112
Carlos Krohmer *(Chief Corp Dev Officer)*

Subsidiaries:

Abix Service S.L.U. (1)
Llacuna 56, Barcelona, 08005, Spain
Tel.: (34) 932246513
Real Estate Manangement Services
N.A.I.C.S.: 531390

Axiare Patrimonio SOCIMI S.A. (1)
Edificio Beatriz Calle Jose Ortega y Gasset 29 Planta 6, 28009, Madrid, Spain
Tel.: (34) 914319317
Web Site: http://www.axiarealestate.com
Sales Range: Less than $1 Million
Real Estate Investment Trust
N.A.I.C.S.: 525990

Riofisa S.A. (1)
Arbea Campus Empresarial Ctra Fuencarral a Alcobendas, M-603, Km 3800, 28108, Alcobendas, Madrid, Spain
Tel.: (34) 916612250
Web Site: http://www.riofisa.com
Sales Range: $500-549.9 Million
Emp.: 100
Commercial & Residential Real Estate Development
N.A.I.C.S.: 531190

Subsidiary (Domestic):

Necsa, Nuevos Espacios Comerciales, S.A. (2)
Paseo De La Castellana 52 3rd Fl, 28046, Madrid, Spain
Tel.: (34) 916612250
Real Estate Management Services
N.A.I.C.S.: 531390

Riofisa Sema, S.L. (1)
Cr De Fuencarral 603, Alcobendas, Spain
Tel.: (34) 916612250
Real Estate Manangement Services
N.A.I.C.S.: 531390

Societe Fonciere Lyonnaise S.A.S. (1)
42 rue Washington, 75008, Paris, France (98.58%)
Tel.: (33) 142972700
Web Site:
https://www.fonciere-lyonnaise.com
Rev.: $258,770,284
Assets: $8,201,259,522
Liabilities: $3,253,539,022
Net Worth: $4,947,720,500
Earnings: ($868,608,014)
Emp.: 77
Fiscal Year-end: 12/31/2023
Real Estate Services
N.A.I.C.S.: 531390
Nicolas Reynaud *(CEO)*

Subsidiary (Domestic):

SCI Paul Cezanne (2)
42 rue Washington, 75008, Paris, France
Tel.: (33) 559300803
Real Estate Manangement Services
N.A.I.C.S.: 531390

Torre Marenostrum, S.L. (1)
Avinguda Diagonal 532, 08006, Barcelona, Spain
Tel.: (34) 934 04 79 00
Real Estate Manangement Services
N.A.I.C.S.: 531390

INMOBILIARIA CRAIGHOUSE SA
El Rodeo 12525 Lo Barnechea, PO Box 20007, Santiago, 7700 494, Chile
Tel.: (56) 27560200
CRAIGHOUSE—(SGO)
Sales Range: Less than $1 Million
Real Estate Investment Services
N.A.I.C.S.: 531210
Antony Fyfe Garcia *(Chm)*

INMOBILIARIA DE DEPORTES LA DEHESA S.A.
Camino Club De Golf 2501, PO Box 212, Santiago, Chile
Tel.: (56) 2166816
DEHESA—(SGO)
Sales Range: Less than $1 Million
Golf Club Operator
N.A.I.C.S.: 713910

INMOBILIARIA DEL SUR, S.A.
C/ Angel Gelan n 2, 41013, Sevilla, Spain
Tel.: (34) 954278446
Web Site:
https://www.grupoinsur.com

INTERNATIONAL PUBLIC

Year Founded: 1945
ISUR—(MAD)
Rev.: $137,518,808
Assets: $517,487,306
Liabilities: $397,438,314
Net Worth: $120,048,992
Earnings: $137,518,808
Fiscal Year-end: 12/31/19
Real Estate Development Services
N.A.I.C.S.: 531390
Ricardo Pumar Lopez *(Chm)*

INMOBILIARIA ESPACIO, S.A
P de la Castellana 259-D Planta 50, Madrid, 28046, Spain
Tel.: (34) 914176930
Web Site:
http://www.inmoespacio.com
Real Estate Services
N.A.I.C.S.: 531390
Angel Lloret Sempere *(Project Mgr)*

INMOBILIARIA MANQUEHUE SA
Av Santa Maria 6350 Piso 4, Vitacura, Chile
Tel.: (56) 227507000
Web Site:
https://www.imanquehue.com
Construction Services
N.A.I.C.S.: 237990
Juan Eduardo Bauza Ramsay *(CEO)*

INMOBILIARIA RAPID S.A.C.
Av Arenales, 1814, Lima, Peru
Tel.: (51) 4705678
Gaming Concession Management Services
N.A.I.C.S.: 713290

INMOBILIARIA SAN PATRICIO SA
Isidora Goyenechea 2800 piso 13, Las Condes, Santiago, Chile
Tel.: (56) 2800480
Web Site: https://www.isanpatricio.cl
Year Founded: 2004
ISANPA—(SGO)
Sales Range: Less than $1 Million
Real Estate Manangement Services
N.A.I.C.S.: 531311

INMOBILIARIA SIXTERRA S.A.
Av Santa Maria 2050, Providencia, Santiago, Chile
Tel.: (56) 24788016
Web Site: https://www.sixterra.cl
SIXTERRA—(SGO)
Sales Range: Less than $1 Million
Investment Management Service
N.A.I.C.S.: 523999
Vicente Navarrete Rolando *(Chm)*

INMOBILIARIA STADIO ITALIANO S.A.
Av Apoquindo 6589, Las Condes, Chile
Tel.: (56) 224847000
Web Site:
https://www.stadioitaliano.cl
Year Founded: 1941
STADITALIA—(SGO)
Sales Range: Less than $1 Million
Real Estate Services
N.A.I.C.S.: 531390

INMOBILIARIA YUGOSLAVA S.A.
Avenida Vitacura 8001, Santiago, Chile
Tel.: (56) 2129727
YUGOSLAVA—(SGO)
Sales Range: Less than $1 Million
Investment Management Service
N.A.I.C.S.: 523999

AND PRIVATE COMPANIES — INNER MONGOLIA OJING SCIENCE & TECHNOLOGY CO., LTD.

Roque Razmilic Tomicic Radovan *(Chm)*

INMODE LTD.
Tavor Building Sha'ar Yokneam, PO Box 533, Yokneam, 2069206, Israel
Tel.: (972) 49096313 II
Web Site: http://www.inmodemd.com
Year Founded: 2008
INMD—(NASDAQ)
Rev.: $492,048,000
Assets: $863,286,000
Liabilities: $75,914,000
Net Worth: $787,372,000
Earnings: $197,919,000
Emp.: 581
Fiscal Year-end: 12/31/23
Healthcare Software Development Services
N.A.I.C.S.: 541511
Moshe Mizrahy *(Co-Founder, Chm & CEO)*

INMOSUPA, SOCIMI, S.A.
Socorro Street No 28 Ground Floor, 15003, A Coruna, Spain
Tel.: (34) 98131000
Web Site: https://www.inmosupa.eu
Year Founded: 2015
MLISP—(EUR)
Rev.: $1,309,817
Assets: $17,527,903
Liabilities: $9,655,209
Net Worth: $7,872,693
Earnings: $101,765
Emp.: 300
Fiscal Year-end: 12/31/22
Real Estate Investment Services
N.A.I.C.S.: 531190
Manuel Casal Villasenin *(Sec)*

INMYSHOW DIGITAL TECHNOLOGY (GROUP) CO., LTD.
No 5 courtyard West Five Street, Chaoyang district, Beijing, 536000, Guangxi, China
Tel.: (86) 1064660106
Web Site: https://www.inmyshow.com
600556—(SHG)
Rev.: $579,698,866
Assets: $800,817,255
Liabilities: $275,698,145
Net Worth: $525,119,110
Earnings: $25,261,077
Fiscal Year-end: 12/31/22
Information Technology Services
N.A.I.C.S.: 541512
Meng Li *(Chm & Gen Mgr)*

INNATE PHARMA S.A.
117 Avenue de Luminy, 13 009, Marseilles, France
Tel.: (33) 430303030 FR
Web Site: https://www.innate-pharma.com
Year Founded: 1999
IPHA—(NASDAQ)
Rev.: $70,837,514
Assets: $255,305,651
Liabilities: $188,795,227
Net Worth: $66,510,424
Earnings: ($71,364,429)
Emp.: 211
Fiscal Year-end: 12/31/22
Biopharmaceutical Research & Development Services
N.A.I.C.S.: 325412
Herve Brailly *(Co-Founder & Chm-Supervisory Bd)*

INNATURE BERHAD
No 5 Jalan USJ 10/1C UEP, 47620, Subang Jaya, Selangor, Malaysia
Tel.: (60) 356324313 MY
Web Site: https://www.innature.com.my
Year Founded: 1984
INNATURE—(KLS)
Rev.: $31,618,624
Assets: $38,555,979
Liabilities: $7,089,735
Net Worth: $31,466,243
Earnings: $4,515,344
Emp.: 632
Fiscal Year-end: 12/31/22
Personal Care Product Distr
N.A.I.C.S.: 456199
Fong Hui Sain *(CEO)*

INNELEC MULTIMEDIA
Centre d Activites de l Ourcq 45 rue Delizy, 93692, Pantin, Cedex, France
Tel.: (33) 148105555 FR
Web Site: https://www.corporate.innelec.com
Year Founded: 1983
ALINN—(EUR)
Sales Range: $150-199.9 Million
Multimedia Product Distr
N.A.I.C.S.: 423990
Denis Thebaud *(Founder & CEO)*

INNER EAST COMMUNITY FINANCE LIMITED.
145 Maling Road, Canterbury, 3126, VIC, Australia
Tel.: (61) 398368029 AU
Web Site: https://iecf.com.au
IEC—(NSXA)
Rev.: $3,381,188
Assets: $4,997,156
Liabilities: $2,423,886
Net Worth: $2,573,271
Earnings: $100,082
Emp.: 22
Fiscal Year-end: 06/30/22
Commericial Banking
N.A.I.C.S.: 522110
Juliann Ruth Byron *(Chm)*

INNER MONGOLIA DAZHONG MINING CO., LTD.
Xiaoshetai Secretary Valley Urad Front Banner, Inner Mongolia, Baotou, 014010, China
Tel.: (86) 4725216664
Web Site: https://www.dzky.cn
Year Founded: 1999
001203—(SSE)
Rev.: $569,800,764
Assets: $1,542,053,916
Liabilities: $670,814,352
Net Worth: $871,239,564
Earnings: $137,132,892
Fiscal Year-end: 12/31/22
Iron Ore Mining Services
N.A.I.C.S.: 212210
Guofeng Niu *(Chm)*

INNER MONGOLIA DIAN TOU ENERGY CORPORATION LIMITED
Huakuang Zhusi Flower Zone Zhelimu Avenue, Huolinguole City, Tongliao, 029200, China
Tel.: (86) 4756196998
002128—(SSE)
Rev.: $3,075,525,283
Assets: $5,281,013,875
Liabilities: $2,128,748,767
Net Worth: $3,152,265,108
Earnings: $317,261,140
Fiscal Year-end: 12/31/20
Coal Product Mfr
N.A.I.C.S.: 324199

INNER MONGOLIA EERDUOSI RESOURCES CO., LTD.
Cashmere Industrial Park Hantai Town, Dongsheng District, Ordos, 017000, China
Tel.: (86) 4778543776
600295—(SHG)
Rev.: $5,109,637,460
Assets: $6,707,314,795
Liabilities: $3,081,780,070
Net Worth: $3,625,534,725
Earnings: $664,439,841
Emp.: 40,000
Fiscal Year-end: 12/31/22
Apparels Mfr
N.A.I.C.S.: 315120
Linxiang Wang *(Chm)*

INNER MONGOLIA ENERGY ENGINEERING CO., LTD.
Harbor Building 29 Midwest Lane Ordos East Street, Inner Mongolia Autonomous Region Saihan, Hohhot, 010010, China
Tel.: (86) 4715202054
Web Site: http://www.en.imeec.cn
Year Founded: 2016
1649—(HKG)
Building Construction Services
N.A.I.C.S.: 236210
Niu Jirong *(Chm)*

INNER MONGOLIA ERDOS RESOURCES CO., LTD.
No 1 Qingfang Street Hantai, Dongsheng Inner Mongolia, Ordos, 017000, China
Tel.: (86) 477 854 3776
Web Site: http://www.chinaerdos.com
Year Founded: 1995
900936—(SHG)
Rev.: $5,588,075,825
Assets: $7,630,961,112
Liabilities: $3,963,060,089
Net Worth: $3,667,901,024
Earnings: $933,174,532
Emp.: 40,000
Fiscal Year-end: 12/31/21
Clothing Apparel Mfr & Distr
N.A.I.C.S.: 315250
Zhen Wang *(Chm & Gen Mgr)*

INNER MONGOLIA FIRST MACHINERY GROUP CO., LTD.
Minzhu Road Qingshan District, Baotou, 014030, China
Tel.: (86) 4723117903
Web Site: http://www.bfcy.cc
600967—(SHG)
Rev.: $2,014,581,362
Assets: $3,268,120,649
Liabilities: $1,725,204,958
Net Worth: $1,542,915,691
Earnings: $115,581,338
Emp.: 9,003
Fiscal Year-end: 12/31/22
Railway Freight Vehicle Mfr
N.A.I.C.S.: 336510
Quanwen Li *(Chm)*

INNER MONGOLIA FURUI MEDICAL SCIENCE CO.,LTD.
7th Floor Building 2 Kunsha Center No 16 Xinyuanli, Chaoyang District, Beijing, 100027, China
Tel.: (86) 1084682800
Web Site: http://www.fu-rui.com
Year Founded: 1998
300049—(CHIN)
Rev.: $141,631,308
Assets: $354,192,696
Liabilities: $97,850,376
Net Worth: $256,342,320
Earnings: $13,740,948
Fiscal Year-end: 12/31/22
Pharmaceuticals Mfr
N.A.I.C.S.: 325412
Crown One *(Chm & Gen Mgr)*

INNER MONGOLIA JUNZHENG ENERGY & CHEMICAL GROUP CO., LTD.
Wuda Industrial Park, Wuhai, 016040, China
Tel.: (86) 4736921012
Web Site: https://www.junzhenggroup.com
Year Founded: 2003
601216—(SHG)
Rev.: $3,012,936,334
Assets: $5,453,828,551
Liabilities: $1,762,314,152
Net Worth: $3,691,514,399
Earnings: $583,696,419
Emp.: 4,000
Fiscal Year-end: 12/31/22
Chemical Products Mfr
N.A.I.C.S.: 325180
Zhang Haisheng *(Chm)*

INNER MONGOLIA LITTLE SHEEP CATERING CHAIN CO., LTD.
No 9 Wulan Avenue, Baotou, 014010, China
Tel.: (86) 472 513 7998
Web Site: http://www.xfy.cn
Year Founded: 1999
Sales Range: $500-549.9 Million
Restaurant
N.A.I.C.S.: 722513

INNER MONGOLIA MENGDIAN HUANENG THERMAL POWER CORPORATION LIMITED
No 218 Xilin South Road, Inner Mongolia, Hohhot, 010020, China
Tel.: (86) 4716222289
Web Site: http://www.nmhdwz.com
Year Founded: 1994
600863—(SHG)
Rev.: $3,238,407,966
Assets: $5,637,655,366
Liabilities: $2,746,292,628
Net Worth: $2,891,362,739
Earnings: $247,385,783
Fiscal Year-end: 12/31/22
Electric Power Generation & Distribution Services
N.A.I.C.S.: 221118
Wang Zhenrui *(Gen Mgr & Dir)*

INNER MONGOLIA NORTH HAULER JOINT STOCK CO., LTD.
Beizhong Road Rare-Earth Zone, Baotou, 014030, Inner Mongolia, China
Tel.: (86) 4722642010
Web Site: https://www.chinanhl.cn
Year Founded: 1988
600262—(SHG)
Rev.: $313,785,534
Assets: $390,503,042
Liabilities: $181,967,273
Net Worth: $208,535,769
Earnings: $16,678,607
Fiscal Year-end: 12/31/22
Heavy Duty Truck Mfr & Distr
N.A.I.C.S.: 336120
Haiquan Guo *(Chm)*

INNER MONGOLIA OJING SCIENCE & TECHNOLOGY CO., LTD.
No 31 Amur South Street, Saihan District Inner Mongolia, Hohhot, 010070, China
Tel.: (86) 4713252496
Web Site: https://www.ojingquartz.com
Year Founded: 2011
001269—(SSE)
Rev.: $201,311,136
Assets: $281,813,688
Liabilities: $121,534,452
Net Worth: $160,279,236
Earnings: $33,469,956

INNER MONGOLIA OJING SCIENCE & TECHNOLOGY CO., LTD.

Inner Mongolia OJing Science & Technology Co., Ltd.—(Continued)
Fiscal Year-end: 12/31/22
Auxiliary Material Mfr
N.A.I.C.S.: 336419
Liang Zhang (Chm)

INNER MONGOLIA PINGZHUANG ENERGY RESOURCES CO., LTD.
Pingzhuang Town, Yuanbaoshan District, Chifeng, 024076, China
Tel.: (86) 47 6332 4281
Web Site: http://pzny.chnenergy.com.cn
000780—(SSE)
Rev.: $308,190,177
Assets: $693,395,343
Liabilities: $143,297,478
Net Worth: $550,097,865
Earnings: ($11,164,662)
Fiscal Year-end: 12/31/19
Coal Mining Services
N.A.I.C.S.: 213113
Xiaohui Xu (Chm)

INNER MONGOLIA TIANSHOU TECHNOLOGY & DEVELOPMENT CO., LTD.
Building B6 Zhengxiang International Plaza No 7 Gangtie Avenue, Qingshan District, Baotou, 100020, China
Tel.: (86) 105 714 3995
000611—(SSE)
Rev.: $1,132,222
Assets: $366,702,007
Liabilities: $199,359,916
Net Worth: $167,342,090
Earnings: ($5,521,688)
Emp.: 141
Fiscal Year-end: 12/31/20
Communication Terminal Mfr
N.A.I.C.S.: 334290
Duanqi Yuan (Deputy Gen Mgr)

INNER MONGOLIA XINGYE MINING CO., LTD.
Xingye Building Yulong Avenue, Xincheng District, Chifeng, 024000, Inner Mongolia, China
Tel.: (86) 4768833387
Web Site: http://www.nmxyky.com
Year Founded: 1994
000426—(SSE)
Rev.: $292,858,956
Assets: $1,351,206,792
Liabilities: $571,096,656
Net Worth: $780,110,136
Earnings: $24,415,560
Fiscal Year-end: 12/31/22
Mining Services
N.A.I.C.S.: 212290
Xingjun Ji (Gen Mgr)

INNER MONGOLIA YILI INDUSTRIAL GROUP CO., LTD.
No 1 Jinshan Avenue, Jinshan Development Zone, Huhhot, 010110, China
Tel.: (86) 4008169999
Web Site: https://www.yili.com
600887—(SHG)
Rev.: $17,293,214,592
Assets: $18,387,528,443
Liabilities: $10,785,836,754
Net Worth: $7,601,691,689
Earnings: $1,324,121,484
Emp.: 59,052
Fiscal Year-end: 12/31/22
Dairy Products
N.A.I.C.S.: 424430
Pan Gang (Chm)

Subsidiaries:

Ausnutria Dairy Corporation Ltd (1)
Block A Building 1 Ausnutria Building Suncity, Purui East Road, Changsha, 410005, Hunan, China
Tel.: (86) 73182229278
Web Site: https://www.ausnutria.com.hk
Sales Range: $75-99.9 Million
Emp.: 512
Dairy Products Mfr
N.A.I.C.S.: 112120
Yuehui Liu (Exec Dir-Recruitment, HR Plng, R&D & Admin-Ausnutria China)

EasiYo Products (UK) Limited (1)
Capital House 4th Floor 85 King William Street, London, EC4N 7BL, United Kingdom
Tel.: (44) 133 285 0468
Web Site: https://uk.easiyo.com
Dairy Product Retailer
N.A.I.C.S.: 424430

Oceania Dairy Limited (1)
Cnr Cooneys Road and State Highway 1, South Canterbury, Glenavy, 7980, New Zealand
Tel.: (64) 36866403
Web Site: http://www.oceaniadairy.co.nz
Milk Distr
N.A.I.C.S.: 424430
Shiqing Jian (Dir-Resident)

PT. Green Asia Food Indonesia (1)
Perwata Tower Lantai 6 Suite A JI Pluit Selatan Raya Kav 1, Penjaringan, Jakarta Utara, 14440, DKI Jakarta, Indonesia
Tel.: (62) 213 002 7643
Web Site: https://www.joyday.com
Dairy Products Mfr
N.A.I.C.S.: 311511

The Chomthana Company Limited (1)
59/1 Moo 7 Pathum Thani-Ladlumkaeo Road Khu Bang Luang, Lad Lum Kaeo, Pathumthani, 12140, Thailand
Tel.: (66) 2 979 4800
Web Site: https://www.chomthana.com
Ice Cream & Frozen Product Mfr
N.A.I.C.S.: 311520

Westland Milk Products Investments Limited (1)
56 Livingstone Street, PO Box 96, Hokitika, 7842, New Zealand
Tel.: (64) 3 756 9800
Web Site: https://www.westland.co.nz
Milk Distr
N.A.I.C.S.: 424430
Richard Wyeth (CEO)

Yili Innovation Centre Europe B.V. (1)
Bronland 12 E-1, 6708 WH, Wageningen, Netherlands
Tel.: (31) 85 044 1190
Web Site: https://www.yili-innovation.com
Dairy Product Mfr & Distr
N.A.I.C.S.: 311511
Hittjo Homan (Mgr-Open Innovation)

INNER MONGOLIA YITAI COAL COMPANY LIMITED
Yitai Building North Tianjiao Road, Dongsheng District, Ordos, 017000, Inner Mongolia, China
Tel.: (86) 4778565688
Web Site: http://www.yitaicoal.com
900948—(SHG)
Rev.: $7,342,283,230
Assets: $11,831,121,954
Liabilities: $4,156,107,914
Net Worth: $7,675,014,040
Earnings: $1,069,967,282
Emp.: 5,345
Fiscal Year-end: 12/31/23
Coal Mining Services
N.A.I.C.S.: 212115
Chunlin Liu (Exec Dir)

INNER MONGOLIA YUAN XING ENERGY CO., LTD.
Boyuan Etuoke West Building 12th Floor, Dongsheng District, Ordos, 017000, China
Tel.: (86) 4778139869
Web Site: http://www.yuanxing.com
Year Founded: 1997
000683—(SSE)
Rev.: $1,542,506,004
Assets: $4,192,655,688
Liabilities: $1,845,278,604
Net Worth: $2,347,377,084
Earnings: $373,424,688
Fiscal Year-end: 12/31/22
Chemical Products Mfr
N.A.I.C.S.: 325199
Weitu Song (Chm)

INNERGEX RENEWABLE ENERGY INC.
1225 Saint - Charles Street West 10th Floor, Longueuil, J4K 0B9, QC, Canada
Tel.: (450) 928-2550
Web Site: https://www.innergex.com
Year Founded: 1990
3IX—(DEU)
Rev.: $732,379
Assets: $6,750,605
Liabilities: $5,840,442
Net Worth: $910,162
Earnings: ($79,902)
Emp.: 602
Fiscal Year-end: 12/31/23
Power Generating Services
N.A.I.C.S.: 238290
Renaud de Batz (Sr VP-Latin America)

Subsidiaries:

Alterra Power Corp. (1)
888 Dunsmuir Street Suite 1100, Vancouver, V6C 3K4, BC, Canada
Tel.: (604) 633-9990
Web Site: http://www.innergex.com
Geothermal Exploration & Mining Services
N.A.I.C.S.: 221118

Subsidiary (Non-US):

HS Orka hf (2)
Svartsengi, 240, Grindavik, Iceland
Tel.: (354) 5209300
Web Site: https://www.hsorka.is
Geothermal Energy Power Plants
N.A.I.C.S.: 221118
Asbjorn Blondal (VP-Project Dev)

Joint Venture (Non-US):

Magma Energy Italia S.R.L. (2)
Via Ernesto Rossi 9, 52100, Arezzo, Italy (45%)
Tel.: (39) 05 753 2641
Web Site: https://www.magmaenergyitalia.it
Geothermal Electric Power Generation Services
N.A.I.C.S.: 221116

INNITY CORPORATION BERHAD
C501 C502 Block C Kelana Square 17 Jalan SS 7/26 Kelana Jaya, 47301, Petaling Jaya, Selangor Darul Ehsan, Malaysia
Tel.: (60) 378805611 MY
Web Site: https://www.innity.com
Year Founded: 1999
INNITY—(KLS)
Rev.: $24,817,695
Assets: $17,795,837
Liabilities: $9,215,517
Net Worth: $8,580,320
Earnings: ($472,187)
Emp.: 300
Fiscal Year-end: 12/31/23
Holding Company; Technology-Based Online Advertising Solutions & Other Internet-Related Services
N.A.I.C.S.: 551112
Chee Leong Phang (Founder & Chm)

Subsidiaries:

Innity Sdn Bhd (1)
C501 & C502 Block C Kelana Sq 17 Jalan SS7/26, Petaling Jaya, 47301, Selangor, Malaysia
Tel.: (60) 378805611
Sales Range: $25-49.9 Million
Emp.: 100
Online Marketing Services
N.A.I.C.S.: 541613
Phang Chee Leong (CEO)

Subsidiary (Non-US):

Innity Digital Media (Thailand) Co. Ltd. (2)
253 Building Asoke 15th Floor Sukhumvit 21 Road, Kongtoey Nua Wattana, Bangkok, 10110, Thailand
Tel.: (66) 2 664 3370
Internet Advertising Services
N.A.I.C.S.: 541810
Itsarapa Sanitprachakorn (Dir-Sls)

Innity Limited (2)
1107 11/F Westlands Centre 20 Westlands Road, Quarry Bay, China (Hong Kong)
Tel.: (852) 2 668 2302
Web Site: http://www.innity.com
Emp.: 20
Holding Company
N.A.I.C.S.: 551112
Andrew Lin (Head-Hong Kong)

Innity Philippines, Inc. (2)
Unit 1104 Jaka Building 6780 Ayala Avenue, Makati Central Bus District, Makati, 1226, Philippines
Tel.: (63) 2 625 0315
Online Advertising Services
N.A.I.C.S.: 541810
Francis Xavier (Acct Mgr)

Innity Singapore Pte Ltd (2)
144 Robinson Road 09-01 Robinson Square, Singapore, 068908, Singapore
Tel.: (65) 6 324 1471
Web Site: http://www.innity.com
Sales Range: $25-49.9 Million
Emp.: 8
Advertising Services
N.A.I.C.S.: 541810

Innity Vietnam Co Ltd (2)
3rd floor Phuong Nam Office Tower 157 Vo Thi Sau street, ward 6 district 3, Ho Chi Minh City, Vietnam
Tel.: (84) 83 820 8286
Web Site: http://www.innity.com
Advertising Services
N.A.I.C.S.: 541810

PT. Media Innity (2)
Plaza Centris 10th Floor JL HR Rasuna Said Kav B-5, Kuningan, Jakarta, 12910, Indonesia
Tel.: (62) 21 522 9628
Internet Advertising Services
N.A.I.C.S.: 541810

INNO INSTRUMENT INC.
30 Songdomirae-ro, Yeonsu-gu, Incheon, 21990, Korea (South)
Tel.: (82) 328375600
Web Site: https://www.innoinstrument.com
Year Founded: 2007
215790—(KRS)
Rev.: $38,235,911
Assets: $98,422,612
Liabilities: $23,542,237
Net Worth: $74,880,375
Earnings: $4,312,080
Emp.: 24
Fiscal Year-end: 12/31/22
Investment Fund Services
N.A.I.C.S.: 525910

Subsidiaries:

INNO Instrument (China) Inc. (1)
6A 82 No 1198 Qinzhou North Road, Shanghai, 200233, China
Tel.: (86) 2164170300
Optical Communication Equipment Distr
N.A.I.C.S.: 423690

INNQ Instrument America Inc. (1)
2010 Valley View Ln Ste 140, Dallas, TX 75234
Tel.: (214) 484-3627
Web Site: http://www.americainno.com
Communication Equipment Repair Services

AND PRIVATE COMPANIES

N.A.I.C.S.: 811210

INNO Instrument Europe GmbH (1)
Otto-Volger-Strasse 3c, 65843, Sulzbach, Germany
Tel.: (49) 61969533130
Measuring & Controlling Equipment Distr
N.A.I.C.S.: 423830

INNO Instrument India Pvt. Ltd. (1)
811 812 Eight Floor Vishal Tower, Janakpuri District Center, New Delhi, 110058, India
Tel.: (91) 9891999981
Optical Communication Equipment Distr
N.A.I.C.S.: 423690

INNO Instrument Malaysia Inc. (1)
No 22A Jalan Kemuning Bayu 33/33B Kemuning Utama, Shah Alam, 40400, Selangor, Malaysia
Tel.: (60) 162929380
Optical Communication Equipment Distr
N.A.I.C.S.: 423690

INNO Instrument Myanmar Inc. (1)
383 A 2nd Floor Innwa 3rd Street Ward 6 South Okkalapa Tsp, Yangon, Myanmar
Tel.: (95) 9450091740
Optical Communication Equipment Distr
N.A.I.C.S.: 423690

INNO Instrument Philippines Inc. (1)
2nd Flr Topy s Place AlcosGlobal IT Park 7 Industria Street, Bagumbayan, Quezon City, 1110, Philippines
Tel.: (63) 9228529545
Optical Communication Equipment Distr
N.A.I.C.S.: 423690

INNO Instrument Vietnam Inc. (1)
Room 1316 KeangNam Landmark 72 Tower E6 Pham Hung Str, Nam Tu Liem Dist, Hanoi, Vietnam
Tel.: (84) 462777771
Optical Communication Equipment Distr
N.A.I.C.S.: 423690

INNO LASER TECHNOLOGY CO., LTD.
No 01 11th Floor Building A Section 1 Chuangzhi Yuncheng Building, Industrial Zone Xili Subdistrict Nanshan District, Shenzhen, 518053, Guangdong, China
Tel.: (86) 75586353200
Web Site: https://www.inno-laser.com
Year Founded: 2011
301021—(CHIN)
Rev.: $44,894,304
Assets: $151,466,328
Liabilities: $11,802,024
Net Worth: $139,664,304
Earnings: $3,168,828
Fiscal Year-end: 12/31/22
Laser Product Mfr
N.A.I.C.S.: 334510
Xiaojie Zhao (Chm & Gen Mgr)

INNO SMART GROUP LIMITED
13th floor Guangdong Investment Tower 148 Connaught Road Central, Hong Kong, China (Hong Kong)
Tel.: (852) 2587 7800   VG
Holding Company
N.A.I.C.S.: 551112
Wai Keung Yue (CEO)

INNO-GENE SA
ul Sciegiennego 20, 60-128, Poznan, Poland
Tel.: (48) 509658006
Web Site: https://www.inno-gene.pl
Research & Development Services
N.A.I.C.S.: 541720
Michal Kaszuba (CEO)

INNO-TECH HOLDINGS LIMITED
Unit 1015 Level 10 Tower 1 Grand Century Place, 193 Prince Edward Road West, Kowloon, China (Hong Kong)
Tel.: (852) 2153 3330   BM

Web Site: http://www.it-holdings.com.hk
Year Founded: 2001
8202—(HKG)
Sales Range: $1-9.9 Million
Emp.: 76
Holding Company
N.A.I.C.S.: 551112
King Hang Lau (Exec Dir)

INNOCAN PHARMA CORPORATION
1015 926-5 Avenue SW, Calgary, T2P 0N7, AB, Canada
Tel.: (403) 777-1519
Web Site: https://www.innocanpharma.com
INNPF—(OTCQB)
Rev.: $196,000
Assets: $12,575,000
Liabilities: $3,564,000
Net Worth: $9,011,000
Earnings: $10,091,000
Emp.: 7
Fiscal Year-end: 12/31/21
Cannabis Product Mfr & Distr
N.A.I.C.S.: 325412
Doug Menzies (Mgr-Exploration)

INNOCARE OPTOELECTRONICS CORPORATION
Room B No 2 Sec 2 Huansi Rd, Southern Taiwan Science park, Tainan City, 74144, Taiwan
Tel.: (886) 67007238
Web Site: https://www.innocare-x.com
Year Founded: 2019
6861—(TAI)
Rev.: $60,077,698
Assets: $74,183,587
Liabilities: $32,169,494
Net Worth: $42,014,093
Earnings: $3,814,971
Emp.: 359
Fiscal Year-end: 12/31/23
Electronic Components Mfr
N.A.I.C.S.: 334419
James Yang (Chm)

INNOCARE PHARMA LIMITED
Building 8 No 8 Life Science Park Road, Zhongguancun Life Science Park Changping, Beijing, 102206, China
Tel.: (86) 1066609999   Ky
Web Site: http://www.innocarepharma.com
Year Founded: 2015
9969—(HKG)
Rev.: $87,806,722
Assets: $1,449,090,583
Liabilities: $375,827,072
Net Worth: $1,073,263,511
Earnings: ($125,479,271)
Emp.: 939
Fiscal Year-end: 12/31/22
Pharmaceutical Product Mfr & Distr
N.A.I.C.S.: 325412
Jasmine Cui (Founder, Chm & CEO)

INNOCEAN WORLDWIDE INC.
Landmark Tower 20F 837-36 Yeoksam-dong, Gangnam-gu, Seoul, 135937, Korea (South)
Tel.: (82) 220162300   KR
Web Site: http://www.innocean.com
Year Founded: 2005
214320—(KRS)
Rev.: $1,342,562,548
Assets: $1,756,539,339
Liabilities: $1,086,206,733
Net Worth: $670,332,607
Earnings: $68,827,987
Emp.: 820
Fiscal Year-end: 12/31/22

Advertising, Marketing & Communications
N.A.I.C.S.: 541890
Kun-Hee Ahn (CEO)

Subsidiaries:

David & Goliath, LLC (1)
909 N Pacific Coast Hwy Ste 700, El Segundo, CA 90245
Tel.: (310) 445-5200
Web Site: https://www.dng.com
Advetising Agency
N.A.I.C.S.: 541810
David Angelo (Founder & Chm)

WELLCOM GROUP LIMITED (1)
46-48 Pyrmont Bridge Road, Pyrmont, 2009, NSW, Australia
Tel.: (61) 293104458
Web Site: http://www.wellcom.com.au
Rev.: $121,105,511
Assets: $74,596,893
Liabilities: $27,431,102
Net Worth: $47,165,791
Earnings: $9,150,465
Emp.: 60,000
Fiscal Year-end: 06/30/2018
Data Management Services
N.A.I.C.S.: 518210
Wayne William Sidwell (Chm)

INNOCOM TECHNOLOGY HOLDINGS, INC.
Unit 2807 28/F 99 Queen's Road, Central, China (Hong Kong)
Tel.: (852) 3102 1602   NV
Web Site: http://www.innocomtechnology.com
Year Founded: 1998
Assets: $1,643
Liabilities: $702,947
Net Worth: ($701,304)
Earnings: ($122,848)
Emp.: 2
Fiscal Year-end: 12/31/16
Mobile Phone Handsets & Components Distr
N.A.I.C.S.: 423690
Eric Chin Pang Tang (Exec Dir)

INNOCONCEPTS N.V.
Esp 430, 5633 AJ, Eindhoven, Netherlands
Tel.: (31) 402647580
Sales Range: $10-24.9 Million
Emp.: 223
Injection Moulding Technology
N.A.I.C.S.: 333248
Nahendra Mehra (CEO)

Subsidiaries:

I-Pac Technologies N.V. (1)
Rivium Quadrant 90, 2909, Capelle aan den IJssel, Netherlands
Tel.: (31) 10 288 43 67
Web Site: http://www.ipactechnologies.com
Plastics Product Mfr
N.A.I.C.S.: 326199

InnoCleaning Concepts Holding B.V. (1)
Esp 430, Eindhoven, 5633 AJ, Netherlands
Tel.: (31) 180744200
Flame Retardant Product Mfr & Sales
N.A.I.C.S.: 325998

InnoEssentials International B.V. (1)
Donk 1B, 2991 LE, Barendrecht, Netherlands
Tel.: (31) 180330550
Web Site: http://www.silkn.eu
Personal Care Products Mfr & Whslr
N.A.I.C.S.: 812199
Oscar Middendorp (Gen Mgr)

INNOCORP LTD.
Plot no 41 Road No 6 IDA Mallapur, Hyderabad, 500076, Andhra Pradesh, India
Tel.: (91) 4065990114
Web Site: https://www.innocorpltd.com

INNODISK CORP.

Year Founded: 1994
531929—(BOM)
Rev.: $71,617
Assets: $430,001
Liabilities: $552,974
Net Worth: ($122,973)
Earnings: ($23,867)
Emp.: 2
Fiscal Year-end: 03/31/22
Plastics Molded Products Mfr
N.A.I.C.S.: 326199
Venkata Garapati Siva Sundara Prasad (Chm)

INNODEP INC.
9F Hansin IT Tower 2 47 Digital-ro 9-gil, Geumcheon-gu, Seoul, 08375, Korea (South)
Tel.: (82) 221096866
Web Site: https://www.innodep.co.kr
Year Founded: 2008
303530—(KRS)
Software Development Services
N.A.I.C.S.: 541511
Seong-Jin Lee (CEO)

INNODIS LTD
Innodis Building, Caudan, Port Louis, Mauritius
Tel.: (230) 2060800
Web Site: https://www.innodisgroup.com
Year Founded: 1973
HWF—(MAU)
Rev.: $132,751,441
Assets: $127,604,218
Liabilities: $76,841,105
Net Worth: $50,763,114
Earnings: $746,810
Emp.: 1,252
Fiscal Year-end: 06/30/22
Animal Feed Mfr & Distr
N.A.I.C.S.: 311119
Hansley Chadee (Sr Mgr-IT)

Subsidiaries:

Meaders Feeds Ltd (1)
Riche Terre Road Riche Terre, Port Louis, Mauritius
Tel.: (230) 249 3860
Web Site: https://www.meadersfeeds.com
Animal Feed Mfr
N.A.I.C.S.: 311119

Poulet Arc-en-Ciel Ltee (1)
Terres Rocheuses, Beau Vallon, Mahebourg, Grand Port, Mauritius
Tel.: (230) 6318869
Emp.: 100
Poultry Farming Services
N.A.I.C.S.: 112990
Gerard Wong Chong (Sr Mgr)

INNODISK CORP.
5F No 237 Sec 1 Datong Rd, Xizhi Dist, New Taipei City, 221, Taiwan
Tel.: (886) 277033000
Web Site: https://www.innodisk.com
Year Founded: 2005
5289—(TPE)
Rev.: $322,147,047
Assets: $290,808,773
Liabilities: $68,208,111
Net Worth: $222,600,663
Earnings: $58,821,499
Emp.: 288
Fiscal Year-end: 12/31/22
Electric Equipment Mfr
N.A.I.C.S.: 334111

Subsidiaries:

Innodisk Europe B.V. (1)
Pisanostraat 57, 5623 CB, Eindhoven, Netherlands
Tel.: (31) 403045400
Computer Hardware Mfr
N.A.I.C.S.: 332510

Innodisk France S.A.S. (1)

INNODISK CORP.

InnoDisk Corp.—(Continued)

Immeuble Arago 1 41 boulevard Vauban,
78280, Guyancourt, France
Tel.: (33) 134895028
Artificial Intelligence Development Services
N.A.I.C.S.: 541715

Innodisk Japan Corporation (1)
2F 1-1-14 Nihonbashi-Ningyocha, Chuo-ku,
Tokyo, 103-0013, Japan
Tel.: (81) 3666701612
Artificial Intelligence Development Services
N.A.I.C.S.: 541715

Innodisk Shenzhen Corporation (1)
807 8 Floor Building B Hengyue Ceriter
Dengilang Road, Nanshan District, Shenzhen, China
Tel.: (86) 75521673689
Artificial Intelligence Development Services
N.A.I.C.S.: 541715

Innodisk USA Corporation (1)
42996 Osgood Rd, Fremont, CA 94539
Tel.: (510) 770-9421
Artificial Intelligence Development Services
N.A.I.C.S.: 541715

INNOGENE CO., LTD.
301 Woolim E-Biz Center 1 28
Digital-Ro 33-Gil, Guro-Gu, Seoul,
Korea (South)
Tel.: (82) 221082294
Web Site:
    https://www.eng.innogene.com
Year Founded: 2005
344860—(KRS)
Medicinal Cosmetic Product Mfr
N.A.I.C.S.: 325620
Kwang-Hun Lee *(CEO)*

INNOGY LIMITED
18 Richardson Street, West Perth,
6005, WA, Australia
Tel.: (61) 864249000   AU
Web Site:
    https://www.innogylimited.com.au
Year Founded: 2016
IOG—(ASX)
Mineral Exploration Services
N.A.I.C.S.: 212390
David Drabble *(CEO)*

INNOKAIZ INDIA LIMITED
New No 43 Old No 22 Flat 1 4th
Floor Real Enclave Josier Street,
Nungambakkam, Chennai, 600034,
Tamil Nadu, India
Tel.: (91) 7358333340
Web Site:
    https://www.innokaizindia.com
Year Founded: 2003
INNOKAIZ—(NSE)
Rev.: $27,029,200
Assets: $6,813,731
Liabilities: $3,516,279
Net Worth: $3,297,452
Earnings: $1,074,099
Fiscal Year-end: 03/31/23
Digital Marketing Services
N.A.I.C.S.: 541810
Balakrishnan Sukumarbalakrishnan
(Mng Dir)

INNOLUX CORPORATION
No 160 Kexue Rd Hsinchu Science
Park Operation Building, Miaoli
County Fab T1/Fab 2, Taipei, 35053,
Taiwan
Tel.: (886) 37586000
Web Site: https://www.innolux.com
Year Founded: 2003
3481—(TAI)
Rev.: $6,924,377,808
Assets: $11,692,024,870
Liabilities: $4,206,977,865
Net Worth: $7,485,047,005
Earnings: ($608,219,016)
Emp.: 41,322
Fiscal Year-end: 12/31/23

Liquid Crystal Display Screen Mfr
N.A.I.C.S.: 334310
Vincent Yu *(VP)*

Subsidiaries:

GIO Optoelectronics Corp.
No 5 Titangang Road, Fenghuali New District, Tainan City, Taiwan
Tel.: (886) 65889999
Web Site: https://www.giotaiwan.com.tw
Emp.: 90
LED Light Distr
N.A.I.C.S.: 423610

Innolux Corporation - Ningbo (1)
No 16 YangZi River North Rd, Ningbo Export Processing Zone, Ningbo, 315800,
China
Tel.: (86) 574 8686 5999
Computer & Electronic Component Mfr
N.A.I.C.S.: 334419

Innolux Europe B.V. (1)
Jupiterstraat 106, 2132 HE, Hoofddorp,
Netherlands
Tel.: (31) 235671050
Sales Range: $25-49.9 Million
Emp.: 5
Computer & Electronic Component Distr
N.A.I.C.S.: 423620
Xinjan Duan *(CEO)*

Subsidiary (Non-US):

Innolux Germany GmbH (2)
Hanns-Martin-Schleyer Strasse 9b-9c,
47877, Willich, Germany
Tel.: (49) 2154814780
Sales Range: $25-49.9 Million
Computer & Electronic Component Distr
N.A.I.C.S.: 423620
Lonnie Xue *(Office Mgr)*

Innolux USA, Inc. (1)
101 Metro Dr Ste 510, San Jose, CA 95110
Tel.: (408) 573-8438
Sales Range: $25-49.9 Million
Emp.: 18
Computer & Electronic Component Distr
N.A.I.C.S.: 423620
Junichi Ishii *(Pres)*

INNOMETRY CO., LTD.
40 Jeongnamsandan 1-gil,
Jeongnam-myeon, Hwaseong,
Gyeonggi-do, Korea (South)
Tel.: (82) 312755174
Web Site: https://www.innometry.com
Year Founded: 2008
302430—(KRS)
Rev.: $58,069,933
Assets: $61,374,142
Liabilities: $18,611,970
Net Worth: $42,762,172
Earnings: $2,059,466
Emp.: 103
Fiscal Year-end: 12/31/22
Imaging Equipment Mfr & Distr
N.A.I.C.S.: 334510
Lee Gapsoo *(CEO)*

INNOPAC HOLDINGS LIMITED
190 Middle Road 19-07 Fortune Centre, Singapore, 188979, Singapore
Tel.: (65) 6 222 1841
Web Site: http://www.innopacific.com
I26—(SES)
Sales Range: $1-9.9 Million
Investment Services
N.A.I.C.S.: 523999
Jenny Woon Chuen Soh *(Gen Mgr-Corp Affairs)*

INNOPRISE PLANTATIONS BERHAD
6th Floor Menara Tun Mustapha Likas Bay, 88400, Kota Kinabalu, Sabah, Malaysia
Tel.: (60) 88326415
Web Site:
    https://www.innoprise.com.my
Year Founded: 1993

INNO—(KLS)
Rev.: $48,681,754
Assets: $87,463,130
Liabilities: $20,443,998
Net Worth: $67,019,132
Earnings: $11,404,179
Emp.: 735
Fiscal Year-end: 12/31/23
Oil Palm Plantations & Log Extraction
Services
N.A.I.C.S.: 311225
Ai Hoon Chan *(Co-Sec)*

Subsidiaries:

Serijaya Industri Sdn. Bhd. (1)
Pejabat Tsh Jln Aps, Tawau, 91009, Sabah,
Malaysia
Tel.: (60) 89914177
Web Site: http://www.innoprise.com.my
Emp.: 200
Log Extraction & Oil Palm Plantation Services
N.A.I.C.S.: 113310

INNORULES CO., LTD.
12F U-Top TechValley 7 Beopwon-ro
6-gil, Songpa-gu, Seoul, Korea
(South)
Tel.: (82) 24162501
Web Site: https://www.innorules.com
Year Founded: 2007
296640—(KRS)
Software Development Services
N.A.I.C.S.: 541511

INNOSIMULATION CO. LTD.
5 Magokjungang 8-ro 7-gil, Gangseo-gu, Seoul, 07794, Korea (South)
Tel.: (82) 23049500
Web Site: https://www.innosim.com
Year Founded: 2000
274400—(KRS)
Emp.: 88
Information Technology Services
N.A.I.C.S.: 541512
In-Jae Seong *(CMO)*

INNOSYS CORP.
1 Sangwon 12-gil Seongdong-gu,
Seoul, Korea (South)
Tel.: (82) 318520102
Year Founded: 1993
056090—(KRS)
Rev.: $31,576,594
Assets: $108,483,845
Liabilities: $64,244,046
Net Worth: $44,239,799
Earnings: ($14,219,820)
Emp.: 120
Fiscal Year-end: 12/31/22
Orthopaedic Product Mfr
N.A.I.C.S.: 339113
Chung Jumi *(CEO)*

INNOTECH CORPORATION
3-17-6 Shinyokohama, Kouhokuku,
Yokohama, 222-8580, Kanagawa,
Japan
Tel.: (81) 454749000
Web Site: https://www.innotech.co.jp
Year Founded: 1987
9880—(TKS)
Rev.: $273,376,380
Assets: $316,176,130
Liabilities: $148,797,710
Net Worth: $167,378,420
Earnings: $9,762,970
Emp.: 1,768
Fiscal Year-end: 03/31/24
Semiconductor Distr & Sales
N.A.I.C.S.: 423830
Takashi Takahashi *(Mng Dir)*

Subsidiaries:

Sanei Hytechs Co., Ltd. (1)
311-3 Koyasu-cho, Higashi-ku, Hamamatsu,
435-0015, Shizuoka, Japan
Tel.: (81) 534651555

Web Site: http://www.sanei-hy.co.jp
Sales Range: $75-99.9 Million
Emp.: 373
Computer Support System Development
Services
N.A.I.C.S.: 541511
Yoshihiro Mabuchi *(Pres & CEO)*

INNOTEK LIMITED
160 Robinson Road No 24-12 SBF
Center, Singapore, 068914, Singapore
Tel.: (65) 65350689   SG
Web Site:
    https://www.innotek.com.sg
Year Founded: 1984
M14—(SES)
Rev.: $138,478,833
Assets: $191,590,995
Liabilities: $60,565,720
Net Worth: $131,025,275
Earnings: $1,671,341
Emp.: 1,590
Fiscal Year-end: 12/31/22
Investment Holding Company; Precision Components Mfr
N.A.I.C.S.: 551112
Yiliang Lou *(CEO)*

Subsidiaries:

**Acrathon Precision Technologies (HK)
Limited** (1)
Unit 06-07 17/F APEC Plaza 49 Hoi Yuen
Road, Kwun Tong, Kowloon, China (Hong
Kong)   (74.32%)
Tel.: (852) 2 764 3862
Web Site: https://www.acrathon.tdk.com.cn
Emp.: 293
Electronic Parts & Equipment Whslr
N.A.I.C.S.: 423690

**Feng Chuan Tooling Company
Limited** (1)
1-7 King Hong Street, 1st Floor Che Wah
Industrial B, Kwai Chung, China (Hong
Kong)
Tel.: (852) 29435833
Web Site: http://www.mansfield.com.hk
Sales Range: $50-74.9 Million
Metals Service Center
N.A.I.C.S.: 423510

Subsidiary (Non-US):

**Feng Chuan Tooling (Dongguan) Co.
Ltd.** (2)
55 Xiang Xin East Road, Yantian Fenggang, Dongguan, 523700, Guangdong,
China
Tel.: (86) 76987513998
Metal Stamping Mfr
N.A.I.C.S.: 332119

Go Smart Development Limited (1)
1/F Che Wah Ind Bldg 1-7 Kin Hong St,
Kwai Chung, China (Hong Kong)
Tel.: (852) 29435833
Electronic Components Mfr
N.A.I.C.S.: 334419

**Magix Mechatronics (Dongguan)
Company Limited** (1)
No 1 Er Heng Dao Xiang Xin East Road He
Dong Industrial Zone, Yantian Fenggang
Town, Dongguan, 523740, Guangdong
Province, China   (64.58%)
Tel.: (86) 7698 203 9188
Web Site: http://www.magix.com.hk
Mechanical & Electro-Mechanical Contract
Mfr
N.A.I.C.S.: 334111

Magnecomp Corporation (1)
38975 Sky Canyon Dr Ste 111, Murrieta,
CA 92563
Tel.: (951) 296-3582
Web Site:
    http://www.magnecompprecision.com
Sales Range: $25-49.9 Million
Computer & Computer Peripheral Equipment & Software Whslr
N.A.I.C.S.: 423430
K. C. Ee *(Mgr-Design Engrg)*

Magnecomp Technology Limited (1)
Unit 2601 B-2 26/F Yen Sheng Centre, 64

Hoi Yuen Road Kwun Tong, Kowloon, China
(Hong Kong) **(74.32%)**
Tel.: (852) 27955238
Sales Range: $25-49.9 Million
Electronic Parts & Equipment Whslr
N.A.I.C.S.: 423690

Mansfield (Thailand) Co. Ltd. (1)
No 7/11 Moo 4 Tambol Phananikhom Amphur, Nikhompattana, Rayong, 21180, Thailand
Tel.: (66) 33010856
Precision Metal Components Mfr
N.A.I.C.S.: 332721

Mansfield Manufacturing (Wuhan) Company Limited (1)
No 169 North Quanli Road, Wuhan Economic and Technological Development Zone, Wuhan, 430056, Hubei, China
Tel.: (86) 2784551088
Precision Metal Components Mfr
N.A.I.C.S.: 332721

Mansfield Manufacturing Co., Ltd. (1)
Room B 17/F Ford Glory Plaza 37 Wing Hong Street, Cheung Sha Wan, Kowloon, China (Hong Kong)
Tel.: (852) 2 489 1968
Web Site: https://www.mansfield.com.hk
Metal Stamping & Die Making
N.A.I.C.S.: 332119

Subsidiary (Domestic):

Magix Mechatronics Company Limited (2)
1-7 King Hong Street, 1st Fl Che Wah Industrial B, Kwai Chung, China (Hong Kong) **(100%)**
Tel.: (852) 29435833
Web Site: http://www.mechatronics.com
Sales Range: $50-74.9 Million
Metals Service Center
N.A.I.C.S.: 423510

Subsidiary (Non-US):

Mansfield (Suzhou) Manufacturing Company Limited (2)
No 2 Jin Wang Road, Xu Shu Guan, Suzhou, 215151, Jiangsu, China
Tel.: (86) 5126 661 7083
Web Site: http://www.mansfield.com.hk
Metal Stamping
N.A.I.C.S.: 332119

Optimal Technology Limited (1)
Unit 2601 B-2 26th Floor Yen Sheng Centre, 64 Hoi Yuen Road Kwun Tong, Kowloon, China (Hong Kong) **(74.32%)**
Tel.: (852) 27955238
Sales Range: $25-49.9 Million
Electronic Parts & Equipment Whslr
N.A.I.C.S.: 423690

Sun Mansfield Manufacturing (Dongguan) Company Limited (1)
Plant I Block 103 106 Xin Yang Road, New Sun Industrial City Lincun Tangxia, Dongguan, 523711, Guangdong, China
Tel.: (86) 76987929299
Precision Metal Components Mfr
N.A.I.C.S.: 332721
David Zhao *(Acct Mgr)*

INNOTHERA SA
22, avenue Aristide Briand, Arcueil, 94110, France
Tel.: (33) 146151900
Web Site: http://www.innothera.fr
Year Founded: 1913
Pharmaceuticals Product Mfr
N.A.I.C.S.: 456110
Arnaud Gobet *(CEO)*

Subsidiaries:

Gibaud SAS (1)
73 rue de la Tour, PO Box 78, 42002, Saint Etienne, Cedex, France
Tel.: (33) 4 77 91 30 30
Web Site: http://www.gibaud.com
Orthopedic Devices Mfr & Distr
N.A.I.C.S.: 339113

Subsidiary (Domestic):

Gibaud Pharma EURL (2)
73 rue de la Tour, 42000, Saint Etienne, Loire, France
Tel.: (33) 477913030
Pharmaceutical Product Whslr
N.A.I.C.S.: 424210

Subsidiary (Non-US):

Gibaud Suisse SA (2)
Rue Gourgas 23, 1205, Geneva, Switzerland
Tel.: (41) 22 328 06 00
Web Site: http://www.gibaud.com
Sales Range: $50-74.9 Million
Emp.: 2
Orthopedic Product Distr
N.A.I.C.S.: 423450

Subsidiary (Domestic):

Tournier Bottu SAS (2)
300 Ave du Formans, 01600, Trevoux, 01600, Ain, France
Tel.: (33) 478 22 67 67
Sales Range: $25-49.9 Million
Emp.: 100
Orthopaedic Product Mfr
N.A.I.C.S.: 339113
Frederic Baugouin *(Mng Dir)*

INNOTHERAPY, INC.
Ace Hightech City2 401 25 Seonyu-ro 13-gil, Yeongdeungpo-gu, Seoul, 07282, Korea (South)
Tel.: (82) 269591338
Web Site:
https://www.innotherapy.com
Year Founded: 2010
246960—(KRS)
Rev.: $283,619
Assets: $23,634,652
Liabilities: $13,534,041
Net Worth: $10,100,610
Earnings: ($4,580,415)
Emp.: 20
Fiscal Year-end: 12/31/22
Medical Device Mfr
N.A.I.C.S.: 339112

Subsidiaries:

InnoTherapy America, Inc. (1)
2050 Center Ave Ste 510, Fort Lee, NJ 07024
Tel.: (201) 944-0445
Medicinal Product Mfr
N.A.I.C.S.: 339112

INNOVA CAPITAL SP. Z O.O.
Rondo ONZ 1 35th Floor, 00-124, Warsaw, Poland
Tel.: (48) 22 544 94 00
Web Site: http://www.innovacap.com
Year Founded: 1994
Privater Equity Firm
N.A.I.C.S.: 523999
Andrzej Bartos *(Sr Partner)*

Subsidiaries:

Bakalland S.A. (1)
Fabryczna 5 Street, 00 446, Warsaw, Poland **(58%)**
Tel.: (48) 22 355 22 00
Web Site: http://www.bakalland.pl
Emp.: 200
Cereals, Baking Products, Dried Fruits & Nuts Mfr
N.A.I.C.S.: 311230
Marek Moczulski *(Pres-Mgmt Bd & CEO)*

Subsidiary (Domestic):

Delecta S.A. (2)
ul Wyszynskiego 14, Wloclawek, 87800, Poland **(100%)**
Tel.: (48) 54 41 26 000
Web Site: http://www.bakalland.pl
Sales Range: $25-49.9 Million
Emp.: 340
Cakes Mixes, Powder Desserts, Baking Ingredients & Ready Made Foods Mfr
N.A.I.C.S.: 311999

Marek Moczulski *(Mng Dir)*

S.C. EnergoBit Group S.A. (1)
Parcul Industrial Tetarom I, str Taietura Turcului nr 47/11, RO 400221, Cluj-Napoca, Romania
Tel.: (40) 264 207 500
Web Site: http://www.energobit.com
Emp.: 1,000
Electric Power Supplier
N.A.I.C.S.: 221121
Carmen Neagu *(CEO)*

Subsidiary (Domestic):

S.C. EnergoBit PROD S.R.L. (2)
Industrial Park Tetarom I, 47/11 Taietura Turcului Street, RO 400221, Cluj-Napoca, Romania
Tel.: (40) 264 207 500
Electrical Transformer Substation Mfr
N.A.I.C.S.: 334417

S.C. EnergoBit Schreder Lighting S.R.L. (2)
Industrial Park Tetarom I, 47/11 Taietura Turcului Street, RO 400221, Cluj-Napoca, Romania
Tel.: (40) 264 207 500
Outdoor Lighting Mfr
N.A.I.C.S.: 335139

S.C. EnergoBit Tavrida S.R.L. (2)
Industrial Park Tetarom I 47/11, Taietura Turcului Street, RO 400221, Cluj-Napoca, Romania
Tel.: (40) 264 207 575
Voltage Equipment Whslr
N.A.I.C.S.: 423610

S.C. Enex S.R.L. (2)
Industrial Park Tetarom I, 47/11 Taietura Turcului Street, RO 400221, Cluj-Napoca, Romania
Tel.: (40) 264 207 500
Electric Power & Methane Gas Supplier
N.A.I.C.S.: 221210

Szpital Polozniczo - Ginekologiczny Ujastek SP. z o.o (1)
ul Ujastek 3, 31-752, Krakow, Poland **(70%)**
Tel.: (48) 12 29 30 999
Specialty Hospitals & Clinics
N.A.I.C.S.: 622310
Martin Raska *(Mng Dir)*

Trimo, d.o.o. (1)
Prijateljeva Cesta 12, 8210, Trebnje, Slovenia **(94%)**
Tel.: (386) 73460200
Web Site: http://www.trimo.eu
Pre-Fabricated Steel Building Materials Mfr
N.A.I.C.S.: 332311
Jacek Janczuk *(Dir-Bus Processes)*

Subsidiary (Non-US):

Trimex GmbH (2)
102 Leopold Strasse, 80802, Munich, Germany
Tel.: (49) 1711949009
Web Site: http://www.trimex-online.de
Pre-Fabricated Steel Building Materials Mfr
N.A.I.C.S.: 332311

Trimo Bulgaria OOD (2)
Tzarigradsko shose Blvd, 1138, Sofia, Bulgaria
Tel.: (359) 29175413
Web Site: http://www.trimo.bg
Steel Products Whslr
N.A.I.C.S.: 423390

Trimo Magyarorszag Ker. Kep. (2)
Fehervari ut 89-95, 1119, Budapest, Hungary
Tel.: (36) 30 619 5918
Web Site: http://www.trimo-group.com
Prefabricated Building Material Whslr
N.A.I.C.S.: 423390

Trimo Polska Sp.z.o.o. (2)
Ul Obrzezna 5, 02-691, Warsaw, Poland
Tel.: (48) 73460200
Web Site: https://www.trimo-group.com
Pre-Fabricated Steel Building Materials Mfr
N.A.I.C.S.: 332311

Trimo UK Ltd. (2)
1-2 Paris Garden, Southwark, London, SE1

8ND, United Kingdom
Tel.: (44) 2078633040
Web Site: http://www.trimo.org.uk
Pre-Fabricated Steel Building Materials Mfr
N.A.I.C.S.: 332311
Mark Lewis *(Dir-Acct)*

Trimo-Inzenjering d.o.o. (2)
Novo naselje 9, 22310, Belgrade, Serbia
Tel.: (381) 22 480 100
Web Site: http://www.trimo.rs
Pre-Fabricated Steel Building Materials Mfr
N.A.I.C.S.: 332311
Thomas Skrlec *(Dir-Sls)*

Trimont, d.o.o. (2)
Cardak bb, 72220, Zavidovici, Bosnia & Herzegovina
Tel.: (387) 32 851 240
Web Site: http://www.trimont.com.ba
Steel Structural Mfr
N.A.I.C.S.: 238190

INNOVA CAPTAB LIMITED
Plot No 320 Industrial Area Phase1, Panchkula, 134109, Haryana, India
Tel.: (91) 1724194500
Web Site:
https://www.innovacaptab.com
Year Founded: 2005
544067—(BOM)
Rev.: $113,392,054
Assets: $85,374,977
Liabilities: $51,862,450
Net Worth: $33,512,527
Earnings: $8,236,025
Emp.: 1,231
Fiscal Year-end: 03/31/23
Pharmaceutical Product Mfr & Distr
N.A.I.C.S.: 325412

INNOVANA THINKLABS LTD.
Plot No D-41 Patrakar Colony Near Jawahar Nagar, Moti Dungri Vistar Yojna Raja Park, Jaipur, 302004, Rajasthan, India
Tel.: (91) 1414919128
Web Site:
https://www.innovanathinklabs.com
INNOVANA—(NSE)
Rev.: $5,640,540
Assets: $14,316,806
Liabilities: $5,555,899
Net Worth: $8,760,907
Earnings: $2,083,272
Emp.: 157
Fiscal Year-end: 03/31/23
Software Development Services
N.A.I.C.S.: 541511
Chandan Garg *(Chm)*

Subsidiaries:

Innovana Fitness Labs Limited (1)
1 KHA 18 Jawahar Nagar, Jaipur, 302004, Rajastan, India
Tel.: (91) 9587896320
Web Site:
https://www.innovanafitnesslabs.com
App Design Services
N.A.I.C.S.: 541490

Innovana Techlabs Limited (1)
Unit No 407 4th Floor Signature Building Block 13B Zone-1 GIFT SEZ, Gandhinagar, 382355, Gujarat, India
Tel.: (91) 7229808887
Web Site:
https://www.innovanatechlabs.com
App Design Services
N.A.I.C.S.: 541490

INNOVASSYNTH INVESTMENTS LIMITED
Flat No C-2/3 KMC-91 Innovassynth Colony, Dist-Raigad, Khopoli, 410203, Maharashtra, India
Tel.: (91) 2192260100
Web Site:
https://www.innovassynthinvest.in
533315—(BOM)
Rev.: $2,675

Innovassynth Investments Limited—(Continued)
Assets: $5,648,179
Liabilities: $609,022
Net Worth: $5,039,157
Earnings: ($215,261)
Emp.: 2
Fiscal Year-end: 03/31/23
Financial Investment Services
N.A.I.C.S.: 523999
S. B. Ghia (Co-Chm & Co-Mng Dir)

INNOVATEC S.P.A.
Via Giovanni Bensi 12/5, 20152, Milan, Italy
Tel.: (39) 0287211700   IT
Web Site: https://www.innovatec.it
Year Founded: 1960
INC—(ITA)
Rev.: $34,875,121
Assets: $136,964,189
Liabilities: $61,480,935
Net Worth: $75,483,254
Earnings: $826,834
Fiscal Year-end: 12/31/20
Integrated Production & Automation Systems
N.A.I.C.S.: 334512
Roberto Maggio (Pres & CEO)

INNOVATION MEDICAL MANAGEMENT CO., LTD.
Pearl Industrial Park, Shanxiahu Town, Shaoxing, 311804, Zhejiang, China
Tel.: (86) 57587160891
Web Site: http://www.chxyl.com
Year Founded: 2003
002173—(SSE)
Rev.: $99,641,880
Assets: $328,488,264
Liabilities: $60,991,164
Net Worth: $267,497,100
Earnings: ($10,347,480)
Fiscal Year-end: 12/31/22
Investment Services
N.A.I.C.S.: 523999
Haijun Chen (Chm & Pres)

INNOVATION REAL ESTATE S.P.A.
Galleria Sala dei Longobardi 2, 20121, Milan, Italy
Tel.: (39) 0286996623   IT
Web Site: http://www.innovationre.it
Sales Range: $10-24.9 Million
Emp.: 70
Real Estate Consulting & Technical Services
N.A.I.C.S.: 531390
Guido Arena (Project Mgr)

INNOVATION SOFTWARE EXPORTS LIMITED
Plot No 51 Anna Salai Semmenchery, OMR, Chennai, 600 119, India
Tel.: (91) 44 24501274
Web Site: http://www.innovationsoft.in
Assets: $42,821
Liabilities: $6,582
Net Worth: $36,239
Earnings: ($7,936)
Fiscal Year-end: 03/31/18
Information Technology Training Services
N.A.I.C.S.: 611420

INNOVATION, INC.
3-10-13 Shibuya TOKYU REIT Shibuya R Building 3F, Shibuya-ku, Tokyo, 150-0002, Japan
Tel.: (81) 357663800
Web Site: https://www.innovation.co.jp

Year Founded: 2000
3970—(TKS)
Rev.: $31,813,930
Assets: $30,921,580
Liabilities: $7,343,710
Net Worth: $23,577,870
Earnings: $1,612,840
Fiscal Year-end: 03/31/24
Business To Business Marketing Services
N.A.I.C.S.: 561422
Naoto Tomida (Pres, CEO & COO)

INNOVATIONSKAPITAL NORDIC ADVISORS AB
Kungsportsplatsen 1, 411 10, Gothenburg, Sweden
Tel.: (46) 31 60 91 90
Web Site: http://www.innkap.se
Year Founded: 1994
Sales Range: $75-99.9 Million
Emp.: 4
Venture Capital Firm
N.A.I.C.S.: 523999
Staffan Ingeborn (Founder & Mng Dir-Investment)

INNOVATIVE COMPOSITES INTERNATIONAL, INC.
33 Davies Avenue Level 1, Toronto, M4M 2A9, ON, Canada
Tel.: (416) 646-0754
Web Site: http://www.innovativecomposite.com
Year Founded: 2007
Sales Range: $1-9.9 Million
Emp.: 34
Transportation, Construction & Fire Fighting Industries Material Mfr
N.A.I.C.S.: 339999
Kenneth A. Keeley (Chm)
Subsidiaries:
Ecoscapes Composites, LLC (1)
174 Millennium Dr, Orangeburg, SC 29115
Tel.: (803) 928-5380
Construction Materials Distr
N.A.I.C.S.: 423320

Eleison Composites, LLC (1)
2851 Prairie St SW, Grandville, MI 49418
Tel.: (616) 249-8657
Sales Range: $1-9.9 Million
Emp.: 25
Plastic Materials/Resins Mfr
N.A.I.C.S.: 325211

Georgia Composites, LLC (1)
430 10th St NW Ste N-102, Atlanta, GA 30318
Tel.: (404) 724-9077
Construction Materials Distr
N.A.I.C.S.: 423320

INNOVATIVE IDEALS & SERVICES (INDIA) LTD.
E-202 2nd floor Sky Park Oshiwara Garden Ajit Glass Road, Oshiwara Goregaon, Mumbai, 400 104, India
Tel.: (91) 2267392121
Web Site: https://www.innovative.in
Year Founded: 1994
541983—(BOM)
Rev.: $849,740
Assets: $4,846,091
Liabilities: $3,085,774
Net Worth: $1,760,318
Earnings: ($674,133)
Emp.: 45
Fiscal Year-end: 03/31/22
Camera Product Mfr
N.A.I.C.S.: 333310
Zafar Inamdar (CFO)

INNOVATIVE PHARMACEUTICAL BIOTECH LIMITED
Unit No 2111 21/F West Tower Shun Tak Centre 168-200 Connaught Rd, Sheung Wan, China (Hong Kong)
Tel.: (852) 2 598 6818
Web Site: http://www.ipb.asia
0399—(HKG)
Rev.: $1,959,077
Assets: $180,986,026
Liabilities: $134,720,126
Net Worth: $46,265,900
Earnings: ($27,363,752)
Emp.: 27
Fiscal Year-end: 03/31/21
Pharmaceutical Products Distr
N.A.I.C.S.: 424210

INNOVATIVE TECH PACK LIMITED
803-805 8th Floor Assotech Business Cresterra Tower 2 Plot No 22, Sector - 135, Noida, 201301, India
Tel.: (91) 1207195236
Web Site: https://itplgroup.com
Year Founded: 1989
523840—(BOM)
Rev.: $19,922,025
Assets: $17,680,395
Liabilities: $11,847,313
Net Worth: $5,833,082
Earnings: ($311,862)
Emp.: 210
Fiscal Year-end: 03/31/21
Packaging Plastic Product Mfr & Distr
N.A.I.C.S.: 326112
Ketineni Sayaji Rao (Chm & Mng Dir)

INNOVATIVE TECHNOLOGY DEVELOPMENT CORPORATION
Floor 4th ITD Building No 1 Sang Tao St, Tan Thuan Dong Ward Dist 7, Ho Chi Minh City, Vietnam
Tel.: (84) 837701114
ITD—(HOSE)
Rev.: $24,351,631
Assets: $23,464,430
Liabilities: $8,623,160
Net Worth: $14,841,270
Earnings: ($1,644,045)
Fiscal Year-end: 12/31/23
Road Construction Services
N.A.I.C.S.: 237310

INNOVATIVE TYRES & TUBES LIMITED
1201-02-03 G I D C Halol, Panchmahal, 389350, Gujarat, India
Tel.: (91) 2676223221
Web Site: https://www.innovativetyres.com
INNOVATIVE—(NSE)
Rev.: $224,003
Assets: $4,320,472
Liabilities: $9,622,481
Net Worth: ($5,302,008)
Earnings: ($6,346,922)
Emp.: 302
Fiscal Year-end: 03/31/23
Tire Product Mfr
N.A.I.C.S.: 326211
Mukesh G. Desai (Chm)

INNOVATIVE-RFK S.P.A.
Via del Carmine 11, Lombardia, 20121, Milan, Italy
Tel.: (39) 0298670065
Web Site: https://www.innovative-rfk.it
Year Founded: 2017
MLIRF—(EUR)
Sales Range: Less than $1 Million
Investment Management Service
N.A.I.C.S.: 525990
Paolo Pescetto (CEO)

INNOVATORS FACADE SYSTEMS LTD.
204/B-65 Station Rd Sector 1 Shanti Nagar Mira Road East, Mira Bhayandar, Thane, 401107, Maharashtra, India
Tel.: (91) 2228112521
Web Site: https://www.innovators.in
Year Founded: 1999
541353—(BOM)
Rev.: $9,072,153
Assets: $22,401,020
Liabilities: $5,980,016
Net Worth: $16,421,004
Earnings: $125,983
Emp.: 113
Fiscal Year-end: 03/31/21
Building Construction Services
N.A.I.C.S.: 236220
Radheshyam Sharma (Chm & Mng Dir)

INNOVAX HOLDINGS LTD.
Unit A-C 20/F Neich Tower 128 Gloucester Road, Wanchai, China (Hong Kong)
Tel.: (852) 2 311 0322   Ky
Web Site: http://www.innovax.hk
2680—(HKG)
Rev.: $12,386,207
Assets: $52,627,967
Liabilities: $22,824,559
Net Worth: $29,803,409
Earnings: $306,972
Emp.: 41
Fiscal Year-end: 02/28/21
Securities Brokerage Services
N.A.I.C.S.: 523150
Chi Man Chung (Chm)

INNOVENT BIOLOGICS, INC.
168 Dongping Street Suzhou Industrial Park, Jiangsu, China
Tel.: (86) 51269566088   Ky
Web Site: http://www.innoventbio.com
1801—(HKG)
Rev.: $639,715,752
Assets: $2,469,473,838
Liabilities: $962,988,998
Net Worth: $1,506,484,840
Earnings: ($305,969,508)
Emp.: 5,294
Fiscal Year-end: 12/31/22
Biopharmaceutical Product Mfr & Distr
N.A.I.C.S.: 325412
Michael Yu De-Chao (Founder, Chm & CEO)
Subsidiaries:
Innovent Biologics (Europe) Limited (1)
1 Kingdom Street Suite 445-446, London, W2 6BD, United Kingdom
Tel.: (44) 7932661726
Pharmaceuticals Product Mfr
N.A.I.C.S.: 325412

Innovent Biologics (Shanghai) Co., Ltd. (1)
T1-11F SOHO Tianshan Plaza 421 Ziyun Road, Changning District, Shanghai, 200050, China
Tel.: (86) 2131837200
Biopharmaceutical Product Mfr
N.A.I.C.S.: 325412
Michael Yu (Founder, Chm, Pres & CEO)

INNOVENTE INC.
116 Rue Saint-Pierre Suite 100, Quebec, G1K 4A7, QC, Canada
Tel.: (418) 692-1011   QC
Web Site: http://www.innovente.ca
Year Founded: 2004
Sales Range: Less than $1 Million
Electricity Production Services
N.A.I.C.S.: 221118
Richard Painchaud (Founder, Pres & CEO)

AND PRIVATE COMPANIES

Subsidiaries:

Innovente Inc. - St-Patrice-de-Beaurivage Factory (1)
270 Chemin Belfast, St-Patrice-de-Beaurivage, Lotbiniere, G0S 1B0, QC, Canada
Tel.: (418) 596-1211
Eletric Power Generation Services
N.A.I.C.S.: 221118

INNOVENTIVE INDUSTRIES LIMITED
Gat No 56/4/5 Pimple Jagtap, Taluka Shirur, Pune, 412208, Maharashtra, India
Tel.: (91) 2137 669001
Web Site: http://www.innoventive.in
Sales Range: $100-124.9 Million
Emp.: 1,230
Steel Products Mfr
N.A.I.C.S.: 331110
Chandu L. Chavan (Chm & Mng Dir)

INNOVENTIVE VENTURE LIMITED
601 & 602 Nucleus Mall 1 Church Road Camp, Pune, 411 001, Maharashtra, India
Tel.: (91) 20 66203549
Web Site: http://www.innoventure.in
Year Founded: 1985
Investment Management Service
N.A.I.C.S.: 523940

INNOVEOX SA
21 rue de la Paix, 75002, Paris, France
Tel.: (33) 1 40 06 07 06
Web Site: http://www.innoveox.com
Sales Range: Less than $1 Million
Emp.: 12
Toxic Waste Treatment
N.A.I.C.S.: 562211
Jean-Christophe Lepine (Chm)

INNOVID CORP.
89 Medinat Hayehudim Street, Herzliya, 4676672, Israel
Tel.: (972) 99703620
Web Site: http://www.ion-am.com
CTV—(NYSE)
Rev.: $127,117,000
Assets: $259,605,000
Liabilities: $53,677,000
Net Worth: $205,928,000
Earnings: ($18,410,000)
Emp.: 531
Fiscal Year-end: 12/31/22
Special Purpose Acquisition Corporation
N.A.I.C.S.: 523999
Anthony Callini (CFO)

Subsidiaries:

Innovid, Inc. (1)
30 Irving Place 12th Fl, New York, NY 10003
Tel.: (212) 966-7555
Web Site: http://www.innovid.com
Motion Picture & Video Production
N.A.I.C.S.: 512110
Beth-Ann Eason (Pres)

INNOVIUM MEDIA PROPERTIES CORP.
130 Adelaide St W Suite 3210, Toronto, M5H 3P5, ON, Canada
Tel.: (416) 862-7444
Web Site: http://www.innovium.ca
Year Founded: 1992
Sales Range: $1-9.9 Million
Emp.: 6
Investment Services
N.A.I.C.S.: 523999
R. Neil Raymond (Chm & CEO)

Subsidiaries:

Innovium Media Properties Corp.- Executive Office (1)
1 Place Ville Marie Suite 3840, Montreal, H3B 4M6, QC, Canada
Tel.: (514) 281-0481
Web Site: http://www.innovium.com
Emp.: 5
Investment Services
N.A.I.C.S.: 523999

INNOVIZ TECHNOLOGIES LTD.
Building C Nitzba 300, Rosh Ha'Ayin, Israel
Tel.: (972) 747003692
Web Site: https://innoviz.tech
INVZ—(NASDAQ)
Rev.: $20,876,000
Assets: $219,234,000
Liabilities: $65,945,000
Net Worth: $153,289,000
Earnings: ($123,454,000)
Emp.: 488
Fiscal Year-end: 12/31/23
High Performance Sensors & Perception Software Mfr
N.A.I.C.S.: 336390
Omer David Keilaf (CEO)

Subsidiaries:

Collective Growth Corporation (1)
1805 W Ave, Austin, TX 78701
Tel.: (512) 358-9085
Rev.: $100,083
Assets: $150,446,064
Liabilities: $145,446,054
Net Worth: $5,000,010
Earnings: ($1,034,535)
Emp.: 4
Fiscal Year-end: 12/31/2020
Investment Services
N.A.I.C.S.: 523999
Geoffrey W. Whaling (Pres)

INNOVOTECH INC.
Suite L131 2011-94 Street, Edmonton, T6N 1H1, AB, Canada
Tel.: (780) 448-0585
Web Site: https://www.innovotech.ca
Year Founded: 2001
IOT—(TSXV)
Rev.: $893,024
Assets: $918,623
Liabilities: $164,565
Net Worth: $754,058
Earnings: ($118,993)
Fiscal Year-end: 12/31/23
Biofilm Contract Research
N.A.I.C.S.: 541715
Bruce Hirsche (Co-Sec)

INNOWATIO S.P.A.
Kilometro Rosso Via Stezzano 87, 24126, Bergamo, Italy
Tel.: (39) 035 3846911
Web Site: http://www.innowatio.it
Energy Development & Management Services
N.A.I.C.S.: 523940
Fabio Leoncini (CEO)

INNOWIRELESS CO., LTD.
Building 190 Seo-hyeon-ro, Bundang-gu, Seongnam, Gyeonggi-do, Korea (South)
Tel.: (82) 317881700
Web Site: https://www.innowireless.co.kr
Year Founded: 2000
073490—(KRS)
Rev.: $101,899,129
Assets: $142,257,780
Liabilities: $41,851,996
Net Worth: $100,405,784
Earnings: $10,316,710
Emp.: 329
Fiscal Year-end: 12/31/22
Communication Equipment Mfr
N.A.I.C.S.: 517112
Young Su Kwak (Pres)

INNOX ADVANCED MATERIALS CO., LTD.
171 Asan Valley-ro, Dunpo-myeon, Asan, 31409, Chungcheongnam-do, Korea (South)
Tel.: (82) 415369999
Web Site: https://www.innoxamc.com
Year Founded: 2017
272290—(KRS)
Rev.: $375,333,705
Assets: $355,822,865
Liabilities: $64,157,888
Net Worth: $291,664,977
Earnings: $65,471,994
Emp.: 743
Fiscal Year-end: 12/31/22
Semiconductor Product Mfr
N.A.I.C.S.: 334413
KyungHoon Kim (Co-CEO)

INNOX CORPORATION
1352 Seokgok-ri, Dunpo-myeon, Asan, 336-871, Chungcheongnam-do, Korea (South)
Tel.: (82) 317279191
Web Site: http://www.innoxcorp.com
Year Founded: 2001
088390—(KRS)
Sales Range: $25-49.9 Million
Emp.: 11
Semiconductor Product Mfr
N.A.I.C.S.: 334413
Won-Jin Lee (Mng Dir)

INNSCOR AFRICA LTD.
Edward Building 1st Street/Nelson Mandela Avenue, PO Box A88 Avondale, Harare, Zimbabwe
Tel.: (263) 4496886
Web Site: http://www.innscorafrica.com
INN—(ZIM)
Rev.: $804,039,805
Assets: $653,843,006
Liabilities: $236,172,140
Net Worth: $417,670,866
Earnings: $37,844,019
Emp.: 10,800
Fiscal Year-end: 06/30/23
Holding Company
N.A.I.C.S.: 551112
Andrew D. Lorimer (Sec-Grp)

Subsidiaries:

Associated Meat Packers (Private) Limited (1)
1 Coventry Road Colcom Complex, Workington, Harare, Zimbabwe
Tel.: (263) 242772685
Web Site: https://www.innscorafrica.com
Meat Processing Services
N.A.I.C.S.: 311612
Lester Jones (Co-CEO)

Colcom Foods Limited (1)
1/3 Coventry Road, PO Box 2474, Workington, Harare, Zimbabwe
Tel.: (263) 242751051
Web Site: http://www.colcom.co.zw
Pork Processing Services
N.A.I.C.S.: 311612
Dino Tumazos (CEO)

Colcom Holdings Limited (1)
1/3 Coventry Road, PO Box 2474, Workington, Harare, Zimbabwe
Tel.: (263) 242751051
Web Site: www.colcomfoods.com
Rev.: $65,954,836
Assets: $46,568,312
Liabilities: $8,872,008
Net Worth: $37,696,304
Earnings: $5,038,436
Emp.: 1,112
Fiscal Year-end: 06/30/2017
Holding Company
N.A.I.C.S.: 551112

Innscor (Pvt) Ltd (1)
Mp5 Westgate S/Centr Lorraine Dr Bluff, Harare, Zimbabwe
Tel.: (263) 332418
Food Products Mfr
N.A.I.C.S.: 311991

Lennard Manufacturing (Pvt) Ltd (1)
22 A Bellevue Rd, Bulawayo, Zimbabwe
Tel.: (263) 978279
Food Products Mfr
N.A.I.C.S.: 311991

Matabeleland Inns (Pvt) Ltd (1)
Cnr Fort St 11th Ave, PO Box 1001, Bulawayo, Zimbabwe
Tel.: (263) 97 8471
Food Products Mfr
N.A.I.C.S.: 311991

Natpak (Pvt) Limited (1)
No 1 Kelso Rd / Stirling Road, PO Box CY303, Workington, Harare, Zimbabwe
Tel.: (263) 242748041
Web Site: https://www.innscorafrica.com
Packing Product Whslr
N.A.I.C.S.: 423840
Guy Martell (Mng Dir)

Tevason Investments (Pvt) Limited (1)
10 Loreley Close, Harare, Zimbabwe
Tel.: (263) 448 7532
Food Products Mfr
N.A.I.C.S.: 311991

INNUOVO TECHNOLOGY CO., LTD.
Building 1 No 196 Industrial Avenue, Hengdian Town Dongyang City, Jinhua, 322118, Zhejiang, China
Tel.: (86) 57986563922
Web Site: https://www.innuovo.com
000795—(SSE)
Rev.: $664,400,880
Assets: $695,601,972
Liabilities: $312,544,440
Net Worth: $383,057,532
Earnings: $36,299,016
Fiscal Year-end: 12/31/22
Aluminium Products Mfr
N.A.I.C.S.: 331313

INOAC CORPORATION
2-13-4 Meieki-minami, Nakamura-ku, Nagoya, 450-0003, Japan
Tel.: (81) 525811086
Web Site: http://www.inoac.co.jp
Year Founded: 1954
Sales Range: $1-4.9 Billion
Emp.: 1,917
Polyurethane, Plastic & Rubber Parts & Products Mfr
N.A.I.C.S.: 326299
Soichi Inoue (Chm & CEO)

Subsidiaries:

BASF INOAC Polyurethanes Ltd. (1)
1-196 Motomiyamichi Kawata, Shinshiro, 441-1347, Aichi, Japan
Tel.: (81) 536235511
Web Site: https://www.bip-jp.com
Sales Range: $25-49.9 Million
Emp.: 100
Polyurethane Foam System Mfr; Owned 50% by BASF Asktiengesellschaft & 50% by Inoac Corporation
N.A.I.C.S.: 326150

CENTURY INOAC CO., LTD. (1)
119/2 Bangbon 5Rd, Kwaeng Bangbon Khet Bangbon, Bangkok, 10150, Thailand
Tel.: (66) 2 892 4755
Office Equipment Mfr & Distr
N.A.I.C.S.: 339940

CHENGDOU INOAC POLYMER PRODUCTS CO., LTD. (1)
688 Ling Chi Road Chengdu Economic & Technological Development Zone, Longquanyi District, Chengdu, 610100, China
Tel.: (86) 28 6598 9709
Polyurethane Foam Mfr
N.A.I.C.S.: 326150

INOAC CORPORATION

INOAC Corporation—(Continued)

Dongguan Inoac (F.K.) Metal & Elastomer Co., Ltd. (1)
Qisha Villa, Shatian Town, Dongguan, 523997, Guangdong, China
Tel.: (86) 769 8880 4001
Automotive Product Mfr & Distr
N.A.I.C.S.: 336390

Dongguan Inoac Kenjou Automotive Co., Ltd. (1)
Huanbao West Road, Shatian Town, Dongguan, Guangdong, China
Tel.: (86) 769 8868 2171
Web Site: http://www.dika.inoac.com
Automotive Product Mfr & Distr
N.A.I.C.S.: 336390
Toyoki Fukuyama (Vice Gen Mgr)

Dongguan Inoac Metal & Elastomer Co., Ltd. (1)
Inoac Villa Qisha Ind Zone, Shatian Town, Dongguan, Guangdong, China
Tel.: (86) 769 8886 3344
Automotive Product Mfr & Distr
N.A.I.C.S.: 336390

Dongguan Inoac Polymer Co., Ltd. (1)
Cha Shan Industrial Park, Dongguan, 523380, Guangdong, China
Tel.: (86) 769 8617 6861
Rubber Product Mfr & Distr
N.A.I.C.S.: 326299

Higashi Nihon Inoac Co. Ltd. (1)
700 Otsuka Ichikawamisato-cho, Nishiyatsushiro, Yamanashi, 409-3611, Japan
Tel.: (81) 55 272 2111
Automotive Products Mfr
N.A.I.C.S.: 336390

Hokkaido Inoac Co., Ltd. (1)
4-1-15 Higashi-Hachijo-Kita, Bibai, 072-0802, Hokkaido, Japan
Tel.: (81) 126 63 4135
Urethane Mfr
N.A.I.C.S.: 326150

Plant (Domestic):

Hokkaido Inoac Co., Ltd. - Minami Plant (2)
Shintomi-cho, Minamibibai-cho, Bibai, 072-0824, Hokkaido, Japan
Tel.: (81) 126 62 0166
Urethane Mfr
N.A.I.C.S.: 326150

INOAC (Thailand) Co., Ltd. (1)
7th Floor Phairojkijja Tower 825 Bangna-Trad Road, Khwaeng Bangna Khet Bangna, Bangkok, 10260, Thailand
Tel.: (66) 2361 4446
Web Site: http://www.inoacthai.co.th
Automotive Product Mfr & Distr
N.A.I.C.S.: 336390

Subsidiary (Domestic):

Inoac Automotive (Thailand) Ltd. (2)
700/416 Moo 7 Amatanakorn Industrial Estate T Donhuaroh A Muang, Chon Buri, 20000, Thailand
Tel.: (66) 3845 4560 2
Web Site: http://www.inoacauto.co.th
Automotive Product Mfr & Distr
N.A.I.C.S.: 336390

INOAC Corporation - Anjo Plant (1)
3-1-36 Imaike, Anjo, 446-8504, Aichi, Japan
Tel.: (81) 566 98 2947
Tiles Mfr
N.A.I.C.S.: 326211

INOAC Corporation - Kikuchi Plant (1)
2000 Akahoshi, Kikuchi, 861-1311, Kumamoto, Japan
Tel.: (81) 968 25 0121
Tiles Mfr
N.A.I.C.S.: 326211

INOAC Corporation - Kira Plant (1)
18 Hachimanyama, Kira-cho, Nishio, 444-0531, Aichi, Japan
Tel.: (81) 563 35 4605
Tiles Mfr
N.A.I.C.S.: 326211

INOAC Corporation - Kitakyushu Plant (1)
54-1 Tomoda Nukazuka, Okagaki, Onga, 811-4213, Fukuoka, Japan
Tel.: (81) 93 282 2511
Tiles Mfr
N.A.I.C.S.: 326211

INOAC Corporation - Nanno Plant (1)
228 Yoshida, Nanno-cho, Kaizu, 503-0536, Gifu, Japan
Tel.: (81) 584 56 1711
Tiles Mfr
N.A.I.C.S.: 326211

INOAC Corporation - Sakurai Plant (1)
8-1 Higashinagasaki, Fujii-cho, Anjo, 444-1195, Aichi, Japan
Tel.: (81) 50 3145 5831
Tiles Mfr
N.A.I.C.S.: 326211

INOAC Corporation - Seino Plant (1)
737-1 Koujimuramae Kouji, Ibi-gun, Ikeda, 503-2404, Gifu, Japan
Tel.: (81) 585 45 7557
Tiles Mfr
N.A.I.C.S.: 326211

INOAC Corporation - Shinshiro Plant (1)
1-196 Hongudo Kawada, Shinshiro, 441-1347, Aichi, Japan
Tel.: (81) 536 23 5512
Tiles Mfr
N.A.I.C.S.: 326211

INOAC Corporation - Taketoyo Plant (1)
9-117 Nashinoki, Taketoyo-cho, Chita, 470-2309, Aichi, Japan
Tel.: (81) 569 74 1811
Tiles Mfr
N.A.I.C.S.: 326211

INOAC Corporation - Toyohashi Plant (1)
4-38 Akemi-cho, Toyohashi, 441-8074, Aichi, Japan
Tel.: (81) 532 23 6145
Tiles Mfr
N.A.I.C.S.: 326211

INOAC Corporation - Ukiha Plant (1)
1266 Miharu, Ukiha-cho, Ukiha, 839-1407, Fukuoka, Japan
Tel.: (81) 943 77 7211
Tiles Mfr
N.A.I.C.S.: 326211

INOAC Corporation - Yana Plant (1)
50 Akaiwa, Tomioka, 441-1335, Aichi, Japan
Tel.: (81) 536 26 1500
Tiles Mfr
N.A.I.C.S.: 326211

INOAC ELASTOMER CO., LTD. (1)
680 Hongo, Ikeda-cho Ibi, Gifu, 503-2417, Japan
Tel.: (81) 585 45 2808
Real Estate Manangement Services
N.A.I.C.S.: 531390

INOAC ENGINEERING CO., LTD. (1)
3 Arashita, Anjo, 446-0026, Aichi, Japan
Tel.: (81) 566 77 8000
Industrial Mold Mfr
N.A.I.C.S.: 333511

INOAC EUROPE GmbH (1)
Birkenwaldstrasse 42A, Stuttgart, Germany
Tel.: (49) 711 28048942
Rubber Products Mfr
N.A.I.C.S.: 326299

INOAC HONG KONG LIMITED (1)
Rm 1318-22 Park-In Commercial Centre 56 Dundas St, Kowloon, China (Hong Kong)
Tel.: (852) 3910 4500
Industrial Supplies Whslr
N.A.I.C.S.: 423840

INOAC Housing & Construction Materials Co., Ltd. (1)
INOAC Hibino Bldg 2F 4-9-27 Taiho, Atsuta-ku, Nagoya, 456-0062, Japan
Tel.: (81) 52 684 0266
Construction Material Mfr & Distr
N.A.I.C.S.: 327120

INOAC INDUSTRIES (THAILAND) CO., LTD. (1)
Kabinburi Industrial Zone 515 Moo 9 Km 12, Kabinburi-Korat Rd, Nongkee Kabin Buri, Prachin Buri, 25110, Thailand
Tel.: (66) 37 204 485
Polyurethane Foam Mfr
N.A.I.C.S.: 326150

INOAC Living Co., Ltd. (1)
1F West-city Bldg 2-9-3 Osaki, Shinagawa-ku, Tokyo, 141-0032, Japan
Tel.: (81) 3 3492 9214
Web Site: http://www.inoac.jp
Emp.: 1,500
Mattress Mfr & Distr
N.A.I.C.S.: 337910
Soichi Inoue (CEO)

INOAC Malaysia SDN. BHD. (1)
No 4 Jalan Riang 21 Kawasan Perindustrian Taman Gembira, Tampoi, 81200, Johor Bahru, Malaysia
Tel.: (60) 7333 4088
Web Site: http://www.inoac.co.jp
Office Equipment Mfr & Distr
N.A.I.C.S.: 339940
Colin Ou Xiang Xin (CEO)

INOAC POLYMER LANKA (PVT) LTD. (1)
No 15 BOI Zone Boralugoda Poruwedanda, Horana, 12432, Sri Lanka
Tel.: (94) 34 2 255944
Polyurethane Foam Mfr
N.A.I.C.S.: 326150

INOAC POLYTEC de MEXICO S.A de C.V. (1)
Carretera Miguel Aleman KM 20 5 Apodaca Nuero Leon, 66600, Mexico, Mexico
Tel.: (52) 81 8221 0101
Plastic Packaging Product Mfr & Distr
N.A.I.C.S.: 326199

INOAC TRADING CO., LTD. (1)
4F West-city Bldg 2-9-3 Osaki, Shinagawa-ku, Tokyo, 141-0032, Japan
Tel.: (81) 50 3135 9910
Paint Distr
N.A.I.C.S.: 424950

INOAC Technical Center, Co., Ltd. (1)
380-5 Horiyamashita, Hadano, 259-1304, Kanagawa, Japan
Tel.: (81) 463 87 6916
Web Site: http://www.inoac.co.jp
Chemical Research & Development Services
N.A.I.C.S.: 541715

INOAC USA, Inc. (1)
1515 Equity Dr Ste 200, Troy, MI 48084
Tel.: (248) 619-7031
Web Site: http://www.inoacusa.com
Automotive Product Mfr & Distr
N.A.I.C.S.: 336390

Subsidiary (Domestic):

INOAC Packaging Group Inc. (2)
901 Nutter Dr, Bardstown, KY 40004
Tel.: (502) 348-5159
Packaging Product Mfr & Distr
N.A.I.C.S.: 326199

Joint Venture (Domestic):

Intertec Systems, LLC (2)
45000 Helm St, Plymouth, MI 48170
Tel.: (248) 254-3300
Automotive Instrument Panels & Systems Mfr
N.A.I.C.S.: 336390

Inoac Tokai (Thailand) Company Limited (1)
157/4 Moo 5 Phaholyothin Road, Lamsai District Wongnoi, Ayutthaya, 13170, Thailand
Tel.: (66) 35 214 949
Rubber Product Mfr & Distr
N.A.I.C.S.: 326299

Inoac Vietnam Co., Ltd. (1)
LOTNo 36 Quang Minh Industrial Zone, Me Linh District, Hanoi, Vietnam

Tel.: (84) 4 3818 2
Office Equipment Mfr & Distr
N.A.I.C.S.: 339940

Inoue Rubber Co., Ltd. (1)
13-4 Meieki Minami 2-Chome, Nakamura-ku, Nagoya, 450-0003, Japan
Tel.: (81) 50 3145 6022
Web Site: http://www.irc-tire.com
Tire Mfr & Distr
N.A.I.C.S.: 326211

JIANG SU INOAC JUTENG POLYMER CO., LTD (1)
18 Jubao Road, Jurong, Jiangsu, China
Tel.: (86) 511 8718 4269
Polymeric Product Mfr & Distr
N.A.I.C.S.: 325998

KOREA INOUE KASEI CO., LTD. (1)
Jayumuyeok 5-gil Bongam-dong Massanhoewon-gu, Changwon, Gyeongsangnam, Korea (South)
Tel.: (82) 55 255 0854
Web Site: http://www.inoackik.com
Emp.: 83
Rubber Product Mfr & Distr
N.A.I.C.S.: 326299
Oya Hideo (CEO)

Kantoh Inoac Co., Ltd. - Saitama Plant (1)
1-603-34 Komatsudai, Hanyu, 348-0038, Saitama, Japan
Tel.: (81) 48 561 6161
Urethane Mfr
N.A.I.C.S.: 326150

Polyfoam Asia Pte Ltd. (1)
1 International Business Park 01-13B The Synergy, Singapore, 609917, Singapore
Tel.: (65) 6 877 9428
Polyurethane Foam Mfr
N.A.I.C.S.: 326150

Rogers Inoac Corporation (1)
9-117 Nashinoki, Chita-gun, Taketoyo, 470-2309, Aichi, Japan (50%)
Tel.: (81) 569741811
Web Site: https://www.poron.jp
Sales Range: $25-49.9 Million
Emp.: 80
Polyurethane Material Mfr
N.A.I.C.S.: 325211
Takashi Ishi (Mgr-Mktg)

SHANGHAI INOAC CORPORATION (1)
3A Zhaofeng Universal Bldg 1800 West Zhongshan Rd, Shanghai, 200235, China
Tel.: (86) 21 6440 0561
Industrial Supplies Whslr
N.A.I.C.S.: 423840

SHANGHAI INOAC ENGINEERING CO., LTD (1)
2Bldg No 3355 Gu Dai Rd, Shanghai, 201100, China
Tel.: (86) 21 5488 5514
Automotive Product Mfr & Distr
N.A.I.C.S.: 336390

SHANGHAI INOAC NEW MATERIAL CO., LTD. (1)
3081 Huhang Road, Xinsi Town Fenxian, Shanghai, 201416, China
Tel.: (86) 21 5749 2777
Plastic Foam Mfr & Distr
N.A.I.C.S.: 326150

SHANGHAI INOUE PACKING PRODUCT CO., LTD (1)
1497 Huhang Road, Fengxian, Shanghai, China
Tel.: (86) 21 5743 1977
Plastic Bottle Mfr & Distr
N.A.I.C.S.: 326160

SUZHOU INOAC ELASTOMER CO., LTD. (1)
198 Yinzhong Road Hedong Industrial Park Wuzhong, Economic Development Zone, Suzhou, 215128, Jiangsu, China
Tel.: (86) 512 6597 6711
Rubber Products Mfr
N.A.I.C.S.: 326299

SUZHOU INOAC TRADING CORPORATION (1)

Rm 2003 20F No 88 Xiandai Avenue Suzhou Industrial Park, Suzhou, 215121, China
Tel.: (86) 512 6280 7921
Industrial Supplies Whslr
N.A.I.C.S.: 423840

Shanghai Inoue Xin Yi Plastics Co., Ltd. (1)
Room 1401 Hanzhong Plaza 158 Hanzhong Road, Shanghai, 200070, China
Tel.: (86) 21 6354 0343
Packaging Bottle Mfr & Distr
N.A.I.C.S.: 327213
Tony Zhang *(Deputy Gen Mgr-Sls)*

Suzhou Inoac Zhongding Office Machine Products Co., Ltd. (1)
29 Tongdun Street, New District, Suzhou, 215129, Jiangsu, China
Tel.: (86) 512 6661 8600
Office Equipment Mfr & Distr
N.A.I.C.S.: 339940

TAIWAN INOAC POLYMER CORPORATION (1)
1F No 25 Sihyuan Rd, Sinjhuang, Taipei, Taiwan
Tel.: (886) 2 8994 2255
Web Site: http://www.inoac.com.tw
Industrial Supplies Whslr
N.A.I.C.S.: 423840

TECHNOFOAM CHINA CO., LTD. (1)
Jingsan Lu Nanhu Lunan, Wuzhong Economic Development Zone, Suzhou, Jiangsu, China
Tel.: (86) 52 65135572
Urethane Foam Mfr
N.A.I.C.S.: 326150

THAI INOAC MOLD CO., LTD. (1)
119/3 Bangbon 5 Rd, Kwaeng Bangbon Khet Bangbon, Bangkok, 10150, Thailand
Tel.: (66) 2 892 4799
Industrial Mold Mfr & Distr
N.A.I.C.S.: 333511

TIANJIN INOAC HUAXIANG AUTOMOTIVE PRODUCTS CO., LTD. (1)
No 8 Kaituo Road TEDA Jinnan Science & Business Park, Jinnan District, Tianjin, 300350, China
Tel.: (86) 22 5883 0381
Automotive Product Mfr & Distr
N.A.I.C.S.: 336390

Tianjin Inoac Polymer Co., Ltd. (1)
No 30 Siwei Road Dongli Economic Development Area, Tianjin, 300300, China
Tel.: (86) 22 5823 8542
Automotive Product Mfr & Distr
N.A.I.C.S.: 336390

Tohoku Inoac Co., Ltd. - Kitakami Plant (1)
43-137 Yamanenashinoki, Aisari-cho, Kitakami, 024-0051, Iwate, Japan
Tel.: (81) 197 81 5765
Automotive Products Mfr
N.A.I.C.S.: 336390

Tohoku Inoac Co., Ltd. - Kogota Plant (1)
28 Nimatasita, Kogota Misato-cho, Toda, 987-0005, Miyagi, Japan
Tel.: (81) 229 34 2111
Automotive Products Mfr
N.A.I.C.S.: 336390

Tohoku Inoac Co., Ltd. - Wakayanagi Plant (1)
123 Higashiwakayanagi, Kawakita Wakayanagi, Kurihara, 989-5501, Miyagi, Japan
Tel.: (81) 228 32 2201
Automotive Products Mfr
N.A.I.C.S.: 336390

Wuxi Inoue Huaguang Automobile Parts Co., Ltd. (1)
Yangshi Town, Wuxi, 214154, Jiangsu, China
Tel.: (86) 510 8355 0915
Automotive Product Mfr & Distr
N.A.I.C.S.: 336390

INOAPPS LIMITED

2 Fountainhall Road, Aberdeen, AB15 4DT, United Kingdom
Tel.: (44) 870 112 2000
Web Site: http://www.inoapps.com
Year Founded: 2006
Sales Range: $10-24.9 Million
IT Services
N.A.I.C.S.: 541512
Andy Bird *(CEO)*

Subsidiaries:

Inoapps Sdn Bhd (1)
Suite 2B-13-3 Level 13 Block 2B Plaza Sentral, Jalan Stesen Sentral 5 KL, 50470, Kuala Lumpur, Malaysia
Tel.: (60) 322988299
Information Technology Consulting Services
N.A.I.C.S.: 541512
Jake Stewart *(Mgr-Delivery-APAC)*

Inoapps Singapore Pte. Ltd (1)
6001 Beach Road 14 - 01 Golden Mile Tower, Singapore, 199589, Singapore
Tel.: (65) 322988299
Information Technology Consulting Services
N.A.I.C.S.: 541512

Microvive Ltd. (1)
Melton Court Gibson Lane, Melton, HU14 3HH, United Kingdom
Tel.: (44) 1482 638549
Web Site: http://www.microvive.com
IT Services
N.A.I.C.S.: 541512
John Edwards *(Mng Dir)*

INOC DEAD SEA LP

Reh Granit 8 Kiriyat Ariye TD 10188, Petah Tiqwa, 4900201, Israel
Tel.: (972) 39229225
Year Founded: 1990
Sales Range: Less than $1 Million
Oil & Gas Exploration Services
N.A.I.C.S.: 213112
Haim Tzuff *(Chm)*

INOEX GMBH

Mashweg 70, 49324, Melle, Germany
Tel.: (49) 5422605070
Web Site: http://www.inoex.de
Year Founded: 1984
Sales Range: $10-24.9 Million
Emp.: 112
Plastic Materials Mfr
N.A.I.C.S.: 326199
Miguel Izquierdo Blanco *(Dir-Sls)*

Subsidiaries:

iNOEX LLC (1)
1861 Charter Ln Ste 111, Lancaster, PA 17601
Tel.: (717) 672-0870
Plastic Product Distr
N.A.I.C.S.: 424610
P. J. Buriak *(Pres)*

iNOEX Trading (Beijing) Co. Ltd. (1)
RM19D CITIC Building No 19 Jianguomenwai Avenue, ChaoYang District, Beijing, 100004, China
Tel.: (86) 1085261852
Plastic Product Distr
N.A.I.C.S.: 424610

INOFORGES

49 Rue de Montdidier, Breteuil, 60120, Clermont, France
Tel.: (33) 344806750
Web Site: http://www.inoforges.com
Rev.: $24,100,000
Emp.: 200
Metal Stamping
N.A.I.C.S.: 332119
Philippe Schops *(Dir)*

Subsidiaries:

Inoforges Polska Sp. z o.o. (1)
ul Przemyslowa 2, 64-130, Rydzyna, Poland
Tel.: (48) 65 528 85 70
Web Site: http://www.inoforges.pl
Emp.: 40

Die Forging Component Mfr
N.A.I.C.S.: 332111

INOS SINMA AD

Dragacevska bb, 31205, Sevojno, Serbia
Tel.: (381) 31 531 048
Year Founded: 1951
Raw Material Recycling Services
N.A.I.C.S.: 423930

INOUE RUBBER (THAILAND) PUBLIC COMPANY LIMITED

258 Soi Rangsit Nakornnayok 49 Prachatipat Thanyaburi, Pathumthani, 12130, Thailand
Tel.: (66) 29960890
Web Site: https://www.ircthailand.com
Year Founded: 1969
IRC—(THA)
Rev.: $150,618,998
Assets: $138,396,112
Liabilities: $30,337,821
Net Worth: $108,058,291
Earnings: $4,393,650
Emp.: 1,288
Fiscal Year-end: 09/30/23
Rubber Tires & Tubes Mfr
N.A.I.C.S.: 326211
Takeshi Arakawa *(Mng Dir)*

Subsidiaries:

Kinno Hoshi Engineering Co., Ltd. (1)
157 Moo 5 Phaholyothin Road, Lamsai Wangnoi, Ayutthaya, 13170, Thailand
Tel.: (66) 35272206
Sales Range: $25-49.9 Million
Emp.: 32
Rubber Processing Services
N.A.I.C.S.: 326299

Toei Inoac Limited (1)
157/1 Moo 5 Phaholyothin Rd, Lamsai Wangnoi, Ayutthaya, 13170, Thailand
Tel.: (66) 3 521 5518
Web Site: http://inoac.co.id
Sales Range: $75-99.9 Million
Emp.: 150
Computer Printer Whslr
N.A.I.C.S.: 423430

INOVALIS REAL ESTATE INVESTMENT TRUST

151 Yonge Street 11th Floor, Toronto, M5C 2W7, ON, Canada
Tel.: (647) 775-8431
Web Site: https://www.inovalisreit.com
Year Founded: 2013
INO.UN—(TSX)
Sales Range: $10-24.9 Million
Real Estate Investment Services
N.A.I.C.S.: 523999
Stephane Amine *(Pres & CEO)*

INOVEST BSC

Bahrain Financial Harbour East Tower 35th Floor, PO Box 18334, Manama, Bahrain
Tel.: (973) 17155777
Web Site: https://www.inovest.bh
INOVEST—(BAH)
Rev.: $8,670,000
Assets: $240,327,000
Liabilities: $71,069,000
Net Worth: $169,258,000
Earnings: $1,107,000
Emp.: 650
Fiscal Year-end: 12/31/22
Real Estate Investment & Financial Services
N.A.I.C.S.: 531390
Bashar Naser Al Tuwaijri *(Vice Chm)*

Subsidiaries:

BIW Business Park Development Company WLL (1)

PO Box 18334, Manama, Bahrain
Tel.: (973) 17468500
Finance Investment Services
N.A.I.C.S.: 523940

Tameer Real Estate Agencies WLL (1)
19th Floor Bahrain Financial Harbour East Tower, PO Box 18334, Manama, Bahrain
Tel.: (973) 17 155 755
Web Site: http://www.tameer.com
Sales Range: $50-74.9 Million
Emp.: 65
Real Estate Agencies
N.A.I.C.S.: 531210

INOVIQ LTD

23 Normanby Road, Notting Hill, 3168, VIC, Australia
Tel.: (61) 395487856
Web Site: https://www.inoviq.com
Year Founded: 2016
IIQ—(ASX)
Rev.: $357,317
Assets: $14,493,658
Liabilities: $1,148,087
Net Worth: $13,345,572
Earnings: ($4,376,569)
Fiscal Year-end: 06/30/24
Laboratory Testing Services
N.A.I.C.S.: 621511
David Williams *(Chm)*

INOVUUS TECHNOLOGIES PTE. LTD.

61 Bukit Batok Crescent 03-03 Heng Loong Building, Singapore, 658078, Singapore
Tel.: (65) 67671767   SG
Web Site: http://www.inovuus.com.sg
Year Founded: 2000
Sales Range: $1-9.9 Million
Emp.: 10
Information Technology Support Services
N.A.I.C.S.: 541519
Gerald Lek *(Exec Dir)*

INOX INDIA LIMITED

9th Floor K P Platina Race Course, Vadodara, 390007, Gujarat, India
Tel.: (91) 2656160100
Web Site: https://www.inoxcva.com
Year Founded: 1976
544046—(BOM)
Rev.: $119,513,090
Assets: $139,963,323
Liabilities: $73,366,008
Net Worth: $66,597,315
Earnings: $18,754,258
Emp.: 1,016
Fiscal Year-end: 03/31/23
Electric Equipment Mfr
N.A.I.C.S.: 331110

INOX LEASING & FINANCE LIMITED

69 Jolly Maker Chambers 2, Nariman Point, Mumbai, 400021, India
Tel.: (91) 2222026314   In
Web Site: http://www.ilfl.co.in
Year Founded: 1995
Rev.: $827,137,897
Assets: $1,692,567,924
Liabilities: $1,238,149,571
Net Worth: $454,418,353
Earnings: $191,543,338
Emp.: 3,500
Fiscal Year-end: 03/31/19
Holding Company
N.A.I.C.S.: 551112
Pavan Kumar Jain *(Mng Dir)*

Subsidiaries:

Gujarat Fluorochemicals Limited (1)
Survey No 16/3 26-27 Village Ranjitnagar Taluka Ghogamba, Panchmahal, 389 380, Gujarat, India   (52.54%)

INOX LEASING & FINANCE LIMITED

INOX Leasing & Finance Limited—(Continued)
Tel.: (91) 2678248153
Web Site: https://www.gfl.co.in
Rev.: $389,240,697
Assets: $814,724,370
Liabilities: $339,849,032
Net Worth: $474,875,337
Earnings: ($30,237,780)
Emp.: 2,220
Fiscal Year-end: 03/31/2021
Refrigerant Gases & Chemicals Mfr
N.A.I.C.S.: 325120
Vivek Kumar Jain *(Mng Dir)*

Subsidiary (Domestic):

INOX Leisure Limited (2)
Viraj Towers 5th Floor Western Express Highway Andheri East, Mumbai, 400 093, India (64.84%)
Tel.: (91) 2240626900
Web Site: http://www.inoxmovies.com
Rev.: $268,045,736
Assets: $534,157,764
Liabilities: $447,094,102
Net Worth: $87,063,662
Earnings: $2,100,784
Emp.: 2,256
Fiscal Year-end: 03/31/2020
Motion Picture Theaters Owner & Operator
N.A.I.C.S.: 512131
Pavan Kumar Jain *(Chm)*

Inox Wind Ltd. (2)
INOX Towers Plot No 17 Sector 16-A, Noida, 201 301, Uttar Pradesh, India
Tel.: (91) 1206149600
Web Site: https://www.inoxwind.com
Rev.: $107,422,388
Assets: $745,891,433
Liabilities: $566,242,295
Net Worth: $179,649,138
Earnings: ($41,921,784)
Emp.: 1,070
Fiscal Year-end: 03/31/2021
Wind Turbine Generator Mfr
N.A.I.C.S.: 333611
Devansh Jain *(Exec Dir)*

INOX SA

Strada Atomistilor nr 12, Ilfov, Magurele, 077125, Romania
Tel.: (40) 214575334
Web Site: http://www.inoxsa.ro
Year Founded: 1937
INOX—(BUC)
Rev.: $1,565,913
Assets: $7,015,470
Liabilities: $3,203,459
Net Worth: $3,812,011
Earnings: $16,708
Emp.: 41
Fiscal Year-end: 12/31/23
Furniture Mfr
N.A.I.C.S.: 337126

INP DEUTSCHLAND GMBH

Werkstrasse 5, 67354, Romerberg, Germany
Tel.: (49) 6232 6869 0 De
Web Site: http://www.inp-e.com
Year Founded: 1989
Sales Range: $50-74.9 Million
Construction & Engineering Services
N.A.I.C.S.: 541330
Georg Jester *(Member-Mgmt Bd)*

Subsidiaries:

INP North America, Inc. (1)
11390 Old Roswell Rd Ste 126, Alpharetta, GA 30009-0000
Tel.: (678) 527-1400
Web Site: http://www.inp-e.com
Engineeering Services
N.A.I.C.S.: 541330
Andreas Droge *(Mng Dir)*

INPAQ TECHNOLOGY CO., LTD.

No11 Ke-Yi St, Miaoli, Chunan, 35059, Taiwan
Tel.: (886) 37585555
Web Site: https://www.inpaqgp.com
6284—(TPE)
Rev.: $196,575,399
Assets: $329,549,354
Liabilities: $146,019,760
Net Worth: $183,529,594
Earnings: $18,465,435
Emp.: 1,866
Fiscal Year-end: 12/31/22
Semiconductor & Related Device Mfr
N.A.I.C.S.: 334413

Subsidiaries:

Inpaq Korea Co., Ltd. (1)
221 Raemian Seocho Univill 1445-4, Seocho-Dong Seocho-Gu, Seoul, 130-070, Korea (South)
Tel.: (82) 25848959
Antenna Product Mfr
N.A.I.C.S.: 334419

Inpaq Technology (China) Co., Ltd. (1)
Antai No 1 road 81 Xishan Economic Development Zone, AnZheng town, Wuxi, 214105, Jiangsu, China
Tel.: (86) 51088785968
Antenna Product Mfr
N.A.I.C.S.: 334419

Inpaq Trading (Shanghai) Co., Ltd. (1)
J2 14th Floor Zhao Feng Universe Building Block No 1800, Zhongshan West Road Xuhui District, Shanghai, 200235, China
Tel.: (86) 2164403187
Antenna Product Mfr
N.A.I.C.S.: 334419

Taiwan Inpaq Electronic Co., Ltd. (1)
1F No 38 Ke-Yi St, Miaoli, Chunan, 35059, Taiwan
Tel.: (886) 37585555
Antenna Product Mfr
N.A.I.C.S.: 334419

INPEX CORPORATION

Akasaka Biz Tower 5-3-1 Akasaka, Minato-ku, Tokyo, 107-6332, Japan
Tel.: (81) 355720200
Web Site: https://www.inpex.co.jp
Year Founded: 2006
1605—(TKS)
Rev.: $12,045,491,920
Assets: $49,931,337,280
Liabilities: $17,538,098,160
Net Worth: $32,393,239,120
Earnings: $2,159,104,640
Emp.: 3,189
Fiscal Year-end: 12/31/21
Oil & Gas Distribution Services
N.A.I.C.S.: 237120
Toshiaki Kitamura *(Chm)*

Subsidiaries:

Azadegan Petroleum Development, Ltd. (1)
Akasaka Biz Tower 5 3 1 Akasaka, Minato ku, Tokyo, 107 6332, Japan
Tel.: (81) 355720320
Web Site: http://www.inpex.co.jp
Sales Range: $50-74.9 Million
Emp.: 20
Oil Field Development Services
N.A.I.C.S.: 213112
Toshiaki Kitamura *(Pres)*

Daiichi Warehouse Co., Ltd. (1)
128 Sunami-cho, Minato-Ku, Nagoya, 455 0056, Aichi, Japan
Tel.: (81) 526610215
Logistic Services
N.A.I.C.S.: 541614

INPEX ABK, Ltd. (1)
Akasaka Biz Tower 5-3-1 Akasaka, Minato-ku, Tokyo, 107 6332, Japan
Tel.: (81) 355720330
Web Site: http://www.inpex.co.jp
Oil Exploration Services
N.A.I.C.S.: 213112
Toshiaki Kitamura *(Pres)*

INPEX Alpha, Ltd. (1)
Akasaka Biz Tower 5 3 1 Akasaka, Minato ku, Tokyo, 107 6332, Japan
Tel.: (81) 355720300
Web Site: http://www.inpex.co.jp
Oil & Gas Exploration Services
N.A.I.C.S.: 213112
Toshiaki Kitamura *(CEO)*

INPEX Browse, Ltd. (1)
Akasaka Biz Tower 5 3 1 Akasaka, Minato ku, Tokyo, 107 6332, Japan
Tel.: (81) 355720350
Web Site: http://www.inpex.co.jp
Sales Range: $50-74.9 Million
Emp.: 20
Oil & Gas Exploration Services
N.A.I.C.S.: 213112
Arihiro Kezuka *(Gen Mgr)*

INPEX Business Services, Ltd. (1)
Akasaka Biz Tower 5-3-1, Akasaka Minato-ku, Tokyo, 107-6332, Japan
Tel.: (81) 355720600
Web Site: https://www.inpex-bs.co.jp
Emp.: 33
Real Estate Services
N.A.I.C.S.: 531390

INPEX Canada, Ltd. (1)
Akasaka Biz Tower 5-3-1 Akasaka, Minato-ku, Tokyo, 107 6332, Japan
Tel.: (81) 355720310
Web Site: http://www.inpex.co.jp
Sales Range: $350-399.9 Million
Emp.: 700
Oil & Gas Exploration Services
N.A.I.C.S.: 213112

INPEX East Arguni, Ltd. (1)
Akasaka Biz Tower 5 3 1 Akasaka, Minato ku, Tokyo, 107 6332, Japan
Tel.: (81) 355720300
Web Site: http://www.inpex.co.jp
Emp.: 500
Oil & Gas Exploration Services
N.A.I.C.S.: 213112

INPEX Engineering (Japan) Co., Ltd. (1)
2-33-26 Amikawara, Chuo-ku, Niigata, 950-0964, Japan
Tel.: (81) 252842311
Web Site: https://www.inpex-eng.co.jp
Emp.: 144
Natural Gas Extraction Services
N.A.I.C.S.: 325120

INPEX Idemitsu Norge AS (1)
Lysaker Torg 25, 1366, Lysaker, Norway
Tel.: (47) 23250500
Web Site: https://inpex-idemitsu.no
Petroleum Extraction Services
N.A.I.C.S.: 211120

INPEX Jawa, Ltd. (1)
Akasaka Biz Tower 5 3 1 Akasaka, Minato ku, Tokyo, 107 6332, Japan
Tel.: (81) 355720300
Web Site: http://www.inpex.co.jp
Sales Range: $350-399.9 Million
Emp.: 1,000
Oil & Gas Exploration Services
N.A.I.C.S.: 213112

INPEX Libya, Ltd. (1)
Akasaka Biz Tower 5 3 1 Akasaka, Minato ku, Tokyo, 107 6332, Japan
Tel.: (81) 355720310
Oil & Gas Exploration Services
N.A.I.C.S.: 213112

INPEX Logistics (Japan) Co., Ltd. (1)
935 Shibukakihama, Ogata-ku, Joetsu, 949-3115, Niigata, Japan
Tel.: (81) 255345670
Web Site: https://www.inpexlogistics.co.jp
Sales Range: $25-49.9 Million
Emp.: 89
Petroleum Products Storage & Transportation Services
N.A.I.C.S.: 486910

INPEX Masela, Ltd. (1)
Akasaka Biz Tower 5 3 1 Akasaka, Minato ku, Tokyo, 107 6332, Japan
Tel.: (81) 355720340
Web Site: http://www.inpex.co.jp
Oil & Gas Exploration Services
N.A.I.C.S.: 213112

INPEX North Caspian Sea, Ltd. (1)
Akasaka Biz Tower 5 3 1 Akasaka, Minato

INTERNATIONAL PUBLIC

Akasaka Biz Tower 5 3 1 Akasaka, Minato ku, Tokyo, 107 6332, Japan
Tel.: (81) 355720320
Web Site: http://www.inpex.co.jp
Sales Range: $750-799.9 Million
Emp.: 1,500
Oil Exploration Services
N.A.I.C.S.: 211120
Toshiaki Kitinura *(Pres)*

INPEX Offshore North Mahakam, Ltd. (1)
Akasaka Biz Tower 5 3 1 Akasaka, Minato ku, Tokyo, 107 6332, Japan
Tel.: (81) 355720334
Web Site: http://www.inpex.co.jp
Sales Range: $200-249.9 Million
Emp.: 300
Oil & Gas Exploration Services
N.A.I.C.S.: 213112

INPEX Offshore Northeast Java, Ltd. (1)
Akasaka Biz Tower 5 3 1 Akasaka, Minato ku, Tokyo, 107 6332, Japan
Tel.: (81) 355720300
Web Site: http://www.inpex.co.jp
Sales Range: $750-799.9 Million
Emp.: 1,500
Oil & Gas Exploration Services
N.A.I.C.S.: 213112
Toshiaki Kitamura *(Pres)*

INPEX Offshore Northeast Mahakam, Ltd. (1)
Akasaka Biz Tower 5 3 1 Akasaka, Minato ku, Tokyo, 107 6332, Japan
Tel.: (81) 355720300
Emp.: 1,000
Oil & Gas Exploration Services
N.A.I.C.S.: 213112
Kieamura Toshiaki *(CEO)*

INPEX Offshore South East Mahakam, Ltd. (1)
Akasaka Biz Tower 5 3 1 Akasaka, Minato ku, Tokyo, 107 6332, Japan
Tel.: (81) 355720300
Web Site: http://www.inpex.co.jp
Sales Range: $50-74.9 Million
Emp.: 15
Oil & Gas Exploration Services
N.A.I.C.S.: 213112
Toshiaki Kitamura *(Pres)*

INPEX Sahul, Ltd. (1)
Akasaka Biz Tower 5 3 1 Akasaka, Minato ku, Tokyo, 107 6332, Japan
Tel.: (81) 355720300
Sales Range: $350-399.9 Million
Emp.: 1,000
Oil & Gas Exploration Services
N.A.I.C.S.: 213112
Takayuki Ueda *(CEO)*

INPEX Solutions, Ltd. (1)
Akasaka Biz Tower 5-3-1, Akasaka Minato-ku, Tokyo, 107-6332, Japan
Tel.: (81) 355720616
Web Site: https://www.inpex-solutions.co.jp
Oil & Natural Gas Services
N.A.I.C.S.: 213112

INPEX Southwest Caspian Sea, Ltd. (1)
Akasaka Biz Tower 5 3 1 Akasaka, Minato ku, Tokyo, 107 6332, Japan
Tel.: (81) 355720320
Web Site: http://www.inpex.co.jp
Oil Exploration Services
N.A.I.C.S.: 213112
Yasushi Okawa *(Gen Mgr)*

INPEX Sumatra, Ltd. (1)
Akasaka Biz Tower 5 3 1 Akasaka, Minato ku, Tokyo, 107 6332, Japan
Tel.: (81) 355720300
Web Site: http://www.inpex.co.jp
Sales Range: $200-249.9 Million
Emp.: 300
Oil & Gas Exploration Services
N.A.I.C.S.: 213112

INPEX Tengah, Ltd. (1)
Akasaka Biz Tower 5 3 1 Akasaka, Minato ku, Tokyo, 107 6332, Japan
Tel.: (81) 355720300
Emp.: 1,000
Oil & Gas Exploration Services
N.A.I.C.S.: 213112

INPEX Timor Sea, Ltd. (1)
Akasaka Biz Tower 5-3-1 Akasaka, Minato-ku, Tokyo, 107 6332, Japan
Tel.: (81) 355720300
Web Site: http://www.inpex.co.jp
Sales Range: $750-799.9 Million
Emp.: 1,500
Oil & Gas Exploration Services
N.A.I.C.S.: 213112
Kimura Hiromi (Mgr)

INPEX Trading, Ltd. (1)
Akasaka Biz Tower 5-3-1 Akasaka, Minato-ku, Tokyo, 107 6332, Japan
Tel.: (81) 355720270
Sales Range: $350-399.9 Million
Emp.: 1,000
Oil & Natural Gas Whslr
N.A.I.C.S.: 213112

INPEX West Arguni, Ltd. (1)
Akasaka Biz Tower 5-3-1 Akasaka, Minato-ku, Tokyo, 107 6332, Japan
Tel.: (81) 355720300
Web Site: http://www.inpex.co.jp
Emp.: 1,000
Oil & Gas Exploration Services
N.A.I.C.S.: 213112

Japan Oil Development Co., Ltd. (1)
Akasaka Biz Tower 5-3-1 Akasaka, Minato-ku, Tokyo, 107 6332, Japan
Tel.: (81) 355720330
Web Site: http://www.jodco.co.jp
Sales Range: $50-74.9 Million
Emp.: 300
Oil Exploration Services
N.A.I.C.S.: 213112
Yoshito Yokote (Mng Dir)

Keiyo Pipeline Co., Ltd. (1)
3-14-1 Tuganodai, Wakaba-ku, Chiba, 264-0033, Japan
Tel.: (81) 432515259
Natural Gas Distribution Services
N.A.I.C.S.: 221210

Minamifuji Pipeline Co., Ltd. (1)
1146-1 Tadehara, Fuji, 416-0931, Shizuoka, Japan
Tel.: (81) 545551211
Gas Pipeline Services
N.A.I.C.S.: 237120

Next Energy Co., Ltd. (1)
Natural Gas Distr
N.A.I.C.S.: 221210

Offshore Iwaki Petroleum Co., Ltd. (1)
Takara Bldg 34-14 Hatagaya 1-chome, Shibuya-ku, Tokyo, 151 0072, Japan
Tel.: (81) 3 5790 1840
Web Site: http://www.inpex.co.jp
Petroleum Product Mfr
N.A.I.C.S.: 211120

Saitama Gas Co., Ltd. (1)
395-1 Isegata, Fukaya, 366-0836, Saitama, Japan
Tel.: (81) 48 571 1335
Web Site: http://www.saitamagas.co.jp
Emp.: 15
Gas Mfr & Distr
N.A.I.C.S.: 325120

Sakata Natural Gas Co., Ltd. (1)
4-5 Higashiohucho, Sakata, 998-0831, Yamagata, Japan
Tel.: (81) 234244111
Web Site: http://www.sakata-n-gas.co.jp
Gas Distr
N.A.I.C.S.: 221210

TELNITE CO., LTD. (1)
3-2-3 Kanda-Jimbocho, Chiyoda-Ku, Tokyo, 101-0051, Japan
Tel.: (81) 358430010
Web Site: https://www.telnite.co.jp
Sales Range: $100-124.9 Million
Emp.: 47
Well Drilling & Civil Engineering Services
N.A.I.C.S.: 213111

Teikoku Oil (Cabinda) Co., Ltd. (1)
Akasaka Biz Tower 5-3-1 Akasaka, Minato-ku, Tokyo, 103 6332, Japan
Tel.: (81) 355720310
Web Site: http://www.inpex.co.jp
Sales Range: $350-399.9 Million
Emp.: 600
Oil Exploration Services
N.A.I.C.S.: 213111
Toshiaki Kitamura (CEO)

Teikoku Oil (North America) Co.,Ltd. (1)
Williams Tower 2800 Post Oak Blvd Ste 2450, Houston, TX 77056
Tel.: (713) 850-8480
Web Site: http://www.inpex.co.jp
Sales Range: $50-74.9 Million
Emp.: 20
Oil Mfr & Distr
N.A.I.C.S.: 213111
Toshito Todoroki (Gen Mgr)

Teikoku Oil (Suriname) Co., Ltd. (1)
Akasaka Biz Tower 5-3-1 Akasaka, Minato-ku, Tokyo, 107 6332, Japan
Tel.: (81) 355720310
Web Site: http://www.inpex.co.jp
Sales Range: $350-399.9 Million
Emp.: 700
Oil Exploration Services
N.A.I.C.S.: 213111

Teikoku Oil (Venezuela) Co., Ltd. (1)
Akasaka Biz Tower 5-3-1 Akasaka, Minato-ku, Tokyo, 107-6332, Japan
Tel.: (81) 355720310
Web Site: http://www.inpex.co.jp
Sales Range: $350-399.9 Million
Emp.: 700
Oil & Gas Exploration Services
N.A.I.C.S.: 213111

Teikoku Oil Algeria Co., Ltd. (1)
Akasaka Biz Tower 5-3-1 Akasaka, Minato-ku, Tokyo, 107 6332, Japan
Tel.: (81) 355720310
Web Site: http://www.inpex.co.jp
Oil & Gas Mfr & Exploration Services
N.A.I.C.S.: 213111

Teikoku Oil Ecuador (1)
Edificio Torre XXI Oficina 2W Av Republica del Salvador 500, E Irlanda, Quito, Ecuador
Tel.: (593) 22240827
Oil Mfr & Distr
N.A.I.C.S.: 213111

Teikoku Oil Nile NQR Co., Ltd. (1)
Akasaka Biz Tower 5-3-1 Akasaka, Minato-ku, Tokyo, 107 6332, Japan
Tel.: (81) 355720310
Web Site: http://www.inpex.co.jp
Sales Range: $350-399.9 Million
Emp.: 1,000
Oil Exploration Services
N.A.I.C.S.: 213111

Teiseki Drilling Co., Ltd. (1)
Lucid Square Shinjuku East 7F 3-21 Okubo 1 Chome, Shinjuku-Ku, Tokyo, 169-0072, Japan
Tel.: (81) 352921711
Web Site: http://www.teiseki-drilling.co.jp
Emp.: 100
Drilling Services
N.A.I.C.S.: 213111
Kuniaki Shimada (Pres)

Teiseki Pipeline Co., Ltd. (1)
6-2 Ookubo 1-Chome, kashiwazaki-shi, Niigata, 945 0851, Japan
Tel.: (81) 257242143
Natural Gas Transportation & Management Services
N.A.I.C.S.: 221210

Teiseki Real Estate Co., Ltd. (1)
3-8 Ogawamachi Kanda, Chiyada-ku, Tokyo, 101 0052, Japan
Tel.: (81) 3 3259 1611
Real Estate Rental & Insurance Agency Services
N.A.I.C.S.: 524210

Toyo Gas Engineering Co., Ltd. (1)
2-33-26 AmiGawara Chuo-ku, Niigata-shi, Niigata, 950 0964, Japan
Tel.: (81) 252842311
Web Site: http://www.inpex.co.jp
Sales Range: $50-74.9 Million
Emp.: 50
Gas Mfr
N.A.I.C.S.: 211120

INPLASTOR AB
Medevivagen 81, PO Box 922, 591 29, Motala, Sweden
Tel.: (46) 141224300 SE
Web Site: http://www.inplastor.se
Year Founded: 1957
Sales Range: $10-24.9 Million
Emp.: 25
Plastic Product Graphic Printing Services
N.A.I.C.S.: 323111
Hakan Kindstrom (Mng Dir)

INPOKOMERC D.D.
Ul Causlije bb, 70 230, Bugojno, Bosnia & Herzegovina
Tel.: (387) 30270006
INPKRK1—(SARE)
Rev.: $94,208
Assets: $1,262,041
Liabilities: $66,573
Net Worth: $1,195,468
Earnings: ($24,848)
Emp.: 2
Fiscal Year-end: 12/31/21
Real Estate Manangement Services
N.A.I.C.S.: 531210

INPOST S.A.
70 route d Esch, 1470, Luxembourg, Luxembourg
Web Site: https://www.inpost.eu
Year Founded: 2006
INPST—(EUR)
Rev.: $8,671
Assets: $10,753
Liabilities: $10,177
Net Worth: $576
Earnings: $560
Emp.: 6,130
Fiscal Year-end: 12/31/22
Online Shopping Services
N.A.I.C.S.: 459999
Rafal Brzoska (CEO)

Subsidiaries:

InPost UK Limited (1)
2nd Floor 16 Dufours Place, London, W1F 7SP, United Kingdom
Tel.: (44) 3303350950
Web Site: https://www.inpost.co.uk
Logistic Services
N.A.I.C.S.: 541614

Locker InPost Italia S.r.l. (1)
Viale Cassala 30, 20143, Milan, Italy
Tel.: (39) 0238582894
Web Site: https://www.inpost.it
Logistic Services
N.A.I.C.S.: 541614

INPRO S.A.
Opata Jacka Rybinskiego 8 Street, 80-320, Gdansk, Oliwa, Poland
Tel.: (48) 583400381
Web Site: https://www.inpro.com.pl
Year Founded: 1987
INP—(WAR)
Rev.: $86,651,845
Assets: $194,912,662
Liabilities: $83,469,908
Net Worth: $111,442,754
Earnings: $12,647,944
Emp.: 276
Fiscal Year-end: 12/31/21
Real Estate Construction Services
N.A.I.C.S.: 236220
Piotr Stefaniak (Member-Mgmt Bd & VP)

Subsidiaries:

Dom Zdrojowy Sp. z o.o (1)
ul Kosciuszki 2a, 84-140, Jastarnia, Poland
Tel.: (48) 58 67 99 100
Web Site: http://www.zdrojowy.com.pl
Emp.: 90
Home Management Services
N.A.I.C.S.: 721110

InBet Sp. z o.o. (1)
ul Przemyslowa 10, 83-050, Kolbudy, Poland
Tel.: (48) 586827765
Web Site: https://www.inbet.com.pl
Emp.: 50
Cement & Concrete Product Mfr
N.A.I.C.S.: 327390

PB Domesta Sp. z o.o. (1)
ul Budowlanych 68 B, 80-298, Gdansk, Poland
Tel.: (48) 58 349 56 65
Web Site: http://www.domesta.com.pl
Residential Building Construction Services
N.A.I.C.S.: 236117

Rugby Prefabrykaty Sp. z o.o. (1)
ul Przemyslowa 10, 83-050, Kolbudy, Poland
Tel.: (48) 58 682 77 62
Web Site: http://www.rugby.com.pl
Construction Materials Mfr
N.A.I.C.S.: 238120

INRETAIL PERU CORP.
Calle Morelli 139, 13, Lima, Peru
Tel.: (51) 12192000
Web Site: https://www.inretail.pe
Year Founded: 2003
INRETC1—(LIM)
Rev.: $4,912,871,018
Assets: $5,305,384,269
Liabilities: $4,090,097,645
Net Worth: $1,215,286,623
Earnings: $102,882,444
Fiscal Year-end: 12/31/21
Grocery Product Distr
N.A.I.C.S.: 445110

INROM CONSTRUCTION INDUSTRIES LTD.
1 Golan Street Golan building, Airport City, Israel
Tel.: (972) 39718181
Web Site: https://www.inrom-group.co.il
Year Founded: 2013
INRM—(TAE)
Rev.: $309,195,740
Assets: $391,178,333
Liabilities: $167,106,504
Net Worth: $224,071,830
Earnings: $53,314,545
Emp.: 870
Fiscal Year-end: 12/31/23
Paint & Coating Manufacturing
N.A.I.C.S.: 325510
Zion Ginat (Chm)

Subsidiaries:

SP Advanced Industries Ltd. (1)
Kibbutz Metzer D N Hefer, Hadera, 3882000, Israel
Tel.: (972) 525589140
Web Site: https://www.sp-i.co.il
Plumbing Services
N.A.I.C.S.: 532490

INS COMMUNICATIONS PTE. LTD.
69 Amoy St, Singapore, 069 888, Singapore
Tel.: (65) 62245583 SG
Web Site: http://www.asiainsurancereview.com
Year Founded: 1990
Sales Range: $25-49.9 Million
Emp.: 25
Publishers of Journals, Magazines & Literary Works
N.A.I.C.S.: 513120
Sheela Suppiah-Raj (Gen Mgr-Bus Dev)

INSA A.D.
Trscanska No 21, 11080, Zemun, Serbia
Tel.: (381) 113713600
Web Site: https://www.insa.rs
Year Founded: 1950

INSA A.D.

Insa a.d.—(Continued)

INSA—(BEL)
Sales Range: $1-9.9 Million
Measuring Instruments Mfr
N.A.I.C.S.: 334515
Jovica Zaric *(Gen Dir, Gen Mgr & Dir)*

INSAN INC
23-26 Sudongnonggong-gil, Sudongmyeon Hamyang-gun, Sudong, Korea (South)
Tel.: (82) 559639991
Web Site: http://www.insanga.co.kr
Year Founded: 2017
Medicine Salt Mfr & Distr
N.A.I.C.S.: 311942
Jung Byung Jo *(Mng Dir)*

Subsidiaries:

INSAN Inc - Insan Bamboo Salt Factory **(1)**
1250-17 Hwasan-ri Hamyang-gun, Sudong, Gyeongsangnam-do, Korea (South)
Tel.: (82) 559639992
Salt Product Mfr
N.A.I.C.S.: 311942

INSAS BERHAD
Suite 23 02 Level 23 The Gardens South Tower Mid Valley City, Lingkaran Syed Putra, 59200, Kuala Lumpur, Malaysia
Tel.: (60) 322829311
Web Site: https://www.insas.net
INSAS—(KLS)
Rev.: $53,557,020
Assets: $668,423,003
Liabilities: $125,593,628
Net Worth: $542,829,375
Earnings: $53,613,945
Emp.: 258
Fiscal Year-end: 06/30/22
Alcoholic Beverages Mfr
N.A.I.C.S.: 424820
Gian Kui Wong *(CEO & Exec Dir)*

Subsidiaries:

Dawnfield Pte. Ltd. **(1)**
2 Ubi View 02 02, Singapore, 408556, Singapore
Tel.: (65) 67415227
Sales Range: $50-74.9 Million
Emp.: 3
Investment Management Service
N.A.I.C.S.: 523999

Divfex Berhad **(1)**
Level 5 Ho Hup Tower 1 Persiaran Jalil 1 Bandar Bukit Jalil, 57000, Kuala Lumpur, Malaysia **(55.62%)**
Tel.: (60) 390783211
Web Site: https://divfex.com
Rev.: $3,942,949
Assets: $13,750,532
Liabilities: $6,322,971
Net Worth: $7,427,561
Earnings: $247,001
Emp.: 90
Fiscal Year-end: 06/30/2022
Investment Holding Services
N.A.I.C.S.: 551112
Seng Chuan Tan *(Exec Dir)*

Hastanas Development Sdn. Bhd. **(1)**
45 5 The Boulevard Mid Valley City, Lingkaran Syed Putra, Kuala Lumpur, 59200, Federal Territory, Malaysia
Tel.: (60) 322848311
Sales Range: $50-74.9 Million
Emp.: 4
Real Estate Property Development Services
N.A.I.C.S.: 531311

Insas Pacific Rent-A-Car Sdn. Bhd. **(1)**
Unit C05-11 Plaza Bukit Jalil No 1 Jalan Persiaran Jalil 1, Bandar Bukit Jalil, 57000, Kuala Lumpur, Malaysia
Tel.: (60) 350332627
Web Site: https://www.iprac.com

Sales Range: $25-49.9 Million
Emp.: 50
Car Rental Services
N.A.I.C.S.: 532111
Jennifer Lam *(Gen Mgr)*

Insas Properties Sdn. Bhd. **(1)**
No 45-5 The Boulevard Mid Valley City, Lingkaran Syed Putra, 59200, Kuala Lumpur, Malaysia
Tel.: (60) 322848311
Web Site: https://www.insasproperty.com
Property Management Services
N.A.I.C.S.: 531311

Insas Technology Berhad **(1)**
D-07-2 Plaza Kelana Jaya Jalan SS7/13A, Kelana Jaya, 47301, Petaling Jaya, Malaysia **(100%)**
Tel.: (60) 78768609
Web Site: https://www.itb.com.my
Software Development, Mobile Technologies & EMS Mfr
N.A.I.C.S.: 513210
Peter Wong Cheng Hin *(Project Mgr)*

Insas Technology Pte. Ltd. **(1)**
2 Ubi View 02 02, Singapore, 408556, Singapore
Tel.: (65) 67476313
Application Software Development Services
N.A.I.C.S.: 541511

Langdale E3 Pte. Ltd. **(1)**
2 Ubi View 02-02 CSE Bldg, Singapore, Singapore
Tel.: (65) 67476313
Web Site: http://www.langdale.net
Wireless Modems & Routers Distr
N.A.I.C.S.: 423430

Magxo Sdn. Bhd. **(1)**
45-11 The Boulevard Midvalley City, Lingkaran Syed Putra, 59200, Kuala Lumpur, Malaysia
Tel.: (60) 322878609
Web Site: http://www.magxo.com
Sales Range: $25-49.9 Million
Emp.: 5
Mobile Communication Carriers
N.A.I.C.S.: 517112

Makan Channel Sdn. Bhd. **(1)**
No 8 Jalan Serendah 26/41 Sekitar 26, 40400, Shah Alam, Selangor, Malaysia
Tel.: (60) 163321735
Web Site: https://www.desiq.my
Consumer Food Distr
N.A.I.C.S.: 424490

Megapolitan Management Services Sdn. Bhd. **(1)**
No 47-5 The Boulevard Mid Valley City, Lingkaran Syed Putra, 59200, Kuala Lumpur, Federal Territory, Malaysia
Tel.: (60) 323919309
Sales Range: $25-49.9 Million
Emp.: 6
Business Management Services
N.A.I.C.S.: 561499

PRAC Transport Sdn. Bhd. **(1)**
Unit C-05-11 Plaza Bukit Jalil No 1 Persiaran Jalil 1, Bandar Bukit Jalil, 57000, Kuala Lumpur, Malaysia
Tel.: (60) 350332627
Web Site: https://practransport.iprac.com
Fleet Rental Services
N.A.I.C.S.: 532112

Valencia Homes Sdn. Bhd. **(1)**
45 5 The Boulevard Midvalley City, Lingkaran Syed Putra, 59200, Kuala Lumpur, Federal Territory, Malaysia
Tel.: (60) 322848311
Web Site: http://www.insas.net
Sales Range: $25-49.9 Million
Emp.: 40
Property Managing Services
N.A.I.C.S.: 531311

VigTech Labs Sdn. Bhd. **(1)**
No 10 Jalan Serendah 26/41 Sekitar 26, Lingkaran Syed Putra, 40400, Shah Alam, Selangor, Malaysia
Tel.: (60) 378768609
Web Site: https://www.vigtech.net
Online Gaming Platform Development Services
N.A.I.C.S.: 541511

INSCAPE CORPORATION
67 Toll Road, Holland Landing, L9N 1H2, ON, Canada
Tel.: (905) 836-7676 ON
Web Site: https://myinscape.com
Year Founded: 1888
INQ—(TSX)
Rev.: $59,310,905
Assets: $29,573,313
Liabilities: $22,785,470
Net Worth: $6,787,844
Earnings: ($4,229,006)
Emp.: 295
Fiscal Year-end: 04/30/20
Workplace Furniture & Storage Designer & Mfr
N.A.I.C.S.: 337211
Bartley Bull *(Chm)*

Subsidiaries:

Inscape (New York) Inc. **(1)**
221 Lister Ave Ste 1, Falconer, NY 14733
Tel.: (716) 665-6210
Sales Range: $50-74.9 Million
Emp.: 110
Partition Wall Office Products
N.A.I.C.S.: 332321
Angie Turner *(Mgr-HR)*

INSCEPTION BIOSCIENCES, INC.
1620 Tech Avenue Unit 1, Mississauga, L4W 5P4, ON, Canada
Tel.: (905) 206-2790
Web Site: https://www.insception.com
Year Founded: 1996
Sales Range: $10-24.9 Million
Emp.: 50
Stem Cell & Cord Blood Storage & Services
N.A.I.C.S.: 621991

Subsidiaries:

Insception Lifebank Cord Blood Program **(1)**
1620 Tech Avenue Unit 1, Mississauga, L4W 5P4, ON, Canada
Web Site: https://www.insception.com
Cryogenic Storage of Umbilical Cord Blood; Clinical Research & Procedures
N.A.I.C.S.: 621511

INSCOBEE INC.
306-2 47 Digital-ro 9-gil, Geumcheongu, Seoul, Korea (South)
Tel.: (82) 16619641
Web Site: https://www.inscobee.com
Year Founded: 1970
006490—(KRS)
Rev.: $58,812,273
Assets: $77,607,962
Liabilities: $29,247,487
Net Worth: $48,360,475
Earnings: ($5,546,252)
Emp.: 58
Fiscal Year-end: 12/31/22
Wristwatch & Automobeil Sales
N.A.I.C.S.: 423940
Yoo Insoo *(Co-CEO)*

INSECTICIDES (INDIA) LIMITED
401-402 Lusa Tower Azadpur Commercial Complex, Delhi, 110033, India
Tel.: (91) 7428208822
Web Site: http://www.insecticidesindia.com
INSECTICID—(NSE)
Rev.: $194,915,666
Assets: $194,641,752
Liabilities: $82,660,551
Net Worth: $111,981,201
Earnings: $12,817,760
Emp.: 355
Fiscal Year-end: 03/31/21
Pesticide Mfr

INTERNATIONAL PUBLIC

N.A.I.C.S.: 325320
Hari Chand Aggarwal *(Chm)*

INSETCO PLC
Finsgate 5-7 Cranwood Street, London, EC1V 9EE, United Kingdom
Tel.: (44) 207 887 7840
Web Site: http://www.insetco.com
Emp.: 4
Life Insurance Settlement Services
N.A.I.C.S.: 524298
Ivan Couchman *(Chm)*

INSIG AI PLC
6 Heddon Street, London, W1B 4BT, United Kingdom
Tel.: (44) 2079350823
Web Site: https://www.insg.ai
Rev.: $1,963,182
Assets: $886,044
Liabilities: $304,452
Net Worth: $581,592
Earnings: ($183,354)
Emp.: 94
Fiscal Year-end: 12/31/18
Venture Capital Investment Services
N.A.I.C.S.: 523999
Richard Bernstein *(CEO)*

Subsidiaries:

Pantheon Leisure plc **(1)**
58 60 Berners Street, London, W1T 3JS, United Kingdom **(62.5%)**
Tel.: (44) 2089548787
Sales Range: $1-9.9 Million
Football Club
N.A.I.C.S.: 711211

Subsidiary (Domestic):

The Elms Group Limited **(2)**
Pynnacles Close 12, Stanmore, HA7 4AF, Middlesex, United Kingdom
Tel.: (44) 20 8954 8787
Web Site: http://www.theelms.co.uk
Sports Club Operator
N.A.I.C.S.: 711211
Jason O Conner *(Mng Dir)*

INSIGHT INC.
N 4W 3 No 1 Chuo-ku, Sapporo, 060-0004, Hokkaido, Japan
Tel.: (81) 112332221
Web Site: http://www.ppi.jp
Year Founded: 1975
Sales Range: $10-24.9 Million
Emp.: 40
Advertising, Sales Promotion & Media Consulting Services
N.A.I.C.S.: 541890
Hajime Asai *(Pres)*

INSIGNIA FINANCIAL LTD.
Tel.: (61) 280162893 AU
Web Site: https://www.insigniafinancial.com.au
IOOFF—(OTCIQ)
Rev.: $1,296,417,210
Assets: $2,396,318,538
Liabilities: $1,031,190,882
Net Worth: $1,365,127,656
Earnings: ($123,732,222)
Emp.: 4,000
Fiscal Year-end: 06/30/24
Investment Management Service
N.A.I.C.S.: 523999
Renato Mota *(CEO & Mng Dir)*

Subsidiaries:

AET Super Solutions Pty Limited **(1)**
PO Box 546, 5001, Adelaide, SA, Australia
Tel.: (61) 300 652 587
Web Site: http://www.aetsupersolutions.com.au
Investment Management Service
N.A.I.C.S.: 523999

Accountplan Pty Limited **(1)**
58 Klingner Rd, Redcliffe, 4020, QLD, Australia

AND PRIVATE COMPANIES

Tel.: (61) 738838999
Web Site: https://accountplan.com.au
Sales Range: $25-49.9 Million
Emp.: 15
Accounting Services
N.A.I.C.S.: 541219

Australian Executor Trustees (NSW) Limited (1)
Level 4 7 Macquarie Place, Sydney, 2000, NSW, Australia
Tel.: (61) 290281051
Investment Management Service
N.A.I.C.S.: 523999
Yvonne Kelaher *(Head-Corp Trust)*

Australian Executor Trustees (SA) Limited (1)
44 Pirie Street, Millers Point, Adelaide, 5000, SA, Australia
Tel.: (61) 290281000
Sales Range: $100-124.9 Million
Emp.: 200
Investment Management Service
N.A.I.C.S.: 523999

Australian Wealth Management Limited (1)
The Bond Level 3 30 Hickson Road, Sydney, 2000, NSW, Australia
Tel.: (61) 290281000
Sales Range: $25-49.9 Million
Emp.: 200
Wealth Management Services
N.A.I.C.S.: 541618
Martin Walsh *(Chm)*

Subsidiary (Domestic):

Bridges Financial Services Pty Limited (2)
The Bond Level 3 30 Hickson Road, Millers Point, 2000, NSW, Australia
Tel.: (61) 1300763359
Sales Range: $25-49.9 Million
Emp.: 15
Financial Management Services
N.A.I.C.S.: 541611

Ord Minnett Management Ltd (2)
Level 8 255 George Street, Sydney, 2000, NSW, Australia
Tel.: (61) 282166300
Web Site: https://www.ords.com.au
Sales Range: $25-49.9 Million
Emp.: 200
Financial Management Consulting Services
N.A.I.C.S.: 541611

Consultum Financial Advisers Pty Ltd (1)
Level 6 161 Collins Street, Melbourne, 3000, VIC, Australia
Tel.: (61) 1800062134
Web Site: https://www.consultum.com.au
Sales Range: $25-49.9 Million
Emp.: 20
Financial Consulting Services
N.A.I.C.S.: 541611
Leigh Sando *(Mgr-South)*

DKN Financial Group Limited (1)
Level 6 161 Collins Street, Melbourne, 3000, VIC, Australia
Tel.: (61) 396670700
Web Site: http://www.dkn.com.au
Sales Range: $25-49.9 Million
Emp.: 40
Financial Services
N.A.I.C.S.: 551112

Executor Trustee Australia Limited (1)
The Bond Level 3 30 Hickson Road, Millers Point, Sydney, 2000, NSW, Australia
Tel.: (61) 290281000
Web Site: https://www.aetlimited.com.au
Sales Range: $100-124.9 Million
Emp.: 250
Investment Management Service
N.A.I.C.S.: 523999

Ord Minnett Financial Planning Pty Limited (1)
Level 8 NAB House 255 George Street, Sydney, 2000, NSW, Australia
Tel.: (61) 282166300
Emp.: 350
Financial Management Services
N.A.I.C.S.: 541611

Ord Minnett Holdings Pty Limited (1)
Level 8 255 George St, Sydney, 2000, NSW, Australia
Tel.: (61) 282166300
Emp.: 200
Investment Consulting Services
N.A.I.C.S.: 523999
Robert Thomson *(Co-Head-Fin)*

Perennial Investment Partners Limited (1)
Level 14 55 Collins Street, Melbourne, 3000, VIC, Australia
Tel.: (61) 288232534
Web Site: http://www.perennial.net.au
Sales Range: $50-74.9 Million
Emp.: 40
Investment Management Service
N.A.I.C.S.: 523999

SMF Wealth Management Pty Limited (1)
Level 9 59 Liverpool Street, PO Box 529, Hobart, 7000, TAS, Australia
Tel.: (61) 362155900
Sales Range: $50-74.9 Million,
Emp.: 280
Investment Management Service
N.A.I.C.S.: 523999
Susan Gillman *(Officer-Fin Plng Support)*

Select Managed Funds Limited (1)
Level 6 161 Collins Streett, Melbourne, 3000, VIC, Australia
Tel.: (61) 392034755
Web Site: http://www.ioof.com.au
Sales Range: $200-249.9 Million
Emp.: 350
Financial Management Services
N.A.I.C.S.: 523999

Snowball Financial Pty. Ltd. (1)
Level 18 50 Bridge Street, Sydney, 2000, NSW, Australia
Tel.: (61) 292501500
Web Site: http://www.outlookfs.com.au
Sales Range: $50-74.9 Million
Emp.: 10
Financial Services
N.A.I.C.S.: 522320

Western Pacific Financial Group Pty. Ltd. (1)
Garden Ofc Park Bldg B, 355 Scarborough Beach Rd, Osborne Park, 6017, Western Australia, Australia
Tel.: (61) 894436833
Web Site: http://www.westernpacific.com.au
Sales Range: $50-74.9 Million
Emp.: 10
Financial Advisory Services
N.A.I.C.S.: 522320
Devi Chhana *(Mgr)*

INSIMBI INDUSTRIAL HOLDINGS LIMITED
359 Crocker Road, Wadeville Extension 4, Germiston, 1422, Gauteng, South Africa
Tel.: (27) 119026930   ZA
Web Site: https://insimbi-group.co.za
Year Founded: 1970
ISB—(JSE)
Rev.: $302,676,570
Assets: $84,119,076
Liabilities: $47,038,995
Net Worth: $37,080,081
Earnings: $5,668,786
Emp.: 468
Fiscal Year-end: 02/28/23
Alloy & Refractory Material Distr
N.A.I.C.S.: 423510

Subsidiaries:

Insimbi Aluminium Alloys Proprietary Limited (1)
13 Lincoln Road Benoni South, Johannesburg, South Africa
Tel.: (27) 117470420
Ferrous Distr
N.A.I.C.S.: 423510

Metlite Alloys Proprietary Limited (1)
13 Glenhurst St Beaconvale, Parow, Cape Town, South Africa
Tel.: (27) 2193279412
Web Site: https://www.metlite.co.za
Alloy Mfr
N.A.I.C.S.: 331314
Valiant Ah Hing *(Mng Dir)*

INSOLATION ENERGY LTD.
G-25 City Center S C Road, Jaipur, 302001, Rajasthan, India
Tel.: (91) 1414019103   In
Web Site: https://www.insolationenergy.in
Year Founded: 2015
543620—(BOM)
Rev.: $33,578,155
Assets: $19,098,939
Liabilities: $12,758,312
Net Worth: $6,340,627
Earnings: $1,280,727
Emp.: 146
Fiscal Year-end: 03/31/23
Solar Panel Mfr
N.A.I.C.S.: 332410

INSOURCE CO., LTD.
Kandabashi Park Bldg 5F 1-19-1 Kanda Nishikicho Chiyoda-ku, Tokyo, 101-0054, Japan
Tel.: (81) 352590070
Web Site: https://secure.insource.co.jp
Year Founded: 2002
6200—(TKS)
Rev.: $76,451,470
Assets: $76,536,550
Liabilities: $20,319,940
Net Worth: $56,216,610
Earnings: $18,972,840
Fiscal Year-end: 09/30/23
Human Resource Consulting Services
N.A.I.C.S.: 541612
Takayuki Funahashi *(Pres & CEO)*

Subsidiaries:

Mitemo Co., Ltd. (1)
3-20 Kanda Ogawamachi, Chiyoda-ku, Tokyo, 101-0052, Japan
Tel.: (81) 335180611
Web Site: https://www.mitemo.co.jp
Business Management Consulting Services
N.A.I.C.S.: 541611
Tetsuya Sawada *(Pres)*

INSPEARIT SAS
21 rue de la Banque, 75002, Paris, France
Tel.: (33) 180068433
Web Site: http://www.inspearit.com
Year Founded: 1989
Sales Range: $25-49.9 Million
Emp.: 170
IT Services
N.A.I.C.S.: 541512
Pascal Chenais *(Chm-Exec Bd)*

INSPEC INC.
79-1 Kakunodate Arayashiki Kakunodate-machi, Semboku-shi, Akita, 014-0341, Japan
Tel.: (81) 187541888
Web Site: https://www.inspec21.com
Year Founded: 1984
6656—(TKS)
Rev.: $22,728,640
Assets: $36,832,400
Liabilities: $17,966,080
Net Worth: $18,866,320
Earnings: $677,600
Emp.: 72
Fiscal Year-end: 04/30/20
Semiconductor Testing Equipment Mfr
N.A.I.C.S.: 334515
Masashi Sugawara *(Pres & CEO)*

INSPIRATION CO., LTD.

Subsidiaries:

Inspec Taiwan Inc. (1)
5F-6 No 60 Nanhua St, Taoyuan, 33042, Taiwan
Tel.: (886) 33391302
Electronic Equipment Distr
N.A.I.C.S.: 423690

Path Imaging Inc. (1)
SANOS Nihonbashi Building 2-34-5 Nihonbashi Ningyocho, Chuo-ku, Tokyo, 103-0013, Aomori, Japan
Tel.: (81) 33 527 2020
Web Site: https://www.pathimaging.jp
Medical Equipment Mfr
N.A.I.C.S.: 334515
Masashi Sugawara *(CEO)*

INSPECS GROUP PLC
7-10 Kelso Place Upper Bristol Road, Bath, BA1 3AU, United Kingdom   UK
Web Site: https://www.inspecs.com
Year Founded: 1988
SPEC—(AIM)
Rev.: $248,577,000
Assets: $292,680,000
Liabilities: $162,590,000
Net Worth: $130,090,000
Earnings: ($7,816,000)
Emp.: 1,732
Fiscal Year-end: 12/31/22
Optical Product Mfr & Distr
N.A.I.C.S.: 326199

Subsidiaries:

BoDe Design GmbH (1)
Hofweg 20, 97737, Gemunden, Germany
Tel.: (49) 93516053620
Web Site: https://www.bode-design.de
Eyewear Mfr
N.A.I.C.S.: 339115

Norville (20/20) Limited (1)
Norville Waterwells Drive Waterwells Business Park, Gloucester, GL2 2AA, United Kingdom
Tel.: (44) 1452528686
Web Site: https://www.norville.co.uk
Optical Lens Mfr & Distr
N.A.I.C.S.: 326199

INSPIRA FINANCIAL INC.
1515A Bayview Avenue Suite 200E, East York, Toronto, M4G 3B5, ON, Canada
Tel.: (416) 865-7209   Ca
Web Site: http://www.inspirafin.ca
Year Founded: 2013
LND—(TSXV)
Rev.: $2,306,558
Assets: $8,517,926
Liabilities: $299,766
Net Worth: $8,218,160
Earnings: ($557,474)
Fiscal Year-end: 02/28/19
Investment Services
N.A.I.C.S.: 523999
Robert Munro *(Founder)*

INSPIRA TECHNOLOGIES OXY B.H.N. LTD.
2 Ha-Tidhar St, Ra'anana, 4366504, Israel
Tel.: (972) 99664488   Il
Web Site: https://inspira-technologies.com
Year Founded: 2018
IINN—(NASDAQ)
Assets: $9,310,000
Liabilities: $3,572,000
Net Worth: $5,738,000
Earnings: ($11,286,000)
Emp.: 37
Fiscal Year-end: 12/31/23
Medical Device Mfr & Distr
N.A.I.C.S.: 339112
Dagi Ben-Noon *(Co-Founder & CEO)*

INSPIRATION CO., LTD.

INSPIRATION CO., LTD.

Inspiration Co., Ltd.—(Continued)
2-11-1 Kitashinagawa Bay Terrace 206, Shinagawa, Tokyo, 140-0001, Japan
Tel.: (81) 367184812
Web Site: http://www.inspiration.co.jp
Year Founded: 1997
Software Development Services
N.A.I.C.S.: 541511

INSPIRATION HEALTHCARE GROUP PLC

Unit 7/8 Commerce Way, Commerce Park, Croydon, CR0 4YL, United Kingdom
Tel.: (44) 3301750000
Web Site: https://www.inspiration-healthcare.com
IHC—(AIM)
Rev.: $55,982,869
Assets: $74,530,682
Liabilities: $26,366,922
Net Worth: $48,163,759
Earnings: $369,300
Emp.: 200
Fiscal Year-end: 01/31/23
Heating Solutions Developer & Manufacturer
N.A.I.C.S.: 334512
Neil J. Campbell *(CEO)*

Subsidiaries:

Airon Corporation (1)
751 North Dr, Melbourne, FL 32934
Tel.: (321) 821-9433
Web Site: http://www.aironusa.com
Rev.: $1,000,000
Emp.: 7
Surgical & Medical Instrument Mfr
N.A.I.C.S.: 339112
G. Eric Gjerde *(Pres & CEO)*

Inspiration Healthcare Limited (1)
2 Satellite Business Village Fleming Way, Crawley, RH10 9NE, West Sussex, United Kingdom
Tel.: (44) 1455840555
Health Care Product Whslr
N.A.I.C.S.: 423450

Viomedex Limited (1)
Unit 13 Swan Barn Business Centre Old Swan Lane, Hailsham, BN27 2BY, East Sussex, United Kingdom
Tel.: (44) 1323446130
Web Site: http://www.viomedex.com
Health Care Product Whslr
N.A.I.C.S.: 423450

INSPIRE FILMS LIMITED

First Floor Kamdhenu Mind Space Malad West, Mumbai, 400064, India
Tel.: (91) 2246095834
Web Site: https://www.inspirefilms.in
Year Founded: 2007
INSPIRE—(NSE)
Emp.: 35
Television Broadcasting Services
N.A.I.C.S.: 516120
Kameswar Subudhi *(CFO)*

INSPIRED EDUCATION HOLDINGS LIMITED

6th Floor 3 Burlington Gardens, London, W1S 3EP, United Kingdom
Tel.: (44) 2038679961
Web Site: http://inspirededu.com
Private School Operator
N.A.I.C.S.: 611699
Nadim M Nsouli *(Founder, Chm & CEO)*

Subsidiaries:

Wey Education plc (1)
10 Orange Street, London, W1S 2SA, United Kingdom
Tel.: (44) 1873 813 900
Web Site: http://www.weyeducation.com
Rev.: $7,934,354
Assets: $10,424,943
Liabilities: $2,871,054
Net Worth: $7,553,889
Earnings: ($898,993)
Emp.: 107
Fiscal Year-end: 08/31/2019
Educational Group Holding Company
N.A.I.C.S.: 551112
Jacqueline Daniell *(CEO)*

Subsidiary (Domestic):

Academy21 Limited (2)
10 Orange Street, London, WC2H 7DQ, United Kingdom
Tel.: (44) 1438535001
Web Site: http://www.academy21.co.uk
Education Services
N.A.I.C.S.: 611710
Sara De Freitas *(Dir-Education)*

Interhigh Education Limited (2)
Lewis Parry House Elvicta Estate, Crickhowell, NP8 1DF, United Kingdom
Tel.: (44) 1873813900
Web Site: http://www.interhigh.co.uk
Education Services
N.A.I.C.S.: 611710
Sara De Freitas *(Dir-Education)*

INSPIRED PLC

Calder House, St Georges Park, Kirkham, PR4 2DZ, Lancashire, United Kingdom
Tel.: (44) 1772689250
Web Site: https://www.inspiredplc.co.uk
INSE—(AIM)
Rev.: $112,062,610
Assets: $192,041,151
Liabilities: $115,005,049
Net Worth: $77,036,102
Earnings: ($4,579,652)
Emp.: 641
Fiscal Year-end: 12/31/22
Management Consulting Services
N.A.I.C.S.: 541618
Paul Connor *(CFO)*

Subsidiaries:

Bluebell Energy Supply Limited (1)
Rift House 200 Eureka park, Ashford, TN25 4AZ, Kent, United Kingdom
Tel.: (44) 1303647657
Web Site: https://bluebellenergy.com
Energy Consulting Services
N.A.I.C.S.: 541690

Businesswise Solutions Limited (1)
The Energy Centre 16 Lindred Road, Lomeshaye Industrial Estate, Nelson, BB9 5SR, United Kingdom
Tel.: (44) 1282611329
Web Site: https://www.businesswisesolutions.co.uk
Energy Consulting Services
N.A.I.C.S.: 541690

Direct Energy Purchasing Limited (1)
29 Progress Business Park Orders Lane Kirkham, Preston, PR4 2TZ, Lancashire, United Kingdom
Tel.: (44) 72674307
Web Site: http://www.directenergypurchasing.com
Sales Range: $25-49.9 Million
Emp.: 20
Energy Consulting Services
N.A.I.C.S.: 541690

Ignite Energy LTD. (1)
The Orangery, East Lockinge, Wantage, OX12 8QH, Oxfordshire, United Kingdom
Tel.: (44) 3330232222
Web Site: https://www.igniteenergy.co.uk
Energy Consulting Services
N.A.I.C.S.: 541690

Inprova Energy Limited (1)
2 Olympic Way Woolston Grange Avenue, Warrington, WA2 0YL, United Kingdom
Tel.: (44) 1925282360
Web Site: https://www.inprova.com
Business Management Consulting Services
N.A.I.C.S.: 541611

Inspired Energy Solutions Limited (1)
29 Progress Business Park Orders Lane, Kirkham, Preston, PR4 2TZ, Lancashire, United Kingdom
Tel.: (44) 1772689250
Web Site: https://inspiredenergy.co.uk
Energy Consulting Services
N.A.I.C.S.: 541690

SystemsLink 2000 Limited (1)
Bedford i-Lab Priory Business Park Stannard Way, Bedford, MK44 3RZ, United Kingdom
Tel.: (44) 1234988855
Web Site: https://systems-link.com
Energy Consulting Services
N.A.I.C.S.: 541690

INSPIREMD, INC.

Menorat Hamaor 4, Tel Aviv, 6744832, Israel
Tel.: (972) 36917691 DE
Web Site: https://www.inspiremd.com
Year Founded: 2008
NSPR—(NASDAQ)
Rev.: $5,171,000
Assets: $24,653,000
Liabilities: $7,260,000
Net Worth: $17,393,000
Earnings: ($18,491,000)
Emp.: 55
Fiscal Year-end: 12/31/22
Holding Company; Medical Device Mfr
N.A.I.C.S.: 551112
Craig Shore *(CFO, Treas & Sec)*

Subsidiaries:

InspireMD Ltd. (1)
4 Menorat Hamaor Street, Tel Aviv, 6744832, Israel
Tel.: (972) 3 691 7691
Web Site: http://www.inspiremd.com
Sales Range: $1-9.9 Million
Medical Device Mfr
N.A.I.C.S.: 339112

INSPIRIT ENERGY HOLDINGS PLC

200 Aldersgate Street, London, EC1A 4HD, United Kingdom
Tel.: (44) 2070489400 UK
Web Site: https://www.inspirit-energy.com
INSP—(AIM)
Assets: $4,466,899
Liabilities: $859,437
Net Worth: $3,607,462
Earnings: ($316,349)
Emp.: 4
Fiscal Year-end: 06/30/22
Holding Company
N.A.I.C.S.: 551112
John Gunn *(Founder, Founder, Chm, Chm & CEO)*

Subsidiaries:

Inspirit Energy Limited (1)
Unit 4 Flockton Park Holbrook Industrial Estate, Sheffield, S20 3FF, South Yorkshire, United Kingdom
Tel.: (44) 114 247 7190
Web Site: http://www.inspiritenergy.com
Power & Heat Generation Equipment Mfr
N.A.I.C.S.: 335999

INSPIRIT MANAGEMENT LTD.

105 Piccadilly London,, Greater London, W1J 7NJ, United Kingdom
Tel.: (44) 2071191610
Web Site: https://inspiritcap.com
Year Founded: 2019
Private Equity
N.A.I.C.S.: 523999

Subsidiaries:

CWind Limited (1)
Ocean House 1 Winsford Way, Chelmsford, CM2 5PD, United Kingdom

INTERNATIONAL PUBLIC

Tel.: (44) 1245702000
Web Site: https://www.cwind.global
Marine & Offshore Wind Services
N.A.I.C.S.: 237130
Joshua Brennan *(Dir-Ops)*

INSPLORION AB

Arvid Wallgrens backe 20, 413 46, Gothenburg, Sweden
Tel.: (46) 313802695
Web Site: https://www.insplorion.com
Year Founded: 2010
7YV—(DEU)
Laboratory Equipment Mfr
N.A.I.C.S.: 334516
Jan Wahlstrom *(Chm)*

INSPUR GROUP LTD.

1036 Langchao Road, Jinan, Shandong, China
Tel.: (86) 53185102127
Web Site: http://www.en.inspur.com
Holding Company
N.A.I.C.S.: 551112
Peter Sun *(Chm & CEO)*

Subsidiaries:

Inspur Digital Enterprise Technology Limited (1)
Room B&C 30/F Tower A Billion Centre 1 Wang K wong Road Kowloon Bay, Kowloon, China (Hong Kong)
Tel.: (852) 27070990
Web Site: http://www.inspur.com.hk
Rev.: $978,109,236
Assets: $676,451,272
Liabilities: $412,784,705
Net Worth: $263,666,567
Earnings: $17,523,184
Emp.: 7,713
Fiscal Year-end: 12/31/2022
IT Consulting & Outsourcing Services
N.A.I.C.S.: 541690
Hailong Dong *(Officer-Compliance)*

Subsidiary (Domestic):

Inspur (HK) Electronics Limited (2)
Room BNC 30Fl Tower A Billion Center, 1 Wang Kwong Rd, Kowloon, China (Hong Kong)
Tel.: (852) 24926516
Web Site: http://www.inspur.com.hk
Emp.: 11
Software Outsourcing & IT Services
N.A.I.C.S.: 541511
Christen Zou *(Pres)*

Subsidiary (Non-US):

Inspur Beijing Genersoft Technology Limited (2)
3rd Fl Luneng Tower No 1 Shangdi Sixth Rd, Haidian District, Beijing, 100085, China
Tel.: (86) 10 8270 1619
Software Outsourcing & IT Services
N.A.I.C.S.: 541511

Inspur Japan Co. Ltd (2)
8th Fl Misumo Suitengu, 2-1 Nihonbashi Nakasu Chuo-ku, Tokyo, 1030008, Japan
Tel.: (81) 3 3523 3981
Web Site: http://www.inspur.co.jp
Software Outsourcing & IT Services
N.A.I.C.S.: 541511

Subsidiary (US):

Inspur Worldwide Services Limited (2)
2002 156th Ave NE Ste 150, Bellevue, WA 98007
Tel.: (425) 336-4713
Web Site: http://www.inspurworld.com
Sales Range: $25-49.9 Million
Emp.: 20
Software Outsourcing & IT Services
N.A.I.C.S.: 541511
Joe Jin *(Gen Mgr)*

Intersource Technology Limited (2)
3200 Wilshire Blvd Ste 1306, Los Angeles, CA 90010-1319
Tel.: (213) 383-1600
Computer System Design Services
N.A.I.C.S.: 541512

Inspur Electronic Information Industry Co., Ltd. (1)
No 801 Caoshanling South Road High-tech Zone, Jinan, 250101, Shandong, China
Tel.: (86) 53181604000
Web Site: https://en.inspur.com
Rev.: $9,761,374,584
Assets: $5,758,285,572
Liabilities: $3,284,610,264
Net Worth: $2,473,675,308
Earnings: $292,081,140
Fiscal Year-end: 12/31/2022
Software Development Services
N.A.I.C.S.: 541511
Peng Zhen *(Chm)*

Inspur Software Co., Ltd. (1)
No 1036 Chaolang Road Hightech Zone, Jinan, 250101, Shandong, China
Tel.: (86) 53185105606
Web Site: http://www.inspur.com
Rev.: $291,223,998
Assets: $643,908,124
Liabilities: $330,804,597
Net Worth: $313,103,527
Earnings: $8,955,077
Fiscal Year-end: 12/31/2022
Software Publisher
N.A.I.C.S.: 513210
Zhao Shaoxiang *(Chm)*

INSPYRE SOLUTIONS INC.
611 Academy Road, Winnipeg, R3N 0E7, MB, Canada
Tel.: (204) 934-1900
Web Site: http://www.inspyresolutions.com
Year Founded: 1994
Sales Range: $25-49.9 Million
Emp.: 250
Contact Center & Back-Office Services for Organizations; Outsourcing
N.A.I.C.S.: 561421
Lynne White *(VP-Client Dev)*

INSTA FINANCE LTD.
Plot 118 Mahapura Main Road Taluka Sevasi, Baroda, 390 021, India
Tel.: (91) 9321891995
Financial Investment Management Services
N.A.I.C.S.: 523940
Satish Vadilal Raval *(Chm & Mng Dir)*

INSTABANK ASA
Drammensveien 175, 0277, Oslo, Norway
Tel.: (47) 21519300
Web Site: https://www.instabank.no
Year Founded: 2016
INSTA—(EUR)
Commercial Banking Services
N.A.I.C.S.: 522110
Robert Berg *(CEO)*

INSTAL KRAKOW S.A.
Ul Konstantego Brandla 1, 30-732, Krakow, Poland
Tel.: (48) 126532347
Web Site: https://www.instalkrakow.pl
INK—(WAR)
Rev.: $106,263,211
Assets: $137,477,134
Liabilities: $48,996,189
Net Worth: $88,480,945
Earnings: $9,099,593
Fiscal Year-end: 12/31/23
Construction Engineering Services
N.A.I.C.S.: 541330
Piotr Juszczyk *(Pres, CEO & Gen Dir)*

INSTALCO AB
Lilla Bantorget 11, 111 23, Stockholm, 111 23, Sweden
Tel.: (46) 707245149
Web Site: https://instalco.se
Year Founded: 2014
INSTAL—(OMX)
Rev.: $1,140,708,271
Assets: $896,625,362
Liabilities: $601,403,055
Net Worth: $295,222,307
Earnings: $51,607,707
Emp.: 5,600
Fiscal Year-end: 12/31/22
Electrical Maintenance Services
N.A.I.C.S.: 811210
Per Sjostrand *(CEO)*

Subsidiaries:

AB Boras Rorinstallationer
Krakeredsvagen 109, 504 46, Boras, Sweden
Tel.: (46) 33414161
Web Site: https://www.abri.nu
Emp.: 27
Plumbing Services
N.A.I.C.S.: 238220

AB Tingstad Rorinstallation (1)
Backa Bergogata 4, 422 46, Hisings Backa, Sweden
Tel.: (46) 31255059
Web Site: http://www.tingstadror.se
Emp.: 20
Plumbing Services
N.A.I.C.S.: 238220

APC Elinstallatoren AB (1)
Jagarvallsvagen 8A, 584 22, Linkoping, Sweden
Tel.: (46) 13362070
Web Site: https://www.apcel.se
Emp.: 30
Electrical Installation Services
N.A.I.C.S.: 238210

Aircano AB (1)
Tantogatan 49, 118 42, Stockholm, Sweden
Tel.: (46) 855632450
Web Site: https://www.aircano.se
Emp.: 30
Ventilation Services
N.A.I.C.S.: 238220

Aktiebolaget Rorlaggaren (1)
Kantyxegatan 25 C, 213 76, Malmo, Sweden
Tel.: (46) 40987860
Web Site: http://www.rorlaggaren.se
Emp.: 160
Electrical Installation Services
N.A.I.C.S.: 238210

Andersen og Aksnes Rorleggerbedrift AS (1)
Nye Vakasvei 8, 1395, Hvalstad, Norway
Tel.: (47) 66798171
Web Site: https://www.aa-ror.no
Emp.: 40
Plumbing Equipment Distr
N.A.I.C.S.: 423720

App Start-Up AB (1)
Hesselmans Torg 5, 131 54, Nacka, Sweden
Tel.: (46) 84522970
Web Site: https://start-up.se
Electrical Installation Services
N.A.I.C.S.: 238210

Aquadus VVS AB (1)
Fabriksgatan 11, 633 46, Eskilstuna, Sweden
Tel.: (46) 16170180
Web Site: https://www.aquadus.se
Emp.: 38
Heat Pump Installation Services
N.A.I.C.S.: 238220

Bakke El-Installasjon AS (1)
Hammerstadgate 19, 2815, Gjovik, Norway
Tel.: (47) 61138750
Web Site: https://bakkeelinst.in
Electrical Installation Services
N.A.I.C.S.: 238210

Bi-Vent AB (1)
Stenbrovagen 19, 253 68, Helsingborg, Sweden
Tel.: (46) 42298585
Web Site: https://www.bi-vent.se
Emp.: 65
Electrical Installation Services
N.A.I.C.S.: 238210

Bogesunds El & Tele AB (1)
Jonkopingsvagen 40, 523 36, Ulricehamn, Sweden
Tel.: (46) 32126270
Web Site: https://www.bogesundsel.se
Emp.: 41
Electrical Installation Services
N.A.I.C.S.: 238210

Christiania Rorleggerbedrift AS (1)
154 Raelingen, Raelingen, Norway
Tel.: (47) 22161616
Web Site: https://crb.no
Apprentice Training Services
N.A.I.C.S.: 611513

Dala Kylmecano AB (1)
Hugo Hedstroms vag 16, 781 72, Borlange, Sweden
Tel.: (46) 243792280
Web Site: https://www.dalakyl.se
Emp.: 15
Construction Contracting Services
N.A.I.C.S.: 236220

Dalab Sverige AB (1)
Kolargatan 1, 784 68, Borlange, Sweden
Tel.: (46) 241794114
Web Site: https://www.dalabgroup.se
Construction Services
N.A.I.C.S.: 236220

Dymont Installation Oy (1)
Katsastustie 8, 61800, Kauhajoki, Finland
Tel.: (358) 405960979
Web Site: https://www.dymont.fi
Utility Contractor Services
N.A.I.C.S.: 237130

El & Sakerhet Sormland AB (1)
Vastgotagatan 18, 641 36, Katrineholm, Sweden
Tel.: (46) 15079420
Web Site: https://www.elosakerhet.se
Emp.: 160
Electrical Installation Services
N.A.I.C.S.: 238210

El Kraft Teknik & Konsult i Sala AB (1)
Josefsdalsvagen 27, 733 37, Sala, Sweden
Tel.: (46) 22410373
Web Site: https://www.ektk.se
Electrical Installation Services
N.A.I.C.S.: 238210

El-Pagarna i Malmo AB (1)
Stekelgatan 5F, 212 23, Malmo, Sweden
Tel.: (46) 40293193
Web Site: http://www.elpagarna.se
Emp.: 45
Electrical Installation Services
N.A.I.C.S.: 238210

Elektrisk AS (1)
Myrens verksted 3 A Bygg D9, 0473, Oslo, Norway
Tel.: (47) 22871600
Web Site: https://www.elektrisk.no
Construction Services
N.A.I.C.S.: 236220

Elektro-Centralen Entreprenad Hisings Backa AB (1)
Exportgatan 38B, 422 46, Hisings Backa, Sweden
Tel.: (46) 317578200
Web Site: http://www.eceab.se
Emp.: 90
Facility Services
N.A.I.C.S.: 561210

Elexpressen i Lund AB (1)
Kalkstensvagen 35, 224 78, Lund, Sweden
Tel.: (46) 46188889
Web Site: https://www.elexpressen.se
Emp.: 22
Electrical Installation Services
N.A.I.C.S.: 238210

Elinstallationer i Karlshamn AB (1)
Solvesborgsvagen 17-19, 374 41, Karlshamn, Sweden
Tel.: (46) 45419505
Web Site: https://elkarlshamn.se
Electrical Installation Services
N.A.I.C.S.: 238210

Elkontakt i Boras AB (1)
Katrinedalsgatan 43, 504 51, Boras, Sweden
Tel.: (46) 33293830
Web Site: http://www.elkontaktab.se
Electrical Supply Distr
N.A.I.C.S.: 444180

Elovent AB (1)
Franskavagen 11, 393 56, Kalmar, Sweden
Tel.: (46) 480797000
Web Site: http://www.elovent.se
Electrical Installation Services
N.A.I.C.S.: 238210

Froland & Noss Elektro AS (1)
Fabrikkgaten 12, 5059, Bergen, Norway
Tel.: (47) 55206420
Web Site: http://www.fnelektro.no
Construction Services
N.A.I.C.S.: 236220

Grevstad & Tvedt AS (1)
Kanalveien 5, 5068, Bergen, Norway
Tel.: (47) 55202000
Web Site: https://www.grevstadtvedt.no
Emp.: 70
Plumbing Construction Services
N.A.I.C.S.: 238220

Grums Ror AB (1)
Sveagatan 148, 664 34, Grums, Sweden
Tel.: (46) 55512405
Web Site: https://grumsror.se
Plumbing & HVAC Construction Services
N.A.I.C.S.: 238220

Henningsons Elektriska AB (1)
Matsarvsvagen 1, 791 27, Falun, Sweden
Tel.: (46) 23792090
Web Site: http://www.henningsonsel.se
Emp.: 125
Electrical Installation Services
N.A.I.C.S.: 238210

Highcon AB (1)
Verkstadsvagen 21, 871 54, Harnosand, Sweden
Tel.: (46) 706668408
Web Site: https://highcon.se
Scaffolding Services
N.A.I.C.S.: 238990

Imes AS (1)
Tromsoysundveien 20B, 9020, Tromsdalen, Norway
Tel.: (47) 77664600
Web Site: https://imes.no
Emp.: 22
Electrical Construction Services
N.A.I.C.S.: 238210

Inlands Luft AB (1)
Bjornavagen 41F, 891 41, Ornskoldsvik, Sweden
Tel.: (46) 66210210
Web Site: https://inlandsluft.se
Electronic Services
N.A.I.C.S.: 238210

Insta El Syd AB (1)
Kaglingevagen 37, 213 76, Malmo, Sweden
Tel.: (46) 406318200
Web Site: http://www.instael.se
Electrical Installation Services
N.A.I.C.S.: 238210

Installationsservice Nicklas Eriksson AB (1)
Kardangatan 3-5, 633 46, Eskilstuna, Sweden
Tel.: (46) 16131365
Web Site: https://installationsservice.com
Electrical Installation Services
N.A.I.C.S.: 238210

Instamate AB (1)
Morabergsvagen 33B, 152 42, Sodertalje, Sweden
Tel.: (46) 859859600
Web Site: https://www.instamate.se
Emp.: 60
Electrical Installation Services
N.A.I.C.S.: 238210

Inva Engineering AS (1)
Nye Vakas vei 14, 1395, Hvalstad, Norway
Tel.: (47) 23174310
Web Site: https://inva.no
Electrical Installation Services
N.A.I.C.S.: 238210

JB Elektro AS (1)
Meierivegen 1, 9152, Sorkjosen, Norway
Tel.: (47) 93834000

INSTALCO AB

INTERNATIONAL PUBLIC

Instalco AB—(Continued)

Web Site: https://jbelektro.no
Emp.: 20
Electrical Broad Mfr & Distr
N.A.I.C.S.: 335999

JN Elinstallatorer AB (1)
Gransbovagen 4, 152 42, Sodertalje, Sweden
Tel.: (46) 855442900
Web Site: https://www.jnel.se
Electrical Installation Services
N.A.I.C.S.: 238210

KWA-Ror i Ystad AB (1)
Norra Zinkgatan 2, 271 39, Ystad, Sweden
Tel.: (46) 411245555
Web Site: https://www.kwaror.se
Heat Pump Distr
N.A.I.C.S.: 423730

Kempes El AB (1)
Foretagsvagen 2, 872 34, Kramfors, Sweden
Tel.: (46) 612599200
Web Site: https://kempesel.se
Electrical Installation Services
N.A.I.C.S.: 238210

Keyvent AB (1)
Bagargatan 4, Alem, 384 92, Kalmar, Sweden
Tel.: (46) 771606160
Web Site: https://keyventost.se
Ventilation Services
N.A.I.C.S.: 238220

Klimateknikk Oslo AS (1)
Sandstuveien 60A, 1184, Oslo, Norway
Tel.: (47) 41578277
Web Site: https://klimateknikk.no
Ventilation Services
N.A.I.C.S.: 238220

Klimatror i Stockholm AB (1)
Elektravagen 64, 126 30, Hagersten, Sweden
Tel.: (46) 86470100
Web Site: https://www.klimatror.se
Plumbing Equipment Distr
N.A.I.C.S.: 423720

Kompressorteknik AB (1)
Butangsgatan 10F, 602 23, Norrkoping, Sweden
Tel.: (46) 11100840
Web Site: https://www.kompressorteknik.se
Refrigeration Compressor Mfr
N.A.I.C.S.: 333415

Kuopion LVI-Talo Oy (1)
Tehdaskatu 24 B, 70620, Kuopio, Finland
Tel.: (358) 407314684
Web Site: https://www.lvi-talo.com
Emp.: 30
HVAC Construction Services
N.A.I.C.S.: 238220

Kyron Sahko Oy (1)
Sahantie 2, 21800, Kyroskoski, Finland
Tel.: (358) 2486450
Web Site: https://www.kyronsahko.fi
Emp.: 80
Electrical Construction Services
N.A.I.C.S.: 238210

LVI-Talo Kannosto Oy (1)
Teollisuustie 18, 39700, Parkano, Finland
Tel.: (358) 34482400
Web Site: https://www.lvi-kannosto.fi
Facility Services
N.A.I.C.S.: 561210

LVI-Urakointi Paavola Oy (1)
Valimotie 1B 6krs, 00380, Helsinki, Finland
Tel.: (358) 207856780
Web Site: https://www.lvi-paavola.com
Emp.: 43
Construction Contracting Services
N.A.I.C.S.: 236220

Larm & Teleteknik i Motala AB (1)
Dynamovagen 11, 591 61, Motala, Sweden
Tel.: (46) 141252530
Web Site: https://www.ltim.se
Fire Alarm Security Services
N.A.I.C.S.: 561621

Liab Instrumenteringar AB (1)
Dagvindsgatan 8, 652 21, Karlstad, Sweden
Tel.: (46) 54853815
Web Site: https://liab.com
Electronic Services
N.A.I.C.S.: 238210

Lidingo Elektriska AB (1)
Stockby Hantverksby 20, 181 75, Lidingo, Sweden
Tel.: (46) 87650218
Web Site: https://lidingoelektriska.se
Emp.: 17
Electrical Installation Services
N.A.I.C.S.: 238210

Lincom AB (1)
Plintgatan 3, 602 23, Norrkoping, Sweden
Tel.: (46) 11362400
Web Site: https://lincom.se
Telecommunication & Information Services
N.A.I.C.S.: 517810

MRM Mining AB / EPS Sweden AB (1)
Fordonsvagen 14, 982 38, Gallivare, Sweden
Tel.: (46) 97022555
Web Site: https://mrmmining.se
Electric Machinery Maintenance Services
N.A.I.C.S.: 926130

MSI- El Motala Stroms Installations AB (1)
Ringtrastvagen 9, 591 37, Motala, Sweden
Tel.: (46) 141252500
Web Site: https://www.msiel.se
Emp.: 60
Building Renovation Services
N.A.I.C.S.: 236118

MSI-Jarn AB (1)
Kungs Starbyvagen 3, 592 91, Vadstena, Sweden
Tel.: (46) 143170700
Web Site: https://www.msijarn.se
Hardware Products Distr
N.A.I.C.S.: 444140

MSI-Ror AB (1)
Ringtrastvagen 9, 591 37, Motala, Sweden
Tel.: (46) 141252525
Web Site: https://www.msiror.se
Plumbing Services
N.A.I.C.S.: 238220

Medby AS (1)
Ostringsvegen 1, Ostre Gausdal, 2651, Oppland, Norway
Tel.: (47) 95232000
Web Site: https://www.medby-as.no
Emp.: 30
Plumbing Services
N.A.I.C.S.: 238220

Melins Platslageri AB (1)
Brovagen 10, 896 31, Husum, Sweden
Tel.: (46) 66310550
Web Site: https://melinsplat.se
Emp.: 11
Ventilation Machine Mfr
N.A.I.C.S.: 335210

Moi Ror AS (1)
Aegirsvei 10, 4632, Kristiansand, Norway
Tel.: (47) 97101330
Web Site: https://www.moi-ror.no
Plumbing Services
N.A.I.C.S.: 238220

Nassjo Teknikprojektering AB (1)
Storgatan 44A, 57132, Nassjo, Sweden
Tel.: (46) 380649400
Web Site: https://teknikproj.se
Emp.: 12
Electrical Installation Services
N.A.I.C.S.: 238210

Nihlen Elmontage AB (1)
Datavagen 59, 436 32, Askim, Sweden
Tel.: (46) 31495094
Web Site: https://nihlenelmontage.se
Emp.: 18
Charging Box Installation Services
N.A.I.C.S.: 238210

Nordpipe Composite Engineering Oy (1)
Borgmastargrundsvagen 19, 68600, Jakobstad, Finland
Tel.: (358) 67818200
Web Site: https://nce.fi
Plastics Product Mfr
N.A.I.C.S.: 326199

ORAB Entreprenad AB (1)
Nobelvagen 2, Box 975, 802 67, Gavle, Sweden
Tel.: (46) 26140920
Web Site: https://www.orab-ab.se
Plumbing Equipment Distr
N.A.I.C.S.: 423720

OVAB Optimal Ventilation AB (1)
Chaufforvagen 11, 831 48, Ostersund, Sweden
Tel.: (46) 63122030
Web Site: https://www.ovab.se
Ventilation Services
N.A.I.C.S.: 238220

Ohmegi Elektro AB (1)
Sollentunavagen 52, 191 40, Sollentuna, Sweden
Tel.: (46) 8969600
Web Site: http://www.ohmegi.se
Emp.: 100
Electrical Installation Services
N.A.I.C.S.: 238210

PeMi Ventilation & Montage AB (1)
Sodra Bergvagen 49, 794 32, Orsa, Sweden
Tel.: (46) 25040020
Web Site: https://pemi.se
Ventilation Services
N.A.I.C.S.: 238220

PoB:s Elektriska AB (1)
Libro Ringvag 13, 752 28, Uppsala, Sweden
Tel.: (46) 184702000
Web Site: https://www.pobel.se
Electrical Installation Services
N.A.I.C.S.: 238210

Rikelektro AB (1)
Spinnvagen 3H, 903 61, Umea, Sweden
Tel.: (46) 730426885
Web Site: https://www.rikelektro.com
Emp.: 37
Construction Contracting Services
N.A.I.C.S.: 236220

Rodens Varme & Sanitet AB (1)
Storstensvagen 12, 761 53, Norrtalje, Sweden
Tel.: (46) 17616900
Web Site: http://www.rodensvarme.se
Electrical Installation Services
N.A.I.C.S.: 238210

Romerike Elektro AS (1)
Myrvangvegen 8, 2040, Klofta, Norway
Tel.: (47) 63947520
Web Site: https://www.romerike-elektro.no
Emp.: 46
Electrical Installation Services
N.A.I.C.S.: 238210

Rorgruppen AB (1)
Sollentunavagen 78, 191 40, Sollentuna, Sweden
Tel.: (46) 84445530
Web Site: https://www.rorgruppen.se
Plumbing Equipment Distr
N.A.I.C.S.: 423720

Rorman i Svedala AB (1)
Foretagsgatan 9A, 233 51, Svedala, Sweden
Tel.: (46) 40400140
Web Site: http://www.rormansvedala.se
Building Renovation Services
N.A.I.C.S.: 236118

Rorteft AS (1)
Floraveien 33, 2007, Kjeller, Norway
Tel.: (47) 63800950
Web Site: https://www.rorteft.no
Emp.: 35
Plumbing Equipment Distr
N.A.I.C.S.: 423720

Rortema i Nykoping AB (1)
Materialvagen 7, 611 45, Nykoping, Sweden
Tel.: (46) 155268333
Web Site: https://www.rortema.com
Plumbing Services
N.A.I.C.S.: 238220

Sahko-Buumi Oy (1)
Orapihlajatie 35, 00320, Helsinki, Finland
Tel.: (358) 400902118
Web Site: https://www.sahko-buumi.fi
Emp.: 30

Electrical Installation Services
N.A.I.C.S.: 238210

Sprinklerbolaget Stockholm AB (1)
Drottninggatan 14a, 733 30, Sala, Sweden
Tel.: (46) 224688066
Web Site: http://www.sprinkerbolaget.se
Construction Services
N.A.I.C.S.: 236220

Sprinklerbolaget Syd i Helsingborg AB (1)
Landskronavagen 7a, 252 32, Helsingborg, Sweden
Tel.: (46) 424000980
Electrical Installation Services
N.A.I.C.S.: 238210

Stockholm Luftkompetens AB (1)
Gavenius vag 2A, 141 60, Huddinge, Sweden
Tel.: (46) 848001720
Web Site: https://stockholmluftkompetens.se
Emp.: 20
Ventilation System Maintenance Services
N.A.I.C.S.: 561790

Sydsvenska Elanlaggningar AB (1)
Elvagen 1, 384 30, Blomstermala, Sweden
Tel.: (46) 49927300
Web Site: https://sse.se
Emp.: 80
Electrical Installation Services
N.A.I.C.S.: 238210

Teknisk Ventilasjon AS (1)
Industriveien 39A, Heimdal, 7080, Trondheim, Norway
Tel.: (47) 72594000
Web Site: https://www.tv-as.no
Ventilation Services
N.A.I.C.S.: 238220

Telefuusio Oy (1)
Hankasuontie 13, 00390, Helsinki, Finland
Tel.: (358) 406602112
Web Site: https://www.telefuusio.fi
Electrical Installation Services
N.A.I.C.S.: 238210
Ruslan Vassiljev (CEO)

Tofta Plat & Ventilation AB (1)
Stengatan 5, 531 55, Lidkoping, Sweden
Tel.: (46) 762098224
Web Site: http://www.toftaplatoventilation.se
Emp.: 15
Sheet Metal Installation Services
N.A.I.C.S.: 238160

Total VVS AS (1)
Tvetenveien 4, 0661, Oslo, Norway
Tel.: (47) 22641900
Web Site: https://www.total-vvs.no
Emp.: 10
Plumbing Contract Services
N.A.I.C.S.: 238220

Trel AB (1)
Tunbytorpsgatan 31, 721 37, Vasteras, Sweden
Tel.: (46) 762394559
Web Site: http://www.3elab.se
Emp.: 26
Construction Services
N.A.I.C.S.: 236220

Tunabygdens VVS Installator AB (1)
Kolargatan 1, 784 68, Borlange, Sweden
Tel.: (46) 243211925
Web Site: http://www.vvsinstallator.com
Electrical Installation Services
N.A.I.C.S.: 238210

Twinputki Oy (1)
Myllynummentie 2, 04250, Kerava, Finland
Tel.: (358) 92797810
Web Site: https://www.twinputki.fi
Emp.: 12
Automatic Sprinkler Services
N.A.I.C.S.: 238220

Uudenmaan LVI-Talo Oy (1)
Kellokukantie 2, 01300, Vantaa, Finland
Tel.: (358) 97530102
Web Site: https://www.lvitalo.fi
Emp.: 50
Construction Services
N.A.I.C.S.: 236220

VVS Metoder i Stockholm AB (1)

AND PRIVATE COMPANIES / INSTITUT MERIEUX

Vastberga Alle 1 A, 126 30, Hagersten, Sweden
Tel.: (46) 855621100
Web Site: https://www.vvsmetoder.se
Emp.: 47
Plumbing Equipment Distr
N.A.I.C.S.: 423720

VVS-Kraft Teknikservice i Stockholm AB (1)
Saldovagen 3, 175 62, Jarfalla, Sweden
Tel.: (46) 856471200
Web Site: http://www.vvskraft.se
Construction Contracting Services
N.A.I.C.S.: 236220

VallaCom AB (1)
Idogatan 5, 582 78, Linkoping, Sweden
Tel.: (46) 13139797
Web Site: https://www.vallacom.se
Emp.: 70
Electronic Equipment Distr
N.A.I.C.S.: 423690

Ventec AS (1)
Bronningsmyr 1, 4790, Lillesand, Norway
Tel.: (47) 37091255
Web Site: https://www.ventec.no
Ventilation Services
N.A.I.C.S.: 238220

Ventilationsforbattringar i Malmo AB (1)
Krusegatan 28, 212 25, Malmo, Sweden
Tel.: (46) 40388600
Web Site: https://www.vfb.to
Emp.: 40
Facility Services
N.A.I.C.S.: 561210

Vito Teknisk Entreprenor AS (1)
Professor Smiths alle 52 B, 3048, Drammen, Norway
Tel.: (47) 32896570
Web Site: https://www.vito-as.no
Construction Services
N.A.I.C.S.: 236220

Voltmen Oy (1)
Hankasuontie 13, 00390, Helsinki, Finland
Tel.: (358) 108320300
Web Site: https://www.voltmen.fi
Electrical Installation Services
N.A.I.C.S.: 238210
Henri Remonen *(Project Mgr)*

INSTALLATIONS ELECTRIQUES PREFABRICATION
Z I Magre 41 Rue Santos Dumont, 87000, Limoges, Haute Vienne, France
Tel.: (33) 555304337
Rev.: $20,300,000
Emp.: 58
Electrical Work
N.A.I.C.S.: 238210
Mustapha Arfaoui *(Pres)*

INSTALLUX SA
Chemin du Bois Rond, 69720, Saint-Bonnet-de-Mure, France
Tel.: (33) 472483131 FR
Web Site: https://www.installux-aluminium.com
Year Founded: 1963
ALLUX—(EUR)
Sales Range: Less than $1 Million
Building Material Mfr & Distr
N.A.I.C.S.: 238290
Christian Canty *(CEO)*

INSTANT GROUP LIMITED
The Blue Fin Building 110 Southwark Street, SE1 0TA, London, United Kingdom
Tel.: (44) 20 8054 3133
Web Site: https://www.theinstantgroup.com
Year Founded: 1999
Emp.: 100
Digital Marketplace, Virtual Offices, Flexible Office Space & Co-working Memberships
N.A.I.C.S.: 513199

Tim Rodber *(CEO)*

Subsidiaries:

Instant Offices Limited (1)
The Blue Fin Building 110 Southwark Street, London, SE1 0TA, United Kingdom
Tel.: (44) 20 8054 3133
Web Site: https://www.instantoffices.com
Emp.: 150
Digital Marketplace, Listing Meeting Rooms, Virtual Offices, Flexible Office Space & Co-working Memberships
N.A.I.C.S.: 513199
Tim Rodber *(CEO)*

Subsidiary (US):

Davinci Virtual, L.L.C. (2)
2150 S 1300 E Ste 200, Salt Lake City, UT 84106
Tel.: (801) 990-9200
Web Site: http://www.davincivirtual.com
Sales Range: $1-9.9 Million
Emp.: 100
Virtual Office Solutions
N.A.I.C.S.: 561499
Martin Senn *(Chm)*

INSTAR GROUP INC.
Toronto Dominion Bank Tower 66 Wellington Street West Suite 3410, Toronto, M5K 1K7, ON, Canada
Tel.: (416) 815-6224
Web Site: http://www.instarinfrastructure.com
Year Founded: 2013
Alternative Investment Management Services
N.A.I.C.S.: 523940
Gregory J. Smith *(Founder, Pres & CEO)*

Subsidiaries:

InstarAGF Asset Management Inc. (1)
Toronto-Dominion Bank Tower 66 Wellington Street West Suite 3410, PO Box 342, Toronto, M5K 1K7, ON, Canada
Tel.: (416) 815-6224
Web Site: https://instarinvest.com
Asset Management Firm
N.A.I.C.S.: 523940
Gregory J. Smith *(Pres & CEO)*

Holding (US):

AMPORTS, Inc. (2)
10060 Skinner Lake Dr Ste 205, Jacksonville, FL 32246
Tel.: (904) 652-2962
Web Site: http://www.amports.com
Marine Port Terminals Operator & Cargo Handling Services
N.A.I.C.S.: 488320
Steve Taylor *(CEO)*

Subsidiary (Domestic):

AMPORTS Atlantic Terminal (3)
2901 Childs St, Baltimore, MD 21226
Tel.: (410) 350-0400
Web Site: http://www.amports.com
Marine Cargo Handling
N.A.I.C.S.: 488320
George Molyneaux *(Gen Mgr)*

Subsidiary (Non-US):

AMPORTS Mexico Altamira Terminal (3)
Validad Mar Caribe 210, Col Puerto Industrial, Altamira, 89603, Mexico
Tel.: (52) 833 260 1147
Web Site: http://www.amports.com
Marine Freight Holding & Receiving Facility
N.A.I.C.S.: 488320

Subsidiary (Domestic):

Benicia Port Terminal Company (3)
1997 Elm Rd, Benicia, CA 94510-2307
Tel.: (707) 745-2394
Web Site: http://www.amports.com
Marine Cargo Handling
N.A.I.C.S.: 488320
Jim Triplett *(Sr VP-West Coast)*

Holding (Domestic):

Windmill Farms (2)
9760 Heron Rd, Ashburn, L0B 1A0, ON, Canada
Tel.: (905) 985-5569
Web Site: http://www.windmillfarms.ca
Mushroom Farming
N.A.I.C.S.: 111411

Subsidiary (US):

Greenwood Mushrooms (3)
749 Norway Rd, Chadds Ford, PA 19317-8222
Tel.: (610) 388-9500
Web Site: http://www.greenwoodmushrooms.com
Farming
N.A.I.C.S.: 111310
Louis Marson Jr. *(Owner)*

Subsidiary (Domestic):

Ostrom Mushroom Farms LLC (4)
8323 Steilacoom Rd SE, Lacey, WA 98513-2057
Tel.: (360) 491-1410
Web Site: http://www.ostrommushrooms.com
Fruit & Vegetable Canning
N.A.I.C.S.: 311421
Dan Cunningham *(Engr-Maintenance)*

INSTARMAC GROUP PLC
Danny Morson Way Birch Coppice Business Park, Dordon, Tamworth, B78 1SE, Staffordshire, United Kingdom
Tel.: (44) 1827254400 UK
Web Site: http://www.instarmac.co.uk
Year Founded: 1977
Construction Materials Mfr
N.A.I.C.S.: 423320
Karen Williams *(Head-HR)*

INSTITUT FUR RUNDFUNKTECHNIK GMBH
Floriansmuehlstrasse 60, D-80939, Munich, Germany
Tel.: (49) 89 32399 0 De
Web Site: http://www.irt.de
Broadcast & Digital Media Services
N.A.I.C.S.: 334290
Klaus Illgner-Fehns *(Mng Dir)*

Subsidiaries:

Hybrid Broadcast Broadband TV (1)
L'Ancienne-Route 17A, Le Grand-Saconnex, CH-1218, Geneva, Switzerland
Tel.: (41) 22 717 2735
Web Site: http://www.hbbtv.org
Broadcast Media Services
N.A.I.C.S.: 516120

INSTITUT IGH D.D.
Janka Rakuse 1, 10000, Zagreb, Croatia
Tel.: (385) 16125125
Web Site: https://www.igh.hr
IGH—(ZAG)
Rev.: $32,458,329
Assets: $22,835,854
Liabilities: $18,555,028
Net Worth: $4,280,826
Earnings: $5,502,815
Emp.: 372
Fiscal Year-end: 12/31/23
Engineering Services
N.A.I.C.S.: 541330
Hrvoje Sironic *(Head-Reg Centre Rijeka)*

Subsidiaries:

Adepto d.o.o. (1)
Janka Rakuse 1, Zagreb, 10000, Croatia
Tel.: (385) 16125125
Engineering Consulting Services
N.A.I.C.S.: 541330
Yuvaraj Raeit *(Gen Mgr)*

Arhitektura Tholos projektiranje d.o.o. (1)
Lopaseiceva 6, 10000, Zagreb, Croatia
Tel.: (385) 14636949
Building Architectural Designing Services
N.A.I.C.S.: 541310

Dubrovacka Investicijska Grupa d.o.o. (1)
Obala Stjepana Radica 2, Dubrovnik, 20000, Dubrovnik-Neretva, Croatia
Tel.: (385) 20358666
Home Management Services
N.A.I.C.S.: 721110

ETZ d.d. (1)
Trg Ante Starcevica 7 II, 31000, Osijek, Croatia
Tel.: (385) 31284511
Sales Range: $25-49.9 Million
Emp.: 20
Engineering Consulting Services
N.A.I.C.S.: 541330

Geotehnika-inzenjering d.o.o. (1)
Gradiscanska 26, 10000, Zagreb, Croatia
Tel.: (385) 1 3909 400
Web Site: http://www.geotehnika-ing.hr
Sales Range: $400-449.9 Million
Construction & Engineering Services
N.A.I.C.S.: 541330

IGH Mostar d.o.o. (1)
Bisce polje bb, 88000, Mostar, Bosnia & Herzegovina
Tel.: (387) 36449880
Web Site: https://www.igh.ba
Sales Range: $25-49.9 Million
Emp.: 37
Construction Engineering Services
N.A.I.C.S.: 541330

Projektni biro Palmoticeva 45 d.o.o. (1)
Janka Rakuse 1, 10000, Zagreb, Croatia
Tel.: (385) 14923125
Web Site: http://www.p45.hr
Sales Range: $25-49.9 Million
Emp.: 24
Engineering Design Services
N.A.I.C.S.: 541330

INSTITUT LORRAIN DE PARTICIPATION SA
3- rue Marconi Batiment Ecotech Metz Technopole, 57070, Metz, Cedex, France
Tel.: (33) 03 87 75 93 50
Web Site: http://www.ilp-sadepar.com
Year Founded: 2010
Investment Management & Advisory Services
N.A.I.C.S.: 523999

INSTITUT MERIEUX
17 rue Bourgelat, 69002, Lyon, France
Tel.: (33) 478877070 FR
Web Site: https://www.institut-merieux.com
Holding Company
N.A.I.C.S.: 551112
Alain Merieux *(Chm)*

Subsidiaries:

Transgene S.A. (1)
400 Boulevard Gonthier d Andernach Parc d Innovation, 67405, Illkirch-Graffenstaden, Cedex, France (53%)
Tel.: (33) 388279100
Web Site: https://www.transgene.fr
Rev.: $8,720,609
Assets: $49,913,898
Liabilities: $32,680,208
Net Worth: $17,233,690
Earnings: $(24,647,312)
Emp.: 158
Fiscal Year-end: 12/31/2023
Biotechnological Services
N.A.I.C.S.: 541714
Christophe Ancel *(VP-Pharmaceutical Ops)*

bioMerieux S.A. (1)
376 Elm Road, 69280, Marcy-l'Etoile, France (58.9%)

INSTITUT MERIEUX

INTERNATIONAL PUBLIC

Institut Merieux—(Continued)
Tel.: (33) 478872000
Web Site: https://www.biomerieux.com
Rev.: $3,965,788,906
Assets: $5,675,804,015
Liabilities: $1,626,375,998
Net Worth: $4,049,428,016
Earnings: $385,927,045
Emp.: 14,600
Fiscal Year-end: 12/31/2023
Biotechnology Research & Development Services
N.A.I.C.S.: 541714
Alexandre Merieux *(Chm & CEO)*

Subsidiary (Non-US):

Applied Maths NV (2)
Keistraat 120, 9830, Sint-Martens-Latem, Belgium
Tel.: (32) 9 2222 100
Web Site: http://www.applied-maths.com
Software Development Services
N.A.I.C.S.: 541511
Koen Janssens *(CEO)*

Subsidiary (Domestic):

Argene SA (2)
Parc Technologique Delta Sud, F 09340, Verniolle, France
Tel.: (33) 561696100
Web Site: http://www.argene.com
Sales Range: $10-24.9 Million
Emp.: 70
Monoclonal Antibodies & Molecular Biological Products Mfr, Researcher & Developer
N.A.I.C.S.: 325414

Subsidiary (US):

Argene Inc. (3)
45 Ramsey Rd Unit 25, Shirley, NY 11967-4712 (100%)
Tel.: (516) 795-5583
Web Site: http://www.argene.com
Sales Range: Less than $1 Million
Emp.: 1
Monoclonal Antibodies & Molecular Biological Products Mfr
N.A.I.C.S.: 424210

Subsidiary (Non-US):

Argene Srl (3)
Via Fratelli Cervi, Res del Poggio, Segrate, Italy
Tel.: (39) 0221711312
Web Site: http://www.argene.com
Biological Product Mfr
N.A.I.C.S.: 325414

Subsidiary (US):

Invisible Sentinel Inc. (2)
3711 Market St Ste 910, Philadelphia, PA 19104-5532
Tel.: (215) 966-6118
Web Site: http://www.invisiblesentinel.com
Electronics Stores
N.A.I.C.S.: 449210
Benjamin J. Pascal *(CEO)*

bioMerieux, Inc. (2)
100 Rodolphe St, Durham, NC 27712
Tel.: (919) 620-2000
Web Site: http://www.biomerieux-usa.com
Sales Range: $100-124.9 Million
Emp.: 500
Designer, Developer, Manufacturer & Marketer of Reagents & Automated Instruments for Medical & Cosmedic Analysis
N.A.I.C.S.: 334510
Stefan Willemsen *(Pres & CEO)*

Subsidiary (Domestic):

Advance Bioscience Laboratories, Inc. (3)
9800 Medical Center Dr Ste D, Rockville, MD 20850-3770
Tel.: (301) 881-5600
Web Site: http://www.ablinc.com
Sales Range: $25-49.9 Million
Emp.: 100
Biomedical Research Services
N.A.I.C.S.: 541714
Thomas VanCott *(Pres & CEO)*

Astute Medical Inc. (3)
3550 General Atomics Ct, San Diego, CA 92121-1122
Tel.: (858) 500-7000
Web Site: http://www.astutemedical.com
Offices of Physical, Occupational & Speech Therapists & Audiologists
N.A.I.C.S.: 621340
Paul H. McPherson *(Co-Founder, CEO & Chief Scientific Officer)*

Silliker Inc. (3)
111 E Wacker Dr Ste 2300, Chicago, IL 60601
Tel.: (708) 957-7878
Web Site: http://www.silliker.com
Sales Range: $10-24.9 Million
Emp.: 50
Food Testing & Consulting Services
N.A.I.C.S.: 541380

INSTITUT NATIONAL DE RECHERCHE POUR L'AGRICULTURE L'ALIMENTATION ET L'ENVIRONNEMENT

147 Rue de l'Universite, 75338, Paris, Cedex 07, France
Tel.: (33) 142759000
Web Site: https://www.inrae.fr
Agriculture, Food and Environment Research Institute
N.A.I.C.S.: 541715

INSTITUT REGIONAL DE DEVELOPPEMENT INDUSTRIEL DE MIDI-PYRENEES

18 place Dupuy, CS 18008, 31080, Toulouse, Cedex 6, France
Tel.: (33) 581 317 320
Web Site: http://www.irdi.fr
Year Founded: 1981
Privater Equity Firm
N.A.I.C.S.: 523999
Thierry Letailleur *(Chm)*

INSTITUT ZA ISPITIVANJE MATERIJALA A.D.

Bulevar vojvode Misica 43 St, 11040, Belgrade, Serbia
Tel.: (381) 112650322
Web Site: https://www.institutims.rs
Year Founded: 1929
INMT—(BEL)
Rev.: $13,134,625
Assets: $19,123,623
Liabilities: $4,188,335
Net Worth: $14,935,288
Earnings: $205,918
Fiscal Year-end: 12/31/23
Construction Research & Development Services
N.A.I.C.S.: 541715
Vencislav Grabulov *(Gen Mgr)*

INSTITUT ZA TRZISNA ISTRAZIVANJA A.D.

Decanska 8, 11000, Belgrade, Serbia
Tel.: (381) 113235197
Web Site: http://www.izit.rs
Year Founded: 1962
IZIT—(BEL)
Rev.: $28,648
Assets: $586,278
Liabilities: $61,589
Net Worth: $524,689
Earnings: ($86,933)
Emp.: 4
Fiscal Year-end: 12/31/22
Market Research Services
N.A.I.C.S.: 541910
Miloje Kanjevac *(Gen Mgr)*

INSTITUTE OF NUCLEAR ENERGY RESEARCH

1000 Wenhua Rd, Jiaan Village Longtan, Taoyuan, 32546, Taiwan
Tel.: (886) 34711400
Year Founded: 1968
Scientific Research & Development Services
N.A.I.C.S.: 541715

INSTITUTION FOR A GLOBAL SOCIETY CORPORATION

4F 1-11-2 EbisuMinami, Shibuya-ku, Tokyo, 150-0022, Japan
Web Site: https://www.i-globalsociety.com
Year Founded: 2010
4265—(TKS)
Rev.: $6,054,760
Assets: $7,218,120
Liabilities: $515,580
Net Worth: $6,702,540
Earnings: ($138,810)
Fiscal Year-end: 03/31/24
Human Resource Consulting Services
N.A.I.C.S.: 541612
Masahiro Fukuhara *(Founder, Chm & CEO)*

INSTITUTO DE CREDITO OFICIAL

Paseo del Prado 4, 28014, Madrid, Spain
Tel.: (34) 915921600
Web Site: http://www.ico.es
Year Founded: 1971
Rev.: $388,705,646
Assets: $35,658,194,648
Liabilities: $29,640,536,230
Net Worth: $6,017,658,419
Earnings: $122,488,047
Emp.: 338
Fiscal Year-end: 12/31/19
Financial Services
N.A.I.C.S.: 523999
Rosario Casero *(Chief Investment Officer)*

INSTITUTO DE DIAGNOSTICO S.A.

Avenida Santa Maria 1810, PO Box 16455, Providencia, Santiago, Chile
Tel.: (56) 3625555
Web Site: http://www.indisa.cl
INDISA—(SGO)
Sales Range: Less than $1 Million
Health Care Srvices
N.A.I.C.S.: 621111
Manuel Serra Cambiaso *(CEO & Gen Mgr)*

INSTITUTO MOVILIZADOR DE FONDOS COOPERATIVOS

Avenida Corrientes 1543, Buenos Aires, C1042AAB, Argentina
Tel.: (54) 1150778080
Web Site: http://www.imfc.com.ar
Year Founded: 1958
Sales Range: $50-74.9 Million
Emp.: 100
Credit Services
N.A.I.C.S.: 522299
Edgardo Form *(Gen Mgr)*

INSTONE REAL ESTATE GROUP SE

Grugaplatz 2-4, 45131, Essen, Germany
Tel.: (49) 201453550
Web Site: https://www.instone.de
Year Founded: 2014
INS—(DEU)
Rev.: $733,164,809
Assets: $2,030,657,910
Liabilities: $1,394,852,633
Net Worth: $635,805,277
Earnings: $20,940,501
Emp.: 468
Fiscal Year-end: 12/31/23
Real Estate Manangement Services
N.A.I.C.S.: 531210

Kruno Crepulja *(Chm-Mgmt Bd & CEO)*

Subsidiaries:

Nyoo Real Estate GmbH (1)
Adolf-Grimme-Allee 3, 50829, Cologne, Germany
Tel.: (49) 2219998530
Web Site: https://www.nyoo-by-instone.de
Real Estate Developing Services
N.A.I.C.S.: 531390

formart Luxemburg S.a r.l. (1)
49 rue Gabriel Lippmann, 6947, Niederanven, Luxembourg
Tel.: (352) 4636841
Web Site: https://www.format.lu
Exhibition & Event Services
N.A.I.C.S.: 561920
Peter Czibula *(Mng Partner)*

INSTRUMATIC, S.A. DE C.V.

Poniente 106 No 39-5 Col Defensores de la Republica, Del Gustavo A Mader, 07780, Mexico, Mexico
Tel.: (52) 5555875744
Web Site: http://www.instrumatic.com.mx
Sales Range: $500-549.9 Million
Emp.: 80
Measuring & Controlling Device Mfr
N.A.I.C.S.: 334519
Salvador Eliseo Fernandez Alvarez *(Gen Mgr)*

INSTRUMENTS NANOTECH SA. DE CV.

Cine Mexicano 202 Int B 103 Col Lomas Estrella, Iztapalapa, 09890, Mexico, Mexico
Tel.: (52) 5543201445
Web Site: http://www.instrumentsnanotech.com
Microscopy Equipment Services
N.A.I.C.S.: 811210

INSUD PHARMA, S.L.

Edificio Nectar c Quintanapalla 2 4th Floor, 28050, Madrid, Spain
Tel.: (34) 913021560
Web Site: https://www.insudpharma.com
Year Founded: 1977
Pharmaceuticals Mfr
N.A.I.C.S.: 325412
Leandro Sigman *(Mng Dir)*

Subsidiaries:

Altian Pharma (1)
13 Avda A 2-95 Zona 2 de, Colonia La Escuadrilla, Mixco, Guatemala
Tel.: (502) 2229 32 00
Pharmaceutical Products Distr
N.A.I.C.S.: 424210

Chem-East (1)
Fo utca 14-18, 1011, Budapest, Hungary
Tel.: (36) 1 275 0336
Pharmaceutical Products Distr
N.A.I.C.S.: 424210

Chemo Argentina (1)
Edificio INSUD Paraguay 1535, C1061 ABC, Buenos Aires, Argentina
Tel.: (54) 11 4872 11 00
Pharmaceutical Products Distr
N.A.I.C.S.: 424210

Chemo Asia (1)
Unit 1001 Tower 2 Kerry Everbright City No 209 Gonghe Road, Shanghai, 20070, China
Tel.: (86) 21 5081 3228
Pharmaceutical Products Distr
N.A.I.C.S.: 424210
Alick Sun *(Mng Dir)*

Chemo Austria (1)
Rivergate I Gate 2/2 OG TOP B I Handelskai 92, 1200, Vienna, Austria
Tel.: (43) 1 890 00 28 18
Pharmaceutical Products Distr
N.A.I.C.S.: 424210

AND PRIVATE COMPANIES

INSURANCE COMPANY LONDON-ALMATY JSC

Chemo France (1)
7 rue Victor Hugo, Sevres, 92310, Paris, France
Tel.: (33) 1 49 66 22 11
Pharmaceutical Products Distr
N.A.I.C.S.: 424210
Marc Bernard *(Mgr-Sls)*

Chemo Iberica SA - Alcala de Henares Facility (1)
Qulmica SintEtica Dulcinea s/n, Alcala de Henares, 28805, Madrid, Spain
Tel.: (34) 91 889 05 77
Pharmaceutical Products Distr
N.A.I.C.S.: 424210

Chemo Iberica SA - Azuqueca de Henares Facility (1)
Avenida Miralcampo 7, Azuqueca de Henares, Guadalajara, Spain
Tel.: (34) 949 34 97 00
Pharmaceutical Products Distr
N.A.I.C.S.: 424210

Chemo Iberica SA - Buenos Aires Facility (1)
Av Directorio 6155, Buenos Aires, C1440ATA, Argentina
Tel.: (54) 11 4630 15 00
Pharmaceutical Products Distr
N.A.I.C.S.: 424210

Chemo Iberica SA - Hyderabad Facility (1)
404-406 Vijay Sai Towers BJP Office, Kukatpally, 500 072, Hyderabad, India
Tel.: (91) 40 2315 4000
Pharmaceutical Products Distr
N.A.I.C.S.: 424210

Chemo Iberica SA - Saronno Facility (1)
Via E H Grieg 13, 21047, Saronno, Italy
Tel.: (39) 02 964 26 401
Pharmaceutical Products Distr
N.A.I.C.S.: 424210

Chemo Iberica SA - Shanghai Facility (1)
1098 yuegong Rd, Jinshan Industrial Zone, Shanghai, China
Tel.: (86) 21 64856008
Pharmaceutical Products Distr
N.A.I.C.S.: 424210

Chemo Lugano (1)
Via F Pelli 17, 6901, Lugano, Switzerland
Tel.: (41) 91 973 21 01
Pharmaceutical Products Distr
N.A.I.C.S.: 424210

Chemo New Jersey (1)
180 Park Ave Ste 101, Florham Park, NJ 07932
Tel.: (973) 324-0200
Web Site: http://www.vitalfourultra.com
Pharmaceutical Products Distr
N.A.I.C.S.: 424210
Nicole Jolly *(Mgr-HR)*

Chemo do Brazil (1)
R Sampaió Viana 253 Conj 14 15, Sao Paulo, Brazil
Tel.: (55) 11 3052 1063
Pharmaceutical Products Distr
N.A.I.C.S.: 424210

Embil Ilac Sanayii Ltd (1)
Maslak Mah Sumer Sokak Ayazaga Ticaret Merkezi No3/9, Sisli, Istanbul, C4C98, Turkiye
Tel.: (90) 212 365 93 30
Web Site: http://www.embil.com
Pharmaceutical Product Mfr & Distr
N.A.I.C.S.: 325412
Elcin Yildiran *(Mng Dir)*

Everett Laboratories, Inc. (1)
29 Spring St, West Orange, NJ 07052
Tel.: (973) 324-0200
Web Site: http://www.everettlabs.com
Sales Range: $10-24.9 Million
Emp.: 60
Pharmaceutical Preparations
N.A.I.C.S.: 325412

Subsidiary (Domestic):

Quinnova Pharmaceuticals, Inc. (2)
2500 York Rd Ste 200, Jamison, PA 18929
Tel.: (215) 860-6253
Web Site: http://www.quinnova.com
Rev.: $2,600,000
Emp.: 30
Pharmaceutical Preparation Mfr
N.A.I.C.S.: 325412
Vincent Manetta *(Dir-Product Dev)*

Exeltis Austria (1)
Rivergate Gate 2 2 OG Top B Handelskai 92, Vienna, 1200, Austria
Tel.: (43) 1 890 00 28 01
Web Site: http://www.exeltis.at
Pharmaceutical Product Mfr & Distr
N.A.I.C.S.: 325412
Ursula Rieder *(Mgr-Sls & Mktg)*

Exeltis Germany GmbH (1)
Adalperostrabe 84, 85737, Ismaning, Germany
Tel.: (49) 89 4520529 0
Web Site: http://www.exeltis.de
Emp.: 70
Pharmaceutical Product Mfr & Distr
N.A.I.C.S.: 325412
Franziska Heydler Jr. *(Mgr-Product)*

Exeltis Project, Inc. (1)
180 Park Ave Ste 101, Florham Park, NJ 07932
Tel.: (973) 324-0200
Pharmaceuticals Mfr
N.A.I.C.S.: 325412

Exeltis Singapore (1)
158 Cecil Street 11-01, 069545, Singapore, Singapore
Tel.: (65) 603 5613 0599
Pharmaceutical Products Distr
N.A.I.C.S.: 424210

Genhelix S.A (1)
Calle Julia Morros s/n parque Tecnologico, Leon, Spain
Tel.: (34) 987 219 558
Pharmaceutical Products Distr
N.A.I.C.S.: 424210

Ordain Health Care Pvt. Ltd. (1)
Sri Devi Temple Tower No 6 2nd Main Road, Sembakkam, Chennai, 600 073, Tamilnadu, India
Tel.: (91) 44 7102 2097
Pharmaceutical Product Mfr & Distr
N.A.I.C.S.: 325412

PT Nufarindo (1)
Jl Raya Mangkang Kulon KM 16 5, Kecamatan Tugu, Semarang, Jawa Tengah, Indonesia
Tel.: (62) 24 8660006
Web Site: http://www.nufarindo.com
Pharmaceutical Product Mfr & Distr
N.A.I.C.S.: 325412
Christopher Tantis *(Mng Dir)*

Sinensix Pharma (Thailand) Co., Ltd. (1)
153/3 Goldenland Building 5th A5 Soi Mahadlekluang 1 Rajdamri Rd, Kwaeng Lumpini Khet Pathumwan, 10330, Bangkok, Thailand
Tel.: (66) 2 684 1127
Pharmaceutical Products Distr
N.A.I.C.S.: 424210

mAbxience Switzerland (1)
Via Maggio 1, 6990, Lugano, Switzerland
Tel.: (41) 1 973 14 23
Web Site: http://www.mabxience.com
Pharmaceutical Product Mfr & Distr
N.A.I.C.S.: 325412
Carlos Banado *(Mng Dir)*

mAbxience Uruguay (1)
Yaguaron 1407 Office 904, Torre de los Profesionales, 11100, Montevideo, Uruguay
Tel.: (598) 2908 8503
Pharmaceuticals Product Mfr
N.A.I.C.S.: 325412

INSUN ENVIRONMENTAL NEW TECHNOLOGY CO., LTD.
240 Dongguk-ro, Insandong-Gu, Goyang, Gyeonggi-do, Korea (South)
Tel.: (82) 319691500
Web Site: http://www.insun.com
Year Founded: 1997
060150—(KRS)
Rev.: $182,251,973
Assets: $422,017,674
Liabilities: $159,823,197
Net Worth: $262,194,477
Earnings: $16,794,360
Emp.: 419
Fiscal Year-end: 12/31/22
Environmental Engineering Services
N.A.I.C.S.: 541330

INSUNG INFORMATION CO., LTD.
28 Wiryeseong-daero 22-gil, Songpa-Gu, Seoul, 05656, Korea (South)
Tel.: (82) 234007000
Web Site: https://www.insunginfo.co.kr
Year Founded: 1992
033230—(KRS)
Rev.: $241,226,332
Assets: $178,309,480
Liabilities: $119,681,676
Net Worth: $58,627,804
Earnings: $655,519
Emp.: 267
Fiscal Year-end: 12/31/22
Information Technology Consulting Services
N.A.I.C.S.: 541512
Jongyun Won *(CEO)*

Subsidiaries:

Insung Digital Co., Ltd. (1)
7th Floor Garak-dong 97 Jung-daero, Songpa-gu, Seoul, 138-720, Korea (South)
Tel.: (82) 221054500
Web Site: http://www.isd.co.kr
Emp.: 73
Information Technology Consulting Services
N.A.I.C.S.: 541512
In-Yung Lee *(CEO)*

INSURAGUEST TECHNOLOGIES INC.
Suite 1140-640 Howe Street, Vancouver, V6C 2T6, BC, Canada
Tel.: (604) 685-4745   BC
Web Site: http://www.insuraguest.com
Year Founded: 2010
ISGIF—(OTCQB)
Rev.: $49,222
Assets: $562,692
Liabilities: $863,885
Net Worth: ($301,193)
Earnings: ($4,070,069)
Fiscal Year-end: 06/30/20
Gold Mining
N.A.I.C.S.: 212220
Logan B. Anderson *(CFO)*

INSURANCE AUSTRALIA GROUP LIMITED
Level 13 Tower Two Darling Park 201 Sussex Street, Sydney, 2000, NSW, Australia
Tel.: (61) 292929222
Web Site: http://www.iag.com.au
IAG—(ASX)
Rev.: $9,389,083,000
Assets: $23,765,141,000
Liabilities: $18,982,394,500
Net Worth: $4,782,746,500
Earnings: $627,612,500
Emp.: 13,650
Fiscal Year-end: 06/30/23
Insurance
N.A.I.C.S.: 524128
Elizabeth Blomfield Bryan *(Chm)*

Subsidiaries:

CGU Insurance Limited (1)
CGU Centre 181 William St, PO Box 2090S, Melbourne, 3000, VIC, Australia
Tel.: (61) 386301000
Web Site: http://www.cgu.com.au
Sales Range: $900-999.9 Million
Emp.: 2,000
N.A.I.C.S.: 524128

IAG New Zealand Limited (1)
NZI Centre 1 Fanshawe Street, Auckland, 1010, New Zealand
Tel.: (64) 99696000
Web Site: https://www.iag.co.nz
Insurance
N.A.I.C.S.: 524126
Alistair Smith *(CFO)*

Lumley Insurance Group Limited (1)
Tel.: (61) 292481111
Insurance Brokerage Services
N.A.I.C.S.: 524210

Subsidiary (Non-US):

Lumley General Insurance (NZ) Limited (2)
Tel.: (64) 93081959
Web Site: http://www.lumley.co.nz
Sales Range: $150-199.9 Million
Insurance Services
N.A.I.C.S.: 524126

New Zealand Insurance Company Ltd. (1)
Private Bag 92130, Auckland, 1142, New Zealand
Tel.: (64) 800694222
Web Site: https://www.nzi.co.nz
Insurance Services
N.A.I.C.S.: 524120
Andrew Beven *(Mgr-Cyber & Liability)*

SGIC General Insurance Limited (1)
80 Flinders St, Adelaide, 5000, SA, Australia
Tel.: (61) 882236858
Web Site: https://www.sgic.com.au
Sales Range: $25-49.9 Million
Emp.: 435
Insurance Services
N.A.I.C.S.: 524126

Swann Insurance (Aust) Pty Ltd. (1)
Locked Bag 3275, Melbourne, 8001, VIC, Australia
Tel.: (61) 1300657318
Web Site: https://www.swanninsurance.com.au
Insurance Services
N.A.I.C.S.: 524126

WFI Insurance Limited (1)
184 Railway Parade, Bassendean, 6054, WA, Australia
Tel.: (61) 892735333
Web Site: http://www.wfi.com.au
Sales Range: $350-399.9 Million
Emp.: 600
Insurance Services
N.A.I.C.S.: 524126
John Ripepi *(CEO)*

INSURANCE COMPANY AMANAT JSC
232 Dostyk ave Medeu district, Almaty, 050051, Kazakhstan
Tel.: (7) 727 244 33 44
Web Site: http://www.a-i.kz
AMIN—(KAZ)
Sales Range: $10-24.9 Million
Insurance Management Services
N.A.I.C.S.: 524298
Anna Nekryukova *(Deputy CEO)*

INSURANCE COMPANY KOMMESK-OMIR JSC
19 Nauryzbai Batyr str, 050000, Almaty, Kazakhstan
Tel.: (7) 7272447400
Web Site: http://www.kommesk-omir.kz
KMSO—(KAZ)
Sales Range: $10-24.9 Million
Insurance Management Services
N.A.I.C.S.: 524298
Eldar S. Abdrazakov *(Chm)*

INSURANCE COMPANY LONDON-ALMATY JSC

INSURANCE COMPANY LONDON-ALMATY JSC

Insurance Company London-Almaty JSC—(Continued)

Al-Farabi Avenue 19/1 Multifunctional Business Center Nurly Tau Block, Nurly Tau Block 3 B 9th Floor, Almaty, Kazakhstan
Tel.: (7) 7273110777
Web Site: http://www.laic.kz
Year Founded: 1997
LNAT—(KAZ)
Insurance Services
N.A.I.C.S.: 524298
Gianna Dauletbaevna Ahmetzhanova *(Chm-Mgmt Bd)*

INSURANCE HOUSE P.S.C.
Finance House Building Zayed 1st Street Khalidiya Area, PO Box 129921, Abu Dhabi, United Arab Emirates
Tel.: (971) 24934444   **AE**
Web Site:
https://www.insurancehouse.ae
Year Founded: 2010
IH—(ABU)
Rev.: $66,143,984
Assets: $59,138,345
Liabilities: $54,009,390
Net Worth: $5,128,955
Earnings: ($11,427,883)
Emp.: 103
Fiscal Year-end: 12/31/23
General Insurance Services
N.A.I.C.S.: 524210
Mohammed Abdulla Alqubaisi *(Chm)*

INSURANCE INCOME STRATEGIES LTD.
Canon s Court 22 Victoria Street, Hamilton, HM12, Bermuda
Tel.: (441) 294 8000   **BM**
Year Founded: 2017
Emp.: 2
Reinsurance Services
N.A.I.C.S.: 524130
Thomas C. Heise *(CEO)*

INSURED GROUP LIMITED
69 Grantham Street, Wembley, 6014, WA, Australia
Tel.: (61) 8 9287 0499
Web Site:
http://www.insuredgroup.co.nz
Sales Range: $1-9.9 Million
Insurance Services
N.A.I.C.S.: 524298
Wayne Robert Miller *(Mng Dir)*

Subsidiaries:
Australian Consolidated Insurance Limited   (1)
The Central Se 40 1 Ricketts Rd, Mount Waverley, 3149, VIC, Australia
Tel.: (61) 395504320
Insurance Services
N.A.I.C.S.: 524298

INSWAVE SYSTEMS CO., LTD.
20th floor Anchor One 39 Gukjegeumyung-ro Yeouido-dong, Yeongdeungpo-gu, Seoul, 07803, Korea (South)
Tel.: (82) 220821400
Web Site: https://www.inswave.com
Year Founded: 2002
450520—(KRS)
Software Development Services
N.A.I.C.S.: 541511

INSYDE SOFTWARE CORPORATION
12F No 161 Sec 2 Minsheng E Rd, Zhongshan District, Taipei, Taiwan
Tel.: (886) 266083688
Web Site: http://www.insyde.com
Year Founded: 1998

Sales Range: $1-9.9 Million
Emp.: 115
Computer Software Development, Installation & Repair
N.A.I.C.S.: 541511
Jeremy Wang *(Founder & CEO)*

Subsidiaries:
Insyde Software Co., Ltd.   (1)
HyunDai 41 Tower Bldg 3815-1 Mok-1 Dong 917-9, Yangcheon-gu, 158-723, Seoul, Korea (South)
Tel.: (82) 221682290
Computer Programming Services
N.A.I.C.S.: 541511

Insyde Software, Inc.   (1)
1400 Computer Dr, Westborough, MA 01581
Tel.: (508) 599-3999
Computer Programming Services
N.A.I.C.S.: 541511
Jeremy Wang *(CEO)*

Insyde Software, Ltd.   (1)
547 Tianmu West Road Building C Unicom International Tower Room 1106, Shanghai, 200070, China
Tel.: (86) 2151871889
Computer Programming Services
N.A.I.C.S.: 541511

Insyde Technology, Inc.   (1)
153 Cordaville Rd, Southborough, MA 01722-1834
Tel.: (508) 983-0983
System Software & Software Engineering Consulting Services
N.A.I.C.S.: 541512
Stephen Gentile *(Pres)*

INT/EXT COMMUNICATIONS AG
Saint Johanns-Vorstadt 22, 4004, Basel, Switzerland
Tel.: (41) 61 264 88 00
Web Site: http://www.int-ext.com
Year Founded: 1993
Sales Range: $10-24.9 Million
Emp.: 9
Public Relations Agency
N.A.I.C.S.: 541820
Marcel Trachsel *(Mng Partner)*

INTA BINA GROUP BERHAD
No 13 15 & 17 1st Floor Jalan SS 15/8A, 47500, Subang Jaya, Selangor, Malaysia
Tel.: (60) 356379093   **MY**
Web Site: https://www.intabina.com
INTA—(KLS)
Rev.: $98,682,211
Assets: $90,099,446
Liabilities: $57,862,006
Net Worth: $32,237,440
Earnings: $2,022,859
Fiscal Year-end: 12/31/22
Building Construction Services
N.A.I.C.S.: 236220
Lim Ooi Joo *(Mng Dir)*

INTACT FINANCIAL CORPORATION
2020 Boulevard Robert-Bourassa 6th floor, Montreal, H3A 2A5, QC, Canada
Tel.: (416) 941-5336   **ON**
Web Site: https://www.intactfc.com
Year Founded: 1991
IFC—(TSX)
Rev.: $8,576,044,680
Assets: $24,711,130,080
Liabilities: $18,017,575,800
Net Worth: $6,693,554,280
Earnings: $576,990,960
Emp.: 16,000
Fiscal Year-end: 12/31/19
Financial Investment Services
N.A.I.C.S.: 523999
Claude Dussault *(Chm)*

Subsidiaries:
Brokerlink Inc.   (1)
700-48 Yonge Street, Toronto, M5E 1G6, ON, Canada
Tel.: (647) 953-5002
Web Site: http://www.brokerlink.ca
Insurance Services
N.A.I.C.S.: 524210
Joe D'Annunzio *(Pres)*

Intact Financial Corporation   (1)
1611 Cramazie Boulevard East 10th Fl, Montreal, H2M 2R9, QC, Canada
Tel.: (514) 985-7111
Sales Range: $200-249.9 Million
Emp.: 300
Property & Casualty Insurance Services
N.A.I.C.S.: 524126

Intact Financial Corporation   (1)
700 University Avenue Suite 1500-A, Toronto, M5G 0A1, ON, Canada
Tel.: (403) 269-7961
Web Site: http://www.intactfc.com
Sales Range: $350-399.9 Million
Emp.: 700
Insurance Services
N.A.I.C.S.: 524128

Intact Insurance Canada   (1)
700 University Avenue, Toronto, M5G 0A1, ON, Canada   (100%)
Tel.: (416) 341-1464
Web Site: http://www.intact.ca
Sales Range: $200-249.9 Million
Emp.: 450
Insurance Brokerage Services
N.A.I.C.S.: 524210

Subsidiary (Domestic):
Anthony Insurance Incorporated   (2)
10 Factory Lane, Saint John's, A1C 6H5, NL, Canada
Tel.: (709) 758-5600
Web Site: http://www.anthonyinsurance.com
Sales Range: $100-124.9 Million
Emp.: 150
Insurance Services
N.A.I.C.S.: 524210

Canadian Direct Insurance Incorporated   (2)
750 Cambie Street Suite 600, Vancouver, V6B 0A2, BC, Canada
Tel.: (604) 699-3878
Web Site: http://www.canadiandirect.com
Insurance Services
N.A.I.C.S.: 524298
Brian Young *(Pres & CEO)*

Compagnie d'Assurance Belair, Inc.
7101 rue Jean-Talon East, Anjou, H1M 3T6, QC, Canada   (100%)
Tel.: (514) 270-9111
Web Site: http://www.belairdirect.com
Sales Range: $350-399.9 Million
Fire Marine & Casualty Insurance
N.A.I.C.S.: 524126

Jevco Insurance Company   (2)
6925 Century Avenue Suite 900, Mississauga, L5N 7K2, ON, Canada
Tel.: (905) 277-9350
Web Site: http://www.jevco.ca
Sales Range: $100-124.9 Million
Emp.: 200
Motorcycle, Fire & Liability Insurance
N.A.I.C.S.: 524126

Novex Insurance Company   (2)
700 University Ave Ste 1600, Toronto, M5G 0A1, ON, Canada
Tel.: (416) 228-2618
General Insurance Services
N.A.I.C.S.: 524113

O'Neil & Co. Ltd.   (2)
39 Renfrew Ave W, PO Box 100, Renfrew, K7V 2Y2, ON, Canada
Tel.: (613) 432-8121
Web Site: http://www.oneilandco.com
Sales Range: $25-49.9 Million
Emp.: 8
Insurance Services
N.A.I.C.S.: 524298

The Nordic Insurance Company of Canada   (2)

INTERNATIONAL PUBLIC

700 University Avenue Suite 1100, Toronto, M5G 0A2, ON, Canada
Tel.: (416) 250-6363
General Insurance Services
N.A.I.C.S.: 524126
Carla Smith *(VP)*

Trafalgar Insurance Company of Canada   (2)
700 University Ave Ste 1500, Toronto, M5G 0A1, ON, Canada
Tel.: (416) 227-6740
Web Site: http://www.trafalgarinsurance.ca
General Insurance Services
N.A.I.C.S.: 524126

Intact Investment Management Inc.   (1)
700 University Ave Ste 1500, Toronto, M5G 0A1, ON, Canada
Tel.: (416) 341-1464
Sales Range: $700-749.9 Million
Emp.: 2,000
Insurance Management Services
N.A.I.C.S.: 524126

OneBeacon Insurance Group, Ltd.   (1)
605 N Hwy 169, Plymouth, MN 55441
Tel.: (952) 852-2431
Web Site: http://www.onebeacon.com
Sales Range: $1-4.9 Billion
Holding Company; Property & Casualty Insurance Carrier
N.A.I.C.S.: 551112
T. Michael Miller *(Pres)*

Subsidiary (Domestic):
OneBeacon U.S. Holdings, Inc.   (2)
605 Hwy 169 N Ste 800, Plymouth, MN 55441
Tel.: (877) 624-7775
Web Site: http://www.onebeacon.com
Holding Company; Property & Casualty Insurance Carrier
N.A.I.C.S.: 551112
T. Michael Miller *(Pres)*

Subsidiary (Domestic):
OneBeacon Insurance Group, LLC   (3)
150 Royall St, Canton, MA 02021
Tel.: (781) 332-7000
Property & Casualty Insurance Carrier
N.A.I.C.S.: 524126
Mike Miller *(Pres)*

RSA Insurance Group plc   (1)
20 Fenchurch Street, London, EC3M 3AU, United Kingdom
Tel.: (44) 1403232323
Web Site: http://www.rsagroup.com
Rev.: $9,785,847,600
Assets: $26,182,159,200
Liabilities: $20,487,192,000
Net Worth: $5,694,967,200
Earnings: $502,342,800
Emp.: 12,378
Fiscal Year-end: 12/31/2019
Holding Company; Property, Casualty, Motor Vehicle & Household Insurance Products & Services
N.A.I.C.S.: 551112
William McDonnell *(Chief Risk Officer)*

Subsidiary (Non-US):
123 Money Limited   (2)
RSA House Sandyford Rd, PO Box 12123, Dundrum, Dublin, D16 FC92, Ireland
Tel.: (353) 1 518 1434
Web Site: https://www.123.ie
Insurance Management Services
N.A.I.C.S.: 524298

Al Ahlia Insurance Company SAOG   (2)
PO Box 1463, 112, Ruwi, Oman
Tel.: (968) 2 476 6800
Web Site: https://www.alahliarsa.com
Non-Life Insurance Services
N.A.I.C.S.: 524128

Subsidiary (Domestic):
British Aviation Insurance Company Limited   (2)
Fitzwilliam House 10 St Mary Axe, London,

AND PRIVATE COMPANIES

EC3A 8EQ, United Kingdom
Tel.: (44) 2073692244
Insurance Management Services
N.A.I.C.S.: 524298

Subsidiary (Non-US):

Coast Underwriters Limited (2)
Suite 2690 650 West Georgia Street, PO Box 11519, Vancouver, V6B 4N7, BC, Canada
Tel.: (604) 683-5631
Web Site: https://www.coastunderwriters.ca
Marine Insurance Claims Services
N.A.I.C.S.: 524126
Kevan Gielty *(Pres & CEO)*

Codan A/S (2)
Gl Kongevej 60, 1790, Copenhagen, Denmark
Tel.: (45) 33555555
Web Site: http://www.codan.dk
Sales Range: $1-4.9 Billion
Emp.: 6,416
Holding Company; Insurance Products & Services
N.A.I.C.S.: 551112

Subsidiary (Domestic):

Codan Forsikring A/S (3)
Gammel Kongevej 60, 1790, Copenhagen, Denmark
Tel.: (45) 33555555
Web Site: http://www.codan.dk
Insurance Products & Services
N.A.I.C.S.: 524126

Subsidiary (Non-US):

Trygg-Hansa Forsakring AB (3)
Flemingatan 18, 106 26, Stockholm, Sweden
Tel.: (46) 752431000
Web Site: http://www.rsagroup.com
Sales Range: $700-749.9 Million
Insurance Services
N.A.I.C.S.: 522299

Subsidiary (Non-US):

D.L. Deeks Insurance Services Inc. (2)
400 - 2255 Sheppard Avenue East, North York, M2J 4Y1, ON, Canada
Web Site: https://www.deeksinsurance.ca
Business Insurance Services
N.A.I.C.S.: 524128
Serge LaPalme *(Chm & CEO)*

Duborgh Skadeforsikring A/S (2)
Kongsgard Alle 53 A, 4632, Kristiansand, Norway
Tel.: (47) 38 09 31 60
Web Site: http://www.duborgh.no
Insurance Brokerage Services
N.A.I.C.S.: 524210

Forsikringsselskabet Privatsikring A/S (2)
Gammel Kongevej 60, 1790, Copenhagen, Denmark
Tel.: (45) 70111707
Web Site: http://www.privatsikring.dk
All Insurance Coverage Services
N.A.I.C.S.: 524114

Insurance Corporation of the Channel Islands Limited (2)
Dixcart House Sir William Place, PO Box 160, Saint Peter Port, GY1 4EY, Guernsey
Tel.: (44) 148 171 3322
Web Site: https://www.insurancecorporation.com
Emp.: 30
Insurance Management Services
N.A.I.C.S.: 524298
Paul Masterton *(Chm)*

L'Union Canadienne, Compagnie D'Assurances (2)
2475 Laurier Blvd, Quebec, G1T 1C4, QC, Canada
Tel.: (418) 622-2040
Web Site: http://www.unioncanadienne.com
Sales Range: $100-124.9 Million
Emp.: 250
Personal & Commercial Insurance Products
N.A.I.C.S.: 524113

Subsidiary (Domestic):

Noble Marine (Insurance Brokers) Limited (2)
Clinton House Lombard Street, Newark, NG24 1XB, Nottinghamshire, United Kingdom
Tel.: (44) 1636707606
Marine Insurance Claims Services
N.A.I.C.S.: 524126
Phil Kilburn *(Gen Mgr & Mgr-Claims)*

Noble Marine (Underwriting Agencies) Limited (2)
Clinton House Lombard Street, Newark, NG24 1XB, Nottinghamshire, United Kingdom
Tel.: (44) 1636707606
Marine Insurance Claims Services
N.A.I.C.S.: 524126

Subsidiary (Non-US):

RSA Actuarial Services (India) Private Limited (2)
1st Floor Building 10C Cyber City Complex DLF Phase II, Gurgaon, 122002, India
Tel.: (91) 1243863000
Household Insurance Product & Services
N.A.I.C.S.: 524126
Devika Sethi *(Mgr)*

RSA Insurance Ireland Limited (2)
Tel.: (353) 1 290 1000
Web Site: https://www.rsagroup.ie
Sales Range: $200-249.9 Million
Emp.: 500
Provision of insurance services
N.A.I.C.S.: 525190

Subsidiary (Domestic):

RSA Law Limited (2)
Leonard House Scotts Quay, Birkenhead, CH41 1FB, United Kingdom
Tel.: (44) 3442454880
Web Site: http://rsalaw.co.uk
Traffic Accident Insurance Services
N.A.I.C.S.: 524298

Subsidiary (Non-US):

Roins Financial Services Limited (2)
18 York St Ste 800, Toronto, M5J 2T8, ON, Canada
Tel.: (416) 366-7511
Web Site: http://www.rsagroup.com
Emp.: 700
Insurance Holding Company
N.A.I.C.S.: 551112

Subsidiary (Domestic):

Royal & Sun Alliance Insurance Company of Canada (3)
700 University Ave Suite 1500A, Toronto, M5G 0A1, ON, Canada
Tel.: (416) 366-7511
Web Site: http://www.rsagroup.ca
Property & Casualty Insurance, Title Insurance & Reinsurance Products & Services
N.A.I.C.S.: 524126

Subsidiary (Domestic):

Canadian Northern Shield Insurance Company (4)
1900-555 West Hastings Street, Vancouver, V6B 4N6, BC, Canada
Tel.: (604) 662-2900
Web Site: http://www.cns.ca
Sales Range: $150-199.9 Million
Casualty & Property Insurance Services
N.A.I.C.S.: 524298

Compagnie d'Assurance du Quebec (4)
1001 de Maisonneuve Boulevard West Suite 1400, Montreal, H3A 3C8, QC, Canada
Tel.: (514) 844-1116
Web Site: http://www.rsagroup.ca
Sales Range: $200-249.9 Million
Emp.: 500
Property & Casualty Insurance Products & Services
N.A.I.C.S.: 524126

Johnson Inc. (4)
10 Factory Lane, PO Box 12049, Saint John's, A1B 1R7, NL, Canada
Tel.: (709) 737-1500
Web Site: http://www.johnson.ca
Sales Range: $900-999.9 Million
Home & Automotive Insurance Products & Services
N.A.I.C.S.: 524126

Western Assurance Company (4)
100 - 2 Prologis Blvd, Mississauga, L5W 0G8, ON, Canada
Tel.: (905) 403-3318
Web Site: https://www.rsagroup.ca
Sales Range: $50-74.9 Million
Emp.: 100
Insurance Services
N.A.I.C.S.: 524128

Subsidiary (Domestic):

Royal & Sun Alliance Insurance plc (2)
St Marks Court Chart Way, Horsham, RH12 1XL, West Sussex, United Kingdom
Tel.: (44) 140 323 2323
Web Site: https://www.rsagroup.com
Sales Range: $900-999.9 Million
Emp.: 2,500
Property & Casualty Insurance & Pension Products & Services
N.A.I.C.S.: 524126

Subsidiary (Non-US):

The Johnson Corporation (2)
10 Factory Ln, Saint John's, A1B 1R7, NL, Canada
Tel.: (709) 737-1500
Investment Management Service
N.A.I.C.S.: 523999

Tower Insurance Company Limited (2)
Jubilee Buildings 1 Victoria street, IM99 1BF, Douglas, Isle of Man
Tel.: (44) 162 464 5900
Web Site: https://www.towerinsurance.co.im
Sales Range: $50-74.9 Million
Emp.: 30
Insurance Services
N.A.I.C.S.: 524298
Emmet McQuillan *(Mng Dir)*

The Guarantee Company of North America (1)
4950 Yonge Street Madison Centre Suite 1400, Toronto, M2N 6K1, ON, Canada
Tel.: (416) 223-9580
Web Site: http://www.theguarantee.com
Rev.: $416,634,807
Assets: $1,230,916,101
Liabilities: $788,017,513
Net Worth: $442,898,588
Earnings: $26,149,438
Emp.: 450
Fiscal Year-end: 12/31/2018
Property, Casualty & Automobile Insurance; Fidelity & Surety Bonds; Credit Insurance Services
N.A.I.C.S.: 524126
Richard Longland *(VP-Natl-Comml & Developer Surety)*

Subsidiary (US):

The Guarantee Company of North America (2)
One Towne Sq Ste 1470, Southfield, MI 48076
Tel.: (248) 281-0281
Web Site: http://www.gcna.com
Sales Range: $50-74.9 Million
Emp.: 47
Property, Casualty & Automobile Insurance; Fidelity & Surety Bonds; Credit Insurance
N.A.I.C.S.: 524126
Sara Schrauben *(CFO & Treas)*

INTACT GOLD CORPORATION

400-837 West Hastings Street, Vancouver, V6C 3N6, BC, Canada
Tel.: (604) 283-1722 BC
Web Site: http://intactgold.com
Year Founded: 2007
ITG—(TSXV)
Rev.: $88
Assets: $528,815
Liabilities: $676,686

Net Worth: ($147,871)
Earnings: ($209,400)
Fiscal Year-end: 03/31/24
Gold Mining Services
N.A.I.C.S.: 212220
Anthony K. Jackson *(Pres & CEO)*

INTAI TECHNOLOGY CORP.

9 Jingke Road, Nantun Dist, Taichung, 408, Taiwan
Tel.: (886) 423595336
Web Site: https://www.intai.com.tw
Year Founded: 1988
4163—(TPE)
Rev.: $75,460,776
Assets: $142,505,831
Liabilities: $71,932,433
Net Worth: $70,573,398
Earnings: $13,058,969
Emp.: 400
Fiscal Year-end: 12/31/22
Fastener Product Mfr
N.A.I.C.S.: 332721
Tsai Yung-Fang *(Chm)*

INTAS PHARMACEUTICALS LTD.

Corporate House Near Sola Bridge S G Highway Thaltej, Ahmedabad, 380 054, Gujarat, India
Tel.: (91) 7961577000
Web Site: https://www.intaspharma.com
Rev.: $99,987,662
Pharmaceuticals Product Mfr
N.A.I.C.S.: 325412

Subsidiaries:

Accord Farma S.A. de C.V. (1)
Plaza Polanco Jaime Balmes 11 piso 3 Int 300 Torre D, Col Los Morales Polanco, Mexico, Plaza Polanco,, Mexico (100%)
Tel.: (52) 555203 4993
Web Site: http://www.accordfarma.com.mx
Sales Range: $25-49.9 Million
Emp.: 5
Pharmaceutical Preparation Mfr
N.A.I.C.S.: 325412

Accord Healthcare Inc. (1)
3100 Steels Avenue East Suite 605, Markham, L3R 8T3, ON, Canada
Tel.: (905) 489-1957
Web Site: http://www.accord-healthcare.com
Pharmaceutical Preparation Mfr
N.A.I.C.S.: 325412
Anthony Grosso *(Head-Scientific Affairs-Europe)*

Accord Healthcare Ltd. (1)
Sage House 319 Pinner Road, North Harrow, London, HA1 4HF, Middlesex, United Kingdom
Tel.: (44) 2088631427
Web Site: http://www.accord-healthcare.com
Sales Range: $25-49.9 Million
Emp.: 80
Pharmaceutical Preparation Mfr
N.A.I.C.S.: 325412

Subsidiary (Non-US):

ACCORD Healthcare Ireland, Ltd. (2)
26 Bullford Business Campus, Kilcoole, Wicklow, Ireland
Tel.: (353) 1 2592020
Web Site: http://www.accord-healthcare.ie
Pharmaceutical Products Distr
N.A.I.C.S.: 424210

Accord GmbH (2)
General-Arnold-Strasse 6, 5020, Salzburg, Austria
Tel.: (43) 662 42 90 90
Web Site: http://www.accord-healthcare.at
Pharmaceutical Products Distr
N.A.I.C.S.: 424210

Accord Healthcare (Kenya) Ltd. (2)
Block No C/3 & C/5-Temple View Apartment Forest Road Parkland, PO Box 1335-00606, Nairobi, Kenya
Tel.: (254) 20 3751439

INTAS PHARMACEUTICALS LTD.

Intas Pharmaceuticals Ltd.—(Continued)
Pharmaceutical Products Distr
N.A.I.C.S.: 424210

Accord Healthcare AB (2)
Erik Dahlbergsgatan 14, 411 26, Gothenburg, Sweden
Tel.: (46) 31 135 525
Pharmaceutical Products Distr
N.A.I.C.S.: 424210

Accord Healthcare B.V. (2)
Winthontlaan 200, Postbus 85183, 3508 AD, Utrecht, Netherlands
Tel.: (31) 30 850 6014
Web Site: http://www.accordhealthcare.nl
Emp.: 5
Pharmaceutical Products Distr
N.A.I.C.S.: 424210
Ynte Postma *(Mgr-Comml)*

Accord Healthcare France SAS (2)
45 rue du Faubourg de Roubaix, 59000, Lille, France
Tel.: (33) 3 20 40 17 70
Web Site: http://www.accord-healthcare-france.fr
Pharmaceutical Products Distr
N.A.I.C.S.: 424210

Accord Healthcare GmbH (2)
Sagewerkstrasse 3, 83395, Freilassing, Germany
Tel.: (49) 8654 77717 0
Web Site: http://www.accord-healthcare.de
Pharmaceutical Products Distr
N.A.I.C.S.: 424210

Accord Healthcare Italia S.R.L. (2)
Palazzo Taurus A/1 Viale Colleoni 1/3/5, 20864, Agrate Brianza, Monza and Brianza, Italy
Tel.: (39) 039 642 151
Web Site: http://www.accord-healthcare.it
Pharmaceutical Products Distr
N.A.I.C.S.: 424210
Piero Bonzano *(Reg Mgr)*

Accord Healthcare OU (2)
Sepapaja 6, 11415, Tallinn, Estonia
Tel.: (372) 662 35 73
Pharmaceutical Products Distr
N.A.I.C.S.: 424210

Accord Healthcare OY (2)
Fredrikinkatu 62 A 3, 00100, Helsinki, Finland
Tel.: (358) 10 231 4180
Web Site: http://www.accord-healthcare.fi
Emp.: 5
Pharmaceutical Products Distr
N.A.I.C.S.: 424210
Matti Eronen *(Mng Dir)*

Accord Healthcare Polska Sp. z o.o. (2)
Tasmowa 7B, 02-677, Warsaw, Poland
Tel.: (48) 225772800
Pharmaceutical Products Distr
N.A.I.C.S.: 424210

Accord Healthcare Pty Ltd. (2)
Unit 702 23 Queens Road, Melbourne, 3004, VIC, Australia
Tel.: (61) 3 9395 7779
Pharmaceutical Products Distr
N.A.I.C.S.: 424210

Accord Healthcare SA (2)
Building 2 Tuscany Office Park 6 Coombe Place, Rivonia, Johannesburg, South Africa
Tel.: (27) 11 234 5701
Web Site: http://www.accord-healthcare.co.za
Pharmaceutical Products Distr
N.A.I.C.S.: 424210
Reshlan Nagoor *(Exec Dir)*

Accord Healthcare bvba (2)
185 Sint-Janstraat, 8700, Tielt, West-Vlaanderen, Belgium
Tel.: (32) 478 93 60 84
Web Site: http://www.accord-healthcare.be
Pharmaceutical Products Distr
N.A.I.C.S.: 424210
Virginie Beernaert *(Mgr-Natl Sls)*

Accord Healthcare, S.L.U. (2)
WTC Moll de Barcelona s/n Edificio Este 6 planta, 08039, Barcelona, Spain
Tel.: (34) 933 010 064
Pharmaceutical Products Distr
N.A.I.C.S.: 424210

Accord Healthcare S.A.C. (1)
Francisco Bolognesi 125 7th Floor, Lima, Peru
Tel.: (51) 14463720
Web Site: http://www.accordhealthcare.pe
Sales Range: $25-49.9 Million
Emp.: 40
Pharmaceutical Preparation Mfr
N.A.I.C.S.: 325412

Accord Pharmaceuticals Ltd (1)
1985 Av Guido Caloi G-01 Jd Sao Luis, 05802-140, Sao Paulo, SP, Brazil (100%)
Tel.: (55) 11 5516 3281
Web Site: http://www.accord-healthcare.com
Sales Range: $25-49.9 Million
Emp.: 6
Pharmaceutical Preparation Mfr
N.A.I.C.S.: 325412

Actavis Ireland Ltd. (1)
7-8 Euro House Euro Business Park, Little Island, Cork, T45K857, Ireland
Tel.: (353) 214619040
Pharmaceutical Products Distr
N.A.I.C.S.: 424210

Actavis UK Limited (1)
Whiddon Valley, Barnstaple, EX32 8NS, Devon, United Kingdom
Tel.: (44) 1271 385 200
Web Site: http://www.accord-healthcare.co.uk
Pharmaceutical Mfr, Marketer & Whslr
N.A.I.C.S.: 325412
Colin Ternent *(Sr Key Acct Exec)*

Astron Research Limited (1)
10th Floor Premier House Opp Gurudwara Sarkhej-Gandhinagar Highway, Bodakdev, Ahmedabad, 380054, Gujarat, India
Tel.: (91) 79 2685 3518
Web Site: http://www.astron-research.com
Emp.: 300
Pharmaceutical Research & Development Services
N.A.I.C.S.: 541715
Nitin Patel *(Mgr-Bus Dev)*

Farmabiot Sa de CV (1)
Parque Industrial Toluca 2000 Calle 2 Lote 11 Mz VI, Toluca, 50200, Mexico, Mexico
Tel.: (52) 722 279 0330
Pharmaceuticals Product Mfr
N.A.I.C.S.: 325412

Intas Biopharmaceuticals Ltd. (1)
Plot No 423/P/A Gidc Moraiya Sarkhej Bavla Highway, Changodar, Sanand, 382213, India
Tel.: (91) 2717 661298
Pharmaceuticals Product Mfr
N.A.I.C.S.: 325412

Intas Pharmaceuticals Ltd. - Ankleshwar Plant (1)
Survey No 44-B, Naldhari Village Valia Taluka, 393135, Bharuch, Gujarat, India
Tel.: (91) 2643 270015
Pharmaceuticals Product Mfr
N.A.I.C.S.: 325412

Intas Pharmaceuticals Ltd. - Dehradun Facility (1)
Camp Road Selaqui, Dehradun, 248001, Uttrakhand, India
Tel.: (91) 135 2698659
Pharmaceuticals Product Mfr
N.A.I.C.S.: 325412

Intas Pharmaceuticals Ltd. - Matoda Facility (1)
Plot No 457 458 Sarkhej Bavla Highway, Matoda Village Sanand Taluka, Ahmedabad, 382210, Gujarat, India
Tel.: (91) 2717 661298
Pharmaceuticals Product Mfr
N.A.I.C.S.: 325412

Intas Pharmaceuticals Ltd. - Moraiya Facility (1)
Plot No 423/P/A/ GIDC Sarkhej-Bavla Highway, Moraiya Sanand Taluka, Ahmedabad, 382 210, Gujarat, India
Tel.: (91) 2717 660100
Pharmaceuticals Product Mfr
N.A.I.C.S.: 325412

Intas Pharmaceuticals Ltd. - PharmEZ Facility (1)
Plot No 5 6 7 Pharmez Sarkhej-Bavla Highway, Matoda Village Sanand Taluka, Ahmedabad, 382 210, Gujarat, India
Tel.: (91) 2717 619100
Pharmaceuticals Product Mfr
N.A.I.C.S.: 325412

Intas Pharmaceuticals Ltd. - Sanand Facility (1)
85 - 87 Kailash Industrial Estate, Iyava Village Sanand Taluka, Ahmedabad, 382210, Gujarat, India
Tel.: (91) 2717 284188
Pharmaceuticals Product Mfr
N.A.I.C.S.: 325412

Intas Pharmaceuticals Ltd. - Sikkim Facility (1)
Near IOC Depo N H No 31A Bhagey Khola, Majhitar, Rangpo, 737132, Sikkim, India
Tel.: (91) 3592 246417
Pharmaceuticals Product Mfr
N.A.I.C.S.: 325412

Intas Pharmaceuticals Ltd. - Vatva Facility (1)
7/3 GIDC Estate B/H Dena Bank Vatva, Ahmedabad, 382445, Gujarat, India
Tel.: (91) 79 25830207
Pharmaceuticals Product Mfr
N.A.I.C.S.: 325412

INTCHAINS GROUP LIMITED

Building 16 Lane 999 Xinyuan South Road, Lin-Gang Special Area Pudong, Shanghai, 201306, China
Tel.: (86) 2158961080
Web Site: https://www.intchains.com
Year Founded: 2017
ICG—(NASDAQ)
Rev.: $96,803,900
Assets: $93,651,145
Liabilities: $5,035,093
Net Worth: $88,616,051
Earnings: $68,966,562
Emp.: 64
Fiscal Year-end: 12/31/21
Software Development Services
N.A.I.C.S.: 541511
Chaowei Yan *(CFO)*

INTCO MEDICAL TECHNOLOGY CO., LTD.

No 18 Qingtian Road, Zibo, 255414, Shandong, China
Web Site:
  https://www.intcomedical.com
300677—(CHIN)
Rev.: $974,502,346
Assets: $3,814,139,335
Liabilities: $1,519,047,630
Net Worth: $2,295,091,706
Earnings: $53,945,212
Emp.: 9,000
Fiscal Year-end: 12/31/23
Medical Product Mfr & Distr
N.A.I.C.S.: 325412
Fangyi Liu *(Chm)*

INTEC CAPITAL LIMITED

708 Manjusha Building 57 Nehru Place, New Delhi, 110019, India
Tel.: (91) 1146522200
Web Site:
  https://www.inteccapital.com
Year Founded: 1994
526871—(BOM)
Rev.: $4,180,153
Assets: $47,675,366
Liabilities: $36,023,887
Net Worth: $11,651,479
Earnings: ($7,965,555)
Emp.: 103
Fiscal Year-end: 03/31/19
Mortgage Loan Brokerage Services
N.A.I.C.S.: 522310
Sanjeev Goel *(Founder & Mng Dir)*

INTERNATIONAL PUBLIC

INTEC INC.

Ushijimashin Machi 5-5, Toyama, 930-8577, Japan
Tel.: (81) 764441111
Web Site: http://www.intec.co.jp
Year Founded: 1964
Emp.: 3,611
Web Technology, Bio-Informatics Technology & Advanced Research Services
N.A.I.C.S.: 541519
Katsuki Kanaoka *(Chm)*

Subsidiaries:

Intec NetCore Inc. (1)
1-3-3 Shinsuna Koto-ku, Tokyo, 136-0075, Japan
Tel.: (81) 356655069
Web Site: http://www.inetcore.com
Sales Range: $350-399.9 Million
Emp.: 2,000
Management Consulting Services
N.A.I.C.S.: 541618

Intec Web And Genome Informatics Corporation (1)
1-3-3 Shinsuna Koto-ku, 136-0075, Tokyo, Japan
Tel.: (81) 356655011
Web Site: http://www.webgen.co.jp
Medical Laboratories
N.A.I.C.S.: 621511

Iuk Inc (1)
Kyohan Kudan Bldg, Tokyo, Chiyoda-Ku, Japan
Tel.: (81) 332621225
Sales Range: $75-99.9 Million
Emp.: 150
Electrical Apparatus & Equipment Wiring Supplies & Construction Material Whslr
N.A.I.C.S.: 423610

INTEC PHARMA LTD.

12 Hartom Street, Har Hotzvim, Jerusalem, 9777512, Israel
Tel.: (972) 25864657
Web Site:
  http://www.intecpharma.com
NTEC—(NASDAQ)
Assets: $20,896,000
Liabilities: $6,363,000
Net Worth: $14,533,000
Earnings: ($14,128,000)
Emp.: 36
Fiscal Year-end: 12/31/20
Pharmaceuticals Mfr
N.A.I.C.S.: 325412
Nir Sassi *(Pres & CFO)*

INTECH BIOPHARM LTD.

3F No 36 Ln 358 Ruiguang Rd Dist, Taipei, 114, Taiwan
Tel.: (886) 277218877
Web Site:
  https://www.intechbiopharm.com
Year Founded: 2010
6461—(TPE)
Rev.: $739,362
Assets: $79,745,521
Liabilities: $47,487,446
Net Worth: $32,258,075
Earnings: ($10,251,602)
Fiscal Year-end: 12/31/22
Pharmaceuticals Product Mfr
N.A.I.C.S.: 325412
Peter Lin *(Chm)*

INTECH LIMITED

3/1-E 1st Floor Bijoy Nagar Purana Paltan, Dhaka, 1000, Bangladesh
Tel.: (880) 1322894550
Web Site:
  https://www.intechworld.net
Year Founded: 2000
INTECH—(CHT)
Rev.: $116,861
Assets: $1,049,610
Liabilities: $1,110,482
Net Worth: ($60,872)

Earnings: ($211,734)
Emp.: 28
Fiscal Year-end: 06/30/23
Internet Solutions Products & Services
N.A.I.C.S.: 541511
Mirza Aminul Islam Beg *(CEO)*

INTECHNOLOGY PLC
Cardale House Cardale Court Beckwith Head Road, Harrogate, HG3 1RY, United Kingdom
Tel.: (44) 1423 877400
Web Site: http://www.intechnologyplc.com
Year Founded: 1983
Sales Range: $1-9.9 Million
Emp.: 43
Information Technology Solutions, Products & Services
N.A.I.C.S.: 541511
Peter Wilkinson *(CEO)*

Subsidiaries:

Inhealthcare Ltd (1)
Cardale House Cardale Court, Harrogate, HG3 1RY, United Kingdom
Tel.: (44) 1423 877400
Web Site: http://www.inhealthcare.co.uk
Emp.: 30
Health Care Srvices
N.A.I.C.S.: 621999

Live-PA Ltd. (1)
Cardale House Cardale Court Beckwith Head Road, Harrogate, HG3 1RY, United Kingdom **(100%)**
Tel.: (44) 1423 877 400
Web Site: http://www.live-pa.com
Wireless Telecommunications
N.A.I.C.S.: 517112
Peter Wilkinson *(Mng Dir)*

Mobile Tornado PLC (1)
Cardale House Cardale Court Beckwith Head rd, Harrogate, HG3 1RY, United Kingdom **(49.99%)**
Tel.: (44) 1423511900
Web Site: http://www.mobiletornado.com
Wireless Telecommunications
N.A.I.C.S.: 517112
Avi Tooba *(CEO)*

INTEGRA CAPITAL MANAGEMENT LIMITED
32 Regal Building Sansad Marg, New Delhi, 110 001, Delhi, India
Tel.: (91) 1123361532
Web Site:
https://www.integraprofit.com
Year Founded: 1990
531314—(BOM)
Rev: $76,949
Assets: $556,563
Liabilities: $4,152
Net Worth: $551,811
Earnings: $52,985
Fiscal Year-end: 03/31/21
Business Management Services
N.A.I.C.S.: 561499
Tarun Vohra *(Chm & Mng Dir)*

INTEGRA CONSTRUCTION KZ LLP
VP 16 12/1 Kunayev Str, Left Riverbank, Nur-Sultan, Kazakhstan
Tel.: (7) 7172 69 55 22 KZ
Web Site: http://www.inconkz.com
Year Founded: 1998
Railway & Highway Construction & Maintenance Contractor
N.A.I.C.S.: 488210
Muradow Khuram *(CEO)*

Subsidiaries:

ZGOP a.d. (1)
Vase Stajica 2/III, 21000, Novi Sad, Serbia **(90%)**
Tel.: (381) 21 489 0112
Web Site: http://www.zgop.rs

Sales Range: Less than $1 Million
Emp.: 280
Railway Infrastructure Development Services
N.A.I.C.S.: 237990
Zoran Stanojevic *(Dir Gen)*

INTEGRA DOCUMENT MANAGEMENT SRL
Vicolo Diomede Pantaleoni 4, 20161, Milan, MI, Italy
Tel.: (39) 02 646702 1 IT
Web Site: http://www.integradm.it
Year Founded: 2001
Sales Range: $25-49.9 Million
Emp.: 600
Document Management & Data Processing Services
N.A.I.C.S.: 518210

INTEGRA GARMENTS & TEXTILES LTD.
Plot No G2-MIDC Industrial Estate Salai Dhaba Butibori, Nagpur, 441 108, India
Tel.: (91) 2266154651
Web Site:
http://www.integragarments.com
Rev.: $337
Assets: $2,821,367
Liabilities: $5,143,653
Net Worth: ($2,322,286)
Earnings: ($333,627)
Fiscal Year-end: 03/31/19
Textile Products Mfr
N.A.I.C.S.: 314999
Jagdish Sharma *(CFO)*

INTEGRA HOLDING AG
Hammerweg 1, CH-8304, Wallisellen, Switzerland
Tel.: (41) 43 233 3010 CH
Web Site: http://www.integra.ch
Year Founded: 1939
Investment Holding Company
N.A.I.C.S.: 551112
Adrian Oehler *(Chm & CEO)*

Subsidiaries:

Aquametro AG (1)
Ringstrasse 75, Therwil, 4106, Switzerland
Tel.: (41) 61 725 1122
Web Site: http://www.aquametro.com
Emp.: 250
Water & Energy Measurement Technology Mfr
N.A.I.C.S.: 334519
Peter Suter *(CEO)*

Subsidiary (Non-US):

Aquametro (China) Pte Ltd. (2)
Tower A Room 2209 No 188 Zhang Yang Road Tomson Centre, 200122, Shanghai, China
Tel.: (86) 21 5012 6401
Electronic Equipment Distr
N.A.I.C.S.: 423610

Aquametro (S.E.A.) Pte Ltd. (2)
190 Woodlands Industrial Park E5 08-17, Woodlands Bizhub, Singapore, 757516, Singapore
Tel.: (65) 6899 1980
Electronic Equipment Distr
N.A.I.C.S.: 423610

Aquametro Belgium Sprl. (2)
Dallaan 67, 1933, Zaventem, Belgium
Tel.: (32) 2241 6201
Electronic Equipment Distr
N.A.I.C.S.: 423610

Aquametro Korea Ltd. (2)
Dennis Kwak 3F 169 Sameo-ro, Haeundae-gu, Busan, 612-857, Korea (South)
Tel.: (82) 51 905 5566
Web Site: http://www.aquametro.co.kr
Emp.: 5
Electronic Equipment Distr
N.A.I.C.S.: 423610
Dennis Kwak *(Mng Dir)*

Aquametro ME JLT (2)
Jumeirah Lake Towers Jumeirah Bay X3 office 1807, PO Box 334132, Dubai, United Arab Emirates
Tel.: (971) 56 7587 801
Electronic Equipment Distr
N.A.I.C.S.: 423610

Aquametro Marine GmbH (2)
Friedrich-Barnewitz-Str 7, Warnemunde, 18119, Rostock, Germany
Tel.: (49) 381 519 64 88 1
Web Site: http://www.aquametro-marine.com
Emp.: 6
Electronic Equipment Distr
N.A.I.C.S.: 423610
Fritz Hauff *(CEO)*

Aquametro Messtechnik GmbH (2)
Kurt-Schumacher-Allee 2, 28329, Bremen, Germany
Tel.: (49) 421 871 640
Electronic Equipment Distr
N.A.I.C.S.: 423610

Aquametro SA (1)
Ringstrasse 75, 4106, Therwil, Switzerland
Tel.: (41) 21 926 77 77
Web Site: http://www.aquametro.com
Electronic Equipment Distr
N.A.I.C.S.: 423610

INTEGRA Biosciences AG (1)
Tardisstrasse 201, Zizers, 7205, Switzerland
Tel.: (41) 81 286 9530
Web Site: http://www.integra-biosciences.com
Laboratory Equipment & Supplies Mfr & Distr
N.A.I.C.S.: 333248

Subsidiary (US):

INTEGRA Biosciences Corp. (2)
2 Wentworth Dr, Hudson, NH 03051
Tel.: (603) 578-5800
Web Site: http://www.integra-biosciences.com
Sales Range: $1-9.9 Million
Emp.: 15
Laboratory Equipment & Supplies Mfr & Distr
N.A.I.C.S.: 333248
Gary Nelson *(Pres)*

Subsidiary (Non-US):

INTEGRA Biosciences Deutschland GmbH (2)
Turmstrasse 11, 78467, Konstanz, Germany
Tel.: (49) 7531 3615 815
Medical Laboratory Equipment Distr
N.A.I.C.S.: 423450

INTEGRA Biosciences Ltd. (2)
Heathrow Business Centre 65 High Street, Egham, TW20 9EY, United Kingdom
Tel.: (44) 7711 607 687
Medical Laboratory Equipment Distr
N.A.I.C.S.: 423450

INTEGRA Biosciences SAS (2)
Avenue du Fief - Parc d'Activites des Bethunes, BP 79570, 95062, Saint Ouen L'Aumone, Cedex, France
Tel.: (33) 1 34 30 76 76
Medical Laboratory Equipment Distr
N.A.I.C.S.: 423450

INTEGRA Engineering India Ltd. (1)
Post Box 55 Halol, District Panchmahals, Chandrapur, 389350, Gujarat, India
Tel.: (91) 267 622 1870
Web Site: http://www.integraengineering.in
Emp.: 200
Textile Machinery & Custom Fabricated Metal Products Mfr
N.A.I.C.S.: 333248
Milind Shingate *(CEO)*

INTEGRA Immobilien AG (1)
Hammerweg 1, 8304, Wallisellen, Switzerland
Tel.: (41) 43 233 3020
Web Site: http://www.integra-immobilien.ch
Real Estate Acquisition, Development & Management Services
N.A.I.C.S.: 531390
Adrian Oehler *(Chm & CEO)*

Micronic Holding B.V. (1)
Platinastraat 51, 8211 AR, Lelystad, Netherlands
Tel.: (31) 320 277067
Web Site: http://www.micronic.com
Medical Laboratory Equipment Distr
N.A.I.C.S.: 423450

Subsidiary (US):

Micronic Manufacturing USA LLC (2)
210 Bridgewater Rd Ste 3, Aston, PA 19014
Tel.: (484) 483-8075
Medical Laboratory Equipment Mfr
N.A.I.C.S.: 339112

Signal AG (1)
Industriezone Kleine Ey, CH-3294, Buren an der Aare, Switzerland
Tel.: (41) 32 352 1111
Web Site: http://www.signal.ch
Traffic Safety Products Mfr
N.A.I.C.S.: 339950

Subsidiary (Domestic):

Segnaletica Mordasini SA (2)
Via Pobbia 4, Sementina, 6514, Bellinzona, Switzerland
Tel.: (41) 91 857 58 92
Web Site: http://www.segnaletica-mordasini.ch
Demarcation Signage Services
N.A.I.C.S.: 541850

Sitek AG (1)
Friedhofstrasse 18, PO Box 112, 2544, Bettlach, Switzerland
Tel.: (41) 32 645 29 29
Web Site: http://www.sitek.ch
Emp.: 30
Industrial Mold Mfr
N.A.I.C.S.: 333511
Monika Heiniger *(Head-Assembly)*

INTEGRA ITC
Gateshead Close, Sandy, SG19 1RS, Beds, United Kingdom
Tel.: 1767692792
Web Site: http://www.integra-ict.co.uk
Sales Range: $50-74.9 Million
Emp.: 62
Wired Telecom & VOIP Services
N.A.I.C.S.: 517111
Pas Ruggerio *(Mng Dir)*

INTEGRA MANAGEMENT LLC
Michurinsky Prospekt Olympic Village 1 bldg 4, 119602, Moscow, Russia
Tel.: (7) 4959330621 Ky
Web Site: http://en.integra.ru
Year Founded: 2004
Sales Range: $500-549.9 Million
Emp.: 8,000
Investment Management Services Oilfield Services
N.A.I.C.S.: 523999
Felix V. Lubashevsky *(Chm-Mgmt Bd & Pres)*

Subsidiaries:

CJSC Uralmash-VNIIBT (1)
27-29/1 bldg 6 Smolenskaya-Sennaya Square, 119121, Moscow, Russia
Tel.: (7) 495 7455600
Oil & Gas Equipment Mfr & Marketer
N.A.I.C.S.: 333132

Subsidiary (Domestic):

CJSC Uralmash - Drilling Equipment (2)
Pervaya Patiletka Square, 620012, Ekaterinburg, Russia
Tel.: (7) 343 3366492
Oil & Gas Equipment Mfr
N.A.I.C.S.: 333132
Sergey A. Luzgin *(Mng Dir)*

OJSC Concern Stromneftemash (2)
Vokazalnaya St 54, 156001, Kostroma, Russia
Tel.: (7) 4942627801
Sales Range: $150-199.9 Million
Emp.: 750
Oil & Gas Equipment Mfr

INTEGRA MANAGEMENT LLC

Integra Management LLC—(Continued)
N.A.I.C.S.: 333132

OJSC NPO Burovaya Technika (2)
9- bld 1 Letnikovskaya str, 115114, Moscow, Russia
Tel.: (7) 4952216171
Web Site: http://www.vniibt.ru
Oil & Gas Machinery Mfr
N.A.I.C.S.: 333132
Garry S. Oganov *(Gen Dir)*

OOO VNIIBT Drilling Instruments (2)
1 Truda St Permskaya Obl, Ocherskyi Pavlovskiy, 617143, Moscow, Russia
Tel.: (7) 342 2252381
Drilling Tools Mfr
N.A.I.C.S.: 333132

LLC Geophyzservis (1)
Sibirskaya st 38, 628183, Miesbach, Russia
Tel.: (7) 3467252689
Oil & Gas Well Drilling Services
N.A.I.C.S.: 213111

LLC Integra-Drilling (1)
Severnaya st 39 building 26, 628617, Nizhnevartovsk, Russia
Tel.: (7) 3466470620
Oil & Gas Well Drilling Services
N.A.I.C.S.: 213111

LLC Obnefteremont (1)
2-P st 2th Promishlennaya, 628606, Nizhnevartovsk, Russia
Tel.: (7) 3466634202
Construction Engineering Services
N.A.I.C.S.: 541330

LLC Smith Drilling Services (1)
Vernadskogo avenue 6, 119311, Moscow, Russia
Tel.: (7) 4956516798
Oil & Gas Well Drilling Services
N.A.I.C.S.: 213111

LLC VNIIBT-Burovoy Instrument (1)
Truda st 1, Pavlovsk, 617160, Saint Petersburg, Russia
Tel.: (7) 3427833882
Web Site: http://www.vniibt-bi.ru
Oil & Gas Well Drilling Services
N.A.I.C.S.: 213111

SIAM Company (1)
Octyabrskaya st 10a Nizhny Novgorod, 634003, Tomsk, Russia
Tel.: (7) 3822900008
Web Site: http://www.siamoil.ru
Industrial Machinery & Tool Mfr
N.A.I.C.S.: 332439

INTEGRA MICRO SYSTEMS (P) LTD.
4 Bellary Road 12th KM, Jakkur, Bengaluru, 560064, India
Tel.: (91) 8028565801   IN
Web Site:
   http://www.integramicro.com
Year Founded: 1982
Software Devolopment
N.A.I.C.S.: 513210
Mahesh Kumar Jain *(Co-Founder, CEO & Mng Dir)*

Subsidiaries:

Jataayu Software (P) Ltd. (1)
Ground Fl 4 Bellary Road 12th KM, Jakkur, Bengaluru, 560064, India
Tel.: (91) 80 8565852
Wireless Internet Communications
N.A.I.C.S.: 517112

INTEGRA RESOURCES CORP.
1050 - 400 Burrard Street, Vancouver, V6C 3A6, BC, Canada
Tel.: (604) 416-0576   ON
Web Site:
   https://www.integraresources.com
Year Founded: 1997
ITRG—(NYSEAMEX)
Rev.: $272,005
Assets: $61,422,237
Liabilities: $40,099,072
Net Worth: $21,323,165
Earnings: ($19,807,021)
Emp.: 39
Fiscal Year-end: 12/31/22
Metal Mining Services
N.A.I.C.S.: 212290
Andree St-Germain *(CFO)*

INTEGRA SWITCHGEAR LIMITED
10 Por Ramangamdi, Por, Vadodara, 391243, Gujarat, India
Tel.: (91) 9426007687
Web Site:
   https://www.integraindia.com
Year Founded: 1994
517423—(BOM)
Assets: $253,876
Liabilities: $140,895
Net Worth: $112,981
Earnings: ($24,393)
Emp.: 2
Fiscal Year-end: 03/31/21
Switchgear Product Mfr
N.A.I.C.S.: 335313
Pankaj Jamnadas Vora *(CFO)*

INTEGRA TELECOMMUNICATION & SOFTWARE LIMITED
Flat No 1311 B Devika Tower 6, Nehru Place New Delhi, Delhi, 110019, India
Tel.: (91) 1141008327
Web Site:
   http://www.integratelesoftware.com
536868—(BOM)
Rev.: $158,570
Assets: $1,546,752
Liabilities: $106,594
Net Worth: $1,440,159
Earnings: $94,184
Emp.: 8
Fiscal Year-end: 03/31/22
Software Development Services
N.A.I.C.S.: 541511
Ramaswamy Narayan Iyer *(Mng Dir)*

INTEGRAFIN HOLDINGS PLC
29 Clements Lane, London, EC4N 7AE, United Kingdom
Tel.: (44) 2076084900
Web Site:
   https://www.integrafin.co.uk
Year Founded: 1999
IHP—(LSE)
Rev.: $151,261,920
Assets: $27,973,038,960
Liabilities: $27,776,941,920
Net Worth: $196,097,040
Earnings: $49,816,800
Fiscal Year-end: 09/30/22
Portfolio Management & Investment Advice
N.A.I.C.S.: 523940
Michael Howard *(Exec Dir)*

Subsidiaries:

Integrated Application Development Pty Ltd (1)
25 Camberwell Road, Hawthorn East, 3123, VIC, Australia
Tel.: (61) 388623222
Web Site: https://www.integradev.com.au
Emp.: 75
Financial Planning & Advice Services
N.A.I.C.S.: 541611

Integrated Financial Arrangements Ltd. (1)
29 Clement's Lane, London, EC4N 7AE, United Kingdom
Tel.: (44) 2076084900
Financial Planning & Advice Services
N.A.I.C.S.: 541611
Richard Cranfield *(Chm)*

INTEGRAGEN SA
5 Rue de Henri Desbrueres Genopole Campus 1 - Bat 8, 700 020, Evry, France
Tel.: (33) 160910900   FR
Web Site: http://www.integragen.com
ALINT—(EUR)
Sales Range: $1-9.9 Million
Biotechnologies Research & Development
N.A.I.C.S.: 541714
Bernard Courtieu *(Chm & CEO)*

Subsidiaries:

IntegraGen, Inc. (1)
485 Massachusetts Ave Ste 300, Cambridge, MA 02139
Web Site: http://www.integragen.com
Biotechnologies Research & Development
N.A.I.C.S.: 541714
Larry Yost *(Gen Mgr)*

INTEGRAL BETONIRCI AD
Cantavirski put bb, 24000, Subotica, Serbia
Tel.: (381) 24 566 229
Web Site: http://www.betonjerka-su.rs
Construction Material Production & Transport
N.A.I.C.S.: 423390
Dragan Jokic *(Mgr-Production)*

INTEGRAL CORPORATION
10F, GranTokyo South Tower 1-9-2 Marunouchi, Chiyoda-ku, Tokyo, 100-6610, Japan
Tel.: (81) 3 6212 6100   JP
Web Site: http://www.integralkk.com
Year Founded: 2007
Privater Equity Firm
N.A.I.C.S.: 523999
Reijiro Yamamoto *(Partner)*

Subsidiaries:

Mamezou Holdings Co., Ltd. (1)
34F Shinjuku Mitsui Bldg 2-1-1 Nishi-Shinjuku, Shinjuku-ku, Tokyo, 163-0434, Japan
Tel.: (81) 3 5339 2100
Web Site: http://www.mamezou-hd.com
Rev.: $221,435,460
Assets: $132,484,380
Liabilities: $53,653,320
Net Worth: $78,831,060
Earnings: $15,057,720
Emp.: 634
Fiscal Year-end: 03/31/2019
Holding Company
N.A.I.C.S.: 551112
Norio Ogiwara *(Chm & Pres)*

Nitto FC Co., Ltd. (1)
1-23 Iroha-cho, Minato-ku, Nagoya, 455-8544, Aichi, Japan
Tel.: (81) 52 6614381
Web Site: http://www.nittofc.co.jp
Rev.: $145,925,040
Assets: $397,619,760
Liabilities: $38,121,840
Net Worth: $359,497,920
Earnings: $8,755,680
Emp.: 303
Fiscal Year-end: 09/30/2018
Fertilizer Mfr & Distr
N.A.I.C.S.: 325314
Kaname Watanabe *(Pres)*

INTEGRAL DIAGNOSTICS LIMITED
Suite 902 Level 9 45 William Street, Melbourne, 3000, VIC, Australia
Tel.: (61) 353390704
Web Site:
   https://www.integraldiagnostics.com
IDX—(ASX)
Rev.: $314,210,399
Assets: $496,982,856
Liabilities: $295,521,024
Net Worth: $201,461,832
Earnings: ($40,531,150)
Emp.: 1,977
Fiscal Year-end: 06/30/24
Health Care Srvices

INTERNATIONAL PUBLIC

N.A.I.C.S.: 621999
Ian Kadish *(CEO & Mng Dir)*

Subsidiaries:

Advanced Women's Imaging Pty. Ltd. (1)
1 Main Drive, Warana, 4575, QLD, Australia
Tel.: (61) 75 436 7550
Web Site:
   https://www.advancedwomensimaging.com
Diagnostic Imaging Services
N.A.I.C.S.: 621512

Central Queensland Radiology Pty. Ltd. (1)
QTV House 5 Aquatic Place, Rockhampton, 4701, QLD, Australia
Tel.: (61) 74 921 8800
Web Site: https://www.cqradiology.com.au
Emp.: 120
Diagnostic Imaging Services
N.A.I.C.S.: 621512

IQ Radiology Pty. Ltd. (1)
Shop 09 Morayfield Village 177-189 Morayfield Road, Morayfield, 4506, QLD, Australia
Tel.: (61) 75 428 4800
Web Site: https://www.iqradiology.com.au
Diagnostic Imaging Services
N.A.I.C.S.: 621512

Sunshine Coast Radiology Pty. Ltd. (1)
60 Wises Rd, Maroochydore, 4558, QLD, Australia
Tel.: (61) 75 430 3900
Web Site: https://www.scradiology.com.au
Diagnostic Imaging Services
N.A.I.C.S.: 621512

Trinity MRI Limited (1)
96C Carlton Gore Rd, Newmarket, Auckland, 1023, New Zealand
Tel.: (64) 9 522 0848
Web Site: https://www.trinitymri.co.nz
Diagnostic Imaging Services
N.A.I.C.S.: 621512

INTEGRAL GVG A.D.
Somborski put 77, Subotica, Serbia
Tel.: (381) 24559167
Year Founded: 1991
IGVG—(BEL)
Sales Range: Less than $1 Million
Building Construction Services
N.A.I.C.S.: 236220
Perica Savic *(Exec Dir)*

INTEGRATED ASSET MANAGEMENT PLC
4 Hill Street, London, W1J 5NE, United Kingdom
Tel.: (44) 2075149200   UK
Web Site:
   http://www.integratedam.com
Year Founded: 1997
Sales Range: $10-24.9 Million
Emp.: 5
Hedge Fund Management Services
N.A.I.C.S.: 525910
John D. S. Booth *(Chm)*

Subsidiaries:

Attica Holdings (UK) Limited (1)
4 Hill St, London, W1J 5NE, United Kingdom
Tel.: (44) 2075149200
Web Site: http://www.ntegratedam.com
Sales Range: $50-74.9 Million
Emp.: 10
Investment Management Service
N.A.I.C.S.: 523940

Integrated Alternative Investments Limited (1)
4 Hill St, Mayfair, London, W1J 5NE, United Kingdom
Tel.: (44) 2075149210
Web Site: http://www.integratedai.com
Sales Range: $50-74.9 Million
Emp.: 10
Investment Management Service
N.A.I.C.S.: 523999

AND PRIVATE COMPANIES
INTEGRATED WASTE SOLUTIONS GROUP HOLDINGS LIMITED

Integrated Financial Products Limited (1)
4 Hill St, London, W1J 5NE, United Kingdom
Tel.: (44) 2075140550
Web Site: http://www.integratedfp.com
Sales Range: $25-49.9 Million
Emp.: 4
Financial Management Services
N.A.I.C.S.: 541611

INTEGRATED CAPITAL SERVICES LIMITED
606 New Delhi House 27 Barakhamba Road, New Delhi, 110 001, India
Tel.: (91) 1143542784
Web Site: https://www.raas.co.in
539149—(BOM)
Rev.: $108,681
Assets: $1,687,113
Liabilities: $583,538
Net Worth: $1,103,575
Earnings: ($616,489)
Fiscal Year-end: 03/31/22
Business Management Consulting Services
N.A.I.C.S.: 541618
Brijinder Bhushan Deora (Chm)

INTEGRATED COIL COATING INDUSTRIES SDN. BHD.
Lot 6479 Lorong Sg Puluh Batu 6 Jalan Kapar, 42100, Kelang, Selangor, Malaysia
Tel.: (60) 3 3291 5189   MY
Year Founded: 2000
Sales Range: $25-49.9 Million
Emp.: 250
Galvanized Iron Steel & Coils Mfr
N.A.I.C.S.: 332999
Arthur Lu Choon Hii (Mng Dir)

INTEGRATED CYBER SOLUTIONS INC.
2600 1066 West Hastings Street, Vancouver, V6E 3X1, BC, Canada
Tel.: (203) 984-7487   BC
Web Site: https://www.integrated-cyber.com
Year Founded: 2021
ICS—(CNSX)
Information Technology Services
N.A.I.C.S.: 541512

INTEGRATED DENTAL HOLDINGS LTD.
Europa House Europa Trading Estate Stoneclough Road Kearsley, Manchester, M26 1GG, United Kingdom
Tel.: (44) 845 647 7364
Web Site: http://www.idhgroup.co.uk
Year Founded: 1996
Sales Range: $300-349.9 Million
Emp.: 3,103
Dental Care Services
N.A.I.C.S.: 621399
Steve Williams (Dir-Clinical Svcs)

INTEGRATED DIAGNOSTICS HOLDINGS PLC
IFC 5, Saint Helier, JE1 1ST, Jersey
Tel.: (44) 1534847000   JE
Web Site: https://www.idhcorp.com
Year Founded: 1979
IDHC—(LSE)
Rev.: $133,381,620
Assets: $186,696,013
Liabilities: $86,371,567
Net Worth: $100,324,445
Earnings: $15,153,651
Emp.: 6,692
Fiscal Year-end: 12/31/23
Healtcare Services
N.A.I.C.S.: 621511
Hend El Sherbini (CEO)

INTEGRATED ELECTRONIC SYSTEMS LAB CO., LTD.
No 188 East End of Huayuan Road, Jinan, 250100, Shandong, China
Tel.: (86) 53188018000
Web Site: https://english.ieslab.cn
Year Founded: 1984
002339—(SSE)
Rev.: $308,755,044
Assets: $543,641,436
Liabilities: $253,770,192
Net Worth: $289,871,244
Earnings: ($3,915,756)
Emp.: 1,500
Fiscal Year-end: 12/31/22
Electrical Automation Equipment & Systems Mfr Including Computer Hardware, Software, System Integration
N.A.I.C.S.: 541512
Wang Liang (Chm)

INTEGRATED FINANCIAL SERVICES LIMITED
304 New Delhi House 27 Barakhamba Road, New Delhi, Delhi, 110001, India
Tel.: (91) 11 43074307
Web Site: http://www.integratedfinancial.in
Year Founded: 1992
Sales Range: Less than $1 Million
Investment Management Service
N.A.I.C.S.: 523999
Subhash Chander Khaneja (Officer-Compliance & Sec)

INTEGRATED GREEN ENERGY SOLUTIONS LTD
Suite 3a 18 Smith Street, Chatswood, 2067, NSW, Australia
Tel.: (61) 2 8920 2300   AU
Web Site: http://www.igesolutions.org
Year Founded: 1988
Sales Range: Less than $1 Million
Mineral Exploration Services
N.A.I.C.S.: 212290
Bevan Dooley (Dir-Chief Technical)

INTEGRATED MEDIA TECHNOLOGY LIMITED
Suite 1401 Level 14 219-227 Elizabeth Street, Sydney, 2000, NSW, Australia
Tel.: (61) 873246018   AU
Web Site: https://www.imtechltd.com
Year Founded: 2008
IMTE—(NASDAQ)
Rev.: $373,676
Assets: $30,134,828
Liabilities: $13,531,649
Net Worth: $16,603,179
Earnings: ($18,350,112)
Emp.: 11
Fiscal Year-end: 12/31/23
Investment Services
N.A.I.C.S.: 523999

INTEGRATED PROTEINS LIMITED
5th Floor City Point Opp Town Hall, Jamnagar, 361 008, Gujarat, India
Tel.: (91) 2882551901
Web Site: https://www.integratedproteins.com
Year Founded: 1992
519606—(BOM)
Rev.: $21,782
Assets: $355,304
Liabilities: $20,540
Net Worth: $334,765
Earnings: $2,894
Fiscal Year-end: 03/31/21
Edible Oil & Deoiled Cake Processing & Whlsr
N.A.I.C.S.: 311224

Arvind Kantilal Shah (Mng Dir)

INTEGRATED RESEARCH LTD
Level 9 100 Pacific Highway, North Sydney, 2060, NSW, Australia
Tel.: (61) 299661066
Web Site: https://www.ir.com
IRI—(ASX)
Rev.: $55,616,987
Assets: $76,245,326
Liabilities: $17,243,590
Net Worth: $59,001,736
Earnings: $18,115,652
Emp.: 142
Fiscal Year-end: 06/30/24
Design, Development & Sale Of Systems & Applications Management Computer Software
N.A.I.C.S.: 423430
Peter Adams (CFO)

Subsidiaries:

Integrated Research UK Limited (1)
Jubilee House Third Avenue Globe Park, Marlow, SL7 1EY, United Kingdom
Tel.: (44) 189 581 7800
Web Site: http://www.prognosis.com
Sales Range: $25-49.9 Million
Emp.: 20
Performance Monitoring & Diagnostic Software Development Services
N.A.I.C.S.: 541511

Integrated Research, Inc. (1)
4700 S Syracuse St Ste 1000, Denver, CO 80237
Tel.: (303) 390-8700
Web Site: https://www.ir.com
Sales Range: $25-49.9 Million
Emp.: 40
Monitoring & Diagnostic Software Development Services
N.A.I.C.S.: 541511

Interactive Quality Services, Inc. (1)
6601 Lyndale Ave S Ste 330, Minneapolis, MN 55423
Tel.: (612) 243-6700
Web Site: http://www.iq-services.com
Emp.: 25
Management Consulting Services
N.A.I.C.S.: 541611
Russ Zilles (CEO)

INTEGRATED SOFTWARE SOLUTIONS PTY. LTD.
Suite 701 3 Spring Street, Sydney, 2000, NSW, Australia
Tel.: (61) 292473122
Web Site: http://www.intsoftsol.com
Year Founded: 2007
Sales Range: $10-24.9 Million
Emp.: 20
Software Developer
N.A.I.C.S.: 334610
Alex Anderson (Mng Dir)

Subsidiaries:

Integrated Software Solutions Ltd (1)
45 Southgate St, Winchester, SO23 9EH, Hampshire, United Kingdom (100%)
Tel.: (44) 1962844060
Web Site: http://www.intsoftsol.com
Software Developer
N.A.I.C.S.: 334610

INTEGRATED SYSTEM CREDIT CONSULTING FINTECH SPA
Via Aldo Barbaro 15, 10143, Turin, Italy
Tel.: (39) 0800936605
Web Site: https://www.isccfintech.it
Year Founded: 2019
ISC—(EUR)
Investment Management Service
N.A.I.C.S.: 523999
Gianluca De Carlo (CEO)

INTEGRATED TECHNOLOGIES LIMITED
C-24 Defence Colony, New Delhi, 110024, India
Tel.: (91) 11 46502740   In
Web Site: http://www.integratedtech.in
Rev.: $915
Assets: $755,276
Liabilities: $791,262
Net Worth: ($35,986)
Earnings: ($146,959)
Fiscal Year-end: 03/31/18
Printed Circuit Board Mfr
N.A.I.C.S.: 334412
Rajeev Bali (CEO & Mng Dir)

INTEGRATED THERMOPLASTICS LIMITED
Plot No 188 Phase-II 2nd Floor, Kamalapuri Colony Extension Srinagar Colony, Hyderabad, 500073, India
Tel.: (91) 4023235200   In
Web Site: https://www.integratedthermo.com
Year Founded: 1994
Rev.: $8,231,452
Assets: $5,296,761
Liabilities: $5,492,569
Net Worth: ($195,809)
Earnings: $245,690
Fiscal Year-end: 03/31/18
Plastic Tank Mfr
N.A.I.C.S.: 326122

INTEGRATED WASTE SOLUTIONS GROUP HOLDINGS LIMITED
Integrated Waste Solutions Building 8 Chun Cheong Street, Tseung Kwan O Industrial Estate, Hong Kong, New Territories, China (Hong Kong)
Tel.: (852) 2 676 8700   Ky
Web Site: http://www.iwsgh.com
Year Founded: 1968
0923—(HKG)
Rev.: $6,620,027
Assets: $111,218,809
Liabilities: $1,947,340
Net Worth: $109,271,469
Earnings: ($3,110,353)
Emp.: 128
Fiscal Year-end: 03/31/21
Holding Company; Waste Management Services
N.A.I.C.S.: 551112
Chris Sui Kin Tam (CFO)

Subsidiaries:

Confidential Materials Destruction Service Limited (1)
5 F Fook Woo Grp Bldg 3 Kui Sik St On Lok Tsuen, Fanling, New Territories, China (Hong Kong)
Tel.: (852) 26768800
Sales Range: $50-74.9 Million
Emp.: 60
Waste Management Services
N.A.I.C.S.: 924110

Huizhou Fook Woo Paper Company Limited (1)
Gaotou Vlg Liangwu Mgmt Zone, Yuanzhou, Huizhou, 516123, Guangdong, China
Tel.: (86) 7526812825
Tissue Paper Products Mfr & Sales
N.A.I.C.S.: 322120

IWS Assorted Paper Company Limited (1)
Integrated Waste Solutions Building 8 Chun Cheong Street, Fanling, New Territories, China (Hong Kong)
Tel.: (852) 26768700
Tissue Paper Products Sales
N.A.I.C.S.: 424130
Iris Lee (Mgr-HR)

IWS Environmental Technologies Limited (1)

INTEGRATED WASTE SOLUTIONS GROUP HOLDINGS LIMITED

Integrated Waste Solutions Group Holdings Limited—(Continued)
5 F Fook Woo Grp Bldg 3 Kui Sik St On Lok Tsuen, Fanling, New Territories, China (Hong Kong)
Tel.: (852) 26768700
Waste Reduction Services
N.A.I.C.S.: 221320

IWS Waste Management Company Limited (1)
Fook Woo Group Building 3 Kui Sik Street, Fanling, New Territories, China (Hong Kong)
Tel.: (852) 26768700
Paper Product Sales & Waste Management Solutions
N.A.I.C.S.: 424130
King Sang Lam *(COO)*

INTEGRATED WIND SOLUTIONS ASA

Stoperigata 2 Aker Brygge, PO Box 1583, Vika, 0250, Oslo, Norway
Tel.: (47) 22014200
Web Site:
  https://www.integratedwind.com
Year Founded: 2020
IWS—(OSL)
Rev.: $24,789,553
Assets: $172,836,175
Liabilities: $40,018,347
Net Worth: $132,817,829
Earnings: ($1,273,473)
Emp.: 190
Fiscal Year-end: 12/31/23
Construction Engineering Services
N.A.I.C.S.: 541330
Christopher Andersen Heidenreich *(COO)*

Subsidiaries:

ProCon Wind Energy A/S (1)
Ankeret 5B, 9220, Aalborg, Denmark
Tel.: (45) 41525300
Web Site: https://www.procon.as
Wind Power Plant Construction Services
N.A.I.C.S.: 237130

ProCon Wind Energy Ltd. (1)
Belasis Hall Tech Park Coxwold way, Billingham, TS23 4EA, United Kingdom
Tel.: (44) 7825448376
Wind Power Plant Construction Services
N.A.I.C.S.: 237130

INTEGRITAS VIAGER SA

8 avenue Mac Mahon, 75017, Paris, France
Tel.: (33) 186982739
Web Site:
  https://www.integritasviager.com
Year Founded: 2020
MLVIE—(EUR)
Real Estate Investment Services
N.A.I.C.S.: 531190

INTEGRUM AB

Krokslatts Fabriker 50, 431 37, Molndal, Sweden
Tel.: (46) 317601060
Web Site: https://www.integrum.se
Year Founded: 1990
INTEG.B—(OMX)
Rev.: $5,260,427
Assets: $4,542,597
Liabilities: $1,577,274
Net Worth: $2,965,323
Earnings: ($261,251)
Emp.: 23
Fiscal Year-end: 04/30/21
Medical Equipment Mfr
N.A.I.C.S.: 339112
Dennis Baecklund *(CFO)*

Subsidiaries:

Integrum Inc. (1)
100 Montgomery St Ste 1780, San Francisco, CA 94104
Medical Device Mfr
N.A.I.C.S.: 339112

INTEGRUM HOLDINGS LP

55 Hudson Yards 47th Fl, New York, 10001, NY, United Kingdom
Tel.: (212) 970-2500
Web Site:
  https://www.integrumholdings.com
Investment Services
N.A.I.C.S.: 523999
Tagar C. Olson *(Founder)*

Subsidiaries:

Evertree Insurance Services, LLC (1)
55 Hudson Yards 47th Fl., New York, NY 10001
Tel.: (947) 237-1961
Web Site: https://www.evertree.co
Emp.: 210
Insurance Brokerage
N.A.I.C.S.: 524210

Subsidiary (Domestic):

Prosper Insurance Group, LLC (2)
1 Columbus St Ste 500, Virginia Beach, VA 23462
Tel.: (757) 248-5973
Web Site:
  http://www.prosperinsurancegroup.com
Sales Range: $25-49.9 Million
Emp.: 14
General Insurance Services
N.A.I.C.S.: 524210
Morgan Coghlan *(Dir-PR)*

INTEK GROUP S.P.A.

Foro Buonaparte 44, 20121, Milan, Italy
Tel.: (39) 02806291
Web Site: https://www.itkgroup.it
Year Founded: 1886
ITK—(ITA)
Rev.: $1,518,083,677
Assets: $2,240,889,876
Liabilities: $1,623,572,512
Net Worth: $617,317,364
Earnings: $38,432,690
Emp.: 2,963
Fiscal Year-end: 12/31/22
Holding Company; Copper & Copper Alloy Products Mfr; Renewable Energy Investment; Private Equity & Real Estate Investment
N.A.I.C.S.: 551112
Diva Moriani *(Deputy Chm)*

Subsidiaries:

Dalian Dashan Chrystallizer Co. Ltd. (1)
No 72 Tianyu Street Economic & Technology Development Zone, Liaoning, Dalian, China
Tel.: (86) 41187341899
Copper Tube Mfr
N.A.I.C.S.: 331420

Dalian Dashan Heavy Machinery Co. Ltd. (1)
No 73 Zhenping Industrial Park Economic & Technology Development Zone, Liaoning, Dalian, China
Tel.: (86) 41187512008
Copper Tube Mfr
N.A.I.C.S.: 331420

ErgyCapital S.p.A. (1)
Via de' Barucci 2,, 50100, Florence, Italy (100%)
Tel.: (39) 0554411411
Web Site: http://www.greenergycapital.com
Power Production & Renewable Energies
N.A.I.C.S.: 221117
Francesco Cursano *(CFO)*

GreenRecycle Srl (1)
Via Cassano 111, 15069, Serravalle Scrivia, Italy
Tel.: (39) 0143686136
Web Site: http://www.greenrecycle.it
Scrap Product Whslr
N.A.I.C.S.: 423930

KME France S.A.S. (1)
11 Bis rue de la Hotel de Ville, 92411, Courbevoie, France
Tel.: (33) 147896868
Web Site: http://www.kme.com
Sales Range: $150-199.9 Million
Emp.: 55
Copper Product Mfr
N.A.I.C.S.: 331420

KME Germany AG (1)
Klosterstrasse 29, 49074, Osnabruck, Germany
Tel.: (49) 5413210
Web Site: http://www.kme.com
Sales Range: $800-899.9 Million
Emp.: 2,000
Copper & Copper Alloy Mfr
N.A.I.C.S.: 331420
Ulrich Becker *(Chm, CEO & Mng Dir)*

Subsidiary (Domestic):

KME Architectural Metals GmbH & Co. KG (2)
Eichendorfweg 10, 48268, Greven, Reckenfeld, Germany
Tel.: (49) 25753090
Web Site: http://www.fricke-greven.com
Sales Range: $25-49.9 Million
Emp.: 45
Roof, Facade & Rainwater System Supplier
N.A.I.C.S.: 332323

KME Europa Metal AG (2)
Klosterstrasse 29, 49074, Osnabruck, Germany
Tel.: (49) 5413210
Web Site: http://www.kme.com
Emp.: 25
Copper Product Mfr
N.A.I.C.S.: 331420

KME Europa Metal AG (2)
Carl Benz Str 13, PO Box 3253, 58706, Menden, Germany
Tel.: (49) 237316101
Web Site: http://www.thecopperlink.com
Sales Range: $75-99.9 Million
Emp.: 350
Copper Product Mfr
N.A.I.C.S.: 331420

KME Germany AG (2)
Frankentalstrasse 5, PO Box 1929, Stolberg, 52222, Germany
Tel.: (49) 24021050
Web Site: http://www.thecopperlink.com
Sales Range: $125-149.9 Million
Emp.: 300
Copper Product Mfr
N.A.I.C.S.: 331420

KME Germany Gmbh & Co. K.G. (1)
Klosterstrasse 29, 49074, Osnabruck, Germany
Tel.: (49) 5413210
Web Site: http://www.kme.com
Emp.: 4,500
Copper & Copper Alloy Product Mfr
N.A.I.C.S.: 331420

Subsidiary (Non-US):

AMT - Advanced Mould Technology India Private Ltd. (2)
2B Dyavasandra Industrial Area 4th Cross Whitefield Road, Mahadevapura, Bengaluru, 560048, India
Tel.: (91) 8043580300
Web Site:
  http://www.advancedmouldtech.com
Metal Coat Mfr
N.A.I.C.S.: 332812

Bertram's GmbH (2)
Stelzhamergasse 4/7, 1030, Vienna, Austria
Tel.: (43) 13332221
Web Site: http://www.bertrams.co.at
Flue Pipe Mfr
N.A.I.C.S.: 332322

Cuprum S.A.U. (2)
Poligono Industrial El Campillo 11 D BJ, Abanto, 48500, Zierbena, Biscay, Spain
Tel.: (34) 946360128
Web Site: http://www.cuprum.es
Copper Alloy Product Mfr
N.A.I.C.S.: 331420

INTERNATIONAL PUBLIC

KME (Suisse) S.A. (2)
Staffelstrasse 10, 8045, Zurich, Switzerland
Tel.: (41) 433882000
Copper Alloy Product Mfr
N.A.I.C.S.: 331420

Subsidiary (US):

KME America Inc. (2)
1000 Jorie Blvd Ste 111, Oak Brook, IL 60523
Tel.: (630) 990-2025
Copper Alloy Product Mfr
N.A.I.C.S.: 331420

Subsidiary (Non-US):

KME Brass France S.A.S. (2)
11 bis rue de Lhotel de ville, 92411, Courbevoie, Cedex, France
Tel.: (33) 147896817
Copper Tube Mfr
N.A.I.C.S.: 331420

Subsidiary (Domestic):

KME Brass Germany Gmbh (2)
Miraustrasse 10-14, 13509, Berlin, Germany
Tel.: (49) 3040970
Copper Tube Mfr
N.A.I.C.S.: 331420

Subsidiary (Non-US):

KME Brass Italy Srl (2)
Via Cassano 113, 15069, Serravalle Scrivia, Italy
Tel.: (39) 0143609377
Copper Tube Mfr
N.A.I.C.S.: 331420

KME Moulds Mexico S.A. de C.V. (2)
Apolo Avenue No 508 Building 16 Module 3, 66350, Santa Catarina, Nuevo Leon, Mexico
Tel.: (52) 8183086810
Copper Alloy Product Mfr
N.A.I.C.S.: 331420

KME Service Russland Ltd. (2)
Highway Kirillovskoe 86 E Vologda Region, Cherepovets, 162604, Russia
Tel.: (7) 8202290704
Copper Alloy Product Mfr
N.A.I.C.S.: 331420

P.H.M. Pehamet Sp.Zo.o. (2)
ul Kosiarzy 2B, 30-733, Krakow, Poland
Tel.: (48) 126532588
Web Site: http://www.pehamet.com.pl
Copper & Brass Product Distr
N.A.I.C.S.: 423510

bvba KME Benelux sprl (2)
p/a Reus Brussels Airport Pegasuslaan 5, 1831, Diegem, Belgium
Tel.: (32) 27092187
Copper Alloy Product Mfr
N.A.I.C.S.: 331420

KME Ibertubos S.A. (1)
Ctra de Sabadell B-140 Km 5, Sta Perpetua De Mogoda, 08130, Barcelona, Spain
Tel.: (34) 935747090
Web Site: http://www.kme-ibertubos.com
Sales Range: $25-49.9 Million
Emp.: 50
Copper Product Mfr
N.A.I.C.S.: 331420
Nuno Alves Moreira *(Pres)*

KME Italy S.p.A. (1)
Via della Repubblica 257, Fornaci di Barga, 55052, Lucca, Italy
Tel.: (39) 05837011
Web Site: http://www.kme.com
Sales Range: $1-4.9 Billion
Emp.: 1,453
Copper Product Mfr
N.A.I.C.S.: 331420

KME LOCSA S.A. (1)
Ctra Palwa Del Rio S N, Bda Electro Mecanica, 14005, Cordoba, Spain
Tel.: (34) 957216609
Web Site: http://www.locsa.es
Sales Range: $50-74.9 Million
Emp.: 180
Copper Product Mfr

AND PRIVATE COMPANIES

N.A.I.C.S.: 331420

KME Metals (Shanghai) Trading Ltd. (1)
Room 2869 Huaihai Plaza 1045 Middle Huai Hai Road, Xuhui District, Shanghai, 200031, China
Tel.: (86) 2133254169
Copper Alloy Product Mfr
N.A.I.C.S.: 331420

KME Spain S.A.U. (1)
Ctra de Sabadell B-140 Km 5, Santa Perpetua de Mogoda, Barcelona, Spain
Tel.: (34) 935747090
Copper Alloy Product Mfr
N.A.I.C.S.: 331420

KME Srl (1)
Via Saviane 6, 50127, Florence, Italy
Tel.: (39) 05544111
Copper Alloy Product Mfr
N.A.I.C.S.: 331420

Valika SAS (1)
149 Avenue du Golf, 34670, Baillargues, France
Tel.: (33) 467708834
Web Site: http://www.valika.com
International Trading Services
N.A.I.C.S.: 522299

INTEKPLUS CO., LTD.
263 Yuseong-gu, Daejeon, 34026, Korea (South)
Tel.: (82) 429309900
Web Site: https://www.intekplus.com
Year Founded: 1995
064290—(KRS)
Rev.: $91,147,769
Assets: $89,137,462
Liabilities: $37,606,817
Net Worth: $51,530,646
Earnings: $12,528,974
Emp.: 341
Fiscal Year-end: 12/31/22
LED Visual Inspection Semiconductor Mfr
N.A.I.C.S.: 334413
Sang-yoon Lee (CEO)

Subsidiaries:

WKK EMS Equipment (Shenzhen) Ltd. (1)
3 F Xinzhou Building South Xinzhou Road, Futian District, Shenzhen, 518048, Guangdong, China
Tel.: (86) 755 8348 8888
Sales Range: $50-74.9 Million
Semiconductor Inspection System Mfr
N.A.I.C.S.: 333242

INTELGENX TECHNOLOGIES CORP.
6420 Abrams, Ville Saint Laurent, H4S 1Y2, QC, Canada
Tel.: (514) 331-7440 DE
Web Site: https://www.intelgenx.com
IGXT—(OTCIQ)
Rev.: $950,000
Assets: $9,190,000
Liabilities: $12,613,000
Net Worth: ($3,423,000)
Earnings: ($10,690,000)
Emp.: 48
Fiscal Year-end: 12/31/22
Drug DeliveryTechnologies
N.A.I.C.S.: 325412
Horst G. Zerbe (Founder)

Subsidiaries:

IntelGenx Corp. (1)
6425 Abrams Ville, Saint Laurent, H4S 1X9, QC, Canada
Tel.: (514) 331-7440
Web Site: http://www.intelgenx.com
Emp.: 11
Drug Mfr
N.A.I.C.S.: 424210
Horst G. Zerbe (Founder)

INTELICARE HOLDINGS LIMITED
Level 1 299 Vincent Street, Leederville, 6007, WA, Australia
Tel.: (61) 1300001145 AU
Web Site: https://www.intelicare.com.au
Year Founded: 2016
ICR—(ASX)
Rev.: $984,282
Assets: $1,618,515
Liabilities: $999,675
Net Worth: $618,839
Earnings: ($1,954,854)
Fiscal Year-end: 06/30/23
Holding Company
N.A.I.C.S.: 551112
Daniel Pilbrow (CEO)

INTELLABRIDGE TECHNOLOGY CORP.
1055 West Georgia Street Roya Centre Suite 1500, PO Box 11117, Vancouver, V6E 4N7, BC, Canada
Tel.: (604) 684-2181
Web Site: https://www.intellabridge.com
Year Founded: 1988
KASHF—(OTCQB)
Rev.: $12,577
Assets: $8,557,052
Liabilities: $140,999
Net Worth: $8,416,053
Earnings: ($1,041,869)
Emp.: 18
Fiscal Year-end: 12/31/21
Software Application Services
N.A.I.C.S.: 541511
John Eagleton (CEO)

INTELLECT DESIGN ARENA LIMITED
Plot No 3/G3 SIPCOT IT Park Siruseri, Chennai, 600 130, India
Tel.: (91) 4467008000
Web Site: https://www.intellectdesign.com
538835—(BOM)
Rev.: $311,573,945
Assets: $394,119,453
Liabilities: $111,752,960
Net Worth: $282,366,494
Earnings: $36,663,081
Emp.: 5,699
Fiscal Year-end: 03/31/23
Financial Support Services
N.A.I.C.S.: 523999
V. V. Naresh (Officer-Compliance, Sec & VP)

Subsidiaries:

Intellect Design Arena Co. Ltd. (1)
M Level HSC Tower 162B Dien Bien Phu Street, Ward 6 District 3, Ho Chi Minh City, Vietnam
Tel.: (84) 439413076
Software Development Services
N.A.I.C.S.: 541511

Intellect Design Arena FZ LLC (1)
Building No 14 Office 118-120 Dubai Internet City, Dubai, United Arab Emirates
Tel.: (971) 44369461
Software Development Services
N.A.I.C.S.: 541511

Intellect Design Arena Inc. (1)
Suite 400 181 University Avenue, Toronto, M5H 3M7, ON, Canada
Tel.: (416) 800-0216
Software Development Services
N.A.I.C.S.: 541511

Intellect Design Arena Limited (1)
Level 21 25 Canada Square, London, E14 5LQ, United Kingdom
Tel.: (44) 2039729486
Software Development Services
N.A.I.C.S.: 541511

Intellect Design Arena Ltd. (1)
100/42 Sathorn Nakorn Tower 23rd Floor North Sathorn Road, Bangkok, 10500, Thailand
Tel.: (66) 20262311
Software Development Services
N.A.I.C.S.: 541511

Intellect Design Arena Ltda. (1)
Nuncio Monsenor Sotero Sanz N 161 Piso 8 Oficina Intellect Providencia, 7500007, Santiago, Chile
Tel.: (56) 227965530
Software Development Services
N.A.I.C.S.: 541511

Intellect Design Arena Phillipines, Inc. (1)
10th Floor Philamlife Tower 8767 Paseo de Roxas, Makati, 1226, Metro Manila, Philippines
Tel.: (63) 253048403
Software Development Services
N.A.I.C.S.: 541511

Intellect Design Arena Pte. Ltd. (1)
No 10 Ubi Crescent 04-48 Lobby C Ubi Tech Park, Singapore, 408564, Singapore
Tel.: (65) 68482870
Software Development Services
N.A.I.C.S.: 541511

Intellect Design Arena Pte. Ltd. (1)
Level 25 Tower 3 300 Barangaroo Avenue, Barangaroo, 2000, NSW, Australia
Tel.: (61) 282774512
Software Development Services
N.A.I.C.S.: 541511

Intellect Design Arena SA (1)
Avenue de la Gare 49 Case Postale 2067, 2001, Neuchatel, Switzerland
Tel.: (41) 327221990
Software Development Services
N.A.I.C.S.: 541511

Intellect Design Arena, Inc. (1)
20 Corporate Pl S, Piscataway, NJ 08854 (100%)
Tel.: (732) 769-1036
Web Site: https://www.intellectdesign.com
Customer Service & Insurance Software Developer
N.A.I.C.S.: 513210
Pranav Pasricha (CEO)

Intellect Design Arena, PT (1)
Menara BCA 50th Fl JI MH Thamrin No 1, Jakarta, 10310, Indonesia
Tel.: (62) 2123584400
Software Development Services
N.A.I.C.S.: 541511

Sonali Polaris FT Ltd. (1)
35 Kemal Ataturk Avenue 7th Floor Abedin Tower, Banani, Dhaka, 1213, Bangladesh
Tel.: (880) 9666910800
Software Development Services
N.A.I.C.S.: 541511

INTELLECTUAL CAPITAL GROUP LTD.
2450 Victoria Park Avenue Suite 200, Toronto, M2J 4A2, ON, Canada
Tel.: (416) 398-1555
Web Site: http://www.intcapgroup.com
Sales Range: Less than $1 Million
Sports & Entertainment Loyalty Program Services
N.A.I.C.S.: 561499
Steven Wise (Chm & CEO)

Subsidiaries:

Seamiles LLC (1)
3020 NE 32nd Ave, Fort Lauderdale, FL 33308
Tel.: (954) 463-5877
Cruise & Vacation Rewards Program Services
N.A.I.C.S.: 561599

INTELLEGO TECHNOLOGIES AB
Nategrand 8, 194 68, Upplands Vasby, Sweden

INTELLIAN TECHNOLOGIES, INC

Tel.: (46) 735344634
Web Site: https://www.intellego-technologies.com
Year Founded: 2011
7RW—(DEU)
Electronic Components Mfr
N.A.I.C.S.: 334419
Claes Lindahl (Founder)

INTELLEX CO., LTD.
Totate International Building 11F 2-12-19 Shibuya, Shibuya-ku, Tokyo, 150-0002, Japan
Tel.: (81) 357667639
Web Site: https://www.intellex.co.jp
Year Founded: 1995
8940—(TKS)
Rev.: $282,260,220
Assets: $269,093,100
Liabilities: $190,619,180
Net Worth: $78,473,920
Earnings: $2,736,540
Emp.: 319
Fiscal Year-end: 05/31/24
Real Estate Services
N.A.I.C.S.: 531390
Takuya Yamamoto (Pres, Founder & Chm)

Subsidiaries:

Intellex Jyu-Han Co., Ltd. (1)
Intellex Aoyama Bldg 7F 9-11-2Chome Shibuya, Shibuya-ku, Tokyo, 150-0002, Japan
Tel.: (81) 357663739
Web Site: http://www.intellex.jp
Sales Range: $50-74.9 Million
Emp.: 10
Real Estate Agency & Sales Planning Services
N.A.I.C.S.: 531210

Intellex Space Plan Co., Ltd. (1)
1-10 1-chome Takaban Meguro-ku, Tokyo, 152-0004, Japan (100%)
Tel.: (81) 120 55 3927
Web Site: http://www.ku-kan.co.jp
Sales Range: $25-49.9 Million
Emp.: 67
Interior Planning & Design Services
N.A.I.C.S.: 541410

INTELLIAN TECHNOLOGIES, INC
18-7 Jinwisandan-ro Jinwi-myeon, Pyeongtaek, 17709, Gyeonggi-do, Korea (South)
Tel.: (82) 313791000
Web Site: https://www.intelliantech.com
Year Founded: 2004
189300—(KRS)
Rev.: $183,669,923
Assets: $284,079,263
Liabilities: $147,013,064
Net Worth: $137,066,199
Earnings: $12,294,400
Emp.: 306
Fiscal Year-end: 12/31/22
Satellite & Antenna Mfr & Distr
N.A.I.C.S.: 334220

Subsidiaries:

Intellian B.V. (1)
Tempelhof 12, 3045 PV, Rotterdam, Netherlands
Tel.: (31) 108208655
Marine Satellite Antenna Mfr
N.A.I.C.S.: 334220

Intellian Ltd. (1)
Grove House 6 Meridians Cross Ocean Village, Southampton, SO14 3TJ, Hampshire, United Kingdom
Tel.: (44) 2380019021
Satellite Antenna System Product Distr
N.A.I.C.S.: 423690

Intellian Singapore Pte Ltd. (1)
26 Boon Lay Way Tradehub21 01-87, Singapore, 609970, Singapore

INTELLIAN TECHNOLOGIES, INC

INTERNATIONAL PUBLIC

Intellian Technologies, Inc—(Continued)
Tel.: (65) 62061030
Web Site: http://www.intelliantech.com
Emp.: 10
Satellite Antenna System Product Distr
N.A.I.C.S.: 423690
Steve Wee *(Dir)*

Intellian Technologies USA, Inc. (1)
11 Studebaker, Irvine, CA 92618
Tel.: (949) 727-4498
Satellite Antenna System Product Distr
N.A.I.C.S.: 423690

Intellian do Brasil Tecnologia Ltda. (1)
Av Pres Vargas 542 sala 2112 20071000, Rio de Janeiro, Brazil
Tel.: (55) 2131762048
Satellite Antenna System Product Distr
N.A.I.C.S.: 423690

INTELLIGENT CLOUD RESOURCES, INC.
2602 Innisfil Road, Mississauga, L5M 4H9, ON, Canada
Tel.: (647) 478-5633   NV
Information Technology Services
N.A.I.C.S.: 541512
Fatima Khan *(Founder)*

INTELLIGENT ENERGY SAVING COMPANY LTD
344-354 Gray's Inn Road, London, WC1X 8BP, United Kingdom
Tel.: (44) 2071642271
Web Site:
http://www.powerperfector.com
Year Founded: 2004
Energy Saving Equipment Mfr
N.A.I.C.S.: 335311
Michael Robertson-Lambert *(Dir-Engrg)*

INTELLIGENT HOSPITAL SYSTEMS INC.
96 Nature Park Way, Winnipeg, R3P 0X8, MB, Canada
Tel.: (204) 943-0066   MB
Web Site:
http://www.intelligenthospitals.com
Automated Hospital Equipment Mfr & Whslr
N.A.I.C.S.: 334510
Niels Erik Hansen *(Pres & CEO)*

Subsidiaries:

Intelligent Hospital Systems, Inc. (1)
1400 Busch Pkwy, Buffalo Grove, IL 60089
Tel.: (847) 808-2600
Web Site: http://www.arxium.com
Pharmaceutical Supply Chain Management Technologies Developer, Mfr & Whslr
N.A.I.C.S.: 423490

INTELLIGENT LIVING APPLICATION GROUP INC.
Unit 2 5/F Block A Profit Industrial Building, 1-15 Kwai Fung Crescent, Kwai Chung, New Territories, China (Hong Kong)
Tel.: (852) 24817938   Ky
Web Site: https://www.i-l-a-g.com
Year Founded: 1981
ILAG—(NASDAQ)
Rev.: $12,158,102
Assets: $21,802,074
Liabilities: $2,350,263
Net Worth: $19,451,811
Earnings: ($1,655,903)
Emp.: 374
Fiscal Year-end: 12/31/22
Holding Company
N.A.I.C.S.: 551112
Bong Yu Lau *(Chm & CEO)*

Subsidiaries:

KAMBO Locksets Limited (1)
Unit 02 5/F Blk A Profit Industrial Building 1-15 Kwai Fung Crescent, Kwai Chung, China (Hong Kong)
Tel.: (852) 24817938
Web Site: http://www.kambo.com.hk
Lockset Mfr & Distr
N.A.I.C.S.: 332510

INTELLIGENT MONITORING GROUP LIMITED
Level 1 672 Murray Street, Perth, 6005, WA, Australia
Tel.: (61) 1300847328
Web Site:
https://www.threatprotect.com.au
IMB—(ASX)
Rev.: $81,327,457
Assets: $103,080,261
Liabilities: $84,727,564
Net Worth: $18,352,698
Earnings: ($1,121,127)
Fiscal Year-end: 06/30/24
Security Services
N.A.I.C.S.: 561621
Demetrios Pynes *(Mng Dir)*

INTELLIGENT ULTRASOUND GROUP PLC
Floor 6A Hodge House 114-116 St Mary Street, Cardiff, CF10 1DY, United Kingdom
Tel.: (44) 2920756534
Web Site:
https://www.intelligentultra.com
Year Founded: 2006
IUG—(AIM)
Rev.: $12,749,306
Assets: $20,214,592
Liabilities: $4,861,146
Net Worth: $15,353,446
Earnings: ($3,766,726)
Emp.: 57
Fiscal Year-end: 12/31/22
Ultrasound Education & Training
N.A.I.C.S.: 611430
Stuart Gall *(CEO)*

Subsidiaries:

Intelligent Ultrasound North America Incorporated (1)
1111 Alderman Dr Ste 230, Alpharetta, GA 30005
Tel.: (770) 777-8191
Medical Device Mfr
N.A.I.C.S.: 339112
Thomas Brown *(VP-Sls-North America)*

INTELLIGENT WAVE INC.
Kayabacho Tower 1-21-2 Shinkawa, Chuo-ku, Tokyo, 104-0033, Japan
Tel.: (81) 362227111
Web Site: https://www.iwi.co.jp
Year Founded: 1984
4847—(TKS)
Sales Range: Less than $1 Million
Computer Software Programming & Support Services
N.A.I.C.S.: 541511
Masaharu Shirasugi *(Auditor)*

Subsidiaries:

INTELLIGENT WAVE KOREA INC. (1)
2F Samsung Bldg 148 Jungdea-ro, Songpa-gu, Seoul, 138-807, Korea (South)
Tel.: (82) 2 406 1513
Software Development Services
N.A.I.C.S.: 541511
Jongkuk Lee *(Mgr-R&D)*

INTELLIPHARMACEUTICS INTERNATIONAL INC.
30 Worcester Road, Toronto, M9W 5X2, ON, Canada
Tel.: (416) 798-3001   Ca
Web Site:
https://www.intellipharma.com
Year Founded: 2009

IPCIF—(OTCQB)
Rev.: $65,728
Assets: $1,432,032
Liabilities: $12,008,767
Net Worth: ($10,576,735)
Earnings: ($2,892,394)
Emp.: 11
Fiscal Year-end: 11/30/22
Holding Company; Pharmaceutical Research & Development
N.A.I.C.S.: 551112
Isa Odidi *(Co-Founder, Chm, CEO & Co-Chief Scientific Officer)*

Subsidiaries:

Intellipharmaceutics Ltd. (1)
30 Worcester Rd, Toronto, M9W 5X2, ON, Canada   (100%)
Tel.: (416) 798-3001
Web Site:
http://www.intellipharmaceutics.com
Sales Range: $25-49.9 Million
Emp.: 30
Pharmaceutical Product Research & Development Services
N.A.I.C.S.: 541715

INTELLIVATE CAPITAL VENTURES LIMITED
301-304 Vipul Agora Mall M G Road, Gurgaon, 122002, Haryana, India
Tel.: (91) 2224391859
Web Site:
https://www.gourmetgateway.co.in
Year Founded: 1982
506134—(BOM)
Rev.: $8,355
Assets: $679,046
Liabilities: $4,745
Net Worth: $674,301
Earnings: ($28,180)
Emp.: 1
Fiscal Year-end: 03/31/22
Investment Advisory Services
N.A.I.C.S.: 523940
Venkateswara Suram Rao *(Exec Dir)*

Subsidiaries:

Aerpace Industries Ltd. (1)
1104 A Wing Naman Midtown 11th Floor Senapati Bapat Marg, Prabhadevi, Mumbai, 400013, India
Tel.: (91) 2224391933
Web Site: https://www.aerpace.com
Rev.: $7,160
Assets: $482,939
Liabilities: $12,838
Net Worth: $470,100
Earnings: ($15,956)
Fiscal Year-end: 03/31/2022
Steel Trading
N.A.I.C.S.: 423510
Leena V. Modi *(Mng Dir)*

Ram Minerals and Chemicals Limited (1)
1514-1515 Kucha Seth Dariba Kalan, Chandni Chowk, Delhi, 110006, India
Tel.: (91) 1140394984
Web Site: http://www.icvlchemicals.com
Rev.: $984,792
Assets: $5,493,925
Liabilities: $1,845,696
Net Worth: $3,648,229
Earnings: $327
Fiscal Year-end: 03/31/2018
Chemical Product Whslr
N.A.I.C.S.: 424690
Suresh Kumar Aggarwal *(Chm & CFO)*

INTEMA INSAAT VE TESISAT MALZEMELERI YATIRIM VE PAZARLAMA A.S
Buyukdere Cad No 193 Levent, Istanbul, Turkiye
Tel.: (90) 2123399000
INTEM—(IST)
Rev.: $4,868,415
Assets: $11,209,747
Liabilities: $10,372,287
Net Worth: $837,460

Earnings: $84,406
Fiscal Year-end: 12/31/20
Household Product Distr
N.A.I.C.S.: 423220
Bulent Eczacibasi *(Chm)*

INTEMA SOLUTIONS INC.
2020 Trans-Canada Hwy Suite 107, Dorval, H9P 2N4, QC, Canada
Tel.: (514) 861-1881   Ca
Web Site:
https://www.reactgaming.ca
Year Founded: 1994
ITMZF—(OTCEM)
Rev.: $99,692
Assets: $11,209,493
Liabilities: $8,694,834
Net Worth: $2,514,659
Earnings: ($4,066,724)
Emp.: 57
Fiscal Year-end: 12/31/21
Helpdesk & Customer Service Solutions
N.A.I.C.S.: 541519
Laurent Benezra *(Pres & CEO)*

INTENSE TECHNOLOGIES LIMITED
Unit 01 The Headquarters 10th floor Wing B Orbit by AuroRealty, Secunderabad, 500 009, Telangana, India
Tel.: (91) 4044558585
Web Site: https://www.in10stech.com
Year Founded: 1989
532326—(BOM)
Rev.: $11,130,535
Assets: $16,079,337
Liabilities: $2,439,526
Net Worth: $13,639,812
Earnings: $1,666,355
Emp.: 696
Fiscal Year-end: 03/31/23
Application Software Development Services
N.A.I.C.S.: 541511
C. K. Shastri *(Founder, Chm & Mng Dir)*

INTER & CO, INC.
Avenida Barbacena No 1 219 22nd Floor, Belo Horizonte, 30190-131, Brazil
Tel.: (55) 3121387974   Ky
Web Site: https://bancointer.com.br
Year Founded: 1994
INTR—(NASDAQ)
Rev.: $725,008,840
Assets: $9,430,820,850
Liabilities: $7,988,188,186
Net Worth: $1,442,632,664
Earnings: ($2,865,077)
Emp.: 4,030
Fiscal Year-end: 12/31/22
Investment Management Service
N.A.I.C.S.: 523999
Guilherme Ximenes De Almeida *(CTO)*

INTER ACTION CORPORATION
1-1 Fukuura, Kanazawa-ku, Yokohama, 236-0004, Kanagawa, Japan
Tel.: (81) 457888373
Web Site: https://www.inter-action.co.jp
7725—(TKS)
Rev.: $51,253,940
Assets: $90,193,450
Liabilities: $17,245,490
Net Worth: $72,947,960
Earnings: $7,482,520
Emp.: 126
Fiscal Year-end: 05/31/24
Semiconductor Mfr
N.A.I.C.S.: 334413
Nobuo Kiji *(Executives)*

INTER CARS S.A.
ul Gdanska 15 Czastkow Mazowiecki, 05-152, Czosnow, Poland
Tel.: (48) 227141710
Web Site:
 https://www.intercars.com.pl
Year Founded: 1990
CAR—(WAR)
Rev.: $2,303,861,289
Assets: $1,162,908,753
Liabilities: $624,896,141
Net Worth: $538,012,612
Earnings: $59,696,726
Fiscal Year-end: 12/31/19
Automobile Parts Mfr
N.A.I.C.S.: 336390
Andrzej Oliszewski *(Chm-Supervisory Bd)*

INTER CONSTRUTORA E INCORPORADORA S.A.
Rua Ataliba De Barros 182 1504, Sao Mateus, Juiz de Fora, 36025-275, MG, Brazil
Tel.: (55) 3232371540
Web Site:
 http://www.interconstrutora.com
Year Founded: 2008
Rev.: $52,801,356
Assets: $101,792,259
Liabilities: $95,761,726
Net Worth: $6,030,533
Earnings: $12,115,410
Fiscal Year-end: 12/31/18
Real Estate Manangement Services
N.A.I.C.S.: 531210
Leonardo Miguel De Lima *(Pres)*

INTER EDITION DIFFUS REVUE JOURN PERIOD
10 Boulevard Des Freres Voisin, Issy-les-Moulineaux, 92130, Hauts De Seine, France
Tel.: (33) 141468888
Rev.: $22,800,000
Emp.: 34
Periodicals
N.A.I.C.S.: 513120
Veronique Depery *(Dir)*

INTER FAR EAST ENERGY CORPORATION PUBLIC COMPANY LIMITED
33/4 Nine Tower Building 29th Floor Rama 9 Road, Huay Kwang, Bangkok, 10310, Thailand
Tel.: (66) 21681378
Web Site: https://www.ifec.co.th
IFEC—(THA)
Sales Range: $50-74.9 Million
Emp.: 400
Energy Services
N.A.I.C.S.: 221117
Thawich Techanawakun *(Vice Chm & CEO)*

Subsidiaries:

Inter Far East (HongKong) Company Limited (1)
33 Soi Ramkamhaeng 22, Ramkamhaeng Rd Huamark, Bangkok, 10240, Thailand
Tel.: (66) 27188000
Stationery Product Mfr
N.A.I.C.S.: 322230

INTER GLOBE FINANCE LIMITED
Aloka House 1st Floor 6b Bentinck Street, Kolkata, 700001, India
Tel.: (91) 3340661215
Web Site: https://www.igfl.co.in
Year Founded: 1992
511391—(BOM)
Rev.: $3,887,613
Assets: $13,784,552
Liabilities: $1,684,210
Net Worth: $12,100,342
Earnings: ($91,068)
Emp.: 9
Fiscal Year-end: 03/31/21
Financial Management & Advisory Services
N.A.I.C.S.: 523999
Navin Jain *(Chm & Mng Dir)*

INTER INDUSTRIES PLUS LTD.
5 HaYotzer Street Zipporit Industrial Zone, Nof HaGalil, Israel
Tel.: (972) 46414555　　Il
Web Site: https://www.interplus.co.il
Year Founded: 1973
ININ—(TAE)
Rev.: $202,625,498
Assets: $149,668,736
Liabilities: $114,154,716
Net Worth: $35,514,021
Earnings: ($9,951,098)
Fiscal Year-end: 12/31/23
Other Electronic Component Manufacturing
N.A.I.C.S.: 334419

INTER STATE OIL CARRIER LTD
Poddar Point 113 Park Street 5th Floor South Wing, Kolkata, 700016, West Bengal, India
Tel.: (91) 3322290588
Web Site: https://www.isocl.in
530259—(BOM)
Rev.: $6,518,749
Assets: $5,243,156
Liabilities: $2,821,755
Net Worth: $2,421,401
Earnings: $372,795
Emp.: 17
Fiscal Year-end: 03/31/22
Oil Transportation Services
N.A.I.C.S.: 213112
Sanjay Jain *(Mng Dir)*

INTER-CONNECTED STOCK EXCHANGE OF INDIA LIMITED
International Infotech Park Tower No 7 5th Floor Sector 30-AVashi Navi, Mumbai, 400 703, India
Tel.: (91) 2227812056　　In
Web Site: http://www.iseindia.com
Year Founded: 1998
Stock Exchange Services
N.A.I.C.S.: 523210

INTER-DELTA TBK
Jl West Motor Style Sunter II, Jakarta, 14330, Indonesia
Tel.: (62) 216523333　　Id
Web Site: https://www.inter-delta.co.id
Year Founded: 1976
INTD—(INDO)
Rev.: $2,846,094
Assets: $2,756,297
Liabilities: $181,305
Net Worth: $2,574,992
Earnings: ($38,057)
Emp.: 39
Fiscal Year-end: 12/31/23
Online Shopping Services
N.A.I.C.S.: 332311
Joe Marco Lesmana *(Chm)*

INTER-GAMMA INVESTMENT COMPANY LTD.
16 Abba Eban Ave, Herzliya Pituach, 4610302, Israel
Tel.: (972) 99521890
Web Site:
 http://www.intergamma.co.il
Year Founded: 1965
Holding Company
N.A.I.C.S.: 551112
Benjamin Lieberman *(Chm)*

Subsidiaries:

Del-Ta Engineering Equipment Ltd (1)
8 Shaul Hamelech blvd, Tel Aviv, 64733, Israel
Tel.: (972) 3 6979750
Broadcasting Equipment Distr
N.A.I.C.S.: 423690

Delta Digital Ltd. (1)
Kefar Neter Industrial Center, POB 3733, 40593, Kfar Netter, Israel
Tel.: (972) 9 8662626
Web Site: http://www.deltadigital.co.il
Photographic Equipment Distr
N.A.I.C.S.: 449210

RAPAC Communication & Infrastructure Ltd. (1)
6 Meir Ariel Netanya Intergama building, PO Box 3805, Kfar Netter, 4059300, Israel　　(56.6%)
Tel.: (972) 36979700
Web Site: https://www.rapac.co.il
Rev.: $160,304,183
Assets: $880,917,516
Liabilities: $678,550,342
Net Worth: $202,367,175
Earnings: $31,168,393
Emp.: 500
Fiscal Year-end: 12/31/2023
All Other Telecommunications
N.A.I.C.S.: 517810
Nechemya Kind *(Deputy CEO)*

Subsidiary (Domestic):

El-Mor Electric Installation & Services (1986) Ltd. (2)
22 Hotzot Hayotzer st, Ashkelon, Israel
Tel.: (972) 86789999
Web Site: https://www.el-mor.co.il
Rev.: $154,918,080
Assets: $146,781,874
Liabilities: $74,007,735
Net Worth: $72,774,139
Earnings: $9,911,590
Emp.: 500
Fiscal Year-end: 12/31/2023
Electrical Contractors & Other Wiring Installation Contractors
N.A.I.C.S.: 238210
Roni Oren *(Chm)*

General Engineers Ltd. (2)
PO Box 3731, Kfar Netter, 40593, Israel　　(100%)
Tel.: (972) 98662828
Web Site: http://www.geneng.com
Sales Range: $25-49.9 Million
Shipping & Mktg Services
N.A.I.C.S.: 483111
Michal Pataelu-Kamay *(CFO)*

TNN Telecom (2)
Netter Ind Center, Netanya, 49517, Israel
Tel.: (972) 732544500
Data Management Services
N.A.I.C.S.: 541513

INTER-M CO., LTD.
73 Hwahap-ro 1402beon-gil, Yangju, 482-060, Gyeonggi-do, Korea (South)
Tel.: (82) 222898145
Web Site: https://inter-m.net
Year Founded: 1983
017250—(KRS)
Rev.: $53,989,594
Assets: $75,267,871
Liabilities: $46,422,200
Net Worth: $28,845,671
Earnings: $926,166
Emp.: 279
Fiscal Year-end: 09/30/22
Audio & Video Equipment Mfr & Whslr
N.A.I.C.S.: 334310
Ju-Bong Kim *(CEO)*

INTER-ROCK MINERALS INC.
5th Floor 2 Toronto Street, Toronto, M5C 2B6, ON, Canada
Tel.: (416) 367-3003
Web Site:
 https://www.interrockminerals.com
Year Founded: 1952
R77—(DEU)
Rev.: $90,529,000
Assets: $27,544,000
Liabilities: $16,800,000
Net Worth: $10,744,000
Earnings: $1,770,000
Fiscal Year-end: 12/31/23
Mineral Exploration Services
N.A.I.C.S.: 212290
Michael B. Crombie *(CEO)*

Subsidiaries:

MIN-AD, Inc. (1)
　　(100%)
Tel.: (775) 623-5944
Web Site: https://min-ad.com
Sales Range: $1-9.9 Million
Emp.: 22
Prepared Feeds, Nec, Nsk
N.A.I.C.S.: 311119

INTER-SCAN SEA & AIR A/S
Kirstinehoej 8, Kastrup, 2770, Copenhagen, Denmark
Web Site: http://www.isa.dk
Year Founded: 1972
Transportation & Logistics Services
N.A.I.C.S.: 488510
Martin Harrsen *(Mgr-Dev)*

INTER-WORLD PAPER OVERSEAS LTD.
10825 Yonge St Suite 205, Richmond Hill, L4C 3E3, ON, Canada
Tel.: (905) 508-8108
Web Site:
 http://www.interworldpaper.com
Sales Range: $10-24.9 Million
Printing & Paper Mfr
N.A.I.C.S.: 424110
David Zeidenberg *(VP-Sls & Mktg)*

INTERA EQUITY PARTNERS OY
Keskuskatu 1A, 00100, Helsinki, Finland
Tel.: (358) 925252200　　SE
Web Site: http://www.interapartners.fi
Year Founded: 2007
Sales Range: $25-49.9 Million
Emp.: 10
Investment Management Service
N.A.I.C.S.: 523940
Tuomas Lang *(Chm)*

Subsidiaries:

Consti Yhtiot Oy (1)
Fabianinkatu, 00130, Helsinki, Finland
Tel.: (358) 207419770
Web Site: http://www.consti.fi
Sales Range: $125-149.9 Million
Building Renovation Services
N.A.I.C.S.: 238220

Oy Orthex AB (1)
Immulantie 166, Lohja, 8500, Finland
Tel.: (358) 1932961
Web Site: http://www.orthexgroup.com
Sales Range: $10-24.9 Million
Household Plastic Product Mfr
N.A.I.C.S.: 326199
Alexander Rosinlaw *(CEO)*

Subsidiary (Non-US):

Orthex Sweden AB (2)
Barebo, SE 335 91, Gnosjo, Sweden
Tel.: (46) 370356000
Web Site: http://www.orthexgroup.com
Kitchen Product Mfr
N.A.I.C.S.: 332215
Fredrik Enarsson *(Bus Mgr)*

INTERACT BRANDING LTD.
The Dock Tobacco Quay Wapping Lane, London, E1W 2SF, United Kingdom
Tel.: (44) 20 7680 4001　　UK

INTERACT BRANDING LTD.

Interact Branding Ltd.—(Continued)

Web Site:
http://www.interactbranding.com
Brand & Marketing Strategy Consulting Services
N.A.I.C.S.: 541613
Patrick Donovan (Co-Founder)

INTERACTIVE FINANCIAL SERVICES LIMITED
CS Jaini Jain Office No 508 Fifth Floor Nehru Nagar, Priviera, Ahmedabad, 380 015, India
Tel.: (91) 7926581240
Web Site:
https://www.ifinservices.com
Year Founded: 1994
539692—(BOM)
Rev.: $142,084
Assets: $673,272
Liabilities: $9,053
Net Worth: $664,219
Earnings: $61,502
Emp.: 7
Fiscal Year-end: 03/31/21
Financial Support Services
N.A.I.C.S.: 523999
Udayan K. Mandavia (Mng Dir)

INTERACTIVE PROSPECT TARGETING LIMITED
46 Gillingham St, London, SW1V 1HU, United Kingdom
Tel.: (44) 2079324139   UK
Web Site: http://www.ipt-ltd.co.uk
Year Founded: 1999
Sales Range: $10-24.9 Million
Emp.: 55
Onling Direct Marketing Solutions
N.A.I.C.S.: 425120
Lionel Thain (CEO)

INTERAMERICAN GAMING, INC.
110 Yonge Street Suite 1602, Toronto, M5C 1T4, ON, Canada
Tel.: (416) 727-6326   NV
Web Site:
http://www.interamerican.com
Year Founded: 1999
Horse Race Track & Casino Operations
N.A.I.C.S.: 711212

INTERAUTO SA
Zac De La Roche 7 Allee Des Rapailles, Epinal, 88000, Vosges, France
Tel.: (33) 329345239
Web Site: http://www.interauto.fr
Rev.: $12,500,000
Emp.: 15
N.A.I.C.S.: 441110
Jean-Pierre Wolf (Chm)

INTERBALANCE GROUP B.V.
Piet Heinkade 55, 1019 GM, Amsterdam, Netherlands
Tel.: (31) 20 676 3993   NI
Web Site: http://www.balance.nl
Holding Company; Staffing & Employment Consulting Services
N.A.I.C.S.: 551112
Arjen Schutte (Gen Dir)

Subsidiaries:

Balance Ervaring op Projectbasis B.V.   (1)
Piet Heinkade 55, 1019 GM, Amsterdam, Netherlands
Tel.: (31) 206763993
Web Site: http://www.balance.nl
Sales Range: $25-49.9 Million
Emp.: 350
Staffing & Employment Consulting Services
N.A.I.C.S.: 561311
Joost Holleman (Dir-Fin)

INTERBRAND EUROPE
Kirchenweg 5, CH-8008, Zurich, Switzerland
Tel.: (41) 44 388 7878
Web Site: http://www.interbrand.ch
Year Founded: 1972
Emp.: 120
Corporate Identity
N.A.I.C.S.: 541810
Jurg Meier (CFO)

Subsidiaries:

Interbrand   (1)
Zirkusweg 1, D-20359, Hamburg, Germany
Tel.: (49) 40 355 366 0
Emp.: 20
N.A.I.C.S.: 541810
Richard Veit (Mng Dir)

Interbrand   (1)
Weinsbergstrasse 118a, D-50823, Cologne, Germany
Tel.: (49) 221 951 72 0
Web Site: http://www.interbrand.ch
Emp.: 40
N.A.I.C.S.: 541810
Walter Brecht (CEO & CEE)

Interbrand   (1)
Sandstrasse 33, D-80335, Munich, Germany
Tel.: (49) 89 520 579 0
Emp.: 25
N.A.I.C.S.: 541810

Interbrand B.V.   (1)
Prof WH Keesomlaan 4, 1183 DJ, Amstelveen, Netherlands
Tel.: (31) 20 5200 800
Emp.: 10
N.A.I.C.S.: 541810

INTERBUD-LUBLIN S.A.
Al Raclawickie 8 lok 39, 20-037, Lublin, Poland
Tel.: (48) 817450797
Web Site:
https://www.interbud.com.pl
Year Founded: 1987
ITB—(WAR)
Rev.: $407,353
Assets: $5,009,012
Liabilities: $2,301,629
Net Worth: $2,707,383
Earnings: $3,722,383
Emp.: 100
Fiscal Year-end: 12/31/23
Construction Services
N.A.I.C.S.: 236117
Thomas Grodzki (Pres)

INTERCAM BANCO, S.A.
Lago Zurich 219 Colonia Ampliacion Granada Piso 3, Mexico, 11529, Mexico
Tel.: (52) 5550333333   MX
Web Site:
https://www.intercam.com.mx
Year Founded: 1996
Rev.: $252,000,840
Assets: $3,211,375,680
Liabilities: $2,708,729,160
Net Worth: $502,646,520
Earnings: $165,683,040
Fiscal Year-end: 12/31/23
Bank Holding Company
N.A.I.C.S.: 551111
Jose Ruben De la Mora Berenguer (Mng Dir)

INTERCAPITAL GROUP LTD.
Bul Maria Luiza 9-11 Business Center Sofia-2000 floor 5, 1000, Sofia, Bulgaria
Tel.: (359) 29876343
Web Site:
https://www.cashterminal.eu
Year Founded: 2009
ICG—(BUL)
Sales Range: Less than $1 Million

Information & Communication Services
N.A.I.C.S.: 517810
Nadejda Bogoeva (CEO)

INTERCAPITAL PROPERTY DEVELOPMENT REIT
6 Dobrudzha Street 1 Fl, 1000, Sofia, Bulgaria
Tel.: (359) 29210516
Web Site: https://www.icpd.bg
Year Founded: 2005
ICPD—(BUL)
Rev.: $5,158,578
Assets: $28,113,431
Liabilities: $11,178,330
Net Worth: $16,935,102
Earnings: $323,363
Fiscal Year-end: 12/31/23
Real Estate Development Services
N.A.I.C.S.: 531390
Radostina Panteleeva (Dir-Investor Relations)

INTERCEDE GROUP PLC
Lutterworth Hall St Marys Road, Lutterworth, LE17 4PS, Leicestershire, United Kingdom
Tel.: (44) 1455558111   UK
Web Site: https://www.intercede.com
Year Founded: 1992
IGP—(AIM)
Rev.: $25,195,708
Assets: $32,428,744
Liabilities: $15,791,498
Net Worth: $16,637,246
Earnings: $7,599,106
Fiscal Year-end: 03/31/24
Software Development Services
N.A.I.C.S.: 541511
Richard A. Parris (Founder)

Subsidiaries:

Intercede Limited   (1)
Lutterworth Hall St Mary's Road, Lutterworth, LE17 4PS, Leicestershire, United Kingdom
Tel.: (44) 1455 558 111
Web Site: http://www.intercede.com
Sales Range: $25-49.9 Million
Emp.: 6
Security Software Development Services
N.A.I.C.S.: 541511

INTERCEPT ENERGY SERVICES INC.
11464 149th Street, Edmonton, T5M 1W7, AB, Canada
Tel.: (778) 370-1372   AB
Web Site:
http://www.interceptenergy.ca
IESCF—(OTCBB)
Sales Range: $1-9.9 Million
Emp.: 10
Oil Field Services
N.A.I.C.S.: 213112
Monita Faris (Sec)

INTERCONNECT VENTURES CORPORATION
666 Burrard Street Suite 500, Vancouver, V6C 3P6, BC, Canada
Tel.: (965) 998-5018   BC
Year Founded: 2011
IVC—(OTCIQ)
Assets: $277,475
Liabilities: $12,728
Net Worth: $264,748
Earnings: ($80,069)
Fiscal Year-end: 12/31/20
Investment Services
N.A.I.C.S.: 523999

INTERCONTINENTAL GOLD AND METALS LTD
Suite 401-217 Queen Street W, Toronto, M5V 0R2, ON, Canada

INTERNATIONAL PUBLIC

Tel.: (647) 985-2785   BC
Web Site:
http://www.intercontinentalgold.com
Year Founded: 1967
ICAU—(TSXV)
Rev.: $78,910,983
Assets: $2,153,417
Liabilities: $5,567,473
Net Worth: ($3,414,056)
Earnings: ($2,432,804)
Fiscal Year-end: 12/31/20
Mineral Exploration Services
N.A.I.C.S.: 213114
Gorden Glenn (Chm, Pres & CEO)

INTERCONTINENTAL HOTELS GROUP PLC
Windsor Dials 1 Arthur Road, Berkshire, Windsor, SL4 1RS, United Kingdom
Tel.: (44) 1753972000   UK
Web Site: https://www.ihgplc.com
Year Founded: 1777
IHG—(NYSE)
Rev.: $4,624,000,000
Assets: $4,813,000,000
Liabilities: $6,759,000,000
Net Worth: ($1,946,000,000)
Earnings: $750,000,000
Emp.: 13,462
Fiscal Year-end: 12/31/23
Holding Company; Hotel Owner, Operator & Franchisor
N.A.I.C.S.: 551112
George Turner (Chief Comml & Tech Officer)

Subsidiaries:

Asia Pacific Holdings Limited   (1)
Broadwater Park, Denham, UB9 5RH, Buckinghamhshire, United Kingdom
Tel.: (44) 1895512000
Emp.: 700
Investment Management Service
N.A.I.C.S.: 523940

BHR Luxembourg S.A.R.L.   (1)
Avenue Monterey 23, Luxembourg, Luxembourg
Tel.: (352) 2626081
Home Management Services
N.A.I.C.S.: 721110

BHR Overseas (Finance) B.V.   (1)
Strawinskylaan 3105-7, 1077 ZX, Amsterdam, Netherlands
Tel.: (31) 206618203
Financial Investment Services
N.A.I.C.S.: 523999

Carter Queenstown 2015 Ltd.   (1)
93 Beach Street, Queenstown, 9300, New Zealand
Tel.: (64) 34410095
Web Site:
http://www.crowneplazaqueenstown.co.nz
Home Management Services
N.A.I.C.S.: 721110

Crowne Plaza Birmingham City Centre   (1)
Central Square, Birmingham, B1 1HH, West Midlands, United Kingdom
Tel.: (44) 1212245000
Home Management Services
N.A.I.C.S.: 721110

Duet India Hotels (Bangalore) Private Ltd   (1)
Plot No 46 Udyug Vihar Phase 4, Gurgaon, 122015, India
Tel.: (91) 1244528777
Sales Range: $10-24.9 Million
Emp.: 40
Home Management Services
N.A.I.C.S.: 721110
Naveen Jain (Pres)

Grand Central Glasgow Hotel OpCo Limited   (1)
99 Gordon St, Glasgow, G1 3SL, United Kingdom
Tel.: (44) 1412213388

AND PRIVATE COMPANIES

Web Site:
http://grandcentral.vocohotels.com
Hotel & Motel Services
N.A.I.C.S.: 721110

H.I. (Ireland) Limited (1)
Northwood Park Santry Demesne, Santry, Dublin, Ireland
Tel.: (353) 18628866
Sales Range: $25-49.9 Million
Emp.: 130
Home Management Services
N.A.I.C.S.: 721110
Garret O'Neill *(Gen Mgr)*

HH Hotels (EMEA) BV (1)
Kingsfordweg 151, 1043 GR, Amsterdam, Netherlands
Tel.: (31) 206618203
Home Management Services
N.A.I.C.S.: 721110

Holiday Inn Cairns Pty Ltd (1)
121-123 The Esplanade & Florence St, PO Box 121, Cairns, 4870, QLD, Australia
Tel.: (61) 740506070
Sales Range: $10-24.9 Million
Emp.: 80
Home Management Services
N.A.I.C.S.: 721110
Faith Brown *(Mgr-HR)*

Holiday Inn Kuala Lumpur Glenmarie (1)
1 Jalan Usahawan U1/8 Seksyen U1 Shah Alam Selengor, Kuala Lumpur, 40250, Malaysia
Tel.: (60) 378025200
Web Site: http://www.holidayinn.com
Sales Range: $50-74.9 Million
Emp.: 300
Hotel Management, Resort & Guest Services
N.A.I.C.S.: 721110

Holiday Inn Mexicana S.A. (1)
Ontario No 1050, 44630, Guadalajara, Mexico
Tel.: (52) 3336485300
Home Management Services
N.A.I.C.S.: 721110

Holiday Inns (Beijing) Ltd. (1)
No 36 Nanwei Road, Xuanwu District, 100050, Beijing, China
Tel.: (86) 10 83157777
Sales Range: $10-24.9 Million
Emp.: 50
Home Management Services
N.A.I.C.S.: 721110

Holiday Inns (Chongqing), Inc. (1)
No 96 Wu Hong Rd Longta Street, Yubei District, Chongqing, 400020, China
Tel.: (86) 2386568888
Sales Range: $50-74.9 Million
Emp.: 320
Home Management Services
N.A.I.C.S.: 721110

Holiday Inns (Macau) Ltd. (1)
Rua De Pequim 82-86 Macau Sar, Macau, China (Macau)
Tel.: (853) 28783333
Sales Range: $10-24.9 Million
Emp.: 100
Home Management Services
N.A.I.C.S.: 721110
Carmond Hui *(Gen Mgr)*

Holiday Inns Holdings (Australia) Pty Ltd. (1)
Level 11 20 Bond Street, Sydney, 2000, NSW, Australia
Tel.: (61) 299358300
Investment Management Service
N.A.I.C.S.: 523940

Holiday Inns de Espana S.A. (1)
Plaza Carlos Trias Bertran 4, Madrid, 28020, Spain
Tel.: (34) 91 210 58 50
Web Site: http://www.ihg.com
Sales Range: $25-49.9 Million
Emp.: 120
Home Management Services
N.A.I.C.S.: 721110

Holiday Inns of America (UK) Ltd. (1)
Two Snowhill Snow Hill Queensway, Birmingham, B4 6GA, Buckinghamshire, United Kingdom
Tel.: (44) 1895512000
Home Management Services
N.A.I.C.S.: 721110

Hoteles Estelar de Colombia S.A. (1)
Av Colombia 2 72, Cali, Colombia
Tel.: (57) 8000978000
Home Management Services
N.A.I.C.S.: 721110

I.H.C. (Thailand) Ltd (1)
973 Phloen Chit Road, Pathum Wan, Bangkok, 10330, Thailand
Tel.: (66) 2 656 0444
Web Site:
http://bangkok.intercontinental.com
Home Management Services
N.A.I.C.S.: 721110

IC Hotels Management (Portugal) Unipessoal, Lda (1)
Praca da Liberdade 25, 4000-322, Porto, Portugal
Tel.: (351) 220035600
Web Site:
http://www.intercontinentalhotel.com
Sales Range: $10-24.9 Million
Emp.: 70
Home Management Services
N.A.I.C.S.: 721110

IC International Hotels Limited Liability Company (1)
Tverskaya Ulitsa 22, 125009, Moscow, Russia
Tel.: (7) 4957878887
Web Site: http://www.icg.com
Home Management Services
N.A.I.C.S.: 721110

IHC London (Holdings) Ltd. (1)
Broadwater Park, Denham, UB9 5HR, Buckinghamshire, United Kingdom
Tel.: (44) 1895 512000
Web Site: http://www.ihc.com
Emp.: 700
Investment Management Service
N.A.I.C.S.: 523940

IHG (Australasia) Limited (1)
230 Victoria Street 13-00 Bugis Junction Towers, Singapore, 188024, Singapore
Tel.: (65) 63956166
Emp.: 180
Home Management Services
N.A.I.C.S.: 721110

IHG (Marseille) SAS (1)
1 Place Daviel, 13002, Marseille, France
Tel.: (33) 413424242
Hotel & Motel Services
N.A.I.C.S.: 721110

IHG (Thailand) Limited (1)
971 973 Ploenchit Road, Lumpini Pathumwan, Bangkok, 10330, Thailand
Tel.: (66) 265603189
Home Management Services
N.A.I.C.S.: 721110
Thomas Schmelter *(Reg Gen Mgr)*

IHG ANA Hotels Holdings Co., Ltd (1)
20th Floor Toranomon Kotoshira Tower 2-8 Toranomon 1-chom, Minato-ku Akasaka, Tokyo, 105-0001, Japan
Tel.: (81) 335059626
Investment Management Service
N.A.I.C.S.: 523940

IHG Franchising Brasil Ltda (1)
Alameda Jau 536 Suite 3S-E, Sao Paulo, 01420-000, Brazil
Tel.: (55) 1131792600
Home Management Services
N.A.I.C.S.: 721110
Francisco Garcia *(Gen Mgr)*

IHG Hotels Management (Australia) Pty Limited (1)
Level 11 20 Bond Street, Sydney, 2000, NSW, Australia
Tel.: (61) 299358300
Sales Range: $25-49.9 Million
Emp.: 45
Home Management Services

N.A.I.C.S.: 721110
Bill Edwards *(Dir-Ops)*

IHG IT Services (India) Private Limited (1)
Bldg No 10 Tower C 11th Fl Dlf Ph-2 Dlf City Phase Ii, Gurgaon, 122008, India
Tel.: (91) 1244821111
Business Process Outsourcing Services
N.A.I.C.S.: 561499

IHG Japan (Osaka) LLC (1)
3-60 Ofukacho, Kita Ward, Osaka, 530-0011, Japan
Tel.: (81) 663745700
Home Management Services
N.A.I.C.S.: 721110

IHG PS Nominees Limited (1)
Broadwater Park, Denham, UB9 5RH, Buckinghamshire, United Kingdom
Tel.: (44) 8719429292
Financial Investment Services
N.A.I.C.S.: 523999

IHG Szalloda Budapest Szolgatato Kft (1)
Budapest Apaczai Csere J u 12-14, 1052, Budapest, Hungary
Tel.: (36) 13276333
Home Management Services
N.A.I.C.S.: 721110

Inter-Continental Hotels (Montreal) Operating Corp. (1)
360 Saint-Antoine Street West, Montreal, H2Y 3X4, QC, Canada
Tel.: (514) 987-9900
Home Management Services
N.A.I.C.S.: 721110
Louis Sudano *(Dir-Association Sls)*

Inter-Continental Hotels (Montreal) Owning Corp. (1)
360 Saint-Antoine Street West, Montreal, H2Y 3X4, QC, Canada
Tel.: (514) 987-9900
Web Site:
http://www.montral.intercontinental.com
Home Management Services
N.A.I.C.S.: 721110

Inter-Continental Hotels (Singapore) Pte Ltd (1)
80 Middle Rd, Singapore, 188966, Singapore
Tel.: (65) 63387600
Web Site: http://www.ihg.com
Emp.: 400
Home Management Services
N.A.I.C.S.: 721110

InterContinental Gestion Hotelera S.L. (1)
Paseo de Recoletos 37 - 41, 28004, Madrid, Spain
Tel.: (34) 917007300
Hotel & Motel Services
N.A.I.C.S.: 721110

InterContinental Grand Stanford Hong Kong (1)
No 70 Mody Rd Tsim Sha Tsui East, Kowloon, China (Hong Kong)
Tel.: (852) 27215161
Web Site:
https://www.hongkong.intercontinent.com
Home Management Services
N.A.I.C.S.: 721110

InterContinental Hotel Berlin GmbH (1)
Budapester Strasse 2, 10787, Berlin, Germany
Tel.: (49) 3026020
Sales Range: $50-74.9 Million
Emp.: 350
Home Management Services
N.A.I.C.S.: 721110

InterContinental Hotel Dusseldorf GmbH (1)
Konigsallee 59, Dusseldorf, 40215, Germany
Tel.: (49) 21182850
Web Site:
http://www.duesseldorf.intercontinent.com
Sales Range: $25-49.9 Million
Emp.: 150
Home Management Services

INTERCONTINENTAL HOTELS GROUP PLC

N.A.I.C.S.: 721110
Aernout de Jong *(Mng Dir)*

InterContinental Hotels Corporation (1)
3 Ravinia Dr Ste 100, Atlanta, GA 30346-2149
Tel.: (770) 604-2000
Rev.: $8,000,000
Emp.: 2,000
Hotel Franchisor & Operator
N.A.I.C.S.: 721110
Elie W. Maalouf *(CEO-Americas)*

Subsidiary (Domestic):

BHR Pacific Holdings, Inc. (2)
3411 Silverside Rd Tatnall Bldg Ste 104, Wilmington, DE 19810
Tel.: (770) 604-5000
Investment Management Service
N.A.I.C.S.: 523940

Barclay Operating Corp. (2)
111 E 48th St Fl 2 Ste 2, New York, NY 10017
Tel.: (212) 755-5900
Web Site: http://www.ihg.com
Emp.: 52
Home Management Services
N.A.I.C.S.: 721110

Bristol Oakbrook Tenant Company (2)
3411 Silverside Rd Tatnall Bldg Ste 104, Wilmington, DE 19810
Tel.: (770) 604-5000
Home Management Services
N.A.I.C.S.: 721110

CDC San Francisco LLC (2)
888 Howard St, San Francisco, CA 94103
Tel.: (415) 616-6512
Sales Range: $50-74.9 Million
Emp.: 350
Home Management Services
N.A.I.C.S.: 721110

Carr 625 First Street LLC (2)
625 1st St, Alexandria, VA 22314
Tel.: (703) 548-6300
Web Site:
http://www.hioldtownalexandriahotel.com
Emp.: 200
Home Management Services
N.A.I.C.S.: 721110

Crowne Plaza LLC (2)
3 Executive Blvd, Suffern, NY 10901
Tel.: (845) 357-4800
Web Site: http://www.cpsuffernhotel.com
Home Management Services
N.A.I.C.S.: 721110

Crowne Plaza Old Town Alexandria (2)
901 N Fairfax St, Alexandria, VA 22314
Tel.: (703) 683-6000
Web Site: http://www.crowneplaza.com
Home Management Services
N.A.I.C.S.: 721110

General Innkeeping Acceptance Corporation (2)
205 Powell Plc, Brentwood, TN 37027
Tel.: (770) 952-9797
Home Management Services
N.A.I.C.S.: 721110

HC International Holdings, Inc (2)
1105 N Market St Ste 1300, Wilmington, DE 19801
Tel.: (302) 427-3888
Investment Management Service
N.A.I.C.S.: 523940

Hoft Properties LLC (2)
3411 Silverside Rd Tatnall Bldg Ste 104, Wilmington, DE 19810
Tel.: (801) 920-8853
Real Estate Development Services
N.A.I.C.S.: 531390

Holiday Pacific Equity Corporation (2)
3411 Silverside Rd Tatnall Bldg Ste 104, Wilmington, DE 19810
Tel.: (770) 604-2000
Financial Investment Services
N.A.I.C.S.: 523999

INTERCONTINENTAL HOTELS GROUP PLC

InterContinental Hotels Group PLC—(Continued)

Holiday Pacific Limited Liability Company (2)
3411 Silverside Rd Tatnall Bldg Ste 104, Wilmington, DE 19810
Tel.: (770) 604-2000
Home Management Services
N.A.I.C.S.: 721110

IHC Buckhead LLC (2)
2985 Gordy Pkwy 1st Fl, Marietta, GA 30066
Tel.: (404) 946-9000
Sales Range: $50-74.9 Million
Emp.: 500
Home Management Services
N.A.I.C.S.: 721110
Kim Lowthers (Dir-Sls & Mktg)

IHC Hopkins (Holdings) Corp. (2)
3411 Silverside Rd Tatnall Bldg Ste 104, Wilmington, DE 19810
Tel.: (770) 604-5000
Investment Management Service
N.A.I.C.S.: 523940

IHC M-H (Holdings) Corp. (2)
3411 Silverside Rd Tatnall Bldg Ste 104, Wilmington, DE 19810
Tel.: (770) 604-5000
Investment Management Service
N.A.I.C.S.: 523940

IHC United States (Holdings) Corp. (2)
3411 Silverside Rd Tatnall Bldg Ste 104, Wilmington, DE 19810
Tel.: (770) 604-5000
Investment Management Service
N.A.I.C.S.: 523940

IHG Franchising LLC (2)
3 Ravinia Dr, Atlanta, GA 30346
Tel.: (770) 604-2000
Web Site: http://www.ihg.com
Home Management Services
N.A.I.C.S.: 721110

IHG Orchard Street Member, LLC (2)
3 Ravinia Dr, Atlanta, GA 30346
Tel.: (770) 604-5000
Home Management Services
N.A.I.C.S.: 721110

IND East Village SD Holdings LLC (2)
3 Ravinia Dr, Atlanta, GA 30346
Tel.: (770) 604-5000
Investment Management Service
N.A.I.C.S.: 523940

Inter-Continental Florida Investment Corp. (2)
3411 Silverside Rd Tatnall Bldg Ste 104, Wilmington, DE 19810
Tel.: (770) 604-5000
Financial Investment Services
N.A.I.C.S.: 523999

Unit (Domestic):

InterContinental - Chicago Magnificent Mile (2)
505 N Michigan Ave, Chicago, IL 60611-3827
Tel.: (312) 944-4100
Web Site: https://www.icchicagohotel.com
Sales Range: $50-74.9 Million
Emp.: 600
Luxury Hotel Operator
N.A.I.C.S.: 721110

InterContinental - The Barclay New York (2)
111 E 48th St, New York, NY 10017-1297
Tel.: (212) 755-5900
Sales Range: $900-999.9 Million
Emp.: 300
Luxury Hotel Operator
N.A.I.C.S.: 721110
Sofia Vandaele (Gen Mgr)

Subsidiary (Domestic):

InterContinental Hotels (Puerto Rico) Inc (2)
5961 Ave Isla Verde, Carolina, PR 00979
Tel.: (787) 791-5000

Web Site: http://www.intercontinental.com
Home Management Services
N.A.I.C.S.: 721110

InterContinental Hotels Group Resources Inc (2)
1275 W 2240 S, Salt Lake City, UT 84119
Tel.: (801) 975-3000
Web Site: http://www.ihg.com
Home Management Services
N.A.I.C.S.: 721110

InterContinental Hotels of San Francisco, Inc. (2)
888 Howard St, San Francisco, CA 94103
Tel.: (415) 616-6500
Web Site: http://www.intercontinental.com
Emp.: 100
Home Management Services
N.A.I.C.S.: 721110

Intercontinental D.C. Operating Corp. (2)
3411 Silverside Rd Tatnall Bldg Ste 104, Wilmington, DE 19810
Tel.: (703) 217-3165
Home Management Services
N.A.I.C.S.: 721110

Intercontinental Overseas Holding Corporation (2)
3411 Silverside Rd Tatnall Bldg Ste 104, Wilmington, DE 19810
Tel.: (770) 604-5000
Investment Management Service
N.A.I.C.S.: 523940

Kimpton Hotel & Restaurant Group, LLC (2)
222 Kearny St Ste 200, San Francisco, CA 94108
Tel.: (415) 397-5572
Web Site: http://www.kimptonhotels.com
Hotels & Restaurants Operations & Management Services
N.A.I.C.S.: 721110
Mike DeFrino (CEO)

Unit (Domestic):

Kimpton Hotel Madera (3)
1310 New Hampshire Ave NW, Washington, DC 20036
Tel.: (202) 296-7600
Web Site: http://www.hotelmadera.com
Emp.: 40
Hotel Services
N.A.I.C.S.: 721110

Subsidiary (Domestic):

Kimpton Mason & Rook Hotel (3)
1430 Rhode Island Ave NW, Washington, DC 20005-5401
Tel.: (202) 742-3100
Hotel Operator
N.A.I.C.S.: 721110

Unit (Domestic):

Surfcomber Hotel (3)
1717 Collins Ave, Miami Beach, FL 33139
Tel.: (305) 532-7715
Web Site: http://www.surfcomber.com
Emp.: 164
Hotel Services
N.A.I.C.S.: 721110

Subsidiary (Domestic):

Louisiana Acquisitions Corp. (2)
3 Ravinia Dr Ste 2900, Atlanta, GA 30346
Tel.: (770) 604-5000
Financial Management Services
N.A.I.C.S.: 523999

PANACON CORP. (2)
444 Saint Charles Ave, New Orleans, LA 70130
Tel.: (504) 585-4361
Home Management Services
N.A.I.C.S.: 721110

PML Services LLC (2)
3 Ravinia Dr, Atlanta, GA 30346
Tel.: (770) 604-5777
Home Management Services
N.A.I.C.S.: 721110

Pershing Associates LP (2)
209 W 3rd St, Greensburg, PA 15601

Tel.: (724) 834-3191
Real Estate Development Services
N.A.I.C.S.: 531390

Powell Pine, Inc. (2)
3 Ravinia Dr Ste 2900, Atlanta, GA 30346-2143
Tel.: (770) 604-5000
Home Management Services
N.A.I.C.S.: 721110

Priscilla Holliday of Texas, Inc. (2)
3 Ravinia Dr Ste 2900, Hidalgo, TX 77056
Tel.: (512) 282-5516
Home Management Services
N.A.I.C.S.: 721110

Resort Services International (Cayo Largo), L.P., S.E. (2)
3 Ravinia Dr, Atlanta, GA 30346-2118
Tel.: (770) 604-5000
Home Management Services
N.A.I.C.S.: 721110

SC Reservations (Philippines) Inc (2)
205 Powell Plc, Brentwood, TN 37027
Tel.: (770) 604-5000
Home Management Services
N.A.I.C.S.: 721110

SCH Insurance Company (2)
30 Main St Ste 500, Burlington, VT 05402-1489
Tel.: (770) 604-5000
Insurance Management Services
N.A.I.C.S.: 524298

SFH Associates L.P. (2)
3 Ravinia Dr, Atlanta, GA 30346-2118
Tel.: (770) 604-5000
Home Management Services
N.A.I.C.S.: 721110

Six Continents Hotels, Inc. (2)
3 Ravinia Dr Ste 100, Atlanta, GA 30346-2149
Tel.: (770) 604-8347
Home Management Services
N.A.I.C.S.: 721110

SixCo North America, Inc. (2)
1105 N Market St Ste 1300, Wilmington, DE 19801
Tel.: (302) 427-3888
Home Management Services
N.A.I.C.S.: 721110

Unit (Domestic):

Staybridge Suites - Torrance/Redondo Beach Hotel (2)
19901 Prairie Ave, Torrance, CA 90503
Tel.: (310) 371-8525
Web Site: http://www.ichotelsgroup.com
Sales Range: $10-24.9 Million
Emp.: 20
Hotel Services
N.A.I.C.S.: 721110

InterContinental Hotels Corporation de Venezuela C.A. (1)
Hotel Tamanaco Inter-Continental Final Av Ppal Mercedes, PO Box 467, Caracas, Venezuela
Tel.: (58) 2129097111
Home Management Services
N.A.I.C.S.: 721110

InterContinental Hotels Group (Asia Pacific) Pte. Ltd. (1)
230 Victoria Street 13-00 Bugis Junction Towers, Singapore, 188024, Singapore
Tel.: (65) 63956166
Sales Range: $25-49.9 Million
Emp.: 150
Home Management Services
N.A.I.C.S.: 721110

InterContinental Hotels Group (Australia) Pty Limited (1)
Level 11 20 Bond Street, Sydney, 2000, NSW, Australia
Tel.: (61) 299358300
Emp.: 45
Home Management Services
N.A.I.C.S.: 721110

InterContinental Hotels Group (Canada) Inc. (1)

INTERNATIONAL PUBLIC

970 Dixon Rd, Etobicoke, M9W 1J9, ON, Canada
Tel.: (416) 675-2347
Home Management Services
N.A.I.C.S.: 721110
Jonathan Lund (VP-Franchise Performance Support)

InterContinental Hotels Group (Espana) SA (1)
Paseo De La Castellana 49, 28046, Madrid, Spain
Tel.: (34) 917007300
Home Management Services
N.A.I.C.S.: 721110

InterContinental Hotels Group (Greater China) Limited (1)
507 South Tower World Finance Center, Harbour City, Kowloon, China (Hong Kong)
Tel.: (852) 27301654
Home Management Services
N.A.I.C.S.: 721110
Eric Koo (Dir-Dev-Shanghai)

InterContinental Hotels Group (New Zealand) Limited (1)
Level 10 55 Shortland Street, Auckland Central, Auckland, 1010, New Zealand
Tel.: (64) 93670203
Emp.: 100
Home Management Services
N.A.I.C.S.: 721110

InterContinental Hotels Group (Shanghai) Ltd (1)
22nd Floor Citigroup Tower No 33 Huayuanshiqiao Road, Pudong New Area, Shanghai, 200120, China
Tel.: (86) 2128933388
Home Management Services
N.A.I.C.S.: 721110

InterContinental Hotels Group Customer Services Ltd. (1)
Broadwater Park, Denham, UB9 5RH, Buckinghamshire, United Kingdom
Tel.: (44) 8719429040
Home Management Services
N.A.I.C.S.: 721110

InterContinental Hotels Group Healthcare Trustee Ltd (1)
Broadwater Park, Denham, UB9 5RH, Buckinghamshire, United Kingdom
Tel.: (44) 1895512000
Emp.: 700
Home Management Services
N.A.I.C.S.: 721110

InterContinental Hotels Group Services Company (1)
Broadwater Park, Denham, UB9 5RH, Buckinghamshire, United Kingdom
Tel.: (44) 1895512000
Emp.: 600
Home Management Services
N.A.I.C.S.: 721110

InterContinental Hotels Italia, Srl (1)
Viale Monte Nero n 84, 20135, Milan, Italy
Tel.: (39) 0667331
Emp.: 100
Home Management Services
N.A.I.C.S.: 721110
Ciro Verrocchi (Pres)

InterContinental Hotels Limited (1)
Broadwater Park, Denham, UB9 5HR, Buckinghamshire, United Kingdom
Tel.: (44) 1895512000
Sales Range: $125-149.9 Million
Emp.: 700
Hotel Franchisor & Operator
N.A.I.C.S.: 721110
Nigel Stocks (Gen Counsel-EMEA & Sr VP)

InterContinental Hotels Management GmbH (1)
Thurn-und-Taxis-Platz 6, 60313, Frankfurt am Main, Germany
Tel.: (49) 6927401451
Home Management Services
N.A.I.C.S.: 721110

KHRG Born LLC (1)
1600 Wewatta St, Denver, CO 80202
Tel.: (303) 323-0024
Web Site: http://www.hotelborndenver.com
Hotel & Motel Services

AND PRIVATE COMPANIES

N.A.I.C.S.: 721110

KHRG La Peer LLC (1)
627 N La Peer Dr, West Hollywood, CA 90069
Tel.: (213) 296-3038
Web Site: https://www.lapeerhotel.com
Hotel & Motel Services
N.A.I.C.S.: 721110

KHRG Palladian LLC (1)
2000 Second Ave, Seattle, WA 98121
Tel.: (206) 448-1111
Web Site: http://www.palladianhotel.com
Hotel & Motel Services
N.A.I.C.S.: 721110

KHRG Palomar Phoenix LLC (1)
2 E Jefferson St, Phoenix, AZ 85004
Tel.: (602) 253-6633
Web Site: http://www.hotelpalomar-phoenix.com
Hotel & Motel Services
N.A.I.C.S.: 721110

KHRG Philly Monaco LLC (1)
433 Chestnut St, Philadelphia, PA 19106
Tel.: (215) 925-2111
Web Site: http://www.monaco-philadelphia.com
Hotel & Motel Services
N.A.I.C.S.: 721110

Oxford Thames Hotel OpCo Limited (1)
Henley Road, Sandford-on-Thames, Denham, OX4 4GX, Oxfordshire, United Kingdom
Tel.: (44) 1865334444
Web Site: http://www.oxfordthames.vocohotels.com
Hotel & Motel Services
N.A.I.C.S.: 721110

President Hotel & Tower Co Ltd. (1)
971 973 Ploenchit Road Lumpini, Pathumwan, Bangkok, 10330, Thailand
Tel.: (66) 26560444
Home Management Services
N.A.I.C.S.: 721110
Chatchawin Charoen-Rajapark *(Owner)*

Raison d'Etre Spas Sweden AB (1)
Grevgatan 15 BV, 114 53, Stockholm, Sweden
Tel.: (46) 87560056
Web Site: https://www.raisondetrespas.com
Spa Services
N.A.I.C.S.: 812199
Anna Bjurstam *(Mng Partner)*

SC Leisure Group Ltd. (1)
Broadwater Park, Denham, UB9 5RH, United Kingdom
Tel.: (44) 1512281048
Home Management Services
N.A.I.C.S.: 721110

Six Continents Hotels de Colombia SA (1)
Calle 49 Sur 45 A 300 Oficina 1102 Envigado, 55422, Antioquia, Colombia
Tel.: (57) 43154464
Home Management Services
N.A.I.C.S.: 721110

Six Continents International Holdings BV (1)
Kingsfordweg 151, 1043 GR, Amsterdam, Netherlands
Tel.: (31) 206618203
Investment Management Service
N.A.I.C.S.: 523940

Societe Nouvelle du Grand Hotel SA (1)
16 Boulevard Sainte Anne, Lisieux, 14300, France
Tel.: (33) 2 31 62 17 53
Home Management Services
N.A.I.C.S.: 721110

Societe des Hotels InterContinental France SNC (1)
Tel.: (33) 155310800
Web Site: http://www.ihg.com
Sales Range: $10-24.9 Million
Emp.: 25
Home Management Services
N.A.I.C.S.: 721110

Southern Pacific Hotel Corporation (BVI) Ltd. (1)
Tortola, Road Town, Virgin Islands (British)
Tel.: (284) 4942233
Home Management Services
N.A.I.C.S.: 721110

St David's Cardiff Hotel OpCo Limited (1)
Havannah Street, Cardiff, CF10 5SD, United Kingdom
Tel.: (44) 2920454045
Web Site: http://stdavids.vocohotels.com
Hotel & Motel Services
N.A.I.C.S.: 721110

TAK How Investment Limited (1)
70 Mody Road, Tsim Sha Tsui, Kowloon, China (Hong Kong)
Tel.: (852) 23691439
Real Estate Agency
N.A.I.C.S.: 531210

White Shield Insurance Company Ltd. (1)
21 Engineer Lane, Gibraltar, Gibraltar
Tel.: (350) 20074015
Sales Range: $50-74.9 Million
Emp.: 60
Insurance Management Services
N.A.I.C.S.: 524298
Paul Savignon *(Dir-Fin)*

Wotton House Hotel OpCo Limited (1)
Guildford Road, Dorking, RH5 6HS, United Kingdom
Tel.: (44) 1306730000
Web Site: http://www.wottonhouse.co.uk
Hotel & Motel Services
N.A.I.C.S.: 721110

Yokohama Grand Intercontinental Hotel Co. Ltd. (1)
1-1-1 Minatomirai, Nishi-ku, Yokohama, 220-8522, Kanagawa, Japan
Tel.: (81) 452232300
Web Site: https://www.icyokohama-grand.com
Sales Range: $50-74.9 Million
Emp.: 500
Home Management Services
N.A.I.C.S.: 721110

INTERCONTINENTAL INTERNATIONAL REAL ESTATE INVESTMENT COMPANY

26 Rigillis 3rd floor, Anaktora, 10674, Athens, Greece
Tel.: (30) 2167000555
Web Site: https://www.ici-reic.com
INTERCO—(ATH)
Rev.: $3,873,602
Assets: $131,173,804
Liabilities: $41,592,399
Net Worth: $89,581,405
Earnings: $1,114,449
Emp.: 4
Fiscal Year-end: 12/31/23
Real Estate Investment Services
N.A.I.C.S.: 531210
Patricia Halikias *(Vice Chm)*

INTERCORP FINANCIAL SERVICES INC.

Torre Interbank Av Carlos Villaran 140, La Victoria, 13, Lima, 13, Peru
Tel.: (51) 16159011 Pa
Web Site: https://www.ifs.com.pe
Year Founded: 2006
IFS—(NYSE)
Rev.: $1,609,441,304
Assets: $23,980,739,084
Liabilities: $21,226,942,996
Net Worth: $2,753,796,088
Earnings: $457,960,497
Emp.: 8,087
Fiscal Year-end: 12/31/22
Financial Services Including Banking, Wealth Management & Insurance
N.A.I.C.S.: 525990
Carlos Rodriguez-Pastor Persivale *(Chm)*

Subsidiaries:

Inteligo Bank Ltd. (1)
Calle 50 con Elvira Mendez Piso 48, PO Box 0823-00585, Torre Financial Center, Panama, Panama
Tel.: (507) 3669600
Banking Services
N.A.I.C.S.: 522110

Interseguro Compania de Seguros S.A. (1)
Av Javier Prado Este No 492 Oficina 2601, San Isidro, Peru
Tel.: (51) 6114700
Web Site: http://www.interseguro.pe
Rev.: $2,116,170,619
Assets: $24,188,265,176
Liabilities: $21,487,242,048
Net Worth: $2,701,023,128
Earnings: $291,278,979
Fiscal Year-end: 12/31/2023
General Insurance Services
N.A.I.C.S.: 524210
Lorena Vallejos *(Owner)*

INTERCORP GROUP

Urb Ses Fontanellas Plaza Calle Es Calo 104, Port d'es Torrent, Ibiza, 7829, Spain
Tel.: (34) 971804060
Web Site: http://www.intercorpgrp.com
Travel & Vacation Services
N.A.I.C.S.: 721199
Michele Warner *(Acct Mgr-Dallas)*

Subsidiaries:

Brantridge Management Limited (1)
Brantridge Park Brantridge Ln, Balcombe, Haywards Heath, United Kingdom
Tel.: (44) 444400251
Sales Range: $25-49.9 Million
Emp.: 30
Management Consulting Services
N.A.I.C.S.: 541611

INTERCOS S.P.A.

Via Marconi 84, 20864, Agrate Brianza, Italy
Tel.: (39) 03965521 IT
Web Site: https://www.intercos-investor.com
Year Founded: 1972
ICOS—(ITA)
Rev.: $1,090,874,269
Assets: $1,082,825,919
Liabilities: $586,590,131
Net Worth: $496,235,788
Earnings: $57,875,041
Emp.: 4,087
Fiscal Year-end: 12/31/23
Cosmetic Product Mfr & Distr
N.A.I.C.S.: 325620
Dario Gianandrea Ferrari *(Chm)*

Subsidiaries:

Ager S.R.L. (1)
Via Santuario delle Grazie Vecchie 1, 20900, Monza, MB, Italy
Tel.: (39) 0392326260
Web Site: https://www.ager.it
Cosmetics Mfr
N.A.I.C.S.: 325620

Biocosmetiques S.A. (1)
Route du Verney 1, 1070, Puidoux, Switzerland
Tel.: (41) 219460000
Cosmetics Mfr
N.A.I.C.S.: 325620

CRB Benelux B.V. (1)
Oxfordlaan 70, 6229, Maastricht, Netherlands
Tel.: (31) 433885850
Web Site: https://www.crbbeneluxbv.com
Cosmetics Mfr
N.A.I.C.S.: 325620

Cosmint S.p.A. (1)
Via XXV Aprile 15, 22077, Olgiate Comasco, CO, Italy
Tel.: (39) 031996711

Cosmetics Mfr
N.A.I.C.S.: 325620

Intercos Asia Pacific Ltd. (1)
Room 1110 11/F 133 Wai Yip Street, Kwun Tong, China (Hong Kong)
Tel.: (852) 35824578
Cosmetics Mfr
N.A.I.C.S.: 325620

Intercos Cosmetics (Suzhou) Co., Ltd. (1)
No 89 Qi Ming Road EPZB Industrial Park, Suzhou, 215126, China
Tel.: (86) 51287178550
Cosmetics Products Mfr
N.A.I.C.S.: 325620

Intercos Paris S.A.R.L. (1)
10 Rue Cimarosa, 75016, Paris, France
Tel.: (33) 153645420
Cosmetics Mfr
N.A.I.C.S.: 325620

Intercos Technology (SIP) Co., Ltd. (1)
No 2 Building No 29 Huahong Street Suzhou Industrial Park, Suzhou, 215126, China
Tel.: (86) 5126260020
Cosmetics Mfr
N.A.I.C.S.: 325620

Tatra Spring Polska Z o.o. (1)
Trakt Lwowski 155, 08-400, Garwolin, Poland
Tel.: (48) 256815559
Cosmetics Products Mfr
N.A.I.C.S.: 325620

INTERCURE LTD.

Ussishkin Street 11, Hadera, 3844346, Israel
Tel.: (972) 774605012 IL
Web Site: http://www.intercure.co
Year Founded: 1994
INCR—(NASDAQ)
Rev.: $120,694,156
Assets: $297,480,334
Liabilities: $135,551,296
Net Worth: $161,929,038
Earnings: $13,584,939
Emp.: 370
Fiscal Year-end: 12/31/22
Biotechnology Research & Development Services
N.A.I.C.S.: 541714
Ehud Barak *(Chm)*

Subsidiaries:

Canndoc Ltd. (1)
85 Medinat Hayehudim, Herzliya, Israel
Tel.: (972) 774605012
Web Site: https://www.canndoc.com
Health Care Srvices
N.A.I.C.S.: 524114

INTEREL HOLDINGS SA

Rue du Luxembourg 22-24, 1000, Brussels, Belgium
Tel.: (32) 2213 1300 BE
Web Site: http://www.interelgroup.com
Year Founded: 2011
Emp.: 60
Holding Company; Public Affairs, Corporate Communications & Association Management Agencies
N.A.I.C.S.: 551112
Karel Joos *(Partner)*

Subsidiaries:

Interel Consulting Inc. (1)
12100 Sunset Hills Rd Ste 130, Reston, VA 20190
Tel.: (703) 234-4050
Web Site: http://www.interelgroup.com
Government Relations & European Affairs Agency
N.A.I.C.S.: 541820
Benno van der Laan *(Dir-Ops)*

Interel Consulting UK Limited (1)
Greencoat House Francis Street, London,

INTEREL HOLDINGS SA

Interel Holdings SA—(Continued)
SW1P 1DH, United Kingdom
Tel.: (44) 20 7592 3800
Public & Corporate Affairs Agency
N.A.I.C.S.: 541820
George McGregor (Mng Partner)

Interel Management Group NV (1)
Rue du Luxembourg 22-24, 1000, Brussels,
Belgium **(100%)**
Tel.: (32) 2213 1300
Emp.: 25
Public Affairs, Corporate Communications &
Association Management Agencies
N.A.I.C.S.: 541820

Subsidiary (Domestic):

Interel Association Management
SA (2)
Rue du Luxembourg 22-24, Brussels, 1000,
Belgium **(100%)**
Tel.: (32) 2213 1300
Web Site: http://www.interelgroup.com
Emp.: 55
Government Relations & European Affairs
Agency
N.A.I.C.S.: 541820
Bob Lewis (Chm & Partner)

Interel European Affairs SA (2)
Rue du Luxembourg 22-24, 1000, Brussels,
Belgium **(100%)**
Tel.: (32) 2213 1300
Government Relations & European Affairs
Agency
N.A.I.C.S.: 541820
Gregoire Poisson (Deputy Mng Partner)

Interel SAS (1)
33 Boulevard Malesherbes, Paris, 75008,
France
Tel.: (33) 1 4544 9535
Web Site: http://www.interelgroup.com
Sales Range: $25-49.9 Million
Emp.: 10
Public Affairs Consultancy Agency
N.A.I.C.S.: 541820
Florence Maisel (Mng Partner)

INTEREUROPA - LOGISTICKE USLUGE A.D.

Zemunska 174, Dobanovci, 11272,
Belgrade, Serbia
Tel.: (381) 11 4426 180
Web Site: http://www.intereuropa.rs
Year Founded: 1994
INEU—(BEL)
Sales Range: $1-9.9 Million
Emp.: 110
Logistic Services
N.A.I.C.S.: 541614
Nemanja Kacavenda (Geh Mgr)

INTEREUROPA D.D.

Vojkovo Nabrezje 32, 6000, Koper,
Slovenia
Tel.: (386) 56641000
Web Site: http://www.intereuropa.si
IEKG—(LJU)
Rev.: $185,126,680
Assets: $270,757,860
Liabilities: $117,411,679
Net Worth: $153,346,180
Earnings: $4,382,303
Emp.: 1,337
Fiscal Year-end: 12/31/20
Freight Transportation Services
N.A.I.C.S.: 488510
Marko Cegnar (Chm-Mgmt Bd)

Subsidiaries:

Interagent d.o.o. (1)
Shipping agency, Vojkovo nabrezje 30, Koper, 6000, Slovenia **(100%)**
Tel.: (386) 56641609
Web Site: http://www.intereuropa.si
Sales Range: $25-49.9 Million
Emp.: 10
Logistics Consulting Servies
N.A.I.C.S.: 541614
Sandi Krizman (Mng Dir)

Intereuropa Global Logistics Service
Albania shpk (1)
Lagja 4 Rruga Skenderbeg Crystal Tower,
Durres, 2000, Albania
Tel.: (355) 52222760
Logistics Consulting Servies
N.A.I.C.S.: 541614

Intereuropa Kosova L.L.C. (1)
Zona Industriale Lidhja e pejes pn, 10000,
Pristina, Kosovo, Serbia **(90%)**
Tel.: (381) 38544561
Sales Range: $25-49.9 Million
Emp.: 52
Transport & Logistic Provider
N.A.I.C.S.: 488999
Arben Mustafa (Mng Dir)

Intereuropa RTC d.d (1)
Halilovici 12, Sarajevo, 71000, Bosnia &
Herzegovina
Tel.: (387) 33468153
Web Site: http://www.intereuropa.ba
Sales Range: $50-74.9 Million
Emp.: 124
Freight Trucking Services
N.A.I.C.S.: 484230

Intereuropa S.A.S. (1)
Nr 17 Rue de lAigue - ZA Portes du Dauphine St Pierr, 69780, Lyon, France
Tel.: (33) 472482897
Web Site: http://www.intereuropa.fr
Sales Range: $25-49.9 Million
Emp.: 10
Support Activities for Transportation
N.A.I.C.S.: 488999

Intereuropa Sajam, d.o.o. (1)
Av Dubrovnik 15, Zagreb, 10020, Croatia
Tel.: (385) 16521247
Web Site: http://www.intereuropa-sajam.hr
Sales Range: $25-49.9 Million
Freight Forwarding Services
N.A.I.C.S.: 488510

Intereuropa Skopje, doo (1)
Bul Vojvodina 7, Skopje, 1000, North Macedonia
Tel.: (389) 22465520
Web Site: http://www.intereuropa.com.mk
Sales Range: $25-49.9 Million
Emp.: 41
Logistic Services
N.A.I.C.S.: 541614

Intereuropa Transport, d.o.o. (1)
Vojkovo Nabrezje 32, 6000, Koper, Slovenia
Tel.: (386) 56641845
Web Site: http://www.intereuropa.si
Sales Range: $25-49.9 Million
Emp.: 15
Logistic Services
N.A.I.C.S.: 541614

Intereuropa logisticke usluge
d.o.o (1)
Josipa Lonçara 3, 10090, Zagreb,
Croatia **(100%)**
Tel.: (385) 13900666
Web Site: http://www.intereuropa.hr
Freight Transportation Arrangement
N.A.I.C.S.: 488510

Interzav, d.o.o. (1)
Vojkovo Nabrezje 32, Koper, 6000, Slovenia
Tel.: (386) 5 664 17 26
Logistics Consulting Servies
N.A.I.C.S.: 541614

Speditions-Partner GmbH Schneider
& Peklar (1)
Objekt 299 Cargo Nord, Airport, 1300, Vienna, Austria
Tel.: (43) 13322322
Web Site: https://www.schneider-peklar.at
Emp.: 50
Support Activities for Transportation
N.A.I.C.S.: 488999
Valentin H. Peklar (Mng Dir)

TFC Zahidtransservice Limited (1)
Svoboda str 4 Minaj, 89424, Mariupol,
Ukraine **(100%)**
Tel.: (380) 312669660
Web Site: http://www.zts.uz.ua
Sales Range: $25-49.9 Million
Emp.: 100
Support Activities for Transportation

N.A.I.C.S.: 488999

INTERFACE CONTRACTS LIMITED

Pennine House Denton Lane, Chadderton, Oldham, OL9 8PU, United
Kingdom
Tel.: (44) 161 620 0698
Web Site:
http://www.interfacecontracts.com
Sales Range: $1-9.9 Million
Emp.: 30
Electrical & Mechanical Contractor
N.A.I.C.S.: 238210
David B. Taylor (Mng Dir)

INTERFACTORY, INC.

4th floor Iidabashi Grand Bloom
2-10-2 Fujimi, Chiyoda-Ku, Tokyo,
102-0071, Japan
Tel.: (81) 352110086
Web Site:
https://www.interfactory.co.jp
Year Founded: 2003
4057—(TKS)
E Commerce Site Operator
N.A.I.C.S.: 332721
Noboru Kaburaki (Founder, Pres &
CEO)

INTERFAX INFORMATION SERVICE

2 Pervaya Tverskaya-Yamskaya Ul,
127006, Moscow, Russia
Tel.: (7) 4992500022
Web Site: http://www.interfax.com
Sales Range: $150-199.9 Million
Emp.: 700
News & Information Products & Services
N.A.I.C.S.: 516210
Vladimir Gerasimov (Exec Dir-Fin &
Bus Info Svc)

Subsidiaries:

Interfax America (1)
7009 S Potomac St Ste 106, Centennial,
CO 80112
Tel.: (303) 368-1421
Web Site: http://www.interfax.com
Sales Range: $550-599.9 Million
News & Information Product & Services
N.A.I.C.S.: 516210
Mikhail Andelman (Gen Mgr)

Interfax Azerbaijan LLC (1)
31 Ul Istiglaliyyat, Baku, AZ1001, Azerbaijan
Tel.: (994) 12 97 35 07
Advertising Agency Services
N.A.I.C.S.: 541810

Interfax China (1)
Ste 1601 Wilson House 19-27 Wyndham
St, Wyndham St, Central, China (Hong
Kong)
Tel.: (852) 25372262
Web Site: http://www.interfax.cn
Sales Range: $25-49.9 Million
Emp.: 40
News & Information Products & Services
N.A.I.C.S.: 516210
Shaun Bowers (Mng Dir)

Interfax Europe (1)
5th Floor 19-21 Great Tower Street, London, EC3R 5AQ, United Kingdom
Tel.: (44) 20 30046200
Sales Range: $50-74.9 Million
Emp.: 5
News & Information Products & Services
N.A.I.C.S.: 516210
Henry Pettit (Exec Dir)

Interfax Germany (1)
54 Taunusstrasse, Frankfurt, 61440, Germany
Tel.: (49) 6171695750
Web Site: http://www.interfax.com
Sales Range: $50-74.9 Million
Emp.: 4
News & Information Products & Services
N.A.I.C.S.: 516210

INTERNATIONAL PUBLIC

Sergey Sosnovsky (Exec Dir)

Interfax Kazakhstan (1)
15 Republic Sq, Almaty, Kazakhstan
Tel.: (7) 27 250 65 16
Web Site: http://www.interfax.kz
Advertising Agency Services
N.A.I.C.S.: 541810
Oksana Sustavova (Dir-Gen)

Interfax Ukraine (1)
8/5a Ul Reitarska, Kiev, 1034, Ukraine
Tel.: (380) 44 270 74 65
Web Site: http://www.en.interfax.com.ua
Advertising Agency Services
N.A.I.C.S.: 541810
Alexander Martynenko (Gen Dir)

Interfax West (Belarus) (1)
3-1110 Ul Bersona, Minsk, 220050, Belarus
Tel.: (375) 17 222 42 75
Advertising Agency Services
N.A.I.C.S.: 541810
Vyatcheslav Zenkovich (Gen Dir)

INTERFIELD GLOBAL SOFTWARE INC.

200 Burrard Street, Suite 1560,, Vancouver, V6C 3L6, BC, Canada
Tel.: (788) 628-8916
Web Site:
https://interfieldsolutions.com
Year Founded: 2014
IFSS—(BZX)
Rev.: $249
Assets: $8,301
Liabilities: $19,759
Net Worth: ($11,459)
Earnings: ($85,137)
Fiscal Year-end: 12/31/19
Mineral Exploration Services
N.A.I.C.S.: 212290
Harold Hemmerich (CEO)

INTERFLEX CO., LTD.

149 Gangchon-ro, Danwon-Gu, Ansan, Gyeonggi, Korea (South)
Tel.: (82) 314365000
Web Site: https://www.interflex.co.kr
Year Founded: 1994
051370—(KRS)
Rev.: $339,558,538
Assets: $220,039,656
Liabilities: $68,322,073
Net Worth: $151,717,583
Earnings: $11,742,147
Emp.: 404
Fiscal Year-end: 12/31/22
Flexible Printed Circuit Board Mfr
N.A.I.C.S.: 334412
Shin Il-Woon (CEO)

INTERFOR CORPORATION

4720 Kingsway, PO Box 49114,
Burnaby, V5H 4N2, BC, Canada
Tel.: (604) 422-3400 BC
Web Site: https://www.interfor.com
Year Founded: 1963
8IF1—(DEU)
Rev.: $2,503,751,384
Assets: $2,567,634,536
Liabilities: $1,260,974,888
Net Worth: $1,306,659,648
Earnings: ($201,466,016)
Emp.: 5,000
Fiscal Year-end: 12/31/23
Sawmill Operator & Lumber Producer
N.A.I.C.S.: 321113
E. Lawrence Sauder (Chm)

Subsidiaries:

EACOM Timber Corporation (1)
1100 Rene Levesque Blvd West Suite 2110,
Montreal, H3B 4N4, QC, Canada
Tel.: (514) 848-6815
Web Site: http://www.eacom.ca
Sales Range: $250-299.9 Million
Emp.: 50
Timber Products Distr
N.A.I.C.S.: 423310
Kevin Edgson (Pres & CEO)

AND PRIVATE COMPANIES

Helifor Industries Limited (1)
828 1200 W 73rd Ave, Vancouver, V6P
6G5, BC, Canada (100%)
Tel.: (604) 269-2000
Web Site: http://www.helifor.com
Sales Range: $25-49.9 Million
Emp.: 25
Sawmills & Lumber Production
N.A.I.C.S.: 321113

Interfor Corp. - Castlegar Division (1)
2705 Arrow Lakes Drive, Castlegar, V1N
4H1, BC, Canada
Tel.: (250) 365-4400
Sawmill Operator
N.A.I.C.S.: 321113

Interfor Corp. - Grand Forks Division (1)
570 68th Ave, PO Box 39, Grand Forks,
V0H 1H0, BC, Canada
Tel.: (250) 443-2400
Sawmill Operator
N.A.I.C.S.: 321113

Interfor Japan Ltd. (1)
Kasahara Bldg 6F 1-7-7 Nihonbashi
Ningyocho, Chuo-ku, Tokyo, 103-0013, Japan
Tel.: (81) 356412351
Web Site: http://www.interfor.com
Emp.: 7
Lumber Whslr
N.A.I.C.S.: 423310

Interfor U.S. Inc. (1)
700 Westpark Dr Ste 100, Peachtree City,
GA 30269
Tel.: (770) 282-3260
Web Site: http://www.interfor.com
Sales Range: $25-49.9 Million
Emp.: 20
Sawmills Operator & Lumber Whslr
N.A.I.C.S.: 423310

Subsidiary (Domestic):

Interfor Cedarprime Inc. (2)
601 W Front St, Sumas, WA 98295-9651
Tel.: (360) 988-2120
Wood Products Mfr
N.A.I.C.S.: 321918

Plant (Domestic):

Interfor U.S. Inc. - Eatonton Division (2)
370 Dennis Station Rd SW, Eatonton, GA
31024
Tel.: (706) 485-4271
Web Site: http://www.interfor.com
Emp.: 100
Sawmill Operator
N.A.I.C.S.: 321113

Interfor U.S. Inc. - Georgetown Division (2)
2701 Indian Hut Rd, Georgetown, SC
29440-9146
Tel.: (843) 546-6138
Sawmill Operator
N.A.I.C.S.: 321113

Interfor U.S. Inc. - Meldrim Division (2)
911 Old River Rd, Meldrim, GA 31302
Tel.: (912) 748-7310
Emp.: 150
Sawmill Operator
N.A.I.C.S.: 321113
Patt Ricks (Gen Mgr)

Interfor U.S. Inc. - Perry Division (2)
903 Jernigan St, Perry, GA 31069-3435
Tel.: (478) 987-2105
Web Site: http://www.interfor.com
Emp.: 130
Sawmill Operator & Lumber Remanufacturing Services
N.A.I.C.S.: 321113

Interfor U.S. Inc. - Preston Division (2)
378 Tolleson Rd, Preston, GA 31824
Tel.: (229) 828-3555
Web Site: http://www.interfor.com
Emp.: 220
Sawmill Operator
N.A.I.C.S.: 321113

Interfor U.S. Inc. - Tacoma Division (2)
901 E 11th St, Tacoma, WA 98421-3002
Tel.: (253) 680-6800
Sawmill Operator
N.A.I.C.S.: 321113

Subsidiary (Domestic):

Keadle Lumber Enterprises, Inc. (2)
889 RailRd St, Thomaston, GA 30286-9652
Tel.: (706) 647-8981
Web Site: http://www.keadlelumber.com
Sales Range: $10-24.9 Million
Emp.: 90
Pine Lumber Products Mfr & Supplier
N.A.I.C.S.: 321113

INTERFUND INVESTMENTS PLC
8 Stasinou Avenue Photiades Business Center Office 202, Nicosia,
1060, Cyprus
Tel.: (357) 22763344
INF—(CYP)
Sales Range: Less than $1 Million
Investment Management Service
N.A.I.C.S.: 525990

INTERGLOBE ENTERPRISES LIMITED
Block 2B DLF Corp Pk, DLF City
Phase III, Gurgaon, 122 002, Haryana, India
Tel.: (91) 1242358201
Web Site: http://www.interglobe.com
Year Founded: 1989
Sales Range: $1-4.9 Billion
Emp.: 6,000
Holding Company; Travel Related Services
N.A.I.C.S.: 551111
Kapil Bhatia (Chm)

Subsidiaries:

InterGlobe Air Transport Ltd. (1)
Sommerville House 50A Bath Road, Hounslow, TW3 3EE, Middlesex, United Kingdom
Tel.: (44) 208 607 4800
Oil Transportation Services
N.A.I.C.S.: 485999

InterGlobe Air Transport Ltd. (1)
Central Wing Ground Floor Thapar House
124, Janpath, New Delhi, 110001, India
Tel.: (91) 11 43513100
Web Site:
http://www.interglobeairtransport.in
Emp.: 5,000
Oil Transportation Services
N.A.I.C.S.: 485999
Ajay Bhatnagar (VP-Passenger Domestic Sls)

InterGlobe Air Transport South Africa (PTY) LTD (1)
Unit 5 West Square Office Park 407 West
Avenue, Ferndale, 2194, Johannesburg,
South Africa
Tel.: (27) 72 382 0978
Oil Transportation Services
N.A.I.C.S.: 485999

InterGlobe Aviation Limited (1)
Level- 1-5 Tower-C Global Business Park M
G Road, Gurgaon, 122 002, Haryana, India
Tel.: (91) 1244352500
Web Site: https://www.goindigo.in
Rev.: $6,750,475,294
Assets: $7,147,714,135
Liabilities: $7,902,293,268
Net Worth: ($754,579,133)
Earnings: ($36,939,311)
Emp.: 32,407
Fiscal Year-end: 03/31/2023
Airline Operator
N.A.I.C.S.: 481111
Sanjay C. Gupta (Chief Compliance Officer, Sec & Sr VP-Engrg)

InterGlobe Technology Quotient Pvt. Ltd. (1)
6th Floor Tower 6 Candor Tech Space Tikri
Sector 48, Gurgaon, 122018, Haryana, India

Tel.: (91) 124 4284800
Web Site: http://www.itq.in
Air Transportation Distr
N.A.I.C.S.: 485999
Anil Parashar (Pres & CEO)

INTERGROUP LIMITED
Level 1 81 Springs Road, East Tamaki, Auckland, 2013, New Zealand
Tel.: (64) 9 271 1458
Web Site: http://www.intergroup.co.nz
Emp.: 500
Environmental Services
N.A.I.C.S.: 541620
Adam Baines (Mgr-Bus Dev)

INTERHIDES PUBLIC COMPANY LIMITED
678 Soi TJC Sukhumvit Rd
Bangpoomai Muang, Samut Prakan,
10280, Thailand
Tel.: (66) 20289728
Web Site: http://www.interhides.com
IHL—(THA)
Rev.: $53,877,278
Assets: $101,334,146
Liabilities: $54,145,492
Net Worth: $47,188,653
Earnings: $490,664
Emp.: 1,100
Fiscal Year-end: 12/31/23
Leather Goods Mfr
N.A.I.C.S.: 316990
Chutima Busayapoka (Deputy Mng Dir)

Subsidiaries:

Inter Green Company Limited (1)
1111/2 Soi Foknung Km 34 Sukhumvit Rd,
Tambon Bangpoomai Amphoe Muang,
Samut Prakan, 10280, Thailand
Tel.: (66) 2028972837
Allied Product Mfr
N.A.I.C.S.: 316990

INTERHOUSE COMPANY
Spg 574 No 5-7 Bunut Jaya Complex
Jalan Tutong, Bandar Seri Begawan,
BF1320, Brunei Darussalam
Tel.: (673) 2653001
Web Site:
http://www.interhouse.com.bn
Year Founded: 1978
Sales Range: $25-49.9 Million
Emp.: 90
Appliance Distr
N.A.I.C.S.: 423620
Steven Goh (Mgr-Bus Dev)

INTERIOR MANUFACTURING GROUP INC
974 Lakeshore Road East, Mississauga, L5E 1E4, ON, Canada
Tel.: (905) 278-9510
Web Site: https://www.imgmfg.com
Sales Range: $10-24.9 Million
Emp.: 250
Store Fixtures
N.A.I.C.S.: 337215
Marcus Pachal (Pres)

INTERIOR ROADS LTD.
1212 McGill Road, Kamloops, V2C
6N6, BC, Canada
Tel.: (250) 374-7238
Web Site:
http://www.interiorroads.com
Year Founded: 1989
Rev.: $42,168,301
Emp.: 250
Road & Bridge Construction Services
N.A.I.C.S.: 237310
Ian Dawson (Pres)

INTERKOS INC.
62 Namdongseo-ro 362 beon-gil

Namdong-gu, Incheon, 21629, Korea
(South)
Tel.: (82) 328158081
Web Site: http://www.interkos.co.kr
Year Founded: 2011
Cosmetic Mfr & Distr
N.A.I.C.S.: 325620
Ju Deok Kim (CEO)

INTERLIFE HOLDINGS CO., LTD.
11th floor Ginza Wall Building 1316
Ginza 6chome, Chuo-ku, Tokyo, 104-0061, Japan
Tel.: (81) 335473227
Web Site: https://www.n-interlife.co.jp
1418—(TKS)
Rev.: $89,518,340
Assets: $57,677,150
Liabilities: $31,890,820
Net Worth: $25,786,330
Earnings: $2,722,560
Fiscal Year-end: 02/29/24
Holding Company; Construction Services
N.A.I.C.S.: 551112
Tadashi Kagawa (Sr Mng Dir)

Subsidiaries:

Sammy Design Co., Ltd. (1)
Higashi-Ikebukuro Building 6F 3-13-2
Higashi-Ikebukuro, Toshima-ku, Tokyo, 170-0013, Japan
Tel.: (81) 368900777
Web Site: http://www.sammydesign.co.jp
Real Estate Manangement Services
N.A.I.C.S.: 531390

INTERLINK COMMUNICATION PUBLIC COMPANY LIMITED
48 Interlink Building Soi Rung
Rueang Ratchadapisek Road Samsen, Huay Khwang, Bangkok, 10310,
Thailand
Tel.: (66) 26661111
Web Site: https://www.interlink.co.th
Year Founded: 2008
ILINK—(THA)
Rev.: $203,327,723
Assets: $380,445,094
Liabilities: $197,408,911
Net Worth: $183,036,183
Earnings: $20,790,617
Emp.: 442
Fiscal Year-end: 12/31/23
Cable Distr
N.A.I.C.S.: 517111
Chalida Anuntarumporn (Co-Pres)

INTERLINK ROADS PTY. LTD.
Toll Plaza M5 SW Motorway, Hammondville, Sydney, 2170, NSW, Australia
Tel.: (61) 298200070
Goods Inspection Services
N.A.I.C.S.: 488490
Miryana Gacevska (CFO)

INTERLINK TELECOM PCL
48/66 Soi Rung-reung Ratchadaphisek Road Samsennok, Huay
Khwang, Bangkok, 10310, Thailand
Tel.: (66) 26662222
Year Founded: 2007
ITEL—(THA)
Rev.: $80,568,046
Assets: $260,710,158
Liabilities: $143,678,651
Net Worth: $117,031,506
Earnings: $8,705,194
Emp.: 775
Fiscal Year-end: 12/31/23
Telecommunication Servicesb
N.A.I.C.S.: 517112
Pakorn Malakul Na Ayudhya (Chm)

INTERLITE AB

INTERLITE AB

Interlite AB—(Continued)
Stureparksvagen 7, 451 55, Uddevalla, Sweden
Tel.: (46) 522 440 880
Web Site: http://www.interlite.se
Emp.: 10
Architectural Lighting & Professional Lighting Equipment Distr
N.A.I.C.S.: 423610
Niclas Arvidsson (Head-Mktg & Sls)

INTERLOGIC REAL ESTATE JSC

ul Asen Yordanov 17 kompleks Sofiya Gardens sgr F et 5 ap 22, 1407, Sofia, Bulgaria
Tel.: (359) 9615999
INTR—(BUL)
Sales Range: Less than $1 Million
Real Estate Management Services
N.A.I.C.S.: 531210
Ana Atanasova Tasheva (Dir-IR)

INTERLOGIC-LEASING SA

Asen Yordanov 17 kompleks Sofiya Gardens sgr F et 5, Sofia, 1407, Bulgaria
Tel.: (359) 29615999
Web Site: http://www.interlogic.bg
INTL—(BUL)
Sales Range: Less than $1 Million
Real Estate Asset Management Services
N.A.I.C.S.: 531390

INTERMAIL A/S

Stamholmen 70, 2650, Hvidovre, Denmark
Tel.: (45) 36863333
Web Site: http://www.intermail.com
IMAIL—(CSE)
Rev.: $17,713,533
Assets: $19,448,424
Liabilities: $15,861,440
Net Worth: $3,586,983
Earnings: $7,235
Emp.: 86
Fiscal Year-end: 09/30/23
Envelope & Packaging Material Mfr
N.A.I.C.S.: 322230

Subsidiaries:

InterMail Danmark A/S (1)
Stamholmen 70, 2650, Hvidovre, Denmark
Tel.: (45) 36863333
Information Technology Services
N.A.I.C.S.: 513210
Anders Ertmann (CEO)

InterMail Sverige AB (1)
Energigatan 10A, 434 37, Kungsbacka, Sweden
Tel.: (46) 30050600
Information Technology Services
N.A.I.C.S.: 513210
Jorgen Eliasson (Project Mgr-IT)

INTERMEDES SAS

60 Rue La Boetie, 75008, Paris, France
Tel.: (33) 145616765
Web Site: http://www.intermedes.com
Sales Range: $10-24.9 Million
Emp.: 40
N.A.I.C.S.: 561510
Karin Rambaud (Mgr-Sls)

INTERMEDIATE CAPITAL GROUP PLC

Procession House 55 Ludgate Hill, London, EC4M 7JW, United Kingdom
Tel.: (44) 203 545 2000   UK
Web Site: http://www.icgam.com
Year Founded: 1988
ICP—(LSE)
Rev.: $1,333,416,812
Assets: $12,046,370,700
Liabilities: $9,328,486,804
Net Worth: $2,717,883,896
Earnings: $712,938,772
Emp.: 525
Fiscal Year-end: 03/31/22
Holding Company; Investment & Asset Management Services
N.A.I.C.S.: 551112
Benoit Durteste (CEO & Chief Investment Officer)

Subsidiaries:

DOC Generici S.r.l. (1)
Via Filippo Turati 40, 20121, Milan, Italy
Tel.: (39) 02655341
Web Site: https://www.docgenerici.it
Sales Range: $200-249.9 Million
Emp.: 180
Generic Pharmaceutical Products Mfr & Distr
N.A.I.C.S.: 325412
Gualtiero Pasquarelli (Mng Dir)

Education Personnel Holdco Limited (1)
Personnel House 99 Bridge Road East, Welwyn Garden City, AL7 1GL, Herts, United Kingdom
Tel.: (44) 1707 386 212
Web Site: http://www.teachingpersonnel.com
Holding Company; Educational Staffing Services
N.A.I.C.S.: 551112
John Bowman (CEO)

Subsidiary (Domestic):

Teaching Personnel Ltd. (2)
99 Bridge Rd E, Welwyn Garden City, AL7 1GL, Herts, United Kingdom
Tel.: (44) 1707386444
Web Site: http://www.teachingpersonnel.com
Emp.: 300
Educational Staffing Services
N.A.I.C.S.: 561311
John Bowman (CEO)

ICG Enterprise Trust plc (1)
Procession House 55 Ludgate Hill, London, EC4M 7JW, United Kingdom
Tel.: (44) 2035452000
Web Site: https://www.icg-enterprise.co.uk
Rev.: $53,130,490
Assets: $1,665,642,273
Liabilities: $32,003,819
Net Worth: $1,633,638,453
Earnings: $22,108,211
Emp.: 635
Fiscal Year-end: 01/31/2024
Open-Ended Investment Fund
N.A.I.C.S.: 525910
Fiona Bell (Principal)

Inenco Group Limited (1)
Ribble House Ballam Road, Lytham Saint Anne's, FY8 4TS, Lancashire, United Kingdom
Tel.: (44) 8451463626
Web Site: https://www.inenco.com
Sales Range: $25-49.9 Million
Energy Management & Procurement Services
N.A.I.C.S.: 221122
Richard Harrison (CEO)

Division (Domestic):

Inenco Direct (2)
The Corn Exchange, Drury Lane, Liverpool, L2 0PH, United Kingdom
Tel.: (44) 8451442244
Web Site: http://www.inencodirect.com
Electricity & Gas Brokering Services
N.A.I.C.S.: 221122
Michael Abbott (Mng Dir)

Intermediate Capital Asia Pacific Limited (1)
Suites 1301 - 1302 AIA Central 1 Connaught Road, Central, China (Hong Kong) (100%)
Tel.: (852) 21437390
Sales Range: $75-99.9 Million
Emp.: 10
Investment Advisory & Management Services

Intermediate Capital Australia Pty. Limited (1)
Level 9 88 Phillip Street, Sydney, 2000, NSW, Australia (100%)
Tel.: (61) 272084418
Web Site: http://www.icgam.com
Emp.: 8
Investment Advisory & Management Services
N.A.I.C.S.: 523940
Ryan Shelswell (COO & Head-Equity & Mezzanine Funds)

Intermediate Capital Beratungsgesellschaft mbH (1)
12 Stockwerk An der Welle 5, 60322, Frankfurt, Germany (100%)
Tel.: (49) 6925497650
Web Site: http://www.icgplc.co.uk
Investment Advisory & Management Services
N.A.I.C.S.: 523940
Jens Tonn (Head-Equity & Mezzanine)

Intermediate Capital Group (Singapore) Pte. Limited (1)
8 Marina View Asia Square Tower 1 Level 32 - 06, Singapore, 018960, Singapore (100%)
Tel.: (65) 68560680
Investment Advisory & Management Services
N.A.I.C.S.: 523940
Escamilla Lin (Mng Dir & Head-Equity & Mezzanine-South East Asia)

Intermediate Capital Group Benelux B.V. (1)
Paulus Potterstraat 20 2hg, 1071 DA, Amsterdam, Netherlands (100%)
Tel.: (31) 203994060
Emp.: 3
Investment Advisory & Management Services
N.A.I.C.S.: 523940
Leo Houtekamer (Gen Mgr)

Intermediate Capital Group Espana S.L.U. (1)
Serrano 30-3, 28001, Madrid, Spain (100%)
Tel.: (34) 810808790
Emp.: 3
Investment Advisory & Management Services
N.A.I.C.S.: 523940
Jaime Chocron (Assoc Dir-Mezzanine-Spain)

Intermediate Capital Group SAS (1)
1 rue de la Paix, 75002, Paris, France (100%)
Tel.: (33) 188888030
Investment Advisory & Management Services
N.A.I.C.S.: 523940

Intermediate Capital Group, Inc. (1)
277 Park Ave, New York, NY 10172
Tel.: (212) 710-9650
Investment Advisory & Management Services
N.A.I.C.S.: 523940
Salvatore Gentile (Mng Dir & Head-North America)

Intermediate Capital Investments Limited (1)
Procession House 55 Ludgate Hill, London, EC4M 7JW, United Kingdom (100%)
Tel.: (44) 2035452000
Emp.: 1,800
Investment Services
N.A.I.C.S.: 523999

Intermediate Capital Managers Limited (1)
Procession House 55 Ludgate Hill, London, EC4M 7JW, United Kingdom (100%)
Tel.: (44) 2035452000
Emp.: 180
Investment Advisory & Management Services
N.A.I.C.S.: 523940

Intermediate Capital Nordic AB (1)
Strandvagen 7A, 114 56, Stockholm, Sweden (100%)

INTERNATIONAL PUBLIC

Tel.: (46) 850243650
Web Site: http://www.icgplc.com
Emp.: 2
Investment Advisory & Management Services
N.A.I.C.S.: 523940
Timo Larjomaa (Head-Equity & Mezzanine)

Longbow Real Estate Capital LLP (1)
42 Wigmore Street, London, W1U 2RY, United Kingdom (51%)
Tel.: (44) 20 3201 7500
Web Site: http://www.icglongbow.co.uk
Emp.: 33
Commercial Property Sector Investment Advisory & Management Services
N.A.I.C.S.: 523940
Kevin Cooper (Co-Founder & Co-Head-Real Estate)

Loparex LLC (1)
1255 Crescent Green Ste 400, Cary, NC 27518
Tel.: (919) 678-7700
Web Site: https://www.loparex.com
Paper & Film Substrate Release Liners Mfr
N.A.I.C.S.: 326112
Charmaine R. Riggins (CEO)

Plant (Domestic):

Loparex LLC - Iowa City Plant (2)
2000 Industrial Park Rd, Iowa City, IA 52240
Tel.: (319) 341-5000
Web Site: http://www.loparex.com
Paper & Film Substrate Release Liners Mfr
N.A.I.C.S.: 326112

Minimax Viking GmbH (1)
Industriestrasse 10/12, Bad Oldesloe, 23840, Germany
Tel.: (49) 4531 803 0
Sales Range: $1-4.9 Billion
Emp.: 6,000
Fire Protection & Life Safety Systems Equipment Mfr
N.A.I.C.S.: 333310
Klaus Hofmann (CEO)

Subsidiary (US):

Consolidated Fire Protection, LLC (2)
153 Technology Dr Ste 200, Irvine, CA 92618
Tel.: (949) 727-3277
Web Site: http://www.cfpfire.com
Fire Protection & Life Safety Systems & Services
N.A.I.C.S.: 561790
Keith Fielding (Pres)

Subsidiary (Domestic):

Cosco Fire Protection, LLC (3)
1075 W Lambert Rd Bldg D, Brea, CA 92821-2944
Tel.: (714) 989-1800
Web Site: https://www.coscofire.com
Sales Range: $75-99.9 Million
Emp.: 100
Fire Protection Systems
N.A.I.C.S.: 922160

Firetrol Protection Systems, Inc. (3)
3696 W 900 S Ste A, Salt Lake City, UT 84104
Tel.: (801) 485-6900
Web Site: https://www.firetrol.net
Sales Range: $1-9.9 Million
Emp.: 35
Fire Sprinkler System Installation
N.A.I.C.S.: 922160
John White (Pres)

Subsidiary (US):

FLAMEX, Inc. (2)
4365 Federal Dr, Greensboro, NC 27410
Tel.: (336) 299-2933
Web Site: https://www.sparkdetection.com
Sales Range: $25-49.9 Million
Emp.: 15
Fire Prevention Equipment Supplier
N.A.I.C.S.: 423720

Subsidiary (Domestic):

Minimax GmbH & Co. KG (2)

Industriestrasse 10/12, 23840, Bad Oldesloe, Germany
Tel.: (49) 45318030
Web Site: http://www.minimax.com
Sales Range: $1-4.9 Billion
Stationary & Mobile Fire Protection Systems Mfr
N.A.I.C.S.: 333310
Volker Bechtloff *(Chm & Mng Dir)*

Subsidiary (Non-US):

Pefipresa S.A. (3)
C/ San Cesareo 22, Poligono Industrial Villaverde, 28021, Madrid, Spain
Tel.: (34) 917109000
Web Site: http://www.pefipresa.com
Fire Protection Systems Mfr
N.A.I.C.S.: 922160

Subsidiary (US):

Viking Group, Inc. (2)
5150 Beltway Dr SE, Caledonia, MI 49316
Tel.: (269) 945-9501
Web Site: http://www.vikinggroupinc.com
Sales Range: $450-499.9 Million
Emp.: 300
Fire Protection Products Mfr
N.A.I.C.S.: 333310
Jeff Norton *(VP-Mktg)*

INTERMEDIATE PETROCHEMICALS INDUSTRIES COMPANY LIMITED
PO Box 2502, Amman, 11181, Jordan
Tel.: (962) 53653334
Web Site: https://www.ipi.com.jo
Year Founded: 1980
IPCH—(AMM)
Rev.: $2,922,915
Assets: $6,890,060
Liabilities: $4,646,175
Net Worth: $2,243,885
Earnings: ($977,721)
Fiscal Year-end: 12/31/20
Petrochemical Products Mfr
N.A.I.C.S.: 325110

INTERMEDICAL CARE & LAB HOSPITAL PUBLIC COMPANY LIMITED
442 Bangwaek Road, Bangwaek Sub district Phasi Charoen District, Bangkok, 10160, Thailand
Tel.: (66) 28650044   TH
Web Site:
 https://www.intermedthai.com
Year Founded: 1996
IMH—(THA)
Rev.: $19,752,808
Assets: $59,392,132
Liabilities: $35,159,733
Net Worth: $24,232,398
Earnings: $635,050
Emp.: 543
Fiscal Year-end: 12/31/23
Health Care Srvices
N.A.I.C.S.: 621610
Thanavath Phonvichai *(Chm)*

Subsidiaries:

Accufas Lab Center Company Limited (1)
442 Bang Waek Road, Bang Waek Subdistrict Phasi Charoen District, Bangkok, 10160, Thailand
Tel.: (66) 286500449
Web Site: http://www.accufas.com
Laboratory Operator
N.A.I.C.S.: 621511

INTERMESTIC INC.
Yubinbango 107-0061 Kita-Aoyama 3-6-1 Oak Omotesando sixth floor, Minato-ku, Tokyo, 150-0001, Japan
Tel.: (81) 354688650
Web Site: http://www.zoff.co.jp
Year Founded: 1993
Sales Range: $25-49.9 Million
Emp.: 30

Eyeglass Retailer
N.A.I.C.S.: 456130
Takeshi Ueno *(Pres)*

INTERMONTE PARTNERS SIM S.P.A.
Galleria De Cristoforis 7/8, 20122, Milan, Italy
Tel.: (39) 0277115
Web Site: https://www.intermonte.it
Year Founded: 1995
INT—(ITA)
Rev.: $38,176,315
Assets: $233,636,262
Liabilities: $172,262,414
Net Worth: $61,373,848
Earnings: $3,318,072
Emp.: 144
Fiscal Year-end: 12/31/23
Investment Banking Services
N.A.I.C.S.: 523150
Alessandro Valeri *(Chm)*

INTERNACIONAL DE CERAMICA, S.A.B. DE C.V.
Av Carlos Pacheco 7200 Madera 65, 31060, Chihuahua, Mexico
Tel.: (52) 6144291111   MX
Web Site:
 http://www.interceramic.com
Year Founded: 1978
CERAMIC—(MEX)
Ceramic Wall & Floor Tile Mfr & Distr
N.A.I.C.S.: 327120
Charbel Christian Harp Calderoni *(Vice Chm)*

Subsidiaries:

Adhesivos y Boquillas Interceramic, S. de R.L. de C.V. (1)
Av Carlos Pacheco No 7200, Chihuahua, Mexico
Tel.: (52) 6144291111
Sales Range: $1-4.9 Billion
Emp.: 3,000
Adhesive Mfr
N.A.I.C.S.: 325520
Victor D. Almeida *(Ceo)*

Interceramic Inc. (1)
2333 S Jupiter Rd, Garland, TX 75041-6007
Tel.: (214) 503-5500
Web Site: http://www.interceramic.com
Sales Range: $50-74.9 Million
Emp.: 250
Ceramic Tile Mfr
N.A.I.C.S.: 327120
Victor Alneiva *(CEO)*

Subsidiary (Domestic):

Interceramic Trading Co. Inc. (2)
700 N Stanton St Ste 220, El Paso, TX 79902-5206   (100%)
Tel.: (915) 533-0267
Non-Durable Goods Whslr
N.A.I.C.S.: 424990

Interceramic de Occidente, S.A. de C.V. (1)
Av Laureles No 175, Zapopan, Mexico   (100%)
Tel.: (52) 3336333616
Sales Range: $50-74.9 Million
Emp.: 100
Brick Stone & Related Construction Material Whslr
N.A.I.C.S.: 423320

Recubrimientos Interceramic, S.A. de C.V. (1)
Av Carlos Pacheco No 7200, 31060, Chihuahua, Mexico
Tel.: (52) 6144291111
Web Site: http://www.interceramic.com
Sales Range: $200-249.9 Million
Emp.: 1,000
Adhesive Mfr
N.A.I.C.S.: 325520

INTERNATIONAL AGENCIES

COMPANY LTD.
131 Al Khalifa Avenue, PO Box 584, 304, Manama, Bahrain
Tel.: (973) 17228855
Web Site: http://www.intercol.com
Year Founded: 1957
Sales Range: $300-349.9 Million
Emp.: 1,000
N.A.I.C.S.: 423990
Sadiq Mohammed Al Baharna *(Founder)*

Subsidiaries:

General Medicals W.L.L. (1)
Mina Salman Industrial Area Block 343 Rd 4306 Bldg 303, PO Box 56, Manama, Bahrain
Tel.: (973) 17727600
Surgical Equipment Whslr
N.A.I.C.S.: 423450

Intercol Contracting Co. Ltd. (1)
PO Box 584, Manama, Bahrain
Tel.: (973) 17813323
Sales Range: $50-74.9 Million
Emp.: 120
Building Work & Contracting Services
N.A.I.C.S.: 238390

International Advertising Agency (1)
Bldg 406 Road 4308 Block 343, PO Box 600, Manama, Bahrain
Tel.: (973) 17825757
Sales Range: $25-49.9 Million
Emp.: 10
Advetising Agency
N.A.I.C.S.: 541810

International Travel Bureau (1)
PO Box 584, Manama, Bahrain
Tel.: (973) 17228833
Sales Range: $25-49.9 Million
Emp.: 8
Travel Agencies
N.A.I.C.S.: 561510

INTERNATIONAL AGRICULTURAL PRODUCTS
79 El Geish Street, Mansoura, Egypt
Tel.: (20) 502312355
Web Site: https://www.mahaseel.com
Year Founded: 1995
IFAP.CA—(EGX)
Sales Range: Less than $1 Million
Agricultural Product Mfr
N.A.I.C.S.: 111998
Abdel Salam Abdel Salam Mustafa Al-Jabali *(Chm)*

INTERNATIONAL AIR TRANSPORT ASSOCIATION
800 Place Victoria, PO Box 113, Montreal, H4Z 1M1, QC, Canada
Tel.: (514) 874-0202
Web Site: http://www.iata.org
Sales Range: $200-249.9 Million
Emp.: 1,332
Transportation Association
N.A.I.C.S.: 813920
Glyn Hughes *(Global Head-Cargo)*

INTERNATIONAL APPLICATIONS LIMITED
18 Wildmere Road Wildmere Industrial Estate, Banbury, OX16 3JU, Oxfordshire, United Kingdom
Tel.: (44) 1295 274004
Web Site: http://www.international-
 applications.com
Year Founded: 2006
Sales Range: $25-49.9 Million
Emp.: 28
Industrial Goods Distribution Services
N.A.I.C.S.: 424990
Karl Durham *(Mng Dir)*

INTERNATIONAL ARABIAN DEVELOPMENT & INVESTMENT TRADING CO.
Paris St - Rawashdeh Complex 11 -

First Floor, PO Box 1465, Amman, 11953, Jordan
Tel.: (962) 5521592
Year Founded: 2004
INMA—(AMM)
Rev.: $308,733
Assets: $9,264,541
Liabilities: $4,677,559
Net Worth: $4,586,982
Earnings: ($90,677)
Emp.: 4
Fiscal Year-end: 12/31/20
Real Estate Development & Financial Investment Services
N.A.I.C.S.: 531390
Shaher Al-Rawashdeh *(Gen Mgr)*

INTERNATIONAL ASSET MANAGEMENT LTD.
11A Regent Street, London, SW1Y 4LR, United Kingdom
Tel.: (44) 2077348488   UK
Web Site: http://www.iam.uk.com
Year Founded: 1989
Sales Range: $25-49.9 Million
Emp.: 36
Hedge Fund Portfolio Management Services
N.A.I.C.S.: 523940
Alan Djanogly *(Co-Founder)*

Subsidiaries:

International Asset Management Limited, LLC (1)
410 Park Ave Ste 520, New York, NY 10022
Tel.: (212) 235-0400
Web Site: http://www.iamlimiteduk.com
Emp.: 5
Portfolio Management Services
N.A.I.C.S.: 523940

INTERNATIONAL ASSET RECONSTRUCTION COMPANY PRIVATE LIMITED
A 601 6th Floor 215 Atrium Kanakia Spaces, Andheri Kurla Road Andheri East, Mumbai, 400093, Maharashtra, India
Tel.: (91) 2267363000
Asset Management Services
N.A.I.C.S.: 523999

INTERNATIONAL BANK FOR ECONOMIC CO-OPERATION
Masha Poryvaeva Str 11, Moscow, 107996, Russia
Tel.: (7) 4956047290
Web Site: http://www.ibec.int
Year Founded: 1963
Commercial Banking Services
N.A.I.C.S.: 522110
Denis Ivanov *(Chm)*

INTERNATIONAL BANK OF AZERBAIJAN
67 Nazami Str, AZ 1005, Baku, Azerbaijan
Tel.: (994) 124930091
Web Site: http://www.ibar.az
Year Founded: 1991
Sales Range: $400-449.9 Million
Emp.: 1,211
Banking Services
N.A.I.C.S.: 522110
Fuad Rafik Islamov *(Mng Dir)*

Subsidiaries:

AzeriCard Ltd. (1)
67 Nizami Str, AZ 1005, Baku, Azerbaijan
Tel.: (994) 124930091
Clearing & Approving Center for Plastic Credit Cards
N.A.I.C.S.: 522210

Inter Protect Re AG (1)
C/O Leonhard Tonz Altenburger Rechtsan-

INTERNATIONAL BANK OF AZERBAIJAN

International Bank of Azerbaijan—(Continued)
walte, Seestrasse 39, Kusnacht, ZH 8700, Switzerland
Tel.: (41) 19148888
Sales Range: $75-99.9 Million
Emp.: 3
Life Insurance
N.A.I.C.S.: 524113

International Bank of
Azerbaijan-Moscow (1)
Tversskaya ul d 6 str 2, 125009, Moscow, Russia
Tel.: (7) 4959338315
Web Site: http://www.ibamoscow.ru
Sales Range: $200-249.9 Million
Emp.: 300
Banking Services
N.A.I.C.S.: 522110
Faud Ragim Abdullaev *(Chm & CEO)*

Subsidiary (Domestic):

The Bank IBA-Moscow LLC (2)
Ul Rochdelskaya 14 P 1, 123022, Moscow, Russia
Tel.: (7) 4950252525
Web Site: http://www.ibam.ru
Commercial Banking Services
N.A.I.C.S.: 522110
Emin Efendiyev *(Chm-Mgmt Bd)*

International Insurance Company (1)
J Jabbarly 40 J, Baku, AZ1065, Azerbaijan
Tel.: (994) 125962202
Web Site: http://www.iic.az
Sales Range: $125-149.9 Million
Emp.: 120
Insurance Services
N.A.I.C.S.: 524126

INTERNATIONAL BASE METALS LIMITED
Suite 201 29 Albert Avenue, Chatswood, 2067, NSW, Australia
Tel.: (61) 0284128110
Web Site:
http://www.interbasemetals.com
Sales Range: Less than $1 Million
Emp.: 25
Metal Mining Services
N.A.I.C.S.: 212290
Barry Neal *(CFO)*

INTERNATIONAL BATTERY METALS LTD.
1140 - 625 Howe Street, Vancouver, V6C 2T6, BC, Canada
Tel.: (778) 939-4228 BC
Web Site:
http://www.ibatterymetals.com
Year Founded: 2010
IBAT—(CNSX)
Assets: $25,622
Liabilities: $5,172
Net Worth: $20,450
Earnings: ($6,286)
Fiscal Year-end: 03/31/24
Gold Mining
N.A.I.C.S.: 212220
Logan Anderson *(CFO)*

INTERNATIONAL BETHLEHEM MINING CORP.
2489 Bellevue Avenue, West Vancouver, V7V 1E1, BC, Canada
Tel.: (604) 922-2030
Web Site:
http://www.bethlehemmining.com
Year Founded: 1995
IBC.H—(TSXV)
Assets: $58,500
Liabilities: $576,958
Net Worth: ($518,458)
Earnings: ($119,595)
Fiscal Year-end: 12/31/23
Mineral Exploration Services
N.A.I.C.S.: 213114
Peter D. Berdusco *(Pres)*

INTERNATIONAL BIOTECHNOLOGY TRUST PLC
1 London Wall Place, London, EC2Y 5AU, United Kingdom
Tel.: (44) 2074217070
Web Site: https://www.ibtplc.com
Year Founded: 1994
IBT—(LSE)
Rev.: $1,071,673
Assets: $378,588,808
Liabilities: $42,909,157
Net Worth: $335,679,651
Earnings: $8,460,383
Fiscal Year-end: 08/31/23
Investment Services
N.A.I.C.S.: 523999
Ailsa Craig *(Mgr-Investment)*

INTERNATIONAL BRANDS PRIVATE LIMITED
3rd Floor One IBL Center Plot No 1 Block 7 & 8, Tipu Sultan Road Off Shahrah-e-Faisal, Karachi, 75530, Pakistan
Tel.: (92) 2137170100
Web Site: http://www.iblgrp.com
Year Founded: 1887
Sales Range: $350-399.9 Million
Holding Company
N.A.I.C.S.: 551112
Rashid Abdulla *(Chm)*

Subsidiaries:

The Searle Company Limited (1)
One IBL Centre 2nd Floor Plot 1 Block 7 and 8, DMCHS Tipu Sultan Road Off Shahra-e-Faisal, Karachi, Pakistan (55.32%)
Tel.: (92) 2137170200
Web Site: https://www.searlecompany.com
Rev.: $122,205,450
Assets: $224,828,948
Liabilities: $110,872,855
Net Worth: $113,956,092
Earnings: $1,485,960
Emp.: 3,840
Fiscal Year-end: 06/30/2023
Pharmaceuticals Product Mfr
N.A.I.C.S.: 325412
S. Nadeem Ahmed *(CEO)*

United Distributors Pakistan
Limited (1)
Plot 105 Mehran Town Sector 7 A Korangi Indistrial Area, Karachi, 74900, Pakistan
Tel.: (92) 2135116823
Web Site: https://www.udpl.com.pk
Rev.: $2,825,663
Assets: $4,507,360
Liabilities: $2,050,117
Net Worth: $2,457,243
Earnings: $1,340,185)
Emp.: 88
Fiscal Year-end: 06/30/2023
Agricultural Products Marketing & Distr
N.A.I.C.S.: 424910
Rashid Abdulla *(Chm)*

INTERNATIONAL BROKERAGE & FINANCIAL MARKETS CO.
Salman Al Qdah Street Across Wakalat Street, PO Box 850757, Amman, 11185, Jordan
Tel.: (962) 5503300
Web Site: http://www.ibfm.jo
IBFM—(AMM)
Rev.: $52,681
Assets: $13,135,055
Liabilities: $4,576,476
Net Worth: $8,558,580
Earnings: ($2,265,350)
Emp.: 27
Fiscal Year-end: 12/31/20
Investment Banking & Asset Management Services
N.A.I.C.S.: 523150
Ayman Saleh *(Mgr-IT)*

INTERNATIONAL BUILDING PRODUCTS LTD.
Global House 95 Vantage Point The Pensett Estate, Kingswinford, DY6 7FT, W Midlands, United Kingdom
Tel.: (44) 1215572831
Web Site: http://www.ibpgroup.com
Emp.: 80
Building Product Mfr
N.A.I.C.S.: 332311
Mano Bakhtiari *(CEO)*

Subsidiaries:

IBP Atcosa, S.I. (1)
Poligono Industrial Quintos-Aeropuerto, 14005, Cordoba, Spain
Tel.: (34) 957 469 600
Web Site: http://www.atcosa.com
Plumbing Fixture Mfr & Distr
N.A.I.C.S.: 332913
Rafael Salamanca Albornoz *(Mgr-Quality)*

IBP Banninger Italia srl (1)
Piazza Meuccio Ruini 9A, 43126, Parma, Italy
Tel.: (39) 0521 299711
Web Site: http://www.ibpbanningeritalia.it
Plumbing Fixture Mfr & Distr
N.A.I.C.S.: 332913

IBP GmbH (1)
Theodor-Heuss-Str 18, 35440, Linden, Germany (100%)
Tel.: (49) 64 03 77 85 0
Sales Range: $25-49.9 Million
Building Product Mfr
N.A.I.C.S.: 332311

MasterFlow Ltd (1)
Block 2 Crossford Court Dane Road, Manchester, M33 7BZ, Lancashire, United Kingdom
Tel.: (44) 845 600 3060
Web Site: http://www.masterflow.uk.com
Plumbing Fixture Mfr & Distr
N.A.I.C.S.: 332913

Roman Dietsche GmbH (1)
Am Elzdamm 7, 79312, Emmendingen, Germany
Tel.: (49) 7641 5807 0
Web Site: http://www.dietsche.de
Bathroom Fixture Mfr & Distr
N.A.I.C.S.: 332999
Claus Eberling *(Co-CEO)*

INTERNATIONAL BUSINESS DIGITAL TECHNOLOGY LIMITED
4/F Block 2 Founder Building 9 Shangdi Fifth Street, Haidian District, Beijing, China
Tel.: (86) 1062982318 Ky
Web Site: http://www.vixtel.com
Year Founded: 2006
1782—(HKG)
Rev.: $14,568,887
Assets: $46,243,829
Liabilities: $5,615,579
Net Worth: $40,628,250
Earnings: ($1,983,150)
Emp.: 299
Fiscal Year-end: 12/31/22
Network Monitoring Services
N.A.I.C.S.: 541512
Yong Yue *(Chm & CTO)*

INTERNATIONAL BUSINESS SETTLEMENT HOLDINGS LIMITED
Room 2310 23rd Floor China Resources Building, 26 Harbour Road, Wanchai, 999077, China (Hong Kong)
Tel.: (852) 2 549 9988 BM
Web Site:
http://www.ibsettlement.com
0147—(HKG)
Rev.: $39,263,576
Assets: $407,557,582
Liabilities: $314,683,082
Net Worth: $92,874,500

INTERNATIONAL PUBLIC

Earnings: ($18,724,156)
Emp.: 185
Fiscal Year-end: 03/31/22
Holding Company
N.A.I.C.S.: 551112
Leong Yuen *(Exec Dir)*

INTERNATIONAL CARDS COMPANY
PO Box 926974, Amman, 11190, Jordan
Tel.: (962) 5660660 JO
Web Site: http://www.kartee.com.jo
Year Founded: 1999
CARD—(AMM)
Rev.: $172,557
Assets: $40,444,765
Liabilities: $21,504,073
Net Worth: $18,940,692
Earnings: ($1,334,891)
Emp.: 85
Fiscal Year-end: 12/31/19
Card Payment & Money Transfer Services
N.A.I.C.S.: 522320

INTERNATIONAL CARE COMPANY S.P.A.
Cassiopea Palace 2 via Paracelsus 24, 20864, Agrate Brianza, MB, Italy
Tel.: (39) 0396056804
Web Site:
https://www.internationalcareco.com
Year Founded: 2018
ICC—(EUR)
Medical Care Management Services
N.A.I.C.S.: 621999
Gualtiero Ventura *(Chm)*

INTERNATIONAL CAVIAR CORPORATION SA
Str Izvorului nr 5, Calan, Hunedoara, Romania
Tel.: (40) 727598746
Web Site: https://www.iccsa.ro
AMAL—(BUC)
Rev.: $177
Assets: $2,381,252
Liabilities: $553,544
Net Worth: $1,827,708
Earnings: ($448,652)
Fiscal Year-end: 12/31/23
Aquaculture Development Services
N.A.I.C.S.: 114111

INTERNATIONAL CERAMIC INDUSTRIES CO. LTD.
Al-Mafraq-Thaghrat Al-jub, PO Box 1177, Amman, 25110, Jordan
Tel.: (962) 26233465
Web Site: http://www.icicjo.com
Year Founded: 1994
ICER—(AMM)
Sales Range: $1-9.9 Million
Emp.: 167
Tiles & Ceramic Ware Marketing & Mfr
N.A.I.C.S.: 327120
Mohammad Al-Haj *(Gen Mgr)*

INTERNATIONAL CHEMICAL INVESTORS S.E.
An der Hauptwache 5, D-60313, Frankfurt, Germany
Tel.: (49) 695069990 De
Web Site: http://www.ic-investors.com
Year Founded: 2004
Sales Range: $700-749.9 Million
Emp.: 5,200
Pharmaceutical & Chemical Investment Services
N.A.I.C.S.: 523999
Achim Riemann *(Mng Dir)*

Subsidiaries:

Allessa GmbH (1)
Alt-Fechenheim 34, 60386, Frankfurt am

AND PRIVATE COMPANIES

Main, Germany
Tel.: (49) 69 4109 01
Web Site: http://www.allessa.com
Emp.: 890
Chemicals Mfr
N.A.I.C.S.: 325199

CarboTech AC GmbH (1)
Eisenstrasse 119, 45139, Essen, Germany
Tel.: (49) 201 2489900
Web Site: http://www.carbotech.de
Emp.: 12
Activated Carbon & Coal Producer for Water & Gas Industries
N.A.I.C.S.: 335991

ENKA International GmbH & Co. KG (1)
Kasinostrasse 19-21, 42103, Wuppertal, Germany
Tel.: (49) 202 322409
Web Site: http://www.enka.de
Premium Viscose Filament Yarn Mfr
N.A.I.C.S.: 313110

Subsidiary (Non-US):

ENKA Italia Srl (2)
Via Bronzino 14, Milan, 20133, Italy
Tel.: (39) 02 2953 4064
Web Site: http://www.enka.de
Viscose Yarn Sales
N.A.I.C.S.: 313110

ICIG Business Services GmbH & Co. KG (1)
Kasinostrasse 19-21, 42103, Wuppertal, Germany
Tel.: (49) 202 322409
IT, Finance & HR Services
N.A.I.C.S.: 561499

Impra Wood Protection Limited (1)
Industrial Estate Park Road, Barrow-in-Furness, LA14 4EQ, Cumbria, United Kingdom
Tel.: (44) 122 987753
Wood Product Mfr & Distr
N.A.I.C.S.: 321999

Miteni S.p.A. (1)
Via Mecenate 90, 20138, Mailand, Italy
Tel.: (39) 02583991
Fluorine Intermediates & Specialty Chemical Mfr & Sales
N.A.I.C.S.: 325998

Nease Corporation (1)
4480 Lake Forest Dr Ste 312, Cincinnati, OH 45242
Tel.: (503) 587-2800
Web Site: http://www.neasecorp.com
Chemical Products Mfr
N.A.I.C.S.: 325998

PPC Potasse et Produits Chimiques S.A.S. (1)
95 rue du General de Gaulle, BP 60090, F 68802, Thann, Cedex, France
Tel.: (33) 3 8938 4600
Web Site: http://www.ppchemcials.com
Potassium & Chlorine Producer
N.A.I.C.S.: 325180

Rutgers Organics GmbH (1)
Oppauer Strasse 43, Mannheim, 68305, Germany
Tel.: (49) 6217654249
Web Site: http://www.ruetgers-organics.de
Sales Range: $25-49.9 Million
Emp.: 100
Organic Wood Preservatives & Fire Retardants Mfr
N.A.I.C.S.: 325510

Synkem S.A.S. (1)
47 rue Longvic, 21300, Chenove, France
Tel.: (33) 380447272
Pharmaceutical Chemicals Mfr
N.A.I.C.S.: 325412

WP Mannheim GmbH (1)
Sandhofer Strasse 96, 68305, Mannheim, Germany
Tel.: (49) 621 7654 0
Chemical Products Mfr
N.A.I.C.S.: 325199

WeylChem Frankfurt GmbH (1)
Stroofstrasse 27, 65933, Griesheim, Germany

Tel.: (49) 69 3800 2110
Web Site: http://www.weylchem.com
Chemical Products Mfr
N.A.I.C.S.: 325998

Subsidiary (Non-US):

HydroChem Italia S.r.l. (2)
30/32 Via Mario Massari, 28886, Pieve Vergonte, Verbano-Cusio-Ossola, Italy
Tel.: (39) 03248601
Web Site: http://www.weylchem.com
Emp.: 110
Mfr of Chlorinated Aromatic Products & Specialty Dichlorotoluenes for Agricultural & Pharmaceutical Markets
N.A.I.C.S.: 325180
Dierlugi Degiovanni *(Gen Mgr)*

Subsidiary (US):

WeylChem US Inc. (2)
2114 Larry Jeffers Rd, Elgin, SC 29045
Tel.: (803) 438-3471
Web Site: http://www.weylchem.com
Chemical Products Mfr
N.A.I.C.S.: 325998
Torrey Adams *(Dir-Sls & Mktg)*

WeylChem Lamotte S.A.S. (1)
Usine de Lamotte Rue du Flottage, 60350, Trosly-Breuil, France
Tel.: (33) 3 44 85 40 00
Chemical Product Mfr & Distr
N.A.I.C.S.: 325998

WeylChem Switzerland Ltd. (1)
Rothausstrasse 61, 4132, Muttenz, Switzerland
Tel.: (41) 61 469 5999
Chemical Product Mfr & Distr
N.A.I.C.S.: 325998

WeylChem Wiesbaden GmbH (1)
Industriepark Kalle Albert Rheingaustrasse 190-196, 65203, Wiesbaden, Germany
Tel.: (49) 611 962 08
Chemical Product Mfr & Distr
N.A.I.C.S.: 325998

INTERNATIONAL COMBUSTION (INDIA) LTD.
Infinity Benchmark 11th Floor Plot No G-1 Block EP GP Sector V, Salt Lake Electronics Complex, Kolkata, 700 091, West Bengal, India
Tel.: (91) 3340803000
Web Site: https://www.intlcombustion.in
505737—(BOM)
Rev.: $27,092,939
Assets: $20,493,344
Liabilities: $8,198,392
Net Worth: $12,294,952
Earnings: $1,007,063
Emp.: 533
Fiscal Year-end: 03/31/23
Geared Motor Machinery Mfr
N.A.I.C.S.: 333612
Sanjay Bagaria *(Chm)*

INTERNATIONAL COMPANY FOR LEASING S.A.E.
9 Abd El Moneim Riad El Mohandeseen, Giza, 12311, Egypt
Tel.: (20) 3336 6808
Web Site: http://www.incolease.com
Year Founded: 1997
ICLE.CA—(EGX)
Sales Range: Less than $1 Million
Financial Lending Services
N.A.I.C.S.: 522291
Yahya Izz Alddin Nour *(CEO & Member-Exec Bd)*

INTERNATIONAL CONGLOMERATE OF DISTRIBUTION FOR AUTOMOBILE HOLDINGS CO., LTD.
234-1 Iinodera-cho, Suzuka, 513-0802, Mie, Japan
Tel.: (81) 593815540
Web Site: https://www.icda.jp

3184—(NGO)
Rev.: $218,704,927
Assets: $131,014,169
Liabilities: $68,093,803
Net Worth: $62,920,366
Earnings: $6,144,696
Emp.: 343
Fiscal Year-end: 03/31/24
Car Dealership
N.A.I.C.S.: 441110

INTERNATIONAL CONSOLIDATED AIRLINES GROUP S.A.
Waterside HAA2, PO Box 365, Harmondsworth, UB7 0GB, United Kingdom
Tel.: (44) 3707020110
Web Site: https://www.iairgroup.com
Year Founded: 2011
IAG—(MAD)
Rev.: $32,512,418,594
Assets: $41,593,994,928
Liabilities: $37,975,493,989
Net Worth: $3,618,500,939
Earnings: $2,930,787,063
Emp.: 71,794
Fiscal Year-end: 12/31/23
Airline Services
N.A.I.C.S.: 551112
Javier Sanchez-Prieto *(Chm/CEO-Iberia)*

Subsidiaries:

Aer Lingus Group DAC (1)
Dublin Airport, Dublin, Ireland (100%)
Tel.: (353) 1 761 7846
Web Site: https://www.aerlingus.com
Passenger & Cargo Air Transportation Services
N.A.I.C.S.: 481111
Meabh Gallagher *(Sec)*

British Airways Interior Engineering Limited (1)
Waterside, PO Box 365, Harmondsworth, UB7 0GB, United Kingdom
Tel.: (44) 1633242100
Emp.: 200
Aircraft Maintenance Services
N.A.I.C.S.: 488190
Sarah Worley *(Mng Dir)*

British Airways PLC (1)
Waterside, PO Box 365, Harmondsworth, West Drayton, UB7 0GB, United Kingdom
Tel.: (44) 2087385100
Web Site: https://www.britishairways.com
Sales Range: $5-14.9 Billion
Emp.: 4,500
Oil Transportation Services
N.A.I.C.S.: 481111
Lynne Embleton *(Dir-Strategy & Bus Units)*

Subsidiary (Domestic):

Avios Group Ltd. (2)
Astral Towers Betts Way, PO Box 365, Waterside, Harmondsworth, UB7 0GB, West Sussex, United Kingdom
Tel.: (44) 344 493 3349
Web Site: https://www.avios.com
Sales Range: $25-49.9 Million
Emp.: 150
Airline Marketing
N.A.I.C.S.: 541613
Andrea Buchett *(Dir-Relationships Mktg & Insight)*

Representative Office (Non-US):

British Airways - Australia Office (2)
L 19 259 George Street, Sydney, 2000, NSW, Australia
Tel.: (61) 61292583200
Web Site: https://www.britishairways.com
Oil Transportation Services
N.A.I.C.S.: 481111

British Airways - Germany Office (2)
Postfach 286118, 28361, Bremen, Germany
Tel.: (49) 1805003419
Sales Range: $25-49.9 Million
Emp.: 20
International & Local Air Travel
N.A.I.C.S.: 481111

INTERNATIONAL CONSOLIDATED AIRLINES GROUP S.A.

Representative Office (US):

British Airways - US Office (2)
PO Box 300686, Jamaica, NY 11430-0686
Tel.: (312) 843-5794
Sales Range: $400-449.9 Million
Emp.: 1,800
Airline Services
N.A.I.C.S.: 481111

Subsidiary (Domestic):

British Airways Holidays Limited (2)
Eighth Floor The Create Building The Boulevard, Crawley, RH10 1DT, West Sussex, United Kingdom (100%)
Tel.: (44) 3444930787
Tour Operations & Packaged Holidays
N.A.I.C.S.: 561520

British Airways Maintenance Cardiff Ltd (2)
Waterside, PO Box 365, Harmondsworth, UB7 0GB, United Kingdom
Tel.: (44) 1446747100
Sales Range: $200-249.9 Million
Emp.: 700
Aircraft Maintenance Services
N.A.I.C.S.: 488190

British Airways Pension Trustees (No 2) Limited (1)
Waterside, PO Box 365, Harmondsworth, UB7 0GB, Middlesex, United Kingdom
Tel.: (44) 2085382100
Sales Range: $50-74.9 Million
Emp.: 10
Pension Funds
N.A.I.C.S.: 525120
Teresa Suriyae *(Mng Dir)*

Compania Auxiliar al Cargo Expres, S.A. (1)
Lg Centro De Carga Aerea Barajas Parce 2-5 Nave, 28042, Madrid, Spain
Tel.: (34) 91 7461860
Marine Cargo Handling Services
N.A.I.C.S.: 488320

Flyline Tele Sales & Services GmbH (1)
Hermann-Kohl-Strasse 3, 28199, Bremen, Germany
Tel.: (49) 4215575001
Web Site: http://www.flyline.de
Travel & Tourism Services
N.A.I.C.S.: 561510
Michael Spring *(Mng Dir)*

IAG Cargo Limited (1)
Heathrow Airport Sealand Road, PO Box 99, Longford Hounslow, London, TW6 2JS, Middlesex, United Kingdom
Tel.: (44) 2088977034
Web Site: https://www.iagcargo.com
Airline Services
N.A.I.C.S.: 488190

Iberia Lineas Aereas de Espana, S.A. (1)
Velazquez 130, 28006, Madrid, Spain
Tel.: (34) 915878787
Web Site: http://www.iberia.com
Sales Range: $5-14.9 Billion
Emp.: 20,103
Passenger & Freight Airline Operator; Airport & Aircraft Management Services
N.A.I.C.S.: 481111

Subsidiary (Domestic):

CACESA-Compania Auxiliar al Cargo Express, S.A. (2)
Barajas Air Cargo Center Calle Golf 23, 28042, Madrid, Spain (75%)
Tel.: (34) 913335450
Web Site: http://www.cacesa.com
Air Cargo Transport Services
N.A.I.C.S.: 481212

Subsidiary (Domestic):

Auxiliar Logistica Aeroportuaria, S.A. (3)
Centro de Carga Aerea Madrid Barajas Parcela 1 3 B, 28042, Madrid, Spain
Tel.: (34) 91 312 01 59
Web Site: http://www.alaer.es
Air Freight Forwarding Services
N.A.I.C.S.: 481112

INTERNATIONAL CONSOLIDATED AIRLINES GROUP S.A.

International Consolidated Airlines Group S.A.—(Continued)

Subsidiary (Domestic):

Cargosur, S.A. (2)
Calle Trespartème 7 3 C Centro de Carga Aerea, Aeropuerto de Madrid Barajas, 28042, Madrid, Spain **(100%)**
Tel.: (34) 913293250
Web Site: http://www.cargosur.com
Air Cargo Transport Services
N.A.I.C.S.: 481112

Branch (US):

Iberia Air Lines of Spain (2)
5835 Blue Lagoon Dr Ste 200, Miami, FL 33126-2062
Tel.: (305) 267-7747
Sales Range: $50-74.9 Million
Emp.: 150
Oil Transportation Services
N.A.I.C.S.: 481211

Subsidiary (Domestic):

Iberia Tecnologia, S.A. (2)
Calle Martinez Villergas 49, 28027, Madrid, Spain
Tel.: (34) 915878787
Air Maintenance Services
N.A.I.C.S.: 488190

Iberia, Lineas Aereas de Espana, Sociedad Anonima Operadora (2)
Calle Velazquez 130, 28006, Madrid, Spain
Tel.: (34) 915878787
Passenger Transport & Other Related Services
N.A.I.C.S.: 488190

Teleflight Limited (1)
4887 Belfort Rd Ste 201, Jacksonville, FL 32256-6036
Tel.: (904) 245-6200
Scheduled Air Transportation Services
N.A.I.C.S.: 481111

The Mileage Company Limited (1)
Astral Towers Betts Way London Rd, Crawley, H102XY, West Sussex, United Kingdom
Tel.: (44) 844 493 3399
Sales Range: $75-99.9 Million
Emp.: 50
Design & Development Services
N.A.I.C.S.: 541490
Andrew Swaffield (Gen Mgr)

Vueling Airlines S.A. (1)
Parque de Negocios Mas Blau II, Pla de l'Estany 5, 08820, El Prat de Llobregat, Spain
Tel.: (34) 900645000
Web Site: http://www.vueling.com
Sales Range: $1-4.9 Billion
Emp.: 3,074
Passenger Air Transportation Services
N.A.I.C.S.: 481111

INTERNATIONAL CONSOLIDATED BUSINESS GROUP PTY LTD.

Level 1/344 St Kilda Rd, Melbourne, 3004, VIC, Australia
Tel.: (61) 396282700
Web Site: https://icbbrands.com
Year Founded: 1989
Consumer Products Merchant Whslr
N.A.I.C.S.: 424490

Subsidiaries:

Multix Pty. Ltd. (1)
Level 1 Building 3 Brandon Office Park, 530-540 Springvale Road, Glen Waverley, 3150, VIC, Australia
Tel.: (61) 395434577
Web Site: http://www.multix.com.au
Sales Range: $25-49.9 Million
Emp.: 30
Plastics Foil & Coated Paper Bag Mfr
N.A.I.C.S.: 322220

INTERNATIONAL CONSTRUCTION DEVELOPMENT COMPANY

Argentina Square Bucharest Avenue Eighth Street No 11, Tehran, Iran
Tel.: (98) 21 87123
Web Site: http://www.icd.co.ir
BSTE—(THE)
Sales Range: Less than $1 Million
Building Construction Services
N.A.I.C.S.: 236220
Mohammad Motevalian (Vice Chm)

INTERNATIONAL CONSTRUCTION TECHNOLOGY CO., LTD.

ES Tower 9 World Cupbuk-ro 58-gil, Mapo-gu, Seoul, Korea (South)
Tel.: (82) 25715977   KR
Web Site:
http://www.interconstech.com
Bridge Construction Services
N.A.I.C.S.: 237310

INTERNATIONAL CONSTRUCTIONS LIMITED

Golden Enclave Corporate Block Tower B1 5th Floor, Hal Old Airport Road, Bengaluru, 560017, India
Tel.: (91) 8049411700
Web Site: http://www.inltd.co.in
Year Founded: 1983
SUBCAPCITY—(NSE)
Rev: $13,717,997
Assets: $19,392,596
Liabilities: $8,330,794
Net Worth: $11,061,801
Earnings: ($1,964,038)
Emp.: 8
Fiscal Year-end: 03/31/23
Construction Services
N.A.I.C.S.: 236210
Anil Kumar Sethi (Mng Dir)

INTERNATIONAL CONTAINER TERMINAL SERVICES, INC.

ICTSI Administration Building Manila International Container Terminal, MICT South Access Road Port of Manila, Manila, 1012, Philippines
Tel.: (63) 282454101   PH
Web Site: https://www.ictsi.com
Year Founded: 1987
ICT—(PHI)
Rev: $1,925,177,360
Assets: $6,266,459,777
Liabilities: $4,754,880,774
Net Worth: $1,511,579,003
Earnings: $477,542,443
Emp.: 7,870
Fiscal Year-end: 12/31/21
Develops, Manages & Operates Container Ports & Terminals
N.A.I.C.S.: 488310
Arthur R. Tabuena (Head-IR & Dir-Treasury)

Subsidiaries:

Baltic Container Terminal Ltd (1)
Kwiatkowskiego Str 60, 81-127, Gdynia, Poland **(100%)**
Tel.: (48) 583506030
Web Site: https://www.bct.gdynia.pl
Emp.: 280
Containers & Port Development
N.A.I.C.S.: 488310

Batumi International Container Terminal LLC (1)
Tel.: (995) 577172728
Web Site: https://www.bict.ge
Cost Management Services
N.A.I.C.S.: 488310

Bauan International Port, Inc (1)
Port Area Barangay San Roque, Bauan, 4201, Batangas, 4201, Philippines **(100%)**
Tel.: (63) 437798241
Sales Range: $25-49.9 Million
Emp.: 30
Marine Cargo Handling
N.A.I.C.S.: 488320

Contecon Manzanillo S.A. (1)
TEC II Zona Norte Puerto de Manzanillo Boulevard, Miguel de la Madrid Hurtado, 28210, Manzanillo, Colima, Mexico
Tel.: (52) 3149800555
Web Site: https://www.contecon.mx
Cost Management Services
N.A.I.C.S.: 488310

Davao Integrated Port and Stevedoring Services Corporation (1)
International Port Of Davao, Davao, Philippines **(90.7%)**
Tel.: (63) 822330283
Emp.: 140
Marine Cargo Handling
N.A.I.C.S.: 488320
Julien Domingo (Gen Mgr)

ICTSI DR Congo S.A. (1)
Avenue Mienze Kiaku NR 1/2 Cellule Oebk Quartier Ville Haute, Commune de Matadi, Brazzaville, Kongo Central, Congo, Republic of
Tel.: (242) 829999527
Cost Management Services
N.A.I.C.S.: 488310

ICTSI South Pacific Limited (1)
Level 1 Harborside West Stanley Esplanade, National Capital District, Port Moresby, 121, Papua New Guinea
Tel.: (675) 3200881
Cost Management Services
N.A.I.C.S.: 488310
Anil Singh (CEO)

ICTSI Warehousing, Inc. (1)
ICTSI Admin Building MICT South Access Road, Manila, 1012, Philippines
Tel.: (63) 22454101
Bonded Warehousing Services
N.A.I.C.S.: 493190

IW Cargo Handlers, Inc. (1)
3rd Floor Room 305 ICTSI Administration Building, MICT South Access Road, Manila, Philippines
Tel.: (63) 22445066
Web Site: http://www.ictsi.com.ph
Marine Cargo Handling Services
N.A.I.C.S.: 488320

Laguna Gateway Inland Container Terminal Inc. (1)
San Cristobal, Calamba, 4027, Laguna, Philippines
Tel.: (63) 559443244
Web Site: https://lgict.com.ph
Cost Management Services
N.A.I.C.S.: 488310

Madagascar International Container Terminal Services Ltd. (1)
10 Rue du Commerce, 501, Ampasimazava, 501, Toamasina, Madagascar
Tel.: (261) 205335204
Web Site: https://www.mictsl.mg
Cost Management Services
N.A.I.C.S.: 488310
Selom Komi Anani (CFO)

Mindanao International Container Terminal Services Inc. (1)
Phividec Industrial Estate, Tagoloan, 9001, Cagayan de Oro, 9001, Misamis Oriental, Philippines
Tel.: (63) 9178204899
Web Site: https://mictsi.com
Cost Management Services
N.A.I.C.S.: 488310
Alvin Dacoroon (Mgr-HRAD)

Motukea International Terminal Limited (1)
Porebada Road 121, National Capital District, 121, Port Moresby, Papua New Guinea
Tel.: (675) 71900395
Cost Management Services
N.A.I.C.S.: 488310
Derrick Takendu (Deputy Mgr-IT)

Naha International Container Terminal, Inc. (1)
1-27-1 Minatomachi, Naha, 900-0001, Okinawa, Japan **(60%)**
Tel.: (81) 988675931
Web Site: http://www.nicti.co.jp
Sales Range: $25-49.9 Million
Emp.: 5
Marine Cargo Handling

INTERNATIONAL PUBLIC

N.A.I.C.S.: 488320

New Muara Container Terminal Services Sdn. Bhd. (1)
Rusahaan Simpang 15 Muara, BT1728, Negara, Brunei Darussallam
Tel.: (673) 2771959
Web Site: https://www.ictsi.com
Sales Range: $25-49.9 Million
Emp.: 100
Container Terminal Operation Services
N.A.I.C.S.: 488490
Rico T. Cruz (Mng Dir)

Operadora Portuaria Centroamericana S.A. (1)
Piso No 26 Nuevos Horizontes Business Center 1ra Calle 3ra Av Bloque S, Col Rancho El Coco Cortes, San Pedro Sula, Honduras
Tel.: (504) 25646770
Web Site: https://www.opc.hn
Cost Management Services
N.A.I.C.S.: 488310
Mariano Turnes (CEO)

PT Makassar Terminal Services Inc. (1)
Jalan Botolempangan 7B, Makassar, Sulawesi Selatan, Indonesia
Tel.: (62) 4113631774
Cost Management Services
N.A.I.C.S.: 488310

PT Perusahaan Bongkar Muat Olah Jasa Andal (1)
Graha Kirana 7th Floor Suite 701 Jl Yos Sudarso No 88, Jakarta Utara, 14350, Indonesia
Tel.: (62) 2165314710
Web Site: http://www.oja.co.id
Cost Management Services
N.A.I.C.S.: 488310

Pakistan International Container Terminal Limited (1)
Plot 25/1-A Street no 5 Muslimabad Society Jamshed Town, Karachi, 74800, Pakistan
Tel.: (92) 2137442366
Web Site: https://www.pict.com.pk
Rev: $43,257,043
Assets: $29,894,190
Liabilities: $22,096,942
Net Worth: $7,797,248
Earnings: $9,819,171
Emp.: 657
Fiscal Year-end: 12/31/2022
Container Port Operation & Services
N.A.I.C.S.: 488310
Hans-Ole Madsen (Chm)

South Cotabato Integrated Port Services, Inc. (1)
Makar Wharf, Port Of General Santos, General Santos, 9500, South Cotabato, Philippines
Tel.: (63) 835546543
Web Site: https://www.scipsi.com
Sales Range: $125-149.9 Million
Emp.: 352
Marine Cargo Handling Services
N.A.I.C.S.: 488320

South Pacific International Container Terminal Limited (1)
Lae Tidal Basin International Terminal Admin Building Bumbu Road, PO Box 3549, 411, Lae, Papua New Guinea
Tel.: (675) 71900982
Web Site: https://ictsispl.com
Cost Management Services
N.A.I.C.S.: 488310
George Gware (Gen Mgr)

Subic Bay International Terminal Corp. (1)
New Container Terminal 1 San Bernardino Road, Subic Port District Subic Bay Freeport Zone, Olongapo, 2222, Zambales, Philippines
Tel.: (63) 472526477
Web Site: https://sbitc.ph
Sales Range: $25-49.9 Million
Emp.: 84
Container Terminal Operation Services
N.A.I.C.S.: 488490
Roberto R. Locsin (Pres)

Subic Bay International Terminal Holdings, Inc. (1)

AND PRIVATE COMPANIES

NCT 1 San Bernardino Road, Subic Bay Free Port Zone, Olongapo, 2222, Zambales, Philippines
Tel.: (63) 472526475
Web Site: http://www.sbitc.net
Sales Range: $50-74.9 Million
Emp: 80
Investment Management Service
N.A.I.C.S.: 523940
Reimond B. Silvestre (Gen Mgr)

Tartous International Container Terminal jsc (1)
Al Mina Street, PO Box 870, Tartous Port, Tartus, 50400, Syria
Tel.: (963) 43328882
Web Site: http://www.ictsi.sy
Emp.: 75
Container Terminal Operation Services
N.A.I.C.S.: 488310

Tecon Suape, S.A. (1)
Avenida Portuaria S/N Porto de Suape, Ipojuca, 55594-000, PE, Brazil
Tel.: (55) 8135275200
Web Site: http://www.teconsuape.com
Container Terminal Operation Services
N.A.I.C.S.: 488310

Terminal Maritima de Tuxpan S.A. de C.V. (1)
Carr A Cobos Km 7 Barra Sur, Tuxpan, 92770, Veracruz, Mexico
Tel.: (52) 7838375060
Cost Management Services
N.A.I.C.S.: 488310

Victoria International Container Terminal Ltd. (1)
78 Webb Dock Drive, Port Melbourne, 3207, VIC, Australia
Tel.: (61) 385479700
Web Site: https://www.vict.com.au
Cost Management Services
N.A.I.C.S.: 488310
Jon Wheeler (Mgr-IT)

Yantai International Container Terminals Limited (1)
158 Gangwan Dadao, Yantai, 264000, Shandong, China
Tel.: (86) 5356745556
Web Site: https://ictsiyantai.com
Cost Management Services
N.A.I.C.S.: 488310

INTERNATIONAL CONVEYORS LIMITED
10 Middleton Row, Kolkata, 700071, India
Tel.: (91) 3322296033
Web Site: https://www.iclbelting.com
509709—(NSE)
Rev.: $24,329,596
Assets: $31,110,739
Liabilities: $10,089,384
Net Worth: $21,021,355
Earnings: $2,268,876
Emp.: 71
Fiscal Year-end: 03/31/21
Conveyor Belts Mfr
N.A.I.C.S.: 333922
Rajendra Kumar Dabriwala (Mng Dir)

Subsidiaries:

IIFL Finance Ltd. (1)
IIFL House Sun Infotech Park Road No 16V Plot No B-23, Thane Industrial Area Wagle Estate, Thane, 400604, India
Tel.: (91) 2241035000
Web Site: https://www.iifl.com
Rev.: $1,012,782,207
Assets: $6,354,693,364
Liabilities: $5,131,488,520
Net Worth: $1,223,204,844
Earnings: $192,740,243
Emp.: 14,937
Fiscal Year-end: 03/31/2023
Holding Company; Financial Services
N.A.I.C.S.: 551112
H. Nemkumar (Pres-Infoline Limited)

Subsidiary (Non-US):

IIFL (Asia) Pte Ltd. (2)
6 Shenton Way 18-08B OUE Downtown 2, Singapore, 068809, Singapore
Tel.: (65) 65116160
Web Site: http://www.iiflcap.com
Sales Range: $50-74.9 Million
Emp.: 15
Insurance Brokerage & Financial Investment Advisory Services
N.A.I.C.S.: 523940
Bharat Himatlal Parajia (Mng Dir)

Subsidiary (Domestic):

IIFL Securities Pte Ltd. (3)
6 Shenton Way 18-08B OUE Downtown 2, Singapore, 2068809, Singapore
Tel.: (65) 65116160
Web Site: http://www.iiflcap.com
Sales Range: $25-49.9 Million
Emp.: 14
Securities & Bond Brokerage Services
N.A.I.C.S.: 523150
Bharat Himatlal Parajia (Mng Dir)

Subsidiary (Domestic):

IIFL Home Finance Limited (2)
Plot No 98 Udyog Vihar Phase IV Sector 18, Gurgaon, 122015, Haryana, India
Tel.: (91) 1244780900
Web Site: https://www.iiflhomeloans.com
Home Loan Services
N.A.I.C.S.: 522390
S. Sridhar (Chm)

IIFL Samasta Finance Limited (2)
73 2nd Floor Lalbagh Road Next to Kia Motors, Bengaluru, 560027, Karnataka, India
Tel.: (91) 18001208868
Web Site: https://iiflsamasta.com
Financial Product Services
N.A.I.C.S.: 522320

India Infoline Finance Limited (2)
12A-10 13th Floor Parinee Crescenzo C-38 and C-39 G Block, Behind MCA Bandra Kurla Complex Bandra East, Mumbai, 400051, India
Tel.: (91) 22 67881000
Web Site: http://www.iiflfinance.com
Sales Range: $300-349.9 Million
Emp.: 7,503
Mortgage & Other Lending Services
N.A.I.C.S.: 522310
V. K. Chopra (Chm)

International Conveyors Australia Pty Limited (1)
Level 48 101 Collins Street, Melbourne, 3000, VIC, Australia
Tel.: (61) 1300737180
Web Site: http://www.internationalconveyors.com.au
Nonwoven Fabric Mfr
N.A.I.C.S.: 313230

INTERNATIONAL CORONA CAPITAL CORP.
7934 Government Road, Burnaby, V5A 2E2, BC, Canada
Tel.: (416) 844-5712 BC
Web Site: http://internationalcorona.com
Year Founded: 2008
IC—(TSXV)
Sales Range: Less than $1 Million
Investment Services
N.A.I.C.S.: 523999
Brian Bosse (CEO)

INTERNATIONAL CSRC INVESTMENT HOLDINGS CO., LTD.
8F 113 Section 2 Zhongshan North Road, Zhongshan District, Taipei, 104, Taiwan
Tel.: (886) 225316556
Web Site: https://www.csrcgroup.com
Year Founded: 1973
2104—(TAI)
Emp.: 1,347
Pharmaceuticals Product Mfr
N.A.I.C.S.: 325412
Po-Sung Huang (Pres)

INTERNATIONAL DATA MANAGEMENT LIMITED
806 Siddhartha 96 Nehru Place, New Delhi, 110 019, India
Tel.: (91) 1126444812 In
Web Site: https://www.idmlimited.in
517044—(BOM)
Assets: $223,041
Liabilities: $523,368
Net Worth: ($300,327)
Earnings: ($12,162)
Fiscal Year-end: 03/31/21
Computer Product Mfr
N.A.I.C.S.: 334118
Kuldeep Singh Pathania (CFO)

INTERNATIONAL DEVELOPMENT & INVESTMENT CORPORATION
National Road No 80 Vam Cong Industrial Park, An Thanh Lap Vo, Binh Thanh, Dong Thap, Vietnam
Tel.: (84) 673680383
Web Site: https://www.idiseafood.com
Year Founded: 2003
IDI—(HOSE)
Rev.: $297,515,047
Assets: $341,030,858
Liabilities: $200,062,709
Net Worth: $140,968,148
Earnings: $3,022,185
Fiscal Year-end: 12/31/23
Real Estate Manangement Services
N.A.I.C.S.: 531390
Van Chung Le (CEO)

INTERNATIONAL DISTRIBUTIONS SERVICES PLC
185 Farringdon Road, London, EC1A 1AA, United Kingdom
Tel.: (44) 8713842656 UK
Web Site: https://www.internationaldistr.com
ROYMY—(OTCIQ)
Rev.: $15,203,231,507
Assets: $11,128,502,903
Liabilities: $6,329,209,796
Net Worth: $4,799,293,108
Earnings: ($1,101,994,446)
Emp.: 152,250
Fiscal Year-end: 03/26/23
Postal Service
N.A.I.C.S.: 491110
Kulbinder Dosanjh (Sec-Grp)

Subsidiaries:

GLS Beteiligungs GmbH (1)
Christstrasse 9, 44789, Bochum, Germany
Tel.: (49) 234 579 7100
Web Site: https://www.gls-beteiligung.de
Renewable Energy Services
N.A.I.C.S.: 221114

GLS General Logistics Systems Hungary Kft. (1)
GLS Europa u 2, 2351, Alsonemedi, Hungary
Tel.: (36) 2 988 6670
Parcel & Express Services
N.A.I.C.S.: 491110

GLS General Logistics Systems Romania Srl (1)
Stefan cel Mare Street no 3, Parc Industrial Selimbsar, 557260, Sibiu, Romania
Tel.: (40) 26 950 1900
Parcel & Express Services
N.A.I.C.S.: 491110

GLS General Logistics Systems Slovakia s.r.o. (1)
Budca 1039, Budca, 962 33, Zvolen, Slovakia
Tel.: (421) 45 524 2500
Parcel & Express Services
N.A.I.C.S.: 491110

General Logistics Systems Austria GmbH (1)
Traunuferstrasse 105a, 4052, Ansfelden, Austria
Tel.: (43) 598760
Parcel Delivery Services
N.A.I.C.S.: 491110

General Logistics Systems B.V. (1)
Breguetlaan 28-30, 1438 BC, Oude Meer, Netherlands
Tel.: (31) 206587777
Web Site: http://www.gls-holding.com
Sales Range: $1-4.9 Billion
Emp.: 14,500
Courier Services & Logistics Solutions
N.A.I.C.S.: 492110
James Rietkerk (Mng Dir)

Subsidiary (Non-US):

GLS Logistics Systems Canada Ltd. (2)
10500 Avenue Ryan, Dorval, H9P 2T7, QC, Canada
Web Site: https://gls-canada.com
Holding Company; Business-to-Business Freight Transportation Arrangement & Logistics Services
N.A.I.C.S.: 551112
Rick Barnes (Pres)

Subsidiary (Domestic):

Dicom Express Inc. (3)
10500 Ave Ryan, Dorval, H9P 2T7, QC, Canada
Web Site: http://www.godicom.com
Business-to-Business Freight Transportation Arrangement & Logistics Services
N.A.I.C.S.: 488510
Pierre Poliquin (Pres)

Subsidiary (US):

Eastern Connection Operating Inc. (3)
70 Industrial Rd, Cumberland, RI 02864
Tel.: (781) 926-7495
Web Site: http://east.dicom.com
Regional Transportation & Logistics Services
N.A.I.C.S.: 492210
James A. Berluti (VP-Sls)

Subsidiary (Domestic):

Rosenau Transport Ltd. (3)
3300 76 Ave NW, Edmonton, T6P 1J4, AB, Canada
Tel.: (800) 371-6895
Web Site: http://www.rosenau.ca
Emp.: 500
Freight & Warehousing Services
N.A.I.C.S.: 484110
Al May (Mgr-Ops-Calgary)

General Logistics Systems Czech Republic s.r.o. (1)
Prumyslova 5619/1, 586 01, Jihlava, Czech Republic
Tel.: (420) 56 777 1111
Parcel & Express Services
N.A.I.C.S.: 491110

General Logistics Systems Finland OY (1)
Rydontie 6, 20360, Turku, Finland
Tel.: (358) 20 758 1250
Parcel & Express Services
N.A.I.C.S.: 491110

General Logistics Systems Germany GmbH & Co. OHG (1)
GLS Germany-Strasse 1-7, 36286, Neuenstein, Germany
Tel.: (49) 667764 690 7000
Parcel & Express Services
N.A.I.C.S.: 491110

General Logistics Systems Ireland Limited (1)
Unit 200 Northwest Business Park, Dublin, D15 K8ND, Ireland
Tel.: (353) 1 860 6200
Parcel & Express Services
N.A.I.C.S.: 491110

General Logistics Systems Poland Spolka z o.o. (1)
Ul Teczowa 10, Gluchowo, 62-052, Komorniki, Poland

3747

INTERNATIONAL DISTRIBUTIONS SERVICES PLC

International Distributions Services plc—(Continued)

Tel.: (48) 46 814 8220
Parcel & Express Services
N.A.I.C.S.: 491110
Tomasz Zwiercan *(Reg Mgr)*

General Logistics Systems Portugal Lda. (1)
Rua da Bica n 10, 2665-608, Venda do Pinheiro, Portugal
Tel.: (351) 21 966 7100
Web Site: https://www.gls-portugal.pt
Parcel & Express Services
N.A.I.C.S.: 491110

General Logistics Systems US, Inc. (1)
7901 Stoneridge Dr Ste 400, Pleasanton, CA 94588-4588 **(100%)**
Web Site: https://www.gls-us.com
Sales Range: $100-124.9 Million
Emp.: 1,900
Ground Delivery & Priority Overnight Delivery Services
N.A.I.C.S.: 488999
Dana Hyatt *(CEO)*

General Logistics Systems, logisticne storitve, d.o.o. (1)
Cesta v Prod 84, 1129, Ljubljana, Slovenia
Tel.: (386) 1 500 1150
Parcel & Express Services
N.A.I.C.S.: 491110

Overnight Services GmbH Vermittlung Ueberregionaler Kurierdienste (1)
Wendenstrasse 349, 20537, Hamburg, Germany
Tel.: (49) 402 385 8585
Web Site: https://www.hamburg-derkurier.de
Courier Track Services
N.A.I.C.S.: 492110

Parcelforce Ltd (1)
6th Fl 29 Wellington St, Leeds, LS1 1AA, United Kingdom **(100%)**
Tel.: (44) 870 606 1666
Web Site: http://www.parcelforce.com
Sales Range: $10-24.9 Million
Emp.: 50
Courier Service
N.A.I.C.S.: 492110
Alistair Cochrane *(Dir-Ops-Worldwide)*

Quadrant Catering Ltd. (1)
Quadrant House 2 Drakes Meadow, Swindon, SN3 3LL, United Kingdom
Tel.: (44) 1793546500
Web Site: http://www.quadrantcatering.co.uk
Sales Range: $125-149.9 Million
Emp.: 2,667
Full-Service Restaurants & Catering Services
N.A.I.C.S.: 722511
Richard Taylor *(Mng Dir)*

Romec Limited (1)
Romec Applicon House Exchange Street, SK3 0EE, Stockport, United Kingdom - England
Tel.: (44) 01614753800
Web Site: http://www.romec.co.uk
Sales Range: $350-399.9 Million
Emp.: 300
Facilities Management Solutions & Building Maintenance Services
N.A.I.C.S.: 561210
Paul Clutterbuck *(Dir-Sls-Building Svcs Installation Product Grp)*

Royal Mail (1)
148 Old St, London, EC1V 9HQ, United Kingdom **(100%)**
Tel.: (44) 2074902888
Web Site: http://www.royalmail.com
Sales Range: $300-349.9 Million
Emp.: 1,600
Mail Distribution Services
N.A.I.C.S.: 492110

Royal Mail Investments Ltd. (1)
Royal Mail House, 148 Old Street Islington, EC1V9HQ, London, United Kingdom
Tel.: (44) 2074498000
Web Site: http://www.royalmail.com
Postal & Courier Services
N.A.I.C.S.: 492110

Storefeeder Ltd. (1)
185 Farringdon Road, London, EC1A 1AA, United Kingdom
Tel.: (44) 115 784 2150
Web Site: http://www.storefeeder.com
E-Commerce Online Services
N.A.I.C.S.: 513210

INTERNATIONAL ENERGY INSURANCE PLC

Plot 171A Moshood Olugbani Str, Victoria Island, Lagos, Nigeria
Tel.: (234) 14616972
Web Site: https://www.ieiplcng.com
Year Founded: 2003
Insurance Management Services
N.A.I.C.S.: 524298
Muhammad Kabiru Ahmad *(Chm)*

INTERNATIONAL ENGINEERING PUBLIC COMPANY LIMITED

408/37 Phaholyothin Place Building 9th Floor, Phaholyothin Road Phayathai, Bangkok, 10400, Thailand
Tel.: (66) 2 619 0199
Web Site: http://www.iec.co.th
Year Founded: 1953
Sales Range: $10-24.9 Million
Emp.: 55
Engineeering Services
N.A.I.C.S.: 541330
Sunjutha Witchawut *(Vice Chm)*

INTERNATIONAL ENTERTAINMENT CORPORATION

Units 2109-10 21st Floor Wing On House No 71 Des Voeux Road, Central, China (Hong Kong)
Tel.: (852) 28698117 Ky
Web Site: http://www.ientcorp.com
Year Founded: 1998
1009—(HKG)
Rev.: $11,031,015
Assets: $241,808,608
Liabilities: $87,561,684
Net Worth: $154,246,924
Earnings: ($33,069,311)
Emp.: 218
Fiscal Year-end: 06/30/22
Investment Holding Company; Hotel Owner & Operator
N.A.I.C.S.: 551112
Stanley Chiu Fai Choi *(Chm)*

INTERNATIONAL EQUITIES CORPORATION LIMITED

Room 6 Seasons of Perth 37 Pier Street, Perth, 6000, WA, Australia
Tel.: (61) 396852988 AU
Web Site: https://internationalequities.com.au
IEQ—(ASX)
Rev.: $1,735,443
Assets: $9,467,147
Liabilities: $5,239,717
Net Worth: $4,227,431
Earnings: ($317,174)
Fiscal Year-end: 06/30/24
Residential Property Development & Management Services
N.A.I.C.S.: 531311
Marcus Peng Fye Tow *(Chm & CEO)*

Subsidiaries:

IEC Real Estate Pty Ltd (1)
Suite 100A/640 Swanston Street, Carlton, 3053, VIC, Australia
Tel.: (61) 39 340 3300
Web Site: https://internationalequities.com.au
Emp.: 5
Real Estate Management Services
N.A.I.C.S.: 531390
Geoff Stidworthy *(Principal)*

Renaissance Australia Pty Ltd (1)
37 Pier St, Perth, 6000, WA, Australia

Tel.: (61) 893257655
Web Site: http://www.renaissanceminerals.com.au
Sales Range: $50-74.9 Million
Emp.: 6
Financial Investment Management Services
N.A.I.C.S.: 523999
Peter Wong *(Mgr)*

Seasons Apartment Hotel Group Pty. Ltd. (1)
348 St Kilda Road, Melbourne, VIC, Australia
Tel.: (61) 396853000
Web Site: https://www.sahg.com.au
Restaurant Operators
N.A.I.C.S.: 722511

INTERNATIONAL FERRO METALS LIMITED

Level 7 99 Macquarie Street, Sydney, 2000, NSW, Australia
Tel.: (61) 2 8226 3323 AU
Web Site: http://www.ifml.com
Sales Range: $1-4.9 Billion
Emp.: 1,215
Iron Ore Mining Services
N.A.I.C.S.: 212210
Jannie Muller *(Dir-Fin)*

INTERNATIONAL FINANCIAL ADVISORS K.S.C.C.

Souq Al-Kabeer Building BlockA - 9th Floor, PO Box 2986, Safat, Kuwait, 13030, Kuwait
Tel.: (965) 1844432
Web Site: https://www.ifakuwait.com
Year Founded: 1974
IFA—(DFM)
Rev.: $62,953,994
Assets: $367,584,670
Liabilities: $145,112,382
Net Worth: $222,472,289
Earnings: $53,423,872
Emp.: 10
Fiscal Year-end: 12/31/23
Financial Advisory Services
N.A.I.C.S.: 523940
Saleh Saleh Al-Selmi *(CEO)*

Subsidiaries:

IFA Hotels & Resorts Co. K.S.C.C. (1)
Al Abdul Razzak Square Souk Al-Kuwait Building Block A 8th Floor, PO Box 4694, Safat, 13047, Kuwait, Kuwait **(58%)**
Tel.: (965) 1844432
Web Site: http://www.ifahotelsresorts.com
Rev.: $128,760,470
Assets: $645,032,555
Liabilities: $525,371,010
Net Worth: $119,661,546
Earnings: $12,918,337
Emp.: 5
Fiscal Year-end: 12/31/2022
Hotels & Resorts Owner & Operator
N.A.I.C.S.: 721110
Talal Jassim Al-Bahar *(Chm & CEO)*

NEOVA INSURANCE CORPORATION (1)
Kozyatagi E-5 Yan Yol uzeri sasmaz Plaza No 6 Kat 3-5 Kadikoy, 34742, Istanbul, Turkiye
Tel.: (90) 216 665 55 55
Web Site: http://www.neova.com.tr
Emp.: 15
Insurance Advisory Services
N.A.I.C.S.: 524298
Fawaz Kh. E. Alsaleh *(Chm)*

UNIVEST Group (1)
Salhiya Complex Gate 8 5th Floor, PO Box 1520, Safat, 13016, Kuwait, Kuwait
Tel.: (965) 2245 8383
Web Site: http://www.univestgroup.com
Holding Company
N.A.I.C.S.: 551112
Abdul Azeez Abdul Raheem *(VP-Fin & Ops)*

United Investments Portugal (1)
Rua Silva Carvalho 234-7, Lisbon, Portugal
Tel.: (351) 28 950 1090
Hotel & Resort Management Services

INTERNATIONAL PUBLIC

N.A.I.C.S.: 721110

INTERNATIONAL FINANCIAL GROUP LTD.

First Canadian Place 100 King Street West Suite 910, Toronto, M5X 1B1, ON, Canada
Tel.: (877) 434-3737
Web Site: http://www.ifg-global.com
Sales Range: $50-74.9 Million
Outsourced Services for Accounting, Finance, IT & Executive Search
N.A.I.C.S.: 561499
Joe Taylor *(Mng Partner)*

Subsidiaries:

RL360 Insurance Co. Ltd. (1)
International House Cooil Road, Douglas, IM2 2SP, Isle of Man
Tel.: (44) 1624681682
Web Site: https://www.rl360.com
Investment Solution Services
N.A.I.C.S.: 523999

INTERNATIONAL FOR MEDICAL INVESTMENT PLC

Amman-Applied Science University Shafa badran, PO BOX 166, Amman, 11931, Jordan
Tel.: (962) 65609999
Year Founded: 1995
ICMI—(AMM)
Rev.: $34,382
Assets: $4,012,606
Liabilities: $908,645
Net Worth: $3,103,961
Earnings: ($101,121)
Emp.: 2
Fiscal Year-end: 12/31/20
Investment Services
N.A.I.C.S.: 523999

INTERNATIONAL FRONTIER RESOURCES CORPORATION

Livingston Place South Tower 1805 222 3rd Avenue SW, Calgary, T2P 0B4, AB, Canada
Tel.: (403) 215-2780 AB
Web Site: https://www.internationalfrontier.com
IFR—(TSXV)
Rev.: $357,004
Assets: $73,745
Liabilities: $563,328
Net Worth: ($489,583)
Earnings: $145,994
Emp.: 4
Fiscal Year-end: 12/31/23
Oil & Gas Exploration & Development Services
N.A.I.C.S.: 541360
Gary Lyons *(Vice Chm)*

INTERNATIONAL GAME TECHNOLOGY PLC

3rd Floor 10 Finsbury Square, London, EC2A 1AF, United Kingdom
Tel.: (44) 2038661240
Web Site: https://www.igt.com
IGT—(NYSE)
Rev.: $4,225,000,000
Assets: $10,433,000,000
Liabilities: $8,454,000,000
Net Worth: $1,979,000,000
Earnings: $275,000,000
Emp.: 10,786
Fiscal Year-end: 12/31/22
Holding Company; Gaming Services
N.A.I.C.S.: 551112
Marco Sala *(Exec Chm)*

Subsidiaries:

GTECH S.p.A. (1)
Viale del Campo Boario 56/D, 00154, Rome, Italy **(100%)**
Tel.: (39) 06518991

AND PRIVATE COMPANIES

Gambling Technologies Developer, Mfr & Marketer; Gaming Services
N.A.I.C.S.: 339999
Walter Bugno (CEO-Intl)

Subsidiary (US):

IGT Global Solutions Corporation (2)
10 Memorial Blvd, Providence, RI 02903 **(100%)**
Tel.: (401) 392-1000
Web Site: http://www.igt.com
Gambling Technologies Developer, Mfr & Marketer; Gaming Services
N.A.I.C.S.: 339999
Robert Vincent (Chm)

Subsidiary (Non-US):

Europrint (Promotions) Limited (3)
Lancaster House, 52 Preston New Road, Blackburn, BB2 6AH, Lancs, United Kingdom **(100%)**
Tel.: (44) 1254588400
Web Site: http://www.igi-europrint.com
Interactive & Promotional Games Developer
N.A.I.C.S.: 513210
Andrew P. Gray (Mng Dir)

GTECH Austria GmbH (3)
Am Seering 13-14, 8141, Unterpremstatten, Austria **(100%)**
Tel.: (43) 3135 55880
Casino Gaming System Developer & Mfr
N.A.I.C.S.: 713290

Subsidiary (Non-US):

GTECH Monaco S.A.M. (4)
7 rue du Gabian Office No 822, 98000, Monaco, Monaco **(98%)**
Tel.: (377) 92056805
Casino Gaming System Mfr
N.A.I.C.S.: 713290
Lavaz Watson (VP-Intl Plng & Strategic Projects)

Subsidiary (Non-US):

GTECH Peru S.A. (3)
Manuel Olguin 501 Office 1001, Monterrico-Surco, Lima, Peru **(98%)**
Tel.: (51) 16183200
Casino Gaming System Developer & Mfr
N.A.I.C.S.: 713290
David Paredes (Fin Dir)

IGT Germany Gaming GmbH (3)
Borsigstrasse 22, Lubeck, 32312, Germany
Tel.: (49) 5741 24099950
Sales Range: $200-249.9 Million
Emp.: 600
Casino Gaming Machine Developer & Mfr
N.A.I.C.S.: 713290
Sylvia Dietz (VP-Global Mktg)

Subsidiary (Domestic):

IGT Indiana, LLC (3)
1302 N Meridian St Ste 100, Indianapolis, IN 46402 **(100%)**
Tel.: (317) 264-4637
Integrated Services for State Lottery
N.A.I.C.S.: 541512
Colin Hadden (COO & Gen Mgr)

Subsidiary (Non-US):

IGT U.K. Limited (3)
1st Floor Building 3 Croxley Green Business Park, Hatters Lane, Watford, WD18 8YG, Herts, United Kingdom
Tel.: (44) 1923 474800
Emp.: 35
Developer of Gaming Technology & Software
N.A.I.C.S.: 513210

International Game Technology (1)
6355 S Buffalo Dr, Las Vegas, NV 89113
Tel.: (702) 669-7777
Web Site: http://www.igt.com
Sales Range: $1-4.9 Billion
Emp.: 600
Computerized Gaming Machines & Systems Products Designer
N.A.I.C.S.: 713290
Dallas Orchard (Sr VP-Global Premium Products)

Subsidiary (Non-US):

Entraction Holding AB (2)
Sveavagen 20, 111 57, Stockholm, Sweden
Tel.: (46) 856488460
Sales Range: $25-49.9 Million
Emp.: 40
Holding Company; Online & Digital Gaming Software
N.A.I.C.S.: 551112

I.G.T. (Australia) Pty Limited (2)
5-13 Rosebery Avenue, Rosebery, 2018, NSW, Australia **(100%)**
Tel.: (61) 2 8345 3000
Web Site: http://www.igt.com.au
Sales Range: $50-74.9 Million
Emp.: 200
Sales of Gaming Machines & Proprietary Software Systems for Computerized Gaming Machine Networks
N.A.I.C.S.: 423440
Emil Paya (Dir-Technical Svcs & Logistics)

Subsidiary (Non-US):

International Gaming Technology (NZ) Ltd. (3)
Unit 4 Birchwood Park 483 Hutt Rd, Lower Hutt, New Zealand **(100%)**
Tel.: (64) 45701777
Web Site: http://www.igt.co.nz
Sales Range: $10-24.9 Million
Emp.: 11
Marketing of Gaming Machines & Proprietary Software Systems for Computerized Gaming Machine Networks
N.A.I.C.S.: 423430
Barry Crossley (Gen Mgr)

Subsidiary (Non-US):

I.G.T. - Argentina S.A. (2)
Emilio Frers 2154, Martinez, 1640, Buenos Aires, Argentina **(100%)**
Tel.: (54) 11 4500 3900
Emp.: 20
Mfr, Designer & Marketer of Gaming Machines & Proprietary Software Systems for Computerized Gaming Machine Networks
N.A.I.C.S.: 334610
Sebastian Villanueva (Reg Mgr-Fin)

Subsidiary (Domestic):

IGT (2)
6355 S Buffalo Dr, Las Vegas, NV 89113-2133
Tel.: (702) 669-7777
Web Site: http://www.igt.com
Sales Range: $25-49.9 Million
Mfr, Developer & Marketer of Electronic Game Promotions; Equipment & Games for the Casino Gaming Industry
N.A.I.C.S.: 339999
Andrew Kertesz (Dir-Engrg-Game Platform)

Unit (Domestic):

International Game Technology - Reno (3)
9295 Prototype Dr, Reno, NV 89521
Tel.: (775) 688-0100
Web Site: http://www.igt.com
Emp.: 2,200
Gaming Machines Mfr
N.A.I.C.S.: 339999
Ryan Keller (Sr Dir-Art)

Subsidiary (Domestic):

VLC, Inc. (3)
Bldg 4-3 2310 University Way, Bozeman, MT 59715-6504
Tel.: (406) 585-6600
Development of Games
N.A.I.C.S.: 481219

Subsidiary (Non-US):

IGT Asia - Macau, S.A. (2)
11th Floor Block O China Civil Bldg Alameda Dr Carlos D'Assumpcao 263, Nape, Macau, China (Macau) **(100%)**
Tel.: (853) 87959500
Sales Range: $25-49.9 Million
Emp.: 30
Gaming Equipment Sales
N.A.I.C.S.: 423440
Mark Michalko (Dir-Sls-Asia)

IGT Asia Pte. Ltd. (2)
1 Changi North Street 1 #02-01, Singapore, 498789, Singapore **(100%)**
Tel.: (65) 6521 6300
Sales Range: $25-49.9 Million
Emp.: 20
Gaming Equipment Sales
N.A.I.C.S.: 423440
Mark Michalko (Dir-Sls-Asia)

Subsidiary (Domestic):

IGT Interactive, Inc. (2)
405 Howard St Ste 600, San Francisco, CA 94105-2674
Tel.: (415) 625-8300
Interactive Gaming Products, Platforms & Services
N.A.I.C.S.: 513210

Subsidiary (Non-US):

IGT Technology Development (Beijing) Co. Ltd. (2)
11th Floor Viva Plaza 29 Suzhou Street, Haidian District, Beijing, 100080, China
Tel.: (86) 1082174800
Gaming Technology Developer
N.A.I.C.S.: 541512

IGT do Brasil Ltda. (2)
Avenida Das Americanas 4200 Bloco 1, Conjunto 114, 22640-102, Rio de Janeiro, Brazil **(100%)**
Tel.: (55) 2133854250
Sales Range: $100-124.9 Million
Mfr & Marketer of Gaming Machines & Proprietary Software Systems for Computerized Gaming Machine Networks
N.A.I.C.S.: 423430
Roberto Quattrini (Country Mgr)

IGT-Canada Inc. (2)
328 Urquhart Ave, Moncton, E1H 2R6, NB, Canada **(100%)**
Tel.: (506) 878-6000
Emp.: 500
Gaming & Video Lottery Products & Software Systems Developer
N.A.I.C.S.: 541512
David Flinn (Reg VP)

IGT-China, Inc. (2)
11th Floor Viva Plaza 29 Suzhou Street, Haidian District, Beijing, 100080, China **(100%)**
Tel.: (86) 1082174800
Gaming Equipment Mfr
N.A.I.C.S.: 713290

IGT-Europe B.V. (2)
Bijlmermeerstraat 30, 2131 HC, Hoofddorp, Netherlands **(100%)**
Tel.: (31) 235687100
Sales Range: $10-24.9 Million
Emp.: 50
Gaming Machines & Proprietary Software Systems Marketer for Computerized Gaming Machine Networks
N.A.I.C.S.: 334610
Michael Kennedy (Mgr-Tech Svc)

IGT-Mexicana de Juegos, S. de R.L. de C.V. (2)
Andres Bello No 45 Piso 14 Col Polanco Chapultepec, Del Miguel Hidalgo, Mexico, 11560, DF, Mexico **(100%)**
Tel.: (52) 5552817024
Emp.: 40
Gaming Machinery & Systems Mfr & Sales
N.A.I.C.S.: 423430
Juan Manuel Rivero (Dir-Intl Ops-Latin America & Caribbean)

International Game Technology-Africa (Pty) Ltd. (2)
2 Brands Hatch Close corner Indianapolis Street, Midrand, 1684, South Africa **(100%)**
Tel.: (27) 113171000
Emp.: 40
Computerized Gaming Machines Mfr & Marketer
N.A.I.C.S.: 423430

INTERNATIONAL GAMES SYSTEM CO., LTD.

No 130 Wugong Road, Wugu District, New Taipei City, 248, Taiwan

INTERNATIONAL GOLDEN GROUP PJSC

Tel.: (886) 222995048
Web Site: https://www.igs.com.tw
Year Founded: 1989
3293—(TPE)
Rev.: $373,573,430
Assets: $443,375,637
Liabilities: $109,969,390
Net Worth: $333,406,247
Earnings: $171,390,270
Emp.: 1,050
Fiscal Year-end: 12/31/22
Software Development Services
N.A.I.C.S.: 541511

INTERNATIONAL GAS PRODUCT SHIPPING JOINT STOCK COMPANY

13th Floor Sofic Building No 10 Thu Thiem Ward, Mai Chi Tho, Ho Chi Minh City, Vietnam
Tel.: (84) 2822205388
Web Site: https://www.gasshipping.com.vn
GSP—(HOSE)
Rev.: $72,724,922
Assets: $62,686,871
Liabilities: $31,414,712
Net Worth: $31,272,160
Earnings: $3,489,146
Fiscal Year-end: 12/31/23
Inland Water Transportation Services
N.A.I.C.S.: 483211
Nguyen Linh Giang (Chm)

INTERNATIONAL GENERAL INSURANCE HOLDINGS LTD.

74 Abdel Hamid Sharaf Street, PO Box 941428, Amman, 11194, Jordan
Tel.: (962) 65622009   BE
Web Site: https://www.iginsure.com
Year Founded: 2001
IGIC—(NASDAQ)
Rev.: $581,847,000
Assets: $1,561,096,000
Liabilities: $1,131,323,000
Net Worth: $429,773,000
Earnings: $85,465,000
Emp.: 355
Fiscal Year-end: 12/31/22
Holding Company
N.A.I.C.S.: 551112
Hatem Wasef Jabsheh (COO)

INTERNATIONAL GOLDEN GROUP PJSC

Floor 28 Nation Towers, PO Box 43999, Abu Dhabi, United Arab Emirates
Tel.: (971) 2 626 6661
Web Site: http://www.iggroup.ae
Year Founded: 2002
Holding Company; Security Defense Products & Systems
N.A.I.C.S.: 551112
Mohammed Hilal Al Kaabi (Founder & Chm)

Subsidiaries:

Boomeranger Boats Oy (1)
Troolitie 12, Valko, 07910, Loviisa, Finland
Tel.: (358) 19515805
Web Site: http://www.boomeranger.fi
Boats Mfr & Whslr
N.A.I.C.S.: 336612

Global Aerospace Logistics LLC (1)
Sw-5 Plot No P2 Street 16, PO Box 128628, Khalifa City, Abu Dhabi, United Arab Emirates
Tel.: (971) 24941111
Web Site: http://www.gal.ae
Emp.: 5,000
Aircraft Equipment & Parts Distr
N.A.I.C.S.: 423860
Stephen Seddon (Mgr-Quality Assurance)

IGG ASELSAN Integrated Systems LLC (1)
Icad1 Musaffah, PO Box 133627, Abu

INTERNATIONAL GOLDEN GROUP PJSC

International Golden Group PJSC—(Continued)
Dhabi, United Arab Emirates
Tel.: (971) 25508808
Web Site: http://www.iais.ae
Aircraft Mfr
N.A.I.C.S.: 336419
Onur Gucun (Mgr-Technical)

INTERNATIONAL GOLDFIELDS LIMITED
Unit 3 32 Harrogate St, West Leederville, 6007, WA, Australia
Tel.: (61) 8 6181 9799
Web Site:
 http://www.internationalgold.com.au
Rev.: $1,793,010
Assets: $816,400
Liabilities: $841,256
Net Worth: ($24,855)
Earnings: $1,389,552
Emp.: 10
Fiscal Year-end: 06/30/18
Gold Exploration & Mining
N.A.I.C.S.: 212220
Jane Flegg (Sec)

INTERNATIONAL GRAPHITE LIMITED
Tel.: (61) 93809277 AU
Web Site:
 https://www.intlgraphite.technology
Year Founded: 2018
H99—(DEU)
Rev.: $35,274
Assets: $11,798,448
Liabilities: $1,550,961
Net Worth: $10,247,486
Earnings: ($1,651,711)
Fiscal Year-end: 06/30/23
Graphite Product Mfr
N.A.I.C.S.: 335991
Andrew Worland (Mng Dir)

INTERNATIONAL HOLDING COMPANY PJSC
PO Box 32619, Abu Dhabi, United Arab Emirates
Tel.: (971) 26448090 AE
Web Site: https://www.ihcuae.com
Year Founded: 1998
IHC—(ABU)
Rev.: $16,356,345,568
Assets: $71,935,642,207
Liabilities: $29,271,865,920
Net Worth: $42,663,776,286
Earnings: $8,970,146,306
Fiscal Year-end: 12/31/23
Holding Company
N.A.I.C.S.: 551112
Somar Ajalyaqin (Vice Chm)

Subsidiaries:

Multiply Group PJSC (1)
Level 13 Al Khatem Tower Abu Dhabi Global Market Square Al Maryah Island, Abu Dhabi, United Arab Emirates (58.74%)
Tel.: (971) 26168200
Web Site: https://multiply.ae
Rev.: $352,335,866
Assets: $11,480,175,639
Liabilities: $3,260,102,116
Net Worth: $8,220,073,523
Earnings: $150,311,249
Fiscal Year-end: 12/31/2023
Investment Management Service
N.A.I.C.S.: 523999
Samia Bouazza (Grp CEO & Mng Dir)

INTERNATIONAL HOLDINGS COMPANY PJSC
13 Al Halawi St - Al Muntazah - Ministries Complex, PO Box 32619, Abu Dhabi, United Arab Emirates
Tel.: (971) 26448090 AE
Web Site: https://www.ihcuae.com
Year Founded: 1999

IHC—(ABU)
Rev.: $16,362,889,742
Assets: $71,964,423,658
Liabilities: $29,283,577,594
Net Worth: $42,680,846,064
Earnings: $8,973,735,261
Emp.: 52,000
Fiscal Year-end: 12/31/23
Holding Company
N.A.I.C.S.: 551112
H. H. Tahnoon Zayed Al Nahyan (Chm)

Subsidiaries:

Abu Dhabi Land General Contracting LLC (1)
Villa 3 Muroor Road Hadbat Al Zaafran, PO Box 3194, Abu Dhabi, United Arab Emirates
Tel.: (971) 2 4488900
Property Development & Construction Services
N.A.I.C.S.: 236116

Alliance Foods Company LLC (1)
New Industrial Area, PO Box 2923, Ajman, United Arab Emirates
Tel.: (971) 6 7435727
Seafood Whslr
N.A.I.C.S.: 424460

Arena Events Group Plc (1)
4 Deer Park Road South Wimbledon, London, SW19 3GY, United Kingdom
Tel.: (44) 2037703838
Web Site: http://www.arenagroup.com
Rev.: $88,912,880
Assets: $162,551,620
Liabilities: $107,539,880
Net Worth: $55,011,740
Earnings: ($15,770,860)
Emp.: 684
Fiscal Year-end: 03/31/2021
Holding Company; Event Design, Engineering & Project Planning
N.A.I.C.S.: 713990
Paul Berger (CEO-Arena-EMEA)

Subsidiary (US):

Ohana Partners, Inc. (2)
454 S Abbott Ave, Milpitas, CA 95035
Tel.: (408) 914-2795
Web Site: http://www.stuartrental.com
Emp.: 150
Consumer Goods Rental
N.A.I.C.S.: 532289
Michael Berman (Pres)

Asmak Quriyat International LLC (1)
Rusayl Industrial Estate Road No 12, PO Box 188, Rusayl, 124, Muscat, Oman
Tel.: (968) 24446360
Sales Range: $25-49.9 Million
Emp.: 24
Seafood Whslr
N.A.I.C.S.: 424460

Asmak Seafood Processing Co. LLC (1)
Delma Island Western region, Abu Dhabi, United Arab Emirates
Tel.: (971) 2 8782161
Sales Range: $100-124.9 Million
Emp.: 400
Seafood Processing Services
N.A.I.C.S.: 311710

Emirates Stallions Properties LLC (1)
Silver wave Tower 4th Floor - unit 404 Meena Street, PO Box 32619, Abu Dhabi, United Arab Emirates
Tel.: (971) 2 6448090
Real Estate Manangement Services
N.A.I.C.S.: 531390

Gulf Dunes Landscaping & Agricultural Services L.L.C. (1)
PO Box 42559, Abu Dhabi, 2, United Arab Emirates
Tel.: (971) 2 6677288
Web Site: http://www.gdlandscapeu.ae
Sales Range: $350-399.9 Million
Emp.: 2,000
Landscaping Services
N.A.I.C.S.: 541320
Matar Suhail Al Yabhouni (Mng Dir)

SHUAA Securities LLC (1)
Corniche Road Abu Dhabi National Islamic Finance Building, PO Box 8206, Penthouse Level, Abu Dhabi, United Arab Emirates
Tel.: (971) 24090700
Web Site: http://www.shuaasecurities.com
Securities Brokerage Services
N.A.I.C.S.: 523150

INTERNATIONAL HOUSEWARES RETAIL COMPANY LIMITED
20/F Tower B South Mark 11 Yip Hing Street, Wong Chuk Hang, Hong Kong, China (Hong Kong)
Tel.: (852) 35123100
Web Site:
 http://www.japanhome.com.hk
Year Founded: 1991
1373—(HKG)
Rev.: $360,314,235
Assets: $226,623,345
Liabilities: $111,311,963
Net Worth: $115,311,383
Earnings: $23,189,063
Emp.: 2,146
Fiscal Year-end: 04/30/23
Houseware Retailer
N.A.I.C.S.: 449129
Lai Ha Ngai (Chm & CEO)

Subsidiaries:

JHC (International) Limited (1)
20/F Tower B Southmark 11 Yip Hing Street Wong Chuk Hang, Hong Kong, China (Hong Kong)
Tel.: (852) 35123100
Home Furniture Distr
N.A.I.C.S.: 449129

Japan Home (Retail) Pte. Ltd. (1)
204 Bedok South Ave 1, Singapore, 469333, Singapore (60%)
Tel.: (65) 62844122
Web Site: http://www.japanhome.com.sg
Home Furniture Distr
N.A.I.C.S.: 449129

INTERNATIONAL HOUSING FINANCE COMPANY LIMITED
Moorti Bunglow No 5 Ashok Nagar Co Op Soc Ltd B/h Sundarvan - ISRO, Satelite, Ahmedabad, 380 015, India
Tel.: (91) 79 65214174
Web Site: http://www.ihfcl.com
Year Founded: 1990
Rev.: $3,797
Assets: $2,433,444
Liabilities: $7,189
Net Worth: $2,426,255
Earnings: ($7,904)
Fiscal Year-end: 03/31/18
Real Estate Development Services
N.A.I.C.S.: 531390
Sandip Bhikhubhai Padsala (Chm)

INTERNATIONAL HUMAN RESOURCES COMPANY
King Abdullah Road / Al Hamra, PO Box 7021, Riyadh, 12482, Saudi Arabia
Tel.: (966) 920000414
Web Site: https://www.ihr.sa
Year Founded: 2005
9545—(SAU)
Human Resource Consulting Services
N.A.I.C.S.: 541612
Ali Ammar Al-Harbi (Founder & Mng Dir)

INTERNATIONAL ICONIC GOLD EXPLORATION CORP.
1200 - 625 Howe Street, Vancouver, V6E 0C3, BC, Canada
Tel.: (236) 266-5174
Web Site: https://www.iconicgold.com

INTERNATIONAL PUBLIC

Year Founded: 2003
ICON—(OTCIQ)
Assets: $3,107,230
Liabilities: $1,351,157
Net Worth: $1,756,073
Earnings: ($520,178)
Fiscal Year-end: 12/31/20
Mineral Exploration Services
N.A.I.C.S.: 213114
Richard R. Walters (Exec VP)

INTERNATIONAL INDUSTRIES LIMITED
101 Beaumont Plaza 10 Beaumont Road, Karachi, 75530, Pakistan
Tel.: (92) 2135680045
Web Site: https://iil.com.pk
Year Founded: 1948
INIL—(PSX)
Rev.: $362,402,348
Assets: $271,150,496
Liabilities: $144,281,253
Net Worth: $126,869,243
Earnings: $16,579,662
Emp.: 2,513
Fiscal Year-end: 06/30/23
Steel & Pipe Mfr
N.A.I.C.S.: 331110
Riyaz T. Chinoy (CEO)

Subsidiaries:

International Steels Limited (1)
101 Beaumont Plaza 10 Beaumont Road, Karachi, 75530, Pakistan
Tel.: (92) 21111019019
Web Site: https://www.isl.com.pk
Steel Products Mfr
N.A.I.C.S.: 332999
Yousuf Husain Mirza (CEO)

INTERNATIONAL INVESTMENT GROUP K.S.C.C.
Kuwait Stock Exchange Building 5th Floor, PO Box 29448, Safat, Kuwait, 13155, Kuwait
Tel.: (965) 22429010
Web Site: http://www.iigkw.com
Year Founded: 1993
Sales Range: Less than $1 Million
Emp.: 56
Investment Services
N.A.I.C.S.: 523999
Abdullah Mohammed Al Refai (CEO)

INTERNATIONAL KNITWEAR LIMITED
F-2A/L S I T E, Karachi, 75730, Pakistan
Tel.: (92) 2132571463
Web Site:
 https://www.internationalknitwear.com
Year Founded: 1990
INKL—(PSX)
Rev.: $3,238,891
Assets: $2,003,519
Liabilities: $1,131,080
Net Worth: $872,439
Earnings: $73,506
Emp.: 191
Fiscal Year-end: 06/30/19
Knitwear Products Mfr
N.A.I.C.S.: 315990
Naeem Shafi (CEO)

INTERNATIONAL LAZAR COMPANY
Street Serelor Number 19 Bascov Locality, Arges County, Bascov, Romania
Tel.: (40) 248 270 700 RO
Web Site: http://www.intlazar.ro
Freight Forwarding Services
N.A.I.C.S.: 484110
Ion Lazar (Mgr)

AND PRIVATE COMPANIES

Subsidiaries:

S.C. B.A.T. BASCOV S.A. (1)
str Paisesti DN nr 5, Bascov, Arges, Romania
Tel.: (40) 248270872
Web Site: http://www.batbascov.ro
Sales Range: $1-9.9 Million
Repairing Services
N.A.I.C.S.: 811198

INTERNATIONAL LEASING & FINANCIAL SERVICES LIMITED
Printers Building 14th Floor 5 Rajuk Avenue, Dhaka, 1000, Bangladesh
Tel.: (880) 29559639
Web Site: http://www.ilfsl.com
Year Founded: 1996
Sales Range: $25-49.9 Million
Emp.: 56
Leasing & Other Financial Services
N.A.I.C.S.: 522291
Mohammed Ibrahim *(Head-Chittagong Branch)*

Subsidiaries:

International Leasing Securities Limited (1)
Printers Bldg 3rd Fl 5 Rajuk Ave, Dhaka, 1000, Bangladesh
Tel.: (880) 27174603
Web Site: http://www.ilfsl.com
Brokerage Services
N.A.I.C.S.: 523150

INTERNATIONAL LEASING & INVESTMENT COMPANY K.S.C.C.
Al-Nassar Tower beside Sheraton Hotel 20th-25th Floors, PO Box 3716, Fahad Al-Salem Street Safat, Kuwait, 13038, Kuwait
Tel.: (965) 2224 5800
Web Site: http://www.ilic.net
Year Founded: 1999
Sales Range: $100-124.9 Million
Leasing, Investment Management & Advisory Services
N.A.I.C.S.: 523999
Azhar Hussein *(VP-Asset Mgmt)*

INTERNATIONAL MEAL COMPANY ALIMENTACAO S.A.
Avenida Doutora Ruth Cardoso 4 777 Conjunto A-12 andar, Jardim Universidade, Pinheiros, 05477-902, Sao Paulo, Brazil
Tel.: (55) 1130419500
Web Site: https://ri.internationalmealco.com
Year Founded: 2006
MEAL3—(BRAZ)
Rev.: $458,803,708
Assets: $564,657,392
Liabilities: $353,868,933
Net Worth: $210,788,459
Earnings: ($17,579,186)
Emp.: 12,000
Fiscal Year-end: 12/31/23
Restaurant & Hotel Operator
N.A.I.C.S.: 722511
Luiz Fernando Ziegler de Saint Edmond *(Chm)*

INTERNATIONAL MEAL COMPANY HOLDINGS S.A.
Avenida das Nacoes Unidas 4 777 Edificio Villa Lobos 12 andar, Alto de Pinheiros, Sao Paulo, Brazil
Tel.: (55) 11 3041 9500
Web Site: http://www.internationalmealco.com
Year Founded: 2006
Sales Range: $1-4.9 Billion
Emp.: 10,000
Restaurant Operators
N.A.I.C.S.: 722511
Andrea Pires *(Chief Procurement Officer)*

INTERNATIONAL METALS MINING CORP
404-999 Canada Place, Vancouver, V6C 3E2, BC, Canada
Tel.: (778) 928-6565   Ca
Web Site: https://internationalmetalscorp.com
Year Founded: 1998
CYNXF—(OTCQB)
Assets: $60,720
Liabilities: $524,331
Net Worth: ($463,611)
Earnings: ($3,271,659)
Fiscal Year-end: 03/31/22
Mineral Exploration Services
N.A.I.C.S.: 213115
Wayne Tisdale *(Chm)*

INTERNATIONAL MINING & INFRASTRUCTURE CORPORATION PLC
40 New Bond Street, London, W1S 2RX, United Kingdom
Tel.: (44) 20 7290 3340   UK
Web Site: http://www.imicplc.com
Emp.: 66
Mining & Related Infrastructure Investment Services
N.A.I.C.S.: 523999
Haresh D. Kanabar *(Chm)*

INTERNATIONAL NETWORK SYSTEM PUBLIC COMPANY LIMITED
3300/106-107 20th Floor Tower B Elephant Tower Phaholyothin Rd, Chom Phon Chatuchak, Bangkok, 10900, Thailand
Tel.: (66) 25137637
Web Site: https://www.itns.co.th
Year Founded: 2002
ITNS—(THA)
Rev.: $20,128,759
Assets: $16,816,776
Liabilities: $3,736,109
Net Worth: $13,080,667
Earnings: $1,834,389
Emp.: 27
Fiscal Year-end: 12/31/23
Information Technology Services
N.A.I.C.S.: 541512

INTERNATIONAL OLYMPIC COMMITTEE
Chateau De Vidy, 1007, Lausanne, Switzerland
Tel.: (41) 216216111
Web Site: http://www.olympic.org
Year Founded: 1894
Sales Range: $50-74.9 Million
Emp.: 400
Olympic Games Administrator
N.A.I.C.S.: 813990
Timo Lumme *(Mng Dir-Television & Mktg Svcs)*

Subsidiaries:

Olympic Broadcasting Services SA (1)
P Recoletos 27 - 5, Madrid, 28004, Spain
Tel.: (34) 91 502 97 00
Web Site: http://www.obs.es
Sales Range: $25-49.9 Million
Emp.: 100
Television-Broadcasting Services
N.A.I.C.S.: 516120
Hein Verbruggen *(Chm)*

INTERNATIONAL PARKSIDE PRODUCTS INC.
304 - 788 Beatty Street, Vancouver, V6B 2M1, BC, Canada
Tel.: (604) 681-6472
Web Site: https://www.lenspen.com
Year Founded: 1983
IPD—(TSXV)
Rev.: $2,649,509
Assets: $936,210
Liabilities: $735,968
Net Worth: $200,243
Earnings: ($77,332)
Fiscal Year-end: 07/31/24
Chemical Products Mfr
N.A.I.C.S.: 325199
Murray Keating *(CEO)*

INTERNATIONAL PAYMENT SOLUTIONS HOLDINGS LIMITED
Room 231-233 Building 2 Phase 1 1 Science Park West Avenue, Hong Kong Science Park, Hong Kong, China (Hong Kong)
Tel.: (852) 2649 6133
Web Site: http://www.ips.com.hk
Year Founded: 2004
Online Payment Processing Services
N.A.I.C.S.: 522320

INTERNATIONAL PERSONAL FINANCE PLC
26 Whitehall Road, Leeds, LS12 1BE, United Kingdom
Tel.: (44) 1135395466
Web Site: https://www.ipfin.co.uk
Year Founded: 1997
IPF—(LSE)
Rev.: $814,819,490
Assets: $1,478,288,311
Liabilities: $916,309,013
Net Worth: $561,979,298
Earnings: $71,699,066
Emp.: 8,855
Fiscal Year-end: 12/31/22
Financial Consulting Services
N.A.I.C.S.: 541611
Gerard Ryan *(CEO)*

Subsidiaries:

IPF Digital AS (1)
Lootsa 5 VIII korrus, 11415, Tallinn, Estonia
Tel.: (372) 6143400
Web Site: https://credit24.ee
Financial Services
N.A.I.C.S.: 523999

IPF Digital Australia Pty. Limited (1)
61-63 Great Buckingham St, Redfern, 2016, NSW, Australia
Tel.: (61) 1800091967
Web Site: https://www.credit24.com.au
Financial Services
N.A.I.C.S.: 523999

IPF Digital Finland Oy (1)
Hameentie 15, 00500, Helsinki, Finland
Tel.: (358) 300300355
Web Site: https://www.credit24.fi
Financial Services
N.A.I.C.S.: 523999

IPF Digital Latvia, SIA (1)
Unijas street 8 k-6, Riga, LV-1084, Latvia
Tel.: (371) 20140014
Web Site: https://www.credit24.lv
Financial Services
N.A.I.C.S.: 523999

IPF Digital Lietuva, UAB (1)
Svitrigailos st 11M, Vilnius, Lithuania
Tel.: (370) 70080020
Web Site: https://www.credit24.lt
Financial Services
N.A.I.C.S.: 523999

IPF Digital Mexico S.A de C.V (1)
Av Insurgentes 1271 Col Extremadura Insurgentes, 03740, Mexico, Mexico
Tel.: (52) 70991111
Web Site: https://www.creditea.mx
Financial Services
N.A.I.C.S.: 523999

IPF Polska sp. z o.o. (1)
Inflancka 4A, 00-189, Warsaw, Poland
Tel.: (48) 222630955
Web Site: https://www.hapipozyczki.pl
Financial Services
N.A.I.C.S.: 523999

International Personal Finance Digital Spain S.A.U (1)
Avenida de la Albufera 153, 28038, Madrid, Spain
Tel.: (34) 911880500
Web Site: http://www.creditea.es
Financial Services
N.A.I.C.S.: 523999

Provident Financial Romania IFN S.A. (1)
Str Serban Voda No 133 Building A Floor 1 Sector 4, 040205, Bucharest, Romania
Tel.: (40) 212757575
Web Site: https://www.provident.ro
Financial Services
N.A.I.C.S.: 523999

Provident Financial Zrt. (1)
Lechner Odon fasor 10/B, 1095, Budapest, Hungary
Tel.: (36) 19999609
Web Site: https://www.provident.hu
Sales Range: $200-249.9 Million
Emp.: 280
Home Loan Providers
N.A.I.C.S.: 522291

Provident Financial s.r.o. (1)
Olbrachtova 9/2006, 14000, Prague, Czech Republic
Tel.: (420) 241029111
Web Site: http://www.provident.cz
Sales Range: $100-124.9 Million
Home Loan Providers
N.A.I.C.S.: 522299

Provident Mexico S.A. de C.V. (1)
Avenida 31 Poniente 4118 Colonia Ampliacion Reforma, San Rafael, CP 72160, Puebla, Mexico
Tel.: (52) 2222735373
Web Site: https://www.provident.com.mx
Home Loan Providing Services
N.A.I.C.S.: 522291

Provident Servicios S.A de C.V. (1)
Blvd Hermanos Serdan 5786 Piso 2, San Rafael, 72020, Puebla, Mexico
Tel.: (52) 2222735353
Web Site: https://www.provident.com.mx
Emp.: 6,000
Business Support Services
N.A.I.C.S.: 813910
Robert Husband *(Mgr)*

Provident Servicios de Agencia S.A de C.V. (1)
Avenida 31 Poniente No 4118 Colonia Ampliacion Reforma, Del Valle, 72160, Puebla, Mexico
Tel.: (52) 2222735361
Web Site: https://www.providentmexico.com.mx
Business Support Services
N.A.I.C.S.: 561499

INTERNATIONAL PETROLEUM LIMITED
32 Harrogate Street, West Leederville, 6007, WA, Australia
Tel.: (61) 8 9388 0744   AU
Web Site: http://www.intlpetroleum.com.au
Sales Range: $1-9.9 Million
Oil & Gas Exploration
N.A.I.C.S.: 211120

Subsidiaries:

VostokNefteGaz LLC (1)
ul Petra Alekseeva D 74, Yakutsk, 677015, Russia
Tel.: (7) 914 226 25 30
Oil & Gas Exploration Services
N.A.I.C.S.: 213112

INTERNATIONAL PLYWOOD (IMPORTERS) LTD.
Innsworth Technology Park, Gloucester, GL3 1DL, United Kingdom
Tel.: (44) 1452 731 493

International Plywood (Importers) Ltd.—(Continued)
Web Site: http://www.plywooduk.com
Year Founded: 1981
Sales Range: $125-149.9 Million
Wood Whslr
N.A.I.C.S.: 423310
David Attwood (Chm)

INTERNATIONAL PRESS SOFTCOM LIMITED
26 Kallang Avenue, Singapore, 339417, Singapore
Tel.: (65) 62983800
Web Site: http://www.ipsoftcom.com
Rev.: $21,695,662
Assets: $39,033,297
Liabilities: $14,549,967
Net Worth: $24,483,329
Earnings: ($7,316,945)
Fiscal Year-end: 12/31/19
Printing Services
N.A.I.C.S.: 323111
Eng Chai Teh (Co-Sec)

Subsidiaries:

IP Media (Xiamen) Co., Ltd. (1)
1 Building No 285 Weng Jiao Road, Hai Cang, Xiamen, 361022, Fujian, China
Tel.: (86) 5926806555
Printing Services
N.A.I.C.S.: 323111

IP Softcom (Australia) Pty Ltd (1)
Unit 22 6-20 Braidwood Street, South Strathfield, Sydney, 2136, NSW, Australia
Tel.: (61) 296422924
Printing Services
N.A.I.C.S.: 323111

IP Softcom (Malaysia) Sdn. Bhd. (1)
No 5 Lorong Jelawat 4, Seberang Jaya Industrial Park Seberang Perai Tengah, 13700, Perai, Pinang, Malaysia
Tel.: (60) 43973555
Supply Chain Management Services
N.A.I.C.S.: 541614

IP Softcom (Shanghai) Co., Ltd. (1)
Room 402 1 Building No 1299 XinJinqiao Road, Pudong, Shanghai, 201206, China
Tel.: (86) 2150322228
Printing Services
N.A.I.C.S.: 323111

IP Softcom (Shenzhen) Co., Ltd. (1)
5F No 13 Hongfa Industrial Estate Jingtang Road Shiyan Street, Baoan, Shenzhen, 518108, Guangdong, China
Tel.: (86) 75527335200
Printing Services
N.A.I.C.S.: 323111

IP Softcom (Xiamen) Co., Ltd. (1)
No 89 Jinshang Road, Xiamen, 361009, China
Tel.: (86) 5925570638
Web Site: http://leithlee.diytrade.com
Plastic Packaging Product Mfr & Distr
N.A.I.C.S.: 326112

International Press Softcom (Vietnam) Co., Ltd. (1)
Lot B54/1 Road No 2E Vinch Loc A Industrial Park, Binch Chanh, Ho Chi Minh City, Vietnam
Tel.: (84) 837656252
Printing Services
N.A.I.C.S.: 323111

Scantrans (India) Pvt. Ltd. (1)
18 and 19 Mahalakshmi Nagar Extn Numbal, Thiruverkadu, Chennai, 600 077, India
Tel.: (91) 4426492057
Web Site: http://www.scantrans.com
Printing Services
N.A.I.C.S.: 323111

INTERNATIONAL PROCESS TECHNOLOGIES LIMITED
Trading State, Farnham, GU9 9NY, Surrey, United Kingdom
Tel.: (44) 1252736800
Web Site: http://www.plascoat.com
Year Founded: 1995
Sales Range: $50-74.9 Million
Emp.: 200
Holding Company
N.A.I.C.S.: 551112
Jeremy Spoke (Chm & CEO)

Subsidiaries:

PLASCOAT EUROPE BV (1)
Meeuwenoordlaan 19, Postbus 9, 3214 ZG, Zuidland, Netherlands
Tel.: (31) 181 45 88 88
Plastic Coating Distr
N.A.I.C.S.: 423840

PLASTIC COATINGS LTD (1)
Ham Lane, Kingswinford, DY6 7JY, West Midlands, United Kingdom
Tel.: (44) 1384 400066
Web Site: http://www.plasticcoatings.co.uk
Emp.: 106
Plastic Coating Distr
N.A.I.C.S.: 423840
Nigel Skidmore (Controller-Fin)

INTERNATIONAL PROSPECT VENTURES LTD.
2864 Chemin Sullivan, Val d'Or, J9P 0B9, QC, Canada
Tel.: (819) 824-2808
Web Site: https://www.iprospectventures.ca
Year Founded: 2010
URANF—(OTCIQ)
Rev.: $150
Assets: $449,847
Liabilities: $142,740
Net Worth: $307,108
Earnings: $9,638
Fiscal Year-end: 12/31/23
Uranium Mining Services
N.A.I.C.S.: 212290
Glenn J. Mullan (Pres & CEO)

INTERNATIONAL PUBLIC PARTNERSHIPS LIMITED
c/o Ocorian Administration Guernsey Limited, PO Box 286, Floor 2 Trafalgar Court Les Banques, Saint Peter Port, GY1 4LY, Guernsey
Tel.: (44) 1481742742 GY
Web Site: https://www.intlpublicpartners.com
Year Founded: 2006
INPP—(LSE)
Rev.: $461,486,998
Assets: $3,894,072,204
Liabilities: $56,860,641
Net Worth: $3,837,211,563
Earnings: $412,644,534
Fiscal Year-end: 12/31/22
Investment Management Service
N.A.I.C.S.: 523999
Michael Gerrard (Chm)

INTERNATIONAL RESEARCH CORPORATION PUBLIC COMPANY LIMITED
199 Column Tower Building 7th Floor Ratchadaphisek Road, Khlong Toei, Bangkok, 10110, Thailand
Tel.: (66) 21718601
Web Site: https://www.ircp.co.th
Year Founded: 1986
IRCP—(THA)
Rev.: $31,396,121
Assets: $31,757,612
Liabilities: $26,132,354
Net Worth: $5,625,257
Earnings: $826,845
Fiscal Year-end: 12/31/20
Intergrated System Design Services
N.A.I.C.S.: 541512
Dan Hetrakul (CEO)

INTERNATIONAL RESORTS COMPANY - KPSC
Kuwait City Trading Area No 9 Souk Al-Safat Bld First Floor, PO Box 4800, Safat, 13048, Kuwait, Kuwait
Tel.: (965) 22446704
Web Site: http://www.irc-kw.com
Year Founded: 1976
Rev.: $16,293,664
Assets: $37,375,561
Liabilities: $7,754,549
Net Worth: $29,621,012
Earnings: $3,788,043
Emp.: 14
Fiscal Year-end: 12/31/18
Real Estate Management Services
N.A.I.C.S.: 531390
Khaled Ali Mohammed Al-Attal (Chm)

INTERNATIONAL RESOURCES GROUP LTD.
20 Cannon Street, London, EC4M 6XD, United Kingdom
Tel.: (44) 2075291111
Web Site: http://www.odgersberndtson.co.uk
Sales Range: $200-249.9 Million
Executive Search Service
N.A.I.C.S.: 541612
Richard Boggis-Rolfe (Chm)

Subsidiaries:

ODGERS BERNDTSON AG (1)
Gartenstrasse 19, PO Box 1973, 8027, Zurich, Switzerland
Tel.: (41) 433443131
Web Site: http://www.odgersberndtson.ch
Employee Recruitment Services
N.A.I.C.S.: 561311
Christoph Bircher (Mng Partner)

Subsidiary (US):

The Talent Advisors, LLC (2)
1 Bromfield St 5th Fl, Boston, MA 02108
Tel.: (617) 431-3230
Web Site: http://www.talentadvisors.net
General Management Consulting Services
N.A.I.C.S.: 541611

ODGERS BERNDTSON Unternehmensberatung GmbH (1)
Olof-Palme-Strasse 15, 60439, Frankfurt am Main, Germany
Tel.: (49) 699577701
Web Site: http://www.odgersberndtson.de
Employee Recruitment Services
N.A.I.C.S.: 561311
Klaus Hansen (Mng Partner)

Odgers Berndtson A/S (1)
Amaliegade 13, Copenhagen, 1256, Denmark
Tel.: (45) 33143636
Web Site: http://www.odgersberndtson.dk
Employee Recruitment Services
N.A.I.C.S.: 561311
Mikael Frederiksen (Partner)

Odgers Berndtson Russia (1)
11 building 8 Baumanskaya st block 4, Moscow, 105005, Russia
Tel.: (7) 4959357654
Web Site: http://www.odgersberndtson.ru
Employee Recruitment Services
N.A.I.C.S.: 561311
Roman Tyshkovskiy (Mng Partner-Exec Search)

Odgers Berndtson SA (Pty) Ltd (1)
7 West Quay Road Ground Floor Block B V&A Waterfront, Cape Town, 8002, South Africa
Tel.: (27) 214181516
Web Site: http://www.odgersberndtson.co.za
Employee Recruitment Services
N.A.I.C.S.: 561311

INTERNATIONAL SCHOOL AUGSBURG ISA GAG
Wernher von Braun Strasse 1a, 86368, Gersthofen, Germany
Tel.: (49) 821455560
Web Site: https://www.isa-augsburg.com
Year Founded: 2005
9JK—(DEU)
Rev.: $7,473,231
Assets: $11,347,831
Liabilities: $5,287,559
Net Worth: $6,060,272
Earnings: $187,659
Emp.: 89
Fiscal Year-end: 12/31/23
Educational Support Services
N.A.I.C.S.: 611710

INTERNATIONAL SHAKE-SPEARE GLOBE CENTRE LTD.
21 New Globe Walk Bankside, London, SE1 9DT, United Kingdom
Tel.: (44) 2079021400
Web Site: http://www.shakespearesglobe.com
Sales Range: $25-49.9 Million
Emp.: 200
Producer of Plays; Educational Services
N.A.I.C.S.: 611699
Patrick Spottiswoode (Dir-Education-Global)

INTERNATIONAL SILICA INDUSTRIES CO.
PO Box 840338, Amman, 11181, Jordan
Tel.: (962) 777407742
Web Site: http://www.silicajo.com
Rev.: $688,946
Assets: $2,492,832
Liabilities: $1,171,793
Net Worth: $1,321,039
Earnings: ($680,924)
Emp.: 40
Fiscal Year-end: 12/31/16
Silica Sand Mining
N.A.I.C.S.: 212322

INTERNATIONAL SINAIA
Str Avram Iancu nr 1, 106100, Sinaia, Romania
Tel.: (40) 344403841
Hotel & Motel Services
N.A.I.C.S.: 721110

INTERNATIONAL SUN GROUP FZCO
Jebel Ali Free Zone, PO Box 61051, Dubai, 61051, United Arab Emirates
Tel.: (971) 48817432
Web Site: http://www.intersunfzco.com
Year Founded: 1967
Sales Range: $400-449.9 Million
Emp.: 40
Food & Petroleum Products Distr
N.A.I.C.S.: 424720
Abdolbari Goozal (Pres)

Subsidiaries:

Azersun Holding (1)
Heydar Aliyev Ave 92a, AZ1029, Baku, Azerbaijan
Tel.: (994) 124041919
Web Site: http://www.azersun.com
Sales Range: $1-4.9 Billion
Investment Management Service
N.A.I.C.S.: 523940
Abdolbari Goozal (Chm & Pres)

Subsidiary (Domestic):

AZERBAIJAN SUGAR PRODUCTION ASSOCIATION (2)
Sabir Fataliyev Str 45, Imishli, Azerbaijan
Tel.: (994) 154 66110
Web Site: http://asib.az
Beet Sugar Mfr
N.A.I.C.S.: 311313
Abdolbari Goozal (Pres)

AND PRIVATE COMPANIES

Plant (Domestic):

Azersun Holding - Khirdalan Cardboard Factory (2)
Passage-Way No 1232 28-32, Xirdalan, Azerbaijan
Tel.: (994) 12 432 16 08
Web Site: http://kartontara.az
Corrugated Cardboard Mfr
N.A.I.C.S.: 322211

Subsidiary (Domestic):

Caucasus Paper Industry (2)
Darnagul 108A, Binagadi District, Baku, Azerbaijan
Tel.: (994) 12 448 06 82
Web Site: http://qafqazkagiz.az
Sales Range: $25-49.9 Million
Sanitary Paper Product Mfr
N.A.I.C.S.: 322291

Qafqaz Konserv Zavodu LLC (2)
Khachmaz Highway 157th km, Baku, Azerbaijan
Tel.: (994) 172 5 56 58
Web Site: http://www.qafqazkonserv.az
Sales Range: $75-99.9 Million
Processed Food Product Mfr
N.A.I.C.S.: 311999

Qafqaz Metal Fabrikasi LLC (2)
Darnagul Settlement 108, Binagadi District, Baku, Azerbaijan
Tel.: (994) 12 448 06 82
Web Site: http://qafqazmetal.az
Metal Tank Mfr
N.A.I.C.S.: 332431

Qafqaz Trade Co. (2)
Xariji Dairavi Str Building 2038, AZ1000, Baku, Azerbaijan
Tel.: (994) 12 514 35 31
General Freight Trucking Services
N.A.I.C.S.: 484110

INTERNATIONAL TOWER HILL MINES LTD.
200 Burrard Street Suite 1570, Vancouver, V6C 3L6, BC, Canada
Tel.: (604) 683-6332 BC
Web Site: https://www.ithmines.com
Year Founded: 1978
THM—(NYSEAMEX)
Rev.: $404,346
Assets: $60,382,590
Liabilities: $288,385
Net Worth: $60,094,205
Earnings: ($3,041,693)
Emp.: 3
Fiscal Year-end: 12/31/22
Gold & Base Metal Mining & Exploration Services
N.A.I.C.S.: 212220
Debbie L. Evans (Sec)

INTERNATIONAL TRAVEL HOUSE LTD
Travel House T - 2 Community Centre Sheikh Sarai Phase - 1, New Delhi, 110017, India
Tel.: (91) 1126017808
Web Site: https://www.intltravelhouse.in
500213—(BOM)
Rev.: $13,173,752
Assets: $18,227,801
Liabilities: $5,228,837
Net Worth: $12,998,963
Earnings: ($1,460,072)
Emp.: 405
Fiscal Year-end: 03/31/22
Travel Services
N.A.I.C.S.: 813410
Nakul Anand (Chm)

INTERNATIONAL TURNKEY SYSTEMS
ITS Tower Mubrak Al Kabeer Street, PO Box 26729, Safat, Kuwait, 13128, Kuwait
Tel.: (965) 2240 9100 KW
Web Site: http://www.its.ws
Year Founded: 1981
Sales Range: $25-49.9 Million
Emp.: 1,100
Comprehensive Solutions for Integrated Information System Services
N.A.I.C.S.: 517810
John Loomis (Mng Dir & Gen Mgr)

Subsidiaries:

Advance Computer Technology (1)
8 El Batal Medhat Abdel Hamid St Off Shehab St, El Mohandessin, Giza, Egypt (100%)
Tel.: (20) 23051801
Web Site: http://www.act-eg.com
Sales Range: $50-74.9 Million
Emp.: 200
Supplier of Information & Communication Technology
N.A.I.C.S.: 334220

INTERNATIONAL ZEOLITE CORP.
2704-401 Bay Street, Toronto, M5H 2Y4, ON, Canada
Tel.: (604) 684-3301 BC
Web Site: https://internationalzeolite.com
Year Founded: 1987
IZCFF—(OTCIQ)
Rev.: $510,682
Assets: $1,015,845
Liabilities: $795,517
Net Worth: $220,328
Earnings: ($671,117)
Fiscal Year-end: 06/30/19
Metal Exploration Services
N.A.I.C.S.: 213114
Ray Paquette (Pres & CEO)

INTERNATIONELLA ENGELSKA SKOLAN I SVERIGE HOLDINGS II AB
Nytorpsvagen 5B, Stockholm, 18371, Sweden
Tel.: (46) 854473530
Rev.: $298,050,487
Assets: $193,002,453
Liabilities: $73,625,790
Net Worth: $119,376,663
Earnings: $16,568,482
Emp.: 3,028
Fiscal Year-end: 06/30/19
Educational Support Services
N.A.I.C.S.: 611710
Anna Sorelius Nordenborg (CEO)

INTERNESENAL HOTELS AD
Bul Aleksandar Makedonski bb, 1000, Skopje, North Macedonia
Tel.: (389) 23133333
Web Site: http://www.hotelcontinental.com.mk
INHO—(MAC)
Rev.: $1,249,492
Assets: $4,212,583
Liabilities: $1,551,961
Net Worth: $2,660,622
Earnings: ($54,832)
Fiscal Year-end: 12/31/23
Hotel & Restaurant Operator
N.A.I.C.S.: 721110

INTERNET INFINITY, INC.
2F Kowa Nibancho Building 11-19 Nibancho, Chiyoda-ku, Tokyo, 102-0084, Japan
Tel.: (81) 368974777
Web Site: https://www.iif.jp
Year Founded: 2001
6545—(TKS)
Rev.: $32,778,990
Assets: $24,794,110
Liabilities: $15,619,430
Net Worth: $9,174,680
Earnings: $859,300
Emp.: 364
Fiscal Year-end: 03/31/24
Health Care Srvices
N.A.I.C.S.: 621610
Keiichi Bekku (Board of Directors, Founder, Chm & Pres)

INTERNET INITIATIVE JAPAN INC.
Iidabashi Grand Bloom 2-10-2 Fujimi, Chiyoda-ku, Tokyo, 102-0071, Japan
Tel.: (81) 352056500
Web Site: https://www.iij.ad.jp
Year Founded: 1992
Rev.: $1,563,329,763
Assets: $1,362,625,513
Liabilities: $705,607,127
Net Worth: $657,018,386
Earnings: $45,367,467
Emp.: 3,203
Fiscal Year-end: 03/31/18
Internet Access & Related Services
N.A.I.C.S.: 541519
Tadaharu Esaka (Mng Exec Officer)

Subsidiaries:

Asia Internet Holding Co., Ltd. (1)
Takebashi Yasuda Bldg 3 13 Kanda Nishiki Cho, Chiyoda-ku, Tokyo, 101-0054, Japan (20.63%)
Tel.: (81) 352596290
Sales Range: $25-49.9 Million
Emp.: 15
Internet Service Provider
N.A.I.C.S.: 517810

IIJ America, Inc. (1)
55 E 59th St Ste 18C, New York, NY 10022 (88.2%)
Tel.: (212) 440-8080
Web Site: http://www.iij-america.com
Sales Range: $25-49.9 Million
Emp.: 25
Internet Access Services
N.A.I.C.S.: 517810
Yasumitsu Iizuka (Pres & CEO)

IIJ Exlayer Inc. (1)
20F Jinbocho Mitsui Building 1-105 Jinbocho Kanda, Chiyoda-Ku, Tokyo, 101-0051, Japan
Tel.: (81) 3 5205 6580
Sales Range: $25-49.9 Million
Emp.: 4
Information Technology Consulting Services
N.A.I.C.S.: 541512
Takahito Akaike (Gen Mgr)

Subsidiary (Non-US):

IIJ Deutschland GmbH (2)
Georg-Glock-Str 8, Dusseldorf, 40474, Germany
Tel.: (49) 211 4570 400
Web Site: http://www.iijeurope.com
System Integration Services
N.A.I.C.S.: 541512

IIJ Europe Limited (2)
15-25 Artillery Lane, London, E1 7LP, United Kingdom
Tel.: (44) 20 7650 5999
Web Site: http://www.iijeurope.com
Sales Range: $10-24.9 Million
Information Technology Consulting Services
N.A.I.C.S.: 541512

IIJ Exlayer Singapore Pte. Ltd (2)
61 Ubi Avenue 1 UB Point, Singapore, 408941, Singapore
Tel.: (65) 6773 6903
Sales Range: $25-49.9 Million
Emp.: 7
Information Technology Consulting Services
N.A.I.C.S.: 541512
Osamu Ono (Mng Dir)

Subsidiary (US):

IIJ Exlayer USA LLC (2)
307 W 38th St Ste 1318, New York, NY 10018
Tel.: (646) 619-1850
Web Site: http://www.iij-exlayer.com

Sales Range: $25-49.9 Million
Information Technology Consulting Services
N.A.I.C.S.: 541512
Hiroaki Yamaguchi (COO)

IIJ Global Solutions Inc. (1)
Jinbo-cho Mitsui Bldg 1-105 Kanda Jinbo-cho, Chiyoda-ku, Tokyo, 101-0051, Japan
Tel.: (81) 3 5217 5080
Web Site: http://www.iijglobal.co.jp
Sales Range: $100-124.9 Million
Emp.: 251
Network Outsourcing Services
N.A.I.C.S.: 517810
Toshinori Iwasawa (CEO)

IIJ Innovation Institute Inc. (1)
Iidabashi Grand Bloom 2-10-2 Fujimi, Chiyoda-ku, Tokyo, 101-0071, Japan (100%)
Tel.: (81) 3 5205 6501
Web Site: http://www.iij-ii.co.jp
Emp.: 3
Internet Research & Development Services
N.A.I.C.S.: 541715

IIJ Media Communications, Inc. (1)
1 105 Kanda Jineo Cho, Chiyoda Ku, Tokyo, 101 0051, Japan (50.1%)
Tel.: (81) 352596210
Web Site: http://www.iij-mc.co.jp
Sales Range: $25-49.9 Million
Emp.: 30
Web Server & Content Service
N.A.I.C.S.: 517810

Internet Multifeed Co. (1)
Otemachi 1st Square East Tower 3F, 1-5-1 Otemachi, Tokyo, 100 0004, Chiyoda-ku, Japan (26%)
Tel.: (81) 332821010
Web Site: http://www.mfeed.co.jp
Sales Range: $25-49.9 Million
Emp.: 20
High Speed Internet Service Provider
N.A.I.C.S.: 517810
Koichi Suzuki (Pres)

Net Care, Inc. (1)
Sumitomo Fudosan Kanda Bldg 2nd Fl Kanda Suda cho, Chiyoda ku, Tokyo, 101 0041, Japan (50%)
Tel.: (81) 352054000
Web Site: http://www.netcare.co.jp
Sales Range: $50-74.9 Million
Emp.: 200
Information Services
N.A.I.C.S.: 517810

Net Chart Japan Inc. (1)
YS Shin-Yokohama Bldg 8F 2-15-10 Shin-Yokohama, Kohoku-Ku, Yokohama, 222-0033, Kanagawa, Japan (100%)
Tel.: (81) 454761411
Web Site: http://www.ncj.co.jp
Emp.: 87
Network Construction Services
N.A.I.C.S.: 541512
Kazuhiro Kusumoto (Pres & CEO)

Trust Networks Inc. (1)
1-105 Kandajimbocho Jimbochomitsui Bldg, Chiyoda-Ku, Tokyo, 101-0051, Japan
Tel.: (81) 352823358
Web Site: http://www.iij.com
Sales Range: $25-49.9 Million
Emp.: 10
Automatic Teller Machine Operator
N.A.I.C.S.: 561499

hi-ho Inc. (1)
1-103 Kandajimbocho Tokyo Park Tower 2f, Chiyoda-Ku, Tokyo, 101-0051, Japan
Tel.: (81) 3 5283 3290
Web Site: http://www.home.hi-ho.ne.jp
Sales Range: $25-49.9 Million
Emp.: 4
Internet Service Provider
N.A.I.C.S.: 517810
Takafumi Yano (Mgr)

INTERNET TECHNOLOGY GROUP LTD.
No 10 Changi South Lane 07-01, Singapore, 486162, Singapore
Tel.: (65) 6543 5805
Web Site: http://www.internettechnology.com
Sales Range: $10-24.9 Million

INTERNET TECHNOLOGY GROUP LTD.

Internet Technology Group Ltd.—(Continued)
Holding Company; Software Development & Information Technology Services
N.A.I.C.S.: 551112
George Ching Wah Goh (Chm)

Subsidiaries:

Promedia Directories Pte Ltd (1)
41 Jalan Pemimpin 03-01 Kong Beng Industrial Building, Singapore, 577186, Singapore
Tel.: (65) 6258 8255
Web Site: http://www.thegreenbook.com
Emp.: 5
Directory Publisher
N.A.I.C.S.: 513140
Francis Teo (Pres & CEO)

INTERNET THAILAND PUBLIC COMPANY LIMITED

1768 Thai Summit Twr Bldg Floors 10-12 and IT Floor Petchburi New Rd, Bang Kapi Subdistrict Huai Khwang District, Bangkok, 10310, Khwang, Thailand
Tel.: (66) 22577000
Web Site: https://www.inet.co.th
Year Founded: 1995
INET—(THA)
Rev.: $60,987,476
Assets: $383,233,733
Liabilities: $306,753,974
Net Worth: $76,479,759
Earnings: $6,837,787
Emp.: 1,201
Fiscal Year-end: 12/31/23
Internet & Network Services
N.A.I.C.S.: 517111
Wanchai Vach-shewadumrong (Deputy Mng Dir)

Subsidiaries:

Mandala Communications Co., Ltd. (1)
1768 Thai Summit Tower 11th Fl New Petchburi Rd Khwaeng Bang Kapi, Khet Huay Khwang, Bangkok, Thailand
Tel.: (66) 22577255
Telecommunication Servicesb
N.A.I.C.S.: 517810

INTERNETQ PLC

The St Botolph Building 138 Houndsditch, London, EC3A 7AR, United Kingdom
Tel.: (44) 2035195250 UK
Web Site: http://www.internetq.com
Year Founded: 2000
Sales Range: $150-199.9 Million
Emp.: 162
Mobile Marketing & Digital Entertainment Services
N.A.I.C.S.: 423620
Panagiotis Dimitropoulos (CEO)

Subsidiaries:

Escape Mobile Dialogue L.T.D. (1)
Troias 17, Athinaion, 11257, Athens, Greece
Tel.: (30) 2108841141
Telecommunication Servicesb
N.A.I.C.S.: 517810

InternetQ Poland Sp. z o.o. (1)
Al Niepodleglosci 18, 02-653, Warsaw, Poland
Tel.: (48) 224895411
Web Site: http://www.internetq.com
Mobile Marketing & Digital Entertainment Services
N.A.I.C.S.: 517810

i-POP Networks Pte Ltd (1)
101B Amoy Street, Singapore, 069921, Singapore
Tel.: (65) 62366 828
Web Site: http://www.i-pop.net
Mobile Telecommunications Services
N.A.I.C.S.: 517112

Subsidiary (Non-US):

P.T. i-POP Indonesia (2)
Mayapada Tower 7th Floor Suite 07-068 Jl Jend Sudirman Kav 28, Jakarta, 12920, Indonesia
Tel.: (62) 21 521 2135
Web Site: http://www.i-pop.net
Mobile Network Services
N.A.I.C.S.: 517112

INTERNETWORKING & BROADBAND CONSULTING CO., LTD.

1-8-8 Shinkawa Chuo-ku, Tokyo, 104-0033, Japan
Tel.: (81) 351172780
Web Site: http://www.ibc21.co.jp
3920—(TKS)
Rev.: $13,471,000
Assets: $23,141,760
Liabilities: $10,188,330
Net Worth: $12,953,430
Earnings: $496,300
Emp.: 17
Fiscal Year-end: 09/30/23
Computer Maintenance & Support, Software Development & Information Processing Services
N.A.I.C.S.: 811210
Atsushi Oshima (Auditor)

INTERNOS REAL LTD.

Broadbent House, 65 Grosvenor St, London, W1K 3JH, United Kingdom
Tel.: (44) 207355 8800
Web Site:
http://www.internosglobal.com
Sales Range: $1-4.9 Billion
Emp.: 85
Privater Equity Firm
N.A.I.C.S.: 523999
Andrew Thornton (CEO)

Subsidiaries:

Internos Global Investors Kapitalverwaltungsgesellschaft mbH (1)
Goetheplatz 4, 60311, Frankfurt am Main, Germany
Tel.: (49) 6950506690
Property Investment Services
N.A.I.C.S.: 531311

INTEROGO HOLDING AG

Bahnhofstrasse 15, CH 8808, Pfaffikon, Switzerland
Tel.: (41) 152153815 NL
Web Site:
http://www.interogoholding.com
Investment Holding Company
N.A.I.C.S.: 551112
Hans Gydell (Chm)

Subsidiaries:

Inter IKEA Centre Group A/S (1)
Amager Strandvej 390, 2770, Kastrup, Denmark (51%)
Tel.: (45) 3262 6880
Web Site: http://www.iicg.com
Emp.: 600
Shopping Center Operator
N.A.I.C.S.: 531190
John Tegner (CEO)

Inter IKEA Systems B.V. (1)
Olof Palmestraat 1, 2616 LN, Delft, Netherlands
Tel.: (31) 15 215 3815
Web Site: http://franchisor.ikea.com
Furniture Store Franchising Services
N.A.I.C.S.: 449110
Torbjorn Loof (CEO)

Nalka Invest AB (1)
Master Samuelsgatan 42, SE-111 57, Stockholm, Sweden
Tel.: (46) 8 551 176 80
Investment Services
N.A.I.C.S.: 523940
Carl Lyth Fried (Mgr-Comm)

Subsidiary (Domestic):

OneMed Group Oy (2)
Svardvagen 3 B, 182 33, Danderyd, Sweden
Tel.: (46) 86115030
Web Site: http://www.onemed.com
Medical Products, Laboratory Supplies & Chemicals Distr
N.A.I.C.S.: 423450
Johan Falk (CEO)

Subsidiary (Non-US):

BATIST Medical SK s.r.o. (3)
Kopcianska 10, 851 01, Bratislava, Slovakia
Tel.: (421) 244888639
Web Site: http://www.batist.com
Emp.: 60
Medical Products, Laboratory Supplies & Chemicals Distr
N.A.I.C.S.: 423450

BATIST Medical a.s. (3)
Nerudova 309, 549 41, Cerveny Kostelec, Czech Republic
Tel.: (420) 491431311
Web Site: http://www.batist.com
Medical Products, Laboratory Supplies & Chemicals Distr
N.A.I.C.S.: 423450
Martina Piskorova (CMO)

Danpleje OneMed A/S (3)
Langebjerg 23, D 4000, Roskilde, Denmark
Tel.: (45) 46 740 030
Web Site: http://www.onemed.com
Sales Range: $25-49.9 Million
Emp.: 10
Medical Products, Laboratory Supplies & Chemicals Distr
N.A.I.C.S.: 327215
Erik Boje (Gen Mgr)

Hand-Prod Sp. z o.o. (3)
ul Tetmajera 79, Krakow, Poland
Tel.: (48) 123450189
Web Site: http://www.hand-prod.com.pl
Medical Products, Laboratory Supplies & Chemicals Distr
N.A.I.C.S.: 423450

OneMed AS (3)
Bolerveien 63, 2020, Skedsmokorset, Norway
Tel.: (47) 63842200
Sales Range: $25-49.9 Million
Emp.: 30
Medical Products, Laboratory Supplies & Chemicals Distr
N.A.I.C.S.: 423450
Tor Schye (Project Mgr)

OneMed OU (3)
Veerenni 38, 76401, Tallinn, Laagri, Estonia
Tel.: (372) 6503630
Web Site: http://www.onemed.ee
Sales Range: $25-49.9 Million
Emp.: 12
Medical Products, Laboratory Supplies & Chemicals Distr
N.A.I.C.S.: 423450

OneMed SIA (3)
Ulmana Gatve 119, 2167, Riga, Marupe, Latvia
Tel.: (371) 67964748
Medical Products, Laboratory Supplies & Chemicals Distr
N.A.I.C.S.: 423450
Olafs Gutmanis (Mng Dir)

Subsidiary (Domestic):

OneMed Sverige AB (3)
Tagenevagen 29, Hisings Karra, 425 37, Gothenburg, Sweden
Tel.: (46) 770111115
Web Site: http://www.onemed.se
Sales Range: $50-74.9 Million
Emp.: 150
Medical Products, Laboratory Supplies & Chemicals Distr
N.A.I.C.S.: 423450
Johan Falk (CEO)

Subsidiary (Non-US):

UAB OneMed (3)
Perkunkiemio g4A, 12128, Vilnius, Lithuania
Tel.: (370) 52462224

INTERNATIONAL PUBLIC

Web Site: http://www.onemed.com
Medical Products, Laboratory Supplies & Chemicals Distr
N.A.I.C.S.: 423450
Tonu Loog (Mng Dir)

WL-Medical Oy (3)
Karvaamokuja 4, 380, Helsinki, Finland
Tel.: (358) 467146850
Medical Products, Laboratory Supplies & Chemicals Distr
N.A.I.C.S.: 423450

Vastint Holding, B.V. (1)
Hettenheuvelweg 51, 1101 BM, Amsterdam, Netherlands
Tel.: (31) 020 584 06
Web Site: http://www.vastint.eu
Emp.: 90
Real Estate Management & Development Services
N.A.I.C.S.: 531390
Steen Sodemann (CEO)

INTEROIL EXPLORATION & PRODUCTION ASA

Advokatfirmaet Schjodt, AS Tordenskiolds gate 12, 160, Oslo, Norway
Tel.: (47) 67518650 NO
Web Site: https://www.interoil.no
Year Founded: 2005
1ZD0—(DEU)
Rev.: $18,999,000
Assets: $34,118,000
Liabilities: $37,094,000
Net Worth: ($2,976,000)
Earnings: ($664,000)
Emp.: 62
Fiscal Year-end: 12/31/22
Oil & Gas Exploration Services
N.A.I.C.S.: 213112
Leandro Carbone (CEO)

INTEROJO CO., LTD.

28 & 25 Sandan-ro 15 Beon-gil, Pyeongtaek, Gyeonggi-do, Korea (South)
Tel.: (82) 316114760
Web Site: https://www.interojo.com
Year Founded: 2000
119610—(KRS)
Rev.: $97,353,499
Assets: $202,308,822
Liabilities: $57,229,030
Net Worth: $145,079,793
Earnings: $18,553,348
Emp.: 641
Fiscal Year-end: 12/31/22
Contact Lens Mfr
N.A.I.C.S.: 339115

INTERORIENT NAVIGATION COMPANY LTD.

142 Franklin Roosevelt, PO Box 51309, CY-3504, Limassol, Cyprus
Tel.: (357) 25840300
Web Site: http://www.interorient.com
Emp.: 3,300
Marine Transportation Services
N.A.I.C.S.: 483111
Themis Papadopoulos (CEO)

Subsidiaries:

INC Navigation Company Philippines Inc. (1)
Unit 1701 17th Floor Raffles Corporate Center F Ortigas Jr Road, Ortigas Center Metro Manila, Pasig, 1605, Philippines
Tel.: (63) 27062190
Web Site:
http://www.interorientshipmanagement.com
Emp.: 1,000
Marine Transportation Services
N.A.I.C.S.: 488330
Themis Papadopoulos (CEO)

Interorient Marine Services (Germany) GmbH & Co. KG (1)
Kajen 12, 20459, Hamburg, Germany
Tel.: (49) 403749470

AND PRIVATE COMPANIES

Marine Transportation Services
N.A.I.C.S.: 488330
Tim Lissow *(Ops Mgr)*

Interorient Navigation (Latvia) Co. Ltd (1)
Ieriku iela 15 Lit 1 stavs 3, Riga, 1084, Latvia
Tel.: (371) 67326021
Marine Transportation Services
N.A.I.C.S.: 488330
Themis Papadopoulos *(CEO)*

Interorient Navigation (St. Petersburg) Inc. (1)
4 Litera A Line 11, Vasilyevsky Island, Saint Petersburg, 199034, Russia
Tel.: (7) 8123268720
Marine Transportation Services
N.A.I.C.S.: 488330
Themis Papadopoulos *(CEO)*

INTERPHARMA PUBLIC COMPANY LIMITED
140/9 ITF Tower 9th Floor Silom Road, Suriyawong Bangrak, Bangkok, 10500, Thailand
Tel.: (66) 26340225　　　　TH
Web Site:
　https://www.interpharma.co.th
Year Founded: 2006
IP—(THA)
Rev.: $52,509,795
Assets: $86,185,392
Liabilities: $24,364,938
Net Worth: $61,820,454
Earnings: $1,719,456
Emp.: 634
Fiscal Year-end: 12/31/23
Pharmaceutical Product Mfr & Distr
N.A.I.C.S.: 325412
Trinnawat Thanitnithiphan *(CEO & Dir)*

Subsidiaries:

Inter Vetta Co., Ltd. (1)
140/9 ITF Tower 9th Floor Silom Road, Suriyawong Bangrak, Bangkok, 10500, Thailand
Tel.: (66) 26340225
Pharmaceuticals Product Mfr
N.A.I.C.S.: 325412

INTERPIPE NYZHNODNIPROVSKY TUBE-ROLLING PLANT PJSC
21 Stoletova Street, Dnepropetrovsk, Ukraine
Tel.: (380) 562359301
NITR—(UKR)
Sales Range: Less than $1 Million
Steel Pole Mfr
N.A.I.C.S.: 331210
Yevgeniy N. Kopayev *(Chm-Mgmt Bd)*

INTERPORT LIMITED
Brandon House Marlowe Way, Croydon, CR0 4XS, United Kingdom
Tel.: (44) 208 6645 988
Web Site:
　http://www.interportltd.co.uk
Year Founded: 1982
Sales Range: $150-199.9 Million
Emp.: 89
Pharmaceutical Product Whslr
N.A.I.C.S.: 424210
H. Patel *(Mng Dir)*

INTERPROGRESSBANK JSC
Starokashirskoe Highway 2 Block 1 Bld 1, 115201, Moscow, Russia
Tel.: (7) 4954110000
Web Site: http://www.ipb.ru
Year Founded: 1973
Sales Range: Less than $1 Million
Financial Processing & Insurance Services
N.A.I.C.S.: 522320

Dmitry Yakovlev *(Chm-Mgmt Bd)*

INTERPROMBANK JSCB
9 Build 1 Gogolevsky Boulevard, Moscow, 119019, Russia
Tel.: (7) 4952322050
Web Site:
　http://www.interprombank.ru
Year Founded: 1995
Sales Range: Less than $1 Million
Financial Consulting Services
N.A.I.C.S.: 541611

INTERPROMET AD
st Ilindenska no 18a, 1200, Tetovo, North Macedonia
Tel.: (389) 44336163　　　　MK
Web Site: https://www.interpromet.mk
Year Founded: 1973
INPR—(MAC)
Rev.: $271,159
Assets: $3,014,704
Liabilities: $24,278
Net Worth: $2,990,426
Earnings: $1,075,787
Fiscal Year-end: 12/31/23
Departmental Store Operator
N.A.I.C.S.: 455110

INTERPUMP GROUP S.P.A.
Via E Fermi 25, 42049, Sant'Ilario d'Enza, RE, Italy
Tel.: (39) 0522904311
Web Site:
　https://www.interpumpgroup.it
Year Founded: 1977
IP—(ITA)
Rev.: $1,589,788,411
Assets: $2,639,843,950
Liabilities: $1,227,396,199
Net Worth: $1,412,447,750
Earnings: $212,818,373
Emp.: 478
Fiscal Year-end: 12/31/20
High Pressure Liquid Pump Mfr & Whslr
N.A.I.C.S.: 333914
Fulvio Montipo *(Chm & CEO)*

Subsidiaries:

Alfa Valvole S.r.l. (1)
Viale del Lavoro 19, Casorezzo, 20003, Milan, Italy
Tel.: (39) 0290296206
Web Site: https://www.alfavalvole.com
Emp.: 100
Ball Valve Mfr
N.A.I.C.S.: 332911

Contarini Leopoldo S.r.l. (1)
Tel.: (39) 0545281111
Web Site: https://contarini.net
Sales Range: $25-49.9 Million
Hydraulic Cylinder Mfr
N.A.I.C.S.: 333995

Subsidiary (Non-US):

Copa Hydrosystem Odd (2)
Tel.: (359) 67062185
Web Site:
　https://www.copahydro.50webs.com
Sales Range: $25-49.9 Million
Emp.: 45
Hydraulic Truck Parts Mfr
N.A.I.C.S.: 336390

Unidro S.a.r.l. (2)
ZI les Epinettes 495 rue de Branmafan, 73230, Barby, France
Tel.: (33) 4 79 71 06 38
Web Site: http://www.unidro-contarini.com
Hydraulic Cylinder Mfr & Distr
N.A.I.C.S.: 333995

Cover S.r.l. (1)
Via G di Vittorio 53, 25125, Brescia, Italy
Tel.: (39) 0303581105
Web Site: http://www.rav.it
Industrial Machinery Goods Mfr
N.A.I.C.S.: 333248

Draintech S.R.L. (1)

Via 1 Maggio 3/5, 40011, Anzola dell'Emila, BE, Italy
Tel.: (39) 051727447
Web Site: https://www.draintech.it
Transmission Gear Mfr
N.A.I.C.S.: 336350

Eurofluid Hydraulic S.r.l. (1)
Via Martiri della Romania 6, Borzano, 42020, Albinea, Italy
Tel.: (39) 0522349017
Web Site: https://www.eurofluid.it
Emp.: 90
Hydraulic Equipment Mfr
N.A.I.C.S.: 333996

FGA S.r.l. (1)
Via Roma 105, 31040, Chiarano, TV, Italy
Tel.: (39) 0422806075
Web Site:
　https://www.fgacostruzionimecca.com
Precision Mechanical Machining Product Mfr
N.A.I.C.S.: 332721

GS-Hydro Denmark AS (1)
Fabriksvej 12, 6000, Kolding, Denmark
Tel.: (45) 75541533
Web Site: https://dk.gshydro.com
Emp.: 400
Pipe & Pipe Fitting Mfr
N.A.I.C.S.: 332919

Galtech Canada Inc. (1)
3100 Jacob Jordan, Terrebonne, J6X 4J6, QC, Canada
Tel.: (450) 477-1076
Web Site: http://www.galtechcanada.com
Hydraulic Directional Control Valve Distr
N.A.I.C.S.: 423840

General Pump Inc. (1)
5909 Stratler St, Salt Lake City, UT 84107-6902　　　　(100%)
Tel.: (801) 262-8436
Web Site: http://www.generalpump.com
Emp.: 3
Pump & Pumping Equipment Mfr
N.A.I.C.S.: 333914

General Technology S.r.l. (1)
Via G B Vico 2, Reggio Emilia, 42124, Parma, Italy　　　　(100%)
Tel.: (39) 0522948011
Web Site: http://www.interpumpgroup.it
Space Research & Technology
N.A.I.C.S.: 927110

HS Penta Africa Pty Ltd (1)
16 Lever Rd Cnr Van Niekerk Rd, Rosslyn, Pretoria, 81, South Africa
Tel.: (27) 12 541 4097
Web Site: http://www.hspentaafrica.co.za
Telescopic Cylinders Mfr
N.A.I.C.S.: 333998

Hammelmann GmbH (1)
Carl-Zeiss-Strasse 6-8, 59302, Oelde, Germany
Tel.: (49) 2522760
Web Site: https://www.hammelmann.com
Water Pump Mfr
N.A.I.C.S.: 333996

Hammelmann Maschinenfabrik GmbH (1)
Carl-Zeiss-Strasse 6-8, 59302, Oelde, Germany　　　　(100%)
Tel.: (49) 2522760
Web Site: http://www.hammelmann.com
Sales Range: $50-74.9 Million
Emp.: 380
Industrial Pump Mfr
N.A.I.C.S.: 333914

Subsidiary (Non-US):

Hammelmann Australia Pty Ltd (2)
1/41 Paringa Road, Murarrie, 4172, QLD, Australia
Tel.: (61) 1300816483
Web Site: https://www.hammelmann.com.au
Sales Range: $25-49.9 Million
Hydraulic Machine Parts Mfr
N.A.I.C.S.: 333248

Subsidiary (US):

Hammelmann Corporation (2)
436 Southpointe Dr, Miamisburg, OH 45342　　　　(100%)

INTERPUMP GROUP S.P.A.

Tel.: (937) 859-8777
Web Site: https://www.hammelmann.com
Sales Range: $25-49.9 Million
Industrial Pump Mfr
N.A.I.C.S.: 333914

Subsidiary (Non-US):

Hammelmann France S.a.r.l. (2)
Tel.: (33) 241371483
Web Site: https://www.hammelmann.com
High Pressure System & Pump Distr
N.A.I.C.S.: 423830

Hammelmann Pumps Systems Co Ltd (2)
No 9 Shuang Chen Front Road, Bei Chen Economic Development Area, Tianjin, 300400, China
Tel.: (86) 2226972658
Web Site: https://www.hammelmann.cn
Sales Range: $25-49.9 Million
Industrial Pump Mfr
N.A.I.C.S.: 333914

Hammelmann S. L. (2)
Pol Ind Valdeconsejo C / Monte Perdido Parc 7A-2B, E-50410, Cuarte de Huerva, Zaragoza, Spain
Tel.: (34) 976504753
Web Site: https://www.hammelmann.com
Hydraulic Industrial Parts Mfr
N.A.I.C.S.: 333248

Hammelmann Swiss GmbH (2)
Sagerainstrasse 8, 3186, Dudingen, Switzerland
Tel.: (41) 764900708
High-Pressure Plunger Pump Distr
N.A.I.C.S.: 423840

Hangzhou Transtecno Power Transmissions Co. Ltd. (1)
No 4 Xiuyan Road Fengdu Industry Zone, Pingyao Town Yuhang District, Hangzhou, 311115, Zhejiang, China
Tel.: (86) 57186920260
Power Transmission System Mfr & Distr
N.A.I.C.S.: 333613

Hydro Service Penta S.p.A (1)
Via Proventa 31, 48018, Faenza, RA, Italy
Tel.: (39) 0546664848
Web Site: http://www.hspenta.it
Hydraulic Cylinder Mfr
N.A.I.C.S.: 333995

I.MEC S.R.L. (1)
Via Umberto Degola 24, 42124, Reggio Emilia, Italy
Tel.: (39) 0522517492
Web Site: https://bitecnology.com
Industry Machinery Mfr
N.A.I.C.S.: 333519

IMM Hydro Est (1)
Catcau Nr 353 Jud, Cluj-Napoca, Romania
Tel.: (40) 264225210
Web Site: https://www.imm-hydroest.ro
Hydraulic Hose Fitting Mfr & Distr
N.A.I.C.S.: 332912

INOXPA Ltd. (1)
Tel.: (7) 4952150242
Web Site: https://www.inoxpa.ru
Machinery & Equipment Distr
N.A.I.C.S.: 423830

Improved Solutions Portugal Unipessoal Ltda. (1)
Av da Industria no 309 Rossio, 3730-600, Vale de Cambra, Portugal
Tel.: (351) 256472722
Web Site: https://www.inoxpa.pt
Water Pump Mfr
N.A.I.C.S.: 333996

Improved Solutions Unipessoal Ltda. (1)
Rua Helipista 648, Algeriz, 3730-266, Vale de Cambra, Portugal
Tel.: (351) 256472722
Web Site: http://www.inoxpa.pt
Machinery & Equipment Mfr
N.A.I.C.S.: 333248

Inoxihp S.r.l. (1)
Via Garibaldi 89, 20834, Nova Milanese, MB, Italy
Tel.: (39) 0362190111
Web Site: https://www.inoxihp.com

INTERPUMP GROUP S.P.A.

Interpump Group S.p.A.—(Continued)
High Pressure Pump Mfr & Distr
N.A.I.C.S.: 333996

Inoxpa (UK) Ltd. (1)
8G The Old Yard Rectory Lane, Brasted, Westerham, TN16 1JP, Kent, United Kingdom
Tel.: (44) 1737378060
Stainless Steel Component & Fluid Handling Equipment Mfr & Distr
N.A.I.C.S.: 333998

Inoxpa Australia Proprietary Ltd. (1)
8 Law Court, Sunshine, 3020, VIC, Australia
Tel.: (61) 1300816483
Web Site: http://www.inoxpa.com.au
Machinery & Equipment Distr
N.A.I.C.S.: 423830

Inoxpa Colombia Sas (1)
Autopista Medellin Km 2 5 Via Parcelas Parque Ciem Oikos Occidente, Bodega G-100 Cota Cundinamarca, Bogota, Colombia
Tel.: (57) 17427577
Web Site: https://www.inoxpa.co
Machinery & Equipment Distr
N.A.I.C.S.: 423830

Inoxpa India Private Ltd. (1)
Survey No 83 Hissa no 2/6/A, Anant Industrial Estate At- Shivane Tal- Haveli Dist, Pune, 411023, Maharashtra, India
Tel.: (91) 2035002300
Web Site: https://www.inoxpa.in
Machinery & Equipment Mfr
N.A.I.C.S.: 333248

Inoxpa Italia S.r.l. (1)
Via Stazione 119/V - loc Ballo, Mirano, 30035, Venice, Italy
Tel.: (39) 041411236
Web Site: https://www.inoxpa.it
Machinery & Equipment Distr
N.A.I.C.S.: 423830

Inoxpa Mexico S.A. de C.V. (1)
Darwin 74 - 301 Anzures, Mexico, Mexico
Tel.: (52) 5637270546
Web Site: https://www.inoxpa.mx
Water Pump Mfr
N.A.I.C.S.: 333996

Inoxpa Middle East FZCO (1)
G - R and D Office 1 Highbay Dubai Silicon Oasis, PO Box 341085, Dubai, United Arab Emirates
Tel.: (971) 43335388
Stainless Steel Component & Fluid Handling Equipment Mfr & Distr
N.A.I.C.S.: 333998

Inoxpa S.A. (1)
Telers 60, Banyoles, 17820, Girona, Spain
Tel.: (34) 972575200
Web Site: https://www.inoxpa.es
Stainless Steel Component & Fluid Handling Equipment Mfr & Distr
N.A.I.C.S.: 333998

Inoxpa Skandinavien A/S (1)
Langballe 2, DK - 8700, Horsens, Denmark
Tel.: (45) 76286900
Web Site: https://www.inoxpa.dk
Machinery & Equipment Distr
N.A.I.C.S.: 423830

Inoxpa Solutions France Sas (1)
ZAC d'Epinay 69 Allee des Caillotieres, F - 69400, Gleize, France
Tel.: (33) 474627100
Web Site: https://www.inoxpa.fr
Machinery & Equipment Mfr
N.A.I.C.S.: 333248

Inoxpa Solutions Srl (1)
str Maria Dragan 21, Chisinau, MD2052, Moldova
Tel.: (373) 69102624
Stainless Steel Component & Fluid Handling Equipment Mfr & Distr
N.A.I.C.S.: 333998

Inoxpa South Africa Proprietary Ltd. (1)
Unit A3 1510 Zeiss Rd Laser Park, Honeydew, 2040, Gauteng, South Africa
Tel.: (27) 117945223

Stainless Steel Component & Fluid Handling Equipment Mfr & Distr
N.A.I.C.S.: 333998

Inoxpa Special Processing Equipment Co. Ltd. (1)
No 200 Fengjin Road, Fengxian District, Shanghai, 201401, China
Tel.: (86) 2167159966
Stainless Steel Component & Fluid Handling Equipment Mfr & Distr
N.A.I.C.S.: 333998

Inoxpa USA Inc. (1)
Tel.: (972) 423-1750
Web Site: https://www.inoxpausa.com
Machinery & Equipment Distr
N.A.I.C.S.: 423830

Inoxpa Ukraine S.L. (1)
Tel.: (380) 445360957
Web Site: https://www.inoxpa.com.ua
Machinery & Equipment Distr
N.A.I.C.S.: 423830

Intecno S.r.l. (1)
Via Caduti di Sabbiuno 9/E, Anzola dell'Emila, BO, Italy
Tel.: (39) 05119985350
Web Site: http://www.intecno-srl.com
Hydraulic Equipment Mfr & Distr
N.A.I.C.S.: 333996
Moreno Ferrari (Gen Mgr)

Interpump Engineering S.r.l. (1)
Via G B Vico 2, 42124, Reggio nell'Emilia, Italy (100%)
Tel.: (39) 0522948511
Web Site: http://www.interpumpgroup.it
Sales Range: $25-49.9 Million
Emp.: 15
Engine Equipment Mfr
N.A.I.C.S.: 333618

Interpump Fluid Solutions Germany GmbH (1)
Eisenweg 5, 58540, Meinerzhagen, Germany
Tel.: (49) 2354708850
Hydraulic Hose & Fitting Mfr
N.A.I.C.S.: 332912

Interpump Hydraulics RUS LLC (1)
St Generala Tyuleneva 4A building 3 room 52, Moscow, Russia
Tel.: (7) 4957804083
Web Site: https://iph-rus.ru
Fluid Power Pump & Motor Mfr
N.A.I.C.S.: 333996

Interpump Hydraulics S.p.A. (1)
(100%)
Tel.: (39) 0516460511
Web Site: https://iph.it
Sales Range: $50-74.9 Million
Emp.: 130
Pump & Pumping Equipment Mfr
N.A.I.C.S.: 333914

Subsidiary (Domestic):

AVI S.r.l. (2)
Via Brescia 7, 20814, Varedo, MB, Italy
Tel.: (39) 0362544765
Web Site: http://www.avi.it
Sales Range: $25-49.9 Million
Hydraulic Industrial & Vehicle Parts Mfr
N.A.I.C.S.: 336390

Subsidiary (Non-US):

Hydrocar Chile S.A. (2)
Los Libertadores Avenue 41 Los Libertadores Industrial Park, 16 500, Colina, Santiago, Chile
Tel.: (56) 229633870
Web Site: https://www.hydrocar.cl
Hydraulic Pump Distr
N.A.I.C.S.: 423840

Subsidiary (Domestic):

Hydrocar Moderna S.p.A. (2)
Via Leonardo Da Vinci 19, Nonantola, Modena, Italy
Tel.: (39) 059896111
Web Site: http://www.webpto.com
Sales Range: $25-49.9 Million
Emp.: 100
Industrial Machinery Mfr
N.A.I.C.S.: 333248

Munerati Luca (Mng Dir)

Hydrocar Roma S.r.l. (2)
Via Tiburtina n 1470 Loc Settecamini, 00131, Rome, Italy
Tel.: (39) 064190708
Web Site: http://www.hydrocar-roma.com
Motor Vehicle Parts Mfr
N.A.I.C.S.: 336390

Hydrometal S.r.l. (2)
Via Carlo Testa 3-b, Soreara di Bomporto, Modena, Italy (100%)
Tel.: (39) 059812511
Web Site: http://www.hydrometal.net
Sales Range: $25-49.9 Million
Emp.: 30
Motor Vehicle Parts Mfr
N.A.I.C.S.: 336390

Hydroven S.r.l. (2)
Via G Matteotti2, Tezze Sul Brenta, 36056, Vicenza, Italy (51%)
Tel.: (39) 0424539381
Web Site: https://www.hydroven.com
Sales Range: $25-49.9 Million
Hydraulic Pumps Mfr
N.A.I.C.S.: 333914

Subsidiary (Non-US):

Interpump Hydraulics (UK) Ltd. (2)
Unit 5 Greenhill Industrial Estate Birmingham Road, Kidderminster, DY10 2RN, United Kingdom
Tel.: (44) 1215501115
Web Site:
https://www.interpumpfluidsolutions.co.uk
Hydraulic Pump Distr
N.A.I.C.S.: 423840

Interpump Hydraulics Brasil Ltda. (2)
Rua Gilberto de Zorzi 525 Forqueta, CX Postal 3544, Caxias do Sul, 95115-730, RS, Brazil
Tel.: (55) 5432897000
Web Site: https://www.interpump.com.br
Hydraulic Cylinder Pump Mfr & Distr
N.A.I.C.S.: 333996

Interpump Hydraulics France S.a.r.l. (2)
Tel.: (33) 387381010
Hydraulic Vehicle Parts Mfr
N.A.I.C.S.: 336390

Interpump Hydraulics India Private Ltd (2)
No 6A Sipcot Industrial Complex, Elasagiri Road Next to Titan Watches, Hosur, 635 126, Tamil Nadu, India
Tel.: (91) 7397734706
Web Site: https://iphindia.co.in
Hydraulic Spare Parts Mfr
N.A.I.C.S.: 336390

Subsidiary (Domestic):

Interpump Hydraulics International S.p.A. (2)
Via Leonardo Da Vinci 17/1, Nonantola, 41015, Modena, Italy
Tel.: (39) 059896111
Automobile Parts Mfr
N.A.I.C.S.: 336390

Subsidiary (Non-US):

Interpump Hydraulics Middle East FZE (2)
Warehouse No RA08SD03 Jebel Ali, PO Box 261466, Dubai, United Arab Emirates
Tel.: (971) 48876784
Web Site: https://www.interpump.ae
Hydraulic Pumps Mfr
N.A.I.C.S.: 333996

Interpump South Africa Pty. Ltd. (2)
Tel.: (27) 118245494
Web Site:
https://www.interpumpsouthafrica.co.za
Hydraulic Cylinder Mfr & Distr
N.A.I.C.S.: 333995
Johan Buys (Mng Dir)

Subsidiary (US):

Muncie Power Products, Inc (2)
201 E Jackson St, Muncie, IN 47305-2834
Tel.: (765) 284-7721
Web Site: https://www.munciepower.com

INTERNATIONAL PUBLIC

Sales Range: Less than $1 Million
Emp.: 100
Pump, Gear & Power Tool Mfr
N.A.I.C.S.: 333996
Kathy White (CFO)

Subsidiary (Domestic):

American Mobile Power Inc. (3)
619 E Jefferson St, Fairmount, IN 46928
Tel.: (765) 948-3401
Web Site:
https://www.americanmobilepower.com
Metal Tank Mfr
N.A.I.C.S.: 332420

Subsidiary (Non-US):

Hydra Dyne Technology Inc. (3)
55 Samnah Crescent, Ingersoll, N5C 3J7, ON, Canada
Tel.: (519) 485-2200
Web Site: https://www.hydradynetech.com
Hydraulic Pumps Mfr
N.A.I.C.S.: 333996

Subsidiary (Non-US):

Wuxi Interpump Weifu Hydraulics Company Ltd. (2)
202 Chengnan Road, New District, Wuxi, 214028, Jiangsu, China
Tel.: (86) 51085368055
Web Site: http://www.iph.net.cn
Hydraulic Cylinder Mfr & Distr
N.A.I.C.S.: 333995

Interpump Piping GS S.r.l. (1)
Tel.: (39) 0872889225
Web Site: https://gshydro.com
Emp.: 400
Power Transmission System Distr
N.A.I.C.S.: 221121

MA Transtecno S.A.P.I. de C.V. (1)
Av Mundial 176 Parque Industrial JM, CP 66600, Apodaca, Nuevo Leon, Mexico
Tel.: (52) 8113340920
Web Site: https://www.transtecno.com
Power Transmission System Distr
N.A.I.C.S.: 221121

Mega Pacific NZ Pty. Ltd. (1)
53 Aviation Avenue, Mount Maunganui, Tauranga, 3116, New Zealand
Tel.: (64) 79287722
Web Site: https://www.megapacific.co.nz
Hydraulic Pump Distr
N.A.I.C.S.: 423840

Mega Pacific Pty. Ltd. (1)
7 Jersey Avenue, Sandgate, Newcastle, 2304, NSW, Australia
Tel.: (61) 249601888
Web Site: https://www.megapacific.com.au
Hydraulic Pump Distr
N.A.I.C.S.: 423840

Modenflex Hydraulics S.r.l. (1)
Via Rosalba Camera 20 1, San Damaso, 41126, Modena, Italy
Tel.: (39) 059 469734
Web Site:
http://www.modenflex.chinaexporter.com
Sales Range: $25-49.9 Million
Hydraulic Telescopic Cylinder Mfr
N.A.I.C.S.: 333995

NLB Corp. (1)
29830 Beck Rd, Wixom, MI 48393-2824 (80%)
Tel.: (248) 624-5555
Web Site: http://www.nlbcorp.com
Sales Range: $50-74.9 Million
Emp.: 165
High Pressure Water Pump Mfr & Distr
N.A.I.C.S.: 333996

Subsidiary (Non-US):

NLB Poland Corp. Sp. Z.o.o. (2)
ul Dzika 6/271, 00-172, Warsaw, Poland
Tel.: (48) 600659910
Industrial Equipment Distr
N.A.I.C.S.: 423830

NLB Corporation Inc. (1)
51701 Grand River Ave, Wixom, MI 48393
Tel.: (248) 624-5555
Web Site: https://www.nlbcorp.com
Water Pump Mfr

AND PRIVATE COMPANIES

N.A.I.C.S.: 333996

Oleodinamica Panni S.r.l. (1)
Via Don Domenico Valente 5, Loc Santa Croce Bigolina, 35013, Cittadella, PD, Italy
Tel.: (39) 0499448900
Web Site: https://www.panni.com
Sales Range: $50-74.9 Million
Industrial Machinery Mfr
N.A.I.C.S.: 333248

Pioli S.r.l. (1)
Via Carlo Carra 1/3/5/7, 42124, Reggio Emilia, RE, Italy
Tel.: (39) 0522941339
Web Site: https://www.piolisrl.it
Galvanic Treatment Metal Mfr
N.A.I.C.S.: 332811

RR France S.a.r.l. (1)
10 ZAC de la Baudiniere, 44470, Thouare-sur-Loire, France
Tel.: (33) 251859272
Web Site: https://www.rrfrance.fr
Power Transmission System Distr
N.A.I.C.S.: 221121

RR Holland BV (1)
Energieweg 34, 4906 CG, Oosterhout, Netherlands
Tel.: (31) 162456397
Web Site: https://en.rrholland.nl
Power Transmission System Distr
N.A.I.C.S.: 221121
Pieter Poppelaars *(CEO)*

RR India Pvt. Ltd. (1)
Tel.: (91) 1147597176
Web Site: https://www.rrindia.com
Facility Management Services
N.A.I.C.S.: 561210

RR Pacific Pty. Ltd. (1)
Unit 1 2 Access Way, Carrum Downs, 3201, VIC, Australia
Tel.: (61) 397751077
Web Site: https://rrpacific.com
Power Transmission System Distr
N.A.I.C.S.: 221121

RR Slovakia A.S. (1)
Na Stepnici 1, 960 01, Zvolen, Slovakia
Tel.: (421) 455479713
Power Transmission System Mfr & Distr
N.A.I.C.S.: 333613

Reggiana Riduttori (Suzhou) Co. Ltd. (1)
101 Building 1 No 99 Fengnan Road, Xiangcheng District, Suzhou, 215134, Jiangsu, China
Tel.: (86) 51288858153
Power Transmission System Distr
N.A.I.C.S.: 221121

Reggiana Riduttori S.r.l. (1)
Via Martiri di Marzabotto 7, San Polo d'Enza, 42020, Reggio Emilia, RE, Italy
Tel.: (39) 0522259111
Web Site: https://www.reggianariduttori.com
Power Transmission System Mfr & Distr
N.A.I.C.S.: 333613

SIT S.p.A. (1)
Viale A Volta 2, 20047, Cusago, MI, Italy (65%)
Tel.: (39) 02891441
Web Site: https://www.sitspa.com
Sales Range: $25-49.9 Million
Power Transmission Equipment Mfr
N.A.I.C.S.: 333613

Servizi Industriali S.r.l. (1)
Via Antica Massa 52, 54033, Carrara, MS, Italy
Tel.: (39) 0585856797
Web Site: https://www.servizindustria.it
Centrifugal Separator Distr
N.A.I.C.S.: 423830

Suministros Franquesa S.A. (1)
Av de Rosa Parks 61, 25005, Lleida, Spain
Tel.: (34) 973232198
Web Site: https://www.frahp.com
Pipe & Pipe Fitting Mfr
N.A.I.C.S.: 332919

Tekno Tubi S.r.l. (1)
Via Dell Artigianato 8, 44047, Sant'Agostino, FE, Italy
Tel.: (39) 053284022
Web Site: https://www.tekno-tubi.it
Hydraulic Equipment Mfr & Distr
N.A.I.C.S.: 333996

Transtecno Aandrijftechniek BV (1)
Tel.: (31) 332047006
Web Site: https://www.transtecnoaandrijftechniek.nl
Power Transmission System Distr
N.A.I.C.S.: 221121

Transtecno BV (1)
Tel.: (31) 334519505
Web Site: https://www.transtecno.com
Power Transmission System Distr
N.A.I.C.S.: 221121

Transtecno Iberica the Modular Gearmotor S.A. (1)
Carrer de la Ciencia 45, Viladecans, 08840, Barcelona, Spain
Tel.: (34) 931598950
Web Site: https://www.transtecno.com
Power Transmission System Distr
N.A.I.C.S.: 221121

Transtecno S.r.l. (1)
Via Caduti di Sabbiuno 11 D/E, 40011, Anzola dell'Emila, BO, Italy
Tel.: (39) 0516425811
Web Site: https://www.transtecno.com
Hydraulic Equipment Mfr & Distr
N.A.I.C.S.: 333996

Tubiflex S.p.A. (1)
Tel.: (39) 0119033201
Web Site: https://www.tubiflex.com
Hydraulic Hose Fitting Mfr & Distr
N.A.I.C.S.: 332912

Unidro Contarini S.A.S. (1)
ZI les Epinettes 495 rue de Branmafan, 73230, Barby, France
Tel.: (33) 479710638
Web Site: https://www.unidro-contarini.com
Hydraulic Component Distr
N.A.I.C.S.: 423720

Waikato Milking Systems Ireland Ltd. (1)
Unit 26 North Point Business Park New Mallow Road, Cork, T23 X9R7, Ireland
Tel.: (353) 212290823
Dairy Farming Machine Mfr
N.A.I.C.S.: 333111

Waikato Milking Systems LP (1)
29 Innovation Way Northgate Business Park, PO Box 20325, Hamilton, 3241, New Zealand
Tel.: (64) 78498755
Web Site: https://waikatomilking.com
Dairy Farming Machine Mfr
N.A.I.C.S.: 333111

Waikato Milking Systems Lease Ltd. (1)
29 Innovation Way Northgate Business Park, PO Box 20325, Hamilton, 3241, New Zealand
Tel.: (64) 78498755
Web Site: https://waikatomilking.com
Dairy Farming Machine Mfr
N.A.I.C.S.: 333111

Walvoil Canada Inc. (1)
3100 Rue Jacob Jordan, Terrebonne, J6X 4J6, QC, Canada
Tel.: (450) 477-1076
Web Site: https://www.walvoilcanada.com
Hydraulic Component Distr
N.A.I.C.S.: 423720

Walvoil Fluid Power (Dongguan) Co., Ltd. (1)
1st Floor the Third Factory Area Sijia, Shijie Town, Dongguan, Guangdong, China
Tel.: (86) 76981816189
Web Site: https://www.walvoil.com.cn
Hydraulic Directional Control Valve Mfr & Distr
N.A.I.C.S.: 332912

Walvoil Fluid Power Australasia Pty. Ltd. (1)
13 Vanessa Way, Delahey, Melbourne, 3037, VIC, Australia
Tel.: (61) 458918750
Hydraulic Directional Control Valve Mfr & Distr
N.A.I.C.S.: 332912

Walvoil Fluid Power France S.a.r.l. (1)
362 rue de Bretagne Vritz, 44540, Vallons-de-L'Erdre, France
Tel.: (33) 241944106
Hydraulic Directional Control Valve Mfr & Distr
N.A.I.C.S.: 332912

Walvoil Fluid Power Korea Llc. (1)
80-15 Oseongsandan 1-ro, Oseong-myeon, Pyeongtaek, 17818, Gyeonggi, Korea (South)
Tel.: (82) 316826030
Web Site: https://www.walvoil.co.kr
Hydraulic Directional Control Valve Mfr & Distr
N.A.I.C.S.: 332912

Walvoil Fluid Power Pvt. Ltd. (1)
No 19 2nd Cross 2nd Main, KIADB Industrial Area Attibele Anekal Taluk, Bengaluru, 562107, India
Tel.: (91) 8041842900
Hydraulic Directional Control Valve Mfr & Distr
N.A.I.C.S.: 332912

Walvoil S.p.A. (1)
Via Adige 13/D, 42124, Reggio Emilia, Italy
Tel.: (39) 0522932411
Web Site: https://www.walvoil.com
Hydraulic Directional Control Valve Mfr & Distr
N.A.I.C.S.: 332912

INTERQUEST GROUP PLC

27 Bush Lane Cannon Green, London, EC4R 0AA, United Kingdom
Tel.: (44) 207 025 0100
Web Site: http://www.interquestgroup.com
Rev.: $183,442,545
Assets: $58,578,790
Liabilities: $28,434,053
Net Worth: $30,144,737
Earnings: $677,258
Emp.: 304
Fiscal Year-end: 12/31/17
Information Technology Recruitment Services
N.A.I.C.S.: 541612
Gary P. Ashworth *(Chm)*

Subsidiaries:

IQ ERP (1)
The Lenz Hornbeam Park Hookstone Rd, Harrogate, HG2 8RE, Yorkshire, United Kingdom
Tel.: (44) 1423874566
Web Site: http://www.itqerp.com
Sales Range: $10-24.9 Million
Emp.: 250
IT Recruitment Services
N.A.I.C.S.: 561311

IQ Technology (1)
The Lenz Hornbeam Park Hookstone Road, Harrogate, HG2 8RE, United Kingdom
Tel.: (44) 1423 878 905
Web Site: http://www.itqtech.com
Sales Range: $25-49.9 Million
Emp.: 25
IT Recruitment Services
N.A.I.C.S.: 561311

Intelect Recruitment Plc (1)
1 New York St, Manchester, M1 4HD, United Kingdom
Tel.: (44) 1612363776
Web Site: http://www.itqanalytics.com
Sales Range: $10-24.9 Million
Emp.: 26
Recruitment Consultancy Services
N.A.I.C.S.: 561311

InterQuest Group (UK) Limited (1)
6 2-7 St Cross Street, London, EC1N 8UA, United Kingdom
Tel.: (44) 2070250100
Web Site: http://www.interquestgroup.com
Sales Range: $10-24.9 Million
Emp.: 30
IT Recruitment Services
N.A.I.C.S.: 561311

Sand Resources Limited (1)
2-4 Heathervale House Vale Ave, Tunbridge Wells, TN1 1DJ, United Kingdom
Tel.: (44) 1892543434
Web Site: http://www.sand-uk.com
Sales Range: $25-49.9 Million
Emp.: 30
Public Sector Recruitment Services
N.A.I.C.S.: 561311

INTERRA ACQUISITION CORPORATION

5/F Manulife Place 348 Kwun Tong Road, Kowloon, China (Hong Kong) Ky
Web Site: https://www.interraacquisition.com
Year Founded: 2022
7801—(HKG)
Investment Management Service
N.A.I.C.S.: 523999

INTERRA COPPER CORP.

Suite 2501 550 Burrard Street, Vancouver, V6C 2B5, BC, Canada
Tel.: (604) 588-2110
Web Site: https://interracopper.com
Year Founded: 2018
IMIMF—(OTCQB)
Assets: $4,493,466
Liabilities: $30,336
Net Worth: $4,463,130
Earnings: ($266,658)
Fiscal Year-end: 12/31/22
Mineral Exploration Services
N.A.I.C.S.: 213115
T. Gregory Hawkins *(Chm)*

INTERRA RESOURCES LIMITED

1 Grange Road 05-04 Orchard Building, Singapore, 239693, Singapore
Tel.: (65) 67321711 SG
Web Site: https://www.interraresources.com
Year Founded: 1973
5GI—(CAT)
Rev.: $10,796,345
Assets: $41,205,386
Liabilities: $10,389,036
Net Worth: $30,816,350
Earnings: ($1,249,345)
Emp.: 500
Fiscal Year-end: 12/31/20
Petroleum Exploration & Production Services
N.A.I.C.S.: 211120
Edwin Soeryadjaya *(Chm)*

INTERRENT REAL ESTATE INVESTMENT TRUST

485 Bank Street Suite 207, Ottawa, K2P 1Z2, ON, Canada
Tel.: (613) 569-5699
Web Site: https://www.interrentreit.com
Year Founded: 2006
IIP.UN—(TSX)
Rev.: $145,341,366
Assets: $3,221,975,854
Liabilities: $1,328,855,907
Net Worth: $1,893,119,947
Earnings: $289,197,964
Emp.: 435
Fiscal Year-end: 12/31/21
Real Estate Investment Services
N.A.I.C.S.: 523999
Mike McGahan *(CEO)*

Subsidiaries:

InterRent No.1 Limited Partnership (1)
5755 SIR Walter Scott, Montreal, QC, Canada
Tel.: (514) 369-1989
Real Estate Investment Services
N.A.I.C.S.: 523999

INTERROLL HOLDING AG

InterRent Real Estate Investment Trust—(Continued)

INTERROLL HOLDING AG
Via Gorelle 3, 6592, Saint Antonino, Switzerland
Tel.: (41) 918502525   CH
Web Site: https://www.interroll.com
INRN—(SWX)
Rev: $600,921,424
Assets: $530,949,500
Liabilities: $177,630,184
Net Worth: $353,319,315
Earnings: $81,245,663
Emp.: 2,206
Fiscal Year-end: 12/31/20
Holding Company; Rollers, Drivers, Conveyors & Modules Mfr
N.A.I.C.S.: 551112
Jens Karolyi (Sr VP-Corp Mktg & People Dev)

Subsidiaries:

IBH ehf.   (1)
Vagnhofoa 21, 110, Reykjavik, Iceland
Tel.: (354) 5626858
Web Site: https://www.ibhehf.is
Motor Engine Mfr
N.A.I.C.S.: 333618

Interroll (Asia) Pte. Ltd   (1)
10 Pandan Crescent 02-04, Singapore, 128466, Singapore
Tel.: (65) 62666322
Sales Range: $25-49.9 Million
Emp.: 15
Industrial Supplies Whslr
N.A.I.C.S.: 423840

Interroll (Korea) Corporation   (1)
11F 178 Pangyoyeok-ro, Bundang-gu, Seongnam, Gyeonggi, Korea (South)
Tel.: (82) 317015778
Electrical Apparatus & Equipment Wiring Supplies
N.A.I.C.S.: 423610

Interroll (Schweiz) AG   (1)
Via Gorelle 3, PO Box 566, 6592, Saint Antonino, Switzerland   (100%)
Tel.: (41) 918502525
Web Site: https://www.interroll.com
Sales Range: $25-49.9 Million
Emp.: 10
Conveyor & Conveying Equipment Mfr
N.A.I.C.S.: 333922

Interroll (Thailand) Co. Ltd   (1)
700/1015 Moo 9 T Map Pong, 20160, Phan Thong, Chonburi, Thailand
Tel.: (66) 38316400
Sales Range: $25-49.9 Million
Emp.: 50
Electrical Appliance Television & Radio Set Whslr
N.A.I.C.S.: 423620
Grisoi Nakapong (Mng Dir)

Interroll Atlanta, LLC   (1)
159 Corporate Dr N, Hiram, GA 30141
Tel.: (770) 799-4210
Web Site: http://www.interroll.us
Conveyor & Module Mfr
N.A.I.C.S.: 333922

Interroll Australia Pty. Ltd.   (1)
70 Keon Parade, Thomastown, 3074, VIC, Australia
Tel.: (61) 394955800
Sales Range: $25-49.9 Million
Emp.: 25
Material Handling Equipment Mfr
N.A.I.C.S.: 333248
Pat Cieri (Mng Dir)

Interroll Automation GmbH   (1)
Dietmar-Hopp St 3, 74889, Sinsheim, Germany
Tel.: (49) 72619380
Sales Range: $50-74.9 Million
Emp.: 160
Conveyor & Conveying Equipment Mfr
N.A.I.C.S.: 333922
Steffen Flender (Mng Dir)

Interroll Automation Ltd.   (1)
Unit 1 Orion Way, Earlstrees Industrial Estate, Kettering, NN15 6NL, Northampton, United Kingdom
Tel.: (44) 1536200322
Web Site: http://www.interroll.com
Sales Range: $25-49.9 Million
Emp.: 20
Conveyor & Conveying Equipment Mfr
N.A.I.C.S.: 333922
Chris Middeton (Mng Dir)

Interroll CZ sro   (1)
Smetanovo nabrezi 12/2158, Breclav, 690 02, Brno, 690 02, Czech Republic   (100%)
Tel.: (420) 519330210
Sales Range: $25-49.9 Million
Emp.: 6
Conveyor & Conveying Equipment Mfr
N.A.I.C.S.: 333922
Fritz Ratschiller (Mng Dir)

Interroll Canada Ltd.   (1)
1201 Gorham Street, Newmarket, L3Y 8Y2, ON, Canada
Tel.: (905) 953-8510
Conveyor & Conveying Equipment Mfr
N.A.I.C.S.: 333922

Interroll Components Canada Ltd   (1)
8900 Keele Street, Unit 2 & 3, Concord, L4K 2N2, ON, Canada
Tel.: (905) 660-4426
Web Site: http://www.interroll.com
Sales Range: $25-49.9 Million
Emp.: 35
Motor & Generator Mfr
N.A.I.C.S.: 335312

Interroll Corporation   (1)
3000 Corporate Dr, Wilmington, NC 28405
Tel.: (910) 799-1100
Web Site: http://www.interroll.com
Sales Range: $50-74.9 Million
Holding Company; Regional Managing Office; Conveyor & Conveying Equipment Mfr
N.A.I.C.S.: 551112

Subsidiary (Domestic):

Interroll Dynamic Storage, Inc.   (2)
232 Duncan Cir, Hiram, GA 30141
Tel.: (770) 943-1541
Web Site: http://www.interroll.us
Sales Range: $25-49.9 Million
Emp.: 10
General Warehouse & Logistics Services
N.A.I.C.S.: 493110

Interroll Engineering West Inc.   (2)
1 Forge Rd, Canon City, CO 81212
Tel.: (719) 275-7471
Web Site: http://www.interroll.us
Sales Range: $10-24.9 Million
Emp.: 125
Conveyor & Other Material Handling Equipment & Components Mfr
N.A.I.C.S.: 333922

Interroll Manufacturing LLC   (2)
3000 Corporate Dr, Wilmington, NC 28405   (100%)
Tel.: (910) 799-1100
Web Site: http://www.interroll.us
Sales Range: $25-49.9 Million
Emp.: 50
Conveyor Components Mfr
N.A.I.C.S.: 333922

Interroll Engineering GmbH   (1)
Hoferhof 16, 42929, Wermelskirchen, Germany   (100%)
Tel.: (49) 2193230
Web Site: http://www.interroll.com
Sales Range: $50-74.9 Million
Emp.: 200
Conveyor & Conveying Equipment Mfr
N.A.I.C.S.: 333922
Armin Lindholm (Mng Dir)

Interroll Engineering Ltd.   (1)
Brunel Road, Corby, NN17 4UX, Northants, United Kingdom
Tel.: (44) 1 536 20 03 22
Sales Range: $25-49.9 Million
Emp.: 25
Material Handling Equipment Mfr
N.A.I.C.S.: 333998
Chris Middleton (Mng Dir)

Interroll Espana S.A.   (1)
C/Artesans 10, 08290, Cerdanyola del Valles, Barcelona, Spain
Tel.: (34) 935912679
Web Site: http://www.interroll.es
Sales Range: $25-49.9 Million
Emp.: 10
Unit-Load Handling, Internal Logistics & Automation in Specific Target Markets; Food Processing, Airport Logistics & Postal Services
N.A.I.C.S.: 541614
Carlos Alvarez Garcia-Lujan (Mng Dir)

Interroll Fordertechnik GmbH   (1)
Hoferhof 16, 42929, Wermelskirchen, Germany
Tel.: (49) 2193230
Sales Range: $75-99.9 Million
Material Handling Equipment Distr
N.A.I.C.S.: 423830

Interroll GmbH   (1)
Hoferhof 16, Wermelskirchen, 42929, Germany   (100%)
Tel.: (49) 2193230
Sales Range: $50-74.9 Million
Emp.: 250
Conveyor & Conveying Equipment Mfr
N.A.I.C.S.: 333922
Armin Lindholm (Gen Mgr)

Interroll Holding GmbH   (1)
Lothforster Str 32-40, 41849, Wermelskirchen, Germany
Tel.: (49) 2432966640
Web Site: http://www.interroll.com
Sales Range: $50-74.9 Million
Emp.: 14
Investment Management Service
N.A.I.C.S.: 523999

Interroll Holding Management (Shanghai) Co., Ltd.   (1)
Room 902 Building A SOHO Zhongshan Plaza No 1055 West Zhongshan Road, Shanghai, 200051, China
Tel.: (86) 2161369183
Conveyor & Module Mfr
N.A.I.C.S.: 333922

Interroll Italia S.r.l   (1)
Via Italo Calvino 7, 20017, Rho, MI, Italy
Tel.: (39) 0293560442
Web Site: http://www.interroll.it
Conveyor & Module Mfr
N.A.I.C.S.: 333922

Interroll Japan Co. Ltd   (1)
Nisso 13 Building 5F 2-5-1, Shin-Yokohama Kohoku-ku, Yokohama, 222-0033, Kanagawa, Japan   (100%)
Tel.: (81) 456205333
Web Site: http://www.interroll.com
Sales Range: $25-49.9 Million
Emp.: 5
Ball & Roller Bearing Mfr
N.A.I.C.S.: 333922

Interroll Joki AS   (1)
Hammerholmen 2-6, DK 2650, Hvidovre, Denmark   (100%)
Tel.: (45) 36883344
Web Site: https://www.interroll.com
Sales Range: $25-49.9 Million
Emp.: 45
Engine Equipment Mfr
N.A.I.C.S.: 333618

Interroll Logistica Ltda.   (1)
Av Vicenzo Granghelli 856, Jaguariuna, 13820-000, Sao Paulo, Brazil
Tel.: (55) 193 114 6666
Web Site: http://www.interroll.com.br
Conveyor & Module Mfr
N.A.I.C.S.: 333922
Marcos Gaio (Mng Dir)

Interroll Lojistik Sistemleri Tic. Ltd.   (1)
Barbaros Mah Kayacan Sok Evren cad No 10B 34746, Atasehir, 34746, Istanbul, Turkiye
Tel.: (90) 2166884280
Emp.: 8
Material Handling Equipment Mfr
N.A.I.C.S.: 333248

Interroll Ltd.   (1)
Unit 1A Orion Way, Earlstrees Industrial Estate, Kettering, NN15 6NL, Northamptonshire, United Kingdom
Tel.: (44) 1536312770
Web Site: https://www.interroll.com
Sales Range: $25-49.9 Million
Emp.: 20
Non-Durable Goods Whslr
N.A.I.C.S.: 424990
Chris Middleton (Mng Dir)

Interroll Management AG   (1)
Zona Industriale, PO Box 566, 6592, Saint Antonino, Switzerland   (100%)
Tel.: (41) 918502560
Web Site: http://www.interroll.com
Sales Range: $25-49.9 Million
Emp.: 70
Conveyor & Conveying Equipment Mfr
N.A.I.C.S.: 333922

Interroll Mexico S. de R.L. de C.V.   (1)
Guillermo Gonzalez Camarena 1600 Interior 3D, Col Santa Fe Del Alvaro Obregon, 01210, Mexico, Edo Mex, Mexico
Tel.: (52) 555 086 3159
Web Site: http://www.interroll.com.mx
Conveyor & Module Mfr
N.A.I.C.S.: 333922
Liczy Pallares (Dir Gen)

Interroll Nordic AS   (1)
Hammerholmen 2-6, DK 2650, Hvidovre, Denmark   (100%)
Tel.: (45) 36883333
Web Site: http://www.interroll.dk
Sales Range: $25-49.9 Million
Emp.: 10
Industrial Supplies Whslr
N.A.I.C.S.: 423840
Erik Kaiser (Mng Dir)

Interroll Polska Sp.z.o.o.   (1)
ul Plochocinska 85, 03-044, Warsaw, Poland   (100%)
Tel.: (48) 227417410
Sales Range: $25-49.9 Million
Emp.: 8
Fur-Bearing Animal & Rabbit Production
N.A.I.C.S.: 112930

Interroll SA
Via Industrie 4, PO Box 566, 6592, Saint Antonino, Switzerland   (100%)
Tel.: (41) 918502560
Sales Range: $25-49.9 Million
Emp.: 60
Conveyor & Conveying Equipment Mfr
N.A.I.C.S.: 333922
Paul Zumbuhl (CEO)

Interroll SA (Proprietary) Ltd.   (1)
1600 Spartan Ext 2, PO Box 327, Isando, 1619, South Africa
Tel.: (27) 112819900
Web Site: http://www.interroll.com
Sales Range: $25-49.9 Million
Emp.: 18
Ball & Roller Bearing Mfr
N.A.I.C.S.: 332991
Hilton Campbell (Mng Dir)

Interroll SAS   (1)
Z I De Kerannou, BP 34, 29250, Saint-Pol-de-Leon, France
Tel.: (33) 298244100
Sales Range: $25-49.9 Million
Emp.: 2
Material Handling Equipment Repair & Maintenance Services
N.A.I.C.S.: 811310
Gilles Calvez (Mng Dir)

Interroll Shenzhen Co., Ltd.   (1)
Block 3-4 HengLing South Road Hengling Industrial Estate, Jinsha Community, Shenzhen, 518117, Guangdong, China
Tel.: (86) 75528224758
Conveyor & Module Mfr
N.A.I.C.S.: 333922
M. K. Lo (Mng Dir)

Interroll Suzhou Co. Ltd.   (1)
Block B C Ecological Science Hub No 1 Ke Zhi Road, Suzhou Industrial Park, Suzhou, 215021, Jiangsu, China   (100%)
Tel.: (86) 51262560383
Web Site: http://www.interroll.com
Sales Range: $50-74.9 Million
Emp.: 120
Plastics Product Mfr
N.A.I.C.S.: 326199

Interroll Trommelmotoren GmbH   (1)
Interroll Center of Excellence for Drum Motors Opelstrasse 3, Baal, 41836, Huckelhoven, Germany   (100%)

AND PRIVATE COMPANIES

Tel.: (49) 243344610
Sales Range: $50-74.9 Million
Emp.: 150
Motor & Generator Mfr
N.A.I.C.S.: 335312

INTERROS HOLDING COMPANY
ul Bolshaya Yakimanka 9, 119180, Moscow, Russia
Tel.: (7) 4957856363　　　　RU
Web Site: http://www.interros.ru
Year Founded: 1990
Emp.: 300
Holding Company; Metallurgy & Mining, Financial Sector, Food & Agriculture, Mass Media, Real Estate & Tourism
N.A.I.C.S.: 551112
Ivan Linkov (Dir-Info & External Comm Dept)

Subsidiaries:

ProfMedia Holding Company　　(1)
17/4 Ostozhenka Str, 119034, Moscow, Russia
Tel.: (7) 495 787 5335
Web Site: http://www.profmedia.ru
Sales Range: $125-149.9 Million
Emp.: 200
Media Holding Company; Radio Stations, Television Networks, Movie Theaters & Magazine Publishing
N.A.I.C.S.: 551112
Olga Paskina (Pres)

Holding (Domestic):

Rambler-Afisha　　(2)
Warsaw Highway 9 BC Danilovskaya Manufacture Series Soldatenkova, Moscow, 115280, Russia
Tel.: (7) 495 785 1700
Web Site: http://www.rambler.ru
Sales Range: $100-124.9 Million
Russian Language Internet Media & Services
N.A.I.C.S.: 513199
Alexander Mamut (Mng Dir)

INTERSERV INTERNATIONAL INC.
4F No 8 Alley 30 Lane 358 Ruiguang Rd, Nei-Hu Dist, Taipei, 11492, Taiwan
Tel.: (886) 287977000
Web Site: http://www.interserv.com.tw
Year Founded: 1989
6169—(TPE)
Rev.: $130,100
Assets: $13,983,304
Liabilities: $3,451,052
Net Worth: $10,532,252
Earnings: $178,501
Fiscal Year-end: 12/31/22
Software Development Services
N.A.I.C.S.: 541511
Su-Yung Hsiang (CEO)

INTERSERVE PLC
Interserve House Ruscombe Park, Reading, RG10 9JU, United Kingdom
Tel.: (44) 1189320123　　　　UK
Web Site: http://www.interserve.com
Year Founded: 1947
ISVJF—(OTCIQ)
Sales Range: Less than $1 Million
Construction, Engineering & Building Maintenance Services
N.A.I.C.S.: 237990
Ian Hayes (Mng Dir-RMD Kwikform)

Subsidiaries:

Adyard Abu Dhabi LLC　　(1)
Plot 10 MW2, PO Box 7604, Mussafah, Abu Dhabi, United Arab Emirates
Tel.: (971) 25547722
Web Site: http://www.adyardabudhabi.com
Drilling Services
N.A.I.C.S.: 213111
Dean Stothard (Gen Mgr)

First Security (Guards) Ltd.　　(1)
First Security 58-59 Myddelton Square, London, EC1R 1TB, United Kingdom
Tel.: (44) 2078375424
Web Site: http://www.first-security.co.uk
Security Consulting Services
N.A.I.C.S.: 561621

Interserve (Defence) Ltd.　　(1)
Capital Tower 91 Waterloo Rd, London, SE1 8RT, United Kingdom　　(100%)
Tel.: (44) 2079022000
Sales Range: $25-49.9 Million
Emp.: 150
Management Services
N.A.I.C.S.: 561110

Interserve Engineering Services Ltd.　　(1)
Intersection House 110 120 Birmingham Rd, West Bromwich, B70 6RP, West Midlands, United Kingdom
Tel.: (44) 1215005000
Construction Engineering Services
N.A.I.C.S.: 541330
Jim Marner (Dir-North East & Newcastle)

Interserve Environmental Services Ltd.　　(1)
Capital Tower 91 Waterloo Road, London, SE1 8RT, United Kingdom
Tel.: (44) 2079022000
Web Site: http://www.interserve.com
Real Estate Manangement Services
N.A.I.C.S.: 531390

Interserve Group Holdings Ltd.　　(1)
Interserve House Ruscombe Park Twyford, Reading, RG10 9JU, Berkshire, United Kingdom
Tel.: (44) 1189320123
Web Site: http://www.interserve.com
Emp.: 90
Financial Investment Management Services
N.A.I.C.S.: 523999

Interserve Healthcare Ltd.　　(1)
Grosvenor House Central Park, Telford, TF2 9TW, Shropshire, United Kingdom
Tel.: (44) 1952278291
Web Site: http://www.interservehealthcare.com
Emp.: 68,000
Women Healthcare Services
N.A.I.C.S.: 621610
Dawn Hamilton (Mgr-Contracts & Bids)

Interserve Industrial Services Ltd　　(1)
Riverside House Littlebrook Complex, Littlebrook Manorway, Dartford, DA1 5PZ, Kent, United Kingdom　　(100%)
Tel.: (44) 1322226000
Web Site: http://www.interservices.co.uk
Sales Range: $10-24.9 Million
Emp.: 50
Provider of Management Services
N.A.I.C.S.: 561110

Interserve Investments plc　　(1)
Interserve House, Ruscombe Pk Twyford, Reading, RG10 9JU, Berkshire, United Kingdom　　(100%)
Tel.: (44) 213318629
Sales Range: $25-49.9 Million
Emp.: 100
Architects
N.A.I.C.S.: 541310

Interserve PFI 2005 Ltd.　　(1)
Interserve House Ruscombe Park, Reading, RG10 9JU, Berkshire, United Kingdom
Tel.: (44) 118 932 0123
Financial Management Services
N.A.I.C.S.: 523999

Interserve Project Services Ltd.　　(1)
395 George Rd, Erdington, B23 7RZ, Birmingham, United Kingdom　　(100%)
Tel.: (44) 213444888
Provider of Management Services
N.A.I.C.S.: 561110

Interserve Security (Fire & Electronics) Ltd.　　(1)
Unit A Melville Court Spilsby Road, Romford, RM3 8SB, Essex, United Kingdom
Tel.: (44) 1708377000

Sales Range: $25-49.9 Million
Emp.: 2
Security System Installation Services
N.A.I.C.S.: 561621

Interserve Security Ltd.　　(1)
Alderstone Road Stadium House Business Centre, Livingston, EH54 7DN, United Kingdom
Tel.: (44) 20 3376 4805
Web Site: http://www.interservesecurity.co.uk
Security System Installation Services
N.A.I.C.S.: 561621

Interserve Specialist Services (Holdings) Ltd.　　(1)
Capital Tower 91 Waterloo Road, London, SE1 8RT, United Kingdom
Tel.: (44) 2079022000
Web Site: http://www.interserve.com
Sales Range: $25-49.9 Million
Emp.: 200
Security System Installation Services
N.A.I.C.S.: 561621

Interserve Technical Services Ltd.　　(1)
Intersection House 110 Birmingham Road, West Bromwich, B70 6RX, West Midlands, United Kingdom
Tel.: (44) 1215005000
Web Site: http://www.interserve.com
Security System Installation Services
N.A.I.C.S.: 561621

Landmarc Support Services Ltd.　　(1)
Building 150 Westdown Camp Tilshead, Salisbury, SP3 4RS, Wiltshire, United Kingdom
Tel.: (44) 8001695110
Web Site: http://www.landmarcsolutions.com
Sales Range: $300-349.9 Million
Emp.: 130
Facility Management Services
N.A.I.C.S.: 561990

Phoenix Fire Services Ltd.　　(1)
5 Moss Avenue Kingsway, Rochdale, OL16 4AA, United Kingdom
Tel.: (44) 7967309008
Web Site: http://www.phoenixfirepro.co.uk
Fire Protection Services
N.A.I.C.S.: 922160
Joanne Hughes (Sec)

RMD Kwikform (South Africa) (Proprietary) Ltd.　　(1)
52 Jakaranda Street Hennopspark, Centurion, Pretoria, 0046, South Africa
Tel.: (27) 12 681 0360
Sales Range: $25-49.9 Million
Emp.: 40
Construction Engineering Services
N.A.I.C.S.: 541330
Johan Smit (Mng Dir)

RMD Kwikform Al Maha Qatar WLL　　(1)
Building No 146 Zone No 40 Al Muntazah Street, PO Box 405, Doha, Qatar
Tel.: (974) 44653034
Formwork & Ground Shoring Services
N.A.I.C.S.: 238190

RMD Kwikform Almoayed Bahrain WLL　　(1)
Flat 34 Building 5 Road 3001 Block 330 Bu Qhazal, PO Box 21475, Manama, Bahrain
Tel.: (973) 17382724
Formwork & Ground Shoring Services
N.A.I.C.S.: 238190

RMD Kwikform Hong Kong Limited.　　(1)
Room 08 17th Floor Silvercord Tower 2, Tsim Sha Tsui, Kowloon, China (Hong Kong)
Tel.: (852) 24154882
Web Site: http://www.rmdhongkong.com
Construction Engineering Services
N.A.I.C.S.: 541330

RMD Kwikform Iberica SA　　(1)
Paseo del Club Deportivo 1 Urbanizacion La Finca, Edif 3 10 Izda, 28223, Pozuelo de Alarcon, Spain
Tel.: (34) 915556104
Web Site: http://www.rmdkwikform.com
Construction Engineering Services

INTERSERVE PLC

N.A.I.C.S.: 541330

RMD Kwikform India Private Ltd.　　(1)
No 407-A/6 Ansal Chamber-II Bhikaji Cama Place, New Delhi, 110066, India
Tel.: (91) 1145027559
Web Site: http://www.rmdkwikform.com
Formwork & Ground Shoring Services
N.A.I.C.S.: 238190
Bellphine Alexander (Sls Dir)

RMD Kwikform Ireland Ltd.　　(1)
Ballyboggan Road, Finglas, Dublin, D11 AKW1, Ireland
Tel.: (353) 1 830 2500
Web Site: http://www.rmdkwikform.com
Sales Range: $25-49.9 Million
Emp.: 10
Construction Engineering Services
N.A.I.C.S.: 237990

RMD Kwikform Ltd　　(1)
Brickyard Road, Walsall, Aldridge, WS9 8BW, Westmidlands, United Kingdom　　(100%)
Tel.: (44) 1922743743
Web Site: http://www.rmdkwikform.com
Sales Range: $25-49.9 Million
Emp.: 100
Contract Builders
N.A.I.C.S.: 236115

Subsidiary (Non-US):

Rapid Metal Developments (Australia) Pty Ltd.　　(2)
66 Bennet Avenue, PO Box 169, Melrose Park, 5039, SA, Australia
Tel.: (61) 881798200
Web Site: http://www.rmdaustralia.com.au
Sales Range: $10-24.9 Million
Emp.: 40
Construction Engineering Services
N.A.I.C.S.: 541330

RMD Kwikform Middle East Head LLC　　(1)
PO Box 5801, Sharjah, United Arab Emirates
Tel.: (971) 6 553 4173
Construction Engineering Services
N.A.I.C.S.: 541330

RMD Kwikform Middle East LLC　　(1)
PO Box 5801, Sharjah, United Arab Emirates
Tel.: (971) 65025888
Formwork & Ground Shoring Services
N.A.I.C.S.: 238190

RMD Kwikform Omen LLC　　(1)
PO Box 889, 100, Muscat, Oman
Tel.: (968) 2449 6037
Construction Engineering Services
N.A.I.C.S.: 541330
Allan Pemberton (Dir-Resident)

RMD Kwikform Philippines Inc.　　(1)
Units 2406 - 2409 Raffles Corporate Centre F Ortigas Jr Road, Ortigas Centre, Pasig, 1605, Philippines
Tel.: (63) 26967635
Web Site: http://www.rmdkwikform.com
Construction Engineering Services
N.A.I.C.S.: 541330

RMD Kwikform Saudi Arabia LLC　　(1)
Al-Bandariyah Center Office No 611 Unit 5 Building No 3194, Al Khobar, 34424-8555, Saudi Arabia
Tel.: (966) 3 882 5444
Construction Engineering Services
N.A.I.C.S.: 237990

RMD New Zealand Pty Ltd　　(1)
101-105 Station Road, PO Box 22316, Otahuhu, Auckland, 1062, New Zealand
Tel.: (64) 92590353
Web Site: http://www.rmdnewzealand.co.nz
Sales Range: $25-49.9 Million
Emp.: 22
Construction Engineering Services
N.A.I.C.S.: 541330

Rapid Metal Developments NZ Ltd.　　(1)
101-105 Station Road, Otahuhu, Auckland, 1062, New Zealand
Tel.: (64) 92590353

INTERSERVE PLC

Interserve Plc—(Continued)

Web Site: http://www.rmdnewzealand.co.nz
Formwork & Ground Shoring Services
N.A.I.C.S.: 238190

The Cheshire & Greater Manchester Community Rehabilitation Company Ltd. (1)
12 Minshull Street, Manchester, M1 3FR, United Kingdom
Tel.: (44) 1442296011
Web Site: http://www.cgmcrc.co.uk
Community Rehabilitation Services
N.A.I.C.S.: 624310
Emma McMahon *(Mgr-Case)*

The Hampshire & Isle of Wight Rehabilitation Company Ltd. (1)
3rd Floor Civic Offices Civic Way, Fareham, PO16 7AZ, Hampshire, United Kingdom
Tel.: (44) 1442295010
Web Site: http://www.hiowcrc.co.uk
Community Rehabilitation Services
N.A.I.C.S.: 624310
Joanna Ranson *(Mgr-Case)*

The Humberside Lincolnshire & North Yorkshire Community Rehabilitation Company Ltd. (1)
West Offices Station Rise, York, YO1 6GA, United Kingdom
Tel.: (44) 1442295400
Web Site: http://www.hlnycrc.co.uk
Community Rehabilitation Services
N.A.I.C.S.: 624310

The Indium Division Company S.L. (1)
Paseo Del Club Deportivo la Finca Ed 3 1 Piso 1, Pozuelo De Alarcon, Madrid, 28223, Spain
Tel.: (34) 915556104
Construction Engineering Services
N.A.I.C.S.: 237990

The Merseyside Community Rehabilitation Company Ltd. (1)
2nd Floor Cunard Building Water Street, Liverpool, L3 1QX, United Kingdom
Tel.: (44) 1513173120
Web Site: http://www.merseysidecrc.co.uk
Community Rehabilitation Services
N.A.I.C.S.: 624310

The West Yorkshire Community Rehabilitation Company Ltd. (1)
1 Burgage Square Merchant Gate Back Lane, Wakefield, WF1 2TS, United Kingdom
Tel.: (44) 1442295015
Web Site: http://www.westyorkshirecrc.co.uk
Community Rehabilitation Services
N.A.I.C.S.: 624310

Translimp Co (1)
C/Juan Ignacio Luca de Tena 8-1 planta, 28027, Madrid, Spain
Tel.: (34) 911712700
Web Site: http://www.translimp-cs.com
Auxiliary Services
N.A.I.C.S.: 541990

Triangle Training Ltd. (1)
6 Priory Close, Tavistock, Devon, PL19 9DH, United Kingdom
Tel.: (44) 1822612222
Web Site: http://www.triangletrainingukltd.co.uk
First Aid Equipment Distr
N.A.I.C.S.: 423450

INTERSERVIS A.D.

Zeleznicka 17, Futog, Serbia
Tel.: (381) 21848878
Year Founded: 1954
INTS—(BEL)
Rev.: $196,363
Assets: $4,191,072
Liabilities: $406,610
Net Worth: $3,784,462
Earnings: $18,095
Emp.: 3
Fiscal Year-end: 12/31/23
Motor Vehicle Parts & Accessory Retailer
N.A.I.C.S.: 441330

Nikola Bozovic *(Exec Dir)*

INTERSHOP COMMUNICATIONS AG

Steinweg 10, 07743, Jena, Germany
Tel.: (49) 3641500
Web Site: https://www.intershop.com
Year Founded: 1992
ISHA—(DEU)
Rev.: $44,216,640
Assets: $48,638,304
Liabilities: $27,266,928
Net Worth: $21,371,376
Earnings: $982,592
Emp.: 288
Fiscal Year-end: 12/31/21
E-Commerce Software Mfr
N.A.I.C.S.: 541512
Christian Oecking *(Chm-Supervisory Bd)*

Subsidiaries:

Intershop Communications AB (1)
PO Box 19506, Stockholm, Sweden (100%)
Tel.: (46) 8307792
Computer & Software Stores
N.A.I.C.S.: 449210

Intershop Communications AG (1)
Joop Geesinkweg 901-999, 1096 AZ, Amsterdam, Netherlands
Tel.: (31) 205617760
Communication Software Development Services
N.A.I.C.S.: 541512

Intershop Communications Asia Limited (1)
Level 19 Two International Finance Centre 8 Finance Street, Central, China (Hong Kong)
Tel.: (852) 1300868197
Communication Software Development Services
N.A.I.C.S.: 541512

Intershop Communications Australia Pty Limited (1)
S 17 L 12 100 Walker St, Sydney, NSW, Australia (100%)
Tel.: (61) 294604667
Computer Related Services
N.A.I.C.S.: 541519

Intershop Communications Ltd. (1)
Wigley Manor Romsey Road, Ower, Romsey, SO51 6AF, Hampshire, United Kingdom
Tel.: (44) 7501383538
Communication Software Development Services
N.A.I.C.S.: 541512

Intershop Communications SARL (1)
18 rue Pasquier, 75008, Paris, France
Tel.: (33) 178414154
Communication Software Development Services
N.A.I.C.S.: 541512

Intershop Communications Singapore Pte Ltd. (1)
10 Hoe Chiang Road, Singapore, Singapore (100%)
Tel.: (65) 63346743
Custom Computer Programming Services
N.A.I.C.S.: 541511

Intershop Communications, Inc. (1)
Tel.: (415) 844-1500
Web Site: http://www.intershop.com
E-Commerce Software Mfr
N.A.I.C.S.: 541512

Sparque B.V. (1)
Leidseveer 2-10, 3511 SB, Utrecht, Netherlands
Tel.: (31) 853019171
Web Site: https://sparque.ai
Information & Technology Services
N.A.I.C.S.: 519290

The Bakery Gmbh (1)
Ann-Luisa Weimer Genthiner Strasse 11, 10785, Berlin, Germany
Tel.: (49) 3028885880

Web Site: https://thebakery.de
Sales Range: $25-49.9 Million
Emp.: 20
Business Software Development Services
N.A.I.C.S.: 541511

INTERSNACK GROUP GMBH & CO. KG

Peter-Mueller-Strasse 3, 40468, Dusseldorf, Germany
Tel.: (49) 211710650
Web Site: http://www.intersnack.com
Sales Range: $1-4.9 Billion
Emp.: 6,000
Holding Company Snack Foods Mfr
N.A.I.C.S.: 551112
Jeff Swan *(Mng Dir-Largo Foods)*

Subsidiaries:

Estrella AB (1)
Angereds Storasvag 71, 424 80, Angered, Sweden
Tel.: (46) 313323000
Web Site: http://www.estrella.se
Food Products Mfr
N.A.I.C.S.: 311999
Sofi Randen *(Mktg Dir)*

Estrella Oy (1)
Perintotie 2C, 01510, Vantaa, Finland
Tel.: (358) 207893680
Web Site: http://www.estrella.fi
Confectionery Food Product Retailer
N.A.I.C.S.: 424450
Pekka Yli-Piipari *(Sls Dir)*

Felix GmbH & Co. KG (1)
Willhoop 3, 22453, Hamburg, Germany
Tel.: (49) 4025329734
Web Site: http://www.felix-hamburg.com
Management Consulting Services
N.A.I.C.S.: 541611

Grefusa, S.L. (1)
Av Llibertat d Ensenyanca 20, Alzira, 46600, Valencia, Spain
Tel.: (34) 962459022
Web Site: http://www.grefusa.com
Food Products Mfr
N.A.I.C.S.: 311999
Rafael Escriba Esteve *(Mgr-Dev)*

Intersnack Adria d.o.o. (1)
Pepe Bukaca 11, Hercegovac, 43284, Bjelovar, Croatia
Tel.: (385) 13333840
Food Products Mfr
N.A.I.C.S.: 311999
Dino Bijac *(Dir-Mktg & R&D)*

Intersnack Bulgaria EOOD (1)
48 Sitnyakovo blv Serdika offices, 1505, Sofia, Bulgaria
Tel.: (359) 29486969
Food Products Distr
N.A.I.C.S.: 424450

Intersnack Cashew Company Pte. (1)
24 Raffles Place Clifford Centre 16-03A, Singapore, 048621, Singapore
Tel.: (65) 63230741
Food Products Mfr
N.A.I.C.S.: 311999
Abel Santos Saez *(COO)*

Intersnack France S.A.S. (1)
Vic sur Aisne, PO Box 1, Montigny Lengrain, 02290, Picardie, France
Tel.: (33) 323554433
Web Site: http://www.intersnack.fr
Food Products Distr
N.A.I.C.S.: 424450
Arnaud Cordelle *(Pres)*

Intersnack Knabber-Geback GmbH & Co. KG (1)
Erna-Scheffler-Strasse 3, 51103, Cologne, Germany
Tel.: (49) 221 4894 0
Web Site: http://www.intersnack.de
Sweet & Salted Snack Food Mfr
N.A.I.C.S.: 311919
Roland Stroese *(Mng Dir)*

Intersnack Magyarorszag Kft. (1)
Aliz u 2, 1117, Budapest, Hungary
Tel.: (36) 6 1 204 5945

INTERNATIONAL PUBLIC

Web Site: http://www.intersnack.hu
Sales Range: $25-49.9 Million
Emp.: 270
Snacks Mfr & Whslr
N.A.I.C.S.: 311919

Intersnack Nederland BV (1)
Havenstraat 62, 7005 AG, Doetinchem, Netherlands
Tel.: (31) 314 370 200
Web Site: http://www.intersnack.nl
Sales Range: $25-49.9 Million
Emp.: 200
Savoury Snacks & Nuts Mfr
N.A.I.C.S.: 311919
Arajan Lammers *(Mng Dir-Ops)*

Intersnack Poland Sp. z o.o. (1)
Niedzwiedz 64, Slomniki, 32 090, Krakow, Poland
Tel.: (48) 12 640 40 00
Web Site: http://www.intersnack.pl
Emp.: 500
Snack Foods Mfr & Whslr
N.A.I.C.S.: 311919

Intersnack Romania S.R.L. (1)
23C Calea Vitan Street 6th floor district 3, 031281, Bucharest, Romania
Tel.: (40) 372734800
Food Products Distr
N.A.I.C.S.: 424450

Intersnack Slovensko, a.s. (1)
Nozdrkovce 1798, 911 04, Trencin, Slovakia
Tel.: (421) 32 652 11 56
Web Site: http://www.slovakiachips.sk
Snack Foods Mfr & Distr
N.A.I.C.S.: 311919

Intersnack Switzerland Ltd. (1)
Route du Mont Carmel 2, 1762, Givisiez, Switzerland
Tel.: (41) 263475080
Web Site: http://www.intersnack.ch
Food Products Distr
N.A.I.C.S.: 424450
Werner Brunner *(Mng Dir)*

Intersnack Ukraine Ltd. (1)
Prospectus M Bazhana 1-M office 22, Kiev, 02068, Ukraine
Tel.: (380) 445319455
Food Products Distr
N.A.I.C.S.: 424450

Intersnack d.o.o. (1)
Brnciceva ulica 29, 1000, Ljubljana, Slovenia
Tel.: (386) 15309260
Web Site: http://www.intersnack.si
Food Products Distr
N.A.I.C.S.: 424450

Intersnack, a.s. (1)
Choustnik 164, 39118, Choustnik, Czech Republic
Tel.: (420) 381 962 149
Web Site: http://www.intersnack.cz
Snack Food Mfr
N.A.I.C.S.: 311919

JSC Estrella Baltics (1)
Kestucio str 59, LT-08124, Vilnius, Lithuania
Tel.: (370) 66516179
Web Site: http://www.estrella.lt
Confectionery Food Product Retailer
N.A.I.C.S.: 424450
Domantas Grigonis *(Mgr-Supply Chain & Engr-R&D)*

KP Snacks Ltd. (1)
Hayes Park Hayes End Road, Hayes, UB4 8EE, Middlesex, United Kingdom
Tel.: (44) 20 8234 5000
Web Site: http://www.kpnuts.com
Sales Range: $450-499.9 Million
Emp.: 1,500
Snack Food Mfr
N.A.I.C.S.: 311919
Nick Bunker *(CEO)*

Kelly Gesellschaft m.b.H (1)
Hermann-Gebauer-Strasse 1, A 1220, Vienna, Austria
Tel.: (43) 5 70 789 0
Web Site: http://www.kelly.at
Sales Range: $125-149.9 Million
Emp.: 323
Snack Foods Mfr & Whslr
N.A.I.C.S.: 311919

AND PRIVATE COMPANIES

Maarud AS (1)
Innspurten 1A, 0663, Oslo, Norway
Tel.: (47) 62968200
Web Site: http://www.maarud.no
Food Products Distr
N.A.I.C.S.: 424450
Jill Hendnes Ovesen *(Acct Mgr)*

Menken Orlando B.V. (1)
Kerketuinenweg 35, 2544 CV, Hague, Netherlands
Tel.: (31) 703082222
Web Site: http://www.menkenorlando.nl
Food Product Retailer
N.A.I.C.S.: 424450
Erik Rotee *(Mktg Mgr)*

Pittjes Vertriebs GmbH (1)
Binnerheide 28, 58239, Schwerte, Germany
Tel.: (49) 23044720
Web Site: http://www.pittjes.de
Roasted Nut & Peanut Mfr
N.A.I.C.S.: 311911

Truller Knabber-Geback GmbH (1)
Erna-Scheffler-Str 3, 51103, Cologne, Germany
Tel.: (49) 22148940
Food Products Mfr
N.A.I.C.S.: 311999

ultje GmbH (1)
Binnerheide 28, 58239, Schwerte, Germany
Tel.: (49) 2304 472 900
Web Site: http://www.ueltje.de
Emp.: 200
Nuts & Nut Products Mfr & Whslr
N.A.I.C.S.: 311911
Guido Wolf *(Mng Dir)*

INTERSPACE CO., LTD.
Shinjuku NS Building 8F 2-4-1 Nishishinjuku, Shinjuku-ku, Tokyo, 163-0808, Japan
Tel.: (81) 353398680
Web Site:
https://www.interspace.ne.jp
Year Founded: 1999
2122—(TKS)
Rev.: $51,643,560
Assets: $78,656,460
Liabilities: $37,676,260
Net Worth: $40,980,200
Earnings: $4,147,650
Emp.: 364
Fiscal Year-end: 09/30/23
Internet Advertising Services
N.A.I.C.S.: 541810
Toshiaki Hirano *(Dir-Internet Ad Div)*

Subsidiaries:

Interspace (Thailand) Co., Ltd. (1)
591 UBC II Building 22nd Floor Room 2205 Sukhumvit Road, North Klongton Wattana, Bangkok, 10110, Thailand
Tel.: (66) 22584970
Web Site: https://interspace.co.th
Online Trading Services
N.A.I.C.S.: 541810

PT. Interspace Indonesia (1)
Menara Anugrah 11th floor Jl Dr Ide Anak Agung Gde Agung Lot 8 6-8 7, Kawasan Mega Kuningan, Jakarta, 12950, Selatan, Indonesia
Tel.: (62) 2157853978
Web Site: https://www.interspace.co.id
Online Trading Services
N.A.I.C.S.: 541830
Takashi Matsuura *(CEO)*

INTERSPED A.D.
Bose Milicevic 4, 24000, Subotica, Serbia
Tel.: (381) 24600900
Web Site: https://www.intersped.co.rs
Year Founded: 1988
Sales Range: Less than $1 Million
Emp.: 7
Goods Warehousing & Storage Services
N.A.I.C.S.: 493190

INTERSPED D.D.
Put zivota 14, 71000, Sarajevo, Bosnia & Herzegovina
Tel.: (387) 33 652 000
Web Site: http://www.intersped-logistics.ba
Year Founded: 1948
Rev.: $754,896
Assets: $2,123,005
Liabilities: $460,106
Net Worth: $1,662,898
Earnings: $97,392
Emp.: 38
Fiscal Year-end: 12/31/18
Logistics Consulting Servies
N.A.I.C.S.: 541614
Midhat Limo *(Gen Dir)*

INTERSPED D.D. TUZLA
ul Bosne Srebrene 56, 75000, Tuzla, Bosnia & Herzegovina
Tel.: (387) 35 366 333
Web Site: http://www.intersped-tz.com
ITRTRK1—(SARE)
Rev.: $650,308
Assets: $2,225,774
Liabilities: $354,527
Net Worth: $1,871,248
Earnings: $44,542
Emp.: 33
Fiscal Year-end: 12/31/20
Transportation Services
N.A.I.C.S.: 488999

INTERSPORT INTERNATIONAL CORPORATION
Wolflistrasse 2, 3006, Bern, Switzerland
Tel.: (41) 319307811
Web Site: http://www.intersport.com
Year Founded: 1968
Sales Range: $5-14.9 Billion
Emp.: 120
Sporting Goods Retailer
N.A.I.C.S.: 459110
Christoph Frechen *(Gen Mgr-Mktg)*

Subsidiaries:

Athlete's Foot Brands, LLC (1)
3200 Windy Hill Rd SE Ste 175 E, Atlanta, GA 30339
Tel.: (770) 514-4500
Web Site: http://www.theathletesfoot.com
Sales Range: $250-299.9 Million
Athletic Shoes & Apparel
N.A.I.C.S.: 458210

INTERSPORT AUSTRIA Ges. m.b.H. (1)
Flugplatzstrasse 10, 4600, Wels, Austria
Tel.: (43) 7242 233 0
Web Site: http://www.intersport.at
Sporting Goods Distr
N.A.I.C.S.: 423910

INTERSPORT BELGIUM CVBA (1)
Atominiumsquare 1, 1020, Brussels, Belgium
Tel.: (32) 24 74 01 70
Web Site: http://www.intersport.be
Emp.: 3
Sporting Goods Distr
N.A.I.C.S.: 423910
Jacky Rihouet *(Pres)*

INTERSPORT Belarus (1)
Petra Glebki str 5, 220121, Minsk, Belarus
Tel.: (375) 17 3621757
Web Site: http://www.intersport.by
Sporting Goods Distr
N.A.I.C.S.: 423910

INTERSPORT CCS, S.A. (1)
Pol Ind Cova Solera C/Roma 14 - 18, Rubi, 8191, Barcelona, Spain
Tel.: (34) 93 588 76 43
Web Site: http://www.intersport.es
Sporting Goods Distr
N.A.I.C.S.: 423910

INTERSPORT CR s.r.o. (1)
Na Strzi 1702/65, 140 62, Prague, Czech Republic
Tel.: (420) 284 683 695
Web Site: http://www.intersport.cz
Emp.: 30
Sporting Goods Distr
N.A.I.C.S.: 485999

INTERSPORT China (1)
6/F South Tower Huacheng International No 162 Wusi Road, Gulou District, Fuzhou, 350003, Fujian, China
Tel.: (86) 591 88600161
Web Site: http://www.intersport.cn
Sporting Goods Distr
N.A.I.C.S.: 423910

INTERSPORT Denmark AS (1)
Hvilehojvej 20, 5220, Odense, Denmark
Tel.: (45) 63 166100
Web Site: http://www.intersport.dk
Sporting Goods Whslr
N.A.I.C.S.: 423910
Mikael Kold *(CEO)*

INTERSPORT Deutschland eG (1)
Wannenackerstrasse 50, 74078, Heilbronn, Germany
Tel.: (49) 7131 2880
Web Site: http://www.intersport.de
Sporting Goods Distr
N.A.I.C.S.: 423910
Veronique Marie Dorsch *(Product Mgr)*

INTERSPORT Egypt (1)
86 El-Nile El Abyad St Lebanon Square, Mohandssien, Giza, Egypt
Tel.: (20) 33054671
Web Site: http://www.intersport.com.eg
Sporting Goods Distr
N.A.I.C.S.: 423910
Mohamed Omran *(Mgr-Procurement)*

INTERSPORT Holland (1)
Koninginneweg 1, 3871 JZ, Hoevelaken, Netherlands
Tel.: (31) 33 258 25 33
Web Site: http://www.intersport.nl
Sporting Goods Distr
N.A.I.C.S.: 423910

INTERSPORT Iceland (1)
Skogarlind 2, 0201, Kopavogur, Iceland
Tel.: (354) 5857220
Web Site: http://www.intersport.is
Sporting Goods Distr
N.A.I.C.S.: 423910

INTERSPORT Italia SpA (1)
Via del Tuscolano 17/2, 40128, Bologna, Italy
Tel.: (39) 051 6381151
Web Site: http://www.intersport.it
Sporting Goods Distr
N.A.I.C.S.: 423910
Antonella Martiniello *(Mgr-Mktg)*

INTERSPORT Morocco (1)
Boulevard de Londres, Casablanca, Morocco
Tel.: (212) 5224 75220
Web Site: http://www.intersport.com
Sporting Goods Distr
N.A.I.C.S.: 423910

INTERSPORT Norway/Gresvig AS (1)
Sagveien 25, PB 2009, 1814, Askim, Norway
Tel.: (47) 23 358500
Web Site: http://www.intersport.com
Sporting Goods Distr
N.A.I.C.S.: 423910

INTERSPORT Russia (1)
54a Mosfilmovskaya str, 119590, Moscow, Russia
Tel.: (7) 495 2320115
Web Site: http://www.intersport.ru
Sporting Goods Distr
N.A.I.C.S.: 423910
Dennis Kozin *(Dir-Mktg)*

INTERSPORT SK s.r.o. (1)
Roznavska 12, 821 04, Bratislava, Slovakia
Tel.: (421) 907 954 504
Web Site: http://www.intersport.sk
Emp.: 4
Sporting Goods Distr
N.A.I.C.S.: 423910

INTERSPORT Schweiz AG (1)
Obere Zollgasse 75, Postfach 1264, 3072, Ostermundigen, Switzerland
Tel.: (41) 31 930 71 11
Web Site: http://www.intersport.ch
Sporting Goods Distr
N.A.I.C.S.: 423910

INTERSPORT Sverige AB (1)
Krokslatts fabriker 34, BOX 114, 431 37, Molndal, Sweden
Tel.: (46) 31 727 87 00
Web Site: http://www.intersport.se
Sporting Goods Distr
N.A.I.C.S.: 423910

INTERSPORT Turkey (1)
Bayar Cad Gulbahar, Kozyatag, Istanbul, Turkiye
Tel.: (90) 216 665 10 00
Web Site: http://www.intersport.com.tr
Sporting Goods Distr
N.A.I.C.S.: 423910

INTERSPORT UK Ltd. (1)
Cranmore Place Cranmore Drive, Shirley, Solihull, B90 4RZ, West Midlands, United Kingdom
Tel.: (44) 121 7112200
Web Site: http://www.intersport.co.uk
Sporting Goods Distr
N.A.I.C.S.: 423910

Intersport Australia Limited (1)
121 Gardenvale Road, Gardenvale, Melbourne, 3185, VIC, Australia
Tel.: (61) 3 9596 2258
Web Site: http://www.intersport.com.au
Sporting Goods Distr
N.A.I.C.S.: 423910
Kevin O'Hanlon *(CEO)*

Intersport France SA (1)
2 Rue Victor Hugo Boite, Postale 500, 91164, Longjumeau, Cedex, France
Tel.: (33) 1 6910 8200
Web Site: http://www.intersport.fr
Sporting Goods Distr
N.A.I.C.S.: 423910
Marjorie Collet *(Mgr-Dev)*

Intersport North America Ltd. (1)
824 41st Ave NE, Calgary, T2E3R3, AB, Canada
Tel.: (403) 717-1485
Web Site: http://www.intersport.ca
Emp.: 100
Sporting Goods Distr
N.A.I.C.S.: 423910
Rob Fulthorpe *(Product Mgr-Hockey, Snowboard & Inline)*

Intersport Polska Sp Z O O (1)
Cholerzyn 382, 32-060, Liszki, Poland
Tel.: (48) 44 48 100
Web Site: http://www.intersport.pl
Sporting Goods Distr
N.A.I.C.S.: 423910

INTERSPORT PSC HOLDING AG
Obere Zollgasse 75, Ostermundigen, 3072, Switzerland
Tel.: (41) 31 9307111
Web Site: http://www.intersport.ch
Holding Company
N.A.I.C.S.: 551112
Patrick Bundeli *(Chm-Mgmt Bd & CEO)*

INTERSTAHL SERVICE GMBH & CO.KG
Am Jakob 2-4, PO Box 4064, Wetter, 58300, Germany
Tel.: (49) 233597960
Web Site: http://www.interstahl.com
Year Founded: 1990
Rev.: $12,138,720
Emp.: 6
Steel Distr
N.A.I.C.S.: 331513

Subsidiaries:

INTERSTAHL Sud GmbH (1)
Dieselstr 2, Donzdorf, 73072, Goppingen, Germany
Tel.: (49) 716294660
Steel Product Distr
N.A.I.C.S.: 423510
Markus Werner *(CEO)*

INTERSTANDARTS AD

INTERSTAHL Service GmbH & Co.KG—(Continued)

INTERSTANDARTS AD
38 Vasil Levski Blvd, 2700, Blagoevgrad, Bulgaria
Tel.: (359) 73884319
Web Site:
https://www.interstandarts.com
INS—(BUL)
Sales Range: Less than $1 Million
Measuring Equipment Mfr & Distr
N.A.I.C.S.: 334515
Ivo Ganovski *(Dir-IR)*

INTERSTATE BANK
15 Shukhov Str, Moscow, 115162, Russia
Tel.: (7) 4952283100
Web Site: http://www.isbnk.org
Year Founded: 1993
Sales Range: Less than $1 Million
Commercial Banking Services
N.A.I.C.S.: 522110
Aleksey Bakulin *(CFO)*

INTERTAINMENT AG
Brienner Strasse 12, 80333, Munich, Germany
Tel.: (49) 89216990
Web Site: http://www.intertainment.de
Year Founded: 1993
ITN—(DEU)
Rev.: $209,735
Assets: $342,200
Liabilities: $12,032,183
Net Worth: ($11,689,983)
Earnings: ($364,277)
Fiscal Year-end: 12/31/23
Commercial Sector Licensing Services
N.A.I.C.S.: 926150
Matthias Gaebler *(Chm-Supervisory Bd)*

INTERTAINMENT MEDIA INC.
1673 Richmond Street Unit 11, PMB #629, London, N6G 2N3, ON, Canada
Tel.: (519) 871-3998 **AB**
Web Site:
http://www.intertainmentmedia.com
Year Founded: 2006
Sales Range: $1-9.9 Million
Emp.: 16
Technology-Based Marketing & Advertising Related Services
N.A.I.C.S.: 541613

Subsidiaries:

Itibiti Systems Inc. (1)
30 W Beaver Creek Rd Units 111, Richmond Hill, L4B 3K1, ON, Canada
Tel.: (905) 763-3510
Web Site: http://www.itibitisystems.com
Sales Range: $25-49.9 Million
Emp.: 12
Packaged Software Publishers
N.A.I.C.S.: 513210

INTERTECH S.A.
Afroditis Rizountos Str 24, 16677, Elliniko, Greece
Tel.: (30) 2109692300
Web Site: https://www.intertech.gr
Year Founded: 1988
INTET—(ATH)
Sales Range: Less than $1 Million
Emp.: 40
Electrical Product Whslr
N.A.I.C.S.: 423610
Ioannis L. Chaloupis *(CEO)*

INTERTEK GROUP PLC
33 Cavendish Square, London, W1G 0PS, United Kingdom
Tel.: (44) 207 396 3400
Web Site: http://www.intertek.com

ITRK—(OTCIQ)
Rev.: $3,783,015,236
Assets: $4,412,182,684
Liabilities: $2,899,275,288
Net Worth: $1,512,907,396
Earnings: $416,412,724
Emp.: 44,063
Fiscal Year-end: 12/31/21
Technical, Scientific & Inspection Services
N.A.I.C.S.: 541380
David E. Reid *(Chm)*

Subsidiaries:

Acumen Security, LLC (1)
2400 Research Blvd Ste 395, Rockville, MD 20850
Tel.: (703) 375-9820
Web Site: https://www.acumensecurity.net
Design Consulting Services
N.A.I.C.S.: 541512

Alchemy Systems Training, Inc. (1)
5301 Riata Park Ct Bldg F, Austin, TX 78727
Tel.: (512) 637-5100
Web Site: https://www.alchemysystems.com
Food & Safety Training Services
N.A.I.C.S.: 611430

American Analytical Chemistry Laboratories (1)
711 Parkland Ct, Champaign, IL 61821
Tel.: (217) 352-6060
Web Site: http://www.intertek.com
Testing Laboratory
N.A.I.C.S.: 541380

Architectural Testing, Inc. (1)
130 Derry Ct, York, PA 17406
Tel.: (717) 764-7700
Web Site: http://www.archtest.com
Emp.: 303
Testing, Product Certification, Engineering, Forensic Investigation & Building Code Compliance Evaluation Services
N.A.I.C.S.: 541380

Caleb Brett - ITS Testing Services UK Ltd. (1)
Caleb Brett House 734 London Road, Grays, West Thurrock, RM20 3NL, Essex, United Kingdom (100%)
Tel.: (44) 1708680200
Web Site: http://www.intertekcb.com
Sales Range: $25-49.9 Million
Emp.: 100
Testing Laboratories
N.A.I.C.S.: 541380

Check Safety First Limited (1)
Check Safety First The Wine Warehouse The Back, Chepstow, NP16 5HH, Monmouthshire, United Kingdom
Tel.: (44) 1291629863
Web Site: https://www.checksafetyfirst.com
Safety Consulting Services
N.A.I.C.S.: 541690

Electronic Warfare Associates-Canada, Ltd. (1)
1223 Michael Street North 2nd Floor, Ottawa, K1J 7T2, ON, Canada
Tel.: (613) 230-6067
Web Site: http://www.ewa-canada.com
Information Assurance Services
N.A.I.C.S.: 611430
Mark Kuske *(Dir)*

Foreign Trade Standards - Intertek Testing Services Hong Kong Ltd. (1)
4F 1 No 46 Min Chuan E Rd, Section 2, Taipei, 104, Taiwan (100%)
Tel.: (886) 225428818
Web Site: http://www.itsfts.com
Testing Laboratories
N.A.I.C.S.: 541380

Genalysis Laboratory Services Pty Limited (1)
544 Bickley Road, Maddington, 6109, WA, Australia
Tel.: (61) 892518100
Web Site: http://www.genalysis.com.au
Sales Range: $75-99.9 Million
Emp.: 300
Testing Laboratory Operating Services

Global X-Ray & Testing Corp. (1)
112 E Service Rd, Morgan City, LA 70380
Tel.: (985) 631-2426
Web Site: http://www.globalxray.com
Non-Destructive Testing Services
N.A.I.C.S.: 541380
Chris Moreau *(Pres)*

Government Services UK (1)
Academy Place 1 to 9 Brook Street, Brook Street, Brentwood, CM14 5NQ, Essex, United Kingdom (100%)
Tel.: (44) 127 722 3400
Web Site: http://www.intertec.com
Testing Laboratories
N.A.I.C.S.: 541380

ITS Testing Holdings Canada Limited (1)
105 - 9000 Bill Fox Way, Burnaby, V5J 5J3, BC, Canada
Tel.: (604) 454-9011
Emp.: 60
Investment Management Service
N.A.I.C.S.: 523999

International Inspection Services Limited (1)
PO Box 6130, Sharjah, 6130, United Arab Emirates
Tel.: (971) 65281804
Web Site: http://www.int-inspec.com
Emp.: 700
Oil & Gas Industry Inspection Services
N.A.I.C.S.: 541990

Intertek (Schweiz) AG (1)
TechCenter Reinach Kagenstrasse 18, 4153, Reinach, Switzerland
Tel.: (41) 616864800
Web Site: https://www.intertek.ch
Laboratory Testing & Inspection Services
N.A.I.C.S.: 541380

Intertek ATI SRL (1)
266-268 Calea Rahovei Street Building 61 1st Floor Sector 5, Bucharest, Romania
Tel.: (40) 214048148
Laboratory Testing & Inspection Services
N.A.I.C.S.: 541380

Intertek Alchemy (1)
5301 Riata Park Ct Bldg F, Austin, TX 78727
Tel.: (512) 637-5100
Web Site: https://www.alchemysystems.com
Workplace Safety Training Services
N.A.I.C.S.: 611430
Erin Silver *(Exec VP-Client Svcs)*

Subsidiary (Non-US):

Catalyst Awareness Inc. (2)
43 Carolinian Lane, Cambridge, N1S 5B5, ON, Canada
Web Site: https://www.intertek.com
Health & Safety Awareness Services
N.A.I.C.S.: 813212

Reima Danmark ApS (2)
Aldersrogade 8, 2100, Copenhagen, Denmark
Tel.: (45) 33 12 19 19
Web Site: http://www.reima.com
Children Apparel Retailer
N.A.I.C.S.: 458110

Reima GmbH (2)
Block R St Annenufer 3, 20457, Hamburg, Germany
Tel.: (49) 406 056 3849
Web Site: http://www.reima.com
Children Apparel Distr
N.A.I.C.S.: 458110

Intertek Angola LDA (1)
Rua General Rocadas N 47, Ingombotas, Luanda, Angola
Tel.: (244) 916990941
Laboratory Testing & Inspection Services
N.A.I.C.S.: 541380

Intertek Aruba N.V. (1)
Lagoheight Straat 28a, San Nicolaas, Aruba
Tel.: (297) 5845434
Laboratory Testing & Inspection Services
N.A.I.C.S.: 541380

Intertek Asset Integrity Management, Inc. (1)

INTERNATIONAL PUBLIC

1450 Lake Robbins Dr Ste 620, The Woodlands, TX 77380
Tel.: (832) 593-0550
Laboratory Testing & Inspection Services
N.A.I.C.S.: 541380

Intertek Caleb Brett (Uruguay) S.A. (1)
Juncal 1305 3th Floor Of 301, 11000, Montevideo, Uruguay
Tel.: (598) 29167340
Laboratory Testing Services
N.A.I.C.S.: 541380

Intertek Caleb Brett Chile S.A. (1)
Coyancura 2283, Providencia, Santiago, Chile
Tel.: (56) 233046100
Laboratory Testing & Inspection Services
N.A.I.C.S.: 541380

Intertek Caleb Brett El Salvador S.A. de C.V. (1)
RASA Industrial Site, Acajutla Industrial Zone Acajutla, Sonsonate, El Salvador
Tel.: (503) 24864300
Laboratory Testing & Inspection Services
N.A.I.C.S.: 541380

Intertek Caleb Brett Panama, Inc. (1)
Zona Procesadora De Exportacion Albrook Edificio No 6, PO Box 832-0095, World Trade Center Ancon, Panama, Panama
Tel.: (507) 2329100
Laboratory Testing & Inspection Services
N.A.I.C.S.: 541380

Intertek Caleb Brett Venezuela C.A. (1)
Av Mohedano Centro Gerencial Mohedano Piso 4 Oficina 4-C, La Castellana, Chacao, Venezuela
Tel.: (58) 2127314224
Laboratory Testing & Inspection Services
N.A.I.C.S.: 541380

Intertek Certification AB (1)
Torshamnsgatan 43, Box 1103, 164 22, Kista, Sweden
Tel.: (46) 87500000
Laboratory Testing & Inspection Services
N.A.I.C.S.: 541380

Intertek Certification AS (1)
Leif Weldings Vei 8, N-3208, Sandefjord, Norway
Tel.: (47) 33420040
Laboratory Testing & Inspection Services
N.A.I.C.S.: 541380

Intertek Certification GmbH (1)
Marie-Bernays-Ring 19a, 41199, Monchengladbach, Germany
Tel.: (49) 2166600745
Testing Laboratory Services
N.A.I.C.S.: 541380

Intertek Certification Japan Limited (1)
4F Hulic Kamiyacho Building 4-3-13 Toranomon, Minato-ku, Tokyo, 105-0001, Japan
Tel.: (81) 336697408
Web Site: https://ba.intertek-jpn.com
Laboratory Testing & Inspection Services
N.A.I.C.S.: 541380

Intertek Consulting & Training (UK) Limited (1)
Exploration Drive Aberdeen Science and Energy Park, Bridge of Don, Aberdeen, AB23 8HZ, United Kingdom
Tel.: (44) 1224708500
Laboratory Testing & Inspection Services
N.A.I.C.S.: 541380

Intertek Consulting & Training Colombia Limitada (1)
Calle 127A 53A - 45 of 1103 Torre 2 57, Distrito Capital, Bogota, Colombia
Tel.: (57) 6015805268
Laboratory Testing & Inspection Services
N.A.I.C.S.: 541380

Intertek Consumer Goods GmbH (1)
Wurzburger Strasse 152, 90766, Furth, Germany
Tel.: (49) 91195035841
Laboratory Testing & Inspection Services
N.A.I.C.S.: 541380

AND PRIVATE COMPANIES   INTERTEK GROUP PLC

Intertek Denmark A/S (1)
Dokhavnsvej 3, PO Box 67, 4400, Kalundborg, Denmark
Tel.: (45) 75726611
Web Site: https://intertek.dk
Laboratory Testing & Inspection Services
N.A.I.C.S.: 541380

Intertek Deutschland GmbH (1)
Stangenstrasse 1, 70771, Leinfelden-Echterdingen, Germany
Tel.: (49) 711273110
Laboratory Testing & Inspection Services
N.A.I.C.S.: 541380

Intertek ETL Semko Oy (1)
Koneenkatu 12 Door K17, PL 1300, 05801, Hyvinkaa, Finland (100%)
Tel.: (358) 20 475 2600
Laboratory Testing Services
N.A.I.C.S.: 541380

Intertek Finance plc (1)
Academy Place 1-9 Brook Street, Brentwood, CM14 5NQ, Essex, United Kingdom
Tel.: (44) 2073963400
Financial Management Services
N.A.I.C.S.: 523999

Intertek France SAS (1)
ZAC Ecoparc 2, 27400, Heudebouville, France
Tel.: (33) 232093636
Web Site: https://www.intertek-france.com
Laboratory Testing & Inspection Services
N.A.I.C.S.: 541380

Intertek Holdings Limited (1)
Academy Place 1-9 Brook Street, Avonmouth, Brentwood, CM14 5NQ, Essex, United Kingdom
Tel.: (44) 1708680248
Emp.: 3
Financial Management Services
N.A.I.C.S.: 523999

Intertek Holdings Nederland BV (1)
Leerlooierstraat 135, Hoogvliet, 3194AB, Rotterdam, 3194 AB, South Holland, Netherlands
Tel.: (31) 104902984
Sales Range: $50-74.9 Million
Emp.: 3
Investment Management Service
N.A.I.C.S.: 523999
D. van Geemen *(Mgr-Fin)*

Intertek Iberica Spain, S.L. (1)
C/ Alameda Recalde 27 5, 48009, Bilbao, Spain
Tel.: (34) 902377388
Web Site: https://www.intertek.es
Laboratory Testing & Inspection Services
N.A.I.C.S.: 541380

Intertek India Private Limited (1)
E-20 Block B1 Mathura Road, Mohan Cooperative Industrial Area, New Delhi, 110044, India
Tel.: (91) 1141595412
Laboratory Testing & Inspection Services
N.A.I.C.S.: 541380

Intertek Industrial Services GmbH (1)
Marie-Bernays-Ring 19a, 41199, Monchengladbach, Germany
Tel.: (49) 216660070
Laboratory Testing & Inspection Services
N.A.I.C.S.: 541380

Intertek Industry & Certification Services (Thailand) Limited (1)
539/2 Gypsum Metropolitan Building 11Fl 11C Sri-Ayudhaya Road, Phaya Thai Subdistrict Ratchathewi District, Bangkok, 10400, Thailand
Tel.: (66) 22484847
Laboratory Testing & Inspection Services
N.A.I.C.S.: 541380

Intertek Industry Services (S) Pte Ltd. (1)
10-09/10 The Strategy, 2 International Business Park, Singapore, 609930, Singapore
Tel.: (65) 67939930
Laboratory Testing & Inspection Services
N.A.I.C.S.: 541380

Intertek Industry Services Brasil Ltda. (1)
Alameda Mamore 503 - 8 Andar, Edificio Icon - Alphaville, Barueri, 06454-040, SP, Brazil
Tel.: (55) 1128420444
Laboratory Testing & Inspection Services
N.A.I.C.S.: 541380

Intertek Industry Services Colombia Limited (1)
Calle 127A 53A - 45 of 1103 Torre 2 57, Bogota, Colombia
Tel.: (57) 6015805268
Laboratory Testing & Inspection Services
N.A.I.C.S.: 541380

Intertek Industry Services Japan Limited (1)
Nihonbashi North Square 1-4-2 Nihonbashi, Horidomecho Chuo-ku, Tokyo, 103-0012, Japan
Tel.: (81) 336697401
Laboratory Testing & Inspection Services
N.A.I.C.S.: 541380

Intertek Industry WLL (1)
Building 400 Road 3207, 332, Manama, Bahrain
Tel.: (973) 17500271
Laboratory Testing & Inspection Services
N.A.I.C.S.: 541380

Intertek Inspection Services Scandinavia AS (1)
Leif Weldings Vei 8, N-3208, Sandefjord, Norway
Tel.: (47) 33420040
Laboratory Testing & Inspection Services
N.A.I.C.S.: 541380

Intertek International France SAS (1)
La Defense - Tour PB5 10eme Etage Aile Ouest 1, Avenue du General de Gaulle, 92800, Puteaux, France
Tel.: (33) 142235002
Laboratory Testing & Inspection Services
N.A.I.C.S.: 541380

Intertek International Gabon SARL (1)
Immeuble Independance 76- Dumez 1er Etage, BP 13312, Libreville, Gabon
Tel.: (241) 1743664
Laboratory Testing & Inspection Services
N.A.I.C.S.: 541380

Intertek International Inc. (1)
790 NW 107 Ave Ste 307, Miami, FL 33172
Tel.: (305) 513-3000
Web Site: http://www.intertek-fts.com
Sales Range: $25-49.9 Million
Emp.: 50
Testing Laboratories & Inspection
N.A.I.C.S.: 541990

Intertek International Limited (1)
Academy Place 1 to 9 Brook Street, Brentwood, CM14 5NQ, Essex, United Kingdom
Tel.: (44) 1277223400
Sales Range: $25-49.9 Million
Emp.: 200
Laboratory Testing Services
N.A.I.C.S.: 541380

Intertek Kalite Servisleri Limited Sirketi (1)
Cevizli Mah Tansel Cad Bulut Plaza No 12-18 Daire 72-73-74, Kat 9 Maltepe, Istanbul, Turkiye
Tel.: (90) 2164450000
Laboratory Testing & Inspection Services
N.A.I.C.S.: 541380

Intertek Korea Industry Service Ltd. (1)
Room 916 Youido Department Building 36-2 Youido-dong, Youngdungpo-ku, Seoul, 150-749, Korea (South)
Tel.: (82) 27806496
Laboratory Testing & Inspection Services
N.A.I.C.S.: 541380

Intertek Libya Technical Services & Consultations Company SpA (1)
PO Box 3788, Gargaresh, Tripoli, Libya
Tel.: (218) 214782550
Laboratory Testing & Inspection Services
N.A.I.C.S.: 541380

Intertek Overseas Holdings Limited (1)
Academy Place 1-9 Brook Street, Brentwood, CM14 5NQ, Essex, United Kingdom
Tel.: (44) 2073963400
Emp.: 50
Investment Management Service
N.A.I.C.S.: 523999

Intertek Pharmaceutical Services (1)
291 Rt 22 E, Whitehouse, NJ 08888
Tel.: (908) 534-4445
Emp.: 40
Pharmaceutical Research, Analysis & Testing Services
N.A.I.C.S.: 541715

Intertek Pharmaceutical Services Immunochemistry (1)
10420 Wateridge Cir, San Diego, CA 92121
Tel.: (858) 558-2599
Web Site: http://www.intertek.com
Sales Range: $1-9.9 Million
Emp.: 80
Testing Laboratories
N.A.I.C.S.: 541380

Intertek Pharmaceutical Services LCMS (1)
1104 Windfield Way, El Dorado Hills, CA 95762
Tel.: (916) 933-1640
Emp.: 120
Testing Laboratories
N.A.I.C.S.: 541380
William Luksemburg *(Pres)*

Intertek Plastics Technology Laboratories (1)
50 Pearl St, Pittsfield, MA 01201
Tel.: (413) 499-0983
Web Site: http://www.intertek.com
Plastics Testing & Inspection Services
N.A.I.C.S.: 541380

Intertek Poland Sp. z o.o. (1)
Ul Oszczepnikow 4, 02-633, Warsaw, Masovian Voivodeship, Poland
Tel.: (48) 228863280
Web Site: https://www.intertek.pl
Laboratory Testing & Inspection Services
N.A.I.C.S.: 541380

Intertek Polychemlab B.V. (1)
Koolwaterstofstraat 1, Postbus 606, 6160 AP, Geleen, Netherlands
Tel.: (31) 881268888
Laboratory Testing & Inspection Services
N.A.I.C.S.: 541380

Intertek Rus JSC (1)
St Elektrozavodskaya D 27 Building 2 2nd Floor, 107023, Moscow, 107023, Russia
Tel.: (7) 4959338545
Laboratory Testing & Inspection Services
N.A.I.C.S.: 541380

Intertek Semko AB (1)
Torshamnsgatan 43, Box 1103, 164 22, Kista, Sweden (100%)
Tel.: (46) 87500000
Web Site: https://www.intertek.se
Sales Range: $75-99.9 Million
Emp.: 300
Testing Laboratories
N.A.I.C.S.: 541380
Par Zetterberg *(Mng Dir)*

Intertek Testing Management Limited (1)
Academy Place 1 9 Brook Street, Brentwood, CM14 5NQ, Essex, United Kingdom
Tel.: (44) 1277223400
Laboratory Testing Services
N.A.I.C.S.: 541380

Intertek Testing Services (France) SARL (1)
Ecoparc 2, 27400, Heudebouville, France
Tel.: (33) 2 32 63 31 42
Testing & Inspection Services
N.A.I.C.S.: 541380

Intertek Testing Services (ITS) Canada Limited (1)
Unit 1 710 South Service Road, Stoney Creek, Hamilton, L8E 5S7, ON, Canada
Tel.: (905) 529-0090
Sales Range: $25-49.9 Million
Emp.: 30
Petroleum Refinery Inspection Services
N.A.I.C.S.: 541380

Intertek Testing Services (Singapore) Pte Limited (1)
Asiawide Industrial Building 5 Pereira Road 06-03, Singapore, 368025, Singapore
Tel.: (65) 63888666
Laboratory Testing Services
N.A.I.C.S.: 541380
Yee Wong Lai *(Mgr-Ops)*

Intertek Testing Services Holdings Limited (1)
Academy Place 1-9 Brook Street, Brentwood, CM14 5NQ, Essex, United Kingdom
Tel.: (44) 2073963400
Sales Range: $50-74.9 Million
Emp.: 50
Financial Management Services
N.A.I.C.S.: 523999

Intertek Testing Services Hong Kong Ltd. (1)
2 Fl Garment Ctr 576 Castle Peak Rd, Kowloon, China (Hong Kong)
Tel.: (852) 21738888
Web Site: https://www.intertek.com.hk
Emp.: 1,600
Testing Laboratories
N.A.I.C.S.: 541380

Subsidiary (US):

Labtest (2)
70 Diamond Rd, Springfield, NJ 07081
Tel.: (973) 346-5500
Web Site: http://www.intertek.com
Sales Range: $25-49.9 Million
Emp.: 60
Testing Laboratories
N.A.I.C.S.: 541715

Intertek Testing Services NA, Inc. (1)
3933 US Rte 11, Cortland, NY 13045
Tel.: (607) 753-6711
Sales Range: $75-99.9 Million
Emp.: 300
Independent Testing Laboratory
N.A.I.C.S.: 541715

Subsidiary (Domestic):

H.P. White Laboratory, Inc. (2)
3114 Scarboro Rd, Street, MD 21154
Tel.: (410) 838-6550
Web Site: http://www.hpwhite.com
Rev.: $7,231,000
Emp.: 20
Testing Laboratories
N.A.I.C.S.: 541380

Unit (Domestic):

Intertek Testing Services NA, Inc. - Commercial & Electrical (2)
16015 Shady Falls Rd, Elmendorf, TX 78112
Tel.: (210) 635-8100
Sales Range: $1-9.9 Million
Emp.: 40
Testing Laboratories
N.A.I.C.S.: 541380
Constance Humphrey *(VP)*

Intertek Testing Services NA, Inc. - RAM Consulting (2)
2107 Swift Dr Ste 200, Oak Brook, IL 60523
Tel.: (630) 481-3111
Web Site: http://www.ram.com
Sales Range: $10-24.9 Million
Emp.: 34
Testing Laboratories
N.A.I.C.S.: 621511

Intertek Testing Services NA, Inc. - Systems Certification, Kentwood (2)
4700 Broadmoor SE - Ste 200, Kentwood, MI 49512
Tel.: (616) 656-7401
Web Site: http://www.intertek.com
Emp.: 175
Testing Laboratories
N.A.I.C.S.: 541330

Intertek Testing Services Philippines, Inc. (1)
Intertek Building 2307 Chino Roces Avenue Extension, Barangay Magallanes, Makati, 1231, Philippines
Tel.: (63) 288195841

INTERTEK GROUP PLC

Intertek Group plc—(Continued)
Laboratory Testing & Inspection Services
N.A.I.C.S.: 541380

Intertek Testing Services Shenzhen Limited (1)
Industry 7th Road, Shekou, Shenzhen, 518067, Guangdong, China
Tel.: (86) 33232633139
Textile Products Testing Services
N.A.I.C.S.: 541380
Ben Lin *(Gen Mgr)*

Intertek Testing Services UK Limited (1)
Caleb Brett Division, Aberdeen, AB21 7GA, United Kingdom
Tel.: (44) 1224 723242
Laboratory Testing Services
N.A.I.C.S.: 541380

Intertek Trinidad Limited (1)
91-92 Union Road, Marabella, San Fernando, Trinidad & Tobago
Tel.: (868) 6580360
Laboratory Testing & Inspection Services
N.A.I.C.S.: 541380

Intertek UK (1)
Intertek House Cleeve Road, Leatherhead, KT22 7SA, Surrey, United Kingdom (100%)
Tel.: (44) 137 237 0900
Web Site: https://www.intertek.com
Sales Range: $25-49.9 Million
Emp.: 60
Testing Laboratories
N.A.I.C.S.: 541380

Intertek UK Holdings Limited (1)
Academy Place 1-9 Brook Street, Brentwood, CM14 5NQ, Essex, United Kingdom
Tel.: (44) 2073963400
Sales Range: $50-74.9 Million
Emp.: 40
Investment Management Service
N.A.I.C.S.: 523999

Intertek USA Inc. (1)
545 E Algonquin Rd, Arlington Heights, IL 60005 (100%)
Tel.: (713) 407-3500
Web Site: http://www.intertek-cb.com
Rev.: $30,000,000
Emp.: 100
Commodities Testing & Inspection Services
N.A.I.C.S.: 926150

Intertek Vietnam Limited (1)
3rd and 4th Floor Au Viet Building 1 Le Duc Tho, Mai Dich Ward Cau Giay District, Hanoi, Vietnam
Tel.: (84) 2437337094
Web Site: https://www.intertek.vn
Laboratory Testing & Inspection Services
N.A.I.C.S.: 541380

Intertek West Lab AS (1)
Energivegen 1, Box 139, 4056, Tananger, Norway
Tel.: (47) 51940100
Web Site: https://www.intertek.no
Sales Range: $25-49.9 Million
Emp.: 12
Laboratory Testing Services
N.A.I.C.S.: 541380
Havard Olsen *(Mng Dir)*

Moody Energy Technical Service Co., Ltd. (1)
Suite B2206 Dongyu Building A1 Shuguangxili, Chaoyang District, Beijing, 100028, China
Tel.: (86) 1058222940
Laboratory Testing & Inspection Services
N.A.I.C.S.: 541380

Professional Service Industries, Inc. (1)
4421 Harrsion St, Hillside, IL 60162
Tel.: (708) 236-0720
Web Site: http://www.psiusa.com
Environmental Engineering Consulting Services
N.A.I.C.S.: 541620
Tom Boogher *(CMO & Exec VP)*

Division (Domestic):

Professional Service Industries, Inc. - Florida (2)
5801 Benjamin Center Dr Ste 112, Tampa, FL 33634
Tel.: (813) 886-1075
Web Site: http://www.psiusa.com
Emp.: 75
Environmental Consulting Services
N.A.I.C.S.: 541620

Professional Service Industries, Inc. - Washington (2)
20508 56th Ave W Ste A, Lynnwood, WA 98036
Tel.: (425) 409-2504
Web Site: http://www.psiusa.com
Environmental Consulting Services
N.A.I.C.S.: 541620

RAM Consulting (1)
Unit 3 G 114 Garment Ctr 576 CastlePek Rd, Kowloon, Hong Kong, China (Hong Kong) (100%)
Tel.: (852) 29263920
Web Site: http://www.itsram.com
Testing Laboratories
N.A.I.C.S.: 541380

Westport Technology Center International (1)
6700 Portwest Dr, Houston, TX 77024
Tel.: (713) 479-8400
Web Site: https://www.intertek.com
Sales Range: $25-49.9 Million
Emp.: 50
Commercial Physical Research
N.A.I.C.S.: 541715

INTERTRADE CO., LTD.
11721 Shinkawa Chuoku Tokyo Kayabacho First Building 3rd floor, Chuo-ku, Tokyo, 104-0033, Japan
Tel.: (81) 335377450
Web Site: https://www.itrade.co.jp
Year Founded: 1999
3747—(TKS)
Rev.: $14,257,990
Assets: $12,216,070
Liabilities: $2,779,280
Net Worth: $9,436,790
Earnings: $255,240
Emp.: 87
Fiscal Year-end: 09/30/23
Business Security Services
N.A.I.C.S.: 561621
Kazuya Nishimoto *(Pres)*

INTERVACC AB
Vastertorpsvagen 135, 129 44, Hagersten, Sweden
Tel.: (46) 812010600
Web Site: https://www.intervacc.se
Year Founded: 2001
IVACC—(NASDAQ)
Rev.: $1,225,191
Assets: $24,823,681
Liabilities: $1,393,314
Net Worth: $23,430,367
Earnings: ($6,009,160)
Emp.: 15
Fiscal Year-end: 12/31/22
Pharmaceuticals Product Mfr
N.A.I.C.S.: 325412
Andreas Andersson *(CEO)*

Subsidiaries:

Nordvacc Lakemedel AB (1)
Vastertorpsvagen 135, 129 44, Hagersten, Sweden
Tel.: (46) 812010650
Web Site: https://www.nordvacc.se
Pharmaceutical Drug Mfr
N.A.I.C.S.: 325412

INTERWOOD DIRECT
5225 Orbitor Dr Unit 23, Mississauga, L4W 4Y8, ON, Canada
Tel.: (416) 250-1665
Web Site: http://www.interwood.com
Year Founded: 1974
Sales Range: Less than $1 Million
Emp.: 9

Proprietary & Licensed Direct Response Products Sales, Marketing & Distribution
N.A.I.C.S.: 455110
Rob Woodrooffe *(Pres)*

Subsidiaries:

Interwood Marketing Limited (1)
2720 Steeles Ave W, Concord, L4K 4N5, ON, Canada
Tel.: (416) 250-1665
Holding Company
N.A.I.C.S.: 551112

INTERWOOD-XYLEMPORIA A.T.E.N.E.
Thesi Kokkinopyrgos Kalimbaki, 19200, Elefsina, Greece
Tel.: (30) 2104145300
Web Site: https://interwood.gr
Year Founded: 2009
XYLEP—(ATH)
Sales Range: $25-49.9 Million
Emp.: 84
Sawn Timber & Timber Products Distr
N.A.I.C.S.: 423990
Pappa Sofia *(Pres)*

INTERWORKS, INC.
NBF Toranomon Building 8F 1-6-21 Nishi-shimbashi, Minato-ku, Tokyo, 105-0003, Japan
Tel.: (81) 3 6823 5400
Web Site: http://interworks.jp
6032—(TKS)
Rev.: $28,857,990
Assets: $25,410,070
Liabilities: $2,301,670
Net Worth: $23,108,400
Earnings: $412,650
Emp.: 120
Fiscal Year-end: 03/31/20
Recruitment Services
N.A.I.C.S.: 561311
Kazuyuki Matsumoto *(Pres)*

INTERWORLD DIGITAL LTD.
701 Arunachal Building 19, Barakhamba Road, New Delhi, 110 001, India
Tel.: (91) 1143571045 In
Web Site: https://www.interworlddigital.in
Year Founded: 1995
Rev.: $6,524
Assets: $21,653,720
Liabilities: $2,503,645
Net Worth: $19,150,075
Earnings: ($216,285)
Emp.: 4
Fiscal Year-end: 03/31/18
Digital Entertainment Services
N.A.I.C.S.: 512132
Rachit Garg *(CFO)*

INTESA SANPAOLO S.P.A.
Piazza San Carlo 156, 10121, Turin, Italy
Tel.: (39) 0115551 IT
Web Site: https://group.intesasanpaolo.com
Year Founded: 2001
ISP—(ITA)
Rev.: $35,903,521,365
Assets: $1,063,660,448,322
Liabilities: $1,055,134,120,912
Net Worth: $8,526,327,410
Earnings: ($8,557,235,899)
Emp.: 94,368
Fiscal Year-end: 12/31/23
Bank Holding Company
N.A.I.C.S.: 551111
Paolo Andrea Colombo *(Deputy Chm)*

Subsidiaries:

Banca CR Firenze S.p.A. (1)
Via Carlo Magno 7, 50127, Florence, Italy

INTERNATIONAL PUBLIC

Tel.: (39) 0800 303 306
Web Site: http://www.bancacrfirenze.it
Sales Range: $350-399.9 Million
Banking Services
N.A.I.C.S.: 522110

Subsidiary (Non-US):

Banca C.R. Firenze Romania S.A. (2)
B-dul Unirii 55, Bucharest, Romania
Tel.: (40) 212011930
Web Site: http://www.bancacrfirenze.ro
Commercial Banking
N.A.I.C.S.: 522110

Cassa di Risparmio della Spezia S.p.A. (2)
C so cavour 86, La Spezia, 19100, Italy
Tel.: (39) 0187773313
Web Site: http://www.carispe.it
Sales Range: $150-199.9 Million
Emp.: 500
Savings Institutions
N.A.I.C.S.: 522180

Centro Leasing Banca S.p.A (2)
Via Santa Caterina d Alessandria 32 34, 50129, Florence, Italy
Tel.: (39) 05549791
Web Site: http://www.centroleasing.it
Credit Bureaus
N.A.I.C.S.: 561450

Citylife S.p.A. (2)
Via delle Panche 140, 50141, Florence, Italy
Tel.: (39) 0554385646
Web Site: http://www.citylife.it
Software Reproducing
N.A.I.C.S.: 334610

Banca Caboto S.p.A. (1)
Via Arigo Boito 7, 20121, Milan, Italy
Tel.: (39) 0280211
Web Site: http://www.caboto.it
Sales Range: $450-499.9 Million
Emp.: 481
Banking Services
N.A.I.C.S.: 522110

Banca IMI (1)
Largo Mattioli 3, 20121, Milan, Italy
Tel.: (39) 0272611
Web Site: http://www.bancaimi.it
Sales Range: $75-99.9 Million
Emp.: 100
Investment Banking
N.A.I.C.S.: 523999

Banca Intesa Servizi Formazione (1)
Indirizzo: Via dell'Industria 1 - Centro Torri 2, 36100, Vicenza, Italy
Tel.: (39) 0444399815
Web Site: http://www.amway.cz
Commercial Bank
N.A.I.C.S.: 522110

Banca Prossima S.p.A. (1)
Piazza Paolo Ferrari 10, 20121, Milan, Italy
Tel.: (39) 0287934511
Web Site: http://www.bancaprossima.com
Investment Banking Services
N.A.I.C.S.: 523150

Banca d'Intermediazione Mobiliare IMI S.p.A (1)
Largo Mattioli 3, 20121, Milan, Italy
Tel.: (39) 0277511
Web Site: http://www.bancaimi.it
Financial Investment Services
N.A.I.C.S.: 523940

Branch (Non-US):

Banca IMI (2)
90 Queen Street, London, EC4N 1SA, United Kingdom
Tel.: (44) 2076513000
Web Site: http://www.bancaimi.it
Sales Range: $25-49.9 Million
Emp.: 50
Investment Services
N.A.I.C.S.: 523940

Subsidiary (US):

Banca IMI Securities Corp. (2)
1 William St, New York, NY 10004

AND PRIVATE COMPANIES

Tel.: (212) 326-1100
Web Site: http://www.bancaimi.com
Sales Range: $25-49.9 Million
Emp.: 40
Financial Investment Services
N.A.I.C.S.: 523150

Banca dell'Adriatico S.p.A. (1)
Via Yuri Gagarin 216, Pesaro, 61122, Italy
Tel.: (39) 07214471
Web Site: http://www.bancadelladriatico.it
Investment Banking Services
N.A.I.C.S.: 523150

Banca di Trento e Bolzano S.p.A. (1)
Via Mantova 19, 38100, Trento, Italy
Tel.: (39) 0461892111
Web Site: http://www.btbonline.it
N.A.I.C.S.: 522299

Bank of Alexandria S.A.E. (1)
49 Kasr El Nil Street, Cairo, Egypt
Tel.: (20) 19033
Web Site: https://www.alexbank.com
Sales Range: $350-399.9 Million
Emp.: 7,000
Commercial Banking Services
N.A.I.C.S.: 522110
Paolo Vivona (CEO & Mng Dir)

Banka Koper d.d. (1)
Pristaniska Ulica 14, 6000, Koper, Slovenia
Tel.: (386) 56661282
Web Site: http://www.banka-koper.si
Sales Range: $350-399.9 Million
Emp.: 800
Banking Services
N.A.I.C.S.: 522320

Subsidiary (Domestic):

Finor Leasing d.o.o. (2)
Pristaniska 14, 6000, Koper, Slovenia
Tel.: (386) 5 666 13 61
Web Site: http://www.finor.si
Sales Range: $50-74.9 Million
Emp.: 12
Financial Lending Services
N.A.I.C.S.: 522220
Zlatko Kustra (Gen Mgr)

Cassa dei Risparmi di Forli e della Romagna S.p.A. (1)
Corso Della Repubblica 14, 47121, Forli, FO, Italy
Tel.: (39) 0543711111
Web Site: http://www.cariromagna.it
Investment Banking Services
N.A.I.C.S.: 523150

Cassa di Risparmio del Friuli Venezia Giulia S.p.A. (1)
Corso Verdi 104, Gorizia, 34170, Italy
Tel.: (39) 04 81 38 13 66
Web Site: http://www.carifvg.it
Investment Banking Services
N.A.I.C.S.: 523150

Cassa di Risparmio del Veneto S.p.A. (1)
Corso Garibaldi 22/26, Padua, 35122, Italy
Tel.: (39) 0498368111
Web Site: http://www.crveneto.it
Investment Banking Services
N.A.I.C.S.: 523150

Cassa di Risparmio di Citta di Castello S.p.A. (1)
Piazza Matteotti 1, Citta di Castello, Perugia, Italy
Tel.: (39) 075 85081
Web Site: http://www.caricast.it
Commercial Banking Services
N.A.I.C.S.: 522110

Centrale Supporti Operativi S.p.A. (1)
Centro Torri Via dell' Industria 1, 36040, Torri di Quartesolo, Vicenza, Italy
Tel.: (39) 0444519111
Financial Services
N.A.I.C.S.: 522299

Colline e oltre S.p.A. (1)
Viale Cesare Battisti 16/B, 27100, Pavia, Italy
Tel.: (39) 03486440379
Web Site: https://collineeoltre.it
Food & Wine Distr

N.A.I.C.S.: 424490

Compagnia Italiana Finanziaria - CIF S.r.l. (1)
Via Guglielmo Marconi 8, 40122, Bologna, Italy
Tel.: (39) 051266784
Financial Management Services
N.A.I.C.S.: 523999

Epsilon Associati SGR S.p.A. (1)
Piazzetta Giordano Dell Amore 3, 20121, Milan, Italy
Tel.: (39) 0288102070
Web Site: http://www.epsilonsgr.it
Investment Banking Services
N.A.I.C.S.: 523150

Eurizon Asset Management Croatia D.O.O. (1)
Ulica Grada 271, Zagreb, 10000, Vukovar, Croatia
Tel.: (385) 16360758
Investment Fund Management Services
N.A.I.C.S.: 525910

Eurizon Asset Management Hungary Ltd. (1)
Petrezselyem u 2-8, 1024, Budapest, Hungary
Tel.: (36) 4232400
Web Site: https://eurizon.hu
Property Management Services
N.A.I.C.S.: 531311

Eurizon Capital S.G.R. S.p.A. (1)
Piazzetta Giordano Dell'Amore 3, 20121, Milan, Italy
Tel.: (39) 0288101
Web Site: http://www.eurizoncapital.com
Investment Fund Management Services
N.A.I.C.S.: 525910
Daniel Gros (Vice Chm)

Subsidiary (Non-US):

Eurizon Capital S.A. (2)
Avenue De La Liberte 8, 1930, Luxembourg, Luxembourg
Tel.: (352) 494930385
Web Site: http://www.eurizoncapital.com
Sales Range: $25-49.9 Million
Emp.: 6
Investment Fund Management Services
N.A.I.C.S.: 523940
Daniel Gros (Vice Chm)

Eurizon Financial Group (1)
Via Hoepli 10, 20121, Milan, Italy
Tel.: (39) 0230511
Web Site: http://www.eurizon.it
Sales Range: $75-99.9 Million
Emp.: 100
Insurance & Financial Products
N.A.I.C.S.: 524298

Eurizon Slj Capital Ltd. (1)
90 Queen Street, London, EC4N 1SA, United Kingdom
Tel.: (44) 2037551442
Web Site: http://www.eurizonsljcapital.com
Banking Services
N.A.I.C.S.: 522110
Mirko Sturmann (COO)

Euro-Tresorerie S.A. (1)
33 Avenue Mac Mahon, 75017, Paris, France
Tel.: (33) 1 56 02 69 69
Web Site: http://www.eurotresorerie.com
Sales Range: $25-49.9 Million
Emp.: 1
Treasury Consulting Services
N.A.I.C.S.: 541618

Fideuram - Intesa Sanpaolo Private Banking S.p.A. (1)
Piazza San Carlo 156, 10121, Turin, Italy
Tel.: (39) 0115773511
Web Site: http://www.fideuram.it
Banking Services
N.A.I.C.S.: 522110

Subsidiary (Non-US):

Fideuram Bank Luxembourg S.A.
9-11 rue Goethe, PO Box 1642, 1016, Luxembourg, Luxembourg
Tel.: (352) 4690901

Web Site: http://www.fideuramgestions.lu
Banking Services
N.A.I.C.S.: 522110

Fideuram Asset Management Uk Ltd. (1)
90 Queen Street, London, United Kingdom
Tel.: (44) 2076536961
Web Site: https://www.fideuramuk.it
Fund Management Services
N.A.I.C.S.: 523940

IMI Investimenti S.p.A. (1)
Via Zamboni 2, Bologna, 40126, Italy
Tel.: (39) 051 6566011
Web Site: http://www.imiinvestimenti.it
Sales Range: $50-74.9 Million
Emp.: 30
Venture Capital Investment Services
N.A.I.C.S.: 523910
Alberto Roversi Monaco (Pres)

Subsidiary (Domestic):

IMI Fondi Chiusi S.G.R. S.p.A. (2)
Via Zamboni 2, 40126, Bologna, Italy
Tel.: (39) 051 6566011
Web Site: http://www.imiinvestimenti.it
Venture Capital Management Services
N.A.I.C.S.: 523910
Leone Sibani (Chm)

Immobiliare Maram S.r.l. (1)
Quintino Sella 2, 95129, Catania, Sicily, Italy
Tel.: (39) 095535506
Sales Range: $75-99.9 Million
Emp.: 9
N.A.I.C.S.: 522299

Insalute Servizi S.p.A. (1)
Via San Francesco d Assisi 10, 10122, Turin, Italy
Tel.: (39) 0800776490
Web Site: https://www.insaluteservizi.com
Health & Medical Insurance Services
N.A.I.C.S.: 524114

Intesa Holding International SA (1)
19-21 Boulevard du Prince Henri, L-1724, Luxembourg, Luxembourg
Intl. Banking
N.A.I.C.S.: 522299

Intesa Leasing SpA (1)
Via Montebello 18, 20121, Milan, Italy
Tel.: (39) 0287968711
Web Site: http://www.leasint.it
Vehicle, Naval Air, Real Estate & Equipment Leasing
N.A.I.C.S.: 532490

Intesa Sanpaolo Bank Albania (1)
Rruga Ismail Qemali No 27, Tirana, Albania
Tel.: (355) 4 2276000
Web Site: http://www.intesasanpaolobank.al
Assets: $884,000,000
Emp.: 550
Banking Services
N.A.I.C.S.: 522110
E. Zigori (Head-HR & Organization Dept)

Intesa Sanpaolo Bank Ireland Plc (1)
3rd Floor Kbc House 4 Georges Dock, Dublin, 1, Ireland
Tel.: (353) 1 6726720
Investment Banking Services
N.A.I.C.S.: 523150

Intesa Sanpaolo Banque (1)
62 Rue de Richelieu, 75002, Paris, France
Tel.: (33) 1 452 37222
Web Site: http://www.intesasanpaolo.com
Local & International Banking Services
N.A.I.C.S.: 522110

Intesa Sanpaolo Brasil S.A. - Banco Multiplo (1)
Avenida Juscelino Kubitschek No 1327 21 Andar Vila Nova Conceicao, Sao Paulo, 04543-011, Brazil
Tel.: (55) 1134653700
Web Site: http://www.intesasanpaolobrasil.com.br
Banking Services
N.A.I.C.S.: 522110

Intesa Sanpaolo Group Services S.c.p.A. (1)
Piazza San Carlo 156, Turin, Italy

INTESA SANPAOLO S.P.A.

Tel.: (39) 0115551
Investment Banking Services
N.A.I.C.S.: 523150

Intesa Sanpaolo Holding International S.A. (1)
Boulevard du Prince Henri 19-21, Luxembourg, 1724, Luxembourg
Tel.: (352) 46 1411
Investment Management Service
N.A.I.C.S.: 523999
Pizzetto Franco (Office Mgr)

Subsidiary (Domestic):

Intesa Sanpaolo Bank Luxembourg S.A. (2)
19-21 Boulevard du Prince Henri, L-1724, Luxembourg, Luxembourg (100%)
Tel.: (352) 46 1411 1
Web Site: http://www.intesasanpaololuxembourg.lu
Rev.: $261,637,239
Assets: $19,250,833,314
Liabilities: $17,133,480,027
Net Worth: $2,117,353,287
Earnings: $130,327,822
Emp.: 169
Fiscal Year-end: 12/31/2016
Corporate Banking & Wealth Management Services
N.A.I.C.S.: 523150
Walter Ambrogi (Deputy Chm)

Intesa Sanpaolo Servitia S.A. (2)
12 Avenue de la Liberte, 1930, Luxembourg, Luxembourg
Tel.: (352) 22 37 56 1
Web Site: http://www.intesasanpaoloservitia.com
Emp.: 150
N.A.I.C.S.: 541511
Jean-Claude Krieger (CEO)

Servitia S.A. (2)
23 BD Du Prince Henri, 1724, Luxembourg
Tel.: (352) 22 37 56 1
Web Site: http://www.servitia.com
Sales Range: $25-49.9 Million
Emp.: 4
Financial Management Services
N.A.I.C.S.: 523999
John Krieger (Gen Mgr)

Intesa Sanpaolo International Value Services d.o.o. (1)
Radnicka cesta 44, 10000, Zagreb, Croatia
Tel.: (385) 16360000
Web Site: https://www.internationalvalueservices.com
Information Technology Services
N.A.I.C.S.: 541519

Intesa Sanpaolo Life Designed activity company (1)
1st Floor International House 3 Harbourmaster Place IFSC, Dublin, Ireland
Tel.: (353) 16617707
Investment Banking Services
N.A.I.C.S.: 524113

Intesa Sanpaolo Previdenza - Societa di Intermediazione Mobiliare S.p.A. (1)
Via Ugo Bassi 8/a, Milan, 20159, Italy
Tel.: (39) 028904031
Insurance Management Services
N.A.I.C.S.: 524298

Intesa Sanpaolo Private Banking S.p.A. (1)
Via Hoepli 10, 20121, Milan, Italy
Tel.: (39) 02 72622811
Web Site: http://www.intesasanpaoloprivatebanking.it
Commercial Banking Services
N.A.I.C.S.: 522110
Giampio Bracchi (Chm)

Intesa Sanpaolo RBM Salute S.p.A. (1)
Via Lazzari 5, Mestre, 30174, Venice, VE, Italy
Tel.: (39) 0412518798
Web Site: https://www.intesasanpaolorbmsalute.com
Health Insurance Services
N.A.I.C.S.: 524114

INTESA SANPAOLO S.P.A.

Intesa Sanpaolo S.p.A.—(Continued)

Intesa Sanpaolo Rent Foryou S.p.A. (1)
Corso England 3, 10138, Rivalta di Torino, Italy
Tel.: (39) 0241279998
Investment Banking Services
N.A.I.C.S.: 524113

Intesa Sanpaolo Romania S.A. (1)
B-dul Revolutiei nr 88, 310025, Arad, Romania
Tel.: (40) 257 308 200
Web Site: http://www.intesasanpaolobank.ro
Investment Banking Services
N.A.I.C.S.: 523150
Ignacio Jaquotot (Chm)

Intesa Sanpaolo Vita S.p.A. (1)
Viale Stelvio 55/57, 20159, Milan, Italy
Tel.: (39) 0230511
Web Site: http://www.intesasanpaolovita.it
Sales Range: $50-74.9 Million
Insurance Services
N.A.I.C.S.: 524298
Vincenzo Russo (Sr Mgr-Risk)

Subsidiary (Non-US):

Intesa Sanpaolo Life Limited (2)
Georges Court Townsend Street, Dublin, 2, Ireland
Tel.: (353) 1 6617707
Web Site: http://www.intesasanpaololife.ie
Sales Range: $25-49.9 Million
Emp.: 50
Fire Insurance Services
N.A.I.C.S.: 524113

Intesa Sec. S.p.A. (1)
Via Monte Di Pieta 8, Milan, 20121, Italy
Tel.: (39) 0287911
Web Site: http://www.intesasec.com
Investment Banking Services
N.A.I.C.S.: 523150

Intessa Preferred Capital Corporation LLC (1)
114 W 47th St Ste 1715, New York, NY 10036
Tel.: (212) 302-8330
Sales Range: $50-74.9 Million
Emp.: 2
Trusts Nec
N.A.I.C.S.: 522110

Leasint S.p.A. (1)
Via Montebello 18, 20121, Milan, Italy
Tel.: (39) 02 879 68 711
Real Estate Lending Services
N.A.I.C.S.: 531190

Mediocredito Italiano S.p.A. (1)
Via Cernaia 8/10, 20121, Milan, Italy
Tel.: (39) 0287940511
Investment Banking Services
N.A.I.C.S.: 523150
Rony Hamaui (Dir Gen)

Mediofactoring S.p.A. (1)
Via Carlo Poma 47/61, 20129, Milan, Italy
Tel.: (39) 0002752631
Web Site: http://www.bancaintesa.it
N.A.I.C.S.: 522299

NH Italia S.r.l. (1)
Via Giovanni Battista Pergolesi 2 A, IT-20122, Milan, Italy
Tel.: (39) 027780721
Web Site: http://www.nh-hotels.it
Sales Range: $50-74.9 Million
Emp.: 70
Holding Company; Hotel Operator; Owned 52.5% by NH Hoteles, S.A. & 47.5% by Intesa Sanpaolo, S.p.A.
N.A.I.C.S.: 551112

PBZ Invest d.o.o. (1)
Ilica 5 - Oktogon, 10000, Zagreb, Croatia
Tel.: (385) 16363699
Web Site: http://www.pbzinvest.hr
Banking Services
N.A.I.C.S.: 522110

PBZ Leasing d.o.o. (1)
Radnicka Cesta 44, 10000, Zagreb, Croatia
Tel.: (385) 16363606
Web Site: http://www.pbz-leasing.hr
Banking Services
N.A.I.C.S.: 522110

Private Equity International S.A. (1)
Boulevard Du Prince Henri 35, Luxembourg, 1724, Luxembourg
Tel.: (352) 26 47 71 1
Web Site: http://www.privateequityinternational.com
Sales Range: $50-74.9 Million
Emp.: 1
Investment Banking Services
N.A.I.C.S.: 523150

Privredna banka Zagreb d.d. (1)
Radnicka cesta 50, 10000, Zagreb, Croatia (76.6%)
Tel.: (385) 1 489 1310
Web Site: http://www.pbz.hr
Sales Range: $600-649.9 Million
Emp.: 3,713
Banking Services
N.A.I.C.S.: 522110
Giovanni Boccolini (Chm-Supervisory Bd)

Subsidiary (Non-US):

Intesa Sanpaolo Banka d.d. Bosna i Hercegovina (2)
ul Obala Kulina Bana 9A, 71 000, Sarajevo, Bosnia & Herzegovina (94.8%)
Tel.: (387) 33497555
Web Site: http://www.intesasanpaolobanka.ba
Rev: $46,495,752
Assets: $1,463,373,698
Liabilities: $1,261,854,218
Net Worth: $201,519,479
Earnings: $11,457,678
Emp.: 562
Fiscal Year-end: 12/31/2020
Banking Services
N.A.I.C.S.: 522110
Almir Krkalic (Pres & Member-Mgmt Bd)

Qingdao Yicai Fund Distribution Co. Ltd. (1)
20F Tower B InterContinental Qingdao No 98 Aomen Road, Qingdao, Shandong, China
Tel.: (86) 53287071088
Web Site: https://www.yitsai.com
Commercial Banking & Wealth Management Services
N.A.I.C.S.: 522110

REYL & Cie (Malta) Ltd. (1)
Swiss Urban Factory - Office 5 Saint Frederick Street 5, Valletta, Malta
Tel.: (356) 22482950
Custody & Depositary Services
N.A.I.C.S.: 524113

Reyl & Co (Uk) Llp (1)
90 Queen Street, London, United Kingdom
Tel.: (44) 2036960300
Custody & Depositary Services
N.A.I.C.S.: 524113

Sanpaolo IMI S.p.A. (1)
Piazza San Carlo 156, Turin, 10121, Italy
Tel.: (39) 0115551
Web Site: http://www.intesasanpaolo.com
Banking Group
N.A.I.C.S.: 522110
Cucchiani Enrico (Gen Mgr)

Subsidiary (Non-US):

CIB Bank (2)
Medve Utca 4-14, H 1027, Budapest, Hungary
Tel.: (36) 14576800
Web Site: http://www.cib.hu
Sales Range: $400-449.9 Million
Emp.: 730
International Banking Services
N.A.I.C.S.: 522299

Sanpaolo IMI Bank Ireland PLC (2)
3rd Fl KBC House, 1, Dublin, Ireland
Tel.: (353) 16726720
Web Site: http://www.intesasanpaolo.com
Sales Range: $50-74.9 Million
Emp.: 27
N.A.I.C.S.: 522299

Branch (Domestic):

Sanpaolo IMI S.p.A. (2)
Viale Dell Arte 25, 00144, Rome, Italy
Tel.: (39) 0000659591
Web Site: http://www.sanpaoloimi.it

Sales Range: $1-4.9 Billion
Emp.: 3,463
Long-Term Lending; Investment Banking; Personal Financial Services
N.A.I.C.S.: 523150

Societa Italiana di Revisione e Fiduciaria - S.I.R.E.F. S.p.A. (1)
Via Dell'Unione 1, 20122, Milan, Italy
Tel.: (39) 02 87947920
Investment Banking Services
N.A.I.C.S.: 523150

Unione di Banche Italiane SpA (1)
Piazza Vittorio Veneto 8, 24122, Bergamo, Italy
Tel.: (39) 035392111
Web Site: http://www.ubibanca.it
Sales Range: $1-4.9 Billion
Banking Services
N.A.I.C.S.: 522110
Andrea Moltrasio (Chm-Supervisory Bd)

Subsidiary (Domestic):

Banca 24-7 S.p.A. (2)
Via Antonio Stoppani 15, Bergamo, 24121, Italy
Tel.: (39) 0353833611
Web Site: http://www.banca247.it
Commercial Banking Services
N.A.I.C.S.: 522110

Banca Popolar e di Ancona S.p.A. (2)
Corso Stamira 14, Ancona, 60122, Italy
Tel.: (39) 07 316471
Web Site: http://www.ubibanca.com
Commercial Banking Services
N.A.I.C.S.: 522110

Banca Regionale Europea S.p.A. (2)
Via Monte di Pieta 7, Milan, 20121, Italy
Tel.: (39) 027212111
Web Site: http://www.brebanca.it
Commercial Banking Services
N.A.I.C.S.: 522110

Banca di San Giorgio S.p.A. (2)
Via CR Ceccardi 1R, 16121, Genoa, Italy
Tel.: (39) 01055241
Web Site: http://www.bancodisangiorgio.it
Sales Range: $100-124.9 Million
Emp.: 200
Commercial Banking Services
N.A.I.C.S.: 522110
Mori Sergio (Gen Dir)

Banca di Valle Camonica S.p.A. (2)
piazza della Repubblica 2, 25043, Breno, Italy
Tel.: (39) 03642391
Web Site: http://www.bancavalle.it
Commercial Banking Services
N.A.I.C.S.: 522110

Banco di Brescia S.p.A. (2)
Corso Martiri Della Liberta 13, Brescia, 25125, Italy
Tel.: (39) 03029921
Web Site: http://www.bancodibrescia.it
Commercial Banking Services
N.A.I.C.S.: 522110

Centrobanca S.p.A. (2)
C so Europa 16, 20122, Milan, Italy
Tel.: (39) 0277811
Web Site: http://www.centrobanca.it
Commercial Banking Services
N.A.I.C.S.: 522110

Subsidiary (Domestic):

Centrobanca Sviluppo Impresa SGR S.p.A. (3)
Corso Europa 16, Milan, 20122, Italy
Tel.: (39) 0277 81 46 30
Commercial Banking Services
N.A.I.C.S.: 522110

Subsidiary (Domestic):

Focus Impresa Srl (2)
Via Amendola 8, 37138, Verona, Italy
Tel.: (39) 045564980
Web Site: http://www.focusimpresa.com
Financial Investment Services
N.A.I.C.S.: 523940

IW Bank S.p.A. (2)

INTERNATIONAL PUBLIC

Piazzale Fratelli Zavattari 12, 20149, Milan, Italy
Tel.: (39) 0274874501
Web Site: http://www.iwbank.it
Commercial Banking Services
N.A.I.C.S.: 522110

Investnet Italia Srl (2)
Via Cavriana 20, 20134, Milan, Italy
Tel.: (39) 027541161
Web Site: http://www.investnet.it
Commercial Banking Services
N.A.I.C.S.: 522110

Prestitalia S.p.A. (2)
Via Ostiense 131/L, 00154, Rome, Italy
Tel.: (39) 06 4203221
Web Site: http://www.prestitalia.it
Securities Brokerage Services
N.A.I.C.S.: 523150

Societa Lombarda Immobiliare S.p.A. (2)
Via Mario Pagano 39, Milan, 20145, Italy
Tel.: (39) 0248009026
Real Estate Investment Services
N.A.I.C.S.: 531390

UBI Banca di Valle Camonica S.p.A. (2)
Piazza della Repubblica 2, Breno, 25043, Brescia, Italy
Tel.: (39) 03642391
Web Site: http://www.bancavalle.it
Sales Range: $50-74.9 Million
Commercial Banking
N.A.I.C.S.: 522110

UBI Banco di Brescia SpA (2)
Corso Martiri Della Liberta 13, 25171, Brescia, Italy
Tel.: (39) 0003029921
Web Site: http://www.bancodibrescia.com
Commercial & Private Banking
N.A.I.C.S.: 522110

UBI Factor S.p.A. (2)
via F lli Gabba 1, Milan, 20121, Italy
Tel.: (39) 0277661
Web Site: http://www.cbifactor.it
Factoring Services
N.A.I.C.S.: 522390
Egidio Tempini (Chm)

UBI Gestioni Fiduciarie Sim S.p.A. (2)
74 Via Cefalonia, Brescia, 25124, Italy
Tel.: (39) 0302455211
Emp.: 20
Financial Management Services
N.A.I.C.S.: 523940
Sebastiano Di Pasquale (Pres)

UBI Insurance Broker Srl (2)
15 Via Calvi Fratelli, 24122, Bergamo, Italy
Tel.: (39) 0354 527 111
Insurance Brokerage Services
N.A.I.C.S.: 524210

UBI Lease Finance 5 Srl (2)
Foro Buonaparte 70, 20121, Milan, Italy
Tel.: (39) 030 2433205
Financial Lending Services
N.A.I.C.S.: 522220

UBI Leasing S.p.A. (2)
via Cefalonia 74, 25124, Brescia, Italy
Tel.: (39) 030 29761
Web Site: http://www.ubileasing.it
Sales Financing & Leasing Services
N.A.I.C.S.: 522220

UBI Pramerica SGR S.p.A. (2)
Via Monte di Pieta 5, 20121, Milan, Italy
Tel.: (39) 0243024 1
Web Site: http://www.ubipramerica.it
Sales Range: $100-124.9 Million
Emp.: 140
Commercial Banking Services
N.A.I.C.S.: 522110
Andrea Pennacchia (Gen Mgr)

UBI Sistemi e Servizi Scpa (2)
Via Kefalonia 62, PO Box 347, 25124, Brescia, Italy
Tel.: (39) 030 247 31
Web Site: http://www.ubibanche.it
Commercial Banking Services
N.A.I.C.S.: 522110

Vseobecna Uverova Banka a.s. (1)

Mlynske Nivy 1, 829 90, Bratislava, Slovakia
Tel.: (421) 248555970
Web Site: http://www.vub.sk
Banking Services
N.A.I.C.S.: 522110

INTESYS S.R.L.
Via Roveggia 122/a, 37136, Verona, Italy
Tel.: (39) 045 503663 IT
Web Site: http://www.intesys.it
Sales Range: $1-9.9 Million
Emp.: 55
Computer Software, Hardware & Accessories Developer & Whslr
N.A.I.C.S.: 423430
Alberto Gaiga *(CEO)*

Subsidiaries:

Intesys Networking S.r.l. (1)
via Roveggia 122 A, Verona, 37136, Italy
Tel.: (39) 045 8205513
Web Site: http://www.intesys.it
Information Technology Consulting; Software Designer & Developer
N.A.I.C.S.: 513210
Romano Rosponi *(Mgr-Network & Security)*

INTICA SYSTEMS SE
Spitalhofstrasse 94, 94032, Passau, Germany
Tel.: (49) 851966920
Web Site: https://intica-systems.com
IS7—(DUS)
Rev.: $95,904,226
Assets: $74,754,076
Liabilities: $51,760,464
Net Worth: $22,993,612
Earnings: ($1,247,373)
Emp.: 741
Fiscal Year-end: 12/31/23
Electronic Components Supplier
N.A.I.C.S.: 334416
Gregor Wasle *(Chm)*

Subsidiaries:

InTiCa Systems s.r.o. (1)
Krumlovska 979, 383 01, Prachatice, Czech Republic
Tel.: (420) 38830200
Automotive Electronic Equipment Mfr
N.A.I.C.S.: 336320

INTIGER GROUP LIMITED
Suite 9 330 Churchill Avenue, Subiaco, 6008, WA, Australia
Tel.: (61) 8 6489 1600 AU
Web Site:
  http://www.intigergrouplimited.com
Year Founded: 2001
Investment Services
N.A.I.C.S.: 523999
Mark Fisher *(Founder)*

Subsidiaries:

Orion Exploration Pty Ltd (1)
Level 9 440 Collins Street, Melbourne, 3000, VIC, Australia
Tel.: (61) 396071322
Uranium Exploration Services
N.A.I.C.S.: 212290

INTOPS CO., LTD.
51 Anyangcheonseo-ro, Manan-Gu, Anyang, 430-817, Gyeonggi-Do, Korea (South)
Tel.: (82) 314414181
Web Site: https://www.intops.co.kr
Year Founded: 1981
049070—(KRS)
Rev.: $854,556,718
Assets: $667,658,511
Liabilities: $106,751,468
Net Worth: $560,907,043
Earnings: $90,652,798
Emp.: 494
Fiscal Year-end: 12/31/22
Communication Equipment Mfr

N.A.I.C.S.: 334220
Jae Kyung Kim *(Chm)*

Subsidiaries:

Mirae Corporation (1)
65 Baekseokgongdan7-ro, Seobuk-gu, Cheonan, 31093, Chungcheongnam-do, Korea (South) **(71.33%)**
Tel.: (82) 416215070
Web Site: https://www.mirae.com
Rev.: $44,471,341
Assets: $108,304,129
Liabilities: $30,433,236
Net Worth: $77,870,893
Earnings: $6,891,055
Emp.: 107
Fiscal Year-end: 12/31/2021
Semiconductor Testing Equipment Mfr
N.A.I.C.S.: 334513
Jong Up Sun *(CEO)*

INTOS ELECTRONIC AG
Siemensstrasse 11, 35394, Giessen, Germany
Tel.: (49) 64197260
Web Site: http://www.intos.de
Year Founded: 1991
Rev.: $11,035,200
Emp.: 30
IT Products & Accessories Distr
N.A.I.C.S.: 423430
Wolfgang Isenberg *(CEO)*

INTOUCH HOLDINGS PLC
87 M Thai Tower 27th Floor Unit 2 All Seasons Place Wireless Road, Subdistrict Pathumwan District, Bangkok, 10330, Thailand
Tel.: (66) 21186900 TH
Web Site:
  https://www.intouchcompany.com
Year Founded: 1983
Television Services
N.A.I.C.S.: 516120
Kan Trakulhoon *(Chm)*

INTOUCH INSIGHT LTD.
400 March Road, Ottawa, K2K 3H4, ON, Canada
Tel.: (613) 270-7916
Web Site:
  https://www.intouchinsight.com
Year Founded: 1992
INXSF—(OTCQX)
Rev.: $18,788,307
Assets: $11,763,809
Liabilities: $7,112,073
Net Worth: $4,651,736
Earnings: ($283,902)
Fiscal Year-end: 12/31/23
Holding Company; Commercial Marketing & Analytics Software Developer, Publisher & Whslr
N.A.I.C.S.: 551112
Michael J. Gaffney *(Chm)*

Subsidiaries:

In-Touch Insight Systems Corp. (1)
1057 521 Corporate Ctr Dr Ste 125, Fort Mill, SC 29707
Tel.: (800) 263-2980
Software Development Services
N.A.I.C.S.: 541511

In-Touch Insight Systems Inc. (1)
400 March Road, Ottawa, K2K 3H4, ON, Canada
Tel.: (613) 270-7900
Web Site: http://www.intouchinsight.com
Insurance Software Development Services
N.A.I.C.S.: 541511

INTRA ENERGY CORPORATION LIMITED
Level 40 2 Park Street, Sydney, 2000, NSW, Australia
Tel.: (61) 282807111 AU
Web Site:
  https://www.intraenergycorp.com.au
Year Founded: 2007

IEC—(ASX)
Rev.: $19,183
Assets: $3,879,145
Liabilities: $751,056
Net Worth: $3,128,089
Earnings: ($756,508)
Fiscal Year-end: 06/30/24
Thermal Coal Exploration Services
N.A.I.C.S.: 212114
Rozanna Lee *(Sec)*

Subsidiaries:

Intrafrican Resources Limited (1)
Level 6 Ken Lee Building 20th Edith Cavell Street, 11302, Port Louis, Mauritius
Tel.: (230) 2108967
Web Site: https://www.intrafrican.com
Gold Mining Services
N.A.I.C.S.: 541330

Tancoal Energy limited (1)
Level 5 Amverton Tower Chole Road, PO Box 23059, Masaki, Dar es Salaam, Tanzania
Tel.: (255) 2222927820
Web Site: https://www.tancoalenergy.co.tz
Coal Exploration Services
N.A.I.C.S.: 213113

INTRACO LIMITED
60 Albert Street, 07-01 OG Albert Complex, Singapore, 189969, Singapore
Tel.: (65) 65866777 SG
Web Site: https://www.intraco.com.sg
Year Founded: 1968
I06—(SES)
Rev.: $120,108,309
Assets: $59,872,756
Liabilities: $13,094,751
Net Worth: $46,778,005
Earnings: $2,434,295
Emp.: 99
Fiscal Year-end: 12/31/23
Investment Holding Company
N.A.I.C.S.: 551112
Colin Low *(Chm)*

Subsidiaries:

INTRACO International Pte Ltd (1)
60 Albert Street#07-01 OG Albert Complex, 189969, Singapore, Singapore
Tel.: (65) 65 86 6777
Fire Protection Products & Services
N.A.I.C.S.: 922160

Subsidiary (Domestic):

K. A. Group Holdings Pte Ltd (2)
10 Ubi Crescent 06-99 Ubi Techpark Lobby E, Singapore, 408564, Singapore **(90%)**
Tel.: (65) 67471747
Web Site: https://www.ka.com.sg
Holding Company
N.A.I.C.S.: 551112
Soh Yong Poon *(CEO)*

Subsidiary (Domestic):

K.A. Builders Construction Pte Ltd (3)
10 Ubi Crescent 06-99 Ubi Techpark Lobby E, Singapore, 408564, Singapore
Tel.: (65) 67471747
Web Site: https://www.ka.com.sg
Fire Protection Product Installation Services
N.A.I.C.S.: 238220

INTRACO REFUELING STATON LTD.
Intraco Centre House 40 Block-J Pragati Sarani, Baridhara, Dhaka, 1212, Bangladesh
Tel.: (880) 29881887
Web Site:
  https://www.intracorefueling.com
Year Founded: 2007
INTRRC—(CHT)
Rev.: $13,066,101
Assets: $16,365,321
Liabilities: $5,056,827
Net Worth: $11,308,493

Earnings: $1,175,751
Emp.: 140
Fiscal Year-end: 06/30/23
Rail Construction Services
N.A.I.C.S.: 488210
Mohammed Riyadh Ali *(Mng Dir)*

Subsidiaries:

Absar & Elias Enterprise Ltd. (1)
Lalkhan Bazar Tiger Pass Road, Tiger Pass More Dist, Chittagong, Bangladesh
Tel.: (880) 1975006062
CNG Refueling Station Services
N.A.I.C.S.: 237120

INTRACOM HOLDINGS S.A.
19th km Markopoulou Ave, Paiania, 19002, Athens, Greece
Tel.: (30) 2106674000
Web Site: https://www.intracom.com
Year Founded: 1977
INTRK—(ATH)
Rev.: $536,092,369
Assets: $941,316,995
Liabilities: $655,363,071
Net Worth: $285,953,924
Earnings: ($12,470,321)
Emp.: 3,013
Fiscal Year-end: 12/31/20
Telecommunication Equipment & Information Systems Mfr
N.A.I.C.S.: 334290
Dimitris Klonis *(Vice Chm & CEO)*

Subsidiaries:

Conklin Corporation (1)
11360 Atlanta Development Center, Duluth, GA 30097
Tel.: (770) 295-2500
Web Site: http://www.conklin-intracom.com
Sales Range: $25-49.9 Million
Emp.: 100
Telecommunications
N.A.I.C.S.: 517810

Eurokat SA (1)
19 km Peania Markopoulo Avenue, Attica, 190 02, Athens, Greece **(82%)**
Tel.: (30) 21066747
Web Site: http://www.intrakat.gr
Computer Equipment & Software Whslr
N.A.I.C.S.: 423430

Fornax ZRT (1)
Taltos u 1, 1123, Budapest, Hungary **(67%)**
Tel.: (36) 1 457 30 00
Web Site: http://www.fornaxzrt.hu
Sales Range: $25-49.9 Million
Emp.: 45
Computer Related Services
N.A.I.C.S.: 541519
Balasy Bulcsu *(CEO)*

Subsidiary (Non-US):

Fornax Informatika d.o.o. (2)
Savska cesta 106, 10000, Zagreb, Croatia **(100%)**
Tel.: (385) 14854264
Web Site: http://fornax-informatika.hr
Sales Range: $25-49.9 Million
Emp.: 3
Computer Related Services
N.A.I.C.S.: 541519

Subsidiary (Domestic):

Fornax Integrator (2)
Taltos u 1, 1123, Budapest, Hungary
Tel.: (36) 14573000
Web Site: http://www.fornax.hu
Telecommunication Servicesb
N.A.I.C.S.: 517810

Fracasso Hellas S.A. (1)
19th km Paiania- Markopoulou Rd, Paiania, 19002, Athens, Attica, Greece
Tel.: (30) 2106674836
Web Site: http://www.fracassohellas.gr
Steel Products Mfr
N.A.I.C.S.: 331210

IC Intracom USA, Inc. (1)

INTRACOM HOLDINGS S.A.

Intracom Holdings S.A.—(Continued)
550 Commerce Blvd, Oldsmar, FL 34677-2810 **(100%)**
Tel.: (813) 855-0550
Web Site: http://portal.icintracom.com
Sales Range: $50-74.9 Million
Emp.: 230
Computer Equipment & Software Mfr & Whslr
N.A.I.C.S.: 334118
Michael Thiel (CEO)

INTRACOM CONSTRUCTIONS SOCIETE ANONYME TECHNICAL & STEEL CONSTRUCTIONS (1)
19th Klm Peania-Markopoul Ave, Peania Attica, 19002, Athens, Greece **(74%)**
Tel.: (30) 2106074700
Web Site: https://www.intrakat.gr
Rev.: $442,364,655
Assets: $1,531,599,382
Liabilities: $1,358,123,215
Net Worth: $173,476,167
Earnings: $3,146,114
Emp.: 3,371
Fiscal Year-end: 12/31/2023
Water & Sewer Line & Related Structures Construction
N.A.I.C.S.: 237110
Konstantinos S. Kokkalis (Vice Chm)

Subsidiary (Non-US):

Intracom Construct SA (2)
142 Gheorghe Titeica street 3rd floor room 4 5 Sector 2, Bucharest, 020304, Romania **(87%)**
Tel.: (40) 213522377
Web Site: http://www.intracat.gr
Sales Range: $25-49.9 Million
Emp.: 35
Residential Construction
N.A.I.C.S.: 236115

Intrakat International Ltd (2)
36 Kypranoros Str 5th Floor, 1061, Nicosia, Cyprus
Tel.: (357) 22391908
Telecommunication Servicesb
N.A.I.C.S.: 517810

Intracom IT Services (1)
Markopoulou Ave, Peania, Athens, 19002, Greece
Tel.: (30) 210 66 79 000
Web Site: http://www.intracom.gr
Emp.: 800
Banking Software Development Services
N.A.I.C.S.: 541511
S. Kokkalis (Chm)

Subsidiary (Domestic):

Data Bank SA (2)
Skiathou 147, 11255, Athens, Greece
Tel.: (30) 210 2005000
Web Site: http://www.databank.com.gr
Sales Range: $25-49.9 Million
Emp.: 5
Mobile Internet Services
N.A.I.C.S.: 517810
George Thanopoulos (Mng Dir)

Subsidiary (Non-US):

Global Net Solutions Ltd (2)
119A Tsarigradsko Shose bul, 1784, Sofia, Bulgaria
Tel.: (359) 29746194
Web Site: http://www.globalnet.bg
Telecommunication Servicesb
N.A.I.C.S.: 517810

Intracom S.A. (1)
19 km Markopoulou Ave, Koropi, Athens, 19400, Greece
Tel.: (30) 210 6678000
Sales Range: $200-249.9 Million
Emp.: 548
Military Communications Equipment Mfr
N.A.I.C.S.: 334290

Intradevelopment SA (1)
19th km Paiania - Markopoulo Av, 190 02, Peania, Attica, Greece
Tel.: (30) 2106674700
Web Site: http://www.intradevelopment.gr
Real Estate Services
N.A.I.C.S.: 531390
Dimitrios S. Theodoridis (Chm)

Intrapower S.A. Energy Projects Company (1)
19th km Markopoulou Ave, Paiania Attiki, 19002, Athens, Greece
Tel.: (30) 2106674501
Web Site: http://intrapower.com.gr
Construction Services
N.A.I.C.S.: 236220
Dimitrios Klonis (Chm)

Thessaloniki Controlled Parking System S.A. (1)
A 1st Vasileos Georgiou Ave, Thessaloniki, Greece
Tel.: (30) 2312315404
Web Site: http://thesi.gr
Parking System Services
N.A.I.C.S.: 812930

Valeu Consulting SA (1)
5/10 Place du Champs de Mars 3rd Floor, 1050, Brussels, Belgium
Tel.: (32) 22381742
Web Site: http://www.valeu-consulting.com
Business Consulting Services
N.A.I.C.S.: 541611

Wemetrix S.A. (1)
19km Markopoulou-Peania Ave, 19002, Peania, Athens, Greece
Tel.: (30) 2106876524
Predictive Analytic Services
N.A.I.C.S.: 518210

INTRACORP PROJECTS LTD.

25 Centurian Drive Suite 204, Markham, L3R 5N8, ON, Canada
Tel.: (905) 940-6555
Web Site: http://www.intracorp.ca
Year Founded: 1994
Rev.: $33,084,940
Emp.: 116
Real Estate Services
N.A.I.C.S.: 531210
Joseph S. Houssian (Founder)

INTRALOT DE PERU S.A.

Av Jose Pardo 434 Piso 11, Miraflores, Lima, 15036, San Borja, Peru
Tel.: (51) 5135502
Web Site: http://www.intralot.com.pe
Lottery & Gambling Services
N.A.I.C.S.: 713290
Jose Armando Estrada Moron (Reg Head)

INTRALOT S.A.

19 km Markopoulou Ave, Attica, 19 002, Peania, Greece
Tel.: (30) 2106156000
Web Site: https://www.intralot.com
IRLTF—(OTCIQ)
Rev.: $98,252,752
Assets: $665,976,689
Liabilities: $760,637,816
Net Worth: ($94,661,127)
Earnings: $15,623,786
Emp.: 1,707
Fiscal Year-end: 12/31/22
Gaming & Betting Systems
N.A.I.C.S.: 713290
Sokratis Kokkalis (Chm & CEO)

Subsidiaries:

Betting Company S.A. (1)
Premetis 3, 15125, Maroussi, Greece
Tel.: (30) 2102800588
Web Site: https://www.betting.gr
Lottery & Gaming Services
N.A.I.C.S.: 713290

Bit8 Ltd. (1)
Level 2 Quantum House Triq ix-Xatt, Gzira, GZR 1052, Malta
Tel.: (356) 20925800
Web Site: https://www.bit8.com
Hostel Services
N.A.I.C.S.: 518210
Vassilis Trochalidis (CEO)

Gaming Solutions International SAC (1)
Av Del Parque Norte, 1180, Lima, San Borja, Peru
Tel.: (51) 15135568
Web Site: https://www.gamingsolutions.com.pe
Sales Range: $50-74.9 Million
Emp.: 3
Gambling Device Suppliers
N.A.I.C.S.: 713290

INTRALOT Beijing Co., Ltd. (1)
Rm 1612-1614 N Real Estate Bldg, 81 Zizhuyuan Rd, Beijing, Haidian, China
Tel.: (86) 1088825330
Sales Range: $50-74.9 Million
Emp.: 11
Gambling Services
N.A.I.C.S.: 713290

Intralot Asia Pacific Ltd. (1)
35 F Cent Plz 18 Harbour Rd, Wanchai, China (Hong Kong)
Tel.: (852) 2 2593 1113
Sales Range: $50-74.9 Million
Emp.: 15
Gambling Services
N.A.I.C.S.: 713290

Intralot Australia Pty Ltd. (1)
Level 4 650 Lorimer Street, PO Box 690, Port Melbourne, 3207, VIC, Australia
Tel.: (61) 1300764495
Web Site: https://www.igsmonitor.com.au
Sales Range: $25-49.9 Million
Lottery & Gambling Services
N.A.I.C.S.: 713290

Intralot Do Brazil Ltda (1)
Av Camilo Di Lellis 348 Fl 2 Rm 201, 83323000, Sao Jose dos Pinhais, Brazil
Tel.: (55) 4130339400
Gambling Services
N.A.I.C.S.: 713290

Intralot Gaming Services Pty. Ltd. (1)
Level 4 650 Lorimer Street, Port Melbourne, 3207, VIC, Australia
Tel.: (61) 1300764495
Web Site: https://www.igsmonitor.com.au
Electronic Device Services
N.A.I.C.S.: 811210

Intralot Inc. (1)
11360 Technology Cir, Duluth, GA 30097
Tel.: (678) 473-7200
Web Site: https://www.intralot.us
Sales Range: $25-49.9 Million
Emp.: 45
Lottery & Gambling Services
N.A.I.C.S.: 713290

Intralot South Africa Ltd. (1)
Athol Ridge Office Park 1st Fl Block B 151, Katherine St Sandton, Sandton, 2196, South Africa
Tel.: (27) 112174650
Web Site: http://www.intralot.com
Sales Range: $25-49.9 Million
Emp.: 20
Lottery & Gambling Services
N.A.I.C.S.: 713290
Yiannis Rondiris (CEO)

Intralot de Chile S.A. (1)
Av Vitacura 2939 Apt 1804, 1801, Santiago, Las Condes, Chile
Tel.: (56) 247031 00
Lottery & Gambling Services
N.A.I.C.S.: 713290

Maltco Lotteries Ltd. (1)
Hal Mann Bldg 2nd Fl St Michael St, Iklin, 1011, Malta
Tel.: (356) 23883000
Web Site: https://www.maltco.com
Lottery & Gambling Services
N.A.I.C.S.: 713290
John Katakis (Co-CEO)

Slovenske Loterie AS (1)
Stara Vajnorska 11, Bratislava, 83104, Slovakia
Tel.: (421) 263824118
Web Site: http://www.vlt.sk
Sales Range: $50-74.9 Million
Emp.: 25
Gambling Services
N.A.I.C.S.: 713290
Jan Hrusaa (Reg Mgr)

Tecno Accion S.A. (1)

INTERNATIONAL PUBLIC

Rivadavia 620 Piso 2, C1002AAR, Buenos Aires, Argentina
Tel.: (54) 1121504400
Web Site: https://www.tecnoaccion.com.ar
Technology Development Services
N.A.I.C.S.: 811210

INTRANCE CO., LTD.

9th floor Ohshita Building 1-16-5 Dogenzaka, Shibuya-ku, Tokyo, 150-0043, Japan
Tel.: (81) 368038100
Web Site: https://www.intrance.jp
Year Founded: 1998
3237—(TKS)
Rev.: $8,540,120
Assets: $7,654,380
Liabilities: $1,969,780
Net Worth: $5,684,600
Earnings: ($918,790)
Emp.: 87
Fiscal Year-end: 03/31/24
Real Estate Development Services
N.A.I.C.S.: 531390
Yuji Hamatani (Chm & Pres)

INTRAPAC CORPORATION

96 Scarsdale Road, Toronto, M3B 2R7, ON, Canada
Tel.: (461) 391-4296
Web Site: http://www.intrapacgroup.com
Aluminum & Laminated Tubes Mfr; Bottles, Jars, Jar Closures & Vials Mfr; Inhaler Cans & Fluoropolymer Coatings Mfr; Pharmaceutical Specialties Mfr
N.A.I.C.S.: 322219
Raymond Grupinski (CEO)

Subsidiaries:

IntraPac Canada Corporation (1)
7250 East Danbro Crescent, Mississauga, L5N 6C2, ON, Canada
Tel.: (905) 812-3955
Web Site: http://www.interpac.com
Emp.: 89
Packaging Products Mfr
N.A.I.C.S.: 326199
Robert Thiesson (Gen Mgr)

IntraPac Corporation (1)
810 N Main St, Harrisonburg, VA 22802-4625
Tel.: (540) 434-4411
Web Site: http://www.intrapacgroup.com
Sales Range: $25-49.9 Million
Emp.: 10
Mfr of Aluminum & Tin Tubes
N.A.I.C.S.: 332999
Randy Churchill (Gen Mgr)

IntraPac Corporation - Envasa Division (1)
600m Oeste de la Clinica Clorito Picado, San Rafael de 5 Esquinas de Tibas, San Jose, Costa Rica
Tel.: (506) 2547 0707
Web Site: http://www.intrapacinternational.com
Emp.: 350
Packaging Products Mfr
N.A.I.C.S.: 326199
Marlon Moreno (Mng Dir)

INTRASENSE SAS

1231 Avenue du Mondial 98, 34000, Montpellier, France
Tel.: (33) 467130134
Web Site: https://www.intrasense.fr
Year Founded: 2004
ALINS—(EUR)
Sales Range: $1-9.9 Million
Medical Software
N.A.I.C.S.: 513210
Stephane Chemouny (Founder, Pres & CEO)

Subsidiaries:

Intrasense SAS - International Division (1)

3 Castex Street, 75004, Paris, France
Tel.: (33) 1 48 04 32 83
Web Site: http://www.intrasense.fr
Emp.: 5
Medical Software
N.A.I.C.S.: 513210

INTRASOFT TECHNOLOGIES LIMITED
Suite 301 145 Rash Behari Avenue, Kolkata, 700 029, India
Tel.: (91) 3340231234
Web Site: https://www.itlindia.com
533181—(BOM)
Rev.: $58,209,579
Assets: $45,127,583
Liabilities: $22,380,008
Net Worth: $22,747,575
Earnings: $1,750,312
Emp.: 33
Fiscal Year-end: 03/31/22
Online Content & Information
N.A.I.C.S.: 519290
Arvind Kajaria *(Co-Founder & Mng Dir)*
Subsidiaries:
123Greetings.com, Inc. (1)
255 Executive Dr Ste 400, New York, NY 11803
Tel.: (212) 246-0044
Web Site: https://www.123greetings.com
Sales Range: $25-49.9 Million
Electronic Greeting Card Service
N.A.I.C.S.: 513191
Eddie Marmol *(Mgr-Bus Dev)*

INTRAVENOUS INFUSIONS PLC
Koforidua Appenteng Street Effiduase EN-055-0741 Block L Plot 7, Koforidua, Ghana
Tel.: (233) 342020151
Web Site: https://www.iil.com.gh
Year Founded: 1969
Pharmaceuticals Product Mfr
N.A.I.C.S.: 325412
Issac Osei *(Chm)*

INTRAWARE INVESTMENTS PUBLIC LTD.
Arsinois 12A, Strovolo, 2006, Nicosia, Cyprus
Tel.: (357) 99 268922
Web Site:
http://www.intrawareinvest.com
INTRA—(CYP)
Rev.: $61,478,074
Assets: $75,733,892
Liabilities: $67,700,016
Net Worth: $8,033,876
Earnings: $7,207,419
Fiscal Year-end: 12/31/19
Investment Services
N.A.I.C.S.: 523940

INTRED S.P.A.
Via Pietro Tamburini 1, 25136, Brescia, Italy
Tel.: (39) 03914143050
Web Site: https://www.intred.it
Year Founded: 1996
ITD—(ITA)
Sales Range: $10-24.9 Million
Broadband Internet Services
N.A.I.C.S.: 517112
Daniele Peli *(Chm & CEO)*

INTREPID METALS CORP.
2400 - 1055 West Georgia Street, Vancouver, V6E 3P3, BC, Canada
Tel.: (702) 990-3512 BC
Web Site:
https://www.intrepidmetals.com
Year Founded: 1978
TRAD—(TSXV)
Rev.: $45,423
Assets: $1,642,722
Liabilities: $278,114
Net Worth: $1,364,608
Earnings: ($1,274,467)
Emp.: 1
Fiscal Year-end: 12/31/23
Mobile Applications & Software Developer
N.A.I.C.S.: 513210
Jay Sujir *(Founder)*

INTRINSIC TECHNOLOGY, LTD.
14 The Parks, Haydock, WA12 0JQ, United Kingdom
Tel.: (44) 8708802792
Year Founded: 1999
Sales Range: $25-49.9 Million
Emp.: 81
IT Services
N.A.I.C.S.: 541512
Mike Mason *(Mng Dir)*

INTRO-VERWALTUNGS GMBH
Schlossweg 2, 91244, Reichenschwand, Germany
Tel.: (49) 9151 86 93 640
Web Site: http://www.introgroup.de
Emp.: 7
Holding Company
N.A.I.C.S.: 551112
Hans Rudolf Woehrl *(CEO)*
Subsidiaries:
INTRO Aviation GmbH (1)
Schlossweg 2, 91244, Reichenschwand, Germany
Tel.: (49) 9151 8693 640
Web Site: http://www.introaviation.com
Consulting Services for Aviation Industry
N.A.I.C.S.: 541618
Hans Rudolf Woehrl *(Partner)*
Subsidiary (Non-US):
Corsair S.A. (2)
2 Charles Lindbergh Avenue, Rungis, 94636, France (53%)
Tel.: (33) 1 49 79 49 59
Oil Transportation Services
N.A.I.C.S.: 488190

INTROL S.A.
Kosciuszki 112, 40-519, Katowice, Poland
Tel.: (48) 327890022
Web Site: https://www.introlsa.pl
Year Founded: 1990
INL—(WAR)
Rev.: $174,562,754
Assets: $131,814,024
Liabilities: $86,498,729
Net Worth: $45,315,295
Earnings: $9,057,165
Emp.: 1,600
Fiscal Year-end: 12/31/23
Industrial Automation Equipments Mfr
N.A.I.C.S.: 334513
Wieslaw Jozef Kapral *(Chm-Supervisory Bd)*
Subsidiaries:
Biuro Inzynierskie Atechem Sp. z o.o. (1)
ul Mostowa 2, 47-223, Kedzierzyn-Kozle, Poland
Tel.: (48) 774813762
Web Site: http://www.atechem.pl
Pressure Equipment Mfr
N.A.I.C.S.: 334512
I4Tech Sp. z o.o. (1)
ul 16 lipca 14, 41-506, Chorzow, Poland
Tel.: (48) 327841800
Web Site: http://www.i4t.pl
Engineeering Services
N.A.I.C.S.: 541330
IB Systems Sp. z o.o. (1)
ul Klinkierowa 7, 60-104, Poznan, Poland
Tel.: (48) 616468500
Web Site: http://www.ibsystems.pl
Automation System Mfr
N.A.I.C.S.: 334512
Sylwester Damiecki *(Project Mgr)*
Introl Automation s.r.o. (1)
Svabinskeho 1700/4, 702 00, Ostrava, Czech Republic
Tel.: (420) 603381153
Web Site: http://www.introl.cz
Automation System Mfr
N.A.I.C.S.: 334513
Robert Sowa *(CEO)*
Introl Automatyka Sp. z o.o. Sp.k. (1)
ul Kosciuszki 112, 40-519, Katowice, Poland
Tel.: (48) 327890030
Web Site: http://www.introlautomatyka.pl
Engineeering Services
N.A.I.C.S.: 541330
Lukasz Stangrecki *(Project Mgr)*
Introl PRO-ZAP Sp. z o.o. (1)
ul Grabowska 47a, 63-400, Ostrow Wielkopolski, Poland
Tel.: (48) 627374150
Engineeering Services
N.A.I.C.S.: 541330
Introl-Energomontaz Sp. z o.o. (1)
ul 16 Lipca 12, 41-506, Chorzow, Poland
Tel.: (48) 327874300
Web Site: http://www.introlenergo.pl
Emp.: 600
Energy System Mfr
N.A.I.C.S.: 335311
Marian Matys *(Mgr-Electrical Design)*
Limatherm Components Sp. z o.o. (1)
ul Zelazna 5, 41-506, Chorzow, Poland
Tel.: (48) 327831600
Engineeering Services
N.A.I.C.S.: 541330
Grzegorz Cisek *(Pres)*
Limatherm S.A. (1)
ul Tarnowska 1, Limanowa, 34-600, Krakow, Poland
Tel.: (48) 183379820
Web Site: http://www.limatherm.pl
Emp.: 500
Pressure Casting Mfr
N.A.I.C.S.: 334512
Marcin Kloss *(Project Mgr)*
Limatherm Sensor Sp. z o.o. (1)
ul Tarnowska 1, Limanowa, 34-600, Krakow, Poland
Tel.: (48) 183379901
Temperature Sensor Mfr
N.A.I.C.S.: 333248
Michal Lesniak *(Mgr-Export)*
PWP Inzynieria sp. z o.o. (1)
ul Katowicka 60, 41-400, Myslowice, Poland
Tel.: (48) 322090188
Web Site: http://www.pwpinzynieria.pl
Wastewater Equipment Mfr
N.A.I.C.S.: 333248
RAControls Sp. z o.o. (1)
ul Kosciuszki 112, 40-519, Katowice, Poland
Tel.: (48) 327887700
Web Site: http://www.racontrols.pl
Electric Drive Mfr
N.A.I.C.S.: 334512
Mariusz Rudzinski *(Acct Mgr)*
Smart in Sp. z o.o. Sp. k. (1)
ul Porcelanowa 23, 40-246, Katowice, Poland
Tel.: (48) 502377695
Web Site: http://www.smart-in.eu
Real Estate Services
N.A.I.C.S.: 531210

INTROMEDIC CO., LTD.
1105 41 Digital-ro 31-gil, Guro-gu, Seoul, 08375, Korea (South)
Tel.: (82) 28019300
Web Site:
https://www.intromedic.com
Year Founded: 2004
150840—(KRS)
Rev.: $9,261,030
Assets: $25,542,700
Liabilities: $11,770,674
Net Worth: $13,772,026
Earnings: ($26,333,134)
Emp.: 62
Fiscal Year-end: 12/31/22
Medical Device Mfr
N.A.I.C.S.: 339112
Yong Seok Cho *(CEO)*
Subsidiaries:
Hyunjin Materials Co., Ltd. (1)
#46754,92 Noksansandan289-ro, Gangseo Gu, 618027, Busan, Korea (South)
Tel.: (82) 516027700
Web Site: http://www.hjmco.co.kr
Rev.: $1,595,571
Assets: $41,640,168
Liabilities: $89,119,413
Net Worth: ($47,479,246)
Earnings: ($4,362,956)
Emp.: 40
Fiscal Year-end: 12/31/2022
Engine Component Mfr
N.A.I.C.S.: 333618
Do-Heon Lee *(CEO)*

INTRON BIOTECHNOLOGY, INC.
Suite 701-704 137 Sagimakgol-ro, Joongwon-gu, Seongnam, 462-120, Gyeonggi-do, Korea (South)
Tel.: (82) 317395678
Web Site: https://www.intron.co.kr
Year Founded: 1999
048530—(KRS)
Rev.: $10,743,352
Assets: $108,115,220
Liabilities: $26,674,241
Net Worth: $81,440,980
Earnings: $4,381,033
Emp.: 88
Fiscal Year-end: 12/31/22
Biotechnology Products Researcher, Developer & Mfr
N.A.I.C.S.: 541714
Kyung-Won Yoon *(CEO & VP)*
Subsidiaries:
iNtRON Biotechnology Inc - Reagent Business Division (1)
1011 137 Sagimakgol-ro, Jungwon-gu, Seongnam, Gyeonggi-do, Korea (South)
Tel.: (82) 31 739 5733
Web Site: http://www.intron.co.kr
Biological Product Mfr
N.A.I.C.S.: 325414

INTRON TECHNOLOGY HOLDINGS LIMITED
Unit 1008-10 10/F Delta House 3 On Yiu Street, Sha Tin, New Territories, China (Hong Kong)
Tel.: (852) 35801700 Ky
Web Site: http://www.intron-tech.com
Year Founded: 2001
1760—(HKG)
Rev.: $678,123,997
Assets: $572,117,785
Liabilities: $270,449,150
Net Worth: $301,668,635
Earnings: $57,719,423
Emp.: 1,359
Fiscal Year-end: 12/31/22
Automotive Electronic Component Mfr & Distr
N.A.I.C.S.: 336390
Wing Ming Luk *(Co-Founder, Chm & Co-CEO)*
Subsidiaries:
Intron Technology (China) Limited (1)
Unit 2217-18 22/F Grandtech Centre 8 On Ping Street New Territories, Sha Tin, China (Hong Kong)
Tel.: (852) 26469030
Industrial Equipment Mfr
N.A.I.C.S.: 333248
Mike Lam *(Sr Mgr-Product Mktg)*

INTRON TECHNOLOGY HOLDINGS LIMITED

Intron Technology Holdings Limited—(Continued)

Shanghai G-Pulse Electronics Technology Company Limited (1)
1F Block 10 Zhongtian Science and Technology Business Park, 787 Kang Qiao Road, Shanghai, 201315, China
Tel.: (86) 2161905968
Web Site: http://www.g-pulse.net
Electric Equipment Mfr
N.A.I.C.S.: 334419

Shanghai Intron Electronics Company Limited (1)
Block 68 Lane 1000 Zhang Heng Road, Pu Dong District, Shanghai, 201203, China
Tel.: (86) 2161681999
Industrial Equipment Mfr
N.A.I.C.S.: 333248

INTRUM AB

Sicklastraket 4 Nacka, 105 24, Stockholm, Sverige, Sweden SE
Tel.: (46) 344552500
Web Site: https://www.intrum.com
INTRUM—(OMX)
Rev.: $2,171,681,120
Assets: $10,853,522,400
Liabilities: $7,839,733,440
Net Worth: $3,013,788,960
Earnings: $413,973,280
Emp.: 9,694
Fiscal Year-end: 12/31/21
Credit Management Services
N.A.I.C.S.: 522390
Per Christofferson (Mng Dir-Secured Assets, M&A & Markets)

Subsidiaries:

AssetGate GmbH (1)
Bismarckplatz 1, 45128, Essen, Germany
Tel.: (49) 20124677280
Web Site: https://www.assetgate.com
Financial Services
N.A.I.C.S.: 523999

Byjuno AG (1)
Industriestrasse 13c, 6300, Zug, Switzerland
Tel.: (41) 412270505
Web Site: http://www.byjuno.ch
Credit Management Services
N.A.I.C.S.: 522390
Christian Stolz (Mng Dir)

Fair Pay Management AB (1)
Marcusplatsen 1a, Nacka, Sweden (100%)
Tel.: (46) 86167820
Web Site: http://www.intrum.com
Emp.: 400
Management Consulting Services
N.A.I.C.S.: 541618
Per-Henrik Persson (Mgr)

I.C.S International Collections Services BV (1)
Johan de Wittlaan 3 - 5, 's-Gravendeel, Netherlands (100%)
Tel.: (31) 704527996
Motor Vehicle Parts Mfr
N.A.I.C.S.: 336390

Inkasso Med AG (1)
Eschenstrasse 12, 8603, Schwerzenbach, Switzerland
Web Site: http://www.inkassomed.ch
Credit Management Services
N.A.I.C.S.: 522390

Intrum A/S (1)
Kirsten Walthers Vej 7, 2500, Valby, Denmark
Tel.: (45) 33697000
Credit Management Services
N.A.I.C.S.: 522390

Intrum AG (1)
Eschenstrasse 12, 8603, Schwerzenbach, Switzerland
Tel.: (41) 448065656
Web Site: https://www.intrum.ch
Credit Management Services
N.A.I.C.S.: 522390

Intrum Austria GmbH (1)
Ares Tower Donau-City-Strasse 11, 1220, Vienna, Austria
Tel.: (43) 1260887747
Web Site: http://www.intrum.at
Financial Services
N.A.I.C.S.: 523999
Marc Knothe (Mng Dir)

Intrum Brasil Consultoria e Participacoes, S.A. (1)
8501 Nacoes Unidas Ave 4th Floor, Pinheiros, 05425-070, Sao Paulo, Brazil
Tel.: (55) 1147655600
Credit Management Services
N.A.I.C.S.: 522390
Ulisses Rodrigues (CEO)

Intrum Corporate SAS (1)
Immeuble Les Passerelles 104 Avenue Albert 1er, 92500, Rueil-Malmaison, France
Tel.: (33) 472801414
Web Site: http://www.intrum.fr
Financial Services
N.A.I.C.S.: 523999

Intrum Data Systems (Deutschland) GmbH (1)
Pallaswiesenstr 180-182, 64293, Darmstadt, Germany (100%)
Tel.: (49) 61518160
Sales Range: $25-49.9 Million
Emp.: 150
Collection Agencies
N.A.I.C.S.: 561440
Thomas Hutter (Gen Mgr)

Intrum Delgivningsservice AB (1)
Box 90296, 120 24, Stockholm, Sweden
Tel.: (46) 86167871
Credit Management Services
N.A.I.C.S.: 522390

Intrum Deutschland GmbH (1)
Donnersbergstrasse 1, 64646, Heppenheim, Germany
Tel.: (49) 62526720
Web Site: http://www.intrum.de
Credit Management Services
N.A.I.C.S.: 522390

Intrum Financial Services GmbH (1)
Donnersbergstrasse 1, 64646, Heppenheim, Germany
Tel.: (49) 62529380100
Credit Management Services
N.A.I.C.S.: 522390

Intrum Global Business Services UAB (1)
Spaudos str 8-1 Duetto 5th Floor, LT-05132, Vilnius, Lithuania
Tel.: (370) 69812967
Credit Management Services
N.A.I.C.S.: 522390
Lina Gelumbauskaite (Dir-HR & Admin)

Intrum Hanseatische InkassoTreuhand GmbH (1)
Eiffestrasse 76, 20537, Hamburg, Germany
Tel.: (49) 402999230
Credit Management Services
N.A.I.C.S.: 522390

Intrum Hellas A.E.D.A.D.P. (1)
109-111 Mesogeion Ave, 115 26, Athens, Greece
Tel.: (30) 2108622000
Web Site: http://www.intrum.gr
Credit Management Services
N.A.I.C.S.: 522390

Intrum Information Services Deutschland GmbH (1)
Donnersbergstrasse 1, 64646, Heppenheim, Germany
Tel.: (49) 6252672050
Credit Management Services
N.A.I.C.S.: 522390

Intrum International S.A. (1)
Juan Esplandiu 11-13 Planta 7, 28007, Madrid, Spain
Tel.: (34) 91 423 4600
Sales Range: $200-249.9 Million
Emp.: 30
Credit Management Services
N.A.I.C.S.: 522390

Intrum Ireland Ltd. (1)
First Floor Block C Ashtown Gate Navan Road, Dublin, D15Y3EK, Ireland
Tel.: (353) 18692226

Web Site: https://www.intrum.ie
Credit Management Services
N.A.I.C.S.: 522390
Phil Hickson (Head-Bus Dev)

Intrum Justitia (Holdings) Ltd (1)
5th Floor The Plaza 100 Old Hall St, Liverpool, L3 9QJ, Merseyside, United Kingdom (100%)
Tel.: (44) 1514727155
Web Site: http://www.intrum.co.uk
Financial Investment
N.A.I.C.S.: 523999

Intrum Justitia A/S (1)
Lyngbyvej 20, 2100, Copenhagen, Denmark
Tel.: (45) 3369 7000
Emp.: 65
Credit Management Services
N.A.I.C.S.: 541611
Morten Engelbaek (Mng Dir)

Intrum Justitia AG (1)
Eschenstrasse 12, 8603, Schwerzenbach, Switzerland (100%)
Tel.: (41) 448065656
Web Site: http://www.intrum.ch
Sales Range: $25-49.9 Million
Emp.: 200
Collection Agencies
N.A.I.C.S.: 561440

Intrum Justitia AS (1)
Rotermanni 8, 10111, Tallinn, Estonia (100%)
Tel.: (372) 6060990
Web Site: http://www.intrum.ee
Sales Range: $10-24.9 Million
Emp.: 30
Business Support Services
N.A.I.C.S.: 561499

Intrum Justitia AS (1)
Nils Hansensv 2, PO Box 6354, Etterstad, Oslo, 654, Norway
Tel.: (47) 23 17 10 00
Credit Management Services
N.A.I.C.S.: 522390

Intrum Justitia BV (1)
Johan de Wittlaan 3, 2517 JR, Hague, Netherlands
Tel.: (31) 70 452 70 00
Sales Range: $200-249.9 Million
Emp.: 284
Credit Management Services
N.A.I.C.S.: 522299

Intrum Justitia Central Europe BV (1)
Johan De Wittlaan 3, 's-Gravendeel, Netherlands (100%)
Tel.: (31) 704527996
Sales Range: $25-49.9 Million
Emp.: 100
Civic & Social Organizations
N.A.I.C.S.: 813410

Intrum Justitia Data Centre BV (1)
Johan De Wittlaan 3-5, Hague, 2517 JR, Zuid-Holland, Netherlands
Tel.: (31) 704527000
Software Development Services
N.A.I.C.S.: 541511

Intrum Justitia Debt Finance Domestic AG (1)
Alpenstrasse 2, 6300, Zug, Switzerland (100%)
Tel.: (41) 417107420
Public Finance Activities
N.A.I.C.S.: 921130

Intrum Justitia Debt Finance Poland Sp. z. o. o (1)
Domaniewska 41, Warsaw, 02-672, Poland
Tel.: (48) 225766580
Financial Management Services
N.A.I.C.S.: 523999

Intrum Justitia Debt Fund 1 Fundusz Inwestycyjny Zamkniety Niestandaryzowany Fundusz Sekurytyzacyjny (1)
ul Domaniewska 41, 02-672, Warsaw, Poland
Tel.: (48) 22 576 66 66
Credit Management Services
N.A.I.C.S.: 522390

INTERNATIONAL PUBLIC

Intrum Justitia Debt Surveillance Sp. z.o.o (1)
Domaniewska 41, Warsaw, 02-672, Poland
Tel.: (48) 22 576 66 66
Credit Management Services
N.A.I.C.S.: 522390

Intrum Justitia Finance Service AG (1)
Eschenstrasse 12, Schwerzenbach, 8603, Switzerland
Tel.: (41) 448065355
Administrative Management & Financial Services
N.A.I.C.S.: 541611

Intrum Justitia Finland Oy (1)
Hitsaajankatu 20, PO Box 47, 811, Helsinki, Finland
Tel.: (358) 9 229 111
Credit Management Services
N.A.I.C.S.: 522390
Tommi Sova (Mng Dir)

Intrum Justitia GmbH (1)
Franz Brotzner Strasse 11, AT 5071, Wals-Siezenheim, Austria (100%)
Tel.: (43) 662835077
Web Site: http://www.intrum.at
Activities Related to Credit Intermediation
N.A.I.C.S.: 522390

Intrum Justitia GmbH (1)
Pallaswiesenstrasse 180-182, 64293, Darmstadt, Germany
Tel.: (49) 6151 816 0
Credit Management Services
N.A.I.C.S.: 541990
Bernard Green (Mng Dir)

Intrum Justitia Hitel Ugyintezo Szolgaltatas Kft (1)
Pap Karoly Utca 4-6, Budapest, Hungary (100%)
Tel.: (36) 614599400
Web Site: http://www.intrum.hu
Collection Agencies
N.A.I.C.S.: 561440

Intrum Justitia Holding GmbH (1)
Pallaswiesenstr 182, Darmstadt, 64293, Germany (100%)
Tel.: (49) 615181600
Holding Company
N.A.I.C.S.: 551112
Gurgen Sonder (Mng Dir)

Intrum Justitia Iberica S.A.U. (1)
Juan Esplandiu 11-13, 28007, Madrid, Spain (100%)
Tel.: (34) 914234600
Sales Range: $75-99.9 Million
Emp.: 300
Collection Agencies
N.A.I.C.S.: 561440
Eoancarlos Gonzalez (Mng Dir)

Intrum Justitia Inkasso Gesellschaft m. b. H. (1)
Karolingerstrasse 36, 5020, Salzburg, Austria (100%)
Tel.: (43) 662835077
Web Site: http://www.intrum.at
Sales Range: $25-49.9 Million
Emp.: 25
Collection Agencies
N.A.I.C.S.: 561440

Intrum Justitia Inkasso GmbH (1)
Pallaswiesenstr 180-182, 64293, Darmstadt, Germany (100%)
Tel.: (49) 61518160
Web Site: http://www.intrum.de
Sales Range: $25-49.9 Million
Emp.: 220
Collection Agencies
N.A.I.C.S.: 561440
Thomas Hutter (Mgr)

Intrum Justitia Inkassosystem AB (1)
Marcusplatsen 1a, 13134, Nacka, Sweden (100%)
Tel.: (46) 86167750
Web Site: http://www.intrum.se
Nondepository Credit Intermediation
N.A.I.C.S.: 522299

Intrum Justitia Ireland Ltd (1)
1st Floor Block C Ashtown Gate IE, D15 Y3EK, Dublin, Ireland (100%)

AND PRIVATE COMPANIES

Tel.: (353) 18692222
Web Site: http://www.intrum.com
Collection Agencies
N.A.I.C.S.: 561440

Intrum Justitia Koveteleskezelo Zrt. (1)
Vaci ut 144-150, 1138, Budapest, Hungary **(100%)**
Tel.: (36) 14599496
Web Site: http://www.intrum.hu
Sales Range: $25-49.9 Million
Emp.: 100
Collection Agencies
N.A.I.C.S.: 561440

Intrum Justitia Licensing AG (1)
Alpenstrasse 2, Zug, Switzerland **(100%)**
Tel.: (41) 448065656
Web Site: http://www.intrum.ch
Emp.: 200
Software Reproducing
N.A.I.C.S.: 921130

Intrum Justitia Ltd (1)
The Plaza 10 Old Hall Street, L39 QJ, Liverpool, United Kingdom **(100%)**
Tel.: (44) 1514727155
Web Site: http://www.intrum.co.uk
Sales Range: $25-49.9 Million
Emp.: 100
Credit Bureaus
N.A.I.C.S.: 561450

Intrum Justitia Nederland BV (1)
PO Box 84096, 2508, 's-Gravendeel, Netherlands **(100%)**
Tel.: (31) 704527000
Sales Range: $50-74.9 Million
Emp.: 100
Activities Related to Credit Intermediation
N.A.I.C.S.: 522390

Intrum Justitia Norge AS (1)
Innspurten 9, 663, Oslo, Norway
Tel.: (47) 23171000
Credit Management Services
N.A.I.C.S.: 522390

Intrum Justitia Oy (1)
Hitsaajankatu 20, 00810, Helsinki, Finland **(100%)**
Tel.: (358) 9229111
Web Site: http://www.intrum.fi
Sales Range: $25-49.9 Million
Emp.: 100
Business Support Services
N.A.I.C.S.: 561499

Intrum Justitia Portugal Unipessoal Lda. (1)
Alameda dos Oceanos 59 Espace Building Piso 1, 1990-207, Lisbon, Portugal **(100%)**
Tel.: (351) 213172216
Web Site: http://www.intrum.pt
Sales Range: $25-49.9 Million
Emp.: 100
Business Support Services
N.A.I.C.S.: 561439

Intrum Justitia S.r.o. (1)
Prosecka 851/64, 190 00, Prague, 9, Czech Republic **(100%)**
Tel.: (420) 277003730
Web Site: http://www.intrum.cz
Collection Agencies
N.A.I.C.S.: 561440

Intrum Justitia SAS (1)
97 Allee Alexandre Borodine, 69795, Saint Priest, France
Tel.: (33) 4 7280 1414
Credit Management Services
N.A.I.C.S.: 522390

Intrum Justitia Sia (1)
Sokarla Olmana 2, 1004, Riga, Latvia **(100%)**
Tel.: (371) 7332877
Web Site: http://www.intrum.lv
Sales Range: $25-49.9 Million
Emp.: 16
Business Support Services
N.A.I.C.S.: 561499

Intrum Justitia Slovakia S. r. o. (1)
CBC1 Karadzicova 8, 82108, Bratislava, Slovakia **(100%)**
Tel.: (421) 257204700
Web Site: http://www.intrumsk.sk

Sales Range: $10-24.9 Million
Emp.: 40
Collection Agencies
N.A.I.C.S.: 561440

Intrum Justitia Sp.zo.o. (1)
Domaniewska 48 Ul Domaniewska 41, 02-672, Warsaw, Poland **(100%)**
Tel.: (48) 225766666
Web Site: http://www.intrum.pl
Sales Range: $75-99.9 Million
Emp.: 300
Collection Agencies
N.A.I.C.S.: 561440

Intrum Justitia SpA (1)
Viale E Jenner 53, 20159, Milan, Italy **(100%)**
Tel.: (39) 02288701
Web Site: http://www.intrum.it
Business Support Services
N.A.I.C.S.: 561499

Intrum Justitia Sverige AB (1)
Sicklastraket 4, 10524, Nacka, Sweden **(100%)**
Tel.: (46) 86167700
Web Site: http://www.intrum.se
Sales Range: $200-249.9 Million
Emp.: 500
Nondepository Credit Intermediation
N.A.I.C.S.: 522299

Intrum Justitia Sweden Holding AB (1)
Marcusplatsen 1a, 10524S, Stockholm, Sweden **(100%)**
Tel.: (46) 86167700
Web Site: http://www.intrum.ie
Sales Range: $75-99.9 Million
Emp.: 300
Management Consulting Services
N.A.I.C.S.: 541618

Intrum Justitia Towarzystwo Funduszy Inwestycyjnych S.A (1)
ul Domaniewska 41, 02-672, Warsaw, Poland **(100%)**
Tel.: (48) 225766580
Emp.: 100
Management Consulting Services
N.A.I.C.S.: 541618

Intrum Lietuva UAB (1)
Spaudos gatve 8 Business house 7th floor, 05132, Vilnius, Lithuania
Tel.: (370) 52045600
Web Site: https://www.intrum.lt
Credit Management Services
N.A.I.C.S.: 522390

Intrum Oy (1)
PO 47, 00811, Helsinki, Finland
Tel.: (358) 9229111
Web Site: https://www.intrum.fi
Debt Collection Services
N.A.I.C.S.: 561440

Intrum Romania SA (1)
Str Dinu Vintila no 11 Floor 1 and 2, 021101, Bucharest, Romania
Tel.: (40) 213653434
Web Site: http://www.intrum.ro
Credit Management Services
N.A.I.C.S.: 522390

Intrum Slovakia s.r.o. (1)
Mytna 48 Blumental offices I, 811 07, Bratislava, Slovakia
Tel.: (421) 242163185
Web Site: http://www.intrum.sk
Credit Management Services
N.A.I.C.S.: 522390

Intrum Sp. z o.o. (1)
Milosza 15, 50-304, Wroclaw, Poland
Tel.: (48) 717116666
Web Site: https://www.intrum.pl
Debt Recovery Services
N.A.I.C.S.: 561440

Intrum Zrt (1)
Fiastyuk utca 4-8, XIII District, Budapest, Hungary
Tel.: (36) 14599496
Web Site: https://www.intrum.hu
Debt Collection Services
N.A.I.C.S.: 561440

Iris Hellas REO S.A. (1)

Dodekanisou 40, 56 728, Thessaloniki, Greece
Tel.: (30) 6946466767
Web Site: https://www.irishellas.com
Debt Collection Services
N.A.I.C.S.: 561440

Lakoingatlan-Forgalmazo Kft (1)
Vaci ut 144-150, 1138, Budapest, Hungary
Tel.: (36) 305093211
Web Site:
 http://www.lakoinforg.ingatlan.com
Real Estate Services
N.A.I.C.S.: 531210

Lindorff AS (1)
Hoffsveien 70 B, 0377, Oslo, Norway
Tel.: (47) 23211000
Web Site: http://www.lindorff.no
Credit Management Services
N.A.I.C.S.: 522390

Mirus International BV (1)
Burg Pabstlaan 10-E2, 2131 XE, Hoofddorp, Netherlands
Tel.: (31) 203050000
Web Site: http://www.mirus.nl
Credit Management Services
N.A.I.C.S.: 522390

Nice Invest Nordic AB (1)
Monarkvagen 3, Varberg, 432 40, Halland, Sweden
Tel.: (46) 340698100
Credit Management Services
N.A.I.C.S.: 522390

Outsourcing Partners N.V (1)
Martelaarslaan 53, PO Box 181, Ghent, 9000, Brussels, Belgium **(100%)**
Tel.: (32) 70660016
Law firm
N.A.I.C.S.: 541199

Portfolio Investment ICAV (1)
25-28 North Wall Quay Dublin 1, Dublin, Ireland
Tel.: (353) 412150005
Web Site:
 https://www.portfolioinvesticav.com
Investment Management Service
N.A.I.C.S.: 523940

SIA Intrum Global Technologies (1)
Ieriku Street 5, Riga, LV-1084, Latvia
Tel.: (371) 25722515
Software Development Services
N.A.I.C.S.: 541511

Schimmelpfeng Creditmanagement GmbH (1)
Pallaswiesenstr 180-182, Darmstadt, 64293, Germany
Tel.: (49) 61518165500
Sales Range: $25-49.9 Million
Emp.: 200
Credit Management Consulting Services
N.A.I.C.S.: 541690
Thomas Hutter *(Gen Mgr)*

Schimmelpfeng Forderungsmanagement GmbH (1)
Pallaswiesenstr 180-182, 64293, Darmstadt, Germany **(100%)**
Tel.: (49) 615142850
Web Site: http://www.schimmelpfeng.com
Sales Range: $25-49.9 Million
Emp.: 200
Collection Agencies
N.A.I.C.S.: 561440

Solutius Belgium N.V (1)
Martelaarslann 53, Gent, 9000, Belgium
Tel.: (32) 2 723 90 60
Sales Range: $100-124.9 Million
Emp.: 120
Credit Management Services
N.A.I.C.S.: 522390
Guy Colpaert *(Gen Mgr)*

UAB Intrum Justitia (1)
A Gostauto 40A, 01112, Vilnius, Lithuania **(100%)**
Tel.: (370) 52490969
Web Site: http://www.intrum.lt
Sales Range: $25-49.9 Million
Emp.: 13
Collection Agencies
N.A.I.C.S.: 561440

INTRUST GROUP OF COMPANIES

Charles House 108-110 Finchley Road, London, NW3 5JJ, United Kingdom
Tel.: (44) 2074672100   UK
Web Site: http://www.intrust.co.uk
Year Founded: 1996
Sales Range: $10-24.9 Million
Emp.: 100
Holding Company; Corporate & Professional Services
N.A.I.C.S.: 551112
Martin Landman *(Founder)*

Subsidiaries:

CYP inTrust Limited (1)
Kyriakou Matsi 3 Roussos Limassol Tower, 5th Floor Office 5C, Limassol, 1340, Cyprus
Tel.: (357) 25875038
Web Site: http://www.cyp-intrust.com
Sales Range: $50-74.9 Million
Emp.: 7
Trust & Banking Services
N.A.I.C.S.: 523150

InTrust Advisors Management Consultancies LLC (1)
Suite 2109 Level 21 Al Habtoor Business Tour, PO Box 52090, Dubai Marina, Dubai, United Arab Emirates
Tel.: (971) 4 453 2633
Web Site: http://www.intrustamc.com
Financial Advisory Services
N.A.I.C.S.: 523940

Intrust Mideast Limited (1)
Office No W2 25&26 Level 1 Incubator Building, Masbar City, Dubai, United Arab Emirates
Tel.: (971) 42045219
Web Site: http://www.intrustmideast.com
Commodity Trading Services
N.A.I.C.S.: 523160

The Benedict Partnership LLP (1)
Ladbroke Suite, 3 Welbeck St, London, W1G 0AR, United Kingdom
Tel.: (44) 2074862200
Web Site: http://www.benedict-
 partnership.co.uk
Consulting Services
N.A.I.C.S.: 541618

inTrust (Manx) Limited (1)
4-8 Hope Street, PO Box 140, Douglas, LM99 1WU, Isle of Man
Tel.: (44) 1624616544
Web Site: http://www.intrust-manx.com
Emp.: 50
Formation & Incorporation of Company Registrations & Trusts
N.A.I.C.S.: 523991
William Leach *(Mng Dir)*

inTrust Limited (1)
4th Floor Portman House 2 Portman Street, London, W1H 6DU, United Kingdom
Tel.: (44) 2074672100
Web Site: http://www.intrust.co.uk
Sales Range: $10-24.9 Million
Emp.: 80
Trust & Banking Services
N.A.I.C.S.: 523991

INTUITION IT SOLUTIONS

Unit 6 Ground Floor Berghem Mews, London, United Kingdom
Tel.: (44) 207 348 5800
Web Site: http://www.intuition-it.com
Year Founded: 2006
Sales Range: $10-24.9 Million
Emp.: 22
Human Resource Consulting Services
N.A.I.C.S.: 541612
Sacha Milojovic *(Founder)*

INTUITIVE INVESTMENTS GROUP PLC

One St Peters Square, Manchester, M2 3DE, United Kingdom
Web Site: https://www.iigplc.com
Year Founded: 2020
IIG—(LSE)
Assets: $13,332,492

INTUITIVE INVESTMENTS GROUP PLC

Intuitive Investments Group Plc—(Continued)
Liabilities: $126,231
Net Worth: $13,206,261
Earnings: ($4,084,827)
Emp.: 5
Fiscal Year-end: 09/30/23
Investment Management Service
N.A.I.C.S.: 523999
M. Gillies *(Sec)*

INUI GLOBAL LOGISTICS CO., LTD.
Plaza Tower Kachidoki 1-13-6 Kachidoki, Chuo-ku, Tokyo, 104-0054, Japan
Tel.: (81) 355488211
Web Site: https://www.inui.co.jp
Year Founded: 1904
9308—(TKS)
Rev.: $194,955,340
Assets: $439,598,050
Liabilities: $230,603,070
Net Worth: $208,994,980
Earnings: $7,892,340
Emp.: 176
Fiscal Year-end: 03/31/24
Shipping Transportation Services
N.A.I.C.S.: 483111
Yamada Haruhiko *(Auditor)*

Subsidiaries:

Inui Transport Co., Ltd. (1)
2-1-10 Shinonome, Koto-ku, Tokyo, 135-0062, Japan
Tel.: (81) 120511254
Web Site: https://www.inui-transport.co.jp
General Freight Trucking Services
N.A.I.C.S.: 484110

INUVIALUIT REGIONAL CORPORATION
107 Mackenzie Road Bag Service 21, Inuvik, X0E 0T0, NT, Canada
Tel.: (867) 777-7000
Web Site:
https://www.irc.inuvialuit.com
Year Founded: 1984
Sales Range: $200-249.9 Million
Holding Company
N.A.I.C.S.: 551112
Duane Ningaqsiq Smith *(Chm & CEO)*

Subsidiaries:

Inuvialuit Development
Corporation (1)
3rd Floor Inuvialuit Corporate Centre 107 Mackenzie Road, Bag Service 7, Inuvik, X0E 0T0, NT, Canada **(100%)**
Tel.: (867) 777-7050
Web Site: http://www.idc.inuvialuit.com
Sales Range: $125-149.9 Million
Emp.: 18
Economic Development Services
N.A.I.C.S.: 926110
Wayne Gordon *(Chm)*

Subsidiary (Domestic):

Arctic Oil and Gas Services Ltd (2)
PO Box 2600, Inuvik, X0E 0T0, NT, Canada
Tel.: (867) 777-8700
Catering Services
N.A.I.C.S.: 722320

Division (Domestic):

IDC Property Management (2)
PO Box 7, Inuvik, X0E 0T0, NT, Canada
Tel.: (867) 777-2419
Property Management Services
N.A.I.C.S.: 531312

Subsidiary (Domestic):

IEG Inc. (2)
1100 550 11 Ave SW, Calgary, T2R 1M7, AB, Canada
Tel.: (403) 291-0777
Web Site: http://www.ieg.ca

Environmental Services
N.A.I.C.S.: 541620

Stanton Group Ltd. (2)
49 Navy Road, Inuvik, X0E 0T0, NT, Canada
Tel.: (867) 777-4381
Sales Range: $10-24.9 Million
Emp.: 40
Food Distr
N.A.I.C.S.: 722310

Inuvialuit Investment Corporation (1)
Bag Service 21, Inuvik, X0E 0T0, NT, Canada
Tel.: (867) 777-2737
Web Site: http://www.irc.inuvialuit.com
Sales Range: $75-99.9 Million
Emp.: 60
Securities Portfolio Management Services
N.A.I.C.S.: 523150
Nellie Cournoyea *(Chm)*

Inuvialuit Petroleum Corporation (1)
100 300-5th Avenue, Calgary, T2P 3C4, AB, Canada
Tel.: (403) 282-8955
Liquefied Petroleum Gas Storage Services
N.A.I.C.S.: 424710

INV, INC.
1-5-6 Higashi-Nihonbashi, Chuo-ku, Tokyo, 103-0004, Japan
Tel.: (81) 36 858 7105
Web Site: http://www.inv.inc
Year Founded: 2020
7338—(TKS)
Rev.: $49,929,440
Assets: $1,213,959,120
Liabilities: $1,101,032,240
Net Worth: $112,926,880
Earnings: $7,821,440
Fiscal Year-end: 03/31/22
Securities Brokerage Services
N.A.I.C.S.: 523150
Takeshi Kawaji *(Pres & CEO)*

Subsidiaries:

Invast Capital Management Co., Ltd. (1)
2-13-2 Higashinihonbashi, Chuo-ku, Tokyo, 103-0004, Japan
Tel.: (81) 366836001
Web Site: http://www.invastcm.jp
Financial Services
N.A.I.C.S.: 523999

INVALDA INVL AB
Gyneju 14, 01109, Vilnius, Lithuania
Tel.: (370) 52790601
Web Site:
https://www.invaldainvl.com
Year Founded: 1991
IVL1L—(VSE)
Rev.: $18,721,635
Assets: $241,151,440
Liabilities: $44,629,464
Net Worth: $196,521,976
Earnings: $50,579,323
Emp.: 124
Fiscal Year-end: 12/31/23
Asset Management Services
N.A.I.C.S.: 523940
Alvydas Banys *(Chm)*

Subsidiaries:

INVL Asset Management UAB (1)
Gyneju str 14, 01109, Vilnius, Lithuania
Tel.: (370) 70055959
Web Site: https//www.invl.com
Asset Management & Life Insurance Services
N.A.I.C.S.: 524113

INVAR BUILDING CORPORATION
220 Duncan Mill Road Suite 301, Toronto, M3B 3J5, ON, Canada
Tel.: (416) 441-9855
Web Site: http://www.invar.ca
Rev.: $82,214,000
Emp.: 18

Commercial & Residential Building Construction Services
N.A.I.C.S.: 236220
Dusty Miklas *(Pres & CEO)*

INVAST SECURITIES CO., LTD.
NBF Toranomon Building 1-6-21 Nishishinbashi, Minato-Ku, Tokyo, 105-0003, Japan
Tel.: (81) 3 35954111
Web Site: http://www.invast.jp
Year Founded: 1960
Rev.: $41,630,700
Assets: $1,007,290,800
Liabilities: $909,587,760
Net Worth: $97,703,040
Earnings: $4,403,160
Emp.: 55
Fiscal Year-end: 03/31/19
Foreign Exchange Margin Transaction Services
N.A.I.C.S.: 522320
Takeshi Kawaji *(Pres & CEO)*

Subsidiaries:

Invast Financial Services Pty Ltd. (1)
Level 27 Aurora Place 88 Phillip Street, Sydney, 2000, NSW, Australia
Tel.: (61) 290831333
Web Site: http://www.invast.com.au
Financial Management Services
N.A.I.C.S.: 523940
Gavin White *(CEO)*

INVECTURE GROUP, S.A. DE C.V.
Montes Urales 750-3 CP, Hidalgo, Mexico, 11000, Mexico
Tel.: (52) 5552010300
Web Site: http://www.invecture.com
Rev.: $600,000,000
Emp.: 10
Alternative Asset Managment Services
N.A.I.C.S.: 523999
Emilio Mitre *(VP)*

Subsidiaries:

Cobre Del Mayo S.A. de C.V. (1)
Localdad Piedras Verdes Conocido S/N, 85779, Sonora, Mexico
Tel.: (52) 662 319 7596
Web Site: http://www.cobredelmayo.com
Copper Mining Services
N.A.I.C.S.: 212230

Frontera Copper Corporation (1)
Suite 1620 1075 West Georgia St, Vancouver, V6E 4A2, BC, Canada
Tel.: (604) 688-1020
Web Site: http://www.fronteracopper.com
Sales Range: $75-99.9 Million
Copper Mining & Exploration
N.A.I.C.S.: 212230

Mayoson, S.A. De C.V. (1)
Jimenez No 203, Mexico, Sonora, Mexico
Tel.: (52) 647 428 3029
Copper Mining Services
N.A.I.C.S.: 212230

INVEKRA S.A.P.I. DE C.V.
Blvd Adolfo Lopez Mateos 314 Piso 1-A Colonia Tlacopac, Del Alvaro Obregon, CP 01049, Mexico, DF, Mexico
Tel.: (52) 402 964 5144 MX
Emp.: 2,900
Holding Company; Pharmaceutical Developer, Mfr & Whslr
N.A.I.C.S.: 551112

Subsidiaries:

Laboratorios Sanfer S.A. de C.V. (1)
Blvd Adolfo Lopez Mateos 314 Piso 1-A Colonia Tlacopac, Del Alvaro Obregon, CP 01049, Mexico, DF, Mexico
Tel.: (52) 402 964 5144
Web Site: http://www.sanfer.com.mx

INTERNATIONAL PUBLIC

Pharmaceutical Developer, Mfr & Whslr
N.A.I.C.S.: 325412

INVEL REAL ESTATE ADVISORS LLP
26 Grosvenor Gardens, Belgravia, London, SW1W 0GT, United Kingdom
Tel.: (44) 20 7529 6602 UK
Web Site:
http://www.invelrealestate.com
Year Founded: 2013
Emp.: 7
Real Estate Investment Services
N.A.I.C.S.: 531390
Christophoros N. Papachristophorou *(Founder & Mng Partner)*

Subsidiaries:

NBG Pangaea Real Estate Investment Company (1)
6 Karageorgi Servias Str, 105 62, Athens, Greece **(98.1%)**
Tel.: (30) 210 334 0011
Web Site: http://www.nbgpangaea.gr
Real Estate Investment Trust
N.A.I.C.S.: 525990
Christophoros N. Papachristophorou *(Vice Chm)*

INVENGO INFORMATION TECHNOLOGY CO., LTD.
27th and 28th Floor High tech Zone Building, No 63 High tech South 10th Road Yuehai Street Nanshan District, Shenzhen, 518052, Guangdong, China
Tel.: (86) 75526711735
Web Site: http://en.invengo.cn
Year Founded: 1999
002161—(SSE)
Rev.: $67,512,744
Assets: $391,473,108
Liabilities: $189,059,832
Net Worth: $202,413,276
Earnings: ($4,214,808)
Emp.: 700
Fiscal Year-end: 12/31/22
Radio Frequency Products Mfr
N.A.I.C.S.: 334220
Chen Guangzhu *(Chm)*

Subsidiaries:

Invengo Technologies SARL (1)
180 Voie Ariane 1, 13600, La Ciotat, France
Tel.: (33) 413961111
Radio Frequency Identification Equipment Distr
N.A.I.C.S.: 423690

INVENIA CO., LTD.
55 Donyu 3-ro, Munsan-eup, Paju, Gyeonggi-Do, Korea (South)
Tel.: (82) 27889100
Web Site:
https://www.inveniacorp.com
Year Founded: 2001
079950—(KRS)
Rev.: $43,613,144
Assets: $87,197,767
Liabilities: $46,962,794
Net Worth: $40,234,972
Earnings: ($777,530)
Emp.: 131
Fiscal Year-end: 12/31/22
LCD & Related Products Mfr
N.A.I.C.S.: 334419
Dongbeum Koo *(Vice Chm & CEO)*

INVENT MEDIC SWEDEN AB
Nytankargatan 4, 223 63, Lund, Sweden
Tel.: (46) 723811710
Web Site: https://www.inventmedic.se
Year Founded: 2005
Medical Device Mfr
N.A.I.C.S.: 339112
Karin Bryder *(CEO)*

INVENTEC BESTA CO., LTD.
2F No 166 Section 4 Chengde Road, Shilin District, Taipei, 114, Taiwan
Tel.: (886) 77265111 TW
Web Site: https://www.besta.com.tw
Year Founded: 1989
8201—(TAI)
Rev.: $16,881,912
Assets: $23,615,258
Liabilities: $6,701,135
Net Worth: $16,914,123
Earnings: ($2,320,710)
Emp.: 1,169
Fiscal Year-end: 12/31/23
Electronic Dictionaries & Related Products Mfr & Marketer
N.A.I.C.S.: 334419

Subsidiaries:

Besta International Trading Pte. Ltd. (1)
109 North Bridge Rd Funan DigitaLife Mall 04 K2, Singapore, 179097, Singapore
Tel.: (65) 63399533
Web Site: http://www.besta.com.sg
Emp.: 3
Electronic Dictionaries & Related Products Distr
N.A.I.C.S.: 423690

INVENTEC CORPORATION
No 66 Hougang St, Shilin Dist, Taipei, 111059, Taiwan
Tel.: (886) 228810721
Web Site: https://www.inventec.com
Year Founded: 1975
2356—(TAI)
Rev.: $16,094,368,883
Assets: $7,494,855,892
Liabilities: $5,610,780,540
Net Worth: $1,884,075,353
Earnings: $188,252,665
Emp.: 19,639
Fiscal Year-end: 12/31/23
Electric Equipment Mfr
N.A.I.C.S.: 334111
Tom-Hwar Cho (Chm)

Subsidiaries:

AIMobile Co., Ltd. (1)
6F No 166 Section 4 Chengde Road, Shilin District, Taipei, 111, Taiwan
Tel.: (886) 277367661
Web Site: http://www.aimobile.com.tw
Electronic Computer Mfr
N.A.I.C.S.: 334111
K. C. Liu (Chm)

E-TON Solar Tech. Co., Ltd. (1)
No 498 Sec 2 Bentian St, Tainan City, 709, Taiwan
Tel.: (886) 63840777
Web Site: http://www.e-tonsolar.com
Solar Energy Equipment Distr
N.A.I.C.S.: 221114
Frank Wen (Chm)

Inventec (Beijing) Electronics Technology Co., Ltd. (1)
A1505 E-Wing Center No 113 Zhichun Rd, Haidian District, Beijing, 100086, China
Tel.: (86) 1064185165
Notebook Computer & Other Electronic Hardware Mfr
N.A.I.C.S.: 334111

Inventec (Chongqing) Corp. (1)
No 66 West Dist II Rd, Shapingba District, Chongqing, China
Tel.: (86) 2365398888
Notebook Computer & Other Electronic Hardware Mfr
N.A.I.C.S.: 334111

Inventec (Chongqing) Service Co., Ltd. (1)
3F Building NO 98 Xiqu Sceond Road, Shapingba District, Chongqing, China
Tel.: (86) 2365398888
Notebook Computer & Other Electronic Hardware Mfr
N.A.I.C.S.: 334111

Inventec (Pudong) Corp. (1)
No 789 Puxing Road, Minhang District, Shanghai, 201114, China
Tel.: (86) 2164298888
Notebook Computer & Other Electronic Hardware Mfr
N.A.I.C.S.: 334111

Inventec (Pudong) Technology Corp. (1)
No 789 Puxing Road, Minhang District, Shanghai, 201114, China
Tel.: (86) 2164298888
Notebook Computer & Other Electronic Hardware Mfr
N.A.I.C.S.: 334111

Inventec (Shanghai) Corp. (1)
No 789 Puxing Road, Shanghai, 201114, China
Tel.: (86) 2164298888
Notebook Computer & Other Electronic Hardware Mfr
N.A.I.C.S.: 334111

Inventec (Shanghai) Service Co., Ltd. (1)
No 789 Puxing Road, Shanghai, 201114, China
Tel.: (86) 2164298888
Notebook Computer & Other Electronic Hardware Mfr
N.A.I.C.S.: 334111

Inventec (Tianjin) Electronics Co. Ltd. (1)
Tel.: (86) 2223000058
Web Site: http://www.inventec.com
Notebooks, Cloud & Mobile Computing & Software Applications
N.A.I.C.S.: 513210

Inventec Appliances (Jiangning) Corp. (1)
No 133 Jiang-Jun Road, Jiangning Economic and Technological Development Zone, Nanjing, 211153, China
Tel.: (86) 2552262313
Wireless Communication Product Mfr & Whslr
N.A.I.C.S.: 334419

Inventec Appliances (Nanchang) Corporation (1)
4th Floor No 698 Jingdong Boulevard High-Tech Zone, Nanchang, Jiangxi, China
Tel.: (86) 7918161688
Wireless Communication Product Mfr & Whslr
N.A.I.C.S.: 334419

Inventec Appliances Corporation (1)
37 Wugong 5th Road, New Taipei Industrial Park wugu District, New Taipei City, 24890, Taiwan
Tel.: (886) 222999329
Web Site: http://www.iac.com.tw
Sales Range: $1-4.9 Billion
Communications, Digital Products & Components Mfr, Researcher, Developer, Servicer & Retailer
N.A.I.C.S.: 334210
David Ho (Pres)

Subsidiary (Non-US):

Inventec Appliances (Pudong) Corporation (IACP) (2)
No 789 Puxing Rd, Minhang District, Shanghai, 201114, China
Tel.: (86) 2154336899
Web Site: http://www.iac.com.tw
Networking & Cellular Devices Mfr
N.A.I.C.S.: 517112

Inventec Appliances (Shanghai) Co., Ltd. (IACS) (2)
No 7 Gui Qing Rd, Shanghai, 200233, China
Tel.: (86) 2164853668
Networking & Cellular Equipments Mfr
N.A.I.C.S.: 517112

Inventec Appliances (Xi an) Corporation (2)
3rd Floor Tang-Xing Digital Tower 6 Tang-Xing Road, Xi an Ntaional High-tech Industrial Development Zone, Xi'an, 710075, China

Tel.: (86) 2988455488
Web Site: http://www.iac.com.tw
Wireless Smart Client Products Mfr
N.A.I.C.S.: 517112

Inventec Hi-Tech Corp. (1)
No 789 Puxing Road, Minhang District, Shanghai, 201114, China
Tel.: (86) 2164298888
Notebook Computer & Other Electronic Hardware Mfr
N.A.I.C.S.: 334111

Inventec Huan Hsin (Zhejiang) Technology Co., Ltd. (1)
No 8 XinDa Road Huimin Avenue, Jiashan County, Shanghai, Zhejiang, China
Tel.: (86) 57389108888
Notebook Computer & Other Electronic Hardware Mfr
N.A.I.C.S.: 334111

Inventec Multimedia & Telecom Corporation (1)
3F No 166 Sec 4 Chengde Road, Shih-Lin District, Taipei, 111, Taiwan
Tel.: (886) 228839898
Web Site: http://www.importek.com
Sales Range: $25-49.9 Million
Emp.: 63
Digital Audio Telecommunications & Multimedia Networking Products Mfr
N.A.I.C.S.: 334210

Subsidiary (Non-US):

Inventec Multimedia & Telecom (Malaysia) Co., Ltd. (2)
Plot 102 Bayan Lepas Industrial Estate, Bayan Lepas, Penang, Malaysia (100%)
Tel.: (60) 4 643 9566
Electronics Mfr
N.A.I.C.S.: 334419

INVENTIS LIMITED
7 Holbeche Rd Arndell Park, Sydney, 2148, NSW, Australia
Tel.: (61) 288080400
Web Site: http://www.inventis.com.au
IVT—(ASX)
Rev.: $9,099,640
Assets: $9,014,206
Liabilities: $11,962,889
Net Worth: ($2,948,683)
Earnings: ($2,286,001)
Emp.: 55
Fiscal Year-end: 06/30/24
Products & Services Mfr
N.A.I.C.S.: 238390
Alfred Kobylanski (CFO & Co-Sec)

Subsidiaries:

Electronic Circuit Designs Pty. Limited (1)
Factory 11 / 30 Perry Street, Matraville, NSW, Australia
Tel.: (61) 293166909
Web Site: https://www.ecd.com.au
Elevator Controller Mfr
N.A.I.C.S.: 333921

Gregory Commercial Furniture Pty Limited (1)
107 Pitt St, Pemulwuy, Sydney, 2000, NSW, Australia
Tel.: (61) 1300003339
Web Site:
    http://www.gregoryaustralia.com.au
Sales Range: $25-49.9 Million
Emp.: 40
Commercial Furnitures Mfr & Supplier
N.A.I.C.S.: 337211
Tony Noun (Founder)

Inventis Technology Pty Limited (1)
Unit 4 2 Southridge Street, Eastern Creek, 2766, NSW, Australia
Tel.: (61) 288080400
Web Site:
    https://www.inventistechnology.com.au
Sales Range: $25-49.9 Million
Electronic Control Systems Mfr & Distr
N.A.I.C.S.: 334512

Subsidiary (Domestic):

Impart Special Products Pty Limited (2)

Unit 4 2 Southridge Street, Eastern Creek, 2766, NSW, Australia
Tel.: (61) 288080400
Web Site: https://www.impartsp.com.au
Emp.: 20
Emergency Control Systems & Accessories Supplier
N.A.I.C.S.: 423610
Debra Cunningham (Mgr-HR)

Opentec Solutions Pty Limited (1)
Block A Unit 40 1-3 Endeavour Rd, Caringbah, 2229, NSW, Australia
Tel.: (61) 295254177
Web Site: http://www.opentec.com.au
Sales Range: $50-74.9 Million
Emp.: 5
Portable Computers Supplier
N.A.I.C.S.: 423430

INVENTIVA S.A
50 rue de Daix, 21121, Dijon, France
Tel.: (33) 380447500 FR
Web Site:
    https://www.inventivapharma.com
IVA—(NASDAQ)
Rev.: $24,997,842
Assets: $75,071,228
Liabilities: $109,640,622
Net Worth: ($34,569,393)
Earnings: ($119,173,322)
Emp.: 120
Fiscal Year-end: 12/31/23
Pharmaceutical Product Mfr & Distr
N.A.I.C.S.: 325412
Frederic Cren (Co-Founder & CEO)

INVENTRONICS (HANGZHOU) CO LTD
Block A No 459 Jianghong Road Changhe Street, Binjiang District, Hangzhou, 310052, Zhejiang, China
Tel.: (86) 57156565800
Web Site: http://www.inventronics-co.com
Year Founded: 2007
300582—(CHIN)
Rev.: $370,602,126
Assets: $538,044,352
Liabilities: $331,005,993
Net Worth: $207,038,359
Earnings: ($24,417,122)
Fiscal Year-end: 12/31/23
Light Emitting Diode Mfr & Distr
N.A.I.C.S.: 334413
Guichao Hua (Founder, Chm & CTO)

INVENTRONICS LIMITED
1420 Van Horne Ave E, Brandon, R7A 7B6, MB, Canada
Tel.: (204) 728-2001 AB
Web Site:
    https://www.inventronics.com
Year Founded: 1970
IVX—(TSXV)
Rev.: $6,689,572
Assets: $4,602,431
Liabilities: $2,477,535
Net Worth: $2,124,896
Earnings: $278,638
Fiscal Year-end: 12/31/23
Custom Enclosures Developer & Mfr for the Communications, Electronics & Other Industries
N.A.I.C.S.: 335999
Dan J. Stearne (Pres & CEO)

INVENTURE GROWTH & SECURITIES LTD
Viraj Tower 201 2nd W E Highway, Andheri E, Mumbai, 400069, Maharashtra, India
Tel.: (91) 2271148500
Web Site:
    https://www.inventuregrowth.com
533506—(BOM)
Rev.: $6,774,577
Assets: $37,492,482
Liabilities: $10,267,161

INVENTURE GROWTH & SECURITIES LTD

Inventure Growth & Securities Ltd—(Continued)

Net Worth: $27,225,321
Earnings: $1,904,571
Emp.: 107
Fiscal Year-end: 03/31/22
Securities & Commodity Brokerage Services
N.A.I.C.S.: 523150
Arvind J. Gala *(CFO)*

Subsidiaries:

Inventure Finance Private Limited (1)
202 Viraj Tower Western Express Highway, Andheri East, Mumbai, 400 093, India
Tel.: (91) 2239548500
Financial Investment Services
N.A.I.C.S.: 523940
Kushal Gada *(Asst Mgr)*

Inventure Merchant Banker Services Private Limited (1)
2nd Floor Viraj Tower W E Highway Andheri East, Mumbai, 400 063, India
Tel.: (91) 2271148500
Financial Investment Services
N.A.I.C.S.: 523940

INVENTUS MINING CORP.

82 Richmond Street East Suite 1, Toronto, M5C 1P1, ON, Canada
Tel.: (647) 258-0395 Ca
Web Site: https://www.inventusmining.com
Year Founded: 2005
GNGXF—(OTCIQ)
Rev.: $15,646
Assets: $689,506
Liabilities: $590,702
Net Worth: $98,804
Earnings: ($3,255,752)
Fiscal Year-end: 12/31/21
Metal Mineral Mining & Exploration Services
N.A.I.C.S.: 212290
Stefan Spears *(Chm & CEO)*

Subsidiaries:

Mount Logan Resources Ltd. (1)
957 Cambrian Heights Dr Suite 101, Sudbury, P3C 5S5, ON, Canada
Tel.: (705) 222-8800
Metal Mining Services
N.A.I.C.S.: 212290

INVERCAP S.A.

Gertrudis Echenique 220 P 7, Las Condes, Santiago, Chile
Tel.: (56) 228186300
Web Site: https://www.invercap.cl
Year Founded: 1994
INVERCAP—(SGO)
Sales Range: Less than $1 Million
Real Estate Development Services
N.A.I.C.S.: 531390
Roberto De Andraca Adriasola *(Chm)*

INVERITE INSIGHTS INC.

World Trade Centre Suite 404-999 Canada Place, Vancouver, V6C 3E2, BC, Canada
Tel.: (778) 897-2172
Web Site: https://www.mymarble.ca
Year Founded: 2016
2V00—(DEU)
Rev.: $806,128
Assets: $2,612,368
Liabilities: $6,780,885
Net Worth: $4,168,517
Earnings: ($3,909,493)
Fiscal Year-end: 12/31/22
Financial Loan Services
N.A.I.C.S.: 522310
Karim Nanji *(CEO)*

Subsidiaries:

Inverite Verification Inc. (1)
Suite 404-999 Canada Place, Vancouver, V6C 3E2, BC, Canada
Web Site: https://www.inverite.ca
Investment Banking & Financial Services
N.A.I.C.S.: 522320

TPFM The Phoenix Fund Management Ltd. (1)
404-999 Canada Place, Vancouver, V6C 3E2, BC, Canada
Tel.: (604) 336-0185
Web Site: http://www.phoenixfund.autopal.info
Financial Investment Services
N.A.I.C.S.: 523999
Mike Marrandino *(Pres & CEO)*

INVERNOVA SA

El Bosque Sur 130, Santiago, 810, Chile
Tel.: (56) 117074900
INVERNOVA—(SGO)
Sales Range: Less than $1 Million
Real Estate Investment Services
N.A.I.C.S.: 531390
Francisco Javier Valdivia Barros *(CEO)*

INVERSIONES AEREAS S.L.

Aerodromo de Mutxamel, Partida La Almaina 92, 03110, Alicante, Spain
Tel.: (34) 965663835 ES
Web Site: http://www.inaer.com
Sales Range: $150-199.9 Million
Emp.: 750
Helicopter Transportation Services
N.A.I.C.S.: 481219
Luis Minano Sanvalero *(CEO)*

Subsidiaries:

Elilario Italia S.p.A. (1)
2 Via Ombrieno, 68, Colico, Lecco, Italy
Tel.: (39) 03419346 11
Web Site: http://www.iner.net
Sales Range: $50-74.9 Million
Emp.: 220
Helicopter Transportation Services
N.A.I.C.S.: 481219

INAER Helicopter Italia S.p.A. (1)
Via Valpetrosa n 1, 20123, Milan, Italy
Tel.: (39) 02 89096967
Web Site: http://www.inaer.it
Emergency Medical Services
N.A.I.C.S.: 624230
Andrea Stolfa *(Pres & CEO)*

Inaer Helicopter France SA (1)
Lieu-dit Le Portaret, 83340, Paris, France
Tel.: (33) 4 98 10 72 72
Web Site: http://www.inaer.fr
Freight Forwarding & Transportation Services
N.A.I.C.S.: 481112
Frederic Goig *(CEO)*

Inaer-Helicopter Portugal Lda (1)
Heliport Salema Place of Salema, Lousa, 2670-769, Loures, Portugal
Tel.: (351) 21 975 92 00
Web Site: http://www.inaerportugal.pt
Freight Forwarding & Transportation Services
N.A.I.C.S.: 481112
Daniel Blanco *(Head-Trng)*

INVERSIONES AGRICOLAS Y COMERCIALES SA

Camino Longitudinal Sur N 5201 KM 23 Nos Casilla 70, Santiago, Chile
Tel.: (56) 23776400
IACSA—(SGO)
Sales Range: Less than $1 Million
Food Product Mfr & Distr
N.A.I.C.S.: 311412
Gonzalo Bofil Velarde *(Chm)*

INVERSIONES ASTRAU SL

Ayala 11, 28001, Madrid, Spain
Tel.: (34) 914263851 ES
Sales Range: $1-9.9 Million
Emp.: 40
Investment & Consulting Services
N.A.I.C.S.: 523940

Alejandro Von Der Pahlen *(Gen Mgr)*

INVERSIONES BRECA SA

Calle Las Begonias 441 Oficina 242, San Isidro, Lima, 27, Peru
Tel.: (51) 1 706 5050
Holding Company
N.A.I.C.S.: 551112
Alex Fort Brescia *(Co-Pres)*

Subsidiaries:

Inversiones Nacionales de Turismo SA (1)
Calle Amador Merino Reyna 551, San Isidro, Lima, Peru
Tel.: (51) 1 7127000
Construction, Operation & Administration of Hotels
N.A.I.C.S.: 721110

Subsidiary (Domestic):

INVERSIONES LA RIOJA S.A. (2)
Calle Amador Merino Reyna 551, San Isidro, Peru
Tel.: (51) 17127000
Web Site: http://www.larioja.com.pe
Hotel Construction, Development & Operations
N.A.I.C.S.: 721110

INVERSIONES CENTENARIO SA

Av Victor Andres Belaunde 147 Centro Empresarial Real, Edificio Real Cuatro, San Isidro, Peru
Tel.: (51) 16169000
Web Site: https://www.centenario.com.pe
Year Founded: 1929
INVCENC1—(LIM)
Rev.: $124,476,561
Assets: $1,293,694,437
Liabilities: $603,751,383
Net Worth: $689,943,054
Earnings: ($26,042,696)
Fiscal Year-end: 12/31/23
Real Estate Manangement Services
N.A.I.C.S.: 531210
Gonzalo Sarmiento Giove *(CEO)*

INVERSIONES COVADONGA SA

Matias Cousino 150 Of 201 Piso 2, PO Box 2397, Santiago, Chile
Tel.: (56) 6985361
COVADONGA—(SGO)
Sales Range: Less than $1 Million
Real Estate Investment Services
N.A.I.C.S.: 531390
Guillermo Pascual Beltran *(Chm)*

INVERSIONES CRECE PYMES CA

Calle Pantin Edif Galerias Pantin Piso 1 Ofic 4 Urb Eduardo Leal, Chacao, Caracas, 1060, Venezuela
Tel.: (58) 2122637126
Web Site: http://www.crecepymes.com
Financial Investment Services
N.A.I.C.S.: 523999

INVERSIONES EQUIPOS Y SERVICIOS SA

Carretera Palmira Pradera Km 6 5, Palmira, Colombia
Tel.: (57) 2532350461
Web Site: http://www.inesa.com.co
INESA—(COLO)
Sales Range: Less than $1 Million
Sugar Cane Mfr
N.A.I.C.S.: 311314

INVERSIONES LA CONSTRUCCION SA

Marchant Pereira 10 Piso 17, Providenci, Santiago, Chile

INTERNATIONAL PUBLIC

Tel.: (56) 4774600
Web Site: http://www.ilcinversiones.cl
Year Founded: 1980
ILC—(SGO)
Rev.: $1,627,156,820
Assets: $17,632,450,446
Liabilities: $16,356,262,185
Net Worth: $1,276,188,261
Earnings: $89,740,397
Emp.: 10,066
Fiscal Year-end: 12/31/23
Financial Consulting Services
N.A.I.C.S.: 541611
T. Patricio Donoso *(Chm)*

INVERSIONES NUTRAVALOR SA

Avenue El Golf 150 Floo3 los condes, Santiago, Chile
Tel.: (56) 223646757 CL
Web Site: https://www.nutravalor.cl
Year Founded: 1956
NUTRAVALOR—(SGO)
Sales Range: Less than $1 Million
Farm Management Services
N.A.I.C.S.: 115116
Patricio Tapia Costa *(CEO & Gen Mgr)*

INVERSIONES SIEMEL SA

Av El Golf 150 Piso 21 Las Condes, Santiago, Chile
Tel.: (56) 224617700
Web Site: https://www.siemel.cl
SIEMEL—(SGO)
Sales Range: Less than $1 Million
Capital Management Services
N.A.I.C.S.: 523940
Andres Lehuede Bromley *(CEO)*

INVERSIONES TRICAHUE S.A.

San Antonio 486 Piso 7 Oficina 72, Santiago, Chile
Tel.: (56) 6326518
TRICAHUE—(SGO)
Sales Range: Less than $1 Million
Investment Services
N.A.I.C.S.: 523999
Claudio Lobos Veliz *(CEO)*

INVERSIONES UNESPA S.A.

Matias Cousino 150 Of 201 Piso 2, Santiago, Chile
Tel.: (56) 6987038
UNESPA—(SGO)
Sales Range: Less than $1 Million
Investment Management Service
N.A.I.C.S.: 523999
Guillermo Pascual Beltran *(Chm)*

INVERSIONES UNION ESPANOLA S.A.

Matias Cousino 150 Of 201 Piso 2, PO Box 2397, Santiago, Chile
Tel.: (56) 6987038
INVIESPA—(SGO)
Sales Range: Less than $1 Million
Investment Management Service
N.A.I.C.S.: 523940
Clemente Cambara Muniz *(Chm)*

INVERSIONES VENECIA SA

K M 6 5 Carretera Palmira AA 101, Pradera, Palmira, Colombia
Tel.: (57) 3108227446
Web Site: http://www.invensa.com.co
INVENSA—(COLO)
Sales Range: Less than $1 Million
Sugar Cane Mfr
N.A.I.C.S.: 311314

INVERTEC FOODS S.A.

Av Kennedy 9070 Of 701, Vitacura, Santiago, Chile
Tel.: (56) 225805300

AND PRIVATE COMPANIES

Web Site:
https://www.invertecfoods.com
Year Founded: 1988
INVERFOODS—(SGO)
Sales Range: Less than $1 Million
Fruit & Vegetable Farming Services
N.A.I.C.S.: 111219
Juan Francisco Zanolli *(Mgr-Comml)*

INVESCO OFFICE J-REIT, INC.
6-10-1 Roppongi, Minato-ku, Tokyo, Japan
Tel.: (81) 3 6447 3395
Web Site: http://www.invesco-reit.co.jp
Year Founded: 2014
3298—(TKS)
Sales Range: $10-24.9 Million
Real Estate Manangement Services
N.A.I.C.S.: 523999
Yoshifumi Matsumoto *(Exec Dir)*

INVEST BANK
Bldg 43 Abdul Hamid Sharaf Street Shmeisani, PO Box 950601, Amman, 11195, Jordan
Tel.: (962) 65001500
Web Site: https://www.investbank.jo
Year Founded: 1982
INVB—(AMM)
Rev.: $99,259,221
Assets: $1,727,026,200
Liabilities: $1,470,765,436
Net Worth: $256,260,765
Earnings: $8,467,251
Emp.: 651
Fiscal Year-end: 12/31/20
Commercial & Investment Banking Services
N.A.I.C.S.: 522110
Bisher Mohammed Jardaneh *(Chm)*

Subsidiaries:

AL TAS-HEELAT Company (1)
Shmesani Ash Sharif Abdul Hamid Sharaf St Building No 52, Amman, Jordan
Tel.: (962) 65671720
Web Site: http://www.altas-heelat.com
Investment Services
N.A.I.C.S.: 523999
Eyad Jarrar *(CEO)*

Al Imdad Company (1)
Air Cargo Road Al Qastal, Amman, Jordan
Tel.: (962) 64711166
Web Site: http://www.imdad.net
Financial Services
N.A.I.C.S.: 522299

Tamkeen Leasing Company (1)
Mecca Street Building Number 244, PO Box 17415, Amman, 11195, Jordan
Tel.: (962) 65502610
Web Site: https://www.tamkeenleasing.com
Investment Services
N.A.I.C.S.: 523999

INVEST BANK P.S.C.
Al Zahra's Street No 105 King Abdul Aziz Road Al-Qasimiya, PO Box 1885, Sharjah, United Arab Emirates
Tel.: (971) 65980555
Web Site: https://www.investbank.ae
Year Founded: 1975
INVESTB—(ABU)
Rev.: $60,202,598
Assets: $2,333,064,020
Liabilities: $2,304,673,910
Net Worth: $28,390,110
Earnings: ($158,994,363)
Emp.: 439
Fiscal Year-end: 12/31/22
Banking Services
N.A.I.C.S.: 522110
Omran Abdulla Omran Taryam *(Deputy Chm)*

INVEST CAPITAL INVESTMENT BANK LIMITED
Flat 2 Plot 38 -C 22nd Commercial Street, Phase II Ext DHA, Karachi, Pakistan
Tel.: (92) 2135205520
Web Site: https://icibl.com
ICIBL—(PSX)
Rev.: $443,043
Assets: $3,915,147
Liabilities: $1,913,028
Net Worth: $2,002,118
Earnings: $322,912
Emp.: 14
Fiscal Year-end: 06/30/23
Investment Banking Services
N.A.I.C.S.: 523150

INVEST NEXUS LIMITED
Office 3928 Level 39 38 Bourke Street, Melbourne, VIC, Australia
Tel.: (61) 3 8459 2137
Investment Services
N.A.I.C.S.: 523999
Guofei Chen *(Chm)*

INVEST NIKAROM SRL
Et 2 Ap 40 Sector 1 Iancu de Hunedoara 42 bis, 011746, Bucharest, Romania
Tel.: (40) 21211 3495 RO
Investment Holding Company
N.A.I.C.S.: 551112
Victor Chumakov *(Owner)*

Subsidiaries:

COS TARGOVISTE S.A. (1)
Soseaua Gaesti nr 9-11, Dambovita, 130087, Targoviste, Romania
Tel.: (40) 245 640 089
Web Site: http://www.cos-tgv.ro
Rolled Steel Products Mfr
N.A.I.C.S.: 331221
Vladimir Gofman *(Gen Mgr)*

Ductil Steel S.A. (1)
1 Aleea Industriilor, 120224, Buzau, Romania
Tel.: (40) 238 405 102
Web Site: http://www.ductilsteel.ro
Steel Wire & Rolled Products Mfr
N.A.I.C.S.: 331221

Industria Sarmei Campia Turzii S.A. (1)
Strada Laminoristilor 145, 405100, Campia Turzii, Judetul Cluj, Romania
Tel.: (40) 264305302
Web Site: https://iswct.ro
Steel Pole Mfr
N.A.I.C.S.: 331222

INVEST PROPERTY REIT
Ul Hristo Botev 20, Vratsa, 3000, Bulgaria
Tel.: (359) 92661686
Web Site: http://www.investproperty.bg
INVE—(BUL)
Sales Range: Less than $1 Million
Real Estate Development Services
N.A.I.C.S.: 531390
Denitza Michailova Petkova *(Chm)*

INVEST TECH PARTICIPACOES E INVESTIMENTOS LTDA.
Rua dos Pinheiros 870 Conjunto 153/154, Sao Paulo, CEP 05422-001, SP, Brazil
Tel.: (55) 11 3199 2199 BR
Web Site: http://www.investtech.com.br
Year Founded: 2004
Rev.: $59,193,600
Privater Equity Firm
N.A.I.C.S.: 523999
Miguel Perrotti *(Co-CEO)*

INVEST-DEVELOPMENT PJSC
Leningrad Prospect str 20 building 1, The Russian Federation, 125040, Moscow, 125040, Russia
Tel.: (7) 8432317287
Web Site: https://www.invest-development.ru
Year Founded: 2014
IDVP—(MOEX)
Sales Range: Less than $1 Million
Real Estate Manangement Services
N.A.I.C.S.: 531210
Vladimir Boychev Shteryanov *(Gen Dir)*

INVEST-IMPORT A.D.
Terazije 5, 11102 Stari Grad, Belgrade, Serbia
Tel.: (381) 113334300
Web Site: https://www.invest-import.co.rs
Year Founded: 1950
INIM—(BEL)
Rev.: $556,486
Assets: $6,486,302
Liabilities: $1,918,238
Net Worth: $4,568,063
Earnings: ($560,248)
Emp.: 15
Fiscal Year-end: 12/31/22
Residential & Non-Residential Buildings Construction
N.A.I.C.S.: 236116
Goran Simic *(Mng Dir)*

INVESTA PROPERTY GROUP
Level 6 Deutsche Bank Pl, 126 Phillip St, Sydney, 2000, New South Wales, Australia
Tel.: (61) 282269300
Web Site: http://www.investa.com.au
Sales Range: $300-349.9 Million
Emp.: 200
Real Estate Services
N.A.I.C.S.: 525990
Ivan Gorridge *(CFO)*

INVESTANCE CONSULTING
7 Rue Leo Delibes, 75016, Paris, France
Tel.: (33) 158186880
Web Site: http://www.investance.com
Rev.: $13,000,000
Emp.: 77
N.A.I.C.S.: 541611
Franck Dahan *(Gen Dir)*

INVESTCORP HOLDINGS B.S.C.
Investcorp House, PO Box 5340, Manama, Bahrain
Tel.: (973) 17532000 BH
Web Site: http://www.investcorp.com
Year Founded: 1982
Rev.: $939,103,080
Assets: $6,307,290,630
Liabilities: $2,951,843,670
Net Worth: $3,355,446,960
Earnings: $329,741,250
Emp.: 430
Fiscal Year-end: 06/30/21
Hedge Funds, Private Equity & Real Estate Investments Portfolio Manager
N.A.I.C.S.: 523940
Hazem Ben-Gacem *(Co-CEO)*

Subsidiaries:

AlixPartners, LLP (1)
909 3rd Ave, New York, NY 10022
Tel.: (212) 490-2500
Web Site: http://www.alixpartners.com
Emp.: 2,000
Management Consulting Services
N.A.I.C.S.: 541618
Fred Crawford *(Mng Dir)*

Subsidiary (Non-US):

AlixPartners Argentina SRL (2)
Avenida Corrientes 1750 Piso 12, C1042AAQ, Buenos Aires, Argentina
Tel.: (54) 11 5031 2900
Financial Advisory Services
N.A.I.C.S.: 523940

AlixPartners UK LLP (2)
6 New Street Square, London, EC4A 3BF, United Kingdom
Tel.: (44) 20 7098 7400
Financial Advisory Services
N.A.I.C.S.: 523940
Nick Wood *(Mng Dir-Merger & Acq Services Practice-EMEA)*

Best in Class Technology Services, LLC (1)
11086 Strang Line Rd, Lenexa, KS 66215
Tel.: (205) 895-8822
Web Site: https://bctsco.com
Sales Range: $125-149.9 Million
Emp.: 700
Commercial HVAC Services
N.A.I.C.S.: 811310
Smitty Belcher *(CEO)*

Subsidiary (Domestic):

Mountain Air Systems, Inc. (2)
430 Commerce Street, Suite 220, Williston, VT 05495
Tel.: (802) 862-6199
Web Site: http://www.masvt.com
Rev.: $5,000,000
Emp.: 45
Site Preparation Contractor
N.A.I.C.S.: 238910

Cambio Healthcare Systems AB (1)
Universitetsvagen 14, 583 30, Linkoping, Sweden
Tel.: (46) 13200300
Web Site: http://www.cambio.se
Emp.: 600
Health Care Solutions Developer
N.A.I.C.S.: 513210
Goran Persson *(Chm)*

Health Plus Management, LLC (1)
50 Charles Lindbergh Blvd, Uniondale, NY 11553
Tel.: (516) 294-4590
Web Site: http://www.healthplusmgmt.com
Emp.: 255
Business Support Services
N.A.I.C.S.: 561499
Stuart Blumberg *(Pres & CEO)*

Subsidiary (Domestic):

Advanced Care Physical Therapy Management LLC (2)
924 Main St, Niagara Falls, NY 14301
Tel.: (716) 282-2888
Web Site: http://www.advancedphysicaltherapy.com
Offices of Physical, Occupational & Speech Therapists & Audiologists
N.A.I.C.S.: 621340
Craig Reinstein *(CEO-Physical Therapist)*

Investcorp Europe Acquisition Corp I (1)
Century Yard Cricket SQ, PO Box 1111, Grand Cayman, Georgetown, KY1-1102, Cayman Islands
Tel.: (345) 9495122
Rev.: $8,091,510
Assets: $271,607,619
Liabilities: $272,007,607
Net Worth: ($399,988)
Earnings: $6,791,890
Emp.: 2
Fiscal Year-end: 12/31/2022
Investment Services
N.A.I.C.S.: 523999
Hazem Ben-Gacem *(Chm)*

Investcorp International Ltd. (1)
48 Grosvenor Street, London, W1K 3HW, United Kingdom (100%)
Tel.: (44) 2076296600
Web Site: http://www.investcorp.com
Sales Range: $75-99.9 Million
Emp.: 75
Private Equity & Hedge Fund Investments
N.A.I.C.S.: 523999
Grahame Ivey *(Mng DirFin-London)*

Holding (Non-US):

Georg Jensen A/S (2)

INVESTCORP HOLDINGS B.S.C.

Investcorp Holdings B.S.C.—(Continued)
Sondre Fasanjev 7, Frederiks Perg, Copenhagen, 2000, Denmark **(79%)**
Tel.: (45) 38149898
Web Site: http://www.georgjensen.com
Emp.: 1,195
Retail Sales of Jewelry & Watches
N.A.I.C.S.: 449129
David Chu (Chief Creative Officer)

Division (Domestic):

Georg Jensen Antiques **(3)**
Amagertorv 4, DK 1160, Copenhagen, Denmark **(100%)**
Tel.: (45) 33140229
Web Site: http://www.georgjensen.com
Sales Range: $25-49.9 Million
Emp.: 4
Antique Porcelain, Silver & Glassware Retailer
N.A.I.C.S.: 459510

Subsidiary (Domestic):

Investcorp Credit Management EU Ltd. **(2)**
Investcorp House 48 Grosvenor Street, London, W1K 3HW, United Kingdom **(100%)**
Tel.: (44) 20 7629 6600
Web Site: http://www.investcorp.com
Debt Securities Dealing Services
N.A.I.C.S.: 523150
David Fewtrell (Dir & Portfolio Mgr)

Holding (Non-US):

SPGPrints B.V. **(2)**
Raamstraat 1-3, 5831 AT, Boxmeer, Netherlands
Tel.: (31) 485 599 555
Web Site: http://www.spgprints.com
Sales Range: $250-299.9 Million
Commercial Printing Machinery & Equipment Mfr & Whslr
N.A.I.C.S.: 333248
Dick Joustra (CEO)

Subsidiary (US):

SPGPrints America, Inc. **(3)**
3201 N Interstate 85, Charlotte, NC 28221
Tel.: (704) 598-7171
Emp.: 70
Commercial Screen Printing Machinery & Equipment Mfr & Whslr
N.A.I.C.S.: 333248
Sangeeta Sachdev (Mng Dir)

Subsidiary (Non-US):

SPGPrints Austria GmbH **(3)**
Kufsteiner Strasse 4, 6336, Langkampfen, Austria
Tel.: (43) 5372 6993 0
Emp.: 100
Laser Engraving Systems Mfr & Whslr
N.A.I.C.S.: 333248

SPGPrints Brasil Ltda. **(3)**
Avenida Comendador Leopoldo Dedini 150, Distrito Industrial Unileste, Piracicaba, 13422-210, SP, Brazil
Tel.: (55) 19 3437 1300
Emp.: 88
Commercial Screen Printing Machinery & Equipment Mfr & Whslr
N.A.I.C.S.: 333248
Jose Junior (Mng Dir)

SPGPrints Japan K.K. **(3)**
Daimel Bldg 7F 3-20-10 Toyosaki, Kita-ku, Osaka, 531-0072, Japan
Tel.: (81) 6 6359 8865
Web Site: http://www.spjprints.co.jp
Sales Range: $25-49.9 Million
Emp.: 5
Commercial Screen Printing Machinery & Equipment Whslr
N.A.I.C.S.: 423830
Tada Masahiro (Mng Dir)

SPGPrints Pakistan (Pvt) Ltd. **(3)**
11 Bangalore Town Cooperative Housing Society, Shahrah-e-Faisal, Karachi, 75350, Pakistan
Tel.: (92) 21 3455 8344
Emp.: 55

Commercial Screen Printing Machinery & Equipment Mfr & Whslr
N.A.I.C.S.: 333248

Stovec Industries Ltd. **(3)**
NIDC Near Lambha Village, Narol Post, Ahmedabad, 382 405, Gujarat State, India
Tel.: (91) 79 2571 0407
Web Site: http://www.stovec.com
Emp.: 160
Commercial Screen Printing Machinery & Equipment Mfr & Whslr
N.A.I.C.S.: 333248
Shailesh Wani (Mng Dir)

Investcorp International, Inc. **(1)**
280 Park Ave, New York, NY 10017
Tel.: (212) 599-4700
Web Site: http://www.investcorp.com
Hedge Funds, Private Equity & Real Estate Investments
N.A.I.C.S.: 523999
Lionel Erdely (Chief Investment Officer & Head-Hedge Funds Grp)

Holding (Domestic):

Aero Products International, Inc. **(2)**
1834 Walden Office Sq 3rd Fl, Schaumburg, IL 60173 **(100%)**
Tel.: (847) 485-3200
Web Site: http://www.thinkaero.com
Sales Range: $50-74.9 Million
Mattress & Bed Mfr
N.A.I.C.S.: 337910

Archway Marketing Services, Inc. **(2)**
19850 S Diamond Lake Rd, Rogers, MN 55374
Tel.: (763) 428-3300
Web Site: http://www.archway.com
Sales Range: $100-124.9 Million
Management Consulting Services
N.A.I.C.S.: 541613

Fortune International, LLC **(2)**
1068 Thorndale Ave, Bensenville, IL 60106
Tel.: (630) 860-7100
Web Site: http://www.fortunefishco.net
Sales Range: $100-124.9 Million
Emp.: 225
Seafood Distr
N.A.I.C.S.: 424420
Sean O'Scannlain (Pres & CEO)

Subsidiary (Domestic):

Boston Sword & Tuna Inc. **(3)**
8 Seafood Way Ste 5-6, Boston, MA 02210-2618
Tel.: (617) 946-9850
Fish & Seafood Merchant Whslr
N.A.I.C.S.: 424460
Mike Scola (CEO)

DArtagnan Inc. **(3)**
280 Wilson Ave, Newark, NJ 07105
Tel.: (973) 344-0565
Web Site: http://www.dartagnan.com
Rev.: $27,204,394
Emp.: 100
Purveyor of Meats, Mushrooms & Organic Poultry
N.A.I.C.S.: 424470

Neesvig's, Inc. **(3)**
4350 Duraform Ln, Windsor, WI 53598-9671
Tel.: (608) 846-1160
Web Site: http://www.neesvigs.com
Meat Processing
N.A.I.C.S.: 311612
Jeffrey Bauer (VP & Controller)

New Orleans Fish House & Seafood, Inc. **(3)**
921 S Dupre St, New Orleans, LA 70125
Tel.: (504) 821-9700
Web Site: http://www.neworleansfishhouse.com
Seafood Product Preparation & Packaging
N.A.I.C.S.: 311710

Seattle Fish Company **(3)**
2800 Guinotte Ave, Kansas City, MO 64120
Tel.: (816) 920-7070
Web Site: http://www.seattlefish.com
Fish & Seafood Merchant Whslr
N.A.I.C.S.: 424460
Scott Godke (Gen Mgr-Kansas City)

Holding (Non-US):

Impero Solutions Limited **(2)**
Oak House Mere Way, Ruddington Fields Business Park, Ruddington, NG11 6JS, Notts, United Kingdom
Tel.: (44) 1509 611 341
Web Site: http://www.imperosoftware.com
Software Publisher
N.A.I.C.S.: 513210
Justin Reilly (CEO)

Subsidiary (Domestic):

Investcorp Technology Ventures, L.P. **(2)**
280 Park Ave 36th Fl, New York, NY 10017
Tel.: (212) 599-4700
Web Site: http://www.investcorp.com
Sales Range: $75-99.9 Million
Equity Investment Firm
N.A.I.C.S.: 523999
Anand Radhakrishnan (Principal)

Holding (Domestic):

S & S Truck Parts, LLC **(3)**
600 W Irving Park Rd, Schaumburg, IL 60193
Tel.: (847) 584-2000
Web Site: http://www.sandstruck.com
Motor Vehicle Supplies & New Parts Merchant Whslr
N.A.I.C.S.: 423120
Rick Hoffman (Partner)

Holding (Domestic):

KSI Trading Corp. **(3)**
100 Wade Ave, South Plainfield, NJ 07080
Tel.: (908) 754-7154
Automotive Parts & Accessories Stores
N.A.I.C.S.: 441330
James White (VP-Strategic Initiatives)

Subsidiary (Domestic):

Re Nu Body Shop Supply, Inc. **(3)**
7270 Epark Circle Dr, Hanover, MD 21076
Tel.: (410) 712-9580
Furniture Merchant Whslr
N.A.I.C.S.: 423210

Holding (Domestic):

Nobel Learning Communities, Inc. **(2)**
1615 W Chester Pike Ste 200, West Chester, PA 19382
Tel.: (484) 947-2000
Web Site: http://www.nobellearning.com
For-Profit Private Education Services
N.A.I.C.S.: 611699
George H. Bernstein (CEO)

Unit (Domestic):

Merryhill Elementary School **(3)**
750 N Capitol Ave, San Jose, CA 95133
Tel.: (408) 254-1282
Web Site: http://www.merryhillschool.com
Emp.: 30
Elementary School
N.A.I.C.S.: 611110
Yesenia Camacho (Office Mgr)

Holding (Domestic):

Sur La Table Inc. **(2)**
5701 6th Ave S Ste 486, Seattle, WA 98108-2514
Tel.: (206) 613-6000
Web Site: http://www.surlatable.com
Kitchenware Stores
N.A.I.C.S.: 449129
Debbie Bronsfield (CFO)

Wells-CTI, Inc. **(2)**
1498 SE Tech Ctr Pl Ste 320, Vancouver, WA 98683
Tel.: (360) 433-6230
Web Site: http://www.wellscti.com
Semiconductor Testing Products Developer & Mfr
N.A.I.C.S.: 334413
Matt Bergeron (Pres & CEO)

Joint Venture (Domestic):

totes Isotoner Corporation **(2)**

INTERNATIONAL PUBLIC

9655 International Blvd, Cincinnati, OH 45246
Tel.: (513) 682-8200
Web Site: http://www.totes-isotoner.com
Sales Range: $150-199.9 Million
Emp.: 1,200
Weather-Resistant Products & Apparel Accessories Mfr & Distr
N.A.I.C.S.: 315990
Douglas P. Gernert (Pres & CEO)

Holding (Non-US):

totes Isotoner (UK) Limited **(3)**
Eastman House Radford Crescent, Billericay, CM12 0DN, Essex, United Kingdom
Tel.: (44) 1277630277
Web Site: http://www.totes.co.uk
Sales Range: $50-74.9 Million
Emp.: 80
Rainwear, Gloves & Umbrellas Distr
N.A.I.C.S.: 424350
Mike Bate (Chm)

totes Isotoner Canada Ltd. **(3)**
426 Watline Avenue, Mississauga, L4Z 1X2, ON, Canada
Tel.: (905) 564-4817
Web Site: https://www.totes-isotoner.ca
Sales Range: $50-74.9 Million
Emp.: 25
Rainwear, Gloves & Umbrellas Distr
N.A.I.C.S.: 424350
Robin Perry (VP & Gen Mgr)

Resultant, LLC **(2)**
111 Monument Circle, Suite 202, Indianapolis, IN 46204
Tel.: (317) 452-1700
Web Site: https://resultant.com
Consulting Firm
N.A.I.C.S.: 541618
Mark Caswell (CEO)

Subsidiary (Domestic):

Tempus Nova, Inc. **(2)**
7800 E Union Ave Ste 850, Denver, CO 80237
Tel.: (973) 652-2216
Web Site: http://www.tempusnova.com
Information Technology Services
N.A.I.C.S.: 541512
Joseph Dellanno (Founder & CTO)

RoadSafe Traffic Systems, Inc. **(1)**
8750 W Bryn Mawr Ave Ste 400, Chicago, IL 60631
Tel.: (773) 724-3300
Web Site: http://www.roadsafetraffic.com
Emp.: 1,000
Pavement Marking, Road Sign Installation & Traffic Control Services
N.A.I.C.S.: 488490
David Meirick (Pres & CEO)

Subsidiary (Domestic):

A Cone Zone, Inc. **(2)**
120 N Joy St, Corona, CA 92879-1320
Tel.: (951) 734-2887
Web Site: http://www.aconezone.com
Security Guards & Patrol Services
N.A.I.C.S.: 561612
Elaine Norland (Owner)

All Star Striping, Inc. **(2)**
1255 W 2550 S Ste B, Ogden, UT 84401-3237
Tel.: (801) 399-0099
Web Site: http://www.allstarstriping.com
Highway, Street & Bridge Construction
N.A.I.C.S.: 237310

BC Cannon Co. Inc. **(2)**
PO Box 3889, Greenville, SC 29608-9608
Tel.: (864) 235-1255
Web Site: http://www.bccannon.com
Highway, Street & Bridge Construction
N.A.I.C.S.: 237310
Dede Vaughn Cannon (CEO)

Bay Area Barricade Service, Inc. **(2)**
1861 Arnold Ind Way, Concord, CA 94520
Tel.: (925) 686-1089
Web Site: http://www.babsinc.com
Sales Range: $1-9.9 Million
Emp.: 12
Miscellaneous Durable Goods Merchant Whslr
N.A.I.C.S.: 423990

AND PRIVATE COMPANIES

Barbara Songster *(Pres)*

Highway Supply, LLC (2)
6221 Chappell Rd NE, Albuquerque, NM 87113
Tel.: (505) 345-8295
Web Site: http://www.highwaysupply.net
Sales Range: $1-9.9 Million
Emp.: 35
Highway And Street Construction
N.A.I.C.S.: 237310
Denis Riddiford *(Principal)*

Liddell Brothers, Inc. (2)
600 Industrial Dr, Halifax, MA 02338
Tel.: (781) 293-2100
Web Site: http://www.liddellbrothers.com
Rev.: $2,700,000
Emp.: 25
Sign Mfr
N.A.I.C.S.: 339950

Western Remac, Inc. (2)
1740 International Pkwy, Woodridge, IL 60517
Tel.: (630) 972-7770
Web Site: http://www.westernremac.com
Rev.: $5,333,333
Emp.: 43
Sign Mfr
N.A.I.C.S.: 339950
Jill Longoria *(Owner & CEO)*

Viz Branz Limited (1)
14 Woodlands Link, Singapore, 738739, Singapore
Tel.: (65) 67566033
Sales Range: $125-149.9 Million
Coffee Tea Cereal & Snack Food Mfr
N.A.I.C.S.: 311920
Ben Chng *(CEO)*

Subsidiary (Non-US):

Bridge Shine Coffee (Shanghai) Co., Ltd. (2)
1000 WuZhong Road, Shanghai, 201103, China
Tel.: (86) 2164015383
Web Site: http://www.bridgeshine.com.cn
Sales Range: $25-49.9 Million
Emp.: 40
Coffee Roasting & Whslr
N.A.I.C.S.: 311920

Bridge Shine Coffee Equipment (Shanghai) Co., Ltd. (2)
1000 WuZhong Road, Shanghai, China
Tel.: (86) 21 6401 0458
Web Site: http://www.bridgeshine.com.cn
Commercial Coffee Makers Mfr
N.A.I.C.S.: 333241

Subsidiary (Domestic):

Gold Roast Food Industry (Singapore) Pte Ltd (2)
14 Woodland Link, Singapore, 738739, Singapore
Tel.: (65) 67566033
Web Site: http://www.goldroast.com.sg
Sales Range: $100-124.9 Million
Emp.: 300
Instant Beverages Mfr & Distr
N.A.I.C.S.: 311920
Ben Chng *(Mng Dir)*

INVESTCORP INDIA ACQUISITION CORP.
Elgin Avenue, PO Box 1111, Georgetown, KY1-1102, Grand Cayman, Cayman Islands
Tel.: (345) 3027387210   Ky
Web Site:
  https://www.investcorpspac.com
Year Founded: 2021
IVCA—(NASDAQ)
Rev.: $10,636,704
Assets: $108,500,889
Liabilities: $110,566,141
Net Worth: ($2,065,252)
Earnings: $8,862,477
Fiscal Year-end: 12/31/23
Investment Management Service
N.A.I.C.S.: 523999

INVESTEC AUSTRALIA PROPERTY FUND
The Chifley Tower 2 Chifley S Level 23, PO Box 4411, Sydney, 2000, NSW, Australia
Tel.: (61) 292936300
IAP—(JSE)
Rev.: $70,710,427
Assets: $839,654,063
Liabilities: $274,434,341
Net Worth: $565,219,722
Earnings: $41,233,237
Fiscal Year-end: 03/31/20
Investment Management Service
N.A.I.C.S.: 525990
Graeme Anthony Katz *(CEO)*

INVESTEC LIMITED
100 Grayston Drive Sandown, Sandton, 2196, South Africa
Tel.: (27) 112867000   ZA
Web Site: http://www.investec.com
Year Founded: 1974
INL—(JSE)
Rev.: $1,976,731,905
Assets: $33,695,486,856
Liabilities: $30,447,353,690
Net Worth: $3,248,133,166
Earnings: $383,189,514
Emp.: 7,400
Fiscal Year-end: 03/31/23
Investment & Asset Management Services
N.A.I.C.S.: 523999
Bernard Kantor *(Mng Dir)*

Subsidiaries:

Gerard Lighting Pty Ltd (1)
Level 2 191 Fullarton Road, Dulwich, 5065, SA, Australia
Tel.: (61) 1300799300
Web Site: http://www.gerardlighting.com.au
Lighting Product Mfr
N.A.I.C.S.: 335131
Les Patterson *(CEO)*

Subsidiary (Domestic):

Austube Pty Limited (2)
23 Foundry Road, Seven Hills, 2147, NSW, Australia
Tel.: (61) 296749122
Web Site: http://www.austube.com.au
Emp.: 60
Tubular Lighting Systems Mfr
N.A.I.C.S.: 335132
Santina Dominguez *(Controller-Fin)*

Crompton Lighting Pty Limited (2)
96-112 Gow St, Padstow, 2211, NSW, Australia
Tel.: (61) 2 9794 9393
Web Site: http://www.crompton.com.au
Sales Range: $50-74.9 Million
Emp.: 40
Lamps & Light Fittings Distr
N.A.I.C.S.: 423690
Margaret Gao *(Mgr-Pur)*

Subsidiary (Non-US):

Gerard Lighting (NZ) Limited (2)
59 Montgomerie Road, Airport Oaks, Auckland, 2022, New Zealand
Tel.: (64) 9 255 0006
Web Site: http://www.gerardlighting.co.nz
Sales Range: $25-49.9 Million
Emp.: 15
Lighting Product Mfr
N.A.I.C.S.: 335131

Subsidiary (Domestic):

Inlite Pty Limited (2)
44-46 Chippen St, Chippendale, 2008, NSW, Australia
Tel.: (61) 283841000
Web Site: http://www.inlite.com.au
Sales Range: $25-49.9 Million
Emp.: 15
Lighting System Installation & Distr
N.A.I.C.S.: 238210
Jarrod Huxtable *(Mgr-Natl Sls)*

Lighting Corporation Pty Limited (2)
12/37 O'Riordan Street, PO Box 7424, Alexandria, 2015, NSW, Australia
Tel.: (61) 283060900
Sales Range: $150-199.9 Million
Lighting Fixture Marketer & Distr
N.A.I.C.S.: 335131

Moonlighting Pty Limited (2)
351 King Street, Melbourne, 3003, VIC, Australia
Tel.: (61) 392352400
Web Site: http://www.moonlighting.com.au
Sales Range: $25-49.9 Million
Emp.: 10
Lighting Fixtures Mfr & Distr
N.A.I.C.S.: 335131

Pierlite Australia Pty Limited (2)
96-112 Gow Street, Padstow, 2211, NSW, Australia
Tel.: (61) 1300799300
Web Site: http://www.pierlite.com.au
Sales Range: $100-124.9 Million
Emp.: 500
Lighting Systems Mfr & Distr
N.A.I.C.S.: 335131
Simon Morrison *(Mgr-Specification)*

Investec Asset Management (Pty) Ltd (1)
100 Grayston Drive, Sandown, Johannesburg, 2196, South Africa
Tel.: (27) 11 286 7000
Web Site:
  http://www.investecmanagement.com
Sales Range: $100-124.9 Million
Emp.: 125
Asset Management Services
N.A.I.C.S.: 523940
Eric Maskalunas *(Reg Dir-North America & Japan)*

Investec Bank (Mauritius) Limited (1)
Office 2 Ground Floor Block 3 The Strand Beau Plan, 21001, Port Louis, Mauritius
Tel.: (230) 2074000
Web Site: https://www.investec.com
Sales Range: $50-74.9 Million
Emp.: 80
Commercial Banking Services
N.A.I.C.S.: 522110
Marc Kahn *(Chief Strategy Officer)*

Investec Fund Managers SA Ltd (1)
100 Grayston Drive Sandown, Sandton, Johannesburg, 2196, Gauteng, South Africa
Tel.: (27) 11 286 7000
Web Site:
  http://www.investecmanagement.com
Mutual Fund Management Services
N.A.I.C.S.: 523940

Investec Private Trust Limited (1)
36 Hans Strijdom Avenue Foreshore, Cape Town, 8000, South Africa
Tel.: (27) 21 416 1000
Commercial Banking Services
N.A.I.C.S.: 522110

Investec Property Group Holdings Ltd (1)
12 Burnett Road, Pretoria, 0083, Gauteng, South Africa
Tel.: (27) 112867000
Financial Investment Management Services
N.A.I.C.S.: 523999

Investec Trust (Mauritius) Limited (1)
Level 8C Cyber Tower II, Ebene, Mauritius
Tel.: (230) 4030400
Financial Management Services
N.A.I.C.S.: 523999
Gordon Stuart *(Mng Dir)*

Investec plc (1)
30 Gresham Street, London, EC2V 7QP, United Kingdom
Tel.: (44) 2075974000
Web Site: http://www.investec.com
Rev.: $5,250,350,117
Assets: $72,088,767,955
Liabilities: $65,119,650,168
Net Worth: $6,969,117,788
Earnings: $829,167,413
Emp.: 1,400
Fiscal Year-end: 03/31/2024
Investment & Asset Management Services
N.A.I.C.S.: 523999
Fani Titi *(Grp CEO)*

Subsidiary (Domestic):

IWI Fund Management Limited (2)
100 Wood Street, London, EC2V 7AN, United Kingdom
Tel.: (44) 20 7072 7500
Web Site: http://iwifm.co.uk
Investment Management Service
N.A.I.C.S.: 523999

Investec Asset Finance plc (2)
2 New Abbey Court Stert Street, Abingdon, OX14 3JF, Oxfordshire, United Kingdom
Tel.: (44) 1235 555 577
Asset Management Services
N.A.I.C.S.: 523940
Mandy Woodford *(Mgr-Bus Dev-Matls Handling)*

Subsidiary (Non-US):

Investec Asset Management Taiwan Limited (2)
Unit B Unit C 49F Taipei 101 Tower 7 Xin Yi Road Sec 5, Taipei, 110, Taiwan
Tel.: (886) 2 8101 0800
Web Site:
  http://www.investecassetmanagement.com
Asset Management Services
N.A.I.C.S.: 523940
Daria Teng *(Gen Mgr)*

Subsidiary (Domestic):

Investec Asset Management US Limited (2)
2 Gresham Street, London, EC2V 7QP, United Kingdom
Tel.: (44) 20 7597 4000
Web Site: http://www.investec.co.uk
Asset Management Services
N.A.I.C.S.: 523940

Subsidiary (Non-US):

Investec Bank (Channel Islands) Limited (2)
Glategny Court Glategny Esplanade, PO Box 188, Saint Peter Port, GY1 3LP, Guernsey
Tel.: (44) 1481 723 506
Web Site: http://www.investec-ci.com
Sales Range: $50-74.9 Million
Emp.: 1
Commercial Banking Services
N.A.I.C.S.: 522110
Stephen Henry *(Mng Dir)*

Investec Bank (Switzerland) AG (2)
Lowenstrasse 29, 8001, Zurich, Switzerland
Tel.: (41) 44 226 1000
Emp.: 30
Commercial Banking Services
N.A.I.C.S.: 522110
Peter Gyger *(Gen Mgr)*

Investec Capital Asia Limited (2)
36/F Two International Finance Centre 8 Finance Street, Central, China (Hong Kong)
Tel.: (852) 3187 5000
Web Site: http://www.accap.com
Sales Range: $50-74.9 Million
Emp.: 20
Investment Banking Services
N.A.I.C.S.: 523150
Chilie Ho *(Gen Mgr-Fin & Ops)*

Investec Experien Pty Limited (2)
31 The Chifley Tower 2 Chifley Square, Sydney, 2000, NSW, Australia
Tel.: (61) 2 9293 2099
Consumer Lending Services
N.A.I.C.S.: 522291

Subsidiary (Domestic):

Investec Fund Managers Limited (2)
PO Box 9042, Chelmsford, CM99 2XL, United Kingdom
Tel.: (44) 20 7597 1900
Web Site:
  http://www.investecassetmanagement.com
Mutual Fund Management Services
N.A.I.C.S.: 523940
Hendrik du Toit *(CEO)*

Investec Group (UK) Plc (2)
2 Gresham Street, London, EC2V 7QP, United Kingdom
Tel.: (44) 20 75974000
Financial Management Services
N.A.I.C.S.: 523999

INVESTEC LIMITED

Investec Limited—(Continued)

Jane Warren *(Head-Digital-Wealth & Investment)*

Investec Holding Company Limited (2)
2 Gresham Street, London, EC2V 7QP, United Kingdom
Tel.: (44) 2075974598
Web Site: http://www.investec.com
Holding Company
N.A.I.C.S.: 551112

Subsidiary (Domestic):

Investec Group Investments (UK) Limited
2 Gresham St, London, EC2V 7QP, United Kingdom
Tel.: (44) 2075974000
Web Site: http://www.investec.com
Sales Range: $150-199.9 Million
Emp.: 500
Privater Equity Firm
N.A.I.C.S.: 523999
David Currie *(Dir-Investment Banking)*

Investec Securities Ltd. (3)
100 Wood Street 9th Floor, London, EC2V 7AN, United Kingdom
Tel.: (44) 2075971234
Web Site: http://www.investec.com
Sales Range: $10-24.9 Million
Emp.: 554
Holding Company; Financial Services
N.A.I.C.S.: 551112
Alex Snow *(CEO)*

Subsidiary (Domestic):

Darwin Strategic Limited (4)
2 Queen Caroline Street, London, W6 9DX, United Kingdom
Tel.: (44) 20 3178 6173
Web Site: http://www.darwin-strategic.com
Equity Financing Services
N.A.I.C.S.: 523999
Anand Sambasivan *(Co-Founder & CEO)*

Evolution Group Services Limited
Clifton St Peters Rd, Bournemouth, United Kingdom (100%)
Tel.: (44) 1202299344
Business Services
N.A.I.C.S.: 561499

Subsidiary (Non-US):

Evolution Watterson Securities Limited (4)
2105-8 21/F Two Exchange Square 8 Connaught Place, Central, China (Hong Kong) (100%)
Tel.: (852) 25251990
Securities Brokerage
N.A.I.C.S.: 523150

Subsidiary (Non-US):

Investec Ireland Limited (2)
The Harcourt Building Harcourt Street, Dublin, Ireland
Tel.: (353) 14210000
Web Site: http://www.investec.ie
Sales Range: $75-99.9 Million
Emp.: 250
Investment Banking Services
N.A.I.C.S.: 523150
Michael Cullen *(CEO)*

Subsidiary (Domestic):

NCB Group Ltd. (3)
3 George's Dock, IFSC, Dublin, 1, Ireland
Tel.: (353) 16115611
Web Site: http://www.ncb.ie
Sales Range: $125-149.9 Million
Emp.: 120
Investment Management Service
N.A.I.C.S.: 523150

Subsidiary (Domestic):

NCB Corporate Finance Limited (4)
3 George's Dock, IFSC, Dublin, 1, Ireland (100%)
Tel.: (353) 16115611
Web Site: http://www.ncb.ie
Investment Advisor
N.A.I.C.S.: 523940

NCB Stockbrokers Limited (4)
3 George's Dock, IFSC, Dublin, 1, Ireland
Tel.: (353) 16115907
Web Site: http://www.ncb.ie
Sales Range: $50-74.9 Million
Domestic & Offshore Fund Listing Services
N.A.I.C.S.: 525910

NCB Ventures Limited (4)
3 George's Dock, IFSC, Dublin, 1, Ireland (100%)
Tel.: (353) 16115611
Web Site: http://www.ncb-ventures.com
Venture Capital Investment Firm
N.A.I.C.S.: 523999

Subsidiary (US):

Investec Securities (US) LLC (2)
10 E 53rd St 22nd Fl, New York, NY 10022
Tel.: (212) 259-5616
Web Site: http://www.investec.com
Securities Brokerage Services
N.A.I.C.S.: 523150
David Rappaport *(CEO & Chief Compliance Officer)*

Subsidiary (Non-US):

Investec Trust (Jersey) Limited (2)
PO Box 344, Saint Helier, JE4 8UW, Jersey
Tel.: (44) 1534 512 512
Emp.: 45
Financial Management Services
N.A.I.C.S.: 523999

Investec Trust (Switzerland) S.A. (2)
1 Rue Eu Pre De La Vbichette, Geneva, 1201, Switzerland
Tel.: (41) 22 807 20 00
Web Site: http://www.investectrust.com
Emp.: 28
Trust Management Services
N.A.I.C.S.: 523940
Paul Douglas *(Gen Mgr)*

Subsidiary (Domestic):

Leasedirect Finance Limited (2)
Dee House Saint David's Park, Ewloe, CH5 3XF, United Kingdom
Tel.: (44) 1244 527300
Web Site: http://www.ldf.co.uk
Emp.: 200
Financial Lending Services
N.A.I.C.S.: 522220
Peter Alderson *(Mng Dir)*

Reichmans Holdings Limited (1)
Grayston Drive, 2196, Sandton, South Africa
Tel.: (27) 11 2868200
Web Site: http://www.reichmanscapital.com
Emp.: 45
Financial Investment Management Services
N.A.I.C.S.: 523999
John Wilks *(Gen Mgr)*

Subsidiary (Domestic):

ReichmansCapital (2)
100 Grayston Drive, Sandown, Sandton, 2196, South Africa
Tel.: (27) 11 286 8275
Web Site: http://www.reichmanscapital.com
Sales Range: $25-49.9 Million
Emp.: 4
Financial Management Services
N.A.I.C.S.: 523999
John Wilks *(Mng Dir)*

INVESTECH HOLDINGS LIMITED

Room 1201 12/F C C Wu Building 302-308 Hennessy Road, Wanchai, China (Hong Kong)
Tel.: (852) 21512413
Web Site: http://www.investech-holdings.com
1087—(HKG)
Rev.: $78,157,732
Assets: $104,796,245
Liabilities: $59,855,188
Net Worth: $44,941,057
Earnings: ($4,635,868)
Emp.: 306

Fiscal Year-end: 12/31/22
Investment Services
N.A.I.C.S.: 523999
Chengye Lu *(Exec Dir)*

Subsidiaries:

Changshu Honglin Connecting-Technology Co., Ltd. (1)
No 8 Liuzhou Road Yushan Industrial Park, Hi-Tech Development Zone, Changshu, Jiangsu, China
Tel.: (86) 512 51538188
Electronic Connector Mfr
N.A.I.C.S.: 334417

Changshu Honglin Electronic Co., Ltd. (1)
No 8 Liuhou Road Yushan Industrial Park, Hi-Tech Development Zone, Changshu, Jiangsu, China
Tel.: (86) 51252150016
Electronic Connector Mfr
N.A.I.C.S.: 334417

Changshu Honglin Wire & Cable Co., Ltd. (1)
No 8 Liuzhou Industrial Park Yushan Industrial Park, Hi-Tech Development Zone, Changshu, Jiangsu, China
Tel.: (86) 512 52059397
Electronic Connector Mfr
N.A.I.C.S.: 334417

Chongqing Honglin Technology Co., Ltd. (1)
1st Hequa Road Yanjia Industry Park, Chongqing, China
Tel.: (86) 2 4072 0888
Electronic Connector Mfr
N.A.I.C.S.: 334417

Dezhou Honglin Electronic Co., Ltd. (1)
Honglin Road Hengyuan Economic Development Zone, Linyi, Dezhou, Shandong, China
Tel.: (86) 534 5055505
Electronic Connector Mfr
N.A.I.C.S.: 334417

Dezhou Jingchen Automotive Electronic Co., Ltd. (1)
Honglin Road Hengyuan Economic Development Zone, Linyi, Dezhou, Shandong, China
Tel.: (86) 534 5055505
Electronic Connector Mfr
N.A.I.C.S.: 334417

Huizhou Honglin Technology Co., Ltd. (1)
Dongxin Street Honglin Industry Park, Dongijiang Hi-Tech Development Zone, Huizhou, Guangdong, China
Tel.: (86) 752 520 3688
Electronic Connector Mfr
N.A.I.C.S.: 334417

Huizhou Youte Electronic Co., Ltd. (1)
Dongxin Street Honglin Industry Park, Dongjiang Hi-Tech Development Zone, Huizhou, Guangdong, China
Tel.: (86) 752 520 3688
Electronic Connector Mfr
N.A.I.C.S.: 334417

Shenzhen HongLin Communication Technology Co., Ltd. (1)
Building 6 No 2 Industrial Industrial Park, Shapuwei Songgang Baoan District, Shenzhen, China
Tel.: (86) 755 26050272
Electronic Connector Mfr
N.A.I.C.S.: 334417

Wafer Systems Limited (1)
Unit 02 13F No 101 Kings Road, North Point, China (Hong Kong)
Tel.: (852) 39000800
Web Site: http://www.wafersystems.com
Networking & Software Development Services
N.A.I.C.S.: 541512
Raymond Lee *(Mgr-Acct)*

Weihai Honglin Electronic Co., Ltd. (1)

INTERNATIONAL PUBLIC

Pudong Road First Industrial park, Economic and Technological Development Zone, Weihai, Shandong, China
Tel.: (86) 6313678598
Web Site: https://www.honglinpowertech.com
Electronic Connector Mfr
N.A.I.C.S.: 334417

Wuhan Honglin Electronic Co., Ltd. (1)
Building 21 Hi-Tech Industrial Park, Economic & Technology Development Zone, Wuhan, Hubei, China
Tel.: (86) 27 84254577
Electronic Connector Mfr
N.A.I.C.S.: 334417

INVESTEKO SA

Polish Army 16G, 41-600, Swietochlowice, Poland
Tel.: (48) 322585580
Web Site: https://www.investeko.pl
Year Founded: 1999
Financial Support Services
N.A.I.C.S.: 541611
Arkadiusz Primus *(Chm)*

INVESTERINGSSELSKABET LUXOR A/S

Frederiksborggade 50 4 sal, 1360, Copenhagen, 1360, Denmark
Tel.: (45) 33325015
Web Site: https://www.luxor.dk
Year Founded: 1973
LUXOR.B—(CSE)
Rev.: $12,714,889
Assets: $151,364,477
Liabilities: $86,710,594
Net Worth: $64,653,883
Earnings: $4,538,387
Emp.: 10
Fiscal Year-end: 09/30/23
Investment Banking & Securities Intermediation
N.A.I.C.S.: 523150
Jannik Rolf Larsen *(CEO)*

INVESTIGATOR RESOURCES LIMITED

47 King Street, PO Box 3235, Norwood, 5067, SA, Australia
Tel.: (61) 873252222
Web Site: https://www.investres.com.au
IVR—(ASX)
Rev.: $108,114
Assets: $23,751,390
Liabilities: $1,070,202
Net Worth: $22,681,188
Earnings: ($1,323,957)
Emp.: 12
Fiscal Year-end: 06/30/24
Metal Mining Services
N.A.I.C.S.: 212290
Melanie Leydin *(CFO & Co-Sec)*

INVESTIGO LTD

1 Broadgate Cir, London, EC2M 2QS, United Kingdom
Tel.: (44) 20 7194 7850
Web Site: http://www.investigo.co.uk
Sales Range: $75-99.9 Million
Emp.: 160
Employment & Recruitment Services
N.A.I.C.S.: 561311
Haresh Vaya *(Dir-Fin)*

Subsidiaries:

Investigo Guildford (1)
3000 Cathedral Hill, Guildford, GU2 7YB, Surrey, United Kingdom
Tel.: (44) 1483 245465
Web Site: http://www.investigo.co.uk
Emp.: 9
Employment & Recruitment Services
N.A.I.C.S.: 561311

Investigo Milton Keynes (1)
Aurora House Deltic Avenue Rooksley

AND PRIVATE COMPANIES

Bradwell Common, Milton Keynes, MK13 8LW, United Kingdom
Tel.: (44) 1908049944
Web Site: http://www.investigo.co.uk
Emp.: 13
Employment & Recruitment Services
N.A.I.C.S.: 561311

Investigo Reading (1)
Davidson House Forbury Square, Reading, RG1 3EU, United Kingdom
Tel.: (44) 1189 001330
Employment & Recruitment Services
N.A.I.C.S.: 561311

Investigo St Albans (1)
Fountain Court 2 Victoria Court, Saint Albans, AL1 3TF, Hertfordshire, United Kingdom
Tel.: (44) 1727 884 768
Web Site: http://www.investigo.co.uk
Emp.: 15
Employment & Recruitment Services
N.A.I.C.S.: 561311

INVESTIMENTOS E PARTICI-PACOES & INFRA-ESTRUTURA SA- INVEPAR
Praia de Botafogo n 501, Botafogo, Rio de Janeiro, 22250-911, RJ, Brazil
Tel.: (55) 22111300   BR
Web Site: http://www.invepar.com.br
Year Founded: 2000
IVPR4B—(BRAZ)
Rev.: $604,029,468
Assets: $3,461,264,700
Liabilities: $4,148,107,975
Net Worth: ($686,843,275)
Earnings: ($49,950,541)
Fiscal Year-end: 12/31/23
Freight Transportation Services
N.A.I.C.S.: 481212
Enio Stein Jr. *(Dir-Investor Relations)*

INVESTIMENTOS E PARTICI-PACOES EM INFRAESTRU-TURA S.A.
Av Almirante Barroso 52 - Sl 801 3001 E 3002, 20031-000, Rio de Janeiro, RJ, Brazil
Tel.: (55) 2122111300
Web Site: http://www.invepar.com.br
Year Founded: 2000
IVPR4B—(BRAZ)
Rev.: $523,954,330,827
Assets: $3,002,410,853,131
Liabilities: $2,406,621,197,709
Net Worth: $595,789,655,422
Earnings: ($43,328,684,428)
Emp.: 8,542
Fiscal Year-end: 12/31/23
Toll Operating Services
N.A.I.C.S.: 488490
Carlos Fernando Costa *(Chm)*

INVESTINDUSTRIAL ACQUISI-TION CORP.
Suite 1 3rd Floor 11-12 St James's Square, London, SW1Y 4LB, United Kingdom
Tel.: (44) 2074003333   Ky
Web Site: http://www.investacquisition.com
Year Founded: 2020
IIACU—(NYSE)
Sales Range: Less than $1 Million
Investment Services
N.A.I.C.S.: 523999
Roberto Ardagna *(CEO)*

Subsidiaries:

Ermenegildo Zegna N.V. (1)
4 W 57th Street New York, Trivero, 13835, Biella, Italy
Tel.: (39) 01575911
Web Site: https://www.zegna.com
Rev.: $2,055,416,577
Assets: $2,986,197,928
Liabilities: $2,013,938,053
Net Worth: $972,259,875
Earnings: $146,407,295
Emp.: 7,201
Fiscal Year-end: 12/31/2023
Men's & Boys' Clothing Mfr
N.A.I.C.S.: 315250
Ermenegildo Zegna *(CEO)*

Subsidiary (US):

Thom Browne, Inc. (2)
100 Hudson St, New York, NY 10013   (85%)
Tel.: (212) 633-1197
Web Site: http://www.thombrowne.com
Chemicals Mfr
N.A.I.C.S.: 325998
Thom Browne *(Founder & Chm)*

INVESTINDUSTRIAL ADVI-SORS LTD.
16 Palace Street, London, SW1E 5JD, United Kingdom
Tel.: (44) 2076642121
Web Site:
  http://www.investindustrial.com
Year Founded: 1990
Investment Company
N.A.I.C.S.: 523940

Subsidiaries:

CEME S.p.a (1)
Viale dell'Industria, 5, Trivolzio, 27020, Italy
Tel.: (39) 038293011
Web Site: https://www.cemegroup.com
Automation Machinery Mfg.
N.A.I.C.S.: 333517

Subsidiary (US):

Procon Products (2)
8697 Oaks Ste 120, Smyrna, TN 37167
Tel.: (615) 355-8000
Web Site: http://www.proconpump.com
Sales Range: $25-49.9 Million
Emp.: 16
Rotary Vane Pumps
N.A.I.C.S.: 333914
Jeff Kulikowski *(Acct Mgr-Key-Global)*

Fassi Gru S.p.A. (1)
via Roma 110, Albino, 24021, Bergamo, Italy
Tel.: (39) 035 776400
Web Site: http://www.fassi.com
Crane Mfr
N.A.I.C.S.: 333924
Giovanni Fassi *(CEO)*

Subsidiary (Non-US):

Cranab AB (2)
Karlsgardsvagen 56, Vindeln, 922 82, Sweden
Tel.: (46) 93313500
Web Site: http://www.cranab.se
Forestry Equipment Mfr
N.A.I.C.S.: 541330
Hans Eliasson *(Chm)*

Unit (Domestic):

Cranab AB - Cranab 1 Factory (3)
Karlsgardsvagen 56, 922 32, Vindeln, Sweden
Tel.: (46) 93314591
Web Site: http://www.cranab.se
Crane, Grapple & Bushcutter Mfr & Whslr
N.A.I.C.S.: 333924

Cranab AB - Cranab 2 Factory (3)
Allan Jonssons vag 4, 922 31, Vindeln, Sweden
Tel.: (46) 93314594
Web Site: http://www.cranab.se
Crane, Grapple & Bushcutter Mfr & Whslr
N.A.I.C.S.: 333924

Subsidiary (Domestic):

Vimek AB (3)
Allan Jonssons vag 11, 922 31, Vindeln, Sweden
Tel.: (46) 93313515
Web Site: http://www.vimek.se
Forestry Machinery Mfr
N.A.I.C.S.: 333112
Urban Lundstrom *(Mgr-After Sls)*

Jacuzzi Brands Corporation (1)
14525 Montevista Ave, Chino, CA 91710
Tel.: (909) 606-7733
Web Site: http://www.jacuzzihottubs.com
Sales Range: $1-4.9 Billion
Emp.: 4,907
Plumbing Products
N.A.I.C.S.: 332913
Charles Huebner *(CEO)*

Subsidiary (Domestic):

BathCraft, Inc. (2)
1610 James P Rodgers Dr, Valdosta, GA 31601-6518
Tel.: (229) 333-0805
Web Site: http://www.bathcraft.com
Sales Range: $10-24.9 Million
Emp.: 600
Whirlpool Bath Mfr
N.A.I.C.S.: 326191
Johnny Hambrick *(VP)*

Gatsby Spas, Inc. (2)
PO Box 5457, Plant City, FL 33563
Tel.: (813) 754-4122
Web Site: http://www.livingthespalife.com
Hot Tubs Mfr
N.A.I.C.S.: 335220

Subsidiary (Non-US):

Jacuzzi Chile S.A. (2)
Av Pedro Aguirre Cerda 6843, Comuna de Cerrillos, Santiago, 7270677, Chile
Tel.: (56) 25922222
Web Site: http://www.jacuzzi.cl
Sales Range: $25-49.9 Million
Emp.: 50
Domestic Pumps & Water Systems, Swimming Pool Equipment, Whirlpool Bathtubs & Spas; Turbines & Centrifugals
N.A.I.C.S.: 333414

Jacuzzi Europe S.p.A. (2)
S S Pontebbana Km 97 200, Valvasone, 33098, Pordenone, Italy
Tel.: (39) 0434859111
Web Site: http://www.jacuzzi.it
Emp.: 150
Domestic Pumps & Water Systems, Swimming Pool Equipment, Whirlpool Bathtubs & Spas; Turbines & Centrifugals
N.A.I.C.S.: 332913

Division (Domestic):

Jacuzzi Hot Tubs (2)
13925 City Center Dr, Chino Hills, CA 91709
Tel.: (909) 606-1416
Web Site: http://www.jacuzzihottubs.com
Sales Range: $100-124.9 Million
Emp.: 1,000
Hot Tubs
N.A.I.C.S.: 339999

Subsidiary (Domestic):

Jacuzzi Inc. (2)
13925 City Center Dr Ste 200, Chino Hills, CA 91709
Tel.: (972) 232-3200
Web Site: http://www.jacuzzi.com
Whirlpool Bath, Spa & Pump Mfr
N.A.I.C.S.: 327110

Jacuzzi Luxury Bath (2)
13925 City Center Dr Ste 200, Chino Hills, CA 91709
Tel.: (909) 247-2920
Web Site: http://www.jacuzzi.com
Rev.: $64,000,000
Emp.: 1,200
Tubs Bath Shower & Laundry Plastics
N.A.I.C.S.: 326191
Joey Davis *(Pres & Gen Mgr)*

Subsidiary (Non-US):

Jacuzzi do Brasil (2)
Rod Waldomiro C Camargo Km 53 5 SP-79, Itu, 13308-900, SP, Brazil
Tel.: (55) 11 2118 7500
Web Site: http://www.jacuzzi.com.br
Domestic Pumps & Water Systems, Swimming Pool Equipment, Whirlpool Bathtubs & Spas; Turbines & Centrifugals
N.A.I.C.S.: 332913

La Doria S.p.A. (1)

INVESTINDUSTRIAL ADVISORS LTD.

Via Nazionale 320, 84012, Angri, Italy   (63.13%)
Tel.: (39) 0815166111
Web Site: https://www.gruppoladoria.it
Rev.: $1,041,710,876
Assets: $881,453,805
Liabilities: $523,478,344
Net Worth: $357,975,461
Earnings: $69,620,328
Emp.: 820
Fiscal Year-end: 12/31/2020
Tomato-Based Products, Canned Fruit, Vegetables, Pasta Products, Fruit Juices & Iced Tea Processor
N.A.I.C.S.: 311421
Antonio Ferraioli *(Chm, Pres & CEO)*

Subsidiary (Non-US):

LDH (La Doria) Ltd (2)
LDH House Parsons Green, Saint Ives, PE27 4AA, Cambridgeshire, United Kingdom   (51%)
Tel.: (44) 1480308800
Web Site: https://www.ldhltd.com
Sales Range: $25-49.9 Million
General Line Grocery Merchant Whslr
N.A.I.C.S.: 424410

Natra S.A. (1)
Edificio Master's I Avda General Peron 38 5th floor, 28020, Madrid, Spain
Tel.: (34) 914178868
Web Site: http://www.natra.es
Sales Range: $450-499.9 Million
Emp.: 1,108
Cocoa Derivates, Chocolate Products & Other Food Processing Technologies Mfr & Sales
N.A.I.C.S.: 311351

Subsidiary (Non-US):

Natra Allcrump (2)
Nijverheidsstraat 13, 2390, Malle, Belgium
Tel.: (32) 33129500
Web Site: http://www.natra.com
Sales Range: $25-49.9 Million
Emp.: 100
Chocolate Mfr
N.A.I.C.S.: 311351
Joris Van Loveren *(Gen Mgr)*

Natra Saint Etienne SAS (2)
95 Rue Jean-Huss, Saint Etienne, France
Tel.: (33) 477431313
Web Site: http://www.natra.es
Chocolate Mfr
N.A.I.C.S.: 311351
Mikel Beitia Larranaga *(Chm)*

Subsidiary (US):

Natra US (2)
1059 Tierra Del Rey Ste II, Chula Vista, CA 91910-7884
Tel.: (619) 397-4120
Chocolate & Confectionery Mfr
N.A.I.C.S.: 311351
Juan Vinolo *(Acct Mgr)*

Subsidiary (Domestic):

NatraZahor (2)
Carretera de Aranzazu S N, PO Box 20560, Onate, Guipuzcoa, 20560, Spain
Tel.: (34) 943716369
Web Site: http://www.natar.as
Sales Range: $100-124.9 Million
Emp.: 420
Chocolate Mfr
N.A.I.C.S.: 311351
Pedro Anduaa *(Mgr-Quality)*

Natracacao (2)
Autovia A3 salida 343 Cami de Torrent S N, PO Box 46930, Quart de Poblet, Valencia, 46930, Spain
Tel.: (34) 961597300
Sales Range: $25-49.9 Million
Emp.: 150
Chocolate Mfr
N.A.I.C.S.: 311351
Chelo Ferrer *(Mng Dir)*

Subsidiary (Non-US):

Natrajacali (2)
Burgsesteenweg 95, PO Box 8450, Bredene, 8450, West Flanders, Belgium
Tel.: (32) 59340335

INVESTINDUSTRIAL ADVISORS LTD.

Investindustrial Advisors Ltd.—(Continued)
Web Site: http://www.natra.es
Sales Range: $25-49.9 Million
Emp.: 100
Chocolate Mfr
N.A.I.C.S.: 311351
Eric Cools *(Mng Dir)*

INVESTING PROFIT WISELY, SL
San Joaquin 1, 28231, Madrid, Spain
Tel.: (34) 911294847
Web Site: http://www.ipw.es
Privater Equity Firm
N.A.I.C.S.: 523940
Diego Santo Domingo Vicario *(Portfolio Mgr)*

INVESTIS HOLDING SA
Neumuhlequai 6, 8001, Zurich, Switzerland
Tel.: (41) 582017240   CH
Web Site:
   https://www.investisgroup.com
Year Founded: 1994
IREN—(SWX)
Rev.: $275,172,333
Assets: $1,917,870,225
Liabilities: $689,739,722
Net Worth: $1,228,130,502
Earnings: ($6,420,252)
Emp.: 1,170
Fiscal Year-end: 12/31/23
Offices of Other Holding Companies
N.A.I.C.S.: 551112
Stephane Bonvin *(Chm-Exec Bd & Co-CEO)*

Subsidiaries:

AGD Renovationen AG   (1)
Hardstrasse 74, 5432, Neuenhof, Switzerland
Tel.: (41) 564064441
Web Site: https://www.agd-renovationen.ch
Residential Remodeling Services
N.A.I.C.S.: 236118

ProLabo Sarl   (1)
Route de l'Etrier 5, 1950, Sion, Switzerland
Tel.: (41) 272033000
Web Site: https://www.prolabo.ch
Material Investigation & Analysis Services
N.A.I.C.S.: 561611

INVESTIS LIMITED
24 Fashion Street, London, E1 6PX, United Kingdom
Tel.: (44) 20 7038 9000
Web Site:
   http://www.investisdigital.com
Year Founded: 2000
Digital Communications Company;
Corporate Websites & IR Webhosting
N.A.I.C.S.: 518210
Claire Price *(CFO)*

Subsidiaries:

Vertical Measures, LLC   (1)
11201 N Tatum Blvd Ste 350, Phoenix, AZ 85028
Tel.: (602) 314-3460
Web Site: http://www.verticalmeasures.com
Advertising & Marketing Services
N.A.I.C.S.: 541810
Arnie Kuenn *(CEO)*

ZOG Digital   (1)
11201 N Tatum Blvd Ste 200, Phoenix, AZ 85028
Tel.: (480) 426-9952
Social Marketing, Design & Development & Search Engine Optimization
N.A.I.C.S.: 541512
Jason Squardo *(COO)*

INVESTISSEMENT QUEBEC
Edifice Iberville I 1195 Avenue Lavigerie Bureau 060, Quebec, Quebec, G1V 4N3, QC, Canada
Tel.: (418) 643-5172   QC
Web Site:
   http://www.investquebec.com
Year Founded: 1971
Sales Range: $450-499.9 Million
Investment Holding Company
N.A.I.C.S.: 551112
Pierre Gabriel Cote *(Pres & CEO)*

Subsidiaries:

Albecour inc.   (1)
380 Saint-Antoine Street West Suite 3000, Montreal, H2Y 3X7, QC, Canada   (100%)
Tel.: (514) 875-1070
Web Site: http://www.albecour.com
Financial Investment Services
N.A.I.C.S.: 523999
Pierre Boisvert *(Gen Mgr)*

Gestion forestiere Lacroix inc.   (1)
592 Chemin Leblanc, Nouvelle, G0C 2G0, QC, Canada   (100%)
Tel.: (418) 794-2852
Web Site: http://www.gflacroix.com
Forestry Services
N.A.I.C.S.: 115310
Giles Landry *(Supvr-Forestry Ops)*

Gestion forestiere du Saint-Maurice inc.   (1)
995 boul Ducharme, La Tuque, G9X 3C3, QC, Canada   (100%)
Tel.: (819) 523-4531
Web Site: http://www.gfsm.ca
Forestry Services
N.A.I.C.S.: 115310

Le Centre d'insemination porcine du Quebec (C.I.P.Q.) inc.   (1)
1485 Saint-Aime, Saint-Lambert, G0S 2W0, QC, Canada   (100%)
Tel.: (418) 889-9748
Web Site: http://www.cipq.com
Emp.: 92
Biotechnology Research & Development Services
N.A.I.C.S.: 541714

Mine Arnaud inc.   (1)
600 rue de la Gauchetiere-Ouest bureau 1500, Montreal, H3B 4L8, QC, Canada   (60.9%)
Tel.: (514) 397-9191
Web Site: http://www.minearnaud.com
Mineral Mining Services
N.A.I.C.S.: 212390

Rexforet inc.   (1)
2954 boulevard Laurier Bureau 590, Quebec, G1V 4T2, QC, Canada   (100%)
Tel.: (418) 659-6318
Web Site: http://www.rexforet.com
Emp.: 12
Financial Investment Services
N.A.I.C.S.: 523999

Varitron Group Inc.   (1)
4811 Chemin de la Sevanne, Longueuil, J3Y 9G1, QC, Canada   (28.3%)
Tel.: (450) 926-1778
Web Site: http://www.varitron.com
Emp.: 250
Electronics Mfr
N.A.I.C.S.: 334419
Michel Farley *(Pres & CEO)*

Subsidiary (US):

Altronics Manufacturing, Inc.   (2)
12 Executive Dr Unit 2, Hudson, NH 03051
Tel.: (603) 577-8855
Web Site: http://www.altronicsmfg.com
Emp.: 50
Mfg Printed Circuit Boards
N.A.I.C.S.: 334412
Michel Farley *(Pres-Mfg)*

INVESTITORI ASSOCIATI SOCIETA DI GESTIONE DEL RISPARMIO (SGR) S.P.A.
Via Gonzaga n 2, 20123, Milan, Italy
Tel.: (39) 028545731
Web Site:
   http://www.investitoriassociati.com
Sales Range: $25-49.9 Million
Emp.: 10
Holding Company
N.A.I.C.S.: 551112
Dario Cossutta *(Sr Partner)*

Subsidiaries:

La Rinascente s.r.l.   (1)
via Washington 70, 20146, Milan, Italy   (46%)
Tel.: (39) 02467711
Web Site: http://www.rinascente.it
Sales Range: $50-74.9 Million
Departmental Store Operator
N.A.I.C.S.: 455110
Victoria Radice *(Pres)*

INVESTMENT & ALLIED ASSURANCE PLC
Plot 248b Muri Okunola Street, Victoria Island, Lagos, Nigeria
Tel.: (234) 1 271 4028
Insurance Management Services
N.A.I.C.S.: 524298

INVESTMENT & CONSTRUCTION JSC NO.18
No 471 Nguyen Trai, Thanh Xuan Nam Ward, Hanoi, Vietnam
Tel.: (84) 38540401
Web Site:
   https://www.licogi18.com.vn
Year Founded: 1961
L18—(HNX)
Rev.: $221,219,700
Assets: $354,681,800
Liabilities: $292,816,900
Net Worth: $61,864,900
Earnings: $3,063,500
Fiscal Year-end: 12/31/22
Civil Engineering Services
N.A.I.C.S.: 237990

INVESTMENT & DEVELOPMENT AGENCY-IRELAND
Wilton Park House Wilton Place, Dublin, Ireland
Tel.: (353) 16034000   IE
Web Site: http://www.idaireland.com
Year Founded: 1959
Sales Range: $50-74.9 Million
Emp.: 239
Promoter of Ireland for Overseas Investment; Economic Development Agency for In-ward Investment to Ireland
N.A.I.C.S.: 926110
Thomas McEvoy *(Mgr-PR)*

Subsidiaries:

IDA Ireland USA Office   (1)
345 Park Ave 17th Fl, New York, NY 10154
Tel.: (212) 750-4300
Web Site: http://www.ida.com
Sales Range: $25-49.9 Million
Emp.: 10
Promoter of Ireland for Overseas Investment; Industrial Development Agency
N.A.I.C.S.: 541611
Emmanuel Dowdall *(Exec VP-North America)*

INVESTMENT & PRECISION CASTINGS LTD.
Nari Road, Bhavnagar, 364 006, Gujarat, India
Tel.: (91) 7069580001
Web Site: https://www.ipcl.in
504786—(BOM)
Rev.: $23,283,788
Assets: $27,410,319
Liabilities: $16,710,357
Net Worth: $10,699,962
Earnings: $758,476
Emp.: 680
Fiscal Year-end: 03/31/23
Casting Mfr
N.A.I.C.S.: 331524
Piyush Indulal Tamboli *(Chm & Mng Dir)*

INTERNATIONAL PUBLIC

INVESTMENT & TRADING OF REAL ESTATE JSC
18 Nguyen Binh Khiem Street Da Kao Ward, District 1, Ho Chi Minh City, Vietnam
Tel.: (84) 838230256
Web Site:
   https://www.intresco.com.vn
ITC—(HOSE)
Rev.: $21,795,459
Assets: $170,987,581
Liabilities: $76,022,652
Net Worth: $94,964,929
Earnings: $3,624,034
Emp.: 72
Fiscal Year-end: 12/31/23
Real Estate Development Services
N.A.I.C.S.: 531390

INVESTMENT AB LATOUR
J A Wettergrens Gata 7, Box 336, 401 25, Gothenburg, Sweden
Tel.: (46) 31891790   SE
Web Site: https://www.latour.se
Year Founded: 1985
LATO—(OMX)
Rev.: $2,393,061,527
Assets: $5,644,534,360
Liabilities: $1,813,950,003
Net Worth: $3,830,584,357
Earnings: $552,698,868
Emp.: 8,448
Fiscal Year-end: 12/31/23
Financial Investment Services
N.A.I.C.S.: 523999
Anders Morck *(CFO)*

Subsidiaries:

720 Degrees Oy   (1)
Mikonkatu 9, 00100, Helsinki, Finland
Tel.: (358) 102087540
Web Site: https://720.io
Facilities Support Services
N.A.I.C.S.: 561210

AAT Alber Antriebstechnik GmbH   (1)
Ehestetter Weg 11, 72458, Albstadt, Germany
Tel.: (49) 743112950
Web Site: https://aat-online.de
Braking Aid Mfr
N.A.I.C.S.: 336340

Ability Lifts Ltd.   (1)
Khepera Business Centre 9 Orgreave Road, Sheffield, S13 9LQ, United Kingdom
Tel.: (44) 2045713357
Web Site: https://www.abilitylifts.co.uk
Elevator Mfr
N.A.I.C.S.: 333921

Atab automationsteknik AB   (1)
Kryptongatan 5B, 431 53, Molndal, Sweden
Tel.: (46) 313401350
Web Site: https://atab.se
Vehicle Material Transport Services
N.A.I.C.S.: 561910

Barcol- Air Group AG   (1)
Wiesenstrasse 5, 8603, Schwerzenbach, Switzerland
Tel.: (41) 582194000
Climate Ceiling Mfr & Distr
N.A.I.C.S.: 335131

Barcol-Air France S.A.S.   (1)
Parc Saint Christophe 10 avenue de I entreprise, 95861, Cergy-Pontoise, Cedex, France
Tel.: (33) 134243526
Mechanical Bolt Product Mfr & Distr
N.A.I.C.S.: 332722

Barcol-Air Italia S.R.L.   (1)
Via Bagutti 14 6900 Lugano, 20145, Milan, Italy
Tel.: (39) 0582194500
Ventilation Machine Mfr
N.A.I.C.S.: 333413

Barcol-Air Production GmbH   (1)
Scharzwaldstrasse 2, 64646, Heppenheim, Germany
Tel.: (49) 625279070

AND PRIVATE COMPANIES

INVESTMENT AB LATOUR

Ventilation Machine Mfr
N.A.I.C.S.: 333413

Caljan AS (1)
Ved Milepaelen 6-8, 8361, Hasselager, Denmark
Tel.: (45) 87387800
Web Site: https://caljan.com
Logistic Services
N.A.I.C.S.: 541614

Caljan Gmbh (1)
Patthorster Strasse 3, 33790, Halle, Germany
Tel.: (49) 614593490
Logistic Services
N.A.I.C.S.: 541614

Caljan Limited (1)
1 Patriot Dr Rooksley Roundabout Bradwell Common, Milton Keynes, MK13 8PU, United Kingdom
Tel.: (44) 1908648900
Logistic Services
N.A.I.C.S.: 541614

Caljan S.A.R.L. (1)
Centre d'Affaires La Boursidiere Rue de La Boursidiere, Batiment Q/R - 1er Etage, 92357, Le Plessis-Robinson, France
Tel.: (33) 698170215
Web Site: https://www.caljan.com
Conveyor Mfr & Distr
N.A.I.C.S.: 333922

Consens GmbH (1)
Widenmayerstr 16, 80538, Munich, Germany
Tel.: (49) 891200500
Web Site: https://www.consens.de
Property Financing Services
N.A.I.C.S.: 522292

Depac Anstalt Gmbh (1)
Wirtschaftspark 44, 9492, Eschen, Liechtenstein
Tel.: (423) 3739700
Web Site: https://www.depac.eu
Elevator Services
N.A.I.C.S.: 236220

Econdition GmbH (1)
Carl-von-Linde-Strasse 25, 85748, Garching, Germany
Tel.: (49) 89326700
Air Conditioning Contracting Services
N.A.I.C.S.: 238220

Elsys AB (1)
Tvistevagen 48, 907 36, Umea, Sweden
Tel.: (46) 90100500
Web Site: https://www.elsys.se
Wireless Sensor Mfr & Distr
N.A.I.C.S.: 334513

Emma Safety Footwear B.V. (1)
Tunnelweg 104, 6468, Kerkrade, Netherlands
Tel.: (31) 455666500
Web Site: https://www.emmasafetyfootwear.com
Footwear Mfr
N.A.I.C.S.: 316210

Esse-Ti S.R.L. (1)
Via G Capodaglio 9 ZI Squartabue, Recanati, 62019, Macerata, Italy
Tel.: (39) 0717506066
Web Site: https://www.esse-ti.it
Software Development Services
N.A.I.C.S.: 541511

Fristads AB (1)
Prognosgatan 24, 504 64, Boras, Sweden
Tel.: (46) 33202200
Clothing & Footwear Distr
N.A.I.C.S.: 424350

Fristads AS (1)
Postboks 325, 1753, Halden, Norway
Tel.: (47) 22418000
Work Wear Mfr
N.A.I.C.S.: 315210

Fristads B.V. (1)
Veldsteen 54, 4815 PK, Breda, Netherlands
Tel.: (31) 765725625
Textile Material Mfr
N.A.I.C.S.: 313310

Fristads Finland Oy (1)
Olavinkatu 5, 57100, Savonlinna, Finland
Tel.: (358) 8104069850
Textile Material Mfr
N.A.I.C.S.: 313310

Fristads GmbH (1)
Oststrasse 41-43, 22844, Norderstedt, Germany
Tel.: (49) 405353470
Work Wear Mfr
N.A.I.C.S.: 315210

HK Instruments OY (1)
Keihastie 7, 40950, Muurame, Finland
Tel.: (358) 143372000
Emp.: 100
Measuring Instrument Mfr & Distr
N.A.I.C.S.: 334513

Hellberg Safety AB (1)
Stakebergsv 2, Stenkullen, 443 61, Lerum, Sweden
Tel.: (46) 30224450
Web Site: https://www.hellbergsafety.com
Communication Equipment Mfr
N.A.I.C.S.: 334290

Hultafors Group Austria GmbH (1)
Gierstergasse 6, 1120, Vienna, Austria
Tel.: (43) 18101728
Functional Technical Workwear Mfr
N.A.I.C.S.: 315210

Hultafors Group Belgium NV (1)
Antwerpsesteenweg 285, 2800, Mechelen, Belgium
Tel.: (32) 15446530
Functional Technical Workwear Mfr
N.A.I.C.S.: 315210

Hultafors Group France SARL (1)
59 Rue des Petits Champs, 75001, Paris, France
Tel.: (33) 153408990
Functional Technical Workwear Mfr
N.A.I.C.S.: 315210

Hultafors Group Ireland Ltd. (1)
Unit B5 Calmount Business Park, Dublin, Ireland
Tel.: (353) 14098400
Functional Technical Workwear Mfr
N.A.I.C.S.: 315210

Hultafors Group Italy s.r.l. (1)
Via Negrelli 13, 39100, Bolzano, BZ, Italy
Tel.: (39) 0471061666
Functional Technical Workwear Mfr
N.A.I.C.S.: 315210

Hultafors Group Logistics Sp. z o.o. (1)
Nowogrodzka 50/515, 00-695, Warsaw, Poland
Tel.: (48) 222951287
Web Site: https://www.hultaforsgroup.pl
Logistic Services
N.A.I.C.S.: 541614

Hultafors Group NL BV (1)
Jean Monnetpark 81, 7336 BB, Apeldoorn, Netherlands
Tel.: (31) 55 599 9860
Web Site: https://www.hultaforsgroup.nl
Functional Technical Workwear Mfr
N.A.I.C.S.: 315210

Hultafors Group Poland Sp. z o.o. (1)
Nowogrodzka 50/515, 00-695, Warsaw, Poland
Tel.: (48) 222951287
Functional Technical Workwear Mfr
N.A.I.C.S.: 315210

Hultafors Group Switzerland AG (1)
Industriestrasse 9, 5432, Neuenhof, Switzerland
Tel.: (41) 564169898
Functional Technical Workwear Mfr
N.A.I.C.S.: 315210

Hultafors Group UK Ltd. (1)
Unit N3 Gate 4 Meltham Mills Ind Estate, Holmfirth, HD9 4DS, United Kingdom
Tel.: (44) 1484854488
Footwear Mfr
N.A.I.C.S.: 316210

Invalifts Ltd. (1)
6 Falcon Park Claymore Tame Valley Ind Est, Tamworth, B77 5DQ, Staffordshire, United Kingdom
Tel.: (44) 1827286860
Web Site: https://www.invalifts.com
Elevator Mfr
N.A.I.C.S.: 333921

LCP S.R.L. (1)
Via F Santi n 15/17/19, MI, 22037, Paderno Dugnano, Italy
Tel.: (39) 029186350
Web Site: https://www.lcppaderno.com
Wood Furniture Mfr & Distr
N.A.I.C.S.: 337122

LSAB Vandra AS (1)
Saeterituse Allikonnu Kula Pohja-Parnumaa vald, 87604, Parnu, Estonia
Tel.: (372) 56267999
Web Site: https://lsab.ee
Woodworking Tools Mfr & Distr
N.A.I.C.S.: 332216

Lahden Terateos OY (1)
Yhdyskatu 35, 15200, Lahti, Finland
Tel.: (358) 38733100
Web Site: https://www.lahdenterateos.fi
Cutting Tool Mfr
N.A.I.C.S.: 333515

Latour Future Solutions AB (1)
J A Wettergrens Gata 7, Box 336, SE-401 25, Gothenburg, Sweden
Tel.: (46) 313812800
Finance Investment Services
N.A.I.C.S.: 523999

Latour-Gruppen AB (1)
Box 336, 401 25, Gothenburg, Sweden
Tel.: (46) 31 891790
Web Site: http://www.investmentablatour.se
Emp.: 5
Holding Company
N.A.I.C.S.: 551112

Subsidiary (Non-US):

Caljan Rite-Hite ApS (2)
Ved Milepaelen 6-8, 8361, Hasselager, Denmark
Tel.: (45) 87 38 78 00
Web Site: http://www.caljanritehite.com
Sales Range: $10-24.9 Million
Emp.: 90
Telescopic Conveying Equipment Mfr
N.A.I.C.S.: 333922
Spencer Roberts (VP-Sls & Mktg)

Subsidiary (Non-US):

Caljan Rite-Hite Benelux BV (3)
Engelenburgstraat 57, 7391 AM, Twello, Netherlands
Tel.: (31) 571 270444
Emp.: 18
Loading Dock Equipment Mfr
N.A.I.C.S.: 238290
Henk van den Dijk (Gen Mgr)

Caljan Rite-Hite GmbH (3)
Industriestrsse 7, 65439, Florsheim, Germany
Tel.: (49) 614593490
Web Site: http://www.caljanritehite.de
Loading Dock Equipment Mfr
N.A.I.C.S.: 238290
Peter Elbaek (Mng Dir)

Caljan Rite-Hite Latvia SIA (3)
Kapsedes iela 2, Liepaja, 3414, Latvia
Tel.: (371) 6348 9530
Sales Range: $10-24.9 Million
Emp.: 80
Loading Dock Equipment Mfr
N.A.I.C.S.: 333922
Gapis Dradaeka (Gen Mgr)

Caljan Rite-Hite Ltd. (3)
37-39 Simpson Road, Fenny Stratford, Milton Keynes, MK1 1BA, United Kingdom
Tel.: (44) 1908 648900
Web Site: http://caljan.com
Sales Range: $10-24.9 Million
Emp.: 15
Loading & Unloading Equipment Mfr
N.A.I.C.S.: 333922

Caljan Rite-Hite S.A.R.L. (3)
8 Rue Georges Besse ZAC du Fosse Pate, Fontenay-le-Fleury, 78330, France
Tel.: (33) 1300 71237
Web Site: http://www.caljanritehite.fr
Sales Range: $10-24.9 Million
Emp.: 8
Conveying Equipment Mfr
N.A.I.C.S.: 333922
Henrik Olesen (Mng Dir)

Subsidiary (Domestic):

Hultafors Group AB (2)
J A Wettergrens gata 7, 42130, Gothenburg, Sweden
Tel.: (46) 337237400
Web Site: https://www.hultafors.se
Holding Company; Hand Tool Mfr & Distr
N.A.I.C.S.: 551112
Peter Edwinson (CFO & Dir-Fin)

Subsidiary (Domestic):

Hultafors AB (3)
Hultaforsvagen 21, 517 96, Hultafors, Sweden (100%)
Tel.: (46) 337237400
Web Site: http://www.hultafors.se
Hand Tool Mfr & Distr
N.A.I.C.S.: 332216

Subsidiary (Non-US):

Fisco Tools Ltd (4)
21 Brook Road, Rayleigh, SS6 7XD, Essex, United Kingdom
Tel.: (44) 1268747074
Web Site: https://www.fisco.co.uk
Sales Range: $25-49.9 Million
Emp.: 10
Measuring Tapes Mfr & Distr
N.A.I.C.S.: 332216

Hultafors Group Danmark AS (4)
Energivej 37, 2750, Ballerup, Denmark
Tel.: (45) 44 86 06 00
Measuring Tape & Equipment Mfr
N.A.I.C.S.: 334519
David Neergaard (Mgr-Sls)

Hultafors Group Finland Oy (4)
Konalantie 47 E, 00390, Helsinki, Finland
Tel.: (358) 207410130
Web Site: https://www.hultaforsgroup.fi
Sales Range: $25-49.9 Million
Emp.: 20
Hand Tool Mfr
N.A.I.C.S.: 332216

Hultafors Group Germany Gmbh (4)
Im Meisenfeld 26, 32602, Vlotho, Germany
Tel.: (49) 52289570
Sales Range: $25-49.9 Million
Emp.: 15
Industrial Machinery Mfr
N.A.I.C.S.: 333248

Hultafors Group Norge AS (4)
Tevlingveien 23, 1081, Oslo, Norway
Tel.: (47) 23068880
Sales Range: $25-49.9 Million
Emp.: 22
Cutting Tool Mfr
N.A.I.C.S.: 333515
Andreas Ytterdal (Gen Mgr)

Subsidiary (Domestic):

Hultafors Group Sverige AB (4)
JA Wettergrens gata 7, Vastra Frolunda, 421 30, Gothenburg, Sweden
Tel.: (46) 337237400
Web Site: https://www.hultafors.se
Hand Tool Mfr & Distr
N.A.I.C.S.: 332216

Subsidiary (Non-US):

Hultafors Norge AS (4)
Brobekkveien 80, 0975, Oslo, Norway (100%)
Tel.: (47) 23068880
Web Site: http://www.hultafors.no
Sales Range: $25-49.9 Million
Emp.: 20
Plastics Plumbing Fixture Mfr
N.A.I.C.S.: 326191

Hultafors Oy (4)
Konalantie 47 E, 00390, Helsinki, Finland (100%)
Tel.: (358) 207410130
Web Site: http://www.hultafors.fi

INVESTMENT AB LATOUR

Investment AB Latour—(Continued)
Sales Range: $50-74.9 Million
Emp.: 120
Construction Materials Whslr
N.A.I.C.S.: 423390

Hultafors Prasident GmbH (4)
Im Meisenfeld 26, 32602, Vlotho, Germany **(100%)**
Tel.: (49) 522895710
Web Site: http://www.hultafors.de
Sales Range: $25-49.9 Million
Emp.: 20
Professional Equipment & Supplies Whslr
N.A.I.C.S.: 423490
Kai Schlossstein *(Mng Dir)*

Hultafors U.M.I. S.r.l. (4)
Bungard Djza106, 002400, Sibiu, Romania **(100%)**
Tel.: (40) 269213771
Measuring & Controlling Device Mfr
N.A.I.C.S.: 334519

Subsidiary (US):

Johnson Level & Tool Mfg. Co., Inc. (4)
6333 W Donges Bay Rd, Mequon, WI 53092
Tel.: (262) 242-1161
Web Site: http://www.johnsonlevel.com
Hand & Edge Tools
N.A.I.C.S.: 332216

Skillers Workwear NA Inc (4)
299A Washington St, Woburn, MA 01801 **(100%)**
Tel.: (781) 933-5400
Sales Range: $25-49.9 Million
Emp.: 4
Mens & Boys Cut & Sew Work Clothing Mfr
N.A.I.C.S.: 315250

Subsidiary (Non-US):

Snickers Original Ltd (4)
Unit N3 Meltham Mills Industrial Estate, Holmfirth, HD9 4DS, United Kingdom
Tel.: (44) 14 8485 4488
Web Site: http://www.snickersworkwear.com
Clothing Accessories Mfr
N.A.I.C.S.: 315990
Alexander Wennergren Helm *(CEO)*

Snickers Original NV (4)
Antwerpsesteenweg 285, Mechelen, 2800, Belgium **(100%)**
Tel.: (32) 15446530
Sales Range: $25-49.9 Million
Emp.: 15
Mens & Boys Clothing & Furnishings Merchant Whslr
N.A.I.C.S.: 424350
Frederik Vannaldetan *(Mng Dir)*

Snickers Original SIA (4)
Pasta Street 12, 3100, Tukums, Latvia **(100%)**
Tel.: (371) 3181209
Web Site: http://www.snickers-workwear.com
Sales Range: $25-49.9 Million
Emp.: 100
Mens & Boys Cut & Sew Work Clothing Mfr
N.A.I.C.S.: 315250

Snickers Production SIA Latvia (4)
12 Pasta Street, Tukums, 3101, Latvia
Tel.: (371) 63124333
Sales Range: $25-49.9 Million
Emp.: 50
Clothing Accessories Mfr
N.A.I.C.S.: 315990

Snickers Workwear Logistics BV (4)
Jaartsveldsstraat S-39, Postbus 362, 7570 AJ, Oldenzaal, Netherlands
Tel.: (31) 541530557
Web Site: http://www.snickers-workwear.com
Sales Range: $25-49.9 Million
Emp.: 50
Mens & Boys Cut & Sew Work Clothing Mfr
N.A.I.C.S.: 315250

Snickers Workwear Tradewear Ltd (4)
Unit B5 Calmount Business Park, Ballymount, Dublin, 12, Ireland

Tel.: (353) 14098400
Web Site: https://www.snickersworkwear.ie
Sales Range: $25-49.9 Million
Emp.: 20
Mens & Boys Cut & Sew Work Clothing Mfr
N.A.I.C.S.: 315250

Subsidiary (Domestic):

Wibe Stegar AB (4)
Telegatan 6, PO Box 145, Nassjo, 57138, Sweden **(100%)**
Tel.: (46) 380556800
Web Site: http://www.hultafors.se
Sales Range: $25-49.9 Million
Emp.: 45
Fabricated Metal Products Mfr
N.A.I.C.S.: 332999

Subsidiary (Domestic):

Latour Industries AB (2)
J A Wettergrens Gata 7, Box 336, 401 25, Gothenburg, Sweden **(100%)**
Tel.: (46) 313812800
Web Site: https://www.latourindustries.se
Emp.: 1,600
Management Consulting Services
N.A.I.C.S.: 541618
Bjorn Lenander *(CEO)*

Subsidiary (Non-US):

Aritco DE GmbH (3)
Stuttgarter Str 19, 72555, Metzingen, Germany
Tel.: (49) 71239597272
Elevator Design Mfr
N.A.I.C.S.: 333921

Aritco HomeLift Ltd. (3)
02-B A102-B Wending Living Style Plaza No 258 Wending Road, Xuhui District, Shanghai, China
Tel.: (86) 53266736895
Elevator Design Mfr
N.A.I.C.S.: 333921

Subsidiary (Domestic):

Aritco Lift AB (3)
Elektronikhojden 14, 175 43, Jarfalla, Sweden
Tel.: (46) 812040100
Elevator Design Mfr
N.A.I.C.S.: 333921

Bastec AB (3)
Hastvagen 4A, 212 35, Malmo, Sweden
Tel.: (46) 103308000
Web Site: https://www.bastec.se
Emp.: 32
Building Automation Equipment Distr
N.A.I.C.S.: 423730

Brickpack AB (3)
Repslagaregatan 12, PO Box 21, 312 21, Laholm, Sweden **(100%)**
Tel.: (46) 4 302 9550
Web Site: https://www.brickpack.se
Sales Range: $25-49.9 Million
Emp.: 40
Bolt Nut Screw Rivet & Washer Mfr
N.A.I.C.S.: 332722

DENSIQ AB (3)
E A Rosengrens gata 18, 421 31, Vastra Frolunda, Sweden
Tel.: (46) 3 189 1600
Web Site: https://www.densiq.com
Gasket & Sealing Device Mfr
N.A.I.C.S.: 339911

Densiq AB (3)
EA Rosengrens Gata 18 Vastra Frolunda, 421 31, Gothenburg, Sweden
Tel.: (46) 31891600
Web Site: https://www.densiq.com
Industrial Equipment Distr
N.A.I.C.S.: 423830

Subsidiary (Non-US):

Densiq AS (3)
Luramyrveien 13, 4313, Sandnes, Norway
Tel.: (47) 53009770
Industrial Equipment Distr
N.A.I.C.S.: 423830

Densiq Oy (3)
Center Gneissikuja 1, 90620, Oulu, Finland
Tel.: (358) 103234660

Industrial Equipment Distr
N.A.I.C.S.: 423830
Olli-Pekka Keranen *(Mgr-Site)*

Subsidiary (Domestic):

Elvaco AB (3)
Kabelgatan 2T, 434 37, Kungsbacka, Sweden
Tel.: (46) 30030270
Web Site: https://www.elvaco.com
Emp.: 60
Communication Equipment Distr
N.A.I.C.S.: 423690
David Vonasek *(CEO)*

Fortiva AB (3)
Jonkopingsvagen 1, Box 914, 571 29, Nassjo, Sweden
Tel.: (46) 380 77177
Drilling Machines Mfr
N.A.I.C.S.: 333131

Subsidiary (Non-US):

Fortiva Danmark A/S (3)
Teknikervej 16, 7000, Fredericia, Denmark
Tel.: (45) 75942122
Web Site: https://www.fortiva.dk
Machine Tool Whslr
N.A.I.C.S.: 423830

Gartec Ltd. (3)
Gartec Lifts Unit 6 Smeaton Cl, Midshires Business Park, Aylesbury, HP19 8HL, Buckinghamshire, United Kingdom
Tel.: (44) 1296397100
Web Site: https://www.gartec.com
Elevator Design Mfr
N.A.I.C.S.: 333921

Granaths Hardmetal AS (3)
Teknikerbej 16, 7000, Fredericia, Denmark **(100%)**
Tel.: (45) 75942122
Web Site: http://www.granath.dk
Sales Range: $25-49.9 Million
Emp.: 9
Industrial Supplies Whslr
N.A.I.C.S.: 423840
Henrik Damsbo *(Mng Dir)*

Subsidiary (Domestic):

Kontikab AB (3)
Industrigatan 1, 441 21, Alingsas, Sweden
Tel.: (46) 32 264 2590
Web Site: https://www.kontikab.com
Leak Detection Machinery Mfr & Distr
N.A.I.C.S.: 334519
Martin Book *(CEO)*

Subsidiary (Non-US):

LSAB Instrument Service (3)
Zheleznodorozhnaya St 11 Korp 12 Lit A P, Pargolovo, Saint Petersburg, 194362, Russia
Tel.: (7) 921 634 55 43
Web Site: http://www.lsab.ru
Emp.: 1
Industrial Machinery Rental Services
N.A.I.C.S.: 532490

LSAB Latvia SIA (3)
Atmodas iela 61 Incukalna Novads, Incukalns, Riga, LV-2141, Latvia
Tel.: (371) 67977356
Web Site: http://www.lsablatvia.lv
Tool Repair Services
N.A.I.C.S.: 811310
Janis Laubergs *(Mgr-Sls)*

LSAB Norge AS (3)
Fossvegen 15, Tangen, 2337, Stange, Norway
Tel.: (47) 62574600
Web Site: http://www.lsab.no
Saw Sharpening Services
N.A.I.C.S.: 811310

Subsidiary (Domestic):

LSAB Vaxjo AB (3)
Radjursvagen 15, 352 45, Vaxjo, Sweden
Tel.: (46) 470748890
Web Site: http://www.lsab.se
Sales Range: $25-49.9 Million
Emp.: 20
Woodworking Machine Tools Mfr
N.A.I.C.S.: 333517

INTERNATIONAL PUBLIC

LSAB Westlings AB (3)
Appelbovagen 41, 780 50, Vansbro, Sweden
Tel.: (46) 28114400
Saw Sharpening Services
N.A.I.C.S.: 811310

Langshyttan Slipservice AB (3)
Svinohed 415, 770 70, Langshyttan, Sweden
Tel.: (46) 225 62 00 0
Web Site: http://www.lsab.se
Rev.: $51,845,500
Emp.: 23
Industrial Tools Repair & Maintenance Services
N.A.I.C.S.: 811310
Staffan Gustafsson *(Mgr-Sls)*

Subsidiary (Non-US):

Machine Trading Team OY Ltd (3)
Puustellintie 4, 00410, Helsinki, Finland **(100%)**
Tel.: (358) 98545640
Web Site: http://www.mteam.fi
Sales Range: $25-49.9 Million
Emp.: 12
Industrial Machinery & Equipment Merchant Whslr
N.A.I.C.S.: 423830

Subsidiary (Domestic):

Morlunda Slipservice AB (3)
Stationsvagen 21, Box 90, 570 84, Hultsfred, Sweden
Tel.: (46) 495 235 15
Industrial Machinery Distr
N.A.I.C.S.: 423830

Noda Intelligent System AB (3)
Biblioteksgatan 4, 374 35, Karlshamn, Sweden
Tel.: (46) 45410271
Web Site: http://www.noda.se
Heating Product Contracting Services
N.A.I.C.S.: 238220
Christian Johansson *(CEO)*

Subsidiary (Non-US):

Pressmaster Gmbh (3)
Krankelsweg 24, 41748, Viersen, Germany
Tel.: (49) 2162 50 22 61
Precision Tool & Cutting Equipment Mfr
N.A.I.C.S.: 333515

Produal A/S (3)
Generatorvej 8H, 2860, Soborg, Denmark
Tel.: (45) 70260304
Electronic Parts Mfr
N.A.I.C.S.: 334419
Martin Lovenfald *(Mgr-Bus Dev)*

Produal Oy (3)
Keltakalliontie 18, 48770, Kotka, Finland
Tel.: (358) 102199100
Electronic Parts Mfr
N.A.I.C.S.: 334419
Pekka Keskiaho *(Dir-Sls)*

Produal S.A.S. (3)
2 Allee Des Sarments Parc Aux Vignes, 77183, Croissy-Beaubourg, France
Tel.: (33) 171405049
Electronic Parts Mfr
N.A.I.C.S.: 334419

Subsidiary (Domestic):

Produal Sverige AB (3)
Solkraftsvagen 16 A, 135 70, Stockholm, Sweden
Tel.: (46) 855598580
Web Site: http://www.produal.se
Building Automation Equipment Mfr
N.A.I.C.S.: 334512
Anselmi Immonen *(CEO)*

REAC AB (3)
J A Wettergrens gata 7, Box 103, 421 30, Vastra Frolunda, Sweden
Tel.: (46) 313509900
Health Care Wheel Chair Mfr
N.A.I.C.S.: 339113
Stefan Andreasson *(Mgr-Sls)*

Subsidiary (Non-US):

Balle A/S (4)
Avnvej 10, 7400, Herning, Denmark

AND PRIVATE COMPANIES — INVESTMENT AB LATOUR

Tel.: (45) 97220252
Web Site: http://www.balle-as.dk
Sales Range: $25-49.9 Million
Emp.: 18
Hospital Beds Mfr & Sales
N.A.I.C.S.: 337211

Balle A/S (4)
Avnvej 10, 7400, Herning, Denmark
Tel.: (45) 97 22 02 52
Web Site: http://www.balle-as.dk
Hospital Beds Mfr & Distr
N.A.I.C.S.: 339113

Subsidiary (Non-US):

Sensir AG (3)
Lettenstrasse 11, 6343, Rotkreuz, Switzerland
Tel.: (41) 417920365
Web Site: http://www.sensir.ch
Optical Sensor Mfr
N.A.I.C.S.: 333310

Sensortec AG (3)
Bahnhofstrasse 87, 3232, Thun, Switzerland
Tel.: (41) 323127000
Web Site: http://www.sensortec.ch
Sensor Material & Component Mfr
N.A.I.C.S.: 334413

Subsidiary (Domestic):

Skandinaviska chuckfabriken AB (3)
Kyrkogatan 27, Tyringe, 282 31, Hassleholm, Sweden
Tel.: (46) 451 55500
Web Site: http://www.chuck.se
Industrial Chucks Mfr
N.A.I.C.S.: 333515
Krister Dolmark *(Gen Mgr)*

Subsidiary (Non-US):

Vandra Saeteritus As (3)
Allikonnu Kula, Vandra vald, EE-87004, Vandra, Parnumaa, Estonia
Tel.: (372) 442 69 60
Sales Range: $25-49.9 Million
Emp.: 50
Industrial Machine Tool Distr
N.A.I.C.S.: 423830

Vimec Srl (3)
Via Parri 7, 42045, Luzzara, RE, Italy
Tel.: (39) 0522970666
Web Site: https://www.vimechomelifts.co.uk
Elevator Services
N.A.I.C.S.: 238290

Subsidiary (Domestic):

MaskinCentrum i Ornskoldsvik AB (2)
Tegelbruksvagen 10, 891 55, Arnasvall, Sweden
Tel.: (46) 66 026 6570
Web Site: https://www.maskincentrum.com
Industrial Machinery & Equipment Merchant Whslr
N.A.I.C.S.: 423830
Mats Jonsson *(Founder, CEO & Mgr-Mktg)*

Nord-Lock AB (2)
Halabacken, Mattmar, 83002, Ostersund, Sweden (100%)
Tel.: (46) 640681180
Web Site: http://www.nord-lock.com
Sales Range: $25-49.9 Million
Emp.: 160
Bolt Nut Screw Rivet & Washer Mfr
N.A.I.C.S.: 332722

Subsidiary (Non-US):

Nord-Lock Benelux BV (3)
Kattegat 22, PO Box 606, 9700 AP, Groningen, Netherlands
Tel.: (31) 505275656
Web Site: https://www.nord-lock.com
Locking Bolt Component Distr
N.A.I.C.S.: 423830

Nord-Lock France S.a.r.l (3)
Parc Technoland ZI Champ Dolin 3 Allee du Lazio, Saint-Priest, 69800, Lyon, France (100%)
Tel.: (33) 43 725 9030
Web Site: https://www.nord-lock.com
Hardware Mfr

N.A.I.C.S.: 332510

Nord-Lock Gmbh (3)
Hauptstrasse 74, 73466, Lauchheim, Germany
Tel.: (49) 736396600
Web Site: https://www.nord-lock.com
Emp.: 2
Screw Locking System Distr
N.A.I.C.S.: 423710

Nord-Lock Holding Gmbh (3)
In Der Waage 10, 73463, Westhausen, Germany
Tel.: (49) 7363 9660 0
Investment Management Service
N.A.I.C.S.: 523999

Subsidiary (US):

Nord-Lock Inc. (3)
1051 Cambridge Dr, Elk Grove Village, IL 60007 (100%)
Tel.: (224) 875-3333
Web Site: http://www.nord-lock.com
Sales Range: $25-49.9 Million
Emp.: 10
Hardware Mfr
N.A.I.C.S.: 332510

Subsidiary (Domestic):

Superbolt Inc. (4)
1000 Gregg St, Carnegie, PA 15106
Tel.: (412) 279-1149
Nut & Bolt Mfr & Distr
N.A.I.C.S.: 332722

Subsidiary (Domestic):

Nord-Lock International AB (3)
J A Wettergrens Gata 7, Box 336, Gothenburg, 421 30, Sweden
Tel.: (46) 31 719 23 00
Securing Bolt System Mfr
N.A.I.C.S.: 332722

Subsidiary (Non-US):

Nord-Lock Japan co, Ltd (3)
1-18-35 Saitoaominami, Nishiku, Minoh, 562-0028, Osaka, Japan
Tel.: (81) 727271069
Web Site: https://www.nord-lock.com
Emp.: 20
Bolts & Screw Joint Distr
N.A.I.C.S.: 423710

Nord-Lock Ltd (3)
Kingsgate House Newbury Road, Andover, SP10 4DU, United Kingdom (100%)
Tel.: (44) 1264 355 400
Sales Range: $25-49.9 Million
Emp.: 7
Bolt Nut Screw Rivet & Washer Mfr
N.A.I.C.S.: 332722

Nord-Lock Oy (3)
Riihitie 2, 05880, Hyvinkaa, Finland (100%)
Tel.: (358) 103275120
Web Site: https://www.nord-lock.com
Sales Range: $25-49.9 Million
Emp.: 3
Hardware Stores
N.A.I.C.S.: 444140

Nord-Lock Poland Sp. Z.o.o. (3)
ul Zeromskiego 94 P 116, 26-600, Radom, Poland
Tel.: (48) 48 360 12 42
Bolt Securing System Distr
N.A.I.C.S.: 423710

Nord-Lock Switzerland Gmbh (3)
Rietwiesstrasse 2, 8735, Sankt Gallenkappel, Switzerland
Tel.: (41) 552846464
Web Site: https://www.nord-lock.com
Sales Range: $25-49.9 Million
Emp.: 38
Roller Bearing Mfr
N.A.I.C.S.: 332991

Nord-Lock s.r.o. (3)
Beethovenova 1169/18, 430 01, Chomutov, Czech Republic
Tel.: (420) 412 150 157
Emp.: 2
Bolt Securing System Distr
N.A.I.C.S.: 423830

Subsidiary (Domestic):

Nordiska Industri AB (2)
J A Wettergrens Gata 7, PO Box 336, 40125, Gothenburg, Sweden (100%)
Tel.: (46) 31891790
Web Site: http://www.latour.se
Sales Range: $75-99.9 Million
Emp.: 4
Industrial Supplies Whslr
N.A.I.C.S.: 423840

Swegon AB (2)
Foreningsgatan 12, SE-535 30, Kvanum, Sweden
Tel.: (46) 51232200
Web Site: http://www.swegon.com
Sales Range: $450-499.9 Million
Emp.: 1,500
Ventilation & Climate Control Systems Mfr
N.A.I.C.S.: 333415
Tony Pettersson *(Dir-Mktg & Bus Dev)*

Subsidiary (Non-US):

Blue Box Air Engineering (India) Pvt. Ltd (3)
204 Tanishka Off W E Highway Akurli Road, Kandivali East, Mumbai, 400 101, India
Tel.: (91) 22 40169381
Web Site: http://www.bluebox.it
Sales Range: $25-49.9 Million
Emp.: 20
Air Conditioning Equipment Mfr
N.A.I.C.S.: 333415

Blue Box Group s.r.l (3)
Via Valletta 5, 30010, Cona, Venice, Italy
Tel.: (39) 0426 921111
Web Site: http://www.bluebox.it
Emp.: 25
Air Conditioning Equipment Mfr
N.A.I.C.S.: 333415

Blue Service s.r.l (3)
Via Mattei 1, 60121, Ancona, Italy
Tel.: (39) 071 207 1420
Web Site: https://www.blueservice-csm.it
Emp.: 2
Safety System Equipment Distr
N.A.I.C.S.: 423830
Claudio Vitali *(Gen Mgr)*

Oy Swegon AB (3)
Bertel Jungin aukio 7, 02600, Espoo, Finland (100%)
Tel.: (358) 102894010
Web Site: https://www.swegon.com
Plumbing Fixture Fitting & Trim Mfr
N.A.I.C.S.: 332913

SAMP S.p.A. (3)
Via Saliceto 15, 40010, Bentivoglio, Italy
Tel.: (39) 0516319411
Web Site: http://www.sampspa.com
Mfr of Metal Working Equipment for Gears & Wire & Cable Manufacturing
N.A.I.C.S.: 332999
Antonio Maccaferri *(Pres)*

Swegon A/S (3)
Vallensbaekvej 20A 3 floor, Abyhoj, 2605, Brondby, Denmark
Tel.: (45) 36369990
Web Site: https://www.swegon.com
Sales Range: $25-49.9 Million
Emp.: 11
Industrial Machinery & Equipment Whslr
N.A.I.C.S.: 423830

Swegon AS (3)
Stanseveien 28, 0976, Oslo, Norway
Tel.: (47) 23338200
Web Site: https://www.swegon.com
Emp.: 37
Ventilation Products Mfr
N.A.I.C.S.: 333415

Swegon BV (3)
Aert Van Nesstraat 1P, 2901 BH, Capelle aan den IJssel, Netherlands
Tel.: (31) 10 258 09 70
Web Site: https://www.swegon.com
Ventilation Products Mfr & Distr
N.A.I.C.S.: 333415

Swegon Belgium S.A. (3)
Rue de Huy 24, 4280, Hannut, Belgium
Tel.: (32) 19 51 93 20
Emp.: 9
Air Conditioning Equipment Mfr & Distr
N.A.I.C.S.: 333415

Swegon Climate Systems Germany GmbH (3)
Carl-von-Linde-Strasse 25, 85748, Garching, Germany (100%)
Tel.: (49) 89326700
Sales Range: $50-74.9 Million
Emp.: 111
Climate Control Systems Mfr
N.A.I.C.S.: 333415

Swegon Eesti OU (3)
Laki 34, Tallinn, 12915, Estonia
Tel.: (372) 514 7326
Web Site: http://www.swegon.ee
Emp.: 2
Air Conditioning Equipment Mfr
N.A.I.C.S.: 333415

Swegon GmbH (3)
Hetmanekgasse 1b/3, 1230, Vienna, Austria (100%)
Tel.: (43) 16091320
Web Site: https://schwank.at
Sales Range: $25-49.9 Million
Emp.: 3
Warm Air Heating & Air-Conditioning Equipment & Supplies Whslr
N.A.I.C.S.: 423730

Swegon Gmbh (3)
Marie-Curie-Str 7, Bergkamen, 59192, Dortmund, Germany
Tel.: (49) 238 995 9770
Web Site: http://www.swegon.de
Sales Range: $25-49.9 Million
Emp.: 5
Air Conditioning Equipment Mfr
N.A.I.C.S.: 333415

Swegon Indoor climate S.A. (3)
Calle Lope De Vega 2 - Plt 2, Las Rozas, 28231, Spain
Tel.: (34) 916347619
Web Site: http://www.swegon.com
Emp.: 7
Air Conditioning Equipment Distr
N.A.I.C.S.: 423730

Swegon Ltd (3)
Swegon Pavilion St Cross Chambers, Upper Marsh Ln, Hoddesdon, EN11 8LQ, Herts, United Kingdom (100%)
Tel.: (44) 1279416087
Web Site: http://www.swegon.co.uk
Sales Range: $25-49.9 Million
Emp.: 20
Industrial Machinery & Equipment Whslr
N.A.I.C.S.: 423830

Subsidiary (Domestic):

Ruskin Air Management Limited (4)
Stourbridge Road, Bridgnorth, WV15 5BB, Shropshire, United Kingdom
Tel.: (44) 1746761921
Web Site: http://www.ruskinuk.co.uk
Emp.: 220
Fire & Smoke Dampers & Air Distribution Products Mfr
N.A.I.C.S.: 332311
Kevin Munson *(Pres)*

Subsidiary (Non-US):

Swegon S.a.r.l. (3)
10 rue Jules Vercruysse, 95100, Argenteuil, France (90%)
Tel.: (33) 130259025
Web Site: http://www.swegon.fr
Sales Range: $25-49.9 Million
Emp.: 15
Industrial Machinery & Equipment Whslr
N.A.I.C.S.: 423830

Swegon SA (3)
Route de Prilly 23, 1023, Crissier, Switzerland (100%)
Tel.: (41) 842000007
Web Site: http://www1.swegon.com
Sales Range: $25-49.9 Million
Emp.: 8
Warm Air Heating & Air-Conditioning Equipment & Supplies Whslr
N.A.I.C.S.: 423730

Swegon Sp.z o.o (3)
ul Owocowa 23, 62-080, Poznan, Poland (100%)
Tel.: (48) 618168700
Web Site: https://www.swegon

INVESTMENT AB LATOUR

Investment AB Latour—(Continued)
Sales Range: $25-49.9 Million
Emp.: 80
Electrical Appliance Television & Radio Set Whslr
N.A.I.C.S.: 423620

Swegon s.r.o. (3)
Lipi 2556/3, Horni Pocernice, 193 00, Prague, Czech Republic
Tel.: (420) 281 863 162
Air Conditioning System Mfr & Distr
N.A.I.C.S.: 333415

MAXAGV AB (1)
Kryptongatan 5B, 431 53, Molndal, Sweden
Tel.: (46) 317975800
Web Site: https://maxagv.com
Elevator Services
N.A.I.C.S.: 236220

Neuffer Fenster & Turen GmbH (1)
Kronprinzstrasse 8, 70173, Stuttgart, Germany
Tel.: (49) 7118 606 0180
Web Site: https://www.neuffer.de
Window Product Distr
N.A.I.C.S.: 423310

Nord-Lock AG (1)
Rietwiesstrasse 2, 8735, Sankt Gallenkappel, Switzerland
Tel.: (41) 552846464
Web Site: https://www.nord-lock.com
Bolt & Screw Mfr
N.A.I.C.S.: 332722

Nord-Lock AS (1)
Leif Weldingsvei 16, 3208, Sandefjord, Norway
Tel.: (47) 67546700
Construction Machinery Mfr
N.A.I.C.S.: 333120

Nord-Lock ApS (1)
Gydevang 39-41, 3450, Allerod, Denmark
Tel.: (45) 38107070
Construction Machinery Mfr
N.A.I.C.S.: 333120

Nord-Lock Canada, Inc. (1)
480 Sovereign Road Units 5-7, London, N6M1A4, ON, Canada
Tel.: (226) 212-4366
Mechanical Bolt Product Mfr & Distr
N.A.I.C.S.: 333415

Nord-Lock Iberia S.L. (1)
Avda Somosierra 22 - E 6 & 7, Reyes Mezzanine, 28703, Madrid, Spain
Tel.: (34) 911859190
Web Site: https://www.nord-lock.com
Bolt & Screw Mfr
N.A.I.C.S.: 332722

Nord-Lock India Pvt. Ltd. (1)
Unit No 206A Wing B1 2nd Floor Boomerang Chandivali Farm Road, Andheri East, Mumbai, 400072, India
Tel.: (91) 8369312918
Construction Machinery Mfr
N.A.I.C.S.: 333120

Nord-Lock Italy s.r.l. (1)
Via Albenga 36/A, 10098, Rivoli, TO, Italy
Tel.: (39) 0119539656
Construction Machinery Mfr
N.A.I.C.S.: 333120

Nord-Lock Korea Co., Ltd. (1)
1101 Centum IS Tower 60 Centum bukdaero, Haeundae-gu, Busan, 48059, Korea (South)
Tel.: (82) 517107910
Construction Machinery Mfr
N.A.I.C.S.: 333120

Nord-Lock Pte. Ltd. (1)
2 International Business Park 03-36 The Strategy, Singapore, 609930, Singapore
Tel.: (65) 65156658
Construction Machinery Mfr
N.A.I.C.S.: 333120

P Lemmens Company S.A. (1)
102 Chaussee de Tirlemont, Sauveniere Industrial Park, 5030, Gembloux, Belgium
Tel.: (32) 81625252
Web Site: http://www.lemmens.com
Machining Equipment Mfr
N.A.I.C.S.: 333517

Produal S.R.L. (1)
Langrain 38, Chiusa, 39043, Bolzano, Italy
Tel.: (39) 03663320970
Web Site: https://www.produal.com
Measuring Instrument Mfr & Distr
N.A.I.C.S.: 334513

Produal Sp. z o.o. (1)
ul Farbiarska 63 B, 02-862, Warsaw, Poland
Tel.: (48) 536036677
Control Devices & Measurement Devices Supplier
N.A.I.C.S.: 423610

Protag Shoe Supply B.V. (1)
Tunnelweg 104, 6268 EK, Kerkrade, Netherlands
Tel.: (31) 455666511
Web Site: https://www.protagshoes.com
Footwear & Boot Distr
N.A.I.C.S.: 424340

Puvab AB (1)
Kallbacksrydsgatan 10, Bramhult, 507 31, Boras, Sweden
Tel.: (46) 3 320 5480
Web Site: http://www.puvab.com
Protective Wear Distr
N.A.I.C.S.: 423990
Acram Badr Marcoff (Mgr-Ops)

S+S Regeltechnik GmbH (1)
Thurn-und-Taxis-Str 22, 90411, Nuremberg, Germany
Tel.: (49) 911519470
Web Site: https://www.spluss.de
Emp.: 86
Semiconductor Materials Mfr & Distr
N.A.I.C.S.: 334513

SCANGRIP North America Inc. (1)
1201 Peachtree St NE Ste 100, Atlanta, GA 30361
Tel.: (310) 866-5607
Web Site: https://us.scangrip.com
Light Emitting Diode Work Light Mfr & Distr
N.A.I.C.S.: 334111

SLT Swegon GmbH (1)
Lenzfeld 8, 49811, Lingen, Germany
Tel.: (49) 591973370
Web Site: https://www.slt-lingen.de
Air Diffuser Product Mfr
N.A.I.C.S.: 333415

Safegard Systems Limited (1)
3 Newbridge Square, Swindon, SN1 1HN, United Kingdom
Tel.: (44) 8006891835
Door Entry & Perimeter Security Services
N.A.I.C.S.: 561621

Scangrip A/S (1)
Rytterhaven 9, 5700, Svendborg, Denmark
Tel.: (45) 63206320
Web Site: https://www.scangrip.com
LED Light Mfr
N.A.I.C.S.: 335131

Stritex LLC (1)
Novakivskoho St 5, Stryi, 82400, Lviv, Ukraine
Tel.: (380) 324552104
Web Site: https://stritex.com.ua
Work Wear Mfr & Distr
N.A.I.C.S.: 315210

Swegon AG (1)
Kernenriedstrasse 1, 3421, Lyss, Switzerland
Tel.: (41) 842000007
Web Site: https://www.swegon.com
Ventilation Machine Mfr
N.A.I.C.S.: 333413

Swegon Blue Box Private Limited (1)
Unit No B-01 ESR-Industrial & Logistic Park Survey No 136/8 138 136/10, 135 Village Usatane Khoni Taloja Road Ambarnath, Thane, 421306, India
Tel.: (91) 2269827777
Web Site: https://www.blueboxcooling.com
Emp.: 3,000
Air Conditioning Equipment Mfr & Distr
N.A.I.C.S.: 333415

Swegon Germany GmbH (1)
Parkring 22, 85748, Garching, Germany
Tel.: (49) 89326700

Web Site: https://www.swegon.com
Ventilation Machine Mfr
N.A.I.C.S.: 333413

Swegon ILTO OY (1)
Asessorinkatu 10, 20780, Kaarina, Finland
Tel.: (358) 207354800
Air Conditioning Contractor Services
N.A.I.C.S.: 238220

Swegon Lidkoping AB (1)
Skepparegatan 6, 531 30, Lidkoping, Sweden
Tel.: (46) 51022800
Air Conditioning Contractor Services
N.A.I.C.S.: 238220

Swegon North America Inc. (1)
355 Apple Creek Blvd, Markham, L3R 9X7, ON, Canada
Tel.: (416) 291-7371
Web Site: http://www.swegonnorthamerica.com
Emp.: 2,100
Building Automation Equipment Distr
N.A.I.C.S.: 423730

Swegon Operations Belgium S.A. (1)
Chaussee de Tirlemont 102, 5030, Gembloux, Belgium
Tel.: (32) 81625252
HVAC Equipment Supplier
N.A.I.C.S.: 423730

Swegon Operations S.R.L. (1)
Via Valletta 5, Cantarana di Cona, 30010, Venice, Italy
Tel.: (39) 042692111
HVAC Equipment Supplier
N.A.I.C.S.: 423730

TKS Heis AS (1)
Torlandsvegen 3, Naerbo, 4365, Stavanger, Norway
Tel.: (47) 40001059
Web Site: https://tksheis.no
Elevator Services
N.A.I.C.S.: 236220

Telesteps AB (1)
Zinkgatan 3, Box 362, 573 24, Tranas, Sweden
Tel.: (46) 140386800
Web Site: https://telesteps.se
Optical Glass Mfr & Distr
N.A.I.C.S.: 334610

Tradeport AB (1)
Matslingan 19A, 187 66, Taby, Sweden
Tel.: (46) 856237400
Web Site: http://www.tradeport.se
Piece & Yard Goods Whslr
N.A.I.C.S.: 424310

VM Kompensator A/S (1)
Industrivej 4, 6622, Baekke, Denmark
Tel.: (45) 38402020
Web Site: https://vmkomp.dk
Rubber & Steel Joints Mfr
N.A.I.C.S.: 325520

Vega S.R.L. (1)
Via degli Appennini 11-13 Contrada Capparuccia, 63845, Ponzano di Fermo, Italy
Tel.: (39) 0734631941
Web Site: https://www.vegalift.it
Elevator Mfr
N.A.I.C.S.: 333921

Vega Style Italia Ltda. (1)
Rua Monsenhor Felipe Diehl 92, Humaita, Porto Alegre, 90240-150, Brazil
Tel.: (55) 5135086018
Web Site: https://www.vegalift.com.br
Elevator System Mfr
N.A.I.C.S.: 333921

Waterloo Air Products Limited (1)
Unit A Vantage Point, Snodland, ME6 5SL, Kent, United Kingdom
Tel.: (44) 1634981500
Air Diffuser Product Mfr
N.A.I.C.S.: 333415

Zent-Frenger GmbH (1)
Schwarzwaldstrasse 2, 64646, Heppenheim, Germany
Tel.: (49) 625279070
Air Conditioning Contractor Services
N.A.I.C.S.: 238220

INTERNATIONAL PUBLIC

bluMartin GmbH (1)
Argelsrieder Feld 1b, 82234, Wessling, Germany
Tel.: (49) 81538890330
Web Site: https://www.blumartin.de
Air Conditioning Contracting Services
N.A.I.C.S.: 238220
Astrid Kahle (Mgr-Mktg)

INVESTMENT AB ORESUND

Norrlandsgatan 15, Box 7621, 103 94, Stockholm, Sweden
Tel.: (46) 8 402 33 00
Web Site: http://www.oresund.se
Investment Holding Company
N.A.I.C.S.: 551112

INVESTMENT BANK OF IRAQ

Sec 21 3 / Str 26 / Hs 14 Al-Harthia Al-Kindi, PO Box 3724, Baghdad, Iraq
Tel.: (964) 17199042
Web Site: https://www.ibi-bankiraq.com
Year Founded: 1993
BIBI—(IRAQ)
Rev.: $9,517,367
Assets: $445,906,688
Liabilities: $265,656,912
Net Worth: $180,249,776
Earnings: $631,980
Fiscal Year-end: 12/31/21
Commercial Banking Services
N.A.I.C.S.: 522110
May Mohammed Yass (Deputy Gen Mgr)

Subsidiaries:

Investment Bank of Iraq - International Division (1)
Bldg 27 Zokak 2 Mahala 902, Hay Al Wihda, Baghdad, Iraq
Tel.: (964) 17199042
Web Site: http://www.ivi-bankiraq.com
Commercial Banking Services
N.A.I.C.S.: 522110

INVESTMENT COMMERCE FISHERIES CORPORATION

A77 / I Road 7 Vinh Loc industrial zone, Binh Tan District, Ho Chi Minh City, Vietnam
Tel.: (84) 2837653145
Web Site: https://www.incomfish.com
Year Founded: 1999
Frozen Seafood Services
N.A.I.C.S.: 311710
Nguyen Thi Kim Xuan (Chm)

INVESTMENT COMPANY GRANDIS CAPITAL LLC

35 Valovaya Str, 115054, Moscow, Russia
Tel.: (7) 4952724407
Web Site: http://www.grandiscapital.ru
Year Founded: 2008
Sales Range: Less than $1 Million
Securities Brokerage Services
N.A.I.C.S.: 523150

INVESTMENT CORPORATION OF DUBAI

Dubai International Financial Gate Village 7 6th Fl, PO Box 333888, Dubai, United Arab Emirates
Tel.: (971) 47071333
Web Site: http://www.icd.gov.ae
Investment Holding Company
N.A.I.C.S.: 551112
Mohammed Bin Rashid Al Maktoum (Chm)

Subsidiaries:

Al Jaber L.E.G.T. Engineering & Contracting L.L.C. (1)

AND PRIVATE COMPANIES

PO Box 27639, Dubai, United Arab Emirates
Tel.: (971) 44290599
Web Site: http://www.alec.ae
Commercial Building Construction
N.A.I.C.S.: 236220
Kez Taylor (CEO)

Aswaaq (1)
Al Mizhar Community Center First floor, PO Box 6767, Dubai, United Arab Emirates
Tel.: (971) 4 423 4444
Web Site: http://www.aswaaq.ae
Convenience Store Operator
N.A.I.C.S.: 445131

Borse Dubai Limited (1)
Level 7 Precinct Bldg 5 Gate District, PO Box 506690, Dubai Intl Fin Ctr, Dubai, United Arab Emirates
Tel.: (971) 4 305 5000
Web Site: http://www.borsedubai.ae
Holding Company
N.A.I.C.S.: 551112
Essa Abdulfattah Kazim Al Mulla (Chm & CEO)

Holding (Domestic):

Dubai Financial Market PJSC (2)
Mezzanine Floor World Trade Center Rashid Tower Sheikh Zayed Road, PO Box 9700, Dubai, United Arab Emirates (80%)
Tel.: (971) 43055555
Web Site: https://www.dfm.ae
Rev.: $149,051,952
Assets: $2,678,288,809
Liabilities: $447,770,917
Net Worth: $2,230,517,892
Earnings: $89,736,170
Emp.: 138
Fiscal Year-end: 12/31/2023
Securities Exchange
N.A.I.C.S.: 523210
Rashid Hamad Al Shamsi (Vice Chm)

NASDAQ Dubai Ltd. (2)
Level 7 The Exchange Building, PO Box 53536, Dubai, United Arab Emirates (66.7%)
Tel.: (971) 43612222
Web Site: http://www.nasdaqdubai.com
Sales Range: $25-49.9 Million
Emp.: 50
Stock Exchange Services
N.A.I.C.S.: 523210
Abdul Wahed Al Fahim (Chm)

DUBAL Holding L.L.C (1)
Tel.: (971) 45089000
Web Site: https://dubalholding.ae
Investment Services
N.A.I.C.S.: 523999
Ahmad Fahad (CEO)

Subsidiary (US):

Thermalex, Inc. (2)
2758 Gunter Park Dr W, Montgomery, AL 36109-1016
Tel.: (334) 272-8270
Web Site: http://www.tmxinc.com
Sales Range: $50-74.9 Million
Aluminum Extruded Product Mfr
N.A.I.C.S.: 331318

Dubai Duty Free (1)
PO Box 831, Dubai, United Arab Emirates
Tel.: (971) 2162453
Web Site: http://www.dubaidutyfree.com
Holding Company
N.A.I.C.S.: 551112
Colm McLoughlin (Vice Chm & CEO)

Galadari Brothers Group (1)
Al Quoz First Industrial Area 138, Dubai, United Arab Emirates
Tel.: (971) 4 338 8800
Web Site: http://www.galadarigroup.com
Holding Company
N.A.I.C.S.: 551112

National Bonds Corporation PJSC (1)
Al Hudaiba Awards Buildings Adjacent to the Union Flag Block C 6th Flo, 2nd December Street, Dubai, United Arab Emirates
Tel.: (971) 4 384 8000
Web Site: http://www.nationalbonds.ae
Financial Investment Services
N.A.I.C.S.: 523940

Khalifa Al-Daboos (Chm)

Ssangyong Engineering & Construction Co., Ltd. (1)
299 Olyympic-ro, Songpa-gu, Seoul, 138-726, Korea (South) (100%)
Tel.: (82) 234337777
Web Site: http://www.ssyenc.com
Sales Range: $800-899.9 Million
Emp.: 1,395
Construction Design & Engineering Services
N.A.I.C.S.: 236220
S. Joon Kim (Chm & CEO)

Subsidiary (Non-US):

PT. SSY Konstruksi Indonesia (2)
Suite 2801 28th Floor Menara Batavia Jl K H Mas Mansyur Kav, 10220, Jakarta, Indonesia
Tel.: (62) 2157950377
Web Site: http://www.ssyenc.com
Emp.: 6
Building Construction Services
N.A.I.C.S.: 236115
Jonghyuk Ahn (Mgr-Mktg)

Ssangyong Engineering & Construction Co., Ltd. (2)
Office No 1 2nd Fl Al-Audhali Building King Abdulla Road, PO Box 1453, Al Khobar, 31952, Eastern Province, Saudi Arabia
Tel.: (966) 138648807
Web Site: http://www.ssyenc.com
Sales Range: $25-49.9 Million
Emp.: 25
Construction Engineering Services
N.A.I.C.S.: 541330

Ssangyong Engineering & Construction Sdn Bhd (2)
18th Fl Ste 18-05 Kenanga Bldg, Jalan Sultan Ismail, Kuala Lumpur, 50250, Malaysia
Tel.: (60) 321454529
Web Site: http://www.ssyenc.co.kr
Sales Range: Less than $1 Million
Emp.: 10
General Construction
N.A.I.C.S.: 236220
Jeongho Seo (Mng Dir)

Ssangyong Engineering And Constructions Company Ltd. (2)
152 Beach Rd 15 04 Gtwy E, Singapore, 189721, Singapore
Tel.: (65) 63361255
Web Site: http://www.ssyenc.com
Sales Range: $25-49.9 Million
Emp.: 50
Real Estate Developers & General Construction
N.A.I.C.S.: 236220
Ahn Kook Jin (Mng Dir)

emaratech (1)
34th floor Business Central Tower A Dubai Internet City, Dubai, United Arab Emirates
Tel.: (971) 4 3913600
Web Site: http://www.emaratech.ae
Financial Investment Services
N.A.I.C.S.: 523940

INVESTMENT FRIENDS CAPITAL S.A.
Tornimae Tn 5 Kesklinna Linnaosa, Harju maakond, 10145, Tallinn, Estonia
Tel.: (372) 243673132
Web Site: http://www.ifcapital.pl
IFC—(WAR)
Rev.: $168,870
Assets: $5,345,069
Liabilities: $5,344
Net Worth: $5,339,725
Earnings: $151,770
Fiscal Year-end: 06/30/23
Investment Management Service
N.A.I.C.S.: 523940
Damian Patrowicz (CEO)

INVESTMENT FRIENDS SE
Tornimae tn 5 Kesklinna linnaosa, Harju maakond, 10145, Tallinn, 10145, Estonia
Tel.: (372) 243660626

Web Site: https://www.ifsa.pl
IFR—(WAR)
Rev.: $9,275,940
Assets: $156,624,780
Liabilities: $5,437,620
Net Worth: $151,187,160
Earnings: $8,209,740
Fiscal Year-end: 12/31/22
Investment Services
N.A.I.C.S.: 523940
Agnieszka Gujgo (Chm, Pres & CEO)

INVESTMENT HOLDING GROUP QPSC
Al-Hodaifi Building Salwa Road, PO Box 22205, West Bay, Doha, Qatar
Tel.: (974) 44681810
Web Site: https://www.ihgqatar.com
Year Founded: 2008
Rev.: $116,861,336
Assets: $375,583,696
Liabilities: $163,544,230
Net Worth: $212,039,466
Earnings: $17,005,986
Fiscal Year-end: 12/31/18
Building Materials Distr
N.A.I.C.S.: 444180
Ghanim Sultan Al Hodifi Al-Kuwari (Chm)

INVESTMENT MANAGEMENT CORPORATION OF ONTARIO
16 York Street, Suite 2400, Toronto, M5J 0E6, ON , Canada
Tel.: (416) 898-3917
Web Site:
https://www.imcoinvest.com
Year Founded: 2016
Emp.: 325
Investment Management
N.A.I.C.S.: 523999

INVESTMENT ONE FINANCIAL SERVICES LIMITED
37 Karimu Kotun Street, Victoria Island, Lagos, Nigeria
Tel.: (234) 1 448 8888
Web Site: http://www.investment-one.com
Year Founded: 2007
Emp.: 60
Investment Banking & Securities Brokerage Services
N.A.I.C.S.: 523150
Nicholas Nyamali (CEO & Grp Mng Dir)

Subsidiaries:

Investment One Funds Management Limited (1)
37 Karimu Kotun Street, Victoria Island, Lagos, Nigeria
Tel.: (234) 14488888
Web Site: http://www.investment-one.com
Financial Services
N.A.I.C.S.: 541611

Investment One Pension Managers Limited (1)
Plot 871 Tafawa Belewa Way Opposite NICON Luxury Hotel Area11, Garki, Abuja, Nigeria
Tel.: (234) 97802508
Web Site: http://www.investment-onepension.com
Pension Fund Services
N.A.I.C.S.: 525110
Alex Okoh (Chm)

Investment One Stockbrokers Int'l Limited (1)
Plot 10 Olaide Benson Street Along Ikorodu Road, Maryland, Lagos, Nigeria
Tel.: (234) 14480848
Web Site: http://www.investment-one.com
Stock Brokerage Services
N.A.I.C.S.: 523150

INVESTMENT RESEARCH

INVESTOR AB

GROUP LIMITED
Level 7 12-26 Swanson Street, Auckland, New Zealand
Tel.: (64) 93040145
Web Site: http://www.irg.co.nz
Sales Range: $1-9.9 Million
Investment & Financial Services
N.A.I.C.S.: 523940
Brent D. King (Mng Dir)

Subsidiaries:

Equity Investment Advisers Limited (1)
Level 7 12-26 Swanson Street, Auckland, 1140, New Zealand
Tel.: (64) 93040145
Web Site: http://www.equity.co.nz
Emp.: 25
Investment Advisory Services
N.A.I.C.S.: 523940
Brent Jing (Mng Dir)

IRG BOP Ltd (1)
Suite 4 Level 1 Durham House 143 Durham Street, Tauranga, 3110, New Zealand
Tel.: (64) 75783863
Web Site: http://www.irgbop.co.nz
Financial Management & Brokerage Services
N.A.I.C.S.: 523940
Andrew Parkinson (Gen Mgr)

INVESTOR AB
Hamngatan 15, 103 32, Stockholm, Sweden
Tel.: (46) 86142000   SE
Web Site:
https://www.investorab.com
Year Founded: 1916
INVE.B—(NASDAQ)
Rev.: $5,586,276,659
Assets: $78,530,819,448
Liabilities: $11,334,869,388
Net Worth: $67,195,950,059
Earnings: $11,877,921,080
Emp.: 16,884
Fiscal Year-end: 12/31/23
Financial Investment Services
N.A.I.C.S.: 551112
Marcus Wallenberg (Vice Chm)

Subsidiaries:

AB Investor Group Finance (1)
Arsenalsgatan 8 C, Stockholm, 11685, Sweden (100%)
Tel.: (46) 86142000
Web Site: http://www.investorab.com
Sales Range: $50-74.9 Million
Emp.: 90
Financial Investment Activities
N.A.I.C.S.: 523999
Borje Ekholm (Mng Dir)

Atlas Antibodies AB (1)
Voltavagen 13A, 168 69, Bromma, Sweden
Tel.: (46) 854595850
Web Site: https://www.atlasantibodies.com
Biotechnology Research Services
N.A.I.C.S.: 541714

Investor Growth Capital AB (1)
Arsenalsgatan 8 C, 103 32, Stockholm, Sweden (100%)
Tel.: (46) 86141800
Web Site:
http://www.investorgrowthcapital.com
Sales Range: $50-74.9 Million
Emp.: 100
Investment Company
N.A.I.C.S.: 523940
Thomas Eklund (Mng Dir)

Subsidiary (Non-US):

Investor Growth Capital Holding BV (2)
Schit Blvd 353, 1118 BG, Schiphol, Netherlands
Tel.: (31) 205776600
Sales Range: $50-74.9 Million
Emp.: 5
Trusts Estates & Agency Accounts
N.A.I.C.S.: 525920

INVESTOR AB

INTERNATIONAL PUBLIC

Investor AB—(Continued)

Subsidiary (US):

Investor Growth Capital, Inc (2)
333 Middlefield Rd Ste 110, Menlo Park, CA 94025
Tel.: (650) 543-8100
Web Site: http://www.investorgrowthcapital.com
Sales Range: $50-74.9 Million
Emp.: 6
Investment Advice
N.A.I.C.S.: 523940
Jose Suarec (Mng Dir)

Patricia Industries AB (1)
Arsenalsgatan 8C, 103 32, Stockholm, Sweden
Tel.: (46) 8614 2000
Web Site: http://www.patriciaindustries.com
Industrial Investment Holding Company
N.A.I.C.S.: 551112
Jacob Wallenberg (Vice Chm)

Holding (US):

Advanced Instruments, LLC (2)
2 Technology Way, Norwood, MA 02062-2633
Tel.: (781) 320-9000
Web Site: http://www.aicompanies.com
Scientific Instruments & Hospital Equipment Mfr
N.A.I.C.S.: 339112
Byron Selman (Pres & CEO)

Subsidiary (Domestic):

D & F Control Systems (3)
6773 Sierra Ct Ste E, Dublin, CA 94568-2650
Tel.: (925) 875-9660
Milk Preservative Tablet Mfr
N.A.I.C.S.: 325412

Fiske Associates (3)
2 Technology Way, Norwood, MA 02062
Tel.: (781) 320-5656
Web Site: http://www.fiskeassociates.com
Sales Range: $10-24.9 Million
Emp.: 80
Mfr of Scientific Instruments
N.A.I.C.S.: 334516

Spiral Biotech, Inc. (3)
2 Technology Way, Norwood, MA 02062 (100%)
Tel.: (781) 320-9000
Sales Range: $25-49.9 Million
Emp.: 80
Mfr of Scientific Instruments
N.A.I.C.S.: 423450
John Coughlin (CEO)

Holding (Non-US):

Laborie Medical Technologies, ULC (2)
6415 Northwest Drive Unit 11, Mississauga, L4V 1X1, ON, Canada (97%)
Tel.: (905) 612-1170
Web Site: http://www.laborie.com
Surgical Instrument Mfr
N.A.I.C.S.: 339112
Holger Furstenberg (Exec VP & Gen Mgr)

Subsidiary (US):

Cogentix Medical, Inc. (3)
5420 Feltl Rd, Minnetonka, MN 55343
Tel.: (952) 426-6140
Holding Company; Medical Device Mfr
N.A.I.C.S.: 551112

Subsidiary (Domestic):

Machida Incorporated (4)
40 Ramland Rd S, Orangeburg, NY 10962 (100%)
Tel.: (845) 365-0600
Borescopes Custom Designer & Mfr
N.A.I.C.S.: 339112

Subsidiary (Non-US):

LABORIE Belgium (3)
BC Wassaland Industriepark West 75, 9100, Saint-Nicolas, Belgium
Tel.: (32) 3 780 1738
Web Site: http://www.laborie.com
Diagnostic Equipment Distr
N.A.I.C.S.: 423450
Ray Laborie (Dir-Intl Dev)

Subsidiary (Domestic):

LABORIE Canada (3)
2101 Boulevard Lapiniere, Brossard, J4W 1L7, QC, Canada
Tel.: (450) 671-5901
Web Site: http://www.laborie.com
Diagnostic Equipment Mfr
N.A.I.C.S.: 334510
Ray Laborie (Dir-Intl Dev)

Subsidiary (Non-US):

LABORIE China (3)
Room 31B Building 3 Century Classic No 45 Xiao Guam Bei Li, Choa Yang District, Beijing, 100029, China
Tel.: (86) 8489 8891
Web Site: http://www.laborie.com
Diagnostic Equipment Distr
N.A.I.C.S.: 423450
Ray Laborie (Dir-Intl Dev)

LABORIE Europe Ltd (3)
Lumonics House Valley Drive, Rugby, CV21 1TQ, Warwickshire, United Kingdom
Tel.: (44) 1788 547888
Diagnostic Equipment Distr
N.A.I.C.S.: 423450

LABORIE France (3)
10 rue de Penthievre, 75008, Paris, France
Tel.: (33) 01 79 75 03 03
Web Site: http://www.laborie.com
Diagnostic Equipment Distr
N.A.I.C.S.: 423450
Ray Laborie (Dir-Intl Devt)

LABORIE Germany (3)
Riemenstrasse 31, 74906, Bad Rappenau, Germany
Tel.: (49) 7264 9598 0
Web Site: http://www.laborie.com
Diagnostic Equipment Distr
N.A.I.C.S.: 423450
Ray Laborie (Dir-Intl Dev)

Subsidiary (US):

Laborie Medical Technologies, Corp. (3)
400 Ave D Ste 10, Williston, VT 05495
Tel.: (800) 522-6743
Web Site: http://www.laborie.com
Diagnostic Equipment Distr
N.A.I.C.S.: 423450
Michael Frazzette (Pres)

Subsidiary (Domestic):

Clinical Innovations, LLC (4)
747 W 4170 S, Murray, UT 84123
Tel.: (888) 268-6222
Web Site: http://www.clinicalinnovations.com
Medical Device Mfr
N.A.I.C.S.: 339112
Ross McQuivey (Chief Medical Officer)

Subsidiary (Non-US):

Medical Measurement Systems B.V. (3)
Colosseum 25, 7521 PV, Enschede, Netherlands
Tel.: (31) 53 4803700
Web Site: http://www.mmsinternational.com
Medical Equipment Mfr & Distr
N.A.I.C.S.: 334510

Subsidiary (Non-US):

MMS Deutschland GmbH (4)
PO Box 10 10 27, 46210, Bottrop, Germany
Tel.: (49) 20 41 55 80 10
Web Site: http://www.mms-deutschland.de
Medical Equipment Mfr & Distr
N.A.I.C.S.: 334510

Subsidiary (US):

Medical Measurement Systems USA, inc. (4)
53 Washington St Ste 400, Dover, NH 03820
Tel.: (603) 750-0037
Web Site: http://www.mmsusa.net
Medical Equipment Mfr & Distr

N.A.I.C.S.: 334510

Subsidiary (Non-US):

Mediwatch UK Ltd. (3)
Lumonics House Valley Drive Swift Valley, Rugby, CV21 1TQ, Warks, United Kingdom
Tel.: (44) 1788547888
Web Site: http://www.laborie.com
Sales Range: $10-24.9 Million
Emp.: 10
Urological Diagnosis & Screening Products Mfr & Supplier
N.A.I.C.S.: 339112

Subsidiary (Domestic):

Mediwatch Biomedical Limited (4)
Lumonics House Valley Drive, Swift Vly Indust Estate, Rugby, CV21 1tq, United Kingdom
Tel.: (44) 1788547888
Emp.: 50
Medical Equipment Mfr
N.A.I.C.S.: 339112
Philip Stimpson (CEO)

Subsidiary (Non-US):

Unisensor AG (3)
Bahnstrasse 12a, 8544, Attikon, Switzerland
Tel.: (41) 52 337 37 01
Web Site: http://www.unisensor.ch
Measuring & Testing Equipment Mfr
N.A.I.C.S.: 334513
Thomas Wetli (Production Mgr)

Holding (Domestic):

Molnlycke Health Care AB (2)
Gamlestadsveien 3C, Gothenburg, 41502, Sweden (96%)
Tel.: (46) 317223000
Web Site: http://www.molnlycke.com
Sales Range: $500-549.9 Million
Emp.: 600
Mfr, Marketing & Sales of Single-Use Products for Surgical Interventions & Wound Care
N.A.I.C.S.: 339113
Michelle Roy (CFO)

Subsidiary (Non-US):

Molnlycke Health Care (3)
Vabaohumuuseumitee 4-67, 13522, Tallinn, Estonia
Tel.: (372) 6711520
Web Site: http://www.molnlycke.ee
Sales Range: $25-49.9 Million
Emp.: 5
Mfr of Surgical Instruments
N.A.I.C.S.: 339112

Molnlycke Health Care (3)
10/3 Toulskaya Str Office building Serpuhovski dvor, 115191, Moscow, Russia
Tel.: (7) 4952322664
Web Site: http://www.molnlycke.com
Surgical & Medical Instrument Mfr
N.A.I.C.S.: 339112

Molnlycke Health Care (3)
301 White Crown Building Sheikh Zayed Road, PO Box 212565, Dubai, United Arab Emirates
Tel.: (971) 43 31 98 84
Web Site: http://www.molnlycke.com
Surgical & Medical Instrument Mfr
N.A.I.C.S.: 339112
Hussain Malkawi (Gen Mgr)

Molnlycke Health Care AG (3)
Heimstrasse 18, 8953, Dietikon, Switzerland
Tel.: (41) 44 744 54 00
Web Site: http://www.molnlycke.com
Surgical Product Mfr
N.A.I.C.S.: 339112

Molnlycke Health Care AS (3)
Grensesvingen 9, PO Box 6229, Etterstad, 0603, Oslo, Norway
Tel.: (47) 22 70 63 70
Web Site: http://www.molnlycke.com
Sales Range: $25-49.9 Million
Emp.: 23
Surgical & Wound Care Product Mfr
N.A.I.C.S.: 339112

Molnlycke Health Care ApS (3)
Gydevang 33, 3450, Allerod, Denmark

Tel.: (45) 48 16 82 68
Web Site: http://www.molnlycke.com
Surgical & Wound Care Product Mfr
N.A.I.C.S.: 339112
Susanne Kopping (Controller)

Molnlycke Health Care Asia-Pacific Pte Ltd (3)
298 Tiong Rd Bahru Rd 07-03 central Plza, Singapore, 168730, Singapore
Tel.: (65) 6438 4008
Web Site: http://www.molnlycke.com
Sales Range: $25-49.9 Million
Emp.: 35
Surgical & Wound Care Product Mfr
N.A.I.C.S.: 339112
Krishnan Nagasubramani (Gen Mgr)

Molnlycke Health Care B.V. (3)
Smederijstraat 2, Postbus 3196, 4800 DD, Breda, Netherlands
Tel.: (31) 76 521 9663
Web Site: http://www.molnlycke.com
Sales Range: $25-49.9 Million
Emp.: 20
Surgical & Wound Care Product Mfr
N.A.I.C.S.: 339112
Jan Timmermen (Gen Mgr)

Molnlycke Health Care GmbH (3)
Wilhelmstrasse 68, AT 1120, Vienna, Austria
Tel.: (43) 12788542
Web Site: http://www.molynlycke.com
Sales Range: $25-49.9 Million
Emp.: 21
Mfr of Surgical Instruments
N.A.I.C.S.: 339112

Molnlycke Health Care GmbH (3)
Max-Planck-Str 15, Postfach 3265, 40682, Erkrath, Unterfeldhaus, Germany
Tel.: (49) 211 92 08 80
Surgical & Wound Care Product Mfr
N.A.I.C.S.: 339112

Molnlycke Health Care Inc. (3)
2010 Winston Park Drive Suite 100, Oakville, L6H 5R7, ON, Canada
Tel.: (905) 829-1502
Web Site: http://www.molnlycke.com
Sales Range: $25-49.9 Million
Emp.: 8
Surgical & Wound Care Product Mfr
N.A.I.C.S.: 339112
Mary McLean (Pres)

Molnlycke Health Care India Pvt, Ltd (3)
Universal Business Centre Second Floor Universal Trade Tower Sector 49, Gurgaon Sohna Road, Gurgaon, 122 018, Haryana, India
Tel.: (91) 124 4696008
Web Site: http://www.molnlycke.com
Sales Range: $25-49.9 Million
Emp.: 12
Surgical & Medical Equipment Mfr
N.A.I.C.S.: 339112
Tejinder Singh Jassal (Gen Mgr)

Molnlycke Health Care Kft (3)
Devai U 26-28 III Em, Budapest, 1134, Hungary
Tel.: (36) 1 477 3080
Web Site: http://www.molnlycke.com
Sales Range: $25-49.9 Million
Emp.: 18
Surgical & Wound Care Product Mfr
N.A.I.C.S.: 339112
Aniko Szeker (Product Mgr)

Molnlycke Health Care Korea Co., Ltd (3)
2 Fl Hansol Richville 46 Wiryeseong Daero, Songpa-gu, Seoul, 05627, Korea (South)
Tel.: (82) 2 3789 1402
Web Site: http://www.molnlycke.com
Emp.: 7
Surgical & Medical Equipment Mfr
N.A.I.C.S.: 339112
Yoon Ju Cho (Mgr-Mktg)

Molnlycke Health Care Ltd. (3)
The Arenson Centre Arenson Way, Dunstable, LU5 5UL, Bedfordshire, United Kingdom
Tel.: (44) 870 60 60 766
Web Site: http://www.molnlycke.com
Surgical & Wound Care Product Mfr
N.A.I.C.S.: 339112

AND PRIVATE COMPANIES

Plant (Domestic):

Molnlycke Health Care Ltd - IRLAM FACTORY (4)
Two Omega Drive, Irlam, Manchester, M445BJ, United Kingdom
Tel.: (44) 161 777 2600
Web Site: http://www.molnlycke.com
Surgical & Wound Care Product Mfr
N.A.I.C.S.: 339112

Molnlycke Health Care Ltd - OLD-HAM FACTORY (4)
Tubiton House Medlock Street, Oldham, OL1 3HS, Lancashire, United Kingdom
Tel.: (44) 161 621 2100
Web Site: http://www.molnlycke.com
Surgical & Wound Care Product Mfr
N.A.I.C.S.: 339112
Phil Hague *(Gen Mgr)*

Subsidiary (Non-US):

Molnlycke Health Care NV/SA (3)
Berchemstadionstraat 72 Bus 2, 2600, Berchem, Antwerpen, Belgium
Tel.: (32) 800 94705
Web Site: http://www.molnlycke.com
Surgical & Medical Equipment Mfr
N.A.I.C.S.: 339112

Molnlycke Health Care OU (3)
Vabaohumuuseumitee 4-67, 13522, Tallinn, Estonia
Tel.: (372) 671 1520
Web Site: http://www.molnlycke.com
Sales Range: $25-49.9 Million
Emp.: 15
Surgical & Medical Equipment Mfr
N.A.I.C.S.: 339112
Stephen Hamlett *(Mgr)*

Molnlycke Health Care Oy (3)
Pitajanmaentie 14 3rd Floor, 00380, Helsinki, Finland
Tel.: (358) 201 622 300
Web Site: http://www.molnlycke.com
Surgical & Medical Equipment Mfr
N.A.I.C.S.: 339112
Markku Iivonen *(Mng Dir & Mgr-Mktg & Pur)*

Molnlycke Health Care Pty. Ltd. (3)
Ste 1 01 10 Tilley Ln, French's Forest, 2086, NSW, Australia
Tel.: (61) 2 9453 1144
Web Site: http://www.molnlycke.com
Sales Range: $25-49.9 Million
Emp.: 55
Medical Equipment Mfr
N.A.I.C.S.: 334510
Georges Magnan *(CEO)*

Molnlycke Health Care S.L. (3)
Avda De Bruselas 38 B - 1a Planta Poligono Ind Arroyo de la Vega, 28108, Alcobendas, Madrid, Spain
Tel.: (34) 91 484 13 20
Web Site: http://www.molnlycke.com
Sales Range: $25-49.9 Million
Surgical & Medical Instrument Mfr
N.A.I.C.S.: 339112
Pierre Guyot *(Pres)*

Molnlycke Health Care SAS (3)
13 Allee du Chateau Blanc, 59290, Wasquehal, France
Tel.: (33) 320 122 555
Web Site: http://www.molnlycke.com
Surgical & Wound Care Product Mfr
N.A.I.C.S.: 339112

Molnlycke Health Care Sdn. Bhd. (3)
First Subang Suite 1108 South Tower Jalan SS15/4G, Subang Jaya, 47500, Selangor, Malaysia
Tel.: (60) 3 5612 2926
Web Site: http://www.molnlycke.com
Sales Range: $25-49.9 Million
Emp.: 8
Surgical & Wound Care Product Mfr
N.A.I.C.S.: 339112
Yew Pun Kai *(Mgr)*

Subsidiary (US):

Molnlycke Health Care US, LLC (3)
5550 Peachtree Pkwy Ste 500, Norcross, GA 30092
Tel.: (864) 260-5920
Web Site: http://www.molnlycke.com
Sales Range: $75-99.9 Million
Surgical & Wound Care Products Mfr & Distr
N.A.I.C.S.: 339113

Subsidiary (Non-US):

Molnlycke Health Care s.r.l. (3)
Via Marsala 40/C, 21013, Gallarate, Varese, Italy
Tel.: (39) 0331 714 011
Web Site: http://www.molnlycke.com
Emp.: 84
Surgical & Wound Care Product Mfr
N.A.I.C.S.: 339112

Holding (Domestic):

Permobil AB (2)
Per Uddens vag 20, 861 36, Timra, Sweden
Tel.: (46) 60595900
Web Site: http://www.permobil.com
Sales Range: $250-299.9 Million
Powered Wheelchair Mfr
N.A.I.C.S.: 339999
Jon Sintorn *(Pres & CEO)*

Subsidiary (Non-US):

Permobil Australia Pty. Ltd. (3)
Unit 312/14-16 Lexington Dr Norwest Business Park, Bella Vista, 2153, NSW, Australia
Tel.: (61) 2 8883 4292
Powered Wheelchair Distr
N.A.I.C.S.: 423450

Subsidiary (US):

Permobil, Inc. (3)
300 Duke Dr, Lebanon, TN 37090-8115
Tel.: (615) 547-1889
Web Site: http://www.permobilus.com
Sales Range: $25-49.9 Million
Powered Wheelchair Mfr & Distr
N.A.I.C.S.: 339999
Larry Jackson *(CEO)*

Subsidiary (Non-US):

Permobil, Ltd. (3)
75 Mary Street Unit 4, Aurora, L4G 1G3, ON, Canada
Tel.: (905) 726-9333
Powered Wheelchair Mfr
N.A.I.C.S.: 423450

Subsidiary (US):

ROHO, Inc. (3)
100 N Florida Ave, Belleville, IL 62221-5429
Tel.: (618) 277-9173
Web Site: http://www.permobilus.com
Medical Seat Cushion, Back Support Systems, Mattresses & Related Support Surface Products Mfr & Distr
N.A.I.C.S.: 326150
Tom Borcherding *(Pres)*

Holding (Domestic):

Piab AB (2)
Sjoflygvagen 35, PO Box 4501, Taby, Stockholm, 18304, Sweden
Tel.: (46) 86302500
Web Site: http://www.piab.com
Business to Business Electronic Markets
N.A.I.C.S.: 425120
Peter Tell *(CTO)*

Subsidiary (US):

Coval Vacuum Technology Inc. (3)
212 Powell Dr Ste 112, Raleigh, NC 27606-1680
Tel.: (919) 233-4855
Web Site: http://www.coval-inc.com
Service Establishment Equipment & Supplies Merchant Whslr
N.A.I.C.S.: 423850
Michel Cecchin *(CEO)*

SAS Automation LLC (3)
1200 S Patton St, Xenia, OH 45385
Tel.: (937) 372-5255
Automation Machinery Mfr
N.A.I.C.S.: 333998

Holding (US):

Sarnova, Inc. (2)
5000 Tuttle Crossing Blvd, Dublin, OH 43016
Tel.: (614) 760-5000
Web Site: http://www.sarnova.com
Holding Company; Specialty Health Care Products Distr
N.A.I.C.S.: 551112
Brian Ellis *(COO)*

Subsidiary (Domestic):

Bound Tree Medical, LLC (3)
5000 Tuttle Crossing Blvd, Dublin, OH 43017
Tel.: (614) 760-5000
Web Site: http://www.boundtree.com
Emergency Medical Equipment Distr
N.A.I.C.S.: 423450

Subsidiary (Non-US):

BTME Group Ltd. (4)
Unit 3 Stag Business Park, Donnington Wood, Telford, TF2 7NA, Shropshire, United Kingdom
Tel.: (44) 1952565668
Web Site: https://btme-group.co.uk
Medical Supplies & Equipment Distr
N.A.I.C.S.: 423450

Subsidiary (Domestic):

Southeastern Emergency Equipment, Inc. (4)
5760 Nc 96 Hwy W, Youngsville, NC 27596-8609
Tel.: (919) 556-1890
Web Site: http://www.seequip.com
Emergency Equipment Distr
N.A.I.C.S.: 423450
Carla Baker *(Pres)*

Subsidiary (Domestic):

Cardio Partners, Inc. (3)
1001 Flagpole Ct, Brentwood, TN 37027-8172
Web Site: https://www.cardiopartners.com
Medical, Dental & Hospital Equipment & Supplies Merchant Whslr
N.A.I.C.S.: 423450
Matt Spencer *(Pres & CEO)*

Subsidiary (Domestic):

One Beat CPR Learning Center, Inc. (4)
3801 SW 47th Ave Ste 505, Davie, FL 33314-2816
Tel.: (954) 321-5305
Web Site: http://www.onebeatcpr.com
Medical, Dental & Hospital Equipment & Supplies Merchant Whslr
N.A.I.C.S.: 423450

Subsidiary (Domestic):

Digitech Computer LLC (3)
480 Bedford Rd Bldg 600 2nd Fl, Chappaqua, NY 10514
Tel.: (914) 741-1919
Web Site: http://www.digitechcomputer.com
Sales Range: $1-9.9 Million
Emp.: 50
Billing Software Solution Services
N.A.I.C.S.: 513210
Mark Schiowitz *(Founder & CEO)*

Tri-anim Health Services, Inc. (3)
5000 Tuttle Crossing Blvd, Dublin, OH 43016
Tel.: (818) 362-6882
Web Site: http://www.tri-anim.com
Medical & Hospital Equipment
N.A.I.C.S.: 423450

Holding (US):

The Braun Corporation (2)
631 W 11th St, Winamac, IN 46996
Tel.: (574) 946-6153
Web Site: http://www.braunability.com
Wheelchair Mfr
N.A.I.C.S.: 339113
Staci L. Kroon *(Pres & CEO)*

Subsidiary (Domestic):

Ability Center (3)
6550 Freeport Blvd, Sacramento, CA 95822-5932
Tel.: (916) 392-1196
Web Site: http://www.abilitycenter.com
Home Health Equipment Rental
N.A.I.C.S.: 532283
Kevin Horn *(Mgr)*

B&D Independence, LLC (3)
1024 Empire St, Mount Carmel, IL 62863
Tel.: (618) 262-7117
Web Site: http://www.bdindependence.com
Wheelchair Mfr
N.A.I.C.S.: 339113

Vectura Fastigheter AB (1)
Arsenalsgatan 8b, 103 32, Stockholm, Sweden
Tel.: (46) 300323500
Web Site: http://www.vectura.se
Real Estate Services
N.A.I.C.S.: 531210

INVESTOR.BG AD

Brussels Blvd 1, 1540, Sofia, Bulgaria
Tel.: (359) 28129812
Web Site: http://www.ibg.bg
Year Founded: 2000
4IN—(BUL)
Sales Range: $1-9.9 Million
Internet Media Services
N.A.I.C.S.: 517810
Lubomir Lekov *(Founder & Chm)*

INVESTORS HOLDING GROUP CO. (K.P.S.C.)

Fahad Al-Salem Street Humood Tower Floor 8 Qeblah, PO Box 2031, Safat, 13021, Kuwait, Kuwait
Tel.: (965) 2 249 2319
Web Site: http://www.ig.com.kw
Year Founded: 1998
INVESTORS—(KUW)
Assets: $785,856,911
Liabilities: $734,141,104
Net Worth: $51,715,807
Earnings: ($41,010,411)
Emp.: 5
Fiscal Year-end: 12/31/20
Holding Company
N.A.I.C.S.: 551112
Ahmad Dawoud Salman Al-Subah *(Chm & CEO)*

INVESTORS HOUSE OYJ

Veturitie 11 T 152, 520, Helsinki, Finland
Tel.: (358) 26336533
Web Site: https://www.investorshouse.fi
Year Founded: 1988
INVEST—(HEL)
Rev.: $8,202,029
Assets: $59,637,384
Liabilities: $24,983,812
Net Worth: $34,653,572
Earnings: $3,464,278
Emp.: 38
Fiscal Year-end: 12/31/22
Real Estate Support Services
N.A.I.C.S.: 531210
Tapani Rautiainen *(Chm)*

INVESTSMART GROUP LTD.

Suite 2 Level 2 66 Clarence Street, Sydney, 2000, NSW, Australia
Tel.: (61) 1300880160
INV—(ASX)
Rev.: $6,747,123
Assets: $7,029,527
Liabilities: $3,993,655
Net Worth: $3,035,872
Earnings: ($510,381)
Emp.: 36
Fiscal Year-end: 06/30/24
Asset Management Services
N.A.I.C.S.: 523940
Paul Clitheroe *(Chm)*

INVESTX CAPITAL LTD.

1185 West Georgia Street Suite

INVESTX CAPITAL LTD.

InvestX Capital Ltd.—(Continued)
1625, Vancouver, V6E 4E6, BC, Canada
Tel.: (778) 383-1028
Web Site: http://www.investx.com
Investment Services
N.A.I.C.S.: 523999
Marcus New (CEO)
Subsidiaries:

Southwest Battery Company (1)
4320 E Broadway, Phoenix, AZ 85040
Tel.: (602) 437-9244
Web Site: http://www.southwestbattery.com
Sales Range: $1-9.9 Million
Emp.: 8
Industrial Storage Battery Distr
N.A.I.C.S.: 423610

INVEX CONTROLADORA, S.A.B. DE C.V.

Boulevard Manuel Avila Camacho Numero 40 Piso 12, Lomas De Chapultepec, 11000, Mexico, DF, Mexico
Tel.: (52) 53503333
Web Site: https://www.invexcontroladora.com
Year Founded: 1994
INVEX—(MEX)
Rev.: $1,153,488,195
Assets: $10,311,690,706
Liabilities: $9,531,405,465
Net Worth: $780,285,241
Earnings: $61,513,086
Emp.: 2,703
Fiscal Year-end: 12/31/23
Financial Services
N.A.I.C.S.: 523999
Juan Bautista Guichard Michel (Chm)

INVEX THERAPEUTICS LIMITED

Level 2 38 Rowland St Subiaco, Perth, 6008, WA, Australia
Tel.: (61) 863820137 AU
Web Site: https://www.invextherapeutics.com
Year Founded: 2019
IXC—(ASX)
Rev.: $819,044
Assets: $14,866,493
Liabilities: $1,025,214
Net Worth: $13,843,280
Earnings: ($5,053,046)
Fiscal Year-end: 06/30/23
Pharmaceutical Product Mfr & Distr
N.A.I.C.S.: 325412
Narelle Warren (CFO)

INVIBES ADVERTISING NV

Technologiepark 82, 9052, Zwijnaarde, Belgium
Tel.: (32) 22744800
Web Site: https://www.invibes.com
Year Founded: 2011
ALINV—(EUR)
Rev.: $31,916,326
Assets: $42,324,760
Liabilities: $18,398,278
Net Worth: $23,926,482
Earnings: $614,858
Emp.: 174
Fiscal Year-end: 12/31/23
Advertising & Marketing Services
N.A.I.C.S.: 541810
Nicolas Pollet (Founder & CEO)

INVICTA HOLDINGS LIMITED

3 Droste Crescent Droste Park Ext 7, Jeppestown, Johannesburg, 2001, South Africa
Tel.: (27) 116207300 ZA
Web Site: http://www.invictaholdings.co.za

IVT—(JSE)
Rev.: $490,504,856
Assets: $538,869,214
Liabilities: $218,687,316
Net Worth: $320,181,898
Earnings: $61,826,342
Fiscal Year-end: 03/31/22
Investment Holding Company
N.A.I.C.S.: 551112
Arnold Goldstone (Exec Dir)
Subsidiaries:

Autobax (Pty.) Ltd. (1)
Unit 7 Lakeside Ind Park Kelly Rd Jet Park, Boksburg, 1459, South Africa
Tel.: (27) 113977409
Web Site: http://www.autobax.co.za
Automobile Parts Distr
N.A.I.C.S.: 423120
John Black (Mng Dir)

Bearing Man 1955 Limited (1)
6 Tetford Circle Millennium Bridge, Durban, 4051, KwaZulu-Natal, South Africa (100%)
Tel.: (27) 315766200
Web Site: http://www.bmgworld.net
Sales Range: $50-74.9 Million
Emp.: 100
Holding Company
N.A.I.C.S.: 551112
Bryan Nichles (CEO)

Subsidiary (Domestic):

Bearing Man (Pty.) Ltd. (2)
Millennium Bridge Business Park Tetford Circle, La Lucia Ridge, Durban, 4320, South Africa
Tel.: (27) 315766200
Web Site: http://www.bmgworld.net
Bearing & Allied Accessories Distr
N.A.I.C.S.: 459999
Abe Bekker (COO)

Affiliate (Non-US):

Bearing Man (Botswana) (Pty) Ltd (3)
Kamushongo Road Plot 14469, Private Bag BR81, Gaborone, Botswana
Tel.: (267) 673972273
Sales Range: $50-74.9 Million
Emp.: 10
Engineering Components Distr
N.A.I.C.S.: 423120

Bearing Man (Swaziland) (Pty) Ltd. (3)
Simunye Street Plot 178/R, Matsapha, M202, Eswatini
Tel.: (268) 25185110
Sales Range: $50-74.9 Million
Emp.: 13
Fasteners & Bearings Distr
N.A.I.C.S.: 423710

Bearing Man Group (Pty) Ltd. (1)
3 Droste Crescent Droste Park, Jeppestown, Johannesburg, 2001, Gauteng, South Africa (100%)
Tel.: (27) 116201500
Web Site: https://www.bmgworld.net
Sales Range: $50-74.9 Million
Emp.: 200
Hydraulic Engineering Components Mfr & Distr
N.A.I.C.S.: 333995

Belt Brokers (Pty.) Ltd. (1)
3 De Kok Street, Vulcania, Brakpan, 1541, South Africa
Tel.: (27) 118455050
Web Site: https://www.beltbrokers.co.za
Conveyor Belt Mfr & Distr
N.A.I.C.S.: 333922

Driveshaft Parts Pty. Ltd. (1)
4 Mopedi Road Sebenze, Edenvale, 1609, Gauteng, South Africa
Tel.: (27) 114528028
Web Site: http://www.driveshaftparts.co.za
Prop Shaft & CV Joint Component Distr
N.A.I.C.S.: 423120

High Power Equipment Africa (Pty.) Ltd. (1)
105 Andre Greyvensteyn Ave, Spartan, Kempton Park, 1619, Gauteng, South Africa

Tel.: (27) 113974670
Web Site: https://www.hpeafrica.co.za
Construction Equipment Distr
N.A.I.C.S.: 423810

Humulani Investments (Pty) Ltd. (1)
3rd Floor Pepkor House 36 Stellenberg Road, Parow Industria, Cape Town, 7493, South Africa (80%)
Tel.: (27) 21 929 4780
Holding Company
N.A.I.C.S.: 551112
Anthony Sinclair (CEO-Capital Equipment Grp)

Subsidiary (Domestic):

CSE Equipment Company (Pty) Ltd. (2)
14 Industry Road, Box 851, Isando, 1600, South Africa
Tel.: (27) 119222000
Web Site: http://www.cse.co.za
Sales Range: $200-249.9 Million
Emp.: 503
Equipment Distr
N.A.I.C.S.: 423810
Brenton Kimp (Mng Dir)

Criterion Equipment (Pty) Ltd. (2)
1 Wrench Road, Isando, Johannesburg, 1600, Gauteng, South Africa
Tel.: (27) 119669700
Web Site: https://www.criterion.co.za
Sales Range: $25-49.9 Million
Emp.: 70
Forklift Truck Distr
N.A.I.C.S.: 423830
Heinrich Frederick (Branch Mgr)

Disa Equipment (Pty) Ltd. (2)
60C Electron Avenue, Isando, 1600, Gauteng, South Africa
Tel.: (27) 119742095
Web Site: https://develonsa.co.za
Sales Range: $25-49.9 Million
Emp.: 20
Construction & Earthmoving Equipments Distr
N.A.I.C.S.: 423810
Darrel Holton (Mng Dir)

Equipment Spare Parts Africa (Pty) Ltd. (2)
3 Hulley Road, PO Box 658, Isando, 1600, South Africa
Tel.: (27) 113981700
Web Site: https://www.espa.co.za
Sales Range: $50-74.9 Million
Emp.: 150
Construction Machinery Parts Distr
N.A.I.C.S.: 423120
Andrew Grobler (Dir-Mktg)

New Holland SA (Pty) Ltd. (2)
14a Industry Road, PO Box 851, Isando, 1600, Gauteng, South Africa
Tel.: (27) 119222137
Web Site: http://www.nhsa.co.za
Sales Range: $125-149.9 Million
Emp.: 50
Agricultural Machinery & Farming Equipments Distr
N.A.I.C.S.: 423820
Jan Barnard (Mgr-Sls-Gauteng & Mpumalanga)

Oscillating Systems Technology Africa (Pty) Ltd. (2)
252 Propshaft Street Samcor Park X1, Silverton, Pretoria, 0127, Gauteng, South Africa
Tel.: (27) 128037254
Web Site: https://www.ost-africa.co.za
Sales Range: $25-49.9 Million
Emp.: 45
Engineering Component Mfr
N.A.I.C.S.: 334511
Nolene Streicher (Mng Dir)

Tiletoria Cape (Pty) Ltd. (2)
43 Paarden Eiland Road Paarden Eiland, Cape Town, 7405, Western Cape, South Africa (60%)
Tel.: (27) 215113125
Web Site: http://www.tiletoria.co.za
Sales Range: $25-49.9 Million
Emp.: 200
Tiles Distr
N.A.I.C.S.: 423320

INTERNATIONAL PUBLIC

Patrick Thonissen (Mng Dir)

Industri Tools & Equipment (Pty.) Ltd. (1)
70 Watt St Meadowdale, Benrose, Germiston, 1614, South Africa
Tel.: (27) 113865811
Web Site: https://www.industri.co.za
Industrial Tool & Equipment Distr
N.A.I.C.S.: 423830

Kian Ann Engineering Limited (1)
Kian Ann Building 7 Changi South Lane, Singapore, 486119, Singapore
Tel.: (65) 6298 1011
Web Site: http://www.kianann.com.sg
Sales Range: $125-149.9 Million
Heavy Machinery Parts & Diesel Engine Components Distr
N.A.I.C.S.: 423120
Florence Fei Lin Low (Mgr-HR & Corp Comm)

Subsidiary (Domestic):

Kian Ann Districentre Pte Ltd (2)
Kian Ann Building 7 Changi South Lane, Singapore, 486119, Singapore
Tel.: (65) 87 1369
Web Site: http://www.kianann.com.sg
Office Rental & Logistics Services
N.A.I.C.S.: 531120
Kevin Cher Chuan Law (Exec Dir)

Subsidiary (Non-US):

Kian Ann Engineering Trading (Shanghai) Co., Ltd. (2)
No 262 Lihang Road Jingqiao Export Processing Zone, Pudong, Shanghai, 201201, China
Tel.: (86) 21 5838 6818
Web Site: http://www.kianann.com.cn
Sales Range: $25-49.9 Million
Emp.: 20
Diesel Engine Components Distr
N.A.I.C.S.: 423120

Subsidiary (Domestic):

Kian Ann Investment Pte. Ltd. (2)
Kian Ann Building 7 Changi South Lane, Singapore, 486119, Singapore
Tel.: (65) 6587 1378
Investment Management Service
N.A.I.C.S.: 523999
Loy Soo Chew (Dir)

Kian Chue Hwa (Industries) Pte Ltd (2)
Kian Ann Building 7 Changi South Lane 02-01, Singapore, 486119, Singapore
Tel.: (65) 6846 9989
Web Site: http://www.kch-ind.com
Sales Range: $25-49.9 Million
Emp.: 21
Commercial & Industrial Vehicle Spare Parts Distr
N.A.I.C.S.: 423120

Subsidiary (Non-US):

PT Haneagle Heavyparts Indonesia (2)
Jl Raya Sentul Babakan Madang Km 2 5, Kabupaten Bogor, Bogor, 16810, Jawa Barat, Indonesia
Tel.: (62) 21 8795 1384
Sales Range: $25-49.9 Million
Emp.: 100
Heavy Machinery & Diesel Engine Parts Distr
N.A.I.C.S.: 423120

Subsidiary (Domestic):

Transmec Engineering Pte Ltd (2)
6 Loyang Walk, Singapore, 508789, Singapore
Tel.: (65) 654 54311
High Precision Mechanical Engineering Parts Mfr
N.A.I.C.S.: 332999

Screen Doctor Pty. Ltd. (1)
3 Hugo Street Krugersdorp North Rant en Daal, PO Box 2264, Krugersdorp, 1751, Gauteng, South Africa
Tel.: (27) 119536285
Web Site: https://www.screendoctor.co.za

AND PRIVATE COMPANIES

Construction Equipment Mfr & Distr
N.A.I.C.S.: 333120

INVICTA PUBLIC AFFAIRS LTD.
5 Coates Crescent, Edinburgh, G12AG, United Kingdom
Tel.: (44) 131 220 0159
Web Site: http://www.invictapa.co.uk
Emp.: 10
Public Affairs & Political Consulting Services
N.A.I.C.S.: 541820
Mark Cummings (Mng Dir)

INVICTUS ENERGY LTD.
Level 1 10 Outram Street, West Perth, 6005, WA, Australia
Tel.: (61) 861025055   AU
Web Site:
  https://www.invictusenergy.com
Year Founded: 2011
IVZ—(ASX)
Rev.: $121,913
Assets: $84,637,535
Liabilities: $2,207,551
Net Worth: $82,429,984
Earnings: ($3,551,312)
Fiscal Year-end: 06/30/24
Investment Services
N.A.I.C.S.: 523999
Joe Mtizwa (Deputy Chm)

INVICTUS MD STRATEGIES CORP.
16th Floor-595 Burrard Street, Vancouver, V7X 1L4, BC, Canada
Tel.: (604) 688-9588   BC
Web Site: http://www.invictus-md.com
Year Founded: 2014
GENE—(OTCIQ)
Rev.: $3,439,662
Assets: $112,809,322
Liabilities: $26,926,075
Net Worth: $85,883,247
Earnings: ($26,157,383)
Emp.: 85
Fiscal Year-end: 01/31/19
Medical Marijuana Advisory Services
N.A.I.C.S.: 561499
Elena Gershtein (CFO-Acting & Controller)

INVIGOR GROUP LIMITED
Level 16 56 Pitt Street, Sydney, 2000, NSW, Australia
Tel.: (61) 2 8251 9600   AU
Web Site:
  http://www.invigorgroup.com
Rev.: $2,419,780
Assets: $5,045,604
Liabilities: $6,864,834
Net Worth: ($1,819,230)
Earnings: ($8,673,515)
Emp.: 144
Fiscal Year-end: 12/31/18
Support Services for Online Marketing, Electronic Commerce & Other Digital Channel Based Activities
N.A.I.C.S.: 541511
Gary Cohen (Chm & CEO)

INVINCIBLE INVESTMENT CORPORATION
41F Roppongi Hills Mori Tower 101 Roppongi 6chome, Minato-ku, Tokyo, Japan
Tel.: (81) 354112731
Web Site: https://www.invincible-inv.co.jp
Year Founded: 2002
8963—(TKS)
Sales Range: $25-49.9 Million
Investment Management Service
N.A.I.C.S.: 523999

Naoki Fukuda (Exec Officer)

INVINITY ENERGY SYSTEMS PLC
3rd floor Standard Bank House 47-49 La Motte Street, Saint Helier, JE2 4SZ, Jersey
Tel.: (44) 2070616233
Web Site: http://www.invinity.com
IES—(AQSE)
Rev.: $3,541,230
Assets: $63,946,905
Liabilities: $23,222,760
Net Worth: $40,724,145
Earnings: ($22,331,430)
Emp.: 79
Fiscal Year-end: 12/31/22
Renewable & Clean Energy Services
N.A.I.C.S.: 541620
Neil O'Brien (Chm)

Subsidiaries:

Camco Advisory Services (Tanzania) Limited   (1)
Opp Mission Mikocheni Hospital Plot No 284A Mikocheni, Dar es Salaam, Tanzania
Tel.: (255) 22 277 3201
Environmental Consulting Services
N.A.I.C.S.: 541620

Camco International Carbon Assets Information Consulting (Beijing) Co. Limited   (1)
Fl 14 Lucky Tower A No 3 N Rd E 3rd Ring Rd, Chaoyang District, Beijing, China
Tel.: (86) 1084481623
Sales Range: $10-24.9 Million
Emp.: 30
Business Service Providers
N.A.I.C.S.: 561439

Camco Services (UK) Limited   (1)
Unit 4 13 27-31 Clerkenwell Close, London, EC1R 0AT, United Kingdom
Tel.: (44) 2071216100
Web Site:
  http://www.camcocleanenergy.com
Sales Range: $25-49.9 Million
Emp.: 10
Environmental Engineering Services
N.A.I.C.S.: 541330

Camco Ventures (China) Limited   (1)
14th Floor Lucky Tower A No 3 North Road East 3rd Ring Road, Chaoyang District, Beijing, 100027, China
Tel.: (86) 1084481623
Sales Range: $25-49.9 Million
Emp.: 50
Environmental Engineering Services
N.A.I.C.S.: 541330

Camco Ventures Limited   (1)
Suite 4 12 31 Clerkenwell Close, London, EC1R 0AT, United Kingdom
Tel.: (44) 2071216100
Sales Range: $25-49.9 Million
Emp.: 30
Gas Emission Reduction Services
N.A.I.C.S.: 541380
Scott McGregor (CEO)

Carbon Asset Management International GmbH   (1)
Burggasse 116, PO Box 1070, Vienna, Austria
Tel.: (43) 152520200
Sales Range: $50-74.9 Million
Emp.: 5
Asset Management & Investment Services
N.A.I.C.S.: 533110

EPES Limited   (1)
Overmoor Farm, Neston, Corsham, SN139TZ, United Kingdom
Tel.: (44) 1225812102
Environmental Consulting Services
N.A.I.C.S.: 541620

ESD Bulgaria Limited   (1)
38 Dondukov Blv Fl 2, Sofia, 1000, Bulgaria
Tel.: (359) 29817041
Web Site: http://www.esdb.bg
Sales Range: $25-49.9 Million
Emp.: 9
Environmental Consulting Services

N.A.I.C.S.: 541620

ESD Partners Limited   (1)
Overmoor Farm, Corsham, SN13 9TZ, United Kingdom
Tel.: (44) 1225812102
Sales Range: $25-49.9 Million
Emp.: 20
Management Consulting Services
N.A.I.C.S.: 541618

INVION LIMITED
722 High Street East Kew, Melbourne, 3102, VIC, Australia
Tel.: (61) 396927222
Web Site:
  https://www.inviongroup.com
Year Founded: 2000
7C8—(DEU)
Rev.: $2,522,116
Assets: $15,355,328
Liabilities: $354,295
Net Worth: $15,001,033
Earnings: ($1,717,322)
Emp.: 4
Fiscal Year-end: 06/30/22
Biopharmaceutical Mfr, Developer & Researcher
N.A.I.C.S.: 325412
Melanie Farris (Sec)

INVISIO A/S
Stamholmen 157, 2650, Hvidovre, 2650, Denmark
Tel.: (45) 72405500
Web Site: https://www.invisio.com
Year Founded: 1999
Rev.: $39,445,215
Assets: $39,578,739
Liabilities: $7,087,899
Net Worth: $32,490,840
Earnings: $5,363,214
Emp.: 85
Fiscal Year-end: 12/31/18
Telecommunication Product Mfr & Distr
N.A.I.C.S.: 334220
Lars Hojgard Hansen (CEO)

Subsidiaries:

Racal Acoustics Ltd.   (1)
Unit 3/4 Waverley Industrial Park Hailsham Drive, Harrow, HA1 4TR, United Kingdom
Tel.: (44) 2085156200
Web Site: http://www.racalacoustics.com
Sales Range: $25-49.9 Million
Emp.: 55
Audio Ancillary & Field Communication Equipment Mfr
N.A.I.C.S.: 334511
James Ewing (Sr VP)

Subsidiary (US):

Racal Acoustics Inc.   (2)
47 Constitution Dr Ste 400, Bedford, NH 03110
Tel.: (603) 488-2800
Web Site: http://www.esterline.com
Sales Range: $10-24.9 Million
Emp.: 5
High-Precision Temperature Sensors Product Mfr
N.A.I.C.S.: 334513

INVISION AG
Speditionstrasse 5, 40221, Dusseldorf, Germany
Tel.: (49) 2117817810
Web Site: http://www.invision.de
IVX—(DEU)
Rev.: $15,569,667
Assets: $20,416,367
Liabilities: $11,820,667
Net Worth: $8,595,700
Earnings: ($4,293,430)
Emp.: 81
Fiscal Year-end: 12/31/22
Workforce Management Software
N.A.I.C.S.: 541511

Matthias Schroer (Deputy Chm-Supervisory Bd)

Subsidiaries:

InVision Software Inc.   (1)
110 Lk Ave S Ste 35, Nesconset, NY 11767-1071
Tel.: (631) 360-3400
Web Site: https://www.invisionsoft.com
Sales Range: $25-49.9 Million
Emp.: 10
Software Development Services
N.A.I.C.S.: 541511

InVision Software Ltd.   (1)
Baskerville House Centenary Sq, Birmingham, B1 2ND, West Midlands, United Kingdom
Tel.: (44) 1215032620
Workforce Management Software Solutions
N.A.I.C.S.: 541511
Chris Dealy (Dir-Sls)

InVision Software SAS   (1)
Immeuble Elysees la Defense, 92977, Paris, France
Tel.: (33) 173294774
Web Site: http://www.invision.fr
Sales Range: $25-49.9 Million
Emp.: 5
Customized Software Solutions
N.A.I.C.S.: 541511

InVision Software, Inc.   (1)
330 N Wabash 23rd Fl, Chicago, IL 60611
Tel.: (312) 868-0262
Information Technology Services
N.A.I.C.S.: 541511

WFM Software AB   (1)
Teatergatan 3 2tr, 111 48, Stockholm, Sweden
Tel.: (46) 86780890
Sales Range: $25-49.9 Million
Emp.: 3
Software Development Services
N.A.I.C.S.: 541511

injixo AG   (1)
Gubelstrasse 12, 6300, Zug, Switzerland
Tel.: (41) 417103145
Information Technology Services
N.A.I.C.S.: 541511

INVISION AG
Grafenaustrasse 7, 6300, Zug, Switzerland
Tel.: (41) 41 729 01 01   CH
Web Site: http://www.invision.ch
Year Founded: 1997
Privater Equity Firm
N.A.I.C.S.: 523999
Frank Becker (Chm & Mng Partner)

Subsidiaries:

ABC Design GmbH   (1)
Dr Rudolf-Eberle Street 29, Albbruck, 79774, Germany
Tel.: (49) 775393930
Web Site: http://www.abc-design.de
Emp.: 40
Kids Products Distr
N.A.I.C.S.: 458110
Bernd Fischer (Mng Dir)

INVISTA S.A.
Stefana Okrzei Ul 1A Ixp, 03-715, Warsaw, Poland
Tel.: (48) 221275422
Web Site: https://www.ntcsa.com.pl
NTC—(WAR)
Assets: $6,298,526
Liabilities: $2,131,098
Net Worth: $4,167,429
Earnings: $1,624,238
Fiscal Year-end: 12/31/23
Financial Services
N.A.I.C.S.: 523999
Tomasz Szczerbatko (Chm-Supervisory Bd)

INVITA AG
Reichsstrasse 78, 58840, Plettenberg, Germany

INVITA AG

Invita AG—(Continued)
Tel.: (49) 2391 601 55 0
Web Site: http://www.invita-ag.de
Year Founded: 2007
Investment & Holding Company
N.A.I.C.S.: 551112
Otto Prange (Chm-Supervisory Bd)

INVITEL LEGACY S.A.
Av Rio Branco 311 - Sala 523/parte, 20040903, Rio de Janeiro, Brazil
Tel.: (55) 2121967200
Financial Management Services
N.A.I.C.S.: 523999
Alberto Ribeiro Guth (Dir-IR)

INVITES BIOCORE CO., LTD.
33 Digital-ro 9-gil, Geumcheon-gu, Seoul, 08511, Korea (South)
Tel.: (82) 220276200
Web Site: https://www.bio-core.com
Year Founded: 2001
216400—(KRS)
Sales Range: $10-24.9 Million
Emp.: 70
Pharmaceuticals Mfr
N.A.I.C.S.: 325412
Hyung-Sik Choi (Pres)

INVITROCUE LIMITED
Level 2 350 Kent Street, Sydney, 2000, NSW, Australia
Tel.: (61) 2 9299 2289
Web Site: http://www.invitrocue.com
Year Founded: 2012
Rev.: $578,305
Assets: $1,043,160
Liabilities: $976,157
Net Worth: $67,004
Earnings: ($1,432,568)
Fiscal Year-end: 06/30/17
Bio-analytic Solutions & Digital Pathology
N.A.I.C.S.: 541714
Steven Boon Sing Fang (Founder)

Subsidiaries:

Invitrocue Pte Ltd. (1)
11 Biopolis Way Helios #12-07/08, Singapore, 138667, Singapore
Tel.: (65) 6460 0497
Biopharmaceutical Products Developer
N.A.I.C.S.: 325412

INVL BALTIC FARMLAND AB
Gyneju Street 14, 01109, Vilnius, Lithuania
Tel.: (370) 52790601
Web Site: https://www.invlbalticfarmland.com
Year Founded: 2014
INL1L—(VSE)
Financial Support Services
N.A.I.C.S.: 541611
Alvydas Banys (Chm)

INVL BALTIC REAL ESTATE AB
Gyneju Street 14, 01109, Vilnius, 01109, Lithuania
Tel.: (370) 52790601
Web Site: https://www.bre.invl.com
Year Founded: 1997
INR1L—(RSE)
Rev.: $4,008,169
Assets: $49,193,068
Liabilities: $23,234,353
Net Worth: $25,958,715
Earnings: $771,608
Emp.: 7
Fiscal Year-end: 12/31/23
Real Estate Development Services
N.A.I.C.S.: 531390
Darius Sulnis (Chm)

Subsidiaries:

SIA Dommo Grupa (1)
Lapegles Stunisi, Olaine Parish, Riga, LV-2127, Latvia
Tel.: (371) 25408238
Web Site: http://www.dommo.lv
Real Estate Development Services
N.A.I.C.S.: 531390

INVL TECHNOLOGY AB
Gyneju Street 14, Vilnius, 01109, Lithuania
Tel.: (370) 5 279 0601
Web Site: http://www.invltechnology.lt
Year Founded: 2015
INC1L—(RSE)
Rev.: $8,462,574
Assets: $43,484,609
Liabilities: $2,062,215
Net Worth: $41,422,394
Earnings: $5,855,020
Emp.: 121
Fiscal Year-end: 12/31/20
Information Technology Services
N.A.I.C.S.: 541512
Kazimieras Tonkunas (Mng Partner)

Subsidiaries:

Acena UAB (1)
Gyneju st 14, Vilnius, LT-01109, Lithuania
Tel.: (370) 52759647
Web Site: http://www.acena.lt
Information Technology Services
N.A.I.C.S.: 541511

BAIP UAB (1)
Gyneju st 14, Vilnius, LT-01109, Lithuania
Tel.: (370) 52190000
Web Site: http://www.baip.lt
Information Technology Services
N.A.I.C.S.: 541511
Vytautas Vaitkevicius (Dir-Bus Dev)

NRD CS UAB (1)
Gyneju st 14, Vilnius, LT-01109, Lithuania
Tel.: (370) 52191919
Web Site: https://www.nrdcs.lt
Information Technology Services
N.A.I.C.S.: 541511

NRD Systems UAB (1)
Gyneju g 14, LT-01109, Vilnius, Lithuania
Tel.: (370) 52310731
Web Site: http://www.nrd.lt
Information Technology Services
N.A.I.C.S.: 541511
Simonas Biskauskas (Project Mgr)

Norway Registers Development AS (1)
Lokketangen 20 B, 1337, Sandvika, Norway
Tel.: (47) 66971403
Web Site: http://www.nrdcompanies.com
Management Consulting Services
N.A.I.C.S.: 541611

Novian Systems, UAB (1)
Gyneju g 14, LT-01109, Vilnius, Lithuania
Tel.: (370) 52734181
Web Site: https://novian.lt
Information Technology Services
N.A.I.C.S.: 541511
Paulius Vaitkevicius (Head-Innovation)

Zissor AS (1)
Bragernes Torg 6, 3017, Drammen, Norway
Tel.: (47) 22838500
Web Site: https://www.zissor.com
Information Technology Services
N.A.I.C.S.: 541511
Tor Arve Vartdal (VP)

INVOCAS GROUP PLC
2nd Fl Capital House 2 Festival Sq, Lothian Road, Edinburgh, EH3 9SU, United Kingdom
Tel.: (44) 1312222460
Web Site: http://www.invocasgroup.com
Sales Range: $10-24.9 Million
Emp.: 100
Business Consulting & Other Related Services
N.A.I.C.S.: 541618

John M. Hall (Chm)

Subsidiaries:

Invocas Business Recovery and Insolvency Limited (1)
2nd Fl Capital House 2 Festival Sq, Edinburgh, EH3 9SU, Scotland, United Kingdom
Tel.: (44) 1312222460
Business Recovery & Insolvency Prevention Services
N.A.I.C.S.: 541611

Invocas Financial Solutions Limited (1)
2nd Fl Capital House Festival Sq Lothian Rd, Edinburgh, Scotland, United Kingdom
Tel.: (44) 1312222460
Web Site: http://www.invocasfinancial.com
Sales Range: $10-24.9 Million
Emp.: 30
Debt Management Services
N.A.I.C.S.: 561440

INVOKE MEDIA
37 Dunlevy Ave, Vancouver, V6A 3A3, BC, Canada
Tel.: (604) 484-8902
Web Site: http://www.invokemedia.com
Advertising Agencies
N.A.I.C.S.: 541810
Kotone Frankowski (Strategist-Social Media Mktg)

Subsidiaries:

Invoke Media (1)
36 E 20th St, New York, NY 10003
Tel.: (646) 775-4169
Advertising Agencies
N.A.I.C.S.: 541810

INVOLVE! ADVERTISING AS
Hoffsveien 1A, 0275, Oslo, Norway
Tel.: (47) 23253600
Web Site: http://www.involve.no
Year Founded: 1992
Sales Range: $25-49.9 Million
Emp.: 14
Advertising Agency Services
N.A.I.C.S.: 541810

INVOLYS
88-90 rue Larbi Doghmi, 20270, Casablanca, Morocco
Tel.: (212) 529310000
Web Site: https://www.involys.com
INV—(CAS)
Sales Range: $1-9.9 Million
Software & Computer Services
N.A.I.C.S.: 541519
Mohamed Bachir Rachdi (Chm & CEO)

INVOMO LTD.
130 City Road, London, EC1V 2NW, United Kingdom
Tel.: (44) 8448888500
Sales Range: $50-74.9 Million
Emp.: 40
Telecommunications Hosting Services
N.A.I.C.S.: 518210
Ravor Mockecc (CEO)

INVU SERVICES LTD.
Blisworth Hill Farm Stoke Road, Blisworth, Northampton, NN7 3DB, United Kingdom
Tel.: (44) 1604878010   UK
Web Site: http://www.invu.net
Year Founded: 1997
Sales Range: $1-9.9 Million
Emp.: 29
Software for Electronic Management of Information & Documents
N.A.I.C.S.: 334610
Ian Smith (Dir-Fin & Gen Mgr)

INZHSYSTEMS LTD.

INTERNATIONAL PUBLIC

Peiraios 24 1st Floor Office 103, Nicosia, Cyprus
Tel.: (357) 22277200
Investment Services
N.A.I.C.S.: 523999

INZI CONTROLS CO., LTD
171 Gunjacheon-ro Siheung-si Sihwa Industrial Complex 2 DA 504, Siheung, 429-849, Gyeonggi-do, Korea (South)
Tel.: (82) 314961726
Web Site: https://www.inzi.co.kr
Year Founded: 1978
023800—(KRS)
Rev.: $437,205,992
Assets: $465,500,331
Liabilities: $307,328,366
Net Worth: $158,171,965
Earnings: $10,668,231
Emp.: 550
Fiscal Year-end: 12/31/22
Automobile Parts Mfr
N.A.I.C.S.: 336390
Goo Yong Jung (Chm & CEO)

Subsidiaries:

INZI Display Co., Ltd. (1)
88 Dongsan-ro, Danwon, Ansan, Gyeonggi-do, Korea (South)
Tel.: (82) 314919771
Web Site: https://www.inzidisplay.co.kr
Television Display & Equipment Mfr
N.A.I.C.S.: 334419

Subsidiary (Domestic):

INZI AMT Co., Ltd (2)
28-156 Bugok industrial complex Songak-ub, Dangjin, Chungnam, Korea (South)
Tel.: (82) 41 359 5000
Web Site: http://www.inziamt.co.kr
Automobile Parts Mfr
N.A.I.C.S.: 336390
Choi Sean-Ho (Pres & CEO)

Plant (Domestic):

INZI Display Co., Ltd. - Anseong Plant (2)
553-1 Banjeri Wongokmyun, Anseong, Anseong, Korea (South)
Tel.: (82) 31 657 8571
Electric Equipment Mfr
N.A.I.C.S.: 334419

INZI Display Co., Ltd. - Yesan Plant (2)
276-1 Gwanjakri, Yesaneup, Yesan, Chungnam, Korea (South)
Tel.: (82) 41 330 3001
Electric Equipment Mfr
N.A.I.C.S.: 334419

Inzi Mobile Solution Co., Ltd. (1)
Rexmall 202-155 Byeongjeomjungang-ro, Hwaseong, 445390, Korea (South)
Tel.: (82) 31 225 6371
Web Site: http://www.inziht.cn
Electronic Equipment & Component Mfr
N.A.I.C.S.: 334419
Ja il You (CEO)

KOHMECA CO., LTD (1)
1236-3 Chongwang-Dong, Siheung, Korea (South)
Tel.: (82) 31 433 6633
Automobile Spare Parts Mfr
N.A.I.C.S.: 336390

Rf Controls Co., Ltd. (1)
Rm 3ba-404 Shihwa Industrial Complex, Siheung, 429450, Korea (South)
Tel.: (82) 313198411
Web Site: http://www.frcontrols.co.kr
Automobile Spare Parts Mfr
N.A.I.C.S.: 336390
Wonki Kim (Gen Mgr)

INZINC MINING LTD.
550 Burrard Street Suite 2300 Bentall 5, Vancouver, V6C 2B5, BC, Canada
Tel.: (604) 687-7211   Ca
Web Site: https://www.inzincmining.com

Year Founded: 1997
32L—(DEU)
Assets: $3,633,972
Liabilities: $58,010
Net Worth: $3,575,962
Earnings: $2,558,976
Fiscal Year-end: 12/31/21
Metal Mining Services
N.A.I.C.S.: 212290
Steve E. Vanry (CFO)

INZISOFT CO., LTD.
16F 131 Teheran-ro, Gangnam-gu, Seoul, 137-070, Seocho-gu, Korea (South)
Tel.: (82) 25719571
Web Site:
   http://www.mobileleader.com
Year Founded: 2000
100030—(KRS)
Rev.: $18,070,718
Assets: $46,775,088
Liabilities: $8,369,122
Net Worth: $38,405,966
Earnings: $3,304,737
Emp.: 152
Fiscal Year-end: 12/31/22
Software Development Services
N.A.I.C.S.: 541511

INZONE GROUP CO., LTD.
Block C Ginza Building No 66 Luoyuan Street, Lixia District, Jinan, 250063, Shandong, China
Tel.: (86) 53186960688
Web Site:
   http://www.yinzuogroup.com
Year Founded: 1993
600858—(SHG)
Rev.: $755,277,490
Assets: $1,581,621,247
Liabilities: $1,248,540,205
Net Worth: $333,081,043
Earnings: ($2,036,109)
Fiscal Year-end: 12/31/22
Departmental Store Operator
N.A.I.C.S.: 455110
Ma Yunpeng (Chm)

IO BIOTECH, INC.
IO Biotech ApS Ole Maaloes Vej 3, 2200, Copenhagen, Denmark
Tel.: (45) 70702980   DE
Web Site: https://www.iobiotech.com
Year Founded: 2021
IOBT—(NASDAQ)
Rev.: $1,239,000
Assets: $151,805,000
Liabilities: $12,951,000
Net Worth: $138,854,000
Earnings: ($71,458,000)
Emp.: 57
Fiscal Year-end: 12/31/22
Biotechnology Research & Development Services
N.A.I.C.S.: 541714
Amy B. Sullivan (CFO)

IOCHPE-MAXION S.A.
Rua Luigi Galvani 146-13 andar, Sao Paulo, 04575-020, Brazil
Tel.: (55) 1155083800   BR
Web Site: https://www.iochpe.com.br
Year Founded: 1918
MYPK3—(BRAZ)
Rev.: $2,673,391,538
Assets: $2,598,115,088
Liabilities: $1,867,876,284
Net Worth: $730,238,804
Earnings: $18,929,050
Emp.: 17,000
Fiscal Year-end: 12/31/23
Railway & Automotive Wheels & Frames Mfr
N.A.I.C.S.: 336390
Nildemar Secches (Vice Chm)

Subsidiaries:

Iochpe-Maxion   (1)
39500 Orchard Hill Pl Ste 500, Novi, MI 48375
Tel.: (734) 737-5000
Web Site: http://www.hayes-lemmerz.com
Sales Range: $1-4.9 Billion
Emp.: 6,400
Supplier of Automotive & Commercial Highway Wheels, Brakes, Suspension & Other Components
N.A.I.C.S.: 336390
Fred Bentley Jr. (CEO-Global Wheel Grp)

Maxion (Nantong) Wheels Co., Ltd.   (1)
No 89 South Tongsheng Rd ETD Zone, Nantong, Jiangsu, China
Tel.: (86) 51385159496
Emp.: 170
Automotive Wheel Mfr
N.A.I.C.S.: 336390

Maxion Componentes Automotivos S.A.   (1)
Rua Haeckel Ben Hur Salvador 100, CEP 32341-000, Contagem, MG, Brazil
Tel.: (55) 3133995000
Web Site: http://www.maxion.ind.br
Sales Range: $200-249.9 Million
Emp.: 1,000
Automobile Parts Mfr
N.A.I.C.S.: 336340

Maxion Componentes Estruturais Ltda.   (1)
Rua Dr Othon Barcellos 83 Centro, 12700-000, Cruzeiro, SP, Brazil   (100%)
Tel.: (55) 231841000
Web Site: http://www.maxioncr.com.br
Sales Range: $800-899.9 Million
Emp.: 3,000
Wheels & Chassis
N.A.I.C.S.: 336340

Maxion Inci Jant Sanayi, A.S.   (1)
Organize Sanayi Bolgesi Mustafa Kemal Bulvari No 2, Manisa, Turkiye
Tel.: (90) 2362261600
Automotive Wheel Mfr
N.A.I.C.S.: 336390

Maxion Jantas Jant Sanayi ve Ticaret A.S.   (1)
Organize Sanayi Bolgesi 2 Kisim Kecilikoyosb Mah Gaziler Cad No 8, Manisa, Turkiye
Tel.: (90) 2362262000
Automotive Wheel Mfr
N.A.I.C.S.: 336390

Maxion Wheels (Thailand) Co. Ltd.   (1)
42 Moo 5 Nongplakradi Rd, Nongplamoh Nongkhae, Saraburi, 18140, Thailand
Tel.: (66) 261501878
Emp.: 500
Automotive Wheel Mfr
N.A.I.C.S.: 336390

Maxion Wheels Akron LLC   (1)
428 Seiberling St, Akron, OH 44306
Tel.: (330) 794-2300
Emp.: 100
Automotive Wheel Mfr
N.A.I.C.S.: 336390

Maxion Wheels Aluminum India Pvt. Ltd.   (1)
Plot No IP-45, Khed City Industrial Park Village Kanhersar Taluka Rajguru Nagar, Pune, 410505, Maharashtra, India
Tel.: (91) 2135305100
Emp.: 540
Automotive Wheel Mfr
N.A.I.C.S.: 336390

Maxion Wheels Czech s.r.o.   (1)
Vratimovska 707, Kuncice, 719 00, Ostrava, Czech Republic
Tel.: (420) 597440111
Web Site: https://www.maxionwheels.com
Emp.: 1,000
Automotive Wheel Mfr
N.A.I.C.S.: 336390

Maxion Wheels Espana S.L.   (1)
Calle de La Lemmerz 41, Poligono Industrial Pont Nou Manresa, 08241, Barcelona, Spain
Tel.: (34) 938753700
Emp.: 230
Automotive Wheel Mfr
N.A.I.C.S.: 336390

Maxion Wheels Italia S.r.l.   (1)
Via Roma 200, Dello, 25020, Brescia, Italy
Tel.: (39) 03099781
Emp.: 355
Automotive Wheel Mfr
N.A.I.C.S.: 336390

Maxion Wheels Japan K.K.   (1)
Yokohama AIOI-cho Bldg 5th Floor 6-104 Aioi cho, Naka-ku, Yokohama, 231-0012, Kanagawa prefecture, Japan
Tel.: (81) 456805807
Emp.: 5
Automotive Wheel Mfr
N.A.I.C.S.: 336390

Maxion Wheels Sedalia LLC   (1)
3610 W Main St, Sedalia, MO 65301
Tel.: (660) 827-3640
Emp.: 300
Automotive Wheel Mfr
N.A.I.C.S.: 336390

Maxion Wheels South Africa (Pty) Ltd.   (1)
3 Botha Avenue Alrode, Alberton, South Africa
Tel.: (27) 119083060
Emp.: 320
Automotive Wheel Mfr
N.A.I.C.S.: 336390

Maxion Wheels Werke GmbH   (1)
Ladestrasse, 53639, Konigswinter, Germany
Tel.: (49) 2223710
Emp.: 540
Automotive Wheel Mfr
N.A.I.C.S.: 336390

Maxion Wheels de Mexico, S. de R.L.de C.V.   (1)
Av Industrial Uno 5701 Robinson, 31074, Chihuahua, Mexico
Tel.: (52) 6144290401
Emp.: 520
Automotive Wheel Mfr
N.A.I.C.S.: 336390

Maxion WheelsHolding GmbH   (1)
Ladestrasse, Konigswinter, Germany
Tel.: (49) 2223710
Web Site: https://www.maxionwheels.com
Emp.: 540
Automobile Parts Mfr & Distr
N.A.I.C.S.: 336390

IOFINA PLC
48 Chancery Lane, London, WC2A 1JF, United Kingdom
Tel.: (44) 2030063135   UK
Web Site: https://www.iofina.com
Year Founded: 2005
IOF—(AIM)
Rev.: $42,200,000
Assets: $52,710,000
Liabilities: $14,740,000
Net Worth: $37,970,000
Earnings: $7,870,000
Fiscal Year-end: 12/31/22
Iodine & Natural Gas Exploration & Production
N.A.I.C.S.: 325998
Thomas M. Becker (Pres & CEO)

Subsidiaries:

Iofina Chemical Inc   (1)
1025 Mary Laidley Dr, Covington, KY 41017
Tel.: (859) 356-8000
Web Site: http://www.iofina.com
Emp.: 35
Natural Gas Mfr
N.A.I.C.S.: 211130
Kurt Jones (COO)

Iofina Inc.   (1)
8480 E Orchard Rd Ste 4900, Greenwood Village, CO 80111
Tel.: (303) 222-1215
Web Site: http://www.iofina.com
Sales Range: $50-74.9 Million
Emp.: 8
Crude Petroleum Mfr
N.A.I.C.S.: 211120

Iofina Natural Gas Inc   (1)
8480 E Orchard Rd Ste 4900, Greenwood Village, CO 80111
Tel.: (303) 222-1215
Web Site: http://www.iofina.com
Emp.: 5
Crude Petroleum Mfr
N.A.I.C.S.: 211120
Tom Becker (Pres)

Iofina Resources, Inc.   (1)
8480 E Orchard Rd Ste 4900, Greenwood Village, CO 80111
Tel.: (303) 222-1215
Iodine Chemical Mfr
N.A.I.C.S.: 325180

IOG PLC
6th Floor 60 Gracechurch Street, London, EC3V 0HR, United Kingdom
Tel.: (44) 2070361400
Web Site: http://www.iog.co.uk
Year Founded: 2011
IOG—(AIM)
Rev.: $95,185,559
Assets: $260,665,236
Liabilities: $257,394,597
Net Worth: $3,270,639
Earnings: ($35,911,386)
Emp.: 56
Fiscal Year-end: 12/31/22
Oil & Gas Exploration
N.A.I.C.S.: 211120
Andrew Hockey (CEO)

IOI CORPORATION BERHAD
IOI City Tower 2 Lebuh IRC IOI Resort City, 62502, Putrajaya, Malaysia
Tel.: (60) 389478888   MY
Web Site: https://www.ioigroup.com
Year Founded: 1969
IOICORP—(KLS)
Rev.: $3,855,728,250
Assets: $4,744,030,500
Liabilities: $1,951,116,750
Net Worth: $2,792,913,750
Earnings: $437,802,750
Emp.: 24,247
Fiscal Year-end: 06/30/22
Holding Company; Palm Oil Producer
N.A.I.C.S.: 551112
Kean Hua Tan (Exec Dir-Oleochemical)

Subsidiaries:

Acidchem (USA) Inc   (1)
201 W Passaic St Ste 100, Rochelle Park, NJ 07662-3128
Tel.: (604) 376-8888
Web Site: http://www.ioioleo.com
Emp.: 4
Chemical Product Whslr
N.A.I.C.S.: 424690

Commercial Wings Sdn Bhd   (1)
Lot S37 2nd Fl IOI Mall Batu 9, Jalan Puchong Bandar, Puchong, 47100, Selangor, Malaysia
Tel.: (60) 358828888
Property Management Services
N.A.I.C.S.: 531312

Derichem (M) Sdn Bhd   (1)
2411 Lorong Perusahaan 1, Prai Industrial Park, Prai, 13600, Penang, Malaysia
Tel.: (60) 43907818
Soap & Detergents Mfr & Whslr
N.A.I.C.S.: 325611

Flora Development Sdn Bhd   (1)
Lot 5465 Persiaran Lebuh Puteri, Bandar Puteri Puchong, 47100, Puchong, Selangor Darul Ehsan, Malaysia
Tel.: (60) 380648899
Web Site: http://www.ioiproperties.co.my
Property Development Services
N.A.I.C.S.: 531312

Gamore Corporation Sdn Bhd   (1)

IOI CORPORATION BERHAD

IOI Corporation Berhad—(Continued)
Level 8 Two Ioi Square Ioi Resort, Putrajaya, 62502, Selangor, Malaysia
Tel.: (60) 389478888
Emp.: 400
Oil Palm Cultivation Services
N.A.I.C.S.: 115112
Ting Hiang How (Mgr-HR)

IOI Bio-Energy Sdn Bhd (1)
Km12 Sg Mowtas Jalan Jaya Chip Batu Sapi, Sandakan, Sabah, Malaysia
Tel.: (60) 89616733
Sales Range: $25-49.9 Million
Emp.: 60
Biomass Mfr
N.A.I.C.S.: 339999
NB Sudhakaran (Gen Mgr)

IOI Commodity Trading Sdn Bhd (1)
Bangunan Ioi No 8 Jalan Kenari 5 Bandar Puchong Jaya Off Jalan Puchong, Puchong, 62502, Selangor, Malaysia
Tel.: (60) 389478668
Palm Oil Refining Services
N.A.I.C.S.: 324110

IOI Edible Oils Sdn Bhd (1)
12Km Sg Mowtas Jalan Jaya Chip Off Jalan Batu Sapi, 90738, Sandakan, Sabah, Malaysia
Tel.: (60) 89616733
Sales Range: $75-99.9 Million
Emp.: 342
Palm Oil Cultivation Services
N.A.I.C.S.: 115112

IOI Landscape Services Sdn Bhd (1)
2-2-1 Level 2 Tower 2 @ PFCC Jalan Puteri 1/2 Bandar Puteri, Bandar Putri Puchong, Puchong, 47100, Selangor, Malaysia
Tel.: (60) 380648999
Landscape Services
N.A.I.C.S.: 561730
Jinaik Gos (Mgr)

IOI Loders Croklaan Oils Sdn Bhd (1)
Plot 8 and 9 Jalan Timah Pasir Gudang Industrial Estate, Pasir Gudang, Johor Bahru, 81700, Johor, Malaysia
Tel.: (60) 73818888
Web Site: http://asia.croklaan.com
Sales Range: $125-149.9 Million
Emp.: 360
Palm Oil Refining Services
N.A.I.C.S.: 324110

IOI Loders Croklaan Procurement Company Sdn Bhd (1)
Level 9 Two IOI Square, Putrajaya, 62502, Malaysia
Tel.: (60) 389478888
Sales Range: $150-199.9 Million
Emp.: 300
Property Development Services
N.A.I.C.S.: 531312

IOI Oleochemical Industries Berhad (1)
2411 Lorong Perusahaan Satu, Prai Industrial Complex, Prai, Penang, 13600, Malaysia (65%)
Tel.: (60) 43768888
Web Site: http://www.ioioleo.com
Chemicals Mfr
N.A.I.C.S.: 325998
Lee Shin Cheng (Chm)

Subsidiary (Domestic):

Palmex Industries Sdn Berhad (2)
302-H-1 Jalan Dato Ismail Hashim, Desaria Sg Ara, 11900, Penang, Malaysia
Tel.: (60) 46469022
Web Site: http://www.talmex-property.com
Sales Range: $25-49.9 Million
Emp.: 13
Civil Engineering Services
N.A.I.C.S.: 541330
Hooi Eow Ang (Gen Mgr)

Pamol Plantations Sdn Bhd (2)
8 1/2 Miles Jalan Mersing, Keluang, 86000, Johor, Malaysia
Tel.: (60) 77875100
Oil Plam Cultivation & Processing Services

N.A.I.C.S.: 115112
Stabilchem (M) Sdn Bhd (2)
2411 Lorong Perusahaan 1 Prai Industrial Park, Perai, 13600, Penang, Malaysia
Tel.: (60) 43907818
Chemical Products Mfr
N.A.I.C.S.: 325199
Lei-Choon Wah (COO)

IOI Speciality Fats Sdn Bhd (1)
Level 29 IOI City Tower 2, Lebuh IRC IOI Resort City, Putrajaya, 62502, Malaysia
Tel.: (60) 389478888
Palm Oil Refining Services
N.A.I.C.S.: 324110

IOI Ventures (L) Berhad (1)
Ioi Resort, Putrajaya, 62502, Malaysia
Tel.: (60) 389478888
Investment Management Service
N.A.I.C.S.: 523999

Maxgrand Sdn Bhd (1)
Level 8 Two Ioi Square Ioi Resort, Putrajaya, 62502, Malaysia
Tel.: (60) 389478888
Oil Palm Cultivation Services
N.A.I.C.S.: 115112

Morisem (Sabah) Sdn Bhd (1)
Level 8 Two Ioi Sq Ioi Resort, Putrajaya, 91109, Selangor, Malaysia
Tel.: (60) 389478888
Palm Oil Refining Services
N.A.I.C.S.: 311225

Nice Skyline Sdn Bhd (1)
No 1 2 Jalan Putra 1/5 Bandar IOI, Segamat, 85000, Johor, Malaysia
Tel.: (60) 79434000
Web Site: http://www.ioijohor.com
Sales Range: $50-74.9 Million
Emp.: 14
Real Estate Property Management Services
N.A.I.C.S.: 531390
Lim Beng Yeang (Gen Mgr)

Paksi Teguh Sdn Bhd (1)
No 23 Jalan Tawas Baru 2, Taman Tasik Damai, Perak, 30010, Malaysia
Tel.: (60) 55281667
Emp.: 10
Property Development Services
N.A.I.C.S.: 531312
Mohamed Izamin (Gen Mgr)

Pan-Century Edible Oils Sdn Bhd (1)
Lot 240 Jalan Timah 3, Pasir Gudang Industrial Estate Pasir Gudang, 81700, Johor Bahru, Johor, Malaysia
Tel.: (60) 72511580
Web Site: http://www.pancentury.com
Chemicals Mfr & Palm Oil Refining Services
N.A.I.C.S.: 324110

Pan-Century Oleochemicals Sdn Bhd (1)
Lot 231 Jalan Pekeliling, Pasir Gudang, Johor Bahru, 81700, Malaysia
Tel.: (60) 72512298
Sales Range: $50-74.9 Million
Emp.: 157
Palm Oil Refining Services
N.A.I.C.S.: 324110

Pine Properties Sdn Bhd (1)
Lebuh IRC IOI Resort City, 62502, Putrajaya, Malaysia
Tel.: (60) 389478899
Property Development Services
N.A.I.C.S.: 531312
Seh Hwan Lim (Sr Mgr-Mktg)

Property Village Berhad (1)
Jalan Putra 4 Bandar Putra, 81000, Kulai, Johor, Malaysia
Tel.: (60) 75995222
Sales Range: $25-49.9 Million
Emp.: 50
Property Development Services
N.A.I.C.S.: 531311

Subsidiary (Domestic):

Baycrest Sdn Bhd (2)
No 1 Lebuh Putra Utama Bandar Putra Kulai, Johor, 62502, Malaysia
Tel.: (60) 76632101
Web Site: http://www.ioicorp.com

Property Development Services
N.A.I.C.S.: 531311
Simon Heng Kwanghock (Gen Mgr)

Resort Villa Development Sdn Bhd (1)
Palm Garden Hotel Ioi Resort, Ioi Resort, Putrajaya, 62502, Malaysia
Tel.: (60) 389432233
Emp.: 100
Property Development Services
N.A.I.C.S.: 531311
Simon Yong (Gen Mgr)

Resort Villa Golf Course Development Sdn Bhd (1)
Ioi Resort City, Putrajaya, 62502, Malaysia
Tel.: (60) 389432233
Sales Range: $75-99.9 Million
Emp.: 180
Golf Course Operation Services
N.A.I.C.S.: 713910
Simon Yong (Gen Mgr)

Subsidiary (Domestic):

ELK-Desa Capital Sdn. Bhd. (2)
No 15 - 17 Jalan Brunei Utara Off Jalan Pudu, 55100, Kuala Lumpur, Federal Territory, Malaysia
Tel.: (60) 330008666
Web Site: https://engage.elk-desa.com.my
Emp.: 204
Automobile Finance & Leasing Services
N.A.I.C.S.: 532120

Very Good Estate Sdn Bhd (1)
Levwl 8 Two Ioi Square Ioi Resort, Putrajaya, Malaysia
Tel.: (60) 389478888
Oil Palm Cultivation Services
N.A.I.C.S.: 115112

Wealthy Growth Sdn Bhd (1)
PTD153338 Jalan Kempas Lama, Taman Kempas Utama, 81300, Johor Bahru, Johor, Malaysia
Tel.: (60) 75582233
Web Site: http://www.kempasutama.com
Sales Range: $50-74.9 Million
Emp.: 10
Property Development Services
N.A.I.C.S.: 531311
Simon Heng (Gen Mgr)

IOI PROPERTIES GROUP BERHAD

Tel.: (60) 389478888
Web Site: https://www.ioiproperties.com.my
IOIPG—(KLS)
Rev.: $548,800,635
Assets: $9,020,960,635
Liabilities: $4,271,635,979
Net Worth: $4,749,324,656
Earnings: $296,372,275
Emp.: 2,647
Fiscal Year-end: 06/30/23
Commercial, Residential & Industrial Property Development & Investment Services
N.A.I.C.S.: 237210
Yeow Seng Lee (Vice Chm)

Subsidiaries:

IOI City Mall Sdn. Bhd. (1)
Unit T2-3A-3 and Unit T2-3A-3A Level 3A IOI City Tower Two Lebuh IRC, IOI Resort City Sepang, 62502, Putrajaya, Selangor, Malaysia
Tel.: (60) 383288900
Web Site: https://www.ioicitymall.com.my
Shopping Mall Services
N.A.I.C.S.: 531120
Sherry Choong (Mgr-Leasing)

IOI Properties (Singapore) Pte. Ltd. (1)
38 Beach Road 34 11 South Beach Tower, Singapore, 189767, Singapore
Tel.: (65) 63381101
Web Site: https://www.ioiproperties.com.sg
Real Estate Services
N.A.I.C.S.: 531210
Swee Ching Ng (Bus Mgr)

Resort Villa Golf Course Berhad (1)
IOI Resort City, 62502, Putrajaya, Malaysia
Tel.: (60) 382136310
Web Site: https://www.palmgarden.net.my
Golf Club Services
N.A.I.C.S.: 713910

IOL CHEMICALS & PHARMACEUTICALS LTD.

85 Industrial Area-A, Ludhiana, 141 003, Punjab, India
Tel.: (91) 1612225531
Web Site: https://www.iolcp.com
Year Founded: 1986
IOLCP—(NSE)
Rev.: $271,809,720
Assets: $219,777,285
Liabilities: $47,728,590
Net Worth: $172,048,695
Earnings: $60,682,440
Emp.: 2,069
Fiscal Year-end: 03/31/21
Industrial Chemicals & Bulk Drugs Supplier & Mfr
N.A.I.C.S.: 325998
Vijay Kumar Garg (Co-Mng Dir)

Subsidiaries:

IOL Chemicals & Pharmaceuticals Ltd - Manufacturing Plant (1)
Trident Complex Mansa Rd, Dhaula, Barnala, 148101, Punjab, India
Tel.: (91) 1679285285
Web Site: http://www.iolcp.com
Pharmaceuticals Mfr
N.A.I.C.S.: 325412

IOMART GROUP PLC

6 Atlantic Quay 55 Robertson Street, Glasgow, G2 8JD, United Kingdom
Tel.: (44) 1419316400
Web Site: https://www.iomart.com
Year Founded: 1998
IOM—(LSE)
Rev.: $139,869,599
Assets: $282,863,312
Liabilities: $121,442,623
Net Worth: $161,420,689
Earnings: $12,757,137
Emp.: 395
Fiscal Year-end: 03/31/22
Web Based Managed Hosting Services
N.A.I.C.S.: 513210
Ian Steele (Chm)

Subsidiaries:

Bytemark Limited (1)
2 Opus Avenue, York, YO26 6BL, United Kingdom
Tel.: (44) 190 489 0890
Web Site: https://www.bytemark.co.uk
Information Technology Services
N.A.I.C.S.: 541519

Cristie Data Limited (1)
Bodley Block 3rd Floor Ebley Mill Ebley Wharf, Stroud, GL5 4UB, United Kingdom
Tel.: (44) 145 331 0050
Web Site: https://www.cristie.co.uk
Information Technology Services
N.A.I.C.S.: 541519
Russ Sampson (Head-Sales)

Easyspace Limited (1)
Lister Pavilion Kelvin Campus, West of Scotland Science Park, Glasgow, G20 0SP, United Kingdom
Tel.: (44) 370 755 5088
Web Site: https://www.easyspace.com
Internet Publishing & Broadcasting Services
N.A.I.C.S.: 516120

Internetters Limited (1)
Lister Pavilion Kelvin Campus, W of Scotland Science Park, Glasgow, G20 0SP, United Kingdom
Tel.: (44) 1419316775
Web Site: http://www.internetters.co.uk
Web Hosting Services
N.A.I.C.S.: 518210

AND PRIVATE COMPANIES — ION INVESTMENT GROUP LTD.

Netintelligence Limited (1)
Lister Pavilion Kelvin Campus, Glasgow,
G20 0SP, United Kingdom
Tel.: (44) 3700500121
Web Site: http://www.netintelligence.com
Sales Range: $25-49.9 Million
Emp.: 140
Networking Services
N.A.I.C.S.: 561621
Angus MacSween (Owner)

SimpleServers Limited (1)
Unit 24 Ffordd Richard Davies, St Asaph
Business ParK, Saint Asaph, LL17 0LJ,
Denbighshire, United Kingdom
Tel.: (44) 203 886 0405
Web Site: https://www.simpleservers.co.uk
Data Processing Services
N.A.I.C.S.: 518210

Sonassi Limited (1)
3rd Floor 11-21 Paul Street, London, EC2A
4JU, United Kingdom
Tel.: (44) 330 043 1625
Web Site: https://www.sonassi.com
Data Management Services
N.A.I.C.S.: 518210

iomart Hosting Limited (1)
11-21 Paul St, London, EC2A 4JU, United
Kingdom
Tel.: (44) 2074484600
Web Site: http://www.iomarthosting.com
Sales Range: $25-49.9 Million
Emp.: 20
Networking Services
N.A.I.C.S.: 518210
Angus MacSween (CEO)

ION BEAM APPLICATIONS, S.A.
Chemin du Cyclotron 3, 1348,
Louvain-la-Neuve, Belgium
Tel.: (32) 10475811 BE
Web Site: https://www.iba-industrial.com
Year Founded: 1986
IOBCF—(OTCIQ)
Rev.: $473,249,807
Assets: $659,595,982
Liabilities: $542,351,253
Net Worth: $117,244,729
Earnings: ($10,056,298)
Emp.: 1,986
Fiscal Year-end: 12/31/23
Cancer Treatment & Diagnostic
Equipment Designer, Mfr & Marketer
N.A.I.C.S.: 334510
Pierre Mottet (Chm)

Subsidiaries:

IBA Dosimetry America Inc. (1)
470 Spring Park Pl Ste 700, Herndon, VA 20170
Tel.: (786) 288-0369
Web Site: http://www.ibadosimetry.com
Medical Diagnostic Mfr & Distr
N.A.I.C.S.: 334510

IBA Dosimetry Co. Ltd. (1)
No 6 Xing Guang Er Jie Beijing OPTO-
Mechatronics Industrial Park, Tongzhou,
Beijing, 101111, China
Tel.: (86) 1080809288
Radiation Therapy Services
N.A.I.C.S.: 541380

IBA Dosimetry Gmbh (1)
Bahnhofstrasse 5, 90592, Schwarzenbruck,
Germany
Tel.: (49) 9 128 6070
Web Site: https://www.iba-dosimetry.com
Emp.: 200
Medical Diagnostic Equipment Mfr & Distr
N.A.I.C.S.: 334510

IBA Dosimetry Ltd. (1)
Bahnhofstrasse 5, 90592, Schwarzenbruck,
Germany
Tel.: (49) 91286070
Web Site: https://www.iba-dosimetry.com
Diagnosis & Cancer Treatment Services
N.A.I.C.S.: 622310

IBA Industrial Inc. (1)
151 Heartland Blvd, Edgewood, NY 11717-8374
Tel.: (631) 254-6800
Web Site: http://www.iba-industrial.com
Electron Beam Accelerator Mfr
N.A.I.C.S.: 334517

IBA Japan KK (1)
Fukoku Seimei Building 17F 2-2-2, Uchisai-
waicho Chiyoda-ku, Tokyo, 100-0011, Japan
Tel.: (81) 362057531
Web Site: https://www.ibajapan.org
Financial Exchange Services
N.A.I.C.S.: 523999

IBA Proton Therapy (1)
3 chemin du Cyclotron, 1348, Louvain-la-
Neuve, Belgium
Tel.: (32) 10475811
Web Site: http://www.iba-protontherapy.com
Emp.: 500
Cancer Treatment Equipment Designer, Mfr
& Marketer
N.A.I.C.S.: 334510

IBA USA Inc. (1)
470 Spring Park Pl - Ste 700, Herndon, VA 20170
Tel.: (571) 449-4992
Cancer & Diagnosis Treatment Services
N.A.I.C.S.: 622310

Ion Beam Applications Co. Ltd. (1)
No 6 Xing Guang Er Jie Beijing Opto
Mechatronics Industrial Park, Tongzhou,
Beijing, 101111, China
Tel.: (86) 10 8080 9288
Medical Diagnostic Equipment Mfr & Distr
N.A.I.C.S.: 334510

Modus Medical Devices Inc. (1)
1570 North Routledge Park, London, N6H 5L6, ON, Canada
Tel.: (519) 438-2409
Web Site: https://modusqa.com
Advanced Radiotherapy Services
N.A.I.C.S.: 621340

Particle Engineering Solutions, LLC (1)
1st Magistralny tupik 5A, Moscow, 123290, Russia
Tel.: (7) 495 6486900
Medical Diagnostic Equipment Distr
N.A.I.C.S.: 423450

Radcal Corp. (1)
426 W Duarte Rd, Monrovia, CA 91016
Tel.: (626) 357-7921
Web Site: http://www.radcal.com
Sales Range: $1-9.9 Million
Emp.: 48
Measuring And Controlling Devices, Nec, N
N.A.I.C.S.: 334519
Melodie Eberhart (Mgr-Corp Accts)

ION EQUITY LIMITED
15 Pembroke St Lower, Dublin, 2, Ireland
Tel.: (353) 16110500 IE
Web Site: http://www.ionequity.com
Year Founded: 2000
Privater Equity Firm
N.A.I.C.S.: 523999
Neil O'Leary (Chm & CEO)

Subsidiaries:

Dealogic Limited (1)
One New Change 3F, London, EC4M 9AF, United Kingdom
Tel.: (44) 20 7440 6000
Web Site: http://www.dealogic.com
Holding Company; Software Developer
N.A.I.C.S.: 551112

Subsidiary (US):

Dealogic LLC (2)
120 BRdway 8/F, New York, NY 10271
Tel.: (212) 577-4400
Web Site: http://www.dealogic.com
Sales Range: $25-49.9 Million
Emp.: 130
Computer System Design Services
N.A.I.C.S.: 541511
Greg Young (Mng Dir)

Subsidiary (Domestic):

Dealogic Limited (2)
1 New Change, London, EC4M 9AF, United Kingdom
Tel.: (44) 2073795650
Web Site: http://www.dealogic.com
Sales Range: $75-99.9 Million
Emp.: 250
Transaction Management Software & Infor-
mation System Solutions
N.A.I.C.S.: 541511

USIT Ireland Ltd. (1)
19-21 Aston Quay, Dublin, Ireland
Tel.: (353) 16021906
Web Site: http://www.usit.ie
Travel Tour Operator
N.A.I.C.S.: 561510

ION EXCHANGE INDIA LTD
Ion House Dr E Moses Road Mahal-
axmi, Mumbai, 400011, India
Tel.: (91) 2262312000
Web Site: https://ionexchangeglobal.com
IONEXCHANG—(NSE)
Rev.: $220,933,918
Assets: $221,868,793
Liabilities: $132,483,965
Net Worth: $89,384,827
Earnings: $22,070,371
Emp.: 1,500
Fiscal Year-end: 03/31/22
Pollution Control Equipments
N.A.I.C.S.: 924110
Rajesh Sharma (Mng Dir & Chm)

Subsidiaries:

Ion Exchange & Company LLC Oman (1)
PO Box 69, Ruwi, 112, Oman
Tel.: (968) 24696354
Web Site: http://www.ionindia.com
Sales Range: $25-49.9 Million
Emp.: 40
Water Purification Services
N.A.I.C.S.: 488390

Ion Exchange Limited (UAE) (1)
WN - 18 Hamriyah Free Zone, PO Box
49247, Sharjah, United Arab Emirates
Tel.: (971) 65261606
Web Site: http://www.ionindia.com
Sales Range: $25-49.9 Million
Emp.: 25
Water Purification Services
N.A.I.C.S.: 488390

Ion Exchange South Africa (1)
PO Box 79597, St Andrews, Bedfordview, 2145, South Africa
Tel.: (27) 114533815
Sales Range: $25-49.9 Million
Emp.: 2
Water Purification Services
N.A.I.C.S.: 488390

PT. Ion Exchange Indonesia (1)
Jln Industri Selatan 4 Blok EE 2C Kawasan
Industri JABABEKA 2, Cikarang Jawa Ba-
rat, 17550, Jakarta, Indonesia
Tel.: (62) 2189329088
Sales Range: $25-49.9 Million
Emp.: 30
Water Purification Services
N.A.I.C.S.: 488390

ION INVESTMENT GROUP LTD.
Minerva House 4th Floor Simmons-
court Road, Dublin, 4, Ireland
Tel.: (353) 12200300 IE
Web Site: http://www.iongroup.com
Investment Holding Company
N.A.I.C.S.: 551112
Andrea Pignataro (Founder & CEO)

Subsidiaries:

Cerved Group S.p.A (1)
Via dell Unione Europea No 6A 6B, San
Donato, 20142, Milan, Italy
Tel.: (39) 0277541
Web Site: http://cerved.com
Rev.: $606,530,705
Assets: $1,853,969,324
Liabilities: $1,224,362,446
Net Worth: $629,606,878
Earnings: $36,150,788
Emp.: 2,600
Fiscal Year-end: 12/31/2020
Holding Company; Credit Information &
Other Financial Services
N.A.I.C.S.: 551112

Subsidiary (Domestic):

Cerved Group SpA (2)
Via dell Unione Europea 6/A-6/B, San Do-
nato Milanese, 20097, Milan, Italy
Tel.: (39) 02 77541
Web Site: http://www.cerved.com
Credit Management Services
N.A.I.C.S.: 561450
Gianandrea De Bernardis (Chm)

Subsidiary (Domestic):

Cerved Credit Management Group Srl (3)
Via San Vigilio n 1, 20142, Milan, Italy (80%)
Tel.: (39) 06 93370200
Credit Management Services
N.A.I.C.S.: 561450
Andrea Mignanelli (Founder & CEO)

Subsidiary (Domestic):

Cerved Credit Management Spa (4)
Via San Vigilio n 1, 20142, Milan, Italy (100%)
Tel.: (39) 06 93370200
Credit Management Services
N.A.I.C.S.: 561450
Andrea Mignanelli (Founder & CEO)

Subsidiary (Domestic):

Cerved Rating Agency S.p.A. (3)
Via San Vigilio n 1, 20142, Milan, Italy (100%)
Tel.: (39) 02 77541
Web Site: http://ratingagency.cerved.com
Credit Rating Assessment Services
N.A.I.C.S.: 561450
Mauro Alfonso (Mng Dir)

Dash Financial Technologies, LLC (1)
250 Park Ave S 9th Fl, New York, NY 10003
Tel.: (312) 986-2006
Web Site: http://www.dashfinancial.com
Financial Investment Services
N.A.I.C.S.: 523999
Peter Maragos (Founder & CEO)

Fidessa Group Holdings Ltd. (1)
C/O Ion 10 Queen Street Place, London,
EC4R 1BE, United Kingdom
Tel.: (44) 2073980200
Rev.: $477,481,900
Assets: $423,004,434
Liabilities: $198,045,420
Net Worth: $224,959,014
Earnings: $48,140,649
Emp.: 1,728
Fiscal Year-end: 12/31/2017
Trading Systems, Market Data & Connectiv-
ity Solutions to Financial Markets Partici-
pants
N.A.I.C.S.: 513210
Neil Griffin (Sec)

Subsidiary (US):

Fidessa Financial Corpration (2)
17 State St Ste 122 42 Fl, New York, NY
10004-1501 (100%)
Tel.: (212) 269-9000
Sales Range: $25-49.9 Million
Emp.: 100
Custom Computer Programming Services
N.A.I.C.S.: 541511
Dorothy Friedman (VP-Mktg-Americas)

Subsidiary (Domestic):

Fidessa Investments Ltd (2)
2 Suffolk Ln, London, United Kingdom (100%)
Tel.: (44) 2071051000

ION INVESTMENT GROUP LTD.

ION Investment Group Ltd.—(Continued)
Sales Range: $50-74.9 Million
Emp.: 30
Investment Advice
N.A.I.C.S.: 523940

Fidessa LatentZero Limited (2)
1 Old Jewry, London, EC2R 8DN, United Kingdom
Tel.: (44) 2071051000
Sales Range: $100-124.9 Million
Emp.: 400
Investment Management Software Publishing Services
N.A.I.C.S.: 513210

Subsidiary (Non-US):

Fidessa Ltd (2)
69th Floor The Center, Central, China (Hong Kong) (100%)
Tel.: (852) 25009500
Sales Range: $25-49.9 Million
Emp.: 50
Software Reproducing
N.A.I.C.S.: 334610
Phill Jeffrey *(Dir-Sls-Asia Pacific)*

Fidessa SAS (2)
8/10 Rue La Mennais, 75008, Paris, France
Tel.: (33) 173033500
Web Site: http://www.fidessa.com
Sales Range: $25-49.9 Million
Emp.: 10
Financial Software Publishing Services
N.A.I.C.S.: 513210

Subsidiary (US):

Fidessa Software Corporation (2)
17 State St Unit 122 42 Fl, New York, NY 10004-1551 (100%)
Tel.: (212) 269-9000
Sales Range: $25-49.9 Million
Emp.: 100
Software Publisher
N.A.I.C.S.: 513210

Subsidiary (Domestic):

Fidessa Software Limited (2)
2 Suffolk Lane, London, EC4R 0AT, United Kingdom
Tel.: (44) 20 79299200
Business Management Software Development Services
N.A.I.C.S.: 541511

Fidessa plc (2)
Dukes Court Duke St, Woking, GU21 5BH, Surrey, United Kingdom
Tel.: (44) 1483206300
Sales Range: $75-99.9 Million
Emp.: 450
Financial Software Development Services
N.A.I.C.S.: 541511

Subsidiary (Non-US):

Fidessa wll (2)
Level 22 West Tower Bahrain Financial Harbour King Faisal Highway, PO Box 20705, Manama, 5830, Bahrain
Tel.: (973) 17502864
Web Site: http://www.fidessa.com
Financial Management Software Publishing Services
N.A.I.C.S.: 513210

ION Group LLC (1)
100 Tournament Dr, Horsham, PA 19044
Tel.: (215) 784-1100
Web Site: http://iongroup.com
Investment Services
N.A.I.C.S.: 523999
Kyle Bennett *(Partner)*

Subsidiary (Domestic):

Allegro Development Corporation (2)
600 N Pearl St Ste 2000, Dallas, TX 75201
Tel.: (214) 237-8000
Web Site: http://www.allegrodev.com
Energy Trading & Risk Management Software Developer
N.A.I.C.S.: 513210
Michael Hinton *(Chief Strategy & Customer Officer)*

Subsidiary (Domestic):

Financial Engineering Associates, Inc. (3)
2100 Milvia St, Berkeley, CA 94704
Tel.: (510) 548-6200
Risk Management Software Developer
N.A.I.C.S.: 513210

ION Trading Ireland Ltd. (1)
4th Floor Minerva House, Simmonscourt Road, Dublin, 4, Ireland
Tel.: (353) 12200300
Web Site: http://www.iontrading.com
Financial Markets Electronic Trading, Position Tracking, Pricing, Risk Management Platform Software Products & Services
N.A.I.C.S.: 518210
Andrea Pignataro *(Founder & CEO)*

ION Trading UK Limited (1)
26th Floor 30 Saint Mary Axe, London, EC3A 8EP, United Kingdom
Tel.: (44) 20 7398 0200
Web Site: http://www.iontrading.com
Financial Markets Electronic Trading, Position Tracking, Pricing, Risk Management Platform Software Products & Services
N.A.I.C.S.: 518210

Subsidiary (Domestic):

Acuris International Limited (2)
10 Queen St Place, London, EC4R 1BE, United Kingdom
Tel.: (44) 20 3741 1000
Web Site: http://www.acuris.com
Holding Company
N.A.I.C.S.: 551111
Hamilton Matthews *(CEO)*

Subsidiary (Domestic):

Mergermarket Limited (3)
10 Queen St Place, London, EC4R 1BE, United Kingdom
Tel.: (44) 2037411007
Web Site: http://www.mergermarket.com
Merger & Acquisition Information Publisher
N.A.I.C.S.: 513140
Ben Rumble *(Head-Sls-EMEA)*

Subsidiary (US):

Mergermarket (U.S.) Ltd (4)
1501 Broadway 8th Fl, New York, NY 10036
Tel.: (212) 686-5606
Web Site: http://www.acuris.com
Merger & Acquisition Information Publisher
N.A.I.C.S.: 513140
Chrissy Carney *(Mgr-PR-Americas)*

Subsidiary (Domestic):

Perfect Information Ltd (3)
Wells Point, 79 Wells Street, London, W1T 3QN, United Kingdom
Tel.: (44) 20 7892 4200
Web Site: http://www.perfectinfo.com
Sales Range: $10-24.9 Million
Emp.: 50
Publishes Online Database of Corporate Financial Information
N.A.I.C.S.: 513140
Greg Simidian *(CEO)*

Subsidiary (Domestic):

FFastFill Limited (2)
30 St Mary Axe, London, EC3A 8EP, United Kingdom
Tel.: (44) 2076658900
Web Site: http://www.ffastfill.com
Business & Domestic Software Development Services
N.A.I.C.S.: 541512

Subsidiary (Non-US):

FFastFill Australia Pty. Ltd. (3)
Level 18 15 Castlereagh St, Sydney, 2000, NSW, Australia
Tel.: (61) 292279400
Packaged Software Publishers
N.A.I.C.S.: 513210
Paul Hatchman *(Mng Dir)*

Subsidiary (Domestic):

FFastFill Post-trade Processing Limited (3)
70 Wilson St, London, EC2A 2DB, United Kingdom
Tel.: (44) 2070657500
Packaged Software Publishers
N.A.I.C.S.: 513210

Subsidiary (Domestic):

Patsystems Limited (2)
120 Leman St, London, SE1 9HA, United Kingdom
Tel.: (44) 2079400490
Web Site: http://www.patsystems.com
Sales Range: $25-49.9 Million
Emp.: 166
Holding Company; Electronic Trading Technology & Services
N.A.I.C.S.: 551112

Subsidiary (Non-US):

Patsystems (Japan) KK (3)
2nd Floor Kakigaracho Bldg 1-10-7 Nihonbashi, Kakigara-cho Chu-ku, Tokyo, 103 0014, Japan
Tel.: (81) 336689388
Electronic Trading Technology & Services
N.A.I.C.S.: 541511

Subsidiary (US):

Patsystems (NA) LLC (3)
200 W Madison St Ste 1400, Chicago, IL 60604
Tel.: (312) 922-7600
Electronic Trading Technology & Services
N.A.I.C.S.: 541511

Subsidiary (Domestic):

Patsystems (UK) Ltd (3)
Riverside House, 2A Southwark Bridge Rd, London, SE1 9HA, United Kingdom
Tel.: (44) 2079400490
Electronic Trading Technology & Services
N.A.I.C.S.: 541511

Subsidiary (Non-US):

Patsystems Hong Kong Limited (3)
Unit 2004 Kinwick Centre 32 Hollywood Road, Central, China (Hong Kong)
Tel.: (852) 2542 2830
Electronic Trading Technology & Services
N.A.I.C.S.: 541511

ION Trading, Inc. (1)
200 N LaSalle St Suite 2200, Chicago, IL 60606-3910 (100%)
Tel.: (312) 559-0250
Web Site: http://www.iontrading.com
Financial Markets Electronic Trading, Position Tracking, Pricing, Risk Management Platform Software Products & Services
N.A.I.C.S.: 518210

Branch (Domestic):

ION Trading, Inc. - New York Office (2)
1345 Ave of the Americas, New York, NY 10105
Tel.: (212) 906-0050
Web Site: http://www.iontrading.com
Financial Markets Electronic Trading, Position Tracking, Pricing, Risk Management Platform Software Products & Services
N.A.I.C.S.: 518210

Subsidiary (Domestic):

Reval.com, Inc. (2)
1345 Ave of the Americas, New York, NY 10105
Tel.: (212) 393-1313
Web Site: http://www.reval.com
Treasury & Risk Management Software Solutions
N.A.I.C.S.: 518210
Patrick Cannon *(Exec VP-Client Svcs)*

Wall Street Systems Inc. (2)
3329 Frost Rd, Mantua, OH 44255
Tel.: (330) 274-8499
Web Site: http://www.wallstreetsystemsinc.com
Sales Range: $10-24.9 Million
Emp.: 30
Contract Hauling Services
N.A.I.C.S.: 484121
John Kabat *(Pres)*

INTERNATIONAL PUBLIC

OpenLink Financial LLC (1)
F8 W Tower 701 RXR Plz, Uniondale, NY 11556
Tel.: (516) 227-6600
Cross-Asset Trading, Risk Management & Related Operational & Portfolio Management Software Publisher
N.A.I.C.S.: 513210
Rich Grossi *(CEO)*

IONA ENERGY INC.
Suite 1600 333-7th Avenue SW, Calgary, T2P 2Z1, AB, Canada
Tel.: (587) 889-8959 **AB**
Web Site: http://www.ionaenergy.com
Year Founded: 2008
IONAF—(OTCIQ)
Sales Range: $75-99.9 Million
Emp.: 14
Oil & Gas Exploration
N.A.I.C.S.: 211120
Adrian Harvey *(Sec)*

Subsidiaries:

Iona Energy Company (UK) Limited (1)
Lower Ground Suite 3 Queen s Gate, Aberdeen, AB12 5XT, United Kingdom
Tel.: (44) 12 2422 8400
Oil & Gas Exploration Services
N.A.I.C.S.: 213112

IONEER LTD
Suite 16 01 Level 16 213 Miller Street, North Sydney, 2060, NSW, Australia
Tel.: (61) 299225800
Web Site: https://www.ioneer.com
INR—(ASX)
Rev.: $74,320
Assets: $152,004,434
Liabilities: $5,620,004
Net Worth: $146,384,430
Earnings: ($7,911,678)
Fiscal Year-end: 06/30/21
Minerals Exploration
N.A.I.C.S.: 213115
Bernard Rowe *(Mng Dir)*

Subsidiaries:

ioneer Rhyolite Ridge LLC (1)
9460 Double R Blvd Ste 200, Reno, NV 89521
Tel.: (775) 382-4800
Lithium & Ion Battery Mfr
N.A.I.C.S.: 325180

IONIC BRANDS CORP.
488-1090 West Georgia Street Suite 488, Vancouver, V6E 3V7, BC, Canada
Tel.: (604) 687-7130 **BC**
Web Site: http://www.ionicbrands.com
Year Founded: 2012
IONKF—(CNSX)
Rev.: $8,967,423
Assets: $6,106,965
Liabilities: $21,494,325
Net Worth: ($15,387,360)
Earnings: ($6,680,742)
Fiscal Year-end: 12/31/20
Nickel & Copper Mining
N.A.I.C.S.: 212230

IONIC RARE EARTHS LIMITED
Level 5 South 459 Collins Street, Melbourne, 3000, VIC, Australia
Tel.: (61) 397763434 **AU**
Web Site: https://www.ionicre.com.au
IXR—(ASX)
Rev.: $3,076,416
Assets: $25,088,953
Liabilities: $709,103
Net Worth: $24,379,850
Earnings: ($14,156,594)
Emp.: 3
Fiscal Year-end: 06/30/24

AND PRIVATE COMPANIES — IPA SYSTEMS LTD.

Mineral Exploration Services
N.A.I.C.S.: 212290
Brett Dickson *(Sec & Dir-Fin)*

Subsidiaries:

Oro Verda SPA (1)
Loteo Puertas Del Sur Calle 1 PJE 8 1571, 346 0000, Talcahuano, 3460000, Maule, Chile
Tel.: (56) 987795910
Web Site: https://www.oro-verde-spa.webnode.cl
Household Cleaning Services
N.A.I.C.S.: 561740

IONICS, INC.
14 Mountain Drive Light Industry & Science Park of the Philippines II, Brgy La Mesa, Calamba, 4027, Laguna, Philippines
Tel.: (63) 495081111
Web Site: https://www.ionicsgroup.com
ION—(PHI)
Rev.: $62,468,000
Assets: $100,928,000
Liabilities: $44,555,000
Net Worth: $56,373,000
Earnings: $2,634,000
Fiscal Year-end: 12/31/21
Electronics Mfr
N.A.I.C.S.: 334413
Ronan R. Andrade *(VP-Fin)*

Subsidiaries:

Iomni Precision, Inc. (1)
No 14 Mountain Drive LISP II, Brgy La Mesa, Calamba, 4027, Laguna, Philippines
Tel.: (63) 495450050
Web Site: https://www.iomni.com.ph
Sales Range: $50-74.9 Million
Emp.: 114
Injection Molded Plastic Products Mfr
N.A.I.C.S.: 326199

Ionics EMS, Inc. (1)
No 14 Mountain Drive, Light Industry and Science Park of the Philippines 2 Brgy La Mesa, Calamba, 4027, Laguna, Philippines
Tel.: (63) 495081111
Web Site: https://www.ionics-ems.com
Electronic Products Mfr
N.A.I.C.S.: 334419

Ionics Properties, Inc. (1)
Blk 2 & 3 Carmelray Industrial Park II Brgy Milagrosa, II Brgy La Mesa, Calamba, 4027, Laguna, Philippines
Tel.: (63) 495081111
Emp.: 1,500
Property Management Services
N.A.I.C.S.: 531312

IONIX SYSTEMS LTD.
Prospect House Taylor Business Park, Warrington, WA3 6HP, Cheshire, United Kingdom
Tel.: (44) 1942 685200
Web Site: http://www.ionix-systems.com
Year Founded: 2009
Sales Range: $25-49.9 Million
Emp.: 6
Electrical Wire System Mfr
N.A.I.C.S.: 335999
Chris Millar *(Gen Mgr)*

IONIX TECHNOLOGY, INC.
Rm 608 Block B Times Square No 50 Pe, Zhongshan District, Dalian, 116001, Liaoning, China
Tel.: (86) 41188079120 NV
Web Site: http://www.iinx-tech.com
Year Founded: 2011
IINX—(OTCEM)
Rev.: $14,328,326
Assets: $21,737,436
Liabilities: $9,886,398
Net Worth: $11,851,038
Earnings: ($406,607)
Fiscal Year-end: 06/30/21

Investment Holding Company
N.A.I.C.S.: 551112
Yang Yan *(Pres & Treas)*

IONOS GROUP SE
Elgendorfer Strasse 57, 56410, Montabaur, Germany
Tel.: (49) 7211705522
Web Site: https://www.ionos-group.com
Year Founded: 1999
IOS—(DEU)
Rev.: $1,536,514,138
Assets: $1,722,712,066
Liabilities: $1,725,713,361
Net Worth: ($3,001,295)
Earnings: $188,048,780
Emp.: 4,364
Fiscal Year-end: 12/31/23
Information Technology Services
N.A.I.C.S.: 541512
Achim Weiss *(CEO)*

Subsidiaries:

CM4all GmbH (1)
Im Mediapark 6a, 50670, Cologne, Germany
Tel.: (49) 22166012000
Web Site: https://www.cm4all.com
Software Development Services
N.A.I.C.S.: 541511

IONOS Cloud Ltd. (1)
Discovery House 154 Southgate Street, Gloucester, GL1 2EX, United Kingdom
Tel.: (44) 1452541285
Web Site: https://www.ionos.co.uk
Hosting Cloud Services
N.A.I.C.S.: 518210

IONOS Cloud S.L.U. (1)
Avenida de La Vega 1 - Veganova Building 3 Floor 5, Alcobendas, 28108, Madrid, Spain
Tel.: (34) 911360000
Web Site: https://www.ionos.es
Hosting Cloud Services
N.A.I.C.S.: 518210

We22 GmbH (1)
Im Mediapark 6a, 50670, Cologne, Germany
Tel.: (49) 22166012000
Software Development Services
N.A.I.C.S.: 541511

we22 Solutions GmbH (1)
Im Mediapark 6a, 50670, Cologne, Germany
Tel.: (49) 22166012000
Emp.: 150
Software Development Services
N.A.I.C.S.: 541511

IOT GROUP LIMITED
Level 3 32 Walker Street, North Sydney, 2060, NSW, Australia
Tel.: (61) 2 8958 2226
Web Site: http://www.ardentresources.com.au
Sales Range: Less than $1 Million
Investment Services
N.A.I.C.S.: 523999
Ian Duffell *(Exec Dir-Bus Strategy)*

IOUPAY LIMITED
Level 10 50 Pitt Street, Sydney, 2000, NSW, Australia
Tel.: (61) 295380802
Web Site: http://www.isentric.com
OVT—(ASX)
Rev.: $4,035,237
Assets: $10,579,598
Liabilities: $3,019,327
Net Worth: $7,560,272
Earnings: ($3,971,740)
Fiscal Year-end: 06/30/24
Software Based Mobility Platform & Services
N.A.I.C.S.: 541511
Chin Wee Lee *(Founder)*

Subsidiaries:

Isentric Sdn. Bhd. (1)
Unit 3-5 Level 3 Menara Ken TTDI No 37, Jalan Burhanuddin Helmi Taman Tun Dr Ismail, 60000, Kuala Lumpur, Selangor, Malaysia
Tel.: (60) 327031606
Software Development Services
N.A.I.C.S.: 541511

PT Isentric Technology Indonesia (1)
Business Park Kebon Jeruk Blok D1-1 Jl Raya Meruya Ilir Kav 88, Meruya Utara - Kembangan, Jakarta Barat, 11620, Indonesia
Tel.: (62) 2158908220
Software Development Services
N.A.I.C.S.: 541511

IP GROUP PLC
2nd Floor 3 Pancras Square King's Cross, London, N1C 4AG, United Kingdom
Tel.: (44) 2074440050 UK
Web Site: https://www.ipgroupplc.com
IPO—(AIM)
Rev.: $8,962,383
Assets: $1,966,422,621
Liabilities: $229,361,272
Net Worth: $1,737,061,348
Earnings: ($434,864,933)
Emp.: 166
Fiscal Year-end: 12/31/22
Financial Investment & Management Services
N.A.I.C.S.: 523999
Alan John Aubrey *(CEO)*

Subsidiaries:

Diurnal Limited (1)
8th Fl Eastgate House 35-43 Newport Rd, Cardiff, CF24 0AB, Wales, United Kingdom
Tel.: (44) 1142755555
Web Site: http://www.diurnal.co.uk
Sales Range: $50-74.9 Million
Emp.: 3
Medicinal Drugs Mfr & Hormone Replacement Therapeutic Services
N.A.I.C.S.: 325412
Richard Ross *(Chief Scientific Officer)*

IPG USA Plan LLC (1)
20645 N Pima Rd Ste 150, Scottsdale, AZ 85255-5597
Tel.: (480) 488-0599
Web Site: https://ipg-us.com
Insurance Brokerage Services
N.A.I.C.S.: 524210
Doug Wright *(Dir-Operations & Partner)*

Ip2ipo Limited (1)
Top Floor 25 Walbrook, London, EC4N 8AF, United Kingdom (100%)
Tel.: (44) 2074440050
Web Site: http://www.ipgroupplc.com
Sales Range: $50-74.9 Million
Emp.: 50
Financial Investment Activities
N.A.I.C.S.: 523999
Allan Abery *(CEO)*

Medella Therapeutics Limited (1)
The Sheffield Bioincubator, 40 Leavygreave Road, Sheffield, S3 7RD, South Yorkshire, United Kingdom
Tel.: (44) 1142755555
Sales Range: $25-49.9 Million
Emp.: 4
Cancer Therapeutic Services
N.A.I.C.S.: 541715
Tim Skerry *(Founder & Chief Scientific Officer)*

Modern Biosciences Plc (1)
60 Cannon Street, London, EC4N6NP, United Kingdom
Tel.: (44) 2070021529
Web Site: http://www.modernbiosciences.com
Drugs & Druggists Sundries Whslr
N.A.I.C.S.: 424210

Parkwalk Advisors Limited (1)
3 Pancras Square King's Cross, London, N1C 4AG, United Kingdom
Tel.: (44) 2077592285
Web Site: https://www.parkwalkadvisors.com
Venture Capital Services
N.A.I.C.S.: 523910
Alastair Kilgour *(Chief Investment Officer)*

Techtran Group Limited (1)
Leeds Innovation Ctr, 103 Clarendon Rd, Leeds, LS2 9DF, United Kingdom (100%)
Tel.: (44) 1133845825
Web Site: http://www.techtrangroup.com
Sales Range: $50-74.9 Million
Emp.: 10
Financial Investment Activities
N.A.I.C.S.: 523999

Top Technology Ventures Limited (1)
24 Cornhill, London, EC3V 3ND, United Kingdom
Tel.: (44) 8450742929
Web Site: http://www.toptechnology.co.uk
Sales Range: $75-99.9 Million
Emp.: 20
Intermediation Services
N.A.I.C.S.: 523910

i2LResearch Limited (1)
Capital Business Park, Cardiff, CF3 2PX, Wentloog, United Kingdom
Tel.: (44) 2922400586
Web Site: http://www.i2lresearch.com
Emp.: 10
Pest Control Services
N.A.I.C.S.: 561710
Peter McEwen *(CEO)*

Subsidiary (US):

i2LResearch USA, Inc. (2)
1430 Joh Ave Stes L M, Baltimore, MD 21227
Tel.: (410) 747-4500
Web Site: http://www.i2lresearch.com
Sales Range: $25-49.9 Million
Emp.: 7
Pest Control Services
N.A.I.C.S.: 541715
James Palczynski *(Partner)*

IPA INVESTMENTS CORPORATION
01 Nguyen Thuong Hien, Hanoi, Vietnam
Tel.: (84) 439410510
Web Site: http://www.ipa.com.vn
Year Founded: 1998
Investment Banking, Advisory & Management Services
N.A.I.C.S.: 523150
Hien Vu *(Chm)*

Subsidiaries:

VNDIRECT Securities Corporation (1)
No 1 Nguyen Thuong Hien Street, Nguyen Du Ward Hai Ba Trung, Hanoi, Vietnam
Tel.: (84) 2439724568
Web Site: http://www.vndirect.com.vn
Rev.: $61,539,554
Assets: $421,385,653
Liabilities: $302,068,459
Net Worth: $119,317,194
Earnings: $14,925,452
Emp.: 593
Fiscal Year-end: 12/31/2018
Investment Banking & Securities Brokerage Services
N.A.I.C.S.: 523150
Pham Minh Huong *(Chm & Chm)*

IPA SYSTEMS LTD.
Oakfield Industrial Estate Stanton Harcourt Road, Eynsham, OX29 4TJ, Oxon, United Kingdom
Tel.: (44) 1242573344
Web Site: http://www.ipasystems.co.uk
Sales Range: $25-49.9 Million
Emp.: 10
Holding Company
N.A.I.C.S.: 551112
Joe McElligott *(Gen Mgr)*

IPA SYSTEMS LTD.

IPA Systems Ltd.—(Continued)
Subsidiaries:

IPA Systems Ltd. UK (1)
The Priory 37 London Rd, Cheltenham,
GL52 6HA, Gloucestershire, United
Kingdom **(100%)**
Tel.: (44) 1242573344
Web Site: http://www.ipasystems.co.uk
Sales Range: $25-49.9 Million
Development, Manufacture & Sales of Integrated Publishing Systems
N.A.I.C.S.: 333248

Subsidiary (US):

alfa CTP Systems, Inc. (2)
554 Clark Rd, Tewksbury, MA 01876
Tel.: (603) 689-1101
Web Site: http://www.alfactp.com
Publishing Technology Developer
N.A.I.C.S.: 334419
Tony Ford (Pres)

Division (Domestic):

alfa CTP Systems, Inc. (3)
1150 Rose Rd, Lake Zurich, IL 60047
Tel.: (847) 427-8800
Web Site: http://www.alfactp.com
Publishing Technology Developer
N.A.I.C.S.: 334419
Tony Ford (Pres)

alfaQuest BV (1)
Energieweg 3, 3542 DZ, Utrecht, Netherlands
Tel.: (31) 346 566 884
Software Solutions Services
N.A.I.C.S.: 541511

alfaQuest, Inc (1)
2100 Golf Rd, Rolling Meadows, IL 60008
Tel.: (847) 427-8800
Software Solutions Services
N.A.I.C.S.: 541511

IPACKETS INTERNATIONAL, INC.
1580-1130 West Pender Street, Vancouver, V6E 4A4, BC, Canada
Tel.: (778) 328-8200
Year Founded: 2004
Communication Equipment Mfr
N.A.I.C.S.: 334290
Naiel Kanno (Pres & CEO)

IPAL S.A.
Americo Vespucio Oriente 1353
ENEA Parque de Negocios, Las Condes, Pudahuel, Chile
Tel.: (56) 224111500
Web Site: https://www.ipal.cl
Year Founded: 1952
IPAL—(SGO)
Sales Range: Less than $1 Million
Food Products Distr
N.A.I.C.S.: 311423
Max Von Bischhoffshausen Velasquez (CEO & Gen Mgr)

IPB PETROLEUM LIMITED
Tel.: (61) 863191900
Web Site: https://www.ipbpet.com.au
Year Founded: 2009
IPB—(ASX)
Rev.: $11,364
Assets: $2,617,859
Liabilities: $48,126
Net Worth: $2,569,733
Earnings: ($1,679,832)
Emp.: 7
Fiscal Year-end: 06/30/24
Oil & Gas Exploration
N.A.I.C.S.: 211120
Brendan Brown (Mng Dir)

IPC CORPORATION LTD.
1 Fusionopolis Place 0320 Galaxis
West Lobby, Singapore, 535224, Singapore
Tel.: (65) 67442688 SG

Web Site: https://www.ipc.com.sg
Year Founded: 1985
AZA—(SES)
Rev.: $2,397,940
Assets: $37,957,282
Liabilities: $5,943,346
Net Worth: $32,013,936
Earnings: ($477,922)
Emp.: 72
Fiscal Year-end: 12/31/23
Computer Hardware & Software Sales; Information Technology & e-Commerce Services; Communications Equipment Sales
N.A.I.C.S.: 423430
Patrick Mia Je Ngiam (Chm & CEO)

Subsidiaries:

Essex Electronics (Singapore) Pte Ltd (1)
23 Tai Seng Dr IPC Bldg, Singapore, 535224, Singapore **(100%)**
Tel.: (65) 67442688
Web Site: http://www.essex.com.sg
Sales Range: $25-49.9 Million
Emp.: 5
Electronic Parts & Equipment Whslr
N.A.I.C.S.: 423690
Benjamin Ngiam (Mng Dir)

Oday Pte. Ltd. (1)
23 Tai Seng Drive 06-00, Singapore, 535224, Singapore
Tel.: (65) 67442688
Web Site: https://www.oday.com.sg
Restaurant Operators
N.A.I.C.S.: 722511

IPC DATA CENTER, INC.
34th Floor RCBC Plaza Tower II,
Ayala Avenue cor Gil Puyat Avenue,
Makati, 1200, Metro Manila, Philippines
Tel.: (63) 28488700 PH
Web Site: http://www.ipc.ph
Year Founded: 2005
Sales Range: $1-9.9 Million
Emp.: 80
Integrated IT & Telecommunications Services
N.A.I.C.S.: 541513

IPCA LABORATORIES LTD.
48 Kandivli Industrial Estate, Kandivli West, Mumbai, 400 067, Maharashtra, India
Tel.: (91) 2266474444 In
Web Site: https://www.ipca.com
IPCALAB—(BOM)
Rev.: $748,406,295
Assets: $828,331,140
Liabilities: $184,572,570
Net Worth: $643,758,570
Earnings: $155,765,610
Emp.: 14,574
Fiscal Year-end: 03/31/21
Pharmaceutical Products Developer, Mfr & Distr
N.A.I.C.S.: 325412
Premchand Godha (Chm, CEO & Co-Mng Dir)

Subsidiaries:

Bayshore Pharmaceuticals LLC (1)
788 Morris Tpke Ste 200, Short Hills, NJ 07078 **(100%)**
Tel.: (973) 315-1818
Pharmaceuticals Distr
N.A.I.C.S.: 424210
Mark Moshier (Pres)

Onyx Scientific Limited (1)
Silverbriar Enterprise Park East, Sunderland, SR5 2TQ, Tyne Wear, United Kingdom
Tel.: (44) 1915166516
Web Site: https://www.onyxipca.com
Chemicals Mfr
N.A.I.C.S.: 325199
Denise Bowser (Comml Dir)

Pisgah Labs, Inc. (1)
795 Old Hndersonville Hwy, Pisgah Forest, NC 28768
Tel.: (828) 884-2789
Web Site: http://www.pisgahlabs.com
Medicinal & Botanical Mfr
N.A.I.C.S.: 325411

Ramdev Chemical Private Limited (1)
125 Kandivli Industrial Estate CTS No 328, Kandivli West, Mumbai, 400 067, India
Tel.: (91) 2262105000
Web Site: http://www.ramdev.com
Pharmaceutical Mfr & Distr
N.A.I.C.S.: 325412

Unichem Laboratories Limited (1)
Unichem Bhavan Prabhat Estate Off S V Road Jogeshwari West, Mumbai, 400 102, India **(52.67%)**
Tel.: (91) 2266888333
Web Site: https://www.unichemlabs.com
Rev.: $175,446,576
Assets: $426,659,961
Liabilities: $77,652,011
Net Worth: $349,007,950
Earnings: $4,685,335
Emp.: 3,090
Fiscal Year-end: 03/31/2021
Pharmaceuticals Mfr
N.A.I.C.S.: 325412
Prakash Amrut Mody (Chm & Mng Dir)

Subsidiary (Non-US):

Niche Generics Limited (2)
Unit 1 Waterloo Farm Courtyard Stotfold Road, Central Bedfordshire, Arlesey, SG15 6XP, United Kingdom
Tel.: (44) 1462833060
Web Site: http://www.nichegenerics.com
Pharmaceuticals Product Mfr
N.A.I.C.S.: 325412
Gerard Cole (Mng Dir)

Unichem (China) Private Limited (2)
Room 1005 Xingsheng Building No 900 East Jiefang Road, Wuxi, 214001, China
Tel.: (86) 51082328705
Chemical Products Mfr
N.A.I.C.S.: 325412

Unichem Farmaceutica Do Brasil Ltda. (2)
Av sete de setembro 1564 Vila Dirce, Diadema, 09912-010, Sao Paulo, Brazil
Tel.: (55) 1140433635
Web Site: https://www.unichembrasil.com.br
Pharmaceuticals Product Mfr
N.A.I.C.S.: 325412
Pinaki Trivedi (Head-Brazil)

Subsidiary (US):

Unichem Pharmaceuticals (USA) Inc. (2)
1 Tower Center Blvd Ste 2200, East Brunswick, NJ 08816
Tel.: (732) 253-5954
Web Site: https://www.unichemusa.com
Pharmaceutical Product Whslr
N.A.I.C.S.: 424210
Scott B. Delaney (Pres & CEO-North America)

IPD GROUP LIMITED
Level 2/43 Newton Rd, PO Box 22, Wetherill Park, 2164, NSW, Australia
Tel.: (61) 1300556601
Web Site:
  https://www.ipdgroup.com.au
Year Founded: 1956
IPG—(ASX)
Sales Range: $25-49.9 Million
Emp.: 160
Designer, Mfr & Supplier of Electrical Products & Accessories
N.A.I.C.S.: 423610
Mohamed Yoossuff (Dir-Fin)

IPE KRYVBASVYBUHPROM, PJSC
40 Kakhovska St c, Krivoy Rog, 50005, Ukraine
Tel.: (380) 56 404 20 02

INTERNATIONAL PUBLIC

Web Site: http://www.ing-org.dp.ua
KVPR—(UKR)
Sales Range: Less than $1 Million
Explosives Mfr
N.A.I.C.S.: 325920

IPECO HOLDINGS LTD.
Aviation Way, Southend-on-Sea, SS2 6UN, Essex, United Kingdom
Tel.: (44) 1702545118
Web Site: www.ipeco.com
Year Founded: 1960
Sales Range: $75-99.9 Million
Emp.: 500
Flight Deck & Cabin Interior Equipment Mfr
N.A.I.C.S.: 336413
Andy Braley (VP-Bus Dev)

Subsidiaries:

Ipeco Holdings Ltd. - Ipeco Composites Division (1)
Unit 15 Windmill Business Park Windmill Road, Clevedon, BS21 6SR, Avon, United Kingdom
Tel.: (44) 1275 335 800
Aircraft Parts Mfr & Whslr
N.A.I.C.S.: 336413

Ipeco Inc. (1)
2275 Jefferson St, Torrance, CA 90501
Tel.: (310) 783-4700
Web Site: http://www.ipeco.co.uk
Emp.: 200
Aircraft Parts Mfr & Whslr
N.A.I.C.S.: 336413
Mike Maracci (Mgr)

IPEK DOGAL ENERJI KAYNAKLARI ARASTIRMA VE URETIM AS
Istanbul Yolu 10 km No 310, Ankara, Turkiye
Tel.: (90) 3125871000
Web Site:
  https://www.ipekenerji.com.tr
Year Founded: 1968
IPEKE—(IST)
Rev.: $183,495
Assets: $451,824
Liabilities: $51,464
Net Worth: $400,361
Earnings: $117,754
Emp.: 2,821
Fiscal Year-end: 12/31/22
Renewable Energy Consulting Services
N.A.I.C.S.: 541690
Ali Altintas (Chm)

Subsidiaries:

Ozdemir Antimuan Madenleri A.S. (1)
Istanbul Yolu 10 km No 310, Batikent, Ankara, Turkiye
Tel.: (90) 3125871078
Web Site: https://www.antimuan.com
Chemical Element Product Mfr
N.A.I.C.S.: 325998

IPERCEPTIONS INC.
3575 Boulevard St-Laurent Suite 310, Montreal, H2X 2T7, QC, Canada
Tel.: (514) 488-3600 Ca
Web Site:
  http://www.iperceptions.com
Year Founded: 1999
Software Solutions Services
N.A.I.C.S.: 513210
Duff Anderson (Founder & Sr VP)

IPERIONX LIMITED
22 Townshend Rd, Subiaco, 6008, WA, Australia
Tel.: (980) 237-8900 AU
Web Site: https://iperionx.com
Year Founded: 2017
IPX—(NASDAQ)
Rev.: $546,029

Assets: $55,435,894
Liabilities: $4,096,299
Net Worth: $51,339,595
Earnings: ($21,843,646)
Emp.: 48
Fiscal Year-end: 06/30/24
Mineral Exploration Services
N.A.I.C.S.: 213114
Patric Glovac (Mng Dir)

Subsidiaries:

IperionX Technology LLC (1)
6325 Huntley Rd, Worthington, OH 43085
Web Site: https://www.hyperionmt.com
Emp.: 2,000
Tungsten Carbide Powder & Cemented Carbide Mfr
N.A.I.C.S.: 331492

IPEX CAPITAL, LTD.
5th Floor Liscartan House, 127-131 Sloane Street, SW1X 9AS, London, United Kingdom - England
Tel.: (44) 2078113838   UK
Web Site: http://www.ipex.com
Year Founded: 2008
Venture Company Financing
N.A.I.C.S.: 523999
Martin Stapleton (Principal)

Subsidiaries:

Aegate Ltd. (1)
Cambridge Technology Centre, Melbourn, SG8 6DP, United Kingdom   (100%)
Tel.: (44) 1763268160
Web Site: http://www.aegate.com
Sales Range: $25-49.9 Million
Emp.: 40
Research & Development in the Physical Engineering & Life Sciences
N.A.I.C.S.: 541715
Peter Fox (CTO)

IPF ELECTRONIC GMBH
Kalver Strasse 27, Ludenscheid, 58515, Germany
Tel.: (49) 235193650
Web Site: http://www.ipf-electronic.de
Year Founded: 1986
Rev.: $13,890,558
Emp.: 107
Electronic Sensors Mfr
N.A.I.C.S.: 423690
Dirk Neuhaus (CEO)

IPGL LIMITED
Level 28 City Point One Ropemaker St, London, EC2Y 9EW, United Kingdom
Tel.: (44) 2075504775   UK
Web Site: http://www.ipgl.co.uk
Emp.: 10
Investment Holding Company
N.A.I.C.S.: 551112
Michael Spencer (Chm)

IPH LIMITED
Level 24 Tower 2 Darling Park 201 Sussex Street, Sydney, 2000, NSW, Australia
Tel.: (61) 293930301
Web Site: http://www.iphltd.com.au
IPH—(ASX)
Rev.: $411,258,011
Assets: $877,003,202
Liabilities: $453,458,866
Net Worth: $423,544,336
Earnings: $40,598,290
Emp.: 1,626
Fiscal Year-end: 06/30/24
Intellectual Property Services
N.A.I.C.S.: 533110
Andrew Blattman (CEO & Mng Dir)

Subsidiaries:

P.T. Spruson Ferguson Indonesia (1)
Graha Paramita 3B Floor Zone D Jl Denpasar Raya Blok D2 Kav 8, Kuningan, Jakarta, Indonesia
Tel.: (62) 212523853
Intellectual Property Services
N.A.I.C.S.: 531311

Pizzeys Pte. Ltd. (1)
152 Beach Road 04-08 Gateway East, Singapore, Singapore
Tel.: (65) 62914261
Intellectual Property Services
N.A.I.C.S.: 531311

ROBIC, LLP (1)
1001 Square Victoria Bloc E - 8th Floor, Montreal, H2Z 2B7, QC, Canada
Tel.: (514) 987-6242
Emp.: 28
Law firm
N.A.I.C.S.: 541110
Bob H. Sotiriadis (Partner & Atty)

Smart & Biggar IP Agency Co. (1)
55 Metcalfe Street Suite 900, Ottawa, K1P 5Y6, ON, Canada
Tel.: (613) 232-2486
Web Site: http://www.smart-biggar.ca
Emp.: 83
Law firm
N.A.I.C.S.: 541110
Glen B. Tremblay (Mng Partner)

Subsidiary (Domestic):

Ridout & Maybee LLP (2)
100 Murray Street 4th Floor, Ottawa, K1N 0A1, ON, Canada
Tel.: (613) 236-1995
Web Site: http://www.ridoutmaybee.com
Emp.: 33
Law firm
N.A.I.C.S.: 541110
Janet M. Fuhrer (Partner)

Spruson & Ferguson (Asia) Pte. Limited (1)
152 Beach Road 37-05/06 Gateway East, Singapore, Singapore
Tel.: (65) 63337200
Intellectual Property Services
N.A.I.C.S.: 531311

Spruson & Ferguson (M) SDN. BHD. (1)
A-33A-07 Level 33A Menara UOA Bangsar No 5 Jalan Bangsar Utama 1, 59000, Kuala Lumpur, Malaysia
Tel.: (60) 322831668
Intellectual Property Services
N.A.I.C.S.: 531311

Spruson & Ferguson Intellectual Property Agency (Beijing) Co. (1)
Room 502 5 F Building 8/Sinotrans Tower A No 5 Anding Road, Chaoyang District, Beijing, China
Tel.: (86) 1082255655
Web Site: https://www.spruson.com
Emp.: 480
Property Management Services
N.A.I.C.S.: 531311

Spruson & Ferguson Lawyers Pty. Limited (1)
Level 24 Tower 2 Darling Park 201 Sussex Street, Sydney, NSW, Australia
Tel.: (61) 293930100
Property Law Services
N.A.I.C.S.: 531312

WiseTime GmbH (1)
Steinerstr 15/A, 81369, Munich, Germany
Tel.: (49) 8989057880
Web Site: https://wisetime.com
Autonomous Timekeeping Services
N.A.I.C.S.: 518210

WiseTime LLC (1)
5255 Ronald Reagan Blvd Ste 100, Johnstown, CO 80534
Tel.: (970) 776-8300
Autonomous Timekeeping Services
N.A.I.C.S.: 518210

Xenith IP Group Pty. Limited (1)
Level 21 60 Margaret Street, Sydney, 2000, NSW, Australia   (100%)
Tel.: (61) 297771122
Web Site: http://www.xenithip.com
Rev.: $98,609,448
Assets: $141,512,203
Liabilities: $43,537,293
Net Worth: $97,974,910
Earnings: ($11,460,715)
Fiscal Year-end: 06/30/2018
Holding Company
N.A.I.C.S.: 551112
Lesley Kennedy (CFO & Sec)

IPLAYCO CORPORATION LTD.
Unit 500 - 26825 56th Avenue, Langley, V4W 3Z9, BC, Canada
Tel.: (604) 607-1111   AB
Web Site: http://www.iplayco.com
Year Founded: 1999
Rev.: $12,989,939
Assets: $11,668,373
Liabilities: $4,992,158
Net Worth: $6,676,215
Earnings: ($1,100,653)
Fiscal Year-end: 09/30/18
Children Play Structures Mfr
N.A.I.C.S.: 333999
Scott C. Forbes (Founder, Pres & CEO)

Subsidiaries:

International Play Company Inc. (1)
Unit 500 - 26825 56th Avenue, Langley, V4W 3Z9, BC, Canada
Tel.: (604) 607-1111
Web Site: https://www.iplayco.com
Sales Range: $25-49.9 Million
Emp.: 4
Playground Equipment Mfr
N.A.I.C.S.: 339920
Scott Forbes (CEO)

IPM HOLDINGS, INC.
Penthouse The Taipan Place F Ortigas Jr Road Ortigas Center, Pasig, Philippines
Tel.: (63) 288176791
Web Site: https://www.ipmholdings.com.ph
Year Founded: 1995
IPM—(PHI)
Rev.: $5,379,871
Assets: $31,315,622
Liabilities: $6,090,149
Net Worth: $25,225,473
Earnings: $672,189
Emp.: 54
Fiscal Year-end: 12/31/20
Investment Management Service
N.A.I.C.S.: 523999
Isabelita P. Mercado (Chm & CEO)

IPN HOLDING B.V.
Voorveste 2, NL-3992 DC, Houten, Netherlands
Tel.: (31) 306382220   NI
Web Site: http://www.ipneurope.com
Sales Range: $50-74.9 Million
Emp.: 200
Holding Company; Flexible Packaging Systems Mfr
N.A.I.C.S.: 551112
Jeroen Gebbink (Chief Comml Officer)

Subsidiaries:

IPN CRM BV (1)
Industrieweg 17a, Kampen, 8263 AB, Netherlands
Tel.: (31) 384298220
Web Site: http://www.ipn-group.com
Sales Range: Less than $1 Million
Emp.: 30
Medical Packaging Systems Mfr
N.A.I.C.S.: 339112
L. Lost (Gen Mgr)

IPN Europe B.V. (1)
Voorveste 1, 3992 DC, Houten, Netherlands
Tel.: (31) 306382220
Web Site: http://www.ipneurope.com
Sales Range: $50-74.9 Million
Emp.: 70
Flexible Packaging Systems Mfr
N.A.I.C.S.: 326199

IPN HealthCare S.A. (1)
Rue Pra de Plan 3, CH-1618, Chatel Saint Denis, Switzerland
Tel.: (41) 219482350
Web Site: http://www.ipnhc.com
Sales Range: $50-74.9 Million
Emp.: 11
Medical Tubing & Accessories Mfr
N.A.I.C.S.: 326220

IPO.GO AG
Im Weiler 11, 78 479, Reichenau, Germany
Tel.: (49) 7534 99 59 987
Web Site: http://www.ipogo.de
Year Founded: 2005
Investor Relations Services
N.A.I.C.S.: 523150
Florian Bozon (Chm-Mgmt Bd)

IPOINT-MEDIA LTD.
22 Ha'Nagar Street, Neve Neeman Industrial Area, Hod Hasharon, 45240, Israel
Tel.: (972) 9 744 2886
Web Site: http://www.ipoint-media.com
Sales Range: $1-9.9 Million
Emp.: 22
Video Calling Application Platform Maker
N.A.I.C.S.: 513210
Avi Kaneti (VP-R&D)

Subsidiaries:

iPoint-media Ltd. (1)
22 Ha Nagar St Neve Neeman Indus Area, Hod Hasharon, 45240, Israel
Tel.: (972) 97442886
Emp.: 20
Mobile Software Development Services
N.A.I.C.S.: 541511
Shmuel Geller (Founder)

IPOPEMA SECURITIES S.A.
ul Prozna 9, 00-107, Warsaw, Poland
Tel.: (48) 222369200
Web Site: https://www.ipopemasecurities.pl
Year Founded: 2005
IPE—(WAR)
Rev.: $65,329,599
Assets: $95,387,379
Liabilities: $67,078,581
Net Worth: $28,308,798
Earnings: $1,526,654
Emp.: 250
Fiscal Year-end: 12/31/22
Investment Banking & Securities Brokerage Services
N.A.I.C.S.: 523150

Subsidiaries:

IPOPEMA Business Consulting Sp. z o.o. (1)
ul Prozna 9, 00-107, Warsaw, Poland
Tel.: (48) 222095007
Web Site: https://www.ipopemabc.pl
Business Consulting Services
N.A.I.C.S.: 541618
Eliza Los-Strychowska (Co-Founder)

IPOPEMA Financial Advisory Sp. z o.o. (1)
Ul Prozna 9, 00-107, Warsaw, Poland
Tel.: (48) 222369268
Financial Investment Services
N.A.I.C.S.: 523999

IPOPEMA Towarzystwo Funduszy Inwestycyjnych S.A. (1)
ul Prozna 9, 00-107, Warsaw, Poland
Tel.: (48) 222369300
Web Site: https://www.ipopematfi.pl
Financial Investment Services
N.A.I.C.S.: 523999

Subsidiary (Domestic):

Fundusz Hipoteczny Dom S.A. (2)
Atrium Plaza Al Jana Pawla II 29, 00-867, Warsaw, Poland
Tel.: (48) 221005000

IPOPEMA SECURITIES S.A.

IPOPEMA Securities S.A.—(Continued)
Web Site: https://www.funduszhipoteczny.pl
Fund Operate Services
N.A.I.C.S.: 523940
Piotr Jakubowski (Mktg Mgr)

IPOSA PROPERTIES SOCIMI, S.A.
Tambre St 1, 28002, Madrid, 28002, Spain
Tel.: (34) 915632998
Web Site: https://www.iposasocimi.com
Year Founded: 2018
MLIPO—(EUR)
Rev.: $2,597,287
Assets: $8,931,077
Liabilities: $2,680,799
Net Worth: $6,250,278
Earnings: $1,576,305
Emp.: 4
Fiscal Year-end: 12/31/22
Real Estate Investment Trust Services
N.A.I.C.S.: 525990
Carlos Rodriguez San Pedro (CEO)

IPRAD SANTE
178 Quai De Jemmapes, 75010, Paris, France
Tel.: (33) 471468000
Web Site: http://www.laboratoiresiprad.com
Sales Range: $10-24.9 Million
Emp.: 25
Toilet Preparations
N.A.I.C.S.: 325620
Pierre-Marie Defrance (Pres)

IPRO DRESDEN
Schnorrstrasse 70, 1069, Dresden, Germany
Tel.: (49) 35146510
Web Site: http://www.ipro-dresden.de
Year Founded: 1949
Sales Range: $25-49.9 Million
Emp.: 350
Construction Services
N.A.I.C.S.: 236220
Lutz Junge (Mng Dir)

IPROLAM SA BUCURESTI
Negustori Str 23-25 sector 2, 23952, Bucharest, Romania
Tel.: (40) 213132610
Web Site: https://www.iprolam.ro
IPRO—(BUC)
Rev.: $2,311,211
Assets: $8,673,942
Liabilities: $5,119,535
Net Worth: $3,554,407
Earnings: $26,573
Emp.: 38
Fiscal Year-end: 12/31/23
Engineering & Technical Support Services
N.A.I.C.S.: 541330
Andrei Mauthner (Pres, Pres & CEO)

IPS CO., LTD
Grand Front Osaka TowerB 16th Fl 3-1 Ofuka-cho, Kita-ku, Osaka, 530-0011, Japan
Tel.: (81) 662926237
Web Site: https://www.ips.ne.jp
Year Founded: 1997
4335—(TKS)
Rev.: $19,462,380
Assets: $16,097,360
Liabilities: $6,866,880
Net Worth: $9,230,480
Earnings: $1,405,720
Emp.: 142
Fiscal Year-end: 06/30/24
Management Consulting Services
N.A.I.C.S.: 541618

Hiroshi Watanabe (CEO)

IPS SECUREX HOLDINGS LIMITED
213 Henderson Road 04-09 Henderson Industrial Park, Singapore, 159553, Singapore
Tel.: (65) 68634385
Web Site: https://www.ips-securex.com
42N—(CAT)
Rev.: $8,553,602
Assets: $9,391,816
Liabilities: $4,255,691
Net Worth: $5,136,125
Earnings: ($1,490,397)
Emp.: 46
Fiscal Year-end: 06/30/23
Integrated Security Solutions
N.A.I.C.S.: 561621
Kelvin Ching Song Lim (CEO)

Subsidiaries:

IPS Securex Pte. Ltd.   (1)
71 Tech Park Crescent, Singapore, 638072, Singapore
Tel.: (65) 66430808
Information Technology Services
N.A.I.C.S.: 541511
Kelvin Lim (CEO-Grp & Exec.Dir)

Securex GS Pte. Ltd.   (1)
213 Henderson Road 03-09, Singapore, 159553, Singapore
Tel.: (65) 67492321
Web Site: https://www.securex-gs.com
Security & Communication System Services
N.A.I.C.S.: 561621
Kendrick Boey (Gen Mgr)

IPSEN S.A.
65 Quai Georges Gorse, 92100, Boulogne-Billancourt, France
Tel.: (33) 158335000
Web Site: http://www.ipsen.com
IPN—(EUR)
Rev.: $3,375,242,823
Assets: $6,823,764,300
Liabilities: $2,696,956,616
Net Worth: $4,126,807,684
Earnings: $669,004,964
Emp.: 5,325
Fiscal Year-end: 12/31/23
Pharmaceuticals Mfr
N.A.I.C.S.: 325412
Antoine Flochel (Vice Chm)

Subsidiaries:

Clementia Pharmaceuticals Inc.   (1)
1000 de la Gauchetiere West Suite 1200, Montreal, H3B 4W5, QC, Canada
Tel.: (514) 940-3600
Web Site: http://www.clementiapharma.com
Assets: $176,844,381
Liabilities: $12,412,420
Net Worth: $164,431,961
Earnings: ($58,126,332)
Emp.: 45
Fiscal Year-end: 12/31/2018
Biotechnology Research & Development Services
N.A.I.C.S.: 541713
Jeffrey Packman (Chief Dev Officer)

Epizyme, Inc.   (1)
400 Technology Sq 4th Fl, Cambridge, MA 02139
Tel.: (617) 229-5872
Web Site: http://www.epizyme.com
Rev.: $37,427,000
Assets: $289,000,000
Liabilities: $309,688,000
Net Worth: ($20,688,000)
Earnings: ($251,122,000)
Emp.: 250
Fiscal Year-end: 12/31/2021
Biopharmaceutical Developer, Researcher & Mfr
N.A.I.C.S.: 325412
Joseph Beaulieu (Treas & Controller)

Ipsen Biopharmaceuticals, Inc.   (1)
2000 Sierra Point Pkwy Ste 400, Brisbane, CA 94005-1849
Tel.: (650) 624-4900
Web Site: http://www.tercica.com
Sales Range: $25-49.9 Million
Emp.: 126
Pharmaceutical Developer
N.A.I.C.S.: 325412
Donald Pearl (VP-Neuroscience Bus Unit)

Ipsen Pharma S.A.S.   (1)
65 Quai George Gorse, 92100, Boulogne-Billancourt, France
Tel.: (33) 158335833
Emp.: 600
Health Care Srvices
N.A.I.C.S.: 621610

Subsidiary (Non-US):

Beaufour Ipsen (Tianjin) Pharmaceutical Co., Ltd.   (2)
Huayuan Industrial Park Road Open 18, Tianjin, 300384, China
Tel.: (86) 2283710343
Pharmaceuticals Product Mfr
N.A.I.C.S.: 325412
Xue Nan (Mgr-SFE)

Subsidiary (Domestic):

Ipsen (Tianjin) Pharmaceutical Trade Co., Ltd.   (3)
Block B2 No 18 Kaihua Road, Huayuan Industrial Zone, Tianjin, 300384, China
Tel.: (86) 2283710343
Pharmaceuticals Product Mfr
N.A.I.C.S.: 325412

Subsidiary (Non-US):

Beaufour Ipsen Farmaceutica Ltda   (2)
Avenida Engenheiro Luiz Carlos Berrini 1297, Cidade Moncoes, Sao Paulo, 04571-010, Brazil
Tel.: (55) 1135439000
Health Care Srvices
N.A.I.C.S.: 621610
Vanessa Fukuda (Mgr-HR)

Ipsen (Beijing) Pharmaceutical Science & Technology Development Co., Ltd.   (2)
1207 12th Floor Building 22 Yard 5 Shuguang Xili, Chaoyang District, Beijing, China
Tel.: (86) 1056307598
Pharmaceuticals Product Mfr
N.A.I.C.S.: 325412

Ipsen Biopharmaceuticals Canada Inc.   (2)
5050 Satellite Drive Suite 500, Mississauga, L4W 0G1, ON, Canada
Tel.: (905) 238-9293
Web Site: https://www.ipsen.com
Pharmaceuticals Product Mfr
N.A.I.C.S.: 325412
Ed Dybka (Gen Mgr)

Ipsen Epe   (2)
63 Agiou Dimitriou, Alimos, 174 56, Athens, Greece
Tel.: (30) 2109858930
Pharmaceuticals Product Mfr
N.A.I.C.S.: 325412

Ipsen Farmaceutica B.V.   (2)
Taurusavenue 33B, 2132 LS, Hoofddorp, Netherlands
Tel.: (31) 235541600
Health Care Srvices
N.A.I.C.S.: 621610
Agathe Schoeman (Bus Mgr)

Subsidiary (Non-US):

Ipsen Pharma GmbH   (3)
Einsteinstrasse 174, 81677, Munich, Germany
Tel.: (49) 89262043289
Biopharmaceutical Product Mfr
N.A.I.C.S.: 325412
Lisa Schonhoff (Mgr-Drug Safety)

Ipsen Ukraine Services LLC   (3)
Street Degtyarivska Bldg 27-T, 04119, Kiev, Ukraine
Tel.: (380) 445026529

INTERNATIONAL PUBLIC

Web Site: http://www.ipsen.com
Pharmaceuticals Product Mfr
N.A.I.C.S.: 325412
Vladimir Ignatov (Gen Mgr)

Subsidiary (Non-US):

Ipsen Korea Ltd.   (2)
11th Floor Kamkoyangjae Tower 262 Gangnam-daero, Gangnam-gu, Seoul, 06265, Korea (South)
Tel.: (82) 24059500
Pharmaceuticals Product Mfr
N.A.I.C.S.: 325412
Minyoung Kim (Gen Mgr)

Ipsen N.V.   (2)
Guldensporenpark 87, 9820, Merelbeke, Belgium
Tel.: (32) 92439600
Health Care Srvices
N.A.I.C.S.: 621610
Thomas Lammens (Mgr-Bus Excellence)

Ipsen OOO   (2)
st. Taganskaya d 17-23 floor 2 room I, Tagansky municipal district, 109147, Moscow, Russia
Tel.: (7) 4952585400
Pharmaceuticals Product Mfr
N.A.I.C.S.: 325412

Ipsen Pharma S.A.   (2)
Torre Realia Placa Europa 4143 7 Planta, L'Hospitalet de Llobregat, 08908, Barcelona, Spain
Tel.: (34) 936858100
Pharmaceuticals Product Mfr
N.A.I.C.S.: 325412

Ipsen Pharma S.R.O.   (2)
Olbrachtova 2006/9, 140 00, Prague, Czech Republic
Tel.: (420) 242481821
Pharmaceuticals Product Mfr
N.A.I.C.S.: 325412
Tereza Kozuska (Dir-HR-Central Europe)

Ipsen Pty Limited   (2)
Level 2 Building 4 Brandon Office Park 540 Springvale Road, Glen Waverley, 3150, VIC, Australia
Tel.: (61) 385448100
Web Site: http://www.ipsen.com
Pharmaceuticals Product Mfr
N.A.I.C.S.: 325412
Tim Dow (Mgr-Regulatory Affairs)

IPSOS S.A.
35 Rue du Val de Marne, 75013, Paris, France
Tel.: (33) 141989000
Web Site: https://www.ipsos.com
Year Founded: 1975
IPS—(EUR)
Rev.: $2,219,139,006
Assets: $2,630,445,157
Liabilities: $1,246,610,662
Net Worth: $1,383,834,495
Earnings: $198,506,616
Emp.: 20,156
Fiscal Year-end: 12/31/22
Market Research
N.A.I.C.S.: 541910
Didier Truchot (Founder & Chm)

Subsidiaries:

Beijing Ipsos Market Consulting Ltd.   (1)
12F Union Plaza No 20 Chaowai St, Chaoyang, Beijing, 100020, China
Tel.: (86) 1065888899
Marketing Research Service
N.A.I.C.S.: 541910

Espaces TV SA   (1)
30 Rue d Orleans, 92200, Neuilly-sur-Seine, France
Tel.: (33) 146431400
Web Site: http://www.espacestv.fr
Television Communication Services
N.A.I.C.S.: 516120

IPSOS Strategic Puls dooel   (1)
Kairska 31, 1000, Skopje, North Macedonia
Tel.: (389) 23092720
Web Site: https://www.ipsos.com

AND PRIVATE COMPANIES — IPSOS S.A.

Advertising & Marketing Services
N.A.I.C.S.: 541810

Intrasonics Limited (1)
Harston Mill Harston, Cambridge,
CB227GG, Cambridgeshire, United Kingdom
Tel.: (44) 1223875200
Web Site: http://www.intrasonics.com
Emp.: 15
Commercial Equipment Whslr
N.A.I.C.S.: 423430

Ipsos (Chile) S.A. (1)
Pedro de Valdivia 555 piso 10, Providencia,
Santiago, Chile
Tel.: (56) 224335000
Web Site: https://www.ipsos.com
Advertising & Marketing Services
N.A.I.C.S.: 541810

Ipsos (Chile) S.A.S (1)
Pedro de Valdivia 555 Piso 7, Santiago,
Chile
Tel.: (56) 24297000
Web Site: http://www.ipsos.cl
Emp.: 200
Marketing Research Service
N.A.I.C.S.: 541910

Ipsos (Malaysia) L.L.C. (1)
A-38-11 & A-39-11 Level 38 & 39 Menara
Uoa Bangsar N 5, Jalan Bangsar Utama 1,
59000, Kuala Lumpur, Malaysia
Tel.: (60) 323023383
Marketing Research Service
N.A.I.C.S.: 541910
Miranda Cheung *(Country Mgr)*

Ipsos (Pty) Ltd. (1)
Building 3 and 4 Prism Business Park Ruby
Close, Fourways, 2055, South Africa
Tel.: (27) 117097800
Advertising & Marketing Services
N.A.I.C.S.: 541810

Ipsos (Suisse) SA (1)
Chemin du Chateau-Bloch 11, Le Lignon,
1219, Geneva, Switzerland
Tel.: (41) 225910600
Web Site: https://www.ipsos.com
Emp.: 100
Marketing Consulting Services
N.A.I.C.S.: 541613
Cees Faber *(Country Mgr)*

Ipsos (Thailand) Ltd (1)
246 Times Square Building Unit 16-01,
16-02 And 16-03 16th Fl, Sukhumvit 12-14
Rd Klongtoey, Bangkok, 10110, Thailand
Tel.: (66) 22500071
Web Site: http://www.ipsos-th.com
Marketing Research Service
N.A.I.C.S.: 541910

Ipsos A/S (1)
Store Kongensgade 1, 1264, Copenhagen,
Denmark
Tel.: (45) 33193900
Web Site: https://www.ipsos.com
Advertising & Marketing Services
N.A.I.C.S.: 541810

Ipsos AOM (1)
Av Reducto 1363, Miraflores, Lima, Peru
Tel.: (51) 16100100
Web Site: https://www.ipsos.com
Marketing Research Service
N.A.I.C.S.: 541910
Alfredo Torres *(CEO)*

Ipsos AOM Bolivia (1)
Calle Fernando Guachalla 384 Esq Av 20
de Octubre, Sopocachi, La Paz, Bolivia
Tel.: (591) 22167676
Marketing Research Service
N.A.I.C.S.: 541910
Luis Garay *(Country Mgr)*

Ipsos AS (1)
Karenlyst Alle 20, 0278, Oslo, Norway
Tel.: (47) 22954700
Advertising & Marketing Services
N.A.I.C.S.: 541810

Ipsos ASI (1)
Calle 74 No 11-81 Piso 5, Bogota,
Colombia (100%)
Tel.: (57) 1 376 9400
Web Site: http://www.ipsos.com
Sales Range: $25-49.9 Million
Emp.: 15
Market Research
N.A.I.C.S.: 541910

Ipsos ASI GmbH (1)
Papenkamp 2-6, 23879, Molln, Germany
Tel.: (49) 4542 801 200
Web Site: http://www.ipsos.com
Sales Range: $75-99.9 Million
Emp.: 400
Marketing Research Service
N.A.I.C.S.: 541910

Ipsos ASI Venezuela CA (1)
Av Francisco de Miranda entre Primera
Avenida y Avenida Andres Bello, Edif Mene
Grande I Piso 1 1-3 Urb Los Palos Grandes
Municipio Chacao, Caracas, 1060, Venezuela
Tel.: (58) 2122832410
Web Site: http://www.ipsos.com
Marketing Research Service
N.A.I.C.S.: 541910

Ipsos America, Inc. (1)
200 Park Ave 11 FL, New York, NY 10016
Tel.: (212) 265-3200
Web Site: https://www.ipsos.com
Marketing Research Service
Maria Perez *(Head-Ipsos.Digital-North America)*

Subsidiary (Domestic):

Ipsos Forward Research, Inc. (2)
12647 Olive Blvd Ste 510, Saint Louis, MO 63141
Tel.: (314) 205-0005
Web Site: http://www.ipsos-na.com
Emp.: 20
Marketing Research Service
N.A.I.C.S.: 541910

Ipsos USA, Inc. (2)
222 S Riverside Plz 4th Fl, Chicago, IL 60606
Tel.: (312) 526-4000
Web Site: http://www.ipsos.com
Media & Advertisement Agency Services
N.A.I.C.S.: 541890
Bhushan Lakhe *(Sr VP)*

Ipsos-FMC, Inc. (2)
3130 Crow Canyon Pl Ste 400, San Ramon, CA 94583-1346
Tel.: (925) 208-3150
Web Site: http://www.ipsos.com
Marketing Research Service
N.A.I.C.S.: 541910

Ipsos-Reid Public Affairs, Inc. (2)
225 108th Av NE Ste 500, Bellevue, WA 98004
Tel.: (425) 455-0810
Web Site: http://www.ipsos.na.com
Emp.: 30
Marketing Research Service
N.A.I.C.S.: 541910
Ninck Mercurio *(Gen Mgr)*

Ipsos Argentina S.A. (1)
Esmeralda 950 13th Floor Capital Federal,
CP 1007, Buenos Aires, Argentina
Tel.: (54) 1147066500
Web Site: https://www.ipsos.com
Marketing Research Service

Ipsos Asia Ltd. (1)
6/F China Life Center Tower A 1 Harbour-
Gate 18 Hung Luen Road, Hung Hom,
China (Hong Kong)
Tel.: (852) 37662288
Web Site: http://www.ipsos.com
Sales Range: $25-49.9 Million
Emp.: 10
Marketing Research Service
N.A.I.C.S.: 541910

Ipsos Australia Pty Ltd (1)
Level 2 51 Berry Street, Sydney, 2060,
NSW, Australia (100%)
Tel.: (61) 299005100
Web Site: http://www.ipsos.com.au
Sales Range: $25-49.9 Million
Emp.: 27
Market Research
N.A.I.C.S.: 541910

Subsidiary (Domestic):

I-View Pty Ltd. (2)
Level 14 168 Walker Stree, North Sydney,
2060, NSW, Australia
Tel.: (61) 290602600
Web Site: http://www.iview.com.au
Marketing Research Service
N.A.I.C.S.: 541910

Ipsos B.V. (1)
Amstelveenseweg 760, 1081 JK, Amsterdam, Netherlands
Tel.: (31) 206070707
Web Site: https://www.ipsos.com
Advertising & Marketing Services
N.A.I.C.S.: 541810

Ipsos Bahnreisenforschung GmbH (1)
Elektrastr 6, 81925, Munchenbernsdorf, Germany
Tel.: (49) 89996001333
Web Site: http://www.bahnreisenforschung.de
Advertising & Marketing Services
N.A.I.C.S.: 541810

Ipsos Belgium SA (1)
Waterloo Office Park 161 Dreve Richelle
Block J, 1410, Waterloo, Belgium
Tel.: (32) 26424711
Web Site: http://www.ipsos.be
Emp.: 10
Marketing Research Service
N.A.I.C.S.: 541910
Gerd Callewaert *(Country Mgr)*

Ipsos Brasil Pesquisas de Mercado Ltda (1)
Avenida Dra Ruth Cardoso n 7221 10 andar Pinheiros, Sao Paulo, CEP 05425-070, Brazil
Tel.: (55) 1121598400
Marketing Research Service
N.A.I.C.S.: 541910

Ipsos Brazil Ltda. (1)
Avda Nove de Julho 4865-7th Fl Conjunto 62A, Itaim Bibi, Sao Paulo, 01407 200, Brazil
Tel.: (55) 1121598400
Web Site: http://www.ipsos.com.br
Emp.: 300
Marketing Research Service
N.A.I.C.S.: 541910

Ipsos Brussels (1)
Breve Richelle 161, PO Box 1410, Waterloo, 14100, Belgium (100%)
Tel.: (32) 25234055
Web Site: http://www.ipsos.com
Sales Range: $25-49.9 Million
Emp.: 65
Market Research
N.A.I.C.S.: 541910

Ipsos CA (1)
Av Francisco de Miranda entre Primera
Avenida y Avenida Andres Bello, Edif Mene
Grande I Piso 1 of 1-3 Urb Los Palos
Grandes Municipio, Caracas, 1060, Venezuela
Tel.: (58) 2122832410
Web Site: https://www.ipsos.com
Advertising & Marketing Services
N.A.I.C.S.: 541810

Ipsos Canada, Inc. (1)
1410 Stanley Street Suite 1100, Montreal,
H3A 1P8, QC, Canada
Tel.: (514) 861-8555
Web Site: http://www.ipsos.ca
Sales Range: $25-49.9 Million
Emp.: 5
Marketing Research Service
N.A.I.C.S.: 541910

Ipsos Co., Ltd. (1)
5th floor Korea Economic Daily 463
Cheongpa-ro, Jung-gu, Seoul, Korea (South)
Tel.: (82) 264645100
Web Site: https://www.ipsos.com
Advertising & Marketing Services
N.A.I.C.S.: 541810

Ipsos Comcon LLC (1)
3 Bld 2 Verhn Krasnoselskaya St, Moscow, 107140, Russia
Tel.: (7) 4959815646
Web Site: https://www.ipsos.com
Advertising & Marketing Services
N.A.I.C.S.: 541810

Ipsos Costa Rica SA (1)
300 Metros Este 100 Metros Norte y 25
Este de la Iglesia, Santa Teresita, San Jose, Costa Rica
Tel.: (506) 22536108
Marketing Research Service
N.A.I.C.S.: 541910
Fernando Estrella *(Country Mgr)*

Ipsos Ecuador SA (1)
Javier Arauz N 36-15 and Aleman, Quito, Ecuador
Tel.: (593) 22464965
Web Site: https://www.ipsos.com
Advertising & Marketing Services
N.A.I.C.S.: 541810

Ipsos France SAS (1)
35 Rue du Val de Marne, 75013, Paris, France
Tel.: (33) 141989000
Web Site: https://www.ipsos.com
Marketing Research Service
N.A.I.C.S.: 541910

Ipsos GmbH (1)
Sachsenstrasse 6, 20097, Hamburg, Germany (100%)
Tel.: (49) 40800960
Web Site: https://www.ipsos.com
Sales Range: $25-49.9 Million
Emp.: 100
Marketing Research Service
N.A.I.C.S.: 541910
Gudrun Witt *(Mgr-Communications)*

Subsidiary (Domestic):

Ipsos Loyalty GmbH (2)
Saca Sen Scrasaen 6, 20097, Hamburg, Germany
Tel.: (49) 40800960
Web Site: http://wwwipsos.com
Marketing Research Service
N.A.I.C.S.: 541910
Peter Bran *(CEO)*

Ipsos Operations GmbH (2)
Sachsenstrasse 6, 20097, Hamburg, Germany
Tel.: (49) 40800960
Web Site: http://www.ipsos.de
Sales Range: $25-49.9 Million
Marketing Research Service
N.A.I.C.S.: 541910
Ralf Ganzenmueller *(Country Mgr)*

Ipsos GmbH (1)
Rotenturmstrasse 16-18/ 7th Floor, 1010, Vienna, Austria
Tel.: (43) 19059939
Advertising & Marketing Services
N.A.I.C.S.: 541810

Ipsos Group (1)
Via Tolmezzo 15, 20132, Milan, Italy
Tel.: (39) 02361051
Web Site: https://www.ipsos.it
Sales Range: $25-49.9 Million
Emp.: 80
Market Research
N.A.I.C.S.: 541910
Nando Pagnoncelli *(Chm)*

Ipsos Group GIE (1)
35 Rue du Val de Marne, Paris, 75013, France
Tel.: (33) 141989000
Marketing Consulting Services
N.A.I.C.S.: 541613
Didier Truchot *(Chm)*

Ipsos Herrarte, S.A. DE C.V. (1)
79 Avenida Norte y 7 Calle PTE No 4109
Cote Escalon, San Salvador, El Salvador
Tel.: (503) 25254900
Advertising & Marketing Services
N.A.I.C.S.: 541810

Ipsos Holding Belgium SA (1)
Boulevard Paepsem 11B, 1070, Anderlecht, Belgium
Tel.: (32) 92162222
Web Site: http://www.ipsos.com
Emp.: 5
Investment Management Service

IPSOS S.A.

Ipsos S.A.—(Continued)
N.A.I.C.S.: 523999

Ipsos Hong Kong Limited (1)
2/F Leighton Centre 77 Leighton Road, Causeway Bay, Hong Kong, China (Hong Kong)
Tel.: (852) 2881 5388
Web Site: http://ipsoshk.com
Emp.: 240
Marketing Research Service
N.A.I.C.S.: 541910

Ipsos Hungary Zrt (1)
Pap Karoly u 4-6, 1139, Budapest, Hungary
Tel.: (36) 14767600
Web Site: https://www.ipsos.com
Advertising & Marketing Services
N.A.I.C.S.: 541810
Andrea Horvath (Acct Mgr)

Ipsos Inc. (1)
7th floor Unit A South Tower Rockwell Business Center Sheridan, Sheridan cor United Streets, Mandaluyong, 1554, Philippines
Tel.: (63) 286333997
Web Site: https://www.ipsos.com
Advertising & Marketing Services
N.A.I.C.S.: 541810

Ipsos Indonesia PT (1)
Gd WKC Lt 2 Jln R P Soerosos No 32, Jakarta, Indonesia
Tel.: (62) 213155970
Sales Range: $25-49.9 Million
Emp.: 80
Marketing Research Service
N.A.I.C.S.: 541910
Iwan Murty (Country Mgr)

Ipsos Insight Corp. (1)
1075 W Georgia Street Suite 1700, Vancouver, V6E 3C9, BC, Canada
Tel.: (778) 373-5000
Web Site: http://www.ipsos.com
Sales Range: $25-49.9 Million
Market Research Services
N.A.I.C.S.: 541910

Ipsos Insight Inc (1)
250 E 5th St Chiquita Ctr, Cincinnati, OH 45202
Tel.: (513) 639-3700
Web Site: http://www.ipsos-insight.com
Marketing Research Service
N.A.I.C.S.: 541910

Ipsos Interactive Services Canada LP (1)
160 Bloor St E 3rd Fl, Toronto, M4W 1B9, ON, Canada
Tel.: (416) 324-2900
Web Site: http://www.ipsos.ca
Sales Range: $75-99.9 Million
Emp.: 30
Marketing Research Service
N.A.I.C.S.: 541910

Ipsos Interactive Services SRL (1)
319G Splaiul Independentei Atrium House Ground floor, 6th District, 060044, Bucharest, Romania
Tel.: (40) 372177231
Advertising & Marketing Services
N.A.I.C.S.: 541810

Ipsos Japan Holding KK (1)
3-5-8 Nakameguro, Meguro-Ku, Tokyo, 153-0061, Japan
Tel.: (81) 357222141
Investment Management Service
N.A.I.C.S.: 523999

Subsidiary (Domestic):

Ipsos JSR KK (2)
3-5-8 Nakameguro, Meguro, Tokyo, 153-0061, Japan
Tel.: (81) 357222141
Web Site: http://www.ipsosjapan.jp
Marketing Research Service
N.A.I.C.S.: 541910
Shunichi Uchida (Country Mgr)

Ipsos KK (1)
6th and 8th Floor Hulic Kamiyacho Building 4-3-13 Toranomon, Minato-ku, Tokyo, 105-0001, Japan
Tel.: (81) 368678001
Advertising & Marketing Services
N.A.I.C.S.: 541810

Ipsos KMG A.S. (1)
Centrum Business Centre Aydinevler Sanayi Cad No 3, 34854, Istanbul, Turkiye
Tel.: (90) 2165871111
Web Site: http://www.ipsos-kmg.com
Marketing Research Service
N.A.I.C.S.: 541910

Ipsos LLC (1)
Level 9A Nam A Bank Tower 201-203 CMT8 Street, Ward 4 District 3, Ho Chi Minh City, Vietnam
Tel.: (84) 2838329820
Web Site: https://www.ipsos.com
Advertising & Marketing Services
N.A.I.C.S.: 541810

Ipsos LLP (1)
5A office 101 Tole bi str Dalich Business Center, Almalinskiy Raion, 50020, Almaty, Kazakhstan
Tel.: (7) 7273560633
Advertising & Marketing Services
N.A.I.C.S.: 541810

Ipsos Limited (1)
6/F China Life Center Tower A One HarbourGate 18 Hung Luen Road, Hung Hom, China (Hong Kong)
Tel.: (852) 28815388
Web Site: https://www.ipsos.com
Advertising & Marketing Services
N.A.I.C.S.: 541810

Ipsos Limited (1)
Block 3 Blackrock Business Park, Dublin, Blackrock, Ireland
Tel.: (353) 14389000
Advertising & Marketing Services
N.A.I.C.S.: 541810

Ipsos Limited (1)
Acorn House 97 James Gichuru Road 200 City Square, Lavington, 68230, Nairobi, Kenya
Tel.: (254) 20386272133
Advertising & Marketing Services
N.A.I.C.S.: 541810

Ipsos Limited (1)
Hse No 4 Farrar Avenue Asylum Down PMB 7 Kanda, Accra, Ghana
Tel.: (233) 302232970
Advertising & Marketing Services
N.A.I.C.S.: 541810

Ipsos Limited (1)
9632 Central Street, PO Box 36605, Chudleigh, Lusaka, Zambia
Tel.: (260) 211295852
Advertising & Marketing Services
N.A.I.C.S.: 541810

Ipsos Loyalty Pty Ltd. (1)
Level 2/51 Berry Street, North Sydney, 2060, NSW, Australia
Tel.: (61) 299005100
Web Site: http://www.ipsos.com.au
Marketing Research Service
N.A.I.C.S.: 541910

Subsidiary (Non-US):

Ipsos ASI Italy (2)
Via Tolmezzo 15, 20132, Milan, Italy
Tel.: (39) 02361051
Web Site: http://www.ipsos.com
Marketing Research Service
N.A.I.C.S.: 541910

Ipsos Ltd. (1)
3rd Floor Padre Pio House Plot 32 Lumumba Avenue, PO Box 21571, Kampala, Uganda
Tel.: (256) 312311509
Web Site: https://www.ipsos.com
Advertising & Marketing Services
N.A.I.C.S.: 541810

Ipsos Ltd. (1)
19th Floor Empire Tower 1 South Sathorn Road, Yannawa Sathorn, Bangkok, 10120, Thailand
Tel.: (66) 20880100
Advertising & Marketing Services
N.A.I.C.S.: 541810

Ipsos Ltd. (1)
Level 3 8 Rockridge Avenue, Penrose, Auckland, 1061, New Zealand

Tel.: (64) 95380500
Advertising & Marketing Services
N.A.I.C.S.: 541810

Ipsos MORI UK Ltd. (1)
3 Thomas More Square, London, E1W 1YW, United Kingdom
Tel.: (44) 2030595000
Advertising & Marketing Services
N.A.I.C.S.: 541810
Steve Duffy (Dir-IT)

Ipsos Markinor Pty Ltd (1)
Cnr Republic Rd & Oak Ave Ferndale, Randburg, Johannesburg, 2123, South Africa
Tel.: (27) 116868400
Web Site: http://www.ipsos-markinor.co.za
Sales Range: $25-49.9 Million
Emp.: 50
Marketing Research Service
N.A.I.C.S.: 541910
Ryan Gould (Country Mgr)

Ipsos Mozambique, Lda (1)
Av Francisco Orlando Magumbwe No 528, Maputo, Mozambique
Tel.: (258) 21497828
Advertising & Marketing Services
N.A.I.C.S.: 541810

Ipsos NORM AB (1)
Halsingegatan 49 5tr, 113 31, Stockholm, Sweden
Tel.: (46) 852248300
Web Site: http://www.norm.ipsos.com
Advertising & Marketing Services
N.A.I.C.S.: 541810

Ipsos NV (Belgium) SA (1)
Rooigemlaan 2, Bus 4, 9000, Gent, Belgium
Tel.: (32) 92162222
Advertising & Marketing Services
N.A.I.C.S.: 541810

Ipsos Napoleon Franco (1)
Calle 74 No 11-81 Piso 5, Bogota, D.C., Colombia
Tel.: (57) 1 376 9400
Web Site: http://www.ipsos.com
Sales Range: $75-99.9 Million
Emp.: 500
Market Research
N.A.I.C.S.: 541910

Holding (Domestic):

Ipsos Napoleon Franco & Co. (2)
Calle 74 No 11 81 5th Fl, Bogota, Colombia
Tel.: (57) 13769400
Sales Range: $25-49.9 Million
Emp.: 60
Consumer Marketing
N.A.I.C.S.: 541910

Branch (Domestic):

Napoleon Franco & Co. (3)
Carrera 43 A No 1A Sur-267, Oficina 403, Medellin, Colombia
Tel.: (57) 42660337
Sales Range: $25-49.9 Million
Emp.: 10
Consumer Marketing
N.A.I.C.S.: 541910

Ipsos Nigeria Limited (1)
No 70 Adeniyi Jones Avenue, Ikeja, Lagos, Nigeria
Tel.: (234) 8066299805
Web Site: https://www.ipsos.com
Advertising & Marketing Services
N.A.I.C.S.: 541810

Ipsos North America (1)
1271 Avenue of the Americas 15th Fl, New York, NY 10020
Tel.: (212) 265-3200
Web Site: http://www.ipsosna.com
Sales Range: $25-49.9 Million
Emp.: 70
Market Research
N.A.I.C.S.: 541910

Subsidiary (Domestic):

Ipsos North America (2)
222 W Adams St Ste 1100, Chicago, IL 60606 (100%)
Tel.: (312) 526-4000
Web Site: http://www.ipsos-na.com

Assembles & Analyzes Marketing Information
N.A.I.C.S.: 541910
Pierre Le Manh (CEO)

Subsidiary (Domestic):

Synovate-Mahwah (3)
1200 MacArthur Blvd 3rd Fl, Mahwah, NJ 07430-2331 (100%)
Tel.: (201) 529-5540
Sales Range: $25-49.9 Million
Emp.: 50
Market Research Services
N.A.I.C.S.: 541910
Jackie Ilacqua (Sr VP)

Synovate-New York (3)
360 Pk Ave S Fl 5, New York, NY 10010 (100%)
Tel.: (212) 293-6100
Sales Range: $25-49.9 Million
Emp.: 75
Market Research Services

Ipsos Norway AS (1)
Karemsyst Alle 20 Skoyen 4th Floor, 278, Oslo, Norway
Tel.: (47) 22 95 47 00
Web Site: http://www.ipsos-mmi.no
Marketing Research Service
N.A.I.C.S.: 541910

Ipsos Novaction KK (1)
Dai 7 Akiyama Bld 5F 5-3 Koujimachi, Chiyoda, Tokyo, 102-0083, Japan
Tel.: (81) 352168860
Web Site: http://www.ipsos-novaction.co.jp
Sales Range: $25-49.9 Million
Emp.: 20
Marketing Research Service
N.A.I.C.S.: 541910

Ipsos OOO Ltd (1)
5 Gamsonovski Lane Bldg 1, 115191, Moscow, Russia
Tel.: (7) 4959815646
Web Site: http://www.ipsos.ru
Emp.: 250
Marketing Research Service
N.A.I.C.S.: 541910
Nadezhda Alexeeva (Dir-Client Strategy)

Ipsos OTX Corp. (1)
10567 Jefferson Blvd, Culver City, CA 90232
Tel.: (310) 736-3400
Web Site: http://www.ipsos-na.com
Sales Range: $25-49.9 Million
Emp.: 130
Marketing Research Service
N.A.I.C.S.: 541910

Ipsos OTX Inc. (1)
1271 Ave Of The Americas 15th Fl, New York, NY 10001
Tel.: (212) 524-8200
Marketing Research Service
N.A.I.C.S.: 541910

Ipsos Observer SA (1)
35 Rue Du Val De Marne, 75013, Paris, France
Tel.: (33) 141989000
Marketing Research Service
N.A.I.C.S.: 541910

Ipsos Observer SA (1)
Olazabal 1371, 1428, Buenos Aires, Argentina
Tel.: (54) 147066500
Advertising & Marketing Services
N.A.I.C.S.: 541810

Ipsos Operaciones SA (1)
Llano Castellano 13-3a, 28034, Madrid, Spain
Tel.: (34) 917672199
Web Site: http://www.ipsos.es
Sales Range: $25-49.9 Million
Emp.: 100
Marketing Research Service
N.A.I.C.S.: 541910

Subsidiary (Domestic):

Ipsos Estudios Internacionales SA (2)
Av Llano Castellano 13-3a, 28034, Madrid, Spain

AND PRIVATE COMPANIES — IPSOS S.A.

Tel.: (34) 917672199
Web Site: https://www.ipsos.es
Emp.: 100
Marketing Research Service
N.A.I.C.S.: 541910
Frances Costa *(Mng Dir)*

Ipsos Operations Canada LP (1)
1285 West Pender St 2nd Flr, Vancouver,
V6E 4B1, BC, Canada
Tel.: (778) 373-5000
Marketing Research Service
N.A.I.C.S.: 541910

Ipsos Opinion y Mercado S.A. (1)
Av Reducto 1363, Miraflores, 18, Lima,
Peru
Tel.: (51) 6100100
Advertising & Marketing Services
N.A.I.C.S.: 541810

Ipsos Opinion y Mercado SA (1)
Avenida Ecuador Waldo Ballivian Street N
540, Sopocachi, La Paz, Bolivia
Tel.: (591) 22167676
Advertising & Marketing Services
N.A.I.C.S.: 541810

Ipsos Panama SA (1)
Edificio PDC Piso 15 Oficina 15-A Calle 56
Este, Panama, Panama
Tel.: (507) 3700600
Web Site: http://www.ipsos.com
Marketing Research Service
N.A.I.C.S.: 541910

Ipsos Polska Sp. Z.o.o. (1)
Ambassador Building Domaniewska 34a,
02-672, Warsaw, Poland (100%)
Tel.: (48) 224487700
Web Site: http://www.ipsos.com
Sales Range: $25-49.9 Million
Emp.: 100
Market Research
N.A.I.C.S.: 541910

Ipsos Portugal (1)
Av Duque D'avila 26 - 3rd Floor, 1000 141,
Lisbon, Portugal (100%)
Tel.: (351) 213583480
Web Site: http://www.ipsos.com
Emp.: 15
Market Research
N.A.I.C.S.: 541910

Ipsos Public Affairs Pty Ltd (1)
Level 2/51 Berry Street, North Sydney,
2061, NSW, Australia
Tel.: (61) 299005100
Web Site: http://www.ipsos.com
Emp.: 50
Marketing Research Service
N.A.I.C.S.: 541910

Ipsos Reid Corp. (1)
1285 West Pender St 2nd Fl, Vancouver,
V6E 4B1, BC, Canada
Tel.: (778) 373-5000
Web Site: http://www.ipsos-na.com
Emp.: 100
Marketing Research Service
N.A.I.C.S.: 541910

Ipsos Research Pvt. Ltd. (1)
Lotus Corporate Park Unit No 1701 17th
floor F Wing Off, Western Express Highway
Goregaon East, Mumbai, 400 063, India
Tel.: (91) 2266208000
Advertising & Marketing Services
N.A.I.C.S.: 541810

Ipsos SA (1)
Calle 31 300 Meters East 100 Meters North
and 25 East Of The Santa, Teresita, San
Jose, Costa Rica
Tel.: (506) 22536108
Advertising & Marketing Services
N.A.I.C.S.: 541810

Ipsos SARL (1)
Cocody 2 Plateaux Rue j 54 Villa Duplex n
69 11, BP 2280, Abidjan, Cote d'Ivoire
Tel.: (225) 22411488
Advertising & Marketing Services
N.A.I.C.S.: 541810

Ipsos SARL (1)
Khairi Building 4th Floor Center Urbain
Nord, 1080, Tunis, Tunisia
Tel.: (216) 71948864
Advertising & Marketing Services

N.A.I.C.S.: 541810

Ipsos SRL (1)
Frank Felix Miranda 47 Naco, Santo Domingo, Dominican Republic
Tel.: (809) 5677005
Web Site: https://www.ipsos.com
Advertising & Marketing Services
N.A.I.C.S.: 541810

Ipsos Saudi Arabia LLC (1)
Samama Al Tahlia Bldg Prince Muhammad
Bin Abdulaziz Rd, PO Box 10042, Riyadh,
11433, Saudi Arabia
Tel.: (966) 920018006
Web Site: https://www.ipsos.com
Advertising & Marketing Services
N.A.I.C.S.: 541810

Ipsos Sdn, Bhd. (1)
23rd Floor Centrepoint North Mid Valley
City, Lingkaran Syed Putra, 59200, Kuala
Lumpur, Malaysia
Tel.: (60) 322893000
Web Site: http://www.ipsos.com
Sales Range: $25-49.9 Million
Emp.: 200
Market Research Services
N.A.I.C.S.: 541910

Ipsos Senegal SASU (1)
Lot 36 SICAP Mermoz VDN 255822, Dakar,
Senegal
Tel.: (221) 338244689
Advertising & Marketing Services
N.A.I.C.S.: 541810

Ipsos Singapore Pte Ltd (1)
3 Killiney Road Unit 05-01 Winsland House
1, Block B 03-26/27/28 Jackson Square,
Singapore, 239519, Singapore
Tel.: (65) 6333 1511
Web Site: http://www.ipsosasiapacific.com
Sales Range: $25-49.9 Million
Emp.: 161
Market Research Services
N.A.I.C.S.: 541910
Katharine Zhou *(Mng Dir)*

Ipsos Sp. z o. o. (1)
Ambassador Building Domaniewska 34A,
02-672, Warsaw, Poland
Tel.: (48) 224487700
Advertising & Marketing Services
N.A.I.C.S.: 541810

Ipsos Srl (1)
Via Mauro Macchi 61, 20124, Milan, Italy
Tel.: (39) 02361051
Marketing Research Service
N.A.I.C.S.: 541910
Nando Pagnoncelli *(Country Mgr)*

Subsidiary (Domestic):

Ipsos Operations Srl (2)
Via Tolmezzo 15, Milan, 20132, Italy
Tel.: (39) 02361051
Marketing Research Service
N.A.I.C.S.: 541910

Ipsos Stat Jordan Ltd. (1)
Arar street Complex No 231 1st and 2nd
floor Wadi Saqra, PO Box 830871, Amman,
11183, Jordan
Tel.: (962) 65697193
Web Site: https://www.ipsos.com
Advertising & Marketing Services
N.A.I.C.S.: 541810

Ipsos Strategic Puls D.o.o. (1)
Bulevar Svetog Petra Cetinjskog 149/1,
81000, Podgorica, Montenegro
Tel.: (382) 20411610
Web Site: https://www.ipsos.com
Advertising & Marketing Services
N.A.I.C.S.: 541810

Ipsos Strategic Puls SAS (1)
35 rue du Val de Marne, 75013, Paris,
France
Tel.: (33) 141989000
Marketing Research Service
N.A.I.C.S.: 541910

Subsidiary (Non-US):

Ipsos Puls doo Split (2)
Sime Ljubica 37, Split, 21000, Croatia
Tel.: (385) 21430430
Marketing Research Service

N.A.I.C.S.: 541910

Subsidiary (Non-US):

Puls Raziskovanje d.o.o (3)
No 152 Martenska, 1000, Ljubljana, Slovenia
Tel.: (386) 59026801
Sales Range: $25-49.9 Million
Emp.: 7
Marketing Research Service
N.A.I.C.S.: 541910

Subsidiary (Non-US):

Ipsos Strategic Marketing d.o.o. (2)
Gavrila Principa 8, 11000, Belgrade, Serbia
Tel.: (381) 113284075
Marketing Research Service
N.A.I.C.S.: 541910
Shane Farrell *(Head-Europe, Middle East & Africa)*

Ipsos Strategic Puls Sa'jewo (1)
Hamdije Kresevljakovica 7c, 71 000, Sarajevo, Bosnia & Herzegovina
Tel.: (387) 33442133
Marketing Research Service
N.A.I.C.S.: 541910

Ipsos Strategic Puls d.o.o.e.l. Skopje (1)
Rampo Levkata 13a, 1000, Skopje, North Macedonia
Tel.: (389) 23092720
Web Site: http://www.ipsos.com
Sales Range: $25-49.9 Million
Emp.: 11
Marketing Research Service
N.A.I.C.S.: 541910

Ipsos Sweden AB (1)
Sankt Goransgatan 63 1tr, Box 12236, 112
33, Stockholm, Sweden
Tel.: (46) 859899800
Web Site: https://www.ipsos.com
Emp.: 80
Marketing Research Service
N.A.I.C.S.: 541910
Pernilla Wrangdahl *(Dir-Human Resources)*

Subsidiary (Domestic):

IB-IMRI (2)
Kopmangatan 1, 871 30, Harnosand, Sweden
Tel.: (46) 611349720
Web Site: http://www.ibimri.se
Emp.: 16
Data Collection Services
N.A.I.C.S.: 518210
Hasse Tjernberg *(Project Mgr)*

Ipsos Taiwan Ltd. (1)
Unit A 25F No 105 Sec 2 Tun Hwa S Rd,
Da-an, Taipei, 106, Taiwan
Tel.: (886) 2 2701 7278
Web Site: http://www.ipsos.com
Financial Transaction Processing Services
N.A.I.C.S.: 522320

Ipsos Tambor SR s.r.o. (1)
Heydukova 12, 811 06, Bratislava, Slovakia
Tel.: (421) 252 932 142
Sales Range: $25-49.9 Million
Emp.: 11
Marketing Research Service
N.A.I.C.S.: 541910
Michal Drobnik *(Country Mgr)*

Ipsos Tambor s.r.o. (1)
Slavonic House entrance E Na Prikope 22,
110 00, Prague, Czech Republic
Tel.: (420) 226 513 111
Web Site: http://www.ipsos.cz
Sales Range: $25-49.9 Million
Emp.: 12
Marketing Research Service
N.A.I.C.S.: 541910

Ipsos Tanzania Limited (1)
Regent Business Park Plot No 172 Regent
Estate-Mikocheni, PO Box 106253, Dar es
Salaam, Tanzania
Tel.: (255) 222775851
Web Site: https://www.ipsos.com
Advertising & Marketing Services
N.A.I.C.S.: 541810

Ipsos Ukraine Llc (1)

6 Vladimirskaya St Office 1, 1025, Kiev,
Ukraine
Tel.: (380) 442799641
Web Site: http://www.ipsos.com.ua
Sales Range: $25-49.9 Million
Emp.: 43
Marketing Research Service
N.A.I.C.S.: 541910
Irina Baleva *(CEO)*

Ipsos Zrt. (1)
Thaly Kalman u 39, 1096, Budapest, Hungary
Tel.: (36) 14767600
Web Site: http://www.ipsos.com
Emp.: 50
Marketing Research Service
N.A.I.C.S.: 541910

Ipsos d.o.o (1)
Budmanijeva 1, 10000, Zagreb, Croatia
Tel.: (385) 16008900
Advertising & Marketing Services
N.A.I.C.S.: 541810

Ipsos d.o.o. (1)
Leskoskova Cesta 9e, 1000, Ljubljana, Slovenia
Tel.: (386) 59026800
Web Site: https://www.ipsos.com
Advertising & Marketing Services
N.A.I.C.S.: 541810

Ipsos d.o.o. (1)
Hamdije Kresevljakovica 7c, 71000, Sarajevo, Bosnia & Herzegovina
Tel.: (387) 33442133
Advertising & Marketing Services
N.A.I.C.S.: 541810

Ipsos, Inc. (1)
463 Calle Fernando Calder, San Juan, PR
00918 (100%)
Tel.: (787) 753-8370
Web Site: http://www.ipsos.com
Emp.: 20
Marketing Research Service
N.A.I.C.S.: 541910

Ipsos, S.A. (1)
13 calle 2-60 Zona 10 Edificio Topacio Azul
Oficina 803 Ciudad de, Guatemala, Guatemala
Tel.: (502) 22699000
Web Site: https://www.ipsos.com
Advertising & Marketing Services
N.A.I.C.S.: 541810

Ipsos-ASI (1)
Av Santa Fe 94 Torre A Piso 7 Col Zedec
Santa Fe, Alvaro Obregon, 1210, Mexico,
Mexico (100%)
Tel.: (52) 5511010000
Web Site: http://www.ipsos.com
Sales Range: $25-49.9 Million
Emp.: 200
Market Research
N.A.I.C.S.: 541910

Ipsos-ASI (1)
Av Nove de Julho 4865 7th floor, Itaim Bibi,
Sao Paulo, 01407-200, Brazil (100%)
Tel.: (55) 1121598400
Web Site: http://www.ipsos.com
Sales Range: $25-49.9 Million
Emp.: 200
Market Research
N.A.I.C.S.: 541910

Ipsos-ASI (1)
Olazabal 1371, Capital Federal,
C1428DGE, Buenos Aires,
Argentina (90%)
Tel.: (54) 1147066500
Sales Range: $25-49.9 Million
Emp.: 200
Market Research
N.A.I.C.S.: 541910
Gonzalo Santamarina *(Country Mgr)*

Ipsos-ASI, Inc. (1)
Corporate Park 301 Merritt 7 4th Fl, Norwalk, CT 06851 (100%)
Tel.: (203) 840-3400
Web Site: http://www.ipsos-asi.com
Sales Range: $25-49.9 Million
Emp.: 50
Market Research
N.A.I.C.S.: 541910
Gerald C. Lukeman *(Chm)*

IPSOS S.A.

Ipsos S.A.—(Continued)

Ipsos-Investigacion de Mercados (1)
Llano Castellano 13- 3, 28034, Madrid, Spain (100%)
Tel.: (34) 917672199
Web Site: http://www.ipsos.com
Sales Range: $25-49.9 Million
Emp.: 180
Market Research
N.A.I.C.S.: 541910

Ipsos-Loyalty, Inc. (1)
Morris Corporate Ctr 2 1 Upper Pond Rd Bldg D 2nd Fl, Parsippany, NJ 07054-1050
Tel.: (973) 658-1700
Web Site: http://www.ipsosna.com
Emp.: 100
Marketing Research Service
N.A.I.C.S.: 541910
Jeff Repace *(Sr VP)*

Ipsos-NPD Canada Inc. (1)
1285 West Pender St Suite 200, Vancouver, V6E 4B1, BC, Canada
Tel.: (778) 373-5000
Web Site: http://www.ipsos.com
Emp.: 85
Marketing Research Service
N.A.I.C.S.: 541910
Michael Rodenburgh *(VP)*

Ipsos-Novaction Latin America (1)
Hegel 221, Colonia Polanco, CP 11560, Mexico, DF, Mexico (100%)
Tel.: (52) 511010000
Sales Range: $25-49.9 Million
Emp.: 200
Provider of Market Research Services
N.A.I.C.S.: 541910

Ipsos-Novaction Latin America (1)
Ave Nove de Julho 4865 4th Fl Conjunto 62A, Itaim Bibi, CEP 01407-200, Sao Paulo, SP, Brazil (100%)
Tel.: (55) 1121598400
Sales Range: $25-49.9 Million
Emp.: 250
Marketing Research
N.A.I.C.S.: 541910
Enrique Biancotti *(CEO-Latin America)*

Ipsos-Novaction Latin America (1)
Olazabal 1371, 1428, Buenos Aires, Argentina (90%)
Tel.: (54) 1147066500
Web Site: https://www.ipsos.com
Sales Range: $25-49.9 Million
Emp.: 95
Market Research
N.A.I.C.S.: 541910
Daniel Finder *(Pres)*

Ipsos-Stat (1)
Ipsos Building, BP 55103, Dekwaneh, Beirut, Lebanon
Tel.: (961) 149 4136
Web Site: http://www.ipsos.com
Sales Range: $25-49.9 Million
Emp.: 85
Market Research
N.A.I.C.S.: 541910

Subsidiary (Non-US):

Ipsos Stat Bahrain W.L.L (2)
Suite 11 Al Ain Bldg Adliya Av Block 334, PO Box 3053, Manama, Bahrain
Tel.: (973) 17827344
Emp.: 1
Marketing Research Service
N.A.I.C.S.: 541910
Bassam Assaad *(Dir-HR)*

Ipsos Stat Fz. LLC (2)
8th Fl Al Thuraya Tower 1, PO Box 71283, Dubai, 71283, United Arab Emirates
Tel.: (971) 44408980
Web Site: http://www.ipsos.com
Emp.: 17
Marketing Research Service
N.A.I.C.S.: 541910

Ipsos-Szonda (1)
Thaly Kalman u 39, Budapest, 1096, Hungary (100%)
Tel.: (36) 14767600
Web Site: http://www.ipsos-szonda.hu
Sales Range: $1-9.9 Million
Emp.: 100
Global Research

N.A.I.C.S.: 541910

Japan Marketing Operations KK (1)
5-2-2 Rinkaicho, Edogawa, Tokyo, 134-0086, Japan
Tel.: (81) 3 6848 7275
Web Site: http://www.jsr-group.jp
Marketing Research Service
N.A.I.C.S.: 541910
Nozomi Horiguchi *(Mgr-Ops)*

Livra Europe Ltd. (1)
3 Thomas More Square, London, E1W 1YW, United Kingdom
Tel.: (44) 2076168420
Sales Range: $25-49.9 Million
Emp.: 3
Marketing Research Service
N.A.I.C.S.: 541910

Marocstat S.A.R.L (1)
16 Rue des Asphodeles Maarif, 20380, Casablanca, Morocco
Tel.: (212) 522985702
Advertising & Marketing Services
N.A.I.C.S.: 541810

Mori Ltd (1)
3 Thomas More Square, London, E1W 1YW, United Kingdom
Tel.: (44) 2031000000
Emp.: 400
Marketing Research Service
N.A.I.C.S.: 541910

Subsidiary (Domestic):

Ipsos MORI (2)
Kings House Kymberley Road, Harrow, HA1 1PT, Mddx, United Kingdom (100%)
Tel.: (44) 2088618000
Web Site: http://www.ipsos-rsl.com
Sales Range: $75-99.9 Million
Emp.: 300
Market Research
N.A.I.C.S.: 541910
Didier Truchot *(CEO & Chm)*

Subsidiary (Non-US):

Ipsos MRBI Ltd (2)
Block 3 Blackrock Business Park Carysfort Avenue, Blackrock, Dublin, Ireland
Tel.: (353) 14389000
Web Site: http://www.ipsosmrbi.com
Sales Range: $25-49.9 Million
Emp.: 25
Marketing Research Service
N.A.I.C.S.: 541910

PT Ipsos Market Research (1)
Mega Plaza Building 6th Floor Jl HR Rasuna Said Kav C-3, Jakarta Selatan, 12920, Indonesia
Tel.: (62) 2152964388
Advertising & Marketing Services
N.A.I.C.S.: 541810

Popcorn Media SA (1)
35 rue du Val de Marne, 75013, Paris, France
Tel.: (33) 156893232
Web Site: https://www.popcorn-media.fr
Software Services
N.A.I.C.S.: 541511

Synovate Holdings BV (1)
Koningin Wilhelminaplein 2-4, Amsterdam, 1062 HK, Netherlands
Tel.: (31) 206070707
Web Site: http://www.ipsos.com
Investment Management Service
N.A.I.C.S.: 523999

Synovate K.K. (1)
Toranomon Marine Bldg, 3 18 19 Toranomon Minato ku, Tokyo, 105-0001, Japan
Tel.: (81) 3 5408 3853
Sales Range: $25-49.9 Million
Emp.: 120
Marketing Research
N.A.I.C.S.: 541910

Synovate Pty. Ltd. (1)
Level 2 85 Coventry St, Melbourne, 3205, VIC, Australia
Tel.: (61) 396949199
Web Site: http://www.synovate.com
Marketing Research
N.A.I.C.S.: 541910

Synthesio, Inc. (1)
35 W 31st St 5th Fl, New York, NY 10001
Tel.: (646) 760-0000
Web Site: http://www.synthesio.com
Emp.: 160
Social Intelligence Platforms
N.A.I.C.S.: 513210
Loic Moisand *(Co-Founder & CEO)*

Subsidiary (Non-US):

Synthesio Paris (2)
35 Rue du Val de Marne, 75001, Paris, France (100%)
Tel.: (33) 141989300
Web Site: http://www.synthesio.com
Social Intelligence Platforms
N.A.I.C.S.: 513210
Nicolas Saintagne *(Mng Dir)*

Synthesio Singapore (2)
3 Killiney Road 05-01 Winsland House 1, Singapore, 239519, Singapore (100%)
Tel.: (65) 68173121
Web Site: http://www.synthesio.com
Social Media Intelligence Platforms
N.A.I.C.S.: 513210
Mathieu Grele *(CFO)*

Synthesio UK (2)
1 Mark Square, London, EC2A 4EG, United Kingdom (100%)
Tel.: (44) 207 5660 400
Web Site: http://www.synthesio.com
Social Media Platform Solutions
N.A.I.C.S.: 513210
Catriona Oldershaw *(Mng Dir)*

Trendtest GmbH (1)
Kolonnenstrasse 26, 10829, Berlin, Germany
Tel.: (49) 30787830
Web Site: https://www.trendtest.de
Sales Range: $25-49.9 Million
Emp.: 12
Marketing Research Service
N.A.I.C.S.: 541910

IPSWICH BUILDING SOCIETY

Freehold House 6-8 The Havens Ransomes Europark, Ipswich, IP3 9SJ, United Kingdom
Tel.: (44) 3301230723
Web Site: http://www.ibs.co.uk
Rev.: $25,084,350
Assets: $882,033,949
Liabilities: $835,183,597
Net Worth: $46,850,352
Earnings: $1,899,197
Emp.: 81
Fiscal Year-end: 11/30/19
Mortgage Lending & Other Financial Services
N.A.I.C.S.: 522310
Alan Harris *(Chm)*

IPTE FACTORY AUTOMATION N.V.

Geleenlaan 5, Genk, 3600, Belgium
Tel.: (32) 89623000 BE
Web Site: http://www.ipte.com
Year Founded: 2010
Sales Range: $250-299.9 Million
Emp.: 500
Automated Electronic & Mechanical Component Mfr
N.A.I.C.S.: 334111
Hubert Baren *(Gen Mgr)*

Subsidiaries:

Connect Group N.V. (1)
Industriestraat 4, 1910, Kampenhout, Belgium (100%)
Tel.: (32) 1 661 8920
Web Site: http://www.connectgroup.com
Sales Range: $100-124.9 Million
Electronics Manufacturing Services
N.A.I.C.S.: 334419
Dominique Moorkens *(Chm)*

Subsidiary (Non-US):

Connect Group GmbH (2)
Daimlerstrasse 10, 72639, Neuffen, Germany (100%)

Tel.: (49) 7022 9446 0
Web Site: http://www.connectgroup.com
Electronics Manufacturing Services
N.A.I.C.S.: 334419
Irmin Mack *(Mng Dir)*

Connect Group Nederland BV (2)
De Run 4281, 5503 LM, Veldhoven, Netherlands (100%)
Tel.: (31) 40 84 44 999
Web Site: http://www.connectgroup.com
Electronics Manufacturing Services
N.A.I.C.S.: 334419
Niels van Zon *(Bus Mgr)*

Connectronics s.r.o. (2)
Billundska 2756, 272 01, Kladno, Czech Republic (100%)
Tel.: (420) 312 518 311
Web Site: http://www.connectgroup.com
Electronics Manufacturing Services
N.A.I.C.S.: 334419

SC Connectronics Romania S.R.L. (2)
Sos Borsului 40, Bihor, 410605, Oradea, Romania (100%)
Tel.: (40) 359 403 250
Web Site: http://www.connectgroup.com
Electronics Manufacturing Services
N.A.I.C.S.: 334419

IPTE AndElec Sarl (1)
3 Impasse Bidault - Z I de la Croix Blanche, 44260, Malville, France
Tel.: (33) 2 40 56 00 66
Automated Electronic & Mechanical Component Mfr
N.A.I.C.S.: 334419

IPTE Automation ou (1)
Peterburi tee 34/11A, 11415, Tallinn, Estonia
Tel.: (372) 6 391 770
Automated Electronic & Mechanical Component Mfr
N.A.I.C.S.: 334419

IPTE Beernem (1)
Wellingstraat 109, 8730, Beernem, Belgium
Tel.: (32) 50 250 810
Automated Electronic & Mechanical Component Mfr
N.A.I.C.S.: 334419

IPTE Germany GmbH (1)
Schleifweg 14, 90562, Heroldsberg, Germany
Tel.: (49) 911 7848 0
Automated Electronic & Mechanical Component Mfr
N.A.I.C.S.: 334419

IPTE Iberia - Automacao Industrial (1)
Rua do Mocambique LT 27 No 323, 3880-106, 3880-106, Ovar, Portugal
Tel.: (351) 256 579 870
Automated Electronic & Mechanical Component Mfr
N.A.I.C.S.: 334419
Rui Homem *(Engr-Project)*

IPTE Industrial Automation (Shanghai) Co. Ltd. (1)
Building C No 88 Lane 3509 South Hongmei Road, 201108, Shanghai, China
Tel.: (86) 21 3350 6805
Automated Electronic & Mechanical Component Mfr
N.A.I.C.S.: 334419
Martin Vilist *(Mgr-Mechanical Engrg)*

IPTE Mexico S. de R.L. de C.V. (1)
Broca 2605-32 Alamo Industrial, Guadalajara, 45593, Mexico
Tel.: (52) 33 36755597
Automated Electronic & Mechanical Component Mfr
N.A.I.C.S.: 334419

IPTE Oradea (1)
Ogorului 146, 410554, Oradea, Bihor, Romania
Tel.: (40) 359 401 260
Automated Electronic & Mechanical Component Mfr
N.A.I.C.S.: 334419
Ovidiu-Ciprin Balint *(Gen Mgr)*

IPTE Platzgummer GmbH (1)

Siemensstrasse 8, 85221, Dachau, Germany
Tel.: (49) 8131 3834 0
Web Site: http://www.ipte.com
Automated Electronic & Mechanical Component Mfr
N.A.I.C.S.: 334419
Vladimir Dobosch *(Mng Dir)*

IPTE Prodel France S.A. (1)
153 rue de Verdun, 60170, Carlepont, France
Tel.: (33) 3 44 75 81 02
Web Site: http://www.ipte.com
Emp.: 50
Automated Electronic & Mechanical Component Mfr
N.A.I.C.S.: 334419
Cherry Sene *(Mng Dir)*

IPTE Spain S.L.U. (1)
C/Ignasi Iglesias 24, 43206, Reus, Spain
Tel.: (34) 977 271 056
Automated Electronic & Mechanical Component Mfr
N.A.I.C.S.: 334419

IPTE USA (1)
5935 Shiloh Rd E - Ste 100, Alpharetta, GA 30005
Tel.: (678) 807-0067
Automated Electronic & Mechanical Component Mfr
N.A.I.C.S.: 334419

IPWA PLC
45 Oba Akran Avenue, PO Box 67, Ikeja, Lagos, Nigeria
Tel.: (234) 08060400004
Web Site: http://www.ipwaplc.com
Year Founded: 1961
Paint & Lacquer Mfr
N.A.I.C.S.: 325510
Sulaimon Ibikunle Tella *(CEO & Mng Dir)*

IQ EQ LUXEMBOURG SA
412F Route d'Esch, Luxembourg, 2086, Luxembourg
Tel.: (352) 466 1111
Web Site: http://iqeq.com
Financial Services
N.A.I.C.S.: 523999
Serge Krancenblum *(Chm)*

Subsidiaries:

Blue River Partners LLC (1)
2777 N Stemmons Fwy Ste 1425, Dallas, TX 75207
Tel.: (415) 906-6060
Web Site: http://www.blueriverpartnersllc.com
Investment Services
N.A.I.C.S.: 523999
Alfred Chao *(Mng Dir)*

IQ GMG INTENSIVE QUALITY GLOBAL MEDICAL GROUP PUBLIC LTD.
Anexartisias 1 & Athenon 79 Nora Court Office 203, Limassol, Cyprus
Tel.: (357) 25817577
Healtcare Services
N.A.I.C.S.: 621610

IQ GROUP HOLDINGS BERHAD
Plot 149 Jalan Sultan Azlan Shah Taman Perindustrian, Bayan Lepas Fasa 1 FTZ, 11900, Bayan Lepas, 11900, Pulau Pinang, Malaysia
Tel.: (60) 46446677
Web Site: https://www.iq-group.com
IQGROUP—(KLS)
Rev.: $31,564,141
Assets: $36,794,744
Liabilities: $7,025,405
Net Worth: $29,769,339
Earnings: ($2,522,714)
Emp.: 650
Fiscal Year-end: 03/31/22

Motion Sensors & Door Entry Products Mfr
N.A.I.C.S.: 334419
Daniel John Beasley *(CEO & Mng Dir)*

Subsidiaries:

Dong Guan Zhong Jia Electronics Co. Ltd. (1)
Huang Tang Village Xin Si District, Heng Li Town, Dongguan, 523460, Guangdong, China
Tel.: (86) 76983739190
Passive Infrared Detectors & Motion Sensor Light Mfr
N.A.I.C.S.: 334290

IQ Group (Dongguan) Ltd. (1)
Xi Xi Industrial Region, Liao Bu Town, Dongguan, Guang Dong, China
Tel.: (86) 76988955688
Security System Mfr
N.A.I.C.S.: 561621

IQ Group Sdn. Bhd. (1)
Plot 149 Jalan Sultan Azlan Shah Taman Perindustrian Bayan Lepas, Fasa 1 FTZ, 11900, Bayan Lepas, Pulau Pinang, Malaysia
Tel.: (60) 46446677
Sales Range: $125-149.9 Million
Emp.: 260
Wireless Data & Infrared Instruments Mfr
N.A.I.C.S.: 334513
Kent Wen-Chin Chen *(Chm)*

IQ Japan Co., Ltd. (1)
6-12-7 Heso, Ritto, 520-3031, Shiga, Japan
Tel.: (81) 775515002
Web Site: http://www.iq-group.com
Sales Range: $50-74.9 Million
Emp.: 6
Security System Distr
N.A.I.C.S.: 423610

IQ INTERNATIONAL AG
Landis Gyr Strasse 1, 6300, Zug, Switzerland
Tel.: (41) 2519801560 CH
Web Site: http://www.iqint.com
Year Founded: 2018
IQL—(DEU)
Sales Range: $1-9.9 Million
Lead Acid Battery Mfr & Distr
N.A.I.C.S.: 335910
George Weiss *(Co-Founder & Chm)*

IQ PARTNERS S.A.
7 Woloska St, 02-675, Warsaw, Poland
Tel.: (48) 225670000
Web Site: http://www.iqpartners.pl
Sales Range: $1-9.9 Million
Emp.: 40
Investment Services
N.A.I.C.S.: 523999

Subsidiaries:

Hub30.com Sp. z.o.o. (1)
Ul Towarowa 1, Olsztyn, 10-416, Poland
Tel.: (48) 89 532 0606
Online Marketing Services
N.A.I.C.S.: 541613

InQbe Sp. z.o.o. (1)
ul Towarowa 1, 10-416, Olsztyn, Poland
Tel.: (48) 89 532 06 06
Web Site: http://www.inqbe.pl
Emp.: 7
Business Management Consulting Services
N.A.I.C.S.: 541611
Wojciech Przylecki *(Chm)*

SEO Power Sp. z.o.o. (1)
ul Towarowa 1, Olsztyn, 10-416, Poland
Tel.: (48) 89 532 06 06
Web Site: http://www.seopower.pl
Search Engine Optimization Services
N.A.I.C.S.: 541512

Tylko Pracownicy S.A. (1)
ul Ciolka 13, 01-402, Warsaw, Poland
Tel.: (48) 224 85 52 00
Web Site: http://www.pracujekupuje.pl
Loyalty Program Operating Services

N.A.I.C.S.: 541611

Ventures Hub Sp. z.o.o. (1)
ul Woloska 7, 02-675, Warsaw, Poland
Tel.: (48) 22 567 00 20
Emp.: 5
Venture Capital Services
N.A.I.C.S.: 523910
Maciej Hazubski *(Chm)*

IQ STUDENT ACCOMMODATION
7th Floor Cottons Centre, Hays Lane, London, SE1 2QG, United Kingdom
Tel.: (44) 2034327296
Web Site: http://www.iqaccommodation.com
Apartment Building & Flats Operator
N.A.I.C.S.: 531110
Matt Merrick *(CEO)*

Subsidiaries:

GCP Student Living plc (1)
Beaufort House 51 New North Road, Exeter, EX4 4EP, United Kingdom
Tel.: (44) 1392477500
Web Site: http://www.graviscapital.com
Sales Range: $25-49.9 Million
Emp.: 128
Real Estate Investment Trust Services
N.A.I.C.S.: 531190
Robert Peto *(Chm)*

IQ3CORP LIMITED
Level 9 85 Castlereagh Street, Sydney, 2000, NSW, Australia
Tel.: (61) 282395400
Web Site: http://www.iq3corp.com
IQ3—(ASX)
Rev.: $5,286,686
Assets: $2,785,114
Liabilities: $3,542,327
Net Worth: ($757,213)
Earnings: ($1,695,269)
Fiscal Year-end: 06/30/20
Life Science Corporate Finance Advisory & Asset Management Services
N.A.I.C.S.: 523940
George J. Syrmalis *(Chm & CEO-Grp)*

IQE PLC
Pascal Close, St Mellons, Cardiff, CF3 0LW, United Kingdom
Tel.: (44) 2920839400 UK
Web Site: https://www.iqep.com
IQE—(AIM)
Rev.: $211,428,932
Assets: $373,781,873
Liabilities: $152,802,323
Net Worth: $220,979,551
Earnings: ($94,093,663)
Emp.: 665
Fiscal Year-end: 12/31/22
Semiconductor Materials
N.A.I.C.S.: 334413
Andrew W. Nelson *(Pres)*

Subsidiaries:

Galaxy Compound Semiconductors, Inc. (1)
9922 E Montgomery Ave Ste 7, Spokane, WA 99206
Tel.: (509) 892-1114
Web Site: https://www.galaxywafer.com
Sales Range: $25-49.9 Million
Emp.: 18
Semiconductors & Related Devices Mfr
N.A.I.C.S.: 334413

IQE (Europe) Ltd (1)
Pascal Close, St Mellons, Cardiff, CF3 0LW, United Kingdom (100%)
Tel.: (44) 92 083 9400
Web Site: http://www.iqep.com
Sales Range: $25-49.9 Million
Emp.: 100
Semiconductor Materials Sales & Manufacture
N.A.I.C.S.: 334413

IQE Inc. (1)
119 Technology Dr, Bethlehem, PA 18015 (100%)
Tel.: (610) 861-6930
Web Site: https://www.iqep.com
Sales Range: $25-49.9 Million
Emp.: 100
Semiconductor Wafers Mfr
N.A.I.C.S.: 334413

IQE KC LLC (1)
200 John Hancock Rd, Taunton, MA 02780
Tel.: (508) 824-6696
Semiconductor Material Mfr
N.A.I.C.S.: 334413

IQE Properties Inc. (1)
119 Technology Dr, Bethlehem, PA 18015
Tel.: (610) 861-6930
Property Development Services
N.A.I.C.S.: 531390

IQE RF LLC (1)
265 Davidson Ave Ste 141, Somerset, NJ 08873-4120
Tel.: (732) 271-5990
Sales Range: $25-49.9 Million
Emp.: 75
Electronic Component Mfr & Distr
N.A.I.C.S.: 334419
Alex Ceruzzi *(Gen Mgr)*

IQE Silicon Compounds Ltd (1)
Beech House Cypress Drive, St Mellons, Cardiff, CF3 0LW, United Kingdom (100%)
Tel.: (44) 2920837500
Web Site: https://www.iqesilicon.com
Sales Range: $25-49.9 Million
Emp.: 19
Mfr of Silicon Epitaxy
N.A.I.C.S.: 334413

IQE Taiwan Corp. (1)
No 2-1 Li-Hsin Rd, Hsinchu Science Park, Hsinchu, 300, Taiwan
Tel.: (886) 35798181
Semiconductor Material Mfr
N.A.I.C.S.: 334413

MBE Technology Pte Ltd (1)
30 Tampines Industrial Ave 3, Singapore, 528775, Singapore (100%)
Tel.: (65) 65009599
Web Site: https://www.mbetech.com
Sales Range: $10-24.9 Million
Emp.: 40
High-Speed Electronic Epitaxial Wafers Mfr
N.A.I.C.S.: 334413

NanoGaN Limited (1)
5-6 Northumberland Buildings Queen Square, Bath, BA1 2JE, United Kingdom
Tel.: (44) 1225383326
Web Site: https://www.nanogan.com
Semiconductor Equipment Mfr
N.A.I.C.S.: 334413

Wafer Technology Ltd. (1)
34 Maryland Road, Tongwell, Milton Keynes, MK15 8HJ, Bucks, United Kingdom (100%)
Tel.: (44) 1908210444
Web Site: https://www.wafertech.co.uk
Semiconductor Material Mfr
N.A.I.C.S.: 334413

IQX LIMITED
Level 9 85 Castlereagh Street, Sydney, 2000, NSW, Australia
Tel.: (61) 2 8239 5400
Web Site: http://www.iqxinvestments.com
Biotechnology & Biopharmaceutical Investment Services
N.A.I.C.S.: 523999
Kosmas Dimitriou *(Chm)*

IQZAN HOLDING BERHAD
Plot 49 and 63 Lorong Perusahaan 2B Kulim Industrial Estate, 09000, Kulim, Kedah, Malaysia
Tel.: (60) 44924422
Web Site: http://www.iretex.com.my
IQZAN—(KLS)
Rev.: $3,489,101
Assets: $17,692,487
Liabilities: $10,335,450

IQZAN HOLDING BERHAD

IQZAN Holding Berhad—(Continued)

Net Worth: $7,357,037
Earnings: $543,704
Emp.: 650
Fiscal Year-end: 03/31/23
Corrugated Paper Box Mfr
N.A.I.C.S.: 322211
Norman Zainuddin (Exec Dir)

Subsidiaries:

Austin Foam Plastics Inc. (1)
2933 A W Grimes Blvd, Pflugerville, TX 78660-5292
Tel.: (512) 251-6300
Web Site: https://www.a-f-p.com
Emp.: 220
Engineered Packaging Solutions
N.A.I.C.S.: 488991

Ire-Tex (Malaysia) Sdn. Bhd. (1)
Plot 118 Jalan Perusahaan Bukit Tengah Industrial Park, 14000, Bukit Mertajam, Penang, Malaysia
Tel.: (60) 55022752
Packaging Products Mfr
N.A.I.C.S.: 326112

Subsidiary (Domestic):

Ire-Tex (KL) Sdn. Bhd. (2)
Lot 14528 Jalan Perusahaan 25, Kampung Idaman Pandamaran, Port Klang, 42000, Selangor, Malaysia
Tel.: (60) 45022752
Web Site: http://www.iretex.com.my
Wooden Crates & Pallets Mfr
N.A.I.C.S.: 321920

Ire-Tex Electronics Sdn. Bhd. (1)
Plot 6 Hilir SG Keluang 4 Phase 4 FIZ, 11900, Bayan Lepas, Penang, Malaysia
Tel.: (60) 4 6447659
Packaging Materials Mfr
N.A.I.C.S.: 326150

Ire-Tex Praha S.R.O. (1)
Vltavinova 1334/3, 326 00, Plzen, Czech Republic
Tel.: (420) 60 252 9025
Web Site: https://www.iretex.cz
Sales Range: $25-49.9 Million
Emp.: 100
Packaging & Logistics Consulting Services
N.A.I.C.S.: 541614
Roman Doubrava (Mgr)

IR JAPAN HOLDINGS, LTD.

26th Floor Kasumigaseki Building 2-5 Kasumigaseki 3-Chome, Chiyoda-ku, Tokyo, 100-6026, Japan
Tel.: (81) 335196750
Web Site: https://www.irjapan.jp
Year Founded: 2015
6035—(TKS)
Rev.: $37,423,346
Assets: $44,069,575
Liabilities: $8,569,380
Net Worth: $35,500,195
Earnings: $5,041,194
Fiscal Year-end: 03/31/24
Holding Company; Investor Relations Services
N.A.I.C.S.: 551112
Takuji Kurio (COO & Exec VP)

Subsidiaries:

IR Japan, Inc. (1)
26th floor Kasumigaseki Building 2-5 Kasumigaseki 3-chome, Chiyoda-ku, Tokyo, 100-6026, Japan **(100%)**
Tel.: (81) 335196720
Web Site: http://www.irjapan.net
Sales Range: $25-49.9 Million
Emp.: 113
Public Relations
N.A.I.C.S.: 541820
Shirou Terashita (Pres & CEO)

IRAN ARGHAM CO.

No 52 West Sepand St Ostad Nejatollahi St, Tehran, Iran
Tel.: (98) 21 88907163
Web Site: http://www.iranargham.com
Year Founded: 1958
Emp.: 656
Electronic Products Mfr
N.A.I.C.S.: 334118

IRAN BEARING & BUSHING CO.

Ground Floor Sarir Building Side by Social Security Clinic & Paykansha, PO Box 19395-3647, 15th Km of Tehran-Karaj Highwa, Tehran, Iran
Tel.: (98) 21 44182554
Web Site: http://www.ibbc-ir.com
Year Founded: 1997
Flange Bearing Mfr
N.A.I.C.S.: 332991
Nader Noori (Mng Dir)

IRAN BEHNOUSH COMPANY

9 km Shahi Lashkari Highway Shahid Pouri St No 5, Tehran, Iran
Tel.: (98) 544556003 201
Web Site: http://www.behnoushiran.com
Year Founded: 1345
BENN1—(THE)
Sales Range: Less than $1 Million
Non-Alcoholic Beverages Mfr
N.A.I.C.S.: 311999

IRAN BOARD

Fibre Iran building No 89 East 10th st Beyhaghi blvd Argentina sq, Tehran, 15156, Iran
Tel.: (98) 21 88733090
Wood Products Mfr
N.A.I.C.S.: 321212

IRAN CABLE COMPANY

K 16 Old Road-Next To Bahman Group, Tehran, Iran
Tel.: (98) 21 66282706
Web Site: http://www.irancable.com
Year Founded: 1965
Emp.: 184
Cable Products Mfr
N.A.I.C.S.: 332618
Mohammad Jafar Safavian (Chm)

IRAN CARBON COMPANY

No 113 South Gandhi St Vanak Sq, 15179-73111, Tehran, 15179-73111, Iran
Tel.: (98) 2188791648
Web Site: http://www.iran-carbon.com
Year Founded: 1972
CRBN—(THE)
Sales Range: Less than $1 Million
Emp.: 251
Carbon Black Mfr
N.A.I.C.S.: 325180

IRAN CASTING INDUSTRIES

4th St Kaveh Industrial City, Tehran, Iran
Tel.: (98) 8642342181
Web Site: http://www.ici-ir.com
Year Founded: 1987
Iron Casting Parts Mfr
N.A.I.C.S.: 331511

IRAN COMBINE MANUFACTURING COMPANY

Qaem Maqam Farahani Street At The Intersection With Matahari Magnolia, Avenu Building 37, Tehran, Iran
Tel.: (98) 2188828505
COMB1—(THE)
Year Founded: 1969
Sales Range: Less than $1 Million
Industrial Machinery Whslr
N.A.I.C.S.: 423830

IRAN COMPRESSOR MANUFACTURING COMPANY PLC

No 141 Bozorgmeh Street Felestin Avenue, Tehran, 14158, Iran
Tel.: (98) 21 6466655
Industrial Refrigeration Mfr
N.A.I.C.S.: 333415
Ahmad Farokh (Mng Dir)

IRAN ELECTRICITY METER MANUFACTURING COMPANY, PLC

No 5 Varsho St Nejatollahi Ave, Tehran, Iran
Tel.: (98) 21 88801958
Web Site: http://www.ski.ir
Year Founded: 1968
Measuring Instruments Mfr
N.A.I.C.S.: 334513
Syed Ali Ameli (CEO)

IRAN FERROALLOY INDUSTRIES CO.

No 6 21st Gandi Ave, PO Box 15815/3169, Tehran, 15178 64613, Iran
Tel.: (98) 21 88779330
Web Site: http://www.iranferroalloys.com
Year Founded: 1986
Ferrosilicon Mfr
N.A.I.C.S.: 331110

IRAN FERROSILICE CO.

No 1902 & 1903 19th Fl Farmanieh Park-Center building 8th Narenjestan, Farmanieh cross-road Pasdaran ave, Tehran, Iran
Tel.: (98) 2172853000
Web Site: https://www.iran-ifc.com
Year Founded: 1982
FRIS1—(THE)
Sales Range: Less than $1 Million
Ferroalloy Metal & Carbon Material Mfr
N.A.I.C.S.: 331110

IRAN INSULATOR COMPANY

No 4 Niloofar Alley Southern Bahar St, Tehran, Iran
Tel.: (98) 21 2283 2040
Web Site: http://www.iraninsulator.com
Year Founded: 1983
Ceramic Insulator Mfr
N.A.I.C.S.: 327110
Mostafa Mohammad (CEO & Mng Dir)

IRAN KHODRO COMPANY

Km 14 Karaj Makhsoos Rd, PO Box 13895-111, Tehran, Iran
Tel.: (98) 2148901
Web Site: https://www.ikco.ir
Year Founded: 1962
IKCO1—(THE)
Sales Range: Less than $1 Million
Automotive Parts Design & Mfr
N.A.I.C.S.: 811198

Subsidiaries:

Iran Khodro Diesel Company (1)
No 32 Mirghasemi Alley Azadi St Azadi Sq, Tehran, Iran
Tel.: (98) 21 66082770
Web Site: http://www.ikd-co.com
Commercial Vehicle Mfr
N.A.I.C.S.: 333924

IRAN MANGANESE MINES COMPANY

4th Unit-No 161-Shekoofeh Alley Apadana Cross Rd-Sajjad St, Isfahan, Iran
Tel.: (98) 311 6410080
Year Founded: 1963

INTERNATIONAL PUBLIC

MNGZ—(THE)
Sales Range: Less than $1 Million
Emp.: 328
Mining Services
N.A.I.C.S.: 212290

IRAN MARITIME INDUSTRIAL COMPANY

No 2 Shafagh St Dadman Blvd Phase 7 Shahrak Ghods, PO Box 14665-495, 14669 56491, Tehran, Iran
Tel.: (98) 21 83362000
Web Site: http://www.sadra.ir
Year Founded: 1968
Ship Building & Repairing Services
N.A.I.C.S.: 336611

IRAN TRACTOR FOUNDRY COMPANY

Sardroud Road, Tabriz, Iran
Tel.: (98) 4151053255
Web Site: https://itf.ir
Year Founded: 1966
RTIR—(THE)
Sales Range: Less than $1 Million
Iran Parts Mfr
N.A.I.C.S.: 331511

IRAN TRACTOR MANUFACTURING COMPANY

PO Box 1966946413, Tehran, Iran
Tel.: (98) 21 2050115
Sales Range: $350-399.9 Million
Tractor Mfr
N.A.I.C.S.: 333924
M. Arabbaghi (Gen Mgr)

IRAN TRANSFO CO.

Molla Sadra St North Shirazi St Hakim Azam St No, PO Box 13145-159, Tehran, Iran
Tel.: (98) 218821091012
Web Site: https://www.iran-transfo.com
TRNS1—(THE)
Sales Range: Less than $1 Million
Transportation Equipment Mfr
N.A.I.C.S.: 336999

IRAN YASA

Fatah Highway km 2 Baghistan Highway, Tehran, Iran
Tel.: (98) 2165609100
Web Site: https://www.iranyasa.ir
YASA1—(THE)
Sales Range: Less than $1 Million
Tire & Tubes Mfr
N.A.I.C.S.: 326211

IRANAIR

Mehrabad Airport, Tehran, 13185-775, Iran
Tel.: (98) 2146625949
Web Site: http://www.iranair.com
Sales Range: $1-4.9 Billion
Emp.: 6,000
Airline
N.A.I.C.S.: 481111
Farzaneh Sharafbafi (CEO)

IRANI PAPEL E EMBALAGEM S.A.

Rua Francisco Lindner 477, Joacaba, 89600-000, SC, Brazil
Tel.: (55) 4935275100
Web Site: https://www.irani.com.br
Year Founded: 1941
RANI3—(BRAZ)
Rev.: $220,050,094
Assets: $396,285,708
Liabilities: $312,978,752
Net Worth: $83,306,956
Earnings: ($19,705,387)
Emp.: 2,120
Fiscal Year-end: 12/31/19

Cellulose Paper, Corrugated Cardboard Sheets, Resins & Furniture Mfr
N.A.I.C.S.: 322211
Sergio Luiz Cotrim Ribas *(CEO & Member-Exec Bd)*
Subsidiaries:

Celulose Irani S.A. - Forest Factory Division (1)
Vila Campina da Alegria, Vargem Bonita, 89600-000, Santa Catarina, Brazil
Tel.: (55) 49 3548 9156
Kraft Paper Mfr
N.A.I.C.S.: 322120

Celulose Irani S.A. - Furniture Commercial and Factory Division (1)
Vila Nova, Rio Negrinho, 89295-000, Santa Catarina, Brazil
Tel.: (55) 47 3203 4500
Kraft Paper Mfr
N.A.I.C.S.: 322120

Celulose Irani S.A. - Packaging Commercial Division (1)
Rodovia Engenheiro Erminio de Oliveira Penteado, Caldeira Indaiatuba, Sao Paulo, Brazil
Tel.: (55) 19 2107 7148
Packaging Services
N.A.I.C.S.: 561910

Celulose Irani S.A. - Packaging Factory Division (1)
Rodovia Engenheiro Erminio de Oliveira Penteado, Caldeira Indaiatuba, Sao Paulo, 13347-600, Brazil
Tel.: (55) 19 2107 00
Packaging Services
N.A.I.C.S.: 561910

Celulose Irani S.A. - Paper Commercial Division (1)
St Geraldo Flausino Gomes, Sao Paulo, Brazil
Tel.: (55) 1155024100
Sales Range: $25-49.9 Million
Emp.: 7
Kraft Paper Mfr
N.A.I.C.S.: 322120

Celulose Irani S.A. - Paper Factory Division (1)
Rodovia BR 153 Km 47 Vila Campina da Alegria, Vargem Bonita, CEP 89600-000, Santa Catarina, Brazil
Tel.: (55) 49 3548 9000
Web Site: http://www.irani.com.br
Kraft Paper Mfr
N.A.I.C.S.: 322120
Agostinho Deon *(Mgr)*

Celulose Irani S.A. - Resins Commercial Division (1)
St Geraldo Flausino Gomes, Sao Paulo, 04575-060, Brazil
Tel.: (55) 11 5502 4128
Kraft Paper Mfr
N.A.I.C.S.: 322120

Celulose Irani S.A. - Resins Factory Division (1)
Rodovia, Balneario Pinhal, Rio Grande, Brazil
Tel.: (55) 5136820100
Resins & Paper Mfr
N.A.I.C.S.: 325211

Habitasul Florestal S.A. (1)
Rua General Joao Manoel 157, Centro, Porto Alegre, 9001 0030, Brazil
Tel.: (55) 5132203535
Web Site: http://www.habitasul.com.br
Sales Range: $25-49.9 Million
Emp.: 25
Kraft Paper Mfr
N.A.I.C.S.: 322120

IRAQ CAPITAL AG
Tannenberg 3, Oberuzwil, CH-9242, Saint Gallen, Switzerland
Tel.: (41) 719501616
Web Site: http://www.iraq-capital.com
Investment Management Service
N.A.I.C.S.: 523999
Konstantin von Reden-Lutcken *(Pres)*

IRAQI AGRICULTURAL PRODUCTS
Al-Nosoor Sequare, Baghdad, Iraq
Tel.: (964) 7802571841
Year Founded: 1984
AIRP—(IRAQ)
Sales Range: Less than $1 Million
Vegetable Farming Services
N.A.I.C.S.: 111219

IRAQI CARPETS & UPHOLSTERY CO.
Al-Dawoudy Sec 622 St 28 Bld 5, Al-Hamra County, Baghdad, Iraq
Tel.: (964) 5553409
Year Founded: 1989
IITC—(IRAQ)
Sales Range: Less than $1 Million
Textile Products Mfr
N.A.I.C.S.: 314999

IRAQI CARTON MAUFACTURERS CO.
Al-Zaafrania Industrial Strip, Baghdad, Iraq
Tel.: (964) 1773 0541
Year Founded: 1978
Carton Mfr
N.A.I.C.S.: 322212

IRAQI COMPANY FOR ENGINEERING WORKS
Al-Wahda Zone Dis 904 St 72, Baghdad, Iraq
Tel.: (964) 1 7181475
Year Founded: 1985
Automobile Parts Mfr
N.A.I.C.S.: 336390

IRAQI COMPANY FOR GENERAL TRANSPORTATION & OIL PRODUCTION
Sec 103 St 17 H 18 Behind Al-Geelany Gas Station, Baghdad, Iraq
Tel.: (964) 1 8153802
Year Founded: 1994
Transportation Support Services
N.A.I.C.S.: 488490

IRAQI DATE PROCESSING & MARKETING CO.
Al-Shaljiah Behind Bratha Mosque, Baghdad, Iraq
Tel.: (964) 1 5225173
Year Founded: 1989
IIDP—(IRAQ)
Sales Range: Less than $1 Million
Date Mfr & Whslr
N.A.I.C.S.: 311423

IRAQI FOR SEED PRODUCTION
Abu-Graib Enterace Of Eger Goof St, Baghdad, Iraq
Tel.: (964) 1 5114141
Year Founded: 1989
Grain Farming Services
N.A.I.C.S.: 111199

IRAQI MIDDLE EAST INVESTMENT BANK
Street 25 Building 14 Arasat, Babel District, Baghdad, Iraq
Tel.: (964) 7704891014
Web Site: http://www.imeib.com
Year Founded: 1993
BIME—(IRAQ)
Sales Range: $25-49.9 Million
Investment Banking Services
N.A.I.C.S.: 523150
Saif Yousif Ghulam Hussein *(Chm)*

IRAY TECHNOLOGY COMPANY LIMITED
Building 45 No 1000 Jinhai Road, Pudong New Area, Shanghai, 201206, China
Tel.: (86) 2150720560
Web Site: https://www.iraygroup.com
Year Founded: 2011
688301—(SHG)
Rev.: $217,495,985
Assets: $816,950,043
Liabilities: $268,870,970
Net Worth: $548,079,073
Earnings: $90,038,576
Fiscal Year-end: 12/31/22
Optical Instrument Mfr
N.A.I.C.S.: 333310
Tie Gu *(Chm & Gen Mgr)*
Subsidiaries:

IRay Imaging LLC (1)
129 Morgan Dr Ste 102, Norwood, MA 02062
Software Development Services
N.A.I.C.S.: 541511

IRay Japan Limited (1)
Room 901 Koyo Bualding 2-2 Sakuragicho, Naka-ku, Yokohama, 231-0062, Kanagawa, Japan
Tel.: (81) 452259682
Software Development Services
N.A.I.C.S.: 541511

IRay Korea Limited (1)
1001 10F 5 Gasan digital 1-ro, Geumcheon-gu, Seoul, 08594, Korea (South)
Tel.: (82) 263356333
Software Development Services
N.A.I.C.S.: 541511

iRay Europe GmbH (1)
In Den Dorfwiesen 14, 71720, Oberstenfeld, Germany
Tel.: (49) 70629778800
X-Ray Detector Mfr
N.A.I.C.S.: 334517

IRB INFRASTRUCTURE DEVELOPERS LTD.
3rd Floor IRB Complex Chandivli Farm Chandivli Village, Andheri East, Mumbai, 400 072, India
Tel.: (91) 2266404220
Web Site: https://www.irb.co.in
532947—(BOM)
Rev.: $867,518,516
Assets: $5,810,343,630
Liabilities: $4,095,133,634
Net Worth: $1,715,209,997
Earnings: $49,330,691
Emp.: 32
Fiscal Year-end: 03/31/22
Infrastructure Construction Services
N.A.I.C.S.: 237310
Virendra Dattatraya Mhaiskar *(Chm & Co-Mng Dir)*
Subsidiaries:

ATR Infrastructure Pvt. Ltd. (1)
IRB Complex Chandivli Farm Chandivli Vlg, Andheri E, Mumbai, 400 072, Maharastra, India
Tel.: (91) 2266404220
Sales Range: $25-49.9 Million
Emp.:
Infrastructure Developers
N.A.I.C.S.: 236117

Aryan Infrastructure Investments Pvt. Ltd. (1)
IRB Complex Chandivli Farm Chandivli Vlg, Andheri E, Mumbai, 400 072, Maharastra, India
Tel.: (91) 2266404220
Construction Services
N.A.I.C.S.: 237990

Aryan Toll Road Pvt. Ltd. (1)
IRB Complex Chandivli Farm Chandivli Vlg, Andheri E, Mumbai, 400 072, Maharastra, India
Tel.: (91) 2266404220
Sales Range: $25-49.9 Million
Emp.: 100
Construction Services
N.A.I.C.S.: 236116

IRB Infrastructure Pvt. Ltd. (1)
IRB Complex Chandivli Farm Chandivli Vlg, Andheri E, Mumbai, 400 072, Maharastra, India
Tel.: (91) 2266404220
Construction Services
N.A.I.C.S.: 236116
Rajinder Pal Singh *(Chm)*

IRB Kolhapur Integrated Road Development Company Pvt. Ltd. (1)
IRB Complex Chandivli Farm Chandivli Vlg, Andheri E, Mumbai, 400 072, Maharastra, India
Tel.: (91) 2266404220
Construction Services
N.A.I.C.S.: 237990

IRB Surat Dahisar Tollway Pvt. Ltd. (1)
IRB Complex Chandivli Farm Chandivli Vlg, Andheri E, Mumbai, 400 072, Maharastra, India (100%)
Tel.: (91) 2266404220
Emp.: 700
Construction Services
N.A.I.C.S.: 237990

Ideal Road Builders Pvt. Ltd (1)
IRB Complex Chandivli Farm, Chandivli Vlg Andheri E, Mumbai, 400072, Maharastra, India
Tel.: (91) 2266404220
Web Site: http://www.irb.com
Sales Range: $200-249.9 Million
Emp.: 1,000
Infrastructure Developers
N.A.I.C.S.: 236117

MMK Toll Road Pvt. Ltd. (1)
IRB Complex Chandivli Farm Chandivli Vlg, Andheri E, Mumbai, 400 072, Maharastra, India
Tel.: (91) 2266404220
Sales Range: $50-74.9 Million
Emp.: 250
Construction Services
N.A.I.C.S.: 237310
Virendra D. Mhaiskar *(Mng Dir)*

Mhaiskar Infrastructure Pvt. Ltd. (1)
IRB Complex Chandivli Farm Chandivli Vlg, Andheri E, Mumbai, 400 072, Maharastra, India
Tel.: (91) 2266404220
Web Site: http://www.rb.co.in
Emp.: 60
Construction Services
N.A.I.C.S.: 236116
Virendra D. Mhaiskar *(Mng Dir)*

NKT Road and Toll Pvt. Ltd. (1)
IRB Complex Chandivli Farm Chandivli Vlg, Andheri E, Mumbai, 400 07, Maharastra, India
Tel.: (91) 2266404220
Construction Services
N.A.I.C.S.: 237310

Thane Ghodbunder Toll Road Pvt. Ltd. (1)
IRB Complex Chandivli Farm Chandivli Vlg, Andheri E, Mumbai, 400 072, Maharastra, India
Tel.: (91) 2266404220
Infrastructure Developers & Consructors
N.A.I.C.S.: 237990

IRB-BRASIL RESSEGUROS S.A.
Av Brigadeiro Faria Lima 4300 Itaim Bibi, Sao Paulo, 04538-133, Brazil
Tel.: (55) 1125880200 BR
Web Site: https://www.irbbrasilre.com
Year Founded: 1939
IRBR3—(BRAZ)
Rev.: $1,035,860,969
Assets: $2,768,350,868
Liabilities: $2,007,299,959
Net Worth: $761,050,908
Earnings: ($22,139,933)
Emp.: 342
Fiscal Year-end: 12/31/23
Reinsurance Services
N.A.I.C.S.: 524130

IRB-BRASIL RESSEGUROS S.A.

IRB-Brasil Resseguros S.A.—(Continued)
Antonio Cassio dos Santos *(Chm)*
Subsidiaries:

IRB Asset Management SA (1)
Av Marechal Camara 171-Castelo, Rio de Janeiro, 20020-901, Brazil
Tel.: (55) 2122720200
Web Site: http://www.irbassetmanagement.com
Asset Management Services
N.A.I.C.S.: 523940
Marcel Leal *(Chief Investment Officer)*

IRC NIC A.D.
Nikole Pasica 50, Uzice, Serbia
Tel.: (381) 31 515 154
Year Founded: 1992
Sales Range: Less than $1 Million
Natural & Technical Science Research & Development Services
N.A.I.C.S.: 541990

IRCE S.P.A.
via Lasie 12/A, 40026, Bologna, Italy
Tel.: (39) 0542661111
Web Site: https://www.irce.it
Year Founded: 1947
IRC—(ITA)
Rev.: $363,669,573
Assets: $257,153,100
Liabilities: $106,541,378
Net Worth: $150,611,721
Earnings: $3,347,832
Emp.: 646
Fiscal Year-end: 12/31/20
Electrical & Energy Services
N.A.I.C.S.: 541690
Filippo Casadio *(Chm)*
Subsidiaries:

DMG Gmbh (1)
Tel.: (49) 6041960530
Rev.: $107,597
Electric Equipment Mfr
N.A.I.C.S.: 335999

FD Sims Ltd (1)
Lions Drive, Shadsworth Business Park, Blackburn, BB1 2QS, Lancanshire, United Kingdom
Tel.: (44) 1254584154
Web Site: https://www.fdsims.com
Sales Range: $25-49.9 Million
Emp.: 48
Electric Equipment Mfr
N.A.I.C.S.: 335999

Irce Ltda (1)
Zona Industrial Norte Rua Anaburgo 3800, Joinville, CEP 89219 630, Santa Catarina, Brazil
Tel.: (55) 4738021204
Winding Wire Mfr
N.A.I.C.S.: 331420

Irce S.L. (1)
C/Pintor Vila Cinca 2-G, 08213, Polinya, Spain
Tel.: (34) 937134320
Winding Wire Mfr
N.A.I.C.S.: 331420

Isodra GmbH (1)
In der Helle 10, 58566, Kierspe, Germany
Tel.: (49) 23597476
Web Site: https://www.isodra.de
Copper Wires Mfr
N.A.I.C.S.: 331420
Gianfranco Sepriano *(Mng Dir)*

Isomet AG (1)
Mattenstrasse 12, CH-8112, Otelfingen, Dielsdorf, Switzerland
Tel.: (41) 448474444
Web Site: https://www.isomet.ch
Sales Range: $25-49.9 Million
Electric Equipment Mfr
N.A.I.C.S.: 335999

SMIT DRAAD Nijmegen B V (1)
Lagelandseweg 11, 6545 CC, Nijmegen, Netherlands
Tel.: (31) 243717010
Web Site: https://www.smitdraad.nl
Sales Range: $1-9.9 Million
Electric Equipment Mfr
N.A.I.C.S.: 335999

Stable Magnet Wire P. Ltd (1)
Plot No 4 Wing II B Cochin Special Economic Zone, Kakkanad, Cochin, 6820347, Kerala, India
Tel.: (91) 4844058076
Web Site: https://www.stablemagnet.com
Electric Equipment Mfr
N.A.I.C.S.: 335999

IRCON INTERNATIONAL LIMITED
C-4 District Centre, Saket, New Delhi, 110017, India
Tel.: (91) 1126530266
Web Site: https://www.ircon.org
Year Founded: 1976
541956—(BOM)
Rev.: $1,035,449,415
Assets: $1,971,928,140
Liabilities: $1,334,916,765
Net Worth: $637,011,375
Earnings: $80,844,855
Emp.: 985
Fiscal Year-end: 03/31/22
Construction & Design Services
N.A.I.C.S.: 541310
Yogesh Kumar Mishra *(Chm, Mng Dir & Dir-Works)*
Subsidiaries:

Ircon Infrastructure & Services Limited (1)
2nd Floor Plot C-4, District Centre Saket, New Delhi, 110 017, India
Tel.: (91) 1129565666
Web Site: https://www.irconisl.com
Construction & Maintenance Services
N.A.I.C.S.: 561790
Yogesh Kumar Misra *(Chm)*

IRDI SORIDEC GESTION SAS
18 place Dominique Martin Dupuy - CS 18008, 31080, Toulouse, Cedex 6, France
Tel.: (33) 5 81 317 320   FR
Web Site: http://www.irdisoridec.fr
Year Founded: 1981
Privater Equity Firm
N.A.I.C.S.: 523999
Bertrand Religieux *(Member-Mgmt Bd)*

IREADER TECHNOLOGY CO., LTD.
2029E 2nd Floor Sihui Building Sihui East, Chaoyang District, Beijing, 100024, China
Tel.: (86) 1059236288
Web Site: http://www.zhangyue.com
Year Founded: 2008
603533—(SHG)
Rev.: $362,571,403
Assets: $477,772,341
Liabilities: $113,169,392
Net Worth: $364,602,949
Earnings: $8,083,839
Fiscal Year-end: 12/31/22
Mobile Software Development Services
N.A.I.C.S.: 513210
Xiangjun Cheng *(Chm & Pres)*

IREKA CORPORATION BERHAD
Level 18 Wisma Kiara Mont No 1 Jalan Kiara Mont Kiara, 50480, Kuala Lumpur, Malaysia
Tel.: (60) 364116388
Web Site: http://www.ireka.com.my
IREKA—(KLS)
Rev.: $1,286,358
Assets: $39,566,829
Liabilities: $49,072,448
Net Worth: ($9,505,619)
Earnings: ($14,594,380)
Emp.: 414
Fiscal Year-end: 06/30/23
Construction & Property Development Services
N.A.I.C.S.: 236118
Yim Cheng Wong *(Sec)*
Subsidiaries:

Ireka Development Management Sdn. Bhd. (1)
Level 18 Wisma Mont' Kiara No 1, Jalan, Kiara Mont' Kiara, 50480, Kuala Lumpur, Malaysia
Tel.: (60) 364116388
Construction Engineering Services
N.A.I.C.S.: 541330
Lai Voon Hon *(Mng Dir)*

Ireka iCapital Sdn. Bhd. (1)
M-2 Kiara II Mezzanine Floor No 1 Jalan Kiara Mont Kiara, 50480, Kuala Lumpur, Malaysia
Tel.: (60) 364116388
Web Site: http://www.ireka.com.my
Emp.: 40
Construction Engineering Services
N.A.I.C.S.: 541330
Leonard Yee *(Mng Dir)*

Meadowfield Sdn. Bhd. (1)
Level 18 Wisma Mont Kiara No 1 Jalan Kiara Mont Kiara, 50480, Kuala Lumpur, Malaysia
Tel.: (60) 364116388
Web Site: https://rimbunkasia.com.my
Real Estate Services
N.A.I.C.S.: 531390

Regalmont (Sabah) Sdn. Bhd. (1)
Pondok Pengawal Lrg Perdana 6 Taman Luyang Perdanab, Kota Kinabalu, Sabah, Malaysia
Tel.: (60) 88266393
Real Estate Manangement Services
N.A.I.C.S.: 531390

IREKS GMBH
Lichtenfelser Str 20, 95326, Kulmbach, Germany
Tel.: (49) 9221 706 0   De
Web Site: http://www.ireks.com
Year Founded: 1856
Sales Range: $300-349.9 Million
Emp.: 2,900
Flavorings, Ice Cream Products, Brewing Malts & Baking Ingredients Mfr
N.A.I.C.S.: 311930
Jurgen Brinkmann *(Mng Dir)*
Subsidiaries:

Dreidoppel GmbH (1)
Ernst-Abbe-Strasse 4-6, D 40764, Langenfeld, Germany
Tel.: (49) 2173 7909 0
Web Site: http://www.dreidoppel.de
Sales Range: $25-49.9 Million
Emp.: 160
Flavoring Syrups & Fruit Pastes, Cream Stabilizers, Cream Fillings, Ice Cream Toppings & Baking Products
N.A.I.C.S.: 311930
Ina Kononenko *(Jr Mgr-Product)*

IREKS (SHANGHAI) FOOD CO., Ltd. (1)
Room 301 Tower 1 German Centre 88 Keyuan Road, Shanghai, 201203, China
Tel.: (86) 2150652833
Web Site: http://www.ireks.cn
Food Products Mfr
N.A.I.C.S.: 311919
Stary Bai *(Mgr-Comml & Admin)*

IREKS France Sarl (1)
269 rue des Brasseries, 54320, Maxeville, France
Tel.: (33) 383174949
Web Site: http://www.ireks.fr
Sales Range: $25-49.9 Million
Emp.: 45
Brewing Malts & Baking Ingredients Mfr & Distr

INTERNATIONAL PUBLIC

N.A.I.C.S.: 311824
LUMEN GmbH (1)
Petzmannsberg 11, 95326, Kulmbach, Germany
Tel.: (49) 92218930
Web Site: http://www.lumen.de
Ice Cream & Other Frozen Dessert Mfr
N.A.I.C.S.: 311520

STAMAG Stadlauer Malzfabrik GesmbH (1)
Smolagasse 1, 1220, Vienna, Austria
Tel.: (43) 1288080
Web Site: http://www.stamag.at
Food Products Mfr
N.A.I.C.S.: 311919

Stadlauer Malzfabrik AG (1)
Smolagasse 1, 1220, Vienna, Austria
Tel.: (43) 1288080
Web Site: https://www.malzfabrik-ag.at
Sales Range: Less than $1 Million
Real Estate Prorperty Leasing Services
N.A.I.C.S.: 531190

IRELAND BLYTH LIMITED
IBL House Caudan Waterfront, Port Louis, Mauritius
Tel.: (230) 2032000   MU
Web Site: http://www.iblgroup.com
Year Founded: 1972
Rev.: $1,042,708,761
Assets: $1,605,208,393
Liabilities: $867,529,838
Net Worth: $737,678,556
Earnings: $37,068,597
Emp.: 26,993
Fiscal Year-end: 06/30/19
Holding Company
N.A.I.C.S.: 551112
Arnaud Lagesse *(CEO)*
Subsidiaries:

Alentaris Ltd. (1)
The Factory Vivea Business Park, Moka, Mauritius
Tel.: (230) 4057100
Web Site: http://www.alentaris.com
Recruitment Services
N.A.I.C.S.: 561311
Thierry Goder *(CEO)*

CIDP Biotech India Private Limited (1)
32-B First Floor Rajendra Nagar Pusa Road, New Delhi, 110005, India
Tel.: (91) 1140793385
Clinical Services
N.A.I.C.S.: 621610

CIDP Biotechnology SRL (1)
15 Strada Albac - Sector 1, Bucharest, 011607, Romania
Tel.: (40) 317181182
Clinical Services
N.A.I.C.S.: 621610

CIDP Singapore Ltd. (1)
21 Biopolis Road Nucleos North Tower 02-01, Singapore, 138567, Singapore
Tel.: (65) 68049599
Research & Development Services
N.A.I.C.S.: 541715

Construction & Material Handling Company Ltd. (1)
Royal Road Cassis, Cassis, Mauritius
Tel.: (230) 207 0500
Web Site: http://www.cmh.mu
Sales Range: $75-99.9 Million
Emp.: 200
Construction & Material Handling Equipments Distr
N.A.I.C.S.: 423810
Fabrizio Merlo *(COO-IBL Engrg Sector)*

DTOS International East Africa (K) Limited (1)
Suite 2 6th Floor Hanover Block 14 Riverside, PO Box 101650, 00101, Nairobi, Kenya
Tel.: (254) 732188537
Financial Services
N.A.I.C.S.: 523999

DTOS Ltd. (1)

AND PRIVATE COMPANIES

10th Floor Standard Chartered Tower, Ebene, Mauritius
Tel.: (230) 4046000
Web Site: http://www.dtos-mu.com
Sales Range: $100-124.9 Million
Emp.: 200
Financial Support Services
N.A.I.C.S.: 523940
Lina How *(Head-Funds & Financial Institutions)*

Subsidiary (Domestic):

DTOS Trustees Ltd. (2)
10th Floor Raffles Towers 19 Cyber City, Ebene, Mauritius
Tel.: (230) 2032020
Sales Range: $75-99.9 Million
Emp.: 200
Trust Management Services
N.A.I.C.S.: 523940

Interface Management Services Ltd. (2)
9th Floor Raffles Tower 19 Cybercity, Ebene, Mauritius
Tel.: (230) 4046030
Web Site: http://www.knightsjohnsmanagement.com
Sales Range: $10-24.9 Million
Emp.: 30
Business Management Services
N.A.I.C.S.: 541611
Mervyn Chan *(Mng Dir)*

Knights & Johns Management Ltd. (2)
9th Floor Raffles Tower 19 Cybercity, Ebene, Mauritius
Tel.: (230) 4046001
Web Site: http://www.knightsjohnsmanagement.com
Sales Range: $10-24.9 Million
Emp.: 30
Business Management Services
N.A.I.C.S.: 561110
Mervyn Chan *(Mng Dir)*

Eagle Insurance Limited (1)
Eagle House, 15 A5 Wall Street, Ebene, Mauritius **(60%)**
Tel.: (230) 4609200
Web Site: http://www.eagle.mu
Rev.: $35,408,243
Assets: $95,761,282
Liabilities: $70,001,451
Net Worth: $25,759,831
Earnings: $150,907
Emp.: 119
Fiscal Year-end: 06/30/2019
Insurance Services
N.A.I.C.S.: 524298
Pierre Ah Soon *(Mgr-Claims)*

Froid des Mascareignes Limited (1)
Freeport Zone 8 Quay D Rd, Port Louis, 11615, Mauritius
Tel.: (230) 2066900
Web Site: http://www.iblgroup.com
Sales Range: $50-74.9 Million
Emp.: 120
Cold Storage & Logistics Services
N.A.I.C.S.: 493120
Maurice Rault *(Mng Dir)*

GSP Co. Ltd. (1)
IBL Zone 4 Riche Terre, Port Louis, Mauritius
Tel.: (230) 2069246
Sales Range: $500-549.9 Million
Emp.: 1,400
Gypsum Building Products Mfr & Installation Services
N.A.I.C.S.: 238310
Eric Hardy *(Gen Mgr)*

GWS Technologies Ltd. (1)
Suite 101 The Catalyst Building Silicon Avenue, Ebene, Mauritius
Tel.: (230) 4650030
Web Site: http://www.gws-technologies.com
Web Hosting Services
N.A.I.C.S.: 518210
Commarmond Jacques David *(Mng Dir)*

Grapevine Concepts Limited (1)
Royal Road, Cassis, Port Louis, Mauritius
Tel.: (230) 2028200
Web Site: http://www.grapevine.mu
Emp.: 43

Website Designing & Hosting Services
N.A.I.C.S.: 518210
Sareeta Goundan *(Gen Mgr)*

Ground 2 Air Ltd. (1)
Cargo Village SSR international Airport, Plaine Magnien, Mauritius
Tel.: (230) 6035900
Web Site: http://www.ground2air.mu
Cargo & Mail Services
N.A.I.C.S.: 491110

I-Telecom Ltd. (1)
Royal Road, Cassis, Mauritius
Tel.: (230) 2028200
Web Site: http://www.iblgroup.com
Internet & Telecommunication Services
N.A.I.C.S.: 517111

IBL Consumer Health Products Ltd. (1)
Les Salines 15 Reserves Street, Port Louis, Mauritius
Tel.: (230) 2033500
Sales Range: $25-49.9 Million
Emp.: 200
Health Food Supplements Blending & Packaging Services
N.A.I.C.S.: 561990
Raffick Beebeejaun *(Mgr-Production)*

IBL Properties Ltd. (1)
Property Management Dr Ferriere Street, Port Louis, Mauritius
Tel.: (230) 2027095
Property Management Services
N.A.I.C.S.: 531312

IBL Reunion s.a.s. (1)
33/35 rue Helene Boucher Zone d'activite, BP 97438, Sainte Exupery, Sainte-Marie, 97438, Reunion
Tel.: (262) 262971500
Sales Range: $25-49.9 Million
Emp.: 18
Courier Service
N.A.I.C.S.: 492110
Daniel Ah Chong *(Gen Mgr)*

IBL Sante s.a.r.l. (1)
4 Rue Pasteur Antanimena, Antananarivo, 101, Madagascar
Tel.: (261) 20 26 381 51
Sales Range: $50-74.9 Million
Emp.: 10
Pharmaceuticals Warehousing & Distr
N.A.I.C.S.: 424210

IBL Travel Limited (1)
John Kennedy St, Caudan, Port Louis, Mauritius
Tel.: (230) 2027330
Web Site: http://www.iblgroup.com
Sales Range: $25-49.9 Million
Emp.: 18
Airline Ticket Booking & Tour Operating Agencies
N.A.I.C.S.: 561520
Irene Legris *(Mgr)*

IBL Treasury Ltd. (1)
3rd Floor IBL House Caudan Waterfront, Port Louis, Mauritius
Tel.: (230) 2032000
Treasury Management Services
N.A.I.C.S.: 523940
Yannick Ulcoq *(Head-Treasury)*

Indian Ocean Logistics Ltd. (1)
6 President John Kennedy Street, Port Louis, Mauritius
Tel.: (230) 2027044
Web Site: http://www.iol.mu
Sales Range: $25-49.9 Million
Emp.: 30
Freight Forwarding Services
N.A.I.C.S.: 488510

Logidis Limited (1)
Logidis Zone 1 IBL Complex Riche Terre, Port Louis, Mauritius
Tel.: (230) 2069600
Web Site: http://www.ibl.com
Sales Range: $25-49.9 Million
Emp.: 50
Warehousing & Distribution Services
N.A.I.C.S.: 493110
Naden Padayachi *(Mgr-Transport & Warehousing)*

Manser Saxon Aluminium Ltd. (1)

Industrial Zone Riche Terre, Port Louis, Mauritius
Tel.: (230) 2069240
Sales Range: $25-49.9 Million
Emp.: 25
Aluminum Openings Mfr & Installation Services
N.A.I.C.S.: 238350
Fabrizio Merloe *(Mng Dir)*

Manser Saxon Contracting Ltd. (1)
IBL Complex Industrial Zone 4 Riche Terre, Port Louis, Mauritius
Tel.: (230) 2069200
Web Site: http://www.mansersaxon.com
Sales Range: $350-399.9 Million
Emp.: 2,000
Building Subcontracting Services
N.A.I.C.S.: 541330
Eric Hardy *(Gen Mgr)*

Subsidiary (Non-US):

Manser Saxon Dubai LLC (2)
Al Quoz Industrial Area, PO Box 113450, Dubai, United Arab Emirates
Tel.: (971) 43382949
Web Site: http://www.mansersaxondubai.com
Sales Range: $25-49.9 Million
Emp.: 150
Interior Design Services
N.A.I.C.S.: 541410

Subsidiary (Domestic):

Manser Saxon Plumbing Ltd (2)
IBL Industrial Zone 4 Riche Terre, Port Louis, Mauritius
Tel.: (230) 2069250
Web Site: http://www.mansersaxon.com
Sales Range: $50-74.9 Million
Emp.: 103
Plumbing Fixtures Installation Services
N.A.I.C.S.: 238220
Eric Hardy *(Mng Dir)*

Tornado Limited (2)
IBL Complex Zone 4 Riche Terre, Port Louis, Mauritius
Tel.: (230) 2069277
Web Site: http://www.mansersaxon.com
Sales Range: $100-124.9 Million
Emp.: 450
Heating, Ventilation & Air Conditioning Systems Installation Services
N.A.I.C.S.: 238220
Julio Francois *(Gen Mgr)*

Marine Biotechnology Products Ltd. (1)
Motorway M3, Riche Terre, Terre Rouge, Mauritius
Tel.: (230) 2047730
Web Site: http://www.mbp.mu
Fish Meal & Crude Fish Oil Mfr
N.A.I.C.S.: 311710

Medical Trading International Ltd (1)
15 Reserves Street, Les Salines, Port Louis, Mauritius
Tel.: (230) 2033506
Sales Range: $75-99.9 Million
Emp.: 150
Pharmaceutical Products Distr
N.A.I.C.S.: 424210
Din Jheelan *(Gen Mgr)*

New Cold Storage Company Limited (1)
Complex 2 Richetrre, Port Louis, Mauritius
Tel.: (230) 2069500
Web Site: http://www.iblbrandactiv.com
Sales Range: $75-99.9 Million
Emp.: 400
Cold Storage Services
N.A.I.C.S.: 493120
Jean-Michel Rouillard *(Gen Mgr)*

Scomat Limitee (1)
Grewals Lane Bell Village, BP 662, Les Pailles, Mauritius
Tel.: (230) 2060444
Web Site: http://www.scomat.com
Sales Range: $75-99.9 Million
Emp.: 150
Industrial Equipments & Parts Distr
N.A.I.C.S.: 423830
Jocelyn Labour *(Gen Mgr)*

IREN S.P.A.

Somatrans Ltd. (1)
Building No 1 Riche Terre Office Park, Phase 1 Riche Terre, Port Louis, Mauritius
Tel.: (230) 2027140
Web Site: http://www.somatrans.mu
Sales Range: $25-49.9 Million
Emp.: 100
Freight Forwarding Services
N.A.I.C.S.: 488510
Robert Hungley *(Mgr-Air & Sea Clearing)*

Systems Building Contracting Ltd. (1)
9B Thomy D Arifat Street, Curepipe, Mauritius
Tel.: (230) 6012400
Web Site: http://www.systemsbuilding.com
Electrical Contractor Services
N.A.I.C.S.: 238210

Thon des Mascareignes Ltee (1)
Marine Road Quay D, Port Louis, 21731, Mauritius
Tel.: (230) 2066800
Web Site: http://www.tdm.mu
Sales Range: $350-399.9 Million
Emp.: 2,000
Tuna Loins Mfr
N.A.I.C.S.: 311710
Patrice Robert *(Mng Dir)*

IREM CO., LTD.

29 Buan Nonggongdanji-gil, Haengan-myeon, Buan, Jeollabuk-do, Korea (South)
Tel.: (82) 25985133
Web Site: http://www.kossen.co.kr
Year Founded: 1974
009730—(KRS)
Rev.: $51,091,848
Assets: $34,911,763
Liabilities: $13,494,041
Net Worth: $21,417,722
Earnings: $2,236,478
Emp.: 81
Fiscal Year-end: 12/31/22
Stainless Steel Pipes
N.A.I.C.S.: 332996

Subsidiaries:

Kossen Co., Ltd. - Buan Factory (1)
29 Buan Nonggongdanji Gil Haengan-Myeon, Buan, Jeonlabuk-do, Korea (South)
Tel.: (82) 635846464
Stainless Steel Wire Mfr
N.A.I.C.S.: 331210

IREN S.P.A.

Via Nubi di Magellano 30, 42 123, Reggio nell'Emilia, Italy
Tel.: (39) 05222971   IT
Web Site: https://www.gruppoiren.it
Year Founded: 1922
IRDEF—(OTCIQ)
Rev.: $4,575,760,219
Assets: $11,734,930,444
Liabilities: $8,340,654,813
Net Worth: $3,394,275,631
Earnings: $325,570,805
Emp.: 8,680
Fiscal Year-end: 12/31/20
Energy, Water & Telecommunications Services
N.A.I.C.S.: 221122
Massimiliano Bianco *(CEO)*

Subsidiaries:

Acquaenna S.c.p.A. (1)
Via S Agata 65/71, 94100, Ravenna, EN, Italy
Tel.: (39) 0935508311
Web Site: https://www.acquaenna.it
Waste Management Services
N.A.I.C.S.: 924110

Alfa Solutions S.p.A. (1)
Viale Bernardino Ramazzini 39/D Innovation Park - Shed 18, 42124, Reggio Emilia, Italy
Tel.: (39) 0522550905
Web Site: https://www.alfa-solutions.it
Emp.: 200
Laboratory Consulting Services

IREN S.P.A.

Iren S.p.A.—(Continued)
N.A.I.C.S.: 541618

Amiat S.p.A. (1)
Via Giordano Bruno 25, 10134, Turin, Italy
Tel.: (39) 0112223111
Web Site: https://www.amiat.it
Waste Collection & Disposal Services
N.A.I.C.S.: 562119

Ireti S.p.A. (1)
Via Piacenza 54, 16138, Genoa, Italy
Tel.: (39) 0105586664
Web Site: https://www.ireti.it
Electricity Distribution Services
N.A.I.C.S.: 221122

Subsidiary (Domestic):

ASM Vercelli S.p.A. (2)
C so Palestro 130, 13100, Vercelli, Italy
Tel.: (39) 0161226611
Web Site: https://www.asmvercelli.it
Electricity & Gas Public Services
N.A.I.C.S.: 926130
Angelo D'Addesio (Pres)

LAB 231 S.R.L. (1)
Strada Traversetolo 20/D, 43123, Parma, Italy
Tel.: (39) 05211471231
Web Site: https://www.lab231.it
Pharma Consulting Services
N.A.I.C.S.: 541690

Maira S.p.A. (1)
Lottulo Hamlet Adrecchio n 7, San Damiano Macra, 12029, Cuneo, Italy
Tel.: (39) 03467973327
Web Site: https://www.mairaspa.it
Environmental Resource Services
N.A.I.C.S.: 541620
Mariano Allocco (Pres)

Subsidiary (Domestic):

Formaira S.r.l. (2)
Borgata Adrecchio n 7-Fraz Lottulo, San Damiano Macra, 12029, Cuneo, Italy
Tel.: (39) 03346334512
Web Site: https://www.formaira.it
Wood Chip Mfr
N.A.I.C.S.: 321113

Manduriambiente S.p.A. (1)
Localita La Chianca, 74024, Manduria, Italy
Tel.: (39) 0999712143
Web Site: https://manduriambiente.com
Waste Management Services
N.A.I.C.S.: 562998

Omnia Power S.R.L. (1)
Via Calabria 4, 21012, Cassano Magnago, Italy
Tel.: (39) 0331206901
Web Site: https://www.omniapower.it
Industrial Automation Services
N.A.I.C.S.: 541330

Re Mat S.R.L. (1)
Via Somalia 4/B, 10127, Turin, TO, Italy
Tel.: (39) 0116065944
Web Site: https://rematsrl.it
Sheet Metal Mfr
N.A.I.C.S.: 332322

Semia Green S.R.L. (1)
Via Simone Martini 57, 53100, Siena, Italy
Tel.: (39) 0577248011
Web Site: https://www.semiagreen.it
Waste Management Services
N.A.I.C.S.: 562998

Studio Alfa S.p.A. (1)
Viale Bernardino Ramazzini 39/D Innovation Park-Shed 18, 42124, Reggio Emilia, Italy
Tel.: (39) 0522550905
Web Site: http://www.studioalfa.it
Emp.: 150
Laboratory & Consulting Services
N.A.I.C.S.: 541690

Subsidiary (Domestic):

Coin Consultech S.r.l. (2)
Via Giovanni Treccani 2/C, 42122, Reggio Emilia, Italy
Tel.: (39) 0522268078
Web Site: http://www.coinconsultech.it
Documentation & Consulting Services
N.A.I.C.S.: 541690

TRM S.p.A. (1)
Via Paolo Gorini 50, 10137, Turin, Italy
Tel.: (39) 0113013701
Web Site: https://www.trm.to.it
Waste Collection & Disposal Services
N.A.I.C.S.: 562119
Pergetti Mauro (CEO)

Uniproject S.R.L. (1)
Via Bonifica 2, 63085, Maltignano, AP, Italy
Tel.: (39) 0736403919
Web Site: https://www.uniproject.it
Environmental Consulting Services
N.A.I.C.S.: 541620

Valdarno Ambiente S.R.L. (1)
Via Lungarno 123, 52028, Terranuova Bracciolini, AR, Italy
Tel.: (39) 0559737161
Web Site: https://www.valdarnoambiente.it
Environmental Consulting Services
N.A.I.C.S.: 541620

IRENE

32 Rue Des Jeuneurs, Paris, 75002, France
Tel.: (33) 144765858
Web Site: http://www.irene.fr
Rev.: $11,800,000
Emp.: 18
N.A.I.C.S.: 512110
Guillaume De Bary (Mng Partner)

IRESS LIMITED

Level 16 385 Bourke Street, Melbourne, 3000, VIC, Australia
Tel.: (61) 390185800
Web Site: https://www.iress.com
IRE—(ASX)
Rev.: $412,528,733
Assets: $667,640,724
Liabilities: $378,027,165
Net Worth: $289,613,559
Earnings: $35,163,827
Emp.: 2,272
Fiscal Year-end: 12/31/22
Business & Financial Products Mfr
N.A.I.C.S.: 561499

Subsidiaries:

IRESS Portal Limited (1)
1 Kingmaker Court Warwick Technology Park, Gallows Hill, Warwick, CV34 6DY, Warks, United Kingdom **(100%)**
Tel.: (44) 1926621644
Web Site: http://exweb.exchange.uk.com
Financial Information & Transaction Service
Software & Online Application Developer
N.A.I.C.S.: 513210

Subsidiary (Domestic):

IRESS FS Ltd. (2)
1 Kingmaker Court Warwick Technology Park, Gallows Hill, Warwick, CV34 6DY, Warks, United Kingdom **(100%)**
Tel.: (44) 1926621644
Web Site: http://www.iress.co.uk
Emp.: 280
Financial Planning, Client Management & Back-Office Administration Software Publisher
N.A.I.C.S.: 513210
Simon Badley (Mng Dir)

IRESS Wealth Management Pty Ltd (1)
Level 18 385th Pourke St, Melbourne, 3000, VIC, Australia
Tel.: (61) 390185800
Web Site: http://www.iress.com.au
Sales Range: $100-124.9 Million
Emp.: 200
Financial Planning Services
N.A.I.C.S.: 523999

OneVue Holdings Limited (1)
Level 5 10 Spring Street, Sydney, 2000, NSW, Australia
Tel.: (61) 1300219787
Web Site: http://www.onevue.com.au
Rev.: $34,747,094
Assets: $78,982,812
Liabilities: $13,268,827
Net Worth: $65,713,985

Earnings: $6,588,254
Fiscal Year-end: 06/30/2019
Holding Company; Wealth Management Services
N.A.I.C.S.: 551112
Lisa McCallum (Exec Gen Mgr-Platform Svcs & Enterprise Relationship Mgmt)

Quant House SAS (1)
86 Boulevard Haussmann, 75008, Paris, France
Tel.: (33) 173023211
Web Site: http://www.quanthouse.com
Investment Advisory Services
N.A.I.C.S.: 523940
Pierre-Francois Feligioni (Co-Founder, Owner & CEO)

IRICO DISPLAY DEVICES CO., LTD.

Chuangye Building Gaoxin 1st Road Hi-tech Zone, Qindu District, Xianyang, 712021, Shaanxi, China
Tel.: (86) 2933132781
Web Site: http://www.chgf.com.cn
Year Founded: 1992
600707—(SHG)
Rev.: $1,258,960,173
Assets: $5,721,866,402
Liabilities: $2,943,251,490
Net Worth: $2,778,614,912
Earnings: ($373,785,811)
Emp.: 6,551
Fiscal Year-end: 12/31/22
Electronic Component Mfr; Television Tubes
N.A.I.C.S.: 334111
Miao Li (Chm & Pres)

IRICO GROUP NEW ENERGY COMPANY LIMITED

Units 16078 16/F Citicorp Centre 18 Whitfield Road Causeway Bay, Hong Kong, China (Hong Kong)
Tel.: (852) 2933825355
Web Site: https://www.irico.com.cn
Year Founded: 2004
0438—(HKG)
Rev.: $346,826,957
Assets: $895,505,476
Liabilities: $625,661,380
Net Worth: $269,844,096
Earnings: $12,528,229
Emp.: 2,120
Fiscal Year-end: 12/31/22
Holding Company; Photovoltaic Glass & Electronics Materials Mfr & Whslr
N.A.I.C.S.: 551112

IRIDGE, INC.

BPR Place Kamiyacho 10F 1-11-9 Azabudai, Minato-ku, Tokyo, 106-0041, Japan
Tel.: (81) 364412325
Web Site: https://iridge.jp
3917—(TKS)
Rev.: $37,756,320
Assets: $36,361,610
Liabilities: $21,660,970
Net Worth: $14,700,640
Earnings: ($7,641,160)
Emp.: 30
Fiscal Year-end: 03/31/24
Mobile Device Application Software
N.A.I.C.S.: 513210
Kentaro Oda (Pres)

IRIS ACQUISITION CORP.

3rd Floor Zephyr House 122 Mary Street, PO Box 10085, Georgetown, KY1-1001, Grand Cayman, Cayman Islands
Tel.: (345) 97143966949
Year Founded: 2020
IRAA—(NASDAQ)
Rev.: $12,661,555
Assets: $15,488,270
Liabilities: $29,321,685

INTERNATIONAL PUBLIC

Net Worth: ($13,833,415)
Earnings: $10,249,254
Emp.: 3
Fiscal Year-end: 12/31/22
Investment Management Service
N.A.I.C.S.: 523999
Lisha Parmar (CFO)

IRIS BUSINESS SERVICES LIMITED

Tower 2 3rd Floor International Infotech Par, Vashi, Navi Mumbai, 400 703, Maharashtra, India
Tel.: (91) 2267301000
Web Site: https://www.irisbusiness.com
IRIS—(NSE)
Rev.: $7,725,187
Assets: $7,761,399
Liabilities: $4,009,388
Net Worth: $3,752,010
Earnings: $370,911
Emp.: 357
Fiscal Year-end: 03/31/21
Software Development Services
N.A.I.C.S.: 513210
S. Swaminatha (Founder & CEO)

Subsidiaries:

IRIS Logix Solutions Private Limited (1)
T231 Tower 2 Third Floor International Infotech Park, Vashi, Navi Mumbai, 400 703, Maharashtra, India
Tel.: (91) 8657554440
Web Site: https://www.easywaybill.in
Software Product Firm Services
N.A.I.C.S.: 541511

IRIS CERAMICA S.P.A.

Via Ghiarola Nuova 119, Fiorano-Modenese, 41042, MO, Italy
Tel.: (39) 0536862111
Web Site: http://www.irisceramica.it
Year Founded: 1961
Sales Range: $650-699.9 Million
Emp.: 3,000
Mineral & Tile Products Mfr
N.A.I.C.S.: 327120
Romano Minozzi (Founder)

IRIS CLOTHINGS LTD.

103/24/1 Foreshore Road, Howrah, 711 102, India
Tel.: (91) 8100074062
Web Site: https://www.irisclothings.in
Year Founded: 2004
IRISDOREME—(NSE)
Rev.: $13,561,321
Assets: $13,105,785
Liabilities: $6,277,693
Net Worth: $6,828,092
Earnings: $990,216
Emp.: 1,381
Fiscal Year-end: 03/31/23
Fabric Product Mfr
N.A.I.C.S.: 313310
Niraj Agarwal (CFO)

IRIS COMPUTERS D.D.

Hiseta br 6, 71 000, Sarajevo, Bosnia & Herzegovina
Tel.: (387) 33200370
IRISRK1—(SARE)
Rev.: $227,313
Assets: $5,688,521
Liabilities: $282,553
Net Worth: $5,405,968
Earnings: $190,296
Fiscal Year-end: 12/31/21
Real Estate Development Services
N.A.I.C.S.: 531390

IRIS CORPORATION BERHAD

IRIS Smart Technology Complex Technology Park Malaysia, Bukit Jalil, 57000, Kuala Lumpur, Malaysia

AND PRIVATE COMPANIES

Tel.: (60) 389960788 MY
Web Site: https://www.iris.com.my
Year Founded: 1994
IRIS—(KLS)
Rev.: $73,835,132
Assets: $111,855,238
Liabilities: $38,780,317
Net Worth: $73,074,921
Earnings: $4,632,804
Emp.: 512
Fiscal Year-end: 03/31/23
Holding Company; Digital Identity, Business, Farming & Environmental Solutions
N.A.I.C.S.: 551112
Poh Yang Hong (Pres & Mng Dir)

Subsidiaries:

IRIS Agrotech Sdn. Bhd. (1)
IRIS Smart Technology Complex Technology Park Malaysia, Bukit Jalil, 57000, Kuala Lumpur, Malaysia (100%)
Tel.: (60) 3 8996 0788
Web Site: http://www.iris.com.my
Agricultural Watering & Feeding Systems Designer & Engineering Services
N.A.I.C.S.: 333111

IRIS Eco Power Sdn. Bhd. (1)
IRIS Smart Technology Complex Technology Park Malaysia, Bukit Jalil, 57000, Kuala Lumpur, Malaysia (100%)
Tel.: (60) 389960788
Web Site: http://www.iris.com.my
Waste Management & Energy Conversion Systems Designer & Engineering Services
N.A.I.C.S.: 238290

IRIS Information Technology Systems Sdn. Bhd. (1)
IRIS Smart Technology Complex Technology Park Malaysia, Bukit Jalil, 57000, Kuala Lumpur, Malaysia (100%)
Tel.: (60) 3 8996 0788
Web Site: http://www.iris.com.my
Image Retrieval Identification Systems Designer, Mfr & Whslr
N.A.I.C.S.: 334118

IRIS KOTO (M) Sdn. Bhd. (1)
http://www.iris.com.my/Food_Agro/main.html, Bukit Jalil, 57000, Kuala Lumpur, Malaysia (51%)
Tel.: (60) 3 8996 0788
Web Site: http://www.iris.com.my
Emp.: 300
Integrated Building Systems Mfr & Whslr
N.A.I.C.S.: 332311
Lawrence Siew (Mng Dir)

Stamford College Berhad (1)
Lot 7A Jalan 223 Section 14, Petaling Jaya, 46100, Selangor Darul Ehsan, Malaysia
Tel.: (60) 379681188
Web Site: http://www.stamford.edu.my
Sales Range: $10-24.9 Million
Education Services
N.A.I.C.S.: 611710

IRIS ENERGY LIMITED

Level 12 44 Market Street, Sydney, 2000, NSW, Australia
Tel.: (61) 279068301 AU
Web Site: https://iren.com
Year Founded: 2018
IREN—(NASDAQ)
Rev.: $184,087,000
Assets: $1,153,033,000
Liabilities: $55,682,000
Net Worth: $1,097,351,000
Earnings: ($28,955,000)
Emp.: 144
Fiscal Year-end: 06/30/24
Cryptocurrency Mining Services
N.A.I.C.S.: 523160
Daniel Roberts (Co-CEO & Co-Founder)

IRIS INFRARED INNOVATION SYSTEMS GMBH

Arenskule 9, 21339, Luneburg, Germany
Tel.: (49) 413124190

Web Site: http://www.iris-gmbh.com
Year Founded: 1990
Sales Range: $25-49.9 Million
Emp.: 10
Measuring & Controlling Devices Mfr
N.A.I.C.S.: 334519
Detlev Koenecke (Co-CEO)

IRIS NATION WORLDWIDE LIMITED

Iris Towers 185 Park St, London, SE1 9DY, United Kingdom
Tel.: (44) 20 7654 7900 UK
Web Site: http://www.iris-worldwide.com
Year Founded: 2000
Sales Range: $25-49.9 Million
Emp.: 350
Advertising Agencies
N.A.I.C.S.: 541810
Stewart Shanley (Founder, Chm & Partner)

Subsidiaries:

Datalytics Ltd (1)
Crossweys House 28 - 30 High Street, Guildford, GU1 3EL, United Kingdom
Tel.: (44) 1483 243390
Web Site: http://www.datalytics.co.uk
Data Management Software Development Services
N.A.I.C.S.: 541511
Stuart Broughton (Co-Mng Partner)

iris Germany GmbH (1)
Briennerstr 53, Munich, 80333, Germany
Tel.: (49) 89 552 790 100
Sales Range: $10-24.9 Million
Emp.: 150
Advetising Agency
N.A.I.C.S.: 541810
Markus Dunz (Mng Dir)

iris Singapore (1)
19 China St, 02-02 Far East Sq, Singapore, 049561, Singapore
Tel.: (65) 6327 6300
Emp.: 60
N.A.I.C.S.: 541810
Craig Mapleston (Chief Growth Officer)

iris Sydney Pty Ltd (1)
Level 2 285A Crown Street, Surry Hills, Sydney, 2010, NSW, Australia
Tel.: (61) 2 9356 9300
Advetising Agency
N.A.I.C.S.: 541810

iris ny (1)
588 Broadway Ste 505, New York, NY 10012
Tel.: (212) 966-1529
Emp.: 35
N.A.I.C.S.: 541810

IRISH CONTINENTAL GROUP PLC

Ferryport Alexandra Road, Dublin, 1, Ireland
Tel.: (353) 16075628 IE
Web Site: https://www.icg.ie
Year Founded: 1972
IR5B—(ISE)
Rev.: $340,345,304
Assets: $711,028,136
Liabilities: $384,439,120
Net Worth: $326,589,016
Earnings: ($23,336,560)
Emp.: 288
Fiscal Year-end: 12/31/20
Marine Transportation of Passengers, Cars & Freight
N.A.I.C.S.: 483211
Eamonn Rothwell (CEO)

Subsidiaries:

Dublin Ferryport Terminals (1)
Container Terminal Breakwater Rd, Dublin, 1, Ireland (100%)
Tel.: (353) 18552222
Vessel Transportation of Passengers, Cars & Freight

N.A.I.C.S.: 483211

Eucon Shipping & Transport Ltd. (1)
Breakwater Road South, Ferryport, Dublin, 1, Ireland (100%)
Tel.: (353) 1 607 5555
Web Site: https://www.eucon.nl
Sales Range: $150-199.9 Million
Emp.: 40
Vessel Transportation of Passengers, Cars & Freight
N.A.I.C.S.: 483211

EuroFeeders Ltd. (1)
Ferry Ln Ste 3 Orwell House, IP113QL, Felixstowe, United Kingdom (100%)
Tel.: (44) 1394676667
Web Site: http://www.eurofeeders.com
Sales Range: $25-49.9 Million
Emp.: 3
Vessel Transportation of Passengers, Cars & Freight
N.A.I.C.S.: 483211

Feederlink B.V. (1)
Seattle W 11, PO Box 53050, 3008HB, Rotterdam, Netherlands (100%)
Tel.: (31) 0104912666
Web Site: http://www.feederlink.com
Sales Range: $25-49.9 Million
Emp.: 16
Vessel Transportation of Passengers, Cars & Freight
N.A.I.C.S.: 483211

Irish Ferries (1)
Alexandra Road, PO Box 19, Ferryport, Dublin, 1, Ireland (100%)
Tel.: (353) 818300400
Web Site: http://www.irishferries.com
Sales Range: $50-74.9 Million
Vessel Transportation of Passengers, Cars & Freight
N.A.I.C.S.: 483211

Irish Ferries (U.K.) Services Limited (1)
The Plaza Suite 4D - 4th Floor 100 Old Hall Street, Liverpool, L3 9QJ, United Kingdom
Tel.: (44) 3717300400
Administrative Services
N.A.I.C.S.: 561110

IRISH RESIDENTIAL PROPERTIES REIT PLC

South Dock House Hanover Quay, Dublin, D02 XW94, Ireland
Tel.: (353) 15180300
Web Site: https://www.iresreit.ie
Year Founded: 2014
RSHPF—(OTCIQ)
Rev.: $96,979,799
Assets: $1,434,620,819
Liabilities: $664,854,841
Net Worth: $769,765,979
Earnings: ($128,064,908)
Emp.: 95
Fiscal Year-end: 12/31/23
Real Estate Investment Services
N.A.I.C.S.: 531390
Margaret Sweeney (CEO)

IRISO ELECTRONICS CO.,LTD

2-13-8 Shinyokohama, Kohoku-ku, Yokohama, 222-0033, Kanagawa, Japan
Tel.: (81) 454783545
Web Site: https://www.irisoele.com
Year Founded: 1966
6908—(TKS)
Rev.: $365,341,310
Assets: $640,218,160
Liabilities: $131,142,400
Net Worth: $509,075,760
Earnings: $36,969,730
Emp.: 3,037
Fiscal Year-end: 03/31/24
Electronic Connector Mfr
N.A.I.C.S.: 334417
Sadao Sato (Chm)

Subsidiaries:

IRISO (SHANGHAI) R&D CENTER CO., LTD. (1)

No 2388 Rongle Dong Road, Songjiang, Shanghai, 201600, China
Tel.: (86) 2157742968
Connector Mfr & Distr
N.A.I.C.S.: 334417

IRISO (SHANGHAI) TRADING CO., LTD. (1)
Room 2202 Building T2 Everbright Anshi Center No 398 Huoshan Road, Yangpu District, Shanghai, 200082, China
Tel.: (86) 2158352770
Connector Mfr & Distr
N.A.I.C.S.: 334417

IRISO Component Co., Ltd. (1)
2-35-8 Kitamikata, Takatu-ku, Kawasaki, 213-0005, Kanagawa, Japan
Tel.: (81) 44 379 4621
Connector Mfr & Distr
N.A.I.C.S.: 334417

IRISO ELECTRONICS (HONG KONG) LTD. (1)
Unit D 12/F Legend Tower, No 7 Shing Yip Street, Kwun Tong, Kowloon, China (Hong Kong)
Tel.: (852) 27502299
Web Site: https://www.irisoele.com
Connector Mfr & Distr
N.A.I.C.S.: 334417

IRISO ELECTRONICS (THAILAND) LTD. (1)
Room 34 3rd Floor 43 Thai CC Tower South Sathorn Road, Yannawa Sathorn, Bangkok, 10120, Thailand
Tel.: (66) 26758559
Web Site: https://www.irisoele.com
Connector Mfr & Distr
N.A.I.C.S.: 334417

IRISO ELECTRONICS CO.,LTD - Ibaraki Plant (1)
714-1 Kamiiwase, Hitachiomiya, 319-2142, Ibaraki, Japan
Tel.: (81) 295522731
Connector Mfr
N.A.I.C.S.: 334417

IRISO ELECTRONICS EUROPE GmbH (1)
Zettachring 10, 70567, Stuttgart, Germany
Tel.: (49) 7114510490
Web Site: https://www.iriso.de
Connector Mfr & Distr
N.A.I.C.S.: 334417
Rolf Aichele (Dir)

IRISO ELECTRONICS PHILIPPINES, INC. (1)
Cavite Economic Zone Lot Nos 10 12 Block 22 Phase IV Rosario, Cavite, 4106, Philippines
Tel.: (63) 464370440
Web Site: https://www.irisoele.com
Connector Mfr & Distr
N.A.I.C.S.: 334417
Gary Mendones (Sr Engr-Technical Dev)

IRISO ELECTRONICS VIETNAM CO., LTD. (1)
Land lot No CN1-1 Tan Truong Industrial Zone, Cam Giang District, Hai Duong, Vietnam
Tel.: (84) 2203570080
Connector Mfr
N.A.I.C.S.: 334417
Kage Morikane (Mgr)

IRISO U.S.A., INC. (1)
34405 W 12 Mile Rd Ste 237, Farmington Hills, MI 48331
Tel.: (248) 324-9780
Web Site: https://www.irisoconnectors.com
Emp.: 21
Connector Mfr & Distr
N.A.I.C.S.: 334417
Aki Ohira (Gen Mgr)

IRS (S) PTE., LTD. (1)
29 International Business Park 05-01 Acer, Building Tower A, Singapore, 609923, Singapore
Tel.: (65) 68624866
Emp.: 15
Connector Mfr & Distr
N.A.I.C.S.: 334417

SHANGHAI IRISO ELECTRONICS CO., LTD. (1)

IRISO ELECTRONICS CO.,LTD

IRISO ELECTRONICS CO.,LTD—(Continued)
No 2388 Rong Le Tong Road, Songjiang, Shanghai, 201600, China
Tel.: (86) 2157742968
Connector Mfr
N.A.I.C.S.: 334417

IRITEL AD BEOGRAD
Batajnicki put 23, 11080, Belgrade, Serbia
Tel.: (381) 113073400
Web Site: https://www.iritel.com
Year Founded: 1967
IRTL—(BEL)
Rev.: $8,548,357
Assets: $13,782,263
Liabilities: $4,994,160
Net Worth: $8,788,104
Earnings: $84,608
Emp.: 146
Fiscal Year-end: 12/31/23
Telecommunication & Electronic Services
N.A.I.C.S.: 517810
Dragan Kovacevic (Gen Mgr)

IRLAB THERAPEUTICS AB
Arvid Wallgrens Backe 20, 413 46, Gothenburg, Sweden
Tel.: (46) 317573800
Web Site: https://www.irlab.se
Year Founded: 2013
IRLAB.A—(OMX)
Rev.: $49,320
Assets: $45,177,901
Liabilities: $2,708,711
Net Worth: $42,469,190
Earnings: ($11,188,998)
Emp.: 18
Fiscal Year-end: 12/31/20
Pharmaceuticals Product Mfr
N.A.I.C.S.: 325412
Nicholas Waters (CEO)

IRM ENERGY LIMITED
4th Floor 8th Block Magnet Corporate Park Nr Sola Bridge, SG Highway Thaltej, Ahmedabad, 380054, Gujarat, India
Tel.: (91) 7949031500
Web Site: https://www.irmenergy.com
Year Founded: 2015
544004—(BOM)
Rev.: $126,665,999
Assets: $93,570,642
Liabilities: $54,112,649
Net Worth: $39,457,993
Earnings: $6,845,376
Fiscal Year-end: 03/31/23
Renewable Energy Services
N.A.I.C.S.: 221210

IRMOVO A.D.
Atar 25, Novi Sad, Serbia
Tel.: (381) 21823151
Year Founded: 1991
IRMV—(BEL)
Rev.: $1,364,983
Assets: $4,631,007
Liabilities: $3,219,601
Net Worth: $1,411,406
Earnings: $6,160
Emp.: 14
Fiscal Year-end: 12/31/23
Cereal Crop Farming Services
N.A.I.C.S.: 111998
Dragan Radivojevic (Gen Dir)

IROC CO., LTD.
Rm 7 4F No 258 Lian Cheng Rd, Chung Ho Dist, New Taipei City, 235, Taiwan
Tel.: (886) 282272928
Web Site: https://zh.i-baas.com
Year Founded: 2003
3555—(TPE)
Rev.: $2,139,180

Assets: $11,525,164
Liabilities: $5,886,948
Net Worth: $5,638,216
Earnings: ($600,118)
Fiscal Year-end: 12/31/23
Electronic Parts Mfr & Distr
N.A.I.C.S.: 334419
K. C. Chou (Chm & CEO)

IRON FORCE INDUSTRIAL CO., LTD.
19F No 98 Sec 1 Xintai 5th Rd, Xizhi Dist, New Taipei City, 221, Taiwan
Tel.: (886) 226962818
Web Site: https://www.irf.biz
Year Founded: 1977
2228—(TAI)
Rev.: $160,052,906
Assets: $200,639,778
Liabilities: $57,941,526
Net Worth: $142,698,252
Earnings: $16,802,936
Emp.: 949
Fiscal Year-end: 12/31/23
Automotive, Display & Houseware Metal Products Mfr
N.A.I.C.S.: 332999
Alan Cheng-I Huang (Chm)

Subsidiaries:

Huzhou Iron Force Metal Products Co., Ltd (1)
Industrial Zone of Luoshe Town, Deqing County, Huzhou, 313218, Zhejiang, China
Tel.: (86) 5728407778
Display Case Mfr
N.A.I.C.S.: 337215

Iron Force Corporation (1)
19f No 98 Sec 1 Sintai 5th Rd Sijhih Dist, New Taipei City, 221, Taiwan
Tel.: (886) 226962818
Display Case Mfr
N.A.I.C.S.: 337215

Iron Force Industrial Co., Ltd. - Nantou Division (1)
No 13 Gongye North Road Nangang Industrial Zone, Nantong, Guangdong, China
Tel.: (86) 492257447
Display Case Mfr
N.A.I.C.S.: 337215

Zhejiang Iron Force Metal Products Co., Ltd. (1)
Industrial Park Lou-She Town De-Qing, Huzhou, Zhejiang, China
Tel.: (86) 5728407106
Display Case Mfr
N.A.I.C.S.: 337215

IRON HORSE CORP.
884 Churchill Avenue South, Ottawa, K1Z5H2, ON, Canada
Tel.: (613) 228-2813
Web Site: http://www.ironhorsegroup.com
Year Founded: 1994
Sales Range: $50-74.9 Million
Emp.: 400
Security & Private Investigation Services
N.A.I.C.S.: 561611
Robin St. Martin (Pres)

IRONBARK ASSET MANAGEMENT PTY. LTD.
Level 13 60 Castlereagh Street, Sydney, 2000, NSW, Australia
Tel.: (61) 2 9256 6350
Web Site: http://www.ironbarkam.com
Investment Services
N.A.I.C.S.: 523150
Chris Larsen (CEO)

Subsidiaries:

Ironbark Asset Management Fund Services Ltd. (1)
Level 13 60 Castlereagh Street, Sydney, 2000, NSW, Australia (100%)

Tel.: (61) 2 9256 6350
Web Site: http://www.ironbark-am.com
Sales Range: $1-4.9 Billion
Investment & Portfolio Management Services
N.A.I.C.S.: 523940

IRONBARK CAPITAL LIMITED
Suite 607 180 Ocean Street, Edgecliff, 2027, NSW, Australia
Tel.: (61) 289170399 AU
Web Site: https://www.ironbarkcapital.com
Year Founded: 2002
IBC—(ASX)
Rev.: $2,360,443
Assets: $40,940,839
Liabilities: $819,979
Net Worth: $40,120,860
Earnings: $1,741,453
Fiscal Year-end: 06/30/24
Investment Management Service
N.A.I.C.S.: 523999
Michael J. Cole (Chm)

IRONBARK ZINC LIMITED
Level 3 22 Railway Road, PO Box 8187, Subiaco, 6008, WA, Australia
Tel.: (61) 861465325 AU
Web Site: https://www.ironbark.gl
IBG—(ASX)
Rev.: $15,528
Assets: $2,265,198
Liabilities: $1,255,335
Net Worth: $1,009,863
Earnings: ($1,050,282)
Fiscal Year-end: 06/30/24
Base Metal Properties Evaluation & Exploration Services
N.A.I.C.S.: 212220
Robert Orr (CFO & Co-Sec)

IRONBRIDGE CAPITAL
Level 10 56 Pitt Street, Sydney, 2000, NSW, Australia
Tel.: (61) 2 9250 8700 AU
Web Site: http://www.ironbridge.com.au
Year Founded: 2003
Private Equity Group
N.A.I.C.S.: 523999
Neil Broekhuizen (Co-CEO & Partner)

Subsidiaries:

Bravura Solutions Limited (1)
Level 6 345 George Street, Sydney, 2000, NSW, Australia
Tel.: (61) 290187800
Web Site: https://www.bravurasolutions.com
Rev.: $203,366,747
Assets: $344,875,144
Liabilities: $88,296,502
Net Worth: $256,578,642
Earnings: $22,929,002
Emp.: 1,500
Fiscal Year-end: 06/30/2022
Financial Software Publisher
N.A.I.C.S.: 513210
Neil Broekhuizen (Chm)

Subsidiary (Non-US):

Bravura Software Solutions (SA) (Proprietary) Limited (2)
Building 2 Country Club Estate Woodlands Drive, Woodmead, 2052, South Africa
Tel.: (27) 112588861
Web Site: http://www.bravurasolutions.com.au
Software Consulting Services
N.A.I.C.S.: 541512

Bravura Solutions (HK) Limited (2)
22nd Floor Room 2207 Tower Two Times Square 1 Matheson Street, Causeway Bay, China (Hong Kong)
Tel.: (852) 37538853
Professional Consulting Services
N.A.I.C.S.: 541618

Bravura Solutions (NZ) Limited (2)
12 14 N crost St, Takapuna, Auckland,

0740, New Zealand
Tel.: (64) 9 489 6174
Web Site: http://www.bravurasolutions.com
Professional Consulting Services
N.A.I.C.S.: 541618

Bravura Solutions (Thailand) Company Limited (2)
4/4-5 Zen World Building Ste 1292 Level 12, Rajdamri Road Lumpini Phatumwan, Bangkok, 10330, Thailand
Tel.: (66) 26979051
Professional Consulting Services
N.A.I.C.S.: 541618

Bravura Solutions (UK) Ltd. (2)
Austin Friars House 2-6 Austin Friars, London, EC2N 2HD, United Kingdom
Tel.: (44) 2079973000
Web Site: http://www.bravurasolutions.com
Sales Range: $50-74.9 Million
Financial Management Software
N.A.I.C.S.: 513210
Nick Parsons (CEO)

Subsidiary (Domestic):

Bravura Solutions Services (UK) Limited (3)
Level 2 Clarence House 131-135 George Street, Edinburgh, EH2 4JS, United Kingdom
Tel.: (44) 131 260 3300
Sales Range: $25-49.9 Million
Emp.: 12
Professional Consulting Services
N.A.I.C.S.: 541618
Emma Carscadden (Gen Mgr)

Subsidiary (Non-US):

Bravura Solutions Luxembourg Holdings S.a.r.l. (2)
19 Rue de Bitbourg, 1273, Luxembourg, Luxembourg
Tel.: (352) 26005 290
Web Site: http://www.bravurasolutions.com
Sales Range: $25-49.9 Million
Emp.: 1
Professional Consulting Services
N.A.I.C.S.: 541618

Bravura Solutions Polska Sp. Z OO (2)
Level 2 Atrium 1 Al Jana Pawla II 17, 00-854, Warsaw, Poland
Tel.: (48) 22 256 0400
Sales Range: $25-49.9 Million
Emp.: 100
Professional Consulting Services
N.A.I.C.S.: 541618
Martin Lawson (Head-Ops)

IRONBRIDGE EQUITY PARTNERS
Bay Adelaide Centre East Tower 22 Adelaide St West Suite 3520, Toronto, M5H 4E3, ON, Canada
Tel.: (416) 863-0105
Web Site: http://www.ironbridgeequity.com
Year Founded: 2005
Privater Equity Firm
N.A.I.C.S.: 523999
Peter Samson (Mng Partner)

IRONVELD PLC
Unit D De Clare House Sir Alfred Owen Way, Pontygwindy Industrial Estate, Caerphilly, CF83 3HU, United Kingdom
Tel.: (44) 2071383204
Web Site: https://www.ironveld.com
IRON—(AIM)
Rev.: $5,431
Assets: $36,074,620
Liabilities: $7,939,947
Net Worth: $28,134,674
Earnings: ($1,101,111)
Emp.: 11
Fiscal Year-end: 06/30/22
Iron Ore Production & Mining
N.A.I.C.S.: 331511
Peter John Cox (Dir-Technical)

IRONWOOD EDUCATION LTD.
KHIL House 1st floor Orchid Hotel Compound Nehru Road Vile Parle East, Near Sathaye College Stop, Mumbai, 400099, India
Tel.: (91) 2226631834
Web Site: http://www.greycellsltd.com
508918—(BOM)
Rev.: $373,846
Assets: $3,296,270
Liabilities: $1,679,182
Net Worth: $1,617,088
Earnings: ($257,084)
Emp.: 12
Fiscal Year-end: 03/31/23
Media & Entertainment Services
N.A.I.C.S.: 518210
Ashwani Kumar Singh (Exec Dir)

Subsidiaries:

EMDI (Overseas) FZ LLC (1)
First Floor F15 Block 13 Knowledge Park, PO Box 500499, Dubai, United Arab Emirates
Tel.: (971) 44332833
Web Site: https://www.emdiworld.ae
Training Services
N.A.I.C.S.: 611430
Alan Gordon (Chm)

IRPC PUBLIC COMPANY LIMITED
299 moo 5 Sukhumvit Rd, Choeng Noen, Rayong, 21000, Thailand
Tel.: (66) 38611333
Web Site: https://www.irpc.co.th
IRPSY—(OTCIQ)
Rev.: $9,338,512,496
Assets: $5,624,158,585
Liabilities: $3,402,015,277
Net Worth: $2,222,143,308
Earnings: ($85,017,334)
Emp.: 4,441
Fiscal Year-end: 12/31/23
Petrochemical & Petroleum Refiner & Mfr
N.A.I.C.S.: 325110
Chansin Treenuchagron (Chm)

Subsidiaries:

IRPC Oil Co., Ltd. (1)
555/2 Energy Complex Building Building B 9th Fl Vibhavadi Rangsit Road, Chatuchak Subdistrict Chatuchak District, Bangkok, 10900, Thailand
Tel.: (66) 27656666
Web Site: http://www.irpc.co.th
Sales Range: $25-49.9 Million
Emp.: 33
Oil Products Whslr
N.A.I.C.S.: 424720

Thai ABS Co., Ltd (1)
26 56 Tpi Tower Chan Tat Mai Rd, Thung Mahamek Sathon, Bangkok, 10120, Thailand
Tel.: (66) 2 678 5000
Plastic Resin Mfr
N.A.I.C.S.: 325211

Subsidiary (Domestic):

IRPC A&L Co., Ltd. (2)
555/2 Energy Complex Building Building B 9th Fl Vibhavadi Rangsit Road, Chatuchak Subdistrict Chatuchak District, Bangkok, 10900, Thailand
Tel.: (66) 27656666
Polymer Material Mfr
N.A.I.C.S.: 325211

IRRAS AB
Vasagatan 16, 111 20, Stockholm, Sweden
Tel.: (46) 102115170
Web Site: http://www.irras.com
Year Founded: 2011
IRRAS—(OMX)
Rev.: $3,746,289
Assets: $16,074,068
Liabilities: $2,395,403
Net Worth: $13,678,665
Earnings: ($15,604,447)
Emp.: 51
Fiscal Year-end: 12/31/22
Medical Device Application Development Services
N.A.I.C.S.: 541511
Kleanthis G. Xanthopoulos (CEO)

Subsidiaries:

IRRAS GmbH (1)
Prielmayerstr 3, 80335, Munich, Germany
Tel.: (49) 8008503501
Medical Device Mfr
N.A.I.C.S.: 339112

IRRAS USA Inc. (1)
11975 El Camino Real Ste 304, San Diego, CA 92130
Medical Device Mfr
N.A.I.C.S.: 339112

IRRC CORPORATION
5F Hongo Center Building 2-27-20 Hongo, Bunkyo-Ku, Tokyo, 113-0033, Japan
Tel.: (81) 358409051
Web Site: https://www.irrc.co.jp
Year Founded: 1995
7325—(TKS)
Rev.: $49,268,620
Assets: $32,250,700
Liabilities: $9,379,760
Net Worth: $22,870,940
Earnings: $124,400
Fiscal Year-end: 06/30/24
Brokerage Investment Services
N.A.I.C.S.: 524210
Katsumoto Ryuji (Founder, Chm, Pres & CEO)

IRSA INVERSIONES Y REPRESENTACIONES SOCIEDAD ANONIMA
Carlos M Della Paolera 261 9th Floor, C1001ADA, Buenos Aires, Argentina
Tel.: (54) 48147800
Web Site: https://www.irsa.com.ar
Year Founded: 1943
IRS—(NYSE)
Rev.: $360,441,246
Assets: $2,459,395,546
Liabilities: $1,195,079,962
Net Worth: $1,264,315,584
Earnings: ($37,084,595)
Emp.: 1,401
Fiscal Year-end: 06/30/24
Real Estate Services
N.A.I.C.S.: 531120
Daniel Ricardo Elsztain (Chief Real Estate Operating Officer)

Subsidiaries:

IRSA Propiedades Comerciales S.A. (1)
Carlos M Della Paolera 261 9th Floor, C1001ADA, Buenos Aires, Argentina
Tel.: (54) 1148147800
Web Site: https://www.irsacp.com.ar
Rev.: $96,213,880
Assets: $2,109,333,560
Liabilities: $1,181,758,990
Net Worth: $927,574,570
Earnings: ($267,964,930)
Emp.: 620
Fiscal Year-end: 06/30/2021
Commercial Real Estate Acquisition, Development & Leasing Services
N.A.I.C.S.: 531120
Daniel Ricardo Elsztain (CEO)

IRTYSH-POLYMETAL JSC
104 B Dostyk ave Medeu district, Almaty, 050010, Kazakhstan
Tel.: (7) 7273560686
Web Site:
http://www.irtishpolimetall.com
IRPM—(KAZ)
Rev.: $13,236,941
Assets: $8,127,986
Liabilities: $7,553,032
Net Worth: $574,954
Earnings: $1,751,691
Fiscal Year-end: 12/31/19
Copper & Gold Mining Services
N.A.I.C.S.: 212290

IRVIN GOODON INDUSTRIES LTD.
PO Box 777, Boissevain, R0K 0E0, MB, Canada
Tel.: (204) 534-2468
Web Site: https://www.goodon.com
Year Founded: 1963
Rev.: $10,259,504
Emp.: 30
Construction Services
N.A.I.C.S.: 236220
Robert Dyck (Partner & Ops Mgr)

IRVING OIL LIMITED
1 Germain Street, Saint John, E2L 4V1, NB, Canada
Tel.: (506) 202-2000
Web Site: http://www.irvingoil.com
Petroleum Products Refining & Distribution Services; Gas Station Operator
N.A.I.C.S.: 324110
Kevin Dumaresque (CFO)

Subsidiaries:

Cobalt Properties Limited (1)
10 Sydney Street, Saint John, E2L 4K1, Canada
Tel.: (506) 202-1000
Web Site: http://www.cobaltproperties.ca
Property Management & Leasing Services
N.A.I.C.S.: 531190
Marc Gosselin (Bus Dev & Leasing)

Irving Blending & Packaging Limited (1)
555 Courtenay Bay Causeway, Saint John, E2L 4E6, NB, Canada
Tel.: (506) 632-7000
Web Site: http://www.irvingblend.com
Liquid Blending & Packaging Services
N.A.I.C.S.: 311225
Grant Ashe (Mgr-Sls)

Ocean Investments Corporation (1)
190 Commerce Way, Portsmouth, NH 03801
Tel.: (603) 559-8736
Web Site: http://www.irvingoil.com
Sales Range: $150-199.9 Million
Emp.: 100
Holding Company of Petroleum Bulk Stations & Terminals
N.A.I.C.S.: 424710
Arthur L. Irving (Owner & Chm)

Subsidiary (Domestic):

Irving Oil Corporation (2)
190 Commerce Way, Portsmouth, NH 03801
Tel.: (603) 559-8736
Web Site: http://www.irvingoil.com
Petroleum Products
N.A.I.C.S.: 424720
Scott Breen (Controller)

IRVING RESOURCES INC.
999 Canada Place Suite 404, Vancouver, V6C 3E2, BC, Canada
Tel.: (604) 682-3234
Web Site:
https://www.irvresources.com
Year Founded: 2015
IRVRF—(OTCQX)
Rev.: $194,739
Assets: $36,847,150
Liabilities: $443,401
Net Worth: $36,403,749
Earnings: ($1,074,406)
Fiscal Year-end: 02/28/23
Copper Ore & Nickel Ore Mining Services
N.A.I.C.S.: 212230

Akiko Levinson (Pres & CEO)

IRWIN INDUSTRIAL LTD.
50 East Beaver Creek Road, Richmond Hill, L4B 1G6, ON, Canada
Tel.: (905) 889-9100
Web Site: http://www.irwin-ind.com
Year Founded: 1970
Rev.: $10,150,526
Emp.: 53
Industrial Electronic Component Mfr
N.A.I.C.S.: 334419
Glenn Irwin (Pres)

IRWIN MITCHELL LLP
Riverside East 2 Millsands, Sheffield, S3 8DT, S Yorkshire, United Kingdom
Tel.: (44) 114 276 7777
Web Site:
http://www.irwinmitchell.com
Year Founded: 1912
Sales Range: $350-399.9 Million
Emp.: 2,500
Law firm
N.A.I.C.S.: 541110
Adrian Budgen (Partner)

IRWIN NATURALS INC.
1030 West Georgia St Stu 918, Burnaby, V3N 1B9, BC, Canada
Tel.: (604) 628-5616
IWIN—(DEU)
Rev.: $100,342,000
Assets: $47,219,000
Liabilities: $24,103,000
Net Worth: $23,116,000
Earnings: $10,114,000
Fiscal Year-end: 12/31/21
Asset Management Services
N.A.I.C.S.: 523940
Irwin Klee (Chm & CEO)

Subsidiaries:

Irwin Naturals (1)
5310 Beethoven St, Los Angeles, CA 90066
Tel.: (310) 306-3636
Web Site: http://www.irwinnaturals.com
Chemicals Mfr
N.A.I.C.S.: 325998

IS DONGSEO CO., LTD.
231 Hakdong-ro, Gangnam-Gu, Seoul, 06053, Korea (South)
Tel.: (82) 232186701
Web Site:
https://www.isdongseo.co.kr
Year Founded: 1989
010780—(KRS)
Rev.: $1,747,565,706
Assets: $2,866,882,212
Liabilities: $1,634,977,340
Net Worth: $1,231,904,872
Earnings: $157,129,196
Emp.: 778
Fiscal Year-end: 12/31/22
Holding Company; Construction Materials, Concrete Products & Ceramic Products Mfr & Distr
N.A.I.C.S.: 551112
Hyuk-Woon Kwon (Pres)

Subsidiaries:

Korea Rental Corporation (1)
10 Yeonmujang 11-gil, Seongdong-gu, Seoul, 135911, Korea (South)
Tel.: (82) 18993945
Web Site: http://www.korearental.co.kr
Sales Range: $150-199.9 Million
Emp.: 149
Information Technology & Other Office Equipment Rental Services
N.A.I.C.S.: 532420

IS FAKTORING A.S.
Is Kuleleri Kule 1 Kat 10, Levent, 34330, Istanbul, Turkiye
Tel.: (90) 8507227777

IS FAKTORING A.S.

Is Faktoring A.S.—(Continued)
Web Site:
http://www.isfaktoring.com.tr
ISFAK—(IST)
Rev.: $87,990,760
Assets: $942,171,642
Liabilities: $856,154,375
Net Worth: $86,017,267
Earnings: $16,454,402
Emp.: 114
Fiscal Year-end: 12/31/21
Financial Investment Services
N.A.I.C.S.: 523999
Omer Karakus *(Gen Mgr)*

IS GAYRIMENKUL YATIRIM ORTAKLIGI A.S.
Is Kuleleri Kule-2 Kat 10-11, Levent, Levent, 34330, Istanbul, Turkiye
Tel.: (90) 2123252350
Web Site: https://www.isgyo.com.tr
Year Founded: 1999
ISGYO—(IST)
Rev.: $42,451,828
Assets: $1,122,834,032
Liabilities: $207,324,698
Net Worth: $915,509,334
Earnings: $106,043,983
Emp.: 70
Fiscal Year-end: 12/31/23
Real Estate Investment Services
N.A.I.C.S.: 531210
Hasan K. Bolat *(CEO)*

IS GIRISIM SERMAYESI YATIRIM ORTAKLIGI A.S.
Is Kuleleri Kule 2 Kat 2 Levent, 34330, Istanbul, Turkiye
Tel.: (90) 2123251744
Web Site: http://www.isgirisim.com.tr
Year Founded: 1993
ISGSY—(IST)
Rev.: $1,756,185
Assets: $21,233,821
Liabilities: $265,951
Net Worth: $20,967,870
Earnings: $911,400
Emp.: 5
Fiscal Year-end: 12/31/21
Financial Investment Services
N.A.I.C.S.: 523999
A. Murat Ozgen *(CEO)*

IS INDUSTRIAL SERVICES AG
Nordring 26, 90408, Nuremberg, Germany
Tel.: (49) 91199350113
Web Site: http://www.is-ag.com
Year Founded: 1990
Rev.: $12,015,359
Emp.: 310
Industrial Engineering Services
N.A.I.C.S.: 541330
Peter Dinstuehler *(Founder, Chm & CEO)*

IS YATIRIM ORTAKLIGI AS
Is Kuleleri Kule-1 Kat 5, Levent, Istanbul, Turkiye
Tel.: (90) 2122841710
Web Site: https://www.isyatort.com.tr
Year Founded: 1995
ISYAT—(IST)
Rev.: $16,566,156
Assets: $17,112,081
Liabilities: $365,837
Net Worth: $16,746,244
Earnings: $4,285,089
Emp.: 5
Fiscal Year-end: 12/31/22
Portfolio Management Services
N.A.I.C.S.: 523940
Kenan Ayvaci *(Deputy Chm)*

ISA HOLDINGS LIMITED
Block 9 Pinewood Office Park 33 Riley Road, Woodmead, Sandton, 2146, South Africa
Tel.: (27) 110327799
Web Site: https://www.isa.co.za
Year Founded: 1998
ISA—(JSE)
Rev.: $5,489,405
Assets: $4,707,904
Liabilities: $1,281,226
Net Worth: $3,426,678
Earnings: $1,608,694
Emp.: 36
Fiscal Year-end: 02/29/24
Investment Management Service
N.A.I.C.S.: 523940
Clifford S. Katz *(CEO)*

Subsidiaries:

Information Security Architects Proprietary Limited (1)
Block 9 Pinewood Office Park 33 Riley Road, Woodmead, Sandton, South Africa
Tel.: (27) 110327799
Web Site: https://www.isa.co.za
Network Security Services
N.A.I.C.S.: 541519

ISA INDUSTRIAL LTD.
Avenida Da Praia Grande N 619 Comercial Si Toi 5 Andar 8, Macau, 999078, China (Macau)
Tel.: (853) 2835 6320
Web Site: http://www.liteleather.com
Year Founded: 1995
Leather Mfr
N.A.I.C.S.: 316990
Thomas Schneider *(Chm)*

Subsidiaries:

Auburn Leather Co. (1)
125 Caldwell St, Auburn, KY 42206
Tel.: (270) 542-4116
Web Site: http://www.auburnleather.com
All Other Leather Good Mfr
N.A.I.C.S.: 316990

ISA INTERNATIONALE INC.
46 Dufflaw Road, Toronto, M6A 2W1, ON, Canada
Tel.: (416) 782-9100
Web Site: http://www.havaseat.com
Year Founded: 1989
Investment Services
N.A.I.C.S.: 523999
Art Sandler *(Founder)*

ISA-TRAESKO GMBH
Oderstrasse 9, 24539, Neumunster, Germany
Tel.: (49) 432198260
Web Site: http://www.isa-traesko.de
Rev.: $21,159,996
Emp.: 64
Footwear Mfr
N.A.I.C.S.: 424340
Carsten Heinz *(Chm-Mgmt Bd)*

Subsidiaries:

ZAPATO Far East Trading Ltd. (1)
Unit 502 Rykadan Capital Tower No 135 Hoi Bun Road, Kwun Tong, Kowloon, China (Hong Kong)
Tel.: (852) 21740888
Footwear Distr
N.A.I.C.S.: 424340

ISAAC ENGINEERING CO., LTD.
15 Gunpo Cheomdan Saneop 1-Ro, Gunpo, 15881, Gyeonggi-do, Korea (South)
Tel.: (82) 313610800
Web Site: https://isaac-eng.com
Year Founded: 2006
351330—(KRS)
Computer System Consultancy Services
N.A.I.C.S.: 541512

C. S. Kim *(Co-CEO)*

ISABELLA OLIVER LTD.
The Postman's Office 30 Leighton Road, Kentish Town, London, NW5 2QE, United Kingdom
Tel.: (44) 20 7284 3001
Web Site:
http://www.isabellaoliver.com
Year Founded: 2003
Sales Range: $10-24.9 Million
Women's Clothing Retailer
N.A.I.C.S.: 458110
Isabella Oliver *(Founder)*

ISAGRI S.A.
Avenue des censives, 60026, Beauvais, France
Tel.: (33) 344068400
Web Site: http://www.isagri.com
Year Founded: 1983
Sales Range: $150-199.9 Million
Emp.: 1,250
Agricultural Software Developer
N.A.I.C.S.: 513210
Jean-Marie Savalle *(CEO)*

Subsidiaries:

Cecurity.com SA (1)
75 Rue Saint Lazare, 75009, Paris, France
Tel.: (33) 156433737
Web Site: http://www.cecurity.com
Sales Range: $1-9.9 Million
Emp.: 10
Data Protection, Legal Archiving & Traceability Software Publisher
N.A.I.C.S.: 513210
Alain Borghesi *(Chm & CEO)*

ISAMU PAINT CO., LTD.
2-15-24 Sagisu, Fukushima-ku, Osaka, 553-0002, Japan
Tel.: (81) 664580036
Web Site: https://www.isamu.co.jp
Year Founded: 1947
4624—(TKS)
Rev.: $52,846,950
Assets: $137,243,430
Liabilities: $23,690,240
Net Worth: $113,553,190
Earnings: $3,437,200
Emp.: 196
Fiscal Year-end: 03/31/24
Paint Mfr & Distr
N.A.I.C.S.: 325510
Kitamura Baisho *(Pres & CEO)*

ISANGO! LTD.
2nd Floor Whitfield Court 32nd Whitfiled Street, London, W1T 2RQ, United Kingdom
Tel.: (44) 203 355 1240
Web Site: http://wwwisango.com
Year Founded: 2007
Travel Arrangement & Reservation Services
N.A.I.C.S.: 561599
Vinay Gupta *(CEO)*

ISANOR INVEST AS
PO Box 113 Grefsen, NO-0409, Oslo, Norway
Tel.: (47) 81500060
Year Founded: 2005
Management Consultancy Services
N.A.I.C.S.: 541618

Subsidiaries:

Sector Alarm AS (1)
PO Box 113 Grefsen, Vitaminveien 1A, 0409, Oslo, Norway
Tel.: (47) 23 39 94 00
Alarm Mfr
N.A.I.C.S.: 334419

ISB CORPORATION
1F Sumitomo Life Gotanda Building

INTERNATIONAL PUBLIC

5-1-11 Osaki, Shinagawa-ku, Tokyo, 141-0032, Japan
Tel.: (81) 334901761
Web Site: https://www.isb.co.jp
Year Founded: 1970
9702—(TKS)
Rev.: $229,630,920
Assets: $127,534,920
Liabilities: $43,724,030
Net Worth: $83,810,890
Earnings: $10,436,480
Emp.: 890
Fiscal Year-end: 12/31/23
IT & Communication Consulting & Solutions Services
N.A.I.C.S.: 541519
Itsuo Wakao *(Pres & CEO)*

Subsidiaries:

ISB Vietnam Company Limited (1)
Unit 3 1 E-town 2 Building 3rd Fl 364 Cong Hoa St, Tan Binh Dist, Ho Chi Minh City, Vietnam
Tel.: (84) 28 381 2715
Web Site: https://www.isb-vietnam.com.vn
Sales Range: $25-49.9 Million
Emp.: 130
Mobile Systems & Business Application Development Services
N.A.I.C.S.: 561110

Knox Data, Corp. (1)
Minamioi 6-20-14 East Square Omori 7F Yubinbango, Shinagawa-ku, Tokyo, 140-0013, Japan
Tel.: (81) 337663735
Web Site: http://www.knox.co.jp
Software Development Services
N.A.I.C.S.: 513210

TAKES Co., Ltd. (1)
3-11-12 Hatchobori 2nd Floor of Daiki Building, Chuo-ku, Tokyo, 104-0032, Japan
Tel.: (81) 362222221
Web Site: http://www.takes.ne.jp
Computer Services
N.A.I.C.S.: 541690
Yoshiaki Tsuneyo *(Pres)*

ISBANK JSC
Nametkina Str 13 D, 117420, Moscow, Russia
Tel.: (7) 4952321234
Web Site: http://www.isbank.com.ru
Year Founded: 1924
Commercial Banking Services
N.A.I.C.S.: 522110
Recep Haki *(Chm-Mgmt Bd)*

ISBIR HOLDING A.S.
Ataturk Bulvari 169/54, Bakanliklar, 06680, Ankara, Turkiye
Tel.: (90) 3124181043
Web Site: http://www.isbir.com.tr
Year Founded: 1968
ISBIR—(IST)
Rev.: $108,036,121
Assets: $123,427,104
Liabilities: $55,314,861
Net Worth: $68,112,243
Earnings: $8,826,828
Fiscal Year-end: 12/31/22
Holding Company
N.A.I.C.S.: 551112

ISC BUSINESS TECHNOLOGY AG
Lagerhausstrasse 3, 8400, Winterthur, Switzerland
Tel.: (41) 522690404
Web Site: https://www.isc.ag
Year Founded: 1994
I5Q1—(DEU)
Emp.: 50
Information Technology Services
N.A.I.C.S.: 541512

ISC CO., LTD.
26 Geumto-ro 40beon-gil, Sujeong-

gu, Seongnam, 13453, Gyeonggi-do, Korea (South)
Tel.: (82) 317777675
Web Site: https://www.isc21.kr
Year Founded: 2001
095340—(KRS)
Rev.: $137,194,260
Assets: $274,917,680
Liabilities: $69,340,869
Net Worth: $205,576,811
Earnings: $33,713,772
Emp.: 222
Fiscal Year-end: 12/31/22
Components for Semiconductor Industry
N.A.I.C.S.: 334413

Subsidiaries:

JSR Microtech Inc. (1)
289-1 Yaenda Hidaka, Saitama, 350-1236, Japan (100%)
Tel.: (81) 429858855
Printed Circuit Boards & IC Testing Fixtures Mfr
N.A.I.C.S.: 334412
Kazuaki Mayumi *(Pres)*

Subsidiary (US):

JSR Micro Inc. (2)
1280 N Mathilda Ave, Sunnyvale, CA 94089 (100%)
Tel.: (408) 543-8800
Web Site: https://www.jsrmicro.com
Emp.: 200
Semiconductor Materials Mfr & Sales
N.A.I.C.S.: 334413
Mark Slezak *(Pres)*

Subsidiary (Non-US):

JSR Micro Korea Co., Ltd. (2)
97 Gwahaksaneop 4-ro Oksan-myeon Heungdeok-gu, 1111-5 Namchon-ri Okasan-myeon, Cheongju, 363911, Chungcheongbuk-do, Korea
(South) (100%)
Tel.: (82) 432193333
Web Site: http://www.jsrmicro.co.kr
Sales Range: $50-74.9 Million
Industrial-Use Chemical Products Mfr & Sales
N.A.I.C.S.: 424690
Atsushi Kumano *(Pres)*

JSR Micro N.V. (2)
Researchpark Haasrode 1019Technologielaan 8, 3001, Leuven, Belgium (100%)
Tel.: (32) 16832832
Web Site: http://www.jsrmicro.be
Sales Range: $25-49.9 Million
Emp.: 120
Semiconductor Materials Mfr & Sales
N.A.I.C.S.: 334413
Bart Denturck *(Pres)*

JSR Micro Taiwan Co., Ltd. (2)
No 11 Kehu 1st Road, Central Taiwan Science Park, Huwei, 63247, Yunlin,
Taiwan (100%)
Tel.: (886) 56323000
Web Site: http://www.jsrmicro.com.tw
Emp.: 175
Flat Panel Display Materials Mfr & Sales
N.A.I.C.S.: 326199
Hiroaki Nemoto *(Pres)*

ISCOOL ENTERTAINMENT SA
43 rue d Aboukir, 75002, Paris, France
Tel.: (33) 1 42 73 74 00
Web Site: http://www.iscoolentertainment.com
Software Development Services
N.A.I.C.S.: 541511
Ludovic Barra *(Mng Dir)*

ISDN HOLDINGS LIMITED
101 Defu Lane 10, Singapore, 539222, Singapore
Tel.: (65) 68440288
Web Site:
https://www.isdnholdings.com

I07—(SES)
Rev.: $258,854,806
Assets: $303,293,948
Liabilities: $121,013,406
Net Worth: $182,280,542
Earnings: $8,461,713
Emp.: 1,138
Fiscal Year-end: 12/31/23
Management Services
N.A.I.C.S.: 541512
Deyang Kong *(Exec Dir)*

Subsidiaries:

A Tracks Pte Ltd (1)
No 10 Kaki Bukit Road 1 01-30 KB Industrial Building, Singapore, 416175, Singapore
Tel.: (65) 68440288
Web Site: http://www.atracks.com.sg
Linear Motor Mfr
N.A.I.C.S.: 335999

AR Robotics and Automation Pte. Ltd. (1)
101 Defu Lane 10, Singapore, 539222, Singapore
Tel.: (65) 96603212
Web Site: https://www.airobot.com.sg
Industrial Automation Services
N.A.I.C.S.: 541511

Air Vacuum Automation Vietnam Company Limited (1)
21/22 Street No 3 Quarter 2, Binh An Ward District 2, Ho Chi Minh City, Vietnam
Tel.: (84) 2836204172
Web Site: http://www.airvacuum.com.vn
Industrial Machinery Mfr
N.A.I.C.S.: 333248
Tuong Nguyen William *(Product Mgr)*

DBASIX Singapore Pte Ltd (1)
55 Cairnhill Road 35-04 Cairnhill Plaza, Singapore, 229666, Singapore
Tel.: (65) 97310288
Web Site: https://www.dbasix.com.sg
Industrial Machinery & Equipment Distr
N.A.I.C.S.: 423810

ERST Asia Pacific Pte. Ltd. (1)
101 Defu Lane 10, Singapore, 539222, Singapore
Tel.: (65) 68440288
Web Site: https://www.erstapac.com
Coating Services
N.A.I.C.S.: 238990

ISDN Software Business Pte. Ltd. (1)
Vertex 33 Ubi Ave 3 Unit 03-38, Singapore, 408868, Singapore
Tel.: (65) 65148389
Web Site: http://www.isdnsoftware.com
Computer Software Services
N.A.I.C.S.: 541511
G. K. Tay *(Gen Mgr)*

Leaptron Engineering Pte Ltd (1)
17 Tai Seng Drive 06-01 Yew Lee Building, Singapore, 535221, Singapore
Tel.: (65) 62889125
Web Site: http://leaptron.com
Automation Engineering Services
N.A.I.C.S.: 541330
Peter Wong *(Mng Dir)*

Portwell Singapore Pte Ltd (1)
No 10 Kaki Bukit Road 1 01-37 KB Industrial Building, Singapore, 416175, Singapore
Tel.: (65) 62985632
Web Site: http://portwell.com.sg
Computer Parts Mfr
N.A.I.C.S.: 334118

Precision Motion Control Pte Ltd (1)
No 10 Kaki Bukit Rd 1 01-40 KB Industrial Building, Singapore, 416175, Singapore
Tel.: (65) 68441928
Web Site: http://www.e-pmc.com.sg
Electromagnetic Product Mfr
N.A.I.C.S.: 334513

Servo Dynamics (H.K.) Limited (1)
Rm 1504 15/F Yuen Long Trading Centre 33 Wang Yip Street West N T, Hong Kong, China (Hong Kong)
Tel.: (852) 24099986
Industrial Product Engineering Services
N.A.I.C.S.: 541330

Servo Dynamics Co., Ltd. (1)
Tel.: (86) 51282079388
Industrial Product Engineering Services
N.A.I.C.S.: 541330

Servo Dynamics Pte Ltd (1)
No 10 Kaki Bukit Road 1 01-30 KB Industrial Building, Singapore, 416175, Singapore
Tel.: (65) 6844 0288
Web Site: http://www.servo.com.sg
Electronic Product Technology Development Services
N.A.I.C.S.: 541330

Subsidiary (Non-US):

Servo Dynamics Engineering Company Limited (2)
4/1B Luong Dinh Cua St, W Binh Khanh Dist 2, Ho Chi Minh City, Vietnam
Tel.: (84) 2837402128
Web Site: http://www.servodynamics.com.vn
Industrial Equipment Distr
N.A.I.C.S.: 423830

Servo Dynamics Sdn. Bhd. (1)
17 Solok Kekabu 1 Permatang Damar Laut, 11960, Bayan Lepas, Penang, Malaysia
Tel.: (60) 46266388
Web Site: http://www.servo.com.my
Industrial Machinery Mfr
N.A.I.C.S.: 333248
Syafiq Aiman *(Engr-Svcs)*

Servo Engineering Sdn. Bhd. (1)
15G Jalan 51/205 Highway Centre, 46050, Petaling Jaya, Selangor, Malaysia
Tel.: (60) 377823540
Web Site: https://www.servo.my
Power Transmission Product Mfr & Distr
N.A.I.C.S.: 333613

TDS Technology (S) Pte Ltd (1)
64 Sungei Kadut Loop 03-00 Hocen Building, Singapore, 729493, Singapore
Tel.: (65) 63661661
Web Site: http://www.tdstech.com
Industrial Control Equipment Mfr & Distr
N.A.I.C.S.: 335314

ISE CHEMICALS CORPORATION
10th Floor Yaesuguchi Daiei Bldg 3-1 Kyobashi 1-chome, Chuo-ku, Tokyo, 104-0031, Japan
Tel.: (81) 332420520
Web Site: https://www.isechem.co.jp
Year Founded: 1927
4107—(TKS)
Rev.: $187,268,170
Assets: $284,181,380
Liabilities: $58,067,100
Net Worth: $226,114,280
Earnings: $26,034,480
Emp.: 325
Fiscal Year-end: 12/31/23
Chemical Business
N.A.I.C.S.: 332710
Takashizu Minato *(Pres & CEO)*

Subsidiaries:

Woodward Iodine Corporation (USA) (1)
Hwy 34 N, Woodward, OK 73801
Tel.: (580) 254-3311
Sales Range: $50-74.9 Million
Emp.: 28
Natural Gas Production Services
N.A.I.C.S.: 211130
Leroy Goodman *(Pres)*

ISE COMMERCE CO., LTD.
4F 633 Samseong-ro, Gangnam-gu, Seoul, 135-090, Korea (South)
Tel.: (82) 221913500
Web Site:
https://www.exiongroup.co.kr
Year Founded: 2001
069920—(KRS)
Rev.: $4,199,704
Assets: $47,397,800
Liabilities: $3,580,103
Net Worth: $43,817,697
Earnings: ($8,513,032)

Emp.: 64
Fiscal Year-end: 12/31/22
Online Shopping Services
N.A.I.C.S.: 459999
Eungsang Kim *(CEO)*

ISEC HEALTHCARE LIMITED
51 Goldhill Plaza 10-07/08, Singapore, 308900, Singapore
Tel.: (65) 62582262
Web Site:
https://www.isechealthcare.com
Year Founded: 2014
40T—(SES)
Rev.: $53,013,709
Assets: $81,123,230
Liabilities: $18,902,522
Net Worth: $62,220,707
Earnings: $9,959,858
Emp.: 275
Fiscal Year-end: 12/31/23
Ophthalmology Services & Surgical Centers
N.A.I.C.S.: 621111
Jun Shyan Wong *(CEO)*

Subsidiaries:

ISEC Myanmar Company Limited (1)
A5 MinYeKyawSwar Street MinYeKyawSwar Business Building, Corner of St John City Mall Lanmadaw Township, Yangon, Myanmar
Tel.: (95) 9448 282 8212
Web Site:
https://www.isecmyanmar.com.mm
Medical Eye Care Services
N.A.I.C.S.: 621320
Shane Thu Aung *(Founder)*

ISEC Sdn. Bhd. (1)
Level 7 8 Centrepoint South The Boulevard, Mid Valley City, 59200, Kuala Lumpur, Malaysia
Tel.: (60) 322848989
Web Site: https://www.isec.my
Medical Eye Care Services
N.A.I.C.S.: 621320

Subsidiary (Domestic):

ISEC (Penang) Sdn. Bhd. (2)
Lot 1047 No 56 Jalan Larut Seksyen 13, Georgetown Daerah Timur Laut, 10050, Pulau Penang, Malaysia
Tel.: (60) 42288802
Medical Eye Care Services
N.A.I.C.S.: 621320

ISEC (Sibu) Sdn. Bhd. (2)
No 20 22 24 Ground Floor Lorong Chew Silk Hiong 7, 96000, Sibu, Sarawak, Malaysia
Tel.: (60) 84220227
Medical Eye Care Services
N.A.I.C.S.: 621320

Southern Specialist Eye Centre Sdn. Bhd. (2)
309 310 Jalan Melaka Raya 1, Taman Melaka Raya, 75000, Melaka, Malaysia
Tel.: (60) 62833510
Medical Eye Care Services
N.A.I.C.S.: 621320
Robert Yeo *(Dir-Center)*

Indah Specialist Eye Centre Sdn. Bhd. (1)
No 75 & 77 Jalan Indah 15/2, Taman Bukit Indah, 81200, Johor Bahru, Malaysia
Tel.: (60) 72395399
Web Site: https://www.indaheye.com
Eye Care Center Services
N.A.I.C.S.: 621320

ISEC SECURITIZADORA S.A.S
R Tabapua 1123 - 21 Floor - Cj 215, 4533004, Sao Paulo, Brazil
Tel.: (55) 1133207474
Web Site:
http://www.isecbrasil.com.br
Financial Services
N.A.I.C.S.: 523999

ISECO SA

Isec Securitizadora S.A.s—(Continued)

ISECO SA
Str Budiului 68, Targu Mures, Mures, Romania
Tel.: (40) 265 267279   RO
Sales Range: Less than $1 Million
Emp.: 3
Motor Vehicle Repair & Maintenance Services
N.A.I.C.S.: 811111

ISEKI & CO., LTD.
5-3-14 Nishi-Nippori, Arakawa-ku, Tokyo, 116-8541, Japan
Tel.: (81) 356047602   JP
Web Site: https://www.iseki.co.jp
Year Founded: 1926
6310—(TKS)
Rev.: $1,204,704,440
Assets: $1,539,253,180
Liabilities: $1,013,068,830
Net Worth: $526,184,350
Earnings: $205,610
Emp.: 5,457
Fiscal Year-end: 12/31/23
Farming Machinery Mfr
N.A.I.C.S.: 333111
Shirou Tomiyasu *(Pres & Exec Officer)*

Subsidiaries:

Dongfeng Iseki Agricultural Machinery Co., Ltd. (1)
15th Floor Block E Donghe Center No 1 Dongfeng 3rd Road, Economic and Technological Development Zone, Wuhan, Hubei, China
Tel.: (86) 2784289919
Web Site: http://www.dfiseki.com
Agricultural Machinery Mfr
N.A.I.C.S.: 333111

H.C. Petersen & Co.s Eftf. A/S (1)
Applicant Landevej 13, 7200, Grindsted, Denmark
Tel.: (45) 76731133
Web Site: https://hcpetersen.dk
Agricultural Equipment Distr
N.A.I.C.S.: 423820

Iseki (Thailand) Co., Ltd. (1)
T-Park Sriracha W2/3 289/6 Moo6 Tambon Surasak Amphur Sriracha, Amphur Muang, Chonburi, Thailand
Tel.: (66) 33005123
Agricultural Machinery Distr
N.A.I.C.S.: 333111

Iseki France S.A.S (1)
Zac des Ribes 27 Avenue des Freres Montgolfier, CS 20024, 63178, Aubiere, Cedex, France
Tel.: (33) 47 391 9351
Web Site: https://www.iseki.fr
Agricultural Machinery Distr
N.A.I.C.S.: 423820

Iseki Kyushu Co., Ltd. (1)
2550 Hirata Mashiki-cho, Kamimashiki-gun, Kumamoto, 861-2212, Japan
Tel.: (81) 96 286 0303
Web Site: https://www.isekikyusyu.co.jp
Agricultural Machinery Mfr
N.A.I.C.S.: 333111

Iseki Maschinen GmbH (1)
Rudolf-Diesel-Strasse 4, 40670, Meerbusch, Germany
Tel.: (49) 21 595 2050
Web Site: https://www.iseki.de
Sales Range: $50-74.9 Million
Farm Machinery & Equipment Mfr
N.A.I.C.S.: 333111

Iseki Tls Co., Ltd. (1)
5-3-14 Nishinippori, Arakawa-ku, Tokyo, 116-8540, Japan
Tel.: (81) 33 805 7955
Web Site: https://www.iseki-tls.co.jp
Emp.: 70
Real Estate Services
N.A.I.C.S.: 531390

Iseki-Changzhou Mfg. Co., Ltd. (1)
No 201 Chaohu Road, State Hi-Tech Development Zone, Changzhou, 213022, Jiangsu, China
Tel.: (86) 519 8512 5808
Web Site: http://www.iseki.cn
Agricultural Machinery Mfr
N.A.I.C.S.: 333111

Iseki-Kumamoto Mfg. Co., Ltd. (1)
1400 Yasunaga Mashiki-machi Kami, Mashiki-gun, Kumamoto, 861-2231, Japan
Tel.: (81) 962865515
Combine Harvesters Mfr
N.A.I.C.S.: 333111

Iseki-Matsuyama Mfg. Co., Ltd. (1)
700 Umaki-cho, Matsuyama, 799-2655, Ehime, Japan
Tel.: (81) 899781211
Agricultural Machinery Mfr
N.A.I.C.S.: 333111

Iseki-Tohoku Co., Ltd. (1)
1-2 Shinminami Naganuma Shimonogo, Iwanuma, 989-2412, Japan
Tel.: (81) 22 324 1111
Web Site: https://www.iseki-touhoku.co.jp
Emp.: 620
Agricultural Machinery Distr
N.A.I.C.S.: 423820

Ist Farm Machinery Co., Ltd. (1)
294/2 Moo 8, Khu Khot Subdistrict Lam Luk Ka, Bangkok, 12130, Thailand   **(81%)**
Tel.: (66) 2 002 0061
Web Site: https://www.iseki-mf.com
Agricultural Machinery Mfr
N.A.I.C.S.: 333111

Kar Wo Limited (1)
Room 23 6/F Metro Centre Phase 2 21 Lam Hing Street, Kowloon, China (Hong Kong)
Tel.: (852) 23807183
Web Site: http://www.karwo.com.hk
Industrial Equipment Whsr
N.A.I.C.S.: 423830

N.V. Iseki Europe S.A. (1)
Planet II Leuvensesteenweg 542-C1, 1930, Zaventem, Belgium
Tel.: (32) 2 725 2280
Web Site: http://www.iseki.com
Sales Range: $25-49.9 Million
Emp.: 7
Farm Machinery
N.A.I.C.S.: 333111

Nara Iseki Sales Co., Ltd. (1)
17-29 Sanwacho, Yamatotakada, 635-0014, Nara, Japan
Tel.: (81) 745228771
Agricultural Machinery Distr
N.A.I.C.S.: 423820

Oy J-Trading AB (1)
Kuriiritie 15, 01510, Vantaa, Finland
Tel.: (358) 207458600
Web Site: https://j-trading.fi
Agricultural Equipment Distr
N.A.I.C.S.: 423820

P.T. Iseki Indonesia (1)
Jl Kraton Industri Raya No 11 Pier, Pasuruan, 67151, Jawa Timur, Indonesia
Tel.: (62) 3434502000
Web Site: https://www.iseki.co.jp
Agricultural Machinery Mfr
N.A.I.C.S.: 333111

Premium Turf-Care Ltd. (1)
3-5 Foxtail Road Ransomes Euro-Park, Ipswich, IP3 9RT, Suffolk, United Kingdom   **(100%)**
Tel.: (44) 1473599266
Agricultural Machinery Mfr
N.A.I.C.S.: 333111

Van der Haeghe B.V. (1)
De Elzenhof 7G, 4191 PA, Geldermalsen, Netherlands
Tel.: (31) 345788104
Web Site: https://www.vanderhaeghe.nl
Agricultural Equipment Distr
N.A.I.C.S.: 423820

Vietnam Engine and Agricultural Machinery Corporation (1)
D D1 Zone, Phu Thuong Ward Tay Ho District, Hanoi, Vietnam
Tel.: (84) 2462800802
Web Site: https://veamcorp.com

Industrial Equipment Mfr
N.A.I.C.S.: 333413

ISELECT LTD.
294 Bay Road, Cheltenham, 3192, VIC, Australia
Tel.: (61) 3 9276 8000   AU
Web Site: http://www.iselect.com.au
ISU—(ASX)
Rev.: $85,024,104
Assets: $132,019,900
Liabilities: $47,197,304
Net Worth: $84,822,596
Earnings: ($3,886,116)
Emp.: 551
Fiscal Year-end: 06/30/21
Health Insurance Services
N.A.I.C.S.: 524298
Brodie Arnhold *(CEO)*

Subsidiaries:

InfoChoice Ltd (1)
Level 13 10 Queens Rd, Melbourne, 3004, VIC, Australia
Tel.: (61) 383916000
Web Site: http://www.infochoice.com.au
Sales Range: $1-9.9 Million
Product & Service Consumer Information
N.A.I.C.S.: 812990

ISELECTION HOLDING
400 Pro Des Anglais, 6203, Nice, Alpes Maritimes, France
Tel.: (33) 492152575
Web Site: http://www.iselection.fr
Rev.: $15,200,000
Emp.: 31
N.A.I.C.S.: 531210

ISETAN MITSUKOSHI HOLDINGS LTD.
Mitsukoshi Isetan Nishi-Shinjuku Building 3-2-5 Nishi-Shinjuku, Shinjuku-ku, Tokyo, 160-0023, Japan
Tel.: (81) 362056003   JP
Web Site: https://www.imhds.co.jp
Year Founded: 2008
3099—(TKS)
Rev.: $3,545,875,010
Assets: $8,097,930,830
Liabilities: $4,126,484,190
Net Worth: $3,971,446,640
Earnings: $367,383,800
Emp.: 388
Fiscal Year-end: 03/31/24
Holding Company; Department Store Operator; Financial & Real Estate Services
N.A.I.C.S.: 551112
Yoshihiro Kasahara *(Pres/CEO-Nagoya Mitsukoshi Ltd)*

Subsidiaries:

Century Trading Co., Ltd. (1)
Shinjuku-Sanchome Kyodo Bldg 2F 3-17-17, Shinjuku-ku, Tokyo, 160-0022, Japan
Tel.: (81) 5031522001
Web Site: http://www.imhds.co.jp
Beverage Product Whslr
N.A.I.C.S.: 424820

Chengdu Isetan Department Store Co., Ltd. (1)
Block B Lidu Plaza 6 Lane Dakejia, Jinjiang-District, Chengdu, Sichuan, China
Tel.: (86) 2862031111
Departmental Store Services
N.A.I.C.S.: 455110

Hakodate Marui Imai Ltd. (1)
32-15 Honmachi, Hakodate, 040-0011, Hokkaido, Japan
Tel.: (81) 138321151
Web Site: https://www.maruiimai.mistore.jp
Emp.: 137
Department Stores Operation Services
N.A.I.C.S.: 455110

Hiroshima Mitsukoshi Ltd. (1)
5-1 Ebisu-cho, Naka-ku, Hiroshima, 730-8545, Japan

INTERNATIONAL PUBLIC

Tel.: (81) 822423111
Departmental Stores Operating Services
N.A.I.C.S.: 455110
Hiroaki Okuda *(Mgr-Gen Affairs)*

IM Food Style Ltd. (1)
Knowledge Park Ochiai Bldg 3F 2-18-20, Nishiochiai Shinjuku-ku, Tokyo, 161-0031, Japan
Tel.: (81) 366298550
Supermarket Store Services
N.A.I.C.S.: 445110

Isetan (China) Co., Ltd. (1)
1038 Nanjing Rd West, Jinan-District, Shanghai, China
Tel.: (86) 2162171111
Departmental Store Services
N.A.I.C.S.: 455110

Isetan (Italia) S.r.l. (1)
Corso Venezia 5, Milan, 20121, Italy
Tel.: (39) 02 76000070
Sales Range: $25-49.9 Million
Emp.: 8
Supermarkets Operation Services
N.A.I.C.S.: 445110

Isetan (Thailand) Co., Ltd. (1)
4/1-4/2 Central World Plaza Rajdamri Road, Pathumwan, Bangkok, 10330, Thailand
Tel.: (66) 2 255 9898
Apparel & Accessories Retailer
N.A.I.C.S.: 458110

Isetan Co., Ltd. (1)
3-14-1 Shinjuku, Shinjuku-Ku, Tokyo, 160-0022, Japan
Tel.: (81) 333521111
Web Site: http://www.isetan.co.jp
Sales Range: $5-14.9 Billion
Emp.: 8,834
Departmental Store Operator
N.A.I.C.S.: 455110
Kunio Ishidaa *(CEO)*

Isetan Kaikan Co., Ltd. (1)
Tel.: (81) 333528711
Web Site: https://isetan.mistore.jp
Bakeries Operating Services
N.A.I.C.S.: 311812

Isetan Mitsukoshi Building Management Service Co., Ltd (1)
8F H&I Bldg 5-17-18 Shinjuku-ku, Tokyo, 160-0022, Japan
Tel.: (81) 3 5273 5770
Web Site: http://www.imbm.co.jp
Property Management Services
N.A.I.C.S.: 531311

Isetan Mitsukoshi Business Support Ltd. (1)
7th floor Mitsukoshi Isetan Nishi-Shinjuku Building 3-2-5, Nishi-Shinjuku Shinjuku-ku, Tokyo, 160-0023, Japan
Tel.: (81) 367305686
Emp.: 525
Logistics Consulting Servies
N.A.I.C.S.: 541614

Isetan Mitsukoshi Direct Shopping Ltd. (1)
2-36-11 Minamisuna, Koto-ku, Tokyo, 136-0076, Japan
Tel.: (81) 3 5857 8550
Television Mail Order Shopping Services
N.A.I.C.S.: 425120

Isetan Mitsukoshi Food Service Ltd. (1)
3-16 Toyomi-cho, Chuo-ku, Tokyo, 104-8570, Japan   **(100%)**
Tel.: (81) 3 3534 6500
Web Site: http://www.im-food.co.jp
Emp.: 513
Supermarket Operator
N.A.I.C.S.: 445110
Takayuki Uchida *(Pres)*

Isetan Mitsukoshi Human Solutions Ltd. (1)
1-8-12 Harumi Building 14th Fl Harumi Island Triton Sq Office Tower Z, Chuo-ku, Tokyo, 104-6214, Japan
Tel.: (81) 5031500060
Recruitment Consulting Services
N.A.I.C.S.: 541612

Isetan Mitsukoshi Innovations Ltd. (1)

AND PRIVATE COMPANIES

5-16-10 Shinjuku, Shinjuku-ku, Tokyo, 160-0022, Japan
Tel.: (81) 358436022
Investment Services
N.A.I.C.S.: 523910

Isetan Mitsukoshi Ltd (1)
3-14-1 Shinjuku, Shinjuku-ku,, Tokyo, Japan
Tel.: (81) 333521111
Retail Services
N.A.I.C.S.: 456120

Subsidiary (Non-US):

Isetan (Singapore) Limited (2)
593 Havelock Rd 04-01 Isetan Office Building, Singapore, 169641,
Singapore (52.73%)
Tel.: (65) 67331111
Web Site: https://www.isetan.com.sg
Rev.: $68,605,620
Assets: $130,970,991
Liabilities: $50,302,961
Net Worth: $80,668,030
Earnings: ($877,831)
Emp.: 289
Fiscal Year-end: 12/31/2023
Departmental Store Services
N.A.I.C.S.: 455110
Toshifumi Hashizume *(Mng Dir)*

Isetan Mitsukoshi Property Design Ltd. (1)
Mitsukoshi Isetan Nishi-Shinjuku Bldg 8F/9F 3-2-5, Nishi-Shinjuku Shinjuku-ku, Tokyo, 160-0023, Japan
Tel.: (81) 366337555
Construction & Design Services
N.A.I.C.S.: 541310

Isetan Mitsukoshi Soleil, Co., Ltd. (1)
Isetan Daini-Bekkan Bldg 4F 5-16-10, Shinjuku Shinjuku-ku, Tokyo, 160-0022, Japan
Tel.: (81) 332252434
Departmental Store Services
N.A.I.C.S.: 455110

Isetan Mitsukoshi System Solutions Ltd. (1)
14th floor Office Tower Z Harumi Island Triton Square 1-8-12 Harumi, Chuo-ku, Tokyo, 104-6214, Japan
Tel.: (81) 366319300
Emp.: 324
Data Processing Services
N.A.I.C.S.: 518210

Isetan Swing Inc (1)
3-14-1 Shinjuku, Shinjuku-ku, Tokyo, 160-0021, Japan
Tel.: (81) 332072851
Sport Facilities Management Services
N.A.I.C.S.: 711310

Isetan Tianjin Co., Ltd. (1)
108 Nanjing Road, Heping-District, Tianjin, China
Tel.: (86) 2227221111
Departmental Store Services
N.A.I.C.S.: 455110

Isetan of Japan Sdn. Bhd. (1)
Lot 10 Shopping Center 50 Jalan Sultan Ismail, 50250, Kuala Lumpur, Malaysia
Tel.: (60) 321417777
Departmental Store Operator
N.A.I.C.S.: 455110

Itm Clover Co., Ltd. (1)
4/1-4/2 Central World Rajadamri Road, Pathuwan, Bangkok, 10330, Thailand
Tel.: (66) 22559898
Departmental Store Services
N.A.I.C.S.: 455110

Iwataya Co., Ltd. (1)
2-5-35 Tenjin, Chuo-ku, Fukuoka, 810-8680, Japan
Tel.: (81) 927211111
Web Site: https://www.iwataya-mitsukoshi.com
Department Stores Operation Services
N.A.I.C.S.: 455110

Leo Mart Co., Ltd. (1)
3rd floor T Building 3-15-16 Shinjuku, Shinjuku-ku, Tokyo, 160-0022, Japan
Tel.: (81) 5031544077
Emp.: 23
Apparel & Accessories Whslr
N.A.I.C.S.: 424350

Leotex Co., Ltd. (1)
2-18-20 Nishiochiai Knowledge Park Ochiai Building, Shinjuku-ku, Tokyo, 135-8415, Japan
Tel.: (81) 5031544073
Emp.: 80
Uniform Clothing Mfr
N.A.I.C.S.: 315210

MI TOMONOKAI Co., Ltd. (1)
1-8-12 Harumi, Chuo-ku, Tokyo, 104-0053, Japan
Tel.: (81) 570057800
Web Site: https://www2.mi-tomonokai.co.jp
Financial Management Services
N.A.I.C.S.: 523999

Mammina Co., Ltd. (1)
Women's Clothing Retailer
N.A.I.C.S.: 458110

Matsuyama Mitsukoshi Ltd. (1)
3-1-1 Ichibancho, Matsuyama, 790-8532, Ehime, Japan
Tel.: (81) 899453111
Web Site: https://www.mitsukoshi.mistore.com
Department Stores Operation Services
N.A.I.C.S.: 455110

Mitsukoshi Isetan Im Facilities Co., Ltd. (1)
1-4-1 Nihonbashi Muromachi, Chuo-ku, Tokyo, 103-8001, Japan
Tel.: (81) 363726170
Building Maintenance Services
N.A.I.C.S.: 561790

Mitsukoshi Isetan Nikko Travel, Ltd. (1)
1-2-4 Nihonbashi Muromachi, Chuo-ku, Tokyo, 103-0022, Japan
Tel.: (81) 332760111
Web Site: https://www.min-travel.co.jp
Tour & Travel Services
N.A.I.C.S.: 561510

Mitsukoshi Kankyo Building Management Co., Ltd. (1)
1F Nippon Building 2-6-2 Otemachi, Chiyoda-ku, Tokyo, 100-0004, Japan
Tel.: (81) 3 3274 7030
Web Site: http://www.mitsukoshi.co.jp
Real Estate Management Services
N.A.I.C.S.: 531390

Mitsukoshi Kankyo Design Co., Ltd. (1)
3-1-19 Higashirokugou, Ota-ku, Tokyo, 144-0046, Japan
Tel.: (81) 3 3736 3254
Interior Design Services
N.A.I.C.S.: 541410

Mitsukoshi, Ltd. (1)
1-4-1 Nihombashi Muromachi, Chuo-ku, Tokyo, 103 8001, Japan
Tel.: (81) 332413311
Web Site: http://www.mitsukoshi.co.jp
Sales Range: $5-14.9 Billion
Emp.: 10,113
Departmental Store Operator
N.A.I.C.S.: 455110

Subsidiary (US):

Mitsukoshi (U.S.A.) Inc. (2)
8063 Beacon Lake Dr Ste 800, Orlando, FL 32809
Tel.: (407) 352-1986
Web Site: https://www.mitsukoshi-orlando.com
Sales Range: $25-49.9 Million
Emp.: 15
Departmental Store Operator
N.A.I.C.S.: 455110

Subsidiary (Domestic):

Mitsukoshi (U.S.A.) Inc.-Orlando Branch (3)
8063 Beacon Lake Dr Ste 800, Orlando, FL 32809
Tel.: (407) 352-1986
Web Site: https://www.mitsukoshi-orlando.com
Sales Range: $25-49.9 Million
Emp.: 10
Departmental Store Operator
N.A.I.C.S.: 455110
Kinnichi Kaneko *(Pres)*

Subsidiary (Non-US):

Mitsukoshi (UK) Ltd. (2)
Dorland House 14 20 Regent St, London, SW1Y 4PH, United Kingdom
Tel.: (44) 2077661000
Web Site: http://www.london-mitsukoshi.co.uk
Sales Range: $25-49.9 Million
Emp.: 100
Departmental Store Operator
N.A.I.C.S.: 455110

Mitsukoshi Enterprises Co., Ltd. (2)
Ste 1610 Tower II Silvercord, 30 Canton Road, Tsim Sha Tsui, Kowloon, China (Hong Kong)
Tel.: (852) 25765222
Sales Range: $50-74.9 Million
Emp.: 200
Departmental Store Operator
N.A.I.C.S.: 455110

Mitsukoshi Espana S.A. (2)
Gran Via 74, 28013, Madrid, Spain
Tel.: (34) 915590051
Sales Range: $25-49.9 Million
Emp.: 20
Departmental Store Operator
N.A.I.C.S.: 455110

Mitsukoshi France S.A. (2)
25 Boulevard Des Capucines, 75002, Paris, France
Tel.: (33) 142615461
Sales Range: $10-24.9 Million
Emp.: 70
Departmental Store Operator
N.A.I.C.S.: 455110

Mitsukoshi Italia S.p.A. (2)
Via Torino 105/106, 00184, Rome, Italy
Tel.: (39) 064817851
Web Site: http://www.mitsukoshi.it
Sales Range: $25-49.9 Million
Emp.: 50
Departmental Store Operator
N.A.I.C.S.: 455110

Joint Venture (Non-US):

Shin Kong Mitsukoshi Department Store Co., Ltd. (2)
No 12 Nanjing West Road, Zhongshan, Taipei, 104, Taiwan
Tel.: (886) 225682868
Web Site: https://www.skm.com.tw
Sales Range: $100-124.9 Million
Emp.: 300
Department Store Operator; Owned by Isetan Misukoski Holdings Ltd. & Shinkong Group
N.A.I.C.S.: 455110

Nagoya Mitsukoshi, Ltd. (1)
3-5-1 Sakae, Naka-ku, Nagoya, 460-8669, Aichi, Japan
Tel.: (81) 522521111
Web Site: http://mitsukoshi.mistore.jp
Sales Range: $1-9.9 Million
Emp.: 700
Departmental Store Operator
N.A.I.C.S.: 455110

Niigata Isetan Mitsukoshi Ltd. (1)
1-6-1 Yachiyo, Chuo-ku, Niigata, 950-8589, Japan
Tel.: (81) 252421111
Departmental Store Operator
N.A.I.C.S.: 455110

Queen's Isetan Co., Ltd. (1)
Nakajima Building 5-11-22, Shinjuku-ku, Tokyo, 160-0022, Japan
Tel.: (81) 3 5368 1200
Web Site: http://www.queens.jp
Sales Range: $200-249.9 Million
Emp.: 558
Supermarket Operating Services
N.A.I.C.S.: 445110
Satoru Ichimori *(Pres)*

Sapporo Marui Mitsukoshi Ltd. (1)
2 Minami-1-jonishi, Chuo-ku, Sapporo, 060-0061, Hokkaido, Japan
Tel.: (81) 112051151
Web Site: https://www.maruimai.com
Department Stores Operation Services
N.A.I.C.S.: 455110

Sapporo Mitsukoshi Ltd. (1)
3-8 Minami-1-jonishi, Chuo-ku, Sapporo, 060-8666, Hokkaido, Japan
Tel.: (81) 112713311
Web Site: https://www.mitsukoshi.transer.com
Supermarket Operating Services
N.A.I.C.S.: 445110

Sendai Mitsukoshi Ltd. (1)
4-8-15 Ichibancho, Aoba-ku, Sendai, 980-8543, Miyagi, Japan
Tel.: (81) 222257111
Departmental Store Operator
N.A.I.C.S.: 455110

Shanghai Mei Long Zhen Isetan Department Store Co., Ltd. (1)
1-7/F Westgate Tower No 1038 Nanjing W Rd, Shanghai, 200041, China
Tel.: (86) 2162721111
Store Operating Services
N.A.I.C.S.: 445110

Shenyang Isetan Co., Ltd. (1)
No 84 Taiyuan North Street, Heping District, Shenyang, China
Tel.: (86) 24 6250 1111
Store Operating Services
N.A.I.C.S.: 445110

Shizuoka Isetan Co., Ltd. (1)
1-7 Gofukucho, Aoi-ku, Shizuoka, 420-0031, Shizuoka-shi, Japan
Tel.: (81) 542512211
Web Site: https://www.isetan.transer.com
Department Stores Operation Services
N.A.I.C.S.: 455110

Studio Alta Co., Ltd. (1)
3-24-3 Shinjuku, Tokyo, 160-0022, Japan
Tel.: (81) 333501200
Photography Studio Management Services
N.A.I.C.S.: 541921

Takamatsu Mitsukoshi Ltd. (1)
7-1 Uchimachi, Takamatsu, 760-8639, Kagawa, Japan
Tel.: (81) 878515151
Department Stores Operation Services
N.A.I.C.S.: 455110

Tianjin Binhai New District Isetan Co., Ltd. (1)
62 Second Avenue, Tianjin Economic-Technological Development Area, Tianjin, China
Tel.: (86) 2265271111
Departmental Store Services
N.A.I.C.S.: 455110

Tianjin Isetan Co., Ltd. (1)
No 108 Nanjing Road, Heping District, Tianjin, 300051, China
Tel.: (86) 2227221111
Web Site: http://www.isetan-tianjin.cn
Departmental Store Operator
N.A.I.C.S.: 455110

Yanlord Isetan Commercial Co., Ltd. (1)
Dongma Road 129, Nankai-District, Tianjin, China
Tel.: (86) 2227188118
Commercial & Corporate Management Consulting Services
N.A.I.C.S.: 541611

ISEWAN TERMINAL SERVICE CO., LTD.

40-7-1 Irifune, Minato-ku, Nagoya, 455-0032, Japan
Tel.: (81) 526615181
Web Site: https://www.isewan.co.jp
Year Founded: 1949
9359—(NGO)
Rev.: $501,858,177
Assets: $392,532,082
Liabilities: $95,379,750
Net Worth: $297,152,333
Earnings: $30,413,749
Emp.: 832
Fiscal Year-end: 03/31/23
Logistic Services
N.A.I.C.S.: 541614

ISEWAN TERMINAL SERVICE CO., LTD.

Isewan Terminal Service Co., Ltd.—(Continued)
Tadashi Ito *(Chm)*
Subsidiaries:

Goyo Kaiun Kaisha, Ltd. (1)
7-40 Irifune 1-Chome, Minato-Ku, Nagoya, 455-0032, Japan
Tel.: (81) 526535411
Emp.: 93
Transportation Services
N.A.I.C.S.: 485999

Isewan (Guangzhou) International Logistics Co., Ltd. (1)
Room 1409 Tower A Center Plaza 161 Linhexi Road, Tianhe District, Guangzhou, 510620, Guangdong, China
Tel.: (86) 2038310161
Automobile Mfr
N.A.I.C.S.: 336110

Isewan (H.K.) Limited (1)
Unit 14 6/F No 883 Cheung Sha Wan Road, Elite Industrial Centre, Kowloon, China (Hong Kong)
Tel.: (852) 25753026
Machinery Mfr
N.A.I.C.S.: 333248

Isewan (Shanghai) International Logistics Co., Ltd. (1)
Room 1101A Trinity Tower No 575 Wu Song Road, Hongkou District, Shanghai, 200080, China
Tel.: (86) 2151088102
Transportation Services
N.A.I.C.S.: 485999

Isewan (Thailand) Co., Ltd. (1)
159/32 Serm-Mit Tower 19th Floor Unit 1903/1 Soi Sukhumvit 21 Road, North-Klongtoey Wattana, Bangkok, 10110, Thailand
Tel.: (66) 26616404
Warehouse Storage Services
N.A.I.C.S.: 493110

Isewan DE Mexico S.A. DE C.V. (1)
Av Circuito Cerezos Norte 103 Col IV Etapa San Francisco de los Romo, Parque Industrial San Francisco, 20304, Aguascalientes, Mexico
Tel.: (52) 4494788200
Machinery Mfr
N.A.I.C.S.: 333248

Isewan Europe GmbH (1)
Kaiserswerther Strasse 115, 40880, Ratingen, Germany
Tel.: (49) 21023700700
Transportation Services
N.A.I.C.S.: 485999

Isewan Taiwan Co., Ltd. (1)
10F-1 No 141 Sec 1 Keelung Rd, Taipei, 11070, Taiwan
Tel.: (886) 227655546
Transportation Services
N.A.I.C.S.: 485999

Isewan U.S.A. Inc. (1)
9101 Southern Pine Blvd Ste 350, Charlotte, NC 28273
Tel.: (704) 521-2825
Machinery Mfr
N.A.I.C.S.: 333248

Kokusai Butsuryu Co., Ltd. (1)
7-40 Irifune 1-Chome, Minato-Ku, Nagoya, 455-0032, Japan
Tel.: (81) 526535411
Emp.: 131
Transportation Services
N.A.I.C.S.: 485999

PT. Isewan Indonesia (1)
Blok AA No 26 Kota Deltamas Desa Sukamahi, Greenland International Industrial Center GIIC Cikarang Pusat, Bekasi, 17530, Indonesia
Tel.: (62) 2150555230
Warehouse Storage Services
N.A.I.C.S.: 493110

Subsidiary (Domestic):

PT.IS Jaya Logistik (2)
Blok AA No 26 Kota Deltamas Desa Sukamahi, Greenland International Industrial Center GIIC Cikarang Pusat, Bekasi, 17530, Indonesia
Tel.: (62) 2150555238
Freight Forwarder Services
N.A.I.C.S.: 488510

ISF LIMITED
Plot No-13 KH No 33/7 Village Amberhai Pole No J967 Sector-19 Dwarka, Som Vihar R K Puram, New Delhi, 110077, India
Tel.: (91) 9105535135
Web Site: https://www.isflimited.in
526859—(BOM)
Rev.: $335,843
Assets: $1,945,085
Liabilities: $92,845
Net Worth: $1,852,240
Earnings: $46,965
Emp.: 10
Fiscal Year-end: 03/31/21
Financial Support Services
N.A.I.C.S.: 523999

ISFAHAN PEGAH DAIRY COMPANY
5th kilometer of Tehran Highway Azadegan Expressway, PO Box 81395376, Isfahan, 81395 386, Iran
Tel.: (98) 311 3802091
Web Site: http://pegahesfahan.pegah.ir
Year Founded: 1976
SPPE—(THE)
Sales Range: Less than $1 Million
Emp.: 224
Dairy Products Mfr
N.A.I.C.S.: 311514

ISFAHAN SAMAN GOSTAR COMPANY
No 20 Towhid Ave, Isfahan, Iran
Tel.: (98) 311 6250040
Web Site: http://www.samangostar.com
Year Founded: 1996
Building Construction Services
N.A.I.C.S.: 236220

ISFELD FORD SALES LTD
32562 South Fraser Way, Abbotsford, V2T 1X6, BC, Canada
Tel.: (604) 857-1327
Web Site: http://www.magnusonford.com
Year Founded: 1977
Rev.: $27,400,000
Emp.: 50
New & Used Car Dealers
N.A.I.C.S.: 441110
Crystal Wu *(Controller)*

ISG PLC
Aldgate House 33 Aldgate High Street, London, EC3N 1AG, United Kingdom
Tel.: (44) 2072471717 UK
Web Site: http://www.isgplc.com
Year Founded: 1994
Rev.: $2,934,836,160
Assets: $1,150,797,840
Liabilities: $1,021,474,080
Net Worth: $129,323,760
Earnings: $30,429,120
Emp.: 2,783
Fiscal Year-end: 12/31/18
Interior Design & Construction Services
N.A.I.C.S.: 541410
Paul Cossell *(CEO)*
Subsidiaries:

Commtech Asia Limited (1)
11A W Sq 318 Hennessy Rd, Wanchai, China (Hong Kong)
Tel.: (852) 25234411
Web Site: http://www.commtechasia.com
Sales Range: $25-49.9 Million
Emp.: 20
Commissioning & Testing Mgmt
N.A.I.C.S.: 541330
Andrew Knellar *(Chm)*

Subsidiary (Non-US):

Commtech Asia (Australia) Pty Ltd. (2)
Ste 601 King York House, 32 York St, Sydney, 2000, NSW, Australia
Tel.: (61) 292622834
Emp.: 10
Commissioning & Testing Mgmt Services
N.A.I.C.S.: 541330
Warren Chamberlain *(Country Mgr)*

Commtech Asia (Japan) Limited (2)
Kamiyacho MT Bldg 7Fl Toranomon, Minato-ku, Tokyo, 105 0001, Japan
Tel.: (81) 357333031
Web Site: http://www.commtechasia.com
Sales Range: $25-49.9 Million
Emp.: 5
Commissioning & Testing Mgmt Services
N.A.I.C.S.: 541330

Commtech Asia (Singapore) Pte Limited (2)
138 Cecil St Ste 10-01 Cecil Ct, Singapore, 069538, Singapore
Tel.: (65) 65366372
Web Site: http://www.commtechasia.com
Sales Range: $25-49.9 Million
Emp.: 15
Commissioning & Testing Mgmt Services
N.A.I.C.S.: 541330
David Armstrong *(Mng Dir)*

ISG (Schweiz) AG (1)
Uetlibergstrasse 132, 8045, Zurich, Switzerland
Tel.: (41) 44 461 0524
Interior Fit Out Services
N.A.I.C.S.: 541410

ISG Asia (1)
1A Lorong Telokc, Singapore, 49014, Singapore
Tel.: (65) 65333833
Web Site: http://www.isgplc.com
Emp.: 100
Property & Construction Services
N.A.I.C.S.: 541330
Gary Allin *(Mng Dir)*

Subsidiary (Non-US):

ISG Asia (Hong Kong) Limited (2)
10/F W Sq 318 Hennessy Rd, Wanchai, China (Hong Kong)
Tel.: (852) 28157338
Web Site: http://www.isgasia.com
Property & Construction Services
N.A.I.C.S.: 541330
Mark Osborne *(Mgr)*

ISG Asia (Japan) Limited (2)
2F, Loy Krathong Toranomon Bldg 4 1 9 Toranomon, Minato-ku, Tokyo, 105 0001, Japan
Tel.: (81) 5733 3040
Property & Construction Services
N.A.I.C.S.: 541330

ISG Asia (Korea) Limited (2)
10F Korea Press Ctr 25 Taepyeongro 1-Ga, Jung-gu, Seoul, 100 745, Korea (South)
Tel.: (82) 2 3700 5800
Property & Construction Services
N.A.I.C.S.: 541330
John Larman *(Mgr)*

ISG Asia (Macau) Limited (2)
Avenida Dos Jardins Do Oceano No 388, Ocean Tower 8 Andar A2, Taipa, Macau, China (Macau)
Tel.: (853) 62946055
Property & Construction Services
N.A.I.C.S.: 541330

Subsidiary (Domestic):

ISG Asia (Singapore) Pte Limited (2)
1A Lorong Telok, Singapore, 049014, Singapore
Tel.: (65) 65333833
Sales Range: $10-24.9 Million
Emp.: 30
Property & Construction Services

INTERNATIONAL PUBLIC

N.A.I.C.S.: 541330
Gary Allin *(Mng Dir)*

Subsidiary (Non-US):

ISG Asia China Limited (2)
7F Zhong Ya Bldg 458 Nois Wulumuqi Rd, Shanghai, 200040, China
Tel.: (86) 2162480666
Sales Range: $10-24.9 Million
Emp.: 50
Property & Construction Services
N.A.I.C.S.: 541330

ISG Asia Investment (Hong Kong) Limited (2)
10 F W Sq 318 Hennessy Rd, Wanchai, China (Hong Kong)
Tel.: (852) 28157338
Web Site: http://www.isgasia.com
Sales Range: $25-49.9 Million
Scientific & Technical Services
N.A.I.C.S.: 541380
Tim Threlkeld *(Mng Dir)*

ISG Asia Malaysia Sdn Bhd (2)
10-1 Jalan 1-76 D, Desa Pandan, Kuala Lumpur, 55100, Malaysia
Tel.: (60) 392813833
Web Site: http://www.isgasia.com
Sales Range: $25-49.9 Million
Emp.: 70
Property & Construction Services
N.A.I.C.S.: 541330
Paul Marshall *(Country Dir)*

ISG Cathedral Limited (1)
Boleyn House St Augustine Bus Pk, Estuary Close, Whitstable, CT5 2QJ, Kent, United Kingdom
Tel.: (44) 1227792000
Web Site: http://www.isgplc.com
Sales Range: $25-49.9 Million
Emp.: 80
Refurbishment & Construction Services
N.A.I.C.S.: 541330
Darren Hill *(Mng Dir)*

ISG Deutschland GmbH (1)
Am Hauptbahnhof 18, 60329, Frankfurt am Main, Germany
Tel.: (49) 6966787590
Web Site: http://www.de.isgplc.com
Sales Range: $25-49.9 Million
Emp.: 20
Property & Construction Services
N.A.I.C.S.: 541330
Michael Schoeneich *(Country Mgr)*

ISG Developments (Southern) Limited (1)
Jackson House 86 Sandyhill Ln, Ipswich, IP3 0NA, Suffolk, United Kingdom
Tel.: (44) 1473335000
Sales Range: $75-99.9 Million
Emp.: 250
Property Development Services
N.A.I.C.S.: 531312

ISG Jackson Special Projects Limited (1)
Jackson House 86 Sandyhill Ln, Ipswich, IP3 0NA, Suffolk, United Kingdom
Tel.: (44) 1473335000
Web Site: http://www.isgjackson.com
Sales Range: $25-49.9 Million
Emp.: 100
Construction Services
N.A.I.C.S.: 541330

Tecton Engineering GmbH (1)
Karl-Marx-Allee 90A, 10243, Berlin, Germany
Tel.: (49) 307 895 4415
Construction Services
N.A.I.C.S.: 236220

ISGEC HEAVY ENGINEERING LTD.
Radaur Road, Yamunanagar, 135001, Haryana, India
Tel.: (91) 1732661062
Web Site: https://www.isgec.com
533033—(BOM)
Rev.: $747,655,941
Assets: $881,832,138
Liabilities: $595,280,049
Net Worth: $286,552,089

Earnings: $34,544,355
Emp.: 2,798
Fiscal Year-end: 03/31/21
Industrial Machinery Mfr
N.A.I.C.S.: 333248
S. K. Khorana (Sec)

Subsidiaries:

Eagle Press & Equipment Co. Limited (1)
5170 O'Neil Drive, Old Castle, N0R 1L0, ON, Canada
Tel.: (519) 737-1593
Web Site: http://www.eaglepresses.com
Construction Machinery Mfr
N.A.I.C.S.: 333120

Isgec Redecam Enviro Solutions Private Limited (1)
A-05 Sector-63, Noida, 201301, UP, India
Tel.: (91) 9205156787
Air Filtration Services
N.A.I.C.S.: 238220

ISGUS GMBH
Oberdorfstr 18-22, 78054, Villingen-Schwenningen, Germany
Tel.: (49) 77203930
Web Site: http://www.isgus.de
Year Founded: 1888
Rev.: $19,278,721
Emp.: 140
Management Consulting Services
N.A.I.C.S.: 541618
Stefan Beetz (Mng Dir)

Subsidiaries:

ISGUS AMERICA LLC (1)
155 Pompton Ave Ste 203, Verona, NJ 07044
Tel.: (973) 239-1440
Web Site: http://www.isgus.com
Management Consulting Services
N.A.I.C.S.: 541613
Craig Smith (Product Mgr & Mgr-Support)

ISGUS GmbH (1)
Zieglergasse 6, 1070, Vienna, Austria
Tel.: (43) 15262877
Web Site: http://www.isgus.at
Management Consulting Services
N.A.I.C.S.: 541613

ISGUS UK Limited (1)
5 Stanton Court Stirling Road South Marston Park, South Marston, Swindon, SN3 4YH, Wiltshire, United Kingdom
Tel.: (44) 1793766211
Web Site: http://www.uk.isgus.com
Management Consulting Services
N.A.I.C.S.: 541613

ISHAAN INFRASTRUCTURES & SHELTERS LIMITED
1111 Shivalik Shilp Iscon Cross Road Satellite, Ahmedabad, 380015, India
Tel.: (91) 7926840162
Web Site: https://ishaaninfra.in
Year Founded: 1995
540134—(BOM)
Rev.: $77,474
Assets: $1,151,244
Liabilities: $203,947
Net Worth: $947,297
Earnings: ($1,738)
Emp.: 8
Fiscal Year-end: 03/31/21
Construction Engineering Services
N.A.I.C.S.: 541330
Jignesh Patel (Officer-Compliance & Sec)

ISHAN DYES & CHEMICALS LIMITED
18 GIDC Phase-1 Vatva, Ahmedabad, 382 445, Gujarat, India
Tel.: (91) 7925832144
Web Site: https://www.ishandyes.com
Year Founded: 1993
531109—(BOM)
Rev.: $11,464,230

Assets: $12,309,440
Liabilities: $3,398,064
Net Worth: $8,911,376
Earnings: $1,748,281
Emp.: 93
Fiscal Year-end: 03/31/21
Chemical Pigment Mfr
N.A.I.C.S.: 325130
Piyushbhai Natvarlal Patel (Chm & Mng Dir)

ISHIGAKI FOODS CO., LTD.
5-18-9 Shirokanedai, Minato-ku, Tokyo, 108-0071, Japan
Tel.: (81) 362772308
Web Site: https://wel-dish.co.jp
Year Founded: 1957
2901—(TKS)
Rev.: $23,348,160
Assets: $9,796,160
Liabilities: $7,356,800
Net Worth: $2,439,360
Earnings: ($1,529,440)
Emp.: 29
Fiscal Year-end: 03/31/22
Food Products Mfr
N.A.I.C.S.: 311999
Shuhei Komatsu (Pres & CEO)

ISHIHARA CHEMICAL CO., LTD.
5-26 Nishiyanagiwara-cho, Hyogo-ku, Kobe, 652-0806, Hyogo, Japan
Tel.: (81) 786814801
Web Site: https://www.unicon.co.jp
Year Founded: 1900
4462—(TKS)
Rev.: $136,860,050
Assets: $184,531,370
Liabilities: $31,800,710
Net Worth: $152,730,660
Earnings: $12,598,660
Emp.: 810
Fiscal Year-end: 03/31/24
Chemicals Mfr
N.A.I.C.S.: 325998
Motoichi Tokizawa (Chm)

Subsidiaries:

Ishihara Chemical (Shanghai) Co., Ltd. (1)
Room2604 The Place Tower B 100 Zun Yi Road, Changning District, Shanghai, 200051, China
Tel.: (86) 2162372150
Plating Chemical Product Mfr
N.A.I.C.S.: 325998

Kizai Corporation (1)
9-10 Nihonbashi Kodenma-cho, Chuo-ku, Tokyo, 103-0001, Japan
Tel.: (81) 336628871
Web Site: https://www.kizai-chem.co.jp
Synthetic Resin & Metal Mfr
N.A.I.C.S.: 325211
Motoichi Tokizawa (Chm)

ISHIHARA SANGYO KAISHA, LTD.
3-15 Edobori 1-chome, Nishi-ku, Osaka, 550-0002, Japan
Tel.: (81) 664441451 JP
Web Site: https://www.iskweb.co.jp
Year Founded: 1920
4028—(TKS)
Rev.: $915,194,160
Assets: $1,482,781,640
Liabilities: $781,354,880
Net Worth: $701,426,760
Earnings: $52,800,680
Emp.: 29
Fiscal Year-end: 03/31/24
Industrial Chemicals; Titanium Dioxide, Agrochemicals, Organic Intermediates, Fertilizer, Magnetic Iron Oxide, Bio-Pharmaceuticals
N.A.I.C.S.: 424690
Yoichi Kobayashi (Mng Exec Officer & Dir-Legal & IP)

Subsidiaries:

AVC Chemical Corporation (1)
RI Chemical Compound No 13 Joe Borris Street, E Rodriguez Jr Ave, Bagong Ilog, Pasig, 1600, Manila, Philippines
Tel.: (63) 2 671 91 57
Web Site: http://www.richem.com.ph
Sales Range: $25-49.9 Million
Emp.: 10
Chemicals Mfr
N.A.I.C.S.: 325998
Neil R. Bueno (Gen Mgr)

ISK Americas, Inc. (1)
7470 Auburn Rd Ste A, Concord, OH 44077-9703 (100%)
Tel.: (440) 357-4600
Web Site: http://www.iskbc.com
Sales Range: $50-74.9 Million
Emp.: 10
Chemical Titanium
N.A.I.C.S.: 325211
Luke Eberly Fichthorn III (Chm)

ISK Biosciences Corporation (1)
7470 Auburn Rd Ste A, Concord, OH 44077-9703
Tel.: (440) 357-4640
Web Site: https://www.iskbc.com
Sales Range: $25-49.9 Million
Emp.: 22
Research Services in Chemistry & Biotechnology
N.A.I.C.S.: 561499
Mark Gelin (Mgr-Intl Registrations)

ISK Biosciences Europe N.V. (1)
Pegasus Park Building 6 4th Floor De Kleetlaan 12-B, Box 9, 1831, Diegem, Belgium (100%)
Tel.: (32) 26278611
Web Site: http://www.iskweb.co.jp
Sales Range: $25-49.9 Million
Emp.: 22
Chemical Products Mfr
N.A.I.C.S.: 325998

ISK Biosciences Korea Ltd. (1)
8 Gangnam-daero 66-gil Kairos Building, Gangnam-gu Yeoksam-dong, Seoul, 135-937, Korea (South)
Tel.: (82) 25551401
Web Site: https://www.iskbio.co.kr
Emp.: 10
Chemical Products Mfr
N.A.I.C.S.: 325998

ISK Korea Corporation (1)
421 Cheonggu Blueville 11-1 Sunae-dong, Bundang-gu, Seongnam, 463-825, Gyeonggi-do, Korea (South)
Tel.: (82) 317786393
Emp.: 4
Chemical Products Mfr
N.A.I.C.S.: 325998
Taesoon Choi (Mgr)

ISK Singapore Pte. Ltd. (1)
39 Tuas W Dr, Singapore, 638406, Singapore (100%)
Tel.: (65) 68645784
Web Site: http://www.isktuas.com
Sales Range: $50-74.9 Million
Emp.: 240
Mfr of Titanium Dioxide
N.A.I.C.S.: 325180
Kazutaka Fujii (Chm)

ISK Taiwan Co., Ltd. (1)
Empire Bldg Fl11-1 87 Sung Chiang Road, Taipei, Taiwan (100%)
Tel.: (886) 225045387
Web Site: http://www.iskweb.co.jp
Sales Range: $25-49.9 Million
Emp.: 10
Mfr of Chemicals
N.A.I.C.S.: 325998

Ishihara Argentina S.A. (1)
Reconquista 656 Piso 9, CP 1003, Buenos Aires, Argentina (100%)
Tel.: (54) 1143127877
Sales Range: $25-49.9 Million
Emp.: 1
Mfr of Chemicals
N.A.I.C.S.: 325998

Ishihara Corporation (U.S.A.) (1)
601 California St Ste 1700, San Francisco, CA 94108

Tel.: (415) 421-8207
Web Site: https://www.ishihara.com
Sales Range: $25-49.9 Million
Emp.: 7
Wholesale of Chemicals
N.A.I.C.S.: 424690
Marvin Hosokawa (Pres)

Ishihara Sangyo Kaisha Limited, Tokyo (1)
1-3-15 Edobori, Nishi-ku, Osaka, 550-0002, Japan (100%)
Tel.: (81) 664441451
Web Site: https://www.iskweb.co.jp
Sales Range: $25-49.9 Million
Emp.: 1,146
Industrial Chemicals; Titanium Dioxide, Agrochemicals, Organic Intermediates, Fertilizer, Magnetic Iron Oxide, Bio-Pharmaceuticals
N.A.I.C.S.: 325180

ISHII FOOD CO., LTD.
2-7-17 Honmachi, Funabashi, 273-8601, Chiba, Japan
Tel.: (81) 474350141
Web Site: https://www.ishiifood.co.jp
Year Founded: 1945
2894—(TKS)
Rev.: $69,352,120
Assets: $53,507,950
Liabilities: $30,895,140
Net Worth: $22,612,810
Earnings: $3,113,310
Emp.: 196
Fiscal Year-end: 03/31/24
Food Products Mfr
N.A.I.C.S.: 311412
Keisuke Kubo (Exec Dir)

ISHII HYOKI CO., LTD.
5 Asahioka, Kannabe-cho, Fukuyama, 720-2113, Hiroshima, Japan
Tel.: (81) 849601247
Web Site: https://www.ishiihyoki.co.jp
Year Founded: 1963
6336—(TKS)
Rev.: $118,608,610
Assets: $118,268,290
Liabilities: $56,684,550
Net Worth: $61,583,740
Earnings: $7,806,090
Emp.: 2,482
Fiscal Year-end: 01/31/24
Electronic Components Mfr
N.A.I.C.S.: 334413
Mineo Ishii (Chm & Pres)

Subsidiaries:

Ishii Hyoki (America), Inc. (1)
1210 E 223rd St Ste 310, Carson, CA 90745
Tel.: (310) 547-8400
Web Site: https://www.hyoki.com
Printed Circuit Boards & Liquid Crystal Display Mfr
N.A.I.C.S.: 334412

Subsidiary (Domestic):

Atlan Dyess Inc. (2)
1911 Windsor Pl, Fort Worth, TX 76110
Tel.: (817) 335-1448
Web Site: http://www.atlandyess.com
Printed Circuit Boards Mfr & Industrial Machinery Supplier
N.A.I.C.S.: 334412

Ishii Hyoki Co., Ltd. - Display Division (1)
Kannabe Industrial Park 5 Asahioka Kannabe-cho, Fukuyama, 720-2113, Hiroshima, Japan
Tel.: (81) 849601200
Sales Range: $100-124.9 Million
Emp.: 400
Electrical & Electronics Peripheral Equipment Parts Mfr
N.A.I.C.S.: 335313

Ishii Hyoki Co., Ltd. - Machinery Division (1)
Kannabe Industrial Park 5 Asahioka

ISHII HYOKI CO., LTD.

Ishii Hyoki Co., Ltd.—(Continued)
Kannabe-cho, Fukuyama, 720-2113, Hiroshima, Japan
Tel.: (81) 849601211
Web Site: https://www.ishiihyoki.co.jp
Industrial Machinery Mfr
N.A.I.C.S.: 333998

Ishii Hyoki Co., Ltd. - Solar System Division (1)
No 5 Asahioka Kannabe-cho, Fukuyama, 720-2113, Hiroshima, Japan
Tel.: (81) 849601248
Sales Range: $100-124.9 Million
Attaching & Cell Cleaning Machinery Mfr
N.A.I.C.S.: 333998

JPN Inc. (1)
Lot 9 Block 13 Cavite Economic Zone, Rosario, 4106, Cavite, Philippines
Tel.: (63) 464371714
Web Site: https://www.jpn-in.com
Sales Range: $50-74.9 Million
Emp.: 200
Industrial Nameplates Mfr
N.A.I.C.S.: 332999
Shinji Hirasaka (Pres)

ISHII IRON WORKS CO., LTD.
26-11 Tsukishima 3-chome, Chuo-ku, Tokyo, 104-0052, Japan
Tel.: (81) 344552505
Web Site: https://www.ishii-iiw.co.jp
Year Founded: 1900
6362—(TKS)
Rev.: $65,914,920
Assets: $138,043,240
Liabilities: $54,558,940
Net Worth: $83,484,300
Earnings: $7,912,170
Fiscal Year-end: 03/31/24
Storage Tank Mfr
N.A.I.C.S.: 237120
Hiroji Ishii (Pres)

Subsidiaries:

IIW Singapore Pte. Ltd. (1)
6001 Beach Road Rm no 12-01 Golden Mile Twr, Singapore, 199589, Singapore
Tel.: (65) 98162760
Storage Tank Distr
N.A.I.C.S.: 423510
Hiroji Ishii (Pres)

ISHIKAWA SEISAKUSHO LTD.
200 Fukudome-cho, Hakusan, 924-0051, Ishikawa, Japan
Tel.: (81) 762771411
Web Site: https://www.ishiss.co.jp
Year Founded: 1937
6208—(TKS)
Rev.: $89,882,780
Assets: $111,041,390
Liabilities: $78,632,560
Net Worth: $32,408,830
Earnings: $1,659,110
Emp.: 274
Fiscal Year-end: 03/31/24
Paper Machinery Mfr & Distr
N.A.I.C.S.: 333248
Ikunori Konagaya (Pres)

ISHITA DRUGS & INDUSTRIES LIMITED
Survey No 179/1 Vasna-Iyava Nr Sanand Toll Plaza, Sarkhej-Viramgam Highway Tal Sanand Dist, Ahmedabad, Gujarat, India
Tel.: (91) 7926468353
Web Site: https://www.ishitadrugs.com
Year Founded: 1992
524400—(BOM)
Rev.: $1,487,471
Assets: $1,382,550
Liabilities: $270,777
Net Worth: $1,111,773
Earnings: $69,981
Emp.: 16
Fiscal Year-end: 03/31/23
Pharmaceutical Product Mfr & Distr
N.A.I.C.S.: 325412
Jagdish Agrawal (Mng Dir)

ISHIZUKA GLASS CO., LTD.
1880 Kawai-cho, Iwakura, 482-8510, Aichi, Japan
Tel.: (81) 587372111
Web Site: http://www.ishizuka.co.jp
Year Founded: 1819
5204—(TKS)
Rev.: $382,600,020
Assets: $608,880,150
Liabilities: $395,046,650
Net Worth: $213,833,500
Earnings: $31,113,270
Emp.: 2,231
Fiscal Year-end: 03/31/24
Glass Products Mfr
N.A.I.C.S.: 327213
Yoshizo Ishizuka (Chm)

Subsidiaries:

Aderia Co., Ltd. (1)
2-1-5 Higashi Nihonbashi, Chuo-ku, Tokyo, 103-0004, Japan
Tel.: (81) 338634821
Web Site: https://www.aderia.jp
Glass Tableware Mfr & Sales
N.A.I.C.S.: 327212

Subsidiary (Non-US):

Aderia Glass (Zhuhai) Co., Ltd. (2)
Jing 18 Road Fine Chemical Area, Gaolan Port Economic Zone, Zhuhai, 519050, Guangdong, China
Tel.: (86) 756 3902886
Glass Tableware Mfr
N.A.I.C.S.: 327212

Far Eastern Ishizuka Green PET Corporation (1)
880 Semino Shimokobashi, Sakai-Machi, Sashima-gun, Ibaraki, 306-0432, Japan
Tel.: (81) 280876222
Web Site: https://www.figp.co.jp
Emp.: 269
Bottle Recycling Services
N.A.I.C.S.: 562920

Hisa Kinzoku Kogyo Co., Ltd. (1)
3-8-31 Kitatsumori, Nishinari-ku, Osaka, 557-0061, Japan
Tel.: (81) 665620121
Web Site: https://www.hisakinzoku.co.jp
Bottle Caps Mfr
N.A.I.C.S.: 326199

Hokuyo Glass Co., Ltd. (1)
4-29-13 Tomita, Aomori-shi, Aomori, 038-0004, Japan
Tel.: (81) 177825183
Glassware Mfr
N.A.I.C.S.: 327212

Ishizuka Butsuryu Service Co., Ltd. (1)
1880 Kawai-cho, Iwakura, 482-8510, Aichi, Japan
Tel.: (81) 587660606
Glass Container Mfr
N.A.I.C.S.: 327213

Ishizuka Glass Co., Ltd. - Fukusaki Plant (1)
498 Saiji Fukusaki-cho, Kanzaaki-gun, Hyogo, 679-2215, Japan
Tel.: (81) 79 022 2681
Web Site: https://www.ishizuka.co.jp
Glassware Mfr
N.A.I.C.S.: 327212

Ishizuka Glass Co., Ltd. - Himeji Plant (1)
1351-1 Imazaike, Shikama-ku, Himeji, 672-8079, Hyogo, Japan
Tel.: (81) 79 235 2551
Web Site: https://www.ishizuka.co.jp
Glassware Mfr
N.A.I.C.S.: 327212

Ishizuka Machine Techno Co., Ltd. (1)
1880 Kawai-cho, Iwakura, 482-8510, Aichi, Japan
Tel.: (81) 587667211
Web Site: https://www.ishizuka.co.jp
Production Machinery & Equipment Mfr
N.A.I.C.S.: 333998

Mie Narumi Corporation (1)
1524-1 Shimogaito Tsuiji Isobe-cho, Shimada, 517-0218, Mie, Japan
Tel.: (81) 599552113
Clays & Stone Mfr
N.A.I.C.S.: 327999

Narumi Corporation (1)
3 Denjiyama Narumi-cho, Midori-ku, Nagoya, 458-8530, Japan
Tel.: (81) 528962192
Web Site: https://www.narumi.co.jp
Emp.: 260
Bone China Dinnerware Mfr
N.A.I.C.S.: 327110

Narumi Shanghai Company Ltd. (1)
Room 1204 12F Zhaofeng Plaza 1027 Changning Road, Changning, Shanghai, 200050, China
Tel.: (86) 2152375038
Tableware Mfr
N.A.I.C.S.: 327110

Narumi Singapore Pte. Ltd. (1)
75 Bukit Timah Road 05-02 Boon Siew Building, Singapore, 229833, Singapore
Tel.: (65) 62203825
Tableware Mfr
N.A.I.C.S.: 327110

Nippon Parison Co., Ltd. (1)
880 Shimokobashi, Sakai-cho Sashima-gun, Ibaraki, Japan
Tel.: (81) 280878404
Web Site: https://www.j-parison.co.jp
Emp.: 317
Bottle Product Mfr & Distr
N.A.I.C.S.: 326160

P.T. Narumi Indonesia (1)
Ejip Industrial Park Plot 7L-1, Cikarang Selatan, Bekasi, 17550, Indonesia
Tel.: (62) 218970905
Pottery & Ceramic Mfr
N.A.I.C.S.: 327110

Sekishou-Unyu Co., Ltd. (1)
1880 Kawai-cho, Iwakura, 482-8510, Aichi, Japan
Tel.: (81) 587383110
Transportation Services
N.A.I.C.S.: 484110

ISHTIAQ TEXTILE MILLS LTD.
35-KM Sheikhupura Rd, Tehsil Jaranwala Distt, Faisalabad, Pakistan
Tel.: (92) 414713183
Web Site: http://www.ishaqtextile.com
Year Founded: 1982
Yarn & Clothing Product Mfr
N.A.I.C.S.: 313310

ISHWARSHAKTI HOLDINGS & TRADERS LIMITED
Seksaria Chambers 5th floor 139 Nagindas Master Road, Fort, Mumbai, 400001, Maharashtra, India
Tel.: (91) 2240500900
Web Site: https://www.ishwarshakti.com
Year Founded: 1983
506161—(BOM)
Rev.: $208,603
Assets: $2,069,165
Liabilities: $372,437
Net Worth: $1,696,728
Earnings: $49,234
Fiscal Year-end: 03/31/21
Holding Company
N.A.I.C.S.: 551112
Vinay K. Seksaria (Dir)

ISIGN MEDIA SOLUTIONS INC.
45A West Wilmot Street Unit 3, Richmond Hill, L4B 2P2, ON, Canada
Tel.: (905) 780-6200
Web Site:
 https://www.isignmedia.com
Year Founded: 2007

INTERNATIONAL PUBLIC

ISD—(OTCIQ)
Rev.: $982
Assets: $183,028
Liabilities: $3,707,065
Net Worth: ($3,524,037)
Earnings: ($918,183)
Fiscal Year-end: 04/30/21
Software Development Services
N.A.I.C.S.: 513210
Alex Romanov (Interim CEO)

Subsidiaries:

iSIGN Media Corp. (1)
45A West Wilmot Street Unit 3, Richmond Hill, L4B 2P2, ON, Canada
Tel.: (905) 780-6200
Web Site: http://www.isignmedia.com
Emp.: 1
Mobile Software Development Services
N.A.I.C.S.: 541511
Jen Kozar (CEO)

ISIK PLASTIK SANAYI VE DIS TICARET PAZARLAMA A.S.
Ihsan Dede Cd Gebze Organize Sanayi Bolgesi No 101, Gebze, 41400, Kocaeli, Turkiye
Tel.: (90) 2627512235
Web Site: https://www.isikplastik.com
Year Founded: 1988
ISKPL—(IST)
Rev.: $24,774,214
Assets: $28,419,965
Liabilities: $8,653,296
Net Worth: $19,766,668
Earnings: $3,012,670
Emp.: 250
Fiscal Year-end: 12/31/22
Plastic Product Distr
N.A.I.C.S.: 326199
Abdullah Ceker (Vice Chm)

ISIKLAR ENERJI VE YAPI HOLDING A.S.
Yakut Street Eryilmaz Plaza No 3 Floor 2, Cubuklu District, 34810, Istanbul, Turkiye
Tel.: (90) 2122903211
Web Site:
 https://www.isiklarenerjiyapi.com.tr
Year Founded: 1982
IEYHO—(IST)
Rev.: $77,503,577
Assets: $109,105,101
Liabilities: $32,089,679
Net Worth: $77,015,423
Earnings: $15,864,420
Fiscal Year-end: 12/31/23
Holding Company
N.A.I.C.S.: 551112
Riza Kutlu Isik (Chm)

ISIKLAR HOLDING A.S.
Cubuklu Mahallesi Cubuklu Mahallesi Orhan Veli Kanik Caddesi, Yakut Sokak No 3 Kat 2 Beykoz, 34810, Istanbul, Turkiye
Tel.: (90) 2122903211
Web Site: http://www.isiklar.com.tr
Year Founded: 1972
Holding Company; Industrial Paper Packaging Products Mfr & Distr
N.A.I.C.S.: 551112
Riza Kutlu Isik (Chm & CEO)

Subsidiaries:

BND Elektrik Uretim A.S. (1)
Genclik Caddesi Isiklar Binasi No 9, 06570, Ankara, Turkiye
Tel.: (90) 312 230 50 33
Web Site: http://www.bndelektrik.com.tr
Power Generation Services
N.A.I.C.S.: 221111
Riza Kutlu Isik (Chm)

Cemas Dokum Sanayi A.S. (1)
Asfalti 12 km, Kirsehir, 40100, Ankara, Turkiye

Tel.: (90) 3862348080
Web Site: http://www.cemas.com.tr
Sales Range: $125-149.9 Million
Emp.: 420
Iron Foundry
N.A.I.C.S.: 331511
Riza Kutlu Isik *(Chm & CEO)*

Isiklar Ambalaj Paz. A.S. - Cumra Factory (1)
Beylik Yeri Mevkii, 42970, Konya, Türkiye
Tel.: (90) 332 458 11 52
Kraft Sack Product Mfr
N.A.I.C.S.: 322211

Isiklar Paper Sack Co. Ltd. (1)
Gulan Street English Village No 254, Erbil, Iraq
Tel.: (964) 750 8683191
Web Site: http://www.isiklarpapersack.com
Emp.: 150
Paper Sack Mfr & Distr
N.A.I.C.S.: 322211

ISIS CONCEPTS HOLDINGS LTD.
57 High St, Tetsworth, 0X9 7BS, Oxfordshire, United Kingdom
Tel.: (44) 1844 280123   UK
Web Site:
http://www.isisconcepts.co.uk
Emp.: 50
Holding Company
N.A.I.C.S.: 551112
Nick Topliss *(Mng Dir)*

Subsidiaries:

Isis Concepts Ltd (1)
57 High Street, Tetsworth, OX9 7BS, Oxfordshire, United Kingdom
Tel.: (44) 1844280123
Web Site: http://www.isisconcepts.co.uk
Sales Range: $25-49.9 Million
Emp.: 40
Furniture Mfr
N.A.I.C.S.: 337127
Nick Topliss *(Gen Mgr)*

ISIS PROJECTS PTY LIMITED
Level 4 29 Christie Street, Saint Leonards, 2065, NSW, Australia
Tel.: (61) 299066977
Web Site: http://www.isis.com.au
Sales Range: $75-99.9 Million
Emp.: 110
Property Solution Services
N.A.I.C.S.: 541312
Michael Barnes *(CEO)*

ISKANDAR WATERFRONT CITY BERHAD
G08 Block 8 Danga Bay Jalan Skudai, 80200, Johor Bahru, Johor Darul Takzim, Malaysia
Tel.: (60) 72333888
Web Site: https://iwcity.com.my
IWCITY—(KLS)
Rev.: $19,546,667
Assets: $309,100,317
Liabilities: $151,464,762
Net Worth: $157,635,556
Earnings: ($6,815,873)
Emp.: 29
Fiscal Year-end: 12/31/22
Property Development & Construction Services
N.A.I.C.S.: 531311
Kang Hoo Lim *(Vice Chm)*

Subsidiaries:

Bayou Bay Development Sdn. Bhd. (1)
G08 Block 8 Danga Bay Jalan Skudai, 81750, Johor Bahru, Johor, Malaysia
Tel.: (60) 73873777
Web Site: http://www.tebrauteguh.com.my
Sales Range: $50-74.9 Million
Emp.: 14
Real Estate Property Development & Hotel Management Services
N.A.I.C.S.: 531210

Tebrau Bay Construction Sdn. Bhd. (1)
Jalan Persiaran Senibong Taman Bayu Senibong, 81750, Johor Bahru, Johor Darul Ta'zim, Malaysia
Tel.: (60) 73873777
Web Site: http://www.tebrauteguh.com.my
Construction Engineering Services
N.A.I.C.S.: 541330

Tebrau Bay Sdn. Bhd. (1)
Go8-Block 8 Danga Bay, Jalan Skudai, 80200, Johor Bahru, Johor, Malaysia (100%)
Tel.: (60) 72333888
Sales Range: $25-49.9 Million
Emp.: 60
Property Development & Construction Services
N.A.I.C.S.: 531311

ISKANDAR WATERFRONT HOLDINGS SDN. BHD.
#G08 Block 8 Danga Bay, Jalan Skudai, Johor Bahru, 80200, Malaysia
Tel.: (60) 7 233 3888
Web Site:
http://www.iskandarwaterfront.com
Holding Company; Real Estate Development
N.A.I.C.S.: 551112
Cheong Meow Yen *(Treas)*

ISKRA, D.D.
Stegne 21, Ljubljana, 1000, Slovenia
Tel.: (386) 15131000
Web Site: http://www.iskra.eu
Year Founded: 1946
Sales Range: $1-9.9 Million
Emp.: 1,200
Electric Equipment Mfr
N.A.I.C.S.: 334419

Subsidiaries:

Iskra EMS, d.o.o. (1)
Trubarjeva 7, 8310, Sentjernej, Slovenia
Tel.: (386) 7 393 48 56
Potentiometers Mfr & Automotive Electromechanical Parts Mfr
N.A.I.C.S.: 336320

Iskra INVEST, d.d. (1)
Stegne 25a, 1521, Ljubljana, Slovenia
Tel.: (386) 15837110
Web Site: http://www.iskrainvest.si
Management Services of Commercial Buildings & Energy; Technical Maintenance Services; Courier & Postal Services; Investment Engineering & Office Equipment Supplies
N.A.I.C.S.: 541618

Iskra India Pvt Ltd. (1)
401 Padmavishwa Oxyrich 2 Rameshwar Nagar Ganagpur Road, Nashik, 422013, Maharashtra, India
Tel.: (91) 253 2346161
Web Site: http://www.iskra.eu
Audio & Video Equipment Whslr
N.A.I.C.S.: 423690
Rahul Eghe *(Dir-Ops)*

Iskra MIS, d.d. (1)
Ljubljanska c 24a, 4000, Kranj, Slovenia
Tel.: (386) 42372112
Web Site: http://www.iskra-mis.si
Mfr of Electrical Components, Including Contactors, Circuit Breakers & Switches
N.A.I.C.S.: 335999
Dusan Sesok *(Gen Mgr)*

Iskra Sistemi, d.d. (1)
Stegne 21, 1000, Ljubljana, Slovenia
Tel.: (386) 15131000
N.A.I.C.S.: 333248

IskraTela L d. o. o. (1)
Ulica Nemanjina br 35, 78250, Laktasi, Bosnia & Herzegovina
Tel.: (387) 51 535 890
Antenna Mfr
N.A.I.C.S.: 334220

Tevis-Agencija za kadre, d.o.o. (1)
Kotnikova 28, 1000, Ljubljana, Slovenia
Tel.: (386) 13083111

Web Site: http://www.tevis-kadri.si
Maintenance & Management of Commercial Buildings, Security Services & Personnel & Consulting Services
N.A.I.C.S.: 561311

ISKRAEMECO, D.D.
Savska loka 4, 4000, Kranj, Slovenia
Tel.: (386) 42064000   SI
Web Site:
http://www.iskraemeco.com
Year Founded: 1945
Measuring & Controlling Devices for Electricity
N.A.I.C.S.: 334515
Bahaa Abdullah *(CFO)*

Subsidiaries:

Iskraemeco (M) Sdn. Bhd. (1)
Lot 115493 Kawasan Perindustrian Pengkalan, Lahat, 31500, Ipoh, Perak, Malaysia
Tel.: (60) 53220233
Electronic Product Distr
N.A.I.C.S.: 423620

Iskraemeco (UK) Ltd. (1)
Building 1010 Cambourne Business Park, Cambourne, Cambridge, CB23 6DP, United Kingdom
Tel.: (44) 1223598551
Electronic Product Distr
N.A.I.C.S.: 423620

Iskraemeco Benelux nv (1)
Industriepark Hulstlo Sint-Jorisstraat 84 Abus 2, 8730, Beernem, Belgium
Tel.: (32) 50550513
Electronic Product Distr
N.A.I.C.S.: 423620

Iskraemeco France sas (1)
65 rue Jean Monnet, 68200, Mulhouse, France
Tel.: (33) 389257008
Electronic Product Distr
N.A.I.C.S.: 423620

Iskraemeco GmbH (1)
Don-Bosco Strasse 8, 96047, Bamberg, Germany
Tel.: (49) 42064180
Electronic Product Distr
N.A.I.C.S.: 423620

Iskraemeco Sarajevo, d.o.o. (1)
Hifzi Bjelevca 13, 71000, Sarajevo, Bosnia & Herzegovina
Tel.: (387) 33775260
Web Site: https://iskraemeco.ba
Electronic Product Distr
N.A.I.C.S.: 423620

Iskraemeco Sverige AB (1)
Knivsmedsgatan 1 SE, 592 30, Vadstena, Sweden
Tel.: (46) 141233750
Electronic Product Distr
N.A.I.C.S.: 423620

ISL CONSULTING LTD
504 Priviera Nehrunagar Circle, Nr Bank Of Baroda, Ahmedabad, 380015, India
Tel.: (91) 7940030352
Web Site: https://www.islconsulting.in
511609—(BOM)
Rev.: $3,467,565
Assets: $1,895,318
Liabilities: $168,683
Net Worth: $1,726,635
Earnings: $205,695
Emp.: 7
Fiscal Year-end: 03/31/22
Commodity Brokerage Services
N.A.I.C.S.: 523160
Bhavesh Premji Mamnia *(Chm)*

ISL ENGINEERING AND LAND SERVICES LTD
7909 51 Ave NW Unit 100, Edmonton, T6E 5L9, AB, Canada
Tel.: (780) 438-9000
Web Site:
https://www.islengineering.com

Year Founded: 1966
Rev.: $27,061,792
Emp.: 190
Engineeering Services
N.A.I.C.S.: 541330
Rod Peacock *(COO)*

ISLAMI BANK BANGLADESH PLC
Islami Bank Tower 40 Dilkusha C/A, GPO Box 233, Dhaka, 1000, Bangladesh
Tel.: (880) 29563040
Web Site:
http://www.islamibankbd.com
ISLAMIBANK—(CHT)
Rev.: $467,467,618
Assets: $16,444,416,425
Liabilities: $15,718,141,065
Net Worth: $726,275,360
Earnings: $5,562,804
Emp.: 18,621
Fiscal Year-end: 12/31/20
Commercial Banking Services
N.A.I.C.S.: 522110
Yousif Abdullah Al-Rajhi *(Vice Chm)*

Subsidiaries:

Islami Bank Securities Limited (1)
20 Dilkusha 5th Floor C/A, Dhaka, 1000, Bangladesh
Tel.: (880) 247119116
Web Site: http://www.ibslbd.com
Brokerage Services
N.A.I.C.S.: 523150
Mohammed Nasir Uddin *(Chm)*

ISLAMI INSURANCE BANGLADESH LIMITED
DR Tower 11th Floor Box Culvert Road, 65 2 2 Purana Paltan, Dhaka, 1000, Bangladesh
Tel.: (880) 8317353
Web Site:
https://www.islamiinsurance.com
Year Founded: 1999
ISLAMIINS—(CHT)
Rev.: $1,863,339
Assets: $15,816,112
Liabilities: $8,612,563
Net Worth: $7,203,549
Earnings: $1,152,480
Emp.: 1,468
Fiscal Year-end: 12/31/22
General Insurance Services
N.A.I.C.S.: 524210
Mohammad Sayeed *(Chm)*

ISLAMIC BANK ZAMAN-BANK JSC
Mashkhur Zhussup St 111A, Ekibastuz, Kazakhstan
Tel.: (7) 7187280000
Web Site: http://www.zamanbank.kz
Year Founded: 1991
Emp.: 100
Investment Banking Services
N.A.I.C.S.: 523150
Tasbulat Abguzhinov *(Chm)*

ISLAMIC CORPORATION FOR THE DEVELOPMENT OF THE PRIVATE SECTOR
Al-Nazlah Al-Yamaniyah, PO Box 54069, Jeddah, 21514, Saudi Arabia
Tel.: (966) 126441644
Web Site: https://icd-ps.org
Year Founded: 1999
Investment Management Service
N.A.I.C.S.: 523999

ISLAMIC FINANCE AND INVESTMENT LIMITED
Impetus Center 3rd Floor 242/B Tejgaon Gulshan Link Road, Tejgaon, Dhaka, 1208, Bangladesh

ISLAMIC FINANCE AND INVESTMENT LIMITED

Islamic Finance and Investment Limited—(Continued)
Tel.: (880) 226603274 BD
Web Site: https://www.ifilbd.com
Year Founded: 2001
ISLAMICFIN—(CHT)
Rev.: $3,174,020
Assets: $124,185,612
Liabilities: $108,247,494
Net Worth: $15,938,118
Earnings: ($2,104,876)
Emp.: 112
Fiscal Year-end: 12/31/23
Financial Services
N.A.I.C.S.: 523999
Maruf Mansur (Deputy Mng Dir)

ISLAMIC HOLDING GROUP (Q.S.C)

Building No 48 Q03 Building First Floor Office No 10, PO Box 12402, Msheireb Downtown-Area No 03 Al Kharaba South-Street No 908, Doha, Qatar
Tel.: (974) 44498832
Web Site: https://www.inma.qa
Year Founded: 2003
IHGS—(QE)
Rev.: $3,679,321
Assets: $125,889,415
Liabilities: $87,005,698
Net Worth: $38,883,717
Earnings: $1,634,918
Emp.: 40
Fiscal Year-end: 12/31/20
Securities Brokerage Services
N.A.I.C.S.: 523150

Subsidiaries:

Islamic Financial Securities Compnay W.L.L. (1)
Bin Al Sheikh Building Grand Hamad Street, PO Box 12402, Doha, Qatar
Tel.: (974) 44498888
Web Site: http://www.islamicbroker.com.qa
Finance Security Services
N.A.I.C.S.: 523150
Yasser Hammad (Mgr)

ISLAND INFORMATION & TECHNOLOGY, INC.

4-B Vernida I Condominium 120 Amorsolo Street Legaspi Village, Makati, Philippines
Web Site: http://www.iiti.ph
Year Founded: 1959
IS—(PHI)
Rev.: $19,718
Assets: $336,277
Liabilities: $2,303,564
Net Worth: ($1,967,287)
Earnings: ($4,097)
Fiscal Year-end: 10/31/23
Internet Technology & Telecommunications Services
N.A.I.C.S.: 517810
James Shih (Chm)

ISLAND PHARMACEUTICALS LIMITED

Suite 201 697 Burke Road, Camberwell, 3124, VIC, Australia
Tel.: (61) 370367675 AU
Web Site: https://www.islandpharma.com
Year Founded: 2017
ILA—(ASX)
Rev.: $7,215
Assets: $1,336,128
Liabilities: $172,032
Net Worth: $1,164,095
Earnings: ($1,845,504)
Fiscal Year-end: 06/30/23
Pharmaceutical Product Mfr & Distr
N.A.I.C.S.: 325412
Cameron Jones (CFO)

ISLANDS WEST MANUFACTURERS LTD.

4247 Douglas St, Victoria, V8X3Y7, BC, Canada
Tel.: (250) 727-0744
Web Site: http://www.islandswest.com
Year Founded: 1982
Rev.: $34,691,035
Emp.: 85
Fruits & Vegetables Distr
N.A.I.C.S.: 424480
Wayne Fatt (Pres)

ISLANDSBANKI HF.

Hagasmara 3, 201, Kopavogur, Iceland
Tel.: (354) 4404000 IS
Web Site: http://www.islandsbanki.is
Year Founded: 1904
Rev.: $528,554,750
Assets: $9,687,553,710
Liabilities: $8,176,551,300
Net Worth: $1,511,002,410
Earnings: $91,227,650
Emp.: 1,076
Fiscal Year-end: 12/31/18
Banking Services
N.A.I.C.S.: 522110
Birna Einarsdottir (CEO)

Subsidiaries:

Allianz Island hf. (1)
Digranesvegi 1, Kopavogur, 200, Iceland
Tel.: (354) 595 3300
Fire Insurance Services
N.A.I.C.S.: 524113

Frumherji hf. (1)
barabakki 3, 109, Reykjavik, Iceland
Tel.: (354) 570 9000
Web Site: http://www.frumherji.is
Vehicle & Electrical Safety Inspection Services
N.A.I.C.S.: 541990

Kreditkort Hf (1)
28 Armula, Reykjavik, Iceland (55%)
Tel.: (354) 5501500
Web Site: http://www.kreditkort.is
Sales Range: $10-24.9 Million
Emp.: 35
Business Support Services
N.A.I.C.S.: 561499

ISLE OF MAN POST OFFICE

Postal Headquarters Spring Valley Industrial Estate, Douglas, IM21AA, Isle of Man
Tel.: (44) 1624698400
Web Site: http://www.iompost.com
Sales Range: $25-49.9 Million
Emp.: 370
Postal Service
N.A.I.C.S.: 491110
Lisa Duckworth (Dir-Comml)

ISM COMMUNICATIONS CORPORATION

The Penthouse Alphaland Southgate Tower, 2258 Chino Roces Ave corner EDSA, 1231, Makati, Philippines
Tel.: (63) 23385599 PH
Web Site: http://www.ismcorp.ph
Sales Range: $10-24.9 Million
Holding Company; Telecommunications Services
N.A.I.C.S.: 551112
Dennis A. Uy (Chm, Pres & CEO)

ISM RESOURCES CORP.

306 1110 Hamilton Street, Vancouver, V6B 2S2, BC, Canada
Tel.: (778) 868-2226 BC
Web Site: https://www.ismresources.com
Year Founded: 2021
DCLI—(CNSX)
Rev.: $25,760

Assets: $8,892,222
Liabilities: $346,781
Net Worth: $8,545,441
Earnings: ($2,518,793)
Emp.: 1
Fiscal Year-end: 01/31/24
Gold Exploration & Mining Services
N.A.I.C.S.: 212220
Jody Bellefleur (CFO)

ISMAIL INDUSTRIES LTD.

17 Banglore Town Main Shara-e-Faisal, Karachi, 75350, Pakistan
Tel.: (92) 2134311172
Web Site: https://www.ismailindustries.com.pk
ISIL—(KAR)
Rev.: $266,501,939
Assets: $196,966,228
Liabilities: $144,770,139
Net Worth: $52,196,089
Earnings: $4,532,729
Emp.: 2,336
Fiscal Year-end: 06/30/19
Candy Exporter & Mfr
N.A.I.C.S.: 311821
Munsarim Saifullah (CEO)

ISMEDIA CO., LTD.

361 Simin-daero, Dongan-gu, Anyang, 14055, Gyeonggi-do, Korea (South)
Tel.: (82) 314278411
Web Site: https://www.ismedia.com
Year Founded: 2002
181340—(KRS)
Rev.: $38,698,084
Assets: $47,178,850
Liabilities: $25,715,259
Net Worth: $21,463,590
Earnings: ($4,952,711)
Emp.: 86
Fiscal Year-end: 12/31/22
Office Automation Equipment Mfr
N.A.I.C.S.: 339940
Kim Jong-Won (VP)

ISMT LIMITED

Lunkad Towers Viman Nagar, Pune, 411 014, India
Tel.: (91) 2041434100
Web Site: https://www.ismt.com
ISMTLTD—(NSE)
Rev.: $354,651,570
Assets: $265,047,510
Liabilities: $63,304,605
Net Worth: $201,742,905
Earnings: $11,976,510
Emp.: 1,878
Fiscal Year-end: 03/31/23
Tube Products Mfr
N.A.I.C.S.: 334419
B. R. Taneja (Mng Dir)

Subsidiaries:

ISMT Europe (1)
PO Box 1, 688 21, Storfors, Sweden
Tel.: (46) 55065500
Web Site: http://www.ismteurope.com
Sales Range: $25-49.9 Million
Emp.: 2
Tube Mfr
N.A.I.C.S.: 331210

ISMT Ltd - Jejuri Steel Plant (1)
Panama House Earlier known as Lunkad Towers Viman Nagar, Village Kolvihre Pune Dist, Pune, 411014, India
Tel.: (91) 2115253335
Web Site: https://www.ismt.co.in
Cylinder Tubes Mfr
N.A.I.C.S.: 326211

ISMT North America (1)
50 Main St Ste 1000-1015, White Plains, NY 10606
Tel.: (914) 500-2216
Web Site: https://www.ismtna.com

INTERNATIONAL PUBLIC

Sales Range: $25-49.9 Million
Seamless Tubes Mfr
N.A.I.C.S.: 331210

ISOCELE

14 Avenue De Savoie, 38110, Saint-Clair-de-la-Tour, Isere, France
Tel.: (33) 474832080
Web Site: http://www.isocele-france.com
Rev.: $10,300,000
Emp.: 29
N.A.I.C.S.: 423830
Maurice Dunand (Mng Dir)

ISODIOL INTERNATIONAL, INC.

Suite 2710 - 200 Granville Street, Vancouver, V6C 1S4, BC, Canada
Tel.: (604) 409-4409 BC
Web Site: http://isodiol.com
Year Founded: 2014
Rev.: $16,307,242
Assets: $17,311,266
Liabilities: $12,229,659
Net Worth: $5,081,606
Earnings: ($92,290,462)
Emp.: 57
Fiscal Year-end: 03/31/19
Pharmaceutical Preparation Mfr
N.A.I.C.S.: 325412
Marcos Agramont (CEO)

Subsidiaries:

Azure Water LLC (1)
1903 Greenleaf Ln, Leesburg, FL 34748
Tel.: (352) 728-5646
Web Site: http://www.azurewater.com
All Other Specialty Food Stores
N.A.I.C.S.: 445298

ISOENERGY LTD.

Suite 2200 HSBC Building 885 West Georgia St, PO Box 10026, Vancouver, V6C 3E8, BC, Canada
Tel.: (778) 379-3211
Web Site: https://www.isoenergy.ca
I01—(DEU)
Rev.: $564,648
Assets: $262,174,901
Liabilities: $33,359,258
Net Worth: $228,815,644
Earnings: ($14,112,014)
Emp.: 14
Fiscal Year-end: 12/31/23
Uranium Exploration Services
N.A.I.C.S.: 212290
Marty Tunney (COO)

Subsidiaries:

Consolidated Uranium Inc. (1)
960-1055 West Hastings St, Vancouver, V6E 2E9, BC, Canada
Tel.: (778) 383-3057
Web Site: http://www.nxgold.ca
Rev.: $33,756
Assets: $1,772,422
Liabilities: $162,522
Net Worth: $1,609,900
Earnings: ($7,959,924)
Fiscal Year-end: 12/31/2019
Metal & Mining Product Services
N.A.I.C.S.: 212290
Greg Duras (CFO)

ISOFOL MEDICAL AB

Biotech Center Arvid Wallgrens Backe 20, 413 46, Gothenburg, Sweden
Tel.: (46) 317972280
Web Site: https://www.isofolmedical.com
Year Founded: 2008
ISOFOL—(OMX)
Rev.: $1,198,872
Assets: $19,993,069
Liabilities: $5,149,531
Net Worth: $14,843,538
Earnings: ($14,963,425)

Emp.: 15
Fiscal Year-end: 12/31/22
Medical Device Mfr
N.A.I.C.S.: 339112
Sven Erickson (Chief Comml Officer)

ISOFOTON
Montalban 9, 28014, Madrid, Spain
Tel.: (34) 914147800
Web Site: http://www.isofoton.com
Sales Range: $400-449.9 Million
Emp.: 815
Photovoltaic & Thermal Solar Energy Equipment Mfr
N.A.I.C.S.: 334419
Pedro Enciso (Chm)

Subsidiaries:

ISOFOTON North America Inc (1)
800 Independence Dr, Napoleon, OH 43545-9192
Tel.: (202) 463-7877
Electronic Components Distr
N.A.I.C.S.: 423690

ISOFTSTONE HOLDINGS LIMITED
Building 16 Dong Qu 10 Xibeiwang Dong Lu, Haidian District, Beijing, 100193, China
Tel.: (86) 10 5874 9000 Ky
Web Site: http://www.isoftstone.com
Year Founded: 2001
Sales Range: $450-499.9 Million
Information Technology Services
N.A.I.C.S.: 541519
Tianwen Liu (Chm & CEO)

ISOLITE INSULATING PRODUCTS CO., LTD.
Nakanoshima Daibiru Room 802 3-3-23 Nakanoshima, Kita-ku, Osaka, 530-6108, Japan
Tel.: (81) 6 7711 5801
Web Site: http://www.isolite.co.jp
Year Founded: 1927
5358—(TKS)
Rev.: $132,548,240
Assets: $198,788,480
Liabilities: $46,444,640
Net Worth: $152,343,840
Earnings: $15,478,320
Emp.: 664
Fiscal Year-end: 03/31/21
Insulating Product Mfr
N.A.I.C.S.: 327120
Eishi Iida (Pres)

Subsidiaries:

ITM Co., Ltd. (1)
20-8 Takeda Kouzaki-machi, Katori, Chiba, Japan
Tel.: (81) 478 70 1123
Web Site: http://www.itm-cf.com
Ceramic Fiber Mfr & Distr
N.A.I.C.S.: 327999

Isolite (Shanghai) Trade Co., Ltd. (1)
Room 574 Building 1 No 188 Aona Road, Pilot Free Trade Zone, Shanghai, China
Tel.: (86) 5126 825 8051
Web Site: http://www.isolite.com.cn
Ceramic Fiber Distr
N.A.I.C.S.: 423320

Isolite Insulating Products Co., Ltd. - Nanao Plant (1)
1 Yo-bu Ishizaki-machi, Nanao, Ishikawa, Japan
Tel.: (81) 767622211
Insulating Fire Brick Mfr
N.A.I.C.S.: 327120

Isolite Insulating Products Co., Ltd. - Otowa Plant (1)
7 Mukaiyama Hagi-cho, Toyokawa, Aichi, Japan
Tel.: (81) 533883111
Insulating Fire Brick Mfr
N.A.I.C.S.: 327120

ISON GROUP
2nd Fl Fedha Plaza Mpaka Road Westlands, PO Box 20976-00100, Nairobi, Kenya
Tel.: (254) 732 198 000
Web Site: http://www.isongrp.com
Holding Company; Information Technology Services
N.A.I.C.S.: 551112
Ramesh Awtaney (Co-Founder & Chm)

Subsidiaries:

ISON Technologies FZ LLC (1)
Office M07 Block B Al Hudaiba Awards Buildings Opp Union House, PO Box 111507, 2nd December Street Al Mina Road Jumeirah 1, Dubai, United Arab Emirates
Tel.: (971) 4 507 9999
Web Site: http://isontechnologies.com
Information Technology Consulting Services
N.A.I.C.S.: 541512
Jitendra Israni (CEO)

ISOPRA CO., LTD.
21 chome Nishikincho Chiyoda Platform Square 1325, Chiyoda-ku, Tokyo, 101-0054, Japan
Tel.: (81) 335189011 JP
Web Site: http://www.isopra.co.jp
Year Founded: 1985
Emp.: 70
Software Develoment
N.A.I.C.S.: 513210
Atsushi Teramura (Rep Dir)

Subsidiaries:

Sophia Holdings Co., Ltd. (1)
5F Kyoritsu Shin-Yokohama Building 2-15-12 Shin-Yokohama, Kohoku-ku, Yokohama, 222-0033, Kanagawa, Japan (66.38%)
Tel.: (81) 362653339
Web Site: https://www.sophia.com
Rev.: $59,694,910
Assets: $51,829,010
Liabilities: $31,278,520
Net Worth: $20,550,490
Earnings: ($661,000)
Emp.: 511
Fiscal Year-end: 03/31/2024
Holding Company
N.A.I.C.S.: 551112

ISOTEAM LTD.
8 Changi North Street 1 ISOTeam Building, Singapore, 498829, Singapore
Tel.: (65) 67470220
Web Site: https://www.isoteam.com.sg
5WF—(CAT)
Rev.: $81,808,077
Assets: $74,846,980
Liabilities: $55,824,379
Net Worth: $19,022,601
Earnings: $848,462
Emp.: 994
Fiscal Year-end: 06/30/23
Building Maintenance, Upgrading & Retrofitting
N.A.I.C.S.: 238190
Anthony Thong huat Koh (Co-Founder & CEO)

Subsidiaries:

Green Pest Management Pte. Ltd (1)
8 Changi North Street 1 ISOTeam Building, Singapore, 498829, Singapore
Tel.: (65) 67450150
Web Site: http://www.isohomecare.com
Residential Building Alteration Services
N.A.I.C.S.: 236118

ISO-Landscape Pte. Ltd. (1)
8 Changi North Street 1 ISOTeam Building, Singapore, 498829, Singapore
Tel.: (65) 67470220
Web Site: https://www.iso-landscape.com.sg
Residential Building Alteration Services
N.A.I.C.S.: 236118

ISOTeam Access Pte. Ltd. (1)
8 Changi North Street 1 ISOTeam Building, Singapore, 498829, Singapore
Tel.: (65) 67470220
Web Site: https://www.isoteamaccess.com.sg
Industrial Machinery Leasing Services
N.A.I.C.S.: 532490

SG Bike Pte. Ltd. (1)
8 Changi North Street 1, Singapore, 498829, Singapore
Tel.: (65) 96412296
Web Site: https://www.sgbike.com.sg
Bicycle Rental Services
N.A.I.C.S.: 532284

Zara@ISOTeam Pte. Ltd. (1)
8 Changi North Street 1 ISOTeam Building, Singapore, 498829, Singapore
Tel.: (65) 65478324
Web Site: https://www.zara-iso.com
Interior Design Services
N.A.I.C.S.: 541410

ISP FINANCE SERVICES LTD.
17 Phoenix Ave 10, Kingston, Jamaica
Tel.: (876) 8697373
Web Site: https://www.ispfinanceservices.com
ISP—(JAM)
Rev.: $2,828,390
Assets: $6,846,955
Liabilities: $3,440,980
Net Worth: $3,405,975
Earnings: $376,958
Emp.: 44
Fiscal Year-end: 12/31/22
Money Lending Services
N.A.I.C.S.: 522310
Dennis Smith (Founder)

ISP GLOBAL LIMITED
3 Ang Mo Kio Street 62 01-39 LINK AMK, Singapore, 569139, Singapore
Tel.: (65) 63481111 Ky
Web Site: http://www.ispg.hk
Year Founded: 2002
8487—(HKG)
Rev.: $29,049,485
Assets: $28,959,487
Liabilities: $18,233,136
Net Worth: $10,726,351
Earnings: ($3,947,441)
Emp.: 160
Fiscal Year-end: 06/30/23
Audio Equipment Distr
N.A.I.C.S.: 423610
Kean Yeow Mong (Exec Dir)

Subsidiaries:

ISPL Pte. Ltd. (1)
3 Ang Mo Kio St 62 01-39, Singapore, 569139, Singapore
Tel.: (65) 63481111
Web Site: https://www.ispl.com
Wireless & Voice Communication Services
N.A.I.C.S.: 517112
Murugaprasath Asokan (Mgr-IT)

ISP HOLDINGS LIMITED
8/F KT336 334 336 Kwun Tong Road, Kwun Tong, Kowloon, China (Hong Kong)
Tel.: (852) 34712340 BM
Web Site: http://www.synergis.com.hk
Year Founded: 1978
2340—(HKG)
Rev.: $28,677,683
Assets: $54,100,035
Liabilities: $28,574,790
Net Worth: $25,525,245
Earnings: $55,684,350
Emp.: 317
Fiscal Year-end: 12/31/22
Asset Management Services
N.A.I.C.S.: 523940

Terence Siu Cheong Leung (Deputy Chm & Mng Dir)

Subsidiaries:

ISP Interiors Limited (1)
7/F Linkchart Centre 2 Tai Yip Street, Kwun Tong, Kowloon, China (Hong Kong)
Tel.: (852) 21022688
Web Site: http://www.isp-hk.com.hk
Investment Holding Services
N.A.I.C.S.: 551112

Laundrimate Service Limited (1)
Tel.: (852) 27577470
Laundry Services
N.A.I.C.S.: 812320

Master Clean Service Limited (1)
Room 22-24 8/F Pacific Trade Centre 2 Kai Hing Road, Kowloon Bay, Kowloon, China (Hong Kong)
Tel.: (852) 36102127
Building Cleaning Services
N.A.I.C.S.: 561720

SecurExpert Solutions Limited (1)
4/F KT 336 334-336 Kwun Tong Road Kwun Tong, Kowloon, China (Hong Kong)
Tel.: (852) 36102111
Web Site: https://www.securexpert.com.hk
Security Services
N.A.I.C.S.: 561612

Synergis Property Management (Shenzhen) Co., Limited (1)
Rm 1003-1004 Shenhua Commercial Bldg Jiabin Rd And Nanhu Rd, Shenzhen, 518001, Guangdong, China
Tel.: (86) 75533206019
Property Management Services
N.A.I.C.S.: 531311

ISPT PTY. LTD.
Level 11 8 Exhibition Street, Melbourne, 3000, VIC, Australia
Tel.: (61) 386016666
Web Site: http://www.ispt.net.au
Year Founded: 1994
Real Estate Investment Services
N.A.I.C.S.: 531210
Rosemary Hartnett (Chm)

ISR IMMUNE SYSTEM REGULATION HOLDING AB
Rorstrandsgatan 58, 113 40, Stockholm, Sweden
Tel.: (46) 705427939
Web Site: http://www.israb.se
ISR—(OMX)
Assets: $4,897,850
Liabilities: $534,710
Net Worth: $4,363,139
Earnings: ($3,794,246)
Emp.: 2
Fiscal Year-end: 12/31/20
Medical Equipment Mfr
N.A.I.C.S.: 339112
Ola Winqvist (CEO)

ISRACANN BIOSCIENCES INC.
1600-595 Burrard Street, Vancouver, V7X 1L3, BC, Canada
Tel.: (604) 394-2551 AB
Web Site: https://isracann.com
Year Founded: 2010
IPOT—(CNSX)
Rev.: $59,240
Assets: $3,442,370
Liabilities: $363,956
Net Worth: $3,078,414
Earnings: ($19,678,468)
Fiscal Year-end: 05/31/21
Technology Services
N.A.I.C.S.: 541519
Fred Stearman (COO)

ISRAEL AEROSPACE INDUSTRIES LTD.
Ben Gurion International Airport, Lod, 70100, Israel
Tel.: (972) 39353111

ISRAEL AEROSPACE INDUSTRIES LTD.

Israel Aerospace Industries Ltd.—(Continued)

Web Site: http://www.iai.co.il
Year Founded: 1953
Sales Range: $1-4.9 Billion
Emp.: 16,000
Land, Sea, Air Systems & Equipment; Space Technologies; Military & Civil; Aircraft, Missiles, Systems & Components for UAV's Research, Design, Development Integration, Test & Mfr, Support & Service
N.A.I.C.S.: 336411
Shalom Hami *(Sec & VP)*

Subsidiaries:

BEDEK Aviation Group (IAI) **(1)**
Ben Gurion Intl Airport, Tel Aviv, 70100, Israel **(100%)**
Tel.: (972) 39353979
Repair, Overhaul, Retrofit, Modification, Conversion, Remanufacture & Customizing of Civil Aircraft, Made up of Four Autonomous Business Divisions
N.A.I.C.S.: 488119

Division (Domestic):

BEDEK Aviation Group - Aircraft Division **(2)**
Ben Gurion International Airport, Tel Aviv, 70100, Israel
Tel.: (972) 39354930
Web Site: http://www.iai.co.il
Aircraft Support Services
N.A.I.C.S.: 336411

BEDEK Aviation Group-Components Division **(2)**
Ben Gurion International Airport, Tel Aviv, 70100, Israel **(100%)**
Tel.: (972) 39353554
Web Site: http://www.iai.co.il
Sales Range: $75-99.9 Million
Emp.: 450
Maintenance, Overhaul, Repair, Modification & Test of Aircraft Accessories & Instruments; Approved by Major Civil & Military Regulatory Agencies & OEMS
N.A.I.C.S.: 336413
Shimon Pritas *(Gen Mgr)*

Division (US):

Empire Aero Center **(2)**
394 Hanger Rd, Rome, NY 13441
Tel.: (315) 838-1501
Sales Range: $25-49.9 Million
Emp.: 200
Aircraft Services
N.A.I.C.S.: 336411

Division (Domestic):

Israel Aircraft, Engines Division/BEDEK Aviation Group **(2)**
Ben Gurion International Airport, Tel Aviv, 70100, Israel **(100%)**
Tel.: (972) 39357064
Web Site: http://www.iai.co.il
Sales Range: $150-199.9 Million
Emp.: 700
Overhaul, Repair, Retrofit & Outfitting & Testing of Civil & Military Engines
N.A.I.C.S.: 336412
Joseph Kazes *(Gen Mgr)*

RAMTA Division Commercial Aircraft Group **(2)**
Industrial Zone, PO Box 323, Beersheba, 84102, Israel **(100%)**
Tel.: (972) 86402250
Web Site: https://www.iai.co.il
Sales Range: $50-74.9 Million
Emp.: 450
Combat Engineering Equipment; Fighting & Support Vehicles; GSE & Aircraft Structures; Including Galleys Composite Materials Design & Manufacture
N.A.I.C.S.: 336411
Hagai Shmuel *(Dir-Mktg)*

Elta Intelligence Radar & AEW Group **(1)**
100 Yitzthak Hanasi Blvd, PO Box 330, Ashdod, 77102, Israel **(100%)**
Tel.: (972) 88572333

Web Site: http://www.elta-iai.com
Sales Range: $1-9.9 Million
Emp.: 2,800
Design & Manufacture of Military Electronics Systems; Air-Land-Sea Radars; EW & ECM; Sigint System; Secure Communications; Computer & ATE; Signal Processing & AI
N.A.I.C.S.: 334511

Engineering Division/Commercial Aircraft Group **(1)**
Ben Gurion International Airport 4400, Tel Aviv, 70100, Israel **(100%)**
Tel.: (972) 39358150
Web Site: http://www.iai.co.il
Sales Range: $200-249.9 Million
Emp.: 850
Design, Analysis, Integration & Testing of Aircraft Systems
N.A.I.C.S.: 336411

IAI ASIA Pte Ltd **(1)**
36 Lorong Serambi, Singapore, 708973, Singapore
Tel.: (65) 63333456
Aerospace & Defense System Distr
N.A.I.C.S.: 423860
Jude Maniam *(Deputy Gen Mgr)*

IAI North America, Inc. **(1)**
1700 N Moore St Ste 1210, Arlington, VA 22209
Tel.: (703) 875-3749
Web Site: http://www.iainorthamerica.com
Aerospace & Defense System Distr
N.A.I.C.S.: 423860

IAI dO BRASIL LTDA **(1)**
SH/SUL Qd 06 Conj A Bloco A Sala 401 Ed Brasil XXI, Brasilia, 70316-102, Brazil
Tel.: (55) 61 3039 8135
Web Site: http://www.iaidobrasil.com.br
Emp.: 4
Aerospace & Defense System Distr
N.A.I.C.S.: 423860
Henrique Gomes *(CEO)*

Israel Aircraft Industries MHT Division **(1)**
Ben Gurion International Airport, Lod, 70100, Israel **(100%)**
Tel.: (972) 39354540
Web Site: http://www.israelaircraftindustries.com
Sales Range: $25-49.9 Million
Emp.: 170
Provision of Custom Multilingual Technical Publications & Training Services
N.A.I.C.S.: 624310
Samuel Nahum *(Gen Mgr)*

Israel Aircraft Industries Maman Division **(1)**
Ben-Gurion Intl Airport, Tel Aviv, 70100, Israel
Tel.: (972) 39353111
Developing, Operating & Maintaining Software for IAI's Activities from the Business & Financial Infrastructure to Design & Production Facilities, Maintenance Services & More
N.A.I.C.S.: 541511
Rami Sarrtani *(Gen Mgr)*

Israel Aircraft Industries Missile & Space Systems Group **(1)**
Yehud Industrial Zone, PO Box 105, Yehud, 5610001, Israel
Tel.: (972) 35314005
Web Site: http://www.iai.co.il
Analysis, Concept, Design, Manufacture & Testing of Electronic Defense & Civil Systems
N.A.I.C.S.: 336414
Jacob Hardy *(Head-Intl Bus Dev)*

Division (Domestic):

Israel Aircraft Industries MBT Division **(2)**
Yehud Industrial Zone, PO Box 105, Yehud, 56000, Israel
Tel.: (972) 35314059
Web Site: http://www.iai.co.il
Design & Manufacture of Smart Bombs, Fire Control Systems, Offensive & Defensive Precision Tactical Battlefield Missiles, Training & Simulator Systems, Civil Satellite Integration & Ground Service

N.A.I.C.S.: 334519
Israel Aircraft Industries MLM Division/Missile & Space Systems Group **(2)**
PO Box 45, Beer-Yaacov, 70350, Israel **(100%)**
Tel.: (972) 89272230
Sales Range: $350-399.9 Million
Emp.: 1,250
Image Processing Systems Mfr
N.A.I.C.S.: 339991
Yoaz Tourgeman *(Gen Mgr)*

Israel Aircraft Industries TAMAM Division/Missile & Space Systems Group **(2)**
IAI/Tamam Division, PO Box 75, Yehud, 56100, Israel
Tel.: (972) 35315205
Web Site: http://www.iai.co.il
Design, Integration & Manufacture of Inertial Measurement, Stabilization Navigation, Optronic Systems & Components for Land, Sea & Air, Manned & Unmanned Platforms
N.A.I.C.S.: 334511

Israel Aircraft, Military Aircraft Group **(1)**
Ben Gurion International Airport, Tel Aviv, 70100, Israel **(100%)**
Tel.: (972) 39354136
Web Site: http://www.seckhaus-ia.co.il
Sales Range: $50-74.9 Million
Emp.: 150
Design, Manufacturing & Upgrading of Manned & Unmanned Aircraft/Helicopters. Made up of Three Autonomous Business Divisions
N.A.I.C.S.: 336411

Lardosa Investments BV **(1)**
De entree 99 -197, 1101 HE, Amsterdam, Netherlands
Tel.: (31) 20 5554466
Investment Management Service
N.A.I.C.S.: 523940

Stark Aerospace, Inc. **(1)**
319 Chrleigh D Ford Jr Dr, Columbus, MS 39701
Tel.: (662) 798-4075
Web Site: http://www.starkaerospace.com
Aerospace & Defense System Distr
N.A.I.C.S.: 423860
Tom Ronaldi *(Pres)*

Systems Missiles & Space Ltd. **(1)**
Altalef 2, Yehud, 5621602, Israel
Tel.: (972) 35315555
Air Vehicle Mfr & Distr
N.A.I.C.S.: 336415
Guy Bar Lev *(Exec VP)*

ISRAEL CANADA TR LTD.

Hamanofim 2 St, Herzliya Pituach, 4672553, Israel
Tel.: (972) 99710900
Web Site: https://www.israel-canada.co.il
ISCN—(TAE)
Rev.: $148,424,435
Assets: $2,326,733,637
Liabilities: $1,498,210,780
Net Worth: $828,522,857
Earnings: ($7,101,838)
Fiscal Year-end: 09/30/23
Real Estate Investment Services
N.A.I.C.S.: 531390
Asaf Touchmair *(Chm)*

ISRAEL CAPITAL CANADA CORP.

Suite 2050 1055 West Georgia Street, PO Box 11121, Vancouver, V6E 3P3, BC, Canada
Tel.: (250) 732-7170
IL.P—(TSXV)
Assets: $340,149
Liabilities: $17,210
Net Worth: $322,939
Earnings: ($91,199)
Fiscal Year-end: 10/31/20
Business Consulting Services

N.A.I.C.S.: 522299
Stephen Davis *(CEO)*

ISRAEL CHINA BIOTECHNOLOGY ICB LTD.

30 Habarzel Street Ramat Hachayal 2Nd Fl Amot Tower, Tel Aviv, Israel
Tel.: (972) 36474840
Web Site: http://www.icbinvest.com
Year Founded: 2018
ICB—(TAE)
Healthcare Investment Services
N.A.I.C.S.: 551112
Huang Qingxi *(Chm & Pres)*

ISRAEL CORPORATION LTD.

Millennium Tower 23 Aranha Street, PO Box 20456, Tel Aviv, 61204, Israel
Tel.: (972) 36844500
Web Site: http://www.israelcorp.com
Year Founded: 1968
ILCO—(TAE)
Rev.: $10,015,000,000
Assets: $13,092,000,000
Liabilities: $7,240,000,000
Net Worth: $5,852,000,000
Earnings: $2,214,000,000
Fiscal Year-end: 12/31/22
Holding Company; Natural Resources & Specialty Chemicals
N.A.I.C.S.: 551112
Aviad Kaufman *(Chm)*

Subsidiaries:

Ceramic Fuel Cells (Powder) Limited **(1)**
Unit 8 Candy Park, Hardknott Rd, Bromborough, CH62 3QB, Wirral, United Kingdom
Tel.: (44) 1513348880
Sales Range: $50-74.9 Million
Emp.: 4
Powder & Ceramic Production Services
N.A.I.C.S.: 212323
Alan Chapman *(Mgr-Tech & Ops)*

IC Green Energy Ltd. **(1)**
Hatichon Tower 19 Ha'arba'a 11th Floor, Tel Aviv, 61204, Israel
Tel.: (972) 3 684 4538
Web Site: http://www.ic-green.com
Energy Investment Services
N.A.I.C.S.: 523999

Subsidiary (US):

Primus Green Energy Inc. **(2)**
219 Homestead Rd, Hillsborough, NJ 08844 **(89%)**
Tel.: (908) 281-6000
Web Site: https://www.primusge.com
Specialty Fuels Mfr
N.A.I.C.S.: 324110

ICL Group Ltd. **(1)**
Millennium Tower 23 Aranha Street, PO Box 20245, Tel Aviv, 61202, Israel **(46.04%)**
Tel.: (972) 36844400
Web Site: http://www.icl-group.com
Rev.: $7,536,000,000
Assets: $11,627,000,000
Liabilities: $5,590,000,000
Net Worth: $6,037,000,000
Earnings: $687,000,000
Emp.: 12,733
Fiscal Year-end: 12/31/2023
Fertilizer & Specialty Chemical Company
N.A.I.C.S.: 325314
Ilana Fahima *(Chief People Officer & Exec VP)*

Subsidiary (Non-US):

Everris International B.V. **(2)**
Nijverheidsweg 1-5, 6422 PD, Heerlen, Netherlands
Tel.: (31) 41 865 5700
Web Site: https://www.everris.com
Emp.: 125
Fertilizer Mfr & Distr
N.A.I.C.S.: 325314

Subsidiary (Non-US):

Everris GmbH **(3)**

AND PRIVATE COMPANIES

Veldhauser Strasse 197, 48527, Nordhorn, Germany
Tel.: (49) 5921713590
Web Site: http://www.everris.com
Emp.: 7
Fertilizer Distr
N.A.I.C.S.: 424690

Subsidiary (Non-US):

ICL Asia Ltd. (2)
Room 2301 23F Allied Kajima Building 138 Gloucester Road, Wanchai, China (Hong Kong)
Tel.: (852) 28277761
Web Site: http://www.icl.com
Emp.: 10
Chemical Products Mfr & Distr
N.A.I.C.S.: 325311
Yaniv Kabalek *(Gen Mgr)*

Group (Domestic):

ICL Industrial Products (2)
Maklef Building Kreutzer Street 1, Beersheba, 8410101, Israel
Tel.: (972) 8 629 7602
Web Site: https://www.icl-ip.com
Sales Range: $550-599.9 Million
Emp.: 1,000
Specialty Chemicals & Fire Retardants Mfr
N.A.I.C.S.: 325199

Subsidiary (Domestic):

Dead Sea Bromine Company Ltd. (3)
Makleff House 12 Kroitzer St, PO Box 180, Beersheba, 84101, Israel
Tel.: (972) 8 629 7057
Web Site: http://www.icl-ip.com
Specialty Chemical Whslr
N.A.I.C.S.: 424690

Subsidiary (US):

ICL Performance Products LP (2)
Creve Coeur IV 622 Emerson Rd, Saint Louis, MO 63141
Tel.: (314) 983-7500
Web Site: http://www.icl-perfproductslp.com
Sales Range: $350-399.9 Million
Emp.: 570
Phosphates, Phosphoric Acid & Phosphorus Chemical Mfr
N.A.I.C.S.: 325180

Subsidiary (Domestic):

ICL Performance Products Inc. (3)
622 Emerson Rd Ste 500, Saint Louis, MO 63141-6742
Tel.: (314) 983-7500
Web Site: http://www.icl-perfproductslp.com
Holding Company; Chemical Products Distr
N.A.I.C.S.: 551112

Subsidiary (Domestic):

ICL IP America Inc., USA (4)
622 Emerson Rd Ste 500, Saint Louis, MO 63141
Tel.: (314) 983-7500
Web Site: http://www.ameribrom.com
Emp.: 300
Chemical Product Whslr
N.A.I.C.S.: 424690

ICL Performance Products LLC (4)
622 Emerson Rd Ste 500, Saint Louis, MO 63141-6742
Tel.: (314) 983-7500
Web Site: http://www.icl-perfproductslp.com
Chemical Products Distr
N.A.I.C.S.: 424690

Division (Domestic):

Halox (5)
1326 Summer St, Hammond, IN 46320
Tel.: (219) 933-1560
Web Site: http://www.halox.com
Sales Range: $25-49.9 Million
Emp.: 25
Inorganic Dye & Pigment Mfr
N.A.I.C.S.: 325130
Linda Arnold *(Mgr-Inside Sls)*

Subsidiary (Non-US):

ICL Trading (HK) Ltd., Hong Kong (2)
Room 2301 23 F Allied Kajima Building 138 Gloucester Road, Wanchai, China (Hong Kong)
Tel.: (852) 28277761
Chemical Products Sales
N.A.I.C.S.: 424690

Iberpotash S.A. (1)
Afueras S/n Suria, 08260, Barcelona, Spain
Tel.: (34) 93 8682803
Web Site: http://www.iberpotash.com
Potash & Fertilizer Mfr & Distr
N.A.I.C.S.: 325314

Oil Refineries Ltd. (1)
PO 4 Israel Central, 31000, Haifa, Israel (37.08%)
Tel.: (972) 48788111
Web Site: http://www.bazan.co.il
Rev.: $10,828,006,000
Assets: $4,526,534,000
Liabilities: $2,782,587,000
Net Worth: $1,743,947,000
Earnings: $441,221,000
Emp.: 1,406
Fiscal Year-end: 12/31/2022
Holding Company; Petroleum Refining, Polmers & Aromatics Mfr
N.A.I.C.S.: 551112
Moshe Kaplinsky *(CEO)*

Subsidiary (Domestic):

Carmel Olefins Ltd. (2)
Hahistadrut Avenue, PO Box 1468, Haifa Bay, Haifa, 31014, Israel
Tel.: (972) 4 846 6003
Web Site: https://www.carmel-olefins.co.il
Sales Range: $1-4.9 Billion
Petrochemical Polymers Mfr
N.A.I.C.S.: 325211

Gadiv Petrochemical Industries Ltd. (2)
Hahistadrut Avenue 81, Haifa, Israel
Tel.: (972) 4 878 8116
Web Site: https://www.gadiv.com
Petrochemical Mfr
N.A.I.C.S.: 325110

Trafico de Mercancias S.A (1)
Muelle de Contradique Norte S/n, 08039, Barcelona, Spain
Tel.: (34) 934421940
Logistics & Shipping Services
N.A.I.C.S.: 541614

Zim Integrated Shipping Services, Ltd. (1)
9 Andrei Sakharov St Matam Center, PO Box 15067, Matam, Haifa, 3190500, Israel
Tel.: (972) 48652000
Web Site: https://www.zim.com
Rev.: $5,162,200,000
Assets: $8,346,000,000
Liabilities: $5,888,000,000
Net Worth: $2,458,000,000
Earnings: ($2,687,900,000)
Emp.: 4,778
Fiscal Year-end: 12/31/2023
Provider of Container Shipping Services
N.A.I.C.S.: 488330
Eyal Ben-Amram *(CIO & Exec VP)*

Subsidiary (Non-US):

Carib Star Shipping Limited (2)
4 Fourth Avenue, Kingston, 13, Jamaica
Tel.: (876) 923 4900
Web Site: http://www.caribstarshipping.com
Sales Range: $25-49.9 Million
Emp.: 38
Marine Cargo Handling Services
N.A.I.C.S.: 488320
Kisha Williams *(Mgr-Traffic & Customer Svc)*

Hellastir Maritime S.A. (2)
4th Floor 85 Akti Miaouli, 18538, Piraeus, Greece
Tel.: (30) 2104290900
Marine Shipping Services
N.A.I.C.S.: 483111

Jamaica Container Repair Services Ltd (2)
14th Avenue N P West, Kingston, Jamaica
Tel.: (876) 937 2096
Container Repair Services
N.A.I.C.S.: 811412

Kingston Logistics Center Ltd (2)
146 First Street Newport West, Kingston, 11, Jamaica
Tel.: (876) 619 2836
Web Site: https://www.klclogistics-jm.com
Logistics Management Services
N.A.I.C.S.: 541614

Omega Depot S.L (2)
Avda Buenos Aires S/n Poligono Industrial Camporroso, 28806, Alcala de Henares, Madrid, Spain
Tel.: (34) 918025891
Web Site: http://www.omegadepot.es
Marine Cargo Handling Services
N.A.I.C.S.: 488320

Sun Cypress Shipping Co. Ltd (2)
Room 2208 22 F One Island East 18 Westlands Road, Quarry Bay, China (Hong Kong)
Tel.: (852) 2 299 5399
Web Site: https://www.suncypress.com
Sales Range: $25-49.9 Million
Emp.: 16
Barge Transportation Services
N.A.I.C.S.: 483211
Forrest Cheng Hing-Leung *(Mng Dir)*

Thai Star Shipping Co (2)
3656/66-68 20th Floor Green Tower Rama 4 Road, Klongton Klong Toey, Bangkok, 10110, Thailand
Tel.: (66) 24943780
Web Site: http://www.thaistarshipping.com
Shipping Services
N.A.I.C.S.: 488330

ZIM Austria Gmbh (2)
Favoritenstrasse 111, 1100, Vienna, Austria
Tel.: (43) 720530420
Sales Range: $25-49.9 Million
Emp.: 5
Marine Cargo Handling Services
N.A.I.C.S.: 488320

ZIM Belgium NV (2)
Ankerrui 9, 2000, Antwerp, Belgium
Tel.: (32) 3 304 1702
Web Site: https://www.zim.com
Emp.: 12
Shipping Transportation Services
N.A.I.C.S.: 488330

ZIM France S.A. (2)
7 Rue Pierre Brossolette, 76600, Le Havre, France
Tel.: (33) 49 191 9134
Web Site: https://www.zim.com
Emp.: 25
Marine Shipping Services
N.A.I.C.S.: 483111

ZIM Germany GmbH (2)
Hammerbrookstrasse 90, 20097, Hamburg, Germany
Tel.: (49) 4 087 8870
Web Site: https://www.zim.com
Emp.: 100
Freight Forwarding Services
N.A.I.C.S.: 488510

ZIM Integrated Shipping Service (Taiwan) Co., Ltd. (2)
11F No 337 Fuxing N Rd, Songshan Dist, Taipei, 105, Taiwan
Tel.: (886) 289781881
Web Site: https://www.zimtaiwan.com
Marine Shipping Services
N.A.I.C.S.: 483111

ZIM Integrated Shipping Services Hellas S.A. (2)
42 26th October str 2nd Floor office 4, 54627, Thessaloniki, Greece
Tel.: (30) 2310 532 8589
Web Site: http://www.zing.com
Sales Range: $25-49.9 Million
Emp.: 40
Marine Shipping Services
N.A.I.C.S.: 483111

ZIM Poland S.P Z.o.o (2)
Podlaska 1, 81-325, Gdynia, Poland
Tel.: (48) 58 690 6305
Web Site: https://www.zim.com
Sales Range: $25-49.9 Million
Emp.: 9
Freight Forwarding Services
N.A.I.C.S.: 488510

ISRAEL OPPORTUNITY ENERGY RESOURCES, LP

Piotr Karczewski *(Mng Dir)*

Zim Netherlands B.V (2)
Waalhaven Zuidzijde 12c, 3088 HH, Rotterdam, Netherlands
Tel.: (31) 10 459 6912
Web Site: http://www.nl.zim.com
Sales Range: $25-49.9 Million
Emp.: 50
Marine Cargo Handling Services
N.A.I.C.S.: 488320
Tim Van Raaij *(Mgr-Sls & Mktg)*

Subsidiary (US):

Zim-American Israeli Shipping Co. (2)
5801 Lake Wright Dr, Norfolk, VA 23502-1862
Tel.: (724) 865-2000
Web Site: http://www.zim.com
Emp.: 400
Container Shipping for Worldwide Importing & Exporting
N.A.I.C.S.: 488510

Division (Domestic):

Zim American Integrated Shipping Co Inc (3)
5801 Lake Wright Dr, Norfolk, VA 23502-1862
Tel.: (757) 228-1300
Web Site: http://www.zim.com
Sales Range: $125-149.9 Million
Emp.: 300
Container Shipping
N.A.I.C.S.: 488510
George Goldman *(Pres)*

ISRAEL EXPORT INSTITUTE

Hamered 29 st beit hata'asia, Tel Aviv, Israel
Tel.: (972) 35142800
Web Site: https://www.export.gov.il
Year Founded: 1958
Consumer Products Distr
N.A.I.C.S.: 423620

ISRAEL LAND DEVELOPMENT URBAN RENEWAL LTD.

30 Sheshet Hayamim Street, Bnei Brak, 5120261, Israel
Tel.: (972) 37962222
Web Site: https://www.ildc.co.il
Year Founded: 1909
ILDR—(TAE)
Oil & Gas Exploration Services
N.A.I.C.S.: 211130
Ofer Nimrodi *(CEO)*

ISRAEL NATURAL GAS LINES LTD.

Kiryat Atidim Migdal Atidim, PO Box 58177, Tel Aviv, 6158101, Israel
Tel.: (972) 36270400
Web Site: http://www.ingl.co.il
Year Founded: 2003
INGL—(TAE)
Natural Gas Distr
N.A.I.C.S.: 221210
Samuel Tordjman *(CEO)*

ISRAEL OPPORTUNITY ENERGY RESOURCES, LP

2 Ben Guroin Rd, Ramat Gan, 52573, Israel
Tel.: (972) 36116111
Web Site: https://www.oilandgas.co.il
Year Founded: 2010
ISOP.L—(TAE)
Assets: $7,257,000
Liabilities: $362,000
Net Worth: $6,895,000
Earnings: ($1,429,000)
Fiscal Year-end: 12/31/22
Oil & Gas Exploration Services
N.A.I.C.S.: 213112
Maya Gottdenker-Firon *(Gen Counsel)*

ISRAEL PETROCHEMICAL ENTERPRISES LTD.

Israel Opportunity Energy Resources, LP—(Continued)

ISRAEL PETROCHEMICAL ENTERPRISES LTD.
8 Shaul Hamelech Blvd, Tel Aviv, Israel
Tel.: (972) 36955559
Web Site: http://www.israel-petro.co.il
Year Founded: 1961
PTCH—(TAE)
Assets: $458,260,250
Liabilities: $177,152,643
Net Worth: $281,107,607
Earnings: $77,503,245
Fiscal Year-end: 12/31/23
Offices of Other Holding Companies
N.A.I.C.S.: 551112
Rafael Arad (CEO)

Subsidiaries:

Oil Refineries Ltd. (1)
PO 4 Israel Central, 31000, Haifa, Israel (30.72%)
Tel.: (972) 48788111
Web Site: http://www.bazan.co.il
Rev.: $10,828,006,000
Assets: $4,526,534,000
Liabilities: $2,782,587,000
Net Worth: $1,743,947,000
Earnings: $441,221,000
Emp.: 1,406
Fiscal Year-end: 12/31/2022
Holding Company; Petroleum Refining, Polmers & Aromatics Mfr
N.A.I.C.S.: 551112
Moshe Kaplinsky (CEO)

Subsidiary (Domestic):

Carmel Olefins Ltd. (2)
Hahistadrut Avenue, PO Box 1468, Haifa Bay, Haifa, 31014, Israel
Tel.: (972) 4 846 6003
Web Site: https://carmel-olefins.co.il
Sales Range: $1-4.9 Billion
Petrochemical Polymers Mfr
N.A.I.C.S.: 325211

Gadiv Petrochemical Industries Ltd. (2)
Hahistadrut Avenue 81, Haifa, Israel
Tel.: (972) 4 878 8116
Web Site: https://www.gadiv.com
Petrochemical Mfr
N.A.I.C.S.: 325110

ISRAEL PORTS DEVELOPMENT & ASSETS COMPANY LTD.
74 Menachem Begin Road, Tel Aviv, 6721516, Israel
Tel.: (972) 35657070
Web Site: http://www.israports.co.il
IPC—(TAE)
Rev.: $461,313,170
Assets: $4,826,102,772
Liabilities: $1,875,876,783
Net Worth: $2,950,225,989
Earnings: $128,854,621
Fiscal Year-end: 09/30/22
Financial Services
N.A.I.C.S.: 523999
Uzi Itzhaki (Chm)

ISRAEL RAILWAYS LTD.
Tel Aviv Central Station, PO Box 18085, Savidor (Arlozorov), Tel Aviv, 61180, Israel
Tel.: (972) 35774000
Web Site: http://www.israrail.org.il
Year Founded: 1998
Sales Range: $75-99.9 Million
Emp.: 1,300
Railway Services
N.A.I.C.S.: 482111
Beni Lavi (Acting CEO)

ISRAEL SHIPYARDS LTD.
Yulius Simon St 53, PO Box 10630, Haifa Bay, 2611702, Israel
Tel.: (972) 48460246
Web Site: https://www.israel-shipyards.com
Year Founded: 1959
ISHI—(TAE)
Rev.: $423,135,509
Assets: $482,014,083
Liabilities: $224,072,382
Net Worth: $257,941,701
Earnings: $26,485,149
Emp.: 320
Fiscal Year-end: 09/30/23
Ship Building & Repairing
N.A.I.C.S.: 336611
Zvi Shechterman (CEO)

ISRAMCO NEGEV 2 LP
Granite 8, PO Box 7313, Petah Tiqwa, 4951407, Israel
Tel.: (972) 39229225
Year Founded: 1989
ISRA—(TAE)
Rev.: $381,631,000
Assets: $1,291,055,000
Liabilities: $704,840,000
Net Worth: $586,215,000
Earnings: $132,522,000
Fiscal Year-end: 12/31/23
Support Activities for Oil & Gas Operations
N.A.I.C.S.: 213112
Haim Tsuf (Chm)

ISRAS INVESTMENT CO., LTD.
Beit Ishers 3 Mount, Tel Aviv, 65816, Israel
Tel.: (972) 37130200
ISRS—(TAE)
Rev.: $144,824,033
Assets: $2,505,599,208
Liabilities: $1,274,635,866
Net Worth: $1,230,963,343
Earnings: $155,899,626
Fiscal Year-end: 12/31/22
Building Construction Services
N.A.I.C.S.: 236210
Adi Dana (CEO)

ISROTEL LTD.
8 Yitzhak Sadeh St, PO Box 50185, Tel Aviv, 68125, Israel
Tel.: (972) 25699017
Web Site: https://www.isrotel.com
Hotel & Restaurant Operator
N.A.I.C.S.: 721110
Lior Raviv (CEO)

ISSTA LINES LTD.
Menorat Hamaor Street 8, Tel Aviv, 67448, Israel
Tel.: (972) 37777222
Web Site: https://www.issta.co.il
Year Founded: 1989
ISTA—(TAE)
Rev.: $112,211,630
Assets: $969,365,919
Liabilities: $551,453,783
Net Worth: $417,912,136
Earnings: $39,190,772
Fiscal Year-end: 12/31/23
Travel Agencies
N.A.I.C.S.: 561510
Amichi Green (Chm)

ISSUNBOU CO., LTD.
Sapporo 2-2 Building 41 Kita 2-jo Nishi 2-chome, Chuo-Ku, Sapporo, 060-0002, Japan
Tel.: (81) 112150127
Web Site: https://www.issun.jp
Year Founded: 2005
7355—(TKS)
Rev.: $8,117,100
Assets: $4,130,080
Liabilities: $3,514,300
Net Worth: $615,780
Earnings: ($31,100)

Emp.: 684
Fiscal Year-end: 07/31/24
Architectural Services
N.A.I.C.S.: 541310

IST LIMITED
A 23 New Office Complex Defence Colony, New Delhi, 110024, India
Tel.: (91) 1126494291
Web Site: https://www.istindia.com
Year Founded: 1977
508807—(BOM)
Rev.: $22,170,262
Assets: $161,588,536
Liabilities: $10,151,355
Net Worth: $151,437,181
Earnings: $11,098,023
Emp.: 400
Fiscal Year-end: 03/31/23
Precision Turned Product Mfr
N.A.I.C.S.: 332721
Suresh Chand Jain (Exec Dir)

ISTARSKA KREDITNA BANKA UMAG D.D.
Ernesta Milosa 1, 52470, Umag, Croatia
Tel.: (385) 52702400
Web Site: https://www.ikb.hr
Year Founded: 1956
IKBA—(ZAG)
Rev.: $12,141,197
Assets: $549,734,043
Liabilities: $499,540,411
Net Worth: $50,193,632
Earnings: $4,502,099
Emp.: 225
Fiscal Year-end: 12/31/19
Financial Banking Services
N.A.I.C.S.: 522110
Miro Dodic (Pres)

ISTITUTO GANASSINI SPA DI RICERCHE BIOCHIMICHE
Via Boncompagni 63, 20139, Milan, Italy
Tel.: (39) 025357041
Web Site: http://www.ganassinicorporate.com
Year Founded: 1930
Pharmaceuticals Mfr
N.A.I.C.S.: 325412

ISTMO COMPANIA DE REASEGUROS, INC.
Costa del Este Av Paseo Roberto Motta Street View of the Pacific, PO Box 0816-03239, No PH-51, Panama, Panama
Tel.: (507) 3062200
Web Site: http://www.istmore.com
Year Founded: 1979
REIS—(PAN)
Sales Range: Less than $1 Million
Reinsurance Services
N.A.I.C.S.: 524130

ISTRABENZ, HOLDINSKA DRUZBA, D.D.
Cesta Zore Perello - Godina 2, 6000, Koper, Slovenia
Tel.: (386) 56621500
Web Site: http://www.istrabenz.si
ITBG—(LJU)
Sales Range: $25-49.9 Million
Emp.: 458
Holding Company; Asset Management
N.A.I.C.S.: 551112
Milan Marinic (Chm-Supervisory Bd)

Subsidiaries:

Istrabenz Hoteli Portoroz, d.o.o. (1)
Obala 33, Portoroz, 6230, Slovenia
Tel.: (386) 56929011
Web Site: http://www.istrabenz.si

INTERNATIONAL PUBLIC

Hotels & Motels
N.A.I.C.S.: 721110
Thies Bruhn (Pres)

Istrabenz Turizem, d.d. (1)
Obala 33, 6320, Portoroz, Slovenia
Tel.: (386) 56929001
Web Site: http://www.lifeclass.net
Sales Range: $50-74.9 Million
Emp.: 400
Hotels & Motels
N.A.I.C.S.: 721110
Andrej Laznik (Chm-Mgmt Bd)

Subsidiary (Non-US):

Thai Si, S.r.l. (2)
Via Gasparotto Vecellio 56 a, Spresiano, 31027, Treviso, Italy
Tel.: (39) 0422881430
Web Site: http://www.thai-si.it
Home Management Services
N.A.I.C.S.: 721110

Zastava Istrabenz Lizing, d.o.o. (1)
Bulevar despota Stefana broj 12, 11000, Belgrade, Serbia
Tel.: (381) 113342644
Web Site: http://zastavaistrabenzlizing.rs
Sales Range: $50-74.9 Million
Emp.: 9
Commercial & Industrial Machinery & Equipment Rental & Leasing
N.A.I.C.S.: 532490
Bozidar Milojicic (Mng Dir)

ISTREET NETWORK LIMITED
Unit No 107 Sonal Industrial Estate Linking Road Kanchpada, Malad West, Mumbai, 400064, India
Tel.: (91) 2227827900
Web Site: https://istreetnetwork.com
Year Founded: 1986
524622—(BOM)
Rev.: $1,103
Assets: $37,791
Liabilities: $233,799
Net Worth: ($196,007)
Earnings: ($28,847)
Emp.: 1
Fiscal Year-end: 03/31/23
Electronic Commerce Services
N.A.I.C.S.: 459999
Pradeep Malu (Co-Founder)

ISTROKAPITAL SE
4 Archibishop Makarios III & Kalogreon Street Nicolaides Sea View City, 5th Floor Flat/Office 506 Block C, 6016, Larnaca, Cyprus
Tel.: (357) 24252636
Web Site: http://www.istrokapital.eu
Year Founded: 1996
Sales Range: $150-199.9 Million
Emp.: 812
Financial & Investment Services
N.A.I.C.S.: 523999

Subsidiaries:

AXON Neuroscience SE (1)
Dvorakovo nabrezie 10, Bratislava, Bratislava, Slovakia
Tel.: (421) 2 2092 1620
Web Site: http://www.axon-neuroscience.eu
Biotechnology Research & Development Services
N.A.I.C.S.: 541714
Michal Novak (Chief Science Officer)

ISTROKAPITAL CZ, a.s. (1)
Prosecka 851/64, Prosek, 190 00, Prague, Czech Republic
Tel.: (420) 226211230
Web Site: http://www.istrokapital.cz
Financial Investment Services
N.A.I.C.S.: 523999

ISTYLE INC.
Ark Mori Building 34th floor 1-12-32 Akasaka, Minato-ku, Tokyo, 107-6034, Japan
Tel.: (81) 355751260
Web Site: https://www.istyle.co.jp

AND PRIVATE COMPANIES

Year Founded: 1999
3660—(TKS)
Rev.: $348,848,700
Assets: $175,037,020
Liabilities: $99,233,880
Net Worth: $75,803,140
Earnings: $7,551,080
Emp.: 1,079
Fiscal Year-end: 06/30/24
Online Cosmetics Sales
N.A.I.C.S.: 456120
Tetsuro Yoshimatsu *(Pres & CEO)*

Subsidiaries:

Cosme Next Co. Ltd. (1)
Ark Mori Building 34th Floor 1-12-32, Akasaka Minato-ku, Tokyo, 107-6034, Japan
Tel.: (81) 355751280
Web Site: http://www.cosmenext.istyle.co.jp
Cosmetic Product Retailer
N.A.I.C.S.: 456120

Cosme.com Inc. (1)
Ark Mori Building 34th Floor 1-12-32, Akasaka Minato-ku, Tokyo, 107-6034, Japan
Tel.: (81) 355751270
Web Site: http://www.cosmecom.istyle.co.jp
Cosmetic Product Retailer
N.A.I.C.S.: 456120

Media Globe Co., Ltd. (1)
1-12-32 Akasaka Ark Mori Building 34F, Minato-ku, Tokyo, 012-3456, Japan
Tel.: (81) 362346220
Web Site: https://www.mediaglobe.co.jp
Cosmetic Product Retailer
N.A.I.C.S.: 456120

i-TRUE Communications Inc. (1)
3rd Floor No 81 Section 2 Nanchang Road, Zhongzheng District, Taipei, 10084, Taiwan
Tel.: (886) 223223778
Web Site: https://www.itrue.com.tw
Online Marketing Services
N.A.I.C.S.: 541613

ISU CHEMICAL CO., LTD.
84 Sapyeong-daero, Seocho-Gu, Seoul, 06575, Korea (South)
Tel.: (82) 25906600
Web Site:
  https://www.isuchemical.com
Year Founded: 1969
005950—(KRS)
Rev.: $1,693,265,764
Assets: $911,254,732
Liabilities: $600,247,668
Net Worth: $311,007,064
Earnings: $21,266,794
Emp.: 467
Fiscal Year-end: 12/31/22
Chemicals Mfr
N.A.I.C.S.: 325199

Subsidiaries:

ISU Abxis Co., Ltd. (1)
Tel.: (82) 316964700
Biotechnology Research & Development Services
N.A.I.C.S.: 541714

ISU Chemical Germany GmbH (1)
Rhenaniastrasse 76-102, 68219, Mannheim, Germany
Tel.: (49) 6214810350
Chemical Products Mfr
N.A.I.C.S.: 325998

ISU Chemical co., Ltd. - Onsan Factory (1)
Hwasan-Ri 857 Onsan-Uep Uljoo-Gun, Ulsan, Korea (South)
Tel.: (82) 52 231 5600
Chemical Products Mfr
N.A.I.C.S.: 325998

ISU Chemical co., Ltd. - Ulsan Factory (1)
Bugok-Dong 156, Nam-Gu, Ulsan, Korea (South)
Tel.: (82) 52 278 2700
Chemical Products Mfr
N.A.I.C.S.: 325998

ISU Engineering & Construction Co., Ltd. (1)
137-714 ISU B/D 84 Sapyeong-daero, Seocho-gu, Seoul, Korea (South)
Tel.: (82) 2 590 6500
Web Site: http://www.isuenc.com
Civil Construction Services
N.A.I.C.S.: 237990
Jhe Min-Ho *(CEO)*

ISU Exaboard Co., Ltd. (1)
274 Byeolmang-ro, Danwon-gu, Ansan, 425110, Korea (South)
Tel.: (82) 313620000
Printed Circuit Board Mfr
N.A.I.C.S.: 334412

ISU Exaflex Co., Ltd. (1)
Nonhyeon-dong Namdong Industrial Complex, Namdong-gu, Incheon, Korea (South)
Tel.: (82) 32 820 1900
Web Site: http://www.isuexaflex.co.kr
Emp.: 231
Printed Circuit Board Mfr
N.A.I.C.S.: 334412

ISU Petasys Corporation (1)
12930 Bradley Ave, Sylmar, CA 91342
Tel.: (818) 833-5800
Printed Circuit Board Mfr
N.A.I.C.S.: 334412
John Stephens *(VP-Sls)*

ISU SYSTEMS CO., LTD (1)
84 Sapyeong-daero, Seocho-gu, Seoul, 137-714, Korea (South)
Tel.: (82) 2 590 6799
Web Site: http://www.isusystem.com
Software Development Services
N.A.I.C.S.: 541511
Kim Yong-Ha *(Pres & CEO)*

ISU Venture Capital Co., Ltd (1)
24 85-gil, Eonju-Ro, Seoul, 6221, Korea (South)
Tel.: (82) 2 3482 2010
Web Site: http://www.isuvc.com
Investment Management Service
N.A.I.C.S.: 523940
Hui-Seob Lee *(CEO)*

ISUPETASYS CO., LTD.
36 Nongong-ro 53-gil Nongong-eup, Dalseong-gun, Daegu, 42981, Korea (South)
Tel.: (82) 536100300
Web Site: https://www.petasys.com
Year Founded: 1972
007660—(KRS)
Rev.: $493,120,049
Assets: $418,792,861
Liabilities: $248,267,225
Net Worth: $170,525,636
Earnings: $78,596,820
Emp.: 967
Fiscal Year-end: 12/31/22
Printed Circuit Board Mfr
N.A.I.C.S.: 334412
Young-joon Seo *(Pres & CEO)*

ISUZU MOTORS LIMITED
6-21-10 Minami-Oi, Shinagawa-ku, Tokyo, 140-8722, Japan
Tel.: (81) 354711141 JP
Web Site: https://www.isuzu.co.jp
Year Founded: 1916
ISU—(DEU)
Rev.: $22,385,928,360
Assets: $21,568,436,610
Liabilities: $10,602,254,920
Net Worth: $10,966,181,690
Earnings: $1,166,281,620
Emp.: 44,495
Fiscal Year-end: 03/31/24
Automobiles & Vehicle Components Mfr
N.A.I.C.S.: 336110

Subsidiaries:

Anadolu Isuzu Otomotiv Sanayi ve Ticaret A.S. (1)
Sekerpinar Mahallesi Otomotiv Caddesi N0 2, Cayirova, 41435, Kocaeli, Turkiye (87%)
Tel.: (90) 850 200 1900
Web Site: https://www.isuzu.com.tr
Sales Range: $200-249.9 Million
Emp.: 802
Mfr & Distribution of Commercial Vehicles
N.A.I.C.S.: 336110
Mehmet K. Eser *(Pres-Automotive Grp)*

Beijing Beiling Special Automobile Co., Ltd. (1)
No 62 Kunming Hu Nanlu, Haidian District, Beijing, China (30%)
Tel.: (86) 88437224
Mfr of Aluminum Van Bodies
N.A.I.C.S.: 336110

DMAX Ltd. (1)
3100 Dryden Rd, Dayton, OH 45439-1622
Tel.: (937) 425-9699
Web Site: https://www.dmaxengines.com
Sales Range: $25-49.9 Million
Emp.: 800
Mfg. & Sales of Diesel Engines
N.A.I.C.S.: 333618
Tomoko Takamatsu *(Coord-Logistics)*

IT Forging (Thailand) Co., Ltd. (ITF) (1)
Siam Eastern Industrial Park 60/7 Moo 3, Mabyangporn sub-district Pluakdaeng district, Rayong, 21140, Thailand (39%)
Tel.: (66) 33 016 7000
Web Site: https://www.itf.co.th
Sales Range: $10-24.9 Million
Emp.: 288
Mfr & Distr of Forgings
N.A.I.C.S.: 333517

Isuzu (China) Holding Co., Ltd. (1)
No1418 Beijing Fortune Building 5 Dong San Huan Bei-Lu, Chao Yang District, Beijing, 100004, China (100%)
Tel.: (86) 106 590 8950
Web Site: http://www.isuzu.com
Sales Range: $25-49.9 Million
Emp.: 9
Investment & Administration Control; Supply/ Import/Export Agent; Other Related Investment & Consulting Activities
N.A.I.C.S.: 336110

Isuzu (Shanghai) Tradetech Co., Ltd. (1)
Room 1407 Waigaoqiao Building Jilong Road, Waigaoqiao Free Trade Zone, Shanghai, 200131, China
Tel.: (86) 2158696111
Web Site: http://www.isuzu.co.jp
Export & Import of Vehicles & Inland Trading
N.A.I.C.S.: 336110

Isuzu Australia Limited (1) (100%)
Tel.: (61) 39 644 6666
Web Site: https://www.isuzu.com.au
Emp.: 55
Import & Sales of Commercial Vehicles & Engines
N.A.I.C.S.: 423110
Phil Taylor *(COO)*

Isuzu Automotive Europe GmbH. (1)
Im Weiherfeld 2, 65462, Ginsheim, Germany
Tel.: (49) 6134 558 528
Light Truck & Pickup Truck Distr
N.A.I.C.S.: 423830

Isuzu Autoparts Manufacturing Corporation (1)
114 N Main Ave Phase III Special Economic Zone Laguna Technopark, Binan, 4024, Luzon, Philippines (100%)
Tel.: (63) 495411464
Sales Range: $100-124.9 Million
Emp.: 400
Mfr of Transmissions
N.A.I.C.S.: 336350

Isuzu Benelux N.V. (1)
Pierstraat 229, 2550, Kontich, Belgium
Tel.: (32) 3 450 1760
Web Site: https://www.isuzu.be
Sales Range: $1-9.9 Million
Emp.: 10
Importer & Seller of Isuzu Vehicles
N.A.I.C.S.: 441227

ISUZU MOTORS LIMITED

Isuzu Commercial Truck of America, Inc. (1)
1400 S Douglass Rd Ste 100, Anaheim, CA 92806
Tel.: (714) 935-9300
Web Site: http://www.isuzucv.com
Sales Range: Less than $1 Million
Emp.: 175
Importation & Distr of Commercial Vehicles & Automotive Components
N.A.I.C.S.: 336110
Joe Totaro *(VP-Mktg)*

Isuzu Commercial Truck of Canada, Inc. (1)
6205 B Airport Road Suite 212, Mississauga, L4V 1E3, ON, Canada
Tel.: (905) 612-0100
Web Site: https://www.isuzutruck.ca
Motor Vehicle Parts Distr
N.A.I.C.S.: 423120
Andy Craig *(Dir-Ops-Canada)*

Isuzu East Africa Ltd. (1)
Enterprise Road off Mombasa Road, PO Box 30527, Nairobi, 00100, Kenya (57.7%)
Tel.: (254) 800724724
Web Site: https://www.isuzu.co.ke
GM & Isuzu Vehicle Products
N.A.I.C.S.: 336110
Susumu Hosoi *(Chm)*

Isuzu Engine Manufacturing Co., (Thailand) Ltd. (1)
Lad Krabang Industrial Estate 122 Moo 4 Chalongkrung Rd, Lamplatew Lad Krabang, Bangkok, 10520, Thailand (7%)
Tel.: (66) 23260916
Sales Range: $25-49.9 Million
Emp.: 80
Mfr of Diesel Engines
N.A.I.C.S.: 333618

Isuzu Hicom Malaysia Sdn. Bhd. (1)
Peramu Jaya Industrial Area, PO Box 6, 26607, Pekan, Pahang Darul Makmur, Malaysia
Tel.: (60) 9 424 3800
Web Site: https://www.isuzu-hicom.com.my
Emp.: 622
Automobile Mfr
N.A.I.C.S.: 336110
Taizo Nakahigashi *(CEO)*

Isuzu LINEX Co., Ltd. (1)
Omori Prime Building 6-21-12 Minamioi, Shinagawa-Ku, Tokyo, 140-0013, Japan
Tel.: (81) 35 753 7721
Web Site: https://www.isuzu-linex.co.jp
Emp.: 761
Logistics Consulting Servies
N.A.I.C.S.: 541614

Isuzu Motors America Inc. (1)
46401 Commerce Ctr Dr, Plymouth, MI 48170-2473 (100%)
Tel.: (734) 582-9470
Web Site: https://www.isuzuengines.com
Sales Range: $25-49.9 Million
Emp.: 150
Importing & Sales of Isuzu Vehicles & Diesel Engines; Sales of SIA-Produced Vehicles; Automobile Research, Design & Controlling
N.A.I.C.S.: 541715
Susumu Hosoi *(Pres)*

Isuzu Motors America Inc. (1)
1400S Douglass Rd Ste 100, Anaheim, CA 92806 (80%)
Tel.: (714) 935-9300
Web Site: https://www.isuzuengines.com
Sales Range: $75-99.9 Million
Emp.: 175
Pickup Trucks, Sports Utility Vehicles, Light/Medium-Duty Trucks & Diesel Engines Distr in the US & Canada
N.A.I.C.S.: 423110
Shawn Skinner *(Pres)*

Isuzu Motors Asia Ltd. (1)
3 Temasek Avenue 22-03 Centennial Tower, Singapore, 039190, Singapore (100%)
Tel.: (65) 6 339 9301
Web Site: http://www.isuzu.co.jp
Sales Range: $300-349.9 Million
Emp.: 20
Control of Business & Distribution in the Asian Area

ISUZU MOTORS LIMITED

Isuzu Motors Limited—(Continued)
N.A.I.C.S.: 423120

Isuzu Motors Chubu Co., Ltd. (1)
5-1-3 Shioya-cho, Minami-ku, Nagoya, Japan
Tel.: (81) 52 823 8558
Web Site: https://www.isuzu-chubu.jp
Emp.: 1,250
Automobiles Engine Distr
N.A.I.C.S.: 423110

Isuzu Motors Co., (Thailand) Ltd. (1)
38 Kor Moo 9 Poochaosamingprai Rd, Samrong-Tai Phrapradaeng, Samut Prakan, 10130, Thailand
Tel.: (66) 2 394 2541 **(71%)**
Web Site: https://www.isuzu-motors.co.th
Sales Range: $100-124.9 Million
Emp.: 5,600
Mfr of Commercial Vehicles
N.A.I.C.S.: 336110

Isuzu Motors Europe Ltd. (1)
Croxley Business Park 24 The Courtyards Hatters Ln, Watford, WD1 8NS, Herts, United Kingdom **(100%)**
Tel.: (44) 1923231580
Web Site: http://www.isuzu.co.uk
Sales Range: $25-49.9 Million
Emp.: 10
Import, Manufacture & Sales of Automobiles, Parts & Accessories
N.A.I.C.S.: 336110

Isuzu Motors Europe NV (1)
Bist 12, 2630, Aartselaar, Belgium
Tel.: (32) 3 870 8180
Web Site: http://www.isuzu-europe.eu
Industrial Diesel Engine Distr
N.A.I.C.S.: 423830

Isuzu Motors Germany GmbH (1)
Im Weiherfeld 2, Ginsheim-Gustavsburg, 65462, Ginsheim, Germany **(100%)**
Tel.: (49) 6 134 5580
Web Site: https://www.isuzu.de
Sales Range: $50-74.9 Million
Emp.: 130
Development, Purchasing & Quality Assurance of Diesel Engines
N.A.I.C.S.: 333618
Matheas Hoffman *(Mgr-IT Sys)*

Isuzu Motors International FZE (1)
S50909 Jafza South, PO Box 263188, Jebel Ali Free Zone, Dubai, United Arab Emirates
Tel.: (971) 4 880 9192
Web Site: https://www.isuzu-intl.com
Motor Vehicle Parts Distr
N.A.I.C.S.: 423120

Isuzu Motors Kinki Co., Ltd. (1)
1-21-10 Yagumo Higashimachi, Moriguchi, 570-0021, Osaka, Japan
Tel.: (81) 66 908 2284
Web Site: https://www.isuzu-kinki.com
Emp.: 1,075
Automotive Repair & Maintenance Services
N.A.I.C.S.: 811198

Isuzu Motors Off-Highway Diesel Engine (Shanghai) Co., Ltd. (1)
5th Floor Jinhongqiao International Center No 523 Loushanguan Road, Changning District, Shanghai, 200051, China
Tel.: (86) 216 236 8395
Web Site: https://www.isuzupowertrain.com
Diesel Engine Mfr & Distr
N.A.I.C.S.: 333618
Shunichi Tokunaga *(Mng Dir)*

Isuzu Motors Syutoken Co., Ltd. (1)
1-18-14 Shinkiba, Koto-ku, Tokyo, 136-0082, Japan
Tel.: (81) 33 522 4700
Web Site: https://www.isuzu-syutoken.co.jp
Car Distr
N.A.I.C.S.: 441120

Isuzu Motors Tokai Co., Ltd. (1)
2-4 Kafukucho, Minami-Ku, Nagoya, 457-0837, Aichi, Japan
Tel.: (81) 526190777
Automobile Mfr
N.A.I.C.S.: 336110

Isuzu Motors de Mexico S. de R.L. (1)
Paseo de la Reforma 350 Piso 18, Colonia Juarez Federal District, 06600, Mexico, Mexico **(51%)**
Tel.: (52) 800 644 7898
Web Site: https://www.isuzumex.com.mx
Sales Range: $1-9.9 Million
Emp.: 70
Import & Sales of Trucks
N.A.I.C.S.: 423110
Jun Narahashi *(Pres)*

Isuzu Network Co., Ltd (1)
Omori Bellport Bldg A 26-1 Minami-Oi 6-chome, Shinagawa-ku, Tokyo, 140-0013, Japan
Tel.: (81) 3 6893 2011
Commercial Vehicle Mfr
N.A.I.C.S.: 336991

Isuzu North America Corporation (1)
1400 S Douglass Rd Ste 100, Anaheim, CA 92806
Tel.: (714) 935-9300
Commercial Vehicle Component Distr
N.A.I.C.S.: 423120

Isuzu Operations (Thailand) Co., Ltd. (1)
1088 Vibhavadi Rangsit Road, Chatuchak, Bangkok, 10900, Thailand
Tel.: (66) 2 966 2626
Web Site: http://www.iot.co.th
Pickup Truck Distr
N.A.I.C.S.: 423110

Isuzu Philippines Corporation (1)
114 Technology Avenue, Laguna Technopark, Binan, 4024, Laguna, Philippines **(35%)**
Tel.: (63) 27 757 6070
Web Site: https://www.isuzuphil.com
Sales Range: $200-249.9 Million
Emp.: 600
Mfg. & Distribution of Vehicles
N.A.I.C.S.: 336110

Isuzu Sales Deutschland GmbH (1)
Schieferstein 11a, 65439, Florsheim, Germany
Tel.: (49) 6145 549 1100
Web Site: https://www.isuzu-sales.de
Import & Sales of Vehicles
N.A.I.C.S.: 423110

Isuzu Technical Center (Thailand) Co., Ltd. (1)
6th Fl Isuzu Bldg 38 Kor Moo 9 Poochaosamingprai Road, Samrong-Tai Phrapradaeng, Samut Prakan, 10130, Thailand **(49%)**
Tel.: (66) 23942541
Web Site: http://www.isuzumotors.co.th
Sales Range: $25-49.9 Million
Emp.: 100
Engineering for Vehicles
N.A.I.C.S.: 333618
Prapsun Leemapakool *(Gen Mgr)*

Isuzu Technical Center Of Asia Co., Ltd. (ITA) (1)
6th Floor 38Kor Moo9 Poochaosamingprai Road, Samrong-Tai, Phra Pradaeng, 10130, Samutprakan, Thailand
Tel.: (66) 2 394 2541
Web Site: http://www.isuzu-ita.com
Sales Range: $1-9.9 Million
Emp.: 100
Vehicle Engineering
N.A.I.C.S.: 541330

Isuzu Truck (UK) Ltd. (1)
Isuzu House 164 Great North Road, Hatfield, AL9 5JN, Hertfordshire, United Kingdom **(100%)**
Tel.: (44) 170 728 2930
Web Site: https://www.isuzutruck.co.uk
Sales Range: $25-49.9 Million
Emp.: 35
Commercial Truck Distr
N.A.I.C.S.: 423110
Lee Barwick *(Mgr-Fleet Sls)*

Isuzu Vietnam Co., Ltd. (1)
695 Quang Trung Street, Ward 8 Go Vap District, Ho Chi Minh City, Vietnam **(35%)**
Tel.: (84) 83 895 9203
Web Site: https://www.isuzu-vietnam.com
Sales Range: $50-74.9 Million
Emp.: 200
Mfr & Distribution of Commercial Vehicles
N.A.I.C.S.: 333310

Jiangling-Isuzu Motors Co., Ltd. (1)
509 North Yingbin Road, Nanchang, 330001, Jaingxi, China **(12.5%)**
Tel.: (86) 7915266000
Mfr & Distribution of Light-Duty Trucks
N.A.I.C.S.: 336120

Malaysian Truck & Bus Sdn. Bhd. (1)
Kawasan Perindustrian Peramu Jaya, PO Box 3, 26607, Pekan, Pahang Darul Makmur, Malaysia **(20%)**
Tel.: (60) 94260339
Sales Range: $400-449.9 Million
Emp.: 1,100
Commercial & Passenger Vehicles Mfr & Distr
N.A.I.C.S.: 336110

P. T. Mesin Isuzu Indonesia (1)
JL Kaliabang No 1 Pondok Ungu Kelurahan Medan Satria Kec, Bekasi Barat, Bekasi, 17031, West Java, Indonesia
Tel.: (62) 21 8879994
Diesel Engine Parts Mfr & Distr
N.A.I.C.S.: 333618

P.T. Isuzu Astra Motor Indonesia (1)
Jl Danau Sunter Utara Blok O-3 Kav 30 Sunter, Jakarta, 14330, Indonesia
Tel.: (62) 21 650 1000
Web Site: https://www.isuzu-astra.com
Automobile Mfr & Distr
N.A.I.C.S.: 336110

QINGLING ISUZU (CHONGQING) ENGINE CO., LTD. (1)
1 Xiexing Road Zhong Liang Shan, Jiu Long Po District, Chongqing, China
Tel.: (86) 23 6525 1782
Engine Mfr & Whslr
N.A.I.C.S.: 333618

Shonan Unitec Co., Ltd. (1)
1919 Kurami, Samukawa-cho, Koza, 253-0101, Kanagawa, Japan
Tel.: (81) 46 773 2000
Web Site: https://www.shonan-unitec.co.jp
Emp.: 739
Automobile Parts Mfr
N.A.I.C.S.: 336390

Subaru of Indiana Automotive, Inc. (1)
5500 State Rd 38 E, Lafayette, IN 47905
Tel.: (765) 449-1111
Web Site: https://www.subaru-sia.com
Sales Range: $25-49.9 Million
Emp.: 34
Mfr of Pickup Trucks Sports Utility Vehicles & Passenger Cars; Joint Venture of Fuji Heavy Industries, Ltd. & Isuzu Motors Limited
N.A.I.C.S.: 336110
Toshiaki Tamegai *(Sr Gen Mgr)*

Taiwan Isuzu Motors Co., Ltd. (1)
363 Sung Chiang Rd, Taipei, 0478, Taiwan **(100%)**
Tel.: (886) 225037221
Web Site: http://www.isuzu.com.tw
Sales Range: $50-74.9 Million
Emp.: 55
Distr of Vehicles
N.A.I.C.S.: 423110

Taiwan Isuzu Motors Co., Ltd. (1)
12th Floor No 51 Hengyang Road, Taipei, Zhongzheng District, Taiwan **(51%)**
Tel.: (886) 2 2758 6870
Web Site: http://www.isuzu.com.tw
Sales Range: $25-49.9 Million
Emp.: 72
Commmercial Vehicles Mfr & Sales; Sales & Export of Auto Parts
N.A.I.C.S.: 336110

Thai International Die Making Co., Ltd. (TDI) (1)
331 Bangpoo Industrial Estate Sukumvit Rd, Amphur Muang, Samut Prakan, 10280, Thailand **(28%)**
Tel.: (66) 23240511
Sales Range: $100-124.9 Million
Emp.: 500
Mfr of Dies & Stamping Parts
N.A.I.C.S.: 333514
Yasuhiro Suzuki *(Mgr)*

Tri Petch Isuzu Sales Co., Ltd. (1)
1088 Vibhavadi Rangsit Rd, Chatuchak, Bangkok, 10900, Thailand
Tel.: (66) 2 966 2111
Web Site: https://www.isuzu-tis.com
Sales Range: $75-99.9 Million
Emp.: 500
Commercial Vehicles & Pickup Trucks Whslr
N.A.I.C.S.: 423110

INTERNATIONAL PUBLIC

ISXIS INVESTMENT PUBLIC LTD.
66 Makarios Ave Kronos Buil Off 44, 1077, Nicosia, Cyprus
Tel.: (357) 22 374536
ISXI—(CYP)
Sales Range: Less than $1 Million
Financial Services
N.A.I.C.S.: 523999
Vrasidas Mavroudes *(Chm)*

IT BANK JSC
Ulitsa Dumskaya D 7, 644024, Omsk, Russia
Tel.: (7) 83812392828
Web Site: http://www.itbank.ru
Sales Range: Less than $1 Million
Commercial Banking Services
N.A.I.C.S.: 522110
Gerald Kowalski *(Chm)*

IT CITY PUBLIC COMPANY LIMITED
The Palladium World Shopping Mall Building B2 Floor Ratchaprarot Road, Makkasan Subdistrict Ratchathewi District, Bangkok, 10400, Thailand
Tel.: (66) 26565030
Web Site: https://www.itcity.co.th
IT—(THA)
Rev.: $239,424,351
Assets: $108,483,913
Liabilities: $74,966,820
Net Worth: $33,517,092
Earnings: $1,382,820
Emp.: 1,361
Fiscal Year-end: 12/31/23
Computer Equipment Distr
N.A.I.C.S.: 423430
Kamol Juntima *(Co-Chm)*

IT HOLDING S.P.A.
Corso Monforte 30, 20122, Milan, Italy
Tel.: (39) 027630391
Web Site: http://www.ittierre.it
Sales Range: $900-999.9 Million
Emp.: 1,783
Holding Company; Luxury Goods Including Ready-To-Wear, Accessories, Eyewear & Perfume
N.A.I.C.S.: 424350
Tonino Perna *(Chm)*

Subsidiaries:

C'N'C CoStume National (1)
Zona industriale, Pettoranello del Molise, 86090, Naples, IS, Italy
Tel.: (39) 08654461
Web Site: http://www.ittierre.it
Clothing Accessories
N.A.I.C.S.: 315990

Ittierre Accessories S.p.A. (1)
Via Serbelloni Gabrio 1, 20122, Milan, Italy
Tel.: (39) 027630031
Clothes Mfr
N.A.I.C.S.: 315250

Ittierre S.p.A. (1)
Zona Industriale, Pettoranello del Molise, Naples, Italy **(100%)**
Tel.: (39) 08654461
Web Site: http://www.ittierre.it
Clothes Mfr
N.A.I.C.S.: 315250
Antonio Bianchi *(Gen Mgr)*

Malo S.p.A. (1)
Via Gattinella 6, Campi Bisenzio, 50013,

AND PRIVATE COMPANIES

Firenze, Italy
Tel.: (39) 027389701
Web Site: http://www.malo.it
Sales Range: $25-49.9 Million
Emp.: 20
Designer Clothing Mfr
N.A.I.C.S.: 424350
Anna Maria Pahzera *(Gen Mgr)*

Manifatture Associate Cashmere USA Inc (1)
17 Battery Pl Fl 5, New York, NY 10004-1179
Tel.: (212) 414-5700
Clothing & Furnishings Merchant Whslr
N.A.I.C.S.: 424350

IT LINK S.A.
67 Avenue de Fontainebleau, Le Kremlin-Bicetre, 94270, Paris, France
Tel.: (33) 153901590
Web Site: https://www.itlink.fr
ALITL—(EUR)
Sales Range: $50-74.9 Million
Emp.: 550
Information Technology Services
N.A.I.C.S.: 541512
Noel Moisan *(Dir-Information Sys)*

Subsidiaries:

IPSIS, SAS (1)
3 square du Chene Germain, 35510, Cesson Sevigne, France
Tel.: (33) 2 99 27 53 27
Emp.: 35
Information Technology Consulting Services
N.A.I.C.S.: 541512
Eric Guillard *(Mgr)*

NRX Company (1)
67 Avenue de Fontainebleau, Le Kremlin-Bicetre, 94270, Paris, France
Tel.: (33) 1 55 43 17 10
Web Site: http://www.nrx.fr
Information Technology Consulting Services
N.A.I.C.S.: 541512

IT LTD
31/F Tower A Southmark 11 Yip Hing St, Wong Chuk Hang, Hong Kong, China (Hong Kong)
Tel.: (852) 31971109
Web Site: http://www.ithk.com
0999—(HKG)
Rev.: $991,245,329
Assets: $1,009,834,089
Liabilities: $705,814,554
Net Worth: $304,019,535
Earnings: ($95,764,326)
Emp.: 7,116
Fiscal Year-end: 02/29/20
Fashion Wear & Accessories
N.A.I.C.S.: 315210
Kar Wai Sham *(Co-Founder, Chm & CEO)*

Subsidiaries:

Blossom Glory Limited (1)
31 F Tower A Southmark 11 Yip Hing St, Hong Kong, China (Hong Kong)
Tel.: (852) 31991991
Web Site: http://www.ithk.com
Sales Range: $200-249.9 Million
Emp.: 700
Fashion Wears & Accessories Retailer
N.A.I.C.S.: 458110

Cheerwood Limited (1)
31 F Tower A 11 Yip Hing St, Wong Chuk Hang, Hong Kong, China (Hong Kong)
Tel.: (852) 31971195
Women's Clothing Store
N.A.I.C.S.: 458110

Chocoolate Limited (1)
Shop L1-30 Festival Walk 80 Tat Chee Avenue, Kowloon Tong, Kowloon, China (Hong Kong)
Tel.: (852) 22657521
Web Site: http://hk.chocoolate.com
Men & Women Clothing Stores
N.A.I.C.S.: 458110

I.T ezhop (HK) Limited (1)
2/F Block B Vita Tower 29 Wong Chuk Hang Road, Wong Chuk Hang, Hong Kong, China (Hong Kong)
Tel.: (852) 800969032
Web Site: http://www.hk.iteshop.com
Apparel Store Retailer
N.A.I.C.S.: 458110

IT TECH PACKAGING, INC.
Science Park Juli Road, Xushui District, Baoding, 072550, Hebei, China
Tel.: (86) 3128698215   CN
Web Site: http://www.itpackaging.cn
Year Founded: 1996
ITP—(NYSEAMEX)
Rev.: $100,352,434
Assets: $204,447,233
Liabilities: $23,123,341
Net Worth: $181,323,892
Earnings: ($16,571,308)
Emp.: 380
Fiscal Year-end: 12/31/22
Paper Products Mfr & Distr
N.A.I.C.S.: 322299
Zhenyong Liu *(Chm & CEO)*

IT/NET GROUP INC.
116 Albert St Ste 300, Ottawa, K1P 5G3, ON, Canada
Tel.: (613) 234-8638
Web Site: http://www.itnet.ca
Year Founded: 1992
Sales Range: $10-24.9 Million
Emp.: 80
IT Management & Technology Consulting Services
N.A.I.C.S.: 541690
Christine Collyer *(VP-Sls & Mktg)*

ITAB SHOP CONCEPT AB
Instrumentvagen 2, Box 9054, SE-550 09, Jonkoping, Sweden
Tel.: (46) 36317300
Web Site: https://itab.com
ITAB—(OMX)
Rev.: $643,269,924
Assets: $615,920,650
Liabilities: $319,106,091
Net Worth: $296,814,559
Earnings: $17,795,761
Emp.: 2,847
Fiscal Year-end: 12/31/22
Shop Fittings, Checkouts, Entrance Systems & Equipment Developer, Mfr & Sales
N.A.I.C.S.: 541310
Anders Moberg *(Chm)*

Subsidiaries:

AO ITAB Shop Concept Russia (1)
Savushkina Street 126 Bld B Office 5-4, 197374, Saint Petersburg, Russia
Tel.: (7) 8122400975
Architectural Services
N.A.I.C.S.: 541310

Competences S.r.L. (1)
Via dell Artigiano 23, Pianoro, 40065, Bologna, Italy
Tel.: (39) 051770991
Web Site: http://www.competences.it
Product Design Services
N.A.I.C.S.: 541420

ITAB Butikkinnredninger AS Oslo (1)
Tel.: (47) 2 323 3530
Web Site: http://www.itabnorge.no
Emp.: 25
Shop Fittings Mfr & Distr
N.A.I.C.S.: 238390

ITAB Butikkinnredninger AS Trondheim (1)
Harald Harfagresgate 9, PO Box 1804 Lade, NO 74 40, Trondheim, Norway
Tel.: (47) 73890660
Web Site: http://www.itabnorge.no
Shop Fittings Mfr & Distr
N.A.I.C.S.: 238390

ITAB Eesti OU (1)
Reti tee 4 Peetri, Harju, EE-75312, Maakond, Estonia
Tel.: (372) 6140325
Architectural Services
N.A.I.C.S.: 541310

ITAB Finland Oy (1)
Haapaniementie 3, 40800, Jyvaskyla, Finland
Tel.: (358) 207121611
Architectural Services
N.A.I.C.S.: 541310

ITAB Germany GmbH (1)
Bonner Str 324, 50968, Cologne, Germany
Tel.: (49) 221376330
Fitting Whslr
N.A.I.C.S.: 423840

Subsidiary (Domestic):

D&L Lichtplanung GmbH (2)
Am Papenbusch 5, 58708, Menden, Germany
Tel.: (49) 237396920
Web Site: http://www.dl-lichtplanung.de
Electronic Product Whslr
N.A.I.C.S.: 423690

ITAB Prolight Germany GmbH (2)
Peutestrasse 51a, 20539, Hamburg, Germany
Tel.: (49) 407804530
Architectural Services
N.A.I.C.S.: 541310

ITAB Guidance AB (1)
Box 9054, 550 09, Jonkoping, Sweden
Tel.: (46) 36317300
Architectural Services
N.A.I.C.S.: 541310

ITAB Harr GmbH (1)
Gewerbepark 5-6, Malschwitz, 02694, Niedergurig, Germany
Web Site: http://www.itab.se
Shop Fittings Design & Installation Services
N.A.I.C.S.: 238390

ITAB Interiors Ltd. (1)
ITAB House Swallowdale Lane, Hemel Hempstead, HP2 7EA, Hertfordshire, United Kingdom
Tel.: (44) 1442419250
Architectural Services
N.A.I.C.S.: 541310

ITAB Lindco AS (1)
PO Box 152, Holmlia, 1203, Oslo, Norway
Tel.: (47) 22754060
Architectural Services
N.A.I.C.S.: 541310

ITAB Mertens N.V. (1)
Terbekehofdreef 51-53, Wilrijk, 2610, Antwerpen, Belgium
Tel.: (32) 38298911
Web Site: http://www.itab.se
Sales Range: $25-49.9 Million
Emp.: 40
Shop Fittings Production & Installation Services
N.A.I.C.S.: 238390

ITAB Pan Oston OY (1)
Teollisuustie 1 Villahde, FIN 15540, Nastola, Finland
Tel.: (358) 3873370
Web Site: http://www.panoston.fi
Sales Range: $25-49.9 Million
Emp.: 25
Shop Fittings Design & Installation Services
N.A.I.C.S.: 238390

ITAB Pharmacy Concept AB (1)
Soder Malarstrand 71, 118 25, Stockholm, Sweden
Tel.: (46) 86690345
Architectural Services
N.A.I.C.S.: 541310

ITAB Prolight AB (1)
Kyrkangsgatan 6, 503 38, Boras, Sweden
Tel.: (46) 33205650
Web Site: http://prolight.se
Emp.: 800
Lighting Fixture Mfr
N.A.I.C.S.: 335132

ITAB Prolight AS (1)
PO Box 6677, Rodelokka, 0502, Oslo, Norway
Tel.: (47) 23233530

ITAB SHOP CONCEPT AB

Architectural Services
N.A.I.C.S.: 541310

ITAB Scanflow AB (1)
Instrumentvagen 2, PO Box 9054, SE 550 09, Jonkoping, Sweden
Tel.: (46) 36317300
Web Site: http://www.itabscanflow.com
Sales Range: $25-49.9 Million
Emp.: 15
Shop Fittings Mfr & Insatallation Services
N.A.I.C.S.: 238390

ITAB Shop Concept A/S (1)
Langvadbjergvej 5-7, 7400, Herning, Denmark
Tel.: (45) 97220811
Architectural Services
N.A.I.C.S.: 541310

ITAB Shop Concept B.V. (1)
Zilverenberg 3 5234 GL, PO Box 31, Woudenberg, 3930, 's-Hertogenbosch, Netherlands
Tel.: (31) 332861236
Web Site: http://www.itab.nl
Sales Range: $25-49.9 Million
Emp.: 75
Shop Fittings Production & Installation Services
N.A.I.C.S.: 238290

ITAB Shop Concept Belgium N.V. (1)
Berchemstadionstraat 76 B1 Antwerpen, 2600, Berchem, Belgium
Tel.: (32) 38298911
Architectural Services
N.A.I.C.S.: 541310

ITAB Shop Concept CZ a.s (1)
Chrudichromska 2364/19, CZ-680 01, Boskovice, Czech Republic
Tel.: (420) 516805900
Architectural Services
N.A.I.C.S.: 541310

ITAB Shop Concept China Co. Ltd. (1)
No 288 Liangang Road, Suzhou New District, Suzhou, 215129, China
Tel.: (86) 51262800616
Architectural Services
N.A.I.C.S.: 541310

ITAB Shop Concept Finland Oy (1)
Ammattikoulunkatu 12, PL 81, FI 04401, Jarvenpaa, Finland
Tel.: (358) 27 482 700
Web Site: http://www.itab.fi
Shop Fittings Production & Installation Services
N.A.I.C.S.: 238390

ITAB Shop Concept Hungary LLC (1)
Madarasz Viktor u 47-49, 1138, Budapest, Hungary
Tel.: (36) 17826785
Architectural Services
N.A.I.C.S.: 541310

ITAB Shop Concept Jonkoping AB (1)
Instrumentvagen 2, PO Box 9054, 553 02, Jonkoping, Sweden
Tel.: (46) 36317300
Web Site: http://www.itabsweden.se
Sales Range: $50-74.9 Million
Emp.: 120
Shop Fittings Design & Installation Services
N.A.I.C.S.: 238390

ITAB Shop Concept Lithuania AB (1)
Draugystes g 12, LT-51260, Kaunas, Lithuania
Tel.: (370) 37490900
Architectural Services
N.A.I.C.S.: 541310

ITAB Shop Concept Nassjo AB (1)
Tel.: (46) 38 051 4175
Web Site: http://www.itabsverige.se
Sales Range: $25-49.9 Million
Emp.: 80
Shop Fittings Design & Installation Services
N.A.I.C.S.: 238390

ITAB Shop Concept Polska Sp Zoo (1)

ITAB SHOP CONCEPT AB

ITAB Shop Concept AB—(Continued)
Wspolna Droga Str 4, Jawczyce, PL-05-850, Ozarow Mazowiecki, Poland
Tel.: (48) 223600780
Architectural Services
N.A.I.C.S.: 541310

ITAB Shop Products A/S (1)
Dybendalsvaenget 3, 2630, Taastrup, Denmark
Tel.: (45) 47174033
Architectural Services
N.A.I.C.S.: 541310

ITAB Shop Products AB (1)
Instrumentvagen 2, PO Box 9054, 553 02, Jonkoping, Sweden
Tel.: (46) 36317300
Web Site: http://www.itabshopproducts.com
Sales Range: $25-49.9 Million
Emp.: 20
Shop Fittings Design & Installation Services
N.A.I.C.S.: 238390

ITAB Sisustus AS (1)
Parnu Mnt 238, EE 11624, Tallinn, Estonia
Tel.: (372) 6140 325
Web Site: http://www.wtc.ee
Shop Fittings Production & Installation Services
N.A.I.C.S.: 238390

ITAB UK Ltd. (1)
ITAB House Swallowdale Lane, Hemel Hempstead, HP2 7EA, Herts, United Kingdom
Tel.: (44) 1442419419
Architectural Services
N.A.I.C.S.: 541310

KB Design AS (1)
Trondheimsveien 156, 0570, Oslo, Norway
Tel.: (47) 23233530
Architectural Services
N.A.I.C.S.: 541310

La Fortezza Asia Sdn Bhd (1)
No 32 Jalan USJ 1/33 Taman Subang Permai, 47500, Subang Jaya, Selangor, Malaysia
Tel.: (60) 380231580
Architectural Services
N.A.I.C.S.: 541310

La Fortezza Middle East DMCC (1)
HDS Business Centre Cluster M, PO Box 487774, Jumeirah Lakes Tower, Dubai, United Arab Emirates
Tel.: (971) 44329552
Architectural Services
N.A.I.C.S.: 541310

La Fortezza Sudamericana S.A. (1)
Luis Maria Drago 208 ex 5530, Villa Granaderos, B1651DNF, San Martin, Buenos Aires, Argentina
Tel.: (54) 114721074546
Architectural Services
N.A.I.C.S.: 541310

Lindco AS (1)
Bjornerudsveien 19, PO Box 152, Holmlia, 1203, Oslo, Norway
Tel.: (47) 22754060
Web Site: http://www.lindco.no
Sales Range: $25-49.9 Million
Emp.: 10
Shop Fittings Design & Installation Services
N.A.I.C.S.: 238390

MB Shop Design AB (1)
Jarnvagsgatan 35, Box 58, 335 04, Hillerstorp, Sweden
Tel.: (46) 370373400
Web Site: http://www.mbshopdesign.se
Metal Product Distr
N.A.I.C.S.: 459999

Subsidiary (Domestic):

Pulverlacken i Hillerstorp AB (2)
Jarnvagsgatan 35, 335 73, Hillerstorp, Sweden
Tel.: (46) 370346290
Web Site: http://www.pulverlacken.se
Indoor & Outdoor Painting Services
N.A.I.C.S.: 238320

Nordic Light (Suzhou) Co., Ltd. (1)
No 53 East Loufeng District, Industrial Park, Suzhou, 215123, China
Tel.: (86) 51265935118
Architectural Services
N.A.I.C.S.: 541310

Nordic Light AB (1)
Svedjevagen 12, 931 36, Skelleftea, Sweden
Tel.: (46) 910733790
Architectural Services
N.A.I.C.S.: 541310

Nordic Light America Inc. (1)
426 McCormick Blvd, Columbus, OH 43213
Tel.: (614) 421-8419
Architectural Services
N.A.I.C.S.: 541310

Nordic Light Group (HK) Co., Ltd. (1)
Rm 1308 13/F Tai Yau Building No 181 Johnston Road, Wanchai, China (Hong Kong)
Tel.: (852) 28387908
Architectural Services
N.A.I.C.S.: 541310

Nordic Light South America SpA (1)
Napoleon 3565 OF 202, 7550219, Las Condes, Santiago, Chile
Tel.: (56) 68990703
Architectural Services
N.A.I.C.S.: 541310

Nuco Lighting Technology Ltd. Co. (1)
Hongxing Village, The 2nd industrial District Songgang Town Baoan District, Shenzhen, 518105, China
Tel.: (86) 51262800616
Web Site: http://www.nucohk.com
Emp.: 350
Lighting Fixture Mfr
N.A.I.C.S.: 335132

Pharmaservice AB (1)
Soder Malarstrand 71, SE 118 25, Stockholm, Sweden
Tel.: (46) 86690345
Web Site: http://www.pharmaservice.se
Sales Range: $25-49.9 Million
Emp.: 5
Pharmaceuticals Mfr & Whslr
N.A.I.C.S.: 325412

Pharmaservice AS (1)
Leif Weldingsvei 20, 3236, Sandefjord, Norway
Tel.: (47) 33448470
Web Site: http://www.pharmaservice.no
Sales Range: $25-49.9 Million
Emp.: 5
Design & Installation Services
N.A.I.C.S.: 541490

Reklamepartner Graphics AS (1)
Floisbonnveien 5, 1412, Sofiemyr, Norway
Tel.: (47) 95849176
Architectural Services
N.A.I.C.S.: 541310

SIA ITAB Shop Concept Latvia (1)
Kleistu Street 18a-2, LV-1067, Riga, Latvia
Tel.: (371) 67686580
Architectural Services
N.A.I.C.S.: 541310

Sintek International AB (1)
Soder Malarstrand 71, SE 118 21, Stockholm, Sweden
Tel.: (46) 86690345
Web Site: http://www.sintek.se
Sales Range: $25-49.9 Million
Emp.: 13
Pharmacy Interior Designing Services
N.A.I.C.S.: 541410

Skelack AB (1)
Servicegatan 15, 931 76, Skelleftea, Sweden
Tel.: (46) 910713550
Web Site: http://www.skelack.se
Lighting Fixture Mfr
N.A.I.C.S.: 335132

ITACONIX PLC
2 Swan Lane, London, EC4R 3TT, United Kingdom
Tel.: (44) 1244283500
Web Site: http://itaconix.com
Year Founded: 2005
ITX—(AIM)
Rev: $5,600,000
Assets: $2,520,000
Liabilities: $3,300,000
Net Worth: ($780,000)
Earnings: ($2,460,000)
Fiscal Year-end: 12/31/22
Polymer Product Mfr
N.A.I.C.S.: 325998
John Roger Shaw (Co-Founder & CEO)

Subsidiaries:

Itaconix Corporation (1)
2 Marin Way, Stratham, NH 03885
Tel.: (603) 775-4400
Polymer Product Mfr
N.A.I.C.S.: 325998

ITALEAF S.P.A.
Strada dello Stabilimento 1, Nera Montoro, 05035, Narni, Italy
Tel.: (39) 0744 7581
Web Site: http://www.italeaf.com
Sales Range: $75-99.9 Million
Emp.: 500
Business Services for Clean Technology & Innovation
N.A.I.C.S.: 561499
Monica Federici (Exec Dir)

ITALGAS S.P.A.
Via Carlo Bo 11, 20143, Milan, Italy
Tel.: (39) 0281872175
Web Site: https://www.italgas.it
Year Founded: 1837
IG—(ITA)
Rev.: $2,506,477,347
Assets: $11,955,947,323
Liabilities: $9,364,824,409
Net Worth: $2,591,122,914
Earnings: $472,714,069
Emp.: 3,639
Fiscal Year-end: 12/31/22
Natural Gas Distribution Services
N.A.I.C.S.: 221210
Alberto Dell'acqua (Chm)

Subsidiaries:

DEDA S.A. (1)
109-111 Mesogeion Avenue & Roussou, 11526, Athens, Attica, Greece
Tel.: (30) 21620004015
Web Site: https://deda.gr
Natural Gas Distribution Network Operator
N.A.I.C.S.: 221210

EDA Attikis S.A. (1)
109-111 Messogion Ave & Rousou, Attica, 11526, Athens, Greece
Tel.: (30) 2130882000
Web Site: https://edaattikis.gr
Natural Gas Distr
N.A.I.C.S.: 486210

Geoside S.p.A. (1)
Via Ettore Cristoni 88, 40033, Casalecchio di Reno, BO, Italy
Tel.: (39) 0516141933
Web Site: https://www.geoside.com
Renewable Energy Services
N.A.I.C.S.: 221114

Italgas Reti S.p.A. (1)
Largo Regio Parco 11, 10153, Turin, Italy
Tel.: (39) 01123941
Natural Gas Distr
N.A.I.C.S.: 486210

Janagas S.R.L. (1)
Via Carlo Bo 11, 20143, Milan, Italy
Tel.: (39) 0800698698
Natural Gas Distr
N.A.I.C.S.: 486210

Medea S.p.A. (1)
Via xxv luglio 160, Cava de'Tirreni, 84013, Salerno, Italy
Tel.: (39) 0894456501
Web Site: https://www.medeaspa.it
Metal Packaging Product Mfr
N.A.I.C.S.: 332431

Seaside S.r.l. (1)
Via Ettore Cristoni 88, 40033, Casalecchio di Reno, BO, Italy
Tel.: (39) 0516141933
Web Site: http://www.sea-side.it
Energy Management Services
N.A.I.C.S.: 238220
Fabrizio Caldi (Dir-Sls & Ops)

Subsidiary (Domestic):

Toscana Energia Green S.p.A. (2)
Via A Bellatalla 1, 56121, Pisa, Italy
Tel.: (39) 050848500
Web Site: http://www.toscanaenergiagreen.it
Heat Management Services
N.A.I.C.S.: 541330

Toscana Energia S.p.A. (1)
Piazza E Mattei n 3, 50127, Florence, Italy (50.66%)
Tel.: (39) 05543801
Web Site: https://www.toscanaenergia.eu
Sales Range: $800-899.9 Million
Emp.: 347
Hydrocarbons Transport & Gas Distribution Services
N.A.I.C.S.: 221210

ITALIA INDEPENDENT GROUP S.P.A.
Via Emilia 16 Venaria Reale, Turin, Italy
Tel.: (39) 0116988600
Web Site: https://www.italiaindependent.com
Year Founded: 2006
Holding Company; Eyewear, Lifestyle Products & Communication Services
N.A.I.C.S.: 551112
Lapo Edovard Elkann (Founder & Chm)

ITALIAN EXHIBITION GROUP SPA
Via Emilia 155, Rimini, 47921, Italy
Tel.: (39) 0440408
Web Site: http://www.iegexpo.it
Year Founded: 1950
Trade Show Organizer
N.A.I.C.S.: 561920
Carlo Costa (CFO)

Subsidiaries:

FB International, Inc. (1)
1 Raritan Rd, Oakland, NJ 07436
Tel.: (201) 337-1985
Web Site: http://www.fbinternational.com
Industrial Design Services
N.A.I.C.S.: 541410
Fabrizio Bartolozzi (Owner)

ITALIAN WINE BRANDS S.P.A.
Viale Abruzzi 94, 20131, Milan, Italy
Tel.: (39) 0230516516
Web Site: https://www.italianwinebrands.it
IWB—(ITA)
Rev.: $404,368,633
Assets: $615,528,280
Liabilities: $419,065,906
Net Worth: $196,462,374
Earnings: $17,855,018
Emp.: 328
Fiscal Year-end: 12/31/21
Wine Product Mfr
N.A.I.C.S.: 312130
Simone Strocchi (Deputy Chm)

Subsidiaries:

Giordano Vini S.p.A. (1)
Via Cane Guido 47bis/50, Diano d'Alba, 12055, Cuneo, CN, Italy
Tel.: (39) 0800900321
Web Site: https://www.giordanovini.it
Winery Product Retailer
N.A.I.C.S.: 424820

Provinco Italia S.p.A. (1)
Via per Marco 12/b, I-38068, Rovereto, TN, Italy
Tel.: (39) 0464557081

ITALIAN-THAI DEVELOPMENT PCL

2034/132-161 Italthai Tower New Petchburi Road, Bangkapi Huaykwang, Bangkok, 10310, Thailand
Tel.: (66) 27161600
Web Site: https://www.itd.co.th
Year Founded: 1958
ITD—(THA)
Rev.: $1,860,760,361
Assets: $3,418,823,055
Liabilities: $3,116,191,069
Net Worth: $302,631,985
Earnings: ($12,305,466)
Emp.: 5,861
Fiscal Year-end: 12/31/23
Civil & Infrastructure Contractors
N.A.I.C.S.: 236210
Nijaporn Charanachitta *(Sr Exec VP)*

Subsidiaries:

Asian Steel Product Co., Ltd (1)
100 Moo 7 Highway No 36 Mabkha Nikompattana, Rayong, 21180, Thailand
Tel.: (66) 38606024
Web Site: https://www.asiansteel.co.th
Sales Range: $50-74.9 Million
Emp.: 120
Steel Pole Mfr
N.A.I.C.S.: 332996

Bhaka Bhumi Development Co., Ltd. (1)
2034/1 48 New Phetchaburi Road, Italthai Tower Building 35th Floor Bang Kapi, Bangkok, 10320, Thailand
Tel.: (66) 27161600
Industrial Building Construction Services
N.A.I.C.S.: 236210

Charoong Thai Wire & Cable Public Company Limited (1)
589/71 Central City Tower Floor 12A Debaratana Road, North Bangna Sub-district Bangna District, Bangkok, 10260, Thailand
Tel.: (66) 27456118
Web Site: https://www.ctw.co.th
Rev.: $169,828,757
Assets: $178,130,252
Liabilities: $66,542,450
Net Worth: $111,587,802
Earnings: ($4,046,742)
Emp.: 746
Fiscal Year-end: 12/31/2023
Electric Wire, Cable & Telephone Cable Mfr
N.A.I.C.S.: 335929
Premchai Karnasuta *(Vice Chm)*

Italian-Thai Development pcl - Equipment Center Pratoonam Pra-in Factory (1)
13/4 Moo 12 Tumbol Klongnueng Ampher, Khlong Luang, 12120, Prathumthani, Thailand
Tel.: (66) 2909 0690 9
Web Site: http://www.itd.co.th
Concrete Products Mfr
N.A.I.C.S.: 327331

Italian-Thai Development pcl - Italian-Thai Industrial Factory (1)
37 Moo 7, Wihan Daeng District Samutprakarn Fabrication Shop, Saraburi, 18150, Thailand
Tel.: (66) 3636531114
Web Site: http://www.itd.co.th
Emp.: 2,000
Concrete Products Mfr
N.A.I.C.S.: 327331

Italian-Thai Development pcl - Pathum Thani Precast Concrete Factory (1)
Vanont Road T61/5 Moo 4 Tiumbol Ban Mai, Pathumthani, 12000, Thailand
Tel.: (66) 29636323
Concrete Products Mfr
N.A.I.C.S.: 327331

Italian-Thai Development pcl - Samutprakarn Fabrication Factory (1)
Samutprakarn Fabrication Shop 37 Moo 7 Wihan, Daeng District, Saraburi, 18150, Thailand
Tel.: (66) 3 653 1114
Web Site: https://www.itd.co.th
Industrial Building Construction Services
N.A.I.C.S.: 236210

Italian-Thai International Co., Ltd. (1)
2034 Italthai Tower New Petchburi Road, Bangkapi Huaykwang, Bangkok, 10310, Thailand
Tel.: (66) 27161600
Web Site: http://www.idt.co.th
Holding Company
N.A.I.C.S.: 551112

Italian-Thai Power Co., Ltd. (1)
2034/161 New Phetchburi Road, Huai Kwang, Bangkok, 10310, Thailand
Tel.: (66) 271611604
Web Site: http://www.itd.co.th
Sales Range: $75-99.9 Million
Emp.: 50
Electric Power Generation & Distribution Services
N.A.I.C.S.: 221122

Italthai Marine Ltd. (1)
389 Soi 11 Italthaithai Taiban Road, T Taiban A Muang, Samut Prakan, 10280, Thailand
Tel.: (66) 23871056
Web Site: https://www.italthaimarine.com
Ship Building & Repair Services
N.A.I.C.S.: 336611

Italthai Trevi Co., Ltd. (1)
42th Floor Ital-Thai Tower 2034/159 New Petchburi Road, Bangkapi Bangkok, 10310, Huaykwang, Thailand
Tel.: (66) 27160074
Web Site: https://www.itt.co.th
Sales Range: $100-124.9 Million
Emp.: 340
Building Foundation Construction Services
N.A.I.C.S.: 238190

Siam Concrete & Brick Products Co., Ltd. (1)
61/2 Moo 4 Tiwanon Road, Ban Mai Sub-district Mueang District, Pathumthani, 12000, Thailand
Tel.: (66) 25012281
Web Site: https://www.scbp-concretethai.com
Sales Range: $50-74.9 Million
Concrete Products Mfr
N.A.I.C.S.: 327390

Siam Pacific Electric Wire & Cable Co., Ltd. (1)
2922/311-312 30th Fl Charn Issara Tower II New Petchburi Rd, Bangkapi Huaykwang, Bangkok, 10310, Thailand
Tel.: (66) 23082091
Web Site: http://www.spewc.com
Sales Range: $25-49.9 Million
Emp.: 50
Coated Wire Mfr
N.A.I.C.S.: 332618

Sin Rae Muangthai Co., Ltd (1)
2034/159 Italthai Tower New Petchburi Road, Kwaeng Bangkapi, Bangkok, Thailand
Tel.: (66) 2716 1600
Construction Engineering Services
N.A.I.C.S.: 237120

TTCL Public Company Limited (1)
159/41-44 Sermmit Tower 27th-30th Floor Sukhumvit 21 Asoke Road, North Klongtoey Wattana, Bangkok, 10110, Thailand
Tel.: (66) 22608505
Web Site: http://www.ttcl.com
Rev.: $211,483,453
Assets: $454,657,828
Liabilities: $356,837,732
Net Worth: $97,820,096
Earnings: $9,744,061
Emp.: 1,012
Fiscal Year-end: 12/31/2021
Engineering Contracting Services
N.A.I.C.S.: 237990
Hironobu Iriya *(Chm, Pres & CEO)*

Thai Maruken Co., Ltd. (1)
19th Floor Thaniya Plaza Building No 52 Silom Rd, Suriyawongse Bangrak, Bangkok, 10500, Thailand
Tel.: (66) 22312226
Web Site: https://www.maruken.co.th
Sales Range: $50-74.9 Million
Emp.: 100
Construction Steel Material Retailer
N.A.I.C.S.: 532412

Thai Pride Cement Co., Ltd. (1)
2034/132-161 Ital-thai Tower 34 Fl, Bangkapi Huaykwang, Bangkok, 10310, Thailand
Tel.: (66) 271607313
Web Site: https://www.tpcc.co.th
Sales Range: $50-74.9 Million
Emp.: 224
Cement Mfr
N.A.I.C.S.: 327310

Plant (Domestic):

Thai Pride Cement Co., Ltd. - Factory (2)
159 Moo 9 Tambol Hinson, Kaeng Khoi, Saraburi, Thailand
Tel.: (66) 36240800
Cement Mfr
N.A.I.C.S.: 327310

ITALMOBILIARE S.P.A.

Via Borgonuovo 20, 20121, Milan, Italy
Tel.: (39) 02290241 IT
Web Site: https://www.italmobiliare.it
Year Founded: 1946
IMSMF—(OTCIQ)
Rev.: $646,594,547
Assets: $2,472,298,267
Liabilities: $604,636,273
Net Worth: $1,867,661,994
Earnings: $93,474,997
Emp.: 1,162
Fiscal Year-end: 12/31/23
Investment Holding Company
N.A.I.C.S.: 551112
Carlo Pesenti *(CEO & COO)*

Subsidiaries:

Callmewine S.r.l. (1)
Via Natale Battaglia 8, 20127, Milan, Italy
Tel.: (39) 0281480430
Web Site: https://www.callmewine.com
Liquor Store Distr
N.A.I.C.S.: 445320

Casa della Salute S.r.l. (1)
Via Balleydier 7, 16149, Genoa, Italy
Tel.: (39) 0109641083
Web Site: https://cds.it
Dental Clinic Services
N.A.I.C.S.: 621210

Clessidra Capital Credit SGR S.p.A. (1)
Indirizzo Piazza Degli Affari 2, 20123, Milan, Italy
Tel.: (39) 028695221
Web Site: https://www.clessidracapitalcredit.it
Investment Banking Services
N.A.I.C.S.: 523150

Clessidra Factoring S.p.A. (1)
Piazza degli Affari 2, 20123, Milan, Italy
Tel.: (39) 0496365800
Web Site: https://www.clessidrafactoring.it
Financial Services
N.A.I.C.S.: 521110
Federico Ghizzoni *(Chm)*

Clessidra Holding S.p.A. (1)
Piazza San Babila 1/3, 20122, Milan, Italy
Tel.: (39) 028695221
Web Site: https://www.clessidragroup.it
Finance Services
N.A.I.C.S.: 921130

Clessidra Private Equity SGR S.p.A (1)
Piazza degli Affari 2, 20123, Milan, Italy (99%)
Tel.: (39) 028695221
Web Site: https://www.clessidraprivateequity.it
Privater Equity Firm
N.A.I.C.S.: 523999

Manuel Catalano *(Mng Dir)*

Joint Venture (Domestic):

Mercury Payment Services S.p.A. (2)
Via Giulio Richard 7, 20143, Milan, Italy
Tel.: (39) 02 891371
Web Site: http://www.mercurypayments.it
Payment Processing Services
N.A.I.C.S.: 522320

Joint Venture (Non-US):

Mercury Processing Services International LLC (2)
Radnicka cesta 50, 10000, Zagreb, Croatia
Tel.: (385) 1 645 60 41
Web Site: http://www.mercury-processing.com
Credit Card Payment Processing Services
N.A.I.C.S.: 522320
Zdenek Houser *(Chm-Mgmt Bd & Gen Dir)*

Subsidiary (Non-US):

Mercury Processing Services International Payment Card Processing & Development Ltd. (3)
Slovenceva Ulica 24, 1000, Ljubljana, Slovenia
Tel.: (386) 1 568 03 00
Web Site: http://www.mercury-processing.com
Credit Card Payment Processing Services
N.A.I.C.S.: 522320

Faerch Italy S.r.l. (1)
Via Industriale 1/3, 25028, Verolanuova, Italy
Tel.: (39) 0309 3681
Web Site: https://www.sirapgroup.com
Fresh Food Distr
N.A.I.C.S.: 424480

Italgen S.p.A. (1)
Via J F Kennedy 37, Villa di Serio, 24020, Bergamo, BG, Italy (100%)
Tel.: (39) 0354216211
Web Site: https://www.italgen.it
Eletric Power Generation Services
N.A.I.C.S.: 221118
Edoardo Maffeis *(Mgr-Energy)*

Italmobiliare International Finance Ltd. (1)
Aib International Centre, Dublin, Ireland
Tel.: (353) 16701278
Financial Management Services
N.A.I.C.S.: 523999

Petruzalek Italia S.r.l. (1)
Via Flero 46 Centro Direzionale Tre Torri, 25125, Brescia, Italy
Tel.: (39) 0345 468 9410
Web Site: https://www.petruzalek.com
Food Packaging Services
N.A.I.C.S.: 561910

Sirap Gema S.p.A. (1)
Via Industriale 1-3, 25028, Verolanuova, Italy
Tel.: (39) 03093681
Web Site: http://www.sirapgema.com
Food Packaging Mfr
N.A.I.C.S.: 326112

Subsidiary (Non-US):

Sirap France SAS (2)
Route Nationale 7, 13550, Noves, France
Tel.: (33) 490242525
Web Site: http://www.sirapgroup.com
Packaging Machinery Supplier
N.A.I.C.S.: 423830

Subsidiary (Domestic):

Sirap Gema - Amprica (2)
Via Bigarello 20, 46050, Castelbelforte, Italy
Tel.: (39) 0376 259411
Web Site: http://www.sirapgroup.com
Emp.: 100
Packaging Products Mfr & Distr
N.A.I.C.S.: 326140
Mirko Negri *(Mgr)*

Sirap Insulation S.r.l. (2)
Via Kennedy 54, Verolanuova, 25028, Italy
Tel.: (39) 030 9368222
Web Site: http://www.sirapgroup.com

ITALMOBILIARE S.P.A.

Italmobiliare S.p.A.—(Continued)

Emp.: 150
Thermal & Acoustic Insulation Product Mfr & Distr
N.A.I.C.S.: 321219
Claudio Marconi *(Gen Mgr)*

Sirap UK Limited (1)
Salters Lane - Sedgefield Co, Durham, TS21 3EE, United Kingdom
Tel.: (44) 174 062 6000
Web Site: http://www.sirapgroup.com
Food Packaging Services
N.A.I.C.S.: 561910

ITALPASTA LIMITED
116 Nuggett Court, Brampton, L6T 5A9, ON, Canada
Tel.: (905) 792-9928
Web Site: http://www.italpasta.com
Year Founded: 1989
Rev.: $88,591,898
Emp.: 230
Pasta Mfr
N.A.I.C.S.: 311824

ITALPINAS DEVELOPMENT CORPORATION
28th Floor Unit 28C BPI Philam-Life building 6811 Ayala Avenue, Makati City, Manila, 1226, Philippines
Tel.: (63) 288930328 **PH**
Web Site: https://www.italpinas.com
Year Founded: 2009
IDC—(PHI)
Rev.: $5,374,134
Assets: $67,188,067
Liabilities: $44,605,573
Net Worth: $22,582,494
Earnings: $3,409,447
Fiscal Year-end: 12/31/23
Real Estate Management Services
N.A.I.C.S.: 531210
Romolo Valentino Nati *(Chm & CEO)*

ITALTILE LIMITED
The Italtile Building 72 Peter Place, Bryanston, 2021, Gauteng, South Africa
Tel.: (27) 115109050
Web Site: https://www.italtile.com
ITE—(JSE)
Rev.: $493,245,598
Assets: $515,901,097
Liabilities: $105,672,852
Net Worth: $410,228,245
Earnings: $87,453,395
Emp.: 2,477
Fiscal Year-end: 06/30/23
Tile & Bathroom Accessories Retailer
N.A.I.C.S.: 423220
Giovanni A. M. Ravazzotti *(Founder)*

ITALY INNOVAZIONI SPA
Circonvallazione Clodia 163 CAP, 195, Rome, Italy
Tel.: (39) 0690288460
Web Site: https://www.italyinnovazioni.com
MLITN—(EUR)
Sales Range: Less than $1 Million
Electrical Products Mfr
N.A.I.C.S.: 335931
Giorgio Rende *(CEO)*

ITALY1 INVESTMENT S.A.
412F route d'Esch, Grand Douchy, L-1741, Luxembourg, Luxembourg
Tel.: (352) 27 12 55 41 **LU**
Web Site: http://www.ita1invest.com
Year Founded: 2010
Investment Services
N.A.I.C.S.: 523999
Vito A. Gamberale *(Chm)*

ITAPEBI GERACAO DE ENERGIA S.A.
Rodovia BR 101 KM 669, Rio Jequitinhonha Itapebi, Itabuna, 45855-000, BA, Brazil
Tel.: (55) 7332862800
Web Site: http://www.itapebi.com.br
Emp.: 100
Hydroelectric Power Generation Services
N.A.I.C.S.: 221111
Marcelo Jose Cavalcanti Lopes *(CEO)*

ITAR-TASS NEWS AGENCY
10 Tverskoy Blvd Bldg 1, 125009, Moscow, Russia
Tel.: (7) 4956923609
Web Site: http://www.tass.com
Year Founded: 1904
Emp.: 1,500
News Agency
N.A.I.C.S.: 516210
Sergey Mikhaylov *(Dir Gen)*

ITAU UNIBANCO HOLDING S.A.
Praca Alfredo Egydio de Souza Aranha 100, Torre Olavo Setubal Parque Jabaquara, Sao Paulo, CEP 04344-902, SP, Brazil
Tel.: (55) 8005700011 **BR**
Web Site: https://www.itau.com.br
Year Founded: 1945
ITUB—(NYSE)
Rev.: $44,348,389,670
Assets: $507,149,267,125
Liabilities: $2,344,050,000,000
Net Worth: $39,694,884,834
Earnings: $6,755,808,156
Emp.: 95,702
Fiscal Year-end: 12/31/23
Bank Holding Company
N.A.I.C.S.: 551111
Roberto Egydio Setubal *(Co-Chm)*

Subsidiaries:

Banco Citicard S.A. (1)
Av Francisco Matarazzo 1400, Torre Milano 17 Andar, Sao Paulo, 04543 906, Brazil
Tel.: (55) 11 3047 9000
Web Site: http://www.credicard.com.br
Credit Card Services
N.A.I.C.S.: 522210

Banco Itau BBA S.A. (1)
Tel.: (55) 1150191549
Web Site: http://www.itau.com.br
Sales Range: $450-499.9 Million
Emp.: 600
Retail, Commercial & Investment Banking Services
N.A.I.C.S.: 522110

Subsidiary (Non-US):

Itau BBA International plc (2)
Web Site: http://www.itau.com.br
Rev.: $163,472,000
Assets: $8,641,932,000
Liabilities: $7,573,116,000
Net Worth: $1,068,816,000
Earnings: $44,698,000
Fiscal Year-end: 12/31/2015
International Banking Services
N.A.I.C.S.: 522110
Flavio Augusto Aguiar de Souza *(CEO)*

Banco Itau Chile (1)
Rosario Norte 660, Las Condes, Santiago, Chile (65.62%)
Tel.: (56) 226608000
Web Site: http://www.itau.cl
Rev.: $4,447,986
Assets: $56,149,072
Liabilities: $51,804,168
Net Worth: $4,644,905
Earnings: $620,704
Emp.: 7,558
Fiscal Year-end: 12/31/2022
Banking, Wealth Management, Investment & Financial Advisory Services
N.A.I.C.S.: 522110
Ricardo Villela Marino *(Vice Chm)*

Subsidiary (Non-US):

Banco Santander Colombia, S.A. (2)
Carrera 7 No 99-53, Centro de Costos, Bogota, Colombia (91.93%)
Tel.: (57) 1 283 7313
Sales Range: $100-124.9 Million
Emp.: 200
Banking Services
N.A.I.C.S.: 522110

Subsidiary (Domestic):

CorpBanca Asesorias Financieras S.A. (2)
Rosario Norte 660 15th Fl, Las Condes, Santiago, Chile
Tel.: (56) 2 660 2185
Web Site: http://www.corpbanca.cl
Financial Advisory Services
N.A.I.C.S.: 523940

Banco Itau Europa Luxembourg, S.A. (1)
33 Boulevard Prince Henri, 1724, Luxembourg, Luxembourg
Tel.: (352) 2233771
Investment & Private Banking
N.A.I.C.S.: 523150

Banco Itau Paraguay S.A. (1)
Avenida Espana y Brasilia 3 andar, Asuncion, Paraguay
Tel.: (595) 21 617 1000
Web Site: http://www.itau.com.py
Emp.: 731
Retail, Commercial & Investment Banking
N.A.I.C.S.: 522110

Banco Itau Uruguay S.A. (1)
Web Site: http://www.bancoitau.com.uy
Emp.: 1,180
Retail, Commercial & Investment Banking
N.A.I.C.S.: 522110

Banco Itaucard S.A. (1)
Alameda Pedro Calil 43 Vila Das Acacias, Poa, 08557-105, Sao Paulo, Brazil
Tel.: (55) 1150199980
Credit Card Services
N.A.I.C.S.: 522210

CitiFinancial Promotora de Negocios e Cobranca Ltda. (1)
Flaquer Senator Street 72, Santo Andre, SP, Brazil
Tel.: (55) 1144277799
Financial Services
N.A.I.C.S.: 523999

INVESTIMENTOS BEMGE S.A.
Pc Alfredo Egydio de Souza Aranha 100 - 7, 4344902, Sao Paulo, Brazil
Tel.: (55) 1150199872
Web Site: http://www.investimentosbemge.com.br
Rev.: $3,492,429
Assets: $29,221,858
Liabilities: $584,187
Net Worth: $28,637,671
Earnings: $2,147,262
Fiscal Year-end: 12/31/2023
Financial Investment Services
N.A.I.C.S.: 523999

Itau CorpBanca Colombia S. A. (1)
Banco Itau Colombia Cra 7 99-53 Piso 21, Bogota, Colombia
Tel.: (57) 5715818181
Commercial Banking Services
N.A.I.C.S.: 522110

Itau Seguros S.A. (1)
Praca Alfredo Egydio de Souza Aranha 100 Torre Olavo Setubal 8 Andar, Sao Paulo, 04344-902, Brazil
Tel.: (55) 1140044828
General Insurance Services
N.A.I.C.S.: 524210

Itau Unibanco S.A (1)
Praca Alfredo Egydio de Souza Aranha 100, Sao Paulo, Brazil
Web Site: http://www.itau.com.br
Banking Services
N.A.I.C.S.: 522110
Milton Maluhy Filho *(CEO)*

Redecard S.A. (1)
Rua Tenente Mauro de Miranda n 36 - Block D2, Sao Paulo, 04345-030, Brazil

INTERNATIONAL PUBLIC

Tel.: (55) 1140014433
Web Site: https://www.userede.com.br
Sales Range: $1-4.9 Billion
Emp.: 1,054
Credit Cards, Debit Cards & Transaction-Related Services
N.A.I.C.S.: 522210

Unibanco-Uniao de Bancos Brasileiros S.A. (1)
Avenida Eusebio Matoso 891, Pinheiros, 05423 901, Sao Paulo, Brazil
Tel.: (55) 1150198111
Foreign Trade & International Banking Institutions
N.A.I.C.S.: 522110

Subsidiary (Domestic):

Banco Bandeirantes (2)
Rua Boa Vista 162 7o andar, Sao Paulo, SP, Brazil
Tel.: (55) 37897737
Provider of Banking Services
N.A.I.C.S.: 522320

Unibanco Leasing S.A. (2)
Alameda Rio Negro 433 - 7 andar, Alphaville, Barueri, 06454-904 SP, Brazil
Tel.: (55) 1172956088
Web Site: http://www.unibanco.com.br
Financial Services
N.A.I.C.S.: 523150

ITAUSA - INVESTIMENTOS ITAU S.A.
Praca Alfredo Egydio de Souza Aranha 100 Torre Olavo Setubal, 04344-902, Sao Paulo, SP, Brazil
Tel.: (55) 1135434782
Web Site: https://www.itausa.com.br
Year Founded: 1975
ITSA4—(BRAZ)
Rev.: $1,472,330
Assets: $21,008,675
Liabilities: $3,649,018
Net Worth: $17,359,657
Earnings: $2,685,412
Emp.: 95,000
Fiscal Year-end: 12/31/23
Investment Management Service
N.A.I.C.S.: 551112
Alfredo Egydio Setubal *(CEO & Officer-IR)*

Subsidiaries:

Alpargatas S.A. (1)
Av das Nacoes Unidas n 14261 Wing A 9th 10th and 11th floors, 04794-000, Sao Paulo, Brazil (27.12%)
Tel.: (55) 1145697322
Web Site: http://www.alpargatas.com.br
Rev.: $919,062,515
Assets: $1,119,566,663
Liabilities: $442,536,376
Net Worth: $677,030,287
Earnings: $64,206,159
Fiscal Year-end: 12/31/2019
Footwear, Sporting Goods & Textiles Mfr
N.A.I.C.S.: 316210
Adalberto Fernandes Granjo *(Chief Legal Affairs Officer)*

Subsidiary (Non-US):

Alpargatas France S.A.R.L. (2)
29 Blvrd, St Martin, 75003, Paris, France
Tel.: (33) 1 42 74 87 40
Web Site: http://www.alpargatas.com.br
Apparel Product Distr
N.A.I.C.S.: 424310

Alpargatas Italy S.R.L. (2)
Via Michelino 30, 40127, Bologna, Italy
Tel.: (39) 0510455127
Web Site: http://www.havaianas-store.com
Apparel Product Distr
N.A.I.C.S.: 424310

Alpargatas Portugal Limited (2)
Savd do Forte n 8 - Piso 2 - Fraccao Q1, Edificio Pujol, 2790-072, Lisbon, Portugal
Tel.: (351) 214 181 931
Web Site: http://www.alpargatas.com.br
Apparel Product Distr
N.A.I.C.S.: 424310

AND PRIVATE COMPANIES — ITC LIMITED

Plant (Domestic):

Alpargatas S.A. - Campina Grande Plant (2)
Av Assis de Chateaubriand 4324, Distrito Industrial, Campina Grande, 58105-421, Paraiba, Brazil
Tel.: (55) 83 3315 4000
Web Site: http://www.alpargatas.com.br
Footwear Product Mfr
N.A.I.C.S.: 316210

Alpargatas S.A. - Dupe Plant (2)
BR 408km 50 5, Carpina, 55819-320, Pernambuco, Brazil
Tel.: (55) 81 3622 8000
Web Site: http://www.alpargatas.com.br
Footwear Product Mfr
N.A.I.C.S.: 316210

Alpargatas S.A. - Joao Pessoa Plant (2)
Rua B1 - 1099 Av das Industrias, Distrito Industrial, Joao Pessoa, 58083-000, Paraiba, Brazil
Tel.: (55) 83 3229 3000
Web Site: http://www.alpargatas.com.br
Footwear Product Mfr
N.A.I.C.S.: 316210

Alpargatas S.A. - Mogi Mirim Plant (2)
Av Joao Pinto 100 Parque das Empresas, Mogi Mirim, Sao Paulo, 13803-360, Brazil
Tel.: (55) 19 3548 3000
Web Site: http://www.alpargatas.com.br
Footwear Product Mfr
N.A.I.C.S.: 316210

Alpargatas S.A. - Santa Rita Plant (2)
Rua/Av Contorno da BR 230 Km 41, s/n - Ligacao Santa Rita, Santa Rita do Sapucai, 58301-645, Paraiba, Brazil
Tel.: (55) 83 3044 8100
Web Site: http://www.alpargatas.com.br
Footwear Product Mfr
N.A.I.C.S.: 316210

Subsidiary (Non-US):

Alpargatas SAIC (2)
Oficina Central Azara 841, Buenos Aires, C1267ABQ, Argentina
Tel.: (54) 11 4124 2400
Web Site: http://www.alpargatas.com.ar
Apparel Product Mfr & Distr
N.A.I.C.S.: 315990
Diego Jose Mohadeb *(Mng Dir & VP)*

Alpargatas Spain S.L.U. (2)
Avenida Arroyo del Santo 4 Bis, 28037, Madrid, Spain
Tel.: (34) 914 009 288
Web Site: http://www.havaianas-store.com
Apparel Product Distr
N.A.I.C.S.: 424310

Alpargatas UK Ltd (2)
24 Bradmore Park Road, Hammersmith, London, W6 0DT, United Kingdom
Tel.: (44) 208 748 0333
Web Site: http://www.havaianas-store.com
Apparel Product Distr
N.A.I.C.S.: 424310

Subsidiary (US):

Alpargatas USA Inc. (2)
33 E 33rd St Ste 501, New York, NY 10016
Tel.: (646) 747-7171
Web Site: http://www.alpargatas.com.br
Apparel Product Distr
N.A.I.C.S.: 424310
Eno Polo *(Pres)*

Duratex S.A. (1)
Avenida Paulista 1938 5 Floor, Sao Paulo, 01310-942, SP, Brazil
Tel.: (55) 1131797530
Web Site: http://www.duratex.com.br
Rev.: $1,405,275
Assets: $2,210,590
Liabilities: $1,213,127
Net Worth: $997,463
Earnings: $87,278
Emp.: 13,241
Fiscal Year-end: 12/31/2020
Metal & Porcelain Plumbing Fixture & Wood Panel Mfr
N.A.I.C.S.: 327110
Juan Fernando Vasquez Duque *(CEO)*

Division (Domestic):

Deca (2)
Av Brasil 1589, Sao Paulo, 01430-001, Brazil
Tel.: (55) 1130882744
Web Site: http://www.deca.com.br
Metal & Ceramic Plumbing Fixture Mfr
N.A.I.C.S.: 327110

Subsidiary (Non-US):

Deca Piazza (2)
Zavaleta 190 1437, Buenos Aires, Argentina
Tel.: (54) 1149090900
Metal & Ceramic Plumbing Fixture Mfr
N.A.I.C.S.: 327110

Subsidiary (US):

Duratex North America Inc. (2)
1208 Eastchester Dr Ste 202, High Point, NC 27265
Tel.: (336) 885-1225
Web Site: http://www.duratex.com
Sales Range: $25-49.9 Million
Emp.: 100
Metal & Ceramic Plumbing Fixture Mfr & Sales
N.A.I.C.S.: 327110

Fabrica Itautec-Jundiai (1)
301 Av Wilhelm Winter Parte Distrito Industrial, Jundiai, CEP 13213-000, Sao Paulo, SP, Brazil (100%)
Tel.: (55) 11 4531 9002
Web Site: http://www.itautec.com.br
Sales Range: $800-899.9 Million
Emp.: 4,000
Mfr of Computers & Electronics
N.A.I.C.S.: 334111

Itausa Empreendimentos S.A. (1)
Av Faria Lima 1309, Pinheiros, Sao Paulo, Brazil (100%)
Web Site: http://www.itausaemp.com.br
Provider of Real Estate Services
N.A.I.C.S.: 531210

ITBOOK HOLDINGS CO., LTD.
2-24 Toyosu 3-chome Toyosu Foresia 9th floor, Kot o-ku, Tokyo, 135-0061, Japan
Tel.: (81) 362648200   JP
Web Site: https://www.itbook-hd.co.jp
Year Founded: 2018
1447—(TKS)
Rev.: $193,474,700
Assets: $119,317,110
Liabilities: $98,693,910
Net Worth: $20,623,200
Earnings: $1,209,630
Fiscal Year-end: 03/31/24
Holding Company
N.A.I.C.S.: 551112
Yutaka Onda *(Chm & CEO)*

Subsidiaries:

IST Co., Ltd. (1)
8th Floor Toko Head Office Building 1-60-11 Yoyogi, Shibuya-ku, Tokyo, 151-0053, Japan
Tel.: (81) 353712560
Web Site: http://ist-global.co.jp
Amusement Equipment Mfr & Distr
N.A.I.C.S.: 315250

ITbook Co., Ltd. (1)
Toyosu Foresia 9th floor 3-2-24 Toyosu, Koto-ku, Tokyo, 135-0061, Japan (100%)
Tel.: (81) 367709971
Web Site: https://www.itbook.co.jp
Rev.: $39,906,840
Assets: $23,659,180
Liabilities: $16,081,600
Net Worth: $7,577,580
Earnings: $812,820
Fiscal Year-end: 03/31/2017
IT Consulting Services
N.A.I.C.S.: 541512

Something Holdings Co., Ltd. (1)
S Building 4F 1-5-25 Kiba, Kouto-ku, Tokyo, 135-0042, Japan (100%)

Tel.: (81) 3 5665 0840
Web Site: http://www.sthd.co.jp
Rev.: $94,119,120
Assets: $50,243,040
Liabilities: $37,979,760
Net Worth: $12,263,280
Earnings: $213,120
Fiscal Year-end: 12/31/2017
Holding Company
N.A.I.C.S.: 551112
Toshimori Mae *(Pres)*

Subsidiary (Domestic):

Something Shikoku Co., Ltd. (2)
255-1 Ichinomiya-cho, Takamatsu, 761-8084, Kagawa, Japan
Tel.: (81) 878136459
Web Site: http://www.st-shikoku.co.jp
Soil Improvement Services
N.A.I.C.S.: 562910

ITC CONCEPTS LTD
Oakwood House 526 Purley Way, Croydon, CR0 4RE, Surrey, United Kingdom
Tel.: (44) 2082961800
Web Site:
   http://www.itcconcepts.co.uk
Year Founded: 1992
Rev.: $31,619,297
Emp.: 42
Refurbishment Services
N.A.I.C.S.: 238990
Ian Conway *(Gen Mgr)*

ITC CONSTRUCTION GROUP
800 - 564 Beatty Street, Vancouver, V6B 2L3, BC, Canada
Tel.: (604) 685-0111
Web Site: https://www.itc-group.com
Year Founded: 1983
Sales Range: $10-24.9 Million
Full-Service Buildings Construction Contractor & Services
N.A.I.C.S.: 236115
Peter P. Rezansoff *(Chm)*

ITC LIMITED
Virginia House 37 J L Nehru Road, Kolkata, 700071, India
Tel.: (91) 3322889371   In
Web Site: https://www.itcportal.com
Year Founded: 1910
ITC—(NSE)
Rev.: $9,539,996,105
Assets: $11,009,671,923
Liabilities: $2,030,596,679
Net Worth: $8,979,075,244
Earnings: $2,488,023,735
Emp.: 24,567
Fiscal Year-end: 03/31/24
Packaged Food Product Mfr
N.A.I.C.S.: 551112
Rajendra Kumar Singhi *(Sec & Exec VP)*

Subsidiaries:

BFIL Finance Limited (1)
5 5 Congree Building Convent Road Colaba, Mumbai, 400039, Maharashtra, India
Tel.: (91) 22 22830148
Financial Management Services
N.A.I.C.S.: 523999

Fortune Park Hotels Limited (1)
ITC Green Centre 10 Institutional Area Sector 32, Gurgaon, 122 001, Haryana, India
Tel.: (91) 1244196666
Web Site: http://www.fortunehotels.in
Sales Range: $200-249.9 Million
Emp.: 2,000
Hotel Operating Services
N.A.I.C.S.: 721110
V. Chandar *(VP-Fin)*

ITC Bhadrachalam Paperboards Ltd. (1)
PO Box 4, Sarapaka Village, Bhadrachalam, 507 128, Telangana, India
Tel.: (91) 8746 242331
Web Site: http://www.itcpspd.com

Specialty Paper Mfr
N.A.I.C.S.: 322299

ITC Hotels Ltd. (1)
P O Hasanpur Tauru, Mewat, Gurgaon, 122105, India
Tel.: (91) 1267285500
Web Site: http://www.itchotels.in
Hotel Owner & Operator
N.A.I.C.S.: 721110

ITC Infotech India Ltd (1)
Virginia House 37 JL Nehru Road, Kolkata, 700 071, India (100%)
Tel.: (91) 3322889371
Web Site: http://www.itcinfotech.com
Custom Computer Programming Services
N.A.I.C.S.: 541511
Rakesh Batra *(CFO)*

Division (US):

ITC Infotech (USA) Inc. (2)
12 N State Route 17 N Ste 303, Paramus, NJ 07652
Tel.: (201) 336-9431
Web Site: http://www.itcinfotech.com
Sales Range: $10-24.9 Million
Emp.: 50
Computer Related Services
N.A.I.C.S.: 541519
L. N. Balaji *(Pres)*

Division (Non-US):

ITC Infotech Denmark (2)
Havnegade 39 3 sal, 1058, Copenhagen, Denmark
Tel.: (45) 33444488
Web Site: http://www.itcinfotech.com
Emp.: 200
Business Process Outsourcing, IT Solutions & Services
N.A.I.C.S.: 519290
Rahul Dasgupta *(Mgr-HR)*

Division (Domestic):

ITC Infotech India Ltd. (2)
No 18 Banaswadi Main Road Maruthiseva Nagar, Pulikeshinagar PO, Bengaluru, 560005, India
Tel.: (91) 8022988331
Web Site: http://www.itcinfotech.com
Business Process Outsourcing, IT Solutions & Services
N.A.I.C.S.: 519290
Sudip Singh *(CEO & Mng Dir)*

Division (Non-US):

ITC Infotech Ltd. (2)
Organizacni Slozka, Londynska 730-59, 120 00, Prague, 2, Czech Republic
Tel.: (420) 21 620 232
Business Process Outsourcing, IT Solutions & Services
N.A.I.C.S.: 519290

ITC Infotech UK Ltd. (2)
Norfolk House, 118 Saxon Gate West, Milton Keynes, MK9 2DN, United Kingdom
Tel.: (44) 1908230055
Web Site: http://www.itcinfotech.com
Sales Range: $25-49.9 Million
Emp.: 100
Business Process Outsourcing, IT Solutions & Services
N.A.I.C.S.: 519290

Landbase India Limited (1)
25 Community Centre, Basant Lok, Vasant Vihar, New Delhi, 110057, India
Tel.: (91) 124 2378841
Web Site: http://www.landbaseindia.com
Real Estate Development & Management Services
N.A.I.C.S.: 531210

Russell Credit Limited (1)
37 J L Nehru Road, Kolkata, 700071, West Bengal, India
Tel.: (91) 3322884086
Investment Management Service
N.A.I.C.S.: 523999

Subsidiary (Non-US):

Technico Pty Limited (2)
PO Box 758, PO Box 758, Moss Vale, 2577, NSW, Australia (100%)

ITC LIMITED

ITC Limited—(Continued)
Tel.: (61) 280147494
Web Site: http://www.technituber.com.au
Sales Range: $25-49.9 Million
Emp.: 2
Crop Farming
N.A.I.C.S.: 111998
Allan Hendry *(Gen Mgr)*

Subsidiary (Non-US):

Technico Agri Sciences Limited (3)
SCO 835 1st 2nd Floor NAC, Manimajra, Chandigarh, 160 101, India
Tel.: (91) 1726619800
Web Site: https://www.technituberindia.com
Sales Range: $25-49.9 Million
Agricultural Seeds Whslr
N.A.I.C.S.: 424590
Sanjeev Madan *(VP-Fin)*

Technico Technologies Inc (3)
12 Airport Road, Hoyt, E5L 2K5, NB, Canada
Tel.: (506) 687-4272
Web Site: https://www.technicotechnologies.ca
Sales Range: $50-74.9 Million
Emp.: 5
Potato Seeds Distr
N.A.I.C.S.: 424910
Sachidanand Madan *(Pres)*

Technico Horticultural (Kunming) Co. Limited (1)
A38 Yanglin Industrial Development Zone, Songming, Kunming, 651700, Yunnan, China
Tel.: (86) 871 7975616
Agricultural Seeds Mfr & Whslr
N.A.I.C.S.: 111211

WelcomHotels Lanka (Private) Limited (1)
21 Galle Face Centre Road, Colombo, Sri Lanka
Tel.: (94) 117877777
Web Site: http://www.sapphireresidences.lk
Hotel & Motel Operator
N.A.I.C.S.: 721110

Wimco Limited (1)
1st Floor Indian Mercantile Chambers Ramjibhai Kamani Marg, Ballard Estate, Mumbai, 400038, Maharashtra, India
Tel.: (91) 2266316600
Web Site: http://www.wimcoltd.tradeindia.com
Safety Matches Mfr
N.A.I.C.S.: 322299

ITC PROPERTIES GROUP LIMITED
30/F Bank of America Tower 12 Harcourt Road, Central, China (Hong Kong)
Tel.: (852) 2 831 8138
Web Site: http://www.itcproperties.com
0199—(HKG)
Rev.: $83,780,507
Assets: $865,468,182
Liabilities: $323,137,076
Net Worth: $542,331,106
Earnings: $68,770,846
Emp.: 243
Fiscal Year-end: 03/31/22
Property Development, Property Investment, Golf & Leisure, Securities Investment, Finance Service Providers
N.A.I.C.S.: 523150
Alan Yiu Lun Chan *(Exec Dir)*

ITCEN CO., LTD.
Banpo-daero 13, Seocho-gu, Seoul, 137-060, Korea (South)
Tel.: (82) 234978300
Web Site: http://www.itcen.co.kr
Year Founded: 2005
124500—(KRS)
Rev.: $2,010,348,708
Assets: $636,995,429
Liabilities: $426,495,901
Net Worth: $210,499,527
Earnings: $23,917,442
Emp.: 182
Fiscal Year-end: 12/31/22
Computer Programming Services
N.A.I.C.S.: 541511
Jin-Mo Kang *(Board of Directors & Chm)*

Subsidiaries:

Goodcen Co., Ltd. (1)
ITcen Building 13 Banpo-daero, Seocho-dong Seocho-gu, Seoul, 06716, Korea (South)
Tel.: (82) 25806500
Web Site: https://www.goodcen.com
Emp.: 109
Computer Integration Services
N.A.I.C.S.: 541512
Kim Myung-Jun *(CEO)*

ITCONS E-SOLUTIONS LIMITED
3rd Floor B-10 Bajaj Bhawan Sector-3 JamnaLal Bajaj Marg, Noida, 201301, India
Tel.: (91) 1204149543
Web Site: https://www.itconsinc.com
Year Founded: 2007
543806—(BOM)
Rev.: $248,478,769
Assets: $68,628,906
Liabilities: $38,201,379
Net Worth: $30,427,528
Earnings: $17,589,993
Fiscal Year-end: 03/31/22
Recruitment Services
N.A.I.C.S.: 561311
Chetan Prakash *(CFO)*

ITD CEMENTATION INDIA LIMITED
9th Floor Prima Bay Tower -B Gate No 5 Saki Vihar Road Powai, Vile Parle East, Mumbai, 400072, India
Tel.: (91) 2266931600
Web Site: https://www.itdcem.co.in
Year Founded: 1978
ITDCEM—(NSE)
Rev.: $374,032,345
Assets: $435,216,163
Liabilities: $289,344,483
Net Worth: $145,871,681
Earnings: $2,177,489
Emp.: 2,051
Fiscal Year-end: 03/31/21
Construction Services
N.A.I.C.S.: 541330
Adun Saraban *(Vice Chm)*

ITE (HOLDINGS) LIMITED
Units C & D 1/F Por Yen Building 478 Castle Peak Road, Kowloon, China (Hong Kong)
Tel.: (852) 2 770 6682
Web Site: http://www.hkite.com
Year Founded: 1997
8092—(HKG)
Rev.: $4,211,969
Assets: $3,798,917
Liabilities: $890,553
Net Worth: $2,908,364
Earnings: $794,799
Emp.: 24
Fiscal Year-end: 03/31/22
Information Technology Consulting Services
N.A.I.C.S.: 541512
Vincent Hon Kwong Lau *(Co-Founder & CEO)*

Subsidiaries:

Quesco Systems Limited (1)
Level 10 Park Building 476 Castle Peak Road, Kowloon, China (Hong Kong)
Tel.: (852) 25270330
Web Site: http://www.quescohk.com
Staffing & Recruitment Services
N.A.I.C.S.: 561320

ITE ELECTRIC SYSTEMS CO PTE LTD
1 Harrison Road 01-01 ITE Electric Building, Singapore, 369652, Singapore
Tel.: (65) 62852233
Sales Range: $25-49.9 Million
Emp.: 30
Electrical Equipment Distr
N.A.I.C.S.: 423610

ITE TECH. INC.
3rd Floor No 13 Chuangxin 1st Road Hsinchu Science and Industrial Park, Hsin-chu, 30076, Taiwan
Tel.: (886) 35798658
Web Site: https://www.ite.com.tw
3014—(TAI)
Rev.: $205,253,369
Assets: $268,623,261
Liabilities: $58,469,470
Net Worth: $210,153,790
Earnings: $51,924,783
Emp.: 439
Fiscal Year-end: 12/31/23
Notebook Computers & Peripherals Mfr
N.A.I.C.S.: 334111

ITECH MINERALS LTD.
Level 3 170 Greenhill Road, Parkside, 5063, SA, Australia
Tel.: (61) 258500000
Web Site: https://www.itechminerals.com.au
Year Founded: 2021
ITM—(ASX)
Rev.: $98,905
Assets: $14,345,601
Liabilities: $556,790
Net Worth: $13,788,811
Earnings: ($594,014)
Fiscal Year-end: 06/30/23
Mineral Exploration Services
N.A.I.C.S.: 212390
Michael Schwarz *(Mng Dir)*

ITEK, INC.
9-15 DongtanSandan 4-Gil, Hwaseong, 18487, Gyeonggi-Do, Korea (South)
Tel.: (82) 3180771500
Web Site: https://www.iteksemi.com
Year Founded: 2005
119830—(KRS)
Rev.: $58,793,488
Assets: $137,305,339
Liabilities: $28,613,584
Net Worth: $108,691,754
Earnings: $16,614,943
Emp.: 284
Fiscal Year-end: 12/31/22
Semiconductor Devices Mfr
N.A.I.C.S.: 334413
Michael Lee *(CEO)*

ITELLO AB
Kungsgatan 44, 111 35, Stockholm, Sweden
Tel.: (46) 850892200
Web Site: http://www.itello.se
Sales Range: $25-49.9 Million
Emp.: 70
Developer of Pension, Insurance & Fund Administration Software
N.A.I.C.S.: 513210
Lars-Inge Berg *(Chm)*

ITEQ CORPORATION
No 17 Daluge Rd, Xinpu Township, Hsin-chu, 305, Taiwan
Tel.: (886) 35887888
Web Site: https://www.iteq.com.tw
Year Founded: 1997

INTERNATIONAL PUBLIC

6213—(TAI)
Rev.: $820,139,248
Assets: $1,091,586,996
Liabilities: $455,861,587
Net Worth: $635,725,408
Earnings: $22,127,145
Emp.: 2,659
Fiscal Year-end: 12/31/23
Fiberglass Mfr
N.A.I.C.S.: 327993
Dennis Chen *(Co-Chm)*

Subsidiaries:

ITEQ Corporation - Taiwan Factory (1)
22 Kung Yen 1st Rd Ping Chen Industry Zone, Ping Chen, Taoyuan, 324, Taiwan
Tel.: (886) 34191130
Web Site: http://www.iteq.com.tw
Sales Range: $125-149.9 Million
Emp.: 300
Wooden Laminates Mfr
N.A.I.C.S.: 321215

ITERA ASA
Nydalsveien 28, PO Box 4814, Nydalen, 0422, Oslo, Norway
Tel.: (47) 23007650
Web Site: https://itera.com
ITERA—(OSL)
Rev.: $67,969,703
Assets: $21,593,479
Liabilities: $17,026,510
Net Worth: $4,566,968
Earnings: $4,709,958
Emp.: 698
Fiscal Year-end: 12/31/22
Communications, Consulting & IT Services
N.A.I.C.S.: 541611
Morten Thorkildsen *(Chm)*

Subsidiaries:

Cicero Consulting AS (1)
Stortingsgata 6, 0161, Oslo, Norway
Tel.: (47) 23007650
Web Site: https://www.cicero.no
Sales Range: $25-49.9 Million
Emp.: 30
Banking & Financial Consulting Services
N.A.I.C.S.: 541618

Compendia AS (1)
Hetlandsgata 9, 4344, Bryne, Norway
Tel.: (47) 51770800
Web Site: https://www.compendia.no
Sales Range: $25-49.9 Million
Emp.: 33
Human Resource Consulting Services
N.A.I.C.S.: 541612
Oddvar Haland *(CEO)*

Itera Consulting AS (1)
Nydalsveien 28, Oslo, 422, Norway
Tel.: (47) 23007650
Web Site: http://www.itera.no
Sales Range: $25-49.9 Million
Emp.: 300
Banking Software Development Services
N.A.I.C.S.: 513210

Itera Consulting Group Denmark ApS (1)
Rentemestervej 2A, 2830, Virum, Denmark
Tel.: (45) 70136100
Web Site: http://www.itera.dk
Sales Range: $25-49.9 Million
Emp.: 20
Information Technology Consulting Solutions
N.A.I.C.S.: 541690

Itera Consulting Group Sweden AB (1)
Hollamdargatan 10, 11124, Stockholm, Sweden
Tel.: (46) 86949015
Web Site: http://www.iteraconsulting.se
Sales Range: $75-99.9 Million
Emp.: 30
Application Software Development Services
N.A.I.C.S.: 541511
Ulf Magnusson *(CEO)*

AND PRIVATE COMPANIES — ITM POWER PLC

Itera Gazette AS (1)
Nydalsveien 28, PO Box 4814, Nydalen, Oslo, 0422, Norway
Tel.: (47) 23179900
Web Site: http://www.iteragazette.no
Sales Range: $25-49.9 Million
Emp.: 30
Advertising Services
N.A.I.C.S.: 541810
Kristian Enger *(Gen Mgr)*

Itera Networks AB (1)
Hollandargatam 10, 164 40, Stockholm, Sweden
Tel.: (46) 856300800
Web Site: http://www.itera.se
Sales Range: $25-49.9 Million
Emp.: 50
Technology Consulting & Hosting Solutions
N.A.I.C.S.: 541690

Itera Networks AS (1)
Ulleval stadion, PO Box 3824, 0805, Oslo, Norway
Tel.: (47) 23008440
Web Site: http://www.networks.no
Sales Range: $25-49.9 Million
Emp.: 90
Data Processing & Consulting Services
N.A.I.C.S.: 518210

Itera Offshoring Services AS (1)
Sognsveien 77 B, Oslo, 0422, Norway
Tel.: (47) 23007650
Web Site: http://www.iteraconsulting.no
Sales Range: $25-49.9 Million
Emp.: 18
Offshore Consulting Services
N.A.I.C.S.: 541611
Arne Mjos *(CEO)*

Promis AS (1)
Stortingsgata 12, PO Box 438, 0161, Oslo, Norway
Tel.: (47) 91341555
Web Site: http://www.promis.no
Business Management Consulting Services
N.A.I.C.S.: 541618
Jorgen Petersen *(CEO)*

ITERUM THERAPEUTICS PLC
Fitzwilliam Court 1st Floor Leeson Close, Dublin, 2, Ireland
Tel.: (353) 16694820   IE
Web Site: https://www.iterumtx.com
Year Founded: 2015
ITRM—(NASDAQ)
Rev.: $503,000
Assets: $66,833,000
Liabilities: $38,834,000
Net Worth: $27,999,000
Earnings: ($44,434,000)
Emp.: 14
Fiscal Year-end: 12/31/22
Pharmaceutical Product Research & Development Services
N.A.I.C.S.: 541714
Corey N. Fishman *(Pres & CEO)*

ITESOFT S.A.
Parc d Andron Le Sequoia, 30470, Aimargues, France
Tel.: (33) 155919898
Web Site: http://www.itesoft.com
Year Founded: 1984
ITE—(EUR)
Rev.: $25,526,512
Assets: $45,390,837
Liabilities: $34,757,964
Net Worth: $10,632,874
Earnings: ($720,977)
Emp.: 186
Fiscal Year-end: 12/31/20
Automated Document Processing & Data Capture Solutions
N.A.I.C.S.: 513210
Didier Charpentier *(Founder & Pres)*

Subsidiaries:

ITESOFT Deutschland GmbH (1)
Graumannsweg 51, 22087, Hamburg, Germany
Tel.: (49) 4041929461

Data Processing & Transformation Services
N.A.I.C.S.: 518210

ITESOFT UK Ltd. (1)
Unit C5 Nib Block C Dukes Court Dukes Street, Woking, GU21 5BH, Surrey, United Kingdom
Tel.: (44) 1252741500
Web Site: http://www.itesoft.co.uk
Data Processing & Transformation Services
N.A.I.C.S.: 518210
Nick Dunnett *(Mng Dir)*

ITFOR INC.
12F Ichibancho Tokyu Bldg 21 Ichibancho, Chiyoda-ku, Tokyo, 102-0082, Japan
Tel.: (81) 352757841
Web Site: https://www.itfor.co.jp
Year Founded: 1972
4743—(TKS)
Rev.: $136,509,720
Assets: $158,613,560
Liabilities: $34,107,600
Net Worth: $124,505,960
Earnings: $18,309,700
Emp.: 592
Fiscal Year-end: 03/31/24
Information Technology Services
N.A.I.C.S.: 541519
Tsunenori Sato *(Pres, Pres, COO, COO & Dir-Rep)*

Subsidiaries:

AISEL Corporation (1)
Ueno Frontier Tower 12F 3-24-6 Ueno, Taito-ku, Tokyo, 110-0005, Japan
Tel.: (81) 35 652 5236
Web Site: http://www.aisel.ne.jp
Emp.: 155
Software Development Services
N.A.I.C.S.: 541511

CSD Co., Ltd. (1)
136-138 Austin Rd, Hong Kong, China (Hong Kong)
Tel.: (852) 26336278
Web Site: http://www.csd-foshan.com
Computer Peripherals Mfr
N.A.I.C.S.: 334118

ITH PHARMA LTD.
Unit 4 Premier Park Premier Park Road, London, NW10 7NZ, United Kingdom
Tel.: (44) 20 8838 8260
Web Site: http://www.ithpharma.com
Year Founded: 2008
Sales Range: $10-24.9 Million
Emp.: 120
Pharmaceutical Product Whslr
N.A.I.C.S.: 424210
Karen Hamling *(Mng Dir)*

ITI GROUP LTD.
Beustweg 12, 8032, Zurich, Switzerland
Tel.: (41) 44 258 8840
Web Site: http://www.itiholdings.com
Emerging Markets Brokerage Firm
N.A.I.C.S.: 523999
Wojciech Kostrzewa *(Pres & CEO)*

Subsidiaries:

URALSIB Securities Ltd. (1)
Level 33 Tower 42 25 Old Broad Street, London, EC2N 1HQ, United Kingdom
Tel.: (44) 20 7562 8010
Web Site: http://www.uralsib.com
Emp.: 20
Online Trading Services
N.A.I.C.S.: 524210
John Lewin *(CEO)*

ITI INDUSTRIAL INVESTMENTS (UK) LTD.
123 Pall Mall, London, SW1Y 5EA, United Kingdom
Tel.: (44) 7802 305579   UK
Investment Services

N.A.I.C.S.: 523999
Chris Heminway *(CEO)*

Subsidiaries:

Hephaestus Holdings Limited (1)
123 Pall Mall, London, SW1Y 5EA, United Kingdom   **(64.23%)**
Tel.: (44) 20 3416 3226
Web Site: http://www.hephaestus-holdings.com
Investment Services
N.A.I.C.S.: 523999
Chris Heminway *(CEO)*

ITI LTD
ITI Bhavan Doorvaninagar, Bengaluru, 560016, Karnataka, India
Tel.: (91) 8025614466
Web Site: http://www.itiltd-india.com
Year Founded: 1948
523610—(BOM)
Rev.: $197,650,635
Assets: $1,295,570,858
Liabilities: $971,474,363
Net Worth: $324,096,495
Earnings: ($49,119,525)
Emp.: 1,975
Fiscal Year-end: 03/31/23
Telecoms Products Mfr
N.A.I.C.S.: 517111
Rajiv Seth *(Gen Mgr-Plant-Mankapur)*

Subsidiaries:

ITI Limited - Bangalore Unit (1)
Dooravaninagar, Bengaluru, 560016, Karnataka, India
Tel.: (91) 8025651340
Web Site: https://www.itiltd.in
Sales Range: $400-449.9 Million
Emp.: 1,000
Microwave Equipment Mfr
N.A.I.C.S.: 335220

ITI Limited - Mankapur Unit (1)
Mankapur plant, Gonda, Mankapur, 271308, UP, India
Tel.: (91) 5265230202
Web Site: https://www.itiltd.in
Sales Range: $400-449.9 Million
Emp.: 1,500
Digital Switches Mfr
N.A.I.C.S.: 334419

ITI Limited - Naini Unit (1)
Naini Plant, Allahabad, 211010, UP, India
Tel.: (91) 5322687481
Web Site: https://www.itiltd.in
Telephone Instruments Mfr
N.A.I.C.S.: 334210

ITI Limited - Pallakad Unit (1)
Kanjikode West, Palakkad, 678623, Kerala, India
Tel.: (91) 4912566004
Web Site: https://www.itiltd.in
Sales Range: $200-249.9 Million
Emp.: 600
Switching Equipment Mfr
N.A.I.C.S.: 334210

ITIM GROUP PLC
2nd Floor Atlas House 173 Victoria Street, London, SW1E 5NH, United Kingdom
Tel.: (44) 2075987700   UK
Web Site: https://www.itim.com
Year Founded: 1993
ITIM—(AIM)
Rev.: $17,715,223
Assets: $25,146,428
Liabilities: $9,396,617
Net Worth: $15,749,811
Earnings: ($865,943)
Emp.: 174
Fiscal Year-end: 12/31/22
Software Development Services
N.A.I.C.S.: 541511

ITL HEALTH GROUP LIMITED
Level 3 10 Moore Street, Canberra, 2601, ACT, Australia
Tel.: (61) 390887991

Web Site: http://www.itlhealthgroup.com
Rev.: $16,673
Assets: $17,902,880
Liabilities: $6,157,286
Net Worth: $11,745,594
Earnings: $2,358,641
Fiscal Year-end: 06/30/18
Health Care & Medical Devices Stores & Mfr
N.A.I.C.S.: 621610
Stephanie Norrell *(Exec Dir)*

Subsidiaries:

ITL Asia Pacific Sdn. Bhd. (1)
2-14 Persiaran Perindustrian, Pengkalan 29A, Ipoh, 31500, Perak, Malaysia
Tel.: (60) 53217586
Web Site: http://www.itlcorporation.com
Sales Range: $50-74.9 Million
Emp.: 200
Medical Devices Design & Mfr
N.A.I.C.S.: 339112
William Mobbs *(Mng Dir)*

ITL Design and Manufacturing Pty Limited (1)
Ste 111 Natl Innovation Ctr Australian Tech Park, 4 Cornwallis St Eveleigh, Sydney, 2015, NSW, Australia
Tel.: (61) 2 83944800
Medical Devices Design & Mfr
N.A.I.C.S.: 339112

ITL North America Inc. (1)
1925 Isaac Newton Sq E Ste 480, Reston, VA 20190
Tel.: (703) 435-6700
Web Site: http://www.itl-limited.com
Emp.: 4
Medical Device Mfr
N.A.I.C.S.: 334510
Michele Loudermilk *(Dir-Admin & Logistics)*

ITL INDUSTRIES LTD.
111 Sector-B Sanwer Road, Industrial Area, Indore, 452 015, MP, India
Tel.: (91) 7317104400
Web Site: https://www.itl.co.in
522183—(BOM)
Rev.: $19,998,752
Assets: $14,963,116
Liabilities: $6,407,938
Net Worth: $8,555,178
Earnings: $1,053,084
Emp.: 271
Fiscal Year-end: 03/31/23
Industrial Machinery Mfr
N.A.I.C.S.: 333248
Rajendra Singh Jain *(Co-Mng Dir)*

ITM ENTREPRISES S.A.
1 Allee Des Mousquetaires Parc De Treville, 91078, Bondoufle, France
Tel.: (33) 169641072   FR
Web Site: http://www.intermarche.com
Year Founded: 1969
Sales Range: $25-49.9 Billion
Emp.: 112,000
Supermarkets, Chain
N.A.I.C.S.: 445110
Philippe Lebreton *(CEO)*

ITM INSTRUMENTS, INC.
16975 Leslie St, Newmarket, L3Y 9A1, ON, Canada
Tel.: (514) 457-7280
Web Site: http://www.itm.com
Year Founded: 1983
Sales Range: $25-49.9 Million
Emp.: 50
Measuring & Controlling Device Mfr
N.A.I.C.S.: 334519
David Reed *(Pres)*

ITM POWER PLC
2 Bessemer Park, Sheffield, S9 1DZ, United Kingdom
Tel.: (44) 1142445111   UK

ITM POWER PLC

ITM Power Plc—(Continued)
Web Site: https://www.itm-power.com
Year Founded: 2004
ITM—(AIM)
Rev.: $7,382,056
Assets: $600,752,504
Liabilities: $82,894,064
Net Worth: $517,858,440
Earnings: ($61,206,816)
Fiscal Year-end: 04/30/22
Energy Storage & Fuel Dispensing Systems Mfr
N.A.I.C.S.: 333310
Graham Cooley *(CEO)*

Subsidiaries:

ITM Power (Research) Ltd (1)
22 Atlas Way, Sheffield, S4 7QQ, United Kingdom
Tel.: (44) 1142445111
Web Site: http://www.itm-power.com
Emp.: 50
Scientific Research & Development Services
N.A.I.C.S.: 541690

ITM Power (Trading) Limited (1)
22 Atlas Way, Sheffield, S4 7QQ, United Kingdom
Tel.: (44) 114 244 5111
Web Site: http://www.itm-power.com
Emp.: 7
Energy Storage System Distr
N.A.I.C.S.: 423830

ITM Power GmbH (1)
Am Muhlgraben 6, 35410, Hungen, Germany
Tel.: (49) 64025197325
Web Site: http://www.itm-power.de
Sales Range: $25-49.9 Million
Emp.: 2
Hydrogen Compressor System Mfr
N.A.I.C.S.: 333248
Calum McConnell *(Mng Dir)*

ITMAX SYSTEM BERHAD

30-3 & 30-G Jalan Radin Bagus 3, Seri Petaling, 57000, Kuala Lumpur, Malaysia
Tel.: (60) 390548333
Web Site: https://www.itmax.com.my
Year Founded: 2001
ITMAX—(KLS)
Rev.: $32,581,846
Assets: $95,339,792
Liabilities: $20,458,642
Net Worth: $74,881,150
Earnings: $13,756,204
Emp.: 172
Fiscal Year-end: 12/31/23
Information Technology Services
N.A.I.C.S.: 541512

ITO EN LTD

3-chome-47-10 Honmachi, Shibuya, Tokyo, 151-8550, Japan
Tel.: (81) 353717111
Web Site: https://www.itoen.co.jp
2593—(TKS)
Rev.: $3,000,272,390
Assets: $2,339,226,120
Liabilities: $1,128,168,360
Net Worth: $1,211,057,760
Earnings: $103,446,500
Emp.: 8,028
Fiscal Year-end: 04/30/24
Beverages Mfr
N.A.I.C.S.: 311421
Daisuke Honjo *(Pres & Exec Officer)*

Subsidiaries:

Distant Lands Trading Co. (1)
801 Houser Way N, Renton, WA 98057
Web Site: https://www.dlcoffee.com
Emp.: 160
Coffee Mfr
N.A.I.C.S.: 311920

ITO EN (Hawaii) LLC (1)
125 Puuhale Rd, Honolulu, HI 96819

Tel.: (808) 847-4477
Web Site: https://itoen-usa.com
Beverage Product Mfr & Distr
N.A.I.C.S.: 312111

ITO EN (North America) INC. (1)
1320 Greenway Dr Ste 700, Irving, NY 75038
Tel.: (718) 250-4000
Web Site: https://itoen.com
Beverages Mfr
N.A.I.C.S.: 312111
Yosuke Honjo *(Pres & CEO)*

ITO EN KANSAI-CHAGYO, LTD. (1)
1-4 Yasakadai 3-chome, Suma-ku, Kobe, 654-0161, Hyogo, Japan
Tel.: (81) 787942811
Web Site: https://www.itoen.co.jp
Green & Barley Tea Mfr
N.A.I.C.S.: 311920

ITO EN SANGYO, LTD. (1)
3272-1 Sakabe Makinohara-shi, Shizuoka, 421-0412, Japan
Tel.: (81) 548290811
Beverages Mfr
N.A.I.C.S.: 424820

ITOEN-ITOCHU MINERAL WATERS CO., LTD. (1)
22 Tansu-cho, Shinjuku-ku, Tokyo, 162-0833, Japan
Tel.: (81) 368665551
Sales Range: $25-49.9 Million
Mineral Water Mfr
N.A.I.C.S.: 312112

Ito En Australia Pty Limited (1)
42 Buckler Rd North, Wangaratta, 3678, VIC, Australia
Tel.: (61) 357213999
Web Site: https://www.itoen.com.au
Sales Range: $25-49.9 Million
Emp.: 11
Green Tea Mfr
N.A.I.C.S.: 311920

PT ITO EN Ultrajaya Wholesale (1)
Talavera Office Park Talavera Suite 21st Floor, Jl Letjen TB Simatupang Kav 22-26 Cilandak, Jakarta Selatan, 12430, Indonesia
Tel.: (62) 2175925236
Web Site: https://www.itoen-ultrajaya.co.id
Beverage Product Distr
N.A.I.C.S.: 424490

Tullys Coffee Japan Co., Ltd. (1)
22 Tansumachi, Shinjuku-ku, Tokyo, 162-0833, Japan
Tel.: (81) 33268828
Web Site: http://www.tullys.co.jp
Sales Range: $100-124.9 Million
Emp.: 991
Coffee Mfr
N.A.I.C.S.: 311920
Yoshio Kobayashi *(Pres)*

ITO YOGYO CO., LTD.

6-3-14 Nakatsu, Kita-ku, Osaka, 531-0071, Japan
Tel.: (81) 647998853
Web Site: https://www.itoyogyo.co.jp
Year Founded: 1950
5287—(TKS)
Sales Range: $10-24.9 Million
Emp.: 116
Concrete Product Mfr & Distr
N.A.I.C.S.: 327390
Hiroshi Hatanaka *(CEO)*

ITOCHU CORPORATION

5-1 Kita-Aoyama 2-chome, Minato-ku, Tokyo, 107-8077, Japan
Tel.: (81) 334972121   JP
Web Site: https://www.itochu.co.jp
Year Founded: 1858
IOC—(DEU)
Rev.: $92,737,705,100
Assets: $95,776,923,610
Liabilities: $56,169,003,800
Net Worth: $39,607,919,810
Earnings: $5,299,699,700
Emp.: 4,190
Fiscal Year-end: 03/31/24

Textile, Machinery, Metals, Grain, Provisions, Forest Products, General Merchandise, Chemical & Energy Products Import & Export Services
N.A.I.C.S.: 522299
Fumihiko Kobayashi *(Sr Mng Exec Officer)*

Subsidiaries:

A2 Healthcare Corporation (1)
20th Floor Reception Sumitomo Fudosan Korakuen Bldg 1-4-1, Koishikawa Bunkyo-ku, Tokyo, 112-0002, Japan
Tel.: (81) 33 830 1122
Web Site: https://www.a2healthcare.com
Emp.: 1,120
Pharmaceuticals Product Mfr
N.A.I.C.S.: 325412
Tadashi Katori *(Pres & CEO)*

ACRONET Corporation (1)
Sumitomo Fudosan Korakuen Building 1-4-1 Koishikawa, Bunkyo-ku, Tokyo, 112-0002, Japan
Tel.: (81) 3 3830 1122
Web Site: http://www.acronet.jp
Sales Range: $75-99.9 Million
Emp.: 481
Medical Software Development Services
N.A.I.C.S.: 541511
Koichi Kato *(Pres & CEO)*

AD Investment Management Co., Ltd. (1)
1-105 Kanda Jimbocho Mitsui Building 17F, Chiyoda-ku, Tokyo, 101-0051, Japan
Tel.: (81) 3 3518 0480
Web Site: http://www.adim.co.jp
Sales Range: $50-74.9 Million
Emp.: 60
Asset Management Services
N.A.I.C.S.: 523940

BMI HOLDINGS CO., LTD. (1)
8-4 Kudan-Minami 2-chome, Chiyoda-ku, Tokyo, 102-0094, Japan
Tel.: (81) 3 3556 3533
Investment Holding Services
N.A.I.C.S.: 523999

Beijing Itochu-Huatang Comprehensive Processing Co., Ltd. (1)
Room 905 9th Floor Building 3 China Central Place No 77 Jianguo Road, Chaoyang District, Beijing, 100025, China
Tel.: (86) 1059947788
Web Site: http://www.mybic.cn
Food Products Distr
N.A.I.C.S.: 424490

Beijing Pacific Logistics Co., Ltd. (1)
No 318 Zhangjiadian Shibalidian, Chaoyang District, Beijing, 100023, China
Tel.: (86) 10 8730 5971
Web Site: http://www.itochu.com.cn
Logistics Consulting Services
N.A.I.C.S.: 541614

C. I. MATEX Corporation (1)
1-18-1 Kyobashi Yaesu Takaracho Bldg 4f, Chuo-ku, Tokyo, 104-0031, Japan
Tel.: (81) 351593750
Emp.: 100
Farm Supplies Whslr
N.A.I.C.S.: 424910
Maru Yayusuko *(Pres)*

C.I. ITOCHU Colombia S.A. (1)
Calle 72 No 10-07 Piso 12 Edificio Liberty Seguros, Bogota, Colombia
Tel.: (57) 1 310 0788
Web Site: http://www.itochu.com.co
Industrial Machinery & Equipment Whslr
N.A.I.C.S.: 423830

C.I. Takiron Corporation (1)
North Gate Building 3-1-3 Umeda, Kita-ku, Osaka, 530-0001, Japan (90.75%)
Tel.: (81) 664533700
Web Site: https://www.takiron-ci.co.jp
Rev.: $1,373,940,480
Assets: $1,423,550,480
Liabilities: $532,458,080
Net Worth: $891,092,400
Earnings: $64,468,800
Emp.: 3,300
Fiscal Year-end: 03/31/2022
Plastics, Metals & Adhesives Mfr

INTERNATIONAL PUBLIC

N.A.I.C.S.: 325211
Yosuke Minamitani *(Chm & CEO)*

Subsidiary (Domestic):

BonPack Co., Ltd. (2)
2-2-3 Yanagibashi Suzuwa Building 4F, Taito-ku, Tokyo, 111-0052, Japan
Tel.: (81) 356875431
Web Site: http://www.bonpk.com
Industrial Machinery Mfr & Distr
N.A.I.C.S.: 333248

Subsidiary (US):

Bonset America Corporation (2)
6107 Corporate Park Dr, Browns Summit, NC 27214
Tel.: (336) 375-0234
Web Site: https://www.bonset.com
Plastic Packaging Film Mfr
N.A.I.C.S.: 326112

Subsidiary (Non-US):

Bonset Latin America S.A. (2)
Camino el Gallo Km 29 100 Route 101 White Clays, Canelones, Uruguay
Tel.: (598) 22889033
Web Site: https://www.bonset.com
Plastic Packaging Film Mfr
N.A.I.C.S.: 326112

Subsidiary (Domestic):

C.I. Takiron Corporation - Aboshi Plant (2)
1455 Kariya Mitsu-cho, Tatsuno, 671-1393, Hyogo, Japan
Tel.: (81) 793221031
Plastics Product Mfr
N.A.I.C.S.: 326199

Plant (Domestic):

C.I. Takiron Corporation - Hiratsuka Factory (2)
2-1 Tamura 3-Chome, Hiratsuka, 254-0013, Kanagawa, Japan
Tel.: (81) 463 55 3050
Web Site: http://www.takiron-ci.co.jp
Plastic Tank Mfr
N.A.I.C.S.: 326122

Subsidiary (Domestic):

C.I. Takiron Corporation - Ibogawa Plant (2)
1228-1 Baba Ibogawa-cho, Tatsuno, 671-1665, Hyogo, Japan
Tel.: (81) 791765556
Plastics Product Mfr
N.A.I.C.S.: 326199

Plant (Domestic):

C.I. Takiron Corporation - Okayama Factory (2)
20-10 Kamiichi, Niimi, 718-0005, Okayama, Japan
Tel.: (81) 867 71 0221
Web Site: http://www.takiron-ci.co.jp
Plastic Tank Mfr
N.A.I.C.S.: 326122

C.I. Takiron Corporation - Shiga Factory (2)
3-1 Maruyama 3-Chome, Konan, 520-3185, Shiga, Japan
Tel.: (81) 748773170
Web Site: http://www.takiron-ci.co.jp
Plastic Tank Mfr
N.A.I.C.S.: 326122
Hisato Abe *(Gen Mgr)*

C.I. Takiron Corporation - Tochigi Factory (2)
2606 Akabane Ichikai-machi, Haga-gun, Tochigi, 321-3426, Japan
Tel.: (81) 285 68 2111
Web Site: http://www.takiron-ci.co.jp
Plastic Tank Mfr
N.A.I.C.S.: 326122

Subsidiary (Domestic):

C.I. Takiron Logistics Co., Ltd. (2)
2-15-1 Konan Shinagawa Intercity Building A, Minato-ku, Tokyo, 108-6031, Japan
Tel.: (81) 367114553
Logistic Services

AND PRIVATE COMPANIES

ITOCHU CORPORATION

CIK NanoTek Corporation (2)
Shinagawa Intercity Tower A 2-15-1 Konan, Minato-ku, Tokyo, 108-6031, Japan (100%)
Tel.: (81) 367114512
Web Site: https://www.cik-nanotek.co.jp
Metallic Oxide Mfr & Whslr
N.A.I.C.S.: 325180
Akihito Funao *(Pres)*

Dailite Co., Ltd. (2)
North Gate Building 3-1-3 Umeda, Kita-Ku, Osaka, 530-0001, Japan
Tel.: (81) 664533700
Plastic Product Mfr & Distr
N.A.I.C.S.: 326199

Dainippon Plastics Co. Ltd. (2)
Sakaisuji Awaji Cho Bldg 1 3, Awajicyo 2 Chome Chuo ku, Osaka, 541 0047, Japan
Tel.: (81) 662033135
Plastics Product Mfr
N.A.I.C.S.: 326199

Daipla Corporation (2)
3-1-3-1 Umeda North Gate Building 16th Floor, Kita-ku, Osaka, Japan
Tel.: (81) 664539270
Web Site: http://www.daipla.co.jp
Plastics Product Mfr
N.A.I.C.S.: 326199

Daipla Wintes Co., Ltd. (2)
5th Floor OS Building 4-247 Sakuragicho, Omiya-ku, Saitama, 330-0854, Japan
Tel.: (81) 486454171
Web Site: http://www.wintes.co.jp
Metal Products Mfr
N.A.I.C.S.: 332999

Hokkaido Sanplus Co., Ltd. (2)
Hokkaido Shinkonishi 1-chome 706-9, Ishikari, 061-3241, Japan
Tel.: (81) 133722911
Web Site: http://www.hsanplus.jp
Industrial Machinery Mfr
N.A.I.C.S.: 333248

Subsidiary (Non-US):

PT. TAKIRON INDONESIA (2)
Jalan Kabupaten Desa Cangkringmalang Kecamatan Beji Kabupaten, Pasuruan, Jawa Timur, Indonesia
Tel.: (62) 34365906061
Emp.: 67
Fabricated Metal Products Mfr
N.A.I.C.S.: 332999
Ken Tsurumoto *(Pres)*

Subsidiary (Domestic):

Rontec Co., Ltd. (2)
2-14-5 Showamachi Kita-Ku, Tokyo, 114-0011, Japan
Tel.: (81) 359012180
Plastic Product Mfr & Distr
N.A.I.C.S.: 326199

Sanwa Signworks Co., Ltd. (2)
3-1-3 Umeda, Kita-ku, Osaka, 530-0001, Japan
Tel.: (81) 664533171
Web Site: https://www.sanwa-signworks.co.jp
Emp.: 146
Construction Materials Distr
N.A.I.C.S.: 423320

Subsidiary (Non-US):

Shanghai C. I. Kasei Trading Company Ltd. (2)
2503B Ruijin Mansion No 205 Maoming South Road, Huangpu District, Shanghai, China
Tel.: (86) 2164671010
Web Site: https://www.takiron-ci.co.jp
Construction Materials Distr
N.A.I.C.S.: 423320

Shanghai CIK Electronics Co., Ltd. (2)
No 1438 Minta Road, Songjiang District, Shanghai, 201617, China
Tel.: (86) 2157845505
Motor & Electronic Device Mfr & Whslr
N.A.I.C.S.: 334419

Shanghai Sanplus Plastic Co., Ltd. (2)
NO 585 East Banqiao RD, Jinshan, Shanghai, 201508, China
Tel.: (86) 2157241808
Construction Materials Distr
N.A.I.C.S.: 423320

Shanghai Takiron Plastics Co., Ltd. (2)
No 1138 Huazhi Road Huaxin Town, Shanghai, China
Tel.: (86) 21 6979 1048
Web Site: http://www.takiron-sh.com.cn
Plastics Product Mfr
N.A.I.C.S.: 326199

Subsidiary (Domestic):

Takiron Engineering Co., Ltd. (2)
2-15-1 Konan, Minato-Ku, Tokyo, 108-6031, Japan
Tel.: (81) 368640330
Plastic Product Mfr & Distr
N.A.I.C.S.: 326199
Kaoru Tateshi *(Gen Mgr)*

Takiron KC Home Improvement Co., Ltd. (2)
2-15-1 Konan Shinagawa Intercity Building A, Minato-ku, Tokyo, 108-6030, Japan
Tel.: (81) 357157700
Construction Materials Distr
N.A.I.C.S.: 423320

Takiron Matex Co., Ltd. (2)
Shinagawa Intercity Building A 15th Floor 2-15-1 Konan, Minato-ku, Tokyo, 108-6015, Japan
Tel.: (81) 357818150
Web Site: https://www.t-matex.co.jp
Emp.: 117
Construction Materials Distr
N.A.I.C.S.: 423320

Takiron Polymer Co., Ltd. (2)
437-1 Imabuku Yame, Fukuoka, 834-0061, Japan
Tel.: (81) 943249151
Plastic Product Mfr & Distr
N.A.I.C.S.: 326199
Kawame Yoshimitsu *(Pres)*

Takiron Protech Co., Ltd. (2)
3-7-1 Higashiokino Higashiomi, Shiga, 527-0033, Japan
Tel.: (81) 748234844
Plastic Product Mfr & Distr
N.A.I.C.S.: 326199

Takiron-Rowland Limited (2)
1455 Mitsucho-kariya, Tatsuno, 671-1393, Hyogo, Japan
Tel.: (81) 793222556
Web Site: https://www.takiron-rowland.co.jp
Resin Plate Mfr
N.A.I.C.S.: 325211

Yokobi Co., Ltd. (2)
20-6 Kita 2 Johigashi, Chuo-ku, Sapporo, 060-0032, Japan
Tel.: (81) 112310111
Web Site: http://www.yokobi.co.jp
Agricultural Material Distr
N.A.I.C.S.: 424590

CAPLAN Corporation (1)
2-6-2 Otemachi, Chiyoda-ku, Tokyo, 100-0004, Japan
Tel.: (81) 367785550
Web Site: http://www.caplan.jp
Sales Range: $150-199.9 Million
Emp.: 938
Human Resource Consulting Services
N.A.I.C.S.: 541612
Masanori Ishida *(Pres & CEO)*

CGB Enterprises Inc. (1)
1127 Hwy 190 E Service Rd, Covington, LA 70433
Tel.: (985) 867-3500
Web Site: https://www.cgb.com
Sales Range: $50-74.9 Million
Emp.: 150
Grain Handling, Storage & Export Services
N.A.I.C.S.: 424510
Kevin D. Adams *(Pres & CEO)*

Subsidiary (Domestic):

CGB Diversified Services, Inc. (2)
1608 B W Lafayette Ave, Jacksonville, IL 62650
Tel.: (217) 479-6000
Web Site: http://www.diversifiedservices.com
Insurance Agencies & Brokerages
N.A.I.C.S.: 524210

Consolidated Grain & Barge Co. (2)
1127 Highway 190 East Service Rd, Covington, LA 70433
Tel.: (985) 867-3500
Web Site: https://www.cgbgrain.com
Agricultural Products Distr & Transporation & Financial Services
N.A.I.C.S.: 488310
Kevin Adams *(Pres & CEO)*

Subsidiary (Domestic):

Colusa Elevator Company (3)
2531 N County Rd 1750, Colusa, IL 62329-0026
Tel.: (217) 755-4221
Web Site: http://www.colusaelevator.com
Sales Range: $10-24.9 Million
Emp.: 12
Grain Storage & Drying Services
N.A.I.C.S.: 493130
Dale Griffiths *(Gen Mgr)*

Plant (Domestic):

Colusa Elevator Company (4)
13 Broadway St, Nauvoo, IL 62354
Tel.: (217) 453-2216
Web Site: http://www.colusaelevator.com
Grain Storage & Drying
N.A.I.C.S.: 493130
Gene McEntee *(Office Mgr)*

Subsidiary (Domestic):

River Bend Transport Company Inc. (2)
300 3 Rivers Pkwy, North Bend, OH 45052-9638
Tel.: (513) 941-1200
Web Site: http://www.riverbendtransport.com
Sales Range: $50-74.9 Million
Emp.: 10
Local & Long Distance Trucking; Freight Forwarding Services
N.A.I.C.S.: 484121
Gregory Beck *(VP)*

CI Shopping Service Co., Ltd. (1)
2-5-1 Kita Aoyama, Minato-ku, Tokyo, 107-8571, Japan
Tel.: (81) 33 497 7943
Web Site: https://www.ciss.co.jp
Apparel Whslr
N.A.I.C.S.: 424350

CI TEXTILE SERVICE CO., LTD. (1)
3-1-3 Umeda inside the North Gate Building, Kita-ku, Osaka, 530-0001, Japan
Tel.: (81) 67 638 2575
Web Site: https://www.citex.co.jp
Emp.: 270
Apparel Distr
N.A.I.C.S.: 424350
Hitoshi Okamoto *(Pres-CI Textile & COO-Apparel Div 1)*

CIECO Exploration and Production (Australia) Pty Limited (1)
Grosvenor Pl L 29 225 George St, Sydney, 2000, NSW, Australia
Tel.: (61) 2 9239 1568
Oil & Gas Exploration Services
N.A.I.C.S.: 213112

CIECO North Sea Ltd. (1)
2-5-1 Kitaaoyama Itochu Bldg 12f, Minato-ku, Tokyo, 107-0061, Japan
Tel.: (81) 334978113
Oil & Gas Exploration Services
N.A.I.C.S.: 213112

CIMCO Co., Ltd. (1)
2-35-13 Kameido, Koto-ku, Tokyo, 136-0071, Japan
Tel.: (81) 3 5626 2311
Web Site: http://www.cimco.co.jp
Livestock Farming Services
N.A.I.C.S.: 112990
Suzuki Tamotsu *(Pres)*

CIPA Lumber Co. Ltd. (1)
797 Carlisle Rd, Annacis Island, Delta, V3M 5P4, BC, Canada
Tel.: (604) 523-2250
Veneer Mfr
N.A.I.C.S.: 321211

CISD (ASIA) CO.,LTD. (1)
28th Floor United Centre 95 Queensway, Admiralty, Central, China (Hong Kong)
Tel.: (852) 2 861 9750
Web Site: https://www.cisd.com.hk
Sales Range: $25-49.9 Million
Emp.: 55
Information Technology Consulting Services
N.A.I.C.S.: 541512
Manabu Igarashi *(Chm)*

Century Medical, Inc. (1)
Gate City Osaki East Tower 22F 1-11-2 Osaki, Shinagawa-ku, Tokyo, 141-8588, Japan
Tel.: (81) 33 491 0161
Web Site: https://www.cmi.co.jp
Emp.: 323
Medical Device Whslr
N.A.I.C.S.: 423450
Takahiko Motani *(Pres & CEO)*

Chemical Logitec Co., Ltd. (1)
16th Floor ITOCHU Building5-1 Kita-Aoyama 2-chome, Minato-ku, Tokyo, 107-0061, Japan
Tel.: (81) 33 497 8020
Web Site: https://tkclt.secure.idchosting.jp
Sales Range: $25-49.9 Million
Emp.: 72
Chemical Products Warehousing & Transportation Services
N.A.I.C.S.: 493190

Cosmos Services (Korea) Co., Ltd. (1)
801 Korean Re Building 80 Susong-dong, Jongno-gu, Seoul, Korea (South)
Tel.: (82) 2 732 2348
General Insurance Services
N.A.I.C.S.: 524210

Cosmos Services Co., Ltd. (1)
28/F United Centre 95 Queensway, Hong Kong, China (Hong Kong)
Tel.: (852) 2 529 8110
Web Site: https://www.cosmos-services.com.hk
Sales Range: $100-124.9 Million
Emp.: 150
General Insurance Services
N.A.I.C.S.: 524210
Kazuhiro Yamamoto *(Pres & Mng Dir)*

DAIICHI TOGYO CO., LTD. (1)
17371 Hichiya, Hyuga, 883-0062, Miyazaki, Japan
Tel.: (81) 982 52 4162
Web Site: http://www.daiichi-togyo.co.jp
Sugar Mfr & Whslr
N.A.I.C.S.: 311313

Daishin Plywood Co., Ltd. (1)
167 Nakagido, Higashi-ku, Niigata, 950-0886, Japan
Tel.: (81) 25 273 4456
Web Site: http://www.daishin-ply.co.jp
Emp.: 197
Plywood Mfr
N.A.I.C.S.: 321211

Descente Ltd. (1)
Web Site: http://www.descente.co.jp
Rev.: $1,054,074,560
Assets: $1,126,510,000
Liabilities: $287,660,560
Net Worth: $838,849,440
Earnings: $60,296,720
Emp.: 3,452
Fiscal Year-end: 03/31/2022
Active Sportswear & Sports Related Products Mfr & Distr
N.A.I.C.S.: 315250
Shuichi Koseki *(Pres)*

Subsidiary (Non-US):

Beijing Descente Co., Ltd. (2)
No 1 Hongda Road North Xihuan Road, Changping Town Changping District, Beijing, 102200, China
Tel.: (86) 1060713541
Sales Range: $25-49.9 Million
Emp.: 175
General Sportswear Mfr & Sales

3835

ITOCHU CORPORATION

ITOCHU Corporation—(Continued)
N.A.I.C.S.: 315250

Subsidiary (Domestic):

Ben-General Corporation (2)
1-11-3 Dogashiba, Tennoji-ku, Osaka, 543-8921, Japan
Tel.: (81) 667346430
Sportswear Product Distr
N.A.I.C.S.: 423910

Descente Apparel Ltd. (2)
Maruito Namba Building 13F 1-2-3 Minatomachi, Naniwa-ku, Osaka, 556-0017, Japan **(100%)**
Tel.: (81) 666334201
Web Site: http://www.descente.co.jp
Sales Range: $200-249.9 Million
Emp.: 600
Mfr of General Sportswear
N.A.I.C.S.: 458110

Subsidiary (Non-US):

Descente Korea, Ltd. (2)
32nd Floor Lotte world Tower 300 Olympic-RO, Songpa-gu, Seoul, 135080, Korea (South) **(100%)**
Tel.: (82) 805655600
Web Site: https://shop.descentekorea.co.kr
Sales Range: $25-49.9 Million
Emp.: 40
Sales of Descente Sportswear
N.A.I.C.S.: 424350

Affiliate (US):

Descente North America, Inc. (2)
334 N Marshall Way, Layton, UT 84041-7346 **(41%)**
Tel.: (801) 317-0017
Web Site: http://www.descente.com
Sales Range: $25-49.9 Million
Emp.: 12
Ski Apparel Mfr & Distr
N.A.I.C.S.: 424350

Subsidiary (Non-US):

Descente North America, Inc. (2)
1445 Charles St, Vancouver, V5L2S7, BC, Canada **(100%)**
Tel.: (604) 254-9100
Web Site: http://www.descente.net
Sales Range: $25-49.9 Million
Emp.: 6
Whslr of Descente Sportswear
N.A.I.C.S.: 424350

Hong Kong Descente Trading Ltd. (2)
Shop G62 and 162 G/F and L1 Mira Place Two 118-130 Nathan Road, Tsim Sha Tsui, Kowloon, China (Hong Kong)
Tel.: (852) 34211626
Web Site: http://www.descente.com.hk
Sales Range: $25-49.9 Million
Emp.: 30
Sportswear Sales
N.A.I.C.S.: 424350
Kenneth Lee (Pres)

Shanghai Descente Commercial Co., Ltd. (2)
Unit 1001 Raffles City Changing Office Tower 1 NO 1133 Changning Road, Shanghai, 200051, China
Tel.: (86) 2162473399
Web Site: http://www.shanghai-descente.com.cn
Sportswear Product Distr
N.A.I.C.S.: 423910

Dole International Holdings, Inc. (1)
Itochu Bldng 9th Fl 5-1 Kita Ayoma 2-Chome Minatoku-Ku, Chiyoda-ku, Tokyo, 107-8077, Japan **(100%)**
Tel.: (81) 334978150
Holding Company
N.A.I.C.S.: 551112
Yutaka Yamamura (Exec VP-Singapore)

Subsidiary (Domestic):

Dole Japan, Inc. (2)
6-2 Sanbancho, Chiyoda-ku, Tokyo, 102-0075, Japan **(100%)**
Tel.: (81) 332371451
Web Site: https://www.dole.co.jp
Sales Range: $75-99.9 Million
Emp.: 187
Production, Processing & Sale of Fresh Fruits & Vegetables
N.A.I.C.S.: 424480

Subsidiary (Non-US):

Dole Lanka (Private) Limited (2)
No 252 Nawala Road, Nawala, Rajagirya, Sri Lanka
Tel.: (94) 772 961 678
Bananas & Tropical Fruit Production
N.A.I.C.S.: 111339

Subsidiary (US):

Dole Packaged Foods, LLC (2)
3059 Towngate Rd Ste 400, Westlake Village, CA 91361
Tel.: (209) 358-5643
Web Site: https://dolesunshine.com
Packaged Fresh & Frozen Fruit Products
N.A.I.C.S.: 311411
Pier Luigi Sigismondi (Pres)

Subsidiary (Non-US):

Dole Packaged Foods Europe SAS (3)
36 rue de Chateaudun, 75009, Paris, France
Tel.: (33) 1 55 27 10 60
Web Site: http://www.doleeurope.com
Sales Range: $25-49.9 Million
Emp.: 25
Fresh Produce Import & Distr
N.A.I.C.S.: 424480
Marc Deschrijver (Gen Mgr)

Division (Domestic):

Dole Packaged Frozen Foods (3)
7916 W Bellevue Rd, Atwater, CA 95301-2655
Tel.: (209) 358-5643
Web Site: http://www.dole.com
Frozen Fruit & Vegetables Producer & Retailer
N.A.I.C.S.: 311411
Jon Rodacy (VP & Gen Mgr)

Subsidiary (Non-US):

Dole Philippines, Inc. (2)
5 F 6750 Office Tower Ayala Avenue, Makati, 1200, Philippines
Tel.: (63) 2 810 2601
Pineapple Farming & Processing
N.A.I.C.S.: 111320
Richard Toman (Pres)

Dole Thailand Ltd. (2)
Panjathani Tower 10th fl 127/11 Nonsee rd Chongnonsee, Yannawa, Bangkok, 10120, Thailand **(64%)**
Tel.: (66) 2686 7676
Web Site: http://www.dole.co.th
Emp.: 7,000
Fruit Producer
N.A.I.C.S.: 111320

Edwin Co., Ltd. (1)
2nd Floor of IK Building 2-24-9, Kamiosaki Shinagawa-ku, Tokyo, 141-8255, Japan
Tel.: (81) 120008503
Web Site: http://edwin.co.jp
Jeans Mfr & Whslr
N.A.I.C.S.: 315210

Family Corporation Inc. (2)
174-2 Nakamura Inamicho, Kako-gun, Hyogo, 675-1122, Japan
Tel.: (81) 794928998
Food Products Distr
N.A.I.C.S.: 424490

FamilyMart Co., Ltd. (1)
msb Tamachi-Tamachi Station Tower S 9F 3-1-21 Shibaura, Minato-ku, Tokyo, 108-0023, Japan **(65.71%)**
Tel.: (81) 364367600
Web Site: https://www.family.co.jp
Rev: $5,591,596,440
Assets: $12,431,380,020
Liabilities: $7,088,362,800
Net Worth: $5,343,017,220
Earnings: $411,052,200
Emp.: 15,139
Fiscal Year-end: 02/28/2019
Convenience Store Operator
N.A.I.C.S.: 445131
Toshio Kato (Exec Officer, Exec Officer, VP & VP)

Subsidiary (US):

FAMIMA CORPORATION (2)
20000 Mariner Ave Ste 100, Torrance, CA 90503-7140
Tel.: (310) 214-1001
Web Site: http://www.familymart-usa.com
Convenience Stores Operating Services
N.A.I.C.S.: 445123
Ryan Umemoto (Area Mgr-Store Dev)

Subsidiary (Domestic):

FamilyMart Co., Ltd. (2)
3-1-21 Shibaura msb Tamachi Tamachi Station Tower S 9th floor, Minato-ku, Tokyo, 108-0023, Japan
Tel.: (81) 120079188
Web Site: http://www.family.co.jp
Emp.: 13,070
Convenience Store Operator
N.A.I.C.S.: 445131
Yong Zhongshan (Chm)

Kanemi Co., Ltd. (2)
3-107 Tokushige, Midori-ku, Nagoya, 458-0815, Aichi, Japan **(45.87%)**
Tel.: (81) 528796111
Web Site: https://www.kanemi-foods.co.jp
Rev.: $746,833,920
Assets: $284,357,160
Liabilities: $73,811,820
Net Worth: $210,545,340
Earnings: $101,843,460
Emp.: 1,286
Fiscal Year-end: 02/28/2019
Boxed Meals Mfr
N.A.I.C.S.: 311991
Masaya Terayama (Pres & CEO)

Subsidiary (Non-US):

Siam FamilyMart Co., Ltd. (2)
Vanit Bldg II 11th Fl 1126/2 New Petchburi Rd, Makkasan Rajchtewi, Bangkok, 10400, Thailand
Tel.: (66) 22541632
Web Site: http://www.familymart.co.th
Sales Range: $400-449.9 Million
Emp.: 1,912
Convenience Store Operator
N.A.I.C.S.: 445131

Subsidiary (Domestic):

famima.com Co., Ltd. (2)
Sunshine 60 3-1-1 Higashi Ikebukuro, Toshima-ku, Tokyo, 170-6018, Japan
Tel.: (81) 359583812
Web Site: http://www.famima.com
Sales Range: $25-49.9 Million
Emp.: 60
Online Shopping Services
N.A.I.C.S.: 425120

First Response Finance Ltd. (1)
5 and 16 Regan Way, Chilwell Beeston, Nottingham, NG9 6RZ, United Kingdom
Tel.: (44) 1159466368
Web Site: http://www.firstresponsefinance.co.uk
Emp.: 300
Automobile Financing Services
N.A.I.C.S.: 522220

Galaxy Management S.A. (1)
3 Quai du Mont Blanc, Geneva, 1201, Switzerland
Tel.: (41) 22 7153000
Crude Oil & Petroleum Products Whslr
N.A.I.C.S.: 424720

Geg Management S.A.M. (1)
7 Rue du Gabian, 98000, Monaco, Monaco
Tel.: (377) 93100150
Sales Range: $50-74.9 Million
Emp.: 70
Crude Oil & Petroleum Products Whslr
N.A.I.C.S.: 424720
Massimo Filosa (Mng Dir)

Guangzhou Global Logistics Corp. (1)
No10 Dongsheng Industrial Zone, Donghuan Panyu, Guangzhou, 511490, Guangdong, China
Tel.: (86) 203 480 6858

INTERNATIONAL PUBLIC

Web Site: http://www.ggl.com.cn
Sales Range: $50-74.9 Million
Emp.: 130
Logistics & Warehousing Services
N.A.I.C.S.: 541614

Hangzhou New Huahai Business & Trading Co., Ltd. (1)
4f No 19 Kai Yuan Road, Shangcheng District, Hangzhou, 310001, Zhejiang, China
Tel.: (86) 571 8708 3497
Cosmetics Whslr
N.A.I.C.S.: 424210

Helmitin Inc. (1)
11110 Airport Rd, Olive Branch, MS 38654
Web Site: https://helmitin.com
Footwear Mfr & Distr
N.A.I.C.S.: 316210

Helmitin Inc. (1)
99 Shorncliffe Road, Toronto, M8Z 5K7, ON, Canada
Tel.: (416) 239-3105
Web Site: http://helmitin.com
Adhesive Mfr
N.A.I.C.S.: 325520

Hexa Americas Inc. (1)
1150 S Vandemark Rd, Sidney, OH 45365
Tel.: (937) 497-7900
Plastic Product Mfr & Distr
N.A.I.C.S.: 326122

I&T Risk Solutions Co., Ltd. (1)
2-5-1 Kita-Aoyama Itochu Building 5th floor, Minato-ku, Tokyo, 107-0061, Japan
Tel.: (81) 33 497 8415
Web Site: https://www.itrs.co.jp
Insurance Agencies Services
N.A.I.C.S.: 524210

I.C. Autohandel Beteiligungen GmbH (1)
Oberhausener Str 2, 40472, Dusseldorf, Germany
Tel.: (49) 21 196 5050
Web Site: https://www.icabgroup.de
Automobile Dealers
N.A.I.C.S.: 441110

IFA Co., LTD. (1)
5-1, Kita-Aoyama 2-chome, Minato-ku, Tokyo, 107-0061, Japan
Tel.: (81) 334976155
Web Site: https://www.ifa-shoes.jp
Sales Range: $25-49.9 Million
Emp.: 36
N.A.I.C.S.: 316210
Noriyuki Tamura (Pres)

IM AUTOTRADE HOLDING G.m.b.H (1)
Millennium Tower Handelskai 94-96, 1200, Vienna, Austria
Tel.: (43) 1 2402 7480
Automobile & Motor Vehicle Whslr
N.A.I.C.S.: 423110

IMECS Co., Ltd. (1)
2-5-1 Kita-Aoyama Itochu Building 18F, Minato-ku, Tokyo, 107-0061, Japan
Tel.: (81) 33 497 8365
Web Site: https://www.imecs.co.jp
Ship Chartering Services
N.A.I.C.S.: 483111

IML Corporation (1)
2-22-3 Shibuya Shibuya Higashiguchi Bldg 9F, Shibuya-ku, Tokyo, 150-0002, Japan
Tel.: (81) 3 6418 6045
Web Site: http://www.imlcorp.jp
Sales Range: $25-49.9 Million
Emp.: 250
Human Resource Consulting Services
N.A.I.C.S.: 541612

ITC Green & Water Corp. (1)
6th Floor Kita-Aoyama Yoshikawa Bldg 12-16 Kita-Aoyama 2-chome, Minato-ku, Tokyo, 107-0061, Japan
Tel.: (81) 3 3497 8377
Web Site: http://www.itcgw.jp
Sales Range: $25-49.9 Million
Emp.: 60
Water Treatment System Installation & Gardening Services
N.A.I.C.S.: 561730

ITC TECHNOLOGY TAIWAN CORPORATION (1)

AND PRIVATE COMPANIES

6F-3 No 30 Taiyuan St, Tai Yuen Hi-Tech Industrial Park, Jhubei, 30288, Hsinchu, Taiwan
Tel.: (886) 3 552 6999
Web Site: https://www.itctw.com.tw
Semiconductor Equipment Whslr
N.A.I.C.S.: 423690

ITOCHU (China) Holding Co., Ltd. (1)
9/F No 3 Office Building China Central Place No 77 Jian Guo Road, Chaoyang District, Beijing, 100025, China
Tel.: (86) 10 6599 7000
Web Site: http://www.itochu.com.cn
Sales Range: $350-399.9 Million
Emp.: 530
Financial Investment Management Services
N.A.I.C.S.: 523999
Sasaki Junichi *(Pres & CEO)*

Subsidiary (Domestic):

IMECS (SHANGHAI) CO., LTD. (2)
Room No 2708 Jingan China Tower No 1701 Beijing Road West, Shanghai, 200040, China
Tel.: (86) 21 6288 6833
Food Products Mfr
N.A.I.C.S.: 311999

ITOCHU (CHONGQING) TRADING CO., LTD. (2)
Room 801 Hilton Chongqing Kingrun Tower No 131 Zhongshan San Road, Yuzhong District, Chongqing, 400015, China
Tel.: (86) 23 8906 7915
Seal Products Distr
N.A.I.C.S.: 423510

ITOCHU (DALIAN) CO., LTD. (2)
20F Liyuan Building No 16 Mingze Street, Zhongshan District, Dalian, 116001, Liaoning, China
Tel.: (86) 411 8360 8000
Seal Products Distr
N.A.I.C.S.: 423510

ITOCHU (QINGDAO) CO., LTD. (2)
23F New World Cyber Port Flagship Tower No 40 Xianggang Zhong Road, Qingdao, 266071, Shandong, China
Tel.: (86) 532 8666 2929
Seal Products Distr
N.A.I.C.S.: 423510

ITOCHU GUANGZHOU LTD. (2)
Room 1006-1007 Goldlion Digital Network Center 138 Tiyu Road E, Tianhe District, Guangzhou, 510620, Guangdong, China
Tel.: (86) 20 8668 0888
Seal Products Distr
N.A.I.C.S.: 423510

ITOCHU SHANGHAI LTD. (2)
56F Shanghai World Financial Center 100 Century Avenue, Pudong New Area, Shanghai, 200120, China
Tel.: (86) 21 6877 6688
Seal Products Distr
N.A.I.C.S.: 423510

Shanghai S.S.I. Auto Textile Inter-Decoration Co., Ltd.
600 Yushu Road, Songjiang District, Shanghai, 201600, China
Tel.: (86) 21 6772 5974
Web Site: http://www.itochu.com.cn
Woven Fabrics Mfr
N.A.I.C.S.: 314999

YIXIN (DALIAN) LOGISTICS CO.,LTD. (2)
20F Liyuan Building No 16 Mingze Street, Zhongshan District, Dalian, 116001, Liaoning, China
Tel.: (86) 411 8360 8000
Web Site: http://www.yixin-dalian.com
Seal Products Distr
N.A.I.C.S.: 423510

ITOCHU (Thailand) Ltd (1)
5th Floor Harindhorn Tower 54 North Sathorn Road, Bangrak, Bangkok, 10500, Thailand
Tel.: (66) 2 266 3086
Web Site: https://www.itochu.co.th
Emp.: 160
Consumer Goods Whslr
N.A.I.C.S.: 423990

ITOCHU AVIATION CO., LTD. (1)
2-9-11 Akasaka 4th floor ORIX Akasaka 2-chome Building, Minato-ku, Tokyo, 107-0052, Japan
Tel.: (81) 36 435 5100
Web Site: https://www.iaj.co.jp
Emp.: 104
New & Used Aircraft Retailer
N.A.I.C.S.: 423860

ITOCHU AirLease B.V. (1)
World Trade Center Strawinskylaan 433, 1077XX, Amsterdam, Netherlands
Tel.: (31) 205753165
Web Site: http://www.itochu.co.jp
Commercial Aircraft Leasing Services
N.A.I.C.S.: 532411

ITOCHU Argentina S.A. (1)
Av del Libertador 602 Piso 15, 1001, Buenos Aires, Argentina
Tel.: (54) 11 5777 7500
Web Site: http://www.itochu.com.ar
Industrial Machinery & Equipment Whslr
N.A.I.C.S.: 423830

ITOCHU Australia Ltd. (1)
Level 23 Gateway Tower 1 Macquarie Place, Sydney, 2000, NSW, Australia
Tel.: (61) 2 9239 1500
Web Site: http://www.itochu.com.au
Iron Ore & Bauxite Mining Services
N.A.I.C.S.: 212210

Subsidiary (Non-US):

ITOCHU New Zealand Ltd. (2)
Floor 21 151 Queen Street, Private Bag 92160, Auckland, New Zealand
Tel.: (64) 9 379 8480
Sales Range: $25-49.9 Million
Emp.: 1
Farm Supplies Distr
N.A.I.C.S.: 424910
Yoshihiro Taniguchi *(Mng Dir)*

ITOCHU Automobile Corporation (1)
Itochu Building 19F 2-5-1 Kita-Aoyama, Minato-ku, Tokyo, 107-0061, Japan
Tel.: (81) 33 497 4700
Web Site: https://www.itac.co.jp
Emp.: 162
Automobile Parts Import & Distr
N.A.I.C.S.: 423120
Naoyo Sode *(Pres)*

ITOCHU BRASIL S.A. (1)
Av Paulista 37 19 Andar Vila Mariana, São Paulo, 01311-902, Brazil
Tel.: (55) 11 3170 8501
Sales Range: $25-49.9 Million
Emp.: 30
Industrial Machinery & Equipment Whslr
N.A.I.C.S.: 423830

ITOCHU CABLE SYSTEMS CORP. (1)
3-20-14 Higashigotanda Takanawa Park Tower, Shinagawa-ku, Tokyo, 141-0022, Japan
Tel.: (81) 36 277 1821
Web Site: https://www.itochu-cable.co.jp
Sales Range: $25-49.9 Million
Emp.: 158
Digital Broadcasting Solutions
N.A.I.C.S.: 516120
Kenji Tsuchiya *(Pres & CEO)*

ITOCHU CHEMICAL FRONTIER Corporation (1)
5-1 Kita-Aoyama 2-chome, Minato-ku, Tokyo, 107-0061, Japan
Tel.: (81) 3 3497 4510
Web Site: http://www.itcchem.co.jp
Emp.: 299
Chemical & Pharmaceutical Products Mfr & Whslr
N.A.I.C.S.: 325180
Toshiro Ikeshiro *(Exec Officer)*

ITOCHU CONSTRUCTION MACHINERY CO., LTD. (1)
PMO NihonbashiMuromachi BLDG 13-7 Nihonbashi-Muromachi 1-chome, Chuo-ku, Tokyo, 103-0023, Japan
Tel.: (81) 33 242 5211
Web Site: https://www.icm.co.jp
Rev.: $372,096,000
Emp.: 127
Construction Machinery Whslr & Rental Services
N.A.I.C.S.: 423810
Jun Ikeno *(Pres)*

ITOCHU Capital Securities, Ltd. (1)
Aoyama-kumano Jinjya bldg 4F 2-22 Jingumae 2-chome, Shibuya-ku, Tokyo, 150-0001, Japan
Tel.: (81) 354138250
Web Site: http://www.itcap.jp
Investment Management Service
N.A.I.C.S.: 523999

ITOCHU Ceratech Corp. (1)
12-8 Shiokusa-cho, Seto, 489-0895, Aichi, Japan
Tel.: (81) 56 121 4131
Web Site: https://www.itc-cera.co.jp
Synthetic Sand Mfr
N.A.I.C.S.: 339999

ITOCHU Chile S.A. (1)
Av Apoquindo N 3472 Piso 13, Las Condes, 7550105, Santiago, Chile
Tel.: (56) 222109200
Web Site: http://www.itochu.co.jp
Sales Range: $25-49.9 Million
Emp.: 15
Industrial Machinery & Equipment Whslr
N.A.I.C.S.: 423830

ITOCHU Corporation - Osaka Headquarters (1)
1-3 Umeda 3-chome, Kita-ku, Osaka, 530-8448, Japan
Tel.: (81) 67 638 2121
Web Site: https://www.itochu.co.jp
Sales Range: $200-249.9 Million
Emp.: 300
Trade Agents & Brokers
N.A.I.C.S.: 425120

ITOCHU Deutschland GmbH (1)
Am Seestern 3, 40547, Dusseldorf, Germany
Tel.: (49) 211 52900
Industrial Machinery & Equipment Whslr
N.A.I.C.S.: 423830

ITOCHU Ecuador S.A. (1)
Edificio MIRAGE Av 12 de Octubre N26-48 y Abraham Lincoln Floor 7, Office 7A, Quito, 170525, Ecuador
Tel.: (593) 23949130
Web Site: http://www.itochu.co.jp
Sales Range: $50-74.9 Million
Emp.: 7
Industrial Machinery & Equipment Whslr
N.A.I.C.S.: 423830

ITOCHU Espana S.A. (1)
Paseo de la Castellana 60 4th Floor, 28046, Madrid, Spain
Tel.: (34) 91 425 0077
Industrial Machinery & Equipment Whslr
N.A.I.C.S.: 423830

ITOCHU Europe PLC (1)
The Broadgate Tower 20 Primrose Street, London, EC2A 2EW, United Kingdom
Tel.: (44) 207 947 8000
Web Site: http://www.itochu.com
Sales Range: $25-49.9 Million
Emp.: 140
Chemical & Plastic Products Distr
N.A.I.C.S.: 424690

Subsidiary (Domestic):

Kwik-Fit Group Limited (2)
ETEL House Avenue One, Letchworth, SG6 2HU, Herts, United Kingdom
Tel.: (44) 1727840206
Web Site: https://www.kwik-fit.com
Holding Company; Automotive Tire & Repair Shops Operator
N.A.I.C.S.: 551112
Kenji Murai *(CEO)*

Subsidiary (Domestic):

Kwik-Fit (GB) Limited (3)
ETEL House Avenue One, Letchworth, SG6 2HU, Herts, United Kingdom (100%)
Tel.: (44) 172 784 0206
Web Site: https://www.kwik-fit.com
Sales Range: $75-99.9 Million
Emp.: 150
Automotive Tire & Repair Shops Operator
N.A.I.C.S.: 811111

ITOCHU CORPORATION

Luke Penn *(Mgr-Corp Accts)*

Unit (Domestic):

Kwik-Fit Fleet (4)
14-18 Fleet Road, Fleet, GU51 4QG, Herts, United Kingdom
Tel.: (44) 125 281 5255
Web Site: https://www.kwik-fit.com
Sales Range: $25-49.9 Million
Emp.: 14
Commercial Fleet Automotive Tire Fitting & Repair Services
N.A.I.C.S.: 811111
Andy Fern *(Dir-Sls)*

Subsidiary (Domestic):

Stapleton's Tyre Services Ltd. (2)
Fourth Avenue, Letchworth, SG6 2TT, Hertfordshire, United Kingdom
Tel.: (44) 146 248 8800
Web Site: https://www.stapletons-tyres.co.uk
Sales Range: $125-149.9 Million
Emp.: 30
Automotive Tires Distr
N.A.I.C.S.: 423130

ITOCHU FASHION SYSTEM Co., Ltd. (1)
Itochu Building 17F 2-5-1 Kita-Aoyama, Minato-ku, Tokyo, 107-0061, Japan
Tel.: (81) 33 497 4000
Web Site: https://www.ifs.co.jp
Sales Range: $25-49.9 Million
Emp.: 85
Fashion Design Services
N.A.I.C.S.: 541490
Takaaki Komatani *(Pres)*

ITOCHU Feed Mills Co., Ltd. (1)
Shinei Building 2-35-13 Kameido, Koto-ku, Tokyo, 136-8511, Japan
Tel.: (81) 35 626 3200
Web Site: https://www.itochu-f.co.jp
Emp.: 241
Animal Feeds Mfr & Whslr
N.A.I.C.S.: 311119
Teruo Fujishima *(Pres)*

ITOCHU Finance (Europe) PLC (1)
The Broadgate Tower 20 Primrose Street, London, EC2A 2EW, United Kingdom
Tel.: (44) 2079478250
Financial Investment Management Services
N.A.I.C.S.: 523999

ITOCHU Finance Corporation (1)
2-5-1 Kitaaoyama Itochu Bldg 3f, Minato-ku, Tokyo, 107-0061, Japan
Tel.: (81) 334978432
Emp.: 4
Consumer Lending Services
N.A.I.C.S.: 522291

ITOCHU Food Sales & Marketing Co., Ltd. (1)
Shin-Aoyama Bldg West Tower 21F 1-1 Minami-Aoyama 1-chome, Minato-ku, Tokyo, 107-0062, Japan
Tel.: (81) 35 771 7266
Web Site: https://www.itochufsm.co.jp
Emp.: 189
Food Products Distr
N.A.I.C.S.: 424490
Hideyori Kondo *(Pres & CEO)*

ITOCHU France S.A.S. (1)
17 square Edouard VII, 75009, Paris, France
Tel.: (33) 145383525
Web Site: http://www.itochu-hightech.com
Emp.: 45
Industrial Machinery & Equipment Whslr
N.A.I.C.S.: 423830

ITOCHU GENERAL SERVICES INC. (1)
2-5-1 Kita Aoyama Itochu Bldg 4F, Minato-ku, Tokyo, 107-0061, Japan
Tel.: (81) 3 3497 7993
Web Site: http://www.igs-inc.co.jp
Facilities Management Services
N.A.I.C.S.: 561210

ITOCHU HOUSING Co., Ltd. (1)
2-9-11 Akasaka 5th floor ORIX Akasaka 2-chome Building, Minato-ku, Tokyo, 107-0052, Japan
Tel.: (81) 36 811 0300

ITOCHU CORPORATION

ITOCHU Corporation—(Continued)

Web Site: https://www.itochu-housing.co.jp
Sales Range: $75-99.9 Million
Emp.: 127
Real Estate Manangement Services
N.A.I.C.S.: 531390

ITOCHU HUMAN RESOURCE SERVICES INC. (1)
2-5-1 Kita-Aoyama Itochu Building 12F,
Minato-ku, Tokyo, 107-0061, Japan
Tel.: (81) 334977993
Web Site: http://www.ihgs.co.jp
Emp.: 200
Human Resource Consulting Services
N.A.I.C.S.: 541612

ITOCHU HUNGARY Kft. (1)
Bajcsy-Zsilinszky ut 12 4th Floor No 401,
1051, Budapest, Hungary
Tel.: (36) 1 429 3071
Sales Range: $50-74.9 Million
Emp.: 8
Industrial Machinery & Equipment Whslr
N.A.I.C.S.: 423830

ITOCHU Hellas Ltd. (1)
Alimou 8, 105-57, Athens, Greece
Tel.: (30) 2103230103
Industrial Machinery & Equipment Whslr
N.A.I.C.S.: 423830

ITOCHU Hong Kong Ltd. (1)
28th Floor United Centre 95 Queensway,
Hong Kong, China (Hong Kong)
Tel.: (852) 25296011
Web Site: http://www.itochu.com.hk
Sales Range: $50-74.9 Million
Emp.: 70
Industrial Machinery Distr
N.A.I.C.S.: 423830
Tokuichiro Yoshimura *(Mng Dir)*

Subsidiary (Domestic):

ADV Advance Systems (Asia) Ltd. (2)
Room 901 9/F International Plaza 20
Sheung Yuet Road, Kowloon Bay, Kowloon, China (Hong Kong)
Tel.: (852) 2796 3395
Web Site: http://www.asal.hk
Light Emitting Diode Displays Mfr
N.A.I.C.S.: 334419

i-LOGISTICS (HK) LTD. (2)
Unit 2007 20F Tower 2 Metro Plaza 223
Hing Fong Road, Kwai Fong, China (Hong Kong)
Tel.: (852) 2376 8108
Logistics Consulting Servies
N.A.I.C.S.: 541614

ITOCHU IRAN Co. Ltd. (1)
2nd Floor No 257 Corner of Golkhaneh St
Nelson Mandela Jordan Ave, PO Box
15815-1876, Tehran, 19158 43153, Iran
Tel.: (98) 212 204 5792
Web Site: http://www.itochu.co.jp
Industrial Machinery & Equipment Whslr
N.A.I.C.S.: 423830

ITOCHU India Pvt. Ltd. (1)
World Trade Tower Ground Floor Barakhamba Lane, New Delhi, 110 001, India
Tel.: (91) 11 2341 1891
Industrial Machinery & Equipment Whslr
N.A.I.C.S.: 423830

ITOCHU Interactive Corp. (1)
3-20-1 Minami Azabu Daiwa Azabu Terrace
3F, Minato-ku, Tokyo, 106-0047, Japan
Tel.: (81) 36 408 1770
Web Site: https://www.market.co.jp
Sales Range: $25-49.9 Million
Emp.: 130
Online Marketing Services
N.A.I.C.S.: 541613

ITOCHU International Inc. (1)
1251 Avenue of the Americas 51st Fl, New
York, NY 10020
Tel.: (212) 818-8000
Web Site: https://www.itochu.com
Sales Range: $1-4.9 Billion
Emp.: 4,671
Holding Company; Textiles; Machinery; Motor Vehicles; Steel & Raw Materials; Non-Ferrous & Light Metals; Grains; Provisions; General Merchandise; Chemicals & Energy
N.A.I.C.S.: 424310
Claire Chino *(Pres & CEO)*

Subsidiary (Domestic):

ATR Wire & Cable Co. Inc. (2)
1857 South Danville, Danville, KY 40422
Tel.: (859) 236-9220
Silo Mfr
N.A.I.C.S.: 331222

Advanced Media Technologies, Inc. (2)
3150 SW 15th St, Deerfield Beach, FL 33442
Tel.: (954) 427-5711
Web Site: https://www.goamt.com
Sales Range: $25-49.9 Million
Emp.: 50
Importation & Distribution of Satellite Receivers
N.A.I.C.S.: 516210
Ken Mosca *(Pres & CEO)*

Alta Forest Product, LLC (2)
810 NW Alta Wy, Chehalis, WA 98532
Tel.: (360) 219-0008
Wood Fence Board Mfr
N.A.I.C.S.: 321999
Kobe Yamamoto *(Pres & CEO)*

Auto Investment Inc. (2)
80 Drivers Way, Pelham, AL 35124
Tel.: (205) 271-2090
Emp.: 55
Motor Vehicle Retailers
N.A.I.C.S.: 441227
Chris Martin *(Gen Mgr)*

CIECO Energy (US) Limited (2)
5555 San Felipe St Ste 620, Houston, TX 77056-2701
Tel.: (713) 547-5601
Oil & Gas Exploration Services
N.A.I.C.S.: 213112

Calwest Compress & Warehouse Co., Inc. (2)
5612 E International Ave, Clovis, CA 93611-9532
Tel.: (559) 275-4702
Cotton Compressing & Warehousing
N.A.I.C.S.: 424590

Chemoil Corporation (2)
4 Embarcadero Ctr Ste 3400, San Francisco, CA 94111-4106
Tel.: (415) 268-2700 (50%)
Web Site: http://www.chemoil.com
Sales Range: $25-49.9 Million
Emp.: 35
Bunkering Petroleum to Barges
N.A.I.C.S.: 424710

Subsidiary (Domestic):

Chemoil Terminals Corporation (3)
4 Embarcadero Ctr Ste 3400, San Francisco, CA 94111-4106
Tel.: (415) 268-2700
Web Site: http://www.chemoil.com
Sales Range: $10-24.9 Million
Emp.: 40
Special Warehousing & Storage
N.A.I.C.S.: 493190

Subsidiary (Domestic):

ITOCHU Automobile America Inc. (2)
33533 W 12 Mile Rd Ste 300, Farmington Hills, MI 48331
Tel.: (248) 479-1400
Sales Range: $25-49.9 Million
Emp.: 15
Motor Vehicle Distr
N.A.I.C.S.: 423110
Tetsushi Miyazawa *(Controller)*

ITOCHU Aviation, Inc. (2)
222 N Sepulveda Blvd Ste 2200, El Segundo, CA 90245-5667
Tel.: (310) 640-2700
Sales Range: $25-49.9 Million
Emp.: 30
Import & Export Aircraft & Parts
N.A.I.C.S.: 423860

Subsidiary (Non-US):

ITOCHU Canada Ltd. (2)
World Trade Centre Suite 590-999 Canada Place, Vancouver, V6C 3E1, BC, Canada
Tel.: (604) 331-5800
Web Site: http://www.itochu.com
Sales Range: $25-49.9 Million
Emp.: 12
General Trading Services
N.A.I.C.S.: 425120

Subsidiary (Domestic):

ITOCHU Chemicals America Inc (2)
360 Hamilton Ave 6th Fl, White Plains, NY 10601
Tel.: (914) 333-7800
Web Site: https://www.itochu-sc.com
Sales Range: $25-49.9 Million
Emp.: 36
Provider of Intermediate, Fine & Specialty Chemicals
N.A.I.C.S.: 424690

Branch (Domestic):

ITOCHU International (2)
1251 Ave of the Americas 51st Fl, New York, NY 10020
Tel.: (212) 818-8000
Web Site: https://www.itochu.com
Sales Range: $50-74.9 Million
Emp.: 4
Crude Oil & Petroleum Products Trading
N.A.I.C.S.: 424310

Subsidiary (Domestic):

Industrious Group Inc. (2)
4259 E 49th St, Cleveland, OH 44125-1001 (100%)
Tel.: (216) 206-0081
Web Site: https://www.enprotech.com
Sales Range: $75-99.9 Million
Emp.: 7
Equipment Repair, Rebuilding & Spare Parts
N.A.I.C.S.: 423830
Chris Pascarella *(Pres & CEO)*

Subsidiary (Domestic):

American Hydro Corporation (3)
135 Stonewood Rd, York, PA 17402
Tel.: (717) 755-5300
Web Site: https://www.ahydro.com
Provider of Hydraulic Equipment Repair Services
N.A.I.C.S.: 811210
Gerry Russell *(Pres & VP-Sls & Mktg)*

Enprotech Industrial Technologies, Inc. - Verson, Danly & NSD Parts (3)
16800 Industrial Pkwy, Lansing, MI 48906
Tel.: (517) 372-0950
Web Site: https://www.enpromech.com
Mechanical Press Parts Mfr & Distr
N.A.I.C.S.: 423830
Chuck Poffley *(COO)*

Subsidiary (Domestic):

Master Halco, Inc. (2)
3010 Lyndon B Johnson Fwy Ste 800, Dallas, TX 75234
Tel.: (714) 385-0091
Web Site: https://www.masterhalco.com
Sales Range: $550-599.9 Million
Emp.: 1,615
Perimeter Security & Fencing Mfr & Wholesale Distr; Vinyl, Wood, Ornamental & Chain Link Fences & Automated Gates for Residential, Commercial, Industrial & High Security Applications
N.A.I.C.S.: 423390

Division (Non-US):

Belair Fence Limited (3)
400 Rue Deslauriers, Saint Laurent, H4N 1V8, QC, Canada
Tel.: (514) 335-4455
Web Site: http://www.fenceonline.com
Sales Range: $25-49.9 Million
Emp.: 40
Fencing Products & Accessories Distr
N.A.I.C.S.: 332618

Branch (Domestic):

Master Halco (3)
9800 Reeves Rd, Tampa, FL 33619-7713
Tel.: (813) 769-2956

INTERNATIONAL PUBLIC

Web Site: https://www.masterhalco.com
Sales Range: $50-74.9 Million
Emp.: 150
Mfr & Distr Fence Systems
N.A.I.C.S.: 331222
Laurinda Citty *(Engr-Network)*

Subsidiary (Domestic):

Midlantic Machinery Company (2)
2240 Bethlehem Pike, Hatfield, PA 19440-1608
Tel.: (215) 822-0145
Web Site: http://www.midlanticmachinery.com
Sales Range: $25-49.9 Million
Emp.: 35
Construction Machinery & Equipment Distr
N.A.I.C.S.: 423810
Mark Jackson *(Dir-Acctg)*

MultiQuip, Inc. (2)
6141 Katella Ave Ste 200, Cypress, CA 90630
Tel.: (310) 537-3700
Web Site: https://www.multiquip.com
Sales Range: $100-124.9 Million
Emp.: 400
Wholesale Distr of General Construction Machinery & Equipment
N.A.I.C.S.: 423810
Kimi Chiba *(CFO & VP-Fin & Admin)*

NAES Corporation (2)
1180 NW Maple St Ste 200, Issaquah, WA 98027
Tel.: (425) 961-4700
Web Site: https://www.naes.com
Power Plant Construction & Maintenance Services
N.A.I.C.S.: 237130
Glen J. Canavera *(Sr VP-Business Development)*

Subsidiary (Domestic):

NAES Power Contractors (3)
167 Anderson Rd, Cranberry Township, PA 16066
Tel.: (724) 716-4095
Web Site: http://www.naes.com
Sales Range: $25-49.9 Million
Emp.: 20
Power Plant & Electric Infrastructure Services
N.A.I.C.S.: 237110
Mike Geyer *(Pres)*

Olsson Industrial Electric, Inc. (3)
1919 Laura St, Springfield, OR 97477
Tel.: (541) 747-8460
Web Site: https://olssonelec.com
Industrial Electrical Contractor & Engineering Services
N.A.I.C.S.: 238210
Ike Olsson *(Pres)*

PurEnergy LLC (3)
4488 Onondaga Blvd, Syracuse, NY 13219 (100%)
Tel.: (315) 448-2266
Web Site: https://www.purenergyllc.com
Sales Range: $1-9.9 Million
Emp.: 12
Management Consulting Services
N.A.I.C.S.: 541614
Don Scholl *(Co-Founder)*

Subsidiary (Domestic):

OILSEEDS INTERNATIONAL LTD. (2)
1 Sansome St Ste 2000, San Francisco, CA 94104
Tel.: (415) 956-7251
Web Site: https://www.oilseedssf.com
Sales Range: $50-74.9 Million
Emp.: 10
Vegetable Oil Whslr
N.A.I.C.S.: 424990

Prominent USA LLC (2)
725 S Figueroa St Ste 3050, Los Angeles, CA 90017
Tel.: (213) 623-4001
Sales Range: $25-49.9 Million
Emp.: 7
Buy & Sell Raw Cotton
N.A.I.C.S.: 424350

AND PRIVATE COMPANIES

Quality Technology International, Inc. (2)
1707 N Randall Rd Ste 300, Elgin, IL 60123
Tel.: (847) 649-9300
Web Site: https://qtitechnology.com
Animal Feed Mfr
N.A.I.C.S.: 311119
Jeffrey Jordan *(Mgr-Sales-Marketing)*

SolarNet, LLC (2)
1500 Valley House Dr Ste 210, Rohnert Park, CA 94928
Tel.: (707) 992-3100
Web Site: http://www.solarnet.us
Solar Electric Power Generation Services
N.A.I.C.S.: 221118

Telerent Leasing Corporation (2)
4191 Fayetteville Rd, Raleigh, NC 27603
Tel.: (919) 772-8604
Web Site: http://www.telerent.com
Sales Range: $10-24.9 Million
Televisions & Air Conditioners Distr to Healthcare & Hospitality Industries
N.A.I.C.S.: 423620
John Woodward *(CFO, Treas & Controller)*

Subsidiary (Domestic):

Digital Networks Group, Inc. (3)
20382 Hermana Cir, Lake Forest, CA 92630
Tel.: (949) 428-6333
Web Site:
http://www.digitalnetworksgroup.com
Emp.: 140
All Other Telecommunications
N.A.I.C.S.: 517810
Mike Stammire *(Founder & Pres)*

Subsidiary (Domestic):

Texmac, Inc. (2)
3001 Stafford Dr, Charlotte, NC 28208-3570
Tel.: (704) 394-0314
Web Site: https://texmac.com
Sales Range: $25-49.9 Million
Emp.: 50
Import & Distribution of Textile Machinery
N.A.I.C.S.: 423830

Tyr Energy, Inc. (2)
7500 College Blvd Ste 400, Overland Park, KS 66210
Tel.: (913) 754-5800
Web Site: https://tyrenergy.com
Power-Related Asset Management, Risk Management & Capacity Services
N.A.I.C.S.: 541618
Garrick Venteicher *(CEO)*

ITOCHU Italiana S.p.A. (1)
Via Hoepli 5, 20121, Milan, Italy
Tel.: (39) 0227701
Web Site: https://www.itochuitaliana.com
Test Equipment Whslr
N.A.I.C.S.: 423830

ITOCHU Kenzai Corporation (1)
5F Nomurafudosan Nihonbashi Honcho Bldg 7-1 Nihonbashi-honcho 2-chome, Chuo-ku, Tokyo, 103-8419, Japan
Tel.: (81) 3 3661 3281
Web Site: http://www.ick.co.jp
Emp.: 608
Wood Products Whslr
N.A.I.C.S.: 423990
Toshiaki Shibata *(Pres & CEO)*

ITOCHU Korea Ltd. (1)
21F 92 Sejong-Daero, Jung-Gu, Seoul, 04525, Korea (South)
Tel.: (82) 26 366 2600
Web Site: https://www.itochu.com
Emp.: 45
International Trading Services
N.A.I.C.S.: 522299
Koji Hasegawa *(Pres & CEO)*

ITOCHU Latin America, S.A. (1)
PH Plaza Canaima 7 Piso Calle Samuel Lewis, Obarrio, Panama, Panama
Tel.: (507) 205 5000
Web Site: http://www.itochu.co.jp
Industrial Machinery & Equipment Distr
N.A.I.C.S.: 423830

ITOCHU Logistics (China) Co., Ltd. (1)
3rd Floor Tianyu Building No55 Jiachuang 2nd Road, Taihu Town Tongzhou District, Beijing, 101111, China
Tel.: (86) 1087305963
Logistic Services
N.A.I.C.S.: 541614

ITOCHU Logistics Corp. (1)
13th Floor Shiodome City Center 5-2 Higashi-Shimbashi 1-chome, Minato ku, Tokyo, 105-7113, Japan (98.97%)
Tel.: (81) 36 254 6100
Web Site: https://www.itclogi.com
Sales Range: $75-99.9 Million
Emp.: 1,075
Logistic Services
N.A.I.C.S.: 541614
Kazuhide Sasa *(Pres & CEO)*

Subsidiary (Non-US):

ITOCHU LOGISTICS (EUROPE) GMBH. (2)
Breitscheider Weg 168-170, 40885, Ratingen, Germany
Tel.: (49) 2102 133890
Logistic Services
N.A.I.C.S.: 541614

ITOCHU LOGISTICS (HK) LTD. (2)
28th Floor The Cameron 33 Cameron Road, Tsimshatsui, Kowloon, China (Hong Kong)
Tel.: (852) 23768185
Web Site: http://www.itochulogistics.com.hk
Logistics Consulting Servies
N.A.I.C.S.: 541614

ITOCHU LOGISTICS (UK) LTD. (2)
Kerry Logistics UK Ltd Unit 7 Vector Park Forest Road, Feltham, TW13 7EJ, United Kingdom
Tel.: (44) 203 1743182
Emp.: 10
Logistics & Freight Forwarding Services
N.A.I.C.S.: 541614

Subsidiary (US):

ITOCHU Logistics (USA) Corp. (2)
1140 Sandhill Ave, Carson, CA 90746
Tel.: (562) 748-4100
Web Site: https://us.itclogi.com
Sales Range: $25-49.9 Million
Emp.: 35
Full-Service Logistics; International Freight
N.A.I.C.S.: 488510
Takashi Tanaka *(Pres)*

Subsidiary (Non-US):

PT. ITOCHU LOGISTICS INDONESIA (2)
The Prime-Office Suites 8th Fl Suite AF JL Yos Sudarso KAV 30 Sunter, Jakarta Utara, 14350, Indonesia
Tel.: (62) 2122655097
Web Site: http://www.ilogi.co.jp
Emp.: 100
Logistics Consulting Servies
N.A.I.C.S.: 541614

Shandong i-Logistics Co., Ltd. (2)
No 378 Longgangshan Road, Qingdao Economic And Technological Development Zone, Qingdao, 266500, Shandong, China
Tel.: (86) 532 8691 1888
Web Site: http://www.shandong-ilogi.com
Warehousing & Freight Forwarding Services
N.A.I.C.S.: 493110

i-LOGISTICS (GUANGZHOU) LTD. (2)
3706B Teemtower 208 Tianhe Road, Guangzhou, 510620, China
Tel.: (86) 20 3878 1722
Web Site: http://www.ilogi.co.jp
Logistics Consulting Servies
N.A.I.C.S.: 541614

i-LOGISTICS (SHANGHAI) CORP. (2)
Room 1015 Shanghai International Trade Center 2201 Yan An Road West, Shanghai, 200336, China
Tel.: (86) 21 6270 1892
Logistics Consulting Servies
N.A.I.C.S.: 541614

i-LOGISTICS (SHANGHAI) FORWARDING CORP. (2)
Room 1001 Shanghai International Trade Center 2201 Yan An Road West, Shanghai, 200336, China
Tel.: (86) 21 6209 2184
Freight Forwarding Services
N.A.I.C.S.: 488510

i-LOGISTICS (SHENZHEN) CORP. (2)
Room 1712 West Tower Shengtang Building No 1 Tairan Ninth Road, Chegongmiao Futian-district, Shenzhen, 518038, China
Tel.: (86) 755 8359 1661
Web Site: http://www.ilogi.co.jp
Logistic Services
N.A.I.C.S.: 541614

ITOCHU MACHINE-TECHNOS CORPORATION (1)
2-14-2 Nagatacho, Chiyoda-ku, Tokyo, 100-0014, Japan
Tel.: (81) 3 3506 3511
Web Site: http://www.itcmt.co.jp
Emp.: 265
Industrial Machinery Whslr
N.A.I.C.S.: 423830
Yoshiaki Hongo *(Pres & CEO)*

Subsidiary (Domestic):

URSCHEL JAPAN CO,. LTD. (2)
Sanno Grand Building 2-14-2 Nagata-cho, Chiyoda-ku, Tokyo, 100-0014, Japan
Tel.: (81) 3 3506 3531
Food Cutters Distr
N.A.I.C.S.: 423440

ITOCHU MIDDLE EAST FZE (1)
201 The Spectrum Building Al Qutaeyat Road, PO Box 3572, Oud Metha, Dubai, United Arab Emirates
Tel.: (971) 4 302 0000
Web Site: http://www.itochu.co.jp
Sales Range: $25-49.9 Million
Emp.: 40
Industrial Machinery & Equipment Whslr
N.A.I.C.S.: 423830

ITOCHU MODEPAL CO., LTD. (1)
Inamura Building 9-10 Nihonbashitomizawa-cho, Chuo-ku, Tokyo, 103-0006, Japan
Tel.: (81) 35 643 3061
Web Site: https://www.itcmpal.co.jp
Sales Range: $25-49.9 Million
Emp.: 70
Apparel Mfr & Whslr
N.A.I.C.S.: 315250

ITOCHU Metals Corporation (1)
Itochu Building 5-1 Kita-Aoyama 2-chome, Minato-ku, Tokyo, 107-8573, Japan
Tel.: (81) 334977137
Web Site: http://www.itochu-metals.co.jp
Sales Range: $75-99.9 Million
Emp.: 227
Metal Processing Services
N.A.I.C.S.: 423510
Seiya Kamanoi *(CFO, Exec Officer & Gen Mgr-Fin & Acctg Div)*

ITOCHU Mexico S.A. de C.V. (1)
Av Paseo de la Reforma N 483-piso 51, Col Cuauhtemoc Delg Cuauhtemoc, 06500, Mexico, Mexico
Tel.: (52) 5553504100
Web Site: http://www.itochu.com.mx
Sales Range: $25-49.9 Million
Emp.: 17
Industrial Machinery & Equipment Whslr
N.A.I.C.S.: 423830

ITOCHU Mineral Resources Development Corporation (1)
2-5-1 Kita-Aoyama, Minato-ku, Tokyo, 107-0061, Japan
Tel.: (81) 334973020
Web Site: http://itochu-mineral.com
Mine Developing & Consulting Services
N.A.I.C.S.: 541690

ITOCHU Minerals & Energy of Australia Pty Ltd (1)
Level 31 Grosvenor Place 225 George Street, Sydney, 2000, NSW, Australia
Tel.: (61) 292391520
Sales Range: $50-74.9 Million
Emp.: 20
Iron Ore & Bauxite Mining Services
N.A.I.C.S.: 212210

ITOCHU Nigeria Ltd. (1)

ITOCHU CORPORATION

No 16 Amodu Ojikutu Street Off Bishop Oluwole Street Victoria Island, Lagos, Nigeria
Tel.: (234) 1 462 7058
Industrial Machinery & Equipment Whslr
N.A.I.C.S.: 423830

ITOCHU Oil Exploration Co., Ltd. (1)
5-1 Kita-Aoyama 2-chome, Minato-ku, Tokyo, 107-0061, Japan
Tel.: (81) 33 497 8113
Web Site: https://www.itochuoil.co.jp
Sales Range: $50-74.9 Million
Emp.: 30
Oil & Natural Gas Exploration Services
N.A.I.C.S.: 213112
Tetsuya Yamada *(Pres & CEO)*

ITOCHU Orico Insurance Services Co., Ltd. (1)
Itochu Building 3rd floor 2-5-1 Kita-Aoyama, Minato-ku, Tokyo, 107-0061, Japan
Tel.: (81) 3 3497 8200
Web Site: http://www.itochuiis.co.jp
General Insurance Services
N.A.I.C.S.: 524210

ITOCHU Petroleum Co., (Singapore) Pte. Ltd. (1)
9 Raffles Place 45-01 Republic Plaza, Singapore, Singapore
Tel.: (65) 62300670
Sales Range: $75-99.9 Million
Emp.: 170
Petroleum Product Whslr
N.A.I.C.S.: 424720
Haruo Maeda *(Mng Dir)*

ITOCHU Plantech Inc. (1)
1-1-1 Minami-Aoyama 11th floor East Building Shin-Aoyama, Minato-ku, Tokyo, 107-0062, Japan
Tel.: (81) 3 5414 8418
Web Site: http://www.itpm.co.jp
Emp.: 92
Industrial Machinery Distr
N.A.I.C.S.: 423830
Ichiro Shimizu *(Pres)*

ITOCHU Plastics Inc. (1)
Tokyu Building 5 4 6F 21 Ichibancho Yubinbango, Chiyoda-ku, Tokyo, 102-0082, Japan
Tel.: (81) 368801600
Web Site: http://www.itc-ps.co.jp
Emp.: 546
Plastic Product Whslr
N.A.I.C.S.: 424610

ITOCHU Plastics Pte., Ltd. (1)
1 Wallich Street 32-03 Guoco Tower, Singapore, 078881, Singapore
Tel.: (65) 6 230 0400
Web Site: https://www.itochuplastics.com
Sales Range: $25-49.9 Million
Emp.: 50
Plastic Resin Whslr
N.A.I.C.S.: 424610

ITOCHU Property Development, Ltd. (1)
ORIX Akasaka 2-chome Bldg 8F Reception 7F 2-9-11 Akasaka, Minato-ku, Tokyo, 107-0052, Japan
Tel.: (81) 36 811 0200
Web Site: https://www.ipd.co.jp
Sales Range: $75-99.9 Million
Emp.: 14
Real Estate Development Services
N.A.I.C.S.: 531390

ITOCHU Pulp & Paper Corp. (1)
Nomura Fudosan Nihonbashi-Honcho Building 8F 7-1 2-Chome, Chuo-Ku, Tokyo, 103-8415, Japan
Tel.: (81) 33 639 7111
Web Site: https://www.itcpp.co.jp
Emp.: 163
Paper Product Distr
N.A.I.C.S.: 424130

ITOCHU REIT Management Co., Ltd. (1)
3F Kojimachi GN Yasuda Building 3-6-5 Kojimachi, Chiyoda-ku, Tokyo, 102-0083, Japan
Tel.: (81) 335563912
Web Site: http://www.itc-rm.co.jp
Asset Management Services
N.A.I.C.S.: 523940
Junichi Shoji *(Pres & CEO)*

ITOCHU CORPORATION

ITOCHU Corporation—(Continued)

ITOCHU Retail Link Corporation (1)
5th Floor Daisan Sakurabashi Bldg 7-1
Hacchobori 4-chome, Chuo-ku, Tokyo, 104-0032, Japan
(100%)
Tel.: (81) 3 6280 0002
Web Site: http://www.itc-rl.co.jp
Emp.: 115
Digital Video Disc Whslr
N.A.I.C.S.: 449210
Masafumi Mizuno (Pres & CEO)

ITOCHU SHOKUHIN Co., Ltd. (1)
2-2-22 Shiromi, Chuo-ku, Osaka, 540-8522, Japan
Tel.: (81) 66 947 9811
Web Site: https://www.itochu-shokuhin.com
Emp.: 1,189
Food Products Whslr & Distr
N.A.I.C.S.: 424490

ITOCHU Singapore Pte. Ltd. (1)
1 Wallich Street 32-03 Guoco Tower, Singapore, 078881, Singapore
Tel.: (65) 6 230 0500
Web Site: http://www.itochu.com
Sales Range: $75-99.9 Million
Emp.: 100
Industrial Machinery & Equipment Whslr
N.A.I.C.S.: 423830

ITOCHU Sugar Co., Ltd. (1)
3 Tamatsuuramachi, Hekinan, 447-8506, Aichi, Japan
(100%)
Tel.: (81) 56 646 0617
Web Site: https://www.itochu-sugar.com
Emp.: 100
Sugar Products Mfr
N.A.I.C.S.: 311313
Hiroshi Takeshi Sato (Pres)

ITOCHU SysTech Corporation (1)
Itoh Bldg 9F 3-6-14 Minami-Honmachi, Chuo-ku, Osaka, 541-0054, Japan
Tel.: (81) 6 6282 1114
Web Site: http://www.itochu-systech.co.jp
Sales Range: $50-74.9 Million
Emp.: 120
Textile Machinery Whslr
N.A.I.C.S.: 423830
Shigenobu Matsumoto (Pres & CEO)

ITOCHU TAIWAN CORPORATION (1)
Fl 16 No 4 Zhongxiao West Road Section 1, Jhongjheng District, Taipei, 10041, Taiwan
Tel.: (886) 2 2312 1112
Web Site: http://www.itochu.com.tw
Industrial Machinery & Equipment Whslr
N.A.I.C.S.: 423830

ITOCHU Techno-Solutions Corporation (1)
Kamiyacho Trust Tower 4-1-1 Toranomon, Minato-ku, Tokyo, 105-6950, Japan
(52.19%)
Tel.: (81) 364036000
Web Site: https://www.ctc-g.co.jp
Rev.: $4,093,596,762
Assets: $3,786,082,650
Liabilities: $1,594,930,650
Net Worth: $2,191,152,000
Earnings: $245,271,360
Emp.: 10,120
Fiscal Year-end: 03/31/2023
Holding Company; Information Technology Product Sales & Support Services
N.A.I.C.S.: 551112
Ichiro Tsuge (Chm)

Subsidiary (Domestic):

CRC Systems Corp. (2)
Kuita Kudam Building 11 5 Fujimi 1 Chome, Chiyoda-ku, Tokyo, Japan
Tel.: (81) 3 6238 5800
Web Site: http://www.crs.co.jp
Telecommunications & Broadcasting Network Services & Software Development
N.A.I.C.S.: 517810

CTC Laboratory Systems Corporation (2)
16-7 Komazawa 1-chome Setagaya Ku, Setagaya-ku, Tokyo, 154-0012, Japan
(80%)
Tel.: (81) 3 3419 9171

Sales Range: $50-74.9 Million
Emp.: 138
Computer & Software Whslr for the Pharmaceutical, Chemical & Food Product Industries; Owned 20% by ITOCHU Corporation
N.A.I.C.S.: 423430

Subsidiary (US):

ITOCHU Techn-Solutions America, Inc. (2)
3945 Freedom Cir Ste 640, Santa Clara, CA 95054
Tel.: (408) 727-8810
Web Site: https://www.ctc-america.com
Sales Range: $25-49.9 Million
Emp.: 40
Information Technology Consulting Services
N.A.I.C.S.: 541512
John Takita (VP-Fin & Enterprise Solutions)

ITOCHU Technology Ventures, Inc. (1)
2-5-1 Kita-Aoyama, Minato-ku, Tokyo, 107-0061, Japan
Tel.: (81) 334978077
Web Site: http://www.techv.co.jp
Sales Range: $50-74.9 Million
Emp.: 15
Venture Capital Investment Services
N.A.I.C.S.: 523910

ITOCHU Textile Prominent (Asia) Ltd. (1)
Unit 2118 21/F Mira Place Tower A 132 Nathan Rd, Tsim Tsa Tsui, China (Hong Kong)
Tel.: (852) 2 376 7300
Web Site: https://www.ipahkg.com.hk
Fabrics Mfr
N.A.I.C.S.: 313310
Morita Hiroshi (Mng Dir)

ITOCHU Tunisia S.A.R.L. (1)
06 Rue Mohamed Ali J'Nah, 1002, Tunis, Tunisia
Tel.: (216) 71 799 688
Industrial Machinery & Equipment Whslr
N.A.I.C.S.: 423830

ITOCHU Urban Community Ltd. (1)
2-7-1 Nihonbashihoncho Nomura Real Estate, Nihonbashihoncho Building 1st and 4th floors Chuo-ku, Tokyo, 103-0023, Japan
Tel.: (81) 33 662 5100
Web Site: https://www.itc-uc.co.jp
Emp.: 2,762
Property Management Services
N.A.I.C.S.: 531012

ITOCHU Venezuela S.A. (1)
Miranda Nucleo A Piso-11 Ave Libertador, Chacao, Caracas, 1060, Venezuela
Tel.: (58) 212 263 3711
Emp.: 12
Industrial Machinery & Equipment Whslr
N.A.I.C.S.: 423830

ITOCHU Windows Co., Ltd. (1)
8th Floor Tokyu Reit Hacchobori Bldg 7-1 Hacchobori 2-chome, Chuo-ku, Tokyo, 104-0032, Japan
Tel.: (81) 3 3553 7690
Web Site: http://www.itcw.co.jp
Insulating Glass Mfr & Whslr
N.A.I.C.S.: 327215

ITOHPIA HOME Co., Ltd. (1)
2-1-10 Nihonbashi, Chuo-ku, Tokyo, 103-0027, Japan
Tel.: (81) 352040711
Web Site: http://www.itohpiahome.co.jp
Residential Construction Services
N.A.I.C.S.: 236116

ITOPIA Asset Management Co., Ltd. (1)
Jinbocho Mitsui Bldg 17F 1-105 Kanda-Jinbocho, Chiyoda-ku, Tokyo, 101-0051, Japan
Tel.: (81) 332199210
Web Site: http://www.itopia-am.com
Asset Management Services
N.A.I.C.S.: 523940
Kenji Kousaka (Pres & CEO)

ITR Corp. (1)
Itochu Corp 2-5-1 Kitaaoyama, Minato-ku, Tokyo, 107-0061, Japan
Tel.: (81) 334976454

Tire Whslr & Retailer
N.A.I.C.S.: 423130

ITS. Farm Co., Ltd. (1)
2-35-13 Kameido, Koto-ku, Tokyo, 136-0071, Japan
Tel.: (81) 3 5609 1839
Web Site: http://www.its-farm.co.jp
Poultry Farming Services
N.A.I.C.S.: 112340
Tanbo Takashi Hisashi (Pres)

JOI'X CORPORATION (1)
Sumitomo Hanzomon Building 3-16 Hayabusa-cho, Chiyoda-ku, Tokyo, 540-0012, Japan
Tel.: (81) 352132500
Web Site: http://www.joix-corp.com
Emp.: 1,041
Apparel Goods Distr
N.A.I.C.S.: 424350

Jamieson Manufacturing Co. (1)
4221 Platinum Way, Dallas, TX 75237
Tel.: (214) 339-8384
Web Site: http://www.jamiesonfence.com
Sales Range: $10-24.9 Million
Emp.: 100
Wire Fence, Gates & Accessories
N.A.I.C.S.: 423390

Japan Aerospace Corporation (1)
20F Shin-Aoyama Buildings West 1-1-1 Minami-Aoyama, Minato-ku, Tokyo, 107-0062, Japan
Tel.: (81) 35 785 5995
Web Site: https://www.j-aero.co.jp
Sales Range: $25-49.9 Million
Emp.: 80
Aircraft Part Mfr
N.A.I.C.S.: 336412
Hitoshi Tanimura (Pres & CEO)

Japan Nutrition Co., Ltd. (1)
New Aoyama Building West Building 22nd Floor Minami-Aoyama, Minato-ku, Tokyo, 107-0062, Japan
Tel.: (81) 3 5771 7890
Web Site: http://www.jnc.co.jp
Livestock Nutritional Supplements Mfr & Distr
N.A.I.C.S.: 311119

Plant (Domestic):

Japan Nutrition Co., Ltd. - Kashima Plant (2)
20-5 Towada, Kamisu, 314-0102, Ibaraki, Japan
Tel.: (81) 299 96 2227
Livestock Nutritional Supplements Mfr & Distr
N.A.I.C.S.: 311119

Leilian Co., Ltd. (1)
3-6-28 Aobadai Sumitomo Real Estate Aobadai Tower 2nd floor, Meguro-ku, Tokyo, 153-0042, Japan
Tel.: (81) 368347201
Web Site: http://www.leilian.co.jp
Sales Range: $400-449.9 Million
Emp.: 1,398
Women's Apparel Stores
N.A.I.C.S.: 458110

Marubeni Itochu Pipe & Tube, Inc. (1)
750 Town & Country Blvd, Houston, TX 77024
Tel.: (281) 368-7000
Web Site: http://www.mitube.com
Sales Range: $25-49.9 Million
Emp.: 50
Steel Pipe & Tube Distr
N.A.I.C.S.: 423510
Mike Lamb (CFO)

Marubeni-Itochu Steel Inc. (1)
Nihonbashi 1-chome Bldg 4-1 Nihonbashi 1-chome 16-18F, Chuo-ku, Tokyo, 103-8247, Japan
(50%)
Tel.: (81) 352043300
Web Site: https://www.benichu.com
Sales Range: $1-4.9 Billion
Emp.: 10,480
Iron & Steel Forging
N.A.I.C.S.: 332111
Tatsuhiko Toshita (Pres & CEO)

Subsidiary (Non-US):

Marubeni-Itochu Steel America, Inc. (2)

INTERNATIONAL PUBLIC

Tel.: (212) 660-6000
Sales Range: $25-49.9 Million
Emp.: 50
Steel Importer & Exporter; Steel Blanking, Cut-to-Length, Laser Welding & Stamping Services
N.A.I.C.S.: 425120
Toshio Namiki (CEO)

Subsidiary (Domestic):

ClarkWestern Building Systems, Inc. (3)
6510 General Dr, Riverside, CA 92509-0103
Tel.: (951) 360-3500
Web Site: http://www.clarkdietrich.com
Sales Range: $25-49.9 Million
Mfr & Developer of Metal Framing
N.A.I.C.S.: 332322

Marubeni-Itochu Tubulars America, Inc. (3)
750 Town and Country Blvd, Houston, TX 77024
Tel.: (281) 368-7000
Web Site: https://www.mitube.com
Sales Range: $25-49.9 Million
Emp.: 50
Steel Tubes Supplier to the Oil & Gas Industry
N.A.I.C.S.: 423510
Taewoo Kim (Mgr-Acctg)

Subsidiary (Domestic):

Sooner Pipe LLC (4)
909 Fannin St Ste 3100, Houston, TX 77010
Tel.: (713) 759-1200
Oil Country Tubular Goods
N.A.I.C.S.: 423830
Joseph C. Ottaviani (VP-Ops)

Subsidiary (Domestic):

A-Z Terminal Corporation (5)
1919 Crosby Dayton Rd, Crosby, TX 77532
Tel.: (281) 328-4877
Web Site: http://www.soonerpipe.com
Sales Range: $1-9.9 Million
Emp.: 35
Oilfield Casing
N.A.I.C.S.: 237120
Joseph C. Ottaviani (VP & Gen Mgr)

Sooner Inc. (5)
909 Fannin St Ste 3100, Houston, TX 77010
Tel.: (888) 487-3557
Web Site: https://www.soonerpipe.com
Sales Range: $50-74.9 Million
Emp.: 93
Oil Tubular Products & General Oil Field Supplies Distr
N.A.I.C.S.: 423830
Dorinda J. Barker (CFO)

Subsidiary (Domestic):

CTAP LLC (6)
2585 Trailridge Dr E, Lafayette, CO 80026
Tel.: (844) 888-2827
Web Site: https://www.ctapllc.com
Industrial Machinery & Equipment Merchant Whslr
N.A.I.C.S.: 423830
Seth Merril (Pres)

Division (Domestic):

Marubeni-Itochu Steel Inc. - Osaka Division (2)
Nakanoshima Festival Tower 26F 2-3-18 Nakanoshima, Kita-ku, Osaka, 530-0005, Japan
Tel.: (81) 676384800
Web Site: http://www.benichu.com
Steel & Steel Products Whslr
N.A.I.C.S.: 423510

NISSIN ADVANCED COATING (TIANJIN) CO.,LTD (1)
No 5 Xiangzun Road, Tianxiang Industrial Park Xiqing Economic Development Area, Tianjin, 300385, China
Tel.: (86) 22 2396 6016
Web Site: http://nissin-coating.com
Food Products Mfr
N.A.I.C.S.: 311999

AND PRIVATE COMPANIES

Naigai Travel Service Co., Ltd. (1)
1-10-7 Dogenzaka, Shibuya-ku, Tokyo, 150-0043, Japan
Tel.: (81) 3 6910 0139
Web Site: http://www.naigainet.co.jp
Travel Arrangement Services
N.A.I.C.S.: 561510

Nippon Access, Inc. (1)
1-1-1 Nishi-Shinagawa, Shinagawa-ku, Tokyo, 141-8582, Japan
Tel.: (81) 3 5435 5800
Web Site: http://www.nippon-access.co.jp
Emp.: 3,992
Food Product Whslr
N.A.I.C.S.: 424490
Junichi Sasaki (Pres)

P.T. Aneka Bumi Pratama (1)
Jl Pulo Kerto RT 04 RW 02 Kec Gandus, Palembang, South Sumatera, Indonesia
Tel.: (62) 711 744 0992
Web Site: https://www.ptabp.co.id
Crumb Rubber Mfr
N.A.I.C.S.: 326299
Hisashi Yajima (Pres)

PT ITOCHU INDONESIA (1)
The Plaza Office Tower 26th Floor Jl MH Thamrin Kav 28-30, Jakarta, 10350, Indonesia
Tel.: (62) 21 2992 2300
Industrial Machinery & Equipment Whslr
N.A.I.C.S.: 423830

PT. SUZUKI Finance Indonesia (1)
Jl Raya Bekasi KM 19 Pulogadung, Jakarta Timur, 12910, Indonesia
Tel.: (62) 2180607000
Web Site: http://www.sfi.co.id
Automobile Financing Services
N.A.I.C.S.: 522220

Plastribution Limited (1)
14 Charter Point Way, Ashby Business Park, Ashby de la Zouch, LE65 1NF, Leicestershire, United Kingdom
Tel.: (44) 153 056 0560
Web Site: https://www.plastribution.co.uk
Plastic Material Distr
N.A.I.C.S.: 424610
Martin White (Sls Mgr-Direct & Distr)

Pocket Card Co., Ltd. (1)
Sumitomo Fudosan Onarimon Tower 1-1-1 Shibakoen, Minato-ku, Tokyo, 105-0011, Japan (36.05%)
Tel.: (81) 33 432 6070
Web Site: https://www.pocketcard.co.jp
Emp.: 410
Credit Card Services
N.A.I.C.S.: 522210
Kenji Imazato (Exec Officer)

Prominent (Europe) Limited (1)
Unit 8 Wheatcroft Business Park Landmere Lane, Edwalton, Nottingham, NG12 4DG, United Kingdom
Tel.: (44) 1159212222
Web Site: http://www.prominent-europe.co.uk
Men Apparel Whslr
N.A.I.C.S.: 424350

Provence Huiles S.A.S. (1)
25 avenue de Rome, 13127, Vitrolles, France
Tel.: (33) 442461107
Web Site: http://provence-huiles.com
Vegetable Oil Mfr
N.A.I.C.S.: 311225

REMEJE PHARMACEUTICALS (CHINA) CO., LTD. (1)
Room 1306-1308 Suite A Aerospace Mansion No 4019 Shennan Ave, Shenzhen, 518048, Guangdong, China (70%)
Tel.: (86) 75588265899
Emp.: 8,000
Pharmaceutical Product Whslr
N.A.I.C.S.: 325412

ROYNE CO., LTD. (1)
1-22-1 Higashigotanda Nippon Life Gotanda East Building 4F, Shinagawa- ku, Tokyo, 141-0022, Osaka, Japan
Tel.: (81) 36 830 7820
Web Site: http://www.royne.co.jp
Sales Range: $150-199.9 Million
Emp.: 170
Woven & Knitted Wear Mfr & Whslr

N.A.I.C.S.: 314999
Masahiko Kinoshita (Pres & CEO)

Ricardo Perez, S.A. (1)
Via Brasil Street and Samuel Lewis Avenue Ricardo Perez SA Building, Obarrio Urbanization Bella Vista Township, Panama, Panama
Tel.: (507) 2107000
Web Site: http://www.toyotarp.com
Automotive Distr
N.A.I.C.S.: 423110

SCABAL JAPAN Co., Ltd. (1)
1st Floor Osaka Keori Kaikan 6-10 Awajimachi 2-chome, Chuo-ku, Osaka, 541-0047, Japan
Tel.: (81) 662322755
Web Site: http://www.scabal.co.jp
Apparel Import & Distr
N.A.I.C.S.: 424350

Samson Holding Ltd. (1)
China Timber Industry City Development Area No 2 Taicheng Road, Jia Shan County, Hangzhou, 314100, Zhejiang, China
Tel.: (86) 57384824666
Web Site: http://www.samsonholding.com
Rev: $598,850,000
Assets: $616,376,000
Liabilities: $301,009,000
Net Worth: $315,367,000
Earnings: $15,125,000
Emp.: 6,100
Fiscal Year-end: 12/31/2022
Holding Company
N.A.I.C.S.: 551112
Samuel Shan Huei Kuo (Co-Founder, Chm & CEO)

Sankei Co., Ltd. (1)
6F KDX Toyosu Grand Square 1-7-12 Shinonome, Koto-ku, Tokyo, 135-0062, Japan
Tel.: (81) 367572782
Web Site: http://www.sankeicoltd.co.jp
Emp.: 1,930
Garments Whslr
N.A.I.C.S.: 424350
Kazuo Oguchi (Pres)

Southwood Export Limited (1)
45 Kekeno Place Awarua, PO Box 7010, Invercargill, 9844, New Zealand
Tel.: (64) 3 218 2073
Web Site: https://www.swel.co.nz
Wood Product Distr
N.A.I.C.S.: 423310
Graeme Manley (Gen Mgr)

TELECOMUNICACIONES Y SERVICIOS CONOSUR LTDA. (1)
Calle Panamericana Norte 6199 Oficina 804 Torre YOEMAR, Conchali, Santiago, Chile
Tel.: (56) 227076800
Web Site: http://www.telconsur.cl
Communication Equipment Installation Services
N.A.I.C.S.: 238210

Taiwan Distribution Center Co., Ltd. (1)
No 1 Hongchang Street Donglinli, Linkou District, New Taipei City, Taiwan
Tel.: (886) 226032801
Web Site: http://www.tdccorp.com.tw
Logistic Services
N.A.I.C.S.: 541614

The Japan Cee-Bee Chemical Co., Ltd. (1)
4th fl Omori Plaza Bldg 28-3 Minami-Oi 3-chome, Shinagawa-ku, Tokyo, 140-0013, Japan
Tel.: (81) 35 767 6431
Web Site: https://www.jcbchem.co.jp
Sales Range: $50-74.9 Million
Emp.: 70
Cleaning Chemicals Distr
N.A.I.C.S.: 424690
Shinji Hamamoto (Pres & CEO)

Toyo Advanced Technologies Co., Ltd. (1)
5-3-38 Ujina-Higashi, Minami-ku, Hiroshima, 734-8501, Japan (70%)
Tel.: (81) 822525230
Web Site: http://www.toyo-at.co.jp
Sales Range: $350-399.9 Million
Emp.: 679
Grinding Machine Mfr

N.A.I.C.S.: 333517
Yasuto Tatsuta (Pres)

Division (Domestic):

Toyo Advanced Technologies Co., Ltd. - Automobile Components Sales Division (2)
5-3-38 Ujina-Higashi, Minami, Japan
Tel.: (81) 82 252 5207
Automobile Component Distr
N.A.I.C.S.: 423120

Toyo Advanced Technologies Co., Ltd. - Hard Coating Sales Division (Hard Coating) (2)
5-3-38 Ujina-Higashi, Minami-ku, Hiroshima, 734-8501, Japan
Tel.: (81) 822525216
Web Site: http://www.toyo-at.co.jp
Die Equipment Distr
N.A.I.C.S.: 423440

Plant (Domestic):

Toyo Advanced Technologies Co., Ltd. - Hiroshima Plant (2)
5-3-38 Ujina-higashi, Minami-ku, Hiroshima, 734-8501, Japan
Tel.: (81) 82 252 5212
Web Site: http://www.toyo-at.co.jp
Industrial Machinery Mfr
N.A.I.C.S.: 333248

Toyo Advanced Technologies Co., Ltd. - Nagoya Plant (Hard coating) (2)
41-1 Aza Hikisawa Kamiya-cho, Kasugai, 480-0304, Aichi, Japan
Tel.: (81) 568 88 5151
Web Site: http://www.toyo-at.co.jp
Industrial Machinery Mfr
N.A.I.C.S.: 333248

Toyo Advanced Technologies Co., Ltd. - Tokyo Plant (Hard coating) (2)
1450-27 Uwanodai, Fukaya, 366-0801, Saitama, Japan
Tel.: (81) 48 571 5216
Industrial Machinery Mfr
N.A.I.C.S.: 333248

UNEX (Guatemala), S.A. (1)
13 Calle 3-40 Zona 10 Edificio Atlantis Nivel 14 Oficina 1402, Guatemala, Guatemala
Tel.: (502) 24270100
Web Site: http://www.unexguatemala.com
Coffee Product Mfr
N.A.I.C.S.: 311920

UNICO CORPORATION (1)
2nd floor Inamura Building 9-10 Nihonbashitomizawa-cho, Chuo-ku, Tokyo, 103-0006, Japan
Tel.: (81) 35 643 2821
Web Site: https://www.uniform.co.jp
Emp.: 86
Apparel Mfr & Whslr
N.A.I.C.S.: 315250

Universal Food Co., Ltd. (1)
2-3-43 Shinsuna, Koto-ku, Tokyo, 136-0075, Japan
Tel.: (81) 356179350
Sales Range: $50-74.9 Million
Emp.: 100
Food Products Distr
N.A.I.C.S.: 424490

VEHICLES MIDDLE EAST FZCO U.A.E. (1)
Office 17602 Jebel Ali Free Zone, Dubai, United Arab Emirates
Tel.: (971) 4 8873280
Motor Vehicle Leasing Services
N.A.I.C.S.: 532120

Wellness Communications Corporation (1)
14th Floor Ark Mori Building 1-12-32 Akasaka, Minato-ku, Tokyo, 107-6014, Japan
Tel.: (81) 355449898
Web Site: http://www.wellcoms.jp
Emp.: 182
Healthcare Software Development Services
N.A.I.C.S.: 541511

Yanase & Co., Ltd. (1)
1-6-38 Shibaura, Minato-ku, Tokyo, 105-8575, Japan

Tel.: (81) 354404755
Web Site: http://www.yanase.co.jp
New & Used Car Retailer
N.A.I.C.S.: 441110

ITOCHU ENEX CO., LTD.

ITOCHU ENEX CO., LTD.
3-2-5 Kasumigaseki, Chiyoda-ku, Tokyo, 100-6028, Japan
Tel.: (81) 342338000 JP
Web Site: https://www.itcenex.com
Year Founded: 1961
8133—(TKS)
Rev.: $6,367,426,220
Assets: $2,936,849,440
Liabilities: $1,666,347,950
Net Worth: $1,270,501,490
Earnings: $91,793,070
Emp.: 5,365
Fiscal Year-end: 03/31/24
Petroleum Products Distr & Gas Station Operator
N.A.I.C.S.: 424720
Kenji Okada (Pres & CEO)

Subsidiaries:

Ecore Co., Ltd. (1)
Tel.: (81) 922828900
Web Site: http://www.ecoregas.jp
Sales Range: $1-4.9 Billion
Emp.: 402
LP Gas & Kerosene Supply Services
N.A.I.C.S.: 457210

Enearc Co., Ltd. (1)
Kasumigaseki Building 29th Floor 3-2-5 Kasumigaseki, Chiyoda-ku, Tokyo, 100-6029, Japan
Tel.: (81) 342338200
Web Site: http://enearc.co.jp
LPG Gas Distribution Services
N.A.I.C.S.: 211130

Enex Asset Management Co., Ltd. (1)
Kasumigaseki Building 29F 3-2-5, Kasumigaseki Chiyoda-ku, Tokyo, 100-6029, Japan
Tel.: (81) 342338320
Web Site: http://www.enex-am.jp
Asset Management Services
N.A.I.C.S.: 523940
Keiichi Matsuzuka (Pres & CEO)

Enex Clean Power Energy Co., Ltd. (1)
1 17 20 Bldg 4th Fl Sumiyoshi Koto, Sumiyoshi, Tokyo, 135 0002, Japan
Tel.: (81) 356007320
Sales Range: $25-49.9 Million
Emp.: 97
Low Emission Vehicles & Fuel Mfr
N.A.I.C.S.: 324110

Enex Life Service Co., Ltd. (1)
3-2-5 Kasumigaseki, Chiyoda-ku, Tokyo, 100-6001, Japan
Tel.: (81) 342338320
Web Site: https://www.enexls.ne.jp
Electric Power Generation Services
N.A.I.C.S.: 221122

Enex Petroleum Sales Nishi-Nihon Co., Ltd. (1)
10 10 Hashimoto cho, Naka ku, Hiroshima, 730 0015, Japan (100%)
Tel.: (81) 825022626
Web Site: http://www.west-enex.com
Sales Range: Less than $1 Million
Emp.: 180
Gasoline Station Services
N.A.I.C.S.: 457120
Tadashi Utsunomiya (CFO)

ITC Enex (Thailand) Co., Ltd. (1)
159/16 Serm-Mit Tower 10th Floor Room No 1016/1, Sukhumvit 21 Road Asoke Khlong Toei Nuea Subdistrict Wattana District, Bangkok, 10110, Thailand
Tel.: (66) 22586951
Renewable Energy Generation Services
N.A.I.C.S.: 221114

ITC Enex Southeast Asia Co., Ltd. (1)
159/16 Serm-Mit Tower 10th Floor Sukhumvit 21 Asoke, Klongtoey Nua Wattana, Bangkok, 10110, Thailand

ITOCHU ENEX CO., LTD.

Itochu Enex Co., Ltd.—(Continued)
Tel.: (66) 22586952
Petroleum Product Distr
N.A.I.C.S.: 424720

Itochu Enex Home-Life Hokkaido Co., Ltd. (1)
Sapporo MN Building 7th floor Kita 1-jo Nishi 3-3, Chuo-ku, Sapporo, 060-0001, Hokkaido, Japan
Tel.: (81) 112422060
Web Site: https://hokkaido.enexhl.jp
Emp.: 242
Petroleum Product Distr
N.A.I.C.S.: 424720

Itochu Enex Home-Life Kansai Co., Ltd. (1)
Shinosakadaiichiseimei Bldg 8f 3 5 24 Miyahara, Yodogawa Ku, Osaka, 100 0003, Osaka, Japan
Tel.: (81) 663960076
Petroleum Product Distr
Fuel Oil Mfr
N.A.I.C.S.: 324110

Itochu Enex Home-Life Nishi-Nihon Co., Ltd. (1)
Hiroshima Intes Building 7F 10-10 Hashimotocho, Naka-ku, Hiroshima, 730-0015, Japan
Tel.: (81) 825022500
Web Site: https://nishi-nihon.enexhl.jp
Emp.: 253
Petroleum Product Distr
N.A.I.C.S.: 424720

Itochu Enex Home-Life Tohoku Co., Ltd. (1)
3 1 35 Ogimachi Miyagino Ku Sendai-shi, Miyagi, 983 0034, Japan
Tel.: (81) 222321811
Web Site: http://www.homelife-tohoku.jp
Petroleum & Petroleum Products Whslr
N.A.I.C.S.: 424720

Itochu Enex Support Co., Ltd. (1)
12F Toranomon Twin Building East 2-10-1 Toranomon, Minato ku, Tokyo, 105-0001, Japan
Tel.: (81) 363278090
Web Site: http://www.itcesp.co.jp
Rev.: $49,467,320
Emp.: 55
Administration Support Services
N.A.I.C.S.: 624190
Ootsubo Yoshi Sung *(Pres)*

Itochu Industrial Gas Co., Ltd. (1)
Kasumigaseki Building 27th Floor 3-2-5, Kasumigaseki Chiyoda-ku, Tokyo, 100-6027, Japan
Tel.: (81) 342338270
Web Site: http://www.iig.co.jp
Emp.: 259
Industrial Gas Mfr
N.A.I.C.S.: 325120
Yozo Taniguchi *(Exec Dir)*

Kokura Kosan Energy Co., Ltd. (1)
Kmm Bldg 2 14 1 Asano, Kokurakita Ku, Fukuoka, 802 0001, Fukuoka, Japan
Tel.: (81) 935113150
Petroleum & Petroleum Products Whslr
N.A.I.C.S.: 424720

Kyushu Energy Co., Ltd. (1)
6-6 Kamoike Shinmachi, Kagoshima, 890-0064, Japan
Tel.: (81) 992976425
Web Site: https://www.kyushu-energy.co.jp
Eletric Power Generation Services
N.A.I.C.S.: 221122

Oita Kyuseki Hanbai Co., Ltd. (1)
Toyomi 5 No 3 chome, Oita, 870 0035, Oita, Japan
Tel.: (81) 97 534 0468
Web Site: http://www.oita-kyuseki.co.jp
Sales Range: $25-49.9 Million
Emp.: 46
Petroleum & Petroleum Products Whslr
N.A.I.C.S.: 424720

Oji-Ltochu Enex Power Retailing Co., Ltd. (1)
Kasumigaseki Building 27th Floor 3-2-5, Kasumigaseki Chiyoda-ku, Tokyo, 100-6027, Japan
Tel.: (81) 342338260

Web Site: http://ojex.net
Eletric Power Generation Services
N.A.I.C.S.: 221122

Passtech Co., Ltd. (1)
11 32 Minamimachi, Osaka, Kishiwada, 596-0060, Japan
Tel.: (81) 724327011
Professional & Management Services
N.A.I.C.S.: 541380

ITOCO, INC.

1-2857 Sherwood Heights Dr, Oakville, L6J 7J9, ON, Canada
Web Site: http://www.itoco.net
ITMC—(OTCIQ)
Assets: $96,000
Liabilities: $1,742,000
Net Worth: ($1,646,000)
Earnings: ($1,418,000)
Fiscal Year-end: 12/31/20
Cannabis Farming Services
N.A.I.C.S.: 111998
Michael Paul *(CEO)*

ITOHAM YONEKYU HOLDINGS INC.

1 6 21 Mita, Tokyo, 153-8587, Meguro, Japan
Tel.: (81) 57238619
Web Site: https://www.itoham-yonekyu-holdings.com
2296—(TKS)
Rev.: $6,316,383,800
Assets: $3,057,587,700
Liabilities: $1,171,582,840
Net Worth: $1,886,004,860
Earnings: $102,805,330
Emp.: 3,000
Fiscal Year-end: 03/31/24
Holding Company
N.A.I.C.S.: 551112
Isao Miyashita *(Pres)*

Subsidiaries:

Itoham Foods, Inc. (1)
4-27 Takahata-cho, Nishinomiya, 663-8586, Hyogo, Japan
Tel.: (81) 798661231
Web Site: https://www.itoham.co.jp
Emp.: 1,881
Meat, Ham & Sausage Processor
N.A.I.C.S.: 311612
Ikurou Shibayama *(CEO)*

Subsidiary (Non-US):

ANZCO Foods Ltd. (2)
5 Robin Mann Place Christchurch Airport, Christchurch, 8053, New Zealand (100%)
Tel.: (64) 33582200
Web Site: https://www.anzcofoods.com
Sales Range: $900-999.9 Million
Emp.: 3,000
Beef & Lamb Products Mfr
N.A.I.C.S.: 311612
Peter Conley *(CEO)*

Subsidiary (Non-US):

ANZCO FOODS TAIWAN LIMITED (3)
2F -203 No 52 Sec 1 Nanjing E Road, Zhongshan Dist, Taipei, 104408, Taiwan
Tel.: (886) 225643185
Food Product Mfr & Distr
N.A.I.C.S.: 311412

Subsidiary (Domestic):

ANZCO Foods Ltd. Canterbury Facility (3)
Seafield Road, Pendarves, Ashburton, 7777, New Zealand
Tel.: (64) 33027699
Food Products Mfr
N.A.I.C.S.: 311991

ANZCO Foods Ltd. Eltham Facility (3)
London Street, Eltham, 4322, New Zealand
Tel.: (64) 67648155
Food Products Mfr
N.A.I.C.S.: 311991

ANZCO Foods Ltd. Green Island Facility (3)
15 Carnforth Street, Green Island, Dunedin, 9018, New Zealand
Tel.: (64) 34788033
Food Products Mfr
N.A.I.C.S.: 311991

ANZCO Foods Ltd. Kokiri Facility (3)
Arnold Valley Road, Kokiri, Greymouth, 7872, New Zealand
Tel.: (64) 37625505
Food Products Mfr
N.A.I.C.S.: 311991

ANZCO Foods Ltd. Manawatu Facility (3)
Ferry Road, Bulls, Manawatu, 4894, New Zealand
Tel.: (64) 63220184
Food Products Mfr
N.A.I.C.S.: 311991

ANZCO Foods Ltd. Marlborough Facility (3)
Alabama Road, Blenheim, 7274, New Zealand
Tel.: (64) 35209347
Food Products Mfr
N.A.I.C.S.: 311991

ANZCO Foods Ltd. Rakaia Facility (3)
Knyvetts Road, Rakaia, 7783, New Zealand
Tel.: (64) 33027802
Food Products Mfr
N.A.I.C.S.: 311991

ANZCO Foods Ltd. Rangitikei Facility (3)
State Highway 1, Marton, 4787, New Zealand
Tel.: (64) 63270010
Food Products Mfr
N.A.I.C.S.: 311991

ANZCO Foods Ltd. Waitara Facility (3)
Stafford Street, Waitara, 4320, New Zealand
Tel.: (64) 67549088
Food Products Mfr
N.A.I.C.S.: 311991

Subsidiary (Non-US):

Anzco Foods (Europe) ltd (3)
Markt 32 bus 1, 9700, Oudenaarde, Belgium
Tel.: (32) 55317312
Food Products Mfr
N.A.I.C.S.: 424470

Anzco Foods (UK) Ltd (3)
Jubilee House 3 The Drive, Great Warley, Brentwood, CM13 3FR, Essex, United Kingdom
Tel.: (44) 1708371803
Food Product Mfr & Distr
N.A.I.C.S.: 311412
Heath Milne *(Gen Mgr)*

Anzco Foods Australia Pty Ltd (3)
Unit 2B 54 Riverside Place, Morningside, Brisbane, 4170, QLD, Australia
Tel.: (61) 733958999
Food Products Distr
N.A.I.C.S.: 424470

Anzco Foods Japan Ltd. (3)
2F Hulic Megro Mita 7-13 Mita 1-chome, Meguro-ku, Tokyo, 153-0062, Japan
Tel.: (81) 357731271
Web Site: https://anzcofoods.com
Food Products Distr
N.A.I.C.S.: 424470

Subsidiary (US):

Anzco Foods North America Inc. (3)
666 Dundee Rd Ste 1605, Northbrook, IL 60062
Tel.: (847) 498-4470
Web Site: http://www.anzcofoods.com
Emp.: 6
Food Product Mfr & Distr
N.A.I.C.S.: 311412
Nick Brander *(Pres)*

Subsidiary (Domestic):

Asakusa Ham Co., Ltd. (2)

1-2-5 Senzoku, Taito-ku, Tokyo, 111-0031, Japan
Tel.: (81) 338762901
Web Site: http://www.asakusa-ham.co.jp
Sales Range: $75-99.9 Million
Emp.: 92
Processed Meat Mfr
N.A.I.C.S.: 311612
Hironobu Fujimoto *(Pres)*

Subsidiary (US):

Calco International, Inc. (2)
2 Denver Highlands 10065 E Harvard Ave Ste 805, Denver, CO 80231 (100%)
Tel.: (303) 671-4550
Web Site: http://www.coloradojijo.com
Sales Range: $50-74.9 Million
Emp.: 4
Export of Beef & Pork to Japan
N.A.I.C.S.: 424470

Subsidiary (Domestic):

Dairyu Inc. (2)
1-34-1 Tobitakyu, Chofu, 182-0036, Tokyo, Japan
Tel.: (81) 424844811
Web Site: http://www.dairyu.net
Sales Range: $50-74.9 Million
Emp.: 150
Chinese Frozen Food Mfr & Whslr
N.A.I.C.S.: 311412

Subsidiary (Non-US):

Five Star Beef Ltd. (2)
Seaside Road Wakanui, PO Box 42, Ashburton, 7740, Mid Canterbury, New Zealand (50%)
Tel.: (64) 33081599
Web Site: http://www.fivestarbeef.co.nz
Sales Range: $10-24.9 Million
Emp.: 24
N.A.I.C.S.: 425120
Ian Andrews *(Gen Mgr)*

Subsidiary (Domestic):

Ih Meat Solutions Co.,Ltd. (2)
Mita 1-6-21, Meguroku, Tokyo, 153-8587, Japan
Tel.: (81) 357236213
Veal Product Mfr
N.A.I.C.S.: 311612

Ito Fresh Salad Co., Ltd. (2)
Mita 1-6-21, Meguroku, Tokyo, 153-8587, Japan
Tel.: (81) 357236887
Fresh Salad Mfr
N.A.I.C.S.: 311991

Subsidiary (US):

Itoham America,Inc. (2)
2640 Murray St, Sioux City, IA 51111
Tel.: (303) 671-4550
Processed Meats Whslr
N.A.I.C.S.: 424470

Subsidiary (Domestic):

Itoham Daily Inc. (2)
Takashimizu Raikozawa 20, Kurihara, 987-2195, Miyagi, Japan
Tel.: (81) 228583111
Processed Meats Mfr & Distr
N.A.I.C.S.: 311612

Plant (Domestic):

Itoham Foods, Inc. - Funabashi Plant (2)
24-28 Takase-cho, Funabashi, 273-0014, Chiba, Japan
Tel.: (81) 474371186
Web Site: http://www.itoham.co.jp
Processed Meat Mfr
N.A.I.C.S.: 311612

Itoham Foods, Inc. - Itoham Daily Otaru Plant (2)
5-61-3 Zenibako, Otaru, 061-3271, Hokkaido, Japan
Tel.: (81) 133721861
Web Site: http://www.itoham.co.jp
Processed Meat Mfr
N.A.I.C.S.: 311612

AND PRIVATE COMPANIES

Itoham Foods, Inc. - Itoham Daily Tohoku Plant (2)
20 Raikozawa Takashimizu, Kurihara, 987-2195, Miyagi, Japan
Tel.: (81) 228 58 3115
Web Site: http://www.itoham.co.jp
Processed Meat Mfr
N.A.I.C.S.: 311612

Itoham Foods, Inc. - Itoham Shokuhin, Oyabe Plant (2)
5068 Nabata, Oyabe, 932-0131, Toyama, Japan
Tel.: (81) 766 69 8888
Web Site: http://www.itoham.co.jp
Processed Meat Mfr
N.A.I.C.S.: 311612

Itoham Foods, Inc. - Kobe Plant (2)
6-20-1 Koyo-cho Nishi, Higashinada-ku, Kobe, 658-0033, Hyogo, Japan
Tel.: (81) 788568600
Web Site: http://www.itoham.co.jp
Sales Range: $25-49.9 Million
Emp.: 250
Processed Meat Mfr
N.A.I.C.S.: 311612

Itoham Foods, Inc. - Nishinomiya Plant (2)
4-27 Takahata-Cho, Nishinomiya, 663-8586, Hyogo, Japan
Tel.: (81) 798641381
Web Site: http://www.itoham.co.jp
Processed Meat Mfr
N.A.I.C.S.: 311612

Itoham Foods, Inc. - Rokko Plant (2)
5-7 Koyo-cho Nishi, Higashinada-ku, Kobe, 658-0033, Hyogo, Japan
Tel.: (81) 788579186
Web Site: http://www.itoham.co.jp
Processed Meat Mfr
N.A.I.C.S.: 311612

Subsidiary (Domestic):

Itoham Foods, Inc. - Tokyo Plant (2)
1-3 Nedo, Kashiwa, 277-0831, Chiba, Japan
Tel.: (81) 471323111
Processed Meat Mfr
N.A.I.C.S.: 311612

Plant (Domestic):

Itoham Foods, Inc. - Toyohashi Plant (2)
73 Aza Fujinami Fujinami-cho, Toyohashi, 441-8686, Aichi, Japan
Tel.: (81) 532 45 1180
Web Site: http://www.itoham.co.jp
Processed Meat Mfr
N.A.I.C.S.: 311612

Subsidiary (Domestic):

Itoham Foods, Inc. - West Kyushu Plant (2)
970-1 Nagano Kiyama-cho, Miyaki-gun, Saga, 841-0202, Japan
Tel.: (81) 942920086
Processed Meat Mfr
N.A.I.C.S.: 311612

Okinawa Fresh Pack Co., Ltd. (2)
2814-2 Chibana, Koza, 904-2143, Okinawa, Japan
Tel.: (81) 989383790
Veal Product Mfr
N.A.I.C.S.: 311612

Sankyo Meat Co., Ltd. (2)
6965 Noikura Ariake-Cho, Shibushi, 899-7402, Kagoshima, Japan
Tel.: (81) 994741118
Web Site: http://www.itoham.co.jp
Emp.: 470
Livestock Farming & Meat Processing Services
N.A.I.C.S.: 112990
Koji Kusumoto (Mng Dir)

Tsukushi Factory Co., Ltd. (2)
2-1-11 Nakanohara, Yahatanishi-ku, Kitakyushu, 807-0078, Fukuoka, Japan
Tel.: (81) 93614373
Web Site: https://www.tsukushi-factory.co.jp
Sales Range: $25-49.9 Million
Emp.: 100
Processed Meat Mfr

N.A.I.C.S.: 311612

Yonekyu Corporation (1)
1259 Okanomiya Terabayashi, Numazu, 410-8530, Shizuoka, Japan (100%)
Tel.: (81) 55 922 5321
Web Site: http://www.yonekyu.co.jp
Emp.: 773
Processed Food Mfr & Whslr
N.A.I.C.S.: 311612

Subsidiary (Domestic):

Gotemba Kogen Brewery, Co., Ltd. (2)
719 Koyama, Gotemba, 412-0033, Shizuoka, Japan
Tel.: (81) 550875500
Web Site: https://www.gkb.co.jp
Beer Brewery Services
N.A.I.C.S.: 312120

I-Pork Corp. (2)
161-1 Toribamachi, Maebashi, 371-0845, Gunma, Japan
Tel.: (81) 272525353
Web Site: http://www.yonekyu.co.jp
Meat Product Distr
N.A.I.C.S.: 424420

Plant (Domestic):

I-Pork Corp. - Honjo Plant (3)
115 Sugiyama, Honjo, 367-0074, Saitama, Japan
Tel.: (81) 495 25 2911
Web Site: http://www.yonekyu.co.jp
Veal Product Mfr
N.A.I.C.S.: 311412

Subsidiary (Domestic):

Marufuji Corp. (2)
2-7-19 Konan, Minato-ku, Tokyo, 108-0075, Japan
Tel.: (81) 3347124014
Web Site: http://www.yonekyu.co.jp
Frozen Food Distr
N.A.I.C.S.: 424420

Nikkoh Food Corp. (2)
1281-6 Souemon, Yaizu, 400-0065, Shizuoka, Japan
Tel.: (81) 54 624 2125
Web Site: http://www.yonekyu.co.jp
Prepared Food Mfr
N.A.I.C.S.: 311991

Plant (Domestic):

Nikkoh Food Corp. - Nenoji Plant (3)
1140-1 Ryoke, Kakegawa, 436-0038, Shizuoka, Japan
Tel.: (81) 537 23 2177
Web Site: http://www.yonekyu.co.jp
Prepared Food Mfr
N.A.I.C.S.: 311991

Subsidiary (Domestic):

Taiyo Pork Corp. (2)
1821-1 Fukamachi, Mihara, 723-0001, Hiroshima, Japan
Tel.: (81) 848365010
Web Site: http://www.yonekyu.co.jp
Meat Product Distr
N.A.I.C.S.: 424420

Subsidiary (US):

YONEKYU U.S.A., INC. (2)
3615 E Vernon Ave, Los Angeles, CA 90058
Tel.: (323) 581-4194
Web Site: http://www.yonekyu.co.jp
Prepared Food Mfr
N.A.I.C.S.: 311991

Plant (Domestic):

Yonekyu Corporation - Fuji Plant (2)
50-15 Hachibudaira Higashino, Sunto-gun, Nagaizumi, 411-0931, Shizuoka, Japan
Tel.: (81) 55 988 3215
Web Site: http://www.yonekyu.co.jp
Prepared Food Mfr
N.A.I.C.S.: 311991

Yonekyu Corporation - Fujiyama Plant (2)
2210-1 Inno Aza Nakamichi-Mura, Gotemba, 412-0008, Shizuoka, Japan
Tel.: (81) 550 89 7641
Web Site: http://www.yonekyu.co.jp
Veal Product Mfr
N.A.I.C.S.: 311412

Subsidiary (Domestic):

Yonekyu Delica Foods Corp. (2)
292-33 Ashitaka, Numazu, 410-0001, Shizuoka, Japan
Tel.: (81) 559252255
Web Site: http://www.yonekyu.co.jp
Prepared Food Mfr
N.A.I.C.S.: 311991

Plant (Domestic):

Yonekyu Delica Foods Corp. - Maebashi Plant (3)
88 Kamiooshimamachi, Maebashi, 379-2153, Gunma, Japan
Tel.: (81) 27 261 7575
Web Site: http://www.yonekyu.co.jp
Prepared Food Mfr
N.A.I.C.S.: 311991

Yonekyu Delica Foods Corp. - Shizuoka Plant (3)
6-7-12 Toro, Suruga, Shizuoka, 422-8033, Japan
Tel.: (81) 54 283 0632
Web Site: http://www.yonekyu.co.jp
Prepared Food Mfr
N.A.I.C.S.: 311991

Subsidiary (Domestic):

Yonekyu Kagayaki Corp. (2)
1263 Kobuchi, Kasukabe, 344-0007, Saitama, Japan
Tel.: (81) 487533929
Web Site: http://www.yonekyu.co.jp
Prepared Food Mfr
N.A.I.C.S.: 311991

Plant (Domestic):

Yonekyu Kagayaki Corp. - Hana Plant (3)
1565-15 Shirakusadai, Fukaya, 369-1106, Saitama, Japan
Tel.: (81) 48 583 3511
Web Site: http://www.yonekyu.co.jp
Prepared Food Mfr
N.A.I.C.S.: 311991

Subsidiary (Domestic):

Yonekyu Oishii Tori Corp. (2)
84-1 Nakao Kotoura-cho, Touhaku-gun, Tottori, 689-2311, Japan
Tel.: (81) 858522165
Web Site: http://www.yonekyu.co.jp
Poultry Processing Services
N.A.I.C.S.: 311615

Plant (Domestic):

Yonekyu Oishii Tori Corp. - Shizuoka Plant (3)
462-1 Kasaume, Iwata, 438-0011, Shizuoka, Japan
Tel.: (81) 538 38 0811
Web Site: http://www.yonekyu.co.jp
Poultry Processing Services
N.A.I.C.S.: 311615

ITOKI CORPORATION
2-5-1 Nihonbashi, Chuo-ku, Tokyo, 103-6113, Japan
Tel.: (81) 369103957
Web Site: https://www.itoki-global.com
Year Founded: 1890
7972—(TKS)
Rev.: $942,863,650
Assets: $832,628,330
Liabilities: $442,685,420
Net Worth: $389,942,910
Earnings: $41,866,450
Emp.: 3,892
Fiscal Year-end: 12/31/23
Furniture Mfr & Sales
N.A.I.C.S.: 337127
Masamichi Yamada (Chm)

Subsidiaries:

Dalton Corporation (1)
5-6-10 Tsukiji Hama Rikyu Parkside Place, Chuo-ku, Tokyo, 104-0045, Japan (85.67%)
Tel.: (81) 33 549 6800
Web Site: https://www.dalton.co.jp
Emp.: 363
Laboratory Equipment Mfr
N.A.I.C.S.: 334510
Takayuki Ando (Pres)

ITOKI (Shanghai) Corporation (1)
1 Fl No 425 Yanping Road, Jingan Dist, Shanghai, 200042, China
Tel.: (86) 2162495533
Rev.: $292,600,000
Emp.: 50
Office Furniture Mfr & Supplier
N.A.I.C.S.: 423210

ITOKI (Suzhou) Furniture Co., Ltd. (1)
No 222 Hufuhuang Rd Suzhang Village, Liuhe Town, Taicang, 215431, Jiangsu, China
Tel.: (86) 51281603000
Web Site: http://www.itoki.jp
Office Furniture Mfr & Supplier
N.A.I.C.S.: 423210

ITOKI (Thailand) Co., Ltd. (1)
972 3rd Fl Rim Klong Samsaen Rd Khwaeng Bangkapi, Khet Huaykwang, Bangkok, Thailand
Tel.: (66) 22465430
Web Site: http://www.itokithai.com
Sales Range: $25-49.9 Million
Emp.: 20
Interior Design & Decoration Services
N.A.I.C.S.: 541410

ITOKI Corporation - International Division (1)
2-5-1 Nihonbashi, Chuou-ku, Tokyo, 103-6113, Japan
Tel.: (81) 369103957
Web Site: http://www.itoki.jp
Office Furniture Mfr & Whslr
N.A.I.C.S.: 423210

ITOKI Systems (Singapore) Pte., Ltd. (1)
133 New Bridge Road 23-09/10 Chinatown Point, Singapore, 059413, Singapore
Tel.: (65) 67326169
Web Site: http://www.itoki.com.sg
Sales Range: $25-49.9 Million
Emp.: 15
Interior Decorators
N.A.I.C.S.: 541410
Y Kida (Mng Dir)

Itoki Corporation - NY Design Branch (1)
1501 Broadway, New York, NY 10036
Tel.: (212) 217-0642
Furniture Product Whslr
N.A.I.C.S.: 423210

Itoki Malaysia Sdn. Bhd. (1)
3A-23A Eco Sky No 972 Batu 61/2 Jalan Sultan Azlan Shah, 68100, Kuala Lumpur, Malaysia
Tel.: (60) 362428670
Web Site: http://itoki-malaysia.com
Furniture Whslr
N.A.I.C.S.: 423210

Itoki Modernform Co., Ltd. (1)
699 Modernform Tower 22nd Floor Srinakarindr Rd, Phatthanakan Suan Luang, Bangkok, 10250, Thailand
Tel.: (66) 27228288
Web Site: https://www.itokimodernform.com
Furniture Product Whslr
N.A.I.C.S.: 423210

Novo Workstyle (China) Co., Ltd. (1)
No 129 HuTaiXin Road, LiuHe Town, Taicang, 215431, Jiangsu, China
Tel.: (86) 51281603000
Furniture Product Whslr
N.A.I.C.S.: 423210

Novo Workstyle (Malaysia) Sdn. Bhd. (1)
3A-23A Eco Sky No 972 Batu 6 1/2, Jalan Sultan Azlan Shah, 68100, Kuala Lumpur, Malaysia

ITOKI CORPORATION

Itoki Corporation—(Continued)
Tel.: (60) 362428670
Furniture Product Whslr
N.A.I.C.S.: 423210

Novo Workstyle HK Limited (1)
3/F Cheung Lee Industrial Bldg 9 Cheung Lee Street, Chai Wan, China (Hong Kong)
Tel.: (852) 28383262
Furniture Product Whslr
N.A.I.C.S.: 423210

PT Itoki Solutions Indonesia (1)
Satrio Tower 14th Floor Unit A Jl Prof Dr Satrio Kav 1-4, Blok C4 Mega Kuningan, South Jakarta, 12950, Indonesia
Tel.: (62) 2125982278
Furniture Product Whslr
N.A.I.C.S.: 423210

Tarkus Interiors Pte. Ltd. (1)
46 Defu Lane 9, Singapore, 539286, Singapore
Tel.: (65) 62856142
Furniture Product Whslr
N.A.I.C.S.: 423210

ITOKURO INC.
4F JR Tokyu Meguro Building 3-1-1 Kamiosaki, Shinagawa-ku, Tokyo, 141-0021, Japan
Tel.: (81) 362301096
Web Site: https://www.itokuro.jp
Year Founded: 2006
6049—(TKS)
Sales Range: $25-49.9 Million
Emp.: 100
Internet Information Services
N.A.I.C.S.: 519290
Takashi Ryoshita (COO)

ITOXI CORP.
5th floor Pamoso Building 427 Dosandaero, Gangnam-gu, Seoul, 06016, Korea (South)
Tel.: (82) 262077114
Web Site: https://www.itoxi.co.kr
Year Founded: 1997
052770—(KRS)
Rev.: $21,582,340
Assets: $10,866,396
Liabilities: $5,247,366
Net Worth: $5,619,030
Earnings: ($312,493)
Emp.: 44
Fiscal Year-end: 12/31/22
Online Game Developing Services
N.A.I.C.S.: 513210
Sung-Jeung Kim (VP)

ITS GROUP SA
42 rue de Bellevue, 92100, Boulogne, France
Tel.: (33) 1 78 89 35 00
Web Site: http://www.itsgroup.com
Year Founded: 2007
Rev.: $153,360,507
Earnings: $7,557,021
Fiscal Year-end: 12/31/18
IT System Design Services
N.A.I.C.S.: 541512
Jean-Michel Benard (Founder, Chm & CEO)

Subsidiaries:

Axialog S.A. (1)
25 Boulevard des Bouvets, 92000, Nanterre, France
Tel.: (33) 155173650
Web Site: http://www.axialog.fr
Sales Range: $25-49.9 Million
Emp.: 300
Software & Engineering Services
N.A.I.C.S.: 541618

ITS Group Benelux SPRL (1)
Rue Royale 146, 1000, Brussels, Belgium
Tel.: (32) 25461990
Information Technology Services
N.A.I.C.S.: 541512
Pieter Van Rossen (Country Mgr)

MIB Suisse SA (1)
Route des Jeunes 59 26, PO Box 1423, 1211, Geneva, Switzerland
Tel.: (41) 223084666
Web Site: http://www.mib-suisse.com
Computer Parts Retailer
N.A.I.C.S.: 423430

ITSUMO, INC.
21F Daiichi Life Hibiya First 1132 Yurakucho, Chiyoda-Ku, Tokyo, 100-0006, Japan
Tel.: (81) 345801365
Web Site:
  https://www.itsumo365.co.jp
Year Founded: 2007
7694—(TKS)
Rev.: $91,621,210
Assets: $49,052,810
Liabilities: $32,878,140
Net Worth: $16,174,670
Earnings: $1,705,380
Emp.: 124
Fiscal Year-end: 03/31/24
E Commerce Site Operator
N.A.I.C.S.: 541511
Mamoru Sakamoto (Founder & Pres)

ITTEFAQ IRON INDUSTRIES LTD.
40-B II Gulberg III, Lahore, Pakistan
Tel.: (92) 4235765021
Web Site:
  https://www.ittefaqsteel.com
Year Founded: 2009
Metal Products Mfr
N.A.I.C.S.: 331110
Shahzad Javed (CEO)

ITTEHAD CHEMICALS LIMITED
39 Empress Road, PO Box 1414, Lahore, 54000, Pakistan
Tel.: (92) 4236306586
Web Site:
  https://www.ittehadchemicals.com
ICL—(KAR)
Rev.: $69,078,755
Assets: $65,496,081
Liabilities: $35,224,735
Net Worth: $30,271,347
Earnings: $4,078,523
Emp.: 485
Fiscal Year-end: 06/30/21
Industrial Chemicals Mfr
N.A.I.C.S.: 327110
Javed Iqbal (CFO)

Subsidiaries:

Chemi Dyestuff Industries (Pvt) Ltd. (1)
D-4 South Avenue Site, Karachi, 75700, Pakistan
Tel.: (92) 21 257 3940
Web Site: https://www.chemidyes.com
Chemical Products Mfr
N.A.I.C.S.: 325998

ITTIHAD SCHOOLS CO P.L.C.
Tareq Area, PO Box 6804, Amman, 11118, Jordan
Tel.: (962) 65153857
ITSC—(AMM)
Sales Range: $10-24.9 Million
Emp.: 718
School Operator
N.A.I.C.S.: 611310
Mohamad Abdullah Abdulhaleem Abu Khadeeja (Gen Mgr-Acting)

ITURAN LOCATION & CONTROL LTD.
3 Hashikma Street, Azour, Tel Aviv, 5800182, Israel
Tel.: (972) 35571333
Web Site: http://www.ituran.com

ITRN—(NASDAQ)
Rev.: $293,072,000
Assets: $290,927,000
Liabilities: $138,068,000
Net Worth: $152,859,000
Earnings: $37,103,000
Emp.: 2,736
Fiscal Year-end: 12/31/22
Wireless Tracking & Communication Solutions
N.A.I.C.S.: 423690
Izzy Sheratzky (Pres)

Subsidiaries:

ERM Electronic Systems Ltd. (1)
16 Hasar Shapira St, Rishon le Zion, 7570418, Israel
Tel.: (972) 39413313
Web Site: https://www.ermtelematics.com
Wireless Telecommunication Services
N.A.I.C.S.: 334220

ITURAN Argentina (1)
Sucre 2480, Lomas de, 1643, San Isidro, Argentina
Tel.: (54) 1148921401
Web Site: http://www.ituran.com.ar
Sales Range: $25-49.9 Million
Emp.: 100
Wireless Tracking & Communication Solutions
N.A.I.C.S.: 541512
Christian Fancceoti (Pres)

ITURAN Brazil (1)
Rua Cenno Sbrighi 170, Agua Branca, CEP 05036-010, Sao Paulo, Brazil
Tel.: (55) 1136169000
Web Site: https://www.ituran.com.br
Wireless Tracking & Communication Solutions
N.A.I.C.S.: 517112

ITURAN USA LifeTrak (1)
1700 NW 64th St Ste 100, Fort Lauderdale, FL 33309
Tel.: (954) 484-3806
Web Site: https://www.ituranusa.com
Sales Range: $10-24.9 Million
Emp.: 30
Security System Services
N.A.I.C.S.: 561621

Mapa Mapping & Publishing Ltd. (1)
29 Ha-Metsuda St, Azor, Israel
Tel.: (972) 36210500
Web Site: www.gisrael.co.il
Books Publishing Services
N.A.I.C.S.: 323117

ITV GMBH
Grafenheider Str 96a, 33729, Bielefeld, Germany
Tel.: (49) 521977190
Web Site: http://www.itv-gmbh.de
Year Founded: 1981
Rev.: $11,724,900
Emp.: 45
Industrial Product Distr
N.A.I.C.S.: 423830
Peter Wittkaemper (CEO & Mgr-Sls)

ITV PLC
White City Place 201 Wood Lane, London, W12 7RU, United Kingdom
Tel.: (44) 4967001
Web Site: https://www.itvplc.com
Year Founded: 2003
ITVPF—(OTCIQ)
Rev.: $4,705,882,353
Assets: $5,648,826,054
Liabilities: $3,280,737,188
Net Worth: $2,368,088,866
Earnings: $549,103,762
Emp.: 6,677
Fiscal Year-end: 12/31/22
Holding Company; Television Production & Broadcasting Services
N.A.I.C.S.: 551112
Pippa Foulds (Dir-IR)

Subsidiaries:

12 Yard Productions Limited (1)

INTERNATIONAL PUBLIC

G7 The Hub 70 Pacific Quay Pacific Drive, Glasgow, G51 1DZ, United Kingdom
Tel.: (44) 141 302 4701
Web Site: https://www.12yard.com
Picture & Video Production Services
N.A.I.C.S.: 512110
Michae Mannes (Deputy Mng Dir)

3 Sixtymedia Ltd. (1)
Quay St, Manchester, M60 9EA, Greater Manchester, United Kingdom (100%)
Tel.: (44) 1619526000
Web Site: http://www.3sixtymedia.com
Sales Range: $50-74.9 Million
Emp.: 100
Television Production Services
N.A.I.C.S.: 512191
Paul Bennett (Mng Dir)

Apple Tree Productions Aps (1)
Store Kongensgade 77 st, 1264, Copenhagen, Denmark
Tel.: (45) 30423600
Web Site: https://appletree.dk
Television Production Services
N.A.I.C.S.: 512110

Bait Studio Limited (1)
GloWorks Porth Teigr Way, Cardiff, CF10 4GA, United Kingdom
Tel.: (44) 292 019 0132
Web Site: https://www.baitstudio.com
Picture & Video Production Services
N.A.I.C.S.: 512110
Peter Rogers (Mng Dir)

Big Talk Productions Limited (1)
26 Nassau Street, London, W1W 7AQ, United Kingdom
Tel.: (44) 207 255 1131
Web Site:
  https://www.bigtalkproductions.com
Picture & Video Production Services
N.A.I.C.S.: 512110
Kenton Allen (CEO)

Bildergarten Entertainment GmbH (1)
Genthiner Strasse 5, 10785, Berlin, Germany
Tel.: (49) 30814920
Web Site: https://bildergarten.tv
Video Production Services
N.A.I.C.S.: 512199

Boom Cymru TV Ltd. (1)
GloWorks Porth Teigr Way Road, Cardiff, CF10 4GA, United Kingdom
Tel.: (44) 292 245 0000
Web Site: https://www.boomcymru.co.uk
Emp.: 200
Picture & Video Production Services
N.A.I.C.S.: 512110
Nia Thomas (Mng Dir)

Cattleya Srl (1)
P le Valerio Massimo 7, 00162, Rome, Italy
Tel.: (39) 0636 7201
Web Site: https://www.cattleya.it
Picture & Video Production Services
N.A.I.C.S.: 512110
Riccardo Tozzi (Founder & Chm)

Circle of Confusion Television Studios LLC (1)
8931 Ellis Ave, Los Angeles, CA 90034
Tel.: (310) 691-7000
Web Site: https://www.circleofconfusion.com
Television Broadcasting Services
N.A.I.C.S.: 516120

Coral Racing Ltd. (1)
Glebe House, Vicarage Drive, Barking, 1G11 7NF, Barring, United Kingdom (100%)
Tel.: (44) 85915151
Web Site: http://www.coral.co.uk
Sales Range: $100-124.9 Million
Emp.: 300
Bookmaker
N.A.I.C.S.: 513130

Crook Productions Limited (1)
3rd Floor 19-21 Great Portland Street, London, W1W 8QB, United Kingdom
Tel.: (44) 2037457828
Web Site:
  https://www.crookproductions.com
Picture & Video Production Services
N.A.I.C.S.: 512110

AND PRIVATE COMPANIES

Gala Leisure Ltd. (1)
New Castle House, Castle Boulevard, Nottingham, NG7 1FT, United Kingdom
Tel.: (44) 1602240333
Web Site: http://www.galacasino.co.uk
Bingo, Casino, Snooker & Ten Pin Bowling
N.A.I.C.S.: 713940

Gear Shop Inc. (1)
1107 Middle River Rd Ste 19, Baltimore, MD 21220
Tel.: (410) 477-4327
Web Site: https://thegearshop1945.com
Auto Parts Distr
N.A.I.C.S.: 423120

ITC Distribution, LLC (1)
8 N Line Rd, Edgartown, MA 02539
Tel.: (508) 693-3028
Web Site: https://www.itcdistributors.com
Food & Grocery Product Distr
N.A.I.C.S.: 424490

ITV America Inc. (1)
420 Lexington Ave Ste 2149, New York, NY 10170
Tel.: (203) 548-8000
Web Site: https://www.itv-america.com
Picture & Video Production Services
N.A.I.C.S.: 512110
David George *(CEO)*

ITV Anglia (1)
Anglia House, Norwich, NR1 3JG, Norfolk, United Kingdom **(100%)**
Tel.: (44) 8448816900
Web Site: http://www.angliatv.co.uk
Sales Range: $50-74.9 Million
Emp.: 200
Television Production & Broadcasting
N.A.I.C.S.: 516120

ITV Breakfast Limited (1)
ITV White City 201 Wood Lane, London, W12 7RU, United Kingdom
Tel.: (44) 2078277000
Television Broadcasting Services
N.A.I.C.S.: 516120

ITV Global Entertainment Limited (1)
ITV Studios Global Entertainment London Television Centre Upper Ground, London, SE1 9LT, United Kingdom
Tel.: (44) 20 7491 1441
Web Site: http://www.itv.com
Emp.: 2,000
Motion Picture Production Services
N.A.I.C.S.: 512110
Augustus Dulgaro *(Exec VP-Asia Pacific)*

ITV Meridian (1)
Television Centre, Southampton, SO14 0PZ, United Kingdom
Tel.: (44) 2380222555
Web Site: http://www.meridiantv.co.uk
Television Production & Broadcasting
N.A.I.C.S.: 516120

ITV Studios Australia Pty Limited (1)
Level 5 Building 61 Fox Studios Australia 38 Driver Avenue, Moore Park, Sydney, 2021, NSW, Australia
Tel.: (61) 29 383 4360
Web Site: https://www.itvstudios.com.au
Picture & Video Production Services
N.A.I.C.S.: 512110
David Mott *(CEO & Mng Dir)*

ITV Studios Germany GmbH (1)
Agrippastrasse 87-93, 50676, Cologne, Germany
Tel.: (49) 2214920480
Web Site: https://www.itvstudios.de
Sales Range: $25-49.9 Million
Motion Picture Production Services
N.A.I.C.S.: 512110

Subsidiary (Domestic):

Kromschroder & Pfannenschmidt GmbH (2)
Lovenicher Weg 28, 50933, Cologne, Germany
Tel.: (49) 221 9643 9770
Web Site: http://www.kromschroederpfannenschmidt.de
Broadcasting Services
N.A.I.C.S.: 516120
Christian Pfannenschmidt *(Partner)*

ITV Studios Holding B.V. (1)
Familie de Mollaan 1, Postbus 28000, 1217 ZB, Hilversum, Netherlands
Tel.: (31) 882483333
Web Site: https://itvstudios.nl
Emp.: 5,000
Television Broadcasting Services
N.A.I.C.S.: 516120

ITV Studios Limited (1)
White City Place 201 Wood Lane, London, W12 7RU, United Kingdom
Tel.: (44) 2071573000
Sales Range: $50-74.9 Million
Emp.: 160
Television Programe Production & Distribution Services
N.A.I.C.S.: 512110
Mike Beale *(Mng Dir-Creative Networks-Nordics & Global)*

ITV Studios Norway AS (1)
Gullhaugveien 1-3, 0484, Oslo, Norway
Tel.: (47) 47696446
Web Site: https://itvstudiosnorway.com
Picture & Video Production Services
N.A.I.C.S.: 512110

ITV Studios Sweden AB (1)
Sodermalarstrand 65, 118 25, Stockholm, Sweden
Tel.: (46) 86426888
Web Site: https://www.itvstudiossweden.com
Picture & Video Production Services
N.A.I.C.S.: 512110

ITV Studios, Inc (1)
15303 Ventura Blvd Bldg C Ste 800, Sherman Oaks, CA 91403
Tel.: (818) 455-4600
Web Site: http://www.itvstudios.com
Sales Range: $25-49.9 Million
Emp.: 40
Broadcasting Services
N.A.I.C.S.: 516120

Subsidiary (Domestic):

Gurney Productions, Inc. (2)
8929 S Sepulveda Blvd Ste 510, Los Angeles, CA 90045 **(100%)**
Tel.: (310) 645-1499
Web Site: http://www.gurneyproductions.com
Sales Range: $1-9.9 Million
Television Production
N.A.I.C.S.: 512110

High Noon Productions, LLC (2)
3035 S Parker Rd Ste 500, Denver, CO 80014 **(60%)**
Tel.: (303) 872-8700
Web Site: https://www.highnoontv.com
Motion Picture & Video Production
N.A.I.C.S.: 512110
Scott Feeley *(Pres)*

ITV Tyne Tees Television (1)
Television House The Watermark Gateshead, Upper Ground, London, NE11 9SZ, United Kingdom
Tel.: (44) 8448815153
Web Site: http://www.itv.com
Television Station
N.A.I.C.S.: 516120

ITV Wales (1)
The Television Ctr Culverhouse Cross, Cardiff, CF5 6XJ, United Kingdom **(100%)**
Tel.: (44) 2920590590
Sales Range: $50-74.9 Million
Emp.: 170
Television Production & Broadcasting
N.A.I.C.S.: 516120

Independent Television News Ltd. (1)
200 Grays Inn Road, London, WC1X 8XZ, United Kingdom
Tel.: (44) 207 833 3000
Web Site: https://www.itn.co.uk
Sales Range: $150-199.9 Million
Television Broadcasting Services
N.A.I.C.S.: 516120
Bryan R. Martin *(CFO)*

Loud Television, LLC (1)
460 W 34th St 5th Fl, New York, NY 10001
Tel.: (646) 459-8180
Web Site: http://www.loudtelevision.com
Picture & Video Production Services
N.A.I.C.S.: 512110

Mammoth Screen Ltd. (1)
Third Floor 142-144 New Cavendish Street, London, W1W 6YF, United Kingdom
Tel.: (44) 207 268 0050
Web Site: https://www.mammothscreen.com
Picture & Video Production Services
N.A.I.C.S.: 512110
Veronica Castillo *(Co-Head-Production)*

MasMedia B.V. (1)
Noorderweg 8, 1221 AA, Hilversum, Netherlands
Tel.: (31) 355288860
Web Site: http://www.masmedia.tv
Picture & Video Production Services
N.A.I.C.S.: 512110

Oxford Scientific Films Limited (1)
4th Floor 21 Berners Street, London, W1T 3LP, United Kingdom
Tel.: (44) 203 551 4600
Web Site: https://www.oxfordscientificfilms.tv
Picture & Video Production Services
N.A.I.C.S.: 512110
Clare Birks *(CEO)*

Plimsoll Productions Limited (1)
Plimsoll Studios 51-55 Whiteladies Road, Bristol, BS8 2LY, United Kingdom
Tel.: (44) 1173072300
Web Site: https://plimsollproductions.com
Television Production Services
N.A.I.C.S.: 512110

Prosper Productions Pty. Ltd. (1)
78 Stirling Highway, North Fremantle, 6160, WA, Australia
Tel.: (61) 893366006
Web Site: https://prospero.com.au
Television Broadcasting Services
N.A.I.C.S.: 516120

Second Act Productions Limited (1)
ITV White City 201 Wood Lane, London, W12 7RU, United Kingdom
Tel.: (44) 2071398639
Web Site: https://www.2ndact.co.uk
Picture & Video Production Services
N.A.I.C.S.: 512110

Sirens Media, LLC (1)
5250 Lankershim Blvd 3rd Fl, North Hollywood, CA 91601
Tel.: (203) 548-8000
Web Site: https://sirensmedia.com
Picture & Video Production Services
N.A.I.C.S.: 512110
Jessica Sebastian *(Pres)*

So Television Limited (1)
1 Boundary Row, London, SE1 8GN, United Kingdom
Tel.: (44) 2079602000
Web Site: https://www.sotelevision.co.uk
Picture & Video Production Services
N.A.I.C.S.: 512110

Talpa Germany Gmbh & Co KG (1)
Genthiner Strasse 5, 10785, Berlin, Germany
Tel.: (49) 30814920
Web Site: http://www.talpa-germany.tv
Picture & Video Production Services
N.A.I.C.S.: 512110
Karsten Roeder *(Co-CEO)*

Talpa Media B.V. (1)
Zevenend 45, 1251 RL, Laren, Netherlands **(100%)**
Tel.: (31) 35 533 3333
Web Site: http://www.talpa.tv
Television Program Creation, Production & Distribution Services
N.A.I.C.S.: 512110
John de Mol *(Founder)*

Tetra Media Studio SAS (1)
60 rue Marcel Dassault, Boulogne-Billancourt, France
Tel.: (33) 155380101
Picture & Video Production Services
N.A.I.C.S.: 512110

The Garden Productions Limited (1)
One America Street, London, SE1 0NE, United Kingdom
Tel.: (44) 207 261 1252
Web Site: https://www.thegarden.tv
Television Broadcasting Services

ITWAY S.P.A.

N.A.I.C.S.: 516120
John Hay *(Chief Creative Officer)*

Twofour America, LLC (1)
15301 Ventura Blvd Bldg D Ste 220, Sherman Oaks, CA 91403
Tel.: (818) 479-4256
Television Broadcasting Services
N.A.I.C.S.: 516120

Twofour Group Ltd. (1)
The Westworks 195 Wood Lane, London, W12 7FQ, United Kingdom
Tel.: (44) 2073472624
Web Site: https://www.twofour.co.uk
Television Production & Distr
N.A.I.C.S.: 512191
Shireen Abbott *(Dir-Production)*

Vorst Media B.V. (1)
Hollandse Kade 34-1, Abcoude, 1391 JM, De Ronde Venen, Netherlands
Tel.: (31) 294236060
Web Site: http://www.vorstmedia.tv
Television Broadcasting Services
N.A.I.C.S.: 516120

World Productions Limited (1)
5th Floor National House 60-66 Wardour Street, London, W1F 0TA, United Kingdom
Tel.: (44) 207 156 6990
Web Site: https://www.world-productions.com
Picture & Video Production Services
N.A.I.C.S.: 512110
Elizabeth Binns *(Head-Production)*

Yellow Productions USA, Inc. (1)
4 N Water St, Nantucket, MA 02554
Tel.: (617) 510-3713
Web Site: https://yellowproductions.com
Television Broadcasting Services
N.A.I.C.S.: 516120

boxclever (1)
Lakeview House Fraser Road, Priory Business Park, Bedford, MK44 3WH, United Kingdom **(100%)**
Tel.: (44) 370 572 5725
Web Site: https://www.boxclever.co.uk
Sales Range: $200-249.9 Million
Emp.: 700
Television & Radio Rental Services
N.A.I.C.S.: 532289
Emma McInnes *(Dir-Quantitative Res-London)*

ITV PUBLIC COMPANY LIMITED
1010 Shinawatra Tower, 3 Viphavadi Rangsit Rd Chatuchak, Bangkok, 10900, Thailand
Tel.: (66) 27911795
Web Site: http://www.itv.co.th
Sales Range: $1-9.9 Million
Television Broadcasting Services
N.A.I.C.S.: 516120
Somkid Wangcherdchuwong *(Chm)*

ITWAY S.P.A.
Viale Achille Papa 30, 20149, Milan, Italy
Tel.: (39) 0544288710
Web Site: https://www.itway.com
Year Founded: 1996
ITW—(ITA)
Rev.: $43,953,797
Assets: $44,199,445
Liabilities: $33,319,695
Net Worth: $10,879,750
Earnings: $1,500,909
Emp.: 50
Fiscal Year-end: 12/31/20
Computer Softwares Mfr
N.A.I.C.S.: 513210
Giovanni Andrea Farina *(Founder, Chm & CEO)*

Subsidiaries:

4 Science S.r.l. (1)
Viale A Papa 30, 20149, Milan, Italy
Tel.: (39) 023 971 0430
Web Site: https://www.4science.it
Research Services
N.A.I.C.S.: 541910

ITWAY S.P.A.

Itway S.p.A.—(Continued)

Cesare Valenti *(CEO)*

Diogene S.r.l. (1)
Viale Felsina 5, 40139, Bologna, Italy
Tel.: (39) 051 54 06 88
Web Site: http://www.diogenenet.com
Human Resource Consultancy Services
N.A.I.C.S.: 541612

Itway France S.A.R.L. (1)
76 rue Thiers, 92100, Boulogne-Billancourt, France
Tel.: (33) 170951500
Web Site: http://www.itway.fr
Computer & Computer Peripheral Equipment & Software Whslr
N.A.I.C.S.: 423430

Itway Hellas S.A. (1)
10 Ag Ioannou str, 15233, Halandri, Greece
Tel.: (30) 2106801013
Web Site: https://itway.gr
Sales Range: $25-49.9 Million
Information Technology Consulting Services
N.A.I.C.S.: 541512

Itway Iberica S.L. (1)
Argenters 4 Edificio 2 Bajos, Parc Tecnologic del Valles, 08290, Barcelona, Spain **(100%)**
Tel.: (34) 935942580
Web Site: http://www.itway.es
Sales Range: $25-49.9 Million
Emp.: 35
Telecommunications Resellers
N.A.I.C.S.: 517121

Itwayvad S.r.l. (1)
Via Braille 15, 48010, Ravenna, Italy **(100%)**
Tel.: (39) 0544288711
Sales Range: $25-49.9 Million
Emp.: 20
Management Consulting Services
N.A.I.C.S.: 541618
Andrea De Marchi *(Mng Dir)*

ITX-AI CO., LTD.

9F Kolon Digital Tower Aston Building 212, Gasandigital 1-ro Geumcheon-gu, Seoul, 08520, Korea (South)
Tel.: (82) 220828500
Web Site: https://www.itxai.com
Year Founded: 1998
099520—(KRS)
Rev.: $20,439,773
Assets: $18,224,423
Liabilities: $3,474,571
Net Worth: $14,749,851
Earnings: $1,022,076
Fiscal Year-end: 12/31/22
Video Surveillance Equipment Mfr
N.A.I.C.S.: 334310
Park Sang Yeol *(CEO)*

IUS SA

Str Harmanului 58, Brasov, Romania
Tel.: (40) 268 333429
Sales Range: $1-9.9 Million
Emp.: 128
Tool Product Mfr
N.A.I.C.S.: 333515

IV PRODUKT AB

Sjouddevagen 7, PO Box 3103, 352 46, Vaxjo, Sweden
Tel.: (46) 470758800
Web Site: http://www.ivprodukt.se
Year Founded: 1969
Sales Range: $25-49.9 Million
Emp.: 200
Ventilation Systems
N.A.I.C.S.: 333413
Mattias Sjoberg *(CEO)*

IV-GROEP B.V.

Tel.: (31) 889433000 Nl
Web Site: https://www.iv.nl
Year Founded: 1949
Emp.: 1,318
Holding Company; Engineering & Technical Consulting Services
N.A.I.C.S.: 551112
Maarten van de Waal *(Chm & CEO)*

Subsidiaries:

IV-Aga Texas LLC (1)
1500 City W Blvd Ste 200, Houston, TX 77042
Tel.: (281) 258-2300
Engineering Consulting Services
N.A.I.C.S.: 541330

Iv-Bouw b.v. (1)
Kelvinring 48, 2952 BG, Alblasserdam, Netherlands
Tel.: (31) 78 699 1899
Web Site: http://www.iv-groep.nl
Commercial, Institutional & Industrial Building Engineering & Technical Consulting Services
N.A.I.C.S.: 541330

Iv-Consult b.v. (1)
Noordhoek 37, Papendrecht, 3351 LD, Netherlands
Tel.: (31) 889433100
Web Site: http://www.iv-groep.nl
Emp.: 80
Offshore & Yard Handling, Static Structures & Special Moving Structures Engineering & Technical Consulting Services
N.A.I.C.S.: 541330
Arie Lanser *(Mng Dir)*

Subsidiary (Non-US):

IV-Consult Sdn Bhd (2)
No 29-4 Jalan SP 2/1 Taman Serdang Perdana - Seksyen 2, 43300, Seri Kembangan, Selangor, Malaysia
Tel.: (60) 3 8941 8807
Engineering Consulting Services
N.A.I.C.S.: 541330

Iv-Industrie b.v. (1)
Meander 651, 6825 ME, Arnhem, Netherlands
Tel.: (31) 88 943 3700
Web Site: http://www.iv-groep.nl
Emp.: 50
Engineering Consulting Services
N.A.I.C.S.: 541330

Iv-Infra b.v. (1)
Fultonbaan 30, 3439 NE, Nieuwegein, Netherlands
Tel.: (31) 889433200
Web Site: http://www.iv-groep.nl
Emp.: 150
Infrastructure & Waterway Engineering & Technical Consulting Services
N.A.I.C.S.: 541330
Rob A. van Bodegraven *(Dir-Ops)*

Subsidiary (US):

Iv-Infra USA, LLC. (2)
3500 N Causeway Blvd Ste 600, Metairie, LA 70002
Tel.: (504) 846-6400
Engineering Consulting Services
N.A.I.C.S.: 541330

Iv-Oil & Gas b.v. (1)
Noordhoek 37, 3351 LD, Papendrecht, Netherlands
Tel.: (31) 78 644 8888
Web Site: http://www.iv-groep.nl
Oil & Gas Structure Engineering & Technical Consulting Services
N.A.I.C.S.: 541330
Wim Bal *(Mng Dir)*

Subsidiary (Domestic):

Escher Process Modules B.V. (2)
Noordhoek 37, 3351 LD, Papendrecht, Netherlands
Tel.: (31) 78 644 8250
Web Site: http://www.escher.nl
Oil & Gas Treatment System Combustion System & Process Vessel Mfr
N.A.I.C.S.: 333248
H. M. Bunschoten *(Mng Dir)*

Iv-Water b.v. (1)
Noordhoek 37, 3351 LD, Papendrecht, Netherlands
Tel.: (31) 889433000
Web Site: http://www.iv-groep.nl
Emp.: 25
Water & Sewer Line Engineering & Technical Consulting Services
N.A.I.C.S.: 541330
Erik Vegt *(Mng Dir)*

IVACON ENGINEERING B.V.

Hoofdweg Westzijde 81, 1175 KM, Lijnden, Netherlands
Tel.: (31) 23 53 44 666 Nl
Web Site: http://www.ivacon.nl
Year Founded: 1980
Sales Range: $1-9.9 Million
Emp.: 50
Concrete Renovation & Repair Services
N.A.I.C.S.: 238110

IVANHOE ELECTRIC INC.

606-999 Canada Place, Vancouver, V6C 3E1, BC, Canada
Tel.: (480) 656-5821 DE
Web Site:
 https://www.ivanhoeelectric.com
Year Founded: 2020
IE—(NYSE)
Rev.: $8,440,000
Assets: $260,486,000
Liabilities: $58,039,000
Net Worth: $202,447,000
Earnings: ($149,813,000)
Emp.: 244
Fiscal Year-end: 12/31/22
Mineral Exploration Services
N.A.I.C.S.: 212323
Robert Martin Friedland *(Exec Chm)*

Subsidiaries:

Kaizen Discovery Inc. (1)
World Trade Centre 606-999 Canada Place, Vancouver, V6C 3E1, BC, Canada **(100%)**
Tel.: (604) 669-6446
Web Site: https://www.kaizendiscovery.com
Rev.: $20,661
Assets: $4,847,030
Liabilities: $3,993,022
Net Worth: $854,008
Earnings: ($2,109,001)
Fiscal Year-end: 12/31/2019
Mineral Exploration Services
N.A.I.C.S.: 213114
Mark Gibson *(COO)*

IVANHOE ENERGY, INC.

999 Canada Place Suite n654, Vancouver, V6C 3E1, BC, Canada
Tel.: (604) 688-8323 YT
Web Site: http://www.ivanhoe-energy.com
Year Founded: 1995
Emp.: 75
Heavy-Oil & Gas Development & Production Services
N.A.I.C.S.: 211120
Michael Silverman *(CTO & Sr VP-Downstream Tech)*

IVANHOE MINES LTD.

654-999 Canada Place, Vancouver, V6C 3E1, BC, Canada
Tel.: (604) 688-6630 YT
Web Site:
 https://www.ivanhoemines.com
IVPAF—(OTCQX)
Rev.: $76,080,000
Assets: $2,444,722,000
Liabilities: $81,868,000
Net Worth: $2,362,854,000
Earnings: ($11,396,000)
Emp.: 750
Fiscal Year-end: 12/31/19
Metal Mining Services
N.A.I.C.S.: 212290
Robert Martin Friedland *(Founder & Co-Chm)*

INTERNATIONAL PUBLIC

Subsidiaries:

Ivanplats Syerston (Pty) Ltd. (1)
L 3 231 Adelaide Terrace, Perth, 6000, WA, Australia
Tel.: (61) 8 9221 4700
Metal Mining Services
N.A.I.C.S.: 212290

IVD MEDICAL HOLDING LIMITED

Rm 1703 Grandtech Centre 8 On Ping St, Sha Tin, China (Hong Kong)
Tel.: (852) 4008209809 Ky
Web Site: http://www.ivdholding.com
Year Founded: 1993
1931—(HKG)
Rev.: $385,932,784
Assets: $605,724,491
Liabilities: $162,978,145
Net Worth: $442,746,346
Earnings: $27,452,412
Emp.: 755
Fiscal Year-end: 12/31/22
Holding Company
N.A.I.C.S.: 551112
Kuk Sing Ho *(Chm & CEO)*

Subsidiaries:

Vastec Medical Limited (1)
Room 1703 Grandtech Centre 8 On Ping Street, Shatin, Hong Kong, New Territories, China (Hong Kong)
Tel.: (852) 28971912
Web Site: http://www.vastec.com.cn
Laboratory Equipment Mfr
N.A.I.C.S.: 334516

IVE GROUP LIMITED

Building B 350 Parramatta Road, Homebush, 2140, NSW, Australia
Tel.: (61) 280204300
Web Site:
 https://www.ivegroup.com.au
IGL—(ASX)
Rev.: $649,591,495
Assets: $443,932,916
Liabilities: $314,004,735
Net Worth: $129,928,181
Earnings: $18,432,963
Emp.: 2,000
Fiscal Year-end: 06/30/24
Commercial Printing
N.A.I.C.S.: 323111
Geoff Selig *(Chm)*

Subsidiaries:

Ovato Limited (1)
8 Priddle Street, Warwick Farm, 2170, NSW, Australia
Tel.: (61) 294126049
Web Site: http://www.ovato.com.au
Rev.: $339,208,403
Assets: $188,309,581
Liabilities: $182,585,376
Net Worth: $5,724,205
Earnings: $51,400,622
Emp.: 1,608
Fiscal Year-end: 06/30/2021
Printed Communication Solutions
N.A.I.C.S.: 323111
Alistair Clarkson *(Gen Counsel & Sec)*

Subsidiary (Domestic):

Bolton Print Pty Ltd (2)
246 Hartley Street, Bungalow, Cairns, 4870, QLD, Australia
Tel.: (61) 7 4035 0500
Web Site: http://www.boltonprint.com.au
Emp.: 50
Commercial Printing Services
N.A.I.C.S.: 323111
Darren McCormick *(Gen Mgr)*

Griffin Press (2)
168 Cross Keys Rd Salisbury S, Adelaide, 5106, South Australia, Australia
Tel.: (61) 882532000
Web Site: http://www.griffinpress.com.au
Sales Range: $50-74.9 Million
Emp.: 140
Books Mfr

AND PRIVATE COMPANIES — IVS GROUP S.A.

N.A.I.C.S.: 328117
Ben Jolly *(Gen Mgr)*

Inprint Pty Ltd (2)
552 Bilsen Rd, Geebung, Brisbane, 4034, QLD, Australia
Tel.: (61) 733601111
Web Site: http://www.inprint.net.au
Commercial Printing Services
N.A.I.C.S.: 323111
Hans Oerlemans *(Gen Mgr)*

Ovato Packaging Pty Ltd (2)
552 Bilsen Road, Geebung, Geebung, 4034, QLD, Australia
Tel.: (61) 733601133
Web Site: https://www.ovato.com.au
Packaging Services
N.A.I.C.S.: 561910
Terry Sharp *(Sls Mgr)*

PEP Central Pty Ltd (2)
552 Bilsen Rd, Geebung, Brisbane, 4034, QLD, Australia
Tel.: (61) 7 3852 9400
Web Site: http://www.pep.net.au
Emp.: 50
Commercial Printing Services
N.A.I.C.S.: 323111

Subsidiary (Non-US):

PMP (NZ) Limited (2)
Ground Floor Old City Markets Building 106 Customs St West, Viaduct Harbour, 1010, Auckland, New Zealand
Tel.: (64) 99793100
Web Site: https://www.pmplimited.co.nz
Sales Range: $50-74.9 Million
Emp.: 150
Printing & Marketing Services
N.A.I.C.S.: 323117

Division (Domestic):

Gordon & Gotch (3)
Ground Fl Old City Markets Bldg 106 Customs St W, PO Box 106603, Viaduct Harbour, Auckland, 1141, New Zealand
Tel.: (64) 99793100
Web Site: http://www.gordongotch.co.nz
Sales Range: $25-49.9 Million
Emp.: 80
Newspaper Book Distribution & Merchandising Services
N.A.I.C.S.: 424920

PMP Distribution (3)
Ground Fl Old City Markets Bldg 106 Customs St W, PO Box 106253, Viaduct Harbour, 1143, Auckland, New Zealand
Tel.: (64) 99793100
Web Site: http://www.gordongotch.co.nz
Printing Services
N.A.I.C.S.: 323111

Subsidiary (Domestic):

PMP Maxum (3)
122 Kerrs Road, PO Box 8178, Manukau, 2241, New Zealand
Tel.: (64) 99793100
Web Site: http://www.pmpmaxum.co.nz
Sales Range: $25-49.9 Million
Printing Services
N.A.I.C.S.: 323111
Tony Edwards *(Gen Mgr)*

Division (Domestic):

PMP Micromarketing (3)
122 Kerrs Road Wiri, PO Box 106253, Viaduct Harbour, Manukau, 2104, New Zealand
Tel.: (64) 99793100
Web Site: http://www.mosaicnz.co.nz
Marketing Services
N.A.I.C.S.: 541910

PMP Print (3)
Ground Fl Old City Markets Bldg 106 Customs St W, PO Box 106253, Auckland, New Zealand
Tel.: (64) 99793100
Web Site: http://www.pmplimited.co.nz
Sales Range: $50-74.9 Million
Emp.: 140
Printing Services
N.A.I.C.S.: 323111
Glen Turnbull *(Mgr-Sls)*

Pareto Phone Pty Limited (1)
Ground Floor 518 Brunswick Street, Fortitude Valley, 4006, QLD, Australia
Tel.: (61) 730154000
Web Site: https://www.paretophone.com
Tele Fundraising Services
N.A.I.C.S.: 561422
Mick Hishon *(Head-Data Svcs & IT)*

Reach Media New Zealand Limited (1)
525 Mount Wellington Highway, Otahuhu, Auckland, 1062, New Zealand
Tel.: (64) 8007322487
Marketing Services
N.A.I.C.S.: 541613

IVECO GROUP N.V.
Via Puglia 35, 10156, Turin, Italy
Tel.: (39) 03351776091
Web Site: https://www.ivecogroup.com
IVG—(EUR)
Industrial Company
N.A.I.C.S.: 236210

Subsidiaries:

Magirus GmbH (1)
Tel.: (49) 7314080
Web Site: https://www.magirusgroup.com
Commercial Vehicles & Trucks Mfr
N.A.I.C.S.: 333924

IVENTA GROUP HOLDING GMBH
Seidengasse 9-11, 1070, Vienna, Austria
Tel.: (43) 1 523 49 44 0   AT
Web Site: http://www.iventa.eu
Year Founded: 1991
Sales Range: $25-49.9 Million
Emp.: 100
Holding Company; Executive Search & Consulting Services, Employer Branding & Media Services
N.A.I.C.S.: 551112
Martin Mayer *(Mng Dir)*

Subsidiaries:

IVENTA Bratislava (1)
Jakubovo 13, 81109, Bratislava, Slovakia
Tel.: (421) 2 5737 3711
Web Site: http://www.iventa.sk
Advertising Agency; Executive Search & Management Consulting Services
N.A.I.C.S.: 541810

IVENTA Bucharest (1)
Str Maria Rosetti nr 8A, et 4 ap 5 sect 2, RO-020485, Bucharest, Romania
Tel.: (40) 21 306 00 00
Web Site: http://www.iventa.co.ro
Sales Range: $10-24.9 Million
Advertising Agency; Executive Search & Management Consulting Services
N.A.I.C.S.: 541810
Robert Koenes *(Dir)*

IVENTA Czech Management Consulting s.r.o. (1)
Jugoslavska 620/29, CZ-120, Prague, 2, Czech Republic
Tel.: (420) 224 915 240
Web Site: http://www.iventa.cz
Advetising Agency
N.A.I.C.S.: 541810

IVENTA Management Consulting GmbH - Graz (1)
Schorgelgasse 10, 8010, Graz, Austria
Tel.: (43) 316 90 80 10 0
Web Site: http://www.iventa.com
Emp.: 4
Executive Search & Management Consulting Services
N.A.I.C.S.: 561312
Edith Baumgartner *(Office Mgr)*

IVENTA Management Consulting GmbH - Linz (1)
Museumstrasse 31, 4020, Linz, Austria
Tel.: (43) 732 90 80 10 0
Web Site: http://www.iventa.eu
Emp.: 4

Executive Search & Management Consulting Services
N.A.I.C.S.: 561312
Irma Brazda *(Mng Dir-HR Consulting)*

IVENTA Management Consulting GmbH - Salzburg (1)
Neutorstrasse 13, 5020, Salzburg, Austria
Tel.: (43) 662 90 80 10 0
Web Site: http://www.iventa.eu
Executive Search & Management Consulting Services
N.A.I.C.S.: 561312

IVISION TECH S.P.A.
Via Alberico Albricci 8, Lombardy, 20122, Milan, Italy
Tel.: (39) 04321483803
Web Site: https://www.ivisiontech.eu
Year Founded: 2020
IVN—(EUR)
Optical Product Mfr
N.A.I.C.S.: 339115
Giulio Vignando *(Officer)*

IVISYS AB
Siktgatan 2, 162 50, Vallingby, Sweden
Tel.: (46) 8 38 20 80
Web Site: http://www.ivisys.com
IVISYS—(OMX)
Sales Range: $1-9.9 Million
Emp.: 15
Machine Vision Inspection Systems Mfr
N.A.I.C.S.: 333248
Jakob Kesje *(Founder)*

IVOCLAR VIVADENT SAS
219 Route de la Chapelle du Puy, 74410, Annecy, Saint Jorioz, France
Tel.: (33) 450886400
Web Site: http://www.ivoclarvivadent.fr
Sales Range: $10-24.9 Million
Emp.: 70
Medical Devices Mfr & Whslr
N.A.I.C.S.: 424210
Sarah Anders *(COO)*

IVORY PROPERTIES GROUP BERHAD
81-11-1 Jalan Dato' Keramat, George Town, 10150, Penang, Malaysia
Tel.: (60) 42108000
Web Site: https://www.ivory.com.my
Year Founded: 1999
IVORY—(KLS)
Rev.: $2,788,360
Assets: $100,463,915
Liabilities: $78,392,169
Net Worth: $22,071,746
Earnings: ($26,594,286)
Emp.: 145
Fiscal Year-end: 03/31/23
Property Development, Management & Construction Services
N.A.I.C.S.: 531311
Eng Hock Low *(CEO)*

Subsidiaries:

Ivory Meadows Sdn. Bhd. (1)
Ivory Tower Penang Times Square 81-11-1, Jalan Dato' Kerama, 10150, George Town, Penang, Malaysia
Tel.: (60) 42108000
Web Site: https://www.ivory.com.my
Emp.: 500
Property Development Services
N.A.I.C.S.: 531390
Low Eng Hock *(Mng Dir)*

IVP LIMITED
Shashikant Narayan Redij Marg Ghorupdeo, Mumbai, 400 033, India
Tel.: (91) 2223787300
Web Site: https://www.ivpindia.com
IVP—(BOM)
Rev.: $76,440,000

Assets: $50,578,710
Liabilities: $38,060,295
Net Worth: $12,518,415
Earnings: $2,406,495
Emp.: 194
Fiscal Year-end: 03/31/22
Foundry Chemicals Mfr
N.A.I.C.S.: 325998
Mandar Joshi *(CEO)*

IVRCL LIMITED
MIHIR H No 8-2-350/5/A/24/1B Panchavati Colony, Road No 2 Banjara Hills, Hyderabad, 500 034, India
Tel.: (91) 4030931111
Web Site: https://www.ivrcl.com
Year Founded: 1987
530773—(BOM)
Rev.: $68,842,820
Assets: $1,065,229,757
Liabilities: $1,767,533,177
Net Worth: ($702,303,420)
Earnings: ($272,840,295)
Fiscal Year-end: 03/31/20
Infrastruture Construction & Engineering
N.A.I.C.S.: 237310
E. Sudhir Reddy *(Chm & Mng Dir)*

Subsidiaries:

Alkor Petroo Limited (1)
129 Level III G S Arkade, Srinagar Colony, Hyderabad, 500073, Andhra Pradesh, India
Tel.: (91) 40 23757719
Oil & Gas Exploration Services
N.A.I.C.S.: 211120

IVRESSE CO., LTD.
Atago Green Hills Mori Tower 25F Atago, Minato, Tokyo, 105-6225, Japan
Tel.: (81) 669441411
Web Site: https://www.ivresse.jp
Year Founded: 1990
7125—(TKS)
Rev.: $7,968,285
Assets: $2,332,342
Liabilities: $2,226,627
Net Worth: $105,715
Earnings: ($548,398)
Fiscal Year-end: 10/31/23
Management Consulting Services
N.A.I.C.S.: 541618

Subsidiaries:

Ivresse Consulting LLC (1)
Atago Green Hills MORI Tower 25F 2-5-1 Atago, Minato-ku, Tokyo, Japan
Tel.: (81) 355799490
Web Site: https://www.ivresseconsulting.co.jp
Advertising Services
N.A.I.C.S.: 541810

Ivresse Hospitality LLC (1)
Atago Green Hills MORI Tower 25F 2-5-1 Atago, Minato-ku, Tokyo, Japan
Tel.: (81) 355799490
Web Site: https://www.ivressehospitality.com
Home Management Services
N.A.I.C.S.: 721110

IVS GROUP S.A.
18 Rue de LEau, L-1449, Luxembourg, Luxembourg
Tel.: (352) 2255051
Web Site: https://www.ivsgroup.it
IVS—(ITA)
Rev.: $587,575,331
Assets: $1,409,159,983
Liabilities: $855,676,349
Net Worth: $553,483,633
Earnings: $6,763,494
Emp.: 3,953
Fiscal Year-end: 12/31/22
Vending Machine Operators
N.A.I.C.S.: 445132
Paolo Covre *(Chm)*

IVS GROUP S.A.

IVS Group S.A.—(Continued)
Subsidiaries:

Aora Vending Sp. z o.o. (1)
Ul Chmielna 73, 00-801, Warsaw, Poland
Tel.: (48) 536425722
Web Site: https://www.aoravending
Welding Machine Distr
N.A.I.C.S.: 423440

Auto-bar S.r.l. (1)
Via Siracusa 3, Albano Laziale, 00041, Rome, Italy
Tel.: (39) 069310085
Web Site: http://www.auto-bar.it
Drink & Non-Food Product Machinery Mfr
N.A.I.C.S.: 333241

Caybe 2 SI (1)
Andra Mari Kalea 1, 48220, Abadiano, Biscay, Spain
Tel.: (34) 946816596
Vending Machine Operators
N.A.I.C.S.: 445132

Cialdamia S.R.L. (1)
Via Bartolomeo Panizza 4, 20144, Milan, MI, Italy
Tel.: (39) 0800867316
Web Site: https://www.cialdamia.it
Food & Beverage Services
N.A.I.C.S.: 722310

Coin Service Empoli S.p.A. (1)
V Volontari Della Liberta int 1, Empoli, Florence, Italy
Tel.: (39) 0571 93 02 41
Vending Machine Operators
N.A.I.C.S.: 445132

Coin Service Nord S.p.A. (1)
Via Andrea Costa 18, Castel Maggiore, 40013, Bologna, Italy
Tel.: (39) 051700250
Web Site: https://www.coinservicebo.it
Transportation Shipping Services
N.A.I.C.S.: 492110

Demomatic S.A. (1)
Via 1 Agosto 3, 6830, Chiasso, Switzerland
Tel.: (41) 916954151
Web Site: https://www.demomatic.ch
Automated Vending Machine Operator
N.A.I.C.S.: 445132

Espressa C&W S.A. (1)
Travessa da Rua Nova de Pereira N 36 C, Vilar, 4485-805, Vila do Conde, Portugal
Tel.: (351) 225420780
Web Site: https://espressa.pt
Information Technology Services
N.A.I.C.S.: 541519

Espressa Coffee & Water S.A. (1)
Reverend Marti Duran 13-15 Pol Ind El Pla, Sant Feliu de Llobregat, 08980, Barcelona, Spain
Tel.: (34) 900800879
Web Site: https://espressa.es
Bakery Product Mfr & Distr
N.A.I.C.S.: 311813

Express S.R.L. (1)
Via De Gasperi 55, 80133, Naples, Italy
Tel.: (39) 0814201811
Web Site: https://expressglobal.com
Logistics Services Provider
N.A.I.C.S.: 488510

Ge.o.s. Sardegna S.R.L. (1)
Prolungamento Via Natta, ZI Elmas, 09122, Cagliari, Italy
Tel.: (39) 07022652
Web Site: https://www.geos-sardegna.it
Bakery Product Mfr & Distr
N.A.I.C.S.: 311813

IVS Italia S.p.A. (1)
Via dell'Artigianato 25, 24068, Bergamo, Seriate, Italy
Tel.: (39) 0257523000
Web Site: https://www.ivsitalia.com
Vending Machine Operators
N.A.I.C.S.: 445132

Subsidiary (Domestic):

DDS S.p.A. (2)
Pontedassio Loc Montanari, 18027, Imperia, Italy
Tel.: (39) 0183 299909

Web Site: http://www.didiesse.com
Vending Machine Operators
N.A.I.C.S.: 445132

Subsidiary (Non-US):

Emmedi S.A. (2)
c/ Mar Cantabrico 6, 28830, San Fernando de Henares, Spain
Tel.: (34) 916762414
Web Site: http://www.ivsiberica.com
Vending Machine Operators
N.A.I.C.S.: 445132

Subsidiary (Domestic):

Eurovending S.r.l. (2)
Via G di Vittorio 31/7, Peschiera Borromeo, 20068, Milan, Italy
Tel.: (39) 0255302239
Web Site: https://www.eurovendingsrl.it
Vending Machine Operators
N.A.I.C.S.: 445132

Subsidiary (Non-US):

IVS France S.A.S. (1)
3 rue Georges Melies, 95240, Cormeilles-en-Parisis, cedex, France
Tel.: (33) 134118080
Web Site: https://www.ivsfrance.com
Vending Machine Operators
N.A.I.C.S.: 445132

Liomatic S.p.A. (1)
Via dell'Artigianato 25, Seriate, 24068, Bergamo, Italy
Tel.: (39) 0800103010
Web Site: https://www.liomatic.it
Food & Drinks Distr
N.A.I.C.S.: 424420

MB WEB S.a.s. (1)
3 Rue Georges Melies, Cormeilles-en-Parisis, 95240, Cormeilles, France
Tel.: (33) 134118080
Automated Vending Machine Operator
N.A.I.C.S.: 445132

Moneynet S.p.A. (1)
Viale Aiace 132/134, 90151, Palermo, PA, Italy
Tel.: (39) 0800822056
Web Site: https://www.moneynet.it
Financial Transaction Processing Services
N.A.I.C.S.: 522320
Marco Di Cosimo (CEO)

Wefor S.r.l. (1)
Via dell'Artigianato 25, Seriate, 24068, Bergamo, Italy
Tel.: (39) 0257523000
Web Site: https://www.wefor.ch
Coffee Machine Distr
N.A.I.C.S.: 423440

IVU TRAFFIC TECHNOLOGIES AG

Bundesallee 88, 12161, Berlin, Germany
Tel.: (49) 30859060
Web Site: https://www.ivu.com
Year Founded: 1976
IVU—(MUN)
Rev.: $135,213,036
Assets: $168,373,291
Liabilities: $81,134,445
Net Worth: $87,238,846
Earnings: $12,562,041
Emp.: 938
Fiscal Year-end: 12/31/23
Software Publishing Services
N.A.I.C.S.: 513210
Martin Muller-Elschner (Chm-Exec Bd)

Subsidiaries:

IVU Austria GmbH (1)
DC Tower 30 Etage Donau-City-Strasse 7, Vienna, 1220, Austria
Tel.: (43) 12055517036
Software Publisher
N.A.I.C.S.: 513210

IVU Benelux B.V. (1)
Wiltonstraat 38-A, 3905 KW, Veenendaal, Netherlands

Tel.: (31) 318453223
Software Publisher
N.A.I.C.S.: 513210

IVU Chile Ltda. (1)
Santa Beatriz 91 Oficina 204, Providencia, 750-0519, Santiago, Chile
Tel.: (56) 982295306
Web Site: http://www.ivuandina.com
Software Publisher
N.A.I.C.S.: 513210

IVU Traffic Technologies Inc. (1)
2612-A 8th St, Berkeley, CA 94710
Tel.: (510) 926-6560
Software Publisher
N.A.I.C.S.: 513210

IVU Traffic Technologies Italia s.r.l. (1)
Via Cristoforo Colombo 283/A, 00147, Rome, Italy
Tel.: (39) 0694429600
Web Site: https://www.ivu.it
Software Publisher
N.A.I.C.S.: 513210

IVU Traffic Technologies Schweiz AG (1)
Zielempgasse 8, 4600, Olten, Switzerland
Tel.: (41) 442621391
Software Publisher
N.A.I.C.S.: 513210

IVU Traffic Technologies UK Ltd. (1)
33 Ludgate Hill, Birmingham, B3 1 EH, United Kingdom
Tel.: (44) 1212381030
Software Publisher
N.A.I.C.S.: 513210

IVY COSMETICS CORPORATION

IVY Building 6-18-3 Akasaka, Minato-ku, Tokyo, 107-8463, Japan
Tel.: (81) 335685151
Web Site: https://www.ivy.co.jp
Year Founded: 1975
49180—(TKS)
Sales Range: $900-999.9 Million
Emp.: 172
Cosmetics Products Mfr
N.A.I.C.S.: 325620
Koji Shirogane (Pres)

Subsidiaries:

IVY Cosmetics Corporation - Kyoto Promotion Division (1)
9F Karasuma-chuo bldg 659 Tearaimizu-cho Nishiki-koji Agaru, Karasuma-dori Nakagyo-ku, Kyoto, Japan
Tel.: (81) 752535770
Cosmetics Products Mfr
N.A.I.C.S.: 325620

IVY Cosmetics Corporation - Kyushu Division (1)
11F Da Vinci Fukuoka-Tenjin 1-9-17 Tenjin Chuuo-ku, Fukuoka, Fukuoka, Japan
Tel.: (81) 927717707
Cosmetics Products Mfr
N.A.I.C.S.: 325620

IVY Cosmetics Corporation - Misato Plant (1)
1028-1 Aza Kanakusa Oaza Inomata Misato-machi Kodama-gun, Saitama, Japan
Tel.: (81) 495764011
Cosmetics Products Mfr
N.A.I.C.S.: 325620

IVY Cosmetics Corporation - Osaka Promotion Division (1)
1F Aqua-dojima/NBF tower 1-4-16 Dojima-hama Kita-ku, Osaka, Osaka, Japan
Tel.: (81) 647961680
Cosmetics Products Mfr
N.A.I.C.S.: 325620

IVY Cosmetics Corporation - San'in Division (1)
3F Nissei Yonago Washington Building 125 Meiji-cho, Yonago, Tottori, Japan
Tel.: (81) 859372456
Cosmetics Products Mfr
N.A.I.C.S.: 325620

INTERNATIONAL PUBLIC

IWABUCHI CORPORATION

167 Kamihongo, Matsudo, 271-0064, Chiba, Japan
Tel.: (81) 473682222
Web Site: https://www.iwabuchi.co.jp
Year Founded: 1969
5983—(TKS)
Rev.: $77,753,530
Assets: $164,942,141
Liabilities: $34,991,731
Net Worth: $129,950,410
Earnings: $4,453,253
Fiscal Year-end: 03/31/24
Hardware Mfr & Distr
N.A.I.C.S.: 332510
Shugo Uchida (Pres & CEO)

Subsidiaries:

Kyowakougyou Co., Ltd. (1)
No 32 1-chome Umemachi, Hana- ku, Osaka, 554-0032, Kanagawa, Japan
Tel.: (81) 664643421
Web Site: http://www.kyo-wa.biz
Emp.: 220
Motor Vehicle Parts Mfr
N.A.I.C.S.: 336350
Kinzo Misumi (Pres)

IWAICOSMO HOLDINGS, INC.

1-8-12 Imabashi, Chuo-ku, Osaka, Japan
Tel.: (81) 662292800
Web Site: https://www.iwaicosmo-hd.jp
8707—(TKS)
Rev.: $158,904,400
Assets: $1,375,633,540
Liabilities: $937,099,700
Net Worth: $438,533,840
Earnings: $36,711,940
Fiscal Year-end: 03/31/24
Holding Company
N.A.I.C.S.: 551112
Yoshiaki Okitsu (CEO & Chm)

Subsidiaries:

IwaiCosmo Securities Co., Ltd. (1)
1-8-12 Imabashi, Chuo-ku, Osaka, 541 0042, Japan
Tel.: (81) 662032331
Sales Range: $450-499.9 Million
Emp.: 740
Financial Services; Securities
N.A.I.C.S.: 523999

IWAKI CO., LTD.

2-6-6 Kanda Suda-cho, Chiyoda-ku, Tokyo, 101-8558, Japan
Tel.: (81) 3 3254 2935   JP
Web Site: http://www.iwakipumps.jp
Year Founded: 1956
Sales Range: $200-249.9 Million
Emp.: 930
Pump & Pumping Equipment Mfr
N.A.I.C.S.: 333914
Shigeru Fujinaka (Co-Pres)

Subsidiaries:

GFTZ IWAKI Engineering & Trading Co., Ltd. (1)
Room 512-8 Fu Ying International Building 166-3 Changgang Zhong Road, Haizhu District, Guangzhou, 510250, Guangdong, China
Tel.: (86) 2084350603
Pump Distr
N.A.I.C.S.: 423830

IWAKI Belgium bvba (1)
Industrieweg 100 IZ Ravenhout 5025, 3980, Tessenderlo, Belgium
Tel.: (32) 13670200
Web Site: http://www.iwaki.be
Pump Distr
N.A.I.C.S.: 423830

IWAKI Nordic A/S (1)
Ronnekrogen 2, 3400, Hillerod, Denmark
Tel.: (45) 4824 2345
Web Site: http://www.iwaki.dk
Pump Distr

AND PRIVATE COMPANIES

IWATANI CORPORATION

N.A.I.C.S.: 423830
Jan Feddersen (CEO)

Subsidiary (Non-US):

IWAKI Norge AS (2)
Bjornerudveien 13, 1266, Oslo, Norway
Tel.: (47) 23384900
Web Site: http://www.iwaki.no
Pump Distr
N.A.I.C.S.: 423830

IWAKI Suomi Oy (2)
Kultasepankatu 4A, 04250, Kerava, Finland
Tel.: (358) 92745810
Web Site: http://www.iwaki.fi
Pump Distr
N.A.I.C.S.: 423830

IWAKI Sverige AB (2)
Enhagslingan 21A, 187 40, Taby, Sweden
Tel.: (46) 851172922
Web Site: http://www.iwaki.se
Pump Distr
N.A.I.C.S.: 423830

IWAKI Pumps (Shanghai) Co., Ltd. (1)
Room D 18/F Block A Jia Fa Mansion 129 Da Tian Road, Jingan District, Shanghai, 200041, China
Tel.: (86) 2162727502
Pump Distr
N.A.I.C.S.: 423830

IWAKI Pumps Taiwan Co., Ltd. (1)
No 31 Sec 3 Chi-Nan Road, Taipei, Taiwan
Tel.: (886) 227765900
Web Site: http://www.iwakipumps.com.tw
Pump Distr
N.A.I.C.S.: 423830

IWAKI Pumps Vietnam Co., Ltd. (1)
The 9th Street Bien Hoa Industrial Zone 1, Dong Nai, Vietnam
Tel.: (84) 613933456
Web Site: http://www.iwakipumps.com.vn
Pump Distr
N.A.I.C.S.: 423830

IWAKI Singapore Pte Ltd. (1)
51 Bukit Batok Crescent 08-13 Unity Centre, Singapore, 658077, Singapore
Tel.: (65) 63162028
Web Site: http://www.iwakipumps.sg
Pump Mfr & Distr
N.A.I.C.S.: 333996
Hiro Miyauchi (Mng Dir)

IWAKIm SDN. BHD. (1)
No 33 Jalan SS 26/15 Taman Mayang Jaya, 47301, Petaling Jaya, Selangor, Malaysia
Tel.: (60) 378038807
Web Site: http://www.iwakipumps.my
Pump Distr
N.A.I.C.S.: 423830

Iwaki (Thailand) Co., Ltd. (1)
1852/4/6 Pattanakarn Road, Suanluang, Bangkok, 10250, Thailand
Tel.: (66) 2 322 2471 4
Web Site: http://www.iwaki.co.th
Pumps & Pumping Equipment Mfr & Distr
N.A.I.C.S.: 333914

Iwaki America Incorporated (1)
5 Boynton Rd, Holliston, MA 01746
Tel.: (508) 429-1440
Web Site: http://www.walchem.com
Sales Range: $25-49.9 Million
Emp.: 100
Pumps & Pumping Equipment Mfr
N.A.I.C.S.: 333914
Richard L. Jewett (Chm)

Unit (Domestic):

Walchem (2)
5 Boynton Rd, Holliston, MA 01746
Tel.: (508) 429-1110
Web Site: http://www.walchem.com
On-line Analytical Instruments & Electronic Metering Pumps Mfr
N.A.I.C.S.: 334513
Tom Malcolm (Mgr-Customer Svc)

Iwaki Co., Ltd. - Miharu Plant (1)
40-1 Oaza Takanosu Azanumanokura, Miharu-cho, Tamura, 963-7725, Fukushima, Japan
Tel.: (81) 247625771
Pumps Mfr
N.A.I.C.S.: 333914

Iwaki Co., Ltd. - Saitama Plant (1)
2-1-4 Hirosedai, Sayama-shi, Saitama, 350-1328, Japan
Tel.: (81) 429545121
Pumps Mfr
N.A.I.C.S.: 333914

Iwaki Europe GmbH (1)
Siemensring 115, 47877, Willich, Germany
Tel.: (49) 2154 9254 10
Web Site: http://www.iwaki.de
Pumps & Pumping Equipment Distr
N.A.I.C.S.: 423830
Akira Aiyama (Founder & Mng Dir)

Iwaki France S.A. (1)
9 rue Joly de Bammeville Parc de la fontaine, de Jouvence, 91460, Marcoussis, France
Tel.: (33) 1 6963 3370
Web Site: http://www.iwaki.fr
Emp.: 15
Pumps & Pumping Equipment Distr
N.A.I.C.S.: 423830
Terry Serre (Pres)

Iwaki Iberica Pumps S.A. (1)
B Ventas 36 Pab 10 Apdo Correos 434, 20305, Irun, Guipuzcoa, Spain
Tel.: (34) 943 630 030
Web Site: http://www.iwaki.es
Pumps & Pumping Equipment Distr
N.A.I.C.S.: 423830

Iwaki Italia S.r.l. (1)
Via Vicenza 232, IT-36077, Altavilla Vicentina, VI, Italy
Tel.: (39) 02 990 3931
Web Site: http://www.iwakipompe.it
Pumps & Pumping Equipment Distr
N.A.I.C.S.: 423830

Iwaki Pumps (UK) Limited (1)
Unit 2 Monkmoor Industrial Estate Monkmoor Road, Shrewsbury, SY2 5TX, Shropshire, United Kingdom
Tel.: (44) 1743 231 363
Web Site: http://www.iwakipumpsltd.co.uk
Emp.: 5
Pumps & Pumping Equipment Distr
N.A.I.C.S.: 423830
R. N. Sterd (Gen Mgr)

Iwaki Pumps Australia Pty. Ltd. (1)
1/7 Salisbury Road, Castle Hill, 2154, NSW, Australia
Tel.: (61) 2 9899 2411
Web Site: http://www.iwaki-pumps.com.au
Pumps & Pumping Equipment Mfr & Distr
N.A.I.C.S.: 333914

Iwaki Pumps Co., Ltd. (1)
Room 503-505 5/F CCT Telecom Bldg 11 Wo Shing Street, Sha Tin, Hong Kong, China (Hong Kong)
Tel.: (852) 2607 1168
Web Site: http://www.iwaki.hk
Emp.: 20
Pumps & Pumping Equipment Mfr & Distr
N.A.I.C.S.: 423830
Jack Lan (Gen Mgr)

IWASAKI ELECTRIC CO., LTD.
1-1-7 Higashi-Nihonbashi, Chuo-ku, Tokyo, 103-0004, Japan
Tel.: (81) 358469010
Web Site: http://www.eye.co.jp
6924—(TKS)
Rev.: $514,830,800
Assets: $634,862,800
Liabilities: $311,221,680
Net Worth: $323,641,120
Earnings: $22,554,400
Emp.: 1,687
Fiscal Year-end: 03/31/22
Lighting Equipment Mfr
N.A.I.C.S.: 335139
Yoshitake Ito (Pres & CEO)

Subsidiaries:

E.G. Technology Management Corporation (1)
42 Indust Way, Wilmington, MA 01887
Tel.: (978) 694-9000
Web Site: http://www.ebeam.com
Sales Range: $25-49.9 Million
Emp.: 60
Patent & Technology Developers
N.A.I.C.S.: 541199

EYE Lighting (Hong Kong) Ltd. (1)
Room 609 Silvercord Tower 2 30 Canton Road, Tsim Sha Tsui, Kowloon, China (Hong Kong)
Tel.: (852) 23688782
Web Site: http://www.eyelighting.com.hk
Sales Range: $50-74.9 Million
Emp.: 5
Lighting Fixtures Import & Distr
N.A.I.C.S.: 423610

EYE Lighting Asia Pacific Pte. Ltd. (1)
21 Kaki Bukit Pl, Eunos Techpark, Singapore, 416199, Singapore
Tel.: (65) 67423611
Sales Range: $25-49.9 Million
Emp.: 13
Lighting Fixture Mfr
N.A.I.C.S.: 335131
Andrew Koh (Mng Dir)

EYE Lighting Australia Pty. Ltd. (1)
15 Industrial Avenue, Wacol, 4076, QLD, Australia
Tel.: (61) 733353555
Web Site: https://www.eyelighting.com.au
Emp.: 50
Lamps Import & Distr
N.A.I.C.S.: 423330
Russell Loane (Mng Dir)

EYE Lighting Europe Ltd. (1)
Unit 2 Chartridge Devp Eskdale Rd, Uxbridge, UB8 2RT, Middlesex, United Kingdom
Tel.: (44) 1895814418
Web Site: http://www.eyelighting.co.uk
Sales Range: $50-74.9 Million
Emp.: 4
Lamp Suppliers
N.A.I.C.S.: 423220
Henry Zimet (Mgr-Sls)

EYE Lighting International of North America, Inc. (1)
9150 Hendricks Rd, Mentor, OH 44060-2146
Tel.: (440) 350-7000
Web Site: https://www.eyelighting.com
Sales Range: $50-74.9 Million
Emp.: 165
High Intensity Discharge Lamps Mfr
N.A.I.C.S.: 335139
Tom Salpietra (Pres & COO)

EYE Lighting New Zealand Ltd. (1)
18 Levene Pl Mt Wellington, Auckland, 1060, New Zealand
Tel.: (64) 92768099
Sales Range: $50-74.9 Million
Emp.: 5
Lamps Import & Distr
N.A.I.C.S.: 423330

Energy Sciences, Inc. (1)
42 Industrial Way, Wilmington, MA 01887
Tel.: (978) 694-9000
Web Site: http://www.ebeam.com
Power Transformer Mfr
N.A.I.C.S.: 335311

Eye Graphics Co., Ltd. (1)
12th Floor Arca East 3-2-1 Kinshi, Sumida-ku, Tokyo, 130-0013, Japan
Tel.: (81) 336256441
Web Site: http://www.eyegraphics.co.jp
Sales Range: $25-49.9 Million
Emp.: 100
UV Irradiation Equipment Mfr & Supplier
N.A.I.C.S.: 334517
Naoya Fujimoto (Pres)

IWASAKI ELECTRIC Co Ltd - International Business Division (1)
Bakurocho-daiichi Bldg 14-16 Nihonbashi-bakurocho, Chuo-ku, Tokyo, 103-0002, Japan
Tel.: (81) 358478630
Web Site: http://www.eye.co.jp
Lighting Fixture Mfr
N.A.I.C.S.: 335132

Ito Denki Hanbai Co., Ltd. (1)
5-17-1 Shiba, Minato-ku, Tokyo, 108-0014, Japan
Tel.: (81) 334550415
Web Site: http://www.hanbai.itodenki-eye.co.jp
Sales Range: $25-49.9 Million
Emp.: 14
Light Fixtures Supplies & Mfr
N.A.I.C.S.: 335132

Iwasaki Electric Engineering Service Co., Ltd. (1)
3361 Shimonaga, Konosu, 369-0113, Saitama, Japan
Tel.: (81) 485471300
Web Site: http://www.eye-es.jp
Lamp Supplies & Mfr
N.A.I.C.S.: 423220

MIK Smart Lighting Network Corporation (1)
4106-73 Oaza Miyota Miyota-machi, Kitasaku-gun, Nagano, Japan (24.5%)
Tel.: (81) 3 6758 6703
Lighting Equipment Designer & Mfr
N.A.I.C.S.: 335139
Shinichi Yamamura (Exec Officer & Dir)

Shanghai Iwasaki Electric Co., Ltd. (1)
6/F suite2612 New Town Center Building 83 Loushanguan Road, Shanghai, 200336, China
Tel.: (86) 2131056379
Web Site: http://www.eye.co.jp
Lamps & Electric Equipment Mfr & Distr
N.A.I.C.S.: 335139

Spectra Lighting Pty. Ltd. (1)
15 Industrial Avenue, Wacol, 4076, QLD, Australia
Tel.: (61) 733353555
Web Site: http://www.spectralighting.com.au
Sales Range: $25-49.9 Million
Emp.: 50
Lighting Fixture Mfr
N.A.I.C.S.: 335131

IWATA SANGYO CO., LTD.
3-26-39 Moroka, Hakata-ku, Fukuoka, 812-0894, Japan
Tel.: (81) 925138181
Web Site:
http://www.iwatasangyo.co.jp
Year Founded: 1971
Food Business Industry
N.A.I.C.S.: 311999
Yotaro Iwata (Pres)

Subsidiaries:

Tokusui Foods Co., Ltd. (1)
3-15-5 Nagahama, Chuo-ku, Fukuoka, 810-0072, Japan
Tel.: (81) 927118692
Fish & Seafood Distr
N.A.I.C.S.: 424460

IWATANI CORPORATION
6-4 Hommachi 3-chome, Chuo-ku, Osaka, 541-0053, Japan
Tel.: (81) 676373131
Web Site: https://www.iwatani.co.jp
Year Founded: 1945
8088—(TKS)
Rev.: $5,604,539,680
Assets: $5,515,324,510
Liabilities: $3,050,257,210
Net Worth: $2,465,067,300
Earnings: $313,069,430
Emp.: 11,332
Fiscal Year-end: 03/31/24
Oil & Gas Refining, Marketing & Distribution, Liquefied Petroleum Gas Dealers & Industrial Gases Supplier
N.A.I.C.S.: 324110
Toshio Watanabe (Vice Chm & Vice Chm)

Subsidiaries:

ATEC MOBILITY Co., Ltd (1)
289 Pangyo-ro, Bundang-gu, Seongnam, 13488, Gyeonggi, Korea (South)

IWATANI CORPORATION

Iwatani Corporation—(Continued)
Tel.: (82) 316988700
Web Site: https://www.atecmobility.co.kr
Rev.: $115,419,553
Assets: $111,739,762
Liabilities: $45,176,430
Net Worth: $66,563,332
Earnings: $3,302,893
Emp.: 167
Fiscal Year-end: 12/31/2022
Transportation Related Services
N.A.I.C.S.: 488999
Shin Seung-Young (CEO)

Atec Co., Ltd. (1)
A-Tech Building 289 Pangyo-ro, Bundang-gu, Seongnam, 13488, Gyeonggi-do, Korea (South)
Tel.: (82) 316988800
Web Site: https://www.atec.kr
Rev.: $70,297,140
Assets: $75,787,746
Liabilities: $7,577,638
Net Worth: $68,210,109
Earnings: $4,111,219
Emp.: 105
Fiscal Year-end: 12/31/2022
Electronic Components Mfr
N.A.I.C.S.: 334118
Lee Sang-Hoon (CEO)

Bangkok Ai-Toa Co., Ltd (1)
1/7 Moo2 Rama 2 Rd Tambol Thasai, Smutsakorn Industrial Estate Amphur Muang, Samut Sakhon, 74000, Thailand
Tel.: (66) 34490729
Web Site: http://www.ai-toa.com
Emp.: 410
Household Furniture Mfr
N.A.I.C.S.: 321999
Masato Kato (Pres)

Dalian Iwatani Trading Co.,Ltd. (1)
Room 1205B Shen Mao Building No 147 Zhongshan Road, Xigang District, Dalian, 116011, Liaoning, China
Tel.: (86) 41183691810
Web Site: https://www.iwatanid.com
Emp.: 17
Industrial Equipments Merchant & Whslr
N.A.I.C.S.: 423840

Dandong Iwatani Toyo Gas Meter Co., Ltd (1)
66 Gucheng Road, Yuanbao District, Dandong, 118003, Liaoning, China
Tel.: (86) 4154250168
Web Site: http://www.iwatani.co.jp
Gas Meters Mfr & Sales
N.A.I.C.S.: 213112

Doral Pty. Ltd. (1)
1 Alumina Road, East Rockingham, Rockingham, 6168, WA, Australia
Tel.: (61) 894392236
Web Site: http://www.doral.com.au
Zircon Sand Product Mfr
N.A.I.C.S.: 327999

Guangzhou Iwatani Trading Co., Ltd (1)
Room 2304-2306 Kaihua International Center No 5 Xiancun Road, Zhujiang New Town Tianhe District, Guangzhou, 510623, Guangdong, China
Tel.: (86) 2038838998
Web Site: https://www.iwatani-gz.com
Sales Range: $25-49.9 Million
Emp.: 40
Industrial Equipments Whslr & Merchant
N.A.I.C.S.: 423840

I.Sydek Original Package Co.,Ltd. (1)
Suite 06 30th Floor Skyline Tower 39 Wang Kwong Road, Kowloon Bay, Kowloon, China (Hong Kong)
Tel.: (852) 28360606
Web Site: https://www.sydek.com
Packaging Materials Mfr
N.A.I.C.S.: 326199

Iwatani Corporation (Korea) Ltd. (1)
11F Youngpoong Building 41 Cheonggyecheon-Ro, Jongno-Ku, Seoul, 03188, Korea (South)
Tel.: (82) 27538381
Web Site: http://www.iwatani.co.jp
Machinery, Welding, Electronic Equipment, Materials & Food Mfr & Distr
N.A.I.C.S.: 333241

Iwatani Corporation - Tokyo Head Office (1)
21-8 Nishi-shimbashi 3-chome, Minato-ku, Tokyo, 105-8458, Japan
Tel.: (81) 354055711
Gas & Oil Producer & Distr
N.A.I.C.S.: 324110

Iwatani Corporation Europe GmbH (1)
Maximilianstrasse 2, 80539, Munich, Germany
Tel.: (49) 8923708080
Web Site: http://www.iwatani.de
Sales Range: $50-74.9 Million
Emp.: 10
Industrial Gases Whslr
N.A.I.C.S.: 213112
Makoto Fujikake (Mng Dir)

Iwatani Corporation Hong Kong Ltd. (1)
Suites 1506-8 15F Tower2 33 Canton road, Tsim Sha Tsui, Kowloon, China (Hong Kong)
Tel.: (852) 21997727
Web Site: https://iwatani.com.hk
Sales Range: $25-49.9 Million
Emp.: 25
Household Products Trading
N.A.I.C.S.: 423310

Iwatani Corporation Singapore Pte. Ltd. (1)
6 Shenton Way OUE Downtown 2 13-11, DBS Bldg Tower Two, Singapore, 068809, Singapore
Tel.: (65) 62208347
Web Site: https://iwatani.com.sg
Sales Range: $25-49.9 Million
Emp.: 20
Household Trading
N.A.I.C.S.: 423310

Iwatani Corporation Taiwan Ltd. (1)
13F Union Commercial Building No137 Nanking E Road Sec 2, Zhongshan Dist, Taipei, 10485, Taiwan
Tel.: (886) 225066955
Web Site: http://en.iwatani.com.tw
Emp.: 13
Household Products Trading
N.A.I.C.S.: 423310

Iwatani Corporation of America (1)
2200 Post Oak Blvd Ste 1150, Houston, TX 77056
Tel.: (713) 965-9970
Web Site: https://www.iwatani.com
Sales Range: $25-49.9 Million
Emp.: 11
Metals Merchant & Whslr
N.A.I.C.S.: 423930

Iwatani Electronics Shanghai Co., Ltd. (1)
Rm 607 6F Shanghai Overseas Chinese Mansion No 129 Yan an W Rd, Jing an Area, Shanghai, 200040, China
Tel.: (86) 21 5239 4409
Web Site: http://www.iwatani.co.jp
Electronic Products Mfr
N.A.I.C.S.: 334419

Iwatani Industrial Gas Pte.Ltd (1)
13 Pioneer Sector 3, Jurong Industrial Estate, Singapore, 628347, Singapore
Tel.: (65) 68622111
Sales Range: $25-49.9 Million
Emp.: 23
Industrial Gas Mfr
N.A.I.C.S.: 325120

Iwatani Nox Gas Pte. Ltd. (1)
13 Pioneer Sector 3, Jurong Industrial Estate, Singapore, 628347, Singapore
Tel.: (65) 68622111
Web Site: http://www.iwatani.com
Sales Range: $25-49.9 Million
Emp.: 11
Industrial Gas Mfr
N.A.I.C.S.: 325120
Manabu Tsuyoshi (Mng Dir)

Shanghai Iwatani Co., Ltd. (1)
Room 18032 Hang Seng Bank Building No 1000 Lujiazui Ring Road, Pudong New District, Shanghai, 200120, China
Tel.: (86) 2168811188
Web Site: https://www.sh-iwatani.com
Industrial Gases Merchant & Whslr
N.A.I.C.S.: 213112
Yasuhiro Tanaki (Pres)

Shougang Motoman Robot Co., Ltd. (1)
No 7 Yongchang N Rd, Beijing Eco & Tech Devel Area, Beijing, 100076, China
Tel.: (86) 1067880547
Web Site: http://www.sg-motoman.com.cn
Industrial Robots Mfr & Sls
N.A.I.C.S.: 335314

Suzhou Iwatani Metal Products Co.,Ltd (1)
Kinken Kogyoen, Taixing Urban Area Industrial Park, Taicang, Jiangsu, China
Tel.: (86) 51253118570
Web Site: http://www.sziwatani.com.cn
Emp.: 85
Stainless Steel Ultra-Precision Slitting Services
N.A.I.C.S.: 332721
Masatoshi Hio (Gen Mgr)

Suzhou Kinsei Matec Co., Ltd. (1)
No 500 Chaohong Road, Suzhou New District, Suzhou, 215129, Jiangsu, China
Tel.: (86) 51266657995
Web Site: http://www.kinseimatec.co.jp
Emp.: 30
Quartz Glass Mfr
N.A.I.C.S.: 327212

IWATSUKA CONFECTIONERY CO., LTD.

9750 Ura Niigata Prefecture, Nagaoka, 949-5492, Japan
Tel.: (81) 258924111
Web Site: http://www.iwatsukaseika.co.jp
Year Founded: 1954
2221—(TKS)
Rev.: $145,420,000
Assets: $566,827,330
Liabilities: $145,069,670
Net Worth: $421,757,660
Earnings: $12,935,770
Emp.: 880
Fiscal Year-end: 03/31/24
Confectionery Product Mfr & Distr
N.A.I.C.S.: 311351
Haruo Maki (Pres)

IWG PLC

22 Grenville Street, Saint Helier, JE4 8PX, Jersey
Tel.: (44) 8554003575 BE
Web Site: https://work.iwgplc.com
Year Founded: 1989
IWG—(LSE)
Rev.: $3,765,754,312
Assets: $10,441,756,885
Liabilities: $10,333,545,554
Net Worth: $108,211,331
Earnings: ($274,984,088)
Emp.: 9,055
Fiscal Year-end: 12/31/23
Holding Company; Workspace Centers Leasing & Business Support Services
N.A.I.C.S.: 551112
Mark Dixon (CEO)

Subsidiaries:

Basepoint Centres Limited (1)
1 Burwood Place, London, W2 2UT, United Kingdom
Tel.: (44) 8006406271
Web Site: https://www.basepoint.co.uk
Real Estate Services
N.A.I.C.S.: 531210
Rebecca Gattinesi (Sls Dir)

HQ Global Workplaces, LLC (1)
15305 Dallas Pkwy Ste 400, Addison, TX 75001-6922
Tel.: (972) 361-8100
Web Site: http://www.hq.com
Rev.: $200,000,000
Emp.: 2,000

INTERNATIONAL PUBLIC

Office & Business Services & Franchises; Leased Executive Suites; Video Conference Centers
N.A.I.C.S.: 531190
D Farley (CEO)

MWB Business Exchange Limited (1)
1 West Garden Place, Kendal Street, London, W2 2AQ, United Kingdom
Tel.: (44) 20 7868 7200
Web Site: http://www.mwbex.com
Sales Range: $25-49.9 Million
Emp.: 100
Office Space Rental Services
N.A.I.C.S.: 561499
Rob Strachan (Dir-Mktg)

Regus Brasil Limitada (1)
Praia de Botafogo 501 1 andar Torre Pao de Acucar, 22250-040, Rio de Janeiro, Brazil
Tel.: (55) 2125866000
Web Site: http://www.regus.com.br
Real-Time Customer Management & Billing Software
N.A.I.C.S.: 541511
Soraya Freitas (Gen Mgr)

Regus Frankfurt Herriot's GmbH & Co., KG (1)
Herriot Strasse 1, Frankfurt, 60528, Germany (100%)
Tel.: (49) 69677330
Web Site: http://www.regus.com
Sales Range: $25-49.9 Million
Emp.: 4
Reseller of Software Products
N.A.I.C.S.: 334610

IWIN

110 Jangansandan 9-ro, Jangan-eup Gijang-gun, Busan, Gijang-gun, Korea (South)
Tel.: (82) 517112222
Web Site: https://www.iwin.kr
Year Founded: 1999
090150—(KRS)
Rev.: $72,424,352
Assets: $136,391,116
Liabilities: $76,252,124
Net Worth: $60,138,992
Earnings: ($3,243,951)
Emp.: 66
Fiscal Year-end: 12/31/22
Automobile Parts Mfr
N.A.I.C.S.: 336360

IWOCA LTD.

39-45 Shaftesbury Avenue, London, W1D 6LA, United Kingdom
Tel.: (44) 20 3397 3375
Web Site: http://www.iwoca.co.uk
Year Founded: 2012
Financial Services
N.A.I.C.S.: 525990
Seema Desai (COO)

IWOW TECHNOLOGY LIMITED

Block 1004 Toa Payoh North 02-17, Singapore, 318995, Singapore
Tel.: (65) 67488123
Web Site: https://www.iwow.com.sg
Year Founded: 1999
NXR—(CAT)
Rev.: $34,386,810
Assets: $29,194,516
Liabilities: $13,390,144
Net Worth: $15,804,372
Earnings: $2,059,281
Emp.: 163
Fiscal Year-end: 03/31/24
Software Development Services
N.A.I.C.S.: 541511
Raymond Bo Jiang Chek (CEO)

IX ACQUISITION CORP.

Arch 124 Salamanca Street, London, SE1 7HX, United Kingdom
Tel.: (44) 2039830450 Ky
Web Site: https://www.ixacq.com

Year Founded: 2021
IXAQ—(NASDAQ)
Rev.: $10,729,865
Assets: $234,668,588
Liabilities: $247,860,182
Net Worth: ($13,191,594)
Earnings: $9,286,803
Emp.: 3
Fiscal Year-end: 12/31/22
Miscellaneous Financial Investment Activities
N.A.I.C.S.: 523999
Guy Willner *(Chm)*

IX BIOPHARMA LTD.
1 Kim Seng Promenade Great World City Office Tower East Tower 14-01, Singapore, 237994, Singapore
Tel.: (65) 62352270   SG
Web Site: https://www.ixbiopharma.com
Year Founded: 2008
42C—(CAT)
Rev.: $4,381,623
Assets: $18,472,027
Liabilities: $6,725,454
Net Worth: $11,746,573
Earnings: ($7,124,861)
Emp.: 55
Fiscal Year-end: 06/30/23
Pharmaceutical Product Mfr & Distr
N.A.I.C.S.: 325412
Eddy Yip hang Lee *(Chm & CEO)*

Subsidiaries:

iX Syrinx Pty Ltd.   (1)
110 Merrindale Drive, Croydon, 3136, VIC, Australia
Tel.: (61) 397374333
Web Site: https://www.ixsyrinx.com
Pharmaceuticals Product Mfr
N.A.I.C.S.: 325412

IX KNOWLEDGE INC.
3-22-23 Kaigan MSC Center Building, Minato-ku, Tokyo, 108-0022, Japan
Tel.: (81) 364007000
Web Site: https://www.ikic.co.jp
Year Founded: 1999
97530—(TKS)
Sales Range: Less than $1 Million
Emp.: 1,221
Information Service Provider
N.A.I.C.S.: 519290
Fumio Ando *(Pres & CEO)*

IXARIS SYSTEMS, LTD.
22 Long Acre, London, WC2E 9LY, United Kingdom
Tel.: (44) 2082965588
Web Site: http://www.ixaris.com
Year Founded: 2002
Sales Range: $10-24.9 Million
Electronic Payment Solutions
N.A.I.C.S.: 513210
Alex Mifsud *(Founder & CEO)*

IXICO PLC
4th Floor Griffin Court 15 Long Lane, London, EC1A 9PN, United Kingdom
Tel.: (44) 2037637499
Web Site: https://www.ixico.com
IXI—(AIM)
Rev.: $12,941,787
Assets: $16,422,981
Liabilities: $4,041,932
Net Worth: $12,381,049
Earnings: $1,292,549
Emp.: 62
Fiscal Year-end: 09/30/20
Drug Development Services
N.A.I.C.S.: 325412
Giulio Cerroni *(CEO)*

IXIR PRODUCTIONS, INC.
4 Rue Santeuil, Nantes, 44000, France
Tel.: (33) 96 707 7099   NV
Year Founded: 2013
Sales Range: Less than $1 Million
Music Artist Manager
N.A.I.C.S.: 711410
Jonathan Azoulay *(Chm, Pres, CEO, CFO, Treas & Sec)*

IXO PRIVATE EQUITY
34 rue de Metz, Toulouse, 31000, France
Tel.: (33) 5 34 417 418
Web Site: http://www.ixope.fr
Year Founded: 2003
Management Company
N.A.I.C.S.: 523940
Olivier Athanase *(Director General)*

IXUP LIMITED
201 Miller Street, North Sydney, 2060, NSW, Australia
Tel.: (61) 282068888   AU
Web Site: https://www.ixup.com
Year Founded: 2011
IXU—(ASX)
Rev.: $4,427,656
Assets: $4,486,632
Liabilities: $2,638,251
Net Worth: $1,848,381
Earnings: ($6,863,220)
Fiscal Year-end: 06/30/24
Data Management Technology Services
N.A.I.C.S.: 518210
Dean Joscelyne *(Founder)*

IYKOT HITECH TOOLROOM LIMITED
131/2 Thiruneermalai Road Nagelkeni Chrompet, Chennai, 600 044, India
Tel.: (91) 4443162280
Web Site: https://iykot.com
Year Founded: 1989
522245—(BOM)
Rev.: $861,132
Assets: $678,964
Liabilities: $116,754
Net Worth: $562,210
Earnings: $4,637
Emp.: 28
Fiscal Year-end: 03/31/21
Injection Mould Mfr
N.A.I.C.S.: 326199
S. Iyempandi *(Co-Mng Dir)*

IYOGIN HOLDINGS CO.,LTD.
1 Minami-Horibata-cho, Matsuyama, Japan
Tel.: (81) 899071034   JP
Web Site: https://www.iyogin-hd.co.jp
Year Founded: 2022
5830—(TKS)
Rev.: $1,274,130,380
Assets: $61,197,924,850
Liabilities: $55,625,516,380
Net Worth: $5,572,408,470
Earnings: $132,200
Emp.: 2,896
Fiscal Year-end: 03/31/24
Bank Holding Company
N.A.I.C.S.: 551111
Kenji Miyoshi *(Pres & CEO)*

Subsidiaries:

Iyo Bank Ltd.   (1)
1 Minamihoribatacho, Matsuyama, Japan
Tel.: (81) 899411141
Web Site: https://www.iyobank.co.jp
Rev.: $1,296,839,280
Assets: $82,713,634,960
Liabilities: $75,629,830,320
Net Worth: $7,083,804,540
Earnings: $255,716,560
Fiscal Year-end: 03/31/2022
Commercial Bank
N.A.I.C.S.: 522110
Iwao Otsuka *(Chm)*

Affiliate (Domestic):

Iyogin Capital Company Limited   (2)
1 Minamihoribata-cho, Matsuyama, 790-8514, Japan
Tel.: (81) 899338804
Web Site: https://www.iyo-capital.co.jp
Investment & Financing Services
N.A.I.C.S.: 523999
Kenichi Oizumi *(CEO)*

Iyogin Computer Service Company Limited   (2)
2-2-5 Takasagomachi, Matsuyama, 790-0822, Japan
Tel.: (81) 899251130
Web Site: https://www.iyoics.co.jp
Emp.: 187
Data Processing Services
N.A.I.C.S.: 518210

Iyogin Leasing Company Limited   (2)
2-5 Otemachi, Matsuyama, 790-0067, Japan
Tel.: (81) 899331220
Web Site: http://www.iyoginlease.co.jp
Sales Range: $125-149.9 Million
Leasing & Financial Services
N.A.I.C.S.: 561499

IZ HAYVANCILIK TARIM VE GIDA SANAYI VE TICARET AS
OtakclarCad No 78 1 Kat D Blok No 38 Eyrup, Istanbul, Turkiye
Tel.: (90) 2126745059
Web Site: http://www.iztarim.com
IZINV—(IST)
Rev.: $539,718
Assets: $9,995,843
Liabilities: $4,263,523
Net Worth: $5,732,321
Earnings: ($168,901)
Fiscal Year-end: 12/31/23
Agricultural Services Including Dairy Farms, Livestock & Crops
N.A.I.C.S.: 112120
David James Price *(Chm)*

IZAFE GROUP AB
David Bagares Gata 3, 111 38, Stockholm, Sweden
Tel.: (46) 8211121
Web Site: https://www.izafe.se
Year Founded: 2008
M02—(STU)
Sales Range: Less than $1 Million
Integrated Security Services
N.A.I.C.S.: 561621
Anders Segerstrom *(CEO)*

IZMIR DEMIR CELIK SANAYI AS
Sair Esref Bulvari No 23, Cankaya, 35210, Izmir, Turkiye
Tel.: (90) 2324415050
Web Site: https://www.izdemir.com.tr
Year Founded: 1975
IZMDC—(IST)
Rev.: $761,271,759
Assets: $357,455,719
Liabilities: $278,693,052
Net Worth: $78,762,667
Earnings: $37,039,005
Emp.: 1,980
Fiscal Year-end: 12/31/22
Steel Products Mfr
N.A.I.C.S.: 331110
Halil Sahin *(Chm)*

Subsidiaries:

Akdemir Celik Sanayi Ve Ticaret A.S.   (1)
Sair Esref Bulvari No 23/4, Cankaya, 35210, Izmir, Turkiye
Tel.: (90) 2324457884
Web Site: https://www.akdemircelik.com.tr
Rolling Mill Machinery Mfr
N.A.I.C.S.: 333519

IDC Liman Isletmeleri A.S.   (1)
Gumruk Cad No 7 Cakmakli, Aliaga, 35800, Izmir, Turkiye
Tel.: (90) 2326255465
Web Site: https://www.idcliman.com.tr
Port Cargo Handling Services
N.A.I.C.S.: 488310

Izdemir Enerji Elektrik Uretim A.S   (1)
Nemrut Cad No 2, Horozgelerini Village Aliaga, 35808, Izmir, Turkiye
Tel.: (90) 2329993535
Web Site: https://www.izdemirenerji.com
Electricity Generation Services
N.A.I.C.S.: 221118

IZMIR FIRCA SANAYI VE TICARET AS
M Kemal Ataturk Bulvari No 18 AOSB PK, Cigli, 35620, Izmir, Turkiye
Tel.: (90) 2323283187
Web Site: https://www.izmirfirca.com.tr
Year Founded: 1993
IZFAS—(IST)
Rev.: $10,674,460
Assets: $8,080,233
Liabilities: $3,616,854
Net Worth: $4,463,379
Earnings: ($926,246)
Fiscal Year-end: 12/31/23
House Cleaning Products Mfr
N.A.I.C.S.: 339994
Orhan Dilberoglu *(Chm)*

IZMO LTD.
177/2C Bilekahalli Industrial Area Banneraghatta Road, Bengaluru, 560 076, India
Tel.: (91) 8067125430
Web Site: https://www.izmoltd.com
IZMO—(NSE)
Rev.: $18,965,469
Assets: $39,295,207
Liabilities: $7,143,333
Net Worth: $32,151,874
Earnings: $3,638,902
Emp.: 259
Fiscal Year-end: 03/31/21
Automotive Solutions Services
N.A.I.C.S.: 561499
Sanjay Soni *(Mng Dir)*

IZOLA BANK P.L.C
53/58 East Street, Valletta, VLT 1251, Malta
Tel.: (356) 27922040
Web Site: http://www.izolabank.com
IB25A—(MAL)
Rev.: $13,147,765
Assets: $494,268,895
Liabilities: $453,393,157
Net Worth: $40,875,738
Earnings: $550,228
Emp.: 54
Fiscal Year-end: 12/31/21
Commercial Banking Services
N.A.I.C.S.: 522110
Andrew Mifsud *(CEO)*

IZOLACIJA HOLDING A.D.
Kumodraska 257, 11000, Belgrade, Serbia
Tel.: (381) 113986615
Web Site: http://www.izolacija.co.rs
Year Founded: 1959
IZLC—(BEL)
Sales Range: Less than $1 Million
Emp.: 48
Holding Company
N.A.I.C.S.: 551112
Ales Slavec *(Exec Dir)*

IZOLACJA JAROCIN S.A.
Ul Poznanska 24-26, 63-200, Jarocin, Poland
Tel.: (48) 627470400
Web Site: https://www.izolacja-jarocin.pl

IZOLACJA JAROCIN S.A.

Izolacja Jarocin S.A.—(Continued)
Year Founded: 1925
IZO—(WAR)
Rev.: $8,410,275
Assets: $4,976,002
Liabilities: $1,149,624
Net Worth: $3,826,378
Earnings: $436,127
Fiscal Year-end: 12/31/22
Asphalt Roofing Material Mfr & Whslr
N.A.I.C.S.: 324121
Piotr Widawski (Chm & CEO)

IZOLIR A.D.
Novosadski put bb, 23000, Zrenjanin, Serbia
Tel.: (381) 23 561 791
Web Site: http://www.izolir.com
Year Founded: 1997
Sales Range: $1-9.9 Million
Emp.: 39
Plastics Product Mfr
N.A.I.C.S.: 326199

IZOPROGRES A.D.
Bacvanska br 21 3rd Floor, 11000, Belgrade, Serbia
Tel.: (381) 11 285 16 41
Web Site: http://www.izoprogres.rs
Year Founded: 1967
Sales Range: $10-24.9 Million
Emp.: 122
Thermal Insulation Mfr
N.A.I.C.S.: 326140

IZOTROPIC CORP.
Suite 424 800-15355 24th Avenue, Surrey, V4A 2H9, BC, Canada
Tel.: (604) 542-9458
Web Site: https://www.izocorp.com
IZO—(CNSX)
Assets: $3,666,276
Liabilities: $132,426
Net Worth: $3,533,851
Earnings: ($3,892,724)
Fiscal Year-end: 04/30/21
Healtcare Services
N.A.I.C.S.: 621610
Jaclyn Thast (Sec)

IZU SHABOTEN RESORT CO., LTD.
7-8-4 Minami-Aoyama, Minato-Ku, Tokyo, 107-0062, Japan
Tel.: (81) 354642380
Web Site: https://www.izu-sr.co.jp
Year Founded: 1976
6819—(TKS)
Rev.: $23,299,760
Assets: $36,319,360
Liabilities: $9,389,600
Net Worth: $26,929,760
Earnings: $1,877,920
Fiscal Year-end: 03/31/22
Entertainment Services
N.A.I.C.S.: 713110
Yukihiro Kitamoto (Pres)

IZUTSUYA CO., LTD.
1-1 Senba-cho, Kokurakita-ku, Kitakyushu, 802-8511, Japan
Tel.: (81) 935222851
Web Site: https://www.izutsuya.co.jp
Year Founded: 1935
8260—(TKS)
Rev.: $514,433,920
Assets: $457,864,000
Liabilities: $370,463,280
Net Worth: $87,400,720
Earnings: $11,335,280
Emp.: 811
Fiscal Year-end: 02/28/22
Departmental Store Operator
N.A.I.C.S.: 455110
Hideo Kageyama (Pres & CEO)

IZVOR A.D.
Vidovdanska 8, 35250, Paracin, Serbia
Tel.: (381) 35 563 926
Web Site: http://www.pekara-izvor.co.rs
Year Founded: 1997
Sales Range: $1-9.9 Million
Emp.: 117
Bakery Products Mfr
N.A.I.C.S.: 311813

J C BAMFORD EXCAVATORS LIMITED
Harewood Estate Leek Road, Cheadle Stoke-on-Trent, Stoke-on-Trent, ST10 2JU, Staffordshire, United Kingdom
Tel.: (44) 1889590312
Web Site: http://www.jcb.com
Year Founded: 1945
Sales Range: $1-4.9 Billion
Emp.: 8,000
Construction Machinery Mfr
N.A.I.C.S.: 333120
Anthony Bamford (Chm)

Subsidiaries:

JCB Finance Ltd (1)
The Mill High Street, Rocester, Stafford, ST14 5JW, United Kingdom
Tel.: (44) 1889 594155
Web Site: http://www.jcb-finance.co.uk
Financial Consulting Services
N.A.I.C.S.: 523940
Tony Whitehurst (Gen Mgr)

JCB Inc. (1)
2000 Bamford Blvd, Pooler, GA 31322
Tel.: (912) 447-2000
Construction Machinery Distr
N.A.I.C.S.: 423810
Richard Fox-Marrs (Pres & CEO)

J CLARK AND SON LIMITED
820 Prospect Street, Fredericton, E3B 4Z2, NB, Canada
Tel.: (506) 452-1010
Web Site: http://www.clarks.ca
Year Founded: 1883
Sales Range: $50-74.9 Million
Emp.: 125
New & Used Car Dealers
N.A.I.C.S.: 441110
Scott Keirstead (Mgr-Sls-Used Car)

J ESCOM HOLDINGS, INC.
Jack Plaza 6-15-11 Akasaka, Minato-Ku, Tokyo, 107-0052, Japan
Tel.: (81) 351140761
Web Site: https://www.j-escom.co.jp
Year Founded: 2005
3779—(TKS)
Rev.: $10,490,070
Assets: $15,685,530
Liabilities: $13,305,930
Net Worth: $2,379,600
Earnings: ($1,949,950)
Fiscal Year-end: 03/31/24
Holding Company
N.A.I.C.S.: 551112
Takenori Minei (Pres)

J MILLIET BERCY BISTROT CASH BBC
65 Rue Baron Le Roy, 75012, Paris, France
Tel.: (33) 144754780
Web Site: http://www.milliet.fr
Rev.: $21,400,000
Emp.: 80
Wine & Distilled Beverages
N.A.I.C.S.: 424820
Patricia Zylberbogen (Pres)

J RENE HEBERT LTEE
300 rue St Sacrement Suite 28, Montreal, H4P 1W3, QC, Canada
Tel.: (514) 281-0112
Web Site: http://www.jrhebert.com
Year Founded: 1951
Rev.: $10,200,000
Emp.: 15
Brokerage & Transportation Services
N.A.I.C.S.: 523150
Francois Dupuis (Pres)

J SAINSBURY PLC
Sainsbury's Store Support Centre 33 Holborn, London, EC1N 2HT, United Kingdom
Tel.: (44) 2076956000 UK
Web Site: https://www.about.sainsburys.co.uk
Year Founded: 1869
JSAIY—(OTCQX)
Rev.: $39,105,523,800
Assets: $32,483,004,400
Liabilities: $23,476,229,000
Net Worth: $9,006,775,400
Earnings: $257,052,600
Emp.: 63,000
Fiscal Year-end: 03/04/23
Supermarket Grocery & Home Improvement Stores, Garden Centers & Filling Stations Owner & Operator; Bacon & Pork Products Mfr
Tim Fallowfield (Sec & Dir-Corp Svcs)

Subsidiaries:

Argos Ltd. (1)
Royal Avenue, Widnes, WA8 8HS, United Kingdom
Tel.: (44) 3456402020
Web Site: https://www.argos.co.uk
Sales Range: $5-14.9 Billion
Emp.: 1,600
Catalog Retailing
N.A.I.C.S.: 425120

Home Retail Group (UK) Limited (1)
489-499 Avebury Boulevard, Saxon Gate West Central, Milton Keynes, MK9 2NW, United Kingdom (100%)
Tel.: (44) 8451240044
Home & General Merchandise Retailer
N.A.I.C.S.: 455219
Steve Carson (Dir-Retail & Customer Ops)

Subsidiary (Domestic):

Argos Business Solutions Limited (2)
489-499 Avebury Boulevard, Milton Keynes, MK9 2NW, United Kingdom
Tel.: (44) 3454217000
Web Site: http://argosforbusiness.co.uk
General Merchandise Retailer
N.A.I.C.S.: 424990

Nectar 360 Limited (1)
33 Holborn, London, EC1N 2HT, United Kingdom
Tel.: (44) 2076956000
Web Site: http://www.nectar360.co.uk
Advertising & Marketing Services
N.A.I.C.S.: 541810
James Moir (Mng Dir)

Premier Incentives Limited (1)
Barwell Mill Road, West Chiltington, Horsham, RH20 2QN, West Sussex, United Kingdom
Tel.: (44) 1798817317
Web Site: http://www.premiumincentives.co.uk
Advertising & Marketing Services
N.A.I.C.S.: 541810

Sainsbury's Supermarkets Ltd. (1)
33 Holborn, London, EC1N 2HT, United Kingdom
Tel.: (44) 800636262
Web Site: http://www.sainsburys.co.uk
Sales Range: $800-899.9 Million
Emp.: 3,000
Supermarket Grocery Store Services
N.A.I.C.S.: 445110
Jeremy Jones (Controller-Dev)

J STEEL COMPANY HOLDINGS INC

INTERNATIONAL PUBLIC

301 60 Sihwa-ro, Danwon-gu, Ansan, Gyeonggi-do, Korea (South)
Tel.: (82) 314990771
Web Site: http://www.jeilsteel.co.kr
Year Founded: 1964
023440—(KRS)
Rev.: $64,537,713
Assets: $104,772,355
Liabilities: $56,319,765
Net Worth: $48,452,590
Earnings: ($20,830,040)
Emp.: 50
Fiscal Year-end: 12/31/22
Rolling Steel Mfr
N.A.I.C.S.: 331221

J TRUST CO., LTD.
Toranomon First Garden 1-7-12 Toranomon, Minato-Ku, Tokyo, 105-0001, Japan
Tel.: (81) 343309100
Web Site: https://www.jt-corp.co.jp
8508—(TKS)
Rev.: $810,238,110
Assets: $8,612,322,260
Liabilities: $7,419,677,910
Net Worth: $1,192,644,350
Earnings: $115,637,900
Emp.: 3,082
Fiscal Year-end: 12/31/23
Renting Services
N.A.I.C.S.: 522291
Nobuyoshi Fujisawa (Chm)

Subsidiaries:

CREDIA CO., LTD. (1)
6F 10-5 Minamimachi, Suruga-ku, Shizuoka, 422-8563, Japan
Tel.: (81) 542021341
Web Site: http://www.credia.jp
Emp.: 42
Financial Management Services
N.A.I.C.S.: 523999
Tomohiko Sato (Pres)

Chinae Savings Bank Co., Ltd. (1)
Donghoon Tower 317 Teheran-ro, Gangnam-gu, Seoul, Korea (South)
Tel.: (82) 2 6711 5005
Web Site: http://www.chinae-bank.co.kr
Banking Services
N.A.I.C.S.: 522110
Yoon Byeong muk (Pres)

J Trust ASIA PTE. LTD. (1)
Tel.: (65) 65355152
Web Site: http://www.jtrustasia.com
Emp.: 5
Investment Management Service
N.A.I.C.S.: 523940
Nobuyoshi Fujisawa (CEO & Mng Dir)

J Trust Royal Bank Ltd. (1)
20 Kramuon Sar & Corner of Street 67, PO Box 624, Doun Penh District, Phnom Penh, Cambodia (55%)
Tel.: (855) 23 999 000
Web Site: http://www.jtrustroyal.com
Emp.: 522
Commercial Banking Services
N.A.I.C.S.: 522110
Leonie Lethbridge (CEO)

LOPRO CORPORATION (1)
12F Shin Osaka Brick Building 1 6 1 Miyahara, Yodogawa ku, Osaka, 5328552, Japan
Tel.: (81) 663930201
Web Site: http://www.lopro.co.jp
Sales Range: $25-49.9 Million
Emp.: 130
Financial Services
N.A.I.C.S.: 522320

Neoline Credit Co., Ltd. (1)
HLMC Building 12F 890-16 Daechi-dong, Gannam-gu, Seoul, Korea (South)
Tel.: (82) 2 3475 9300
Web Site: http://www.neolinecredit.com
Financial Management Services
N.A.I.C.S.: 523999
Takashi Watanabe (Pres)

Nexus Bank Co., Ltd. (1)
Akasaka Enoki-Zaka Building 11F 1-7-1

Akasaka, Minato-ku, Tokyo, 105-0001, Japan
Tel.: (81) 352595300
Web Site: http://www.nbank.co.jp
Rev: $7,583,590
Assets: $27,565,020
Liabilities: $8,097,110
Net Worth: $19,467,910
Earnings: ($2,778,510)
Fiscal Year-end: 01/31/2020
Software System Services
N.A.I.C.S.: 541512
Yoshito Fukuyama *(Chm)*

Rakuten KC Co., Ltd. (1)
Rakuten KC Kaikan 3-4-2 Hakata Ekimae, Hakata-ku, Fukuoka, 812-8524, Japan (97.3%)
Tel.: (81) 924515971
Web Site: http://www.rakuten-kc.co.jp
Sales Range: $500-549.9 Million
Emp.: 617
Credit Card Issuing & Loan Services
N.A.I.C.S.: 522210

Subsidiary (Domestic):

Kajiyama Warehouse Co., Ltd. (2)
1-15 Dairi Moto-machi, Moji-ku, Fukuoka, 800-0062, Japan (100%)
Tel.: (81) 933813810
Sales Range: $600-649.9 Million
Emp.: 2,000
Credit Card Business
N.A.I.C.S.: 522210
Raii Yamagata *(Mng Dir)*

J WAY CO., LTD.
1110-22 1F Oryong-dong Buk-gu, Gwangju, Korea (South)
Tel.: (82) 234008500
Web Site: http://www.jway.kr
058420—(KRS)
Rev.: $1,066,211
Assets: $847,260
Liabilities: $4,591,046
Net Worth: ($3,743,786)
Earnings: ($963,463)
Emp.: 2
Fiscal Year-end: 12/31/22
Movie Distribution Services
N.A.I.C.S.: 512120

J&E DAVY HOLDINGS LIMITED
Davy House 49 Dawson Street, Dublin, D02 PY05, Ireland
Tel.: (353) 16797788
Web Site: http://www.davy.ie
Year Founded: 1926
Sales Range: $125-149.9 Million
Emp.: 500
Stock Broking Services
N.A.I.C.S.: 523150
Tony Garry *(CEO)*

Subsidiaries:

Davy Securities Ltd (1)
Davy House 49 Dawson Street, Dublin, Ireland
Tel.: (353) 1 679 7788
Web Site: http://www.davy.ie
Emp.: 680
Securities Brokerage Services
N.A.I.C.S.: 523150
Brian McKiernan *(CEO)*

J&F INVESTIMENTOS S.A.
Av Marginal Direita do Tiete 500-Vila, Jaguara, Sao Paulo, 05118-100, Brazil
Tel.: (55) 1125050400 BR
Web Site: http://www.jfinvest.com.br
Year Founded: 1953
Investment Holding Services
N.A.I.C.S.: 551112
Joesley Mendonca Batista *(Partner)*

Subsidiaries:

Ambar Energia Ltda (1)
Av Marginal Direita do Tiete 500 Vila Jaguara, Sao Paulo, 05118-100, Brazil
Tel.: (55) 1136681175
Web Site: http://ambarenergia.com.br
Electric Power Distr
N.A.I.C.S.: 221116

J&J DENHOLM LTD.
18 Woodside Crescent, Glasgow, G3 7UL, United Kingdom
Tel.: (44) 1413532090
Web Site: http://www.denholm-group.co.uk
Year Founded: 1866
Sales Range: $350-399.9 Million
Emp.: 1,400
Holding Company; Shipping, Logistics, Seafood & Industrial Services
N.A.I.C.S.: 551112
John S. Denholm *(Chm)*

Subsidiaries:

Ably Resources Ltd. (1)
105 West George Street, Glasgow, G2 1PD, United Kingdom
Tel.: (44) 141 271 6000
Web Site: http://www.ablyresources.com
Emp.: 10
Employee Placement Services
N.A.I.C.S.: 561311

Denholm Industrial Services Ltd. (1)
Abbey Manor Business Centre Preston Road, Yeovil, BA20 2EN, Somerset, United Kingdom
Tel.: (44) 1935420081
Web Site: http://www.denholm-industrial.com
Sales Range: $25-49.9 Million
Emp.: 6
Vessel Cleaning, Coating, Inspection, Operations & Maintenance Services
N.A.I.C.S.: 488390
John Moore *(Mng Dir)*

Denholm Logistics Ltd. (1)
Water Street, PO Box 28, Liverpool, L69 2BW, United Kingdom
Tel.: (44) 1512844000
Web Site: http://www.denholm-logistics.co.uk
Sales Range: $25-49.9 Million
Emp.: 40
Logistic Services
N.A.I.C.S.: 541614
Niall Denholm *(Mng Dir)*

Joint Venture (Domestic):

Denholm Barwil Ltd. (2)
Liner House Test Road Eastern Docks, Southampton, SO14 3GE, United Kingdom (60%)
Tel.: (44) 2380713140
Web Site: http://www.denholm-barwil.com
Sales Range: $25-49.9 Million
Ships Agency Services
N.A.I.C.S.: 488390
Gary Tranter *(Mng Dir)*

Subsidiary (Domestic):

Denholm Forwarding (2)
Enterprise House 168-170 Upminster Road, Upminster, RM14 2RB, Essex, United Kingdom
Tel.: (44) 1708449100
Web Site: http://www.denholm-forwarding.co.uk
Sales Range: $25-49.9 Million
Emp.: 15
Freight Forwarding & Freight Management Services
N.A.I.C.S.: 483111

Denholm Handling Ltd (2)
Stopgate Lane Simonswood, Kirkby, Liverpool, L33 4YA, United Kingdom
Tel.: (44) 1515474141
Web Site: http://www.denholm-handling.co.uk
Logistics Services Including Handling & Storage
N.A.I.C.S.: 488390
Martin Hall *(Mng Dir)*

Denholm Transport Ltd. (2)
India Buildings Water Street, PO Box 28, Liverpool, L69 2BW, United Kingdom
Tel.: (44) 1512272050
Web Site: http://www.denholm-transport.co.uk
Sales Range: $25-49.9 Million
Container Transportation & Cargo Distribution Services
N.A.I.C.S.: 488390
Dave Carse *(Mng Dir)*

Affiliate (Domestic):

Lacy & Middlemiss Shipbrokers Ltd. (2)
Marlborough House 102-110 High Street, Shoreham-by-Sea, BN43 5DB, West Sussex, United Kingdom
Tel.: (44) 1273461464
Web Site: http://www.lacy.co.uk
Sales Range: $25-49.9 Million
Emp.: 6
Inland Shipping Services
N.A.I.C.S.: 483211

Denholm MacNamee Limited (1)
Souterford Avenue Inverurie Business Park, Inverurie, AB51 0ZJ, Aberdeenshire, United Kingdom
Tel.: (44) 1467 629933
Web Site: http://www.denholm-macnamee.com
Oilfield Cleaning Services
N.A.I.C.S.: 213112
Andrew Rettie *(Mgr-Sls Dev)*

Denholm Seafoods Ltd. (1)
11 Timber Bush, Edinburgh, EH6 6QH, Scotland, United Kingdom
Tel.: (44) 1315549400
Web Site: http://www.denholm-seafoods.com
Sales Range: $25-49.9 Million
Emp.: 3
Seafood Processor
N.A.I.C.S.: 311710

Subsidiary (Domestic):

Cawoods (Fishcurers) Ltd. (2)
Estate Road 6, South Humberside Indus Estate, Grimsby, DN31 2TG, United Kingdom
Tel.: (44) 1472342248
Web Site: http://www.cawoodsfish.com
Sales Range: $10-24.9 Million
Emp.: 30
Seafood Processor Service
N.A.I.C.S.: 311710
Suki Dulai *(Mng Dir)*

Denholm Fishselling Ltd. (2)
12 Timber Bush, Edinburgh, EH6 6QH, Scotland, United Kingdom
Tel.: (44) 1315549400
Web Site: http://www.cawoodsfish.com
Fish Sales & Distr; Vessel Management Services
N.A.I.C.S.: 424460

Denholm Shipping Company (1)
78 Cornhill Union Building 78 Corn Hill, London, EC3V3QQ, United Kingdom
Tel.: (44) 2073377070
Web Site: http://www.denshipco.co.uk
Sales Range: $50-74.9 Million
Emp.: 6
Ship Owning, Broking, Commercial Management, Consulting & Vessel Technical Management Services
N.A.I.C.S.: 441222
Duncan Brown *(Mng Dir)*

Denholm Yam (1)
PO Box 94243, Abu Dhabi, United Arab Emirates
Tel.: (971) 2 659 3333
Steel Structure Fabrication Services
N.A.I.C.S.: 237120
Jad Ayoub *(Project Mgr)*

Denholm Zholdas LLP (1)
45 Abylkhair Khan Avenue, Atyrau, 060011, Kazakhstan
Tel.: (7) 7122 760 166
Web Site: http://www.denholmzholdas.kz
Human Resource Training & Consulting Services
N.A.I.C.S.: 541612
Gus Gill *(Dir-Fin)*

Petrasco Services Ltd (1)
Freight House Kirkhill Place, Dyce, AB21 0GU, Aberdeenshire, United Kingdom
Tel.: (44) 1224 337733
Web Site: http://www.petrasco.co.uk
International Freight Forwarding Services
N.A.I.C.S.: 488510

Relay Engineering Limited (1)
S167 South Yard HM Naval Base Devonport, Plymouth, PL2 2BG, United Kingdom
Tel.: (44) 1752 606206
Web Site: http://www.relay-engineering.com
Emp.: 50
Engineering Consulting Services
N.A.I.C.S.: 541330
Paul Fisher *(Mng Dir)*

SDL Denholm Limited (1)
5 Sabir Street, Old City, AZ1000, Baku, Azerbaijan
Tel.: (994) 12 4978750
Web Site: http://www.denholm-oilfield.az
Emp.: 4,000
Marine Engineering Services
N.A.I.C.S.: 541330
Elchin Ibrahimov *(Mgr-IT & Plng)*

J&PARTNERS L.P.
Suite 805 8/F ICBC Tower Citibank Plaza, 3 Garden Road, Central, China (Hong Kong)
Tel.: (852) 2878 7321
Web Site: http://www.jandpartners.com
Privater Equity Firm
N.A.I.C.S.: 523999
Jimmy Budiarto *(Founder & Partner)*

Subsidiaries:

PT J Resources Asia Pasifik Tbk (1)
Equity Tower 48th Floor Sudirman Central Business District Lot 9, Jl Jenderal Sudirman Kav 52-53 Jakarta Selatan, Jakarta, 12190, Indonesia
Tel.: (62) 215153335
Web Site: https://www.jresources.com
Rev.: $170,145,810
Assets: $858,524,541
Liabilities: $475,565,221
Net Worth: $382,959,320
Earnings: $581,876
Emp.: 573
Fiscal Year-end: 12/31/2023
Silver & Gold Exploration & Mining
N.A.I.C.S.: 212220
Edi Permadi *(Chm)*

Subsidiary (Domestic):

PT J Resources Nusantara (2)
Equity Tower 48th Floor Sudirman Central Business District Lot 9, Jl Jenderal Sudirman Kav 52-53 Jakarta Selatan, Jakarta, 12190, Indonesia
Tel.: (62) 21 515 3335
Emp.: 150
Holding Company
N.A.I.C.S.: 551112
Jimmy Budiarto *(Pres)*

Subsidiary (Domestic):

PT J Resources Bolaang Mongondow (3)
J1 Kol Sugiono No 24 Kotabangun, 95712, Kotamobagu, Indonesia (80%)
Tel.: (62) 43421018
Web Site: http://www.jresources.com
Gold Ore Mining
N.A.I.C.S.: 212220

Subsidiary (Non-US):

Specific Resources Sdn. Bhd. (3)
Penjom Gold Mine Empang Jalih, PO Box 49, Kuala Lipis, 27207, Pahang, Malaysia (100%)
Tel.: (60) 93227288
Gold Ore Mining
N.A.I.C.S.: 212220
Jesper Christan *(Gen Mgr)*

J&R HALL TRANSPORT INC.
RR 3 552 Piper St, Ayr, N0B 1E0, ON, Canada
Tel.: (519) 632-7429
Web Site: http://www.jrhall.ca
Year Founded: 1947

J&R HALL TRANSPORT INC.

J&R Hall Transport Inc.—(Continued)

Sales Range: $10-24.9 Million
Truck Transportation Services
N.A.I.C.S.: 484122
Jeff Hall *(Pres)*

J&T FINANCE GROUP SE
Dvorakovo nabrezie 8, 811 02, Bratislava, Slovakia
Tel.: (421) 259418111
Web Site: http://www.jtfg.com
Year Founded: 1994
Sales Range: $1-4.9 Billion
Emp.: 8,869
Investment Services
N.A.I.C.S.: 523999
Jozef Tkac *(Chm)*

Subsidiaries:

Elektrarny Opatovice, a.s. (1)
Opatovice Nad Labem, Pardubice, 532 13, Czech Republic
Tel.: (420) 466843111
Web Site: http://www.eop.cz
Emp.: 300
Generates & Sells Electricity
N.A.I.C.S.: 221122
Miloslav Decker *(Dir-Project Dev)*

J&V ENERGY TECHNOLOGY CO., LTD.
4F-1 No 1 Jihu Rd, Neihu Dist, Taipei, Taiwan
Tel.: (886) 226570355
Web Site: https://global.jv-holding.com
Year Founded: 2016
6869—(TAI)
Rev.: $221,837,037
Assets: $286,931,216
Liabilities: $150,910,979
Net Worth: $136,020,238
Earnings: $33,240,327
Emp.: 395
Fiscal Year-end: 12/31/23
Solar Energy Services
N.A.I.C.S.: 237130

J-BASE, INC.
1-2-15 Kakyoin, Aoba-Ku, Sendai, 980-0021, Japan
Tel.: (81) 120610534
Web Site: http://www.j-base.net
Year Founded: 2018
5073—(TKS)
Construction Services
N.A.I.C.S.: 236220
Junya Takahashi *(Founder & Pres)*

J-GROUP HOLDINGS CORP.
284 Sakae 3chome, Naka-ku, Nagoya, 460-0008, Aichi, Japan
Tel.: (81) 522430026
Web Site: https://www.jgroup.jp
Year Founded: 1997
3063—(TKS)
Rev.: $73,969,970
Assets: $64,866,410
Liabilities: $53,557,860
Net Worth: $11,308,550
Earnings: $1,751,230
Fiscal Year-end: 02/29/24
Holding Company
N.A.I.C.S.: 551112
Akinari Nakagawa *(Pres)*

J-HOLDINGS CORP.
7F Azabu Inoue Building 1-7-11 AzabuJuban, Minato-Ku, Tokyo, 106-0045, Japan
Tel.: (81) 364303461
Web Site: https://www.jholdings.co.jp
Year Founded: 1993
2721—(TKS)
Rev.: $1,240,750
Assets: $2,346,790
Liabilities: $347,410
Net Worth: $1,999,380
Earnings: ($2,098,640)
Fiscal Year-end: 12/31/23
Construction Services
N.A.I.C.S.: 237990
Shinji Ueno *(Pres)*

Subsidiaries:

J-Sports Corp. (1)
5th floor Shimbashi Square Building 5-10-10 Shimbashi, Minato-ku, Tokyo, 105-0004, Japan
Tel.: (81) 364303484
Web Site: http://www.j-spo.co.jp
Football Court Development Services
N.A.I.C.S.: 237990

Synergy Consulting Co., Ltd. (1)
5th Floor Shimbashi Square Building 5-14-10 Shimbashi, Minato-ku, Tokyo, 105-0004, Japan
Tel.: (81) 364303463
Web Site: http://sc225.jp
Real Estate Consulting Service
N.A.I.C.S.: 531210

J-HORIZONS TRAVEL (M) SDN. BHD.
Lot L4-C Level 4 The Weld No 76, Jalan Raja Chulan, 50200, Kuala Lumpur, Malaysia
Tel.: (60) 321610922
Web Site: http://www.j-horizons.com.my
Year Founded: 1970
Sales Range: $10-24.9 Million
Emp.: 24
Tour & Travel Agency Services
N.A.I.C.S.: 561520
Shinya Hori *(Mng Dir)*

J-LEASE CO., LTD.
6-22-1 Nishi-Shinjuku Shinjuku Square Tower 2nd floor, Shinjuku-ku, Tokyo, 163-1102, Japan
Tel.: (81) 359091241
Web Site: https://www.j-lease.jp
Year Founded: 2004
7187—(TKS)
Rev.: $87,384,200
Assets: $76,583,460
Liabilities: $45,998,990
Net Worth: $30,584,470
Earnings: $11,825,290
Emp.: 404
Fiscal Year-end: 03/31/24
Real Estate Rental Services
N.A.I.C.S.: 531210
Shigeharu Nakashima *(Sr Mng Dir)*

Subsidiaries:

Asumirai Co., Ltd. (1)
Brother Hakata Ekimae Building 5F 2-3-12 Hakata Ekimae, Hakata-ku, Fukuoka, 812-0011, Japan
Tel.: (81) 924333711
Real Estate Manangement Services
N.A.I.C.S.: 531210

J-MAX CO., LTD.
130-1 Otsusaka, Kamiishizu-Cho Gifu, Ogaki, 503-1601, Japan
Tel.: (81) 584463191
Web Site: https://www.jp-jmax.co.jp
Year Founded: 1952
3422—(TKS)
Rev.: $359,233,670
Assets: $341,988,180
Liabilities: $198,181,020
Net Worth: $143,807,160
Earnings: ($6,781,860)
Emp.: 1,427
Fiscal Year-end: 03/31/24
Automobile Body Mfr
N.A.I.C.S.: 336211
Eiji Yamazaki *(Pres)*

Subsidiaries:

Guangzhou Marujun Co., Ltd. (1)
No 8 Yongsheng Road Yonghe Economic Zone, Economic and Technological Development Zone, Guangzhou, China
Tel.: (86) 2032225188
Web Site: http://www.gz-gmax.cn
Emp.: 827
Stamping Mold Mfr
N.A.I.C.S.: 333511

Thai Marujun Co., Ltd. (1)
62 Moo 6 Ban Nongsamak Khokyae, Nongkhae Industrial Estate, Nongkhae, 18230, Saraburi, Thailand
Tel.: (66) 363742617
Web Site: http://www.marujun.co.th
Automobile Parts Mfr
N.A.I.C.S.: 336390

Wuhan Marujun Co., Ltd. (1)
No 223 Juufeng Street Wuhan East Lake Hi-Tech Development Zone, Wuhan, 430250, Hubei, China
Tel.: (86) 2787905900
Automobile Parts Mfr
N.A.I.C.S.: 336390

J-OIL MILLS INC.
St Luke's Tower 8-1 Akashi-cho, Chuo-ku, Tokyo, 104-0044, Japan
Tel.: (81) 351487100
Web Site: https://www.j-oil.com
Year Founded: 2002
2613—(TKS)
Rev.: $1,614,948,590
Assets: $1,177,194,730
Liabilities: $502,637,620
Net Worth: $674,557,110
Earnings: $44,895,120
Emp.: 1,275
Fiscal Year-end: 03/31/24
Oil Product Mfr & Distr
N.A.I.C.S.: 311225
Fuminao Hachiuma *(Chm, Pres & CEO)*

J-STAR CO. LTD.
6th floor New International Building 3-4-1 Marunouchi, Chiyoda, Tokyo, 100-0005, Japan
Tel.: (81) 3 6269 9701
Web Site: http://www.j-star.co.jp
Year Founded: 2006
Private Investment Firm
N.A.I.C.S.: 523999
Gregory Rokuro Hara *(Mng Partner & Head-Investment)*

J-STAR HOLDING CO., LTD.
7/F-1 No 633 Sec 2 Taiwan Blvd, Xitun District, Taichung, 407, Taiwan
Tel.: (886) 423229900
Year Founded: 2016
Rev.: $22,178,572
Assets: $28,592,759
Liabilities: $19,373,708
Net Worth: $9,219,051
Earnings: $1,110,146
Emp.: 901
Fiscal Year-end: 12/31/20
Holding Company
N.A.I.C.S.: 551112
Jing-Bin Chiang *(CEO & Chm)*

J-STREAM INC.
Shiba 256 Square Bldg 6F 2-5-6 Shiba, Minato-ku, Tokyo, 105-0014, Japan
Tel.: (81) 357657000
Web Site: https://www.stream.co.jp
Year Founded: 1997
4308—(TKS)
Rev.: $74,468,260
Assets: $82,638,220
Liabilities: $10,780,910
Net Worth: $71,857,310
Earnings: $1,969,780
Fiscal Year-end: 03/31/24
Media Streaming Services
N.A.I.C.S.: 518210
Toshio Ishimatsu *(Pres)*

INTERNATIONAL PUBLIC

Subsidiaries:

CROSSCO Co., Ltd. (1)
7-18-23 Roppongi, Minato-ku, Tokyo, 106-0032, Japan
Tel.: (81) 364471920
Sales Range: $25-49.9 Million
Emp.: 86
Video Production & Communication Services
N.A.I.C.S.: 512199
Kengo Kaketa *(Pres & CEO)*

InnoQos Corporation (1)
4-14-7 Nihonbashi Honcho, chuo-ku, Tokyo, 103-0023, Japan (90%)
Tel.: (81) 3 6712 9523
Web Site: http://www.innoqos.jp
Emp.: 11
Internet Broadcasting Services
N.A.I.C.S.: 516210
Masaki Inomata *(Pres & CEO)*

J. ASTAPHAN & CO (1970) LTD
65 King George V Street, PO Box 75, Roseau, Dominica
Tel.: (767) 4483221
Web Site: http://www.astaphans.com
Year Founded: 1970
Sales Range: $10-24.9 Million
Emp.: 450
Supermarket & Department Store Owner & Operator
N.A.I.C.S.: 445110
W. A. Astaphan *(Chm)*

J. BAUER GMBH & CO. KG
Molkerei Bauer Strasse 1 10, 83512, Wasserburg am Inn, Germany
Tel.: (49) 80711090
Web Site: http://www.bauer-milch.de
Year Founded: 1887
Rev.: $583,728,220
Emp.: 600
Cheese Mfr
N.A.I.C.S.: 311513
Markus Bauer *(Mng Dir)*

Subsidiaries:

Bauer Frischdienst GmbH (1)
Priener Strasse 2, 83512, Berlin, Germany
Tel.: (49) 80719030101
Web Site: http://www.bauer-frischdienst.de
Dairy Products Mfr
N.A.I.C.S.: 112120

Heideblume Molkerei Elsdorf Rotenburg AG (1)
Molkereistrasse 6, 27404, Elsdorf, Germany
Tel.: (49) 428693000
Web Site: http://www.elsdorfer.de
Dairy Products Mfr
N.A.I.C.S.: 112120
Dirk Wagner *(Acct Mgr)*

Immergut GmbH & Co. KG (1)
Bahnhofstrasse 22, 36381, Schluchtern, Germany
Tel.: (49) 66611550
Web Site: http://www.immergut.de
Dairy Products Mfr
N.A.I.C.S.: 112120

Marker Fine Food GmbH (1)
Grosser Kamp 7, 22885, Barsbuttel, Germany
Tel.: (49) 406706181
Web Site: http://www.maerkerfinefood.de
Dairy Products Mfr
N.A.I.C.S.: 112120

Stannecker GmbH (1)
Am Steinbach 16, 94496, Ortenburg, Germany
Tel.: (49) 854296010
Web Site: http://www.stannecker.de
Food Product Mfr & Distr
N.A.I.C.S.: 311412

Walhalla Delikatessen GmbH (1)
Benzstrasse 5, 93092, Barbing, Germany
Tel.: (49) 9401528330
Web Site: http://www.walhalla-delikatessen.de

AND PRIVATE COMPANIES

Food Product Mfr & Distr
N.A.I.C.S.: 311412

J. BOUTARI & SON HOLDING S.A.
20th Km Marathonos Ave, 19009, Pikermi, Greece
Tel.: (30) 210 6605200
Web Site: http://www.boutarigroup.gr
Year Founded: 1879
Emp.: 104
Wine & Distilled Beverage Mfr
N.A.I.C.S.: 424820

Subsidiaries:

J. Boutari & Son Wineries S.A. (1)
20th km Marathonos Avenue, Pikermi, 19009, Athens, Greece
Tel.: (30) 2106605200
Web Site: http://www.boutari.gr
Wine Mfr
N.A.I.C.S.: 312130

J. ESTINA CO., LTD.
Romanson Building 53, Yangjae-daero 62-gil Songpa-gu, Seoul, Korea (South)
Tel.: (82) 809980077
Web Site: https://www.jestina.com
Year Founded: 1988
026040—(KRS)
Rev.: $59,734,318
Assets: $45,396,199
Liabilities: $9,696,044
Net Worth: $35,700,155
Earnings: $1,003,061
Emp.: 323
Fiscal Year-end: 12/31/22
Jewelry & Watch Mfr
N.A.I.C.S.: 339910
Gi-mun Kim *(Chm)*

J. FRONT RETAILING CO., LTD.
10-1 Ginza 6-chome, Chuo-ku, Tokyo, Japan
Tel.: (81) 368657621 JP
Web Site: https://www.j-front-retailing.com
Year Founded: 2007
JFROF—(OTCIQ)
Rev.: $3,208,765,120
Assets: $11,547,339,760
Liabilities: $8,042,018,160
Net Worth: $3,505,321,600
Earnings: $41,827,280
Emp.: 7,302
Fiscal Year-end: 02/28/22
Holding Company; Retail Department Stores Owner & Operator
N.A.I.C.S.: 551112
Kozo Makiyama *(Sr Mng Exec Officer)*

Subsidiaries:

Angel Park Co., Ltd. (1)
3-16-10 Sakae Sakikyuya Odori Park Hisaya Square/Angel Square, Sakikyuya Odori Park Naka-ku, Nagoya, 460-0008, Aichi, Japan
Tel.: (81) 522615746
Web Site: http://www.angelpark.co.jp
Parking Services
N.A.I.C.S.: 812930

Central Park Building Co., Ltd. (1)
15-6 Koseidori Nishi 3-chome, Okazaki, 444-0059, Aichi, Japan
Tel.: (81) 564231321
Web Site: http://www.j-front-retailing.com
Real Estate Leasing & Parking Services
N.A.I.C.S.: 531110

Consumer Product End-Use Research Institute Co., Ltd. (1)
2-1-1 Edobori 20th floor reception 21st floor Edobori Center Building, Nishi-ku, Osaka, 550-0002, Japan
Tel.: (81) 664454670
Web Site: http://www.shoukaken.jp

Sales Range: $25-49.9 Million
Merchandise Testing & Quality Control Services
N.A.I.C.S.: 561990

Daimaru Kogyo, Ltd. (1)
Yushutsu Seni Kaikan 3-4F 3-4-9 Bingo-Machi, Chuo-ku, Osaka, 541-0051, Japan
Tel.: (81) 662051000
Web Site: http://www.daimarukogyo.co.jp
Sales Range: $750-799.9 Million
Emp.: 341
General Commodities Distr
N.A.I.C.S.: 423930
Tsuneichirou Nagano *(Pres & CEO)*

Daimaru Matsuzakaya Department Stores Co., Ltd. (1)
18-11 Kiba 2-chome, Koto-ku, Tokyo, 135-0042, Japan
Tel.: (81) 368950816
Sales Range: $1-4.9 Billion
Emp.: 6,000
Department Stores
N.A.I.C.S.: 455110

Subsidiary (Domestic):

Daimaru COM Development Inc. (2)
2nd Floor Daimaru Kitasumiyamachi Building 7-3 Nishishinsaibashi, 1-chome Chuo-ku, Osaka, 542-0086, Japan
Tel.: (81) 6 6245 8481
Web Site: http://www.j-front-retailing.com
Real Estate Leasing & Tenant Services
N.A.I.C.S.: 531110

Subsidiary (Non-US):

Daimaru Kogyo (Thailand) Co., Ltd. (2)
Unit 1902 19th Floor Sathorn Square Office Building 98 North Sathorn, Kwaeng Silom Khet Bangrak, Bangkok, 10500, Thailand
Tel.: (66) 21632903
Electronic Product Distr
N.A.I.C.S.: 423690

Daimaru Kogyo International Trading (Shangai) Co., Ltd. (2)
6th Floor Hang Seng Bank Tower 1000 Lujiazui Ring Rd, Pudong New Area, Shanghai, China
Tel.: (86) 2168413588
Electronic Product Distr
N.A.I.C.S.: 423690

Subsidiary (Domestic):

Daimaru Matsuzakaya Sales Associates Co. Ltd. (2)
2-1 Konyamachi, Takatsuki, 569-8522, Osaka, Japan
Tel.: (81) 72 684 8145
Employee Leasing Services
N.A.I.C.S.: 561330

Daimaru Matsuzakaya Tomonokai, Co., Ltd. (2)
1-7-1 Shinsaibashisuji, Chuo-ku, Osaka, 542-0083, Japan (100%)
Tel.: (81) 662711231
Web Site: https://www.dmtomonokai.co.jp
Cash & Carry Stores Operation Services
N.A.I.C.S.: 561990
Ikeda Akira *(CEO)*

Matsuzakaya - Nagoya (2)
3-16-1 Sakae, Naka-ku, Nagoya, 460-8430, Japan (100%)
Tel.: (81) 522511111
Web Site: https://www.matsuzakaya.co.jp
Department Stores Owner & Operator
N.A.I.C.S.: 455110

Shimonoseki Daimaru, Inc. (2)
4-10 Takezaki-cho, Shimonoseki, 750-8503, Yamaguchi, Japan
Tel.: (81) 832321111
Web Site: http://www.daimaru.shimonoseki.ne.jp
Department Stores Operation Services
N.A.I.C.S.: 455110
Satoshi Nishio *(President & Dir)*

The Daimaru Home Shopping, Inc. (2)
4th Floor Higashikobe Center Building 6-26 Motoyama Minamimachi, 8-chome

Higashinada-ku, Kobe, 658-0015, Hyogo, Japan
Tel.: (81) 78 441 8800
Web Site: http://www.dmall.jp
Online Shopping Services
N.A.I.C.S.: 561990

The Daimaru, Inc. (2)
1-7-1 Shinsaibashisuji 1-chome, Chuo-ku, Osaka, 542-8501, Japan (100%)
Tel.: (81) 662711231
Web Site: http://www.daimaru.co.jp
Sales Range: $5-14.9 Billion
Department Store & Supermarket Operator
N.A.I.C.S.: 455110
Tsutomu Okuda *(Chm & CEO)*

Tottori Daimaru Co., Ltd. (2)
2-151 Imamachi, Tottori, 680-8601, Japan
Tel.: (81) 857 25 2111
Web Site: http://www.daimaru-tottori.co.jp
Departmental Store Operator
N.A.I.C.S.: 455110

Daimaru Osaka Shinsaibashi Store Co., Ltd. (1)
Shinsaibashisuji 1-chome, Chuo-ku, Osaka, 542-8501, Japan
Tel.: (81) 6 6271 1231
Departmental Store Operations
N.A.I.C.S.: 445110

J. Front Design & Construction Co., Ltd. (1)
16/17F Harumi Island Triton Square Office Tower W Bldg 1-8-8 Harumi, Tokyo, 104-0053, Japan
Tel.: (81) 368906710
Web Site: http://www.jfdc.co.jp
Sales Range: $100-124.9 Million
Emp.: 280
Interior Design & Construction Engineering Services
N.A.I.C.S.: 541330
Sadayuki Aiukawaa *(Pres)*

J. Front Foods Co., Ltd. (1)
Nakanoshima 101 3-92 Nakanoshima, Kita-ku, Osaka, 530-0005, Japan
Tel.: (81) 672200290
Web Site: http://www.j-frontfoods.co.jp
Sales Range: $100-124.9 Million
Emp.: 604
Restaurant Operating Services
N.A.I.C.S.: 721110

JFR Card Co., Ltd. (1)
2-1 Konyamachi, Takatsuki, 542-8551, Osaka, Japan
Tel.: (81) 664453462
Web Site: https://www.jfr-card.co.jp
Emp.: 275
Credit Card Issuing Services
N.A.I.C.S.: 522210

JFR Consulting Co. Ltd. (1)
Yanmar Tokyo Building 1-1 Yaesu 2-chome, Chuo-ku, Tokyo, 104-0028, Japan
Tel.: (81) 3 3241 1408
Web Site: http://www.j-front-retailing.com
Cost Reduction Consulting Services
N.A.I.C.S.: 541611

JFR Create Co., Ltd. (1)
2-1 Konyamachi Matsuzakaya Takatsuki store 5th Floor, Takatsuki, 569-8522, Osaka, Japan
Tel.: (81) 726848068
Departmental Store Services
N.A.I.C.S.: 455110

JFR Information Center Co., Ltd. (1)
1-3-24 Oisaka, Tennoji-ku, Osaka, 543-0062, Japan
Tel.: (81) 667753700
Web Site: https://www.jfr-ic.jp
Emp.: 98
Information Services
N.A.I.C.S.: 519290

JFR Kodomo Mirai Co., Ltd. (1)
Daimaru Matsuzakaya Kids Duo International Aobadai 4-11 Enokigaoka, Aoba-ku, Yokohama, 227-0063, Kanagawa, Japan
Tel.: (81) 368950258
Electronic Products Mfr
N.A.I.C.S.: 334419

JFR Office Support Co., Ltd. (1)
Daimaru Kitasumiyamachi Bldg 7-3 Nishishinsaibashi 1-chome, Chuo-ku, Osaka,

J. FRONT RETAILING CO., LTD.

542-0086, Japan
Tel.: (81) 662815040
Business Processing Services
N.A.I.C.S.: 561439

JFR Service Co. Ltd. (1)
2-1 Konyamachi, Takatsuki, 569-8522, Osaka, Japan
Tel.: (81) 726817245
Web Site: https://www.jfrservice.co.jp
Emp.: 326
Leasing & Parking Management Services
N.A.I.C.S.: 812930

Kochi Daimaru Co., Ltd. (1)
1-6-1 Obiyamachi, Kochi, 780-8566, Kochi Prefecture, Japan
Tel.: (81) 888225111
Web Site: https://www.kochi-daimaru.co.jp
Department Stores Operation Services
N.A.I.C.S.: 455110

Neuve A Co., Ltd. (1)
Shibuya First Place 10th Floor 8-16 Shinsencho, Shibuya-ku, Tokyo, 150-0045, Japan
Tel.: (81) 3 5428 2600
Web Site: http://www.neuve-a.com
Emp.: 580
Departmental Store Operator
N.A.I.C.S.: 455110
Hideki Noguchi *(Auditor)*

PT. Daimaru Kogyo (1)
19th Floor Summitmas I, JI Jend Sudirman Kav 61-62, Jakarta, 12190, Indonesia
Tel.: (62) 215200066
Web Site: https://www.dkin.co.id
Electronic Products Mfr
N.A.I.C.S.: 334419

Parco (Singapore) Pte Ltd. (1)
1 Wallich Street 14-01 GUOCO Tower, Singapore, 078881, Singapore
Tel.: (65) 65959100
Web Site: http://www.parco.com.sg
Departmental Store Operator
N.A.I.C.S.: 455110

Parco Co., Ltd. (1)
Shibuya First Place Bldg 8-16 Shinsen-cho, Shibuya-ku, Tokyo, Japan
Tel.: (81) 334775710
Web Site: http://www.parco.co.jp
Rev.: $815,119,140
Assets: $2,494,843,140
Liabilities: $1,345,056,660
Net Worth: $1,149,786,480
Earnings: $30,532,200
Emp.: 651
Fiscal Year-end: 02/28/2019
Construction Services
N.A.I.C.S.: 236220
Kozo Makiyama *(Pres & Exec Officer)*

Parco Digital Marketing Co., Ltd. (1)
Shibuya First Place 8-16 Shinsencho, Shibuya-ku, Tokyo, 150-0045, Japan
Tel.: (81) 334778910
Web Site: https://www.parco-digital.co.jp
Emp.: 77
Digital Marketing Services
N.A.I.C.S.: 541613

Parco Space Systems Co., Ltd. (1)
8-16 Shinsen-cho Shibuya First Place, Shibuya-ku, Tokyo, 150-0045, Japan
Tel.: (81) 354596811
Web Site: https://www.parco-space.co.jp
Emp.: 1,144
Building Maintenance Services
N.A.I.C.S.: 561790

Taiwan Daimaru Kogyo, Ltd. (1)
Room709 No 142 Sec 3 Minquan E Rd, Songshan Dist, Taipei, 10542, Taiwan
Tel.: (886) 227187215
Web Site: https://www.twdk.com.tw
Electronic Products Mfr
N.A.I.C.S.: 334419
Hiroshi Inoue *(CEO)*

The Hakata Daimaru, Inc. (1)
1-4-1 Tenjin, Chuo-ku, Fukuoka, 810-8717, Japan
Tel.: (81) 927128181
Web Site: https://www.daimaru.co.jp
Emp.: 310
Departmental Store Operator
N.A.I.C.S.: 455110
Kazuyo Yunoki *(Pres)*

J. J. FINANCE CORPORATION LIMITED

J. Front Retailing Co., Ltd.—(Continued)

J. J. FINANCE CORPORATION LIMITED
3C Park Plaza South Block 71 Park Street, Kolkata, 700 016, India
Tel.: (91) 3322291083
Web Site: https://www.jjfc.co.in
Year Founded: 1982
523062—(BOM)
Rev.: $91,584
Assets: $1,390,909
Liabilities: $100,321
Net Worth: $1,290,588
Earnings: $44,361
Emp.: 3
Fiscal Year-end: 03/31/21
Electric Power Generation & Financial Services
N.A.I.C.S.: 221118
Ankita Nigam *(Sec)*

J. KUMAR INFRAPROJECTS LTD.
J Kumar House CTS No 448 448/1 449 Subhash Road, Vile Parle East, Mumbai, 400057, Maharashtra, India
Tel.: (91) 2268717900
Web Site: https://www.jkumar.com
JKIL—(NSE)
Rev.: $354,372,236
Assets: $497,544,507
Liabilities: $239,984,076
Net Worth: $257,560,430
Earnings: $8,724,343
Emp.: 6,876
Fiscal Year-end: 03/31/21
Heavy Construction & Engineering Services
N.A.I.C.S.: 237990
Jagadishkumar M. Gupta *(Chm)*

J. MACEDO S.A.
R Benedito Macedo 79 Quayside, 60180415, Fortaleza, CE, Brazil
Tel.: (55) 8540066000
Web Site: http://www.jmacedo.com.br
Year Founded: 1939
J.MACEDO—(BRAZ)
Rev.: $663,685,315
Assets: $421,656,465
Liabilities: $207,129,726
Net Worth: $214,526,738
Earnings: $87,288,614
Fiscal Year-end: 12/31/23
Food Product Mfr & Distr
N.A.I.C.S.: 311824
Jose Honorio Goncalves De Tofoli *(CEO)*

J. MALUCELLI HOLDING SA
Rodovia do Cafe 315 KM 0 5 Mossungue, Curitiba, Brazil
Tel.: (55) 41 33515577
Web Site: http://www.jmalucelli.com.br
Year Founded: 1966
Holding Company
N.A.I.C.S.: 551112
Alexandre Malucelli *(Pres)*

Subsidiaries:

JMalucelli Equipamentos Ltda (1)
Rod do Cafe n 425 - BR 277 - Km 0 5, Curitiba, 82 305-100, Brazil
Tel.: (55) 41 3351 5522
Web Site: http://www.jmalucelliequipamentos.com.br
Construction Machinery & Equipment Distr
N.A.I.C.S.: 423810

JMalucelli Previdencia (1)
Rua Comendador Araujo 143 - 20 andar, Centro, Curitiba, 80 420-900, Parana, Brazil
Tel.: (55) 41 3351 9963
Financial Consulting Services
N.A.I.C.S.: 523940

JMalucelli Seguradora S.A (1)
Rua Visconde de Nacar 1440 - 3 Andar, Centro, Curitiba, Parana, Brazil
Tel.: (55) 41 3281 9100
Web Site: http://www.jmalucelliseguradora.com.br
General Insurance Services
N.A.I.C.S.: 524210
Joao Possiede *(Pres)*

Parana Banco SA (1)
Visconde de Nacar Street 1441, 80410-201, Curitiba, Parana, Brazil
Tel.: (55) 8006456090
Web Site: http://www.paranabanco.com.br
Credit, Insurance & Investment Services
N.A.I.C.S.: 522110
Cristiano Malucelli *(Chm)*

J. MICHAELS, INC.
100 Ronson Drive, Toronto, M9W 1B6, ON, Canada
Tel.: (416) 674-7433
Web Site: http://www.jmichaels.ca
Rev.: $20,000,000
Emp.: 200
Women's Clothing Retailer
N.A.I.C.S.: 458110
James H. Michaels *(CEO)*

J. MURPHY & SONS LIMITED
Hiview House Highgate Road, London, NW5 1TN, United Kingdom
Tel.: (44) 20 7267 4366
Web Site: http://www.murphygroup.com
Year Founded: 1992
Sales Range: $1-4.9 Billion
Emp.: 3,500
Construction Engineering Services
N.A.I.C.S.: 541330
Stuart Rothery *(Dir-Water)*

Subsidiaries:

Land & Marine Engineering Ltd. (1)
Dock Road North, Bromborough, CH62 4LN, Wirral, United Kingdom
Tel.: (44) 151 641 5600
Web Site: http://www.landandmarine.com
Emp.: 200
Engineeering Services
N.A.I.C.S.: 541330
Andrew A. Ball *(Mng Dir)*

Subsidiary (Domestic):

Protech Engineering Ltd (2)
Unit 29 Palmerston Business Park, Palmerston Drive, Fareham, PO14 1DJ, Hampshire, United Kingdom
Tel.: (44) 1329 221775
Web Site: http://www.protech-engineering.co.uk
Engineeering Services
N.A.I.C.S.: 541330

Pipeline Testing Services (1)
31 Smallwood St, Underwood, 4119, QLD, Australia
Tel.: (61) 7 3841 5100
Engineeering Services
N.A.I.C.S.: 541330

Surerus Murphy JV (1)
2200 605 - 5th Avenue SW, Calgary, T2P 3H5, AB, Canada
Tel.: (403) 930-1358
Web Site: https://www.surerus-murphy.com
Pipeline Construction Services
N.A.I.C.S.: 237120

J. P. BACHEM VERLAG GMBH
Ursulaplatz 1, Cologne, 50668, Germany
Tel.: (49) 2211619900
Web Site: http://www.bachem.de
Year Founded: 1818
Sales Range: $25-49.9 Million
Emp.: 170
Sheet-Fed & Web Offset Printing Services
N.A.I.C.S.: 323111
Claus Bachem *(CEO)*

J. R. FOODS LIMITED
J K Towers 100 Feet Road, Pondicherry, 605013, Tamil Nadu, India
Tel.: (91) 4132640427
Web Site: http://www.jrfoods.in
530915—(BOM)
Rev.: $220,721
Assets: $1,715,873
Liabilities: $9,328,806
Net Worth: $(7,612,933)
Earnings: $(704,176)
Emp.: 6
Fiscal Year-end: 03/31/22
Vegetable Oil Mfr & Whslr
N.A.I.C.S.: 325411
Dinesh Kothari *(Exec Dir)*

J. RETTENMAIER & SOHNE GMBH & CO. KG
Holzmuhle 1, Rosenberg, 73479, Germany
Tel.: (49) 79671520
Web Site: http://www.jrs.de
Year Founded: 1878
Sales Range: $300-349.9 Million
Emp.: 1,300
Organic Fiber Mfr
N.A.I.C.S.: 325220
Josef Rettenmaier *(Sr Mgr)*

Subsidiaries:

J. Rettenmaier & Sohne GmbH & Co. KG - Heilbronn Plant (1)
Kalistr 57, 74076, Heilbronn, Germany
Tel.: (49) 7131 7623 0
Organic Fiber Mfr
N.A.I.C.S.: 325220

J. Rettenmaier Benelux (1)
Zonnehorst 17, 7207, Zutphen, Netherlands
Tel.: (31) 575 510333
Organic Fiber Distr
N.A.I.C.S.: 424590

J. Rettenmaier Latinoamericana Ltda. (1)
Avenida Deputado Osvaldo Morais e Silva 55 Galpao 10, 09991-190, Diadema, Sao Paulo, Brazil
Tel.: (55) 11 4051 3234
Organic Fiber Distr
N.A.I.C.S.: 424590

J. Rettenmaier USA, LP (1)
16369 US Hwy 131 S, Schoolcraft, MI 49087
Tel.: (269) 679-2340
Web Site: http://www.jrsusa.com
Sales Range: $1-9.9 Million
Emp.: 43
Cellulosic Manmade Fibers
N.A.I.C.S.: 325220
Thorsten Willmann *(CEO)*

JRS Pharma LP (1)
2981 Route 22 Ste 1, Patterson, NY 12563-2563
Tel.: (845) 878-3414
Organic Fiber Distr
N.A.I.C.S.: 424590
Craig Scott *(Assoc Dir-Quality)*

Plant (Domestic):

JRS Pharma LP - Cedar Rapids Plant (2)
801 1st St SW, Cedar Rapids, IA 52404-2145
Tel.: (319) 398-3833
Organic Fiber Mfr
N.A.I.C.S.: 325220

JRS Pharma OY (1)
Maitotie 4, 15560, Nastola, Finland
Tel.: (358) 3 875100
Web Site: http://www.jrspharma.de
Emp.: 20
Organic Fiber Distr
N.A.I.C.S.: 424590
Jurki Kuoctmen *(Mng Dir)*

JRS Prozesstechnik GmbH & Co KG (1)
Calenberger Muhle 1, 30982, Pattensen, Germany

INTERNATIONAL PUBLIC

Tel.: (49) 5069 9407 0
Web Site: http://www.alt.jrs.de
Plastic Recycling Services
N.A.I.C.S.: 325991

JRS Schweiz AG (1)
Eulerstr 55, 4051, Basel, Switzerland
Tel.: (41) 61 272 22 00
Organic Fiber Distr
N.A.I.C.S.: 424590

OOO Rettenmaier Rus (1)
Leninskaya Sloboda Ul 19 building 1, 115280, Moscow, Russia
Tel.: (7) 495 2760640
Organic Fiber Distr
N.A.I.C.S.: 424590
Vladimir Leontiev *(Product Mgr)*

RS Ceska a Slovenska republika, org. slozka (1)
J Kociana 1095, 27201, Kladno, Czech Republic
Tel.: (420) 326 538100 6
Organic Fiber Distr
N.A.I.C.S.: 424590

Rettenmaier (Shanghai) Fiber Trading Co., Ltd. (1)
Crystal Century Tower Room 14B 14/F No 567 Weihai Road, Shanghai, 200041, China
Tel.: (86) 21 52341188
Organic Fiber Distr
N.A.I.C.S.: 424590

Rettenmaier Austria GmbH & Co.KG (1)
Gesslgasse 7/1, 1230, Vienna, Austria
Tel.: (43) 188 606880
Organic Fiber Distr
N.A.I.C.S.: 424590

Rettenmaier France SARL (1)
Les Tanneries Royales 20 Quatar Rue Schnapper, Saint Germain-en-Laye, 78100, France
Tel.: (33) 1 30 61 86 10
Web Site: http://www.jrs.eu
Emp.: 18
Organic Fiber Distr
N.A.I.C.S.: 424590
Laurent Ouvrard *(Gen Mgr)*

Rettenmaier Iberica S.L. y Cia. S. Com (1)
Travesera de Gracia No 56 2 Piso, 08006, Barcelona, Spain
Tel.: (34) 933 262888
Organic Fiber Distr
N.A.I.C.S.: 424590

Rettenmaier India Pvt Ltd. (1)
G-6 Eternity Mall Lbs Marg West Teen Hath Naka, Thane, Maharashtra, India
Tel.: (91) 22 40243821
Web Site: http://www.rettenmaierindia.tradeindia.com
Organic Fiber Mfr & Distr
N.A.I.C.S.: 325220
Rohit P. Raut *(Gen Mgr)*

Rettenmaier Italia Srl & C. Sas (1)
Via Bresiya 37a, 25014, Castenedolo, Italy
Tel.: (39) 030 7870410
Organic Fiber Distr
N.A.I.C.S.: 424590

Rettenmaier Japan Co., Ltd. (1)
Kanda-Ogawamachi Bldg 3F 3-26-8 Kanda Ogawamachi, Chiyoda-ku, Tokyo, Japan
Tel.: (81) 35259 6050
Web Site: http://www.jrsj.co.jp
Organic Fiber Distr
N.A.I.C.S.: 424590

Rettenmaier Mexicana S.A. de C.V. (1)
Plasticos No 30 Col Santa Clara Coatitla, Ecatepec, 55540, Mexico
Tel.: (52) 5537 740710
Organic Fiber Distr
N.A.I.C.S.: 424590

Rettenmaier Polska Sp. z o.o. (1)
Bitwy Warszawskiej 1920r 7B, Warsaw, 02366, Poland
Tel.: (48) 22 6085100
Web Site: http://www.jrs.de
Plastics Product Mfr
N.A.I.C.S.: 326199

AND PRIVATE COMPANIES

Rettenmaier UK Ltd. (1)
Church House 48 Church St, Reigate, RH2 0SN, Surry, United Kingdom
Tel.: (44) 1737222323
Sales Range: $150-199.9 Million
Emp.: 6
Organic Fiber Mfr
N.A.I.C.S.: 325220

J. ROMERO & ASSOCIATES
205 Nicanor Garcia Corner Constellation Sts, Bel-Air Village, Makati, 1209, Philippines
Tel.: (63) 28906583
Web Site: http://www.jromero.com.ph
Year Founded: 1959
Sales Range: $10-24.9 Million
Emp.: 75
N.A.I.C.S.: 541810
Andre S. Kahn (Pres)

J. S. REDPATH LIMITED
710 McKeown Avenue, PO Box 810, North Bay, P1B 7M2, ON, Canada
Tel.: (705) 474-2461
Web Site: http://www.redpathmining.com
Year Founded: 1962
Rev.: $110,000,000
Emp.: 6,200
Mining Services
N.A.I.C.S.: 213114
George B. Flumerfelt (Pres & CEO)

J. SCHNEIDER ELEKTROTECHNIK GMBH
Helmholtzstr 13, 77652, Offenburg, Germany
Tel.: (49) 7812060
Web Site: http://www.j-schneider.de
Year Founded: 1939
Sales Range: $25-49.9 Million
Emp.: 190
Industrial Products Mfr
N.A.I.C.S.: 333248
Bettina Schneider (Co-Mng Dir)

Subsidiaries:

J. Schneider Elektrotechnik GmbH Factory II
Werner-von-Siemens-Str 12, 77656, Offenburg, Germany
Tel.: (49) 7812060
Electronic Components Mfr
N.A.I.C.S.: 333248

J. Schneider Power Supplies Inc. (1)
4240 Carson St, Denver, CO 80239
Tel.: (303) 407-0490
Electronic Components Mfr
N.A.I.C.S.: 333248
Sebastian Eschmann (Mgr-Production)

J. SMART & CO. (CONTRACTORS) PLC
28 Cramond Road South, Edinburgh, EH4 6AB, United Kingdom
Tel.: (44) 1313362181
Web Site: https://www.jsmart.co.uk
Year Founded: 1947
SMJ—(LSE)
Rev.: $16,106,146
Assets: $183,699,474
Liabilities: $27,890,828
Net Worth: $155,808,646
Earnings: $248,360
Fiscal Year-end: 07/31/23
Building & Public Works Contracting Services
N.A.I.C.S.: 236220
David William Smart (Chm & Co-Mng Dir)

Subsidiaries:

C. & W. Assets Limited (1)
14 Links Pl, Edinburgh, EH6 7EZ, Scotland, United Kingdom
Tel.: (44) 1315532716
Property Management Services

N.A.I.C.S.: 531311

Concrete Products (Kirkcaldy) Limited (1)
Hayfield Pl Hayfield Indus Estate, Kirkcaldy, KY2 5DH, Scotland, United Kingdom
Tel.: (44) 1592261326
Sales Range: $25-49.9 Million
Emp.: 16
Concrete Products Mfr
N.A.I.C.S.: 327390
Ian McGlasham (Gen Mgr)

McGowan & Co. (Contractors) Limited (1)
28 Cramond Rd S, Edinburgh, EH4 6AB, Scotland, United Kingdom
Tel.: (44) 1313362181
Web Site: http://www.jsmart.co.uk
Sales Range: $25-49.9 Million
Emp.: 35
Building Contracting Services
N.A.I.C.S.: 236220

Thomas Menzies (Builders) Limited (1)
Hayfield Place, Hayfield Industrial Estate, Kirkcaldy, KY2 5DH, Fife, United Kingdom
Tel.: (44) 159 226 4712
Web Site: https://www.tmenzies.co.uk
Sales Range: $25-49.9 Million
Emp.: 50
Civil Engineering Services
N.A.I.C.S.: 541330

J. TAPARIA PROJECTS LIMITED
3 Synagogue Street 3rd Floor, Kolkata, 700 001, India
Tel.: (91) 3322305244
Web Site: http://www.jtapariaprojects.com
Year Founded: 1980
538539—(BOM)
Rev.: $15,244
Assets: $2,135,138
Liabilities: $19,166
Net Worth: $2,115,972
Earnings: ($2,408)
Fiscal Year-end: 03/31/21
Business Support Services
N.A.I.C.S.: 561499
Sanjit Dhawa (Mng Dir)

J. TECHNOLOGY CO., LTD.
75 number72road Jungmun tourism road, Seogwipo, Jeju, Korea (South)
Tel.: (82) 0269252176
Year Founded: 1998
035480—(KRS)
Casino Hotel Operator
N.A.I.C.S.: 721120

J. WAGNER AG
Industriestr 22, Postfach 109, 9450, Altstatten, Switzerland
Tel.: (41) 717572211
Web Site: http://www.wagner-group.com
Sales Range: $450-499.9 Million
Emp.: 1,800
Mfr of Paints & Coatings
N.A.I.C.S.: 325510

Subsidiaries:

J. Wagner GmbH (1)
Otto-Lilienthal-Str 18, Markdorf, 88677, Germany
Tel.: (49) 75445050
Web Site: http://www.wagner-group.com
Sales Range: $100-124.9 Million
Emp.: 350
Fluid Power Pump & Motor Mfr
N.A.I.C.S.: 333996
Thorsten Koch (CEO)

Wagner Australia Pty. Ltd. (1)
14-16 Kevlar Close, Braeside, 3195, VIC, Australia
Tel.: (61) 395872000
Web Site: http://www.wagneraustralia.com.au
Emp.: 17

Paint & Coating Mfr
N.A.I.C.S.: 325510
Hamesh Kapadia (Controller-Fin)

Wagner Colora Srl (1)
Via Fermi 3, Burago Molgora, 20040, Milan, Italy
Tel.: (39) 039625021
Web Site: http://www.wagnercolora.com
Pump & Pumping Equipment Mfr
N.A.I.C.S.: 333914

Wagner Spray Tech Corporation (1)
1770 Fernbrook Ln, Plymouth, MN 55447-4661
Tel.: (763) 553-7000
Web Site: http://www.wagnerspraytech.com
Sales Range: $50-74.9 Million
Emp.: 180
Paint Spraying Equipment Mfr & Marketer
N.A.I.C.S.: 333912
Jackie McMartin (Grp VP-HR)

Subsidiary (Domestic):

Titan Tool, Inc. (2)
107 Bauer Dr, Oakland, NJ 07436
Tel.: (201) 337-1240
Web Site: http://www.titantool.com
Sales Range: $75-99.9 Million
Mfr of Paint Spraying Systems for Contractors
N.A.I.C.S.: 333912

Wagner Spray Tech Do Brasil Ltda (1)
Av Ataulfo De Paiva 253, Rio de Janeiro, Brazil
Tel.: (55) 2125237804
Business Support Services
N.A.I.C.S.: 561499

Wagner Spraytech (Shanghai) Co Ltd. (1)
No 395 Jiangchang Xi Road, Shibei Industrial Park, Shanghai, 200436, China (100%)
Tel.: (86) 2166521858
Web Site: http://www.wagner-spraytech.com.cn
Sales Range: $25-49.9 Million
Emp.: 30
Industrial Machinery & Equipment Whslr
N.A.I.C.S.: 423830

Wagner Spraytech (UK) Ltd. (1)
The Coach House 2 Main Rd, Middleton Cheney, Banbury, OX17 2ND, Oxfordshire, United Kingdom (100%)
Tel.: (44) 1295714200
Web Site: http://www.wagner-group.de
Sales Range: $50-74.9 Million
Emp.: 8
Industrial Machinery & Equipment Whslr
N.A.I.C.S.: 423830
Ian Pocock (Office Mgr)

Wagner Spraytech Benelux B.V. (1)
De Heldinnenlaan 200, Utrecht, 3543 MB, Netherlands
Tel.: (31) 302414155
Web Site: http://www.wagner-wsb.eu
Sales Range: $25-49.9 Million
Emp.: 40
Electrical Apparatus & Equipment Wiring Supplies & Construction Material Whslr
N.A.I.C.S.: 423610

Wagner Spraytech Iberica, S.A. (1)
Ctra N-340 M 1245 4, Molinsde Rei, 8750, Barcelona, Spain
Tel.: (34) 936800028
Sales Range: $25-49.9 Million
Emp.: 20
Paint & Coating Mfr
N.A.I.C.S.: 325510
Celso Rodriguez (Dir-Mktg)

Wagner Spraytech Japan Ltd. (1)
2-35 Shinden-Nishimachi Daito-Shi, 574-0057, Osaka, Japan (100%)
Tel.: (81) 728743560
Web Site: http://www.Wagner-japan.co.jp
Sales Range: $25-49.9 Million
Emp.: 30
Electrical Equipment & Component Mfr
N.A.I.C.S.: 335999
Gerhard Tellbuscher (Pres)

Wagner Spraytech Scandinavia A/S (1)

Helgeshoj Alle 28, Taastrup, 2630, Arhus, Denmark
Tel.: (45) 43271818
Web Site: http://www.wagner-group.dk
Sales Range: $50-74.9 Million
Emp.: 10
Construction & Mining Machinery & Equipment Whslr
N.A.I.C.S.: 423810
Pol Antras (Gen Mgr)

Wagner Sverige AB (1)
Muskotgatan 19, 25466, Helsingborg, Sweden
Tel.: (46) 42150020
Sales Range: $50-74.9 Million
Emp.: 7
Electrical Apparatus & Equipment Wiring Supplies & Construction Material Whslr
N.A.I.C.S.: 423610

Wagner Systems, Inc. (1)
300 Airport Rd Unit 1, Elgin, IL 60123
Tel.: (630) 784-8900
Web Site: http://www.wagnersystemsinc.com
Sales Range: $25-49.9 Million
Emp.: 12
Commercial & Service Industry Machinery Mfr
N.A.I.C.S.: 333310
Matthias Koehler (Gen Mgr)

Wagner s.r.o. (1)
Nedasovska Str 345, 155 21, Prague, 5, Zlicin, Czech Republic
Tel.: (420) 2 579 52351
Web Site: http://www.wagner-group.biz
Industrial Machinery & Equipment Whslr
N.A.I.C.S.: 423830

Wagner- Hosokawa Micron Ltd. (1)
No 9 1-Chome Shodai Tajka Hirakata-Shi, Osaka, 573-1132, Japan (80%)
Tel.: (81) 728566751
Web Site: http://www.hosokawamicron.co.jp
Sales Range: $25-49.9 Million
Emp.: 12
Paint Varnish & Supplies Merchant Whslr
N.A.I.C.S.: 424950
Tetsuo Unemoto (Pres)

J.A.G. MINES LTD.
620 Saint-Jacques St Suite 110, Montreal, H3C 1C7, QC, Canada
Tel.: (514) 849-7336
Web Site: http://www.minesjag.com
Year Founded: 1976
Sales Range: Less than $1 Million
Mineral Exploration Services
N.A.I.C.S.: 213114
Pierre Gevry (Pres & CFO)

Subsidiaries:

Olitra Inc. (1)
620 Saint-Jacques St Suite 110, Montreal, H3C 1C7, QC, Canada
Tel.: (514) 849-7336
Web Site: http://www.olitrainc.com
Oil & Gas Property Development Services
N.A.I.C.S.: 213112

J.D DEVELOPMENT CO., LTD.
9F -1 No 151 Zhongzheng 4th Rd, Qianjin Dist, Kaohsiung, 801, Taiwan
Tel.: (886) 72167569
Web Site: https://j-d.com.tw
Year Founded: 1970
4402—(TPE)
Rev.: $2,516,727
Assets: $16,594,558
Liabilities: $1,074,430
Net Worth: $15,520,128
Earnings: ($650,544)
Emp.: 9
Fiscal Year-end: 12/31/23
Artificial & Synthetic Fiber Mfr
N.A.I.C.S.: 325220
Tang Cheng (Chm)

J.D. IRVING, LIMITED
300 Union St, PO Box 5777, Saint John, E2L 4M3, NB, Canada
Tel.: (506) 632-7777

J.D. IRVING, LIMITED

J.D. Irving, Limited—(Continued)

Web Site: http://www.jdirving.com
Year Founded: 1882
Sales Range: $1-4.9 Billion
Emp.: 15,000
Holding Company; Sawmills & Home Improvement Stores; Shipbuilding & Construction
N.A.I.C.S.: 551112

Subsidiaries:

Irving Pulp and Paper Ltd. (1)
408 Mill St W, PO Box 3007, Saint John, E2M 3H1, NB, Canada
Tel.: (506) 635-6666
Web Site: http://www.irvingpulp.com
Rev.: $81,600,000
Emp.: 250
Producer of Kraft Pulp
N.A.I.C.S.: 322110

J.E.M. CAPITAL, INC.
5B Prat Building 13 Prat Avenue, Tsim Sha Tsui, Kowloon, China (Hong Kong)
Tel.: (852) 3957 0379   DE
JEMC—(OTCIQ)
Assets: $12,000
Liabilities: $132,456
Net Worth: ($120,456)
Earnings: ($34,296)
Emp.: 2
Fiscal Year-end: 12/31/19
Investment Services
N.A.I.C.S.: 523999
MingJing Xia (Chm & CFO)

J.E.T.CO., LTD.
6078 Shinjo Kanayama Satoshocho, Asakuchi-gun, Okayama, 719-0302, Japan
Tel.: (81) 865694080
Web Site: https://www.globaljet.jp
6228—(TKS)
Rev.: $177,136,560
Assets: $204,007,660
Liabilities: $116,013,670
Net Worth: $87,993,990
Earnings: $11,705,590
Emp.: 1,427
Fiscal Year-end: 12/31/23
Semiconductor Device Mfr & Distr
N.A.I.C.S.: 334413

J.F. MOORE LITHOGRAPHERS INC.
124 Milner Avenue, Toronto, M1S 3R2, ON, Canada
Tel.: (416) 291-2012
Web Site:
http://www.jfmoorelitho.com
Rev.: $15,233,171
Emp.: 59
Printing Services
N.A.I.C.S.: 323111
Dean Baxendale (Pres & CEO)

J.G. NIEDEREGGER GMBH & CO. KG
Breite Strasse 89, Lubeck, Germany
Tel.: (49) 451 5301127
Web Site: http://www.niederegger.de
Year Founded: 1806
Confectionery Mfr
N.A.I.C.S.: 311340
Holger Strait (Mng Dir)

J.G. RIVE-SUD FRUITS & LEGUMES
1963 Patrick Farrar, Chambly, J3L 4N7, QC, Canada
Tel.: (450) 447-3092
Web Site: http://www.jgrive-sud.com
Year Founded: 1984
Rev.: $12,087,703
Emp.: 200
Fruits & Vegetables Distr
N.A.I.C.S.: 424480
Pierre Pouliot (Dir-Sls)

J.H. MCNAIRN LIMITED
125 Consumers Drive, Whitby, L1N 1C4, ON, Canada
Tel.: (905) 668-7533
Web Site:
http://www.mcnairnpackaging.com
Year Founded: 1882
Rev.: $28,517,944
Emp.: 180
Food Products Mfr
N.A.I.C.S.: 311991
Ken Miller (Chm & CEO)

J.J. EXPORTERS LTD.
64 Bright Street, Kolkata, 700 019, India
Tel.: (91) 3340713125
Web Site: http://www.jjexporters.com
530049—(BOM)
Sales Range: $1-9.9 Million
Textile Products Distr
N.A.I.C.S.: 314999

Subsidiaries:

OOO JJ Home (1)
Building 2 Entrance 15 Suite 701B, Leninsky District-Rumyantsev, 142784, Moscow, Russia
Tel.: (7) 495 744 16 32
Web Site: http://www.jjhome.ru
Sales Range: $25-49.9 Million
Emp.: 4
Silk Fabric Mfr & Whslr
N.A.I.C.S.: 313210

Spin International Inc. (1)
240 W 37th St Rm 503, New York, NY 10018-5772
Tel.: (212) 967-8071
Emp.: 2
Silk Fabric Mfr & Whslr
N.A.I.C.S.: 313210
Agarwal Sanjay (Mgr)

J.K. INTERNATIONAL PTY. LTD.
49 Suscatand Street, Rocklea, 4106, QLD, Australia
Tel.: (61) 732741023
Web Site: http://www.jki.com.au
Year Founded: 1979
Marine Shipping Services
N.A.I.C.S.: 488320
Sandeep Mohan (Gen Mgr)

J.K. SPINNING MILLS LTD.
29 KM Sheikhupura Road, Khurrianwala, Faisalabad, Pakistan
Tel.: (92) 41240101116
Web Site: https://www.jkgroup.net
Year Founded: 1958
JKSM—(PSX)
Rev.: $129,973,069
Assets: $98,980,223
Liabilities: $54,052,901
Net Worth: $44,927,321
Earnings: $6,547,814
Emp.: 3,218
Fiscal Year-end: 06/30/23
Yarn & Clothing Material Mfr
N.A.I.C.S.: 314999
Jawed Anwar (Chm)

J.L. DE BALL CANADA INC.
835 Blvd Industriel, Granby, J2J 1A5, QC, Canada
Tel.: (450) 378-7978
Rev.: $20,000,000
Emp.: 176
Woven Apparel & Upholstery Fabrics Mfr
N.A.I.C.S.: 313210
Paul Flay (Pres)

J.L. MORISON (INDIA) LTD.
Rasoi Court 20 Sir R N Mukherjee Road, Kolkata, 700 001, India
Tel.: (91) 3322480114
Web Site: https://www.jlmorison.com
506522—(BOM)
Rev.: $18,152,797
Assets: $28,622,649
Liabilities: $4,950,926
Net Worth: $23,671,722
Earnings: $1,274,456
Emp.: 393
Fiscal Year-end: 03/31/23
Personal Care Product Mfr
N.A.I.C.S.: 325620
Sohan H. Sarda (CEO)

J.L. RICHARDS & ASSOCIATES LIMITED
864 Lady Ellen Place, Ottawa, K1Z 5M2, ON, Canada
Tel.: (613) 728-3571
Web Site: http://www.jlrichards.ca
Year Founded: 1955
Rev.: $16,465,713
Emp.: 150
Architectural & Engineering Services
N.A.I.C.S.: 541330

J.M. BASTILLE ACIER INC.
396 rue Temiscouata CP 744, Riviere-du-Loup, G5R 3Z3, QC, Canada
Tel.: (418) 862-3346
Web Site: http://www.jmbastille.com
Year Founded: 1958
Rev.: $10,796,631
Emp.: 70
New & Waste Metal Recycling Service & Whslr
N.A.I.C.S.: 423930

J.P. MORGAN FUTURES CO., LIMITED
J78 1/F 171 Haibin Road, Nansha District, Guangzhou, 511458, Guangdong, China
Tel.: (86) 21 5200 3602
Financial Investment Services
N.A.I.C.S.: 523999

J.POND PRECISION TECHNOLOGY CO., LTD.
Room 201 Building 1 No 1 R&D 1 Road Songshan Lake, Hi-tech Industrial Park, Dongguan, 523808, Guangdong, China
Tel.: (86) 76981238666
Web Site: https://www.jpond.com.cn
Year Founded: 2007
301326—(CHIN)
Rev.: $95,520,225
Assets: $227,080,295
Liabilities: $38,995,211
Net Worth: $188,085,084
Earnings: ($7,859,634)
Fiscal Year-end: 12/31/23
Precision Product Mfr & Distr
N.A.I.C.S.: 332721
Yunfeng Xin (Chm)

Subsidiaries:

J.Pond Precision Metal Stamping (Dongguan) Co., Ltd. (1)
Building 7 No 77 Jian an Road, Chang an, Dongguan, Guanddong, China
Tel.: (86) 76989617778
Machine Part Mfr
N.A.I.C.S.: 333517

Just Technology(Kunshan)Co.,Ltd. (1)
No 258 Chenjiabang road, Development District, Kunshan, China
Tel.: (86) 51257126991
Machine Part Mfr
N.A.I.C.S.: 333517

Ruitai New Material Technology (Dongguan) Co., Ltd. (1)
Dongshen Road De Li Xin Industrial Park Building A Floor 1 & 2, Chen Wubei Cun Changpin, Dongguan, China
Tel.: (86) 76982206123
Machine Part Mfr
N.A.I.C.S.: 333517

Someway New Material (Kunshan) Co., Ltd. (1)
No 336 Honghu Road, Penglang, Kunshan, China
Tel.: (86) 51257559368
Machine Part Mfr
N.A.I.C.S.: 333517

J.S. CORRUGATING MACHINERY CO., LTD.
Light Machinery Industrial Park Economic Development Zone, Jingmen, 431899, Hubei, China
Tel.: (86) 2783320271
Web Site:
http://www.jspackmach.com
Year Founded: 1993
000821—(SSE)
Rev.: $683,426,484
Assets: $1,398,947,004
Liabilities: $926,979,768
Net Worth: $471,967,236
Earnings: $42,392,376
Fiscal Year-end: 12/31/22
Packaging & Printing Machine Mfr
N.A.I.C.S.: 333993
Li Jian (Chm & Pres)

Subsidiaries:

J. S. Machine India Private Limited (1)
Plot No 628 Sector III Pithampur Industrial Area Pithampur, Dhar, 454775, Madhya Pradesh, India
Tel.: (91) 7024111555
Web Site: https://www.jsmachineindia.com
Corrugated Packaging Machinery Distr
N.A.I.C.S.: 423830

J.S. JOHNSON & COMPANY LIMITED
34 Collins Avenue, PO Box N-8337, Nassau, Bahamas
Tel.: (242) 3972100   BS
Web Site: http://www.jsjohnson.com
Year Founded: 1919
JSJ—(BISX)
Rev.: $119,634,447
Assets: $122,281,418
Liabilities: $64,868,519
Net Worth: $57,412,899
Earnings: $12,257,874
Emp.: 160
Fiscal Year-end: 12/31/23
Insurance Brokerage Services
N.A.I.C.S.: 524210
Alister I. McKellar (Mng Dir)

J.S.B. CO., LTD.
655 Inabado-cho Shimogyo-ku, Kyoto, 600-8415, Japan
Tel.: (81) 753412728
Web Site: https://www.jsb.co.jp
Year Founded: 1976
3480—(TKS)
Rev.: $452,207,290
Assets: $472,520,140
Liabilities: $252,425,270
Net Worth: $220,094,870
Earnings: $33,854,750
Emp.: 1,191
Fiscal Year-end: 10/31/23
Apartment Rental Services
N.A.I.C.S.: 531110

J.S.P. PROPERTY PUBLIC COMPANY LIMITED
No 41/1 Soi Rama 2 Soi 54 Samae-Dam, Bang Khun Thian, Bangkok, 10150, Thailand
Tel.: (66) 28978888

Web Site: http://www.jsp.co.th
JSP—(THA)
Rev.: $14,298,612
Assets: $42,004,525
Liabilities: $9,803,077
Net Worth: $32,201,448
Earnings: $989,271
Fiscal Year-end: 12/31/21
Commercial & Residential Property Developer
N.A.I.C.S.: 237210
Vacharin Duangdara *(Chm)*

J.W. CONSTRUCTION HOLDING S.A.
ul Radzyminska 326 Zabki, 05-091, Warsaw, Poland
Tel.: (48) 22 771 77 77
Web Site: http://www.jwc.pl
Year Founded: 1993
JWC—(WAR)
Rev.: $159,118,839
Assets: $438,679,846
Liabilities: $247,333,395
Net Worth: $191,346,451
Earnings: $16,665,252
Emp.: 538
Fiscal Year-end: 12/31/19
Holding Company
N.A.I.C.S.: 551112
Jozef Kazimierz Wojciechowski *(Chm-Supervisory Bd)*

J2 MANAGEMENT CORPORATION
200 Yorkland Blvd Suite 800, Toronto, M2J 5C1, ON, Canada
Tel.: (416) 438-6650
Web Site:
  http://www.agsautomotive.com
Year Founded: 1947
Sales Range: $150-199.9 Million
Emp.: 1,200
Holding Company
N.A.I.C.S.: 551112
Joe Loparco *(Co-Pres)*

Subsidiaries:

AGS Automotive Systems, Inc. - Cambridge Plant (1)
560 Conestoga Blvd, Cambridge, N1R 7L7, ON, Canada
Tel.: (519) 621-7953
Automobile Parts Mfr
N.A.I.C.S.: 336390

AGS Automotive Systems, Inc. - Oshawa Plant (1)
901 Simcoe St S, Oshawa, L1H 4L2, ON, Canada
Tel.: (905) 571-2121
Automobile Parts Mfr
N.A.I.C.S.: 336390

AGS Automotive Systems, Inc. - Windsor Plant (1)
275 Eugenie St E, Windsor, N8X 2X9, ON, Canada
Tel.: (519) 969-5193
Automobile Parts Mfr
N.A.I.C.S.: 336390

Tiercon (1)
591 Arvin Avenue, Stoney Creek, L8E 5N7, ON, Canada
Tel.: (905) 643-4176
Web Site: http://www.tiercon.com
Sales Range: $200-249.9 Million
Emp.: 300
Paint & Coating Mfr
N.A.I.C.S.: 325510
Terry Kotwa *(Mgr)*

J2L HOLDING AB
Hovslagargatan 5B, Stockholm, Sweden
Tel.: (46) 8 463 06 00
Web Site: http://www.j2l.se
Year Founded: 2009
Holding Company
N.A.I.C.S.: 551112
Johan Lindh *(Co-Founder & CEO)*

Subsidiaries:

AB Sigfrid Stenberg (1)
Vasavagen 3D, 554 54, Jonkoping, Sweden **(100%)**
Tel.: (46) 36 30 44 00
Web Site: http://www.stenbergs.se
Sales Range: $50-74.9 Million
Emp.: 130
Industrial Machinery & Equipment Whslr
N.A.I.C.S.: 423830

Subsidiary (Non-US):

Flextek A/S (2)
Kildeparken 30, 8722, Hedensted, Denmark **(100%)**
Tel.: (45) 76413413
Web Site: http://www.flextek.dk
Sales Range: $25-49.9 Million
Emp.: 40
Industrial Machinery & Equipment Whslr
N.A.I.C.S.: 423830
Peter Jorgensen *(CEO)*

Dorato Tools AB (1)
Kungsgatan 90, 632 21, Eskilstuna, Sweden
Tel.: (46) 16167290
Web Site: http://www.d-tools.se
Cutting Tool Distr
N.A.I.C.S.: 333517

EuroMaskin AB (1)
Vasavagen 3D, 554 54, Jonkoping, Sweden
Tel.: (46) 36129400
Industrial Machinery Mfr
N.A.I.C.S.: 333998

JA MITSUI LEASING, LTD.
Ginza Mitsui Building 8-13-1 Ginza, Chuo-ku, Tokyo, 104-0061, Japan
Tel.: (81) 3 6775 3000
Web Site:
  http://www.jamitsuilease.co.jp
Year Founded: 2008
Leasing, Installment Sales & Financing Services
N.A.I.C.S.: 532490
Shuzo Furuya *(Pres)*

Subsidiaries:

First Financial Corporate Services, Inc. (1)
711 Kimberly Ave Ste160, Placentia, CA 92870
Tel.: (714) 626-0330
Web Site: http://www.ffcsi.com
Computer Rental & Leasing Services
N.A.I.C.S.: 532420
Richard Stebbins *(Co-Founder & Co-Pres)*

JA Mitsui Leasing USA Holdings, Inc. (1)
286 Madison Ave 12th Fl, New York, NY 10017
Tel.: (212) 557-9450
Leasing, Installment Sales & Financing Services
N.A.I.C.S.: 532490

JA SOLAR TECHNOLOGY CO., LTD.
No 8 Building Nuode Center No 1 Courtyard East Auto Museum Road, Fengtai District, Beijing, 100160, China
Tel.: (86) 1063611888
Web Site: https://www.jasolar.com.cn
Year Founded: 2000
002459—(SSE)
Rev.: $11,292,115,806
Assets: $14,758,178,182
Liabilities: $9,496,197,261
Net Worth: $5,261,980,920
Earnings: $974,674,693
Emp.: 50,258
Fiscal Year-end: 12/31/23
Heavy Duty Equipment Mfr
N.A.I.C.S.: 333120
Baofang Jin *(Founder & Chm)*

Subsidiaries:

Beijing Huasuitong Boring Equipment Co., Ltd. (1)
Room 702 Fortune International Center Daliushu Road, Haidian District, Beijing, 100081, China **(55.4%)**
Tel.: (86) 1062122321
Web Site: http://www.huasuitong.com
Sales Range: $25-49.9 Million
Emp.: 30
Tunneling Equipments Mfr & Sales
N.A.I.C.S.: 333248

JA Solar Australia Pty. Ltd. (1)
C PKF Newcastle 755 Hunter Street, Newcastle, 2302, NSW, Australia
Tel.: (61) 283280488
Solar Equipment Mfr & Whslr
N.A.I.C.S.: 334413

JA Solar Brazil Co., Ltd. (1)
Rua Barao do Triunfo 612 CJ 604 Brooklin, Sao Paulo, Brazil
Tel.: (55) 1123720795
Solar Equipment Mfr & Whslr
N.A.I.C.S.: 334413

JA Solar GmbH (1)
Am Dorfteich 75, Kritzow / OT Gasoline, 19386, Munich, Germany
Tel.: (49) 3873156497
Electronic Parts Whslr
N.A.I.C.S.: 423690

JA Solar Holdings Co., Ltd. (1)
Building No 8 Noble Center, Automobile Museum East Road Fengtai, Beijing, 100070, China
Tel.: (86) 10 6361 1888
Web Site: http://www.jasolar.com
Sales Range: $1-4.9 Billion
Emp.: 20,000
Holding Company; Solar Cells Mfr
N.A.I.C.S.: 551112
Wei Shan *(CTO)*

Subsidiary (Domestic):

JA Solar Technology YangZhou Co., Ltd. (2)
No 1 Jianhua Rd Bali Town, Economic Development Zone, Yangzhou, 225000, Jiangsu, China
Tel.: (86) 514 8554 8888
Solar Photovoltaic Products Mfr
N.A.I.C.S.: 334413

Subsidiary (US):

JA Solar USA Inc (2)
2570 N 1st St Ste 360, San Jose, CA 95131
Tel.: (408) 586-0000
Solar Photovoltaic Products Mfr
N.A.I.C.S.: 334413

Subsidiary (Domestic):

JingAo Solar Co., Ltd. (2)
Jinglong Industrial Park Jinglong St, Ningjin, 055550, Hebei, China
Tel.: (86) 3195806783
Sales Range: $800-899.9 Million
Emp.: 3,000
Solar Photovoltaic Products Mfr
N.A.I.C.S.: 334413

Shanghai JA Solar PV Technology Co., Ltd. (2)
No 36 Jiang Chang San Rd, Zhabei, Shanghai, 200436, China
Tel.: (86) 2160955888
Web Site: http://www.jasolar.com
Solar Photovoltaic Products Mfr
N.A.I.C.S.: 334413

JA Solar Japan Limited (1)
2-5-2 Marunouchi Mitsubishi Building 9th Floor 960, Chiyoda-ku, Tokyo, Japan
Tel.: (81) 352196133
Solar Equipment Mfr & Whslr
N.A.I.C.S.: 334413

JA Solar Korea Co., Ltd. (1)
Room 705 Gwanghwamun Office Building, Sinmun-ro 1-ga Jongno-gu, Seoul, Korea (South)
Tel.: (82) 7043883888
Solar Equipment Mfr & Whslr
N.A.I.C.S.: 334413

JA Solar Mexico Co., Ltd. (1)
Avenida Paseo De la Reforma 107 Int 601, Colonia Tabacalera, Cuauhtemoc, Mexico
Tel.: (52) 15582487373
Solar Equipment Mfr & Whslr
N.A.I.C.S.: 334413

JA-CO WELDING & CONSULTING LTD.
1304 8th Street, Nisku, T9E 7M1, AB, Canada
Tel.: (780) 955-2251
Web Site:
  http://www.jacowelding.com
Year Founded: 1987
Rev.: $13,041,743
Emp.: 150
Steel Fabrication Services
N.A.I.C.S.: 238120
Jason Adams *(Mgr-API & Quality Control)*

JAA - SERBIAN AUTHORS AGENCY
38 Majke Jevrosime Street, 11000, Belgrade, Serbia
Tel.: (381) 113225902
Web Site:
  https://www.autorskaagencija.com
Year Founded: 1955
JAAB—(BEL)
Rev.: $546,784
Assets: $1,775,227
Liabilities: $360,288
Net Worth: $1,414,939
Earnings: $61,543
Emp.: 4
Fiscal Year-end: 12/31/23
Law firm
N.A.I.C.S.: 541199

JAAMDAROU CO.
No 711 Seventeen Km Fath Express way Karaj Road, Tehran, Iran
Tel.: (98) 21 4492 2371
Web Site: http://ww.jaamdarou.com
JAMD—(THE)
Sales Range: Less than $1 Million
Emp.: 159
Laminate Tube Products Mfr
N.A.I.C.S.: 322219
M. H. E. Zargar *(Head-Boarder)*

JAANH, INC.
203 Gangchon-ro, Danwon-gu, Ansan, Gyeonggi-do, Korea (South)
Tel.: (82) 313647400
Web Site: http://www.hansolcnp.com
Year Founded: 1996
221610—(KRS)
Rev.: $12,105,765
Assets: $88,161,568
Liabilities: $40,841,404
Net Worth: $47,320,163
Earnings: ($9,897,182)
Emp.: 64
Fiscal Year-end: 12/31/20
Paint & Coating Mfr
N.A.I.C.S.: 325510
Sichan An *(CEO)*

JAARBEURS HOLDING B.V.
Jaarbeursplein 6, 3521 AL, Utrecht, Netherlands
Tel.: (31) 302955911 NI
Web Site: http://www.jaarbeurs.nl
Sales Range: $200-249.9 Million
Emp.: 709
Holding Company
N.A.I.C.S.: 551112
A. Brienen *(CEO)*

Subsidiaries:

Jaarbeurs Utrecht B.V. (1)
Jaarbeursplein, 3521 AL, Utrecht, Netherlands **(100%)**
Tel.: (31) 302955911

JAARBEURS HOLDING B.V.

Jaarbeurs Holding B.V.—(Continued)
Web Site: http://www.jaarbeurs.nl
Sales Range: $100-124.9 Million
Emp.: 400
Accommodate Cater & Facilitate Public & Business Event Services
N.A.I.C.S.: 561210

Subsidiary (Domestic):

VNU Exhibitions Europe BV (2)
Jaarbeursplein 6, Utrecht, 3521, Netherlands
Tel.: (31) 302952700
Web Site: http://www.vnuexhibitions.com
Sales Range: $25-49.9 Million
Emp.: 180
Convention & Trade Show Planning & Marketing Services
N.A.I.C.S.: 561920
Ton Otten (CEO)

JAB HOLDING COMPANY S.A.R.L.
Oudeweg 147, 2031 CC, Haarlem, Netherlands
Tel.: (31) 23 230 2200
Web Site: http://www.jabholco.com
Investment Holding Company
N.A.I.C.S.: 551112
Peter G. Harf (Chm & Mng Partner)

Subsidiaries:

Coty, Inc. (1)
350 5th Ave, New York, NY 10118 **(60%)**
Tel.: (212) 389-7300
Web Site: https://www.coty.com
Rev: $6,118,000,000
Assets: $12,082,500,000
Liabilities: $8,070,800,000
Net Worth: $4,011,700,000
Earnings: $109,400,000
Emp.: 11,791
Fiscal Year-end: 06/30/2024
Cosmetics & Fragrances Mfr
N.A.I.C.S.: 325620
Peter G. Harf (Chm)

Subsidiary (Non-US):

Bourjois Limited (2)
Bourjois House Queensway, Croydon, CR9 4DL, United Kingdom
Tel.: (44) 2086887131
Web Site: http://www.bourjois.co.uk
Cosmetics & Beauty Product Mfr & Whslr
N.A.I.C.S.: 456120
Katheline Vandal (Brand Mgr)

Bourjois S.a.r.l. (2)
Burgstrasse 26, Glarus, 8750, Switzerland
Tel.: (41) 556401467
Cosmetics Products Mfr
N.A.I.C.S.: 325620

Coty (Schweiz) AG (2)
Boesch 80b, Postfach 143, CH 6331, Hunenberg, Switzerland
Tel.: (41) 417850000
Sales Range: $25-49.9 Million
Emp.: 50
Perfumes & Cosmetics Marketing & Sales
N.A.I.C.S.: 456120

Coty Argentina S.A. (2)
Olga Cossettini 1545 Piso 3 Sur, Buenos Aires, C1107CEK, Argentina
Tel.: (54) 11 4129 2900
Web Site: http://www.coty.com
Perfumes & Cosmetics Sales & Marketing
N.A.I.C.S.: 456120

Coty Asia Pte. Ltd. (2)
12 Tai Seng Street Suite06-01, Singapore, 534118, Singapore
Tel.: (65) 67422260
Cosmetic Product Whslr
N.A.I.C.S.: 325620
Ted Bacay (Reg Mng Dir)

Coty Australia Pty. Limited (2)
1 Market Street Level 31, Sydney, 2000, NSW, Australia
Tel.: (61) 282639914
Web Site: http://www.cotyaustralia.com.au
Perfumes & Cosmetics Marketing & Sales
N.A.I.C.S.: 456120

Coty Austria GmbH, wien (2)
Technologiestr 101 Wienerberstr 41, 1120, Vienna, Austria
Tel.: (43) 181005030
Pharmaceutical Products Distr
N.A.I.C.S.: 424210
Martina Kashofer (Mgr-Mktg Trade)

Coty B.V. (2)
Oudeweg 147, Haarlem, 2031 CC, Netherlands
Tel.: (31) 232302200
Pharmaceutical Product Whslr
N.A.I.C.S.: 424210
Roel Vree (Area Mgr-Amsterdam)

Coty Benelux B.V. (2)
Oudeweg 147, Haarlem, 2031CC, Netherlands
Tel.: (31) 232302200
Web Site: http://www.coty.com
Emp.: 80
Perfumes & Cosmetics Marketing & Sales
N.A.I.C.S.: 456120

Coty Benelux N.V./S.A. (2)
Z.3 Doornveld 174, 1731, Zellik, Belgium
Tel.: (32) 24816760
Web Site: http://www.coty.com
Sales Range: $25-49.9 Million
Emp.: 15
Perfumes & Cosmetics Sales & Marketing
N.A.I.C.S.: 456120
Frank Pierik (Gen Mgr)

Coty Brands Group Limited (2)
Eureka Park, Ashford, TN25 4AQ, Kent, United Kingdom
Tel.: (44) 1233625076
Skin Care Product Mfr
N.A.I.C.S.: 325620

Coty Canada Inc. (2)
1255 Rte Transcanadienne Bureau 200, Dorval, H9P 2V4, QC, Canada
Tel.: (514) 421-5050
Pharmaceutical Product Whslr
N.A.I.C.S.: 424210
Amaury De Vallois (Gen Mgr)

Coty Ceska Republika, k.s. (2)
Na Okraji 335/42, 16200, Prague, Czech Republic
Tel.: (420) 233020111
Emp.: 80
Perfumes & Cosmetics Sales & Marketing
N.A.I.C.S.: 456120
Daniel Naxera (Mng Dir)

Coty Colombia Ltda. (2)
Ci 4 s43AA-30 Of 401, Medellin, Colombia
Tel.: (57) 43120499
Cosmetics Products Mfr
N.A.I.C.S.: 325620

Coty Cosmeticos Chile Limitada (2)
Avenida Vitacura 2909 Oficina 417, Comuna Las Condes, Santiago, Chile
Tel.: (56) 233 57 63 6
Perfumes & Cosmetics Sales & Marketing
N.A.I.C.S.: 456120

Coty Cosmetics Romania SRL (2)
42 44 Soseaua Bucuresti Ploiesti, 013696, Bucharest, Romania
Tel.: (40) 213169351
Web Site: http://www.coty.com
Perfumes & Cosmetics Marketing & Sales
N.A.I.C.S.: 456120

Coty Deutschland GmbH (2)
Rheinstrasse 4E, Mainz, 55116, Germany
Tel.: (49) 61313060
Web Site: http://www.coty.com
Sales Range: $50-74.9 Million
Emp.: 130
Fragrances & Cosmetics Mfr, Marketer & Distr
N.A.I.C.S.: 325620
Joachim Lubig (Mng Dir)

Subsidiary (Domestic):

Dr. Scheller Cosmetics AG (3)
Schillerstrasse 21, 73054, Eislingen, Wurttemberg, Germany **(100%)**
Tel.: (49) 7221 688 150
Web Site: http://www.coty.com
Sales Range: $50-74.9 Million
Cosmetics, Perfumes, Shampoo & Toothpaste Mfr & Distr
N.A.I.C.S.: 325620

Subsidiary (Non-US):

Dr. Scheller Cosmetics Polska Sp. z o.o. (4)
ul Kamienskiego 201-219, 51126, Wroclaw, Lower Silesian, Poland
Tel.: (48) 71 320 79 80
Web Site: http://www.dr-scheller-cosmetics.pl
Sales Range: $10-24.9 Million
Emp.: 35
Cosmetic Product Whslr
N.A.I.C.S.: 456120

Subsidiary (Domestic):

Lady Manhattan Cosmetics GmbH (4)
Heiligenwiesen 26, 70327, Stuttgart, Baden-Wurttemberg, Germany
Tel.: (49) 7161803249
Cosmetics Mfr
N.A.I.C.S.: 325620

Subsidiary (Non-US):

Coty France S.A.S. (2)
14 rue du Quatre Septembre, Paris, 75002, France
Tel.: (33) 158717200
Pharmaceutical Product Whslr
N.A.I.C.S.: 424210
Remi Frayssinet (Dir-Fin)

Coty Geneva S.A. (2)
Chemin de la Papeterie 1, PO Box 594, Versoix, 1290, Switzerland
Tel.: (41) 225918100
Web Site: http://www.coty.com
Sales Range: $25-49.9 Million
Emp.: 20
Perfumes & Cosmetics Marketing & Sales
N.A.I.C.S.: 456120
Peggy Elfrode (Mng Dir)

Coty Geneva S.A. Versoix (2)
Chemin De La Papeterie 1, Versoix, 1290, Switzerland
Tel.: (41) 585918100
Cosmetic Product Distr
N.A.I.C.S.: 456120
Jolanda Antunes (Office Mgr-Svcs)

Coty Germany GmbH (2)
Rheinstrabe 4 E, Fort Malakoff-Park, 55116, Mainz, Germany
Tel.: (49) 61313060
Web Site: http://www.lancaster-beauty.de
Skin Care Products Distr
N.A.I.C.S.: 424210
Leonhard Zastrow (Sr VP-R&D)

Coty Hellas S.A. (2)
5 Kalyftaki St, 14564, Kifissia, Greece
Tel.: (30) 2111887141
Cosmetic Product Whslr
N.A.I.C.S.: 325620
Eftihia Mageira (Gen Mgr)

Coty Hungary Kft. (2)
91 Vaci ut, Budapest, 1139, Hungary
Tel.: (36) 18872400
Web Site: http://www.cotyhungary.com
Emp.: 44
Perfumes & Cosmetics Marketing & Sales
N.A.I.C.S.: 456120
Beata Lakatos (Mng Dir)

Coty Ireland Ltd. (2)
Unit A1 Nutgrove Office Pk, Rathfarnham, Dublin, 14, Ireland
Tel.: (353) 12961606
Web Site: http://www.coty.com
Emp.: 12
Perfumes & Cosmetics Marketing & Sales
N.A.I.C.S.: 456120
Sarah Bean (Gen Mgr)

Coty Italia S.p.A. (2)
Via Serrenteaporti 8, 20154, Milan, Italy
Tel.: (39) 02623181
Perfumes & Cosmetics Marketing & Sales
N.A.I.C.S.: 456120

Coty Manufacturing UK Ltd. (2)
Bradfield Road, Eureka Park, Ashford, TN25 4AQ, Kent, United Kingdom
Tel.: (44) 1233625076
Web Site: http://www.coty.com

INTERNATIONAL PUBLIC

Sales Range: $100-124.9 Million
Emp.: 300
Perfumes & Cosmetics Mfr
N.A.I.C.S.: 325620

Coty Mexico, S.A. de C.V. (2)
Barranca del Muerto No 329 Planta Baja, Col San Jose Insurgentes, Mexico, DF, Del Benito Juarez, Mexico
Tel.: (52) 5530674200
Web Site: http://www.coty.com
Emp.: 73
Perfumes & Cosmetics Sales & Marketing
N.A.I.C.S.: 456120
Jean Marc Apfel (Gen Mgr)

Coty Middle East FZCO (2)
Plot No B34S22, PO Box 261125, Jebel Ali Free Zone, Dubai, United Arab Emirates
Tel.: (971) 48045900
Perfumes & Cosmetics Marketing & Sales
N.A.I.C.S.: 456120

Coty Polska Sp z o.o. (2)
Ul Domaniewska 34a, 02-672, Warsaw, Poland
Tel.: (48) 224310431
Web Site: http://www.coty.pl
Sales Range: $25-49.9 Million
Emp.: 115
Perfumes & Cosmetics Marketing & Sales
N.A.I.C.S.: 456120
Monika Rut (Mng Dir)

Coty Prestige (Taiwan) Ltd. (2)
5f-7 188 Sec 5 Nanjing E Rd, Taipei, 10571, Taiwan
Tel.: (886) 225285928
Cosmetic Product Distr
N.A.I.C.S.: 456120
Melody Ma (Gen Mgr)

Coty Prestige Austria Handelsgesellschaft m.b.H. (2)
Euro Plaza Gebaude E 5. Stock, Wienerbergstrasse 41, A 1120, Vienna, Austria
Tel.: (43) 6131 306 0
Web Site: http://www.coty.com
Perfumes & Cosmetics Sales & Marketing
N.A.I.C.S.: 456120

Coty Prestige Espana - Surcursal em Portugal (2)
Av Antonio De Aguiar Augusto 19 4 Dto Room B, 1050-012, Lisbon, Portugal
Tel.: (351) 214126360
Pharmaceutical Product Whslr
N.A.I.C.S.: 424210
Clara Alonso (Dir-HR-Spain & Portugal)

Coty Prestige Hellas S.A. (2)
655 Kalisdaki Street, 14564, Kifissia, Greece
Tel.: (30) 2107204141
Perfumes & Cosmetics Marketing & Sales
N.A.I.C.S.: 456120

Coty Prestige Portugal (2)
Rua Dr Antonio Loureiro Borges Edifico 2 Piso 0, Miraflores, 1499 030, Alges, Portugal
Tel.: (351) 214126360
Web Site: http://www.coty.com
Perfumes & Cosmetics Marketing & Sales
N.A.I.C.S.: 456120

Coty Prestige Southeast Asia (M) Sdn. Bhd. (2)
12 Tai Seng Street Ste 06-01, Singapore, 534118, Singapore
Tel.: (65) 67422260
Perfumes & Cosmetics Marketing & Sales
N.A.I.C.S.: 456120

Subsidiary (Domestic):

Coty Puerto Rico Inc. (2)
Metro Office Park Ste 8 Colgate Palmolive Bldg Ste 100, Guaynabo, PR 00968
Tel.: (787) 775-0606
Emp.: 16
Cosmetic Product Whslr
N.A.I.C.S.: 325620
Yimar Carrion (Dir-Comml)

Subsidiary (Non-US):

Coty S.A.S. (2)
14 rue du Quatre Septembre, Paris, 75002, France
Tel.: (33) 158717200

AND PRIVATE COMPANIES — JAB HOLDING COMPANY S.A.R.L.

Sales Range: $75-99.9 Million
Emp.: 300
Perfumes & Cosmetics Sales & Marketing
N.A.I.C.S.: 456120
Odile Mathoulin *(CEO)*

Coty Services U.K. Ltd. (2)
St Georges House 5 St Georges Rd, Wimbledon, London, SW19 4DR, United Kingdom
Tel.: (44) 2089711300
Cosmetics Products Mfr
N.A.I.C.S.: 325620
James Watling *(Dir-IT-Solution Design Mfg Europe)*

Coty Services and Logistics GmbH (2)
Rheinstr 4E, 55116, Mainz, Germany
Tel.: (49) 6131306473
Skin Care Products Distr
N.A.I.C.S.: 424210
Fredrik Handel *(Dir-Warehousing & Distr)*

Coty Slovenska Republika s.r.o. (2)
Ladislava Derera 18, Bratislava, 37, Slovakia
Tel.: (421) 254793888
Web Site: http://www.coty.sk
Sales Range: $25-49.9 Million
Emp.: 30
Perfumes & Cosmetics Marketing & Sales
N.A.I.C.S.: 456120
Jere Henerryeh *(Mgr-Slovakia)*

Coty Spain S.L. (2)
Calle de la Marina 16-18 Planta 16, 08005, Barcelona, Spain
Tel.: (34) 933163700
Perfumes & Cosmetics Mfr & Marketer
N.A.I.C.S.: 325620

Coty UK Ltd. (2)
5 St George's Rd St George's House, Wimbledon, London, SW19 4DR, United Kingdom
Tel.: (44) 2089711300
Sales Range: $25-49.9 Million
Emp.: 250
Perfumes & Cosmetics Marketing & Sales
N.A.I.C.S.: 456120
Esra Erkal-Paler *(Chief Global Corp Affairs Officer)*

Subsidiary (Domestic):

Coty US LLC (2)
1400 Broadway Rd, Sanford, NC 27332
Tel.: (919) 895-5374
Cosmetic Product Mfr & Whslr
N.A.I.C.S.: 325620
William Murphy *(Mgr-Mfg)*

Coty-OPI Inc. (2)
13034 Saticoy St, North Hollywood, CA 91605-3510
Tel.: (818) 759-2400
Web Site: http://www.opi.com
Sales Range: $100-124.9 Million
Emp.: 450
Cosmetics & Nail Products Mfr & Marketer
N.A.I.C.S.: 325620
Miriam Schaeffer *(Treas)*

Subsidiary (Non-US):

Else France S.A.S. (2)
56 Quai De Dion Bouton, Puteaux, 92800, France
Tel.: (33) 899868051
Cosmetic Product Whslr
N.A.I.C.S.: 325620

Fragrance Production S.A.S. (2)
ZI Edmond Poillot, B P 855, 28011, Chartres, France
Tel.: (33) 237917878
Web Site: http://www.coty.com
Sales Range: $100-124.9 Million
Emp.: 300
Perfumes & Cosmetics Mfr
N.A.I.C.S.: 325620

OPI Japan KK (2)
Minami-Aoyama Minato-ku 3-1-3 Spline Aoyama Tokyu building, Tokyo, 107-0062, Japan
Tel.: (81) 357723922
Web Site: http://www.opijapan.com
Dental Equipment & Supplies Mfr
N.A.I.C.S.: 339114

Ron Anderskow *(Pres & CEO)*

PT StarAsia Distributions (2)
No 23 Wijaya Kusuma, Grogol Petamburan Komplek Perkantoran Kota Grogol Permai Blok G, Jakarta, Indonesia
Tel.: (62) 2156980233
Fragrance Distr
N.A.I.C.S.: 456120
Fitri Tjandra *(Gen Mgr-Ops)*

Subsidiary (Domestic):

Philosophy Inc. (2)
3809 E Watkins St, Phoenix, AZ 85034
Tel.: (480) 794-8701
Web Site: http://www.philosophy.com
Sales Range: $200-249.9 Million
Emp.: 125
Skincare & Facial Cosmetic Mfr
N.A.I.C.S.: 424210

Rimmel Inc. (2)
2 Park Ave Rm 1800, New York, NY 10016
Tel.: (212) 479-4300
Cosmetic & Skincare Product Mfr & Whslr
N.A.I.C.S.: 325620

Subsidiary (Non-US):

StarAsia (Malaysia) Sdn. Bhd. (2)
Lot 44 Jalan E1/4, Kawasan Perusahaan Taman Ehsan Jaya, Kuala Lumpur, 52100, Malaysia
Tel.: (60) 362742097
Cosmetic Product Whslr
N.A.I.C.S.: 325620
Calvin Lim *(Mgr-Natl Sls)*

Suzhou Jiahua Biochemistry Co. (2)
Lili Industrial Park fenhu Economic, Wujiang, 215212, China
Tel.: (86) 51263628616
Commercial Banking Services
N.A.I.C.S.: 325620
Ice Liu *(Engr-EHS)*

Einstein Noah Restaurant Group, Inc. (1)
555 Zang St Ste 300, Lakewood, CO 80228
Tel.: (303) 568-8000
Web Site: http://www.einsteinnoah.com
Holding Company; Coffee & Bagel Restaurants Franchisor & Operator
N.A.I.C.S.: 551112
Mike Tettersfield *(Pres & CEO)*

Subsidiary (Domestic):

Einstein & Noah Corp. (2)
555 Zang St Ste 300, Lakewood, CO 80228
Tel.: (303) 568-8000
Sales Range: $25-49.9 Million
Emp.: 400
Owner & Franchisor of Bagel Restaurants
N.A.I.C.S.: 722511
Mike Tettersfield *(Pres & CEO)*

Manhattan Bagel Company, Inc. (2)
555 Zang St Ste 300, Lakewood, CO 80228
Tel.: (303) 568-8000
Web Site: http://www.manhattanbagel.com
Bagel Restaurants Operator
N.A.I.C.S.: 722515
Mike Tetterssield *(Pres & CEO)*

Independence Pet Holdings, Inc. (1)
11333 N Scottsdale Rd Ste 160, Scottsdale, AZ 85254
Tel.: (866) 901-2739
Web Site: https://www.independencepetholding.com
Holding Company
N.A.I.C.S.: 551112
Dirk Beeckman *(Chm)*

Subsidiary (Domestic):

Independence American Holdings Corp. (2)
485 Madison Ave Fl 14, New York, NY 10022-5819
Tel.: (212) 355-4141
Investment Management Service
N.A.I.C.S.: 551112

Subsidiary (Domestic):

IHC Specialty Benefits, Inc. (3)
860 Blue Gentian Rd Ste 330, Eagan, MN 55121

Tel.: (651) 332-8900
Web Site: http://www.ihcspecialty.com
Insurance Brokerage Services
N.A.I.C.S.: 524210
David T. Kettig *(CEO & COO)*

IPA Family, LLC (3)
2502 N Rocky Point Dr Ste 100, Tampa, FL 33607
Tel.: (813) 983-2990
Web Site: http://www.ipafamily.com
Emp.: 25
Insurance Brokerage Services
N.A.I.C.S.: 524210
David W. Keeler *(Pres)*

Independence American Insurance Company (3)
485 Madison Ave, New York, NY 10022
Tel.: (212) 355-4141
Web Site: http://www.independenceamerican.com
Property & Casualty Insurance Products & Services
N.A.I.C.S.: 524126
Roy T. K. Thung *(CEO)*

Subsidiary (Domestic):

Pets Best Insurance Services, LLC (2)
10840 Ballantyne Commons Pkwy, Charlotte, NC 28277
Tel.: (877) 738-7237
Web Site: http://www.petsbest.com
Pet Insurance
N.A.I.C.S.: 524210
Chris Middleton *(Sr VP & Gen Mgr)*

JAB Holdings B.V. (1)
Oudeweg 147, 2031 CC, Haarlem, Netherlands **(100%)**
Tel.: (31) 23 230 2883
Web Site: http://www.jabholco.com
Holding Company
N.A.I.C.S.: 551112
Peter G. Harf *(Sr Partner)*

JAB Luxury GmbH (1)
Via Industria 1, 6987, Caslano, Switzerland **(100%)**
Tel.: (41) 916129212
Web Site: http://www.jabholco.com
Sales Range: $125-149.9 Million
Emp.: 200
Holding Company; Luxury Goods Retailer
N.A.I.C.S.: 551112
Peter G. Harf *(Chm)*

Subsidiary (Domestic):

Bally Schuhfabriken AG (2)
Via Industria 1, 6987, Caslano, Switzerland
Tel.: (41) 916129111
Web Site: http://www.bally.com
Sales Range: $150-199.9 Million
Emp.: 955
Men's & Women's Shoes, Apparel, Accessories & Other Luxury Goods Designer & Retailer
N.A.I.C.S.: 458210
Frederic de Narp *(CEO)*

Subsidiary (Non-US):

Bally Australia Pty. Ltd. (3)
8 Canal Road, Saint Peters, 2044, NSW, Australia
Tel.: (61) 295192433
Sales Range: $1-9.9 Million
Emp.: 10
Luxury Goods & Accessories Retailer
N.A.I.C.S.: 459999

Bally France SAS (3)
52/54 Avenue Capitaine Glarner, 93400, Saint-Ouen, France
Tel.: (33) 149211313
Web Site: http://www.bally.fr
Sales Range: $50-74.9 Million
Emp.: 150
Luxury Goods & Accessories Retailer
N.A.I.C.S.: 459999

Bally GC Retail Co. Limited (3)
16/F One Peking Road, Tsimshatsui, Kowloon, China (Hong Kong)
Tel.: (852) 21963111
Web Site: http://www.experience.bally.com

Sales Range: $25-49.9 Million
Emp.: 60
Luxury Goods & Accessories Retailer
N.A.I.C.S.: 459999
Dinesh Tandon *(CEO)*

Bally GmbH (3)
Karntner Strasse 9, 1010, Vienna, Austria
Tel.: (43) 15121461
Web Site: http://experience.bally.com
Sales Range: $25-49.9 Million
Emp.: 12
Mfr of Footwear
N.A.I.C.S.: 316210

Subsidiary (US):

Bally North America, Inc. (3)
750 Lexington Ave 25th Fl, New York, NY 10022
Tel.: (212) 446-3930
Web Site: http://www.bally.com
Rev: $100,500,000
Emp.: 137
Luxury Goods & Accessories Retailer
N.A.I.C.S.: 459999
Mimmo Mariottini *(CEO-Americas)*

Subsidiary (Non-US):

Bally Singapore Pte Ltd. (3)
2 Leng Kee Road, 04-11 Thye Hong Centre, Singapore, 159086, Singapore
Tel.: (65) 67375554
Web Site: http://www.Bally.com
Sales Range: $25-49.9 Million
Emp.: 60
Luxury Goods & Accessories Retailer
N.A.I.C.S.: 459999
Danial Chua *(Area Mgr-Retail)*

Bally UK Sales Ltd. (3)
116 New Bond St, London, W1S 1EN, United Kingdom
Tel.: (44) 2074089877
Web Site: http://www.bally.com
Sales Range: $25-49.9 Million
Emp.: 15
Luxury Goods & Accessories Retailer
N.A.I.C.S.: 459999
Anne-Marie Gaultier *(VP-Global Mktg & Comm)*

Keurig Dr Pepper Inc. (1)
53 S Ave, Burlington, MA 01803 **(64.56%)**
Tel.: (781) 418-7000
Web Site: https://www.keurigdrpepper.com
Rev: $14,814,000,000
Assets: $52,130,000,000
Liabilities: $26,454,000,000
Net Worth: $25,676,000,000
Earnings: $2,181,000,000
Emp.: 28,100
Fiscal Year-end: 12/31/2023
Holding Company; Coffee, Tea & Soft Drink Mfr, Bottler & Whslr
N.A.I.C.S.: 551112
Robert James Gamgort *(Exec Chm)*

Subsidiary (Domestic):

Bai Brands LLC (2)
1800 E State St Ste 153, Hamilton, NJ 08609-2020
Tel.: (609) 586-0500
Web Site: http://www.drinkbai.com
Sales Range: $100-124.9 Million
Beverages Mfr
N.A.I.C.S.: 312111
Ben Weiss *(Founder)*

Plant (Domestic):

Big Red/Seven Up Bottling Group (2)
2120 Grand Ave Pkwy Ste 200, Austin, TX 78728
Tel.: (512) 385-4477
Sales Range: $75-99.9 Million
Emp.: 150
Soft Drink Bottler
N.A.I.C.S.: 312111

Big Red/Seven Up Bottling Group (2)
3127 Cabaniss Pkwy, Corpus Christi, TX 78415-5907
Tel.: (361) 851-9977
Web Site: http://www.dpsg.com

3861

JAB HOLDING COMPANY S.A.R.L.

JAB Holding Company S.a.r.l.—(Continued)
Sales Range: $25-49.9 Million
Emp.: 85
Soft Drink Bottler
N.A.I.C.S.: 312111
Maribel Munoz (Office Mgr)

Subsidiary (Non-US):

Canada Dry Mott's Inc. (2)
200 Matheson Boulevard West Suite 104,
30 Eglinton 3600, Mississauga, L5R 3E7,
ON, Canada
Tel.: (905) 712-4121
Rev.: $228,000,000
Emp.: 80
Soft Drink, Fruit Juice & Bottled Water Mfr
N.A.I.C.S.: 312112
Carol-Anne Gower (VP-Mktg & Bus Dev)

Plant (Domestic):

Dr Pepper Snapple Group, Inc. (2)
401 N Railroad Ave, Northlake, IL 60164-1671
Tel.: (708) 947-5000
Web Site:
http://www.drpeppersnapplegroup.com
Carbonated & Non-Carbonated Soft Drink Bottler
N.A.I.C.S.: 312111
Terry Graham (Pres & CQO)

Dr Pepper Snapple Group, Inc. - Williamson (2)
4363 Rte 104, Williamson, NY 14589-9332
Tel.: (315) 589-4911
Web Site:
http://www.drpeppersnapplegroup.com
Sales Range: $100-124.9 Million
Emp.: 400
Mfr & Distr of Branded Apple Juice & Applesauce Products
N.A.I.C.S.: 311411
Rodger Collins (Pres)

Subsidiary (Domestic):

Dr. Pepper/Seven Up, Inc. (2)
5301 Legacy Dr, Plano, TX 75024-3109
Tel.: (972) 673-7000
Web Site: http://www.brandspeoplelove.com
Emp.: 750
Holding Company; Soft Drink Mfr
N.A.I.C.S.: 551112
Charles Alfaro (VP-Corp Commun)

Subsidiary (Domestic):

Dr. Pepper/Seven Up Manufacturing Company (3)
5950 Sherry Ln Ste 500, Dallas, TX 75265-5024
Tel.: (214) 330-0491
Sales Range: $1-4.9 Billion
Soft Drink Bottler
N.A.I.C.S.: 312111
Tammy Atwell (Admin Asst)

Plant (Domestic):

Dr. Pepper/Seven Up Bottling Group (4)
915 N Ed Carey Dr, Harlingen, TX 78550-9203
Tel.: (956) 423-2705
Sales Range: $350-399.9 Million
Emp.: 80
Soft Drinks Mfr
N.A.I.C.S.: 312111

Dr. Pepper/Seven Up Bottling Group (4)
2875 Prune Ave, Fremont, CA 94539
Tel.: (510) 770-8777
Sales Range: $125-149.9 Million
Emp.: 600
Soft Drink Bottling Services
N.A.I.C.S.: 312111
Robert Love (Branch Mgr-Sls)

Dr. Pepper/Seven Up Bottling Group Midwest Division (4)
545 E 32nd St, Holland, MI 49423-5411
Tel.: (616) 396-1281
Sales Range: $250-299.9 Million
Soft Drink Bottler
N.A.I.C.S.: 312111

Dr. Pepper/Seven-Up Bottling Group of St. Louis (4)
555 James S McDonnell Blvd, Hazelwood, MO 63042-2401
Tel.: (314) 895-7400
Sales Range: $25-49.9 Million
Emp.: 50
Soft Drink Bottler
N.A.I.C.S.: 312111
Robert Matson (VP & Gen Mgr)

Subsidiary (Domestic):

Keurig Green Mountain, Inc. (2)
33 Coffee Ln, Waterbury, VT 05676
Tel.: (866) 574-5653
Web Site:
http://www.keuriggreenmountain.com
Coffee & Other Brewing Products Mfr & Distr
N.A.I.C.S.: 311920
Derek Hopkins (Chief Comml Officer)

Subsidiary (Non-US):

Keurig Canada Inc. (3)
3700 Jean-Rivard, Montreal, H1Z 4K3, QC, Canada
Tel.: (514) 593-7711
Web Site: http://corp.keurig.ca
Holding Company; Coffee & Other Brewing Products Mfr
N.A.I.C.S.: 551112
Stephane Glorieux (Pres)

Subsidiary (Domestic):

Keurig, Incorporated (3)
63 South Ave, Burlington, MA 01803 (100%)
Tel.: (781) 928-0162
Web Site: http://www.keurig.com
Sales Range: $100-124.9 Million
Single-Serving Coffee Products Mfr
N.A.I.C.S.: 311920
Andrew Loucks (Pres-Appliances)

Subsidiary (Domestic):

Snapple Beverage Corp. (2)
5301 Legacy Dr, Plano, TX 75024
Tel.: (972) 673-7000
Web Site: http://www.snapple.com
Emp.: 1,100
Fruit Juice & Soft Drink Mfr
N.A.I.C.S.: 312111
Steve Jarmon (VP-Mktg & Community Ventures)

Subsidiary (Domestic):

Southeast-Atlantic Beverage Corp. (2)
6001 Bowdendale Ave, Jacksonville, FL 32216-6041
Tel.: (904) 739-1000
Web Site:
http://www.drpeppersnapplegroup.com
Rev.: $172,000,000
Emp.: 400
Non-Alcoholic Bottling & Distribution Network
N.A.I.C.S.: 312111

Splash Transport, Inc. (2)
5301 Legacy Dr, Plano, TX 75024
Tel.: (972) 673-7000
Freight Transportation Services
N.A.I.C.S.: 484121

National Veterinary Associates, Inc. (1)
29229 Canwood St Ste 100, Agoura Hills, CA 91301
Tel.: (805) 777-7722
Web Site: http://www.nvaonline.com
Veterinary Hospital
N.A.I.C.S.: 541940
Stanley R. Creighton (Founder)

Subsidiary (Domestic):

Quartz Mountain Animal Hospital, Inc. (2)
8875 E Via Linda, Scottsdale, AZ 85258
Tel.: (480) 860-1433
Web Site:
http://www.quartzmountainhospital.com
Sales Range: $1-9.9 Million
Emp.: 9
Animal Hospital
N.A.I.C.S.: 541940

Mark Weaver (Founder)

Westside Animal Hospital, Inc. (2)
4550 Illinois Rd, Fort Wayne, IN 46804
Tel.: (260) 432-1542
Web Site: http://www.westsidevets.com
Sales Range: $25-49.9 Million
Emp.: 15
Animal Hospital Services, Pets & Other Animal Specialties
N.A.I.C.S.: 541940

Oak 1753 B.V. (1)
Oosterdokstraat 80, 1011 DK, Amsterdam, Netherlands (56%)
Tel.: (31) 207 240 2486
Web Site:
http://www.jacobsdouweegberts.com
Sales Range: $5-14.9 Billion
Holding Company; Tea & Coffee Mfr
N.A.I.C.S.: 551112
Luc Volatier (Sr VP-Ops)

Subsidiary (Non-US):

Balirny Douwe Egberts A.S. (2)
K Zizkovu 9, Prague, 190 009, Czech Republic
Tel.: (420) 266311683
Sales Range: $100-124.9 Million
Emp.: 250
Coffee & Tea Mfr
N.A.I.C.S.: 311920

Subsidiary (Domestic):

CoffeeCompany Holding B.V. (2)
's-Gravenhekje 1-A, Amsterdam, 1011 TG, Netherlands
Tel.: (31) 204282248
Web Site: http://www.coffeecompany.nl
Sales Range: $50-74.9 Million
Emp.: 10
Holding Company; Coffee Shop Franchisor & Operator
N.A.I.C.S.: 551112

The Coffee Company B.V. (3)
's-Gravenhekje 1-A, Amsterdam, 1011 TG, Netherlands
Tel.: (31) 204282248
Web Site: http://www.coffeecompany.nl
Emp.: 500
Coffee Shop Franchisor & Operator
N.A.I.C.S.: 722515
Stefan Swart (Gen Mgr)

Subsidiary (Non-US):

D.E. Master Blenders 1753 - Spain (2)
Pol Industrial de la Zona Franca, ES-08040, Barcelona, Spain
Tel.: (34) 934628400
Sales Range: $100-124.9 Million
Emp.: 226
Coffee & Tea
N.A.I.C.S.: 311920

Subsidiary (Domestic):

Sara Lee Finance Spain S.L. (3)
Street Josep Pla 2 B2 Built Torres Diagonal Litoral, Barcelona, 08019, Spain
Tel.: (34) 934628400
Consumer Goods Distr
N.A.I.C.S.: 424490

Subsidiary (Non-US):

Decotrade GmbH (2)
Baarerstrasse 12, 6300, Zug, Switzerland
Tel.: (41) 41 710 95 15
Web Site: http://www.decotrade.ch
Sales Range: $25-49.9 Million
Emp.: 32
Coffee Roasters
N.A.I.C.S.: 311920

Kaffehuset Friele A/S (2)
Midtunhaugen 6, Nesttun, Bergen, 5224, Norway
Tel.: (47) 55 92 66 00
Food Products Mfr
N.A.I.C.S.: 311999

Subsidiary (Domestic):

Koninklijke Douwe Egberts B.V. (2)

INTERNATIONAL PUBLIC

Vleutensevaart 100, PB 2, Utrecht, 3532 AD, Netherlands
Tel.: (31) 302979111
Web Site: http://www.demb.com
Food Products Mfr
N.A.I.C.S.: 311999
Frederic Larmuseau (CEO)

Subsidiary (Non-US):

Douwe Egberts N.V. (3)
Potaarde Z N, Grimbergen, 1850, Belgium
Tel.: (32) 22600611
Web Site: http://www.douwe-egberts.be
Sales Range: $150-199.9 Million
Coffee & Tea Producer
N.A.I.C.S.: 311920
Joke Maes (Dir-HR)

Subsidiary (Domestic):

Douwe Egberts Coffee Systems BVBA (4)
Potaarde, 1850, Grimbergen, Belgium
Tel.: (32) 22600611
Food Products Mfr
N.A.I.C.S.: 311999

Douwe Egberts Operating Service BVBA (4)
Potaarde, Grimbergen, 1850, Belgium
Tel.: (32) 22600611
Web Site: http://www.demb.com
Food Products Merchant & Whslr
N.A.I.C.S.: 424490

Subsidiary (Non-US):

Douwe Egberts Professional Germany GmbH (3)
Friedrich Koenig Strasse 35, 55129, Mainz, Germany
Tel.: (49) 613150690
Web Site:
http://www.douweegbertsprofessional.com
Sales Range: $75-99.9 Million
Emp.: 190
Bakery Products Mfr
N.A.I.C.S.: 311919
Udo Leunissen (Mng Dir)

Subsidiary (Domestic):

Coffenco International GmbH (4)
Friedrich-Koenig-Strasse 35, Mainz, 551299, Germany
Tel.: (49) 61315069770
Web Site: http://www.slee.de
Sales Range: $50-74.9 Million
Emp.: 120
Coffee & Tea Producer
N.A.I.C.S.: 311920

Fairwind GmbH (4)
Edmund Rumpler Starassen 6, Cologne, 40589, Germany
Tel.: (49) 220397980
Sales Range: $10-24.9 Million
Emp.: 1
Bakery Products Producer
N.A.I.C.S.: 311919

Sara Lee Coffee & Tea Germany GmbH (4)
Edmund Rumpler Str 6, Cologne, 51149, Germany
Tel.: (49) 220397980
Food Products Mfr
N.A.I.C.S.: 311920

Subsidiary (Domestic):

Jacobs Douwe Egberts NL B.V. (3)
Vleetenvaart 35, 3532 AD, Utrecht, Netherlands
Tel.: (31) 800 0221121
Web Site: http://www.de.nl
Coffee Mfr
N.A.I.C.S.: 311920

Subsidiary (Domestic):

Douwe Egberts Coffee Treatment & Supply BV (4)
Leeuwarderweg 1, Joure, 8501 ZD, Netherlands
Tel.: (31) 513488200
Web Site: http://www.douweegberts.com
Food Products Mfr
N.A.I.C.S.: 311999

AND PRIVATE COMPANIES — JAB HOLDING COMPANY S.A.R.L.

Jos Van Wilsum *(Plant Mgr)*

Douwe Egberts Van Nelle Participations BV (4)
Vleutensevaart 100, Utrecht, 3532 AD, Netherlands
Tel.: (31) 302927311
Web Site: http://www.de.nl
Emp.: 500
Food Products Mfr
N.A.I.C.S.: 311999
Luc Van Gorp *(Mgr-HR)*

Subsidiary (Non-US):

Oldtown Berhad (4)
No 2 Jalan Portland Tasek Industrial Estate, 31400, Ipoh, Perak, Malaysia
Tel.: (60) 5 546 5128
Web Site: http://www.oldtown.com.my
Holding Company; Coffee Mfr & Distr
N.A.I.C.S.: 311920
Siew Heng Lee *(Mng Dir)*

Subsidiary (Domestic):

Connecezone Sdn Bhd. (5)
25-01 Jalan Kenari 19a Bandar Puchong Jaya, Selangor, 47100, Kuala Lumpur, Malaysia
Tel.: (60) 3 8076 7823
Coffee Outlet Operator
N.A.I.C.S.: 722515

Emperor's Kitchen Sdn Bhd (5)
No 896 Jln Subang 10 Taman Perindustrian Subang, Subang Jaya, 47600, Malaysia
Tel.: (60) 3 8060 5454
Food Products Mfr
N.A.I.C.S.: 311999
Catherine Chee *(Mng Dir)*

Esquire Chef Sdn Bhd (5)
No 98 Psn Bercham Selatan 20 Taman Bercham Indah, Ipoh, 31400, Malaysia
Tel.: (60) 5 548 4882
Food Products Mfr
N.A.I.C.S.: 311999

Subsidiary (Non-US):

Super Group Ltd. (4)
30 Tuas Link 2 JDE Building, Singapore, 638568, Singapore
Tel.: (65) 67533088
Web Site: https://www.supereveryday.sg
Rev.: $1,587,144,010
Assets: $1,077,166,480
Liabilities: $420,492,877
Net Worth: $656,673,603
Earnings: $223,870,077
Emp.: 3,900
Fiscal Year-end: 12/31/2022
Food Products & Beverages Mfr
N.A.I.C.S.: 311999

Subsidiary (Non-US):

Maison du Cafe Coffee Systems France SNC (2)
Paris Nord II Batiment Le Rimbaud 22 Avenue des Nations, Villepinte, 93420, France
Tel.: (33) 149898400
Web Site: http://www.maisonducafe.com
Coffee Mfr
N.A.I.C.S.: 311920

Subsidiary (Domestic):

Marander Assurantie Compagnie BV (2)
Vleutensevaart 35, Utrecht, 3532 AD, Netherlands
Tel.: (31) 302972697
Food Products Mfr
N.A.I.C.S.: 311999

Subsidiary (Non-US):

Prima-Sara Lee Coffee & Tea Poland Sp. z o.o. (2)
ul Rubiez 46, Poznan, 61-612, Poland
Tel.: (48) 618220305
Web Site: http://www.primafinezja.pl
Food Products Mfr
N.A.I.C.S.: 311999
Peter Kokcenceske *(Gen Mgr)*

Santora Kaffee GmbH (2)
Liebhartsgasse 55-57, 1160, Vienna, Austria
Tel.: (43) 01404180
Web Site: http://www.santora.at
Sales Range: $25-49.9 Million
Emp.: 40
Coffee Roasters
N.A.I.C.S.: 311920

Sara Lee (Malaysia) Sdn. Bhd. (2)
201 1/F Kompleks Penchala, 50 Jalan Penchala, Petaling Jaya, Selangor, Malaysia
Tel.: (60) 377112888
Sales Range: $300-349.9 Million
Household & Body Care Products Sales & Mfr
N.A.I.C.S.: 456120

Sara Lee Baltic, s.i.a. (2)
59 Slokas, Riga, 1007, Latvia
Tel.: (371) 67783360
Web Site: http://www.merrild.lv
Sales Range: $25-49.9 Million
Emp.: 5
Food Products Mfr
N.A.I.C.S.: 311999
Dzintars Licis *(Mgr)*

Sara Lee Coffee & Tea France SNC (2)
Paris Nord Ii Le Rimbaud 22 Avenue Des Nations, Villepinte, 93420, France
Tel.: (33) 149898400
Coffee & Tea Mfr
N.A.I.C.S.: 311920

Sara Lee Coffee and Tea Hellas S.A. (2)
100 Kifissou Ave Egaleo, 122-41, Athens, Greece
Tel.: (30) 2105699300
Web Site: http://www.saraleect.gr
Sales Range: $50-74.9 Million
Emp.: 100
Coffee Processing & Tea Blending Services
N.A.I.C.S.: 311920
Luc Volatier *(Sr VP-Intl Supply Chain & Ops)*

Sara Lee Czech Republic, s.r.o. (2)
The zizkovu 282 / 9, Prague, 190 00, Czech Republic
Tel.: (420) 266720333
Web Site: http://www.saralee.cz
Food Products Mfr
N.A.I.C.S.: 311999

Sara Lee Group (Australia) Pty. Ltd. (2)
35-37 Ryde Road, Pymble, 2073, NSW, Australia
Tel.: (61) 295513000
Web Site: http://www.saralee.com.au
Holding Company
N.A.I.C.S.: 551112

Subsidiary (Domestic):

Sara Lee Australia Pty Ltd. (3)
37 Ryde Rd, Pymble, 2073, NSW, Australia
Tel.: (61) 295513000
Web Site: http://www.demb.com
Food Products Merchant & Whslr
N.A.I.C.S.: 424490

Division (Domestic):

Sara Lee Food Holdings Pty. Ltd. (4)
35-37 Ryde Road, Pymble, 2073, NSW, Australia
Tel.: (61) 295513000
Web Site: http://www.saralee.com.au
Sales Range: $300-349.9 Million
Emp.: 665
Holding Company; Food Mfr
N.A.I.C.S.: 551112

Subsidiary (Non-US):

Sara Lee New Zealand Limited (3)
9 Gladding Place, Manukau, 2241, Auckland, New Zealand
Tel.: (64) 99151600
Web Site: http://www.saralee.com
Emp.: 5
Coffee & Tea Distr
N.A.I.C.S.: 311999
Craig Jamieson *(Gen Mgr)*

Subsidiary (Non-US):

Sara Lee Hong Kong Ltd. (2)
Room 1204-05 12th Floor Allied Kajima Building, 138 Gloucester Road, Wanchai, China (Hong Kong)
Tel.: (852) 28208621
Food Products Mfr
N.A.I.C.S.: 311999

Sara Lee Hungary Kave es Tea Kft (2)
Vaci 22-24, H 1132, Budapest, Hungary (100%)
Tel.: (36) 12379298
Web Site: http://www.saralee.hu
Sales Range: $350-399.9 Million
Emp.: 300
Food Brokers; Coffee Roaster
N.A.I.C.S.: 445298

Sara Lee Japan, Ltd. (2)
35 Shinamo-machi, Shinjuku-ku, Tokyo, 160-0016, Japan
Tel.: (81) 353612800
Web Site: http://www.saralee.com
Sales Range: $25-49.9 Million
Emp.: 80
Underwear Sales
N.A.I.C.S.: 315120

Sara Lee UK Holdings Limited (2)
225 Bath Rd, Slough, SL1 4AB, Berks, United Kingdom (100%)
Tel.: (44) 753523971
Sales Range: $250-299.9 Million
Holding Company
N.A.I.C.S.: 551112

Subsidiary (Domestic):

Douwe Egberts Coffee Systems Ltd (3)
225 Bath Road, Slough, SL1 4AU, Berks, United Kingdom
Tel.: (44) 8452711818
Food Products Mfr
N.A.I.C.S.: 311999

Subsidiary (US):

Tea Forte, Inc. (2)
23 Bradford St, Concord, MA 01742
Tel.: (978) 369-7777
Web Site: http://www.teaforte.com
Sales Range: $10-24.9 Million
Emp.: 30
Tea Mfr
N.A.I.C.S.: 311920
Peter Hewitt *(Founder)*

Panera Bread Company (1)
3630 S Geyer Rd Ste 100, Saint Louis, MO 63127
Tel.: (314) 984-1000
Web Site: http://www.panerabread.com
Sales Range: $1-4.9 Billion
Bakery Cafes Owner, Operator & Franchisor
N.A.I.C.S.: 722511
Ronald M. Shaich *(Founder)*

Branch (Domestic):

Panera Bread Company (2)
3056 Columbus Ctr, Bloomington, IN 47401
Tel.: (812) 375-9421
Web Site: http://www.panerabread.com
Owner, Operator & Franchisor of Bakery Cafes
N.A.I.C.S.: 722513

Panera Bread Company (2)
1700 N Moore St, Arlington, MA 22209
Tel.: (703) 812-4690
Web Site: http://www.panerabread.com
Owner, Operator & Franchisor of Bakery Cafes
N.A.I.C.S.: 722513

Panera Bread Company (2)
3083 E Main St, Mohegan Lake, NY 12401
Tel.: (914) 528-0014
Web Site: http://www.panerabread.com
Owner, Operator & Franchisor of Bakery Cafes
N.A.I.C.S.: 722513

Panera Bread Company (2)
7224 Eastchase Pkwy, Montgomery, AL 36117
Tel.: (334) 274-9170
Web Site: http://www.panerabread.com

Owner, Operator & Franchisor of Bakery Cafes
N.A.I.C.S.: 722513

Panera Bread Company (2)
2100 Henderson Mill Rd, Atlanta, GA 30345
Tel.: (770) 414-4664
Web Site: http://www.panerabread.com
Owner, Operator & Franchisor of Bakery Cafes
N.A.I.C.S.: 722513

Panera Bread Company (2)
1935 Calle Barcelona, Carlsbad, CA 92009
Tel.: (760) 635-0026
Web Site: http://www.panerabread.com
Owner, Operator & Franchisor of Bakery Cafes
N.A.I.C.S.: 722513

Subsidiary (Non-US):

Panera Bread ULC (2)
322 Yonge St, Toronto, M5B 1R8, ON, Canada
Tel.: (416) 205-9371
Web Site: http://www.panerabread.com
Fresh Bakery Products Mfr
N.A.I.C.S.: 311812

Subsidiary (Domestic):

Paradise Bakery & Cafe, Inc. (2)
618 E 400 S, Salt Lake City, UT 84102
Tel.: (801) 746-6990
Web Site: http://www.paradisebakery.com
Owner, Operator & Franchisor of Bakery Cafes
N.A.I.C.S.: 722513

Peet's Coffee & Tea, Inc. (1)
1400 Park Ave, Emeryville, CA 94608-3520 (77.1%)
Tel.: (510) 594-2100
Web Site: http://www.peets.com
Sales Range: $200-249.9 Million
Emp.: 811
Coffee Roaster & Online Merchant
N.A.I.C.S.: 311920
Olivier Goudet *(Chm)*

Subsidiary (Domestic):

Caribou Coffee Company, Inc. (2)
3900 Lakebreeze Ave N, Brooklyn Center, MN 55429 (95.16%)
Tel.: (763) 592-2200
Web Site: http://www.cariboucoffee.com
Sales Range: $200-249.9 Million
Emp.: 1,737
Coffeehouse Operator
N.A.I.C.S.: 722515
Chad Trewick *(Sr Dir-Coffee & Tea Ops)*

Intelligentsia Coffee, Inc. (2)
3123 N Broadway St, Chicago, IL 60657-4522
Tel.: (773) 348-8058
Web Site: http://www.intelligentsiacoffee.com
Coffee & Tea Bar & Retail Store
N.A.I.C.S.: 722515
Waldemar Colon *(Gen Counsel & VP-Ops)*

Mighty Leaf Tea Company (2)
100 Smith Ranch Rd Ste 120, San Rafael, CA 94903
Web Site: http://www.mightyleaf.com
Sales Range: $1-9.9 Million
Emp.: 50
Tea & Related Products Mfr & Whslr
N.A.I.C.S.: 311920
Radha Ahuja *(Mgr-Retail Bus Dev)*

Pret A Manger (Europe) Ltd (1)
75b Verde 10 Bressenden Place, London, SW1E 5DH, United Kingdom
Tel.: (44) 2078278000
Web Site: http://www.pret.co.uk
Sales Range: $150-199.9 Million
Emp.: 2,000
Sandwich Shops Operator
N.A.I.C.S.: 722513
Julian Metcalfe *(Co-Founder)*

Subsidiary (Domestic):

Eat Ltd (2)
140 Aldersgate Street, London, EC1A 4HY, United Kingdom
Tel.: (44) 20 8900 6404

JAB HOLDING COMPANY S.A.R.L.

JAB Holding Company S.a.r.l.—(Continued)

Web Site: http://www.eat.co.uk
Specialty Food Retailer
N.A.I.C.S.: 445298

Subsidiary (US):

Pret A Manger (2)
853 Broadway Ste 701, New York, NY
10003-4722 **(100%)**
Tel.: (212) 997-5520
Web Site: http://www.pret.com
Sales Range: $10-24.9 Million
Emp.: 25
Sandwich Shop
N.A.I.C.S.: 722511

Subsidiary (Non-US):

Pret A Manger (Hong Kong) Ltd (2)
Room 1503 15/F 18 Hysan Avenue Causeway Bay, Hong Kong, China (Hong Kong)
Tel.: (852) 2520 0445
Web Site: http://www.pret.com.hk
Emp.: 300
Restaurant Operators
N.A.I.C.S.: 722513
Sarah Lee (Mng Dir)

JABA I INVERSIONES INMO-BILIARIAS SOCIMI SA

Maria de Molina 37 Bis, 28006, Madrid, Spain
Tel.: (34) 915619066
Web Site:
  https://www.jabaholdings.com
YABA—(MAD)
Sales Range: Less than $1 Million
Real Estate Investment Trust Services
N.A.I.C.S.: 531210
Walid Tawfiq Shakir Fakhouri (Chm & CEO)

JABAL OMAR DEVELOPMENT COMPANY

Jabal omar project, PO Box 56968, Al Shubaikah district, Makkah, 21955, Saudi Arabia
Tel.: (966) 125478888
Web Site: https://jabalomar.com.sa
Year Founded: 2006
4250—(SAU)
Rev.: $353,783,371
Assets: $7,275,192,244
Liabilities: $3,882,530,661
Net Worth: $3,392,661,583
Earnings: $9,994,400
Emp.: 171
Fiscal Year-end: 12/31/23
Real Estate Developers
N.A.I.C.S.: 237210
Ziyad Othman Al-Hogail (Co-Chm)

JABER EBNE HAYYAN PHARMACEUTICAL CO.

km 5 of special Karaj road corner of Besharti Som St, PO Box 13185-1739, Tehran, Iran
Tel.: (98) 2144503323
Web Site: https://www.jaber-pharma.com
Year Founded: 1961
Pharmaceuticals Product Mfr
N.A.I.C.S.: 325412
Masoud Amanlou (Chm)

JABUKA A.D

Trg Marala Tita 65 Postanski fah 85, 26000, Pancevo, Serbia
Tel.: (381) 132314236
Web Site:
  https://www.skrobarajabuka.rs
Year Founded: 1999
Sales Range: $10-24.9 Million
Emp.: 166
Starch Product Mfr
N.A.I.C.S.: 311221

JAC RECRUITMENT CO., LTD.

14F Jinbocho Mitsui Building 1-105 Kanda Jinbocho, Chiyoda-ku, Tokyo, 101-0051, Japan
Tel.: (81) 352599221
Web Site: http://corp.jac-recruitment.jp
Year Founded: 1988
2124—(TKS)
Rev.: $244,427,750
Assets: $166,742,620
Liabilities: $44,674,090
Net Worth: $122,068,530
Earnings: $42,384,020
Emp.: 1,952
Fiscal Year-end: 12/31/23
Recruitment Services
N.A.I.C.S.: 561320
Hiromi Tazaki (Chm)

Subsidiaries:

C.C. Consulting Co., Ltd. (1)
Jinbocho Mitsui Bldg 15F 1-105 Kanda Jinbocho, Chiyoda-ku, Tokyo, 101-0051, Japan
Tel.: (81) 35 217 3900
Web Site: https://www.ccconsulting.jp
Online Recruitment Services
N.A.I.C.S.: 561311
Toshihide Horiguchi (Mng Dir)

JAC Recruitment (Germany) GmbH (1)
Berliner Allee 47, 40212, Dusseldorf, Germany
Tel.: (49) 2119425480
Web Site: https://www.jac-recruitment.de
Recruitment Services
N.A.I.C.S.: 561311

JAC Recruitment (UK) Limited (1)
2nd Floor 64 London Wall, London, EC2M 5TP, United Kingdom
Tel.: (44) 2073822400
Web Site: https://www.jac-recruitment.co.uk
Recruitment Services
N.A.I.C.S.: 561311

JAC Recruitment Hong Kong Ltd. (1)
Rooms 601-5 6/F Tai Yau Building 181 Johnston Road, Wanchai, China (Hong Kong)
Tel.: (852) 25856700
Web Site: http://www.jac-recruitment.hk
Recruitment Services
N.A.I.C.S.: 561311

JAC Recruitment India Pvt. Ltd. (1)
502A 5th Floor Global Foyer Golf Course Road, Gurgaon, 122002, Haryana, India
Tel.: (91) 1244174330
Web Site: https://www.jac-recruitment.in
Recruitment Services
N.A.I.C.S.: 561311

JAC Recruitment Pte. Ltd. (1)
1 Raffles Place 42-01 One Raffles Place Tower 1, Singapore, 048616, Singapore
Tel.: (65) 62246864
Web Site: https://www.jac-recruitment.sg
Recruitment Services
N.A.I.C.S.: 561311

VantagePoint K.K. (1)
Roppongi Hills North Tower 3F 6-2-31 Roppongi, Minato-ku, Tokyo, 106-0032, Japan
Tel.: (81) 354134433
Web Site: https://www.vpointcareers.com
Online Recruitment Services
N.A.I.C.S.: 561311
Shaun Sundberg (Mng Partner)

JACCS CO., LTD.

Ebisu Neonart 1-18 Ebisu 4-chome, Shibuya-ku, Tokyo, 150-8932, Japan
Tel.: (81) 354481311
Web Site: https://www.jaccs.co.jp
Year Founded: 1948
8584—(TKS)
Rev.: $1,221,409,020
Assets: $24,969,902,950
Liabilities: $23,393,814,550
Net Worth: $1,576,088,400
Earnings: $157,119,700
Emp.: 6,097
Fiscal Year-end: 03/31/24
Credit Card Issuer
N.A.I.C.S.: 522210
Yasuyoshi Itagaki (Chm & CEO)

Subsidiaries:

JACCS Finance (Cambodia) Plc (1)
Canadia Tower 20 Floor Street Preah Angdoung, Sangkat Wat Phnom Khan Daun Penh, Phnom Penh, Cambodia
Tel.: (855) 1002 397 7265
Web Site: https://www.jaccs.com.kh
Financial Services
N.A.I.C.S.: 541611
Thun Sophy (Mgr-Credit)

JACCS International Vietnam Finance Co., Ltd. (1)
15th Floor Centec Tower 72-74 Nguyen Thi Minh Khai, Vo Thi Sau Ward District 3, Ho Chi Minh City, Vietnam
Tel.: (84) 285 404 3870
Web Site: https://www.jaccs.com.vn
Financial Services
N.A.I.C.S.: 541611

PT JACCS Mitra Pinasthika Mustika Finance Indonesia (1)
Gedung Lippo Kuningan Lantai 25 Jalan H R Rasuna Said, Kav B-12 Karet Kuningan Kota, Jakarta Selatan, Indonesia
Tel.: (62) 150 0309
Web Site: https://www.jaccs-mpmfinance.com
Financial Services
N.A.I.C.S.: 541611

JACK CEWE LTD.

1850 Hillside Ave, Coquitlam, V3K 1K5, BC, Canada
Tel.: (604) 526-0751
Web Site: https://www.cewe.com
Year Founded: 1953
Rev.: $30,256,843
Emp.: 200
General Construction Services
N.A.I.C.S.: 237310
Kirsten Wilson (Pres)

JACK CHIA INDUSTRIES (THAILAND) PUBLIC COMPANY LIMITED

114/1 Soi Chalongkrung 31, Lat Krabang District, Bangkok, 10520, Thailand
Tel.: (66) 20120012
Web Site: https://www.jackchia.co.th
Year Founded: 1966
JCT—(THA)
Rev.: $26,438,875
Assets: $45,804,244
Liabilities: $6,496,965
Net Worth: $39,307,280
Earnings: $2,777,032
Fiscal Year-end: 12/31/23
Pharmaceutical Product Mfr & Distr
N.A.I.C.S.: 325412
Tin Lung Chong (Chm)

JACK MAY CHEVROLET BUICK GMC LIMITED

3788 Prince of Wales Drive, Ottawa, K2C 3H1, ON, Canada
Tel.: (613) 692-3553
Web Site: http://www.jackmay.com
Year Founded: 1990
Rev.: $17,053,290
Emp.: 48
New & Used Car Dealers
N.A.I.C.S.: 441110
Nathan Ames (Mgr-Sls-New Car)

JACK TECHNOLOGY CO., LTD.

181 Qiyihe Rd Linhai, Taizhou, 317000, Zhejiang, China
Tel.: (86) 57688177782
Web Site: https://www.chinajack.com
Year Founded: 1995

INTERNATIONAL PUBLIC

603337—(SHG)
Rev.: $772,433,247
Assets: $1,201,120,329
Liabilities: $583,245,285
Net Worth: $617,875,044
Earnings: $69,303,658
Emp.: 3,000
Fiscal Year-end: 12/31/22
Sewing Machine Mfr & Distr
N.A.I.C.S.: 333248
Ruan Jixiang (Chm & Gen Mgr)

Subsidiaries:

Taizhou Topcut-Bullmer Mechanical & Electrical Co., Ltd. (1)
No 181 Qiyihe Road Jiangnan Street, Linhai, 317000, China
Tel.: (86) 57689399566
Sewing machines Mfr
N.A.I.C.S.: 333248

JACK VICTOR LIMITED

1250 St Alexandre Street, Montreal, H3B 3H6, QC, Canada
Tel.: (514) 866-4891
Web Site: http://www.jackvictor.com
Year Founded: 1913
Apparel Mfr & Distr
N.A.I.C.S.: 315990
Alan Victor (Pres & CEO)

JACKA RESOURCES LTD.

Level 11 London House 216 St Georges Terrace, Perth, 6000, WA, Australia
Tel.: (61) 8 9481 0389
Web Site:
  http://www.jackaresources.com.au
Rev.: $58,537
Assets: $668,142
Liabilities: $753,333
Net Worth: ($85,191)
Earnings: ($481,288)
Fiscal Year-end: 06/30/18
Oil & Gas Exploration Services
N.A.I.C.S.: 211120
Stephen Brockhurst (Sec)

JACKON AS

Sorkilen 3, 1621, Gressvik, Norway
Tel.: (47) 69 36 33 00
Web Site: http://www.jackon.no
Insulation & Polystyrene Products Mfr
N.A.I.C.S.: 326140

Subsidiaries:

ThermiSol Finland Oy (1)
Toravantie 18, FIN 38210, Sastamala, Finland
Tel.: (358) 108419200
Web Site: http://www.thermisol.fi
Produces & Markets Expanded Polystyrene Products in Finland
N.A.I.C.S.: 326140
Veli Ollila (Mng Dir)

JACKPOT DIGITAL INC.

Suite 575 510 Burrard Street, Vancouver, V6C 3A8, BC, Canada
Tel.: (604) 681-0204
Web Site:
  https://www.jackpotdigital.com
JPOTF—(OTCQB)
Rev.: $478,170
Assets: $2,410,712
Liabilities: $7,828,478
Net Worth: ($5,417,766)
Earnings: ($2,995,947)
Emp.: 23
Fiscal Year-end: 12/31/20
Software Development Services
N.A.I.C.S.: 541511
Jacob H. Kalpakian (Pres & CEO)

Subsidiaries:

MT Ventures Inc. (1)
1111 E Lincolnway Ste 211, Cheyenne, WY 82001

Tel.: (307) 222-0327
Gaming Software Development Services
N.A.I.C.S.: 541511

JACKSON INVESTMENTS LIMITED
Room No 310/A 7/A Bentick Street
3rd Floor, Kolkata, 700 001, West Bengal, India
Tel.: (91) 22430153
Web Site:
https://www.jacksoninvestltd.com
Year Founded: 1982
Rev.: $672,556
Assets: $4,523,372
Liabilities: $696
Net Worth: $4,522,675
Earnings: $8,702
Emp.: 9
Fiscal Year-end: 03/31/19
Financial Investment Services
N.A.I.C.S.: 523999
Rajeev Ghosh *(CFO)*

JACKSPEED CORPORATION LIMITED
221 Henderson Road 06-15, Singapore, 159557, Singapore
Tel.: (65) 62730386   SG
Web Site: http://www.jackspeed.com
Year Founded: 1993
J17—(SES)
Rev.: $24,914
Assets: $536,029
Liabilities: $763,275
Net Worth: $(227,246)
Earnings: ($385,035)
Fiscal Year-end: 02/28/21
Leather Seat Trim Product Mfr
N.A.I.C.S.: 316990
Kian Peng Yap *(Deputy Chm & CEO)*

Subsidiaries:

Index Credit Pte Ltd (1)
210 Turf Club Road, Lot B69/B72/B73/B75 Car Mall At Grandstand, Singapore, 287995, Singapore
Tel.: (65) 63562988
Web Site: http://www.indexgroup.com.sg
Automotive Finance Services
N.A.I.C.S.: 522220

J.V. (Thailand) Co., Ltd. (1)
700/768 Moo 1 Amata Nakorn Industrial Estate Tambol Panthong Amphur, Phan Thong, 20160, Chonburi, Thailand
Tel.: (66) 384470114
Leather Goods Distr
N.A.I.C.S.: 424990

Jackspeed Leather Special Manufacturer (M) Sdn. Bhd. (1)
No 21 Jalan 20 Taman Sri Kluang, Kluang, 86000, Johor, Malaysia
Tel.: (60) 77721412
Automotive Leather Good & Seat Mfr
N.A.I.C.S.: 316990

Jackspeed Singapore Pte. Ltd. (1)
221 Henderson Road 06-15, Singapore, 159557, Singapore
Tel.: (65) 62730386
Leather Goods Mfr
N.A.I.C.S.: 316990

Ultimate Vehicle Pty Ltd (1)
29 Sir Laurence Drive, Seaford, 3198, VIC, Australia
Tel.: (61) 397735275
Web Site: http://www.ultimatevehicle.com.au
Motor Vehicle Parts Mfr
N.A.I.C.S.: 336390

JACKSTONES, INC.
593 Antonio Drive Bagumbayan, Taguig, 1630, Philippines
Tel.: (63) 82779455
Web Site:
https://www.jackstonesinc.com
Year Founded: 1964
JAS—(PHI)
Rev.: $293,378
Assets: $2,858,690
Liabilities: $2,525,280
Net Worth: $333,410
Earnings: ($70,842)
Emp.: 4
Fiscal Year-end: 12/31/20
Other Holding Company
N.A.I.C.S.: 551112
Aleta So Tanenglian *(Vice Chm)*

JACKY'S ELECTRONICS LLC
Office No 2001 & 2002 Twin Towers Deira, PO Box 13745, Dubai, 13745, United Arab Emirates
Tel.: (971) 42594040
Web Site: http://www.jackys.com
Year Founded: 1970
Sales Range: $125-149.9 Million
Emp.: 600
Household Appliance, Electronic & Office Equipment Retailer
N.A.I.C.S.: 459410
Jacky Panjabi *(Founder & Mng Dir)*

Subsidiaries:

JACKY'S ELECTRONICS (S) PTE. LTD. (1)
Henderson Industrial Park Block 219 02-02 Henderson Road, Singapore, 159556, Singapore
Tel.: (65) 6273 8055
Web Site: http://www.jackys.com
Sales Range: $50-74.9 Million
Emp.: 7
Printing Equipment Distr
N.A.I.C.S.: 423830
Jacky Panjabi *(Mng Dir)*

JACKY'S INTERNATIONAL LTD. (1)
7th Floor Suite A Alpha House 27-33 Nathan Road, Tsim Sha Tsui, Kowloon, China (Hong Kong)
Tel.: (852) 2739 0333
Sales Range: $25-49.9 Million
Emp.: 15
Printing Equipment Distr
N.A.I.C.S.: 423830
Manoj Panjabi *(Exec Dir)*

JACOBIO PHARMACEUTICALS GROUP CO., LTD.
Building F2 No 88 Kechuang 6th Street, Beijing Economic Development Zone, Beijing, China
Tel.: (86) 1056315466   Ky
Web Site:
http://www.jacobiopharma.com
Year Founded: 2015
1167—(HKG)
Pharmaceutical Product Mfr & Distr
N.A.I.C.S.: 325412
Yinxiang Wang *(Chm & CEO)*

JACOBS & THOMPSON INC.
89 Kenhar Drive, Toronto, M9L 2R3, ON, Canada
Tel.: (416) 749-0600
Web Site: http://www.foamparts.com
Year Founded: 1947
Sales Range: $25-49.9 Million
Emp.: 100
Automotive Foam Sealant Mfr
N.A.I.C.S.: 325998
Christopher Brand *(Co-Owner)*

JACOBS CAPITAL (PTY) LTD.
5 Ennisdale Dr, Durban North, Durban, 4051, Kwazulu-Natal, South Africa
Tel.: (27) 31 573 2558   ZA
Web Site:
http://www.jacobscapital.co.za
Year Founded: 2002
Emp.: 50
Investment & Business Advisory Services
N.A.I.C.S.: 523940
Wessel Jacobs *(CEO)*

Subsidiaries:

Evowood Pty. Limited (1)
1 Nelson Road 2nd Floor Buckhurst Building, Westville, 3630, KwaZulu-Natal, South Africa
Tel.: (27) 871501510
Web Site: http://www.evowood.co.za
Hardboard & Soft Board Mfr
N.A.I.C.S.: 321113
Urekha Venketas *(Mgr-Comml Relationship)*

JACOBS HOLDING AG
Seefeldquai 17, CH-8034, Zurich, Switzerland
Tel.: (41) 443881200   CH
Web Site:
https://www.jacobsholding.com
Year Founded: 1994
Rev.: $46,145,233
Assets: $1,664,645,233
Liabilities: $102,994,457
Net Worth: $1,561,650,776
Emp.: 31
Fiscal Year-end: 12/31/21
Holding Company
N.A.I.C.S.: 551112
Michael Tuchschmid *(CFO & Sec)*

Subsidiaries:

Barry Callebaut AG (1)
Hardturmstrasse 181, 8005, Zurich, Switzerland (51%)
Tel.: (41) 432040404
Web Site: https://www.barry-callebaut.com
Rev.: $11,557,007,890
Assets: $16,868,008,219
Liabilities: $13,706,085,445
Net Worth: $3,161,922,775
Earnings: $212,454,657
Emp.: 13,000
Fiscal Year-end: 08/31/2024
Chocolate & Chocolate-Related Products Mfr & Distr
N.A.I.C.S.: 311351
Patrick G. De Maeseneire *(Chm)*

Subsidiary (Non-US):

Barry Callebaut Canada Inc. (2)
2950 Nelson Street, Saint-Hyacinthe, J2S 1Y7, QC, Canada (100%)
Tel.: (450) 774-9131
Web Site: http://www.barry-callebaut.com
Sales Range: $150-199.9 Million
Emp.: 600
Chocolate Product Mfr
N.A.I.C.S.: 311352
Sebastian Gilbert *(Plant Mgr)*

Barry Callebaut France SAS (2)
5 boulevard Michelet, BP 8, Hardricourt, 78250, Meulan, France (100%)
Tel.: (33) 130228400
Sales Range: $50-74.9 Million
Emp.: 200
Chocolate & Chocolate Related Products Mfr
N.A.I.C.S.: 311352
Aurelie Hristov *(Mgr-R&D)*

Barry Callebaut UK Ltd. (2)
Wildmere Road Industrial Estate, Banbury, OX16 3UU, Oxfordshire, United Kingdom
Tel.: (44) 1295224700
Sales Range: $25-49.9 Million
Emp.: 250
Mfr of Chocolate Confectionery & Coatings
N.A.I.C.S.: 311352

Subsidiary (US):

Barry Callebaut USA, LLC (2)
600 W Chicago Ave Ste 860, Chicago, IL 60610
Tel.: (312) 496-7300
Web Site: http://www.barry-callebaut.com
Cocoa, Chocolates & Confectionery Products Mfr & Distr
N.A.I.C.S.: 311351
Mike Schrauth *(VP & Gen Mgr-Gourmet)*

Plant (Domestic):

Barry Callebaut USA LLC (3)
400 Industrial Park Rd, Saint Albans, VT 05478-1875

Tel.: (802) 524-9711
Web Site: http://www.barry-callebaut.com
Sales Range: $25-49.9 Million
Emp.: 200
Mfr of Cocoa & Chocolate Products
N.A.I.C.S.: 311351

Barry Callebaut USA LLC (3)
1500 Suckle Hwy, Pennsauken, NJ 08110-1432 (100%)
Tel.: (856) 663-2260
Web Site: http://www.barry-callebaut.com
Sales Range: $25-49.9 Million
Emp.: 100
Chocolate Product Mfr
N.A.I.C.S.: 311351
Bill Hayes *(Plant Mgr)*

Oral Hammaslaakarit Oyj (1)
Tekniikantie 4A, 02150, Espoo, Finland
Tel.: (358) 10 400 3010
Web Site: http://www.oral.fi
Dental Care Services
N.A.I.C.S.: 339116
Minna Lonnqvist *(Dir-Comm)*

Subsidiary (Domestic):

Oral Hammaslaakarit - Itakeskus (2)
Tallinnanaukio 4 B, 00930, Helsinki, Finland
Tel.: (358) 10 400 3460
Web Site: http://www.oral.fi
Dental Care Services
N.A.I.C.S.: 339116

Oral Hammaslaakarit - Vantaa (2)
Kielotie 14 B, 01300, Vantaa, Finland
Tel.: (358) 10 400 3480
Web Site: http://www.oral.fi
Dental Care Services
N.A.I.C.S.: 621999

JACOBSON PHARMA CORPORATION LIMITED
Unit 2313-18 23/F Tower 1 Millennium City 1 388 Kwun Tong Road, Kwun Tong, Kowloon, China (Hong Kong)
Tel.: (852) 2 267 2298   Ky
Web Site:
http://www.jacobsonpharma.com
2633—(HKG)
Rev.: $205,793,136
Assets: $613,369,549
Liabilities: $231,851,224
Net Worth: $381,518,326
Earnings: $24,210,191
Emp.: 1,736
Fiscal Year-end: 03/31/22
Pharmaceutical Product Mfr & Distr
N.A.I.C.S.: 325412
Derek Kwong Yip Sum *(Founder, Chm & CEO)*

Subsidiaries:

APT Pharma Limited (1)
3-6/F 8/F 10-12/F Tai Fung Indl Bldg 61 Hung To Rd, Kwun Tong, China (Hong Kong)
Tel.: (852) 23417878
Pharmaceutical Product Mfr & Distr
N.A.I.C.S.: 325412

Dickson Warehousing Limited (1)
10/F Kerry Warehouse 36-42 Shan Mei Street Fotan, Sha Tin, New Territories, China (Hong Kong)
Tel.: (852) 26903637
Sales Range: $25-49.9 Million
Emp.: 30
Warehouse Operating Services
N.A.I.C.S.: 493110
Jackson Yam *(Mgr)*

Ho Chai Kung Medicine Manufactory Limited (1)
Flat A2 8/F Block A Texaco Road Industrial Centre 256-264 Texaco Road, Tsuen Wan, NT, China (Hong Kong)
Tel.: (852) 2 408 6373
Web Site: https://www.hochaikung.com.hk
Pharmaceutical Product Mfr & Distr
N.A.I.C.S.: 325412

Jacobson Medical (Hong Kong) Limited (1)

JACOBSON PHARMA CORPORATION LIMITED

Jacobson Pharma Corporation Limited—(Continued)

15/F China Trade Center 122-124 Wai Yip Street, Kwun Tong, Kowloon, China (Hong Kong)
Tel.: (852) 28271616
Pharmaceutical Products Distr
N.A.I.C.S.: 424210

Jean-Marie Pharmacal Company Limited **(1)**
12 Dai Fu Street 1/F Tai Po Industrial Estate, Tai Po, New Territories, China (Hong Kong)
Tel.: (852) 24088356
Web Site: https://www.jmp.com.hk
Emp.: 160
Pharmaceutical Product Mfr & Distr
N.A.I.C.S.: 325412

Jetstar Company Limited **(1)**
Rm A 16/F Marvel Indl Bldg Blk A, Kwai Chung, China (Hong Kong)
Tel.: (852) 24227700
Pharmaceutical Product Mfr & Distr
N.A.I.C.S.: 325412

Karen Pharmaceutical Company Limited **(1)**
17/F Success Industrial Bldg, Tuen Mun, China (Hong Kong)
Tel.: (852) 24073695
Pharmaceutical Product Mfr & Distr
N.A.I.C.S.: 325412

Li Chung Shing Tong (Holdings) Limited **(1)**
2 and 3/F Flat C and D 4/F Complex I, Tai Po, China (Hong Kong)
Tel.: (852) 25643536
Pharmaceutical Product Mfr & Distr
N.A.I.C.S.: 325412

Li Chung Shing Tong (S) Pte Limited **(1)**
8 Marina Boulevard, Singapore, 018981, Singapore
Tel.: (65) 62744887
Pharmaceutical Products Distr
N.A.I.C.S.: 424210

Marching Pharmaceutical Limited **(1)**
Rm 5-6 9/F Vigor Indl Bldg Blk B, Tsing Yi, China (Hong Kong)
Tel.: (852) 24326993
Pharmaceutical Product Mfr & Distr
N.A.I.C.S.: 325412

Neochem Pharmaceutical Laboratories Limited **(1)**
12 Kut Shing St 1/F, Decca Industrial Centre, Chai Wan, China (Hong Kong)
Tel.: (852) 25562922
Pharmaceutical Product Mfr & Distr
N.A.I.C.S.: 325412

Vickmans Laboratories Limited **(1)**
2/F China Trade Centre No 122-124 Wai Yip Street, Kwun Tong, China (Hong Kong)
Tel.: (852) 27260302
Web Site: http://www.vickmans.com
Pharmaceutical Product Mfr & Distr
N.A.I.C.S.: 325412

Vincents Pharma Trading Company Limited **(1)**
Rm 7 12/F Hang Wai Indl Ctr Blk C, Tuen Mun, China (Hong Kong)
Tel.: (852) 24938177
Pharmaceutical Products Distr
N.A.I.C.S.: 424210

JACQUES BOGART SA

13 rue Pierre Leroux, 75007, Paris, France
Tel.: (33) 153775555 **FR**
Web Site: https://www.groupe-bogart.com
Year Founded: 1975
JBOG—(EUR)
Sales Range: $250-299.9 Million
Cosmetic Product Mfr & Distr
N.A.I.C.S.: 456120

JACQUES GEORGES DURAND INDUSTRIES, S.A.

41 Avenue du General De Gaulle, Arques, 62510, France
Tel.: (33) 321930000
Sales Range: $1-4.9 Billion
Emp.: 4,500
Holding Company
N.A.I.C.S.: 551112

Subsidiaries:

ARC International SA **(1)**
41 avenue du General De Gaulle, F-62510, Arques, France
Tel.: (33) 321930000
Web Site: http://www.arc-international.com
Sales Range: $1-4.9 Billion
Glassware & Crystal Mfr, Distr & Retailer
N.A.I.C.S.: 327215
Patrick Gournay (Chm-Mgmt Bd & CEO)

Division (US):

ARC International North America Inc. **(2)**
901 S Wade Blvd, Millville, NJ 08332
Tel.: (856) 825-5620
Web Site: http://www.arc-intl.com
Holding Company; Glass & Crystal Ware Mfr & Distr
N.A.I.C.S.: 551112
William Calvert (Controller)

Subsidiary (Domestic):

Durand Glass Manufacturing Co. **(3)**
901 S Wade Blvd, Millville, NJ 08332
Tel.: (856) 327-4800
Web Site: http://www.arc-intl.com
Sales Range: $300-349.9 Million
Emp.: 1,000
Glassware Mfr & Distr
N.A.I.C.S.: 327212
William Calvert (Controller)

JACQUET METAL SERVICE SA

7 rue Michel Jacquet, CS 40087, F-69802, Saint Priest, Cedex, France
Tel.: (33) 472232350 **FR**
Web Site:
https://www.jacquetmetals.com
JCQ—(EUR)
Rev: $2,896,048,996
Assets: $1,855,339,953
Liabilities: $1,126,980,358
Net Worth: $728,359,594
Earnings: $193,870,063
Emp.: 3,060
Fiscal Year-end: 12/31/22
Steel Products & Stainless Steel Products Distr
N.A.I.C.S.: 423510
Eric Jacquet (Chm & CEO)

Subsidiaries:

Abraservice Belgium SA **(1)**
Rue du Parc Industriel 5, 4480, Engis, Belgium
Tel.: (32) 42758250
Stainless Steel Mfr
N.A.I.C.S.: 331110
Alexandre Ferreira Marum (Gen Mgr)

Abraservice Czech S.r.o. **(1)**
Otmarov 57, Otmarov, 66457, Brno, Czech Republic
Tel.: (420) 544423930
Stainless Steel Mfr
N.A.I.C.S.: 331110

Abraservice Portugal Lda **(1)**
Rua da Zona Industrial n 105 Lote D, VILA MAIOR, 4525-540, Santa Maria da Feira, Portugal
Tel.: (351) 256026014
Stainless Steel Mfr
N.A.I.C.S.: 331110

Aceros IMS Int., S.A. **(1)**
Barrio Astola 7, 48220, Abadiano, Vizcaya, Spain
Tel.: (34) 946204000
Web Site: http://www.acerosims.com
Engineering & Abrasion-Resistant Steel Products Distr
N.A.I.C.S.: 423510

Subsidiary (Non-US):

IMS Portugal SA **(2)**
Edificio IMS - Rua da Tapada Nova Capa Rota Linho, Capa Rota Linho Sintra, Sintra, 2710-297, Portugal **(100%)**
Tel.: (351) 219109910
Web Site: http://www.imsportugal.com
Sales Range: $25-49.9 Million
Emp.: 50
Distr of Engineering & Corrosion-Resistant Steel Products
N.A.I.C.S.: 423510

CL Staal b.v. **(1)**
Stationsplein 4 N, 3331 LL, Zwijndrecht, Netherlands **(100%)**
Tel.: (31) 786117150
Web Site: http://www.clstaal.nl
Sales Range: $25-49.9 Million
Emp.: 9
Distr of Corrosion & Abrasion Resistant Steel Products
N.A.I.C.S.: 423510
J. J. M. Sassen (Gen Mgr)

Detail Inox SAS **(1)**
553 route des Gorges du Sierroz - ZI, 73100, Gresy-sur-Aix, France
Tel.: (33) 479885000
Web Site: https://www.detail-inox.fr
Stainless Steel Mfr
N.A.I.C.S.: 331110
Raphaelle Alberti (Mgr)

Finkenholl Stahl Service Center GmbH **(1)**
Bahnstrasse 38, 44793, Bochum, Germany
Tel.: (49) 2343340
Web Site: https://www.finkenholl-stahl.de
Stainless Steel Mfr
N.A.I.C.S.: 331110

France Inox SAS **(1)**
1901 route de Maremne, Sausbosse, 40180, Saint-Paul-les-Dax, France
Tel.: (33) 558564456
Web Site: https://www.francinox.com
Stainless Steel Mfr
N.A.I.C.S.: 331110

Gunther Schramm GmbH **(1)**
Heidenheimer Str 65, 73447, Oberkochen, Germany
Tel.: (49) 7364240
Web Site: https://www.gs-stahl.de
Stainless Steel Mfr
N.A.I.C.S.: 331110

IMS Austria GmbH **(1)**
Industriestrasse 3, Inzersdorf, 4565, Vienna, Austria
Tel.: (43) 1725500
Web Site: https://www.ims-austria.com
Stainless Steel Mfr
N.A.I.C.S.: 331110
Herbert Zraunig (CEO)

IMS Belgium s.a./n.v. **(1)**
Oudemanstraat 17, 1840, Londerzeel, Belgium
Tel.: (32) 52307100
Web Site: https://www.ims-belgium.biz
Sales Range: $25-49.9 Million
Emp.: 40
Steel Product Distr
N.A.I.C.S.: 423510

IMS France SAS **(1)**
ZI Chemin du Jacloret, 95820, Bruyeres-Sur-Oise, France
Tel.: (33) 130283200
Web Site: https://www.imsfrance.com
Emp.: 200
Special Engineering, Abrasion & Corrosion Resistant Steels Distr
N.A.I.C.S.: 423510

Subsidiary (Domestic):

Calibracier SAS **(2)**
ZI des Forges -Route de Foecy, 18100, Vierzon, France **(100%)**
Tel.: (33) 248530170
Web Site: https://calibracier.com
Precision Straightening of Special Steels
N.A.I.C.S.: 423510

Eurallliage SAS **(2)**
19 rue Maurice Petit, BP 7031, 69360, Serezin-du-Rhone, Cedex, France **(100%)**

INTERNATIONAL PUBLIC

Tel.: (33) 472730054
Web Site: https://www.euralliage.com
Steel Product Distr
N.A.I.C.S.: 423510

Produr SAS **(2)**
153 Rue Aristide Berges, PO Box 29402, 73094, Chambery, Cedex, France **(100%)**
Tel.: (33) 479620673
Web Site: http://www.wa-produr.com
Steel Product Distr
N.A.I.C.S.: 423510

IMS Nederland BV **(1)**
Gildenweg 21, 3334 KC, Zwijndrecht, Netherlands
Tel.: (31) 786230600
Web Site: https://www.ims-nederland.biz
Stainless Steel Mfr
N.A.I.C.S.: 331110

IMS Rhein-Main GmbH **(1)**
Otto-Hahn-Strasse 10, 35501, Butzbach, Germany
Tel.: (49) 603374500
Web Site: http://www.ims-rhein-main.de
Stainless Steel Mfr
N.A.I.C.S.: 331110
Klaus Scheu (Mng Dir)

IMS SpA **(1)**
Via A Polini 450, 20862, Arcore, MB, Italy
Tel.: (39) 03961831
Web Site: https://www.ims.it
Emp.: 150
Engineering, Corrosion/Abrasion-Resistant, Steel Products Distr
N.A.I.C.S.: 423510

Subsidiary (Non-US):

IMS Ozel Celik Ticaret Ltd Sirketi **(2)**
GEPOSB 13 Cad No 3, Gebze, 41400, Kocaeli, Turkiye **(100%)**
Tel.: (90) 2626580440
Web Site: http://www.imscelik.com.tr
Distr of Structural & Engineering Steels, Abrasion Resistant Steels, Tool Steels, Tubes & Chromed Bars
N.A.I.C.S.: 423510

IMS UK Limited **(1)**
Arley Road, Saltley, Birmingham, B8 1BB, United Kingdom
Tel.: (44) 1213263100
Web Site: http://www.abraservice.com
Sales Range: $25-49.9 Million
Emp.: 17
Special Steel Trading
N.A.I.C.S.: 423510

International Metal Service Nord GmbH **(1)**
Eupener Strasse 70, 40472, Dusseldorf, Germany
Tel.: (49) 2115092000
Web Site: https://imetals.de
Emp.: 425
Stainless Steel Mfr
N.A.I.C.S.: 331110
Torsten Moller (Mng Dir)

International Metal Service Trade GmbH **(1)**
Eupener Strasse 70, 40472, Dusseldorf, Germany
Tel.: (49) 2115092000
Web Site: http://www.ims-trade.com
Stainless Steel Mfr
N.A.I.C.S.: 331110
Martin Kasnitz (Mng Dir)

Intra Metals BV **(1)**
Pedro de Medinalaan 65, 1086 XP, Amsterdam, Netherlands
Tel.: (31) 202380376
Web Site: https://www.intrametals.com
Stainless Steel Mfr
N.A.I.C.S.: 331110
Daphne Helmstrijd (Mng Dir)

JACQUET Benelux SA **(1)**
Z I des Hauts Sarts Rue de l'Abbaye 85, 4040, Herstal, Liege, Belgium **(100%)**
Tel.: (32) 42400990
Web Site: https://benelux.myjacquet.com
Sales Range: $25-49.9 Million
Stainless Steel & Nickel Alloy Mfr
N.A.I.C.S.: 331110

JACQUET Deutschland GmbH **(1)**

AND PRIVATE COMPANIES

JACQUET METAL SERVICE SA

Karl-Winnacker-Str 22, 36396, Steinau, Germany
Tel.: (49) 6663911120
Web Site:
    https://deutschland.myjacquet.com
Emp.: 20
Stainless Steel & Nickel Alloy Mfr & Distr
N.A.I.C.S.: 331110
Eric Jacquet *(Mng Dir)*

JACQUET Finland Oy (1)
Kaapelikatu 1, FI 05800, Hyvinkaa, Finland **(78.95%)**
Tel.: (358) 192121200
Sales Range: $25-49.9 Million
Emp.: 20
Steel Product Distr
N.A.I.C.S.: 423510
Ilkka Jauhiainen *(Mng Dir)*

JACQUET Iberica S.A. (1)
Pol Ind Valdemuel Aptdo 31, Epila, 50290, Zaragoza, Spain **(70%)**
Tel.: (34) 976817645
Web Site: https://iberica.myjacquet.com
Steel Product Distr
N.A.I.C.S.: 423510

JACQUET Italtaglio Srl (1)
Via Astico 1, 36010, Carre, VI, Italy **(85%)**
Tel.: (39) 0445315154
Web Site: https://italtaglio.myjacquet.com
Steel Products Whslr
N.A.I.C.S.: 423510

JACQUET Lyon SASU (1)
ZA de Grammont 9 rue Garibaldi, 69800, Saint-Priest-en-Jarez, Cedex, France
Tel.: (33) 478210040
Web Site: https://lyon.myjacquet.com
Sales Range: $50-74.9 Million
Steel Product Distr
N.A.I.C.S.: 423510

JACQUET Metallservice GmbH (1)
Kleinreith Gewerbepark 8, Ohlsdorf, 4694, Gmunden, Austria **(75%)**
Tel.: (43) 7612714460
Web Site:
    https://metallservice.myjacquet.com
Sales Range: $25-49.9 Million
Steel Product Distr
N.A.I.C.S.: 423510
Jean-Luc Vogt *(Mng Dir)*

JACQUET Mid Atlantic Inc. (1)
500 Keystone Blvd, Limerick, PA 19468 **(75%)**
Tel.: (484) 945-1075
Web Site: http://www.myjacquet.com
Sales Range: $25-49.9 Million
Emp.: 20
Stainless Steel & Nickel Alloy Mfr & Distr
N.A.I.C.S.: 331110

Subsidiary (Domestic):

JACQUET Houston Inc. (2)
6707 Willowbrook Park, Houston, TX 77066 **(80%)**
Tel.: (281) 397-9920
Web Site: http://www.myjacquet.com
Sales Range: $25-49.9 Million
Emp.: 11
Stainless Steel & Nickel Alloy Distr
N.A.I.C.S.: 331110

JACQUET Midwest Inc. (2)
1908 DeKoven Ave, Racine, WI 53403 **(95%)**
Tel.: (262) 898-1381
Web Site: http://www.myjacquet.com
Sales Range: $25-49.9 Million
Emp.: 12
Stainless Steel & Nickel Alloy Mfr & Distr
N.A.I.C.S.: 331110
Linda Hanson *(Office Mgr)*

JACQUET Southeast Inc. (2)
11301 Downs Rd, Pineville, NC 28134 **(80%)**
Tel.: (704) 588-3778
Web Site: http://www.myjacquet.com
Sales Range: $25-49.9 Million
Emp.: 6
Metals Service Center
N.A.I.C.S.: 423510

JACQUET West Inc. (2)
22400 Lucerne St, Carson, CA 90745 **(80%)**
Tel.: (310) 684-4370
Web Site: http://www.myjacquet.com
Sales Range: $25-49.9 Million
Emp.: 9
Stainless Steel & Nickel Alloy Distr
N.A.I.C.S.: 331110

JACQUET Nordpol Sp. z o.o. (1)
ul Zalogowa 6, PL 80 557, Gdansk, Poland **(90%)**
Tel.: (48) 585220066
Sales Range: $50-74.9 Million
Emp.: 3
Steel Product Distr
N.A.I.C.S.: 423510
Andrzej Zastawny *(Mgr)*

JACQUET Osiro AG (1)
Industriestrasse 105, 4147, Aesch, Basel-Land, Switzerland **(51%)**
Tel.: (41) 617568989
Web Site: https://osiro.myjacquet.com
Sales Range: $25-49.9 Million
Emp.: 10
Stainless Steel & Nickel Alloy Distr
N.A.I.C.S.: 331110

JACQUET Portugal Lda (1)
Alameda D Pedro V n24 4 Esq Frt, PT 4400 115, Vila Nova de Gaia, Portugal **(51%)**
Tel.: (351) 223743595
Sales Range: $50-74.9 Million
Emp.: 5
Steel Product Distr
N.A.I.C.S.: 423510
Jose Alberto *(Gen Mgr)*

JACQUET Sverige AB (1)
Sveavagen 33, 544 50, Hjo, Sweden **(100%)**
Tel.: (46) 50312030
Web Site: https://sverige.myjacquet.com
Sales Range: $25-49.9 Million
Steel Product Distr
N.A.I.C.S.: 423510

JACQUET UK Ltd (1)
Rockingham House, Wentworth Park Industrial Estate Wentworth Way Tankersley, Barnsley, S75 3DH, United Kingdom **(76%)**
Tel.: (44) 1226745000
Web Site: http://uk.myjacquet.com
Sales Range: $25-49.9 Million
Steel Product Distr
N.A.I.C.S.: 423510

JACQUET s.r.o. (1)
CP 57, Bechovice, 664 57, Prague, Czech Republic **(80%)**
Tel.: (420) 544423950
Web Site: https://sro.myjacquet.com
Sales Range: $50-74.9 Million
Emp.: 4
Steel Product Distr
N.A.I.C.S.: 423510
Ivan Burda *(Mng Dir)*

JMS Adriatic d.o.o. (1)
Cesta Borisa Kidrica 41C, 4270, Jesenice, Slovenia
Tel.: (386) 45809320
Web Site:
    http://www.jmsnetworkformetals.com
Stainless Steel Mfr
N.A.I.C.S.: 331110
Sebastian Mohar *(Mng Dir)*

JMS Danmark ApS (1)
Lindvedvej 71, 5260, Odense, Denmark
Tel.: (45) 61194036
Web Site: https://jmsdanmark.dk
Stainless Steel Mfr
N.A.I.C.S.: 331110
Bent Edal Pedersen *(Mgr)*

JMS Metals Asia Pte. Ltd. (1)
51 Goldhill Plaza 21-02/05, Singapore, 308900, Singapore
Tel.: (65) 91091909
Stainless Steel Mfr
N.A.I.C.S.: 331110

Jacquet International SAS (1)
7 rue Michel Jacquet, CS 40087, 69802, Saint Priest, Cedex, France
Tel.: (33) 472232327

Web Site:
    https://international.myjacquet.com
Stainless Steel Mfr
N.A.I.C.S.: 331110

Jacquet Montreal Inc. (1)
89 rue Morane, Laval, H7M 1R6, QC, Canada
Tel.: (514) 631-6833
Web Site: http://montreal.myjacquet.com
Stainless Steel Mfr
N.A.I.C.S.: 331110
Victoria Stamper *(Branch Mgr)*

Jacquet Nederland BV (1)
Volume 119B, 1446 WH, Purmerend, Netherlands
Tel.: (31) 299479879
Web Site: https://nederland.myjacquet.com
Stainless Steel Mfr
N.A.I.C.S.: 331110
Ron Kras *(Mng Dir)*

Jacquet Nova SR (1)
Via Giovanni Pascoli 1/C, Basiano, 20060, Cambiago, MI, Italy
Tel.: (39) 0249751687
Web Site: https://nova.myjacquet.com
Stainless Steel Mfr
N.A.I.C.S.: 331110
Michele La Piscopia *(Mgr-Comml)*

Jacquet Paris SAS (1)
ZI Les Carreaux 1 Ancien Chemin de Reims, 77440, Lizy-sur-Ourcq, France
Tel.: (33) 160017580
Web Site: https://paris.myjacquet.com
Stainless Steel Mfr
N.A.I.C.S.: 331110

Jacquet Polska Sp z o.o. (1)
Ul Karola Miarki 36, 41-400, Myslowice, Poland
Tel.: (48) 322221553
Web Site: https://jacquet.pl
Stainless Steel Mfr
N.A.I.C.S.: 331110

Jacquet Shanghai Co. Ltd. (1)
No 6688 East Yinggang Road, Qingpu Industrial Zone, Shanghai, China
Tel.: (86) 2159757755
Stainless Steel Mfr
N.A.I.C.S.: 331110

Noxon Stainless B.V. (1)
Vossenbeemd 51, 5705 CL, Helmond, Netherlands **(100%)**
Tel.: (31) 492582111
Web Site: http://www.noxon.nl
Emp.: 90
Distr of Stainless Steel Pipes, Tubes, Valves, Bars, Sheets, Profiles & Plates
N.A.I.C.S.: 423510
Coen Van Lieshout *(Mgr-Sls)*

Rolark Edmonton Inc. (1)
6704-59 Street NW, Edmonton, T6B 3N6, AB, Canada
Tel.: (780) 989-1183
Stainless Steel Mfr
N.A.I.C.S.: 331110
Rad Matjevic *(CEO & Gen Mgr)*

STAPPERT Deutschland GmbH (1)
Willstatterstrasse 13, 40549, Dusseldorf, Germany
Tel.: (49) 21152790
Web Site: http://deutschland.stappert.biz
Stainless Steel Mfr
N.A.I.C.S.: 331110
Jens Munchow *(Mng Dir)*

STAPPERT France SAS (1)
13 rue Charlemagne, 02200, Soissons, France
Tel.: (33) 323735000
Web Site: https://france.stappert.biz
Stainless Steel Mfr
N.A.I.C.S.: 331110
Luc Thonnat *(Mng Dir)*

STAPPERT Intramet SA (1)
5 Rue du Parc Industriel, 4480, Engis, Belgium
Tel.: (32) 42758211
Web Site: https://intramet.stappert.biz
Stainless Steel Mfr
N.A.I.C.S.: 331110

STAPPERT Magyarorszag Kft (1)
Retifarkas utca 1, 1172, Budapest, Hungary
Tel.: (36) 614342424
Web Site: https://magyarorszag.stappert.biz
Stainless Steel Mfr
N.A.I.C.S.: 331110
Zoltan Cseke *(Mgr-Quality)*

STAPPERT Noxon BV (1)
Gerstdijk 4, 5704 RG, Helmond, Netherlands
Tel.: (31) 492582111
Web Site: http://www.noxon.stappert.biz
Stainless Steel Mfr
N.A.I.C.S.: 331110
Mark Dankers *(Mng Dir)*

STAPPERT Sverige AB (1)
Gamla Slatthultsvagen 3, 343 34, Almhult, Sweden
Tel.: (46) 47648550
Web Site: https://sverige.stappert.biz
Stainless Steel Mfr
N.A.I.C.S.: 331110
Fredrik Wallman *(Sls Mgr)*

STAPPERT UK Ltd. (1)
Unit 7 Severnbridge Industrial Estate, Caldicot, Newport, NP26 5PW, United Kingdom
Tel.: (44) 1217400175
Web Site: https://uk.stappert.biz
Stainless Steel Mfr
N.A.I.C.S.: 331110
Keith Bonnington *(Mng Dir)*

Stappert Deutschland GmbH (1)
Willstatterstrasse 13, 40549, Dusseldorf, Germany
Tel.: (49) 21152790
Web Site: http://www.stappert.de
Sales Range: $150-199.9 Million
Emp.: 80
Steel Products Processing & Sales
N.A.I.C.S.: 423510
Wolfgang Hartmann *(Mng Dir)*

Subsidiary (Non-US):

Fleischmann Spezialstahl-Handel GmbH (2)
Gewerbepark B17/I/Objekt 1, 2524, Teesdorf, Austria **(100%)**
Tel.: (43) 2253903130
Web Site: http://www.fls.at
Sales Range: $25-49.9 Million
Emp.: 63
Corrosion Resistant Steel Products Distr
N.A.I.C.S.: 423510
Harald Ebenberger *(Mng Dir)*

Subsidiary (Domestic):

Hoselmann Stahl GmbH (2)
Ludwig-Barnay-Strasse 8, 30175, Hannover, Germany **(100%)**
Tel.: (49) 511280410
Web Site: http://www.hoselmann.de
Distr of Engineering Steels
N.A.I.C.S.: 423510
Andreas Lippmann *(Mng Dir)*

Subsidiary (Non-US):

Rev es Tarsai Nemesacel Kereskedelmi Kft. (2)
Retifarkas utca 1, Budapest, 1172, Hungary **(100%)**
Tel.: (36) 14342424
Web Site: http://www.stappert.de
Sales Range: $25-49.9 Million
Emp.: 55
Corrosion & Abrasion-Resistant Steel Products
N.A.I.C.S.: 423510

STAPPERT Ceska republika spol. s r.o. (2)
Otmarov 57, 664 57, Menin, Czech Republic
Tel.: (420) 544423911
Web Site: https://cz.stappert.biz
Corrosion Resistant Steel Products Distr
N.A.I.C.S.: 423510
Jaroslav Komarek *(Branch Mgr)*

STAPPERT Polska Sp. Z o.o. (2)
ul A Gaudiego 18, 44-109, Gliwice, Poland **(100%)**
Tel.: (48) 323447300
Web Site: https://polska.stappert.biz

JACQUET METAL SERVICE SA

Jacquet Metal Service SA—(Continued)
Corrosion-Resistant & Abrasion-Resistant Steel Products Distr
N.A.I.C.S.: 423510

Speciastal AB (2)
Statthultsvagen 3, Box 82, S 343 21, Almhult, Sweden (100%)
Tel.: (46) 47548550
Web Site: http://www.specialstal.se
Distr of Corrosion Resistant Steel Products
N.A.I.C.S.: 423510

Stappert Slovensko A.s. (2)
Simonovska 37, 971 71, Novaky, Slovakia
Tel.: (421) 465183420
Web Site: https://slovensko.stappert.biz
Corrosion Resistant Steel Products Distr
N.A.I.C.S.: 423510

UAB Stappert Lietuva (2)
R Kalantos g 49B, Kaunas, LT 52303, Lithuania (100%)
Tel.: (370) 37473509
Web Site: http://www.stappert.biz
Sales Range: $25-49.9 Million
Emp.: 15
Steel Product Distr
N.A.I.C.S.: 331513

Trinox SA (1)
Z I en Vannel, 1880, Bex, Switzerland
Tel.: (41) 244631209
Web Site: http://www.trinox.ch
Sales Range: $50-74.9 Million
Emp.: 5
Steel Product Distr
N.A.I.C.S.: 423510

JACS UK LTD.
Unit 16 Hercules Way, Bowerhill Ind Est, Melksham, SN12 6TS, Wiltshire, United Kingdom
Tel.: (44) 1225 700 202
Web Site: http://www.jacsuk.com
Year Founded: 2000
Sales Range: $50-74.9 Million
Emp.: 7
Recycled Plastic Products Distr
N.A.I.C.S.: 424610
Jeff Payne *(Partner & Mng Dir)*

JADAR A.D.
Tpr Byka Kapaunha 66, 15300, Loznica, Serbia
Tel.: (381) 15 877 111
Web Site: http://www.jadar.rs
Year Founded: 1946
Sales Range: Less than $1 Million
Emp.: 39
Grocery Store Operator
N.A.I.C.S.: 445110

JADASON ENTERPRISES LTD
No 3 Kaki Bukit Crescent 03-01, Singapore, 416237, Singapore
Tel.: (65) 63831800 SG
Web Site: https://www.jadason.com
Year Founded: 1980
J03—(SES)
Rev.: $16,605,317
Assets: $16,166,023
Liabilities: $12,876,619
Net Worth: $3,289,404
Earnings: ($6,038,022)
Emp.: 86
Fiscal Year-end: 12/31/23
Industrial Machinery Distr
N.A.I.C.S.: 423830
Chi Wai Fung *(CEO)*

Subsidiaries:

Jadason Enterprises (HK) Limited (1)
Block A 3/F Hop Hing Industrial Building No 702 Castle Peak Road, Kowloon, China (Hong Kong)
Tel.: (852) 27421771
Web Site: https://www.jadason.com
Industrial Machinery Distr
N.A.I.C.S.: 423830

Jadason Enterprises (Japan) Limited (1)
Takenaka Charme-602 3-1-3, Asakusabashi Taito-ku, Tokyo, 111-0053, Japan
Tel.: (81) 368264880
Industrial Machinery Distr
N.A.I.C.S.: 423830

Jadason Enterprises (Thailand) Limited (1)
184/1 Forum Tower Building Ground Floor Ratchadapisek Road, Huikwang, Bangkok, 10320, Thailand
Tel.: (66) 26452229
Industrial Machinery Distr
N.A.I.C.S.: 423830

JADAWEL INTERNATIONAL COMPANY LIMITED
PO Box 61539, Riyadh, 11575, Saudi Arabia
Tel.: (966) 4631760
Web Site: http://www.jadawelinternational.com
Year Founded: 1984
Sales Range: $400-449.9 Million
Emp.: 1,200
Residential Community Developer & Operator
N.A.I.C.S.: 531311
Sheikh Mohammed Issa Alljadar *(Pres)*

JADE ART GROUP INC.
35 Baita Zhong Road, Yujiang, 335200, Jiangxi, China
Tel.: (86) 6462006328 NV
JADA—(OTCIQ)
Sales Range: $25-49.9 Million
Emp.: 35
Wood Carving Services
N.A.I.C.S.: 321999
Hua-Cai Song *(CEO)*

JADE BIRD FIRE CO., LTD.
Beida Qingniao Building No 207 Chengfu Road, Haidian, Beijing, 100871, China
Tel.: (86) 1062758875
Web Site: http://www.jbufa.com
Year Founded: 2001
002960—(SSE)
Rev.: $646,172,748
Assets: $1,131,315,120
Liabilities: $289,605,888
Net Worth: $841,709,232
Earnings: $79,976,052
Fiscal Year-end: 12/31/22
Fire Safety System Installation Services
N.A.I.C.S.: 238210
Weimin Cai *(Chm)*

Subsidiaries:

Jade Bird Fire Alarm International (Europe) S.L. (1)
Carrer de Tarragona 157, 08014, Barcelona, Spain
Tel.: (34) 936403414
Security System Services
N.A.I.C.S.: 561621

MPower Electronics, Inc. (1)
3046 Scott Blvd, Santa Clara, CA 95054
Tel.: (408) 320-1266
Gas Detector Mfr
N.A.I.C.S.: 334519
Hong T. Sun *(Pres)*

JADE LEADER CORP.
Suite 1620 734 - 7th Avenue SW, Calgary, T2P 3E8, AB, Canada
Tel.: (403) 233-0464 AB
Web Site: https://jadeleader.com
Year Founded: 1995
MCKRF—(OTCIQ)
Rev.: $1,266
Assets: $1,172,129
Liabilities: $269,108
Net Worth: $903,021
Earnings: ($309,072)
Fiscal Year-end: 09/30/23
Copper & Gold Exploration Services
N.A.I.C.S.: 212230
Jean Pierre Jutras *(Pres)*

JADE MARVEL GROUP BERHAD
Unit 31-16-3 Lebuh Nipah 5, Bayan Lepas, 11950, Penang, Malaysia
Tel.: (60) 46046899
Web Site: https://xinsynergy.com.my
XIN—(KLS)
Rev.: $14,938,073
Assets: $46,102,482
Liabilities: $5,497,050
Net Worth: $40,605,431
Earnings: ($2,326,040)
Emp.: 25
Fiscal Year-end: 03/31/24
Asphalt Mixes Mfr
N.A.I.C.S.: 423320
Yong Chee Goh *(Exec Dir)*

JADE MOUNTAIN ACQUISITION CORP.
5/F-4 No. 89 Songren Road, Xinyi District, Taipei, Taiwan
Tel.: (886) 2 7713 7952
Year Founded: 2021
JMACU—(NASDAQ)
Investment Services
N.A.I.C.S.: 523999
Hong-Jung Chen *(Chm & CEO)*

JADE POWER TRUST
100 Adelaide Street West Suite 301, Toronto, M5H 4H1, ON, Canada
Tel.: (416) 342-1091
Web Site: https://www.jadepower.com
JPWR.UN—(TSXV)
Assets: $3,095,524
Liabilities: $839,557
Net Worth: $2,255,967
Earnings: ($517,007)
Fiscal Year-end: 12/31/23
Investment Management Service
N.A.I.C.S.: 525990

JADE ROAD INVESTMENTS LIMITED
29/F Infinitus Plaza 199 Des Voeux Road, Central, China (Hong Kong)
Tel.: (852) 37963503 VG
Web Site: http://jaderoadinvestments.com
1CP0—(DEU)
Rev.: $2,833,000
Assets: $20,317,000
Liabilities: $5,193,000
Net Worth: $15,124,000
Earnings: ($52,904,000)
Fiscal Year-end: 12/31/22
Investment Services
N.A.I.C.S.: 523999

JADESTONE ENERGY PLC
3 Anson Road 13-01 Springleaf Tower, Singapore, 079909, Singapore
Tel.: (65) 63240359 UK
Web Site: https://www.jadestone-energy.com
Year Founded: 2021
JSE—(AIM)
Holding Company; Oil & Natural Gas Extraction
N.A.I.C.S.: 551112
Bert-Jaap Dijkstra *(CFO & Exec Dir)*

Subsidiaries:

Jadestone Energy (Australia) Pty. Ltd. (1)
The Atrium Building Level 2 168 St Georges Terrace, PO Box 5388, Perth, 6000, WA, Australia
Tel.: (61) 894866600
Oil & Gas Exploration Services
N.A.I.C.S.: 213112

Jadestone Energy (Singapore) Pte. Ltd. (1)
3 Anson Road 13-01 Springleaf Tower, Singapore, 079909, Singapore
Tel.: (65) 63240359
Oil & Gas Exploration Services
N.A.I.C.S.: 213112

Jadestone Energy Inc. (1)
3 Anson Road No 13-01 Springleaf Tower, Singapore, 079909, Singapore
Tel.: (65) 63240359
Web Site: https://www.jadestone-energy.com
Rev.: $217,938,000
Assets: $609,714,000
Liabilities: $449,072,000
Net Worth: $160,642,000
Earnings: ($60,908,000)
Fiscal Year-end: 12/31/2020
Holding Company; Oil & Gas Exploration Services
N.A.I.C.S.: 551112
Bert-Jaap Dijkstra *(CFO)*

Jadestone Energy Sdn. Bhd. (1)
Suite 13 5 Level 13 Menara IMC No 8 Jalan Sultan Ismail, 50250, Kuala Lumpur, Malaysia
Tel.: (60) 320225600
Oil & Gas Exploration Services
N.A.I.C.S.: 213112

JADI IMAGING HOLDINGS BERHAD
No 1 Jalan Peguam U1/25A Seksyen U1 Hicom-Glenmarie Industrial Park, 40150, Shah Alam, Selangor, Malaysia
Tel.: (60) 378040333
Web Site: https://www.jadi.com.my
JADI—(KLS)
Rev.: $10,657,417
Assets: $34,175,160
Liabilities: $7,911,130
Net Worth: $26,264,030
Earnings: ($1,946,727)
Fiscal Year-end: 03/31/22
Toner Mfr
N.A.I.C.S.: 325992
Poh Yen Lim *(Co-Sec)*

Subsidiaries:

Jadi Imaging Technologies Sdn. Bhd. (1)
No 1 Jalan Peguam U1/25A Seksyen U1 Hicom-Glenmarie Industrial Park, 40150, Shah Alam, Selangor, Malaysia
Tel.: (60) 378040333
Sales Range: $75-99.9 Million
Emp.: 220
Toners Mfr & Distr
N.A.I.C.S.: 325130

JADRAN A.D.
Kornetska 2, 11000, Belgrade, Serbia
Tel.: (381) 11 2781 333
Web Site: http://www.jadran-bg.rs
Civil Engineering Services
N.A.I.C.S.: 541330

JADRAN AD
ul Proleterska br 41, Nova Gajdobra, 21431, Serbia
Tel.: (381) 2 176 2883
Web Site: http://www.jadranad.com
Year Founded: 1989
JDNG—(BEL)
Sales Range: Less than $1 Million
Cereal Crop Farming Services
N.A.I.C.S.: 111998
Branko Zoric *(CEO)*

JADRAN D.D. CRIKVENIC
Bana Jelacica 16, 51260, Crikvenica, Croatia

Tel.: (385) 51800480
Web Site: https://www.jadran-crikvenica.hr
JDRN—(ZAG)
Rev.: $35,792,030
Assets: $153,229,937
Liabilities: $77,435,699
Net Worth: $75,794,238
Earnings: ($5,257,755)
Emp.: 293
Fiscal Year-end: 12/31/23
Hotels (except Casino Hotels) & Motels
N.A.I.C.S.: 721110

Subsidiaries:

Club Adriatic d.o.o. (1)
Kralja Petra Kresimira IV 11, Baska Voda, Dalmatia, Croatia
Tel.: (385) 51800480
Web Site: http://www.club-adriatic.hr
Tourism Services
N.A.I.C.S.: 561510
Miro Boric (Dir-Ops)

JADRAN GALENSKI LABORATORIJ D.D.
Svilno 20, 51000, Rijeka, Croatia
Tel.: (385) 51660700
Web Site: http://www.jgl.hr
Year Founded: 1991
3JDG2—(ZAG)
Rev.: $232,794,129
Assets: $302,110,626
Liabilities: $148,191,641
Net Worth: $153,918,984
Earnings: $21,616,595
Emp.: 1,254
Fiscal Year-end: 12/31/23
Drugs & Druggists' Sundries Merchant Wholesalers
N.A.I.C.S.: 424210
Ivo Usmiani (Pres)

JADRAN TVORNICA CARAPA D.D.
Vinka Zganeca 2, 10 040, Zagreb, Croatia
Tel.: (385) 12961400
Web Site: https://www.jadran-carapa.hr
Year Founded: 1930
JDTC—(ZAG)
Sales Range: Less than $1 Million
Women Hosiery Product Retailer
N.A.I.C.S.: 458110

JADRANSKA BANKA D.D. SIBENIK
Ante Starcevica 4, 22000, Sibenik, Croatia
Tel.: (385) 22242242
Web Site: http://www.jadranska-banka.hr
JDBA-R-A—(ZAG)
Sales Range: $25-49.9 Million
Emp.: 247
Banking & Financial Services
N.A.I.C.S.: 523150

JADRANSKI NAFTOVOD, JOINT STOCK COMPANY
Miramarska Cesta 24, 10000, Zagreb, Croatia
Tel.: (385) 13039999
Web Site: https://www.janaf.hr
Year Founded: 1974
JNAF—(ZAG)
Rev.: $169,255,989
Assets: $809,017,552
Liabilities: $34,195,827
Net Worth: $774,821,724
Earnings: $57,371,675
Emp.: 435
Fiscal Year-end: 12/31/23
Crude Oil Transportation Services
N.A.I.C.S.: 486110

Ivan Lucic (Dir-Economics & Fin Div)

JADRANSKO OSIGURANJE D.D.
Listopadska 2, 10 000, Zagreb, Croatia
Tel.: (385) 1 303 6666
Web Site: http://www.jadransko.hr
Year Founded: 1991
Insurance Management Services
N.A.I.C.S.: 524298
Sanja Coric (Chm)

JADROAGENT D.D.
Trg Ivana Koblera 2, POB 120, 51000, Rijeka, Croatia
Tel.: (385) 51780300
Web Site: https://www.jadroagent.hr
Year Founded: 1947
JDGT—(ZAG)
Sales Range: Less than $1 Million
Freight Forwarding Services
N.A.I.C.S.: 488510
Mario Stefanic (Gen Dir)

JADROPLOV LTD.
Obala kneza Branimira 16, 21000, Split, Hrvatska, Croatia
Tel.: (385) 21302690
Web Site: https://www.jadroplov.com
Year Founded: 1947
Emp.: 50
Ship Repairing Services
N.A.I.C.S.: 336611
Goran Matesic (Supervisory Bd of Dirs & Chm-Supervisory Bd)

JADWA INVESTMENT COMPANY
PO Box 60677, Riyadh, 11555, Saudi Arabia
Tel.: (966) 112791111
Web Site: http://www.jadwa.com
Year Founded: 2006
Privater Equity Firm
N.A.I.C.S.: 523999
Tariq Al Sudairy (CEO & Mng Dir)

Subsidiaries:

Saudi Mechanical Industries Co. (1)
Second Industrial City Street No 234, Riyadh, Saudi Arabia
Tel.: (966) 112651979
Web Site: http://www.smi.com.sa
Steel Works & Rolling Mills, Pumps & Pumping Equipment Mfr
N.A.I.C.S.: 333914
Ahmad A. Khraishi (COO)

JADWA REIT SAUDI FUND
Sky Towers 4th Floor king Fahad Road Olaya Area, PO Box 60677, Riyadh, 11555, Saudi Arabia
Tel.: (966) 112791111
Web Site: https://www.jadwa.com
4342—(SAU)
Rev.: $215,240,098
Assets: $578,619,814
Liabilities: $132,820,556
Net Worth: $445,799,258
Earnings: $133,424,387
Emp.: 116
Fiscal Year-end: 12/31/22
Real Estate Investment Services
N.A.I.C.S.: 531190

JAEGER LIMITED
2nd Floor The Lab 11 Evesham Street, London, W11 4AJ, United Kingdom
Tel.: (44) 1234567890   UK
Web Site: http://www.jaeger.co.uk
Year Founded: 2011
Holding Company; Men's & Women's Apparel Retailer
N.A.I.C.S.: 551112
Ken Pratt (CFO)

Subsidiaries:

The Jaeger Company's Shops Limited (1)
2nd Floor The Lab 11 Evesham Street, London, W11 4AJ, United Kingdom
Tel.: (44) 1234567890
Web Site: http://www.jaeger.co.uk
Men's & Women's Fashion Retailer
N.A.I.C.S.: 458110
Sheila McKain-Waid (Creative Dir)

JAEGER RESOURCES CORP.
9320 49th St NW, Edmonton, T6B 2L7, AB, Canada
Tel.: (780) 465-4129   Ca
Web Site: https://www.jaegerresources.com
Year Founded: 1993
JAEG—(TSXV)
Assets: $302,129
Liabilities: $395,400
Net Worth: ($93,271)
Earnings: ($93,443)
Fiscal Year-end: 11/30/22
Mineral Exploration Services
N.A.I.C.S.: 213114
Russel J. Renneberg (Chm)

Subsidiaries:

Nueva California S.A. (1)
Calle 12 30 356, Medellin, Colombia
Tel.: (57) 44482950
Gold Mining Services
N.A.I.C.S.: 212220

JAEREN SPAREBANK
Postboks 325, 4349, Bryne, Norway
Tel.: (47) 51779100
Web Site: http://www.jaerensparebank.no
JAEREN—(OSL)
Sales Range: Less than $1 Million
Banking Services
N.A.I.C.S.: 522110

JAEYOUNG SOLUTEC CO., LTD.
7-6 Songdo-dong, Yeonsu-gu, Incheon, 406-840, Korea (South)
Tel.: (82) 328500700
Web Site: https://www.jysolutec.com
Year Founded: 1984
049630—(KRS)
Rev.: $91,715,626
Assets: $154,463,881
Liabilities: $106,446,432
Net Worth: $48,017,448
Earnings: ($8,613,230)
Emp.: 107
Fiscal Year-end: 12/31/22
Photographic Equipment Mfr
N.A.I.C.S.: 333310
Hak Kwon Kim (CEO)

Subsidiaries:

Jaeyoung Solutec Co., Ltd. - Chiba Factory (1)
580-1 Ogi, Sanmu, 289-1211, Chiba, Japan
Tel.: (81) 434972244
Photographic & Photocopying Equipment Mfr
N.A.I.C.S.: 333310

JAFCO GROUP CO., LTD.
Toranomon Hills Mori Tower 24F 1-23-1 Toranomon, Minato-ku, Tokyo, 105-6324, Japan
Tel.: (81) 352237536   JP
Web Site: https://www.jafco.co.jp
Year Founded: 1973
8595—(TKS)
Rev.: $161,568,230
Assets: $1,094,219,400
Liabilities: $184,425,610
Net Worth: $909,793,790
Earnings: $49,535,340
Emp.: 159

Fiscal Year-end: 03/31/24
Equity Investment Firm
N.A.I.C.S.: 523999
Shinichi Fuki (Chm, Pres & CEO)

Subsidiaries:

JAFCO America Ventures Inc. (1)
505 Hamilton Ave Ste 310, Palo Alto, CA 94301
Tel.: (650) 463-8800
Web Site: http://www.iconventures.com
Sales Range: $50-74.9 Million
Emp.: 20
Equity Investment Firm
N.A.I.C.S.: 523999
Tsunesaburo Sugaya (Gen Partner & Head-Bus Dev)

JAFCO Investment (Korea) Co., Ltd. (1)
18/F Korea City Air Tower 159-9 Samseong-dong, Gangnam-gu, Seoul, 135-973, Korea (South)
Tel.: (82) 2 2016 6100
Emp.: 4
Investment Management Service
N.A.I.C.S.: 523940
Richard Joung (Gen Mgr)

JAFCO INVESTMENT (ASIA PACIFIC) LTD
10 Marine Boulevard #33-05 Marina Bay Financial Centre Tower 2, Singapore, 018983, Singapore
Tel.: (65) 62246383
Year Founded: 1990
Privater Equity Firm
N.A.I.C.S.: 523940
Jerry Cai (Mng Dir & Head-China)

JAFRON BIOMEDICAL CO., LTD.
No 98 Technology Six Road Hightech Zone, Zhuhai, 519085, China
Tel.: (86) 7563689708
Web Site: https://www.jafroninternational.com
Year Founded: 1989
300529—(CHIN)
Rev.: $349,798,176
Assets: $760,044,168
Liabilities: $255,944,988
Net Worth: $504,099,180
Earnings: $124,891,416
Emp.: 1,100
Fiscal Year-end: 12/31/22
Medical Equipment Mfr & Distr
N.A.I.C.S.: 339112
Dong Fan (Chm)

JAG BERHAD
D65-3A Block D Jaya One 72A Jalan Universiti, 46200, Petaling Jaya, Selangor Darul Ehsan, Malaysia
Tel.: (60) 374972558   MY
Web Site: https://www.jagb.com.my
Year Founded: 1997
JAG—(KLS)
Rev.: $53,776,235
Assets: $55,214,776
Liabilities: $10,150,784
Net Worth: $45,063,992
Earnings: $2,037,931
Fiscal Year-end: 12/31/22
Investment Holding Services
N.A.I.C.S.: 551112
Siew Ching Tan (Chm)

Subsidiaries:

Jaring Metal Industries Sdn. Bhd. (1)
No 7 9 Jalan Sungai Kayu Ara 32/37 Taman Perindustrian Berjaya, Seksyen 32, 40460, Shah Alam, Selangor Darul Ehsan, Malaysia
Tel.: (60) 357408823
Web Site: https://www.jaringmetal.com
Emp.: 150
Waste Management Services
N.A.I.C.S.: 562998

JAG BERHAD

JAG Berhad—(Continued)

Kok Kar Ng *(Founder)*

JAGAN LAMPS LIMITED
Narela Piao Manihari Road Kundli, Sonipat, 131028, Haryana, India
Tel.: (91) 8814805077
Web Site: https://www.jaganlamps.com
Year Founded: 1993
530711—(BOM)
Rev.: $5,714,741
Assets: $4,762,352
Liabilities: $1,485,834
Net Worth: $3,276,518
Earnings: $319,477
Emp.: 139
Fiscal Year-end: 03/31/23
Automotive Bulb Mfr & Whslr
N.A.I.C.S.: 335139
Ashish Aggarwal *(Chm & Mng Dir)*

JAGATJIT INDUSTRIES LIMITED
Jagatjit Nagar Hamira, Kapurthala, 144802, Punjab, India
Tel.: (91) 812783112
Web Site: https://www.jagatjit.com
Year Founded: 1944
507155—(BOM)
Rev.: $75,599,712
Assets: $60,883,608
Liabilities: $52,985,004
Net Worth: $7,898,604
Earnings: $865,368
Emp.: 1,563
Fiscal Year-end: 03/31/23
Alcoholic Beverages Mfr
N.A.I.C.S.: 325193
Ravi Manchanda *(Mng Dir)*

Subsidiaries:

Jagatjit Industries Limited - Plant I (1)
Jagatjit Nagar, Kapurthala, 144 802, Punjab, India
Tel.: (91) 181 2783112
Sales Range: $25-49.9 Million
Emp.: 100
Liquor & Dairy Product Mfr
N.A.I.C.S.: 311999

Milkfood Limited (1)
5th Floor Bhandari House 91 Nehru Place, New Delhi, 110 019, India
Tel.: (91) 1126460670
Web Site: https://www.milkfoodltd.com
Rev.: $50,272,950
Assets: $42,244,020
Liabilities: $25,997,790
Net Worth: $16,246,230
Earnings: $333,060
Emp.: 180
Fiscal Year-end: 03/31/2021
Milk Production Services
N.A.I.C.S.: 112120
Sudhir Avasthi *(CEO)*

JAGENBERG AG
Kleinewefersstr 1, 47803, Krefeld, Germany
Tel.: (49) 21519340990
Web Site: http://www.jagenberg.com
Year Founded: 1878
Sales Range: $25-49.9 Million
Emp.: 9
Machinery Mfr
N.A.I.C.S.: 333310
Jan Kleinewefers *(Chm-Supervisory Bd)*

Subsidiaries:

Jagenberg Paper Systems GmbH (1)
Neuer Weg 24, 47803, Krefeld, Germany
Tel.: (49) 21514124950
Industrial Machinery Distr
N.A.I.C.S.: 423830

Jagenberg Textile GmbH & Co. KG (1)
Monforts Quartier 33 Schwalmstrasse 301, 41238, Monchengladbach, Germany
Tel.: (49) 2161599730
Industrial Machinery Distr
N.A.I.C.S.: 423830
Erich W. Broker *(CEO)*

Jagenberg, Inc. (1)
175 Freshwater Blvd, Enfield, CT 06082
Tel.: (860) 741-2501
Web Site: http://translate.google.com
Mfr of Coaters Winders Sheeters Folding Carton Gluers Packaging Lines Diecutters
N.A.I.C.S.: 333993

Kampf (Hong Kong) Ltd (1)
Room 803 8/F Wanchai Commercial Centre 194-204 Johnston Road, Wanchai, China (Hong Kong)
Tel.: (852) 2882 1136
Web Site: http://www.kampf.de
Industrial Machinery & Equipment Whslr
N.A.I.C.S.: 423830

Kampf Machinery (Shanghai) Co., Ltd. (1)
No 1212 Lixue Road, Malu Town Jiading District, 201801, Shanghai, China
Tel.: (86) 2159518028
Industrial Machinery Distr
N.A.I.C.S.: 423830

Kampf Machinery Corporation (1)
Kennedy Industrial Park 900 River St Unit H, Windsor, CT 06095
Tel.: (860) 640-0040
Web Site: http://www.kampfusa.com
Sales Range: $50-74.9 Million
Industrial Machinery & Equipment Whslr
N.A.I.C.S.: 423830

Kampf Machinery India Pvt. Ltd. (1)
508 Atlantis Heights Sarabhai Compound Near Genda Circle, Vadodara, 390007, Gujarat, India
Tel.: (91) 9624044922
Industrial Machinery Distr
N.A.I.C.S.: 423830

Kampf Schneid- und Wickeltechnik GmbH And Co, KG (1)
Muhlener Strasse 36-42, Wiehl-Muhlen, 51674, Wiehl, Germany
Tel.: (49) 2262810
Web Site: http://www.kampf.de
Commercial & Service Industry Machinery Mfr
N.A.I.C.S.: 333310
Lutz Busch *(Mng Dir)*

Kampf WT LLC. (1)
1655 Murfreesboro Rd Ste A, Nashville, TN 37217
Tel.: (615) 361-4140
Web Site: http://www.kampfwt.com
Industrial Machinery Distr
N.A.I.C.S.: 423830

Kleinewefers Beteiligungs-GmbH (1)
Kempener Allee 30, 47803, Krefeld, Germany
Tel.: (49) 215189470
Web Site: http://www.kleinewefers.net
Engineering Services
N.A.I.C.S.: 541330

Kusters Zima Corporation (1)
101 Zima Park Dr, Spartanburg, SC 29301
Tel.: (864) 576-0660
Web Site: http://www.kusterszima.com
Sales Range: $25-49.9 Million
Emp.: 70
Textile Machinery Mfr
N.A.I.C.S.: 333248
Ken Kruse *(Pres & CEO)*

Lebbing engineering & consulting GmbH (1)
Konrad-Zuse-Strasse 16, Bocholt, 46397, Germany
Tel.: (49) 287124120
Web Site: http://www.lebbing.com
Engineeering Services
N.A.I.C.S.: 541330

MQ Management GmbH & Co.KG (1)
Schwalmstrasse 301, 41238, Monchenglad-bach, Germany
Tel.: (49) 215193409922
Web Site: http://www.monforts-quartier.de
Asset Management Services
N.A.I.C.S.: 531390

Maschinen Ritter Wickeltechnik GmbH (1)
Alfred-Nobel-Str 2, 51588, Numbrecht, Germany
Tel.: (49) 229390800
Industrial Machinery Distr
N.A.I.C.S.: 423830

TAG Composites & Carpets GmbH (1)
Glockenspitz 36, 47800, Krefeld, Germany
Tel.: (49) 21515850
Web Site: http://www.tag-krefeld.de
Carpet Mfr
N.A.I.C.S.: 321999

JAGJANANI TEXTILES LIMITED
SCOs 33-34 RIICO Shopping Complex Bagru Extn 1 Bagru, Jaipur, 303007, Rajasthan, India
Tel.: (91) 1414104745
Web Site: https://www.jagjanani.com
532825—(BOM)
Sales Range: Less than $1 Million
Cotton Yarn Mfr
N.A.I.C.S.: 313110
Ajay Sharma *(Compliance Officer)*

JAGRAN PRAKASHAN LIMITED
Jagran Building 2 Sarvodaya Nagar, Kanpur, 208005, India
Tel.: (91) 5122216161
Web Site: https://www.jplcorp.in
532705—(BOM)
Rev.: $183,074,442
Assets: $407,865,549
Liabilities: $105,469,496
Net Worth: $302,396,053
Earnings: $10,689,820
Emp.: 4,953
Fiscal Year-end: 03/31/21
Newspaper Publishers
N.A.I.C.S.: 513110
Mahendra Mohan Gupta *(Chm & Mng Dir)*

Subsidiaries:

Music Broadcast Limited (1)
5th Floor RNA Corporate Park Off Western Express Highway, Kalanagar Bandra East, Mumbai, 400 051, India
Tel.: (91) 2266969010
Web Site: https://www.radiocity.in
Rev.: $26,205,228
Assets: $78,675,043
Liabilities: $15,759,271
Net Worth: $62,915,772
Earnings: $412,433
Emp.: 430
Fiscal Year-end: 03/31/2023
Radio Broadcasting Services
N.A.I.C.S.: 516210
Prashant Domadia *(CFO)*

JAGSON AIRLINES LIMITED
18-B SDA Complex Kasumati, Shimla, 171009, India
Tel.: (91) 11 23721593
Web Site: http://www.jagson-id.wix.com
Year Founded: 1994
Rev.: $341
Assets: $647,710
Liabilities: $2,161,759
Net Worth: ($1,514,049)
Earnings: ($17,234)
Fiscal Year-end: 03/31/18
Passenger Air Transportation Services
N.A.I.C.S.: 481111
Jagdish Pershad Gupta *(Chm & Mng Dir)*

INTERNATIONAL PUBLIC

JAGSONPAL FINANCE & LEASING LTD
C-30 Ground Floor Friends Colony East, New Delhi, 110065, India
Tel.: (91) 1149025758
Web Site: https://www.jagsonpal.co.in
Year Founded: 1991
530601—(BOM)
Rev.: $6,238
Assets: $105,178
Liabilities: $32,321
Net Worth: $72,857
Earnings: ($7,634)
Fiscal Year-end: 03/31/23
Financial Management Services
N.A.I.C.S.: 523999
Kanwarpal Singh Kochhar *(Chm & Mng Dir)*

JAGSONPAL PHARMACEUTICALS LIMITED
T-210 J Shahpur Jat, New Delhi, 110049, India
Tel.: (91) 1146181100
Web Site: https://www.jagsonpal.com
507789—(NSE)
Rev.: $26,254,260
Assets: $22,413,628
Liabilities: $5,770,305
Net Worth: $16,643,322
Earnings: $2,328,458
Emp.: 2,500
Fiscal Year-end: 03/31/21
Drugs & Pharmaceuticals Mfr
N.A.I.C.S.: 325412
Sanjiv Kumar Dudeja *(CFO)*

JAGUAR FINANCIAL CORPORATION
2708 Yonge Street, PO Box 1251, Toronto, M4P 3E5, ON, Canada
Tel.: (416) 201-1206   QC
Web Site: http://www.jaguarfinancial.ca
Year Founded: 1956
JFC—(TSXV)
Assets: $192,601
Liabilities: $81,431
Net Worth: $111,169
Earnings: ($185,965)
Emp.: 3
Fiscal Year-end: 12/31/19
Merchant Banking Services
N.A.I.C.S.: 523150

JAGUAR MINING INC.
First Canadian Place 100 King Street West 56th Floor, Toronto, M5X 1C9, ON, Canada
Tel.: (416) 847-1854   ON
Web Site: https://jaguarmining.com
Year Founded: 2002
JAG—(OTCIQ)
Rev.: $97,234,000
Assets: $200,915,000
Liabilities: $72,335,000
Net Worth: $128,580,000
Earnings: ($148,000)
Emp.: 1,141
Fiscal Year-end: 12/31/19
Gold Mining Services
N.A.I.C.S.: 212220
Hashim Ahmed *(CFO)*

Subsidiaries:

Mineracao Serras do Oeste Ltda. (1)
Rod CabeCa de Boi - Zona Rural, 34505-970, Belo Horizonte, Minas Gerais, Brazil
Tel.: (55) 31 3232 8300
Gold Ore Mining Services
N.A.I.C.S.: 212220

JAGUAR RESOURCES INC.
Suite 730 1015 4th Street SW, Calgary, T2R 1J4, AB, Canada

Tel.: (403) 975-4009 AB
Web Site:
http://www.jaguarresources.com
Year Founded: 2012
Assets: $141,219
Liabilities: $12,795,132
Net Worth: ($12,653,913)
Earnings: ($1,790,484)
Fiscal Year-end: 12/31/17
Oil & Gas Exploration
N.A.I.C.S.: 211120
Corbin Blume *(CEO-Interim)*

JAHANGIR SIDDIQUI & CO. LTD.
20th Floor The Center Plot No 28 SB-5 Abdullah Haroon Road, Karachi, Pakistan
Tel.: (92) 21111574111 PK
Web Site: https://www.js.com
Year Founded: 1991
JSCL—(PSX)
Rev.: $530,391,037
Assets: $4,421,928,305
Liabilities: $4,154,886,052
Net Worth: $267,042,253
Earnings: $40,949,285
Emp.: 177
Fiscal Year-end: 12/31/23
Bank Holding Company
N.A.I.C.S.: 551111
Suleman Lalani *(CEO)*

Subsidiaries:

Credit Chex (Private) Limited (1)
Suit 111 Office Wing Park Towers Shahrah e-Firdous Block-5 Clifton, Karachi, Pakistan
Tel.: (92) 21 5290021
Web Site: http://www.credit-chex.com
Risk Management Solution Services
N.A.I.C.S.: 541611

JS Bank Limited (1)
Shaheen Commercial Complex Dr Ziauddin Ahmed Road, PO Box 4847, Karachi, 74200, Sindh, Pakistan (64.49%)
Tel.: (92) 21111572265
Web Site: https://www.jsbl.com
Rev.: $75,083,451
Assets: $3,047,493,124
Liabilities: $2,922,033,475
Net Worth: $125,459,649
Earnings: ($1,652,556)
Emp.: 4,904
Fiscal Year-end: 12/31/2019
Investment Banking Services
N.A.I.C.S.: 523150
Kalim-Ur Rahman *(Chm)*

Subsidiary (Domestic):

JS Global Capital Limited (2)
14th 16th and 17th Floor The Centre Plot No 28 SB-5, Abdullah Haroon Road, Karachi, Pakistan
Tel.: (92) 21111574111
Web Site: https://www.jsgcl.com
Rev.: $3,391,491
Assets: $26,351,543
Liabilities: $11,967,465
Net Worth: $14,384,078
Earnings: $304,280
Emp.: 185
Fiscal Year-end: 12/31/2019
Investment Banking, Brokerage & Investment Advisory Services
N.A.I.C.S.: 523150
Muhammad Kamran Nasir *(CEO)*

JS Infocom Limited (1)
20th Floor The Center Plot No 28 SB-5 Shahrah-e-Faisal, Abdullah Haroon Road Saddar, Karachi, 75530, Pakistan
Tel.: (92) 21111574111
Web Site: https://www.jsinfocom.com
Telecommunication Servicesb
N.A.I.C.S.: 517111
Hasan Shahid *(CEO)*

JS International Limited (1)
Unit B 3 Regal Way, Watford, WD24 4YJ, United Kingdom
Tel.: (44) 1923209440
Web Site: https://www.jsint.com
Sports Product Retailer
N.A.I.C.S.: 459110

JS Investments Limited (1)
19th Floor The Centre Plot No 28 SB-5 Abdullah Haroon Road, Saddar, Karachi, 75600, Pakistan (52.02%)
Tel.: (92) 21111222626
Web Site: https://www.jsil.com
Rev.: $1,280,100
Assets: $16,499,443
Liabilities: $4,812,209
Net Worth: $11,687,233
Earnings: ($557,995)
Emp.: 119
Fiscal Year-end: 12/31/2019
Investment Banking Services
N.A.I.C.S.: 523150
Kamran Jafar *(Chm)*

Quality 1 Petroleum (Private) Limited (1)
4th Floor 22 East Saeed Plaza Jinnah Avenue Blue Area, Islamabad, Pakistan
Tel.: (92) 51287006364
Web Site: https://www.q1petroleum.com
Petroleum Product Mfr
N.A.I.C.S.: 324199

JAHEN HOUSEHOLD PRODUCTS CO., LTD.
Jiangnan Huoju Industrial Zone, Licheng District, Quanzhou, 362005, Fujian, China
Tel.: (86) 59522463333
Web Site: http://www.jahenjh.com
Year Founded: 2005
300955—(SSE)
Rev.: $147,640,428
Assets: $216,267,948
Liabilities: $77,479,740
Net Worth: $138,788,208
Earnings: $9,781,668
Fiscal Year-end: 12/31/22
Household Appliance Mfr & Distr
N.A.I.C.S.: 335220
Bensheng Zeng *(Chm)*

Subsidiaries:

Shanghai Jiaheng Daily Chemical Co., Ltd. (1)
1069 Taogan Road, Songshan Town Songjiang District, Shanghai, 201602, China
Tel.: (86) 213 373 0666
Plastic Packaging Materials Mfr
N.A.I.C.S.: 326112

Tianjin Jiaheng Plastics Co., Ltd. (1)
No 36 Jisheng Street No 3 Road TEDA, Tianjin, China
Tel.: (86) 228 898 8808
Plastic Packaging Materials Mfr
N.A.I.C.S.: 326112

Zhejiang Jiaheng Packaging Technology Co., Ltd. (1)
No 138 Changsheng Road Weitang Street, Jiashan, 314100, Zhejiang, China
Tel.: (86) 5738 412 1192
Plastic Packaging Materials Mfr
N.A.I.C.S.: 326112

Zhuhai Jiaheng Daily Chemical Co., Ltd. (1)
Anyu Industrial Park Nangang East Road, Nanshui Town, Zhuhai, 519050, China
Tel.: (86) 756 771 6788
Plastic Packaging Materials Mfr
N.A.I.C.S.: 326112

JAHNS & FRIENDS
Heerdter Sandberg 32, 40549, Dusseldorf, Germany
Tel.: (49) 211559620 De
Web Site:
http://www.jahnsandfriends.de
Year Founded: 1985
Sales Range: $10-24.9 Million
Emp.: 30
Consumer Marketing, Direct Marketing, Sales Promotion
N.A.I.C.S.: 541810
Rudolf Jahns *(Mng Dir)*

JAHORINA OC A.D
Olimpijska bb, Jahorina, 71423, Pale, Bosnia & Herzegovina
Tel.: (387) 57270090
Web Site: https://www.oc-jahorina.com
OCJH-R-A—(BANJ)
Sales Range: Less than $1 Million
Tourism & Recreational Services
N.A.I.C.S.: 561520

JAHR TOP SPECIAL VERLAG GMBH & CO. KG
Troplowitzstrasse 5, 22529, Hamburg, Germany
Tel.: (49) 40 389 06 0 De
Web Site: http://www.jahr-tsv.de
Year Founded: 2000
Sales Range: $25-49.9 Million
Emp.: 150
Magazine Publisher
N.A.I.C.S.: 513120
Alexandra Jahr *(Mng Dir)*

JAHWA ELECTRONICS CO., LTD
1217 Chungcheong-daero Bugimyeon, Cheongwon-gu, Cheongju, 363-922, chungcheongbuk-do, Korea (South)
Tel.: (82) 432107114
Web Site: http://www.jahwa.co.kr
Year Founded: 1981
033240—(KRS)
Rev.: $224,219,788
Assets: $387,939,913
Liabilities: $124,737,925
Net Worth: $263,201,988
Earnings: ($29,285,965)
Emp.: 939
Fiscal Year-end: 12/31/22
Electronic Components Mfr
N.A.I.C.S.: 334419
Sang-Myeon Kim *(Chm)*

Subsidiaries:

JA HWA ELECTRONICS (M) SDN, BHD (1)
Lot No 61 Senawang Industrial Park, 70400, Seremban, Negeri Sembilan, Malaysia
Tel.: (60) 6 678 3302
Emp.: 36
Electronic Components Distr
N.A.I.C.S.: 423690
Kim Deesan *(Mng Dir)*

JAI BALAJI INDUSTRIES LTD
5 Bentinck Street, Kolkata, 700 001, West Bengal, India
Tel.: (91) 3322489808
Web Site:
https://www.jaibalajigroup.com
532976—(BOM)
Rev.: $637,918,240
Assets: $405,288,443
Liabilities: $632,265,611
Net Worth: ($226,977,169)
Earnings: $6,560,545
Emp.: 3,063
Fiscal Year-end: 03/31/22
Steel Mfrs
N.A.I.C.S.: 331110
Ajay Kumar Tantia *(Compliance Officer & Sec)*

JAI CORP LTD
603 Embassy Centre 6th Floor Plot No 207 Block III Backbay Reclamation, Nariman Point, Mumbai, 400 021, India
Tel.: (91) 2235215146
Web Site:
https://www.jaicorpindia.com
Year Founded: 1985
512237—(BOM)
Rev.: $84,556,290
Assets: $205,364,250
Liabilities: $6,779,955
Net Worth: $198,584,295
Earnings: ($1,850,940)
Emp.: 700
Fiscal Year-end: 03/31/23
Steel Mfrs
N.A.I.C.S.: 339999
Virendra Jain *(Vice Chm)*

Subsidiaries:

Oasis Holding FZC (1)
PO Box 121943, Sharjah, United Arab Emirates
Tel.: (971) 443702010
Investment Management Service
N.A.I.C.S.: 523940

Urban Infrastructure Venture Capital Limited (1)
46-47 Maker Chambers VI Nariman Point, Mumbai, 400 021, India
Tel.: (91) 2266696110
Web Site: http://urbaninfra.com
Sales Range: $50-74.9 Million
Emp.: 5
Venture Capital Management Services
N.A.I.C.S.: 523910
Anand Jain *(Chm)*

JAI MATA GLASS LTD.
Village Tipra Tehsil Barotiwala, Solan, 174103, India
Tel.: (91) 41536830 In
Web Site:
http://www.jaimataglass.com
Year Founded: 1981
Rev.: $136,648
Assets: $714,858
Liabilities: $328,845
Net Worth: $386,012
Earnings: $77,162
Fiscal Year-end: 03/31/18
Designed Glass Mfr
N.A.I.C.S.: 327212
Chander Mohan Marwah *(Mng Dir)*

JAIC CO., LTD.
1-101 Jimbocho Kanda, Chiyoda-Ku, Tokyo, 101-0051, Japan
Tel.: (81) 352827600
Web Site: https://www.jaic-g.com
Year Founded: 1991
7073—(TKS)
Rev.: $21,182,689
Assets: $19,213,743
Liabilities: $13,108,688
Net Worth: $6,105,055
Earnings: $925,008
Emp.: 43
Fiscal Year-end: 01/31/23
Educational Support Services
N.A.I.C.S.: 611710
Takeshi Sato *(Chm & Pres)*

Subsidiaries:

JAIC Business Service Co., Ltd. (1)
2F Medical Friend Building 3-2-4 Kudankita, Chiyoda-ku, Tokyo, 102-0073, Japan
Tel.: (81) 332218533
Asset Management & Accounting Services
N.A.I.C.S.: 541219

JAIHIND PROJECTS LTD.
3rd Floor Venus Atlantis Corporate Park Nr Prahladnagar AUDA Garden, Anandnagar Road Satellite, Ahmedabad, 380 015, Gujarat, India
Tel.: (91) 79 4050 1300
Web Site: http://www.jpl.in
Sales Range: $1-9.9 Million
Construction Engineering Services
N.A.I.C.S.: 237990
Jheel Sanjhira *(Sec)*

Subsidiaries:

Jaihind Green Energy Ltd. (1)
3rd Floor Venus Atlantis Corporate Park Near Prahlad Nagar Auda Garden, Anand

JAIHIND PROJECTS LTD.

Jaihind Projects Ltd.—(Continued)
Nagar Road, Ahmedabad, 380 015, Gujarat, India
Tel.: (91) 79 40501300
Sales Range: $25-49.9 Million
Emp.: 30
Solar Power Plant Construction Services
N.A.I.C.S.: 237130

JAIHIND SYNTHETICS LIMITED

103 Shreenath Saidarshan Dattapada Road, Borivali west, Mumbai, 400066, Maharashtra, India
Tel.: (91) 2228676010
Web Site: https://www.jaihindltd.co.in
Year Founded: 1986
514312—(BOM)
Rev.: $24,744
Assets: $2,125,437
Liabilities: $81,812
Net Worth: $2,043,626
Earnings: $744
Fiscal Year-end: 03/31/21
Textile Products Mfr
N.A.I.C.S.: 314999
Dinesh Jayantlal Doshi (Exec Dir)

JAIN IRRIGATION SYSTEMS LIMITED

Jain Plastic Park NH No 6 Bambhori, Jalgaon, 425 001, Maharashtra, India
Tel.: (91) 2572258011
Web Site: https://www.jains.com
500219—(BOM)
Rev.: $698,330,281
Assets: $1,333,616,322
Liabilities: $694,064,890
Net Worth: $639,551,432
Earnings: $100,832,340
Emp.: 6,551
Fiscal Year-end: 03/31/23
Irrigation System & Farm Machinery Whslr
N.A.I.C.S.: 221310
Ashok Bhavarlal Jain (Chm)

Subsidiaries:

Agri-Valley Irrigation LLC (1)
3168 W Belmont Ave, Fresno, CA 93726
Tel.: (559) 486-1412
Web Site: https://agrivalley.com
Irrigation Design & Engineering Services
N.A.I.C.S.: 221310
Larry Rompal (Owner & CEO)

Irrigation Design & Construction, LLC (1)
808 Merced St, Newman, CA 95360
Tel.: (209) 862-4900
Web Site: https://idcsupply.com
Irrigation Systems
N.A.I.C.S.: 221310
Mike Conrad (Co-Founder)

JISL Global SA (1)
Tel.: (41) 327290909
Irrigation Systems Mfr
N.A.I.C.S.: 332322

JISL Systems SA (2)
Tel.: (41) 327290909
Irrigation Systems Mfr & Distr
N.A.I.C.S.: 332322

Jain (Americas), Inc. (1)
1000 Sheridan St, Chicopee, MA 01022
Tel.: (614) 850-9400
Sales Range: $1-9.9 Million
Emp.: 81
Construction Materials Mfr & Whslr
N.A.I.C.S.: 423390

Subsidiary (Domestic):

Cascade Specialties Inc. (2)
71449 Rail Loop Dr, Boardman, OR 97818
Tel.: (541) 481-2522
Web Site: http://www.cascadespec.com
Onion & Garlic Products Mfr
N.A.I.C.S.: 111219

Jack Sollazzo (Chm)

Jain Irrigation, Inc. (2)
2851 E Florence Ave, Fresno, CA 93721
Tel.: (559) 485-7171
Irrigation System Whslr
N.A.I.C.S.: 221310

Subsidiary (Domestic):

ET Water Systems, Inc. (3)
6 Hamilton Landing Ste 175, Novato, CA 94949
Tel.: (415) 945-9383
Web Site: https://jainsusa.com
Cloud-Based Irrigation System Developer
N.A.I.C.S.: 518210
Pat McLntyre (Chm & CEO)

Unit (Domestic):

Jain Irrigation, Inc. (3)
740 Water St, Watertown, NY 13601
Tel.: (315) 755-4400
Web Site: https://jainsusa.com
Greenhouse Watering System Mfr & Whslr
N.A.I.C.S.: 221310

Subsidiary (Domestic):

Nucedar Mills Inc (2)
1000 Sheridan St, Chicopee, MA 01022
Tel.: (413) 593-8883
Web Site: http://www.jainbuildingproducts.com
Emp.: 25
Building Materials Mfr
N.A.I.C.S.: 326199

Jain (Europe) Ltd. (1)
Regal House 3rd Floor 70 London Road, Twickenham, TW1 3QS, Middle Sex, United Kingdom
Tel.: (44) 2088918700
Web Site: http://www.jains.com
Sales Range: $25-49.9 Million
Emp.: 15
Irrigation Systems Mfr & Sales
N.A.I.C.S.: 332322
Ashish Gagi (VP)

NaanDan Jain Australia Pty Ltd (1)
214-216 Hammond Road, Dandenong, 3175, VIC, Australia
Tel.: (61) 397671222
Web Site: https://www.naandanjain.com.au
Sales Range: $50-74.9 Million
Emp.: 6
Irrigation Systems Distr
N.A.I.C.S.: 423820

NaanDan Jain Iberica S.C. (1)
P I La Redonda calle XIV 26, Santa Maria del Aguila, 04710, El Ejido, Almeria, Spain
Tel.: (34) 950582121
Web Site: http://www.naandanjain.es
Sales Range: $25-49.9 Million
Emp.: 35
Irrigation Systems Mfr & Distr
N.A.I.C.S.: 327332
Carlos Lavilla (Gen Mgr)

NaanDan Jain Irrigation CS Ltd (1)
Kibbutz Naan, Naan, 76829, Israel
Tel.: (972) 89442180
Irrigation Systems Mfr
N.A.I.C.S.: 333111
Avner Hermoni (CEO)

Subsidiary (Domestic):

NaanDan Agro-Pro Ltd (2)
Kibbutz Naan M P Ayalon, 76829, Naan, Israel
Tel.: (972) 89442789
Irrigation Systems Mfr & Distr
N.A.I.C.S.: 333111

Subsidiary (Non-US):

NaanDan Jain Mexico, S.A. De C.V. (2)
Circuito Interior 130 A Parque Industrial Millennium, 78395, San Luis Potosi, Mexico
Tel.: (52) 4445008400
Web Site: https://www.naandanjain.com.mx
Irrigation Equipment Mfr
N.A.I.C.S.: 333111
Avner Hermoni (CEO)

NaanDan Jain Peru S.A.C. (2)
Centro Logistico BSF Bodega C-6 Panamericana Sur N 2001 Km 38, Punta Hermosa, Lima, Peru
Tel.: (51) 16176060
Web Site: http://www.naandanjain.pe
Irrigation Systems Mfr
N.A.I.C.S.: 221310
Ian Vega (Mgr-Mktg)

NaanDan Jain srl (1)
Via Del Tecchione 18, 20098, San Giuliano Milanese, Milano, Italy
Tel.: (39) 0255603877
Web Site: http://www.naandanjain.com
Sales Range: $25-49.9 Million
Emp.: 15
Irrigation Systems Mfr & Distr
N.A.I.C.S.: 327332
Fernando S. Ondarza (Gen Mgr)

NaanDanJain France SAS (1)
12 Bis rue Seveso, 31150, Fenouillet, France
Tel.: (33) 561998509
Web Site: http://www.naandanjain.com
Irrigation System & Farm Machinery Mfr & Whslr
N.A.I.C.S.: 327332
Anthony Seches (Gen Mgr)

Sleaford Quality Foods Limited, (1)
Woodbridge Road, East Road Industrial Estate, Sleaford, NG34 7JX, Lincolnshire, United Kingdom
Tel.: (44) 1529305000
Web Site: http://www.sleafordqf.com
Sales Range: $25-49.9 Million
Emp.: 90
Food Processing & Sales
N.A.I.C.S.: 311423
Anthony Ware (Mgr-Export)

JAIN MARMO INDUSTRIES LTD.

N H 8 Sukher, Udaipur, 313 001, Rajasthan, India
Tel.: (91) 2942441666
Web Site: https://www.jainmarmo.com
Year Founded: 1981
539119—(BOM)
Rev.: $216,093
Assets: $938,615
Liabilities: $410,729
Net Worth: $527,886
Earnings: ($12,285)
Emp.: 11
Fiscal Year-end: 03/31/21
Marble Blocks, Slabs & Tiles Mfr & Distr
N.A.I.C.S.: 212311
Sidharth Jain (Mng Dir)

JAINAM FERRO ALLOYS (I) LIMITED

Plot No 130137 Sector C Urla Industrial Area, Raipur, 492003, Chhattisgarh, India
Tel.: (91) 7714700109
Web Site: https://www.jainamferro.com
Year Founded: 2014
JAINAM—(NSE)
Rev.: $31,005,683
Assets: $13,434,698
Liabilities: $2,979,426
Net Worth: $10,455,272
Earnings: $2,787,279
Emp.: 103
Fiscal Year-end: 03/31/23
Fabricated Structural Metal Mfr
N.A.I.C.S.: 332312

JAINCO PROJECTS (INDIA) LIMITED

2 Clive Ghat Street 4th Floor Room No 4A, Kolkata, 700001, West Bengal, India
Tel.: (91) 3322213549
Web Site: https://www.jainco.in
Year Founded: 1991

INTERNATIONAL PUBLIC

526865—(BOM)
Rev.: $38,895
Assets: $2,105,881
Liabilities: $829,351
Net Worth: $1,276,530
Earnings: $863
Emp.: 4
Fiscal Year-end: 03/31/23
Building Materials Whslr
N.A.I.C.S.: 423390
Mant Agarwal (Compliance Officer)

JAINEX AAMCOL LIMITED

L-3 MIDC Industrial Area Chikalthana, Nariman Point, Aurangabad, 431210, Maharashtra, India
Tel.: (91) 2406614480
Web Site: https://www.jainexaamcol.com
Year Founded: 1947
505212—(BOM)
Rev.: $1,640,798
Assets: $1,878,636
Liabilities: $1,373,867
Net Worth: $504,769
Earnings: $15,798
Emp.: 94
Fiscal Year-end: 03/31/21
Cutting Tool Mfr
N.A.I.C.S.: 333515
Bhagat Singh Dugar (Chm)

Subsidiaries:

JAINEX AAMCOL LIMITED - AURANGABAD WORKS (1)
L-3 MIDC Industrial Area, Chilkalthana, Aurangabad, 431210, Maharashtra, India
Tel.: (91) 240 6614480
Cutting Tool Mfr
N.A.I.C.S.: 333515

JAIPAN INDUSTRIES LIMITED

17/1 Cama Industrial Estate Walbhat Road, Goregaon East, Mumbai, 400063, Maharashtra, India
Tel.: (91) 8928227717
Web Site: https://jaipanonline.com
Year Founded: 1984
505840—(BOM)
Rev.: $3,191,530
Assets: $2,985,091
Liabilities: $1,057,813
Net Worth: $1,927,277
Earnings: $27,940
Fiscal Year-end: 03/31/22
Home Appliance Mfr
N.A.I.C.S.: 332215
Jaynarayan O. Agarwal (Chm)

JAIPRAKASH ASSOCIATES LIMITED

Sector 128, Noida, 201304, Uttar Pradesh, India
Tel.: (91) 1204609000
Web Site: https://www.jalindia.com
JPASSOCIAT—(NSE)
Rev.: $898,918,020
Assets: $4,963,370,685
Liabilities: $4,752,975,045
Net Worth: $210,395,640
Earnings: ($90,298,845)
Emp.: 6,252
Fiscal Year-end: 03/31/21
Construction Engineering Services
N.A.I.C.S.: 541330
Manoj Gaur (Chm & CEO)

Subsidiaries:

Bhilai Jaypee Cement Limited (1)
Village and Post Babupur, Distt Satna, Bhilai, 485112, India
Tel.: (91) 7672415500
Cement Mfr
N.A.I.C.S.: 327310

Jaiprakash Associates Limited - Jaypee Balaji Cement Plant (1)
Survey No 99 Vill Budawada, Mandal-

Jaggiyapet, Jaggaiahpeta, 521175, Andhra Pradesh, India
Tel.: (91) 8654 285011
Cement Mfr
N.A.I.C.S.: 327310

Jaiprakash Associates Limited - Jaypee Cement Blending Unit (1)
Sadwa Khurd Paragana Arail, Bara, Allahabad, Uttar Pradesh, India
Tel.: (91) 9956290958
Cement Mfr
N.A.I.C.S.: 327310

Jaiprakash Associates Limited - Jaypee Cement Grinding Unit (1)
Asan Kalan Madlauda, Khukhrana, Panipat, 132103, Haryana, India
Tel.: (91) 1802520160
Cement Mfr
N.A.I.C.S.: 327310

Jaiprakash Associates Limited - Jaypee Himachal Cement Grinding & Blending Unit (1)
Vill Tikari Pandiyana Khilian, Nalagarh, Solan, 174101, Himachal Pradesh, India
Tel.: (91) 1795229100
Cement Mfr
N.A.I.C.S.: 327310

Jaiprakash Associates Limited - Jaypee Himachal Cement Plant (1)
Village Baga, Arki, Solan, 171 102, Himachal Pradesh, India
Tel.: (91) 1796 223300
Cement Mfr
N.A.I.C.S.: 327310

Jaiprakash Associates Limited - Jaypee Rewa Plant (1)
Jaypee Nagar, Rewa, 486 450, Madhya Pradesh, India
Tel.: (91) 7662 400700
Cement Mfr
N.A.I.C.S.: 327310

Jaiprakash Associates Limited - Jaypee Roorkee Cement Grinding Unit (1)
Vill Nalherideh Nalhera Anantpur, Roorkee, Haridwar, 247667, Uttarakhand, India
Tel.: (91) 1332231941
Cement Mfr
N.A.I.C.S.: 327310

Jaiprakash Associates Limited - Jaypee Sidhi Cement Plant (1)
Jaypee Vihar, Majhigawan, Sidhi, 486 776, India
Tel.: (91) 7802 276701
Cement Mfr
N.A.I.C.S.: 327310
Prabhakar Mishra (Sr Mgr-HR)

Jaiprakash Associates Limited - Jaypee Sikandarabad Cement Grinding Unit (1)
19 -20 Industrial Area, Bulandshahr, Sikandrabad, 203205, Uttar Pradesh, India
Tel.: (91) 5735222573
Cement Mfr
N.A.I.C.S.: 327310

Jaiprakash Power Ventures Ltd. (1)
JA House 63 Basant Lok, Vasant Vihar, New Delhi, 110057, India (76.02%)
Tel.: (91) 1149828500
Web Site: https://www.jppowerventures.com
Rev.: $468,059,865
Assets: $2,319,638,685
Liabilities: $916,137,495
Net Worth: $1,403,501,190
Earnings: $38,415,195
Emp.: 1,766
Fiscal Year-end: 03/31/2021
Hydroelectric Power Generation
N.A.I.C.S.: 221111
Suren Jain (Mng Dir & CFO)

Subsidiary (Domestic):

Andhra Cements Limited (2)
Durga Cement Works, Sri Durgapuram Srinagar Dachepalli, Guntur, 522 414, Andhra Pradesh, India
Tel.: (91) 8649257413
Web Site: https://www.andhracements.com
Rev.: $212,189

Assets: $128,176,940
Liabilities: $221,038,299
Net Worth: ($92,861,360)
Earnings: ($27,987,359)
Emp.: 306
Fiscal Year-end: 03/31/2021
Cement Mfr
N.A.I.C.S.: 327310

Jaypee Fertilizers & Industries Limited (1)
Sector-134 near-yamuna express way village, Wazidpur, 201 304, Noida, Uttar Pradesh, India
Tel.: (91) 9953791909
Emp.: 300
Fertilizer Mfr
N.A.I.C.S.: 325314
Umesh Saxena (Deputy Gen Mgr-Ops)

Jaypee Infratech Limited (1)
Sector-128, Dist Gautam Buddh Nagar, Noida, 201304, Uttar Pradesh, India
Tel.: (91) 1204609000
Web Site: https://www.jaypeeinfratech.com
Rev.: $263,529,672
Assets: $3,349,467,534
Liabilities: $3,550,346,338
Net Worth: ($200,878,804)
Earnings: ($315,012,670)
Emp.: 171
Fiscal Year-end: 03/31/2020
Infrastructure Construction Services
N.A.I.C.S.: 237310
Manoj Gaur (Chm & Mng Dir)

Jaypee Sports International Limited (1)
Jaya Holy International Jaypee Sports City Sector-95 Bunhar, Express Way, Delhi, 9892, Uttar Pradesh, India
Tel.: (91) 22535962182
Web Site: https://www.jaypeesports.com
Sports Event Management Services
N.A.I.C.S.: 711310
Sameer Gaur (CEO & Mng Dir)

Kanpur Fertilizers & Chemicals Limited (1)
Sector-128, Noida, 201304, Uttar Pradesh, India
Tel.: (91) 1204609000
Web Site: https://kfclkanpur.com
Fertilizer Mfr
N.A.I.C.S.: 325314
Manoj Gaur (Chm)

JAIZ BANK PLC
Ground Floor Kano House 73 Ralph Shodeinde Street Central, Business District, Abuja, Nigeria
Tel.: (234) 7080635500
Web Site:
 https://www.jaizbankplc.com
Year Founded: 2011
JAIZBANK—(NIGE)
Rev.: $24,744,286
Assets: $281,141,574
Liabilities: $147,574,733
Net Worth: $133,566,841
Earnings: $5,093,507
Emp.: 821
Fiscal Year-end: 12/31/22
Financial Banking Services
N.A.I.C.S.: 522110
Umaru Abdul Mutallab (Chm)

JAKHARIA FABRIC LTD.
H N 1224 Deoji Nagar Near Shanti Sagar Building, Narpoli Village Bhiwandi District, Thane, 421302, India
Tel.: (91) 2522278892
Web Site:
 https://www.jakhariafabric.com
Year Founded: 1987
JAKHARIA—(NSE)
Rev.: $10,472,394
Assets: $7,978,203
Liabilities: $5,754,739
Net Worth: $2,223,464
Earnings: ($260,584)
Emp.: 146
Fiscal Year-end: 03/31/23
Textile Mfr

N.A.I.C.S.: 314999
Nitin Shah (Mng Dir)

Subsidiaries:

Jakharia Synthetics Pvt. Ltd. (1)
H N 1224 Deoji Nagar Near Shanti Sagar Building, Narpoli Village Bhiwandi District, Thane, 421302, India
Tel.: (91) 2522278479
Synthetic Fabric Mfr & Distr
N.A.I.C.S.: 325220

JAKOB MULLER AG
Schulstrasse 14, Frick, 5070, Switzerland
Tel.: (41) 62 8655 111
Web Site: http://www.mueller-frick.com
Private Investment Firm
N.A.I.C.S.: 523999

Subsidiaries:

Benninger AG (1)
Fabrikstrasse, 9240, Uzwil, Switzerland
Tel.: (41) 719558585
Web Site: http://www.benningergroup.com
Textile Finishing & Cord Production Range Mfr
N.A.I.C.S.: 333248

Subsidiary (Non-US):

Benninger Automation GmbH (2)
Schopfheimerstrasse 89, 79669, Zell, Germany
Tel.: (49) 7625 131 0
Web Site: http://www.benningergroup.com
Textile Machinery Distr
N.A.I.C.S.: 423830
Jurgen Zah (CEO-Automation Div)

Benninger India Private Ltd. (2)
415 Sunshine Plaza, Naigaon Cross Road Near Avon, 400 014, Mumbai, India
Tel.: (91) 2224175361
Web Site: http://www.benningergroup.com
Textile Finishing & Cord Production Range Mfr
N.A.I.C.S.: 333248
Cavale N. Guruprasad (Gen Mgr)

JAKOB WINTER GMBH
Eisenstrasse 3, 65428, Russelsheim, Germany
Tel.: (49) 615263070
Web Site: http://www.jakob-winter.com
Year Founded: 1886
Sales Range: $10-24.9 Million
Emp.: 40
Musical Instrument Case & Specialty Case Mfr
N.A.I.C.S.: 339999
Joachim Winter (Mng Dir)

JAKPAISAN ESTATE PUBLIC COMPANY LIMITED
153/3 Moo6 Tumbon Bangpoon Umpher, Muamg, Pathumthani, 12000, Thailand
Tel.: (66) 21571958 TH
Web Site:
 https://www.jakpaisanestate.com
Year Founded: 2003
JAK—(THA)
Rev.: $8,237,388
Assets: $23,653,427
Liabilities: $10,213,873
Net Worth: $13,439,554
Earnings: $927,145
Emp.: 36
Fiscal Year-end: 12/31/23
Real Estate Development Services
N.A.I.C.S.: 531390
Admiral Na Arreenich (Chm)

JAKS RESOURCES BERHAD
Unit B-09-28 Tower B Pacific Towers Jalan 13/6 Section 13, 46200, Petaling Jaya, Selangor, Malaysia

Tel.: (60) 376603333
Web Site: https://www.jaks.com.my
JAKS—(KLS)
Rev.: $20,031,697
Assets: $503,454,890
Liabilities: $216,759,031
Net Worth: $286,695,859
Earnings: $7,729,063
Emp.: 124
Fiscal Year-end: 12/31/22
Pipes Mfr
N.A.I.C.S.: 331210
Oi Wah Leong (Sec)

Subsidiaries:

Integrated Pipe Industries Sdn. Bhd. (1)
Jln Haji Abdul Manan Off Jln Meru, Meru, 41050, Selangor, Malaysia
Tel.: (60) 333920153
Web Site: http://www.jaks.com.my
Sales Range: $25-49.9 Million
Emp.: 18
Steel Pole Mfr
N.A.I.C.S.: 332919

JAKS Sdn. Bhd. (1)
Lot 526 Persiaran Subang Permai Sungai Penaga Industrial Park Usj 1, Subang Jaya, 47600, Petaling Jaya, Selangor, Malaysia
Tel.: (60) 356331988
Sales Range: $75-99.9 Million
Emp.: 300
Construction Engineering Services
N.A.I.C.S.: 541330
Ang Lam Poah (Dir-Sls)

JAKS Steel Industries Sdn. Bhd. (1)
Lot 526 Persiaran Subang Permai Sungai Penaga Industrial Park USJ 1, 47600, Subang Jaya, Selangor Darul Ehsan, Malaysia
Tel.: (60) 356348891
Sales Range: $50-74.9 Million
Emp.: 200
Construction Steel & Metal Products Mfr
N.A.I.C.S.: 331110

JAL GROUP ITALIA S.R.L.
Via Borgomanero 50, IT-28045, Paruzzaro, NO, Italy
Tel.: (39) 0322539111 IT
Web Site: http://www.jal-group.com
Year Founded: 2005
Sales Range: $200-249.9 Million
Emp.: 4,500
Holding Company; Safety Footwear Mfr & Distr
N.A.I.C.S.: 551112

Subsidiaries:

Jallatte S.A.S. (1)
5 Rue du Fort - Pierre Jallatte, BP 5, 30170, Saint Hippolyte-du-Fort, France
Tel.: (33) 466806300
Web Site: http://www.jallatte.fr
Sales Range: $100-124.9 Million
Emp.: 370
Safety Footwear Mfr
N.A.I.C.S.: 316210

JALAN TRANSOLUTIONS (INDIA) LTD.
2F-CS-38 Second Floor Ansal Plaza Vaishali, Ghaziabad, 201010, India
Tel.: (91) 1204257719
Web Site:
 https://www.jalantransolutions.com
Year Founded: 2003
JALAN—(NSE)
Rev.: $1,181,044
Assets: $3,149,008
Liabilities: $6,075,691
Net Worth: ($2,926,683)
Earnings: ($1,583,430)
Emp.: 3
Fiscal Year-end: 03/31/23
Freight Forwarding & Logistics Consulting Services
N.A.I.C.S.: 488510
Rajesh Jalan (Mng Dir)

JALCO HOLDINGS INC.

JALCO Holdings Inc.—(Continued)

JALCO HOLDINGS INC.
8F Nihonbashi Central Square
2-16-11 Nihonbashi, Chuo-ku, Tokyo,
103-0027, Nihonbashi, Japan
Tel.: (81) 332745240
Web Site: https://www.jalco.co.jp
Year Founded: 2011
6625—(TKS)
Rev.: $84,198,180
Assets: $479,899,220
Liabilities: $353,344,160
Net Worth: $126,555,060
Earnings: $27,464,550
Emp.: 16
Fiscal Year-end: 03/31/24
Holding Company; Electronic Parts & Equipment Mfr
N.A.I.C.S.: 551112
Junichi Tanabe *(Board of Directors & Pres)*

Subsidiaries:

PT JALCO ELECTRONICS INDONESIA (1)
Karawang International Industrial City Blok C-6 Jalan Toll Jakarta, Cikampek Km 47, Karawang, Jawa Barat, Indonesia
Tel.: (62) 21 890 1508
Web Site: http://www.jalco.co.jp
Electronic Components Mfr
N.A.I.C.S.: 334419

JALLON SAS
Z I Montmartin 2 Rue Marcel Merieux, Corbas, 69960, Venissieux, France
Tel.: (33) 472901550
Web Site: http://jallon-sas.bee27.com
Rev.: $24,500,000
Emp.: 80
Packaged Frozen Goods
N.A.I.C.S.: 424420
Jacques Jaquemot *(Dir)*

JALPAC INDIA LTD.
903/911 Tolstoy House 15 Tolstoy Marg, New Delhi, 110001, India
Tel.: (91) 1123712242
523230—(BOM)
Sales Range: $1-9.9 Million
Packaging Film Mfr
N.A.I.C.S.: 326112
Madhukar Jalan *(Mng Dir)*

JAMAICA BROILERS GROUP LIMITED
Content McCook's Pen St Catherine, Spanish Town, Jamaica
Tel.: (876) 9434376 JM
Web Site:
https://www.jamaicabroilers.com
Year Founded: 1958
JBG—(JAM)
Rev.: $607,989,119
Assets: $564,563,988
Liabilities: $363,123,250
Net Worth: $201,440,738
Earnings: $39,871,222
Fiscal Year-end: 04/27/24
Broiler Meat Production & Distr
N.A.I.C.S.: 112320
Robert E. Levy *(Chm)*

Subsidiaries:

Farmers Pride, Inc. (1)
154 W Main St, Fredericksburg, PA 17026
Tel.: (717) 865-6626
Web Site: http://www.bellandevans.com
Poultry Product Distr
N.A.I.C.S.: 311615
Scott Sechler Jr. *(Exec VP)*

International Poultry Breeders LLC (1)
1235 Perry Batts Rd, Norman Park, GA 31771
Tel.: (229) 769-3410

Web Site:
https://internationalpoultrybreeders.com
Egg Production Services
N.A.I.C.S.: 112310

Jamaica Broilers Group Limited - JAMAICA EGG SERVICES DIVISION (1)
White Marl, Spanish Town, Jamaica
Tel.: (876) 749 5433
Egg Distr
N.A.I.C.S.: 424440

Master Blend Feeds Limited (1)
Bodles PO BOX 24, PO Box 24, Old Harbour, Jamaica
Tel.: (876) 983 2305
Property Rental Services
N.A.I.C.S.: 531190

WINCORP International Inc. (1)
10025 NW 116th Way Ste 9, Medley, FL 33178
Tel.: (305) 887-4000
Web Site: http://www.wincorpintl.com
Emp.: 22
Farm Equipment Whslr
N.A.I.C.S.: 423820
Stephen D. E. Levy *(Pres)*

JAMAICA MONEY MARKET BROKERS LIMITED
6 Haughton Terrace, Kingston, 10, Jamaica
Tel.: (876) 9985662 JM
Web Site: http://jm.jmmb.com
Year Founded: 1992
Rev.: $72,256,823
Assets: $2,057,634,403
Liabilities: $171,993,715
Net Worth: $1,885,640,688
Earnings: $11,130,969
Fiscal Year-end: 03/31/22
Money Market Brokerage
N.A.I.C.S.: 523150
Keith Duncan *(CEO)*

Subsidiaries:

JMMB Insurance Brokers Ltd (1)
8 Dominica Drive, New Kingston, Kingston, 5, Jamaica
Tel.: (876) 9205040
Health Insurance Brokerage Services
N.A.I.C.S.: 524210

JMMB International Limited (1)
Reduit, Gros Islet, Saint Lucia
Tel.: (758) 458 1046
Web Site: http://www.jmmb.com
Investment Management Service
N.A.I.C.S.: 523999
Carolyn Dacoste *(Gen Mgr)*

JMMB Securities Limited (1)
6 Haughton Terrace, Kingston, 10, Jamaica
Tel.: (876) 920 5040
Web Site: http://www.jmmbsecurities.com
Investment Services
N.A.I.C.S.: 523999

JAMAICA NATIONAL BUILDING SOCIETY
2-4 Constant Spring Road, Kingston, 10, Jamaica
Tel.: (876) 9261344
Web Site: http://www.jnbs.com
Sales Range: $150-199.9 Million
Emp.: 500
Financial & Mortgage Services
N.A.I.C.S.: 522180
Earl Jarrett *(CEO)*

Subsidiaries:

JN Fund Managers Limited (1)
17 Belmont Road, Kingston, Jamaica
Tel.: (876) 929 2289
Web Site: http://www.jnfunds.com
Sales Range: $50-74.9 Million
Emp.: 40
Financial Management Services
N.A.I.C.S.: 523999

JNBS Foundation (1)
32 1/2 Duke Street, Kingston, Jamaica

Tel.: (876) 922 4931
Web Site: http://www.jnfoundation.com
Sales Range: $10-24.9 Million
Emp.: 10
Social Welfare Services
N.A.I.C.S.: 624190
Earl Jarrett *(Chm)*

Management Control Systems Limited (1)
10-12 Grenada Crescent, Kingston, Jamaica
Tel.: (876) 929 8661
Web Site: http://www.mcsystems.com
Information Technology Consulting Services
N.A.I.C.S.: 541512
Diane Smith-Sears *(Gen Mgr)*

National Building Society Of Cayman (1)
29 Elgin Avenue, PO Box 504, Georgetown, KY1-1106, Cayman Islands
Tel.: (345) 946 3030
Web Site: http://www.nbsc.com.ky
Home Loan Providers
N.A.I.C.S.: 522299
Dunbar McFarlane *(Gen Mgr)*

The Creative Unit Limited (1)
1 Holborn Road, Kingston, Jamaica
Tel.: (876) 926 4414
Advetising Agency
N.A.I.C.S.: 541810
Terence Tracey *(Dir-Art)*

Total Credit Services Limited (1)
26 Trafalgar Road, Kingston, Jamaica
Tel.: (876) 920 6573
Sales Range: $50-74.9 Million
Emp.: 18
Property Management Services
N.A.I.C.S.: 531311

JAMAICA PEGASUS HOTEL
81 Knutsford Boulevard, Kingston, 5, Jamaica
Tel.: (876) 926 36919
Web Site:
http://www.jamaicapegasus.com
Hotel Owner & Operator
N.A.I.C.S.: 721110

JAMAICA STOCK EXCHANGE
40 Harbour Street, Kingston, Jamaica
Tel.: (876) 9673271
Web Site: http://www.jamstockex.com
Sales Range: $10-24.9 Million
Stock Exchange Services
N.A.I.C.S.: 523210
Marlene Street-Forrest *(Mng Dir)*

JAMAICAN TEAS LTD.
2 Bell Road, Kingston, 11, Jamaica
Tel.: (876) 6569491
Web Site:
https://www.jamaicanteas.com
Year Founded: 1967
JAMT—(JAM)
Rev.: $17,498,677
Assets: $33,851,855
Liabilities: $7,647,618
Net Worth: $26,204,237
Earnings: $1,208,227
Emp.: 140
Fiscal Year-end: 09/30/23
Food Mfr
N.A.I.C.S.: 311999
John Mahfood *(CEO)*

Subsidiaries:

QWI Investment Limited (1)
2 Bell Road, Kingston, Jamaica
Tel.: (876) 65694912
Web Site: https://www.qwiinvestments.com
Cement Mfr
N.A.I.C.S.: 327310
John Jackson *(Chm)*

JAMCO CORPORATION
1-100 Takamatsu-cho, Tachikawa, 190-0011, Tokyo, Japan
Tel.: (81) 425039900

INTERNATIONAL PUBLIC

Web Site: https://www.jamco.co.jp
Year Founded: 1955
7408—(TKS)
Rev.: $423,033,390
Assets: $715,307,760
Liabilities: $615,688,450
Net Worth: $99,619,310
Earnings: $11,303,100
Emp.: 2,692
Fiscal Year-end: 03/31/24
Aircraft Interior Parts Mfr & Whslr
N.A.I.C.S.: 336413
Toshikazu Kimura *(Sr Mng Exec Officer & Chief Compliance Officer-PR & Corp Admin)*

Subsidiaries:

JAMCO AEROMANUFACTURING Co. Ltd. (1)
7-101-36 Medeshimadai, Natori, 981-1251, Miyagi, Japan
Tel.: (81) 227841570
Aircraft Engine Parts Mfr
N.A.I.C.S.: 336412

JAMCO AEROTECH CO., LTD. (1)
26 Shin-izumi, Narita, 286-0825, Chiba, Japan
Tel.: (81) 476409540
Aircraft Maintenance Services
N.A.I.C.S.: 488190

JAMCO Philippines Inc. (1)
Bldg 1-A Berthaphil V Gil Puyat Ave, Clark Special Economic Zone, Pampanga, 2023, Philippines
Tel.: (63) 454991515
Web Site: https://www.jamcophilippines.com
Aircraft Interior Components Mfr
N.A.I.C.S.: 336413
Keiji Ozawa *(Pres)*

JAMCO SINGAPORE PTE LTD. (1)
8 Loyang Lane, Singapore, 508915, Singapore
Tel.: (65) 64170560
Web Site: http://www.sinjam.com.sg
Aircraft Interior Product Mfr
N.A.I.C.S.: 336413
Hiroshi Uchijo *(Pres)*

JAMCO TECHNICAL CENTER Co., Ltd. (1)
6-11-25 Osawa, Mitaka, Tokyo, Japan
Tel.: (81) 422319139
Aircraft Maintenance Services
N.A.I.C.S.: 488190

Jamco America, Inc. (1)
1018 80th St SW, Everett, WA 98203
Tel.: (425) 347-4735
Web Site: https://www.jamco-america.com
Emp.: 400
Aircraft Maintenance Services
N.A.I.C.S.: 488190
Kazuo Nishimiya *(Chm & CEO)*

MRO Japan Co., Ltd. (1)
260 Omine, Naha, 901-0196, Okinawa, Japan
Tel.: (81) 988517660
Web Site: https://www.mrojpn.co.jp
Emp.: 390
Aircraft Maintenance Services
N.A.I.C.S.: 488190

Miyazaki JAMCO Corporation (1)
Tel.: (81) 985646022
Web Site: http://www.miyazaki-jamco.co.jp
Aircraft Interior Product Mfr
N.A.I.C.S.: 336360

Nakajo JAMCO Corporation (1)
9-113 Shimizu, Tainai, 959-2600, Niigata, Japan
Tel.: (81) 254440066
Web Site: http://www.jamco.co.jp
Aircraft Interior Product Mfr
N.A.I.C.S.: 336413

Niigata JAMCO Corporation (1)
341-1 Kamitsubone Tsubone, Murakami, Niigata, 958-0822, Japan
Tel.: (81) 254521188
Web Site: http://www.niigata-jamco.co.jp
Aircraft Interior Product Mfr
N.A.I.C.S.: 336360

AND PRIVATE COMPANIES

SINGAPORE JAMCO SERVICES PTE LTD. (1)
9 Loyang Way, Singapore, 508722, Singapore
Tel.: (65) 67186550
Aircraft Maintenance Services
N.A.I.C.S.: 488190

Tokushima JAMCO Corporation (1)
5F Pinefield 3-40-7 Matsubara, Setagaya, Tokyo, 156-0043, Japan
Tel.: (81) 333254411
Aircraft Maintenance Services
N.A.I.C.S.: 488190

JAMES & JENKINS LTD
Station Road Llandaff North, Clifton, Cardiff, CF14 2FB, United Kingdom
Tel.: (44) 2920304020
Web Site: http://www.jamesandjenkins.co.uk
Sales Range: $10-24.9 Million
Emp.: 65
New & Used Car Dealers
N.A.I.C.S.: 441110
Mike O'Shea (Mgr-Sls)

JAMES BAY RESOURCES LIMITED
110 Yonge St suite 501, Toronto, M5C 1T4, ON, Canada
Tel.: (416) 366-4200
Web Site: https://www.jamesbayresource.com
Year Founded: 2007
JMBRF—(OTCIQ)
Assets: $1,160,591
Liabilities: $1,433,766
Net Worth: ($273,175)
Earnings: ($1,719,292)
Fiscal Year-end: 12/31/22
Mineral Exploration Services
N.A.I.C.S.: 213114
Stephen Shefsky (Co-Founder, Pres & CEO)

Subsidiaries:

James Bay Energy Nigeria Limited (1)
2 Obudu Close Osborne Foreshore Estate, Ikoyi, Lagos, Nigeria
Tel.: (234) 12773900
Metal Mining Services
N.A.I.C.S.: 213114
Afolabi Omoni (Office Mgr)

JAMES BRADEN FORD LTD.
505 Canatara Court, Kingston, K7M 7L1, ON, Canada
Tel.: (613) 384-4854
Web Site: http://www.jamesbradenford.ca
Year Founded: 1984
Rev.: $16,780,375
Emp.: 36
New & Used Car Dealers
N.A.I.C.S.: 441110

JAMES CROPPER PLC
Burneside Mills, Kendal, LA9 6PZ, Cumbria, United Kingdom
Tel.: (44) 1539722002
Web Site: https://jamescropper.com
Year Founded: 1845
CRPR—(AIM)
Rev.: $143,464,842
Assets: $126,103,676
Liabilities: $78,836,012
Net Worth: $47,267,664
Earnings: $1,843,784
Emp.: 587
Fiscal Year-end: 03/26/22
Paper & Paper Products Mfr
N.A.I.C.S.: 322299
Mark A. J. Cropper (Chm)

Subsidiaries:

James Cropper Converting Limited (1)
Tel.: (44) 1539818210
Web Site: http://www.cropper.com
Sales Range: $125-149.9 Million
Emp.: 496
Coated & Laminated Packaging Paper & Plastics Film Mfr
N.A.I.C.S.: 322220

James Cropper Speciality Papers Limited (1)
Burneside Mills, Kendal, LA9 6PZ, Cumbria, United Kingdom (100%)
Tel.: (44) 1539818240
Web Site: http://www.jamescropper.com
Sales Range: $125-149.9 Million
Emp.: 450
Paperboard Mills
N.A.I.C.S.: 322130

Papermilldirect.com Limited (1)
Westmorland Business Park, Kendal, LA9 6NP, Cumbria, United Kingdom (100%)
Tel.: (44) 1539735252
Web Site: http://www.papermilldirect.co.uk
Sales Range: $25-49.9 Million
Emp.: 520
Other Direct Selling Establishments
N.A.I.C.S.: 423690

Technical Fiber Products Inc (1)
679 Mariaville Rd, Schenectady, NY 12306
Tel.: (518) 280-8500
Web Site: https://www.tfpglobal.com
Nonwoven Mats Mfr
N.A.I.C.S.: 313230

Technical Fibre Products Limited (1)
Burneside Mills, Kendal, LA9 6PZ, Cumbria, United Kingdom (100%)
Tel.: (44) 1539818220
Web Site: http://www.tfpglobal.com
Sales Range: $25-49.9 Million
Emp.: 100
Nonwoven Fabric Mills
N.A.I.C.S.: 313230

Joint Venture (US):

Electro Fiber Technologies LLC (2)
679 Mariaville Rd, Schenectady, NY 12306
Tel.: (518) 280-8500
Web Site: http://www.electrofibertechnologies.com
Noncellulosic Organic Fiber Mfr; Owned 50% by Thermion Systems International, Inc. & 50% by James Cropper Plc
N.A.I.C.S.: 325220

JAMES DURRANS & SONS LIMITED
Phoenix Works Thurlstone, Sheffield, S36 9QU, South Yorkshire, United Kingdom
Tel.: (44) 1226 370000
Web Site: http://www.durrans.co.uk
Year Founded: 1863
Sales Range: $100-124.9 Million
Emp.: 178
Carbonaceous Material Whslr
N.A.I.C.S.: 424690
Alexander Brown (Mgr-Product)

Subsidiaries:

Carbon International Ltd (1)
Anchor Road, Bilston, WV14 9NZ, W Midlands, United Kingdom
Tel.: (44) 1902492770
Web Site: http://www.carboninternational.co.uk
Chemical Products Mfr
N.A.I.C.S.: 325199

Durrans RMS (Pty) Ltd (1)
Corner 15th and All Black Road, Boksburg, South Africa
Tel.: (27) 119170702
Web Site: http://www.rmsproducts.co.za
Chemical Product Mfr & Distr
N.A.I.C.S.: 325199

James Durrans (Tianjin) Coatings Ltd (1)
Huangshan Road No 1116, Binhai New District, Tianjin, 300451, China
Tel.: (86) 2225215337
Web Site: http://www.durrans.com.cn
Refractory Material Mfr & Distr
N.A.I.C.S.: 327120

James Durrans GmbH (1)
Am Niederheiderhof 3, 47877, Willich, Germany
Tel.: (49) 215495840
Chemical Products Distr
N.A.I.C.S.: 424690

MPM-Durrans Refracoat PVT Ltd (1)
275 Avm Campus Shanti Nagar Godown No Shanti Nagar, Pollachi, 642001, Tamil Nadu, India
Tel.: (91) 4222454191
Refractory Material Mfr & Distr
N.A.I.C.S.: 327120

JAMES E. WAGNER CULTIVATION CORP.
PO Box 46015, Kitchener, N2E 4J3, ON, Canada
Web Site: https://www.jwc.ca
Year Founded: 2007
JWCA—(TSX)
Rev.: $2,158,946
Assets: $22,166,915
Liabilities: $10,602,694
Net Worth: $11,564,221
Earnings: ($7,080,194)
Emp.: 85
Fiscal Year-end: 09/30/19
Pharmaceutical Products Distr
N.A.I.C.S.: 424210
Nathan Woodworth (Pres & CEO)

JAMES FISHER & SONS PUBLIC LIMITED COMPANY
Fisher House Michaelson Road, PO Box 4, Barrow-in-Furness, LA14 1HR, Cumbria, United Kingdom
Tel.: (44) 1229615400   UK
Web Site: https://www.james-fisher.com
FSJ—(LSE)
Rev.: $670,849,452
Assets: $848,439,228
Liabilities: $562,503,396
Net Worth: $285,935,832
Earnings: ($38,287,704)
Emp.: 2,662
Fiscal Year-end: 12/31/21
Marine Engineering Services
N.A.I.C.S.: 541330
Stuart Charles Kilpatrick (Dir-Grp Fin)

Subsidiaries:

Buchan Technical Services Limited (1)
Fisher Offshore North Meadows, Oldmeldrum, AB51 0GQ, Aberdeenshire, United Kingdom
Tel.: (44) 1651873932
Web Site: http://www.fisheroffshore.com
Sales Range: $50-74.9 Million
Oil & Gas Field Equipment Sales & Rental Services
N.A.I.C.S.: 423720

Cattedown Wharves Limited (1)
Cattedown Wharves, Plymouth, Devon, United Kingdom
Tel.: (44) 1752665231
Web Site: http://www.cattwharves.co.uk
Sales Range: $25-49.9 Million
Emp.: 25
Marine Cargo Handling
N.A.I.C.S.: 488320

Cowan Manufacturing Pty. Limited (1)
9A Walker Street, PO Box 185, Warners Bay, Lake Macquarie, 2282, NSW, Australia
Tel.: (61) 249546588
Web Site: http://www.cowanmfg.com.au
Emp.: 25
Sheet Metal Work Mfg
N.A.I.C.S.: 332322

Electricity Distribution Services Limited (1)
18 Three Point Business Park Charles Lane Haslingden, Rossendale, BB4 5EH, Lancashire, United Kingdom
Tel.: (44) 1706231067
Offshore Infrastructure Services
N.A.I.C.S.: 236220

Everard (Guernsey) Limited (1)
Francis House Sir William Place, PO Box 112, Saint Peter Port, GY1 4EA, Guernsey
Tel.: (44) 1481 731 024
Web Site: http://www.bachmannhr.com
Sales Range: $25-49.9 Million
Emp.: 4
Payroll Processing Services
N.A.I.C.S.: 541214
Nicholas Saul (Gen Mgr)

Fender Care Marine (Asia Pacific) Pte Ltd (1)
39 Tuas West Avenue, Singapore, 638442, Singapore
Tel.: (65) 62729167
Sales Range: $25-49.9 Million
Emp.: 25
Marine Engineering Services
N.A.I.C.S.: 541330
Ashley Mawby (Reg Mng Dir)

Fender Care Marine Products (Asia Pacific) Pte. Limited (1)
39 Tuas West Avenue, Singapore, 638442, Singapore
Tel.: (65) 62729167
Marine Products Distr
N.A.I.C.S.: 423860

FenderCare Australia Pty Ltd (1)
Tel.: (61) 89 412 9999
Web Site: http://www.fendercare.com.au
Sales Range: $25-49.9 Million
Marine Engineering Services
N.A.I.C.S.: 541330

FenderCare Marine Limited (1)
Enterprise House Harveys Lane, Seething, Norfolk, NR15 1EN, United Kingdom
Tel.: (44) 1508482666
Web Site: http://www.fendercare.com
Sales Range: $25-49.9 Million
Emp.: 100
Other Marine Fishing
N.A.I.C.S.: 114119

Division (Domestic):

E. J. Bean & Co. (2)
Enterprise House Harveys Lane, Seething, Norfolk, NR15 1EN, United Kingdom
Tel.: (44) 1508483703
Web Site: http://www.fendercare.com
Sales Range: $25-49.9 Million
Emp.: 100
Fabricated Structural Metal Mfr
N.A.I.C.S.: 332312

FenderCare Marine Solutions Ltd (2)
Enterprise House, Harveys Lane Seething, Norfolk, NR15 1EN, United Kingdom
Tel.: (44) 1508482691
Web Site: http://www.fendercare.com
Sales Range: $25-49.9 Million
Emp.: 70
Engineered Wood Member Mfr
N.A.I.C.S.: 321215

FenderCare Naval Solutions Ltd (2)
Enterprise House, Harveys Lane Seething, Norfolk, NR15 1EN, United Kingdom
Tel.: (44) 1508482691
Web Site: http://www.fendercare.com
Sales Range: $25-49.9 Million
Emp.: 50
Marine Cargo Handling
N.A.I.C.S.: 488320

Hippo Marine Ltd (2)
Enterprise House Harvey Lane Seething, Norfolk, NR15 1EN, United Kingdom
Tel.: (44) 1752843333
Web Site: http://www.fendercare.com
Sales Range: $25-49.9 Million
Emp.: 100
Polystyrene Foam Product Mfr
N.A.I.C.S.: 326140

Turners Marine Trading Ltd (2)
Enterptise House, Harveys Lane Seething, Norfolk, NR15 1EN, United Kingdom
Tel.: (44) 1508483705
Web Site: http://www.sendercire.com
Sales Range: $50-74.9 Million
Emp.: 150
Marine Cargo Handling

JAMES FISHER & SONS PUBLIC LIMITED COMPANY

James Fisher—Sons Public Limited Company—(Continued)
N.A.I.C.S.: 488320
Eric Pleane (Mng Dir)

Fendercare Marine Ghana Limited (1)
11 Aduemi Close, PO Box CT 3104, North Kaneshie, Accra, Ghana
Tel.: (233) 302797555
Marine Products Distr
N.A.I.C.S.: 423860

GMC Produkt AS (1)
Dusavikveien 19, Stavanger, 4007, Norway
Tel.: (47) 51 54 54 00
Lifting Equipment Whslr
N.A.I.C.S.: 423830

High Technology Sources Limited (1)
Michaelson Road, PO Box 4, Cumbria, Barrow-in-Furness, LA14 1HR, United Kingdom
Tel.: (44) 1235514200
Web Site: http://hightechsource.co.uk
Pharmaceuticals Product Mfr
N.A.I.C.S.: 325412

JFD Australia Pty. Ltd. (1)
Unit 13 21-25 Monro Avenue Kirrawee, Sydney, 2232, NSW, Australia
Tel.: (61) 295453500
Engineering & Technical Services
N.A.I.C.S.: 541330

JFD Ortega B.V. (1)
Vliegveldstraat 100-b515, 7524PK, Enschede, Netherlands
Tel.: (31) 613980787
Web Site: https://www.ortega-submersibles.com
Boat Mfr
N.A.I.C.S.: 336612

JFD Singapore Pte. Ltd. (1)
19 Loyang Lane, Singapore, 508929, Singapore
Tel.: (65) 65462844
Engineering & Technical Services
N.A.I.C.S.: 541330

JFD Sweden AB (1)
Rindo Vastra, 185 41, Vaxholm, Sweden
Tel.: (46) 854131880
Web Site: https://www.jfdglobal.com
Diving Equipment Mfr & Distr
N.A.I.C.S.: 339920

James Fisher (Crewing Services) Limited (1)
Fisher House Michaelson Rd, Barrow-in-Furness, LA14 1HR, Cumbria, United Kingdom
Tel.: (44) 1229615400
Freight Transportation Services
N.A.I.C.S.: 483111

James Fisher (Logistics) Limited (1)
Fisher House, PO Box 4, Barrow-in-Furness, LA14 1HR, Cumbria, United Kingdom
Tel.: (44) 1229615400
Web Site: http://www.james-fisher.co.uk
Other Support Activities for Water Transportation
N.A.I.C.S.: 488390

James Fisher (Shipping Services) Limited (1)
Fisher House Michaelson Road, PO Box 4, Barrow-in-Furness, LA14 1HR, Cumbria, United Kingdom
Tel.: (44) 1229615400
Sales Range: $25-49.9 Million
Emp.: 100
Navigational Services to Shipping
N.A.I.C.S.: 488330

James Fisher Asset Information Services Limited (1)
Level 4 City Wharf, Shiprow, Aberdeen, AB11 5BY, United Kingdom
Tel.: (44) 1224355880
Freight Forwarding Services
N.A.I.C.S.: 488510

James Fisher Australia Pty Ltd (1)
54 Bushland Ridge Bibra Lake, Perth, 6163, WA, Australia

Tel.: (61) 861644400
Web Site: http://www.james-fisher.com
Marine Engineering Services
N.A.I.C.S.: 541330

James Fisher Defence Limited (1)
Fisher House Michaelson Road, PO Box 4, Barrow-in-Furness, LA141HR, Cumbria, United Kingdom
Tel.: (44) 1229615400
Sales Range: $25-49.9 Million
Emp.: 150
Engineeering Services
N.A.I.C.S.: 541330

James Fisher Defence North America Limited (1)
1801 Robert Fulton Dr Ste 400, Reston, VA 20191
Tel.: (757) 955-8556
Submarine Rescue Services
N.A.I.C.S.: 488330
Keith Lehnhardt (Gen Mgr)

James Fisher Defence Sweden Aktiebolag (1)
Rindo Vastra, 185 41, Vaxholm, Sweden
Tel.: (46) 854131880
Submarine Rescue Services
N.A.I.C.S.: 488330

James Fisher Everard Limited (1)
Third Floor 68 Cornhill, London, EC3V 3QX, United Kingdom
Tel.: (44) 2076149500
Web Site: http://www.jfeverard.co.uk
Sales Range: $25-49.9 Million
Emp.: 12
Deep Sea Freight Transportation
N.A.I.C.S.: 483111

James Fisher MFE Limited (1)
Fisher House, PO Box 4, Barrow-in-Furness, LA14 1HR, Cumbria, United Kingdom
Tel.: (44) 1651871454
Web Site: https://www.jfsubseaexcavation.com
Subsea Excavation Services
N.A.I.C.S.: 238910
Kenneth R. Mackie (Co-Founder & Mng Dir)

James Fisher MIMIC Limited (1)
Unit 1 Enterprise House, Manchester Science Park Pencro, Manchester, M15 6SE, United Kingdom
Tel.: (44) 1612321414
Web Site: http://www.jfmimic.co.uk
Sales Range: $25-49.9 Million
Emp.: 14
Other Management Consulting Services
N.A.I.C.S.: 541618

James Fisher Marine Services Limited (1)
Fisher House Michaelson Road, PO Box 4, Barrow-in-Furness, LA14 1HR, Cumbria, United Kingdom
Tel.: (44) 1229615400
Emp.: 10
Marine Freight Transportation Services
N.A.I.C.S.: 483211

James Fisher Nuclear GmbH (1)
Uwestrasse 12, 22525, Hamburg, Germany
Tel.: (49) 40228613999
Web Site: http://www.jfnhamburg.com
Contamination & Clearance Product Distr
N.A.I.C.S.: 423860
Ingo Kolln (Mng Dir)

James Fisher Offshore Limited (1)
North Meadows Oldmeldrum, Inverurie, AB51 0GQ, Aberdeenshire, United Kingdom
Tel.: (44) 1651873932
Web Site: https://www.fisheroffshore.com
Marine Hydraulic & Air Winches Supplier
N.A.I.C.S.: 333998

James Fisher Offshore Malaysia Sdn. Bhd. (1)
Plo 209 Jalan Rasau Block 12 Kompleks Perindustrian Tanjung Langsat, 81700, Pasir Gudang, Johor, Malaysia
Tel.: (60) 197228744
Offshore Infrastructure Services
N.A.I.C.S.: 236220

James Fisher Rumic Limited (1)
Fisher House, PO Box 4, Barrow-in-Furness, LA14 1HR, Cumbria, United Kingdom
Tel.: (44) 1229615456
Web Site: https://www.rumic.co.uk
Sales Range: $25-49.9 Million
Other Management Consulting Services
N.A.I.C.S.: 541618

James Fisher Subsea Excavation Mexico S.A. de C.V. (1)
Calle 55 num 107 Colonia Miamimi, 24115, Ciudad del Carmen, Campeche, Mexico
Tel.: (52) 9382860285
Subsea Excavation Services
N.A.I.C.S.: 238910
Jose Luis Oviedo (Country Mgr)

James Fisher Subsea Excavation Pte. Limited (1)
133 Cecil Street 16-01 Keck Seng Tower, Singapore, 069535, Singapore
Tel.: (65) 68873613
Subsea Excavation Services
N.A.I.C.S.: 238910

James Fisher Tankships Holdings Limited (1)
Fisher House Michaelson Rd, Barrow-in-Furness, LA14 1HR, United Kingdom
Tel.: (44) 1229615400
Emp.: 100
Other Holding Companies Offices
N.A.I.C.S.: 551112

James Fisher Technologies LLC (1)
5821 Langley Ave, Loveland, CO 80538
Tel.: (720) 408-0100
Web Site: https://www.jftechgroup.com
Engineering & Technical Services
N.A.I.C.S.: 541330
Scott Adams (CEO)

James Fisher Testing Services (Ireland) Limited (1)
Zone 5 Unit D Clonminam Industrial Estate, Co Laois, Portlaoise, Ireland
Tel.: (353) 578664885
Non-Destructive Testing Services
N.A.I.C.S.: 541380

Maritime Engineers Pty Ltd (1)
8A Sparks Road, Henderson, 6166, WA, Australia
Tel.: (61) 89 335 3250
Web Site: https://www.maritime-engineers.com.au
Marine Engineering Services
N.A.I.C.S.: 541330

Martek Marine Limited (1)
Adwick Park, Manvers Swinton, Rotherham, S63 5AB, United Kingdom
Tel.: (44) 170959922
Web Site: https://www.martek-marine.com
Marine Engineering Services
N.A.I.C.S.: 541330

Martek-Marine (Asia Pacific) Pte Ltd. (1)
1 Raffles Place Tower 2 Level 19-61 and 20-61, Singapore, 048616, Singapore
Tel.: (65) 68085862
Marine Engineering Services
N.A.I.C.S.: 541330

Mojo Maritime France SAS (1)
3 rue de Fracne Comte - CS 50311, 50103, Cherbourg, France
Tel.: (33) 240990041
Marine Engineering Services
N.A.I.C.S.: 541330

Mojo Maritime Limited (1)
Units 5C and D Falmouth Business Park Bickland Water Road, Falmouth, TR11 4SZ, United Kingdom
Tel.: (44) 1326218218
Web Site: http://www.mojomaritime.com
Marine Engineering Services
N.A.I.C.S.: 541330

Remote Marine Systems Limited (1)
Derwent Rd, York Rd Business Park North, YO17 6YB, Malton, United Kingdom - England
Tel.: (44) 1653690001
Web Site: http://www.rmsltd.com
Sales Range: $25-49.9 Million
Emp.: 43
Measuring & Controlling Device Mfr

INTERNATIONAL PUBLIC

N.A.I.C.S.: 334519

RigCool Australia Pty Ltd (1)
23 Sparks Road, Henderson, 6166, Perth, Australia
Tel.: (61) 8 9437 4555
Web Site: http://www.rigcoolaustralia.com.au
Oil,Heat Suppression Safety System Mfr & Distr
N.A.I.C.S.: 333132

RigCool Limited (1)
Unit 4 Fisher Offshore Base North Meadows, Oldmeldrum, AB51 0GQ, Aberdeenshire, United Kingdom
Tel.: (44) 1651 871430
Web Site: http://www.rigcoolltd.com
Sales Range: $25-49.9 Million
Emp.: 2
Oil & Gas Industries Safety System Distr
N.A.I.C.S.: 423830
Keith Moyse (Dir-Ops)

Rotos 360 Limited (1)
Kirkley Business Park Maconochie Way Horn Hill, Lowestoft, NR33 0PX, United Kingdom
Tel.: (44) 1472907720
Web Site: https://www.rotos360.co.uk
Wind Turbine Installation Mfr
N.A.I.C.S.: 333611
Simon Sanderson (Dir-Technical)

Scan Tech AS (1)
Finnestadsvingen 23, 4004, Stavanger, Norway
Tel.: (47) 51545400
Web Site: https://www.scan-tech.no
Emp.: 60
Marine Engineering Services
N.A.I.C.S.: 541330

ScanTech Offshore Ltd (1)
Unit 4 Fisher Offshore Base, North Meadows, Oldmeldrum, AB51 0GQ, Aberdeenshire, United Kingdom
Tel.: (44) 1651871440
Web Site: https://www.scantechoffshore.com
Sales Range: $25-49.9 Million
Engineeering Services
N.A.I.C.S.: 541330

Scantech Offshore Pty. Ltd. (1)
23 Sparks Road Henderson, Perth, 6166, WA, Australia
Tel.: (61) 861644400
Offshore Infrastructure Services
N.A.I.C.S.: 236220

Servicos Maritimos Continental S.A. (1)
Alameda Lieutenant Celio 150, Granja dos Cavaleiros, Macae, 930043, RJ, Brazil
Tel.: (55) 2233123350
Web Site: https://smcontinental.com
Port Maintenance Services
N.A.I.C.S.: 488310

Strainstall Group Ltd. (1)
9-10 Mariners Way, Cowes, PO31 8PD, United Kingdom
Tel.: (44) 1983203600
Web Site: http://www.strainstall.com
Sales Range: $25-49.9 Million
Emp.: 60
Sensors & Control Systems Mfr
N.A.I.C.S.: 334511

Subsidiary (Domestic):

Scotload Ltd (2)
Unit 14 Enterprise Drive, Westhill, Aberdeen, AB32 6TQ, United Kingdom
Tel.: (44) 1224 877007
Web Site: http://www.scotload.com
Sales Range: $25-49.9 Million
Emp.: 6
Load Transducers Mfr
N.A.I.C.S.: 334519
Simon Everett (Mng Dir)

Subsidiary (Non-US):

Strainstall AS (2)
Smidsrodveien 95, 3120, Notteroy, Norway
Tel.: (47) 33346100
Web Site: http://www.strainstall.no
Emp.: 1
Winch Monitoring & Control System Whslr

AND PRIVATE COMPANIES

N.A.I.C.S.: 423830
Bogdan Planinc *(Gen Mgr)*

Strainstall Malaysia SDN BHD (2)
Ground Floor 8 Lorong Universiti B Section 16, 46200, Petaling Jaya, Senalgor Darul Ehsan, Malaysia
Tel.: (60) 380604450
Web Site:
http://www.strainstallmalaysia.com.my
Sales Range: $25-49.9 Million
Emp.: 16
Geotechnical Instrumentation Mfr
N.A.I.C.S.: 333310

Subsidiary (Domestic):

Strainstall UK Limited (2)
9 10 Mariners Way, Cowes, PO31 8PD, Hampshire, United Kingdom
Tel.: (44) 983203600
Web Site: http://www.strainstall.com
Sales Range: $10-24.9 Million
Emp.: 50
Stress Analysis Service for Load Measurement & Monitoring
N.A.I.C.S.: 541511

Strainstall Singapore Pte. Ltd. (1)
25 North Bridge Road Level 7, Singapore, 179104, Singapore
Tel.: (65) 65614628
Structural Monitoring Services
N.A.I.C.S.: 561621

JAMES HALSTEAD PLC

Beechfield Hollinhurst Road, Radcliffe, Manchester, M26 1JN, United Kingdom
Tel.: (44) 1617672500
Web Site:
https://www.jameshalstead.com
JHD—(LSE)
Rev.: $347,422,901
Assets: $312,177,704
Liabilities: $83,061,173
Net Worth: $229,116,531
Earnings: $52,477,250
Emp.: 819
Fiscal Year-end: 06/30/24
Commercial Flooring Manufacturer
N.A.I.C.S.: 321918
Gordon R. Oliver *(Dir-Fin)*

Subsidiaries:

Falck Design AB (1)
Energigatan 9, PO Box 102 51, 434 37, Kungsbacka, Halland, Sweden
Tel.: (46) 30015820
Web Site: https://polyflor.se
Sales Range: $25-49.9 Million
Emp.: 3
Vinyl Flooring Coverings Mfr
N.A.I.C.S.: 326199

Halstead Flooring Concepts Pty Limited (1)
59-65 Wedgewood Rd, Hallam, 3803, VIC, Australia
Tel.: (61) 392154400
Floor Coverings Whslr
N.A.I.C.S.: 423220
Mark Halstead *(Gen Mgr)*

Karndean International GmbH (1)
Wankelstrasse 50, 50996, Cologne, Germany
Tel.: (49) 2236966330
Web Site: http://www.karndean.de
Sales Range: $25-49.9 Million
Emp.: 100
Floor Covering Mfr
N.A.I.C.S.: 326199
Stephan Wolff *(CEO)*

Polyflor (M) Sdn Bhd (1)
Lot 2D Jalan Kilang 51/215 Section 51, 46050, Petaling Jaya, Selangor, Malaysia
Tel.: (60) 130 080 7788
Flooring Material Whslr
N.A.I.C.S.: 449121

Polyflor Canada Inc. (1)
3209 Orlando Drive, Mississauga, L4V 1C5, ON, Canada
Tel.: (905) 364-3000
Web Site: https://www.polyflor.ca

Flooring Material Whslr
N.A.I.C.S.: 449121

Polyflor FZE (1)
Office No LB16112 Jafza 16 Building Jebel Ali Free Zone, Dubai, United Arab Emirates
Tel.: (971) 50 406 8114
Flooring Material Mfr & Whslr
N.A.I.C.S.: 321918

Polyflor India Pvt Limited (1)
B-506 Knox Plaza Adjacent to Grand Hometel Hotel, Mindspace Malad West, Mumbai, 400 064, India
Tel.: (91) 224 023 2485
Flooring Material Whslr
N.A.I.C.S.: 449121

Polyflor Limited (1)
Radcliffe New Road, PO Box 3, Whitefield, M45 7NR, Greater Manchester, United Kingdom
Tel.: (44) 161 767 1111
Web Site: https://www.polyflor.com
Sales Range: $50-74.9 Million
Emp.: 150
Commercial Floor Coverings Mfr
N.A.I.C.S.: 326199
Geoffrey Halstead *(Mng Dir)*

Polyflor New Zealand Limited (1)
2 Narek Place, Manukau, 2104, Auckland, New Zealand
Tel.: (64) 800765935
Web Site: https://www.polyflor.co.nz
Sales Range: $25-49.9 Million
Emp.: 20
Flooring Materials Mfr
N.A.I.C.S.: 326199
Glenn Richardson *(Reg Mgr-North)*

JAMES HARDIE INDUSTRIES PLC

Europa House 2nd Floor Harcourt Center Harcourt Street, Dublin, D02 WR20, Ireland
Tel.: (353) 14116924   NL
Web Site:
https://www.ir.jameshardie.com.au
Year Founded: 2001
JHX—(NYSE)
Rev.: $3,614,700,000
Assets: $4,243,200,000
Liabilities: $2,910,300,000
Net Worth: $1,332,900,000
Earnings: $459,100,000
Emp.: 5,196
Fiscal Year-end: 03/31/22
Holding Company; Fibre Cement Building Products Mfr & Distr
N.A.I.C.S.: 551112
Sean Gadd *(Exec VP-Comml-North America)*

Subsidiaries:

James Hardie 117 Pty Ltd (1)
Level 3 22 Pitt Street, Sydney, 2000, NSW, Australia
Tel.: (61) 282745239
Cement Mfr
N.A.I.C.S.: 327310

James Hardie Australia Pty. Ltd. (1)
Level 3 22 Pitt Street, Sydney, 2000, NSW, Australia (100%)
Tel.: (61) 282745274
Web Site: http://www.jameshardie.com
Sales Range: $150-199.9 Million
Emp.: 397
Fibre Cement Building Products Mfr & Distr
N.A.I.C.S.: 327999

James Hardie Batiment S.A.S. (1)
1 rue de l Union, 92500, Rueil-Malmaison, France
Tel.: (33) 170373635
Web Site: https://www.jameshardie.fr
Construction & Renovation Services
N.A.I.C.S.: 541330

James Hardie Building Products Inc. (1)
26300 La Alameda Ste 400, Mission Viejo, CA 92691-6380
Tel.: (949) 348-1800
Web Site: https://www.jameshardie.com

Sales Range: $1-4.9 Billion
Emp.: 1,809
Fibre Cement Building Products Mfr & Distr
N.A.I.C.S.: 327999

Plant (Domestic):

James Hardie Building Products (2)
10901 Elm Ave, Fontana, CA 92337-7327
Tel.: (909) 356-6300
Web Site: http://www.jameshardie.com
Sales Range: $50-74.9 Million
Emp.: 150
Fibre Cement Building Products Mfr & Distr
N.A.I.C.S.: 327999

James Hardie Philippines, Inc. (1)
Barangay San Isidro, 4025, Cabugao, Laguna, Philippines (100%)
Tel.: (63) 28702500
Web Site: http://www.jameshardie.com.ph
Sales Range: $75-99.9 Million
Emp.: 167
Fibre Cement Building Products Mfr & Distr
N.A.I.C.S.: 327999

James Hardie Research (Holdings) Pty Ltd (1)
Level 3 22 Pitt St, Sydney, 2000, NSW, Australia
Tel.: (61) 282745239
Investment Management Service
N.A.I.C.S.: 523999

James Hardie Research Pty Ltd (1)
Level 3 18-22 Pitt Street, Sydney, 2000, NSW, Australia
Tel.: (61) 282745274
Building Material Mfr & Distr
N.A.I.C.S.: 327120

JAMES HOTELS LIMITED

Block 10 Sector 17-A, Chandigarh, 160017, India
Tel.: (91) 1726600000
Web Site:
http://www.jameshotels.co.in
526558—(BOM)
Hotel Operator
N.A.I.C.S.: 721110

JAMES L. WILLIAMS PTY. LTD.

51 N Gate Dr, Thomastown, 3074, VIC, Australia
Tel.: (61) 394642202
Web Site:
http://www.jlwilliams.com.au
Year Founded: 1926
Sales Range: $25-49.9 Million
Emp.: 300
Plumbing, Heating, Refrigeration & General Construction Services
N.A.I.C.S.: 238220
Allen Lee Williams *(Mng Dir)*

JAMES LATHAM PLC

Unit C2 Breakspear Way, Breakspear Park, Hemel Hempstead, HP2 4TZ, United Kingdom
Tel.: (44) 1442849100
Web Site:
https://www.lathamtimber.co.uk
LTHM—(LSE)
Rev.: $523,221,841
Assets: $305,233,106
Liabilities: $82,606,400
Net Worth: $222,626,706
Earnings: $61,969,056
Emp.: 498
Fiscal Year-end: 03/31/22
Importer & Distr of Hardwoods & Softwoods, Plywood, Panel Products & Related Sheet Materials
N.A.I.C.S.: 321211
David A. Dunmow *(Sec & Dir-Fin)*

Subsidiaries:

Abbey Wood Agencies Limited (1)
Unit 143 Grange Drive Baldoyle Industrial Estate, Dublin, D13 W9V2, Ireland
Tel.: (353) 1 839 3435
Web Site: https://www.abbeywoods.ie

JAMES LATHAM PLC

Timber & Panel Distr
N.A.I.C.S.: 423310

James Latham Gateshead Ltd (1)
Nest Road, Felling Industrial Estate, Gateshead, NE10 0LU, United Kingdom (100%)
Tel.: (44) 1914694211
Sales Range: $25-49.9 Million
Emp.: 16
Wheat Farming
N.A.I.C.S.: 111140
Jeff Hall *(Mng Dir)*

James Latham Leeds (1)
Topcliffe Close Capitol Park East Tingley, Longlands, Leeds, WF3 1DR, West Yorkshire, United Kingdom (100%)
Tel.: (44) 1133870830
Web Site: http://www.lathams.co.uk
Sales Range: $25-49.9 Million
Emp.: 40
Lumber Plywood Millwork & Wood Panel Merchant Whslr
N.A.I.C.S.: 423310

James Latham Purfleet Ltd (1)
Unit 22/24 Purfleet Industrial Park Juliette Way, Aveley South Ockendon, Purfleet, RM15 4YD, Essex, United Kingdom
Tel.: (44) 1708864477
Web Site: http://www.lathams.co.uk
Sales Range: $50-74.9 Million
Emp.: 80
Lumber Plywood Millwork & Wood Panel Merchant Whslr
N.A.I.C.S.: 423310

James Latham Thurrock Ltd (1)
Unit 4 Dolphin Way, Purfleet, RM19 1NZ, Essex, United Kingdom
Tel.: (44) 1708869800
Web Site: http://www.lathamtimber.co.uk
Sales Range: $25-49.9 Million
Emp.: 40
Lumber Plywood Millwork & Wood Panel Merchant Whslr
N.A.I.C.S.: 423310

James Latham Wigston Ltd (1)
Unit A Devana Avenue Optimus Point, Glenfield, Leicester, LE3 8JS, United Kingdom
Tel.: (44) 1162889161
Web Site: http://www.lathamtimber.co.uk
Sales Range: $25-49.9 Million
Emp.: 25
Lumber Plywood Millwork & Wood Panel Merchant Whslr
N.A.I.C.S.: 423310

James Latham Yate Ltd (1)
Unit 14 Apollo Park Armstrong Way, Yate, Bristol, BS37 5AH, United Kingdom (100%)
Tel.: (44) 1454315421
Web Site: http://www.lathams.co.uk
Sales Range: $10-24.9 Million
Emp.: 35
Forest Nurseries & Gathering of Forest Products
N.A.I.C.S.: 113210

James Lathams Dudley Ltd (1)
Unit 3 Yorks Park Blowers Green Road, Dudley, DY2 8UL, West Midlands, United Kingdom
Tel.: (44) 1384234444
Web Site: http://www.lathamtimber.co.uk
Sales Range: $25-49.9 Million
Emp.: 18
Lumber Plywood Millwork & Wood Panel Merchant Whslr
N.A.I.C.S.: 423310

James Lathams Eastleigh Ltd (1)
Unit 6 Goodwood Rd Boyatt Wood, Hampton, PO15 5AP, United Kingdom (100%)
Tel.: (44) 1329854800
Web Site: http://www.lathams.co.uk
Sales Range: $25-49.9 Million
Emp.: 15
Wood Products Mfr
N.A.I.C.S.: 321999
Kelly Oleson *(Mgr-Sls)*

James Lathams Hemel Hempstead Ltd (1)
Unit 2 Swallow Park Finway Road, Hemel Hempstead, HP2 7QU, Hertfordshire, United Kingdom (100%)
Tel.: (44) 1442849000

JAMES LATHAM PLC

James Latham Plc—(Continued)

Web Site: http://www.lathamtimber.co.uk
Sales Range: $25-49.9 Million
Emp.: 50
Lumber Plywood Millwork & Wood Panel Merchant Whslr
N.A.I.C.S.: 423310

LDT (1)
5B The Old Yard Rectory Lane, Brasted, Westerham, TN16 1JP, Kent, United Kingdom (100%)
Tel.: (44) 1959561777
Web Site: https://www.directtimber.co.uk
Sales Range: $50-74.9 Million
Emp.: 8
Timbers Sales & Distr
N.A.I.C.S.: 423310
Neil Gaines *(Mgr-Sls)*

Lathams Limited (1)
Unit 2 Swallow Park Finway Road, Hemel Hempstead, HP2 7QU, Hertfordshire, United Kingdom
Tel.: (44) 144 284 9000
Timber & Panel Distr
N.A.I.C.S.: 423310

Lathams ltd (1)
111 E K St, Munday, TX 76371 (100%)
Tel.: (940) 422-4094
Lumber Plywood Millwork & Wood Panel Merchant Whslr
N.A.I.C.S.: 423310

JAMES PASCOE LIMITED

29 Union Street, Newton, Auckland, 1145, New Zealand
Tel.: (64) 9 377 8351 NZ
Web Site: http://www.pascoes.co.nz
Year Founded: 1906
Sales Range: $1-4.9 Billion
Emp.: 9,000
Jewelry Stores
N.A.I.C.S.: 458310
David Norman *(Co-Owner & Mng Dir)*

JAMES REED & PARTNERS PLC

Academy Court 94 Chancery Lane, London, WC 2A1DT, United Kingdom
Tel.: (44) 2082744467
Web Site: http://www.reedglobal.com
Sales Range: $400-449.9 Million
Holding Company
N.A.I.C.S.: 551112
James Reed *(Chm & CEO)*

JAMES RICHARDSON & SONS, LIMITED

3000 One Lombard Place, Winnipeg, R3B 0Y1, MB, Canada
Tel.: (204) 953-7970
Web Site: https://www.jrsl.ca
Year Founded: 1857
Sales Range: $1-4.9 Billion
Emp.: 1,300
Grain Whslr; Real Estate, Investments & Oil & Gas Developer
N.A.I.C.S.: 424510
Hartley T. Richardson *(Pres & CEO)*

Subsidiaries:

Bison Transport, Inc. (1)
1001 Sherwin Rd, Winnipeg, R3H 0T8, MB, Canada
Tel.: (204) 833-0000
Web Site: http://www.bisontransport.com
Sales Range: $150-199.9 Million
Emp.: 1,650
Freight & Truckload Services
N.A.I.C.S.: 484121
Don Streuber *(Chm)*

Subsidiary (US):

Pottle's Transportation Inc. (2)
15 Page Rd W, Hermon, ME 04401
Tel.: (207) 947-2179
Web Site: http://www.pottlestrans.com
Contract Haulers
N.A.I.C.S.: 484121
Barry E. Pottle *(Pres & CEO)*

Richardson Centre Limited (1)
615-One Lombard Place, Winnipeg, R3B 0X3, MB, Canada
Tel.: (204) 934-5728
Web Site: http://www.richardsoncentre.ca
Real Estate Manangement Services
N.A.I.C.S.: 531390
Mark Rzadki *(VP)*

Richardson International Limited (1)
2800 One Lombard Place, Winnipeg, R3B 0X8, MB, Canada
Tel.: (204) 934-5961
Web Site: https://www.richardson.ca
Agricultural Products Processor, Producer, Distr & Whslr
N.A.I.C.S.: 424510
Curt Vossen *(Pres & CEO)*

Richardson Oilseed Limited (1)
2415 2A Ave N, Lethbridge, T1J 3Y4, AB, Canada
Tel.: (403) 329-5500
Oilseed Farming Services
N.A.I.C.S.: 111120

Subsidiary (US):

Italgrani USA Inc. (2)
7900 Van Buren St, Saint Louis, MO 63111
Tel.: (314) 638-1447
Web Site: http://www.italgraniusa.com
Sales Range: $125-149.9 Million
Emp.: 80
Durum Wheat Miller
N.A.I.C.S.: 311211
James Meyer *(Pres)*

Richardson Pioneer Limited (1)
3655 Quance Street, Regina, S4V 3A4, SK, Canada
Tel.: (306) 751-7700
Web Site: http://www.richardsonpioneer.ca
Food Product Whslr
N.A.I.C.S.: 424420
Blair Swarbrick *(Mgr-Mktg)*

JAMES SOUTHALL & COMPANY LTD.

Peachman Way Broadland Business Park, Norwich, NR7 0WF, United Kingdom
Tel.: (44) 1603437909 UK
Web Site: http://www.startriteshoes.com
Holding Company
N.A.I.C.S.: 551112

Subsidiaries:

Start-Rite Shoes Ltd. (1)
Peachman Way Broadland Business Park, Norwich, NR7 0WF, United Kingdom
Tel.: (44) 3445617263
Web Site: http://www.startriteshoes.com
Sales Range: $25-49.9 Million
Emp.: 110
Footwear Mfr
N.A.I.C.S.: 316210
Ian Watson *(CEO)*

JAMESON RESOURCES LIMITED

Deutsche Bank Place Level 4 126-130 Phillip, Sydney, 2000, NSW, Australia
Tel.: (61) 892004473
Web Site: https://www.jamesonresources.com
JAL—(ASX)
Rev.: $5,639
Assets: $31,174,196
Liabilities: $288,681
Net Worth: $30,885,515
Earnings: ($900,948)
Emp.: 4
Fiscal Year-end: 06/30/24
Minerals Exploration
N.A.I.C.S.: 212323
Terry Arthur Palm *(Dir-Operations, Interim CEO & Chm)*

Subsidiaries:

NWP Coal Canada Ltd. (1)

Suite 810 789 West Pender Street, Vancouver, V6C 1H2, BC, Canada
Tel.: (604) 629-8605
Web Site: https://www.nwpcoal.com
Coal Mining Services
N.A.I.C.S.: 213113

JAMESON, GILROY, AND B & L LIVESTOCK LTD.

780 Home St, PO Box 40, Moose Jaw, S6H 4N7, SK, Canada
Tel.: (306) 692-4911
Web Site: http://www.jglcattle.com
Year Founded: 1979
Sales Range: $200-249.9 Million
Emp.: 22
Livestock Services
N.A.I.C.S.: 424520
Tom Hansen *(Controller)*

JAMIESON WELLNESS, INC.

1 Adelaide Street East Suite 2200, Toronto, M5C 2V9, ON, Canada
Tel.: (416) 960-0052
Web Site: https://www.jamiesonwellness.com
Year Founded: 1922
2JW—(DEU)
Rev.: $510,588,235
Assets: $863,530,922
Liabilities: $500,172,921
Net Worth: $363,358,000
Earnings: ($7,710,489)
Emp.: 307
Fiscal Year-end: 12/31/23
Health Product Mfr & Distr
N.A.I.C.S.: 325411
Mike Pilato *(Pres & CEO)*

Subsidiaries:

Jamieson Laboratories Ltd. (1)
4025 Rhodes Drive, Windsor, N8W 5B5, ON, Canada
Vitamin & Mineral Supplement Retailer
N.A.I.C.S.: 456191

Nutrawise Health & Beauty LLC (1)
9600 Toledo Way, Irvine, CA 92618
Web Site: https://www.youtheory.com
Health Product Mfr & Distr
N.A.I.C.S.: 325411

JAMIESON'S PET FOOD DISTRIBUTORS LTD.

7471 Vantage Way, Delta, V4G 1C9, BC, Canada
Tel.: (604) 940-9787
Web Site: http://www.jamiesonspetfood.com
Year Founded: 1974
Rev.: $10,759,648
Emp.: 15
Pet Food Whslr
N.A.I.C.S.: 459910
Bob Spires *(Pres)*

JAMMU & KASHMIR BANK LTD.

M A Road, Srinagar, 190 001, Jammu & Kashmir, India
Tel.: (91) 1942481930
Web Site: https://www.jkbank.com
J&KBANK—(NSE)
Rev.: $1,205,724,675
Assets: $16,417,247,096
Liabilities: $15,488,737,460
Net Worth: $928,509,637
Earnings: $58,482,988
Emp.: 11,727
Fiscal Year-end: 03/31/21
Banking Services
N.A.I.C.S.: 522110
Parvez Ahmed *(Co-Chm)*

JAMNA AUTO INDUSTRIES LTD.

Jai Spring Road, Yamunanagar, 135 001, India

INTERNATIONAL PUBLIC

Tel.: (91) 1732251810
Web Site: https://www.jaispring.com
JAMNAAUTO—(NSE)
Rev.: $235,106,358
Assets: $162,871,309
Liabilities: $69,412,175
Net Worth: $93,459,134
Earnings: $19,219,773
Emp.: 1,573
Fiscal Year-end: 03/31/22
Automobile Parts Mfr
N.A.I.C.S.: 336390
Randeep Singh Jauhar *(Vice Chm)*

Subsidiaries:

Jamna Auto Industries Ltd - Plant I (1)
Jai Spring Road, Yamunanagar, 135001, Haryana, India
Tel.: (91) 173225181014
Web Site: http://www.jaispring.com
Sales Range: $25-49.9 Million
Emp.: 54
Leaf Spring Design & Mfr
N.A.I.C.S.: 332613

Jamna Auto Industries Ltd - Plant II (1)
U - 27 to 29 Industrial Area Bhind, Malanpur, 477116, Madhya Pradesh, India
Tel.: (91) 7539283396
Web Site: http://www.jaispring.in
Leaf Spring Design & Mfr
N.A.I.C.S.: 332613

Jamna Auto Industries Ltd - Plant III (1)
Plot No 22 to 25 Sengundram Village, Maraimalai Nagar Industrial Complex Singaperumal Koil Post, Chennai, 603204, Tamil Nadu, India
Tel.: (91) 4427463800
Web Site: http://www.jaispring.in
Sales Range: $100-124.9 Million
Emp.: 300
Leaf Spring Design & Mfr
N.A.I.C.S.: 332613

JAMSHRI REALTY LIMITED

5 Motimahal 195 J Tata Road, Churchgate, Mumbai, 400020, Maharashtra, India
Tel.: (91) 2243152400
Web Site: https://www.jamshri.in
Year Founded: 1907
502901—(BOM)
Rev.: $273,497
Assets: $3,639,719
Liabilities: $2,878,773
Net Worth: $760,946
Earnings: ($486,227)
Emp.: 13
Fiscal Year-end: 03/31/21
Textile Products Mfr
N.A.I.C.S.: 313310
Prem Ratan Damani *(Chm & Co-Mng Dir)*

JAMUNA BANK PLC

2 Dilkusha C/A, Dhaka, 1000, Bangladesh
Tel.: (880) 9570912
Web Site: https://www.jamunabankbd.com
JAMUNABANK—(DHA)
Rev.: $128,829,628
Assets: $3,071,919,604
Liabilities: $2,825,011,281
Net Worth: $246,908,323
Earnings: $29,144,598
Emp.: 3,346
Fiscal Year-end: 12/31/21
Commercial Banking Services
N.A.I.C.S.: 522110
Shaheen Mahmud *(Chm)*

JAMUNA OIL COMPANY LIMITED

Jamuna Bhaban Agrabad C/A, Chittagong, Bangladesh

Tel.: (880) 2333320181
Web Site:
   https://www.jamunaoil.gov.bd
Year Founded: 1964
JAMUNAOIL—(CHT)
Rev.: $14,300,451
Assets: $1,002,869,581
Liabilities: $792,798,184
Net Worth: $210,071,396
Earnings: $31,557,044
Emp.: 477
Fiscal Year-end: 06/30/23
Petroleum Whslr
N.A.I.C.S.: 424720
A. B. M. Azad *(Chm)*

JAN KELLEY MARKETING
1005 Skyview Dr Ste 322, Burlington, L7P 5B1, ON, Canada
Tel.: (905) 631-7934   ON
Web Site:
   http://www.jankelleymarketing.com
Year Founded: 2001
Rev.: $10,000,000
Emp.: 63
Advetising Agency
N.A.I.C.S.: 541810
Jim Letwin *(Pres & CEO)*

JANA SMALL FINANCE BANK
The Fairway Business Park First Floor Survey No 10/1 11/2 and 12/2B, Koramangala Inner Ring Road Next to EGL Business Park Challaghatta, Bengaluru, 560071, India
Tel.: (91) 80 46020100
Web Site: http://www.janabank.com
Year Founded: 2006
Sales Range: $400-449.9 Million
Emp.: 16,357
Financial Services
N.A.I.C.S.: 522291
Ramesh Ramanathan *(Chm)*

JANAKI FINANCE COMPANY LIMITED
Station Road, Janakpurdham, Nepal
Tel.: (977) 41590587
Web Site:
   https://www.jfcjanakpur.com
JFL—(NEP)
Sales Range: Less than $1 Million
Investment Advisory Services
N.A.I.C.S.: 523940
Sunil Shah *(Head-Accounts & HR Dept)*

JANANA DE MALUCHO TEXTILE MILLS LIMITED
, Habibabad, Kohat, Pakistan
Tel.: (92) 922862161   PK
Web Site: http://www.jdm.com.pk
Year Founded: 1960
JDMT—(PSX)
Rev.: $21,644,480
Assets: $34,666,938
Liabilities: $11,038,067
Net Worth: $23,628,871
Earnings: ($288,793)
Emp.: 1,275
Fiscal Year-end: 06/30/23
Textile Products Mfr
N.A.I.C.S.: 314999
Raza Kuli Khan Khattak *(Chm)*

JANASHAKTHI INSURANCE PLC
No 75 Kumaran Ratnam Road, PO Box 1672, 2, Colombo, Sri Lanka
Tel.: (94) 2636636
Web Site:
   https://www.janashakthi.com
Year Founded: 1992
JINS.N0000—(COL)
Rev.: $14,162,057
Assets: $111,794,117
Liabilities: $63,632,245
Net Worth: $48,161,872
Earnings: $12,772,070
Emp.: 357
Fiscal Year-end: 12/31/23
General Insurance Services
N.A.I.C.S.: 524113
Ramesh Schaffter *(Exec Dir)*

JANATA INSURANCE COMPANY LTD.
GA/95/D Link Road Middle Badda, Gulshan-1, Dhaka, 1212, Bangladesh
Tel.: (880) 2222262181
Web Site: https://jiclbd.com
Year Founded: 1986
JANATAINS—(CHT)
Rev.: $238,973
Assets: $13,077,918
Liabilities: $6,815,887
Net Worth: $6,262,031
Earnings: $815,164
Emp.: 208
Fiscal Year-end: 12/31/23
Insurance Services
N.A.I.C.S.: 524298
Belal Ahmed *(Chm)*

JANCO HOLDINGS LIMITED
Unit 1608 16th Floor Tower A Manulife Financial Centre No 223, Wai Yip Street Kwun Tong, Kowloon, China (Hong Kong)
Tel.: (852) 25757883   Ky
Web Site:
   http://www.jancofreight.com
Year Founded: 1990
8035—(HKG)
Rev.: $65,365,680
Assets: $44,731,463
Liabilities: $34,297,373
Net Worth: $10,434,090
Earnings: $681,233
Emp.: 179
Fiscal Year-end: 12/31/22
Freight Forwarding Services
N.A.I.C.S.: 488510
Chin Hung Ng *(Chm & CEO)*

Subsidiaries:

Janco E-commerce Solutions Limited   (1)
Unit 1608 16/F Tower A Manulife Financial Centre 223 Wai Yip Street, Kwun Tong, Kowloon, China (Hong Kong)
Tel.: (852) 25757883
Web Site:
   https://www.jancoecommerce.com
Emp.: 120
Ecommerce Services
N.A.I.C.S.: 541511

Transpeed Hong Kong Limited   (1)
Unit 1002B 10/FL Hutchison Logistics CTR, Terminal 4 Kwai Chung Container Port S NT, Hong Kong, China (Hong Kong)
Tel.: (852) 21872472
Air Freight Forwarding Services
N.A.I.C.S.: 481112

JANFUSUN FANCYWORLD CORP.
No 67 Dahukou, Yongguang Village Gukeng Yownship, Yun-lin, Taiwan
Tel.: (886) 55825789
Web Site:
   https://www.janfusun.com.tw
Year Founded: 1986
5701—(TPE)
Rev.: $14,807,054
Assets: $83,755,245
Liabilities: $68,311,072
Net Worth: $15,444,173
Earnings: ($2,712,472)
Fiscal Year-end: 12/31/22
Amusement Park Operator
N.A.I.C.S.: 713110
Chen Jing-Cun *(Founder)*

JANGADA MINES PLC
Level 1 20 North Audley Street, London, W1K 6LX, United Kingdom
Tel.: (44) 2039406625   UK
Web Site:
   https://www.jangadamines.com
Year Founded: 2015
JAN—(AIM)
Assets: $4,994,000
Liabilities: $134,000
Net Worth: $4,860,000
Earnings: ($936,000)
Emp.: 1
Fiscal Year-end: 12/31/22
Mineral Exploration Services
N.A.I.C.S.: 212290
Brian McMaster *(Chm)*

JANGHO GROUP COMPANY LIMITED
Building 5 ID Park South Shunxi Road, Shunyi District, Beijing, 101300, China
Tel.: (86) 1060411166
Web Site: https://en.jangho.com
Year Founded: 1999
601886—(SHG)
Rev.: $2,535,119,094
Assets: $3,781,238,437
Liabilities: $2,713,101,450
Net Worth: $1,068,136,987
Earnings: $68,665,344
Emp.: 4,848
Fiscal Year-end: 12/31/22
Structural Curtain Wall Products Mfr
N.A.I.C.S.: 332312
Liu Zaiwang *(Chm)*

Subsidiaries:

Jangho Curtain Wall Hongkong Ltd   (1)
Room 1101-03 11F Fullerton Centre No 19 Hung To Street Kwun Tong Road, 57 Hung To Road Kwun Tong, Kowloon, China (Hong Kong)
Tel.: (852) 34991645
Structural Curtain Wall Products Mfr
N.A.I.C.S.: 332312

Vision Eye Institute Limited   (1)
Ground floor 600 St Kilda Rd, Melbourne, 3004, VIC, Australia
Tel.: (61) 395212175
Web Site:
   http://www.visioneyeinstitute.com.au
Ophthalmic Services
N.A.I.C.S.: 339112
James Thiedeman *(CEO)*

JANGWON TECH CO., LTD.
14-9 7th Industrial Complex Road Gumi-si, Gumi, Gyeongsangbuk-do, Korea (South)
Tel.: (82) 544628896
Web Site:
   https://www.jangwontech.net
Year Founded: 2000
174880—(KRS)
Rev.: $52,624,240
Assets: $66,399,236
Liabilities: $12,653,765
Net Worth: $53,745,471
Earnings: ($22,063,128)
Emp.: 107
Fiscal Year-end: 12/31/22
Metal Die-Casting Services
N.A.I.C.S.: 331523
Jin-myung Kim *(CEO)*

Subsidiaries:

Jangwon Tech Co., Ltd. - Second Plant   (1)
86-26 1 Gongdan-ro, Gumi, Gyeongsangbuk-do, Korea (South)
Tel.: (82) 7075458824
Automotive Components Mfr
N.A.I.C.S.: 336310

Jangwon Tech Co., Ltd. - Third Plant   (1)
35 1 Gongdan-ro 2-gil, Gumi, Gyeongbuk, Korea (South)
Tel.: (82) 540000000
Metal Die Casting Products Mfr
N.A.I.C.S.: 331523

JANICO INVESTMENTS LTD.
928 Marion Street, Winnipeg, R2J 0K8, MB, Canada
Tel.: (204) 949-7280
Web Site: http://www.janicofuels.com
Year Founded: 1996
Rev.: $21,606,095
Emp.: 34
Fuel Distr
N.A.I.C.S.: 457210
Kim Robertson *(Mgr-Pine Falls)*

JANISON EDUCATION GROUP LIMITED
Tel.: (61) 266529850   AU
Web Site: https://www.janison.com
Year Founded: 1998
JAN—(ASX)
Rev.: $28,752,884
Assets: $32,816,082
Liabilities: $11,039,745
Net Worth: $21,776,337
Earnings: ($5,403,352)
Emp.: 146
Fiscal Year-end: 06/30/24
Digital Education & Learning Services
N.A.I.C.S.: 611710
Wayne Houlden *(Founder & Vice Chm)*

Subsidiaries:

Academic Assessment Services Pty. Ltd.   (1)
Level 1 80 Bay Street, Ultimo, NSW, Australia
Tel.: (61) 299044933
Web Site:
   https://www.academicassessment.com.au
Educational Support Services
N.A.I.C.S.: 611710

UNSW Global Pty. Ltd.   (1)
12-22 Rothschild Avenue, Rosebery, 2018, NSW, Australia
Tel.: (61) 289362200
Web Site:
   http://www.unswglobal.unsw.edu.au
Educational Support Services
N.A.I.C.S.: 611710
Sarah Lightfoot *(CEO)*

JANIVO HOLDING BV
Sparrenheuvel 36, 3708 JE, Zeist, Netherlands
Tel.: (31) 30 693 7500
Emp.: 13
Privater Equity Firm
N.A.I.C.S.: 523999
Joost E. Tjaden *(Mng Dir)*

JANJ A.D.
I Sipovacke Brigade 1, 70270, Sipovo, Bosnia & Herzegovina
Tel.: (387) 50373210
JANJ—(BANJ)
Sales Range: Less than $1 Million
Emp.: 1
Roof Covering Services
N.A.I.C.S.: 238160
Milenko Smanja *(Pres)*

JANKO STAJACIC A.D.
Karadordeva br 53, 11550, Lazarevac, Serbia
Tel.: (381) 11 8123 987
Web Site:
   http://www.jankostajcic.com
Year Founded: 1979
Sales Range: Less than $1 Million
Emp.: 1
Driving School Operator

JANKO STAJACIC A.D.

Janko Stajacic a.d.—(Continued)
N.A.I.C.S.: 611692

JANOME SEWING MACHINE CO., LTD.
31 1 Kyobashi 3 Chome Chuo Ku, Tokyo, 104 8311, Japan
Tel.: (81) 332772033
Web Site: http://www.janome.com
Year Founded: 1921
Sales Range: $400-449.9 Million
Emp.: 1,000
Mfr of Household & Industrial Sewing Machines & Patterns
N.A.I.C.S.: 335220
Sunitezu Kato (Pres)

Subsidiaries:

Comercial Janome Latin America Limitada (1)
Av Santa Isabel 1012, Providencia, Santiago, Chile
Tel.: (56) 222472750
Web Site: http://www.janome.cl
Sewing Machines Distr
N.A.I.C.S.: 423830

Elna Interntional Corp. SA (1)
Rue Veyrot 14, 1217, Meyrin, Geneve, Switzerland
Tel.: (41) 228848666
Web Site: http://www.elna.ch
Sewing Machines Distr
N.A.I.C.S.: 423830

Jamac Inc. (1)
c/o Janome America 10 Industrial Ave Ste 2, Mahwah, NJ 07430
Tel.: (201) 825-3200
Coated & Laminated Paper Mfr
N.A.I.C.S.: 322220

Janome (Thailand) Co. Ltd. (1)
312 Moo 1 Sukaphiban 8 Road T Bueng, Si Racha, 20230, Chonburi, Thailand
Tel.: (66) 38480131
Web Site: http://www.janome.co.jp
Sewing Needlework & Piece Goods Stores
N.A.I.C.S.: 459130
Asai Koichi (Mng Dir)

Janome America, Inc. (1)
10 Industrial Ave, Mahwah, NJ 07430 (100%)
Tel.: (201) 825-3200
Web Site: http://www.janome.com
Sales Range: $25-49.9 Million
Emp.: 50
Sewing Machine Mfr & Distr
N.A.I.C.S.: 423620

Janome Australia Pty Ltd. (1)
1-15 Mills Street, Cheltenham, 3192, VIC, Australia
Tel.: (61) 385863100
Web Site: http://www.janome.com.au
Sewing Machines Distr
N.A.I.C.S.: 423830
Shinichi Ohashi (Mng Dir)

Janome Canada Ltd. (1)
Unit 3 6620 Kitimat Road, Mississauga, L5N2B8, ON, Canada
Tel.: (905) 821-0266
Web Site: http://www.janome.ca
Sales Range: $25-49.9 Million
Emp.: 9
Store Retailers
N.A.I.C.S.: 459999
Terri Baillie (Gen Mgr)

Janome Credia Co., Ltd. (1)
1-9-4 Edagawa Sumitomofudosantoyosutk Bldg, Tokyo, 135-0051, Japan
Tel.: (81) 356347111
Web Site: http://www.janomecredia.co.jp
Application Software Development Services
N.A.I.C.S.: 541511

Janome Deutschland GmbH (1)
Opelstrasse 20-22, 64546, Morfelden-Walldorf, Germany
Tel.: (49) 6105406360
Sewing Machines Distr
N.A.I.C.S.: 423830

Janome Diecasting (Thailand) Co., Ltd. (1)
Saha Group Industrial Park Kabinburi 124 Moo 1 Suwannasorn Rd, Kabinburi, Amphur Muang, 25110, Prachinburi, Thailand
Tel.: (66) 37290001
Die Cast Mfr
N.A.I.C.S.: 333515

Janome Europe B.V. (1)
Bijlmerm eerstraat 22, 2131HG, Hoofddorp, Netherlands
Tel.: (31) 235575559
Web Site: http://www.janome.nl
Sales Range: $50-74.9 Million
Emp.: 6
Piece Goods Notions & Other Dry Goods Merchant Whslr
N.A.I.C.S.: 424310

Janome Industrial Equipment (Shanghai) Co., Ltd. (1)
B211 2633 Yan'an Road W, Changning District, Shanghai, China
Tel.: (86) 2162788225
Web Site: http://www.janomeie.com.cn
Sewing Machines Distr
N.A.I.C.S.: 423830

Janome Industrial Equipment (Taiwan) Co., Ltd. (1)
6F-6 No 8 Zihciang South Road, Jhubei, 30264, Hsinchu, Taiwan
Tel.: (886) 36683949
Web Site: http://www.janome.tw
Sewing Machines Distr
N.A.I.C.S.: 423830

Janome Industrial Equipment USA, Inc (1)
Fortune Business Campus 1831 Howard St Unit D, Elk Grove Village, IL 60007
Tel.: (847) 357-8870
Sewing Machines Distr
N.A.I.C.S.: 423830

Janome Mexico Servicios Limitada S de RL de CV (1)
Insurgentes Sur 1768 Piso 1, Colonia Florida Delegación Alvaro obregon, 01030, Mexico, Mexico
Tel.: (52) 54488670
Web Site: http://www.janome.com.mx
Sewing Machine Maintenance & Mfr
N.A.I.C.S.: 333248

Janome New Zealand Ltd. (1)
Unit 5 325 Ti Rakau Dr, East Tamaki, Auckland, New Zealand
Tel.: (64) 92650250
Web Site: http://www.janome.co.nz
Sewing Machines Distr
N.A.I.C.S.: 423830

Janome Taiwan Co. Ltd. (1)
No 101 Jifung Road, Wufung, Taichung, Taiwan
Tel.: (886) 4 2339 3301
Web Site: http://www.janome.co.jp
Sewing Needlework & Piece Goods Stores
N.A.I.C.S.: 459130

Janome UK Ltd. (1)
Janome Centre Southside, Stockport, SK6 2SP, Cheshire, United Kingdom
Tel.: (44) 1616666011
Web Site: http://www.janome.co.uk
Sewing Machines Distr
N.A.I.C.S.: 423830

Janome do Brasil Comercio de Maquinas Ltda. (1)
R Padre Antonio Tomas 159, Agua Branca, 05003-010, Sao Paulo, Brazil
Tel.: (55) 1136756754
Web Site: http://www.janome.com.br
Sewing Machines Distr
N.A.I.C.S.: 423830

Sun Planning Co., Ltd. (1)
2670-1 Shinohara Ryuo-cho, Nakakoma Gun, Yamanashi, Japan
Tel.: (81) 337581261
Sewing machines Mfr
N.A.I.C.S.: 339999

JANOSCHKA GMBH

Mattweg 1, 77971, Kippenheim, Germany
Tel.: (49) 78258490
Web Site: http://www.janoschka.com
Year Founded: 1976
Sales Range: $25-49.9 Million
Emp.: 1,300
Prepress Printing & Packaging Development Services
N.A.I.C.S.: 323120
Alexander Janoschka (CEO)

Subsidiaries:

Fentsch Packaging Solutions GmbH (1)
Osterfeldstrasse 90, Ismaning, 85737, Germany
Tel.: (49) 899607950
Web Site: http://www.fentsch.de
Sales Range: $25-49.9 Million
Emp.: 25
Flexible Packaging Mfr
N.A.I.C.S.: 322220
Rainer Geiger (Mng Dir)

Janoschka Barcelona S.L. (1)
Nave 5 Calle Industria Esquina Avinguda de l'Ebre, Palau-solita, 8184, Palau de Plegamans, Spain
Tel.: (34) 938 64 09 10
Offset Printing Services
N.A.I.C.S.: 323111
Michael Janoschka (Mng Dir)

Janoschka Espana S.L. (1)
Carretera CV-50 Alzira-Tavernes Km 18 1, Alzira, 46600, Valencia, Spain
Tel.: (34) 962 45 53 50
Offset Printing Services
N.A.I.C.S.: 323111
Jose M. Jimenez (Mng Dir)

Janoschka Graphic Services India Private Ltd. (1)
386 Sane Guruji Premises Vir Savarkar Marg, Prabhadevi, Mumbai, 400025, India
Tel.: (91) 22 71 00 02 47
Prepress Printing Services
N.A.I.C.S.: 323120
Shailesh Dahitule (Mgr-Ops)

Janoschka Graphics France S.A.S. (1)
Z E Les Savis, 16160, Gond-Pontouvre, France
Tel.: (33) 5 45 91 21 21
Digital Printing Services
N.A.I.C.S.: 323111
Thierry Lafarge (Acct Mgr)

Janoschka Izmir AS (1)
Sok No 16 Aosb, Cigli, 10000, Izmir, Turkiye
Tel.: (90) 232 376 7005
Offset Printing Services
N.A.I.C.S.: 323111
Emre Candan (Plant Mgr)

Janoschka Kippenheim GmbH (1)
Mattweg 1, 77971, Kippenheim, Germany
Tel.: (49) 7825 8490
Prepress Printing Services
N.A.I.C.S.: 323120
Stefan Hilss (Mng Dir)

Janoschka Mexico SAPI de C.V. (1)
Km 18 8 Carr Fed Mexico-Puebla, Col Los Reyes Acaquilpan, La Paz, 56400, Mexico
Tel.: (52) 55 5856 3241
Emp.: 25
Graphic Printing Services
N.A.I.C.S.: 323111
Gerd Wiedermann (Dir-Tech)

Janoschka Pavlovsk Ltd. (1)
Pavlovskaya Str 9, Gatschinsky District, Kommunar, Leningrad, Russia
Tel.: (7) 8123364168
Emp.: 100
Commercial Printing Services
N.A.I.C.S.: 323111
Lutz Braune (Mng Dir)

Janoschka Polska Sp. z o.o. (1)
Ul Kard S Wyszynskiego 13, 05530, Gora Kalwaria, Poland
Tel.: (48) 227271706
Web Site: http://www.janoschka.pl
Sales Range: $25-49.9 Million
Emp.: 30
Rotogravure Cylinder Mfr

INTERNATIONAL PUBLIC

N.A.I.C.S.: 333248
Peter Haller (Mng Dir)

Janoschka Portugal Lda. (1)
Av Marechal Gomes da Costa 29 E, 1800-255, Lisbon, Portugal
Tel.: (351) 218 31 04 00
Prepress Printing Services
N.A.I.C.S.: 323120
Jose Miguel Jimenez (Mng Dir)

Nord Helio Service SAS (1)
Route Nationale Fosse 7 de Vermelles, 62670, Mazingarbe, France
Tel.: (33) 321448686
Web Site: http://www.janoschka.com
Sales Range: $50-74.9 Million
Emp.: 20
Prepress Printing & Packaging Development Services
N.A.I.C.S.: 323120
Philippe Fromentin (Mng Dir)

Packpool Medien GmbH (1)
Im Oberdorf 22, 77948, Friesenheim, Germany
Tel.: (49) 7821954190
Web Site: http://www.packpool.de
Sales Range: $50-74.9 Million
Emp.: 100
Prepress & Packaging Design & Consulting Services
N.A.I.C.S.: 323120

Subsidiary (Non-US):

Packpool Swiss GmbH (2)
Nauenstrasse 41, 4052, Basel, Switzerland
Tel.: (41) 612011020
Web Site: http://www.packpool.ch
Prepress & Packaging Design Services
N.A.I.C.S.: 323120

Repro-Form GmbH (1)
Am Bauhof 16, Dieburg, 64807, Germany
Tel.: (49) 607161760
Web Site: http://www.reproform.janoschka.com
Sales Range: $25-49.9 Million
Emp.: 30
Packaging Design Services
N.A.I.C.S.: 322220
Bernhard Volmer (Mng Dir)

JANSER GMBH

Boblinger Strasse 91, 71139, Ehningen, Germany
Tel.: (49) 70341270
Web Site: http://www.janser.com
Year Founded: 1961
Rev: $25,315,948
Emp.: 80
Professional Tool Mfr
N.A.I.C.S.: 333515

Subsidiaries:

JANSER, spol. s r.o. (1)
Kremnicka 1401/13, 14100, Prague, Czech Republic
Tel.: (420) 246061410
Web Site: http://www.janser.cz
Industrial Machinery Distr
N.A.I.C.S.: 423830

JH. JANSER KFT (1)
Hangar u 4, 1108, Budapest, Hungary
Tel.: (36) 14334361
Web Site: http://www.janser.hu
Industrial Machinery Distr
N.A.I.C.S.: 423830

Janser GmbH (1)
Bahnhofstrasse 37, 4860, Lenzing, Austria
Tel.: (43) 7672951540
Web Site: http://www.janser.at
Industrial Machinery Distr
N.A.I.C.S.: 423830

Janser Polska Sp. z o.o. (1)
ul Powstancow Wlkp 5, Lipno k, 64-111, Leszno, Poland
Tel.: (48) 655340680
Web Site: http://www.janser.com.pl
Industrial Machinery Distr
N.A.I.C.S.: 423830

Janser S.A. (1)
Parc d'activites de la Mossig, BP 24, 67521, Marlenheim, Cedex, France

Tel.: (33) 388592820
Web Site: http://www.janser.fr
Industrial Machinery Distr
N.A.I.C.S.: 423830

Janser Slovenija (1)
Poljska cesta 19, 3210, Slovenske Konjice, Slovenia
Tel.: (386) 37580720
Web Site: http://www.prenova.si
Industrial Machinery Distr
N.A.I.C.S.: 423830

Janser Spol. s.r.o. (1)
Vajnorska 135, 831 04, Bratislava, Slovakia
Tel.: (421) 265424600
Web Site: http://www.janser.sk
Industrial Machinery Distr
N.A.I.C.S.: 423830

Janser UK Ltd. (1)
Coombs wood business park, Coombs wood way, Halesowen, B62 8BH, United Kingdom
Tel.: (44) 1215615888
Web Site: http://www.janser-uk.co.uk
Industrial Machinery Distr
N.A.I.C.S.: 423830

Janser d.o.o. (1)
Nasicka 16, 10000, Zagreb, Croatia
Tel.: (385) 13692177
Web Site: http://www.janser.hr
Industrial Machinery Distr
N.A.I.C.S.: 423830

JANTSA JANT SANAYI VE TIC. A.S.
Umurlu Organize Sanayi Bolgesi, Umurlu, 09630, Aydin, Turkiye
Tel.: (90) 256 259 11 25
Web Site: http://www.jantsa.com
Year Founded: 1977
Wheel Mfr & Distr
N.A.I.C.S.: 326211
Tamer Cercioglu *(Dir-Export Sls)*

Subsidiaries:

Jantesa Mexico, S.A. de C.V. (1)
Calle General Mariano Escobedo 510
Miguel Hidalgo, 11590, Mexico, Mexico
Tel.: (52) 5550912587
Wheel Distr
N.A.I.C.S.: 423120

Jantsan Jant Pazarlama ve Tic. A.S. (1)
Gorece Cumhuriyet Mah Cevre Yolu Bulvarn No 45/A, Menderes, Izmir, Turkiye
Tel.: (90) 2327827171
Web Site: http://www.jantsan.com.tr
Wheel Distr
N.A.I.C.S.: 423120

JANUS CORPORATION LIMITED
513 Stanford Building Link Road, Andheri West, Mumbai, 400053, India
Tel.: (91) 2262363222
Web Site:
  https://www.januscorporation.in
Year Founded: 1998
542924—(BOM)
Rev.: $4,313,735
Assets: $2,034,731
Liabilities: $252,052
Net Worth: $1,782,679
Earnings: $43,493
Emp.: 9
Fiscal Year-end: 03/31/23
Construction Services
N.A.I.C.S.: 236210

JANUS HENDERSON GROUP PLC
201 Bishopsgate, London, EC2M 3AE, United Kingdom
Tel.: (44) 2078181818 JE
Web Site:
  http://www.janushenderson.com
Year Founded: 2008
JHG—(NYSE)
Rev.: $2,101,800,000
Assets: $6,496,600,000
Liabilities: $1,958,300,000
Net Worth: $4,538,300,000
Earnings: $392,000,000
Emp.: 2,200
Fiscal Year-end: 12/31/23
Holding Company; Investment Management Services
N.A.I.C.S.: 551112
Roger Thompson *(CFO)*

Subsidiaries:

Henderson Equity Partners Limited (1)
201 Bishopsgate, London, EC2M 3AE, United Kingdom
Tel.: (44) 2078181818
Web Site: https://www.janushenderson.com
Financial Investment Management Services
N.A.I.C.S.: 523999

Henderson Global Investors (Holdings) Limited (1)
201 Bishopsgate, London, EC2M 3AE, United Kingdom
Tel.: (44) 2078181818
Web Site: https://www.janushenderson.com
Financial Management Services
N.A.I.C.S.: 523999

Henderson Global Investors (International Holdings) BV (1)
Gustav Mahlerlaan 1212, 1081 LA, Amsterdam, Netherlands
Tel.: (31) 206750146
Web Site: https://www.janushenderson.com
Asset Management Services
N.A.I.C.S.: 541618

Henderson Global Investors (North America) Inc. (1)
737 N Michigan Ave Ste 1700, Chicago, IL 60611
Tel.: (312) 397-1122
Sales Range: $50-74.9 Million
Emp.: 45
Financial Investment Activities
N.A.I.C.S.: 523999

Subsidiary (Domestic):

Geneva Capital Management, LLC (2)
411 E Wisconsin Ave Ste 2320, Milwaukee, WI 53202
Tel.: (414) 224-6002
Web Site: https://www.genevacap.com
Investment Advice
N.A.I.C.S.: 523940
W. Scot Priebe *(Mng Principal & Portfolio Mgr)*

Henderson Holdings Group BV (1)
Gustav Mahlerlaan 1212, Amsterdam, 1081 LA, Netherlands
Tel.: (31) 206750146
Web Site: https://www.janushenderson.com
Investment Management Service
N.A.I.C.S.: 523999

Janus Henderson Administration UK Limited (1)
201 Bishopgate, London, EC2M 3AE, United Kingdom (100%)
Tel.: (44) 2078181818
Web Site: https://www.janushenderson.com
Financial Investment Activities
N.A.I.C.S.: 523999

Janus Henderson Fund Management UK Limited (1)
201 Bishopgate, London, EC2M 3AE, United Kingdom (100%)
Tel.: (44) 2078181818
Web Site: https://www.janushenderson.com
Financial Investment Activities
N.A.I.C.S.: 523999

Janus Henderson Investors (Hong Kong) Limited (1)
Suites 706 -707 Chater House 8 Connaught Road, Central, China (Hong Kong) (100%)
Tel.: (852) 31217000
Web Site: https://www.janushenderson.com
Financial Investment Activities
N.A.I.C.S.: 523999

Janus Henderson Investors (Singapore) Limited (1)
#34-03/04 138 Market Street CapitaGreen, Singapore, 048946, Singapore (100%)
Tel.: (65) 68131000
Web Site: https://www.janushenderson.com
Financial Investment Activities
N.A.I.C.S.: 523999

Janus Henderson Investors UK Limited (1)
201 Bishopegates, London, EC2M 3AE, United Kingdom
Tel.: (44) 2078181818
Web Site: https://www.janushenderson.com
Fund Management & Investment Services
N.A.I.C.S.: 523940

Janus Henderson UK (Holdings) Limited (1)
201 Bishopsgate, London, EC2M 3AE, United Kingdom
Tel.: (44) 2078181818
Web Site: https://www.janushenderson.com
Investment Management Service
N.A.I.C.S.: 523999

Janus Henderson US (Holdings) Inc. (1)
151 Detroit St, Denver, CO 80206
Web Site: https://www.janushenderson.com
Investment Management Service
N.A.I.C.S.: 523999

Subsidiary (Domestic):

Janus Henderson Investors US LLC (2)
151 Detroit St, Denver, CO 80206-4921
Tel.: (800) 525-3713
Investment Management Service
N.A.I.C.S.: 523940

Janus Index & Calculation Services LLC (1)
17 Old Kings Hwy S Ste 100, Darien, CT 06820
Tel.: (800) 525-3713
Web Site: https://janussg-mc.com
Capital Investment Financial Services
N.A.I.C.S.: 523910

Kapstream Capital Pty Limited (1)
Level 5 151 Macquarie Street, Sydney, 2000, NSW, Australia
Tel.: (61) 292340000
Web Site: https://kapstream.com
Capital Investment Financial Services
N.A.I.C.S.: 523910

Perkins Investment Management LLC (1)
311 S Wacker Dr Ste 6000, Chicago, IL 60606 (100%)
Investment Management Service
N.A.I.C.S.: 523940

JANUS HENDERSON INVESTORS
201 Bishopsgate, London, EC2M 3AE, United Kingdom
Tel.: (44) 2078181818 UK
Web Site:
  https://www.janushenderson.com
BIT—(NZX)
Rev.: $51,340,824
Assets: $2,042,142,579
Liabilities: $194,739,137
Net Worth: $1,847,403,442
Earnings: ($243,264,050)
Fiscal Year-end: 10/31/22
Investment Banking Services
N.A.I.C.S.: 523150
Sue Inglis *(Chm)*

JAPAN AIRLINES CO., LTD.
Nomura Real Estate Bldg 2-4-11 Higashi-Shinagawa, Shinagawa-ku, Tokyo, 140-8637, Japan
Tel.: (81) 367333062
Web Site: https://www.jal.com
Year Founded: 1951
JAL—(DEU)
Rev.: $10,918,992,900
Assets: $17,511,423,520
Liabilities: $11,242,863,070
Net Worth: $6,268,560,450
Earnings: $631,479,740
Emp.: 36,500
Fiscal Year-end: 03/31/24
Airline Transportation & Support Services; Hotel Operator
N.A.I.C.S.: 481111
Yoshiharu Ueki *(Chm)*

Subsidiaries:

AirFlite Japan Corp. (1)
206 Imazu-Cho, Nagasaki, 856-0818, Japan
Tel.: (81) 0957521660
Sales Range: $25-49.9 Million
Emp.: 45
Cultural Activities & Publishing Services
N.A.I.C.S.: 513199

Airport Ground Service Co., Ltd. (1)
Nihon Kuko 1 Technical Cente 3 6 8 Hanedakukor, Tokyo, 144-0041, Japan (100%)
Tel.: (81) 357563965
Web Site: http://www.agsgroup.co.jp
Sales Range: $150-199.9 Million
Emp.: 1,000
Air Courier Services
N.A.I.C.S.: 492110

Axess International Network, Inc. (1)
Sea Fort Square Center Building 2-3-12 Higashishinagawa, Shinagawa-Ku, Tokyo, 140-8619, Japan (75%)
Tel.: (81) 354607012
Web Site: http://www.axess.co.jp
Sales Range: $25-49.9 Million
Emp.: 250
Air Connectivity & Ticketing Services
N.A.I.C.S.: 541511

Chitose Airport Fuelling Facilities Co., Ltd. (1)
1387 1 Chitose, Hokkaido, 066-0044, Japan (60%)
Tel.: (81) 123463456
Web Site: http://www.jal.com
Sales Range: $25-49.9 Million
Emp.: 4
Aircraft Fuel Services
N.A.I.C.S.: 457210

Euro Creative Tours (U.K.) Ltd. (1)
4th Floor Standon House 21 Mansell Street, London, E1 8AA, United Kingdom (65.5%)
Tel.: (44) 207 850 4403
Web Site: https://www.ectuk.com
Sales Range: $10-24.9 Million
Emp.: 40
Travel Management Services
N.A.I.C.S.: 561599

Global Building Co., Ltd. (1)
2 4 11 Shinagawa Ku, Tokyo, 140-0002, Japan (100%)
Tel.: (81) 354606820
Web Site: http://www.jal.com
Sales Range: $50-74.9 Million
Emp.: 6
Real Estate & Construction Services
N.A.I.C.S.: 531390

Ground Air Service Co., Ltd. (1)
2 2 5 Kuko, Ikeda, Osaka, 563-0034, Japan (100%)
Tel.: (81) 668566500
Web Site: http://www.jal.com
Sales Range: $125-149.9 Million
Emp.: 417
Baggage Handling Services
N.A.I.C.S.: 488119

Hokkaido Air Service Co., Ltd. (1)
Ryokaku Terminal Building 3F, Chitose, Hokkaido, 066-0012, Japan (65%)
Tel.: (81) 123465570
Web Site: http://www.jal.com
Sales Range: $75-99.9 Million
Emp.: 241
Airport Support Services & Store Operator
N.A.I.C.S.: 488119

International Catering Ltd. (1)
Horton Road, Colnbrook, Slough, SL3 0BG, United Kingdom
Tel.: (44) 1753 686 366
Web Site: http://www.jal.com
Sales Range: $50-74.9 Million
Emp.: 350
Catering Services

JAPAN AIRLINES CO., LTD.

Japan Airlines Co., Ltd.—(Continued)
N.A.I.C.S.: 722320

International In-Flight Catering Co., Ltd. (1)
310 Rodgers Blvd Honolulu International Airport, Honolulu, HI 96819 **(56.7%)**
Tel.: (808) 836-2431
Sales Range: $25-49.9 Million
Emp.: 136
Catering Services
N.A.I.C.S.: 722320
Randall Chin *(Mgr-Ops)*

J. Inter Co., Ltd. (1)
World Trade Center Building Bekkan, 2 4 1 Hamamatsu-Cho, Minato-Ku, Tokyo, 105-0013, Japan **(100%)**
Tel.: (81) 354701250
Web Site: http://www.jal.com
Sales Range: $25-49.9 Million
Emp.: 9
Hotel & Travel Services
N.A.I.C.S.: 721110

J. Pro Co., Ltd. (1)
6-1-1 Heiwajima TRC Center Building 4th floor, Ota-Ku, Tokyo, 143-0006, Japan **(100%)**
Tel.: (81) 35 753 0505
Web Site: https://www.j-pro.co.jp
Sales Range: $10-24.9 Million
Emp.: 30
Hotel & Travel Services
N.A.I.C.S.: 721110

JAL ABC, Inc. (1)
Round Cross Tsukiji Bldg 3-9-9 Tsukiji, Chuo-Ku, Tokyo, 104-0045, Japan **(51%)**
Tel.: (81) 33 545 1143
Web Site: https://www.jalabc.com
Sales Range: $25-49.9 Million
Emp.: 95
Luggage Delivery Services
N.A.I.C.S.: 488119

JAL Academy Co., Ltd. (1)
1-31 Minami Aoyama 3, Minatoku, Tokyo, 107-0062, Japan **(100%)**
Tel.: (81) 354122672
Web Site: http://www.jaca.co.jp
Sales Range: $100-124.9 Million
Emp.: 290
Cultural Activities & Publishing Services
N.A.I.C.S.: 513199

JAL Aeroparts Co., Ltd. (1)
2 3 3 Shiba, Tokyo, 105-0014, Japan **(100%)**
Tel.: (81) 354435561
Sales Range: $50-74.9 Million
Emp.: 60
Aircraft Parts & Equipment Whslr
N.A.I.C.S.: 423830

JAL Airtech Co., Ltd. (1)
3 F Maintenance Center Annex Building 3-5-7 Haneda-Kuko, Ota-ku, Tokyo, 144-0041, Japan **(70%)**
Tel.: (81) 357563491
Web Site: http://www.jalairtech.com
Sales Range: $50-74.9 Million
Emp.: 200
Aircraft Maintenance Services
N.A.I.C.S.: 811310
Kudo Nobuo *(Pres)*

JAL Aviation Technologies Co., Ltd. (1)
735 1 Hisashigetomi Kichioka, Taiei-Machi, Katori-Gun, Chiba, 287-0225, Japan **(100%)**
Tel.: (81) 478736432
Sales Range: $200-249.9 Million
Emp.: 780
Aircraft Maintenance Services
N.A.I.C.S.: 811310

JAL Brand Communications Co., Ltd. (1)
Shinagawa 2-4-11 Nomura Real Estate Agency Tennozu Building Higashi, Shinagawa-ku, Tokyo, 140-8643, Japan **(100%)**
Tel.: (81) 35 460 3971
Web Site: https://www.jalbrand.co.jp
Sales Range: $50-74.9 Million
Emp.: 176
Cultural Activities & Publishing Services

N.A.I.C.S.: 513199

JAL Capital Co., Ltd. (1)
2 4 11 Higashishinagawa, Shinagawa-Ku, Tokyo, 140-8653, Japan **(100%)**
Tel.: (81) 354607253
Sales Range: $50-74.9 Million
Emp.: 62
Financial Services
N.A.I.C.S.: 523999

JAL Cargo Sales Co., Ltd. (1)
4-11 Higashi-shinagawa 2-chome, Shinagawa-ku, Tokyo, 140-8637, Japan **(100%)**
Tel.: (81) 354605747
Web Site: http://www.jal.com
Sales Range: $50-74.9 Million
Emp.: 110
Air Cargo Services
N.A.I.C.S.: 481112

JAL Construction Co., Ltd. (1)
1 7 1 Haneda Airport Ota-Ku, Tokyo, 144-0041, Japan **(91%)**
Tel.: (81) 337476439
Web Site: http://www.jal.com
Sales Range: $50-74.9 Million
Emp.: 58
Real Estate & Construction Services
N.A.I.C.S.: 531390

JAL Hawaii, Incorporated (1)
Honolulu International Airport 300 Rodgers Blvd Ste 21, Honolulu, HI 96819 **(100%)**
Tel.: (808) 831-4111
Web Site: http://www.jal.co.jp
Sales Range: $50-74.9 Million
Emp.: 105
Airport Services
N.A.I.C.S.: 488119

JAL Hotels Co., Ltd. (1)
JAL Bldg 2 4 11 Higashi-Shinagawa, Shinagawa-Ku, Tokyo, 140-0002, Japan **(90.7%)**
Tel.: (81) 334583910
Web Site: http://www.jalhotels.com
Sales Range: $200-249.9 Million
Emp.: 208
Hotel & Travel Services
N.A.I.C.S.: 721110
Marcel Van Aelst *(Pres & CEO)*

Subsidiary (Domestic):

Hotel Nikko Chitose (2)
4 4 Honcho, Chitose-shi, Hokkaido, 066-8520, Japan **(85.3%)**
Tel.: (81) 123221121
Web Site: http://www.breezbay-group.com
Sales Range: $10-24.9 Million
Emp.: 60
Hotel Services
N.A.I.C.S.: 721110
Sera Masaki *(Gen Mgr)*

Hotel Nikko Osaka Co., Ltd. (2)
1-3-3 Nishi-Shinsaibashi, Chuo-ku, Osaka, 542-0086, Japan **(100%)**
Tel.: (81) 66 244 1111
Web Site: https://www.hno.co.jp
Sales Range: $50-74.9 Million
Hotel Services
N.A.I.C.S.: 721110

Subsidiary (US):

Hotel Nikko of San Francisco, Inc. (2)
222 Mason St, San Francisco, CA 94102 **(100%)**
Tel.: (415) 403-1800
Web Site: https://www.hotelnikkosf.com
Sales Range: $50-74.9 Million
Hotel Services
N.A.I.C.S.: 721110

Subsidiary (Non-US):

Hotel Royal - Nikko Taipei (2)
37-1 Chung Shan North Road Section 2, Taipei, 104, Taiwan
Tel.: (886) 225423266
Web Site: http://www.royal-taipei.com.tw
Hotel Operator
N.A.I.C.S.: 721110

Subsidiary (Domestic):

JAL Shuri Kanko Co., Ltd. (2)

1-132-1 Shuriyamagawacho, Naha, 903-8601, Okinawa, Japan **(57.9%)**
Tel.: (81) 988865454
Sales Range: $25-49.9 Million
Emp.: 248
Hotel Services
N.A.I.C.S.: 721110
Touru Ishiduka *(Pres)*

Narita Nikko Hotel Co., Ltd. (2)
500 Tokko, Narita, 286-0106, Japan **(100%)**
Tel.: (81) 47 632 0032
Web Site: https://www.nikko-narita.com
Sales Range: $25-49.9 Million
Emp.: 250
Hotel Services
N.A.I.C.S.: 721110

Okuma Beach Land Co., Ltd. (2)
913 Aza Okuma, Kunigami-son, Koza, 905-1412, Okinawa, Japan **(94.4%)**
Tel.: (81) 980412222
Web Site: http://www.jalokuma.co.jp
Sales Range: $25-49.9 Million
Emp.: 210
Hotel Services
N.A.I.C.S.: 721110

Subsidiary (Non-US):

The Montcalm London (2)
2 Wallenberg Place, Top of Park Lane Marble Arch, London, W1H 7TN, United Kingdom **(100%)**
Tel.: (44) 207 958 3200
Web Site: https://www.montcalm.co.uk
Sales Range: $10-24.9 Million
Emp.: 85
Hotel Services
N.A.I.C.S.: 721110
Sabine Altschaeffr *(Mng Dir)*

Subsidiary (Domestic):

Tokyo Humania Enterprise, Inc. (2)
1 9 1 Daiba, Tokyo, 135-8625, Minato-Ku, Japan
Tel.: (81) 355005500
Web Site: http://www.hnt.co.jp
Sales Range: $50-74.9 Million
Emp.: 500
Hotel Services
N.A.I.C.S.: 721110
Manabu Inoue *(Pres)*

JAL Information Technology Co., Ltd. (1)
3-1-1 Shibaura msb Tamachi Tamachi Station Tower N 12F, Minato-ku, Tokyo, 108-0023, Japan
Tel.: (81) 35 445 7000
Web Site: https://www.jalinfotec.co.jp
Sales Range: $350-399.9 Million
Emp.: 1,245
Aeronautical Systems Developer
N.A.I.C.S.: 541511

JAL Kansai Aircargo System Co., Ltd. (1)
JALKAS Imported Cargo Building 1 South Senshu Airport, Sennan, 549-0021, Osaka, Japan **(54.3%)**
Tel.: (81) 72 455 3660
Web Site: https://www.jalkas.co.jp
Sales Range: $50-74.9 Million
Emp.: 163
Air Cargo Services
N.A.I.C.S.: 481112

JAL Livre Co., Ltd. (1)
2 4 11 JAL Bldg, Shinagawa-Ku, Tokyo, 140-8637, Japan **(100%)**
Tel.: (81) 354603662
Web Site: http://www.jal.com
Sales Range: $50-74.9 Million
Emp.: 100
Financial Services
N.A.I.C.S.: 523999
Morikazu Saito *(Mgr)*

JAL Maintenance Service Co., Ltd. (1)
Haneda Airport 1-5-1 aircraft building 2F Yubinbango, Ota-ku, Tokyo, 144-0041, Japan **(100%)**
Tel.: (81) 337473715
Web Site: http://www.jmsweb.co.jp
Sales Range: $200-249.9 Million
Emp.: 600
Aircraft Maintenance Services

N.A.I.C.S.: 811310

JAL Narita Aircraft Maintenance Co., Ltd. (1)
1-1 Makiba Goryo Sanrizuka, Narita, Chiba, 286-0116, Japan **(100%)**
Tel.: (81) 476323967
Web Site: http://www.jalnam.co.jp
Sales Range: $400-449.9 Million
Emp.: 1,500
Aircraft Maintenance Services
N.A.I.C.S.: 811310

JAL Navia Fukuoka Co., Ltd. (1)
1 15 6 Tenjin, Chuo-Ku, Fukuoka, 810-0001, Japan **(100%)**
Tel.: (81) 927336100
Web Site: http://www.jal.co.jp
Sales Range: $75-99.9 Million
Emp.: 281
Travel Agency Services
N.A.I.C.S.: 561510

JAL Navia Osaka Co., Ltd. (1)
2-2-8 Dojimahama Osaka Center Toyobo Bldg 3rd Fl, Osaka, 530-0004, Japan **(100%)**
Tel.: (81) 3 3284 2557
Web Site: http://www.jal.co.jp
Sales Range: $150-199.9 Million
Emp.: 1,600
Travel Agency & Insurance Services
N.A.I.C.S.: 561510

JAL Navia Sapporo Co., Ltd. (1)
North 1 & East 7 Mitsui Building 1003 4-2-12 Kita-ku, Sapporo, 060-0002, Japan **(100%)**
Tel.: (81) 112327257
Web Site: http://www.jal.co.jp
Sales Range: $25-49.9 Million
Emp.: 100
Travel Agency Services
N.A.I.C.S.: 561510
Yugi Nakano *(Pres)*

JAL Navia Tokyo Co., Ltd. (1)
2-4-11 Higashi Shinagawa Shinagawa Ku, Tokyo, 140-8659, Japan **(100%)**
Tel.: (81) 354605692
Web Site: http://www.jalnavia.co.jp
Sales Range: $150-199.9 Million
Emp.: 1,000
Travel Agency Services
N.A.I.C.S.: 561510
Uji Nakano *(Pres)*

JAL Passenger Services America, Inc. (1)
300 Continental Blvd Ste 620, El Segundo, CA 90245 **(100%)**
Tel.: (310) 322-9684
Web Site: http://www.jpsa.us
Sales Range: $75-99.9 Million
Emp.: 130
Reservation Call Center Services
N.A.I.C.S.: 488190

JAL Plaza Co., Ltd. (1)
1st Floor Yurakucho Denki Building, 1 7 1 Yurakucho Chiyoda-ku, Tokyo, 100-0006, Japan **(100%)**
Tel.: (81) 332870068
Web Site: http://www.jalplaza.co.jp
Sales Range: $125-149.9 Million
Emp.: 389
Airline Ticket Services
N.A.I.C.S.: 488119

JAL Royal Catering Co., Ltd. (1)
1-720 Goryobokujo Sanrizuka Narita, Chiba, 286-0111, Japan **(51%)**
Tel.: (81) 476321311
Sales Range: $25-49.9 Million
Emp.: 150
Catering Services
N.A.I.C.S.: 722320
Hidemasa Ishikawa *(Mng Dir)*

JAL Sales Co., Ltd. (1)
2-4-11 Higashi Shinagawa Nomura Real Estate King Island Bldg, Hikaru 21 order Shinagawa-Ku, Tokyo, 140-0002, Japan **(100%)**
Tel.: (81) 367208520
Web Site: http://www.jalsales.com
Sales Range: $250-299.9 Million
Emp.: 735
Hotel & Travel Services
N.A.I.C.S.: 721110

AND PRIVATE COMPANIES

JAPAN AIRLINES CO., LTD.

JAL Satellite Travel Co., Ltd. (1)
Room 501B 5/F Eastmark 21 Sheung Yuet Road, Kowloon, China (Hong Kong) **(100%)**
Tel.: (852) 3 429 1288
Web Site: https://www.jalselect.com.hk
Sales Range: $10-24.9 Million
Emp.: 45
Travel Agency Services
N.A.I.C.S.: 561510

JAL Simulator Engineering Co., Ltd. (1)
JAL Technical Center 2 3-6-8 Hanedakuko, Ota-Ku, Tokyo, 144-0041, Japan **(100%)**
Tel.: (81) 357563007
Web Site: http://www.jalsim.com
Sales Range: $50-74.9 Million
Emp.: 130
Aircraft Simulator Engineering Services
N.A.I.C.S.: 336413

JAL Sky Service Co., Ltd. (1)
1 1 Furugome, Chiba, 282-0004, Japan **(100%)**
Tel.: (81) 476343976
Web Site: http://www.jalsky.co.jp
Sales Range: $450-499.9 Million
Emp.: 1,000
Passenger Transport & Lounge Services
N.A.I.C.S.: 488119
Hirokazu Jo (Mgr)

JAL Sunlight Co., Ltd. (1)
2 4 11 JAL Building, Shinagawa-Ku, Tokyo, 140-0002, Japan **(100%)**
Tel.: (81) 54606871
Web Site: http://www.jal.com
Sales Range: $25-49.9 Million
Emp.: 98
Cultural Activities & Publishing Services
N.A.I.C.S.: 513199

JAL Techno Service Co., Ltd. (1)
Nikkokitai Building, 1-5-1 Hanedakuko, Ota-Ku, Tokyo, 144-0041, Japan **(100%)**
Tel.: (81) 337472587
Web Site: http://www.jaltechno.com
Sales Range: $25-49.9 Million
Emp.: 30
Aircraft Maintenance Services
N.A.I.C.S.: 811310

JAL Tokyo Aircraft Maintenance Co.,Ltd. (1)
Haneda Airport 3-5-1 Ota-Ku, Tokyo, 144-0041, Japan **(100%)**
Tel.: (81) 357562253
Web Site: http://www.japanairlines.com
Sales Range: $400-449.9 Million
Emp.: 1,600
Aircraft Maintenance Services
N.A.I.C.S.: 811310
Atofhifuke Satoshi (Mgr)

JAL Tours Co., Ltd. (1)
2-4-11 Higashi shinagawa, Tokyo, 140-8658, Shinagawa-Ku, Japan **(100%)**
Tel.: (81) 357158120
Web Site: http://www.jal.co.jp
Sales Range: $75-99.9 Million
Emp.: 379
Hotel & Travel Services
N.A.I.C.S.: 721110

JAL Travel Hokkaido Co., Ltd. (1)
West 7 North 1 Jhouku, Chuo-Ku Sapporo, Sapporo, 060-0001, Japan **(100%)**
Tel.: (81) 112001222
Web Site: http://www.jaltravel-h.com
Sales Range: $75-99.9 Million
Emp.: 288
Hotel & Travel Services
N.A.I.C.S.: 721110

JAL Wave Co., Ltd. (1)
JAL Operation Centre 44, Narita Airport, Narita, 282-0004, Chiba, Japan **(100%)**
Tel.: (81) 476343185
Sales Range: $50-74.9 Million
Emp.: 170
Flight Operation & Load Control Services
N.A.I.C.S.: 488119

JALUX Inc. (1)
Shinagawa Season Terrace 1-2-70 Konan, Minato-ku, Tokyo, 108-8209, Japan
Tel.: (81) 354607200
Web Site: http://www.jalux.com
Rev.: $327,274,234
Assets: $374,957,939
Liabilities: $200,681,467
Net Worth: $174,276,472
Earnings: ($4,116,519)
Emp.: 1,905
Fiscal Year-end: 03/31/2022
Holding Company; Aviation Industry Support, Insurance, Real Estate, Facility Support, Retail Store Operation, Food & Beverage Distribution Services
N.A.I.C.S.: 551112
Shigeki Yamazaki (Exec Officer & Pres-Food & Beverage Unit)

Subsidiary (Non-US):

J Value Co., Ltd. (2)
87 Soi Akapat Thonglor 13 Sukhumvit 55 Road, Klongtan-Nua Wattana, Bangkok, 10110, Thailand
Tel.: (66) 20592616
Web Site: https://www.jvalue.co.th
Emp.: 25
Food Product Whslr
N.A.I.C.S.: 424490
Haruo Endo (Pres)

Subsidiary (Domestic):

JAL-DFS Co., Ltd. (2)
Morita Bldg 5F 959 Hanazakicho, Chiba, 286-0033, Japan
Tel.: (81) 476228571
Web Site: http://www.jaldfs.co.jp
Sales Range: $50-74.9 Million
Emp.: 153
Duty Free Sales Services
N.A.I.C.S.: 455219
Seiji Nakamura (CEO)

Subsidiary (Non-US):

JALUX ASIA Ltd. (2)
159/14 Serm-Mit Tower 9th Floor Room 915 Sukhumvit 21 Asoke Road, North Klongtoey Wattana, Bangkok, 10110, Thailand
Tel.: (66) 225865313
Web Site: http://www.as.jalux.com
Sales Range: $25-49.9 Million
Emp.: 50
Processed Foodstuffs Distr
N.A.I.C.S.: 424420
Taichi Saito (Pres)

Subsidiary (Domestic):

JALUX Airport Inc. (2)
3 3 2 Haneda Airport, Terminal 5F Ota-Ku, Tokyo, Japan
Tel.: (81) 357569110
Web Site: http://www.jalux.com
Sales Range: $250-299.9 Million
Emp.: 1,000
Airport Shop Management Services
N.A.I.C.S.: 459420

Subsidiary (US):

JALUX Americas, Inc. (2)
390 Sepulveda Blvd Ste 3000, El Segundo, CA 90245
Tel.: (310) 524-1000
Sales Range: $50-74.9 Million
Emp.: 75
Aircraft Parts, Food, Wine & General Merchandise Distribution Services
N.A.I.C.S.: 423990

Subsidiary (Non-US):

JALUX Europe Ltd. (2)
Mimosa House, 12 Princes St, London, W1B 2LL, United Kingdom
Tel.: (44) 2074081020
Sales Range: $25-49.9 Million
Emp.: 10
Airport Shop Management Services
N.A.I.C.S.: 488119

Subsidiary (Domestic):

JALUX Fresh Foods, Inc. (2)
2-3-1 Higashigotanda Sompo Japan Gotanda Joint Building, Shinagawa-ku, Tokyo, 141-0022, Japan
Tel.: (81) 363678837
Web Site: http://www.jaluxff.com
Emp.: 25
Fruit & Vegetable Distr
N.A.I.C.S.: 445230

Subsidiary (Non-US):

JALUX HONG KONG Co., Ltd. (2)
1908 19/F Miramar Tower 132 Nathan Road, Harbour City, Tsim Tsa Tsui, Kowloon, China (Hong Kong)
Tel.: (852) 2827 0163
Web Site: http://www.hk.jalux.com
Airline Cabin Service Items & Meals Supplier
N.A.I.C.S.: 722310

JALUX Inc. (2)
Davidson House Forbury Square, Reading, RG1 3EU, Berkshire, United Kingdom
Tel.: (44) 1189000983
Airport Business Development Services
N.A.I.C.S.: 488119

Subsidiary (Domestic):

JALUX Insurance & Service Inc. (2)
2-5-5 Higashi-Shinagawa Harbor One Building 6F, Shinagawa-ku, Tokyo, Japan
Tel.: (81) 120258400
Web Site: http://www.jaluxhs.com
Life Insurance Agency Services
N.A.I.C.S.: 524210

Subsidiary (Non-US):

JALUX SHANGHAI Co., Ltd. (2)
Room 702 Huaihai Plaza No 1045 Huaihai Zhong Rd, Shanghai, 200031, China
Tel.: (86) 2134060663
Web Site: http://www.sh.jalux.com
Sales Range: $25-49.9 Million
Emp.: 30
Food & Beverage Whslr
N.A.I.C.S.: 424490
Hidekazu Nagai (CEO)

Subsidiary (Domestic):

JALUX Style Inc. (2)
Next Site Kamata Building 4F 1-2-5 Kamatahoncho, Ota-ku, Tokyo, 144-0053, Japan
Tel.: (81) 337305661
Web Site: http://www.jaluxstyle.com
Leather Goods Mfr & Distr
N.A.I.C.S.: 316990
Naoto Yokoyama (Mgr-Product Dev)

Subsidiary (Non-US):

JRE Development Co., Ltd. (2)
159 Serm-Mit Tower 9th Floor Room 915 Sukhumvit 21 Road, North Klongtoey Wattana, Bangkok, 10110, Thailand
Tel.: (66) 22586530
Web Site: http://jre.jalux.com
Apartment Development Services
N.A.I.C.S.: 531110

Jalux Singapore Pte. Ltd. (2)
1 Fullerton Road 02-01 One Fullerton, Singapore, 049213, Singapore
Tel.: (65) 68325102
Web Site: https://www.sg.jalux.com
Asset Management Services
N.A.I.C.S.: 523940
Hidebumi Mori (Pres)

Subsidiary (Domestic):

Japan Airport Delica Inc. (2)
1-8-2 Haneda Airport, Ota-ku, Tokyo, 144-0041, Japan
Tel.: (81) 357087790
Web Site: http://www.airdeli.co.jp
Food Products Mfr
N.A.I.C.S.: 311999

JTA Information & Communication Co., Ltd (1)
3- 24 Yamashita-Cho, Naha, Okinawa, 900-0027, Japan **(100%)**
Tel.: (81) 988577811
Web Site: http://www.jtainfocom.co.jp
Sales Range: $25-49.9 Million
Emp.: 20
Aeronautical Systems Developer
N.A.I.C.S.: 541511

JTA Southern Sky Service Co., Ltd. (1)
497 Okinawa Ishigaki, Naha, 907002, Japan **(100%)**
Tel.: (81) 980823200
Web Site: http://www.jal.
Sales Range: $25-49.9 Million
Emp.: 243
Travel Agency Services
N.A.I.C.S.: 561510

Jalcard, Inc. (1)
Nomura Real Estate Agency Tennozu Building 2-4-11 Higashi-Shinagawa, Shinagawa-Ku, Tokyo, 140-8656, Japan **(100%)**
Tel.: (81) 35 460 5131
Web Site: https://www.jalcard.jal.co.jp
Sales Range: $700-749.9 Million
Emp.: 800
Credit Card Services
N.A.I.C.S.: 522210

Jalpak Co., Ltd. (1)
Trade Pia Odaiba Minato-Ku 2 3 1 Daiba, Tokyo, 135-8660, Japan **(78.6%)**
Tel.: (81) 355200550
Rev.: $1,010,000,000
Emp.: 400
Hotel & Travel Services
N.A.I.C.S.: 721110

Subsidiary (Non-US):

Jalpak International (Europe) B.V. (2)
4th Floor Standon House 21 Mansell Street, 5 Hanover Square, London, E1 8AA, United Kingdom **(100%)**
Tel.: (44) 207 264 5190
Web Site: https://www.jalpak.co.uk
Sales Range: $125-149.9 Million
Tour Operating Services
N.A.I.C.S.: 561520

Subsidiary (Non-US):

Jalpak International (Austria) Ges.M.B.H. (3)
Karntner Strasse 11, 1010, Vienna, Austria **(75%)**
Tel.: (43) 15127580
Web Site: http://www.jreast.co.jp
Sales Range: $25-49.9 Million
Emp.: 10
Tour Operating Services
N.A.I.C.S.: 561520

Jalpak International (Germany) GmbH (3)
Immermannstrasse 45, 40210, Dusseldorf, Germany **(100%)**
Tel.: (49) 2111686117
Web Site: http://www.jaltour.de
Sales Range: $10-24.9 Million
Emp.: 15
Tour Operating Services
N.A.I.C.S.: 561520
Andrea Deckelmann (Mgr)

Subsidiary (Non-US):

Jalpak International (France) S.A.S. (2)
4 Rue de Ventadour, 75001, Paris, France **(100%)**
Tel.: (33) 14 455 1530
Web Site: https://www.jaltour.fr
Sales Range: $10-24.9 Million
Emp.: 37
Tour Operating Services
N.A.I.C.S.: 561520

Jalpak International Asia Pte. Ltd. (2)
111 North Bridge Road, 26 03 Peninsula Plaza, Singapore, 179098, Singapore **(100%)**
Tel.: (65) 63386002
Sales Range: $10-24.9 Million
Emp.: 30
Tour Operating Services
N.A.I.C.S.: 561520

Subsidiary (Non-US):

Jalpak International Hong Kong Co., Ltd. (3)
, 9 A 24 Tower China Hong Kong C, Kowloon, China (Hong Kong) **(100%)**
Tel.: (852) 21117574
Travel Agency Services
N.A.I.C.S.: 561599

Subsidiary (Non-US):

Jalpak de Mexico SA de CV (2)

JAPAN AIRLINES CO., LTD.

Japan Airlines Co., Ltd.—(Continued)

Paseo de La Reforma 505 Piso 36, Torre Mayor, Col Cuauhtemoc, CP 06500, Mexico, DF, Mexico
Tel.: (52) 5555147520 **(100%)**
Sales Range: $10-24.9 Million
Emp.: 40
Tour Operating Services
N.A.I.C.S.: 561520

Subsidiary (US):

Micronesian Hospitality, Inc. **(2)**
360 Chalan Pasaheru Rte 10 A, Tamuning, GU 96913 **(62.6%)**
Tel.: (671) 646-6300
Web Site: http://www.jal.com
Sales Range: $25-49.9 Million
Emp.: 90
Tour Operating Services
N.A.I.C.S.: 561520
Norie Nakajima (Office Mgr)

Subsidiary (Non-US):

P.T. Taurina Travel Jaya **(2)**
Wisma KEIAI 3rd Floor Jl Gendral Sudirman Kav 3-4, Jakarta, 10220, Indonesia **(51%)**
Tel.: (62) 21 251 0550
Web Site: https://www.jalan-tour.com
Sales Range: $10-24.9 Million
Emp.: 50
Tour Operating Services
N.A.I.C.S.: 561520

Subsidiary (US):

Tour Create, Inc. **(2)**
2270 Kalakaua Ave Ste 1707, Honolulu, HI 96815 **(100%)**
Tel.: (808) 923-5599
Sales Range: $25-49.9 Million
Emp.: 5
Tour Operating Services
N.A.I.C.S.: 561520

Jalsky Hakodate Co., Ltd. **(1)**
7 1 6 Daido Seimei Building, Hokkaido, Wakamatsu, Hakodate, 040-0063, Japan **(100%)**
Tel.: (81) 138275401
Web Site: http://www.jal.com
Sales Range: $10-24.9 Million
Emp.: 45
Travel Agency Services
N.A.I.C.S.: 561599

Jalsky Kanazawa Co., Ltd. **(1)**
Komatsu Airport 50, Ukiyanagimachi, Komatsu, 923-0993, Ishikawa, Japan **(100%)**
Tel.: (81) 761235126
Web Site: http://www.jal.co.jp
Sales Range: $25-49.9 Million
Emp.: 47
Cargo Handling Services
N.A.I.C.S.: 488119

Jalsky Kansai Co., Ltd. **(1)**
Sennan Gun Tajiri Cho, Quanzhou Airport, Osaka, 549-0011, Japan **(100%)**
Tel.: (81) 724553568
Web Site: http://www.jal.co.jp
Sales Range: $200-249.9 Million
Emp.: 527
Airport Passenger Services
N.A.I.C.S.: 488119

Jalsky Kyushu Co., Ltd. **(1)**
Hakata-Ku Oaza 767 1, Fukuoka, 812-0003, Japan **(100%)**
Tel.: (81) 926226283
Sales Range: $200-249.9 Million
Emp.: 500
Airport Lounge Services
N.A.I.C.S.: 488119
Satoru Nakamura (CEO)

Jalsky Osaka Co., Ltd. **(1)**
Osaka International Airport Nisimati 3 Chome 555, Osaka, 560-0036, Japan **(100%)**
Tel.: (81) 668568398
Web Site: http://www.jal.co.jp
Sales Range: $75-99.9 Million
Emp.: 200
Travel Agency Services
N.A.I.C.S.: 561520
Teiji Murayama (Pres)

Jalsky Sapporo Co., Ltd. **(1)**
Chitose Airport, Hokkaido, 066-0012, Japan **(100%)**
Tel.: (81) 123452211
Web Site: http://www.jal.co.jp
Sales Range: $125-149.9 Million
Emp.: 250
Airport Passenger Services
N.A.I.C.S.: 488119
Hideto Ace (Gen Mgr)

Jalsky Sendai Co., Ltd. **(1)**
Natori-Sendai Airport, Migagi, Natori, 989-2401, Miyagi, Japan **(100%)**
Tel.: (81) 223836568
Web Site: http://www.jal.co.jp
Sales Range: $25-49.9 Million
Emp.: 44
Airport Cargo Handling Services
N.A.I.C.S.: 488119

Jalsky Tokyo Co., Ltd. **(1)**
Haneda Airport 3 3 2, Tokyo, 144-0041, Japan **(100%)**
Tel.: (81) 357563349
Web Site: http://www.jal.com
Sales Range: $1-4.9 Billion
Emp.: 2,600
Passenger Handling Services
N.A.I.C.S.: 488119
Hiroai Kapo (Pres)

Jaltos Co., Ltd. **(1)**
2139-1 Komaino, Narita, 286-0121, Chiba, Japan **(100%)**
Tel.: (81) 476328056
Web Site: http://www.jalcargoservice.com
Sales Range: $200-249.9 Million
Emp.: 60
Air Cargo Services
N.A.I.C.S.: 481112
Hidehiko Itani (Pres)

Japan Airlines Co., Ltd. - Los Angeles Representative Office **(1)**
300 Continental Blvd Ste 401, El Segundo, CA 90245-5046
Tel.: (310) 606-6609
Sales Range: $50-74.9 Million
Emp.: 150
Air Transportation
N.A.I.C.S.: 481111

Japan Airlines Co., Ltd. - New York Representative Office **(1)**
461 5th Ave, New York, NY 10017
Tel.: (212) 310-1337
Web Site: http://www.jal.com
Sales Range: $200-249.9 Million
Emp.: 900
Scheduled Passenger & Cargo International Airline
N.A.I.C.S.: 488119

Japan Airlines Domestic Co., Ltd. **(1)**
4-11 Higashi-shinagawa 2-chome, Shinagawa-Ku, Tokyo, 140-8637, Japan
Tel.: (81) 3 5460 3191
Air Transportation; Domestic
N.A.I.C.S.: 481111

Subsidiary (Domestic):

Asia Creative Tours Co., Ltd. **(2)**
Landmark Plaza Building 3F, 1 6 7 Shibakoen Minato-Ku, Tokyo, 105-0011, Japan **(100%)**
Tel.: (81) 335785262
Web Site: http://www.jal.com
Sales Range: $10-24.9 Million
Emp.: 10
Hotel & Travel Services
N.A.I.C.S.: 721110

Hokkaido Air System Co., Ltd. **(2)**
New Chitose Airport Terminal, Chitose, Hokkaido, 066-0012, Japan **(51%)**
Tel.: (81) 123465533
Sales Range: $25-49.9 Million
Emp.: 92
Oil Transportation Services
N.A.I.C.S.: 481111
Nishimura Kimitoshi (Pres)

J-Air Co., Ltd. **(2)**
4-10-2 Kanon-shin-machi, Nishi-ku, Hiroshima, 733-0036, Japan **(100%)**
Tel.: (81) 822346168

Sales Range: $50-74.9 Million
Emp.: 130
Oil Transportation Services
N.A.I.C.S.: 481111

JAL Express Co., Ltd. **(2)**
Kukoshisetu Osaka Sogo Building 2-2-5 Kuko, Ikeda, 563-0034, Osakafu, Japan **(100%)**
Tel.: (81) 668577378
Web Site: http://www.jal.co.jp
Sales Range: $200-249.9 Million
Emp.: 870
Oil Transportation Services
N.A.I.C.S.: 481111

Jalways Co., Ltd. **(2)**
Spheretower Tennoz 23F 2-8 Higashi-Shinagawa 2-chome, Tokyo, 140-0002, Japan **(100%)**
Tel.: (81) 354606830
Sales Range: $800-899.9 Million
Emp.: 3,048
Oil Transportation Services
N.A.I.C.S.: 481111

Japan Air Commuter Co., Ltd. **(2)**
87-4 Mizobe Town, Mizobecho-Fumoto, Kirishima, Kagoshima, Japan **(60%)**
Tel.: (81) 995582151
Web Site: http://www.jac.co.jp
Sales Range: $200-249.9 Million
Emp.: 445
Oil Transportation Services
N.A.I.C.S.: 481111

Ryukyu Air Commuter Co., Ltd. **(2)**
31 Yamashitacho, Naha, 900-0027, Okinawa, Japan **(70.3%)**
Tel.: (81) 988589664
Web Site: http://www.rac.churashima.net
Sales Range: $25-49.9 Million
Emp.: 70
Oil Transportation Services
N.A.I.C.S.: 481111
Mashmr Kamiyama (Pres)

Japan Airlines Management Corp. **(1)**
Bldg 151 JFK Airport, Jamaica, NY 11430 **(100%)**
Tel.: (718) 244-5140
Web Site: http://www.jmcjfk.com
Sales Range: $50-74.9 Million
Emp.: 4
Real Estate Services
N.A.I.C.S.: 531390
Jack Weber (Mgr)

Japan Airport Fueling Service Co., Ltd. **(1)**
Keisei Narita Higashiguchi Morita Bldg 6F 959 Hanazaki-cho, Room 5014, Narita, 286-0033, Chiba, Japan
Tel.: (81) 47 685 6185
Web Site: https://www.jafsnet.co.jp
Sales Range: $50-74.9 Million
Emp.: 172
Aircraft Fueling Services
N.A.I.C.S.: 457210
Kimitoshi Nishimura (Mng Dir)

Japan TransOcean Air Co., Ltd. **(1)**
3-24 Yamashita-cho, Naha, 900-0027, Okinawa, Japan **(51.1%)**
Tel.: (81) 988572112
Sales Range: $200-249.9 Million
Emp.: 716
Oil Transportation Services
N.A.I.C.S.: 481111

Jupiter Global Limited **(1)**
Room 2616-18 26/F The Metropolis Tower 10 Metropolis Drive, Hung Hom, Kowloon, China (Hong Kong) **(80%)**
Tel.: (852) 2 735 1886
Web Site: https://www.jupiter-groups.com
Sales Range: $50-74.9 Million
Emp.: 800
Holding Company; Global Logistics Services
N.A.I.C.S.: 551112

Subsidiary (Non-US):

Data & Jupiter Freight (Beijing) Co., Ltd. **(2)**
Room 5E Block A Guo Men Mansion No 1 Zuo Jia Zhuang, Chao Yang District, Beijing, 100028, China

INTERNATIONAL PUBLIC

Tel.: (86) 106 466 7790
Web Site: https://www.data-jupiter.com
Sales Range: $25-49.9 Million
Cargo Transportation Services
N.A.I.C.S.: 488320

Subsidiary (Domestic):

Jupiter Air (Hong Kong) Ltd. **(2)**
Room 2616-18 26/F The Metropolis Tower 10 Metropolis Drive, Kowloon, NT, China (Hong Kong)
Tel.: (852) 27137552
Web Site: http://www.jupiterhkg.com.hk
Sales Range: $25-49.9 Million
Emp.: 10
Air Courier Services
N.A.I.C.S.: 492110

Subsidiary (Non-US):

Jupiter Air Oceania Ltd. **(2)**
Unit 3 55 Kent Road, Mascot, 2020, NSW, Australia
Tel.: (61) 283378900
Web Site: http://www.jupiterair.com.au
Sales Range: $25-49.9 Million
Air Courier Services
N.A.I.C.S.: 492110

Jupiter Air Services (Malaysia) Sdn. Bhd. **(2)**
Lot F1-46 Klas Forwarders Building, Klas Cargo Complex International Airport, Sepang, 64000, Selangor, Malaysia
Tel.: (60) 387788448
Web Site: http://www.jupiter-groups.com
Sales Range: $25-49.9 Million
Emp.: 10
Freight Transportation Services
N.A.I.C.S.: 488510
Shinju Yagisawa (Gen Mgr)

Jupiter Japan Co., Ltd. **(2)**
1-18-10 Saga Sagacho Building 2nd Annex 4th Floor, Koto-ku, Tokyo, 135-0031, yubinbango, Japan
Tel.: (81) 35 621 8625
Web Site: https://jupiter-japan.jp
Air Courier Services
N.A.I.C.S.: 492110

Affiliate (Non-US):

Jupiter Pacific Forwarding Joint Venture Co., Ltd. **(2)**
112 Hong Ha Street, Ward 2 Tan Binh District, Ho Chi Minh City, 70000, Vietnam
Tel.: (84) 283 845 4940
Web Site: http://www.jupiterpacific.com.vn
Sales Range: $10-24.9 Million
Emp.: 50
Air & Sea Courier Services
N.A.I.C.S.: 492110

Subsidiary (Non-US):

Jupiter Singapore Pte Ltd. **(2)**
7 Airline Road 05-15 Cargo Agents Building E, Changi Cargo Agents Megaplex 1, Singapore, 819834, Singapore
Tel.: (65) 6 545 0531
Web Site: https://www.jupiterair.com.sg
Sales Range: $10-24.9 Million
Emp.: 20
Air Courier Services
N.A.I.C.S.: 492110

Mercury International Co., Ltd. **(2)**
Sumitomo Fudosan Shibazono Building 4F, 2 10 1 Shibakouen Minato-Ku, Tokyo, 105-0011, Japan
Tel.: (81) 357773734
Web Site: http://www.jupiter-groups.com
Sales Range: $25-49.9 Million
Emp.: 10
Air Courier Services
N.A.I.C.S.: 492110

Subsidiary (US):

Micom America, Inc. **(2)**
460 South Hindry Ave Unit C, Inglewood, CA 90301-2045
Tel.: (310) 670-5123
Web Site: http://www.jupiter-groups.com
Sales Range: $10-24.9 Million
Air Courier Services
N.A.I.C.S.: 492110

AND PRIVATE COMPANIES

Subsidiary (Non-US):

Sirius Air International Ltd. (2)
Unit 3 Horton Road, Colnbrook, Slough,
SL3 OBB, Berks, United Kingdom
Tel.: (44) 1753 689 212
Web Site: http://www.jupiter-groups.com
Freight Transportation Services
N.A.I.C.S.: 488510

Kansai Airport Ground Service Co., Ltd. (1)
Quanzhou Airport South 1, Sennan, Osaka, 549-0021, Japan (100%)
Tel.: (81) 724553346
Web Site: http://www.kgs-kankuu.com
Sales Range: $200-249.9 Million
Emp.: 691
Baggage Handling Services
N.A.I.C.S.: 488119

Narita Logistic Terminal Co., Ltd. (1)
2139 1 Tennamino Komaino, Narita, Chiba, 282-0021, Japan (100%)
Tel.: (81) 476327132
Web Site: http://www.jal.com
Sales Range: $50-74.9 Million
Emp.: 156
Air Cargo Services
N.A.I.C.S.: 481112

New Tokyo Service Co., Ltd. (1)
141 Narita International Airport, Narita, 282-0004, Chiba, Japan (100%)
Tel.: (81) 476 21 1234
Web Site: http://www.tfk.co.jp
Sales Range: $250-299.9 Million
Emp.: 945
Equipment Washing & General Cleaning
N.A.I.C.S.: 488119
Makoto Fukada (Pres)

Nikko Hotels International-USA (1)
222 Mason St, San Francisco, CA 94102-2115
Tel.: (415) 394-1111
Web Site: http://www.hotelnikkoss.com
Sales Range: $125-149.9 Million
Emp.: 330
Hotel
N.A.I.C.S.: 481111
Joseph Curran (VP-Sls & Mktg)

Nitto Aircraft Maintenance Co., Ltd. (1)
1-11-1 Haneda Airport, Ota-Ku, Tokyo, 144-0041, Japan (100%)
Tel.: (81) 337476007
Sales Range: $50-74.9 Million
Emp.: 170
Aircraft Maintenance Services
N.A.I.C.S.: 488119

Okinawa Airport Service Co., Ltd. (1)
403 Kagamizu, Naha, 901-0142, Okinawa, Japan (100%)
Tel.: (81) 988521996
Web Site: http://www.jal.com
Sales Range: $50-74.9 Million
Emp.: 196
Freight & Fuel Supply Services
N.A.I.C.S.: 488119
Osamu Yushima (Pres)

Okinawa Fueling Facilities Co., Ltd. (1)
306-1 Naha, Naha, 901-0142, Okinawa, Japan (60%)
Tel.: (81) 988576982
Fuel Operating System Mfr
N.A.I.C.S.: 333248

Osaka Airport Transport Co., Ltd. (1)
3-555 Hotarugaike Nishimachi, Toyonaka, 560-0036, Osaka, Japan
Tel.: (81) 66 844 1124
Web Site: https://www.okkbus.co.jp
Sales Range: $125-149.9 Million
Emp.: 294
Limousine Service
N.A.I.C.S.: 485320

JAPAN AIRPORT TERMINAL CO., LTD.
Terminal 1 3-3-2 Haneda Airport, Ota-ku, Tokyo, 144-0041, Japan
Tel.: (81) 357578000
Web Site: https://www.tokyo-airport-bldg.co.jp
Year Founded: 1953
9706—(TKS)
Rev.: $1,438,190,580
Assets: $3,043,396,030
Liabilities: $1,945,898,070
Net Worth: $1,097,497,960
Earnings: $127,275,550
Emp.: 272
Fiscal Year-end: 03/31/24
Aviation Support Services
N.A.I.C.S.: 488190
Isao Takashiro (Chm & CEO)

Subsidiaries:

Big Wing Co., Ltd. (1)
Tel.: (81) 357578283
Emp.: 60
Marketing & Advertising Services
N.A.I.C.S.: 541890
Tsukasa Koga (Pres & CEO)

CTT Co., Ltd. (1)
709-9 Kichioka, Narita, Chiba, Japan
Tel.: (81) 476737220
Janitorial Services
N.A.I.C.S.: 561720

Cosmo Enterprise Co., Ltd. (1)
164 Furugome, Narita, 282-0004, Chiba, Japan
Tel.: (81) 476328600
Emp.: 317
Frozen Food Mfr & Distr
N.A.I.C.S.: 311412
Masao Saida (Vice Chm)

Hamashin Co., Ltd. (1)
Suisanto C-17 3-2-8, Tokai Ota-ku, Tokyo, Japan
Tel.: (81) 354926130
Marine Product Whslr
N.A.I.C.S.: 423910

Haneda Future Research Institute Incorporated (1)
Terminal 1 3-3-2 Haneda Airport, Ohta-ku, Tokyo, 144-0041, Japan
Tel.: (81) 357578070
Web Site: https://www.haneda-the-future.com
Office Administrative Services
N.A.I.C.S.: 561110

Japan Airport Techno Co., Ltd. (1)
3-3-2 Haneda Airport, Ota-ku, Tokyo, 144-0041, Japan
Tel.: (81) 357578551
Emp.: 358
International Airport Operation Services
N.A.I.C.S.: 488119

Japan Duty Free Fa-So-La Isetan Mitsukoshi Co., Ltd. (1)
4-8-12 Ginza Kochiwa Building 7F, Chuo-ku, Tokyo, 104-0061, Japan
Tel.: (81) 355246610
Emp.: 56
Tax Preparation Services
N.A.I.C.S.: 485310

Kaikan Kaihatsu Co., Ltd. (1)
Dai-ichi Dendo Kaikan Tsukiji Hongwanji Temple 3-15-1 Tsukiji, Chuo-ku, Tokyo, Japan
Tel.: (81) 335440551
Restaurant Services
N.A.I.C.S.: 722511

Sakura Shokai Co., Ltd. (1)
14-11 Keihinjima 2-chome, Ota-ku, Tokyo, Japan
Tel.: (81) 357551415
Airport Clean Center Services
N.A.I.C.S.: 488119

Tokyo International Air Terminal Corporation (1)
2-6-5 Haneda Airport, Ota-ku, Tokyo, 144-0041, Japan
Tel.: (81) 364285931
Web Site: https://www.tiat.co.jp
Emp.: 62
International Airport Operation Services
N.A.I.C.S.: 488119

JAPAN ANIMAL REFERRAL MEDICAL CENTER CO., LTD.
2-5-8 Kuji Takatsu-ku, Kawasaki, 213-0032, Kanagawa, Japan
Tel.: (81) 448501320
Web Site: http://www.jarmec.co.jp
6039—(TKS)
Rev.: $28,224,700
Assets: $57,969,700
Liabilities: $32,778,990
Net Worth: $25,190,710
Earnings: $2,227,570
Emp.: 217
Fiscal Year-end: 03/31/24
Animal Hospital & Medical Services
N.A.I.C.S.: 541940
Hidehiro Hirao (Pres & Dir-Rep)

JAPAN ASIA GROUP LIMITED
Kokusai Building 1-1 Marunouchi 3-chome, Chiyoda-ku, Tokyo, 100-0005, Japan
Tel.: (81) 3 4476 8000
Web Site: http://www.japanasiagroup.jp
Year Founded: 1988
3751—(TKS)
Rev.: $882,293,280
Assets: $1,544,782,800
Liabilities: $1,296,616,640
Net Worth: $248,166,160
Earnings: ($3,000,800)
Emp.: 4,765
Fiscal Year-end: 03/31/21
Scientific Consulting Services
N.A.I.C.S.: 541690
Tetsuo Yamashita (Chm, Pres & CEO)

Subsidiaries:

GEOSOL Beteiligungsgesellschaft mbH (1)
Cicerostrasse 37, 10709, Berlin, Germany
Tel.: (49) 30 89 40 86 0
Web Site: http://www.geosol.de
Emp.: 425
Solar Electric Power Generation Services
N.A.I.C.S.: 221114
Andreas Steinberg (Mng Dir)

GEOSOL Italia S.r.l. (1)
Piazza Scipione Ammirato 4, 00179, Rome, Italy
Tel.: (39) 064 567 5500
Web Site: https://www.geosol-italia.it
Solar Electric Power Generation Services
N.A.I.C.S.: 221114

JAG Field Co., Ltd. (1)
Nagoya Mitsui Building Main Building 15F 1-24-30 Meiekiminami, Nakamura-ku, Nagoya, 450-0003, Japan
Tel.: (81) 525892822
Web Site: http://www.jag-fld.com
Engineeering Services
N.A.I.C.S.: 541330

JAG Forest Co., Ltd. (1)
3-1-1 Marunouchi, Chiyoda-ku, Tokyo, 100-0005, Japan
Tel.: (81) 344768024
Web Site: http://www.jagforest.co.jp
Forest Management Services
N.A.I.C.S.: 115310

JAG Seabell Co., Ltd. (1)
Kokusai Building 1-1 Marunouchi 3-chome, Chiyoda-ku, Tokyo, 100-0005, Japan
Tel.: (81) 363640954
Web Site: http://www.jagseabell.jp
Eletric Power Generation Services
N.A.I.C.S.: 221118
Satoshi Watanabe (Pres)

Japan Asia Asset Management Co., Ltd. (1)
1-14-1 Shintomi, Chuo-ku, Tokyo, 104-0041, Japan
Tel.: (81) 3 5542 7000
Asset Management Services
N.A.I.C.S.: 523940
Akiho Kumagai (Pres)

Japan Asia Financial Service Co., Ltd. (1)
3-1-1 Marunouchi International Building, Chiyoda-ku, Tokyo, 100-0005, Japan
Tel.: (81) 34 476 8080
Web Site: https://www.ja-fs.jp
Financial Management Services
N.A.I.C.S.: 523999
Tatsuro Yamakawa (Pres)

KHC Ltd. (1)
2-2 Hanazono-cho, Akashi, 673-0015, Japan
Tel.: (81) 789298315
Web Site: https://www.khc-ltd.co.jp
Rev.: $66,509,820
Assets: $99,315,250
Liabilities: $57,044,300
Net Worth: $42,270,950
Earnings: $2,346,550
Emp.: 120
Fiscal Year-end: 03/31/2024
Real Estate Development Services
N.A.I.C.S.: 531311
Yoshiaki Kiyomi (Chm)

KOKUSAI BEIJING LIMITED (1)
Room A560 Floor5 16 YongAnDongli, ChaoYang District, Beijing, China
Tel.: (86) 10 65637740
Business Consulting Services
N.A.I.C.S.: 541611
Yasuchika Fujiwara (Mng Dir)

KOKUSAI LAND (VIETNAM) LIMITED (1)
Suite 2708 Saigon Trade Center 37 Ton DucThang Street, District 1, Ho Chi Minh City, Vietnam
Tel.: (84) 8 3910 3101
Web Site: http://www.kl-vn.com
Construction Management Consulting Services
N.A.I.C.S.: 541618
Naomiki Kanamaru (Chm)

Kimura Sangyo Co., Ltd. (1)
4-9-2 Honcho-Nihonbashi, chuo-ku, Tokyo, 103-0023, Japan
Tel.: (81) 336633551
Web Site: http://www.kimsco.co.jp
Emp.: 31
Health & Personal Care Services
N.A.I.C.S.: 456199
Sadakatsu Kimura (Pres)

Kokusai Bunkazai Co., Ltd. (1)
2-3-4 Higashigotanda, Shinagawa-ku, Tokyo, 141-0022, Japan
Tel.: (81) 33 473 1221
Web Site: https://www.k-bunka.co.jp
Scientific Consulting Services
N.A.I.C.S.: 541690
Norimi Oyama (Pres)

Meiji Consultant Co., Ltd. (1)
1-21-1 Minami 7 West, Chuo-ku, Sapporo, 064-0807, Hokkaido, Japan
Tel.: (81) 115520122
Web Site: http://www.meicon.co.jp
Engineeering Services
N.A.I.C.S.: 541330

Ryukyu Kokusai Kogyo Co., Ltd. (1)
1831-1 Oroku, Naha, 901-0152, Okinawa, Japan
Tel.: (81) 98 989 8019
Scientific Consulting Services
N.A.I.C.S.: 541690

Sakazume Seizaisho Co., Ltd. (1)
3858 Yasuda, Agano, 959-2221, Niigata Prefecture, Japan
Tel.: (81) 250682250
Web Site: http://s-seizai.com
Wood Processing Services
N.A.I.C.S.: 423310

TDS Co., Ltd. (1)
2-5-5 Shinmei-cho, Okaya, 394-0004, Nagano Prefecture, Japan
Tel.: (81) 266234517
Web Site: http://www.tdsjp.co.jp
DC Solenoid Assembly Product Mfr & Distr
N.A.I.C.S.: 332911
Takihiko Takahashi (Pres)

JAPAN ASIA INVESTMENT CO., LTD.
2F Medical Friend Building 3-2-4

JAPAN ASIA INVESTMENT CO., LTD.

Japan Asia Investment Co., Ltd.—(Continued)
Kudn-kita, Chiyoda-ku, Tokyo, 102-0073, Japan
Tel.: (81) 332598518
Web Site: https://www.jaic-vc.co.jp
Year Founded: 1981
8518—(TKS)
Rev.: $16,154,840
Assets: $111,021,560
Liabilities: $70,489,040
Net Worth: $40,532,520
Earnings: ($11,237,000)
Emp.: 38
Fiscal Year-end: 03/31/24
Investment & Financial Services
N.A.I.C.S.: 523999
Keizai Doyukai *(Founder)*

Subsidiaries:

DFJ JAIC Venture Partners, LLC (1)
2882 Sandhill Rd Ste 210, Menlo Park, CA 94025
Tel.: (650) 617-9000
Web Site: http://www.dfjjaic.com
Sales Range: $50-74.9 Million
Emp.: 4
Investment Management Service
N.A.I.C.S.: 523150
Quaeed Motiwala *(Mng Dir)*

JAIC (Thailand) Co., Ltd. (1)
14th Fl C Rm Thanapoom Tower 1550 New Petchuburi Rd, Makasan, Bangkok, 10400, Thailand
Tel.: (66) 22070216
Sales Range: $50-74.9 Million
Emp.: 2
Financial Investment Advisory Services
N.A.I.C.S.: 523940

JAIC Asia Holdings Pte. Ltd. (1)
20 Cecil St Ste 15-02 Equity Plz, Singapore, 049705, Singapore
Tel.: (65) 65570559
Sales Range: $50-74.9 Million
Emp.: 5
Investment Management Service
N.A.I.C.S.: 523999

JAIC International (Hong Kong) Co., Ltd. (1)
Ste 1112 Two Pacific Pl, 88 Queensway Admiralty, Hong Kong, China (Hong Kong)
Tel.: (852) 25093011
Web Site: http://www.jaic-vc.co.jp
Investment Management Service
N.A.I.C.S.: 523150

JAIC Securities Co., Ltd. (1)
4th Fl Seiko Takebashi Kyodo Bldg 11 Nishiki-cho 3-chome, Chiyoda-ku, Tokyo, 101 0054, Japan
Tel.: (81) 3 3518 0930
Equity Fund Management Services
N.A.I.C.S.: 525910

Japan Asia Investment (China) Co., Ltd. (1)
5F GIFC 1438 Hongqiao Road, 1376 Nangjing W Rd, Shanghai, 201103, China
Tel.: (86) 2161976238
Web Site: http://www.jaic-vc.co.jp
Investment Management Service
N.A.I.C.S.: 523150

Japan Private Equity Co., Ltd (1)
2-15-6 Misakicho Kanda K-STAGE 5F, Chiyoda ku, Tokyo, 101-0061, Japan **(49.2%)**
Tel.: (81) 332381726
Web Site: https://www.private-equity.co.jp
Equity Fund Management Services
N.A.I.C.S.: 525910
Shinichi Hoda *(Pres)*

PT. JAIC Indonesia (1)
Wisma Nugra Santana 10th Fl, Jl. Jend. Sudirman Kav 7-8, Jakarta, 10220, Indonesia
Tel.: (62) 215702525
Web Site: http://www.jaic.co.id
Sales Range: $50-74.9 Million
Emp.: 4
Investment Management Service
N.A.I.C.S.: 523150
Vincent Ng *(Mgr)*

JAPAN AUTO LEASING INC.

545 King Street North, Waterloo, N2L 5Z6, ON, Canada
Tel.: (519) 746-4120
Web Site: http://www.waterloohonda.com
Year Founded: 1979
Rev.: $17,438,860
Emp.: 40
New & Used Car Dealers
N.A.I.C.S.: 441110
Lothar Quak *(Gen Mgr-Sls)*

JAPAN AVIATION ELECTRONICS INDUSTRY, LTD.

21-1 Dogenzaka 1-Chome, Shibuya-ku, Tokyo, 150-0043, Japan
Tel.: (81) 337802711
Web Site: https://www.jae.com
Year Founded: 1953
6807—(TKS)
Rev.: $1,492,412,410
Assets: $1,560,237,620
Liabilities: $722,023,520
Net Worth: $838,214,100
Earnings: $80,939,450
Emp.: 791
Fiscal Year-end: 03/31/24
Aviation Electronics Systems & Components Mfr
N.A.I.C.S.: 334419
Tsutomu Onohara *(Chm & Pres)*

Subsidiaries:

JAE Business Support, Ltd. (1)
3-1-1 Musashino, Akishima, 196-8555, Tokyo, Japan
Tel.: (81) 42 549 9662
Web Site: http://www.jbs.jae.co.jp
Sales Range: $25-49.9 Million
Emp.: 129
Engineeering Services
N.A.I.C.S.: 541330

JAE Dongguan Service Co., Ltd. (1)
Rm801 8/f Changan Taishang Bldg Dezhengzhong Road, Changan Town, Dongguan, 523850, Guangdong, China
Tel.: (86) 76985356736
Electronic Components Mfr
N.A.I.C.S.: 334419

JAE Electronics, Inc. (1)
142 Technology Dr Ste 100, Irvine, CA 92618-2430 **(100%)**
Tel.: (949) 753-2600
Web Site: http://www.jaeusa.com
Sales Range: $25-49.9 Million
Emp.: 60
Marketing & Sales of Electronic Equipment, Aeronautical Equipment, Switches & Connectors
N.A.I.C.S.: 423690

JAE Engineering, Ltd. (1)
1 1 Musashino 3 Chome, Akishima Shi, Tokyo, 196 8555, Japan **(100%)**
Tel.: (81) 42 549 9112
Web Site: http://www.jae.com
Sales Range: $25-49.9 Million
Emp.: 200
Engineering Design of Electronic Equipment & Devices & Development of Related Software
N.A.I.C.S.: 811210

JAE Europe, Ltd. (1)
Royal Pavilion Tower 3 First Floor Wellesley Road, Aldershot, GU11 1PZ, Hampshire, United Kingdom **(100%)**
Tel.: (44) 1252551100
Web Site: http://www.jae.co.uk
Sales Range: $25-49.9 Million
Emp.: 21
Import, Export & Marketing of Electronic Parts & Related Products
N.A.I.C.S.: 423690

JAE Foods, Ltd. (1)
1-1 Musashino 3-chome, Akishima, Tokyo, 196-8555, Japan
Tel.: (81) 425464878
Food Supplier
N.A.I.C.S.: 445298

JAE Fuji, Ltd. (1)
8154-35 Uenohara, Uenohara, 409-0112, Yamanashi, Japan
Tel.: (81) 554205611
Web Site: https://www.jae.com
Sales Range: $25-49.9 Million
Emp.: 195
Design & Production of Various Molds & Assembling Equipment
N.A.I.C.S.: 333514

JAE Hakko, Ltd. (1)
6-1-1 Sakaemachi, Tachikawa, 190-0003, Tokyo, Japan
Tel.: (81) 425387751
Web Site: https://www.jae.com
Emp.: 59
Electronic Connectors Distr
N.A.I.C.S.: 423690

JAE Hirosaki, Ltd. (1)
5-5-1 Seinofukuro, Hirosaki, 036-8666, Aomori, Japan
Tel.: (81) 172333111
Web Site: http://www.hae.co.jp
Sales Range: $200-249.9 Million
Emp.: 775
Production & Marketing of Electronic Equipment & Parts
N.A.I.C.S.: 334220

JAE Hong Kong, Ltd. (1)
Units 1810-1813 Level 18 Tower 1 Grand Century Place 193 Prince, PO Box 177, Edward Road West Mongkok, Kowloon, China (Hong Kong) **(100%)**
Tel.: (852) 27237782
Web Site: http://www.jae.com
Emp.: 100
Purchase & Marketing of Precision Electric & Electronic Equipment & Components
N.A.I.C.S.: 449210

JAE Korea, Inc. (1)
5th floor Industry-Academic Cooperation Foundation Building, 329 Gangnam-daero Seocho-gu, Seoul, 1337-31, Korea (South) **(100%)**
Tel.: (82) 26230110
Web Site: https://www.jaekr.com
Sales Range: $25-49.9 Million
Emp.: 24
Import, Export & Marketing of Electronic Parts & Related Products
N.A.I.C.S.: 423690

JAE Oregon, Inc. (1)
11555 SW Leveton Dr, Tualatin, OR 97062-6000 **(100%)**
Tel.: (503) 692-1333
Web Site: http://www.jaeoregon.com
Sales Range: $50-74.9 Million
Emp.: 250
Production & Marketing of Electric & Electronic Equipment & Parts
N.A.I.C.S.: 334417

JAE Philippines, Inc. (1)
JAE Philippines Building Linares Extension, Gateway Business Park Javalera General Trias, Cavite, 4107, Philippines **(100%)**
Tel.: (63) 464330285
Sales Range: $25-49.9 Million
Emp.: 1,000
Production & Marketing of Electronic Components & Related Products
N.A.I.C.S.: 334419
Shinichi Kimura *(Pres)*

JAE Shanghai Co., Ltd. (1)
8F Jin Hong Qiao Business Building No 8 555 Gubei Road, Chang Ning District, Shanghai, 200051, China
Tel.: (86) 2162360322
Aviation Electronics Systems & Components Mfr
N.A.I.C.S.: 334419

JAE Shinshu, Ltd. (1)
800 Kamikatagiri Matsukawa-cho, Shimoina-gun, Nagano, 399-3301, Japan **(100%)**
Tel.: (81) 265373111
Web Site: https://www.jae.com
Sales Range: $50-74.9 Million
Emp.: 229
Production & Marketing of Aerospace Electronic Equipment & Parts
N.A.I.C.S.: 334511

JAE Singapore Pte. Ltd. (1)

INTERNATIONAL PUBLIC

33 Tannery Lane 02-01 Hoesteel Industrial Building, Singapore, 347789, Singapore **(100%)**
Tel.: (65) 67481332
Web Site: http://www.jae-connector.com
Sales Range: $25-49.9 Million
Emp.: 15
Production & Marketing of Connectors & Switches
N.A.I.C.S.: 335931
Tasumi Miyauchi *(Mng Dir)*

JAE Taiwan, Ltd. (1)
35 20th Rd Industrial Park, Taichung, 40850, Taiwan **(100%)**
Tel.: (886) 423593411
Web Site: http://www.jae.com.tw
Sales Range: $1-9.9 Million
Emp.: 400
Production & Marketing of Various Kinds of Electric & Electronic Precision Connectors & Cable Harnessing
N.A.I.C.S.: 335931
Kono Toru *(Pres)*

JAE Tijuana, S.A. de C.V. (1)
Calle Cerro Colorado 16650 Int 1 y 2 Colonia Ninos Heroes este, Baja California, 22120, Tijuana, Mexico
Tel.: (52) 6646897484
Web Site: http://www.jaeoregon.com
Sales Range: $200-249.9 Million
Emp.: 1,000
Aviation Electronics Systems & Components Mfr
N.A.I.C.S.: 334419

JAE Wujiang Co., Ltd. (1)
859 Pangjin Road Wujiang Economic and Technological Development Zone, Suzhou, Jiangsu, 215200, China
Tel.: (86) 51263496123
Aviation Electronics Systems & Components Mfr
N.A.I.C.S.: 334419

JAE Wuxi Co., Ltd. (1)
33 Xiqin Road, Xinwu District, Wuxi, 214028, Jiangsu, China
Tel.: (86) 51085215888
Aviation Electronics Systems & Components Mfr
N.A.I.C.S.: 334419

JAE Yamagata, Ltd. (1)
4102-6 Takadaishinden Izumida, Shinjo, 999-5103, Yamagata, Japan
Tel.: (81) 233241111
Web Site: https://www.jae.com
Sales Range: $100-124.9 Million
Emp.: 425
Production, Processing & Marketing of Electronic Parts, Precision Tools & Machinery Components
N.A.I.C.S.: 336411

Jae Houston, LLC (1)
1100 W Park 1 Dr, Sugar Land, TX 77478-2578
Tel.: (281) 325-5760
Electronic Equipment Distr
N.A.I.C.S.: 423690
Antonio Serra *(Plant Mgr)*

Japan Aviation Electronics Industry, Ltd. - Aerospace Sales Division (1)
1-19 Aobadai 3-chome, Shibuya-ku, Tokyo, 150-0043, Japan
Tel.: (81) 337802925
Web Site: http://www.jae.com
Aircraft Equipment Distr
N.A.I.C.S.: 423860

Japan Aviation Electronics Industry, Ltd. - Akishima Plant (1)
1-1 Musashino 3-chome, Akishima, 196-8555, Tokyo, Japan
Tel.: (81) 42 549 9112
Web Site: http://www.jae.co.jp
Electronic Connector Mfr
N.A.I.C.S.: 334417

Japan Aviation Electronics Industry, Ltd. - International Operations Planning Division (1)
1-19 Aobadai 3-chome, Meguro-ku, Tokyo, 153-8539, Japan
Tel.: (81) 337802768
Electronic Connector Mfr
N.A.I.C.S.: 334417

AND PRIVATE COMPANIES

Japan Aviation Electronics Industry, Ltd. - User Interface Solutions Division
1-19 Aobadai 3-chome, Meguro-ku, Tokyo, 153-8539, Japan
Tel.: (81) 337802843
Web Site: http://www.jae.co.jp
Aviation Software Development Services
N.A.I.C.S.: 541511

Meiyu-Giken Co., Ltd. (1)
2 1 Katayama cho, Fukui, 910-3611, Japan
Tel.: (81) 776985512
Web Site: http://www.meiyu-giken.co.jp
Industrial Equipment Mfr
N.A.I.C.S.: 333248

Nikko Logistics Corp. (1)
10-40 Musashino 2-chome, Akishima, 196-0021, Japan (100%)
Tel.: (81) 425421070
Sales Range: $75-99.9 Million
Emp.: 150
Warehousing & Logistics Services
N.A.I.C.S.: 484121

JAPAN BEST RESCUE SYSTEM CO., LTD.
Urban Net Fushimi Bldg 5F 1-10-20 Nishiki, Naka-ku, Nagoya, Japan
Tel.: (81) 52 8830791
Web Site: http://www.jbr.co.jp
Year Founded: 1997
2453—(TKS)
Rev.: $130,292,800
Assets: $272,734,000
Liabilities: $159,787,760
Net Worth: $112,946,240
Earnings: $542,080
Emp.: 344
Fiscal Year-end: 09/30/21
Rescue Services
N.A.I.C.S.: 624230
Nobuhiro Sakakibara (Pres & CEO)

JAPAN CABLECAST INC.
1-6-7 Kudanminami Chiyodakaikan 8F, Chiyoda-ku, Tokyo, 102-0074, Japan
Tel.: (81) 3 6910 2900
Web Site: http://www.cablecast.co.jp
Year Founded: 2002
Sales Range: $25-49.9 Million
Emp.: 62
Cable Television Broadcaster
N.A.I.C.S.: 516210
Okuma Shigetaka (Pres & CEO)

JAPAN CASH MACHINE CO., LTD.
2-11-18 Nambanaka, Naniwa-ku, Osaka, 556-0011, Japan
Tel.: (81) 666438400 JP
Web Site: https://www.jcm-hq.co.jp
Year Founded: 1955
6418—(TKS)
Rev.: $208,942,100
Assets: $315,283,780
Liabilities: $125,874,230
Net Worth: $189,409,550
Earnings: $21,687,410
Emp.: 564
Fiscal Year-end: 03/31/24
Money Handling Machinery Mfr
N.A.I.C.S.: 333310
Yojiro Kamihigashi (Pres)

Subsidiaries:

J-Cash Machine (Thailand) Co., Ltd. (1)
42 Tower Room 701 7th Floor 65 Soi Sukhumvit 42 Kluaynamthai, Sukhumvit Rd Prakanong Klongtoey, Bangkok, 10110, Thailand
Tel.: (66) 27123155
Web Site: https://www.jcm-thai.co.th
Software Development Services
N.A.I.C.S.: 541511

JCM American Corporation (1)
925 Pilot Rd, Las Vegas, NV 89119

Tel.: (702) 651-0000
Web Site: https://am-en.jcmglobal.com
Sales Range: $50-74.9 Million
Emp.: 100
Currency Validation Services
N.A.I.C.S.: 522390
Hikaru Izawa (Pres)

JCM Gold (HK) Ltd. (1)
Unit 1-7 3/F Favor Industrial Center 2-6 Kin Hong Street, Kwai Chung, New Territories, China (Hong Kong)
Tel.: (852) 24297187
Web Site: https://www.jcmgold.com.hk
Emp.: 25
Billing Machines Distr
N.A.I.C.S.: 423420

JCM Meiho Co., Ltd. (1)
2-23-2 Higashinihonbashi JCM Higashinihonbashi Building, Chuo-ku, Tokyo, 103-0004, Japan
Tel.: (81) 358091182
Web Site: http://www.jcm-meiho.com
Sales Range: Less than $1 Million
Emp.: 300
Amusement Park Equipment Mfr
N.A.I.C.S.: 713990
Akio Someno (Pres)

JCM Techno Support Co., Ltd. (1)
2-4-21 Hirano-Baba, Hirano-ku, Osaka, 547 0048, Japan
Tel.: (81) 6 6760 2300
Electronic Machinery Repair & Maintenance Services
N.A.I.C.S.: 811310

JCM United Kingdom Ltd. (1)
Unit B Third Avenue, Denbigh West Business Park Bletchley, Milton Keynes, MK1 1DH, Buckinghamshire, United Kingdom
Tel.: (44) 1908377331
Web Site: http://www.jcm-uk.com
Sales Range: $25-49.9 Million
Emp.: 4
Cash Registers Mfr
N.A.I.C.S.: 333310
Takatomo Imai (Mng Dir)

Japan Cash Machine Co., Ltd. - Nagahama Plant (1)
1 Aza Shichinotsubo, Shichijo-cho, Nagahama, 526-0817, Shiga, Japan
Tel.: (81) 749650311
Web Site: http://www.jcm-hq.co.jp
Electric Component Whslr
N.A.I.C.S.: 423690
Yojiro Kamihigashi (Pres)

JAPAN COMMUNICATIONS, INC.
4-1-28 Toranomon, Minato-ku, Tokyo, 105-0001, Japan
Tel.: (81) 357761700 JP
Web Site: http://www.j-com.co.jp
Year Founded: 1996
Sales Range: $25-49.9 Million
Emp.: 105
Mobile Data & Voice Communications Services
N.A.I.C.S.: 517112
Frank Seiji Sanda (Founder, Chm & CEO)

Subsidiaries:

Arxceo Corporation
2 Midtown Plz Ste 1740 1349 W Peachtree, Atlanta, GA 30309
Tel.: (404) 347-8362
Web Site: http://www.arxceo.com
Sales Range: $25-49.9 Million
Emp.: 13
Custom Computer Programming Services
N.A.I.C.S.: 541511

Communications Security & Compliance Technologies Inc. (1)
1349 W Peachtree St Ste 1740, Atlanta, GA 30309
Tel.: (404) 347-8350
Web Site: http://www.contournetworks.com
Communications Security & Compliance
N.A.I.C.S.: 517112
Marc Winn (CEO)

Computer & Communication Technologies, Inc. (1)
61 Inverness Dr E Ste 250, Englewood, CO 80112 (100%)
Tel.: (303) 708-9228
Web Site: http://www.cctus.com
Sales Range: $25-49.9 Million
Emp.: 25
Develops Systems for Data Communication Services & Develops & Operates Billing System
N.A.I.C.S.: 541519

INCOM Co., Ltd. (1)
Plaza Edogawabashi 1-23-6 Sekiguchi Bunkyo-ku, Tokyo, 112-8712, Japan
Tel.: (81) 332607871
Sales Range: $25-49.9 Million
Emp.: 20
Trade Reference Sources
N.A.I.C.S.: 513140
Ichiro Suzuki (Pres)

JAPAN CORPORATE NEWS NETWORK (JCN) K.K.
MA Minami Azabu Bldg 3F, 4-14-2 Minami Azabu Minato-ku, Tokyo, 106-0047, Japan
Tel.: (81) 357911821
Web Site: http://www.japancorp.net
Year Founded: 2001
Sales Range: $10-24.9 Million
Emp.: 50
Business & Financial News Publisher
N.A.I.C.S.: 516210
Bruce Porter (Mng Dir)

JAPAN CREATIVE PLATFORM GROUP CO., LTD.
18F Ueno Frontier Tower 3-24-6 Ueno, Taito-ku, Tokyo, 110-0005, Japan
Tel.: (81) 358173061
Web Site: https://www.jcpg.co.jp
Year Founded: 1972
7814—(TKS)
Rev.: $530,658,140
Assets: $535,663,680
Liabilities: $423,173,740
Net Worth: $112,489,940
Earnings: $17,781,720
Emp.: 3,222
Fiscal Year-end: 12/31/23
Commercial Gravure Printing
N.A.I.C.S.: 323111
Ichiro Fujita (Pres)

Subsidiaries:

Sakae Shokai Co., Ltd. (1)
2-5-28 Shigita, Joto-ku, Osaka, 536-0015, Japan (70%)
Tel.: (81) 669320261
Real Estate Leasing
N.A.I.C.S.: 531190
Koichi Nishimura (Pres)

JAPAN CURRENT CO., LTD.
1-11-30 Nagatacho South Hill, Nagatacho Chiyoda-ku, Tokyo, Japan
Tel.: (81) 367570170
Web Site: http://www.japan-current.com
Emp.: 100
Digital Marketing Services
N.A.I.C.S.: 541810
Nobuyuki Kitahara (Pres)

JAPAN DIGITAL LABORATORY CO., LTD.
1-2-3 Shinsuna, Koto-ku, Tokyo, 136-8640, Japan
Tel.: (81) 3 56063111
Web Site: http://www.jdl.co.jp
Year Founded: 1968
Electronic Computer Mfr & Software Development Services
N.A.I.C.S.: 334111
Kazuo Maezawa (Founder & Pres)

JAPAN DISPLAY INC.

JAPAN DISPLAY INC.
Landic 2nd Bldg 3-7-1 Nishishimbashi, Minato-ku, Tokyo, 105-0003, Japan
Tel.: (81) 367328100 JP
Web Site: https://www.j-display.com
Year Founded: 2012
6740—(TKS)
Rev.: $1,580,801,330
Assets: $1,480,567,290
Liabilities: $914,348,080
Net Worth: $566,219,210
Earnings: ($292,908,930)
Emp.: 4,320
Fiscal Year-end: 03/31/24
Small & Medium Display Mfr
N.A.I.C.S.: 335999
Takahisa Hashimoto (Vice Chm)

Subsidiaries:

JDI China Inc. (1)
Unit 09-12 31F Raffles City Changning Office Tower 1, No 1133 Changning Road, Shanghai, 200051, China
Tel.: (86) 2160919750
Mobile Device Screen Distr
N.A.I.C.S.: 423690
Jessie Heah (Gen Mgr)

JDI Display America, Inc. (1)
181 Metro Dr Ste 279, San Jose, CA 95110
Tel.: (408) 501-3720
Mobile Device Screen Distr
N.A.I.C.S.: 423690
Naoto Oki (Dir-Sls)

Subsidiary (Domestic):

KOE Americas Inc. (2)
3555 Koger Blvd #110, Duluth, GA 30096
Tel.: (770) 409-3000
Web Site: https://www.koe.j-display.com
LCD Display Mfr
N.A.I.C.S.: 334419
Dan Mead (CEO)

JDI Europe GmbH (1)
Ridlerstrasse 57, 80339, Munich, Germany
Tel.: (49) 891890840
Web Site: https://www.jdi-europe.com
Mobile Device Screen Distr
N.A.I.C.S.: 423690
Holger Gerkens (Pres)

JDI Hong Kong Limited (1)
6F North Tower World Finance Centre Harbour City Canton Road, Tsimshatsui, Kowloon, China (Hong Kong)
Tel.: (852) 21523825
Mobile Device Screen Distr
N.A.I.C.S.: 423690
Yoshihisa Komori (Gen Mgr)

JDI Korea Inc. (1)
807 ILSHIN Bldg 38 Mapo-daero, Mapo-gu, Seoul, 04174, Korea (South)
Tel.: (82) 27885600
Mobile Device Screen Distr
N.A.I.C.S.: 423690

JDI Taiwan Inc. (1)
7F No 36 Ruihu St, Neihu Dist, Taipei, 114, Taiwan
Tel.: (886) 226596808
Mobile Device Screen Distr
N.A.I.C.S.: 423690

Nanox Philippines Inc. (1)
Civil Aviation Complex Near Clark South Interchange, Clark Freeport Zone Clarkfield, Pampanga, 2023, Philippines (81%)
Tel.: (63) 455985600
Web Site: http://www.nanox.co.jp
Sales Range: $800-899.9 Million
Emp.: 4,000
Liquid Crystal Display Panel Mfr
N.A.I.C.S.: 334419

PrimusTech Pte. Ltd. (1)
07-01/02 Techlink 31 Kaki Bukit Rd 3, Singapore, 417818, Singapore
Tel.: (65) 65110082
Web Site: https://primustech.com.sg
Engineeering Services
N.A.I.C.S.: 541330

Shenzhen JDI Inc. (1)
No 9 East Lanzhu Road Pingshan New Dis-

JAPAN DISPLAY INC.

Japan Display Inc.—(Continued)
trict, Shenzhen, 518118, China
Tel.: (86) 755 84630388
Mobile Device Screen Mfr
N.A.I.C.S.: 334419

Suzhou JDI Devices Inc. (1)
No 162 Zhongxin Avenue West Suzhou Industrial Park, Suzhou, China
Tel.: (86) 512 67610111
Mobile Device Screen Mfr
N.A.I.C.S.: 334419

Taiwan Display Inc. (1)
7F No 36 Ruihu St Neihu Dist, Taipei, 114, Taiwan (100%)
Tel.: (886) 2 2659 6808
Web Site: http://www.tdi.j-display.com
Mobile Device Screen Design & Assembly Services
N.A.I.C.S.: 334419
Jeff Hsu (Chm & CEO)

ThinkTron Limited (1)
Room 309 Excellence Research Building 3rd Floor No 18 Siyuan Street, Zhongzheng District, Taipei, 10087, Taiwan
Tel.: (886) 289783797
Web Site: http://www.thinktronltd.com
Geospatial Information Services
N.A.I.C.S.: 541370

JAPAN DRILLING CO., LTD.
Shin-Horidome Bldg 5F-6F 2-4-3 Nihonbashi Horidome-cho, Chuo-ku, Tokyo, 103-0012, Japan
Tel.: (81) 358475850
Web Site: http://www.jdc.co.jp
Year Founded: 1968
Sales Range: $150-199.9 Million
Emp.: 550
Offshore Drilling Services
N.A.I.C.S.: 213111
Minoru Murata (Pres)

Subsidiaries:

P.T. Japan Drilling Indonesia (1)
17th floor Wisma Keiai Jl Jenderal Sudirman Kav 3 - 4, Kel Karet Tengsin Kec Tanah Abang, Jakarta, 10220, Indonesia
Tel.: (62) 21 572 3027
Web Site: http://jdi.co.id
Offshore Drilling Services
N.A.I.C.S.: 213111

Pars Drilling Kish Co., Ltd. (1)
96a Koosha St, PO Box 79415-164, Amir Kabir Sq, Kish, Iran
Tel.: (98) 764 442 2062
Offshore Drilling Services
N.A.I.C.S.: 213111

JAPAN ECOSYSTEM CO., LTD.
JES Ichinomiya Building 2-2-2 Honcho, Ichinomiya, 491-0859, Aichi, Japan
Tel.: (81) 586255788
Web Site: https://www.jp-eco.co.jp
Year Founded: 1998
9249—(TKS)
Rev.: $54,327,090
Assets: $60,034,410
Liabilities: $27,496,950
Net Worth: $32,537,460
Earnings: $6,266,580
Emp.: 509
Fiscal Year-end: 09/30/23
Transportation Services
N.A.I.C.S.: 488490

JAPAN ELECTRONIC MATERIALS CORPORATION
2-5-13 Nishinagasu-cho, Amagasaki, 660-0805, Hyogo, Japan
Tel.: (81) 664822007
Web Site: https://www.jem-net.co.jp
Year Founded: 1960
6855—(TKS)
Rev.: $115,417,210
Assets: $229,823,090
Liabilities: $66,754,390
Net Worth: $163,068,700
Earnings: $4,111,420
Fiscal Year-end: 03/31/24
Semiconductor Testing Component Mfr & Distr
N.A.I.C.S.: 334413
Kazumasa Okubo (Pres & CEO)

Subsidiaries:

JEM (HONG KONG) CO., LTD. (1)
Suite 2408 24/F Lippo Centre Tower2 89 Queensway, Tsim Sha Tsui, Hong Kong, China (Hong Kong)
Tel.: (852) 25372146
Electronic Chip Whslr
N.A.I.C.S.: 423690

JEM AMERICA CORP. (1)
3000 Laurelview Ct, Fremont, CA 94538
Tel.: (510) 683-9234
Electronic Chip Whslr
N.A.I.C.S.: 423690
Kaz Okubo (Chm & CEO)

JEM EUROPE S.A.R.L. (1)
le Solaris Zone de Pre' Milliet 667 Rue Aristide Berge's, 38330, Montbonnot-Saint-Martin, France
Tel.: (33) 476529194
Web Site: https://www.jem-europe.com
Electronic Equipment Whslr
N.A.I.C.S.: 423690

JEM KOREA CO., Ltd. (1)
1st fl IH Bldg 7 Samsung 1-ro 3-gil, Seocho-gu, Hwaseong, 18449, Gyeonggi-do, Korea (South)
Tel.: (82) 313085400
Electric Equipment Mfr
N.A.I.C.S.: 335999

JEM SHANGHAI CO., LTD. (1)
D6-8B-1B No 211 Fute Rd N Pilot F T Z, Shanghai, 200131, China
Tel.: (86) 2158682700
Electronic Equipment Whslr
N.A.I.C.S.: 423690

JEM TAIWAN PROBE CORP. (1)
6F No 35 Hsin Tai Road, Jhubei, Hsin Chu Hsien, Taiwan
Tel.: (886) 35545257
Electric Equipment Mfr
N.A.I.C.S.: 335999
Ryan Chuang (Mgr)

Japan Electronic Materials Corporation - Kumamoto Plant (1)
1396-5 Sosaki Shichijo-machi, Kikuchi, 861-1344, Kumamoto, Japan
Tel.: (81) 968264101
Electric Equipment Mfr
N.A.I.C.S.: 335999

JAPAN ELEVATOR SERVICE HOLDINGS CO., LTD.
6-3-1 Suishacho Toyohira-ku, Sapporo, Hokkaido, 062-0912, Japan
Web Site: http://www.jes24.co.jp
Year Founded: 1994
6544—(TKS)
Rev.: $279,047,760
Assets: $215,082,790
Liabilities: $104,107,500
Net Worth: $110,975,290
Earnings: $29,844,150
Emp.: 1,997
Fiscal Year-end: 03/31/24
Elevator Maintenance Services
N.A.I.C.S.: 238290
Katsushi Ishida (Founder & CEO)

Subsidiaries:

Elevator Media Co., Ltd. (1)
Tokyo Tatemono Nihonbashi Bldg 5F 1-3-13 Nihonbashi, Chuo-ku, Tokyo, 103-0027, Japan
Tel.: (81) 362621640
Elevator Maintenance Services
N.A.I.C.S.: 811310

Japan Elevator Parts Co., Ltd. (1)
JES Innovation Center 5-6-50 Nikura, Wako, 351-0115, Saitama, Japan
Tel.: (81) 484869200
Elevator Maintenance Services
N.A.I.C.S.: 811310

Japan Elevator Service Hokkaido Co., Ltd. (1)
6-3-1 Suishacho, Toyohira-ku, Sapporo, 062-0912, Hokkaido, Japan
Tel.: (81) 118188888
Elevator Maintenance Services
N.A.I.C.S.: 811310

Japan Elevator Service Jyonan Co., Ltd. (1)
Towa Higashi Kanda Bldg 8F 1-11-2 Higashi Kanda, Chiyoda-ku, Tokyo, 101-0031, Japan
Tel.: (81) 338518251
Elevator Maintenance Services
N.A.I.C.S.: 811310

Japan Elevator Service Jyosai Co., Ltd. (1)
Shinjuku Fukuchi Bldg 3F 6-29-8 Shinjuku, Shinjuku-ku, Tokyo, 160-0022, Japan
Tel.: (81) 351557521
Elevator Maintenance Services
N.A.I.C.S.: 811310

Japan Elevator Service Kanagawa Co., Ltd. (1)
Urban Center Yokohama West 12F 3-33-8 Tsuruyacho, Kanagawa-ku, Yokohama, 221-0835, Kanagawa, Japan
Tel.: (81) 454100333
Elevator Maintenance Services
N.A.I.C.S.: 811310

Japan Elevator Service Kansai Co., Ltd. (1)
Wakita Fujimura Midosuji Bldg 4F 4-2-14 Fushimimachi, Chuo-ku, Osaka, 541-0044, Japan
Tel.: (81) 661255001
Elevator Maintenance Services
N.A.I.C.S.: 811310

Japan Elevator Service Tokai Co., Ltd. (1)
Toyoshima Bldg 14F 2-15-15 Nishiki, Naka-ku, Nagoya, 460-0003, Aichi, Japan
Tel.: (81) 522658000
Elevator Maintenance Services
N.A.I.C.S.: 811310

JAPAN ENGINE CORPORATION
1 Minamifutami Futami-cho, Akashi, 674-0093, Hyogo, Japan
Tel.: (81) 789490800
Web Site: https://www.j-eng.co.jp
Year Founded: 1920
6016—(TKS)
Rev.: $127,427,520
Assets: $168,528,800
Liabilities: $104,011,600
Net Worth: $64,517,200
Earnings: $5,304,640
Emp.: 345
Fiscal Year-end: 03/31/22
Diesel Engine Mfr & Distr
N.A.I.C.S.: 333618

JAPAN EXCELLENT, INC.
1-15-9 Minami Aoyama, Minato-ku, Tokyo, Japan
Tel.: (81) 354127911
Web Site: https://www.excellent-reit.co.jp
Year Founded: 2006
8987—(TKS)
Sales Range: $75-99.9 Million
Real Estate Manangement Services
N.A.I.C.S.: 523999
Hidehiko Ogawa (Exec Dir)

JAPAN EXCHANGE GROUP, INC.
2-1 Nihombashi Kabuto-cho, Chuo-ku, Tokyo, 103-8224, Japan
Tel.: (81) 336661361 JP
Web Site: https://www.jpx.co.jp
Year Founded: 2013
OSCUF—(OTCIQ)
Rev.: $1,010,477,310

INTERNATIONAL PUBLIC

Assets: $533,312,164,470
Liabilities: $531,074,243,210
Net Worth: $2,237,921,260
Earnings: $402,033,420
Emp.: 214
Fiscal Year-end: 03/31/24
Holding Company; Securities Exchanges Operator
N.A.I.C.S.: 551112
Atsushi Tabata (CFO & Exec Officer-Treasury, Corp Comm & IR)

Subsidiaries:

Japan Securities Clearing Corporation (1)
2-1 Nihombashi Kabuto-cho, Chuo-ku, Tokyo, 103-0026, Japan
Tel.: (81) 33 665 1234
Web Site: https://www.jpx.co.jp
Sales Range: $50-74.9 Million
Emp.: 50
Securities Transaction Clearing Services
N.A.I.C.S.: 522320
Masaki Shizuka (Sr Exec VP)

Osaka Securities Exchange Co., Ltd. (1)
8-16 Kitahama 1-chome, Chuo-ku, Osaka, 541-0041, Japan
Tel.: (81) 647060800
Sales Range: $200-249.9 Million
Emp.: 125
Derivative Securities Exchange Operator
N.A.I.C.S.: 523210
Masayuki Murata (Exec Officer-Equities)

Tokyo Stock Exchange, Inc. (1)
2-1 Nihombashi Kabutocho, Chuo-ku, Tokyo, 103-8220, Japan
Tel.: (81) 33 666 0141
Web Site: http://www.tse.or.jp
Sales Range: $500-549.9 Million
Emp.: 800
Securities Exchange Operator
N.A.I.C.S.: 523210

JAPAN EXTERNAL TRADE ORGANIZATION
Ark Mori Building 6F 12 32 Akasaka 1 chome, Minato ku, Tokyo, 107-6006, Japan
Tel.: (81) 335825511
Web Site: http://www.jetro.go.jp
Year Founded: 2003
Sales Range: $350-399.9 Million
Emp.: 1,730
Trade Promotion Solutions
N.A.I.C.S.: 323120
Nobuhiko Sasaki (Chm)

Subsidiaries:

JETRO, New York (1)
1221 Avenue of the Americas 42nd Fl, New York, NY 10020
Tel.: (212) 997-0400
Web Site: http://www.jetro.go.jp
Sales Range: $25-49.9 Million
Emp.: 50
Japan External Trade Promoter
N.A.I.C.S.: 926110
Masaki Fujihara (Dir-Bus Dev)

JAPAN FAWICK CO., LTD.
Nihonbashi Muromachi Building 6F 3-3-16 Nihonbashi-Hongokucho, Chuo-Ku, Tokyo, 103-0021, Japan
Tel.: (81) 362626171
Web Site: http://www.fawick.co.jp
Year Founded: 1952
Sales Range: $25-49.9 Million
Emp.: 25
Industrial Products Mfr
N.A.I.C.S.: 333248

Subsidiaries:

R.I.K. (THAILAND) Co., Ltd. (1)
370/3 Fair Tower 2nd Sukhumvit 50 Sukhumvit Road, Prakhanong Klongtoey, Bangkok, 10260, Thailand
Tel.: (66) 27427423
Web Site: http://www.rikind.com

Industrial Machinery Distr
N.A.I.C.S.: 423830
Sariya thawon (Country Mgr)

R.I.K. Industries Pte. Ltd. (1)
2-6-1 Nakase Mihama-ku Wbg Marib West 22f, Chiba, 261-0023, Japan
Tel.: (81) 432971800
Industrial Machinery Mfr
N.A.I.C.S.: 333998

RIK Industries (1)
1 Sunview Road Eco-Tech Sunview 06-15, Singapore, 627615, Singapore
Tel.: (65) 67751121
Web Site: http://www.rikind.com
Sales Range: $25-49.9 Million
Emp.: 10
Mfr of Industrial Clutches & Brakes
N.A.I.C.S.: 335314

JAPAN FOODS HOLDING LTD.
420 North Bridge Road 02-01 North Bridge Centre, Singapore, 188727, Singapore
Tel.: (65) 63339781
Web Site: https://www.jfh.com.sg
5OI—(CAT)
Rev.: $58,193,405
Assets: $67,150,056
Liabilities: $42,904,039
Net Worth: $24,246,017
Earnings: $3,058,170
Emp.: 534
Fiscal Year-end: 03/31/23
Restaurant Franchise
N.A.I.C.S.: 722511
Siew Geen Fong (Head-Operations)

JAPAN FOUNDATION ENGINEERING CO., LTD.
1-9-14 Tenma, Kita-ku, Osaka, 530-0037, Japan
Tel.: (81) 663515621
Web Site: https://www.jafec.co.jp
Year Founded: 1935
1914—(TKS)
Rev.: $155,830,750
Assets: $217,065,790
Liabilities: $72,042,390
Net Worth: $145,023,400
Earnings: $6,160,520
Fiscal Year-end: 03/31/24
Construction Engineering Services
N.A.I.C.S.: 541330

Subsidiaries:

Jafec USA, Inc. (1)
2025 Gateway Pl Ste 230, San Jose, CA 95110
Tel.: (408) 467-2240
Web Site: https://www.jafecusa.com
Engineeering Services
N.A.I.C.S.: 541330

JAPAN GOLD CORP.
Suite 650 669 Howe St, Vancouver, V6C 0B4, BC, Canada
Tel.: (778) 725-1491
Web Site: https://www.japangold.com
Year Founded: 2014
JGLDF—(OTCQB)
Rev.: $9,804
Assets: $25,323,619
Liabilities: $863,579
Net Worth: $24,460,040
Earnings: ($2,602,485)
Fiscal Year-end: 12/31/21
Mineral Exploration Services
N.A.I.C.S.: 213115
John Graham Proust (Chm & CEO)

Subsidiaries:

Japan Gold KK (1)
Suite 401 ARK Hills Executive Tower Akasaka 1-14-5, Minato-ku, Tokyo, Japan
Tel.: (81) 365508735
Gold Mining Services
N.A.I.C.S.: 212220

JAPAN HOSPICE HOLDINGS, INC.
3-3-1 Marunouchi, Chiyoda-Ku, Tokyo, 100-0005, Japan
Tel.: (81) 363684154
Web Site: https://www.jhospice.co.jp
Year Founded: 2017
7061—(TKS)
Rev.: $69,985,390
Assets: $107,484,400
Liabilities: $88,398,120
Net Worth: $19,086,280
Earnings: $4,828,290
Emp.: 1,477
Fiscal Year-end: 12/31/23
Holding Company
N.A.I.C.S.: 551112
Tadashi Takahashi (Chm & Pres)

JAPAN HOTEL REIT INVESTMENT CORPORATION
Ebisu Neonart 118 Ebisu 4chome, Shibuya-ku, Tokyo, 150-0013, Japan
Tel.: (81) 364220530
Web Site: https://www.jhrth.co.jp
Year Founded: 2005
8985—(TKS)
Rev.: $106,919,040
Assets: $2,845,048,830
Liabilities: $1,242,023,250
Net Worth: $1,603,025,580
Earnings: $19,151,070
Fiscal Year-end: 12/31/22
Real Estate Investment Trust Services
N.A.I.C.S.: 531120
Kaname Masuda (Exec Dir)

JAPAN INDUSTRIAL PARTNERS, INC.
Meiji Yasuda Life Insurance Building 15F 2-1-1 Marunouchi, Chiyoda-ku, Tokyo, 100 0005, Japan
Tel.: (81) 362665781   JP
Web Site: http://www.jipinc.com
Sales Range: $25-49.9 Million
Emp.: 30
Private Equity Investment Firm
N.A.I.C.S.: 523999
Hidemi Moue (Pres)

Subsidiaries:

KH Neochem Co., Ltd. (1)
NBF Nihonbashi-Muromachi Center Building 3-2-15 Nihonbashi-Muromachi, Chuo-ku, Tokyo, 103-0022, Japan
Tel.: (81) 335103550
Web Site: http://www.khneochem.co.jp
Emp.: 557
Petrochemicals Mfr & Distr
N.A.I.C.S.: 325110
Makoto Kikkawa (Pres & CEO)

Subsidiary (Non-US):

KH Neochem Singapore (2)
260 Orchard Road The Heeren Ste 12-04, Singapore, 238855, Singapore
Tel.: (65) 67334948
Web Site: http://www.khneochem.sg
Sales Range: $25-49.9 Million
Emp.: 5
Pharmaceutical & Food Additive Developer & Mfr
N.A.I.C.S.: 325412

Subsidiary (US):

Kyowa Hakko Chemical Americas, Inc. (2)
1515 E Woodfield Rd Ste 710, Schaumburg, IL 60173
Tel.: (847) 517-8800
Web Site: http://www.khc-americas.com
Industrial Chemicals Mfr & Distr
N.A.I.C.S.: 355998

Nippon Avionics Co., Ltd. (1)
4475 Ikonobe-cho, Tsuzuki-ku, Yokohama, 224-0053, Japan   (50.1%)
Tel.: (81) 452870300

Web Site: https://www.avio.co.jp
Rev.: $119,343,550
Assets: $181,960,080
Liabilities: $87,404,030
Net Worth: $94,556,050
Earnings: $14,204,890
Emp.: 578
Fiscal Year-end: 03/31/2024
Electrical Equipment Mfr & Whslr
N.A.I.C.S.: 335999
Masato Takeuchi (Pres)

Toshiba Corporation (1)
1-1 Shibaura 1-chome, Minato-ku, Tokyo, 105-8001, Japan
Tel.: (81) 334574511
Web Site: https://www.global.toshiba
Rev.: $24,103,080,690
Assets: $25,376,551,560
Liabilities: $15,789,781,170
Net Worth: $9,586,770,390
Earnings: $907,528,410
Emp.: 106,648
Fiscal Year-end: 03/31/2023
Audio Systems, Semiconductors, Transportation Equipment, Utility Products & Telecommunications Equipment Mfr
N.A.I.C.S.: 334310
Taro Shimada (Pres & CEO)

Subsidiary (Non-US):

Changzhou Toshiba Transformer Co., Ltd. (2)
86 Long Jiang Zhong Rd, Changzhou, 213002, Jiangsu, China   (62.8%)
Tel.: (86) 51983256016
Sales Range: $100-124.9 Million
Emp.: 300
Power Transformer Mfr
N.A.I.C.S.: 334416

Subsidiary (Domestic):

D.T. Circuit Technology Co., Ltd. (2)
2 1 Toshiba, Fuchu, 183-8511, Tokyo, Japan   (49%)
Tel.: (81) 423621048
Web Site: http://uk.computers.toshiba-europe.com
Sales Range: $100-124.9 Million
Emp.: 310
Printed Circuit Boards Designer, Developer & Mfr
N.A.I.C.S.: 334412

Subsidiary (Non-US):

Dalian Toshiba Television Co., Ltd. (2)
8 An Shan St Dalian Economic And Technical Development Zone, Dalian, 116600, China
Tel.: (86) 41187328866
Sales Range: $50-74.9 Million
Emp.: 200
Television Mfr
N.A.I.C.S.: 334310

Dalian Toshiba Televison Co., Ltd. (2)
9/F Senmao Building No 147 Zhongshan Road, Xigang, Dalian, 116600, China   (100%)
Tel.: (86) 41183686882
Web Site: http://www.toshiba.co.jp
Sales Range: $400-449.9 Million
Emp.: 1,001
Mfr of Color TVs
N.A.I.C.S.: 334310

Subsidiary (Domestic):

Device Link Corporate (2)
18 13 Sotokanda, Chiyoda Ku, Tokyo, 101 0021, Japan   (100%)
Tel.: (81) 332574020
Sales Range: $25-49.9 Million
Emp.: 60
Sales of Semiconductor & LCD Products
N.A.I.C.S.: 334419

Enterprise Business System Solution Co. (2)
3 16 33 Roppongi Minato-ku, Tokyo, 106 0032, Japan   (60%)
Tel.: (81) 355617676
Web Site: http://www.ebss.co.jp
Sales Range: Less than $1 Million
Emp.: 100

Provider of System Integration & Consultation
N.A.I.C.S.: 541512

Fukuoka Toshiba Corporation (2)
Toshiba Fukuoka Building 11F 2-4-1 Nagahama Tyuou-ku, Fukuoka-shi, Fukuoka, 812 0072, Japan   (60%)
Tel.: (81) 925151600
Software Mfr
N.A.I.C.S.: 334413

Subsidiary (Non-US):

GE Toshiba Turbine Components de Mexico S.R.L. de C.V. (2)
230 Industrial Park National, Cienegade Flores, Monterrey, 65550, NL, Mexico
Tel.: (52) 1 81 8154 1412
Sales Range: $100-124.9 Million
Emp.: 320
Mfr of Turbine Components
N.A.I.C.S.: 333611

Subsidiary (Domestic):

Hamaoka Toshiba Electronics Corp. (2)
Sakura 4231 Hamaoka Cho Ogasa Gun, Shizuoka, 437 1604, Japan   (100%)
Tel.: (81) 537862815
Mfr & Sales of Semiconductor Materials
N.A.I.C.S.: 334413

Subsidiary (Non-US):

Hangzhi Machinery & Electronics Co., Ltd. (2)
27 Jiao Gong Rd, Hangzhou, 310012, Zhejiang, China   (100%)
Tel.: (86) 57188072428
Web Site: http://www.toshiba.com.cn
Sales Range: $400-449.9 Million
Emp.: 1,226
Mfr of Electronic & Mechanical Components
N.A.I.C.S.: 333613

Affiliate (Non-US):

Hanji Electronic Engineering Co., Ltd. (2)
2017 Kec Bldg 275-7 Yang Jae-Dong, Seocho-ku, Seoul, Korea (South)
Tel.: (82) 258949958
Sales Range: $50-74.9 Million
Emp.: 6
Electronics Mfr
N.A.I.C.S.: 334417

Joint Venture (Non-US):

Henan Pinggao Toshiba High-Voltage Switchgear Co., Ltd. (2)
Dongduan Jianshe Road, Pingdingshan, 467013, Henan, China
Tel.: (86) 3753988888
Sales Range: $25-49.9 Million
Emp.: 27
High-Voltage Switchgear Mfr
N.A.I.C.S.: 335313

Subsidiary (Domestic):

Himeji Toshiba E.P. Corporation (2)
1000 Hamada, Aboshi, 671-1242, Hyogo, Japan   (100%)
Tel.: (81) 72745194
Web Site: http://www3.toshiba.co.jp
Sales Range: $50-74.9 Million
Emp.: 230
Mfr & Sales of Lead Frames for Semiconductor Devices, Parts for Electronic Devices & Precision Molds
N.A.I.C.S.: 334413
Ushijima Tomomi (Pres & CEO)

Japan Semionductor Corporation (2)
6-6 Kita Kogyo-Danchi, Kitakami, 024-8510, Iwate, Japan   (100%)
Tel.: (81) 197713003
Web Site: http://www.jsemicon.co.jp
Emp.: 2,200
Electronic Components Mfr
N.A.I.C.S.: 334419
Kazuya Mori (Pres)

Kaga Toshiba Electronics Company (2)
1 1 Aza Iwauchi Tatsukuchi Machi, Nomi, 923 1293, Ishikawa, Japan   (100%)

JAPAN INDUSTRIAL PARTNERS, INC.   INTERNATIONAL PUBLIC

Japan Industrial Partners, Inc.—(Continued)
Tel.: (81) 761515511
Web Site: http://www.toshiba-kaga.co.jp
Emp.: 1,400
Electric Machines Parts, Appliances & Discrete Devices Mfr
N.A.I.C.S.: 334413
Takashi Fujiwara *(Mng Dir)*

Kawamata Seiki Co., Ltd. (2)
36-1 Azahosoiri Ooaza Tsurusawa, Date-gun, Fukushima, 960 1406, Japan **(90%)**
Tel.: (81) 245653111
Web Site: http://www.kawamataseiki.co.jp
Sales Range: $25-49.9 Million
Emp.: 223
Mfr & Sale of Small Motors, Power Generators
N.A.I.C.S.: 335312

Kitashiba Electric Co., Ltd. (2)
9 Tennohara Matsukawa Machi, Fukushima shi, Fukushima, 960 1292, Japan **(79%)**
Tel.: (81) 245372121
Web Site: http://www.kitashiba.co.jp
Sales Range: $200-249.9 Million
Emp.: 850
Mfr & Sale of Power Transformers, Distribution Transformers, Small Sized Motors
N.A.I.C.S.: 335311
Yoshitomo Kanno *(Pres)*

Affiliate (Non-US):

Korea Electronic Material Co., Ltd. (2)
712 3 Kozandong Namdong Ku 148 Block 16 Lot, Namdong Kogyo 2 Danchi, 405310, Incheon, Korea (South) **(100%)**
Tel.: (82) 328144115
Sales Range: $50-74.9 Million
Emp.: 102
Mfr of Tungsten Molybdenum Wires & Assembly Parts; Ceramic Parts
N.A.I.C.S.: 331491

Subsidiary (Non-US):

Landis+Gyr AG (2)
Alte Steinhauserstrasse 18, 6330, Cham, Switzerland
Tel.: (41) 9356000
Web Site: http://www.landisgyr.com
Sales Range: $1-4.9 Billion
Emp.: 300
Energy Measurement Equipment Mfr
N.A.I.C.S.: 334515
Andreas Umbach *(Chm)*

Subsidiary (Non-US):

Landis+Gyr (3)
1 Lysander Drive Northfields Industrial Estate, Market Deeping, Peterborough, PE6 8FB, United Kingdom
Tel.: (44) 1778349700
Web Site: http://www.landisgyr.co.uk
Sales Range: $100-124.9 Million
Energy Measurement Equipment Mfr
N.A.I.C.S.: 334515

Landis+Gyr (Pty.) Ltd. (3)
2 Slate Avenue N1 Business Park, PO Box 4052, Kosmosdal Ext 7, Centurion, 0157, Gauteng, South Africa **(75%)**
Tel.: (27) 126453100
Web Site: http://www.za.landisgyr.com
Sales Range: $50-74.9 Million
Emp.: 200
Energy Measurement Equipment Mfr
N.A.I.C.S.: 334515
Connel Ngcukana *(CEO)*

Landis+Gyr A.E. (3)
78 Km National Rd, Athens, 20100, Corinth, Greece
Tel.: (30) 2741041200
Web Site: http://www.landisgyr.com
Sales Range: $100-124.9 Million
Energy Measurement Equipment Mfr
N.A.I.C.S.: 334515
Dimitrios Avrampos *(Mng Dir)*

Landis+Gyr A/S (3)
Skovlytoften 33, Holte, 2840, Denmark
Tel.: (45) 70212530
Web Site: http://www.landisgyr.dk
Sales Range: $25-49.9 Million
Emp.: 18
Energy Measurement Equipment Mfr

Landis+Gyr AB (3)
Forskarvagen 1, 70226, Orebro, Sweden
Tel.: (46) 703392500
Web Site: http://www.landisgyr.se
Energy Measurement Equipment Mfr
N.A.I.C.S.: 334515

Landis+Gyr AS (3)
Bryggegata 6, PO Box 2051 Vilka, 125, Oslo, Norway
Tel.: (47) 66983952
Web Site: http://www.landisgyr.com
Sales Range: $25-49.9 Million
Emp.: 14
Energy Measurement Equipment Mfr
N.A.I.C.S.: 334515

Landis+Gyr B.V. (3)
Tielweg 10, 2803 PK, Gouda, Netherlands
Tel.: (31) 182540888
Web Site: http://www.landisgyr.com
Sales Range: $25-49.9 Million
Emp.: 10
Energy Measurement Equipment Mfr
N.A.I.C.S.: 334515

Landis+Gyr GmbH (3)
Altmannsdorfer Strasse 76, A 1120, Vienna, Austria
Tel.: (43) 18022022
Web Site: http://www.landisgyr.at
Sales Range: $25-49.9 Million
Emp.: 9
Energy Measurement Equipment Mfr
N.A.I.C.S.: 334515
Werner Wagner *(Gen Mgr)*

Landis+Gyr GmbH (3)
Humboldtstrasse 64, 90459, Nuremberg, Germany
Tel.: (49) 9117237036
Web Site: http://www.landisgyr.de
Sales Range: $50-74.9 Million
Emp.: 130
Energy Measurement Equipment Mfr
N.A.I.C.S.: 334515

Subsidiary (US):

Landis+Gyr Inc. (3)
6436 County Rd 11, Pequot Lakes, MN 56472
Tel.: (218) 562-4877
Web Site: http://www.landisgyr.com
Emp.: 150
Energy Measurement Equipment Mfr
N.A.I.C.S.: 334515

Subsidiary (Non-US):

Landis+Gyr N.V. (3)
AA Tower Technologiepark 122, 9052, Beersel, Belgium
Tel.: (32) 92980721
Web Site: http://www.landisgyr.com
Sales Range: $25-49.9 Million
Emp.: 8
Energy Measurement Equipment Mfr
N.A.I.C.S.: 334515

Landis+Gyr Oy (3)
Salvesenintie 6, 40420, Jyska, Finland
Tel.: (358) 14660100
Web Site: http://www.landisgyr.fi
Sales Range: $75-99.9 Million
Emp.: 140
Energy Measurement Equipment Mfr
N.A.I.C.S.: 334515

Landis+Gyr S.A.S. (3)
77 81 Bd de la Republique, 92257, La Garenne-Colombes, France
Tel.: (33) 156058597
Web Site: http://www.landisgyr.fr
Sales Range: $50-74.9 Million
Emp.: 110
Energy Measurement Equipment Mfr
N.A.I.C.S.: 334515
Christian Huguet *(CEO)*

Landis+Gyr S.A.U. (3)
Carretera De La Esclusa 11 Galia Puerto, E 41011, Seville, Spain
Tel.: (34) 954998820
Web Site: http://www.landisgyr.es
Sales Range: $25-49.9 Million
Emp.: 14
Energy Measurement Equipment Mfr
N.A.I.C.S.: 334515

Landis+Gyr S.p.A (3)
Via Del Plebiscito 102, 00186, Rome, Italy
Tel.: (39) 0622406203
Web Site: http://www.landisgyr.it
Energy Measurement Equipment Mfr
N.A.I.C.S.: 334515

Landis+Gyr Sp.z o.o (3)
Al Jerozolimskie 212, 02-486, Warsaw, Poland
Tel.: (48) 22 576 8930
Web Site: http://www.landisgyr.pl
Sales Range: $25-49.9 Million
Emp.: 10
Energy Measurement Equipment Mfr
N.A.I.C.S.: 334515

Landis+Gyr d.o.o. (3)
Poslovna cona A2, Sencur, 4208, Slovenia
Tel.: (386) 4 2790 500
Web Site: http://www.landisgyr.si
Sales Range: $25-49.9 Million
Emp.: 40
Energy Measurement Equipment Mfr
N.A.I.C.S.: 334515

Landis+Gyr s.r.o (3)
Plzenska 5a cp 3185, 150 00, Prague, Czech Republic
Tel.: (420) 251119511
Web Site: http://www.landisgyr.cz
Sales Range: $25-49.9 Million
Emp.: 30
Energy Measurement Equipment Mfr
N.A.I.C.S.: 334515

Landis+Gyr-Alexandria (3)
60 O Riordan Street, Alexandria, 2015, NSW, Australia
Tel.: (61) 296907333
Web Site: http://www.landisgyr.com
Sales Range: $50-74.9 Million
Emp.: 230
Energy Measurement Equipment Mfr
N.A.I.C.S.: 334515

Joint Venture (Domestic):

NEC Space Technologies, Ltd. (2)
1-10 Nissin-cho, Fuchu, 183-8551, Tokyo, Japan
Tel.: (81) 423544000
Web Site: http://www.ntspace.co.jp
Sales Range: Less than $1 Million
Emp.: 515
Testing Space Communication Equipment Mfr
N.A.I.C.S.: 334290
Kunio Kondo *(Pres)*

Subsidiary (Non-US):

Nanjing Postel Wong Zhi Telecommunications Co., Ltd. (2)
No1 South zhongshan Road, Nanjing, 210005, China **(67%)**
Tel.: (86) 2586890070
Web Site: http://www.toshiba.com.cn
Sales Range: $25-49.9 Million
Emp.: 50
Mfr of Cellular Phones
N.A.I.C.S.: 517111

Ningbo Toshiba Huatong Switchgear Co., Ltd. (2)
No15 Hangda Road, Hangzhou, Ningbo, 310007, Zhejiang, China **(100%)**
Tel.: (86) 57128953610
Web Site: http://www.toshiba.com
Sales Range: $25-49.9 Million
Emp.: 50
Mfr of Vacuum Circuit Breakers
N.A.I.C.S.: 334220

Subsidiary (Domestic):

Nishishiba Electric Co., Ltd. (2)
1000 Hamada Aboshi Ku, Himeji, 671 1280, Japan **(100%)**
Tel.: (81) 792712448
Web Site: http://www.nishishiba.co.jp
Sales Range: $200-249.9 Million
Emp.: 600
Mfr & Sale of Diesel Generating Sets, Controllers, Switchboards, Ventilating Fans, Compressors
N.A.I.C.S.: 335313
Tetsuji Takatsuji *(Pres & CEO)*

Nisshiba Electric Co., Ltd. (2)
1000 Hamada, Aboshi-ku, Himeji, 671-1280, Japan
Tel.: (81) 792712448
Web Site: https://www.nishishiba.co.jp
Emp.: 700
Electric Generator Mfr & Distr
N.A.I.C.S.: 335312
Tetsuji Takatsuji *(Pres & CEO)*

Subsidiary (Non-US):

P.T. Toshiba Display Devices Indonesia (2)
East Jakarta Industrial Park Plot 3G Lemah Abang, Bekasi, 17550, Jawa Barat, Indonesia **(100%)**
Tel.: (62) 218970505
Web Site: http://www.asia.toshiba.com
Sales Range: $750-799.9 Million
Emp.: 2,000
Mfr Color Picture Cathode-Ray Tubes
N.A.I.C.S.: 423610
Fumio Otani *(Mng Dir)*

P.T. Tosjaya Abadi Ventura (2)
Jalan Kali Besar Barat No 40, Jakarta, 11230, Indonesia **(100%)**
Tel.: (62) 216916254
Web Site: http://www.toshiba.co.jp
Electronic & Computer Mfr
N.A.I.C.S.: 334110

PT. Toshiba Visual Media Network Indonesia (2)
Setiabudi Atrium Building Lt 5 Suite 508A-510 Jl HR Rasuna Said Kav 62, Jakarta, 12920, Indonesia **(51%)**
Tel.: (62) 215223880
Web Site: http://www.asia.toshiba.com
Electronic Components Mfr
N.A.I.C.S.: 334419

Affiliate (Non-US):

Schneider Toshiba Inverter Europe S.A.S. (2)
33 Rue Andre Blanchet, 27120, Pacy-sur-Eure, France **(60%)**
Tel.: (33) 232781140
Sales Range: $100-124.9 Million
Emp.: 300
Mfr of Inverters
N.A.I.C.S.: 335999

Subsidiary (Non-US):

Shenyang Neusoft Business Software Co., Ltd. (2)
Neusoft Park No 2 Xinxiu Street, Hunnan, Shenyang, 110179, China **(100%)**
Tel.: (86) 83667788
Sales Range: $50-74.9 Million
Emp.: 150
Mfr of Computer Software
N.A.I.C.S.: 449210

Subsidiary (Domestic):

Shibaula Mechatronics Ltd. (2)
5-14-33 Higashihakugaya, Ebina, 243 0401, Kanagawa, Japan **(47%)**
Tel.: (81) 462318111
Sales Range: $100-124.9 Million
Emp.: 500
Mfr & Sale of Industrial Automation Machinery, Tube Manufacturing Machines, Vacuum Pumps, Industrial Robots, Bonders & Mounters
N.A.I.C.S.: 333248

Shibaura Machine Co., Ltd. (2)
2068-3 Ooka Numazu-shi, Shizuoka-ken, Numazu, 410-8510, Japan **(33%)**
Tel.: (81) 559265141
Web Site:
https://www.shibaura-machine.co.jp
Rev.: $1,061,916,330
Assets: $1,673,466,920
Liabilities: $935,096,870
Net Worth: $738,370,050
Earnings: $118,451,200
Emp.: 3,057
Fiscal Year-end: 03/31/2024
Machine Tools, Plastic Processing Machines, Industrial Machinery & Hydraulic Equipment Mfr
N.A.I.C.S.: 333517
Yukio Iimura *(Chm)*

Subsidiary (Non-US):

TOSHIBA MACHINE (SHANGHAI) CO., LTD. (3)

AND PRIVATE COMPANIES

JAPAN INDUSTRIAL PARTNERS, INC.

4788 Jin Du Road Xinhuang Industrial Zone, Shanghai, 201108, China
Tel.: (86) 2154425455
Sales Range: $75-99.9 Million
Emp.: 30
Injection Molding Machine Mfr
N.A.I.C.S.: 333248
Nishizawa Makoto (Pres)

Subsidiary (Domestic):

SHANGHAI TOSHIBA MACHINE CO., LTD. (4)
4788 Jin Du Road Xinzhuang Industry Zone, Shanghai, 201108, China
Tel.: (86) 2154420606
Injection Molding Machine Mfr
N.A.I.C.S.: 333248

TOSHIBA MACHINE (SHENZHEN) CO., LTD. (4)
Room 608 Building 2 Animation Park Yuehai Road Nanhai Street, Nanshan District, Shenzhen, 518054, China
Tel.: (86) 75586250599
Web Site: http://www.toshiba-machine.co.jp
Emp.: 30
Injection Molding Machine Mfr
N.A.I.C.S.: 333248
Shinji Tanabe (Mng Dir)

Subsidiary (Non-US):

TOSHIBA MACHINE (THAILAND) CO., LTD. (4)
127/28 Panjathanee Tower 23rd Floor Nonthree Road Khwaeng Chong, Nonthree Khet Yannawa, Bangkok, 10120, Thailand
Tel.: (66) 26810158
Web Site:
http://www.toshibamachineth.co.th
Injection Molding Machine Mfr
N.A.I.C.S.: 333248
Koichi Kawauchi (Mng Dir)

Subsidiary (Domestic):

TMT SERVICE & ENGINEERING CO LTD (5)
39M 6 Phaholyothin Rd Thumbol Klongnueng, Amphur Klongluang, Pathumthani, 12120, Thailand
Tel.: (66) 25162930
Web Site: http://www.toshiba-machine.co.jp
Injection Molding Machine Mfr
N.A.I.C.S.: 333248

Subsidiary (Non-US):

TOSHIBA MACHINE (VIETNAM) CO., LTD. (4)
2nd Floor VIT Tower No 519 Kim Ma Street Ngoc Khanh Ward, Ba Dinh District, Hanoi, Vietnam
Tel.: (84) 422208700
Sales Range: $25-49.9 Million
Emp.: 1
Injection Molding Machine Mfr
N.A.I.C.S.: 333248

TOSHIBA MACHINE HONG KONG LTD (4)
Suite 1508 15th Floor Tower 3 China Hong Kong City 33 Canton Road, Tsim Sha Tsui, Kowloon, China (Hong Kong)
Tel.: (852) 27351868
Sales Range: $25-49.9 Million
Emp.: 5
Injection Molding Machine Mfr
N.A.I.C.S.: 333248
Sheila Kelleher (Mng Dir & Gen Mgr)

TOSHIBA MACHINE S.E ASIA PTE. LTD. (4)
No 24 Tuas Avenue 4, Singapore, 639374, Singapore
Tel.: (65) 68611455
Injection Molding Machine Mfr
N.A.I.C.S.: 333248
H. Miyama (Mng Dir)

TOSHIBA MACHINE TAIWAN CO,. LTD. (4)
No 62 Lane 188 Jui-Kuang Road, Nei-Hu District, Taipei, 11491, Taiwan
Tel.: (886) 226596558
Sales Range: $25-49.9 Million
Emp.: 9
Injection Molding Machine Mfr

N.A.I.C.S.: 333248

Plant (Domestic):

TOSHIBA MACHINE CO., LTD - GOTEMBA PLANT (3)
1-120 Komakado, Gotemba, 412-0038, Shizuoka-ken, Japan
Tel.: (81) 550873555
Die Cast & Injection Molding Products Mfr
N.A.I.C.S.: 333514

TOSHIBA MACHINE CO., LTD - SAGAMI PLANT (3)
4-29-1 Hibarigaoka, Zama, 228-0003, Kanagawa-ken, Japan
Tel.: (81) 462582801
Injection Molding Machine Mfr
N.A.I.C.S.: 333248

Plant (Non-US):

TOSHIBA MACHINE CO., LTD. - SHANGHAI PLANT (3)
4788 Jin Du Road Xinhuang Industrial Zone, Shanghai, 201108, China
Tel.: (86) 2154425455
Web Site: http://www.toshiba-machine.co.jp
Sales Range: $100-124.9 Million
Emp.: 300
Die Casting & Injection Molding Products Mfr
N.A.I.C.S.: 333514
Nisizawa Makoto (Gen Mgr)

Subsidiary (Non-US):

Toshiba Machine (Chennai) Pvt. Ltd. (3)
No 65 PO Box No 5 Chennai-Bangalore Highway, Chembarambakkam, Chennai, 600123, India
Tel.: (91) 44 26812000
Sales Range: $25-49.9 Million
Emp.: 250
Injection Molding Machine Mfr
N.A.I.C.S.: 333248
Kailas Parameswaran (Mng Dir)

Toshiba Machine (Europe) GmbH (3)
Oskar-Messter-Strasse 22, 85737, Ismaning, Germany
Tel.: (49) 8995094990
Web Site: http://www.toshiba-machine.de
Injection Molding Machine Mfr
N.A.I.C.S.: 333248

Toshiba Machine Company Canada Ltd. (3)
6 Shields Ct, Markham, L3R 4S1, ON, Canada
Tel.: (905) 479-9111
Web Site: https://shibaura-machine.ca
Sales Range: $25-49.9 Million
Emp.: 15
Machine Tools Mfr
N.A.I.C.S.: 333517
Matt Nicholson (Coord-Inside Sls & Customer Svc)

Subsidiary (Domestic):

Shibaura Mechatronics Corporation (2)
2 5 1 Kasama, Sakae Ku, Yokohama, 247-8610, Japan (40%)
Tel.: (81) 458972421
Web Site: http://www.shibaura.co.jp
Sales Range: $200-249.9 Million
Emp.: 1,260
Mfr of Semiconductor, FPD, Media Device & Manufacturing Automation Systems & Components
N.A.I.C.S.: 334413

TFPD Corporation (2)
50 Kamiyobe, Yobe Ku, Himeji, 671 1285, Hyogo, Japan (100%)
Tel.: (81) 792721211
Sales Range: $100-124.9 Million
Emp.: 500
Mfr of TFT-LCD's
N.A.I.C.S.: 334419

Subsidiary (Non-US):

TMST Tibbi Sistemler Pazarlama Ticaret ve Servis A.S. (2)
Alemdag Cad No 46 Masaldan Is Merkezi E Blok No 10 Camlica, Uskudar, 34746, Istanbul, Turkiye
Tel.: (90) 2164618830
Web Site: http://www.toshiba-turkey.com
Medical Equipment Mfr
N.A.I.C.S.: 334510

TNB Bilgisayar Sistemleri A.S. (2)
Burhanniye Mah Nehset Bey sok, Uskudar, 34676, Istanbul, Turkiye
Tel.: (90) 2164224050
Computer Component Mfr
N.A.I.C.S.: 334118

TOSHIBA TEC FRANCE IMAGING SYSTEMS S.A. (2)
Parc Euro Channel Rue Bleriot, 76370, Neuville-les-Dames, France
Tel.: (33) 235067000
Web Site: http://www.toshibatec-teis.com
Sales Range: $100-124.9 Million
Emp.: 23
Photographic Machinery Mfr
N.A.I.C.S.: 333310
Verna Alain (Gen Mgr)

Taiwan Toshiba International Procurement Corp. (2)
Hung Kuo Building 18F-D No 167 Duen-hua N Rd, Sung-Shan Chiu, Taipei, 105, Taiwan (100%)
Tel.: (886) 2 8770 3888
Web Site: http://www.toshiba.co.jp
Sales Range: $25-49.9 Million
Emp.: 40
Procurer of Electronic Components
N.A.I.C.S.: 334419

Affiliate (Non-US):

Thai Toshiba Electric Industries Co., Ltd. (2)
129 1 5 Tivanon Rd, Nonthaburi, 11000, Thailand (100%)
Tel.: (66) 25890161
Web Site: http://www.toshiba.com
Sales Range: $50-74.9 Million
Emp.: 200
Mfr & Sales of Home Electrical Appliances & Motors
N.A.I.C.S.: 449210

Topcon Europe Positioning B.V. (2)
Essebaan 11, 2908 LJ, Capelle aan den IJssel, Netherlands
Tel.: (31) 104585077
Web Site: http://www.topcon-positioning.eu
Global Positioning System Mfr
N.A.I.C.S.: 334511
Ray O'Connor (Pres & CEO)

Subsidiary (Non-US):

Toshiba (Australia) Pty., Ltd. (2)
12-24 Talavera Rd, PO Box 350, Ryde, 2113, NSW, Australia (100%)
Tel.: (61) 1300794202
Web Site: http://www.toshiba.com.au
Sales Range: $75-99.9 Million
Emp.: 430
Mfr & Sales of Information Systems, Electronic Imaging Equipment & Medical Equipment
N.A.I.C.S.: 541512

Division (Domestic):

Toshiba-Medical Division (3)
11A Gibbon Rd, North Ryde, 2113, NSW, Australia
Tel.: (61) 288676200
Web Site: http://www.toshiba.com.au
Sales Range: $75-99.9 Million
Emp.: 400
N.A.I.C.S.: 456199

Subsidiary (Non-US):

Toshiba (China) Co., Ltd. (2)
Room 501 Tower W2 Oriental Plaza 1, East Chang Ave, Beijing, 100738, China
Tel.: (86) 1085183111
Web Site: http://www.toshiba.com.cn
Sales Range: $25-49.9 Million
Emp.: 80
Mfr of Household Audio & Video Equipment
N.A.I.C.S.: 334310

Subsidiary (Domestic):

Toshiba Akita Denki Co., Ltd. (2)
3 1 47 Sanno, Akita, 010 0915, Japan
Tel.: (81) 188623421
Sales Range: $25-49.9 Million
Emp.: 16
Sale & Maintenance of Electronic Equipment
N.A.I.C.S.: 811210

Subsidiary (US):

Toshiba America, Inc. (2)
1251 Avenue of the Americas Ste 4110, New York, NY 10020
Tel.: (212) 596-0600
Web Site: http://www.toshiba.com
Sales Range: $1-4.9 Billion
Emp.: 9,500
Holding Company; TVs, Radios, Tape Recorders, CD Players, Stereos, Microwave Ovens, VCRs, Video Cameras & Coffee Makers Mfr
N.A.I.C.S.: 334310
Cheryl L. Roberts (CFO & Sr VP)

Subsidiary (Domestic):

Enceratec, Inc. (3)
1414 Franklin St, Columbus, IN 47201-5716
Tel.: (812) 377-3188
Web Site: http://www.enceratec.com
Sales Range: $25-49.9 Million
Emp.: 3
Sales of Fine Ceramic Components
N.A.I.C.S.: 423840

Group (Domestic):

OCZ Storage Solutions, Inc. (3)
6373 San Ignacio Ave, San Jose, CA 95119
Tel.: (408) 733-8400
Web Site: http://www.ocz.com
Rev: $333,964,000
Assets: $78,830,000
Liabilities: $52,525,000
Net Worth: $26,305,000
Earnings: ($125,786,000)
Emp.: 597
Fiscal Year-end: 02/28/2013
Computer Memory Components Developer
N.A.I.C.S.: 334112
Bob Roark (VP-Power Mgmt)

Subsidiary (Domestic):

Firepower Technology, Inc. (4)
2101 Las Palmas Dr Ste C, Carlsbad, CA 92011
Tel.: (760) 931-5700
Web Site:
http://www.pcpowerandcooling.com
Computer Power Supplies
N.A.I.C.S.: 334118
Tiffiney S. Gustafson (Mgr-Ops)

Subsidiary (Non-US):

Indilinx Co, Ltd. (4)
607 C-dong Techno Park, 145 Yatap-dong Bundang-gu, Seongnam, Gyeonggi-do, Korea (South)
Tel.: (82) 317096321
Computer Storage Device Mfr
N.A.I.C.S.: 334112

OCZ Technology Limited (4)
25 Milton Pk, Abingdon, OX14 4SH, Oxon, United Kingdom
Tel.: (44) 1235824900
Sales Range: $25-49.9 Million
Emp.: 50
Semiconductor Research & Development
N.A.I.C.S.: 541715

Subsidiary (Domestic):

Toshiba America Business Solutions, Inc. (3)
25530 Commercentre Dr, Lake Forest, CA 92630 (100%)
Tel.: (949) 462-6000
Web Site: http://business.toshiba.com
Plain Paper Copiers, Digital Copiers & Facsimiles Mfr
N.A.I.C.S.: 423420
Larry White (Pres & CEO)

Branch (Domestic):

Toshiba America Business Solutions - Arlington Heights (4)

JAPAN INDUSTRIAL PARTNERS, INC.

Japan Industrial Partners, Inc.—(Continued)
3860 North Ventura Dr, Arlington Heights, IL 60004-7951
Tel.: (847) 439-3200
Sales Range: $25-49.9 Million
Emp.: 90
Consumer Electronic Equipment
N.A.I.C.S.: 449210

Toshiba America Business Solutions - Atlanta (4)
6025 The Corners Pkwy Ste 207, Norcross, GA 30092
Tel.: (770) 446-2009
Rev.: $7,300,000
Emp.: 85
Mfr of Copiers, Business Machines & Equipment
N.A.I.C.S.: 449110

Toshiba America Business Solutions - Chicago (4)
8770 W Bryn Mawr Ave Ste 700, Chicago, IL 60631-3515
Tel.: (773) 380-6000
Web Site: http://www.toshiba.com
Sales Range: $25-49.9 Million
Emp.: 8
Mfr of Copiers & Facsimile Systems
N.A.I.C.S.: 333310

Toshiba America Business Solutions - Denver (4)
1101 W 48th Ave, Denver, CO 80221 (100%)
Tel.: (303) 262-5800
Rev.: $10,200,000
Emp.: 25
Fax Machines, Photocopiers & Other Office Equipment Whslr
N.A.I.C.S.: 532420
John Kouri (Gen Mgr)

Division (Domestic):

Toshiba America Business Solutions - Electronic Imaging Division (4)
4855 Peachtree Industrial Blvd Ste 210, Norcross, GA 30092-3014
Tel.: (770) 209-8540
Copiers & Facsimilie Systems
N.A.I.C.S.: 423490

Branch (Domestic):

Toshiba America Business Solutions - Irving (4)
8100 Jetstar Ste 100, Irving, TX 75063
Tel.: (972) 386-1860
Sales Range: $1-9.9 Million
Emp.: 52
Office Equipment Merchant Whslr
N.A.I.C.S.: 423420
Angie Adkins (Gen Mgr)

Toshiba America Business Solutions - Las Vegas (4)
6560 S Tioga Way Ste 150, Las Vegas, NV 89113
Tel.: (702) 878-9751
Web Site: http://www.toshiba.com
Sales Range: $1-9.9 Million
Emp.: 30
Sales & Service Business Equipment
N.A.I.C.S.: 449210

Toshiba America Business Solutions - Lees Summit (4)
2732 NE Independence Ave, Lees Summit, MO 64064
Tel.: (816) 483-1840
Web Site: http://www.tbsmoks.toshiba.com
Sales Range: $1-9.9 Million
Emp.: 60
Office Equipment Merchant Whslr
N.A.I.C.S.: 423420
Steve McCluhan (Pres)

Toshiba America Business Solutions - Mitchell (4)
901 N Foster St, Mitchell, SD 57301-2108 (100%)
Tel.: (605) 996-7731
Web Site: http://www.toshiba.com
Sales Range: $50-74.9 Million
Emp.: 150
Mfr of Toner
N.A.I.C.S.: 334111

Toshiba America Business Solutions - Mount Gilead (4)
400 N Main St, Mount Gilead, NC 27306-9038
Tel.: (910) 439-6906
Web Site: http://www.tbscmg.toshiba.com
Sales Range: $25-49.9 Million
Emp.: 90
Wholesale of Electronic Components & Accessories
N.A.I.C.S.: 459999

Toshiba America Business Solutions - Parsippany (4)
959 US Hwy 46 5th Fl, Parsippany, NJ 07054-3409
Tel.: (973) 316-2700
Web Site: http://www.eid.toshiba.com
Mfr of Computers & Peripherals
N.A.I.C.S.: 334111

Toshiba America Business Solutions - Richland Hills (4)
7427 Airport Freeway, Richland Hills, TX 76118
Tel.: (817) 654-3191
Web Site: http://www.business.toshiba.com
Emp.: 8
Office Equipment Merchant Whslr
N.A.I.C.S.: 423420
Butch Skelton (Mgr)

Toshiba America Business Solutions - Saint Paul (4)
960 Blue Gentien, Saint Paul, MN 55121
Tel.: (651) 644-3830
Sales Range: $50-74.9 Million
Emp.: 130
Computers, Peripherals & Software
N.A.I.C.S.: 423430

Toshiba America Business Solutions - San Antonio (4)
14607 San Pedro Ave Ste 120, San Antonio, TX 78232
Tel.: (210) 357-2600
Web Site: http://www.ocs.toshiba.com
Sales Range: $10-24.9 Million
Emp.: 175
Business Machines & Equipment Whslr
N.A.I.C.S.: 459999
Joe Lemoine (Gen Mgr)

Toshiba America Business Solutions - Tamarac (4)
6401 Nob Hill Rd, Tamarac, FL 33321
Tel.: (954) 428-1300
Web Site: http://www.business.toshiba.com
Sales Range: $25-49.9 Million
Emp.: 150
Office Equipment Whslr
N.A.I.C.S.: 423420
Bob Greenhalgh (Pres)

Division (Domestic):

Toshiba Electronic Imaging Division (4)
959 US Hwy 46 5th Fl, Parsippany, NJ 07054-3409
Tel.: (973) 316-2700
Copiers & Facsimile Systems
N.A.I.C.S.: 423420

Subsidiary (Domestic):

Toshiba Business Solutions of NY & NJ (5)
3075 Veterans Memorial Hwy, Ronkonkoma, NY 11779
Tel.: (631) 567-9400
Web Site: http://www.tbsnynj.toshiba.com
Rev.: $21,200,000
Emp.: 20
Office Equipment
N.A.I.C.S.: 423420
Dimitrios Soursos (Gen Mgr)

Subsidiary (Domestic):

Toshiba America Capital Corporation (3)
1251 Avenue of the Americas Fl 41, New York, NY 10020
Tel.: (212) 596-0620
Web Site: http://www.toshiba.com
Financial Services
N.A.I.C.S.: 334310

Toshiba America Consumer Products, LLC (3)
82 Totowa Rd, Wayne, NJ 07470-3114 (100%)
Tel.: (973) 628-8000
Web Site: http://www.tacp.toshiba.com
Sales Range: $10-24.9 Million
Emp.: 100
Televisions, DVD Players, Air Conditioners, Industrial Video Systems, Satellite Receivers, Lamps & Other Consumer Electronics
N.A.I.C.S.: 334310

Division (Domestic):

Toshiba America Consumer Products-Latin America (4)
15801 NW 49th Ave Ste 1, Miami, FL 33014
Tel.: (305) 625-3217
Media Equipment Mfr
N.A.I.C.S.: 334310

Subsidiary (Domestic):

Toshiba America Electronic Components, Inc. (3)
19900 Macarthur Blvd Ste 400, Irvine, CA 92612-8434 (100%)
Tel.: (949) 623-2900
Web Site: http://www.toshiba.com
Sales Range: $200-249.9 Million
Emp.: 712
Mfr of Microelectronics
N.A.I.C.S.: 334419
Hideya Yamaguchi (Exec VP)

Division (Domestic):

Toshiba America Electronic Components, Inc. - Advanced Materials Division (4)
290 Donald Lynch Blvd Ste 201, Marlborough, MA 01752
Tel.: (508) 303-5041
Web Site: http://www.toshiba.com
Electronic Components Mfr
N.A.I.C.S.: 334419

Toshiba America Electronic Components, Inc. - Storage Products Business Unit (4)
2610 Orchard Pkwy, San Jose, CA 95134
Tel.: (408) 526-2400
Web Site: http://www.toshiba.com
Electronic Storage Device Mfr
N.A.I.C.S.: 334112

Division (Domestic):

Toshiba America Electronics (4)
2610 Orchard Pkwy, San Jose, CA 95134 (100%)
Tel.: (408) 526-2400
Web Site: http://www.toshiba.com
Sales Range: $50-74.9 Million
Emp.: 200
N.A.I.C.S.: 334310

Toshiba Disk Products Division (4)
5241 California Ave Ste 100, Irvine, CA 92617-3052
Tel.: (949) 583-3000
Web Site: http://www.toshiba.com
Mfr of Electronic Components
N.A.I.C.S.: 541820

Subsidiary (Domestic):

Toshiba America Medical Systems, Inc. (3)
2441 Michelle Dr, Tustin, CA 92780-7047 (100%)
Tel.: (714) 730-5000
Web Site: http://www.medicaltoshiba.com
Sales Range: $200-249.9 Million
Emp.: 920
Computer Tomography (CT), Magnetic Resonance Imaging (MRI), Ultrasound Equipment, X-Ray Diagnostic Imaging Systems & Nuclear Medicine Device Mfr
N.A.I.C.S.: 423450
Mark G. Mindell (VP-HR & IT)

Subsidiary (Domestic):

Applied Super Conetics, Inc. (4)
2441 Michelle Dr, Tustin, CA 92780-7047

INTERNATIONAL PUBLIC

Tel.: (858) 452-3400
Sales Range: $25-49.9 Million
Emp.: 40
MRI Magnets
N.A.I.C.S.: 332999

Subsidiary (Domestic):

Toshiba America Research, Inc. (3)
1251 Avenue Of The Americas Ste 4110, New York, NY 10020-4110
Tel.: (973) 829-3951
Web Site: http://www.tari.toshiba.com
N.A.I.C.S.: 334310

Toshiba International Corp., Industrial Products Div. (3)
13131 W Little York Rd, Houston, TX 77041 (100%)
Tel.: (713) 466-0277
Web Site: http://www.toshiba.com
Sales Range: $400-449.9 Million
Emp.: 1,100
Industrial Equipment & Power Plant Systems Mfr
N.A.I.C.S.: 335312

Toshiba International Corporation (3)
13131 W Little York Rd, Houston, TX 77041
Web Site: http://www.toshiba.com
Semiconductor Devices Mfr
N.A.I.C.S.: 334413

Division (Domestic):

Toshiba International Corporation - Industrial Systems Division (4)
13131 W Little York Rd, Houston, TX 77041
Tel.: (713) 466-0277
Web Site: http://www.toshiba.com
Industrial Machinery Mfr
N.A.I.C.S.: 333248

Toshiba International Corporation - LED Display Systems Division (4)
10435 Okanella Ste 100, Houston, TX 77041
Tel.: (713) 466-0277
Web Site: http://www.toshiba.com
Light Emitting Diode Embedded Display Mfr
N.A.I.C.S.: 334419
Ken Honeycut (Mgr)

Subsidiary (Domestic):

Toshiba Logistics America, Inc. (3)
9740 Irvine Blvd, Irvine, CA 92618
Tel.: (949) 455-2194
Web Site: http://www.toshiba.com
Sales Range: $1-9.9 Million
Emp.: 17
Freight Transportation Arrangement
N.A.I.C.S.: 488510

Toshiba Machine Company America Ltd. (3)
755 Greenleaf Ave, Elk Grove Village, IL 60007
Tel.: (847) 709-7000
Web Site: http://www.toshiba-machine.com
Sales Range: $25-49.9 Million
Emp.: 100
Injection Molding Machine Mfr
N.A.I.C.S.: 333248
Tom McKevitt (VP & Gen Mgr)

Subsidiary (Non-US):

Toshiba Asia Pacific Pte., Ltd. (2)
152 Beach Rd 1600 Gtwy E, Singapore, 189721, Singapore (100%)
Tel.: (65) 62970990
Web Site: http://www.asia.toshiba.com
Sales Range: $350-399.9 Million
Emp.: 50
Electrical Equipment Services
N.A.I.C.S.: 334419
Shoji Yoshioka (Pres & Dir-Singapore)

Subsidiary (Non-US):

CET Toshiba (Langfang) Arrester Co., Ltd. (3)
Huiyuan Road 2 Economic & Technical Development Zone, Langfang, 065001, Hebei, China
Tel.: (86) 3166071801
Electric Equipment Mfr
N.A.I.C.S.: 335999

Dalian Toshiba Broadcasting Systems Co., Ltd. (3)
No 33-17-12 Dalian Industrial Park Dalian Development Zone, Dalian, China
Tel.: (86) 41187648090
Web Site: http://www.toshiba.co.jp
Television Broadcasting Services
N.A.I.C.S.: 516120
Fatofi Imamura *(Pres)*

Guangzhou Toshiba Baiyun Control System Engineering Co., Ltd. (3)
18 Daling South-Road Industrial Park of Shenshan Town, Guangzhou, 510460, China
Tel.: (86) 2026261282
Electronic Control System Mfr
N.A.I.C.S.: 334519

Plant (Non-US):

Toshiba (Vietnam) Home Appliances Co., Ltd. - Ben Cat Factory (3)
Tan Dinh Ward, Ben Cat, Binh Duong, Vietnam
Tel.: (84) 6503560768
Web Site: http://www.asia.toshiba.com
Household Appliances Mfr
N.A.I.C.S.: 335220

Subsidiary (Non-US):

Toshiba Baiyun Vacuum Interrupters (Jinzhou) Co., Ltd. (3)
No 2 Section 2 Chongqing Road, Guta District, Jinzhou, 121001, Liaoning, China
Tel.: (86) 4164162122
Electronic Components Mfr
N.A.I.C.S.: 334419

Toshiba Consumer & Lighting Products Trading (shanghai) Co., Ltd. (3)
No 11 Xi Ya Road Shanghai Waigaoqiao Free Trade Zone, Shanghai, China
Tel.: (86) 2162789535
Sales Range: $25-49.9 Million
Emp.: 11
Lighting Equipment Mfr
N.A.I.C.S.: 335139
Hiroshi Abe *(Gen Mgr)*

Toshiba Digital Media Network Korea Corp. (3)
26F Gangnam Finance Center 737 Yeoksam-dong, Gangnam-gu, Seoul, 135-984, Korea (South)
Tel.: (82) 234041200
Web Site: http://www.toshiba.co.kr
Electronic Product Distr
N.A.I.C.S.: 423690

Toshiba Electronics (Dalian) Co., Ltd. (3)
14/F Senmao Building 147 Zhongshan Road, Xigang Dist, Dalian, 116011, China
Tel.: (86) 41183686882
Web Site: http://www.toshiba.com.cn
Sales Range: $25-49.9 Million
Emp.: 1
Semiconductor Equipment Distr
N.A.I.C.S.: 423690

Toshiba Electronics (Shanghai) Co., Ltd. (3)
5th Floor Wheelock Square 1717 Nanjing West Road Jingan Area, Shanghai, 200040, China
Tel.: (86) 2160900610
Web Site: http://www.toshiba.co.jp
Electronic Components Mfr
N.A.I.C.S.: 334419

Toshiba Electronics (Shenzhen) Co., Ltd. (3)
28/F Excellence Times Square Bldg 4068 Yi Tian Road, Fu Tian District, Shenzhen, 518048, China
Tel.: (86) 75523996897
Sales Range: $25-49.9 Million
Electronic Components Mfr
N.A.I.C.S.: 334419
Makoto Mizuma *(Gen Mgr)*

Toshiba Electronics Service (Thailand) Co., Ltd. (3)
135 Moo 5 Bangkadi Industrial Park Tivanon Road Tambol Bangkadi, Amphur Muang, Pathumthani, 12000, Thailand
Tel.: (66) 25011634

Web Site: http://www.asia.toshiba.com
Electronic Equipment Repair & Maintenance Services
N.A.I.C.S.: 811210

Toshiba Hangzhou Co., Ltd. (3)
M12-19-1 Hangzhou Export Processing Zone of Zhejiang, Hangzhou, China
Tel.: (86) 57186714411
Web Site: http://www.toshiba.co.jp
Electronic Components Mfr
N.A.I.C.S.: 334419

Toshiba Home Appliances Sales (Nanhai) Co., Ltd. (3)
BOC Building Floor 11th Nanhai Street 31 Guicheng, Nanhai, Foshan, 528200, Guangdong, China
Tel.: (86) 75786291981
Electric Appliances Mfr
N.A.I.C.S.: 335210

Toshiba Hydro Power (Hangzhou) Co., Ltd. (3)
1 Gongren Rd Fuchunjiang, Tonglu, 311504, Zhejiang, China
Tel.: (86) 57156982000
Web Site: http://www.toshiba.co.jp
Hydroelectric Power Generation Services
N.A.I.C.S.: 221111

Toshiba Lighting & Display Systems (Shanghai) Co., Ltd. (3)
1st Floor No 168 Meisheng Road Waigaoqiao Free Trade Zone, Shanghai, 200131, China
Tel.: (86) 2168431048
Web Site: http://www.toshiba.co.jp
Display Lighting Equipment Mfr
N.A.I.C.S.: 335139

Toshiba Lighting (Beijing) Co., Ltd. (3)
Room 1756 Office Building Beijing Nikko New Century Hotel, Haidian District, Beijing, 100044, China
Tel.: (86) 1068492228
Electric Lamp Mfr
N.A.I.C.S.: 335139

Toshiba Lighting (Fuzhou) Co.,Ltd. (3)
180 Huagong Road Jinan Area, Fuzhou, 350014, Fujian, China
Tel.: (86) 59183625618
Web Site: http://www.lighting.toshiba.com.cn
Sales Range: $75-99.9 Million
Emp.: 40
Electric Lamp Mfr
N.A.I.C.S.: 335139
Takashi Yorifuji *(Gen Mgr)*

Toshiba Products & Services (Shanghai) Co., Ltd. (3)
1605 16/F Shanghai Times Square Office 93 Huaihaizhong Road, Shanghai, China
Tel.: (86) 2163911188
Electronic Products Mfr
N.A.I.C.S.: 334419

Toshiba Visual Imaging Systems (Shenzhen) Ltd. (3)
No 117-118 Block 1 1001 Honghua Road Futian Free Trade Zone, Shenzhen, 518038, China
Tel.: (86) 75583480376
Medical Equipment Mfr
N.A.I.C.S.: 339112

Subsidiary (Non-US):

Toshiba Asia Pacific Pte., Ltd. (TAPL) (2)
19 Fl Panorama Tower 34th St Corner Lane A Bgc, 6815 Ayala Ave, Makati, Manila, Philippines (100%)
Tel.: (63) 28191048
Web Site: http://taplasia.toshiba.co.jp
Sales Range: $25-49.9 Million
Emp.: 5
Mfr of Electronic Components
N.A.I.C.S.: 334419

Subsidiary (Domestic):

Toshiba Battery Co., Ltd. (2)
4 10 Minami Shinagawa 3 Chome, Tokyo, 140 0004, Shinagawa-ku, Japan (100%)
Tel.: (81) 354793883

Sales Range: $25-49.9 Million
Emp.: 100
Manganese & Silver Batteries Mfr
N.A.I.C.S.: 335910

Toshiba Business And Life Service Corporation (2)
7-1 Nisshincho, Kawasaki-ku, Kawasaki, 210-0024, Kanagawa, Japan
Tel.: (81) 442303355
Web Site: http://www.tbls.toshiba.co.jp
Emp.: 2,166
Real Estate Brokerage & Business Solutions Services
N.A.I.C.S.: 523160
Yuichi Funada *(Dir)*

Subsidiary (Non-US):

Toshiba Capital (Asia) Ltd. (2)
20 Pasir Panjang Road, Singapore, 117439, Singapore (100%)
Tel.: (65) 785252
Web Site: http://www.toshiba.com
Sales Range: $25-49.9 Million
Emp.: 17
Provider of Electrical Related Services
N.A.I.C.S.: 811114

Subsidiary (Domestic):

Toshiba Capital Corporation (2)
Toshiba Bldg 1 1 1 Shibaura Minato-ku, Tokyo, 105 6691, Japan (100%)
Tel.: (81) 334573952
Web Site: http://www.toshiba.com
Sales Range: $50-74.9 Million
Emp.: 6
Provider of Fund Raising & Management Services
N.A.I.C.S.: 523940

Toshiba Components Co., Ltd. (2)
647 Mobara, Mobara, 297 8555, Chiba, Japan (75%)
Tel.: (81) 475228700
Sales Range: $200-249.9 Million
Emp.: 700
Mfr & Sale of Rectifiers, Airtight Terminals, Printed Circuit Boards & Other Electric Parts
N.A.I.C.S.: 334413
Hiroyuki Matsumoto *(Pres)*

Subsidiary (Non-US):

Toshiba Compressor (Taiwan) Corp. (2)
6F No 66 Sec 1 Shin Sheng North Rd, Taipei, Taiwan (100%)
Tel.: (886) 225813639
Sales Range: $50-74.9 Million
Emp.: 250
Mfr of Rotary Compressors
N.A.I.C.S.: 333912

Subsidiary (Domestic):

Toshiba Computer Technology Corp. (2)
2-9 Suehiro-cho, Oume-shi, Tokyo, 198 8710, Japan (100%)
Tel.: (81) 428341833
Web Site: http://www.toshiba-tcot.co.jp
Sales Range: $100-124.9 Million
Emp.: 472
Computers & Related Products Mfr
N.A.I.C.S.: 334118
Isao Morita *(Mng Dir)*

Toshiba Consumer Marketing Corporation (2)
Kita 3 28 Nangodori 20 Chome, Shiroishi Ku, Sapporo, 003-0023, Hokkaido, Japan
Tel.: (81) 118682111
Sales Range: $25-49.9 Million
Emp.: 100
Sales of Home Electric Appliances
N.A.I.C.S.: 449210

Toshiba Consumer Marketing Corporation (2)
6 1 21 Meike, Niigata, 950 8606, Japan (100%)
Tel.: (81) 252821653
Sales Range: $25-49.9 Million
Emp.: 100
Sales of Home Electric Appliances
N.A.I.C.S.: 449210

Toshiba Consumer Marketing Corporation (2)
25 1 Ekimae Honcho Kawasaki ku Kawasaki-shi, Kawasaki, 2108543, Kanagawa, Japan (100%)
Tel.: (81) 3 3457 4511
Web Site: http://www.toshiba.co.jp
Sales of Home Electric Appliances
N.A.I.C.S.: 449210

Toshiba Consumer Marketing Corporation (2)
4 2 12 Honmachi, Chuo Ku, Osaka, 541 0053, Japan (100%)
Tel.: (81) 662448700
Sales of Home Electric Appliances
N.A.I.C.S.: 449210

Toshiba Consumer Marketing Corporation (2)
Kawasaki Ekimaehon Building 25-1 Ekimaehon, Kawasaki, Kawasaki, 210-8543, Kanagawa, Japan
Tel.: (81) 443317350
Web Site: http://www.toshiba.co.jp
Home Electric Appliances Whslr
N.A.I.C.S.: 449210
Koichi Suezawa *(Pres)*

Toshiba Consumer Marketing Corporation (2)
2 2 22 Asahimachi, Takamatsu, 760 0065, Kagawa, Japan (100%)
Tel.: (81) 878516161
Sales of Home Electric Appliances
N.A.I.C.S.: 449210

Subsidiary (Non-US):

Toshiba Consumer Products (Thailand) Co., Ltd. (2)
144 1 Moo 5 Bangkadi Industrial Park Tivanon Rd, Tambol Bangkadi, Pathumthani, 12000, Thailand (100%)
Tel.: (66) 25011400
Web Site: http://www.toshiba.com
Sales Range: $200-249.9 Million
Emp.: 1,100
Mfr of Refrigerators & Washing Machines
N.A.I.C.S.: 335220

Plant (Domestic):

Toshiba Corporation - Fuchu Complex Factory (2)
1 Toshiba-cho, Fuchu, 183-8511, Tokyo, Japan
Tel.: (81) 423332011
Emp.: 1,000
Consumer Electronics Product Mfr
N.A.I.C.S.: 334419

Toshiba Corporation - Fukaya Complex Factory (2)
1-9-2 Hatara-cho, Fukaya, 366-8510, Saitama, Japan
Tel.: (81) 485742014
Web Site: http://www.toshiba.co.jp
Electronic Products Mfr
N.A.I.C.S.: 334419
Ichimiya Atsushi *(Gen Mgr)*

Toshiba Corporation - Kashiwazaki Operations Factory (2)
931-21 Oaza Karuigawa, Kashiwazaki, 945-1396, Niigata, Japan
Tel.: (81) 257201048
Web Site: http://www.toshiba.co.jp
Consumer Electronic Component Mfr
N.A.I.C.S.: 334419

Toshiba Corporation - Keihin Product Operations Factory (2)
2-4 Suehiro-cho, Tsurumi-ku, Yokohama, 230-0045, Kanagawa, Japan
Tel.: (81) 455105016
Consumer Electronics Mfr
N.A.I.C.S.: 334310

Toshiba Corporation - Komukai Complex Factory (2)
1 Komukaitoshiba-cho, Saiwai-ku, Kawasaki, 212-8581, Kanagawa, Japan
Tel.: (81) 445485003
Electronic Products Mfr
N.A.I.C.S.: 334419

Toshiba Corporation - Mie Operations Factory (2)

JAPAN INDUSTRIAL PARTNERS, INC.

Japan Industrial Partners, Inc.—(Continued)

2121 Oaza Nao, Asahi-cho, Mie, 510-8521, Japan
Tel.: (81) 593766001
Sales Range: $25-49.9 Million
Emp.: 100
Consumer Electronics Mfr
N.A.I.C.S.: 334220
Maruo Tatsuya *(Gen Mgr)*

Toshiba Corporation - Oita Operations Factory (2)
3500 Oaza Matsuoka, Oita, 870-0197, Japan
Tel.: (81) 975246000
Web Site: http://www.toshiba.co.jp
Electronic Components Mfr
N.A.I.C.S.: 334419

Toshiba Corporation - Ome Complex Factory (2)
2-9 Suehiro-cho, Ome, 198-8710, Tokyo, Japan
Tel.: (81) 428341000
Web Site: http://www.toshiba.co.jp
Emp.: 150
Electronic Products Mfr
N.A.I.C.S.: 334419

Toshiba Corporation - West Turbine Works (2)
1-9 Suehiro-cho, Tsurumi-ku, Yokohama, 230-0045, Kanagawa, Japan
Tel.: (81) 455105016
Web Site: http://www.toshiba.co.jp
Consumer Electronics Mfr
N.A.I.C.S.: 334310

Toshiba Corporation - Yokkaichi Operations Factory (2)
800 Yamanoisshiki-cho, Yokkaichi, 512-8550, Mie, Japan
Tel.: (81) 593301001
Web Site: http://www.toshiba.co.jp
Consumer Electronics Mfr
N.A.I.C.S.: 334310

Toshiba Corporation - Yokohama Complex Factory (2)
8 Shinsugita-cho, Isogo-ku, Yokohama, 235-8522, Kanagawa, Japan
Tel.: (81) 457703111
Web Site: http://www.toshiba.co.jp
Electronic Products Mfr
N.A.I.C.S.: 334419

Subsidiary (Non-US):

Toshiba Dalian Co. Ltd. (2)
6 An Shan St Dalian Economic & Technical, Development Zone, Dalian, 116600, Liaoning, China
Tel.: (86) 41187614111
Web Site: http://www.toshiba.co.jp
Sales Range: $400-449.9 Million
Emp.: 2,112
Mfr of Small Industrial Motors, Diffraction Yokes, Printed Circuit Board Units & Delay Lines
N.A.I.C.S.: 336320

Affiliate (Non-US):

Toshiba Data Dynamics Pte. Ltd. (2)
Data Dynamics Bldg, 10 Kallang Sector, Singapore, 349280, Singapore (100%)
Tel.: (65) 67418181
Web Site: http://www.toshibadata.com
Sales Range: $150-199.9 Million
Emp.: 270
Telecommunications & IT Products Distr
N.A.I.C.S.: 423420

Subsidiary (Domestic):

Toshiba Digital Media Engineering Corp. (2)
3-3-5 Shin-machi, Ome, 198 0024, Tokyo, Japan (100%)
Tel.: (81) 428334111
Web Site: http://www.toshiba-dme.co.jp
Sales Range: $400-449.9 Million
Emp.: 1,644
Developer & Designer of PCs & Related Products
N.A.I.C.S.: 334111

Subsidiary (Non-US):

Toshiba Digital Media Network Taiwan Corporation (2)

12F No 10 Sec 3 Min Sheng E Rd, Taipei, 10480, Taiwan (100%)
Tel.: (886) 225135999
Web Site: http://www.sdttoshiba.com.tw
Sales Range: $50-74.9 Million
Emp.: 68
Mfr & Distr of DVD Recorders & Hard Disk Drives
N.A.I.C.S.: 334610

Toshiba Display Devices (Thailand) Co., Ltd. (2)
142 Moo 5 Bangkadi Industrial Park Tivanon Rd, Pathumthani, 12000, Thailand (93%)
Tel.: (66) 25011200
Web Site: http://www.toshiba.com
Sales Range: $800-899.9 Million
Emp.: 3,890
Mfr of Color Picture Tubes & Color Display Tubes
N.A.I.C.S.: 334419

Subsidiary (Domestic):

Toshiba Electric Service Corp. (2)
Shinjuku Daiichiseimei Bldg, 2 7 1 Nishishinjuku Shinjuku K, Tokyo, 35322 5051, Japan (100%)
Tel.: (81) 353225051
Sales Range: $200-249.9 Million
Emp.: 645
Transformers, Circuit Breakers & Related Products Mfr
N.A.I.C.S.: 335313
Yoshida Satoshi *(Gen Mgr)*

Toshiba Electronic Devices & Storage Corporation (2)
1-1 Shibaura 1-Chome, Minato-ku, Tokyo, 105-0023, Japan
Tel.: (81) 334574511
Semiconductor Technologies Developer
N.A.I.C.S.: 334413
Hiroshi Fukuchi *(Pres & CEO)*

Subsidiary (Domestic):

NuFlare Technology, Inc. (3)
8-1 Shinsugita-cho, Isogo-ku, Yokohama, 235-8522, Kanagawa, Japan (84.66%)
Tel.: (81) 453709127
Web Site: http://www.nuflare.co.jp
Rev.: $523,867,320
Assets: $916,428,060
Liabilities: $256,352,700
Net Worth: $660,075,360
Earnings: $75,805,020
Emp.: 626
Fiscal Year-end: 03/31/2019
Semiconductor Devices Mfr
N.A.I.C.S.: 334413
Shigeki Sugimoto *(Pres)*

Subsidiary (Domestic):

Toshiba Electronic Engineering Corporation (2)
8 Shin Sugita Cho, Isogo-ku, Yokohama, 235 8522, Kanagawa, Japan (100%)
Tel.: (81) 457703370
Web Site: http://www.toshiba.co.jp
Emp.: 50
Design of Laser Equipment, Electron Tubes, Electronic Devices & Manufacturing Systems for Electron Tubes & Electronic Devices; Physical & Chemical Analysis
N.A.I.C.S.: 334419
Eiji Kamohara *(Mgr)*

Subsidiary (Non-US):

Toshiba Electronics Asia (Singapore) Pte. Ltd. (2)
438 B Alexandra Rd 06 08 12, Singapore, 119968, Singapore (100%)
Tel.: (65) 062785252
Web Site: http://www.semicon.toshiba.co.jp
Sales Range: $50-74.9 Million
Emp.: 135
Sales of Electronic Components
N.A.I.C.S.: 449210

Toshiba Electronics Asia, Ltd. (2)
Level 11 Tower 2 Grand Century Pl No 93 Prince Edward Rd W Monko, Kowloon, Hong Kong (China (Hong Kong)) (100%)
Tel.: (852) 023756111
Web Site: http://www.toshiba-electronics.com.hk

Sales Range: $50-74.9 Million
Emp.: 150
Sales of Color TVs, Audio/Video Products & Home Electric Appliances
N.A.I.C.S.: 449210

Division (Non-US):

Toshiba Electronics Asia (3)
Room 1403C Tower 5D1 Liangmaqiao Diplomatic Office Building, No 19 Dongfangdong Road Chaoyang, Beijing, 100600, China (100%)
Tel.: (86) 1085323834
Web Site: http://www.semicon.toshiba.com.cn
Sales Range: $25-49.9 Million
Emp.: 10
Mfr of Electronic Components
N.A.I.C.S.: 334419

Toshiba Electronics Asia (3)
Room 4 DE 24F International Financial Centre, 59 Xiang Gang Zhong Road, Qingdao, 266071, Shandong, China (100%)
Tel.: (86) 532 8579 3328
Web Site: http://www.semicon.toshiba.co.jp
Mfr of Electronic Components
N.A.I.C.S.: 334419

Subsidiary (Non-US):

Toshiba Electronics Korea Corporation (2)
27F ASEM Tower 517, Seocho-ku, Seoul, 6164, Korea (South) (100%)
Tel.: (82) 234844334
Web Site: http://www.toshiba.co.jp
Sales Range: $75-99.9 Million
Emp.: 120
N.A.I.C.S.: 334220

Toshiba Electronics Korea Corporation (2)
891 Samsung Life Insurance Daechi Tower 20 F, Daechi Dong Gangnam Gu, Seoul, 135 738, Korea (South) (100%)
Tel.: (82) 234844334
Electronic Equipment Sales
N.A.I.C.S.: 334220

Toshiba Electronics Taiwan Corp. (2)
10th Floor Union Enterprise Plaza Building No 10, Ming Sheng East Road Sec 3, Taipei, 109, Taiwan
Tel.: (886) 225149988
Web Site: http://www.toshiba.com
Sales Range: $50-74.9 Million
Emp.: 163
Sales of Electronic Components
N.A.I.C.S.: 449210

Toshiba Electronics Trading (Malaysia) Sdn. Bhd. (2)
Ste W1203 Wisma Consplant No 1 Jalan SS 16-4 Subang Jaya, Subang Jaya, 7500, Selangor, Malaysia (100%)
Tel.: (60) 356316311
Web Site: http://www.semicon.toshiba.co.jp
Sales Range: $25-49.9 Million
Emp.: 40
Mfr of Electronic Components
N.A.I.C.S.: 334419
Osamu Yoshida *(Mng Dir)*

Division (Domestic):

Toshiba Electronics Trading (Malaysia) Sdn. Bhd. (3)
Ste 13-1 13th Floor Menara Penang Garden 42-A Jalan Sultan Ahmad Shah, 10050, Penang, Malaysia (100%)
Tel.: (60) 42268523
Web Site: http://www.toshiba.com.my
Sales Range: $25-49.9 Million
Emp.: 11
Mfr of Electronic Components
N.A.I.C.S.: 334419

Subsidiary (Domestic):

Toshiba Elevator & Building Systems Corporation (2)
6-5-27 Kita Shinagawa, Shinagawa-ku, Tokyo, 141 0001, Japan (100%)
Tel.: (81) 354233333
Web Site: http://www.toshiba-elevator.co.jp
Sales Range: $100-124.9 Million
Emp.: 300

INTERNATIONAL PUBLIC

Mfr, Sales, Installation, Maintenance, Parts Supply & Repair of Elevators & Escalators
N.A.I.C.S.: 333921

Affiliate (Non-US):

MS Elevators Sdn. Bhd. (3)
Suite 13-1 13th Floor Menara Penang Garden 42-A, 10050, Penang, Malaysia
Tel.: (60) 42268523
Web Site: http://www.msee.com.my
Sales Range: $25-49.9 Million
Emp.: 200
Mfr of Elevators & Escalators
N.A.I.C.S.: 333921

Subsidiary (Non-US):

PT. TOSHINDO ELEVATOR UTAMA (3)
Kokan Permata Kelapa Gading Blok F No 15-17 Jl Boulevard Bukit, Gading Raya Kelapa Gading, Jakarta, 14240, Indonesia
Tel.: (62) 2145858300
Elevator Mfr
N.A.I.C.S.: 333921

TOSHIBA ELEVATOR (INDIA) PVT., LTD (3)
Level 4 Dynasty Business Park Andheri Kurla Road, Andheri East, Mumbai, 400059, India
Tel.: (91) 2240309492
Web Site: http://www.toshiba-elevator.co.jp
Sales Range: $25-49.9 Million
Emp.: 20
Elevator & Escalator Installation Services
N.A.I.C.S.: 238290

TOSHIBA ELEVATOR KOREA INC. (3)
891 Samsung Life Insurance Daechi Tower 20f, Seoul, 135-738, Korea (South)
Tel.: (82) 234844334
Web Site: http://www2.toshiba-elevator.co.jp
Elevator Mfr
N.A.I.C.S.: 333921

Toshiba Elevator (China) Co.,Ltd. (3)
No 685 Yunchuan Road, Baoshan District, Shanghai, 201901, China
Tel.: (86) 2156808888
Elevator Repair Services & Mfr
N.A.I.C.S.: 333921

Subsidiary (Non-US):

Toshiba Elevator Shenyang Co., Ltd. (2)
Room1801 18F Tower C President Mansion No 69 Heping North Street, Heping, Shenyang, 110000, China (100%)
Tel.: (86) 2431873325
Web Site: http://www.toshiba-elevator.co.jp
Sales Range: $200-249.9 Million
Emp.: 825
Mfr of Elevators & Escalators
N.A.I.C.S.: 333921

Subsidiary (Domestic):

Toshiba Energy Systems & Solutions Corporation (2)
72-34 Horikawa-cho, Saiwai-ku, Kawasaki, 212-8585, Kanagawa, Japan
Tel.: (81) 443310625
Web Site: http://www.toshiba-energy.com
Emp.: 7,200
Development, Manufacture & Sales of Energy Business Products, Systems & Services
N.A.I.C.S.: 221113
Mamoru Hatazawa *(Pres & CEO)*

Subsidiary (Domestic):

Nuclear Fuel Industries Ltd. (3)
4-33-5 Tsurumi Chuo, Tsurumi-ku, Yokohama, 230-0051, Japan (100%)
Tel.: (81) 455006300
Web Site: http://www.nfi.co.jp
Sales Range: $150-199.9 Million
Water Reactor Nuclear Fuel Mfr
N.A.I.C.S.: 332410
Kenichi Kitagawa *(Pres & CEO)*

Plant (Domestic):

Nuclear Fuel Industries Ltd. - Kumatori Works (4)

1-950 Asashironishi Kumatori-cho, Sennan-gun, Osaka, 590-0481, Japan
Tel.: (81) 724523901
Sales Range: $75-99.9 Million
Emp.: 35
Water Reactor Nuclear Fuel Mfr
N.A.I.C.S.: 332410

Nuclear Fuel Industries Ltd. - Tokai Works (4)
3135-41 Muramatsu Tokai-mura, Naka-gun, Ibaraki, 319-1196, Japan
Tel.: (81) 292878201
Sales Range: $25-49.9 Million
Emp.: 25
Fuel Products Mfr
N.A.I.C.S.: 324199
Shinsuke Matsumoto *(Pres)*

Subsidiary (Non-US):

Toshiba Europe (Switzerland) GmbH (2)
Chriesbaumstrasse 4, 8604, Volketswil, Switzerland
Tel.: (41) 449085630
Web Site: http://www.toshiba.ch
Sales Range: $25-49.9 Million
Emp.: 4
Digital Camera Mfr
N.A.I.C.S.: 333310

Toshiba Gulf Fze (2)
Besides Jasza Post Office Jebel Ali, PO Box 61028, Jebel Ali, 61028, Dubai, United Arab Emirates **(100%)**
Tel.: (971) 48817789
Web Site: http://www.toshiba.com
Sales Range: $25-49.9 Million
Emp.: 33
Mfr of Consumer Electronics & Industrial Power Equipment
N.A.I.C.S.: 333612

Subsidiary (Domestic):

Toshiba Hokuto Electronics Corporation (2)
1975 23-chome Minami 5-jodori, Asahikawa, 078-8335, Hokkaido, Japan
Tel.: (81) 166314721
Web Site: http://www.hokuto.co.jp
Sales Range: $125-149.9 Million
Black & White TV Picture Tubes, Incandescent Lamps, Flexible Circuit Board Mfr & Sales
N.A.I.C.S.: 334419
Norio Murakawa *(Pres & CEO)*

Toshiba Hokuto Electronics Corporation (2)
23 1975 Minamigojodori, Asahikawa, Hokkaido, 078 8335, Japan **(100%)**
Tel.: (81) 066314721
Web Site: http://www3.toshiba.co.jp
Mfr & Sales of Black & White TV Picture Tubes, Magnetrons for Microwave Ovens & Flexible Printed Circuit Boards
N.A.I.C.S.: 334412

Toshiba Home Appliances Corporation (2)
Toshiba Shoheizaka Bldg 3F 2-15 Stokanda 2-chome, Chiyoda-Ku, Tokyo, 101-0021, Japan
Tel.: (81) 332575879
Web Site: http://www.toshiba-denchi.jp
Household Appliances Mfr
N.A.I.C.S.: 335220

Toshiba Home Technology Corporation (2)
2570-1 Oaza Urasuda Kamo, Niigata, 959 1393, Japan **(100%)**
Tel.: (81) 256532511
Sales Range: $100-124.9 Million
Emp.: 300
Household Appliances Mfr
N.A.I.C.S.: 449210

Subsidiary (Non-US):

Toshiba Hong Kong Limited. (2)
16th Fl Evergain Ctr 28 On Muk St, Sha Tin, NT, China (Hong Kong) **(100%)**
Tel.: (852) 29560222
Web Site: http://www.toshiba.com.hk
Sales Range: $25-49.9 Million
Emp.: 40
Mfr of Consumer Products

N.A.I.C.S.: 449210

Subsidiary (Domestic):

Toshiba IT & Control Systems Corporation (2)
17F 6-24-1 Nishi-Shinjuku, Shinjuku-ku, Tokyo, 160-0023, Japan **(100%)**
Tel.: (81) 345746877
Web Site: http://www.toshiba-itc.com
Sales Range: $150-199.9 Million
Emp.: 1,000
Industrial-Use & Public-Use Control Systems & Information Processing Systems Designer, Mfr, Sales & Servicer
N.A.I.C.S.: 541512

Toshiba Industrial Products Manufacturing Corporation (2)
2121 Oaza Nao, Asahi, 510 8521, Mie, Japan **(100%)**
Tel.: (81) 593766301
Web Site: http://www.toshiba.sankiki.co.jp
Sales Range: $400-449.9 Million
Emp.: 1,050
Motors Developer, Mfr & Transformers; Motor Control Centers
N.A.I.C.S.: 335311
Tatsuya Maruo *(Pres)*

Toshiba Industrial Products Sales Corporation (2)
4-9-11 Nihonbashi-honcho, Chuo-ku, Tokyo, 103 0023, Japan **(100%)**
Tel.: (81) 356445501
Web Site: http://www.tips.toshiba.com.au
Sales Range: $250-299.9 Million
Emp.: 600
Domestic Sales & Service of Industrial Machinery
N.A.I.C.S.: 423830

Subsidiary (Non-US):

Toshiba Information Equipment (Philippines), Inc. (2)
103 East Main Ave Extension Special Export Processing Zone, Laguna Technopark, Binan, 4024, Laguna, Philippines **(100%)**
Tel.: (63) 28095183
Web Site: http://www.toshiba.co.jp
Sales Range: $400-449.9 Million
Emp.: 1,500
Mfr Of DVD-ROMs & CD-ROMs
N.A.I.C.S.: 334112
Minodu Iriko *(Pres)*

Toshiba Information Systems (UK) Ltd. (2)
Toshiba Court Weybridge Business Park Addlestone Road, KT15 2UL, Weybridge, Surrey, United Kingdom - England
Tel.: (44) 8448478944
Web Site: http://www.toshiba.co.uk
Information Technology Consulting Services
N.A.I.C.S.: 541512

Toshiba Information, Industrial and Power Systems Taiwan Corporation (2)
6F No 66 Sector 1 Shin Sheng N Rd, Taipei, Taiwan
Tel.: (886) 225813639
Electric Equipment Mfr
N.A.I.C.S.: 335999

Toshiba Infrastructure Systems South America Ltd. (2)
Eng Luis Carlos Berrini Ave, 1511 Brooklin Novo, 04571-011, Sao Paulo, SP, Brazil **(100%)**
Tel.: (55) 3133296650
Web Site: http://www.toshiba.com.br
Sales Range: $200-249.9 Million
Emp.: 841
Transmission, Distribution, Transportation, Industry & Smart Grid Solutions
N.A.I.C.S.: 335311

Subsidiary (Domestic):

Toshiba Insurance Service Corporation (2)
Ginza Toshiba Building 5 2 1 Ginza, Chuo Ku, Tokyo, 104 0061, Japan **(100%)**
Tel.: (81) 332893800
Sales Range: $100-124.9 Million
Emp.: 200
Insurance Agents

N.A.I.C.S.: 524298

Subsidiary (Non-US):

Toshiba International (Europe) Ltd (2)
2 Floor 3 Furzeground Way Stockley Park, Uxbridge, UB11 1EZ, Middlesex, United Kingdom **(100%)**
Tel.: (44) 1895427400
Web Site: http://www.toshiba.co.uk
Sales Range: $25-49.9 Million
Emp.: 15
Heavy Electrical Apparatus, Generators & Motors Mfr
N.A.I.C.S.: 335312
Akira Abe *(Mng Dir)*

Subsidiary (Non-US):

Toshiba Electronics Europe GmbH (3)
Hansallee 181, Dusseldorf, 40549, Germany **(100%)**
Tel.: (49) 21152960
Web Site: http://www.toshiba-components.com
Sales Range: $25-49.9 Million
Sales of Electronic Components
N.A.I.C.S.: 449210

Subsidiary (Non-US):

Toshiba Electronics Espana S.A. (4)
Parque Empresarial San Fernando, 1st Planta Edificio Europa, E 28831, Madrid, Spain **(100%)**
Tel.: (34) 916606798
Web Site: http://www.toshibacomponents.com
Sales Range: $25-49.9 Million
Emp.: 4
Sales of Electronic Components
N.A.I.C.S.: 449210
Alfonso Rubio *(Gen Mgr)*

Toshiba Electronics Europe GmbH (4)
First Floor Delta House The Crescent, Southwood Business Park, Farnborough, GU14 ONL, Hampshire, United Kingdom **(100%)**
Tel.: (44) 8700602370
Web Site: http://www.toshiba-components.com
Sales Range: $25-49.9 Million
Emp.: 16
Sales of Electronic Components
N.A.I.C.S.: 449210

Toshiba Electronics France S.A.R.L. (4)
Immeuble Robert Schuman 3 Rue De Rome, F 93561, Rosny-sous-Bois, Cedex, France **(100%)**
Tel.: (33) 0148124812
Web Site: http://www.toshiba.fr
Sales Range: $25-49.9 Million
Emp.: 13
Electronic Components Mfr
N.A.I.C.S.: 449210

Toshiba Electronics Italiana S.R.L. (4)
Centro Direzionale Colleoni Pallazzo Perseo 3, I 20041, Agrate Brianza, Milano, Italy **(100%)**
Tel.: (39) 0003968701
Web Site: http://www.toshiba.it
Sales Range: $25-49.9 Million
Emp.: 15
Color TV Sets & VCR Sales
N.A.I.C.S.: 449210

Toshiba Electronics Scandinavia AB (4)
Gustavslundsvagen 18 5th Fl, S 167 15, Bromma, Sweden **(100%)**
Tel.: (46) 87040900
Web Site: http://www.toshiba.com
Sales Range: $25-49.9 Million
Emp.: 45
Sales of Electronic Components
N.A.I.C.S.: 449210

Subsidiary (Domestic):

Toshiba International (Europe) Ltd. (3)
Albany 71 79 State Rd, West Drayton, UB7

7LT, Middlesex, United Kingdom **(100%)**
Tel.: (44) 1895427400
Web Site: http://www.toshiba-europe.com
Sales Range: $25-49.9 Million
Sales of Power & Industrial Equipment
N.A.I.C.S.: 423830

Toshiba International Finance (UK) plc (3)
100 Ludgate Hill 6th Fl, London, EC4M 7RE, United Kingdom **(100%)**
Tel.: (44) 2073326200
Sales Range: $75-99.9 Million
Emp.: 5
Financial Transactions & Investments
N.A.I.C.S.: 522299

Subsidiary (Non-US):

Toshiba International Finance (Netherlands) B.V. (4)
Zilverstraat 1, 2718 RP, Zoetermeer, South Holland, Netherlands **(100%)**
Tel.: (31) 793689222
Web Site: http://www.toshiba.com
Sales Range: $10-24.9 Million
Financial Services
N.A.I.C.S.: 522299

Subsidiary (Non-US):

Toshiba Medical Systems Europe B.V. (3)
Zilverstraat 1, Zoetermeer, 2718 RP, South Holland, Netherlands **(100%)**
Tel.: (31) 793689222
Sales of Medical Equipment
N.A.I.C.S.: 423450
Chikao Kamijima *(Mng Dir)*

Subsidiary (Non-US):

Toshiba Medical France S.A. (4)
7 Rue Ampere, PO Box 14, F 92802, Puteaux, Cedex, France **(100%)**
Tel.: (33) 0147282500
Web Site: http://www.toshiba.fr
Sales Range: $25-49.9 Million
Sales of Medical Equipment
N.A.I.C.S.: 423450

Toshiba Medical Systems AG (4)
Kreuzlenstrasse 5, CH 8618, Oetwil am See, Switzerland **(100%)**
Tel.: (41) 19296666
Web Site: http://www.toshiba.com
Sales Range: $25-49.9 Million
Emp.: 30
Sales of Medical Equipment
N.A.I.C.S.: 423450

Toshiba Medical Systems GmbH (4)
Hellerbergstrasse 4, D 41460, Neuss, Germany **(100%)**
Tel.: (49) 213118090
Web Site: http://www.toshiba-medical.com
Sales Range: $50-74.9 Million
Sales of Medical Equipment
N.A.I.C.S.: 423450
Willem De Bouter *(Mng Dir-Fin)*

Toshiba Medical Systems GmbH (4)
Industriezentrum No Sud Ricoweg 40, Wiener Neudorf, 2351, Austria **(100%)**
Tel.: (43) 223661623
Sales Range: $25-49.9 Million
Emp.: 20
Sales of Medical Equipment
N.A.I.C.S.: 423450
Paula Angoluan *(Mng Dir)*

Toshiba Medical Systems Ltd. (4)
Boundary Code Gatwick Rd, Crawley, RH10 9AX, W Sussex, United Kingdom **(100%)**
Tel.: (44) 293653700
Web Site: http://www.toshiba-europe.com
Sales Range: $25-49.9 Million
Emp.: 20
Sales of Medical Equipment
N.A.I.C.S.: 423450

Toshiba Medical Systems NV/SA (4)
Bijkhoevelaan 32 C, 2110, Wijnegem, Antwerp, Belgium **(100%)**
Tel.: (32) 33262323
Sales Range: $25-49.9 Million
Emp.: 30
Sales of Medical Equipment
N.A.I.C.S.: 423450

JAPAN INDUSTRIAL PARTNERS, INC.

Japan Industrial Partners, Inc.—(Continued)

Toshiba Medical Systems S.A. (4)
Carretera De Fuencarral No 46, 28108, Madrid, Spain **(100%)**
Tel.: (34) 914905850
Sales Range: $50-74.9 Million
Medical Equipment Rental
N.A.I.C.S.: 423450

Toshiba Medical Systems S.R.L. (4)
Via Canton 115, 00144, Rome, Italy **(100%)**
Tel.: (39) 06520771
Web Site: http://www.toshiba.it
Sales Range: $50-74.9 Million
Sales of Medical Equipment
N.A.I.C.S.: 423450

Toshiba Medical Systems Sweden (4)
Sisjo Kullegata 8, 421 32, Vastra Frolunda, Sweden
Tel.: (46) 313898040
Web Site: http://www.toshiba-medical.se
Sales Range: $25-49.9 Million
Emp.: 14
Medical Equipment Distr
N.A.I.C.S.: 423450
Frank Zingaropoli (CEO)

Subsidiary (Domestic):

Toshiba Research Europe, Ltd. (3)
208 Cambridge Science Park, Milton Rd, Cambridge, CB4 0GZ, United Kingdom **(100%)**
Tel.: (44) 1223436900
Web Site: http://www.toshiba-europe.com
Sales Range: $10-24.9 Million
Emp.: 50
Provider of Research Services
N.A.I.C.S.: 541715
Roberto Cipolli (Mng Dir)

Subsidiary (Domestic):

Toshiba Europe Research Ltd. (4)
208 Cambridge Science Park Milton Rd, Cambridge, CB4 0GZ, United Kingdom **(100%)**
Tel.: (44) 1223436900
Web Site: http://www.toshiba-europe.com
Sales Range: $10-24.9 Million
Emp.: 50
Provider of Research Services
N.A.I.C.S.: 541715

Toshiba-Telecommunications Research Laboratory (4)
32 Queen Square, Bristol, BS1 4ND, United Kingdom **(100%)**
Tel.: (44) 1179060700
Web Site: http://www.toshiba.com
Sales Range: $10-24.9 Million
Emp.: 40
Cellular & Wireless Research Services
N.A.I.C.S.: 541715

Subsidiary (Non-US):

Toshiba Semiconductor GmbH (3)
Grotrian Steinwegstrasse 10, 38112, Braunschweig, Germany **(100%)**
Tel.: (49) 53131990
Web Site: http://www.toshiba.com
Sales Range: $25-49.9 Million
Mfr of Semiconductors
N.A.I.C.S.: 334413

Subsidiary (Non-US):

Toshiba International Corporation Pty., Ltd. (2)
11A Gibbon Road, Sydney, 2153, NSW, Australia **(100%)**
Tel.: (61) 297686600
Web Site: http://www.toshiba.com.au
Sales Range: $50-74.9 Million
Emp.: 80
Mfr of Industrial Equipment & Systems
N.A.I.C.S.: 333310
Stephen Bartlett (Mgr-Sls)

Subsidiary (Domestic):

Toshiba KN System Co., Ltd. (2)
4 9 11 Nihonbashi Honcho, Chuo Ku, Tokyo, 103 0023, Japan
Tel.: (81) 357932933
Web Site: http://www.toshiba-kn.co.jp
Development & Sale of Computer Software; Data Processing Services
N.A.I.C.S.: 513210

Toshiba Kyushu Marketing Co., Ltd. (2)
2 4 1 Nagahama, Chuo Ku, Fukuoka, 810 0072, Japan
Tel.: (81) 99 751 2380
Web Site: http://www.toshiba.co.jp
Sales of Home Electric Appliances
N.A.I.C.S.: 449210

Toshiba Lighting & Technology Corporation (2)
2-13 Minami Shinagawa 2-Chome, Shinagawa-ku, Tokyo, 140 8660, Japan **(100%)**
Tel.: (81) 354638800
Web Site: http://www.tlp.co.jp
Sales Range: $800-899.9 Million
Emp.: 2,800
Mfr & Sales of Lamps, Lighting Fixtures, Airport Lighting Systems, Stage & Studio Lighting Systems, Large Screen Color Display Systems, Ballasts, Wiring Devices, Intercoms & Parts for Copiers
N.A.I.C.S.: 335131

Toshiba Location Information Co., Ltd. (2)
4 5 11 Shiba, Minato Ku, Tokyo, 108 0014, Japan **(100%)**
Tel.: (81) 354397088
Provider of System Integration for Location Information Systems
N.A.I.C.S.: 541512

Toshiba Logistics Corporation (2)
Sumitomo Higashi Shinbasi Bldg 3 10 14 Hamamatsu Cho 1 Chome, Tokyo, 105 0013, Japan **(100%)**
Tel.: (81) 354258401
Web Site: http://www.toshiba-logi.co.jp
Sales Range: $150-199.9 Million
Emp.: 1,000
Provider of Transportation & Warehousing Services
N.A.I.C.S.: 493110

Toshiba Material Sales Co., Ltd. (2)
8 Shinsugita-cho, Yokohama, 224 8534, Japan **(100%)**
Tel.: (81) 457703100
Web Site: http://www.toshiba-tmat.co.jp
Sales Range: $25-49.9 Million
Emp.: 30
Sales of Metal Materials & Parts
N.A.I.C.S.: 423930
Katsuaki Aoki (Pres & CEO)

Toshiba Materials Co., Ltd. (2)
1-1 Shibaura 1-Chome, Minato-ku, Tokyo, 105-8001, Japan
Tel.: (81) 334574874
Web Site: http://www.toshiba-tmat.co.jp
Sales Range: $100-124.9 Million
Emp.: 485
Ceramic Tile Mfr
N.A.I.C.S.: 327120
Katsuaki Aoki (Pres)

Subsidiary (Non-US):

Toshiba Electronics Asia (Hong Kong), Ltd. (3)
Level 11 Tower 2 Grand Century Place No 193 Prince Edward Road West, Mongkok, Kowloon, China (Hong Kong)
Tel.: (852) 2375 6111
Emp.: 10
Consumer Electronics Mfr
N.A.I.C.S.: 334220

Subsidiary (Non-US):

Toshiba Medical Systems Asia Pte., Ltd. (2)
Block 211 Henderson Rd 08 02, Singapore, 159552, Singapore **(100%)**
Tel.: (65) 62729766
Web Site: http://www.toshiba.com
Sales Range: $25-49.9 Million
Emp.: 30
Provider of Electrical Equipment Services
N.A.I.C.S.: 811114
Kuan Yong Kuan (Pres)

Toshiba Medical do Brasil Ltda. (2)
Rua Marcelo Moraes Cordeiro 110, Taboao da Serra, 1147884350, Sao Paulo, Brazil **(100%)**
Tel.: (55) 1147884350
Sales Range: $50-74.9 Million
Emp.: 95
Sales of Medical Equipment
N.A.I.C.S.: 423450

Subsidiary (Domestic):

Toshiba Memory Advanced Package Corporation (2)
3500 Oaza Matsuoka, Oita, 870 0197, Japan **(100%)**
Tel.: (81) 97 524 6000
Sales Range: $200-249.9 Million
Emp.: 600
Semiconductor Mfr
N.A.I.C.S.: 334413

Subsidiary (Non-US):

Toshiba Memory Semiconductor Taiwan Corporation (2)
17F Union Enterprise Plaza Bldg, 109 Min Sheng East Rd Sec 3, Taipei, 10544, Taiwan
Tel.: (886) 225149988
Web Site: http://www.toshiba-corp.com.tw
Sales Range: $25-49.9 Million
Emp.: 21
Mfr of Semiconductors
N.A.I.C.S.: 334413

Subsidiary (Domestic):

Toshiba Metal Parts Co., Ltd. (2)
782 Hirosaka Paishi Cho Ibogun, Hyogo, 671 1571, Japan
Tel.: (81) 792771737
Web Site: http://www.toshiba.co.jp
Mfr of Parts for Electron Tubes, Electric Appliances & Automobiles
N.A.I.C.S.: 334419

Joint Venture (Domestic):

Toshiba Mitsubishi-Electric Industrial Systems Corporation (2)
Square Garden 3-1-1, Kyobashi Chuo-ku, Tokyo, 104-0031, Japan
Tel.: (81) 332775511
Sales Range: $600-649.9 Million
Emp.: 1,943
N.A.I.C.S.: 238210

Subsidiary (Domestic):

Toshiba Multi Media Devices Co., Ltd. (2)
19 Aza Minase Oaza Fukihata Goshogawara, Aomori, 037 0003, Japan **(100%)**
Tel.: (81) 0173352255
Sales Range: $100-124.9 Million
Emp.: 400
Mfr of Optical Disc Drives
N.A.I.C.S.: 334610

Toshiba Multimedia Devices Co., Ltd. (2)
19 Aza Minase Oaza Fukihata, Aomori, Japan **(100%)**
Tel.: (81) 173352255
Web Site: http://www.toshiba.co.jp
Sales Range: $100-124.9 Million
Emp.: 450
Mfr & Sales of Audio Equipment
N.A.I.C.S.: 334310

Toshiba Nishi Nihon Service & Engineering Co., Ltd. (2)
21 10 Higashiueno 2 Chome, Taitou ku, Tokyo, 110 0015, Japan
Tel.: (81) 358187880
Provider of Computer System After-Sales Service
N.A.I.C.S.: 541512

Toshiba Osaka Building Co., Ltd. (2)
6F 2 12 Honmachi 4 Chome, Chuo Ku, Osaka, 541-0053, Japan
Tel.: (81) 662442790
Web Site: http://www.toshiba.co.jp
Management & Leasing of Real Estate
N.A.I.C.S.: 531210

Toshiba Ou Denki Co., Ltd. (2)
Wakabayashi Ku, Sendai, 984 0042, Japan

INTERNATIONAL PUBLIC

Tel.: (81) 222357261
Sales & Maintenance of Electric Machines
N.A.I.C.S.: 811210

Subsidiary (Non-US):

Toshiba Personal Computer & Network (Shanghai) Co., Ltd. (2)
5F Wheelock Square 1717 West Nanjing Road, Jingan, Shanghai, 200040, China **(100%)**
Tel.: (86) 2160900610
Web Site: http://www.toshiba.co.jp
Sales Range: $50-74.9 Million
Emp.: 124
Personal Computer Sales
N.A.I.C.S.: 334111

Subsidiary (Domestic):

Toshiba Personal Computer System Corp. (2)
20 7 Masago 5 Chome Mihama Kau Chibachi Shi, Mihama Ku, Chiba, 261 8580, Japan **(100%)**
Tel.: (81) 432792622
Web Site: http://www.toshiba-tops.co.jp
Sales Range: $150-199.9 Million
Emp.: 200
PCs & Related Products Developer, Mfr, Sales & Maintainer
N.A.I.C.S.: 334111

Toshiba Plant Systems & Services Corporation (2)
4-36-5 Tsurumichuo, Tsurumi-ku, Yokohama, 230-8691, Kanagawa, Japan **(100%)**
Tel.: (81) 455007050
Web Site: http://www.toshiba-tpsc.co.jp
Rev.: $2,212,805,340
Assets: $2,485,067,400
Liabilities: $1,063,988,280
Net Worth: $1,421,079,120
Earnings: $130,047,240
Emp.: 4,319
Fiscal Year-end: 03/31/2019
Provider of Consultation on Electrical Machinery & Facilities & Computer System Design
N.A.I.C.S.: 541511
Koichi Kamei (Exec VP)

Subsidiary (Non-US):

Toshiba Portugal (2)
Lagoas Park Edificio 1 Piso 3, 2740-264, Porto Salvo, Portugal
Tel.: (351) 707265265
Household Appliances Mfr
N.A.I.C.S.: 335220
Joao Amaral (Gen Mgr)

Toshiba Rus LLC. (2)
2nd Floor Naberezhnaya Tower-B 18 Krasnopresnenskaya Naberezhnaya, 123317, Moscow, Russia
Tel.: (7) 4956428910
Web Site: http://www.toshiba.com.ru
Household Appliances Mfr
N.A.I.C.S.: 335220

Toshiba Sales & Services Sdn. Bhd. (2)
Lot 5 And 7 Jalan Jurunilai U 1 20 Hicom Glenmarie Indus Pk, 40150, Shah Alam, Selangor, Malaysia **(70%)**
Tel.: (60) 355692190
Web Site: http://www.toshiba.com.my
Sales Range: $25-49.9 Million
Emp.: 80
Sales of Color TVs, Audio/Video Products & Home Electrical Appliances
N.A.I.C.S.: 449210

Subsidiary (Domestic):

Toshiba Sangyo Kiki System Corporation (2)
Nakamura Ku, Nagoya, 450 0003, Japan **(100%)**
Tel.: (81) 525411048
Web Site: http://www.toshiba-tips.co.jp
Sales Range: $25-49.9 Million
Emp.: 70
Sale & Maintenance of Electric Machines
N.A.I.C.S.: 811210

Subsidiary (Non-US):

Toshiba Semiconductor (Thailand) Co., Ltd. (2)

AND PRIVATE COMPANIES

JAPAN INDUSTRIAL PARTNERS, INC.

572 Moo 7 304 Industrial Park, Thatoom Srimahaphot, Bangkok, 25140, Prachinburi, Thailand
Tel.: (66) 037284900
Web Site: http://asia.toshiba.com
Emp.: 500
Semiconductor Mfr
N.A.I.C.S.: 333242
Yasuo Ashizawa (Pres)

Subsidiary (Domestic):

Toshiba Service & Engineering Co., Ltd. (2)
2 21 10 Higashi Ueno, Taito Ku, Tokyo, 110 0015, Japan (100%)
Tel.: (81) 358187880
Sales Range: $25-49.9 Million
Emp.: 100
Provider of Computer System After-Sales Service
N.A.I.C.S.: 541512

Toshiba Shikoku Service & Engineering Co. Ltd. (2)
2 2 29 Asahi Machi, Takamatsu, 760 0065, Kagawa, Japan (100%)
Tel.: (81) 878225415
Sales Range: $25-49.9 Million
Emp.: 75
Provider of Computer System After-Sales Service
N.A.I.C.S.: 541512

Toshiba Shomei Precision Corporation (2)
1 1 Aza Machida Tsuchifune, Fukushima shi, Fukushima, 960 2152, Japan (100%)
Tel.: (81) 245935550
Web Site: http://www.toshiba-tosp.co.jp
Sales Range: $50-74.9 Million
Emp.: 200
Mfr & Sales of Light Bulb Bases & Precision Press Machinery
N.A.I.C.S.: 335139

Toshiba Socio-Engineering Co., Ltd. (2)
70 Yanagi Cho, Saiwai Ku, Kawasaki, 210 8501, Kanagawa, Japan (100%)
Tel.: (81) 445555952
Developer of Analog & Digital Copiers; Automation Equipment for Banks & Railways
N.A.I.C.S.: 333310

Subsidiary (Non-US):

Toshiba Storage Device (Phillippines), Inc. (2)
42nd Level GT Tower International 6815 Ayala Avenue, Metro Manila, Makati, 1226, Philippines
Tel.: (63) 28191048
Electronic Components Mfr
N.A.I.C.S.: 334419

Subsidiary (Domestic):

Toshiba Storage Device Corporation (2)
1-1-1 Shibaura, Minato-Ku, Tokyo, 105-8001, Japan
Tel.: (81) 334574511
Computer Storage Device Mfr
N.A.I.C.S.: 334112

Toshiba System Technology Corp. (2)
Toshiba Fuchu South Building C 1-13, Toshiba-cho, Fuchu, 183-8511, Tokyo, Japan (100%)
Tel.: (81) 423336868
Web Site: http://www3.toshiba.co.jp
Emp.: 900
Electric Power System Engineering Services
N.A.I.C.S.: 221122
Yoko Abe (Pres & CEO)

Subsidiary (Non-US):

Toshiba TEC Spain Imaging Systems (2)
Parque Empresarial San Fernando - Edificio Europa 1a Planta, Madrid, 28830, Spain
Tel.: (34) 917037200
Sales Range: $25-49.9 Million
Emp.: 25
Printer Mfr
N.A.I.C.S.: 334118

Toshiba TEC Suisse AG (2)
Herostrasse 7, 8048, Zurich, Switzerland
Tel.: (41) 444397171
Web Site: http://www.toshibatec.ch
Emp.: 83
Photocopy Machine & Printer Mfr
N.A.I.C.S.: 333310

Subsidiary (Domestic):

Toshiba TLC, Inc. (2)
3 27 2 Nakasaiwai Cho, Saiwai Ku, Kawasaki, 210-0012, Kanagawa, Japan (100%)
Tel.: (81) 445441136
Web Site: http://www.toshiba-tbls.co.jp
Sales Range: $650-699.9 Million
Emp.: 2,500
Provider of Consumer Goods, Recreational Facilities Management, Civil Engineering, Construction, Plumbing, Electrical, Temporary Employee Services, Copying, Printing & Data Processing
N.A.I.C.S.: 532289

Toshiba Tec Corporation (2)
Gate City Ohsaki West Tower 1-11-1 Osaki, Shinagawa-ku, Tokyo, 141-8562, Japan (52.9%)
Tel.: (81) 368309100
Web Site: https://www.toshibatec.co.jp
Rev.: $3,623,172,350
Assets: $2,230,934,490
Liabilities: $1,594,814,530
Net Worth: $636,119,960
Earnings: ($44,333,270)
Emp.: 19,493
Fiscal Year-end: 03/31/2024
Cash Register & Office Machinery Mfr
N.A.I.C.S.: 333310
Hironobu Nishikori (Co-Pres & Co-CEO)

Subsidiary (Non-US):

TEC ELECTRONICA, S.A. de C.V. (3)
Dr Marquez No 19 Col Doctores, 6720, Mexico, Mexico
Tel.: (52) 5541604200
Web Site: http://www.tecelectronica.com.mx
Sales Range: $25-49.9 Million
Emp.: 10
Electronic Components Mfr
N.A.I.C.S.: 334419
Juan Valadez (Mgr-Mktg)

TOSHIBA TEC KOREA CO., LTD. (3)
4th Floor Juyeon Building 209 Seogye-dong, Yongsan-gu, Seoul, 140-710, Korea (South)
Tel.: (82) 232790001
Web Site: http://www.toshibateckorea.com
Sales Range: $25-49.9 Million
Emp.: 45
Electronic Components Mfr
N.A.I.C.S.: 334419

TOSHIBA TEC SINGAPORE PTE LTD (3)
2 Ang Mo Kio Street 62, Singapore, 569138, Singapore
Tel.: (65) 64819488
Web Site: http://www.tecsg.com.sg
Sales Range: $150-199.9 Million
Emp.: 600
Electronic Components Mfr
N.A.I.C.S.: 334419
Takeshi Hiyoshi (Pres & CEO)

Toshiba TEC Australia Pty. Ltd. (3)
Building C 12-24 Talavera Road, North Ryde, 2113, NSW, Australia
Tel.: (61) 299001300
Web Site: http://www.toshibatec.com.au
Electronic Cash Register System Installation Services & Distr
N.A.I.C.S.: 238210

Toshiba TEC Canada Inc (3)
191 McNabb Street, Markham, L3R 8H2, ON, Canada
Tel.: (905) 470-3500
Web Site: http://www.toshibateccanada.com
Printer Mfr
N.A.I.C.S.: 334118

Toshiba TEC Germany Imaging Systems GmbH (3)

Carl-Schurz-Strasse 7, 41460, Neuss, Germany
Tel.: (49) 213112450
Web Site: http://www.electronicimaging.toshiba-europe.com
Sales Range: $125-149.9 Million
Emp.: 20
Printer & Fax Machinery Distr
N.A.I.C.S.: 423430
Michael Becker (Pres & COO)

Subsidiary (US):

Toshiba Tec America Retail Information Systems, Inc. (3)
4401 A Bankers Cir, Atlanta, GA 30360-2709
Tel.: (770) 449-3040
Rev.: $50,000,000
Emp.: 50
Cash Register & Office Machinery Mfr
N.A.I.C.S.: 333310

Subsidiary (Non-US):

Toshiba Tec Malaysia Sdn Bhd (3)
No 4 Jalan Saudagar U1 16 Seksyen U1 Hicom Glemarie Industrial Park, 40150, Shah Alam, Selangor Darul Ehsan, Malaysia
Tel.: (60) 355687788
Web Site: http://www.toshibatec.com.my
Emp.: 750
Computer & Computer Peripheral Equipment & Software Whslr
N.A.I.C.S.: 423430

Subsidiary (Domestic):

Tele Dynamics Global Com Sdn. Bhd (4)
Level 4 Wisma Avon Lot 13A Jalan 219 Seksyen 51A, 46100, Petaling Jaya, Selangor Darul Ehsan, Malaysia
Tel.: (60) 379661888
Web Site: http://www.fdgc.com.my
Computer & Computer Peripheral Equipment & Software Whslr
N.A.I.C.S.: 423430

Subsidiary (Non-US):

Toshiba Tec Netherlands Retail Information Systems B.V. (3)
Softwareweg 3, 3821 BN, Amersfoort, Netherlands
Tel.: (31) 334538100
Sales Range: $25-49.9 Million
Emp.: 85
Cash Register & Office Machinery Mfr
N.A.I.C.S.: 333310

Subsidiary (Non-US):

Toshiba Tec Nordic AB (2)
Klovinpellontie 3, 02180, Espoo, Finland
Tel.: (358) 105685000
Web Site: http://fi.toshibatec.eu
Photocopy Machinery Mfr
N.A.I.C.S.: 333310

Subsidiary (Domestic):

Toshiba Technical Services International Corporation (2)
7-10-18 Ginza, Chuo-ku, Tokyo, 104, Japan
Tel.: (81) 335725781
Web Site: http://www.tic.toshiba.com
International Maintenance & Consulting Services for Electric Machinery & Facilities
N.A.I.C.S.: 811210

Subsidiary (Non-US):

Toshiba Technology Development (Shanghai) Co., Ltd. (2)
23rd Fl HSBC Tower, 101 Yin Cheng E Rd Pudong New, Shanghai, 200120, China (100%)
Tel.: (86) 2168410666
Web Site: http://www.toshiba.com
Sales Range: $25-49.9 Million
Emp.: 57
Mfr of Household Audio & Video Equipment
N.A.I.C.S.: 334310

Subsidiary (Domestic):

Toshiba Teli Corp. (2)

4 7 1 Asahigaoka Hino, Tokyo, 191-0065, Japan (75%)
Tel.: (81) 425898771
Web Site: http://www.toshiba-teli.co.jp
Emp.: 400
Mfr & Sales of Wireless Communications Equipment, Video Cameras for Broadcast, Medical & Industrial Use & Industrial Electronic Devices
N.A.I.C.S.: 334220

Affiliate (Non-US):

Toshiba Thailand Co., Ltd. (2)
201 Vibhavadee Rangsit Rd, Bangkok, 10900, Thailand (100%)
Tel.: (66) 25117999
Web Site: http://www.toshiba.co.th
Sales Range: $50-74.9 Million
Emp.: 210
Sales of Color TVs, Audio/Video Products & Home Electric Appliances
N.A.I.C.S.: 449210

Subsidiary (Domestic):

Toshiba Tourist Corporation (2)
Toshiba Bldg 1 1 1 Shibaura, Minato Ku, Tokyo, 105 6691, Japan
Tel.: (81) 334578051
Web Site: http://www.toshiba-tourist.co.jp
International Travel Agency & Travel Insurance
N.A.I.C.S.: 561510

Toshiba Trading Inc. (2)
Seavans N Bldg 16F 1-2-1 Shibaura, Minato-Ku, Tokyo, 105-6791, Japan
Tel.: (81) 334572760
Web Site: http://www.toshiba-tti.co.jp
Sales Range: $75-99.9 Million
Emp.: 126
Home Appliance Distr
N.A.I.C.S.: 423620

Subsidiary (Non-US):

Toshiba Transmission and Distribution Brazil Ltd. (2)
Rodovia Fernao Dias 3045-Bandeirantes, Contagem, 32240-090, Minas Gerais, Brazil
Tel.: (55) 3133296666
Sales Range: $200-249.9 Million
Emp.: 100
Electric Power Transmission Equipment Mfr
N.A.I.C.S.: 333613
Robson Tadeu Lage Alves (VP)

Toshiba Transmission and Distribution Systems Brazil Ltd. (2)
Maria Lucia Locher de Athayde Street 10511, Curitiba, 81450-010, Parana, Brazil
Tel.: (55) 4130255111
Web Site: http://www.toshiba-tstb.com.br
Sales Range: $100-124.9 Million
Emp.: 35
Electric Power Transmission Equipment Mfr
N.A.I.C.S.: 333613
Koji Kotani (Mng Dir)

Subsidiary (Domestic):

Toshiba Video Products Japan Co., Ltd. (2)
1 1 Shibaura 1 Chome, Minato-ku, Tokyo, 105 6691, Japan (100%)
Tel.: (81) 334574511
Web Site: http://www.toshiba.co.jp
Mfr of TVs. & VCRs
N.A.I.C.S.: 334310

Subsidiary (Non-US):

Toshiba Vietnam Consumer Products Co., Ltd. (2)
Floor 17 Centec Tower 72 - 74 Nguyen Thi Minh Khai, Ward 6 District 3 City, NIL, Ho Chi Minh City, Vietnam (100%)
Tel.: (84) 2838242818
Web Site: http://www.toshiba.com.vn
Sales Range: $50-74.9 Million
Emp.: 200
Mfr & Sales of Color TVs
N.A.I.C.S.: 334220

Subsidiary (Domestic):

Toshiba Visual-Equipment Corporation (2)
2 29 8 Kamishiba Cho Higashi, Fukaya,

JAPAN INDUSTRIAL PARTNERS, INC.

Japan Industrial Partners, Inc.—(Continued)
366 0051, Saitama, Japan **(100%)**
Tel.: (81) 485724621
Web Site: http://www.toshiba.co.jp
Sales Range: $100-124.9 Million
Emp.: 400
Mfr of Color TV Sets & Displays, TV Stands & Cabinets, Plastic & Pressed Parts for TVs & Other Equipment
N.A.I.C.S.: 334220

Subsidiary (Non-US):

Toshiba de Columbia C.A. **(2)**
Edificio World Trade Ctr Torre A Piso 6 Oficina 731 Calle 100, Bogota, Colombia **(100%)**
Tel.: (57) 16361849
Web Site: http://www.toshiba.com
Sales Range: $25-49.9 Million
Emp.: 5
Mfr of Household Audio & Video Equipment
N.A.I.C.S.: 334310

Toshiba de Mexico, S.A. de C.V. **(2)**
Sierra Candela 111 6 Piso Col Lomas De Chapultepec, 11000, Mexico, Districto Federal, Mexico **(100%)**
Tel.: (52) 5552496500
Web Site: http://www.toshiba.com.mx
Sales Range: $25-49.9 Million
Emp.: 200
Mfr of Portable Personal Computers & Consumer Products
N.A.I.C.S.: 334111
Carlos Canales (CEO)

Toshiba de Venezuela C.A. **(2)**
Torre Delta Piso 2 Oficinas C Y D Av Francisco De Miranda, Caracas, 68421, Venezuela **(100%)**
Tel.: (58) 26932814
Web Site: http://www.toshibalatino.com
Sales Range: $25-49.9 Million
Emp.: 5
Mfr of Household Audio & Video Equipment
N.A.I.C.S.: 334310

Toshiba do Brasil S.A. **(2)**
Estrada dos Alvarengas 5500, Sao Bernardo do Campo, 09850 550, SP, Brazil **(100%)**
Tel.: (55) 1143587199
Web Site: http://www.toshiba.com
Sales Range: $200-249.9 Million
Emp.: 1,000
Mfr of Generators, Motors, Transformers, Switch Panels, Control Panels & Inverters
N.A.I.C.S.: 335312

Toshiba of Canada, Ltd. **(2)**
75 Tiverton Court, Markham, L3R 8H2, ON, Canada **(100%)**
Tel.: (905) 470-3500
Web Site: http://www.toshiba.ca
Sales Range: $100-124.9 Million
Emp.: 350
Mfr of Personal Computers; Consumer Electronic Products & Medical Equipment
N.A.I.C.S.: 334111
Mini Saluja (Product Mgr)

Unit (Non-US):

Toshiba of Europe Ltd. - New Lighting Systems **(2)**
Gustavslundsvagen 151 5th Floor S-167, PO Box 15031, Bromma, 16715, Sweden
Tel.: (46) 87040900
Web Site: http://www.toshiba.eu
Emp.: 18
Lighting Equipment Mfr
N.A.I.C.S.: 335139
Richard Karsten (Gen Mgr)

Subsidiary (Non-US):

Tsurong Xiamen Xiangyu Trading Co., Ltd. **(2)**
14G International Bank Bldg, Xiamen, 361001, Fujian, China **(100%)**
Tel.: (86) 922261398
Web Site: http://www.toshiba-electronics.com
Sales Range: $25-49.9 Million
Emp.: 12
Electronic Component Sales
N.A.I.C.S.: 334419

Affiliate (Non-US):

Zhuhai Xujizhi Power System Automation Co. Ltd. **(2)**
Nanping Scientific & Technological Indus Garden, Pingbei 12 Rd, Zhuhai, 519060, Guangdong, China
Tel.: (86) 7568681166
Web Site: http://www.toshiba.co.jp
Sales Range: $25-49.9 Million
Emp.: 43
Mfr of Distribution Automation Systems
N.A.I.C.S.: 238210

JAPAN INNOVATIONS CO., LTD.
Toranomon Building 3-18-6 Toranomon, Minato-ku Asahi, Tokyo, 105-0001, Japan
Tel.: (81) 368092721 JP
Web Site: https://jic.co.jp
Year Founded: 1951
Water Supply & Irrigation Systems Mfr
N.A.I.C.S.: 221310
Akio Kamakawa (Mng Dir)

JAPAN INSULATION CO., LTD.
Beside Kiba 2-17-16 Kiba, Koto-ku, Tokyo, 135-0042, Japan
Tel.: (81) 358758842
Web Site: http://www.jic-bestork.co.jp
Year Founded: 1914
5368—(TKS)
Rev.: $82,869,570
Assets: $119,746,760
Liabilities: $31,635,460
Net Worth: $88,111,300
Earnings: $6,444,750
Emp.: 354
Fiscal Year-end: 03/31/24
Insulating Material Mfr & Distr
N.A.I.C.S.: 321999
Ken-Ichi Ohashi (Chm)

JAPAN INVESTMENT ADVISER CO., LTD.
Kasumigaseki Common Gate West Tower 21F 3-2-1 Kasumigaseki, Chiyoda-ku, Tokyo, 100-0013, Japan
Tel.: (81) 368046805
Web Site: https://www.jia-ltd.com
Year Founded: 2006
7172—(TKS)
Rev.: $154,689,620
Assets: $1,501,307,500
Liabilities: $1,155,237,510
Net Worth: $346,069,990
Earnings: $16,725,310
Fiscal Year-end: 12/31/23
Financial & Investment Services
N.A.I.C.S.: 525990
Naoto Shiraiwa (Pres & CEO)

Subsidiaries:

Adler Solar Works Co., Ltd. **(1)**
Fontana Shin Yokohama Bldg 9F Shinyokohama 2-17-2, Kohoku-ku, Yokohama, 2220033, Japan
Tel.: (81) 455959385
Web Site: https://adlersolarworks.co.jp
Construction Services
N.A.I.C.S.: 236220

Finspire Inc. **(1)**
Kasumigaseki Common Gate West Tower 21F 3-2-1 Kasumigaseki, Chiyoda -ku, Tokyo, 100-0013, Japan
Tel.: (81) 55216005
Web Site: https://finspire.co.jp
Container Rental & Leasing Services
N.A.I.C.S.: 532289

Iter Corporation **(1)**
3-2-1 Kasumigaseki Tokyo Kasumigaseki Common Gate West Building 21st, Chiyoda-ku, Tokyo, 100-0012, Japan
Tel.: (81) 368046805
Web Site: https://www.iter.co.jp
Software Development Services
N.A.I.C.S.: 541511

JIA Trust Co., Ltd. **(1)**
21st Floor Kasumigaseki Common Gate West Building, 3-2-1 Kasumigaseki Chiyoda-ku, Tokyo, 100-0013, Japan
Tel.: (81) 362058550
Web Site: https://www.jiatrust.co.jp
Investment Trust Services
N.A.I.C.S.: 525920

JP Lease Products & Services Co., Ltd. **(1)**
Kasumigaseki Common Gate West Tower 21F 3-2-1, Kasumigaseki Chiyoda-ku, Tokyo, 100-0013, Japan
Tel.: (81) 36 206 1394
Web Site: https://www.jlps.co.jp
Financial Services
N.A.I.C.S.: 541611

Nihon Securities Journal Inc. **(1)**
2-16-1 Nihonbashi Kayabacho, Chuo-ku, Tokyo, 103-0025, Japan
Tel.: (81) 12 081 7240
Web Site: https://www.nsjournal.jp
Newspaper Publishers
N.A.I.C.S.: 513110

JAPAN INVESTMENT CORPORATION
Tokyo Toranomon Global Square 9F Reception 8F 1-3-1 Toranomon, Minato-ku, Tokyo, 105-0001, Japan
Tel.: (81) 352187300 JP
Web Site: https://www.j-ic.co.jp
Year Founded: 2009
Investment Holding Company
N.A.I.C.S.: 551112
Keisuke Yokoo (Pres & CEO)

Subsidiaries:

INCJ, Ltd. **(1)**
1-4-1 Marunouchi, Chiyoda-ku, Tokyo, 100-0005, Japan
Tel.: (81) 352187200
Web Site: http://www.incj.co.jp
Investment Fund Services
N.A.I.C.S.: 523999
Toshiyuki Shiga (Chm & CEO)

Joint Venture (US):

Ambry Genetics Corp. **(2)**
15 Argonaut, Aliso Viejo, CA 92656 **(40%)**
Tel.: (949) 900-5500
Web Site: http://www.ambrygen.com
Genetics Testing Laboratory
N.A.I.C.S.: 541380
Aaron Elliott (CEO)

JIC Capital, Ltd. **(1)**
Tokyo Toranomon Global Square 8F, 1-3-1, Toranomon, Minato-ku, Tokyo, Japan
Tel.: (81) 55327086
Web Site: https://www.jiccapital.co.jp
Supplies Risk Capital
N.A.I.C.S.: 561621

JAPAN LAND LIMITED
8 Temasek Blvd 39-01 Suntec Tower 3, 038988, Singapore, Singapore
Tel.: (65) 65358722
Web Site:
 http://www.japanlandltd.com
Sales Range: $1-9.9 Million
Property Development Services
N.A.I.C.S.: 531312
Tet Sin Leow (Mng Dir)

Subsidiaries:

Japan Asia (Vietnam) Company Ltd. **(1)**
Saigon Trade Center 27F 37 Ton Duc Thang Street, District 01, Ho Chi Minh City, Vietnam
Tel.: (84) 839110741
Web Site: http://www.japanasialand.com
Construction Management Services
N.A.I.C.S.: 236116

Japan Asia Land Limited **(1)**
Yusen Building 5F 3-2 Marunouchi 2-chome, Chiyoda-ku, Tokyo, 100-0005, Japan
Tel.: (81) 332118787

INTERNATIONAL PUBLIC

Web Site: http://www.japanasialand.com
Real Estate Manangement Services
N.A.I.C.S.: 531210

JAPAN LIFELINE CO., LTD.
Tennoz Ocean Square 25F 2-2-20 Higashishinagawa, Shinagawa-ku, Tokyo, 140-0002, Japan
Tel.: (81) 367115200
Web Site:
 https://www.japanlifeline.com
Year Founded: 1981
7575—(TKS)
Rev.: $339,648,240
Assets: $485,894,490
Liabilities: $101,840,270
Net Worth: $384,054,220
Earnings: $49,674,150
Emp.: 1,216
Fiscal Year-end: 03/31/24
Medical Device Distr
N.A.I.C.S.: 423450
Keisuke Suzuki (Pres & CEO)

Subsidiaries:

JUNKEN MEDICAL Co., Ltd. **(1)**
14f Tennoz Central Tower 2-2-24 Higashishinagawa Shinagawa, Tokyo, Japan
Tel.: (81) 354950590
Web Site: http://www.jun-ken.co.jp
Medical Equipment Mfr & Distr
N.A.I.C.S.: 339112
Kunio Kuwahara (Pres)

Synexmed (Hong Kong) Limited **(1)**
8/F Tower 2 Admiralty Centre 18 Harcourt Road Admiralty, Hong Kong, China (Hong Kong)
Tel.: (852) 39753122
Web Site: http://www.synexmed.com
Medical Device Mfr & Distr
N.A.I.C.S.: 339112
Jizelle Wong (Accountant)

JAPAN LOGISTIC SYSTEMS CORP.
Shinbashi Sumitomo Bldg 5113 Shinbashi, Minato-ku, Tokyo, 105-0004, Japan
Tel.: (81) 334336711
Web Site: https://www.logitem.co.jp
Year Founded: 1944
9060—(TKS)
Rev.: $416,244,920
Assets: $316,407,480
Liabilities: $217,865,600
Net Worth: $98,541,880
Earnings: $3,298,390
Emp.: 3,737
Fiscal Year-end: 03/31/24
Logistics Consulting Servies
N.A.I.C.S.: 541614
Hirotake Nakanishi (Pres)

Subsidiaries:

CLK Cold Storage Company Limited **(1)**
Lot B2 Tan Dong Hiep B Industrial Park, Tan Dong Hiep Ward, Di An, Binh Duong, Vietnam
Tel.: (84) 2743795623
Web Site: https://clk.com.vn
Warehouse & Storage Services
N.A.I.C.S.: 493110

Fukuoka Logistic Systems Corp. **(1)**
369-8 Ino Umi-cho, Kasuya-gun, Fukuoka, 811-2104, Japan
Tel.: (81) 929311665
Web Site: http://www.f-logitem.co.jp
Freight Transportation Services
N.A.I.C.S.: 488510

Hanshin Logi-Support Corp. **(1)**
3-2-1 Nishinomiyahama, Nishinomiya, 662-0934, Hyogo, Japan
Tel.: (81) 798381173
Cargo Vehicle Transportation Services
N.A.I.C.S.: 488490

Hanshin Logistic Systems Corp. **(1)**
9-27 Tsutoogo-cho, Nishinomiya, 663-8243,

AND PRIVATE COMPANIES

Hyogo, Japan
Tel.: (81) 798339271
Web Site: http://www.hanshin-logitem.jp
Emp.: 355
Cargo Transportation Services
N.A.I.C.S.: 484121
Takashi Mochizuki (Pres)

L & K Trading Co., Ltd. (1)
8F APEX Building - 121 Bui Thi Xuan, Hai Ba Trung Dist, Hanoi, Vietnam
Tel.: (84) 2439364650
Merchandising Retailer
N.A.I.C.S.: 455219

Logistics Mates Corp. (1)
2-16-37 Takanawa, Minato-ku, Tokyo, 108-0074, Japan
Tel.: (81) 366878951
Web Site: https://www.logismate.co.jp
Logistics Consulting Servies
N.A.I.C.S.: 541614
Munetake Horio (Pres)

Logitem (Cambodia) Co., Ltd. (1)
Room 106 515 Monivong Boulevard Sagkat Boeung Keng Kong 2, Khan Chamkarmon, Phnom Penh, Cambodia
Tel.: (855) 23218684
Web Site: https://www.logitemvietnam.com
Passenger Transport Services
N.A.I.C.S.: 485999

Logitem (Thailand) Co., Ltd. (1)
75/22 27 Richmond Tower 11F Soi 26 Sukhumvit Road Klongton Kongtoey, Bangkok, 10110, Thailand
Tel.: (66) 2 260 8293
Cargo Transportation Services
N.A.I.C.S.: 484121

Subsidiary (Domestic):

Trancom Bangkok Co., Ltd. (2)
11th Floor Sermmit Tower Unit 1102/5 159/18 Soi Asoke Sukhumvit 21 Rd, NorthKlongtoey Wattana, Bangkok, 10110, Thailand
Tel.: (66) 26616787
Cargo Transportation Services
N.A.I.C.S.: 484121

Logitem Engineering Corp. (1)
Ariake Logistics Center 1-3-33 Ariake, Koto-ku, Tokyo, 135-0063, Japan
Tel.: (81) 335275320
Web Site: https://www.logitem-engineering.jp
Emp.: 30
Construction Services
N.A.I.C.S.: 236220

Logitem Hong Kong Co., Ltd. (1)
Unit 2006 20/F Telford House 12-16 Wang Hoi Road, Kowloon Bay, China (Hong Kong)
Tel.: (852) 25270511
Web Site: http://www.logitem-hk.com
Customs Consulting Services
N.A.I.C.S.: 541614

Logitem International Corp. (1)
Tel.: (81) 367445481
Web Site: http://www.logitem-inter.co.jp
Freight Transportation Services
N.A.I.C.S.: 488510

Logitem Keikabin Corp. (1)
1-31-5 Nakaikegami, Ota-ku, Tokyo, 146-0081, Japan
Tel.: (81) 357486206
Web Site: https://www.logitem-keikabin.jp
Cargo Transportation Services
N.A.I.C.S.: 484121

Logitem Laos GLKP Co., Ltd. (1)
2F KP-Nissei CoLtd No 380 Road No 9 Ban Meuang Neu, Kaysone Phomvihanh District, Savannakhet, Lao People's Democratic Republic
Tel.: (856) 41213102
Cargo Transportation Services
N.A.I.C.S.: 484121

Logitem Myanmar Co., Ltd. (1)
B4-F Building B 4F LL Town Tharkayta No 53/62 Myanma Gon Yi Street, Tharkayta Industrial Zone Tharkayta Township, Yangon, Myanmar
Tel.: (95) 9250408926
Cargo Transportation Services

N.A.I.C.S.: 484121

Logitem Shanghai Corp. (1)
Building No 155 Futeyi Rd Waigaoqiao Free Trade Zone, Shanghai, 200131, China
Tel.: (86) 2158682295
Cargo Transportation Services
N.A.I.C.S.: 484121

Logitem Shanghai Warehouse Corp. (1)
No 28 Taiqiao Road, Jinqiao Pudong New Area, Shanghai, 201206, China
Tel.: (86) 2158996376
Web Site: https://www.logitem.co.jp
Cargo Transportation Services
N.A.I.C.S.: 484121

Logitem Taiwan Co., Ltd. (1)
No 21 Lane 61 Sec 1 Kuang-fu Road, San-chung, New Taipei City, Taiwan
Tel.: (886) 229955299
Cargo Transportation Services
N.A.I.C.S.: 484121

Logitem Trading (Thailand) Co., Ltd. (1)
75/27 Richmond Tower 11th Floor Soi Sukhumvit 26 Ari Sukhumvit Road, Klongton Klongtoey, Bangkok, 10110, Thailand
Tel.: (66) 22583036
Trading Services
N.A.I.C.S.: 425120

Logitem Vietnam Corp. (1)
Lot No 6 Quang Minh Industrial Zone Me Linh Dist, Hanoi, Vietnam
Tel.: (84) 435250698
Cargo Transportation Services
N.A.I.C.S.: 484121

Logitem Vietnam Corp. No. 1 (1)
No 6 Le Van Thiem Thanh Xuan Trung Dist, Hanoi, Vietnam
Tel.: (84) 435582131
Real Estate Rental & Leasing Services
N.A.I.C.S.: 531190
Shunsuke Saito (Pres)

Logitem Vietnam Corp. No. 2 (1)
Lot No 8A Noi Bai Industrial Zone Soc Son Dist, Hanoi, Vietnam
Tel.: (84) 437689881
Cargo Transportation Services
N.A.I.C.S.: 484121
Nguyen Hieu Vu (Mgr-WH Section)

Logitem Vietnam Holding & Investment Company Limited (1)
14F TTC Tower 19 Duy Tan St, Dich Vong Hau Ward Cau Giay Dist, Hanoi, Vietnam
Tel.: (84) 2437950212
Web Site: http://www.logitemvietnam.com
Investment & Fund Management Services
N.A.I.C.S.: 523940

Logitem Vietnam North Service Co., Ltd. (1)
2F Thang Long Tower 98A Nguy Nhu Kon Tum St, Nhan Chinh Ward Thanh Xuan Dist, Hanoi, Vietnam
Tel.: (84) 2435582131
Passenger Transport Services
N.A.I.C.S.: 485999

Logitem Vietnam South Service Co., Ltd. (1)
30 Duong so 5, An Phu Dist 2, Ho Chi Minh City, Vietnam
Tel.: (84) 2837442281
Passenger Transport Services
N.A.I.C.S.: 485999

Logitem Vietnam Trading Co., Ltd. (1)
HDTC Bld 9F 36 Bui Thi Xuan Ben Thanh Ward Dist 1, Ho Chi Minh City, Vietnam
Tel.: (84) 839251022
Cargo Transportation Services
N.A.I.C.S.: 484121
Takashi Iijima (Pres)

JAPAN LOGISTICS FUND, INC.
3-2-1 Nishikanda, Chiyoda-Ku, Tokyo, 101-0065, Japan
Tel.: (81) 332387171
Web Site: https://www.8967.jp
8967—(TKS)
Rev.: $137,880,120

Assets: $2,439,394,230
Liabilities: $1,159,262,230
Net Worth: $1,280,132,000
Earnings: $89,425,840
Fiscal Year-end: 07/31/20
Investment Management Service
N.A.I.C.S.: 525990

JAPAN M&A SOLUTION INCORPORATED
3-3-8 Kojimachi, Chiyoda-ku, Tokyo, Japan
Tel.: (81) 362610403
Web Site: https://www.jpmas.jp
Year Founded: 2019
9236—(TKS)
Emp.: 23
Investment Management Service
N.A.I.C.S.: 523999

JAPAN MATERIAL CO., LTD.
3098-22 Nagai Komono-cho, Mie-gun, Mie, 510-1311, Japan
Tel.: (81) 593993821
Web Site: https://j-materials.jp
Year Founded: 1997
6055—(NGO)
Rev.: $321,057,062
Assets: $372,824,474
Liabilities: $56,207,450
Net Worth: $316,617,024
Earnings: $37,713,898
Emp.: 1,657
Fiscal Year-end: 03/31/24
Industrial Gas Mfr
N.A.I.C.S.: 325120
Hisao Tanaka (Pres)

Subsidiaries:

C'set Co., Ltd. (1)
8F Hamamatsu Station South Bldg 350-5 Suhayamacho, Chuo-ku, Hamamatsu, 430-0926, Shizuoka, Japan
Tel.: (81) 534509957
Web Site: https://www.3dtascal.com
Sales Range: $25-49.9 Million
Emp.: 5
Software Development Services
N.A.I.C.S.: 541511
Yoshinori Sakaguchi (CEO)

PEK Co., Ltd. (1)
4th Floor Royal Court Bldg 2-5 Kurumano-cho nishi 2-chome, Sakai-ku, Sakai, 590-0940, Osaka, Japan
Tel.: (81) 722286882
Web Site: https://www.j-materials.jp
Plumbing & Electrical Maintenance Services
N.A.I.C.S.: 811114

TAIWAN MATERIAL TECHNOLOGY Co., Ltd. (1)
No 57 Lane 128 Fu Ya-Rd, Si Tun District, Taichung, Taiwan
Tel.: (886) 4246 16227
Gas Management Services
N.A.I.C.S.: 213112

TOWA SHOKO Co., Ltd. (1)
18-1 Nishishin-machi, Omuta, 836-0031, Fukuoka, Japan
Tel.: (81) 944 53 3771
Plumbing Machinery Mfr
N.A.I.C.S.: 332913

JAPAN MEAT CO., LTD.
2-30 Wholesale Town, Tsuchiura, 300-0847, Ibaki, Japan
Tel.: (81) 29 846 3539
Web Site: http://www.japanmeat.co.jp
Year Founded: 1978
Meat, General Food, Vegetables, Fresh Fish & VegetableRetailer
N.A.I.C.S.: 445240
Masahiro Sakai (Pres)

Subsidiaries:

AMS Corporation (1)
3-15 Shibaura 6th floor, Minato-ku, Tokyo, 108-0023, Japan   (72.91%)
Tel.: (81) 3 3451 7030

JAPAN PC SERVICE CO., LTD.

Web Site: http://www.ams-jp.com
Data Entry Services, Pay Staffing, Groupware Sales & Sublease Business
N.A.I.C.S.: 518210
Toshihiko Koganei (Mng Dir)

JAPAN MEDICAL DYNAMIC MARKETING, INC.
12-2 Ichigayadaimachi, Shinjuku-ku, Tokyo, 162-0066, Japan
Tel.: (81) 333416545
Web Site: https://www.jmdm.co.jp
Year Founded: 1973
7600—(TKS)
Rev.: $153,199,970
Assets: $208,115,850
Liabilities: $38,880,020
Net Worth: $169,235,830
Earnings: $8,401,310
Emp.: 511
Fiscal Year-end: 03/31/24
Medical Equipment Mfr & Whslr
N.A.I.C.S.: 339112
Masao Okawa (Pres)

JAPAN METROPOLITAN FUND INVESTMENT CORPORATION
Tokyo Building 2-7-3 Marunouchi, Chiyoda-ku, Tokyo, 100-6420, Japan
Tel.: (81) 352937080   JP
Web Site: https://www.jmf-reit.com
8953—(TKS)
Sales Range: Less than $1 Million
Investment Management Service
N.A.I.C.S.: 525990
Masahiko Nishida (Exec Officer)

JAPAN OIL TRANSPORTATION CO., LTD.
16F Tokyo Gate City Osaki West Tower 1-11-1 Osaki, Shinagawa-ku, Tokyo, 141-0032, Japan
Tel.: (81) 354967671
Web Site: https://www.jot.co.jp
Year Founded: 1946
9074—(TKS)
Rev.: $231,250,850
Assets: $271,598,290
Liabilities: $106,308,630
Net Worth: $165,289,660
Earnings: $7,627,940
Fiscal Year-end: 03/31/24
Oil Transportation Services
N.A.I.C.S.: 484110
Toru Kurimoto (Chm)

Subsidiaries:

JK Trans Co., Ltd. (1)
1-5 Tanabe Shinden, Kawasaki-ku, Kawasaki, Japan
Tel.: (81) 443286625
Web Site: https://www.jktrans.co.jp
Emp.: 190
Petroleum Product Transportation Services
N.A.I.C.S.: 486910
Wataru Amano (Pres)

Kinki Oil Transportation Co., Ltd. (1)
1-20 Amagasuka Shinmachi, Yokkaichi, 510-8002, Mie, Japan
Tel.: (81) 593632500
Web Site: https://kinseki.co.jp
Emp.: 92
Petroleum Product Transportation Services
N.A.I.C.S.: 486910
Keiji Oki (Pres)

New J's Co., Ltd. (1)
3-2-15 Ogoso, Yokkaichi, 510-0958, Mie, Japan
Tel.: (81) 593491800
Web Site: https://newjs.co.jp
Emp.: 50
Petroleum Product Transportation Services
N.A.I.C.S.: 486910
Yasuhiko Shin (Pres)

JAPAN PC SERVICE CO., LTD.
933 Hiroshibacho Suita, Osaka, 564-0052, Japan

JAPAN PC SERVICE CO., LTD.

Japan PC Service Co., Ltd.—(Continued)
Tel.: (81) 667344985
Web Site: https://www.j-pcs.jp
Sales Range: $10-24.9 Million
Emp.: 197
Computer Repair Services
N.A.I.C.S.: 811210
Nobuyuki Ieki *(Pres & CEO)*

JAPAN PETROLEUM EXPLORATION CO. LTD.

SAPIA Tower 1-7-12 Marunouchi, Chiyoda-ku, Tokyo, 100-0005, Japan
Tel.: (81) 362687000
Web Site: https://www.japex.co.jp
1662—(TKS)
Rev.: $2,153,954,430
Assets: $4,368,734,080
Liabilities: $815,369,940
Net Worth: $3,553,364,140
Earnings: $354,699,210
Emp.: 1,641
Fiscal Year-end: 03/31/24
Oil & Gas Extraction Services
N.A.I.C.S.: 211120
Osamu Watanabe *(Chm)*

Subsidiaries:

Akita Natural Gas Pipeline Co., Ltd. (1)
85-2 Hirune, Terauchi, Akita, 011-0901, Japan
Tel.: (81) 188624966
Web Site: https://apl-gas.co.jp
Emp.: 10
Oil & Gas Services
N.A.I.C.S.: 213112

Canada Oil Sands Co., Ltd. (1)
Sapia Tower 1-7-12 Marunouchi, Chiyoda-ku, Tokyo, 100-0005, Japan
Tel.: (81) 362687150
Industrial Oil Product Mfr
N.A.I.C.S.: 324191

Fukushima Gas Power Co., Ltd. (1)
Sapia Tower 1-7-12 Marunouchi, Chiyoda-ku, Tokyo, 100-0005, Japan
Tel.: (81) 362687390
Web Site: https://www.f-gp.co.jp
Gas Power Distr
N.A.I.C.S.: 221112

GEOSYS, Inc. (1)
7F Otomo Building 1-5-18 Otsuka, Bunkyo-ku, Tokyo, 112-0012, Japan
Tel.: (81) 359405951
Emp.: 33
Surveying Equipment Distr
N.A.I.C.S.: 423490

Geophysical Surveying Co., Ltd. (1)
2nd floor Ebara Building 1-5-7 Kajicho, Chiyoda-ku, Tokyo, 101-0044, Japan
Tel.: (81) 352946711
Emp.: 72
Geophysical Surveying Services
N.A.I.C.S.: 541360
Kazuhiko Tezuka *(Pres)*

JAPEX SKS Corporation (1)
Sakura Shimbashi Building7F 2-6-1 Shimbashi, Minato-ku, Tokyo, 105-0004, Japan
Tel.: (81) 352518001
Oil & Gas Services
N.A.I.C.S.: 213112

JAPEX UK E&P Ltd. (1)
One Marischal Square Centre 5083 Broad Street, Aberdeen, AB10 1BL, United Kingdom
Tel.: (44) 1224602311
Oil & Gas Services
N.A.I.C.S.: 213112

JGI, Inc. (1)
Meikei Building 1-5-21 Otsuka, Bunkyo-ku, Tokyo, 112-0012, Japan
Tel.: (81) 359788021
Emp.: 115
Geophysical Surveying Services
N.A.I.C.S.: 541360
Susumu Abe *(Pres)*

Japex (U.S.) Corp. (1)
5051 Westheimer Ste 425, Houston, TX 77056
Tel.: (713) 334-9800
Petroleum Product Mfr & Distr
N.A.I.C.S.: 324199
Yuka Iwai *(Mgr-Admin & Acctg)*

Japex Energy Co., Ltd. (1)
16F Ueno Frontier Tower 3-24-6 Ueno, Taito-ku, Tokyo, 110-0005, Japan
Tel.: (81) 362842572
Web Site: https://www.japex-en.co.jp
Emp.: 35
Petroleum Product Distr
N.A.I.C.S.: 424720

Japex Garraf Ltd. (1)
Sapia Tower 1-7-12 Marunouchi, Chiyoda-ku, Tokyo, 100-0005, Japan
Tel.: (81) 362687210
Oil & Gas Services
N.A.I.C.S.: 213112

Japex Offshore Ltd. (1)
Sapia Tower 1-7-12 Marunouchi, Chiyoda-ku, Tokyo, 100-0005, Japan
Tel.: (81) 362687400
Web Site: https://www.jpo.co.jp
Emp.: 54
Oil & Gas Services
N.A.I.C.S.: 213112

Japex Pipeline Ltd. (1)
2-2-83 Higashizao, Nagaoka, 940-0029, Niigata, Japan
Tel.: (81) 258311456
Web Site: https://www.japex-jpl.co.jp
Emp.: 165
Oil & Gas Services
N.A.I.C.S.: 213112

Kangean Energy Indonesia Ltd. (1)
The Convergence Indonesia Lt 29 Rasuna Epicentrum Jl H R Rasuna Said, Jakarta Selatan, 12940, Indonesia
Tel.: (62) 2125504880
Oil & Gas Services
N.A.I.C.S.: 213112

North Japan Oil Co., Ltd. (1)
2-14-5 Yamai-cho, Sakata, 998-0838, Yamagata, Japan
Tel.: (81) 234240321
Web Site: https://www.kitanihonoil.co.jp
Emp.: 26
Oil & Gas Services
N.A.I.C.S.: 213112

North Japan Security Service Co., Ltd. (1)
19-1 Kasayanagi, Kita-ku, Niigata, 950-3312, Japan
Tel.: (81) 253862151
Integrated Security Services
N.A.I.C.S.: 561621

SK Engneering Co., Ltd. (1)
6th floor JMF Building Kanda 01 2-1-15 Iwamoto-cho, Chiyoda-ku, Tokyo, 101-0032, Japan
Tel.: (81) 35820195
Web Site: https://sk-eng.co.jp
Oil & Gas Services
N.A.I.C.S.: 213112

Sakhalin Oil & Gas Development Co., Ltd. (1)
Toranomon 2-chome Tower 2-3-17 Toranomon, Minato-ku, Tokyo, 105-0001, Japan
Tel.: (81) 355121501
Oil & Gas Services
N.A.I.C.S.: 213112

Shirone Gas Co., Ltd. (1)
4-2-4 Suidocho, Tsubame, 959-1262, Niigata, Japan
Tel.: (81) 256617511
Emp.: 46
Industrial Gas Product Mfr & Distr
N.A.I.C.S.: 325120

Tohoku Natural Gas Co., Inc. (1)
Jozenji-dori Square Building 4F 3-1-11 Kokubu-cho, Aoba-ku, Sendai, 980-0803, Miyagi, Japan
Tel.: (81) 222253621
Web Site: https://www.tng-gas.co.jp
Industrial Gas Product Mfr
N.A.I.C.S.: 325120

Universe Gas & Oil Company, Inc. (1)
Sapia Tower 1-7-12 Marunouchi, Chiyoda-ku, Tokyo, 100-0005, Japan
Tel.: (81) 362687191
Oil & Gas Services
N.A.I.C.S.: 213112

JAPAN POST HOLDINGS CO., LTD.

2-3-1 Otemachi, Chiyoda-ku, Tokyo, 100-8791, Japan
Tel.: (81) 334770111 JP
Web Site: https://www.japanpost.jp
Year Founded: 2006
6178—(TKS)
Rev.: $109,043,012,320
Assets: $2,941,238,766,400
Liabilities: $2,799,049,430,320
Net Worth: $142,189,336,080
Earnings: $4,856,310,800
Emp.: 2,031
Fiscal Year-end: 03/31/22
Holding Company
N.A.I.C.S.: 551112
Kunio Tanigaki *(Sr Mng Exec Officer)*

Subsidiaries:

Japan Post Bank Co., Ltd. (1)
2-3-1 Otemachi, Chiyoda-ku, Tokyo, 100-8793, Japan
Tel.: (81) 120108420
Web Site: https://www.jp-bank.japanpost.jp
Rev.: $17,527,776,660
Assets: $1,546,131,813,900
Liabilities: $1,481,962,442,870
Net Worth: $64,169,371,030
Earnings: $337,110
Emp.: 11,345
Fiscal Year-end: 03/31/2024
Investment Products & Services
N.A.I.C.S.: 523999
Masaya Touma *(Exec Officer)*

Japan Post Co., Ltd. (1)
2-3-1 Otemachi, Chiyoda-ku, Tokyo, 100-8792, Japan (100%)
Tel.: (81) 334770111
Web Site: http://www.post.japanpost.jp
Sales Range: $15-24.9 Billion
Emp.: 194,842
Postal Products & Services
N.A.I.C.S.: 491110
Tomohiro Yonezawa *(Sr Exec VP)*

Subsidiary (Domestic):

JP Media Direct Co., Ltd. (2)
5F Toranomon NN Building 1-21-17 Toranomon, Minato-ku, Tokyo, 105-0001, Japan
Tel.: (81) 351576071
Emp.: 174
Advetising Agency
N.A.I.C.S.: 541810
Taku Kageshima *(COO)*

Subsidiary (Non-US):

Toll Holdings Limited (2)
380 St Kilda Rd, Melbourne, 3004, VIC, Australia
Tel.: (61) 396942888
Web Site: https://www.tollgroup.com
Sales Range: $5-14.9 Billion
Emp.: 40,000
Holding Company; Freight Logistics & Forwarding Services
N.A.I.C.S.: 551112
Mal Grimmond *(Dir-Domestic Forwarding Div)*

Subsidiary (Non-US):

BALtrans Exhibition & Removal Ltd (3)
Unit 2606-10 26/F Tower 1 Ever Gain Plaza 88 Container Port Road, Kwai Chung, New Territories, China (Hong Kong)
Tel.: (852) 2798 6628
Web Site: http://www.baltrans-exhibition.com
Sales Range: $25-49.9 Million
Emp.: 14
Logistics Solutions & Freight Forwarding for Exhibitions
N.A.I.C.S.: 541614

INTERNATIONAL PUBLIC

Subsidiary (Non-US):

BALtrans International Cargo Ltd (4)
B 11 & B15 16/F Han Wei Plaza No 7 Guang Hua Road, Chao Yang District, Beijing, 100004, China
Tel.: (86) 10 6561 4171
Web Site: http://www.bim.com.hk
Sales Range: $25-49.9 Million
Emp.: 20
Freight Forwarding Services
N.A.I.C.S.: 488510

Subsidiary (Domestic):

BALtrans International Moving Ltd (4)
14/F Tower 1 Ever Gain Plaza 88 Container Port Road, Kwai Chung, New Territories, China (Hong Kong)
Tel.: (852) 27562882
Web Site: https://www.bim.com.hk
Packaging, Moving & Storage Services
N.A.I.C.S.: 561910
Lawrence Chan *(Sls Mgr)*

Subsidiary (Non-US):

BALtrans Logistics Ltd (4)
Emp.: 22
Logistics Consulting Servies
N.A.I.C.S.: 541614
May Kwok *(Gen Mgr)*

Subsidiary (Non-US):

DPEX Worldwide Express (S) Pte. Ltd. (3)
25 Changi South Street 1, Singapore, 486059, Singapore
Tel.: (65) 67818888
Web Site: http://www.dpex.com
Courier Service
N.A.I.C.S.: 492110

Subsidiary (Domestic):

DPEX Logistics Pte Ltd (4)
25 Changi South Street 1, SB Building, Singapore, 486059, Singapore
Tel.: (65) 67818888
Logistics Consulting Servies
N.A.I.C.S.: 541614
Taychoon Heng Donald *(CEO)*

Subsidiary (Non-US):

DPEX Worldwide (HK) Limited (4)
Unit 1 & 2 G/F Well Fung Industrial Centre 68 Ta Chuen Ping Street, Kwai Chung, New Territories, China (Hong Kong)
Tel.: (852) 8106 3232
Web Site: http://www.dpex.com
Sales Range: $25-49.9 Million
Emp.: 30
Courier Service
N.A.I.C.S.: 492110

Subsidiary (Non-US):

Dynamic Airmaster (Hong Kong) Limited (3)
Unit A-B 1/F Sunshine Kowloon Bay Cargo Centre 59 Tai Yip Street, Kowloon Bay, Kowloon, China (Hong Kong)
Tel.: (852) 2796 3191
Web Site: http://www.supremelog.com.hk
Air Freight Transportation Services
N.A.I.C.S.: 481212
Natalie Suen *(Asst Mgr-Ops)*

Dynamic Logistics (Hong Kong) Ltd (3)
12/F Tower II Enterprise Square, 9 Sheung Yuet Road, Kowloon, China (Hong Kong)
Tel.: (852) 3622 5528
Emp.: 10
Freight Forwarding Services
N.A.I.C.S.: 488510
Frederick Leung *(Gen Mgr)*

Oil Tex (Thailand) Co. Ltd (3)
95/16 Moo 6 Tambol Plutaluang, Amphur Sattahip, Chon Buri, 20180, Thailand (60%)
Tel.: (66) 3870 1992
Web Site: http://www.tollgroup.com
Logistics Consulting Services for Offshore Oil & Gas Industry
N.A.I.C.S.: 541614

AND PRIVATE COMPANIES — JAPAN POST HOLDINGS CO., LTD.

PT Toll Indonesia (3)
6/F Graha Lestari Building 48 Jl Kesehatan
Raya, Jakarta, 10160, Indonesia **(51%)**
Tel.: (62) 213451726
Web Site: http://www.tollgroup.com
Emp.: 130
Logistics Consulting Services
N.A.I.C.S.: 541614

Joint Venture (Domestic):

PrixCar Services Pty. Ltd. (3)
Gate 3 120-124 Foundation Road, Altona
North, Truganina, 3029, VIC,
Australia **(50%)**
Tel.: (61) 1300660616
Automobile Transport, Logistics & Storage
Services
N.A.I.C.S.: 541614

Subsidiary (Domestic):

PrixCar Transport Services Pty.
Ltd. (4)
810-848 Kororoit Creek Road, Altona North,
Melbourne, 3025, VIC, Australia
Tel.: (61) 1300 660 616
Web Site:
  http://www.prixcartransport.com.au
Automobile Transport Services
N.A.I.C.S.: 541614

Subsidiary (Domestic):

R & H Transport Services Pty
Ltd (3)
Lot 7 Old Punt Rd, Tomago, 2322, NSW,
Australia
Tel.: (61) 2 4964 8293
Freight Forwarding Services
N.A.I.C.S.: 488510

Subsidiary (Non-US):

SAT Albatross Sea Air Transport
FZE (3)
M-02 Makeen Building Airport Road, PO
Box 54769, Dubai, United Arab
Emirates **(100%)**
Tel.: (971) 46057900
Web Site: http://www.sat-albatros.com
Emp.: 15
Sea & Air Freight Transportation Services
N.A.I.C.S.: 483111
Oliver Bursch *(CEO & Sr VP)*

Subsidiary (Domestic):

ST Logistics (Australia) Pty Ltd (3)
Level 7 380 St Kilda Road, Melbourne,
3004, VIC, Australia
Tel.: (61) 396942888
Web Site: http://www.tollgroup.com
Emp.: 200
Logistics Consulting Servies
N.A.I.C.S.: 541614

Stream Solutions (Holdings) Pty
Ltd (3)
65 Fennell Street, Port Melbourne, 3207,
VIC, Australia
Tel.: (61) 3 9676 1240
Web Site: http://www.stream.net.au
Communications Solutions, Including Design, Print Management, Promotional Products & Logistic Services
N.A.I.C.S.: 323113
Clive Steele *(Gen Mgr)*

Subsidiary (Non-US):

Toll (New Zealand) Ltd (3)
 (100%)
Tel.: (64) 99289500
Web Site: http://www.tollgroup.com
Freight Transport & Logistics Services
N.A.I.C.S.: 541614
Grant Lemin *(Gen Mgr-Freight Forwarding)*

Subsidiary (Domestic):

Toll Networks (NZ) Limited (4)
339 Neilson Street, Onehunga, Auckland,
New Zealand **(100%)**
Tel.: (64) 9928 9500
Logistic Services
N.A.I.C.S.: 541614
Jon Adams *(Gen Mgr)*

Subsidiary (Non-US):

Toll Express (Asia) Pte Ltd (3)
5 Clementi Loop, Singapore, 129816, Singapore
Tel.: (65) 6542 7733
Sales Range: $25-49.9 Million
Emp.: 200
Freight Transport Services
N.A.I.C.S.: 541614

Toll Express Japan Co., Ltd. (3)
3-4-8 Honmachi Tokyo Tatemono Honmachi
Building 7th floor, Chuo-ku, Osaka, 541-0053, Japan
Tel.: (81) 67 167 8700
Web Site: https://www.tollexpressjapan.com
Emp.: 3,889
Logistics & Freight Forwarding Services
N.A.I.C.S.: 541614
Satoru Kawakami *(Exec Officer)*

Subsidiary (Domestic):

Toll Pty Limited (3)
Level 7 380 Saint Kilda Road, Melbourne,
3004, VIC, Australia **(100%)**
Tel.: (61) 396942888
Web Site: http://www.tollgroup.com
Freight Transportation, Distribution & Logistics Services
N.A.I.C.S.: 541614
Michael Byrne *(Mng Dir)*

Subsidiary (Non-US):

Toll (Asia) Pte. Ltd. (4)
Toll Global Forwarding 5 Clementi Loop
Level 2M, Singapore, 129816,
Singapore **(100%)**
Tel.: (65) 69042700
Web Site: http://www.toll.com.sg
Sales Range: $75-99.9 Million
Emp.: 110
Holding Company; Logistics, Supply Chain
& Freight Management Services
N.A.I.C.S.: 551112
Vincent Phang *(Dir-Global Logistics-Singapore)*

Subsidiary (Domestic):

ST Logistics Pte. Ltd. (5)
Toll City 60 Pioneer Road, Singapore,
628509, Singapore
Tel.: (65) 65597266
Sales Range: $300-349.9 Million
Emp.: 1,000
Mfr of Computer Related Equipment
N.A.I.C.S.: 334112
Vincent Phang *(CEO)*

Subsidiary (US):

Plexis Services Inc. (6)
815 W Arbor Vitae St, Inglewood, CA 90301
Freight Forwarding Services
N.A.I.C.S.: 488510
Ferry Soen *(Sr Mgr-Ops & Compliance)*

Subsidiary (Domestic):

ST Healthcare Pte. Ltd. (6)
Toll City 60 Pioneer Road, Singapore,
628509, Singapore
Tel.: (65) 64880644
Web Site: http://www.sthealthcare.com.sg
Sales Range: $10-24.9 Million
Emp.: 80
Healthcare Solutions & Logistics Services
N.A.I.C.S.: 541614
Chien Her Tang *(Head-Vertical)*

Subsidiary (Domestic):

Toll Logistics (Asia) Limited (5)
5 Clementi Loop, Singapore, 129816,
Singapore **(100%)**
Tel.: (65) 64622288
Web Site: http://www.tollgroup.com
Emp.: 100
Logistics, Supply Chain & Freight Management Services
N.A.I.C.S.: 541614
Chris Pearce *(CEO-Global Logistics)*

Subsidiary (Non-US):

Toll (India) Logistics Pvt Ltd (6)
9A Puzhal Ambattur Road, Puzhal, Chennai, 600066, Tamil Nadu, India **(100%)**

Tel.: (91) 9909910437
Web Site: http://www.tollgroup.com
Logistics Consulting Servies
N.A.I.C.S.: 541614

Subsidiary (Domestic):

Toll (SCL) Ltd (6)
5 Clementi Loop, Singapore, 129816,
Singapore **(100%)**
Tel.: (65) 64622288
Sales Range: $75-99.9 Million
Emp.: 350
Logistics Consulting Services
N.A.I.C.S.: 541614

Subsidiary (Non-US):

Toll (Taiwan) Ltd (6)
No 108 Baolin Road, Linkou District, New
Taipei City, 24451, Taiwan **(100%)**
Tel.: (886) 2 8601 3288
Web Site: http://www.tollgroup.com
Sales Range: $25-49.9 Million
Emp.: 13
Logistic Services
N.A.I.C.S.: 541614

Toll Global Logistics Lanka (Pvt)
Ltd (6)
No 46 Vauxhall Street, Colombo, Sri
Lanka **(100%)**
Tel.: (94) 11 4723 939
Web Site: http://www.tollgroup.com
Sales Range: $25-49.9 Million
Emp.: 105
Logistics Consulting Servies
N.A.I.C.S.: 541614
Prasad Jayasuriya *(Gen Mgr)*

Toll Global Logistics Vietnam
Limited (6)
Unit 801 10 Pho Quang Street, Tan Binh
District, Ho Chi Minh City, Vietnam
Tel.: (84) 2839976115
Web Site: http://www.tollgroup.com
Emp.: 25
Logistics Consulting Servies
N.A.I.C.S.: 541614

Subsidiary (Domestic):

Toll Integrated Feeder Pte Ltd (6)
21 Jalan Buroh 07-00 Logistics 21, Singapore, 619478, Singapore **(100%)**
Tel.: (65) 6210 2121
Logistic Services
N.A.I.C.S.: 541614

Subsidiary (Non-US):

Toll Integrated Logistics (M) Sdn
Bhd (6)
Tel.: (60) 333222800
Logistics Consulting Servies
N.A.I.C.S.: 541614

Toll Logistics (Thailand) Co., Ltd. (6)
49/1 Moo 1 Bangna-Trad Highway Km 21,
Bangsaothong District, Samut Prakan,
10540, Thailand **(100%)**
Tel.: (66) 2769 8900
Web Site: http://www.tollgroup.com
Logistics Consulting Services
N.A.I.C.S.: 541614
Samphan Aranyanart *(Sr VP-Automotive)*

Subsidiary (Domestic):

Toll Warehouse (Thailand)
Limited (7)
One Pacific Place 14FL/16FL 140
Sukhumvit Road, Klongtoey, Bangkok,
10110, Thailand **(100%)**
Tel.: (66) 27698900
Web Site: https://www.tollgroup.com
General Warehousing & Storage Services
N.A.I.C.S.: 493110
Graham Spillane *(Reg Mgr-Mekong Sub-Region & Indonesia)*

Subsidiary (Domestic):

Toll Offshore Petroleum Services Pte
Ltd (6)
Loyang Offshore Supply Base Loyang Crescent Blk 103 TOPS Ave 1 08-01, Singapore, 508988, Singapore **(100%)**
Tel.: (65) 65452541
Web Site: http://www.tollgroup.com

Offshore Logistics Services
N.A.I.C.S.: 541614

Subsidiary (Domestic):

Toll Aviation Pty Ltd (4)
1-7 Chloris St, Brisbane Airport, Brisbane,
4007, QLD, Australia
Tel.: (61) 738604477
Web Site: http://www.tollaviation.com
Chartered Freight Air Transportation Services
N.A.I.C.S.: 481212
Mark Delany *(Gen Mgr-Helicopters)*

Subsidiary (Non-US):

Toll Global Forwarding Limited (4)
14/F Tower 1 Ever Gain Plaza 88 Container
Port Road, Kwai Chung, New Territories,
China (Hong Kong) **(100%)**
Tel.: (852) 27577111
Web Site: https://www.tollgroup.com
Holding Company; Freight Forwarding &
Logistics Support Services
N.A.I.C.S.: 551112
Tom Thompson *(CIO)*

Subsidiary (Non-US):

PT Toll Global Forwarding
Indonesia (5)
 (100%)
Tel.: (62) 2134835311
Freight Forwarding & Logistics Consulting
Services
N.A.I.C.S.: 541614

Toll Global Forwarding (Beijing)
Ltd (5)
Room 508 2/F Guomen Building No 1 Zuojiazhuang Road, Chaoyang District, Beijing,
100028, China **(100%)**
Tel.: (86) 1084483436
Web Site: http://www.tollgroup.com
Freight Forwarding Services
N.A.I.C.S.: 488510

Toll Global Forwarding (France)
SAS (5)
Parc Mail Batiment X Pulsar 24a Ave De La
Demi Lune, 93290, Roissy-en-France, Cedex, France **(100%)**
Tel.: (33) 148630969
Web Site: http://www.tollgroup.com
Emp.: 25
Freight Forwarding Services
N.A.I.C.S.: 488510

Toll Global Forwarding (Germany)
GmbH (5)
Parsevalstrasse 11, 40468, Dusseldorf,
Germany
Tel.: (49) 211 171 4920
Web Site: http://www.tollgroup.com
Emp.: 40
Freight Forwarding Services
N.A.I.C.S.: 488510
Uwe Jacobsen *(Mng Dir)*

Subsidiary (Domestic):

Toll Global Forwarding (Hong Kong)
Limited (5)
14/F Tower 1 Ever Gain Plaza, 88 Container Port Road, Kwai Chung, New Territories, China (Hong Kong) **(100%)**
Tel.: (852) 3402 1500
Web Site: http://www.tollglobe.com
Sales Range: $200-249.9 Million
Emp.: 300
Freight Forwarding & Logistics Support Services
N.A.I.C.S.: 488510
Michael Pereira *(Head-Air Freight-Greater China)*

Subsidiary (Non-US):

Toll Global Forwarding (India) Private
Ltd (5)
The Qube A-803 M V Road Off International
Airport Approach Road, Marol Andheri East,
Mumbai, 400059, Maharashtra,
India **(100%)**
Tel.: (91) 22 42522100
Web Site: http://www.tollgroup.com
Freight Forwarding Services
N.A.I.C.S.: 488510

3901

JAPAN POST HOLDINGS CO., LTD.

Japan Post Holdings Co., Ltd.—(Continued)

Toll Global Forwarding (Ireland) Ltd (5)
Eversheds 1 Earlsfort Centre, Earlsfort Terrace, Dublin, 2, Ireland **(100%)**
Tel.: (353) 1 8444 811
Web Site: http://www.tollgroup.com
Freight Forwarding Services
N.A.I.C.S.: 488510

Toll Global Forwarding (Malaysia) Sdn Bhd (5)
B-10-1 & 2 10th Floor North Tower Tower B BBT One The Towers, Lebuh Batu Nilam 2 Bandar Bukit Tinggi, 41200, Kelang, Selangor, Malaysia
Tel.: (60) 3 3322 2901
Web Site: http://www.tollgroup.com
Sales Range: $25-49.9 Million
Emp.: 70
Freight Forwarding Services
N.A.I.C.S.: 488510

Toll Global Forwarding (Shenzhen) Ltd (5)
Room 4101-4105 Panglin Plaza 2002 Jiabin Road, Luohu District, Shenzhen, 518001, Guangdong, China **(100%)**
Tel.: (86) 755 2518 9644
Web Site: http://www.tollgroup.com
Freight Forwarding Services
N.A.I.C.S.: 488510

Toll Global Forwarding (Singapore) Pte Ltd (5)
Block 511 Kampong Bahru Road #02-04 Keppel Distripark, Singapore, 486153, Singapore **(100%)**
Tel.: (65) 6542 7733
Web Site: http://www.tollgroup.com
Emp.: 53
Freight Forwarding Services
N.A.I.C.S.: 488510
Jason Wilson *(Gen Mgr-Southeast Asia)*

Toll Global Forwarding (Taiwan) Ltd (5)
6F No 301 Sec 2 Tiding Blvd, Nei-Hu District, Taipei, 11493, Taiwan **(100%)**
Tel.: (886) 226587777
Web Site: http://www.tollgroup.com
Freight Forwarding Services
N.A.I.C.S.: 488510
Lilian Chen *(Mgr)*

Toll Global Forwarding (UAE) LLC (5)
Outside Cargo Village Next to Aramex Makeen Building, Dubai, 5599, United Arab Emirates **(100%)**
Tel.: (971) 4 28228 88
Web Site: http://www.tollgroup.com
Freight Forwarding Services
N.A.I.C.S.: 488510
Sachu Simon *(Mng Dir-Indian Sub-Continent & Middle East)*

Subsidiary (US):

Toll Global Forwarding (USA) Inc. (5)
70 Sunrise Hwy Ste 517, Valley Stream, NY 11581 **(100%)**
Tel.: (718) 723-2333
Web Site: http://www.tollgroup.com
Freight Forwarding & Logistics Support Services
N.A.I.C.S.: 488510
Myles O'Brien *(Pres & CEO)*

Subsidiary (Domestic):

FMI International, LLC (6)
800 Federal Blvd, Carteret, NJ 07008
Tel.: (718) 723-2333
Web Site: http://www.fmiint.com
Logistics Consulting Servies
N.A.I.C.S.: 541614
Neil Devine *(VP-Fin)*

Plant (Domestic):

FMI International, LLC - Carteret Facility (7)
800 Federal Blvd, Carteret, NJ 07008
Tel.: (732) 750-9000
Web Site: http://www.tollgroup.com
Logistics Consulting Servies
N.A.I.C.S.: 541614
Jim Lake *(Mgr-Warehouse)*

FMI International, LLC - Miami Facility (7)
2100 NW 129th Ave Ste 100, Doral, FL 33172
Tel.: (305) 769-1442
Web Site: http://www.tollgroup.com
Logistics Consulting Servies
N.A.I.C.S.: 541614
Joe Abbate *(Asst VP)*

Subsidiary (Non-US):

Toll Global Forwarding (Canada) Ltd (6)
7380 Bren Rd Unit 1, Mississauga, L4T 1H4, ON, Canada **(100%)**
Tel.: (905) 672-1477
Web Site: http://www.tollgroup.com
Emp.: 8
Freight Forwarding Services
N.A.I.C.S.: 488510

Subsidiary (Non-US):

Toll Global Forwarding Cooperatief U.A. (5)
Leisteen 1, 2132 ME, Hoofddorp, Netherlands
Tel.: (31) 20 6543100
Freight Transport & Logistics Consulting Services
N.A.I.C.S.: 541614

Subsidiary (Domestic):

Toll Global Forwarding (Netherlands) B.V. (6)
Leisteen 1, 2132 ME, Hoofddorp, Netherlands **(100%)**
Tel.: (31) 20 6543 100
Web Site: http://www.tollgroup.com
Sales Range: $25-49.9 Million
Emp.: 15
Freight Forwarding & Logistics Services
N.A.I.C.S.: 488510
Marinus Uleman *(Mng Dir)*

Subsidiary (Non-US):

Toll Global Forwarding AB (6)
Stigbergsliden 5, Box 12177, 414 63, Gothenburg, Sweden **(100%)**
Tel.: (46) 31 14 11 11
Web Site: http://www.tollgroup.com
Sales Range: $25-49.9 Million
Emp.: 77
Freight Transport & Logistics Consulting Services
N.A.I.C.S.: 541614
Per Andersson *(Mng Dir)*

Subsidiary (Non-US):

Toll Global Forwarding Group (UK) Limited (5)
Australis House Unit 2 Heron Way, Feltham, TW14 0AR, Middlesex, United Kingdom
Tel.: (44) 2088187800
Web Site: http://www.tollgroup.com
Freight Forwarding Services
N.A.I.C.S.: 488510
Mark Kurzeja *(Mng Dir)*

Subsidiary (Domestic):

Genesis Forwarding Group Limited (6)
Australis House Unit 2 Heron Way, Feltham, TW14 0AR, Middlesex, United Kingdom
Tel.: (44) 208 818 7800
Web Site: http://www.tollgroup.com
Emp.: 25
Freight Forwarding Services
N.A.I.C.S.: 488510
James Francis Irving *(Dir-Comml)*

Toll Global Forwarding (UK) Ltd (6)
Australis House Unit 2 Heron Way, Feltham, TW14 0AR, Middlesex, United Kingdom **(100%)**
Tel.: (44) 208 818 7800
Web Site: http://www.tollgroup.com
Freight Forwarding Services
N.A.I.C.S.: 488510
Mark Kurzeja *(Mng Dir)*

Toll Perishables (UK) Limited (6)
Australis House Unit 2, Heron Way, Feltham, TW14 0AR, Middlesex, United Kingdom
Tel.: (44) 208 818 7800
Emp.: 12
Freight Forwarding Services
N.A.I.C.S.: 488510
Shaun Reed *(Dir-Fin)*

Subsidiary (Domestic):

Toll Personnel Pty Ltd (4)
15 Berry Street, Granville, 2142, NSW, Australia **(100%)**
Tel.: (61) 2 9091 6300
Web Site: http://www.tollgroup.com
Emp.: 200
Recruitment & Staffing Services
N.A.I.C.S.: 561320
Grahame Doyle *(Exec Gen Mgr)*

Toll Properties Pty Ltd (4)
Level 7 380 St Kilda Road, Melbourne, 3004, VIC, Australia
Tel.: (61) 396942888
Emp.: 200
Investment Management Service
N.A.I.C.S.: 523999

Division (Domestic):

Toll Resources & Government Logistics (4)
Level 7 380 Saint Kilda Road, Melbourne, 3004, VIC, Australia
Tel.: (61) 396942888
Web Site: http://www.tollgroup.com
Sales Range: $25-49.9 Million
Emp.: 50
Oil & Gas, Mining & Chemical Industries Logistics Services
N.A.I.C.S.: 541614
David Jackson *(CEO)*

Subsidiary (Domestic):

Toll Energy & Marine Logistics Pty Ltd (5)
Level 4 30 The Esplanade, Perth, 6000, WA, Australia
Tel.: (61) 893460400
Web Site: http://www.tollgroup.com
Emp.: 80
Logistics & Project Management Services for Oil & Gas Industry
N.A.I.C.S.: 541614
Scott Woodward *(Gen Mgr)*

Toll Remote Logistics Pty Ltd (5)
Level 9 145 Eagle Street, Brisbane, 4001, QLD, Australia
Tel.: (61) 7 3339 6500
Web Site: http://www.tollgroup.com
Emp.: 50
Logistics Consulting Servies
N.A.I.C.S.: 541614

Subsidiary (Domestic):

Toll Transport Pty. Limited (4)
Level 8 380 Saint Kilda Road, Melbourne, 3004, VIC, Australia
Tel.: (61) 396942888
Web Site: http://www.tollgroup.com
Freight Trucking & Rail Transport Services
N.A.I.C.S.: 484122
Tim Kehoe *(Exec Gen Mgr-Toll Liquids)*

Unit (Domestic):

Toll Fast (5)
65 Fennell Street, Port Melbourne, 3207, VIC, Australia **(100%)**
Tel.: (61) 396761200
Web Site: http://www.tollfast.com.au
Sales Range: $75-99.9 Million
Emp.: 500
Supply Chain Delivery Solutions; Courier Delivery Services
N.A.I.C.S.: 492110
Mark Gillett *(Gen Mgr & Mgr-Sls & Mktg-Natl)*

Subsidiary (Domestic):

Toll IPEC Pty Ltd (5)
11-25 Toll Drive, Altona North, Altona, 3025, VIC, Australia
Tel.: (61) 3 8368 1200

INTERNATIONAL PUBLIC

PT Toll
Web Site: http://www.tollgroup.com
Express Road Freight Services & Logistics
N.A.I.C.S.: 492110
David Cook *(Gen Mgr-Sls & Mktg)*

Subsidiary (Domestic):

Victorian Express Pty Ltd (6)
Building 3 77-125 Princes Highway, Dandenong, 3175, VIC, Australia
Tel.: (61) 387913800
Parcel Delivery Services
N.A.I.C.S.: 492110
Bill Smith *(Mgr-B2C Ops)*

Unit (Domestic):

Toll Intermodal (5)
Level 10 390 Saint Kilda Road, Melbourne, 3004, VIC, Australia
Tel.: (61) 396942888
Web Site: http://www.tollgroup.com
Road, Rail & Shipping Freight Transportation Services
N.A.I.C.S.: 488510
Mark Benbow *(Mgr-Sls-Queensland)*

Toll NQX (5)
59 Forest Way, Karawatha, Brisbane, 4117, QLD, Australia
Tel.: (61) 7 3089 7444
Web Site: http://www.tollgroup.com
Sales Range: $600-649.9 Million
Emp.: 100
General Freight Trucking & Logistics Services
N.A.I.C.S.: 488510
Michael Rose *(Mgr-QA)*

Subsidiary (Domestic):

Toll North Pty. Ltd. (5)
59 Forest Way, Karawatha, Brisbane, QLD, Australia **(100%)**
Tel.: (61) 732750400
Web Site: http://www.toll.com.au
General & Specialized Trucking, Rail & Coastal Freight Transportation Services
N.A.I.C.S.: 488510

Unit (Domestic):

Toll Shipping (5)
108 Webb Dock Drive, PO Box 420, Port Melbourne, 3207, VIC, Australia
Tel.: (61) 392998400
Web Site: http://www.tollgroup.com
Sales Range: $50-74.9 Million
Emp.: 200
Coastal Freight Transportation & Logistics Services
N.A.I.C.S.: 488510

Japan Post Information Technology Co., Ltd. (1)
6-27-30 Shinjuku 7th floor of Shinjuku East Side Square, Shinjuku-ku, Tokyo, 160-0022, Japan
Tel.: (81) 345118000
Emp.: 251
Information Technology Consulting Services
N.A.I.C.S.: 541512
Toshinobu Yukawa *(CEO)*

Japan Post Insurance Co., Ltd. (1)
OTEMACHI PLACE WEST TOWER 3-1 Otemachi 2chome, Chiyoda-ku, Tokyo, 100-8794, Japan
Tel.: (81) 334770111
Web Site: https://www.jp-life.japanpost.jp
Rev.: $44,578,725,740
Assets: $402,257,492,390
Liabilities: $379,811,624,550
Net Worth: $22,445,867,840
Earnings: $310,670
Emp.: 18,427
Fiscal Year-end: 03/31/2024
Insurance Services
N.A.I.C.S.: 524298
Masaaki Horigane *(Deputy Pres & Exec Officer)*

JAPAN POWER GENERATION LIMITED
Near Jia Bagga Railway Station Chowk Araian Off Raiwind Road, Lahore, Pakistan
Tel.: (92) 425835864
Web Site: http://www.jpglpk.com

JPGL—(LAH)
Emp.: 38
Electric Power Generating & Supplying Services
N.A.I.C.S.: 221111
Amjad Awan (CEO)

JAPAN PRIME REALTY INVESTMENT CORPORATION
4-16 Yaesu 1-chome, Chuo-ku, Tokyo, 103-0028, Japan
Tel.: (81) 332311051
Web Site: https://www.jpr-reit.co.jp
Year Founded: 2001
8955—(TKS)
Sales Range: $125-149.9 Million
Real Estate Investment Services
N.A.I.C.S.: 523999
Sosuke Yasuda (Supervising Officer)

JAPAN PROCESS DEVELOPMENT CO., LTD.
Gate City Osaki West Tower 22F
1-11-1 Osaki, Shinagawa-ku, Tokyo, 141-0032, Japan
Tel.: (81) 345312111
Web Site: https://www.jpd.co.jp
Year Founded: 1967
96510—(TKS)
Rev.: $58,956,062
Assets: $81,341,262
Liabilities: $14,760,489
Net Worth: $66,580,773
Earnings: $4,506,112
Emp.: 609
Fiscal Year-end: 05/31/23
Software Development Services
N.A.I.C.S.: 513210
Yoshiaki Kamiishi (Pres)

Subsidiaries:

IPD Dalian Engineering Limited (1)
Room 201H Building 17 Software Park No 267 Wuyi Road High-tech Park, Dalian, 116023, Liaoning, China
Tel.: (86) 41139707366
Web Site: https://www.ipdchina.net
Emp.: 110
Software Development Services
N.A.I.C.S.: 541511
Yoshiaki Kamiishi (Pres)

JAPAN PROPERTY MANAGEMENT CENTER CO., LTD.
Shin-Nisseki Building 3-4-2
Marunouchi, Chiyoda-ku, Tokyo, 100-0005, Japan
Tel.: (81) 362685225
Web Site: https://www.jpmc.jp
Year Founded: 2002
3276—(TKS)
Rev.: $406,632,770
Assets: $128,697,680
Liabilities: $67,418,810
Net Worth: $61,278,870
Earnings: $12,882,530
Emp.: 90
Fiscal Year-end: 12/31/23
Real Estate Management
N.A.I.C.S.: 531311

JAPAN PULP AND PAPER COMPANY LIMITED
Forefront Tower 3-12-1 Kachidoki, Chuo-ku, Tokyo, 104-8656, Japan
Tel.: (81) 335348522
Web Site: https://www.kamipa.co.jp
Year Founded: 1845
8032—(TKS)
Rev.: $3,531,260,300
Assets: $2,463,183,450
Liabilities: $1,548,709,780
Net Worth: $914,473,670
Earnings: $68,459,770
Emp.: 4,157
Fiscal Year-end: 03/31/24
Import, Export, Sale & Distribution of Paper, Paperboard, Pulp, Paper-Related Products, Plastics & Waste Paper-Related Machinery; Real Estate Leasing
N.A.I.C.S.: 322120
Mitsutoshi Imamura (Exec VP-Global Bus & Specialties)

Subsidiaries:

Aarque Group Limited (1)
2a Waipareira Ave, Henderson, Auckland, 0610, New Zealand
Tel.: (64) 508227783
Web Site: http://graphics.aarque.co.nz
Digital Printer Distr
N.A.I.C.S.: 423430

Akazawa Paper Co., Ltd. (1)
2-22-50 Mitake, Morioka, 020-0122, Iwate, Japan
Tel.: (81) 196411081
Web Site: http://www.akazawa-group.com
Emp.: 21
Household Paper Product Distr
N.A.I.C.S.: 424130

Arise Innovation, Inc. (1)
FOREFRONT TOWERII 3-13-1 kachidoki, Chuo-ku, Tokyo, 104-0054, Japan
Tel.: (81) 355349967
Web Site: https://en.ariseinnovation.co.jp
IT Services
N.A.I.C.S.: 541511
Makoto Shimizu (CEO)

Ball & Doggett Group Pty. Ltd. (1)
Rear Factory 41-45 Mills Road, Braeside, 3195, VIC, Australia
Tel.: (61) 387943469
Paper Product Distr
N.A.I.C.S.: 424130

Ball & Doggett Pty. Ltd. (1)
221-251 Discovery Road, Dandenong South, 3175, VIC, Australia
Tel.: (61) 387943550
Web Site: https://www.ballanddoggett.com.au
Paper Product Distr
N.A.I.C.S.: 424130

Corelex Doh-Ei Co., Ltd. (1)
283 Hirafu Kutchan-cho, Abuta-gun, Hokkaido, 044-0077, Japan
Tel.: (81) 136232323
Bathroom Tissue Mfr
N.A.I.C.S.: 322120

Corelex San-Ei Co., Ltd. (1)
775-1 Agoyama, Fujinomiya, 418-0037, Shizuoka, Japan
Tel.: (81) 544230303
Paper Product Mfr & Distr
N.A.I.C.S.: 333243

Corelex Shin-Ei Co., Ltd. (1)
575-1 Nakanogo, Fuji, 421-3306, Shizuoka, Japan
Tel.: (81) 545562513
Household Paper Products Mfr
N.A.I.C.S.: 424130

Cosmo Paper Trading Co., Ltd (1)
2nd floor Forefront Tower 3-12-1 Kachidoki, Chuo-ku, Tokyo, 104-0054, Japan
Tel.: (81) 335208571
Web Site: https://www.cosmo-p.jp
Emp.: 26
Paper Product Distr
N.A.I.C.S.: 424130

Eco Paper JP Co., Ltd. (1)
82-1 Higashi Haruokacho, Owariasahi, 488-0031, Aichi, Japan
Tel.: (81) 561 53 3315
Printing Paper Mfr & Distr
N.A.I.C.S.: 322299

Eco-Port Kyushu Co., Ltd. (1)
1-4-10 Shinminato, Nishi-ku, Kumamoto, 861-5274, Japan
Tel.: (81) 962883588
Web Site: https://www.eco-port.jp
Paper Product Mfr & Distr
N.A.I.C.S.: 322120

Fine Paper Takeo (M) Sdn. Bhd. (1)
51 Jalan 10/91 Taman Shamelim Perkasa, 56100, Kuala Lumpur, Malaysia (100%)
Tel.: (60) 392861890
Web Site: http://www.takeo.com.my
Sales Range: $25-49.9 Million
Emp.: 10
Paper & Newsprint Production
N.A.I.C.S.: 322120
K. C. Chong (CEO)

Fukudasansho Co., Ltd. (1)
2-14-1 Chizadori, Minami-ku, Nagoya, 457-0071, Japan
Tel.: (81) 528252111
Web Site: http://www.fukudasansho.co.jp
Paper Product Mfr & Distr
N.A.I.C.S.: 322120

GOKURA Co., Ltd. (1)
887 Muramatsucho, Shikokuchuo, 799-0401, Ehime, Japan
Tel.: (81) 896242520
Paper & Packaging Materials Distr
N.A.I.C.S.: 424110

Gould International UK Limited (1)
Brunswick House Regent Park 299 Kingston Road, Leatherhead, KT22 7LU, Surrey, United Kingdom
Tel.: (44) 1372376133
Paper Product Distr
N.A.I.C.S.: 424130

Gould Papiers France Sarlu (1)
159 rue de Rome, 75017, Paris, France
Tel.: (33) 143188400
Web Site: https://www.gould-papiersfrance.com
Printing Paper Supply Services
N.A.I.C.S.: 424130
Didier Amsellem (Comml Dir)

Gould Publication Papers UK Limited (1)
Brunswick House Regent Park 299 Kingston Road, Leatherhead, KT22 7LU, Surrey, United Kingdom
Tel.: (44) 1372626071
Web Site: http://www.gouldpublicationpapers.co.uk
Paper Product Distr
N.A.I.C.S.: 424130
Dominic Blakey (Mng Dir)

Hakozaki Kami Ryutsu Center Co., Ltd. (1)
5-6-3 Hakozakifuto, Higashi-ku, Fukuoka, 812-0051, Japan
Tel.: (81) 926312124
Warehouse & Storage Services
N.A.I.C.S.: 493110

Harlech PPM Limited (1)
Brunswick House Regent Park 299 Kingston Road, Leatherhead, KT22 7LU, Surrey, United Kingdom
Tel.: (44) 1372626071
Web Site: http://www.harlechppm.co.uk
Paper Product Distr
N.A.I.C.S.: 424130

Hokkai Shigyo Co., Ltd. (1)
2-5-13 Ryutsu Danchi, Asahikawa, 079-8442, Hokkaido, Japan
Tel.: (81) 166485011
Web Site: https://www.hokkai-shigyoh.com
Emp.: 30
Recycled Paper Whslr
N.A.I.C.S.: 423930

Honshu Electrical Materials Sales Co., Ltd. (1)
JP Building 1-6-10 Kawaramachi, Chuo-ku, Osaka, 541-0048, Japan
Tel.: (81) 662030145
Web Site: https://www.honden.co.jp
Electrical Material Distr
N.A.I.C.S.: 423610

Itabashi Kyoudo Sagyo Co., Ltd. (1)
No 8 6-1-7 Takashimadaira, Itabashi-ku, Tokyo, 175-0082, Japan
Tel.: (81) 339751624
Logistic Services
N.A.I.C.S.: 488510

Itabashi Paper Distribution Center Co., Ltd. (1)
6-4 Takashimadaira, Itabashi-ku, Tokyo, 175-0082, Japan
Tel.: (81) 339752128
Warehouse & Storage Services
N.A.I.C.S.: 493110

JH Recycle Co., Ltd. (1)
8-1 Henjohara, kamihobara Hobaramachi, Date, 960-0684, Fukushima, Japan
Tel.: (81) 245744822
Paper Product Mfr & Distr
N.A.I.C.S.: 322120

JK Recycle Co., Ltd. (1)
1-27-9 Higashi nippori, Arakawa-ku, Tokyo, Japan
Tel.: (81) 485401561
Web Site: https://www.jkr.jp
Paper Recycling Services
N.A.I.C.S.: 562111

JP Asian Electronics Materials (M) Sdn. Bhd. (1)
Level 33 Ilham Tower No 8 Jalan Binjai, 50450, Kuala Lumpur, Malaysia
Tel.: (60) 321696318
Web Site: https://www.kamipa.co.jp
Electronic Product Distr
N.A.I.C.S.: 423690

JP CORELEX (Vietnam) Co., Ltd. (1)
Road B1 Section B Pho Noi A Industrial Park, Lac Hong Commune Van Lam District, Hung Yen, Vietnam
Tel.: (84) 2213587065
Paper Product Mfr & Distr
N.A.I.C.S.: 322120

JP Corelex Holdings Co., Ltd. (1)
575-1 Nakanogo, Fuji, 421-3306, Shizuoka, Japan
Tel.: (81) 545562525
Business Management Services
N.A.I.C.S.: 541611

JP Hokkai Co., Ltd. (1)
4th floor Maruit Sapporo Building Kita 2-jo Nishi 1-1, Chuo-ku, Sapporo, Hokkaido, Japan
Tel.: (81) 118877785
Web Site: https://www.jphokkai.co.jp
Emp.: 7
Paper Product Mfr & Distr
N.A.I.C.S.: 322120

JP Household Supply Co., Ltd (1)
12th Fl Forefront Tower 3-12-1 Kachidoki, Chuo-Ku, Tokyo, 104-0054, Japan
Tel.: (81) 362049591
Web Site: https://www.jphs.co.jp
Emp.: 16
Household Paper Product Distr
N.A.I.C.S.: 424130

JP Loginet Co., Ltd. (1)
4th floor Forefront Tower 3-12-1 Kachidoki, Chuo-ku, Tokyo, Japan
Tel.: (81) 355484055
Web Site: https://www.jploginet.co.jp
Emp.: 33
Warehouse & Storage Services
N.A.I.C.S.: 493110

JP Resources Co., Ltd. (1) (100%)
Tel.: (81) 3332701311
Sales Range: $25-49.9 Million
Emp.: 85
N.A.I.C.S.: 423930

JP Transport Service Co., Ltd. (1)
5-6 Nishimizue, Edogawa-ku, Tokyo, 134-0015, Japan
Tel.: (81) 358781260
Truck Transportation Services
N.A.I.C.S.: 484110

JPP Far East (S) Pte. Ltd. (1)
No 9 3rd Chin Bee Rd, Jurong, 618685, Singapore (100%)
Tel.: (65) 62615277
Web Site: http://www.jpp.com.sg
Sales Range: $25-49.9 Million
Emp.: 30
Newsprint Production
N.A.I.C.S.: 322120

JPTS Electronics Materials (Shanghai) Co., Ltd. (1)
Room 1118 Shanghai International Trade Centre No 2201 Yan An W Road, Shanghai, 200336, China
Tel.: (86) 2158682021

JAPAN PULP AND PAPER COMPANY LIMITED

Japan Pulp and Paper Company Limited—(Continued)
Web Site: https://www.kamipa.co.jp
Electronic Equipment Distr
N.A.I.C.S.: 423690

JRS Resources, Inc. (1)
408 East Alondra Ave, Compton, CA 90221
Tel.: (310) 886-0948
Paper Product Mfr & Distr
N.A.I.C.S.: 322120

Japan Pulp & Paper (Australia) Pty. Ltd. (1)
Level 12 141 Walker Street, North Sydney, 2060, NSW, Australia
Tel.: (61) 280996088
Web Site: http://www.kamipa.co.jp
Sales Range: $50-74.9 Million
Emp.: 3
Printing & Writing Paper Whslr
N.A.I.C.S.: 424110

Japan Pulp & Paper (Korea) Co., Ltd. (1)
9th floor Flour Mill Hall 8 Sowol-ro, Jung-gu, Seoul, Korea (South)
Tel.: (82) 27736122
Web Site: https://www.ovolkorea.com
Household Paper Product Distr
N.A.I.C.S.: 424130

Japan Pulp & Paper (M) Sdn. Bhd. (1)
Business Suite 19A-22-1 Level 22 UOA Centre 19 Jalan Pinang, 50450, Kuala Lumpur, Malaysia (100%)
Tel.: (60) 321813383
Web Site: http://www.pamika.co.jp
Sales Range: $25-49.9 Million
Emp.: 7
Newsprint Production
N.A.I.C.S.: 322120

Japan Pulp & Paper (Shanghai) Co., Ltd. (1)
Room 1116 Shanghai International Trade Centre No 2201 Yan An W Road, Shanghai, 200336, China
Tel.: (86) 2162702325
Web Site: http://www.jppchina.com
Sales Range: $25-49.9 Million
Emp.: 30
Domestic Sale & Import & Export of Paper, Paperboard, Converted Products, Pulp & Related Merchandise
N.A.I.C.S.: 424120

Japan Pulp & Paper (Taiwan) Co., Ltd. (1)
10F No 111 Songjiang Rd, Zhongshan Dist, Taipei, Taiwan
Tel.: (886) 225170070
Paper Product Mfr & Distr
N.A.I.C.S.: 322120

Japan Pulp & Paper (Thailand) Co., Ltd. (1)
98 Sathorn Square Office Tower 17th Floor Unit 1704 North Sathorn Road, Silom BangRak, Bangkok, 10500, Thailand
Tel.: (66) 26310112
Web Site: http://www.kamipa.co.jp
Sales Range: $25-49.9 Million
Emp.: 5
Pulp & Paper Mfr
N.A.I.C.S.: 322120
Maki Kobayashi *(Mng Dir)*

Japan Pulp & Paper (U.S.A.) Corp. (1)
1111 Corporate Center Dr Ste 202, Monterey Park, CA 91754
Tel.: (323) 889-7750
Web Site: https://www.jppusa.com
Sales Range: $25-49.9 Million
Emp.: 15
Newsprint Production
N.A.I.C.S.: 322120

Japan Pulp & Paper Co., (H.K.) Ltd. (1)
11th Fl Park Ave Tower, 2-3 Moreton Terrace, Causeway Bay, China (Hong Kong) (100%)
Tel.: (852) 25762636
Web Site: https://www.kamipa.co.jp
Sales Range: $25-49.9 Million
Emp.: 100
Paper & Newsprint Production
N.A.I.C.S.: 322120

Japan Pulp & Paper Co., Ltd. (1)
Floor 11 Ladeco Building No 266 Doi Can Street, Ba Dinh District, Hanoi, Vietnam
Tel.: (84) 2437954253
Paper Product Mfr & Distr
N.A.I.C.S.: 322120

Japan Pulp & Paper GmbH (1)
Immermannstrasse 14-16, 40210, Dusseldorf, Germany (100%)
Tel.: (49) 21116040
Web Site: https://www.jpd.de
Emp.: 18
Paper & Newsprint Production
N.A.I.C.S.: 322120

JasmineSoft Co., Ltd. (1)
1-25-15 Ujidomari, Ginowan, 901-2227, Okinawa, Japan
Tel.: (81) 988906036
Web Site: https://www.jasminesoft.co.jp
Software Services
N.A.I.C.S.: 541511

KCT Trading Private Limited (1)
25 Braboume Road, Kolkata, 700001, West Bengal, India
Tel.: (91) 3340051701
Web Site: https://www.kctpaper.com
Emp.: 90
Paper Product Distr
N.A.I.C.S.: 424130
Priya Saran Chaudhri *(Vice Chm & Mng Dir)*

Kawabe Biomass Power Generation Co., Ltd. (1)
252-1 Kamikawabe, Kawabecho Kamo, Gifu, 509-0302, Japan
Tel.: (81) 574532576
Biomass Power Generation Services
N.A.I.C.S.: 221117

Kosoku Paper Ltd. (1)
10/F G Golden Bear Ind Ctr, 2 Cheung Fai Road, Tsuen Wan, NT, China (Hong Kong)
Tel.: (852) 25411627
Web Site: https://www.kosoku.com.hk
Sales Range: $25-49.9 Million
Emp.: 17
Printing & Writing Paper Whslr
N.A.I.C.S.: 424110

Koyosha Co., Ltd. (1)
2-3-14 Saiwaicho Daito Bldg 203, NaniwaKu, Osaka, 556-0021, Japan
Tel.: (81) 665670467
Printing Paper & Paperboard Distr
N.A.I.C.S.: 424110

Kurashi Net JP Co., Ltd. (1)
12th Floor Forefront Tower 3-12-1 Kachidoki, Chuo-ku, Tokyo, 104-0054, Japan
Tel.: (81) 362049750
Household Paper Product Distr
N.A.I.C.S.: 424130

Kyoto Kami Shoji Co., Ltd. (1)
Tel.: (81) 753251810
Web Site: http://www.kyokami.ec-net.jp
Household Paper Product Mfr & Distr
N.A.I.C.S.: 322120

Maruni Chikiriya Co., Ltd. (1)
134-1 Tonyamachi, Ueda, 386-0041, Nagano, Japan
Tel.: (81) 268248111
Household Paper Product Distr
N.A.I.C.S.: 424130

Matsue Biomass Power Co., Ltd. (1)
899-7 Oicho, Matsue, 690-0832, Shimane, Japan
Tel.: (81) 852390391
Web Site: http://www.nakabayashi.co.jp
Renewable Energy Generation Services
N.A.I.C.S.: 221114

Mikunishiko Co., Ltd. (1)
3-7-35 Wakamatsucho Higashi, Tondabayashi, 584-0023, Osaka, Japan
Tel.: (81) 721 26 1045
Web Site: http://www.mikunishiko.co.jp
Emp.: 60
Laminating & Coating Paper Products Mfr
N.A.I.C.S.: 322299
Seijiro Tominaga *(Pres)*

Nabiace Co., Ltd. (1)
2-12 Nagatsukacho, Kasugai, 486-0934, Aichi, Japan
Tel.: (81) 568316161
Web Site: https://www.nabiace.jp
Emp.: 228
Corrugated Board Mfr & Distr
N.A.I.C.S.: 322211

Nanko Paper Center Co., Ltd. (1)
6-4-36 Nankonaka, Suminoe-Ku, Osaka, 559-0033, Japan
Tel.: (81) 666142552
Emp.: 4
Paper Products Mfr
N.A.I.C.S.: 322299

Noda Bio Power JP Co., Ltd. (1)
Noda-mura 22 Chiwari 52-3, Kunohe-gun, Noda, 028-8201, Iwate, Japan
Tel.: (81) 194754666
Web Site: http://www.noda-bio.jp
Renewable Energy Generation Services
N.A.I.C.S.: 221114

OVOL ICT Solutions Co., Ltd. (1)
15th floor Forefront Tower 3-12-1 Kachidoki, Chuo-ku, Tokyo, 104-0054, Japan
Tel.: (81) 335343670
Web Site: https://www.icts.ovol.jp
Emp.: 180
Computer Distr
N.A.I.C.S.: 423430

OVOL Malaysia Sdn. Bhd. (1)
Subang 1 Block B Lot 36545 Jalan TS 6/1 Taman Perindustrian Subang, Subang Jaya, 47510, Petaling Jaya, Selangor, Malaysia
Tel.: (60) 356225522
Web Site: https://www.ovol.com.my
Paper Product Distr
N.A.I.C.S.: 424130

OVOL Singapore Pte. Ltd. (1)
76 Pioneer Road 05-05 Mapletree Logistics Hub, Singapore, 639577, Singapore
Tel.: (65) 67380888
Web Site: https://www.ovol.com.sg
Paper Product Distr
N.A.I.C.S.: 424130

Osaka Kami Kyodo Soko Co., Ltd. (1)
23-53 Takaramachi, Higashiosaka, 579-8025, Osaka, Japan
Tel.: (81) 729821161
Warehouse & Storage Services
N.A.I.C.S.: 493110

PT. Oriental Asahi JP Carton Box (1)
Jl Irian II-I Blok AB2 Kawasan Industri MM2100, Desa Danau Indah Cikarang Barat, Bekasi, 17520, Jawa Barat, Indonesia
Tel.: (62) 218980503
Web Site: http://www.kamipa.co.jp
Sales Range: $125-149.9 Million
Emp.: 300
Corrugated & Solid Fiber Boxes Mfr
N.A.I.C.S.: 322211

Price & Pierce Oy (1)
Hietalahdenranta 13, 00180, Helsinki, Finland
Tel.: (358) 968187399
Web Site: http://www.price-pierce.fi
Paper Product Distr
N.A.I.C.S.: 424130

Repasys Co., Ltd. (1)
3-2-1 Hakata Ekimae, Hakata-ku, Fukuoka, 812-0011, Japan
Tel.: (81) 924183161
Web Site: https://www.repasys.jp
Emp.: 27
Paper Recycling Services
N.A.I.C.S.: 562111

Safeshred Co., Inc. (1)
5928 S Malt Ave, Commerce, CA 90040-3504
Tel.: (323) 721-4300
Web Site: http://www.safeshred.com
Sales Range: $25-49.9 Million
Emp.: 50
Paper & Newsprint Production
N.A.I.C.S.: 322120

Sanpei Kogyo Co., Ltd. (1)
1 kokan-cho, Fukuyama, 721-0931, Hiroshima, Japan
Tel.: (81) 849412440
Web Site: http://www.sanpeikogyo.co.jp
Emp.: 242
Paper Products Mfr
N.A.I.C.S.: 333243
Tomozo Omoto *(Chm & CEO)*

Sapporo Kami Ryutsu Center Co., Ltd. (1)
14-516-4 hassamukyujyo, Nishi-ku, Sapporo, 063-0829, Hokkaido, Japan
Tel.: (81) 116623177
Warehouse & Storage Services
N.A.I.C.S.: 493110

Seihoku Paper Depot Co., Ltd. (1)
6-5-4 Takashimadaira, Itabashi-ku, Tokyo, 175-0082, Japan
Tel.: (81) 339751200
Web Site: http://seihoku-depot.co.jp
Emp.: 20
Warehouse & Storage Services
N.A.I.C.S.: 493110

Shanghai JP Co., Ltd. (1)
No 173 Hongcao Rd, Shanghai, 200233, China
Tel.: (86) 2164089900
Web Site: http://www.shangui.com
Sales Range: Less than $1 Million
Emp.: 5
Paper Products Mfr; Joint Venture of Japan Pulp & Paper Limited & Nippon Paper Industries Co., Ltd.
N.A.I.C.S.: 322120

Showa Packaging Industry Co., Ltd. (1)
1631-1 Takenami, Takenami-cho, Ena, 509-7122, Gifu, Japan
Tel.: (81) 573282321
Web Site: http://www.showa-hoso.co.jp
Cardboard Sheet Mfr
N.A.I.C.S.: 322211

Spicers Paper (Malaysia) Sdn Bhd (1)
Paper Products Distributor, Subang Jaya, 47500, Selangor, Malaysia
Tel.: (60) 356225522
Paper Product Distr
N.A.I.C.S.: 424130
Roger Lim *(Gen Mgr)*

Spicers Paper (Singapore) Pte Ltd (1)
3 Gul Crescent, Singapore, 629519, Singapore
Tel.: (65) 67380888
Printing Paper & Paperboard Distr
N.A.I.C.S.: 424110
Tony Lim *(Dir-Mktg)*

Sun Energy Hirono Co., Ltd. (1)
39-39-35 Taneichi, Hironocho, Kunohe, 028-7911, Iwate, Japan
Tel.: (81) 194691226
Renewable Energy Generation Services
N.A.I.C.S.: 221114

Tai Tak Paper (Shenzhen) Co., Ltd. (1)
Room 2111-13 Changping Business Building Honghua Road, Futian Free Trade Zone, Shenzhen, 518038, China
Tel.: (86) 75582788644
Web Site: http://www.taitak.hk
Pulp & Paper Products Mfr
N.A.I.C.S.: 322299

Tai Tak Paper Co., Ltd. (1) (100%)
Tel.: (852) 25727546
Web Site: http://www.taitak.hk
Sales Range: $25-49.9 Million
Emp.: 22
Newsprint Production
N.A.I.C.S.: 322120

Tai Tak Takeo Fine Paper Co., Ltd. (1)
Flat 401 & 409 4/F Block B Sea View Estate Watson Rd, North Point, China (Hong Kong) (100%)
Tel.: (852) 28073002
Web Site: http://www.ttf.com.hk
Sales Range: $25-49.9 Million
Emp.: 19
Paper & Newsprint Production

AND PRIVATE COMPANIES

N.A.I.C.S.: 322120

Taiho Paper Co., Ltd. (1)
252-1 Kamikawabe Kawabe-cho, Kamo-gun, Gifu, 509-0302, Japan
Tel.: (81) 574532626
Web Site: http://www.taihopaper.jp
Emp.: 90
Corrugated Board Mfr
N.A.I.C.S.: 322211

Taiwan Electro-Materials Co., Ltd. (1)
No 25 Shindu Rd Chien Chen District, Kaohsiung, Taiwan
Tel.: (886) 78136311
Web Site: http://www.kamipa.co.jp
Sales Range: $25-49.9 Million
Emp.: 30
Paper Mills
N.A.I.C.S.: 322120

Talico, S.A. de C.V. (1)
Calle Leibnitz 20 Piso 12, Colonia Anzures, Mexico, 11590, DF, Mexico **(100%)**
Tel.: (52) 5552552500
Sales Range: $25-49.9 Million
Emp.: 10
Paper & Newsprint Production
N.A.I.C.S.: 322120

Thai Pex Co., Ltd. (1)
Bangna Central City Tower 1 Office 1093 144 Bangna Trad Road KM 3, Banga Prakhanong, Bangkok, 10260, Thailand
Tel.: (66) 27456444
Web Site: http://www.kamipa.co.jp
Paper Mfr
N.A.I.C.S.: 322120

Tokyo Sangyo Yoshi Co., Ltd. (1)
Nihombashi Nichigin-Dori Building 4-6-7 Nihombashi Hongokucho, Chuo-ku, Tokyo, 103-0021, Japan
Tel.: (81) 332700432
Web Site: https://www.tsy.co.jp
Electrical Material Distr
N.A.I.C.S.: 423610
Kosuke Kikuchi *(Pres)*

Weiss McNair, LCC (1)
100 Loren Ave, Chico, CA 95928
Tel.: (530) 891-6214
Web Site: http://www.weissmcnair.com
Sales Range: $1-9.9 Million
Emp.: 45
Hand & Edge Tool Mfr
N.A.I.C.S.: 332216

Wotai Paper (Shenzhen) Co., Ltd. (1)
Tong He Ind Building, Ping Di Town Long Gang District, Shenzhen, China
Tel.: (86) 75584069691
Paper Product Mfr & Distr
N.A.I.C.S.: 322120

Yamato Inc. (1)
1-13-21 Shintomi, Chuo-ku, Tokyo, 104-0041, Japan
Tel.: (81) 3 3551 8281
Paper Product Distr
N.A.I.C.S.: 424130

Yoshimoto Yoshiten Co., Ltd. (1)
1-13-21 Shintomi, Chuo-ku, Tokyo, 104-0041, Japan
Tel.: (81) 335514141
Household Paper Product Distr
N.A.I.C.S.: 424130

JAPAN PURE CHEMICAL CO LTD
3-10-18 Kitamachi, Nerima-ku, Tokyo, 179-0081, Japan
Tel.: (81) 335501048   JP
Web Site: https://www.netjpc.com
Year Founded: 1971
4973—(TKS)
Rev.: $160,900,960
Assets: $156,322,320
Liabilities: $28,072,000
Net Worth: $128,250,320
Earnings: $7,647,200
Emp.: 47
Fiscal Year-end: 03/31/21
Electronic Components Mfr
N.A.I.C.S.: 334417

Shigeki Shimizu *(Pres)*

JAPAN REAL ESTATE INVESTMENT CORPORATION
3-1-34 Minami-aoyama, Chiyoda-ku, Tokyo, 107-0062, Japan
Tel.: (81) 332117921
Web Site: https://www.j-re.co.jp
Year Founded: 2001
8952—(TKS)
Sales Range: $200-249.9 Million
Real Estate Investment Services
N.A.I.C.S.: 523999
Noritada Terasawa *(Exec Dir)*

JAPAN REGISTRY SERVICES CO., LTD.
Chiyoda First Bldg East 13F 3-8-1, Nishi-Kanda Chiyoda-ku, Tokyo, 101-0065, Japan
Tel.: (81) 352158451
Web Site: http://www.jprs.co.jp
Year Founded: 2000
Emp.: 102
Internet Infrastructure Services
N.A.I.C.S.: 518210
Koki Higashida *(Pres)*

JAPAN RELIANCE SERVICE CORPORATION
3-1-3 Higashiikebukuro, Toshima-Ku, Tokyo, 170-8630, Japan
Tel.: (81) 359527211
Web Site: https://www.trsc.co.jp
Year Founded: 1971
4664—(TKS)
Rev.: $53,498,498
Assets: $27,756,847
Liabilities: $14,165,837
Net Worth: $13,591,010
Earnings: $1,618,764
Fiscal Year-end: 03/31/24
Human Resource Consulting Services
N.A.I.C.S.: 541612
Hiroo Kanai *(Pres)*

JAPAN RESISTOR MFG CO., LTD.
2315 Kitano, Nanto, 939-1897, Toyama, Japan
Tel.: (81) 337629516
Web Site: https://www.jrm.co.jp
6977—(TKS)
Rev.: $50,877,840
Assets: $54,203,050
Liabilities: $39,044,630
Net Worth: $15,158,420
Earnings: $595,560
Fiscal Year-end: 12/31/23
Electronic Component Mfr & Distr
N.A.I.C.S.: 334419
Hitoshi Kimura *(Pres)*

Subsidiaries:

JRM (Shanghai) Electronics Manufacturing Co., Ltd. (1)
No 3 4 Standard Factory No 8 Rongxiang Road, Songjiang Export Processing Zone, Shanghai, 201611, China
Tel.: (86) 2157749696
Web Site: http://www.jrm.co.jp
Electronic Components Mfr
N.A.I.C.S.: 334419

JRM (Thailand) Co., Ltd. (1)
2/3 Moo 14 Bangna Towers A 2nd Floor Unit No 208, Bangna-Trad Rd KM 6 5 Bangkaew Bangplee, Samut Prakan, 10540, Thailand
Tel.: (66) 23120288
Electronic Product Whslr
N.A.I.C.S.: 423690

JRM Group Co., Ltd. (1)
3 and 4 Drayton Fields Rutherford Way, Daventry, NN11 8XW, United Kingdom
Tel.: (44) 132 730 7150
Web Site: https://www.jrm-group.com

Electronic Components Mfr
N.A.I.C.S.: 334419
Jason King *(Mng Dir)*

Japan Resistor Sales Co., Ltd. (1)
3-6-20 Minami Ohi, Shinagawa, Tokyo, 140-0013, Japan
Tel.: (81) 332981061
Sales Range: $50-74.9 Million
Emp.: 7
Electronic Components Distr
N.A.I.C.S.: 423690

Microjenics Inc. (1)
1-10 Mishima-Machi, Tonami, 939-1365, Japan
Tel.: (81) 763333550
Electronic Components Mfr
N.A.I.C.S.: 334419

Shanghai JRM Trading Co., Ltd. (1)
Room 823 No T2 Lane 166 Minhong Road, Minhang District, Shanghai, 201100, China
Tel.: (86) 2164833623
Electronic Product Whslr
N.A.I.C.S.: 423690

JAPAN SECURITIES FINANCE CO., LTD.
1-2-10 Nihonbashi-Kayabacho, Chuo-ku, Tokyo, 103-0025, Japan
Tel.: (81) 336663184
Web Site: https://www.jsf.co.jp
Year Founded: 1927
8511—(TKS)
Rev.: $330,552,880
Assets: $90,852,896,650
Liabilities: $89,897,050,990
Net Worth: $955,845,660
Earnings: $53,078,300
Emp.: 247
Fiscal Year-end: 03/31/24
Financial Investment Services
N.A.I.C.S.: 523999
Eizo Kobayashi *(Co-Chm)*

Subsidiaries:

JSF Information Technology (1)
Edobashi Building 1-20-5 Nihonbashi, Chuo-ku, Tokyo, 103-0027, Japan **(82.5%)**
Tel.: (81) 332423121
Web Site: https://www.jsfit.co.jp
Sales Range: $50-74.9 Million
Emp.: 324
Data Processing Related Business
N.A.I.C.S.: 518210

JSF Trust and Banking Co., Ltd. (1)
1-2-4 Nihonbashi Kayabacho, Chuo-ku, Tokyo, 103-0025, Japan **(100%)**
Tel.: (81) 356423070
Web Site: https://www.jsftb.co.jp
Sales Range: $50-74.9 Million
Emp.: 40
Security Brokers
N.A.I.C.S.: 523150

Japan Securities Agents, Ltd. (1)
1-2-4 Kayabacho Nihonbashi, Chuo-ku, Tokyo, 103-8202, Japan **(40%)**
Tel.: (81) 352172153
Web Site: https://www.jsa-hp.co.jp
Sales Range: $200-249.9 Million
Transfer of Certificates & Other Related Business
N.A.I.C.S.: 523910

Nihon Building Co. Ltd. (1)
1-2-14 Kayabacho Nihonbashi, Chuo-ku, Tokyo, 103-0025, Japan **(100%)**
Tel.: (81) 362773001
Web Site: https://www.nichi-bldg.co.jp
Sales Range: $50-74.9 Million
Emp.: 15
Maintenance & Leasing of Real Estate Offices
N.A.I.C.S.: 531210

JAPAN SYSTEM TECHNIQUES CO., LTD.
27th Floor Taiyo Life Shinagawa Building 2-16-2 Konan, Minato-ku, Tokyo, 108-8288, Japan
Tel.: (81) 367182771
Web Site: https://www.jast.jp

JAPAN TOBACCO INC.

Year Founded: 1973
4323—(TKS)
Rev.: $173,069,630
Assets: $132,345,420
Liabilities: $48,319,100
Net Worth: $84,026,320
Earnings: $13,788,460
Emp.: 1,847
Fiscal Year-end: 03/31/24
Software Development Services
N.A.I.C.S.: 541511
Takeaki Hirabayashi *(Pres & CEO)*

Subsidiaries:

GuiLin Anxin Software Co., Ltd. (1)
Guilin High-Tech Development Zone Creative Industry Park 1-2 4th Floor, Guilin, 541002, China
Tel.: (86) 7735863688
Information Technology Consulting Services
N.A.I.C.S.: 541512

JAST Techniques Pte. Ltd. (1)
Web Site: http://www.jast.com.sg
Information Technology Consulting Services
N.A.I.C.S.: 541512
Nakanishi Yoshiki *(Mng Dir)*

Subsidiary (Non-US):

JASTEC Thailand Co., Ltd. (2)
UM Tower Building 25th Floor Room A49 No 9/257 Ramkhamhaeng Road, Suan Luang, Bangkok, 10250, Thailand
Tel.: (66) 2061941619
Information Technology Consulting Services
N.A.I.C.S.: 541512

NewNeeds Co., Ltd. (1)
29th floor Nakanoshima Festival Tower 2-3-18 Nakanoshima, Kita-ku, Osaka, 530-0005, Japan
Tel.: (81) 645601015
Emp.: 95
Software Development Services
N.A.I.C.S.: 541511

Shanghai Jiafeng Information Technology Co., Ltd. (1)
Room 3201 Junling Plaza No 500 North Chengdu Road, Shanghai, 200003, China
Tel.: (86) 2158430699
Web Site: https://www.jastsh.com
Information Technology Consulting Services
N.A.I.C.S.: 541512

JAPAN TOBACCO INC.
1-1 Toranomon 4-chome, Minato-ku, Tokyo, 105-6927, Japan
Tel.: (81) 366362914   JP
Web Site: https://www.jt.com
Year Founded: 1985
JAPAF—(OTCIQ)
Rev.: $18,771,563,954
Assets: $48,114,271,298
Liabilities: $22,263,660,763
Net Worth: $25,850,610,535
Earnings: $3,186,573,274
Emp.: 53,239
Fiscal Year-end: 12/31/23
Tobacco, Food & Pharmaceutical Products Mfr
N.A.I.C.S.: 312230
Mutsuo Iwai *(Deputy Chm)*

Subsidiaries:

Akros Pharma Inc. (1)
302 Carnegie Ctr Ste 300, Princeton, NJ 08540-6237
Tel.: (609) 919-9570
Web Site: https://www.akrospharma.com
Sales Range: $25-49.9 Million
Emp.: 42
Research & Development of Pharmaceutical Products
N.A.I.C.S.: 541715
Hideshi Sunada *(Pres & CEO)*

Fuji Flavor Co., Ltd., (1)
3-5-8 Midorigaoka, Hamura, 205-8503, Tokyo, Japan
Tel.: (81) 425541201
Web Site: http://www.fjf.co.jp
Insect Pheromone Trap Mfr

JAPAN TOBACCO INC.

Japan Tobacco Inc.—(Continued)
N.A.I.C.S.: 325320
Junji Ueno *(Pres)*

Division (Domestic):

Fuji Flavor Co., Ltd. - Ecology & Pheromone Division (2)
3-5-8 Midorigaoka, Hamura, 205-8503, Tokyo, Japan
Tel.: (81) 42 555 5186
Insect Pheromone Trap Mfr
N.A.I.C.S.: 114210
Yasukawa Shintaro *(Mgr-Sls)*

Fuji Flavor Co., Ltd. - Flavor Division (2)
3-5-8 Midorigaoka, Hamura, 205-8503, Tokyo, Japan
Tel.: (81) 42 555 5100
Web Site: http://www.fjf.co.jp
Emp.: 100
Insect Pheromone Trap Mfr
N.A.I.C.S.: 114210

Fuji Flavor Co., Ltd. - Planning & General Administration Division (2)
3-5-8 Midorigaoka, Hamura, 205-8503, Tokyo, Japan
Tel.: (81) 42 554 1201
Web Site: http://www.fjf.co.jp
Sales Range: $50-74.9 Million
Emp.: 110
Insect Pheromone Trap Mfr
N.A.I.C.S.: 325320

Fuji Flavor Co., Ltd. - Tobacco Flavor Division (2)
3-5-8 Midorigaoka, Hamura, 205-8503, Tokyo, Japan
Tel.: (81) 42 554 1203
Emp.: 100
Insect Pheromone Trap Mfr
N.A.I.C.S.: 114210

JT (UK) Ltd. (1)
Members Hill Brooklands Road, Weybridge, KT13 0QU, Surrey, United Kingdom
Tel.: (44) 1932372000 **(100%)**
Web Site: http://www.jti.com
Sales Range: $25-49.9 Million
Mfr & Sale of Tobacco, Food & Pharmaceutical Products; Agribusiness; Real Estate & Engineering Services
N.A.I.C.S.: 459991

JT Engineering Inc. (1)
Seisan Gijutsu Center 3f, Sumida-Ku, Tokyo, 130-0003, Japan
Tel.: (81) 356107601
Engineering Services
N.A.I.C.S.: 541330

JT International S.A. (1)
8 rue Kazem-Radjavi, 1202, Geneva, Switzerland
Tel.: (41) 22 703 0777
Web Site: https://www.jti.com
Sales Range: $150-199.9 Million
Emp.: 600
Tobacco Products Mfg & Distr
N.A.I.C.S.: 312230
Eddy Pirard *(Pres & CEO)*

Subsidiary (Non-US):

CJSC - JTI Marketing & Sales (2)
28 32 floor Mercury City Tower 15 1st Krasnogvardeysky proezd, 123100, Moscow, Russia
Tel.: (7) 4996770000
Web Site: http://www.jti.com
Sales Range: $300-349.9 Million
Tobacco Product Mfr & Distr
N.A.I.C.S.: 312230

Subsidiary (Non-US):

Austria Tabak GmbH (3)
Koppstrasse 116, 1160, Vienna, Austria
Tel.: (43) 1313420
Sales Range: $75-99.9 Million
Emp.: 300
Tobacco Mfr
N.A.I.C.S.: 111910
Stefan Fitz *(Pres-Asia Pacific Reg)*

Subsidiary (Domestic):

CJSC Liggett-Ducat (3)
61/4 Kashirskoye Shosse, Moscow, 115563, Russia
Tel.: (7) 495 728 73 00
Web Site: http://www.jti.com
Tobacco Mfr
N.A.I.C.S.: 111910

Subsidiary (Non-US):

Gallaher France EURL (3)
77 Rue Marcel Dassault, 92100, Boulogne, Billancourt, France
Tel.: (33) 147619797
Sales Range: $25-49.9 Million
Emp.: 100
Tobacco Mfr
N.A.I.C.S.: 111910

Gallaher Spain SA (3)
18 Pl Espana, 28008, Madrid, Spain
Tel.: (34) 915488594
Tobacco Mfr
N.A.I.C.S.: 111910

JT International Co. (Cyprus) Ltd. (3)
Limassol Avenue 209, Dhali Industrial Area, 2540, Nicosia, Cyprus
Tel.: (357) 22480708
Web Site: http://www.jti.com
Tobacco Products Mfr & Distr
N.A.I.C.S.: 312230

JTI Ireland Ltd. (3)
1st Floor 4-6 River Walk Citywest Business Campus, Dublin, Ireland
Tel.: (353) 14040200
Web Site: http://www.jti.com
Sales Range: $300-349.9 Million
Mfr, Marketing & Distribution of Tobacco Products
N.A.I.C.S.: 312230

JTI Sweden (3)
Tel.: (46) 456 0000
Web Site: http://www.jtisweden.com
Emp.: 160
Tobacco Mfr
N.A.I.C.S.: 111910

Tobaccoland Automaten GmbH & CO KG (3)
Krahnendonk 121 a b, 41066, Monchengladbach, Germany
Tel.: (49) 21616950
Web Site: http://www.tobaccoland.de
Tobacco Mfr
N.A.I.C.S.: 111910

Subsidiary (Non-US):

JT International (Philippines), Inc. (2)
Penthouse W Office Building 28th St corner 11th Ave, Bonifacio Global City, Taguig, 1634, Philippines
Tel.: (63) 2 620 2500
Web Site: https://www.jti.com
Sales Range: $10-24.9 Million
Tobacco Product Mfr & Distr
N.A.I.C.S.: 312230

JT International (Singapore) Pte. Ltd. (2)
438B Alexandra Road 07-09/12 Alexandra Technopark Block B, Winslad House 1, Singapore, 119968, Singapore
Tel.: (65) 6 738 7978
Web Site: http://www.jti.com
Tobacco Product Mfr & Distr
N.A.I.C.S.: 312230

JT International (Thailand) Limited (2)
38th Flr Bhiraj Tower at Emquartier 689 Klongtoey Nuea, Wattana, Bangkok, 10110, Thailand
Tel.: (66) 2 204 6994
Web Site: http://www.jti.com
Sales Range: $25-49.9 Million
Tobacco Product Mfr & Distr
N.A.I.C.S.: 312230

JT International Business Services Ltd. (2)
Orange Media City UK, Salford, M50 2HF, United Kingdom
Tel.: (44) 1618690600
Web Site: http://www.jti.com

Sales Range: $25-49.9 Million
Tobacco Product Mfr & Distr
N.A.I.C.S.: 312230

JT International Company Netherlands bv (2)
Bella Donna 4, 1181 RM, Amstelveen, Netherlands
Tel.: (31) 20 721 3500
Web Site: https://www.jti.com
Sales Range: $25-49.9 Million
Tobacco Product Mfr & Distr
N.A.I.C.S.: 312230

JT International Company Ukraine CJSC (2)
19 G Skovorody Street, 04070, Kiev, Ukraine
Tel.: (380) 44 490 7800
Web Site: https://www.jti.com
Sales Range: $25-49.9 Million
Tobacco Product Mfr & Distr
N.A.I.C.S.: 312230

JT International France (2)
35 Rue des Abondances, 92513, Boulogne-Billancourt, Cedex, France
Tel.: (33) 14 699 4600
Web Site: http://www.oasis.fr.gti.com
Sales Range: $25-49.9 Million
Emp.: 17
Tobacco Product Mfr & Distr
N.A.I.C.S.: 312230

JT International Germany GmbH (2)
Im MediaPark 4e, 50670, Cologne, Germany
Tel.: (49) 2 211 6460
Web Site: http://www.jti.com
Emp.: 100
Tobacco Product Mfr & Distr
N.A.I.C.S.: 312230

JT International Hellas AEBE (2)
40 2km Attiki Odos SEA Mesogeion, Paiania, 190 02, Athens, Greece
Tel.: (30) 210 745 5700
Web Site: https://www.jti.com
Emp.: 300
Tobacco Product Mfr & Distr
N.A.I.C.S.: 312230

JT International Iberia SL (2)
Avda Juan Carlos I n 29 planta 4a and 5a, 35019, Las Palmas, Spain
Tel.: (34) 92 849 5800
Web Site: https://www.jti.com
Sales Range: $25-49.9 Million
Tobacco Product Mfr & Distr
N.A.I.C.S.: 312230

JT International India Pte Limited (2)
3rd Floor Residency Road No 138 Raheja Paramount, 560025, Bengaluru, Karnataka, India
Tel.: (91) 8041818899
Web Site: http://www.jti.com
Sales Range: $10-24.9 Million
Emp.: 50
Tobacco Product Mfr & Distr
N.A.I.C.S.: 312230

JT International Italia srl (2)
Via Crocefisso 27, 20122, Milan, Italy
Tel.: (39) 02583471
Web Site: http://www.jti.com
Sales Range: $25-49.9 Million
Emp.: 110
Tobacco Product Mfr & Distr
N.A.I.C.S.: 312230

JT International Korea, Inc. (2)
12F Jongno Tower 51, Jongno-gu, Seoul, 03161, Korea (South)
Tel.: (82) 2 732 5711
Web Site: http://www.oasis.jti.com
Sales Range: $75-99.9 Million
Emp.: 500
Tobacco Product Mfr & Distr
N.A.I.C.S.: 312230

JT International Marketing & Sales doo (2)
Trgovacka 2, 11030, Belgrade, Serbia
Tel.: (381) 11 2399 764
Tobacco Product Mfr & Distr
N.A.I.C.S.: 312230

JT International Romania srl (2)
9-9A Bd Dimitrie Pompei, District 2, 020335,

INTERNATIONAL PUBLIC

Bucharest, Romania
Tel.: (40) 212043111
Web Site: http://www.jti.com
Emp.: 1,000
Tobacco Product Mfr & Distr
N.A.I.C.S.: 312230

JT International TABANDOR SA (2)
Carrer de les Escoles, Sant Julia de Loria, Andorra
Tel.: (376) 876500
Web Site: http://www.jti.com
Tobacco Products Mfr & Distr
N.A.I.C.S.: 312230

JT International Trading Sdn Bhd (2)
6th Floor Menara Manulife RB No 6 Jalan Gelenggang Damansara Heights, 50490, Kuala Lumpur, Malaysia
Tel.: (60) 320949011
Web Site: http://www.jti.com
Sales Range: $150-199.9 Million
Emp.: 300
Tobacco Product Mfr & Distr
N.A.I.C.S.: 312230

JT International d.o.o. (2)
Kongressi trg 3, Brigade 25, 1000, Ljubljana, Slovenia
Tel.: (386) 12442620
Web Site: http://www.jti.com
Sales Range: $25-49.9 Million
Emp.: 5
Tobacco Product Mfr & Distr
N.A.I.C.S.: 312230

JT International do Brasil Ltda (2)
Presidente Juscelino Kubitschek 1600 Avenue 9th floor - Vila Olimpia, Sao Paulo, 04543-000, Brazil
Tel.: (55) 113 080 1962
Web Site: https://www.jti.com
Sales Range: $25-49.9 Million
Tobacco Product Mfr & Distr
N.A.I.C.S.: 312230

JT International spol sro (2)
Na Pankraci 1683/127, 140 00, Prague, Czech Republic
Tel.: (420) 221416777
Web Site: http://www.jti.com
Sales Range: $10-24.9 Million
Emp.: 180
Tobacco Products Mfr & Distr
N.A.I.C.S.: 312230

JT Tobacco International Taiwan Corp. (2)
2 Hsin Yi road, Taipei, Taiwan
Tel.: (886) 2 2720 2450
Sales Range: $25-49.9 Million
Emp.: 133
Tobacco Product Mfr & Distr
N.A.I.C.S.: 312230

JTI (Vietnam) Pte. Ltd. (2)
9th Floor Pearl Plaza Building 561A Dien Bien Phu Street, Ward 25 Binh Thanh District, Ho Chi Minh City, Vietnam
Tel.: (84) 83 899 0088
Web Site: http://www.jti.com
Tobacco Product Mfr & Distr
N.A.I.C.S.: 312230

JTI Tutun Urunleri Pazarlama as (2)
Capak Mahallesi 2561 Sokak no 12, Torbali, 35860, Izmir, Turkiye
Tel.: (90) 2328500000
Web Site: http://www.jti.com
Sales Range: $25-49.9 Million
Emp.: 2,400
Tobacco Product Mfr & Distr
N.A.I.C.S.: 312230

JTI-MacDonald Corp. (2)
1 Robert Speck Parkway Suite 1601, Mississauga, L4Z 0A2, ON, Canada
Tel.: (905) 804-7300
Web Site: http://www.jti.com
Sales Range: $25-49.9 Million
Emp.: 500
Tobacco Product Mfr & Distr
N.A.I.C.S.: 312230

JT Logistics Co., Ltd (1)
5-1 Nampeidaicho Nihontabakoshibuya Bldg 5f, Shibuya-Ku, Tokyo, 150-0036, Japan
Tel.: (81) 334965110
Logistics Consulting Servies

AND PRIVATE COMPANIES   **JAPAN TRUSTEE SERVICES BANK, LTD.**

N.A.I.C.S.: 541614

JT Pharma Alliance Co., Ltd (1)
Jt Bldg, Minato-Ku, Tokyo, 105-8422, Japan
Tel.: (81) 355724212
Emp.: 1
Pharmaceuticals Product Mfr
N.A.I.C.S.: 325412

JTI Tutun Urunleri Sanayi A.S (1)
Capak Mahallesi 2561 Sokak No 12,
35860, Izmir, Turkiye
Tel.: (90) 2328500000
Web Site: http://www.jti.com
Tobacco Product Distr
N.A.I.C.S.: 424940

Japan Filter Technology, Ltd. (1)
1-17-7 Yokokawa, Sumida-ku, Tokyo, 130-8603, Japan
Tel.: (81) 36 740 6707
Web Site: https://www.jft-l.co.jp
Emp.: 600
Tobacco Product Mfr
N.A.I.C.S.: 312230
Hiroshi Hasuike *(Pres)*

TS Network Co., Ltd (1)
4-17-7 Asakusabashi TS Bldg, Taito-Ku,
Tokyo, 111-0053, Japan
Tel.: (81) 338617431
Tobacco Product Distr
N.A.I.C.S.: 424940

TableMark Co., Ltd. (1)
6-4-10 Tsukiji, Chuo-ku, Tokyo, 104-0045, Japan
Tel.: (81) 57 002 6800
Web Site: https://www.tablemark.co.jp
Emp.: 3,691
Food Products Mfr & Distr
N.A.I.C.S.: 311999
Masashi Kagawa *(CEO)*

Vector Group Ltd. (1)
4400 Biscayne Blvd, Miami, FL 33137
Tel.: (305) 579-8000
Web Site: https://www.vectorgroupltd.com
Rev.: $1,441,009,000
Assets: $908,591,000
Liabilities: $1,716,468,000
Net Worth: ($807,877,000)
Earnings: $158,701,000
Emp.: 536
Fiscal Year-end: 12/31/2022
Holding Company; Tobacco Products
N.A.I.C.S.: 551112
Howard M. Lorber *(Pres & CEO)*

Subsidiary (Domestic):

Multi Soft II, Inc. (2)
3535 Quakerbridge Rd Ste 103, Hamilton, NJ 08619
Tel.: (609) 631-7401
Assets: $4,544
Liabilities: $1,158,176
Net Worth: ($1,153,632)
Earnings: ($119,620)
Emp.: 2
Fiscal Year-end: 01/31/2024
Investment Services
N.A.I.C.S.: 523999
J. Bryant Kirkland III *(Chm, Pres & CEO)*

New Valley LLC (2)
4400 Biscayne Blvd, Miami, FL 33137
Tel.: (305) 579-8000
Web Site: https://www.newvalley.com
Emp.: 12
Real Estate Holding Company
N.A.I.C.S.: 237210

Subsidiary (Domestic):

ALKI Corporation (3)
1105 N market St, Wilmington, DE 19801
Tel.: (302) 478-6160
Real Estate
N.A.I.C.S.: 531390

Douglas Elliman Realty, LLC (3)
575 Madison Ave, New York, NY 10022 (100%)
Tel.: (212) 891-7000
Web Site: http://www.elliman.com
Real Estate Support Services
N.A.I.C.S.: 531210
Steven James *(Pres)*

Douglas Elliman, LLC (3)
575 Madison Ave, New York, NY 10022 (70.59%)
Tel.: (212) 891-7000
Web Site: http://www.elliman.com
Offices of Real Estate Agents & Brokers
N.A.I.C.S.: 531210
Howard M. Lorber *(Chm)*

Subsidiary (Domestic):

Douglas Elliman Property Management (4)
675 3rd Ave, New York, NY 10017
Tel.: (212) 370-9200
Web Site: https://www.ellimanpm.com
Sales Range: $75-99.9 Million
Emp.: 340
Residential Management Services
N.A.I.C.S.: 541611
James V. O'Connor *(Pres)*

Majestic Properties, LLC (4)
PO Box 175, Rensselaer, IN 47978
Web Site:
   https://www.majesticproperties.net
Real Estate Brokerage
N.A.I.C.S.: 531210
Donald Kleinkort *(Owner)*

Subsidiary (Domestic):

VGR Holding LLC (2)
4400 Biscayne Blvd, Miami, FL 33137 (100%)
Tel.: (305) 579-8000
Sales Range: $1-9.9 Million
Emp.: 12
Holding Company
N.A.I.C.S.: 551112
Bennett S. LeBow *(Chm)*

Subsidiary (Domestic):

Liggett Group LLC (3)
100 Maple Ln, Mebane, NC 27302 (100%)
Tel.: (212) 687-8080
Web Site:
   http://www.liggettvectorbrands.com
Cigarette Mfr & Retailer
N.A.I.C.S.: 312230
James A. Taylor *(Sr Exec VP-Sls & Mktg)*

Subsidiary (Domestic):

Epic Holdings Inc. (4)
209 A St Bldg 3411, Wilmington, DE 19810
Tel.: (302) 478-6160
Sales Range: $250-299.9 Million
Emp.: 100
Holding Company
N.A.I.C.S.: 551112
Janine Walter *(Chief Talent Officer-Stamford)*

Subsidiary (Domestic):

Eve Holdings Inc. (5)
1105 N Market St 1300, Wilmington, DE 19810
Tel.: (302) 478-6160
Sales Range: $50-74.9 Million
Holding Company
N.A.I.C.S.: 722320

Subsidiary (Domestic):

Liggett Vector Brands Inc. (3)
3800 Paramount Pkwy Ste 250, Morrisville, NC 27560-6951
Tel.: (919) 990-3500
Web Site:
   http://www.liggettvectorbrands.com
Emp.: 41
Sale & Distribution of Tobacco Products
N.A.I.C.S.: 424940

Vector Tobacco Inc. (3)
3800 Paramount Pkwy Ste 250, Morrisville, NC 27560-6951
Tel.: (212) 687-8080
Web Site:
   http://www.liggettvectorbrands.com
Sale & Distribution of Tobacco
N.A.I.C.S.: 424940

JAPAN TRANSCITY CORPORATION

1-1 2 Chome Kasumi, Yokkaichi, 510-8651, Mie, Japan
Tel.: (81) 593635211   JP
Web Site: https://www.trancy.co.jp
Year Founded: 1895
9310—(NGO)
Rev.: $809,745,396
Assets: $1,059,286,126
Liabilities: $469,890,850
Net Worth: $589,395,276
Earnings: $30,611,158
Emp.: 2,505
Fiscal Year-end: 03/31/24
Warehouse & Transportation Services
N.A.I.C.S.: 493110
Ken Ogawa *(Bd of Dirs & Chm)*

Subsidiaries:

J Trans KK (1)
2-16-13 Obata, Yokkaichi, 510-0875, Mie, Japan (60%)
Tel.: (81) 593450738
Web Site: http://www.jsr-log.co.jp
Sales Range: $25-49.9 Million
Emp.: 33
Freight Forwarding, Warehousing & Delivery Management
N.A.I.C.S.: 488510

Japan Transcity Corporation - Overseas Business Management Division (1)
6-6 Chitose-cho, Yokkaichi, 510-8651, Mie, Japan
Tel.: (81) 593535236
Business Management Services
N.A.I.C.S.: 561499

Japan Transcity Corporation - SCM Division (1)
4 780-4 Shinkonishi, Ishikari, 061-3241, Japan
Tel.: (81) 13 374 4581
Web Site: https://www.trancy.co.jp
Warehousing & Logistics Services
N.A.I.C.S.: 493110

Japan Transcity Corporation - Sales Development Division (1)
6-6 Chitose-cho, Yokkaichi, 510-8651, Mie, Japan
Tel.: (81) 593535245
Web Site: http://www.trancity.com.jp
General Warehousing Services
N.A.I.C.S.: 493110

Japan Transcity Corporation - Sales Promotion Division (1)
3-23-17 Takanawa, Minato-ku, Tokyo, 108-0074, Japan
Tel.: (81) 364090380
Web Site: http://www.trancy.co.jp
Sales Range: $25-49.9 Million
Emp.: 40
Logistic Services
N.A.I.C.S.: 541614

PT.Naditama-Trancy Logistics Indonesia (1)
Wisma 46 Kota Bni Suite 36 05 36th Floor
Jl Jend Sudirman Kav 1, Jakarta, 10220, Indonesia
Tel.: (62) 21 573 1580
Web Site: https://www.trancy.co.jp
Freight Forwarding Services
N.A.I.C.S.: 488510

Trancy Logistics (Europe) GmbH (1)
Immermannstr 50-52, Dusseldorf, Germany
Tel.: (49) 2115504190
Web Site: http://www.trancyamerica.com
Sales Range: $25-49.9 Million
Emp.: 8
Scheduled Freight Air Transportation
N.A.I.C.S.: 481112
Ryusuke Matsuhashi *(Mng Dir)*

Trancy Logistics (H.K.) Ltd (1)
Office D 20 / F Kings Tower 111 King Lam Street, Cheung Sha Wan, Kowloon, China (Hong Kong)
Tel.: (852) 2 530 4735
Web Site: http://www.trancy.com.hk
Sales Range: $25-49.9 Million
Emp.: 8
Scheduled Freight Air Transportation
N.A.I.C.S.: 481112

Trancy Logistics (Malaysia) Sdn. Bhd (1)
A-3A-6 Block A No 1 Jalan PJS 8/15 Dataran Mentari, 46150, Petaling Jaya, Selangor, Malaysia
Tel.: (60) 35 637 2111
Web Site: https://www.trancy.com.my
Sales Range: $25-49.9 Million
Emp.: 60
Scheduled Freight Air Transportation
N.A.I.C.S.: 481112

Trancy Logistics (Philippines), Inc (1)
Ramon Magsaysay Building 1680 Roxas Blvd, Malate, Manila, 1004, Metro Manila, Philippines (100%)
Tel.: (63) 2 521 1584
Web Site: https://trancy.com.ph
Sales Range: $25-49.9 Million
Emp.: 30
Scheduled Freight Air Transportation
N.A.I.C.S.: 481112

Trancy Logistics (Singapore) Pte Ltd (1)
20 Gul Rd # 0400, Singapore, 629345, Singapore (100%)
Tel.: (65) 62206769
Sales Range: $25-49.9 Million
Emp.: 2
General Warehousing & Storage
N.A.I.C.S.: 493110

Trancy Logistics (Thailand) Co., Ltd. (1)
888/187-189 Mahatun Plaza 18FL Ploenchit Rd, 18th Floor F1 Ploenchit Road, Bangkok, 10330, Pathumwan, Thailand
Tel.: (66) 2 253 6782
Web Site: http://www.trancyamerica.com
Sales Range: $25-49.9 Million
Emp.: 30
Transportation, Freight Forwarding & Warehousing
N.A.I.C.S.: 481112
Kenji Kawamura *(Mng Dir)*

Trancy Logistics America (1)
1670 Dolwick Dr Ste 8, Erlanger, KY 41018
Tel.: (859) 282-7780
Web Site: https://www.trancyamerica.com
Sales Range: $25-49.9 Million
Emp.: 80
Scheduled Freight Air Transportation
N.A.I.C.S.: 481112

Trancy Logistics Mexico S.A. de C.V. (1)
Av Universidad 815-301 Bosques Del Prado Sur, 20130, Aguascalientes, Mexico
Tel.: (52) 449 996 1901
Web Site: http://www.trancy.co.jp
Emp.: 3
Warehousing & Logistics Services
N.A.I.C.S.: 493110
Takaya Abe *(Gen Mgr)*

Trancy Logistics(Shanghai)Co.,Ltd. (1)
Room 3201-3203 Tower 1 Kerry Everbright City No 218 Tian Mu Road West, Shanghai, 200070, China
Tel.: (86) 21 6353 6060
Warehousing & Logistics Services
N.A.I.C.S.: 541614

Trancy Logistics(Vietnam)Co.,Ltd. (1)
22nd Floor Icon 4 Tower 243A De La Thanh, Dong Da, Hanoi, Vietnam
Tel.: (84) 243 772 6870
Web Site: https://www.trancy.co.jp
Emp.: 20
Warehousing & Transportation Services
N.A.I.C.S.: 493110

JAPAN TRUSTEE SERVICES BANK, LTD.

Harumi Island Triton Square Tower
1-8-11 Harumi 1-Chome, Chuo-ku, Tokyo, 104-6107, Japan
Tel.: (81) 362202300
Web Site:
   http://www.japantrustee.co.jp
Year Founded: 2000
Investment Banking & Securities Trading Services
N.A.I.C.S.: 523150

JAPAN TRUSTEE SERVICES BANK, LTD.

Japan Trustee Services Bank, Ltd.—(Continued)
Masatoshi Noguchi *(Deputy Pres)*
Subsidiaries:

Trust & Custody Services Bank, Ltd. (1)
Tower Z Harumi Island Triton Square
Harumi 1-8-12 Chuo-ku, Tokyo, 104-6228, Japan
Tel.: (81) 3 6220 4000
Web Site: http://www.tcsb.co.jp
Sales Range: $200-249.9 Million
Emp.: 671
Investment Banking
N.A.I.C.S.: 523150
Nobumitsu Watanabe *(Pres & CEO)*

JAPAN WASTE CORPORATION
2-12-10 Nihonbashi Kayabacho, Chuo-ku, Tokyo, 103-0025, Japan
Tel.: (81) 366612327
Web Site: https://www.japanwaste.co.jp
Year Founded: 2008
Sales Range: $350-399.9 Million
Emp.: 1,200
Environmental Services
N.A.I.C.S.: 541620
Subsidiaries:

Taiyo Chemical Co., Ltd. (1)
1-1-1 Nishiura, Funabashi, 273-0017, Chiba, Japan
Tel.: (81) 474351817
Waste Water Treatment Services
N.A.I.C.S.: 562211

JAPANET HOLDINGS CO., LTD.
Hiumachi, Sasebo, Nagasaki, Japan
Tel.: (81) 956261300   JP
Web Site: https://corporate.japanet.co.jp
Year Founded: 2007
Holding Company
N.A.I.C.S.: 551112
Akito Takada *(Pres & CEO)*
Subsidiaries:

Japanet Broadcasting Co., Ltd. (1)
Shinkawa Chuo-ku, Tokyo, Japan (100%)
Tel.: (81) 956261300
Television Broadcasting Services
N.A.I.C.S.: 516120

JAPAUL GOLD & VENTURES PLC
Japaul House Plot 8 Dr Nurudeen Olowopopo Avenue, Central Business District Agidingbi Alausa Ikeja, Lagos, Nigeria
Tel.: (234) 8062377018
Web Site: https://www.japaulgroup.com
Year Founded: 1994
JAPAULGOLD—(NIGE)
Rev.: $1,007,067
Assets: $9,768,443
Liabilities: $9,862,029
Net Worth: ($93,586)
Earnings: $115,458
Emp.: 104
Fiscal Year-end: 12/31/22
Marine Offshore Construction Services
N.A.I.C.S.: 488320
Akinloye Daniel Oladapo *(CEO & Mng Dir)*

JAPAUTO MOTO
43 Avenue De La Grande Armee, Paris, 75116, France
Tel.: (33) 144173610
Rev.: $15,800,000
Emp.: 41
N.A.I.C.S.: 441227

Cedric Vilaseca *(Pres)*

JAPRA AD
Blatna bb, 79200, Novi Grad, Bosnia & Herzegovina
Tel.: (387) 52759100
Web Site: http://www.fortisgroup.ba
Year Founded: 1957
JAPR—(BANJ)
Sales Range: Less than $1 Million
Emp.: 37
Mineral Exploration Services
N.A.I.C.S.: 213114

JARA CORPORATION
1F Yaesu KT Building 1-1-8 Yaesu, Chuo-ku, Tokyo, 103-0028, Japan
Tel.: (81) 3 3548 3010   JP
Web Site: http://www.jara.co.jp
Year Founded: 2003
Sales Range: $25-49.9 Million
Emp.: 40
Recycling Services
N.A.I.C.S.: 423930
Takashi Kitajima *(Pres)*

JARDINE MATHESON HOLDINGS LIMITED
4th Floor Jardine House 33-35 Reid Street, Hamilton, HM12, Bermuda
Tel.: (441) 2920515   BM
Web Site: https://www.jardines.com
Year Founded: 1995
JMHBD—(BERM)
Rev.: $36,049,000,000
Assets: $89,182,000,000
Liabilities: $33,251,000,000
Net Worth: $55,931,000,000
Earnings: $2,362,000,000
Emp.: 443,000
Fiscal Year-end: 12/31/23
Holding Company
N.A.I.C.S.: 551112
Benjamin William Keswick *(Chm)*
Subsidiaries:

Jardine Matheson Limited (1)
48th Floor Jardine House, GPO Box 70, Hong Kong, China (Hong Kong) (100%)
Tel.: (852) 28438288
Web Site: https://www.jardines.com
Sales Range: $75-99.9 Million
Emp.: 70
Investment Management & Administrative Services; Corporate Office
N.A.I.C.S.: 523940
Y. K. Pang *(Deputy Chm & Deputy Mng Dir)*

Subsidiary (Non-US):

Jardine Matheson (China) Ltd. (2)
Rm 528 5/F China World Office 1 China World Trade Centre, Chaoyang District, Beijing, 100004, China (100%)
Tel.: (86) 1065052801
Sales Range: $50-74.9 Million
Emp.: 5
Investment Management & Administrative Services
N.A.I.C.S.: 523940

Jardine Matheson (Malaysia) Sdn Bhd (2)
Suite 7 01 Level 7 Wisma EandC No 2 Lorong Dungun Kiri, Bukit Damansara, 50490, Kuala Lumpur, Malaysia (100%)
Tel.: (60) 320942168
Web Site: http://www.jardines.com
Investment Management & Administrative Services
N.A.I.C.S.: 523940
Rossana Annizah Rashidi *(Chm)*

Jardine Matheson (Singapore) Ltd. (2)
239 Alexandra Rd 3rd Fl, Singapore, 159930, Singapore (100%)
Tel.: (65) 62205111
Sales Range: $50-74.9 Million
Emp.: 4
Investment Management & Administrative Services

N.A.I.C.S.: 523940
Boon Yoon Chiang *(Chm & Mng Dir)*

Jardine Matheson (Thailand) Ltd. (2)
21st Fl Times Sq Bldg 246 Sukhumvit Rd, Klong Toey, Bangkok, 10110, Thailand (100%)
Tel.: (66) 22540675
Sales Range: $50-74.9 Million
Emp.: 4
Investment Management & Administrative Services
N.A.I.C.S.: 523940

Jardine Matheson (Vietnam) Ltd. (2)
Unit 14 3 14th Floor E town Central Building 11 Doan Van Bo Street, Ward 12 District 4, Ho Chi Minh City, 70000, Vietnam
Tel.: (84) 2838222344 (100%)
Web Site: http://www.jardines.com
Investment Management & Administrative Services
N.A.I.C.S.: 523940

Jardine Matheson Australia Pty. Ltd. (2)
Level 11 66 Clarence Street, Sydney, 2000, NSW, Australia (100%)
Tel.: (61) 292908100
Web Site: http://www.jlta.com.au
Sales Range: $200-249.9 Million
Investment Management & Administrative Services
N.A.I.C.S.: 523940

Jardine Matheson Europe B.V. (2)
Atrium Building Strawinskylaan 3007, 1077 ZX, Amsterdam, Netherlands (100%)
Tel.: (31) 204700258
Web Site: http://www.jardine.com
Sales Range: $50-74.9 Million
Emp.: 2
Investment Management & Administrative Services
N.A.I.C.S.: 523940
Judith Hope *(Mng Dir)*

Jardine Matheson International Services Ltd. (2)
4th Floor Jardine House 33-35 Reid Street, PO Box HM 1068, Hamilton, HM 12, Bermuda
Tel.: (441) 2920515
Sales Range: $25-49.9 Million
Emp.: 4
Investor Relations & Corporate Services
N.A.I.C.S.: 561499

Group (Domestic):

Jardine Motors Group Ltd. (2)
25th Floor Devon House Taikoo Place 979 King's Road Quarry Bay, 979 King's Road, Hong Kong, China (Hong Kong) (100%)
Tel.: (852) 25792888
Holding Company; New Car Dealerships & Automotive Repair Stations Owner & Operator
N.A.I.C.S.: 551112
Adam Keswick *(CEO)*

Subsidiary (Non-US):

PT. Tunas Ridean Tbk (3)
Jl Raya Pasar Minggu No 7, Jakarta, 12740, Indonesia (100%)
Tel.: (62) 217944788
Web Site: http://www.tunasgroup.com
Sales Range: Less than $1 Million
Emp.: 300
Automotive Retailer
N.A.I.C.S.: 441110

Subsidiary (Domestic):

Zung Fu Company Ltd. (3)
60 Ka Yip Street, PO Box 209, Chai Wan, Hong Kong, China (Hong Kong) (75%)
Tel.: (852) 25046140
Web Site: http://www.zungfu.com
Sales Range: $250-299.9 Million
Motor Car Dealers & Importers
N.A.I.C.S.: 441110

Subsidiary (Domestic):

Jardine Pacific Holdings Ltd (2)
25/f Devon Hse Taikoo Plc, Quarry Bay, China (Hong Kong)
Tel.: (852) 25792888
Web Site: https://www.jardines.com

INTERNATIONAL PUBLIC

Investment Management Service
N.A.I.C.S.: 523999

Group (Domestic):

Jardine Pacific Ltd. (2)
48th Floor Jardine House, G PO Box 70, Hong Kong, China (Hong Kong) (100%)
Tel.: (852) 28438288
Web Site: http://www.jardines.com
Holding Company; Inland Water Freight Transportation, Engineering, Construction, Restaurants & IT Services
N.A.I.C.S.: 551112

Joint Venture (Domestic):

Gammon Construction Ltd. (3)
22/F Tower 1 The Quayside 77 Hoi Bun Road, Kwun Tong, Kowloon, China (Hong Kong) (50%)
Tel.: (852) 25168823
Sales Range: $1-4.9 Billion
Emp.: 7,000
Construction Services
N.A.I.C.S.: 236220
Patricia Or *(Exec Dir-Fin, Risk Mgmt, & Information Mgmt-Gammon Capital)*

Subsidiary (Domestic):

Hong Kong Air Cargo Terminals Ltd. (3)
SuperTerminal 1 9 Chun Wan Road, Hong Kong International Airport, Hong Kong, China (Hong Kong) (100%)
Tel.: (852) 27531010
Web Site: https://www.hactl.com
Sales Range: $25-49.9 Million
Air Cargo Terminal Operator
N.A.I.C.S.: 488119
Wilson Kwong *(CEO)*

Subsidiary (Domestic):

Hong Kong Air Cargo Industry Services Limited (4)
5/F North Office Block SuperTerminal 1, Hong Kong International Airport, Hong Kong, China (Hong Kong) (100%)
Tel.: (852) 27532973
Web Site: http://www.hacis.com
Air Cargo Logistics Support & IT Services
N.A.I.C.S.: 488190

Subsidiary (Non-US):

SuperLink Logistics (Shenzhen) Co., Ltd. (5)
Room 7B6 Block 20 The Grand No 1, HuangYuYuan, Shenzhen, Futian, China (100%)
Tel.: (86) 755 8302 1821
Web Site: http://www.hacis.com
Intermodal Freight Logistics Services
N.A.I.C.S.: 541614

Subsidiary (Non-US):

Jardine Distribution, Inc. (3)
2/F Jardine Building JM Compound Faraday corner Osmena Highway, Makati, 1234, Philippines
Tel.: (63) 288436011
Web Site: http://www.jardinedistribution.com
Sales Range: $25-49.9 Million
Agricultural & Construction Chemical Whslr
N.A.I.C.S.: 424690

Jardine OneSolution (2001) Pte. Ltd. (3)
67 Ubi Avenue 1 02 01, Singapore, 408942, Singapore (100%)
Tel.: (65) 65519611
Web Site: http://www.jos.com.sg
Sales Range: $25-49.9 Million
Emp.: 180
Information Technology Solutions & Services
N.A.I.C.S.: 541519
Andrew Tan *(Mng Dir)*

Unit (Domestic):

JOS Distribution (4)
55 Ubi Avenue 1 Unit 03-15, Singapore, 408935, Singapore
Tel.: (65) 6551 9611
Web Site: http://www.jos.com.sg

AND PRIVATE COMPANIES

JARDINE MATHESON HOLDINGS LIMITED

Computer Services; Communications Systems Engineering; Facilities Management; Business Data Processing Services & Systems Integration
N.A.I.C.S.: 518210

Subsidiary (Domestic):

Jardine OneSolution (China) Limited (3)
19 F Tower One Millennium City 1 388 Kwun Tong Road, Kowloon, China (Hong Kong)
Tel.: (852) 2565 2011
Web Site: http://www.jos.com
Software Development Services
N.A.I.C.S.: 541511

Jardine OneSolution (HK) Limited (3)
19 F Tower One Millennium City 1 388 Kwun Tong Road, Kowloon, China (Hong Kong)
Tel.: (852) 2565 2011
Web Site: http://www.jos.com
Information Technology Consulting Services
N.A.I.C.S.: 541512

Subsidiary (Non-US):

Jardine Pacific (Thailand) Ltd (3)
24/F Time Square Building 246 Sukhumvit Road, Klongtoey, Bangkok, 10110, Thailand
Tel.: (66) 2 253 7890
Marine Shipping Services
N.A.I.C.S.: 488390

Subsidiary (Domestic):

Jardine Restaurant Group (3)
Shop 2 G/F Shatin Park Stage 1 8-12 Sha Kok Street, Sha Tin, China (Hong Kong)
Tel.: (852) 2647 8044
Web Site: http://www.pizzahut.com.hk
Restaurant Management Services
N.A.I.C.S.: 722511

Joint Venture (Domestic):

Jardine Schindler Group (3)
29 F Devon House Taikoo Place 979 King's Road, Quarry Bay, China (Hong Kong)
Tel.: (852) 25168168
Web Site: https://www.jardineschindler.com
Holding Company; Lift, Escalator & Moving Walkway Designer, Mfr, Installation & Maintenance Services
N.A.I.C.S.: 551112

Subsidiary (Non-US):

Jardine Schindler (Thai) Ltd. (4)
Times Square Building 20th Floor 246 Sukhumvit Road, Klongtoey, Bangkok, 10110, Thailand
Tel.: (66) 26851600
Web Site: https://www.schindler.com
Sales Range: $25-49.9 Million
Elevators, Escalators & Passenger Conveyors
N.A.I.C.S.: 333921

Jardine Schindler Elevator Corporation (4)
20th/F Tower 1 Insular Life Corporate Centre Insular Life Drive, Filinvest Corporate City Alabang, Muntinlupa, 1781, Philippines
Tel.: (63) 286836800
Web Site: https://www.schindler.ph
Sales Range: $25-49.9 Million
Elevators, Escalators & Passenger Conveyors
N.A.I.C.S.: 333921

Myanmar Jardine Schindler Ltd. (4)
No 1/4 Parami Road, Hlaing Township, Yangon, 11051, Myanmar
Tel.: (95) 1654855
Web Site: https://www.schindler.com
Sales Range: $25-49.9 Million
Emp.: 250
Elevators, Escalators & Passenger Conveyors
N.A.I.C.S.: 333921

Subsidiary (Non-US):

Jardine Shipping Hub Services Pte. Ltd. (3)
60 Alexandra Terrace 10-22 Lobby D The Comtech, Singapore, 118502, Singapore
Tel.: (65) 6323 2716
Web Site: http://www.jardine-shipping.com
Sales Range: $25-49.9 Million
Emp.: 100
Marine Shipping Services
N.A.I.C.S.: 488390

Jardine Shipping Services (Malaysia) Sdn Bhd (3)
Suite 6 01 Level 6 Intan Melinium Square 2 Jalan Batai Laut 4, Taman Intan, 41300, Kelang, Selangor, Malaysia
Tel.: (60) 3 3258 5388
Web Site: http://www.jardine-shipping.com
Sales Range: $25-49.9 Million
Emp.: 75
Marine Shipping Services
N.A.I.C.S.: 488390
Ajay Bhosle (Country Mgr)

Jardine Shipping Services (Vietnam) Ltd (3)
3rd Floor Gemadept Tower 2bis-4-6 Le Thanh Ton Street, Ben Nghe Ward District 1, Ho Chi Minh City, Vietnam
Tel.: (84) 8 3827 9350
Web Site: http://www.jardine-shipping.com
Sales Range: $25-49.9 Million
Emp.: 33
Marine Shipping Services
N.A.I.C.S.: 488390
Nga Nguyen (Country Mgr)

Subsidiary (Domestic):

Jardine Travel Limited (3)
Room 2101-2103 21/F Yardley Commercial Building 3 Connaught Road West, Sheung Wan, China (Hong Kong)
Tel.: (852) 3164 9888
Web Site: http://www.jardinetravel.com
Sales Range: $10-24.9 Million
Emp.: 50
Travel Management Services
N.A.I.C.S.: 561510
Susanna Chan (Mgr-Sls & Mktg)

RoomPlus (Self Storage) Limited (3)
338 Kwun Tong Road, Kwun Tong, Kowloon, China (Hong Kong)
Tel.: (852) 23317331
Web Site: http://www.roomplus.com.hk
Self Storage Facilities
N.A.I.C.S.: 531130

The Jardine Engineering Corporation Ltd. (3)
5/F Tower A Manulife Financial Centre 223-231 Wai Yip Street, Kwun Tong, Kowloon, China (Hong Kong) (100%)
Tel.: (852) 28071717
Web Site: http://www.hk.jec.com
Sales Range: $100-124.9 Million
Engineeering Services
N.A.I.C.S.: 541330

Subsidiary (Non-US):

Jardine, Matheson & Co., Ltd. (2)
3rd Floor No 1 Zhong Zheng Rd, Xin-Zhuang Dist, New Taipei City, 24243, Taiwan (100%)
Tel.: (886) 280699005
Web Site: http://www.jardines.com
Sales Range: $50-74.9 Million
Emp.: 50
Investment Management & Administrative Services
N.A.I.C.S.: 523940

Matheson & Co., Ltd. (2)
12 Upper Grosvenor Street, London, W1K 2ND, United Kingdom (100%)
Tel.: (44) 2078168100
Web Site: https://www.matheson.co.uk
Sales Range: $50-74.9 Million
Emp.: 27
Investment Management & Administrative Services
N.A.I.C.S.: 523940

Jardine Strategic Holdings Ltd. (1)
4th Floor Jardine House 33-35 Reid Street, Hamilton, HM 12, Bermuda
Tel.: (441) 2920515
Web Site: http://www.jardines.com
Investment Holding Company
N.A.I.C.S.: 551112
Y. K. Pang (Deputy Chm & Deputy Mng Dir)

Holding (Domestic):

DFI Retail Group Holdings Limited (2)
Jardine House 33-35 Reid Street, PO Box HM 1068, Hamilton, Bermuda
Tel.: (441) 2920515
Web Site: http://www.dairyfarmgroup.com
Rev.: $9,169,900,000
Assets: $7,111,100,000
Liabilities: $6,123,000,000
Net Worth: $988,100,000
Earnings: $30,400,000
Emp.: 213,000
Fiscal Year-end: 12/31/2023
Supermarket & Hypermarket Operator
N.A.I.C.S.: 445110

Subsidiary (Non-US):

Dairy Farm International Holdings Limited (3)
11/F Devon House Taikoo Place 979 King's Road, PO Box 286, Quarry Bay, Hong Kong, China (Hong Kong)
Tel.: (852) 22991888
Web Site: http://www.dairyfarmgroup.com
Grocery Retailer
N.A.I.C.S.: 445110
Ian McLeod (Co-CEO)

Dairy Farm Management Limited (3)
11 F Devon House Taikoo Place 979 Kings Road, PO Box 286, Quarry Bay, China (Hong Kong) (100%)
Tel.: (852) 22991888
Web Site: http://www.dairyfarmgroup.com
Sales Range: $50-74.9 Million
Holding Company; Corporate Office
N.A.I.C.S.: 551112

Subsidiary (Non-US):

Asia Investment and Supermarket Trading Do. Ltd. (4)
2/F Phuong Long Building 506 Nguyen Dinh Chieu Street, Ward 4 District 3, Ho Chi Minh City, Vietnam
Tel.: (84) 838328272
Supermarket Operator
N.A.I.C.S.: 445110
Paul Sheldrake (Mng Dir)

Cold Storage Singapore (1983) Pte. Ltd. (4)
21 Tampines North Drive 2 03-01, Singapore, 528765, Singapore (100%)
Tel.: (65) 68918000
Web Site: http://www.coldstorage.com.sg
Sales Range: $100-124.9 Million
Supermarkets Franchisor & Operator; Perishable Food & General Grocery Distr
N.A.I.C.S.: 445110

DFI Home Furnishings Taiwan Ltd (4)
4 F 1 Zhong Zheng Road, Xinzhuang District, New Taipei City, 24243, Taiwan
Tel.: (886) 280699005
Web Site: http://www.ikea.com.tw
Home Furniture Distr
N.A.I.C.S.: 423210

DFI Lucky Private Ltd (4)
#01 Street 55P Sangkat Tuek Thia, Khan Sen Sok, Phnom Penh, Cambodia
Tel.: (855) 23885722
Supermarket Operator
N.A.I.C.S.: 445110
Paul Sheldrake (Mng Dir)

Affiliate (Non-US):

Foodworld Supermarkets Pvt. Ltd. (4)
No 740 Eswari industrial Estate Gate No 2 Hullimavu, Bannerghatta Rd, Bengaluru, 560 076, India (49%)
Tel.: (91) 8032466544
Web Site: http://www.foodworld.in
Sales Range: $25-49.9 Million
Supermarkets Franchisor & Operator
N.A.I.C.S.: 445110

Subsidiary (Non-US):

GCH Retail (Malaysia) Sdn. Bhd. (4)
Mezzanine Floor Giant Hypermarket Shah Alam Stadium Lot 2 Persiaran, Sukan Seksyen 13, 40100, Shah Alam, Selangor, Malaysia (100%)
Tel.: (60) 377239396
Web Site: http://www.giant.com.my
Sales Range: $25-49.9 Million
Emp.: 100
Supermarkets & Hypermarkets Franchisor & Operator
N.A.I.C.S.: 445110

Giant TMC (B) Sdn Bhd (4)
Giant Hypermarket Tasik Rimba Lot 58865 Kampong Rimba, Mukim Gadong Bandar Seri Begawan, BE 3119, Negara, Brunei Darussalam
Tel.: (673) 2460820
Supermarket Operator
N.A.I.C.S.: 445110
Marius Knight (Mng Dir)

Guangzhou Sai Yi Convenience Stores Ltd. (4)
3/F Guangdong Mechanical Sub-Building 185 Yue Hua Road, Yue Xiu District, Guangzhou, 510030, China (65%)
Tel.: (86) 2083647118
Web Site: http://www.dairyfarmgroup.com
Convenience Store Operator
N.A.I.C.S.: 445131

Guardian Health and Beauty Sdn Bhd (4)
Mezzanine Floor Giant Hypermarket Shah Alam Stadium, Lot 2 Persiaran Sukan Seksyen 13, 40100, Shah Alam, Selangor Darul Ehsan, Malaysia
Tel.: (60) 355448400
Pharmaceutical Product Retailer
N.A.I.C.S.: 456110
Loi Liang Tok (Mng Dir)

Mannings Guangdong Retail Company Ltd (4)
2 F Guangdong Mechanical Main-Building 185 Yue Hua Road, Yue Xiu District, Guangzhou, 510030, China
Tel.: (86) 2083181388
Web Site: http://www.mannings.com.cn
Health & Beauty Care Product Retailer
N.A.I.C.S.: 456120

Subsidiary (Domestic):

Maxim's Caterers Ltd. (4)
18/F Maxim's Centre No 17 Cheung Shun Street, Cheung Sha Wan, Kowloon, China (Hong Kong) (50%)
Tel.: (852) 21011333
Web Site: http://www.maxims.com.hk
Restaurant
N.A.I.C.S.: 722511

Subsidiary (Non-US):

PT. Hero Supermarket Tbk (4)
Graha HERO CBD Bintaro Jaya Sektor 7 Blok B7/7, Pondok Jaya, Tangerang, 15224, Banten, Indonesia (94%)
Tel.: (62) 2183788388
Web Site: http://www.hero.co.id
Sales Range: $50-74.9 Million
Emp.: 150
Supermarkets, Convenience Stores, Health & Beauty Stores Franchisor & Operator
N.A.I.C.S.: 445110
Ingemar Patrik Lindvall (Chm)

Subsidiary (Domestic):

The Dairy Farm Company, Ltd. (4)
5 F Devon House Taikoo Place 979 Kings Road, Quarry Bay, China (Hong Kong)
Tel.: (852) 22993888
Web Site: http://www.dairyfarmgroup.com
Holding Company; Supermarkets, Health & Beauty, Convenience & Home Furnishing Stores
N.A.I.C.S.: 551112

Unit (Domestic):

The Dairy Farm Co., Ltd. - 7-Eleven (5)
5/F Devon House Taikoo Place, 979 King's Road, Quarry Bay, China (Hong Kong) (100%)
Tel.: (852) 22991711
Web Site: http://www.7-eleven.com.hk
Convenience Store Operator
N.A.I.C.S.: 445131

JARDINE MATHESON HOLDINGS LIMITED

Jardine Matheson Holdings Limited—(Continued)
Glyn Hughuf *(Mng Dir)*

The Dairy Farm Co., Ltd. - Mannings (5)
8/F Devon House Taikoo Place 979 King's Road, Quarry Bay, China (Hong Kong) **(100%)**
Tel.: (852) 22993398
Web Site: http://www.mannings.com.hk
Sales Range: $500-549.9 Million
Health & Beauty Stores Operator
N.A.I.C.S.: 456110

Subsidiary (Domestic):

Wellcome Company Limited (4)
5/F Devon House Taikoo Place 979 King's Road, Quarry Bay, China (Hong Kong) **(100%)**
Tel.: (852) 22993838
Web Site: http://www.wellcome.com.hk
Supermarkets Franchisor & Operator; Branded Foodstuffs Mfr & Distr
N.A.I.C.S.: 445110
Jessie Chan *(Mgr-Human Resources)*

Subsidiary (Non-US):

Wellcome Taiwan Company Ltd. (4)
2/F 175 Hua Ling St, Shin Lin, Taipei, 111, Taiwan **(100%)**
Tel.: (886) 228839489
Web Site: http://www.wellcome.com.tw
Supermarkets Franchisor & Operator
N.A.I.C.S.: 445110

Holding (Domestic):

Hongkong Land Holdings Limited (2)
Jardine House 33-35 Reid Street, Hamilton, HM EX, Bermuda
Tel.: (441) 2920515
Web Site: http://www.hkland.com
Rev.: $2,244,400,000
Assets: $42,596,800,000
Liabilities: $9,293,400,000
Net Worth: $33,303,400,000
Earnings: $199,600,000
Emp.: 2,841
Fiscal Year-end: 12/31/2022
Holding Company; Property Investment, Development & Management Services
N.A.I.C.S.: 551112
Ben Keswick *(Chm)*

Subsidiary (Non-US):

Hongkong Land Limited (3)
8th Floor One Exchange Square, Hong Kong, China (Hong Kong)
Tel.: (852) 28428428
Web Site: https://www.hkland.com
Sales Range: $350-399.9 Million
Property Investment, Development & Management Services; Corporate Office
N.A.I.C.S.: 531390
John R. Witt *(Chm)*

Subsidiary (Non-US):

HKL (Esplanade) Pte Limited (4)
One Raffles Quay 22-10 South Tower, Singapore, 048583, Singapore
Tel.: (65) 62381121
Web Site: http://www.hkland.com
Property Management Services
N.A.I.C.S.: 531312

Hongkong Land (Asia Management) Limited (4)
Suite 204 2nd Floor Central Building 31 Hai Ba Trung Hoan, Kiem District, Hanoi, Vietnam
Tel.: (84) 438251480
Sales Range: $25-49.9 Million
Emp.: 55
Real Estate Services
N.A.I.C.S.: 531390
Caoly Anh *(Gen Dir)*

Hongkong Land (Beijing) Management Co Ltd
Room 303 Block 26 Central Park No 6 Chaoyangmenwai Avenue, Chaoyang District, Beijing, 100020, China
Tel.: (86) 1065970921
Web Site: http://www.hkland.com
Property Investment & Management Services

N.A.I.C.S.: 523999

Hongkong Land (Chongqing) Management Co Ltd (4)
7/F Zone D Neptune Building No 62 Star Light Road, New North Zone, Chongqing, 401147, China
Tel.: (86) 23670330168
Web Site: http://www.hkland.com
Sales Range: $75-99.9 Million
Emp.: 110
Investment & Property Management Services
N.A.I.C.S.: 523999

Hongkong Land (Singapore) Pte. Limited (4)
One Raffles Quay 22-10 South Tower, Singapore, 48583, Singapore **(100%)**
Tel.: (65) 62381121
Sales Range: $25-49.9 Million
Emp.: 40
Real Estate Development Services
N.A.I.C.S.: 531390

Subsidiary (Domestic):

MCL Land Limited (5)
One Raffles Quay 19-10 South Tower, Singapore, 048583, Singapore **(100%)**
Tel.: (65) 62381121
Web Site: https://www.mclland.com.sg
Sales Range: $450-499.9 Million
Residential Property Development
N.A.I.C.S.: 531311
Tong Voon Lee *(COO)*

Subsidiary (Non-US):

MCL Land (Pantai View) Sdn. Bhd. (6)
Bintang Condominium No 88 Jln Bukit Pantai, 59100, Kuala Lumpur, Malaysia
Tel.: (60) 322828501
Property Management Services
N.A.I.C.S.: 531311

Subsidiary (Domestic):

The Hongkong Land Property Company, Limited (4)
8th Floor One Exchange Square, Central, China (Hong Kong)
Tel.: (852) 28428428
Web Site: http://www.hkland.com
Real Estate Development Services
N.A.I.C.S.: 531390

Group (Non-US):

Jardine Cycle & Carriage Limited (2)
239 Alexandra Road, Singapore, 159930, Singapore **(70%)**
Tel.: (65) 64733122
Web Site: http://www.jcclgroup.com
Rev.: $21,793,500,000
Assets: $29,303,200,000
Liabilities: $12,853,700,000
Net Worth: $16,449,500,000
Earnings: $2,455,900,000
Emp.: 240,000
Fiscal Year-end: 12/31/2022
Motor Vehicle Dealer & Distr
N.A.I.C.S.: 423110
Benjamin William Keswick *(Chm)*

Subsidiary (Domestic):

Cycle & Carriage Automotive Pte. Ltd. (3)
239 Alexandra Road, Singapore, 159930, Singapore
Tel.: (65) 64719111
Web Site: http://www.cyclecarriage.com
Automotive Distr
N.A.I.C.S.: 423110

Subsidiary (Non-US):

Cycle & Carriage Bintang Berhad (3)
Lot 19 Jalan 51A/219 Off Federal Highway, 46100, Petaling Jaya, Selangor Darul Ehsan, Malaysia **(88.03%)**
Tel.: (60) 378661100
Web Site: http://www.cyclecarriage.com.my
Rev.: $254,453,018
Assets: $123,995,025
Liabilities: $64,376,235
Net Worth: $59,618,790

Earnings: $1,186,763
Emp.: 704
Fiscal Year-end: 12/31/2021
Motor Vehicle Retailers
N.A.I.C.S.: 423120
Kok Leong Yeap *(Co-Sec)*

Subsidiary (Domestic):

Cycle & Carriage Bintang (Perak) Sdn. Bhd. (4)
75 Jalan Kuala Kangsar, 30010, Ipoh, Perak, Malaysia
Tel.: (60) 55064266
Vehicle Parts Retailer
N.A.I.C.S.: 441330

Subsidiary (Domestic):

Cycle & Carriage France Pte Ltd (3)
239 Alexandra Rd, Singapore, 159930, Singapore
Tel.: (65) 64792792
Automobile Dealers
N.A.I.C.S.: 441110

Cycle & Carriage Industries Pte Ltd (3)
301 Alexandra Rd, Singapore, 159968, Singapore
Tel.: (65) 62981818
Web Site: http://www.cyclecarriage.com.sg
Emp.: 300
Automotive Distr
N.A.I.C.S.: 423110
Teo Collin *(Head-Sls)*

Cycle & Carriage Kia Pte Ltd (3)
239 Alexandra Road, Singapore, 159931, Singapore
Tel.: (65) 64278800
Web Site: http://www.cyclecarriage.com
Automobile Parts Distr
N.A.I.C.S.: 423120

Diplomat Parts Pte Ltd (3)
209 Pandan Gardens, Singapore, 609339, Singapore
Tel.: (65) 65695041
Web Site: http://www.diplomatparts.com
Automobile Parts Sales & Maintenance Services
N.A.I.C.S.: 423120

Republic Auto Pte Ltd (3)
600 Sin Ming Avenue, Singapore, 575733, Singapore
Tel.: (65) 69328788
Web Site: http://www.republicauto.com.sg
Used Car Sales & Maintenance Services
N.A.I.C.S.: 441120

Holding (Domestic):

Mandarin Oriental International Limited (2)
Jardine House 33-35 Reid Street, Hamilton, HM 12, Bermuda
Tel.: (441) 2920140
Web Site: http://www.mandarinoriental.com
Rev.: $454,100,000
Assets: $4,252,700,000
Liabilities: $955,100,000
Net Worth: $3,297,600,000
Earnings: ($49,400,000)
Emp.: 12,681
Fiscal Year-end: 12/31/2022
Holding Company; Hotel & Resort Management Services
N.A.I.C.S.: 551112
Christoph Mares *(COO)*

Subsidiary (Non-US):

Mandarin Oriental Hotel Group Limited (3)
281 Gloucester Road, Causeway Bay, China (Hong Kong) **(100%)**
Tel.: (852) 28948888
Web Site: http://www.mandarinoriental.com
Sales Range: $1-4.9 Billion
Hotel & Resort Management Services; Corporate Office
N.A.I.C.S.: 561110
Christoph Mares *(COO)*

Subsidiary (Non-US):

MOHG Hotel (Paris) Sarl (4)
251 rue Saint-Honore, 75001, Paris, France
Tel.: (33) 170987888

INTERNATIONAL PUBLIC

Web Site: http://www.mandarinoriental.com
Sales Range: $10-24.9 Million
Emp.: 150
Home Management Services
N.A.I.C.S.: 722511

Subsidiary (US):

Mandarin Oriental Hotel Company, Inc. (4)
345 California St Ste 1250, San Francisco, CA 94104-2622
Tel.: (415) 772-8800
Web Site: http://www.mandarinoriental.com
Sales Range: $25-49.9 Million
Emp.: 25
Hotel Management Services; Regional Managing Office
N.A.I.C.S.: 561110

Branch (Domestic):

Mandarin Oriental Hotel Company, Inc. - New York Office (5)
888 7th Ave Ste 510, New York, NY 10106
Tel.: (212) 207-8880
Web Site: http://www.mandarinoriental.com
Sales Range: $50-74.9 Million
Emp.: 14
Hotel Management Services; Regional Managing Office
N.A.I.C.S.: 561110

Subsidiary (Domestic):

Mandarin Oriental Hotel Group International Limited (4)
7/F The Excelsior, Causeway Bay, China (Hong Kong)
Tel.: (852) 0028959288
Sales Range: $10-24.9 Million
Emp.: 100
Home Management Services
N.A.I.C.S.: 721110
Edouard Ettedgui *(Grp CEO)*

Subsidiary (Non-US):

Mandarin Oriental Hyde Park Limited (4)
66 Knightsbridge, London, SW1X 7LA, United Kingdom
Tel.: (44) 2072352000
Web Site: http://www.mandarinoriental.com
Home Management Services
N.A.I.C.S.: 721110

Mandarin Oriental Tokyo KK (4)
2-1-1 Nihonbashi Muromachi, Chuo-ku, Tokyo, 103-8328, Japan
Tel.: (81) 332708800
Web Site: http://www.mandarinoriental.com
Home Management Services
N.A.I.C.S.: 721110

Manila Mandarin Hotel Incorporated (4)
Makati Ave Paseo de Roxas, Makati, 1226, Metro Manila, Philippines
Tel.: (63) 27508888
Web Site: http://www.mandarinoriental.com
Home Management Services
N.A.I.C.S.: 721110

Affiliate (Non-US):

OHTL Public Company Limited (4)
48 Oriental Avenue, Bang Rak, Bangkok, Thailand **(40%)**
Tel.: (66) 26599000
Web Site: http://www.mandarinoriental.com
Rev.: $30,443,198
Assets: $224,645,920
Liabilities: $153,886,190
Net Worth: $70,759,729
Earnings: ($15,997,634)
Emp.: 1,000
Fiscal Year-end: 12/31/2020
Luxury Hotel Operator
N.A.I.C.S.: 721110
Nijaporn Charanachitta *(Chm)*

Subsidiary (Non-US):

P.T. Jaya Mandarin Agung (4)
Jalan M H Thamrin, PO Box 3392, Jakarta, 10310, Indonesia
Tel.: (62) 2139838888
Web Site: http://www.mandarinoriental.com
Home Management Services

N.A.I.C.S.: 721110
Maximilian von Reden *(Gen Mgr)*

Societe Immobiliere de Mandarin Oriental (Geneva) SA (4)
Quai Turrettini 3, Geneva, 1201, Switzerland
Tel.: (41) 229090000
Web Site: http://www.mandarinoriental.com
Emp.: 200
Real Estate Manangement Services
N.A.I.C.S.: 531390

Societe pour l'Exploitation de Mandarin Oriental (Geneva) SA (4)
Quai Turrettini 1, 1201, Geneva, Switzerland
Tel.: (41) 229090000
Web Site: http://www.mandarinoriental.com
Emp.: 200
Restaurant Management Services
N.A.I.C.S.: 722511

JARIR MARKETING COMPANY
PO Box 3196, Riyadh, 11471, Saudi Arabia
Tel.: (966) 920000089
Web Site: https://www.jarir.com
Year Founded: 1974
4190—(SAU)
Rev.: $2,504,119,184
Assets: $1,135,177,710
Liabilities: $654,832,956
Net Worth: $480,344,754
Earnings: $258,568,458
Emp.: 5,601
Fiscal Year-end: 12/31/22
Office & School Products Suppliers
N.A.I.C.S.: 459410

Subsidiaries:

Jarir Marketing Company Bahrain (1)
999 Rd, 4653, Manama, Bahrain
Tel.: (973) 77997755
Engineering Equipment Mfr & Distr
N.A.I.C.S.: 333924

JARLLYTEC CO., LTD.
No 13 Wu-Gong 5th RD, Hsin Chung Dist, New Taipei City, Taiwan
Tel.: (886) 222982666
Web Site: https://www.jarlly.com
3548—(TPE)
Rev.: $219,510,615
Assets: $283,051,371
Liabilities: $139,895,601
Net Worth: $143,155,770
Earnings: $14,819,373
Fiscal Year-end: 12/31/22
Financial Consulting Services
N.A.I.C.S.: 541611
Chang Tai-Yuan *(Gen Mgr)*

Subsidiaries:

Dong Guan Jarlly Electronics Co., Ltd. (1)
NO 12 Xin Gui Road, Lin Cun Tang Xia Town, Dongguan, 523711, Guangdong, China
Tel.: (86) 76938895958
Metal Products Mfr
N.A.I.C.S.: 332312

Jarlly Technology (Shanghai) Co., Ltd. (1)
NO 639 Guangzhong Road, Zhuanqiao Town Minhang District, Shanghai, 201308, China
Tel.: (86) 2131066699
Metal Products Mfr
N.A.I.C.S.: 332312

Jarson Precision Technology Co., Ltd. (1)
No 59 Wuquan 7th Road, Wugu District, New Taipei City, Taiwan
Tel.: (886) 222980926
Metal Products Mfr
N.A.I.C.S.: 332312

Xiamen Jarlly Electronics Co., Ltd. (1)
1633-4 Jicheng Road, Tong'an District, Xiamen, 361100, Fujian, China
Tel.: (86) 5927232123
Metal Products Mfr
N.A.I.C.S.: 332312

JARVIS PLC
Meridian House The Crescent, York, YO24 1AW, United Kingdom
Tel.: (44) 1904712712 UK
Web Site: http://www.jarvisplc.com
Year Founded: 1950
Sales Range: $450-499.9 Million
Emp.: 2,930
Holding Company; Railway Services
N.A.I.C.S.: 551112
Graham Denton *(Grp Fin Dir)*

Subsidiaries:

Jarvis Construction (UK) Limited (1)
Meridian House The Crescent, York, YO24 1AW, United Kingdom (100%)
Tel.: (44) 1904712667
Sales Range: $75-99.9 Million
Emp.: 500
Construction Related Services on Both a Traditional Design & Build Basis & as a Component for PFI Packages
N.A.I.C.S.: 541330

Jarvis Estates Limited (1)
Meridian House The Crescent, York, YO24 1AW, United Kingdom (100%)
Tel.: (44) 1904712667
Sales Range: $25-49.9 Million
Emp.: 50
Property Holding Company
N.A.I.C.S.: 551112

Jarvis Fastline Limited (1)
Frogmore Park, Watton-at-Stone, SG14 3RU, Herts, United Kingdom (100%)
Tel.: (44) 1920832800
Sales Range: $25-49.9 Million
Emp.: 50
Rail Infrastructure Services, Comprising Maintenance, Track Renewals, Signaling Electrification & Other Rail Projects
N.A.I.C.S.: 488210

Jarvis Projects Limited (1)
Frogmore Park, Watton-at-Stone, SG14 3RU, Herts, United Kingdom (100%)
Tel.: (44) 1920832800
Sales Range: $25-49.9 Million
Emp.: 30
Provides Property & Construction Related Services; Focuses on Turnkey Projects (Including PFI) & Niche Markets
N.A.I.C.S.: 541330

JARVIS SECURITIES PLC
78 Mount Ephraim, Tunbridge Wells, TN4 8BS, Kent, United Kingdom
Tel.: (44) 1892510515 UK
Web Site: https://www.jarvissecurities.co.uk
Year Founded: 1984
JIM—(LSE)
Rev.: $18,111,985
Assets: $15,681,666
Liabilities: $6,747,868
Net Worth: $8,933,798
Earnings: $7,548,923
Emp.: 57
Fiscal Year-end: 12/31/20
Stock Brokerage Services
N.A.I.C.S.: 523150
Andrew James Grant *(Chm & CEO)*

JAS ASSET PUBLIC COMPANY LIMITED
No 87 The Jas Ramintra Building 3rd Floor Room A315 Ladplakhao Road, Bang Khen District Anusawari Subdistrict, Bangkok, 10220, Thailand
Tel.: (66) 20121277
Web Site: https://www.jasasset.co.th
J—(THA)
Rev.: $16,123,559
Assets: $172,905,521
Liabilities: $87,816,214
Net Worth: $85,089,062
Earnings: $5,622,307
Emp.: 269
Fiscal Year-end: 12/31/23
Property Development
N.A.I.C.S.: 531390
Sukont Kanjana-Huttakit *(Chm)*

JASA KITA BERHAD
No 8 3rd Floor Jalan Segambut, 51200, Kuala Lumpur, Malaysia
Tel.: (60) 361951888
Web Site: https://www.jasakita.com.my
JASKITA—(KLS)
Rev.: $4,789,689
Assets: $13,972,661
Liabilities: $295,424
Net Worth: $13,677,237
Earnings: $110
Emp.: 46
Fiscal Year-end: 03/31/23
Engineering & Electric Motors Mfr
N.A.I.C.S.: 334515
Hin Weng Woo *(Exec Dir)*

Subsidiaries:

Jasa Kita Berhad - Factory (1)
Lot 10245 Jalan Batu Caves, Gombak, Batu Caves, 68100, Selangor Darul Ehsan, Malaysia
Tel.: (60) 361883795
Web Site: http://www.jasakita.com.my
Power Tool Mfr
N.A.I.C.S.: 333991

Jasa Kita Trading Sdn. Bhd. (1)
No 8 3rd Floor Jalan Segambut, Kuala Lumpur, 51200, Wilayah Persekutuan, Malaysia
Tel.: (60) 361951888
Web Site: http://www.jasakita.com.my
Sales Range: $50-74.9 Million
Emp.: 100
Power Tools & Industrial Equipments Distr
N.A.I.C.S.: 423710
Robert Tan *(Mng Dir)*

JASCH INDUSTRIES LIMITED
43/5 Bahalgarh Road, Sonipat, 131021, Haryana, India
Tel.: (91) 302216666
Web Site: https://www.jaschindustries.com
Year Founded: 1985
500220—(BOM)
Rev.: $20,660,341
Assets: $10,259,244
Liabilities: $3,487,303
Net Worth: $6,771,940
Earnings: $1,941,289
Emp.: 233
Fiscal Year-end: 03/31/24
Coated Fabric Mfr
N.A.I.C.S.: 313310
Jai Kishan Garg *(Chm & Mng Dir)*

JASCO ELECTRONICS HOLDINGS LIMITED
Cnr Alexandra Avenue & 2nd Street Halfway House, Midrand, 1685, Gauteng, South Africa
Tel.: (27) 112661500
Web Site: http://www.jasco.co.za
JSC—(JSE)
Rev.: $45,191,458
Assets: $24,773,904
Liabilities: $19,798,231
Net Worth: $4,975,673
Earnings: ($1,086,904)
Emp.: 393
Fiscal Year-end: 06/30/22
Electronic & Electrical Products Design & Mfr
N.A.I.C.S.: 334416
Warren A. Prinsloo *(CFO)*

Subsidiaries:

Jasco Electronics (1)
Cnr Alexandra Avenue and 2nd Street Halfway House, Midrand, 1685, Gauteng, South Africa
Tel.: (27) 112661500
Web Site: http://www.jasco.co.za
Sales Range: $25-49.9 Million
Emp.: 258
Technology Systems, Solutions & Integration Services
N.A.I.C.S.: 519290
Paul Fick *(Grp CTO)*

Subsidiary (Domestic):

Spescom Mobile Solutions (Proprietary) Limited (2)
PO Box 288, Midrand, 1685, Gauteng, South Africa
Tel.: (27) 112661500
Sales Range: $25-49.9 Million
Emp.: 200
Mobile Software Development Services
N.A.I.C.S.: 541511

Jasco Electronics Holdings Limited - Scafell Division (1)
20 The Hwy, Florida, 1708, Gauteng, South Africa
Tel.: (27) 116725198
Web Site: http://www.scafell.co.za
Sales Range: $25-49.9 Million
Emp.: 12
Security System Mfr
N.A.I.C.S.: 334290
Peter Achterberg *(COO)*

Jasco Trading (Pty) Limited (1)
12 Delphi Street Eastgate Ext 18, Sandton, Gauteng, South Africa
Tel.: (27) 117190000
Web Site: http://www.webb.co.za
Sales Range: $50-74.9 Million
Emp.: 12
Telecommunication Equipments & Accessories Whslr
N.A.I.C.S.: 423510
Paul Richards *(Mng Dir-Div)*

TeleSciences (Pty) Ltd. (1)
Conor Alexandra 2nd Half Way House, Midrand, 1632, Gauteng, South Africa
Tel.: (27) 118483900
Web Site: http://www.telesciences.co.za
Sales Range: $50-74.9 Million
Emp.: 200
Telecommunication Support Services
N.A.I.C.S.: 517810

Telesto Communications (Pty) Ltd (1)
Cambridge Office Park Building 26 First Floor No 5 Bauhinia Street, Centurion, 0169, Gauteng, South Africa
Tel.: (27) 126653010
Sales Range: $25-49.9 Million
Emp.: 9
Call Center Operation Services
N.A.I.C.S.: 561422

JASENOVO A.D.
Karadordeva 4, Nova Varos, Serbia
Tel.: (381) 3361479
Year Founded: 1994
JSNV—(BEL)
Sales Range: Less than $1 Million
Emp.: 12
Home Management Services
N.A.I.C.S.: 721110
Milinko Konatar *(Exec Dir)*

JASH DEALMARK LIMITED
C/18 Mulund Sahakar Vishwa CHS Nahur Road Sarvodaya Nagar Mulund W, Mumbai, 400 080, Maharashtra, India
Tel.: (91) 2225911914
Web Site: http://www.jashdealmark.co.in
Rev.: $53,498,394
Assets: $23,642,513
Liabilities: $20,362,541
Net Worth: $3,279,972
Earnings: $189,301
Emp.: 10
Fiscal Year-end: 03/31/18

JASH DEALMARK LIMITED

Jash Dealmark Limited—(Continued)
International Goods Trading Services
N.A.I.C.S.: 522299

JASH ENGINEERING LIMITED
31 Sector-C Sanwer Road Industrial Area, Indore, 452015, Madhya Pradesh, India
Tel.: (91) 7312720143
Web Site: https://www.jashindia.com
Year Founded: 1948
JASH—(NSE)
Rev.: $49,782,111
Assets: $53,775,985
Liabilities: $25,153,552
Net Worth: $28,622,433
Earnings: $6,198,813
Emp.: 575
Fiscal Year-end: 03/31/23
Industrial Valve Mfr
N.A.I.C.S.: 333310
Choksi Patel *(Mng Dir)*

Subsidiaries:

Jash USA Inc. (1)
Tel.: (281) 962-6369
Web Site: https://rodneyhunt.com
Water Control Gate Mfr
N.A.I.C.S.: 332911

Rodney Hunt Inc. (1)
46 Mill St, Orange, MA 01364
Tel.: (281) 962-6369
Web Site: https://www.rodneyhunt.com
Steel Component Mfr
N.A.I.C.S.: 331110

Shivpad Engineers Pvt. Ltd. (1)
Plot 3/86-E ATC Road 2nd Main Road, Ambattur Industrial Estate, Chennai, 600 058, Tamil Nadu, India
Tel.: (91) 4448606201
Web Site: https://www.shivpad.com
Water Treatment Equipment Mfr
N.A.I.C.S.: 333310

JASMINE INTERNATIONAL PUBLIC COMPANY LIMITED
200 29 th-30 th Floor Moo 4 Chaengwatana Road, Pakkred District, Nonthaburi, 11120, Thailand
Tel.: (66) 21003000
Web Site: https://www.jasmine.com
Year Founded: 1982
JASUF—(OTCIQ)
Rev.: $591,954,768
Assets: $2,208,868,794
Liabilities: $2,233,565,201
Net Worth: ($24,696,407)
Earnings: ($24,404,487)
Emp.: 723
Fiscal Year-end: 12/31/23
Telecommunication Servicesb
N.A.I.C.S.: 517121
Saijai Kitsin *(Pres & CEO-Acting)*

Subsidiaries:

ACeS Regional Service Co., Ltd. (1)
200 Moo 4 Jasmine International Tower 7th Fl Chaengwatana Road, Pakkret, Nonthaburi, 11120, Thailand
Tel.: (66) 25024000
Web Site: http://www.acesthailand.com
Sales Range: $25-49.9 Million
Emp.: 50
Cellular Telecommunications
N.A.I.C.S.: 517112

Acumen Co., Ltd. (1)
200 Moo 4 7th Fl Jasmine International Tower Chaengwatana Rd, Pakkred Subdistrict Pakkred District, Nonthaburi, 11120, Thailand
Tel.: (66) 21003000
Web Site: http://www.acumen.co.th
Satellite Telecommunications
N.A.I.C.S.: 517410

In Cloud Co., Ltd. (1)
200 Moo 4 Chaengwatana Rd, Pakkred Sub-district Pakkred District, Nonthaburi, 11120, Thailand
Tel.: (66) 21004400
Broadband Network Providing Services
N.A.I.C.S.: 517111

JasTel Network Co., Ltd. (1)
200 Moo4 7th Fl Jasmine International Tower Chaengwattana Rd, Pakkret, Pakkret, 11120, Nonthaburi, Thailand
Tel.: (66) 2 100 3183
Web Site: https://www.jastel.co.th
Telecommunication Network Services
N.A.I.C.S.: 517810
Pete Bodharamik *(Pres)*

Jasmine Internet Co., Ltd. (1)
200 Moo 4 8th Fl Chaengwatana Rd, Pakkred Sub-district Pakkred District, Nonthaburi, 11120, Thailand
Tel.: (66) 25023700
Web Site: https://www.ji-net.com
Internet Services
N.A.I.C.S.: 517810

Jasmine Submarine Telecommunications Co., Ltd. (1)
200 7th Floor Moo 4 Chaengwatana Road, Pakkred Sub-district Pakkred District, Nonthaburi, 11120, Thailand
Tel.: (66) 21003183
Web Site: http://www.jasmine.com
Submarine Fiber Optic Cable Network
N.A.I.C.S.: 335921

Premium Asset Co., Ltd. (1)
200 Moo 4 Chaengwatana Rd, Pakkred Sub-district Pakkred District, Nonthaburi, 11120, Thailand
Tel.: (66) 21003000
Space Rental Management Services
N.A.I.C.S.: 531120

Siam Teltech Computer Co., Ltd. (1)
200 Moo 4 Jasmin International Building Tumbol, Pak Kret Amphoe, Pak Kret, 11120, Nonthaburi, Thailand
Tel.: (66) 25023000
Web Site: http://www.stcc.jasmine.com
Computer Data Networking Services
N.A.I.C.S.: 541519

Smart Highway Co., Ltd. (1)
200 Moo 4 Chaengwatana Rd, Pakkred Sub-district Pakkred District, Nonthaburi, 11120, Thailand
Tel.: (66) 21003000
Data Communication Services
N.A.I.C.S.: 517810

Thai Long Distance Telecommunications Co., Ltd. (1)
200 Moo 4 Chaengwatana Rd, Pakkred Sub-district Pakkred District, Nonthaburi, 11120, Thailand
Tel.: (66) 21003183
Broadband Network Providing Services
N.A.I.C.S.: 517111

JASMINE TECHNOLOGY SOLUTION PUBLIC COMPANY LIMITED
200 Moo 4 9th Floor Jasmine International Tower Chaengwatana Road, Tambon Pakkret Amphoe Pakkret, Nonthaburi, 11120, Thailand
Tel.: (66) 21008300
Web Site: https://www.jts.co.th
Year Founded: 2004
JTS—(THA)
Rev.: $69,173,209
Assets: $67,506,950
Liabilities: $52,011,160
Net Worth: $15,495,790
Earnings: $177,670
Emp.: 295
Fiscal Year-end: 12/31/23
Telecommunication System Design Services
N.A.I.C.S.: 517810
Sang Do Lee *(Pres)*

JASON CO., LTD.
2-8-5 Otsugaoka, Kashiwa, 277-0921, Chiba, Japan
Tel.: (81) 471930911
Web Site: https://www.jason.co.jp
Year Founded: 1973
3080—(TKS)
Rev.: $203,766,600
Assets: $76,330,940
Liabilities: $32,940,140
Net Worth: $43,390,800
Earnings: $4,268,180
Emp.: 182
Fiscal Year-end: 02/29/24
General Merchandise Store Owner & Operator
N.A.I.C.S.: 455219
Masahiko Ota *(Chm & Pres)*

JASON FURNITURE HANGZHOU CO LTD
Jason Building No 599 Dongning Road, Jianggan District, Hangzhou, 310017, China
Tel.: (86) 57188603816
Web Site: http://www.kukahome.com
Year Founded: 2006
603816—(SHG)
Rev.: $2,528,666,745
Assets: $2,261,231,014
Liabilities: $987,307,514
Net Worth: $1,273,923,500
Earnings: $254,411,511
Fiscal Year-end: 12/31/22
Furniture Mfr & Distr
N.A.I.C.S.: 337121
Chen Bangdeng *(Sec)*

JASON MARINE GROUP LIMITED
194 Pandan Loop No 06-05 Pantech Business Hub, Singapore, 128383, Singapore
Tel.: (65) 64777700
Web Site: https://www.jason.com.sg
Year Founded: 1976
5PF—(CAT)
Rev.: $25,680,622
Assets: $25,576,880
Liabilities: $9,339,014
Net Worth: $16,237,866
Earnings: $133,383
Emp.: 142
Fiscal Year-end: 03/31/24
Marine Services
N.A.I.C.S.: 488320
Joseph Chew Tuck Foo *(Founder, Chm & CEO)*

Subsidiaries:

Jason (Shanghai) Co., Ltd. (1)
16H New Shanghai City Bldg 33 He Nan Rd S, Shanghai, 200002, China
Tel.: (86) 2163375966
Web Site: http://www.jason.com.sg
Sales Range: $25-49.9 Million
Emp.: 20
Marine Communication & Navigation Equipments Distr
N.A.I.C.S.: 423690

Jason Electronics (Pte) Ltd (1)
194 Pandan Loop Unit 06-05 Pantech Business Hub, Singapore, 128383, Singapore
Tel.: (65) 64777700
Web Site: http://www.jason.com.sg
Emp.: 160
Communication Equipment Whslr
N.A.I.C.S.: 423690

Jason Electronics (Thailand) Co., Ltd. (1)
113/6 Soi Latplakhao 24 Kasit-Nawamin Road, Jorakhae-bua Latphrao, Bangkok, 10230, Thailand
Tel.: (66) 2553 2290
Web Site: http://www.jason.com.sg
Communication Equipment Sales
N.A.I.C.S.: 334290

Jason Elektronik (M) Sdn. Bhd. (1)
B-UG-2 Zenopy Shoplot Jalan Lestari Perdana LP7/4 Bandar Putra Permai, 43300, Seri Kembangan, Selangor, Malaysia
Tel.: (60) 182885628
Web Site: http://www.jason.com.sg

INTERNATIONAL PUBLIC

Communication Equipment Maintenance & Sales
N.A.I.C.S.: 423690

Jason Marine Electronics Spain, S.L. (1)
Juan Perez Arriete S/N Edificio Nexus Oficina B1 1, 11204, Algeciras, Spain
Tel.: (34) 856034035
Electronic Equipment Repair Services
N.A.I.C.S.: 811310

Marine Innovation Pte. Ltd. (1)
194 Pandan Loop 06-01 Pantech Business Hub, Singapore, 128383, Singapore
Tel.: (65) 64777737
Web Site: https://www.marinov.com.sg
Consumer Products Distr
N.A.I.C.S.: 423990
Dominic Oliver *(Sls Dir)*

PT. Jason Elektronika (1)
Jalan Gunung Sahari Raya No 2 Komp Marina Mangga Dua Blok F 20, Jakarta, 11410, Indonesia
Tel.: (62) 21 641 5491
Web Site: http://www.jason.com.sg
Sales Range: $50-74.9 Million
Emp.: 10
Communication Equipment Whslr
N.A.I.C.S.: 423690
Danny Santoso *(Mgr-Ops)*

JASON PARQUET HOLDINGS LIMITED
16 Tampines St 92 JP Building, Singapore, 528873, Singapore
Tel.: (65) 6783 2727
Web Site: http://www.jasonparquet.com
Year Founded: 1987
Sales Range: $10-24.9 Million
Timber Flooring Services
N.A.I.C.S.: 238330
Andrew Loke *(Controller)*

JASON SHIPPING ASA
Ruselokkveien 6, 0251, Oslo, Norway
Tel.: (47) 92608912
Web Site: http://www.jason-shipping.com
Sales Range: Less than $1 Million
Emp.: 4
Holding Company; Shipping & Other Water-Related Transportation Services
N.A.I.C.S.: 551112
Siv Jonland Staubo *(Chm)*

JASPER INVESTMENTS LIMITED
1 Kallang Junction 06-01 Vanguard Campus, 04-08C Sime Darby Centre, Singapore, 339263, Singapore
Tel.: (65) 31058628   SG
Web Site: http://www.jasperinvests.com
Year Founded: 1987
FQ7—(SES)
Assets: $259,000
Liabilities: $1,248,000
Net Worth: ($989,000)
Earnings: ($607,000)
Emp.: 2
Fiscal Year-end: 03/31/24
Investment Holding Company
N.A.I.C.S.: 551112
Michael Wai Kwong Chan *(Chm)*

JASPER MINING CORPORATION
Suite 501 888 4th Avenue SW, Calgary, T2P 0V2, AB, Canada
Tel.: (403) 297-9480   AB
Web Site: http://www.jaspermining.com
Year Founded: 1994
JAMGF—(OTCIQ)
Rev.: $1,201,229
Assets: $7,088,473

Liabilities: $4,261,786
Net Worth: $2,826,687
Earnings: $901,254
Emp.: 5
Fiscal Year-end: 12/31/23
Mineral Exploration Services
N.A.I.C.S.: 213114
Gordon F. Dixon *(Pres & CEO)*

JASTECH LTD.
433-15 Sandong-ro, Eumbong-myeon, Asan, 403858, Chungcheongnam-do, Korea (South)
Tel.: (82) 414215000
Web Site: https://www.jastech.co.kr
090470—(KRS)
Rev.: $110,401,748
Assets: $145,970,460
Liabilities: $30,863,812
Net Worth: $115,106,649
Earnings: $21,128,536
Emp.: 252
Fiscal Year-end: 12/31/22
Electronic Component Mfr & Distr
N.A.I.C.S.: 334419
Jae-Song Chung *(Chm & CEO)*

JASTRZEBSKA SPOLKA WE-GLOWA S.A.
Aleja Jana Pawla II 4, 44-330, Jastrzebie-Zdroj, Poland
Tel.: (48) 327564113
Web Site: https://www.jsw.pl
Year Founded: 1993
JSW—(WAR)
Rev.: $2,279,556,066
Assets: $3,923,702,768
Liabilities: $1,596,908,963
Net Worth: $2,326,793,805
Earnings: $170,760,352
Emp.: 30,629
Fiscal Year-end: 12/31/19
Coking Coal Producer
N.A.I.C.S.: 324199
Artur Dyczko *(Member-Mgmt Bd & VP-Technical & Operational Matters)*

Subsidiaries:

Advicom Sp. z o.o. (1)
Armii Krajowej 56, 44-330, Jastrzebie-Zdroj, Poland
Tel.: (48) 324762345
Web Site: http://www.advicom.pl
Information Technology Consulting Services
N.A.I.C.S.: 541512

Carbotrans Sp. z o.o. (1)
Ul Pawliczka 1, 41-800, Zabrze, Poland
Tel.: (48) 323702054
Web Site: http://www.carbotrans.eu
Road Transport Services
N.A.I.C.S.: 484110

Centralne Laboratorium Pomiarowo-Badawcze Sp. z o.o. (1)
ul Rybnicka 6, 44-335, Jastrzebie-Zdroj, Poland
Tel.: (48) 327565296
Laboratory Testing Services
N.A.I.C.S.: 541380

Dzwigi Sp. z o.o. (1)
11 Listopada 71 Woj Slaskie, 44-335, Jastrzebie-Zdroj, Poland
Tel.: (48) 324762534
Web Site: http://www.jzr-dzwigi.eu
Lifting Equipment Handling Services
N.A.I.C.S.: 811310

Fundacja JSW SA (1)
ul Armii Krajowej 56, 44-330, Jastrzebie-Zdroj, Poland
Tel.: (48) 327564820
Web Site: http://www.fundacjajsw.pl
Charity Services
N.A.I.C.S.: 813219

Hawk-e Sp. z o.o. (1)
Al Krakowska 2A, 02-284, Warsaw, Poland
Tel.: (48) 222903332
Web Site: http://www.hawk-e.pl
Consulting Services
N.A.I.C.S.: 541611

JSU Sp. z o.o. (1)
ul Rybnicka 6, 44-335, Jastrzebie-Zdroj, Poland
Tel.: (48) 327565377
Web Site: http://www.jsu.pl
Insurance Services
N.A.I.C.S.: 524210

JSW IT SYSTEMS Sp. z o.o. (1)
ul Armii Krajowej 56, 44-330, Jastrzebie-Zdroj, Poland
Tel.: (48) 327002710
Web Site: http://www.jswits.pl
IT Services
N.A.I.C.S.: 541511

JSW KOKS S.A. (1)
ul Pawliczka 1, 41-800, Zabrze, Poland
Tel.: (48) 327575900
Web Site: http://www.jswkoks.pl
Coal Mining Services
N.A.I.C.S.: 212115

JSW Logistics Sp. z o.o. (1)
ul Ignacego Paderewskiego 41, 40-282, Katowice, Poland
Tel.: (48) 327295450
Web Site: http://www.jswlogistics.pl
Railway Logistics Services
N.A.I.C.S.: 488510

JSW Ochrona Sp. z o.o. (1)
ul Armii Krajowej 39, 44-330, Jastrzebie-Zdroj, Poland
Tel.: (48) 324795620
Web Site: http://www.jswochrona.pl
Security Services
N.A.I.C.S.: 561612

JSW Szkolenie i Gornictwo Sp. z o.o. (1)
ul Weglowa 4, 44-268, Jastrzebie-Zdroj, Poland
Tel.: (48) 327561620
Web Site: http://www.jswsig.pl
Mining Training Center Services
N.A.I.C.S.: 611430

Jastrzebska Spolka Kolejowa Sp. z o.o. (1)
Towarowa 1, Jastrzebie-Zdroj, 44-330, Poland
Tel.: (48) 324759580
Railway Maintenance Services
N.A.I.C.S.: 488210

Jastrzebskie Zaklady Remontowe Sp. z o.o. (1)
ul Weglowa 4, 44-268, Jastrzebie-Zdroj, Poland
Tel.: (48) 327215100
Web Site: http://www.jzr.pl
Mining Machinery Mfr
N.A.I.C.S.: 333131

Koksownia Przyjazn Sp. z o.o. (1)
ul Koksownicza 1, 42-523, Dabrowa Gornicza, Poland
Tel.: (48) 32 757 50 00
Web Site: http://www.przyjazn.com.pl
Sales Range: $450-499.9 Million
Emp.: 200
Coke Mfr
N.A.I.C.S.: 324199
Edward Szlek *(Chm-Mgmt Bd & Gen Dir)*

Polski Koks S.A. (1)
421 Street 42, 4282, Katowice, Poland
Tel.: (48) 32 357 09 00
Web Site: http://www.polskikoks.pl
Sales Range: $25-49.9 Million
Emp.: 30
Coal Distr
N.A.I.C.S.: 423520

Przedsiebiorstwo Budowy Szybow S.A. (1)
ul Hutnicza 5-9, 42-600, Tarnowskie Gory, Poland
Tel.: (48) 327365000
Web Site: http://www.jswpbsz.pl
Underground Construction Services
N.A.I.C.S.: 237130

Przedsiebiorstwo Gospodarki Wodnej i Rekultywacji S.A. (1)
ul Chlebowa 22, 44-335, Jastrzebie-Zdroj, Poland
Tel.: (48) 324763073
Web Site: http://www.pgwir.pl
Sewage Discharge Services
N.A.I.C.S.: 221320

ZREM-BUD Sp. z o.o. (1)
ul Koksownicza 1, 42-523, Dabrowa Gornicza, Poland
Tel.: (48) 327575123
Web Site: http://www.zrem-bud.pl
Machine Repair Services
N.A.I.C.S.: 811310

JASUINDO TIGA PERKASA TBK
Jalan Raya Betro No 21 Sedati Sidoarjo, Surabaya, 61253, Jawa Timur, Indonesia
Tel.: (62) 318910919
Web Site: https://www.jasuindo.com
Year Founded: 1990
JTPE—(INDO)
Rev.: $149,119,878
Assets: $116,227,932
Liabilities: $45,760,271
Net Worth: $70,467,661
Earnings: $14,650,904
Emp.: 541
Fiscal Year-end: 12/31/23
Payment Protection Services
N.A.I.C.S.: 522210
Lukito Budiman *(Fin Dir & Sec)*

JATALIA GLOBAL VENTURES LIMITED
500 5th Floor ITL Twin Tower Netaji Subhash Place Pitampura, New Delhi, 110 034, Delhi, India
Tel.: (91) 9911149069
Web Site: https://www.jatalia.in
Year Founded: 1987
519319—(BOM)
Rev.: $26,035
Assets: $410,222
Liabilities: $631,991
Net Worth: ($221,769)
Earnings: ($2,294,955)
Emp.: 2
Fiscal Year-end: 03/31/23
Software Development Services
N.A.I.C.S.: 541511
Anshu Jain *(Chm & Compliance Officer)*

JATCORP LIMITED
Suite 306 521 Toorak Road, Toorak, 3142, VIC, Australia
Tel.: (61) 280980232
Web Site: https://www.jatenergy.com
Year Founded: 2007
JAT—(ASX)
Rev.: $29,004,926
Assets: $17,467,768
Liabilities: $11,735,612
Net Worth: $5,732,156
Earnings: ($7,670,917)
Fiscal Year-end: 06/30/22
Biodiesel & Biodiesel Feedstock Producer
N.A.I.C.S.: 325414
Wilton Yao *(Mng Dir)*

Subsidiaries:

Australian Natural Milk Association Pty Ltd (1)
29 Paramount Boulevard, Derrimut, Melbourne, 3030, VIC, Australia
Tel.: (61) 393638988
Web Site: http://www.anmadairy.com.au
Dairy Products Mfr
N.A.I.C.S.: 311511

JATEC ELECTRIC LTD.
100 2304 119th St NE, Edmonton, T6S 1B3, AB, Canada
Tel.: (780) 466-5832
Web Site: http://www.jatec.ca
Year Founded: 1984
Rev.: $12,961,678
Emp.: 75
Electrical Contracting & Installation Services
N.A.I.C.S.: 238210
Jim Allen *(CEO)*

JATET PETRO TECHNOLOGY PLC
No 6 Block 0812 Chaowai SOHO A Room B Chaowai Street, Chaoyang District, Beijing, China
Tel.: (86) 1059003358
Web Site: http://www.jatet.net
Year Founded: 1996
Oil & Gas Exploration Services
N.A.I.C.S.: 213112
Wusheng Zhang *(Pres & CEO)*

JATOM SYSTEMS INC.
99 Michael Cowpland Drive, Kanata, K2M 1X3, ON, Canada
Tel.: (613) 591-5910
Web Site: http://www.jsitelecom.com
Year Founded: 1979
Rev.: $39,336,074
Emp.: 140
Telecommunication Servicesb
N.A.I.C.S.: 517810

JATTASHANKAR INDUSTRIES LIMITED
11 Parasrampuria Apartment Film City Road Gokuldham, Goregaon East, Mumbai, 400 063, India
Tel.: (91) 2228414262
Web Site: https://www.jsil.in
Year Founded: 1988
514318—(BOM)
Rev.: $1,958,144
Assets: $2,101,061
Liabilities: $205,839
Net Worth: $1,895,222
Earnings: $62,958
Fiscal Year-end: 03/31/23
Polyester Yarn Mfr
N.A.I.C.S.: 313110
Sharad Poddar *(Exec Dir)*

JAUHARABAD SUGAR MILLS LIMITED
125-B Quaid-e-Azam Industrial Estate Kot Lakh Pat, Lahore, Pakistan
Tel.: (92) 4235213491
Web Site: https://jsml.com.pk
Year Founded: 1968
JSML—(PSX)
Rev.: $24,598,071
Assets: $43,460,849
Liabilities: $11,976,081
Net Worth: $31,484,768
Earnings: $753,768
Emp.: 623
Fiscal Year-end: 09/30/23
Sugar Mfr
N.A.I.C.S.: 311314
Muhammad Usman Afzaal *(Head-Internal Audit)*

JAUNATO
Z Artisanale Grossines Rue Des Entrepreneurs, Marennes, 17320, Lyon, France
Tel.: (33) 546858050
Rev.: $20,100,000
Emp.: 41
Grocery Stores
N.A.I.C.S.: 445110
Arnaud Noel *(Pres)*

JAUSS POLYMERS LIMITED
Plot No-51 Roz Ka Meo Industrial Area Sohna, Gurgaon, 122103, India
Tel.: (91) 1126427394   In

JAUSS POLYMERS LIMITED

Jauss Polymers Limited—(Continued)
Web Site:
    https://www.jausspolymers.com
Year Founded: 1989
526001—(BOM)
Assets: $1,295,876
Liabilities: $33,279
Net Worth: $1,262,598
Earnings: ($34,207)
Emp.: 2
Fiscal Year-end: 03/31/22
Plastic Bottle & Container Mfr
N.A.I.C.S.: 326160
Ketineni Sayaji Rao *(Chm & Mng Dir)*

JAVED OMER VOHRA & COMPANY LIMITED
507-511 5th Fl Pakistan Stock Exchange Building II Chundrigar Rd, Karachi, 74000, Sindh, Pakistan
Tel.: (92) 21 32424051
Web Site: http://www.jovcoltd.com
Year Founded: 1992
JOVC—(KAR)
Sales Range: Less than $1 Million
Financial Consultancy & Brokerage Services
N.A.I.C.S.: 523150
Muhammad Bilal Vohra *(CEO)*

JAWALA INC.
H-7-10 Block H Aeropod Commercial Square Tanjung Aru Kepayan, 88100, Kota Kinabalu, Sabah, Malaysia
Tel.: (60) 88252323
Web Site: https://www.jawalainc.com
Year Founded: 2017
1J7—(CAT)
Rev.: $2,371,017
Assets: $12,955,147
Liabilities: $2,997,462
Net Worth: $9,957,686
Earnings: ($189,912)
Emp.: 130
Fiscal Year-end: 07/31/23
Forest Management Services
N.A.I.C.S.: 111421
Jema Anton Khan *(Chm & CEO)*

JAXON MINING INC.
1100 - 1111 Melville Street, Vancouver, V6E 3V6, BC, Canada
Tel.: (604) 424-4488
Web Site:
    https://www.jaxonmining.com
Year Founded: 2006
JXMNF—(OTCIQ)
Rev.: $94
Assets: $6,184,393
Liabilities: $693,954
Net Worth: $5,490,438
Earnings: ($754,157)
Emp.: 8
Fiscal Year-end: 01/31/22
Gold Mining & Exploration Services
N.A.I.C.S.: 212220
John King Burns *(Chm, Chm & CEO)*

JAXSTA LIMITED
Level 1 113-115 Oxford Street, Darlinghurst, 2010, NSW, Australia
Tel.: (61) 283171000
Web Site: http://www.jaxsta.com
VNL—(ASX)
Rev.: $3,319,052
Assets: $11,672,482
Liabilities: $7,884,452
Net Worth: $3,788,030
Earnings: ($11,275,168)
Fiscal Year-end: 06/30/24
Music Database Platform
N.A.I.C.S.: 512230
Jacqui Louez Schoorl *(Co-Founder, CEO & Exec Dir)*

JAY BHARAT MARUTI LTD
Plot No 9 Institutional Area Sector 44, Gurgaon, 122003, Haryana, India
Tel.: (91) 1244674500
Web Site: https://www.jbmgroup.com
JAYBARMARU—(NSE)
Rev.: $272,182,583
Assets: $336,329,571
Liabilities: $234,553,096
Net Worth: $101,776,475
Earnings: $6,729,505
Emp.: 1,981
Fiscal Year-end: 03/31/21
Automotive Product Mfr
N.A.I.C.S.: 336110
S. K. Arya *(Chm & Mng Dir)*

JAY ENERGY & S. ENERGIES LIMITED
C-327 SidhiVinayak Tower S.G. Highway Makarba, Ahmedabad, 380051, Gujarat, India
Tel.: (91) 99989 43518
Assets: $965,964
Liabilities: $19,519
Net Worth: $946,446
Earnings: ($17,759)
Fiscal Year-end: 03/31/16
Financial Investment Services
N.A.I.C.S.: 523999
Amul Gandhi *(Compliance Officer)*

JAY MART PUBLIC COMPANY LIMITED
187 189 Jaymart Building Ramkhamhaeng Road Rat Phatthana, Sapansoong, Bangkok, 10240, Thailand
Tel.: (66) 23088196
Web Site: https://www.jaymart.co.th
JMART—(THA)
Rev.: $401,199,663
Assets: $1,816,898,125
Liabilities: $861,508,610
Net Worth: $955,389,515
Earnings: $17,490,658
Emp.: 1,041
Fiscal Year-end: 12/31/23
Mobile Phones & Accessories Retailer
N.A.I.C.S.: 517112
Pisnu Pong-Acha *(Chm)*

Subsidiaries:

JMT Network Services Company Limited (1)
187 Jaymart Bldg 4-6 FL Ramkhamhaeng Rd, Rat Phatthana Sapansoong, Bangkok, 10240, Thailand
Tel.: (66) 23089999
Web Site: https://www.jmtnetwork.co.th
Rev.: $148,487,494
Assets: $1,239,037,018
Liabilities: $441,879,396
Net Worth: $797,157,621
Earnings: $60,532,958
Emp.: 2,137
Fiscal Year-end: 12/31/2023
Debt Management Services
N.A.I.C.S.: 561440
Adisak Sukumwittaya *(Chm)*

JAY SHREE TEA & INDUSTRIES LTD
Industry House 15th Floor 10 Camac Street, Kolkata, 700 017, India
Tel.: (91) 3322827534
Web Site:
    https://www.jayshreetea.com
JAYSREETEA—(NSE)
Rev.: $112,325,817
Assets: $128,989,825
Liabilities: $96,049,863
Net Worth: $32,939,962
Earnings: $346,792
Emp.: 19,341
Fiscal Year-end: 03/31/21
Tea & Chemical Exporter
N.A.I.C.S.: 424690
D. P. Maheshwari *(Mng Dir)*

JAY USHIN LTD
GP-14 HSIIDC Industrial Estate Sector-18, Gurgaon, 122001, Haryana, India
Tel.: (91) 1244623400
Web Site: https://www.jpmgroup.co.in
513252—(BOM)
Rev.: $91,306,966
Assets: $46,266,074
Liabilities: $34,597,631
Net Worth: $11,668,443
Earnings: $1,629,646
Emp.: 366
Fiscal Year-end: 03/31/22
Switches, Body Parts & Security Systems Mfr
N.A.I.C.S.: 334419
Ashwani Minda *(CEO & Mng Dir)*

JAYA HIND INDUSTRIES GROUP
Mumbai-Pune Akurdi, Pune, Maharashtra, India
Tel.: (91) 20 2747 3981
Web Site: http://www.jayahind.com
Holding Company
N.A.I.C.S.: 551112

JAYA HOLDINGS LIMITED
13 Tuas Crescent, Singapore, 638707, Singapore
Tel.: (65) 62651010
Web Site:
    http://jayaholdings.creaworld.sg
Year Founded: 1981
Sales Range: Less than $1 Million
Holding Company
N.A.I.C.S.: 551112
George Richard Horsington *(Pres-Offshore & Bus Dev)*

JAYA KONSTRUKSI MANGGALA PRATAMA TBK
Kantor Taman Bintaro Jaya Gedung B Jalan Bintaro Raya, Jakarta, 12330, Indonesia
Tel.: (62) 217363939
Web Site:
    https://www.jayakonstruksi.com
JKON—(INDO)
Rev.: $295,396,130
Assets: $285,496,380
Liabilities: $87,129,842
Net Worth: $198,366,538
Earnings: $15,703,453
Emp.: 869
Fiscal Year-end: 12/31/23
Building Construction Services
N.A.I.C.S.: 236210
Sutopo Kristanto *(Chm)*

Subsidiaries:

PT Jaya Beton Indonesia (1)
Jalan Letjen S Parman Kav 17-18, Palmerah, Jakarta Barat, Indonesia
Tel.: (62) 5902385
Construction Engineering Services
N.A.I.C.S.: 541330

Subsidiary (Domestic):

PT Jaya Celcon Prima (2)
Jl Raya Tangerang - Serang Km 22, Cikupa, Tangerang, 15710, Indonesia
Tel.: (62) 2159 622 6061
Web Site: https://www.jayacelcon.com
Celcon Block Mfr
N.A.I.C.S.: 327331

PT Jaya Daido Concrete (1)
Jalan Jenderal Gatot Soebroto Km 8 5 Desa Kadu Jaya, Tangerang, Indonesia
Tel.: (62) 215902385
Concrete Products Mfr
N.A.I.C.S.: 327390

PT Jaya Teknik Indonesia (1)
Gedung Jaya Teknik Jalan Johar No 10, Jakarta, Indonesia
Tel.: (62) 23555999

INTERNATIONAL PUBLIC

Construction Engineering Services
N.A.I.C.S.: 541330

Subsidiary (Domestic):

PT Jaya Multi Sarana Indonesia (2)
Jalan Johar Number 10 Kelurahan Kebon Sirih, Menteng, Jakarta Pusat, 10340, Jakarta, Indonesia
Tel.: (62) 212 355 5999
Web Site: https://www.jayamultisarana.com
Construction Services
N.A.I.C.S.: 541330

PT Jaya Trade Indonesia (1)
Jalan Kramat Raya No 144, Jakarta, 10430, Indonesia
Tel.: (62) 3159999
Construction Engineering Services
N.A.I.C.S.: 541330

Subsidiary (Domestic):

PT Kenrope Sarana Pratama (2)
Jl Raya Narogong KM 13, Cikiwul, Bekasi, Indonesia
Tel.: (62) 2182600519
Asphalt Material Mfr
N.A.I.C.S.: 324121

PT Kenrope Utama Sentul (2)
Jl Tengsaw No 18 Kp Sabur RT 02 RW 05, Tarikolot Citeureup, Bogor, 16810, Jawa Barat, Indonesia
Tel.: (62) 2187943161
Asphalt Material Mfr
N.A.I.C.S.: 324121

PT Sarana Aceh Utama (2)
Kompleks Pelabuhan Malahayati Jl Laksamana Malahayati KM 32, 5 Gampong Lamreh Kec Kab Aceh Besar, Mesjid Raya, 23381, Aceh, Indonesia
Tel.: (62) 65 163 6049
Web Site: https://www.saranaaceh.com
Asphalt Material Mfr
N.A.I.C.S.: 324121
Hannimi Nasution *(Gen Mgr)*

PT Sarana Jambi Utama (2)
Jl Lintas Timur Aur Duri KM 16 No 49, Jambi, Indonesia
Tel.: (62) 74 158 2270
Web Site: https://www.saranajambi.com
Asphalt Material Mfr
N.A.I.C.S.: 324121
Lukman Alwi *(Gen Mgr)*

PT Sarana Mbay Utama (2)
Jl Gatot Subroto KM 4 RT/RW 032/016, Ende Timur, Mautapaga, Ende Flores, Indonesia
Tel.: (62) 38121904
Asphalt Material Mfr
N.A.I.C.S.: 324121
My Doni Musdi *(Gen Mgr)*

PT Sarana Sampit Mentaya Utama (2)
Jl CPO Tanjung Kalaf RT18 Kumai Hulu, Pangkalan Bun, Indonesia
Tel.: (62) 53229444
Web Site: http://www.saranasampit.com
Asphalt Material Mfr
N.A.I.C.S.: 324121

JAYA REAL PROPERTY TBK
CBD Emerald Blok CE/A No 1 Boulevard Bintaro Jaya, Tangerang, 15227, Indonesia
Tel.: (62) 217458888
Web Site:
    https://www.jayaproperty.com
JRPT—(INDO)
Rev.: $162,586,730
Assets: $857,655,981
Liabilities: $255,607,956
Net Worth: $602,048,026
Earnings: $66,520,479
Emp.: 444
Fiscal Year-end: 12/31/23
Real Estate Investment Services
N.A.I.C.S.: 531390
Trisna Muliadi *(Pres)*

Subsidiaries:

PT Jaya Gardenpolis (1)

AND PRIVATE COMPANIES

Jl Raya Pasar Kemis Taman Merpat Boulevard, Pasar Kemi, Tangerang, 15660, Indonesia
Tel.: (62) 215908888
Real Estate Services
N.A.I.C.S.: 531390

JAYA TIASA HOLDINGS BERHAD
No 1-9 Pusat Suria Permata Lorong Upper Lanang 10A, 96000, Sibu, Sarawak, Malaysia
Tel.: (60) 84213255
Web Site: https://www.jayatiasa.net
JTIASA—(KLS)
Rev.: $180,942,222
Assets: $413,650,794
Liabilities: $122,056,085
Net Worth: $291,594,709
Earnings: $32,127,407
Emp.: 2,881
Fiscal Year-end: 06/30/23
Timber Product Mfr
N.A.I.C.S.: 423990
Ung Huong Ngu (Sec)

Subsidiaries:

Rimbunan Hijau Plywood Sdn. Bhd. (1)
No 1-9 Pusat Suria Permata Upper Lanang 10 A, Lorong Upper Lanan, Sibu, 96000, Sarawak, Malaysia
Tel.: (60) 84213255
Web Site: http://www.jayatiasa.net
Sales Range: $50-74.9 Million
Emp.: 220
Plywood Panels Mfr
N.A.I.C.S.: 321211

JAYABHARAT CREDIT LTD.
19-20 Rajabhadur Mansion No 22 4th Floor Opp SBI Main Branch, Near Stock Exchange Mumbai Samachar Marg, Mumbai, 400 023, India
Tel.: (91) 2222643022
Web Site:
https://www.jayabharat.com
Year Founded: 1943
501311—(BOM)
Rev.: $103,807
Assets: $6,247
Liabilities: $7,054,913
Net Worth: ($7,048,666)
Earnings: ($179,330)
Emp.: 4
Fiscal Year-end: 03/31/23
Financial Credit Management Services
N.A.I.C.S.: 522180
Hinal R. Mehta (Compliance Officer & Sec)

JAYANT AGRO ORGANICS LTD
701 Tower A Peninsula Business Park Senapati Bapat Marg, Lower Parel W, Mumbai, 400013, India
Tel.: (91) 2240271300
Web Site:
https://www.jayantagro.com
Year Founded: 1992
JAYAGROGN—(NSE)
Rev.: $223,889,876
Assets: $91,824,335
Liabilities: $36,522,946
Net Worth: $55,301,192
Earnings: $7,185,429
Emp.: 372
Fiscal Year-end: 03/31/21
Castor Oil & Derivatives Mfr
N.A.I.C.S.: 311224
Dinesh M. Kapadia (Compliance Officer, Officer-Nodal & Sec)

Subsidiaries:

Ihsedu Agrochem Pvt. Ltd. (1)
701 Tower A Peninsula Business Park Senapati Bapat Marg Lower Parel W, Mumbai, 400 013, Maharashtra, India
Tel.: (91) 2240271300
Web Site: https://www.jayantagro.com
Castor Oil Mfr
N.A.I.C.S.: 311225

Jayant Agro-Organics Limited - Unit 1 (1)
Plot No 602 Behind G A C L, PO Petrochemicals, Baroda, 391 346, Gujarat, India
Tel.: (91) 2652230350
Web Site: http://www.jayantagro.com
Sales Range: $25-49.9 Million
Emp.: 150
Castor Oil Mfr
N.A.I.C.S.: 311225
Hemant V. Udeshi (Mng Dir)

Jayant Agro-Organics Limited - Unit 2 (1)
Plot No 602 Behind GACL, PO Petrofils, Baroda, 391 347, Gujarat, India
Tel.: (91) 265 2230350
Web Site: http://www.jayantagro.com
Emp.: 300
Castor Oil Mfr
N.A.I.C.S.: 311225
Hemant V. Udeshi (Mng Dir)

JAYANT INFRATECH LIMITED
Mangal Smriti Bajpai Ground Tilak Nagar, Bilaspur, 495001, Chhattisgarh, India
Tel.: (91) 77730156888
Web Site:
https://www.jayantinfra.com
Year Founded: 2003
543544—(BOM)
Rev.: $5,224,543
Assets: $6,032,636
Liabilities: $2,856,651
Net Worth: $3,175,985
Earnings: $427,013
Emp.: 3
Fiscal Year-end: 03/31/23
Information Technology Services
N.A.I.C.S.: 541512

JAYASWAL NECO INDUSTRIES LIMITED
F-8 MIDC Industrial Area Hingna Road, Nagpur, 440016, Maharashtra, India
Tel.: (91) 7104237276
Web Site: https://www.necoindia.com
Year Founded: 1975
JAYNECOIND—(BOM)
Rev.: $496,955,864
Assets: $786,520,344
Liabilities: $896,591,705
Net Worth: ($110,071,361)
Earnings: ($205,359,527)
Emp.: 3,566
Fiscal Year-end: 03/31/20
Iron Castings & Pig Iron Mfr & Sales
N.A.I.C.S.: 331511
P. K. Bhardwaj (CFO)

JAYATMA ENTERPRISES LIMITED
2nd Floor 1 Laxminagar Besides Naranpura Post Office, Naranpura, Ahmedabad, 380013, Gujarat, India
Tel.: (91) 7922167030
Web Site:
http://www.jayatmaspinners.com
539005—(BOM)
Rev.: $97,236
Assets: $880,343
Liabilities: $64,241
Net Worth: $816,102
Earnings: $43,355
Emp.: 3
Fiscal Year-end: 03/31/23
Cotton & Fabric Trading Services
N.A.I.C.S.: 424990
Nirav Kalyanbhai Shah (CEO)

JAYATMA INDUSTRIES LTD.
4th Floor 1 Laxminagar Coop Hou Soc Ltd Bs Naranpura post office, Ahmedabad, 380002, Gujarat, India
Tel.: (91) 7922167030
Web Site:
https://www.jayatmaindustries.com
531323—(BOM)
Rev.: $20,464,337
Assets: $3,959,178
Liabilities: $2,301,734
Net Worth: $1,657,444
Earnings: $36,538
Emp.: 5
Fiscal Year-end: 03/31/22
Cotton & Yarn Mfr
N.A.I.C.S.: 313110
Janak Gautambhai Nanavaty (Chm)

JAYBHARAT TEXTILES & REAL ESTATE LIMITED
Village Salvav N H No 8 Taluka Pardi Near Vapi Dist Valsad, Vapi, Gujarat, 396191, India
Tel.: (91) 22 24955321
Year Founded: 1985
Sales Range: $10-24.9 Million
Real Estate Management Services & Textile Product Mfr
N.A.I.C.S.: 531390
RajivKumar Baijnath Gupta (Exec Dir)

JAYCO CORPORATION PTY. LTD.
1 Jayco Drive, Dandenong South, 3175, VIC, Australia
Tel.: (61) 297922000
Web Site: http://www.jayco.com.au
Year Founded: 1975
Emp.: 1,000
Automotive Retailer
N.A.I.C.S.: 441110
Colin Kerr (Mgr-Maintenance)

JAYCORP BERHAD
Lot 17 03 17th Floor Menara KH Jalan Sultan Ismail, 50250, Kuala Lumpur, Malaysia
Tel.: (60) 321458108
Web Site:
https://www.jaycorp.com.my
JAYCORP—(KLS)
Rev.: $47,139,683
Assets: $53,136,931
Liabilities: $10,758,519
Net Worth: $42,378,413
Earnings: $4,273,228
Emp.: 1,193
Fiscal Year-end: 07/31/23
Rubberwood Furniture Mfr
N.A.I.C.S.: 424990
Ayk Ke Yeo (Mng Dir)

Subsidiaries:

Digital Furniture Sdn. Bhd. (1)
Lot 158 Parit Seri Jalan Parit Ulu Jalan Jeram Bakri Batu 5, 84000, Muar, Johor, Malaysia
Tel.: (60) 124298355
Web Site:
https://www.digitalfurniture.com.my
Emp.: 500
Wooden Furniture Mfr
N.A.I.C.S.: 337122

Jaycorp Home Furnishings Inc. (1)
1 Jalan Wawasan 12 Sri Gading Industrial Area, 83300, Batu Pahat, Johor, Malaysia
Tel.: (60) 74559988
Web Site: http://www.jaycorphomes.com
Sales Range: $25-49.9 Million
Emp.: 100
Furniture Mfr & Distr
N.A.I.C.S.: 337121
Pohpeot Lin (Mng Dir)

P.T. Tiga Mutiara Nusantara (1)
Jl Iskandar Muda No 115, 20113, Medan, North Sumatra, Indonesia (51%)
Tel.: (62) 614524833
Web Site: http://www.jaycorp.com.my

Pressure Treatment & Kiln-Drying of Rubberwood
N.A.I.C.S.: 322220

Pine Packaging (M) Sdn. Bhd. (1)
JA 1880 Batu 22 1/2 Parit Perawas, 77400, Kampong Sungai Rambai, Melaka, Malaysia
Tel.: (60) 62650333
Web Site:
https://www.pinepackaging.com.my
Corrugated Carton Box Mfr
N.A.I.C.S.: 322211

Yeo Aik Hevea (M) Sdn. Bhd. (1)
No 11656 Jln Industri A2, Kawasan Perindustrian Gerisek, 84700, Kampong Gerisek, Johor, Malaysia
Tel.: (60) 69727178
Timber Logging Services
N.A.I.C.S.: 113110
Liong Yeo Eck (Mng Dir)

Yeo Aik Wood Sdn. Bhd. (1)
JA 1880 Batu 22 1/2 Parit Perawas, 77400, Kampong Sungai Rambai, Melaka, Malaysia
Tel.: (60) 62650111
Web Site: https://www.yeoaik.com
Emp.: 400
Furniture Mfr & Distr
N.A.I.C.S.: 337121
A. K. Yeo (Mng Dir)

Subsidiary (Domestic):

Winshine Industries Sdn. Bhd. (2)
No 1 Jalan Wawasan 12, Sri Gading Industrial Area, 83300, Batu Pahat, Johor, Malaysia
Tel.: (60) 74559988
Web Site: https://www.mywinshine.com
Sales Range: $100-124.9 Million
Emp.: 350
Furniture Mfr & Distr
N.A.I.C.S.: 337126

JAYDEN RESOURCES INC.
1055 West Hastings Street Suite 2250, Vancouver, V6E 2E9, BC, Canada
Tel.: (604) 688-9588 BC
Web Site:
https://www.jaydenresources.com
JDN—(TSXV)
Rev.: $6,340
Assets: $6,628,595
Liabilities: $251,918
Net Worth: $6,376,677
Earnings: ($485,128)
Emp.: 1
Fiscal Year-end: 12/31/22
Gold & Silver Mining Services
N.A.I.C.S.: 212220
Herrick Lau (CFO)

JAYEX TECHNOLOGY LIMITED
Jayex Healthcare Level 4 100 Albert Road, Melbourne, 3205, VIC, Australia
Tel.: (61) 1300799365
Web Site: http://www.jayex.com
JHL—(ASX)
Sales Range: $1-9.9 Million
Healthcare Technology Services
N.A.I.C.S.: 621999

JAYFER AUTOMOTIVE GROUP (MARKHAM) INC
5426 Hwy 7 East, Markham, L3P 1B7, ON, Canada
Tel.: (905) 294-1210
Web Site:
https://www.markhammazda.ca
Year Founded: 2000
Rev.: $23,735,971
Emp.: 50
New & Used Car Dealers
N.A.I.C.S.: 441110

JAYJUN COSMETIC INC.

JAYJUN COSMETIC INC.

Jayjun Cosmetic Inc.—(Continued)
526 Nonhyeon-ro, Gangnam-gu, Seoul, Korea (South)
Tel.: (82) 808812001 KR
Web Site: https://www.jayjun.co.kr
Year Founded: 2014
025620—(KRS)
Rev.: $4,790,870
Assets: $37,112,849
Liabilities: $5,220,107
Net Worth: $31,892,742
Earnings: ($16,646,401)
Emp.: 40
Fiscal Year-end: 12/31/22
Cosmetic Product Mfr & Distr
N.A.I.C.S.: 325620
Jin-Hyung Lee (CEO)

JAYKAY ENTERPRISES LTD.
Kamla Tower, Kanpur, 208001, Uttar Pradesh, India
Tel.: (91) 5122371478
Web Site: https://www.jaykayenterprises.com
Year Founded: 1943
500306—(BOM)
Rev.: $2,024,145
Assets: $18,012,854
Liabilities: $1,627,913
Net Worth: $16,384,941
Earnings: $2,399,752
Emp.: 45
Fiscal Year-end: 03/31/22
Synthetic Fiber Mfr
N.A.I.C.S.: 325220
Ashok Gupta (Mng Dir)

JAYMAN MASTERBUILT, INC.
200 3132 118 Ave SE, Calgary, Y2Z 3X1, AB, Canada
Tel.: (403) 258-3772
Web Site: https://www.jayman.com
Year Founded: 1980
Rev.: $66,779,775
Emp.: 300
Building Construction Services
N.A.I.C.S.: 444110
Jay Westman (Chm & CEO)

JAYNE INDUSTRIES INC.
550 Seaman St, Stoney Creek, L8E 3X7, ON, Canada
Tel.: (905) 643-9200
Web Site: http://www.jayneindustries.com
Year Founded: 1966
Rev.: $20,479,131
Emp.: 64
Hardware Supplier
N.A.I.C.S.: 423710
Chris Pirie (Pres)

JAYRIDE GROUP LIMITED
Level 2 11-17 York Street, Sydney, 2000, NSW, Australia
Tel.: (61) 6464806835 AU
Web Site: https://www.jayride.com
Year Founded: 2012
JAY—(ASX)
Rev.: $3,384,715
Assets: $4,996,778
Liabilities: $3,609,203
Net Worth: $1,387,575
Earnings: ($5,320,605)
Fiscal Year-end: 06/30/23
Transportation Services
N.A.I.C.S.: 481111
Rod Cuthbert (Chm)

JAYSHREE CHEMICALS LTD.
31 Chowringhee Road, Kolkata, 700 016, West Bengal, India
Tel.: (91) 3371500500
Web Site: https://www.jayshreechemicals.com
506520—(BOM)
Rev.: $1,233,439
Assets: $2,996,079
Liabilities: $1,327,834
Net Worth: $1,668,245
Earnings: ($24,195)
Emp.: 8
Fiscal Year-end: 03/31/23
Caustic Soda Mfr
N.A.I.C.S.: 325180
Shree Kumar Bangur (Chm)

JAYSYNTH DYESTUFF (INDIA) LTD.
301 Sumer Kendra Pandurang Budhkar Marg, Worli, Mumbai, 400 018, India
Tel.: (91) 224 938 4200
Web Site: http://www.jaysynth.com
Year Founded: 1985
506910—(BOM)
Rev.: $17,356,794
Assets: $16,036,925
Liabilities: $4,516,373
Net Worth: $11,520,551
Earnings: $615,915
Emp.: 109
Fiscal Year-end: 03/31/21
Chemical Products Mfr
N.A.I.C.S.: 325998
Parag Sharadchandra Kothari (Chm & Mng Dir)

JAYUD GLOBAL LOGISTICS LIMITED
4th Floor Building 4 Shatoujiao Free Trade Zone Shenyan Road, Yantian District, Shenzhen, China
Tel.: (86) 75525595406
Web Site: https://www.jayud.com
Year Founded: 2009
JYD—(NASDAQ)
Rev.: $83,590,380
Assets: $26,174,739
Liabilities: $23,605,365
Net Worth: $2,569,374
Earnings: $1,578,876
Emp.: 192
Fiscal Year-end: 12/31/21
Logistic Services
N.A.I.C.S.: 541614
Jianhong Huang (COO)

JAYWING PLC
Albert Works 71 Sidney Street, Sheffield, S1 4RG, United Kingdom
Tel.: (44) 3333706500
Web Site: https://www.jaywing.com
JWNG—(AIM)
Rev.: $27,396,592
Assets: $28,845,772
Liabilities: $30,360,768
Net Worth: ($1,514,996)
Earnings: ($15,927,327)
Emp.: 300
Fiscal Year-end: 03/31/23
Digital Marketing & Digital Commerce Services
N.A.I.C.S.: 541810
Andrew Fryatt (CEO)

Subsidiaries:

Bloom Media (UK) Ltd. (1)
Globe Point Third Floor 1 Globe Road, Marshall Street, Leeds, LS11 5FD, United Kingdom
Tel.: (44) 3333706500
Web Site: http://www.bloomagency.co.uk
Emp.: 20
Digital Marketing Services
N.A.I.C.S.: 541810
Matt Martin (Dir-Creative)

Frank Digital Pty Limited (1)
Suite 301 2 Elizabeth Plaza, North Sydney, 2060, NSW, Australia
Tel.: (61) 29 692 0200
Web Site: https://www.frankdigital.com.au

Marketing Consulting Services
N.A.I.C.S.: 541613

JAZAN DEVELOPMENT AND INVESTMENT COMPANY
Corniche Road, PO Box 127, Jazan, Saudi Arabia
Tel.: (966) 173222162
Web Site: https://www.jazadco.com.sa
Year Founded: 1993
6090—(SAU)
Rev.: $20,768,882
Assets: $170,074,131
Liabilities: $24,337,488
Net Worth: $145,736,643
Earnings: $4,398,750
Emp.: 325
Fiscal Year-end: 12/31/22
Financial Investment Services
N.A.I.C.S.: 523999
Ahmed Mohammed Al-Sanea (Chm)

JAZEERA AIRWAYS COMPANY KSC
Road 55 Exit Road 100 Airport District, PO Box 29288, Compared to Hall ceremonies Al Safat, Kuwait, 13153, Kuwait
Tel.: (965) 22054944
Web Site: https://www.jazeeraairways.com
Year Founded: 2004
JAZEERA—(KUW)
Rev.: $591,882,109
Assets: $884,324,843
Liabilities: $765,610,384
Net Worth: $118,714,459
Earnings: $65,268,273
Emp.: 1,200
Fiscal Year-end: 12/31/22
Oil Transportation Services
N.A.I.C.S.: 481111
Marwan Marzouk Jassim Boodai (Chm)

JAZZ HIPSTER CORPORATION
2F No 512 Yuanshan Road, Zhonghe, 235, Taiwan
Tel.: (886) 222225678
Web Site: http://www.jazzhipster.com.tw
Year Founded: 1981
6247—(TPE)
Rev.: $23,576,792
Assets: $45,080,458
Liabilities: $25,529,478
Net Worth: $19,550,979
Earnings: ($2,816,859)
Fiscal Year-end: 12/31/20
Home Appliance Distr
N.A.I.C.S.: 449129
Yue-Hua Hsu Huang (Chm)

JAZZ PHARMACEUTICALS PLC
Fifth Floor Waterloo Exchange Waterloo Road, Dublin, D04 E5W7, Ireland
Tel.: (353) 16347800
Web Site: http://www.jazzpharmaceuticals.com
Year Founded: 2005
JAZZ—(NASDAQ)
Rev.: $3,834,204,000
Assets: $11,393,359,000
Liabilities: $7,656,362,000
Net Worth: $3,736,997,000
Earnings: $414,832,000
Emp.: 2,800
Fiscal Year-end: 12/31/23
Biopharmaceutical Developer, Mfr & Marketer
N.A.I.C.S.: 325412
Bruce C. Cozadd (Chm & CEO)

INTERNATIONAL PUBLIC

Subsidiaries:

GW Pharmaceuticals plc (1)
Sovereign House Vision Park Chivers Way, Histon, CB24 9BZ, Cambridge, United Kingdom
Tel.: (44) 1223266800
Web Site: https://www.gwpharm.com
Rev.: $527,205,000
Assets: $939,511,000
Liabilities: $198,421,000
Net Worth: $741,090,000
Earnings: ($58,128,000)
Emp.: 1,161
Fiscal Year-end: 12/31/2020
Pharmaceutical Preparation Mfr
N.A.I.C.S.: 325412
Chris Tovey (COO)

Subsidiary (Domestic):

GW Pharma Limited (2)
1 Cavendish Place, London, W1G 0QF, United Kingdom
Tel.: (44) 2072910555
Pharmaceuticals Product Mfr
N.A.I.C.S.: 325412

Subsidiary (US):

Greenwich Biosciences (2)
5750 Fleet St Ste 200, Carlsbad, CA 92008
Tel.: (760) 795-2200
Web Site: http://www.greenwichbiosciences.com
Pharmaceuticals Product Mfr
N.A.I.C.S.: 325412
Justin Gover (CEO)

Gentium S.R.L. (1)
Piazza XX Settembre 2, Villa Guardia, 22079, Como, Italy
Tel.: (39) 0315373200
Web Site: https://www.jazzpharma.com
Pharmaceutical Medical Product Mfr
N.A.I.C.S.: 325411

Gentium SpA (1)
Piazza XX Settembre 2 Villa Guardia, 22079, Como, Italy
Tel.: (39) 0315373200
Sales Range: $50-74.9 Million
Emp.: 76
Therapeutic Agent Discovery, Research, Development & Mfr
N.A.I.C.S.: 325411

Jazz Pharmaceuticals UK Limited (1)
Wing B Building 5700 Spires House John Smith Drive, Oxford Business Park South, Oxford, OX4 2RW, United Kingdom
Tel.: (44) 1865 405 000
Web Site: http://www.jazzpharma.com
Oncology, Pain Control & Critical Care Pharmaceutical Products Mfr
N.A.I.C.S.: 325412

Jazz Pharmaceuticals, Inc. (1)
3170 Porter Dr, Palo Alto, CA 94304
Tel.: (650) 496-3777
Web Site: http://www.jazzpharmaceuticals.com
Sales Range: $150-199.9 Million
Emp.: 242
Biopharmaceutical Developer, Mfr & Marketer
N.A.I.C.S.: 325412
Kim Sablich (Exec VP & Gen Mgr-US)

Subsidiary (Domestic):

Jazz Pharmaceuticals Commercial Corp (2)
1818 Market St Ste 2350, Philadelphia, PA 19103
Tel.: (215) 832-3750
Pharmaceutical Preparation Mfr
N.A.I.C.S.: 325412

Branch (Domestic):

Jazz Pharmaceuticals, Inc. - Philadelphia (2)
1818 Market St Ste 2350, Philadelphia, PA 19103
Tel.: (215) 832-3750
Web Site: http://www.jazzpharmaceuticals.com

AND PRIVATE COMPANIES

Sales Range: $50-74.9 Million
Emp.: 200
Biopharmaceutical Developer & Mfr
N.A.I.C.S.: 325412

JB CHEMICALS & PHARMACEUTICALS LTD.
Neelam Centre B Wing 4th Floor
Hind Cycle Road, Worli, Mumbai,
400030, India
Tel.: (91) 2224822222
Web Site: https://jbpharma.com
Year Founded: 1976
JBCHEPHARM—(NSE)
Rev.: $2,571,831
Assets: $478,895,839
Liabilities: $128,388,656
Net Worth: $350,507,183
Earnings: $66,260,073
Emp.: 5,311
Fiscal Year-end: 03/31/24
Pharmaceuticals Mfr
N.A.I.C.S.: 325412
Bharat P. Mehta *(Exec Dir-Plng & Dev)*

Subsidiaries:

Biotech Laboratories (Pty.) Ltd. (1)
Ground Floor Block K West Central Park
400 16th Road, Randjespark, Midrand,
1685, South Africa
Tel.: (27) 118483050
Web Site: https://www.biotech.co.za
Pharmaceutical Product Retailer
N.A.I.C.S.: 456110
Stewart Barker *(CEO)*

J. B. Healthcare Pvt. Ltd. (1)
204 Investment House B H Padmachambers, Opp Gandhigram Rly Station,
Ahmedabad, Gujarat, India
Tel.: (91) 79 26580369
Web Site: http://www.jbhealthcare.co.in
Healtcare Services
N.A.I.C.S.: 621610

JB FINANCIAL GROUP CO., LTD.
566 Baekje-daero, Deokjin-gu,
Jeonju, 561-711, Jeollabuk-do, Korea
(South)
Tel.: (82) 221282714   KR
Web Site: https://www.jbfg.com
Year Founded: 2013
175330—(KRS)
Rev.: $2,520,606,268
Assets: $47,061,420,958
Liabilities: $43,264,121,254
Net Worth: $3,797,299,705
Earnings: $434,942,773
Emp.: 99
Fiscal Year-end: 12/31/23
Financial Investment Services
N.A.I.C.S.: 551111

Subsidiaries:

JB Asset Management Co., Ltd. (1)
7F Hanyang-Securities Bldg 7
Gukjegeumyung-ro 6-gil, Yeongdeungpo-gu,
Seoul, Korea (South)
Tel.: (82) 237825000
Web Site: http://www.jbam.co.kr
Asset Management Services
N.A.I.C.S.: 531390
Hyuk Joon Lee *(Mng Dir)*

JeonBuk Bank (1)
JeonBuk Bank Bldg 669-2 Geumam
1-dong, Deokjin-gu, Jeonju, Jeollabuk-do,
Korea (South)
Tel.: (82) 2 1588 4477
Web Site: http://www.jbbank.co.kr
Commericial Banking
N.A.I.C.S.: 522110
Han Kim *(Chm & CEO)*

Kwangju Bank Co., Ltd. (1) (100%)
225 Jebong-ro, Dong-gu, Gwangju, 501730,
Korea (South)
Tel.: (82) 62 239 5000
Web Site: http://www.pib.kjbank.com
Rev.: $834,450,663

Assets: $22,002,714,289
Liabilities: $20,515,206,159
Net Worth: $1,487,508,130
Earnings: $126,931,782
Emp.: 1,623
Fiscal Year-end: 12/31/2017
Commericial Banking
N.A.I.C.S.: 522110

Subsidiary (Non-US):

Morgan Stanley Gateway Securities
JSC (2)
No 8 Thien Quang Str, Hai Ba Trung Dist,
Hanoi, Vietnam
Tel.: (84) 439429775
Web Site: http://www.msgs.com.vn
Investment Advisory Services
N.A.I.C.S.: 523940
Ronald Whatt Soon Ong *(Chm)*

JB FOODS LIMITED
80 Robinson Road 17-02, Singapore,
68898, Singapore
Tel.: (65) 62228008
Web Site: https://www.jbcocoa.com
BEW—(SES)
Rev.: $595,786,000
Assets: $744,742,000
Liabilities: $567,651,000
Net Worth: $177,091,000
Earnings: $1,895,000
Emp.: 802
Fiscal Year-end: 12/31/23
Cocoa Processor & Mfr
N.A.I.C.S.: 311351
How Keong Tey *(CEO)*

Subsidiaries:

JB Cocoa Foods (China) Co., Ltd. (1)
No 1188 Xin Ming Road, Pinghu Economic
Development Zone, Jiaxing, 314200, Zhejiang, China
Tel.: (86) 57385085601
Farm Product Distr
N.A.I.C.S.: 424590

JB Cocoa Sdn Bhd (1)
Lot CP1 Jalan Tanjung A/6, Pelabuhan Tanjung Pelepas Gelang Patah, 81560, Johor,
Malaysia
Tel.: (60) 75042888
Cocoa Powder Mfr
N.A.I.C.S.: 311351
Ariel Loh *(Asst Mgr-Pur)*

JB Cocoa, Inc. (1)
757 3rd Ave Ste 2012, New York, NY 10017
Tel.: (646) 216-6722
Farm Product Distr
N.A.I.C.S.: 424590

PT. Jebe Trading Indonesia (1)
Kawasan Industri Maspion Blok SE JI Raya
Manyar KM 25, Sukomulyo - Manyar,
Gresik, 61151, East Java, Indonesia
Tel.: (62) 313958688
Farm Product Distr
N.A.I.C.S.: 424590

JB GLOBAL LTD.
Unit 5 Haven works Tewkesbury
Road, Cheltenham, GL51 9AA,
United Kingdom
Tel.: (44) 844 977 3300
Web Site:
    http://www.oakfurnitureland.co.uk
Year Founded: 2004
Sales Range: $10-24.9 Million
Emp.: 297
Electronic Shopping Services
N.A.I.C.S.: 449110
Ross Lawson *(Head-IT)*

Subsidiaries:

Oak Furniture Land Ltd (1)
Unit 2a Reading Gate Retail Park, Reading,
RG2 0QG, Berkshire, United Kingdom
Tel.: (44) 1184027555
Web Site: http://www.oakfurnitureland.co.uk
Emp.: 650
Furniture Distr
N.A.I.C.S.: 423210

JB HI-FI LIMITED
Podium Level 60 City Road, Southbank, 3006, VIC, Australia
Tel.: (61) 385307333   AU
Web Site: http://www.jbhifi.com.au
JBH—(ASX)
Rev.: $6,405,181,598
Assets: $2,328,124,990
Liabilities: $1,287,059,290
Net Worth: $1,041,065,701
Earnings: $293,002,136
Emp.: 15,000
Fiscal Year-end: 06/30/24
Retailing of Electrical Products
N.A.I.C.S.: 238210
Richard Murray *(CEO)*

Subsidiaries:

Clive Anthonys Pty Ltd (1)
111 Cranbourne Rd, Frankston, 3199, VIC,
Australia
Tel.: (61) 387880000
Web Site: http://www.cliveanthonys.com.au
Consumer Electronics Retailer
N.A.I.C.S.: 449210

JB Hi-Fi (A) Pty Ltd (1)
Level 4 Ofc Tower 2 Chadstone Pl Chadstone Shopping Ctr, Chadstone, Melbourne,
3148, VIC, Australia
Tel.: (61) 385307333
Consumer Electronics Retailer
N.A.I.C.S.: 449210

JB Hi-Fi Group (NZ) Limited (1)
12-1 Wagener Place, Saint Lukes, Auckland, 1025, New Zealand
Tel.: (64) 98154610
Web Site: http://www.jbhifi.co.nz
Sales Range: $25-49.9 Million
Emp.: 40
Household Appliance Retailer
N.A.I.C.S.: 423620
Rod Korff *(Gen Mgr-Buying)*

JB Hi-Fi Group Pty Ltd (1)
Level 4 Office Tower 2 Chadstone Shopping
Ctr, Chadstone, Melbourne, 3148, VIC, Australia
Tel.: (61) 385307333
Sales Range: $50-74.9 Million
Emp.: 250
Consumer Electronics Retailer
N.A.I.C.S.: 449210

JB Hi-Fi Insurance Replacements (1)
58-76 Stephenson St, Richmond, 3121,
VIC, Australia
Tel.: (61) 385307590
Web Site:
    http://www.rocketreplacements.com.au
Sales Range: $150-199.9 Million
Emp.: 300
Consumer Electronics Distr
N.A.I.C.S.: 423620

The Good Guys Discount Warehouses (Australia) Pty. Ltd. (1)
PO Box 5190, South Melbourne, 3205, VIC,
Australia
Tel.: (61) 1300942765
Web Site: https://www.thegoodguys.com.au
Online Electrical Appliance Retailer
N.A.I.C.S.: 449210
Richard Murray *(CEO)*

JB LAVERDURE INC.
400 Cremazie W, Montreal, H2P
1C7, QC, Canada
Tel.: (514) 382-7520
Web Site: http://www.jblaverdure.com
Rev.: $34,691,035
Emp.: 100
Fruits & Vegetables Whslr
N.A.I.C.S.: 424480
Jean-Francois Laverdure *(Pres)*

JB WATER & VACUUM SERVICE
10302 123 Street, Grande Prairie,
T8V 8B8, AB, Canada
Tel.: (780) 539-9951
Web Site: http://www.jbwater.com

JBCC HOLDINGS INC.

Year Founded: 1978
Rev.: $11,200,000
Emp.: 95
Vacuum & Water Trucks Transportation Services
N.A.I.C.S.: 488390
Art Bain *(Owner & Pres)*

JB&ZJMY HOLDING COMPANY
No 149 Beijing Road, Fengtai District
10, Beijing, 89128, China
Tel.: (86) 18511635616   NV
Web Site: http://www.dove-diamonds.com
Year Founded: 2006
JBZY—(OTCEM)
Sales Range: Less than $1 Million
Emp.: 2
Diamond & Precious Stones Mining & Wholesale Distribution Services
N.A.I.C.S.: 212311
DeQun Wang *(Pres, CEO & CFO)*

JBB BUILDERS INTERNATIONAL LIMITED
No 20-01 Jalan Sri Perkasa 2/18 Taman Tampoi Utama, 81200, Johor
Bahru, Johor, Malaysia
Tel.: (60) 72414998   Ky
Web Site: https://www.jbb.com.my
Year Founded: 2012
1903—(HKG)
Rev.: $46,012,254
Assets: $46,242,764
Liabilities: $18,072,892
Net Worth: $28,169,871
Earnings: ($1,735,263)
Emp.: 55
Fiscal Year-end: 06/30/23
Construction Engineering Services
N.A.I.C.S.: 541330
Say Piyu Dato'Ng *(Chm)*

JBCC HOLDINGS INC.
2-2-1 Yaesu Central Tower 13th floor,
Tokyo Midtown Yaesu Chuo-ku, Tokyo, 104-0028, Japan
Tel.: (81) 357145111
Web Site: https://www.jbcchd.co.jp
Year Founded: 1964
9889—(TKS)
Rev.: $430,932,340
Assets: $245,938,270
Liabilities: $105,951,690
Net Worth: $139,986,580
Earnings: $21,066,070
Emp.: 1,962
Fiscal Year-end: 03/31/24
Holding Company
N.A.I.C.S.: 551112
Takashi Yamada *(Chm)*

Subsidiaries:

Central Information Systems Co., Ltd. (1)
Glass City Sakae 9th floor 3-11-31 Sakae,
Naka-ku, Nagoya, 460-0008, Japan
Tel.: (81) 522612182
Web Site: https://www.cisjp.com
Software Services
N.A.I.C.S.: 541511
Hiroshi Fukuda *(Pres & CEO)*

General Business Services Co., Ltd. (1)
2 3F Chiyoda-Kaikan blg 1-6-17 Kudan-Minami, Chiyoda-ku, Tokyo, 102-0074, Japan
Tel.: (81) 352165500
Web Site: http://www.gbs.co.jp
Emp.: 108
Application Software Development Services
N.A.I.C.S.: 541511
Hiroyuki Utsumi *(CEO)*

JB Advanced Technology Corporation (1)
580 Horikawa-cho, Saiwai-ku, Kawasaki,

JBCC HOLDINGS INC.

JBCC Holdings Inc.—(Continued)
212-8505, Kanagawa, Japan
Tel.: (81) 442808611
Web Site: https://www.jbat.co.jp
Emp.: 183
Software Services
N.A.I.C.S.: 541511
Masami Yoshimatsu (Pres & CEO)

JBCC (Thailand) Co., Ltd. (1)
18th Fl UBCII Building 591 Sukhumvit Rd
Soi 33 North Klongton, Wattana, Bangkok, 10110, Thailand
Tel.: (66) 26622217
Web Site: https://www.jbcchd.co.jp
Emp.: 18
Software Distr
N.A.I.C.S.: 423430
Shoichi Isono (Mng Dir)

JBCN (Shanghai) Information Technology Co., Ltd. (1)
601 Tianshan Rd Rm 1301 Changning Dist
Shanghai, Shanghai, 200336, China
Tel.: (86) 2162419334
Information Technology Services
N.A.I.C.S.: 541512

SOLNET Corporation (1)
2-8-13 Chuo, Yahatahigashi-ku, Kitakyushu, 805-0019, Fukuoka, Japan
Tel.: (81) 936717827
Web Site: https://www.solnet-dot.com
Emp.: 140
Software Services
N.A.I.C.S.: 541511

iGUAZU Corporation (1)
21F West Bldg Solid Square 580 Horikawa-cho, Saiwai-ku, Kawasaki, 212-0013, Kanagawa, Japan
Tel.: (81) 442808500
Emp.: 342
Computer Distr
N.A.I.C.S.: 423430

JBF INDUSTRIES LTD

Survey No 273 Village Athola Silvassa Dadra & Nagar Haveli, Gujarat, 396230, India
Tel.: (91) 2602642745
Web Site: https://jbfindustries.co.in
Year Founded: 1982
JBFIND—(BOM)
Rev.: $302,508,570
Assets: $487,406,010
Liabilities: $461,121,570
Net Worth: $26,284,440
Earnings: $26,416,845)
Emp.: 2,602
Fiscal Year-end: 03/31/21
Polyester Chips Mfr
N.A.I.C.S.: 339999
Bhagirath C. Arya (Chm)

Subsidiaries:

JBF Bahrain S.P.C (1)
PO Box 50397, Al-Hidd, Bahrain
Tel.: (973) 17181500
Web Site: http://jbfbahrain.com
Photographic Film Mfr
N.A.I.C.S.: 325992

JBF RAK LLC (1)
Al Jazeera Al Hamra, PO Box 6574, Ras al Khaimah, United Arab Emirates
Tel.: (971) 72047100
Web Site: http://www.jbfrak.com
Sales Range: $200-249.9 Million
Emp.: 900
Polyester Resin Mfr
N.A.I.C.S.: 325211
Bhagirath C. Arya (Chm)

JBM AUTO LTD.

610 Hemkunt Chambers 89 Nehru Place, New Delhi, 110 019, India
Tel.: (91) 1244674500
Web Site: https://www.jbm-group.com
Year Founded: 1990
JBMA—(NSE)
Rev.: $272,182,583
Assets: $336,329,571
Liabilities: $234,553,096

Net Worth: $101,776,475
Earnings: $6,729,505
Emp.: 1,981
Fiscal Year-end: 03/31/21
Tools & Die Mfr
N.A.I.C.S.: 333514
Vivek Gupta (CFO, Officer-Compliance & Sec)

Subsidiaries:

INDO Toolings Private Limited (1)
Survey No 113/2 A Village - Harnia Khedi Opp Veterinary College, A B Road, Indore, 453446, MP, India
Tel.: (91) 7324276824
Web Site: https://indotoolings.com
Air Tank & Fuel Tank Mfr
N.A.I.C.S.: 332420

JBS FOODS INTERNATIONAL B.V.

Bankrashof 3 5th Floor, 1183 NP, Amstelveen, Netherlands
Tel.: (31) 20 656 4707   NL
Year Founded: 2016
Emp.: 171,966
Food Product Mfr & Distr
N.A.I.C.S.: 311412
Russell Colaco (CFO)

JBS S.A.

Avenida Marginal Direita do Tiete 500, Vila Jaguara, Sao Paulo, SP, Brazil
Tel.: (55) 31444224   BR
Web Site: https://jbs.com.br
Year Founded: 1953
JBSS3—(BRAZ)
Rev.: $72,918,123,000
Assets: $42,577,834,000
Liabilities: $32,870,048,000
Net Worth: $9,707,786,000
Earnings: $131,735,000
Emp.: 272,565
Fiscal Year-end: 12/31/23
Food Products Distr
N.A.I.C.S.: 424470
Wesley Mendonca Batista (Founder)

Subsidiaries:

Excelsior Alimentos S.A. (1)
Rua Barao do Arroio Grande 192, Bairro Arroio Grande, Santa Cruz do Sul, 96830-504, RS, Brazil
Tel.: (55) 5121068800
Web Site: https://excelsior.com.br
Rev.: $39,752,595
Assets: $29,676,623
Liabilities: $10,903,452
Net Worth: $18,773,171
Earnings: $3,159,579
Emp.: 359
Fiscal Year-end: 12/31/2023
Meat Product Mfr & Whslr
N.A.I.C.S.: 311999
Renato Jackisch (Dir-IR)

JBS Australia Pty Limited (1)
1 Lock Way, Riverview, 4303, QLD, Australia
Tel.: (61) 738102100
Web Site: http://www.jbsaa.com.au
Sales Range: $450-499.9 Million
Meat Packer & Exporter
N.A.I.C.S.: 424470

Subsidiary (Domestic):

Huon Aquaculture Group Limited (2)
Hideaway Bay Head Office, PO Box 42, Dover, 7117, TAS, Australia
Tel.: (61) 362958111
Web Site: http://www.huonaqua.com.au
Rev.: $344,639,158
Assets: $488,751,835
Liabilities: $300,485,927
Net Worth: $188,265,908
Earnings: ($98,125,187)
Emp.: 797
Fiscal Year-end: 06/30/2021
Seafood Production
N.A.I.C.S.: 112511

Peter Bender (CEO & Mng Dir)

Subsidiary (Domestic):

Huon Aquaculture Company Pty. Ltd. (3)
PO Box 42, Dover, 7117, TAS, Australia
Tel.: (61) 362958111
Emp.: 800
Seafood Product Mfr
N.A.I.C.S.: 311710

Subsidiary (Domestic):

P&M Quality Smallgoods Pty Ltd. (2)
18 Hume Highway, Chullora, 2190, NSW, Australia
Tel.: (61) 2 9742 0000
Web Site: http://www.primo.com.au
Poultry Slaughtering & Processing; Packaged Frozen Food
N.A.I.C.S.: 311615

Subsidiary (Non-US):

Scott Technology Limited (2)
630 Kaikorai Valley Road, Private Bag 1960, Dunedin, 9054, New Zealand   (51.9%)
Tel.: (64) 800552280
Web Site: https://www.scottautomation.com
Rev.: $160,003,589
Assets: $151,348,086
Liabilities: $83,226,675
Net Worth: $68,121,411
Earnings: $9,232,057
Emp.: 656
Fiscal Year-end: 08/31/2023
Automated Production, Process Machinery Mfr & Sales
N.A.I.C.S.: 333310
Stuart McLauchlan (Chm)

Subsidiary (Domestic):

Rocklabs Limited (3)
63 Tidal Road, Mangere, Auckland, 2022, New Zealand
Tel.: (64) 96347696
Web Site: http://www.scottautomation.com
Laboratory Equipment Mfr
N.A.I.C.S.: 334516
Mike Lynn (Gen Mgr)

Scott Fabtech (3)
630 Kaikorai Valley Road, PO Box 1960, Dunedin, 9054, New Zealand
Tel.: (64) 34788110
Web Site: http://www.scottautomation.com
Metal Fabrication
N.A.I.C.S.: 332999

Subsidiary (US):

Scott Systems International, Inc. (3)
Ste 214 1611 Stemmons Frwy, Carrollton, TX 75006   (100%)
Tel.: (858) 732-3001
Automated Production & Process Machinery Sales & Service
N.A.I.C.S.: 423830

Unit (Domestic):

RobotWorx (4)
370 W Fairground St, Marion, OH 43302
Tel.: (740) 251-4312
Web Site: http://www.robots.com
Emp.: 50
Industrial Robotic Systems Distr & Installation Services
N.A.I.C.S.: 423830

Subsidiary (US):

Transbotics Corp. (3)
2205 Beltway Blvd Ste 100, Charlotte, NC 28214
Tel.: (704) 362-1115
Web Site: http://www.scottautomation.com
Automated Guided Vechicles Design, Development & Support Services
N.A.I.C.S.: 541330
Claude Imbleau (CEO)

Subsidiary (Domestic):

Tatiara Meat Company Pty. Ltd. (2)
69 York St, Melbourne, 3205, Victoria, Australia

INTERNATIONAL PUBLIC

Tel.: (61) 3 8646 9500
Web Site: http://www.tatiara.com.au
Sales Range: $200-249.9 Million
Emp.: 500
Animal Slaughtering; Lamb
N.A.I.C.S.: 311611

JBS Global UK Limited (1)
Imperial Place Elstree Way, Borehamwood, WD6 1JN, Hertfordshire, United Kingdom
Tel.: (44) 20 8369 5310
Web Site: http://www.jbsglobal.co.uk
Meat Product Mfr & Distr
N.A.I.C.S.: 311613

JBS USA Food Company (1)
1770 Promontory Cir, Greeley, CO 80634
Tel.: (970) 506-8000
Web Site: http://www.jbssa.com
Food Mfr
N.A.I.C.S.: 311999

JBS USA Holdings, Inc. (1)
1770 Promontory Cir, Greeley, CO 80634   (100%)
Tel.: (970) 506-8000
Web Site: http://www.jbsswift.com
Sales Range: $1-4.9 Billion
Emp.: 31,900
Holding Company; Meat Processor & Products Distr
N.A.I.C.S.: 551112
Andre Nogueira De Souza (Pres & CEO)

Subsidiary (Domestic):

JBS USA, LLC (2)
1770 Promontory Cir, Greeley, CO 80634
Tel.: (970) 506-8000
Web Site: http://www.jbssa.com
Sales Range: $5-14.9 Billion
Emp.: 15,000
Meat Processor & Products Distr
N.A.I.C.S.: 311612
Wesley Mendonca Batista Filho (CEO)

Unit (Domestic):

JBS USA, LLC - Four Star Beef, Green Bay (3)
1330 Lim Kiln Rd, Green Bay, WI 54311
Tel.: (920) 468-4000
Web Site: http://www.fourstarbeef.com
Trucking Service
N.A.I.C.S.: 484230
Hicham Timejardine (Gen Mgr)

JBS USA, LLC - Four Star Beef, Plainwell (3)
Eleven 11th St, Plainwell, MI 49080-0247
Tel.: (269) 685-6886
Web Site: http://www.fourstarbeef.com
Beef Packing & Processing
N.A.I.C.S.: 311611
Jim Reed (Gen Mgr)

JBS USA, LLC - Four Star Beef, Souderton (3)
249 Allentown Rd, Souderton, PA 18964
Tel.: (215) 723-5555
Web Site: http://www.fourstarbeef.com
Meat Packing & Rendering Services
N.A.I.C.S.: 311611

JBS USA, LLC - Four Star Beef, Tolleson (3)
651 S 91st Ave, Tolleson, AZ 85353
Tel.: (623) 936-7177
Web Site: http://www.fourstarbeef.com
Beef Packaging & Processing
N.A.I.C.S.: 311611
Scott Weeden (Controller)

Subsidiary (Domestic):

Plumrose USA Inc. (3)
1901 Butterfield Rd Ste 305, Downers Grove, IL 60515
Tel.: (732) 624-4040
Web Site: http://www.plumroseusa.com
Veal Product Mfr
N.A.I.C.S.: 311612
Thomas Lopez (Pres & COO)

Plant (Domestic):

JBS USA, LLC - Hyrum (2)
410 N 200 W, Hyrum, UT 84319-1024
Tel.: (435) 245-6456
Web Site: http://www.jbssa.com

AND PRIVATE COMPANIES — JCB CO., LTD.

Sales Range: $300-349.9 Million
Emp.: 1,100
Meat Processing
N.A.I.C.S.: 311612

JBS USA, LLC - Worthington (2)
Hwy 60 N, Worthington, MN 56187-0369
Tel.: (507) 372-2121
Web Site: http://www.jbssa.com
Sales Range: $300-349.9 Million
Emp.: 2,200
Pork Plant
N.A.I.C.S.: 311611
Bob Krebs *(Plant Mgr)*

Subsidiary (Domestic):

Pilgrim's Pride Corporation (2)
1770 Promontory Cir, Greeley, CO
80634-9038 (80.2%)
Tel.: (970) 506-8000
Web Site: https://www.pilgrims.com
Rev: $17,362,217,000
Assets: $9,810,361,000
Liabilities: $6,465,784,000
Net Worth: $3,344,577,000
Earnings: $321,574,000
Emp.: 61,200
Fiscal Year-end: 12/31/2023
Poultry Processing Services
N.A.I.C.S.: 311615
Gilberto Tomazoni *(Chm)*

Subsidiary (Domestic):

Gold'n Plump Farms, LLC (3)
4150 2nd St S Ste 200, Saint Cloud, MN 56301-7314
Tel.: (320) 251-3570
Web Site: http://www.goldnplump.com
Holding Company; Chicken Production, Processor & Whslr
N.A.I.C.S.: 551112
Peggy Brown *(Dir-HR)*

Subsidiary (Domestic):

Gold'n Plump Poultry, LLC (4)
4150 2nd St Ste 200, Saint Cloud, MN 56301
Tel.: (320) 251-3570
Web Site: http://www.goldnplump.com
Poultry Processing & Chicken Product Whslr
N.A.I.C.S.: 311615

Subsidiary (Non-US):

Grupo Pilgrim's Pride Funding Holdings, S. de R.L. de C.V. (3)
Privada De Los Industriales No 115, Queretaro, 76100, Queretaro, Mexico
Tel.: (52) 4422383500
Investment Management Service
N.A.I.C.S.: 551112

Incubadora Hidalgo S. de R.L. de C.V. (3)
Priv De Los Industriales No 115, Queretaro, 76100, Queretaro, Mexico
Tel.: (52) 4421032200
Poultry Product Distr
N.A.I.C.S.: 424440

Moy Park Limited (3)
The Food Park 39 Seagoe Industrial Estate, Craigavon, BT63 5QE, Armagh, United Kingdom
Tel.: (44) 28 3835 2233
Web Site: http://www.moypark.com
Emp.: 800
Food Processing Services
N.A.I.C.S.: 311999
Janet McCollum *(CEO)*

Subsidiary (Domestic):

PFS Distribution Company (3)
3420 Avenue F, Arlington, TX 76011
Tel.: (817) 652-8712
Poultry Product Distr
N.A.I.C.S.: 424440

PPC Transportation Company (3)
110 S Texas St, Pittsburg, TX 75686
Tel.: (903) 434-1806
Transportation Services
N.A.I.C.S.: 488999

PPC of Alabama, Inc. (3)
7004 1st N Ave, Birmingham, AL 35206

Tel.: (205) 836-3636
Poultry Product Distr
N.A.I.C.S.: 424440

Plant (Domestic):

Pilgrim's Pride - Athens (3)
898 Barber St, Athens, GA 30601-2030
Tel.: (706) 425-7500
Sales Range: $250-299.9 Million
Emp.: 1,500
Poultry Processing Services
N.A.I.C.S.: 311615

Pilgrim's Pride - Canton (3)
654 Univeter Rd, Canton, GA 30115-9091
Tel.: (678) 493-3000
Sales Range: $125-149.9 Million
Emp.: 800
Poultry Processing Services
N.A.I.C.S.: 311615
Matt Westbrooks *(Mgr-Quality Control)*

Pilgrim's Pride - Chattanooga (3)
1300 Market St, Chattanooga, TN 37402-4401
Tel.: (423) 756-2471
Sales Range: $250-299.9 Million
Emp.: 1,600
Poultry Slaughtering & Processing Services
N.A.I.C.S.: 311615

Pilgrim's Pride - Elberton (3)
1129 Old Middleton Rd, Elberton, GA 30635
Tel.: (706) 283-3821
Sales Range: $150-199.9 Million
Emp.: 600
Poultry Processing Services
N.A.I.C.S.: 311615

Pilgrim's Pride - Enterprise (3)
4693 County Rd 636, Enterprise, AL 36330
Tel.: (334) 347-0515
Sales Range: $125-149.9 Million
Emp.: 800
Poultry Processing Services
N.A.I.C.S.: 311615

Pilgrim's Pride - Gainesville (3)
949 Industrial Blvd, Gainesville, GA 30501
Tel.: (770) 536-3413
Sales Range: $250-299.9 Million
Emp.: 1,150
Poultry Processing Services
N.A.I.C.S.: 112390
Mike MacCordy *(Plant Mgr)*

Pilgrim's Pride - Mount Pleasant (3)
1000 S O'Tyson Ave, Mount Pleasant, TX 75455
Tel.: (903) 575-1000
Sales Range: $25-49.9 Million
Emp.: 250
Processor of Poultry
N.A.I.C.S.: 311611
Daniel Torres *(Coord-Safety)*

Pilgrim's Pride - Natchitoches (3)
7088 Hwy 1 Byp, Natchitoches, LA 71457
Tel.: (318) 352-9600
Sales Range: $50-74.9 Million
Emp.: 500
Poultry Processing Services
N.A.I.C.S.: 311615

Branch (Domestic):

Pilgrim's Pride Corp. (3)
244 Perimeter Center Pkwy NE, Atlanta, GA 30346-2302
Tel.: (770) 393-5000
Sales Range: $10-24.9 Million
Emp.: 30
Poultry Processing Services
N.A.I.C.S.: 311615

Subsidiary (Domestic):

Pilgrim's Pride Corporation of West Virginia, Inc. (3)
129 Potomac Ave, Moorefield, WV 26836-1246
Tel.: (304) 538-7811
Emp.: 1,100
Poultry Product Distr
N.A.I.C.S.: 424440
Tracy Sherman *(Mgr-HR)*

Subsidiary (Non-US):

Tulip Ltd. (3)

Seton House Warwick Technology Park, Gallows Hill, Warwick, CV34 6DA, United Kingdom
Tel.: (44) 1926 475680
Web Site: http://www.tulipltd.co.uk
Food Products Processing Services
N.A.I.C.S.: 311999
Andrew Cracknell *(CEO)*

Tyson de Mexico, S. de R.L. de C.V. (3)
Calle Valle del Guadiana No 294, Parque Industrial Gomez Palacio, Gomez Palacio, CP 35078, Durango, Mexico
Tel.: (52) 871 749 2000
Web Site: http://www.tyson.com.mx
Sales Range: $650-699.9 Million
Emp.: 5,400
Holding Company; Poultry Processing & Whslr
N.A.I.C.S.: 551112
Rick Thomason *(Pres & Gen Mgr)*

Montana Alimentari S.p.A. (1)
Via Marconi 3, 46040, Gazoldo degli Ippoliti, Italy
Tel.: (39) 03766801
Web Site: http://www.montanafood.it
Meat Processing
N.A.I.C.S.: 311613

Rigamonti Salumificio S.p.A. (1)
Via Stelvio 973, 23020, Montagna, Italy
Tel.: (39) 0342535111
Web Site: http://www.rigamontisalumificio.it
Food Mfr
N.A.I.C.S.: 311999

JBT TRANSPORT
235 Waydom Drive RR #1, Ayr, N0B 1E0, ON, Canada
Tel.: (519) 622-3604
Web Site: http://www.jbttransport.com
Year Founded: 2002
Transportation Services
N.A.I.C.S.: 488999
Kelly Gates *(Controller)*

JC AB
Box 161 42, 435 85, Stockholm, Sweden
Tel.: (46) 841052220
Web Site: http://www.jc.se
Sales Range: $200-249.9 Million
Emp.: 550
Denim Clothing
N.A.I.C.S.: 424350
Iliya Meric *(Owner & CEO)*

Subsidiaries:

JC Jeans & Clothes Oy (1)
Korkeavuorenkatu 34, Helsinki, Finland
Tel.: (358) 988171616
Web Site: http://www.jc.fi
Sales Range: $25-49.9 Million
Emp.: 200
Family Clothing Stores
N.A.I.C.S.: 458110

JC CHEMICAL CO., LTD.
Hwasan-Ri 354 Onsan-Eup Ulju-Gun, Ulsan, 689-896, Korea (South)
Web Site: http://www.jcchemical.co.kr
Year Founded: 2006
137950—(KRS)
Rev.: $392,448,066
Assets: $236,270,029
Liabilities: $126,498,956
Net Worth: $109,771,073
Earnings: $14,716,067
Emp.: 85
Fiscal Year-end: 12/31/22
Crude Oil Mfr
N.A.I.C.S.: 325194
Sahho Yoom *(CEO)*

JC CLARK LTD.
130 Adelaide Street West Suite 3400, Toronto, M5H 3P5, ON, Canada
Tel.: (416) 361-6144 ON
Web Site: http://www.jcclark.com
Year Founded: 2001

Equity Investment Firm
N.A.I.C.S.: 523999
Colin Stewart *(CEO & Portfolio Mgr)*

Subsidiaries:

Arbor Memorial Services Inc. (1)
2 Jane Street, Toronto, M6S 4W8, ON, Canada
Tel.: (416) 763-4531
Web Site: https://www.arbormemorial.com
Sales Range: $250-299.9 Million
Emp.: 1,550
Crematories, Funeral Homes & Cemeteries Operator
N.A.I.C.S.: 812220

JC FINANCE & TAX INTERCONNECT HOLDING LTD.
No 333 Nanxiang West Road Economic Development Zone, Dafeng District, Yancheng, 224100, Jiangsu, China
Tel.: (86) 51583282838
Web Site: http://www.fengdong.com
Year Founded: 1989
002530—(SSE)
Rev.: $171,247,284
Assets: $377,018,928
Liabilities: $157,865,760
Net Worth: $219,153,168
Earnings: ($47,818,836)
Fiscal Year-end: 12/31/22
Investment Services
N.A.I.C.S.: 523999
Wenming Zhu *(Chm & Gen Mgr)*

Subsidiaries:

Nanjing Fengdong Heat Treatment Engineering Co., Ltd. (1)
Industry Park Yongyang Town, Lishui county, Nanjing, Jiangsu, China
Tel.: (86) 2557208966
Heating Furnaces Mfr
N.A.I.C.S.: 333415

JC INTERNATIONAL GROUP LTD
Level 9 115 Pitt Street, Sydney, 2000, NSW, Australia
Tel.: (61) 282630515
Web Site: http://www.jcigroup.com.au
Year Founded: 2003
Rev.: $60,381,691
Assets: $58,400,025
Liabilities: $22,874,770
Net Worth: $35,525,255
Earnings: $5,547,390
Fiscal Year-end: 12/31/17
Construction Engineering Services
N.A.I.C.S.: 541330

Subsidiaries:

Anhui Jiancheng International Economic & Technical Cooperation Co., Ltd (1)
Dangtu County Gushu Industrial Park concentration area, Ma'anshan, 243100, Anhui, China
Tel.: (86) 5556871512
Web Site: http://jcgc.cc
Engineering Consulting Services
N.A.I.C.S.: 541330

JCB CO., LTD.
Aoyama Rise Square 5-1-22 Minami Aoyama, Minato-ku, Tokyo, 107 8686, Japan
Tel.: (81) 422761700
Sales Range: $1-4.9 Billion
Emp.: 2,787
Credit Card Operations & Services, Including Financing, Credit Guarantee, Collections, Gift Cards & Certificate Issuing & Sales
N.A.I.C.S.: 522210
Takao Kawanishi *(Co-Chm)*

JCB CO., LTD.

JCB Co., Ltd.—(Continued)

Subsidiaries:

JCB Card International (Korea) Co., Ltd. **(1)**
6F Seoul Center Bldg 91-1, Sogong-Dong Jung-Gu, Seoul, 4533, Korea (South)
Tel.: (82) 2 757 3068
Credit card operations
N.A.I.C.S.: 522320

JCB International (Eurasia) LLC **(1)**
Kievskaya st 7 entrance 7 floor12, 121059, Moscow, Russia
Tel.: (7) 4956471036
Credit card operations
N.A.I.C.S.: 522320

JCB International (Micronesia) Ltd. **(1)**
Comete Building 2F 1245 Pale San Vitores Rd, Tumon, GU 96913
Tel.: (671) 646-0993
Credit card operations
N.A.I.C.S.: 522320
Satomi McCarthy *(Mgr)*

JCB International Asia Pacific Pte. Ltd. **(1)**
230 Orchard Road 10-234/236 Faber House, Singapore, Singapore
Tel.: (65) 6738 0321
Credit card operations
N.A.I.C.S.: 522320

JCB International Business Consulting (Shanghai) Co., Ltd. **(1)**
Room A01 8th Floor Tower AB Office Park No 10, Jintong West Road Chaoyang District, Beijing, 100020, China
Tel.: (86) 10 8590 6860
Credit card operations
N.A.I.C.S.: 522320

JCB International Co., Ltd. **(1)**
5-1-22 Minami Aoyama, Minato-Ku, Tokyo, 107 8686, Japan
Tel.: (81) 357785483
Web Site: http://www.jcbinternational.com
Sales Range: $700-749.9 Million
Emp.: 2,300
Consumer Credit Services
N.A.I.C.S.: 522210

Subsidiary (Non-US):

JCB International (Asia) Ltd.-Tsim Sha Tsui Office **(2)**
1003 10th Fl Wai Fung Plz, 664 Mathan Rd, Hong Kong, China (Hong Kong) **(100%)**
Tel.: (852) 23667203
Web Site: http://www.jcbinternational.com
Sales Range: $25-49.9 Million
Emp.: 30
Provider of Consumer Credit
N.A.I.C.S.: 522291

JCB International (Deutschland) GmbH **(2)**
7 Kaiser Strasse 4, 60313, Frankfurt, Germany **(100%)**
Tel.: (49) 69292057
Web Site: http://www.jcbinternational.com
Sales Range: $50-74.9 Million
Emp.: 10
Provider of Consumer Credit Cards
N.A.I.C.S.: 522210

JCB International (Europe) Limited **(2)**
30 Eastbourne Terrace, 1 Harbor Exchange Sq, London, W2 6LA, United Kingdom **(100%)**
Tel.: (44) 2075120588
Web Site: http://www.jcbinternational.com
Sales Range: $10-24.9 Million
Emp.: 30
Provider of Consumer Credit Cards
N.A.I.C.S.: 522210
Devadas Vassanth *(Gen Mgr)*

JCB International (Italy) S.p.A. **(2)**
Via Sallustiana 26, 00187, Rome, Italy **(100%)**
Tel.: (39) 064814405
Web Site: http://www.jcbinternational.com
Sales Range: $50-74.9 Million
Emp.: 7
Consumer Credit Cards
N.A.I.C.S.: 522210
Francesco Maroldi *(Gen Mgr)*

JCB International (Oceania) Pty Ltd. **(2)**
Level 18 44 Market Street, Sydney, 2000, NSW, Australia
Tel.: (61) 292638000
Web Site: http://www.jcbinternational.com
Sales Range: $50-74.9 Million
Emp.: 10
Provider of Consumer Credit
N.A.I.C.S.: 522291

JCB International (Oceania) Pty Ltd.-Gold Coast **(2)**
Ste 14 Level 1 The Forum, 26 Orchid Ave, Gold Coast, 4217, GLD, Australia **(100%)**
Tel.: (61) 755925911
Web Site: http://www.jcbinternational.com.au
Sales Range: $50-74.9 Million
Emp.: 6
Provider of Consumer Credit
N.A.I.C.S.: 522291

JCB International (Singapore) Pte. Ltd. **(2)**
230 Orchard Rd No 10-234/236, Feber House, Singapore, 238854, Singapore **(100%)**
Tel.: (65) 67380321
Web Site: http://www.jcbi.com.jp
Sales Range: $50-74.9 Million
Emp.: 20
Provider of Consumer Credit
N.A.I.C.S.: 522291
Vincent Ling *(Mng Dir)*

JCB International (Taiwan) Co., Ltd. **(2)**
6F D 44 Chungshan North Road Sec 2, Taipei, 104, Taiwan
Tel.: (886) 225310055
Web Site: http://www.jcbinternational.com.tw
Sales Range: $50-74.9 Million
Emp.: 11
Provider of Consumer Credit
N.A.I.C.S.: 522291

Subsidiary (US):

JCB International Credit Card Co., Ltd. **(2)**
800 W 6th St Ste 200, Los Angeles, CA 90017-2915
Tel.: (213) 629-8111
Web Site: http://www.jcbusa.com
Sales Range: $25-49.9 Million
Emp.: 40
Provider of Consumer Credit
N.A.I.C.S.: 522320
Thomas Wright *(Pres & COO)*

JCB International Holding (Thailand) Co., Ltd. **(1)**
500 Ploenchit Road Lumpini Pathumwan, 9th Floor Amarin Plaza Building, Bangkok, 10330, Thailand
Tel.: (66) 2 256 9151
Emp.: 40
Credit card operations
N.A.I.C.S.: 522320
Naoya Michishima *(Mng Dir)*

JCB International do Brasil Administradora de Cartoes de Pagamento Ltda. **(1)**
Av Engenheiro Luiz Carlos Berrini 1748, 905/907 Brooklin Novo, Sao Paulo, 04571-000, Brazil
Tel.: (55) 11 3385 1333
Credit card operations
N.A.I.C.S.: 522320

P.T. JCB International Indonesia **(1)**
Wisma Nusantara International 4th Floor, M H Thamrin No 59, Jakarta, 10350, Indonesia
Tel.: (62) 21 3193 8104
Credit card operations
N.A.I.C.S.: 522320

JCBNEXT BERHAD

8th floor Wisma JcbNext 27 Lorong Medan Tuanku 1, 50300, Kuala Lumpur, 50300, Malaysia
Tel.: (60) 326922333
Web Site: https://www.jcbnext.com
Year Founded: 1995
JCBNEXT—(KLS)
Rev.: $2,374,458
Assets: $80,900,160
Liabilities: $2,069,768
Net Worth: $78,830,392
Earnings: $7,724,542
Emp.: 14
Fiscal Year-end: 12/31/23
Recruitment Services
N.A.I.C.S.: 541612
Yit Chan Tai *(Co-Sec)*

Subsidiaries:

Autoworld.com.my Sdn. Bhd. **(1)**
7 Lorong Medan Tuanku 1 Off Jln Sultan Ismail, 50300, Kuala Lumpur, Federal Territory, Malaysia
Tel.: (60) 321760333
Web Site: http://www.autoworld.com.my
Online Automobile Dealers
N.A.I.C.S.: 423110

Enerpro Pte. Ltd. **(1)**
10 Anson Road, 05 20 International Plaza, Singapore, 079903, Singapore
Tel.: (65) 63241169
Web Site: http://www.enerpro.com.sg
Human Resource Consulting Services
N.A.I.C.S.: 541612

JCDECAUX S.A.

17 Rue Soyer, 92200, Neuilly-sur-Seine, France
Tel.: (33) 130797979
Web Site: http://www.jcdecaux.com
Year Founded: 1964
DEC—(OTCIQ)
Rev.: $3,638,260,294
Assets: $10,217,904,847
Liabilities: $7,958,383,929
Net Worth: $2,259,520,919
Earnings: $264,377,967
Emp.: 11,096
Fiscal Year-end: 12/31/23
Outdoor Advertising & Media Services
N.A.I.C.S.: 541850
Jean-Claude Decaux *(Founder)*

Subsidiaries:

AFA JCDecaux AS **(1)**
Industriholmen 82, Hvidovre, 2650, Denmark **(100%)**
Tel.: (45) 36 34 24 00
Web Site: http://www.afajcdecaux.dk
Sales Range: $25-49.9 Million
Emp.: 100
Providers of Outdoor & Out-of-Home Media Services
N.A.I.C.S.: 541830

AFA JCDecaux Iceland **(1)**
Vesturvor 30 B, 200, Kopavogur, Iceland **(100%)**
Tel.: (354) 562 42 43
Sales Range: Less than $1 Million
Emp.: 7
Provider of Outdoor & Out-of-Home Media Services
N.A.I.C.S.: 541830
Einar Hermannsson *(Mng Dir)*

APN Outdoor Pty. Ltd. **(1)**
Level 4 33 Saunders St, Pyrmont, 2009, NSW, Australia
Tel.: (61) 285693000
Sales Range: $25-49.9 Million
Publisher
N.A.I.C.S.: 513120
Andrew Hines *(COO)*

Subsidiary (Domestic):

Jcdecaux Australia Trading Pty Ltd **(2)**
Level 6 1 York Street, Sydney, 2000, NSW, Australia
Tel.: (61) 285693000
Web Site: http://www.apnoutdoor.com.au
Outdoor Advertising Services
N.A.I.C.S.: 541850

Jessica Clayton *(Acct Mgr-Independent Media Agency Sls)*

The Australasian Advertising Company Pty Limited **(2)**
Level 4 33 Saunders Street, Pyrmont, 2009, NSW, Australia
Tel.: (61) 285693000
Web Site: http://www.apnoutdoor.com.au
Advertising Services
N.A.I.C.S.: 541850
Richard Harling *(CEO)*

Arge Autobahnwerbung GmbH **(1)**
Litfassstrasse 6, 1030, Vienna, Austria
Tel.: (43) 6643309275
Web Site: http://www.autobahnwerbung.com
Advertising Services
N.A.I.C.S.: 541810

Avenir **(1)**
17 rue Soyer, 92200, Neuilly-sur-Seine, France **(100%)**
Tel.: (33) 1 30 79 37 37
Web Site: http://www.jcdecaux.fr
Sales Range: $75-99.9 Million
Emp.: 3,000
Provider of Outdoor & Out-of-Home Media Services
N.A.I.C.S.: 541830

Avenir Praha & JCDecaux Neonlight **(1)**
Saldova 12, Prague, 18600, Czech Republic
Tel.: (420) 225 001 300
Web Site: http://www.jcdecaux.cz
Emp.: 100
Provider of Outdoor & Out-of-Home Media Services
N.A.I.C.S.: 541830
Pavel Slaby *(Mng Dir)*

Clear Channel Italy Outdoor SRL **(1)**
Via Cellini 66, 35027, Noventa Padovana, Italy
Tel.: (39) 0498955200
Web Site: http://www.clearchannel.it
Sales Range: $50-74.9 Million
Emp.: 40
Advertising Services
N.A.I.C.S.: 541890

Cyclocity Inc. **(1)**
3-23 kanda nishiki-cho, chiyoda-ku, Tokyo, 101-0054, Japan
Tel.: (81) 352172510
Web Site: https://www.en.cyclocity.jp
Bike Parking Services
N.A.I.C.S.: 812930

Die Draussenwerber GmbH **(1)**
An der Spreeschanze 6, 13599, Berlin, Germany
Tel.: (49) 30338995050
Web Site: http://www.draussenwerber.de
Advertising Services
N.A.I.C.S.: 541810

Gewista Werbegesellschaft.mbH **(1)**
Litfassstrasse 6, 1031, Vienna, Austria
Tel.: (43) 1795970
Web Site: https://www.gewista.at
Emp.: 343
Outdoor Advertising Services
N.A.I.C.S.: 541850
Kurt Sonnleitner *(CFO)*

Subsidiary (Non-US):

JCDecaux Hungary Zrt **(2)**
Ganz utca 16 Residence Office Building 2 4th floor, 1027, Budapest, Hungary
Tel.: (36) 12087301
Web Site: http://www.jcdecaux.hu
Advertising Services
N.A.I.C.S.: 541810
Timea Samu *(CEO)*

Gigaboard Polska Sp Zoo **(1)**
Radarowa Street 62A, 02-137, Warsaw, Poland
Tel.: (48) 223378855
Outdoor Advertising Services
N.A.I.C.S.: 541850
Iwona Bonder *(Acct Mgr)*

IGPDecaux SpA **(1)**
Centro Direzionale Milanofior Strada 3 - Palazzo B10, 20090, Assago, Italy
Tel.: (39) 02654651

AND PRIVATE COMPANIES

JCDECAUX S.A.

Web Site: http://www.igpdecaux.it
Sales Range: $25-49.9 Million
Emp.: 200
Provider of Outdoor & Out-of-Home Media Services
N.A.I.C.S.: 541830
Fabrizio du Chene de Vere *(CEO)*

IPDecaux Inc. (1)
51-1 Umyeon-dong, Seocho-gu, Seoul, 137-900, Korea (South)
Tel.: (82) 2 3497 0700
Web Site: http://www.jcdecaux.co.kr
Sales Range: $25-49.9 Million
Emp.: 50
Provider of Outdoor & Out-of-Home Media Services
N.A.I.C.S.: 541830
Jouyoung Kim *(Mng Dir)*

Infoscreen Austria GmbH (1)
Hainburger Strasse 11, 1030, Vienna, Austria
Tel.: (43) 171052000
Web Site: http://www.infoscreen.at
Advertising Services
N.A.I.C.S.: 541810
Stefanie Paffendorf *(Dir-Editorial Dept)*

Ispa Bratislava Spol Sro (1)
Kopcianska 92, 851 01, Bratislava, Slovakia
Tel.: (421) 268207502
Web Site: http://www.jcdecaux.sk
Construction Maintenance Services
N.A.I.C.S.: 561790

JCDecaux (1)
6 Sandyford Park Burton Hall Rd, Leopardstown, Dublin, 18, Ireland
Tel.: (353) 1 2958 170
Web Site: http://www.jcdecaux.ie
Sales Range: $50-74.9 Million
Emp.: 62
Provider of Outdoor & Out-of-Home Media Services
N.A.I.C.S.: 541830

JCDecaux (1)
6 Sandyford Park Burton Hall Rd, Leopardstown, Dublin, 18, Ireland
Tel.: (353) 1 295 8170
Web Site: http://www.jcdecaux.ie
Sales Range: $25-49.9 Million
Emp.: 7
Outdoor & Media Services
N.A.I.C.S.: 541850
Joanne Grant *(Mng Dir)*

JCDecaux (1)
991 Great West Road, Brentford, TW8 9DN, Middlesex, United Kingdom
Tel.: (44) 2083267720
Web Site: http://www.jcdecaux.co.uk
Sales Range: $25-49.9 Million
Emp.: 80
Provider of Outdoor & Out-of-Home Media Services
N.A.I.C.S.: 541830

JCDecaux Advertising India Pvt Ltd. (1)
153 3rd Floor Phase -III, Okhla Industrial Estate, New Delhi, 110020, India
Tel.: (91) 1140653000
Web Site: http://www.jcdecaux.co.in
Advertising Services
N.A.I.C.S.: 541810
Mahesh Kumar *(Ops Mgr)*

JCDecaux Airport Espana (1)
Avd de Aragon 328 Poligono Industrial Las Mercedes, CP 28022, Madrid, Spain
Tel.: (34) 918 374 100
Web Site: http://www.jcdecaux.es
Sales Range: $75-99.9 Million
Emp.: 450
Outdoor & Out-of-Home Media Services
N.A.I.C.S.: 541830
Isabel Lopez Ortuno *(Co-Dir Gen)*

JCDecaux Airport France (1)
17 rue Soyer, 92200, Neuilly-sur-Seine, France **(100%)**
Tel.: (33) 130794949
Web Site: http://www.jcdecauxairport.fr
Sales Range: $150-199.9 Million
Emp.: 300
Provider of Outdoor & Out-of-Home Media Services
N.A.I.C.S.: 541830

JCDecaux Airport Polska Sp z o.o. (1)
Ul Radarowa 62A, 02-137, Warsaw, Poland
Tel.: (48) 223313320
Web Site: http://www.jcdecauxairport.com.pl
Airport Advertising Services
N.A.I.C.S.: 541850
Mariola Drezek *(Acct Mgr-Sls)*

JCDecaux Airport Portugal (1)
Avenida Infante D Henrique Lote 312, Lisbon, 1950-421, Portugal
Tel.: (351) 21 831 14 30
Web Site: http://www.jcdecaux.com
Sales Range: $25-49.9 Million
Emp.: 6
Provider of Outdoor & Out-of-Home Media Services
N.A.I.C.S.: 541830

JCDecaux Airport UK (1)
Summit House 27 Sale Pl, London, W2 IYR, United Kingdom **(100%)**
Tel.: (44) 2072988100
Web Site: http://www.jcdecauxairport.co.uk
Sales Range: $25-49.9 Million
Emp.: 100
Provider of Outdoor & Out-of-Home Media Services
N.A.I.C.S.: 541830

JCDecaux Angola Limitada. (1)
Bairro do Benfica Talhao N 09-I, Municipio do Belas, Luanda, Angola
Tel.: (244) 929246850
Outdoor Advertising Services
N.A.I.C.S.: 541850
Rui Puna *(Ops Mgr)*

JCDecaux Argentina/ Uruguay (1)
Talcahuano 833 - 9B, Ciudad de, 1004, Buenos Aires, Argentina
Tel.: (54) 11 52390070
Web Site: http://www.jcdecaux.com
Sales Range: $25-49.9 Million
Emp.: 12
Provider of Outdoor & Out-of-Home Media Services
N.A.I.C.S.: 541830

JCDecaux Australia (1)
Units 2&3 182 190 Euston Rd, Alexandria, Sydney, 2015, NSW, Australia **(100%)**
Tel.: (61) 2 95576555
Web Site: http://www.jcdecaux.com.au
Sales Range: $25-49.9 Million
Emp.: 108
Provider of Outdoor & Out-of-Home Media Services
N.A.I.C.S.: 541830

JCDecaux Belgium (1)
Allee Verte 50, 1000, Brussels, Belgium
Tel.: (32) 2 274 11 11
Web Site: http://www.jcdecaux.be
Sales Range: $25-49.9 Million
Emp.: 150
Provider of Outdoor & Out-of-Home Media Services
N.A.I.C.S.: 541830
Wim Jansen *(CEO)*

JCDecaux Billboard (1)
Allee Verte 50, 1000, Brussels, Belgium **(100%)**
Tel.: (32) 2 274 11 11
Web Site: http://www.jcdecaux.be
Sales Range: $25-49.9 Million
Emp.: 80
Provider of Outdoor & Out-of-Home Media Services
N.A.I.C.S.: 541830
Wim Jansen *(CEO)*

JCDecaux Botswana (Pty) Limited (1)
Plot 157 Unit 5 Gaborone International Commerce Park, Gaborone, Botswana
Tel.: (267) 3922340
Outdoor Advertising Services
N.A.I.C.S.: 541850
Modisa Maphanyane *(Sls Mgr)*

JCDecaux Chile S.A. (1)
Andres Bellos 2777 Oficina 602 Tore le Industria, Las Condes, Santiago, Chile **(100%)**
Tel.: (56) 2 203 03 24
Web Site: http://www.jcdecaux.com
Sales Range: $25-49.9 Million
Emp.: 85
Provider of Outdoor & Out-of-Home Media Services
N.A.I.C.S.: 541830

JCDecaux China Group Marketing (1)
21/F V-CAPITAL Bldg, No 333 Xianxia Rd, Shanghai, 200336, China
Tel.: (86) 21 6290 0101
Web Site: http://www.jcdecaux.com.cn
Sales Range: $125-149.9 Million
Emp.: 300
Advertising Services
N.A.I.C.S.: 541870
Stephen Wong *(CEO)*

Branch (Domestic):

Beijing Top Result Public Transportation Advertising Co., Ltd. Wuhan Branch
25F Jianyin Bldg, 709 Jianshe Ave, Wuhan, 430015, China
Tel.: (86) 27 8555 1618
Advertising Services
N.A.I.C.S.: 541870

Guangzhou Yongtong Metro Ads Co., Ltd. (2)
Unit 05-09 27/F HNA Tower No 8 Linhe Zhong Road, Tianhe District, Guangzhou, 510610, China
Tel.: (86) 2037183000
Web Site: http://www.jcdecaux.com.cn
N.A.I.C.S.: 541870

JCDecaux Advertising Co Ltd. Chengdu Branch (2)
B1501 Air China Century Ctr, No 3 Hangkong Road, Chengdu, 610041, China
Tel.: (86) 28 8602 9977
Advertising Services
N.A.I.C.S.: 541870

JCDecaux Advertising Co., Ltd. - Chongquing Branch (2)
40/F YingLi IFC No 28 MinQuan Road, Yu Zhong District, Chongqing, 400010, China
Tel.: (86) 2363936989
Web Site: http://www.jcdecaux.com.cn
Sales Range: $25-49.9 Million
Emp.: 40
N.A.I.C.S.: 541870

JCDecaux Momentum Shanghai Airport Advertising Co., Ltd. (2)
8/F Erdos International plaza No 1118 South Pudong Rd, Shanghai, 200122, China
Tel.: (86) 2138600000
Web Site: http://www.samdecaux.com
Sales Range: $25-49.9 Million
Advertising Services
N.A.I.C.S.: 541870
Stephane Chanut *(Gen Mgr)*

Branch (Non-US):

JCDecaux Pearl & Dean Ltd (2)
20/F Berkshire House Taikoo Place 25 Westlands Road, Quarry Bay, China (Hong Kong)
Tel.: (852) 2111 0111
Web Site: http://www.jcdecaux-transport.com.hk
Sales Range: $50-74.9 Million
Emp.: 150
N.A.I.C.S.: 541870

Branch (Domestic):

Nanjing MPI Public Transport Advertising Co., Ltd. (2)
22/F Golden Eagle Plaza No 89 Han Zhong Rd, Nanjing, 210029, China
Tel.: (86) 25 8471 1070
Web Site: http://www.jcdecaux.com.cn
Public Transport Media Services
N.A.I.C.S.: 541870

JCDecaux Deutschland/Abribus Citymedia (1)
Oskar Jager Str 48A, 50825, Cologne, Germany
Tel.: (49) 221 54 68 50
Web Site: http://www.jcdecaux.de

Provider of Outdoor & Out-of-Home Services
N.A.I.C.S.: 541830
Dieter Keppler *(CEO)*

JCDecaux Digital Vision (HK) Ltd. (1)
20/F Berkshire House 25 Westlands Road, Quarry Bay, China (Hong Kong)
Tel.: (852) 39603333
Marketing Services
N.A.I.C.S.: 541613

JCDecaux Dominicana, SAS (1)
Av Ortega y Gasset 16-Esquina Roberto Pastoriza, Santo Domingo, Dominican Republic
Tel.: (809) 8095675528
Advertising Services
N.A.I.C.S.: 541810
Eury Vasquez Diaz *(Gen Mgr)*

JCDecaux Ecuador SA (1)
Av Luis Orrantia Gonzalez entre Av Miguel H Alcivar y Av, Juan Tanca Marengo Manzana, Guayaquil, Ecuador
Tel.: (593) 45010101
Advertising Services
N.A.I.C.S.: 541810

JCDecaux Eesti OU (1)
Tartu mnt 18, Tallinn, Estonia
Tel.: (372) 6309940
Web Site: http://www.jcdecaux.ee
Emp.: 30
Advertising Services
N.A.I.C.S.: 541810
Kristiina Sepp *(Gen Mgr)*

JCDecaux El Salvador, S.a. De C.V. (1)
Rua Deocleciana 53/59, Sao Paulo, SP, Brazil
Tel.: (55) 1122221516
Web Site: http://www.jcdecaux.com.br
Outdoor Advertising Services
N.A.I.C.S.: 541850

JCDecaux Espana SLU (1)
Avenida de Aragon 328, Poligono Industrial Las Mercedes, 28022, Madrid, Spain
Tel.: (34) 918374100
Advertising Services
N.A.I.C.S.: 541810

JCDecaux Eswatini (Proprietary) Limited (1)
Unit No 2 at Lot 443 8th Street, Nkosing Phile Building Industrial Site, Matsapha, Eswatini
Tel.: (268) 25187836
Outdoor Advertising Services
N.A.I.C.S.: 541850
Chandre Fortune-Barbosa *(Country Mgr)*

JCDecaux Finland Oy (1)
Mekaanikonkatu 11, PO Box 53, 8210, Helsinki, Finland **(100%)**
Tel.: (358) 207 758 200
Web Site: http://www.jcdecaux.fi
Rev: $48,913,752
Emp.: 100
Providers of Outdoor & Out-of-Home Media Services
N.A.I.C.S.: 541830

JCDecaux France SAS (1)
Avenue Sainte Apolline, 78370, Plaisir, Cedex, France
Tel.: (33) 130797979
Web Site: http://www.jcdecaux.fr
Advertising Services
N.A.I.C.S.: 541810

JCDecaux Guatemala, S.A. (1)
6a Avenida 14-50 zona 10, Guatemala, Guatemala
Tel.: (502) 23670840
Advertising Services
N.A.I.C.S.: 541810
Fernando E. Mansilla *(Gen Dir)*

JCDecaux Ireland Ltd. (1)
6 Sandyford Park Burton Hall Road, Leopardstown, Dublin, D18 AT28, Ireland
Tel.: (353) 12958170
Web Site: http://www.jcdecaux.ie
Outdoor Advertising Services
N.A.I.C.S.: 541850
Tony O'Flanagan *(Mktg Dir)*

JCDECAUX S.A. — INTERNATIONAL PUBLIC

JCDecaux S.A.—(Continued)

JCDecaux Israel Ltd. (1)
Ha-Psagot 4, Petach Tikva, 4951623, Israel
Tel.: (972) 36490490
Web Site: http://www.jcdecaux.co.il
Outdoor Advertising Services
N.A.I.C.S.: 541850

JCDecaux Korea Inc. (1)
38-21 Baumoe-ro 11an-gil, Seocho-Gu, Seoul, Korea (South)
Tel.: (82) 234970700
Web Site: http://www.jcdecaux.co.kr
Advertising Services
N.A.I.C.S.: 541810

JCDecaux Latvija SIA (1)
9-3 Kr Valdemara Street, Riga, LV-1010, Latvia
Tel.: (371) 67320717
Advertising Services
N.A.I.C.S.: 541810

JCDecaux Lesotho (Pty) Ltd. (1)
14 / 15 Lioli Street, Maseru West Industrial Area, Maseru, Lesotho
Tel.: (266) 22326936
Outdoor Advertising Services
N.A.I.C.S.: 541850

JCDecaux Lietuva UAB (1)
Vilniaus g 31, LT-01402, Vilnius, Lithuania
Tel.: (370) 52730917
Advertising Services
N.A.I.C.S.: 541810
Jurate Mizare *(Mng Dir)*

JCDecaux Ltd. (1)
991 Great West Road, Brentford, TW8 9DN, Middlesex, United Kingdom
Tel.: (44) 2083267777
Web Site: http://www.jcdecaux.co.uk
Outdoor Advertising Services
N.A.I.C.S.: 541850

JCDecaux Macau Ltd. (1)
Alameda Dr Carlos D Assumpcao No 258, Edificio Kin Heng Long Plaza 21 Andar G, Macau, China (Macau)
Tel.: (853) 28721292
Advertising Services
N.A.I.C.S.: 541810
Grover Ho *(Assoc Dir)*

JCDecaux Madagascar SA (1)
Batiment Sirius Zone Galaxy Andraharo 101, Antananarivo, Madagascar
Tel.: (261) 693934141
Outdoor Advertising Services
N.A.I.C.S.: 541850
Jerry Rafidimanana *(Office Mgr)*

JCDecaux Mestsky Mobiliar spol s.r.o. (1)
Krizikova 34/148, Prague, 186 00, Czech Republic
Tel.: (420) 225 001 300
Web Site: http://www.jcdecaux.cz
Sales Range: $25-49.9 Million
Emp.: 80
Provider of Outdoor & Out-of-Home Media Services
N.A.I.C.S.: 541850
Pavel Slaby *(CEO)*

JCDecaux Middle East FZ-LLC (1)
Boutique Offices Villa No 03, PO Box 214810, Dubai, United Arab Emirates
Tel.: (971) 44398400
Advertising Services
N.A.I.C.S.: 541810
Martin Sabbagh *(CEO)*

Subsidiary (Non-US):

JCDecaux ATA Saudi LLC (2)
King s Road Tower 8th floor-Office 804 King Abdulaziz Road Malek Road, PO Box 24842, Ash Shati District, Jeddah, 21456, Saudi Arabia
Tel.: (966) 126928504
Advertising Services
N.A.I.C.S.: 541810
Mohammed Imran *(Ops Mgr)*

JCDecaux Mobilier Urbain (1)
17 rue Soyer, 92 200, Neuilly-sur-Seine, France **(100%)**
Tel.: (33) 130797969
Web Site: http://www.jcdecaux-mu.fr
Sales Range: Less than $1 Million
Emp.: 300
Provider of Outdoor & Out-of-Home Media Services
N.A.I.C.S.: 541830
Jean Muller *(COO)*

JCDecaux Mongolia LLC (1)
Blue sky Tower No 707 Peace Avenue 17 1st Khoroo, Sukhbaatar District, Ulaanbaatar, Mongolia
Tel.: (976) 70077707
Web Site: http://www.jcdecaux.mn
Advertising Services
N.A.I.C.S.: 541810

JCDecaux Nederland B.V. (1)
Barbara Strozzilaan 374, 1112 AA, Amsterdam, Netherlands
Tel.: (31) 206607500
Web Site: http://www.jcdecaux.nl
Sales Range: $25-49.9 Million
Emp.: 190
Provider of Outdoor & Out-of-Home Media Services
N.A.I.C.S.: 541830
Bart Devries *(Dir-Sls & Mktg)*

JCDecaux Neonlight (1)
17 rue Soyer, 92000, Neuilly-sur-Seine, France **(100%)**
Tel.: (33) 1 30 79 49 59
Web Site: http://www.jcdecaux-artvertising.com
Sales Range: $75-99.9 Million
Emp.: 300
Provider of Outdoor & Out-of-Door Media Serivces
N.A.I.C.S.: 541830

JCDecaux Neonlight (1)
Allee Verte 50, 1000, Brussels, Belgium
Tel.: (32) 2 274 11 11
Web Site: http://www.jcdecaux.be
Sales Range: $25-49.9 Million
Emp.: 150
Provider of Outdoor & Out-of-Home Media Services
N.A.I.C.S.: 541830
Wim Jansen *(CEO)*

JCDecaux Neonlight Poland (1)
Radarowa 62A, 02511, Warsaw, Poland
Tel.: (48) 223313320
Web Site: http://www.jcdecaux.com.pl
Sales Range: $25-49.9 Million
Emp.: 5
Provider of Outdoor & Out-of-Home Media Services
N.A.I.C.S.: 541830

JCDecaux Neonlight Sp Zoo (1)
Radarowa Street 62A, 02-137, Warsaw, Poland
Tel.: (48) 225751380
Outdoor Advertising Services
N.A.I.C.S.: 541850
Joanna Sadowska *(Gen Mgr)*

JCDecaux Nigeria Outdoor Advertising Ltd. (1)
17b Bishop Aboyade Cole Street Victoria Island, Lagos, Nigeria
Tel.: (234) 9087431284
Outdoor Advertising Services
N.A.I.C.S.: 541850
Omoniyi Dada *(Mgr-Site Acquisition & Regulatory)*

JCDecaux Norge (1)
Gullhaugveien 7, PO Box 4314, 0402, Oslo, Norway
Tel.: (47) 23 00 75 00
Web Site: http://www.jcdecaux.no
Sales Range: $1-9.9 Million
Emp.: 60
Provider of Outdoor & Out-of-Home Media Services
N.A.I.C.S.: 541830
Oyvind Markussen *(Mng Dir)*

JCDecaux North America Inc. (1)
3 Park Ave 33rd Fl, New York, NY 10016
Tel.: (646) 834-1200
Web Site: http://www.jcdecauxna.com
Sales Range: $25-49.9 Million
Emp.: 180
Outdoor, Out-of-Home Media
N.A.I.C.S.: 541810
Jean-Luc Decaux *(Co-CEO)*

JCDecaux One-Stop Shop (1)
Summit House 27 Sale Pl, London, W2 1YR, United Kingdom
Tel.: (44) 2072988000
Web Site: http://www.jcdecaux.co.uk
Sales Range: $25-49.9 Million
Emp.: 5
Provider of Outdoor & Out-of-Home Media Services
N.A.I.C.S.: 541830

JCDecaux Out Of Home FZ-LLC (1)
Office 107 Park Rotana Office Building Two-four54 Campus Khalifa Park, PO Box 77869, Off Salam Street, Abu Dhabi, United Arab Emirates
Tel.: (971) 44398404
Airport Transportation Services
N.A.I.C.S.: 485999
Wissam Zaatar *(Mng Dir)*

JCDecaux Outdoor Advertising Ltd. (1)
Plot No BC404 Along Mahatma Gandhi Road Mount Pleasant, Blantyre, Malawi
Tel.: (265) 885503888
Outdoor Advertising Services
N.A.I.C.S.: 541850
Khwesi Msusa *(Gen Mgr)*

JCDecaux Panama, S.A. (1)
Costa del Este Calle 1ra Edificio East Coast 141, Parque Industrial, Panama, Panama
Tel.: (507) 2327748
Advertising Services
N.A.I.C.S.: 541810
Monica Mitrotti *(Mgr-Treasury)*

JCDecaux Peru SAC (1)
Av Alfredo Benavides 1579 Office 1001, Miraflores, Lima, Peru
Tel.: (51) 17150208
Outdoor Advertising Services
N.A.I.C.S.: 541850
Felipe Romero Dacal *(Comml Dir)*

JCDecaux Portugal (1)
Estrada Nacional 115-5 Granja do Alpriate, 1950 421, Vialonga, Portugal
Tel.: (351) 218311360
Web Site: http://www.jcdecaux.pt
Sales Range: $25-49.9 Million
Emp.: 50
Provider of Outdoor & Out-of-Home Media Services
N.A.I.C.S.: 541830

JCDecaux Portugal & JCDecaux Publicidade Luminosa (1)
Avenida Infante D Henrique Lote 312, P 1950 002, Lisbon, Portugal **(100%)**
Tel.: (351) 218317500
Web Site: http://www.jcdecaux.com
Provider of Outdoor & Out-of-Home Media Services
N.A.I.C.S.: 541830

JCDecaux Publicidad Luminosa (1)
Calle Botanica 172-174 Pol Ind Gran Via Sur, L'Hospitalet de Llobregat, 08908, Barcelona, Spain
Tel.: (34) 933 357 110
Web Site: http://www.jcdecaux.es
Sales Range: $150-199.9 Million
Emp.: 580
Provider of Outdoor & Out-of-Home Media Services
N.A.I.C.S.: 541830
Jean-Louis Paccalin *(Mng Dir)*

JCDecaux Singapore Pte. Ltd. (1)
8 Temasek Boulevard 33-02 Suntec City Tower 3, Singapore, 038988, Singapore
Tel.: (65) 63336639
Web Site: http://www.jcdecaux.com.sg
Outdoor Advertising Services
N.A.I.C.S.: 541850
Audrey Soh *(Mgr-HR & Admin)*

JCDecaux Slovakia (1)
Kopcianska 92, 851 01, Bratislava, Slovakia
Tel.: (421) 2 63 811 916
Web Site: http://www.jcdecaux.com
Sales Range: $25-49.9 Million
Emp.: 40
Provider of Outdoor & Out-of-Home Media Services
N.A.I.C.S.: 541830
Milos Karpati *(Dir-Sls)*

JCDecaux South Africa (Pty) Ltd. (1)
Block E 392 Main Street, Bryanston, 2191, Gauteng, South Africa
Tel.: (27) 115141400
Outdoor Advertising Services
N.A.I.C.S.: 541850
Jenny Pillay *(Head-HR)*

JCDecaux Spain (1)
Avd de Aragon 328 Pol Ind, Las Mercedes, 28022, Madrid, Spain **(100%)**
Tel.: (34) 918 374 100
Web Site: http://www.jcdecaux.es
Sales Range: $75-99.9 Million
Emp.: 450
Provider of Outdoor & Out-of-Home Services
N.A.I.C.S.: 541830
Isabel Lopez Ortuno *(Mng Dir)*

JCDecaux Sverige AB (1)
Stureplan 13, 111 45, Stockholm, Sweden
Tel.: (46) 8 474 83 00
Web Site: http://www.jcdecaux.se
Sales Range: $25-49.9 Million
Emp.: 120
Outdoor & Out-of-Home Media Services
N.A.I.C.S.: 541830
Gauthier Alby *(CFO)*

JCDecaux Tanzania Ltd. (1)
Plot No 278 Halle Selassie Road, Masaki, Dar es Salaam, Tanzania
Tel.: (255) 765350828
Outdoor Advertising Services
N.A.I.C.S.: 541850
Godfrey Lyimo *(Fin Mgr)*

JCDecaux Top Media Honduras S.A. (1)
Col Alameda Ave Julio Lozano Diaz Edif Paviole 2nd Floor, Tegucigalpa, Honduras
Tel.: (504) 2239749900
Outdoor Advertising Services
N.A.I.C.S.: 541850
David Alfredo Pineda Mendoza *(Mng Dir)*

JCDecaux Top Media Servicios De Panama, S.A. (1)
Industrial Park First Street, Costa del Este, Panama, Panama
Tel.: (507) 2707000
Outdoor Advertising Services
N.A.I.C.S.: 541850

JCDecaux UK (1)
991 Great W Rd, Brentford, TW89 DN, United Kingdom
Tel.: (44) 2083267777
Web Site: http://www.jcdecaux.co.uk
Sales Range: $75-99.9 Million
Emp.: 500
Provider of Outdoor & Out-of-Home Media Services
N.A.I.C.S.: 541830
Spencer Berwin *(Co-CEO)*

JCDecaux Uganda Outdoor Advertising Ltd. (1)
Plot 78 Kira Road 1st Floor Media Plaza, Kampala, Uganda
Tel.: (256) 414510488
Outdoor Advertising Services
N.A.I.C.S.: 541850

JCDecaux United (1)
25 Chapel St Capital House, London, NW1 5DH, United Kingdom **(100%)**
Tel.: (44) 2072988000
Web Site: http://www.jcdecaux.co.uk
Sales Range: $25-49.9 Million
Emp.: 200
Provider of Outdoor & Out-of-Home Media Services
N.A.I.C.S.: 541830

JCDecaux Uruguay SA (1)
Av Rondeau 1978, 11800, Montevideo, Uruguay
Tel.: (598) 29242935
Advertising Services
N.A.I.C.S.: 541810
Marcelo Petruccelli *(Mng Dir)*

JCDecaux Uz. Jv Ltd. (1)
Gospitalny Block 12, Mirabad, Tashkent, 100015, Uzbekistan
Tel.: (998) 781500050
Web Site: http://www.jcdecaux.uz
Outdoor Advertising Services

AND PRIVATE COMPANIES

JCDecaux Zambia Ltd. (1)
Stand No 25086 Off Parliament Lane Olympia Park, Lusaka, Zambia
Tel.: (260) 211220978
Outdoor Advertising Services
N.A.I.C.S.: 541850
Simba A. Banda *(Ops Mgr)*

JCDecaux Zimbabwe (Pvt) Ltd. (1)
9B Townsend Road, Emerald Hill, Harare, Zimbabwe
Tel.: (263) 772490736
Outdoor Advertising Services
N.A.I.C.S.: 541850
Victor Shambare *(Gen Mgr)*

JCDecaux do Brasil, Ltda (1)
Rua Jeronimo da Veiga No 45-11 andar Itaim Bibi, CEP 04536 000, Sao Paulo, Brazil (100%)
Tel.: (55) 11 30 89 68 24
Web Site: http://www.jcdecaux.com.br
Provider of Outdoor & Out-of-Home Media Serivces
N.A.I.C.S.: 541830

Kulturformat GmbH (1)
Litfassstrasse 6, 1030, Vienna, Austria
Tel.: (43) 17962640
Web Site: http://www.kulturformat.at
Outdoor Advertising Services
N.A.I.C.S.: 541850
Daniela Grill *(Mng Dir)*

MCDecaux Inc. (1)
Nishimoto Kosan Nishiki-cho Bldg 6Fl 23 Kanda Nishiki-cho 3-chome, Chiyoda-ku, Tokyo, 101-0054, Japan
Tel.: (81) 352 172 520
Web Site: http://www.mcdecaux.co.jp
Sales Range: $25-49.9 Million
Emp.: 45
Provider of Outdoor & Out-of-Home Media Services
N.A.I.C.S.: 541830

Progress Aussenwerbung GmbH (1)
Rottfeld 3, 5020, Salzburg, Austria
Tel.: (43) 6624392240
Web Site: http://www.progress-werbung.at
Outdoor Advertising Services
N.A.I.C.S.: 541850
Cornelia Hutter *(Head-Analog, Sls, Support & Disposition)*

Progress Werbeland Werbe. GmbH (1)
Freistadter Str 313 - 315/2 Stock, 4040, Linz, Austria
Tel.: (43) 732736437
Web Site: http://www.progress.at
Outdoor Advertising Services
N.A.I.C.S.: 541850

Top Media Nicaragua, S.A. (1)
Reparto San Juan Kindergarten Preschool 1 Block East 1 Block North, Managua, Nicaragua
Tel.: (505) 22703990
Outdoor Advertising Services
N.A.I.C.S.: 541850

UDC JCDecaux (1)
Blvd Avila Camacho Colonias Lomas de Chapultepec, Delegacion Miguel Hidalgo, 11000, Mexico, DF, Mexico
Tel.: (52) 55 52 81 77 43
Web Site: http://www.udcmx.com
Provider of Outdoor & Out-of-Home Media Services
N.A.I.C.S.: 541830

Usp Werbegesellschaft.mbH (1)
Freistadter Strasse 313 - 315, 4040, Linz, Austria
Tel.: (43) 732667766
Web Site: http://www.usp-aussenwerbung.at
Outdoor Advertising Services
N.A.I.C.S.: 541850

Wall GmbH (1)
Friedrichstrasse 118, 10117, Berlin, Germany
Tel.: (49) 30338990
Web Site: http://www.wall.de
Advertising Services
N.A.I.C.S.: 541810
Sophie Smikalla *(Mgr-Digital)*

JCE GROUP AB
Hogasplatsen 3, SE 412 56, Gothenburg, Sweden
Tel.: (46) 31 759 55 00
Web Site: http://www.jcegroup.se
Year Founded: 1971
Emp.: 10
Investment Firm; Holding Company
N.A.I.C.S.: 551112
Hampus Ericsson *(Chm, Pres & CEO)*

Subsidiaries:

Bruks Siwertell Group AB (1)
P.O Box 566 Gunnarstorp, SE-267 25, Bjuv, Sweden (52%)
Tel.: (46) 4285800
Web Site: https://bruks-siwertell.com
Emp.: 500
Machinery Mfg
N.A.I.C.S.: 333924
Peter Jonsson *(CEO)*

Subsidiary (US):

West Salem Machinery Co (2)
665 Murlark Ave NW, Salem, OR 97304
Tel.: (503) 364-2213
Web Site: http://www.westsalem.com
Rev.: $9,225,000
Emp.: 75
All Other Miscellaneous Fabricated Metal Product Mfr
N.A.I.C.S.: 332999
Mark Lyman *(Owner)*

JCET GROUP CO., LTD.
275 Middle Binjiang Rd, Jiangyin, Jiangsu, China
Tel.: (86) 51086854189
Web Site: https://www.jcetglobal.com
Year Founded: 1972
600584—(SHG)
Rev.: $4,740,188,787
Assets: $5,532,845,531
Liabilities: $2,073,005,789
Net Worth: $3,459,839,741
Earnings: $453,630,743
Emp.: 23,000
Fiscal Year-end: 12/31/22
Electronic Components Mfr
N.A.I.C.S.: 334413
Li Zheng *(CEO)*

Subsidiaries:

Jiangyin Changdian Advanced Packaging Co., Ltd. (1)
No 78 Changshan Rd, Jiangyin, Jiangsu, China
Tel.: (86) 51068830101
Web Site: http://www.jcap.cn
Emp.: 1,000
Semiconductor & Related Device Mfr
N.A.I.C.S.: 334413

STATS ChipPAC Semiconductor (Jiangyin) Co., Ltd. (1)
No 78 Changshan Rd, Jiangyin, 214437, Jiangsu, China
Tel.: (86) 51068835858
Semiconductor Components Mfr
N.A.I.C.S.: 334413

SanDisk Semiconductor (Shanghai) Co., Ltd. (1)
No 388 Jiang Chuan East Road, Minhang District, Shanghai, 200241, China (80%)
Tel.: (86) 2160905555
Web Site: http://www.sandisk.de
Flash Memory Data Storage Products Sales & Services
N.A.I.C.S.: 423430

JCH SYSTEMS INC.
JC Hyun Building 74 Saechang-ro 45-gil, Yongsan-gu, Seoul, Korea (South)
Tel.: (82) 221059100
Web Site: https://www.jchyun.com
Year Founded: 1991
033320—(KRS)
Rev.: $153,832,950
Assets: $123,211,571
Liabilities: $36,836,852
Net Worth: $86,374,719
Earnings: $296,924
Emp.: 95
Fiscal Year-end: 12/31/22
Computer & Computer Peripheral Equipment Whslr
N.A.I.C.S.: 423430
Hyeon Bae Cha *(Chm & CEO)*

JCHX MINING MANAGEMENT CO., LTD.
No 28 Shuiyuan West Road economic development zone, Miyun District, Beijing, 101500, China
Tel.: (86) 1083203999
Web Site: https://www.jchxmc.com
Year Founded: 1997
603979—(SHG)
Rev.: $751,822,330
Assets: $1,582,391,833
Liabilities: $713,436,465
Net Worth: $868,955,368
Earnings: $85,609,209
Emp.: 7,600
Fiscal Year-end: 12/31/22
Mining Construction & Development Services
N.A.I.C.S.: 236210
Wu Shao *(Exec VP & Chief Engr)*

JCK HOSPITALITY PUBLIC COMPANY LIMITED
TFD Building No 18 Soi Sathorn 11 yaeg 9 Khwaeng yannava, Sathorn, Bangkok, 10120, Thailand
Tel.: (66) 22869959 TH
Web Site: http://jckhgroup.com
Year Founded: 2004
JCKH—(THA)
Rev.: $11,606,636
Assets: $43,747,514
Liabilities: $30,314,064
Net Worth: $13,433,451
Earnings: $(3,177,952)
Emp.: 673
Fiscal Year-end: 12/31/23
Fast Food Restaurant Owner & Operator
N.A.I.C.S.: 722513
Apichai Taechaubol *(Chm & Chm)*

JCK INTERNATIONAL PUBLIC LIMITED COMPANY
18 Soi Sathorn 11 Yaek 9 TFD Building Yannawa, Sathorn, Bangkok, 10120, Thailand
Tel.: (66) 26764031 TH
Web Site: https://www.tfd-factory.com
Year Founded: 1977
JCK—(THA)
Rev.: $82,915,431
Assets: $278,999,288
Liabilities: $193,295,812
Net Worth: $85,703,476
Earnings: $16,993,889
Emp.: 108
Fiscal Year-end: 12/31/23
Real Estate Development Services
N.A.I.C.S.: 531390
Apichai Taechaubol *(Chm)*

Subsidiaries:

Total Industrial Services Company Limited (1)
10th Fl JC Kevin Tower 26 Narathiwat, Ratchanakarin Rd Yannawa, Sathorn, 10120, Bangkok, Thailand
Tel.: (66) 267640315
Sales Range: $25-49.9 Million
Emp.: 62
Factory Construction & Rental Services
N.A.I.C.S.: 236210

JCL AG
Liebenauer Tangente 4 6, 8041, Graz, Liebenau, Austria
Tel.: (43) 316 9190 6100
Web Site: http://www.jcl-logistics.com
Sales Range: $750-799.9 Million
Emp.: 1,900
Logistic Services
N.A.I.C.S.: 541614
Stephan Joebstl *(CEO)*

JCP ENTREPRISE
6 Rue Paul Heroult, 92563, Rueil-Malmaison, France
Tel.: (33) 141448888
Web Site: http://www.jcpentreprise.com
Year Founded: 1987
Sales Range: $25-49.9 Million
Emp.: 100
Painting & Paper Hanging Product Mfr
N.A.I.C.S.: 238320
Dominique Pigeon *(Mgr-Admin)*

JCR PHARMACEUTICALS CO., LTD.
3-19 Kasuga-cho Ashiya, Hyogo, 659-0021, Japan
Tel.: (81) 797328591
Web Site: https://www.jcrpharm.co.jp
Year Founded: 1975
4552—(TKS)
Rev.: $283,377,310
Assets: $675,713,860
Liabilities: $302,414,110
Net Worth: $373,299,750
Earnings: $36,401,270
Emp.: 997
Fiscal Year-end: 03/31/24
Pharmaceutical Mfr & Distr; Medical Devices & Laboratory Instruments Distr
N.A.I.C.S.: 325412
Hiroshi Yoshimoto *(Sr VP, Head-Production Div & Exec Dir-Production Div)*

Subsidiaries:

Chromatech Co., Ltd. (1)
Shinjung 2-dong, Yancheon-gu, 89-106, Seoul, Korea (South)
Tel.: (82) 2 2644 1991
Laboratory Equipment Distr
N.A.I.C.S.: 423490

Family Health Rental Co., Ltd. (1)
3-15-8 Ninomiyacho, Chuo-Ku, Kobe, 651-0093, Hyogo, Japan
Tel.: (81) 782714566
Laboratory Equipment Distr
N.A.I.C.S.: 423450

JCR Pharmaceuticals Co., Ltd. - Kobe Nishi Plant (1)
2-2-10 Murotani, Nishi-ku, Kobe, 651-2241, Hyogo, Japan
Tel.: (81) 789927888
Web Site: https://www.jcrpharm.co.jp
Pharmaceuticals Product Mfr
N.A.I.C.S.: 325412

JCR Pharmaceuticals Co., Ltd. - Kobe Plant (1)
1-6-6 Murotani, Nishi-ku, Kobe, 651-2241, Hyogo, Japan
Tel.: (81) 789972626
Web Site: https://www.jcrpharm.co.jp
Pharmaceuticals Product Mfr
N.A.I.C.S.: 325412

JCR Pharmaceuticals Co., Ltd. - Murotani Plant (1)
1-2-3 Murotani, Nishi-ku, Kobe, 651-2241, Hyogo, Japan
Tel.: (81) 789905515
Web Site: https://www.jcrpharm.co.jp
Pharmaceuticals Product Mfr
N.A.I.C.S.: 325412

JCR Pharmaceuticals Co., Ltd. - Seishin Plant (1)
3-2-61 Takatsukadai, Nishi-ku, Kobe, 651-

JCR PHARMACEUTICALS CO., LTD.

JCR Pharmaceuticals Co., Ltd.—(Continued)
2271, Hyogo, Japan
Tel.: (81) 789914461
Web Site: https://www.jcrpharm.co.jp
Pharmaceuticals Product Mfr
N.A.I.C.S.: 325412

JCT ELECTRONICS LIMITED
124 Janpath Thapar House, New Delhi, 110001, India
Tel.: (91) 11 4353 4242
Web Site: http://www.jctel.com
Sales Range: $100-124.9 Million
Color Picture Tube Mfr
N.A.I.C.S.: 334419

JCT LIMITED
G T Road Phagwara, Kapurthala, 144401, Punjab, India
Tel.: (91) 1824521500
Web Site: https://www.jct.co.in
500223—(BOM)
Rev.: $115,878,140
Assets: $117,404,646
Liabilities: $69,365,355
Net Worth: $48,039,291
Earnings: $1,313,772
Emp.: 3,969
Fiscal Year-end: 03/31/22
Textiles & Yarn Mfr
N.A.I.C.S.: 314999
Vinod Kumar Singhal *(CFO)*

Subsidiaries:

JCT Ltd - Filament Plant (1)
Dharamshala Road, Chohal, Hoshiarpur, 146024, Punjab, India
Tel.: (91) 9872766441
Web Site: http://www.jct.co.in
Nylon & Polyester Products Mfr
N.A.I.C.S.: 314999

JCT Ltd - Textile Plant (1)
G T Rd, 144401, Phagwara, Punjab, India
Tel.: (91) 182430500007
Web Site: http://www.jctltd.com
Apparels Mfr
N.A.I.C.S.: 315990

JCT600 LIMITED
137 Sticker Lane, Bradford, BD4 8RR, United Kingdom
Tel.: (44) 1274 777600
Web Site: http://www.jct600.co.uk
Year Founded: 1946
Sales Range: $1-4.9 Billion
Emp.: 1,802
New & Used Car Dealer
N.A.I.C.S.: 441110
Neill Richards *(Dir-Fleet Sls)*

JCU CORPORATION
TIXTOWER UENO 16F 8-1 Higashi-ueno 4-chome, Taito-ku, Tokyo, 110-0015, Japan
Tel.: (81) 368957001
Web Site: https://www.jcu-i.com
4975—(TKS)
Rev.: $164,317,990
Assets: $328,127,010
Liabilities: $48,854,510
Net Worth: $279,272,500
Earnings: $36,553,300
Emp.: 538
Fiscal Year-end: 03/31/24
Chemical Equipment Mfr
N.A.I.C.S.: 332813

Subsidiaries:

JCU (SHANGHAI) TRADING CO., LTD. (1)
Bldg 10 2338 Duhui Road, Minhang, Shanghai, 201108, China
Tel.: (86) 2133587543
Web Site: https://www.jcu-china.com
Industrial Chemical Distr
N.A.I.C.S.: 424690

JCU CHEMICALS INDIA PVT. LTD. (1)
Unit No 2201A 22nd Floor WTC Bangalore Brigade Gateway, Rajanagar Extention Malleswaram, Bengaluru, 560055, Karnataka, India
Tel.: (91) 9136646180
Web Site: https://www.jcu-i.com
Industrial Chemical Distr
N.A.I.C.S.: 424690

JCU Corporation - Niigata Plant (1)
Section C Southern Industrial Park 144-7 Rokkanno Ishibashi-shinden, Joetsu, 942-0023, Niigata, Japan
Tel.: (81) 255459989
Web Site: https://www.jcu-i.com
Industrial Chemicals Mfr
N.A.I.C.S.: 325998

JCU INTERNATIONAL, INC. (1)
49108 Wixom Tech Dr, Wixom, MI 48393
Tel.: (248) 313-6630
Web Site: https://www.jcu-i.com
Industrial Chemical Distr
N.A.I.C.S.: 424690

JCU KOREA CORPORATION (1)
Room 904 O'Biztower Pyeongchon 126 Beolmal-ro, Dongan-gu, Anyang, Gyeonggi-do, Korea (South)
Tel.: (82) 313892095
Industrial Chemical Mfr & Distr
N.A.I.C.S.: 325998

Subsidiary (Domestic):

JCU KOREA CORPORATION - Cheonan Factory (2)
96 5sandan 1-ro Seongnam-myeon, Dongnam-gu, Cheonan, Chungcheongnam-do, Korea (South)
Tel.: (82) 415664095
Web Site: https://www.jcu-i.com
Industrial Chemicals Mfr
N.A.I.C.S.: 325998

JCU Shenzhen Technology Corporation (1)
Bldg 10 Shiguan Industrial Park Gongming, Guangming District, Shenzhen, China
Tel.: (86) 75581738651
Web Site: http://www.jcu-t.com
Metal Surface Coating Services
N.A.I.C.S.: 332812

PT. JCU Indonesia (1)
Jl Pinang Blok F 16-15C Delta Silikon 3 Lippo Cikarang, Bekasi, 17550, Indonesia
Tel.: (62) 2129288430
Web Site: https://www.jcu-i.com
Plating Machine Distr
N.A.I.C.S.: 423830

JCURVE SOLUTIONS LIMITED
Level 8 9 Help St, Chatswood, 2067, NSW, Australia
Tel.: (61) 291292900 AU
Web Site: https://www.jcurvesolutions.com
Year Founded: 1997
JCS—(ASX)
Rev.: $8,506,231
Assets: $5,399,213
Liabilities: $3,878,795
Net Worth: $1,520,418
Earnings: ($1,271,737)
Fiscal Year-end: 06/30/24
Software Solutions & Services
N.A.I.C.S.: 513210
Katrina Doring *(COO)*

Subsidiaries:

JCurve Solutions Philippines Inc. (1)
Unit 10A 5th Ave cor 26th St, Metro, Manila, Philippines
Tel.: (63) 285488282
Business Software Development Services
N.A.I.C.S.: 541511

Resource Systems & Services Pty Ltd (1)
Level 1 1254 Hay St, West Perth, 6005, WA, Australia
Tel.: (61) 892276233
Web Site: http://www.stratatel.com.au

Sales Range: $25-49.9 Million
Emp.: 80
Software Solutions Provider
N.A.I.C.S.: 541511

JCY INTERNATIONAL BERHAD
No 1 Jalan Firma 3, Kawasan Perindustrian Tebrau IV, 81100, Johor, Malaysia
Tel.: (60) 73525822
Web Site: https://www.jcyinternational.com
Year Founded: 1994
JCY—(KLS)
Rev.: $100,606,984
Assets: $167,885,926
Liabilities: $23,154,921
Net Worth: $144,731,005
Earnings: ($19,111,958)
Emp.: 3,677
Fiscal Year-end: 09/30/23
Hard Disk Drive Mechanical Components Mfr
N.A.I.C.S.: 334610
Rozali Mohamed Ali *(Chm)*

Subsidiaries:

JCY HDD Technology Sdn Bhd (1)
No 1 Jalan Firma 3 Kawasan Perindustrian Tebrau 4, Johor Bahru, 81100, Malaysia
Tel.: (60) 73525822
Hard Disk Drive Component Mfr & Distr
N.A.I.C.S.: 334112

JD HEALTH INTERNATIONAL INC.
Block C Building 2 Jingdong Headquarters No 20 Kechuang 11 Street, Yizhuang Economic & Technological Development Zone Daxing District, Beijing, 101111, China Ky
Web Site: https://ir.jdhealth.com
Year Founded: 2018
6618—(HKG)
Rev.: $7,160,445,542
Assets: $9,388,294,520
Liabilities: $2,526,851,776
Net Worth: $6,861,442,744
Earnings: $58,714,515
Emp.: 2,739
Fiscal Year-end: 12/31/22
Health Care Srvices
N.A.I.C.S.: 621610
Dong Cao *(CFO)*

JD LOGISTICS, INC.
8th Floor Building B No 20 Kechuang 11 Street, Yizhuang Economic & Technological Development Zone Daxing District, Beijing, China Ky
Web Site: https://ir.jdl.com
Year Founded: 2012
2618—(HKG)
Rev.: $23,070,546,079
Assets: $15,632,160,639
Liabilities: $7,965,230,671
Net Worth: $7,666,929,968
Earnings: $161,607,637
Emp.: 457,015
Fiscal Year-end: 12/31/23
Freight Transportation Services
N.A.I.C.S.: 488510
Shan Su *(CFO)*

Subsidiaries:

Kuayue-Express Group Co., Ltd. (1)
Headquarters Building of Express Group No 4 Terminal, Baoan International Airport Baoan District, Shenzhen, Guangdong, China
Tel.: (86) 95324
Web Site: https://www.ky-express.com
Logistic Services
N.A.I.C.S.: 541614

JD ORGOCHEM LIMITED
301 Sumer Kendra Pandurang Budhkar Marg, Worli, Mumbai, 400 018, India
Tel.: (91) 2230423048
Web Site: https://www.jdorgochem.com
524592—(BOM)
Rev.: $269,985
Assets: $794,634
Liabilities: $3,326,129
Net Worth: ($2,531,494)
Earnings: ($116,307)
Emp.: 4
Fiscal Year-end: 03/31/21
Dyes & Pigments Mfr & Sales
N.A.I.C.S.: 325130
Parag Sharadchandra Kothari *(Chm)*

Subsidiaries:

Jaysynth Anthraquinones Ltd. (1)
301 Sumer Kendra Pandurang Budhkar Marg, Mumbai, 400 018, India
Tel.: (91) 22 30423048
Web Site: http://www.jaysynth.com
Colouring Pigment & Dye Mfr
N.A.I.C.S.: 325130
Uday Kumar *(Gen Mgr)*

JD WETHERSPOON PLC
Wetherspoon House Reeds Crescent, Watford, WD24 4QL, United Kingdom
Tel.: (44) 923477777
Web Site: https://www.jdwetherspoon.com
JDW—(LSE)
Rev.: $1,048,913,375
Assets: $2,728,552,860
Liabilities: $2,359,284,247
Net Worth: $369,268,612
Earnings: ($245,821,995)
Emp.: 23,322
Fiscal Year-end: 07/25/21
Pubs & Hotels Owner & Operator
N.A.I.C.S.: 722410
Tim Martin *(Founder & Chm)*

JD.COM, INC.
JD Building No 18 Kechuang 11 Street BDA, Yizhuang Economic and Technological Development Zone, Beijing, 101111, China
Tel.: (86) 4006065500 Ky
Web Site: https://www.jd.com
JD—(NASDAQ)
Rev.: $150,180,272,486
Assets: $87,084,348,693
Liabilities: $46,133,141,338
Net Worth: $40,951,207,355
Earnings: $3,220,120,735
Emp.: 517,124
Fiscal Year-end: 12/31/23
Ecommerce Services
N.A.I.C.S.: 449210
Richard Qiangdong Liu *(Founder & Chm)*

Subsidiaries:

JD.com International Limited (1)
Suite 1203 12/F Ruttonjee House 11 Duddell Street, Central, China (Hong Kong)
Tel.: (852) 1089127407
Online Shopping Services
N.A.I.C.S.: 423620

Subsidiary (Non-US):

Beijing Jingdong Century Trade Co., Ltd. (2)
Room B168 Building 2 No 99 Kechuang 14 Street, Beijing Economic & Technological Development Zone, Beijing, China
Tel.: (86) 58955008
Online Shopping Services
N.A.I.C.S.: 423620

JDA GROUP LTD.
Windhill Manor Leeds Rd, Shipley, BD18 1BP, West Yorkshire, United Kingdom
Tel.: (44) 113 290 4290

JDC CORPORATION
4-3-13 Toranomon, Minato-ku, Tokyo, 105-8467, Japan
Tel.: (81) 334033311
Web Site: https://www.jdc-corporation.com
Year Founded: 1951
1887—(TKS)
Rev.: $896,983,610
Assets: $962,924,970
Liabilities: $509,538,460
Net Worth: $453,386,510
Earnings: $(47,532,510)
Emp.: 1,094
Fiscal Year-end: 05/31/24
Building Construction Services
N.A.I.C.S.: 236220
Takeo Asakura *(Pres & CEO)*

Subsidiaries:

Kokudo BuilACE Corporation (1)
Web Site: http://www.kokudoace.co.jp
Construction & Renovation Services
N.A.I.C.S.: 236220

Kokudo Kaihatsu Industry Co., Ltd. (1)
Tel.: (81) 462213388
Web Site: http://www.kokudo-kk.co.jp
Construction & Renovation Services
N.A.I.C.S.: 236220

JDC GROUP AG
Kormoranweg 1, 65201, Wiesbaden, Germany
Tel.: (49) 6118905750 De
Web Site: http://www.jdcgroup.de
JDC—(DEU)
Rev.: $189,545,518
Assets: $156,639,153
Liabilities: $98,465,204
Net Worth: $58,173,949
Earnings: $4,150,551
Emp.: 394
Fiscal Year-end: 12/31/23
Investment Banking, Advisory & Other Financial Services
N.A.I.C.S.: 523150
Sebastian Grabmaier *(Chm-Mgmt Bd & CEO)*

Subsidiaries:

BB-Wertpapierverwaltungsgesellschaft mbH (1)
Dollgast-Str 12, 86199, Augsburg, Germany
Tel.: (49) 8211598906
Web Site: https://www.bbwv.de
Financial Institution Services
N.A.I.C.S.: 523999

FINUM.Private Finance AG (1)
Krugerstrasse 13/4 OG, 1010, Vienna, Austria
Tel.: (43) 1534190
Web Site: https://www.finum.at
Financial Institution Services
N.A.I.C.S.: 523999

JDC plus GmbH (1)
Sohnleinstrasse 8, 65201, Wiesbaden, Germany
Tel.: (49) 6113353150
Web Site: https://www.jdc.plus
Financial Insurance Services
N.A.I.C.S.: 524210

Jung, DMS & Cie. AG (1)
Widenmayerstrasse 36, 80538, Munich, Germany
Tel.: (49) 6113353500
Web Site: https://www.jungdms.de

Sales Range: $75-99.9 Million
Emp.: 15
Investment Services
N.A.I.C.S.: 523940
Sebastian Grabmaier *(CEO)*

MORGEN & MORGEN GmbH (1)
Elisabethenstrasse 20, 65428, Russelsheim, Germany
Tel.: (49) 614292520
Web Site: https://morgenundmorgen.com
Emp.: 50
Software Development Services
N.A.I.C.S.: 541511

benefit consulting GmbH (1)
Krugerstrasse 13/4 OG, 1010, Vienna, Austria
Tel.: (43) 15325666
Web Site: https://www.benefit.at
Insurance Services
N.A.I.C.S.: 524210

JDE PEET'S N.V.
Oosterdoksstraat 80, 1011 DK, Amsterdam, Netherlands
Tel.: (31) 205581753 Nl
Web Site: https://www.jdepeets.com
Year Founded: 2015
JDEP—(EUR)
Rev.: $8,839,844,593
Assets: $24,974,098,856
Liabilities: $12,978,631,556
Net Worth: $11,995,467,300
Earnings: $392,834,017
Emp.: 13,421
Fiscal Year-end: 12/31/23
Beverage Product Mfr & Distr
N.A.I.C.S.: 312111
Evert Meindertsma *(Chief Supply Officer)*

Subsidiaries:

Jacobs Douwe Egberts Au Pty. Ltd. (1)
Level 1 80 Pacific Highway, Sydney, 2060, NSW, Australia
Tel.: (61) 1300331753
Web Site: https://www.jacobsdouweegberts.com.au
Coffee Mfr
N.A.I.C.S.: 311920

Jacobs Douwe Egberts Be B.V.B.A. (1)
Buro & Design Center Esplanade 1, PO Box 18, B-1020, Brussels, Belgium
Tel.: (32) 24901500
Tea & Coffee Distr
N.A.I.C.S.: 423620

Jacobs Douwe Egberts De GmbH (1)
Langemarckstrasse 16, 28199, Bremen, Germany
Tel.: (49) 8005736736
Web Site: https://www.jacobskaffee.de
Coffee Mfr
N.A.I.C.S.: 311920

Jacobs Douwe Egberts Dk ApS (1)
Nyvang 16, 5500, Middelfart, Denmark
Tel.: (45) 79313838
Web Site: https://www.jdeprofessional.dk
Coffee Mfr
N.A.I.C.S.: 311920

Jacobs Douwe Egberts Es S.L.U. (1)
Josep Pla No 2 Torre Diagonal Mar B-2, 08019, Barcelona, Spain
Tel.: (34) 934628400
Web Site: https://www.jdeprofessional.es
Coffee Mfr
N.A.I.C.S.: 311920

Jacobs Douwe Egberts Fr S.A.S. (1)
30 Bis Rue de Paradis, 75010, Paris, France
Tel.: (33) 155771515
Web Site: https://www.jacobsdouweegberts.fr
Coffee Mfr
N.A.I.C.S.: 311920

Jacobs Douwe Egberts Gb Ltd. (1)

Horizon Honey Lane Hurley, Maidenhead, SL6 6RJ, Berkshire, United Kingdom
Tel.: (44) 8081008787
Web Site: https://www.jacobsdouweegberts.co.uk
Coffee Mfr
N.A.I.C.S.: 311920

Jacobs Douwe Egberts Kazakhstan LLP (1)
Tole Bi Str 101, 50012, Almaty, Kazakhstan
Tel.: (7) 88000700350
Web Site: https://www.jacobscoffee.kz
Coffee Mfr
N.A.I.C.S.: 311920

Jacobs Douwe Egberts Norge AS (1)
Midtunhaugen 6, 5224, Nesttun, Norway
Tel.: (47) 80080015
Web Site: https://www.jdeprofessional.no
Coffee Mfr
N.A.I.C.S.: 311920

Jacobs Douwe Egberts Pl Sp. z o.o. (1)
Tasmowa 7, 02-677, Warsaw, Poland
Tel.: (48) 801800312
Web Site: https://www.kawajacobs.pl
Coffee Mfr
N.A.I.C.S.: 311920

Jacobs Douwe Egberts Pro Nl B.V. (1)
Vleutensevaart 35, 3532 AD, Utrecht, Netherlands
Tel.: (31) 302977000
Web Site: https://www.jacobsdouweegberts.nl
Tea & Coffee Distr
N.A.I.C.S.: 423620

Jacobs Douwe Egberts Ro S.r.l. (1)
169A Calea Floreasca Floreasca Business Park Building A 1st Floor, 014459, Bucharest, Romania
Tel.: (40) 213808595
Tea & Coffee Distr
N.A.I.C.S.: 423620

JDM JINGDA MACHINE(NINGBO) CO.,LTD
No 377 Jinshan Road, Ningbo, 315033, Zhejiang, China
Tel.: (86) 57487562525
Web Site: https://www.nbjingda.com
Year Founded: 1990
603088—(SHG)
Rev.: $91,322,562
Assets: $188,427,414
Liabilities: $97,380,233
Net Worth: $91,047,182
Earnings: $20,037,593
Emp.: 900
Fiscal Year-end: 12/31/22
Heat Exchange Equipment Mfr & Distr
N.A.I.C.S.: 333248
James Marriner *(Dir-Sls-Global,UK)*

Subsidiaries:

JDM JingDa Machine Americas Inc. (1)
11601 Pellicano Dr Ste D9, El Paso, TX 79936
Tel.: (915) 307-6957
Heat Exchange Equipment Mfr
N.A.I.C.S.: 333248
Gordon Butler *(Mgr-Ops)*

JDM TECHNOLOGY GROUP
1788 West Broadway Suite 902, Vancouver, V6J 1Y1, BC, Canada
Tel.: (800) 665-8966
Web Site: http://jdmtechnologygroup.com
Year Founded: 1984
Computer Software Publisher
N.A.I.C.S.: 513210
Jim McFarlane *(CEO)*

Subsidiaries:

ConEst Software Systems (1)

592 Harvey Rd, Manchester, NH 03103
Tel.: (603) 437-9353
Web Site: http://www.conest.com
Software & Cabling Sales
N.A.I.C.S.: 541511

Vision InfoSoft Corp. (1)
1915 Aston Ave, Carlsbad, CA 92008-7307
Tel.: (760) 579-0334
Web Site: http://www.visioninfosoft.com
Material Billing Software Publisher
N.A.I.C.S.: 513210

JDW SUGAR MILLS LTD.
Tel.: (92) 4236664891
Web Site: https://www.jdw-group.com
JDWS—(PSX)
Rev.: $371,911,541
Assets: $211,790,110
Liabilities: $141,517,468
Net Worth: $70,272,642
Earnings: $10,122,320
Emp.: 5,868
Fiscal Year-end: 09/30/23
Crystalline Sugar Production & Sales
N.A.I.C.S.: 111930
Muhammad Rafique *(CFO & Fin Dir-Grp)*

Subsidiaries:

Faruki Pulp Mills Limited (1)
19-A Street 1 Link 6 Cavalry Grounds, Lahore, Pakistan
Web Site: http://www.farukipulpmills.com
Paper Pulp Mfr & Distr
N.A.I.C.S.: 322120
Saleem Akbar Faruki *(Founder)*

Subsidiary (Domestic):

Faruki Pulp Mills Limited - Gujrat Mill (2)
20th KM Gujrat-Sargodha Road Mangowal, Gujrat, Pakistan
Tel.: (92) 533545207
Web Site: https://farukipulpmills.com
Paper Pulp Mfr
N.A.I.C.S.: 322120

JE CLEANTECH HOLDINGS LIMITED
3 Woodlands Sector 1, Singapore, 738361, Singapore
Tel.: (65) 63684198 Ky
Web Site: https://www.jecleantech.sg
Year Founded: 2019
JCSE—(NASDAQ)
Rev.: $14,065,846
Assets: $26,775,011
Liabilities: $14,483,344
Net Worth: $12,291,667
Earnings: $899,924
Emp.: 102
Fiscal Year-end: 12/31/22
Holding Company
N.A.I.C.S.: 551112
Jia Kwang Long *(CFO)*

JEAN CACHAREL
36 rue Tronchet, 75009, Paris, France
Tel.: (33) 142683888
Web Site: http://www.cacharel.com
Year Founded: 1962
Sales Range: $25-49.9 Million
Emp.: 50
Perfumes, Women's & Children's Clothing Designer & Retailer
N.A.I.C.S.: 315250
Jean Bousquet *(Chm)*

JEAN CO., LTD.
6F No 300 Yangguang Street, Neihu District, Taipei, 114, Taiwan
Tel.: (886) 800244288
Web Site: https://www.jean.com.tw
Year Founded: 1986
2442—(TAI)
Rev.: $81,839,756
Assets: $546,374,943

Jean Co., Ltd.—(Continued)
Liabilities: $380,360,527
Net Worth: $166,014,415
Earnings: $13,959,449
Fiscal Year-end: 12/31/23
Liquid Crystal Display Mfr
N.A.I.C.S.: 334118
Chuan-Chieh Lin *(Chm & CEO)*

Subsidiaries:

Jet Optoelectronics Co., Ltd. (1)
7F 300 Yangguang St, Neihu Dist, Taipei, 11491, Taiwan
Tel.: (886) 25 582 1818
Web Site: https://www.jet-opto.com.tw
Automotive Services
N.A.I.C.S.: 488490

JEAN EGRETEAUD
18 Ave Antoine Becquerel Parc Industriel Bersol 1, 33600, Bordeaux, Pessac, France
Tel.: (33) 56 46 70 70
Web Site:
    http://www.centreporsche.fr
Rev.: $22,600,000
Emp.: 20
Porsche Automotive Dealer
N.A.I.C.S.: 441110
Ronan Chabot *(Pres)*

JEAN LAIN ENTREPRISES
Z Industrie Des Landier 158 Rue Des Epinettes, BP 117, 73006, Chambery, Cedex, France
Tel.: (33) 479683333
Web Site: http://www.jeanlain-
    loisirs.com
Year Founded: 1966
Rev.: $20,600,000
Emp.: 20
New & Used Car Dealers
N.A.I.C.S.: 441110
Alexandre Lain *(Mng Partner)*

JEBILS FINANCE LIMITED
New Road, PO Box 19385, Kathmandu, Nepal
Tel.: (977) 14220426
Web Site: http://www.jebils.com
JEFL—(NEP)
Merchant Banking Services
N.A.I.C.S.: 523150
Binod Kumar Manandhar *(Chm)*

JEBSEN & JESSEN (SEA) PTE LTD
2 Corporation Road Suite 03-06 Corporation Place Main Lobby, Singapore, 618494, Singapore
Tel.: (65) 63053888
Web Site: http://www.jjsea.com
Year Founded: 1895
Sales Range: $200-249.9 Million
Emp.: 4,400
Diversified Business Enterprise
N.A.I.C.S.: 813910
J. Heinrich Jessen *(Chm)*

Subsidiaries:

JJ-Lapp Cable (S) Pte Ltd (1)
9 Tuas South Street 3, Singapore, 638017, Singapore
Tel.: (65) 65086200
Wire & Cable Distr
N.A.I.C.S.: 423510
Richard Ng *(Gen Mgr)*

JJ-PUN (S) Pte Ltd (1)
Building No 1 5th Floor Myanmar Info-Tech, Hlaing Township, Yangon, Myanmar
Tel.: (95) 12305135
Chemical Products Distr
N.A.I.C.S.: 424690
Philipp Hoffmann *(Gen Mgr)*

JJ-Pun (S) Pte Ltd (1)
Building No 1 5th floor Myanmar Info-Tech Phase-3, Universitys Hlaing Campus Hlaing Township, Yangon, Myanmar
Tel.: (95) 12305135
Wireless Telecommunication Services
N.A.I.C.S.: 517112
Soe Moe Min Oo *(Gen Mgr-Infrastructure Dev)*

Jebsen & Jessen Business Services (M) Sdn. Bhd. (1)
No 7-13A-01 Level 13A, Jalan Pengaturcara U1/51A Seksyen U1, 40150, Shah Alam, Selangor, Malaysia
Tel.: (60) 350306333
Cable System & Cable Accessory Product Mfr
N.A.I.C.S.: 335929
Michelle Pereira *(Gen Mgr)*

Jebsen & Jessen Business Services (S) Pte. Ltd. (1)
2 Corporation Road 03-06 Corporation Place Main Lobby, Singapore, 618494, Singapore
Tel.: (65) 63053888
Cable System & Cable Accessory Product Mfr
N.A.I.C.S.: 335929
Linda Anthonius *(Gen Mgr)*

Jebsen & Jessen Business Services (T) Ltd. (1)
23/110-117 Sorachai Building 29th Floor Soi Sukhumvit 63 Ekamai, Sukhumvit Road Klongton Nua Wattana, Bangkok, 10110, Thailand
Tel.: (66) 27878888
Cable System & Cable Accessory Product Mfr
N.A.I.C.S.: 335929
Itchaya Savanayana *(Gen Mgr)*

Jebsen & Jessen Cambodia Ltd (1)
2nd Floor Delano Center 144 Street 169, Phnom Penh, Cambodia
Tel.: (855) 12 20 1359
Chemical Products Distr
N.A.I.C.S.: 424690
Alex Spitzy *(Gen Mgr)*

Jebsen & Jessen Chemicals (M) Sdn Bhd (1)
16A Jalan 51A/225, 46100, Petaling Jaya, Malaysia
Tel.: (60) 3 7861 6788
Chemical Products Distr
N.A.I.C.S.: 424690

Jebsen & Jessen Chemicals (P) Inc (1)
Unit 704 PhilPlans Corporate Centre 1012 Triangle Drive Bonifacio, 1634, Taguig, Philippines
Tel.: (63) 2 786 7700
Chemical Products Distr
N.A.I.C.S.: 424690
Jessica Huang-Lara *(Mng Dir)*

Jebsen & Jessen Chemicals (T) Ltd (1)
23 110-117 Sorachai Building 25th-29th Floor, Soi Sukhumvit 63 Sukhumvit Road, 10110, Bangkok, Thailand
Tel.: (66) 2 787 8700
Chemical Products Distr
N.A.I.C.S.: 424690
Ben Hopkins *(Mng Dir)*

Jebsen & Jessen Chemicals Vietnam Co Ltd (1)
Unit 1205 Sailing Tower 111A Pasteur Street, District 1, Ho Chi Minh City, Vietnam
Tel.: (84) 8 3823 8181
Chemical Products Distr
N.A.I.C.S.: 424690
Kenneth Jul Jensen *(Gen Dir)*

Jebsen & Jessen Communication Solutions (M) Sdn Bhd (1)
Level 11 1st Ave Bandar Utama, 47800, Petaling Jaya, Selangor, Malaysia
Tel.: (60) 3 7884 6388
Telecommunication Servicesb
N.A.I.C.S.: 517810

Jebsen & Jessen Ingredients (P) Inc. (1)
11th Avenue Corner 38th Street 5th Floor Orion Building, Bonifacio Global City, Taguig, 1634, Manila, Philippines
Tel.: (63) 27867700
Cable System & Cable Accessory Product Mfr
N.A.I.C.S.: 335929
Raque Patdu *(Mgr-Fin & Admin)*

Jebsen & Jessen Packaging (M) Sdn Bhd (1)
Lot 3297 Jalan Permata 2/1 Arab Malaysian Industrial Park, 71800, Nilai, Negeri Sembilan, Malaysia
Tel.: (60) 6 799 2271
Packaging Product Distr
N.A.I.C.S.: 423840

Jebsen & Jessen Packaging Vietnam Co Ltd (1)
Lot K-1 Que Vo Industrial Park, Bac Ninh, Hanoi, Vietnam
Tel.: (84) 241 3634 21
Packaging Product Distr
N.A.I.C.S.: 423840

Jebsen & Jessen Technology (S) Pte Ltd (1)
18 Enterprise Road, Singapore, 629824, Singapore
Tel.: (65) 6305 3688
Web Site: http://www.jjsea.com
Emp.: 40
Industrial Supplies Whslr
N.A.I.C.S.: 423840

Jebsen & Jessen Vietnam Co Ltd (1)
Unit 1206 12th Floor Sailing Tower 111A Pasteur Street, Dist 1, Ho Chi Minh City, Vietnam
Tel.: (84) 8 6288 7688
Telecommunication Servicesb
N.A.I.C.S.: 517810

Jebsen Jessen Offshore Pte Ltd (1)
11 Tuas Crescent, Singapore, 638705, Singapore
Tel.: (65) 6779 3595
Web Site: http://www.offshore.jjsea.com
Offshore Engineering Services
N.A.I.C.S.: 541330
Ronald Wong *(Gen Mgr-Sls & Mktg)*

Subsidiary (Non-US):

Jebsen & Jessen Offshore FZE (2)
PO Box 261553, Jebel Ali, Dubai, United Arab Emirates
Tel.: (971) 4 8806349
Web Site: http://www.offshore.jjsea.com
Emp.: 7
Offshore Engineering Services
N.A.I.C.S.: 541330
Ambreas Zam Brank *(Area Mgr)*

Labplas Sdn Bhd (1)
Lot 1563 Kg Industrial Area 131/2 Miles Jalan Kusta Off, Jalan Sungai Buloh, 47000, Sungai Buloh, Selangor, Malaysia
Tel.: (60) 3 6157 5555
Packaging Product Distr
N.A.I.C.S.: 423840
Phoelen Ghwe *(Mng Dir)*

MHE-Demag (P) Inc (1)
Main Avenue Severina Diamond Industrial Estate Km 16, West Service Road South Expressway, 1700, Paranaque, Philippines
Tel.: (63) 27867500
Industrial Equipment Mfr
N.A.I.C.S.: 333310
Marc von Grabowski *(Pres)*

MHE-Demag Australia Pty Ltd (1)
92 Long Street, Smithfield, 2164, NSW, Australia
Tel.: (61) 296099500
Industrial Equipment Distr
N.A.I.C.S.: 423810

MHE-Demag Malaysia Sdn Bhd (1)
PT 79 Jalan 26/6 Sec 26 Kawasan Perindustrian Hicom, 40000, Shah Alam, Selangor, Malaysia
Tel.: (60) 355170888
Industrial Equipment Mfr
N.A.I.C.S.: 333310
Frankie Chan *(Mng Dir)*

MHE-Demag Taiwan Company Limited (1)
5F-3 No 286 Xinya Rd, Qianzhen, Kaohsiung, Taiwan
Tel.: (886) 79708900
Industrial Equipment Distr
N.A.I.C.S.: 423810
Raymond Ng *(Pres)*

MHE-Demag Vietnam Company Limited (1)
No 15 VSIP Street 2 Vietnam Singapore Industrial Park, Thuan An, Binh Duong, Vietnam
Tel.: (84) 6503784080
Industrial Equipment Mfr
N.A.I.C.S.: 333310

Mongolian Star Melchers Co., Ltd. (1)
MSM Building Chinggis avenue-62, Khan Uul, Ulaanbaatar, Mongolia
Tel.: (976) 11342175
Web Site: http://www.msmgroup.mn
Automobile Parts Distr
N.A.I.C.S.: 423110

PT Jebsen & Jessen Business Services (I) (1)
Graha Inti Fauzi 7th Floor Jl Buncit Raya No 22, 12510, Jakarta, Indonesia
Tel.: (62) 2127537088
Cable System & Cable Accessory Product Mfr
N.A.I.C.S.: 335929
Linda Anthonius *(Pres)*

PT Jebsen & Jessen Chemicals Indonesia (1)
Graha Inti Fauzi 7th Floor Jl Buncit Raya No 22, 12510, Jakarta, Indonesia
Tel.: (62) 21 2753 7177
Chemical Products Distr
N.A.I.C.S.: 424690

JEDINSTVO A.D.
Prvomajska bb Street, 31205, Sevojno, Serbia
Tel.: (381) 31532911
Web Site:
    https://www.mppjedinstvo.co.rs
Year Founded: 1947
JESV—(BEL)
Sales Range: $25-49.9 Million
Emp.: 1,000
Holding Company
N.A.I.C.S.: 551112
Mica Micic *(Chm/Chm-Supervisory Bd & Gen Mgr)*

JEDINSTVO A.D.
Vrsacka 45, Vlajkovac, Serbia
Tel.: (381) 13 891 513
Year Founded: 1989
JDVL—(BEL)
Sales Range: Less than $1 Million
Emp.: 5
Cereal Crop Farming Services
N.A.I.C.S.: 111998
Igor Kojic *(Exec Dir)*

JEDINSTVO GP A.D.
Patrijarha Gavrila Dozica 56, 78400, Gradiska, Bosnia & Herzegovina
Tel.: (387) 51813215
Web Site: https://gpjedinstvo.ba
Year Founded: 1963
JDNS-L1—(BANJ)
Rev.: $5,195,665
Assets: $11,288,625
Liabilities: $7,872,448
Net Worth: $3,416,177
Earnings: $319,778
Emp.: 67
Fiscal Year-end: 12/31/12
Civil Engineering Construction Services
N.A.I.C.S.: 237990
Nikola Dubravac *(Chm-Mgmt Bd)*

JEDINSTVO-METALOGRADNJA A.D.
Prvomajska bb, 31205, Sevojno, Serbia

AND PRIVATE COMPANIES — JENAX INC.

Tel.: (381) 31531952
Web Site: https://www.j-metalogradnja.rs
Year Founded: 1991
JMSE—(BEL)
Rev.: $6,471,484
Assets: $4,082,703
Liabilities: $1,894,551
Net Worth: $2,188,152
Earnings: $245,888
Emp.: 118
Fiscal Year-end: 12/31/23
Building Architectural Designing Services
N.A.I.C.S.: 541310
Dejan Stevanovic *(Mng Dir)*

JEERAN HOLDING COMPANY K.S.C.C.
PO Box 23495, Safat, 13095, Kuwait
Tel.: (965) 4747188
Web Site:
http://www.jeeranholding.com
Year Founded: 2001
Sales Range: $150-199.9 Million
Emp.: 2,116
Investment Services
N.A.I.C.S.: 523999
Abdul Jalil Hussein Ali Hussein *(Deputy Chm)*

Subsidiaries:

United Gulf Construction Co. W.L.L. (1)
PO Box 23495, Safat, Kuwait, 13095, Kuwait
Tel.: (965) 2474 7188
Web Site: http://www.ugcc.com
Sales Range: $350-399.9 Million
Commercial & Civil Engineering Services
N.A.I.C.S.: 541330

JEEVAN SCIENTIFIC TECHNOLOGY LIMITED
Plot No 1 and 2 Sai Krupa Enclave Near Lanco Hills, Goloconda Post, Hyderabad, 500 008, Telangana, India
Tel.: (91) 4067364700
Web Site:
https://www.jeevanscientific.com
Year Founded: 1999
538837—(BOM)
Rev.: $4,514,942
Assets: $7,989,855
Liabilities: $2,120,952
Net Worth: $5,868,904
Earnings: ($371,454)
Emp.: 251
Fiscal Year-end: 03/31/23
Health Care Development Services
N.A.I.C.S.: 541714
Sreerama Koteswara Rao Surapaneni *(Chm)*

Subsidiaries:

Enhops, Inc. (1)
7924 Preston Rd Ste 350, Plano, TX 75024
Tel.: (973) 457-0830
Software Testing Services
N.A.I.C.S.: 541511

JEFF'S BRANDS LTD.
3 Hanechoshet Street, Tel Aviv, 6971068, Israel
Tel.: (972) 36899124 II
Web Site: https://www.railvision.io
Year Founded: 2021
JFBR—(NASDAQ)
Rev.: $5,859,000
Assets: $15,775,000
Liabilities: $2,954,000
Net Worth: $12,821,000
Earnings: ($2,201,000)
Emp.: 9
Fiscal Year-end: 12/31/22
Holding Company
N.A.I.C.S.: 551112
Naor Bergman *(COO)*

JEFFERSON AUTOMOTIVE GROUP
58 Nepean Highway, Mentone, 3194, VIC, Australia
Tel.: (61) 395812525
Web Site:
http://www.jeffersonford.com.au
Automotive Retailer
N.A.I.C.S.: 441110
Glenn Barrand *(Controller-Fin)*

JEFMAG
41 Boulevard Des Marchandises, L'Herbergement, 85260, Nantes, France
Tel.: (33) 251428672
Web Site: http://www.jefmag.fr
Rev.: $21,400,000
Emp.: 120
Fabricated Structural Metal
N.A.I.C.S.: 332312
Thierry Beaumont *(Pres)*

JEI CORPORATION
55-5 Hyehwa-Dong, Chongno-Gu, Seoul, 110-530, Korea (South)
Tel.: (82) 2367001145 KR
Web Site: http://www.jei.com
Year Founded: 1977
Sales Range: $300-349.9 Million
Emp.: 1,500
Production of Printed Materials
N.A.I.C.S.: 323120
Sung Hoon Park *(Chm & Pres)*

Subsidiaries:

JEI America, Inc. (1)
440 Sylvan Ave, Englewood, NJ 07632
Tel.: (201) 567-0677
Web Site: http://www.jeilearning.com
Sales Range: $25-49.9 Million
Emp.: 5
Production of Printed Materials
N.A.I.C.S.: 513130
Dae Kim *(Mng Dir)*

JEI Corporation Japan (1)
Funabori 1 1 26 627, Edogawa gu, Tokyo, 13 0091, Japan
Tel.: (81) 56052394
Web Site: http://www.jei-edu.com
Production of Printed Materials
N.A.I.C.S.: 513130

JEI Self Learning Systems New Zealand (1)
U4 11A Kitirawa Rd, Remuera, Auckland, New Zealand (100%)
Tel.: (64) 95225456
Sales Range: $25-49.9 Million
Emp.: 23
Production of Printed Materials
N.A.I.C.S.: 513130

JEI Self-Learning Systems, Inc. (1)
4221 Wilshire Blvd Ste 224, Los Angeles, CA 90010-3512 (100%)
Tel.: (323) 936-3300
Web Site: http://www.jeilearning.com
Sales Range: $25-49.9 Million
Emp.: 10
Production of Printed, Educational Materials
N.A.I.C.S.: 513130
Cho Park *(Pres)*

JEIL PHARMA HOLDINGS, INC.
343 Sapyeong-daero, Seocho-gu, Seoul, 06543, Korea (South)
Tel.: (82) 25497451
Holding Company; Pharmaceutical Preparations
N.A.I.C.S.: 551112
Sang-Cheol Han *(CEO)*

Subsidiaries:

Jeil Pharmaceutical Co., Ltd. (1)
343 Sapyeong-daero, Seocho-gu, Seoul, 06543, Korea (South) (61.13%)
Tel.: (82) 2 549 7451
Web Site: http://www.jeilpharm.co.kr
Pharmaceuticals Product Mfr
N.A.I.C.S.: 325411
Soo Han Seung *(Chm & CEO)*

Plant (Domestic):

Jeil Pharmaceutical Co., Ltd. - Yongin Factory (2)
7 Cheongganggachang-ro Baegam-myeon Cheoin-gu, Yongin, 17172, Gyeonggi-do, Korea (South)
Tel.: (82) 313324457
Pharmaceuticals Product Mfr
N.A.I.C.S.: 325412

JEIL TECHNOS CO., LTD.
7 Jangheung-ro 39 Beon-Gil, Nam-Gu, Pohang, Gyeongsangbuk-do, Korea (South)
Tel.: (82) 542782841
Web Site: https://www.jeil21c.co.kr
Year Founded: 2000
038010—(KRS)
Rev.: $165,394,309
Assets: $141,805,582
Liabilities: $76,974,056
Net Worth: $64,831,526
Earnings: $8,345,844
Emp.: 196
Fiscal Year-end: 12/31/22
Steel Products Mfr
N.A.I.C.S.: 331110
Jeil Technos *(CEO)*

JEJU BEER CO., LTD.
62-11 Geumneungnonggong-gil, Hallim-eub, Jeju, Korea (South)
Tel.: (82) 647989800
Web Site: https://www.jejubeer.co.kr
Year Founded: 2015
276730—(KRS)
Rev.: $18,384,946
Assets: $47,515,704
Liabilities: $21,170,089
Net Worth: $26,345,615
Earnings: ($18,994,256)
Emp.: 125
Fiscal Year-end: 12/31/22
Beverage Product Mfr
N.A.I.C.S.: 312130

JEJU SEMICONDUCTOR CO.
A-2F 330 Cheomdan-ro, Jeju, 690-029, Jeju-do, Korea (South)
Tel.: (82) 647401700
Web Site: https://www.jeju-semi.com
Year Founded: 2000
080220—(KRS)
Rev.: $134,243,066
Assets: $134,991,135
Liabilities: $25,538,707
Net Worth: $109,452,429
Earnings: $18,662,499
Emp.: 96
Fiscal Year-end: 12/31/22
Semiconductor Memory Chips Mfr
N.A.I.C.S.: 334413

JEJUAIR, CO., LTD.
64 Sindae-ro, Jeju, Jeju-do, Korea (South)
Tel.: (82) 7074201986
Web Site: http://www.jejuair.net
Year Founded: 2005
089590—(KRS)
Rev.: $538,820,013
Assets: $1,276,014,978
Liabilities: $1,040,837,281
Net Worth: $235,177,697
Earnings: ($133,354,004)
Emp.: 2,833
Fiscal Year-end: 12/31/22
Airport Cargo Handling Services
N.A.I.C.S.: 488119

JELEN D.D.
Mestni trg 2, 3210, Slovenske Konjice, Slovenia
Tel.: (386) 37575700
Hotel Owner & Operator
N.A.I.C.S.: 721110
Franc Tomazic *(Gen Dir)*

JELSINGRAD LIVAR LIVNICA CELIKA A. D.
Brace Podgornika br 8, 78000, Banja Luka, Republika Srpska, Bosnia & Herzegovina
Tel.: (387) 51344540
Web Site:
https://www.livnicajelsingrad.com
Year Founded: 1937
JLLC—(BANJ)
Sales Range: $10-24.9 Million
Emp.: 237
Steel & Iron Foundry
N.A.I.C.S.: 331513
Jordanka Milinovic *(Sec)*

JEMA DISTRIBUTION
14 Avenue De L Europe, 67390, Marckolsheim, Bas Rhin, France
Tel.: (33) 388586230
Sales Range: $10-24.9 Million
Emp.: 50
Grocery Stores
N.A.I.C.S.: 445110
Jerome Schickler *(Pres)*

JEMBAS ASSISTENCIA TECNICA, LDA
Largo do Soweto N 88, Luanda, Angola
Tel.: (244) 222637000
Web Site: http://www.jembas.com
Year Founded: 1989
Sales Range: $300-349.9 Million
Emp.: 1,290
Communication, Electronic & Industrial Products Mfr
N.A.I.C.S.: 811210
Etienne Albert Brechet *(Pres & CEO)*

JEMS COATING LIMITED
210 Jacob Keffer Pkwy, Concord, L4K 4W3, ON, Canada
Tel.: (905) 303-7433 ON
Web Site:
http://www.jemscoating.com
Year Founded: 1981
Metal Finishing Services
N.A.I.C.S.: 212290
Robert German *(Pres)*

JEMTEC INC.
Suite 200 38 Fell Avenue, North Vancouver, V7P 3S2, BC, Canada
Web Site: https://www.jemtec.ca
JTC—(TSXV)
Rev.: $1,104,918
Assets: $1,870,758
Liabilities: $171,036
Net Worth: $1,699,721
Earnings: ($150,231)
Fiscal Year-end: 07/31/23
Compliance Monitoring Solutions
N.A.I.C.S.: 561990
Jeremy N. Kendall *(Chm)*

JENAX INC.
109 Dongseong-Ro, Busanjin -Gu, Busan, 614865, Korea (South)
Tel.: (82) 518046500
Web Site: http://www.shineworld.com
Year Founded: 1991
065620—(KRS)
Rev.: $3,096,583
Assets: $21,311,337
Liabilities: $20,039,606
Net Worth: $1,271,731
Earnings: ($9,201,642)

JENAX INC.

JENAX Inc.—(Continued)
Emp.: 46
Fiscal Year-end: 12/31/19
Stainless Steel Wire Mfr
N.A.I.C.S.: 331222
L. H. Shin (CEO)

JENBURKT PHARMACEUTI-CALS LTD
Nirmala Apartments 93 J P Road
Andheri W, Mumbai, 400058, India
Tel.: (91) 2267603603
Web Site: https://www.jenburkt.com
524731—(BOM)
Rev.: $17,010,059
Assets: $17,002,830
Liabilities: $2,328,685
Net Worth: $14,674,144
Earnings: $2,950,303
Emp.: 724
Fiscal Year-end: 03/31/23
Pharmaceutical Formulations & Healthcare Products Mfr & Marketing
N.A.I.C.S.: 325412
Ashish Rasiklal Shah (Compliance Officer & Sec)

JENERATION ACQUISITION CORP.
Suite 6901-06 8 Finance Street, Two International Finance Centre, Central, China (Hong Kong)
Tel.: (852) 3898 0300
Year Founded: 2021
JACAU—(NASDAQ)
Investment Services
N.A.I.C.S.: 523999
Jason Tan (CEO)

JENERS DRUCKGUSSTECH-NIK GMBH
Kruppstrasse 51, 42489, Wulfrath, Germany
Tel.: (49) 205877850
Web Site: http://www.jeners.com
Year Founded: 1925
Rev.: $37,243,800
Emp.: 70
Die Cast Components Mfr
N.A.I.C.S.: 331523
Carl Jeners (Founder)

JENKEM TECHNOLOGY CO., LTD.
3/F Building C-1 Northern Territory 66 Xixiaokou Road, Zhongguancun Dongsheng Science & Technology Park Haidian District, Beijing, 100192, China
Tel.: (86) 1062983737
Web Site: https://www.jenkemusa.com
Year Founded: 2001
688356—(SHG)
Rev.: $57,171,442
Assets: $182,879,410
Liabilities: $10,923,359
Net Worth: $171,956,051
Earnings: $26,231,339
Fiscal Year-end: 12/31/22
Chemical Product Mfr & Distr
N.A.I.C.S.: 325520

Subsidiaries:

JenKem Technology USA, Inc. (1)
4105 W Spring Creek Pkwy Ste 606B, Plano, TX 75024
Tel.: (972) 673-0603
Web Site: http://www.jenkemusa.com
Polymer Product Mfr & Distr
N.A.I.C.S.: 325998

JENN FENG INDUSTRIAL TOOLS CO., LTD.
No 33 Ln 433 Sec 2 Zhongzheng Rd, Taoyuan City Zhongli Dist, Taoyuan, 32051, Taiwan
Tel.: (886) 34904111
Web Site: https://www.jennfeng.com
1538—(TAI)
Rev.: $6,357,500
Assets: $10,799,830
Liabilities: $3,682,592
Net Worth: $7,117,237
Earnings: ($923,804)
Fiscal Year-end: 12/31/23
Light Emitting Diode Lights Mfr
N.A.I.C.S.: 334413

JENNER CHEVROLET BUICK CORVETTE GMC
1730 Island Hwy, Victoria, V9B 1H8, BC, Canada
Tel.: (250) 474-1211
Web Site: http://www.jennerchev.com
Year Founded: 1981
Sales Range: $10-24.9 Million
Emp.: 40
New & Used Car Dealers
N.A.I.C.S.: 441110
Fred Jenner (Gen Mgr)

JENOBA CO., LTD.
1-34-4 Kandasuda-cho, Chiyoda-ku, Tokyo, 101-0041, Japan
Tel.: (81) 352096885
Web Site: https://www.jenoba.jp
Year Founded: 1997
5570—(TKS)
Information Technology Services
N.A.I.C.S.: 541512
Satoshi Togami (Sr Mng Dir)

JENOPTIK AG
Carl Zeiss Strasse 1, 07743, Jena, Germany
Tel.: (49) 3641650
Web Site: https://www.jenoptik.com
JEN—(DUS)
Rev.: $1,176,780,614
Assets: $1,840,051,942
Liabilities: $850,333,138
Net Worth: $989,718,803
Earnings: $79,997,459
Emp.: 4,415
Fiscal Year-end: 12/31/23
Laser & Optics, Sensors & Mechatronics Technologies Mfr
N.A.I.C.S.: 334511
Matthias Wierlacher (Chm-Supervisory Bd)

Subsidiaries:

ESW Extel Systems Wedel Gesellschaft fur Ausrustung mbH (1)
Industrialstrasse 33, D 22876, Wedel, Germany (100%)
Tel.: (49) 4103600
Web Site: http://www.esw-wedel.de
Sales Range: $200-249.9 Million
Emp.: 600
Mfr of Aircraft Parts
N.A.I.C.S.: 336413

ESW Gmbh (1)
Industriestrasse 33, 22876, Wedel, Germany
Tel.: (49) 4103 60 5900
Sales Range: $200-249.9 Million
Emp.: 900
Civil Engineering Services
N.A.I.C.S.: 237990

Subsidiary (Domestic):

VINCORION Power Systems GmbH (2)
Sudliche Romerstrasse 12-18, 86972, Altenstadt, Germany
Tel.: (49) 88617100
Web Site: http://www.lechmotoren.de
Sales Range: $25-49.9 Million
Emp.: 150
Electronic Components Mfr

ESW Gmbh I Sensorik (1)
Pruessingstrasse 41, 07745, Jena, Germany
Tel.: (49) 3641653041
Sales Range: $800-899.9 Million
Emp.: 3,000
Semiconductor Devices Mfr
N.A.I.C.S.: 334413
Swen Schumann (Mgr-Sls)

Electroop S.A (1)
Lagranje 30, Alcobendas, 28108, Spain
Tel.: (34) 91 490 23 49
Web Site: http://www.electroop.es
Electric Equipment Mfr
N.A.I.C.S.: 335999

Five Lakes Automation, LLC (1)
24975 Trans-x Rd, Novi, MI 48375
Tel.: (248) 344-2150
Web Site: http://www.fivelakesautomation.com
Computer Software & Packaging Services
N.A.I.C.S.: 513210

Hommel-Etamic America Corp (1)
1505 W Hamlin Rd, Rochester Hills, MI 48309
Tel.: (248) 853-5888
Web Site: http://www.jenoptik.com
Optical Instrument Mfr
N.A.I.C.S.: 333310

Hommel-Etamic Espana S.A (1)
Principe de Vergara 126 1 F, 28002, Madrid, Spain
Tel.: (34) 914840219
Sales Range: $25-49.9 Million
Emp.: 5
Semiconductor Devices Mfr
N.A.I.C.S.: 334413
Antonio Martinez (Mng Dir)

Hommel-Etamic France SA (1)
ZAC des Longchamps 1 rue des Longchamps Saint Martin des Entrees, BP 61080, 14400, Bayeux, France
Tel.: (33) 231513751
Web Site: http://www.jenoptik.com
Emp.: 55
Precision Product Mfr
N.A.I.C.S.: 332721
Mark Schuch (Gen Mgr)

INNOVAVENT GmbH (1)
Reinhard-Rube Str 4, 37077, Gottingen, Germany
Tel.: (49) 55 190 0470
Web Site: https://www.innovavent.com
Semiconductor Devices Mfr
N.A.I.C.S.: 334413
Hans-Jurgen Kahlert (Mng Dir-Mktg & Sls)

JENOPTIK (Shanghai) Precision Instruments and Equipment Co., Ltd. (1)
Building 15 No 3999 Xiupu Road, Shanghai, 201315, China
Tel.: (86) 2138252380
Web Site: http://www.hommel-china.com
Sales Range: $25-49.9 Million
Emp.: 90
Electric Equipment Mfr
N.A.I.C.S.: 334515

JENOPTIK Advanced Systems, LLC (1)
6940 Commerce Ave, El Paso, TX 79915
Tel.: (915) 775-1803
Laser Optical & Optoelectronic System Mfr
N.A.I.C.S.: 333310

JENOPTIK Automotive North America, LLC (1)
1500 W Hamlin Rd, Rochester Hills, MI 48309
Tel.: (248) 853-5888
Laser Optical & Optoelectronic System Mfr
N.A.I.C.S.: 333310

JENOPTIK Benelux B.V. (1)
Christiaan Huygensweg 3, 5151 DM, Drunen, Netherlands
Tel.: (31) 857435700
Measuring Instrument Mfr & Distr
N.A.I.C.S.: 334513

JENOPTIK Components LLC (1)
BC Pulkovo Sky Office B-916 Vnukovskaya Str 2, 196210, Saint Petersburg, Russia

INTERNATIONAL PUBLIC

Tel.: (7) 8126105050
Web Site: http://www.jenoptik-components.ru
Sales Range: $50-74,9 Million
Emp.: 3
Laser Component Distr
N.A.I.C.S.: 423990

JENOPTIK Laser Technologies USA Corp (1)
8020 Kensington Ct, Brighton, MI 48116
Tel.: (248) 446-9540
Web Site: http://www.jenoptik.com
Sales Range: $25-49.9 Million
Emp.: 8
Semiconductor Devices Mfr
N.A.I.C.S.: 334413

JENOPTIK Optical Systems, LLC (1)
16490 Innovation Dr, Jupiter, FL 33478-6428
Tel.: (561) 881-7400
Measuring Instrument Mfr & Distr
N.A.I.C.S.: 334513

JENOPTIK Power Systems GmbH (1)
Sudliche Romerstrasse 12 - 18, 86972, Altenstadt, Germany
Tel.: (49) 88617100
Laser Optical & Optoelectronic System Mfr
N.A.I.C.S.: 333310

JENOPTIK Traffic Solutions Switzerland AG (1)
Industriepark 11, 8610, Uster, Switzerland
Tel.: (41) 432882828
Web Site: https://www.jenoptik.ch
Traffic Monitoring System Mfr
N.A.I.C.S.: 334290

JENOPTIK Traffic Solutions UK Ltd. (1)
Ten Watchmoor Park Riverside Way, Camberley, GU15 3YL, Surrey, United Kingdom
Tel.: (44) 1183130333
Web Site: https://www.jenoptik.co.uk
Traffic Control System Design Mfr
N.A.I.C.S.: 334290

Jenoptik Automatisierungstechnik Gmbh (1)
Konrad-Zuse-Str 6, 07745, Jena, Germany
Tel.: (49) 364 165 2532
Web Site: http://www.automation-jenoptik.de
Optoelectronic Product Mfr
N.A.I.C.S.: 334419

Jenoptik Diode Lab Gmbh (1)
Max-Planck-Strasse 2, 12489, Berlin, Germany
Tel.: (49) 306779870
Web Site: http://www.diodelab.com
Semiconductor Equipment Mfr
N.A.I.C.S.: 334413

Jenoptik Industrial Metrology Germany GmbH (1)
Drachenloch 5, 78052, Villingen-Schwenningen, Germany
Tel.: (49) 77 216 8130
Web Site: https://www.jenoptik.com
Sales Range: $50-74.9 Million
Emp.: 150
Gauging Instruments Mfr
N.A.I.C.S.: 334519

Subsidiary (Non-US):

Etamic SA (2)
Zone d'Activites de Damigny, Saint-Martin-des-Entrees, Bayeux, 14400, France
Tel.: (33) 231513770
Web Site: http://www.etamic.com
Sales Range: $25-49.9 Million
Emp.: 50
Production Measurement Device Mfr
N.A.I.C.S.: 334519

Jenoptik Japan Co Ltd (1)
2-3-8 Shin-Yokohama, Kohoku-ku, Yokohama, 222-0033, Kanagawa, Japan (100%)
Tel.: (81) 456709140
Web Site: https://www.jenoptik.co.jp
Sales Range: $50-74.9 Million
Emp.: 7
Lasers Distr
N.A.I.C.S.: 423440

AND PRIVATE COMPANIES

Jenoptik Katasorb GmbH (1)
Konrad-Zuse Strasse 6, 07745, Jena,
Germany (100%)
Tel.: (49) 3641652532
Web Site: http://www.jenoptik.com
Sales Range: $50-74.9 Million
Emp.: 570
Industrial Waste Gas Purification Processes
N.A.I.C.S.: 562112

Subsidiary (US):

Jenoptik Optical Systems, Inc. (2)
16490 Innovation Dr, Jupiter, FL 33478-6428
Tel.: (561) 881-7400
Web Site: http://www.jenoptik-inc.com
Sales Range: $25-49.9 Million
Emp.: 40
Custom Optical Assemblies Mfr & Designer
N.A.I.C.S.: 333310
Rob Allen (VP-Fin-Micro Optics)

Jenoptik Korea Corporation Ltd (1)
91 Hyeongoksandan-ro 93beon-gil
Cheongbuk-myeon, 17812, Pyeongtaek,
Gyeonggi, Korea (South)
Tel.: (82) 31 646 4021
Web Site: https://www.jenoptik.co.kr
Sales Range: $25-49.9 Million
Emp.: 12
Lasers Distr
N.A.I.C.S.: 423440

Jenoptik Optical Systems GmbH (1)
Am Sandberg 2, Triptis, 07819, Jena, Germany
Tel.: (49) 364 824 5450
Web Site: http://www.jenoptik.com
Sales Range: $200-249.9 Million
Emp.: 700
Semiconductor Devices Mfr
N.A.I.C.S.: 334413

Jenoptik Robot GmbH (1)
Opladener Strasse 202, 40789, Monheim
am Rhein, Germany
Tel.: (49) 217339402400
Web Site: http://www.jenoptik.com
Traffic Surveillance Equipment Developer &
Mfr
N.A.I.C.S.: 335999

Subsidiary (Non-US):

ROBOT Nederland B.V. (2)
Veertels 4, 5133 NL, Riel, Netherlands
Tel.: (31) 13 5772233
Web Site: http://www.robot-nederland.nl
Traffic Surveillance Equipment Developer &
Mfr
N.A.I.C.S.: 335999

Jenoptik SSC Gmbh (1)
Carl-zeiss-str 1, Jena, 07743, Germany
Tel.: (49) 3641652305
Sales Range: $800-899.9 Million
Emp.: 3,000
Electronic Products Mfr
N.A.I.C.S.: 334419

Jenoptik UK Limited (1)
4 3 Frimley Business Park, Frimley, GU16
7SG, Surrey, United Kingdom (92%)
Tel.: (44) 1183130333
Web Site: https://www.jenoptik.co.uk
Traffic Management Products Mfr
N.A.I.C.S.: 334290
Geoff Collins (Dir-Sls & Mktg)

OTTO Vision Technology GmbH (1)
Im Steinfeld 3, 07751, Jena, Germany
Tel.: (49) 364167150
Web Site: http://www.otto-jena.de
Optical Inspection Control System Mfr
N.A.I.C.S.: 333310
Reinhard Otto (Mng Dir)

OVITEC GmbH (1)
Im Steinfeld 3, 07751, Jena, Germany
Tel.: (49) 364167150
Web Site: http://www.ovitec.de
Optical Inspection Control System Mfr
N.A.I.C.S.: 333310

Prodomax Automation Ltd. (1)
455 Welham Road, Barrie, L4N 8Z6, ON,
Canada
Tel.: (705) 726-5841
Web Site: https://www.prodomax.com

Industrial Flexible Automation Systems Designer, Mfr & Whslr
N.A.I.C.S.: 333519
Carolyn Garvey (Co-CEO)

Radarlux Radar Systems GmbH (1)
Rottgerweg 10, 51371, Leverkusen, Germany
Tel.: (49) 2142064940
Web Site: http://www.radarlux.com
Emp.: 3,500
Traffic & Speed Monitoring Equipment Mfr
N.A.I.C.S.: 334511

SwissOptic (Wuhan) Co., Ltd. (1)
No 1 2nd Road Huagong Park Eastlake
High Technology Development Zone, Wuhan, 430223, China
Tel.: (86) 2787928588
Emp.: 120
Optical Glass Mfr & Distr
N.A.I.C.S.: 334610

SwissOptic AG (1)
Heinrich-Wild-Strasse 210, 9435, Heerbrugg, Switzerland
Tel.: (41) 717470420
Measuring Instrument Mfr & Distr
N.A.I.C.S.: 334513

TRIOPTICS Berlin GmbH (1)
Strandbaddamm 6, 22880, Wedel, Germany
Tel.: (49) 4103180060
Web Site: https://trioptics.com
Optical Lens Mfr
N.A.I.C.S.: 339115

Traffipax, LLC (1)
16490 Innovation Dr, Jupiter, FL 33478-6428
Tel.: (561) 881-7400
Laser Optical & Optoelectronic System Mfr
N.A.I.C.S.: 333310

Trioptics GmbH (1)
Strandbaddamm 6, 22880, Wedel, Germany
Tel.: (49) 4103180060
Measuring Instrument Mfr & Distr
N.A.I.C.S.: 334513

Trioptics Japan Co., Ltd. (1)
4-6-25 Nakada, Suruga-ku, Shizuoka, 422-8041, Shizuoka, Japan
Tel.: (81) 542034555
Web Site: https://www.trioptics.jp
Optical Lens Mfr
N.A.I.C.S.: 339115

Trioptics Korea Co., Ltd. (1)
Room 701 Building 101 Digital Empire 2 88
Shinwon-ro 486, Sindong Yeongtong-gu,
Suwon, Gyeonggi-do, Korea (South)
Tel.: (82) 316957450
Web Site: https://www.trioptics.co.kr
Optical Glass Mfr & Distr
N.A.I.C.S.: 334610

Trioptics Singapore Pte. Ltd. (1)
12 Woodlands Square 10-70 Tower 1, Singapore, 737715, Singapore
Tel.: (65) 65134188
Web Site: https://trioptics.com.sg
Measuring Instrument Mfr & Distr
N.A.I.C.S.: 334513

Trioptics Taiwan Ltd. (1)
4F-2 No 5 Andong Road, Chungli Dist,
Taoyuan, 32063, Taiwan
Tel.: (886) 34620405
Optical Glass Mfr & Distr
N.A.I.C.S.: 334610

VINCORION Advanced Systems GmbH (1)
Feldstrasse 155, 22880, Wedel, Germany
Tel.: (49) 4103600
Laser Optical & Optoelectronic System Mfr
N.A.I.C.S.: 333310

JENSCARE SCIENTIFIC CO., LTD.
Block B-5 777 4th Binhai Road,
Hangzhou Bay New Area, Ningbo,
Zhejiang, China
Tel.: (86) 57463935666 CN
Web Site: https://en.jenscare.com
Year Founded: 2011
9877—(HKG)
Rev.: $8,338,301

Assets: $219,293,916
Liabilities: $8,932,449
Net Worth: $210,361,467
Earnings: ($67,552,434)
Emp.: 292
Fiscal Year-end: 12/31/22
Medical Device Mfr
N.A.I.C.S.: 339112
Fei Pan (VP)

Subsidiaries:

Ningbo Diochange Medical Technology Co., Ltd. (1)
Block B-6 777 4th Binhai Road Hangzhou
Bay New Area, Ningbo, Zhejiang, China
Tel.: (86) 57463865666
Medical Device Mfr
N.A.I.C.S.: 339112

JENSEN-GROUP N.V.
Neerhonderd 33, BE-9230, Wetteren,
Oost-Vlaanderen, Belgium
Tel.: (32) 93338330 BE
Web Site: https://www.jensen-group.com
Year Founded: 1990
JEN—(EUR)
Rev.: $301,211,121
Assets: $341,928,505
Liabilities: $174,833,823
Net Worth: $167,094,683
Earnings: $9,337,080
Emp.: 1,239
Fiscal Year-end: 12/31/20
Holding Company; Commercial &
Heavy-Duty Laundry Machinery Mfr
N.A.I.C.S.: 551112

Subsidiaries:

JENSEN Industrial Group A/S (1)
Industrivej 2, 3700, Ronne, Denmark
Tel.: (45) 56943121
Web Site: http://www.jensen.com
Laundry Machinery Mfr
N.A.I.C.S.: 333310

Subsidiary (Non-US):

JENSEN GmbH (2)
Jorn-Jensen-Str 1, 31177, Harsum, Germany
Tel.: (49) 51272100
Sales Range: $75-99.9 Million
Emp.: 240
Laundry Equipment Sales & Maintenance
Services
N.A.I.C.S.: 423850
Christoph Ansorge (Gen Mgr)

JENSEN Italia S.r.l. (1)
Strada Provinciale Novedratese 46, 22060,
Novedrate, Como, Italy
Tel.: (39) 031789119
Web Site: https://www.jensen-group.com
Laundry Equipment Sales & Maintenance
Services
N.A.I.C.S.: 423850

JENSEN Laundry Systems Australia Pty. Ltd. (1)
Unit 16 38-46 South Street, Rydalmere,
2116, NSW, Australia
Tel.: (61) 298490000
Web Site: http://www.jensen-group.com
Laundry Machinery Mfr & Distr
N.A.I.C.S.: 333310

JENSEN UK Ltd. (1)
Unit 5 Network 11 Thorpe Way, Industrial
Estate, Banbury, OX16 4XS, Oxfordshire,
United Kingdom
Tel.: (44) 1295226226
Web Site: http://www.jensen-group.com
Sales Range: $25-49.9 Million
Laundry Machine Distr
N.A.I.C.S.: 423850

Jensen USA, Inc. (1)
99 Aberdeen Loop, Panama City, FL
32405 (100%)
Tel.: (850) 271-5959
Web Site: https://www.jensenusa.com
Sales Range: $50-74.9 Million
Emp.: 60

Commercial & Heavy-Duty Laundry Machinery Mfr
N.A.I.C.S.: 333310
Simon Nield (Pres)

JENSON & NICHOLSON INDIA LTD
617 Bestech Business Tower Sector-48 Sohna Road, Gurgaon, 122 018,
Haryana, India
Tel.: (91) 1244017402
Web Site: http://www.jnpaints.com
Year Founded: 1922
Rev.: $5,731,612
Assets: $2,410,115
Liabilities: $55,353,052
Net Worth: ($52,942,937)
Earnings: ($1,520,621)
Emp.: 211
Fiscal Year-end: 03/31/17
Paints Mfr
N.A.I.C.S.: 325510

JENTAYU SUSTAINABLES BERHAD
Unit 25-01 Level 25 Menara Felda 11
Persiaran KLCC, 50088, Kuala Lumpur, Malaysia
Tel.: (60) 392127878
Web Site: https://jentayu-sustainables.com
JSB—(KLS)
Rev.: $9,024,550
Assets: $41,729,524
Liabilities: $15,633,862
Net Worth: $26,095,661
Earnings: ($1,090,582)
Emp.: 203
Fiscal Year-end: 06/30/23
Building Materials Distr
N.A.I.C.S.: 444110
Abu Sahid Mohamed (Chm)

JENTECH PRECISION INDUSTRIAL CO., LTD.
No 40 Keji 1st Rd, Gueishan,
Taoyuan, 333, Taiwan
Tel.: (886) 32115678
Web Site: https://www.jentech.com.tw
Year Founded: 1987
3653—(TAI)
Rev.: $394,475,409
Assets: $518,187,266
Liabilities: $114,698,580
Net Worth: $403,488,686
Earnings: $73,635,695
Emp.: 1,779
Fiscal Year-end: 12/31/23
Metal Stamping Mfr
N.A.I.C.S.: 332119
Chung-Hsin Chao (Chm)

Subsidiaries:

Wuxi Jentech Precision Industrial Co., Ltd (1)
2-1 Junshan Rd, Wuxi National High & New
Industrial Development Zone, Wuxi,
214028, Jiangsu, China
Tel.: (86) 510 8522 7688
Web Site: http://www.jentech.com.tw
Metal Stamping Mfr
N.A.I.C.S.: 332119

JEOL LTD.
3-1-2 Musashino Akishima, Tokyo,
196-8558, Japan
Tel.: (81) 425431111
Web Site: https://www.jeol.com
Year Founded: 1949
6951—(TKS)
Rev.: $1,152,360,960
Assets: $1,521,707,930
Liabilities: $692,067,000
Net Worth: $829,640,930
Earnings: $143,463,440
Emp.: 3,435
Fiscal Year-end: 03/31/24

JEOL LTD.

JEOL Ltd.—(Continued)

Analytical, Electron Optics, Medical & Semiconductor Equipment Mfr & Sales
N.A.I.C.S.: 334516
Gon-Emon Kurihara (Chm & CEO)

Subsidiaries:

CeSPIA Inc. (1)
18th Floor of Otemachi Nomura Building 2-1-1 Otemachi, Chiyoda-ku, Tokyo, 100-0004, Japan
Tel.: (81) 362625959
Web Site: http://www.cespia.co.jp
New Drug Development Consulting Services
N.A.I.C.S.: 541690

Integrated Dynamic Electron Solutions, Inc. (1)
Web Site: http://www.ides-inc.com
Electron Microscopes Provider
N.A.I.C.S.: 811210

JEOL (Australasia) Pty. Ltd. (1)
Suite 1 Level 2 18 Aquatic Drive, Frenchs Forest, Sydney, 2086, NSW, Australia (100%)
Tel.: (61) 294513855
Sales Range: $1-9.9 Million
Emp.: 6
Laboratory Analytical Instruments
N.A.I.C.S.: 334516

JEOL (BEIJING) CO., LTD. (1)
2nd Floor South Building Zhongke Resources Building, No 6 South Third Street Zhongguancun Haidian District, Beijing, 100190, China
Tel.: (86) 10 6804 6321
Web Site: http://www.jeol.com.cn
Industrial Machinery Mfr & Distr
N.A.I.C.S.: 333248

JEOL (Europe) B.V. (1)
Lireweg 4, 2153 PH, Nieuw-Vennep, Netherlands (100%)
Tel.: (31) 252623500
Web Site: https://www.jeolbenelux.com
Sales Range: $25-49.9 Million
Emp.: 20
Laboratory Analytical Instruments
N.A.I.C.S.: 334516
Marc Mine (Dir-Svc)

JEOL (Europe) SAS (1)
Allee de Giverny, 78290, Croissy-sur-Seine, France (100%)
Tel.: (33) 130153737
Web Site: http://www.jeol.fr
Sales Range: $25-49.9 Million
Emp.: 48
Provider of Laboratory Analytical Instruments
N.A.I.C.S.: 334516

JEOL (Germany) GmbH (1)
Gute Anger 30, 85356, Freising, Germany (100%)
Tel.: (49) 816198450
Web Site: http://www.jeol.de
Sales Range: $25-49.9 Million
Emp.: 100
Laboratory Analytical Instruments Sales & Service
N.A.I.C.S.: 334516

JEOL (Italia) S.p.A. (1)
Palazzo Pacinotti - Milano 3 City Via Ludovico il Moro 6/A, 20080, Basiglio, MI, Italy
Tel.: (39) 029041431
Web Site: http://www.jeol.it
Analytical Laboratory Instruments
N.A.I.C.S.: 334516

JEOL (Malaysia) Sdn Bhd (1)
508 Block A Level5 Kelana Business Center 97 Jalan SS7/2 Kelana Jaya, 47301, Petaling Jaya, Selangor, Malaysia
Tel.: (60) 374927722
Sales Range: $25-49.9 Million
Emp.: 17
Laboratory Instrument Mfr
N.A.I.C.S.: 334516

JEOL (Nordic) AB (1)
Hammarbacken 6A, PO Box 716, 191 27, Sollentuna, Sweden
Tel.: (46) 8282800
Electron Microscope Mfr
N.A.I.C.S.: 333310

JEOL (RUS) LLC. (1)
Office 351 floor 3 23 Novoslobodskaya St, 127055, Moscow, Russia
Tel.: (7) 4957487791
Web Site: http://jeolrus.com
Emp.: 10
Industrial Machinery Mfr & Distr
N.A.I.C.S.: 333248

JEOL (Skandinaviska) A.B. (1)
Hammerbacken 6A, Box 716, Sollentuna, 191 27, Sweden (100%)
Tel.: (46) 8282800
Web Site: http://www.jeoleuro.com
Sales Range: $25-49.9 Million
Emp.: 15
Laboratory Analytical Instruments Sales & Service
N.A.I.C.S.: 334516
Siegfried Falch (Mng Dir)

JEOL (U.K.) Ltd. (1)
JEOL House Silver Court Watchmead, Welwyn Garden City, AL7 1LT, Hertfordshire, United Kingdom (100%)
Tel.: (44) 1707377117
Web Site: http://www.jeoluk.com
Sales Range: $25-49.9 Million
Emp.: 60
Provider of Laboratory Analytical Instruments
N.A.I.C.S.: 334516

JEOL Asia Pte. Ltd. (1)
2 Corporation Rd, Ste 01-12 Corporation Pl, Singapore, 618494, Singapore (100%)
Tel.: (65) 659989
Web Site: https://www.jeol.com
Sales Range: $25-49.9 Million
Emp.: 20
Laboratory Analytical Instruments
N.A.I.C.S.: 334516
Takeuchi Chihiro (Mng Dir)

JEOL Asia(Thailand)Co., Ltd. (1)
36C CRC Tower All Seasons Place 87/2 Wireless Road Lumpini, Phatumwan, Bangkok, 10330, Thailand
Tel.: (66) 262531023
Electron Microscope Mfr
N.A.I.C.S.: 333310

JEOL BRASIL Instrumentos Cientificos Ltda. (1)
Av Jabaquara 2958-5 andar-cj 52, 04046 500, Sao Paulo, 04046-500, Brazil
Tel.: (55) 1150704000
Sales Range: $25-49.9 Million
Emp.: 14
Scientific Instrumentation Machinery Distr
N.A.I.C.S.: 423830
Andre Maeda Oyama (Office Mgr)

JEOL Canada, Inc. (1)
3275 1ere Rue Local 8, Saint-Hubert, J3Y 8Y6, QC, Canada
Tel.: (450) 676-8776
Electron Microscope Mfr
N.A.I.C.S.: 333310

JEOL DATUM Shanghai.Co., Ltd. (1)
Rm 1507 & 1508 Benben Mansion No 300 Xikang Rd, Jing'an Area, Shanghai, 200040, China
Tel.: (86) 21 5836 6350
Sales Range: $25-49.9 Million
Emp.: 24
Scientific Instrument Distr
N.A.I.C.S.: 423490
Jozsef Fekete (Gen Mgr)

JEOL Gulf FZCO (1)
Dubai Airport Free Trade Zone West Wing 5WA NoG12, PO Box No 371107, Dubai, United Arab Emirates
Tel.: (971) 46091497
Electron Microscope Mfr
N.A.I.C.S.: 333310

JEOL India Pvt. Ltd. (1)
Unit No305 3rd Floor ABW Elegance Tower, Jasola District Centre, New Delhi, 110 025, India
Tel.: (91) 1145958000
Electron Microscope Mfr
N.A.I.C.S.: 333310

JEOL Korea Ltd. (1)
7th floor Dongwoo Building 1443 Yangjaedaero, Gil-dong Gangdong-Gu, Seoul, 05355, Korea (South) (100%)
Tel.: (82) 25115501
Web Site: http://www.jeol.co.kr
Sales Range: $25-49.9 Million
Emp.: 60
Laboratory Analytical Instruments
N.A.I.C.S.: 334516

JEOL Resonance Inc. (1)
3-1-2 Musashino, Akishima, 196-8558, Tokyo, Japan
Tel.: (81) 425422234
Emp.: 144
Electron Microscope Mfr
N.A.I.C.S.: 333310
Takahiro Anai (Pres)

JEOL Shanghai Semiconductors Ltd. (1)
Building No 3 No 589 QuWu Rd, Pudong Nan Road, Shanghai, China
Tel.: (86) 2168880770
Semiconductor Mfr
N.A.I.C.S.: 334413

JEOL TECHNOSERVICE CO., LTD. (1)
3-1-2 Musashino, Akishima, 196-8558, Tokyo, Japan
Tel.: (81) 425422127
Web Site: https://www.jeol-tcn.co.jp
Sales Range: $1-9.9 Million
Emp.: 219
Multilingual Translation Services
N.A.I.C.S.: 541930
Kouji Matsumoto (Pres)

JEOL Taiwan Semiconductors Ltd. (1)
No 198 Xingong 2nd Rd, East Dist, Zhubei, 302004, Hsinchu, Taiwan
Tel.: (886) 35715656
Web Site: http://www.jeol.co.jp
Semiconductor Mfr
N.A.I.C.S.: 334413

JEOL USA, Inc. (1)
11 Dearborn Rd, Peabody, MA 01960-3823 (100%)
Tel.: (978) 535-5900
Web Site: https://www.jeolusa.com
Sales Range: $75-99.9 Million
Emp.: 300
Distribution of Electron Microscopes & Scientific Instruments
N.A.I.C.S.: 423490
Collette Hanlon (Dir-HR)

JEOL de Mexico S.A. de C.V. (1)
Arkansas 11 Piso 2 Colonia Napoles Delegacion Benito Juarez, Colonia Hipodromo, 03810, Mexico, DF, Mexico (100%)
Tel.: (52) 5554485900
Web Site: http://www.jeol.com.mx
Sales Range: $25-49.9 Million
Emp.: 15
Laboratory Analytical Instruments
N.A.I.C.S.: 334516

System In Frontier Inc. (1)
4F Shinsuzuharu Bldg 2-8-3, Akebono-cho, Tachikawa, 190-0012, Tokyo, Japan
Tel.: (81) 425264360
Web Site: https://www.sifi.co.jp
Emp.: 55
Computer System Services
N.A.I.C.S.: 541512

YAMAGATA CREATIVE CO., LTD. (1)
1655 Aza Qobotoke Ooaza Yamaguchi, Yamaguchi, Tendo, 994-0101, Yamagata, Japan
Tel.: (81) 23 6582811
Emp.: 8
Laboratory Measuring Equipment Mfr
N.A.I.C.S.: 333248
Masao Kuga (Pres)

JEONGMOON INFORMATION CO., LTD.
15-20 Dongtansandan 8-gil, Dongtanmyeon, Hwaseong, Gyeonggi-do, Korea (South)
Tel.: (82) 313769494
Web Site: https://www.jmikorea.co.kr
Year Founded: 1993
033050—(KRS)
Rev.: $49,797,847
Assets: $65,553,647
Liabilities: $33,162,156
Net Worth: $32,391,491
Earnings: $1,902,784
Emp.: 86
Fiscal Year-end: 12/31/22
LCD Products Mfr
N.A.I.C.S.: 334413
Chung Kwang-Hoon (Chm & CEO)

Subsidiaries:

JMIMX S.A. de C.V. (1)
Jardines Del Valle 1151, 32551, Ciudad Juarez, Chihuahua, Mexico
Tel.: (52) 6566401350
Web Site: https://www.jmimx.com
Computer Peripherals Mfr
N.A.I.C.S.: 334118

JEONJINBIO CO., LTD.
295 Seongseo Gongdan Buk-Ro, Dalseo-Gu, Daegu, Korea (South)
Tel.: (82) 535937191
Web Site: https://www.jjbious.com
Year Founded: 2004
110020—(KRS)
Rev.: $5,978,133
Assets: $13,704,151
Liabilities: $6,411,335
Net Worth: $7,292,816
Earnings: ($2,419,410)
Emp.: 45
Fiscal Year-end: 12/31/22
Chemicals Mfr
N.A.I.C.S.: 325998
Tae-Hoon Lee (CEO)

JEONWOO PRECISION CO., LTD.
24 Gongdan 8-ro Jillyang-eup, Gyeongsan, Gyeongsangbuk-do, Korea (South)
Tel.: (82) 538595400
Web Site: http://www.jwjm.com
Year Founded: 1992
Automobile Parts Mfr & Distr
N.A.I.C.S.: 332510
Dong Jin Kim (Pres & CEO)

Subsidiaries:

Jeonwoo Precision Co., Ltd. - China Factory (1)
No 9 Donglin Lianfa Chengxiang Zhentaicang, Jiangsu, China
Tel.: (86) 51253442323
Automobile Parts Mfr
N.A.I.C.S.: 332510

JEOTEX, INC.
7895 Transmere Drive Suite 207, Mississauga, L5S 1V9, ON, Canada
Tel.: (905) 712-0505
Web Site: http://www.datawinc.com
Sales Range: $10-24.9 Million
Wireless Web Products Mfr
N.A.I.C.S.: 334220
Sunit Singh Tuli (Co-Founder, Pres & CEO)

JERAISY GROUP
790 King Fahad Rd, PO Box 317, Riyadh, 11411, Saudi Arabia
Tel.: (966) 14198000
Web Site: http://www.jeraisy.com
Year Founded: 1958
Sales Range: $500-549.9 Million
Emp.: 4,000
Office Furniture Mfr
N.A.I.C.S.: 334118
Abdul Rahman Ali Al Jeraisy (Owner & Chm)

AND PRIVATE COMPANIES

Subsidiaries:

Computer Paper Product Co. (1)
PO Box 355711, Riyadh, 11383, Saudi Arabia
Tel.: (966) 11 2651818
Web Site: http://www.cppc-jeraisy.com
Paper Products Mfr
N.A.I.C.S.: 322299

Jeraisy CardTec (1)
PO Box 477, Industrial City, 11383, Riyadh, Saudi Arabia
Tel.: (966) 012650098
Web Site: http://www.jeraisycardtec.com
Sales Range: $25-49.9 Million
Emp.: 100
Plastic Card Mfr
N.A.I.C.S.: 326199

Jeraisy Computer & Communication Services (1)
792 King Fahad Road, PO Box 317, 11411, Riyadh, Saudi Arabia
Tel.: (966) 14198000
Web Site: http://www.jeraisy.com
Sales Range: $550-599.9 Million
Emp.: 1,500
Hardware & Software Distr
N.A.I.C.S.: 423430

Jeraisy Computer Paper Products Co. (1)
PO Box 355711, Riyadh, 11383, Saudi Arabia
Tel.: (966) 112651818
Web Site: https://www.cppc-jeraisy.com
Label & Adhesive Distr
N.A.I.C.S.: 424690

Riyadh House Company (1)
King Fahd Road Building 970, Riyadh, Saudi Arabia
Tel.: (966) 14198000
Web Site: https://beta.rhc.com.sa
Office Equipment Distr
N.A.I.C.S.: 423420

Riyadh House Establishment (1)
PO Box 317, Riyadh, 11411, Saudi Arabia
Tel.: (966) 4198000
Web Site: http://www.rhc.com.sa
Office Equipment Importer, Whslr & Distr
N.A.I.C.S.: 423420

Steelcase Jeraisy Ltd. (1)
3rd Industrial City, PO Box 102, Riyadh, 11383, Saudi Arabia
Tel.: (966) 1 2650031
Web Site: http://www.steelcasejeraisy.com
Office Furniture Mfr
N.A.I.C.S.: 337214

JERASIA CAPITAL BERHAD

Nos 2-8 Lorong 6E/91Taman Shamelin Perkasa, Batu 3 1/2 Jalan Cheras, 56100, Kuala Lumpur, Wilayah Persekutuan, Malaysia
Tel.: (60) 39 283 7518
Web Site: http://corporate.jerasia.com.my
JERASIA—(KLS)
Rev.: $33,288,616
Assets: $39,847,565
Liabilities: $69,101,782
Net Worth: ($29,254,218)
Earnings: ($41,623,377)
Emp.: 832
Fiscal Year-end: 11/30/21
Apparels Mfr
N.A.I.C.S.: 458110
Pronob Kumar sen Gupta *(Mng Dir-Grp)*

Subsidiaries:

Canteran Apparel Sdn. Bhd. (1)
28 Jalan Bakau Kluang, 86000, Keluang, Bohor, Malaysia
Tel.: (60) 77733688
Sales Range: $100-124.9 Million
Emp.: 400
Fashion Apparels Mfr
N.A.I.C.S.: 315990
Yap Fung Kong *(Mng Dir)*

Subsidiary (Non-US):

Canteran Apparel (Cambodia) Co., Ltd. (2)
No 97 Street Chomchao Trapang Thloeung Village Sangkat Chomchao, Khan Dangkor, 12301, Phnom Penh, Cambodia
Tel.: (855) 23424277
Fashion Apparels Mfr
N.A.I.C.S.: 315250

Jerasia Apparel Sdn. Bhd. (1)
Nos 2-8 Lorong 6E/91 Taman Shamelin Perkasa Batu 3 1/2 Jalan Cheras, 56100, Kuala Lumpur, Wilayah Persekutuan, Malaysia
Tel.: (60) 392837518
Apparels Whslr & Retailer
N.A.I.C.S.: 424350

JERICH INTERNATIONAL GMBH

Feldbacherstrasse 19, A-8200, Gleisdorf, Austria
Tel.: (43) 3112 4000 0
Web Site: http://www.jerich.com
Year Founded: 1969
Logistics & Supply Chain Management Services
N.A.I.C.S.: 541614
Herbert Jerich *(Mgr)*

Subsidiaries:

Jerich Austria GmbH (1)
Feldbacherstrasse 19, A-8200, Gleisdorf, Austria
Tel.: (43) 3112 4000 0
Web Site: http://www.jerich.com
Logistics & Supply Chain Management Services
N.A.I.C.S.: 541614

Subsidiary (Domestic):

Management Transport & Logistik GmbH (2)
Grazer Strasse 10, 8130, Frohnleiten, Austria
Tel.: (43) 312626110
Process Physical Distribution & Logistics Consulting Services
N.A.I.C.S.: 541614

JERICHO ENERGY VENTURES INC.

1055 W Georgia Street Suite 2100, PO BOX 11110, STN Royal Centre, Vancouver, V6E 3P3, BC, Canada
Tel.: (604) 343-4534
Web Site: https://jerichoenergyventures.com
JEV—(TSXV)
Rev.: $73,000
Assets: $19,021,451
Liabilities: $5,641,878
Net Worth: $13,379,573
Earnings: ($7,321,633)
Fiscal Year-end: 12/31/23
Oil & Gas Exploration
N.A.I.C.S.: 211120
Brian Williamson *(Pres & CEO)*

JERNBANEVERKET

Stortorvet 7, Oslo, 2308, Norway
Tel.: (47) 22455000
Web Site: http://www.jerbaneverket.no
Sales Range: $750-799.9 Million
Emp.: 3,200
Railway Stations & Terminals Developer & Operator
N.A.I.C.S.: 485112
Elizabeth Inger *(CEO & Dir Gen)*

JERONIMO MARTINS SGPS SA

Rua Actor Antonio Silva n 7, 1649-033, Lisbon, Portugal
Tel.: (351) 217532000
Web Site: https://www.jeronimomartins.com
Year Founded: 1792
JMT—(EUR)
Rev.: $20,872,197,049
Assets: $10,920,730,258
Liabilities: $8,424,665,345
Net Worth: $2,496,064,913
Earnings: $471,200,133
Emp.: 115,428
Fiscal Year-end: 12/31/19
Food Products Mfr
N.A.I.C.S.: 551112
Rita Fragoso *(Head-Media)*

Subsidiaries:

Desimo-Desenvolvimento e Gestao Imobiliaria, Lda. (1)
Rua Tierno Galvan Torre 3 9th Fl, Lisbon, 1099 008, Portugal (100%)
Tel.: (351) 217532000
N.A.I.C.S.: 455219

Fima/VG Distribuicao de Produtos Alimentares, Lda. (1)
Largo Monterroio Mascarenhas 1, 1070-184, Lisbon, Portugal
Tel.: (351) 213892000
Web Site: http://www.unilever.com
Sales Range: $100-124.9 Million
Emp.: 500
Food & Personal Care Product Mfr
N.A.I.C.S.: 311999

Hussel Iberia-Chocolates e Confeitaria, S.A. (1)
Rua Dof Userdiz 25 B, Lisbon, 1349 024, Portugal
Tel.: (351) 213613300
N.A.I.C.S.: 455219

JMR-Gestao de Empresas de Retalho, SGPS, S.A. (1)
Rua Actor Antonio Silva 7, 1600-404, Lisbon, Portugal (51%)
Tel.: (351) 217532000
Web Site: http://www.jeronimomartins.pt
Food Distr & Manufacturing
N.A.I.C.S.: 311999

Subsidiary (Domestic):

EVA-Sociedade de Investimentos Mobiliaros e Imobiliarios, Lda. (2)
Rua 31 de Janeiro, no. 81-A, 3o Esq., Funchal, Madeira Islands, Portugal (89%)
Tel.: (351) 217526180
Food Mfr
N.A.I.C.S.: 311999

Gestiretalho-Gestao e Consultadoria para a Distribuicao a Retalho, S.A. (2)
Rua Antonio Actor Silva 7, 1600-404, Lisbon, Portugal (100%)
Tel.: (351) 217532000
Web Site: http://www.jernimomartin.com
Sales Range: $75-99.9 Million
Emp.: 300
Engineering Consulting
N.A.I.C.S.: 541330

Subsidiary (Domestic):

Pingo Doce-Distribuicao Alimentar, S.A. (3)
Rua Actor Antonio Silva, 7-A B 1600, Lisbon, Portugal
Tel.: (351) 217532000
Web Site: http://www.pingo-martins.pt
Provider of Grocery Store Services
N.A.I.C.S.: 445110

Subsidiary (Domestic):

Bento & Martins, Lda. (4)
Rua Tierno Galvan Torre 3 Piso 9J, 1070-274, Lisbon, Portugal (51%)
Distr of Food
N.A.I.C.S.: 445110

Feira Nova-Hipermercados, S.A. (4)
Rua Actor Antonio Silva 7, 1070 274, Lisbon, Portugal (65%)
Tel.: (351) 217532000
Convenience Store
N.A.I.C.S.: 457110

Supertur-Imobiliaria, Comercio e Turismo, S.A. (4)
Rua Actor Antonio Silva 7, 1600-404, Lisbon, Portugal (91%)
Tel.: (351) 217532000
Tourist Offices
N.A.I.C.S.: 561520
Pedro Santos *(Gen Mgr)*

Jeronimo Martins Dystrybucja S.A. (1)
ul Zniwna 5, 62 025, Kostrzyn, Poland
Tel.: (48) 616548001
Web Site: http://www.biedronka.pl
Supermarket Chain Operator
N.A.I.C.S.: 445110

Jeronimo Martins-Distribuicao de Produtos de Consumo, Lda. (1)
Rua Actor Antonio Silva n 7, 1649-033, Lisbon, Portugal (100%)
Tel.: (351) 217532000
Web Site: http://www.jeronimomartins.pt
Sales Range: $450-499.9 Million
Emp.: 1,500
Consumer Products Distr
N.A.I.C.S.: 455219

Jeronimo Martins-Servicos, S.A. (1)
Rua Actor Antonio Silva 7, 1600-404, Lisbon, Portugal (100%)
Tel.: (351) 217532000
Web Site: http://www.jeronimomartins.pt
Sales Range: $250-299.9 Million
Emp.: 600
N.A.I.C.S.: 457110

Lillywhites Ltd. (1)
24 36 Regent St, London, SW1Y 4QF, United Kingdom (100%)
Tel.: (44) 3443325602
Web Site: https://www.lillywhites.com
Sports Equipment & Clothing Retailer
N.A.I.C.S.: 459110

Recheio-Distribuicao, Lda. (1)
Rua Tierno Galvan, Torre 3, Piso 9J, 1070-274, Lisbon, Portugal (60%)
Grocery Stores
N.A.I.C.S.: 445110

Subsidiary (Domestic):

Bivol-Utilidades, Equipamentos e Invest. Imobiliarios, Lda. (2)
Rua Jose Falcao no 3-1o Esq, Lisbon, Portugal (75%)
Provider of Business Services
N.A.I.C.S.: 561499

PSQ-Sociedade de Investimentos Mobiliarios e Imobiliarios, Lda. (2)
Rua 31 de Janeiro 81-A 3o Esq, Funchal, Madeira Islands, Portugal (75.5%)
Provider of International Trade Services
N.A.I.C.S.: 522299

Recheio Cash & Carry S.A. (2)
Rua Actor Antonio Silva 7, 1600 404, Lisbon, Portugal (99.66%)
Tel.: (351) 217532000
Web Site: http://www.jeronimomartins.pt
Sales Range: $75-99.9 Million
Emp.: 500
Variety Stores
N.A.I.C.S.: 445110

Santa Maria Manuela Turismo, S.A. (1)
Rua Actor Antonio Silva no 7, 1649-033, Lisbon, Portugal
Tel.: (351) 938040843
Web Site: https://www.santamariamanuela.pt
Electric Utility Services
N.A.I.C.S.: 221122

Victor Guedes-Industria e Comercio, S.A. (1)
Largo Monterroio de Mascarenhas, Lisbon, P-1070-184, Portugal (100%)
Sales Range: $25-49.9 Million
Emp.: 150
Producer of Butter & Oils
N.A.I.C.S.: 311512

JERRY FORD SALES LTD.

5098 4 Avenue, Edson, T7E1L9, AB, Canada

JERRY FORD SALES LTD.

Jerry Ford Sales Ltd.—(Continued)
Tel.: (780) 723-4441
Web Site: http://www.jerryford.com
Year Founded: 1973
Rev.: $10,675,190
Emp.: 29
New & Used Car Dealers
N.A.I.C.S.: 441110
Cathy Pasychny (Pres)

JERSEY ELECTRICITY PLC
The Powerhouse Queens Road, PO Box 45, Saint Helier, JE4 8NY, Jersey
Tel.: (44) 1534505460
Web Site: https://www.jec.co.uk
JEL—(LSE)
Rev.: $157,886,897
Assets: $449,690,735
Liabilities: $144,787,932
Net Worth: $304,902,802
Earnings: $14,431,962
Emp.: 374
Fiscal Year-end: 09/30/23
Electricity Distr
N.A.I.C.S.: 221122
Phil Austin (Chm)

Subsidiaries:

Jendev (1)
The Powerhouse Queens Road, PO Box 45, Queens Rd, Saint Helier, JE4 8NY, Jersey
Tel.: (44) 153 450 5350
Web Site: https://www.jendev.com
Sales Range: $25-49.9 Million
Emp.: 8
Custom Computer Programming Services
N.A.I.C.S.: 541511
Gary Parsons (Mng Dir)

Jersey Deep Freeze Limited (1)
Unit 3 Block D 19 Oxford Rd, Saint Helier, JE2 4LJ, Jersey (60%)
Tel.: (44) 1534768621
Sales Range: $25-49.9 Million
Emp.: 10
Plumbing Heating & Air-Conditioning Contractors
N.A.I.C.S.: 238220

JERSEY OIL & GAS PLC
Ground Floor 5 St Andrew's Place, Saint Helier, JE2 3RP, Jersey
Tel.: (44) 1534858622   UK
Web Site: https://www.jerseyoilandgas.com
Year Founded: 2014
JOG—(AIM)
Assets: $35,041,781
Liabilities: $1,104,252
Net Worth: $33,937,529
Earnings: ($7,123,301)
Emp.: 14
Fiscal Year-end: 12/31/23
Oil & Gas Distribution Services
N.A.I.C.S.: 221210
Andrew Benitz (CEO)

JERUSALEM INSURANCE COMPANY
Shmeisani Abdul Hameed Sharaff St, PO Box 20094, Amman, 11118, Jordan
Tel.: (962) 65693161
Web Site: https://jico.jo
Year Founded: 1975
JERY—(AMM)
Rev.: $30,573,068
Assets: $52,044,462
Liabilities: $31,842,261
Net Worth: $20,202,200
Earnings: $1,687,085
Emp.: 93
Fiscal Year-end: 12/31/20
Insurance Services
N.A.I.C.S.: 524298
Khaled Mohammad Alayyan (Chm)

JERUSALEM PHARMACEUTICALS CO.
Po Box 3570 Lamalarebella Naballas Road, PO Box 3570, Al-Bireh, Palestine
Tel.: (970) 22406550
Web Site: http://wwwjepharm.ps
Rev.: $8,000,000
Emp.: 240
Pharmaceuticals Mfr
N.A.I.C.S.: 325412
Mohamed Masrouji (Chm)

JERUSALEM POST PUBLICATIONS LTD.
The Jerusalem Post Building, PO Box 81, Jerusalem, 91000, Israel
Tel.: (972) 25315666
Web Site: http://www.jpost.com
Year Founded: 1932
Sales Range: $25-49.9 Million
Emp.: 150
Newspaper Publishers
N.A.I.C.S.: 513110
David Horovitz (Editor-in-Chief)

JERUSALEM REAL ESTATE INVESTMENT COMPANY P.L.C.
Ersal St, PO Box 1876, Ramallah, Palestine
Tel.: (970) 22965215
Year Founded: 1996
JREI—(PAL)
Sales Range: Less than $1 Million
Real Estate Investment Services
N.A.I.C.S.: 531390

JERUSALEM TECHNOLOGY INVESTMENTS LTD.
Beit Ayalon 16th floor 12 Abba Hillel Silver St, PO Box 3306, Ramat Gan, 52136, Israel
Tel.: (972) 3 6486154
Web Site: http://www.jtechinv.com
Financial Investment Services
N.A.I.C.S.: 523999
Tsvika Ben-Porat (CEO & Mng Partner)

JERVOIS GLOBAL LIMITED
Suite 203 1-11 Gordon Street, Cremorne, 3121, VIC, Australia
Tel.: (61) 395830498
Web Site: https://www.jervoismining.com.au
JRV—(OTCIQ)
Rev.: $2,497,013
Assets: $93,996,189
Liabilities: $9,142,179
Net Worth: $84,854,010
Earnings: ($6,817,559)
Fiscal Year-end: 06/30/20
Gold Production & Mineral Exploration
N.A.I.C.S.: 212390
Bryce Crocker (CEO)

Subsidiaries:

eCobalt Solutions Inc. (1)
Suite 1810 - 999 West Hastings Street, Vancouver, V6C 2W2, BC, Canada (100%)
Tel.: (604) 682-6229
Web Site: http://www.ecobalt.com
Metal Mining & Exploration Services
N.A.I.C.S.: 212290
E. Rick Honsinger (Sr VP)

Subsidiary (Domestic):

Coronation Mines Limited (2)
999 Hastings Street West Suite 1810, Vancouver, V6C 2W2, BC, Canada
Tel.: (604) 682-6229
Web Site: http://www.formationmetals.com
Sales Range: $50-74.9 Million
Emp.: 4
Mining Services
N.A.I.C.S.: 212290

Subsidiary (Non-US):

Minera Terranova S.A. de C.V. (2)
Independencia 718-108, 76000, San Luis Potosi, Mexico
Tel.: (52) 444 812 5959
Gold Mining Services
N.A.I.C.S.: 212220

JES INTERNATIONAL HOLDINGS LIMITED
10 Bukit Batok Crescent 04-06 The Spire, Singapore, 658079, Singapore
Tel.: (65) 62259949   SG
Web Site: http://www.jes-intl.com
Year Founded: 2006
EG0—(SES)
Sales Range: $75-99.9 Million
Ship Building Services
N.A.I.C.S.: 336611
Daizhong Zheng (Mgr-Technical)

JESCO HOLDINGS, INC.
JESCO Shin-nakano Building 4-3-4 Chuo, Nakano-ku, Tokyo, 164-0011, Japan
Tel.: (81) 333520811
Web Site: https://www.jesco.co.jp
1434—(TKS)
Rev.: $92,080,880
Assets: $110,305,480
Liabilities: $68,345,360
Net Worth: $41,960,120
Earnings: $6,294,640
Emp.: 13
Fiscal Year-end: 08/31/24
Holding Company
N.A.I.C.S.: 551112
Toshihiro Matsumoto (Chm & CEO)

Subsidiaries:

JESCO CNS CO., LTD. (1)
4-3-4 Chuo Nakano-Ku, Tokyo, 164-0011, Japan
Tel.: (81) 363048021
Wireless Communication Equipment Mfr
N.A.I.C.S.: 334220
Eisaku Akiyama (Mng Dir)

Jesco Hoa Binh Engineering JSC (1)
9th Floor South Building - 60 Truong Son Street Ward 2 Tan Binh Dist, Ho Chi Minh City, Vietnam
Tel.: (84) 838489192
Web Site: http://www.jescohoabinh.com
Air Conditioning System Installation Services
N.A.I.C.S.: 238220
Quoc Duy Le (Chm)

Jescobina M Sdn. Bhd. (1)
Wisma Low Siew Eng, Kuala Lumpur, 56100, Malaysia
Tel.: (60) 392006313
Electrical Contracting Services
N.A.I.C.S.: 238210

JESS-LINK PRODUCTS CO., LTD.
9F No 176 Jian 1st Rd, Zhonghe Dist, New Taipei City, 235, Taiwan
Tel.: (886) 282271658
Web Site: http://www.jpcco.com.tw
6197—(TAI)
Rev.: $162,272,632
Assets: $175,088,747
Liabilities: $61,158,080
Net Worth: $113,930,667
Earnings: $21,593,871
Fiscal Year-end: 12/31/23
Electronics & Computer Peripherals Mfr
N.A.I.C.S.: 334112

Subsidiaries:

ASKA TECHNOLOGIES (KS) INC. (1)
No 536 Gucheng Road, Bacheng Town, Kunshan, Jiangsu, China

INTERNATIONAL PUBLIC

Tel.: (86) 51257650288
Web Site: http://www.jpcco.com.tw
Sales Range: $200-249.9 Million
Emp.: 1,000
Connector Mfr
N.A.I.C.S.: 334417

CELESTA INTERNATIONAL ELECTRONICS CO., LTD. (1)
3F Building 2 Yizhongli Industry Park Langshan 1 Rd, Northern Area Shenzhen Hi-Tech Industrial Park, Shenzhen, Guangdong, China
Tel.: (86) 75586141678
Web Site: http://www.celesta.com.cn
Sales Range: $25-49.9 Million
Emp.: 50
Electronic Components Mfr
N.A.I.C.S.: 334419

HUNG FU(SAMOA) INTERNATIONAL CO.,LTD (1)
Chu Tang Chin Chiao Tang Industrial Zone, FengGang, Dongguan, Guangdong, China
Tel.: (86) 769 87757688
Web Site: http://www.jpcco.com.tw
Sales Range: $400-449.9 Million
Emp.: 1,800
Electronic Products Mfr
N.A.I.C.S.: 334417

Hung Dun Electronics Co., Ltd. (1)
Chu Tang Chin Chiao Tang Industrial Zone, Feng Ging, Dongguan, 518048, Guangdong, China
Tel.: (86) 769 8775 7688
Web Site: http://www.hungfu.com.tw
Electrical Cable Distr
N.A.I.C.S.: 423610

Hung Fu Electronics Co., Ltd. (1)
1st Floor No 362-1 Section 2 Zhongshan Road, Zhonghe District, Taipei, 235, Taiwan
Tel.: (886) 222446100
Web Site: http://www.hungfu.com.tw
Electrical Cables Mfr
N.A.I.C.S.: 423610

JPC CABLE & WIRE INC. (1)
Tu Qiao Qing Xi Town, Dongguan, Guang Dong, China
Tel.: (86) 769 82015341
Web Site: http://www.jpcco.com.tw
Sales Range: $50-74.9 Million
Emp.: 150
Electronic Products Mfr
N.A.I.C.S.: 334417

Tai Kun (DG) Electronics Hardware Co., Limited (1)
No 4 ChangQing 3 Road LuDong administration Region, HuMeng Town, Dongguan, 523907, GuangDong, China
Tel.: (86) 769 85158202
Sales Range: $25-49.9 Million
Emp.: 80
Metal Processing Services
N.A.I.C.S.: 331420

TopSeed Technology Corp. (1)
9F 3 No 16 Jian Ba Road, Zhonghe, Chung Ho, Taipei, 235, Taiwan
Tel.: (886) 282263811
Web Site: http://www.topseed.com.tw
Consumer Electronics Product Mfr
N.A.I.C.S.: 334290

JESSOPS PLC
Jessop House 98 Scudamore Road, Leicester, LE3 1TZ, United Kingdom
Tel.: (44) 3448004444
Web Site: http://www.jessops.com
Sales Range: $350-399.9 Million
Emp.: 2,322
Photographic Equipment Retailer
N.A.I.C.S.: 449210
Andrew Hannan (Dir-Buying)

Subsidiaries:

The Jessop Group Limited (1)
98 Scudamore Rd, Leicester, LE3 1TZ, Leicestershire, United Kingdom
Tel.: (44) 1162326000
Web Site: http://www.jessops.com
Sales Range: $50-74.9 Million
Emp.: 90
Photo Imaging Products Retailer

AND PRIVATE COMPANIES   JETPAK TOP HOLDING AB

N.A.I.C.S.: 423410
Trevor Moore *(CEO)*

JESSY VENTURES CORP.
605-815 Hornby Street, Vancouver, V6Z 2E6, BC, Canada
Tel.: (778) 388-5258
W85—(DEU)
Assets: $1,449,495
Liabilities: $72,916
Net Worth: $1,376,579
Earnings: ($530,137)
Emp.: 6
Fiscal Year-end: 04/30/24
Business Consulting Services
N.A.I.C.S.: 522299
Anthony Zelen *(CEO)*

JET AIRWAYS (INDIA) LTD.
Siroya Centre Sahar Airport Road Andheri East, Mumbai, 400 099, Maharashtra, India
Tel.: (91) 2261211000   In
Web Site: https://www.jetairways.com
Year Founded: 1993
532617—(BOM)
Sales Range: $1-4.9 Billion
Airline Transportation & Leasing Services
N.A.I.C.S.: 481111
Prabh Sharan Singh *(Chief Digital Officer)*

JET ALU MAROC SA
78 Quartier Industriel de Takadoum, Rabat, Morocco
Tel.: (212) 537 74 92 92
Web Site: http://www.jet-contractors.com
Year Founded: 1992
Aluminium Products Mfr
N.A.I.C.S.: 332999
Mohamed Adil Rtabi *(Chm, CEO & Mng Dir)*

JET FREIGHT LOGISTICS LIMITED
705-706 Wing C Pramukh Plaza Cardinal Gracias Road, Chakala Andheri East, Mumbai, 400099, India
Tel.: (91) 2261043700
Web Site: https://www.jfll.com
Year Founded: 1986
543420—(BOM)
Rev.: $51,801,668
Assets: $19,058,227
Liabilities: $11,289,938
Net Worth: $7,768,290
Earnings: ($50,007)
Emp.: 237
Fiscal Year-end: 03/31/23
Logistic Services
N.A.I.C.S.: 481112
Richard Francis Theknath *(Chm & Mng Dir)*

JET INFRAVENTURE LTD
Office No 1 1st Floor Nandanvan Apartment E Wing Kandivali Link Road, Opp Laljipada Police Chowki Kandivali W, Mumbai, 400 067, India
Tel.: (91) 2228676233
Web Site: https://www.jetinfra.com
Year Founded: 2001
538794—(BOM)
Rev.: $68,646
Assets: $1,087,041
Liabilities: $335,993
Net Worth: $751,048
Earnings: ($53,204)
Emp.: 5
Fiscal Year-end: 03/31/21
Residential & Commercial Construction
N.A.I.C.S.: 236116
George Mattappilly *(Chm)*

JET INTERNATIONAL TRAVEL CO., LTD.
359/2-3 Soi Ekamai Sukhumvit 63 Rd, Klongton Nua Wattana, Bangkok, 10110, Thailand
Tel.: (66) 27115454
Web Site: http://www.jetintertravel.com
Year Founded: 1983
Provider of Travel Agency Services
N.A.I.C.S.: 561510

JET KNITWEARS LTD.
119/410 B1 Darshanpurwa, Kanpur, Uttar Pradesh, India
Tel.: (91) 9621363636
Web Site: https://www.jetlycot.com
JETKNIT—(NSE)
Rev.: $4,383,059
Assets: $4,856,328
Liabilities: $2,226,305
Net Worth: $2,630,022
Earnings: $145,243
Emp.: 49
Fiscal Year-end: 03/31/23
Textile Product Mfr & Distr
N.A.I.C.S.: 313310
Balram Kumar Narula *(Mng Dir)*

JET2 PLC
Low Fare Finder House Leeds Bradford Airport, Leeds, LS19 7TU, United Kingdom
Tel.: (44) 8716640300   UK
Web Site: https://www.jet2plc.com
Year Founded: 1971
JET2—(AIM)
Rev.: $6,247,076,850
Assets: $5,617,342,710
Liabilities: $4,360,853,070
Net Worth: $1,256,489,640
Earnings: $360,911,880
Fiscal Year-end: 03/31/23
Aviation Services & Fresh Food Distr
N.A.I.C.S.: 481111
Stephen Heapy *(CEO)*

Subsidiaries:

Fowler Welch-Coolchain BV   (1)
Herenlaan 27, 3155 DC, Maasland, Netherlands
Tel.: (31) 174631888
Web Site: http://www.fowler-welch.co.uk
Sales Range: $25-49.9 Million
Emp.: 4
Food Transport & Distribution
N.A.I.C.S.: 488510
Bas de Koning *(Gen Mgr)*

JETBEST CORP.
No 173 2 Dahu Rd, Xiangshan Dist, Hsinchu, 30093, Taiwan
Tel.: (886) 35181666
Web Site: https://www.jetbest.com
4741—(TPE)
Rev.: $22,653,034
Assets: $36,535,097
Liabilities: $7,352,500
Net Worth: $29,182,597
Earnings: $1,387,800
Emp.: 200
Fiscal Year-end: 12/31/22
Inkjet Inks Mfr
N.A.I.C.S.: 325910
Yi Ching Lu *(Chm & Gen Mgr)*

JETCAM INTERNATIONAL LTD.
9 Blvd Charles 3rd, Monaco, MC98000, Monaco
Tel.: (377) 97971640
Web Site: http://www.jetcam.com
Year Founded: 1986
Sales Range: $1-9.9 Million
Software Development Services
N.A.I.C.S.: 541512
Martin Bailey *(Gen Mgr)*

JETCON CORPORATION LIMITED
2 Sandringham Ave 10, Kingston, Jamaica
Tel.: (876) 9202277
Web Site:
    https://www.jetconcars.com
Year Founded: 1991
JETCON—(JAM)
Rev.: $4,367,177
Assets: $4,510,609
Liabilities: $759,000
Net Worth: $3,751,609
Earnings: ($46,740)
Emp.: 30
Fiscal Year-end: 12/31/20
Automotive Retailer
N.A.I.C.S.: 441110
Andrew Jackson *(Mng Dir)*

JETEC ELECTRONICS CO., LTD.
No 11 Furen Street, West District, Taichung, 403, Taiwan
Tel.: (886) 423729418   TW
Web Site: http://www.jetec.com.tw
Year Founded: 1983
Industrial Sensory & Measurement Equipment Distr
N.A.I.C.S.: 423830
Kuan Pin Chen *(CEO)*

JETEMA CO., LTD.
1283-4 Gagok-Ri Jijeong-Myeon, Wonju, Gangwon-do, Korea (South)
Tel.: (82) 25721331
Web Site: http://www.jetema.com
Year Founded: 2009
216080—(KRS)
Rev.: $35,277,259
Assets: $144,467,210
Liabilities: $100,789,160
Net Worth: $43,678,049
Earnings: $1,115,988
Emp.: 193
Fiscal Year-end: 12/31/22
Pharmaceutical Product Mfr & Distr
N.A.I.C.S.: 325412
Kim Jaeyoung *(Pres & Co-CEO)*

JETION SOLAR HOLDINGS LIMITED
No 1011 Zhencheng Road, Shengang, Jiangyin, Jiangsu, China
Tel.: (86) 51086687300   CN
Web Site: http://www.jetionsolar.com
Year Founded: 2004
Sales Range: $150-199.9 Million
Solar Cell Mfr
N.A.I.C.S.: 334413
Wen Yan Xu *(CEO)*

Subsidiaries:

Jetion Solar Holdings Limited - Nantong Factory   (1)
Haian Industry Park, Hai'an, Nantong, 226600, Jiangsu, China
Tel.: (86) 513 88785988
Solar Cell Mfr
N.A.I.C.S.: 334413

JETIX EUROPE
Bergweg 50, 1217, Hilversum, Netherlands
Tel.: (31) 2082223600
Web Site: http://www.jetixeurope.com
Rev.: $187,838,000
Assets: $358,330,000
Liabilities: $109,015,000
Net Worth: $249,315,000
Earnings: $19,759,000
Fiscal Year-end: 09/30/05
Broadcasting Services
N.A.I.C.S.:

JETKING INFOTRAIN LTD.
434 Bussa Udyog Bhavan T J Road Near Sewri Bus Terminus, Sewri W, Mumbai, 400015, India
Tel.: (91) 7666830000
Web Site: https://www.jetking.com
517063—(BOM)
Rev.: $2,451,185
Assets: $6,012,511
Liabilities: $655,555
Net Worth: $5,356,956
Earnings: $236,978
Emp.: 121
Fiscal Year-end: 03/31/22
Educational Support Services
N.A.I.C.S.: 611710
Suresh G. Bharwani *(Chm & Co-Mng Dir)*

JETMALL SPICES & MASALA LIMITED
No 33/1 Ritherdon Road, Vepery, Chennai, 600007, Tamil Nadu, India
Tel.: (91) 9884066677
Web Site: https://jetmallltd.in
Year Founded: 1947
543286—(BOM)
Rev.: $473,473
Assets: $1,235,106
Liabilities: $69,708
Net Worth: $1,165,398
Earnings: $35,070
Fiscal Year-end: 03/31/23
Food Products Distr
N.A.I.C.S.: 424420
Ratanchand Lodha *(Mng Dir)*

JETPAK TOP HOLDING AB
Tornvagen 17A, Box 3009, Arlanda, 190 60, Solna, 169 03, Sweden
Tel.: (46) 855585220
Web Site: https://jetpakgroup.com
Year Founded: 1979
JETPAK—(OMX)
Rev.: $114,198,207
Assets: $120,610,301
Liabilities: $41,589,630
Net Worth: $79,020,671
Earnings: $8,141,092
Emp.: 230
Fiscal Year-end: 12/31/22
Logistic Services
N.A.I.C.S.: 488510
Kenneth Marx *(CEO)*

Subsidiaries:

Jetpak Belgium B.V.   (1)
Bedrijvenzone Machelen Cargo 733, 1830, Machelen, Belgium
Tel.: (32) 23002424
Airport Shuttle Services
N.A.I.C.S.: 531190

Jetpak Goteborg AB   (1)
Kryptongatan 14, 431 53, Molndal, Sweden
Tel.: (46) 31670400
Freight Transportation Services
N.A.I.C.S.: 561910

Jetpak Group AB   (1)
Tornvagen 17A, Arlanda, 19060, Stockholm, Sweden
Tel.: (46) 775700000
Web Site: https://jetpak.com
Courier Service
N.A.I.C.S.: 513199

Jetpak Handling A/S   (1)
Kystvejen 16B, 2770, Kastrup, Denmark
Tel.: (45) 36321100
Courier Service
N.A.I.C.S.: 513199

Jetpak Helsinki OY   (1)
Rahtikuja 1A, 01530, Vantaa, Finland
Tel.: (358) 97277180
Freight Transportation Services
N.A.I.C.S.: 561910

Jetpak Malmo AB   (1)
Travbanegatan 4, 213 77, Malmo, Sweden
Tel.: (46) 4080000
Freight Transportation Services

JETPAK TOP HOLDING AB

Jetpak Top Holding AB—(Continued)
N.A.I.C.S.: 561910

Jetpak Oslo AS (1)
Fridtjof Nansensvej, 2060, Gardermoen, Norway
Tel.: (47) 91509899
Freight Transportation Services
N.A.I.C.S.: 561910

Jetpak Stockholm AB
Solna Strandvag 3, 171 54, Solna, Sweden
Tel.: (46) 812021405
Freight Transportation Services
N.A.I.C.S.: 561910

JETWAY INFORMATION CO., LTD.
9F No 207 Sec 3 Beixin Rd, Xindian Dist, Taipei, 23143, Taiwan
Tel.: (886) 289132711
Web Site: https://www.jetwayipc.com
6161—(TPE)
Rev.: $49,610,973
Assets: $59,539,769
Liabilities: $13,680,649
Net Worth: $45,859,120
Earnings: $4,386,599
Fiscal Year-end: 12/31/20
Electronic Computer Mfr
N.A.I.C.S.: 334111

JETWELL COMPUTER CO., LTD.
No 1163 Minzu 1st Rd, Zuoying Dist, Kaohsiung, 81368, Taiwan
Tel.: (886) 73458011
Web Site: http://www.jetwell.com.tw
Year Founded: 1991
3147—(TPE)
Rev.: $130,454,065
Assets: $98,543,016
Liabilities: $56,873,669
Net Worth: $41,669,347
Earnings: $9,411,131
Fiscal Year-end: 12/31/23
Information Technology Services
N.A.I.C.S.: 541512
Chih-Chung Li *(Chm)*

JETWING SYMPHONY PLC
Jetwing House II 4626 Nawam Mawatha, 2, Colombo, 2, Sri Lanka
Tel.: (94) 112345700
Web Site: https://www.jetwinghotels.com
Year Founded: 2007
JETS—(COL)
Rev.: $7,043,557
Assets: $34,693,654
Liabilities: $23,635,664
Net Worth: $11,057,990
Earnings: ($2,104,440)
Emp.: 690
Fiscal Year-end: 03/31/23
Hotel & Restaurant Operator
N.A.I.C.S.: 721110
Shiromal Cooray *(Chm)*

JEUDAN A/S
Bredgade 30, Koebenhavn K, 1260, Copenhagen, Denmark
Tel.: (45) 70106070
Web Site: https://www.jeudan.dk
JDAN—(CSE)
Rev.: $289,476,350
Assets: $5,362,814,892
Liabilities: $3,437,282,054
Net Worth: $1,925,532,838
Earnings: $486,022,486
Emp.: 637
Fiscal Year-end: 12/31/22
Real Estate Services
N.A.I.C.S.: 531210

JEUGIA CORPORATION
4F Sound Stage 61 Benkeiishi-Cho Sanjodori Teramachi Nishiiru, Nakagyo-ku, Kyoto, 604-8036, Japan
Tel.: (81) 75 2551566
Web Site: http://www.jeugia.co.jp
Year Founded: 1952
Rev.: $66,853,740
Assets: $45,934,200
Liabilities: $25,821,000
Net Worth: $20,113,200
Earnings: $199,320
Fiscal Year-end: 03/31/19
Musical Instrument Store Operator
N.A.I.C.S.: 459140

JF TECHNOLOGY BERHAD
Lot 6 Jalan Teknologi 3/6 Taman Sains Selangor 1 Kota Damansara, 47810, Petaling Jaya, Selangor, Malaysia
Tel.: (60) 361408668
Web Site: https://www.jf-technology.com
JFTECH—(KLS)
Rev.: $9,597,672
Assets: $31,641,058
Liabilities: $3,485,926
Net Worth: $28,155,132
Earnings: $2,488,042
Emp.: 134
Fiscal Year-end: 06/30/23
Holding Company; Electronic Products & Components Mfr
N.A.I.C.S.: 551112
Wei Kuong Foong *(Mng Dir)*

Subsidiaries:

J Foong Technologies Sdn. Bhd. (1)
Lot 6 Jalan Teknologi 3/6 Taman Sains Selangor 1, Kota Damansara, 47810, Petaling Jaya, Selangor, Malaysia
Tel.: (60) 361408668
Interconnect Test Probe Mfr
N.A.I.C.S.: 334516

JF Microtechnology Sdn. Bhd. (1)
Lot 6 Jalan Teknologi 3/6 Taman Sains Selangor 1 Kota Damansara, Petaling Jaya, 47810, Selangor, Malaysia
Tel.: (60) 361408668
Web Site: http://www.jf-technology.com
Emp.: 80
Electronic Components Mfr
N.A.I.C.S.: 334419

JF WEALTH HOLDINGS LTD.
3-5/F Yintech Finance Center 88 Xumin East Road, Qingpu District, Shanghai, China
Tel.: (86) 62160150919
9636—(HKG)
Rev.: $283,460,103
Assets: $208,850,356
Liabilities: $127,737,459
Net Worth: $81,112,898
Earnings: $70,561,478
Emp.: 2,375
Fiscal Year-end: 12/31/22
Holding Company
N.A.I.C.S.: 551112
Di Qian *(CFO)*

JFE HOLDINGS, INC.
2-2-3 Uchisaiwaicho, Chiyoda-ku, Tokyo, 100-0011, Japan
Tel.: (81) 335974321
Web Site: https://www.jfe-holdings.co.jp
Year Founded: 2002
5411—(TKS)
Rev.: $34,204,317,520
Assets: $38,040,312,040
Liabilities: $21,260,688,230
Net Worth: $16,779,623,810
Earnings: $1,304,952,810
Emp.: 62,218
Fiscal Year-end: 03/31/24
Holding Company
N.A.I.C.S.: 551112
Yoshihisa Kitano *(Pres & CEO)*

Subsidiaries:

AGRICOMPASS Inc. (1)
2-6-2 Otemachi Nihon Bldg, Chiyoda-Ku, Tokyo, 100-0004, Japan
Tel.: (81) 3 3242 8527
Web Site: http://www.agricompass.co.jp
Agricultural Supplies Distr
N.A.I.C.S.: 424910

California Steel Industries, Inc. (1)
1 California Steel Way, Fontana, CA 92335 (50%)
Tel.: (909) 350-6300
Web Site: https://www.californiasteel.com
Emp.: 1,000
Flat Rolled Steel & Steel Pipe Products Mfr; Owned 50% by Companhia Vale do Rio Doce & 50% by JFE Steel Corporation
N.A.I.C.S.: 331221
Ricardo Bernardes *(CFO & Exec VP-Comml)*

DAIWA KOHTAI CO., LTD. (1)
Nihonbashi Tachibana Building 3-6-11 Higashi Nihonbashi, Chuo-Ku, Tokyo, 103-0004, Japan
Tel.: (81) 356406311
Web Site: https://www.daiwa-kohtai.co.jp
Emp.: 150
Steel Product Distr
N.A.I.C.S.: 423510

DAIWA STEEL CORP. (1)
1-1 Mizushimakawasakidoori, Kurashiki, 712-8074, Okayama, Japan
Tel.: (81) 864474224
Web Site: http://www.daiwa-steel.com
Steel Products Mfr & Distr
N.A.I.C.S.: 331110

Fuji Kako Co., Ltd. (1)
90 Maeda, Fuji, 416-8655, Shizuoka, Japan
Tel.: (81) 545611370
Web Site: http://www.fujikako.co.jp
Emp.: 130
Synthetic Resin Pipe Mfr
N.A.I.C.S.: 326122

GALVATEX CORP. (1)
3 Takaya Shinmachi, Ichikawa, 272-0011, Chiba, Japan
Tel.: (81) 473281171
Web Site: https://www.gtx.co.jp
Emp.: 188
Steel Pipe & Tube Mfr
N.A.I.C.S.: 331210

JAPAN RECYCLING CO. (1)
1 Kawasakicho Jfe Steal Higashinihon Seitetsusho Chibachikunai, Chuo-Ku, Chiba, 260-0835, Japan
Tel.: (81) 432624716
Industrial Waste Recycling Services
N.A.I.C.S.: 562920

JFE ADVANTECH CO., LTD. (1)
3-48 Takahata-cho, Nishinomiya, 663-8202, Hyogo, Japan
Tel.: (81) 358255577
Web Site: http://www.jfe-advantech.co.jp
Emp.: 290
Ultrasonic Measurement System Mfr
N.A.I.C.S.: 334519
Takuya Yoshii *(Pres)*

JFE Advanced Light Corporation (1)
2-1 Suehirocho Jfe Engineering Nigo-Kan 1f, Tsurumi-Ku, Yokohama, 230-0045, Kanagawa, Japan
Tel.: (81) 45 505 7467
Web Site: http://www.jfe-adv.co.jp
Street Lighting Installation Services
N.A.I.C.S.: 238210

JFE BARS & SHAPES CORP. (1)
Shimbashi Sumitomo Bldg 5th floor 5-11-3 Shimbashi, Minato-Ku, Tokyo, 105-0004, Japan
Tel.: (81) 357773811
Web Site: https://www.jfe-bs.co.jp
Emp.: 870
Steel Billets Mfr
N.A.I.C.S.: 331110
Makoto Watanabe *(Pres)*

JFE Business Support Yokohama Corporation (1)
2-1 Suehirocho, Tsurumi-Ku, Yokohama, 230-0045, Kanagawa, Japan

INTERNATIONAL PUBLIC

Tel.: (81) 455058942
Web Site: https://www.jfe-bsy.co.jp
Emp.: 253
Information Technology Support Services
N.A.I.C.S.: 561990

JFE CHEMICAL CORPORATION (1)
4F JFE Kuramae Bldg 2-17-4 Kuramae, Taito-ku, Tokyo, 111-0051, Japan
Tel.: (81) 358206500
Web Site: https://www.jfe-chem.com
Emp.: 583
Specialty Chemicals Mfr & Whslr
N.A.I.C.S.: 325998

Plant (Domestic):

JFE CHEMICAL CORPORATION - Chiba Plant (2)
1 Kawasaki-cho, Chuo-ku, Chiba, 260-0835, Japan
Tel.: (81) 43 262 2088
Web Site: http://www.jfe-chem.com
Specialty Chemicals Mfr
N.A.I.C.S.: 325998

JFE CHEMICAL CORPORATION - Kasaoka Plant (2)
9-2 Kokan-cho, Kasaoka, 714-0063, Okayama, Japan
Tel.: (81) 865 66 3911
Web Site: http://www.jfe-chem.com
Chemical Products Mfr
N.A.I.C.S.: 325998

JFE CHEMICAL CORPORATION - Keihin Plant (2)
1-1 Ogishima, Kawasaki-ku, Kawasaki, 210-0855, Kanagawa, Japan
Tel.: (81) 44 322 1754
Chemical Products Mfr
N.A.I.C.S.: 325998

Subsidiary (Domestic):

JFE CHEMICAL CORPORATION - Kurashiki Plant (2)
1 Mizushima Kawasaki-dori, Kurashiki, 712-8074, Okayama, Japan
Tel.: (81) 864473805
Chemical Products Mfr
N.A.I.C.S.: 325998

JFE Civil Engineering & Construction Corp. (1)
2-17-4 Kuramae JFE Kuramae Building 5F, Taito-Ku, Tokyo, 111-0051, Japan
Tel.: (81) 338643670
Web Site: https://www.jfe-civil.com
Emp.: 735
Civil Engineering Construction Services
N.A.I.C.S.: 237990

JFE Container Co., Ltd. (1)
9F Sarugakucho SS Bldg 1-5-15 Sarugakucho, Chiyoda-ku, Tokyo, 101-0064, Japan
Tel.: (81) 352818512
Web Site: http://www.jfecon.jp
Rev.: $265,880,560
Assets: $386,861,200
Liabilities: $91,137,200
Net Worth: $295,724,000
Earnings: $17,724,080
Fiscal Year-end: 03/31/2021
Metal Container Mfr & Whlsr
N.A.I.C.S.: 332431
Shichinobu Nasu *(Pres & CEO)*

JFE ELECTRICAL & CONTROL SYSTEMS, INC. (1)
1-9-9 Shibadaimon Nomurafudosanshibadaimon Bldg 10f, Minato-Ku, Tokyo, 105-0012, Japan
Tel.: (81) 354058855
Web Site: http://www.jfe-densei.co.jp
Mechanical Engineering Services
N.A.I.C.S.: 541330

JFE ELECTRICAL STEEL CO., LTD. (1)
1-6-20 Dojima Doshima Abanza 10f, Kita-Ku, Osaka, 530-0003, Japan
Tel.: (81) 663420630
Iron & Steel Products Mfr
N.A.I.C.S.: 331110

JFE Engineering Corporation (1)
2-2-3 Uchisaiwaicho 22nd floor of Hibiya Kokusai Building, Chiyoda-ku, Tokyo, 100-

AND PRIVATE COMPANIES

JFE HOLDINGS, INC.

0011, Japan **(100%)**
Tel.: (81) 335397250
Web Site: http://www.jfe-eng.co.jp
Emp.: 10,000
Steelmaking, Engineering, Information Technology, LSIs & Urban Development
N.A.I.C.S.: 541330
Hajime Oshita *(Pres & CEO)*

Subsidiary (US):

AnyTech Inc. **(2)**
14433 Settlers Landing Way, North Potomac, MD 20878
Tel.: (301) 294-6206
Web Site: http://www.anytech-inc.com
Engineering Services
N.A.I.C.S.: 541330

Subsidiary (Domestic):

Asukasoken Co., Ltd. **(2)**
4-1-8 Higashi-Shinagawa, Shinagawa-ku, Tokyo, 140-0002, Japan
Tel.: (81) 334740881
Web Site: http://www.asksoken.co.jp
Emp.: 299
Gas Pipeline Construction Services
N.A.I.C.S.: 237120

Joint Venture (Non-US):

Companhia Nipo-Brasileira de Pelotizacao-NIBRASCO **(2)**
Ponta Do Tubarao, PO Box 334, 29090-900, Vitoria, Espirito Santo, Brazil **(50%)**
Tel.: (55) 2733335179
Web Site: http://www.cale.com
Iron Ore Pellet Manufacturer
N.A.I.C.S.: 212210

Subsidiary (Domestic):

J Farm Corporation **(2)**
6-312 Kashiwahara, Tomakomai, 059-1362, Hokkaido, Japan
Tel.: (81) 144841850
Web Site: http://www.jfarm-tomakomai.co.jp
Agricultural Product Mfr & Distr
N.A.I.C.S.: 333111

Subsidiary (Non-US):

J&M Steel Solutions Co., Ltd. **(2)**
No 237 Shukhinthar Mayopat Road Block No 10, Thaketa Township, Yangon, Myanmar
Tel.: (95) 194101234
Web Site: https://www.jandmss.com
Emp.: 600
Steel Sheet Mfr
N.A.I.C.S.: 332322

Subsidiary (Domestic):

J&T Recycling Corporation **(2)**
3-1 Benten-cho, Tsurumi-ku, Yokohama, 230-0044, Kanagawa, Japan
Tel.: (81) 455023860
Web Site: https://www.jt-kankyo.co.jp
Emp.: 1,009
General Domestic Waste Services
N.A.I.C.S.: 562119
Tetsuo Tsuyuguchi *(Pres)*

Affiliate (Non-US):

JFE Engineering (M) Sdn. Bhd. **(2)**
Suite 9 01 9 02 9th Floor Menara JKG No 282 Jalan Raja Laut, 50350, Kuala Lumpur, Malaysia **(100%)**
Tel.: (60) 322027272
Web Site: https://www.jfem.com.my
Emp.: 40
Steel Production
N.A.I.C.S.: 324199
Shu Suesiro *(Mng Dir)*

Subsidiary (Non-US):

JFE Engineering Consulting (Shanghai) Co., Ltd. **(2)**
Rm 1501 Ruijin Mansion No 205 Maoming South Road, Luwan, Shanghai, 200020, China
Tel.: (86) 2164730777
Web Site: http://www.jfe-eng.co.jp
Engineeering Services
N.A.I.C.S.: 541330
Hideki Ipo *(Mng Dir)*

Branch (Non-US):

JFE Engineering Corporation-Yangon Branch **(2)**
05-05 05-06 Union Business Centre Nat Mauk Road Bo Cho Quarter, Bahan T/S, Yangon, Myanmar **(100%)**
Tel.: (95) 18603457
Web Site: http://www.nkk.co.jp
Steel Products Mfr
N.A.I.C.S.: 324199

Subsidiary (Domestic):

JFE Environmental Service Corporation **(2)**
6F Building 1 JFE Engineering 3 Bentencho, Tsurumi-ku, Yokohama, 230-0044, Kanagawa, Japan
Tel.: (81) 455022226
Web Site: http://www.jfe-esc.co.jp
General Domestic Waste Services
N.A.I.C.S.: 562119

JFE KANKYO Corporation **(2)**
3-1 Bentencho, Tsurumi-ku, Yokohama, 230-0044, Kanagawa, Japan
Tel.: (81) 455057949
Web Site: http://www.jfe-kankyo.co.jp
Sales Range: $150-199.9 Million
Emp.: 830
Industrial Waste Management Services
N.A.I.C.S.: 562998
Masaaki Sakurai *(Pres & Dir)*

JFE Pipeline Engineering Corporation **(2)**
3-1 Bentencho, Tsurumi-ku, Yokohama, 230-0044, Kanagawa, Japan
Tel.: (81) 455057958
Web Site: http://www.jpe-corp.jp
Gas Pipeline Construction Services
N.A.I.C.S.: 237120

Subsidiary (Non-US):

JFE Techno Manila, Inc. **(2)**
23rd flr Robinsons Cyberscape Alpha Bldg Sapphire and Garnet Rd, Ortigas Center, Pasig, 1605, Philippines
Tel.: (63) 286542548
Web Site: https://www.jfetechnomanila.com
Engineering Services
N.A.I.C.S.: 541330
Makoto Yamagishi *(Pres)*

Subsidiary (Domestic):

Mie Data Craft Co., Ltd. **(2)**
1 Kumoide Kokancho, Tsu, 514-0301, Mie, Japan
Tel.: (81) 592463700
Web Site: https://www.mdc-web.com
Emp.: 52
Document Management Services
N.A.I.C.S.: 541611

Subsidiary (US):

NKK-Steel Engineering, Inc. **(2)**
910 Sheraton Dr Ste 400, Mars, PA 16046-9414
Tel.: (412) 772-3242
Web Site: http://www.jfe-holdings.co.jp
N.A.I.C.S.: 324199

Subsidiary (Non-US):

PT. JFE Engineering Indonesia **(2)**
Tel.: (62) 2127881740
Web Site: http://www.jfeei.co.id
Gas Pipeline Construction Services
N.A.I.C.S.: 237120

Standardkessel Baumgarte Holding GmbH **(2)**
Web Site: http://www.standardkessel-baumgarte.com
Engineeering Services
N.A.I.C.S.: 541330

Standardkessel Power Systems Holding GmbH **(2)**
Baldusstrasse 13, 47138, Duisburg, Germany **(100%)**
Tel.: (49) 2034520
Web Site: http://www.standardkessel-baumgarte.com
Emp.: 225

Holding Company; Industrial Boiler Systems & Components Mfr, Whslr, Installation & Maintenance Services
N.A.I.C.S.: 551112
Lutz Reinery *(Member-Mgmt Bd)*

Subsidiary (Domestic):

Baumgarte Boiler Systems GmbH **(3)**
Senner Strasse 115, Bielefeld, 33647, Germany
Tel.: (49) 52194060
Boiler Technologies
N.A.I.C.S.: 332410

Subsidiary (Non-US):

Environment & Power Company Ltd. **(3)**
8147 King Faisal St, Al-Rawabi District, Al Khobar, 34421, Saudi Arabia
Tel.: (966) 38588510
Engineeering Services
N.A.I.C.S.: 541330

Subsidiary (Domestic):

Standardkessel Baumgarte Contracting GmbH **(3)**
Baldusstr 13, 47138, Duisburg, Germany
Tel.: (49) 2034520
Power Plant Construction Services
N.A.I.C.S.: 237990
Mario Scharf *(Mgr)*

Subsidiary (Non-US):

Standardkessel Baumgarte UK Ltd. **(3)**
Century Business Centre Manvers Way, Rotherham, S63 5DA, United Kingdom
Tel.: (44) 1709300160
Power Plant Construction Services
N.A.I.C.S.: 237990

Standardkessel GmbH **(3)**
Tel.: (49) 2034520
Web Site: http://www.standardkessel-baumgarte.com
Industrial Boiler, Plants & Components Mfr
N.A.I.C.S.: 332410
Thomas Fink *(Member-Mgmt Bd)*

Subsidiary (Domestic):

Urban Energy Corporation **(2)**
2-1 Suehiro-cho, Tsurumi-ku, Yokohama, 230-8611, Japan
Tel.: (81) 455057878
Web Site: http://www.u-energy.jp
Eletric Power Generation Services
N.A.I.C.S.: 221118

JFE GALVANIZING & COATING CO., LTD. **(1)**
1-11-2 Osaki Gate City Osaki East Tower 9f, Shinagawa-Ku, Tokyo, 141-0032, Japan
Tel.: (81) 334931200
Web Site: http://www.jfe-kouhan.co.jp
Emp.: 493
Coated Steel Sheet Mfr & Distr
N.A.I.C.S.: 331110

JFE KOZAI CORP. **(1)**
4-10-4 Hatchobori 7th floor of Hulic Hatchobori second building, Chuo-Ku, Tokyo, 104-0032, Japan
Tel.: (81) 3 3553 5111
Web Site: http://www.jfe-kozai.com
Emp.: 263
Steel Products Mfr
N.A.I.C.S.: 331110

JFE LEASE SYSTEM CORP. **(1)**
2-17-4 Kuramae, Taito-ku, Tokyo, 111-0051, Japan
Tel.: (81) 3 3864 5235
Construction Engineering Services
N.A.I.C.S.: 541330

JFE LIFE CORPORATION **(1)**
2-17-4 Kuramae JFE Kuramae Building 7F, Taito-Ku, Tokyo, 111-0051, Japan
Tel.: (81) 338645200
Web Site: https://www.jfe-life.co.jp
Sales Range: $200-249.9 Million
Emp.: 745
General Insurance Services
N.A.I.C.S.: 524210

JFE MATERIAL CO., LTD. **(1)**
2-9-38 Shosei-machi, Imizu, 934-8550, Toyama, Japan
Tel.: (81) 766844490
Web Site: https://www.jfe-mineral.co.jp
Sales Range: $50-74.9 Million
Emp.: 220
Metal Smelting & Refining Services
N.A.I.C.S.: 331410
Nishimura Hiropumi *(Pres)*

JFE MECHANICAL CO., LTD. **(1)**
2-17-4 Kuramae, Taito-ku, Tokyo, 111-0051, Japan
Tel.: (81) 338643865
Web Site: http://www.jfe-m.co.jp
Emp.: 2,600
Mechanical Engineering, Civil & Steel Structure Construction Services
N.A.I.C.S.: 541330
Hidenori Yasuoka *(Pres)*

JFE METAL PRODUCTS & ENGINEERING INC. **(1)**
1-2-70 Konan 11F Shinagawa Season Terrace, Minato-ku, Tokyo, 103-0012, Japan
Tel.: (81) 356441200
Web Site: https://www.jfe-kenzai.co.jp
Building Materials Mfr
N.A.I.C.S.: 332311

JFE MINERAL COMPANY, LTD. **(1)**
5th Floor Sumitomofudosan Shibakoen First Building 8-2 Shiba 3-chome, Minato-ku, Tokyo, 105-0014, Japan
Tel.: (81) 354455200
Web Site: https://www.jfe-mineral.co.jp
Emp.: 100
Mineral Mining Services
N.A.I.C.S.: 212290

Unit (Domestic):

JFE MINERAL COMPANY, LTD. - ADVANCED MATERIALS WORKS **(2)**
1 Niihamacho, Chuo-ku, Chiba, 260-0835, Japan
Tel.: (81) 43 262 8792
Web Site: http://www.jfe-mineral.co.jp
Mineral Mining Services
N.A.I.C.S.: 212390

Plant (Domestic):

JFE MINERAL COMPANY, LTD. - CHIBA PLANT **(2)**
1 Kawasaki-cho, Chuo-ku, Chiba, 260-0835, Japan
Tel.: (81) 43 262 2360
Iron & Steel Mfr
N.A.I.C.S.: 331110

JFE MINERAL COMPANY, LTD. - FUKUYAMA PLANT **(2)**
1 Kokan-cho, Fukuyama, 721-0931, Hiroshima, Japan
Tel.: (81) 84 941 2333
Iron & Steel Mfr
N.A.I.C.S.: 331110

Unit (Domestic):

JFE MINERAL COMPANY, LTD. - IIDE MINING WORKS **(2)**
1211 Tenoko Iidemachi, Nishiokitama-gun, Yamagata, 999-1111, Japan
Tel.: (81) 238 75 2011
Emp.: 700
Silica Sand Mining Services
N.A.I.C.S.: 212322
Asai Junji *(Mgr)*

Plant (Domestic):

JFE MINERAL COMPANY, LTD. - KEIHIN PLANT **(2)**
1-1 Ogishima, Kawasaki-ku, Kawasaki, 210-0868, Kanagawa, Japan
Tel.: (81) 44 277 7697
Iron & Steel Mfr
N.A.I.C.S.: 331110

JFE MINERAL COMPANY, LTD. - KURASHIKI PLANT **(2)**
1 Kawasaki-Dori Mizushima, Kurashiki, 712-8074, Okayama, Japan
Tel.: (81) 86 447 4481
Calcium Silicate Fertilizer Mining Services
N.A.I.C.S.: 212390

JFE HOLDINGS, INC.

JFE Holdings, Inc.—(Continued)

Unit (Domestic):

JFE MINERAL COMPANY, LTD. - MUSASHINO MINING WORKS (2)
2160 Shimoshiraiwa Kaminaguri, Hanno, 357-0111, Saitama, Japan
Tel.: (81) 42 979 0082
Construction Material Mining Services
N.A.I.C.S.: 212321

JFE MINERAL COMPANY, LTD. - TOCHIGI MINING WORKS (2)
153 Fukahodo, Kanuma, 322-0302, Tochigi, Japan
Tel.: (81) 289753911
Web Site: http://www.jfe-mineral.co.jp
Silica Sand Mining Services
N.A.I.C.S.: 212322

Plant (Domestic):

JFE MINERAL COMPANY, LTD. - TSUKUMI PLANT (2)
6-7 Gounomototown, Tsukumi, 879-2471, Oita, Japan
Tel.: (81) 972 82 2643
Web Site: http://www.jfe-mineral.co.jp
Limestone Mining Services
N.A.I.C.S.: 212312

Unit (Domestic):

JFE MINERAL COMPANY, LTD. - YOSII MINING WORKS (2)
811 Kamishigi Yoshii-cho, Ibara, 714-2232, Okayama, Japan
Tel.: (81) 866740111
Web Site: http://www.jfe-mineral.co.jp
Limestone Mining Services
N.A.I.C.S.: 212312

JFE Mie Tech. Service Corporation (1)
1 Kumozukokancho, Tsu, 514-0301, Mie, Japan
Tel.: (81) 59 246 3550
Web Site: http://www.jfe-mts.co.jp
Business Support Services
N.A.I.C.S.: 561990
Takashi Kazumy (Gen Mgr)

JFE PIPE FITTING MFG. CO., LTD. (1)
Tel.: (81) 724450285
Web Site: http://www.jfe-pf.co.jp
Industrial Machinery Mfr & Distr
N.A.I.C.S.: 333248

JFE PLASTIC RESOURCE CORPORATION (1)
5-1 Mizuecho, Kawasaki-ku, Kawasaki, 210-0866, Kanagawa, Japan
Tel.: (81) 442995193
Web Site: https://www.jfe-plr.co.jp
Sales Range: $25-49.9 Million
Emp.: 70
Plastic Waste Recycling Services & Equipment Distr
N.A.I.C.S.: 562920
Nozomu Tamura (Pres)

JFE PRECISION CO., LTD. (1)
2-3 Kamiosemachi, Higashi-Ku, Niigata, 950-0063, Japan
Tel.: (81) 25 274 3181
Steel Products Mfr
N.A.I.C.S.: 331110

JFE SEKKEI LTD. (1)
2-17-4 Kuramae JFE Kuramae Building 3F, Taito-Ku, Tokyo, 111-0051, Japan
Tel.: (81) 358353201
Web Site: https://www.jfe-sekkei.co.jp
Emp.: 219
Civil Engineering Services
N.A.I.C.S.: 237990

JFE Shoji Trade Corporation (1)
1-9-5 Otemachi Otemachi Financial City North Tower, Chiyoda-ku, Tokyo, 100-8070, Japan (100%)
Tel.: (81) 3 5203 5053
Web Site: http://www.jfe-shoji.co.jp
Emp.: 8,565
Steel Trading, Heavy Machinery, Chemicals, Food & Construction Materials
N.A.I.C.S.: 331110
Junji Yamada (Mng Exec Officer)

Subsidiary (Domestic):

Aichi Kanzai Kogyo Corporation (2)
3-1 Kawasaki-cho, Handa, 475-0832, Aichi, Japan
Tel.: (81) 569242870
Steel Pipe Distr
N.A.I.C.S.: 423510

Subsidiary (Non-US):

Dongguan JFE Shoji Steel Products Co., Ltd. (2)
No 2 Zhenrong North Road, Wusha Community Changan Town, Dongguan, 523860, Guangdong, China
Tel.: (86) 76985543072
Steel Material Distr
N.A.I.C.S.: 423510

Guangzhou JFE Shoji Steel Products Co., Ltd. (2)
B-04 International Industry Park, Shilou Town Panyu District, Guangzhou, 511447, Guangdong, China
Tel.: (86) 2034861111
Steel Material Distr
N.A.I.C.S.: 423510

Subsidiary (Domestic):

Hanwa Kozai Co., Ltd. (2)
4th Floor Shin Osaka Dai3 Building 1-8-24 Nishimiyahara, Yodogawa-ku, Osaka, 532-0004, Japan
Tel.: (81) 663923031
Steel Material Distr
N.A.I.C.S.: 423510

Hokuriku Kogyo Corporation (2)
3545-2 Oiwake, Namerikawa, 939-0808, Toyama, Japan
Tel.: (81) 764755959
Steel Material Distr
N.A.I.C.S.: 423510

Hokuriku Steel Co., Ltd. (2)
He 106-20 Dorin-machi, Nomi, 929-0125, Ishikawa, Japan
Tel.: (81) 761551383
Steel Plate Distr
N.A.I.C.S.: 423510

Hoshi Kinzoku Corporation (2)
1-6-20 Dojima, Kita-ku, Osaka, 530-0003, Japan
Tel.: (81) 663482501
Steel Pipe Distr
N.A.I.C.S.: 423510

Subsidiary (US):

JFE Shoji America, LLC (2)
45 Broadway Fl 18 Atrium, New York, NY 10006
Tel.: (212) 841-7400
Emp.: 15
Trade Management Services
N.A.I.C.S.: 425120
Akira Yano (Mgr)

Subsidiary (Domestic):

JFE Shoji Coil Center Corporation (2)
7 Torihama-cho, kanazawa-ku, Yokohama, 236-0002, Kanagawa, Japan
Tel.: (81) 457711429
Steel Plate Distr
N.A.I.C.S.: 423510

JFE Shoji Cormec Co., Ltd. (2)
158-1 Yomogida Ishimori Nakada-cho, Tome, 987-0601, Miyagi, Japan
Tel.: (81) 220342011
Web Site: http://www.jfe-cormec.com
Emp.: 50
Electrical Equipment Mfr & Distr
N.A.I.C.S.: 335999

JFE Shoji Electrical Steel Co., Ltd. (2)
1-6-20 Dojima, Kita-ku, Osaka, 530-0003, Japan
Tel.: (81) 663420630
Steel Plate Distr
N.A.I.C.S.: 423510

JFE Shoji Electronics Corporation (2)
Shin-Otemachi Bldg 6th Floor 2-1 Otemachi 2-chome, Chiyoda-ku, Tokyo, 100-0004, Japan
Tel.: (81) 352035630
Web Site: https://www.jfe-shoji-ele.co.jp
Emp.: 189
Semiconductor Product Mfr
N.A.I.C.S.: 334413
Takaaki Yanagisawa (Pres)

JFE Shoji Jutaku Shizai Corporation (2)
6th Floor JFE Shoji Building 7-1 Otemachi 2-chome, Chiyoda-ku, Tokyo, 100-0004, Japan
Tel.: (81) 352036162
Building Materials Distr
N.A.I.C.S.: 423310

JFE Shoji Kohnan Steel Center Co., Ltd. (2)
43-1 Uozakihama-machi, Higashinada-ku, Kobe, 658-0024, Hyogo, Japan
Tel.: (81) 784536081
Steel Plate Distr
N.A.I.C.S.: 423510

JFE Shoji Machinery & Materials Corporation (2)
1st Floor JFE Shoji Building 7-1 Otemachi 2-chome, Chiyoda-ku, Tokyo, 100-0004, Japan
Tel.: (81) 352036230
Petroleum Product Distr
N.A.I.C.S.: 424720

JFE Shoji Matech Inc. (2)
3rd Floor JFE Shoji Building 7-1 Otemachi 2-chome, Chiyoda-ku, Tokyo, 100-0004, Japan
Tel.: (81) 352036280
Building Materials Distr
N.A.I.C.S.: 423310

JFE Shoji Service Corporation (2)
1st Floor JFE Shoji Building 7-1 Otemachi 2-chome, Chiyoda-ku, Tokyo, 100-0004, Japan
Tel.: (81) 352035330
Contracting Services
N.A.I.C.S.: 236220

JFE Shoji Steel Construction Materials Corporation (2)
10th Floor JFE Shoji Building 7-1 Otemachi 2-chome, Chiyoda-ku, Tokyo, 100-0004, Japan
Tel.: (81) 352036080
Steel Plate Distr
N.A.I.C.S.: 423510

Subsidiary (Non-US):

JFE Shoji Steel Hai Phong Co., Ltd. (2)
No 2 Road No 5 VSIP, Thuy Nguyen District Dinh Vu-Cat Hai Economic Zone, Haiphong, Vietnam
Tel.: (84) 2253959916
Steel Material Distr
N.A.I.C.S.: 423510

JFE Shoji Steel India Private Limited (2)
Plot No F-42 Ranjangaon Industrial Area Ranjangaon MIDC, Village Koregaon Taluka Shirur, Pune, 412220, Maharashtra, India
Tel.: (91) 2138665700
Steel Material Distr
N.A.I.C.S.: 423510

JFE Shoji Steel Malaysia Sdn. Bhd. (2)
PT 5021 Jalan 27/90 Section 27, Hicom Industrial Area, 40400, Shah Alam, Selangor, Malaysia
Tel.: (60) 351911125
Web Site: https://www.jssm.com.my
Sales Range: $50-74.9 Million
Emp.: 200
Steel Processing
N.A.I.C.S.: 331513

JFE Shoji Steel Philippines, Inc. (2)
107 Trade Ave Laguna Technopark, Bo Loma, Binan, 4024, Laguna, Philippines
Tel.: (63) 495412404
Web Site: https://jssp.ph
Sales Range: $25-49.9 Million
Emp.: 105
Steel Processing & Sales

INTERNATIONAL PUBLIC

N.A.I.C.S.: 331513

JFE Shoji Steel Service Center Bajio, S.A.P.I. de C.V. (2)
Camino El Refugio-Colonia El Nuevo Refugio, km 1 200 del Ejido Menores Silao de la Victoria, 36294, Guanajuato, Mexico
Tel.: (52) 4728009800
Steel Material Distr
N.A.I.C.S.: 423510

JFE Shoji Steel Vietnam Co., Ltd. (2)
Lot 202 Amata Industrial Park, Long Binh Ward, Bien Hoa, Dong Nai, Vietnam
Tel.: (84) 2513936461
Web Site: https://www.jssv.com.vn
Steel Products Mfr
N.A.I.C.S.: 331210

JFE Shoji Steel de Mexico S.A. de C.V. (2)
Paseo Cucapah 10515 El Lago, 22210, Tijuana, BC, Mexico
Tel.: (52) 6649694300
Web Site: https://www.jfe-shoji-steel-america.com
Sales Range: Less than $1 Million
Emp.: 165
Steel Processing & Sales Company
N.A.I.C.S.: 331513

Subsidiary (Domestic):

JFE Shoji Terre One Corporation (2)
4th Floor JFE Shoji Building 7-1 Otemachi 2-chome, Chiyoda-ku, Tokyo, 100-0004, Japan
Tel.: (81) 352036270
Civil Engineering Material Distr
N.A.I.C.S.: 423390

JFE Shoji Tinplate Center Corporation (2)
6-2 Shindenasahimachi, Daito, 574-0053, Osaka, Japan
Tel.: (81) 728709731
Steel Plate Distr
N.A.I.C.S.: 423510

Subsidiary (Non-US):

JFE Shoji Trade Australia Pty. Ltd. (2)
Suite 3/B Level 33 52 Martin Place, Sydney, 2000, NSW, Australia
Tel.: (61) 292219440
Web Site: http://www.jfe-shoji.co.jp
Sales Range: $50-74.9 Million
Emp.: 9
Trader of Steel, Heavy Machinery, Chemicals, Food & Construction Materials
N.A.I.C.S.: 424690

JFE Shoji Trade Corp. (2)
10 Anson Road 19-16 International Plaza, Singapore, 079903, Singapore
Tel.: (65) 62209188
Web Site: http://www.jfe-shoji.com.sg
Sales Range: $50-74.9 Million
Emp.: 7
Trader of Steel, Heavy Machinery, Chemicals, Food & Construction Materials
N.A.I.C.S.: 424690
Naosuke Oda (Pres & CEO)

JFE Shoji Trade Do Brasil Ltda. (2)
Av Paulista 509 Conj 301, Bela Vista, Sao Paulo, 01311-910, Brazil
Tel.: (55) 1132847839
Web Site: http://www.jfe-shoji.co.jp
Sales Range: $50-74.9 Million
Emp.: 3
Metals Service Center
N.A.I.C.S.: 423510

JFE Shoji Trade Korea Ltd. (2)
16th Floor Young Poong Building 41 Cheonggyecheon-ro, Jongno-gu, Seoul, 03188, Korea (South)
Tel.: (82) 239977275
Web Site: http://www.jfe-shoji.co.jp
Sales Range: $50-74.9 Million
Emp.: 25
Steel, Heavy Machinery, Chemicals, Food & Construction Materials
N.A.I.C.S.: 424690

JFE Shoji Trade Philippines, Inc. (2)
17th Floor 6788 Ayala Avenue Oledan

Square, Makati, 1223, Manila, Philippines
Tel.: (63) 288923691
Web Site: http://www.jfe-shoji.com
Emp.: 20
Trader of Steel, Heavy Machinery, Chemicals, Food & Construction Materials
N.A.I.C.S.: 424690
Takeo Inoue *(Pres)*

JFE Shoji Trade Thailand, Ltd. (2)
Ramaland Bldg 18th Floor 952 Rama IV Road Suriyawongse, Bangrak, Bangkok, 10500, Thailand
Tel.: (66) 26329200
Web Site: http://www.jfe-shoji.co.jp
Sales Range: Less than $1 Million
Emp.: 25
Trader of Steel, Heavy Machinery, Chemicals, Food & Construction Materials
N.A.I.C.S.: 424690

Subsidiary (Domestic):

JFE Shoji Zosen Kako Corporation (2)
111 Mukaishima-cho, Onomichi, 722-0073, Hiroshima, Japan
Tel.: (81) 848206011
Steel Plate Mfr & Distr
N.A.I.C.S.: 332313

Subsidiary (Non-US):

JFE Trade Hong Kong Ltd. (2)
Unit 1115 11/F The Metropolis Tower 10 Metropolis Drive, Hung Hom, Kowloon, China (Hong Kong)
Tel.: (852) 22359500
Web Site: http://www.jfe-shoji.co.jp
Sales Range: $25-49.9 Million
Emp.: 10
Steel, Heavy Machinery, Chemicals, Food & Construction Materials
N.A.I.C.S.: 331110

JY Steel Processing Co., Ltd. (2)
Quan Goi, Hung Thinh commune Binh Giang District, Hai Duong, Vietnam
Tel.: (84) 2203777808
Web Site: http://www.jysp.com.vn
Emp.: 30
Construction Materials Mfr
N.A.I.C.S.: 324122
Hideki Okuyama *(Gen Dir)*

Jiangsu JFE Shoji Steel Products Co., Ltd. (2)
Broom Hill Road On the 11th, Hi-tech Park Economic Development Zone, Jiangyin, 214429, Jiangsu, China
Tel.: (86) 51086199500
Web Site: https://www.ksj-js.com
Emp.: 190
Steel Sheet Mfr & Distr
N.A.I.C.S.: 332322

Subsidiary (Domestic):

K&I Tubular Corporation (2)
2-1 Otemachi 2-Chome, Chiyodaku, Tokyo, Japan
Tel.: (81) 332798751
Web Site: https://www.kitc.co.jp
Emp.: 23
Steel Pipe & Tube Distr
N.A.I.C.S.: 423510
Shigeki Tashiro *(Pres)*

Kadota Kozai Corporation (2)
4-3-52 Higashimon-cho, Imabari, 794-0033, Ehime, Japan
Tel.: (81) 898221917
Steel Plate Distr
N.A.I.C.S.: 423510

Kadowaki Steel Material's Corporation (2)
4-43 Masago-cho, Naka-ku, Yokohama, 231-0016, Kanagawa, Japan
Tel.: (81) 452264436
Steel Material Distr
N.A.I.C.S.: 423510

Subsidiary (Non-US):

Kawarin Enterprise Pte Ltd. (2)
144 Gul Circle, Jurong, 629603, Singapore
Tel.: (65) 68615508
Web Site: http://www.kawarin.com.sg

Sales Range: $50-74.9 Million
Emp.: 100
Steel Processing & Sales
N.A.I.C.S.: 523160

Kawasho Food Corporation (2)
Tel.: (81) 352031001
Web Site: http://www.kawasho-foods.co.jp
Sales Range: $25-49.9 Million
Emp.: 72
Foodstuff Mfr
N.A.I.C.S.: 445298
Shinzo Sekiguchi *(Pres)*

Subsidiary (Non-US):

Marushin Canneries (M) Sdn. Bhd. (3)
Plo 213 1 Jalan Timah Kawasan Perindustrian, 81700, Pasir Gudang, Johor, Malaysia
Tel.: (60) 72514802
Web Site: https://www.king-cup.com
Sales Range: $75-99.9 Million
Emp.: 100
Food Manufacturing & Sales
N.A.I.C.S.: 311423

Subsidiary (Domestic):

Kita-Kanto Steel Corporation (2)
1-3-50 Higashionuma-cho, Hitachi, 316-0023, Ibaraki, Japan
Tel.: (81) 294360885
Steel Material Distr
N.A.I.C.S.: 423510

Kohnan Blanking Service Corporation (2)
43-1 Uozakihama-machi, higashinada-ku, Kobe, 658-0024, Hyogo, Japan
Tel.: (81) 784356031
Steel Material Distr
N.A.I.C.S.: 423510

Subsidiary (Non-US):

Kuroda Precision Industries (M) Sdn BHD (2)
Block C Lot 3 Solok Waja 3, Bukit Raja Industrial Park, 41050, Klang, Selangor, Malaysia
Tel.: (60) 333413790
Web Site: http://www.kuroda-precision.com
Emp.: 87
Mfr High-Precision Metal Dies
N.A.I.C.S.: 333514

Subsidiary (Domestic):

Kyushu-Tech Corporation (2)
13 Meishihama, Tamana-gun Nagasumachi, Kumamoto, 869-0111, Japan
Tel.: (81) 968783717
Steel Plate Distr
N.A.I.C.S.: 423510

Mitsuwa Tekken Corporation (2)
20 Sitinohematitatenogashira, kamikitagun, Aomori, 039-2505, Japan
Tel.: (81) 176626211
Steel Frame Mfr
N.A.I.C.S.: 332321

Mizushima Metal Products Corporation (2)
1-4 Mizushimakawasakidori, Kurashiki, 712-8074, Okayama, Japan
Tel.: (81) 864406322
Steel Plate Distr
N.A.I.C.S.: 423510

Mizushima Steel Corporation (2)
1-4 Mizushimakawasakidori, Kurashiki, 712-8074, Okayama, Japan
Tel.: (81) 864474737
Steel Plate Distr
N.A.I.C.S.: 423510

Nagano Can Corporation (2)
4057-1 Matsukawa Ogawara-cho, Suzaka, 382-0001, Nagano, Japan
Tel.: (81) 262451502
Container Mfr
N.A.I.C.S.: 327213

Naigai Steel Corporation (2)
1-1950 Mizushima-nishidori, Kurashiki, 712-8073, Okayama, Japan
Tel.: (81) 864483688
Industrial Machinery Mfr & Distr
N.A.I.C.S.: 333248

Subsidiary (Non-US):

New Bangpoo Manufacturing Co., Ltd. (2)
635 Bangpoo Industrial Estate Soi6 Sukhumvit Rd Tambon Preaksa, Muang District, Samut Prakan, 10280, Thailand
Tel.: (66) 23240062
Web Site: http://www.newbangpoo.com
Emp.: 130
Steel Structure Manufacturing Company
N.A.I.C.S.: 331513

Subsidiary (Domestic):

Niigata Steel Corporation (2)
1421 Inokobashinden, Sanjo, 959-1151, Niigata, Japan
Tel.: (81) 256456666
Steel Plate Distr
N.A.I.C.S.: 423510

Ohmi sangyo Co., Ltd. (2)
4-13-13 Tsurumachi, Taisho-ku, Osaka, 551-0023, Japan
Tel.: (81) 643943500
Web Site: https://www.ohmi-sangyo.co.jp
Emp.: 105
Iron Plate Distr
N.A.I.C.S.: 423510

Subsidiary (Non-US):

PT. JFE Shoji Steel Indonesia (2)
MM2100 Industrial Town Block B-4-2, Cibitung, Bekasi, Jawa Barat, Indonesia
Tel.: (62) 218980903
Steel Material Distr
N.A.I.C.S.: 423510

Subsidiary (US):

R. Bourgeois JFE Shoji Magnetic Lamination, Inc. (2)
301 E Ocean Blvd Ste 1750, Long Beach, CA 90802
Tel.: (562) 637-3500
Lamination Core Distr
N.A.I.C.S.: 423310

Subsidiary (Domestic):

Shin Nihon Kogyo Corporation (2)
2763-9 Uenodai Otsu Tosejima, Nishi Aizumachi Yama-Gun, Fukushima, 969-4401, Japan
Tel.: (81) 241453040
Construction Material Mfr & Distr
N.A.I.C.S.: 327120

Showa Kigyo Corporation (2)
2-7-33 Nagisa, Matsumoto, 390-0841, Nagano, Japan
Tel.: (81) 263257373
Steel Pipe Distr
N.A.I.C.S.: 423510

Subsidiary (Non-US):

Steel Alliance Service Center Co., Ltd. (2)
Hemaraj Eastern Seaboard Industrial Estate 500/95 Moo 3 Tasit, Pluak Daeng, 21140, Rayong, Thailand
Tel.: (66) 33659014
Steel Material Distr
N.A.I.C.S.: 423510

Subsidiary (Domestic):

Taisei Kogyo Corporation (2)
2-12-3 Takaokahigashi, Naka-ku, Hamamatsu, 433-8117, Shizuoka, Japan
Tel.: (81) 534361815
Steel Plate Distr
N.A.I.C.S.: 423510

Tochigi Shearing Corporation (2)
1-22 Owada, Moka, 321-4508, Tochigi, Japan
Tel.: (81) 285731101
Web Site: http://www.tochis.co.jp
Machine Frame Mfr
N.A.I.C.S.: 333248

Tohsen Corporation (2)
9th Floor JFE Shoji Building 7-1 Otemachi 2-chome, Chiyoda-ku, Tokyo, 100-0004, Japan
Tel.: (81) 352031071
Steel Product Mfr & Distr

N.A.I.C.S.: 331210

Toyo Kinzoku Corporation (2)
712-9 Hinode-cho, Isesaki, 372-0022, Gunma, Japan
Tel.: (81) 270269035
Steel Plate Distr
N.A.I.C.S.: 423510

Yashimanada Corporation (2)
Dojima Plaza Building 1-5-30 Dojima, Kita-ku, Osaka, 530-0003, Japan
Tel.: (81) 663480710
Web Site: https://www.yashimanada.co.jp
Emp.: 80
Steel Sheet Distr
N.A.I.C.S.: 423510

Subsidiary (Non-US):

Zhejiang JFE Shoji Steel Products Co., Ltd. (2)
No 1199 Xingxing Third Road, Pinghu Economic Development Zone, Pinghu, Zhejiang, China
Tel.: (86) 57385095111
Web Site: http://www.ksz-zj.com.cn
Steel Sheet Mfr & Distr
N.A.I.C.S.: 332322

JFE Steel Corporation (1)
2-2-3 Uchisaiwaicho, Chiyoda-ku, Tokyo, 100-0011, Japan (100%)
Tel.: (81) 335973111
Web Site: http://www.jfe-steel.co.jp
Sales Range: $25-49.9 Million
Emp.: 45,844
Steel Milling & Steel Sheet, Plate, Pipe, Wire & Flat Rolled Products Mfr
N.A.I.C.S.: 331221
Yoshihisa Kitano *(Pres & CEO)*

Joint Venture (Non-US):

DJ Galvanizing (2)
300 Sprucewood Avenue, Windsor, N9C 3Y6, ON, Canada
Tel.: (519) 250-2100
Sales Range: $25-49.9 Million
Emp.: 100
Hot-Dip Galvanizing Services; Owned 50% by Dofasco, Inc. & 50% by JFE Steel Corporation
N.A.I.C.S.: 331221
Paul Dunmore *(Pres)*

Subsidiary (Domestic):

Gecoss Corporation (2)
2-5-1 Koraku, Bunkyo-ku, Tokyo, 112-0004, Japan
Tel.: (81) 366997401
Web Site: https://www.gecoss.jp
Rev: $847,362,340
Assets: $707,560,840
Liabilities: $291,269,650
Net Worth: $416,291,190
Earnings: $29,176,540
Emp.: 1,385
Fiscal Year-end: 03/31/2024
Construction Machinery Lease & Whlsr
N.A.I.C.S.: 532412
Manabu Umakoshi *(Pres & CEO)*

Subsidiary (Non-US):

Gecoss Vietnam Company Limited (2)
Unit 503 5th Floor TMS Building-172 Hai Ba Trung Street, Da Kao Ward District 1, Ho Chi Minh City, Vietnam
Tel.: (84) 2839101844
Construction Materials Distr
N.A.I.C.S.: 423310

Guangzhou JFE Steel Sheet Co., Ltd. (2)
Shiliuyong, Wanqingsha Town Nansha District, Guangzhou, 511464, China
Tel.: (86) 2084953388
Web Site: http://www.gjss.com.cn
Steel Sheet Mfr & Distr
N.A.I.C.S.: 332322

Hojalata Y Laminados S.A. (2)
Calle 17 No 43F - 122 Medellan, Antioquia, Colombia
Tel.: (57) 42619898
Web Site: http://www.holasa.com.co
Electrolytic Tinplate Mfr & Distr
N.A.I.C.S.: 332313

JFE HOLDINGS, INC.

JFE Holdings, Inc.—(Continued)

JFE Consulting (Shanghai) Co., Ltd. (2)
Room 801 Building A Far East International Plaza 319 Xianxia Road, Shanghai, 200051, China **(100%)**
Tel.: (86) 2162351345
Web Site: http://www.jfe-steel.co.jp
Sales Range: $25-49.9 Million
Emp.: 7
Mfr of Steel Products
N.A.I.C.S.: 331221

Subsidiary (Domestic):

JFE Logistics Corp. (2)
1-9-5 Otemachi Financial City North Tower 25th Fl Otemachi, Chiyoda-Ku, Tokyo, 100-0004, Japan
Tel.: (81) 3 6214 9700
Web Site: http://www.jfe-logistics.co.jp
Rev.: $179,700,000,000
Emp.: 4,295
Fiscal Year-end: 03/31/2017
Logistics Consulting Servies
N.A.I.C.S.: 541614
Yasushi Yamamura (Pres & CEO)

JFE Plant Engineering Co., Ltd. (2)
2-17-4 Kuramae JFE-Kuramae Bld 8th Floor, Taito-ku, Tokyo, 111-0051, Japan
Tel.: (81) 338643865
Web Site: https://www.jfe-planteng.co.jp
Emp.: 3,777
Engineeering Services
N.A.I.C.S.: 541330
Itaru Hishinuma (Pres)

JFE STEEL PIPE CO., LTD. (2)
1 Niihamacho, Chuo-Ku, Chiba, 260-0826, Japan
Tel.: (81) 432624375
Steel Pipe & Tube Mfr
N.A.I.C.S.: 331210

Subsidiary (US):

JFE Steel America, Inc. (2)
600 3rd Ave 12th Fl, New York, NY 10016
Tel.: (212) 310-9320
Web Site: http://www.jfe-steel.co.jp
Sales Range: $25-49.9 Million
Emp.: 9
Processor of Steel
N.A.I.C.S.: 541618

JFE Steel America, Inc. (2)
750 Town & Country Blvd Ste 705, Houston, TX 77024 **(100%)**
Tel.: (713) 532-0052
Web Site: http://www.jfe-steel.co.jp
Sales Range: $25-49.9 Million
Emp.: 6
Refiner of Steel
N.A.I.C.S.: 423510

Subsidiary (Non-US):

JFE Steel Corporation (2)
15th Floor The Broadgate Tower 20 Primrose Street, London, EC2A 2EW, United Kingdom **(100%)**
Tel.: (44) 2074260166
Web Site: http://www.jfe-steel.co.jp
Sales Range: $25-49.9 Million
Emp.: 7
Mfr of Steel Products
N.A.I.C.S.: 331221

JFE Steel Corporation (2)
16 Raffles Quay No 1503 Hong Leong Bldg, Singapore, 048581, Singapore **(100%)**
Tel.: (65) 62201174
Web Site: http://www.jfe-steel.co.jp
Sales Range: $25-49.9 Million
Emp.: 10
Mfr of Steel Products
N.A.I.C.S.: 331221

JFE Steel Corporation (2)
22 Fl Abdulrahim Pl 990 Rama IV Rd Silom, Bangrak, Bangkok, 10500, Thailand **(100%)**
Tel.: (66) 26361886
Web Site: http://www.jfe-steel.co.jp
Sales Range: $25-49.9 Million
Emp.: 13
Mfr of Steel Products
N.A.I.C.S.: 331221

JFE Steel Corporation (2)
6th Floor Summitmas II JL Jendral Sudirman Kav 61-62, Jakarta, 12190, Indonesia **(100%)**
Tel.: (62) 215226405
Web Site: http://www.jfe-steel.co.jp
Sales Range: $25-49.9 Million
Emp.: 9
Mfr of Steel Products
N.A.I.C.S.: 331221

JFE Steel Corporation (2)
23rd Floor 6788 Ayala Avenue Oledan Square, Makati, 1226, Philippines **(100%)**
Tel.: (63) 288867432
Web Site: http://www.jfe-steel.co.jp
Sales Range: $25-49.9 Million
Emp.: 7
Mfr of Steel Products
N.A.I.C.S.: 331221

JFE Steel Galvanizing (Thailand) Ltd. (2)
500/94 Moo 3 T Tasit A, Pluakdaeng, Rayong, 21140, Thailand
Tel.: (66) 3301071518
Web Site: https://www.jsgt.co.th
Steel Sheet Mfr & Distr
N.A.I.C.S.: 332322
Shigeru Kuroda (Pres)

JFE Steel do Brasil Ltda (2)
Praia de Botafogo 228 Setor B Salas 508 509, Botafogo, Rio de Janeiro, 22250-040, Brazil
Tel.: (55) 2125531132
Web Site: http://www.jfe-steel.co.jp
Sales Range: $25-49.9 Million
Emp.: 100
Steel Mfrs
N.A.I.C.S.: 331221

Subsidiary (Domestic):

JFE Systems, Inc. (2)
Seavans South Building 1-2-3 Shibaura, Minato-ku, Tokyo, 105-0023, Japan
Tel.: (81) 354182400
Web Site: https://www.jfe-systems.com
Rev.: $410,038,130
Assets: $310,108,150
Liabilities: $111,583,410
Net Worth: $198,524,740
Earnings: $32,845,090
Emp.: 1,864
Fiscal Year-end: 03/31/2024
Information Technology Services
N.A.I.C.S.: 541512
Takumi Kamijo (Sr Mng Exec Officer)

JFE Techno-Design Corporation (2)
2-7-1 Otemachi, Chiyoda-ku, Tokyo, 100-004, Japan **(100%)**
Tel.: (81) 3 3510 3400
Web Site: http://www.jfe-tec.co.jp
Sales Range: $125-149.9 Million
Emp.: 1,458
Structural Design & Analysis Services
N.A.I.C.S.: 541490
Seishi Tsuyama (Pres & Dir)

Mizushima Eco-Works Co., Ltd. (2)
1-14-5 Mizushima Kawasaki-dori, Kurashiki, 712-8074, Okayama, Japan
Tel.: (81) 864473255
Web Site: https://www.m-ecoworks.net
Emp.: 6
General Domestic Waste Services
N.A.I.C.S.: 562119

Subsidiary (Non-US):

Philippine Sinter Corporation (2)
23rd Floor Oledan Square 6788 Ayala Avenue, Makati, 1226, Philippines
Tel.: (63) 28867421
Web Site: http://www.psc.ph
Sales Range: $50-74.9 Million
Emp.: 10
Iron Ore Mining Services
N.A.I.C.S.: 212210

Thai Coated Steel Sheet Co., Ltd. (2)
28/1 PrapawitBuilding 8th Floor Surasak Rd, Silom Bangrak, Bangkok, Thailand
Tel.: (66) 26300390
Web Site: https://www.thaicoat.com
Steel Sheet Mfr & Distr
N.A.I.C.S.: 332322

Mitsuru Nishikawa (Co-Pres)

JFE TECHNO-RESEARCH CORP (1)
2-7-1 Otemachi, Chiyoda-ku, Tokyo, 100-0004, Japan
Tel.: (81) 335103400
Web Site: http://www.jfe-tec.co.jp
Emp.: 1,419
Industrial Material Research Services
N.A.I.C.S.: 541715
Saiji Matsuoka (Pres)

JFE TUBIC CORP. (1)
1-1 Kawasaki-cho, Handa, 475-8611, Aichi, Japan
Tel.: (81) 569242920
Web Site: https://www.tubic.com
Emp.: 100
Steel Pipe & Pipe Fitting Mfr
N.A.I.C.S.: 331210

JFE Techno-wire CORP. (1)
1 Shinhama-cho, Chuo-Ku, Chiba, 260-0826, Japan
Tel.: (81) 432622164
Web Site: https://www.jfe-techno-wire.co.jp
Emp.: 126
Steel Wire Mfr & Distr
N.A.I.C.S.: 331222
Eiichi Shiokawa (CEO)

JFE Technophenix Co., Ltd. (1)
387-1 Miho, Shimizu-Ku, Shizuoka, 424-0901, Japan
Tel.: (81) 543342152
Steel Products Mfr
N.A.I.C.S.: 331110

JFE Technos Corporation (1)
2-1 Suehirocho, Tsurumi-Ku, Yokohama, 230-0045, Kanagawa, Japan
Tel.: (81) 455057370
Web Site: https://www.jfe-technos.co.jp
Emp.: 681
Industrial Machinery Maintenance Services
N.A.I.C.S.: 811310
Matsumoto Koji (Pres)

JFE Tsu Technical Works Co., Ltd. (1)
1 Kumozukokancho, Tsu, 514-0301, Mie, Japan
Tel.: (81) 592463495
Fabricated Metal Mfr
N.A.I.C.S.: 332999

JFE URBAN RECYCLE CORP. (1)
6-1 Mizue-cho, Kawasaki-Ku, Kawasaki, 210-0866, Kanagawa, Japan
Tel.: (81) 442705370
Web Site: https://www.urrec.co.jp
Sales Range: $25-49.9 Million
Emp.: 110
Industrial Waste Disposal Services
N.A.I.C.S.: 562211

JFE WELDED PIPE MANUFACTURING CO., LTD. (1)
7-1 Anezaki kaigan, Ichihara, 299-0107, Chiba, Japan
Tel.: (81) 436628111
Web Site: https://www.jfe-wp.co.jp
Emp.: 449
Welded Pipe Mfr & Distr
N.A.I.C.S.: 331210

JFE WING CORP. (1)
6-3 Mizue-cho, Kawasaki-Ku, Kawasaki, 210-0866, Kanagawa, Japan
Tel.: (81) 442703561
Web Site: http://www.jfewing.co.jp
Steel Products Mfr
N.A.I.C.S.: 331110

JFE West Japan GS Co., Ltd. (1)
1 Kokancho, Fukuyama, 721-8510, Hiroshima, Japan
Tel.: (81) 849437358
Web Site: http://www.jfe-steel.co.jp
Steel Products Mfr
N.A.I.C.S.: 331110

JFE West Technology Co.,Ltd. (1)
1 Kokancho, Fukuyama, 721-0931, Hiroshima, Japan
Tel.: (81) 84 941 1506
Web Site: http://www.jfe-fst.co.jp
Emp.: 950
Railway Support Services

INTERNATIONAL PUBLIC

N.A.I.C.S.: 488210

JMU Defense Systems Co., Ltd. (1)
1180 Amarube-shirno, Maizuru, 625-8501, Kyoto, Japan
Tel.: (81) 773628760
Defense Equipment Distr
N.A.I.C.S.: 423910

JP Steel Plantech Co. (1)
Kaneko 2nd Building 4-11F 2-6-23, Shin-yokohama Kohoku-ku, Yokohama, 222-0033, Japan
Tel.: (81) 454713911
Web Site: http://steelplantech.com
Sales Range: $75-99.9 Million
Emp.: 367
Steel Plant Engineering Services
N.A.I.C.S.: 541330
Norio Ao (Gen Mgr-Iron, Steel Making & Continuous Casting Plant Sector)

Subsidiary (Non-US):

JP Steel Plantech (Shanghai) Co., Ltd. (2)
Shanghai Strength Plaza 11C-D No 3 600, Tianshan Road, Shanghai, China
Tel.: (86) 2152061956
Web Site: http://www.spco-sh.cn
Steel Products Mfr
N.A.I.C.S.: 331110

Japan Marine United Corporation (1)
Yokohama Blue Avenue Building 4-4-2 Minatomirai, Nishi-ku, Yokohama, 220-0012, Japan **(45.9%)**
Tel.: (81) 452647200
Web Site: https://www.jmuc.co.jp
Emp.: 6,000
Ships & Patrol Vessels Mfr
N.A.I.C.S.: 336611
Kotaro Chiba (Pres & CEO)

Subsidiary (Non-US):

IMBV B.V. (2)
De Linie 3 - I, 2905 AX, Capelle aan den IJssel, Netherlands
Tel.: (31) 104116406
Web Site: https://www.imbvrotterdam.com
Sales Range: $25-49.9 Million,
Emp.: 17
Technical & Navigation Services to Ships
N.A.I.C.S.: 488330
Y. Okita (Mng Dir)

IMCS Marine (Shanghai) Co., Ltd. (2)
Room No 706-707 Information Tower No 1403 Minsheng Road, Pudong New Area, Shanghai, 200135, China
Tel.: (86) 2163518029
Web Site: http://www.ihi-imcs.cn
Sales Range: $25-49.9 Million
Emp.: 41
Consulting & Engineering for Shipbuilding, Ship Repair & Supply of Marine Equipment
N.A.I.C.S.: 336611
Wang Kegui (Mng Dir)

IMES Pte. Ltd. (2)
27 Tanjong Kling Road, Singapore, 628052, Singapore
Tel.: (65) 62687360
Web Site: http://www.imes.com.sg
Sales Range: $25-49.9 Million
Emp.: 60
Marine Engineering
N.A.I.C.S.: 541330
Nakashima Tomohiro (Mng Dir)

KAWASAKI KOKAN CO., LTD, (1)
25 Suzukawa, Isehara, 259-1146, Kanagawa, Japan
Tel.: (81) 463943992
Web Site: http://www.kawasakikokan.co.jp
Sales Range: $25-49.9 Million
Emp.: 80
Steel Pipe & Pipe Fitting Mfr
N.A.I.C.S.: 331210
Obuchi Toshisuke (Gen Mgr)

MIZUSHIMA FERROALLOY CO., LTD. (1)
1-1 Kawasakidori Mizushima, Kurashiki, 712-8513, Okayama, Japan
Tel.: (81) 864444241
Web Site: http://www.mizukin.co.jp

AND PRIVATE COMPANIES

Sales Range: $50-74.9 Million
Emp.: 195
Ferromanganese Mfr & Distr
N.A.I.C.S.: 331110

MIZUSHIMA RIVERMENT CORP. (1)
1 Mizushimakawasakidoori, Kurashiki, 712-8074, Okayama, Japan
Tel.: (81) 864474607
Emp.: 14
Steel Products Mfr
N.A.I.C.S.: 331110
Masaru Yotsuyanagi *(Pres)*

Nippon Chutetsukan K.K. (1)
1 Showanuma Shobu-cho, Kuki, 346-0193, Saitama, Japan
Tel.: (81) 480851101
Web Site: https://www.nichu.co.jp
Rev.: $111,437,990
Assets: $135,220,770
Liabilities: $70,634,460
Net Worth: $64,586,310
Earnings: $3,139,750
Emp.: 313
Fiscal Year-end: 03/31/2024
Iron Product & Plastic Pipe Mfr & Whlsr
N.A.I.C.S.: 331511
Shuichi Kusaka *(Pres & Chm)*

Nippon Chuzo K.K. (1)
2-1 Shiraishicho, Kawasaki-ku, Kawasaki, 210-9567, Japan
Tel.: (81) 443223751
Web Site: https://www.nipponchuzo.co.jp
Rev.: $105,707,120
Assets: $155,526,690
Liabilities: $76,993,280
Net Worth: $78,533,410
Earnings: $4,303,110
Fiscal Year-end: 03/31/2024
Casting Product Mfr & Whlsr
N.A.I.C.S.: 331110
Masaru Washio *(Pres & Pres)*

RIVER STEEL CO., LTD. (1)
1 Shin-Isogocho, Isogo-Ku, Yokohama, 235-8505, Kanagawa, Japan
Tel.: (81) 457576111
Web Site: http://www.river-steel.co.jp
Emp.: 150
Steel Products Mfr & Distr
N.A.I.C.S.: 331110
Makoto Shibata *(Pres)*

Recycling Management Japan, Inc. (1)
3-1 Bentencho, Tsurumi-ku, Yokohama, Kanagawa, Japan
Tel.: (81) 45 511 2951
Web Site: http://www.jfe-rmj.co.jp
Industrial Waste Recycling Services
N.A.I.C.S.: 562920

Universal Marine Systems Corporation (1)
1 Ariake Nagasumachi Universal Zosen Ariake Kojo, Tamana, 869-0113, Kumamoto, Japan
Tel.: (81) 968 65 7267
Web Site: http://www.jmusystems.co.jp
Marine Software Development Services
N.A.I.C.S.: 541511
Noda Shi *(Pres)*

JFLA HOLDINGS INC.
1-5-6 Nihonbashi-kakigara-cho, Chuo-ku, Tokyo, 103-0014, Japan
Tel.: (81) 364593231
Web Site: https://www.j-fla.com
Year Founded: 2007
3069—(TKS)
Rev.: $448,832,220
Assets: $273,680,440
Liabilities: $217,667,300
Net Worth: $56,013,140
Earnings: ($4,084,980)
Fiscal Year-end: 03/31/24
Restaurant Operators
N.A.I.C.S.: 722511
Shusaku Higaki *(Pres & CEO)*

Subsidiaries:

DOSANKO CORP. (1)
1-5-6 Kakigara-cho, Nihonbashi Chuo-ku, Tokyo, 103-0014, Japan
Tel.: (81) 363118900
Web Site: https://www.dskgroup.co.jp
Restaurant Management Services
N.A.I.C.S.: 722513
Masanori Morishita *(CEO)*

Japan Food & Liquor Alliance Inc. (1)
1850 Noumako Shodoshima-cho, Shodoshima, 761-4498, Kagawa, Japan
Tel.: (81) 879 821705
Web Site: http://www.j-fla.com
Rev.: $234,677,740
Assets: $247,088,540
Liabilities: $174,642,680
Net Worth: $72,445,860
Earnings: $1,013,840
Emp.: 642
Fiscal Year-end: 09/30/2017
Food Product & Alcohol Mfr
N.A.I.C.S.: 311941
Shusaku Higaki *(Pres & CEO)*

Subsidiary (Domestic):

Arcane Ltd. (2)
Morita Building 1-5-6 Nihonbashi Kakigaracho, Chuo-ku, Tokyo, 103-0014, Japan
Tel.: (81) 336646551
Emp.: 126
Wine Distr
N.A.I.C.S.: 424820
Shusaku Higaki *(Pres)*

Subsidiary (Non-US):

Arcane s.a.r.l. (3)
71 rue de Commerce, 75015, Paris, France
Tel.: (33) 142610042
Emp.: 3
Wine Distr
N.A.I.C.S.: 424820
Pierre Payen *(Gen Mgr)*

Subsidiary (Domestic):

Morita Co., Ltd. (2)
1-7-34 Sakae, Naka-ku, Nagoya, 460-0008, Aichi, Japan
Tel.: (81) 522291600
Web Site: https://moritakk.com
Sales Range: $10-24.9 Million
Emp.: 371
Food Mfr
N.A.I.C.S.: 311942
Shusaku Higaki *(Pres & CEO)*

Pacific Paradise Foods, Inc. (1)
8940 Sorensen Ave Ste 1, Santa Fe Springs, CA 90670
Tel.: (562) 946-9429
Seafood Warehouse Services
N.A.I.C.S.: 493120

Sushi Bar Atari-Ya Limited (1)
1 Station Parade Uxbridge Road Ealing, London, United Kingdom
Tel.: (44) 2088963175
Web Site: http://www.sushibaratariya.co.uk
Restaurant Management Services
N.A.I.C.S.: 722513

T&S Enterprises (London) Limited (1)
458 Heather Park Drive, Wembley, HA0 1SS, Middlesex, United Kingdom
Tel.: (44) 2089001100
Seafood Distr
N.A.I.C.S.: 424460
Kazuo Tasaka *(Chm)*

JG SUMMIT HOLDINGS, INC.
43F Robinsons Equitable Tower ADB Ave cor P Poveda St, Ortigas Center, Pasig, Metro Manila, Philippines
Tel.: (63) 86337631
Web Site: https://www.jgsummit.com.ph
JGSHF—(OTCIQ)
Rev.: $6,210,511,291
Assets: $2,026,848,802
Liabilities: $12,046,189,307
Net Worth: $8,036,089,495
Earnings: $603,511,161
Emp.: 25,979
Fiscal Year-end: 12/31/23
Air Transportation & Power Generation Services
N.A.I.C.S.: 221111
James L. Go *(Chm)*

Subsidiaries:

Cebu Air, Inc. (1)
Basement 2 R 01 02 Robinsons Galleria Cebu General Maxilom corner, Osmena Boulevard Barangay Tejero, Cebu, 6000, Philippines **(66.7%)**
Tel.: (63) 288027000
Web Site: http://www.cebupacificair.com
Rev.: $1,635,868,157
Assets: $3,379,697,709
Liabilities: $3,293,427,783
Net Worth: $86,269,925
Earnings: $143,047,114
Emp.: 5,471
Fiscal Year-end: 12/31/2023
Oil Transportation Services
N.A.I.C.S.: 481111
Lance Y. Gokongwei *(Chm, Co/Co-Pres, CEO & CEO)*

Affiliate (Domestic):

Aviation Partnership (Philippines) Corporation (2)
8006 Domestic Road, Pasay, 1301, Philippines **(100%)**
Tel.: (63) 28876214
Aviation Support Services
N.A.I.C.S.: 488119
Vairappan Ganesan *(Gen Mgr)*

JG Summit Petrochemical Corporation (1)
9F-11F Robinsons Cyberscape Gamma Bldg Topaz and Ruby Roads, Ortigas Center Brgy San Antonio, Pasig, 1605, Philippines
Tel.: (63) 28 230 5000
Web Site: https://www.jgspetrochem.com
Polymer Chemical Mfr
N.A.I.C.S.: 325998

Oriental Petroleum & Minerals Corporation (1)
34th Floor Robinsons Equitable Tower, ADB Avenue Ortigas Center, Pasig, 1600, Metro Manila, Philippines
Tel.: (63) 26337631
Web Site: https://www.opmc.com.ph
Rev.: $3,020,421
Assets: $89,829,583
Liabilities: $3,044,640
Net Worth: $86,784,943
Earnings: $3,896,582
Fiscal Year-end: 12/31/2022
Petroleum & Mineral Resources Exploration Company; Petroleum Product Mfr
N.A.I.C.S.: 324199
James L. Go *(Chm & CEO)*

Robinsons Land Corporation (1)
Level 2 Galleria Corporate Center EDSA cor Ortigas Ave, Quezon City, 1100, Philippines
Tel.: (63) 283971888
Web Site: https://www.robinsonsland.com
Rev.: $809,647,319
Assets: $3,975,662,278
Liabilities: $1,565,613,954
Net Worth: $2,410,048,325
Earnings: $198,070,985
Emp.: 2,810
Fiscal Year-end: 12/31/2022
Real Estate Services
N.A.I.C.S.: 531312
Lance Y. Gokongwei *(Chm)*

Universal Robina Corporation (1)
6th Floor Tera Tower Bridgetowne E Rodriguez Jr Avenue C5 Road, Ugong Norte, Quezon City, 1110, Metro Manila, Philippines
Tel.: (63) 285169888
Web Site: https://www.urc.com.ph
Rev.: $2,859,379,021
Assets: $3,255,424,718
Liabilities: $1,116,003,177
Net Worth: $2,139,421,541
Earnings: $229,387,014
Emp.: 1,212
Fiscal Year-end: 12/31/2023
Food Mfr
N.A.I.C.S.: 311999
Lance Y. Gokongwei *(Chm)*

Joint Venture (Domestic):

Nissin-Universal Robina Corporation (2)
9th floor Tera Tower Bridgetowne C5 Road, Ugong Norte, Quezon City, 1110, Philippines **(51%)**
Tel.: (63) 26713944
Web Site: http://www.urc.com.ph
Sales Range: $25-49.9 Million
Mfr & Sales of Instant Noodles
N.A.I.C.S.: 311824

JGC HOLDINGS CORPORATION

JGC HOLDINGS CORPORATION
2-3-1 Minatomirai, Nishi-ku, Yokohama, 220 6001, Japan
Tel.: (81) 456821111
Web Site: https://www.jgc.com
Year Founded: 1928
VJC—(DEU)
Rev.: $5,503,452,950
Assets: $5,237,076,560
Liabilities: $2,673,156,710
Net Worth: $2,563,919,850
Earnings: ($51,756,300)
Emp.: 7,876
Fiscal Year-end: 03/31/24
Engineering & Construction Contractor
N.A.I.C.S.: 541330
Yutaka Yamazaki *(Co-Pres, Sr Exec Officer & Sr Gen Mgr-Process Tech Div)*

Subsidiaries:

Al Asilah Desalination Company Saoc (1)
PO Box 703, 112, Ruwi, Oman
Tel.: (968) 24597510
Engineeering Services
N.A.I.C.S.: 541330

JGC (U.S.A.), Inc. (1)
10370 Richmond Ave Ste 800, Houston, TX 77042-4135 **(100%)**
Tel.: (713) 789-1441
Web Site: http://www.jgc.co.com
Sales Range: $50-74.9 Million
Emp.: 10
Procurement Services of U.S.-Made Equipment & Materials for Various Chemical Plants
N.A.I.C.S.: 423830

Subsidiary (Domestic):

JGC Energy Development (USA) Inc. (2)
3151 Briarpark Dr Suite 400, Houston, TX 77042
Tel.: (832) 487-9965
Web Site: http://www.jgc.co.jp
Oil & Gas Exploration Services
N.A.I.C.S.: 213112
Masato Kato *(Pres)*

JGC Algeria S.P.A. (1)
Alger tour CMA-CGM 2e etage Quartier des affaires, Bab Ezzouar, 16024, Algiers, Algeria
Tel.: (213) 23924959
Web Site: http://www.jgc-algeria.com
Engineering & Construction Services
N.A.I.C.S.: 541330
Terumasa Ono *(CEO)*

JGC America, Inc. (1)
3151 Briarpark Dr Ste 400, Houston, TX 77042
Tel.: (832) 591-2000
Web Site: https://www.jgcamerica.com
Engineeering Services
N.A.I.C.S.: 541330
Eiki Furuta *(Pres)*

JGC Arabia Limited (1)
PO Box 2414, Al Khobar, Saudi Arabia
Tel.: (966) 138965055
Engineeering Services
N.A.I.C.S.: 541330

JGC Catalysts & Chemicals Ltd (1)
16th Floor Solid Square East Tower 580 Horikawa-cho, Saiwai-ku, Kawasaki, 212-0013, Kanagawa, Japan
Tel.: (81) 44 556 9137
Web Site: https://www.jgccc.com

JGC HOLDINGS CORPORATION

JGC Holdings Corporation—(Continued)
Sales Range: $200-249.9 Million
Emp.: 52
Petrochemical Mfr
N.A.I.C.S.: 325110
Toshiharu Hirai *(Pres)*

JGC Construction International Pte. Ltd. (1)
31 International Business Park 01-12/13,
Singapore, 609921, Singapore
Tel.: (65) 65611255
Web Site: http://www.jci.sg
Engineering & Construction Services
N.A.I.C.S.: 541330

JGC Corporation (UK) Ltd. (1)
7 E Kellogg Twr Greenford Rd, Greenford,
UB6 0JA, United Kingdom **(100%)**
Tel.: (44) 2088727851
Sales Range: Less than $1 Million
Emp.: 5
Equipment & Materials Procurement
N.A.I.C.S.: 541330

JGC Corporation Europe B.V. (1)
Scheveningseweg 58, 2517 KW, Hague,
Netherlands **(100%)**
Tel.: (31) 703066500
Web Site: http://www.jgc.nl
Sales Range: $25-49.9 Million
Emp.: 5
Provider of Procurement Services
N.A.I.C.S.: 541330

JGC Engineering Consultants (Shanghai) Co., Ltd. (1)
1502-1504 Pos Plaza 1600 Century Avenue, Pudong New Area, Shanghai,
201220, China **(100%)**
Tel.: (86) 2150589881
N.A.I.C.S.: 541330

JGC Evergreen Ltd. (1)
2 Donskaya, 680000, Khabarovsk, Russia
Tel.: (7) 84212390149
Web Site: http://j-eve.ru
Vegetable Mfr
N.A.I.C.S.: 334512

JGC Gulf International Co., Ltd. (1)
12th Floor Adil Kashoggi Building Custodian of Two Holy Mosque Road, PO Box 2257,
Custodian of Two Holy Mosque Road, Al Khobar, 31952, Saudi Arabia
Tel.: (966) 13 806 9999
Web Site: https://www.jgc.com.sa
Engineering & Construction Services
N.A.I.C.S.: 541330
Sachio Kaneko *(Pres & CEO)*

JGC Information Systems Co., Ltd. (1)
3-6-3 Minatomirai, Nishi-ku, Yokohama, 220 0012, Japan **(100%)**
Tel.: (81) 453457000
Web Site: http://www.jsys.co.jp
Sales Range: $125-149.9 Million
Emp.: 400
Systems Management & Operations, Consulting Services; Software Development & Customization
N.A.I.C.S.: 541512
Akiyoshi Nakajima *(Pres)*

JGC Italy S. R. L. (1)
Via Lallio n35 Frazione Sforzatica, 24044,
Dalmine, Italy
Tel.: (39) 035373705
Engineeering Services
N.A.I.C.S.: 541330

JGC Japan Corporation (1)
2-3-1 Minato Mirai, Nishi-ku, Yokohama,
220-6001, Kanagawa, Japan
Tel.: (81) 456821111
Engineering Services
N.A.I.C.S.: 541330
Shoji Yamada *(Pres)*

JGC Korea Corporation (1)
KSCFC Building 21th Floor 15 Boramae-ro 5-gil, Dongjak-Gu, Seoul, Korea (South)
Tel.: (82) 2 831 7316
Web Site: http://www.jgckorea.co.kr
Emp.: 81
Engineering & Construction Services
N.A.I.C.S.: 541330
Hiroshi Nonaka *(Pres & CEO)*

JGC Middle East Fze (1)
PO Box 18414, Jebel Ali, Dubai, United Arab Emirates
Tel.: (971) 48812102
Engineering Services
N.A.I.C.S.: 541330

JGC Nigeria Ltd. (1)
109 Awolowo Rd SW Ikoyi Maku House 5th Fl, PO Box 52159, Falomo Ikoyi, Lagos, Nigeria **(100%)**
Tel.: (234) 12690597
Design & Construction of Petroleum Refining, Petrochemical & Gas Processing Plants
N.A.I.C.S.: 324110

JGC Oceania Pty. Ltd. (1)
Exchange Tower Suite 1724 Level 17 2 The Esplanade, Perth, 6000, WA, Australia
Tel.: (61) 861461334
Engineeering Services
N.A.I.C.S.: 541330

JGC PLANTECH AOMORI Co., Ltd. (1)
1-89 Yaeihei Rokkasho-mura, Kamikita-gun, Aomori, 039-3212, Japan
Tel.: (81) 175711515
Web Site: https://www.a-plantech.co.jp
Industrial Plant Construction Services
N.A.I.C.S.: 237990

JGC Philippines, Inc. (1)
2109 Prime Street, Madrigal Business ParkAlabang, Muntinlupa, 1780, Metro Manila, Philippines **(95%)**
Tel.: (63) 288766000
Web Site: https://www.jgc.com.ph
Sales Range: $200-249.9 Million
Emp.: 800
Design & Construction of Petroleum Refining, Petrochemical & Gas Processing Plants
N.A.I.C.S.: 324110

JGC Plantech Co., Ltd. (1)
1-13-10 Saido, Konan-ku, Yokohama, 233 0008, Japan
Tel.: (81) 457433377
Web Site: http://www.plantech.co.jp
Sales Range: $25-49.9 Million
Emp.: 245
Testing Laboratories
N.A.I.C.S.: 541380

JGC Singapore Pte. Ltd. (1)
31 International Business Park Unit 01-12, Singapore, 609921, Singapore **(100%)**
Tel.: (65) 62270122
Sales Range: $75-99.9 Million
Emp.: 300
Consulting, Design, Procurement & Construction for Various Plants & Facilities
N.A.I.C.S.: 541330
Satoshi Hasegawa *(Gen Mgr)*

JGC Technical Assistance Services Philippines, Inc. (1)
Unit 02 12th Floor Bank of Makati Building, Ayala Avenue Extension, Makati, Philippines
Tel.: (63) 28899440
Engineeering Services
N.A.I.C.S.: 541330

JGC Trading & Services Co., Ltd. (1)
Queen's Tower A 2-3-1 Minato Mirai, Nishi-ku, Yokohama, 220-6001, Japan
Tel.: (81) 45 682 8692
Web Site: https://www.jgctrading.com
Emp.: 30
Machinery Equipment Distr
N.A.I.C.S.: 423830
Kenichi Hanahara *(Pres)*

JGC Vietnam Co., Ltd. (1)
Unit 1709 17F Keangnam Hanoi Landmark Tower, Lot E6 Cau Giay New Urban Area Me Tri Ward Nam Tu Liem District, Hanoi, Vietnam
Tel.: (84) 2437940520
Web Site: http://jgcvietnam.vn
Engineeering Services
N.A.I.C.S.: 541330

JGC-ITC Rabigh Utility Co., Ltd. (1)
2-3-1 Minatomirai, Nishil-ku, Yokohama,
220-0012, Kanagawa, Japan
Tel.: (81) 456821111
Power Generation Services

N.A.I.C.S.: 221118

Japan Fine Ceramics Co., Ltd. (1)
10 Akedori, Izumi-ku, Sendai, 981-3206, Miyagi, Japan
Tel.: (81) 22 378 7825
Web Site: https://www.japan-fc.co.jp
Emp.: 480
Engineering Ceramics Mfr
N.A.I.C.S.: 327910
Shigeru Adachi *(Pres)*

Japan NUS Co., Ltd. (1)
Loop X Building 8F, Kaigan 3 Chome Minato Ku, Tokyo, 108 0022, Japan **(80%)**
Tel.: (81) 354401851
Web Site: http://www.janus.co.jp
Sales Range: $25-49.9 Million
Emp.: 150
Nuclear & Environmental Engineering & Consulting
N.A.I.C.S.: 541330
Yukio Kishimoto *(Pres)*

Nikki Business Services Co., Ltd. (1)
1-22-8 Saido, Konan-ku, Yokohama, 233 0008, Japan
Tel.: (81) 457317411
Web Site: http://www.nikki-business.co.jp
Sales Range: $25-49.9 Million
Emp.: 100
Building Maintenance & Office Support Services
N.A.I.C.S.: 561499
Yasuhiro Doi *(Pres)*

Nikki Construction Co., Ltd. (1)
3-17 Egasaki-cho, Tsurumi-ku, Yokohama, 230-0002, Japan
Tel.: (81) 45 571 7841
Construction Engineering Services
N.A.I.C.S.: 541330

P.T. Pertafenikki Engineering (1)
Jl Mampang Prapatan Raya Kav 66, Jakarta, 12790, Selatan, Indonesia **(100%)**
Tel.: (62) 217993848
Web Site: http://www.pertafenikki.com
Sales Range: $25-49.9 Million
Emp.: 200
N.A.I.C.S.: 541330

PT. JGC INDONESIA (1)
Jl TB Simatupang 7B, Cilandak, Jakarta, 12430, Indonesia
Tel.: (62) 212 997 6500
Web Site: https://www.jgc-indonesia.com
Sales Range: $150-199.9 Million
Emp.: 1,000
Construction Engineering Services
N.A.I.C.S.: 541330
Nurdin Haris *(Pres)*

Technoserve Co., Inc. (1)
12th Floor Bank of Makati Building, Ayala Avenue Extension, Makati, Philippines
Tel.: (63) 28899440
Engineeering Services
N.A.I.C.S.: 541330

JH EDUCATIONAL TECHNOLOGY INC.
No 618 Liuweng Road, Liushi Town,
Yueqing, Zhejiang, China Ky
Web Site:
https://www.jheduchina.com
Year Founded: 2017
1935—(HKG)
Rev.: $120,921,716
Assets: $576,496,594
Liabilities: $105,310,423
Net Worth: $471,186,171
Earnings: $69,618,271
Emp.: 2,219
Fiscal Year-end: 12/31/23
Information Technology Services
N.A.I.C.S.: 541512
Cheung Chan *(CFO)*

JHANDEWALAS FOODS LIMITED
B-70 First Floor Upasana House
Janta Store Bapu Nagar, Jaipur, 302 015, Rajasthan, India
Tel.: (91) 1412703308 In
Web Site: https://www.namans.co.in

INTERNATIONAL PUBLIC

540850—(BOM)
Rev.: $3,853,334
Assets: $4,734,220
Liabilities: $8,231,413
Net Worth: ($3,497,192)
Earnings: ($2,534,234)
Emp.: 70
Fiscal Year-end: 03/31/21
Dairy Product Mfr & Distr
N.A.I.C.S.: 311512
Raakesh B. Kulwal *(Chm & Mng Dir)*

JHAVERI CREDITS & CAPITAL LIMITED
B-2 907-912 Palladium B/H Divya Bhaskar Press, Prahladnagar In Nr Vodafone House, Ahmedabad, 380015, India
Tel.: (91) 9712000637
Web Site:
https://www.jhavericredits.com
Year Founded: 1993
531550—(BOM)
Rev.: $1,308,721
Assets: $1,630,970
Liabilities: $606,824
Net Worth: $1,024,146
Earnings: $37,073
Emp.: 10
Fiscal Year-end: 03/31/22
Commodity Broking Services
N.A.I.C.S.: 523160
Kamlesh J. Jhaveri *(Exec Dir)*

JHAVERI FLEXO INDIA LTD.
9th Floor Gold Crest 10th Road J V P D Scheme Near HSBC Bank, Vile Parle West, Mumbai, 400049, India
Tel.: (91) 22 61512121
Web Site:
http://www.jhaveriflexo.com
Year Founded: 1998
Sales Range: $50-74.9 Million
Flexible Packaging Film Mfr
N.A.I.C.S.: 326112
Sandeep Jhaveri *(Mng Dir)*

Subsidiaries:

Jhaveri Flexo India Ltd. - AURANGABAD FACTORY (1)
GUT 74 Farola Paithan Road, Aurangabad, 431 105, Maharashtra, India
Tel.: (91) 2431251663
Packaging Product Distr
N.A.I.C.S.: 423840

Jhaveri Flexo India Ltd. - DAPADA FACTORY (1)
Survey No 135/2 Village Dapada Khanvel Road, Silvassa, 396 230, India
Tel.: (91) 2602699084
Packaging Product Distr
N.A.I.C.S.: 423840

Jhaveri Flexo India Ltd. - LUHARI FACTORY (1)
188/2/1 Village Luhari Opp Govt Tourism Resort, Silvassa, 396 230, India
Tel.: (91) 2602993437
Packaging Product Distr
N.A.I.C.S.: 423840

JHEN VEI ELECTRONIC CO., LTD.
6F No 18 Ln 609 Sec 5 Chongxin Rd, Sanchong Dist, New Taipei City, 24159, Taiwan
Tel.: (886) 229996166
Web Site: https://www.jve-tech.com
3520—(TPE)
Rev.: $31,381,359
Assets: $45,152,612
Liabilities: $19,761,655
Net Worth: $25,390,958
Earnings: $3,355,126
Fiscal Year-end: 12/31/22
Cable Socket Mfr
N.A.I.C.S.: 335931
Liang-Chuan Wei *(Chm & Pres)*

JHM CONSOLIDATION BERHAD
15-1-21 Bayan Point Medan Kampung Relau, 11900, Penang, Malaysia
Tel.: (60) 46465121 MY
Web Site: https://www.jhm.net.my
Year Founded: 2005
JHM—(KLS)
Rev.: $67,637,319
Assets: $101,941,655
Liabilities: $32,120,827
Net Worth: $69,820,828
Earnings: $3,111,244
Emp.: 1,259
Fiscal Year-end: 12/31/23
Investment Holding Services
N.A.I.C.S.: 551112
King Seng Tan *(CEO-Grp)*

Subsidiaries:

JHM Consolidation Berhad - Kedah Darul Aman Factory (1)
A95 & A96 Jalan 2A-3 Kawasan Perusahaan Miel Sungai Lalang, Sungai Petani Darul Aman, 08000, Kedah, Malaysia
Tel.: (60) 44427820
Electronic Components Mfr
N.A.I.C.S.: 334419

JHM Consolidation Berhad - Sungai Petani Factory (1)
A95 & A96 Jalan 2A-3 Kawasan Perusahaan MIEL Sungai Lalang, 08000, Sungai Petani, Kedah, Malaysia
Tel.: (60) 44427820
Investment Holding Company Services
N.A.I.C.S.: 551112

Mace Instrumentation Sdn. Bhd. (1)
Plot 6692 Lorong Perusahaan 5 Kawasan Perusahaan Kulim, 09000, Kulim, Kedah, Malaysia
Tel.: (60) 44891688
Web Site: http://www.misb.net.my
Metal Fabrication Product Mfr
N.A.I.C.S.: 332312
Allen Tan *(Dir-Mktg)*

JHM DEVELOPMENT SA
ul European Union 18, 96-100, Skierniewice, Poland
Tel.: (48) 833 95 89
Web Site: http://www.jhmdevelopment.pl
Real Estate Developer & Property Manager
N.A.I.C.S.: 236117
Regina Biskupska *(Chm-Mgmt Bd)*

JHS SVENDGAARD LABORATORIES LIMITED
Trilokpur Road Kheri Tehsil Nahan Distt Sirmour, Kala Amb, 173030, Himachal Pradesh, India
Tel.: (91) 1702302100
Web Site: https://www.svendgaard.com
Year Founded: 1997
532771—(BOM)
Rev.: $13,261,123
Assets: $28,318,062
Liabilities: $6,700,725
Net Worth: $21,617,337
Earnings: ($2,011,306)
Emp.: 11
Fiscal Year-end: 03/31/23
Oral Care Product Mfr
N.A.I.C.S.: 339999
Nikhil Nanda *(Mng Dir)*

JHSF PARTICIPACOES S.A.
Av Magalhaes de Castro 4800 Cidade Jardim, Sao Paulo, SP, Brazil
Tel.: (55) 1137021900
Web Site: https://jhsf.com.br
Year Founded: 1972
JHSF3—(BRAZ)
Rev.: $284,849,030
Assets: $1,980,312,956
Liabilities: $1,046,660,561
Net Worth: $933,652,395
Earnings: $88,998,228
Fiscal Year-end: 12/31/23
Residential & Commercial Property Developer & Manager
N.A.I.C.S.: 237210
Jose Auriemo Neto *(Chm)*

Subsidiaries:

Shopping Bela Vista Ltda. (1)
Castello Branco Highway Km 102 5, Porto Feliz, Sao Paulo, Brazil
Tel.: (55) 1532619900
Real Estate Services
N.A.I.C.S.: 531390

Shopping Ponta Negra S.A. (1)
Av Coronel Teixeira 5705, Ponta Negra, 69037-000, Manaus, 69037-000, Amazonas, Brazil
Tel.: (55) 9236677200
Web Site: https://www.shoppingpontanegra.com.br
Business Center Services
N.A.I.C.S.: 561439

JI TECH CO., LTD.
16 Junggado-gil 884-8 Osikdo-dong, Gunsan, Jeollabuk-do, Korea (South)
Tel.: (82) 637310088
Web Site: https://www.ji-tech.co.kr
Year Founded: 2014
417500—(KRS)
Semiconductor Device Mfr & Distr
N.A.I.C.S.: 334413

JI YAO HOLDING GROUP CO., LTD.
No 6 Huancheng North Road, Meihekou, Tonghua, 135000, Jilin, China
Tel.: (86) 4008125557 CN
Web Site: https://www.jiyaogroup.com
Year Founded: 2000
300108—(CHIN)
Rev.: $48,749,101
Assets: $269,558,941
Liabilities: $383,243,667
Net Worth: ($113,684,725)
Earnings: ($49,200,257)
Fiscal Year-end: 12/31/23
Chemicals Mfr
N.A.I.C.S.: 325998

JI'AN MANKUN TECHNOLOGY CO., LTD.
No 191 Torch Avenue, Jinggangshan Economic & Technological Development Zone, Jian, 343100, Jiangxi, China
Tel.: (86) 75529889502
Web Site: https://www.mankun.com
Year Founded: 2008
301132—(CHIN)
Rev.: $171,407,591
Assets: $320,602,267
Liabilities: $80,416,746
Net Worth: $240,185,520
Earnings: $15,462,183
Fiscal Year-end: 12/31/23
Circuit Board Mfr & Distr
N.A.I.C.S.: 334412
Juncheng Hong *(Chm)*

JI-HAW INDUSTRIAL CO., LTD.
No 53 Baoxing Rd, Xindian Dist, New Taipei City, 23145, Taiwan
Tel.: (886) 229189189
Web Site: https://www.jh.com.tw
3011—(TAI)
Rev.: $37,630,039
Assets: $54,353,378
Liabilities: $25,632,590
Net Worth: $28,720,788
Earnings: ($4,296,936)
Emp.: 680
Fiscal Year-end: 12/31/23
Connectors & Electric Wires Mfr
N.A.I.C.S.: 335931

Subsidiaries:

J.B.T. Industrial Co., Ltd. (1)
No 53 Pao Hsin Road, Hsin Tien, 231, Taipei, Taiwan
Tel.: (886) 2 29189189
Web Site: http://www.jihaw.com
Sales Range: $125-149.9 Million
Emp.: 500
Connectors & Electric Wires Mfr
N.A.I.C.S.: 331318
Chia-Hsin Wu *(Gen Mgr)*

Ji-Haw America, Inc. (1)
3545 Lomita Blvd Unit B, Torrance, CA 90505
Tel.: (310) 534-9002
Electronic Connector Mfr
N.A.I.C.S.: 334417

Ji-Haw Electronics (Kunshan) Co., Ltd. (1)
No288 Jin-Hao Road, Economic & Technology Zone, Kunshan, Jiangsu, China
Tel.: (86) 51257330288
Emp.: 1,650
Electronic Connector Mfr
N.A.I.C.S.: 334417

Ji-Haw Opto-Electrical (Auhui) Co., Ltd. (1)
Chuzhou Industrial Park, Dingyuan County, Anhui, China
Tel.: (86) 5505429787
Emp.: 1,000
Electronic Connector Mfr
N.A.I.C.S.: 334417

Ji-Haw Opto-Electrical (Kunshan) Co., Ltd. (1)
No 18 Jiang Feng Road, Kunshan Economic Technology Development Zone Zhangpu Complex Area, Kunshan, 225300, Jiangsu, China
Tel.: (86) 51257452388
Web Site: http://www.jh.com.tw
Emp.: 2,500
Connector Mfr
N.A.I.C.S.: 334417

JIA GROUP HOLDINGS LIMITED
2205 Universal Trade Centre 3 Arbuthnot Road, Central, China (Hong Kong)
Tel.: (852) 22007000 Ky
Web Site: http://www.jiagroup.co
8519—(HKG)
Rev.: $27,668,138
Assets: $12,566,018
Liabilities: $12,931,178
Net Worth: ($365,160)
Earnings: ($2,932,500)
Emp.: 252
Fiscal Year-end: 12/31/22
Restaurant Management Services
N.A.I.C.S.: 722511
Cherry Suet Yee Wan *(Exec Dir)*

Subsidiaries:

Duddell's Hong Kong Limited (1)
Level 3 1 Duddell Street, Central, China (Hong Kong)
Tel.: (852) 25259191
Cultural & Art Services
N.A.I.C.S.: 711510

JIA WEI LIFESTYLE, INC.
14F 4 No 296 Sec 4 Xinyi Rd, Daan Dist, Taipei, 10679, Taiwan
Tel.: (886) 277335368
Web Site: http://www.jiaweils.com
Year Founded: 2005
3557—(TAI)
Rev.: $155,414,560
Assets: $163,797,240
Liabilities: $86,632,490
Net Worth: $77,164,751
Earnings: $12,636,547
Fiscal Year-end: 12/31/23
Optical Film Mfr for Liquid Crystal Displays
N.A.I.C.S.: 333310
Shuo-Tsan Chen *(Chm)*

JIA YAO HOLDINGS LIMITED
Suite 3212 32nd Floor Tower One Times Square No 1 Matheson Street, Causeway Bay, China (Hong Kong)
Tel.: (852) 34264784 Ky
Web Site: http://www.jiayaoholdings.com
Year Founded: 1992
1626—(HKG)
Rev.: $135,958,165
Assets: $150,619,576
Liabilities: $96,928,931
Net Worth: $53,690,645
Earnings: $1,547,208
Emp.: 1,275
Fiscal Year-end: 12/31/22
Paper Cigarette & Other Paper Packaging Mfr
N.A.I.C.S.: 322299
Yoong An Yang *(Chm)*

JIACHEN HOLDING GROUP LIMITED
No 18 Changhong East Road Henglin Town, Wujin, Changzhou, Jiangsu, China
Tel.: (86) 51988501140 Ky
Web Site: http://www.jiachencn.com.cn
Year Founded: 1991
1937—(HKG)
Rev.: $31,908,708
Assets: $62,873,366
Liabilities: $19,756,246
Net Worth: $43,117,121
Earnings: $1,508,879
Emp.: 175
Fiscal Year-end: 12/31/22
Holding Company
N.A.I.C.S.: 551112
Min Shen *(Chm)*

JIADING INTERNATIONAL GROUP HOLDINGS LIMITED
Room 8212 Unit 01 82/F International Commerce Centre, 1 Austin Road West, Kowloon, China (Hong Kong)
Tel.: (852) 35838488 BM
Web Site: http://www.code-hk.com
8153—(HKG)
Rev.: $8,241,822
Assets: $18,307,421
Liabilities: $9,371,816
Net Worth: $8,935,605
Earnings: ($5,716,523)
Emp.: 56
Fiscal Year-end: 03/31/22
Tobacco Machinery Mfr
N.A.I.C.S.: 333248
Gelin Guo *(Chm & Compliance Officer)*

JIAHE FOODS INDUSTRY CO., LTD.
127 Wufang Rd, Wujiang, Suzhou, 215200, Jiangsu, China
Tel.: (86) 4008899300
Web Site: https://www.jiahefoods.com
Year Founded: 2001
605300—(SHG)
Rev.: $340,840,684
Assets: $436,796,166
Liabilities: $152,971,767
Net Worth: $283,824,399
Earnings: $16,199,254
Fiscal Year-end: 12/31/22
Food Product Mfr & Distr
N.A.I.C.S.: 311421
Xinrong Liu *(Founder, Chm, Pres & Gen Mgr)*

Jiahe Foods Industry Co., Ltd.—(Continued)

JIAHUA STORES HOLDINGS LIMITED
4/F Jiahua Ming Yuan No. 2146 Xinhu Road, Baoan District, Shenzhen, China
Tel.: (86) 75527927950 Ky
Web Site: http://www.szbjh.com
Year Founded: 1995
0602—(HKG)
Rev.: $47,072,189
Assets: $125,858,210
Liabilities: $107,408,387
Net Worth: $18,449,824
Earnings: ($15,148,739)
Emp.: 618
Fiscal Year-end: 12/31/22
Investment Management Service
N.A.I.C.S.: 523940
Lu Kun Zhuang (Founder & Chm)

JIAJIA FOOD GROUP CO., LTD.
Zhanqian Road, Ningxiang, Changsha, 410600, China
Tel.: (86) 73181820107
Web Site: http://www.jiajiagroup.com
Year Founded: 1996
002650—(SSE)
Rev.: $236,729,844
Assets: $389,621,232
Liabilities: $66,497,652
Net Worth: $323,123,580
Earnings: ($11,180,052)
Fiscal Year-end: 12/31/22
Seasoning Product Mfr
N.A.I.C.S.: 311942
Zhou Jianwen (Chm & Gen Mgr)

JIAJIAFU MODERN AGRICULTURE LIMITED
Suite 402 368 Sussex Street, Sydney, 2000, NSW, Australia
Tel.: (61) 280754595 AU
Web Site: http://www.jjfma.com
Year Founded: 2015
Rev.: $41,005,775
Assets: $36,948,361
Liabilities: $4,179,681
Net Worth: $32,768,681
Earnings: $4,667,222
Fiscal Year-end: 06/30/18
Fruit & Vegetable Mfr & Distr
N.A.I.C.S.: 311411
Qingkai Li (Chm & CEO)

JIAJIAYUE GROUP CO LTD
No 53 Daqing Road Economic and Technological, Weihai, 264200, Shandong, China
Tel.: (86) 6313855555
Web Site: https://en.jiajiayue.com.cn
Year Founded: 1981
603708—(SHG)
Rev.: $2,553,008,019
Assets: $2,018,339,505
Liabilities: $1,729,678,804
Net Worth: $288,660,701
Earnings: $7,588,760
Fiscal Year-end: 12/31/22
Supermarket Operator
N.A.I.C.S.: 445110
Wang Peihuan (Chm & Gen Mgr)

JIALIJIA GROUP CORPORATION LIMITED
Room 402 Unit B Guanghua Community Guanghua Road, Tianning District, Changzhou, 213000, Jiangsu, China
Tel.: (86) 51989801180 NV
Year Founded: 2015
RZZN—(OTCIQ)
Assets: $3,869,990
Liabilities: $3,519,700
Net Worth: $350,290
Earnings: ($314,141)
Fiscal Year-end: 12/31/21
Electronic Toy Distr
N.A.I.C.S.: 423920
Na Jin (CEO, CFO & Sec)

JIAMEI FOOD PACKAGING (CHUZHOU) CO., LTD.
No 189 Wuhu East Road, Chuzhou, 239000, Anhui, China
Tel.: (86) 5506821909
Web Site: http://www.chinafoodpack.com
Year Founded: 2011
002969—(SSE)
Rev.: $418,483,260
Assets: $629,100,108
Liabilities: $295,328,592
Net Worth: $333,771,516
Earnings: $2,391,012
Fiscal Year-end: 12/31/22
Packaging Product Mfr & Distr
N.A.I.C.S.: 333993
Min Chen (Chm & Gen Mgr)

JIAN EPAYMENT SYSTEMS LIMITED
Suite 1501A 15/F Tower 1 China Hong Kong City 33 Canton Road, Tsim Sha Tsui, Kowloon, China (Hong Kong)
Tel.: (852) 1065992650 Ky
Web Site: http://www.jianepayment.com
Rev.: $594,936
Assets: $4,984,260
Liabilities: $2,718,793
Net Worth: $2,265,467
Earnings: ($1,152,507)
Emp.: 17
Fiscal Year-end: 12/31/18
Information Management Services
N.A.I.C.S.: 541512
Tien Tzu Liang (CFO & Sec)

JIAN SIN INDUSTRIAL CO., LTD.
No 3 Zhangbin E 1st Rd, Xianxi Township Zhanghua County, Hsien, 507, Taiwan
Tel.: (886) 47582899
Web Site: https://www.rostawheels.com.tw
Year Founded: 1978
4502—(TPE)
Rev.: $46,253,166
Assets: $80,756,840
Liabilities: $59,964,012
Net Worth: $20,792,827
Earnings: ($759,278)
Emp.: 393
Fiscal Year-end: 12/31/22
Aluminum Product Mfr & Distr
N.A.I.C.S.: 331110
Li-Wen Tsai (Chm & Pres)

JIANA SCIENCE AND TECHNOLOGY CO., LTD.
7CDE A Jinfeng Building, Futian District, Shenzhen, 518031, Guangdong, China
Tel.: (86) 75583581568 Ky
Year Founded: 2018
Rev.: $3,538,125
Assets: $10,214,107
Liabilities: $4,855,058
Net Worth: $5,359,049
Earnings: $1,556,684
Emp.: 16
Fiscal Year-end: 04/30/19
Holding Company
N.A.I.C.S.: 551112
Fengzhen Zhu (Chm & CEO)

JIANG XI SANXI MEDTEC CO., LTD.
No 999 Fushan Avenue Xiaolan Economic Development Zone, Nanchang, 330200, Jiangxi, China
Tel.: (86) 79185950275
Web Site: https://www.sanxin-med.com
300453—(CHIN)
Rev.: $187,574,400
Assets: $250,830,216
Liabilities: $88,610,652
Net Worth: $162,219,564
Earnings: $25,922,052
Fiscal Year-end: 12/31/22
Medicinal Product Mfr
N.A.I.C.S.: 339112
Yixin Peng (Chm)

JIANGBO PHARMACEUTICALS, INC.
25 Haihe Rd Laiyang Economic Development Zone, Laiyang City, Yantai, 265200, Shandong, China
Tel.: (86) 5357282997 FL
Web Site: http://www.jiangbopharma.com
Year Founded: 2001
Sales Range: $75-99.9 Million
Emp.: 934
Pharmaceutical Mfr & Sales
N.A.I.C.S.: 325412
Wubo Cao (Chm)

JIANGLING MOTORS CORPORATION, LTD
No 2111 Yingbin Middle Avenue, Nanchang, 330200, Jiangxi, China
Tel.: (86) 79185266000
Web Site: http://www.jmc.com.cn
Year Founded: 1993
200550—(SSE)
Rev.: $4,226,079,312
Assets: $3,856,552,128
Liabilities: $2,559,164,868
Net Worth: $1,297,387,260
Earnings: $128,473,020
Emp.: 11,024
Fiscal Year-end: 12/31/22
Commercial Vehicle Mfr
N.A.I.C.S.: 336110
Qiu Tiangao (Chm)

JIANGLONG SHIPBUILDING CO., LTD.
No 1 Guizhu Road, Shenwan Town, Zhongshan, 528462, Guangdong, China
Tel.: (86) 13923360365
Web Site: https://en.jianglong.cn
Year Founded: 2003
300589—(CHIN)
Rev.: $167,163,358
Assets: $336,982,414
Liabilities: $212,573,778
Net Worth: $124,408,636
Earnings: $6,207,865
Fiscal Year-end: 12/31/23
Boat Mfr & Distr
N.A.I.C.S.: 336612
Yan Zhiqing (Chm & Gen Mgr)

Subsidiaries:

Jianglong Boat Polytron Technologies Inc (1)
Yacht Industrial Zone Pingsha Town Jinwan District, Zhuhai, 519050, China
Tel.: (86) 7567754888
Boat Mfr
N.A.I.C.S.: 336611

JIANGMEN KANHOO INDUSTRY CO., LTD.
No 22 JiaoXing South Road Jiaotou, Jianghai District, Jiangmen, 529040, Guangdong, China
Tel.: (86) 7503863800
Web Site: http://www.keheng.com.cn
300340—(CHIN)
Rev.: $556,285,860
Assets: $593,965,008
Liabilities: $561,226,536
Net Worth: $32,738,472
Earnings: ($64,637,352)
Emp.: 260
Fiscal Year-end: 12/31/22
Rare Earth Luminescent Materials Mfr
N.A.I.C.S.: 335999
Tang Xiulei (Sec)

JIANGNAN GROUP LIMITED
53 Xinguandonglu Guanlin Town, Yixing, Jiangsu, China
Tel.: (86) 85239983097 Ky
Web Site: http://www.jiangnangroup.com
1366—(HKG)
Rev.: $2,043,084,460
Assets: $2,416,404,219
Liabilities: $1,429,849,331
Net Worth: $986,554,888
Earnings: $25,968,329
Emp.: 3,440
Fiscal Year-end: 12/31/20
Wire & Cable Mfr
N.A.I.C.S.: 335921
Yafang Xia (Exec VP)

Subsidiaries:

Wuxi Jiangnan Cable Co., Ltd. (1)
Official Town Road 53 New Official, Guanlin Town, Yixing, 214251, China
Tel.: (86) 510 8720 1739
Wire & Cable Product Mfr & Distr
N.A.I.C.S.: 335929

JIANGNAN MOULD & PLASTIC TECHNOLOGY CO., LTD.
No 8 Changqin Road, Zhouzhuang Town, Jiangyin, 214423, Jiangsu, China
Tel.: (86) 51086222318
Web Site: https://www.000700.com
Year Founded: 1988
000700—(SSE)
Rev.: $1,075,965,228
Assets: $1,309,029,228
Liabilities: $890,199,180
Net Worth: $418,830,048
Earnings: $69,761,952
Emp.: 2,300
Fiscal Year-end: 12/31/22
Automotive Plastic Product Mfr
N.A.I.C.S.: 326199
Cao Kebo (Chm & Gen Mgr)

Subsidiaries:

Beijing Beiqi Mould & Plastic Technology Co., Ltd. (1)
No1 Yuzheng Road, Caiyu Technical Economic Development Area Caiyu Town Daxing District, Beijing, 102606, China
Tel.: (86) 1080278488
Plastic Mfr
N.A.I.C.S.: 326199

Jiangyin Daoda Automobile Decorative Parts Co., Ltd. (1)
58 Youjiaba Street, Zhouxi Zhouzhuang, Jiangyin, 214423, China
Tel.: (86) 51086906728
Plastic Mfr
N.A.I.C.S.: 326199

Jiangyin Degi Tec Casting Co., Ltd. (1)
No 8 Chang Qing Road, Zhou Zhuang, Jiangyin, 214423, Jiang Su, China
Tel.: (86) 51068978696
Web Site: http://www.degitec-jiangyin.com
Plastic Mfr
N.A.I.C.S.: 326199

Minghua De Mexico S.A. De C.V. (1)

Av Munich 640 Parque Ind Logistik, Villa de Reyes, 79526, San Luis Potosi, Mexico
Tel.: (52) 4448335567
Plastic Mfr
N.A.I.C.S.: 326199

Minghua USA, Inc. (1)
1000 Robinson Rd, Greer, SC 29651
Tel.: (864) 479-0162
Web Site: http://admin13628.wixsite.com
Plastic Mfr & Distr
N.A.I.C.S.: 326199

Shanghai Mingchen Mould & Plastic Technology Co., Ltd. (1)
No 900 Jinhai Road Pudong New Area, Shanghai, China
Automobile Parts Mfr
N.A.I.C.S.: 336390

Shenyang Daoda Automobile Decorative Parts Co., Ltd. (1)
9 Liubei Street, Economical and Technological Development Area Xihe, Shenyang, 110000, China
Tel.: (86) 2431220900
Plastic Mfr
N.A.I.C.S.: 326199

Shenyang Minghua Mould & Plastic Technology Co., Ltd. (1)
Automobile Parts Mfr
N.A.I.C.S.: 336390

Wuhan Mingjie Mould & Plastic Co., Ltd. (1)
No 38 Xinghua Road Economical and Technological Development Zone, Hubei, 200137, China
Tel.: (86) 2158342784
Automobile Parts Mfr
N.A.I.C.S.: 336390

Wuxi Mingci Cardiovascular Hospital Co., Ltd. (1)
No 599 Zhongnan Road, Liangxi District, Wuxi, 214000, China
Tel.: (86) 51068585999
Plastic Mfr
N.A.I.C.S.: 326199

Yantai Mingyue Mould & Plastic Co., Ltd. (1)
No 135 Fuxin Road Shangzhuang Industrial Zone Fushan District, Yantai, Shandong, China
Tel.: (86) 5356988618
Automobile Parts Mfr
N.A.I.C.S.: 336390

JIANGNAN YIFAN MOTOR CO., LTD.
No 7 Yanyu Road Yanqiao Industrial Park, Huishan, Wuxi, 214174, Jiangsu, China
Tel.: (86) 13395158800
Web Site: https://www.yifanmotor.com
Year Founded: 2011
301023—(CHIN)
Rev.: $24,587,760
Assets: $124,521,112
Liabilities: $10,429,507
Net Worth: $114,091,605
Earnings: $6,705,394
Emp.: 350
Fiscal Year-end: 12/31/23
Motor Product Mfr & Distr
N.A.I.C.S.: 335312
Jincheng Liu (Chm)

JIANGSHAN OUPAI DOOR INDUSTRY CO., LTD.
No 8 Yudashan Village, Yutou Village Hecun Town, Quzhou, 324100, Zhejiang, China
Tel.: (86) 5704729200
Web Site: http://www.oupaigroup.com
Year Founded: 2006
603208—(SHG)
Rev.: $450,532,410
Assets: $627,016,418
Liabilities: $420,474,132
Net Worth: $206,542,286
Earnings: ($41,910,453)
Fiscal Year-end: 12/31/22
Wooden Door Mfr & Distr
N.A.I.C.S.: 321911
Wu Shuigen (Chm)

JIANGSU AIDEA PHARMACEUTICAL CO., LTD.
No 69 New Ganquan West Road, Hanjiang, Yangzhou, 225008, Jiangsu, China
Tel.: (86) 51487530666
Web Site: http://www.aidea.com.cn
Year Founded: 2009
688488—(SHG)
Rev.: $34,288,390
Assets: $232,390,333
Liabilities: $64,054,762
Net Worth: $168,335,571
Earnings: ($17,438,059)
Fiscal Year-end: 12/31/22
Pharmaceutical Product Mfr & Distr
N.A.I.C.S.: 325412
Heliang Fu (Chm, CEO & Gen Mgr)

Subsidiaries:

Nanjing Accelas Pharmaceutical Co., Ltd. (1)
315 Room F7 No 9 Weidi Road, Xianlin University City Qixia District, Nanjing, China
Tel.: (86) 2585578729
Biopharmaceutical Research & Development Services
N.A.I.C.S.: 541714

Yangzhou Aidea Pharmaceutical Co., Ltd. (1)
No 69 New Ganquan West Road, Hanjiang Zone, Yangzhou, Jiangsu, China
Tel.: (86) 51487414925
Pharmaceutical Preparation Mfr
N.A.I.C.S.: 325412

JIANGSU ALCHA ALUMINIUM GROUP CO., LTD.
West of Baimao Town, Changshu, 215532, Jiangsu, China
Tel.: (86) 51252899988
Web Site: http://www.alcha.com
Year Founded: 2002
002160—(SSE)
Rev.: $952,587,324
Assets: $1,175,226,624
Liabilities: $671,297,328
Net Worth: $503,929,296
Earnings: ($52,707,564)
Emp.: 2,300
Fiscal Year-end: 12/31/22
Aluminum Foil Product Mfr
N.A.I.C.S.: 331315
Shi Ying (Chm)

JIANGSU ALLFAVOR INTELLIGENT CIRCUITS TECHNOLOGY CO., LTD.
No 7 Kongjia Road, Lishui Economic & Technological Development Zone, Nanjing, 211200, Jiangsu, China
Tel.: (86) 2557422058
Web Site: https://www.allfavorpcb.com
Year Founded: 2006
300964—(CHIN)
Rev.: $71,963,746
Assets: $185,488,168
Liabilities: $45,230,183
Net Worth: $140,257,985
Earnings: $679,845
Fiscal Year-end: 12/31/23
Circuit Board Mfr & Distr
N.A.I.C.S.: 334412
Xiaojun Dong (Chm)

Subsidiaries:

Allfavor Circuits (Shenzhen) Co., Ltd. (1)
No 9 Xingda Road Yanluo Street, Baoan District, Shenzhen, China
Tel.: (86) 75523491986
Printed Circuit Board Distr
N.A.I.C.S.: 423690

Zhuhai Allfavor Electronic Co., Ltd. (1)
No 28 Yingyue Road, Sanzao Town Jinwan District, Zhuhai, China
Tel.: (86) 7567514848
Printed Circuit Board Distr
N.A.I.C.S.: 423690

JIANGSU ALPHAMAB BIO-PHARMACEUTICALS CO., LTD.
175 Fangzhou Road, Suzhou Industrial Park, Suzhou, 215127, China
Tel.: (86) 51262850800 Ky
Web Site: https://www.alphamabonc.com
Year Founded: 2008
9966—(HKG)
Rev.: $25,562,322
Assets: $324,426,925
Liabilities: $85,775,997
Net Worth: $238,650,927
Earnings: ($49,903,868)
Emp.: 472
Fiscal Year-end: 12/31/22
Biotechnology Research & Development Services
N.A.I.C.S.: 541714
Ting Xu (Founder)

JIANGSU AMER NEW MATERIAL CO., LTD
No 1 East Zhongshan Road, Rugao, 226500, Jiangsu, China
Tel.: (86) 51387530125
Web Site: http://www.cjdg.com
Year Founded: 1994
002201—(SSE)
Rev.: $202,489,092
Assets: $334,927,008
Liabilities: $188,317,116
Net Worth: $146,609,892
Earnings: $5,082,480
Fiscal Year-end: 12/31/22
Fiberglass Product Mfr & Distr
N.A.I.C.S.: 327212
Wang Wenyin (Chm)

JIANGSU ANKURA INTELLIGENT POWER CO., LTD
No 100 Tianmu Lake Avenue Tianmu Lake Industrial Park, Liyang, 213333, Jiangsu, China
Tel.: (86) 51987983111
Web Site: https://www.ankura.com.cn
Year Founded: 2006
300617—(CHIN)
Rev.: $134,996,077
Assets: $486,330,584
Liabilities: $100,241,931
Net Worth: $386,088,653
Earnings: $28,855,320
Fiscal Year-end: 12/31/23
Cable Connector Mfr & Distr
N.A.I.C.S.: 333248
Chen Xiaoling (Chm & Gen Mgr)

JIANGSU AOYANG HEALTH INDUSTRY CO., LTD.
No 018 Zhenzhong Road Tangshi, Yangshe Town, Zhangjiagang, 215618, Jiangsu, China
Tel.: (86) 51258598699
Web Site: http://aykj.215600.net
Year Founded: 2001
002172—(SSE)
Rev.: $283,791,924
Assets: $380,207,412
Liabilities: $376,432,056
Net Worth: $3,775,356
Earnings: ($2,160,756)
Fiscal Year-end: 12/31/22
Chemical Fiber Mfr & Distr
N.A.I.C.S.: 327999
Xueru Shen (Chm & Gen Mgr)

JIANGSU APON MEDICAL TECHNOLOGY CO., LTD.
East of Yongtong Avenue Rudong Economic Development Zone, Nantong, 226400, China
Tel.: (86) 51380158888
Web Site: https://www.apon.com.cn
Year Founded: 2001
300753—(CHIN)
Rev.: $59,462,715
Assets: $121,070,857
Liabilities: $22,870,829
Net Worth: $98,200,028
Earnings: $1,165,872
Fiscal Year-end: 12/31/23
Medical Equipment Mfr & Distr
N.A.I.C.S.: 339113
Wang Ningyu (Chm)

JIANGSU ASIA-PACIFIC LIGHT ALLOY TECHNOLOGY CO., LTD.
No 58 Lihe East Road, Xinwu District, Wuxi, 214111, Jiangsu, China
Tel.: (86) 51088278652
Web Site: https://www.yatal.com
002540—(SSE)
Rev.: $944,741,772
Assets: $896,015,952
Liabilities: $114,507,432
Net Worth: $781,508,520
Earnings: $94,928,652
Fiscal Year-end: 12/31/22
Precision Aluminum Tubes & Aluminum Extruded Products Mfr
N.A.I.C.S.: 331318
Fuhai Zhou (Chm)

Subsidiaries:

Asia-Pacific Light Alloy (Nantong) Technology Co., Ltd. (1)
No 29 Haifang Road Haian Economic Development Zone, Jiangsu, China
Tel.: (86) 51388271111
Web Site: https://www.aplah.com
Aluminium Products Mfr
N.A.I.C.S.: 331313

Jiangsu APH Metal Printing Technology Co., Ltd. (1)
No 102 Xinjin Road, Wuxi New District, Jiangsu, China
Tel.: (86) 51081892568
Web Site: http://www.aph3d.com
Machine Tool Mfr & Distr
N.A.I.C.S.: 333517

Jiangsu Asia-Pacific AnsindarAluminium Co., Ltd. (1)
No 8 Chunhui middle road, Xishan economic developing zone Xishan district, Wuxi, 214101, Jiangsu, China
Tel.: (86) 51088265153
Web Site: https://www.ansindar.cn
Aluminium Products Mfr
N.A.I.C.S.: 331318

Wuxi Hatal Aluminium Co., Ltd. (1)
No 72 Zhouxin East Road, Binhu District, Wuxi, 214111, Jiangsu, China
Tel.: (86) 51085069506
Aluminium Products Mfr
N.A.I.C.S.: 331318

JIANGSU AZURE CORPORATION
No 10 Xinjing Middle Road, Zhangjiagang, Suzhou, 215618, Jiangsu, China
Tel.: (86) 51258161276
Web Site: http://www.aucksun.com
Year Founded: 2007
002245—(SSE)
Rev.: $882,430,848
Assets: $1,589,867,136
Liabilities: $579,641,400
Net Worth: $1,010,225,736

Jiangsu Azure Corporation—(Continued)
Earnings: $53,118,936
Emp.: 3,000
Fiscal Year-end: 12/31/22
Steel & Aluminum Alloy Plate Logistics Services
N.A.I.C.S.: 331315
Chen Kai (Chm, Pres & Gen Mgr)

JIANGSU BAICHUAN HIGH-TECH NEW MATERIALS CO.,LTD.
No 55 Jianshe Road, Yunting Subdistrict, Jiangyin, 214422, Jiangsu, China
Tel.: (86) 51081629979
Web Site: https://www.bcchem.com
Year Founded: 2002
002455—(SSE)
Rev.: $579,996,612
Assets: $1,413,818,172
Liabilities: $994,433,544
Net Worth: $419,384,628
Earnings: $19,069,128
Fiscal Year-end: 12/31/22
Chemical Products Mfr
N.A.I.C.S.: 325998
Zheng Tiejiang (Chm)

JIANGSU BAOLI INTERNATIONAL INVESTMENT CO., LTD.
Jiangyin Yunting Industrial Park, Jiangyin, 201107, Jiangsu, China
Tel.: (86) 51086017008
Web Site: https://en.baoligroups.com
Year Founded: 2002
300135—(SSE)
Rev.: $346,595,652
Assets: $331,259,760
Liabilities: $193,389,768
Net Worth: $137,869,992
Earnings: ($24,126,336)
Fiscal Year-end: 12/31/22
Asphalt Material Mfr
N.A.I.C.S.: 324121
Zhou Wenbin (Chm & Gen Mgr)

JIANGSU BEIREN ROBOT SYSTEM CO., LTD.
No 1 Qingqiu Lane, Suzhou Industrial Park, Suzhou, China
Tel.: (86) 4001016959
Web Site: http://www.br-robot.com
Year Founded: 2011
688218—(SHG)
Rev.: $90,000,150
Assets: $232,381,268
Liabilities: $99,474,657
Net Worth: $132,906,611
Earnings: $3,335,382
Fiscal Year-end: 12/31/21
Application Development Services
N.A.I.C.S.: 541511
Lin Tao (Founder & CTO)

JIANGSU BIDE SCIENCE & TECHNOLOGY CO., LTD.
No 27 Yuexiang Road, Yuecheng Town, Jiangyin, 214404, Jiangsu, China
Tel.: (86) 51086581042
Web Site: http://www.bidekeji.com
Year Founded: 2002
605298—(SHG)
Rev.: $32,227,837
Assets: $160,744,957
Liabilities: $24,167,249
Net Worth: $136,577,708
Earnings: $6,606,775
Emp.: 292
Fiscal Year-end: 12/31/22
Railroad Equipment Mfr
N.A.I.C.S.: 336510
Jianqun Wang (Chm & Gen Mgr)

JIANGSU BIOPERFECTUS TECHNOLOGIES CO., LTD.
2nd Floor Block 10 No 188 Xinjun Ring Road, Pujiang High-Tech Park Caohejing Development Area Minhang, Shanghai, 201114, China
Tel.: (86) 2154847326
Web Site: https://www.bioperfectus.com
Year Founded: 2010
688399—(SHG)
Rev.: $777,084,909
Assets: $686,696,400
Liabilities: $156,244,098
Net Worth: $530,452,302
Earnings: $256,637,216
Fiscal Year-end: 12/31/22
Medical Product Mfr & Distr
N.A.I.C.S.: 339112
Yongsheng Fang (Chm)

JIANGSU BOAMAX TECHNOLOGIES GROUP CO., LTD.
8th Floor Building N Zendai Himalaya No 2 Minzhi Road, Yuhuatai District, Nanjing, 210012, Jiangsu, China
Tel.: (86) 2552201300
Web Site: https://www.boamax.com
Year Founded: 2001
002514—(SSE)
Rev.: $96,037,812
Assets: $328,797,144
Liabilities: $128,668,176
Net Worth: $200,128,968
Earnings: $4,261,140
Emp.: 2,000
Fiscal Year-end: 12/31/22
Sheet Metal Products Mfr
N.A.I.C.S.: 332322
He Deyong (Chm & Pres)

JIANGSU BOILN PLASTICS CO., LTD.
No 1 Xingyu west road, Jinfeng Town, Zhangjiagang, 215626, Jiangsu, China
Tel.: (86) 51258956098
Web Site: http://www.boiln.com
Year Founded: 2006
301003—(SSE)
Rev.: $72,506,772
Assets: $161,350,488
Liabilities: $6,535,620
Net Worth: $154,814,868
Earnings: $15,932,592
Fiscal Year-end: 12/31/22
Plastic Product Mfr & Distr
N.A.I.C.S.: 326199
Feng Lv (Chm & Gen Mgr)

JIANGSU BOJUN INDUSTRIAL TECHNOLOGY CO., LTD.
No 88 LongJiang Road, Development Zone, Kunshan, 215300, Jiangsu, China
Tel.: (86) 51236689825
Web Site: http://www.sh-bojun.com
Year Founded: 2011
300926—(SSE)
Rev.: $195,283,764
Assets: $432,978,156
Liabilities: $253,977,984
Net Worth: $179,000,172
Earnings: $20,766,564
Fiscal Year-end: 12/31/22
Automotive Parts Mfr & Distr
N.A.I.C.S.: 336390
Yalin Wu (Chm & Gen Mgr)

JIANGSU BOQIAN NEW MATERIALS CO., LTD.
No 23 Jiangshan Avenue, High-tech Development Zone, Suqian, 223800, Jiangsu, China
Tel.: (86) 52780805772
Web Site: http://www.boqianpvm.com
Year Founded: 2010
605376—(SHG)
Rev.: $104,816,182
Assets: $291,688,525
Liabilities: $54,535,558
Net Worth: $237,152,967
Earnings: $21,548,760
Fiscal Year-end: 12/31/22
Metal Product Mfr & Distr
N.A.I.C.S.: 331491
Liping Wang (Chm)

Subsidiaries:

Ningbo Guangxin Import & Export Co., Ltd. (1)
Shiqi Street, Haishu District, Ningbo, Zhejiang, China
Tel.: (86) 57428827207
Nanometer Metal Powder Distr
N.A.I.C.S.: 424690

Ningbo Guangxin Nano Materials Co., Ltd. (1)
Shiqi Street, Haishu District, Ningbo, Zhejiang, China
Tel.: (86) 57428827522
Laboratory Equipment Mfr
N.A.I.C.S.: 334516

JIANGSU BOXIN INVESTING & HOLDINGS CO., LTD.
16th Floor Building B3 Gusu Software Park No 8 Zhujiawan Street, Gusu District, Suzhou, 215008, Jiangsu, China
Tel.: (86) 51268856070
Web Site: http://www.toppers.com.cn
Year Founded: 1993
600083—(SHG)
Rev.: $54,264,305
Assets: $154,322,303
Liabilities: $114,920,896
Net Worth: $39,401,407
Earnings: $8,684,976
Fiscal Year-end: 12/31/22
Holding Company
N.A.I.C.S.: 551112
Wang Wei (Chm)

JIANGSU BROADCASTING CABLE INFORMATION NETWORK CORPORATION LIMITED
Jiangsu Cable Tri-Network Integration Hub Center No 101, Yunlianghe West Road Qilin Technology Innovation Park, Nanjing, 210046, Jiangsu, China
Tel.: (86) 2583187799
Web Site: http://www.jscnnet.com
Year Founded: 2008
600959—(SHG)
Rev.: $1,053,818,658
Assets: $5,184,483,478
Liabilities: $1,980,311,575
Net Worth: $3,204,171,903
Earnings: $45,898,557
Fiscal Year-end: 12/31/22
Television & Radio Broadcasting Services
N.A.I.C.S.: 516120

JIANGSU CANLON BUILDING MATERIALS CO., LTD.
No 8 Hengtong Rd, Qidu Town Wujiang Dist, Suzhou, 215234, Jiangsu, China
Tel.: (86) 51263809938
Web Site: https://www.canlon.com
Year Founded: 2011
300715—(CHIN)
Rev.: $394,470,947
Assets: $918,961,289
Liabilities: $576,211,547
Net Worth: $342,749,742
Earnings: $3,188,450
Fiscal Year-end: 12/31/23
Asphalt Coating Material Mfr & Distr
N.A.I.C.S.: 324122

JIANGSU CANOPUS WISDOM MEDICAL TECHNOLOGY CO., LTD.
No 24-4 Changyang Road, West Taihu Science and Technology Industrial Part Wujin District, Changzhou, 213115, Jiangsu, China
Tel.: (86) 51986687028
Web Site: https://www.dx-med.com
Year Founded: 2001
301290—(CHIN)
Rev.: $62,070,840
Assets: $334,682,712
Liabilities: $25,279,020
Net Worth: $309,403,692
Earnings: $14,392,404
Fiscal Year-end: 12/31/22
Medical Device Mfr & Distr
N.A.I.C.S.: 339112
Shiping Wan (Chm)

JIANGSU CAS-IGBT TECHNOLOGY CO., LTD.
Linghu Road 200 Chinese Secsor Network International, Innovation Park Building D2 Drive Five, Wuxi, 214135, Jiangsu, China
Tel.: (86) 51081884888
Web Site: http://www.cas-junshine.com
Year Founded: 2011
Electronic Chips Research & Developer
N.A.I.C.S.: 334419

JIANGSU CHANGBAO STEEL TUBE CO., LTD.
No 558 Yanling East Road, Changzhou, 213018, Jiangsu, China
Tel.: (86) 51988813911
Web Site: https://www.cbsteeltube.com
Year Founded: 1958
002478—(SSE)
Rev.: $873,759,744
Assets: $1,029,888,756
Liabilities: $364,528,944
Net Worth: $665,359,812
Earnings: $66,132,612
Emp.: 2,000
Fiscal Year-end: 12/31/22
Steel Tube Mfr
N.A.I.C.S.: 331210
Jian Cao (Chm)

JIANGSU CHANGHAI COMPOSITE MATERIALS CO., LTD.
308 Changhong East Road, Changzhou, China
Tel.: (86) 51988708813
Web Site: https://www.changhaigfrp.com
Year Founded: 2000
300196—(CHIN)
Rev.: $423,591,012
Assets: $781,897,428
Liabilities: $185,830,632
Net Worth: $596,066,796
Earnings: $114,748,920
Emp.: 242
Fiscal Year-end: 12/31/22
Fiberglass Materials Mfr
N.A.I.C.S.: 339999

JIANGSU CHANGLING HYDRAULIC CO., LTD.
No 855 Yungu Road, Yunting Town, Jiangyin, Jiangsu, China
Tel.: (86) 51080287803
Web Site: https://www.changlingmach.cn
Year Founded: 2006

AND PRIVATE COMPANIES

605389—(SHG)
Rev.: $125,848,017
Assets: $288,843,179
Liabilities: $29,024,471
Net Worth: $259,818,708
Earnings: $17,848,645
Fiscal Year-end: 12/31/22
Hydraulic Parts Mfr & Distr
N.A.I.C.S.: 333611
Jifa Xia (Chm)

JIANGSU CHANGQING AGRO-CHEMICAL CO., LTD.
No 1006 Wenchang East Road, Yangzhou, 225000, Jiangsu, China
Tel.: (86) 51486168288
Web Site: https://www.jscq.com
Year Founded: 2001
002391—(SSE)
Rev.: $595,800,036
Assets: $1,049,346,792
Liabilities: $396,507,852
Net Worth: $652,838,940
Earnings: $36,833,940
Emp.: 1,800
Fiscal Year-end: 12/31/22
Agricultural Chemical Mfr
N.A.I.C.S.: 325920
Qingzhu Kong (VP-Foreign Trade Dept)

JIANGSU CHANGSHU AUTOMOTIVE TRIM GROUP CO., LTD.
No 288 Haiyu North Road, Changshu, 215500, Jiangsu, China
Tel.: (86) 51252330018
Web Site: http://www.caip.com.cn
Year Founded: 1992
603035—(SHG)
Rev.: $514,660,377
Assets: $1,198,767,759
Liabilities: $547,731,793
Net Worth: $651,035,965
Earnings: $71,845,039
Fiscal Year-end: 12/31/22
Passenger Car Equipment Mfr & Distr
N.A.I.C.S.: 336320
Luo Xiaochun (Chm & Gen Mgr)

Subsidiaries:

Beijing Changchun Automotive Parts Co., Ltd. (1)
No 3 Ruihe East 1 Road Beijing Economic Technical Development Zone, Beijing, 100176, China
Tel.: (86) 1056916932
Automotive Interior Mfr & Distr
N.A.I.C.S.: 336360

Changchun Changchun Automotive Interiors Co., Ltd. (1)
No 199 Xiangfan Road Changchun Economic Technology Development Zone, Changchun, 130033, Jilin, China
Tel.: (86) 43181929619
Automotive Interior Mfr & Distr
N.A.I.C.S.: 336360

Chengdu Suchun Automotive Parts Co., Ltd (1)
Tel.: (86) 2888491937
Automotive Interior Mfr & Distr
N.A.I.C.S.: 336360

Shenyang Changchun Automotive Parts Co., Ltd (1)
No 188 Jianshe Road Dadong District, Shenyang, 110122, Liaoning, China
Tel.: (86) 2431398069
Automotive Interior Mfr & Distr
N.A.I.C.S.: 336360

Wuhu Changchun Automotive Interiors Co., Ltd (1)
No 12-10 Yinhe North Road Wuhu Economic Technology Development Zone, Wuhu, 241009, Anhui, China
Tel.: (86) 5535801809
Automotive Interior Mfr & Distr
N.A.I.C.S.: 336360

JIANGSU CHANGSHU RURAL COMMERCIAL BANK CO., LTD.
No 58 Xinshiji Dadao, Changshu, 215500, JiangSu, China
Tel.: (86) 512962000
Web Site: http://www.csrcbank.com
601128—(SHG)
Rev.: $1,366,622,037
Assets: $46,308,211,952
Liabilities: $42,551,713,281
Net Worth: $3,756,498,671
Earnings: $454,350,631
Emp.: 7,376
Fiscal Year-end: 12/31/23
Commercial Banking Services
N.A.I.C.S.: 522110

JIANGSU CHENGXING PHOSPH-CHEMICALS CO., LTD.
No 618 Meiyuan Road, Jiangyin, 214432, Jiangsu, China
Tel.: (86) 51080622222
Web Site: https://www.cxpcchina.com
Year Founded: 1984
600078—(SHG)
Rev.: $637,072,469
Assets: $791,451,143
Liabilities: $436,396,278
Net Worth: $355,054,864
Earnings: $73,208,575
Emp.: 10,000
Fiscal Year-end: 12/31/22
Chemicals Mfr
N.A.I.C.S.: 325998
Li Xingxing (Chm)

Subsidiaries:

Yunnan Mile Phosphorus Electricity Co., Ltd. (1)
Baishapo, Zhuyuan Town Mile County, Mile City, 652304, Yunnan, China
Tel.: (86) 8736379977
Power Engineering Services
N.A.I.C.S.: 541330

Yunnan Xuanwei Phosphorus Electricity Co., Ltd. (1)
Industrial Park, Yangchang Town Xuanwei, Qujing, Yunnan, China
Tel.: (86) 8747973131
Emp.: 1,000
Power Engineering Services
N.A.I.C.S.: 541330

JIANGSU CHINAGREEN BIOLOGICAL TECHNOLOGY CO., LTD.
No 88 Lvdu Avenue, Siyang County, Suqian, 223700, Jiangsu, China
Tel.: (86) 52785302330
Web Site: http://www.chinagreenbio.com
Year Founded: 2010
300970—(SSE)
Rev.: $105,523,236
Assets: $278,042,544
Liabilities: $64,277,928
Net Worth: $213,764,616
Earnings: $10,986,300
Fiscal Year-end: 12/31/22
Mushroom Production Services
N.A.I.C.S.: 111411
Yangchao Yu (Chm & Gen Mgr)

JIANGSU CHUANZHIBOKE EDUCATION TECHNOLOGY CO., LTD.
1F Jinyanlong Office Building Jiancaicheng West Road, Changping District, Beijing, 100096, China
Tel.: (86) 1082939940
Web Site: http://www.itcast.cn
Year Founded: 2012
003032—(SSE)
Rev.: $112,715,928
Assets: $258,543,792
Liabilities: $70,659,108
Net Worth: $187,884,684
Earnings: $25,382,916
Fiscal Year-end: 12/31/22
Educational Support Services
N.A.I.C.S.: 611710
Huoming Li (Chm & Gen Mgr)

JIANGSU CHUNLAN REFRIGERATING EQUIPMENT CO., LTD.
1 Chunlan Rd, Taizhou, Jiangsu, China
Tel.: (86) 52386993086
Web Site: https://www.chunlan.com
600854—(SHG)
Rev.: $39,568,525
Assets: $339,003,017
Liabilities: $45,645,683
Net Worth: $293,357,334
Earnings: $17,249,979
Fiscal Year-end: 12/31/22
Refrigerator Equipment Mfr
N.A.I.C.S.: 335220

JIANGSU CNANO TECHNOLOGY CO., LTD.
No 113 Qinglongshan Road, New District, Zhenjiang, 212000, Jiangsu, China
Tel.: (86) 14088260918
Web Site: https://www.cnanotechnology.com
Year Founded: 2011
688116—(SHG)
Rev.: $258,550,475
Assets: $570,407,882
Liabilities: $215,397,271
Net Worth: $355,010,610
Earnings: $59,557,722
Fiscal Year-end: 12/31/22
Application Development Services
N.A.I.C.S.: 541511
Tao Zheng (Chm & Gen Mgr)

JIANGSU DAGANG CO., LTD.
11th Floor Jingkai Building No 401 Gangnan Road, Zhenjiang New District, Zhenjiang, 212132, Jiangsu, China
Tel.: (86) 51188901888
Web Site: https://www.dggf.cn
Year Founded: 2000
002077—(SSE)
Rev.: $79,926,912
Assets: $621,431,460
Liabilities: $137,759,076
Net Worth: $483,672,384
Earnings: $6,866,964
Fiscal Year-end: 12/31/22
Construction Engineering Services
N.A.I.C.S.: 541330
An Mingliang (Chm)

JIANGSU DAYBRIGHT INTELLIGENT ELECTRIC CO., LTD.
No 223 Jiangjun Avenue, Jiangning District, Nanjing, 211100, China
Tel.: (86) 2587163336
Web Site: https://www.daybright.cn
Year Founded: 2011
300670—(CHIN)
Rev.: $62,370,253
Assets: $302,870,051
Liabilities: $199,944,730
Net Worth: $102,925,321
Earnings: ($20,362,600)
Fiscal Year-end: 12/31/23
Electrical Equipment Mfr & Distr
N.A.I.C.S.: 335313
Chen Jie (Chm & Gen Mgr)

JIANGSU DEWEI ADVANCED MATERIALS CO., LTD.
E 99 Shanan Rd, Shaxi Town, Taicang, 215421, Jiangsu, China
Tel.: (86) 51253229367
Web Site: http://www.chinadewei.com
Year Founded: 1995
300325—(CHIN)
Rev.: $137,083,115
Assets: $405,287,945
Liabilities: $364,120,418
Net Worth: $41,167,527
Earnings: ($107,988,536)
Emp.: 300
Fiscal Year-end: 12/31/20
Polymer Materials Mfr for Cables & Wires
N.A.I.C.S.: 325998

JIANGSU DINGSHENG NEW MATERIAL JOINT-STOCK CO., LTD.
Jingkou Economic Development Zone, Zhenjiang, 212141, Jiangsu, China
Tel.: (86) 51185580854
Web Site: http://www.dingshengxincai.com
Year Founded: 2003
603876—(SHG)
Rev.: $3,033,377,802
Assets: $3,082,350,150
Liabilities: $2,195,633,985
Net Worth: $886,716,165
Earnings: $193,970,968
Emp.: 2,600
Fiscal Year-end: 12/31/22
Aluminum Product Mfr & Distr
N.A.I.C.S.: 331313
Xianhai Zhou (Chm)

Subsidiaries:

SLIM Aluminium S.p.A. (1)
Piazzale dell'Alluminio, 04012, Cisterna di Latina, Italy
Tel.: (39) 06968301
Emp.: 430
Rolled Aluminum Products Mfr
N.A.I.C.S.: 331318

JIANGSU DONGGUANG MICRO-ELECTRONICS CO., LTD.
42 Lv Yuan Road Industrial Park of Environmental Science & Tech, Yixing, Jiangsu, China
Tel.: (86) 510 87138935
Web Site: http://www.jsdgme.com
Year Founded: 1998
Sales Range: $150-199.9 Million
Semiconductor Devices & Integrated Circuits Mfr
N.A.I.C.S.: 334413
Jianping Shen (Chm)

JIANGSU EASTERN SHENGHONG CO., LTD.
No 73 East Market Road, Shengze Town Wujiang District, Suzhou, 215228, Jiangsu, China
Tel.: (86) 51263573480
Web Site: http://www.jsessh.com
Year Founded: 1998
000301—(SSE)
Rev.: $3,489,664,170
Assets: $9,642,058,388
Liabilities: $6,187,500,758
Net Worth: $3,454,557,631
Earnings: $48,461,855
Fiscal Year-end: 12/31/20
Eletric Power Generation Services
N.A.I.C.S.: 221117
Gaoxiong Ji (Deputy Chm & Deputy Gen Mgr)

JIANGSU EAZYTEC CO., LTD.
No 298 Xingye Road Xinjie Street, Yixing, 214205, Jiangsu, China

JIANGSU EAZYTEC CO., LTD.

Jiangsu Eazytec Co., Ltd.—(Continued)
Tel.: (86) 51080322888
Web Site: http://www.eazytec.com
Year Founded: 2008
688258—(SHG)
Rev.: $39,596,001
Assets: $168,453,886
Liabilities: $31,315,518
Net Worth: $137,138,368
Earnings: $7,161,102
Fiscal Year-end: 12/31/22
Information Technology Services
N.A.I.C.S.: 541512
Qian Xie (Chm & Gen Mgr)

JIANGSU ETERN COMPANY LIMITED

Luxu Section North Side 74K.318 National Road, Lili Town Wujiang District, Wujiang, 215211, Jiangsu, China
Tel.: (86) 51263272395
Web Site:
 https://www.yongding.com.cn
Year Founded: 1994
600105—(SHG)
Rev.: $593,555,658
Assets: $1,114,815,017
Liabilities: $657,430,525
Net Worth: $457,384,492
Earnings: $31,740,523
Fiscal Year-end: 12/31/22
Cable & Communication Equipment Mfr
N.A.I.C.S.: 335929
Mo Siming (Chm & Pres)

Subsidiaries:

Beijing Etern Zhiyuan Network Technology Co., Ltd. (1)
Room 1504 15th floor Yingu Building No 9 North FourthRing West Road, Haidian District, Beijing, China
Tel.: (86) 1082525868
Web Site: https://www.bjydzy.com
Telecommunication & Information Services
N.A.I.C.S.: 517810

JIANGSU EXPRESSWAY COMPANY LIMITED

No 6 Xianlin Avenue, Nanjing, 210049, Jiangsu, China
Tel.: (86) 2584362700
Web Site:
 http://www.jsexpressway.com
600377—(SHG)
Rev.: $1,861,086,675
Assets: $11,015,551,652
Liabilities: $5,687,325,053
Net Worth: $5,328,226,599
Earnings: $522,865,774
Emp.: 4,798
Fiscal Year-end: 12/31/22
Passenger Transportation, Real Estate & Investment Management
N.A.I.C.S.: 523940
Yong Xiang Qian (Gen Mgr)

JIANGSU FASTEN COMPANY LIMITED

No 165 Chengjiang Middle Road, Jiangyin, 214434, Jiangsu, China
Tel.: (86) 51086119890
Web Site: http://www.fasten.com.cn
Year Founded: 1993
000890—(SSE)
Rev.: $95,132,232
Assets: $258,208,236
Liabilities: $228,450,456
Net Worth: $29,757,780
Earnings: ($1,590,732)
Fiscal Year-end: 12/31/22
Metal Products Mfr
N.A.I.C.S.: 331110
Chen Mingjun (Chm & Gen Mgr)

JIANGSU FEILIKS INTERNATIONAL LOGISTICS INC.

No 999 Meigui Road Economic and Technical Development Zone, Kunshan, 215300, Jiangsu, China
Tel.: (86) 51257352888
Web Site: https://www.feiliks.com
Year Founded: 1993
300240—(CHIN)
Rev.: $950,853,384
Assets: $519,513,696
Liabilities: $278,701,020
Net Worth: $240,812,676
Earnings: $15,108,444
Emp.: 3,000
Fiscal Year-end: 12/31/22
Cargo Terminal Storage Service, Container Transportation, Inland Freight Service, International Freight Forwarding
N.A.I.C.S.: 493190
Qin Yao (Chm)

Subsidiaries:

HuaiAn Feili Supply Chain Management Co., Ltd. (1)
Huaian Economic And Technical Development Zone, Huai'an, Jiangsu, China
Tel.: (86) 517 83730013
Web Site: http://www.feiliks.com
Supply Chain Management Services
N.A.I.C.S.: 541618

Suzhou Feili Supply Chain Management Co., Ltd. (1)
No 8 Modern Logistics Building Weisheng Road SuZhou Industrial Park, Suzhou, JiangSu, China
Tel.: (86) 512 62584946
Web Site: http://www.feiliks.com
Logistics Consulting Servies
N.A.I.C.S.: 541614

Suzhou Tanji Electronic Technology Co., Ltd. (1)
Processing Zone Economic And Technology Development Zone, 21530, Suzhou, China
Tel.: (86) 512 50130512
Logistics Consulting Servies
N.A.I.C.S.: 541614
Grant Yan (Mgr)

JIANGSU FENGSHAN GROUP CO., LTD.

1903 Central International Plaza 105-6 North Zhongshan Road, Nanjing, China
Tel.: (86) 2586558671
Web Site: https://www.fschem.com
Year Founded: 1988
603810—(SHG)
Rev.: $239,967,538
Assets: $374,474,515
Liabilities: $149,938,608
Net Worth: $224,535,907
Earnings: $13,931,794
Fiscal Year-end: 12/31/22
Agrochemical Mfr & Distr
N.A.I.C.S.: 325320
Fengshan Yin (Founder & Chm)

JIANGSU FEYMER TECHNOLOGY CO., LTD.

No 1 Fenghuang South Road, Feymer Technology Administrative District Fenghuang Town, Zhangjiagang, 215613, Jiangsu, China
Tel.: (86) 4009280389
Web Site: https://www.feymer.com
Year Founded: 2010
688350—(SHG)
Rev.: $238,225,357
Assets: $356,893,964
Liabilities: $134,867,819
Net Worth: $222,026,145
Earnings: $18,001,007
Fiscal Year-end: 12/31/22
Chemical Product Mfr & Distr
N.A.I.C.S.: 325520
Yixin Xiong (Chm & Gen Mgr)

JIANGSU FINANCIAL LEASING CO., LTD.

8F-9F 11F-19F 25F-33F Building 1 No 99 Jialingjiang East Street, Jianye District, Nanjing, 210019, Jiangsu, China
Tel.: (86) 2586816906
Web Site: http://www.jsleasing.cn
Year Founded: 1985
600901—(SHG)
Rev.: $603,737,794
Assets: $15,214,860,708
Liabilities: $12,985,365,641
Net Worth: $2,229,495,067
Earnings: $317,520,065
Fiscal Year-end: 12/31/21
Financial Services
N.A.I.C.S.: 532412
Xiangen Xiong (Chm)

JIANGSU FLAG CHEMICAL INDUSTRY CO., LTD.

309 Changfenghe Road New Material Science and Technology Park, Jiangbei, Nanjing, 210047, Jiangsu, China
Tel.: (86) 2558375015
Web Site: https://en.flagchem.com
Year Founded: 2003
300575—(CHIN)
Rev.: $336,633,373
Assets: $543,186,757
Liabilities: $223,850,243
Net Worth: $319,336,514
Earnings: $26,990,114
Fiscal Year-end: 12/31/23
Agrochemical Mfr & Distr
N.A.I.C.S.: 325311
Wu Yaojun (Chm & Gen Mgr)

Subsidiaries:

Hualan Glory Chemical Co., Ltd. (1)
2 Yannan Avenue, Salt Chemical New Material Industrial Park, Huai'an, Jiangsu, China
Tel.: (86) 51787238698
Agrochemical Product Mfr
N.A.I.C.S.: 325320

Jiangsu Flagchem International Co., Ltd. (1)
Building 2 Jiangsu Software Park 6 Suyuan Road, Xuanwu District, Nanjing, Jiangsu, China
Tel.: (86) 2586890329
Agrochemical Product Mfr
N.A.I.C.S.: 325320

JIANGSU GENERAL SCIENCE TECHNOLOGY CO., LTD

Next to Jin Gang Road, Dong Gang Town, Wuxi, 214199, Jiangsu, China
Tel.: (86) 4006858183
Web Site: https://en.ty-tyre.com
Year Founded: 2002
601500—(SHG)
Rev.: $578,514,522
Assets: $1,290,846,712
Liabilities: $685,713,586
Net Worth: $605,133,126
Earnings: $2,381,465
Fiscal Year-end: 12/31/22
Tire Mfr & Distr
N.A.I.C.S.: 326211
Gu Cui (Chm)

JIANGSU GIAN TECHNOLOGY CO., LTD.

No 59 Zonglv Road Zhonglou Economic Development Zone, Changzhou, 213014, Jiangsu, China
Tel.: (86) 51969890866
Web Site: http://www.jsgian.com
Year Founded: 2004
300709—(CHIN)
Rev.: $309,247,584
Assets: $453,243,300
Liabilities: $164,820,895
Net Worth: $288,422,404

INTERNATIONAL PUBLIC

Earnings: $23,418,848
Fiscal Year-end: 12/31/23
Industrial Molding Machinery Mfr
N.A.I.C.S.: 333248
Mingxi Wang (Chm, Pres & Gen Mgr)

JIANGSU GOODWE POWER SUPPLY TECHNOLOGY CO., LTD.

No 93 Tayuan Road, New District, Suzhou, 215011, Jiangsu, China
Tel.: (86) 51269582201
Web Site:
 https://www.goodwe.com.cn
Year Founded: 2010
688390—(SHG)
Rev.: $661,317,205
Assets: $814,143,981
Liabilities: $493,874,634
Net Worth: $320,269,346
Earnings: $91,160,063
Emp.: 3,000
Fiscal Year-end: 12/31/22
Power Supply Equipment Mfr & Distr
N.A.I.C.S.: 335312
Min Huang (Chm & Gen Mgr)

JIANGSU GUOJING HOLDING GROUP CO., LTD.

7, Yanzhengzhong Avenue Hutang Town Wujin District, Changzhou, 213000, Jiangsu, China
Tel.: (86) 05198580905
Emp.: 100
Investment Management
N.A.I.C.S.: 523999

JIANGSU GUOMAO REDUCER CO., LTD.

No 98 Longqian Road Wujin Hi-tech Industrial Development Zone, Changzhou, 213164, Jiangsu, China
Tel.: (86) 51969878020
Web Site:
 http://www.guomaoglobal.com
Year Founded: 2013
603915—(SHG)
Rev.: $378,628,951
Assets: $651,929,583
Liabilities: $191,702,820
Net Worth: $460,226,763
Earnings: $58,111,012
Emp.: 3,500
Fiscal Year-end: 12/31/22
Motor Product Mfr
N.A.I.C.S.: 335312
Guozhong Xu (Chm)

JIANGSU GUOTAI INTERNATIONAL GROUP CO., LTD.

31F Guotai Building Renmin Middle Road, Zhangjiagang, 215600, Jiangsu, China
Tel.: (86) 51258696853
Web Site: http://www.gtiigm.com
Year Founded: 1998
002091—(SSE)
Rev.: $6,011,874,648
Assets: $5,532,533,604
Liabilities: $2,827,142,136
Net Worth: $2,705,391,468
Earnings: $242,118,396
Emp.: 5,550
Fiscal Year-end: 12/31/22
Chemical Products Mfr
N.A.I.C.S.: 325998
Zhang Ziyan (Chm)

JIANGSU GUOXIN CORP., LTD.

No 88 Changjiang Road, Xuanwu District, Nanjing, 210005, Jiangsu, China
Tel.: (86) 2584679116
Web Site:
 http://www.saintymarine.com.cn
Year Founded: 2003

AND PRIVATE COMPANIES

002608—(SSE)
Rev.: $4,554,410,328
Assets: $11,629,979,244
Liabilities: $6,273,180,108
Net Worth: $5,356,799,136
Earnings: $9,571,068
Fiscal Year-end: 12/31/22
Ship Builder & Operator
N.A.I.C.S.: 336611
Xu Wenjin (Chm)

JIANGSU HAGONG INTELLIGENT ROBOT CO., LTD.
No 15 Shuangliang Road, Lingang Subdistrict Jiangyin, Jiangsu, 100029, China
Tel.: (86) 1060181838
Web Site: http://en.hgzngroup.com
Year Founded: 1980
000584—(SSE)
Sales Range: $100-124.9 Million
Holding Company; One-stop Industrial Robotic Platform
N.A.I.C.S.: 551112
Di Ai (Bd of Dirs & Chm)

JIANGSU HAILI WIND POWER EQUIPMENT TECHNOLOGY CO., LTD.
North of Jinshajiang Road and East of Jinggangshan Road, Rudong Economic and Technological Development Zone, Jiangsu, 226400, China
Tel.: (86) 51380152296
Web Site: https://www.jshlfd.com
Year Founded: 2009
301155—(CHIN)
Rev.: $229,236,696
Assets: $996,157,656
Liabilities: $202,826,052
Net Worth: $793,331,604
Earnings: $28,793,232
Fiscal Year-end: 12/31/22
Electronic Component Mfr & Distr
N.A.I.C.S.: 334419
Shijun Xu (Chm)

JIANGSU HANSOH PHARMACEUTICAL GROUP CO., LTD.
No 9 Dongjin Road Huaguoshan Avenue, Lianyungang, Jiangsu, China
Tel.: (86) 51883096666   CN
Web Site: https://www.hansoh.cn
Year Founded: 1995
3692—(HKG)
Rev.: $1,299,070,946
Assets: $4,154,004,071
Liabilities: $1,018,350,548
Net Worth: $3,135,653,522
Earnings: $357,740,779
Emp.: 10,523
Fiscal Year-end: 12/31/22
Pharmaceutical Product Mfr & Distr
N.A.I.C.S.: 325412

JIANGSU HANVO SAFETY PRODUCT CO., LTD.
128 Jinshajiang Road Rudong New Development Zone, Nantong, 226400, Jiangsu, China
Tel.: (86) 51381901801
Web Site: https://www.hanvosafety.com
Year Founded: 2004
300952—(SSE)
Rev.: $125,394,048
Assets: $212,274,972
Liabilities: $62,350,236
Net Worth: $149,924,736
Earnings: $17,086,680
Emp.: 1,500
Fiscal Year-end: 12/31/22
Safety Gloves Product Mfr
N.A.I.C.S.: 339113
Xian Hua Wang (Founder)

JIANGSU HENGLI HYDRAULIC CO., LTD.
No 98 Longqian Road Wujin Hi-tech Industrial Development Zone, Changzhou, 213164, Jiangsu, China
Tel.: (86) 51981689797
Web Site: http://www.henglicn.com
Year Founded: 2005
601100—(SHG)
Rev.: $1,426,265,596
Assets: $1,889,391,848
Liabilities: $473,843,292
Net Worth: $1,415,548,557
Earnings: $412,686,456
Emp.: 6,000
Fiscal Year-end: 12/31/21
Oil Cylinder Mfr
N.A.I.C.S.: 333995
Liping Wang (Chm)

Subsidiaries:

Hengli America Corporation   (1)
580 W Crossroads Pkwy Bolingbrook, Chicago, IL 60440
Tel.: (630) 995-3674
Hydraulic Pump & Cylinder Distr
N.A.I.C.S.: 423830

Hengli Hydraulic India System Solutions Pvt. Ltd.   (1)
PAP - B - 67/1 Bhamboli Varale Chakan MIDC Phase II, Pune, India
Tel.: (91) 9845673856
Hydraulic Pump & Cylinder Distr
N.A.I.C.S.: 423830

InLine Hydraulik GmbH   (1)
Sperenberger Str 13, 12277, Berlin, Germany
Tel.: (49) 30720880
Web Site: https://www.inlinehydraulik.com
Hydraulic Equipment Mfr & Distr
N.A.I.C.S.: 333914

Shanghai Lixin Hydraulic Co., Ltd.   (1)
No 81 Zhuhang Road, Minhang District, Shanghai, 200237, China
Tel.: (86) 21 64761280
Web Site: http://www.shlixin.com
Hydraulic Components Mfr
N.A.I.C.S.: 332911

JIANGSU HENGRUI MEDICINE CO., LTD.
No 7 Kunlunshan Road, Lianyungang Economic and Technological Development Zone, Lianyungang, Jiangsu, China
Tel.: (86) 4008283900
Web Site: https://www.hengrui.com
Year Founded: 1970
600276—(SHG)
Rev.: $2,987,048,006
Assets: $5,946,643,278
Liabilities: $553,436,161
Net Worth: $5,393,207,116
Earnings: $548,445,138
Emp.: 24,000
Fiscal Year-end: 12/31/22
Pharmaceuticals Product Mfr
N.A.I.C.S.: 325412
Zhou Yunshu (Chm & Gen Mgr)

JIANGSU HENGSHUN VINEGAR-INDUSTRY CO., LTD.
No 66 Hengshun Avenue, Dantu New Town, Zhenjiang, 212028, Jiangsu, China
Tel.: (86) 51185307777
Web Site: http://www.zjhengshun.com
Year Founded: 1993
600305—(SHG)
Rev.: $300,318,408
Assets: $416,665,754
Liabilities: $104,140,731
Net Worth: $312,525,023
Earnings: $19,374,372
Fiscal Year-end: 12/31/22
Seasoning Product Mfr & Distr
N.A.I.C.S.: 311941
Hang Zhuhong (Chm)

JIANGSU HIGH HOPE INTERNATIONAL GROUP CORPORATION
91 Bai Xia Road, Nanjing, 225500, Jiangsu, China
Tel.: (86) 2584691000
Web Site: http://www.high-hope.com
Year Founded: 1996
600981—(SHG)
Rev.: $6,705,409,637
Assets: $3,510,396,377
Liabilities: $2,684,811,159
Net Worth: $825,585,219
Earnings: ($70,183,952)
Fiscal Year-end: 12/31/22
Textile Product Trading Services
N.A.I.C.S.: 314999
Yang Chengming (Chm)

Subsidiaries:

High Hope Aglory Limited   (1)
No 91 Baixia Road Huihong Building 16-19 Floors, Nanjing, 210001, Jiangsu, China
Tel.: (86) 25 469 1300
Web Site: https://www.aglory.com
Emp.: 170
Textile Products Mfr
N.A.I.C.S.: 314999

High Hope Group Jiangsu Tongtai Co., Ltd.   (1)
No 50 Zhong Hua Road, Nanjing, 210001, China
Tel.: (86) 2552327222
Textile Products Mfr
N.A.I.C.S.: 314999

High Hope International Group Jiangsu Medicines and Health Products Import & Export Co., Ltd.   (1)
10-11/f High Hope Mansion 91 Bai Xia Road, Nanjing, 210001, China
Tel.: (86) 2584691899
Web Site: https://www.mehecojs.cn
Pharmaceutical Products Distr
N.A.I.C.S.: 424210

High Hope Intl Group Jiangsu Asset Management Co., Ltd.   (1)
High Hope Mansion 91 Bai Xia Road, Nanjing, 210001, China
Tel.: (86) 2584691212
Textile Products Mfr
N.A.I.C.S.: 314999

High Hope Intl Group Jiangsu Champion Holdings Ltd.   (1)
High Hope Building No 91 Baixia Rd, Nanjing, 210001, China
Tel.: (86) 258 469 1099
Web Site: https://www.hhchampion.com
Textile Products Mfr
N.A.I.C.S.: 314999

High Hope Intl Group Jiangsu Medicines & Health Products Import & Export Corp. Ltd.   (1)
12-14/F High Hope Mansion 91 Bai Xia Road, Nanjing, 210001, China
Tel.: (86) 258 677 0363
Web Site: https://www.jiangsulight.cn
Textile Products Mfr
N.A.I.C.S.: 314999

High Hope Zhongding Corporation   (1)
No 100 Jian Ye Road, Nanjing, 210004, China
Tel.: (86) 255 800 6166
Web Site: https://www.jslgroup.com
Textile Products Mfr
N.A.I.C.S.: 314999

High Hope Zhongtian Corporation   (1)
15 Hubu Street, Nanjing, China
Tel.: (86) 2586895000
Web Site: https://www.jstex.com
Textile Products Mfr
N.A.I.C.S.: 314999

Jiangsu Animals By-Products Import & Export Group Corporation   (1)
No 50 Zhonghua Road, Nanjing, 210001, China
Tel.: (86) 2552306185
Textile Products Mfr
N.A.I.C.S.: 314999

Jiangsu Cereals, Oils & Foodstuffs Import & Export Group Corp.   (1)
No 528 Taiping Road, Nanjing, 210001, China
Tel.: (86) 2552851799
Textile Products Mfr
N.A.I.C.S.: 314999

Jiangsu High Hope Arser Co., Ltd.   (1)
7/F Huihong No 91 Jianye Road, Nanjing, 210004, China
Tel.: (86) 2584216287
Web Site: https://www.arserwood.com
Plywood Mfr
N.A.I.C.S.: 321212

Jiangsu High Hope Baby Co., Ltd.   (1)
No 91 Baixia Road, Nanjing, 210001, China
Tel.: (86) 2552328275
Textile Products Mfr
N.A.I.C.S.: 314999

Jiangsu High Hope Cold Chain Logistics Co., Ltd.   (1)
No 136 Jingang Road, Dagang New District, Zhenjiang, 212132, Jiangsu, China
Web Site: http://www.hhcold.com
Logistic Services
N.A.I.C.S.: 541614

Jiangsu High Hope Convention & Exhibition Corp.   (1)
35th Floor 50 Zhonghua Road, Nanjing, 210001, Jiangsu, China
Tel.: (86) 2552236117
Textile Products Mfr
N.A.I.C.S.: 314999

Jiangsu High Hope International Group Laiyinda Co., Ltd.   (1)
High Hope International Commercial Building 181 Hunan Road, Nanjing, 210009, China
Tel.: (86) 2583171516
Textile Products Mfr
N.A.I.C.S.: 314999

Jiangsu High Hope International Group Sunshine Import & Export Corporation   (1)
17/F Jiangsu International Business Mansion 50 Zhonghua Road, Nanjing, 210001, China
Tel.: (86) 2552851352
Web Site: http://www.jssunshine.com
Textile Products Mfr
N.A.I.C.S.: 314999

Jiangsu High Hope Venture Co., Ltd.   (1)
Building No 91 Building China 12-13 Huihong Baixia Road, Nanjing, 210001, China
Tel.: (86) 2586770716
Textile Products Mfr
N.A.I.C.S.: 314999

JIANGSU HONGDE SPECIAL PARTS CO., LTD.
Group 4, Qiqiao Village Xingren Town Tongzhou District, Nantong, 226352, Jiangsu, China
Tel.: (86) 51380600008
Web Site: https://www.nt-casting.com
Year Founded: 1994
301163—(CHIN)
Rev.: $98,175,267
Assets: $187,673,788
Liabilities: $31,162,113
Net Worth: $156,511,676
Earnings: $6,869,169
Fiscal Year-end: 12/31/23
Steel Product Mfr & Distr
N.A.I.C.S.: 331210
Jinde Yang (Chm)

JIANGSU HONGDOU INDUS-

JIANGSU HONGDOU INDUS—(CONTINUED)

TRIAL CO., LTD.
26-28F Building A Hongdou Fortune Plaza No 19 Tonghui Street, Core District Xidong New Town Business District, Wuxi, 214105, Jiangsu, China
Tel.: (86) 51066868422
Web Site:
  https://www.hongdou.com.cn
Year Founded: 1995
600400—(SHG)
Rev.: $328,730,356
Assets: $665,068,103
Liabilities: $237,358,569
Net Worth: $427,709,534
Earnings: $2,111,532
Fiscal Year-end: 12/31/22
Apparel Mfr & Distr
N.A.I.C.S.: 315990
Zhou Hongjiang (Chm)

JIANGSU HONGTIAN TECHNOLOGY CO., LTD.
No 16 West Henggang Street Yangchenghu Industrial Park, Xiangcheng District, Suzhou, 215138, Jiangsu, China
Tel.: (86) 51288180808
Web Site: https://www.douson.cn
Year Founded: 2001
603800—(SHG)
Rev.: $307,413,227
Assets: $519,049,758
Liabilities: $349,399,496
Net Worth: $169,650,262
Earnings: $14,945,145
Fiscal Year-end: 12/31/22
Oil & Gas Field Equipment Mfr
N.A.I.C.S.: 333132
Zhao Weibin (Chm)

Subsidiaries:

Suzhou Baoforging Co., Ltd.   (1)
No 18 Changtai Road, Dongqiao Town Xiangcheng District, Suzhou, China
Tel.: (86) 51265085929
Web Site: http://en.baoforging.cn
Emp.: 300
Oil & Gas Field Machinery & Equipment Mfr
N.A.I.C.S.: 333132

Suzhou Douson Valve Co., Ltd.   (1)
Guijia Alley 42 Xinglong Street Suzhou Industrial Park, Jiangsu, China
Tel.: (86) 51269369380
Web Site: http://www.dousonvalve.com
Emp.: 270
Industrial Valve Mfr
N.A.I.C.S.: 332911

USA Master Valve Co., Ltd.   (1)
23555 Clay Rd, Katy, TX 77493
Tel.: (832) 838-4999
Web Site: http://www.mastervalveusa.com
Oil & Gas Field Machinery & Equipment Mfr
N.A.I.C.S.: 333132

JIANGSU HONGTU HIGH TECHNOLOGY CO., LTD.
4F No 68 Ruanjian Avenue Yuhuatai District, Nanjing, 210012, Jiangsu, China
Tel.: (86) 2583274777
Web Site: http://www.hiteker.com.cn
600122—(SHG)
Rev.: $341,912,629
Assets: $1,566,563,057
Liabilities: $1,445,110,426
Net Worth: $121,452,631
Earnings: ($339,491,911)
Fiscal Year-end: 12/31/20
Electronics Mfr
N.A.I.C.S.: 335999
Yan Alan (Chm)

JIANGSU HOPERUN SOFTWARE CO., LTD.
No 168 Software Avenue, Yuhuatai District, Nanjing, 210012, Jiangsu, China
Tel.: (86) 2552668518
Web Site: http://www.hoperun.com
Year Founded: 2006
300339—(CHIN)
Rev.: $417,649,284
Assets: $674,654,292
Liabilities: $224,568,396
Net Worth: $450,085,896
Earnings: $14,799,564
Emp.: 1,800
Fiscal Year-end: 12/31/22
Software Publisher
N.A.I.C.S.: 513210
Hongwei Zhou (Chm, Pres & Gen Mgr)

Subsidiaries:

Beijing UISF Information Technology Co., Ltd.   (1)
2/F Building 5 No 11 Hepingli East Street Dongcheng District, Beijing, 100013, China
Tel.: (86) 1056753666
Software Development Services
N.A.I.C.S.: 513210

Guangzhou HopeRun Software Co., Ltd   (1)
Room 508 No 1023 Gaopu Road Tianhe District, Guangzhou, China
Tel.: (86) 2087096935
Software Development Services
N.A.I.C.S.: 513210

Hoperun Software Singapore Pte. Ltd.   (1)
152 Beach Road 13-06 Gateway East, Singapore, 189721, Singapore
Tel.: (65) 63919100
Software Development Services
N.A.I.C.S.: 513210

Hoperun Technology Corporation   (1)
2 Burlington Woods Dr Ste 100, Burlington, MA 01803
Tel.: (781) 202-9120
Web Site: https://www.hoperun.net
Software Development Services
N.A.I.C.S.: 513210

Shanghai HopeRun Information Technology & Services Co., Ltd   (1)
Building 82 No 1198 Qinzhou North Road Xuhui District, Shanghai, 200235, China
Tel.: (86) 2160927008
Software Development Services
N.A.I.C.S.: 513210

Xi'an HopeRun Software Information Technology Co., Ltd   (1)
11-12/F Tower A Jiayu Mainsion No 58 Jinye 1st Road Gaoxin District, Xi'an, China
Tel.: (86) 2968713333
Software Development Services
N.A.I.C.S.: 513210

JIANGSU HUACHANG CHEMICAL CO., LTD.
No 1 Nanhai Road Yangtze River International Chemical Industrial Park, Zhangjiagang, 215634, Jiangsu, China
Tel.: (86) 51258686806
Web Site:
  https://www.huachangchem.cn
Year Founded: 1970
002274—(SSE)
Rev.: $1,269,913,788
Assets: $1,166,858,784
Liabilities: $452,034,648
Net Worth: $714,824,136
Earnings: $122,444,244
Fiscal Year-end: 12/31/22
Chemical Fertilizer Mfr & Distr
N.A.I.C.S.: 325311

JIANGSU HUAHONG TECHNOLOGY STOCK CO., LTD.
No 1118 Chengyang Road, Zhouzhuang Town, Jiangyin, 214423, Jiangsu, China
Tel.: (86) 51080629680
Web Site: https://www.asiabaler.com
Year Founded: 2004
002645—(SSE)
Rev.: $1,038,278,124
Assets: $790,745,920
Liabilities: $239,386,029
Net Worth: $551,359,891
Earnings: $81,512,316
Fiscal Year-end: 12/31/21
Recycling Resource Process Equipment Mfr
N.A.I.C.S.: 333519
Shiyong Hu (Board of Directors & Pres)

JIANGSU HUALAN NEW PHARMACEUTICAL MATERIAL CO., LTD.
No 1488 Zhencheng Road, Shengang Town, Jiangyin, 214443, Jiangsu, China
Tel.: (86) 51068951553
Web Site:
  https://www.hualannpm.com
Year Founded: 1992
301093—(CHIN)
Rev.: $87,735,648
Assets: $381,911,745
Liabilities: $31,746,521
Net Worth: $350,165,224
Earnings: $16,609,563
Emp.: 800
Fiscal Year-end: 12/31/23
Pharmaceutical Product Mfr & Distr
N.A.I.C.S.: 325412
Yimin Hua (Chm & Gen Mgr)

JIANGSU HUASHENG TIANLONG PHOTOELECTRIC CO., LTD.
No 318 Huacheng Road Economic Development Zone, Jintan City, Changzhou, 213200, Jiangsu, China
Tel.: (86) 51982330395
Web Site: http://www.hstl.cn
Year Founded: 2001
300029—(CHIN)
Rev.: $35,049,456
Assets: $33,798,492
Liabilities: $29,607,552
Net Worth: $4,190,940
Earnings: $1,687,608
Emp.: 780
Fiscal Year-end: 12/31/22
Photovoltaic Equipment Mfr
N.A.I.C.S.: 334413
Guo Tairan (Chm & Gen Mgr)

JIANGSU HUAXICUN CO., LTD.
No 88 Jingbang Road Huaxi Industrial Park, Huashi Town, Jiangyin, 214420, Jiangsu, China
Tel.: (86) 51086217149
Web Site:
  https://www.jshuaxicun.com
Year Founded: 1999
000936—(SSE)
Rev.: $411,012,576
Assets: $896,865,372
Liabilities: $188,121,960
Net Worth: $708,743,412
Earnings: $29,342,196
Fiscal Year-end: 12/31/22
Textile Chemical Fiber Product Mfr
N.A.I.C.S.: 325220
Xie'En Wu (Chm)

JIANGSU HUAXIN NEW MATERIAL CO., LTD.
No 18 the Pearl River Road, Xinyi, 221400, Jiangsu, China
Tel.: (86) 51681639993
Web Site:
  https://www.huaxinfilms.com
Year Founded: 1999
300717—(CHIN)
Rev.: $46,065,345
Assets: $108,286,565
Liabilities: $13,387,074
Net Worth: $94,899,490
Earnings: $5,772,202
Fiscal Year-end: 12/31/23
Card Material Mfr & Distr
N.A.I.C.S.: 326199
Zhenbin Li (Chm, Pres & Gen Mgr)

JIANGSU HUIFENG BIO-AGRICULTURE CO., LTD.
South of Wanggang Gate, Dafeng, 224100, Jiangsu, China
Tel.: (86) 51585055512
Web Site: https://www.hfagro.com
Year Founded: 1989
002496—(SSE)
Sales Range: $800-899.9 Million
Pesticide Mfr
N.A.I.C.S.: 325320

Subsidiaries:

Shanghai Dibai Plant Protection Co., Ltd   (1)
14 F No 986 Hejing Road, Jiading District, Shanghai, 201800, China
Tel.: (86) 2159561999
Agricultural Products Sales
N.A.I.C.S.: 424910

JIANGSU INNOVATIVE ECOLOGICAL NEW MATERIALS LTD.
16 Kaixuan West Road Economic Development Zone, Yixing, 214200, China
Tel.: (86) 51087869999
2116—(HKG)
Rev.: $36,108,493
Assets: $48,786,052
Liabilities: $6,598,800
Net Worth: $42,187,252
Earnings: $1,608,703
Emp.: 59
Fiscal Year-end: 12/31/22
Investment Services
N.A.I.C.S.: 523940
Xiaojun Ge (Chm & CEO)

JIANGSU JIANGNAN HIGH POLYMER FIBER CO., LTD.
Jiangnan Building No 7 Suyang Road, Huangdai Town Xiangcheng District, Suzhou, 215143, Jiangsu, China
Tel.: (86) 51265481181
Web Site: https://www.jngx.cn
Year Founded: 1984
600527—(SHG)
Rev.: $116,667,626
Assets: $351,093,155
Liabilities: $21,564,963
Net Worth: $329,528,193
Earnings: $11,729,142
Emp.: 700
Fiscal Year-end: 12/31/22
Timber Product Mfr
N.A.I.C.S.: 325220
Wang Hongxing (Chm-Supervisory Bd)

JIANGSU JIANGNAN WATER CO., LTD.
No 66 Yangtze River Road, Binjiang, Jiangyin, 214432, Jiangsu, China
Tel.: (86) 51086276771
Web Site: http://www.jsjnsw.com
Year Founded: 2003
601199—(SHG)
Rev.: $178,029,531
Assets: $821,897,276

AND PRIVATE COMPANIES

Liabilities: $331,754,824
Net Worth: $490,142,451
Earnings: $39,371,010
Fiscal Year-end: 12/31/22
Tap Water Production & Supply Services
N.A.I.C.S.: 221310
Feng Hua (Chm)

JIANGSU JIANGYIN RURAL COMMERCIAL BANK.
No 1 Chengjiang Middle Road, Jiangyin, 214431, Jiangsu, China
Tel.: (86) 51086851978
Web Site: http://www.jybank.com.cn
Year Founded: 2001
002807—(SSE)
Rev.: $530,699,364
Assets: $23,692,696,560
Liabilities: $21,668,756,148
Net Worth: $2,023,940,412
Earnings: $226,894,824
Fiscal Year-end: 12/31/22
Banking Services
N.A.I.C.S.: 523150
Song Ping (Chm)

JIANGSU JIBEIER PHARMACEUTICAL CO., LTD.
High-tech Industrial Development Zone, Zhenjiang, 212000, Jiangsu, China
Tel.: (86) 51188898101
Web Site: http://www.jibeier.com.cn
Year Founded: 2001
688566—(SHG)
Rev.: $91,924,176
Assets: $275,826,344
Liabilities: $37,942,398
Net Worth: $237,883,946
Earnings: $21,715,359
Fiscal Year-end: 12/31/22
Pharmaceutical Product Mfr & Distr
N.A.I.C.S.: 325412
Zhongyi Geng (Chm & Gen Mgr)

JIANGSU JIEJIE MICROELECTRONICS CO LTD
3000 Qiantangjiang Road Economic Development Zone, Qidong, 226200, Jiangsu, China
Tel.: (86) 51368528666
Web Site: http://www.en.jjwdz.com
Year Founded: 1995
300623—(SSE)
Rev.: $256,020,804
Assets: $1,070,524,728
Liabilities: $476,349,120
Net Worth: $594,175,608
Earnings: $50,466,780
Fiscal Year-end: 12/31/22
Semi Conductor Component Mfr & Distr
N.A.I.C.S.: 333248
Jian Huang (Vice Chm, Pres & Gen Mgr)

JIANGSU JINGXUE INSULATION TECHNOLOGY CO., LTD.
No 18 Fengze Road, Wujin West Taihu Science and Technology Industrial Park, Changzhou, 213149, Jiangsu, China
Tel.: (86) 51988061278
Web Site: https://www.jingxue.com
Year Founded: 1993
301010—(CHIN)
Rev.: $162,267,323
Assets: $255,701,450
Liabilities: $138,561,225
Net Worth: $117,140,225
Earnings: $5,379,493
Emp.: 500
Fiscal Year-end: 12/31/23
Insulation Material Mfr
N.A.I.C.S.: 326140
Fuzhong Jia (Chm & Gen Mgr)
Subsidiaries:
Dalian Jingxue Insulation Technology Co., Ltd. (1)
1St Floor No 92-2 West Tieshan Road, Dalian Economic & Technological Development Zone, Dalian, Liaoning, China
Tel.: (86) 41188530530
Nonmetallic Mineral Product Mfr
N.A.I.C.S.: 327999

Shanghai Jingxue Insulation Technology Co., Ltd. (1)
Room 20B No 4 Lane 600 Tianshan Road, Changning District, Shanghai, China
Tel.: (86) 2162330808
Nonmetallic Mineral Product Mfr
N.A.I.C.S.: 327999

JIANGSU JINGYUAN ENVIRONMENTAL PROTECTION CO., LTD.
109 Tongxin Road, Chongchuan District, Nantong, 226014, Jiangsu, China
Tel.: (86) 2038857862
Web Site: https://www.jsjyep.com
Year Founded: 1999
688096—(SHG)
Rev.: $72,206,934
Assets: $240,845,516
Liabilities: $120,038,869
Net Worth: $120,806,646
Earnings: $7,390,361
Fiscal Year-end: 12/31/22
Environmental Protection Equipment Mfr & Distr
N.A.I.C.S.: 334512
Wulin Li (Chm & Gen Mgr)

JIANGSU JINJI INDUSTRIAL CO., LTD.
No 10 Xingang Road, Taixing Economic & Development Zone, Taixing, 225404, Jiangsu, China
Tel.: (86) 52387671590
Web Site: https://www.jinjidyes.com
Year Founded: 1999
300798—(SSE)
Rev.: $126,413,352
Assets: $310,854,024
Liabilities: $118,374,048
Net Worth: $192,479,976
Earnings: $1,064,232
Fiscal Year-end: 12/31/22
Dyes Product Mfr
N.A.I.C.S.: 325194
Weiguo Zhao (Chm & Gen Mgr)

JIANGSU JINLING SPORTS EQUIPMENT CO., LTD.
No 88 Xingyuan Road, Nanfeng Town, Zhangjiagang, 215600, Jiangsu, China
Tel.: (86) 51258983911
Web Site: http://www.jlsports.com
Year Founded: 2004
300651—(CHIN)
Rev.: $72,379,928
Assets: $184,778,171
Liabilities: $67,797,063
Net Worth: $116,981,108
Earnings: $9,524,164
Fiscal Year-end: 12/31/23
Sport Equipment Mfr & Distr
N.A.I.C.S.: 339920
Chunrong Li (Chm)

JIANGSU JINSHENG INDUSTRY CO., LTD.
98 Huacheng Road, Jintan, Changzhou, 213200, Jiangsu, China
Tel.: (86) 519 8231 4836 CN
Web Site: http://www.cn-jtmw.com
Year Founded: 1954
Sales Range: $1-4.9 Billion
Emp.: 5,000
Textile & Other Industrial Machinery Mfr & Distr
N.A.I.C.S.: 333998
Xueping Pan (Pres & CEO)
Subsidiaries:
Saurer AG (1)
Bleikenstrasse 11, Wattwil, 9630, Switzerland
Tel.: (41) 71 987 4444
Web Site: http://www.saurer.com
Sales Range: $1-4.9 Billion
Emp.: 80
Textile Processing Equipment & Components Mfr & Distr
N.A.I.C.S.: 333248
Clement Woon (CEO)

Subsidiary (Non-US):
Saurer Components GmbH (2)
Maria-Merian-Strasse 8, 70736, Fellbach, Germany
Tel.: (49) 711 585 21 0
Textile Machinery Mfr
N.A.I.C.S.: 333248

Saurer Components Pte Ltd. (2)
151 Gul Circle, Jurong, 629608, Singapore
Tel.: (65) 869231
Web Site: http://www.saurer.com
Sales Range: $25-49.9 Million
Textile Machinery Components Mfr
N.A.I.C.S.: 333248
Chun Tap Chan (Mng Dir)

Saurer Fibrevision Ltd. (2)
Heather Close 10, Macclesfield, SK11 0LR, Cheshire, United Kingdom
Tel.: (44) 1625 425355
Web Site: http://www.fibrevision.co.uk
Sensors & On Line Monitoring Equipment Mfr
N.A.I.C.S.: 334513

JIANGSU JIUWU HITECH CO.,LTD.
No 9 Yuansi Road, Pukou District, Nanjing, 211808, Jiangsu, China
Tel.: (86) 2558109595
Web Site: http://www.jiuwu.com
Year Founded: 1997
300631—(CHIN)
Rev.: $106,623,380
Assets: $266,633,543
Liabilities: $94,772,894
Net Worth: $171,860,649
Earnings: $6,387,618
Fiscal Year-end: 12/31/23
Ceramic Membrane Mfr
N.A.I.C.S.: 327110
Dang Jianbing (Chm & Gen Mgr)

JIANGSU JUJIE MICROFIBER TECHNOLOGY GROUP CO., LTD.
No 68 Jiaotong Road, Songling Town Wujiang District, Suzhou, 215222, Jiangsu, China
Tel.: (86) 51263366336
Web Site: https://www.jujie.com
Year Founded: 2000
300819—(SSE)
Rev.: $84,982,716
Assets: $146,549,520
Liabilities: $30,049,812
Net Worth: $116,499,708
Earnings: $5,161,104
Fiscal Year-end: 12/31/22
Textile Product Mfr & Distr
N.A.I.C.S.: 313310
Hongtian Zhong (Chm & Gen Mgr)

JIANGSU KANION PHARMACEUTICAL CO., LTD.
No 58 Kangyuan Road Economic and development zone, Jiangning Industrial town Lianyun District, Lianyungang, 222000, Jiangsu, China
Tel.: (86) 51885521948

JIANGSU LANFENG BIO-CHEMICAL CO., LTD.

Web Site: https://www.kanion.com
Year Founded: 1975
600557—(SHG)
Rev.: $610,862,415
Assets: $954,130,910
Liabilities: $261,398,349
Net Worth: $692,732,561
Earnings: $60,999,223
Emp.: 5,000
Fiscal Year-end: 12/31/22
Pharmaceutical Product Mfr & Distr
N.A.I.C.S.: 325412
Wei Xiao (Chm, Pres & Gen Mgr)

JIANGSU KING'S LUCK BREWERY JOINT-STOCK CO., LTD.
No 1 Jinshiyuan Avenue, Gaogou Town Lianshui County, Huai'an, 223411, Jiangsu, China
Tel.: (86) 51782433619
Web Site: http://www.jinshiyuan.com.cn
Year Founded: 1997
603369—(SHG)
Rev.: $1,107,479,819
Assets: $2,552,993,038
Liabilities: $999,504,497
Net Worth: $1,553,488,541
Earnings: $351,391,618
Emp.: 4,000
Fiscal Year-end: 12/31/22
Distilled Spirit Product Mfr & Distr
N.A.I.C.S.: 312140
Gu Xiangyue (Chm & Gen Mgr)

JIANGSU KUANGSHUN PHOTOSENSITIVITY NEW-MATERIAL STOCK CO., LTD.
Huacheng Road 18 Qingyang Industriarea, Jiangyin, 214401, Jiangsu, China
Tel.: (86) 51068826620
Web Site: https://www.kuangshun.com
Year Founded: 2006
300537—(CHIN)
Rev.: $69,900,948
Assets: $174,585,996
Liabilities: $83,543,616
Net Worth: $91,042,380
Earnings: ($4,491,396)
Fiscal Year-end: 12/31/22
Printing Ink Mfr & Distr
N.A.I.C.S.: 325910
Youming Li (Chm, Pres & Gen Mgr)
Subsidiaries:
Jiangsu Kuangshun Photosensitivity New-Material Stock Co., Ltd. - Guangzhou Division (1)
No 12 105 Bridge Street Grass River Road Two street, Riverside Village Panyu District Guangzhou city, Guangzhou, China
Tel.: (86) 2084554228
Photosensitive Material Mfr
N.A.I.C.S.: 325992

JIANGSU LANFENG BIO-CHEMICAL CO., LTD.
No 2 Ningxia road Economic Development Zone, Xinyi, Jiangsu, 221400, China
Tel.: (86) 51688920479
Web Site: http://www.jslanfeng.com
Year Founded: 1990
002513—(SSE)
Rev.: $202,911,696
Assets: $207,165,816
Liabilities: $156,960,180
Net Worth: $50,205,636
Earnings: ($45,024,876)
Emp.: 1,340
Fiscal Year-end: 12/31/22
Fungicides, Insecticides, Herbicides & Phosgene Intermediates Mfr
N.A.I.C.S.: 325320

JIANGSU LANFENG BIO-CHEMICAL CO., LTD.

Jiangsu Lanfeng Bio-chemical Co., Ltd.—(Continued)

Zhenhua Yang (Chm)

JIANGSU LEIKE DEFENSE TECHNOLOGY CO., LTD.
Jianhua Road South Jiandong Village Lijia Town, Wujin District, Changzhou, 213161, Jiangsu, China
Tel.: (86) 1068916700
Web Site: http://www.racodf.com
002413—(SSE)
Rev.: $191,466,288
Assets: $835,160,976
Liabilities: $242,430,084
Net Worth: $592,730,892
Earnings: ($131,295,060)
Emp.: 524
Fiscal Year-end: 12/31/22
Investment Services
N.A.I.C.S.: 523999

Subsidiaries:

Changzhou Changfa Refrigeration Technology Co., LTD, - Lijia Factory (1)
Changfa Industry Park Lijia Town, Changzhou, Jiangsu, China
Tel.: (86) 51986239560
Heat Exchanger Mfr
N.A.I.C.S.: 332410

JIANGSU LEILI MOTOR CORPORATION LIMITED
No 19th Qianjiatang Road, Wujin District, Changzhou, 213011, Jiangsu, China
Tel.: (86) 51988770606
Web Site: https://www.czleili.com
Year Founded: 1993
300660—(CHIN)
Rev.: $433,354,251
Assets: $810,900,282
Liabilities: $270,679,797
Net Worth: $540,220,485
Earnings: $44,667,408
Emp.: 3,737
Fiscal Year-end: 12/31/23
Motor Equipment Mfr & Distr
N.A.I.C.S.: 335312
Su Jianguo (Chm)

Subsidiaries:

Changzhou ChengLi Electrical Equipment Co., Ltd. (1)
No 18 Xin4 Rd, Xinbei District Electronic Technology Industrial Park, Changzhou, Jiangsu, China
Tel.: (86) 51985486097
Motor Product Mfr
N.A.I.C.S.: 335312

Changzhou Gongli Metal Product Technology Co., Ltd. (1)
High-tech zone, Wujin, Jiangsu, China
Tel.: (86) 51986408036
Motor Product Mfr
N.A.I.C.S.: 335312

Changzhou Leili S & T Co., Ltd. (1)
No18 Xin4 Rd, Xinbei District Electronic Technology Industrial Park, Changzhou, Jiangsu, China
Tel.: (86) 51988375176
Micro-Motor Product Mfr
N.A.I.C.S.: 336320

Wuxi Leili Controls Technology Co., Ltd. (1)
No 306 Building B1 No 999 Gaolang East Road, Binghu District, Wujin, Jiangsu, China
Tel.: (86) 51068795166
Motor Product Mfr
N.A.I.C.S.: 335312

JIANGSU LETTALL ELECTRONICS CO., LTD.
No 8 Xufeng Road Industrial Concentration Zone, Xushe Town, Yixing, 214241, Jiangsu, China
Tel.: (86) 51080333705
Web Site: https://www.lettall.com
Year Founded: 1991
603629—(SHG)
Rev.: $284,369,698
Assets: $403,966,560
Liabilities: $174,379,201
Net Worth: $229,587,359
Earnings: $9,254,677
Emp.: 2,000
Fiscal Year-end: 12/31/22
Electronic Product Mfr & Distr
N.A.I.C.S.: 333415

JIANGSU LIANCE ELECTROMECHANICAL TECHNOLOGY CO., LTD.
2368-2370 West Renmin Road, Qidong, 226200, Jiangsu, China
Tel.: (86) 51385636573
Web Site: https://www.qdceqi.com
Year Founded: 2002
688113—(SHG)
Rev.: $52,439,723
Assets: $159,283,870
Liabilities: $47,688,039
Net Worth: $111,595,831
Earnings: $11,404,144
Emp.: 300
Fiscal Year-end: 12/31/22
Electrical Equipment Mfr & Distr
N.A.I.C.S.: 335999
Aiguo Zhao (Chm & Gen Mgr)

JIANGSU LIANFA TEXTILE CO., LTD.
No 88 Henglian Road, Haian Town, Nantong, 226600, Jiangsu, China
Tel.: (86) 51381819196
Web Site: https://www.lianfa.cn
Year Founded: 1955
002394—(SSE)
Rev.: $314,114,112
Assets: $826,211,880
Liabilities: $263,337,048
Net Worth: $562,874,832
Earnings: $15,941,016
Emp.: 10,000
Fiscal Year-end: 12/31/22
Textile Spinning, Yarn Dyeing, Weaving, Finishing & Garment Manufacturing Services
N.A.I.C.S.: 313110
Qinglong Xue (Pres)

Subsidiaries:

Huaian Lianfa Textiles Co., Ltd. (1)
No 137 Easten Road of Chengan Road, Huai'an, Lianshui County, China
Tel.: (86) 51782381237
Emp.: 370
Yarn-Dye Fabric Product Mfr
N.A.I.C.S.: 313310

Lianfa Textile (H.K.) Ltd. (1)
Suite 04-06 25/F Laford Centre 838 Lai Chi Kok Road, Kowloon, China (Hong Kong)
Tel.: (852) 23713255
Textile Products Distr
N.A.I.C.S.: 424310

Lianfa Textile Europe Srl (1)
Via Canova Antonio 1 Cassola, 36022, Vicenza, Italy
Tel.: (39) 0424220648
Textile Products Distr
N.A.I.C.S.: 424310

JIANGSU LIANHUAN PHARMACEUTICAL CO., LTD.
No 9 Jiankang 1st Road Biological Health Industry Park, Yangzhou, 225127, Jiangsu, China
Tel.: (86) 51487813082
Web Site: http://www.lhpharma.com
Year Founded: 2000
600513—(SHG)
Rev.: $274,504,015
Assets: $381,177,450
Liabilities: $182,689,449
Net Worth: $198,488,001
Earnings: $19,848,418
Emp.: 1,100
Fiscal Year-end: 12/31/22
Pharmaceutical Product Mfr & Distr
N.A.I.C.S.: 325412
Chunlai Xia (Chm)

JIANGSU LIANYUNGANG PORT CO., LTD.
No 8 Port 4th Road Miaoling Port Area, Lianyun District, Lianyungang, 222042, Jiangsu, China
Tel.: (86) 51882387588
Web Site: http://www.jlpcl.com
Year Founded: 2001
601008—(SHG)
Rev.: $313,350,434
Assets: $1,292,224,457
Liabilities: $529,941,583
Net Worth: $762,282,874
Earnings: $22,318,293
Emp.: 1,273
Fiscal Year-end: 12/31/22
Cargo Transportation Services
N.A.I.C.S.: 488320
Yang Long (Chm)

JIANGSU LIBA ENTERPRISE JOINT-STOCK CO., LTD.
88 Huaxi Rd Industrial Park for Environmental Science & Technology, Yixing, 214205, Jiangsu, China
Tel.: (86) 51068535700
Web Site: https://www.jsliba.com
Year Founded: 1994
603519—(SHG)
Rev.: $198,864,582
Assets: $258,694,764
Liabilities: $78,376,573
Net Worth: $180,318,191
Earnings: $79,266,400
Emp.: 300
Fiscal Year-end: 12/31/22
Household Appliance Mfr & Distr
N.A.I.C.S.: 335220
Song Jianrui (Chm & Gen Mgr)

JIANGSU LIDAO NEW MATERIAL CO., LTD.
No 1959 longcheng Avenue, Changzhou, 213012, Jiangsu, China
Tel.: (86) 51983250280
Web Site: https://www.jsldxcl.com
Year Founded: 2004
603937—(SHG)
Rev.: $225,030,298
Assets: $263,558,487
Liabilities: $42,927,637
Net Worth: $220,630,850
Earnings: $12,336,471
Emp.: 300
Fiscal Year-end: 12/31/22
Aluminum Product Mfr & Distr
N.A.I.C.S.: 331315
Cai Zhengguo (Chm & Gen Mgr)

JIANGSU LIHUA ANIMAL HUSBANDRY STOCK CO., LTD.
500 Weihe West Village Luxi Village, Niutang Town, Changzhou, 213168, China
Tel.: (86) 51986355611
Web Site: http://www.lihuamuye.com
Year Founded: 1997
300761—(CHIN)
Rev.: $2,162,624,548
Assets: $1,924,662,643
Liabilities: $827,896,680
Net Worth: $1,096,765,963
Earnings: ($61,609,086)
Fiscal Year-end: 12/31/23
Animal Feeding Product Mfr
N.A.I.C.S.: 311119

INTERNATIONAL PUBLIC

Lili Cheng (Chm & Pres)

JIANGSU LINYANG ENERGY CO., LTD.
No 666 Linyang Road, Qidong, 226299, Jiangsu, China
Tel.: (86) 2150196552
Web Site: https://www.linyang.com
Year Founded: 1995
601222—(SHG)
Rev.: $694,128,909
Assets: $2,990,596,813
Liabilities: $903,182,558
Net Worth: $2,087,414,255
Earnings: $120,182,035
Emp.: 300
Fiscal Year-end: 12/31/22
Electro Technical Instrument Mfr & Whslr
N.A.I.C.S.: 334515
Yonghua Lu (Founder, Chm & Pres)

Subsidiaries:

Jiangsu Lucala Lighting Technology Co., Ltd. (1)
Qidong No 612 Huashird, Qidong, Jiangsu, China
Tel.: (86) 51383615785
Light Emitting Diode Mfr & Distr
N.A.I.C.S.: 334413

Linyang International Co., Ltd. (1)
Floor 18 Zendai Wudaokou Plaza No 1199 Minsheng Road Pudong, Shanghai, 200120, China
Tel.: (86) 2150196556
Light Emitting Diode Distr
N.A.I.C.S.: 423690

JIANGSU LIXING GENERAL STEEL BALL CO., LTD.
No 68 Xingyuan Avenue Rucheng Street, Rucheng Town, Rugao, 226500, Jiangsu, China
Tel.: (86) 51387513793
Web Site: https://www.jgbr.com.cn
Year Founded: 2000
300421—(CHIN)
Rev.: $137,711,340
Assets: $251,023,968
Liabilities: $72,831,096
Net Worth: $178,192,872
Earnings: $8,752,536
Emp.: 560
Fiscal Year-end: 12/31/22
Ball Bearing Mfr
N.A.I.C.S.: 332991
Shi Xianggui (Chm)

JIANGSU LOPAL TECHNOLOGY CO., LTD.
No 6 Hengtong Avenue Enonomic & Technological Development Zone, Nanjing, Jiangsu, China
Tel.: (86) 2585802178
Web Site: https://www.lopaltrading.com
Year Founded: 2003
603906—(SHG)
Rev.: $1,975,658,677
Assets: $2,062,570,279
Liabilities: $1,275,001,505
Net Worth: $787,568,774
Earnings: $105,710,516
Fiscal Year-end: 12/31/22
Automotive Lubricant Mfr & Distr
N.A.I.C.S.: 324191

JIANGSU LUOKAI MECHANICAL & ELECTRICAL CO., LTD.
No 101 Yong anli Road, Luoyang Town Wujin District, Changzhou, China
Tel.: (86) 51988790029
Web Site: https://www.lk-jd.com
Year Founded: 1970

AND PRIVATE COMPANIES — **JIANGSU PHOENIX PUBLISHING & MEDIA CORPORATION LTD.**

603829—(SHG)
Rev.: $225,949,314
Assets: $299,974,540
Liabilities: $154,692,130
Net Worth: $145,282,410
Earnings: $10,580,558
Emp.: 670
Fiscal Year-end: 12/31/22
Circuit Breaker Product Mfr
N.A.I.C.S.: 335313
Zang Wenming *(Vice Chm & Gen Mgr)*

JIANGSU MAIXINLIN AVIATION SCIENCE & TECHNOLOGY CORP.
No 1009 Xihong Road, Taihu street, Suzhou, 215104, Jiangsu, China
Tel.: (86) 51266591666
Web Site: https://www.maixinlin.com
Year Founded: 2010
688685—(SHG)
Rev.: $45,491,074
Assets: $126,870,593
Liabilities: $24,907,873
Net Worth: $101,962,720
Earnings: $5,963,293
Fiscal Year-end: 12/31/22
Aerospace Parts Mfr
N.A.I.C.S.: 334511
Youzhi Zhang *(Chm & Gen Mgr)*

JIANGSU MAYSTA CHEMICAL CO., LTD.
7 F and 8 F building A3 Huizhi Science and Technology Park, No 8 Hengtai Road Nanjing Economic and Technological Development Zone, Nanjing, 210046, China
Tel.: (86) 2585576548
Web Site: https://www.maysta.com
Year Founded: 2000
603041—(SHG)
Rev.: $69,748,951
Assets: $221,674,499
Liabilities: $28,542,183
Net Worth: $193,132,317
Earnings: $11,081,856
Fiscal Year-end: 12/31/22
Silicone Surfactant Mfr & Distr
N.A.I.C.S.: 325199
Yu Sun *(Chm, Pres & Gen Mgr)*

Subsidiaries:

Maysta International Ltd.   (1)
Suite C Elmwood Court Tytherington Business Park Springwood Way, Macclesfield, SK10 2XF, Cheshire, United Kingdom
Tel.: (44) 1625380560
Silicone Surfactant Mfr
N.A.I.C.S.: 325199
Steve Hulme *(VP-Comml Ops)*

JIANGSU NANDASOFT TECHNOLOGY COMPANY LIMITED
Block 1 No 19 South QingJiang Road, Gulou District, Nanjing, 210036, China
Tel.: (86) 2568528888   CN
Web Site: http://www.nandasoft.com
8045—(HKG)
Rev.: $43,640,532
Assets: $151,589,880
Liabilities: $125,169,689
Net Worth: $26,420,191
Earnings: ($3,879,814)
Emp.: 265
Fiscal Year-end: 12/31/22
Software Development Services
N.A.I.C.S.: 541511
Zhengrong Wu *(VP)*

Subsidiaries:

Jiangsu Chang Tian Zhi Yuan Transportation Technology Co., Ltd.   (1)
19th Floor Shunyu Building No 19 Bailongjiang East Street, Jianye District, Nanjing, China
Tel.: (86) 2586667369
Web Site: https://www.itssky.com
Transportation Equipment Mfr
N.A.I.C.S.: 334290

JIANGSU NANFANG BEARING CO., LTD.
No 9 Longxiang Road Wujin Hi-Tech Development Zone, Changzhou, 213164, Jiangsu, China
Tel.: (86) 51986552111
Web Site: https://www.nf-precision.com
Year Founded: 1998
002553—(SSE)
Rev.: $92,378,947
Assets: $195,747,395
Liabilities: $29,883,066
Net Worth: $165,864,329
Earnings: $3,753,980
Fiscal Year-end: 12/31/23
Needle Bearing Mfr
N.A.I.C.S.: 332991

JIANGSU NANFANG MEDICAL CO., LTD.
No 1 Guoxiang Road Wujin Economic Development Zone, Changzhou, 213149, Jiangsu, China
Tel.: (86) 51986362360
Web Site: https://www.nfmedical.com.cn
Year Founded: 1990
603880—(SHG)
Rev.: $76,569,836
Assets: $204,595,668
Liabilities: $117,339,426
Net Worth: $87,256,241
Earnings: ($2,056,677)
Fiscal Year-end: 12/31/22
Transdermal Product Mfr & Distr
N.A.I.C.S.: 339113
Ping Li *(Chm, Pres & Gen Mgr)*

JIANGSU NATA OPTO-ELECTRONIC MATERIAL CO., LTD.
No 67 Pingsheng Road Suzhou Industrial Park, Suzhou, 215126, Jiangsu, China
Tel.: (86) 51262520998
Web Site: https://www.sonatamaterials.com
Year Founded: 2000
300346—(CHIN)
Rev.: $222,004,692
Assets: $746,164,224
Liabilities: $376,210,224
Net Worth: $369,954,000
Earnings: $26,216,892
Emp.: 180
Fiscal Year-end: 12/31/22
High Purity Metal Organic Compounds Mfr
N.A.I.C.S.: 325998
Feng Jiansong *(Chm)*

JIANGSU NEW ENERGY DEVELOPMENT CO., LTD.
9-10F Guoxin Building No 88 Changjiang Road, Nanjing, 210005, Jiangsu, China
Tel.: (86) 2584736307
Web Site: http://www.jsne.com.cn
Year Founded: 2002
603693—(SHG)
Rev.: $276,738,340
Assets: $2,225,392,931
Liabilities: $1,242,598,856
Net Worth: $982,794,075
Earnings: $66,821,513
Fiscal Year-end: 12/31/22
Solar Electric Power Generation Services
N.A.I.C.S.: 221114
Zhu Yousheng *(Chm & Sec-Party Committee)*

JIANGSU NEWAMSTAR PACKAGING MCHNRY CO LTD
No 8 Xinjing East Road, Economic and Technological Development Zone, Zhangjiagang, 215618, Jiangsu, China
Tel.: (86) 51258699111
Web Site: https://www.newamstar.com
300509—(CHIN)
Rev.: $130,798,775
Assets: $293,115,132
Liabilities: $197,202,648
Net Worth: $95,912,484
Earnings: $3,279,382
Fiscal Year-end: 12/31/23
Food Packing Machine Mfr & Distr
N.A.I.C.S.: 321920

JIANGSU NHWA PHARMACEUTICAL CORPORATION LTD.
No 31 West Longhu Road Economic Development Zone, Xuzhou, 221004, Jiangsu, China
Tel.: (86) 51687767115
Web Site: https://www.nhwa-group.com
Year Founded: 1978
002262—(SSE)
Rev.: $603,510,804
Assets: $910,037,700
Liabilities: $125,937,396
Net Worth: $784,100,304
Earnings: $126,490,572
Emp.: 4,000
Fiscal Year-end: 12/31/22
Pharmaceuticals Product Mfr
N.A.I.C.S.: 325412
Pengsheng Sun *(Chm)*

Subsidiaries:

Jiangsu Farever Pharma. Co., Ltd.   (1)
No 18 Yangshan Road, Economic Development Zone, Xuzhou, 221004, Jiangsu, China
Tel.: (86) 51687733171
Web Site: http://www.farever.cn
Chemical Products Mfr
N.A.I.C.S.: 325199

JIANGSU NONGHUA INTELLIGENT AGRICULTURE TECHNOLOGY CO., LTD.
7th Floor China International Trade Building No 50 Zhonghua Road, Nanjing, 224003, Jiangsu, China
Tel.: (86) 2552308859
Web Site: https://www.jccief.org.cn
000816—(SSE)
Rev.: $170,577,576
Assets: $480,638,340
Liabilities: $124,717,320
Net Worth: $355,921,020
Earnings: ($3,605,472)
Fiscal Year-end: 12/31/22
Engine Mfr
N.A.I.C.S.: 336310
Jun Jia *(Chm & Gen Mgr)*

JIANGSU OLIVE SENSORS HIGH-TECH CO LTD
No 158 Xiangyuan Road, HanJiang Industrial District, Yangzhou, 225127, Jiangsu, China
Tel.: (86) 51482775359
Web Site: https://yos.net.cn
300507—(CHIN)
Rev.: $157,958,683
Assets: $404,534,102
Liabilities: $110,821,076
Net Worth: $293,713,026
Earnings: $17,447,160
Fiscal Year-end: 12/31/23
Automobile Parts Mfr & Distr
N.A.I.C.S.: 332510

JIANGSU PACIFIC PRECISION FORGING
Shuangdeng Avenue No 198, Jiangyan District, Taizhou, 225500, Jiangsu, China
Tel.: (86) 52380512685
Web Site: https://www.ppforging.com
Year Founded: 1992
300258—(CHIN)
Rev.: $296,261,989
Assets: $881,138,951
Liabilities: $352,074,632
Net Worth: $529,064,319
Earnings: $33,467,115
Emp.: 800
Fiscal Year-end: 12/31/23
Automobile Forging Parts Mfr
N.A.I.C.S.: 331110
Xia Hanguan *(Chm & Gen Mgr)*

Subsidiaries:

Ningbo Pacific E-Control System Ltd.   (1)
No 600 Jingang Road, Beilun District, Ningbo, 315800, China
Tel.: (86) 57486966522
Iron & Steel Product Mfr
N.A.I.C.S.: 331110

JIANGSU PACIFIC QUARTZ CO., LTD.
Pacific Quartz Industrial Park, Pingming Town Donghai County, Lianyungang, 222342, Jiangsu, China
Tel.: (86) 51883062922
Web Site: https://www.quartzpacific.com
Year Founded: 1992
603688—(SHG)
Rev.: $281,384,864
Assets: $517,465,021
Liabilities: $56,314,314
Net Worth: $461,150,708
Earnings: $147,727,841
Fiscal Year-end: 12/31/22
Quartz Mining Services
N.A.I.C.S.: 212390
Liwen Zhang *(Fin Mgr)*

JIANGSU PARKTEC PARKING EQUIPMENT CO., LTD.
32-9 Tongsheng South Road, Economic and Technological Development Zone, Nantong, Jiangsu, China
Tel.: (86) 51380770888
Web Site: http://www.parktec-parking.com
Parking Services
N.A.I.C.S.: 812930

JIANGSU PHOENIX PROPERTY INVESTMENT CO., LTD.
6F Phoenix International Mansion No 389 Central Road, Nanjing, 210037, Jiangsu, China
Tel.: (86) 2583566283
600716—(SHG)
Rev.: $85,301,087
Assets: $1,142,697,025
Liabilities: $423,990,338
Net Worth: $718,706,687
Earnings: $54,946,453
Fiscal Year-end: 12/31/22
Real Estate Property Development Services
N.A.I.C.S.: 531390
Bi Sheng *(Sec)*

JIANGSU PHOENIX PUBLISHING & MEDIA CORPORATION LTD.

JIANGSU PHOENIX PUBLISHING & MEDIA CORPORATION LTD.

Jiangsu Phoenix Publishing & Media Corporation Ltd.—(Continued)

Block B Fenghuang Plaza No 1 Hunan Road, Nanjing, 210009, China
Tel.: (86) 2551883338
Web Site: http://www.ppm.cn
Year Founded 1999
601928—(SHG)
Rev.: $1,908,857,789
Assets: $4,170,204,029
Liabilities: $1,705,783,679
Net Worth: $2,464,420,351
Earnings: $292,283,723
Fiscal Year-end: 12/31/22
Books Publishing Services
N.A.I.C.S.: 513130
Wang Yixuan (Vice Chm & VP)

Subsidiaries:

Beijing Fonghong Media Ltd. (1)
7F Tower B Beichen Century Center No 8 Beichen West Rd, Chaoyang District, Beijing, 100101, China
Tel.: (86) 1064959786
Books Publishing Services
N.A.I.C.S.: 513130
Zhang Xiaobo (Mng Dir)

Hachette-Phoenix Cultural Development (Beijing) Co., Ltd. (1)
24 Jia Shijia Hutong, Dongcheng District, Beijing, 100010, China
Tel.: (86) 1065950366
Web Site: http://www.hachette-phoenix.com
Emp.: 13
Books Publishing Services
N.A.I.C.S.: 513130
Xu Gefei (Gen Mgr)

Jiangsu New Trade Import & Export Corp. (1)
34 Baiziting, Nanjing, 210009, China
Tel.: (86) 2558502796
Books Publishing Services
N.A.I.C.S.: 513130
Jin Guohua (Gen Mgr)

Jiangsu People's Publishing House Ltd. (1)
8-9F Tower A 1 Hunan Road, Nanjing, 210009, China
Tel.: (86) 2583658050
Books Publishing Services
N.A.I.C.S.: 513130

Jiangsu People's Publishing Ltd. (1)
1 Hunan Road, Nanjing, 210009, China
Tel.: (86) 2583658094
Books Publishing Services
N.A.I.C.S.: 513130
Xu Hai (Pres)

Jiangsu Phoenix Education Development Ltd. (1)
23F Tower B 1 Hunan Road, Nanjing, 210009, China
Tel.: (86) 2583657727
Textbook Distr
N.A.I.C.S.: 424920

Jiangsu Phoenix Vocational Education Books Ltd. (1)
Tower B 1 Hunan Road, Nanjing, 210009, China
Tel.: (86) 2583658823
Comic Book & Education Book Publisher
N.A.I.C.S.: 513130

Jiangsu Xinhua Distribution Group Ltd. (1)
34 Baiziting, Nanjing, 210009, China
Tel.: (86) 2551883305
Books Publishing Services
N.A.I.C.S.: 513130

PPM International (Australia) Ltd. (1)
Level 39 385 Bourke Street, Melbourne, 3000, Australia
Tel.: (61) 384592230
Web Site: http://www.ippmi.com.au
Books Publishing Services
N.A.I.C.S.: 513130

Phoenix Books Ltd. (1)
Room 1101 Tower C 1 Hunan Road, Nanjing, 210009, China
Tel.: (86) 2583303410

Web Site: http://www.fhcbs.com
Books Publishing Services
N.A.I.C.S.: 513130

Phoenix Digital Media Ltd. (1)
8F Tower B No 1 Hunan Road, Nanjing, 210009, China
Tel.: (86) 2583657882
Web Site: http://www.ppmit.cn
Digital Publishing Services
N.A.I.C.S.: 513199

Phoenix Digital Printing Ltd. (1)
517 A 9th Ave, San Mateo, CA 94402
Tel.: (650) 343-8747
Web Site: http://www.phoenixdp.com
Commercial Printing Services
N.A.I.C.S.: 323111

Phoenix Education Development Ltd. (1)
23F Tower B 1 Hunan Road, Nanjing, 210009, China
Tel.: (86) 2583657720
Books Publishing Services
N.A.I.C.S.: 513130
Hu Xiaodong (Gen Mgr)

Phoenix Education Publishing Ltd. (1)
19th Floor Building A No 1 Hunan Road, Nanjing, 210009, China
Tel.: (86) 83658888
Web Site: https://www.1088.com.cn
Books Publishing Services
N.A.I.C.S.: 513130

Phoenix Fine Arts Publishing Ltd. (1)
Tower B 1 Hunan Road, Nanjing, 210009, China
Tel.: (86) 2568155684
Books Publishing Services
N.A.I.C.S.: 513130
Ge Qingwen (Pres)

Phoenix International Publications Inc. (1)
8501 W Higgins Rd Ste 300, Chicago, IL 60631
Tel.: (312) 739-3725
Web Site: https://www.pikidsmedia.com
Books Publishing Services
N.A.I.C.S.: 513199

Phoenix Juvenile & Children's Publishing Ltd. (1)
1 Hunan Road, Nanjing, 210009, China
Tel.: (86) 2583658161
Web Site: http://www.sushao.com.cn
Emp.: 160
Books Publishing Services
N.A.I.C.S.: 513130
Zhang Shengyong (Pres)

Phoenix Legend Films Ltd. (1)
10F 1 Hunan Road, Nanjing, 210009, China
Tel.: (86) 2583320333
Web Site: http://www.plfilms.cn
Film Production & Distribution Services
N.A.I.C.S.: 512110
Jiang Hao (Mng Dir)

Phoenix Media Publishing Ltd. (1)
No 1 Hunan Road, Nanjing, 210009, China
Tel.: (86) 2583211799
Books Publishing Services
N.A.I.C.S.: 513130
Xu Chenmin (Mng Dir)

Phoenix Science Press Ltd. (1)
18th Floor Phoenix Plaza No 1 Hunan Road, Nanjing, 210009, China
Tel.: (86) 2586634269
Web Site: https://www.pspress.cn
Books Publishing Services
N.A.I.C.S.: 513130

Phoenix Vocational Education Books Ltd. (1)
9F Tower B 1 Hunan Road, Nanjing, 210009, China
Tel.: (86) 2583658823
Books Publishing Services
N.A.I.C.S.: 513130
Zhu Yongzhen (Gen Mgr)

Phoenix Xinhua Printing Ltd. (1)
Yaoxin Av 399 Xingang, Nanjing, 210038, China
Tel.: (86) 2583247965

Web Site: http://www.pxprint.cn
Book Printing Services
N.A.I.C.S.: 323117
Zhang Zai Jian (Chm)

Phoenix-Power Cultural Development Ltd. (1)
Building 15 6th Yard Yuan Zhong Yuan Financial Street, Tongzhou District, Beijing, 101100, China
Tel.: (86) 1085376703
Books Publishing Services
N.A.I.C.S.: 513130
He Pengfei (Mng Dir)

Xanadu Publishing (Australia) Ltd. (1)
Level 39 385 Bourke Street, Melbourne, 3000, VIC, Australia
Tel.: (61) 384592230
Web Site: https://ippmi.com.au
Text Book Mfr & Distr
N.A.I.C.S.: 314910

Xanadu Publishing Ltd. (1)
25 Wharf Street, London, SE8 3GG, United Kingdom
Tel.: (44) 7463675656
Books Publishing Services
N.A.I.C.S.: 513130
Sun Qian (VP)

Yilin Press Ltd. (1)
1504 Tower A 1 Hunan Road, Nanjing, 210009, China
Tel.: (86) 2583658388
Web Site: http://www.yilin.com
Books Publishing Services
N.A.I.C.S.: 513130
Gu Aibin (Pres)

JIANGSU PROTRULY TECHNOLOGY GROUP CO., LTD.

589 Binjiang Road, Jiangyin, Jiangsu, China
Tel.: (86) 519 83978328
Web Site: http://www.protruly.com.cn
Year Founded: 1997
Sales Range: $100-124.9 Million
Electronic Vision Products Mfr
N.A.I.C.S.: 334419
Lihong Ding (Chm & Sec-Interim)

JIANGSU PROVINCIAL AGRICULTURAL RECLAMATION & DEVELOPMENT CO., LTD.

12th Floor Suken Building No 136 Hengshan Road, Jianye District, Nanjing, 210019, Jiangsu, China
Tel.: (86) 2587772112
Web Site: https://www.skiad.com.cn
Year Founded: 2011
601952—(SHG)
Rev.: $1,786,911,755
Assets: $2,048,510,496
Liabilities: $1,106,275,847
Net Worth: $942,234,649
Earnings: $116,005,177
Fiscal Year-end: 12/31/22
Agricultural Develpment Services
N.A.I.C.S.: 115112
Zhu Yadong (Chm)

JIANGSU RAINBOW HEAVY INDUSTRIES CO., LTD.

No 9 Zhenxing West Road, Nantong Economic and Technological Development Zone, Nantong, 226010, Jiangsu, China
Tel.: (86) 51385328000
Web Site: https://www.rainbowco.com.cn
Year Founded: 2003
002483—(SSE)
Rev.: $726,457,680
Assets: $1,455,181,416
Liabilities: $878,290,452
Net Worth: $576,890,964
Earnings: $7,462,260
Emp.: 1,500
Fiscal Year-end: 12/31/22

INTERNATIONAL PUBLIC

Heavy Machinery Mfr
N.A.I.C.S.: 333924
Liu Zhongqiu (Chm)

Subsidiaries:

Jiangsu Greenwise Environmental Protection Technology Co., Ltd. (1)
Suzhou Industrial Park Ren Ai Road Dushu Lake Higher Education Dist, No 150 Nanjing University Suzhou High-Tech Institute 5th Floor Block A, Suzhou, Jiangsu, China
Tel.: (86) 51262869887
General Purpose Machinery Mfr
N.A.I.C.S.: 333998

Nantong Rainbow Heavy Machineries Co., Ltd. (1)
NO 88 Rongsheng Road Chenqiao Nantong Marine Equipment Industrial, Equipment Industrial Zone, Nantong, 226013, Jiangsu, China
Tel.: (86) 5138 010 1000
Web Site: http://www.rhm.rainbowco.com.cn
Industrial Machinery & Equipment Distr
N.A.I.C.S.: 423830
Miser Liu (Dir-Quality)

Nantong Rainbow Marine Technology Co., Ltd. (1)
1504 Room International Trade Center No 88 Chongchuan Road, Nantong, Jiangsu, China
Tel.: (86) 51355083600
General Purpose Machinery Mfr
N.A.I.C.S.: 333998

Nantong Rainbow Offshore & Engineering Equipments Co., Ltd. (1)
No 3333 Haigong Road, Qidong, 226255, Jiangsu, China
Tel.: (86) 51383623000
Web Site: https://roc.rainbowco.com.cn
Ship Building Equipment Mfr
N.A.I.C.S.: 336611

Nantong Runhope Environment Technology Co., Ltd. (1)
Room 2709 Buliding 3 Jiangcheng Park, No 1088 Jiangcheng Road Su-Tong Science and Technology Park, Nantong, Jiangsu, China
Tel.: (86) 51380100386
General Purpose Machinery Mfr
N.A.I.C.S.: 333998

JIANGSU RECBIO TECHNOLOGY CO., LTD.

No 888 Yaocheng Avenue China Medical City, High-tech District, Taizhou, Jiangsu, China
Tel.: (86) 52386818860 CN
Web Site: https://www.recbio.cn
Year Founded: 2012
2179—(HKG)
Rev.: $22,674,008
Assets: $353,854,888
Liabilities: $100,586,808
Net Worth: $253,268,080
Earnings: ($112,761,947)
Emp.: 532
Fiscal Year-end: 12/31/22
Information Technology Services
N.A.I.C.S.: 541512
Jianhui Zhang (Chief Medical Officer)

JIANGSU RIJIU OPTOELECTRONICS JOINTSTOCK CO., LTD.

No 509 Jinzhou Road, Zhouzhuang Town, Kunshan, 215325, Jiangsu, China
Tel.: (86) 51283639999
Web Site: https://www.rnafilms.cn
Year Founded: 2010
003015—(SSE)
Rev.: $65,867,256
Assets: $183,737,268
Liabilities: $36,094,032
Net Worth: $147,643,236
Earnings: $5,600,556
Fiscal Year-end: 12/31/22
Electronic Product Mfr & Distr

AND PRIVATE COMPANIES

N.A.I.C.S.: 334419
Chao Chen *(Chm & Gen Mgr)*

JIANGSU RIYING ELECTRONICS CO., LTD.
Fangmao Village Hengshanqiao Town Economic Development Zone, Changzhou, Jiangsu, China
Tel.: (86) 51968850588
Web Site: https://www.riyingcorp.com
Year Founded: 1998
603286—(SHG)
Rev.: $99,885,530
Assets: $164,533,272
Liabilities: $97,073,248
Net Worth: $67,460,024
Earnings: ($2,430,029)
Emp.: 1,200
Fiscal Year-end: 12/31/22
Electronic Automotive Component Mfr
N.A.I.C.S.: 336320
RongZhu Shi *(Chm & CEO)*

JIANGSU RONGTAI INDUSTRY CO., LTD.
No 8 Lehe Road, Jiangdu, Yangzhou, Jiangsu, China
Tel.: (86) 51485335333
Web Site: https://www.rtco.com.cn
Year Founded: 2000
605133—(SHG)
Rev.: $216,960,036
Assets: $495,637,146
Liabilities: $229,633,143
Net Worth: $266,004,002
Earnings: $18,763,070
Fiscal Year-end: 12/31/22
Automotive Parts Mfr & Distr
N.A.I.C.S.: 336390
Chengliang Xia *(Chm & Gen Mgr)*

Subsidiaries:

Rongtai Industrial Development Leon S. de R.L. de C.V. (1)
Paseo de las Colinas No 104-140, Parque Industrial Colinas de Leon, 37668, Guanajuato, Mexico
Tel.: (52) 4773432600
Auto Machine Parts Mfr
N.A.I.C.S.: 333511

Zhuhai Rongtai Precision Die Casting Co., Ltd. (1)
16 Honghui Road, Shuanglin District Liangang Industrial Park, Zhuhai, Guangdong, China
Tel.: (86) 7567252832
Auto Machine Parts Mfr
N.A.I.C.S.: 333511

JIANGSU RUITAI NEW ENERGY MATERIALS CO., LTD.
Guotai Building No 109 Renmin Middle Road, Zhangjiagang, 215600, Jiangsu, China
Tel.: (86) 51256375311
Web Site: https://www.rtxc.com
Year Founded: 2017
301238—(CHIN)
Rev.: $861,348,384
Assets: $1,432,671,084
Liabilities: $447,592,392
Net Worth: $985,078,692
Earnings: $109,076,760
Fiscal Year-end: 12/31/22
Battery Product Mfr
N.A.I.C.S.: 335910
Ziyan Zhang *(Chm)*

Subsidiaries:

Zhangjiagang Guotai Huarong New Chemical Materials Co., Ltd. (1)
No 35 Nanhai Road Yangtze River, International Chemical Industrial Park Zhangjiagang, Jiangsu, 215634, China
Tel.: (86) 51256357882
Web Site: https://www.gthr.com.cn
Marketing Consulting Services
N.A.I.C.S.: 541613

JIANGSU RUTONG PETRO-MACHINERY CO.,LTD
No 33 Huaihe Road New Area Rudong Economic Development Zone, Nantong, 226400, Jiangsu, China
Tel.: (86) 51381907806
Web Site: http://www.rutong.com
Year Founded: 1958
603036—(SHG)
Rev.: $43,093,506
Assets: $192,912,071
Liabilities: $21,381,558
Net Worth: $171,530,513
Earnings: $11,392,590
Emp.: 650
Fiscal Year-end: 12/31/22
Petroleum Drilling Equipment Mfr & Distr
N.A.I.C.S.: 333132
Caihong Cao *(Chm & Vice Chm)*

JIANGSU SAFETY GROUP CO.,LTD
No 151 FuRong 3 Road XiShan Economic Development Zone, Xishan District, Wuxi, 214192, Jiangsu, China
Tel.: (86) 51082451189
Web Site: https://www.safety-rope.com
Year Founded: 2005
603028—(SHG)
Rev.: $111,750,762
Assets: $169,718,117
Liabilities: $73,666,308
Net Worth: $96,051,810
Earnings: ($11,160,171)
Fiscal Year-end: 12/31/22
Elevator Rope Mfr & Distr
N.A.I.C.S.: 333921
Fan Qing *(Chm)*

JIANGSU SAINTY CORP., LTD.
Building B No 21 SoftwareAvenue, Yuhuatai District, Nanjing, 210012, Jiangsu, China
Tel.: (86) 2552875682
Web Site: https://www.esaintycorp.com
Year Founded: 1979
600287—(SHG)
Rev.: $575,018,042
Assets: $541,155,120
Liabilities: $276,296,193
Net Worth: $264,858,928
Earnings: $8,426,359
Fiscal Year-end: 12/31/22
Apparel Product Whslr
N.A.I.C.S.: 424310
Hua Yisong *(Gen Mgr)*

Subsidiaries:

Hongze Sainty Fortune Garment Manufacturing Co., Ltd. (1)
No 4 East 5th Avenue Hongze Industrial Park, Jiangsu, China
Tel.: (86) 51787216212
Emp.: 360
Apparels Mfr
N.A.I.C.S.: 315250

Jiangsu Sainty Apparel Co., Ltd. (1)
No 2099 integrity avenue high-tech Park, Jiangning District, Nanjing, Jiangsu, China
Tel.: (86) 2557917666
Apparel Mfr & Whslr
N.A.I.C.S.: 315250

Jiangsu Sainty Chemical Storage Co., Ltd. (1)
East Side of North Zhonghua Road Bonded Logistics West Park, Zhangjiagang, Jiangsu, China
Tel.: (86) 51255371728
Chemical Products Distr
N.A.I.C.S.: 424690

Jiangsu Sainty Eagle & Mfg Co., Ltd. (1)
Room 608 Building B No 21 Software Avenue, Nanjing, Jiangsu, China
Tel.: (86) 2552875516
Web Site: http://www.saintyeagle.com
Emp.: 48
Apparel Mfr & Distr
N.A.I.C.S.: 315250
Feng Qiu *(Gen Mgr)*

Jiangsu Sainty Food Trade Co., Ltd. (1)
13th Floor No 98 Jianye Road, Nanjing, Jiangsu, China
Tel.: (86) 2584440272
Wine Distr
N.A.I.C.S.: 424820

Jiangsu Sainty Fortune Co., Ltd. (1)
Room 303 Building B No 21 Software Avenue, Nanjing, Jiangsu, China
Tel.: (86) 2552875226
Garments Whslr
N.A.I.C.S.: 424350

Jiangsu Sainty Handsome Co., Ltd. (1)
Room 207 Building B No 21 Software Avenue, Nanjing, 210012, Jiangsu, China
Tel.: (86) 2552875273
Web Site: http://www.sainty-pharma.com.cn
Pharmaceutical Product Mfr & Distr
N.A.I.C.S.: 325412
Leon Wang *(Gen Mgr)*

Jiangsu Sainty Jintan Garments Co., Ltd. (1)
No 218 Hua Cheng Road, Jintan, Jiangsu, China
Tel.: (86) 51982312612
Apparel Mfr & Whslr
N.A.I.C.S.: 315250

Jiangsu Sainty Land-up Pro-Trading Co., Ltd. (1)
Room 601 Building B No 21 Software Avenue, Nanjing, Jiangsu, China
Tel.: (86) 2552875616
Garment Mfr & Whslr
N.A.I.C.S.: 315250

Jiangsu Sainty Saintek Company Limited (1)
15th Floor No 239 Xindu Building Hongwu Road, Nanjing, Jiangsu, China
Tel.: (86) 2584567399
Garment Mfr & Whslr
N.A.I.C.S.: 315250

Jiangsu Sainty Suits Co., Ltd. (1)
No 8 Taishan Road, Jianye District, Nanjing, Jiangsu, China
Tel.: (86) 2586410008
Apparel Mfr & Whslr
N.A.I.C.S.: 315250

STIG JIANGSU LIGHT & TEXTILE IMP. & EXP. CO., LTD (1)
F6 A No 21 Ningnan Road, Nanjing, 210010, Jiangsu, China
Tel.: (86) 2552876207
Emp.: 100
Apparel Whslr
N.A.I.C.S.: 424350

Sainty (HK) Company Limited (1)
ROOM 03 11th Floor Heng Yi Jewelry Centre Hok Yuen Street East 4, Hong Kong, China (Hong Kong)
Tel.: (852) 28656612
Apparel Distr
N.A.I.C.S.: 424320

JIANGSU SANFANGXIANG CO., LTD.
Zhouzhuang Town, Jiangyin, Jiangsu, China
Tel.: (86) 51086229006
Web Site: http://www.jssfx.com
600370—(SHG)
Rev.: $3,206,332,743
Assets: $2,019,200,017
Liabilities: $1,071,853,502
Net Worth: $947,346,515
Earnings: $114,879,211
Emp.: 7,000
Fiscal Year-end: 12/31/22
Textile Product Mfr & Whslr
N.A.I.C.S.: 313310

Bian Fuhou *(Gen Mgr)*

JIANGSU SEAGULL COOLING TOWER CO., LTD.
No 16 Xiangyun Road Wujin Economic Development Zone, Changzhou, 213149, Jiangsu, China
Tel.: (86) 4001391116
Web Site: https://www.seagull-ct.cn
Year Founded: 1997
603269—(SHG)
Rev.: $190,127,939
Assets: $370,943,315
Liabilities: $236,805,772
Net Worth: $134,137,542
Earnings: $10,354,823
Fiscal Year-end: 12/31/22
Cooling Tower Equipment Mfr & Distr
N.A.I.C.S.: 333415
Jin Ao Da *(Chm)*

Subsidiaries:

Seagull Cooling Technologies (Asia Pacific) Sdn. Bhd. (1)
Suite 6-4 Level 6 Menara Millennium No 8 Jalan Damanlela, Pusat Bandar Damansara, 50490, Kuala Lumpur, Malaysia
Tel.: (60) 327326978
Web Site: https://sap-ct.com
Cooling Tower Mfr
N.A.I.C.S.: 333415

Seagull Cooling Technologies (Thailand) Co., Ltd. (1)
111/56 Soi Ramintra 64 Ramintra Road, Kannayao Sub-district Kannayao District, Bangkok, 10230, Thailand
Tel.: (66) 20377228
Cooling Tower Mfr
N.A.I.C.S.: 333415

Truwater Cooling Towers Sdn. Bhd. (1)
Executive Suite 702 Block B Kelana Business Centre No 97 Jalan SS 7/2, Kelana Jaya, 47301, Petaling Jaya, Selangor, Malaysia
Tel.: (60) 378808800
Web Site: https://www.truwater.com.my
Cooling Tower Construction Services
N.A.I.C.S.: 237130

JIANGSU SENXUAN PHARMACEUTICAL & CHEMICAL CO., LTD.
Hongqiao Industrial Park, Taixing, Jiangsu, 225453, China
Tel.: (86) 52387484267
Web Site: http://www.senxuan.cn
Pharmaceuticals & Agrochemicals Preparation & Mfr
N.A.I.C.S.: 325412

Subsidiaries:

Jinghua Pharmaceutical Group Co., Ltd (1)
No 20 3 Haibin Road Yanhai Economic Development Zone, Nantong, 226407, Jiangsu, China
Tel.: (86) 51385609405
Web Site: https://www.jinghuapharm.com
Rev.: $208,021,045
Assets: $438,266,136
Liabilities: $52,391,743
Net Worth: $385,874,394
Earnings: $34,083,801
Fiscal Year-end: 12/31/2023
Pharmaceuticals Mfr
N.A.I.C.S.: 325412

JIANGSU SHAGANG CO., LTD.
Shagang Building, Jinfeng Town, Zhangjiagang, 215625, Jiangsu, China
Tel.: (86) 51258987088
Web Site: https://www.shaganggf.com
Year Founded: 1999
002075—(SSE)
Rev.: $2,551,522,896
Assets: $2,367,012,024

JIANGSU SHAGANG CO., LTD.

Jiangsu Shagang Co., Ltd.—(Continued)
Liabilities: $992,128,176
Net Worth: $1,374,883,848
Earnings: $63,615,240
Fiscal Year-end: 12/31/22
Ferrous Metal Product Smelting Services
N.A.I.C.S.: 332111
Ji Yongxin (Chm)

JIANGSU SHAGANG GROUP LTD.
Jin Feng, Zhangjiagang, 215625, Jiangsu, China
Tel.: (86) 51258568800
Web Site: http://www.sha-steel.com
Year Founded: 1975
Sales Range: $15-24.9 Billion
Emp.: 30,000
Steel Pipe, Wire & Bar Mfr
N.A.I.C.S.: 331210
Wenrong Shen (Chm)

Subsidiaries:

Chongqing Shagang Modern Logistics Co., Ltd. (1)
Rm No 16-5 of 2nd Unit No 10 Fengtian Avenue, Shapingba District, Chongqing, China
Tel.: (86) 23 65012212
Steel Products Mfr
N.A.I.C.S.: 331210

Dongbei Special Steel Group Co., Ltd. (1)
No 18 South Hebin Road, Dengshahe Coastal Industrial Zone Jinzhou New District, Dalian, 116105, Liaoning, China
Tel.: (86) 41182510800
Web Site: https://www.dtsteel.com
Rolled Steel Shape Mfr
N.A.I.C.S.: 331221

Nanjing Shagang Materials Trade Co., Ltd. (1)
Rm No 1502 Steel Digital Port No 201 Yanjiang Road, Nanjing, China
Tel.: (86) 25 58788310
Steel Products Mfr
N.A.I.C.S.: 331210

Shagang (Australia) Co., Ltd. (1)
Level 20 77 St Georges TCE, Perth, 6000, WA, Australia
Tel.: (61) 893257718
Steel Product Distr
N.A.I.C.S.: 423510

Shagang International (Singapore) Pte. Ltd. (1)
3 Church Street No 2202 Samsung Hub, Singapore, 049483, Singapore
Tel.: (65) 62210617
Steel Product Distr
N.A.I.C.S.: 423510

Shagang Intl. (Singapore) Co., Ltd. (1)
3 Church Street 22-02 Samsung hub, Singapore, Singapore
Tel.: (65) 62218257
Steel Product Distr
N.A.I.C.S.: 423510

Shagang Intl. Middle East Co., Ltd. (1)
Unit610 One Lake Plaza Cluster T Jumeirah Lakes Towers, Dubai, United Arab Emirates
Tel.: (971) 45667712
Steel Product Distr
N.A.I.C.S.: 423510

Shagang Mining (Australia) Pty Ltd (1)
Lvl20/ 77 St Georges Tce, Perth, 6000, WA, Australia
Tel.: (61) 8 9325 7718
Steel Product Distr
N.A.I.C.S.: 423510

Shagang South Asia (Hongkong) Trade Co., Ltd. (1)
Unit2506-7 25/F Harbour Centre 25 Harbour Road, Wanchai, China (Hong Kong)
Tel.: (852) 28875081
Steel Product Distr
N.A.I.C.S.: 423510

Shagang South-Asia (Hong Kong) Co., Ltd. (1)
Unit 2506-7 25/F Harbour Centre 25Harbour Road, Wanchai, China (Hong Kong)
Tel.: (852) 288775081
Steel Products Mfr
N.A.I.C.S.: 331210

Shagang Steel & Iron Trade Co., Ltd. (1)
Room 1403 Shagang Building, Jinfeng Town, Zhangjiagang, Jiangsu, China
Tel.: (86) 51258568268
Steel Product Distr
N.A.I.C.S.: 423510

Suzhou Shagang Materials Trade Co., Ltd. (1)
Rm No 311 No 2928 Xihuan Road, Jinchang District, Suzhou, China
Tel.: (86) 512 65890020
Steel Products Mfr
N.A.I.C.S.: 331210

Taizhou Shagang Materials Trade Co., Ltd. (1)
No 1358 Workers West Road, Jiaojiang District, Taizhou, China
Tel.: (86) 576 88685028
Steel Products Mfr
N.A.I.C.S.: 331210

Wuxi Shagang Materials Trade Co., Ltd. (1)
Rm No 621 of Building B Guolian Metallic Material Market No 168 Qianga, Beitang District, Wuxi, China
Tel.: (86) 510 82828373
Steel Products Mfr
N.A.I.C.S.: 331210

Zhejiang Shagang Materials Trade Co., Ltd. (1)
Rm No 86 of 21st Building Yangguangqingchen Jianye Road No 152, Jiangbei District, Ningbo, China
Tel.: (86) 574 87635290
Steel Products Mfr
N.A.I.C.S.: 331210

Zhenjiang Shagang Materials Trade Co., Ltd. (1)
Rm No 3308 of Huilong Mansion No 88 Jinqiao Road, Zhenjiang, China
Tel.: (86) 511 89982118
Steel Products Mfr
N.A.I.C.S.: 331210

JIANGSU SHEMAR ELECTRIC CO., LTD.
66 Haiwei Road Sutong Science and Technology Industrial Park, Nantong, 226553, Jiangsu, China
Tel.: (86) 51380575299
Web Site: https://www.shemar.com.cn
Year Founded: 1996
603530—(SHG)
Rev.: $103,531,409
Assets: $296,167,145
Liabilities: $72,823,992
Net Worth: $223,343,153
Earnings: $6,897,318
Fiscal Year-end: 12/31/22
Electrical Equipment Mfr & Distr
N.A.I.C.S.: 335999
Bin Ma (Chm & Gen Mgr)

JIANGSU SHENTONG VALVE CO., LTD.
Nanyang Industrial Park, Qidong, 226232, Jiangsu, China
Tel.: (86) 51383335899
Web Site: https://www.stfm.cn
Year Founded: 2001
002438—(SSE)
Rev.: $274,489,020
Assets: $814,339,656
Liabilities: $399,676,680
Net Worth: $414,662,976
Earnings: $31,948,020
Emp.: 400
Fiscal Year-end: 12/31/22
Valve Mfr
N.A.I.C.S.: 332911
Jianxin Wu (Pres & CEO)

Subsidiaries:

Wuxi Flange Forging Co., Ltd. (1)
Emp.: 350
Forging Flange Mfr
N.A.I.C.S.: 333517

JIANGSU SHUANGXING COLOR PLASTIC NEW MATERIALS CO., LTD.
No 1 Jingtou Street Color Sculpture Industrial Park, Suqian, 223808, China
Tel.: (86) 52784253088
Web Site: https://www.cpp.com.cn
002585—(SSE)
Rev.: $851,062,680
Assets: $1,719,647,280
Liabilities: $354,948,048
Net Worth: $1,364,699,232
Earnings: $98,070,804
Emp.: 1,000
Fiscal Year-end: 12/31/22
Plastic Packaging Films Mfr
N.A.I.C.S.: 322220
Peifu Wu (Chm & Gen Mgr)

JIANGSU SIDIKE NEW MATERIALS SCIENCE & TECHNOLOGY CO., LTD.
No 11 Qingdao West Road, Taicang, Suzhou, 215400, Jiangsu, China
Tel.: (86) 51253372222
Web Site: https://www.sidike.com
Year Founded: 2006
300806—(SSE)
Rev.: $263,557,476
Assets: $936,845,676
Liabilities: $633,924,252
Net Worth: $302,921,424
Earnings: $23,590,008
Fiscal Year-end: 12/31/22
Aluminium Products Mfr
N.A.I.C.S.: 331313
Chuang Jin (Chm & Gen Mgr)

JIANGSU SIHUAN BIOENGINEERING CO., LTD.
No 10 Dingshan Road, Binjiang Development Zone Jiangyin City, Wuxi, 214434, Jiangsu, China
Tel.: (86) 51086408558
Year Founded: 1992
000518—(SSE)
Rev.: $32,595,675
Assets: $91,517,363
Liabilities: $20,518,733
Net Worth: $70,998,629
Earnings: ($10,421,730)
Fiscal Year-end: 12/31/23
Medicinal Product Mfr
N.A.I.C.S.: 325414
Yu Guo (Acting Sec & Gen Mgr)

JIANGSU SINOJIT WIND ENERGY TECHNOLOGY CO., LTD.
No 8 Naxiang Road Industrial Concentration Zone Yunting Street, Jiangyin, 214422, Jiangsu, China
Tel.: (86) 51086157378
Web Site: https://www.sinojit.com
Year Founded: 2003
601218—(SHG)
Rev.: $247,353,280
Assets: $543,043,894
Liabilities: $148,675,541
Net Worth: $394,368,353
Earnings: $21,808,613
Fiscal Year-end: 12/31/22
Wind Turbine Parts Mfr & Whslr
N.A.I.C.S.: 333611

JIANGSU SKYRAY INSTRUMENT CO., LTD.
1888 West Zhonghuayuan Rd, Yushan, Kunshan, Jiangsu, China
Tel.: (86) 4007102888
Web Site: https://www.skyray-instrument.com
300165—(CHIN)
Rev.: $181,064,052
Assets: $532,482,444
Liabilities: $313,155,180
Net Worth: $219,327,264
Earnings: ($14,556,672)
Fiscal Year-end: 12/31/22
Analytical & Testing Instruments Mfr
N.A.I.C.S.: 334516

Subsidiaries:

Beijing Bandwise Technology Development Co., Ltd. (1)
Add 202 Units 4th Building of Courtyard Technical Building, 8th courtyard of west Haidian Disctrict, Beijing, 102200, China
Tel.: (86) 1069706470
Web Site: http://bandwise.com.cn
Measuring Instrument Mfr & Distr
N.A.I.C.S.: 334516

Skyray Instruments USA, Inc (1)
10875 Plano Rd Ste 130, Dallas, TX 75238
Tel.: (972) 638-9035
Measuring Instrument Mfr & Distr
N.A.I.C.S.: 334516

Skyray Korea Co., Ltd. (1)
2501 Hyundai 41 Tower 917-9 Mok-dong, Yangcheon-gu, Seoul, Korea (South)
Tel.: (82) 220615540
Measuring Instrument Mfr & Distr
N.A.I.C.S.: 334516

JIANGSU SMARTWIN ELECTRONICS TECHNOLOGY CO., LTD.
1-3F Building 01 West Side of West Ring Road, Jurong Economic Development Zone, Zhenjiang, 212499, Jiangsu, China
Tel.: (86) 13380151126
Web Site: https://www.cnsmartwin.com
Year Founded: 2009
301106—(CHIN)
Rev.: $80,289,760
Assets: $191,293,760
Liabilities: $28,485,028
Net Worth: $162,808,732
Earnings: $9,991,831
Emp.: 1,350
Fiscal Year-end: 12/31/22
Electronic Component Mfr & Distr
N.A.I.C.S.: 334419
Faxiang Ying (Chm)

JIANGSU SOPO CHEMICAL CO., LTD.
No 101 Qiusuo Road, Jingkou District, Zhenjiang, 212006, Jiangsu, China
Tel.: (86) 51188995001
Web Site: http://www.sopo.com.cn
Year Founded: 1996
600746—(SHG)
Rev.: $1,006,957,743
Assets: $870,158,091
Liabilities: $100,797,204
Net Worth: $769,360,887
Earnings: $70,922,007
Fiscal Year-end: 12/31/22
Chemical Product Mfr & Distr
N.A.I.C.S.: 325998
Shao Shouyan (Chm)

JIANGSU SUNSHINE CO., LTD.
Sunshine Industrial Park Xinqiao

AND PRIVATE COMPANIES — JIANGSU WUZHONG PHARMACEUTICAL DEVELOPMENT CO., LTD.

Town, Jiangyin, 214426, Jiangsu, China
Tel.: (86) 51086121888
Web Site: http://www.china-sunshine.com
Year Founded: 1986
600220—(SHG)
Rev.: $279,843,525
Assets: $666,085,512
Liabilities: $327,774,555
Net Worth: $338,310,957
Earnings: $16,462,981
Emp.: 15,000
Fiscal Year-end: 12/31/22
Textile Product Mfr & Distr
N.A.I.C.S.: 314999

JIANGSU SUYAN JINGSHEN CO., LTD.
No 18 Huaxi Road, Huaian District, Huai'an, 223200, Jiangsu, China
Tel.: (86) 51785998513
Web Site: http://www.jsjsyh.com
Year Founded: 2009
603299—(SHG)
Rev.: $838,061,078
Assets: $1,364,934,500
Liabilities: $614,272,899
Net Worth: $750,661,601
Earnings: $112,870,789
Emp.: 2,300
Fiscal Year-end: 12/31/22
Chemical Product Mfr & Distr
N.A.I.C.S.: 325998
Wu Xufeng (Chm)

JIANGSU SUZHOU RURAL COMMERCIAL BANK CO., LTD
No 1777 Zhongshan South Road Wujiang District, Suzhou, 215200, Jiangsu, China
Tel.: (86) 51263965383
Web Site: https://www.szrcb.com
603323—(SHG)
Rev.: $566,857,840
Assets: $25,311,025,724
Liabilities: $23,299,342,794
Net Worth: $2,011,682,930
Earnings: $210,846,683
Fiscal Year-end: 12/31/22
Commercial Bank Services
N.A.I.C.S.: 522110

JIANGSU TIANMU LAKE TOURISM CO., LTD.
No 1 Huanhu West Road Tianmu Lake Tourism Holiday Resort, Liyang, 213333, Jiangsu, China
Tel.: (86) 51987980000
Web Site: https://www.tmhtour.com
Year Founded: 1992
603136—(SHG)
Rev.: $51,747,481
Assets: $221,134,044
Liabilities: $40,714,540
Net Worth: $180,419,504
Earnings: $2,851,089
Emp.: 600
Fiscal Year-end: 12/31/22
Tourism Management Services
N.A.I.C.S.: 561591
Meng Guangcai (Chm, Vice Chm & Pres)

JIANGSU TIMES TEXTILE TECHNOLOGY CO., LTD.
No 666 Yishou Road Rucheng Town, Chengbei Subdistrict Rugao County, Rugao, 226572, Jiangsu, China
Tel.: (86) 51387770989
Web Site: https://www.times-clothing.com
Year Founded: 1992
001234—(SSE)
Rev.: $104,179,608
Assets: $155,352,600
Liabilities: $31,320,432
Net Worth: $124,032,168
Earnings: $10,789,740
Fiscal Year-end: 12/31/22
Apparel Product Mfr & Distr
N.A.I.C.S.: 315990
Biao Lu (Chm)

JIANGSU TOLAND ALLOY CO., LTD.
No 9 Fenglin Avenue, Danyang, 212352, Jiangsu, China
Tel.: (86) 51186456067
Web Site: https://tolandalloys.com
Year Founded: 1991
300855—(SSE)
Rev.: $144,946,152
Assets: $264,847,752
Liabilities: $55,914,300
Net Worth: $208,933,452
Earnings: $35,773,920
Fiscal Year-end: 12/31/22
Alloy Product Mfr
N.A.I.C.S.: 331420
Baifang Wan (Chm & Gen Mgr)

JIANGSU TONGDA POWER TECHNOLOGY CO., LTD.
No 58 Xingshi Road, Sian Town Tongzhou, Nantong, 226352, Jiangsu, China
Tel.: (86) 513 86212995
Web Site: http://www.tdchina.com
Sales Range: $125-149.9 Million
Emp.: 1,490
Generator & Motor Machinery Mfr
N.A.I.C.S.: 335312
Yan Hua (Interim Chm & CEO)

Subsidiaries:

Jiangsu Fusson Mould Technology Co., Ltd. (1)
No 18 Xingshi Road, Sian Town, Nantong, Jiangsu, China
Tel.: (86) 51382590008
Web Site: http://www.fusson.cn
Emp.: 110
Motor Equipment Mfr & Distr
N.A.I.C.S.: 335312

JIANGSU TONGGUANG ELECTRONIC WIRE & CABLE CORP., LTD.
No 169 Bohai Road, Haimen District, Nantong, 226103, Jiangsu, China
Tel.: (86) 51382263991
Web Site: https://www.tgjt.cn
Year Founded: 2000
300265—(CHIN)
Rev.: $292,470,048
Assets: $396,854,640
Liabilities: $195,931,008
Net Worth: $200,923,632
Earnings: $11,472,084
Emp.: 800
Fiscal Year-end: 12/31/22
Optical Cables & Wires Mfr
N.A.I.C.S.: 335921
Zhong Zhang (Chm & Gen Mgr)

Subsidiaries:

Jiangsu Tongguang Optical Fiber Cable Co., Ltd (1)
3966 Dasheng Rd, Haimen, 226100, Jiangsu, China
Tel.: (86) 51382298811
Cable Product Mfr & Distr
N.A.I.C.S.: 331222

Jiangsu Tongguang Transmission Lines Technology Co., Ltd (1)
3966 Dasheng Rd, Haimen, 226100, Jiangsu, China
Tel.: (86) 51382298811
Cable Product Mfr & Distr
N.A.I.C.S.: 331222

JIANGSU TONGLI RISHENG MACHINERY CO., LTD.
Dangui Road Economic Development Zone, Danyang, 212300, Jiangsu, China
Tel.: (86) 51185166666
Web Site: https://www.jstljx.com
Year Founded: 2003
605286—(SHG)
Rev.: $344,312,678
Assets: $409,613,434
Liabilities: $150,015,729
Net Worth: $259,597,705
Earnings: $20,261,938
Fiscal Year-end: 12/31/22
Escalator Mfr & Distr
N.A.I.C.S.: 333921
Guoping Li (Chm & Gen Mgr)

JIANGSU TONGLING ELECTRIC CO., LTD.
No 666 Gangmao Road Yangzhong Economic Development Zone, Zhenjiang, 212200, Jiangsu, China
Tel.: (86) 51188368553
Web Site: https://www.jstl.com.cn
Year Founded: 1984
301168—(CHIN)
Rev.: $216,954,859
Assets: $460,504,604
Liabilities: $164,784,267
Net Worth: $295,720,337
Earnings: $23,237,887
Emp.: 1,200
Fiscal Year-end: 12/31/23
Electrical Component Mfr & Distr
N.A.I.C.S.: 335210
Rongfei Yan (Chm)

JIANGSU TONGRUN EQUIPMENT TECHNOLOGY CO., LTD.
No 536 Tonggang Road, Haiyu Town, Changshu, 215517, Jiangsu, China
Tel.: (86) 51252346618
Web Site: https://www.tongrunindustries.com
Year Founded: 2002
002150—(SSE)
Rev.: $235,595,412
Assets: $301,430,376
Liabilities: $53,448,876
Net Worth: $247,981,500
Earnings: $20,925,216
Emp.: 1,000
Fiscal Year-end: 12/31/22
Metal Products Mfr
N.A.I.C.S.: 332999
Lu Chuan (Chm)

JIANGSU TONGXINGBAO INTELLIGENT TRANSPORTATION TECHNOLOGY CO., LTD.
Building 31 No 2 Zidong Road, Qixia District, Nanjing, 210019, Jiangsu, China
Tel.: (86) 2583485958
Web Site: https://www.jstxb.com
Year Founded: 2016
301339—(CHIN)
Rev.: $104,451,803
Assets: $778,309,758
Liabilities: $399,513,816
Net Worth: $378,795,943
Earnings: $26,895,084
Fiscal Year-end: 12/31/23
Transportation Services
N.A.I.C.S.: 483211
Wang Mingwen (Chm)

JIANGSU TRANSIMAGE TECHNOLOGY CO., LTD.
No 33 Limbo Road Gaoyou Economic Development Zone, Gaoyou, 225600, Jiangsu, China
Tel.: (86) 51484606288
Web Site: http://www.transimage.cn
Year Founded: 2007
002866—(SSE)
Rev.: $280,618,884
Assets: $502,695,180
Liabilities: $214,277,076
Net Worth: $288,418,104
Earnings: $16,148,808
Fiscal Year-end: 12/31/22
Electronic Parts Mfr & Distr
N.A.I.C.S.: 334412
Weimin Zou (Chm, Pres & Gen Mgr)

JIANGSU WANLIN MODERN LOGISTICS CO., LTD.
Tel.: (86) 52389112000
Web Site: http://www.china-wanlin.com
Year Founded: 2011
603117—(SSE)
Rev.: $62,619,804
Assets: $333,396,648
Liabilities: $137,570,940
Net Worth: $195,825,708
Earnings: ($84,004,128)
Fiscal Year-end: 12/31/22
Wood Agency Procurement Logistics Services
N.A.I.C.S.: 541614
Fan Jibo (Chm)

Subsidiaries:

Jiangsu Wanlin Wood Industrial Park Co., Ltd. (1)
Room A-B 8F World Trade Center Building No 68 Renmin Zhong Road, Jingjiang, 214500, Jiangsu, China
Tel.: (86) 52389112222
Logistic Services
N.A.I.C.S.: 541614

Jingjiang Yingli Port Co., Ltd. (1)
No 1 Liuzhugang Road Xingang Industrial Park, Jingjiang, 214513, Jiangsu, China
Tel.: (86) 52384099006
Logistic Services
N.A.I.C.S.: 541614

Shanghai Mailin International Trade Co., Ltd. (1)
37F SIIC Building No 18 Cao Xi Bei Rd, Shanghai, 200030, China
Tel.: (86) 2164695696
Logistic Services
N.A.I.C.S.: 541614

Wanlin International(H.K.)Co., Ltd. (1)
Room 11 9F Wayson Comm Bldg No 28 Connaught Rd West, Sheung Wan, China (Hong Kong)
Tel.: (852) 28757805
Logistic Services
N.A.I.C.S.: 541614

JIANGSU WUJIN STAINLESS STEEL PIPE GROUP CO., LTD
No 1 Wucheng West Road, Changzhou, 213111, Jiangsu, China
Tel.: (86) 4009288688
Web Site: https://www.wjss.com.cn
Year Founded: 1970
603878—(SHG)
Rev.: $397,383,344
Assets: $535,918,566
Liabilities: $173,569,598
Net Worth: $362,348,967
Earnings: $30,206,990
Emp.: 1,300
Fiscal Year-end: 12/31/22
Steel Pipe Mfr & Distr
N.A.I.C.S.: 331210
Zhu Qi (Chm)

JIANGSU WUZHONG PHARMACEUTICAL DEVELOPMENT CO., LTD.
988 Dongfang Avenue, Suzhou, 215128, Jiangsu, China
Tel.: (86) 51266981888
Web Site: https://www.600200.com

JIANGSU WUZHONG PHARMACEUTICAL DEVELOPMENT CO., LTD.

Jiangsu Wuzhong Pharmaceutical Development Co., Ltd.—(Continued)
Year Founded: 1994
600200—(SHG)
Rev.: $284,483,085
Assets: $548,926,345
Liabilities: $292,896,541
Net Worth: $256,029,804
Earnings: ($10,698,101)
Fiscal Year-end: 12/31/22
Precious Metal Product Mfr & Distr
N.A.I.C.S.: 332999
Qian Qunying *(Chm, Vice Chm & Pres)*

JIANGSU XIEHE ELECTRONIC CO., LTD.
No 4 Tangtou Road, Henglin Town Wujin District, Changzhou, 213101, Jiangsu, China
Tel.: (86) 51988506113
Web Site: http://www.xiehepcb.com
Year Founded: 2000
605258—(SHG)
Rev.: $96,550,118
Assets: $200,224,243
Liabilities: $38,354,837
Net Worth: $161,869,406
Earnings: $7,096,757
Emp.: 700
Fiscal Year-end: 12/31/22
Electronic Product Mfr & Distr
N.A.I.C.S.: 334419
Nanguo Zhang *(Chm)*

JIANGSU XINQUAN AUTOMOTIVE TRIM CO., LTD.
No 555 Huanghe West Road, Xinbei District, Changzhou, 213022, Jiangsu, China
Tel.: (86) 51985120170
Web Site: http://www.xinquan.cn
Year Founded: 2001
603179—(SHG)
Rev.: $975,315,978
Assets: $1,310,300,325
Liabilities: $730,530,445
Net Worth: $579,769,880
Earnings: $66,069,039
Emp.: 1,500
Fiscal Year-end: 12/31/22
Automotive Body Parts Mfr & Distr
N.A.I.C.S.: 336370
Zhihua Tang *(Chm, Pres & Gen Mgr)*

JIANGSU XINRI E-VEHICLE CO., LTD.
No 501 Xishan Road Anzhen, Xishan District, Wuxi, 214106, Jiangsu, China
Tel.: (86) 51088109820
Web Site: https://www.sunraev.com
Year Founded: 2007
603787—(SHG)
Rev.: $688,468,108
Assets: $465,704,652
Liabilities: $303,140,982
Net Worth: $162,563,670
Earnings: $22,769,300
Emp.: 5,000
Fiscal Year-end: 12/31/22
Electric Vehicle Parts Mfr & Distr
N.A.I.C.S.: 336320
Chongshun Zhang *(Chm)*

JIANGSU XIUQIANG GLASS WORK CO., LTD.
No 28 Jiangshandadao Road Suyu, High-Tech Industry Developing District, Suqian, 223801, Jiangsu, China
Tel.: (86) 52780300160
Web Site: https://www.jsxq.com
Year Founded: 2001
300160—(CHIN)
Rev.: $211,591,224
Assets: $389,447,136
Liabilities: $74,135,412
Net Worth: $315,311,724
Earnings: $25,850,448
Emp.: 1,100
Fiscal Year-end: 12/31/22
Glass Products Mfr
N.A.I.C.S.: 327212
Gao Ying *(Sec & Rep-Securities Affairs)*

JIANGSU YABANG DYESTUFF CO., LTD.
No 105 Renmin West Road, Niutang Town Wujing District, Changzhou, 213163, Jiangsu, China
Tel.: (86) 51988316008
Web Site: http://www.yabangdyes.com
Year Founded: 2006
603188—(SHG)
Rev.: $135,670,472
Assets: $355,207,956
Liabilities: $163,683,627
Net Worth: $191,524,329
Earnings: ($98,119,537)
Fiscal Year-end: 12/31/22
Textile Dye Mfr & Distr
N.A.I.C.S.: 325998
Yunxia Xu *(Chm & Gen Mgr)*

JIANGSU YANGDIAN SCIENCE & TECHNOLOGY CO., LTD.
690 Tianmu Road Economic Development Zone, Jiangyan, Taizhou, 225500, Jiangsu, China
Tel.: (86) 52388857703
Web Site: https://www.jsyddq.cn
Year Founded: 1993
301012—(CHIN)
Rev.: $89,141,364
Assets: $133,257,852
Liabilities: $45,912,204
Net Worth: $87,345,648
Earnings: $9,257,976
Fiscal Year-end: 12/31/22
Electronic Component Mfr & Distr
N.A.I.C.S.: 334419
Zhao Henglong *(Gen Mgr)*

JIANGSU YANGHE BREWERY JOINT-STOCK CO., LTD.
118 Middle Road, Yanghe Town, Suqian, Jiangsu, China
Tel.: (86) 2586438732 CN
Web Site: https://www.yangheglobal.com
Year Founded: 2002
002304—(SSE)
Rev.: $4,226,727,960
Assets: $9,542,180,700
Liabilities: $2,869,747,920
Net Worth: $6,672,432,780
Earnings: $1,316,647,332
Emp.: 30,000
Fiscal Year-end: 12/31/22
Production & Distribution of Liquor & Related Products
N.A.I.C.S.: 312120

JIANGSU YANGNONG CHEMICAL CO., LTD.
No 39 Wenfeng Road, Yangzhou, 225009, Jiangsu, China
Tel.: (86) 51485889958
Web Site: https://www.yangnongchem.com
Year Founded: 1999
600486—(SHG)
Rev.: $2,219,830,592
Assets: $2,077,002,289
Liabilities: $878,062,765
Net Worth: $1,198,939,524
Earnings: $251,907,140
Emp.: 3,000
Fiscal Year-end: 12/31/22
Pesticide Mfr & Whslr
N.A.I.C.S.: 325320
Wu Xiaoju *(Sec-Party Committee & Gen Mgr)*

Subsidiaries:

Youth Chemical Co. Ltd. (1)
Yangzhou Chemical Industry Park, Yangzhou, China
Tel.: (86) 51483299500
Web Site: http://www.youthchem.com
Pesticide Mfr & Distr
N.A.I.C.S.: 325320

JIANGSU YAWEI MACHINE TOOL CO., LTD.
Xiancheng Industrial Park Huanghainan Road, Jiangdu District, Yangzhou, 225200, Jiangsu, China
Tel.: (86) 51486880508
Web Site: https://www.yawei.cc
Year Founded: 1956
002559—(SSE)
Rev.: $256,953,060
Assets: $592,243,704
Liabilities: $336,263,616
Net Worth: $255,980,088
Earnings: $1,051,596
Emp.: 1,300
Fiscal Year-end: 12/31/22
Machine Tools Mfr
N.A.I.C.S.: 333517
Leng Zhibin *(Chm & Gen Mgr)*

Subsidiaries:

Jiangsu Yawei Stock Co.,Ltd. (1)
Xiancheng Industrial Zone Huanghai South Rd, Jiangdu, Yangzhou, 225200, China
Tel.: (86) 51486880508
Web Site: http://www.yaweigroup.cc
Metal Sheet Mfr
N.A.I.C.S.: 332999

JIANGSU YIDA CHEMICAL CO., LTD.
No 1 Qiuzhuang Xishiqiao, Jiangyin, 214441, Jiangsu, China
Tel.: (86) 51086601707
Web Site: https://www.yidachem.com
Year Founded: 1996
300721—(CHIN)
Rev.: $255,518,605
Assets: $371,363,716
Liabilities: $195,051,812
Net Worth: $176,311,903
Earnings: ($4,970,864)
Emp.: 500
Fiscal Year-end: 12/31/22
Chemical Products Mfr
N.A.I.C.S.: 325199
Liu Zhun *(Chm & Gen Mgr)*

Subsidiaries:

Jilin Yida Chemical Co., Ltd. (1)
No 1 Street Jiuzhan Economic and Technological Development Zone, Jilin, China
Tel.: (86) 43263058009
Chemical Products Mfr
N.A.I.C.S.: 325998

JIANGSU YIKE FOOD GROUP CO., LTD.
North of Huashan Road High-tech Industrial Development Zone, Suqian High-tech Industrial Development Zone, Suqian, 223800, Jiangsu, China
Tel.: (86) 52788207929
Web Site: https://www.ecolovo.com
Year Founded: 2004
301116—(CHIN)
Rev.: $2,627,538,264
Assets: $688,379,796
Liabilities: $405,037,152
Net Worth: $283,342,644
Earnings: $7,264,296
Fiscal Year-end: 12/31/22
Food Product Mfr & Distr
N.A.I.C.S.: 333241

INTERNATIONAL PUBLIC

Liyu Tian *(Chm)*

JIANGSU YINHE ELECTRONICS CO., LTD.
No 188 NanHuan Road, ZhangJiaGang City, Zhangjiagang, 215611, Jiangsu, China
Tel.: (86) 51258449242 CN
Web Site: https://www.yinhe.com
Year Founded: 1975
002519—(SSE)
Rev.: $184,016,664
Assets: $509,983,344
Liabilities: $74,449,908
Net Worth: $435,533,436
Earnings: $27,487,512
Emp.: 500
Fiscal Year-end: 12/31/22
Digital TV Receiver Equipment, Case, Cabinets & Sheet Metal Products Mfr
N.A.I.C.S.: 334419
Wu Jianming *(Chm & Gen Mgr)*

Subsidiaries:

Fujian Junpeng Communication Technology Co., Ltd. (1)
18-19 Taijiang Industrial Park Jinshan Development Zone, Fuzhou, 350000, Fujian, China
Tel.: (86) 13489895909
Electronic Components Mfr
N.A.I.C.S.: 334419

Hefei Tongzhi Electromechanical Control Technology Co., Ltd. (1)
Electro Mechanical Product Mfr
N.A.I.C.S.: 334514

Jiangsu Yinhe Tongzhi New Energy Technology Co., Ltd. (1)
No 188 Nanhuan Road, Tangqiao Town, Zhangjiagang, 215611, Jiangsu, China
Tel.: (86) 51258449208
Electronic Components Mfr
N.A.I.C.S.: 334419

Luoyang Jiasheng Power Supply Technology Co., Ltd. (1)
F4 Block C Huojuyuan Yanguang Road Luoyang Hi-tech Zone, Luoyang, 471003, China
Tel.: (86) 37965189955
Electronic Components Mfr
N.A.I.C.S.: 334419

JIANGSU YINREN GROUP CO., LTD.
5F Yinren Building 99 Xianqian West Street, Wuxi, Jiangsu, China
Tel.: (86) 510 8275 2111 CN
Web Site: http://www.yrg-china.com
Year Founded: 2000
Holding Company; Real Estate & Diamonds
N.A.I.C.S.: 551112
Xiaoan Shen *(Pres)*

JIANGSU YITONG HIGH-TECH CO., LTD.
No 28 Tonglin Road, Changshu, 215500, Jiangsu, China
Tel.: (86) 51252818000
Web Site: https://www.yitong-group.com
300211—(CHIN)
Rev.: $47,481,876
Assets: $83,252,988
Liabilities: $10,646,532
Net Worth: $72,606,456
Earnings: $3,522,636
Emp.: 450
Fiscal Year-end: 12/31/22
Broadcast Television Equipment Mfr
N.A.I.C.S.: 334220

JIANGSU YOKE TECHNOLOGY CO., LTD.
Jingxi North Road Economic Devel-

AND PRIVATE COMPANIES

opment Zone, Yixing, 214203, Jiangsu, China
Tel.: (86) 51087126528
Web Site: https://www.yokechem.com
Year Founded: 1997
002409—(SSE)
Rev.: $597,990,276
Assets: $1,487,717,712
Liabilities: $345,690,072
Net Worth: $1,142,027,640
Earnings: $73,606,104
Emp.: 250
Fiscal Year-end: 12/31/22
Phosphate Flame Retardant, Polyurethane Catalyst & Silicone Surfactant Mfr
N.A.I.C.S.: 325998
Shen Qi *(Chm & Gen Mgr)*

Subsidiaries:

UP Chemical Co. Ltd. (1)
81 Sandan-ro 197beon-gil, Pyeongtaek, Gyeonggi-do, Korea (South)
Tel.: (82) 31 611 8900
Web Site: http://www.upchem.co.kr
Semiconductor Material Mfr
N.A.I.C.S.: 334413
Soo-Ick Sohn *(CEO)*

Plant (Domestic):

UP Chemical Co. Ltd. - Pyeongtaek Plant (2)
455-91 Dongsak-ro, Pyeongtaek, Gyeonggi-do, Korea (South)
Tel.: (82) 316115400
Web Site: http://www.upchem.co.kr
Semiconductor Product Mfr
N.A.I.C.S.: 334413

JIANGSU YUEDA GROUP CO., LTD.
No 2 East Road Shiji Avenue, Yancheng, 224007, Jiangsu, China
Tel.: (86) 51588202867
Web Site: https://www.yueda.com
600805—(SHG)
Rev.: $431,487,950
Assets: $1,125,250,907
Liabilities: $460,779,350
Net Worth: $664,471,557
Earnings: $13,220,569
Emp.: 40,000
Fiscal Year-end: 12/31/22
Automobile Parts Mfr & Distr
N.A.I.C.S.: 336390

JIANGSU YUNYI ELECTRIC CO., LTD.
26 Huangshan Road, Tongshan Area, Xuzhou, 221116, Jiangsu, China
Tel.: (86) 51683913580
Web Site: https://www.yunyi-china.net
Year Founded: 2000
300304—(CHIN)
Rev.: $164,899,800
Assets: $465,937,056
Liabilities: $100,574,136
Net Worth: $365,362,920
Earnings: $19,109,844
Emp.: 1,600
Fiscal Year-end: 12/31/22
Automotive Electronic Product Mfr
N.A.I.C.S.: 336320
Fu Hongling *(Chm & Gen Mgr)*

JIANGSU YUNYONG ELECTRONICS & TECHNOLOGY CO., LTD.
No 16 Taian Road, Hailing District, Taizhou, 225314, Jiangsu, China
Tel.: (86) 52386658773
Web Site: http://www.yytek.com
Year Founded: 2010
688060—(SHG)
Rev.: $37,321,367
Assets: $153,448,987
Liabilities: $15,286,935
Net Worth: $138,162,052
Earnings: $2,352,683
Fiscal Year-end: 12/31/22
Electronic Product Mfr & Distr
N.A.I.C.S.: 334419
Nan Gao *(Chm & Gen Mgr)*

JIANGSU YUXING FILM TECHNOLOGY CO., LTD.
No 8-8 West Tongzi River Road Zhonglou Development Zone, Changzhou, 213023, Jiangsu, China
Tel.: (86) 51981681538
Web Site: https://www.bopet-film-china.com
Year Founded: 2004
300305—(CHIN)
Rev.: $261,982,188
Assets: $431,509,572
Liabilities: $154,296,792
Net Worth: $277,212,780
Earnings: $19,477,692
Emp.: 500
Fiscal Year-end: 12/31/22
Polyester Film Mfr
N.A.I.C.S.: 322220
Wang Jianxin *(Chm)*

JIANGSU YUYUE MEDICAL EQUIPMENT & SUPPLY CO., LTD.
Zhenxin Road South Yunyang Industrial Park, Danyang, 212300, Jiangsu, China
Tel.: (86) 51186900876
Web Site: http://www.yuyue.com.cn
Year Founded: 2007
002223—(SSE)
Rev.: $997,075,872
Assets: $2,119,367,484
Liabilities: $706,040,712
Net Worth: $1,413,326,772
Earnings: $223,943,616
Fiscal Year-end: 12/31/22
Medical Equipment Mfr
N.A.I.C.S.: 339112
Chen Jian *(Sec & VP)*

Subsidiaries:

Shanghai Yu Yue Medical Equipment Co., Ltd. (1)
273 Siping Road, Shanghai, 200081, China
Tel.: (86) 2165757288
Medical Equipment Mfr
N.A.I.C.S.: 339112

Yuwell Germany GmbH (1)
Gotenstr 3, Tuttlingen, 78532, Germany
Tel.: (49) 74629463050
Web Site: http://www.yuwell.com
Emp.: 10
Medical Equipment Mfr
N.A.I.C.S.: 339112
Jurgen Bucher *(Gen Mgr)*

JIANGSU ZEYU INTELLIGENT ELECTRIC POWER CO., LTD.
Building 1-4 No 279 Zhonghuan Road, Chongchuan District, Nantong, 226002, Jiangsu, China
Tel.: (86) 51385359899
Year Founded: 2011
301179—(CHIN)
Rev.: $146,997,452
Assets: $441,962,686
Liabilities: $114,280,281
Net Worth: $327,682,405
Earnings: $35,490,765
Fiscal Year-end: 12/31/23
Electrical Component Mfr & Distr
N.A.I.C.S.: 335210
Jian Zhang *(Chm)*

JIANGSU ZHANGJIAGANG RURAL COMMERCIAL BANK CO., LTD
No 66 Renmin Middle Road, Zhangjiagang, 215600, Jiangsu, China
Tel.: (86) 51256961859
Web Site: https://www.zrcbank.com
002839—(SSE)
Rev.: $677,762,748
Assets: $26,329,599,504
Liabilities: $24,121,699,992
Net Worth: $2,207,899,512
Earnings: $236,155,608
Fiscal Year-end: 12/31/22
Banking Services
N.A.I.C.S.: 523150
Ying Ji *(Chm)*

JIANGSU ZHENGDAN CHEMICAL INDUSTRY CO., LTD.
No 18 Songlinshan Road International Chemical Industrial Park, Zhenjiang New District, Zhenjiang, 212004, Jiangsu, China
Tel.: (86) 51188059005
Web Site: https://www.zhengdanchem.com
Year Founded: 2007
300641—(CHIN)
Rev.: $216,601,468
Assets: $310,967,264
Liabilities: $95,018,818
Net Worth: $215,948,445
Earnings: $1,390,908
Fiscal Year-end: 12/31/23
Chemical Product Mfr & Distr
N.A.I.C.S.: 325211
Cao Zhengguo *(Chm)*

JIANGSU ZHENJIANG NEW ENERGY EQUIPMENT CO., LTD.
No 2608 Zhencheng Road, Jiangyin, 214441, Jiangsu, China
Tel.: (86) 51086605508
Web Site: https://www.zjavim.com
Year Founded: 2004
603507—(SHG)
Rev.: $407,733,604
Assets: $767,706,961
Liabilities: $446,315,257
Net Worth: $321,391,704
Earnings: $13,287,049
Fiscal Year-end: 12/31/22
Wind Power Equipment Mfr
N.A.I.C.S.: 335312
Hu Zhen *(Chm)*

JIANGSU ZHONGCHAO HOLDING CO., LTD.
No 999 Zhenfeng East Road Xijiao Industrial Park, Yixing, 21422, Jiangsu Province, China
Tel.: (86) 5108769677
Web Site: https://www.zckggf.com
002471—(SSE)
Rev.: $827,093,592
Assets: $795,073,968
Liabilities: $598,029,588
Net Worth: $197,044,380
Earnings: ($6,733,584)
Emp.: 1,300
Fiscal Year-end: 12/31/22
Electric Wire & Cables Mfr
N.A.I.C.S.: 335921
Fei Yang *(Chm)*

Subsidiaries:

Connect Cable Accessories Co., Ltd. (1)
No 8 Changxing Road, Xushe Industrial Concentration District Yixing, Wuxi, Jiangsu, China
Tel.: (86) 51087694555
Web Site: https://www.jsconnect.com
Power Cable Equipment Mfr
N.A.I.C.S.: 335999

Jiangsu Changfeng Cable Co., Ltd. (1)
Guanlin Town Industrial Zone, Yixing City, Wuxi, 214252, Jiangsu, China (90%)
Tel.: (86) 51087298645
Web Site: http://www.cfalloy.com
Cable Mfr
N.A.I.C.S.: 335921

Jiangsu Yuanfang Cable Factory Co., Ltd. (1)
Guanfeng Road, Guanlin Town, Yixing, 214252, Jiangsu, China
Tel.: (86) 51087290353
Web Site: https://www.yuanfang-cn.com
Cable Mfr
N.A.I.C.S.: 335921

Nanjing Zhongchao New Materials Corporation (1)
No 31 Wutai Road, Dongba town Gaochun District, Nanjing, 211301, Jiangsu, China
Tel.: (86) 2568618183
Web Site: https://www.zcnewmaterials.com
Polyolefin Compound Mfr
N.A.I.C.S.: 325211

Wuxi City Heng Hui Cable Co., Ltd. (1)
No 1 Jinfeng Road Fengyi, Guanlin Town, Yixing, 214252, China
Tel.: (86) 51087295158
Web Site: http://www.hhdl.cn
Cable Mfr
N.A.I.C.S.: 335921

Wuxi Xizhou Magnet Wires Co., Ltd. (1)
No 231-5 Chengnan Road, High-Tech Development Zone, Wuxi, Jiangsu, China
Tel.: (86) 51085362205
Web Site: http://www.xizhou.com.cn
Cable Mfr
N.A.I.C.S.: 335921

JIANGSU ZHONGLI GROUP CO., LTD.
No 8 Changkun Rd, Changshu, 215500, Jiangsu, China
Tel.: (86) 51252578888
Web Site: https://www.zhongli.com
Year Founded: 1988
002309—(SSE)
Rev.: $1,146,490,956
Assets: $1,341,058,680
Liabilities: $1,203,329,088
Net Worth: $137,729,592
Earnings: ($68,095,404)
Fiscal Year-end: 12/31/22
Communication Equipment Mfr
N.A.I.C.S.: 334290
Wang Weifeng *(Chm & Gen Mgr)*

Subsidiaries:

Changshu Zhonglian Photoelectric New Material Co., Ltd. (1)
No 8 Changkun Road Zhongli Industry Park, Southeast Economic Development Zone, Changshu, Jiangsu, China
Tel.: (86) 51252578915
Web Site: http://jszl.com.cn
Plastic Material Mfr & Distr
N.A.I.C.S.: 325211

Changzhou Marine Cable Co., Ltd. (1)
NO 8 East Beitanghe Road, Changzhou, Jiangsu, China
Tel.: (86) 117858899782
Web Site: https://www.cmc-cable.com
Marine Cable Mfr
N.A.I.C.S.: 335921

Ningxia Zhongsheng Cable Technology Co., Ltd. (1)
No 8 Zhongli Road, Shizuishan Economic and Technological Development Zone Ningxia, Yinchuan, China
Tel.: (86) 18895026632
Web Site: http://www.zhongli-nx.com
Marine Cable Mfr
N.A.I.C.S.: 335921

Suzhou Cableplus Technologies Co., Ltd. (1)

JIANGSU ZHONGLI GROUP CO., LTD.

Jiangsu Zhongli Group Co., Ltd.—(Continued)
No 7 Nanxin Road Changkun Industrial Park, Shajiabang, Changshu, Jiangsu, China
Tel.: (86) 51252579665
Web Site: http://www.cableplus-sz.com
Other Machinery Mfr
N.A.I.C.S.: 333248

Suzhou Talesun Solar Technology Co., Ltd. (1)
No 1 Talesun Road, Shajiabang, Changshu, 215542, Jiangsu, China
Tel.: (86) 51282355888
Web Site: http://global.talesun.com
Solar PV Panel Mfr
N.A.I.C.S.: 334413

JIANGSU ZHONGNAN CONSTRUCTION GROUP CO., LTD.
No 899 Shanghai Road Haimen City, Nantong, 226124, Jiangsu, China
Tel.: (86) 51368702888
Web Site: http://www.zhongnanconstruction.cn
000961—(SSE)
Rev.: $8,288,697,924
Assets: $43,063,810,920
Liabilities: $38,675,893,932
Net Worth: $4,387,916,988
Earnings: ($1,287,555,048)
Fiscal Year-end: 12/31/22
Property Development Services
N.A.I.C.S.: 531311
Jinshi Chen *(Chm & Gen Mgr)*

JIANGSU ZHONGSHE GROUP CO., LTD.
No 1 Xingyang Road, Binhu District, Wuxi, 214081, Jiangsu, China
Tel.: (86) 51083278988
Web Site: http://www.jszs-group.com
Year Founded: 1987
002883—(SSE)
Rev.: $104,805,792
Assets: $175,561,776
Liabilities: $72,995,364
Net Worth: $102,566,412
Earnings: $7,258,680
Fiscal Year-end: 12/31/22
Landscape Development Services
N.A.I.C.S.: 541320
Gu Xiaojun *(Chm)*

JIANGSU ZHONGSHENG GAOKE ENVIRONMENTAL CO., LTD
Jingtang industrial concentration area Xushe town, Yixing, 214244, Jiangsu, China
Tel.: (86) 4009672778
Web Site: https://www.jsgaoke.com
002778—(SSE)
Rev.: $101,318,256
Assets: $206,364,132
Liabilities: $112,589,568
Net Worth: $93,774,564
Earnings: ($4,968,756)
Fiscal Year-end: 12/31/22
Industrial & Automobile Oil Mfr & Distr
N.A.I.C.S.: 324191

JIANGSU ZHONGTIAN TECHNOLOGY CO., LTD.
No 88 Qixin Road Economic and Technological Development Zone, Nantong, 226009, Jiangsu, China
Tel.: (86) 51383599505
Web Site: http://www.zttcable.com
Year Founded: 1990
600522—(SHG)
Rev.: $5,654,010,043
Assets: $6,833,292,359
Liabilities: $2,438,424,589
Net Worth: $4,394,867,771
Earnings: $451,218,812
Emp.: 16,000
Fiscal Year-end: 12/31/22
Fiber Optic Cable Mfr
N.A.I.C.S.: 335921
Jiping Xue *(Chm)*

Subsidiaries:

Demirer Kablo Tesisleri SAN. Ve TIC. A.S (1)
Dereboyu Cad Meydan Sok Beybi Giz Plaza No 1 Kat 30, Sariyer, 34398, Istanbul, Turkiye
Tel.: (90) 2122615163
Web Site: http://www.demirerkablo.com.tr
Emp.: 277
Telecommunication Cable Accessory Mfr
N.A.I.C.S.: 335929

PT ZTT Cable Indonesia (1)
Tower 33rd Floor Unit 7 Central Park Jl S Parman 28, Tanjung Duren, Jakarta Barat, 11470, Indonesia
Tel.: (62) 2129337670
Web Site: http://www.zttindonesia.com
Power Grid & Accessory Mfr
N.A.I.C.S.: 335999
Chairul Anwar *(Mgr-Mktg)*

ZTT India Private Limited (1)
956 Jeedi Drive Sector 28 Sri City Satyavedu Mandal, Chittoor, 517 646. AP, India
Tel.: (91) 7995024587
Web Site: http://www.zttindia.com
Emp.: 500
Optical Fiber Cable Mfr
N.A.I.C.S.: 335921
Sankar Nandhu *(Sr Mgr-Fin, Costing & Comml)*

JIANGSU ZIJIN RURAL COMMERCIAL BANK CO., LTD.
381 Jiangdong Middle Road, Jianye District, Nanjing, 210019, Jiangsu, China
Tel.: (86) 2588866792
Web Site: http://www.zjrcbank.com
Year Founded: 2011
601860—(SHG)
Rev.: $632,748,683
Assets: $31,550,987,473
Liabilities: $29,150,547,332
Net Worth: $2,400,440,141
Earnings: $224,664,851
Fiscal Year-end: 12/31/22
Commercial & Financial Banking Services
N.A.I.C.S.: 522110
Wenxiong Shi *(Pres)*

JIANGSU ZITIAN MEDIA TECHNOLOGY CO., LTD.
In Forging Industrial Park of Economic Development Zone, Rugao, 226578, Jiangsu, China
Tel.: (86) 51382155555
Web Site: http://www.ntdy.com.cn
Year Founded: 2000
300280—(CHIN)
Rev.: $245,125,764
Assets: $655,696,080
Liabilities: $316,411,056
Net Worth: $339,285,024
Earnings: $24,529,284
Fiscal Year-end: 12/31/22
Hydraulic Press Mfr & Whslr
N.A.I.C.S.: 333998

JIANGSU ZONGYI CO., LTD.
Zongyi Digital City, Xingdong Town Tongzhou District, Nantong, 226371, Jiangsu, China
Tel.: (86) 51386639999
Web Site: http://www.600770.com
Year Founded: 1987
600770—(SHG)
Rev.: $52,716,746
Assets: $768,946,258
Liabilities: $116,813,109
Net Worth: $652,133,149
Earnings: ($44,991,629)
Fiscal Year-end: 12/31/22
Solar Cell Mfr & System Design Services
N.A.I.C.S.: 334413
Shengda Zan *(Chm)*

Subsidiaries:

Zongyi Solar (America) Limited (1)
PO Box 302, Alpine, NJ 07620
Tel.: (201) 767-1922
Web Site: http://www.zongyisolar.com
Solar Cell & Module Distr
N.A.I.C.S.: 423690

JIANGXI BAISHENG INTELLIGENT TECHNOLOGY CO., LTD.
No 1220 Xiaolan Middle Avenue, Xiaolan Economic & Technological Development Zone Nanchang County, Nanchang, 330052, Jiangxi, China
Tel.: (86) 79187389020
Web Site: https://www.bisensa.com
Year Founded: 1999
301083—(CHIN)
Rev.: $54,684,648
Assets: $143,588,169
Liabilities: $27,584,127
Net Worth: $116,004,042
Earnings: $4,955,746
Fiscal Year-end: 12/31/23
Industrial Machinery Mfr & Distr
N.A.I.C.S.: 333248
Liu Rungen *(Chm & Gen Mgr)*

JIANGXI BANK CO., LTD.
No 699 Financial Street, Honggutan New District, Nanchang, 330038, Jiangxi, China
Tel.: (86) 956055 CN
Web Site: https://www.jx-bank.com
Year Founded: 2015
1916—(HKG)
Rev.: $2,947,097,790
Assets: $72,386,400,200
Liabilities: $65,813,568,725
Net Worth: $6,572,831,476
Earnings: $224,712,868
Emp.: 5,221
Fiscal Year-end: 12/31/22
Commercial Banking Services
N.A.I.C.S.: 522110
Xiaoming Chen *(Chm)*

JIANGXI BLACK CAT CARBON BLACK CO., LTD.
Liyao, Changjiang District, Jingdezhen, 333000, Jiangxi, China
Tel.: (86) 7988399125
Web Site: https://www.blackcat.com.cn
Year Founded: 2001
002068—(SSE)
Rev.: $1,388,991,240
Assets: $1,180,672,740
Liabilities: $698,511,060
Net Worth: $482,161,680
Earnings: $1,242,540
Fiscal Year-end: 12/31/22
Chemical Products Mfr
N.A.I.C.S.: 335991
Wang Yao *(Chm)*

JIANGXI CHANGJIU BIOCHEMICAL INDUSTRY CO., LTD.
Room 805 8th Floor Chamber of Commerce Building No 31 Changzheng Avenue, Zhanggong District, Ganzhou, 200232, Jiangxi, China
Tel.: (86) 2180231198
Web Site: http://www.600228.net
Year Founded: 1999
600228—(SHG)
Rev.: $71,695,092
Assets: $192,848,919
Liabilities: $31,825,184
Net Worth: $161,023,735
Earnings: $9,552,058
Emp.: 2,000
Fiscal Year-end: 12/31/22
Chemical Product Mfr & Distr
N.A.I.C.S.: 325180
Guobao Xiong *(VP)*

JIANGXI CHANGYUN CO., LTD.
No 1 Pingan West 2nd Street Jiulong Lake Management Office, Xinjian District, Nanchang, 330038, Jiangxi, China
Tel.: (86) 79188283082 CN
Web Site: https://www.jxcy.com.cn
Year Founded: 1993
600561—(SHG)
Rev.: $203,806,760
Assets: $671,865,190
Liabilities: $500,643,220
Net Worth: $171,221,970
Earnings: ($20,765,272)
Fiscal Year-end: 12/31/22
Road Passenger Transportation Services
N.A.I.C.S.: 485210
Wang Xiao *(Chm)*

JIANGXI CHENGUANG NEW MATERIALS CO., LTD.
High-tech Industrial Park, Hukou County, Jiujiang, 332500, Jiangxi, China
Tel.: (86) 2558991889
Web Site: https://www.cgsilane.com
Year Founded: 2006
605399—(SHG)
Rev.: $273,322,801
Assets: $343,878,772
Liabilities: $35,640,652
Net Worth: $308,238,119
Earnings: $89,670,588
Fiscal Year-end: 12/31/22
Chemical Product Mfr & Distr
N.A.I.C.S.: 325520
Qiao Yuliang *(Deputy Gen Mgr)*

JIANGXI COPPER COMPANY LIMITED
No 7666 Changdong Avenue, Nanchang, Jiangxi, China
Tel.: (86) 79182710117
Web Site: https://en.jxcc.com
Year Founded: 1979
600362—(SHG)
Rev.: $72,260,261,437
Assets: $23,281,859,963
Liabilities: $12,655,383,211
Net Worth: $10,626,476,753
Earnings: $900,685,243
Emp.: 24,831
Fiscal Year-end: 12/31/23
Copper Mining Services
N.A.I.C.S.: 212230
Liang Qing *(Exec Dir)*

Subsidiaries:

Beijing JCC Marketing & Sales Company Limited (1)
Room 1101 Towerb Xinsheng Plaza No 5 Financial Street, Xicheng, Beijing, China
Tel.: (86) 1066555353
Copper Mfr & Distr
N.A.I.C.S.: 331420

JCC Copper Strip Company Limited (1)
No 979 Gaoxin Dadao Nangchang State, High-Tech Industry Development Zone, Nanchang, Jiangxi, China
Tel.: (86) 79188198313
Copper Mfr & Distr
N.A.I.C.S.: 331420

AND PRIVATE COMPANIES

JCC Financial Co., Ltd. (1)
No 527 North Erqi Road, Nanchang, Jiangxi, China
Tel.: (86) 79188602206
Financial Services
N.A.I.C.S.: 541611

Jiangxi Copper CorpJiangxi Copper Corporation Material & Equipment Company (1)
JCC International Plaza No 7666 East Chang Road, Nanchang, Jiangxi, China
Tel.: (86) 79182710409
Copper Mfr & Distr
N.A.I.C.S.: 331420

Jiangxi Copper International Trading Co., Ltd. (1)
7th Floor No 16 Dongfang Road, Pudong District, Shanghai, China
Tel.: (86) 2150431800
Copper Mfr & Distr
N.A.I.C.S.: 331529
Yiwei Mao (Dir-Bus)

Shanghai Jiangxi Copper Marketing Co., Ltd. (1)
1st Floor No 16 Dongfang Road, Pudong, Shanghai, China
Tel.: (86) 2150431800
Copper Mfr & Distr
N.A.I.C.S.: 331420

Thermonamic Electronics(Jiangxi) Corp., Ltd. (1)
No 1129 Gaoxin Road Torch Hi-Tech Zone, Nanchang, 330096, Jiangxi, China
Tel.: (86) 79188198288
Web Site: http://www.thermonamic.com
Electronic Equipment Mfr & Distr
N.A.I.C.S.: 334419

JIANGXI EVERBRIGHT MEASUREMENT & CONTROL TECHNOLOGY CO., LTD.
No 999 Gaoxin 4th Road, High-tech Industrial Development Zone, Nanchang, 330029, Jiangxi, China
Tel.: (86) 79188193001
Web Site: https://www.rym.com.cn
Year Founded: 2006
300906—(SSE)
Rev.: $15,999,984
Assets: $128,958,804
Liabilities: $13,236,912
Net Worth: $115,721,892
Earnings: $4,297,644
Fiscal Year-end: 12/31/22
Measuring Instruments Mfr
N.A.I.C.S.: 334513
Jie Tao (Chm & Gen Mgr)

JIANGXI FIRSTAR PANEL TECHNOLOGY CO LTD
No 3505 Jianan Avenue Sanjia Street, Taizhou Bay New District, Taizhou, 318014, Zhejiang, China
Tel.: (86) 57681866333
Web Site: https://www.first-panel.com
Year Founded: 2003
300256—(CHIN)
Rev.: $98,149,337
Assets: $303,530,877
Liabilities: $98,538,336
Net Worth: $204,992,541
Earnings: ($70,824,746)
Emp.: 300
Fiscal Year-end: 12/31/23
Glass Protection Screen Mfr
N.A.I.C.S.: 335999
Ying Guangjie (Chm & Gen Mgr)

JIANGXI FUXIANG PHARMACEUTICAL CO., LTD.
No 2 Yuli Industrial Zone, Changjiang District, Jingdezhen, 330029, Jiangxi, China
Tel.: (86) 7982699911   CN
Web Site: https://www.fushine.cn
Year Founded: 2002
300906—(CHIN)
Rev.: $231,275,304
Assets: $710,400,132
Liabilities: $332,774,676
Net Worth: $377,625,456
Earnings: ($19,862,388)
Fiscal Year-end: 12/31/22
Pharmaceutical Product Mfr & Distr
N.A.I.C.S.: 325412
Jianhua Bao (Pres)

JIANGXI GANFENG LITHIUM CO., LTD.
Xinyu High-Tech Development Zone, Chengdong, Xinyu, 338000, Jiangxi, China
Tel.: (86) 7906415606
Web Site: http://www.ganfenglithium.com
Year Founded: 2000
1772—(HKG)
Rev.: $4,543,090,524
Assets: $12,696,319,921
Liabilities: $5,452,763,486
Net Worth: $7,243,556,436
Earnings: $638,428,362
Emp.: 14,481
Fiscal Year-end: 12/31/23
Lithium Chloride, Lithium Fluoride, Lithium Carbonate, Lithium Hydroxide & Lithium Magnesium Alloy Mfr
N.A.I.C.S.: 325999
Liang Bin Li (Chm & Pres)

Subsidiaries:

Fengxin Ganfeng Lithium Co., Ltd. (1)
Fengxin County Industrial Park, Fengxin County, Yichun, 330700, Jiangxi, China
Tel.: (86) 7954605430
Sales Range: $100-124.9 Million
Emp.: 500
Lithium Batteries Mfr
N.A.I.C.S.: 335910

Minera Exar S. A. (1)
Carrilo Palm 54 PB San Salvador, La Puntilla, Salta, Jujuy, Argentina   (46.7%)
Tel.: (54) 3884831000
Web Site: http://www.mineraexar.com.ar
Lithium & Potassium Mining Services
N.A.I.C.S.: 212390
Waldo A. Perez (Pres & CEO)

JIANGXI GANNENG CO., LTD.
No 199 Huoju Avenue Hi-Tech Development Zone, Nanchang, 330096, Jiangxi, China
Tel.: (86) 79188109899
Web Site: http://www.000899.com
Year Founded: 1997
000899—(SSE)
Rev.: $581,642,100
Assets: $1,659,820,032
Liabilities: $994,767,696
Net Worth: $665,052,336
Earnings: $1,495,260
Fiscal Year-end: 12/31/22
Eletric Power Generation Services
N.A.I.C.S.: 221111
Wanbo Chen (Chm & Sec-Party Committee)

JIANGXI GANYUE EXPRESSWAY CO., LTD.
No 367 Chaoyangzhou Middle Road, Xihu District, Nanchang, 330096, Jiangxi, China
Tel.: (86) 79186539322
Web Site: https://www.600269.cn
Year Founded: 1998
600269—(SHG)
Rev.: $948,878,953
Assets: $4,859,900,595
Liabilities: $2,232,701,565
Net Worth: $2,627,199,030
Earnings: $97,714,623
Fiscal Year-end: 12/31/22
Toll Collection Services
N.A.I.C.S.: 488490
Han Feng (Chm)

JIANGXI GETO NEW MATERIALS CORPORATION LIMITED
Guangchang Industrial Park, Guangchang County, Fuzhou, 344900, Jiangxi, China
Tel.: (86) 7943637898
Web Site: https://geto.en.alibaba.com
Year Founded: 2011
300986—(SSE)
Rev.: $307,961,535
Assets: $697,355,310
Liabilities: $471,943,748
Net Worth: $225,411,562
Earnings: ($6,233,017)
Emp.: 2,000
Fiscal Year-end: 12/31/23
Aluminium Products Mfr
N.A.I.C.S.: 331313
Weiquan Gao (Chm)

JIANGXI GLOBAL CHEMICAL INDUSTRIAL CO., LTD
Industrial Zone of Economic Development, 336000, Yichun, China
Tel.: (86) 7953666923   CN
Web Site: http://www.globalchemi.com
Sales Range: $1-9.9 Million
Emp.: 120
Epichlorohydrin & Dichloro-Propanol Mfr
N.A.I.C.S.: 325998
Chao Ge (Mgr)

JIANGXI GUOGUANG COMMERCIAL CHAINS CO., LTD.
No 8 Wentianxiang Avenue, Qingyuan District, Jian, 330096, Jiangxi, China
Tel.: (86) 7968117072
Web Site: http://www.jxggls.com
Year Founded: 2005
605188—(SHG)
Rev.: $315,892,559
Assets: $374,382,651
Liabilities: $219,304,196
Net Worth: $155,078,455
Earnings: $2,640,854
Fiscal Year-end: 12/31/22
Departmental Store Operator
N.A.I.C.S.: 455110
Jingen Hu (Chm)

JIANGXI GUOTAI GROUP CO., LTD.
No 699 Gaoxin Avenue Nanchang High-tech Industrial Development Zone, Nanchang, 330096, Jiangxi, China
Tel.: (86) 79188110756
Web Site: https://www.jxgtjtgw.com
Year Founded: 2006
603977—(SHG)
Rev.: $302,209,470
Assets: $694,295,999
Liabilities: $230,801,988
Net Worth: $463,494,012
Earnings: $20,178,120
Fiscal Year-end: 12/31/22
Explosive Product Mfr & Distr
N.A.I.C.S.: 325920
Xuqing Xiong (Chm)

JIANGXI HAIYUAN COMPOSITES TECHNOLOGY CO.,LTD.
No 2 Tieling North Road, Jingxi Minhou, Fuzhou, 350101, Fujian, China
Tel.: (86) 59183850998
Web Site: https://www.haiyuan-group.com
Year Founded: 1988
002529—(SSE)
Rev.: $51,097,176
Assets: $178,892,064
Liabilities: $95,391,972
Net Worth: $83,500,092
Earnings: ($21,008,052)
Emp.: 1,000
Fiscal Year-end: 12/31/22
Hydraulic Forming Equipment & Related Devices Mfr
N.A.I.C.S.: 333248
Gan Shengquan (Chm & Gen Mgr)

JIANGXI HENGDA HI-TECH CO., LTD.
No 88 Jinlu North Road High-tech Zone, Nanchang, 330096, Jiangxi, China
Tel.: (86) 7918194572
Web Site: http://www.heng-da.com
Year Founded: 1994
002591—(SSE)
Rev.: $52,484,328
Assets: $141,615,864
Liabilities: $40,516,632
Net Worth: $101,099,232
Earnings: ($8,760,960)
Emp.: 330
Fiscal Year-end: 12/31/22
Corrosion-Proof & Abrasion Resistant Materials Including Paints, Coatings, Spraying Wires, Linings & Ceramic Sheets Mfr
N.A.I.C.S.: 325510
Xinghe Zhu (Chm)

JIANGXI HONGCHENG ENVIRONMENT CO., LTD.
No 98 Guanying Road, Xihu District, Nanchang, 330038, Jiangxi, China
Tel.: (86) 79185234708
Web Site: http://www.jxhcsy.com
Year Founded: 2001
600461—(SHG)
Rev.: $1,091,764,243
Assets: $2,934,281,629
Liabilities: $1,798,248,395
Net Worth: $1,136,033,234
Earnings: $132,765,076
Fiscal Year-end: 12/31/22
Water Supply Services
N.A.I.C.S.: 221310
Shao Tao (Chm & Gen Mgr)

JIANGXI HONGDU AVIATION INDUSTRY CO., LTD.
High-tech Industrial Development Zone Flying South Point, Nanchang, Jiangxi, China
Tel.: (86) 79187669749
600316—(SHG)
Rev.: $1,017,990,305
Assets: $2,419,679,237
Liabilities: $1,675,605,246
Net Worth: $744,073,991
Earnings: $19,778,555
Emp.: 10,000
Fiscal Year-end: 12/31/22
Aircraft Parts Mfr & Distr
N.A.I.C.S.: 336413
Deng Feng (Sec)

JIANGXI HUANGSHANGHUANG GROUP FOOD CO., LTD.
No 66 Hongzhou Avenue Xiaolan Economic Development Zone, Nanchang County, Nanchang, 330052, Jiangxi, China
Tel.: (86) 79185985546
Web Site: http://www.jxhsh.com.cn
Year Founded: 1999
002695—(SSE)
Rev.: $274,303,692
Assets: $420,742,296
Liabilities: $86,322,132

JIANGXI HUANGSHANGHUANG GROUP FOOD CO., LTD.

Jiangxi Huangshanghuang Group Food Co., Ltd.—(Continued)
Net Worth: $334,420,164
Earnings: $4,327,128
Emp.: 600
Fiscal Year-end: 12/31/22
Meat & Poultry Production & Distribution
N.A.I.C.S.: 311612
Jun Chu *(Chm & Gen Mgr)*

JIANGXI HUAWU BRAKE CO., LTD.
No 26 Torch Avenue High-tech Industrial Park, Yichun, 331100, Jiangxi, China
Tel.: (86) 7956201884
Web Site: https://www.hua-wu.com
300095—(CHIN)
Rev.: $203,052,096
Assets: $540,325,188
Liabilities: $211,954,860
Net Worth: $328,370,328
Earnings: $12,636,000
Emp.: 800
Fiscal Year-end: 12/31/22
Industrial Brake & Controlling Equipment Mfr
N.A.I.C.S.: 335314
Zhang Jing *(Deputy Gen Mgr)*

JIANGXI HUNGPAI NEW MATERIAL CO., LTD.
Industrial 9th Road, Tashan Industrial Park Leping City, Jingdezhen, 333332, Jiangxi, China
Tel.: (86) 7986885888
Web Site: https://www.hungpai.net
Year Founded: 2005
605366—(SHG)
Rev.: $238,346,971
Assets: $403,786,413
Liabilities: $121,982,216
Net Worth: $281,804,197
Earnings: $49,473,633
Emp.: 1,000
Fiscal Year-end: 12/31/22
Chemical Product Mfr & Distr
N.A.I.C.S.: 325520
Jinshu Ji *(Chm & Gen Mgr)*

JIANGXI JDL ENVIRONMENTAL PROTECTION CO., LTD.
No 459 Industrial Avenue Changhou Foreign Investment Development Zone, New District, Nanchang, 330100, Jiangxi, China
Tel.: (86) 79183775088
Web Site: http://www.jdlhb.com
Year Founded: 2004
688057—(SHG)
Rev.: $111,052,960
Assets: $525,848,123
Liabilities: $66,420,643
Net Worth: $459,427,480
Earnings: $42,643,538
Fiscal Year-end: 12/31/22
Water Pollution Control Equipment Mfr & Distr
N.A.I.C.S.: 333248
Zhimin Liao *(Chm & Gen Mgr)*

Subsidiaries:
JDL International Environmental Protection Inc. (1)
149 W Harvard St Ste 301, Fort Collins, CO 80525
Tel.: (970) 632-5350
Water Pollution Control Equipment Mfr
N.A.I.C.S.: 334519

JIANGXI JOVO ENERGY CO., LTD.
Room 2116 Building A Yaozhong Plaza No 9 Linhe West Road, Tianhe District, Guangzhou, 510610, Guangdong, China
Tel.: (86) 2038107688
Web Site: https://www.jovo.com.cn
Year Founded: 2008
605090—(SHG)
Rev.: $3,363,091,084
Assets: $1,587,832,937
Liabilities: $579,600,122
Net Worth: $1,008,232,814
Earnings: $153,025,526
Emp.: 230
Fiscal Year-end: 12/31/22
Energy Distribution Services
N.A.I.C.S.: 221122
Jianguo Zhang *(Chm & Gen Mgr)*

JIANGXI LIANCHUANG OPTO-ELECTRONIC SCIENCE & TECHNOLOGY CO., LTD.
No 168 Jingdong Avenue High-tech Industrial Development Zone, Nanchang, 330096, Jiangxi, China
Tel.: (86) 79188161979
Web Site: http://www.lianovation.com
Year Founded: 1999
600363—(SHG)
Rev.: $465,244,912
Assets: $984,540,455
Liabilities: $394,396,334
Net Worth: $590,144,120
Earnings: $37,547,242
Fiscal Year-end: 12/31/22
Electronic Components Mfr
N.A.I.C.S.: 334419
Wu Rui *(Chm & Pres)*

Subsidiaries:
Jiangxi Linktrend Cable Tech Co., Ltd. (1)
No 16-18 Jingju Road High-tech Zone, Jian, 343100, Jiangxi, China
Tel.: (86) 7968323450
Web Site: http://linktrendcable.tomos-group.com
Communication & Energy Wire Mfr
N.A.I.C.S.: 335929

Xiamen Hualian Electronics Co., Ltd. (1)
No 502 Qianpu Road, Siming District, Xiamen, China
Tel.: (86) 5926037466
Web Site: http://www.xmhl.com
Semiconductor & Related Device Mfr
N.A.I.C.S.: 334413

JIANGXI SELON INDUSTRIAL CO., LTD.
Shilong Science and Technology Park Leping Industrial Park, Leping City, Jingdezhen, 333000, Jiangxi, China
Tel.: (86) 7986735688
Web Site: http://www.chinaseloin.com
Year Founded: 2003
002748—(SSE)
Rev.: $363,877,488
Assets: $297,611,496
Liabilities: $104,068,692
Net Worth: $193,542,804
Earnings: $25,294,464
Emp.: 1,140
Fiscal Year-end: 12/31/22
Chemicals Mfr
N.A.I.C.S.: 325998
Yiyun Liu *(Vice Chm & Pres)*

JIANGXI SPECIAL ELECTRIC MOTOR CO., LTD.
No 581 Huancheng South Road, Yichun, 336000, Jiangxi, China
Tel.: (86) 7953272270
Web Site: https://www.jiangte.com
Year Founded: 1995
002176—(SSE)
Rev.: $922,694,760
Assets: $1,014,989,508
Liabilities: $411,105,240
Net Worth: $603,884,268
Earnings: $326,623,752
Emp.: 3,000
Fiscal Year-end: 12/31/22
Electric Motor Mfr
N.A.I.C.S.: 335312
Hu Chunhui *(Chm)*

JIANGXI SYNERGY PHARMACEUTICAL CO., LTD.
Jiangxi Fengxin Industrial Park, Fengxin, Yichun, 330700, Jiangxi, China
Tel.: (86) 7954605771
Web Site: https://www.jxsynergy.com
Year Founded: 2004
300636—(CHIN)
Rev.: $101,713,236
Assets: $453,739,782
Liabilities: $140,144,426
Net Worth: $313,595,356
Earnings: $14,927,748
Fiscal Year-end: 12/31/23
Pharmaceutical Preparation Mfr & Distr
N.A.I.C.S.: 325411
Pang Zhengwei *(Chm & Gen Mgr)*

JIANGXI TIANLI TECHNOLOGY, INC.
9th Floor Building 6 No 30 Shixing Street, Shijingshan District, Beijing, 100144, China
Tel.: (86) 1057551169
Web Site: https://www.ihandy.cn
300399—(CHIN)
Rev.: $63,195,444
Assets: $76,029,408
Liabilities: $6,657,768
Net Worth: $69,371,640
Earnings: $2,369,952
Emp.: 240
Fiscal Year-end: 12/31/22
Mobile Information Application
N.A.I.C.S.: 334220

JIANGXI WANNIANQING CEMENT CO., LTD.
No 399 Jingdong Avenue, High-tech Industrial Development Zone, Nanchang, 330096, Jiangxi, China
Tel.: (86) 79188160975
Web Site: https://www.wnq.com.cn
Year Founded: 1997
000789—(SSE)
Rev.: $1,583,940,852
Assets: $2,557,927,944
Liabilities: $1,089,591,048
Net Worth: $1,468,336,896
Earnings: $54,493,452
Fiscal Year-end: 12/31/22
Cement Mfr
N.A.I.C.S.: 327310
Li Shifeng *(Sec-Party & Gen Mgr)*

JIANGXI XINYU GUOKE TECHNOLOGY CO., LTD.
Songshanjiang Village, Guanchao Town Xiannuhu District, Xinyu, 338018, Jiangxi, China
Tel.: (86) 7906331188
Web Site: https://www.jx9394.com
Year Founded: 2008
300722—(SSE)
Rev.: $47,841,300
Assets: $96,630,300
Liabilities: $20,634,588
Net Worth: $75,995,712
Earnings: $9,321,156
Fiscal Year-end: 12/31/22
Electronic Equipment Mfr & Whslr
N.A.I.C.S.: 334511
Yuan Yougen *(Chm & Sec-Party Committee)*

JIANGXI ZHENGBANG TECHNOLOGY CO., LTD.
No 569 Aixihu 1st Road, Nanchang, Jiangxi, China
Tel.: (86) 79186397834
Web Site: https://www.zhengbang.com
002157—(SHG)
Rev.: $2,023,871,616
Assets: $3,293,659,044
Liabilities: $4,888,093,392
Net Worth: ($1,594,434,348)
Earnings: ($1,879,555,860)
Emp.: 35,800
Fiscal Year-end: 12/31/22
Animal Feedstuffs Mfr
N.A.I.C.S.: 311119
Cheng Fangui *(Chm)*

JIANGYIN ELECTRICAL ALLOY CO., LTD.
No 398 Century Avenue North Section, Zhouzhuang Town, Jiangyin, 214423, Jiangsu, China
Tel.: (86) 51086979398
Web Site: http://www.cn-dghj.com
Year Founded: 1985
300697—(CHIN)
Rev.: $336,972,681
Assets: $219,795,425
Liabilities: $70,746,349
Net Worth: $149,049,076
Earnings: $19,098,880
Fiscal Year-end: 12/31/23
Metal Products Mfr
N.A.I.C.S.: 331420
Chen Lijiao *(Chm)*

JIANGYIN HAIDA RUBBER AND PLASTIC CO., LTD.
585 Yungu Road, Changshou Zhouzhuang Town, Jiangyin, 214424, Jiangsu, China
Tel.: (86) 51086231958
Web Site: https://www.haida.cn
Year Founded: 1998
300320—(CHIN)
Rev.: $369,247,788
Assets: $467,894,232
Liabilities: $172,892,772
Net Worth: $295,001,460
Earnings: $14,472,432
Fiscal Year-end: 12/31/22
Rubber & Plastic Products Mfr
N.A.I.C.S.: 326299
Zhenyu Qian *(Chm & Gen Mgr)*

JIANGYIN HENGRUN HEAVY INDUSTRIES CO., LTD.
A Area European Industrial Zone, ZhouZhuang Town, Jiangyin, Jiangsu, China
Tel.: (86) 51086221155
Web Site: https://www.hrflanges.com
603985—(SHG)
Rev.: $273,049,120
Assets: $605,727,973
Liabilities: $128,684,687
Net Worth: $477,043,286
Earnings: $13,309,415
Emp.: 800
Fiscal Year-end: 12/31/22
Steel Products Mfr
N.A.I.C.S.: 331110

Subsidiaries:
Jiangyin Hengrun Ring Forging Co., Ltd. (1)
181 Zhuhuang Road Zhutang Industrial Zone, Jiangyin, 214415, Jiangsu, China
Tel.: (86) 51086396878
Web Site: https://www.hengrun-forging.com
Emp.: 800
Wind Tower Flange Mfr
N.A.I.C.S.: 332919

JIANGYIN JIANGHUAMICRO

AND PRIVATE COMPANIES

ELCTRONIC MATERIALS CO., LTD.
No 581 Changshou Yungu Road, Zhouzhuang Town, Jiangyin, 214423, Jiangsu, China
Tel.: (86) 51086239858
Web Site:
https://www.jianghuamem.com
Year Founded: 2001
603078—(SHG)
Rev.: $106,467,161
Assets: $344,458,979
Liabilities: $167,780,271
Net Worth: $176,678,708
Earnings: $12,540,239
Fiscal Year-end: 12/31/21
Wet Electronic Chemical Mfr & Distr
N.A.I.C.S.: 325180
Fuhua Yin *(Chm & Gen Mgr)*

JIANGYIN PIVOT AUTOMOTIVE PRODUCTS CO., LTD.
1 Mona Road, Huaxi Village Huashi Town, Jiangyin, 214421, Jiangsu, China
Tel.: (86) 51086218226
Web Site:
https://www.pivotautomotive.com
Year Founded: 2009
301181—(CHIN)
Rev.: $80,415,718
Assets: $223,718,112
Liabilities: $25,493,972
Net Worth: $198,224,140
Earnings: $20,956,620
Emp.: 260
Fiscal Year-end: 12/31/23
Automobile Parts Mfr & Distr
N.A.I.C.S.: 336211
Qi Zhao *(Chm)*

JIANGZHONG PHARMACEUTICAL CO., LTD.
No 788 Huoju Avenue High-Tech Zone, Nanchang, 330096, Jiangxi, China
Tel.: (86) 79188169323
Web Site: http://www.jzjt.com
Year Founded: 1996
600750—(SHG)
Rev.: $535,154,467
Assets: $876,609,738
Liabilities: $245,458,751
Net Worth: $631,150,987
Earnings: $83,686,641
Fiscal Year-end: 12/31/22
Pharmaceutical Mfr & Whslr
N.A.I.C.S.: 325412
Xiaojun Li *(CFO)*

JIANKUN INTERNATIONAL BERHAD
L21-03 Level 21 PJX-HM Shah Tower No 16A Persiaran Barat, 46050, Petaling Jaya, Selangor Darul Ehsan, Malaysia
Tel.: (60) 379323666
Web Site: https://jki.com.my
Year Founded: 1983
JIANKUN—(KLS)
Rev.: $1,725,073
Assets: $26,701,391
Liabilities: $6,813,967
Net Worth: $19,887,423
Earnings: ($3,655,505)
Emp.: 10
Fiscal Year-end: 12/31/22
Investment Holding Company; Property Development
N.A.I.C.S.: 551112
Siang Chai Lim *(Chm)*

Subsidiaries:

Continental Series Sdn Bhd (1)
No 5 Jalan Pelabur 23/1, Shah Alam, 40300, Selangor, Malaysia
Tel.: (60) 355410612
Web Site: http://www.tenco.com.my
Emp.: 100
Investment Management Service
N.A.I.C.S.: 523999

Ferndale Direct Sdn Bhd (1)
No 5 Jalan Pelabur 23/1, Shah Alam, 40300, Selangor, Malaysia
Tel.: (60) 355410612
Air Conditioning Equipments Mfr & Distr
N.A.I.C.S.: 333415

Mas-Be Travel Services Sdn Bhd (1)
31 1st Fl Wisma Malaysia Beijing Jalan Maharajalela, Kuala Lumpur, 50150, Malaysia
Tel.: (60) 321429668
Web Site: http://www.mbts.com.my
Sales Range: $25-49.9 Million
Emp.: 20
Travel Touring Services
N.A.I.C.S.: 561510
Yeo Soat Luang *(Mng Dir)*

Ridgemonde Chemicals & Resins Sdn Bhd (1)
Lot 5 Jalan Pelabur Section 23/1, Shah Alam, 40300, Selangor, Malaysia
Tel.: (60) 355410612
Web Site: http://www.tenco.com.my
Sales Range: $25-49.9 Million
Emp.: 100
Synthetic Resin Emulsions Mfr
N.A.I.C.S.: 325212

Tenco Industries Sdn Bhd (1)
5 Jalan Pelabur 23/1, 40300, Shah Alam, Selangor, Malaysia
Tel.: (60) 355410612
Web Site: http://www.tenco.com.my
Sales Range: $50-74.9 Million
Paint & Chemicals Distr
N.A.I.C.S.: 424950

Westech Chemicals Sdn Bhd (1)
5 Jalan Pelabur 23/1, 40300, Shah Alam, Selangor, Malaysia
Tel.: (60) 35 541 0612
Web Site:
https://m.westechchemicals.com.my
Sales Range: $25-49.9 Million
Chemical Distr
N.A.I.C.S.: 424690

Wilron Products Sdn Bhd (1)
5 Jalan Pelabur 23/1, Shah Alam, 43000, Selangor, Malaysia
Tel.: (60) 355410612
Sales Range: $25-49.9 Million
Emp.: 100
Industrial Adhesives Mfr
N.A.I.C.S.: 325520
Vicky Lim *(Dir-Ops)*

JIANMIN PHARMACEUTICAL GROUP CO., LTD.
No 484 Yingwu Avenue, Hanyang District, Wuhan, 430052, Hubei, China
Tel.: (86) 2784523350
Web Site: https://www.whjm.com
Year Founded: 1993
600976—(SHG)
Rev.: $511,168,390
Assets: $482,647,366
Liabilities: $220,403,430
Net Worth: $262,243,936
Earnings: $57,222,702
Fiscal Year-end: 12/31/22
Pharmaceutical Product Mfr & Distr
N.A.I.C.S.: 325412
He Qin *(Chm)*

JIANPU TECHNOLOGY INC.
21/F Internet Finance Center Danling Street, Beijing, China
Tel.: (86) 1083023688   KY
Web Site: http://www.jianpu.ai
Year Founded: 2011
JT—(NYSE)
Rev.: $148,068,924
Assets: $129,015,424
Liabilities: $71,218,847
Net Worth: $57,796,577
Earnings: ($3,744,739)

Emp.: 393
Fiscal Year-end: 12/31/23
Financial Management Services
N.A.I.C.S.: 551112
David Daqing Ye *(Co-Founder, Chm & CEO)*

JIANZHI EDUCATION TECHNOLOGY GROUP COMPANY LIMITED
27/F Tower A Yingdu Building Zhichun Road, Haidian District, Beijing, 100086, China
Tel.: (86) 1058732560   Ky
Web Site: https://www.jianzhi-jiaoyu.com
Year Founded: 2018
JZ—(NASDAQ)
Rev.: $60,995,878
Assets: $21,002,246
Liabilities: $23,386,210
Net Worth: ($2,383,964)
Earnings: ($53,003,609)
Emp.: 59
Fiscal Year-end: 12/31/22
Educational Support Services
N.A.I.C.S.: 611710
Peixuan Wang *(Founder & Chm)*

JIANZHONG CONSTRUCTION DEVELOPMENT LIMITED
Jinlan Building 33 Zhaoqiang Road, Mawei, Fuzhou, Fujian, China
Tel.: (86) 59138110555   Ky
Web Site:
http://www.jianzhongdev.com
Year Founded: 2012
0589—(HKG)
Rev.: $73,654,121
Assets: $232,380,392
Liabilities: $123,995,243
Net Worth: $108,385,150
Earnings: ($30,336,930)
Emp.: 256
Fiscal Year-end: 12/31/22
Construction Management Services
N.A.I.C.S.: 236116
Minghong Xun *(Chm)*

JIAOZUO WANFANG ALUMINUM MANUFACTURING CO., LTD.
Jiaoxin Road South Side, Daiwang Town Macun District, Jiaozuo, 454005, Henan, China
Tel.: (86) 3912535596
Web Site: http://www.jzwfly.cn
Year Founded: 1996
000612—(SSE)
Rev.: $937,323,036
Assets: $1,100,790,756
Liabilities: $357,329,232
Net Worth: $743,461,524
Earnings: $42,552,432
Aluminum Product Smelting Services
N.A.I.C.S.: 331314
Jiao Jifang *(CFO & Deputy Gen Mgr)*

JIASHILI GROUP LIMITED
No 18 Gangkou Road, Changsha, Kaiping, Guangdong, China
Tel.: (86) 7502207363
Web Site: http://www.gdjsl.com
1285—(HKG)
Rev.: $233,676,144
Assets: $295,837,261
Liabilities: $152,424,418
Net Worth: $143,412,844
Earnings: $7,722,562
Emp.: 2,453
Fiscal Year-end: 12/31/22
Snacks & Bakery Products Mfr
N.A.I.C.S.: 311919
Xianming Huang *(Chm & CEO)*

JIAYOU INTERNATIONAL LOGISTICS CO., LTD.

JIAWEI RENEWABLE ENERGY CO., LTD.
33A China Energy Storage Building No 3099 Keyuannan Road, Nanshan District, Shenzhen, 518063, Guangdong, China
Tel.: (86) 75526902682
Web Site: https://www.jiawei.com
Year Founded: 1993
300317—(CHIN)
Rev.: $70,942,716
Assets: $328,010,904
Liabilities: $74,374,092
Net Worth: $253,636,812
Earnings: $12,825,540
Emp.: 1,920
Fiscal Year-end: 12/31/22
Photovoltaic Lighting Products Mfr
N.A.I.C.S.: 335139
Kongxian Ding *(Chm)*

Subsidiaries:

Jiawei Technology (HK) Ltd. (1)
1505 Star House 3 Salisbury Road, Tsim Sha Tsui, Kowloon, China (Hong Kong)
Tel.: (852) 2 736 2080
Web Site: http://www.jiawei.com
Photovoltaic Lighting Product Mfr
N.A.I.C.S.: 335132

Jiawei Technology (USA) Ltd. (1)
2305 Lincoln Ave, Hayward, CA 94545
Tel.: (510) 887-8815
Web Site: http://www.jiaweisolar.com
Emp.: 15
Solar Energy Equipment Distr
N.A.I.C.S.: 423720
Leslie Conover *(Mgr-Natl Acct)*

Xiamen Jiawei Solar Energy Technology Co., Ltd. (1)
Xiang Ming Road Xiamen Torch Hi-tech Zone, Xiang Industrial District 3, Xiamen, China
Tel.: (86) 5923757221
Web Site: http://www.jiawei.com
Solar Energy Equipment Distr
N.A.I.C.S.: 423690

JIAXING GAS GROUP CO., LTD.
Building NO 3 Hualong Plaza NO 32 Qinyi Road, Jiaxing, Zhejiang, China
Web Site: https://www.jiaxinggas.com
Year Founded: 1985
9908—(HKG)
Rev.: $409,349,108
Assets: $367,570,337
Liabilities: $219,639,455
Net Worth: $147,930,882
Earnings: $34,685,562
Emp.: 408
Fiscal Year-end: 12/31/23
Natural Gas Distribution Services
N.A.I.C.S.: 221210
Lianqing Sun *(CEO)*

JIAYIN GROUP INC.
26th Floor Building No 1 428 South Yanggao Road, Youyou Century Plaza Pudong New Area, Shanghai, 200122, China
Tel.: (86) 2161906826
Web Site: https://www.jiayinfintech.cn
Year Founded: 2017
JFIN—(NASDAQ)
Rev.: $501,213,339
Assets: $462,827,493
Liabilities: $272,616,818
Net Worth: $190,210,675
Earnings: $180,735,402
Emp.: 796
Fiscal Year-end: 12/31/22
Holding Company
N.A.I.C.S.: 551112
Dinggui Yan *(Founder, Chm & CEO)*

JIAYOU INTERNATIONAL LOGISTICS CO., LTD.

JIAYOU INTERNATIONAL LOGISTICS CO., LTD.

Floor 23-24 Building 2 Financial Street ChangAn Centre, No 26 Chengtong Street, Beijing, 100043, China
Tel.: (86) 1088998888
Web Site: https://www.jyinternational.com.cn
Year Founded: 2005
603871—(SHG)
Rev.: $678,055,342
Assets: $752,027,862
Liabilities: $158,632,512
Net Worth: $593,395,349
Earnings: $95,576,303
Fiscal Year-end: 12/31/22
Transportation Services
N.A.I.C.S.: 541614
Han Jinghua *(Chm)*

Subsidiaries:

JR Global Logistics, Inc. (1)
Unit 8 / 10 Bradford St, Alexandria, 2015, NSW, Australia
Tel.: (61) 296671809
Web Site: https://www.jrglobal.com.au
Freight Transportation Services
N.A.I.C.S.: 488320
Josette Robert *(Mng Dir)*

JIAYU HOLDING CO., LTD.

No 1 Niufu Road Niulanshan, Shunyi District, Beijing, 101301, China
Tel.: (86) 1069415566
Web Site: http://en.jiayu.com.cn
Year Founded: 1987
300117—(CHIN)
Rev.: $274,278,420
Assets: $638,191,008
Liabilities: $634,595,364
Net Worth: $3,595,644
Earnings: ($10,489,284)
Emp.: 1,170
Fiscal Year-end: 12/31/22
Energy-Saving Doors, Windows & Curtain Walls Mfr & Installation Services
N.A.I.C.S.: 332321
Zhang Guofeng *(Chm)*

Subsidiaries:

Guangdong Jiayu Door, Window & Curtain Wall Co., Ltd. (1)
Tai Mei Zhen Ban Qiao Industrial Zone Boluo Town, Huizhou, Guangdong, China
Tel.: (86) 7526306700
Curtain Wall Mfr
N.A.I.C.S.: 332323

JIAYUAN INTERNATIONAL GROUP LIMITED

Suite 1403 9 Queens Road, Central, China (Hong Kong)
Tel.: (852) 3 951 8888 Ky
Web Site: http://www.jiayuanintl.com
2768—(HKG)
Rev.: $2,813,423,574
Assets: $11,075,397,537
Liabilities: $8,400,699,030
Net Worth: $2,674,698,507
Earnings: $541,014,080
Emp.: 7,137
Fiscal Year-end: 12/31/20
Property Development Services
N.A.I.C.S.: 531210
Tin Ching Shum *(Founder & Chm)*

JIAYUAN SCIENCE & TECHNOLOGY CO., LTD.

4F Building No 01 No 20 Jitai Road Chengdu High-tech Zone, China Sichuan Pilot Free Trade Zone, Chengdu, 610097, Sichuan, China
Tel.: (86) 2886938681
Web Site: https://www.scjydz.com
Year Founded: 1994
301117—(CHIN)
Rev.: $32,027,155
Assets: $200,506,492
Liabilities: $16,243,437
Net Worth: $184,263,056
Earnings: ($753,930)
Fiscal Year-end: 12/31/23
Information Technology Services
N.A.I.C.S.: 541512
Jin Wang *(Chm & Gen Mgr)*

JIAYUAN SERVICES HOLDINGS LIMITED

Floor 3 Rome Metropolis No 899 Wanghu Road, Nanhu, Jiaxing, Zhejiang, China
Tel.: (86) 57382815595 Ky
Web Site: http://www.jy-fw.cn
Year Founded: 2004
1153—(HKG)
Holding Company
N.A.I.C.S.: 551112
Hongge Zhu *(CEO)*

JIAYUAN.COM INTERNATIONAL LTD.

15/F Anhua Development Building No 35 Anding Road, Chaoyang District, Beijing, China
Tel.: (86) 4001520005 Ky
Web Site: http://www.jiayuan.com
Online & Offline Dating Services
N.A.I.C.S.: 812990

Subsidiaries:

Jiangsu Five Star Appliance Co., Ltd. (1)
1-21 Overseas Chinese Building No 241 Zhongshan North Road, Nanjing, 210009, Jiangsu, China
Tel.: (86) 2583758046
Web Site: http://www.5star.cn
Electronics & Appliances Retailer
N.A.I.C.S.: 449210
Yiqing Pan *(Pres)*

JIBANNET HOLDINGS CO. LTD.

Shinjuku 5-2-3, Shinjuku-ku, Tokyo, 160-0022, Japan
Tel.: (81) 362651803
Web Site: https://jiban-holdings.jp
6072—(TKS)
Rev.: $12,406,970
Assets: $10,576,000
Liabilities: $2,273,840
Net Worth: $8,302,160
Earnings: ($627,950)
Emp.: 25
Fiscal Year-end: 03/31/24
Engineeering Services
N.A.I.C.S.: 541330
Tsuyoshi Yamamoto *(Founder, Pres & CEO)*

JICHODO CO., LTD.

16-2 Tode, Shinichi-cho, Fukuyama, 729-3193, Hiroshima, Japan
Tel.: (81) 847518113
Web Site: https://www.jichodo.co.jp
Year Founded: 1960
3597—(TKS)
Rev.: $104,887,860
Assets: $258,839,080
Liabilities: $20,451,360
Net Worth: $238,387,720
Earnings: $12,533,300
Emp.: 196
Fiscal Year-end: 06/30/24
Apparel Distr
N.A.I.C.S.: 458110
Masaki Idehara *(Co-Pres)*

JIFFY INTERNATIONAL AS

Markensgate 2 A, PO Box 359, 4663, Kristiansand, Norway
Tel.: (47) 38105670 NO
Web Site: http://www.jiffygroup.com
Year Founded: 1955
Sales Range: $50-74.9 Million
Emp.: 220
Garden Product Supply Services
N.A.I.C.S.: 551112
Aarstin Knugson *(Mng Dir)*

Subsidiaries:

Jiffy AS (1)
Industrivej 4, 8550, Ryomgaard, Denmark
Tel.: (45) 86394388
Farm Supply Merchant Whslr
N.A.I.C.S.: 424910

Jiffy France S.A.R.L (1)
3 Rue de l'Herberie, 1600, Trevoux, France
Tel.: (33) 474088855
Farm Supply Merchant Whslr
N.A.I.C.S.: 424910

Jiffy Preforma Production K.K (1)
1657-1 Hazawa-cho, Kanagawa-ku, Yokohama, 221-0863, Japan
Tel.: (81) 453738520
Farm Supply Merchant Whslr
N.A.I.C.S.: 424910

Jiffy Products (UK) Ltd. (1)
PO Box 329, Winchester, SO23 9WQ, United Kingdom
Tel.: (44) 8703667930
Farm Supply Merchant Whslr
N.A.I.C.S.: 424910

Jiffy Products Espana S.L.U. (1)
Carretera Estacion KM4 W30, Puerto Lumbreras, 30891, Murcia, Spain
Tel.: (34) 968402623
Farm Supply Merchant Whslr
N.A.I.C.S.: 424910

Jiffy Products GmbH (1)
Postfatch 1240, 23872, Molln, Germany
Tel.: (49) 45428003678
Farm Supply Merchant Whslr
N.A.I.C.S.: 424910

Jiffy Products International AS (1)
Stensrudv. 8, N 2335, Stange, Norway
Tel.: (47) 62573800
Web Site: http://www.jisseygroupt.com
Sales Range: $25-49.9 Million
Emp.: 50
Mfr, Developer & Marketer of Garden Supply Products
N.A.I.C.S.: 325314

Subsidiary (US):

Jiffy Products of America, Inc. (2)
5401 Baumhart Rd Ste B, Lorain, OH 44053
Tel.: (440) 282-2818
Sales Range: $25-49.9 Million
Emp.: 35
Container-Based Plant Propagation Products
N.A.I.C.S.: 444240
Susan Diaz *(Mgr-Customer Svc & Coord-Sls)*

Subsidiary (Domestic):

Ferry-Morse Seed Company (3)
600 Stethen Beale Dr, Fulton, KY 42041
Tel.: (270) 472-3400
Web Site: http://www.ferry-morse.com
Sales Range: $75-99.9 Million
Marketing of Vegetable, Flower & Lawn Seeds for the Home Gardener
N.A.I.C.S.: 424910

Jiffy Products International B.V. (1)
Port no M089 Appelweg 3, 4782 PX, Moerdijk, Netherlands
Tel.: (31) 168413500
Farm Supply Merchant Whslr
N.A.I.C.S.: 424910

Jiffy Products N.B Ltd (1)
161 Atlantic Lane, PO Box 2004, Pokemouche, Gloucester, E8P 2M4, NB, Canada
Tel.: (506) 336-2284
Farm Supply Merchant Whslr
N.A.I.C.S.: 424910
Gino Roy *(Mgr-Supply Chain, Retail, and Special Projects)*

INTERNATIONAL PUBLIC

Jiffy Products S.L. (Private) Ltd. (1)
Mirigama Export Processing Zone Plot 27 C, Mirigama, Sri Lanka
Tel.: (94) 332276401
Farm Supply Merchant Whslr
N.A.I.C.S.: 424910
Sandeeptha Gamalath *(Mng Dir)*

JIG-SAW INC.

8 3 Square North Building 7F 32 N8W3, Kita-ku, Sapporo, 060-0808, Hokkaido, Japan
Tel.: (81) 354423957
Web Site: https://www.jig-saw.com
3914—(TKS)
Rev.: $22,971,600
Assets: $24,758,280
Liabilities: $6,402,270
Net Worth: $18,356,010
Earnings: $3,254,310
Emp.: 50
Fiscal Year-end: 12/31/23
Computer Related Services
N.A.I.C.S.: 541519
Masunaru Yamakawa *(Pres & CEO)*

JIG.JP CO., LTD.

5-23-5 Sendagaya Yoyogi East 4th floor, Shibuya-ku, Tokyo, 151-0051, Japan
Web Site: https://www.jig.jp
Year Founded: 2003
5244—(TKS)
Rev.: $80,952,670
Assets: $37,776,150
Liabilities: $16,267,210
Net Worth: $21,508,940
Earnings: $8,024,540
Emp.: 99
Fiscal Year-end: 03/31/24
Software Development Services
N.A.I.C.S.: 541511

JIGAR CABLES LIMITED

Plot No 164/15 G I D C - II Jamwadi, Gondal, Rajkot, 360 311, Gujarat, India
Tel.: (91) 2825221422
Web Site: https://www.sigmacab.com
540651—(BOM)
Rev.: $1,770,855
Assets: $2,774,881
Liabilities: $777,327
Net Worth: $1,997,555
Earnings: $46,246
Emp.: 13
Fiscal Year-end: 03/31/22
Electric Equipment Mfr & Distr
N.A.I.C.S.: 335929
Vijay Gopalbhai Shingala *(Chm & Mng Dir)*

JIGSY.COM

101 100 East Jensen Avenue, PO Box 656, Parksville, V9P 2G7, BC, Canada
Tel.: (250) 954-5537
Web Site: http://www.jigsy.com
Content Management Software & Website Development
N.A.I.C.S.: 513210
Dave Shworan *(Owner & CEO)*

JIGYASA INFRASTRUCTURE LIMITED

108-109 Vardhman Appenzerl Plaza Mayur Vihar- Phase III, New Delhi, 110 037, India
Tel.: (91) 1132318522 In
Web Site: http://www.jigyasainfra.com
Real Estate Support Services
N.A.I.C.S.: 531390
Sanjay Kumar Singh *(Exec Dir)*

JIH LIN TECHNOLOGY CO., LTD.

No 58 Central Road, Nanzi Dist, Kaohsiung, 811, Taiwan
Tel.: (886) 73658828
Web Site: https://www.jihlin.com.tw
5285—(TAI)
Rev.: $167,812,937
Assets: $169,183,355
Liabilities: $75,351,447
Net Worth: $93,831,907
Earnings: $5,841,819
Emp.: 764
Fiscal Year-end: 12/31/23
Semiconductor Components Mfr
N.A.I.C.S.: 334413
Shang-Ming Tsai *(Gen Mgr)*

Subsidiaries:

Jinan Jihlong Technology Co., Ltd. (1)
No 5 Taixing West Street, Jiyang County, Jinan, Shandong, China
Tel.: (86) 53184239588
Semiconductor Lead Frame Mfr
N.A.I.C.S.: 334413

Malaysian SH Precision Sdn. Bhd. (1)
Pt 111 Senawang Industrial Estate Darul Khusus, 70450, Seremban, Malaysia
Tel.: (60) 66774911
Semiconductor Lead Frame Mfr
N.A.I.C.S.: 334413

Suzhou SH Precision Co., Ltd. (1)
No 48 Tinglan Lane Xinglong Street, Suzhou Industrial Park, Suzhou, Jiangsu, China
Tel.: (86) 51262831110
Semiconductor Lead Frame Mfr
N.A.I.C.S.: 334413

JIHUA GROUP CORPORATION LIMITED
Hongshan Farm, Xiaoshan, Hangzhou, 311234, Zhejiang, China
Tel.: (86) 57122898000
Web Site: https://www.jihuadyes.com
601718—(SHG)
Rev.: $2,167,186,264
Assets: $3,885,049,537
Liabilities: $1,493,879,784
Net Worth: $2,391,169,753
Earnings: $31,117,203
Emp.: 2,000
Fiscal Year-end: 12/31/22
Dyestuff, Dye Intermediate, Paint & Chemical Mfr & Distr
N.A.I.C.S.: 325130
Shao Hui *(Pres)*

Subsidiaries:

Hangzhou Jihua Polymer Material Co., Ltd. (1)
No 1766-1 New Century Avenue Linjiang Industrial Park, Xiaoshan District, Hangzhou, 311234, Zhejiang, China
Tel.: (86) 57122898389
Emp.: 107
Chemical Products Mfr
N.A.I.C.S.: 325998

JIIN YEEH DING ENTERPRISE CO., LTD.
No 599 Sec 6 Xibin Road, Nangang Village Xiangshan District, Hsinchu, Taiwan
Tel.: (886) 35182368
Web Site: https://www.jyd.com.tw
Year Founded: 1997
8390—(TPE)
Rev.: $113,352,406
Assets: $99,570,522
Liabilities: $17,549,229
Net Worth: $82,021,293
Earnings: $9,740,581
Fiscal Year-end: 12/31/22
Petrochemical Products Mfr
N.A.I.C.S.: 325110
Rui-Yuan Chuang *(Pres)*

JIK INDUSTRIES LIMITED
Pada No 3 Balkum, Thane W, Thane, 400 608, Maharashtra, India
Tel.: (91) 2225426356
Web Site: https://www.jik.co.in
Year Founded: 1990
JIKIND—(BOM)
Rev.: $109,034
Assets: $14,080,544
Liabilities: $17,124,731
Net Worth: ($3,044,187)
Earnings: ($72,520)
Emp.: 18
Fiscal Year-end: 03/31/20
Glassware Mfr
N.A.I.C.S.: 327212
Rajendra G. Parikh *(Chm & Mng Dir)*

JIKAI EQUIPMENT MANUFACTURING CO., LTD.
No 418 Xiangjiang Road, National New Hi-Tech Industrial Development Zone, Shijiazhuang, 050035, Hebei, China
Tel.: (86) 31185323556
Web Site: https://en.sjzzm.com
Year Founded: 2003
002691—(SSE)
Rev.: $46,180,368
Assets: $165,424,896
Liabilities: $36,672,480
Net Worth: $128,752,416
Earnings: $1,891,188
Emp.: 730
Fiscal Year-end: 12/31/22
Coal Mining Equipment Mfr & Distr
N.A.I.C.S.: 333131
Feng Fan *(Chm)*

JILGYUNGYI CO., LTD.
32 Saimdang-ro Seocho-gu, Seoul, Korea (South)
Tel.: (82) 7089525702
Cleanser Product Mfr & Distr
N.A.I.C.S.: 325611
Choi Won-Seog *(CEO)*

JILIN AODONG PHARMACEUTICAL GROUP CO., LTD.
No 2158 Aodong Street, Dunhua City, Jilin, 133700, China
Tel.: (86) 4336238973
Web Site: https://www.jlaod.com
000623—(SSE)
Rev.: $402,696,684
Assets: $4,376,630,232
Liabilities: $678,475,980
Net Worth: $3,698,154,252
Earnings: $250,001,856
Fiscal Year-end: 12/31/22
Pharmaceuticals Mfr
N.A.I.C.S.: 325412
Xiu Lin Li *(Chm)*

JILIN CHEMICAL FIBRE CO., LTD.
No 216 Kunlun Street Economic and Technological Development Zone, Jilin, 132115, Jilin, China
Tel.: (86) 4323502452
Web Site: http://www.jlhxjt.com
Year Founded: 1960
000420—(SSE)
Rev.: $515,217,456
Assets: $1,476,190,872
Liabilities: $868,180,248
Net Worth: $608,010,624
Earnings: ($12,839,580)
Fiscal Year-end: 12/31/22
Chemical Fiber Mfr & Distr
N.A.I.C.S.: 327999

Subsidiaries:

Jilin Qifeng Chemical Fiber Co., Ltd. (1)
No 516-1 jiuzhan Street, Jilin, China (97.31%)
Tel.: (86) 432 63502305
Web Site: http://www.qifengfiber.com
Sales Range: $200-249.9 Million
Timber Product Mfr
N.A.I.C.S.: 325220
Xuefeng Yang *(Gen Mgr)*

JILIN CHENGCHENG GROUP CO., LTD.
29 Wilder Street Jilin Chuanying, Shenzhen, 518034, China
Tel.: (86) 755 83558842
600247—(SHG)
Rev.: $1,992,610
Assets: $139,239,048
Liabilities: $148,354,217
Net Worth: ($9,115,169)
Earnings: ($12,192,106)
Fiscal Year-end: 12/31/19
Real Estate Manangement Services
N.A.I.C.S.: 531390
Fangwen Shen *(Gen Mgr)*

JILIN EXPRESSWAY CO., LTD.
No 4488 Pudong Road Economic & Technology Development Zone, Changchun, 130033, Jilin, China
Tel.: (86) 43184664798
Web Site: http://www.jlgsgl.com
Year Founded: 2010
601518—(SHG)
Rev.: $204,863,368
Assets: $846,826,461
Liabilities: $171,319,885
Net Worth: $675,506,576
Earnings: $55,266,747
Fiscal Year-end: 12/31/22
Toll Highway Operator
N.A.I.C.S.: 488490
Jiang Tao *(Chm)*

JILIN HOROC NONFERROUS METAL GROUP CO., LTD.
No 5 Red Zhen Ji ICP, Panshi, 000619, China
Tel.: (86) 43265610634 CN
Web Site: http://www.jljn.com
Sales Range: $1-4.9 Billion
Emp.: 10,000
Metal Mining & Production
N.A.I.C.S.: 212230
Guangping Xu *(Chm & Gen Mgr)*

Subsidiaries:

Jilin Jien Nickel Industry Co., Ltd. (1)
No 54 Hongqi Avenue Hongqiling County, Panshi, 132311, Jilin, China
Tel.: (86) 432 65610792
Nickel Mining & Production
N.A.I.C.S.: 212230

Subsidiary (Non-US):

Jien Canada Mining Ltd. (2)
200 Burrard Street Suite 1550, Vancouver, V6C 3L6, BC, Canada (100%)
Tel.: (604) 683-8083
Holding Company; Nickel Ore Mining
N.A.I.C.S.: 551112

Subsidiary (Domestic):

Canadian Royalties Inc. (3)
2772 Chemin Sullivan, Val d'Or, J9P 0B9, QC, Canada
Tel.: (819) 824-1030
Web Site: http://www.canadianroyalties.com
Sales Range: Less than $1 Million
Emp.: 150
Nickel & Copper Mining Services
N.A.I.C.S.: 212230
C. Jens Zinke *(VP-Bus Dev)*

Jien Nunavik Mining Exploration Ltd. (3)
147 Av Cartier Suite 301, Pointe-Claire, H9S 4R9, QC, Canada
Tel.: (514) 505-3521
Nickel Mining

N.A.I.C.S.: 212230

JILIN JIAN YISHENG PHARMACEUTICAL CO., LTD.
17 20 Wenhua East Road, Jian, 134200, Jilin, China
Tel.: (86) 435622247
Web Site: https://www.yisheng-pharm.com
002566—(SSE)
Rev.: $116,537,616
Assets: $416,512,044
Liabilities: $100,692,072
Net Worth: $315,819,972
Earnings: $11,667,240
Emp.: 1,780
Fiscal Year-end: 12/31/22
Pharmaceutical Mfr & Distr
N.A.I.C.S.: 325412
Yisheng Zhang *(Chm)*

JILIN JINGUAN ELECTRIC CO LTD
Shuangyang Economic Development Zone, No 4 Yanshou Road, Changchun, 130600, Jilin, China
Tel.: (86) 43184158222
Web Site: https://www.jljgdq.cn
Year Founded: 2006
300510—(CHIN)
Rev.: $164,681,397
Assets: $542,174,370
Liabilities: $165,425,747
Net Worth: $376,748,622
Earnings: $3,592,548
Fiscal Year-end: 12/31/23
Electrical Switch Gear Equipment Mfr & Distr
N.A.I.C.S.: 335313

JILIN JIUTAI RURAL COMMERCIAL BANK
No 2559 Weishan Road High tech Zone, Changchun, 130012, Jilin, China
Tel.: (86) 43189250628 CN
Web Site: https://www.jtnsh.com
Year Founded: 2008
6122—(HKG)
Rev.: $2,019,330,518
Assets: $37,486,905,160
Liabilities: $34,872,748,981
Net Worth: $2,614,156,178
Earnings: $234,752,310
Emp.: 6,605
Fiscal Year-end: 12/31/22
Commercial Banking Services
N.A.I.C.S.: 522110
Luo Hui *(Chm-Supervisory Bd)*

JILIN JLU COMMUNICATION DESIGN INSTITUTE CO., LTD
7th Floor Building 9 Lakeside Eslite No 488 Qianjin Street, Chaoyang District, Changchun, 130012, Jilin, China
Tel.: (86) 43185175230
Web Site: https://www.jlucdi.com
Year Founded: 1985
300597—(CHIN)
Rev.: $78,206,526
Assets: $202,418,028
Liabilities: $49,640,540
Net Worth: $152,777,488
Earnings: $529,342
Fiscal Year-end: 12/31/23
Communication Network Design Services
N.A.I.C.S.: 541430
Zhou Wei *(Chm)*

JILIN LIYUAN PRECISION MANUFACTURING CO., LTD.
No 5729 Xining Road Economic Development Zone, Jilin, 136200, Liaoyuan, China
Tel.: (86) 4373171666

JILIN LIYUAN PRECISION MANUFACTURING CO., LTD.

Jilin Liyuan Precision Manufacturing Co., Ltd.—(Continued)
Web Site: https://www.liyuanlvye.com
002501—(SSE)
Rev.: $71,333,028
Assets: $263,674,008
Liabilities: $87,442,524
Net Worth: $176,231,484
Earnings: ($57,027,672)
Emp.: 1,000
Fiscal Year-end: 12/31/22
Aluminium Products Mfr
N.A.I.C.S.: 331318

JILIN OLED MATERIAL TECH CO., LTD.
19/F Hongqi Building 5666 Silicon Valley Street, High-tech District, Changchun, 130000, Jilin, China
Tel.: (86) 43185834771
Web Site: https://www.jl-oled.com
Year Founded: 2005
688378—(SHG)
Rev.: $64,422,470
Assets: $301,632,482
Liabilities: $67,180,866
Net Worth: $234,451,615
Earnings: $15,868,584
Fiscal Year-end: 12/31/22
Electronic Products Mfr
N.A.I.C.S.: 334419
Jingquan Xuan *(Chm & Gen Mgr)*

JILIN POWER SHARE CO., LTD.
No 9699 Renmin Avenue, Changchun, 130022, Jilin, China
Tel.: (86) 43181150932
Web Site: http://www.cpijl.com
000875—(SSE)
Rev.: $2,070,607,236
Assets: $9,902,387,517
Liabilities: $7,141,742,994
Net Worth: $2,760,644,523
Earnings: $93,004,403
Fiscal Year-end: 12/31/22
Electric Power Generation & Distribution Services
N.A.I.C.S.: 221116
Yiyong Liu *(Deputy Gen Mgr)*

JILIN PROVINCE CHUNCHENG HEATING COMPANY LIMITED
No 28 Block B Nanhu Road Community No 998 Nanhu Road, Nanguan District, Changchun, Jilin, China
Tel.: (86) 963963　　　　CN
Web Site: https://www.cc-tp.com.cn
Year Founded: 2017
1853—(HKG)
Rev.: $232,320,603
Assets: $426,672,084
Liabilities: $298,641,122
Net Worth: $128,030,962
Earnings: $16,099,384
Emp.: 1,562
Fiscal Year-end: 12/31/22
Heating Contractor Services
N.A.I.C.S.: 238220
Wan Tao *(Sec)*

JILIN PROVINCE HUINAN CHANGLONG BIO-PHARMACY COMPANY LIMITED
Pharmaceutical Industrial Park Huinan Economic Development Zone, Chaoyang Town Huinan County, Tonghua, 135100, Jilin, China
Tel.: (86) 4358218333　　CN
Web Site: https://www.jlchanglong.com
Year Founded: 1989
8049—(HKG)
Rev.: $118,158,674
Assets: $333,146,876
Liabilities: $106,780,237
Net Worth: $226,366,639
Earnings: $27,176,526
Emp.: 823
Fiscal Year-end: 12/31/22
Pharmaceutical Product Mfr & Distr
N.A.I.C.S.: 325412
Hong Zhang *(Chm, Chm, Compliance Officer, Compliance Officer & Exec Dir)*

JILIN PROVINCE XIDIAN PHARMACEUTICAL SCI-TECH DEVELOPMENT CO., LTD.
No 777 Xidian Street, Panshi Economic Development Zone, Panshi, 132300, Jilin, China
Tel.: (86) 43265888277
Web Site: https://www.xidianyy.com
Year Founded: 1990
301130—(CHIN)
Rev.: $35,867,988
Assets: $142,786,800
Liabilities: $10,068,084
Net Worth: $132,718,716
Earnings: $5,717,088
Fiscal Year-end: 12/31/22
Pharmaceutical Product Mfr & Distr
N.A.I.C.S.: 325412
Jun Zhang *(Chm & Gen Mgr)*

JILIN QUANYANGQUAN CO., LTD.
No 1399 Yanan Street, Chaoyang District, Changchun, 130012, Jilin, China
Tel.: (86) 43188912969
Web Site: https://www.jlsg.com.cn
Year Founded: 1998
600189—(SHG)
Rev.: $178,168,555
Assets: $687,592,082
Liabilities: $432,657,861
Net Worth: $254,934,220
Earnings: $8,023,832
Emp.: 6,325
Fiscal Year-end: 12/31/22
Lumber & Paper Products Mfr
N.A.I.C.S.: 115310
Wang Jinhui *(Gen Mgr & Deputy Sec-Party Committee)*

JILIN SINO-MICROELECTRONICS CO., LTD.
No 99 Shenzhen Street High-tech Zone, Jilin, 132013, Jilin, China
Tel.: (86) 43264678411
Web Site: https://www.hwdz.com.cn
Year Founded: 1965
600360—(SHG)
Rev.: $274,221,474
Assets: $969,060,639
Liabilities: $513,459,901
Net Worth: $455,600,738
Earnings: $8,107,932
Emp.: 2,300
Fiscal Year-end: 12/31/22
Semiconductor Device Mfr & Whslr
N.A.I.C.S.: 334413
Shengdong Yu *(Chm, CEO & Gen Mgr)*

Subsidiaries:
Guangzhou Sino-Microelectronics Co., Ltd. (1)
No 15th Baoying St, GZ Economy and Technology Development Area, Guangzhou, 510730, China
Tel.: (86) 2082211088
Web Site: http://www.gz-sm.net
Semiconductor & Related Device Mfr
N.A.I.C.S.: 334413

JILIN YATAI (GROUP) CO., LTD.
No 1801 Jilin Road, Erdao District, Changchun, 130031, Jilin, China
Tel.: (86) 43184958888
Web Site: http://www.yatai.com
Year Founded: 1993
600881—(SHG)
Rev.: $1,820,667,411
Assets: $7,538,200,816
Liabilities: $5,878,552,296
Net Worth: $1,659,648,519
Earnings: ($484,989,743)
Fiscal Year-end: 12/31/22
Cement Mfr & Whslr
N.A.I.C.S.: 327310
Shanglong Song *(Chm & Pres)*

Subsidiaries:
Jilin Yatai (Group) Building Materials Investment Co., Ltd. (1)
Yatai Building No 1801 Jilin Road, Changchun, 130031, Jilin, China
Tel.: (86) 43184974500
Web Site: http://www.en.yataijcgs.com
Cement Mfr
N.A.I.C.S.: 327320

Jilin Yatai (Group) Pharmaceutical Investment Co., Ltd. (1)
YATAI Tower No 1801 Jilin Avenue, Changchun, China
Tel.: (86) 43184971088
Cement Mfr
N.A.I.C.S.: 327320

Jilin Yatai Construction Engineering Co., Ltd. (1)
4 Floor Ming Di 9 Dong Windsor Heights Hefei Road, Economic Development Zone, Changchun, Jilin, China
Tel.: (86) 43184950545
Cement Mfr
N.A.I.C.S.: 327320

Jilin Yatai Real Estate Development Co., Ltd. (1)
YATAI Tower No 1801 Jilin Avenue, Changchun, 130031, China
Tel.: (86) 431 84958888
Web Site: http://www.en.yataidc.com
Real Estate Manangement Services
N.A.I.C.S.: 531210
Dongyang Han *(Gen Mgr)*

JILIN ZIXIN PHARMACEUTICAL INDUSTRIAL CO., LTD.
No 137 East First Street, Nanguan District, Changchun, 130041, Jilin, China
Tel.: (86) 43181916633
Web Site: http://www.jilinzixin.com
002118—(SSE)
Rev.: $43,747,583
Assets: $1,610,044,055
Liabilities: $1,036,928,344
Net Worth: $573,115,711
Earnings: ($108,124,893)
Fiscal Year-end: 12/31/20
Pharmaceuticals Mfr
N.A.I.C.S.: 325412
Feng Youshun *(Chm & Gen Mgr)*

JIM HATHEWAY FORD SALES LIMITED
76 Robert Angus Drive, Amherst, B4H 4R7, NS, Canada
Tel.: (902) 667-6000
Web Site: http://www.hathewayford.com
Year Founded: 1993
Rev.: $12,015,640
Emp.: 35
New & Used Car Dealers
N.A.I.C.S.: 441110
Leslie Beaton *(Mgr-Fin Svcs)*

JIM MACDONALD MOTORS LTD
1324 Kings Highway, Fort Frances, P9A 2X6, ON, Canada
Tel.: (807) 274-5321

INTERNATIONAL PUBLIC

Web Site: http://www.jimmacdonaldmotors.ca
Rev.: $11,911,458
Emp.: 26
New & Used Car Dealers
N.A.I.C.S.: 441110
Ron MacKinnon *(Mgr-Internet)*

JIM PENNEY LIMITED
105 Laurel Road, Gander, A1V 0A9, NL, Canada
Tel.: (709) 256-4821
Web Site: http://jimpenneyford.com
Rev.: $16,084,816
Emp.: 35
New & Used Car Dealers
N.A.I.C.S.: 441110
Dorothy Lawton *(Mgr-Svc)*

JIM WILSON CHEVROLET BUICK GMC
20 Mulcahy Court, Orillia, L3V 7W7, ON, Canada
Tel.: (705) 329-2000
Web Site: http://www.jimwilsonchevrolet.com
Year Founded: 1992
Rev.: $16,084,816
Emp.: 35
New & Used Car Dealers
N.A.I.C.S.: 441110
Matt French *(Mgr-Sls)*

JIMDO GMBH
Stresemannstr 375, 22761, Hamburg, Germany
Tel.: (49) 40 8 22 44 997
Web Site: http://www.jimdo.com
Year Founded: 2007
Sales Range: $1-9.9 Million
Emp.: 30
Software Publisher & Website Developer
N.A.I.C.S.: 513210
Fridtjof Detzner *(Co-Founder)*

Subsidiaries:
Jimdo Inc. (1)
548 Market St Ste 56907, San Francisco, CA 94104
Tel.: (415) 727-0774
Web Designing Services
N.A.I.C.S.: 541511
Stephen Belomy *(CEO)*

JIMOTO HOLDINGS, INC.
1-1 Ichibancho 2-chom Sendai Bank Building 9th floor, Aoba-ku, Sendai, 980-8656, Japan
Tel.: (81) 227220011　　JP
Web Site: https://www.jimoto-hd.co.jp
Year Founded: 2012
7161—(TKS)
Rev.: $250,796,620
Assets: $17,720,253,250
Liabilities: $17,167,485,390
Net Worth: $552,767,860
Earnings: ($155,083,820)
Fiscal Year-end: 03/31/24
Bank Holding Company
N.A.I.C.S.: 551111
Takashi Suzuki *(Chm)*

Subsidiaries:
Kirayaka Bank, Ltd. (1)
2-3-2 Hatagocho, Yamagata, 990-0047, Japan (100%)
Tel.: (81) 236310001
Web Site: http://www.kirayaka.co.jp
Sales Range: $700-749.9 Million
Emp.: 963
Banking Services
N.A.I.C.S.: 522110
Makoto Suzuki *(Exec Mng Dir)*

The Sendai Bank, Ltd. (1)
2-1-1 Ichibancho, Aoba-ku, Sendai, 980-8656, Miyagi, Japan (100%)
Tel.: (81) 22 225 8241

Web Site: http://www.sendaibank.co.jp
Sales Range: $350-399.9 Million
Emp.: 756
Retail & Commercial Banking
N.A.I.C.S.: 522110
Takashi Suzuki (Pres)

JIMOTY, INC.
1-2-10 Nishigotanda, Shinagawa-Ku, Tokyo, 141-0031, Japan
Tel.: (81) 366302450
Web Site: https://jmty.jp
Year Founded: 2011
7082—(TKS)
Application Development Services
N.A.I.C.S.: 541511
Takahiro Kato (Chm & Pres)

JIMU GROUP LIMITED
Suite 2207 22/F Prudential Tower The Gateway Harbour City, Kowloon, China (Hong Kong)
Tel.: (852) 27893123   Ky
Web Site: http://www.jimugroup.hk
Year Founded: 2009
8187—(HKG)
Rev.: $4,003,500
Assets: $3,770,685
Liabilities: $3,613,223
Net Worth: $157,463
Earnings: ($674,220)
Emp.: 16
Fiscal Year-end: 12/31/22
Footwear Distr
N.A.I.C.S.: 424340
Kin Wai Ho (CEO)

JIN AIR CO., LTD.
453 Gonghang-Daero, Gangseo-Gu, Seoul, 157-841, Korea (South)
Tel.: (82) 16006200
Web Site: http://www.jinair.com
Year Founded: 2008
272450—(KRS)
Rev.: $455,159,658
Assets: $592,043,712
Liabilities: $508,406,152
Net Worth: $83,637,560
Earnings: ($37,899,518)
Emp.: 1,758
Fiscal Year-end: 12/31/22
Passenger Air Transport Services
N.A.I.C.S.: 481111
Jeong-Cheol Lee (Gen Mgr)

JIN MEDICAL INTERNATIONAL LTD.
No 33 Lingxiang Road, Wujin District, Changzhou, Jiangsu, China
Tel.: (86) 51989607972   Ky
Web Site: http://ir.zhjmedical.com
Year Founded: 2020
Rev.: $15,110,510
Assets: $20,815,216
Liabilities: $10,012,753
Net Worth: $10,802,463
Earnings: $2,205,998
Emp.: 263
Fiscal Year-end: 09/30/20
Holding Company
N.A.I.C.S.: 551112
Erqi Wang (Chm & CEO)

JIN TONG LING TECHNOLOGY GROUP CO., LTD.
No 135 Mid Zhongxiu Road, Nantong, 226001, Jiangsu, China
Tel.: (86) 51385198522
Web Site: https://www.jtltech.cn
Year Founded: 1993
300091—(CHIN)
Rev.: $204,243,993
Assets: $766,451,811
Liabilities: $494,408,135
Net Worth: $272,043,676
Earnings: ($71,201,182)
Fiscal Year-end: 12/31/23

Fan & Fluid Machinery Mfr
N.A.I.C.S.: 333413
Zhang Jianhua (Chm)

JIN WAN HONG INTERNATIONAL HOLDING LIMITED
Room 1101 Block E Guang Hua Yuan, 2031 Bin He Nan Road FuTian District, Shenzhen, China
Tel.: (86) 189 4831 9148   NV
Year Founded: 2014
Liabilities: $59,281
Net Worth: ($59,281)
Earnings: ($35,443)
Fiscal Year-end: 05/31/18
Holding Company
N.A.I.C.S.: 551112
Shu Feng Lu (Chm & Pres)

JIN YANG PHARMACEUTICAL CO. LTD
Jinyang Pharm Building 231 Hyoryeong-ro, Seocho-gu, Seoul, 06671, Korea (South)
Tel.: (82) 234700300
Web Site: https://www.jinyangpharm.com
Year Founded: 1971
007370—(KRS)
Rev.: $58,494,644
Assets: $87,778,311
Liabilities: $28,278,179
Net Worth: $59,500,132
Earnings: $9,440,534
Emp.: 219
Fiscal Year-end: 12/31/22
Pharmaceutical Product Mfr & Distr
N.A.I.C.S.: 325412
Yoon Hwan Choi (Chm, Pres & CEO)

Subsidiaries:

Jin Yang Pharmaceutical Co. Ltd - Ansan Factory   (1)
627 Byeolmang-ro, Danwon-gu, Ansan, 425-866, Gyeonggi-do, Korea (South)
Tel.: (82) 31 494 8196
Pharmaceuticals Product Mfr
N.A.I.C.S.: 325412

JINAN ACETATE CHEMICAL CO., LTD.
Room 409 Unit 2 Building 7 Shangang Xintiandi No 61 Gongye South Road, Lixia District, Jinan, Shandong, China
Tel.: (86) 53188164818   CN
Web Site: https://www.acetatechemical.com
Year Founded: 1999
4763—(TAI)
Rev.: $311,241,069
Assets: $370,095,809
Liabilities: $173,664,729
Net Worth: $196,431,080
Earnings: $47,402,877
Emp.: 180
Fiscal Year-end: 12/31/19
Acetate Tow Mfr & Distr
N.A.I.C.S.: 325220

Subsidiaries:

Acetek Material Co., Ltd.   (1)
Room 409 Unit 2 Building 7 Shangang Xintiandi No 61 Gongye South Road, Lixia District, Jinan, Shandong, China
Tel.: (86) 53188164818
Web Site: http://en.acetekmaterial.cn
Cellulose Acetate Mfr
N.A.I.C.S.: 325211

JINAN GUOJI GROUP CO., LTD.
33 Baosheng Road Songjiang Industrial Zone, Shanghai, 201613, China
Tel.: (86) 2157747138
Web Site: https://www.goldenmax.cn
Year Founded: 2000

002636—(SSE)
Rev.: $527,960,160
Assets: $876,595,824
Liabilities: $357,692,868
Net Worth: $518,902,956
Earnings: $12,228,840
Emp.: 1,460
Fiscal Year-end: 12/31/22
Copper Clad Laminates Mfr
N.A.I.C.S.: 334413

JINAN HIGH TECH DEVELOPMENT CO., LTD.
Main office building Longao Tianjie No 1577 Longao North Road, Lixia District, Jinan, 250101, Shandong, China
Tel.: (86) 53186171188
Web Site: https://jngxfz.com
Year Founded: 1993
600807—(SHG)
Rev.: $167,260,889
Assets: $721,092,058
Liabilities: $621,661,832
Net Worth: $99,430,226
Earnings: ($126,396,718)
Fiscal Year-end: 12/31/20
Real Estate Property Development Services
N.A.I.C.S.: 531120
Wang Chengdong (Chm)

Subsidiaries:

Australia Minjar Gold Pty Ltd.   (1)
Level 3 66 Kings Park Road, West Perth, 6005, WA, Australia
Tel.: (61) 892128900
Web Site: https://www.minjargold.com.au
Gold Ore Mining Services
N.A.I.C.S.: 212220
Max Ji (Vice Chm)

JINBANG STEEL CO., LTD.
605 Ho-Dong, Pohang, Kyungsangbyk-Do, Korea (South)
Tel.: (82) 542895700   KR
Web Site: http://www.jinbangsteel.com
Year Founded: 1987
Sales Range: $25-49.9 Million
Emp.: 160
Produces Steel Tubes, Main Frames of Buildings, Steel Materials & Scaffolding Equipment
N.A.I.C.S.: 331210
Jung Tae Jung (Pres)

JINCHI BIOTECH LIMITED
8 Baofeng Road, Wulingyuan District, Zhangjiajie, 427400, Hunan, China
Tel.: (86) 731 89792662
Web Site: http://www.jinchishengwu.com
Year Founded: 2009
Biotechnology Products Developer
N.A.I.C.S.: 541714
Haibo Zhang (Chm)

JINCHUAN GROUP INTERNATIONAL RESOURCES CO. LTD.
Unit 3101 31/F United Centre 95 Queensway Admiralty, Hong Kong, China (Hong Kong)
Tel.: (852) 39197268
Web Site: http://www.jinchuan-intl.com
2362—(HKG)
Rev.: $881,598,000
Assets: $2,029,528,000
Liabilities: $863,438,000
Net Worth: $1,166,090,000
Earnings: $6,864,000
Emp.: 1,598
Fiscal Year-end: 12/31/22
Investment Services
N.A.I.C.S.: 523940

Tianpeng Gao (CEO)

Subsidiaries:

Cheng Ming Ming's Beauty World Limited   (1)
Units 801-4 8/F Miramar Tower 132-134 Nathan Road, Tsim Sha Tsui, Kowloon, China (Hong Kong)
Tel.: (852) 27398833
Beauty Salon Operating Services
N.A.I.C.S.: 812112
Vivien Fok (Gen Mgr)

Metorex (Proprietary) Limited   (1)
The Mall Offices 5th Floor 11 Cradock Ave cnr Baker Street, Rosebank, 2196, South Africa
Tel.: (27) 112154000
Web Site: https://www.metorexgroup.com
Copper Mining Services
N.A.I.C.S.: 212230

Ruashi Mining SAS   (1)
Ruashi Mine Site Luano, Lubumbashi, Congo, Democratic Republic of
Tel.: (243) 819782744
Copper Mining Services
N.A.I.C.S.: 212230
Ghislain Kayumba (Officer-Comm)

JINCHUAN GROUP LIMITED
98 Jinchuan Road, Jinchang, Gansu, China
Tel.: (86) 935 8811111
Web Site: http://www.jnmc.com
Sales Range: $5-14.9 Billion
Emp.: 31,000
Nickel, Copper & Cobalt Mining Services; Chemical Mfr
N.A.I.C.S.: 212230
Jianke Gao (Asst Gen Mgr)

Subsidiaries:

Albidon Limited   (1)
Level 1 8 Colin Street, West Perth, 6005, WA, Australia   (100%)
Tel.: (61) 892114600
Web Site: http://www.albidon.com
Sales Range: $25-49.9 Million
Emp.: 313
Nickel Mining & Other Support Services
N.A.I.C.S.: 212230

Subsidiary (Domestic):

Albidon Australia Pty Ltd   (2)
12 Walker Ave, West Perth, 6005, WA, Australia
Tel.: (61) 892114600
Nickel Mining & Exploration Services
N.A.I.C.S.: 212230

Subsidiary (Non-US):

Albidon Zambia Limited   (2)
Kafue/Mazabuka Road, Lusaka, Zambia
Tel.: (260) 213235190
Nickel Ore Mining Services
N.A.I.C.S.: 212230

Metorex Limited   (1)
5th Floor The Mall Offices 11 Cradock Avenue, Rosebank, 2196, Johannesburg, South Africa
Tel.: (27) 112154000
Web Site: http://www.metorexgroup.com
Sales Range: $500-549.9 Million
Emp.: 40
Base Metal Producer Services
N.A.I.C.S.: 213114
Lloyd Bradford (Mgr-Metallurgical)

Subsidiary (Non-US):

Chibuluma Mines plc   (2)
South Downs Airport Rd, PO Box 260499, Lufwanyama, Kalulushi, Copperbelt, Zambia   (85%)
Tel.: (260) 2749110
Copper Mining
N.A.I.C.S.: 212230

Subsidiary (Domestic):

Copper Resources Corporation   (2)
Cradock Hts 2nd Fl 21 Cradock Ave, Rose-

JINCHUAN GROUP LIMITED

Jinchuan Group Limited—(Continued)
bank, Johannesburg, 2196, Gauteng, South
Africa (100%)
Tel.: (27) 118803155
Sales Range: $25-49.9 Million
Copper Mining
N.A.I.C.S.: 212230

Division (Domestic):

Metorex Limited - Consolidated
Murchison Division (2)
Farm Josephine 777 LT, Phalaborwa, Limpopo, South Africa
Tel.: (27) 153188000
Antimony & Gold Mining Services
N.A.I.C.S.: 212220

Subsidiary (Domestic):

Ruashi Holdings (Pty) Limited (2)
11 Cradock Ave, Johannesburg, 2196, Gauteng, South Africa (100%)
Tel.: (27) 118803155
Sales Range: $550-599.9 Million
Emp.: 1,165
Holding Company; Copper Mining
N.A.I.C.S.: 551112

JINCOSTECH CO., LTD.
2-604 31 Gunjacheon-ro 237beon-gil, Siheung, Gyeonggi-do, Korea (South)
Tel.: (82) 314335575
Web Site: https://www.jincostech.com
Year Founded: 2010
250030—(KRS)
Cosmetic Product Mfr & Distr
N.A.I.C.S.: 325620

JINDAL CAPITAL LTD.
201 Aggarwal Plaza Sector-9, Delhi, 110085, India
Tel.: (91) 1145578272
Web Site: https://www.jindalcapital.in
Year Founded: 1994
530405—(BOM)
Rev: $602,809
Assets: $1,226,074
Liabilities: $162,702
Net Worth: $1,063,372
Earnings: $14,395
Fiscal Year-end: 03/31/23
Investment Management Service
N.A.I.C.S.: 523999
Pawan Kumar Jindal (Chm & Mng Dir)

JINDAL COTEX LIMITED
Mandiala Kalan P O Bija Tehsil Khanna, Ludhiana, 141412, Punjab, India
Tel.: (91) 1612511840
Web Site:
https://www.jindalcotex.com
Rev.: $37,167,425
Assets: $100,974,068
Liabilities: $105,932,916
Net Worth: ($4,958,848)
Earnings: ($4,400,726)
Emp.: 774
Fiscal Year-end: 03/31/18
Synthetic, Cotton & Blended Yarns Mfr
N.A.I.C.S.: 313110
Sandeep Jindal (Mng Dir & Compliance Officer)

JINDAL DRILLING & INDUSTRIES LTD
Plot No 30 Institutional Sector-44, Gurgaon, 122001, Haryana, India
Tel.: (91) 1242574325
Web Site: https://www.jindal.com
JINDALDRIL—(NSE)
Rev.: $55,411,752
Assets: $249,101,348
Liabilities: $96,002,675
Net Worth: $153,098,673
Earnings: ($801,705)
Emp.: 689

Fiscal Year-end: 03/31/21
Offshore Drilling Services
N.A.I.C.S.: 213111
Raghav Jindal (Mng Dir)

JINDAL HOLDINGS LIMITED
Jindal Centre 12 Bhikaiji Cama Place, New Delhi, 110066, India
Tel.: (91) 02527220022
Web Site: http://www.jindalsteel.com
Year Founded: 1970
Sales Range: $5-14.9 Billion
Holding Company
N.A.I.C.S.: 551112
Prithviraj Jindal (Mng Dir)

Subsidiaries:

HEXA TRADEX Limited (1)
Jindal Centre 12 Bhikaiji Cama Place, New Delhi, 110066, India
Tel.: (91) 1126188345
Web Site: https://www.hexatradex.com
Rev.: $7,969,340
Assets: $46,247,619
Liabilities: $5,077,894
Net Worth: $41,169,724
Earnings: $6,763,791
Emp.: 3
Fiscal Year-end: 03/31/2019
Steel Mfr & Distr
N.A.I.C.S.: 331110
Raj Kamal Agarwal (Chm)

JSW Energy Limited (1)
JSW Centre Bandra Kurla Complex Bandra East, Mumbai, 400 051, India
Tel.: (91) 2242861000
Rev.: $1,302,925,484
Assets: $5,843,978,179
Liabilities: $3,597,808,285
Net Worth: $2,246,169,894
Earnings: $177,461,783
Emp.: 2,310
Fiscal Year-end: 03/31/2023
Electric Power Distr
N.A.I.C.S.: 221112
Sajjan Jindal (Chm & Co-Mng Dir)

Subsidiary (Domestic):

JSW Energy (Ratnagiri) Ltd. (2)
2nd Fl Kasturi Plz Desai Niwas Juna Mal Naka, Ratnagiri, 415612, Maharashtra, India
Tel.: (91) 2352271617
Eletric Power Generation Services
N.A.I.C.S.: 221112

JSW Power Trading Company Ltd (2)
NBCC Tower Bhikaji Cama Pl, New Delhi, 110066, India
Tel.: (91) 1141619673
Web Site: http://www.jsw.in
Sales Range: $50-74.9 Million
Emp.: 15
Electric Power Trading Services
N.A.I.C.S.: 221122

JSW Holdings Ltd. (1)
Bandra Kurla Complex, Near MMRDA Grounds Bandra East, Mumbai, 400 051, India
Tel.: (91) 2242861000
Rev.: $48,769,834
Assets: $2,642,410,431
Liabilities: $315,223,847
Net Worth: $2,327,186,584
Earnings: $39,745,231
Emp.: 2
Fiscal Year-end: 03/31/2023
Holding Company; Investment Services
N.A.I.C.S.: 551112
Sajjan Jindal (Chm)

Jindal Iron & Steel Company Limited (1)
Jindal Mansion 5-A G Deshmukh Marg, Mumbai, 400 026, India
Tel.: (91) 22 2351 3000
Web Site: http://www.jisco.com
Iron & Steel Products Mfr
N.A.I.C.S.: 332111
Sajjan Jindal (Chm & Mng Dir)

Jindal SAW Limited (1)
Jindal Centre 12 Bhikaiji Cama Place, New Delhi, 110066, India
Tel.: (91) 1161462220
Web Site: https://www.jindalsaw.com
Rev.: $2,163,703,051
Assets: $2,188,825,370
Liabilities: $1,316,180,637
Net Worth: $872,644,734
Earnings: $53,086,614
Emp.: 7,517
Fiscal Year-end: 03/31/2023
Cold Rolled Stainless Steel & Nickel Alloys Mfr
N.A.I.C.S.: 331110
Prithavi Raj Jindal (Chm)

Subsidiary (US):

Jindal Tubular USA LLC (2)
13092 Sea Plane Rd, Bay Saint Louis, MS 39520
Tel.: (228) 533-7779
Web Site: http://www.jindalsaw.com
Pipes Mfr
N.A.I.C.S.: 331210

Subsidiary (Domestic):

SATHAVAHANA ISPAT LIMITED (2)
505 5th floor Block-1 Divyashakti Complex Ameerpet, Hyderabad, 500016, Telangana, India
Tel.: (91) 4023730812
Web Site: https://www.sathavahana.com
Rev.: $5,220,730
Assets: $86,260,464
Liabilities: $222,015,227
Net Worth: ($135,754,763)
Earnings: ($14,707,871)
Emp.: 11
Fiscal Year-end: 03/31/2022
Iron & Metallurgical Coke Mfr
N.A.I.C.S.: 331110
A. S. Rao (Vice Chm)

Jindal Stainless Ltd. (1)
O P Jindal marg, Hisar, 125 005, Haryana, India
Tel.: (91) 1662222471
Web Site: https://www.jindalstainless.com
Rev.: $1,669,307,640
Assets: $1,465,260,615
Liabilities: $1,025,951,745
Net Worth: $439,308,870
Earnings: $57,256,290
Emp.: 1,685
Fiscal Year-end: 03/31/2021
Stainless Steel Mfr
N.A.I.C.S.: 331513
Tarun Kumar Khulbe (Exec Dir)

Subsidiary (Domestic):

Austenitic Creations Private Limited (2)
12 Bhikaji Cama Pl Jindal Ctr, New Delhi, 110066, India
Tel.: (91) 1126188340
Web Site: http://www.artdinox.com
Stainless Steel Mfr
N.A.I.C.S.: 331110

Jindal Architecture Limited (2)
64-65 Udyog Vihar Phase-IV, Gurgaon, 122001, Haryana, India
Tel.: (91) 9953230199
Web Site: http://www.jindalarc.in
Sales Range: $25-49.9 Million
Emp.: 30
Stainless Steel Mfr
N.A.I.C.S.: 331110

Jindal Stainless Steelway Limited (2)
Plot No 64 2nd Fl, Udyog Vihar Phase IV, Gurgaon, 122016, Haryana, India
Tel.: (91) 1244127700
Web Site: http://www.jindalstainless.com
Sales Range: $25-49.9 Million
Emp.: 70
Stainless Steel Mfr
N.A.I.C.S.: 331513
Payoj Jindal (Gen Mgr-Mktg)

Jindal Steel & Power Ltd. (1)
Jindal Centre 12 Bhikaiji Cama Place, New Delhi, 110 066, India
Tel.: (91) 1126188340
Web Site: https://www.jindalsteelpower.com
Rev.: $6,374,402,184
Assets: $8,386,809,384

INTERNATIONAL PUBLIC

Liabilities: $3,673,299,688
Net Worth: $4,713,509,696
Earnings: $385,739,768
Emp.: 6,399
Fiscal Year-end: 03/31/2023
Iron & Steel Producer; Power Generation
N.A.I.C.S.: 332111
Naveen Jindal (Chm)

Subsidiary (Domestic):

Jindal Power Limited (2)
Jindal Centre, 12 Bhikaiji Cama Place, New Delhi, 110 066, India (100%)
Tel.: (91) 1141462000
Web Site: http://www.jindalpower.com
Sales Range: $400-449.9 Million
Emp.: 600
Thermal Power Generation
N.A.I.C.S.: 221118
Naveen Jindal (Chm)

UMI Special Steel Ltd. (2)
P-9 Darga Road, Kolkata, 700071, India
Tel.: (91) 33 2262 5223
Steel Mfrs
N.A.I.C.S.: 332111

Subsidiary (Non-US):

Wollongong Coal Limited (2)
7 Princes Highway cnr Bellambi Lane, Corrimal, Wollongong, 2518, NSW, Australia
Tel.: (61) 242236800
Web Site:
http://www.wollongongcoal.com.au
Rev.: $21,352,645
Assets: $645,547,181
Liabilities: $708,210,382
Net Worth: ($62,663,201)
Earnings: ($57,664,943)
Emp.: 70
Fiscal Year-end: 03/31/2018
Coking Coal Producer
N.A.I.C.S.: 212115
Sanjay Sharma (Sec)

JINDAL HOTELS LTD
Grand Mercure Vadodara Surya Palace Sayajiganj, Vadodara, 390020, Gujarat, India
Tel.: (91) 2652226000
Web Site:
http://www.suryapalace.com
Year Founded: 1987
507981—(BOM)
Rev.: $4,148,563
Assets: $12,058,219
Liabilities: $9,766,425
Net Worth: $2,291,794
Earnings: ($327,996)
Emp.: 186
Fiscal Year-end: 03/31/22
Home Management Services
N.A.I.C.S.: 721110
Piyush D Shah (Mng Dir)

JINDAL LEASEFIN LIMITED
110 Babar Road Opp World Trade Center, New Delhi, 110001, India
Tel.: (91) 1123412636
Web Site: https://jindalleasefin.in
539947—(BOM)
Rev.: $27,189
Assets: $1,085,549
Liabilities: $5,962
Net Worth: $1,079,587
Earnings: $26,577
Fiscal Year-end: 03/31/22
Consumer Lending Services
N.A.I.C.S.: 522291

JINDAL PHOTO LTD.
Plot Number 12 Sector B 1 Local Shopping Complex Vasant Kunj, New Delhi, 110070, India
Tel.: (91) 1140322100
Web Site:
https://www.jindalphoto.com
532624—(BOM)
Rev.: $51,420
Assets: $14,396,832
Liabilities: $10,983,008

Net Worth: $3,413,824
Earnings: ($608,435)
Emp.: 2
Fiscal Year-end: 03/31/21
Photographic & Allied Products Mfr
N.A.I.C.S.: 333310
Ashok Yadav *(Compliance Officer & Sec)*

JINDAL POLY FILMS LTD.
Plot No 12 Sector B-1 Local Shopping Complex Vasant Kunj, New Delhi, 110070, India
Tel.: (91) 1140322100
Web Site: https://www.jindalpoly.com
Year Founded: 1985
JINDALPOLY—(NSE)
Rev.: $576,800,229
Assets: $657,613,798
Liabilities: $297,009,149
Net Worth: $360,604,649
Earnings: $107,955,434
Emp.: 1,858
Fiscal Year-end: 03/31/21
Polyester Film Mfr
N.A.I.C.S.: 326113
Sanjeev Kumar *(Compliance Officer & Sec)*

Subsidiaries:

Apeldoorn Flexible Packaging B.V.
Laan Van Westenenk 11, 7336 AZ, Apeldoorn, Netherlands
Tel.: (31) 55 599 6600
Web Site: https://www.afpfilm.com
Sales Range: $100-124.9 Million
Emp.: 230
Plastic Flexible Packaging & Pallet Wrapping Material Mfr
N.A.I.C.S.: 326112
Paul F. T. Kommerkamp *(Mgr-Customer Svc & Bus Dev)*

Jindal Films Europe S.a.r.l (1)
11 Rue de l'Industrie, 8399, Windhof, Luxembourg
Tel.: (352) 45 10 22 211
Steel Pole Mfr
N.A.I.C.S.: 331210
Paul Smeaton *(Mgr-Sls)*

JINDAL POLY INVESTMENT & FINANCE COMPANY LIMITED
Plot No 12 Sector B-1 Local Shopping Complex Vasant Kunj, New Delhi, 110 070, India
Tel.: (91) 1140322100
Web Site: https://www.jpifcl.com
Year Founded: 2012
JPOLYINVST—(NSE)
Rev.: $145,045
Assets: $69,378,527
Liabilities: $126,931,009
Net Worth: ($57,552,481)
Earnings: ($4,234,967)
Emp.: 2
Fiscal Year-end: 03/31/21
Investment Management Service
N.A.I.C.S.: 523940
Ghanshyam Dass Singhal *(Mng Dir)*

Subsidiaries:

Jindal India Thermal Power Limited (1)
Habitat India 1st Floor C-3 Qutub Institutional Area Katwaria Sarai, New Delhi, 110016, India
Tel.: (91) 1140841950
Web Site: https://www.jitpl.com
Steel Pipe & Cold Rolled Steel Mfr
N.A.I.C.S.: 331210

JINDAL WORLDWIDE LIMITED
Jindal House Opp D-Mart IOC Petrol Pump Lane Shivranjani, Shyamal 132 Ft Ring Road Satellite, Ahmedabad, 380015, Gujarat, India
Tel.: (91) 7971001500

Web Site: https://www.jindaltextiles.com
Year Founded: 1976
531543—(BOM)
Rev.: $282,759,586
Assets: $228,962,083
Liabilities: $140,239,991
Net Worth: $88,722,093
Earnings: $15,795,330
Emp.: 3,000
Fiscal Year-end: 03/31/23
Textile Products Mfr
N.A.I.C.S.: 314999
Amit Yanunadutt Agrawal *(Mng Dir)*

JINDALEE RESOURCES LIMITED
Level 2 9 Havelock Street, West Perth, 6005, WA, Australia
Tel.: (61) 893217550
Web Site: http://www.jindalee.net
JLL—(ASX)
Rev.: $13,144
Assets: $13,636,463
Liabilities: $1,108,054
Net Worth: $12,528,410
Earnings: ($3,130,314)
Fiscal Year-end: 06/30/24
Minerals Exploration
N.A.I.C.S.: 212220
Patricia Anne Farr *(Sec)*

JINDO CO., LTD.
75 Gasan Digital 1-ro, Geumcheon-gu, Seoul, 153-802, Korea (South)
Tel.: (82) 28508200
Web Site: https://www.jindofand.co.kr
Year Founded: 2006
088790—(KRS)
Rev.: $48,640,851
Assets: $99,096,998
Liabilities: $19,195,928
Net Worth: $79,901,070
Earnings: $3,506,405
Emp.: 136
Fiscal Year-end: 12/31/22
Fur Garment Mfr & Whslr
N.A.I.C.S.: 315250
Oh-Sik Yim *(Chm)*

JINDUICHENG MOLYBDENUM GROUP CO., LTD.
No 67 Dongfeng Street High tech industrial development zone, Weinan, 714000, Shaanxi, China
Tel.: (86) 9132939201
Web Site: https://en.jdcmmc.com
Year Founded: 1958
601958—(SHG)
Rev.: $1,221,670,494
Assets: $2,215,362,977
Liabilities: $286,625,268
Net Worth: $1,928,737,709
Earnings: $75,806,776
Fiscal Year-end: 12/31/21
Molybdenum Mining & Processing Services
N.A.I.C.S.: 212290

Subsidiaries:

Yukon Zinc Corporation (1)
Suite 705 - 1030 West Georgia Street, Vancouver, V6E 2Y3, BC, Canada
Tel.: (604) 682-5474
Web Site: http://www.yukonzinc.com
Sales Range: $50-74.9 Million
Emp.: 20
Base & Precious Metal Exploration & Development Services; Owned by Jinduicheng Molybdenum Group Co., Ltd. & Northwest Nonferrous International Investment Company, Ltd.
N.A.I.C.S.: 212290

JINFA LABI MATERNITY & BABY ARTICLES CO., LTD.
No 107 Jinan Road Xipuxi, Jinping

District, Shantou, 515061, Guangdong, China
Tel.: (86) 75482526666
Web Site: https://www.stjinfa.com
002762—(SSE)
Rev.: $34,448,544
Assets: $132,485,652
Liabilities: $9,353,448
Net Worth: $123,132,204
Earnings: ($12,388,896)
Fiscal Year-end: 12/31/22
Infant Articles Mfr & Distr
N.A.I.C.S.: 316210
Haoliang Lin *(Chm)*

JING KING TECH HOLDINGS PTE LTD.
22/F Remington Centre 23 Hung To Road, Kwun Tong, Hong Kong, China (Hong Kong)
Tel.: (852) 23443170
Web Site: http://www.jingking.com
Year Founded: 1984
Emp.: 2,000
Payment & Telecommunication Smart Card Mfr
N.A.I.C.S.: 513210
Lennon Tan *(Chm & CEO)*

Subsidiaries:

DataPost Pte Ltd (1)
10 Eunos Road 8 02-36, Singapore Post Centre, Singapore, 408600, Singapore
Tel.: (65) 6845 6543
Web Site: http://www.datapost.com.sg
Business Printing & Mailing Solutions
N.A.I.C.S.: 561410
Knight Liew *(Mgr-IT Infrastructure)*

Subsidiary (Non-US):

Novation Solutions Limited (2)
22/F Remington Centre 23 Hung To Road, Kwun Tong, China (Hong Kong)
Tel.: (852) 3699 3111
Web Site: http://www.novsn.com
Document Management Services
N.A.I.C.S.: 561410

Jing King Tech Holdings Pte Ltd. - Dongguan Plant (1)
J 109 Luyuan Road Keyuan City, Tangxia, Dongguan, 523718, China
Tel.: (86) 76982991018
Chip Mfr
N.A.I.C.S.: 334413

Jing King Tech Holdings Pte Ltd. - Shenzhen Plant (1)
Jing King Group Plaza Pingxin Avenue Shangmugu Industrial Zone, Pinghu, Shenzhen, 518111, China
Tel.: (86) 75584255088
Chip Mfr
N.A.I.C.S.: 334413

JINGBO TECHNOLOGY, INC.
Building B8 China Zhigu Yinhu Street, Fuyang District, Hangzhou, 310000, Zhejiang, China
Tel.: (86) 57187197085 NV
Year Founded: 2015
SVMB—(OTCIQ)
Rev.: $1,583,637
Assets: $12,866,660
Liabilities: $31,568,840
Net Worth: ($18,702,180)
Earnings: ($5,482,077)
Emp.: 1
Fiscal Year-end: 02/29/24
Technical Support Services
N.A.I.C.S.: 541990
Zhang Guowei *(Chm, Pres, CEO & CFO)*

JINGGONG STEEL BUILDING GROUP
29F Asia Financial Center No 999 Li An Road, MinhangDistrict, Shanghai, 201199, China

Tel.: (86) 31215588
Web Site: https://www.600496.com
Year Founded: 1999
600496—(SHG)
Rev.: $2,192,794,845
Assets: $3,075,984,779
Liabilities: $1,951,770,249
Net Worth: $1,124,214,530
Earnings: $99,135,022
Emp.: 7,000
Fiscal Year-end: 12/31/22
Steel Products Mfr
N.A.I.C.S.: 331110

JINGJIN EQUIPMENT CO., LTD.
Jinghua Road, Dezhou Econ Develop Zone, Dezhou, 253034, Shandong, China
Tel.: (86) 5342556198
Web Site: https://topfilterpress.com
Year Founded: 1988
603279—(SHG)
Rev.: $797,772,653
Assets: $1,119,916,676
Liabilities: $556,270,346
Net Worth: $563,646,330
Earnings: $117,082,185
Emp.: 4,873
Fiscal Year-end: 12/31/22
Industrial Machinery Product Mfr & Distr
N.A.I.C.S.: 333248
Guiting Jiang *(Chm & Gen Mgr)*

JINGLV ENVIRONMENT SCIENCE & TECHNOLOGY CO., LTD.
No 517 Tuohe Road, Xinzhan District, Hefei, 230012, Anhui, China
Tel.: (86) 55164282862
Web Site: https://www.jlhoe.com
Year Founded: 2002
001230—(SSE)
Rev.: $177,183,396
Assets: $391,301,820
Liabilities: $157,969,656
Net Worth: $233,332,164
Earnings: $17,425,044
Fiscal Year-end: 12/31/22
Environmental Consulting Services
N.A.I.C.S.: 541620
Yu Xiaoxia *(Chm)*

JINGRUI HOLDINGS LIMITED
Room 09 43/F China Resources Building 26 Harbour Road, Wanchai, China (Hong Kong)
Tel.: (852) 23276858 Ky
Web Site: http://www.jingruis.com
Year Founded: 1993
1862—(HKG)
Rev.: $1,110,270,002
Assets: $6,614,222,098
Liabilities: $5,715,845,039
Net Worth: $898,377,059
Earnings: ($600,614,352)
Emp.: 3,082
Fiscal Year-end: 12/31/22
Holding Company
N.A.I.C.S.: 551112
Hao Yan *(Co-Founder, Co-Chm & CEO)*

JINGWEI INTERNATIONAL LIMITED
Unit 701-702 Building 14 Software Park Keji Yuan Second Road, Nanshan District, Shenzhen, 518057, China
Tel.: (86) 755 83437888 NV
Sales Range: $25-49.9 Million
Emp.: 371
Data Mining & Interactive Marketing Services
N.A.I.C.S.: 518210

JINGWEI INTERNATIONAL LIMITED—(Continued)

George Du (Chm, Pres & CEO)

JINGYE GROUP
2/F Jingye Group Office Building
Nandian Town, Pingshan County,
Shijiazhuang, Hebei, China
Tel.: (86) 0311 82870906
Web Site: http://jingyesteel.com.cn
Iron & Steel Mills & Ferroalloy Mfr
N.A.I.C.S.: 331110
Ganpo Li (Chm)

Subsidiaries:

British Steel Limited (1)
Brigg Road, Scunthorpe, DN16 1BP, N Lincolnshire, United Kingdom
Tel.: (44) 1724 404 040
Web Site: http://www.britishsteel.co.uk
Steel & Ferroalloy Mfr
N.A.I.C.S.: 331110
Roland Junck (Chm)

Subsidiary (Non-US):

FNsteel BV (2)
Rapenburg 1, 2952 AP, Alblasserdam,
Netherlands
Tel.: (31) 786923100
Web Site: http://www.fnsteel.eu
Nonferrous Metal Refinement & Rolling
N.A.I.C.S.: 331491

JINGYOU TIMES INFORMATION TECHNOLOGY DEVELOPMENT CO., LTD.
3rd Floor Building A Intl Tech Innovat Park 1 Shangdi Information Road,
Haidian District, Beijing, 100085,
China
Tel.: (86) 10 8282 6669 CN
Web Site:
   http://www.jingyougroup.com
Data Collection, Processing Integration, Processing Analysis & Systems Services
N.A.I.C.S.: 518210

JINHAI INTERNATIONAL GROUP HOLDINGS LIMITED
21B Senoko Loop, Singapore,
758171, Singapore
Tel.: (65) 63639982 Ky
Web Site: http://www.jin-hai.com.hk
2225—(HKG)
Rev.: $34,570,931
Assets: $47,125,653
Liabilities: $18,730,592
Net Worth: $28,395,062
Earnings: ($3,114,444)
Emp.: 636
Fiscal Year-end: 12/31/23
Construction Support Services
N.A.I.C.S.: 561320

JINHE BIOTECHNOLOGY CO., LTD.
1-7-2 Building 27 Zone B3 Xinghai
Plaza, Shahekou District, Dalian,
116023, Liaoning, China
Tel.: (86) 4713291630
Web Site: https://www.jinhe.com.cn
Year Founded: 1990
002688—(SSE)
Rev.: $298,028,484
Assets: $632,583,432
Liabilities: $292,082,544
Net Worth: $340,500,888
Earnings: $10,605,816
Emp.: 1,640
Fiscal Year-end: 12/31/22
Veterinary Medicine Mfr
N.A.I.C.S.: 325412
Wang Dongxiao (Chm)

Subsidiaries:

Pharmgate LLC (1)
1800 Sir Tyler Dr, Wilmington, NC 28405
Tel.: (800) 380-6099
Web Site: https://pharmgate.com
Biological Product Mfr
N.A.I.C.S.: 325414
Colin Gray (Pres & CEO)

Subsidiary (Domestic):

Protatek International, Inc. (2)
540 W Iron Ave Ste 106, Mesa, AZ 85210
Tel.: (480) 545-8499
Web Site: http://www.protatek.com
Biological Product Mfr
N.A.I.C.S.: 325414

JINHONG FASHION GROUP CO., LTD.
No 240 Chating East Street, Jianye
District, Nanjing, 210017, Jiangsu,
China
Tel.: (86) 2584736763
Web Site: http://www.v-grass.com
Year Founded: 2003
603518—(SSE)
Rev.: $547,489,168
Assets: $858,058,854
Liabilities: $424,108,007
Net Worth: $433,950,847
Earnings: $10,026,554
Fiscal Year-end: 12/31/22
Women Apparel Mfr & Distr
N.A.I.C.S.: 315250
Wang Zhiqin (Chm & Gen Mgr)

JINHUA CAPITAL CORPORATION
303-570 Granville Street, Vancouver,
V6C 3P1, BC, Canada
Tel.: (604) 687-2580 AB
Year Founded: 2009
JHC—(TSXV)
Rev.: $31,173
Assets: $726,788
Liabilities: $638,454
Net Worth: $88,335
Earnings: ($1,693,159)
Fiscal Year-end: 12/31/23
Investment Services
N.A.I.C.S.: 523999
Negar Adam (CEO & CFO)

JINHUA CHUNGUANG TECHNOLOGY CO., LTD.
No 1399 Huatai Road, Wucheng District, Jinhua, 321000, Zhejiang, China
Tel.: (86) 57982237057
Web Site: https://www.chinacgh.com
Year Founded: 2000
603657—(SHG)
Rev.: $269,767,242
Assets: $305,558,038
Liabilities: $150,835,216
Net Worth: $154,722,822
Earnings: $13,807,596
Fiscal Year-end: 12/31/22
Rubber & Plastic Product Mfr & Distr
N.A.I.C.S.: 326220
Zhengming Chen (Chm & Pres)

Subsidiaries:

CGH Industry Sdn Bhd (1)
PLO 673 Jalan Haji Saat, Taman Perindustrian Jalan Sungai Tiram, 81800, Ulu Tiram, Johor, Malaysia
Tel.: (60) 78614650
Steel Pole Mfr
N.A.I.C.S.: 331222

CGH Technology (Vietnam) Company Limited (2)
Workshop ATDN 01 land lot no 01/10 Road 7 Giang Dien IP, An Vien Commune Trang Bom District, Dong Nai, Vietnam
Tel.: (84) 2513678899
Plastics Product Mfr
N.A.I.C.S.: 326199

Suntone Technology Company Limited (1)
No 11B No 3 Streed Nhon Trach 2-Nhon Phu Industrial Zone, Nhon Trach District, Phu Hoi, Dong Nai, Vietnam
Tel.: (84) 2512814410
Electronic Payment Services
N.A.I.C.S.: 522320

Suzhou K&H Rubber & Plastic Co., Ltd. (1)
No 685 Xu Kou Zhen Xu Shi Road, Suzhou, Jiangsu, China
Tel.: (86) 51266939371
Steel Pole Mfr
N.A.I.C.S.: 331222

Suzhou Suntone Technology Manufacturing Co., Ltd. (1)
No 499 Fan Feng Road, Xukou Town, Suzhou, China
Tel.: (86) 51266539888
Electronic Material Mfr & Distr
N.A.I.C.S.: 334419

JINHUI HOLDINGS COMPANY LIMITED
26th Floor Yardley Commercial Building 1-6 Connaught Road West, Hong
Kong, China (Hong Kong)
Tel.: (852) 25450951
Web Site: https://www.jinhuiship.com
0137—(HKG)
Rev.: $151,627,080
Assets: $565,506,998
Liabilities: $142,318,688
Net Worth: $423,188,310
Earnings: ($8,947,823)
Emp.: 618
Fiscal Year-end: 12/31/22
Ship Chartering Services
N.A.I.C.S.: 483112
Suk Lin Ho (Sec)

Subsidiaries:

Jinhui Shipping & Transportation Limited (1)
26th Floor Yardley Commercial Building 1-6 Connaught Road West, Hong Kong, China (Hong Kong)
Tel.: (852) 2 545 0951
Web Site: https://www.jinhuiship.com
Marine Transportation Services
N.A.I.C.S.: 483111

JINHUI LIQUOR CO., LTD.
Fujia Town Hui County, Longnan,
742308, China
Tel.: (86) 9397551826
Web Site: http://www.jinhuijiu.com
Year Founded: 2009
603919—(SHG)
Rev.: $282,447,229
Assets: $575,003,286
Liabilities: $132,596,189
Net Worth: $442,407,097
Earnings: $39,346,047
Fiscal Year-end: 12/31/22
Liquor Mfr & Distr
N.A.I.C.S.: 312130
Zhou Zhigang (Chm & Pres)

JINJIAN CEREALS INDUSTRY CO., LTD.
No 158 Chongde Road, Economic
and Technological Development
Zone, Changde, 415001, Hunan,
China
Tel.: (86) 4001880099
Web Site: https://www.jjmy.cn
Year Founded: 1998
600127—(SHG)
Rev.: $900,254,853
Assets: $270,807,774
Liabilities: $169,387,138
Net Worth: $101,420,636
Earnings: ($7,135,114)
Fiscal Year-end: 12/31/22
Grain & Oil Product Mfr & Whslr
N.A.I.C.S.: 111191
Su Zhen (Chm)

Subsidiaries:

Hunan Jinjian Import & Export Co., Ltd. (1)
Jinjian Industry City, Deshan Economic Developing Area, Changde, Hunan, China
Tel.: (86) 7362588293
Web Site: http://www.cnjjmy.com
Oilseed & Grain Farming Services
N.A.I.C.S.: 111191

JINKE PROPERTY GROUP CO., LTD.
10F Dikuang Mansion, Chongqing,
401121, China
Tel.: (86) 2363023656
Web Site: http://www.jinke.com
000656—(SSE)
Rev.: $7,702,607,952
Assets: $42,054,823,512
Liabilities: $36,595,185,588
Net Worth: $5,459,637,924
Earnings: ($3,003,442,416)
Emp.: 200,000
Fiscal Year-end: 12/31/22
Property Management Services
N.A.I.C.S.: 523940
Huang Hongyun (Chm)

JINKE SMART SERVICES GROUP CO., LTD.
Building A4 East Zone Jinke Shiniancheng, No 480 Panxi Road Shimahe Street Jiangbei District,
Chongqing, China
Tel.: (86) 2388259666 CN
Web Site:
   http://www.jinkeservice.com
Year Founded: 2000
9666—(HKG)
Property Management Services
N.A.I.C.S.: 531311
Shaofei Xia (Chm)

JINKO POWER TECHNOLOGY CO., LTD.
Jinko Center No 1 Lane 1466 Shenchang Road, Minhang District,
Shanghai, 201106, China
Tel.: (86) 2151808666
Web Site:
   https://www.jinkopower.com
Year Founded: 2011
601778—(SHG)
Rev.: $448,786,719
Assets: $5,250,963,650
Liabilities: $3,494,691,051
Net Worth: $1,756,272,600
Earnings: $29,378,475
Fiscal Year-end: 12/31/22
Electronic Product Mfr & Distr
N.A.I.C.S.: 334419
Xiande Li (Chm)

JINKOSOLAR HOLDING CO., LTD.
1 Yingbin Road, Shangrao Economic
Development Zone, Shangrao,
334100, Jiangxi, China
Tel.: (86) 7938469699 Ky
Web Site: http://www.jinkosolar.com
JKS—(NYSE)
Rev.: $16,432,015,812
Assets: $18,807,020,519
Liabilities: $14,163,945,918
Net Worth: $4,643,074,601
Earnings: $893,408,562
Emp.: 57,397
Fiscal Year-end: 12/31/23
Silicon Wafers, Solar Cells & Solar Modules Mfr
N.A.I.C.S.: 335311
Charlie Haiyun Cao (CFO)

Subsidiaries:

Zhejiang Jinko Solar Co., Ltd. (1)
No 58 Yuanxi Rd Yuanhua Indus Park,

Haining, Zhejiang, China
Tel.: (86) 57387985678
Solar Cell Mfr
N.A.I.C.S.: 334413

JINLEI TECHNOLOGY CO., LTD.
No 18 Shuangyuan Street, Gangcheng District, Jinan, 271105, Shandong, China
Tel.: (86) 53176492211
Web Site: https://www.jinleiwind.com
Year Founded: 2006
300443—(CHIN)
Rev.: $254,345,832
Assets: $689,921,388
Liabilities: $183,655,836
Net Worth: $506,265,552
Earnings: $49,479,768
Emp.: 420
Fiscal Year-end: 12/31/22
Wind Power Equipment Mfr
N.A.I.C.S.: 333611
Tinglei Yi (Chm)

JINLI GROUP HOLDINGS LIMITED
11 F No 189 boai 1st Rd, Sanmin Dist, Kaohsiung, 111, Taiwan
Tel.: (886) 73223642
Web Site: https://www.jinli.net.cn
8429—(TAI)
Rev.: $6,649,595
Assets: $217,143,858
Liabilities: $21,301,692
Net Worth: $195,842,166
Earnings: ($6,292,718)
Emp.: 135
Fiscal Year-end: 12/31/22
Shoe Mfr
N.A.I.C.S.: 316210
Chun-Lung Chong (Chm & Gen Mgr)

Subsidiaries:

Aiqi (Fujian) Shoes Model Co., Ltd. (1)
Meiling Street, Shuanggou Industrial Zone, Jinjiang, Fujian, China
Tel.: (86) 59585655777
Sports & Casual Shoe Mfr
N.A.I.C.S.: 316210

Gold Apple (HK) Int'l Trading Co. Limited (1)
Room 1613 16/F Wellborne Commercial Centre 8 Java Road, North Point, China (Hong Kong)
Tel.: (852) 22050229
Holding Company
N.A.I.C.S.: 551112
Chun Lung Chong (Chm)

Subsidiary (Non-US):

Changtai Golden Apple Co., Ltd. (2)
Changtai Economic Development Zone, Xingtai Industrial Park, Zhangzhou, Fujian, China
Tel.: (86) 59585655777
Sports & Casual Shoe Mfr
N.A.I.C.S.: 316210

Golden Apple (China) Co., Ltd. (2)
Meiling Street, Shuanggou Industrial Zone, Jinjiang, Fujian, China
Tel.: (86) 59585655777
Sports & Casual Shoe Mfr
N.A.I.C.S.: 316210

Leads Bio Co., Ltd. (1)
9 -1F No 128 Section 3 Minsheng East Road, Songshan District, Taipei, Taiwan
Tel.: (886) 225467700
Sports & Casual Shoe Mfr
N.A.I.C.S.: 316210

JINLIHUA ELECTRIC CO., LTD.
JinDong Economic Development Zone, Jinhua, 321037, Zhejiang, China
Tel.: (86) 57982913599
Web Site: https://www.jlhdq.com

Year Founded: 2003
300069—(CHIN)
Rev.: $16,905,564
Assets: $54,371,304
Liabilities: $19,267,092
Net Worth: $35,104,212
Earnings: ($3,839,940)
Emp.: 230
Fiscal Year-end: 12/31/22
Power Transmission Mfr
N.A.I.C.S.: 335311
Han Changan (Chm)

Subsidiaries:

Jiangxi Qianglian Electric Porcelain Co., Ltd. (1)
Luxi Electric Porcelain Industry Area, Pingxiang, Jiangxi, China
Tel.: (86) 7997516826
Web Site: http://www.jxqldc.com
Electric Insulator Mfr & Distr
N.A.I.C.S.: 327110

JINLING HOTEL CORPORATION LTD.
No 2 Hanzhong Road, Nanjing, 210005, Jiangsu, China
Tel.: (86) 2584711888
Web Site: http://www.jinlinghotel.com
Year Founded: 2002
601007—(SHG)
Rev.: $198,643,873
Assets: $575,712,797
Liabilities: $249,235,258
Net Worth: $326,477,539
Earnings: $5,843,939
Emp.: 1,273
Fiscal Year-end: 12/31/22
Hotel Owner & Operator
N.A.I.C.S.: 721110
Bi Jinbiao (Chm & Sec-Party Committee)

Subsidiaries:

Jinling Hotels & Resorts Corporation (1)
No 2 Hanzhong Road, Nanjing, 210005, China
Tel.: (86) 258 476 3008
Web Site: http://www.jinlinghotels.com
Hotel & Resort Operator
N.A.I.C.S.: 721120

JINLING PHARMACEUTICAL COMPANY LIMITED
No 238 Zhongyang Road, Nanjing, 210009, Jiangsu, China
Tel.: (86) 2583118511
Web Site: https://www.jlyy1999.com
Year Founded: 1998
000919—(SSE)
Rev.: $375,004,188
Assets: $637,886,340
Liabilities: $128,648,520
Net Worth: $509,237,820
Earnings: $14,781,312
Fiscal Year-end: 12/31/22
Pharmaceuticals Mfr
N.A.I.C.S.: 325412
Chen Sheng (Chm)

JINLONG MACHINERY & ELECTRONICS CO., LTD.
Xingke Industrial Park No 5 Xinxia Road Huaide Community, Humen Town, Dongguan, 523926, Guangdong, China
Tel.: (86) 76981008096
Web Site: http://en.kotl.com.cn
Year Founded: 1993
300032—(CHIN)
Rev.: $541,674,432
Assets: $452,636,964
Liabilities: $288,183,636
Net Worth: $164,453,328
Earnings: $7,269,912
Emp.: 832

Fiscal Year-end: 12/31/22
Mini Motor Mfr & Sales
N.A.I.C.S.: 335312
Xu Gaojin (Chm & Gen Mgr)

JINLONGYU GROUP CO., LTD.
Jinlongyu Industrial Park No 288 Jihua Road Jihua Street, Longgang District, Shenzhen, 518112, Guangdong, China
Tel.: (86) 4008588688
Web Site: https://www.szjly.com
Year Founded: 1996
002882—(SSE)
Rev.: $557,804,988
Assets: $393,046,992
Liabilities: $110,677,320
Net Worth: $282,369,672
Earnings: $31,150,548
Emp.: 700
Fiscal Year-end: 12/31/22
Electrical Cable Mfr & Distr
N.A.I.C.S.: 335929
Zheng Youshui (Chm)

JINMAO (CHINA) HOTEL INVESTMENTS AND MANAGEMENT LIMITED
8F Jin Mao Tower 88 Century Avenue, Pudong New Area, Shanghai, 200121, China
Tel.: (86) 21 50476688
Web Site: http://www.jinmao88.com
Real Estate Investment
N.A.I.C.S.: 525990

JINNENG GROUP CO., LTD.
82 Kaihuasi Street, Taiyuan, 030002, China
Tel.: (86) 35 1311 1666   CN
Web Site: http://www.jinnengjt.com
Year Founded: 2013
Holding Company; Energy & Electric Power Generation Assets Operator
N.A.I.C.S.: 551112
Peiyi Feng (Deputy Gen Mgr)

JINNENG HOLDING SHANXI ELECTRIC POWER CO., LTD.
No 10 South 1st Street Jinyang Street, Taiyuan, 030006, Shanxi, China
Tel.: (86) 3517785998
Web Site: https://jksxpower.jnkgjtnews.com
Year Founded: 1993
000767—(SSE)
Rev.: $2,838,852,703
Assets: $8,843,616,990
Liabilities: $7,335,386,501
Net Worth: $1,508,230,489
Earnings: ($95,831,817)
Fiscal Year-end: 12/31/22
Electric Power Distribution Services
N.A.I.C.S.: 221122
Shi Lijun (Chm & Gen Mgr)

JINNENG SCIENCE & TECHNOLOGY CO., LTD.
No 1 West Road Industrial Park, Qihe County, Dezhou, 251199, Shandong, China
Tel.: (86) 5342159822
Web Site: https://www.jin-neng.com
Year Founded: 1998
603113—(SHG)
Rev.: $2,358,814,868
Assets: $2,292,144,131
Liabilities: $1,069,619,569
Net Worth: $1,222,524,562
Earnings: $34,984,114
Emp.: 3,000
Fiscal Year-end: 12/31/22
Chemical Product Mfr & Distr
N.A.I.C.S.: 325180
Qin Qingping (Chm)

JINPU LANDSCAPE ARCHITECTURE CO., LTD.
No 70 Runqi Road, Dongshan Subdistrict Jiangning District, Nanjing, 211100, Jiangsu, China
Tel.: (86) 2587763739
Web Site: https://www.nj-jp.com
Year Founded: 1998
301098—(CHIN)
Rev.: $137,036,016
Assets: $371,150,208
Liabilities: $214,185,816
Net Worth: $156,964,392
Earnings: $10,558,080
Fiscal Year-end: 12/31/22
Architectural Services
N.A.I.C.S.: 541310
Yisen Wang (Chm)

JINRO DISTILLERS CO., LTD.
594 Byeolmang-ro, Danwon-gu, Ansan, Gyeonggi-do, Korea (South)
Tel.: (82) 314912675
Web Site: https://www.cleancohol.com
Year Founded: 1966
018120—(KRS)
Rev.: $76,383,084
Assets: $71,349,391
Liabilities: $13,239,492
Net Worth: $58,109,899
Earnings: $2,764,688
Emp.: 61
Fiscal Year-end: 12/31/22
Methanol Mfr
N.A.I.C.S.: 325193
Jong Sik Kim (CEO)

JINS HOLDINGS INC.
Yasuda Sequence Tower 1 Kanda Nishiki-cho 3-chome, Chiyoda-ku, Tokyo, 101-0054, Japan
Tel.: (81) 352757001   JP
Web Site: https://jinsholdings.com
Year Founded: 1988
3046—(TKS)
Rev.: $516,253,780
Assets: $336,159,900
Liabilities: $176,971,440
Net Worth: $159,188,460
Earnings: $29,053,620
Emp.: 3,485
Fiscal Year-end: 08/31/24
Eyewear Retailer
N.A.I.C.S.: 456130
Paul Nixon (Chief Creative Officer-Global)

Subsidiaries:

JINS Eyewear US, Inc. (1)
151 Powell St, San Francisco, CA 94102
Tel.: (415) 391-2481
Web Site: http://www.jins.com
Eyewear Distr
N.A.I.C.S.: 456130
Jin Mario Arai (Pres)

JINSHANG BANK CO., LTD.
No 59 Changfeng Street, Xiaodian District, Taiyuan, 030000, Shanxi, China
Tel.: (86) 3517812583   CN
Web Site: https://www.jshbank.com
Year Founded: 1998
2558—(HKG)
Rev.: $1,608,172,907
Assets: $50,025,619,046
Liabilities: $46,590,084,321
Net Worth: $3,435,534,725
Earnings: $276,992,551
Emp.: 4,429
Fiscal Year-end: 12/31/23
Bank Holding Company
N.A.I.C.S.: 551111
Qiang Hao (Chm)

JINSUNG T.E.C. INC

JINSUNG T.E.C. INC

JinSung T.E.C. Inc—(Continued)

3 Segyosandan-ro, Pyeongtaek, 17843, Gyeonggi-do, Korea (South)
Tel.: (82) 316586588
Web Site: https://www.jinsungtec.com
Year Founded: 1982
036890—(KRS)
Rev.: $414,957,773
Assets: $308,846,870
Liabilities: $148,171,579
Net Worth: $160,675,291
Earnings: $34,845,654
Emp.: 233
Fiscal Year-end: 12/31/22
Construction Machinery Mfr
N.A.I.C.S.: 333120
Woo Suk Yoon *(Chm)*

Subsidiaries:

JINSUNG GEORGIA, LLC (1)
5385 Rafe Banks Dr, Flowery Branch, GA 30542
Tel.: (770) 476-7188
Web Site: http://www.jsamerica.net
Emp.: 12
Construction Machinery Distr
N.A.I.C.S.: 423840
Jin Whan Ahn *(Gen Mgr)*

JINSUNG T.E.C. (YANTAI) CO., LTD. (1)
NO 99 XiangfuJie, Fushan, Yantai, Shandong, China
Tel.: (86) 5356303802
Construction Machinery Distr
N.A.I.C.S.: 423840

JinSung Japan Corp. (1)
1-16-1 Funamasa Bldg 5F, Kitashinagawa, Shinagawa, 140-0001, Tokyo, Japan
Tel.: (81) 3 5781 0445
Construction Machinery Distr
N.A.I.C.S.: 423840

JinSung T.E.C. Inc - No. 2 Plant (1)
35 Segyosandan-ro 22beon-gil, Pyeongtaek, Gyeonggi-do, Korea (South)
Tel.: (82) 31 653 0100
Construction Machinery Mfr
N.A.I.C.S.: 333120

JINTAI ENERGY HOLDINGS LIMITED

Golden Phoenix Building No 111 Liyi Road Lijin County, Dongying, Shandong, China
Tel.: (86) 35794636 Ky
Web Site:
  http://www.jintaienergy.com
2728—(HKG)
Rev.: $21,100,154
Assets: $73,101,085
Liabilities: $58,883,339
Net Worth: $14,217,746
Earnings: ($5,726,214)
Emp.: 159
Fiscal Year-end: 12/31/22
Communication & Multimedia Products Sales
N.A.I.C.S.: 334220

Subsidiaries:

DongGuan Shinhint Audio Technology Limited (1)
No 683 Zhen Au Middle Road Sha Tou South District Changan Town, Dongguan, Guangdong, China
Tel.: (86) 76989883333
Speaker Mfr
N.A.I.C.S.: 334310
Frank Fang *(Head-Project Mgmt Dept)*

JINTAI MINING GROUP, INC.

48 Qiaodong Road Sien Town, Huanjiang County, Hechi, 547100, Guangxi, China
Tel.: (86) 7782205911 DE
Web Site: http://www.jintaimining.com
Sales Range: $25-49.9 Million
Emp.: 621

Exploration, Mining, Leaching, Smelting & Other Processing Operations of Zinc & Lead
N.A.I.C.S.: 212230
Kuizhong Cai *(Chm, Founder & Pres)*

JINUSHI CO., LTD.

6F Yodoyabashi Mitsui Building 1-1 Imabashi 4-chome, Chuo-ku, Osaka, 541-0042, Japan
Tel.: (81) 647067501
Web Site: https://www.jinushi-jp.com
Year Founded: 2000
3252—(NGO)
Rev.: $208,767,757
Assets: $670,512,058
Liabilities: $462,378,593
Net Worth: $208,133,465
Earnings: $31,113,314
Emp.: 100
Fiscal Year-end: 12/31/23
Real Estate Services
N.A.I.C.S.: 531390
Tetsuya Matsuoka *(CEO)*

Subsidiaries:

Kumagai Australia Finance Pty. Ltd. (1)
Level 9 71 Walker Street, North Sydney, 2060, NSW, Australia
Tel.: (61) 299552066
Real Estate Services
N.A.I.C.S.: 531210

Kumagai Australia Pty. Ltd. (1)
Level 9 71 Walker Street, North Sydney, 2060, NSW, Australia
Tel.: (61) 299552066
Property Investment Management Services
N.A.I.C.S.: 523940

New Real Property Corporation (1)
4-2-22 Kudankita, Chiyoda-ku, Tokyo, 102-0073, Japan
Tel.: (81) 332622005
Web Site: http://www.new-rp.co.jp
Real Estate Services
N.A.I.C.S.: 531210
Yukinori Nagaoka *(Pres)*

JINXIANDAI INFORMATION INDUSTRY CO., LTD.

2101 East Area 21F Building 2 Aosheng Building No 1166 Xinluo Avenue, High-tech Zone, Jinan, 250101, Shandong, China
Tel.: (86) 53188870618
Web Site: http://www.jxdinfo.com
Year Founded: 2001
300830—(SSE)
Rev.: $88,147,332
Assets: $192,340,980
Liabilities: $22,476,636
Net Worth: $169,864,344
Earnings: $8,026,668
Fiscal Year-end: 12/31/22
Information Technology Services
N.A.I.C.S.: 541512
Feng Li *(Chm & Pres)*

JINXIN FERTILITY GROUP LIMITED

No 301 North Jingsha Road, Jinjiang, Chengdu, Sichuan, China
Tel.: (86) 17711055657 Ky
Web Site: http://www.jxr-fertility.com
Year Founded: 2003
1951—(HKG)
Rev.: $331,972,852
Assets: $2,138,577,995
Liabilities: $912,166,024
Net Worth: $1,226,411,971
Earnings: $16,560,040
Emp.: 3,158
Fiscal Year-end: 12/31/22
Health Care Srvices
N.A.I.C.S.: 621610
Bin Wang *(Chm)*

Subsidiaries:

HRC Fertility Management, LLC (1)
55 S Lk Ave 9th Fl, Pasadena, CA 91101
Tel.: (626) 440-9161
Web Site: https://www.havingbabies.com
Fertility Clinic Operator
N.A.I.C.S.: 621410

JINXUAN COKING COAL LIMITED

T4-1802-1812 Huarun building No-1 Changxin road, Wanbailin District, Taiyuan, Shanxi, China
Tel.: (86) 351 702 0402 Ky
Year Founded: 2017
Rev.: $154,490
Assets: $3,733,614
Liabilities: $3,455,332
Net Worth: $278,282
Earnings: ($671,074)
Emp.: 13
Fiscal Year-end: 12/31/21
Coke Mfr & Distr
N.A.I.C.S.: 324199
Xiangyang Guo *(CEO & Chm)*

JINYOUNG CO., LTD.

129 Majung-ro, Seo-gu, Incheon, Korea (South)
Tel.: (82) 325621924
Web Site: https://www.jyp21.co.kr
Year Founded: 1996
285800—(KRS)
Automobile Parts Mfr & Distr
N.A.I.C.S.: 336110
Soojung Lee *(Mng Dir)*

JINYU BIO-TECHNOLOGY CO., LTD.

No 1 Jinyu Street Shaerqin Industrial Park, Hohhot, 010111, China
Tel.: (86) 4718166957
Web Site: http://www.jinyu.com.cn
Year Founded: 1993
600201—(SHG)
Rev.: $214,625,170
Assets: $897,062,634
Liabilities: $145,971,002
Net Worth: $751,091,632
Earnings: $29,578,981
Emp.: 1,060
Fiscal Year-end: 12/31/22
Pharmaceutical Product Mfr & Real Estate Management Services
N.A.I.C.S.: 325412
Zhang Chongyu *(Chm)*

Subsidiaries:

The Spirit Jinyu Biological Pharmaceutical Co., LTD (1)
No 58 Eerduosi West Street Yuquan, Hohhot, 10030, China
Tel.: (86) 4713683492
Web Site: http://www.jinyubaoling.com.cn
Emp.: 600
Pharmaceuticals Distr
N.A.I.C.S.: 424210
Wang Yoongsheng *(Gen Mgr)*

JINYUAN ENVIRONMENTAL PROTECTION CO., LTD.

30th Floor Building 1 Runhe Xinyada Creative Center, No 1750 Jianghong Road Binjiang District, Hangzhou, 310052, Zhejiang, China
Tel.: (86) 57186602265 HK
Web Site: http://www.jysn.com
Year Founded: 1992
000546—(SSE)
Sales Range: $750-799.9 Million
Construction Materials Mfr
N.A.I.C.S.: 327310
Hui Zhao *(Chm & Gen Mgr)*

JINZAI FOOD GROUP CO., LTD.

46F Block A Wanda Plaza, Kaifu District, Changsha, 410005, Hunan, China
Tel.: (86) 73189822256
Web Site:
  https://en.jinzaifood.com.cn
Year Founded: 2010
003000—(SSE)
Rev.: $205,269,012
Assets: $181,987,884
Liabilities: $44,220,384
Net Worth: $137,767,500
Earnings: $17,502,264
Fiscal Year-end: 12/31/22
Packaged Food Product Mfr & Distr
N.A.I.C.S.: 311991
Jinsong Zhou *(Founder, Chm & Gen Mgr)*

JINZHOU CIHANG GROUP CO., LTD.

19F Nanyin Mansion No 2, Dongsanhuan North Road Chaoyang District, Beijing, 100027, China
Tel.: (86) 106 410 6338
Web Site: http://www.goldzb.com
000587—(SSE)
Rev.: $57,905,720
Assets: $803,189,636
Liabilities: $751,426,106
Net Worth: $51,763,531
Earnings: $6,906,707
Fiscal Year-end: 12/31/20
Jewelry Product Mfr
N.A.I.C.S.: 339910
Yaowen Zhu *(Chm)*

JINZHOU PORT CO., LTD.

No 1 Section 1 Jingang Street Binhai New Area, Economic and Technological Development Zone, Jinzhou, 121007, Liaoning, China
Tel.: (86) 4163586039
Web Site:
  https://www.jinzhouport.com
Year Founded: 1986
600190—(SHG)
Rev.: $415,299,536
Assets: $2,481,584,995
Liabilities: $1,532,805,894
Net Worth: $948,779,100
Earnings: $17,925,387
Fiscal Year-end: 12/31/22
Cost Management Services
N.A.I.C.S.: 488310
Yin Shihui *(Chm)*

JINZI HAM COMPANY LTD.

No 1000 Jinfan Street Industrial Park, Jinhua, 321016, Zhejiang, China
Tel.: (86) 57982262717
Web Site: http://www.jinzichina.com
Year Founded: 1994
002515—(SSE)
Rev.: $62,414,820
Assets: $222,694,056
Liabilities: $8,557,380
Net Worth: $214,136,676
Earnings: $6,883,812
Emp.: 230
Fiscal Year-end: 12/31/22
Ham Products Mfr & Distr
N.A.I.C.S.: 311612
Ren Qifeng *(Chm)*

JIO FINANCIAL SERVICES LTD.

1st floor, Building 4NA, Maker Maxity, Bandra Kurla Complex, Bandra East, Mumbai, 400 051, India
Tel.: (91) 0223555409
Web Site: https://www.jfs.in
Year Founded: 2023
543940—(BOM)
Rev.: $222,370,382
Assets: $17,368,623,426

AND PRIVATE COMPANIES

Liabilities: $685,250,349
Net Worth: $16,683,373,076
Earnings: $192,380,571
Emp.: 584
Fiscal Year-end: 03/31/24
Financial Services
N.A.I.C.S.: 523999
Mukesh D. Ambani (Founder)

JIONTO ENERGY INVESTMENT CO., LTD.
No 9 Yuhua West Road, Shijiazhuang, 050051, Hebei, China
Tel.: (86) 31185518600
Web Site: https://www.jei.com.cn
Year Founded: 1994
000600—(SSE)
Rev.: $2,570,138,532
Assets: $5,130,520,668
Liabilities: $3,390,457,824
Net Worth: $1,740,062,844
Earnings: $14,459,796
Fiscal Year-end: 12/31/22
Eletric Power Generation Services
N.A.I.C.S.: 221118
Wang Shuanghai (Chm)

JIPANGU INC.
Ebisu Prime Square Bld 12F 1-1-39 Hiroo Shibuya-ku, Tokyo, 150-0012, Japan
Tel.: (81) 3 5468 3690
Web Site: http://www.jipangu.co.jp
Year Founded: 1995
Sales Range: $50-74.9 Million
Emp.: 183
Gold Ore Mining
N.A.I.C.S.: 212220
Tamisuke Matsufuji (Pres & CEO)

Subsidiaries:

Florida Canyon Mining, Inc. (1)
600 S Humboldt Rd, Imlay, NV 89418
Tel.: (775) 538-7300
Gold Mining Services
N.A.I.C.S.: 212220
Deborah Davis (Mgr-HR)

JISHANYE, INC.
3F No 10 Yuanxi 2nd Rd Agricultural Biotechnology Park, Ping-tung, 908, Taiwan
Tel.: (886) 87621913
Year Founded: 2012
Enzyme Product Distr
N.A.I.C.S.: 325411
Chun-Hao Chang (Chm, Pres & CEO)

JISHI MEDIA CO., LTD.
Jishi Media Information Hub No 999 Hemei Road Jingyue Development Zone, Changchun, 130117, Jilin, China
Tel.: (86) 43188789022
Web Site: http://www.jishimedia.com
Year Founded: 2001
601929—(SHG)
Rev.: $254,544,793
Assets: $2,062,582,578
Liabilities: $1,077,230,878
Net Worth: $985,351,700
Earnings: ($59,619,849)
Emp.: 7,300
Fiscal Year-end: 12/31/22
Cable Television Broadcasting Services
N.A.I.C.S.: 334220
Xuesong Gao (Board of Directors & Deputy Gen Mgr)

JITF INFRALOGISTICS LIMITED
A-1 UPSIDC Industrial Area Nandgaon Road Kosi Kalan, Mathura, 281403, Uttar Pradesh, India
Tel.: (91) 5662232426
Web Site: https://www.jindalinfralogistics.com
Year Founded: 2008
540311—(BOM)
Rev.: $192,285,942
Assets: $402,950,195
Liabilities: $502,265,608
Net Worth: ($99,315,413)
Earnings: ($12,845,837)
Emp.: 5
Fiscal Year-end: 03/31/23
Transportation Services
N.A.I.C.S.: 541614
Alok Kumar (Officer-Compliance & Sec)

Subsidiaries:

Timarpur-Okhla Waste Management Company Private Limited - Old NDMC Compost Plant (1)
Behind Crri Jasola, New Delhi, 110020, Delhi, India
Tel.: (91) 1126843044
Biomass Electric Power Generation Services
N.A.I.C.S.: 221117

JIU RONG HOLDINGS LTD
Flat 8 49th Floor Office Tower Convention Plaza 1 Harbour Road, Wanchai, China (Hong Kong)
Tel.: (852) 26886312   Ky
Web Site: http://www.jiurongkg.com
2358—(HKG)
Rev.: $106,831,868
Assets: $376,918,815
Liabilities: $316,285,680
Net Worth: $60,633,135
Earnings: ($11,494,253)
Emp.: 479
Fiscal Year-end: 12/31/22
Digital Television Mfr & Distr
N.A.I.C.S.: 334310
Jianwen Yin (Exec Dir)

JIU ZUN DIGITAL INTERACTIVE ENTERTAINMENT GROUP HOLDINGS LIMITED
Suite 1801 R&F To-win Building 30 Huaxia Road, Zhujiang New Town, Guangzhou, China
Tel.: (86) 2083513011   Ky
Web Site: http://www.jiuzundigital.com
Year Founded: 2011
1961—(HKG)
Rev.: $26,073,125
Assets: $39,094,442
Liabilities: $4,428,841
Net Worth: $34,665,601
Earnings: $156,734
Emp.: 51
Fiscal Year-end: 12/31/20
Holding Company
N.A.I.C.S.: 551112
Lu Jian (Exec Dir)

JIUGUI LIQUOR CO., LTD.
Jiuguijiu Industrial Park, Zhenwuying Village, Xiangxi, 416000, Hunan, China
Tel.: (86) 73188186030
Web Site: http://www.jiuguijiu000799.com
Year Founded: 1997
000799—(SSE)
Rev.: $568,677,564
Assets: $819,139,932
Liabilities: $236,166,840
Net Worth: $582,973,092
Earnings: $147,251,520
Fiscal Year-end: 12/31/22
Liquor Product Mfr
N.A.I.C.S.: 312140
Gao Feng (Chm)

JIUJIANG SHANSHUI TECHNOLOGY CO., LTD.
Jishan Industrial Park, Pengze County, Jiujiang, 332700, Jiangxi, China
Tel.: (86) 7922310368
Web Site: https://www.jjsskj.com
Year Founded: 2012
301190—(CHIN)
Rev.: $69,758,648
Assets: $345,269,140
Liabilities: $60,221,183
Net Worth: $285,047,957
Earnings: $2,965,423
Fiscal Year-end: 12/31/23
Chemical Product Mfr & Distr
N.A.I.C.S.: 327120
Guorong Huang (Chm & Gen Mgr)

JIUJIUWANG FOOD INTERNATIONAL LIMITED
Xukeng Industrial Park Luoshan Street, Jinjiang, Fujian, China
Tel.: (86) 59588187888   Ky
Web Site: https://en.jiujiuwang.com
Year Founded: 1999
1927—(HKG)
Rev.: $57,669,929
Assets: $101,569,803
Liabilities: $41,011,100
Net Worth: $60,558,704
Earnings: $2,461,472
Emp.: 406
Fiscal Year-end: 12/31/22
Confectionary Product Mfr
N.A.I.C.S.: 311352
Kan Chen (CFO)

JIUMAOJIU INTERNATIONAL HOLDINGS LIMITED
No 668 West Huangpu Avenue Race Track Food Street F2 8-9, Tianhe, Guangzhou, Guangdong, China
Tel.: (86) 2037873399   Ky
Web Site: https://www.ir.jiumaojiu.com
Year Founded: 2005
9922—(HKG)
Rev.: $562,403,369
Assets: $759,152,909
Liabilities: $309,994,776
Net Worth: $449,158,133
Earnings: $7,807,644
Emp.: 16,190
Fiscal Year-end: 12/31/22
Holding Company
N.A.I.C.S.: 551112
Yihong Guan (Chm & CEO)

JIUSHENG ELECTRIC CO., LTD.
1000 Xifeng Road, Economy & Technology Development Area, Huzhou, 313099, Zhejiang, China
Tel.: (86) 5722228372
Web Site: https://www.teccable.com
Year Founded: 2004
301082—(CHIN)
Rev.: $282,287,267
Assets: $427,353,013
Liabilities: $273,911,844
Net Worth: $153,441,169
Earnings: $7,137,380
Emp.: 500
Fiscal Year-end: 12/31/23
Wire Product Mfr & Distr
N.A.I.C.S.: 335921
Jianhua Zhang (Chm & Gen Mgr)

Subsidiaries:

Zhejiang Jiusheng Cross-Linked Cable Co., Ltd. (1)
1 Baishaling, Lanxi, Zhejiang, China
Tel.: (86) 57988804208
Cable Wire Mfr
N.A.I.C.S.: 332618

JIUTIAN CHEMICAL GROUP LIMITED
9 Raffles Place 26-01 Republic Plaza Tower I, Singapore, 048619, Singapore
Tel.: (65) 62363333
Year Founded: 2004
C8R—(CAT)
Rev.: $84,304,648
Assets: $181,558,028
Liabilities: $73,693,662
Net Worth: $107,864,366
Earnings: ($48,835,070)
Emp.: 542
Fiscal Year-end: 12/31/23
Chemical Products Mfr
N.A.I.C.S.: 325998
Pan Mi Keay (Sec)

JIUZHITANG CO., LTD.
No 339 Tongzipo West Road, Changsha, 410205, Hunan, China
Tel.: (86) 73184499738
Web Site: https://www.hnjzt.com
Year Founded: 1999
000989—(SSE)
Rev.: $425,871,108
Assets: $735,474,168
Liabilities: $176,378,904
Net Worth: $559,095,264
Earnings: $50,452,740
Fiscal Year-end: 12/31/22
Pharmaceuticals Mfr
N.A.I.C.S.: 325412
Sun Guangyuan (Chm)

Subsidiaries:

Jiuzhitang Maker (Beijing) Cell Technology Co., Ltd. (1)
Tel.: (86) 1064654791
Web Site: http://en.jztmaker.com
Pharmaceuticals Product Mfr
N.A.I.C.S.: 325412

Stemedica Cell Technologies, Inc. (1)
6350 Nancy Ridge Dr Ste 106, San Diego, CA 92121
Tel.: (858) 658-0910
Web Site: https://www.stemedica.com
Biopharmaceutical Product Development Services
N.A.I.C.S.: 541714
Nikolai I. Tankovich (Pres & Chief Medical Officer)

JIUZI HOLDINGS, INC.
No 168 Qianjiang Nongchang Gengwen Road, 15th Floor Economic and Technological development Zone, Hangzhou, 310000, Zhejiang, China
Tel.: (86) 57182651956   Ky
Year Founded: 2019
JZXN—(NASDAQ)
Rev.: $5,931,000
Assets: $11,390,076
Liabilities: $7,090,760
Net Worth: $4,299,316
Earnings: ($9,853,772)
Emp.: 33
Fiscal Year-end: 10/31/23
Holding Company
N.A.I.C.S.: 551112
Shuibo Zhang (Chm & CEO)

JIWANRAM SHEODUTTRAI INDUSTRIES LIMITED
30D Jawaharlal Nehru Road, Kolkata, 700016, India
Tel.: (91) 3340169500
Web Site: https://www.jiwanramgroup.com
Year Founded: 1997
JIWANRAM—(NSE)
Rev.: $5,145,705
Assets: $14,728,636
Liabilities: $8,888,968
Net Worth: $5,839,667

Jiwanram Sheoduttrai Industries Limited—(Continued)
Earnings: $489,621
Emp.: 157
Fiscal Year-end: 03/31/23
Safety Wear Product Mfr
N.A.I.C.S.: 332911
Alok Prakash *(Mng Dir)*

JIWOO ELECTRONICS CO., LTD.
110-1 Gyesan-ro, Gyeyang-gu, Incheon, Korea (South)
Tel.: (82) 325564177   KR
Web Site: http://www.jiwooelec.co.kr
Year Founded: 1998
Power Generating Equipment Mfr
N.A.I.C.S.: 335312
Jongduk Kwon *(CEO)*

JIYA ECO-PRODUCTS LIMITED
Survey Number 202/2 Navagam, Taluka Vallabhipur, Bhavnagar, 364313, India
Tel.: (91) 9879219898
Web Site: https://www.jiyaeco.com
Rev.: $30,598,234
Assets: $20,564,646
Liabilities: $9,700,117
Net Worth: $10,864,529
Earnings: $2,619,251
Emp.: 37
Fiscal Year-end: 03/31/19
Bio-fuel Mfr
N.A.I.C.S.: 324199
Bhavesh J. Kakdiya *(Chm & Mng Dir)*

JIYI HOLDINGS LIMITED
No 2 Xianzi Middle Road, Meixian District, Meizhou, Guangdong, China
Tel.: (86) 7536116988   Ky
Web Site: http://www.jiyihousehold.com
Year Founded: 1997
1495—(HKG)
Rev.: $78,590,725
Assets: $190,781,276
Liabilities: $63,704,675
Net Worth: $127,076,602
Earnings: ($5,604,206)
Emp.: 33
Fiscal Year-end: 12/31/22
Holding Company
N.A.I.C.S.: 551112
Wei Hou *(Chm & CEO)*

JIYUAN PACKAGING HOLDINGS LIMITED
No 197 Sec 1 Funong St, East District, T'ainan, 701, Taiwan
Tel.: (886) 62895658
Web Site: http://www.jypkg.com
8488—(TAI)
Rev.: $125,361,845
Assets: $173,408,182
Liabilities: $96,148,857
Net Worth: $77,259,325
Earnings: ($3,860,525)
Fiscal Year-end: 12/31/23
Packaging Product Mfr & Distr
N.A.I.C.S.: 326199
Han-Ching Lin *(Chm)*

JIZHONG ENERGY RESOURCES CO., LTD.
No 191 Zhongxing West Street, Xingtai, 054000, Hebei, China
Tel.: (86) 3192068242
Web Site: http://www.jznygf.com
Year Founded: 1999
000937—(SSE)
Rev.: $5,059,504,944
Assets: $7,228,691,964
Liabilities: $3,728,272,860
Net Worth: $3,500,419,104
Earnings: $625,859,676
Emp.: 46,000
Fiscal Year-end: 12/31/22
Coal Mining & Processing
N.A.I.C.S.: 212115
Yan Yunsheng *(Chm)*

Subsidiaries:

HeBei Jinniu Chemical Industry Co., Ltd. (1)
21F Aoyi Building No 98 Huanghe Avenue, Yuhua District, Shijiazhuang, 050000, Hebei, China   **(56.04%)**
Tel.: (86) 31186861889
Web Site: https://www.hbjnhg.com
Chemical Product Mfr & Distr
N.A.I.C.S.: 325180
Qi Yongxue *(Gen Mgr)*

JJ ENTERTAINMENT SE
Schlehenweg 10, 30855, Langenhagen, Germany
Tel.: (49) 1732591919
Web Site: http://www.jj-entertainment.com
JJSE—(VIE)
Sales Range: Less than $1 Million
Information Technology Management Services
N.A.I.C.S.: 541512
Peter Hufnagel *(CEO & Mng Dir)*

JJM CONSTRUCTION LTD.
8218 River Way, Delta, V4G 1C4, BC, Canada
Tel.: (604) 946-0978
Web Site: https://www.jjmconstruction.com
Year Founded: 1988
Rev.: $55,500,000
Emp.: 400
Construction Services
N.A.I.C.S.: 237310
Craig Peddie *(VP-Estimating & Construction Svcs)*

JK CEMENT LTD
Kamla Tower, Kanpur, 208001, India
Tel.: (91) 5122371478
Web Site: https://www.jkcement.com
Year Founded: 1975
JKCEMENT—(NSE)
Rev.: $1,175,901,253
Assets: $1,592,837,108
Liabilities: $1,036,233,415
Net Worth: $556,603,693
Earnings: $50,246,328
Emp.: 3,767
Fiscal Year-end: 03/31/23
Cement Mfr
N.A.I.C.S.: 325520
Anil Kumar Agrawal *(Sr VP-Tax & Mgmt Svcs)*

Subsidiaries:

Acro Paints Limited (1)
19 DDA Community Center Okhla Phase -1, New Delhi, 110020, India
Tel.: (91) 1149220051
Web Site: https://www.acropaints.net
Architectural Paint Mfr & Distr
N.A.I.C.S.: 325510

J.K. Cement Works (Fujairah) FZC (1)
The Citadel Tower Office 2007-2008, PO Box 123 630, Business Bay, Dubai, United Arab Emirates
Tel.: (971) 42797303
Web Site: https://www.jkcementuae.com
Cement Mfr
N.A.I.C.S.: 327310

JK Maxx Paint Limited (1)
Prism Tower 6th Floor Ninaniya Estate, Gwal Pahari, Gurugram, 122102, Haryana, India
Tel.: (91) 18002034555
Web Site: https://jkmaxxpaints.com
Architectural Paints Mfr & Distr
N.A.I.C.S.: 325510

JK HOLDINGS CO., LTD.
Wood Land Tower 1-7-22 Shinkiba, Koto-ku, Tokyo, 136-8405, Japan
Tel.: (81) 355343807
Web Site: https://www.jkhd.co.jp
Year Founded: 1949
9896—(TKS)
Rev.: $2,570,695,100
Assets: $1,550,468,040
Liabilities: $1,133,330,770
Net Worth: $417,137,270
Earnings: $33,373,890
Emp.: 3,368
Fiscal Year-end: 03/31/24
Holding Company
N.A.I.C.S.: 551112
Takashi Yoshida *(Chm)*

Subsidiaries:

Interra Bronz (Shanghai) Building Materials Co., Ltd. (1)
Rm2205 Yintong Mansion No 988 Dingxi Road, Changning District, Shanghai, China
Tel.: (86) 2164270609
Plywood & Housing Related Equipment Mfr & Whslr
N.A.I.C.S.: 321999

Interra Jk Singapore Pte., Ltd. (1)
18 Robinson Road Level 15-01, Singapore, 048547, Singapore
Tel.: (65) 69557651
Plywood & Housing Related Equipment Mfr & Whslr
N.A.I.C.S.: 321999

Interra USA, Inc. (1)
900 SW 16th St Ste 125, Renton, WA 98057
Tel.: (425) 277-7850
Web Site: http://interra-usa.com
Building Material Mfr & Distr
N.A.I.C.S.: 327120
Masanori Katsumata *(Pres)*

Japan Kenzai Co., Ltd. (1)
Lot 1296 1st Floor, Jalan Merpati, 98000, Miri, Malaysia
Tel.: (60) 137376139
Plywood & Housing Related Equipment Mfr & Whslr
N.A.I.C.S.: 321999

KEYTEC Co., Ltd. (1)
Shinkiba Tower 8th floor 1-7-22 Shinkiba, Koto-ku, Tokyo, 136-0082, Japan
Tel.: (81) 355343741
Web Site: https://www.key-tec.co.jp
Emp.: 200
Plywood Mfr
N.A.I.C.S.: 423310
Shigeru Yoshida *(Chm)*

Subsidiary (Domestic):

Akita Glulam Co., Ltd. (2)
1 Nanatsudate Hanaoka-Machi, Odate, 017-0005, Akita Prefecture, Japan **(100%)**
Tel.: (81) 186461100
Web Site: http://www.akita-glulam.com
Glue laminated Product Mfr
N.A.I.C.S.: 321215

Rus Interra Inc. (1)
3A office 201 Building Business Cooperation Center, St Sukhanova, 690091, Vladivostok, Russia
Tel.: (7) 4232444900
Web Site: http://rus-interra.com
Emp.: 6
Construction Materials Whslr
N.A.I.C.S.: 423310

JK LAKSHMI CEMENT LTD
Nehru House 4 Bahadur Shah Zafar, Marg, New Delhi, 110 002, India
Tel.: (91) 1133001142
Web Site: https://www.jklakshmicement.com
JKLAKSHMI—(NSE)
Rev.: $655,210,920
Assets: $721,570,395
Liabilities: $433,917,120
Net Worth: $287,653,275
Earnings: $55,334,370

Emp.: 1,677
Fiscal Year-end: 03/31/21
Cement Mfr
N.A.I.C.S.: 325520
Shailendra Chouksey *(Exec Dir)*

JK PAPER LTD
Nehru House 3rd Floor 4 Bahadur Shah Zafar Marg, New Delhi, 110002, India
Tel.: (91) 1133001112
Web Site: https://www.jkpaper.com
JKPAPER—(NSE)
Rev.: $406,374,150
Assets: $894,738,390
Liabilities: $550,634,175
Net Worth: $344,104,215
Earnings: $32,312,280
Emp.: 2,655
Fiscal Year-end: 03/31/21
Printing Paper Mfr & Sales
N.A.I.C.S.: 322299
Suresh Chander Gupta *(Officer-Compliance, Sec & VP)*

Subsidiaries:

JK Paper Ltd - JK Paper Mills (1)
Jaykaypur, Rayagada, 765 017, Orissa, India
Tel.: (91) 685 623 3303
Web Site: https://www.jkpaper.com
Paper Products Mfr
N.A.I.C.S.: 322130

JK TECHNOLOGY PTE. LTD.
61 Kaki Bukit Avenue 1 02-13 Shun Li Industrial Park, Singapore, 417943, Singapore
Tel.: (65) 6841 6868   SG
Web Site: http://www.jktech.com.sg
Year Founded: 1990
Sales Range: $1-9.9 Million
Emp.: 70
Information Technology Equipment Whslr & Integration Services
N.A.I.C.S.: 541512
Eugene Yew Jin Ang *(Mng Dir)*

JK TYRE & INDUSTRIES LTD.
Patriot House 3 Bahadur Shah Zafar Marg, New Delhi, 110 002, India
Tel.: (91) 1133001112
Web Site: https://www.jktyre.com
530007—(BOM)
Rev.: $1,640,664,480
Assets: $1,671,804,225
Liabilities: $1,269,474,570
Net Worth: $402,329,655
Earnings: $27,469,260
Emp.: 5,904
Fiscal Year-end: 03/31/22
Automobile Mfr
N.A.I.C.S.: 336110
Raghupati Singhania *(Chm & Co-Mng Dir)*

Subsidiaries:

Compania Hulera Tacuba, S.A. De C.V. (1)
Inmobiliaria Santa Lucia No 311 Santa Cruz Acayucan, Azcapotzalco, 2770, Mexico, Mexico
Tel.: (52) 55 53540200
Emp.: 1
Automotive Tire Mfr
N.A.I.C.S.: 326211
Juan Carlos *(Dir-Fin)*

Florence Investech Limited (1)
7 Council House Street, Kolkata, 700 001, West Bengal, India
Tel.: (91) 33 22486181
Web Site: http://www.florenceinvestech.co.in
Sales Range: $1-9.9 Million
Emp.: 2
Hybrid Seed Mfr & Distr
N.A.I.C.S.: 111199
Kailash Chand Jain *(CFO)*

JK Agri Genetics Ltd. (1)

7 Council House Street, Kolkata, 700 001, India
Tel.: (91) 3322486181
Web Site: https://www.jkagri.com
Rev.: $24,398,130
Assets: $39,684,168
Liabilities: $24,020,658
Net Worth: $15,663,509
Earnings: ($1,294,719)
Emp.: 311
Fiscal Year-end: 03/31/2023
Oilseed Processing Services
N.A.I.C.S.: 311224
Bharat Hari Singhania (Chm)

JK Tornel S.A. de C.V. (1)
Santa Lucia No 311 Acayucan Delegacion, Azcapotzalco, Mexico, Mexico
Tel.: (52) 15553540200
Web Site: http://jktornel.com.mx
Tiles Mfr
N.A.I.C.S.: 326211

JK WOHNBAU AG
Leopold Strasse 8, 80802, Munich, Schwabing, Germany
Tel.: (49) 893899840
Web Site: http://www.ifiria.at
Year Founded: 1995
Sales Range: $10-24.9 Million
Emp.: 40
Residential Property Developer
N.A.I.C.S.: 236117
Joseph L. Kastenberger (CEO)

JKG LAND BERHAD
27th Floor Menara JKG No 282 Jalan Raja Laut, 50350, Kuala Lumpur, Malaysia
Tel.: (60) 327758688
Web Site: https://www.jkgland.com
Year Founded: 1986
JKGLAND—(KLS)
Rev.: $22,638,519
Assets: $169,542,646
Liabilities: $53,250,159
Net Worth: $116,292,487
Earnings: $5,336,720
Fiscal Year-end: 01/31/23
Property Development Services
N.A.I.C.S.: 531312
Geok Heok Lim (Co-Sec)

JKL PARTNERS, INC.
4th Floor 36 87-gil Therean-ro, Gangnam-du, Seoul, 06164, Korea (South)
Tel.: (82) 220165900
Web Site: http://www.jklpartners.co.kr
Year Founded: 2001
Privater Equity Firm
N.A.I.C.S.: 523999
Jang Keun Jeong (CEO)

Subsidiaries:

Lotte Non-Life Insurance Co., Ltd. (1)
3 Sowol-ro Jung-gu, Seoul, 100-778, Korea (South) (54%)
Tel.: (82) 215883344
Web Site: http://www.lotteins.co.kr
Sales Range: Less than $1 Million
Non-Life Insurance Services
N.A.I.C.S.: 524126
Hyun-Soo Kim (CEO)

JKN GLOBAL GROUP PUBLIC COMPANY LIMITED
818 JKN Empire Building Moo 2, Samrong Nuea Subdistrict Mueang Samut Prakan District, Samut Prakan, 10270, Thailand
Tel.: (66) 20217799
Web Site: http://www.jknglobal.com
JKN—(THA)
Rev.: $73,174,052
Assets: $273,709,457
Liabilities: $198,858,911
Net Worth: $74,850,546
Earnings: ($62,124,015)
Fiscal Year-end: 12/31/23
Advertising & Marketing Services
N.A.I.C.S.: 541810
Jakkaphong Jakrajutatip (CEO & Mng Dir)

JKP JABLANICA D.D.
ul Omladinsko setaliste bb, 88420, Jablanica, Bosnia & Herzegovina
Tel.: (387) 36 752 378
JABLRK4—(SARE)
Sales Range: Less than $1 Million
Emp.: 70
Water Purification & Supply Services
N.A.I.C.S.: 221310
Mesud Tucakovic (Pres)

JKP VODOVOD I KANALIZACIJA D.D.
Varda 40 D, 88 400, Konjic, Bosnia & Herzegovina
Tel.: (387) 36727576
VKNKRK1—(SARE)
Rev.: $845,035
Assets: $2,178,659
Liabilities: $195,975
Net Worth: $1,982,684
Earnings: ($57,345)
Emp.: 44
Fiscal Year-end: 12/31/20
Waste Water Disposal Services
N.A.I.C.S.: 221320

JKR EXCAVATING LTD.
Bay 105 220 3rd Street NE, Black Diamond, T0L 0H0, AB, Canada
Tel.: (403) 933-3008
Web Site: http://www.jkrexcavating.com
Year Founded: 1998
Rev.: $13,650,357
Emp.: 30
Excavation & Underground Services
N.A.I.C.S.: 238910
Don Beaton (Pres)

JKX OIL & GAS PLC
6 Cavendish Square, London, W1G 0PD, United Kingdom
Tel.: (44) 2073234464
Web Site: http://www.jkx.co.uk
JKX—(LSE)
Rev.: $69,623,000
Assets: $219,398,000
Liabilities: $42,536,000
Net Worth: $176,862,000
Earnings: $19,868,000
Emp.: 530
Fiscal Year-end: 12/31/20
Oil & Gas Exploration & Production
N.A.I.C.S.: 211120
Charles Valceschini (Chm)

Subsidiaries:

JKX (Nederland) B.V. (1)
Rokin 55, 1012KK, Amsterdam, Netherlands
Tel.: (31) 206715603
Oil & Gas Exploration Services
N.A.I.C.S.: 211120

Subsidiary (Domestic):

JKX Hungary B.V. (2)
Jan van Goyen Quay 8, HP 1075, Amsterdam, North Holland, Netherlands
Tel.: (31) 20 5214866
Oil & Gas Exploration Services
N.A.I.C.S.: 211120

Poltava Petroleum Company (1)
153 Frunze St 5th Fl, 36002, Poltava, Ukraine
Tel.: (380) 532501317
Web Site: http://www.ppc.net.ua
Oil & Gas Exploration Services
N.A.I.C.S.: 211120

JL MAG RARE-EARTH CO., LTD.
West Jinling Road Development Zone, Ganzhou, 341000, Jiangxi, China
Tel.: (86) 7978068888
Web Site: https://www.jlmag.com.cn
Year Founded: 2008
300748—(CHIN)
Rev.: $941,985,701
Assets: $1,665,685,663
Liabilities: $674,502,762
Net Worth: $991,182,901
Earnings: $79,396,131
Fiscal Year-end: 12/31/23
Magnetic Material Mfr & Distr
N.A.I.C.S.: 333611

JLA INFRAVILLE SHOPPERS LTD
402 Bijith Tower Babusapalya Horamavu, Green Glen Layout Bellandur, Bengaluru, 560043, KA, India
Tel.: (91) 8299590971
Web Site: https://jlainfraville.com
538670—(BOM)
Rev.: $57,690
Assets: $1,046,423
Liabilities: $18,425
Net Worth: $1,027,998
Earnings: $4,833
Fiscal Year-end: 03/31/21
Internet Retailer
N.A.I.C.S.: 423910
Jawahar Lal Agarwal (Exec Dir)

JLC RENOV
Parc d'Activites 1035 rue de Gautray, 45590, Orleans, France
Tel.: (33) 238630303
Web Site: http://www.jlc-renov.fr
Year Founded: 1994
Rev.: $21,819,508
Emp.: 170
Painting & Paper Hanging
N.A.I.C.S.: 238320
Jean-Luc Cheymol (Founder & Dir)

JLEN ENVIRONMENTAL ASSETS GROUP LIMITED
1 Royal Plaza Royal Avenue, Saint Peter Port, GY1 2HL, Guernsey
Tel.: (44) 2035303600
Web Site: https://www.jlen.com
Year Founded: 2013
JLEN—(LSE)
Rev.: $136,890,937
Assets: $1,031,413,784
Liabilities: $3,178,490
Net Worth: $1,028,235,294
Earnings: $124,084,827
Emp.: 347
Fiscal Year-end: 03/31/23
Investment Management Service
N.A.I.C.S.: 523940
Richard Morse (Chm)

Subsidiaries:

Codford Biogas Limited (1)
Codford Biogas Ltd Malmpit Hill, Codford, Warminster, Wiltshire, United Kingdom
Tel.: (44) 1985850582
Web Site: https://codfordbiogas.co.uk
Food Waste Recycling Services
N.A.I.C.S.: 562119

JLG GROUP PLC
1 Charterhouse Mews Farringdon, London, EC1M 6BB, United Kingdom
Tel.: (44) 2031997114
Web Site: http://www.thejust-group.com
Holding Company
N.A.I.C.S.: 551112
John Davies (Founder & CEO)

Subsidiaries:

City Fuel Services Limited (1)
155 Fairfield Road, Droylsden, Manchester, M43 6AX, United Kingdom
Tel.: (44) 1616412918
Web Site: http://www.cityfuelservices.co.uk
Fuel Retailer
N.A.I.C.S.: 457110

Pure World Energy Limited (1)
Spaces-1650 Arlington Business Park, Theale, Reading, RG7 4SA, Berkshire, United Kingdom
Tel.: (44) 1184620258
Web Site: http://www.pureworldenergy.com
Renewable Energy Services
N.A.I.C.S.: 221114

JLH S A
Lieu Dit Saint Nicolas, Lonlay L Abbaye, 61700, Flers, Orne, France
Tel.: (33) 233306868
Sales Range: $10-24.9 Million
Emp.: 52
Holding Companies
N.A.I.C.S.: 551112

JLK, INC.
204 10 Yangcheongsongdae-gil Ochang-eup, Cheongwon-Gu, Cheongju, Chungcheongbuk-do, Korea (South)
Tel.: (82) 7046514051
Web Site: https://www.jlkgroup.com
Year Founded: 2014
322510—(KRS)
Rev.: $2,619,559
Assets: $27,865,722
Liabilities: $15,134,087
Net Worth: $12,731,636
Earnings: ($6,911,934)
Emp.: 82
Fiscal Year-end: 12/31/22
Software Development Services
N.A.I.C.S.: 541511
Yoo Kwang Hyun (Deputy Dir)

JLOGO HOLDINGS LTD.
124 Lorong 23 Geylang 10-01 and 10-02 Arcsphere, Singapore, 388405, Singapore
Tel.: (65) 68873350
Web Site: https://www.jlogoholdings.com
Year Founded: 2002
8527—(HKG)
Rev.: $12,915,247
Assets: $6,685,602
Liabilities: $9,317,579
Net Worth: ($2,631,978)
Earnings: ($3,728,698)
Emp.: 239
Fiscal Year-end: 12/31/23
Restaurant Operators
N.A.I.C.S.: 722511
Yeun Ching Low (Exec Dir)

JLS CO., LTD.
227 Yeongdong-daero, Gangnam-Gu, Seoul, Korea (South)
Tel.: (82) 16440500
Web Site: https://www.gojls.com
Year Founded: 1993
040420—(KRS)
Rev.: $84,977,282
Assets: $76,456,787
Liabilities: $16,795,082
Net Worth: $59,661,706
Earnings: $10,202,445
Emp.: 588
Fiscal Year-end: 12/31/22
Educational Service Provider
N.A.I.C.S.: 611710
Jeong-Hum Park (CEO)

JLT MOBILE COMPUTERS AB
Isbjornsvagen 3, SE-352 45, Vaxjo, Sweden

JLT MOBILE COMPUTERS AB

JLT Mobile Computers AB—(Continued)
Tel.: (46) 470530300
Web Site: https://www.jltmobile.com
Year Founded: 1994
JLT—(OMX)
Rev.: $15,762,548
Assets: $11,660,344
Liabilities: $6,047,749
Net Worth: $5,612,596
Earnings: $495,471
Emp.: 31
Fiscal Year-end: 12/31/22
Computer Mfr
N.A.I.C.S.: 334111
Per Holmberg (CEO)

Subsidiaries:

JLT Mobile Computers Sweden AB (1)
Isbjornsvagen 3, 352 45, Vaxjo, Sweden
Tel.: (46) 470530300
Web Site: https://jltmobile.com
Computer Hardware Mfr & Distr
N.A.I.C.S.: 334111

JLT Mobile Computers, Inc. (1)
8945 S Harl Ave Ste 112, Tempe, AZ 85284 (100%)
Tel.: (480) 705-4200
Web Site: http://www.jltmobile.com
Computer Mfr
N.A.I.C.S.: 334111
Eric Miller (CEO)

JM AB

Gustav III s boulevard 64, 169 74, Solna, Sweden
Tel.: (46) 87828700
Web Site: https://www.jm.se
Rev.: $1,672,387,850
Assets: $2,461,909,240
Liabilities: $1,698,215,820
Net Worth: $763,693,420
Earnings: $163,541,420
Emp.: 2,559
Fiscal Year-end: 12/31/19
Residential Property Development & Management
N.A.I.C.S.: 531311
Johan Skoglund (Pres & CEO)

Subsidiaries:

Boratt AB (1)
Landsvägen 50 A, PO Box 6048, 17106, Solna, Sweden
Tel.: (46) 86266630
Web Site: http://www.boratt.se
Sales Range: $50-74.9 Million
Emp.: 8
Real Estate Property Lessors
N.A.I.C.S.: 531190
Maria Forsman (Mgr-Mktg)

JM Construction S.A. (1)
Avenue Louise 287 Bte 1, Brussels, 1050, Belgium (100%)
Tel.: (32) 26461112
Web Site: http://www.jmconstruction.be
Sales Range: $25-49.9 Million
Emp.: 9
Heavy & Civil Engineering Construction
N.A.I.C.S.: 237990
Christofer Lee (Gen Mgr)

JM Danmark A/S (1)
Nyroksgaei 14, 1602, Copenhagen, Denmark
Tel.: (45) 33457000
Sales Range: $25-49.9 Million
Emp.: 35
Heavy & Civil Engineering Construction
N.A.I.C.S.: 237990

JM Entreprenad AB (1)
Strandbergsgatan 57, 16982, Stockholm, Sweden
Tel.: (46) 87828700
Web Site: http://www.jm-entreprenad.se
Sales Range: $75-99.9 Million
Emp.: 400
Engineeering Services
N.A.I.C.S.: 541330
Gohan Skoglund (Gen Mgr)

JM Norge AS (1)
Mustads vei 1 0283, Oslo, Norway
Tel.: (47) 67 17 60 00
Web Site: http://www.jm.no
Residential Building Construction Services
N.A.I.C.S.: 236117
Magnus Berg (Mng Dir)

JM Suomi Oy (1)
Sinimaentie 8B, Espoo, 2630, Finland
Tel.: (358) 947302610
Web Site: http://www.jmoy.fi
Sales Range: $25-49.9 Million
Emp.: 10
Heavy & Civil Engineering Construction
N.A.I.C.S.: 237990
Lars Svard (Mng Dir)

OIE AS (1)
Gamleveien 2, Rasta, 1476, Lorenskog, Norway
Tel.: (47) 67 91 12 00
Property Development Services
N.A.I.C.S.: 531390

Seniorgarden AB (1)
Landsvagen 50 A, PO Box 6048, 171 06, Solna, Sweden
Tel.: (46) 86266630
Web Site: http://www.seniorgarden.se
Sales Range: $50-74.9 Million
Emp.: 500
Senior Care & Special Needs Housing & Assisted Living Services
N.A.I.C.S.: 623990
Tomas Eriksson (CEO)

JM BRUNEAU SAS

Z D''activite Courtaboeuf, Villebon-Sur-Yvette, France
Tel.: (33) 164460202
Web Site: http://www.bruneau.fr
Stationery & Office Supplies Merchant Whslr
N.A.I.C.S.: 424120
Nicolas Potier (CEO)

Subsidiaries:

JM Bruneau Espana SAU (1)
C/ Bergueda 1 Edificio Prima Muntas - Puerta A, 08820, Barcelona, Spain
Tel.: (34) 902 2250 22
Web Site: http://www.bruneau.es
Stationery & Office Supplies Merchant Whslr
N.A.I.C.S.: 424120

Subsidiary (Non-US):

Office Depot Italia S.r.l. (2)
Strada 1 Palazzo E3, Milanofiori, 20090, Milan, Italy
Tel.: (39) 0282285500
Web Site: http://www.officedepot.eu
Office Supplies Retailer
N.A.I.C.S.: 459410

JM CAPITAL II CORP.

135 Yorkville Ave Suite 900, Toronto, M5R 0C7, ON, Canada
Tel.: (416) 972-9993
Year Founded: 2012
JCI.H—(TSXV)
Assets: $2,029
Liabilities: $327,804
Net Worth: ($325,775)
Earnings: ($35,652)
Fiscal Year-end: 12/31/23
Investment Services
N.A.I.C.S.: 523999

JM EDUCATION GROUP

36 Jalan SS 15/8, 47500, Subang Jaya, Selangor Darul Ehsan, Malaysia
Tel.: (60) 356334732
Web Site: http://www.jmeducationgroup.com
Rev.: $2,321,319
Assets: $3,521,640
Liabilities: $644,142
Net Worth: $2,877,498
Earnings: $143,930

Fiscal Year-end: 12/31/19
Placement Services
N.A.I.C.S.: 561311

Subsidiaries:

Miraj Academy Sdn Bhd (1)
No 15A & 17A Jalan Wawasan 4/6 Bandar Baru Ampang, 68000, Ampang, Selangor, Malaysia
Tel.: (60) 342707428
Web Site: http://www.miraj.edu.my
Education Services
N.A.I.C.S.: 611710
Nur Farahellyna Jafri (Asst Dir-Academic)

JM FINANCIAL LTD.

7th Floor Cnergy Appasaheb Marathe Marg Prabhadevi, Mumbai, 400 025, India
Tel.: (91) 2266303030
Web Site:
https://www.jmfinancialservices.in
Year Founded: 1986
JMFINANCIL—(NSE)
Rev.: $513,687,720
Assets: $3,523,679,250
Liabilities: $1,450,399,860
Net Worth: $2,073,279,390
Earnings: $135,458,505
Emp.: 1,786
Fiscal Year-end: 03/31/22
Financial Services
N.A.I.C.S.: 522291
Manish Sheth (Co-Mng Dir, CFO-Grp & CEO-Home Loans)

Subsidiaries:

JM Financial Asset Management Private Limited (1)
Office B 8th Floor Cnergy Appasaheb Marathe Marg, Prabhadevi, Mumbai, 400025, Maharastra, India
Tel.: (91) 2261987777
Web Site: https://www.jmfinancialmf.com
Financial Services
N.A.I.C.S.: 522320

JM Financial Home Loans Limited (1)
Suashish Ii Park Plot No 68E Off Datta Pada Road Borivali East, Mumbai, 400066, India
Tel.: (91) 8069935050
Web Site:
https://jmcustportal.jmflhomeloans.com
Investment Bank Financial Services
N.A.I.C.S.: 523150

JM Financial Institutional Securities Private Limited (1)
51 Maker Chamber 3, Nariman Point, Mumbai, 400021, Maharashtra, India
Tel.: (91) 2266303050
Web Site:
https://www.jmfinancialasksecurities.in
Institutional Securities Services
N.A.I.C.S.: 561612

JM Financial Overseas Holdings Private Limited (1)
Suite 2004 Level 2 Alexander House 35 Cybercity, Ebene, Mauritius
Tel.: (230) 4645100
Web Site:
Investment Bank Financial Services
N.A.I.C.S.: 523150

JM Financial Securities Inc. (1)
2500 Plz 5 Harborside Financial Ctr, Jersey City, NJ 07311
Tel.: (201) 633-3610
Investment Bank Financial Services
N.A.I.C.S.: 523150

JM Financial Services Private Limited (1)
1st & 2nd Floor Suashish IT Park Plot No 68 E Off Datta Pada Road, Borivali East, Mumbai, 400 066, Maharastra, India
Tel.: (91) 2267617000
Web Site: http://www.jmfinancialservices.in
Sales Range: $50-74.9 Million
Emp.: 30
Financial Consulting Services
N.A.I.C.S.: 522320

JM Financial Singapore Pte. Limited (1)
16 Raffles Quay 20-01 Hong Leong Building, Singapore, 048581, Singapore
Tel.: (65) 64221888
Investment Bank Financial Services
N.A.I.C.S.: 523150

JM FINANCIAL MUTUAL FUND

Office B 8th Floor Cnergy Appasaheb Marathe Marg Prabhadevi, Mumbai, 400 025, India
Tel.: (91) 2261987777
Web Site:
http://www.jmfinancialmf.com
Year Founded: 1993
Sales Range: $125-149.9 Million
Emp.: 250
Mutual Fund Investment Services
N.A.I.C.S.: 525910
Shalini Tibrewala (Mgr-Fund-Debt)

JM HOLDINGS CO., LTD.

2-3-30 Oroshimachi, Tsuchiura, 300-0847, Ibaraki, Japan
Tel.: (81) 298463539
Web Site:
https://www.japanmeat.co.jp
Year Founded: 2019
3539—(TKS)
Rev.: $1,071,898,820
Assets: $443,852,980
Liabilities: $171,616,020
Net Worth: $272,236,960
Earnings: $33,992,300
Emp.: 1,444
Fiscal Year-end: 07/31/24
Convenience Food Retailer
N.A.I.C.S.: 445131
Tomoyuki Sakamoto (Pres & CEO)

JM TELECOM(CORP.)

122-6 Youngcheon-ri, Dongtan-myeon, Hwaseong, Gyeonggi-do, Korea (South)
Tel.: (82) 313719313
Web Site: https://www.jmtkorea.com
Year Founded: 1998
094970—(KRS)
Rev.: $69,490,072
Assets: $106,100,140
Liabilities: $26,695,886
Net Worth: $79,404,254
Earnings: $22,564,126
Emp.: 15
Fiscal Year-end: 12/31/22
Electronic Products Mfr
N.A.I.C.S.: 339999
Jung Soo Youn (Co-CEO)

Subsidiaries:

JMT SK S.r.o (1)
Priemyselna, 920 01, Hlohovec, Slovakia
Tel.: (421) 337352711
Printed Circuit Board Mfr & Distr
N.A.I.C.S.: 334412

JMACS JAPAN CO., LTD.

2-2-2 Dojima, Kita-ku, Osaka, 530-0003, Japan
Tel.: (81) 68855
Web Site: https://www.jmacs-j.co.jp
Year Founded: 1965
5817—(TKS)
Rev.: $46,309,120
Assets: $82,686,560
Liabilities: $39,736,400
Net Worth: $42,950,160
Earnings: $358,160
Emp.: 144
Fiscal Year-end: 02/28/22
Electric Wire & Cabel Mfr
N.A.I.C.S.: 332618

Subsidiaries:

Nihon Electric Wire & Cable Co., Ltd. - Hyogo Factory (1)

AND PRIVATE COMPANIES

275-122 Aza-Kidani Shinjyo, Kato, 673-1324, Hyogo, Japan
Tel.: (81) 795460436
Cable Mfr
N.A.I.C.S.: 335921

JMAX GLOBAL DISTRIBUTORS INC.
8680 Cambie St, Vancouver, V6P 6M9, BC, Canada
Tel.: (604) 688-3657
Year Founded: 1966
Sales Range: $10-24.9 Million
Emp.: 66
Apparel Distr
N.A.I.C.S.: 315990
Michael Fugman (Pres)

JMAX INTERNATIONAL LIMITED
Office 08 on 22nd Floor China Shipbuilding Tower, No 650 Cheung Sha Wan Road, Kowloon, China (Hong Kong)
Tel.: (852) 23230835
Web Site: http://www.jmaxintl.com
Year Founded: 2016
Rev.: $5,055,265
Assets: $5,575,465
Liabilities: $1,771,197
Net Worth: $3,804,268
Earnings: ($3,713,393)
Emp.: 10
Fiscal Year-end: 03/31/20
Holding Company
N.A.I.C.S.: 551112
Chee Boon Chiew (Chm & CEO)

JMC CORPORATION
1F Sumitomo Real Estate ShinYokohama Building 255 ShinYokohama, Kohoku-ku, Yokohama, 222-0033, Kanagawa, Japan
Tel.: (81) 454775757
Web Site: https://www.jmc-rp.co.jp
Year Founded: 1992
5704—(TKS)
Sales Range: $10-24.9 Million
Emp.: 81
Cast Products Mfr
N.A.I.C.S.: 331524
Daichi Watanabe (Pres & CEO)

JMC PROJECTS INDIA LTD
A-104 Shapath-4 Opp Karnavati Club S G Road, Ahmedabad, 380 015, India
Tel.: (91) 7968161500
Web Site: http://www.jmcprojects.com
522263—(BOM)
Rev.: $545,187,412
Assets: $734,831,566
Liabilities: $659,404,690
Net Worth: $75,426,876
Earnings: $166,894
Emp.: 3,600
Fiscal Year-end: 03/31/20
Construction Factories Offices & Commercial
N.A.I.C.S.: 236115
Devendra Raj Mehta (Chm)

JMD VENTURES LIMITED
Unit No 323 324 3rd Floor Bldg No 9, Laxmi Plaza New Link Road Andheri W, Mumbai, 400 053, India
Tel.: (91) 2265653451
Web Site: https://www.jmdlimited.com
Rev.: $6,264,840
Assets: $6,284,291
Liabilities: $164,022
Net Worth: $6,120,269
Earnings: ($317,250)
Emp.: 16
Fiscal Year-end: 03/31/18
Motion Picture Development Services

N.A.I.C.S.: 512199
Shiv Kumar Ramnath Yadav (CFO)
Subsidiaries:

JMD Medico Services Limited (1)
323 and 324 3rd Floor Building Number 9 Laxmi Plaza New Link Road, Andheri W, Mumbai, 400053, India
Tel.: (91) 7506886666
Web Site: http://www.jmdmedico.com
Ayurvedic Product Mfr
N.A.I.C.S.: 325411
Jagdish Prasad Purohit (Chm)

JMG CORPORATION LIMITED
574 Second Floor Chirag Delhi Main Road, New Delhi, 110017, India
Tel.: (91) 1141834411
Web Site: https://www.jmg-corp.in
Year Founded: 1989
523712—(BOM)
Rev.: $864,350
Assets: $1,436,356
Liabilities: $225,327
Net Worth: $1,211,030
Earnings: ($174,299)
Emp.: 3
Fiscal Year-end: 03/31/21
Security Brokerage Services
N.A.I.C.S.: 523150
Atul Kumar Mishra (Mng Dir)

JMI SYRINGES & MEDICAL DEVICES LIMITED
Unique Heights Level-11 117 Kazi Nazrul Islam Avenue, Dhaka, 1217, Bangladesh
Tel.: (880) 255138723
Web Site: https://www.jmigroup-bd.com
JMISMDL—(CHT)
Rev.: $16,249,334
Assets: $27,761,766
Liabilities: $3,728,816
Net Worth: $24,032,950
Earnings: ($1,388,357)
Emp.: 1,075
Fiscal Year-end: 06/30/23
Disposable Syringe Mfr
N.A.I.C.S.: 339112
Muhammad Tarek Hossain Khan (CFO & Sec)

JMICRON TECHNOLOGY CORPORATION
1F No 13 Innovation Road 1 Hsinchu Science Park, Hsinchu, Taiwan
Tel.: (886) 35797389
Web Site: https://www.jmicron.com
Year Founded: 2001
4925—(TAI)
Semiconductor Product Mfr
N.A.I.C.S.: 334413
Tim Liu (Chm & Pres)

JMJ FINTECH LIMITED
Shop No 3 1st Floor Adhi Vinayaga Complex No 3 Bus Stand, Gopalsamy Temple Street Ganapaty, Coimbatore, 641006, India
Tel.: (91) 7395922292
Web Site: https://jmjfintechltd.com
Year Founded: 1982
538834—(BOM)
Rev.: $232,891
Assets: $1,689,825
Liabilities: $108,940
Net Worth: $1,580,885
Earnings: ($35,663)
Emp.: 5
Fiscal Year-end: 03/31/21
Investment Banking Services
N.A.I.C.S.: 523150
Stanley Gilbert Felix Melkhasingh (Mng Dir)

JMMB BANK (JAMAICA) LIMITED
6-8 Grenada Way, Kingston, 5, Jamaica
Tel.: (876) 998 5662   JM
Web Site: http://www.jmmb.com
Sales Range: $10-24.9 Million
Commercial Banking Services
N.A.I.C.S.: 522110
Dennis L. Harris (Chm)
Subsidiaries:

Capital & Credit Merchant Bank Limited (1)
6-8 Grenada Way 5, Kingston, Jamaica
Tel.: (876) 960 5320
Web Site: http://ccmb.capital-credit.com
Sales Range: $50-74.9 Million
Emp.: 99
Commercial Banking Services
N.A.I.C.S.: 522110
Ryland T. Campbell (Chm, Grp Pres & CEO)

Subsidiary (Domestic):

Capital & Credit Securities Limited (2)
10-16 Grenada Way 5, Kingston, Jamaica
Tel.: (876) 9461770
Web Site: http://ccsl.capital-credit.com
Sales Range: $50-74.9 Million
Emp.: 99
Securities Brokerage Services
N.A.I.C.S.: 523150
Christopher Walker (Gen Mgr)

JMMB GROUP LTD.
6 Haughton Terrace, Kingston, 10, Jamaica
Tel.: (876) 9985662
Web Site: https://www.jm.jmmb.com
JMMBGL—(JAM)
Rev.: $265,408,007
Assets: $4,415,308,389
Liabilities: $4,057,737,432
Net Worth: $357,570,956
Earnings: $77,511,967
Emp.: 351
Fiscal Year-end: 03/31/24
Investment Management Service
N.A.I.C.S.: 525990
Archibald Campbell (Chm)

JMS CO., LTD.
12-17 Kako-machi, Naka-ku, Hiroshima, 730-8652, Japan
Tel.: (81) 822435844
Web Site: https://www.jms.cc
Year Founded: 1965
7702—(TKS)
Rev.: $431,580,120
Assets: $559,926,490
Liabilities: $290,588,820
Net Worth: $269,337,670
Earnings: ($237,960)
Emp.: 5,283
Fiscal Year-end: 03/31/24
Medical Equipment & Pharmaceuticals Mfr & Sales
N.A.I.C.S.: 325412
Hiroaki Okukubo (Pres)
Subsidiaries:

BIONIC Medizintechnik GmbH (1)
Max-Planck-Str 21, 61381, Friedrichsdorf, Germany
Tel.: (49) 617275760
Web Site: https://www.bionic-jms.com
Emp.: 30
Blood Transfusion Equipments Mfr
N.A.I.C.S.: 339112

J.M.S.(K) Medical Supply Co., Ltd. (1)
128 Gasan Digital 2-ro, Gasan-dong Geumcheon-gu, Seoul, Korea (South)
Tel.: (82) 28560518
Web Site: http://www.jmsk.co.kr
Medicine Distr
N.A.I.C.S.: 423450

JMS REKLAMGARDEN AB

JMS CO. LTD. - Chiyoda Plant (1)
10 Shinujigami, Kitahiroshima-cho, Yamagata, 731-1514, Hiroshima, Japan
Tel.: (81) 826722611
Web Site: http://www.jms.cc
Sales Range: $75-99.9 Million
Emp.: 150
Medical Equipment Mfr & Whslr
N.A.I.C.S.: 423450

JMS CO. LTD. - Izumo Plant (1)
127-1 Shimogoshi-cho, Izumo, 693-0032, Shimane, Japan
Tel.: (81) 853230211
Medical Equipment Mfr & Whslr
N.A.I.C.S.: 423450

JMS CO. LTD. - Miyoshi Plant (1)
350 Yamaga Shijikkan-machi, Miyoshi, 728-0016, Hiroshima, Japan
Tel.: (81) 824637141
Web Site: http://www.jms.cc
Medical Equipment Mfr & Whslr
N.A.I.C.S.: 423450

JMS CO. LTD. - Ono Plant (1)
1990 Ono Hatsukaichi, Hatsukaichi, 739-0407, Hiroshima, Japan
Tel.: (81) 822435844
Web Site: http://www.jms.cc
Sales Range: $25-49.9 Million
Emp.: 15
Medical Equipment Mfr & Whslr
N.A.I.C.S.: 423450

JMS Dalian Medical Supply Co., Ltd. (1)
No 25 Huanghaixi Road, Dalian Economic & Technical Development Zone, Dalian, 116600, Liaoning, China
Tel.: (86) 41187611733
Web Site: http://www.jmsdl.com
Sales Range: $200-249.9 Million
Emp.: 700
Medical Equipment Mfr & Sales
N.A.I.C.S.: 339112

JMS Healthcare (Thailand) Co., Ltd. (1)
559/31 Moo 7 Bangpleeyai, Bang Phli, 10540, Samutprakarn, Thailand
Tel.: (66) 23994585
Medicine Mfr
N.A.I.C.S.: 325412

JMS Healthcare Phl, Inc. (1)
Lot 2-B-1 Phase 1B, First Philippine Industrial Park Special Economic Zone, Tanauan, Batangas, Philippines
Tel.: (63) 433021200
Medicine Mfr
N.A.I.C.S.: 325412

JMS North America Corporation (1)
22320 Foothill Blvd Ste 350, Hayward, CA 94541
Tel.: (510) 888-9090
Sales Range: $25-49.9 Million
Emp.: 10
Medical Equipment Mfr & Suppliers
N.A.I.C.S.: 339112

JMS Service Co., Ltd. (1)
2-38-9 Kawauchi, Asaminami-ku, Hiroshima, 731-0102, Japan
Tel.: (81) 829620532
Medicine Mfr
N.A.I.C.S.: 325412

JMS Singapore Pte. Ltd. (1)
440 Ang Mo Kio Industrial Park 1, Singapore, 569620, Singapore
Tel.: (65) 64571176
Web Site: https://www.jmss.com.sg
Emp.: 1,800
Medical Device Mfr
N.A.I.C.S.: 423450

Pt. Jms Batam (1)
Kawasan Industri Batamindo Blok 211, Jalan Beringin, Batam, 29433, Muka Kuning, Indonesia
Tel.: (62) 770611807
Medicine Mfr
N.A.I.C.S.: 325412

JMS REKLAMGARDEN AB
Modemgatan 10, 235 39, Vellinge, Sweden

JMS REKLAMGARDEN AB

JMS Reklamgarden AB—(Continued)
Tel.: (46) 40 42 90 00
Web Site: http://www.jms.se
Printing Services
N.A.I.C.S.: 323111
Stefan Mannfalk *(Owner)*

JNBY DESIGN LIMITED

3/F Blue Ocean Times Building No 39 Yile Road, Xihu District, Hangzhou, Zhejiang, China
Tel.: (86) 57187382221 Ky
Web Site: http://www.jnbygroup.com
Year Founded: 1994
3306—(HKG)
Rev.: $625,995,836
Assets: $597,493,720
Liabilities: $339,340,233
Net Worth: $258,153,488
Earnings: $85,624,932
Emp.: 1,497
Fiscal Year-end: 06/30/22
Apparel Mfr & Distr
N.A.I.C.S.: 315990
Jian Wu *(Chm)*

Subsidiaries:

Hangzhou Huikang Huazhuo Import & Export Trade Co., Ltd. (1)
No 350 Hongda Rd Qiaonan Zone, Hangzhou, 310012, Zhejiang, China
Tel.: (86) 57187205013
Apparel Product Distr
N.A.I.C.S.: 424350

JNC CORPORATION

Shin Otemachi Building 2-2-1 Otemachi Chiyoda-Ku, Tokyo, 100-8105, Japan
Tel.: (81) 332436370
Web Site: https://www.jnc-corp.co.jp
Emp.: 100
Chemicals Mfr
N.A.I.C.S.: 325998

JNE WELDING

3915 Thatcher Avenue, Saskatoon, S7R 1A3, SK, Canada
Tel.: (306) 242-0884
Web Site: http://www.jnewelding.com
Year Founded: 1980
Rev.: $21,699,444
Emp.: 150
Fabricated Steel Mfr
N.A.I.C.S.: 332312
Jim Nowakowski *(Founder)*

JNK GLOBAL CO., LTD.

10F Building A 43 Changeop-ro, Sujeong-gu, Seongnam, 13449, Gyeonggi-do, Korea (South)
Tel.: (82) 316279300
Web Site: https://jnk-global.com
Year Founded: 1998
126880—(KRS)
Rev.: $151,178,897
Assets: $183,675,235
Liabilities: $96,881,481
Net Worth: $86,793,754
Earnings: $5,667,592
Emp.: 66
Fiscal Year-end: 12/31/22
Heaters & Air-Cooled Condensers Mfr & Installer
N.A.I.C.S.: 333415
Bang-Hee Kim *(Pres & CEO)*

JNTC CO., LTD.

81-9 Gunae-Gil Jeongnam-Myeon, Hwaseong, 18516, Gyeonggi-do, Korea (South)
Tel.: (82) 313542590
Web Site: https://www.thejntc.com
Year Founded: 1996
204270—(KRS)
Rev.: $123,736,407
Assets: $400,745,967
Liabilities: $143,949,531
Net Worth: $256,796,436
Earnings: ($45,062,383)
Emp.: 348
Fiscal Year-end: 12/31/22
Electronic Components Mfr
N.A.I.C.S.: 334419

JNU GLOBAL INC.

6-7F Star-Valley Building Gasan-Dong, Geumcheon-Gu, Seoul, 153-777, Korea (South)
Tel.: (82) 2 2109 1400
Web Site: http://www.cnbtec.com
Year Founded: 1999
Sales Range: $25-49.9 Million
Emp.: 143
Surveillance Product Mfr
N.A.I.C.S.: 334220
Sae Young Hong *(CEO)*

JOACHIM HERZ STIFTUNG

Langenhorner Chaussee 384, 22419, Hamburg, Germany
Tel.: (49) 40 533 295 0
Web Site: https://www.joachim-herz-stiftung.de
Year Founded: 2008
Emp.: 100
Education Services
N.A.I.C.S.: 611710
Joachim Herz *(Founder)*

Subsidiaries:

VTG Aktiengesellschaft (1)
Nagelsweg 34, D-20097, Hamburg, Germany
Tel.: (49) 4023540
Web Site: http://www.vtg.de
Rev.: $1,214,630,040
Assets: $3,695,997,030
Liabilities: $2,737,589,244
Net Worth: $958,407,786
Earnings: $81,574,266
Emp.: 1,527
Fiscal Year-end: 12/31/2017
Holding Company; Railway Freight & Tanker Transportation Logistics & Railcar Rental Services
N.A.I.C.S.: 551112
Heiko Fischer *(Chm-Exec Bd & CEO)*

Subsidiary (Non-US):

CIT Rail Holdings (Europe) SAS (2)
40 Rue La Boetie, 75008, Paris, France
Tel.: (33) 145615620
Holding Company
N.A.I.C.S.: 551112

Subsidiary (Domestic):

VOTG Tanktainer GmbH (2)
Nagelsweg 34, 20097, Hamburg, Germany **(58.35%)**
Tel.: (49) 40280590
Sales Range: $50-74.9 Million
Emp.: 170
Tank Container Railcar Rental & Logistics Services
N.A.I.C.S.: 532411

Subsidiary (US):

VOTG North America Inc. (3)
109 E Evans St, West Chester, PA 19380 **(100%)**
Tel.: (610) 429-5440
Emp.: 15
Tank Container Railcar Rental & Logistics Services
N.A.I.C.S.: 532411
Lars Schuster *(Mng Dir)*

Representative Office (Non-US):

VTG Deutschland GmbH - Belgium Representative Office (2)
Uitbreidingstraat 66, 2600, Berchem, Belgium
Tel.: (32) 32868430
Web Site: http://www.vtg.com
Sales Range: $25-49.9 Million
Emp.: 3
Freight Railcar Rental Services

N.A.I.C.S.: 532411

VTG Deutschland GmbH - Netherlands Representative Office (2)
Waalhaven Z z 19 Port City II 3rd Floor, Port #2235, Rotterdam, 3089GH, Netherlands
Tel.: (31) 102642525
Web Site: http://www.vtg.com
Sales Range: $75-99.9 Million
Emp.: 4
Freight Railcar Rental Services
N.A.I.C.S.: 532411

Subsidiary (US):

VTG Rail (2)
103 W Vandalia Ste 200, Edwardsville, IL 62025
Tel.: (618) 343-0600
Web Site: http://www.vtg.com
Sales Range: $25-49.9 Million
Emp.: 13
Rail Cars Leasing Services
N.A.I.C.S.: 488210

Subsidiary (Non-US):

VTG Rail Espana S.L. (2)
C/ Acanto 22 - 7th floor, 28045, Madrid, Spain
Tel.: (34) 915510804
Web Site: http://www.vtg.com
Sales Range: $25-49.9 Million
Emp.: 15
Railway Freight Transportation Logistics & Railcar Rental Services
N.A.I.C.S.: 488510

JOANNE FABRICS INC.

2610 Sheridan Garden Drive, Oakville, L6J 7Z4, ON, Canada
Tel.: (905) 491-3900 Ca
Web Site: http://www.jffabrics.com
Year Founded: 1977
Fabric Distr
N.A.I.C.S.: 424310

JOAO FORTES ENGENHARIA S.A.

Av Das Americas 3443 Bloco 3 Loja 108/10, Rio de Janeiro, 22631003, Brazil
Tel.: (55) 2135014900
Web Site: https://www.joaofortes.com.br
Year Founded: 1950
JFEN3—(BRAZ)
Rev.: $14,998,659
Assets: $188,966,048
Liabilities: $336,908,520
Net Worth: ($147,942,471)
Earnings: ($9,377,022)
Fiscal Year-end: 12/31/23
Real Estate Development Services
N.A.I.C.S.: 531390
Antonio Jose de Almeida Carneiro *(Chm)*

JOB SOLUTION SWEDEN HOLDING AB

Landsvagen 57, 172 65, Sundbyberg, Sweden
Tel.: (46) 102040004
Web Site: https://www.jobsolutionholding.se
Year Founded: 2015
JOBS—(OMX)
Rev.: $7,324,240
Assets: $9,755,396
Liabilities: $6,133,977
Net Worth: $3,621,419
Earnings: $149,900
Emp.: 570
Fiscal Year-end: 12/31/23
Holding Company
N.A.I.C.S.: 551112
Carl Renman *(Chm)*

JOBAN KAIHATSU CO., LTD.

INTERNATIONAL PUBLIC

1 Tatsunokuchi Jobanyumoto-machi, Iwaki, 972-8321, Fukushima, Japan
Tel.: (81) 246721111
Web Site: http://www.jobankaihatsu.co.jp
Year Founded: 1960
Rev.: $172,411,800
Assets: $162,482,040
Liabilities: $81,222,900
Net Worth: $81,259,140
Earnings: $10,355,580
Fiscal Year-end: 03/31/19
Civil Engineering Services
N.A.I.C.S.: 237990
Junichi Takagi *(Pres)*

JOBAN KOSAN CO., LTD.

50 Warabihira Tokiwa Fujiwara-cho, Iwaki, 972-8326, Fukushima, Japan
Tel.: (81) 246309066
Web Site: https://www.joban-kosan.com
Year Founded: 1944
9675—(TKS)
Rev.: $98,363,410
Assets: $319,388,590
Liabilities: $248,879,720
Net Worth: $70,508,870
Earnings: $6,173,740
Emp.: 593
Fiscal Year-end: 03/31/24
Tourism Services & Coal Product Whlsr
N.A.I.C.S.: 721110
Kazushi Sekine *(Pres)*

JOBEN BIO-MEDICAL CO., LTD.

No 9 Shennong E Rd Agricultural Biotechnology Park, Dehe Village Changzhi, Ping-tung, 908, Taiwan
Tel.: (886) 87620778
Web Site: http://www.jobenbio.com
Year Founded: 2012
Herbal Medicine Mfr
N.A.I.C.S.: 325411
Huang Wen-Tien *(Chm)*

JOBINDEX A/S

Holger Danskes Vej 91, 2000, Frederiksberg, Denmark
Tel.: (45) 38323355
Web Site: http://www.jobindex.dk
JOBNDX—(OMX)
Rev.: $46,198,141
Assets: $60,217,536
Liabilities: $36,619,129
Net Worth: $23,598,407
Earnings: $9,692,910
Emp.: 190
Fiscal Year-end: 12/31/20
Online Job Search Engine
N.A.I.C.S.: 541890
Kaare Danielsen *(Founder & CEO)*

JOBSERVE LTD.

Tower Business Park Kelvedon Road, Colchester, CO5 0LX, United Kingdom
Tel.: (44) 1621817335
Web Site: http://www.jobserve.com
Year Founded: 1993
Sales Range: $10-24.9 Million
Emp.: 80
Internet Recruitment Services
N.A.I.C.S.: 541612
Robbie Cowling *(Founder & CEO)*

Subsidiaries:

ComputerJobs.com, Inc. (1)
1995 N Park Pl St 375, Atlanta, GA 30339
Tel.: (770) 850-0045
Web Site: http://www.computerjobs.com
Online Employment Services for IT Professionals & Employers
N.A.I.C.S.: 561311
Richard Padgett *(Pres)*

AND PRIVATE COMPANIES

JOCHU TECHNOLOGY CO., LTD.
No 42 Kuangfu Rd, Hsin Chu Industrial park Hukou, Hsinchu, 303, Taiwan
Tel.: (886) 35981919
Web Site: https://www.jochu.com
Year Founded: 2000
3543—(TAI)
Semiconductor Devices Mfr
N.A.I.C.S.: 334413
Shu-I Li (Chm)

JOCKEY CLUB RACECOURSES LTD.
75 High Holborn, London, WC1V 6LS, United Kingdom
Tel.: (44) 207 611 1800
Web Site: http://www.thejockeyclub.co.uk
Year Founded: 1964
Racecourse Operator
N.A.I.C.S.: 713990
Paul Fisher (Mng Dir)

JOE HOLDING BERHAD
Lot 5031 5032 Jalan Teratai Off Jalan Meru, 41050, Klang, Selangor, Malaysia
Tel.: (60) 333927180
Web Site: https://www.joeholding.com.my
Year Founded: 1968
7096—(KLS)
Rev.: $4,650,030
Assets: $59,223,780
Liabilities: $3,984,998
Net Worth: $55,238,783
Earnings: ($8,130,375)
Emp.: 67
Fiscal Year-end: 03/31/22
Batteries Mfr
N.A.I.C.S.: 335910
Lock Yong Gan (Exec Dir)
Subsidiaries:

GP Autobat Sdn. Bhd. (1)
Lot 5031 & 5032 Jalan Teratai Off Jalan Meru, 41050, Klang, Selangor, Malaysia
Tel.: (60) 333927180
Web Site: http://www.gp-products.com
Emp.: 24
Batteries Mfr & Sales
N.A.I.C.S.: 335910
Poh Weng Choon (Mng Dir)

JOE KOZEK SAWMILLS LTD.
1792 Camozzi Road, Revelstoke, V0E 2S1, BC, Canada
Tel.: (250) 837-6041
Web Site: https://www.kozeksawmills.com
Year Founded: 1955
Sales Range: Less than $1 Million
Emp.: 20
Custom-Cut Lumber & Timber
N.A.I.C.S.: 113110
Joe Kozek (Gen Mgr-Sls)

JOEONE CO., LTD.
JOEONE Industrial Park Economic & Technological Development Zone, Quanzhou, 362005, Fujian, China
Tel.: (86) 59522351111
Web Site: https://www.joeone.cn
601566—(SHG)
Rev.: $367,860,720
Assets: $796,342,299
Liabilities: $273,132,194
Net Worth: $523,210,105
Earnings: ($13,116,000)
Fiscal Year-end: 12/31/22
Apparel Mfr & Retailer
N.A.I.C.S.: 315250
Lin Congying (Chm)

JOH. BERENBERG, GOSSLER & CO.
Neuer Jungfernstieg 20, 20354, Hamburg, Germany
Tel.: (49) 40350600
Web Site: http://www.berenberg.de
Year Founded: 1590
Rev.: $23,889,179
Emp.: 370
Private Banking House
N.A.I.C.S.: 522180
Gerd Simon (CIO)
Subsidiaries:

Berenberg Bank (1)
Neuer Jungfernstieg 20, 20354, Hamburg, Germany (100%)
Tel.: (49) 40350600
Web Site: http://www.berenbergbank.de
Sales Range: Less than $1 Million
Private Bank
N.A.I.C.S.: 522180
Jason Rand (Head-Electronic Trading & Distr-Global)

Subsidiary (Non-US):
Berenberg Bank (2)
46 Pl Guillame, Luxembourg, 1648, Luxembourg (100%)
Tel.: (352) 466380
Web Site: http://www.berenbergbank.lu
Sales Range: $50-74.9 Million
Emp.: 5
Banking Services
N.A.I.C.S.: 522110

Subsidiary (Domestic):
Berenberg Capital Management GmbH (2)
Neuer Jungfernstieg 20, Hamburg, 20354, Germany (100%)
Tel.: (49) 4035060508
Web Site: http://www.berenbergbank.de
Asset Management of Special Funds & Advisory Instituional Sales
N.A.I.C.S.: 523999
Hannwalter Peter (Chm)

Berenberg Consult GmbH (2)
Neuer Jungfernstieg 20, 20354, Hamburg, Germany (100%)
Tel.: (49) 40350600
Web Site: http://www.berenbergconsult.de
Sales Range: Less than $1 Million
Emp.: 400
Corporate Finance Consulting
N.A.I.C.S.: 523940
Claus Budelmann (Chm)

Berenberg Capital Markets LLC (1)
255 State St, Boston, MA 02109
Tel.: (617) 589-4900
Emp.: 10
Financial Advisory Services
N.A.I.C.S.: 523940

Berenberg Finanzanlagen (1)
Neuer Jungfernstieg 20, 20354, Hamburg, Germany (100%)
Tel.: (49) 40350600
Sales Range: Less than $1 Million
Private Equity & Asset Management
N.A.I.C.S.: 531390

Berenberg Treuhand GmbH (1)
Neuer Jungfernstieg 20, 20354, Hamburg, Germany (100%)
Tel.: (49) 40350600
Web Site: http://www.berenberg.de
Sales Range: Less than $1 Million
Emp.: 400
Administration of & Advice on Trusts
N.A.I.C.S.: 525990
Claus Budelmann (Chm)

JOHAN HOLDINGS BERHAD
11th Floor Wisma E&C No 2 Lorong Dungun Kiri Damansara Heights, 50490, Kuala Lumpur, Malaysia
Tel.: (60) 320921858 MY
Web Site: http://www.johanholdings.com
JOHAN—(KLS)
Rev.: $23,594,053
Assets: $236,509,816
Liabilities: $220,925,382
Net Worth: $15,584,433
Earnings: ($4,205,555)
Emp.: 351
Fiscal Year-end: 01/31/20
Ceramic Floor & Wall Tiles Mfr & Distr
N.A.I.C.S.: 327120
Yong Fah Teh (Sec)
Subsidiaries:

Diners Club (Malaysia) Sdn. Bhd. (1)
Suite 21-02 Level 21 Menara Tan & Tan 207 Jalan Tun Razak, PO Box 11095, 50400, Kuala Lumpur, Malaysia
Tel.: (60) 321611322
Web Site: http://www.dinersclub.com.my
Sales Range: $100-124.9 Million
Credit Card Providers
N.A.I.C.S.: 522210

Diners World Travel (Malaysia) Sdn. Bhd. (1)
Suite 21-02 Level 21 Menara Tan & Tan 207 Jalan Tun Razak, 50400, Kuala Lumpur, Federal Territory, Malaysia
Tel.: (60) 321640068
Sales Range: $10-24.9 Million
Emp.: 30
Travel Tour Operating Agencies
N.A.I.C.S.: 561520

J Capital Investments Pte Ltd (1)
250 North Bridge Road 37-03 Raffles City Tower, Singapore, 179101, Singapore
Tel.: (65) 68936631
Web Site: http://www.dinerstravel.com.sg
Sales Range: $25-49.9 Million
Travel Tour Operating Services
N.A.I.C.S.: 561520

Johan Investment Private Limited (1)
7500e Beach Rd 03-201 The Plz, Singapore, 199595, Singapore
Tel.: (65) 62944222
Sales Range: $100-124.9 Million
Emp.: 220
Investment Management Service
N.A.I.C.S.: 523999

Johan Management Services Sdn. Bhd. (1)
11th Floor Wisma E and C No 2 Lorong Dungun Kiri, Damanasara Heights, 50490, Kuala Lumpur, Malaysia
Tel.: (60) 320921858
Web Site: https://www.johanmanagement.com.my
Sales Range: $10-24.9 Million
Secretarial & Management Services
N.A.I.C.S.: 561499

Lumut Park Resort Sdn. Bhd. (1)
Lot 203 & 366 Jalan Iskandar Shah, 32200, Lumut, Perak Darul Ridzuan, Malaysia
Tel.: (60) 56804230
Web Site: https://orientstar.com.my
Sales Range: $25-49.9 Million
Resort Management Services
N.A.I.C.S.: 721110

William Jacks & Co. (Singapore) Pte. Ltd. (1)
18 Kaki Bukit Road 3 05-16 Entrepreneur Business Centre, Singapore, 415978, Singapore
Tel.: (65) 67489818
Web Site: http://www.naturesfarm.com
Sales Range: $50-74.9 Million
Emp.: 100
Health Foods Whslr
N.A.I.C.S.: 424490

William Jacks & Company (Malaysia) Sendirian Berhad (1)
11th Floor Wisma E&C No 2 Lorong Dungun Kiri, Damansara Heights, 50490, Kuala Lumpur, Selangor, Malaysia
Tel.: (60) 320921858
Web Site: http://www.johanholdings.com
Sales Range: $25-49.9 Million
Emp.: 300
Building Product Distr
N.A.I.C.S.: 444180

JOHLER NORDDRUCK GMBH
Gadelander Strasse 77, 24539, Neumunster, Germany
Tel.: (49) 43218750 De
Web Site: http://www.johlerdruck.de
Year Founded: 1876
Sales Range: $25-49.9 Million
Emp.: 110
Newspaper Supplement & Catalogue Printing Services
N.A.I.C.S.: 323111
Franz-Hermann Enk (Mng Dir)
Subsidiaries:

Nord Offset Druck GmbH (1)
Gadelander Strasse 77, 24359, Neumunster, Germany
Tel.: (49) 4321875156
Web Site: http://www.nord-offset.de
Sales Range: $10-24.9 Million
Envelope, Magazines & Periodical Printing Services
N.A.I.C.S.: 323111

JOHN AYLING & ASSOCIATES LIMITED
27 Soho Square, London, W1D 3QR, United Kingdom
Tel.: (44) 207 439 6070 UK
Web Site: http://www.jaa-media.co.uk
Year Founded: 1978
Sales Range: $100-124.9 Million
Emp.: 37
N.A.I.C.S.: 541870
John Ayling (Chm & Mng Dir)

JOHN BENJAMINS BV
Klaprozenweg 75G, 1033 NN, Amsterdam, Netherlands
Tel.: (31) 206304747
Web Site: http://www.benjamins.com
Sales Range: $1-9.9 Million
Emp.: 20
Academic Book & Antiquarian Bookseller Publisher
N.A.I.C.S.: 513130
Subsidiaries:

John Benjamins Antiquariat B.V. (1)
Club Rozen Wag, PO Box 36224, 1020ME, Amsterdam, Netherlands (100%)
Tel.: (31) 206304747
Web Site: http://www.benjamins.nl
Book Publishers
N.A.I.C.S.: 513130
John Benjamins (Mng Dir)

John Benjamins North America Inc. (1)
763 N 24th St, Philadelphia, PA 19130 (100%)
Tel.: (215) 769-3444
Web Site: http://www.benjamins.com
Publishers of Books & Publishing Services
N.A.I.C.S.: 513130

JOHN BRIDGEMAN LIMITED
Level 9 123 Eagle Street, Brisbane, 4000, QLD, Australia
Tel.: (61) 1300108495 AU
Web Site: http://www.johnbridgeman.com.au
Year Founded: 2015
Rev.: $42,149,232
Assets: $74,216,304
Liabilities: $35,447,574
Net Worth: $38,768,730
Earnings: ($13,012,851)
Fiscal Year-end: 06/30/18
Investment Management Service
N.A.I.C.S.: 523940
Stuart McAuliffe (Mng Dir)

JOHN BROWN VOEST GMBH
Torgauer Strasse 330-334, D-04347, Leipzig, Germany
Tel.: (49) 341 2673 600
Web Site: http://www.jbv.griesemann-gruppe.de

JOHN BROWN VOEST GMBH

John Brown Voest GmbH—(Continued)
Engineeering Services
N.A.I.C.S.: 541330
Thomas Dolezych *(Mgr-Project)*
Subsidiaries:

Exyte Central Europe GmbH (1)
Loewentorbogen 9B, 70376, Stuttgart,
Germany **(100%)**
Tel.: (49) 71188041800
Web Site: http://www.mwgroup.net
Life Science Industry Consulting, Engineering, Construction Management, Compliance Validation & Facility Support Contract Services
N.A.I.C.S.: 238990

JOHN BULL COMPANY LIMITED
284 Bay Street, PO Box N-3737,
Nassau, Bahamas
Tel.: (242) 0003224253
Web Site: http://www.johnbull.com
Year Founded: 1929
Sales Range: $75-99.9 Million
Emp.: 270
Jewelry Store Owner & Operator
N.A.I.C.S.: 458310
Fred Hazelwood *(Pres)*

JOHN E. FELLS & SONS LTD.
Fells House Prince Edward Street,
Berkhamsted, HP4 3EZ, Herts,
United Kingdom
Tel.: (44) 1442 870900
Web Site: http://www.fells.co.uk
Year Founded: 1858
Sales Range: $50-74.9 Million
Emp.: 50
Wine Importer & Distr
N.A.I.C.S.: 424820
Steve Moody *(Mng Dir)*

JOHN HOGG & CO. LTD.
1-6 St Helen Business Park, Holywood, BT18 9HQ, Co Down, United
Kingdom
Tel.: (44) 2890222200
Web Site: http://www.johnhogg.com
Year Founded: 1890
Sales Range: $150-199.9 Million
Holding Company
N.A.I.C.S.: 551112
Colin Cairns *(Grp Dir-Fin)*
Subsidiaries:

Ulster Weavers Home Fashion
Ltd (1)
1-6 St Helens Business Pk, Donegall Rd,
Holywood, BT18 9HQ, County Down,
United Kingdom **(100%)**
Tel.: (44) 2890329494
Web Site: http://www.ulsterweavers.com
Sales Range: $25-49.9 Million
Emp.: 200
Apparel & Linens Mfr
N.A.I.C.S.: 313210
Kenneth Webb *(Mng Dir)*

Subsidiary (Domestic):

Moygashel Furnishings (2)
Moygashel Mills, Dungannon, BT71 7QS,
United Kingdom **(100%)**
Tel.: (44) 2887722231
Web Site: http://www.moygashel.com
Mfr & Conversion of Fabric for Furnishings
N.A.I.C.S.: 313310

Ulster Weavers (2)
245 Castlewellan Rd, Banbridge, BT32
3SG, United Kingdom **(100%)**
Tel.: (44) 2840624490
Web Site:
 http://www.ulsterweaversapparel.com
Sales Range: $25-49.9 Million
Emp.: 25
Dyeing, Finishing & Weaving of Woven
Fabrics for Apparel
N.A.I.C.S.: 313310

JOHN KEELLS HOLDINGS PLC
No 117 Sir Chittampalam A Gardiner
Mawatha, 2, Colombo, Sri Lanka
Tel.: (94) 112306000 **LK**
Web Site: https://www.keells.com
Year Founded: 1979
JKH—(COL)
Rev.: $679,234,458
Assets: $2,855,745,165
Liabilities: $1,563,055,235
Net Worth: $1,292,689,930
Earnings: $21,018,740
Emp.: 13,889
Fiscal Year-end: 03/31/21
Holding Company
N.A.I.C.S.: 551112
Dilani Alagaratnam *(Pres-HR, Legal, Secretarial, Corp Comm & Sustainablity)*
Subsidiaries:

AuxiCogent Holdings Private
Limited (1)
IFS Court 28 Cybercity, Ebene, Mauritius
Tel.: (230) 467 3000
Investment Management Service
N.A.I.C.S.: 523999

AuxiCogent International (Pvt)
Ltd (1)
IFS Court 28 Cybercity, Ebene, 72201,
Mauritius
Tel.: (230) 467 3000
Business Processing Services
N.A.I.C.S.: 561499

Ceylon Cold Stores PLC (1)
Tel.: (94) 112318798
Web Site: https://www.elephanthouse.lk
Rev.: $419,923,145
Assets: $238,773,809
Liabilities: $175,269,056
Net Worth: $63,504,754
Earnings: $8,364,129
Emp.: 7,568
Fiscal Year-end: 03/31/2023
Beverages Mfr
N.A.I.C.S.: 312111
Daminda Gamlath *(Pres)*

Ceylon Holiday Resorts Ltd. (1)
Bentota Beach Hotel, Bentota, Sri Lanka
Tel.: (94) 34 2275176
Web Site: http://www.johnkeellshotels.com
Emp.: 290
Resort Operating Services
N.A.I.C.S.: 721110
Sanjeeva Pereira *(Gen Mgr)*

Cinnamon Hotels Management
Ltd. (1)
Cinnamon Lakeside Commercial Complex
No 117, Sir Chittampalam A Gardinar Mawatha, 02000, Colombo, Sri Lanka
Tel.: (94) 112161161
Web Site:
 https://vouchers.cinnamonhotels.com
Hotel Services
N.A.I.C.S.: 721110

Fantasea World Investments (Pte)
Ltd (1)
2nd Floor H Maizan Building, Sosun Magu,
Male, Maldives
Tel.: (960) 3336000
Hotel Operating Services
N.A.I.C.S.: 721110

Habarana Lodge Ltd. (1)
PO Box 2, Habarane, Sri Lanka
Tel.: (94) 66 2270011
Home Management Services
N.A.I.C.S.: 721110

Habarana Walk Inn Ltd. (1)
PO Box 1, Habarane, Sri Lanka
Tel.: (94) 66 2270046
Hotel Operating Services
N.A.I.C.S.: 721110

InfoMate (Pvt) Ltd. (1)
No 04 Leyden Bastian Street, Colombo, 01,
Sri Lanka
Tel.: (94) 11 214 9700
Web Site: https://www.infomateworld.com

Business Process Outsourcing Services
N.A.I.C.S.: 561499

Jaykay Marketing Services (Pvt)
Ltd. (1)
No148 Vauxhall Street, Colombo, 2, Sri
Lanka
Tel.: (94) 11 230 3500
Web Site: https://www.keellssuper.com
Emp.: 4,500
Supermarket Operating Services
N.A.I.C.S.: 445110
Charitha Subasinghe *(CEO)*

John Keells Computer Services (Pvt)
Ltd. (1)
 (100%)
Web Site: http://www.jkcsworld.com
Sales Range: $50-74.9 Million
Emp.: 200
Software Reproducing
N.A.I.C.S.: 334610

John Keells Conventions (Pvt)
Ltd. (1)
130 Glennie Street, Colombo, Sri
Lanka **(100%)**
Tel.: (94) 112306000
Web Site: http://www.jkconventions.com
Management Consulting Services
N.A.I.C.S.: 541618

John Keells International (Pvt)
Ltd. (1)
No 130 Glennie Street, Colombo, Sri Lanka
Tel.: (94) 112306000
Administrative Management Services
N.A.I.C.S.: 541611

John Keells Maldivian Resorts (Pte)
Ltd. (1)
2nd Floor H Maizan Building, Sosun Magu,
Male, 20252, Maldives
Tel.: (960) 3336000
Hotel Services
N.A.I.C.S.: 721110

John Keells Office Automation Pvt
Ltd. (1)
90 Union Place, Colombo, 02, Sri
Lanka **(100%)**
Tel.: (94) 11 231 3000
Web Site: https://www.jkoa.com
Sales Range: $50-74.9 Million
Emp.: 174
Automatic Vending Machine Mfr
N.A.I.C.S.: 333310

John Keells Properties Ja-ela (Pvt.)
Ltd. (1)
No 186 Vauxhall Street, Colombo, Sri
Lanka
Tel.: (94) 112152152
Real Estate Services
N.A.I.C.S.: 531390

John Keells Residential Properties
(Pvt) Ltd. (1)
No 186 Vauxhall Street, Colombo, 02, Sri
Lanka
Tel.: (94) 11 215 2100
Web Site: http://www.onthree20.com
Sales Range: $50-74.9 Million
Emp.: 100
Property Development Services
N.A.I.C.S.: 531390
Suresh Rajendra *(Pres)*

John Keells Stock Brokers (Pvt)
Ltd. (1)
Financial Investment Activities
N.A.I.C.S.: 523999

John Keels Logistics (Pvt) Ltd (1)
No 11 York Street, Colombo, 01, Sri
Lanka **(100%)**
Tel.: (94) 11 247 5574
Web Site: https://www.keellslogistics.com
Sales Range: $25-49.9 Million
Emp.: 60
Supply Chain Management & Forwarding
N.A.I.C.S.: 488510
Suranga S. Aththanayaka *(Head-Sls & Mktg)*

Kandy Walk Inn Ltd. (1)
Cinnamon Citadel Kandy 124 Srimath Kuda
Ratwatte Mawatha, Kandy, Sri Lanka
Tel.: (94) 812234365
Home Management Services

INTERNATIONAL PUBLIC

N.A.I.C.S.: 721110

Keells Food Products PLC (1)
No 16 Minuwangoda Road, Ekala, Ja-Ela,
Sri Lanka
Tel.: (94) 112236317
Web Site: https://www.keellsfoods.lk
Rev.: $21,451,583
Assets: $14,322,742
Liabilities: $7,304,747
Net Worth: $7,017,995
Earnings: $46,420
Emp.: 543
Fiscal Year-end: 03/31/2023
Processed Meat Mfr
N.A.I.C.S.: 311612
K. A. V. Fernando *(Mgr-Factory-Pannala)*

Keells Hotel Management Services
Ltd. (1)
130 Glennie Street, Colombo, 02, Sri
Lanka **(100%)**
Tel.: (94) 112439049
Web Site: http://www.johnkeellshotels.com
Hotels & Motels
N.A.I.C.S.: 721110

Lanka Marine Services (Pvt.)
Ltd. (1)
No 04 Leyden Bastian Road, 01000, Colombo, Sri Lanka
Tel.: (94) 112475414
Web Site: https://www.lankamarine.com
Bunkering Services
N.A.I.C.S.: 424720
Anushka Weeraratne *(CEO)*

Mack Air Ltd. (1)
No 11 York Street, 01000, Colombo, Sri
Lanka **(100%)**
Tel.: (94) 117441441
Sales Range: $25-49.9 Million
Emp.: 60
Support Activities for Air Transportation
N.A.I.C.S.: 488190

Mack Air Services Maldives (Pte)
Ltd. (1)
4th Floor Sto Aifaanu Building, Boduthakurufaanu, Magu, Maldives
Tel.: (960) 3334708
Web Site: http://www.johnkeellsairlines.com
Sales Range: $25-49.9 Million
Emp.: 12
Airport Operations
N.A.I.C.S.: 488119

Mackinnon & Keells Financial Services Ltd. (1)
130 Glennie St, Colombo, 00200, Sri Lanka
Tel.: (94) 112475502
Financial Investment Activities
N.A.I.C.S.: 523999

Mackinnon Mackenzie and Co (Shipping) Ltd. (1)
11 York Street, Colombo, Sri Lanka
Tel.: (94) 112475200
Sales Range: $25-49.9 Million
Emp.: 60
Navigational Services to Shipping
N.A.I.C.S.: 488330

Mackinnon Mackenzie and Co of
Ceylon Ltd. (1)
130 Glennie Street, Colombo, Sri Lanka
Tel.: (94) 112306000
Management Consulting Services
N.A.I.C.S.: 541618

Mackinnons Tours Ltd. (1)
130 Glennie Street, Colombo, Sri
Lanka **(100%)**
Tel.: (94) 112306000
Tour Operator
N.A.I.C.S.: 561520

Mackinnons Travels (Pvt) Ltd (1)
No 11 York Street, Colombo, 01, Sri Lanka
Tel.: (94) 11 231 8600
Web Site:
 https://www.mackinnonstravels.com
Sales Range: $25-49.9 Million
Emp.: 7
Travel Agency Services
N.A.I.C.S.: 561510
Sanjay Weerkoon *(CEO)*

Mortlake Ltd (1)

AND PRIVATE COMPANIES

No 148 Vauxhall Street, Colombo, Sri Lanka
Tel.: (94) 11 2475308
Investment Management Service
N.A.I.C.S.: 523999

Nature Odyssey (Pvt) Ltd. (1)
Sir Chittampalam A Gardiner Mawatha, Colombo, 2, Sri Lanka **(100%)**
Tel.: (94) 11 230 6442
Web Site: https://www.natureodyssey.com
Sales Range: $75-99.9 Million
Emp.: 500
Tour Operator
N.A.I.C.S.: 561520

Nexus Networks (Pvt) Limited (1)
148, Vauxhall Street, 02, Colombo, Sri Lanka
Tel.: (94) 777733833
Web Site: http://www.mynexuscard.com
Sales Range: $25-49.9 Million
Emp.: 15
Holding Company
N.A.I.C.S.: 551112

Serene Holidays (Pvt) Ltd. (1)
204 Accord Commercial Complex Opp Station, Goregaon E, Mumbai, 400 063, India
Tel.: (91) 2242105210
Web Site: http://www.sereneholidays.com
Sales Range: $25-49.9 Million
Emp.: 15
Tour Operating Services
N.A.I.C.S.: 561520

The Colombo Ice Company (Pvt.) Ltd. (1)
Block B6 Seethawaka Export Processing Zone, Awissawella, Colombo, Sri Lanka
Tel.: (94) 362030600
Supermarket Services
N.A.I.C.S.: 445110

Tranquility (Pte) Ltd (1)
2nd Floor H Maizan Building, Sosun Magu, Male, Maldives
Sales Range: $50-74.9 Million
Emp.: 300
Hotel Operating Services
N.A.I.C.S.: 721110

Travel Club (Pte) Ltd (1)
2nd Floor H Maizan Building, Sosun Magu, Male, Maldives
Tel.: (960) 3336000
Sales Range: $150-199.9 Million
Emp.: 30
Boat Club Operating Services
N.A.I.C.S.: 711211
V. Premkumar *(Gen Mgr)*

Union Assurance PLC (1)
20 St Michaels Road, 3, Colombo, 3, Sri Lanka
Tel.: (94) 112990990
Web Site: https://www.unionassurance.com
Rev.: $55,507,650
Assets: $252,884,415
Liabilities: $205,569,781
Net Worth: $47,314,633
Earnings: $9,144,519
Emp.: 659
Fiscal Year-end: 12/31/2022
Life & General Insurance Services
N.A.I.C.S.: 524113
Iroshini Tittagalla *(Gen Mgr-Life Ops)*

Walkers Tours Ltd. (1)
117 Sir Chittampalam A Gardiner Mawatha, Colombo, 02, Sri Lanka
Tel.: (94) 768511264
Web Site: https://www.walkerstours.com
Tour Operator
N.A.I.C.S.: 561520

Waterfront Properties (Pvt.) Ltd. (1)
No 5 Justice Akbar Mawatha, Slave Island, 02, Colombo, Sri Lanka
Tel.: (94) 112152152
Supermarket Services
N.A.I.C.S.: 445110

Whittall Boustead (Travel) Ltd. (1)
No 117 Sir Chittampalam A Gardiner Mawatha, Colombo, 02, Sri Lanka **(100%)**
Tel.: (94) 112306356
Web Site: https://www.whittallstravels.com
Tour Operator
N.A.I.C.S.: 561520

Whittall Boustead Ltd. (1)
130 Glennie Street, Colombo, Sri Lanka
Tel.: (94) 112306000
Holding Company
N.A.I.C.S.: 551112

Division (Domestic):

Whittall Boustead (Pvt) Ltd - Cargo Division (2)
No 148 Vauxhall Street, Colombo, Sri Lanka
Tel.: (94) 11 2475299
Freight Forwarding Services
N.A.I.C.S.: 488510

Yala Village (Pvt) Ltd. (1)
PO Box 1 Kirinda, Kirinda, Tissamaharama, Sri Lanka
Tel.: (94) 47 2239449
Hotel Operating Services
N.A.I.C.S.: 721110

JOHN KEELLS HOTELS PLC
117 Sir Chittampalam A Gardiner Mawatha, 02, Colombo, 02, Sri Lanka
Tel.: (94) 11242110115
Year Founded: 1979
KHL—(COL)
Rev.: $95,986,818
Assets: $289,924,883
Liabilities: $181,411,844
Net Worth: $108,513,039
Earnings: ($1,106,967)
Emp.: 2,450
Fiscal Year-end: 03/31/23
Hotel & Restaurant Operator
N.A.I.C.S.: 721110
K. N. J. Balendra *(Chm)*

JOHN LAING GROUP PLC
1 Kingsway, London, WC2B 6AN, United Kingdom
Tel.: (44) 2079013200 UK
Web Site: http://www.laing.com
Year Founded: 2006
Investment Holding Company
N.A.I.C.S.: 551112
Mark Westbrook *(Sr Mng Dir)*

Subsidiaries:

John Laing Limited (1)
1 Kingsway, London, WC2B 6AN, United Kingdom
Tel.: (44) 2079013200
Web Site: http://www.laing.com
Investment Holding Company
N.A.I.C.S.: 551112

JOHN LEWIS OF HUNGERFORD PLC
Grove Technology Park, Wantage, OX12 9FA, Oxfordshire, United Kingdom
Tel.: (44) 1235760030
Web Site: http://www.john-lewis.co.uk
JLH—(AIM)
Rev.: $14,018,634
Assets: $11,615,699
Liabilities: $9,714,264
Net Worth: $1,901,435
Earnings: $18,409
Emp.: 55
Fiscal Year-end: 06/30/22
Kitchen Furniture Manufacturer
N.A.I.C.S.: 337122
John L. Lewis *(Founder)*

JOHN LEWIS PARTNERSHIP PLC
171 Victoria Street, London, SW1E 5NN, United Kingdom
Tel.: (44) 2078281000
Web Site: http://www.johnlewispartners.co.uk
Year Founded: 1864
Rev.: $14,878,117,382
Assets: $8,010,181,142
Liabilities: $4,685,348,742
Net Worth: $3,324,832,400
Earnings: $98,095,246
Emp.: 60,800
Fiscal Year-end: 01/26/19
Department Stores & Supermarket Operator
N.A.I.C.S.: 455110
John Lewis *(Head-Brand Mktg)*

Subsidiaries:

John Lewis plc (1)
171 Victoria St, London, SW1E 5NN, United Kingdom **(100%)**
Tel.: (44) 2078281000
Web Site: http://www.johnlewis.com
Sales Range: $5-14.9 Billion
Emp.: 3,000
Department Stores
N.A.I.C.S.: 455110
John Vary *(Partner)*

Subsidiary (Domestic):

Herbert Parkinson Limited (2)
Harvest Mill Monton Road, Darwen, BB3 0HR, Lancashire, United Kingdom
Tel.: (44) 1254771614
Web Site: http://www.herbertparkinson.com
Sales Range: $25-49.9 Million,
Emp.: 300
Weaver & Curtain, Duvet & Pillow Mfr
N.A.I.C.S.: 314120
Stuart McDonald *(Head-Branch)*

Waitrose Limited (2)
Bond Way, Bracknell, RG12 1RQ, Berkshire, United Kingdom
Tel.: (44) 1344862374
Web Site: http://www.waitrose.com
Supermarket & Specialist Store
N.A.I.C.S.: 445110
Ross Avery *(Fin Dir)*

JOHN M HENDERSON & CO LTD.
Kings Works Sir William Smith Road, Kirkton Industrial Estate, Arbroath, DD11 3RD, Angus, United Kingdom
Tel.: (44) 1241870774
Web Site: http://www.johnmhenderson.com
Year Founded: 1866
Rev.: $12,411,773
Emp.: 92
Industrial Machinery Mfr
N.A.I.C.S.: 333248
Gary McCombie *(Mng Dir)*

JOHN MATTSON FASTIGHETS AB
Larsbergsvagen 10, Box 100 35, 181 10, Lidingo, Sweden
Tel.: (46) 86133500
Web Site: https://www.johnmattson.se
Year Founded: 1965
JOMA—(OMX)
Rev.: $60,595,232
Assets: $1,445,629,107
Liabilities: $890,086,778
Net Worth: $555,542,329
Earnings: ($124,615,326)
Emp.: 46
Fiscal Year-end: 12/31/23
Real Estate Manangement Services
N.A.I.C.S.: 531210
Siv Malmgren *(CEO)*

JOHN MCASLAN PARTNERS LIMITED
7-9 William Road, London, NW1 3ER, United Kingdom
Tel.: (44) 20 7313 6000
Web Site: http://www.mcaslan.co.uk
Year Founded: 1984
Sales Range: $10-24.9 Million
Emp.: 90
Architectural Services
N.A.I.C.S.: 541310
Robert Torday *(Dir-Mktg & Comm)*

JOHN SWIRE & SONS LIMITED

JOHN MITCHELL HAULAGE & WAREHOUSING
Earls Road Industrial Estate, Grangemouth, FK3 8XA, Stirlingshire, United Kingdom
Tel.: (44) 132448651
Web Site: http://www.johnmitchell.co.uk
Year Founded: 1956
Sales Range: $10-24.9 Million
Emp.: 140
Transportation & Warehousing Services
N.A.I.C.S.: 493110
Iain Mitchell *(Mng Dir)*

JOHN NOLAN ASSOCIATES LTD
42 Upper Churchtown Rd, Churchtown, Dublin, 14, Ireland
Tel.: (353) 868161808
Web Site: http://www.johnnolanassociates.com
Sales Range: $10-24.9 Million
Property Surveying Services
N.A.I.C.S.: 541370
John Nolan *(Mng Dir)*

JOHN SMEDLEY LTD.
Lea Mills, Matlock, DE4 5AG, Derbyshire, United Kingdom
Tel.: (44) 1629534571 UK
Web Site: http://www.johnsmedley.com
Year Founded: 1784
Sales Range: $10-24.9 Million
Emp.: 450
Men's & Women's Knitwear Mfr
N.A.I.C.S.: 315120
Kristen Hayden *(Mgr-Sls-Womenswear)*

JOHN SWIRE & SONS LIMITED
Swire House 59 Buckingham Gate, London, SW1E 6AJ, United Kingdom
Tel.: (44) 2078347717
Web Site: https://www.swire.com
Year Founded: 1816
Sales Range: $5-14.9 Billion
Emp.: 41,000
Holding Company; Property, Aviation, Beverages, Marine Services, Trading & Industrial Operations
N.A.I.C.S.: 551112
Barnaby Swire *(Chm)*

Subsidiaries:

Ethos International Limited (1)
301-2 Oxford House 979 Kings Road Taikoo Place, Hong Kong, China (Hong Kong)
Tel.: (852) 2840 8600
Web Site: http://www.ethosintl.com
Professional Training Services
N.A.I.C.S.: 611430

Finlay Airline (Agencies) Ltd (1)
186 Vauxhall Street, PO Box 211Colombo, Colombo, 00200, Sri Lanka
Tel.: (94) 11 472 5200
Logistics Consulting Servies
N.A.I.C.S.: 541614

Finlay Beverages Limited (1)
Elmsall Way Dale Lane Industrial Estate, South Elmsall, Pontefract, WF9 2XS, West Yorkshire, United Kingdom
Tel.: (44) 1977 655500
Web Site: http://www.finlay.net
Emp.: 180
Tea Packaging & Labeling Services
N.A.I.C.S.: 561910
Ian Bryson *(Mng Dir)*

Finlay Flowers BV (1)
Jupiter 185, 2675 LV, Honselersdyk, Netherlands
Tel.: (31) 174 210500
Flower Farming Services
N.A.I.C.S.: 111422

JOHN SWIRE & SONS LIMITED

John Swire & Sons Limited—(Continued)

Finlay Hull Limited (1)
60 Lime Street, Hull, HU8 7AF, United Kingdom
Tel.: (44) 1482 225 960
Emp.: 50
Tea Mfr
N.A.I.C.S.: 311920
Gay Chambers *(Mng Dir)*

Finlay Properties (Pvt) Ltd (1)
09/7 Negombo Road, Welisara, Sri Lanka
Tel.: (94) 11 4828400
Warehousing & Logistics Consulting Services
N.A.I.C.S.: 493110

Finlay Tea Solutions (US) Inc (1)
23 Vreeland Rd Ste 290, Florham Park, NJ 07932-1510
Tel.: (973) 539-8030
Tea Whslr
N.A.I.C.S.: 424490

Finlay Teas (Pvt) Ltd (1)
PO Box 1, Haldummulla, Sri Lanka
Tel.: (94) 57 2268191
Tea & Tea Product Mfr & Distr
N.A.I.C.S.: 311920

Finlay Vietnam Company Limited (1)
6th Floor 61/33 Lac Trung Vinh Thuy Ward, Hai Ba Trung District, Hanoi, Vietnam
Tel.: (84) 36368000
Tea Whslr
N.A.I.C.S.: 424490

Finlays Horticulture Holdings Ltd. (1)
Flamingo House Cockerell Close, Stevenage, SG1 2NB, United Kingdom
Tel.: (44) 1438 375100
Holding Company
N.A.I.C.S.: 551112

Finlays Horticulture Kenya Ltd. (1)
Unit B Ngong Road, PO Box 10222, Nairobi Business Park, 00400, Nairobi, Kenya
Tel.: (254) 20 387 3800
Flower Farming Services
N.A.I.C.S.: 111422
Jacob Wanyonyi *(Mgr-Flowers Production)*

Finlays Horticulture South Africa Ltd (1)
PO Box 663, Tarlton, Krugersdorp, 1749, Gauteng, South Africa
Tel.: (27) 11 952 1088
Flower Farming Services
N.A.I.C.S.: 111422

HSE Group Pty Ltd (1)
161 Great Eastern Highway, PO Box 504, Belmont, 6104, WA, Australia
Tel.: (61) 8 9450 9800
Web Site: http://www.hsegroup.com.au
Commercial Equipment Rental Services
N.A.I.C.S.: 532490

Hapugastenne Plantations Ltd (1)
Finlay House, Colombo, Sri Lanka
Tel.: (94) 34297500
Tea Farming Services
N.A.I.C.S.: 111998

James Finlay (Blantyre) Ltd (1)
Gate 149 BCA Hill, Plot LE 460-505, Limbe, Malawi
Tel.: (265) 991 247494
Tea Whslr
N.A.I.C.S.: 424490

James Finlay Mombasa Ltd (1)
Mashundu Street, PO Box 84619, Mombasa, Kenya
Tel.: (254) 412 224057
Tea Whslr
N.A.I.C.S.: 424490
Winnie Nasurutia *(Mgr-Trading)*

John Swire & Sons (China) Limited (1)
Unit 1405 14/F One Indigo 20 Jiuxianqiao Road, Chaoyang District, Beijing, 100016, China
Tel.: (86) 10 8486 3321
Aircraft Engineering Services
N.A.I.C.S.: 541330

John Swire & Sons (Green Investments) Ltd (1)
236-240 Biggar Road, Newarthill, Motherwell, ML1 5FA, United Kingdom
Tel.: (44) 1698 863000
Web Site: http://www.argentenergy.com
Biodiesel Mfr
N.A.I.C.S.: 324110
Andrew Hunter *(Chm)*

John Swire & Sons (PNG) Limited (1)
PO Box 1, National Capital District 121, Port Moresby, Papua New Guinea
Tel.: (675) 322 0222
Aircraft Engineering Services
N.A.I.C.S.: 541330

John Swire & Sons (S.E. Asia) Pte Limited (1)
300 Beach Road 12-06 The Concourse, Singapore, 199555, Singapore
Tel.: (65) 6571 0351
Web Site: http://www.swire.com
Aircraft Engineering Services
N.A.I.C.S.: 541330
Mary Tan *(Sec)*

John Swire & Sons Inc. (1)
PO Box 140, Milford, DE 19963-0140
Tel.: (302) 422-7536
Web Site: http://www.swire.com
Refrigerated Warehousing Services
N.A.I.C.S.: 493120

John Swire & Sons Pty Ltd (1)
Level 16 Aurora Place 88 Phillip Street, Sydney, 2000, NSW, Australia
Tel.: (61) 292729272
Web Site: http://www.swire.com.au
Sales Range: $25-49.9 Million
Emp.: 1,500
Logistics & Mining Services
N.A.I.C.S.: 541614
Jeffery Cundle *(CEO)*

Subsidiary (Domestic):

Kalari Holdings Pty Ltd (2)
164 Garden Street, Portland, 3305, VIC, Australia
Tel.: (61) 355220130
Web Site: http://www.kalari.com.au
Sales Range: $50-74.9 Million
Emp.: 120
Holding Company
N.A.I.C.S.: 551112

Omniflora Blumen Center GmbH (1)
Odenwaldstrasse 7-9, 63263, Neu-Isenburg, Germany
Tel.: (49) 6102 7115
Web Site: http://www.omniflora.de
Flower Farming Services
N.A.I.C.S.: 111422

Swire Cold Storage Pty., Ltd. (1)
100-130 Abbotts Rd, Dandenong, VIC, Australia
Tel.: (61) 387959967
Web Site: http://www.swirecoldstorage.com.au
Sales Range: $25-49.9 Million
Emp.: 50
Cold Storage & Transportation Services
N.A.I.C.S.: 493120
Peter Manolidis *(Mgr-Site)*

Swire Group Taiwan (1)
39/F Taipei 101 Tower Nd 7 Sec 5 Xinyi Road, Taipei, 11049, Taiwan
Tel.: (886) 2 8101 5188
Aircraft Engineering Services
N.A.I.C.S.: 541330

Swire International Travel Services Ltd. (1)
Room 704 7/F 18 Chang An East Road Sec 1, Taipei, '00104, Taiwan
Tel.: (886) 2 2536 0100
Web Site: http://www.swiretravel.com.tw
Travel Agency
N.A.I.C.S.: 561510

Subsidiary (Non-US):

Quadrant Pacific Limited (2)
PO Box 919, Nelson, 7040, New Zealand
Tel.: (64) 3 546 7176
Web Site: http://www.quadrantpacific.co.nz
Logistics Consulting Servies
N.A.I.C.S.: 541614

Captain Gus D'Mello *(Mgr-Ops)*

Swire Oilfield Services Ltd. (1)
Swire House Souter Head Rd, Altens, Aberdeen, AB1 4LF, United Kingdom (100%)
Tel.: (44) 1224872707
Web Site: http://www.swireos.com
Emp.: 200
Engineereing Services
N.A.I.C.S.: 561990
Roy Burrell *(Gen Mgr & Dir-UK)*

Subsidiary (Non-US):

Swire Oilfield Services A/S (2)
PO Box 121, Stavanger, 4098, Tananger, Norway
Tel.: (47) 51653800
Web Site: http://www.swireos.com
Emp.: 200
Offshore Cargo Carrying Services
N.A.I.C.S.: 488999
Kjell Steine *(Dir-Comml)*

Swire Oilfield Services Do Brasil LTDA (2)
Av Prefeito Aristeu Ferreira da Silva, 2950 Novo Cavaleiros, Macae, Brazil
Tel.: (55) 22 2106 1050
Offshore Cargo Carrying Services
N.A.I.C.S.: 488999
Licia Rocha *(Mgr-Comml)*

Swire Oilfield Services India Private Ltd. (2)
105 Mahinder Chambers WT Patil Marg, Chembur, Mumbai, 400 071, India
Tel.: (91) 22 6758 2700
Offshore Cargo Carrying Services
N.A.I.C.S.: 488999
Paresh Mahulkar *(Mgr-Comml)*

Subsidiary (US):

Swire Oilfield Services L.L.C (2)
28420 Hardy Toll Rd, Spring, TX 77373
Tel.: (281) 210-5598
Offshore Cargo Carrying Services
N.A.I.C.S.: 488999
Mike Perera *(Gen Mgr-Offshore)*

Subsidiary (Non-US):

Swire Oilfield Services PTE Ltd. (2)
Loyang Offshore Supply Base 103 TOPS Ave 1 Unit 03-03, Mailbox No 5052, 25 Loyang Crescent, Singapore, 508988, Singapore
Tel.: (65) 6632 1900
Web Site: http://www.swire.com
Emp.: 30
Offshore Cargo Carrying Services
N.A.I.C.S.: 488999
Gary Lindsay *(Mgr-Comml)*

Swire Oilfield Services PTY Ltd. (2)
7 Hopetoun Place, Welshpool, 6106, WA, Australia
Tel.: (61) 8 6254 4600
Emp.: 20
Offshore Cargo Carrying Services
N.A.I.C.S.: 488999
Teresa Soanes *(Gen Mgr-Australasia)*

Swire Pacific Limited (1)
33/F One Pacific Place 88 Queensway, GPO Box 1, Hong Kong, China (Hong Kong) (65%)
Tel.: (852) 28408888
Web Site: http://www.swirepacific.com
Rev.: $11,651,437,116
Assets: $55,563,280,381
Liabilities: $15,186,524,723
Net Worth: $40,376,755,658
Earnings: $801,180,876
Emp.: 80,000
Fiscal Year-end: 12/31/2022
Real Estate Property, Aviation, Trading Industry, Marine Services & Beverages
N.A.I.C.S.: 713990
Merlin Bingham Swire *(Chm)*

Subsidiary (Non-US):

Coca-Cola Beverages Vietnam Ltd. (2)
10th Floor The Metropolitan 235 Dong Khoi, District 1, Ho Chi Minh City, Vietnam
Tel.: (84) 1900555584
Web Site: https://en.cocacolavietnam.com
Soft Drinks Mfr

N.A.I.C.S.: 312111

Joint Venture (Non-US):

Crown Vinalimex Packaging Ltd. (2)
Km 24 Highway 1, Quat Dong, Houng Tin Hatay, Hanoi, Vietnam
Tel.: (84) 34852003
Sales Range: $25-49.9 Million
Emp.: 88
Packaging Products for Consumer Goods; Joint Venture of Crown Cork & Seal Co., Inc. & Swire Pacific Limited Mfr
N.A.I.C.S.: 326199

Subsidiary (Non-US):

Finlays Colombo Limited (2)
Finlay House 186 Vauxhall Street, Colombo, 00200, Sri Lanka
Tel.: (94) 112421931
Web Site: http://www.finlays.lk
Sales Range: $25-49.9 Million
Emp.: 734
Diversified Holding Company
N.A.I.C.S.: 551112
N. K. H. Ratwatte *(Exec Dir)*

Joint Venture (Domestic):

HUD Group (2)
TYTL 108RP Sai Tso Wan Road, Tsing Yi, New Territories, China (Hong Kong) (50%)
Tel.: (852) 2 431 2828
Web Site: https://www.hud.com.hk
Ship Building, Maintenance & Repair Services
N.A.I.C.S.: 336611

Subsidiary (Domestic):

HongKong Salvage & Towage (3)
2/F HUD Administration Building Sai Tso Wan Road, Sai Tso Wan Road, Tsing Yi, New Territories, China (Hong Kong)
Tel.: (852) 2 427 7477
Web Site: http://www.hud.com.hk
Sales Range: $25-49.9 Million
Emp.: 50
Shipbuilding & Repair Services
N.A.I.C.S.: 336611

Subsidiary (Domestic):

Hong Kong Aircraft Engineering Co., Ltd. (2)
80 South Perimeter Road Hong Kong International Airport Lantau, Hong Kong, China (Hong Kong) (100%)
Tel.: (852) 2767 6142
Web Site: http://www.haeco.com
Rev.: $1,861,160,700
Assets: $1,795,778,250
Liabilities: $876,457,500
Net Worth: $919,320,750
Earnings: $44,270,700
Emp.: 605,755
Fiscal Year-end: 12/31/2017
Aeronautical Engineering Services
N.A.I.C.S.: 541330
Christopher Patrick Gibbs *(Grp Dir-Components & Engine Svcs)*

Subsidiary (US):

TIMCO Aviation Services, Inc. (3)
623 Radar Rd, Greensboro, NC 27410-6221
Tel.: (336) 668-4410
Web Site: http://www.haeco.aero
Maintenance Repair & Overhaul Services for Planes & Equipment
N.A.I.C.S.: 488999
Keith Statzer *(Gen Mgr-Greensboro MRO Facility)*

Division (Domestic):

HAECO Cabin Systems (4)
10262 Norris Ave, Pacoima, CA 91331-2217 (100%)
Tel.: (818) 896-2938
Web Site: http://www.haeco.aero
Sales Range: $25-49.9 Million
Emp.: 300
Aircraft Seats Mfr
N.A.I.C.S.: 336413
Jeff Luedeke *(VP-Sls)*

TIMCO Aerosystems (4)

AND PRIVATE COMPANIES

815 Radar Rd, Greensboro, NC 27410
Tel.: (336) 668-4410
Web Site: http://www.timco.aero
Aviation Engineering Services
N.A.I.C.S.: 541330
Rick Salanitri *(Pres)*

TIMCO Engine Center (4)
3921 Arrow St, Oscoda, MI 48750-2212
Tel.: (989) 739-2194
Web Site: http://www.timco.aero
Rev.: $3,800,000
Emp.: 50
Aircraft Maintenance & Repair Services
N.A.I.C.S.: 488190
Dennis Little *(Gen Mgr)*

Subsidiary (US):

Swire Coca-Cola, USA (2)
12634 S 265 West, Draper, UT 84020
Tel.: (801) 816-5300
Web Site: http://www.swirecc.com
Emp.: 6,000
Beverages Mfr, Marketer & Distr
N.A.I.C.S.: 312111
Scarlett Foster-Moss *(VP-PR & Govt Affairs)*

Subsidiary (Non-US):

Swire Cold Storage Vietnam Co., Ltd. (2)
18 Street No 6, Song Than I Industrial Park, Di An, Binh Duong, Vietnam
Tel.: (84) 650790015
Web Site: http://www.spcs.com.vn
Sales Range: $25-49.9 Million
Emp.: 200
Cold Storage Services
N.A.I.C.S.: 493120

Subsidiary (Domestic):

Swire Properties Limited (2)
64/F One Island East Taikoo Place 18 Westlands Road, Quarry Bay, Hong Kong, China (Hong Kong)
Tel.: (852) 28443888
Web Site: https://www.swireproperties.com
Sales Range: $1-4.9 Billion
Emp.: 5,000
Real Estate Development Services
N.A.I.C.S.: 236220
Guy Martin Coutts Bradley *(CEO)*

Subsidiary (Non-US):

Swire Resources (Shanghai) Trading Company Limited (2)
15/F 1089 Zhongshan No 2 Road (S), Xuhuiyuan Building, Shanghai, 200030, China (100%)
Tel.: (86) 2161211000
Web Site: http://www.swire.com
Marketing, Distribution & Retailing of Branded Sports & Casual Footwear, Apparel & Accessories
N.A.I.C.S.: 424340

Swire Shipping Pte Ltd (2)
300 Beach Road #27-01 The Concourse, Singapore, 199555, Singapore
Tel.: (65) 6603 9400
Web Site: http://www.swireshipping.com
Holding Company; Freight Shipping Services
N.A.I.C.S.: 551112
Stuart Jones *(Dir-Fleet)*

Subsidiary (Non-US):

Furness Withy (Chartering) Ltd. (3)
Finsbury House 23 Finsbury Circus, London, EC2M 7EA, United Kingdom
Tel.: (44) 2073775757
Freight & Cargo Transport Agents
N.A.I.C.S.: 488320

Subsidiary (Non-US):

Furness Withy (Australia) Pty. Limited (4)
484 St Kilda Rd, 3004, Melbourne, VIC, Australia
Tel.: (61) 398678288
Freight Transportation
N.A.I.C.S.: 488510

Subsidiary (US):

Westwood Shipping Lines (3)
1019 39th Ave SE Ste 210, Puyallup, WA 98374
Tel.: (253) 200-3800
Web Site: http://www.wsl.com
Container Transport Services
N.A.I.C.S.: 483111
Jack Mahoney *(Pres & CEO)*

Subsidiary (Domestic):

Swire Travel Ltd. (2)
6/F East Wing Warwick House Taikoo Place, 979 King's Road, Quarry Bay, China (Hong Kong)
Tel.: (852) 25796688
Web Site: http://www.swiretravel.com
Emp.: 400
Travel Management Services
N.A.I.C.S.: 561599
Andrew Leung *(Mng Dir)*

Subsidiary (Non-US):

Swire (Beijing) Air Service Limited (3)
No 7 San Feng North Road Room 1105-1106 11/F YOU Town Center Tower B, Chaoyang District, Beijing, 100020, China
Tel.: (86) 10 5737 3788
Travel Agency
N.A.I.C.S.: 561510
Henry Tuen *(Asst Mgr-Corp Travel)*

Swire International(Shanghai)Air Service Ltd. (3)
No 928 LiuZhou Road Room1001 Belile Intl Plaza, Xuhui District, Shanghai, 200233, China
Tel.: (86) 21 5198 1988
Travel Agency
N.A.I.C.S.: 561510
James Tang *(Gen Mgr)*

United States Cold Storage, Inc. (1)
201 Laurel Rd Fl 4, Voorhees, NJ 08043-2329
Tel.: (856) 354-8181
Web Site: http://www.uscoldstorage.com
Sales Range: $25-49.9 Million
Emp.: 30
Public Refrigerated Warehouse Operator
N.A.I.C.S.: 493120
James Slamon *(CFO & VP)*

WesTech Engineering, Inc. (1)
3665 SW Temple, Salt Lake City, UT 84115-4523
Tel.: (801) 290-1218
Web Site: http://www.westech-inc.com
Sales Range: $75-99.9 Million
Emp.: 500
Mfr of Service Industry Machinery
N.A.I.C.S.: 333310
Mark Biesinger *(Chief Engr-Process)*

Xiamen James Finlay Trading Co, Ltd. (1)
1806 Baoxian Dasha 68 Hubin Bei Lu, Xiamen, 360012, Fujian, China
Tel.: (86) 592 531 6278
Emp.: 4
Tea Whslr
N.A.I.C.S.: 424490
Sally Henderson *(Gen Mgr)*

Yunnan Taikoo Flowers Limited (1)
Xiao Pu Xiao Jie Town, Song Ming County, Kunming, 651708, Yunnan, China
Tel.: (86) 871 798 1179
Flower Farming Services
N.A.I.C.S.: 111422
Michelle He *(Mgr-Post Harvest)*

JOHN WOOD GROUP PLC

Sir Ian Wood House Hareness Road, Altens Industrial Estate, Aberdeen, AB12 3LE, United Kingdom
Tel.: (44) 1224851000 UK
Web Site: https://www.woodplc.com
Year Founded: 1982
WG—(LSE)
Rev.: $5,900,700,000
Assets: $7,660,600,000
Liabilities: $4,018,700,000
Net Worth: $3,641,900,000
Earnings: ($127,700,000)
Emp.: 2,000

Fiscal Year-end: 12/31/23
Holding Company; Oil & Natural Gas Support Services
N.A.I.C.S.: 551112
Roy Alexander Franklin *(Chm)*

Subsidiaries:

Amec Foster Wheeler Limited (1)
4th Floor Old Change House 128 Queen Victoria Street, London, EC4V 4BJ, United Kingdom
Tel.: (44) 2074297500
Web Site: http://www.woodplc.com
Holding Company; Construction & Civil Engineering Services
N.A.I.C.S.: 551112

Subsidiary (Non-US):

AMEC (South Korea) (2)
J-Tower 4/F 538 Sinsa-dong, Gangnam-gu, Seoul, 135-889, Korea (South)
Tel.: (82) 2 3014 8100
Project Management Consulting Services
N.A.I.C.S.: 541618

AMEC (United Arab Emirates) (2)
International Tower 5th Floor Capital Centre(Adjacent ADNEC) 24th, Karama Street, Abu Dhabi, United Arab Emirates
Tel.: (971) 2 6519800
Project Management Consulting Services
N.A.I.C.S.: 541618

AMEC Cade Ingenieria y Desarrollo de Proyectos Ltda. (2)
Av Larrain 5862 Piso 11, La Reina, Santiago, 7870154, Santiago, Chile
Tel.: (56) 2 640 6600
Engineeering Services
N.A.I.C.S.: 541330

AMEC Cade Servicios de Ingenieria Ltda. (2)
Av Larrain 5862 Piso 11, La Reina, Santiago, Santiago, Chile
Tel.: (56) 2 6406600
Engineeering Services
N.A.I.C.S.: 541330
Sergio Rosales *(Gen Mgr)*

AMEC Engineering & Consulting (Shanghai) Co., Ltd (2)
Project Execution Center No 42 Beisuitanghe Road, Jinshan District, Shanghai, 201209, China
Tel.: (86) 21 5739 8999
Project Management Consulting Services
N.A.I.C.S.: 541618

AMEC Environment & Infrastructure GmbH (2)
Facility Point Meander 251, Arnhem, 6825 MC, Netherlands
Tel.: (31) 88 217 4100
Engineering Consulting Services
N.A.I.C.S.: 541618

AMEC Foster Wheeler (Peru) S.A. (2)
Calle Las Begonias 441 Piso 8, San Isidro, Lima, 27, Peru
Tel.: (51) 1 622 3555
Project Management Consulting Services
N.A.I.C.S.: 541618

Subsidiary (Domestic):

AMEC Foster Wheeler Energy Limited (2)
Shinfield Pk, Reading, RG2 9FW, Berkshire, United Kingdom (100%)
Tel.: (44) 1189131234
Web Site: http://www.woodplc.com
Engineering & Construction Services
N.A.I.C.S.: 541330

Subsidiary (Non-US):

AMEC Foster Wheeler NCL Limited (2)
700 University Avenue 4th Floor, Toronto, M5G 1X6, ON, Canada
Tel.: (416) 592-2102
Engineering, Project Management & Consulting Services
N.A.I.C.S.: 541330

JOHN WOOD GROUP PLC

Subsidiary (Domestic):

AMEC Foster Wheeler Nuclear UK Limited (2)
2 Booths Hall, Chelford Rd, Knutsford, WA16 8QZ, Cheshire, United Kingdom (100%)
Tel.: (44) 1565 652 100
Web Site: http://www.amecnnc.com
Rev.: $150,520,326
Emp.: 500
Engineering Consulting Services
N.A.I.C.S.: 541330

Subsidiary (Non-US):

AMEC GRD SA B.V (2)
Facility Point Meander 251, 6825 MC, Arnhem, Netherlands
Tel.: (31) 882174100
Project Engineering & Technical Services
N.A.I.C.S.: 541330

AMEC Inc. (2)
2020 Winston Park Drive Suite 700, Oakville, L6H 6X7, ON, Canada (100%)
Tel.: (905) 829-5400
Engineering, Construction, Environment & Systems Technology Operations
N.A.I.C.S.: 541330

AMEC International Ingenieria y Construccion Limitada (2)
Avenida Presidente Riesco 5335, Las Condes, 7550123, Santiago, Chile
Tel.: (56) 2 2957 7700
Engineeering Services
N.A.I.C.S.: 541330

AMEC NSS Limited (2)
700 University Avenue 4th Floor, Toronto, M5G 1X6, ON, Canada
Tel.: (416) 592-7000
Nuclear Management Consulting Services
N.A.I.C.S.: 541690

Subsidiary (Domestic):

AMEC Offshore Services Ltd (2)
Edison Way Gapton Hall Industrial Estate, Great Yarmouth, NR31 0NG, United Kingdom
Tel.: (44) 1493 412200
Web Site: http://www.woodplc.com
Survey & Offshore Facilities Engineering Services
N.A.I.C.S.: 541330

Subsidiary (Non-US):

AMEC Philippines (2)
8th FL Filinvest 1 Bldg North Gate Cyberaone Alabang, Commerce Avenue Filinvest, Muntinlupa, 1981, Philippines
Tel.: (63) 2 7711532
Engineeering Services
N.A.I.C.S.: 541330

Subsidiary (Domestic):

AMEC Process & Energy Ltd. (2)
60 London Wall, Isrington, London, EC2M 5TQ, United Kingdom (100%)
Tel.: (44) 32151700
Offshore Engineering Specialists
N.A.I.C.S.: 541330

Subsidiary (Non-US):

AMEC Services Ltd. (2)
Insular Life Corporate Center Level 22 Tower 1 Corporate Corner, Alabang, Muntinlupa, 1780, Philippines
Tel.: (63) 2 7711532
Engineering, Project Management & Consulting Services
N.A.I.C.S.: 541330

AMEC South Africa (2)
Building 2, Silver Stream Business Park 10 Muswell Road South, Johannesburg, 2021, South Africa
Tel.: (27) 11 840 7300
Engineeering Services
N.A.I.C.S.: 541330

AMEC Zektin Pty Limited (2)
Level 3 171 Collins Street, Melbourne, 3000, VIC, Australia
Tel.: (61) 3 9944 5500
Environmental Consulting Services

3981

JOHN WOOD GROUP PLC

John Wood Group PLC—(Continued)
N.A.I.C.S.: 541620

Amec Azerbaijan (2)
Demirchi Tower 10th floor Khojaly ave 37, Baku, AZ1025, Azerbaijan
Tel.: (994) 412 465 7615
Web Site: http://www.woodplc.com
Project Management Consulting Services
N.A.I.C.S.: 541618

Amec Foster Wheeler Americas Limited (2)
2020 Winston Park Dr Ste 700, Oakville, L6H 6X7, ON, Canada **(100%)**
Tel.: (905) 829-5400
Electrical & Mechanical Engineering Consultant
N.A.I.C.S.: 541330

Unit (Domestic):

AMEC Inc. - St. John's (3)
133 Crosbie Rd, Saint John's, A1B 1H3, NL, Canada
Tel.: (709) 724-1900
Engineering Consultancy Services
N.A.I.C.S.: 541330

AMEC Inc. - Vancouver (3)
111 Dunsmuir Ste 400, Vancouver, V6B 5W3, BC, Canada
Tel.: (604) 664-4367
Web Site: http://www.woodplc.com
Engineeering Services
N.A.I.C.S.: 541330

Subsidiary (Domestic):

AMEC Technologies Limited (3)
210 Colonnade Rd S Ste 300, Ottawa, K2E 7L5, ON, Canada
Tel.: (613) 727-0658
Web Site: http://www.woodplc.com
Environmental Services
N.A.I.C.S.: 541620

Branch (Domestic):

Amec Foster Wheeler Americas Limited (3)
900 AMEC Pl 801 6th Ave SW, Calgary, T2P 3W3, AB, Canada **(100%)**
Tel.: (403) 298-4170
Engineering Services
N.A.I.C.S.: 541330

Subsidiary (Domestic):

Amec Foster Wheeler Environment & Infrastructure
1003 53rd Avenue N, Calgary, T2E 6X9, AB, Canada **(100%)**
Tel.: (403) 235-8108
Provider of Environmental & Geotechnical Engineering Services; Engineering, Scientific & Contracting Services; Air, Water, Soil & Groundwater Assessment, Site Remediation & Materials Testing
N.A.I.C.S.: 541330

Teshmont Consultants LP
1190 Waverley St, Winnipeg, R3T 0P4, MB, Canada **(100%)**
Tel.: (204) 284-8100
Web Site: http://www.teshmont.com
Electrical Engineering Consultants; Joint Venture with Stantec & Manitoba Hydro

Transtech Interactive Training Inc. (3)
1111 Dunsmuir St Ste 400, Vancouver, V6B 5W3, BC, Canada **(100%)**
Tel.: (604) 664-4367
Provider of Training Services
N.A.I.C.S.: 624310

Wood Environment and Infrastructure Solutions (3)
5681 70 St NW, Edmonton, T6B 3P6, AB, Canada **(100%)**
Tel.: (780) 436-2152
Web Site: http://www.woodplc.com
Surveying Services
N.A.I.C.S.: 541360

Subsidiary (Non-US):

Amec Foster Wheeler Australia Pty. Ltd. (2)
Level 7 197 St Georges Terrace, Perth, 6000, WA, Australia
Tel.: (61) 893474777
Web Site: http://www.woodplc.com
Mineral Resource & Waste-to-Resource Projects Designer, Engineering & Construction Services
N.A.I.C.S.: 541330

Amec Foster Wheeler Bimas Birlesik Insaat ve Muhendislik A.S. (2)
Kucukbakkalkoy Mahallesi Merdivenkoyyolu Cad Cardak Sok No 1 A Plaza, Atasehir, 34750, Istanbul, Turkiye
Tel.: (90) 2166650000
Project Engineering & Technical Services
N.A.I.C.S.: 541330

Amec Foster Wheeler Colombia SAS (2)
Carrera 11 A No 96-51 Floor 3 4 5, Bogota, 110111, Colombia
Tel.: (57) 1593 0593
Web Site: http://www.woodplc.com
Construction Engineering Services
N.A.I.C.S.: 541330

Amec Foster Wheeler Consulting Poland Sp. z o.o. (2)
ul Chmielna 132/134, 00-805, Warsaw, Poland
Tel.: (48) 4895330
Project Engineering & Technical Services
N.A.I.C.S.: 541330

Amec Foster Wheeler E & I GmbH (2)
Weserstr 4, 60329, Frankfurt am Main, Germany
Tel.: (49) 69 756 0070
Environmental Consulting Services
N.A.I.C.S.: 541620

Amec Foster Wheeler Energy & Partners Engineering Company (2)
Majd Business Center Formerly Karawan Towers King Faisal Road, Al Khobar, 31952, Saudi Arabia
Tel.: (966) 136685555
Project Engineering & Technical Services
N.A.I.C.S.: 541330

Amec Foster Wheeler Engineering AG (2)
Lohweg 6, 4054, Basel, Switzerland
Tel.: (41) 61 283 2200
Construction Engineering Services
N.A.I.C.S.: 541330

Amec Foster Wheeler Fired Heaters, Ltd. (2)
Ste 200-4954 Richard Rd SW, Calgary, T3E 6L1, AB, Canada **(100%)**
Tel.: (403) 255-3447
Engineering & Construction Services
N.A.I.C.S.: 541330

Amec Foster Wheeler France S.A. (2)
14 place de la Coupole, Charenton-le-Pont, 94220, Paris, France **(100%)**
Tel.: (33) 1 53 88 50 00
Engineering & Construction Services
N.A.I.C.S.: 541330

Amec Foster Wheeler Holding (Thailand) Limited (2)
1st Floor Talaythong Tower 53 Moo 9 Sukhumvit Road Thungsukla, Sriracha, Chon Buri, 20230, Thailand
Tel.: (66) 38344300
Project Engineering & Technical Services
N.A.I.C.S.: 541330

Amec Foster Wheeler Iberia S.A. (2)
Calle Gabriel Garcia Marquez 2, Las Rozas, 28232, Madrid, Spain **(100%)**
Tel.: (34) 913362500
Sales Range: $150-199.9 Million
Engineering & Construction Services
N.A.I.C.S.: 541330

Amec Foster Wheeler India Private Limited (2)
6th Floor Zenith Building Ascendas IT Park CSIR Rd, Taramani, Chennai, 600 113, Tamil Nadu, India
Tel.: (91) 4466223100
Project Engineering & Technical Services

N.A.I.C.S.: 541330

Amec Foster Wheeler International Ingenieria y Construccion Limitada (2)
Avenida Presidente Riesco 5335 8th Floor, Las Condes, 7550123, Santiago, Chile
Tel.: (56) 229577700
Project Engineering & Technical Services
N.A.I.C.S.: 541330

Amec Foster Wheeler Italiana, S.R.L. (2)
Via Sebastiano Caboto 15, Corsico, 20094, Milan, Italy **(100%)**
Tel.: (39) 0244861
Web Site: http://www.fwc.com
Engineering & Construction Services
N.A.I.C.S.: 541330

Subsidiary (US):

Amec Foster Wheeler North America Corp. (2)
53 Frontage Rd, Hampton, NJ 08827-9000
Tel.: (908) 730-4000
Web Site: http://www.woodplc.com
Construction Engineering Services
N.A.I.C.S.: 541330
Charles Bill (Dir-Comml)

Subsidiary (Domestic):

AMEC Foster Wheeler AES, Inc. (3)
40 Shuman Blvd Ste 340, Naperville, IL 60563
Tel.: (630) 357-8880
Web Site: http://www.woodplc.com
Engineering Services
N.A.I.C.S.: 541330

AMEC Foster Wheeler Environment & Infrastructure, Inc. (3)
1105 Lakewood Pkwy Ste 300, Alpharetta, GA 30009
Tel.: (770) 360-0600
Sales Range: $1-4.9 Billion
Emp.: 7,000
Engineering, Environmental & Remedial Construction Services
N.A.I.C.S.: 541330
Lawrence J. White (CIO & Sr VP)

AMEC Foster Wheeler Kamtech, Inc. (3)
1979 Lakeside Pkwy Ste 400, Tucker, GA 30084
Tel.: (770) 688-2500
Construction Services
N.A.I.C.S.: 322211

AMEC Geomatrix Consultants, Inc. (3)
180 Grand Ave Ste 1100, Oakland, CA 94612
Tel.: (510) 663-4100
Engineering & Technical Consulting Services
N.A.I.C.S.: 541330

Amec Foster Wheeler Constructors, Inc. (3)
53 Frontage Rd, Hampton, NJ 08827 **(100%)**
Tel.: (908) 730-4000
Web Site: http://www.woodplc.com
Heavy Construction Services
N.A.I.C.S.: 237990

Amec Foster Wheeler Inc. (3)
53 Frontage Rd, Hampton, NJ 08827-9000 **(100%)**
Tel.: (908) 730-4000
Web Site: http://www.woodplc.com
Cogeneration Facilities Construction Services
N.A.I.C.S.: 236220

Amec Foster Wheeler USA Corporation (3)
6223 W Sam Houston Pkwy N, Houston, TX 77041 **(100%)**
Tel.: (713) 538-9700
Web Site: http://www.woodplc.com
Engineering & Construction Services
N.A.I.C.S.: 541330

Foster Wheeler LLC (3)
Perryville Corporate Park, Clinton, NJ 08809

INTERNATIONAL PUBLIC

Tel.: (908) 730-4000
Holding Company; Power Plant Construction Engineering Services
N.A.I.C.S.: 551112

Subsidiary (Non-US):

Amec Foster Wheeler Service (Thailand) Limited (2)
10th Floor SJ Infinite I Business Complex 349 Vibhavadi-Rangsit Road, Chompol Chatuchak, Bangkok, 10900, Thailand **(100%)**
Tel.: (66) 20233860
Engineering & Project Management Services
N.A.I.C.S.: 541330

Amec Foster Wheeler Venezuela, C.A. (2)
Av Francisco de Miranda Ofic 903 Torre Cavendes Los Palos Grande, Piso 9, Caracas, 1060, Venezuela
Tel.: (58) 2127501172
Project Engineering & Technical Services
N.A.I.C.S.: 541330

Branch (Domestic):

Amec Foster Wheeler plc (2)
Booths Park Chelford Road, Knutsford, WA16 8QZ, United Kingdom
Tel.: (44) 1565652100
Emp.: 60
Management Consulting Services
N.A.I.C.S.: 541618

Subsidiary (Non-US):

Amec New Zealand Limited (2)
Level 5 21 Pitt St, PO Box 5647, Auckland, 1141, New Zealand
Tel.: (64) 9 300 9700
Engineeering Services
N.A.I.C.S.: 541330

Amec Romania (2)
184 Calea Dorobantilor Et 2 Ap 3 Sector 1, Bucharest, 10583, Romania
Tel.: (40) 21 231 63 27
Engineeering Services
N.A.I.C.S.: 541330

Amec Russia (2)
113/1 Leninsky Prospect Office E-100 Park Place, Moscow, 117198, Russia
Tel.: (7) 495 662 3617
Project Management Consulting Services
N.A.I.C.S.: 541618

Amec Singapore Pte Ltd (2)
991E Alexandra Rd Unit 01-25, Singapore, 119973, Singapore
Tel.: (65) 6423 9180
Project Management Consulting Services
N.A.I.C.S.: 541618

Baymont Malaysia Sdn. Bhd. (2)
Level 18 Naza Tower Platinum Park 10 Persiaran KLCC, 50088, Kuala Lumpur, Malaysia
Tel.: (60) 3 9212 4600
Engineeering Services
N.A.I.C.S.: 541330

CHANGZHOU AMEC GROUP CO., LTD (2)
No 62 Xinggang Rd, Changzhou, 213023, Jiangsu, China
Tel.: (86) 51983978000
Web Site: http://www.amecco.com
Asset Management Services
N.A.I.C.S.: 523940

Foster Wheeler (Philippines) Corporation
12th Floor Net One Center 26th Street Corner 3r Crescent Park West, Metro Manilla Bonifacio Global City, Taguig, 1634, Philippines
Tel.: (63) 43 723 0720
Construction Engineering Services
N.A.I.C.S.: 541330

Subsidiary (Domestic):

Foster Wheeler AG (2)
Shinfield Park, Reading, RG2 9FW, Berks, United Kingdom
Tel.: (44) 118913 1234
Web Site: http://www.fwc.com

AND PRIVATE COMPANIES

Emp.: 13,311
Holding Company; Engineering, Construction & Other Related Technical Services
N.A.I.C.S.: 551112

Subsidiary (Non-US):

Foster Wheeler Arabia, Ltd. (2)
Majd Business Center King Faisal Road, Al Khobar, 31952, Saudi Arabia (100%)
Tel.: (966) 13 6685555
Engineering & Construction Services
N.A.I.C.S.: 541330

Foster Wheeler Asia Pacific Pte. Ltd (2)
991e Alexandra Road 01-25 Block 7, Singapore, 119973, Singapore
Tel.: (65) 65018888
Construction Engineering Services
N.A.I.C.S.: 541330

Foster Wheeler Bimas A.S. (2)
Kucukbakkalkoy Mahallesi Merdivenkoyyolu Cad Cardak, Sok No 1 A Plaza 34750 Atasehir, Istanbul, 81090, Turkiye (100%)
Tel.: (90) 216 665 0000
Engineering & Construction Services
N.A.I.C.S.: 541330

Foster Wheeler Energy Management (Shanghai) Company Limited (2)
3rd Floor Building 3A Tianhua Technology Information Park No 299 Lon, Xuhui District, Shanghai, China
Tel.: (86) 21 3469 7300
Construction Engineering Services
N.A.I.C.S.: 541330

Foster Wheeler OOO (2)
Office A-404 Park Place 113/1, Leninsky Prospekt, Moscow, 117198, Russia
Tel.: (7) 4956623617
Construction Engineering Services
N.A.I.C.S.: 541330

Foster Wheeler Power Group Asia Limited (2)
Project Execution Center No 42 Beisuitanghe Road, Jinshan District, Shanghai, China
Tel.: (86) 21 5739 8999
Construction Engineering Services
N.A.I.C.S.: 541330

Foster Wheeler South Africa (PTY) Limited (2)
2nd Road Halfway House, Midrand, 1685, South Africa
Tel.: (27) 11 690 0400
Construction Engineering Services
N.A.I.C.S.: 541330

MDM Engineering Group Limited (2)
382 Jan Smuts Avenue Craighall Park, Johannesburg, 2196, South Africa
Tel.: (27) 119934300
Minerals Process Engineering & Project Management Services
N.A.I.C.S.: 541330

PT AMEC Berca Indonesia (2)
CCM Building 4th Floor Jl Cikini Raya No 95, Jakarta, 10330, Indonesia
Tel.: (62) 213159040
Engineeering Services
N.A.I.C.S.: 541330

PT Amec Foster Wheeler Indonesia (2)
Perkantoran Pulo Mas Blok VII No 2, Pulogadung, Jakarta Timur, 13260, Indonesia
Tel.: (62) 214895322
Project Engineering & Technical Services
N.A.I.C.S.: 541330

PT Foster Wheeler O&G Indonesia (2)
Perkantoran Pulo Mas Blok VII No 2 Jl Perintis kemerdekaan, Pulogading East Jakarta, Jakarta, 13260, Indonesia
Tel.: (62) 21 489 5322
Construction Engineering Services
N.A.I.C.S.: 541330

Subsidiary (Domestic):

Performance Improvements (PI) Group Limited (2)
15 Justice Mill Lane, Aberdeen, AB11 6EQ, United Kingdom
Tel.: (44) 1224 851000
Design & Production Optimization Consultancy Services
N.A.I.C.S.: 541618

Performance Improvements (PI) Limited (2)
15 Justice Mill Lane, Aberdeen, AB11 6EQ, United Kingdom
Tel.: (44) 1224 851000
Oil & Gas Engineering Consulting Services
N.A.I.C.S.: 541690

Primat Recruitment Limited (2)
Lingfield Point, Darlington, DL1 1RW, United Kingdom
Tel.: (44) 1325 744400
Human Resource Consulting Services
N.A.I.C.S.: 541612

Wood Environment & Infrastructure Solutions UK Limited (2)
Partnership House Regent Farm Road, Gosforth, Newcastle upon Tyne, NE3 3AF, United Kingdom
Tel.: (44) 800 371733
Web Site: http://www.woodplc.com
Environmental & Engineering Consulting Services
N.A.I.C.S.: 541620

Wood and Company Limited (2)
Sandiway House Littledales Lane, Northwich, CW8 2YA, United Kingdom
Tel.: (44) 1606 883885
Project Management & Consulting Services
N.A.I.C.S.: 541618

Subsidiary (Non-US):

World Services Italiana S.r.l. (2)
Via Sebastiano Caboto 15, Corsico, 20094, Italy
Tel.: (39) 0244861
Construction Engineering Services
N.A.I.C.S.: 541330

Bauunternehmung Kittelberger GmbH i.L (1)
Bruesseler Str 6, 67657, Kaiserslautern, Germany
Tel.: (49) 6314140160
Project Engineering & Technical Services
N.A.I.C.S.: 541330

CEC Controls Company S.R.L (1)
Bulevardul Tudor Vladimirescu 22 Sector 5 Green Gate Office Building, Office 516 Campus 2 5th floor, Bucharest, Romania
Tel.: (40) 723670674
Industrial Maintenance Services
N.A.I.C.S.: 811310

Ethos Energy Group Limited (1)
Ethos House Craigshaw Business Park Craigshaw Road, Aberdeen, AB12 3QH, United Kingdom (51%)
Tel.: (44) 1224367200
Web Site: https://ethosenergy.co
Oil & Gas Rotating Equipment Services
N.A.I.C.S.: 811310
Ana B. Amicarella (CEO)

Hexagon Sociedad Anonima (1)
INCAT Camp Bioko Norte, Malabo, Equatorial Guinea
Tel.: (240) 522307
Engineering Consulting Services
N.A.I.C.S.: 541330

ISI Mustang (Argentina) S.A. (1)
Pedro Molina 714, 5500, Mendoza, Argentina
Tel.: (54) 2614252439
Project Engineering & Technical Services
N.A.I.C.S.: 541330

J P Kenny Engineering Limited (1)
John Wood House Greenwell Road, Aberdeen, AB12 3AX, Scotland, United Kingdom (100%)
Tel.: (44) 1224851000
Web Site: http://www.woodgroupkenny.com
Sales Range: $1-4.9 Billion
Emp.: 5,000
Holding Company
N.A.I.C.S.: 551112
Bob MacDonald (CEO)

JOHN WOOD GROUP PLC

Subsidiary (Non-US):

Wood Group Integrity Management Pty. Ltd. (2)
5th Floor Wood Group House 432 Murray Street, Perth, 6000, WA, Australia
Tel.: (61) 863142400
Web Site: http://www.wgim.com
Emp.: 200
Oil & Gas, Mining, Water & Power Generation Industries Engineering & Project Management Services
N.A.I.C.S.: 541330
Mark Linton (Mng Dir)

Division (Domestic):

Wood Group Kenny (2)
Compass Point 79-87 Kingston Road, Staines-upon-Thames, TW18 1DT, Mddx, United Kingdom
Tel.: (44) 1784417200
Web Site: http://www.woodgroupkenny.com
Sales Range: $125-149.9 Million
Emp.: 500
Oil & Gas Pipeline & Subsea Engineering Services Contractor
N.A.I.C.S.: 238990
Gerwyn Williams (Grp Mng Dir)

Subsidiary (US):

J P Kenny Inc. (3)
15115 Park Row 3rd Fl, Houston, TX 77084
Tel.: (281) 675-1000
Sales Range: $75-99.9 Million
Emp.: 150
Oil & Gas Pipeline & Subsea Engineering Services Contractor
N.A.I.C.S.: 238990
Alan Brackenridge (Pres & COO)

Subsidiary (Non-US):

J P Kenny Pty. Ltd. (3)
Wood Group House 432 Murray St, Perth, 6000, WA, Australia
Tel.: (61) 863142000
Web Site: http://www.jpkenny.com
Sales Range: $25-49.9 Million
Emp.: 200
Oil & Gas Pipeline & Subsea Engineering Services Contractor
N.A.I.C.S.: 238990
Phil Brown (Dir-Ops)

M&O Pacific Limited (1)
26 - 32 Manadon Street, PO Box 265, New Plymouth, New Zealand
Tel.: (64) 67511101
Project Engineering & Technical Services
N.A.I.C.S.: 541330

PSJ Fabrications Ltd. (1)
Murdock Road, Bedford, MK41 7PT, United Kingdom
Tel.: (44) 1234268484
Web Site: http://www.psjfabrications.com
Metal Fabrication Mfr
N.A.I.C.S.: 332312

PSN Overseas Holding Company Limited (1)
International Tower 5th Floor Capital Centre Adjacent ADNEC, 24th Karama Street, Abu Dhabi, United Arab Emirates
Tel.: (971) 26519800
Project Engineering & Technical Services
N.A.I.C.S.: 541330

PSN Production Services Network Philippines Corp. (1)
12th Floor Net One Center 26th Street Corner 3r Crescent Park West, Metro Manilla Bonifacio Global City, Taguig, 1634, Philippines
Tel.: (63) 437230720
Project Engineering & Technical Services
N.A.I.C.S.: 541330

PT Australian Skills Training (1)
Green Town Warehouse No 3 - 4 Bengkong, Batam, Riau, Indonesia
Tel.: (62) 778425969
Project Engineering & Technical Services
N.A.I.C.S.: 541330

Procesos y Disenos Energeticos S.A.S. (1)

Carrera 11 A No 96-51 Floor 3 4 5, Bogota, Colombia
Tel.: (57) 15930593
Project Engineering & Technical Services
N.A.I.C.S.: 541330

Production Services Network (UK) Limited (1)
15 Justice Mill Lane, Aberdeen, AB11 6EQ, United Kingdom
Tel.: (44) 1224 777 777
Web Site: http://www.woodgroup-psn.com
Sales Range: $5-14.9 Billion
Oil & Natural Gas Well Operation & Maintenance Services
N.A.I.C.S.: 213112
Sue MacDonald (Grp Head-HR)

Subsidiary (US):

Swaggart Brothers Inc. (2)
31989 Feedville Rd, Stanfield, OR 97875-7875
Tel.: (541) 564-9000
Web Site: http://www.swaggartbrothers.com
Construction Services
N.A.I.C.S.: 236115
Doug Doyle (CFO)

Wood Group Production Services, Inc. (2)
17000 Katy Freeway Ste 150, Houston, TX 77094
Tel.: (281) 647-8300
Web Site: http://www.wgps.com
Oil & Natural Gas Well Operation & Maintenance Services
N.A.I.C.S.: 213112

Subsidiary (Domestic):

Duval Lease Service, LLC (3)
202 N Norton Rd, Freer, TX 78357
Tel.: (361) 394-7273
Sales Range: $200-249.9 Million
Emp.: 300
Oil & Gas Market Machinery Maintenance, Installation & Fabrication Services
N.A.I.C.S.: 213112
Rene A. Casas (Pres)

Branch (Domestic):

Wood Group Production Services, Inc. - Houma (3)
182 Equity Blvd, Houma, LA 70360
Tel.: (985) 868-4116
Web Site: http://www.wgps.com
Rev.: $14,740,758
Emp.: 350
Oil & Natural Gas Well Operation & Maintenance Services
N.A.I.C.S.: 213112
Lee Gautreaux (Mgr-Ops)

Production Services Network Holdings Corp. (1)
585 ME National Road HW Barangay, Alangilan, Batangas, Philippines
Tel.: (63) 437230720
Project Engineering & Technical Services
N.A.I.C.S.: 541330

Rider Hunt International (Australia) Pty. Ltd. (1)
Level 11 171 Collins St, Melbourne, 3000, VIC, Australia
Tel.: (61) 392116420
Professional Consultancy Services
N.A.I.C.S.: 541618

Rider Hunt International South Africa (Pty.) Ltd (1)
Building 2 Silver Stream Business Park 10 Muswell Road South, Johannesburg, 2021, South Africa
Tel.: (27) 118407300
Professional Consultancy Services
N.A.I.C.S.: 541618

Shanahan Engineering Ltd (1)
West Pier Business Campus Block 1- 3rd Floor Old Dunleary Road, Dun Laoghaire, Dublin, Ireland
Tel.: (353) 1 280 9888
Web Site: https://www.shanahanengineering.com
Emp.: 2
Construction Engineering Services
N.A.I.C.S.: 541330

JOHN WOOD GROUP PLC

John Wood Group PLC—(Continued)
James Greaney (CEO)

The Automated Technology Group (Slovakia) s.r.o. (1)
Pri Jelsine 3636/1, Nitra, 949 01, Slovakia
Tel.: (421) 373215100
Industrial Maintenance Services
N.A.I.C.S.: 811310

The Automated Technology Group Limited
Wrest Park, Silsoe, Bedford, MK45 4HS, United Kingdom
Tel.: (44) 1582400690
Web Site: http://www.the-atg.com
Industrial Maintenance Services
N.A.I.C.S.: 811310
Andy Robinson (CEO)

Wood E&IS GmbH (1)
Weserstr 4, 60329, Frankfurt am Main, Germany
Tel.: (49) 697560070
Project Engineering & Technical Services
N.A.I.C.S.: 541330

Wood Group Colombia S.A. (1)
Carrera 11 A 93-67 Edificio Parque Ejecutivo Oficina 501, Bogota, Colombia
Tel.: (57) 1 6212425
Industrial Gas & Turbine Overhaul Repair & Maintenance Services
N.A.I.C.S.: 811310

Wood Group Engineering (North Sea) Limited (1)
John Wood House Greenwell Road, East Tullosuni, Aberdeen, AB12 3AX, United Kingdom
Tel.: (44) 1224 851 000
Emp.: 3,000
Oil & Gas Field Construction Engineering Services
N.A.I.C.S.: 237120
Robert Keiller (CEO)

Wood Group France SAS (1)
60 rue de la Chaussee d'Antin, 75009, Paris, France
Tel.: (33) 144885710
Project Engineering & Technical Services
N.A.I.C.S.: 541330

Wood Group Kazakhstan LLP (1)
46 Satpayev St, Atyrau, 060011, Kazakhstan
Tel.: (7) 7122909800
Project Engineering & Technical Services
N.A.I.C.S.: 541330

Wood Group Kenny India Private Limited (1)
Vatika Business Centre Vatika Atrium 3rd Floor Block B Sector - 53, Golf Course Road, Gurgaon, 122002, India
Tel.: (91) 1244311111
Project Engineering & Technical Services
N.A.I.C.S.: 541330

Wood Group Kenny Ireland Limited (1)
Galway Technology Park, Parkmore, Galway, Ireland
Tel.: (353) 91481210
Project Engineering & Technical Services
N.A.I.C.S.: 541330

Wood Group Norway AS (1)
Fokserodveien 12, Sandefjord, 3241, Norway
Tel.: (47) 33446600
Project Engineering & Technical Services
N.A.I.C.S.: 541330

Wood Group PSN Uganda Limited (1)
Plot 18 Shimoni Road, PO Box 30330, Kampala, Uganda
Tel.: (256) 793244954
Project Engineering & Technical Services
N.A.I.C.S.: 541330

Wood Group Somias SPA (1)
Route des salines, PO Box 67, Annaba, Algeria
Tel.: (213) 38539319
Web Site: http://www.wgsomias.com
Industrial Maintenance Services
N.A.I.C.S.: 811310

Wood Group Trinidad & Tobago Limited (1)
6A Queens Park West Victoria Avenue, Port of Spain, Trinidad & Tobago
Tel.: (868) 6256810
Project Engineering & Technical Services
N.A.I.C.S.: 541330

Wood Group USA, Inc. (1)
17420 Katy Freeway Ste 300, Houston, TX 77094
Tel.: (281) 828-3500
Web Site: http://www.woodgroup.com
Sales Range: $25-49.9 Million
Emp.: 40
Holding Company; Corporate Office
N.A.I.C.S.: 551112
Carolyn Smith (Dir-Corp Comm-Eastern Hemisphere)

Subsidiary (Domestic):

CEC Controls Company, Inc. (2)
14555 Barber Ave, Warren, MI 48088
Tel.: (586) 779-0222
Web Site: https://www.ceccontrols.com
Control Panel Mfr
N.A.I.C.S.: 335313

Cape Software, Inc. (2)
17325 Park Row Dr, Houston, TX 77084
Tel.: (281) 600-3637
Web Site: http://www.capesoftware.com
Engineeering Services
N.A.I.C.S.: 541330

Deepwater Specialists Inc (2)
1215 Prytania St Ste 401, New Orleans, LA 70130
Tel.: (504) 523-3334
Web Site: http://www.deepwaterspecialists.com
Facilities Commissioning Services
N.A.I.C.S.: 561210
Bryan Broussard (Pres)

Elkhorn Holdings Inc. (2)
71 Allegiance Cir, Evanston, WY 82930-3823
Tel.: (307) 789-1595
Web Site: http://www.elkhornconstruction.com
Sales Range: $100-124.9 Million
Provider of Heavy Construction Services
N.A.I.C.S.: 237990
Sean Sullivan (Chm, Pres & CEO)

Subsidiary (Domestic):

Eagle Pipeline Construction, Inc. (3)
11917 E FM 917, Alvarado, TX 76009
Tel.: (817) 506-7750
Web Site: http://www.eaglepipeline.com
Sales Range: $1-9.9 Million
Pipeline Construction Services
N.A.I.C.S.: 237120
Scott Chisum (Bus Unit Mgr)

Elkhorn Construction Inc. (3)
71 Allegiance Cir, Evanston, WY 82930-3823
Tel.: (307) 789-1595
Web Site: http://www.elkhornconstruction.com
Sales Range: $25-49.9 Million
Emp.: 130
Heavy Construction Services
N.A.I.C.S.: 237990
Mitch Midcap (Pres)

HOAD, Inc. (3)
4057 Camelot Cir, Longmont, CO 80504
Tel.: (720) 438-2000
Web Site: http://www.hoadinc.com
Measuring Equipment Mfr
N.A.I.C.S.: 334519
Kevin Craft (Gen Mgr)

Division (Domestic):

HOAD, Inc. - San Juan Division (4)
1700 N 1st St, Bloomfield, NM 87413
Tel.: (505) 634-4100
Measuring Equipment Mfr
N.A.I.C.S.: 334519
Dave Gerg (Area Mgr)

Subsidiary (Domestic):

Infinity Construction Services, LP (2)
622 Commerce Ave, Clute, TX 77531
Tel.: (979) 388-8579
Web Site: http://www.infinitycs.us
Chemical Plant & Refinery Construction
N.A.I.C.S.: 237990
Calvin Shiflet (Mgr-Construction-Coatings Grp)

Ingenious Inc. (2)
10700 Richmond Ave Ste 108, Houston, TX 77042-4905
Tel.: (832) 844-0082
Web Site: http://www.ingeniousinc.com
Engineering Services
N.A.I.C.S.: 541330
Bharat Kamdar (Co-Founder & Pres)

Kelchner, Inc. (2)
50 Advanced Dr, Springboro, OH 45066
Tel.: (937) 704-9890
Web Site: http://www.kelchner.com
Sales Range: $75-99.9 Million
Emp.: 375
Construction Services
N.A.I.C.S.: 237990
Troy Norvell (Pres)

Producers Assistance Corporation (2)
1400 Broadfield S 300, Houston, TX 77084
Tel.: (281) 676-9000
Web Site: http://www.pachouston.com
Oil & Gas Industry Maintenance Services
N.A.I.C.S.: 213112
Mitchell Fralick (Pres & CEO)

Swaggart Logging & Excavation LLC (2)
15862 SW 72nd Ave Ste 150, Portland, OR 97224
Tel.: (503) 639-3400
Project Engineering & Technical Services
N.A.I.C.S.: 541330

Wood Group Mustang, Inc. (2)
17325 Park Row, Houston, TX 77084
Tel.: (832) 809-8000
Web Site: http://www.mustangeng.com
Construction Engineering Services
N.A.I.C.S.: 541330
Kent McAllister (Pres-Offshore Bus)

Joint Venture (Domestic):

Wood Group Pratt & Whitney Industrial Turbine Services, LLC (2)
1460 Blue Hills Ave, Bloomfield, CT 06002
Tel.: (860) 286-4600
Web Site: https://www.wgpw.com
Sales Range: $10-24.9 Million
Emp.: 85
Industrial & Aero Turbine Overhaul & Technical Support Services; Owned 51% by United Technologies Corporation & 49% by John Wood Group PLC
N.A.I.C.S.: 811310
George T. Gaudette (Pres)

Wood Sardegna S.r.l. (1)
Via Sebastiano Caboto 15, Corsico, 20094, Milan, Italy
Tel.: (39) 0244861
Project Engineering & Technical Services
N.A.I.C.S.: 541330

JOHNAN ACADEMIC PREPARATORY INSTITUTE, INC.
222 Ekimae Honmachi, Kawasaki-ku, Kawasaki, 210-0007, Kanagawa, Japan
Tel.: (81) 442461951
Web Site: https://www.johnan.co.jp
Year Founded: 1982
4720—(TKS)
Rev.: $38,675,110
Assets: $32,223,750
Liabilities: $19,783,730
Net Worth: $12,440,020
Earnings: ($806,420)
Fiscal Year-end: 03/31/24
Education Services
N.A.I.C.S.: 611691
Katsumi Shimomura (Pres & CEO)

JOHNS LYNG GROUP LIMITED
1 Williamsons Road, Doncaster, 3108, VIC, Australia

INTERNATIONAL PUBLIC

Tel.: (61) 392720000 AU
Web Site: https://johnslyng.com.au
Year Founded: 1953
JLG—(ASX)
Rev.: $773,827,860
Assets: $524,891,050
Liabilities: $217,546,353
Net Worth: $307,344,696
Earnings: $42,256,590
Emp.: 2,300
Fiscal Year-end: 06/30/24
Building Restoration Services
N.A.I.C.S.: 236118
Lindsay Barber (COO)

Subsidiaries:

Dressed For Sale Australia Pty. Ltd. (1)
7 Myer Court, Beverley, Adelaide, 5009, SA, Australia
Tel.: (61) 883333443
Web Site: http://www.dressedforsale.com.au
Home Product Whslr
N.A.I.C.S.: 423620

Steamatic of Nashville, LLC (1)
2219 Dunn Ave, Nashville, TN 37211
Tel.: (615) 256-7447
Web Site: https://steamatictn.com
Restoration & Cleaning Services
N.A.I.C.S.: 561720

JOHNS LYNG GROUP LIMITED
1 Williamsons Road, Doncaster, VIC, Australia
Tel.: (61) 92720000
Web Site: http://www.johnslyng.com.au
Integrated Building Services
N.A.I.C.S.: 236220
Scott Didier (CEO)

Subsidiaries:

Reconstruction Experts Inc. (1)
5300 Vivian St, Arvada, CO 80002
Tel.: (303) 783-2562
Web Site: http://www.reconstructionexperts.net
Commercial & Institutional Building Construction
N.A.I.C.S.: 236220

Subsidiary (Domestic):

Advanced Roofing & Sheet Metal (2)
2320 Bruner Ln, Fort Myers, FL 33912
Tel.: (239) 939-4412
Web Site: http://www.advancedroofingsheetmetal.com
Sales Range: $1-9.9 Million
Emp.: 80
Roofing Contractors
N.A.I.C.S.: 238160
Michael Shephard (Pres)

Steamatic, Inc. (1)
3333 Quorum Dr Ste 280, Fort Worth, TX 76137
Tel.: (817) 632-1555
Web Site: http://www.steamatic.com
Carpet, Furniture & Drapery Cleaning Processes, Air Duct Cleaning & Fire & Water Damage Restoration Mfr & Franchiser
N.A.I.C.S.: 533110
Bill Sims (Chm)

JOHNS OF NOTTINGHAM LTD
622 640 Woodborough Road, Nottingham, NG3 5FS, United Kingdom
Tel.: (44) 1159624131
Web Site: http://www.johnsofnottingham.co.uk
Year Founded: 1909
Sales Range: $10-24.9 Million
Emp.: 120
Commercial Painting Contracting Services
N.A.I.C.S.: 238320
Russell Chapman (Mng Dir)

AND PRIVATE COMPANIES

JOHNSON & JOHNSON MEDICAL, INC
1234 Chanlon, Berlin, Germany
Tel.: (49) 555 1212
Sales Range: $10-24.9 Million
Medical Device Mfr
N.A.I.C.S.: 339112
Tanya Hurst *(Pres)*

JOHNSON AND PHILLIPS (PAKISTAN) LIMITED
C-10 South Avenue S I T E, PO Box 3603, Karachi, 75700, Pakistan
Tel.: (92) 2132560030
Web Site:
   http://www.johnsonphillips.pk
JOPP—(KAR)
Rev.: $29,280
Assets: $3,566,981
Liabilities: $2,524,689
Net Worth: $1,042,292
Earnings: ($254,876)
Emp.: 8
Fiscal Year-end: 06/30/19
Electrical Power Equipment Mfr
N.A.I.C.S.: 335312
Zainab Anis Mianoor *(Chm)*

Subsidiaries:

Elmetec (Pvt) Limited (1)
App 211 Second Floor Al-Safa Heights-1 F-11 Markaz, Islamabad, Pakistan
Tel.: (92) 3337147042
Electrical Distribution Equipment Mfr
N.A.I.C.S.: 335999

JOHNSON CHEMICAL PHARMACEUTICAL WORKS CO., LTD.
31 Sec 4 San Ho Road, San Chung District, New Taipei City, 241, Taiwan
Tel.: (886) 229894756
Web Site:
   https://www.jcpjohnson.com.tw
Year Founded: 1959
4747—(TPE)
Rev.: $15,466,685
Assets: $32,492,887
Liabilities: $5,239,158
Net Worth: $27,253,729
Earnings: $2,027,671
Emp.: 157
Fiscal Year-end: 12/31/22
Pharmaceutical Product Mfr & Distr
N.A.I.C.S.: 325412
Pai-Hsiung Huang *(Chm & CEO)*

JOHNSON CONTROLS INTERNATIONAL PLC
1 Albert Quay, Cork, T12 X8N6, Ireland
Tel.: (353) 214235000   IE
Web Site:
   http://www.johnsoncontrols.com
Year Founded: 1885
JCI—(NYSE)
Rev.: $26,793,000,000
Assets: $42,242,000,000
Liabilities: $24,548,000,000
Net Worth: $17,694,000,000
Earnings: $1,849,000,000
Emp.: 100,000
Fiscal Year-end: 09/30/23
Holding Company; Building Control Equipment, Batteries & Distributed Energy Storage Products Mfr
N.A.I.C.S.: 551112
George R. Oliver *(Chm & CEO)*

Subsidiaries:

Creativesystems - Sistemas E Servicos De Consultoria, S.A. (1)
Fundoes Street 151, 3700-121, Sao Joao da Madeira, Portugal
Tel.: (351) 256303150
Web Site: http://www.creativesystems.eu
Infrastrcuture Management Services

N.A.I.C.S.: 561110

FM:Systems Group, LLC (1)
2301 Sugar Bush Rd, Raleigh, NC 27612
Tel.: (919) 790-5320
Web Site: https://fmsystems.com
Computer Facilities Management Services
N.A.I.C.S.: 541513
Kurt von Koch *(CEO)*

First Choice Facilities Limited (1)
Security House The Summit, Hanworth Road, Sunbury-on-Thames, TW16 5DB, Middlesex, United Kingdom
Tel.: (44) 1895814912
Building Maintenance Services
N.A.I.C.S.: 561790

Infrared Systems Group Ltd. (1)
3M Centre Cain Road, Bracknell, RG12 8HT, Berkshire, United Kingdom
Tel.: (44) 1268527700
Imaging Equipment Mfr
N.A.I.C.S.: 811210
J M Thompstone *(Dir)*

Infrared Systems Group, LLC (1)
305 Petty Rd Ste B, Lawrenceville, GA 30043
Tel.: (678) 442-1234
Fire Security Equipment Mfr
N.A.I.C.S.: 423690

Johnson Controls, Inc. (1)
5757 N Green Bay Ave, Glendale, WI 53209
Tel.: (414) 524-4500
Web Site: https://www.johnsoncontrols.com
Automotive Battery & Interior Systems Designer & Mfr; Facility Heating, Ventilation, Air Conditioning, Lighting, Fire & Safety Systems Designer, Mfr & Installer
N.A.I.C.S.: 333415
George R. Oliver *(Chm & CEO)*

Subsidiary (Domestic):

Lux Products Corp. (2)
4747 S Broad St Bldg 101 Ste 330, Philadelphia, PA 19112
Tel.: (856) 234-8803
Web Site: http://www.luxproducts.com
Instruments & Related Products Mfr for Measuring, Displaying & Controlling Industrial Process Variables
N.A.I.C.S.: 334513

Trion, Inc. (2)
101 McNeill Rd, Sanford, NC 27330-9451
Tel.: (919) 775-2201
Web Site: http://www.trioniaq.com
Electronic Air Cleaners Mfr
N.A.I.C.S.: 333413
Mike Howell *(Natl Sls Mgr)*

York International Corporation (2)
507 E Michigan St, Milwaukee, WI 53202
Tel.: (717) 771-7890
Web Site: http://www.johnsoncontrols.com
Facility Heating, Ventilation, Air Conditioning, Refrigeration, Lighting, Security & Fire Management Control Equipment Whslr, Systems Engineering & Maintenance Services
N.A.I.C.S.: 423720

Subsidiary (Non-US):

Arduman Klima Sanayi Servisi AS (3)
Cetin Emec Bulvari 2 Cadde No 4/2, Ovecler, Ankara, 06520, Turkiye
Tel.: (90) 3124726114
Web Site: http://www.johnsoncontrols.com.tr
Heat, Ventilation, Refrigeration & Air Conditioning Equipment Mfr, Distr & Servicing
N.A.I.C.S.: 333415

BGIS Global Integrated Solutions Canada LP (3)
4175 14th Avenue, PO Box 4800, Markham, L3R 0J2, ON, Canada
Tel.: (905) 943-4100
Web Site: https://www.bgis.com
Workspace Management Services
N.A.I.C.S.: 561210
Gordon Hicks *(CEO)*

Subsidiary (Domestic):

Evcon Industries, Inc. (3)

3110 N Mead St, Wichita, KS 67219-4057
Tel.: (405) 364-4040
Web Site: http://www.johnsoncontrols.com
Heating, Ventilation, Refrigeration & Air Conditioning Equipment Mfr
N.A.I.C.S.: 333415

Subsidiary (Non-US):

Johnson Controls - Egypt (3)
47th Building Section 1 City Center, Cairo, 11853, Egypt   **(100%)**
Tel.: (20) 225370131
Web Site:
   http://middleeast.johnsoncontrols.com
Heat, Ventilation, Refrigeration & Air Conditioning Equipment Distr & Servicing
N.A.I.C.S.: 333415

Johnson Controls BE Argentina S.r.l. (3)
Thames 139, Boulogne, Buenos Aires, B1609JU, Argentina
Tel.: (54) 1140064900
Web Site: http://www.johnsoncontrols.com
Refrigerator Equipment Mfr
N.A.I.C.S.: 333415

Johnson Controls Bulgaria EOOD (3)
102 Oborishte str., Sofia, 1505, Bulgaria
Tel.: (359) 29803040
Web Site: http://www.johnsoncontrols.com
Provider of Heat, Ventilation, Refrigeration & Air Conditioning Equipment
N.A.I.C.S.: 333415

Johnson Controls Chile S.A. (3)
Avenida Los Maitenes Oriente 1261 Pudahuel, Consorcio Industrial Enea, 1261, Santiago, Chile
Tel.: (56) 24272100
Web Site: http://www.johnsoncontrols.com
Heating, Ventilation, Refrigeration & Air Conditioning Equipment Mfr
N.A.I.C.S.: 333415

Johnson Controls Co., Ltd. (3)
Sasazuka NA Building 1-50-1 Sasazuka Shibuya-ku, Tokyo, 151 0073, Japan
Tel.: (81) 357386100
Web Site: http://www.johnsoncontrols.com
Heat, Ventilation, Refrigeration & Air Conditioning Equipment Servicing, Mfr & Whslr
N.A.I.C.S.: 333415

Johnson Controls Colombia Limitada (3)
Calle 25D No 100-12, Bogota, Colombia
Tel.: (57) 1742366000
Web Site: http://www.johnsoncontrols.com
Heat, Ventilation, Refrigeration & Air Conditioning Services & Equipment Mfr
N.A.I.C.S.: 333415

Johnson Controls Czech sro. (3)
Libalova 1/2348, 149 00, Prague, Czech Republic
Tel.: (420) 241029601
Web Site: http://www.johnsoncontrols.com
Heat, Ventilation, Refrigeration & Air Conditioning Equipment Mfr & Distr
N.A.I.C.S.: 333415

Johnson Controls Denmark ApS (3)
Christian Xs Vej 201, PO Box 1810, 8270, Hojbjerg, Denmark
Tel.: (45) 87367000
Heat, Ventilation, Refrigeration & Air Conditioning Equipment Mfr
N.A.I.C.S.: 333415

Johnson Controls FZE (3)
Industrial Area 1 near Flaknaz Warehouse Plot B354 Al Quoz, PO Box 31065, Dubai, United Arab Emirates
Tel.: (971) 43817000
Web Site: http://www.johnsoncontrols.com
Refrigeration & Air Conditioning Equipment Mfr & Distr
N.A.I.C.S.: 333415

Johnson Controls Finland Oy (3)
Hankasuontie 10, FIN 00390, Helsinki, Finland
Tel.: (358) 505621613
Web Site: http://www.sabroe.com
Refrigeration & Air Conditioning Equipment Mfr
N.A.I.C.S.: 333415

JOHNSON CONTROLS INTERNATIONAL PLC

Unit (Domestic):

Johnson Controls Fire & Security Solutions (3)
4100 Guardian St Ste 200, Simi Valley, CA 93063-3391   **(100%)**
Tel.: (805) 522-5555
Web Site: http://www.johnsoncontrols.com
Electronic Access Control, Fire Protection & Security Management Systems
N.A.I.C.S.: 423690

Johnson Controls Inc.- Normal, Oklahoma (3)
5005 York Dr, Norman, OK 73069
Tel.: (405) 364-4040
Web Site: http://www.johnsoncontrols.com
Mfr of Residential & Light Commercial Air Conditioning, Furnaces & Heat Pumps
N.A.I.C.S.: 424490

Subsidiary (Non-US):

Johnson Controls Industries (3)
14 rue de Bel Air Zone Industrielle, PO Box 70309, 44473, Carquefou, Nantes, France
Tel.: (33) 240306200
Web Site: http://www.johnsoncontrols.fr
Industrial & Commercial Fans, Blowers & Ventilation Equipment Mfr,
N.A.I.C.S.: 333413

Johnson Controls International KFT (3)
1097 Gubacsi ut 6, 1097, Budapest, Hungary
Tel.: (36) 1 459 3700
Building Efficiencies; Heat, Ventilation, Refrigeration & Air Conditioning Equipment Mfr & Distr
N.A.I.C.S.: 333415

Johnson Controls International Romania S.R.L. (3)
Strada Drajna 5, 060764, Bucharest, Romania
Tel.: (40) 0213304047
Heat, Ventilation, Refrigeration & Air Conditioning Equipment Mfr & Servicing
N.A.I.C.S.: 333415

Johnson Controls Korea Ltd. (3)
34 KT & G Euljiro Tower 34 Mareonnae-ro, Jung-gu, Seoul, 04555, Korea (South)
Tel.: (82) 15889117
Web Site: http://www.johnsoncontrols.com
Heat, Ventilation, Refrigeration & Air Conditioning Equipment Mfr & Distr
N.A.I.C.S.: 333415

Johnson Controls L.P. (3)
7400 Birchmount Rd, Markham, L3R 5V4, ON, Canada   **(100%)**
Tel.: (905) 475-7610
Facility Environmental Controls Systems & Equipment Mfr
N.A.I.C.S.: 334512

Johnson Controls Limited (3)
4 Kilmartin Place, Tannochside Business Park, Uddingston, G71 5PH, Gaslow, United Kingdom
Tel.: (44) 1236784120
Web Site: http://www.johnsoncontrols.com
Refrigeration & Air Conditioning Equipment Mfr & Whslr
N.A.I.C.S.: 333415

Johnson Controls Limited (3)
Unit 1 Russel Square, Basildon, SS15 6RZ, Essex, United Kingdom
Tel.: (44) 1268246000
Web Site: http://www.johnsoncontrols.com
Industrial & Commercial Cooling & Ventilation Equipment Mfr & Distr
N.A.I.C.S.: 333415

Johnson Controls Ltd. (3)
7-8 Eaves Ct, Sittingbourne, ME10 3RY, Kent, United Kingdom
Tel.: (44) 01795472361
Web Site: http://www.johnsoncontrols.com
Refrigeration & Air Conditioning Equipment Whslr
N.A.I.C.S.: 333415

Johnson Controls Portugal Be, Lda. (3)
Av do Forte no 12, 2790-072, Lisbon, Carnaxide, Portugal

JOHNSON CONTROLS INTERNATIONAL PLC

Johnson Controls International plc—(Continued)
Tel.: (351) 219533810
Web Site: http://www.johnsoncontrols.com
Refrigeration & Air Conditioning Equipment Mfr & Whslr
N.A.I.C.S.: 333415

Johnson Controls Systems & Service AB (3)
Ursviksvagen 127, 174 46, Sundbyberg, Sweden
Tel.: (46) 77 164 8000
Web Site: http://www.johnsoncontrols.com
Heat, Ventilation, Refrigeration & Air Conditioning Equipment Mfr
N.A.I.C.S.: 333415

Johnson Controls Systems & Service GmbH (3)
Fuggerstrasse 1, Leipzig, D-04158, Germany
Tel.: (49) 341353060
Web Site: http://www.johnsoncontrols.com
Sales Range: $50-74.9 Million
Emp.: 120
Heating, Ventilation, Air Conditioning & Refrigeration Equipment Mfr
N.A.I.C.S.: 333415

Subsidiary (Domestic):

Johnson Controls Systems & Service GmbH (4)
Carnotstrasse 4, Hamburg, D-10587, Germany
Tel.: (49) 303908030
Web Site: http://www.johnsoncontrols.com
Heat, Ventilation, Refrigeration & Air Conditioning Equipment Mfr
N.A.I.C.S.: 333415

Johnson Controls Technischer Service GmbH (4)
Ohmstrasse 10, 63225, Langen, Germany
Tel.: (49) 6103981717
Web Site: http://www.johnsoncontrols.com
Heating, Ventilation, Air Conditioning & Refrigeration Equipment & Systems Repair & Maintenance
N.A.I.C.S.: 238220

Subsidiary (Non-US):

Johnson Controls Systems & Service Italia S.r.l. (3)
Via Alessandro Manzoni 44, Cusano Milanino, 20095, Milan, Italy
Tel.: (39) 02280421
Web Site: http://www.johnsoncontrols.com
Heat, Ventilation, Refrigeration & Air Conditioning Equipment Mfr & Servicing
N.A.I.C.S.: 333415
Francesco Rossi (Mgr-Product Mktg & Solutions)

Johnson Controls Venezuela S.A. (3)
Calle El Arenal Parcela No 136, Caracas, 1080, Venezuela
Tel.: (58) 2129527890
Web Site: http://www.johnsoncontrols.com
Heat, Ventilation, Refrigeration & Air Conditioning Equipment & Controls Systems Distr
N.A.I.C.S.: 333415

Johnson Controls York Marine ApS (3)
Christian Xs Vej 201, 8260, Hojbjerg, Denmark
Tel.: (45) 87363500
Web Site: http://www.johnsoncontrols.com
Provider of Heat, Ventilation, Refrigeration & Air Conditioning Equipment
N.A.I.C.S.: 333415

Johnson Controls, AO (3)
Poklonnaya St 14, 121170, Moscow, Russia
Tel.: (7) 4952326660
Web Site: http://www.johnsoncontrols.com
Heat, Ventilation, Refrigeration & Air Conditioning Services & Equipment Mfr
N.A.I.C.S.: 333415

Branch (Domestic):

Johnson Controls, Inc. - Dallas Office (3)
3021 W Bend Dr, Irving, TX 75063
Tel.: (972) 460-6703
Web Site: http://www.johnsoncontrols.com
Heating, Ventilation, Air-Conditioning, Refrigeration & Security Systems Whslr & Services Contractor
N.A.I.C.S.: 423720

Johnson Controls, Inc. - Little Rock Office
10600 Colonel Glenn Rd Ste 200, Little Rock, AR 72204
Tel.: (501) 224-5580
Web Site: http://www.johnsoncontrols.com
Heating, Ventilation, Air-Conditioning, Refrigeration & Security Systems Whslr & Services Contractor
N.A.I.C.S.: 423720

Johnson Controls, Inc. - Louisville Office (3)
9410 Bunsen Pkwy, Louisville, KY 40220-4209
Tel.: (502) 671-7300
Web Site: http://www.johnsoncontrols.com
Sales Range: $25-49.9 Million
Emp.: 150
Heating, Ventilation, Air-Conditioning, Refrigeration & Security Systems Whslr & Services Contractor
N.A.I.C.S.: 423720

Johnson Controls, Inc. - Shreveport Office (3)
531 W 61st St, Shreveport, LA 71106-2508
Tel.: (318) 868-8884
Heating, Ventilation, Air-Conditioning, Refrigeration & Security Systems Whslr & Services Contractor
N.A.I.C.S.: 423720

Subsidiary (Non-US):

Preston Refrigeration Limited (3)
Chantry Industrial Estate Kingsbury Road, Sutton Coldfield, B76 9EE, Curdworth, United Kingdom
Tel.: (44) 1675470899
Web Site: http://www.prestoncompressors.com
Refrigeration & Air Conditioning Equipment Remanufacturing
N.A.I.C.S.: 333415

Sabroe UK (3)
Unit E Chanty Industrial Estate Kingsbury Rd, Sutton Coldfield, B76 9EF, United Kingdom
Tel.: (44) 1675477214
Web Site: http://www.sabroe.com
Sales Range: $10-24.9 Million
Emp.: 14
Refrigeration Compressors & Equipment Mfr
N.A.I.C.S.: 333415

Supremeair (Pty) Limited (3)
43 11th Road KEW, PO Box 391465, 2018, Bramley, South Africa
Tel.: (27) 0117860868
Web Site: http://www.supremeair.co.za
Air Conditioning Maintenance & Services
N.A.I.C.S.: 238220

York Air Conditioning & Refrigeration (Thailand) Co., Ltd. (3)
69/154 Nawamin 48 Aleey Khlong Kum Bueng Kum, Rama 9 Road, Bangkok, 10240, Thailand
Tel.: (66) 27940101
Heat, Ventilation, Refrigeration & Air Conditioning Equipment Mfr & Distr
N.A.I.C.S.: 333415

York Guangzhou Air Conditioning & Refrigeration Co., Ltd. (3)
Xuetian Longshan Town, Fogang, Guangzhou, 511685, Guangdong, China
Tel.: (86) 76334688315
Heat, Ventilation, Refrigeration & Air Conditioning Equipment Mfr
N.A.I.C.S.: 333415

York Industrial (Thailand) Co., Ltd. (3)
Export Privilege Zone Phase II 49/40 Moos 5 Sriracha, Tambon Tungsukla Ampher, Chon Buri, 20230, Thailand (100%)
Tel.: (66) 38493400
Heat, Ventilation, Refrigeration & Air Conditioning Equipment Mfr
N.A.I.C.S.: 333415

York International GesmbH (3)
Gnigler Str, 5020, Salzburg, Austria
Tel.: (43) 662882544
Web Site: http://www.york.com
Heat, Ventilation, Refrigeration & Air Conditioning Equipment Mfr
N.A.I.C.S.: 333415

York International Ltd. (3)
2-2323 Winston Pk Dr, Oakville, L6H 6R7, ON, Canada
Tel.: (905) 829-1411
Web Site: http://www.york.com
Heat, Ventilation, Refrigeration & Air Conditioning Equipment Mfr
N.A.I.C.S.: 333415

York International, S.A. de C.V. (3)
Carretera Miguel Aleman Km. 11.2, Apodaca, 66600, NL, Mexico
Tel.: (52) 8181546000
Heat, Ventilation, Refrigeration & Air Conditioning Equipment Mfr
N.A.I.C.S.: 333415

York Refrigeration Philippines, Inc. (3)
81 Dr Arcadio Santos Ave, San Antonio, Paranaque, 1715, Metro Manila, Philippines (100%)
Tel.: (63) 288204258
Heat, Ventilation, Refrigeration & Air Conditioning Equipment Mfr
N.A.I.C.S.: 333415

Mid Atlantic GI Consultants (1)
537 Stanton Christiana Rd Ste 203, Newark, DE 19713
Tel.: (302) 225-2380
Web Site: http://www.midatlanticgi.com
Biomedical Engineering Services
N.A.I.C.S.: 811210

SA Oktopus NV (1)
Avenue Louise 331, Louizalaan-Brussels, 1050, Brussels, Belgium
Tel.: (32) 25420542
Web Site: http://www.oktopus.be
Remote Sensing Services
N.A.I.C.S.: 541360

Shanghai Jindun Fire-Fighting Intelligence Science and Technology Co., Ltd. (1)
No 88 College Town Pudong Road wansong, Shanghai, 201318, China
Tel.: (86) 2168189000
Web Site: http://en.shjd-intel.com
Fire Safety Services
N.A.I.C.S.: 561990

ShopperTrak Central Europe GmbH (1)
Kronenstr 12, 10117, Berlin, Germany
Tel.: (49) 3092102380
Web Site: http://de.shoppertrak.com
Retail Consulting Services
N.A.I.C.S.: 541618

Shoppertrak Iberica SL (1)
C / Jose Echegaray 8, Business Park Alvia Ed, 28232, Madrid, Spain
Tel.: (34) 916404490
Web Site: http://es.shoppertrak.com
Electrical Equipment Maintenance Services
N.A.I.C.S.: 811310

Shoppertrak Limited (1)
Yorke House Arleston Way, Solihull, B90 4LH, United Kingdom
Tel.: (44) 1217121488
Web Site: http://uk.shoppertrak.com
Retail Management Consulting Services
N.A.I.C.S.: 541611
Nick Pompa (CEO)

Synchrony, Inc. (1)
4655 Technology Dr, Salem, VA 24153
Tel.: (540) 444-4200
Web Site: http://www.synchrony.com
Automatic Environmental Control Mfr
N.A.I.C.S.: 334512
Margaret M. Keane (Pres & CEO)

Tyco International Management Company, LLC (1)
9 Roszel Rd, Princeton, NJ 08540
Tel.: (609) 720-4200
Web Site: http://www.tyco.com

INTERNATIONAL PUBLIC

Sales Range: $300-349.9 Million
Emp.: 1,000
Holding Company; Corporate Office
N.A.I.C.S.: 551112

Subsidiary (Non-US):

ADT Trustees Limited (2)
Security House The Summit, Hanworth Road, Sunbury-on-Thames, TW165DB, United Kingdom
Tel.: (44) 8083024346
Web Site: http://www.adt.co.uk
Fire Protection & Integrated Services
N.A.I.C.S.: 922160
Anton Bernard Alphonsus (Sec)

AIM Nederland B.V. (2)
PO Box 285, 2900 AG, Capelle aan den IJssel, Netherlands
Tel.: (31) 884604616
Web Site: http://www.aim-services.nl
Automatic Identification System Mfr & Distr
N.A.I.C.S.: 334519

Beijing Master Systems Engineering Co., Ltd (2)
Room 659 6th Floor Block B Chaowai SOHO Building No. 2 Chaowai St, Chaoyang, Beijing, 100020, China
Tel.: (86) 1065881188
Web Site: http://www.master.com.cn
Engineeering Services
N.A.I.C.S.: 541330

Bentel Security S.r.l. (2)
Via Gabbiano 22 Zona Industriale S Scolastica, 64013, Corropoli, Teramo, Italy
Tel.: (39) 0861839060
Web Site: http://www.bentelsecurity.com
Intrusion Security & Fire Alarm Control Equipment Mfr
N.A.I.C.S.: 334290

CIPE Belgium (2)
Humaniteitslaan 241, 1620, Drogenbos, Belgium
Tel.: (32) 25583600
Security Service Systems Provider
N.A.I.C.S.: 561621

CKS Systeme GmbH (2)
Dieselstrasse 9, Meppen, 49716, Germany
Tel.: (49) 59318400
Web Site: http://www.tyco.de
Security System Installation Services
N.A.I.C.S.: 238210

COSMOS Feuerloeschgeraetebau GmbH (2)
Industriestrasse 13, 68526, Ladenburg, Germany
Tel.: (49) 62032007
Web Site: http://www.cosmos-feuerloescher.de
Security Service Systems Provider
N.A.I.C.S.: 561621
Jurgen Joseph (Mng Dir)

Subsidiary (Domestic):

Central CPVC Corporation (2)
245 Swancott Rd, Madison, AL 35756
Tel.: (256) 464-5633
Fluid Power Valves & Hose Fittings Mfr
N.A.I.C.S.: 332912

Central Sprinkler Company (2)
1400 Pennbrook Pkwy, Lansdale, PA 19446
Tel.: (215) 362-0700
Fire Protection Equipments Distr
N.A.I.C.S.: 423850

Chemguard, Inc. (2)
1 Stanton St, Marinette, WI 54146-2542
Tel.: (817) 473-9964
Web Site: http://www.chemguard.com
Fire Protection Equipment Mfr
N.A.I.C.S.: 333998
John Vieweger (Dir-Foam Bus-Americas)

Subsidiary (Domestic):

Haz-Tank Fabricators, Inc. (3)
PO Box 591, Milwaukee, WI 53201
Tel.: (817) 473-9964
Bladder Tank Mfr
N.A.I.C.S.: 326226

Subsidiary (Non-US):

Controlled Electronic Management Systems Limited (2)

AND PRIVATE COMPANIES — JOHNSON CONTROLS INTERNATIONAL PLC

195 Airport Road West, Belfast, BT3 9ED, United Kingdom
Tel.: (44) 2890456767
Web Site: http://www.cemsys.com
Access Control & Integrated Security Management System Provider
N.A.I.C.S.: 561621

Digital Security Controls, Inc. (2)
3301 Langstaff Road, Concord, ON, Canada
Tel.: (905) 760-3000
Web Site: http://www.dsc.com
Home Security System Mfr
N.A.I.C.S.: 423690

FLN Feuerloschgerate Neuruppin Vertriebs-GmbH (2)
Martin-Ebell-Str 4, 16816, Neuruppin, Germany
Tel.: (49) 33916890
Web Site: http://www.fln-neuruppin.de
Fire Protection & Integrated Services
N.A.I.C.S.: 922160

Feuerloeschgeraete GmbH Neuruppin (2)
Martin Ebell Str 4, 16816, Neuruppin, Brandenburg, Germany
Tel.: (49) 93 42 92 64 0
Web Site: http://www.fln-neuruppin.de
Security Service Systems Provider
N.A.I.C.S.: 561621

Fire Equipment de Mexico, S.A. de C.V. (2)
Poniente 122 No 513 Col Barrio Coltongo, 02630, Mexico, Mexico
Tel.: (52) 5553688888
Web Site: http://www.fireequipmentmexico.com
Fire Protection Equipment Mfr
N.A.I.C.S.: 339999

First City Care (London) plc (2)
Little Ridge, Welwyn Garden City, AL7 2BH, Hertfordshire, United Kingdom
Tel.: (44) 1707364800
Web Site: http://www.firstcitycare.co.uk
Industrial Machinery System Installation Services
N.A.I.C.S.: 238210

Helmut Geissler Glasinstrumente GmbH (2)
Leonhard-Karl-Strasse 33, 97877, Wertheim, Germany
Tel.: (49) 93 42 92 64 0
Web Site: http://www.geisslerglass.com
Sprinkler Bulb Mfr
N.A.I.C.S.: 335139

Isogard SAS (2)
78 Rue Gustave Delory, 59810, Lesquin, France
Tel.: (33) 970809180
Household Durable Product Distr
N.A.I.C.S.: 423990

Johnson Controls Integrated Fire and Security Corporation Servicios, S.A. (2)
Calle Pollensa Cr Coruna Km 23 500 Edif Ecu 1 S/N, Las Rozas De Madrid, Madrid, 28290, Spain
Tel.: (34) 902444440
Web Site: http://www.tyco.es
Fire Protection & Integrated Services
N.A.I.C.S.: 922160
Ricardo Arroyo *(Sr Dir-Sls BT&S Continental Europe & Gen Mgr-Iberia)*

Johnson Controls International Korea Co., Ltd. (2)
34 Mareonnae-ro, Jung-gu, Seoul, 34903, Korea (South)
Tel.: (82) 15889117
Web Site: http://www.dbefire.com
Fire Detection Alarm System Mfr & Distr
N.A.I.C.S.: 334519
Bradley Buckwalter *(CEO)*

Johnson Controls Marine Services (Seaplus) Co., Ltd. (2)
32 Noksandandan 165-ro 14 beon-gil, GangSeo-gu, Busan, 46752, Korea (South)
Tel.: (82) 519703987
Fire Fighting System & Safety Equipments Mfr
N.A.I.C.S.: 332919

Johnson Controls Marine Services Company Limited (2)
21 Noksandandan 261-ro 13 beon-gil, Gangseo-gu, Busan, 46753, Korea (South)
Tel.: (82) 51 8995304
Marine Transportation Services
N.A.I.C.S.: 488390

Johnsons Control Systems and Service GmbH (2)
Waltherstrasse 51, 51069, Cologne, Germany
Tel.: (49) 221 67850
Security Service Systems Provider
N.A.I.C.S.: 561621

LPG America Latina Sociedad Anonima (2)
Juan Benito Blanco 3302, Montevideo, 11300, Uruguay
Tel.: (598) 26227840
Security Service Systems Provider
N.A.I.C.S.: 561621
Jose Carlos Rodriguez *(Gen Mgr)*

LPG Tecnicas en Extincion de Incendios, S.L. (2)
Mestre Joan Corrales 107-109, 8950, Esplugues de Llobregat, Barcelona, Spain
Tel.: (34) 934802925
Fire Protection & Integrated Services
N.A.I.C.S.: 922160

Macron Safety Systems (UK) Limited (2)
Burlingham House Hewett Road Gapton Hall Industrial Estate, Great Yarmouth, NR31 0NN, Norfolk, United Kingdom
Tel.: (44) 1493 417600
Web Site: http://www.hygood.com
Emp.: 100
Fire Protection & Suppression Product Mfr
N.A.I.C.S.: 339999
Robert Wade *(Dir)*

Subsidiary (Domestic):

Master Protection, LP (2)
13050 Metro Pkwy Ste 1, Fort Myers, FL 33966-4800
Tel.: (239) 896-1680
Web Site: http://www.firemasterweb.com
Fire Protection Equipment Mfr
N.A.I.C.S.: 922160
Bob Rice *(Gen Mgr)*

Subsidiary (Non-US):

Obsidian HCM Medical Holdings Ireland Limited (2)
1 Albert Quay Cork, Dublin, 2, Ireland
Tel.: (353) 906441400
Investment Management Service
N.A.I.C.S.: 523940

P2i Fire Protection Systems, Lda. (2)
Rua Zona Industrial, Casais da Serra, 2665-305, Lisbon, Miharado, Portugal
Tel.: (351) 219751322
Web Site: http://www.p2i.pt
Sales Range: $25-49.9 Million
Emp.: 7
Fire Extinguishing Products Mfr
N.A.I.C.S.: 922160

Protector Technologies BV (2)
Kopersteden 1, Enschede, 7547 TJ, Overijssel, Netherlands
Tel.: (31) 102730397
Fire Extinguisher Mfr
N.A.I.C.S.: 339999

Subsidiary (Domestic):

Proximex Corporation (2)
300 Santana Row Ste 200, San Jose, CA 95128
Tel.: (408) 215-9000
Web Site: http://www.proximex.com
Software Development Services
N.A.I.C.S.: 541511

Subsidiary (Non-US):

Rindin Enterprises Pty. Limited (2)
137 Mccredie Rd, Guildford, 2161, NSW, Australia
Tel.: (61) 287182191
Web Site: http://www.3mscott.com
Security System Service Provider
N.A.I.C.S.: 561621

Sabo Foam Srl (2)
Via Caravaggi, 24040, Levate, Bergamo, Italy
Tel.: (39) 035 2057011
Web Site: http://www.sabofoam.com
Foam Products Mfr
N.A.I.C.S.: 326140

Scott Health & Safety Limited (2)
3m Centre Cain Road, Bracknell, RG12 8HT, Berkshire, United Kingdom
Tel.: (44) 1695 727171
Web Site: http://www.3mscott.com
Fire Extinguisher Mfr
N.A.I.C.S.: 339999

Shanghai Eagle Safety Equipment Ltd. (2)
Room 1119, 200 Yincheng Rd, Pudong, Shanghai, 201206, China
Tel.: (86) 2138789588
Respiratory Protective Equipment Mfr
N.A.I.C.S.: 334510

Subsidiary (Domestic):

ShopperTrak RCT Corporation (2)
233 S Wacker Dr 41st Fl, Chicago, IL 60606
Tel.: (312) 529-5300
Web Site: http://www.shoppertrak.com
Software Solutions
N.A.I.C.S.: 513210

Shurjoint America, Inc. (2)
1380 Beverage Dr Ste P, Stone Mountain, GA 30083
Tel.: (770) 817-0444
Web Site: http://www.shurjoint.com
Emp.: 3
Mechanical Piping Component Mfr
N.A.I.C.S.: 331511

Subsidiary (Non-US):

Shurjoint Taiwan, Inc. (2)
11 F-2 No 175 Zhongzheng 2nd Rd Lingya, Kaohsiung, 80274, Taiwan
Tel.: (886) 72253768
Web Site: http://www.shurjoint.com
Hardware & Coupling Products Mfr
N.A.I.C.S.: 331511

Swiss Alertis AG (2)
Bahnweg 11, CH-8808, Pfaffikon, Switzerland
Tel.: (41) 444372020
Web Site: http://www.swissalertis.ch
Security System Services
N.A.I.C.S.: 561621

Thorn Security (Hong Kong) Limited (2)
11/F & 12/F Millennium City 6 392 Kwun Tong Road, Kwun Tong, Kowloon, China (Hong Kong)
Tel.: (852) 25900012
Web Site: http://www.johnsoncontrols.com
Security Control Equipment Distr
N.A.I.C.S.: 423690

Total Feuerschutz GmbH (2)
Industriestrasse 13, Ladenburg, 68526, Germany
Tel.: (49) 6203750
Web Site: http://www.tyco.de
Fire Protection & Integrated Services
N.A.I.C.S.: 922160

Tyco (China) Investment Co., Ltd. (2)
Room 1C104, Block 11 Block 518 Fuquan North Road, Changning, Shanghai, 200233, China
Tel.: (86) 2161135588
Fire Protection & Integrated Services
N.A.I.C.S.: 922160

Tyco Building Services Products (Germany) GmbH (2)
Senefelder Strasse 2, Rodgau, 63110, Germany
Tel.: (49) 6106 84455
Totalizing Fluid Meter Mfr
N.A.I.C.S.: 334514

Tyco Building Services Products (Hungary) Kft (2)
Etele Ut 59-61, Budapest, 1119, Hungary
Tel.: (36) 1481 1383
Web Site: http://www.tfppemea.com
Fire Protection System Installation Services
N.A.I.C.S.: 238310

Tyco Building Services Products (Italy) S.r.l. (2)
Via Xx Settembre 75, Nerviano, 20017, Italy
Tel.: (39) 0331589222
Fire Detection & Alarm System Distr
N.A.I.C.S.: 423610

Tyco Building Services Products (Norway) AS (2)
Kabelgata 8, 0580, Oslo, Norway
Tel.: (47) 67917700
Security System Installation Services
N.A.I.C.S.: 238210

Tyco Building Services Products (Sweden) AB (2)
Tradgardsgatan 10, PO Box 145, 36030, Lammhult, Kronoberg, Sweden
Tel.: (46) 472269980
Security Service Systems Provider
N.A.I.C.S.: 561621

Tyco Building Services Products (UK) Limited (2)
Security House The Summit, Hanworth Road, Sunbury-on-Thames, M40 2WL, Mddx, United Kingdom
Tel.: (44) 1618750400
Web Site: http://www.tyco-fire.com
Security Service Systems Provider
N.A.I.C.S.: 561621

Tyco Building Services Products S.A.S. (2)
5 Rue des Chardonnerets 14aBP 51275, 95957, Roissy-en-France, France
Tel.: (33) 148178727
Web Site: http://www.tyco-fire.com
Fire Protection & Building Construction Services
N.A.I.C.S.: 339999

Subsidiary (Domestic):

Tyco Electronics (US), Inc. (2)
15 Hampshire St, Mansfield, MA 02048
Tel.: (508) 261-8000
Fire Protection Consulting Services
N.A.I.C.S.: 922160

Subsidiary (Non-US):

Tyco Europe S.A.S. (2)
1 Rue Henri Giffard, Montigny Le Bretonneux, Yvelines, 78180, France
Tel.: (33) 130695400
Fire Detection & Alarm System Distr
N.A.I.C.S.: 423610
Jordi Andreu Serra-Roca *(Pres)*

Tyco Fire & Building Products Asia Pte. Ltd. (2)
2 Serangoon North Avenue 5 07-01 Fu Yu Building, Singapore, 554911, Singapore
Tel.: (65) 65774360
Web Site: http://www.tyco-fire.com
Fire Protection Equipment Mfr
N.A.I.C.S.: 339999

Tyco Fire & Integrated Solutions (Slovakia) s.r.o. (2)
Hontianska 1274/7, Bratislava, 821 09, Slovakia
Tel.: (421) 258104000
Fire Protection & Integrated Services
N.A.I.C.S.: 922160

Tyco Fire & Integrated Solutions s.r.o. (2)
Novodvorska 994, Prague, 142 00, Czech Republic
Tel.: (420) 239045100
Web Site: http://www.tycofis.cz
Security System Installation Services
N.A.I.C.S.: 238210

Tyco Fire & Security GmbH (2)
Victor von Bruns-Strasse 21, Neuhausen am Rheinfall, 8212, Switzerland
Tel.: (41) 526330244
Fire Protection & Integrated Services
N.A.I.C.S.: 922160

JOHNSON CONTROLS INTERNATIONAL PLC

Johnson Controls International plc—(Continued)

Group (Domestic):

Tyco Fire & Security LLC (2)
6600 Congress Ave, Boca Raton, FL 33487
Tel.: (561) 705-0168
Web Site: http://www.tycois.com
Fire Protection Equipment Mfr & Distr
N.A.I.C.S.: 334519

Subsidiary (Non-US):

ADT Fire and Security Limited (3)
ADT House Block 9A Beckett Way Parkwest Business Park, Dublin, 12, Ireland
Tel.: (353) 16205888
Web Site: http://www.adt.ie
Electronic Security System Mfr & Distr
N.A.I.C.S.: 334290

ADT Fire and Security plc (3)
Security House The Summit Hanworth Road, Sunbury-on-Thames, TW16 5DB, Mddx, United Kingdom
Tel.: (44) 1932743333
Web Site: http://www.adt.co.uk
Security, Fire Detection & Protection Products Whslr
N.A.I.C.S.: 561621

ADT Group Sp. z o.o. (3)
ul Poleczki 35, 02-822, Warsaw, Poland (100%)
Tel.: (48) 223783450
Web Site: http://adtg.pl
Security Services
N.A.I.C.S.: 561621

ADT Hong Kong Limited (3)
11/F & 12/F Millennium City 6 392 Kwun Tong Road, Kwun Tong, Kowloon, China (Hong Kong) (100%)
Tel.: (852) 25900012
Web Site: http://www.johnsoncontrols.com
Sales of Electronic Article Surveillance Equipment
N.A.I.C.S.: 449210

Digital Security Controls (3)
3301 Langstaff Rd, Concord, L4K 4L2, ON, Canada
Tel.: (905) 760-3000
Web Site: http://www.dsc.com
Digital Security Systems
N.A.I.C.S.: 561621

Subsidiary (Domestic):

Exacq Technologies, Inc. (3)
11955 Exit Five Pkwy Bldg 3, Fishers, IN 46037
Tel.: (317) 845-5710
Web Site: http://www.exacq.com
Video Management Systems Mfr
N.A.I.C.S.: 928110

Subsidiary (Non-US):

Johnson Control & Integrated Solutions France (3)
1 rue Giffard, 78067, Saint-Quentin-en-Yvelines, France
Tel.: (33) 139307300
Web Site: http://www.tyco.fr
Fire Extinguishing & Detection Products Distr
N.A.I.C.S.: 423990

Johnson Controls Integrated Fire & Security N.V. (3)
Leuvensesteenweg 510, Zaventem, 1930, Belgium
Tel.: (32) 2 467 78 11
Web Site: http://www.tyco.be
Fire Protection Equipment Mfr
N.A.I.C.S.: 334290

Mather & Platt Ireland Limited (3)
1 Albert Quay, Cork, Ireland
Tel.: (353) 014966077
Fire Detection, Alarm, Fire Supression & Integrated Security Applications & Services
N.A.I.C.S.: 922160

Subsidiary (Domestic):

Sensormatic Electronics, LLC (3)
6600 Congress Ave, Boca Raton, FL 33487
Tel.: (561) 912-6000
Web Site: http://www.sensormatic.com

Electronic Article Surveillance Equipment, Integrated Electronic Security Systems, Access Control, Exception Monitoring & Video Surveillance
N.A.I.C.S.: 561621

Subsidiary (Non-US):

Keeper-Grupo Sensormatic S.A. (4)
Profesor Conradi Facundo Machain No 6680, Asuncion, Paraguay (100%)
Tel.: (595) 21503609
Web Site: http://keeper.com.py
Security Services
N.A.I.C.S.: 561621
Graciela Medal Trinidad (Pres)

Sensormatic Argentina S.A. (4)
Thames 139, Boulogne Sur Mer, Buenos Aires, Argentina (100%)
Tel.: (54) 11 4006 4900
Electronic Security Mfr
N.A.I.C.S.: 561621

Sensormatic Electronics Corporation (Ireland) Limited (4)
Johnson Controls International 1 Albert Quay, Cork, 180014, Ireland
Tel.: (353) 214801000
Web Site: http://www.sensormatic.com
Security Service Systems Provider
N.A.I.C.S.: 561621

Branch (Domestic):

Sensormatic Electronics, LLC - Lithia Springs (4)
2600 Westpoint Dr, Lithia Springs, GA 30122
Tel.: (678) 505-2079
Web Site: http://www.sensormatic.com
Security Products
N.A.I.C.S.: 561621

Subsidiary (Non-US):

Sensormatic Hong Kong Limited (4)
RM 304 Shui Hing Ctr 13 Sheung Yuet Rd, Kowloon, China (Hong Kong)
Tel.: (852) 27580020
Web Site: http://www.sensormatic.com
Fire Detection & Alarm System Distr
N.A.I.C.S.: 423610

Sensormatic Moscow (4)
12 Krasnopresnenskaya Nab Office 505, 123610, Moscow, Russia (100%)
Tel.: (7) 4952326660
Web Site: http://www.sensormatic.com
Security Products
N.A.I.C.S.: 561621
Ruslan Nikitin (Gen Mgr)

Sensormatic Proteccao Contra Furto, Lda (4)
Praca Jose Queiros 1 Fracco n 5 Piso 3, 1801-802, Lisbon, Portugal
Tel.: (351) 217 51 05 60
Fire Protection Equipment Mfr
N.A.I.C.S.: 339999

Subsidiary (Domestic):

Sensormatic del Caribe, Inc. (4)
Amelia Industrial Park #45 Diana St, Guaynabo, PR 00968 (100%)
Tel.: (787) 782-7373
Electronics Distr
N.A.I.C.S.: 423690

Subsidiary (Non-US):

Sensormatic do Brasil Eletronica Ltda. (4)
R Joao BAtista da Silva, Nonoai, Porto Alegre, 90820-190, RS, Brazil
Tel.: (55) 800892003
Web Site: http://www.sensormatic.com.br
Electronic Article Surveillance Equipment Sales & Service
N.A.I.C.S.: 449210

Subsidiary (Non-US):

Signature Security Group Holdings Pty Limited (3)
Unit 38 38-46 South Street, Rydalmere, 2116, NSW, Australia
Tel.: (61) 300655994
Electronic Security System Monitoring Services

N.A.I.C.S.: 561621

Subsidiary (Domestic):

Signature Security Group Pty Limited (4)
362 Oxford St, Leederville, 6007, WA, Australia
Tel.: (61) 892736888
Electronic Security System Services
N.A.I.C.S.: 561621

Subsidiary (Domestic):

SimplexGrinnell LP (3)
50 Technology Dr, Westminster, MA 01441-0001
Tel.: (978) 731-2500
Web Site: http://www.simplex-fire.com
Fire Detection Systems, Fire Alarms, Fire Sprinklers, Fire Extinguishers & Fire Suppression Systems Mfr
N.A.I.C.S.: 922160

Subsidiary (Domestic):

Grinnell LLC (4)
1802 SW 2nd St, Pompano Beach, FL 33069
Tel.: (954) 781-0866
Web Site: http://www.grinnell.com
Industrial Valve Mfr
N.A.I.C.S.: 332911

Simplex Time Recorder Co. (4)
50 Technology Dr, Westminster, MA 01441
Tel.: (978) 731-2500
Web Site: http://www.simplex-fire.com
Security Alarm Services
N.A.I.C.S.: 561612

Branch (Non-US):

SimplexGrinnell (4)
765 Godin Ave, Vanier, G1M 2WA, QC, Canada
Tel.: (418) 681-4242
Web Site: http://www.tycosimplexgrinnell.com
Communications Equipment
N.A.I.C.S.: 334290

SimplexGrinnell (4)
2400 Skymark Avenue, Mississauga, L4W 5K5, ON, Canada (100%)
Tel.: (905) 212-4600
Web Site: http://www.simplex-fire.com
Fire Protection & Alarm Equipment Distr
N.A.I.C.S.: 922160

Branch (Domestic):

Tyco SimplexGrinnell (4)
283 Gibraltar Rd, Horsham, PA 19044
Tel.: (215) 347-6500
Web Site: http://www.tycosimplexgrinnell.com
Fire & Safety Products
N.A.I.C.S.: 922160

Tyco SimplexGrinnell (4)
10550 Commerce Pkwy, Miramar, FL 33025-9998
Tel.: (954) 431-3700
Web Site: http://www.simplexgrinnell.com
Firefighting Equipment
N.A.I.C.S.: 922160

Subsidiary (Non-US):

Tyco Fire & Integrated Solutions (Norway) AS (3)
Stalfara 26, PO Box 47, Kalbakken, 0901, Oslo, Norway
Tel.: (47) 95198271
Web Site: http://www.tyco.no
Fire Protection Equipment Mfr
N.A.I.C.S.: 334290

Tyco Fire & Integrated Solutions (Schweiz) AG (3)
Bahnweg 11, Pfaffikon, 8808, Switzerland
Tel.: (41) 584454000
Web Site: http://www.tyco.ch
Audio System Installation Services
N.A.I.C.S.: 238210

Tyco Fire & Integrated Solutions (UK) Limited (3)
Tyco Park Grimshaw Lane Newton Heath, Manchester, M40 2WL, United Kingdom

INTERNATIONAL PUBLIC

Tel.: (44) 1216231000
Web Site: http://www.tycofis.co.uk
Fire Protection Equipment Mfr
N.A.I.C.S.: 339999

Tyco Fire & Integrated Solutions France S.A.S. (3)
1 Rue Henry Giffard, 78180, Montigny-le-Bretonneux, France
Tel.: (33) 139307300
Web Site: http://www.tyco.fr
Fire & Security System Services
N.A.I.C.S.: 561621

Tyco Fire & Integrated Systems (Guangzhou) Co., Ltd. (3)
Room 908 TP Plaza No 109 Liuhua Road, Linhe, Guangzhou, 510010, Guangdong, China
Tel.: (86) 2086006030
Web Site: http://www.tyco-fire.com
Fire Protection Equipment Mfr
N.A.I.C.S.: 339999

Tyco Fire & Security Czech Republic s.r.o. (3)
Prumyslova 1306/7, 102 00, Prague, Czech Republic
Tel.: (420) 246039270
Fire Security Equipment Mfr
N.A.I.C.S.: 423690

Tyco Fire & Security Finance S.C.A. (3)
29 Avenue de la Porte-Neuve, Luxembourg, 2227, Luxembourg
Tel.: (352) 26637851
Fire Safety Services
N.A.I.C.S.: 561990

Tyco Fire & Security Holding Germany GmbH (3)
Am Schimmersfeld 5-7, Ratingen, 40880, Germany
Tel.: (49) 210255100
Web Site: http://www.tyco.de
Holding Company
N.A.I.C.S.: 551112

Tyco Fire & Security Nederland BV (3)
Vlierbaan 6-12, Capelle aan den IJssel, 2908 LR, South Holland, Netherlands
Tel.: (31) 882602600
Web Site: http://www.tyco.nl
Security System Services
N.A.I.C.S.: 561621

Tyco Fire & Security Pty. Limited (3)
38 South Street, Rydalmere, 2116, NSW, Australia (100%)
Tel.: (61) 294142444
Fire Safety Products & Services
N.A.I.C.S.: 922160

Unit (Domestic):

Wormald Australia Pty. Ltd. (4)
91 Derby St, PO Box 7241, Silverwater, 2128, NSW, Australia
Tel.: (61) 133166
Web Site: http://www.wormald.com.au
Electronic Article Surveillance Systems
N.A.I.C.S.: 449210

Subsidiary (Non-US):

Tyco Fire & Security Services International Trading (Shanghai) Co. Ltd. (3)
2F W Building 1 Lane 955 Jin Hai Road, Pudong, Shanghai, 200233, China
Tel.: (86) 2161633373
Web Site: http://www.tyco-fire.com
Security System Service Provider
N.A.I.C.S.: 561621

Tyco Fire Products Manufacturing Limited (3)
Security House The Summit Hanworth Road Sunbury-o-Thames, London, TW16 5DB, Mddx, United Kingdom
Tel.: (44) 1614293400
Web Site: http://www.tyco.com
Fire Protection Equipment Mfr
N.A.I.C.S.: 339999

Subsidiary (Domestic):

Tyco Fire Products, LP (3)

AND PRIVATE COMPANIES — JOHNSON CONTROLS INTERNATIONAL PLC

1400 Pennbrook Pkwy, Lansdale, PA 19446
Tel.: (215) 362-0700
Web Site: http://www.tyco-fire.com
Fire Protection Equipment, Valves & Building Products Mfr
N.A.I.C.S.: 922160

Subsidiary (Non-US):

Ansul Mexico, S.A. de C.V. (4)
Tlalnepantla, Mexico, 54090, Mexico
Tel.: (52) 5553212356
Web Site: http://www.ansul.com
Fire Suppression & Control Products Mfr
N.A.I.C.S.: 334519

Spraysafe Automatic Sprinklers Limited (4)
Security House The Summit, Hanworth Road, Sunbury, TW16 5DB, Mddx, United Kingdom
Tel.: (44) 01618750500
Fire Sprinker Systems
N.A.I.C.S.: 922160

Branch (Domestic):

Tyco Fire Protection Products (4)
1 Stanton St, Marinette, WI 54143-2542
Tel.: (715) 735-7411
Web Site: http://www.ansul.com
Fire Suppression & Control Products Mfr
N.A.I.C.S.: 922160
Jim Cox *(Sr Mgr-Mktg Comm)*

Tyco Fire Protection Products (4)
260 Central Casting Dr, Anniston, AL 36206-8534
Tel.: (256) 238-0579
Web Site: http://www.tyco-fire.com
Fire Protection Products
N.A.I.C.S.: 922160

Subsidiary (Non-US):

Tyco Fire, Security & Services Pte. Ltd. (3)
31 International Business Park Level 03-02, Singapore, 609921, Singapore
Tel.: (65) 6389 8999
Web Site: http://www.tyco-fire.com
Emp: 300
Security System Installation Services
N.A.I.C.S.: 238210

Tyco Integrated Fire & Security (3)
Vlierbaan 6-12, PO Box 285, 2900 AG, Capelle aan den IJssel, Netherlands
Tel.: (31) 882602600
Web Site: http://www.tyco.nl
Protective Services
N.A.I.C.S.: 561612
Ton Vlot *(Sr Controller & Mgr- FP&A)*

Subsidiary (Non-US):

ADT Security Services (4)
Boulevard d/Humanite 241a, 1620, Drogenbos, Belgium
Tel.: (32) 025581414
Web Site: http://security.adt.com
Electronic Article Surveillance Sales
N.A.I.C.S.: 449210

Subsidiary (Non-US):

Tyco Integrated Fire & Security Austria GmbH (3)
Wehlistrabe 27b, 1200, Vienna, Austria
Tel.: (43) 574740
Web Site: http://www.tyco-austria.at
Fire Safety Equipment Distr
N.A.I.C.S.: 424690
Rudolf Deussner *(Reg Mgr-Ops)*

Subsidiary (Domestic):

Tyco Integrated Security LLC (3)
6600 Cngress Ave, Boca Raton, FL 33431
Web Site: http://www.tycois.com
Commercial Security Products & Services
N.A.I.C.S.: 561621

Subsidiary (Non-US):

ADT Deutschland GmbH (4)
Am Schimmersfeld 5-7, Ratingen, 40880, Germany
Tel.: (49) 210271410
Web Site: http://www.tyco.de

Electronic Security System Installation Services & Mfr
N.A.I.C.S.: 238210

ADT Integrated Solutions, S.A. de C.V. (4)
Av. Insurgentes Sur No. 1106 Tlacoquemecatl del Valle, Benito Juarez, Mexico, 03720, Mexico
Tel.: (52) 5554888000
Electronic Product Distr
N.A.I.C.S.: 423620

ADT Private Security Services de Mexico, S.A. de C.V. (4)
Av de los Insurgentes Sur 1106 Iacoquemecatl del Valle, Benito Juarez, Mexico, 3200, Mexico
Tel.: (52) 5554888000
Web Site: http://www.adt.com.mx
Security System Installation Services
N.A.I.C.S.: 238210

ADT Security Deutschland GmbH (100%)
Am Schimmersseld 5-7 Ratingen, 40880, Essen, Germany
Tel.: (49) 40733640
Web Site: http://www.tyco.de
Electronic Security Products Sales
N.A.I.C.S.: 449210

ADT Security Services, S.A. (4)
Av Alfredo Arocena 1626, 1500, Montevideo, Uruguay
Tel.: (598) 800 8238
Web Site: http://www.adt.com.uy
Security Services
N.A.I.C.S.: 561621
Marcelo Montero *(Mng Dir)*

ADT Security Services, S.A. (4)
100 mts South of the American Embassy Office 104 2nd floor, Pavas, San Jose, Costa Rica
Tel.: (506) 22956500
Web Site: http://www.adt.co.cr
Fire Detection & Alarm System Distr
N.A.I.C.S.: 423610

ADT Service-Center GmbH (4)
Am Schimmersfeld 5, 40880, Ratingen, Germany
Tel.: (49) 2102 71410
Security Service Systems Provider
N.A.I.C.S.: 561621

ADT Services (M) Sdn Bhd. (4)
Southgate Commercial Centre Level 8 Block E-8-2 3&4 No 2 Jalan Dua, Off Jalan Chan, 55200, Kuala Lumpur, Malaysia
Tel.: (60) 392361800
Web Site: http://www.adt.my
Electronic Security System Designer & Installation Services
N.A.I.C.S.: 561621

ADT Servicos de Monitoramento Ltda. (4)
Rua Werner Siemens 111 Predio 20 Terreo, Rio de Janeiro, 05069-010, Sao Paulo, Brazil
Web Site: http://www.adt.com.br
Fire Security Equipment Mfr
N.A.I.C.S.: 423690

Advanced Independent Monitoring Limited (4)
PO Box 519, Manchester, M60 2LY, United Kingdom
Tel.: (44) 8448001643
Web Site: http://www.aim-monitoring.co.uk
Alarm System Monitoring Services
N.A.I.C.S.: 561621
Scott Kent *(Mgr-Ops-UK-Natl)*

Johnson Controls Integrated Fire & Security (Portugal), Unipessoal Lda (4)
Ed Entreposto-Pr Jose Queiros n 1, Fraccao 5 piso 3, 1800-237, Lisbon, Portugal
Tel.: (351) 217510560
Web Site: http://www.tyco.pt
Security Service Systems Provider
N.A.I.C.S.: 561621

Tyco Integrated Fire & Security Canada, Inc. (4)
5800 Henri-Bourassa Blvd W, Saint-Laurent, Montreal, H4R 1V9, QC, Canada

Tel.: (514) 737-5505
Web Site: http://www.tycoifs.ca
Security Service Systems Provider
N.A.I.C.S.: 561621

Subsidiary (Domestic):

Tyco Integrated Fire & Security (5)
2400 Skymark Ave, Mississauga, L4W 5K5, ON, Canada
Tel.: (905) 212-4400
Web Site: http://www.tycoifs.ca
Electronic Security & Access Control Systems
N.A.I.C.S.: 561621

Subsidiary (Non-US):

Tyco Safety Products (Shanghai) Co., Ltd. (3)
Zone B Building 2 88 Wansong Road Shuyuan Town, Pudong, Shanghai, China
Tel.: (86) 2161135588
Web Site: http://www.tyco-tsp.com
Fire Alarm Distr
N.A.I.C.S.: 423690

Tyco Safety Products (Shenyang) Co., Ltd. (3)
33 Shiji Rd, Hunnan, Shenyang, 110179, Liaoning, China
Tel.: (86) 2483780100
Electrical Equipment Distr
N.A.I.C.S.: 335999

Tyco Safety Products France SARL (3)
1 Rue Henri Giffard, 78180, Montigny-le-Bretonneux, France
Tel.: (33) 139307300
Electronic Fire Protection Equipment Mfr
N.A.I.C.S.: 334290

Wormald Engineering Services Ltd. (3)
704-730 King's Rd, Tsat Tsz Mui, North Point, China (Hong Kong)
Tel.: (852) 27642511
Fire & Detection Systems Design, Engineering & Installation
N.A.I.C.S.: 541330
Lawrence Cheng *(Mng Dir)*

Wormald Italiana S.p.A. (3)
Via Ettore Ponti 55, 20143, Milan, Italy
Tel.: (39) 0289125500
Fire Alarm & Protection Equipment Distr
N.A.I.C.S.: 922160

Subsidiary (Non-US):

Tyco Fire & Security S.p.A. (2)
Viale dell Innovazione 3, 20126, Milan, Italy
Tel.: (39) 02818061
Fire Detection & Alarm System Distr
N.A.I.C.S.: 423610

Tyco Fire, Security & Services Malaysia Sdn Bhd (2)
Luxor Tech Center Level 2 1A Technology Road 3/4 Selangor Science, Pju 5 Kota Damansara, 47810, Petaling Jaya, Selangor, Malaysia
Tel.: (60) 376284300
Web Site: http://www.johnsoncontrols.com
Fire Protection & Integrated Services
N.A.I.C.S.: 922160

Tyco Holding VIII (Denmark) ApS (2)
Tuborg Havnevej 19, 2900, Hellerup, Denmark
Tel.: (45) 70 22 65 12
Investment Management Service
N.A.I.C.S.: 523940

Tyco Integrated Fire & Security (Schweiz) AG (2)
Winkelstrasse 2, CH-4622, Egerkingen, Switzerland
Tel.: (41) 584454800
Web Site: http://www.tyco.ch
Alarm System Security System Services
N.A.I.C.S.: 561621

Tyco International Pty Limited (2)
38 South Street, Rydalmere, 2116, NSW, Australia (100%)
Tel.: (61) 299477244
Electronics, Flow Control & Medical Products

N.A.I.C.S.: 335999

Tyco International of Canada Ltd. (2)
2400 Skymark Avenue, Mississauga, L4W 5K5, ON, Canada
Tel.: (905) 212-4600
Web Site: http://www.tycoifs.ca
Fire Detection & Alarm System Distr
N.A.I.C.S.: 423610

Tyco New Zealand Limited (2)
8 Henderson Place, Onehunga, Auckland, 1061, New Zealand
Tel.: (64) 80049676253
Web Site: http://www.wormald.co.nz
Fire Production & Extinguisher Material Designer & Mfr
N.A.I.C.S.: 339999

Tyco Safety Products Canada Ltd. (2)
3301 Langstaff Rd, Concord, L4K 4L2, ON, Canada
Tel.: (905) 760-3000
Fire Detection & Alarm System Distr
N.A.I.C.S.: 423610

Tyco Service & Montage GmbH (2)
Strabburger Strabe 1, 6184, Kabelsketal, Germany
Tel.: (49) 6203750
Alarm System Monitoring Services
N.A.I.C.S.: 561621

Branch (Domestic):

Tyco Service & Montage GmbH - Merseburg (3)
Simon-Hoffmann-Str 1, 06217, Merseburg, Germany
Tel.: (49) 346173740
Fire Security Equipment Mfr
N.A.I.C.S.: 423690

Subsidiary (Non-US):

Tyco Services S.A. (2)
Diagonal 92 17a - 42 Oficina 201, Bogota, Cundinamarca, Colombia
Tel.: (57) 16553600
Security System Installation Services
N.A.I.C.S.: 238210

Tyco Services S.A. (2)
Alfredo Barros Errazuriz No 1973, 7500550, Santiago, Chile
Tel.: (56) 224104900
Web Site: http://tycoifs.cl
Fire Protection & Integrated Services
N.A.I.C.S.: 922160

Visonic Ltd. (2)
24 Habarzel St, Tel Aviv, 69710, Israel
Tel.: (972) 36456789
Web Site: http://www.visonic.com
Wireless Security, Automation & Control Solutions
N.A.I.C.S.: 561621

Subsidiary (Non-US):

Johnson Controls International Sp.z.o.o. (3)
Ul Krakowiakow 50, 02-255, Warsaw, Poland
Tel.: (48) 532300801
Web Site: http://www.visonic.com.pl
Wireless Security, Automation & Control Solutions
N.A.I.C.S.: 561621

Visonic Iberica De Seguridad, S.L. (3)
Calle Isla de Palma 32 N 7 Pol Ind Norte, S Sebastian de los Reyes, 28700, Madrid, Spain
Tel.: (34) 916502472
Web Site: http://www.visonic-iberica.es
Wireless Security, Automation & Control Solutions
N.A.I.C.S.: 561621

Subsidiary (US):

Visonic Inc. (3)
65 West Dudley Town Rd, Bloomfield, CT 06002
Tel.: (860) 243-0833
Web Site: http://www.visonic.com

JOHNSON CONTROLS INTERNATIONAL PLC

Johnson Controls International plc—(Continued)
Wireless Security, Automation & Control Solutions
N.A.I.C.S.: 561621

Subsidiary (Non-US):

Visonic Limited (3)
Heathrow Boulevard 3 282 bath Road, Sipson, West Drayton, UB7 0DQ, United Kingdom
Tel.: (44) 2087505660
Web Site: http://www.visonic.com
Wireless Security, Automation & Control Solutions
N.A.I.C.S.: 561621

Visonic Sicherheitstechnik GmbH (3)
Kirchfeldstr 118, D-40215, Dusseldorf, Germany
Tel.: (49) 2116006960
Web Site: http://www.visionic.de
Wireless Security, Automation & Control Solutions
N.A.I.C.S.: 561621

Subsidiary (Non-US):

WOPF Befestigungselemente GmbH (2)
Luner Rennbahn 22, Luneburg, 21339, Germany
Tel.: (49) 413130110
Fire Detection & Alarm System Distr
N.A.I.C.S.: 423610

Wormald Holdings (U.K.) Ltd. (2)
Tyco Park Grimshaw Lane Newton Heath, Manchester, M40 2WL, United Kingdom
Tel.: (44) 1614554655
Fire Protection Equipment Mfr & Distr
N.A.I.C.S.: 334519

Westfire Sudamerica S.R.L. (1)
Joaquin V Gonzalez 425, San Juan, 15047, Argentina
Tel.: (54) 2644273550
Electronic Security System Services
N.A.I.C.S.: 334290

Westfire Sudamerica SpA (1)
El Salitre, 7735, Antofagasta, Chile
Tel.: (56) 552592960
Fire Safety Services
N.A.I.C.S.: 561990
Nielsen Carrasco (Mgr-Contract)

JOHNSON ELECTRIC HOLDINGS LIMITED

6/F 12 Science Park East Avenue, Hong Kong Science Park, Sha Tin, NT, China (Hong Kong)
Tel.: (852) 2 663 6688   HK
Web Site:
http://www.johnsonelectric.com
Year Founded: 1959
0179—(HKG)
Rev.: $3,446,055,000
Assets: $4,338,776,000
Liabilities: $1,837,062,000
Net Worth: $2,501,714,000
Earnings: $152,195,000
Emp.: 35,000
Fiscal Year-end: 03/31/22
Micromotors Designer, Mfr & Marketer
N.A.I.C.S.: 811114
James Randolph Dick (CIO & Sr VP)

Subsidiaries:

AML Systems SAS (1)
6 place de la Madeleine, 75008, Paris, France
Tel.: (33) 180907907
Web Site: http://www.aml-systems.com
Automotive Lighting Components Designer, Mfr & Whslr
N.A.I.C.S.: 335139
Jacques Le Morvan (Pres)

Chengdu Zheng Heng Automobile Parts Co., Ltd. (1)
Nan Feng Industrial City Da Feng, Chengdu, 610504, Si Chuan, China
Tel.: (86) 28 83912135

Web Site: http://www.zhengine.com
Sales Range: $200-249.9 Million
Emp.: 600
Cylinder Block Mfr
N.A.I.C.S.: 333995

Fu Wang Electric Manufacturing Company Limited (1)
6/F Johnson Bldg 6-22 Dai Shun St Tai Po Indl Est, Tai Po, New Territories, China (Hong Kong)
Tel.: (852) 24240763
Electronic Components Mfr

Fully Motor Co. Limited (1)
6/F Johnson Building 6-22 Dai Shun Street, Tai Po Industrial Estate, Tai Po, New Territories, China (Hong Kong)
Tel.: (852) 2424 0763
Web Site: http://www.fullymotor.com
Sales Range: $200-249.9 Million
Emp.: 600
Commercial Motor Mfr
N.A.I.C.S.: 335312

Plant (Non-US):

Fully Motor Co. Limited - China Factory (2)
No 9 Yi Heng Dao He Dong Industrial District Xiang Xin Dong Road, Yan Tian Fenggang, Dongguan, Guangdong, China
Tel.: (86) 769 87773227
Industrial Machinery Mfr
N.A.I.C.S.: 333248

Gate France SAS (1)
Zone Industrielle La Girard, 73660, Saint-Remy-de-Maurienne, France
Tel.: (33) 4 79 83 13 52
Sales Range: $25-49.9 Million
Emp.: 80
Automobile Parts Mfr
N.A.I.C.S.: 336390
Ang Peres (Gen Mgr)

Gate S.r.l. (1)
Corso Alessandria 395, 14100, Asti, AT, Italy
Tel.: (39) 0141444111
Electric Equipment Mfr
N.A.I.C.S.: 334419

Halla Stackpole Corporation (1)
101 Gwahaksaneop 5-ro Ochang-eup, Cheongwon-gu, Cheongju, 363-885, Chungcheongbuk, Korea (South)   (80%)
Tel.: (82) 432417114
Web Site: https://www.hallastackpole.co.kr
Automotive Components Mfr
N.A.I.C.S.: 336390

Johnson Electric (Beihai) Co., Ltd. (1)
Block A6-4 Export Processing Zone, Beihai, 536000, Guangxi, China
Tel.: (86) 7793807050
Electronic Component Mfr & Distr
N.A.I.C.S.: 334419

Johnson Electric (Jiangmen) Co., Ltd. (1)
888 Donghai Road, Jianghai District, Jiangmen, Guangdong, China
Tel.: (86) 7503202888
Electrical & Electronic Parts Mfr
N.A.I.C.S.: 336320

Johnson Electric (Nanjing) Co., Ltd. (1)
Tel.: (86) 2557422000
Industrial Machinery Mfr
N.A.I.C.S.: 333248

Johnson Electric (Shenzhen) Co. Ltd. (1)
Xin Er Industrial Village, Shajing Town Baoan, Shenzhen, 518125, China
Tel.: (86) 75529900437
Motor & Generator Mfr
N.A.I.C.S.: 335312

Johnson Electric Automotivo Brasil Ltda. (1)
Av Governador Mario Covas Junior 2755, Portao, Aruja, 07412-000, SP, Brazil
Tel.: (55) 1124315600
Electrical & Electronic Parts Mfr
N.A.I.C.S.: 336320

Johnson Electric Doo (1)
Vazduhoplovaca bb, 18000, Nis, Serbia
Tel.: (381) 18506100
Electrical & Electronic Parts Mfr
N.A.I.C.S.: 336320

Johnson Electric Engineering Limited (1)
Tai Po Indl Est Johnson Bldg 6-22 Dai Shun St, Tai Po, New Territories, China (Hong Kong)
Tel.: (852) 26636688
Electric Motor Mfr
N.A.I.C.S.: 335312
Patrick Wang Shui-Chung (CEO)

Johnson Electric Germany GmbH & Co. KG (1)
Am Kreyenhof 10-12, D 26127, Oldenburg, Germany
Tel.: (49) 44134030
Web Site: http://www.johnsonmotion.com
Sales Range: $100-124.9 Million
Emp.: 300
Mfr of Electronic Microswitches
N.A.I.C.S.: 334220

Johnson Electric Hatvan Kft (1)
Szepes Bela u 7, 3000, Hatvan, Hungary
Tel.: (36) 37 544 100
Automotive Components Mfr
N.A.I.C.S.: 336390

Johnson Electric Industrial Manufactory, Limited (1)
6/F Hong Kong Science Park 12 Science Park East Ave, Sha Tin, New Territories, China (Hong Kong)
Tel.: (852) 26636688
Web Site: http://www.johnsonelectric.com
Automotive Spare Parts Whslr
N.A.I.C.S.: 423120
Patrick Wang (CEO)

Johnson Electric International (AT) GmbH (1)
Linzer Bundesstrasse 101, 5023, Salzburg, Austria
Tel.: (43) 662884910
Electronic Components Distr
N.A.I.C.S.: 423690

Johnson Electric International (IT) S.r.l. (1)
Via Alvise Cadamosto 3, 20094, Corsico, MI, Italy
Tel.: (39) 02486921
Electrical & Electronic Parts Mfr
N.A.I.C.S.: 336320

Johnson Electric International (UK) Limited (1)
Metropolitan House Longrigg Road, Swalwell, Newcastle upon Tyne, NE16 3AS, United Kingdom
Tel.: (44) 8448112130
Sales Range: $50-74.9 Million
Emp.: 8
Electronic Components Distr
N.A.I.C.S.: 423690

Johnson Electric International AG (1)
Freiburgstrasse 33, 3280, Murten, Switzerland
Tel.: (41) 266727111
Electronic Component Mfr & Distr
N.A.I.C.S.: 334419

Johnson Electric International France S.a.r.l (1)
Le Mermoz 53 avenue Jean Jaures, 93350, Le Bourget, France
Tel.: (33) 180907974
Electrical & Electronic Parts Mfr
N.A.I.C.S.: 336320

Johnson Electric International Limited (1)
6/F Hong Kong Science Park 12 Science Park East Ave, Sha Tin, New Territories, China (Hong Kong)
Tel.: (852) 26636688
Electronic Component Mfr & Distr
N.A.I.C.S.: 334419

Johnson Electric Korea (Industry) (1)
6th Floor Find Building 304 Sinbanpo-ro,
Seocho-gu, Seoul, 06533, Korea (South)
Tel.: (82) 25188351
Sales Range: $50-74.9 Million
Emp.: 3
Industrial Component Distr
N.A.I.C.S.: 423830
Tony Kim (Gen Mgr)

Johnson Electric North America Inc. (1)
Johnson Bldg 10 Progress Dr, Shelton, CT 06484
Tel.: (203) 447-5362
Web Site: http://www.johnsonelectric.com
Sales Range: $25-49.9 Million
Emp.: 18
Power Tools, Business Equipment, Personal Products, Home Appliances & Audio Visuals
N.A.I.C.S.: 423610

Johnson Electric Ozd Kft (1)
Bolyki T u 44, 3600, Ozd, Hungary
Tel.: (36) 48 570 300
Electronic Components Mfr
N.A.I.C.S.: 334419

Johnson Electric Poland Sp.z o.o. (1)
Ul Jozefa Cieszkowskiego 26, 42-500, Bedzin, Silesian, Poland
Tel.: (48) 322952700
Electric Equipment Mfr
N.A.I.C.S.: 334419

Johnson Electric Private Limited (1)
Survey No 88 90 Meppur Thangal Road, Madavilagam Village Thirumazhisai, Chennai, 602 103, Tamil Nadu, India
Tel.: (91) 4443912800
Web Site: http://www.johnsonelectric.com
Sales Range: $25-49.9 Million
Emp.: 300
Electric Equipment Mfr
N.A.I.C.S.: 334419

Johnson Electric Saint Remy SAS (1)
La Girard, 73660, Saint-Remy-de-Maurienne, France
Tel.: (33) 479831352
Electrical & Electronic Parts Mfr
N.A.I.C.S.: 336320

Johnson Electric Shanghai (Industry) (1)
No 1 Lane 10800 Songze Avenue Qingpu Industrial Zone, Shanghai, 201700, China
Tel.: (86) 75529900437
Industrial Electronic Component Distr
N.A.I.C.S.: 423690

Johnson Electric World Trade Ltd. (1)
6 22 Dai Shun St Tai Po Industrial Est, Tai Po, China (Hong Kong)   (100%)
Tel.: (852) 26636688
Web Site: http://www.johnsonelectric.com
Sales Range: $50-74.9 Million
Emp.: 200
Provider of Electronic Components
N.A.I.C.S.: 334220
Patrick Wang (Chm & CEO)

Johnson Medtech (HK) Limited (1)
6/F 12 Science Park East Avenue Hong Kong Science Park, Sha Tin, New Territories, China (Hong Kong)
Tel.: (852) 26636688
Electrical & Electronic Parts Mfr
N.A.I.C.S.: 336320

Johnson Medtech LLC (1)
801 Scholz Dr, Vandalia, OH 45377
Tel.: (978) 946-2600
Web Site: https://www.johnsonmedtech.com
Medical Device Mfr
N.A.I.C.S.: 339112

M.M.A. (Manufactura de Motores Argentinos) S.r.l. (1)
Av Benito Perez Galdos 8180, Pablo Podesta, B1687, Buenos Aires, Argentina
Tel.: (54) 1147394848
Electrical & Electronic Parts Mfr
N.A.I.C.S.: 336320

Nanomotion Ltd. (1)
6 Carmel St Mordot HaCarmel Industrial Park, PO Box 623, Yokneam, 20692, Israel
Tel.: (972) 732498000

Web Site: https://www.nanomotion.com
Sales Range: $25-49.9 Million
Emp.: 60
Electronic Motion Platform Equipment Mfr
N.A.I.C.S.: 334419
Alan Feinstein *(VP-Sls & Mktg)*

Parlex Dynaflex Corporation (1)
1756 Junction Ave, San Jose, CA 95112-1018
Tel.: (408) 441-8713
Web Site: http://www.parlex.com
Sales Range: $25-49.9 Million
Emp.: 40
Electronic Component Mfr & Distr
N.A.I.C.S.: 334419
Martin Smallen *(Gen Mgr)*

Parlex USA (1)
801 Scholz Dr, Vandalia, OH 45377
Tel.: (937) 898-3621
Web Site: http://www.parlex.com
Sales Range: $50-74.9 Million
Emp.: 160
Mfr & Designer of Flexible Circuits, Laminated Cables, Value-Added Assemblies & Polymer Thick Film Products
N.A.I.C.S.: 334418

Subsidiary (Non-US):

Parlex (Shanghai) Electronics Co. Ltd. (2)
No 1 Lane 10800 Songze Avenue Qingpu Industrial Zone, Shanghai, 201700, China
Tel.: (86) 2169228900
Web Site: http://www.parlex.com
Electronic Component Mfr & Distr
N.A.I.C.S.: 334419

Stackpole International (1)
1325 Cormorant Road, Ancaster, L9G 4V5, ON, Canada
Tel.: (905) 304-9455
Web Site: https://www.stackpole.com
Automotive Gears Mfr
N.A.I.C.S.: 333612
Peter Ballantyne *(Pres & CEO)*

Plant (Domestic):

Stackpole Ltd. - Mississauga, Engineered Products Division (2)
2400 Royal Windsor Drive, Mississauga, L5J 1K7, ON, Canada
Tel.: (905) 403-0550
Web Site: http://www.stackpole.com
Automotive Engine Components Mfr
N.A.I.C.S.: 336310

Stackpole Ltd. - Mississauga, Powder Metal Division (2)
2430 Royal Windsor Drive, Mississauga, L5J 1K7, ON, Canada
Tel.: (905) 822-6015
Web Site: http://www.stackpole.com
Automotive Gears for Transmission & Engine Applications Mfr
N.A.I.C.S.: 336310

Stackpole Ltd. - Stratford, Powder Metal Division (2)
128 Monteith Avenue, Stratford, N5A 6T7, ON, Canada
Tel.: (519) 271-6060
Web Site: http://www.stackpole.com
Metal Components for Transmission & Engine Applications Mfr
N.A.I.C.S.: 332311

Stackpole International Fluid Power Solutions (Changzhou) Co., Ltd. (1)
Building A2 Fengshu Industrial Zone No 7 Xinhui Road, Wujin, Changzhou, 213164, Jiangsu, China
Tel.: (86) 51981663716
Engineered Fluid Power Mfr
N.A.I.C.S.: 333996

Stackpole International Otomotiv Urunleri Limited Sirketi (1)
Ege Serbest Bolgesi Cinar Sk No 11, Gaziemir, 35410, Izmir, Türkiye
Tel.: (90) 2324559000
Web Site: http://www.stackpole.com.tr
Engine & Automotive Metal Component Mfr
N.A.I.C.S.: 333618

Stackpole International Powder Metal, Ltd. (1)
1325 Cormorant Road, Ancaster, L9G 4V5, ON, Canada
Tel.: (905) 304-9455
Engineered Fluid Power Mfr
N.A.I.C.S.: 333996

Stackpole Powertrain International GmbH (1)
Campus-Boulevard 30, 52074, Aachen, Germany
Tel.: (49) 24146367033
Engineered Fluid Power Mfr
N.A.I.C.S.: 333996

V Motor Limited (1)
6/F Hong Kong Science Park 12 Science Park E Ave, Sha Tin, New Territories, China (Hong Kong)
Tel.: (852) 26636672
Electronic Motor Whslr
N.A.I.C.S.: 423690

JOHNSON HEALTH TECH. CO., LTD.
No 999 Sec 2 Dongda Rd, Daya Dist, Taichung, 428314, Taiwan
Tel.: (886) 425667100
Web Site:
  http://www.johnsonhealthtech.com
Year Founded: 1975
1736—(TAI)
Rev.: $1,244,957,702
Assets: $1,191,073,568
Liabilities: $875,515,746
Net Worth: $315,557,822
Earnings: $23,200,136
Emp.: 1,278
Fiscal Year-end: 12/31/23
Fitness Equipment Mfr
N.A.I.C.S.: 423910
May Lo *(VP)*

Subsidiaries:

Fuji Medical Instruments MFG. Co., Ltd. (1)
14F Oe Bldg 1-22 Noninbashi 1-chome, Chuo-ku, Osaka, 540-0011, Japan
Tel.: (81) 647930611
Web Site: https://www.fujiiryoki.com
Emp.: 769
Massage Chair Mfr & Distr
N.A.I.C.S.: 337127

Johnson Fitness (Malaysia) Sdn. Bhd. (1)
Lot 557D Jalan Subang 3 Subang Jaya Industrial Estate, 47610, Subang Jaya, Selangor, Malaysia
Tel.: (60) 380230161
Web Site: https://johnsonfitness.com.my
Fitness Equipment Mfr & Distr
N.A.I.C.S.: 339920

Johnson Health Care Co., Ltd. (1)
Chuo-odori FN Building 7F 1-3-8, Tokiwamachi Chuo-ku, Osaka, 540-0028, Japan
Tel.: (81) 669498797
Web Site: https://www.synca-wellness.us
Medical Equipment Mfr & Distr
N.A.I.C.S.: 339112

Johnson Health Tech Australia Pty. Ltd. (1)
6B Hazelwood Dr, Morwell, 3840, VIC, Australia
Tel.: (61) 351363100
Web Site: http://www.jhta.com.au
Sales Range: $25-49.9 Million
Emp.: 40
Fitness Equipment Mfr
N.A.I.C.S.: 339920

Johnson Health Tech France S.A.S. (1)
Rue des Ormes, 78550, Houdan, France
Tel.: (33) 130686280
Cardiovascular & Weight Training Equipment Distr
N.A.I.C.S.: 423490

Johnson Health Tech North America Inc (1)
1600 Landmark Dr, Cottage Grove, WI 53527-8967
Tel.: (608) 839-1240
Web Site:
 http://www.us.corporate.johnsonfitness.com
Sales Range: $25-49.9 Million
Fitness Equipment Distr
N.A.I.C.S.: 423910

Johnson Health Tech Philippines, Inc. (1)
Unit 1401-1402 The Orient Square Building F Ortigas Jr Road, Ortigas Center Metro Manila, Pasig, 1605, Philippines
Tel.: (63) 253103878
Fitness Equipment Mfr & Distr
N.A.I.C.S.: 339920

Johnson Health Tech Retail Inc. (1)
1600 Landmark Dr, Cottage Grove, WI 53527
Tel.: (211) 6088391240
Web Site:
 https://www.johnsonhealthtech.com
Fitness Equipment Mfr
N.A.I.C.S.: 423910

Subsidiary (Domestic):

BowFlex Inc. (2)
17750 SE 6th Way, Vancouver, WA 98683
Tel.: (360) 859-2900
Web Site: https://www.nautilusinc.com
Rev.: $205,964,000
Assets: $86,307,000
Liabilities: $110,120,000
Net Worth: ($23,813,000)
Earnings: ($90,370,000)
Emp.: 46
Fiscal Year-end: 03/31/2024
Marketer of Consumer Health & Fitness Products
N.A.I.C.S.: 339920
Jeffery L. Collins *(VP & Gen Mgr-Intl & Comml Specialty)*

Group (Domestic):

Nautilus Health & Fitness Group (3)
1886 Prairie Way, Louisville, CO 80027
Tel.: (303) 939-0100
Web Site: http://www.nautilus.com
Rev.: $200,000,000
Emp.: 200
Exercise Equipment Mfr
N.A.I.C.S.: 423910

Subsidiary (Non-US):

Octane Fitness International, B.V. (3)
Rivium Westlaan 15, 2909 LD, Capelle aan den IJssel, Netherlands
Tel.: (31) 102662412
Sports & Athletic Goods Mfr
N.A.I.C.S.: 339920
Leo Schreuders *(Mng Dir)*

Octane Fitness UK Ltd (3)
13-21 High Street, Guildford, GU1 3DL, Surrey, United Kingdom
Tel.: (44) 7799475366
Sports & Athletic Goods Distr
N.A.I.C.S.: 459110
Neil Campbell *(Mng Dir)*

Subsidiary (Domestic):

Octane Fitness, LLC (3)
7601 Northland Dr N Ste 100, Brooklyn Park, MN 55428
Tel.: (763) 391-0228
Web Site: https://www.octanefitness.com
Sales Range: $50-74.9 Million
Exercise Equipment Designer, Mfr & Distr
N.A.I.C.S.: 339920

Johnson Health Tech Romania S.A. (1)
Str Drumul Garii nr 64, 077145, Otopeni, Romania
Tel.: (40) 746279350
Fitness Equipment Mfr & Distr
N.A.I.C.S.: 339920

Johnson Health Tech. GmbH (1)
Europaallee 51, 50226, Frechen, Germany
Tel.: (49) 22349997100
Cardiovascular & Weight Training Equipment Distr
N.A.I.C.S.: 423490

Johnson Health Tech. Poland Sp. z o.o. (1)
Gate One Business Park sector C ul Dzialkowa 62, 02-234, Warsaw, Poland
Tel.: (48) 222809430
Fitness Equipment Mfr & Distr
N.A.I.C.S.: 339920

World of Leasing GmbH (1)
Ganseberg 5, 22926, Ahrensburg, Germany
Tel.: (49) 41026672620
Web Site: https://www.world-of-leasing.de
Rental & Leasing Services
N.A.I.C.S.: 532490

JOHNSON MATTHEY PLC
5th Floor 25 Farringdon Street, London, EC4A 4AB, United Kingdom
Tel.: (44) 2072698000 UK
Web Site: https://www.matthey.com
Year Founded: 1817
JMPLY—(OTCIQ)
Rev.: $18,543,799,400
Assets: $8,728,612,200
Liabilities: $5,575,682,000
Net Worth: $3,152,930,200
Earnings: $342,736,800
Emp.: 12,600
Fiscal Year-end: 03/31/23
Precious Metals, Catalysts & Fine Chemicals Mfr
N.A.I.C.S.: 325998
Patrick Thomas *(Chm)*

Subsidiaries:

Applied Utility Systems, Inc. (1)
31 Journey Ste 250, Aliso Viejo, CA 92656
Tel.: (949) 297-5200
Web Site: http://www.matthey.com
Fossil Fuels Engineered Solutions
N.A.I.C.S.: 541330

Davy Process Technology Limited (1)
10 Eastbourne Terrace, London, W2 6LG, United Kingdom
Tel.: (44) 207 957 4120
Web Site: http://www.davyprotech.com
Sales Range: $50-74.9 Million
Emp.: 150
Petrochemical Mfr
N.A.I.C.S.: 325110
Antoine Bordet *(Pres)*

Finex Oy (1)
Seppolantie 1, 48230, Kotka, Finland
Tel.: (358) 103277400
Web Site: http://www.finex.fi
Pharmaceuticals Product Mfr
N.A.I.C.S.: 325412

INTERCAT Inc. (1)
2399 Hwy 34 Ste C-1, Manasquan, NJ 08736-1500
Tel.: (732) 223-4644
Sales Range: $50-74.9 Million
Emp.: 150
Fluid Cracking Catalyst Additives Mfr & Developer
N.A.I.C.S.: 325520

Subsidiary (Non-US):

INTERCAT Equipment Mumbai Pvt Ltd (2)
904 Gunjan Towers, Alembic Gorwa Road, Mumbai, 390 023, India
Tel.: (91) 2653922750
Web Site: http://www.intercatinc.com
Sales Range: $25-49.9 Million
Emp.: 7
Fluid Cracking Catalyst Additives Mfr & Developer
N.A.I.C.S.: 325180

INTERCAT Europe b.v. (2)
Stationsstraat 50, 3451 BZ, Vleuten, Netherlands (100%)
Tel.: (31) 306777010
Web Site: http://www.intercatinc.com
Rev.: $2,795,522
Emp.: 7
Fluid Cracking Catalyst Additives Mfr & Developer
N.A.I.C.S.: 325998

Johnson Matthey & Brandenberger AG (1)
Glattalstrasse 18, PO Box 485, 8052, Zu-

JOHNSON MATTHEY PLC — INTERNATIONAL PUBLIC

Johnson Matthey PLC—(Continued)

rich, Switzerland **(100%)**
Tel.: (41) 443071919
Web Site: https://www.johnson-matthey.ch
Sales Range: $25-49.9 Million
Emp.: 25
Petroleum Trading
N.A.I.C.S.: 424720

Johnson Matthey & Co. GmbH. (1)
Steckhovengasse 12, A1132, Vienna, Austria **(100%)**
Tel.: (43) 18779890
Web Site: http://www.matthey.com
Sales Range: $50-74.9 Million
Emp.: 150
Chemical Preparation Plant
N.A.I.C.S.: 325998

Johnson Matthey (Aust) Ltd (1)
64 Lillee Crescent, Tullamarine, Melbourne, 3043, VIC, Australia
Tel.: (61) 3 9344 7700
Web Site: http://www.matthey.com.au
Sales Range: $25-49.9 Million
Emp.: 23
Metal Products Mfr
N.A.I.C.S.: 332999

Johnson Matthey (Pty.) Limited (1)
Cnr Henderson and Premier Road Germiston South, Germiston Ext 7, Germiston, 1401, Gauteng, South Africa **(100%)**
Tel.: (27) 113458500
Web Site: http://www.matthey.com
Sales Range: $25-49.9 Million
Emp.: 450
Refining & Mechanical Production
N.A.I.C.S.: 331314

Johnson Matthey (Shanghai) Chemicals Limited (1)
No 588 Dongxing Rd Songjiang Industrial Zone, Shanghai, 201613, China
Tel.: (86) 2123099888
Specialty Chemicals Mfr
N.A.I.C.S.: 325180

Johnson Matthey (Zhangjiagang) Environmental Protection Technology Co., Ltd. (1)
No 9 Dongxin Road Yangzijiang International, Chemical Industrial Park, Jiangsu, 215635, China
Tel.: (86) 2123099888
Catalyst & Pharmaceutical Material Mfr
N.A.I.C.S.: 325998

Johnson Matthey AB (1)
Victor Hasselblads gata 8S-421, 31 Vastra Frolunda, 421 31, Gothenburg, Sweden **(100%)**
Tel.: (46) 31893700
Web Site: http://www.matthey.com
Sales Range: $1-9.9 Million
Emp.: 40
Trading
N.A.I.C.S.: 325130

Johnson Matthey Argentina S.A. (1)
Calle 7 Parcela 2 Nro 194 Parque Industrial, Pilar, B1629MXA, Buenos Aires, Argentina
Tel.: (54) 2322529999
Sales Range: $50-74.9 Million
Emp.: 150
Motor Vehicle Parts And Accessories
N.A.I.C.S.: 336390

Johnson Matthey Argillon (Shanghai) Emission Control Technologies Ltd. (1)
298 East RongLe Road, Song Jiang Industrial Zone, Shanghai, 201613, China
Tel.: (86) 2137745800
Chemical Products Mfr
N.A.I.C.S.: 325998

Johnson Matthey Battery Materials GmbH (1)
Ostenriederstr 15, 85368, Moosburg, Germany
Tel.: (49) 15116147811
Catalyst & Pharmaceutical Material Mfr
N.A.I.C.S.: 325998

Johnson Matthey Battery Materials Ltd. (1)
280 Avenue Liberte, Candiac, J5R 6X1, QC, Canada
Tel.: (514) 906-1396
Catalyst & Pharmaceutical Material Mfr
N.A.I.C.S.: 325998

Johnson Matthey Belgium BVBA (1)
Regus Brussels Airport Pegasuslaan 5, 1831, Diegem, Belgium
Tel.: (32) 27092098
Catalyst & Pharmaceutical Material Mfr
N.A.I.C.S.: 325998

Johnson Matthey Brasil Ltda. (1)
Avenida Macuco 726 - 12 andar, Moema, Sao Paulo, 04523-001, SP, Brazil
Tel.: (55) 1135836866
Catalyst & Pharmaceutical Material Mfr
N.A.I.C.S.: 325998

Johnson Matthey Catalog Co. (1)
26 Parkridge Rd, Ward Hill, MA 01835-8042
Tel.: (978) 521-6300
Web Site: http://www.alfa.com
Sales Range: $50-74.9 Million
Emp.: 140
Mail Order Catalog
N.A.I.C.S.: 424690
Barry Singelais (Dir-Res Chemical)

Johnson Matthey Catalysts (1)
Belasis Avenue, PO Box 1, Billingham, TS23 1LB, United Kingdom **(100%)**
Tel.: (44) 164 255 3601
Web Site: http://www.jmcatalysts.com
Sales Range: $25-49.9 Million
Specialty Catalysts for Polymers, Chemicals & Edible Oils Mfr
N.A.I.C.S.: 325998

Subsidiary (Domestic):

Johnson Matthey Chemical Catalysts (2)
Pimlico Industrial Area West Bradford Road, Clitheroe, BB7 4QB, Lancs, United Kingdom
Tel.: (44) 120 042 2493
Web Site: https://www.matthey.com
Sales Range: $50-74.9 Million
Emp.: 200
Develop & Manufacture Chemical Catalysts
N.A.I.C.S.: 325180

Subsidiary (Non-US):

Johnson Matthey Chemicals India Private Ltd. (2)
Plot No 6A MIDC Industrial Estate, Dist Raigad, Taloja, 410 208, Maharashtra, India
Tel.: (91) 222 740 1427
Web Site: http://jmindia.co.in
Catalysts Mfr
N.A.I.C.S.: 325998

Subsidiary (Domestic):

Johnson Matthey Fuel Cells Limited (2)
Lydiard Fields, Great Western Way, Swindon, SN5 8AT, United Kingdom
Tel.: (44) 179 375 5600
Web Site: http://www.jmfuelcells.com
Sales Range: $25-49.9 Million
Emp.: 100
Supplier of Fuel Cell Components for Hydrogen & Methanol Fuelled Systems
N.A.I.C.S.: 336390

Subsidiary (US):

Johnson Matthey Fuel Cells NA (3)
1397 King Rd, West Chester, PA 19380
Tel.: (610) 232-1900
Supplier of Fuel Cell Components for Hydrogen & Methanol Fuelled Systems
N.A.I.C.S.: 336390
Bill Scilingo (Mgr-Ops)

Subsidiary (Non-US):

Johnson Matthey PCT (2)
8908 60th Avenue, Edmonton, T6E 6A6, AB, Canada
Tel.: (780) 469-0055
Web Site: http://www.johnsonmatthey.com
Sales Range: $25-49.9 Million
Emp.: 4
Specialty Catalysts for Polymers, Chemicals & Edible Oils Mfr
N.A.I.C.S.: 325998
Ben Zimmerman (Reg Mgr)

Subsidiary (US):

Johnson Matthey PCT (2)
4106 New W Dr, Pasadena, TX 77507-1882
Tel.: (281) 291-7769
Web Site: https://matthey.com
Catalysts & Radio-Isotope Technology Mfr
N.A.I.C.S.: 325199

Johnson Matthey PCT (2)
2 Transam Plz Dr, Oakbrook Terrace, IL 60181-4823
Tel.: (630) 268-6300
Web Site: http://www.jmcatalysts.com
Sales Range: $25-49.9 Million
Emp.: 26
Catalysts Mfr
N.A.I.C.S.: 424690

Subsidiary (Non-US):

Tracerco (2)
9 1173 Michener Rd, Sarnia, M7S 5G5, ON, Canada **(100%)**
Tel.: (519) 332-6160
Web Site: http://www.tracerco.com
Sales Range: $25-49.9 Million
Emp.: 3
Chemical Catalysts Mfr
N.A.I.C.S.: 325998
Mike Boones (Reg Mgr)

Johnson Matthey Catalysts (Germany) GmbH (1)
Bahnhofstrasse 43, 96257, Redwitz an der Rodach, Germany
Tel.: (49) 957481249
Web Site: http://www.johnson-matthey.de
Pharmaceuticals Product Mfr
N.A.I.C.S.: 325412

Johnson Matthey Catalysts Korea Limited (1)
759 - 9 Gumui-Ri Jangan-Myeon, Hwaseong, 445941, Gyeonggi, Korea (South)
Tel.: (82) 313591614
Web Site: http://www.matthey.co.kr
Sales Range: $25-49.9 Million
Emp.: 50
Chemical Products Mfr
N.A.I.C.S.: 325998
Sean Gilgunn (Gen Mgr)

Johnson Matthey Catalysts LLC (1)
Transportny proezd 1, 660027, Krasnoyarsk, Russia
Tel.: (7) 3912748709
Catalyst & Pharmaceutical Material Mfr
N.A.I.C.S.: 325998

Johnson Matthey Chemicals GmbH (1)
Wardstrasse 17, 46446, Emmerich am Rhein, Germany
Tel.: (49) 2822 9141 0
Web Site: http://www.johnson-matthey.de
Sales Range: $25-49.9 Million
Emp.: 100
Chemical Products Mfr
N.A.I.C.S.: 325199

Johnson Matthey DOOEL Skopje (1)
TIDZ Skopje 1, Ilinden, 1041, Skopje, North Macedonia
Tel.: (389) 23251301
Catalyst & Pharmaceutical Material Mfr
N.A.I.C.S.: 325998

Johnson Matthey GmbH (1)
Otto-Volger-Strasse-9 B Taunus, 65843, Sulzbach, Germany
Tel.: (49) 619 670 3820
Web Site: https://www.johnson-matthey.de
Specialty Chemicals Mfr
N.A.I.C.S.: 325998

Johnson Matthey Italia S.r.l. (1)
Corso Trapani 16, 10139, Turin, TO, Italy
Tel.: (39) 0110202693
Catalyst & Pharmaceutical Material Mfr
N.A.I.C.S.: 325998

Johnson Matthey Japan G.K. (1)
5123 Kitsuregawa, Sakura, 329-1412, Tochigi, Japan
Tel.: (81) 28 686 5781
Web Site: https://www.jmj.co.jp
Metal Products Mfr

Johnson Matthey Korea Limited (1)
Lotte Castle 101-2803 109 Mapo-daero, Mapo-gu, Seoul, 04146, Korea (South)
Tel.: (82) 23263891
Catalyst & Pharmaceutical Material Mfr
N.A.I.C.S.: 325998

Johnson Matthey Limited (1)
130 Glidden Rd, Brampton, L6W 3M8, ON, Canada **(100%)**
Tel.: (905) 453-6120
Web Site: http://www.johnsonmatthey.com
Sales Range: $25-49.9 Million
Emp.: 85
Mechanical Production & Refining
N.A.I.C.S.: 331314

Johnson Matthey Limited (1)
Naas Industrial Estate, Kildare, Naas, W91 E409, Ireland
Tel.: (353) 872734923
Catalyst & Pharmaceutical Material Mfr
N.A.I.C.S.: 325998

Johnson Matthey Pharmaceutical Materials-USA (1)
2003 Nolte Dr, West Deptford, NJ 08066
Tel.: (856) 384-7001
Web Site: https://matthey.com
Sales Range: $50-74.9 Million
Emp.: 140
Mfr & Developer of Anticancer & Antiviral Drugs, Organic Pharmaceutical Products & Bactericides
N.A.I.C.S.: 325412

Division (Domestic):

Johnson Matthey Pharma Services (2)
25 Patton Rd, Devens, MA 01434-3803
Tel.: (978) 784-5000
Web Site: http://www.jmpharmaservices.com
Sales Range: $50-74.9 Million
Emp.: 140
Research & Development of Pharmaceutical Products
N.A.I.C.S.: 325412

Johnson Matthey Pharmaceutical Services (Yantai) Co., Ltd. (1)
Wuxi Rd 9 Bajiao Industrial Park Yantai Economic and Development Zone, Yantai, Shandong, China
Tel.: (86) 5353975153
Catalyst & Pharmaceutical Material Mfr
N.A.I.C.S.: 325998

Johnson Matthey Piezo Products GmbH (1)
Bahnhofstr 43, 96257, Redwitz an der Rodach, Germany
Tel.: (49) 957481453
Web Site: http://www.piezoproducts.com
Piezoelectric Ceramic & Component Mfr
N.A.I.C.S.: 327110

Johnson Matthey Poland Spolka z ograniczona odpowiedzialnoscia (1)
Ul Alberta Einsteina 6, 44-109, Gliwice, Poland
Tel.: (48) 327902600
Catalyst & Pharmaceutical Material Mfr
N.A.I.C.S.: 325998

Johnson Matthey SA (1)
13 Rue Dela Perdrix ZI Paris Nord 2, 96596, Roissy-en-France, CDG Cedex, France **(100%)**
Tel.: (33) 148172199
Web Site: http://www.matthey.com
Sales Range: $25-49.9 Million
Emp.: 20
Chemical Preparations Mfr
N.A.I.C.S.: 325998

Johnson Matthey Sdn. Bhd. (1)
PT 3349 Jalan Permata 1/2 Arab-Malaysian Industrial Park, 71800, Nilai, Negeri Sembilan, Malaysia
Tel.: (60) 6 798 2888
Web Site: http://www.intranet.matthey.com
Metal Products Mfr
N.A.I.C.S.: 332999

Johnson Matthey Stationary Emissions Control LLC (1)

900 Forge Ave Ste 100, Audubon, PA
19403-2305
Tel.: (484) 320-2125
Web Site: https://www.jmsec.com
Pollution Control Services
N.A.I.C.S.: 924110

Johnson Matthey Trading (Shenzhen) Ltd (1)
Suites S-V 8th Floor Building A Fortune Plaza Shennan Road, Futian, 7060, Shenzhen, China
Tel.: (86) 755 8282 8538
Web Site: http://www.matthey.com.hk
Chemical Products Mfr
N.A.I.C.S.: 325998

Johnson Matthey Vehicle Testing & Dev. LLC (1)
12600 Universal Dr, Taylor, MI 48180
Tel.: (734) 946-9856
Automotive Research & Development Services
N.A.I.C.S.: 541715

Johnson Matthey de Mexico, S.A. de C.V. (1)
Av La Canada No 1 Parque Ind Bernardo Quintana, El Marquez, Queretaro, 76246, Mexico
Tel.: (52) 4422381400
Sales Range: $50-74.9 Million
Emp.: 220
Chemical Products Mfr
N.A.I.C.S.: 325199

Macfarlan Smith Limited (1)
10 Wheatfield Road, Edinburgh, EH11 2QA, United Kingdom
Tel.: (44) 131 337 2434
Web Site: http://www.macsmith.com
Pharmaceuticals Product Mfr
N.A.I.C.S.: 325412

Precious Metal Products Division (1)
Orchard Road, Royston, SG8 5HE, Hertfordshire, United Kingdom
Tel.: (44) 1763253000
Web Site: http://www.matthey.com
Sales Range: $650-699.9 Million
Emp.: 1,200
Production of Precious Metal & Fabricated Products; Platinum Marketing & Distribution; Colours & Enamels Production; Gold & Silver Refining
N.A.I.C.S.: 921110
John Walker (Mng Dir)

Subsidiary (Domestic):

Johnson Matthey Noble Metals (2)
Orchard Road, Royston, SG8 5HE, Hertfordshire, United Kingdom (100%)
Tel.: (44) 1763253000
Web Site: http://www.noble.matthey.com
Sales Range: $25-49.9 Million
Emp.: 170
Mfr of Industrial Products from Platinum Metals
N.A.I.C.S.: 332999
Garry Crooks (Mgr-Sls & Mktg-Chemical Products)

Subsidiary (US):

Johnson Matthey Inc. (3)
435 Devon Park Dr Ste 600, Wayne, PA 19087
Tel.: (610) 971-3000
Web Site: http://matthey.com
Refines & Fabricates Platinum Group Metals; Platinum Chemicals, Catalysts, Lab Apparatus, Wire, Sheet, Automotive Converters, Transfers & Colors Mfr
N.A.I.C.S.: 332999

Subsidiary (Domestic):

Johnson Matthey Refining, Inc. (4)
4601 W 2100 S, Salt Lake City, UT 84120 (100%)
Tel.: (801) 972-6466
Emp.: 900
Refining of Gold & Silver
N.A.I.C.S.: 331410

Subsidiary (US):

Johnson Matthey Inc. - Downingtown (3)
498 Acorn Ln, Downingtown, PA 19335-3075 (100%)
Tel.: (610) 873-3200
Web Site: http://www.matthey.com
Sales Range: $25-49.9 Million
Emp.: 22
Cyclic Crudes & Intermediates
N.A.I.C.S.: 331492

Subsidiary (Domestic):

Johnson Matthey Plc (3)
Orchard Road, Royston, SG8 5HE, Herts, United Kingdom (100%)
Tel.: (44) 176 325 3000
Web Site: http://www.colours.matthey.com
Mfr of Colours & Pigments for Ceramics
N.A.I.C.S.: 325130
Maurits van Tol (CTO)

Subsidiary (Domestic):

Johnson Matthey PLC-Colours & Coatings Division (2)
Blythe Business Park Sandon Road, Cresswell, Stoke-on-Trent, ST11 9RD, Staffs, United Kingdom (100%)
Tel.: (44) 1782384100
Web Site: http://www.glassmatthey.com
Sales Range: $50-74.9 Million
Emp.: 150
Mfr of Colors & Pigments for Ceramics
N.A.I.C.S.: 325130

Subsidiary (Non-US):

Johnson Matthey B.V. (3)
Fregatweg 38, 6222 NZ, Maastricht, Netherlands (100%)
Tel.: (31) 433525400
Web Site: http://www.colours.matthey.com
Sales Range: $50-74.9 Million
Mfr of Ceramic Colors & Pigments
N.A.I.C.S.: 325130
Zamder Heyden (Mng Dir)

Subsidiary (US):

Johnson Matthey Metal Products (3)
1401 King Rd, West Chester, PA 19380-1467 (100%)
Tel.: (610) 648-8000
Sales Range: $75-99.9 Million
Liquid Gold & Ceramic Colors
N.A.I.C.S.: 325180
Jim D. Malanga (Gen Mgr-North America)

S.A. Johnson Matthey NV (1)
8 Ave De Bale, 1140, Brussels, Belgium (100%)
Tel.: (32) 27290711
Web Site: http://www.matthey.com
Sales Range: $100-124.9 Million
Emp.: 285
Mechanical Production
N.A.I.C.S.: 333613

StePac L.A. Limited (1)
Tefen Industrial Park Building 12, PO Box 73, Migdal Tefen, 2495900, Israel
Tel.: (972) 46123500
Web Site: http://www.stepac.com
Fresh Fruits & Vegetables Packaging Services
N.A.I.C.S.: 115114

Subsidiary (Non-US):

StePac Brasil Ltda (2)
Rua Itapolis 1921 Consolacao, Sao Paulo, 01245-000, Brazil
Tel.: (55) 11 3596 7450
Web Site: http://www.stepac.com
Corrugated Board & Boxes Mfr
N.A.I.C.S.: 322211

Tracerco Europe BVBA (1)
Z 3 Doornveld 115, 1731, Zellik, Belgium
Tel.: (32) 24658520
Oil & Energy Services
N.A.I.C.S.: 213112

Tracerco Norge AS (1)
Kokstadflaten 35, 5257, Kokstad, Norway
Tel.: (47) 55365540
Oil & Energy Services
N.A.I.C.S.: 213112

Tracerco Radioactive Diagnostic Services Canada Inc. (1)
8908 60th Avenue NW, Edmonton, T6E
6A6, AB, Canada
Tel.: (780) 469-0055
Oil & Energy Services
N.A.I.C.S.: 213112

Tracerco do Brasil - Diagnosticos de Processos Industriais Ltda. (1)
Estrada dos Bandeirantes 1793, Taquara, Rio de Janeiro, 22775-111, RJ, Brazil
Tel.: (55) 2133856800
Oil & Energy Services
N.A.I.C.S.: 213112

JOHNSON PHARMACARE LIMITED
Regus 1101-1106 Earth Arise 11th Floor Sarkhej Gandhinagar Highway, Makarba, Ahmedabad, 380015, Gujarat, India
Tel.: (91) 7926405831
Web Site:
  https://www.johnsonpharma.shop.in
Year Founded: 1994
532154—(BOM)
Rev.: $302,967
Assets: $7,173,455
Liabilities: $345,423
Net Worth: $6,828,032
Earnings: ($154,835)
Fiscal Year-end: 03/31/23
Securities Brokerage Services
N.A.I.C.S.: 523150
Ramanlal Nagjibhai Trivedi (CFO)

JOHNSON SERVICE GROUP PLC
Johnson House Abbots Park, Monks Way, Preston Brook, WA7 3GH, Cheshire, United Kingdom
Tel.: (44) 1928704600   UK
Web Site: https://www.jsg.com
JSG—(AIM)
Rev.: $592,359,471
Assets: $647,992,630
Liabilities: $292,678,793
Net Worth: $355,313,837
Earnings: $34,627,504
Fiscal Year-end: 12/31/23
Holding Company; Textile Rentals & Dry Cleaning Services
N.A.I.C.S.: 551112
Yvonne May Monaghan (CFO)

Subsidiaries:

Bourne Textile Services Limited (1)
Cherry Holt Road, Bourne, PE10 9LA, United Kingdom
Tel.: (44) 1778420900
Web Site: http://www.bournegroup.co.uk
Textile Mfr
N.A.I.C.S.: 314999

Caterers Linen Supply Limited (1)
6-8 Jackson Way Great Western Industrial Park Windmill Lane, Southall, UB2 4SF, Middlesex, United Kingdom
Tel.: (44) 2088435810
Web Site: http://www.caterslinen.co.uk
Laundry Services
N.A.I.C.S.: 812320

Chester Laundry Limited (1)
56 St Marks Rd, Chester, CH4 8DQ, Cheshire, United Kingdom
Tel.: (44) 1244681300
Web Site:
  http://www.chesterlaundryservices.co.uk
Laundry Services
N.A.I.C.S.: 812320

Greenearth Cleaning Limited (1)
51 W 135th St, Kansas City, MO 64145-1289
Web Site:
  https://www.greenearthcleaning.com
Laundry Services
N.A.I.C.S.: 812320
Tim Maxwell (Pres)

Johnsons Hotel Linen Limited (1)
Monks Way, Preston Brook, Runcorn, WA7 3GH, United Kingdom
Tel.: (44) 1928704625
Web Site:
  https://www.johnsonshotellinen.com
Laundry Services
N.A.I.C.S.: 812320

Johnsons Hotel, Restaurant and Catering Linen Limited (1)
Innovation House First Floor Wincombe Lane, Shaftesbury, SP7 8FG, Dorset, United Kingdom
Tel.: (44) 1747851585
Web Site: https://www.johnsons-stalbridge.com
Laundry Services
N.A.I.C.S.: 812320

Johnsons Textile Services Limited (1)
Pittman Way off Olivers Place Eastway, Fulwood, Preston, PR2 9ZD, Lancs, United Kingdom (100%)
Tel.: (44) 800592254
Web Site:
  https://www.johnsonsworkwear.com
Sales Range: $25-49.9 Million
Emp.: 60
Work Uniforms & Protectivewear Sales & Rental Services; Commercial & Industrial Laundry Services
N.A.I.C.S.: 812331

Division (Domestic):

Johnsons Stalbridge Linen Services (2)
23 Wincombe Business Park, Shaftesbury, SP7 9QJ, Dorset, United Kingdom
Tel.: (44) 1747851585
Web Site: http://www.johnsons-stalbridge.com
Hospitality Industry Linen Supply & Laundry Services
N.A.I.C.S.: 812331

Lilliput (Dunmurry) Limited (1)
Lilliput Services 9 City Business Park, Derriaghy, Belfast, BT17 9GX, United Kingdom
Tel.: (44) 2890618555
Web Site: https://www.lilliputservices.com
Laundry Services
N.A.I.C.S.: 812320

London Linen Supply Limited (1)
6-8 Jackson Way, Great Western Industrial Park Windmill Lane, London, UB2 4SF, United Kingdom
Tel.: (44) 208 574 5569
Web Site: https://www.johnsons-londonlinen.co.uk
Laundry Services
N.A.I.C.S.: 812320

London Workwear Rental Limited (1)
6-8 Jackson Way Great Western Industrial Park, Windmill Lane, London, UB2 4SF, Middlesex, United Kingdom
Tel.: (44) 2085740559
Web Site: http://www.londonworkwear.co.uk
Laundry Services
N.A.I.C.S.: 812320

JOHNSTON BUILDERS LTD.
#201 265 Carleton Drive, Saint Albert, T8N 4J9, AB, Canada
Tel.: (780) 460-0441
Web Site:
  http://www.johnstonbuilders.net
Year Founded: 1990
General Contracting Services
N.A.I.C.S.: 238190
Scott Forbes (Coord-Occupational Health & Safety)

JOHNSTON MOTOR SALES CO. LTD
1350 Upper James Street, Hamilton, L9C3B4, ON, Canada
Tel.: (905) 388-5502
Web Site: http://johnstonmotor.com
Year Founded: 1923
Rev.: $28,394,289
Emp.: 60
New & Used Car Dealers
N.A.I.C.S.: 441110
Jim Johnston (Pres)

JOHOR CORPORATION

Johor Corporation—(Continued)

JOHOR CORPORATION
Level 11 Menara KOMTAR, Johor Bahru City Centre, 80000, Johor Bahru, Johor, Malaysia
Tel.: (60) 72192692
Web Site: http://www.jcorp.com.my
Year Founded: 1968
Rev.: $1,351,434,240
Assets: $5,508,490,240
Liabilities: $3,328,291,840
Net Worth: $2,180,198,400
Earnings: $59,919,360
Emp.: 61,872
Fiscal Year-end: 12/31/18
Holding Company
N.A.I.C.S.: 551112
Ali Hamsa (Deputy Chm)

Subsidiaries:

Akli Resources Sdn Bhd (1)
Lot 2135 Jalan Johor, 81990, Kota Tinggi, Johor, Malaysia
Tel.: (60) 7 882 8200
Professional Training Services
N.A.I.C.S.: 611430

Ayamas Shoppe Sdn Bhd (1)
Lot PT 20153 Jalan Pelabuhan Utara, Klang, 42000, Malaysia
Tel.: (60) 3 3166 2281
Convenience Food Distr
N.A.I.C.S.: 445131

Convenue Marketing Sdn Bhd (1)
Suites 1A & 1C Tingkat 20 Menara Komtar, Johor Bahru City Centre, 80000, Johor Bahru, Johor Darul Takzim, Malaysia
Tel.: (60) 7 222 1767
Web Site: http://www.convenue.com.my
Event Management Services
N.A.I.C.S.: 711310
Hana Abdul Rahim (Sec)

Epasa Shipping Agency Sdn Bhd (1)
PLO 559 Jalan Keluli Kawasan Perindustrian, Pasir Gudang, 81700, Malaysia
Tel.: (60) 7 251 1771
Emp.: 30
Freight Forwarding Services
N.A.I.C.S.: 488510
Norrah Abdul Jalil (CEO)

Healthcare Technical Services Sdn. Bhd. (1)
Level 17 Menara KPJ 238 Jalan Tun Razak, 50400, Kuala Lumpur, Malaysia (70%)
Tel.: (60) 326816222
Web Site: https://www.htssb.com
Hospital Construction & Engineering Services
N.A.I.C.S.: 236220

Hotel Selesa (JB) Sdn Bhd (1)
Jalan Dato Abdullah Tahir, 80300, Johor Bahru, Johor Darul Takzim, Malaysia
Tel.: (60) 7 332 3999
Web Site:
http://www.johorbahru.selesahotels.com
Hotel Operator
N.A.I.C.S.: 721110

IPPJ Sdn Bhd (1)
20th Floor Komtar, 80000, Johor Bahru, Johar, Malaysia
Tel.: (60) 7 222 1767
Web Site: http://www.ippj.com.my
Entrepreneurial Training Services
N.A.I.C.S.: 611430

JTP Trading Sdn Bhd (1)
39A Jalan Perang, Taman Pelangi, 80400, Johor Bahru, Malaysia
Tel.: (60) 7 333 3777
Web Site: http://www.jtp.com.my
Fruit Distr
N.A.I.C.S.: 424480

Johor Land Berhad (1)
Kompleks Mutiara Johor Land Jalan Bukit Mutiara Bandar Dato Onn, 81100, Johor Bahru, Johor, Malaysia
Tel.: (60) 7 356 4888
Web Site: http://www.jland.com.my
Emp.: 20

Property Development Services
N.A.I.C.S.: 531210
Kamaruzzaman Abu Kassim (Chm)

Subsidiary (Domestic):

Advance Development Sdn Bhd (2)
10th Floor Komtar Jalan Wong Ah Fook, 80000, Johor Bahru, Malaysia
Tel.: (60) 7 863 2692
Property Development Services
N.A.I.C.S.: 531210

Johor Skills Development Centre Sdn Bhd (1)
PLO 2 Jalan Perak 4, Kawasan Perindustrian Pasir Gudang, 81700, Pasir Gudang, Johor, Malaysia
Tel.: (60) 7 2521606
Web Site: http://www.puspatri.edu.my
Emp.: 45
Professional Training Services
N.A.I.C.S.: 611430
Jaapar Samat (CEO & Mng Dir)

Kulim (Malaysia) Berhad (1)
d/a Ulu Tiram Estate, KB 705, 80990, Johor Bahru, Johor, Malaysia
Tel.: (60) 78611611
Web Site: http://www.kulim.com.my
Rev.: $293,964,738
Assets: $1,628,468,974
Liabilities: $787,277,741
Net Worth: $841,191,233
Earnings: $(26,743,477)
Emp.: 9,135
Fiscal Year-end: 12/31/2019
Holding Company; Palm Oil & Oleochemical Production; Oil & Gas Exploration
N.A.I.C.S.: 551112
Amran Zakaria (Head-HR Div)

Subsidiary (Domestic):

EPA Management Sdn Bhd (2)
Ulu Tiram Estate KB 735, Johor Bahru, 80990, Malaysia
Tel.: (60) 7 861 1611
Holding Company
N.A.I.C.S.: 551112

Kumpulan Bertam Plantations Berhad (2)
Ladang Sepang Loi, 85007, Segamat, Johor, Malaysia
Tel.: (60) 7 937 1080
Palm Oil Mfr
N.A.I.C.S.: 311224

Subsidiary (Non-US):

PT Surya Panen Subur (2)
Jalan Raya Pasar Minggu 15 Kelurahan Pancoran, Kecamatan Pancoran Jakarta Selatan Jakarta, Jakarta, 13930, Indonesia (95%)
Tel.: (62) 214616555
Oil Palm Planting & Production
N.A.I.C.S.: 115112

Subsidiary (Domestic):

Sindora Berhad (2)
9C 9th Floor Menara Ansar, 65 Jalan Trus, 80000, Johor Bahru, Johor, Malaysia (100%)
Tel.: (60) 72215459
Web Site: http://www.sindora.com.my
Sales Range: $100-124.9 Million
Emp.: 2,379
Oil Palm & Rubber Tree Plantations & Palm Oil Processing Mill Owner & Operator; Equity Investment Firm
N.A.I.C.S.: 113210

Skellerup Industries (Malaysia) Sdn. Bhd. (2)
Ulu Tiram Estate, KB 705, 80990, Johor Bahru, Johor, Malaysia (100%)
Tel.: (60) 78611808
Web Site: http://www.skellerup.com.my
Balloons, Swim Caps, Pool Socks & Other Rubber Products Mfr
N.A.I.C.S.: 326299
Mohd Amran A. Kadir (Gen Mgr)

Kulim Livestock Sdn Bhd (1)
K B 537, Kluang, 86009, Malaysia
Tel.: (60) 7 781 6602
Livestock Management Services
N.A.I.C.S.: 112111

Pinnacle Platform Sdn Bhd (1)
No 27B & 27C Jalan Harmonium 33/1, Taman Desa Tebrau, 81000, Johor Bahru, Malaysia
Tel.: (60) 7 3520222
Web Site: http://www.pplatformsb.com
Emp.: 15
Software Development Services
N.A.I.C.S.: 541511
Rahman Mokhtar (CEO)

Pro Corporate Management Services Sdn Bhd (1)
Menara Ansar 65 Jalan Trus Suite 12B Level 12, 80000, Johor Bahru, Johor, Malaysia
Tel.: (60) 7 2267692
Business Management Services
N.A.I.C.S.: 561110

QSR Brands (M) Holdings Sdn. Bhd. (1)
Tower 1 Level 2 Vsquare PJ City Centre Jalan Utara, 46200, Petaling Jaya, Selangor, Malaysia (51%)
Tel.: (60) 379338888
Web Site: http://www.qsrbrands.com
Holding Company; Fast Food Restaurant Operator & Franchisor
N.A.I.C.S.: 551112
Kamaruzzaman Abu Kassim (Chm)

Subsidiary (Domestic):

Ayamas Food Corporation Sdn. Bhd. (2)
Lot PT 20153, Jalan Pelabuhan Utara, 42000, Kelang, Selangor Darul Ehsan, Malaysia (100%)
Tel.: (60) 3 367 0836
Poultry Hatcheries, Feedmills, Breeding Farms & Processing Plants Operator
N.A.I.C.S.: 311615

Kentucky Fried Chicken (Malaysia) Sdn. Bhd. (2)
Level 16 Wisma KFC, No 17 Jalan Sultan Ismail, 50250, Kuala Lumpur, Malaysia
Tel.: (60) 320263388
Web Site: http://www.kfc.com.my
Franchise Fast Food Restaurant Chain Operator
N.A.I.C.S.: 722513

Pizza Hut Restaurants Sdn. Bhd. (2)
Tower 1 VSquare PJ City Centre Level 7 Jalan Utara, 46200, Petaling Jaya, Selangor Darul Ehsan, Malaysia (100%)
Tel.: (60) 1300882525
Web Site: http://www.pizzahut.com.my
Franchise Pizzeria Restaurant Chain Operator
N.A.I.C.S.: 722513
Jean Ler (CMO-Bernama)

Subsidiary (Non-US):

Pizza Hut Singapore Pte. Ltd. (3)
17 Kallang Junction 01-01, Singapore, 339274, Singapore (100%)
Tel.: (65) 62967691
Web Site: http://www.pizzahut.com.sg
Sales Range: $25-49.9 Million
Emp.: 200
Franchise Pizzeria Restaurant Chain Operator
N.A.I.C.S.: 722513
Padmanabhan Rangappa (Gen Mgr)

Rasamas Holding Sdn Bhd (1)
Ground Floor Lot 7 No 300 Jalan Lagenda 1 Legenda Height, 08000, Sungai Petani, Kedah, Malaysia
Tel.: (60) 19 3513948
Web Site: http://www.rasamas.com.my
Restaurant Operators
N.A.I.C.S.: 722511

Sibu Island Resorts Sdn Bhd (1)
Pulau Sibu Tengah, Mersing, Johor, Malaysia
Tel.: (60) 7 799 5555
Web Site:
http://www.sibuislandresort.com.my
Hotel Operator
N.A.I.C.S.: 721110

Special Appearance Sdn Bhd (1)
No 15-02 Jalan Harmonium 33/1, Taman Desa Tebrau, 81100, Johor Bahru, Malaysia

INTERNATIONAL PUBLIC

Tel.: (60) 7 352 6100
Event Management Services
N.A.I.C.S.: 711310
Azman Miskon (Pres)

Syarikat Pengangkutan Maju Berhad (1)
No 24 Jalan Petaling Kawasan Perindustrian Larkin, 80530, Johor Bahru, Malaysia
Tel.: (60) 7 2370271
Web Site: http://www.majujc.com.my
Tour Operator
N.A.I.C.S.: 561599

TPM Technopark Sdn Bhd (1)
11th Floor Menara KOMTAR Johor Bahru City Centre, 80000, Johor Bahru, Johor, Malaysia
Tel.: (60) 7 222 6922
Web Site:
http://www.tpmtechnopark.com.my
Real Estate Development Services
N.A.I.C.S.: 531390
Ibrahim Abdul Samad (Exec Dir)

Tanjung Langsat Port Sdn Bhd (1)
Tanjung Langsat Industrial Complex TLP Building, PO Box 160, 81707, Pasir Gudang, Malaysia
Tel.: (60) 7 254 2692
Freight Transportation Services
N.A.I.C.S.: 483111

Tanjung Tuan Hotel Sdn Bhd (1)
No 80 22nd Floor Menara Safuan Jalan Ampang, 50450, Kuala Lumpur, Wilayah Persekutuan, Malaysia
Tel.: (60) 3 2715 0343
Hotel Operator
N.A.I.C.S.: 721110

Tepak Marketing Sdn Bhd (1)
PLO 398 Kilang Siapbina Pkenj Jalan Perak, Pasir Gudang, 81700, Malaysia
Tel.: (60) 7 251 2917
Emp.: 100
Food Products Distr
N.A.I.C.S.: 424420
Sulaiman Suhsuhaimi (Gen Mgr)

The Secret of Secret Garden Sdn Bhd (1)
Unit D7-3-2 Block D7 Pusat Perdagangan Dana 1, Jalan PJU 1A/46, 47301, Petaling Jaya, Selangor, Malaysia
Tel.: (60) 3 7734 0815
Web Site: http://www.secretgarden.com.my
Personal Care Product Mfr
N.A.I.C.S.: 325620

JOIGNET
Rue Chasse Maree, Bezu St Eloi, 27660, Paris, France
Tel.: (33) 232552733
Rev.: $22,900,000
Emp.: 39
Dairy Products Distr
N.A.I.C.S.: 424430
Jean-Jacques Joignet (Dir-Sls)

JOINCARE PHARMACEUTICAL INDUSTRY GROUP CO., LTD
Joincare Pharmaceutical Group Building No 17 Langshan Road, North District High-tech Zone Nanshan District, Shenzhen, 518057, Guangdong, China
Tel.: (86) 75586252368
Web Site: https://www.joincare.com
Year Founded: 1992
600380—(SHG)
Rev.: $2,406,842,535
Assets: $5,016,387,219
Liabilities: $1,924,747,250
Net Worth: $3,091,639,969
Earnings: $210,964,450
Emp.: 13,000
Fiscal Year-end: 12/31/22
Pharmaceutical Product Mfr & Distr
N.A.I.C.S.: 325412
Baoguo Zhu (Chm)

Subsidiaries:

Jiaozuo Joincare Biological Product Co., Ltd (1)

Wan Fang Industrial Area, Ma Village, Ji-aozuo, 454171, Henan, China
Tel.: (86) 591 83549501
Pharmaceutical Product Mfr & Distr
N.A.I.C.S.: 325412

Shenzhen Haibin Pharmaceutical Co., Ltd (1)
No 2003 Shayan Road, Yantian District, Shenzhen, China
Tel.: (86) 75525225349
Web Site: https://www.szhaibin.com
Emp.: 500
Pharmaceutical Product Mfr & Distr
N.A.I.C.S.: 325412

Shenzhen Taitai Pharmaceutical Co., Ltd (1)
23/F Office Tower Xin Xing Square Di Wang Commercial Centre, 5002 Shen Nan Dong Road, Shenzhen, China
Tel.: (86) 755 82463888
Pharmaceuticals Product Mfr
N.A.I.C.S.: 325412

TIC Industrial Co., Ltd (1)
No 27 Nanjiang Road Nanjiang Industril Park, Sihui, Guangdong, China
Tel.: (86) 758 3855345
Emp.: 200
Pharmaceuticals Product Mfr
N.A.I.C.S.: 325412

Xinxiang Haibin Pharmaceutical Co., Ltd (1)
Dedong Street Of Development High-Tech Industrial Zone, Xinxiang, 453007, Henan, China
Tel.: (86) 3732412881
Pharmaceuticals Product Mfr
N.A.I.C.S.: 325412

JOINDRE CAPITAL SERVICES LTD.
2932 3rd Floor 915 Bansilal Building Homi Modi Street, Mumbai, 400 023, India
Tel.: (91) 2240334567
Web Site: https://www.joindre.com
Year Founded: 1995
531861—(BOM)
Rev.: $3,511,879
Assets: $13,566,667
Liabilities: $4,872,046
Net Worth: $8,694,621
Earnings: $372,860
Emp.: 67
Fiscal Year-end: 03/31/23
Financial Services
N.A.I.C.S.: 522320
Anil Devichand Mutha (Chm)

JOINN LABORATORIES (CHINA) CO., LTD.
No 5 Rongjingdong St Beijing Economic and Development Area, Beijing, 100176, China
Tel.: (86) 10 6786 9966   CN
Web Site: http://www.joinnlabs.com
Year Founded: 1995
603127—(SHG)
Pharmaceutical Development Services
N.A.I.C.S.: 541714
Yuxia Feng (Co-Founder, Chm & Exec Dir)

Subsidiaries:

Biomedical Research Models, Inc. (1)
57 Union St, Worcester, MA 01608
Tel.: (508) 459-7544
Web Site: http://www.biomere.com
Research & Development Services in Biotechnology
N.A.I.C.S.: 541714
Mark Nedelman (CEO)

Joinn Laboratories CA Inc. (1)
Building C 2600 Hilltop Dr, Richmond, CA 94806
Tel.: (510) 408-7722
Health Care Srvices

N.A.I.C.S.: 621610

Joinn MedSafe Co., Ltd. (1)
705 Floor 6 Building 3 No 93 Courtyard Jianguo Road, Chaoyang District, Beijing, China
Tel.: (86) 1058203380
Health Care Srvices
N.A.I.C.S.: 621610

JOINSOON ELECTRONICS MANUFACTURING CO., LTD.
19th Floor No 79 Section 1 Xintai 5th Road, Xizhi District, New Taipei City, 221, Taiwan
Tel.: (886) 226984882
Web Site: https://www.jem.com.tw
Year Founded: 1977
3322—(TPE)
Rev.: $86,479,755
Assets: $81,029,422
Liabilities: $36,807,304
Net Worth: $44,222,118
Earnings: $4,861,333
Fiscal Year-end: 12/31/22
Semiconductor & Related Device Mfr
N.A.I.C.S.: 334413
Chin-Hsiung Huang (Chm & CEO)

JOINT ANALYTICAL SYSTEMS GMBH
Carl-Zeiss-Str 49, Moers, 47455, Germany
Tel.: (49) 28419871100
Web Site: http://www.jas.de
Year Founded: 1995
Rev.: $10,042,032
Emp.: 30
Analytical Equipment Mfr
N.A.I.C.S.: 334516
Robert Schyschka (Mgr-Bus Dev-Asia)

JOINT RESOURCES JSC
58 Azerbaev str, 50059, Almaty, 050059, Kazakhstan
Tel.: (7) 272582725
JRES—(KAZ)
Assets: $907,973
Liabilities: $21,799
Net Worth: $886,174
Earnings: $87,543
Fiscal Year-end: 12/31/23
Financial Investment Services
N.A.I.C.S.: 523940

JOINT STOCK COMMERCIAL BANK INVESTMENT AND DEVELOPMENT OF VIETNAM
BIDV tower 194 Tran Quang Khai, Hoan Kiem, Hanoi, Vietnam
Tel.: (84) 2422200588   VN
Web Site: https://bidv.com.vn
Year Founded: 1957
BID—(HOSE)
Rev.: $12,111,071,900
Assets: $212,060,938,400
Liabilities: $201,641,938,900
Net Worth: $10,418,999,500
Earnings: $1,815,850,200
Emp.: 28,435
Fiscal Year-end: 12/31/22
Commercial Banking Services
N.A.I.C.S.: 522110
Vo Bich Ha (Chm-Supervisory Bd)

Subsidiaries:

Bank for Investment & Development of Cambodia PLC (1)
No 235 Preah Norodom Blvd, Sangkat Tonle Bassac Khan Chamkamorn, Phnom Penh, Cambodia
Tel.: (855) 23210044
Web Site: http://www.bidc.com.kh
Commercial Banking Services
N.A.I.C.S.: 522110
Le Kim Hoa (Chm)

Cambodia - Vietnam Insurance Plc. (1)
8th Floor Building No 398 Monivong Blvd Sangkat BeungKeng Kang 1, Khan Chamkar Mon, Phnom Penh, Cambodia
Tel.: (855) 23212000
Web Site: http://www.cvi.com.kh
Insurance Services
N.A.I.C.S.: 524210
Tran Trung Tinh (Co-Founder & Chm)

Lao-Viet J.V. Bank (1)
44 LaneXang Avenue Ban Hatsady Tay Chanthabouly, Vientiane, Lao People's Democratic Republic
Tel.: (856) 2 125 1418
Web Site: https://www.laovietbank.com.la
Commercial Banking Services
N.A.I.C.S.: 522110
Nguyen Van Binh (Member-Mgmt Bd & Gen Dir)

JOINT STOCK COMMERCIAL BANK OF VIETNAM
198 Tran Quang Khai Street, Hoan Kiem District, Hanoi, Vietnam
Tel.: (84) 835899000
Web Site: https://tuyendung.vietcombank.com
Year Founded: 1963
VCB—(HOSE)
Rev.: $5,362,086,900
Assets: $183,961,319,800
Liabilities: $177,791,705,900
Net Worth: $6,169,613,900
Earnings: $3,303,320,300
Emp.: 21,670
Fiscal Year-end: 12/31/23
Commercial Banking Services
N.A.I.C.S.: 522110
Pham Quang Dung (Gen Dir)

Subsidiaries:

Vietcombank An Giang (1)
30-32 Hai Ba Trung Street, My Long Ward, Long Xuyen, An Giang, Vietnam
Tel.: (84) 2963898999
Web Site: http://www.vietcombank.com.vn
Banking Services
N.A.I.C.S.: 522110

Vietcombank Asset Management Company (1)
53 Tran Nhat Duat Street, Ho Chi Minh City, Vietnam
Tel.: (84) 88480813
Banking Services
N.A.I.C.S.: 522110

Vietcombank Binh Duong (1)
314 Binh Duong Boulevard, Phu Hoa Ward, Thu Dau Mot, Binh Duong, Vietnam
Tel.: (84) 2743831227
Web Site: http://www.vietcombank.com.vn
Banking Services
N.A.I.C.S.: 522110

Vietcombank Binh Tay (1)
129-129A Hau Giang Street, Ward 5 District 6, Ho Chi Minh City, Vietnam
Tel.: (84) 2839600477
Web Site: http://www.vietcombank.com.vn
Banking Services
N.A.I.C.S.: 522110

Vietcombank Ca Mau (1)
07 An Duong Vuong Street, Ward 7, Ca Mau, Vietnam
Tel.: (84) 2903575857
Web Site: http://www.vietcombank.com.vn
Banking Services
N.A.I.C.S.: 522110

Vietcombank Can Tho (1)
03-05-07 Hoa Binh Street, Tan An Ward Ninh Kieu District, Can Tho, Vietnam
Tel.: (84) 2923820445
Web Site: http://www.vietcombank.com.vn
Banking Services
N.A.I.C.S.: 522110

Vietcombank Da Nang (1)
140 Le Loi Street, Da Nang, Vietnam
Tel.: (84) 511823503
Web Site: http://www.vietcombank.com.vn
Banking Services

N.A.I.C.S.: 522110

Vietcombank Daklak (1)
06 Tran Hung Dao Street, Thang Loi Ward, Buon Ma Thuot, Daklak, Vietnam
Tel.: (84) 2623818444
Web Site: http://www.vietcombank.com.vn
Banking Services
N.A.I.C.S.: 522110

Vietcombank Dong Nai (1)
53-55 Vo Thi Sau Street, Quyet Thang Ward, Bien Hoa, Dong Nai, Vietnam
Tel.: (84) 2513823666
Web Site: http://www.vietcombank.com.vn
Sales Range: $100-124.9 Million
Banking Services
N.A.I.C.S.: 522110

Vietcombank Gia Lai (1)
33 Quang Trung Street, Hoi Thuong Ward, Pleiku, Gia Lai, Vietnam
Tel.: (84) 2693875566
Web Site: http://www.vietcombank.com.vn
Banking Services
N.A.I.C.S.: 522110

Vietcombank Ha Tinh (1)
15 Phan Dinh Phung Street, Ha Tinh, Vietnam
Tel.: (84) 39857003
Banking Services
N.A.I.C.S.: 522110

Vietcombank Hai Duong (1)
66 Nguyen Luong Bang Street, Binh Han Ward, Hai Duong, Hai Duong Province, Vietnam
Tel.: (84) 3203891131
Web Site: http://www.vietcombank.com.vn
Banking Services
N.A.I.C.S.: 522110
Nguyen Thi (Deputy Gen Dir)

Vietcombank Hai Phong (1)
275 Lach Tray Street, Dang Giang Ward Ngo Quyen District, Haiphong, Vietnam
Tel.: (84) 2253842658
Web Site: http://www.vietcombank.com.vn
Banking Services
N.A.I.C.S.: 522110

Vietcombank Hanoi (1)
344 Ba Trieu, Hanoi, Vietnam
Tel.: (84) 49746666
Web Site: http://www.vcbhanoi.com.vn
Banking Services
N.A.I.C.S.: 522110

Vietcombank Ho Chi Minh City (1)
VBB Tower 05 Me Linh Square, Ben Nghe Ward District 1, Ho Chi Minh City, Vietnam
Tel.: (84) 2838297245
Web Site: http://www.vietcombank.com.vn
Banking Services
N.A.I.C.S.: 522110

Vietcombank Hue (1)
78 Hung Vuong Street, Hue, Vietnam
Tel.: (84) 54824572
Banking Services
N.A.I.C.S.: 522110

Vietcombank Kien Giang (1)
2 Mac Cuu Phuong Vinh Thanh, Kien Giang, Vietnam
Tel.: (84) 773862749
Banking Services
N.A.I.C.S.: 522110

Vietcombank Leasing Corp. (1)
10 Thuyen Quang, Hanoi, Vietnam
Tel.: (84) 48221644
Loan Services
N.A.I.C.S.: 522310

Vietcombank Nha Trang (1)
21 Le Thanh Phuong Street, Van Thang Ward, Nha Trang, Khanh Hoa, Vietnam
Tel.: (84) 2583826279
Web Site: http://www.vietcombank.com.vn
Banking Services
N.A.I.C.S.: 522110

Vietcombank Quang Ngai (1)
345 Hung Vuong Street, Tran Phu Ward, Quang Ngai, Vietnam
Tel.: (84) 2553828578
Web Site: http://www.vietcombank.com.vn
Banking Services
N.A.I.C.S.: 522110

Joint Stock Commercial Bank of Vietnam—(Continued)

Vietcombank Quang Ninh (1)
172 Le Thanh Tong, Ha Long, Quang Ninh, Vietnam
Tel.: (84) 33825509
Web Site: http://www.vietcombank.com.vn
Banking Services
N.A.I.C.S.: 522110

Vietcombank Quy Nhon (1)
152 Le Loi Street, Quy Nhon, Vietnam
Tel.: (84) 563821498
Web Site: http://www.vietcombank.com.vn
Banking Services
N.A.I.C.S.: 522110

Vietcombank Securities Company (1)
12th - 17th Floor Vietcombank Tower 198 Tran Quang Khai, Hoan Kiem District, Hanoi, Vietnam
Tel.: (84) 439366990
Web Site: http://www.vcbs.com.vn
Securities Investment Services
N.A.I.C.S.: 523150

Vietcombank Tan Thuan (1)
Tan Thuan Export Processing Zone, District 7, Ho Chi Minh City, Vietnam
Tel.: (84) 87701634
Banking Services
N.A.I.C.S.: 522110

Vietcombank Thai Binh (1)
No 75 Le Loi Street, Le Hong Phong, Thai Binh, Vietnam
Tel.: (84) 363836994
Web Site: http://www.vietcombank.com.vn
Banking Services
N.A.I.C.S.: 522110

Vietcombank Vinh (1)
198 Tran Quang Khai, Hoan Kiam, Hanoi, Vietnam
Tel.: (84) 49343137
Web Site: http://www.vietcombank.com.vn
Banking Services
N.A.I.C.S.: 522110

Vietnam Finance Company Ltd (1)
16th Floor Golden Star Building, 20 Lockhard Road, Hong Kong, China (Hong Kong)
Tel.: (852) 28653905
Sales Range: $50-74.9 Million
Emp.: 10
Financial Services
N.A.I.C.S.: 523999

JOINT-STOCK COMPANY KAZAKHSTAN ELECTRICITY GRID OPERATING COMPANY
59 Tauelsizdik Ave, Astana Almaty district, Z00T2D0, Nur-Sultan, Kazakhstan
Tel.: (7) 7172693824
Web Site: https://www.kegoc.kz
Year Founded: 1997
KEGC—(KAZ)
Rev.: $485,791,217
Assets: $2,206,100,329
Liabilities: $744,705,123
Net Worth: $1,461,395,206
Earnings: $59,808,615
Emp.: 4,312
Fiscal Year-end: 12/31/22
Electric Power Generation & Distr
N.A.I.C.S.: 221118
Bakytzhan Kazhiyev (Chm-Mgmt Bd)

JOINTECA EDUCATION SOLUTIONS LTD
53B Geeta Enclave Nr Dr V K Garg Krishna Nagar, Mathura, 281004, Uttar Pradesh, India
Tel.: (91) 9149311933
Web Site: https://jointeca.com
534659—(BOM)
Rev.: $4,162
Assets: $1,522,461
Liabilities: $178,785
Net Worth: $1,343,676
Earnings: ($109,485)
Emp.: 47
Fiscal Year-end: 03/31/21
IT Solutions & Software
N.A.I.C.S.: 541519
Vishal Mishra (Mng Dir)

JOINTOWN PHARMACEUTICAL GROUP CO., LTD.
1610 Block B Madison Building No 8 Longyang Avenue, Hanyang District, Wuhan, Hubei, China
Tel.: (86) 13971717367
Web Site: https://www.jointownpharma.com
Year Founded: 1985
600998—(SHG)
Rev.: $19,715,556,501
Assets: $12,955,005,044
Liabilities: $8,927,569,900
Net Worth: $4,027,435,144
Earnings: $292,728,735
Emp.: 25,000
Fiscal Year-end: 12/31/22
Pharmaceutical & Medical Equipment Mfr & Whslr
N.A.I.C.S.: 325412
Baolin Liu (Chm)

JOKWANG I.L.I CO., LTD.
37 Sanmakgongdanbuk 10-gil, Yangsan, Gyeongsangnam-do, Korea (South)
Tel.: (82) 553600200
Web Site: https://www.jokwang.co.kr
Year Founded: 1968
044060—(KRS)
Rev.: $23,563,023
Assets: $89,190,621
Liabilities: $18,939,513
Net Worth: $70,251,107
Earnings: ($11,623,819)
Emp.: 168
Fiscal Year-end: 12/31/22
Industrial Valve Mfr
N.A.I.C.S.: 332911
Seongho Yang (CEO)

JOLIMARK HOLDINGS LIMITED
Unit 01 23A Floor K Wah Centre 191 Java Road, North Point, China (Hong Kong)
Tel.: (852) 25582457
Web Site: http://www.jolimark.com
2028—(OTCIQ)
Rev.: $38,656,264
Assets: $49,373,754
Liabilities: $27,763,901
Net Worth: $21,609,853
Earnings: ($5,539,571)
Emp.: 768
Fiscal Year-end: 12/31/22
Holding Company; Projectors, Printers & Tax Control Equipments Mfr
N.A.I.C.S.: 551112
Guo Liang Ou (Exec Dir)

Subsidiaries:

Jiangmen Kong Yue Jolimark Information Technology Limited (1)
Kong Yue Industrial Park 18 Kongyue Road, Jiangmen, 529141, China
Tel.: (86) 7506391898
Web Site: http://www.jolimark.com
Emp.: 100
Business Equipment Mfr & Distr
N.A.I.C.S.: 333248

Jolimark (S) Pte. Ltd. (1)
194 Pandan Loop 06-13 Pantech Business Hub, Singapore, 128383, Singapore
Tel.: (65) 68721112
Computer Peripheral Equipment Distr
N.A.I.C.S.: 423430

Xin Yue Logistics Limited (1)
255 Kings Road, North Point, China (Hong Kong)
Tel.: (852) 25586611
Logistics Consulting Servies
N.A.I.C.S.: 541614

JOLINA CAPITAL INC.
8000 Langelier Ofc 800, Montreal, H1P 3K2, QC, Canada
Tel.: (514) 328-6662
Year Founded: 1995
Sales Range: $25-49.9 Million
Emp.: 100
Investment Services
N.A.I.C.S.: 523999
Lino Saputo (Pres)

JOLLIBEE FOODS CORPORATION
10th Floor Jollibee Plaza F Ortigas Jr Road Ortigas Center, Pasig, 1605, Philippines
Tel.: (63) 26341111 PH
Web Site: https://privacy.jollibee.com.ph
Year Founded: 1975
JBFCF—(OTCIQ)
Sales Range: $1-4.9 Billion
Food Service
N.A.I.C.S.: 722511
William Tan Untiong (Corporate Secretary)

Subsidiaries:

International Coffee & Tea, LLC (1)
5700 Wilshire Blvd, Los Angeles, CA 90036
Tel.: (310) 237-2326
Web Site: http://www.coffeebean.com
Coffee Shops Owner, Operator & Franchisor; Coffee & Tea Mfr & Whslr
N.A.I.C.S.: 722515
David De Candia (Dir-Tea)

Jollibee Vietnam Co., Ltd (1)
5 Floor SCIC Buiding 16 Truong Dinh, District 3, Ho Chi Minh City, Vietnam (100%)
Tel.: (84) 2839309081
Web Site: http://www.jollibee.com.vn
Restaurant & Fast Food Services
N.A.I.C.S.: 722511

Red Ribbon Bakeshop (USA), Inc. (1)
6877 Mission St, Daly City, CA 94014-2034 (100%)
Tel.: (650) 755-2376
Web Site: https://www.redribbonbakeshop.us
Emp.: 16
Commercial Bakeries
N.A.I.C.S.: 311812

JOLLIVILLE HOLDINGS CORPORATION
4/F 20 Lansbergh Place 170 Tomas Morato Ave, corner Scout Castor St, Quezon City, 1103, Philippines
Tel.: (63) 23733038 PH
Web Site: https://www.joh.ph
Year Founded: 1986
JOH—(PHI)
Rev.: $26,595,638
Assets: $128,876,219
Liabilities: $64,665,715
Net Worth: $64,210,504
Earnings: $8,920,328
Emp.: 109
Fiscal Year-end: 12/31/21
Holding Company
N.A.I.C.S.: 551112
Ortrud T. Yao (CFO, Chief Compliance Officer, Treas & Sec)

Subsidiaries:

Philippine H2O Ventures Corp. (1)
GGDC Administrative Services Building Clark Global City Clark Freeport, Pampanga, Philippines
Tel.: (63) 8838 1985
Web Site: http://phresorts.com
Sales Range: Less than $1 Million
Holding Company; Water Supply
N.A.I.C.S.: 551112

Subsidiary (Domestic):

Metro Agoo Waterworks, Inc. (2)
Room 1 2nd Floor Agoo Commercial Center, Agoo, 2504, La Union, Philippines
Tel.: (63) 23733038
Water Distribution Services
N.A.I.C.S.: 221310

JOLLY BOARD LTD.
501 Rewa Chambers 31 Sir Vithaldas Thackersey Marg, Mumbai, 400 020, India
Tel.: (91) 22 22078531
Web Site: http://www.jollyboard.com
Construction Board Mfr & Exporter
N.A.I.C.S.: 321219
Rashmi Jolly (Exec Dir)

JOLODA HYDRAROLL LIMITED
51 Speke Road, Liverpool, L192NY, United Kingdom
Tel.: (44) 1514278954
Web Site: http://www.joloda.com
Logistic Services
N.A.I.C.S.: 541614
Mike Molesworth (Chm)

Subsidiaries:

Loading Automation, Inc. (1)
3310 Enterprise Dr, Wilmington, NC 28405
Tel.: (910) 791-2125
Web Site: http://www.loading-automation.com
Rev.: $10,000,000
Emp.: 12
Freight Transportation Arrangement
N.A.I.C.S.: 488510
Brett Murrill (Pres)

JOLT CAPITAL SAS
76-78 rue Saint-Lazare, 75009, Paris, France
Tel.: (33) 1 84 79 11 80
Web Site: http://www.jolt-capital.com
Year Founded: 2011
Privater Equity Firm
N.A.I.C.S.: 523999
Giacomo Del Grande (CFO)

Subsidiaries:

Alpha MOS SA (1)
Immeuble Le Colombus 4 rue Brindejonc des Moulinais, 31500, Toulouse, France
Tel.: (33) 562475380
Web Site: http://www.alpha-mos.com
Sales Range: $1-9.9 Million
Analytical Laboratory Instrument Mfr
N.A.I.C.S.: 334516
Pierre Sbabo (CEO)

Subsidiary (Non-US):

Alpha M.O.S. Japan K.K. (2)
Takanawa 1 - chome No 5 No 4, Minato-Ku, Tokyo, 108-0074, Japan
Tel.: (81) 3 5475 3291
Web Site: http://www.alpha-mos.com
Analytical Instrument Mfr
N.A.I.C.S.: 334516
John Christoff Mifsud (Pres)

Subsidiary (US):

Alpha MOS America Inc (2)
7502 Connelley Dr Ste 110, Hanover, MD 21076-1705
Tel.: (410) 553-9736
Web Site: http://www.alpha-mos.com
Analytical Instrument Distr
N.A.I.C.S.: 423490

Subsidiary (Non-US):

Alpha MOS China (2)
Rm 701 & 706 No 1968 GongHe Xin Road, LifeHub Daning Jing an District, Shanghai, 200072, China
Tel.: (86) 21 6209 3271
Web Site: http://www.alpha-mos.com
Analytical Instrument Mfr
N.A.I.C.S.: 334516

AND PRIVATE COMPANIES

JOLYWOOD SUZHOU SUN-WATT CO., LTD.
No 2 Zhongxing Road Changkun Industrial Park, Shajiabang Town, Changshu, 215542, Jiangsu, China
Tel.: (86) 51283818381
Web Site: https://www.jolywood.cn
Year Founded: 2008
300393—(SSE)
Rev.: $1,344,581,316
Assets: $2,387,260,512
Liabilities: $1,737,042,840
Net Worth: $650,217,672
Earnings: $56,355,156
Emp.: 250
Fiscal Year-end: 12/31/22
Photovaltaic Encapsulation Materials Mfr
N.A.I.C.S.: 334419
Cao Lu *(Chm)*

Subsidiaries:

Filmcutter Advanced Material S.r.l. (1)
Via Giulio Natta 10, 36075, Montecchio Maggiore, Vicenza, Italy
Tel.: (39) 0444492111
Web Site: http://www.filmcutterpv.com
Electronic Components Mfr
N.A.I.C.S.: 334419

Suzhou Central Min Lai Solar Power Co., Ltd. (1)
Room 501 Seat B No 1799 Wuzhong Road, Minhang District, Shanghai, China
Tel.: (86) 2161673366
Web Site: http://www.jolywood.cn
Emp.: 2,000
Semiconductor & Related Device Mfr
N.A.I.C.S.: 334413

Suzhou Central Photovoltaic New Material Limited (1)
No 2 Zhongxing Road Chang Kun Industrial Park, Sha Jia Bang Town, Changzhou, Jiangsu, China
Tel.: (86) 51283818381
Semiconductor & Related Device Mfr
N.A.I.C.S.: 334413

Taizhou Zhong Lai Photoelectric Technology Co., Ltd. (1)
Jiangyan Road Economic Development Zone, Kaiyang, Taizhou, Jiangsu, China
Tel.: (86) 52380612391
Semiconductor & Related Device Mfr
N.A.I.C.S.: 334413

JOMAX DRILLING (1988) LTD.
Sun Life Plaza North Tower Suite 1750 140 4 Avenue SW, Calgary, T2P 3N3, AB, Canada
Tel.: (403) 265-5312
Web Site: http://www.jomax.ca
Year Founded: 1972
Drilling Contracting Services
N.A.I.C.S.: 213111
Eric Markham *(VP-Sls & Mktg)*

JONDETECH SENSORS AB
Drottning Kristinas Vag 45, 104 32, Stockholm, Sweden
Tel.: (46) 738109310
Web Site: https://jondetech.com
Year Founded: 2008
9X60—(DEU)
Rev.: $112,177
Assets: $6,485,397
Liabilities: $1,301,447
Net Worth: $5,183,950
Earnings: ($3,821,947)
Emp.: 7
Fiscal Year-end: 12/31/23
Software Development Services
N.A.I.C.S.: 541511
Dean Tosic *(CEO)*

JONES PACKAGING INC.
3000 Page Street, London, N5V 5H3, ON, Canada
Tel.: (519) 451-2100
Web Site: https://www.jonespackaging.com
Year Founded: 1920
Rev.: $65,905,207
Emp.: 420
Folding Cartons & Other Packaging Products Mfr
N.A.I.C.S.: 322212

JONES TECH PLC
No 3 Donghuan Middle Road Economic and Technological Development Zone, Beijing, 100176, China
Tel.: (86) 1067860832
Web Site: http://www.jones-corp.com
Year Founded: 1997
300684—(CHIN)
Rev.: $177,176,863
Assets: $318,628,095
Liabilities: $51,731,529
Net Worth: $266,896,566
Earnings: $10,388,603
Fiscal Year-end: 12/31/23
Shielding Material Mfr & Distr
N.A.I.C.S.: 335991
Wu Xiaoning *(Chm)*

JONIX SPA
Viale Spagna 31/33, Veneto Tribano, 35020, Padua, Italy
Tel.: (39) 0499588511
Web Site: https://www.investor.jonixair.com
Year Founded: 2013
JNX—(EUR)
Biotechnology Research & Development Services
N.A.I.C.S.: 541714

JONJEE HI-TECH INDUSTRIAL & COMMERCIAL HOLDING CO., LTD.
No 1 Chubang Road Zhongshan Torch Development Zone, Zhongshan, 528437, Guangdong, China
Tel.: (86) 76085596818
Web Site: https://www.jonjee.com
Year Founded: 1993
600872—(SHG)
Rev.: $749,882,156
Assets: $873,762,075
Liabilities: $387,299,044
Net Worth: $486,463,031
Earnings: ($83,151,661)
Emp.: 78,000
Fiscal Year-end: 12/31/22
Holding Company
N.A.I.C.S.: 551112
Guo Yihang *(Sec)*

JONJUA OVERSEAS LIMITED
545 Jubilee Walk Sector 70, Mohali, 160071, Punjab, India
Tel.: (91) 9872172032
Web Site: https://www.jonjua.com
Year Founded: 1993
542446—(BOM)
Consulting Services
N.A.I.C.S.: 541611
Ranbir Kaur Jonjua *(CFO)*

JOONG ANG ENERVIS CO., LTD.
82 Hannam-daero, Yongsan-gu, Seoul, 140894, Korea (South)
Tel.: (82) 7087074500
Web Site: http://www.enervis.co.kr
Year Founded: 1946
000440—(KRS)
Rev.: $54,933,208
Assets: $48,644,484
Liabilities: $3,529,652
Net Worth: $45,114,832
Earnings: $383,563
Emp.: 72
Fiscal Year-end: 12/31/22
Petroleum Product Whslr
N.A.I.C.S.: 424720

JOONGANG ADVANCED MATERIALS CO., LTD
B-617 Hagui-ro 282, Dongan-gu, Anyang, Gyeonggi-do, Korea (South)
Tel.: (82) 7051533200
Web Site: https://www.joonganglivingtech.com
Year Founded: 1980
051980—(KRS)
Rev.: $21,018,613
Assets: $27,532,285
Liabilities: $10,856,025
Net Worth: $16,676,260
Earnings: ($14,436,897)
Emp.: 104
Fiscal Year-end: 12/31/22
Window & Door Mfr
N.A.I.C.S.: 332321

JOONGANG MEDIA NETWORK CO. LTD.
2-6 Sunhwa-dong Jung-gu, Seoul, 100-732, Korea (South)
Tel.: (82) 2200006219
Web Site: http://koreajoongangdaily.joins.com
Sales Range: $400-449.9 Million
Emp.: 1,600
Holding Company: Newspaper Publisher
N.A.I.C.S.: 551112
Bang Jeong-Lim *(Mgr-Circulation & Mktg)*

Subsidiaries:

JoongAng Daily News California Inc. (1)
690 Wilshire Pl, Los Angeles, CA 90005
Tel.: (213) 368-2500
Web Site: http://www.koreadaily.com
Rev.: $23,000,000
Emp.: 400
Publisher of Newspapers
N.A.I.C.S.: 513110

JOOYONTECH CO., LTD.
5F 134 Yanghwa-ro, Mapo-gu, Seoul, 04038, Korea (South)
Tel.: (82) 221221000
Web Site: https://www.jooyon.co.kr
Year Founded: 1988
044380—(KRS)
Rev.: $51,134,037
Assets: $40,836,863
Liabilities: $8,973,135
Net Worth: $31,863,729
Earnings: ($4,323,184)
Emp.: 96
Fiscal Year-end: 12/31/22
Computer & Computer Peripheral Product Mfr
N.A.I.C.S.: 334111
Heui Ra Kim *(CEO)*

Subsidiaries:

Jooyontech Co., Ltd. - Goyang Factory (1)
38-19 Gongneungcheon-ro 71beon-gil, Ilsandong-gu, Goyang, 10260, Gyeonggi-do, Korea (South)
Tel.: (82) 221221000
Electronic Equipment Mfr & Distr
N.A.I.C.S.: 334419

JORDAN AHLI BANK
Shmeisani - Commercial Area Yaqoub Sarouf Street, PO Box 3103, Amman, 11181, Jordan
Tel.: (962) 5638800   JO
Web Site: https://www.ahli.com
Year Founded: 1955
AHLI—(AMM)
Rev.: $210,094,099
Assets: $4,007,541,279
Liabilities: $3,559,480,995
Net Worth: $448,060,284
Earnings: $13,466,828
Emp.: 1,374
Fiscal Year-end: 12/31/20
Commercial Banking Services
N.A.I.C.S.: 522110
Mohammad Musa Daoud *(CEO & Gen Mgr)*

Subsidiaries:

Ahli Brokerage Company (1)
Ground Floor Ahli Bank Building Salwa Road, PO Box 24177, Doha, Qatar
Tel.: (974) 40110333
Web Site: https://www.ahlibrokerage.com.qa
Financial Brokerage Services
N.A.I.C.S.: 523999
Emad Abbas *(Mgr-Compliance)*

Ahli Fintech Company Ltd. (1)
King Hussein Business Park Building 19 Floor 1, Amman, Jordan
Tel.: (962) 65656300
Web Site: https://ahlifintech.com
Financial Technology Software & Hardware Services
N.A.I.C.S.: 541519

Ahli Microfinance Company (1)
King Abdullah II St, Jandaweel building 449, Amman, 11115, Jordan
Tel.: (962) 797530530
Web Site: https://amc.com.jo
Emp.: 260
Financial Loan Services
N.A.I.C.S.: 522291
Marwan Shahatit *(Gen Mgr)*

JORDAN CEMENT FACTORIES COMPANY PSC
Fuhis Shaker circle head office building, PO Box 930019, Amman, 11193, Jordan
Tel.: (962) 65600600
Year Founded: 1951
JOCM—(AMM)
Rev.: $104,056,495
Assets: $159,611,161
Liabilities: $254,601,901
Net Worth: ($94,990,740)
Earnings: $2,170,024
Emp.: 369
Fiscal Year-end: 12/31/23
Cement Mfr & Whslr
N.A.I.C.S.: 327310
Sama'an Sama'an *(Gen Mgr)*

JORDAN CHEMICAL INDUSTRIES CO. LTD
Jabal Al-Hussein Khalid Bin Al-Waleed St., PO Box 3380, 11181, Amman, Jordan
Tel.: (962) 64622964
Web Site: http://www.hypex.com.jo
JOIC—(AMM)
Sales Range: $1-9.9 Million
Emp.: 182
Household & Fabric Care Liquid Products Mfr & Sales
N.A.I.C.S.: 335210
Ahmad Al-Taher *(Gen Mgr)*

JORDAN COMMERCIAL BANK
King Abdallah II Street 8th Circle Building Number 384, PO Box 9989, 11191, Amman, 11191, Jordan
Tel.: (962) 65203000
Web Site: https://www.jcbank.com.jo
Year Founded: 1977
JCBK—(AMM)
Rev.: $99,574,635
Assets: $1,906,945,296
Liabilities: $1,710,235,761
Net Worth: $196,709,535
Earnings: $724,265
Emp.: 703
Fiscal Year-end: 12/31/20
Banking Services
N.A.I.C.S.: 522110

JORDAN COMMERCIAL BANK

Jordan Commercial Bank—(Continued)
Ayman Haza Barakat Al-Majali (Vice Chm)

JORDAN DAIRY
K Hussein St, PO Box 3474, Amman, 11118, Jordan
Tel.: (962) 780011111
Web Site: https://jordandairy.com
Year Founded: 1968
JODA—(AMM)
Rev.: $25,998,904
Assets: $30,679,667
Liabilities: $14,885,300
Net Worth: $15,794,367
Earnings: $313,586
Emp.: 256
Fiscal Year-end: 12/31/20
Dairy Products Mfr
N.A.I.C.S.: 311514
Raed Rashid (Gen Mgr)

JORDAN DECAPOLIS PROPERTIES PLC
Arjan Area Near Ministry of Interior, PO Box 212466, Abdali, Amman, 11121, Jordan
Tel.: (962) 65664109
Web Site: https://www.jdp.jo
Year Founded: 1982
JDPC—(AMM)
Rev.: $792,317
Assets: $116,354,122
Liabilities: $43,757,027
Net Worth: $72,597,096
Earnings: ($5,133,686)
Emp.: 43
Fiscal Year-end: 12/31/20
Real Estate Development Services
N.A.I.C.S.: 531390

JORDAN EMIRATES INSURANCE P.S.C.
Amman Shemesani, PO Box 925383, Amman, 11190, Jordan
Tel.: (962) 65681444
Web Site: http://www.joemirates.com
Insurance Services
N.A.I.C.S.: 524298
Mohamed Al Mazrooei (Chm)

JORDAN EXPRESS TOURIST TRANSPORTATION COMPANY
Amman 7th Circle, PO Box 3515, Amman, 11821, Jordan
Tel.: (962) 65664141
Web Site: https://www.jett.com.jo
Year Founded: 1964
JETT—(AMM)
Rev.: $17,495,082
Assets: $34,697,155
Liabilities: $11,406,605
Net Worth: $23,290,551
Earnings: ($6,195,334)
Emp.: 324
Fiscal Year-end: 12/31/20
Bus Transportation Services
N.A.I.C.S.: 485113

Subsidiaries:
JETT for Tourism & Travel Company (1)
PO Box 3515, Amman, 11821, Jordan
Tel.: (962) 6 464 8470
Web Site: https://www.jtt.com.jo
Transport & Tourism Services
N.A.I.C.S.: 561510

JORDAN FRENCH INSURANCE CO. (P.L.C.)
Al-Shemisani Al Shareef Abd Al Hameed Sharaf St, PO Box 3272, Building No 124, Amman, 11181, Jordan
Tel.: (962) 65600200
Web Site: https://jofico.jo
Year Founded: 1976
JOFR—(AMM)
Rev.: $44,460,440
Assets: $53,743,387
Liabilities: $36,632,838
Net Worth: $17,110,549
Earnings: ($1,453,007)
Emp.: 97
Fiscal Year-end: 12/31/22
Insurance Services
N.A.I.C.S.: 524298
Ayoub Wael Zurub (Exec Mgr)

JORDAN INDUSTRIAL RESOURCES CO. LTD.
Abdullah II Ibn Al Hussein Industrial City, PO Box 170, Amman, 11512, Jordan
Tel.: (962) 64023652
Web Site: https://www.joirco.com
Year Founded: 1992
JOIR—(AMM)
Rev.: $854,724
Assets: $13,233,782
Liabilities: $2,431,070
Net Worth: $10,802,712
Earnings: ($11,343,406)
Emp.: 3
Fiscal Year-end: 12/31/20
Vegetable Oil Mfr
N.A.I.C.S.: 311224

JORDAN INSURANCE COMPANY
3rd Circle, PO Box 279, Amman, 11118, Jordan
Tel.: (962) 64634161
Web Site: https://www.jicjo.com
Year Founded: 1951
JOIN—(AMM)
Rev.: $55,073,775
Assets: $126,525,579
Liabilities: $70,102,927
Net Worth: $56,422,652
Earnings: $4,247,817
Emp.: 221
Fiscal Year-end: 12/31/20
Insurance & Reinsurance Services
N.A.I.C.S.: 524113
Othman M. Bdeir (Chm)

JORDAN INTERNATIONAL INSURANCE CO.
221 Zahran Street, PO Box 3253, Amman, 11181, Jordan
Tel.: (962) 65901150
Web Site: https://www.newtoninsurance.com
Year Founded: 1996
JIJC—(AMM)
Rev.: $31,663,126
Assets: $52,729,394
Liabilities: $23,835,295
Net Worth: $28,894,099
Earnings: ($188,124)
Emp.: 91
Fiscal Year-end: 12/31/21
Insurance Services
N.A.I.C.S.: 524298
Mahmood Matarneh (Gen Mgr)

JORDAN INTERNATIONAL INVESTMENT CO.
6th Circle - Zahran Street - Building Num 221, PO Box 840536, Amman, 11181, Jordan
Tel.: (962) 65925301
Web Site: http://www.jiig.com
Year Founded: 2006
JIIG—(AMM)
Rev.: $55,281
Assets: $13,113,951
Liabilities: $28,367
Net Worth: $13,085,584
Earnings: ($126,491)
Emp.: 13
Fiscal Year-end: 12/31/20
Real Estate Development Services
N.A.I.C.S.: 531390

JORDAN INTERNATIONAL TRADING CENTER CO., LTD.
Dhahiyat Al Rasheed - Jordan Islamic Bank Complex - 3rd Floor, PO Box 926848, Amman, 11190, Jordan
Tel.: (962) 65150302
Web Site: https://www.profile.jitco.com
Year Founded: 1982
JITC—(AMM)
Rev.: $10,904,861
Assets: $11,267,221
Liabilities: $3,873,528
Net Worth: $7,393,693
Earnings: $362,209
Emp.: 77
Fiscal Year-end: 12/31/20
Household Electrical Appliance Whslr
N.A.I.C.S.: 423620
Khamis Ashour (Gen Mgr)

JORDAN INVESTMENT & TOURISM TRANSPORT CO
Airport street, PO Box 83, Amman, 11831, Jordan
Tel.: (962) 65850430
Web Site: https://www.npsc.com.jo
ALFA—(AMM)
Rev.: $11,858,884
Assets: $20,996,620
Liabilities: $16,579,225
Net Worth: $4,417,395
Earnings: $1,100,835
Emp.: 108
Fiscal Year-end: 12/31/23
Tourist Transportation Services
N.A.I.C.S.: 561510

JORDAN INVESTMENT TRUST P.L.C.
3rd Circle - Abed Al Minem Riad street, PO Box 911447, Amman, 11191, Jordan
Tel.: (962) 65508888
Web Site: https://www.jordinvest.com.jo
Year Founded: 1998
JOIT—(AMM)
Rev.: $229,204
Assets: $45,822,737
Liabilities: $1,935,675
Net Worth: $43,887,062
Earnings: ($1,472,880)
Emp.: 7
Fiscal Year-end: 12/31/20
Financial Investment Services
N.A.I.C.S.: 523999
Shadi Al-Majali (Chm)

JORDAN KUWAIT BANK PLC
62 Ummaya Bin Abed Shams Street Abdali, PO Box 9776, Amman, 11191, Jordan
Tel.: (962) 65629400
Web Site: https://www.jkb.com
Year Founded: 1976
JOKB—(AMM)
Rev.: $356,973,233
Assets: $7,398,987,069
Liabilities: $6,372,588,422
Net Worth: $1,026,398,647
Earnings: $127,026,921
Emp.: 1,467
Fiscal Year-end: 12/31/23
Commercial & Investment Banking Services
N.A.I.C.S.: 522110
Abdel Karim Alawi Kabariti (Chm)

Subsidiaries:
United Financial Investments Co. (1)
Abd Al Aziz Al Thaalibi St 13, PO Box

INTERNATIONAL PUBLIC

927250, Amman, 11192, Jordan
Tel.: (962) 65105111
Web Site: https://www.ufico.com
Sales Range: $50-74.9 Million
Emp.: 15
International Financial Services
N.A.I.C.S.: 522299
Naser M. Al-Amad (CEO)

JORDAN LOAN GUARANTEE CORPORATION
24 Prince Shaker Bin Zaid Street Shmeisani, PO Box 830703, Amman, 11183, Jordan
Tel.: (962) 65625400
Web Site: https://www.jlgc.com
JLGC—(AMM)
Rev.: $6,328,986
Assets: $1,100,874,216
Liabilities: $1,048,373,200
Net Worth: $52,501,015
Earnings: $909,761
Emp.: 53
Fiscal Year-end: 12/31/20
Loan & Credit Guarantee
N.A.I.C.S.: 541990
Maher Shiekh Hassan (Chm)

Subsidiaries:
Amman Chamber of Commerce Limited (1)
9 Prince Shaker Bin Zaid St Shmeisani, PO Box 287, Amman, 11118, Jordan
Tel.: (962) 795347222
Web Site: https://www.ammanchamber.org.jo
Promotes Participation & Mutual Respect Services
N.A.I.C.S.: 813319

Amman Chamber of Industry Ltd. (1)
Zahran Street, PO Box 1800, Jabal Amman, Amman, 11118, Jordan
Tel.: (962) 64643001
Web Site: https://aci.org.jo
Loan Guarantee Services
N.A.I.C.S.: 522390

Association of Banks in Jordan Ltd. (1)
62 Mousa Ibn Nosair Street Wadi Saqra, PO Box 926174, Amman, 11190, Jordan
Tel.: (962) 65008686
Web Site: https://abj.org.jo
Loan Guarantee Services
N.A.I.C.S.: 522390

Berne Union Limited (1)
1st Floor 231 - 232 The Strand, London, WC2R 1DA, United Kingdom
Tel.: (44) 2078411110
Web Site: https://www.berneunion.org
Non-Profit Organisation Services
N.A.I.C.S.: 813410

European Institute of the Mediterranean S.L. (1)
Carrer Girona 20, 08010, Barcelona, Spain
Tel.: (34) 932449850
Web Site: https://www.iemed.org
Loan Guarantee Services
N.A.I.C.S.: 522390

Global Network of Guarantee Institutions B.V. (1)
Avenue d'Auderghem 22-28, 1040, Brussels, Belgium
Tel.: (32) 26405177
Web Site: https://www.aecm.eu
Non-Profit Organisation Services
N.A.I.C.S.: 813410

Jordan Businessmen Associations Co., Ltd. (1)
Queen Rania Al-Abdallah Street Jordan University ST, Behind Al-Manaser Gas Station Jamal Ahmad Al-Qudah Street-Villa No 11, Amman, Jordan
Tel.: (962) 65373355
Web Site: https://en.jba.com.jo
Emp.: 292
Banking & Insurance Services
N.A.I.C.S.: 524210

Jordan Export Portal Ltd. (1)

PO Box 830432, Amman, 11183, Jordan
Tel.: (962) 65685603
Web Site: https://www.jordanexporters.org
Non-Profit Organisation Services
N.A.I.C.S.: 813410

Jordan Exporters Association Ltd. (1)
PO Box 830432, Amman, 11183, Jordan
Tel.: (962) 65685603
Web Site: https://www.jordanexporters.org
Loan Guarantee Services
N.A.I.C.S.: 522390

The Euro-Mediterranean Guarantee Network S.L. (1)
Sant Antoni Maria Claret 167, 08025, Barcelona, Spain
Tel.: (34) 934462414
Web Site: https://www.emgn.eu
Non-Profit Organisation Services
N.A.I.C.S.: 813410

JORDAN MARBLE COMPANY
Abu Alanda Hizam Road, PO Box 620628, Behind Al Qadessieh Garage, Amman, 11162, Jordan
Tel.: (962) 64163070
Web Site: http://www.jordan-marble.com
Year Founded: 1998
JMCO—(AMM)
Sales Range: $1-9.9 Million
Marble Processing & Supplier
N.A.I.C.S.: 423390
Hani Al Zammar (Gen Mgr)

Subsidiaries:

Al-Nabeel For Marble & Granite Company (1)
PO Box 620628, Amman, 11162, Jordan
Tel.: (962) 6 4200633
Emp.: 25
Construction Materials Distr
N.A.I.C.S.: 423390
Nabel Zammar (Owner)

JORDAN MASAKEN FOR LAND DEVELOPMENT & INDUSTRIAL PROJECTS
Al Madina Al Munawwarah St Masaken 1 Complex 156, PO Box 5821, 5th Floor Office No 505, Amman, 11953, Jordan
Tel.: (962) 65542756
Web Site: https://www.masaken.jo
Year Founded: 2008
MSKN—(AMM)
Rev.: $650,195
Assets: $13,359,019
Liabilities: $2,083,523
Net Worth: $11,275,496
Earnings: ($307,662)
Fiscal Year-end: 12/31/20
Real Estate Development Services
N.A.I.C.S.: 531390
Yahya Abdullah Mohammed Ismaik (Chm)

JORDAN MORTGAGE REFINANCING COMPANY LTD
15 Al-Mahdi Bin Baraka St Shmeisani West, PO Box 94743, Amman, 11194, Jordan
Tel.: (962) 65601417
Web Site: https://www.jmrc.com.jo
Year Founded: 1996
JMRC—(AMM)
Rev.: $44,389,839
Assets: $857,706,299
Liabilities: $831,471,239
Net Worth: $26,235,060
Earnings: $4,684,644
Emp.: 26
Fiscal Year-end: 12/31/20
Financial Services
N.A.I.C.S.: 541611
Tawfiq Mokahal (Vice Chm)

JORDAN NATION SHIPPING LINES P.L.C
Wadi Saqra Street Bldg No 51, PO Box 5406, Amman, 11183, Jordan
Tel.: (962) 65511500
Web Site: https://www.jnslgroup.com
Year Founded: 1976
SHIP—(AMM)
Rev.: $8,393,381
Assets: $55,514,160
Liabilities: $13,122,708
Net Worth: $42,391,452
Earnings: $5,425,288
Emp.: 17
Fiscal Year-end: 12/31/22
Shipping Services
N.A.I.C.S.: 488510
Ahmad Armoush (Chm)

Subsidiaries:

Arab Ship Management Ltd. (1)
PO Box 941340, Amman, 11194, Jordan
Tel.: (962) 6 5525182
Web Site: http://www.asm.com.jo
Marine Engineering Services
N.A.I.C.S.: 541330
Ahmad Armoush (Chm)

Jordan Academy for Maritime Studies (1)
PO Box 2793, Amman, 11118, Jordan
Tel.: (962) 6 5240102
Web Site: http://www.jams.edu.jo
Marine Engineering Educational Services
N.A.I.C.S.: 611710
Mustafa A. Massad (Pres)

Jordan Group For Shipping Agencies Co. Ltd. (1)
Nasir Bin Jameel Street - Building No 51, PO Box 940816, Jordan National Shipping Lines Building, Amman, 11194, Jordan
Tel.: (962) 65537276
Web Site: https://www.jgsa.com.jo
Marine Shipping Services
N.A.I.C.S.: 483111
Amjad M. Walid Jabri (Gen Mgr)

Jordan International Chartering Company (1)
PO Box 910527, Amman, 11191, Jordan
Tel.: (962) 6 5671474
Web Site: http://www.jicc.jo
Sales Range: $25-49.9 Million
Emp.: 10
Marine Shipping Services
N.A.I.C.S.: 483111
Murad Dakhqan (Gen Mgr)

JORDAN PAPER & CARDBOARD FACTORIES CO. PLC
Awajan-Zarqa, PO Box 1051, Zarqa, 13110, Jordan
Tel.: (962) 53656666
Web Site: http://www.jordanpaper.com
Year Founded: 1973
JOPC—(AMM)
Sales Range: $1-9.9 Million
Emp.: 127
Paperboard & Corrugated Box Mfr
N.A.I.C.S.: 322212
Usama Al-Alami (Gen Mgr)

JORDAN PETROLEUM REFINERY COMPANY
Amman First Circle Rainbow Street, Amman, Jordan
Tel.: (962) 64630151
Web Site: https://www.jopetrol.com.jo
Year Founded: 1961
JOPT—(AMM)
Rev.: $1,350,196,910
Assets: $1,542,980,086
Liabilities: $1,238,349,853
Net Worth: $304,630,233
Earnings: ($20,138,740)
Emp.: 3,298
Fiscal Year-end: 12/31/20
Petroleum Refinery Services
N.A.I.C.S.: 324110

Abed Al-Rahim Boucai (Vice Chm)

JORDAN PHOSPHATE MINES COMPANY LTD.
7 Al-Sharif Al-Radhi Street Shmeisani Amman, PO Box 30, Amman, 11118, Jordan
Tel.: (962) 65607141
Web Site: https://www.jpmc.com.jo
Year Founded: 1949
JOPH—(AMM)
Rev.: $1,734,246,609
Assets: $3,026,406,593
Liabilities: $650,672,966
Net Worth: $2,375,733,627
Earnings: $630,400,675
Emp.: 2,155
Fiscal Year-end: 12/31/23
Phosphate Mining
N.A.I.C.S.: 212390
Adel Al-Sharkas (Vice Chm)

Subsidiaries:

Indo-Jordan Chemicals Company Limited (1)
PO BOX 17028, Amman, 11195, Jordan (87.03%)
Tel.: (962) 65537217
Web Site: https://www.ijcltd.com
Sales Range: $125-149.9 Million
Emp.: 350
Phosphatic Fertilizer Mfr
N.A.I.C.S.: 325312

Indo-Jordan Chemicals Company Limited - Ma'an Factory (1)
PO Box 254, Ma'an, Jordan
Tel.: (962) 32132798
Chemical Products Mfr
N.A.I.C.S.: 325998

Nippon Jordan Fertilizers Company Limited (1)
Tel.: (962) 65691717
Web Site: https://www.njfc-jo.com
Fertilizer Product Distr
N.A.I.C.S.: 424910
H. E. Mohammad Thneibat (Chm)

JORDAN PIPES MANUFACTURING CO., LTD.
Al Hashmiyah, Zarqa, Jordan
Tel.: (962) 53811001
Web Site: http://www.jopipes.com
Year Founded: 1968
JOPI—(AMM)
Rev.: $1,746,266
Assets: $8,466,595
Liabilities: $4,960,809
Net Worth: $3,505,785
Earnings: ($1,126,363)
Emp.: 37
Fiscal Year-end: 12/31/20
Steel Pole Mfr
N.A.I.C.S.: 331210
Khair Abu Sa'alik (Gen Mgr)

JORDAN POULTRY PROCESSING & MARKETING CO LTD.
Amman - Aean Ghazal, PO Box 499, Amman, 11118, Jordan
Tel.: (962) 5052554
Web Site: http://www.hammoudeh.com
JPPC—(AMM)
Rev.: $48,633,557
Assets: $122,045,032
Liabilities: $94,680,107
Net Worth: $27,364,925
Earnings: ($5,053,554)
Emp.: 251
Fiscal Year-end: 12/31/20
Poultry Production Services
N.A.I.C.S.: 112390

Subsidiaries:

Jordan Chemicals Company Ltd. (1)
PO Box 17028, Amman, Jordan
Tel.: (962) 65537217

Web Site: https://ijcltd.com
Acid Mfr
N.A.I.C.S.: 325199

Jordan Feed Company (1)
Hazaa Al Qedyan St, PO Box 340526, Amman, Jordan
Tel.: (962) 64892853
Animal Feed Mfr
N.A.I.C.S.: 311119

JORDAN PRESS FOUNDATION PLC
Queen Rania Street, PO Box 6372, Amman, 11118, Jordan
Tel.: (962) 65600800
Web Site: https://www.alrai.com
Year Founded: 1971
PRES—(AMM)
Rev.: $11,983,651
Assets: $46,690,819
Liabilities: $29,296,008
Net Worth: $17,394,811
Earnings: ($10,769,154)
Emp.: 606
Fiscal Year-end: 12/31/19
Newspaper Publishers
N.A.I.C.S.: 513110

JORDAN PROJECTS FOR TOURISM DEVELOPMENT COMPANY
Zahran St - building No 188, PO Box 941299, Amman, 11194, Jordan
Tel.: (962) 6 2003355
Year Founded: 2001
JPTD—(AMM)
Sales Range: $10-24.9 Million
Emp.: 463
Tourism Development Services
N.A.I.C.S.: 926110
Mazen Hamoud (Gen Mgr)

JORDAN REFLEKTOREN GMBH & CO. KG
Schneiderstr 76, 40764, Langenfeld, Germany
Tel.: (49) 21732790
Web Site: http://www.jordan-reflektoren.de
Year Founded: 1924
Rev.: $43,774,900
Emp.: 147
Reflector Distr
N.A.I.C.S.: 423690
Martina Zallar (Head-Customer Svc)

Subsidiaries:

Jordan Reflectors Ltd. (1)
9 - 10 Seax Way Southfields Industrial Park, Basildon, SS15 6SW, Essex, United Kingdom
Tel.: (44) 1268415828
Web Site: http://www.jordanreflectors.co.uk
Reflector Lighting Mfr & Distr
N.A.I.C.S.: 335139
David Wright (Mng Dir)

JORDAN STEEL
PO Box 35165, Amman, 11180, Jordan
Tel.: (962) 4619380
Web Site: https://www.jordansteelplc.com
Year Founded: 1993
JOST—(AMM)
Rev.: $10,414,802
Assets: $88,946,564
Liabilities: $54,940,181
Net Worth: $34,006,383
Earnings: ($5,883,440)
Emp.: 617
Fiscal Year-end: 12/31/20
Iron & Steel Products Mfr
N.A.I.C.S.: 331110
Mu'taz Ghaleb Abu Hasan (CEO)

JORDAN TELECOM

JORDAN TELECOM

Jordan Telecom—(Continued)
The Boulevard Black Iris Street, PO Box 1689, Abdali, Amman, 11118, Jordan
Tel.: (962) 64606666
Web Site: https://www.orange.jo
Year Founded: 1971
JTEL—(AMM)
Rev.: $447,203,049
Assets: $977,332,656
Liabilities: $590,894,976
Net Worth: $386,437,680
Earnings: $24,685,692
Emp.: 1,623
Fiscal Year-end: 12/31/20
Telecommunication Services
N.A.I.C.S.: 517111
Shabib Farah Ammari (Chm)

JORDAN TRADE FACILITIES COMPANY PLC
Shmeisani - Abd Alhamid Sharaf str Building Num 52, Po Box 941493, Amman, 11194, Jordan
Tel.: (962) 65671720
Web Site: https://www.altas-heelat.com
Year Founded: 1983
JOTF—(AMM)
Rev.: $11,386,125
Assets: $86,649,278
Liabilities: $40,262,539
Net Worth: $46,386,740
Earnings: $3,724,347
Emp.: 77
Fiscal Year-end: 12/31/20
Financial Services
N.A.I.C.S.: 522220

JORDAN WOOD INDUSTRIES CO.
Naur - Mukabalain - Ras Al-Aein Road, PO Box 5272, Amman, 11183, Jordan
Tel.: (962) 4201171
Web Site: http://www.jwico.com
Year Founded: 1975
WOOD—(AMM)
Rev.: $7,787,661
Assets: $10,526,935
Liabilities: $13,448,936
Net Worth: ($2,922,001)
Earnings: ($3,597,226)
Emp.: 346
Fiscal Year-end: 12/31/20
Furniture Mfr
N.A.I.C.S.: 337211

JORDAN WORSTED MILLS COMPANY
7 King Hussein St Ar Rusaifah Awajan, PO Box 6060, 18 Allal Al Fasi St Ground Floor Shmeisani, Amman, 11118, Jordan
Tel.: (962) 53743428
Web Site: https://www.jowm-jo.com
Year Founded: 1962
JOWM—(AMM)
Rev.: $6,847,854
Assets: $78,588,615
Liabilities: $1,480,783
Net Worth: $77,107,832
Earnings: $2,290,165
Emp.: 155
Fiscal Year-end: 12/31/20
Fiber Fabric Mfr
N.A.I.C.S.: 313230
Samir Alamat (Gen Mgr)

JORDANIAN CO. FOR DEVELOPING AND FINANCIAL INVESTMENT
Um Uthaina - Opposite to Crowne Plaza Hotel - Djibouti Street, PO Box 8057, Amman, 13162, Jordan
Tel.: (962) 795201489
Year Founded: 1981
JDFI—(AMM)
Assets: $3,165,456
Liabilities: $993,216
Net Worth: $2,172,240
Earnings: ($399,698)
Emp.: 13
Fiscal Year-end: 12/31/20
Matches & Match Box Mfr
N.A.I.C.S.: 325998

JORDANIAN DUTY FREE SHOPS
PO Box 941601, Amman, 11194, Jordan
Tel.: (962) 65206666
Web Site: http://www.jdfshops.com
Year Founded: 1997
JDFS—(AMM)
Rev.: $37,043,899
Assets: $80,633,515
Liabilities: $12,122,124
Net Worth: $68,511,391
Earnings: $300,858
Emp.: 688
Fiscal Year-end: 12/31/20
Retail Stores
N.A.I.C.S.: 459999
Haitham Al-Majali (CEO)

JORDANIAN ELECTRIC POWER COMPANY LIMITED
Makkah St Raghadan building, PO Box 618, Amman, 11118, Jordan
Tel.: (962) 65503600
JOEP—(AMM)
Rev.: $1,269,073,846
Assets: $1,488,299,425
Liabilities: $1,301,348,836
Net Worth: $186,950,589
Earnings: $14,214,719
Emp.: 2,185
Fiscal Year-end: 12/31/21
Electric Power Distribution & Transmission Services
N.A.I.C.S.: 221122
Hassan Abdullah (Gen Mgr)

JORDANIAN EXPATRIATES INVESTMENT HOLDING PLC
Abdali - Professional Union Building - 8th Floor, PO Box 930220, Amman, 11193, Jordan
Tel.: (962) 5693044
Web Site: https://www.jeihldng.com
Year Founded: 1988
JEIH—(AMM)
Rev.: $1,071,057
Assets: $24,524,608
Liabilities: $906,405
Net Worth: $23,618,203
Earnings: $131,631
Emp.: 7
Fiscal Year-end: 12/31/20
Investment Management Service
N.A.I.C.S.: 523999
Khaled Kamel Abu Nahl (Chm)

JORDANIAN MANAGEMENT & CONSULTANCY COMPANY
Al Sharif Abdul Hamid Sharif Street - Adnan Center, Building 65 First Floor - next to Al Rajhi Bank, Amman, Jordan
Tel.: (962) 65683565
Web Site: https://jomc.net
Year Founded: 2006
JOMC—(AMM)
Rev.: $3,366,561
Assets: $11,393,563
Liabilities: $2,429,967
Net Worth: $8,963,596
Earnings: $640,330
Emp.: 8
Fiscal Year-end: 12/31/20
Financial Management Consulting Services
N.A.I.C.S.: 541611
Walid Wael Zaarb (Chm)

JORDANIAN MUTUAL FUNDS MANAGEMENT COMPANY
Airport Road - Madaba Bridge, PO Box 921513, Rum Group for Transportation and Tourism Investment Company Complex, Amman, 11192, Jordan
Tel.: (962) 64290499
FUND—(AMM)
Assets: $10,302,823
Liabilities: $1,741,717
Net Worth: $8,561,106
Earnings: ($531,272)
Emp.: 7
Fiscal Year-end: 12/31/20
Financial Investment Services
N.A.I.C.S.: 523999
Ahmad Khalil (Gen Mgr)

JORDANIAN REALESTATE COMPANY FOR DEVELOPMENT PLC
Shafa Badran - Haman Real Estate Complex, PO Box 3568, Opposite the Main Gate of the University of Applied Sciences, Amman, 11953, Jordan
Tel.: (962) 65236400
Year Founded: 2005
JRCD—(AMM)
Rev.: $1,583,746
Assets: $51,862,251
Liabilities: $2,016,615
Net Worth: $49,845,636
Earnings: $364,291
Emp.: 16
Fiscal Year-end: 12/31/20
Real Estate Manangement Services
N.A.I.C.S.: 531390

JORJIN TECHNOLOGIES, INC.
17F No 239 Sec 1 Datong Rd, Xizhi Dist, New Taipei City, 22161, Taiwan
Tel.: (886) 226490055
Web Site: https://www.jorjin.com
Year Founded: 1997
4980—(TAI)
Hardware Product Mfr
N.A.I.C.S.: 332510
Hsien-Chang Wang (VP)

JORUDAN CO., LTD.
5-10 Shinjuku 2-chome, Shinjuku-ku, Tokyo, 160-0022, Japan
Tel.: (81) 353694051
Web Site: https://www.jorudan.co.jp
Year Founded: 1979
3710—(TKS)
Rev.: $20,378,880
Assets: $36,860,160
Liabilities: $6,083,040
Net Worth: $30,777,120
Earnings: ($821,280)
Fiscal Year-end: 09/30/24
Custom Computer Programming Services
N.A.I.C.S.: 541511

JOS INTERNATIONAL BREWERIES PLC
1 Brewery Road, Plateau, Jos, Nigeria
Tel.: (234) 463951
Alcoholic Beverages Whslr
N.A.I.C.S.: 424820
Musa Garba Izam (Chm)

JOS. SCHNEIDER OPTISCHE WERKE GMBH

INTERNATIONAL PUBLIC

Ringstrasse 132, 55543, Bad Kreuznach, Germany
Tel.: (49) 6716010
Web Site: http://www.schneiderkreuznach.com
Year Founded: 1913
Sales Range: $50-74.9 Million
Emp.: 350
Provider of Optical Services
N.A.I.C.S.: 811210
Thomas Kessler (Mng Dir-Bingen)

Subsidiaries:

ISK Optics GmbH (1)
Anna-Vandenhoeck-Ring 5, PO Box 200155, 37081, Gottingen, Germany
Tel.: (49) 551 50 58 3
Web Site: http://www.isk-optics.de
Optical Equipment Mfr
N.A.I.C.S.: 333310
Wolfgang Selzer (Pres)

PENTACON GmbH (1)
Foto- und Feinwerktechnik Enderstrasse 92, 01277, Dresden, Germany
Tel.: (49) 351 2589 213
Web Site: http://www.pentacon.de
Emp.: 100
Camera Mfr
N.A.I.C.S.: 333310
Thomas Aurich (Head-Mktg)

Schneider Asia Pacific Ltd. (1)
20/F Central Tower 28 Queens Road, Central, China (Hong Kong)
Tel.: (852) 8302 0301
Web Site: http://www.schneider-asiapacific.com
Optical Equipment Mfr
N.A.I.C.S.: 333310
Shawn Liu (Mng Dir)

Subsidiary (Non-US):

Schneider Optical Technologies (Shenzhen) Co. Ltd. (2)
Rm A505 Yingdali Science Park Hongmian Rd, Futian Free Trade Zone, Shenzhen, 518038, China
Tel.: (86) 755 8832 1170
Web Site: http://www.schneideropticaltech.cn
Optical Equipment Mfr
N.A.I.C.S.: 333310
Shawn Liu (Gen Mgr)

Schneider Optics Inc. (1)
285 Oser Ave, Hauppauge, NY 11788
Tel.: (631) 761-5000
Web Site: http://www.schneideroptics.com
Sales Range: $25-49.9 Million
Emp.: 21
Photographic Cameras, Projectors, Equipment & Supplies Mfr
N.A.I.C.S.: 423410
Dwight Lindsey (CEO)

JOSANICA A.D.
Save Kovacevica bb, Novi Pazar, Serbia
Tel.: (381) 20315530
Year Founded: 2010
JSNC—(BEL)
Sales Range: Less than $1 Million
Emp.: 18
Hardware Product Whslr
N.A.I.C.S.: 423710

JOSAPAR - JOAQUIM OLIVEIRA S/A PARTICIPACOES
Av Carlos Gomes 651 - 5 Floor, 90480003, Porto Alegre, RS, Brazil
Tel.: (55) 5132273219
Web Site: http://www.josapar.com.br
Year Founded: 1922
JOPA4—(BRAZ)
Rev.: $378,819,460
Assets: $426,883,848
Liabilities: $293,222,673
Net Worth: $133,661,175
Earnings: $3,978,835
Emp.: 1,240
Fiscal Year-end: 12/31/23

Food Product Mfr & Whslr
N.A.I.C.S.: 311999
Augusto Lauro de Oliveira Jr. (Exec VP)

JOSE DE MELLO, SGPS, S.A.
Avenida 24 de Julho 24, 1200-480, Lisbon, Portugal
Tel.: (351) 21 391 6000 PT
Web Site: http://www.josedemello.pt
Year Founded: 1988
Rev.: $1,966,798,919
Assets: $5,100,438,206
Liabilities: $4,640,798,388
Net Worth: $459,639,818
Earnings: $72,425,826
Emp.: 12,614
Fiscal Year-end: 12/31/18
Holding Services
N.A.I.C.S.: 551112

Subsidiaries:

Bondalti Capital, S.A. (1)
Lagoas Park-Edificio 6 2 B, 2740-244, Porto Salvo, Portugal
Tel.: (351) 210058600
Web Site: https://www.bondalti.com
Chemical Mfr & Distr
N.A.I.C.S.: 325998

Brisa Group S.A. (1)
Quinta da Torre da Aguilha - Edificio Brisa, 2785-599, Sao Domingos de Rana, Portugal
Tel.: (351) 214448500
Web Site: https://www.brisa.pt
Road Construction Services
N.A.I.C.S.: 237310
Vasco de Mello (Chm)

Companhia Uniao Fabril SGPS S.A. (1)
Lagoas Park-Edificio 6 2, 2740-244, Porto Salvo, Portugal
Tel.: (351) 210 058 600
Web Site: http://www.cuf-sgps.pt
Industrial Chemicals Mfr
N.A.I.C.S.: 325199

Subsidiary (Domestic):

Aquatro - Projectos e Engenharia, S.A. (2)
Largo Alex Herculano Pq Emp Quimiparque - Cp 5108, Barreiro 2830, Setubal, Portugal
Tel.: (351) 212067650
Health Care Srvices
N.A.I.C.S.: 621491

Subsidiary (Non-US):

Electroquimica del Noroeste, S.A. (2)
Lugar Lourizan s/n, Pontevedra, 36153, Spain
Tel.: (34) 98 685 39 09
Industrial Chemical Distr
N.A.I.C.S.: 424690

Subsidiary (Domestic):

Quimigest - Soc. Quimica de Prestacao de Servicos, S.A. (2)
Qta Industria, 3860-680, Estarreja, Portugal
Tel.: (351) 234 810 300
Industrial Chemical Distr
N.A.I.C.S.: 424690

Renoeste - Valorizacao de Recursos Naturais, S.A. (2)
R da Mata do Urso 3105, Pombal, 3105-057, Portugal
Tel.: (351) 236 952 645
Industrial Chemical Distr
N.A.I.C.S.: 424690

Jose de Mello Imobiliaria, SGPS, S.A. (1)
Avenida 24 de Julho 24, 1200-480, Lisbon, Portugal
Tel.: (351) 21 391 6000
Real Estate Investment, Development & Project Management Services
N.A.I.C.S.: 531390

Jose de Mello Saude, S.G.P.S., S.A. (1)
Av do Forte n 3 Edificio Suecia III Piso 2, 2790-073, Carnaxide, Portugal
Tel.: (351) 21 002 5100
Web Site: http://www.josedemellosaude.pt
Healthcare Services
N.A.I.C.S.: 621491
Salvador Maria Guimaraes Jose de Mello (CEO)

Subsidiary (Domestic):

Clinica CUF Alvalade, S.A. (2)
Rua Professor Fernando da Fonseca, 1600-618, Lisbon, Portugal
Tel.: (351) 210 019 500
Web Site: http://www.cufalvalade.pt
Healthcare Services
N.A.I.C.S.: 621491

Clinica CUF Belem, S.A. (2)
R Manuel Maria Viana 4, 1300-383, Lisbon, Portugal
Tel.: (351) 21 361 2300
Web Site: http://www.cufbelem.pt
Healthcare Services
N.A.I.C.S.: 621491
Maria Ines Murteira Bleck (Pres)

Escala Braga - Sociedade Gestora do Estabelecimento, S.A. (2)
Lugar Sete Fontes Apartado 2056, 4710-243, Braga, Portugal
Tel.: (351) 253027000
Industrial Chemical Distr
N.A.I.C.S.: 424690

Escala Vila Franca - Sociedade Gestora do Estabelecimento, S.A. (2)
Estrada Nacional 1, 2600-009, Vila Franca de Xira, Portugal
Tel.: (351) 263 006 652
Hospital Management Services
N.A.I.C.S.: 622110

Hospital CUF Cascais, S.A. (2)
R Fernao Lopes 60 Cobre, 2750-663, Cascais, Portugal
Tel.: (351) 211 141 400
Web Site: http://www.cufcascais.pt
Healthcare Services
N.A.I.C.S.: 621491
Maria Ines Murteira Bleck (Pres)

Hospital CUF Descobertas, S.A. (2)
R Mario Botas Parque das Nacoes, 1998-018, Lisbon, Portugal
Tel.: (351) 210 025 200
Web Site: http://www.cufdescobertas.pt
Healtcare Services
N.A.I.C.S.: 621491
Salvador Maria Guimaraes Jose de Mello (Pres)

Hospital CUF Infante Santo, S.A. (2)
Trav do Castro 3, 1350-070, Lisbon, Portugal
Tel.: (351) 213 926 100
Web Site: http://www.cufinfantesanto.pt
Hospital Management Services
N.A.I.C.S.: 622110
Salvador Jose de Mello (Pres)

Hospital CUF Porto, S.A. (2)
Estrada da Circunvalacao 14341, 4100-180, Porto, Portugal
Tel.: (351) 220 039 000
Web Site: http://www.cufportohospital.pt
Hospital Management Services
N.A.I.C.S.: 622110

Hospital CUF Torres Vedras, S.A. (2)
R Joao Carlos Junior 5, 2560-253, Torres Vedras, Portugal
Tel.: (351) 261 008 000
Web Site: http://www.cuftorresvedras.pt
Hospital Management Services
N.A.I.C.S.: 622110
Maria Ines Murteira Bleck (Pres)

Sagies - Seguranca, Higiene e Saude no Trabalho, S.A. (2)
Rua D Luis I 19 4 andar, 1200-149, Lisbon, Portugal
Tel.: (351) 218 823 600
Healtcare Services
N.A.I.C.S.: 621491

Ravasqueira S.A. (1)
Monte da Ravasqueira, 7040-121, Evora, Portugal
Tel.: (351) 266490200
Web Site: https://www.ravasqueira.com
Wine Mfr & Retailer
N.A.I.C.S.: 312130

JOSEF MANNER & COMP AG
Wilhelminenstrabe 6, 1170, Vienna, Austria
Tel.: (43) 1488220
Web Site: https://www.manner.com
Year Founded: 1890
MAN—(VIE)
Sales Range: $1-4.9 Billion
Emp.: 700
Confectionary Product Mfr
N.A.I.C.S.: 311351

Subsidiaries:

Josef Manner s.r.o. (1)
Olomoucka 1159/40, 618 00, Brno, Czech Republic
Tel.: (420) 548 140 226
Confectionery Product Distr
N.A.I.C.S.: 424450

JOSEF MEISSNER GMBH & CO. KG
Bayenthalgurtel 16-20, 50968, Cologne, Germany
Tel.: (49) 22137920
Web Site: http://www.josefmeissner.com
Year Founded: 1926
Rev.: $51,037,800
Emp.: 70
Chemical Products Mfr
N.A.I.C.S.: 325998
Rolf Meissner (Mng Dir)

Subsidiaries:

RHE Handel Engineering GmbH & Co. KG (1)
Alte Heerstr 34, Saint Augustin, 53757, Germany
Tel.: (49) 22419070
Engineeering Services
N.A.I.C.S.: 541330

JOSER
Rn 19 Lieu Dit Les Boulbenes Rte De Nailloux, 31810, Toulouse, France
Tel.: (33) 561082626
Sales Range: $10-24.9 Million
Emp.: 43
Grocery Stores
N.A.I.C.S.: 445110
Josephine Chrestia (Mng Dir)

JOSERA GMBH & CO. KG
Industriegebiet Sud, 63924, Kleinheubach, Germany
Tel.: (49) 9371940950
Web Site: http://www.josera.de
Year Founded: 1963
Rev.: $135,211,273
Emp.: 175
Animal Feed Mfr
N.A.I.C.S.: 311119
Burkard Erbacher (Owner)

JOSHIN DENKI CO., LTD.
1-6-5 Nipponbashi-Nishi, Naniwa-ku, Osaka, 556-8550, Japan
Tel.: (81) 666311221
Web Site: https://www.joshin.co.jp
Year Founded: 1950
8173—(TKS)
Rev.: $2,668,404,120
Assets: $1,538,642,750
Liabilities: $847,150,820
Net Worth: $691,491,930
Earnings: $32,329,510
Emp.: 218
Fiscal Year-end: 03/31/24
Electronic Appliance Whslr

N.A.I.C.S.: 423620

JOSHUA GOLD RESOURCES INC.
20-1033 Pattullo Avenue, Woodstock, N4V 1C8, ON, Canada
Tel.: (226) 888-5610 NV
Web Site: https://www.joshuagoldresource.com
Year Founded: 2009
JSHG—(OTCIQ)
Assets: $110,188
Liabilities: $1,463,282
Net Worth: ($1,353,094)
Earnings: ($1,067,042)
Fiscal Year-end: 12/31/21
Mineral Mining & Exploration Services
N.A.I.C.S.: 212220
Dino Micacchi (CFO, Treas & Sec)

JOSTS ENGINEERING COMPANY LIMITED
Great Social Building 60 Sir Phirozeshah Mehta Road, PO Box No 243, Mumbai, 400001, Maharashtra, India
Tel.: (91) 2222704071
Web Site: https://www.josts.com
Year Founded: 1907
505750—(BOM)
Rev.: $13,168,715
Assets: $10,217,475
Liabilities: $5,881,266
Net Worth: $4,336,209
Earnings: $476,071
Emp.: 241
Fiscal Year-end: 03/31/21
Material Handling, Industrial Finishing & Engineered Products
N.A.I.C.S.: 423830
Anjan Nag (Head-Electrical)

Subsidiaries:

MHE Rentals India Private Limited (1)
C 7 Road No 12, Wagle Industrial Estate, Thane, 400 604, Maharashtra, India
Tel.: (91) 2262674000
Web Site: http://www.mherentals.com
Industrial Equipment Maintenance Services
N.A.I.C.S.: 811310
Dalip Singh (Gen Mgr)

JOTECH METAL FABRICATION INDUSTRIES SDN. BHD.
20 & 22 Jalan Masyhur 1, Taman Perindustrian Cemerlang, Ulu Tiram, 81800, Johor Darul Takzim, Malaysia
Tel.: (60) 7 861 6613
Web Site: http://www.jotech.com.my
Metal Stamping
N.A.I.C.S.: 332119
Siok Hui Lim (Mng Dir)

Subsidiaries:

GuangDong Jotech Kong Yue Precision Industries Ltd (1)
Kong Yue Industrial Park 18 Kong Yue Road, Xin Hui District, Jiangmen, Guang-Dong, China (60%)
Tel.: (86) 750 639 0222
Web Site: http://www.jotech.com.my
Metal Stamping
N.A.I.C.S.: 332119
Siok Hui Lim (Mng Dir)

PT Indotech Metal Nusantara (1)
Kawasan Industri KIIC Lot C-7C Jl Tol Jakarta Cikampek KM 47, Teluk Jambe, Karawang, 41361, Jawa Barat, Indonesia (100%)
Tel.: (62) 218904587
Web Site: http://www.jotech.com.my
Metal Stamping
N.A.I.C.S.: 332119
Indra S. Susanto (Pres)

JOTUN A/S

JOTUN A/S

Jotun A/S—(Continued)

Hystadveien 167, 3209, Sandefjord, Norway
Tel.: (47) 33457000   **NO**
Web Site: http://www.jotun.com
Year Founded: 1926
Rev.: $2,231,475,175
Assets: $2,172,840,226
Liabilities: $1,084,553,522
Net Worth: $1,088,286,705
Earnings: $175,943,795
Emp.: 10,007
Fiscal Year-end: 12/31/19
Paint, Coatings & Powder Coatings Mfr
N.A.I.C.S.: 325510
Morten Fon *(Pres & CEO)*

Subsidiaries:

Chokwang Jotun Ltd. (1)
96 Gwahaksandan 1-ro, Gangseo-gu, Busan, 46742, Korea (South) **(50%)**
Tel.: (82) 517976000
Web Site: http://www.jotun.com
Rev.: $3,537,400
Emp.: 30
Sales of Marine & Heavy Duty Paint
N.A.I.C.S.: 424950
Anthony Wong *(Pres)*

El-Mohandes Jotun S.A.E. (1)
Florida Tower El Sheikh Aly Gad El Haq Street, Masaken Sheraton Heliopolis 4th Floor, Cairo, Egypt
Tel.: (20) 2 2265 1800
Coating Distr
N.A.I.C.S.: 424950

Jotun (Deutschland) GmbH (1)
Haferweg 38, 22769, Hamburg, Germany **(100%)**
Tel.: (49) 40851960
Web Site: http://www.jotun.com
Sales Range: $25-49.9 Million
Emp.: 30
Sales of Marine Paints, Heavy Duty Coatings, Unsaturated Polyester, Gelcoats, Powder coatings
N.A.I.C.S.: 424950

Jotun (Ireland) Ltd. (1)
Unit K7 Marina Commercial Park Centre Park Road, Park Rd, Cork, Ireland **(100%)**
Tel.: (353) 214965955
Web Site: http://www.jotun.com
Sales Range: $25-49.9 Million
Marine & Protective Coating Mfr & Distr
N.A.I.C.S.: 325510

Jotun (Malaysia) Sdn. Bhd. (1)
Lot 7 Persiaran Perusahaan Section 23, PO Box 7050, 40300, Shah Alam, Selangor, Malaysia **(59%)**
Tel.: (60) 351235500
Web Site: http://www.jotun.com
Sales Range: $25-49.9 Million
Emp.: 280
Decorative & Marine Paints, Heavy Duty Coatings
N.A.I.C.S.: 325510

Jotun (Philippines) Inc. (1)
27 Millennium Drive Light Industry and Science Park III Brgy, Santa Anastacia, Santo Tomas, Batangas, Philippines
Tel.: (63) 27761337
Web Site: http://www.jotun.com
Emp.: 49
Coating Distr
N.A.I.C.S.: 424950

Jotun (Singapore) Pte. Ltd. (1)
37 Tuas View Crescent, Singapore, 637236, Singapore **(100%)**
Tel.: (65) 65088288
Web Site: http://www.jotun.sg
Sales Range: $25-49.9 Million
Emp.: 165
Mfr & Sale of Decorative Paints & Marine & Protective Coatings
N.A.I.C.S.: 325510

Jotun Abu Dhabi (LLC) (1)
Mussafah Industrial Area West 4, PO Box 3714, Abu Dhabi, 3714, United Arab Emirates **(43%)**
Tel.: (971) 25510300

Jotun Algerie SARL (1)
1 Coop El Amel 3, Dely Ibrahim, 16320, Algiers, Algeria
Tel.: (213) 98 2505 059
Coating Distr
N.A.I.C.S.: 424950

Jotun Australia Pty. Ltd. (1)
9 Cawley Road, Yarraville, 3013, VIC, Australia **(100%)**
Tel.: (61) 393140722
Web Site: http://www.jotun.com
Sales Range: $10-24.9 Million
Develops, Produces & Sells Powder Coatings for Decorative & Functional Applications
N.A.I.C.S.: 325510

Jotun B.V. (1)
Curieweg 11B, PO Box 208, 3200 AE, Spijkenisse, Netherlands **(100%)**
Tel.: (31) 181678300
Web Site: http://www.jotun.com
Sales Range: $50-74.9 Million
Emp.: 15
Mfr, Developer & Marketer of Products for the Protection & Decoration of Surfaces in Home, Marine & Industrial Use
N.A.I.C.S.: 531120
Willem Antheunissen *(Gen Mgr)*

Jotun Bangladesh Ltd. (1)
House No 6 7th Floor Road 2B Block J Baridhara, Nearest Land Mark American Centre or Japanese School, Dhaka, 1212, Bangladesh
Tel.: (880) 2 9856886
Web Site: http://www.jotun.com
Emp.: 15
Paint Distr
N.A.I.C.S.: 424950

Jotun Boya San. ve Ticaret A.S. (1)
Balabandere Caddesi Hilpark Suites Sitesi No 10 Istinye-Sariyer, Istanbul, 344600, Türkiye **(100%)**
Tel.: (90) 2122797878
Web Site: http://www.jotun.com
Sales Range: $25-49.9 Million
Sales of Marine Paints & Heavy Duty Coatings
N.A.I.C.S.: 325510

Jotun Brasil Imp. Exp. & Industria de Tintas Ltda. (1)
Estrada Ademar Ferreira Torres 250, Caluge-Itaborai, Rio de Janeiro, 24808-520, Brazil **(100%)**
Tel.: (55) 21 3147 3850
Web Site: http://www.jotun.com
Marine & Protective Coatings Mfr & Distr
N.A.I.C.S.: 325510

Jotun Bulgaria EOOD (1)
414 Okolovrasten Pat Str Bers Building, 1532, Kazichene, Bulgaria
Tel.: (359) 2 920 11 23
Coating Distr
N.A.I.C.S.: 424950

Jotun Coatings (Zhangjiagang) Co. Ltd (1)
No 15 Changjiang Road Jiangsu Yangtze River, Free Trade Zone, Zhangjiagang, 215634, Jiangsu, China
Tel.: (86) 512 5893 7988
Coating Distr
N.A.I.C.S.: 424950

Jotun Cyprus Ltd (1)
PO Box 52177, 4061, Limassol, Cyprus
Tel.: (357) 25 374455
Coating Distr
N.A.I.C.S.: 424950
Frank Montague *(Mgr-Marine Sls)*

Jotun Danmark A/S (1)
Jernet 6, 6000, Kolding, Denmark **(100%)**
Tel.: (45) 76303200
Web Site: http://www.jotun.com
Sales Range: $10-24.9 Million
Emp.: 40
Paint & Coating Mfr
N.A.I.C.S.: 325510

Jotun France S.A. (1)
22-24 Rue Du President Wilson Bat A, 92300, Levallois-Perret, France **(99%)**
Tel.: (33) 145193880
Web Site: http://www.jotun.com
Sales Range: $1-9.9 Million
Emp.: 15
Service, Stocking & Sales of Marine, Heavy-Duty Decorative Paints
N.A.I.C.S.: 424950
Jean-Sraneois Ferrer *(Mng Dir)*

Jotun Hellas Ltd. (1)
33 Zeppou Street, Glyfada, 16675, Greece **(100%)**
Tel.: (30) 2104285980
Web Site: http://www.jotun.com
Sales Range: $25-49.9 Million
Emp.: 50
Marine Paint Anodes Protective Coating & Powder Coating Mfr
N.A.I.C.S.: 325510

Jotun Iberica S.A. (1)
Estrada Vale de Mulatas Warehouse no 5, 2910-383, Setubal, Portugal **(100%)**
Tel.: (351) 265708910
Web Site: http://www.jotun.com
Sales Range: $25-49.9 Million
Marine & Protective Coating Mfr & Distr
N.A.I.C.S.: 325510

Jotun Iberica S.A. (1)
Poligon Industrial Santa Rita Calle Estatica 3, 8755, Barcelona, Spain **(100%)**
Tel.: (34) 937711800
Web Site: http://www.jotun.es
Sales Range: $50-74.9 Million
N.A.I.C.S.: 325510

Jotun India Pvt. Ltd. (1)
502 5th Floor Boston House Suren Road Behind Cinemax Theatre, Mumbai, 400 099, Maharashtra, India
Tel.: (91) 22 67872100
Coating Distr
N.A.I.C.S.: 424950
Richard Chapman *(Mng Dir)*

Jotun Italia S.p.A. (1)
Via O Petronio 8 Z I Noghere, 34015, Muggia, Trieste, Italy **(100%)**
Tel.: (39) 0404606965
Web Site: http://www.jotun.com
Sales Range: $10-24.9 Million
Sales of Marine Paints
N.A.I.C.S.: 424950

Jotun Ocean Paint Co. Ltd. (1)
Huakeng Rd Wenchong, Huangpu, Guangzhou, 510725, China **(51%)**
Tel.: (86) 2082360908
Web Site: http://www.jotun.com
Sales Range: $125-149.9 Million
Emp.: 300
N.A.I.C.S.: 325510

Jotun Paints (1)
Cureaweg 11B, Postbus 208, 3208 KJ, Spijkenisse, Netherlands **(100%)**
Tel.: (31) 181678300
Web Site: http://www.jotun.nl
Sales Range: $25-49.9 Million
Emp.: 20
Paints, Varnishes, Lacquers, Enamels & Allied Products
N.A.I.C.S.: 325510
Willem Antheunissen *(Gen Mgr)*

Jotun Paints (H.K.) Ltd. (1)
Rm 1208 12 F Stanhope House 734, Kings Road, Quarry Bay, China (Hong Kong) **(100%)**
Tel.: (852) 25276466
Web Site: http://www.jotun.com
Rev.: $4,877,600
Emp.: 7
Marine Paints & Heavy Duty Coatings Sales
N.A.I.C.S.: 424950

Jotun Paints (Vietnam) Co. Ltd. (1)
No 1 Street 10 Song Than 1 Industrial Zone, Di An, 650, Binh Duong, Vietnam **(100%)**
Tel.: (84) 2743742206
Web Site: http://www.jotun.com
Sales Range: $1-9.9 Million
Mfr & Sales of Decorative Paints, Also Marine, Protective & Powder Coatings
N.A.I.C.S.: 325510

Jotun Paints Co, L.L.C. (1)
Rusayl Industrial Estate Road No 10, PO Box 672, 111, Muscat, Oman **(57%)**
Tel.: (968) 2444 9700
Web Site: http://www.jotun.com
Sales Range: $25-49.9 Million
Mfr & Sales of Decorative Paints, Marine & Protective Coatings
N.A.I.C.S.: 325510

Jotun Paints OOO (1)
Varshavskaya Str 23/2 ofc 75, 196128, Saint Petersburg, Russia
Tel.: (7) 812 640 0080
Coating Distr
N.A.I.C.S.: 424950
Korkut Kulbul *(Gen Mgr)*

Jotun Paints South Africa (Pty) Ltd. (1)
Wimbledon Rd, PO Box 187, Blackheath, Cape Town, 7581, South Africa **(100%)**
Tel.: (27) 219418800
Web Site: http://www.jotun.com
Sales Range: $50-74.9 Million
Paint & Coating Mfr
N.A.I.C.S.: 325510

Jotun Paints, Inc. (1)
9203 Hwy 23, Belle Chasse, LA 70037
Tel.: (504) 394-3538
Web Site: http://www.jotun.com
Sales Range: $25-49.9 Million
Emp.: 100
Protective Coatings Mfr & Retailer
N.A.I.C.S.: 325510

Branch (Domestic):

Jotun Paints, Inc. - Houston (2)
842 W Sam Houston Pkwy N City Centre 3 Ste 300, Houston, TX 77024
Tel.: (713) 860-8241
Web Site: http://www.jotun.com
Sales Range: $50-74.9 Million
Emp.: 8
Mfr of Powder Coatings
N.A.I.C.S.: 424690

Jotun Polska Sp. z.o.o. (1)
ul Magnacka 15, Kowale, 80-180, Gdansk, Poland **(100%)**
Tel.: (48) 585551515
Web Site: http://www.jotun.com
Sales Range: $25-49.9 Million
Emp.: 40
Decorative Paint Marine & Protective Coating Sale Mfr
N.A.I.C.S.: 325510

Jotun Powder Coatings (CZ) a.s. (1)
Na Rovnem 866, 400 04, Trmice, Czech Republic **(100%)**
Tel.: (420) 477828969
Web Site: http://www.jotun.com
Sales Range: $25-49.9 Million
Powder Coating Mfr
N.A.I.C.S.: 325510

Jotun Powder Coatings (M) Sdn. Bhd. (1)
Lot 7 Persiaran Perusahaan Seksyen 23, PO Box 7057, 40300, Shah Alam, Selangor, Malaysia **(100%)**
Tel.: (60) 355190898
Web Site: http://www.jotun.com
Sales Range: $25-49.9 Million
Emp.: 93
Powder Coating Mfr
N.A.I.C.S.: 325510

Jotun Powder Coatings (N) AS (1)
PO Box 2130, Stubberod, 3255, Larvik, Norway **(100%)**
Tel.: (47) 33164000
Web Site: http://www.jotun.com
Sales Range: $10-24.9 Million
Powder Coating Mfr
N.A.I.C.S.: 325510

Jotun Powder Coatings Bulgaria Ltd. (1)
Sofia Ring Logistics Park Krivina area 454 B Okolovrasten put, 1588, Sofia, Bulgaria **(100%)**
Tel.: (359) 29201123
Web Site: http://www.jotun.com
Sales Range: $25-49.9 Million
Powder Coating Mfr
N.A.I.C.S.: 325510

AND PRIVATE COMPANIES — JOWAT SE

Jotun Powder Coatings Pakistan (Pvt) Lda. (1)
2 KM Defence Road off 9 Km Raiwind Rd, Adjacent Valencia Homes Gate, Lahore, 54770, Pakistan
Tel.: (92) 42 35323500 3
Coating Distr
N.A.I.C.S.: 424950
Per Arne Langnes (Office Mgr)

Jotun Powder Coatings Saudi Arabia Ltd., Co. (1)
Building No 3078 Unit 1 Ad, PO Box 10830, Dammam, 34326, Saudi Arabia (54%)
Tel.: (966) 138121259
Web Site: http://www.jotun.com
Sales Range: $25-49.9 Million
Mfr & Sales of Decorative Paints & Powder Coatings
N.A.I.C.S.: 325510

Jotun Powder Coatings U.A.E. LLC (1)
Fraser Suites Hotel SIDRA Towers 11th Floor Al Sufouh Road, PO Box 51033, Dubai, United Arab Emirates (47%)
Tel.: (971) 43472515
Web Site: http://www.jotun.com
Sales Range: $50-74.9 Million
N.A.I.C.S.: 325510
Ram Ramnath (VP)

Jotun Saudia Co. Ltd. (1)
Phase 3 Industrial Estate, PO Box 34698, 21478, Jeddah, Saudi Arabia
Tel.: (966) 126350535
Web Site: http://www.jotun.com
Sales Range: $1-9.9 Million
Emp.: 60
Decorative & Marine Paints & Heavy Duty Coatings
N.A.I.C.S.: 325510

Jotun Sverige AB (1)
Klangfargsgatan 13, 421 52, Vastra Frolunda, Sweden (100%)
Tel.: (46) 31696300
Web Site: http://www.jotun.com
Sales Range: $25-49.9 Million
Decorative Paint & Marine & Protective Coating Sale & Mfr
N.A.I.C.S.: 325510

Jotun Thailand Ltd. (1)
Amata Nakorn Ind Estate BIPII 700/353 Moo 6, Tumbol Donhualoh Amphur Muang, Chon Buri, 20000, Thailand (95%)
Tel.: (66) 20229888
Web Site: http://www.jotun.co.th
Rev.: $17,768,400
Emp.: 170
Decorative & Marine Paint Heavy Duty Coating Mfr
N.A.I.C.S.: 325510

Jotun Toz Boya San. ve Tic. A.S. (1)
Yeni Camlik Cad Ayaz Sok Ovalar Is Merkezi No 2 K 4, 4 Levent, Istanbul, 34418, Turkiye (100%)
Tel.: (90) 2122797878
Web Site: http://www.jotun.com.tr
Sales Range: $50-74.9 Million
Emp.: 200
N.A.I.C.S.: 325510

Jotun U.A.E. Ltd. (LLC) (1)
Alquoz Industrial 2, PO Box 3671, Dubai, United Arab Emirates (100%)
Tel.: (971) 43395000
Rev.: $28,529,200
Emp.: 148
Mfr of Decorative & Marine Paints, Heavy Duty Coatings
N.A.I.C.S.: 325510
Biren Aurora (Gen Mgr)

Jotun do Brazil Ltda. (1)
Rue Mexico 21 6 Andar, Rio de Janeiro, 20031 144, Brazil (100%)
Tel.: (55) 2127761313
N.A.I.C.S.: 325510

Nor-Maali Oy (1)
Vanhatie 20, 15240, Lahti, Finland (33%)
Tel.: (358) 3874650
Web Site: http://www.nor-maali.fi
Sales Range: $25-49.9 Million
Mfr of Paints
N.A.I.C.S.: 325510
Markku Tuominen (Dir-Offering & Products)

P.T. Jotun Powder Coatings Indonesia (1)
Jl Raya Legok Km 6 8 No 68, Legok, Tangerang, 15820, Indonesia
Tel.: (62) 21 546 8435
Coating Distr
N.A.I.C.S.: 424950

Ratinjat Saudia Co. Ltd. (1)
Jeddah Industrial City Phase 3, PO Box 34698, Jeddah, 21478, Saudi Arabia (40%)
Tel.: (966) 26361271
Coating Material Mfr
N.A.I.C.S.: 325510

Red Sea Paints Co. Ltd. (1)
Jeddah Industrial City Phase 3, PO Box 34698, Jeddah, 21478, Saudi Arabia (40%)
Tel.: (966) 2 635 0535
Web Site: http://www.jotun.com
Sales Range: $50-74.9 Million
Decorative Paints Mfr
N.A.I.C.S.: 325510

Scanox AS (1)
Linnesstranda 2, Gullaug, 3426, Lier, Norway (100%)
Tel.: (47) 32244300
Web Site: http://www.scanox.no
Sales Range: $25-49.9 Million
Powder Coating Mfr
N.A.I.C.S.: 325510

JOUDER PRECISION INDUSTRY (KUNSHAN) CO., LTD
No 1123 Mid-Yingbin Road, Kunshan, 215316, Jiangsu, China
Tel.: (86) 51257796000
Web Site: https://www.jouder.com
Year Founded: 2000
300549—(CHIN)
Rev.: $48,137,234
Assets: $96,616,945
Liabilities: $19,252,012
Net Worth: $77,364,933
Earnings: $2,441,522
Fiscal Year-end: 12/31/23
Precision Product Mfr & Distr
N.A.I.C.S.: 332721
Zeng Zhengxiong (Chm)

JOUFFRUIT
La Tapy Lhttp://joues Vigneres Domaine de la Tapy 2313 Route d'Avignon, 84300, Cavaillon, Vaucluse, France
Tel.: (33) 490713094
Web Site: http://www.jouffruit.com
Year Founded: 1953
Sales Range: $25-49.9 Million
Emp.: 10
Fresh Fruits & Vegetables
N.A.I.C.S.: 424480
Christian Jouffret (Mng Partner)

JOULES LIMITED
Joules Building The Point Rockingham Road, Market Harborough, LE16 7QU, Leicestershire, United Kingdom
Tel.: (44) 3452507160
Web Site: http://www.joules.com
Year Founded: 1989
JOUL—(AIM)
Rev.: $276,608,289
Assets: $137,532,581
Liabilities: $71,364,609
Net Worth: $66,167,972
Earnings: $12,885,629
Fiscal Year-end: 05/26/19
Infant Clothing Retailer
N.A.I.C.S.: 424350
Tom Joule (Founder & Chief Brand Officer)

JOURDAN PLC
Elm House Elmer Street North, Grantham, NG31 6RE, Lincolnshire, United Kingdom
Tel.: (44) 1476403456   UK
Web Site: http://www.jourdanplc.co.uk
Year Founded: 1926
Sales Range: Less than $1 Million
Emp.: 6
Holding Company
N.A.I.C.S.: 551112
J. David Abell (Chm)

Subsidiaries:

Clinipak Limited (1)
Beech House Knaves Beech Business Ctr, Davies Way Loudwater, High Wycombe, HP10 9SD, United Kingdom
Tel.: (44) 1628810626
Web Site: http://www.clinipak.co.uk
Medical Equipments Mfr & Distr
N.A.I.C.S.: 423450
Craig Lewis (Mng Dir)

Nelsons Labels (Manchester) Limited (1)
Unit 3 Wharfside Commerce Park Waterside, Manchester, M17 1WD, United Kingdom
Tel.: (44) 1618734500
Web Site: http://www.nelsons-labels.co.uk
Sales Range: $25-49.9 Million
Emp.: 30
Garment Design & Print Solution Services
N.A.I.C.S.: 541490

JOURDAN RESOURCES INC.
198 Davenport Road, Toronto, M5R 1J2, ON, Canada
Tel.: (647) 477-2382   ON
Web Site: https://jourdaninc.com
Year Founded: 1970
Z36—(DEU)
Rev.: $24,377
Assets: $2,279,115
Liabilities: $270,369
Net Worth: $2,008,746
Earnings: ($3,977,687)
Fiscal Year-end: 12/31/23
Mineral Exploration Services
N.A.I.C.S.: 213114
Roger Marcel Lemaitre (VP & Head-Mining)

JOURDENESS GROUP LIMITED
No 816 Sec 1 Zhongqing Rd, North Dist, Taichung, 404, Taiwan
Tel.: (886) 422922999   Ky
Web Site: http://www.jourdeness.com.tw
Year Founded: 2010
4190—(TAI)
Rev.: $97,312,531
Assets: $256,907,247
Liabilities: $188,948,094
Net Worth: $67,959,152
Earnings: ($8,437)
Fiscal Year-end: 12/31/23
Cosmetic Product Mfr & Distr
N.A.I.C.S.: 325620
Cheng-Hsiung Chen (Chm)

Subsidiaries:

Bio-Jourdeness Cosmetic Co. (MY) Sdn. Bhd. (1)
38-1 Jalan USJ 10/1E USJ 10, 47610, Subang Jaya, Selangor, Malaysia
Tel.: (60) 356210213
Web Site: https://jourdeness.com.my
Beauty Product Mfr
N.A.I.C.S.: 325620

JOURNEO PLC
Unit 3 Fullwood Close, Aldermans Green Industrial Estate, Coventry, CV2 2SS, United Kingdom
Tel.: (44) 2036519166
Web Site: https://www.journeo.com
JNEO—(AIM)
Rev.: $26,663,721
Assets: $19,323,403
Liabilities: $16,611,967
Net Worth: $2,711,437
Earnings: $1,139,864
Emp.: 106
Fiscal Year-end: 12/31/22
Auto Parts & Security Products Sales
N.A.I.C.S.: 423120
Russ C. Singleton (CEO)

Subsidiaries:

21st C Scandinavia AB (1)
Varuvagen 9, 125 30, Alvsjo, Sweden
Tel.: (46) 8210065
CCTV Installation & Project Management Services
N.A.I.C.S.: 561621

JOURNEY ENERGY INC.
Suite 700 Centre 10 517 10th Avenue SW, Calgary, T2R 0A8, AB, Canada
Tel.: (403) 294-1635
Web Site: https://www.journeyenergy.ca
Year Founded: 2007
JOY—(TSX)
Rev.: $56,572,143
Assets: $225,040,834
Liabilities: $240,547,189
Net Worth: ($15,506,354)
Earnings: ($44,295,823)
Emp.: 40
Fiscal Year-end: 12/31/20
Oil Exploration & Production Services
N.A.I.C.S.: 211120
Alex G. Verge (Pres & CEO)

JOUVE, SA
11 Boulevard De Sebastopol, 75001, Paris, France
Tel.: (33) 1 44 76 54 40   FR
Web Site: http://www.jouve.com
Year Founded: 2000
Data Processing & Internet Content Services
N.A.I.C.S.: 518210
Thibault Lanxade (Pres & CEO)

Subsidiaries:

Six Red Marbles, LLC (1)
10 City Sq, Charlestown, MA 02129
Tel.: (857) 588-9000
Web Site: http://www.sixredmarbles.com
Rev.: $1,918,000
Emp.: 7
Periodical Publishers
N.A.I.C.S.: 513120
John Kenney (Exec VP-Bus Dev)

JOWAT SE
Ernst-Hilker-Strasse 10-14, PO Box 1953, 32758, Detmold, Germany
Tel.: (49) 52317490   De
Web Site: http://www.jowat.com
Year Founded: 1919
Sales Range: $150-199.9 Million
Emp.: 1,100
Adhesive Mfr
N.A.I.C.S.: 325520
Klaus Kullmann (Mng Dir-Sls & Mktg)

Subsidiaries:

Jowat (Beijing) Adhesives Co. Ltd. (1)
No 18 Zhongguancun East Road Intelli Center Room A1202, Haidian District, 100083, Beijing, China
Tel.: (86) 1082600876
Web Site: http://www.jowat.com.cn
Adhesive Distr
N.A.I.C.S.: 424690
Sophia Liu (Mgr-Supply Chain)

Jowat (Malaysia) Sdn. Bhd. (1)
No 5 Jalan Taming 2A Taming Jaya Industrial Park, Balakong, Selangor, Malaysia
Tel.: (60) 389622800
Adhesive Distr
N.A.I.C.S.: 424690
Ragunathan Naraina (Project Mgr)

Jowat Adhesives India Pvt. Ltd. (1)

JOWAT SE

Jowat SE—(Continued)
Shiv Chamber Office no 201 / 202 Sector 11, CBD Belapur, Mumbai, Maharastra, India
Tel.: (91) 9167551315
Adhesive Distr
N.A.I.C.S.: 424690

Jowat Atasoy Yapistirici Urunler Ti-caret A.S. (1)
Anonim Sirketi Inonu Mahallesi Kartal Caddesi No 48, Atasehir, Istanbul, Turkiye
Tel.: (90) 2166614315
Web Site: http://www.jowat.com.tr
Adhesive Distr
N.A.I.C.S.: 424690
cihad Atasoy (General Mgr)

Jowat Canada Ltd. (1)
PO Box 149, Mississauga, L5M 2B7, ON, Canada
Tel.: (336) 434-9154
Adhesive Distr
N.A.I.C.S.: 424690

Jowat Chile SPA (1)
La Dehesa 181 Piso 10 Of 1007, Lo Barnechea, Santiago, Chile
Tel.: (56) 223787566
Adhesive Distr
N.A.I.C.S.: 424690

Jowat Corporation (1)
5608 Uwharrie Rd, Archdale, NC 27263
Tel.: (336) 434-9000
Web Site: http://www.jowat.com
Adhesive Distr
N.A.I.C.S.: 424690
Todd Leach (Engr-Technical Svcs)

Jowat France sarl (1)
Immeuble Le Saint Amour 95 rue Pouilly, 71000, Macon, France
Tel.: (33) 385209292
Web Site: http://www.jowat.fr
Adhesive Distr
N.A.I.C.S.: 424690
Christophe Magnin (Mng Dir)

Jowat Italia s.r.l. (1)
Via dell Artigianato 3, Osio Sotto, Bergamo, Italy
Tel.: (39) 0350272310
Industrial Adhesive Distr
N.A.I.C.S.: 424690

Jowat Manufacturing (SEA) Sdn. Bhd. (1)
6 Jalan Taming 2a Taming Jaya Industrial Park, 43300, Balakong, Selangor, Malaysia
Tel.: (60) 389626300
Adhesive Distr
N.A.I.C.S.: 424690
Willi Wiens (Mng Dir)

Jowat Middle East FZE (1)
Q3-17 SAIF Zone, PO Box 120801, Sharjah, United Arab Emirates
Tel.: (971) 65579092
Adhesive Distr
N.A.I.C.S.: 424690
Fabian Heiliger (Gen Mgr)

Jowat Nederland B.V. (1)
Ootmarsumseweg 283, 7666 NB, Fleringen, Netherlands
Tel.: (31) 541670629
Web Site: http://www.jowat.nl
Adhesive Distr
N.A.I.C.S.: 424690

Jowat Polska sp. z o.o. sp. k. (1)
ul Poznanska 15, Sady, Poznan, Poland
Tel.: (48) 618147287
Web Site: http://www.jowat.com.pl
Adhesive Distr
N.A.I.C.S.: 424690

Jowat Scandinavia AB (1)
Hanogatan 11, Malmo, Sweden
Tel.: (46) 40461190
Web Site: http://www.jowat.se
Adhesive Distr
N.A.I.C.S.: 424690
Christer Ekstrand (Mng Dir)

Jowat Swiss AG (1)
Schiltwaldstrasse 33, Buchrain, Switzerland
Tel.: (41) 414451111
Web Site: http://www.jowat.ch

Adhesive Distr
N.A.I.C.S.: 424690

Jowat UK Ltd. (1)
Lymedale Business Centre/Lymed Bus Park Hooters Hall Road, Newcastle-under-Lyme, ST5 9QF, Staffordshire, United Kingdom
Tel.: (44) 1782565265
Web Site: http://www.jowat.co.uk
Adhesive Distr
N.A.I.C.S.: 424690
Craig Boulton (Mng Dir)

Jowat Universal Adhesives Australia Pty. Ltd. (1)
U 2 12 Kerr Rd, Ingleburn, 2565, NSW, Australia
Tel.: (61) 296053477
Adhesive Distr
N.A.I.C.S.: 424690

Jowat de Mexico S. de R.L. de C.V. (1)
Durango No 263 Piso 8, Mexico, Mexico
Tel.: (52) 5552117514
Adhesive Distr
N.A.I.C.S.: 424690
Alejandro Oviedo (Mgr-Natl Sls)

JOWELL GLOBAL LTD.
No 285 Jiangpu Road 2nd Floor, Yangpu District, Shanghai, 200082, China
Tel.: (86) 2155210174 Ky
Year Founded: 2019
JWEL—(NASDAQ)
Rev.: $160,009,293
Assets: $35,297,927
Liabilities: $10,084,608
Net Worth: $25,213,319
Earnings: ($11,519,933)
Emp.: 154
Fiscal Year-end: 12/31/23
Holding Company
N.A.I.C.S.: 551112
Zhiwei Xu (Chm & CEO)

JOY KIE CORPORATION LIMITED.
16F Guangxin building Xintang Road, Shangcheng District, Hangzhou, 310000, Zhejiang, China
Tel.: (86) 18667107197
Web Site:
https://www.joykiebikes.com
Year Founded: 2000
300994—(CHIN)
Rev.: $333,597,420
Assets: $244,110,672
Liabilities: $78,514,488
Net Worth: $165,596,184
Earnings: $23,567,544
Emp.: 500
Fiscal Year-end: 12/31/22
Bicycle Product Mfr & Distr
N.A.I.C.S.: 336991
Zheng Li (Chm)

Subsidiaries:

Hangzhou Joyshine Imp.& Exp. Co., Ltd. (1)
Room 808 Zhongmin Building No 8 Guodong Yuan Road, Hangzhou, China
Tel.: (86) 57187273599
Web Site: https://www.cnjoyshine.com
Motorcycle & Bicycle Parts Mfr
N.A.I.C.S.: 336991

JOY REALTY LIMITED
301 Nestor Court Adj to Vinayak chs Baji Prabhu Deshpande Marg Pond, Gavthan Vile Parle, Mumbai, 400 056, Maharashtra, India
Tel.: (91) 9558780710
Web Site: https://www.joyrealty.in
508929—(BOM)
Rev.: $65,016
Assets: $1,540,891
Liabilities: $2,585,347
Net Worth: ($1,044,456)

Earnings: ($92,119)
Emp.: 710
Fiscal Year-end: 03/31/22
Real Estate Related Services
N.A.I.C.S.: 531390
Bhavin Soni (Mng Dir)

JOY SPREADER GROUP INC.
27/F Wangjing Jinhui Building, Chaoyang District, Beijing, China
Tel.: (86) 1087726988 Ky
Web Site:
https://www.joyspreader.com
Year Founded: 2008
6988—(HKG)
Rev.: $649,736,348
Assets: $238,830,498
Liabilities: $37,405,907
Net Worth: $201,424,591
Earnings: ($101,376,794)
Emp.: 91
Fiscal Year-end: 12/31/23
Information Technology Services
N.A.I.C.S.: 541512
Jiaxin Qin (Sec)

JOYAS INTERNATIONAL HOLDINGS LIMITED
Room 1415 14/F Leighton Centre 77 Leighton Road, Phase 2 Nos 42-46 Tai Lin Pai Road New Territories, Causeway Bay, China (Hong Kong)
Tel.: (852) 26205298 BM
Web Site: https://www.joyasint.com
E9L—(SES)
Rev.: $501,840
Assets: $3,390,735
Liabilities: $1,938,638
Net Worth: $1,452,098
Earnings: $131,963
Emp.: 14
Fiscal Year-end: 12/31/22
Metal Gift Products, Jewelry & Packaging Products Mfr, Distr & Sales
N.A.I.C.S.: 339910
Gwendolyn Jong Yuh Gn (Sec)

JOYAS MANUFACTURING LIMITED
Room 217 2/F Hong Kong Spinners Industrial Building Phase 6, 481-483 Castle Peak Rd, Cheung Sha Wan, Kowloon, China (Hong Kong)
Tel.: (852) 24080880
Web Site: http://www.joyas.hk
Year Founded: 1991
Sales Range: $25-49.9 Million
Emp.: 30
Metal Products Mfr & Distr
N.A.I.C.S.: 332999

Subsidiaries:

Joyas Manufacturing International Ltd (1)
18 F Jinwei Bldg No 4051 Jiabin Rd, Luohu Dist, Shenzhen, Guangdong, China
Tel.: (86) 75525469352
Sales Range: $25-49.9 Million
Metal Products Mfr & Distr
N.A.I.C.S.: 332999

JOYCE BOUTIQUE HOLDINGS LIMITED
26/F One Island South 2 Heung Yip Road, Wong Chuk Hang, Hong Kong, China (Hong Kong)
Tel.: (852) 21135288 BM
Web Site: http://www.joyce.com
Year Founded: 1970
Rev.: $110,126,693
Assets: $87,863,777
Liabilities: $26,008,908
Net Worth: $61,854,869
Earnings: ($7,002,064)
Emp.: 399
Fiscal Year-end: 03/31/18
Cosmetic & Fashion Product Retailer

INTERNATIONAL PUBLIC

N.A.I.C.S.: 456120

JOYCE CORPORATION LTD
30-32 Guthrie Street, Osborne Park, 6017, WA, Australia
Tel.: (61) 894451055 AU
Web Site:
http://www.joycecorp.com.au
JYC—(ASX)
Rev.: $97,161,458
Assets: $61,989,850
Liabilities: $36,069,044
Net Worth: $25,920,807
Earnings: $11,706,063
Fiscal Year-end: 06/30/24
Investment Services; Bedding & Bedroom Furniture Retailer
N.A.I.C.S.: 337122
Anthony Mankarios (Exec Dir)

Subsidiaries:

Bedshed Franchising Pty. Ltd. (1)
467 Scarborough Beach Rd, Osborne Park, 6107, WA, Australia
Tel.: (61) 894453444
Web Site: https://www.bedshed.com.au
Sales Range: $25-49.9 Million
Emp.: 21
Bedroom Furniture Mfr & Retail Services
N.A.I.C.S.: 337121
Rod Parker (Mgr-Bus Dev)

JOYCITY CORPORATION
10F Bundang First Tower 55 Bundang-ro, Bundang-Gu, Seongnam, 13591, Gyeonggi-do, Korea (South)
Tel.: (82) 317896500
Web Site: https://corp.joycity.com
Year Founded: 1994
067000—(KRS)
Rev.: $125,618,874
Assets: $189,951,062
Liabilities: $114,112,968
Net Worth: $75,838,094
Earnings: $2,449,475
Emp.: 322
Fiscal Year-end: 12/31/22
Online Game Mfr & Whslr
N.A.I.C.S.: 541511
Cho Seong-Won (CEO)

JOYFUL HONDA CO., LTD.
1-16-2 Fujisaki, Tsuchiura, 300-0813, Ibaraki, Japan
Tel.: (81) 298222215
Web Site:
https://www.joyfulhonda.com
3191—(TKS)
Rev.: $1,342,927,560
Assets: $1,465,355,340
Liabilities: $512,859,420
Net Worth: $952,495,920
Earnings: $39,719,040
Emp.: 4,892
Fiscal Year-end: 06/20/19
Miscellaneous Retail Stores
N.A.I.C.S.: 459999
Takashi Inaba (Mng Exec Officer & Mgr-Reform Div)

Subsidiaries:

Joyful Athletic Club Co., Ltd. (1)
4-11-7 Nakamuraminami, Tsuchiura, 300-0843, Ibaraki, Japan
Tel.: (81) 298428387
Web Site: http://www.joyful-athleticclub.co.jp
Emp.: 260
Sports Product Distr
N.A.I.C.S.: 423910
Yukio Adachi (Pres & CEO)

JOYVIO FOOD CO., LTD.
Room 21403-21405 Science and Technology Business Park No 2 Xinye Road, High-tech Industrial Development Zone Xinjiang, Shihezi, China

Tel.: (86) 9932087700
Web Site: https://en.joyviofood.com
Year Founded: 2003
300268—(CHIN)
Rev.: $634,564,139
Assets: $1,375,346,572
Liabilities: $1,314,517,218
Net Worth: $60,829,354
Earnings: ($162,196,677)
Fiscal Year-end: 12/31/23
Agricultural Machinery Mfr
N.A.I.C.S.: 333111
Chen Shaopeng (Chm)

Subsidiaries:

Australis Seafoods S.A. (1)
Cerro El Plomo 5680 Of 403 Las Condes, Santiago, Chile
Tel.: (56) 22995800
Web Site: http://www.australis-seafoods.com
Rev.: $407,286,000
Assets: $784,158,000
Liabilities: $410,362,000
Net Worth: $373,796,000
Earnings: $65,825,000
Emp.: 2,373
Fiscal Year-end: 12/31/2019
Aquaculture Services
N.A.I.C.S.: 112519
Jie Tang (Chm)

Subsidiary (US):

Trapananda Seafarms LLC (2)
175 SW 7th St Ste 1102, Miami, FL 33130
Tel.: (786) 708-0188
Seafood Whslr
N.A.I.C.S.: 424460
Rick Cano (Mng Dir)

JOYWARE ELECTRONICS CO., LTD.
15th-20th Floor No 1819 Xixing Road Xixing Street, Binjiang District, Hangzhou, 310051, Zhejiang, China
Tel.: (86) 57188373153
Web Site: http://www.joyware.com
Year Founded: 2000
300270—(CHIN)
Rev.: $49,644,036
Assets: $152,543,196
Liabilities: $46,201,428
Net Worth: $106,341,768
Earnings: $686,556
Emp.: 463
Fiscal Year-end: 12/31/22
Security Protection Video Monitoring Transmission Technology Products Mfr
N.A.I.C.S.: 334310
Li Yice (Chm)

JOYY INC.
30 Pasir Panjang Road 15-31A Mapletree Business City, Singapore, 117440, Singapore
Tel.: (65) 2082120000 Ky
Web Site: https://www.joyy.com
Year Founded: 2005
YY—(NASDAQ)
Rev.: $2,267,870,000
Assets: $8,483,865,000
Liabilities: $3,193,849,000
Net Worth: $5,290,016,000
Earnings: $272,418,000
Emp.: 6,292
Fiscal Year-end: 12/31/23
Rich Communication & Social Platform
N.A.I.C.S.: 513210
David Xueling Li (CEO & Chm)

JP AUTOCESTE FBIH D.O.O.
Adema Buca 20, 88 000, Mostar, Bosnia & Herzegovina
Tel.: (387) 36512300
Web Site: http://www.jpautoceste.ba
Road Construction Services
N.A.I.C.S.: 237310

Marin Jelcic (Exec Dir-Mgmt & Maintenance)

JP BODEN & CO. LTD.
Boden House Victoria Road, London, NW10 6NY, United Kingdom
Tel.: (44) 208 328 7000
Web Site: http://www.boden.co.uk
Year Founded: 1991
Sales Range: $250-299.9 Million
Emp.: 800
Apparel & Accessories Retailer
N.A.I.C.S.: 424350
John Peter Boden (Chm & Mng Dir)

JP ELEKTROPRIVREDA BIH D.D.
Vilsonovo Setaliste 15, 71000, Sarajevo, Bosnia & Herzegovina
Tel.: (387) 3 375 1000
Web Site: http://www.epbih.ba
JPESR—(SARE)
Rev.: $655,469,247
Assets: $4,332,889,506
Liabilities: $2,447,880,609
Net Worth: $1,885,008,897
Earnings: $5,977,655
Emp.: 4,232
Fiscal Year-end: 12/31/20
Electric Power Production & Distribution Services
N.A.I.C.S.: 221111
Salkic Senad (Exec Dir-Capital Investments)

Subsidiaries:

TTU Energetik d.o.o. (1)
18 Hrvatske Brigade 25, 75000, Tuzla, Bosnia & Herzegovina
Tel.: (387) 35291140
Web Site: https://www.ttuenergetik.ba
Industrial Machinery Mfr
N.A.I.C.S.: 333248

JP ELEKTROPRIVREDA HZHB D.D. MOSTAR
Ulica kralja Petra Kresimira IV 6-A, 88000, Mostar, Bosnia & Herzegovina
Tel.: (387) 36 335 705
Web Site: http://www.ephzhb.ba
JPEMR—(SARE)
Rev.: $194,680,210
Assets: $970,735,313
Liabilities: $498,311,369
Net Worth: $472,423,944
Earnings: $516,134
Emp.: 2,192
Fiscal Year-end: 12/31/20
Eletric Power Generation Services
N.A.I.C.S.: 221118

JP GROUP LTD
JP House Green Lane Business Park Green Lane, Tewkesbury, GL20 8SJ, Gloucestershire, United Kingdom
Tel.: (44) 1684271200
Web Site: http://www.jpconstruction.co.uk
Year Founded: 1969
Rev.: $33,341,935
Emp.: 150
Petrol Forecourt Construction Services
N.A.I.C.S.: 237120
John Parrott (Founder & Chm)

JP HOLDINGS, INC.
Orchid Building 7F 2-38-2 Meieki, Nakamura-ku, Nagoya, 450-0002, Aichi, Japan
Tel.: (81) 570001335
Web Site: https://www.jp-holdings.co.jp
2749—(TKS)
Rev.: $250,228,160
Assets: $243,836,290

Liabilities: $137,362,410
Net Worth: $106,473,880
Earnings: $19,360,690
Emp.: 4,023
Fiscal Year-end: 03/31/24
Holding Company; Day Care Services; Arcades & Vending Machines; Food Services
N.A.I.C.S.: 551112
Koichiro Furukawa (Pres)

Subsidiaries:

Cohas Vietnam Co., Ltd. (1)
16 Ly Thuong Kiet, Thach Thang Hai Chau, Da Nang, Vietnam
Tel.: (84) 2363981167
Web Site: http://www.cohasjapan.vn
Child Day Care Services
N.A.I.C.S.: 624410

J Cast Inc. (1)
Royal Bldg 1F 12-8 Nibancho, Chiyoda-ku, Tokyo, 102-0084, Japan
Tel.: (81) 332642591
Web Site: https://en.j-cast.co.jp
Magazine Publishing Services
N.A.I.C.S.: 513120
Masao Ninagawa (Pres)

JP HT D.D. MOSTAR
Kneza Branimira bb, 88000, Mostar, Bosnia & Herzegovina
Tel.: (387) 3 639 5000
Web Site: http://www.hteronet.ba
HTKMR—(SARE)
Rev.: $115,148,970
Assets: $262,485,296
Liabilities: $53,445,529
Net Worth: $209,039,767
Earnings: $30,510
Emp.: 1,345
Fiscal Year-end: 12/31/20
Telecommunication Servicesb
N.A.I.C.S.: 517810

JP KOMUS A.D.
Vasilija Ostroskog 5, 89230, Bileca, Bosnia & Herzegovina
Tel.: (387) 59380777
KOBI—(BANJ)
Sales Range: $350-399.9 Million
Sanitation & Remediation Services
N.A.I.C.S.: 562910

JP NELSON EQUIPMENT PTE LTD
30 Benoi Road, Singapore, 629900, Singapore
Tel.: (65) 6368 9991
Web Site: http://www.jpnelson.com.sg
Year Founded: 1992
Sales Range: $100-124.9 Million
Emp.: 500
Engineering, Construction, Oil, Gas & Shipyard Equipment Leasing, Sales & Services
N.A.I.C.S.: 423830
Harry Yong (Gen Mgr)

Subsidiaries:

Antar Cranes Services Pte. Ltd. (1)
16 Senoko Drive, Singapore, 758203, Singapore
Tel.: (65) 67568821
Web Site: http://www.antarcranes.com.sg
Emp.: 80
Hiring, Trading, Repairs & Servicing of Cranes for Construction
N.A.I.C.S.: 532412
Andrew Tan (Asst Gen Mgr)

JP Nelson (Malaysia) Sdn Bhd (1)
No 174 Jalan Rumbia 2 Kawasan Perindustrian, Tanjung Langsat, 81700, Johor, Malaysia
Tel.: (60) 7 353 9991
Web Site: http://www.jpnelson.com.sg
Emp.: 40
Construction Equipment Distr

N.A.I.C.S.: 423810

JP Nelson (Taiwan) Corporation (1)
5F No 57 Sec 1 Chongqing S Road, Taipei, Taiwan
Tel.: (886) 2 2388 1991
Construction Equipment Distr
N.A.I.C.S.: 423810

JP Nelson (Thailand) Limited (1)
999/1 M007 Tumbol Bangpla Aumphur, Bang Phli, 10540, Samutprakarn, Thailand
Tel.: (66) 2 170 7328
Construction Equipment Distr
N.A.I.C.S.: 423810

JP Nelson Access Equipment Pte Ltd (1)
5 Pioneer Sector 1, Singapore, 628417, Singapore
Tel.: (65) 6896 9991
Web Site: http://www.jpnelson.com.sg
Construction Equipment Distr
N.A.I.C.S.: 423810
Bryan Chew (Gen Mgr)

JP VODOVOD I KANALIZACIJA D.O.O.
Ul 211 Oslobodilacke brigade bb, 75350, Srebrenica, Bosnia & Herzegovina
Tel.: (387) 35644214
Web Site: http://www.vikze.ba
VIKSR—(SARE)
Rev.: $1,200,576
Assets: $1,979,433
Liabilities: $1,406,768
Net Worth: $572,665
Earnings: $11,640
Emp.: 50
Fiscal Year-end: 12/31/20
Waste Water Disposal Services
N.A.I.C.S.: 221320

JP/POLITIKEN HUS A/S
Radhuspladsen 37, 1785, Copenhagen, Denmark
Tel.: (45) 33118511 DK
Web Site: http://www.polciken.dk
Sales Range: $300-349.9 Million
Emp.: 1,400
Newspaper & Book Publishing
N.A.I.C.S.: 513110
Torsten Bjerre Rasmussen (COO & Exec VP)

Subsidiaries:

Infomedia A/S (1)
Pilestrde 58 3, 1112, Copenhagen, Denmark
Tel.: (45) 33471450
Web Site: http://www.infomedia.dk
Sales Range: $50-74.9 Million
Emp.: 120
Media Intelligence Products & Services
N.A.I.C.S.: 513199
Tim Wolff Jacobse (Pres & CEO)

JPAK GROUP INC.
15 Xinghua Road, Qingdao, 266401, Shandong, China
Tel.: (86) 532 8463 0577 NV
Web Site: http://www.chinarmp.com
Sales Range: $50-74.9 Million
Emp.: 417
Aseptic Liquid Food & Beverage Cartons Developer, Mfr & Marketer
N.A.I.C.S.: 322211

JPEL PRIVATE EQUITY LIMITED
Ground Floor Cambridge House Le Truchot, Saint Peter Port, GY1 1WD, Guernsey GY
Web Site: https://www.jpelonline.com
Year Founded: 2005
JPEL—(LSE)
Rev.: $1,724,000
Assets: $41,844,000
Liabilities: $496,000
Net Worth: $41,348,000

JPEL PRIVATE EQUITY LIMITED

JPEL Private Equity Limited—(Continued)

Earnings: ($3,398,000)
Fiscal Year-end: 06/30/23
Investment Management Service
N.A.I.C.S.: 523999

JPIMEDIA HOLDINGS LIMITED
3F 1 King William Street, London,
EC4N 7AF, United Kingdom
Tel.: (44) 308 6657 81
Web Site: http://www.jpimedia.co.uk
Year Founded: 2018
Holding Company
N.A.I.C.S.: 551112
Peter McCall *(Sec & Dir-Legal & Corpo Affairs)*

Subsidiaries:

JPIMedia Limited (1)
3F 1 King William Street, London, EC4N 7AF, United Kingdom
Tel.: (44) 308 6657 81
Holding Company
N.A.I.C.S.: 551112

Subsidiary (Domestic):

Johnston Press plc (2)
Orchard Brae House 30 Queensferry Road, Edinburgh, EH4 2HS, United Kingdom
Tel.: (44) 1313117500
Sales Range: $250-299.9 Million
Newspaper Publishing & Internet Services
N.A.I.C.S.: 513110

Subsidiary (Domestic):

Ackrill Media Group (3)
1 Cardale Park, Harrogate, HG3 1RZ, N Yorkshire, United Kingdom (100%)
Tel.: (44) 423564321
Web Site: http://www.harriogatetoday.com
Sales Range: $25-49.9 Million
Emp.: 100
Newspaper Publishing
N.A.I.C.S.: 513110

Ackrill Newspapers Ltd (3)
9 Westgate, Wetherby, LS22 6LL, West Yorkshire, United Kingdom
Tel.: (44) 1937 582663
Newspaper Publishing Services
N.A.I.C.S.: 513110

Angus County Press Ltd (3)
13 Swan Street, Brechin, DD9 6EE, Angus, United Kingdom
Tel.: (44) 1356 622767
Web Site:
http://www.brechinadvertiser.co.uk
Emp.: 2
Newspaper Publishing Services
N.A.I.C.S.: 513110

Bedfordshire Newspapers Ltd (3)
Media House, 39 Uppr George St, Luton, LU1 2RD, Bed, United Kingdom (100%)
Tel.: (44) 582798501
Web Site: http://www.lutontoday.co.uk
Sales Range: $25-49.9 Million
Emp.: 70
Newspaper Publishers
N.A.I.C.S.: 513110
Poul Gibson *(Mng Dir)*

Blackpool Gazette & Herald Ltd (3)
Avroe House Avroe Crescent Block2, Blackpool Business Ctr, Blackpool, FY42DP, Lancs, United Kingdom (100%)
Tel.: (44) 1253400888
Web Site: http://www.blackpoolgazette.co.uk
Sales Range: $50-74.9 Million
Emp.: 200
Newspaper Publishers
N.A.I.C.S.: 513110
Darren Russell *(Mng Dir)*

Subsidiary (Non-US):

Donegal Democrat Ltd (3)
Larkin House, Oldtown, Letterkenny, Ireland
Tel.: (353) 74 97 40160
Web Site: http://www.donegaldemocrat.com
Sales Range: $25-49.9 Million
Emp.: 2
Newspaper Publishing Services
N.A.I.C.S.: 513110

Michael Daly *(Editor-in-Chief)*

Dundalk Democrat Ltd (3)
7 Crowe Street, Dundalk, Ireland
Tel.: (353) 42 9334058
Web Site: http://www.dundalkdemocrat.ie
Sales Range: $25-49.9 Million
Emp.: 1
Newspaper Publishing Services
N.A.I.C.S.: 513110

Subsidiary (Domestic):

East Lancashire Newspapers Ltd (3)
Bull Street, Burnley, BB11 1DP, United Kingdom (100%)
Tel.: (44) 1282426161
Web Site: http://www.burnleyeapress.net
Sales Range: $25-49.9 Million
Emp.: 15
Newspaper Publishers
N.A.I.C.S.: 513110
Gary Fearon *(Mng Dir)*

East Midlands Newspapers Ltd (3)
57 Priestgate, Peterborough, PE1 1JW, Cambs, United Kingdom (100%)
Tel.: (44) 1733555111
Web Site: http://www.peterborough.co.uk
Sales Range: $50-74.9 Million
Emp.: 150
Newspaper Publishers
N.A.I.C.S.: 513110

Galloway Gazette Ltd (3)
71 Victoria Street, Newton Stewart, DG8 6NL, United Kingdom
Tel.: (44) 1671 402503
Web Site: http://www.gallowaygazette.com
Emp.: 6
Newspaper Publishing Services
N.A.I.C.S.: 513110

Subsidiary (Non-US):

Isle of Man Newspapers Ltd (3)
Publishing House Peel Road, Douglas, IM1 5PZ, Isle of Man
Tel.: (44) 1624 695697
Web Site: http://www.iomtoday.co.im
Newspaper Publishing Services
N.A.I.C.S.: 513110
Richard Butt *(Editor)*

Subsidiary (Domestic):

Johnston (Falkirk) Ltd (3)
Redbrae Rd, Camelon, Falkirk, FK1 4ZA, Scotland, United Kingdom (100%)
Tel.: (44) 324624959
Web Site: http://www.falkirktoday.co.uk
Sales Range: $25-49.9 Million
Emp.: 100
Newspaper Publishers
N.A.I.C.S.: 513110

Johnston Letterbox Direct Ltd (3)
1 Cardale Park Beckwithead Road, Harrogate, HG3 1RZ, North Yorkshire, United Kingdom
Tel.: (44) 1423 524161
Web Site: http://www.letterboxdirect.co.uk
Sales Range: $25-49.9 Million
Emp.: 2
Leaflets & Brochures Publishing Services
N.A.I.C.S.: 513120

Johnston Publishing Ltd (3)
Peterborough Webb Est Oundle Rd, Peterborough, PE2 9QR, Cambshire, United Kingdom
Tel.: (44) 131 225 3361
Web Site:
http://www.johnstonpublishing.com
Newspaper Publishing Services
N.A.I.C.S.: 513110

Subsidiary (Non-US):

Kilkenny People Publishing Ltd (3)
34 High Street, Kilkenny, Ireland
Tel.: (353) 56 772 1015
Web Site: http://www.kilkennypeople.ie
Sales Range: $25-49.9 Million
Emp.: 15
Newspaper Publishing Services
N.A.I.C.S.: 513110

Subsidiary (Domestic):

Lancashire Evening Post Ltd (3)

Stuart House 89 Caxton Road, Fulwood, Preston, PR2 9ZB, Lancashire, United Kingdom
Tel.: (44) 01772254841
Web Site: http://www.lep.co.uk
Newspaper Publishers
N.A.I.C.S.: 513110

Lancashire Publications Ltd (3)
Martland Mill, Martland Mill Lane, Wigan, WN5 0LX, Lancashire, United Kingdom
Tel.: (44) 01942228000
Web Site: http://www.wigantoday.net
Newspaper Publishers
N.A.I.C.S.: 513110

Lancaster & Morecambe Newspapers Ltd (3)
12 Victoria St, Morecambe, LA4 4AG, United Kingdom (100%)
Tel.: (44) 524833111
Web Site:
http://www.morecambetoday.co.uk
Newspaper Publishers
N.A.I.C.S.: 513110

Subsidiary (Non-US):

Leinster Express Newspapers Ltd (3)
Dublin Road, Portlaoise, Ireland
Tel.: (353) 57 86 21666
Web Site: http://www.leinsterexpress.ie
Sales Range: $25-49.9 Million
Emp.: 25
Newspaper Publishing Services
N.A.I.C.S.: 513110
Emer Egan *(Mgr-Bus Dev)*

Leinster Leader Ltd (3)
18/19 South Main Street, Naas, Kildare, Ireland
Tel.: (353) 4 589 7302
Web Site: http://www.leinsterleader.ie
Emp.: 3
Newspaper Publishing Services
N.A.I.C.S.: 513110
Laura Coates *(Mng Editor)*

Leitrim Observer Ltd (3)
3 Hartley Business Park, Carrick-on-Shannon, Ireland
Tel.: (353) 71 96 20025
Web Site: http://www.leitrimobserver.ie
Emp.: 12
Newspaper Publishing Services
N.A.I.C.S.: 513110

Limerick Leader Ltd (3)
54 O'Connell Street, Limerick, Ireland
Tel.: (353) 61 214500
Web Site: http://www.limerickleader.ie
Newspaper Publishing Services
N.A.I.C.S.: 513110

Subsidiary (Domestic):

Lincolnshire Newspapers Ltd (3)
Boston Standard Morgan House, Gilbert Drive, Boston, PE21 7TQ, Lincolnshire, United Kingdom
Tel.: (44) 01205311433
Web Site: http://www.bostonstandard.co.uk
Newspaper Publishers
N.A.I.C.S.: 513110

Subsidiary (Non-US):

Longford Leader Ltd (3)
Leader House Dublin Road, Longford, Ireland
Tel.: (353) 43 33 45241
Web Site: http://www.longfordleader.ie
Sales Range: $25-49.9 Million
Emp.: 15
Newspaper Publishing Services
N.A.I.C.S.: 513110
Alan Walsh *(Editor)*

Subsidiary (Domestic):

Morton Newspapers Ltd (3)
52 Oldtown Street, Cookstown, BT80 8EF, United Kingdom
Tel.: (44) 2886762288
Sales Range: $25-49.9 Million
Emp.: 12
Newspaper Publishing Services
N.A.I.C.S.: 513110

North Notts Newspapers Ltd (3)

INTERNATIONAL PUBLIC

121 Newgate Ln, Mansfield, NG18 2PA, Nottinghamshire, United Kingdom (100%)
Tel.: (44) 623456789
Web Site: http://www.mansfieldtoday.co.uk
Sales Range: $25-49.9 Million
Emp.: 100
Newspaper Publishers
N.A.I.C.S.: 513110
Haroldine LockWood *(Mgr)*

Northampton Chronicle & Echo (3)
Upper Mounts, Northampton, NN1 3HR, United Kingdom (100%)
Tel.: (44) 1604 467000
Web Site:
http://www.northamptonchron.co.uk
Emp.: 30
Newspaper Publishers
N.A.I.C.S.: 513110
Graham Tebbutt *(Editor-Communities Content)*

Northants Evening Telegraph (3)
Ise Park Rothwell Rd, Kettering, NN16 8GA, Northamptonshire, United Kingdom (100%)
Tel.: (44) 1604 467000
Web Site: http://www.northantset.co.uk
Emp.: 20
Newspaper Publishers
N.A.I.C.S.: 513110

Northeast Press Ltd (3)
2nd Floor Alexander House 1 Mandarin Road, Pennywell, Sunderland, TH4 5RA, United Kingdom (100%)
Tel.: (44) 1915015800
Web Site: http://www.sunderlandecho.co.uk
Sales Range: $50-74.9 Million
Emp.: 150
Newspaper Publishers
N.A.I.C.S.: 513110

Peterboro Web Ltd (3)
Oundle Rd, Peterborough, PE2 9QH, Cambridgeshire, United Kingdom
Tel.: (44) 1733 342525
Newspaper Publishing Services
N.A.I.C.S.: 513110

Portsmouth Publishing & Printing Ltd (3)
Lake Road, Portsmouth, PO1 4EZ, Hants, United Kingdom
Tel.: (44) 23 9229 6111
Web Site: http://www.portsmouth.co.uk
Newspaper Publishing Services
N.A.I.C.S.: 513110

Premier Newspapers Ltd (3)
Napier House Auckland Park, Mount Farm, Bletchley, MK1 1BU, Bucks, United Kingdom (100%)
Tel.: (44) 1908651200
Web Site: http://www.miltonkeynes.co.uk
Sales Range: $25-49.9 Million
Emp.: 100
Newspaper Publishers
N.A.I.C.S.: 513110
Chris Pennock *(Mng Dir)*

Sheffield Newspapers Ltd (3)
York St, Sheffield, S1 1PU, South Yorkshire, United Kingdom (100%)
Tel.: (44) 142767676
Web Site: http://www.sheffieldtoday.co.uk
Sales Range: $100-124.9 Million
Emp.: 300
Newspaper Publishers
N.A.I.C.S.: 513110
John Bills *(Mng Dir)*

South Yorkshire Newspapers Ltd (3)
Sunny Bar, Doncaster, DN1 1NB, Yorkshire, United Kingdom (100%)
Tel.: (44) 302819111
Web Site: http://www.doncastertoday.co.uk
Sales Range: $25-49.9 Million
Emp.: 100
Newspaper Publishers
N.A.I.C.S.: 513110

Stornoway Gazette Ltd (3)
10 Francis Street, Stornoway, HS12XE, United Kingdom
Tel.: (44) 1851 702687
Web Site:
http://www.stornowaygazette.co.uk
Emp.: 13
Newspaper Publishing Services

Strachan & Livingston Ltd (3)
23 Kirk Wynd, Kirkcaldy, KY1 1EP, Fife, United Kingdom
Tel.: (44) 592261451
Web Site: http://www.fifetoday.co.uk
Newspaper Publishers
N.A.I.C.S.: 513110

Sussex Newspapers Ltd (3)
14-16 Market Square, Horsham, RH12 1HD, West Sussex, United Kingdom (100%)
Tel.: (44) 1403751200
Web Site: http://www.horshamtoday.co.uk
Newspaper Publishers
N.A.I.C.S.: 513110
Olivia Lerche *(Editor-Health)*

The Bucks Herald (3)
Ground Floor Gatehouse Way, Aylesbury, HP19 8DB, United Kingdom (100%)
Tel.: (44) 1296 619735
Web Site: http://www.bucksherald.co.uk
Sales Range: $25-49.9 Million
Emp.: 30
Newspaper Publishers
N.A.I.C.S.: 513110

The Halifax Evening Courier Ltd (3)
Courier Buildings, PO Box 19, King Cross St, Halifax, HX35AF, Yorkshire, United Kingdom (100%)
Tel.: (44) 1422260200
Web Site: http://www.halifaxcourier.co.uk
Sales Range: $50-74.9 Million
Emp.: 150
Newspaper Publishers
N.A.I.C.S.: 513110

The Scotsman Publications Ltd (3)
Barclay House 108 Holyrood Road, Edinburgh, EH8 8AS, United Kingdom
Tel.: (44) 131 620 8620
Web Site: http://www.scotsman.com
Newspaper Publishing Services
N.A.I.C.S.: 513110

Tweeddale Press Ltd (3)
90 Marygate, Berwick-upon-Tweed, TD15 1BW, Northumberland, United Kingdom (100%)
Tel.: (44) 289306677
Sales Range: $25-49.9 Million
Emp.: 20
Newspaper Publishers
N.A.I.C.S.: 513110

Wilfred Edmunds Ltd (3)
1 floor Spire walk, off Derby Road, Chesterfield, S40 4WJ, Derbyshire, United Kingdom
Tel.: (44) 1246 504500
Web Site: http://www.derbyshiretime.co.uk
Emp.: 3
Newspaper Publishing Services
N.A.I.C.S.: 513110

Yorkshire Post Newspapers Ltd. (3)
Wellington St, PO Box 168, Leeds, LS1 1RF, United Kingdom (100%)
Tel.: (44) 32432701
Web Site: http://www.yorkshiretoday.co.uk
Rev.: $261,347,000
Emp.: 800
Holding Company
N.A.I.C.S.: 551112

JPMORGAN ASIA GROWTH & INCOME PLC
25 Bank St, Canary Wharf, London, E14 5JP, United Kingdom
Tel.: (44) 2077424000 UK
Year Founded: 1837
JAGI—(LSE)
Rev.: $10,701,549
Assets: $487,891,251
Liabilities: $1,067,168
Net Worth: $486,824,083
Earnings: ($96,554,258)
Fiscal Year-end: 09/30/22
Miscellaneous Financial Investment Activities
N.A.I.C.S.: 523999
Bronwyn Curtis *(Chm)*

JPMORGAN CLAVERHOUSE INVESTMENT TRUST PLC
25 Bank St, Canary Wharf, London, E14 5JP, United Kingdom
Tel.: (44) 2077424000
Web Site: http://www.jpmclaverhouse.co.uk
JCH—(LSE)
Assets: $549,504,945
Liabilities: $48,673,845
Net Worth: $500,831,100
Earnings: ($42,458,625)
Fiscal Year-end: 12/31/22
Other Financial Vehicles
N.A.I.C.S.: 525990
William Meadon *(Mgr-Fund)*

JPMORGAN ELECT PLC
60 Victoria Embankment, London, EC4Y 0JP, United Kingdom
Tel.: (44) 2077424000
Year Founded: 1999
JPE—(LSE)
Rev.: $142,261,902
Assets: $557,384,792
Liabilities: $10,223,632
Net Worth: $547,161,160
Earnings: $139,125,568
Fiscal Year-end: 08/31/21
Asset Management Services
N.A.I.C.S.: 523940
Alan Hodson *(Chm)*

JPMORGAN EMERGING EUROPE, MIDDLE EAST & AFRICA SECURITIES PLC
60 Victoria Embankment, London, EC4Y 0JP, United Kingdom
Tel.: (44) 1268444470 UK
Year Founded: 2002
JEMA—(LSE)
Rev.: $823,024
Assets: $24,352,436
Liabilities: $520,071
Net Worth: $23,832,366
Earnings: ($10,098)
Fiscal Year-end: 10/31/23
Investment Management Service
N.A.I.C.S.: 523999
Eric Sanderson *(Chm)*

JPMORGAN EUROPEAN INVESTMENT TRUST PLC
60 Victoria Embankment, London, EC4Y 0JP, United Kingdom
Tel.: (44) 2077424000
Web Site: http://www.jpmeuropean.co.uk
Year Founded: 1929
JETI—(LSE)
Assets: $510,611,338
Liabilities: $80,838,649
Net Worth: $429,772,689
Earnings: ($90,220,494)
Fiscal Year-end: 03/31/20
Investment Management Service
N.A.I.C.S.: 523940
Josephine Dixon *(Chm)*

JPMORGAN GLOBAL CORE REAL ASSETS LIMITED
Level 3 Mill Court La Charrotterie, Saint Peter Port, GY1 1EJ, Guernsey GY
Web Site: https://www.am.jpmorgan.com
Year Founded: 2019
JARA—(LSE)
Rev.: $13,368,111
Assets: $280,919,057
Liabilities: $429,040
Net Worth: $280,490,017
Earnings: $32,168,460
Fiscal Year-end: 02/28/22
Asset Management Services
N.A.I.C.S.: 523999

JPMORGAN GLOBAL EMERGING MARKETS INCOME TRUST PLC
60 Victoria Embankment, London, EC4Y 0JP, United Kingdom
Tel.: (44) 2077426000
JEMI—(LSE)
Rev.: $26,823,812
Assets: $595,712,840
Liabilities: $41,334,681
Net Worth: $554,378,159
Earnings: $32,135,996
Fiscal Year-end: 07/31/24
Investment Management Service
N.A.I.C.S.: 525990
Omar Negyal *(Mgr-Fund)*

JPMORGAN GLOBAL GROWTH & INCOME PLC
60 Victoria Embankment, London, EC4Y 0JP, United Kingdom
Tel.: (44) 2077424000
Web Site: http://am.jpmorgan.com
JGGI—(LSE)
Rev.: $58,289,939
Assets: $3,667,668,093
Liabilities: $209,702,982
Net Worth: $3,457,965,110
Earnings: $697,951,212
Fiscal Year-end: 06/30/24
Investment Management Service
N.A.I.C.S.: 523940

JPMORGAN JAPAN SMALL CAP GROWTH & INCOME PLC
60 Victoria Embankment, London, EC4Y 0JP, United Kingdom
Tel.: (44) 2077424000
Year Founded: 2000
Investment Management Service
N.A.I.C.S.: 523940

JPMORGAN SMALLER COMPANIES INVESTMENT TRUST PLC
60 Victoria Embankment, Hauptsitz, London, EC4Y 0JP, United Kingdom
Tel.: (44) 207 742 4000 UK
Web Site: http://am.jpmorgan.com
Year Founded: 1990
JMI—(LSE)
Sales Range: $1-9.9 Million
Investment Management Service
N.A.I.C.S.: 523940
Michael Quicke *(Chm)*

JPMORGAN US SMALLER COMPANIES INVESTMENT TRUST PLC
25 Bank St, Canary Wharf, London, E14 5JP, United Kingdom
Tel.: (44) 2077424000 UK
JUSC—(LSE)
Assets: $359,880,510
Liabilities: $30,979,740
Net Worth: $328,900,770
Earnings: ($30,148,635)
Fiscal Year-end: 12/31/22
Portfolio Management & Investment Advice
N.A.I.C.S.: 523940
Don San Jose *(Mgr-Portfolio)*

JPP HOLDING CO., LTD.
Rm 1112 No 152 Songjiang Rd Zhongshan Dist, Taipei, 10458, Taiwan
Tel.: (886) 225415566
Web Site: http://www.jppholding.com
Year Founded: 1998
5284—(TAI)
Rev.: $73,558,093
Assets: $148,310,273
Liabilities: $70,929,753
Net Worth: $77,380,520
Earnings: $13,043,428
Emp.: 1,371
Fiscal Year-end: 12/31/23
Electronic Equipment Mfr & Distr
N.A.I.C.S.: 336320
Kuo-Sung Chung *(Chm & Mng Dir)*

Subsidiaries:

Jinpao Precision Industry Co., Ltd (1)
631 Soi 12 Moo 4 Bangpoo Industrial Estate T Phraeksa, Amphur Muang, Samutprakarn, Thailand
Tel.: (66) 27093687
Electronic Parts Distr
N.A.I.C.S.: 423690

Subsidiary (Non-US):

Jinpao Precision Japan Co., Ltd. (2)
Vision Center Nihonbashi Fukushima Bldg 2F 1-5-3 Nihonbashimuromachi, Chuo-ku, Tokyo, 103-0022, Japan
Tel.: (81) 368691099
Electronic Parts Distr
N.A.I.C.S.: 423690

Spem Aero S.A.S. (1)
6 Rue du Castelmouly, 65200, Bagneres-de-Bigorre, France
Tel.: (33) 562913232
Surface Treatment Services
N.A.I.C.S.: 213113

JPT SECURITIES LIMITED
SKIL House 209 Bank Street Cross Lane, Fort, Mumbai, 400 023, Maharashtra, India
Tel.: (91) 2266199000 In
Web Site: https://www.jptsecurities.com
Year Founded: 1994
530985—(BOM)
Rev.: $57,912
Assets: $920,174
Liabilities: $400,901
Net Worth: $519,274
Earnings: ($14,590)
Emp.: 3
Fiscal Year-end: 03/31/23
Financial Services
N.A.I.C.S.: 523999
J. Alexander *(Chm)*

JQW PLC
1-4/F Buildings 12c, Guangling Information Industry Park, Yangzhou, 225000, Jiangsu, China
Tel.: (86) 514 89712888 JE
Web Site: http://www.jqw.com
Sales Range: $125-149.9 Million
Ecommerce Services
N.A.I.C.S.: 521110
Yongde Cai *(Chm)*

JR GLOBAL REIT CO., LTD.
100 Eulji-Ro, Jung-Gu, Seoul, Korea (South)
Tel.: (82) 220087060
Web Site: https://www.jrglobalreit.com
Year Founded: 2019
348950—(KRS)
Real Estate Services
N.A.I.C.S.: 531210
Ah-Ram Yoo *(Mgr)*

JR HOLDING ASI S.A.
Ul Grzegorzecka 67d/105, 31-559, Krakow, Poland
Tel.: (48) 126540519
Web Site: https://www.jrholdingasi.pl
Year Founded: 2003
JRH—(WAR)
Assets: $74,913,087
Liabilities: $24,598,470
Net Worth: $50,314,616
Earnings: ($9,376,123)
Fiscal Year-end: 12/31/23
Holding Company
N.A.I.C.S.: 551112

JR HOLDING ASI S.A.

JR Holding ASI S.A.—(Continued)
Artur Jedynak *(Partner & VP)*

JRI INDUSTRIES & INFRA-STRUCTURE LIMITED
1 Borkar Compound Western Highway E Highway, Borivali E, Mumbai, 400 066, India
Tel.: (91) 22 28872717
Web Site: http://www.jrilimited.com
Year Founded: 1964
Rev.: $16,836
Assets: $3,237,678
Liabilities: $21,831
Net Worth: $3,215,847
Earnings: $3,719
Fiscal Year-end: 03/31/18
Infrastructure Development Services
N.A.I.C.S.: 237990
Shankarrao Ambrushi Borkar *(Mng Dir)*

JRJ VENTURES LLP
61 Conduit Street, London, W1S 2GB, United Kingdom
Tel.: (44) 207 220 2300
Web Site: http://www.jrjgroup.com
Privater Equity Firm
N.A.I.C.S.: 523999
Roger Nagioff *(Founding Partner)*

Subsidiaries:

Demica Limited (1)
3 More London Riverside, London, SE1 2AQ, United Kingdom
Tel.: (44) 20 7450 2500
Web Site: http://www.demica.com
Sales Range: $10-24.9 Million
Emp.: 15
Information Technology Consulting Services
N.A.I.C.S.: 541512
Kishore Patel *(Sr Architect-Technical)*

Marex Spectron Group Ltd. (1)
155 Bishopsgate, London, EC2M 3TQ, United Kingdom
Tel.: (44) 20 7655 6000
Web Site: http://www.marexspectron.com
Financial & Marketing Services
N.A.I.C.S.: 541613
Ian Lowitt *(Grp CEO)*

Subsidiary (Domestic):

CSC Commodities UK Ltd. (2)
155 Bishopsgate, London, EC2M 3TQ, United Kingdom
Tel.: (44) 2076504303
Web Site: http://www.csc-commodities.com
Real Estate Services
N.A.I.C.S.: 531210
Alan Newman *(Head-Mktg)*

Division (US):

Rosenthal Collins Group, LLC (2)
216 W Jackson Blvd, Chicago, IL 60606-6909
Tel.: (312) 460-9200
Web Site: http://www.rcgdirect.com
Sales Range: $75-99.9 Million
Emp.: 400
Commodity Contracts Brokers & Dealers
N.A.I.C.S.: 523160
Leslie Rosenthal *(Principal)*

Subsidiary (Domestic):

MG Financial LLC (3)
40 Exchange Pl 12th Fl, New York, NY 10005
Tel.: (212) 835-0100
Web Site: http://www.mgforex.com
Sales Range: $25-49.9 Million
Emp.: 35
Foreign Exchange Trading Services
N.A.I.C.S.: 523160

JRSIS HEALTH CARE CORPORATION
No 38 South Street, Hulan District, Harbin, 150025, Heilongjiang, China
Tel.: (86) 45156888933 FL

Web Site: http://www.jhcc.cn
JRSS—(OTCIQ)
Rev.: $44,391,171
Assets: $75,692,752
Liabilities: $42,590,572
Net Worth: $33,102,180
Earnings: $2,232,261
Emp.: 963
Fiscal Year-end: 12/31/21
Hospital Operator
N.A.I.C.S.: 622110
Junsheng Zhang *(Pres & Chm)*

Subsidiaries:

Harbin Jiarun Hospital Co., Ltd (1)
South St Hulan, Harbin, Heilongjiang, China
Tel.: (86) 45156888966
Healtcare Services
N.A.I.C.S.: 339112

JS CORPORATION
JS Building 138 Wiryeseongdaero, Songpa-gu, Seoul, 06339, Korea (South)
Tel.: (82) 220403400
Web Site: https://www.jskor.com
Year Founded: 1988
194370—(KRS)
Rev.: $747,875,807
Assets: $409,400,164
Liabilities: $213,448,623
Net Worth: $195,951,541
Earnings: $49,545,169
Emp.: 125
Fiscal Year-end: 12/31/22
Apparel Product Mfr & Distr
N.A.I.C.S.: 315990
Jae Seong Hong *(Chm & CEO)*

Subsidiaries:

JS Vina Ltd. (1)
400 2F Nguyen Thi Thap, Tan Quy Ward Dist 7, Ho Chi Minh City, Vietnam
Tel.: (84) 28377555724
Web Site: https://www.jsvina.com
Construction Services
N.A.I.C.S.: 236220

JS GLOBAL LIFESTYLE COMPANY LIMITED
21/F 238 Des Voeux Road Central, Sheung Wan, China (Hong Kong)
Tel.: (852) 23108035 Ky
Web Site: https://www.jsgloballife.com
Year Founded: 2018
JGLCF—(OTCIQ)
Rev.: $5,041,210,000
Assets: $4,635,815,000
Liabilities: $2,571,166,000
Net Worth: $2,064,649,000
Earnings: $357,503,000
Emp.: 5,661
Fiscal Year-end: 12/31/22
Holding Company; Small Household Appliance Mfr & Whslr
N.A.I.C.S.: 551112
Xuning Wang *(Chm & CEO)*

Subsidiaries:

Joyoung Co., Ltd. (1)
No 28038 Jingshi Road, Huaiyin District, Jinan, 250022, Shandong, China (67.07%)
Tel.: (86) 57181639093
Web Site: https://www.joyoung.com
Rev.: $1,428,807,276
Assets: $993,296,304
Liabilities: $526,261,320
Net Worth: $467,034,984
Earnings: $74,341,800
Emp.: 3,500
Fiscal Year-end: 12/31/2022
Holding Company; Kitchen Appliances Mfr
N.A.I.C.S.: 551112
Xuning Wang *(Chm)*

JSA SERVICES LTD.

Radius House 51 Clarendon Road, Watford, WD17 1HP, Herts, United Kingdom
Tel.: (44) 800 25 26 40
Web Site: http://www.jsagroup.co.uk
Year Founded: 1989
Payroll & Accounting Services
N.A.I.C.S.: 541214
Ben Dunn *(Mng Dir)*

JSC AVANGARD
78 Oktyabrskaya, st Safonovo Smolensk region, Smolensk, 215500, Russia
Tel.: (7) 4812268605
Web Site: http://www.avangard-plastik.ru
Year Founded: 1962
Engineeering Services
N.A.I.C.S.: 541330
Gorelyi Konstantin Aleksandrovich *(Dir Gen)*

JSC BANK OF GEORGIA
29a Gagarin Str, Tbilisi, 0160, Georgia
Tel.: (995) 32 2444256 GE
Web Site: http://bankofgeorgia.ge
Year Founded: 1994
Banking Services
N.A.I.C.S.: 522110
Irakli Gilauri *(CEO)*

Subsidiaries:

Galt & Taggart (1)
79 D Aghmashenebeli Avenue, Tbilisi, 0179, Georgia (100%)
Tel.: (995) 322 401 111
Web Site: http://www.gt.ge
Brokerage & Asset Management Services
N.A.I.C.S.: 523150
Irakli Kirtava *(Gen Dir)*

Georgian Leasing Company Ltd. (1)
No 3/5 Tatishvili St, Tbilisi, 0179, Georgia
Tel.: (995) 322 44 44 02
Web Site: http://www.leasing.ge
Machinery Equipment Leasing Services
N.A.I.C.S.: 532490

JSC Georgian Card (1)
Beliashvili Str 106, Tbilisi, Georgia (55.4%)
Tel.: (995) 32317040
Web Site: http://www.gc.ge
Rev.: $6,705,774
Assets: $20,168,260
Liabilities: $9,754,698
Net Worth: $10,413,563
Earnings: $649,941
Fiscal Year-end: 12/31/2018
Credit Card Services
N.A.I.C.S.: 522210
Irakli Kodua *(CEO)*

JSC BELON
ul 1 Teleut 27/2 room 1, Kemerovo Region, 652607, Belovo, 652607, Russia
Tel.: (7) 3845228357 RU
Web Site: https://www.belon.ru
Year Founded: 1991
BLNG—(MOEX)
Sales Range: Less than $1 Million
Coal Mining Services
N.A.I.C.S.: 212115

JSC BENNET DISTRIBUTORS
Metalo Str 2b, LT02190, Vilnius, Lithuania
Tel.: (370) 52131611
Web Site: http://www.bennet.lt
Year Founded: 1991
Sales Range: $50-74.9 Million
Alcoholic Drinks & Tobacco Products Distr
N.A.I.C.S.: 424810
Marek Kuklis *(Gen Mgr)*

JSC BOROVICHI REFRACTORIES PLANT

INTERNATIONAL PUBLIC

Mezhdunarodnaya Str 1, 174411, Borovichi, Novgorod, Russia
Tel.: (7) 8166492500
Web Site: http://www.oaobko.ru
Year Founded: 1857
Sales Range: $125-149.9 Million
Emp.: 5,500
Clay Refractories Mfr
N.A.I.C.S.: 327120
Anatoly V. Mozhzherin *(Gen Dir)*

Subsidiaries:

Trade House BRP, Ltd. (1)
8 Koltsova St, Borovichi, 174411, Russia
Tel.: (7) 8166492413
Web Site: http://www.borovichi-nov.ru
Sales Range: $25-49.9 Million
Emp.: 35
Marketing & Sales of Refractory Materials
N.A.I.C.S.: 327120
Edward V. Bulin *(Gen Mgr)*

JSC BUSINESS COMPUTER CENTER
Kantemirovskaya st 20, 194100, Saint Petersburg, Russia
Tel.: (7) 812 327 4444 RU
Web Site: http://www.bcc.ru
Year Founded: 1994
Emp.: 900
Information Technology & Systems Integration Services
N.A.I.C.S.: 238990
Michael Talov *(VP)*

JSC CAUCASUS ENERGY & INFRASTRUCTURE
74 Chavchavadze Ave Floor 9, Tbilisi, 0162, Georgia
Tel.: (995) 32 223 4994
Web Site: http://www.cei.ge
Year Founded: 2007
Sales Range: Less than $1 Million
Energy & Infrastructure Development & Construction Services
N.A.I.C.S.: 237990
Tamaz Mikadze *(CEO)*

JSC COMMERCIAL PORT OF VLADIVOSTOK
9 Strelnikova St, 690950, Vladivostok, Russia
Tel.: (7) 4232495222
Web Site: http://www.vladcomport.ru
Year Founded: 1897
Sales Range: $150-199.9 Million
Emp.: 540
Marine Cargo Handler
N.A.I.C.S.: 488320
Vyecheslav M. Pertsev *(Dir Gen & CEO)*

JSC GK KHIMIK
Fontanka River 110, St. Petersburg, 190013, Russia
Tel.: (7) 812336575 RU
Web Site: https://himik.ru
Emp.: 100
Chemical Products Mfr & Distr
N.A.I.C.S.: 325998

Subsidiaries:

OOO Telko (1)
room 95 pom 1-H Professora Popova str 37/IV, 197136, Saint Petersburg, Russia
Tel.: (7) 8126022420
Sales Range: $25-49.9 Million
Emp.: 50
Chemical Products Distr
N.A.I.C.S.: 424690

JSC HOLDING KAZEXPORTASTYK
1/1 Otyrar str, Nur-Sultan, 010000, Kazakhstan
Tel.: (7) 7172 320432

AND PRIVATE COMPANIES

Web Site:
   http://www.kazexportastyk.kz
Year Founded: 1999
Holding Company
N.A.I.C.S.: 551112

JSC INPROM
Ulitsa Marshala Zhukova 2-A, Taganrog, 347942, Rostov Oblast, Russia
Tel.: (7) 8634322133
Web Site: http://www.inprom.ru
Year Founded: 1996
Sales Range: $450-499.9 Million
Emp.: 50
Metal Servicing Center & Supplier
N.A.I.C.S.: 423510
Igor Konovalov *(Chm, CEO & Dir Gen)*

JSC INTER RAO UES
St Bolshaya Pirogovskaya 27 building 2, Moscow, 119435, Russia
Tel.: (7) 4956648840   RU
Web Site: https://interrao.lt
IRAO—(MOEX)
Rev.: $13,285,353,240
Assets: $11,654,823,210
Liabilities: $3,355,996,620
Net Worth: $8,298,826,590
Earnings: $1,016,513,550
Emp.: 48,450
Fiscal Year-end: 12/31/20
Eletric Power Generation Services
N.A.I.C.S.: 221118
Igor Ivanovich Sechin *(Chm)*

Subsidiaries:

Bashkir Heat Distribution System, LLC (1)
Ulyanovykh street 59, Ufa, 450112, Bashkortostan, Russia
Tel.: (7) 347 269 23 29
Eletric Power Generation Services
N.A.I.C.S.: 221118
Vladislav Nikolaevich Shamin *(CTO)*

Joint-Stock Company Inter RAO - Electricity Plants (1)
Bolshaya Pirogovskaya Str 27/1, 119435, Moscow, Russia
Tel.: (7) 4956647680
Web Site: http://irao-generation.ru
Electricity Power Supply Services
N.A.I.C.S.: 221118

LLC Bashkir Generation Company (1)
R Zorge street 3, 450059, Ufa, Russia
Tel.: (7) 3472228625
Web Site: http://www.bgkrb.ru
Eletric Power Generation Services
N.A.I.C.S.: 221118

Limited Liability Company Inter RAO - Export (1)
Bolshaya Pirogovskaya Str 27 build 4 floor 2 office premises III, Room 27, 119435, Moscow, Russia
Tel.: (7) 4956648840
Web Site: http://irao-export.ru
Construction Project Management Services
N.A.I.C.S.: 236220
Oleg Tarasov *(Dir-Legal & Corp Affairs)*

Open Joint-Stock Company Eastern Energy Company (1)
50 let Oktyabrya Street 13/1, Amur, 675000, Blagoveshchensk, Amur, Russia
Tel.: (7) 4162222641
Web Site: http://eastern-ec.ru
Electricity Trading Services
N.A.I.C.S.: 221122

Open Joint-Stock Company Tambov Power Supply Company (1)
Sovetskaya st 104/14, Tambov, 392000, Russia
Tel.: (7) 4752713430
Web Site: https://www.tesk.su
Emp.: 284
Electricity Power Supply Services
N.A.I.C.S.: 221118

Open Joint-Stock Company Territorial Generating Company No. 11 (1)
10 Partizanskaya st, 644037, Omsk, Russia
Tel.: (7) 3812944759
Web Site: http://ww.tgk11.com
Electricity Power Supply Services
N.A.I.C.S.: 221118
Vladislav Polochansky *(CEO)*

RAO Nordic Oy (1)
Tammasaarenkatu 1, 00180, Helsinki, Finland (100%)
Tel.: (358) 9 773 81 000
Web Site: http://www.raonordic.com
Emp.: 15
Energy Trading
N.A.I.C.S.: 221122
Oleg Zakataev *(Mng Dir)*

Holding (Non-US):

AB INTER RAO Lietuva (2)
A Tumeno str 4 Block B, LT-01109, Vilnius, Lithuania (51%)
Tel.: (370) 52421121
Web Site: https://www.interrao.lt
Rev.: $355,033,695
Assets: $72,861,451
Liabilities: $40,138,022
Net Worth: $32,723,429
Earnings: $19,762,169
Emp.: 43
Fiscal Year-end: 12/31/2019
Electric Power Distr
N.A.I.C.S.: 221122
Giedrius Balciunas *(CEO & Dir Gen)*

Subsidiary (Non-US):

INTER RAO Eesti OU (3)
Peterburi tee 47, 11415, Tallinn, Estonia (100%)
Tel.: (372) 6225865
Web Site: http://www.interrao.ee
Electricity Supplier
N.A.I.C.S.: 221122
Diana Jashina *(Mng Dir)*

IRL Polska Sp. z o.o. (3)
Twarda 18, 00-105, Warsaw, Poland (100%)
Tel.: (48) 222026931
Web Site: http://www.irlpolska.pl
Electricity Supplier
N.A.I.C.S.: 221122
Anna Radziwonko *(Mng Dir)*

SIA INTER RAO Latvia (3)
76 Gustava Zemgala Ave, Riga, 1039, Latvia (100%)
Tel.: (371) 6711 44 70
Web Site: http://www.interrao.lv
Emp.: 5
Electricity Supplier
N.A.I.C.S.: 221122

Subsidiary (Domestic):

UAB Vydmantai Wind Park (3)
A Tumeno g 4, 01109, Vilnius, Lithuania
Tel.: (370) 5 242 11 21
Web Site: http://www.vwp.lt
Wind Electric Power Generation
N.A.I.C.S.: 221115

Telasi JSC (1)
Vani Str 3, 0154, Tbilisi, Georgia
Tel.: (995) 32 277 99 99
Web Site: http://www.telasi.ge
Sales Range: Less than $1 Million
Electric Power Distribution Services
N.A.I.C.S.: 221122
Sergey Kobtsev *(Dir Gen & Member-Exec Bd)*

JSC KRASNOKAMSK METAL MESH WORKS
23 Shosseynaya St, Krasnokamsk, Perm, Russia
Tel.: (7) 3427320192
Web Site: https://www.rosset-kzms.com
Year Founded: 1942
KZMS—(MOEX)
Sales Range: Less than $1 Million
Wire Product Mfr
N.A.I.C.S.: 332618

JSC LATVIJAS GAZE
6 Aristida Briana Street, Riga, 1001, Latvia
Tel.: (371) 67869866
Web Site: https://www.lg.lv
Year Founded: 1991
GZE1R—(RSE)
Rev.: $176,420,135
Assets: $180,734,077
Liabilities: $42,653,715
Net Worth: $138,080,362
Earnings: ($62,822,607)
Emp.: 115
Fiscal Year-end: 12/31/23
Natural Gas Distribution Services
N.A.I.C.S.: 221210
Aigars Kalvitis *(Chm)*

JSC LINDEKS
K Ulmana gatve 2, 1004, Riga, Latvia
Tel.: (371) 7066300
Web Site: http://www.lindeks.lv
Year Founded: 1991
Rev.: $40,000,000
Emp.: 250
Forestry & Timber Production
N.A.I.C.S.: 113210
Janis Leitans *(Dir-Eastern European Resources Procurement & Mfg)*

JSC MOTOVILIKHINSKIYE ZAVODY
35 1905 Goda St, 614014, Perm, Perm Krai, Russia
Tel.: (7) 342 260 73 03
Web Site: http://www.mz.perm.ru
Year Founded: 1736
Sales Range: Less than $1 Million
Emp.: 8,000
Metallurgical Product Mfr
N.A.I.C.S.: 331110
Alexander Anokhin *(Dir Gen)*

JSC NATIONAL ATOMIC COMPANY KAZATOMPROM
17/12 Syganak Street, Z05T1X3, Nur-Sultan, Z05T1X3, Kazakhstan
Tel.: (7) 458180   KZ
Web Site:
   https://www.kazatomprom.kz
Year Founded: 1997
KZAP—(KAZ)
Rev.: $2,238,654,354
Assets: $4,969,663,700
Liabilities: $1,176,221,994
Net Worth: $3,793,441,707
Earnings: $1,057,562,274
Emp.: 20,799
Fiscal Year-end: 12/31/22
Uranium & Other Related Products Miner, Refiner & Distr; Nuclear, Geothermal, Solar & Water Power Generation
N.A.I.C.S.: 212290
Neil Longfellow *(Chm)*

Subsidiaries:

High Technology Institute LLP (1)
168 Bogenbay Batyr street, 050012, Almaty, Kazakhstan
Tel.: (7) 7273436145
Web Site: https://iht.kazatomprom.kz
Emp.: 423
IT Services
N.A.I.C.S.: 541519
Kopbaeva Maria Petrovna *(Deputy Gen Dir-R&D)*

JV Inkai LLP (1)
Madeli Kozha st 1G Business Center ESKO 5th Floor, Shymkent, 160021, Kazakhstan
Tel.: (7) 7252997182
Web Site: https://inkai.kazatomprom.kz
Emp.: 757
Natural Uranium Mining Services
N.A.I.C.S.: 212290

JV SARECO LLP (1)
62 Satpayev Ave, Nur-Sultan, 70005, Kazakhstan (51%)
Tel.: (7) 7232 20 37 55
Emp.: 235
Rare Earth Metals Production
N.A.I.C.S.: 325180
Anton V. Manych *(Gen Dir)*

KAP-Technology JSC (1)
E 10 Str Bld 17/12 6th Floor, Nur-Sultan, Kazakhstan
Tel.: (7) 7172459705
Emp.: 378
Cyber Security & Automation Services
N.A.I.C.S.: 541512
Aldongarov Alibek Mansurovich *(Gen Dir)*

Kazatomprom-Damu LLP (1)
st Kunaev 8, Esil district, Nur-Sultan, 010000, Kazakhstan (90%)
Tel.: (7) 7172591554
Web Site: http://damu.kazatomprom.kz
Emp.: 800
Investment Consulting Services
N.A.I.C.S.: 523940
Karibjanov Nurbek Djanibekovich *(Gen Dir)*

Korgan-Kazatomprom LLP (1)
Mankent Street 12, Shymkent, 160009, Kazakhstan
Tel.: (7) 7252998970
Web Site:
   http://www.korgan.kazatomprom.kz
Natural Uranium Mining Services
N.A.I.C.S.: 212290

ULBA-CHINA Co. Ltd. (1)
Room 603 No 139 Futexiyi Road, China Shanghai Pilot Free Trade Zone, Shanghai, 200131, China
Tel.: (86) 2158668919
Web Site: http://www.ulba.cn
Natural Uranium Mining Services
N.A.I.C.S.: 212290
N. R. Mussin *(Gen Dir)*

UMP JSC (1)
102 Abay Avenue, Ust'-Kamenogorsk, 070005, Kazakhstan
Tel.: (7) 7232298103
Web Site: http://www.ulba.kz
Uranium, Beryllium & Tantalum Products Processing & Production Services
N.A.I.C.S.: 331110

Ulba FA LLP (1)
Abai Ave 102 3rd floor, 070005, Ust'-Kamenogorsk, Kazakhstan
Tel.: (7) 7232505757
Web Site: http://www.ulba-fa.kz
Fuel Assemble Component Mfr
N.A.I.C.S.: 336310

Ulba Metallurgical Plant JSC (1)
102 Abay Avenue, Oskemen, 070005, Kazakhstan (90.18%)
Tel.: (7) 7232298103
Web Site: http://www.ulba.kz
Emp.: 3,953
Chemical Products Mfr
N.A.I.C.S.: 325180
Yuri V. Shakhvorostov *(Gen Dir)*

Uranenergo LLP (1)
Street Tolstogo - 60 Reception desk, 160000, Shymkent, Kazakhstan
Tel.: (7) 7252998983
Web Site:
   https://www.uranenergo.kazatomprom.kz
Emp.: 167
Natural Uranium Mining Services
N.A.I.C.S.: 212290
Akhanov Beibut Muzarafovich *(Gen Dir)*

Volkovgeology JSC (1)
Bogenbai batyr st 168, Almaty, 050012, Kazakhstan (90%)
Tel.: (7) 7273436000
Web Site: https://www.vg.kz
Metal Ore Mining Services
N.A.I.C.S.: 212290

JSC NATIONAL COMPANY KAZMUNAYGAS
D Kunayev street 8, 10000, Nur-Sultan, Kazakhstan
Tel.: (7) 7172786101   KZ
Web Site: https://www.kmg.kz
Year Founded: 2002

JSC NATIONAL COMPANY KAZMUNAYGAS

JSC National Company KazMunayGas—(Continued)
KMGZ—(KAZ)
Rev.: $21,959,134,207
Assets: $37,231,704,754
Liabilities: $15,154,315,549
Net Worth: $22,077,389,204
Earnings: $2,945,572,649
Emp.: 44,688
Fiscal Year-end: 12/31/22
Oil & Natural Gas Exploration & Production Services
N.A.I.C.S.: 211120
Christopher John Walton (Chm)

Subsidiaries:

JSC KazMunaiGas Exploration Production (1)
17 Kabanbai Batyr ave, Nur-Sultan, 010000, Kazakhstan (58%)
Tel.: (7) 7172979997
Web Site: http://www.kmgep.kz
Rev.: $2,271,002,550
Assets: $6,436,951,800
Liabilities: $539,740,200
Net Worth: $5,897,211,600
Earnings: $401,306,800
Fiscal Year-end: 12/31/2016
Oil & Gas Exploration & Production Services
N.A.I.C.S.: 211120
Assel Kaliyeva (Head-IR)

Joint Venture (Non-US):

PetroKazakhstan Inc. (2)
Sun Life Plz N Tower, Calgary, T2P 3N3, AB, Canada
Tel.: (403) 221-8435
Web Site: http://www.petrokazakhstan.com
Sales Range: $1-4.9 Billion
Oil & Gas Exploration, Acquisition & Refinement; Owned 67% by China National Petroleum Corporation & 33% by JSC KazMunayGas Exploration
N.A.I.C.S.: 211120

KMG Drilling&Services LLP (1)
Kunaev str 8 Block B 14th floor Business Center, Astana, 010000, Nur-Sultan, Kazakhstan
Tel.: (7) 7172975999
Web Site: https://kmg-ds.kz
Drilling Services
N.A.I.C.S.: 213111

KazMorTransFlot LLP (1)
14 microdistrict building No 70, 130000, Aktau, Kazakhstan
Tel.: (7) 7292535890
Web Site: https://www.kmtf.kz
Sea Freight Transportation Services
N.A.I.C.S.: 483111
Bisaliyev Berik Karlovich (Deputy Gen Dir-Bus Dev)

KazMunayGas Onimdery LLP (1)
8 Kunayev Ave Emerald Towers Block B 1 Turan Ave, 010000, Nur-Sultan, Kazakhstan
Tel.: (7) 7172974408
Web Site: http://www.azskmg.kz
Oil Product Retailer
N.A.I.C.S.: 424720

KazMunayTeniz LLP (1)
Building 70 14th, micro district, 130000, Aktau, Mangistauskaya, Kazakhstan
Tel.: (7) 7292202901
Web Site: https://www.kazmunayteniz.kz
Oil & Gas Services
N.A.I.C.S.: 213112
Anshibayev Amantai Muratovich (Gen Dir)

JSC NPO NAUKA

3rd Yamskogo Polya Str ten 2, 125124, Moscow, 125124, Russia
Tel.: (7) 4957753110
Web Site: https://www.npo-nauka.ru
NAUK—(MOEX)
Sales Range: Less than $1 Million
Aircraft Mfr
N.A.I.C.S.: 336411
Evgeny Merkulov (Chm-Mgmt Bd & Gen Dir)

JSC PHARMSTANDARD

5B Likhachevsky proezd, Dolgoprudny, Moscow, 141701, Russia
Tel.: (7) 4959700030 RU
Web Site: http://www.pharmstd.com
Sales Range: $1-4.9 Billion
Emp.: 6,966
Pharmaceuticals Mfr
N.A.I.C.S.: 325412
Victor Kharitonin (Chm & Exec Dir)

Subsidiaries:

PHS-Tomskhimpharm JSC (1)
211 Prospekt Lenina Tomsk Region, 634009, Tomsk, Russia
Tel.: (7) 3822402856
Web Site: http://pharmstd.com
Emp.: 396
Pharmaceutical Preparation Mfr
N.A.I.C.S.: 325412
Vadim Danilov (Gen Dir)

Pharmstandard-UfaVITA JSC (1)
28 Khudayberdina str, 450077, Ufa, Russia
Tel.: (7) 3472729285
Web Site: http://pharmstd.com
Emp.: 175
Pharmaceutical Preparation Mfr
N.A.I.C.S.: 325412
Vladimir Kreyman (Dir Gen)

JSC PRIMORSK SHIPPING CORPORATION

Administrativny Gorodok Nakhodka 4, 692900, Nakhodka, Primorsky Krai, Russia
Tel.: (7) 4236694505 RU
Sales Range: $650-699.9 Million
Emp.: 2,700
Liquid Bulk Cargo Shipping & Marine Transportation Services
N.A.I.C.S.: 488320

Subsidiaries:

PRISCO (Singapore) Pte. Ltd. (1)
8 Temasek Boulevard, 24-02 Suntec Tower 3, Singapore, 038988, Singapore
Tel.: (65) 63336455
Sales Range: $25-49.9 Million
Emp.: 30
Other Support Activities for Water Transportation
N.A.I.C.S.: 488390
Alexander Migunov (Mng Dir)

JSC QUADRA-POWER GENERATION

Timiryazeva Street 99v, 300012, Tula, Russia
Tel.: (7) 4872 25 44 59
Web Site: http://www.quadra.ru
Year Founded: 2005
TGKD—(MOEX)
Sales Range: $800-899.9 Million
Emp.: 12,762
Eletric Power Generation Services
N.A.I.C.S.: 221118
Ekaterina Mikhailovna Salnikova (Chm)

JSC REFSERVICE

5 Building 2 Orlikov Lane, 107228, Moscow, Russia
Tel.: (7) 49 262 12 15
Web Site: http://www.refservice.ru
Year Founded: 2006
Sales Range: $450-499.9 Million
Emp.: 1,800
Railway Transportation of Perishable Goods
N.A.I.C.S.: 488510
Igor Bogdan (Gen Dir)

JSC ROSSETI

4 Belovezhskaya st, Moscow, 121353, Russia
Tel.: (7) 4959955333 RU
Web Site: http://www.rosseti.ru
Year Founded: 2008
RSTI—(MOEX)
Rev.: $16,608,319,020
Assets: $42,737,709,270
Liabilities: $17,186,095,620
Net Worth: $25,551,613,650
Earnings: $1,698,359,960
Emp.: 217,500
Fiscal Year-end: 12/31/19
Electric Power Generation & Distribution Services
N.A.I.C.S.: 221112
Andrey Murov (Member-Mgmt Bd)

Subsidiaries:

JSC Electrical Equipment maintenance factory RETO (1)
St Starokashirskoe Highway Building 4a, Moscow, 115201, Russia
Tel.: (7) 4993461165
Web Site: https://zreto.ru
Electric Equipment Mfr
N.A.I.C.S.: 335999

JSC Interregional Distribution Grid Company of North-West (1)
Constitution Square 3 A Office 16N, 196247, Saint Petersburg, Russia (55.38%)
Tel.: (7) 8123051000
Web Site: http://www.mrsksevzap.ru
Rev.: $678,234,867
Assets: $671,642,083
Liabilities: $433,123,849
Net Worth: $238,518,233
Earnings: ($11,891,329)
Emp.: 15,000
Fiscal Year-end: 12/31/2021
Electricity Transmission Services
N.A.I.C.S.: 221121
Zhdanova Irina Grigoryevna (Head)

JSC Lenenergo (1)
Gakkelevskaya Street 21A, 197227, Saint Petersburg, Russia
Tel.: (7) 8125958613
Web Site: http://www.rosseti-lenenergo.ru
Rev.: $1,259,523,288
Assets: $3,164,834,906
Liabilities: $1,082,637,309
Net Worth: $2,082,197,597
Earnings: $208,152,812
Emp.: 7,881
Fiscal Year-end: 12/31/2021
Electricity Distribution Services
N.A.I.C.S.: 221122
Ryumin Andrey Valerevich (CEO)

JSC Tyumenenergo (1)
Universitetskaya str 4 Khanty-Mansijsk Autonomous District, Tyumen Region, 628406, Surgut, Russia
Tel.: (7) 3462 77 63 50
Web Site: http://www.te.ru
Sales Range: $500-549.9 Million
Emp.: 7,503
Electric Power Distribution Services
N.A.I.C.S.: 221122
Savchuk Sergey (Mgr-Repair & Strengthing)

JSC Yantarenergo (1)
Teatralnaya Str 34, Kaliningrad, 236022, Russia
Tel.: (7) 4012576459
Eletric Power Generation Services
N.A.I.C.S.: 221112

Joint-Stock Company Tomsk Distribution Company (1)
36 Kirova ul, Tomsk, 634041, Russia
Tel.: (7) 3822 43 19 92
Web Site: http://www.trk.tom.ru
Electric Power Distribution Services
N.A.I.C.S.: 221122
Petrov Oleg Valentinovich (Gen Dir)

Kubanenergo PJSC (1)
2A Stavropolskaya street, Krasnodar, 350033, Russia
Tel.: (7) 8612122403
Web Site: https://rosseti-kuban.ru
Rev.: $833,308
Assets: $1,300,752
Liabilities: $694,745
Net Worth: $606,007
Earnings: $68,921
Emp.: 8,753
Fiscal Year-end: 12/31/2023

INTERNATIONAL PUBLIC

Electric Energy Distribution Services
N.A.I.C.S.: 221122
Alexander Ilich Gavrilov (Chm)

Nedvizhimost of the South Energy Engineering Center Open Joint-Stock Company (1)
Prospekt Budennovsky 2 Korp 105, Rostovna-Donu, Russia
Tel.: (7) 495 926 35 05
Electric Power Distribution Services
N.A.I.C.S.: 221122

Nedvizhimost of the Volga Region Energy Engineering Center Open Joint-Stock Company (1)
Ul Samarskaya 203B, Samara, 443001, Russia
Tel.: (7) 495 926 35 05
Electric Power Distribution Services
N.A.I.C.S.: 221122

Northwest Energy Engineering Center Open Joint-Stock (1)
111/3 Nevsky Prospekt, 191036, Saint Petersburg, Russia
Tel.: (7) 812 449 35 30
Electric Power Distribution Services
N.A.I.C.S.: 221122

OJSC Interregional Distribution Grid Company of the South (1)
49 Bolshaya Sadovaya Street, Rostov-on-Don, 115035, Krasnodar, Russia
Tel.: (7) 8632385464
Web Site: http://www.mrsk-yuga.ru
Rev.: $613,218,259
Assets: $598,209,003
Liabilities: $532,882,874
Net Worth: $65,326,129
Earnings: ($52,641,239)
Emp.: 13,686
Fiscal Year-end: 12/31/2019
Electric Energy Distribution Services
N.A.I.C.S.: 221122
Timur Ulyumdzhievich Alaev (Deputy Dir Gen & Member-Mgmt Bd)

OJSC Interregional Distributive Grid Company of Urals (1)
140 Ulitsa Mamina Sibiryaka, Ekaterinburg, 620026, Russia (51.52%)
Tel.: (7) 343 215 26 00
Web Site: http://www.mrsk-ural.ru
Sales Range: $1-4.9 Billion
Energy Distribution Services
N.A.I.C.S.: 221122
Yuri Vyacheslavovich Lebedev (COO)

PJSC Federal Grid Company Rosseti (1)
5A Akademika Chelomeya str, 117630, Moscow, Russia
Tel.: (7) 4957109333
Web Site: http://www.fsk-ees.ru
Rev.: $3,196,484,880
Assets: $18,051,928,260
Liabilities: $5,242,146,840
Net Worth: $12,809,781,420
Earnings: $799,983,300
Emp.: 21,687
Fiscal Year-end: 12/31/2020
Electric Power Distribution Services
N.A.I.C.S.: 221122
Andrey Y. Murov (Gen Dir)

PJSC IDGC of Northern Caucasus (1)
13a Podstantsionnaya Str, Pyatigorsk, 357506, Stavropol, Russia
Tel.: (7) 8793346680
Web Site: http://www.rossetisk.ru
Electric Power Distribution Services
N.A.I.C.S.: 221122
Ivanov Vitaliy Valerievich (Chm & Gen Dir)

PJSC IDGC of Siberia (1)
144a Bograda street, Krasnoyarsk, 660021, Russia
Tel.: (7) 391 274 41 74
Web Site: http://www.mrsk-sib.ru
Sales Range: Less than $1 Million
Power Generation & Distribution Services
N.A.I.C.S.: 221118
Pavel Evgenevich Akilin (Chm-Exec Bd & Gen Dir)

PJSC Rosseti Moscow Region (1)
2nd Paveletsky PR d 3 P 2, 115114, Moscow, Russia

Tel.: (7) 4956624070
Web Site: http://www.rossetimr.ru
Emp.: 15,448
Electric Power Distribution Services
N.A.I.C.S.: 221122
Sinyutin Petr Alekseyevich *(Dir Gen)*

Public Joint Stock Company Rosseti Centre (1)
Malaya Ordynka 15, 119017, Moscow, 119017, Russia
Tel.: (7) 4957479292
Web Site: https://www.mrsk-1.ru
Sales Range: $1-4.9 Billion
Emp.: 30,337
Electric Power Distribution
N.A.I.C.S.: 221122
Olga Dmitriyevna Lezhneva *(Head-Customer Relationship Mgmt)*

Public Joint Stock Company Rosseti Volga (1)
42/44 Pervomayskaya street, 410031, Saratov, 410031, Russia (50.4%)
Tel.: (7) 8452302930
Web Site: https://www.rossetivolga.ru
Rev.: $1,557,093,856
Assets: $1,764,731,555
Liabilities: $878,425,235
Net Worth: $886,306,320
Earnings: $107,854,648
Emp.: 22,345
Fiscal Year-end: 12/31/2019
Power Transmission & Power Networks Process Connection Services
N.A.I.C.S.: 221122
Kazakov Alexander Ivanovich *(Chm)*

Rosseti Northern Caucasus, PJSC (1)
13a Podstantsionnaya Str, Pyatigorsk, 357506, Stavropol, 357506, Russia
Tel.: (7) 8793346680
Web Site: https://www.rossetisk.ru
Emp.: 8,733
Electric Power Distribution Services
N.A.I.C.S.: 221122
Viktor Mikhailovich Abaimov *(Deputy Gen Dir & Chief Engr)*

Rosseti Volga PJSC (1)
42 44 Pervomayskaya Street, 410031, Saratov, 410031, Russia (67.63%)
Tel.: (7) 8452302632
Web Site: https://www.rossetivolga.ru
Rev.: $833,262,801
Assets: $775,849,923
Liabilities: $320,113,406
Net Worth: $455,736,517
Earnings: $32,145,189
Emp.: 19,800
Fiscal Year-end: 12/31/2023
Electric Power Transmission Services
N.A.I.C.S.: 221121
Vladimir Borisovich Ponomarev *(Deputy Gen Dir-Safety)*

Sibenergosetproekt LLC. (1)
Pr-t Dimitrova d 7, 630132, Novosibirsk, Russia
Tel.: (7) 383 222 63 69
Electric Power Distribution Services
N.A.I.C.S.: 221122

Tyvaenergosbyt Open Joint-Stock Company (1)
St Factory 2 A, Kyzyl, 667010, Tuva, Russia
Tel.: (7) 394 225 6033
Web Site: http://www.tuvaensb.ru
Eletric Power Generation Services
N.A.I.C.S.: 221118

Yantarenergo Open Joint-Stock Company (1)
34 Teatralnaya St, Kaliningrad, 236000, Russia
Tel.: (7) 4012 53 55 14
Web Site: http://www.yantene.ru
Electric Power Generation & Distribution Services
N.A.I.C.S.: 221118

JSC RUSSIAN RAILWAYS
Novaya Basmannaya 2, Moscow, 107174, Russia
Tel.: (7) 4992621628   RU
Web Site: http://eng.rzd.ru
Rev.: $40,446,233,080
Assets: $83,295,529,690
Liabilities: $40,146,069,910
Net Worth: $43,149,459,780
Earnings: $2,512,053,940
Fiscal Year-end: 12/31/19
Railway Operator
N.A.I.C.S.: 482111
Olga Gnedkova *(Deputy Mng Dir)*

Subsidiaries:

GEFCO S.A. (1)
77 81 Rue Des Lilas Espange, BP 313, 92402, Courbevoie, Cedex, France (75%)
Tel.: (33) 149052121
Web Site: http://www.gefco.net
Sales Range: $5-14.9 Billion
Emp.: 11,200
Freight Transportation & Logistics Services
N.A.I.C.S.: 488510
Luc Nadal *(Chm-Mgmt Bd & CEO)*

Affiliate (Non-US):

Algai OOO (2)
Building 1 Entrance 9 8th Floor Business Park Rumyantsevo, Leninsky Area, Moscow, 142784, Russia
Tel.: (7) 495 642 68 88
Web Site: http://www.algai.ru
Automotive Logistics Services
N.A.I.C.S.: 541614

Subsidiary (Non-US):

GEFCO (Portugal) Transitarios, LDA. (2)
Rua Dr Antonio Loureiro Borges Edificio n 1 Arquiparque Piso 1, 1499-016, Alges, Portugal
Tel.: (351) 21 416 98 00
Web Site: http://pt.gefco.net
Freight Transportation & Logistics Services
N.A.I.C.S.: 488510

GEFCO (SUISSE) SA (2)
Route de France 85 H, 2916, Fahy, Switzerland
Tel.: (41) 32 476 01 10
Web Site: http://www.ch.gefco.net
Logistics Consulting Services
N.A.I.C.S.: 541614

GEFCO ARGENTINA S.A. (2)
Av Alicia Moreau De Justo 1930 - Piso 2 Of 207 Puerto Madero, Dock 15 - Puerto Madero, C1107AFN, Buenos Aires, Argentina
Tel.: (54) 11 4000 6080
Web Site: http://ar.gefco.net
Freight Transportation & Logistics Services
N.A.I.C.S.: 488510

GEFCO BENELUX S.A. (2)
Rue Du Parc Industriel 27, 7822, Ghislenghien, Belgium
Tel.: (32) 68 250 241
Web Site: http://benelux.gefco.net
Freight Transportation & Logistics Services
N.A.I.C.S.: 488510

GEFCO Baltic SIA (2)
15 P Brieza iela, Riga, 1010, Latvia
Tel.: (371) 66010950
Web Site: http://www.baltic.gefco.net
Emp.: 40
Freight Transportation & Logistics Services
N.A.I.C.S.: 488510

GEFCO CESKA REPUBLICA s.r.o. (2)
Sokolovska 668/136D, 186 00, Prague, Czech Republic
Tel.: (420) 226222701
Web Site: http://cz.gefco.net
Freight Transportation & Logistics Services
N.A.I.C.S.: 488510

GEFCO DEUTSCHLAND GmbH (2)
Kurhessenstrasse 13, 64546, Morfelden, Germany
Tel.: (49) 610520080
Web Site: http://de.gefco.net
Freight Transportation & Logistics Services
N.A.I.C.S.: 488510
Frank Erhardt *(Mng Dir)*

GEFCO DO BRASIL Ltda (2)
Rua do Mercado 20 - Centro, 20010 007, Rio de Janeiro, Brazil
Tel.: (55) 21 2103 8100
Sales Range: $50-74.9 Million
Emp.: 20
Freight Transportation & Logistics Services
N.A.I.C.S.: 488510

GEFCO ESPANA S.A. (2)
C/ Manises 3, Pozuelo de Alarcon, 28224, Madrid, Spain
Tel.: (34) 91 347 3200
Freight Transportation & Logistics Services
N.A.I.C.S.: 488510

GEFCO Forwarding International B.V. (2)
Contour Avenue 51, 2133 LD, Hoofddorp, Netherlands
Tel.: (31) 20 654 34 44
Web Site: http://www.gefco.net
Logistics Consulting Services
N.A.I.C.S.: 541614

Subsidiary (Non-US):

GEFCO Forwarding UK Ltd (3)
Unit 1 Mereside Park Shield Road, Ashford, TW15 1BL, Middlesex, United Kingdom
Tel.: (44) 1784421030
Logistics Consulting Services
N.A.I.C.S.: 541614
Maria Holmes-Keeling *(Mgr-Mktg-GEFCO UK Ltd)*

GRoss LOGISTICS Inc. (3)
207A Sky Freight Center NAIA Avenue, Sto Nino, Paranaque, 1704, Philippines
Tel.: (63) 2 851 2181
Web Site: http://www.grosslogistics.com.ph
Logistics Consulting Services
N.A.I.C.S.: 541614

Subsidiary (Non-US):

GEFCO HONG KONG Company Limited (2)
Rm 4118-4122 41/F Metroplaza Twr 1 223 Hing Fong Rd, Kwai Fong, Kwai Chung, China (Hong Kong)
Tel.: (852) 23687155
Freight Transportation & Logistics Services
N.A.I.C.S.: 488510

GEFCO ITALIA S.p.A. (2)
Via Palizzi 89, 20157, Milan, Italy
Tel.: (39) 02 39 013 1
Freight Transportation & Logistics Services
N.A.I.C.S.: 488510

GEFCO MIDDLE EAST FZE (2)
Tower 18 Office LB181807, PO Box 263226, Jebel Ali, Dubai, United Arab Emirates
Tel.: (971) 48895566
Web Site: http://dubai.gefco.net
Logistics Consulting Services
N.A.I.C.S.: 541614
Herve Bernhard *(Mgr-Fin)*

GEFCO Magyarorszag Kft (2)
Bocskai ut 134-146, 1113, Budapest, Hungary
Tel.: (36) 1 7663900
Web Site: http://hu.gefco.net
Sales Range: $25-49.9 Million
Freight Transportation & Logistics Services
N.A.I.C.S.: 488510

GEFCO Mexico SA de CV (2)
Monte Elbruz 132 - Despacho 401, Col Polanco Reforma Mexico, 11550, Mexico, Mexico
Tel.: (52) 55 5282 3583
Web Site: http://mx.gefco.net
Freight Transportation Services
N.A.I.C.S.: 488510

GEFCO Osterreich GmbH (2)
Andromeda-Tower Donau-City-Strasse 6, Vienna, 1220, Austria
Tel.: (43) 5 7897 0
Freight Transportation & Logistics Services
N.A.I.C.S.: 488510

GEFCO PARTICIPACOES Ltda (2)
Praca XV De Novembro 20 Salas 401 E 402 - Parte, Rio de Janeiro, 20010-010, Brazil
Tel.: (55) 2121038100
Freight Transportation & Logistics Services
N.A.I.C.S.: 488510

GEFCO POLSKA Sp. z.o.o. (2)
Pl Bankowy 2, 00-095, Warsaw, Poland
Tel.: (48) 22 531 21 77
Freight Transportation & Logistics Services
N.A.I.C.S.: 488510

GEFCO PREVOZNISTVO IN LOGISTICA d.o.o. (2)
Ankaranska Cesta 7 B, 6000, Koper, Slovenia
Tel.: (386) 5 66 38 770
Sales Range: $25-49.9 Million
Emp.: 16
Freight Transportation & Logistics Services
N.A.I.C.S.: 488510
Frederik Nartus *(Gen Mgr)*

GEFCO Romania S.R.L. (2)
2C George Constantinescu street 4th floor, 2nd district, 020339, Bucharest, Romania
Tel.: (40) 21 300 88 86
Web Site: http://ro.gefco.net
Sales Range: $25-49.9 Million
Freight Transportation & Logistics Services
N.A.I.C.S.: 488510
Jerome Chevrolet *(Gen Dir)*

GEFCO Russia (2)
8 Preobrazhenskaya Ploshchad, 107061, Moscow, Russia
Tel.: (7) 4959813100
Web Site: http://ru.gefco.net
Logistics Consulting Services
N.A.I.C.S.: 541614
Valeriya Seledkova *(Gen Dir)*

GEFCO TASIMACILIK VE LOJISTIK ANONIM SIRKETI (2)
Kayisdagi Cad Karaman Ciftlik Yolu N 45 Kar Plaza E Blok Kat 13, Icerenkoy, Istanbul, 34752, Turkiye
Tel.: (90) 216 5783500
Sales Range: $50-74.9 Million
Emp.: 150
Freight Transportation & Logistics Services
N.A.I.C.S.: 488510
Fulvio Villa *(CEO)*

GEFCO Tunisie SA (2)
Zone Portuaire de Rades, 2040, Rades, Tunisia
Tel.: (216) 31348048
Web Site: http://tn.gefco.net
Freight Transportation Services
N.A.I.C.S.: 488510

GEFCO U.K. Ltd. (2)
376-378 Chiswick High Road, London, W4 5TF, United Kingdom
Tel.: (44) 208 742 2220
Web Site: http://uk.gefco.net
Sales Range: $100-124.9 Million
Emp.: 45
Freight Transportation & Logistics Services
N.A.I.C.S.: 488510
John Stocker *(Dir-Comml)*

GEFCO UKRAINE LLC (2)
110 Zhylianska street 7th floor, Kiev, 01032, Ukraine
Tel.: (380) 44 287 88 89
Web Site: http://ua.gefco.net
Sales Range: $25-49.9 Million
Freight Transportation & Logistics Services
N.A.I.C.S.: 488510
William Jean Gerald Leclere *(Gen Mgr)*

Gefco Bulgaria Ltd (2)
5 Lachezar Stanchev str Sopharma Business Towers Building B 15th floor, 1797, Sofia, Bulgaria
Tel.: (359) 29694961
Web Site: http://bg.gefco.net
Emp.: 80
Logistics Consulting Services
N.A.I.C.S.: 541614
Krum Donchev *(Mgr-Mktg & Sls)*

Gefco Slovakia S.r.o. (2)
1 Plynarenska Bbbc Building No 1, 821 09, Bratislava, Slovakia
Tel.: (421) 2 32 13 29 10
Web Site: http://sk.gefco.net
Logistics Consulting Services
N.A.I.C.S.: 541614
Richard Krchnak *(Supvr-WRP)*

JSC BetElTrans (1)
Novaya Basmannaya 9/2-4 building 6, 107078, Moscow, Russia

JSC RUSSIAN RAILWAYS

JSC Russian Railways—(Continued)
Tel.: (7) 4956631133
Web Site: http://www.beteltrans.ru
Concrete Tie & Bar Mfr
N.A.I.C.S.: 327390

JSC Federal Freight (1)
Kuibyshev Street 44, 620026, Yekaterinburg, Russia **(100%)**
Tel.: (7) 3433807144
Web Site: http://www.railfgk.ru
Railway Freight Transportation Services
N.A.I.C.S.: 482111

JSC Federal Passenger Company (1)
34 Masha Poryvayeva Street, Moscow, 107078, Russia **(100%)**
Tel.: (7) 499 260 84 74
Railway Transportation Services
N.A.I.C.S.: 482111
Mikhail Akulov (CEO)

JSC Kaluga plant Remputmash (1)
lane Podkopaevsky 4 building B, 109028, Moscow, Russia
Tel.: (7) 495 663 3216
Web Site: http://www.rempm.ru
Emp.: 100
Freight Transportation Services
N.A.I.C.S.: 488510

JSC RZD Logistics (1)
34 bldg 1 Mashi Poryvaevoy str, 107078, Moscow, Russia
Tel.: (7) 4959886868
Web Site: http://www.rzdlog.com
Freight Forwarding Services
N.A.I.C.S.: 488510
Dmitry Murev (CEO)

JSC RZD Trading Company (1)
5 building 3 Volochaevskaya str, 111033, Moscow, Russia
Tel.: (7) 4952527081
Web Site: http://www.tdrzd.ru
Rail Transportation Support Services
N.A.I.C.S.: 488210
Pavel Shishkin (Accountant)

JSC RZDstroy (1)
Elizavetinsky lane 12 bldg 1, 105005, Moscow, Russia **(100%)**
Tel.: (7) 84992603432
Web Site: http://www.rzdstroy.ru
Transportation Infrastructure Construction Services
N.A.I.C.S.: 237990

JSC RailTransAuto (1)
6 Building 2 Dokuchaev Pereulok, 107078, Moscow, Russia **(51%)**
Tel.: (7) 495 777 02 55
Web Site: http://www.railtransauto.ru
Motor Vehicle Rail Transportation Services
N.A.I.C.S.: 482111

JSC Roszheldorproject (1)
Kalanchjovskaya ul 29, 107078, Moscow, Russia
Tel.: (7) 4956601520
Web Site: http://www.rzdp.ru
Construction Project Survey & Design Services
N.A.I.C.S.: 541330
Tikhonov Alexei (Gen Dir)

JSC TransTeleCom Company (1)
Testovskaya str 8 entrance 3, Moscow, 123112, Russia
Tel.: (7) 495 784 66 70
Web Site: http://www.ttk.ru
Sales Range: $800-899.9 Million
Telecommunication Servicesb
N.A.I.C.S.: 517111

JSC United Transport and Logistics Company (1)
Sadovaya-Chernogryazskaya str 8/7, 107078, Moscow, Russia
Tel.: (7) 4959959591
Web Site: http://www.utlc.com
Emp.: 700
Freight Forwarding Services
N.A.I.C.S.: 488510
Grom Aleksey Nikolaevich (Chm-Mgmt Bd & Pres)

JSC Zheldoripoteka (1)
st Electrozavodskaya 32A, 107023, Moscow, Russia
Tel.: (7) 495 788 1930
Web Site: http://www.zdi.ru
Residential Housing Construction Services
N.A.I.C.S.: 236116

OJSC Carriage Repair Company - 2 (1)
st Nizhnyaya Krasnoselskaya 40/12 bldg 2, 105066, Moscow, Russia
Tel.: (7) 499 260 50 50
Web Site: http://www.vrk2.ru
Rail Repair Services
N.A.I.C.S.: 488210

OJSC Carriage Repair Company - 3 (1)
Protopopovskiy lane, 129090, Moscow, Russia
Tel.: (7) 499 260 30 20
Web Site: http://www.vrk-3.ru
Rail Repair Services
N.A.I.C.S.: 488210

OJSC High-speed Rail Lines (1)
Mashi Poryvaevoy str 34, 107078, Moscow, Russia
Tel.: (7) 495 789 9870
Web Site: http://www.eng.hsrail.ru
Rail Line Construction Services
N.A.I.C.S.: 237990
Georgy Petrushenko (CEO)

JSC SIAULIU PLENTAS
Isradeju st 11, Siauliai, Lithuania
Tel.: (370) 41540601
Web Site: http://www.splentas.lt
Sales Range: $25-49.9 Million
Emp.: 390
Road Construction Services
N.A.I.C.S.: 237310
Juozas Aleksa (Gen Mgr)

JSC SLAVNEFT-YANOS
Moskovskiy prospect b 130, 150023, Yaroslavl, 150023, Russia
Tel.: (7) 4852498100
Web Site: https://www.yanos.slavneft.ru
Year Founded: 1961
JNOS—(MOEX)
Sales Range: Less than $1 Million
Emp.: 3,230
Oil Production Services
N.A.I.C.S.: 213112
Karpov Nikolay Vladimirovich (Gen Dir & Member-Mgmt Bd)

JSC SOFRINSKY EXPERIMENTAL MECHANICAL PLANT
Kraynaya Street 2, Pushkin District, Sofrino, 141270, Moscow, Russia
Tel.: (7) 495 5434231
Web Site: http://www.se-mz.ru
Emp.: 150
Metal Tank Mfr
N.A.I.C.S.: 332431
Anatoly Borisovich Kostenko (CEO)

JSC SUEK
53/7 Dubininskaya str, 115054, Moscow, Russia
Tel.: (7) 4957952538 RU
Coal Mining & Distribution
N.A.I.C.S.: 212115

JSC TBC BANK
7 Marjanishvili St, 0102, Tbilisi, Georgia
Tel.: (995) 322272727
Web Site: http://www.tbcbank.ge
Year Founded: 1913
Sales Range: $10-24.9 Million
Emp.: 350
Banking Services
N.A.I.C.S.: 522110
Vakhtang Butskhrikidze (CEO)

Subsidiaries:

Bank Constanta (1)
117 Tsereteli Avenue, Tbilisi, 0119, Georgia
Tel.: (995) 32 2 401 401
Commercial Banking Services
N.A.I.C.S.: 522110
Badri Japaridze (Chm)

JSC TEMIRBANK
68/74 Abai Ave, 050008, Almaty, Kazakhstan
Tel.: (7) 7272587888 RU
Web Site: http://www.temirbank.kz
Year Founded: 1992
Sales Range: $200-249.9 Million
Emp.: 2,200
Investment Banking Services
N.A.I.C.S.: 523150

JSC ZALIV SHIPYARD
Tankistov 4, 98310, Kerch, Crimea, Ukraine
Tel.: (380) 6561 33055 RU
Web Site: http://www.zaliv.com
Year Founded: 1938
Ship Building & Repair Services
N.A.I.C.S.: 336611
Nikolay Kuzmenko (Chm-Supervisory Bd)

Subsidiaries:

NorYards AS (1)
Thormohlensg 53 C, 1201, Bergen, Norway **(70%)**
Tel.: (47) 55542500
Holding Company; Ship Building & Repair Services
N.A.I.C.S.: 551112
Johannes D. Neteland (CEO)

Subsidiary (Domestic):

NorYards BMV AS (2)
Damsgardsveien 229, 5163, Laksevag, Norway
Tel.: (47) 55 54 24 00
Ship Building & Repair Services
N.A.I.C.S.: 336611
Terje Sjumarken (Mng Dir)

NorYards Fosen AS (2)
Kvithyll, 7100, Rissa, Norway
Tel.: (47) 73858600
AV Price: Range: $50-74.9 Million
Emp.: 260
Ship Building & Repair Services
N.A.I.C.S.: 336611
Arnar Utseth (CEO)

JSC ZVEZDA
123 Babushkina St, 192012, Saint Petersburg, 192012, Russia
Tel.: (7) 8123620747
Web Site: https://www.zvezda.spb.ru
Year Founded: 1932
ZVEZ—(MOEX)
Sales Range: Less than $1 Million
Diesel Engine Mfr
N.A.I.C.S.: 333618
Skvortsov Petr Petrovich (Gen Dir)

JSCB ALMAZERGIENBANK JSC
1 Lenin Avenue, 677000, Yakutsk, Russia
Tel.: (7) 4112342222
Web Site: http://www.albank.ru
Sales Range: Less than $1 Million
Commercial Banking Services
N.A.I.C.S.: 522110

JSCB FORSHTADT JSC
Chkalova Street 35/1, 460058, Orenburg, Russia
Tel.: (7) 3532980400
Web Site: http://www.forshtadt.ru
Year Founded: 1992
Sales Range: Less than $1 Million
Commercial Banking Services
N.A.I.C.S.: 522110
Sokolov Alexander Pavlovich (Chm)

INTERNATIONAL PUBLIC

JSCB PERESVET PJSC
Krasnopresnenskaya Nab 14, Moscow, 123100, Russia
Tel.: (7) 4959740409
Web Site: http://www.bank-peresvet.ru
Sales Range: Less than $1 Million
Investment Brokerage Services
N.A.I.C.S.: 523150

JSCB PRIMORYE
Svetlanskaya st 47, Vladivostok, 690091, Russia
Tel.: (7) 4232260600
Web Site: https://www.primbank.ru
Year Founded: 1994
PRMB—(MOEX)
Sales Range: Less than $1 Million
Commercial Banking Services
N.A.I.C.S.: 522110
Zverev Andrey Nikolaevich (Chm)

JSCB TRANSSTROIBANK JSC
94 Dubininskaya St, 115093, Moscow, Russia
Tel.: (7) 4957863773
Web Site: http://www.transstroybank.ru
Year Founded: 1994
Sales Range: Less than $1 Million
Commercial Banking Services
N.A.I.C.S.:

JSCO SEVASTOPOL MARINE PLANT
13 Geroyev Sevastopolya Street, 99001, Sevastopol, Ukraine
Tel.: (380) 692559950
Web Site: http://www.sevmorzavod.com
Sales Range: $25-49.9 Million
Emp.: 160
Ship Building, Repairing, Mechanical Engineering & Stevedoring Services
N.A.I.C.S.: 336611
Gorelik Valeriy Borisovich (Deputy Chm-Supervisory Bd)

JSE LIMITED
JSE Limited One Exchange Square Gwen LaneSandown, Sandton, 2196, South Africa
Tel.: (27) 115207000 ZA
Web Site: https://www.jse.co.za
Year Founded: 1887
JSE—(JSE)
Rev.: $153,276,145
Assets: $3,256,185,729
Liabilities: $3,017,316,163
Net Worth: $238,869,566
Earnings: $45,255,116
Emp.: 542
Fiscal Year-end: 12/31/23
Securities & Commodities Exchange
N.A.I.C.S.: 523210
John H. Burke (Dir-Issuer Regulation)

Subsidiaries:

JSE Private Placements Proprietary Limited (1)
One Exchange Square 2 Gwen Lane, Sandown, Sandton, South Africa
Tel.: (27) 715634126
Web Site: https://www.jseprivateplacements.co.za
Financial Services
N.A.I.C.S.: 523999

JSE Trustees (Pty) Limited (1)
1 Exchange Square 2 Gwen Lane, Sandton, 2196, Gauteng, South Africa **(100%)**
Tel.: (27) 115207000
Web Site: http://www.jse.co.za
Sales Range: $200-249.9 Million
Emp.: 400
Financial Trust Services
N.A.I.C.S.: 523991

JSL CONSTRUCTION & DEVELOPMENT CO., LTD.
11F-2 No 166 Section 4 Zhongxiao East Road, Daan District, Taipei, 10688, Taiwan
Tel.: (886) 287736688
Web Site: https://www.isanlin.com
Year Founded: 1986
2540—(TAI)
Rev.: $264,981,906
Assets: $1,162,880,070
Liabilities: $870,253,801
Net Worth: $292,626,268
Earnings: $49,304,030
Fiscal Year-end: 12/31/23
Construction Engineering Services
N.A.I.C.S.: 237990
Zhu Wenyu *(Chm)*

JSL INDUSTRIES LIMITED
N H No 8, Mogar, 388 340, Anand, 388 340, Gujarat, India
Tel.: (91) 2692280224
Web Site: https://www.jslmogar.com
Year Founded: 1966
504080—(BOM)
Rev.: $7,681,713
Assets: $5,708,003
Liabilities: $1,628,825
Net Worth: $4,079,178
Earnings: $376,591
Emp.: 65
Fiscal Year-end: 03/31/22
Motor Mfr
N.A.I.C.S.: 333996
Rahul Nanubhai Amin *(Chm)*

JSL S.A.
Rua Doutor Renato Paes de Barros 1017 13 andar - Itaim Bibi, Sao Paulo, 04530-001, Brazil
Tel.: (55) 1131544000
Web Site: https://www.jsl.com.br
JSLGY—(OTCIQ)
Rev.: $1,354,041,544
Assets: $2,125,251,012
Liabilities: $1,827,894,340
Net Worth: $297,356,671
Earnings: $62,884,645
Emp.: 16,000
Fiscal Year-end: 12/31/23
Transportation & Logistics Services
N.A.I.C.S.: 488999
Fernando Antonio Simoes *(CEO)*

Subsidiaries:

Movida Participacoes S.A. (1)
Rua Dr Renato Paes de Barros n 1017 9th floor Itaim Bibi, Sao Paulo, 04530-001, Brazil
Tel.: (55) 1135281121
Web Site: https://ri.movida.com.br
Rev.: $1,914,453,884
Assets: $5,234,595,673
Liabilities: $4,682,460,265
Net Worth: $552,135,407
Earnings: $110,959,418
Emp.: 5,400
Fiscal Year-end: 12/31/2022
Automobile Rental Services
N.A.I.C.S.: 532111
Fernando Antonio Simoes *(Chm)*

JSPV CO LTD
98 Yeomjak-Li Doonpo-Myeon, Asan, Chungcheongnam-do, Korea (South)
Tel.: (82) 415490600
Web Site: http://www.jspv.co.kr
Year Founded: 2008
Power Generator Mfr & Distr
N.A.I.C.S.: 335999
Jung-Hyun Lee *(CEO)*

JSR CORP.
Shiodome Sumitomo Bldg 1-9-2 Higashi-Shimbashi, Minato-ku, Tokyo, 105-8640, Japan
Tel.: (81) 362183500
Web Site: https://www.jsr.co.jp
Year Founded: 1957
4185—(TKS)
Rev.: $3,300,850,960
Assets: $7,834,711,280
Liabilities: $3,820,037,760
Net Worth: $4,014,673,520
Earnings: $361,093,040
Emp.: 9,696
Fiscal Year-end: 03/31/22
Synthetic Rubber Mfr
N.A.I.C.S.: 325212
Koichi Kawasaki *(Exec Mng Officer)*

Subsidiaries:

Crown Bioscience, Inc. (1)
333 Keelung Road, Xinyi District, Taipei, 11012, Taiwan
Tel.: (886) 277181690
Web Site: https://www.crownbio.com
Drug Discovery & Development Services
N.A.I.C.S.: 541713
Eva Ho *(CFO)*

D-Mec Ltd. (1)
Shiodome Sumitomo Building 1-9-2, Higashi-Shinbashi Minato-ku, Tokyo, 105-0021, Japan (100%)
Tel.: (81) 362183582
Web Site: https://www.d-mec.co.jp
Commissioned 3D Models, Solid Modeling Systems & Optically-Hardened Resins Sales
N.A.I.C.S.: 424610

EUV Resist Manufacturing & Qualification Center N.V. (1)
Technologielaan 8, 3001, Leuven, Belgium
Tel.: (32) 16832832
Semiconductor Material Mfr
N.A.I.C.S.: 334413

Elastomix Co., Ltd. (1)
100 Kawajiri-cho, Yokkaichi, 510-0871, Mie, Japan (98.51%)
Tel.: (81) 593452022
Sales Range: $50-74.9 Million
Emp.: 269
Crumb Rubber Mfr
N.A.I.C.S.: 326299

Subsidiary (Non-US):

Elastomix (Foshan) Co., Ltd. (2)
(98.51%)
Tel.: (86) 75787380386
Web Site: http://www.emixfs.com
Sales Range: $25-49.9 Million
Emp.: 90
Crude Rubber Products Compounding & Sales
N.A.I.C.S.: 326299

Elastomix (Thailand) Co., Ltd. (2)
No 7/116 Moo 4 Tumbol-Mapyangporn, Pluakdaeng, Rayong, 21140, Thailand
Tel.: (66) 3801638190
Web Site: https://www.elastomix.co.th
Emp.: 335
Raw Rubber Mfr & Sales
N.A.I.C.S.: 326299
Kazuhiko Nishihara *(Pres)*

Elastomix Mexico, S.A. de C.V. (1)
Rio San Lorenzo No 619 Modulo 1, Parque Tecnoindustrial Castro del Rio, 36810, Irapuato, Guanajuato, Mexico
Tel.: (52) 4626074900
Rubber Product Distr
N.A.I.C.S.: 423840

Emulsion Technology Co., Ltd. (1)
1-6-16 Obata, Yokkaichi, 510-0875, Mie, Japan (100%)
Tel.: (81) 593450022
Web Site: http://www.etec.jsr.co.jp
Emp.: 245
Crude Latex Compounding & Sales
N.A.I.C.S.: 326199

Goko Trading Co., Ltd. (1)
Onest Shin-Osaka Square 9F 4-5-36 Miyahara, Yodogawa-ku, Osaka, 532-0003, Japan
Tel.: (81) 661525430
Chemical Products Distr
N.A.I.C.S.: 424690

JM Energy Corporation (1)
8565 Nishi-ide Ooizumi-cho, Hokuto, 409-1501, Yamanashi, Japan
Tel.: (81) 551 38 8008
Web Site: http://www.jmenergy.co.jp
Lithium Ion Capacitor Mfr
N.A.I.C.S.: 334416

Division (Domestic):

JM Energy Corporation - Corporate Planning Division (2)
8565 Nishiide Oizumi-cho, Hokuto, 409-1501, Yamanashi, Japan
Tel.: (81) 551 38 8008
Web Site: http://www.jmenergy.co.jp
Emp.: 160
Electronic Capacitor Mfr
N.A.I.C.S.: 334416
Mikio Yamachika *(Pres)*

JM Energy Corporation - Manufacturing Division (2)
8565 Nishi-ide Ooizumi-cho, Hokuto, 409-1501, Yamanashi, Japan
Tel.: (81) 551 38 8170
Electronic Capacitor Mfr
N.A.I.C.S.: 334416
Mikio Yamachika *(Pres)*

JN System Partners Co., Ltd. (1)
2nd floor Sumitomo Fudosan Toyosu TK Building 1-9-4 Edagawa, Koto-ku, Tokyo, 135-0051, Japan
Tel.: (81) 366665891
Web Site: https://www.jnsp.co.jp
Emp.: 121
Computer System Design Services
N.A.I.C.S.: 541512

JSR (Shanghai) Co., Ltd. (1)
Rm 606 SMEG PLAZA 1386 Hongqiao Road, Shanghai, 200051, China
Tel.: (86) 2162787600
Liquid Crystal Display Mfr
N.A.I.C.S.: 334419

JSR Active Innovation Fund, LLC (1)
1-9-2 Higashi-Shimbashi, Minato-ku, Tokyo, 105-0021, Japan
Tel.: (81) 362183558
Investment Services
N.A.I.C.S.: 523999

JSR America, Inc. (1)
5300 Dupont Cir, Milford, OH 45150 (100%)
Tel.: (513) 421-6166
Web Site: http://www.jsra.com
Sales Range: $25-49.9 Million
Emp.: 5
Synthetic Rubber Sales
N.A.I.C.S.: 325212
Yuji Hongu *(Pres)*

Subsidiary (Domestic):

KBI Biopharma, Inc. (2)
1101 Hamlin Rd, Durham, NC 27704 (90%)
Tel.: (919) 479-9898
Web Site: http://www.kbibiopharma.com
Emp.: 250
Biopharmaceutical Contract Developer & Mfr
N.A.I.C.S.: 541715
Kathy S. Lee *(Sr VP-Quality & Regulatory)*

JSR BST Elastomer Co., Ltd. (1)
175 Sathorn City Tower 10th Fl South Sathorn Road, Tungmahamek Sathorn, Bangkok, 10120, Thailand
Tel.: (66) 26796644
Web Site: http://www.jbe.co.th
Rubber Product Mfr & Distr
N.A.I.C.S.: 326220

JSR Business Service Co., Ltd. (1)
1-9-2 Higashi-Shimbashi, Minato-ku, Tokyo, 105-0021, Japan (100%)
Tel.: (81) 362183771
Business Support Services
N.A.I.C.S.: 561499

JSR Corp. - Chiba Plant (1)
5 Chigusakaigan, Ichihara, 299-0108, Chiba, Japan
Tel.: (81) 436 62 4161
Web Site: http://www.jsr.co.jp
Synthetic Rubber Mfr

JSR Corp. - Kashima Plant (1)
34-1 Tohwada, Kamisu, 314-0102, Ibaraki, Japan
Tel.: (81) 299 96 2511
Web Site: http://www.jsr.co.jp
Synthetic Rubber Mfr
N.A.I.C.S.: 325212

JSR Corp. - Yokkaichi Plant (1)
100 Kawajiricho, Yokkaichi, 510-8552, Mie, Japan
Tel.: (81) 593458000
Synthetic Rubber Mfr
N.A.I.C.S.: 325212

JSR Elastomer America, Inc. (1)
5300 Dupont Cir Bldg 16 Ste D, Milford, OH 45150
Tel.: (513) 421-6166
Rubber Product Distr
N.A.I.C.S.: 423840

JSR Elastomer Europe GmbH (1)
Am Seestern 8, 40547, Dusseldorf, Germany
Tel.: (49) 2117306690
Rubber Product Distr
N.A.I.C.S.: 423840

JSR Elastomer India Private Limited (1)
Unit 506 Vatika City Point MG Road, Gurgaon, 122002, Haryana, India
Tel.: (91) 1244867530
Rubber Product Distr
N.A.I.C.S.: 423840

JSR Elastomer Korea Co., Ltd. (1)
Gwanghwamun Bldg 15th Floor 149 Sejong-daero, Jongno-gu, Seoul, 110-730, Korea (South)
Tel.: (82) 23992731
Rubber Product Distr
N.A.I.C.S.: 423840

JSR Electronic Materials Korea Co., Ltd. (1)
Samwhan HIPEX A-610 240, Pangyoyeok-ro Bundanggu, Seongnam, 13493, Gyeonggi, Korea (South)
Tel.: (82) 316984420
Semiconductor Material Distr
N.A.I.C.S.: 423690

JSR Engineering Co., Ltd. (1)
100 Kawajiri-cho, Yokkaichi, 510-0871, Mie, Japan (100%)
Tel.: (81) 593458100
Web Site: http://www.j-eng.jsr.co.jp
Emp.: 190
Engineeering Services
N.A.I.C.S.: 541330
Etsuo Noda *(Pres)*

JSR Life Sciences Corporation (1)
25 Miyukigaoka, Tsukuba, 305-0841, Ibaraki, Japan
Tel.: (81) 298561106
Research & Development Services
N.A.I.C.S.: 541714

JSR Logistics & Customer Center Co., Ltd. (1)
100 Kawajiri-cho, Yokkaichi, 510-8552, Mie Prefecture, Japan
Tel.: (81) 593566652
Logistics Management Services
N.A.I.C.S.: 541614

JSR Micro (Changshu) Co., Ltd. (1)
No 101 Changchun Rd, Riverside Industrial Park Economic Development Zone, Changshu, Jiangsu, China
Tel.: (86) 51252648000
Display Material Mfr
N.A.I.C.S.: 334419

Subsidiary (US):

PreClinOmics, Inc. (2)
7918 Zionville Rd, Indianapolis, IN 46278
Tel.: (317) 872-6001
Research & Development in Biotechnology
N.A.I.C.S.: 541714

JSR Micro Kyushu Co., Ltd. (1)
1580-1 Kamiizumi Kuboizumi-cho, Saga, 849-0902, Japan (100%)
Tel.: (81) 952983001

JSR Corp.—(Continued)
Web Site: https://www.jmq.jsr.co.jp
Emp.: 120
Semiconductors Mfr for Flat Panel Displays
N.A.I.C.S.: 334413

JSR Optech Tsukuba Co., Ltd. (1)
57-1 Sawabe Tsuchiura, Ibaraki, 300-4104, Japan **(100%)**
Tel.: (81) 298625781
Web Site: http://www.jsrot.co.jp
Sales Range: $25-49.9 Million
Emp.: 50
Optical Fiber Coating Materials Mfr
N.A.I.C.S.: 326199
Takashi Ukachi (Pres)

JSR Trading (Shanghai) Co., Ltd. (1)
603 SMEG Plaza 1386 Hongqiao Road, Shanghai, 200051, China
Tel.: (86) 2162953340
Emp.: 20
Chemical Products Distr
N.A.I.C.S.: 424690
Oyanage Keiya (Mgr)

JSR Trading Bangkok Co., Ltd. (1)
163 Thai Samut Bldg 17th Floor Room 17C Surawongse Road, Suriyawongse Bangrak, Bangkok, 10500, Thailand
Tel.: (66) 22367291
Chemical Products Distr
N.A.I.C.S.: 424690

JSR Trading Co., Ltd. (1)
Shiodome City Center 9F Reception 8F 1-5-2 Higashi Shimbashi, Minato-ku, Tokyo, 105-7109, Japan **(100%)**
Tel.: (81) 362183800
Web Site: https://eneos-materials-trading.com
Chemicals, Machinery, Household Products, Food & Beverage Distr
N.A.I.C.S.: 424690

JSR Trading Vietnam Co., Ltd. (1)
1713 Skyline Service Office Prime Centre Building, 53 Quang Trung Street Hai Ba Trung District, Hanoi, Vietnam
Tel.: (84) 2473000072
Rubber Product Distr
N.A.I.C.S.: 423840

JSRT Mexico S.A. de C.V. (1)
Rio San Lorenzo No 619 Modulo 1, Parque Tecnoindustrial Castro del Rio, 36810, Irapuato, Guanajuato, Mexico
Tel.: (52) 4626074929
Rubber Product Distr
N.A.I.C.S.: 423840

Japan Butyl Co., Ltd. (1)
10-3 Ukishimacho, Kawasaki-ku, Kawasaki, 210-0862, Kanagawa, Japan **(50%)**
Tel.: (81) 442887351
Web Site: http://www.j-butyl.co.jp
Sales Range: $50-74.9 Million
Emp.: 177
Butyl Rubber Production & Sales
N.A.I.C.S.: 326299

Japan Coloring Co., Ltd. (1)
4-6 Tomarikoyanagicho, Yokkaichi, 510-0883, Mie, Japan **(75%)**
Tel.: (81) 593467161
Web Site: https://www.japan-coloring.co.jp
Emp.: 270
Synthetic Resin Coloring & Colored Products Mfr
N.A.I.C.S.: 325130
Junpei Sako (Pres)

Kumho Polychem Co., Ltd. (1)
8F East Wing Signature Tower 100 Cheonggyecheon-ro, Jung-gu, Seoul, Korea (South) **(50%)**
Tel.: (82) 269613750
Web Site: https://www.polychem.co.kr
Emp.: 226
Rubber Production & Sales
N.A.I.C.S.: 325212
Sungyu Kim (CEO)

Kyushu Gomu Kako Co., Ltd. (1)
1250 Murata-cho, Tosu, Saga, 841-0072, Japan **(99.77%)**
Tel.: (81) 942834696
Web Site: http://www.jsr.co.jp
Crude Rubber Compounding & Sales
N.A.I.C.S.: 325212

LEXI Co., Ltd. (1)
2-11-1 Sugamo, Toshima-ku, Tokyo, 170-0002, Japan
Tel.: (81) 353944833
Web Site: https://www.lexi.co.jp
Medical Device Distr
N.A.I.C.S.: 423450
Zen Komiya (Pres)

MBL Beijing Biotech Co., Ltd. (1)
Room 1606 16th Floor Xueyuan International Building No 1 Zhichun Road, Haidian District, Beijing, 100191, China
Tel.: (86) 1082899503
Web Site: http://www.mbl-chinawide.cn
In-Vitro Diagnostics Mfr
N.A.I.C.S.: 325413

MBL Hangzhou Biotech Co., Ltd. (1)
501F No 22 XinYan Road, Yuhang Economic and Technological Development Zone Yuhang District, Hangzhou, Zhejiang, China
Tel.: (86) 57186108768
Web Site: http://www.mbl-h.com
Diagnostics Material Mfr
N.A.I.C.S.: 325413

Medical & Biological Laboratories Co., Ltd. (1)
Sumitomo Fudosan Shiba Daimon 2-chome Building 2-11-8 Shiba Daimon, Minato-ku, Tokyo, 105-0012, Aichi, Japan **(100%)**
Tel.: (81) 366846860
Web Site: https://www.mbl.co.jp
Sales Range: $50-74.9 Million
Emp.: 474
Medical & Biological Products Whslr
N.A.I.C.S.: 325413
Kimimasa Yamada (Pres & CEO)

Subsidiary (Domestic):

G&G Science Co., Ltd. (2)
4-1-1 Misato Matsukawa-Cho, Fukushima, 960-1242, Japan
Tel.: (81) 245372350
Web Site: https://www.gandgscience.co.jp
Gene Diagnostic Research & Development Services
N.A.I.C.S.: 541715

Glyence Co., Ltd. (2)
407 Ikou-renkei Incubator 2-22-8 Chikusa, Chikusa-ku, Nagoya, 464-0858, Japan
Tel.: (81) 52 745 7377
Web Site: http://www.glyence.com
Biotechnology Research & Development Services
N.A.I.C.S.: 541714
Uichiro Yabe (Pres)

MBL Venture Capital Co., Ltd. (2)
Ogawa Bldg 2F 1-2-2 Uchikanda, Chiyoda-ku, Tokyo, 101-0047, Japan
Tel.: (81) 332948880
Web Site: http://www.mblvc.co.jp
Investment Management Service
N.A.I.C.S.: 523940

Subsidiary (US):

MBL-BION (2)
455 State St Ste 100, Des Plaines, IL 60016
Tel.: (847) 635-9732
Pharmaceutical Product Mfr & Whslr
N.A.I.C.S.: 325412
Melinda Ascher (COO)

PT. Elastomix Indonesia (1)
Jl Mitra Raya Selatan III Blok H-8 Desa Parungmulya Kec, Ciampel, Karawang, Indonesia
Tel.: (62) 2678638110
Rubber Product Distr
N.A.I.C.S.: 423840

Rapithela Corporation (1)
93-1 Kano, Okegawa, 363-0001, Saitama, Japan
Tel.: (81) 487833579
Computer System Design Services
N.A.I.C.S.: 541512

Selexis SA (1)
Route de la Galaise 36, 1228, Plan-les-Ouates, Switzerland
Tel.: (41) 223089360
Web Site: http://www.selexis.com
Biopharmaceutical Product Mfr
N.A.I.C.S.: 325412
J. D. Mowery (CEO)

Techno Polymer Guangzhou Co., Ltd. (1)
Room 4104 China Shine Plaza 3-15 Linhe Xi Road, Guangzhou, 510075, China
Tel.: (86) 20 3810 3655
Web Site: http://www.techpo.co.jp
Polymer Resin Mfr
N.A.I.C.S.: 325211

Techno Polymer Shanghai Technical Development Co., Ltd. (1)
207 Zhongqing Road, Maqiao Minhang, Shanghai, 201111, China
Tel.: (86) 21 5457 3262
Plastic Polymer Mfr
N.A.I.C.S.: 325211

Techno-UMG Co., Ltd. (1)
Shiodome Sumitomo Building 22F 1-9-2 Higashi-Shimbashi, Minato, Tokyo, 105-0021, Japan **(51%)**
Tel.: (81) 362183880
Web Site: https://www.t-umg.com
Styrene Resin Mfr & Whslr
N.A.I.C.S.: 325211
Masaaki Mori (Exec VP)

Subsidiary (Non-US):

Techno-UMG (Shanghai) Co., Ltd. (1)
Room 2507-08 The Place Tower A 100 Zunyi Road, Shanghai, 200051, China
Tel.: (86) 2162953327
Web Site: http://www.t-umg.com
Synthetic Resin Sales
N.A.I.C.S.: 424690

Subsidiary (US):

Techno-UMG America, Inc. (2)
5405 Dupont Cir Ste E, Milford, OH 45150
Tel.: (513) 248-2033
Web Site: http://www.t-umg.com
Plastics Sales & Services
N.A.I.C.S.: 424610

Subsidiary (Non-US):

Techno-UMG Asia Co., Ltd. (2)
968 28th Floor U-Chuliang Foundation Building Rama 4 Road silom, Bangkok, 10500, Thailand
Tel.: (66) 26367569
Web Site: http://www.t-umg.com
Sales Range: $25-49.9 Million
Emp.: 20
Synthetic Resin Sales
N.A.I.C.S.: 424690
Takao Nagai (Mng Dir)

Techno-UMG Hong Kong Co., Ltd. (2)
Room 1002 10/F Tower 2 Lippo Centre 89 Queensway, Admiralty, Kowloon, China (Hong Kong)
Tel.: (852) 25217622
Web Site: http://www.t-umg.com
Chemical & Allied Products Merchant Whslr
N.A.I.C.S.: 424690
Louis Lo (Mng Dir)

Techno-UMG Shanghai Technical Center Co., Ltd. (2)
207 Zhongqing Road Maqiao, Minhang, Shanghai, 201111, China
Tel.: (86) 21 5457 3262
Synthetic Resin Research & Development
N.A.I.C.S.: 541715

Techno-UMG Europe GmbH (1)
Berliner Allee 29, 40212, Dusseldorf, Germany
Tel.: (49) 21154235720
Rubber Product Distr
N.A.I.C.S.: 423840

Tianjin Kuo Cheng Rubber Industry Co., Ltd. (1)
No 28 Jinkaido, Jinghai Economic Development Zone, Tianjin, China
Tel.: (86) 2259792025
Web Site: https://ja.tjguocheng.com
Rubber Product Mfr & Distr
N.A.I.C.S.: 326220

JSS CORPORATION
9F Kincho Tosabori Building 1-4-11 Tosabori, Nishi-ku, Osaka, 550-0001, Japan
Tel.: (81) 664496121
Web Site: https://www.jss-group.co.jp
Year Founded: 1976
6074—(TKS)
Sales Range: $75-99.9 Million
Emp.: 511
Swimming Instruction & Swimming Products Sales
N.A.I.C.S.: 611699
Takao Fujiki (Pres & CEO)

JST TRANSFORMATEURS SA
84 avenue Paul Santy, 69008, Lyon, Cedex 08, France
Tel.: (33) 478778800
Web Site: https://www.jst-transformers.eu
Year Founded: 1917
Sales Range: $75-99.9 Million
Transformer Mfr
N.A.I.C.S.: 335311
Eric Lajus (Pres)

Subsidiaries:

American JST Corp. (1)
7301 Ranch Rd 620 N Ste 155-384, Austin, TX 78726
Tel.: (512) 968-4202
Web Site: http://www.american-jst.com
Emp.: 1
Transformer Whslr
N.A.I.C.S.: 423610
Scott Becker (VP)

JSTI GROUP CO., LTD.
No.8 East Funchunjiang Road, Jianye District, Nanjing, 210017, Jiangsu, China
Tel.: (86) 2586576555
Web Site: https://www.jsti.com
Year Founded: 1978
300284—(SSE)
Rev.: $726,240,330
Assets: $2,190,358,615
Liabilities: $989,638,354
Net Worth: $1,200,720,261
Earnings: $45,353,035
Fiscal Year-end: 12/31/23
Engineering Consulting Services
N.A.I.C.S.: 541330
Guanhua Fu (Chm)

JSW PACIFIC CORP.
3F-3 No 700 Zhongzheng Rd, Zhonghe Dist, New Taipei City, Taiwan
Tel.: (886) 282278582
Web Site: https://www.jswpac.com
5251—(TPE)
Rev.: $9,602,039
Assets: $17,515,680
Liabilities: $3,348,185
Net Worth: $14,167,495
Earnings: ($598,443)
Fiscal Year-end: 12/31/22
Electronic Components Mfr
N.A.I.C.S.: 334419

JSW STEEL LTD.
JSW Centre Bandra Kurla Complex Near MMRDA Grounds Bandra East, Mumbai, 400 051, India
Tel.: (91) 2242861000
Web Site: https://www.jsw.in
500228—(NSE)
Rev.: $10,342,080,000
Assets: $18,454,800,000
Liabilities: $13,411,440,000
Net Worth: $5,043,360,000
Earnings: $548,660,000
Emp.: 13,209
Fiscal Year-end: 03/31/20
Steel Products Mfr

AND PRIVATE COMPANIES   JTB CORP.

N.A.I.C.S.: 331210
Sajjan Jindal *(Co-Mng Dir)*

Subsidiaries:

Amba River Coke Limited (1)
JSW Centre Bandra Kurla Complex Bandra East, Mumbai, 400 051, India
Tel.: (91) 2242865114
Iron & Steel Product Mfr
N.A.I.C.S.: 331110

GSI Lucchini S.p.A (1)
Largo Caduti sul Lavoro 21, 57025, Piombino, LI, Italy
Tel.: (39) 056564661
Web Site: http://www.gsilucchini.it
Steel Products Mfr
N.A.I.C.S.: 331210

JSW Infrastructure Ltd. (1)
JSW Centre Bandra Kurla Complex, Mumbai, 400 051, India
Tel.: (91) 2242861000
Web Site: http://www.jsw.in
Transportation Terminal Construction Services
N.A.I.C.S.: 236220
N. K. Jain *(Chm)*

Subsidiary (Domestic):

Navkar Corporation Ltd. (1)
13 th Floor Goodwill Infinity Plot No E/3A Sector - 12, Kharghar, Navi Mumbai, 410 210, Maharashtra, India (70.4%)
Tel.: (91) 2248006500
Web Site: https://www.navkarcorp.com
Rev.: $91,987,609
Assets: $340,269,794
Liabilities: $92,511,210
Net Worth: $247,758,584
Earnings: $2,174,349
Emp.: 516
Fiscal Year-end: 03/31/2021
Marine Cargo Handling Services
N.A.I.C.S.: 488320
Shantilal J. Mehta *(Chm & Mng Dir)*

JSW Ispat Special Products Limited. (1)
Bandra Kurla Complex, Bandra, Mumbai, 400051, India
Tel.: (91) 2242861000
Web Site: https://www.aionjsw.in
Rev.: $273,379,194
Assets: $670,998,714
Liabilities: $428,071,944
Net Worth: $242,926,770
Earnings: $(509,391,216)
Emp.: 2,295
Fiscal Year-end: 03/31/2019
Minerals Product Mfr
N.A.I.C.S.: 327999
Ravichandar Moorthy Dhakshana *(Exec Dir)*

Subsidiary (Domestic):

MPDL Ltd. (2)
Monnet House 11 Masjid Moth, Greater Kailash Part - II, New Delhi, 110048, India
Tel.: (91) 1129223112
Web Site: https://www.monnetgroup.com
Rev.: $1,880,115
Assets: $23,944,344
Liabilities: $10,018,764
Net Worth: $13,925,580
Earnings: $(461,171)
Emp.: 11
Fiscal Year-end: 03/31/2023
Sugar Mfr
N.A.I.C.S.: 311813
Subhash Kumar Singh *(CFO)*

Monind Ltd. (2)
Urla Industrial Complex Plot No 216 Sector-C, Raipur, 493221, Chattisgarh, India
Tel.: (91) 1129218542
Web Site: http://www.monnetgroup.com
Rev.: $996
Assets: $3,700,925
Liabilities: $21,187,639
Net Worth: $(17,486,715)
Earnings: $233,947
Emp.: 2
Fiscal Year-end: 03/31/2021
Iron & Steel Products Mfr
N.A.I.C.S.: 331210
Mahesh Kumar Sharma *(CFO)*

Monnet Industries Ltd. (2)
Monnet House 11 Masjid Moth Greater Kailash Part-2, New Delhi, 110 048, India
Tel.: (91) 1129218542
Steel Products Mfr
N.A.I.C.S.: 331110

Rameshwaram Steel & Power Pvt. Ltd. (2)
Indira Chowk Bailadula, Raigarh, 496 001, Chhattisgarh, India
Tel.: (91) 9893629840
Sponge Iron Mfr
N.A.I.C.S.: 331110

JSW Steel Italy Piombino S.p.A. (1)
Largo Caduti sul Lavoro 21, 57025, Piombino, LI, Italy
Tel.: (39) 056564111
Iron & Steel Product Mfr
N.A.I.C.S.: 331110

JSW Steel USA Inc. (1)
5200 E McKinney Rd, Baytown, TX 77523 (100%)
Tel.: (281) 383-3300
Steel Pole Mfr
N.A.I.C.S.: 331210
Indresh Butra *(Pres)*

JT CORPORATION
135 4sandan 3-ro Jiksan-eup, Seobuk-gu, Cheonan, 31040, Chungcheongnam-do, Korea (South)
Tel.: (82) 7041720100
Web Site: http://www.jtcorp.co.kr
Year Founded: 1998
089790—(KRS)
Rev.: $62,785,710
Assets: $62,002,775
Liabilities: $20,122,766
Net Worth: $41,880,009
Earnings: $11,535,393
Emp.: 134
Fiscal Year-end: 12/31/22
Semiconductor Equipment Mfr
N.A.I.C.S.: 333242
Jun Yoo *(CEO)*

JTB CORP.
JTB Building 2-3-11 Higashi-Shinagawa Shinagawa-ku, Tokyo, 140-8602, Japan
Tel.: (81) 57023489
Web Site: http://www.jtb.co.jp
Year Founded: 1912
Emp.: 29,153
Travel Agency
N.A.I.C.S.: 561510
Hiromi Tagawa *(Chm)*

Subsidiaries:

City Circle UK Ltd. (1)
4 Millington Road, Hyde Park Hayes, Hayes, UB3 4AZ, Middlesex, United Kingdom
Tel.: (44) 20 8561 2112
Web Site: http://www.citycircleuk.com
Emp.: 40
Travel Tour Operator Service
N.A.I.C.S.: 561520
Neil Pegg *(Mng Dir)*

Dynasty Travel International Pte. Ltd. (1)
35 New Bridge Road Dynasty Travel Hub, Singapore, Singapore
Tel.: (65) 6532 3833
Web Site: http://www.dynastytravel.com.sg
Travel Agency
N.A.I.C.S.: 561510
Alicia Seah *(Dir-Mktg Comm)*

JCOM China Co., Ltd. (1)
Room3011 Chang Fu Gong Office Building No 26 Jian Guo Men Wai Avenue, Beijing, China
Tel.: (86) 10 6513 7078
Web Site: http://www.jcomchina.com
Travel Tour Operator
N.A.I.C.S.: 561520
Yamasaki Michinori *(Chm)*

JTB (GUANGZHOU) International Tours Co., LTD. (1)
RM923-924 Tower A China Shine Plaza No 9 LinHe West RD, Guangzhou, 510610, China
Tel.: (86) 20 3810 3181
Travel Agency
N.A.I.C.S.: 561510
Chen Liang *(Mgr)*

JTB (Hong Kong) Ltd (1)
Suites 710-716 7th Floor Wharf T&T Centre 7 Canton Road, Kowloon, China (Hong Kong)
Tel.: (852) 2731 7166
Travel Tour Operator
N.A.I.C.S.: 561520

JTB (Thailand) Limited (1)
54 Harindhorn Building 4th Fl room 4B North Sathorn Road Silom, Bangrak, Bangkok, Thailand
Tel.: (66) 2 3444600
Web Site: http://www.jtbthailand.com
Travel Agency
N.A.I.C.S.: 561510
Tsuyoshi Matsuda *(Sr Mgr)*

JTB Americas, Ltd. (1)
19700 Mariner Ave, Torrance, CA 90503
Tel.: (310) 303-3750
Web Site: http://www.jtbamericas.com
Travel Tour Operator
N.A.I.C.S.: 561520
Jun Takeda *(Gen Mgr)*

Subsidiary (Domestic):

JTB Hawaii, Inc. (2)
818 Pine St, Honolulu, HI 96817
Tel.: (808) 397-5000
Web Site: http://www.jtb-hawaii.com
Emp.: 650
Travel Agency
N.A.I.C.S.: 561510
Tsukasa Harufuku *(Pres & CEO)*

Subsidiary (Domestic):

JTB Hawaii Travel, LLC (3)
2155 Kalakaua Ave 9th Fl, Honolulu, HI 96815
Tel.: (808) 922-0200
Travel Agency
N.A.I.C.S.: 561510
Masato Tezuka *(Pres)*

Tachibana Enterprises, LLC (3)
735 Iwilei Rd Ste 330, Honolulu, HI 96817
Tel.: (808) 738-3000
Web Site: http://www.tachibana.com
Travel Tour Operator
N.A.I.C.S.: 561520
Tatsuo Watanabe *(Pres)*

Subsidiary (Non-US):

JTB International (Canada), Ltd. (1)
8899 Odlin Crescent, Richmond, V6X 3Z7, BC, Canada
Tel.: (604) 276-0300
Web Site: http://www.jtb.ca
Emp.: 57
Travel Tour Operator
N.A.I.C.S.: 561520
Nobuo Watanabe *(Pres)*

Subsidiary (Domestic):

TPI Travel (Canada), Ltd. (3)
8899 Odlin Cres, Richmond, V6X 3Z7, BC, Canada
Tel.: (604) 276-2221
Travel Tour Operator
N.A.I.C.S.: 561520

Subsidiary (Domestic):

Lassen Tour & Travel, Inc. (2)
391 Sutter St Ste 504, San Francisco, CA 94108
Tel.: (415) 421-2171
Web Site: http://www.lassentours.com
Emp.: 42
Travel Agency
N.A.I.C.S.: 561510
Jack Swen *(Pres)*

Sunrise Plaza Transportation of Nevada, Co. (2)
4047 Ponderosa Way, Las Vegas, NV 89118
Tel.: (702) 732-0456
Travel Tour Operator
N.A.I.C.S.: 561520

JTB Australia Pty. Ltd. (1)
Level 18 456 Kent Street, Sydney, 2000, NSW, Australia
Tel.: (61) 2 9510 0100
Web Site: http://www.jtbaustralia.com.au
Emp.: 70
Travel Tour Operator
N.A.I.C.S.: 561520
Toshiya Yamada *(Mgr-Div)*

JTB Europe Ltd (1)
Horatio House 77-85 Fulham Palace Road, London, W6 8JA, United Kingdom
Tel.: (44) 20 8237 1600
Web Site: http://www.jtb-europe.com
Travel Tour Operator
N.A.I.C.S.: 561520

JTB Germany GmbH (1)
Rossmarkt 15, 60311, Frankfurt am Main, Germany
Tel.: (49) 69 921877 20
Web Site: http://www.jtbgermany.com
Travel Agency
N.A.I.C.S.: 561510

JTB Greece Ltd. (1)
4 Filellinon street, Syntagma, Athens, 10557, Attica, Greece
Tel.: (30) 210 3215835
Web Site: http://www.jtb.gr
Emp.: 11
Travel Agency
N.A.I.C.S.: 561510
George Karagiannis *(Gen Mgr)*

JTB India Private Limited (1)
406 4th Floor Sewa Corporate Park MG Road, Gurgaon, 122001, Haryana, India
Tel.: (91) 124 449 7750
Web Site: http://www.jtb-india.com
Emp.: 24
Travel Agency
N.A.I.C.S.: 561510
Norio Nakamura *(Pres & CEO)*

JTB Italy srl (1)
Piazza San Bernardo 106, 00187, Rome, Italy
Tel.: (39) 06 4890 4745
Web Site: http://www.viaggigiappone.com
Travel Agency
N.A.I.C.S.: 561510
Christian Fiorentino *(Mgr-Pur & Booking Team)*

JTB New Zealand Ltd (1)
Level 5 191 Queen street, PO Box 4345, Auckland, New Zealand
Tel.: (64) 9 309 7696
Web Site: http://www.jtbtravel.co.nz
Emp.: 31
Travel Agency
N.A.I.C.S.: 561510

JTB Pte. Ltd. (1)
2 Orchard Turn B4-29 ION Orchard, Singapore, 238801, Singapore
Tel.: (65) 6595 0600
Web Site: http://www.jtb.com.sg
Travel Agency
N.A.I.C.S.: 561510
Fong Chan *(Mgr)*

JTB Switzerland S.A. (1)
3F Rue De Lausanne 69, 1202, Geneva, Switzerland
Tel.: (41) 22 7163 405
Travel Tour Operator
N.A.I.C.S.: 561520

JTB Taiwan Ltd. (1)
1F No 56 Sec 2 Zhongshan N Rd, Zhongshan Dist, Taipei, 00104, Taiwan
Tel.: (886) 22568 2111
Web Site: http://www.jtbtaiwan.com
Travel Agency
N.A.I.C.S.: 561510

JTB USA (1)
810 7th Ave 34th Fl, New York, NY 10019
Tel.: (212) 698-4900
Package, Convention, Group & Individual Tours
N.A.I.C.S.: 561510

JTB CORP.

INTERNATIONAL PUBLIC

JTB Corp.—(Continued)

JTB Viajes Spain, S.A. (1)
Santa Engracia 151, Madrid, 28003, Spain (100%)
Tel.: (34) 915931400
Web Site: http://www.jpak.es
Sales Range: $25-49.9 Million
Emp.: 11
Tour Operating Services
N.A.I.C.S.: 561520
Takagi Toru *(Gen Mgr)*

Japan Travel Bureau (Malaysia) Sdn. Bhd. (1)
Unit 16 05-16 07 Level 16 Amoda Building 22 Jalan Imbi, 55100, Kuala Lumpur, Malaysia
Tel.: (60) 3 2141 9991
Web Site: http://www.jtbmalaysia.com
Travel Tour Operator
N.A.I.C.S.: 561520

Kuoni Global Travel Services AG (1)
Elias-Canetti-Strasse 2, 8050, Zurich, Switzerland (100%)
Tel.: (41) 443252111
Web Site: http://www.kuoniglobaltravelservices.com
Group Travel Arrangement & Reservation Services
N.A.I.C.S.: 561599
Reto Wilhelm *(CEO)*

Subsidiary (Non-US):

Kuoni Destination Management A/S (2)
Amager Strandvej 60 1 Floor, DK-2300, Copenhagen, Denmark
Tel.: (45) 70232321
Web Site: http://www.kuoniglobaltravelservices.com
Tour Operating Services
N.A.I.C.S.: 561520
Carsten Jensen *(Mgr)*

Kuoni Destination Management B.V. (2)
Eurocenter II Barbara Strozzilaan 384, 1083 HN, Amsterdam, Netherlands
Tel.: (31) 207184655
Web Site: http://www.kuoni-meetings-events.com
Tour Operating Services
N.A.I.C.S.: 561520
Maxime Toldre *(Mgr)*

Kuoni Destination Management Ges.m.b.H (2)
Lerchenfelder Gurtel 43 A, 1160, Vienna, Austria
Tel.: (43) 1 319 76 90
Web Site: http://www.kuoni-meetings-events.com
Travel & Tour Operating Services
N.A.I.C.S.: 561510
Andreas Scholten *(Country Mgr)*

Kuoni Destination Management S.L. (2)
Calle Virgen de los Peligros 3 1, 28013, Madrid, Spain
Tel.: (34) 915245660
Web Site: http://www.kuoni-meetings-events.com
Tour Operating Services
N.A.I.C.S.: 561520
Carlos Sabate *(Mgr)*

Kuoni Destination Management S.p.A. (2)
Viale Castro Pretorio 124 1, 00185, Rome, Italy
Tel.: (39) 0649227700
Web Site: http://www.kuoni-meetings-events.com
Tour & Travel Operating Services
N.A.I.C.S.: 561520

Subsidiary (US):

Kuoni Holding Delaware, LLC (2)
5 Penn Plz Fl 5, New York, NY 10001
Tel.: (212) 596-1000
Web Site: http://www.kuoniglobaltravelservices.com
Investment Management Service
N.A.I.C.S.: 523999
Melissa Wakeford *(Partner-HR Bus)*

My Bus (Italy) s.r.l. (1)
Via Vittorio Emanuele Orlando 73, 00185, Rome, Italy
Tel.: (39) 06 482 5560
Travel Tour Operator
N.A.I.C.S.: 561520

OY Tumlare Corporation AB (1)
Kalevankatu 20, 00100, Helsinki, Finland
Tel.: (358) 9 622 6650
Travel Tour Operator
N.A.I.C.S.: 561520

PT. JTB Indonesia (1)
Jl Bypass Ngurah Rai No 88 Lelan Abian, Kuta, 80363, Bali, Indonesia
Tel.: (62) 6272 9159
Travel Tour Operator
N.A.I.C.S.: 561520
Eiji Imamiya *(Mgr-Sls)*

Star Holiday Mart Pte Ltd (1)
Blk 203 Henderson Industrial Park 02-04, Singapore, 159546, Singapore
Tel.: (65) 6735 9009
Web Site: http://www.starmart.com.sg
Travel Agency
N.A.I.C.S.: 561510
Michael Chong *(Bus Mgr-Global)*

Tour East Singapore (1996) Pte Ltd (1)
1 Magazine Road 07-05/06 Central Mall Office Tower, Singapore, 059567, Singapore
Tel.: (65) 6735 1221
Web Site: http://www.toureast.net
Tour Operator
N.A.I.C.S.: 561520
Shigeyuki Suzuki *(Pres & CEO)*

Subsidiary (Non-US):

Tour East (2009) Sdn Bhd (2)
Unit 10 05-10 06 10th Fl Amoda 22 Jalan Imbi, 55100, Kuala Lumpur, Malaysia
Tel.: (60) 327100108
Web Site: http://www.toureast.net
Sales Range: $25-49.9 Million
Emp.: 11
Travel Tour Operating Agencies
N.A.I.C.S.: 561520
Stephen Chan *(Gen Mgr)*

Tour East (Hong Kong) Limited (2)
Suites 805-806 8th Floor World Finance Centre South Tower Harbour City, Tsimshatsui, Kowloon, China (Hong Kong)
Tel.: (852) 23663111
Tour Operator Services
N.A.I.C.S.: 561520

Tour East Australia Pty Limited (2)
Suite 2 Level 2 189 Kent St, Sydney, 2000, NSW, Australia
Tel.: (61) 283145800
Web Site: http://www.toureast.com.au
Travel Tour Operating Agency Services
N.A.I.C.S.: 561520
Dennis Choo *(Mng Dir)*

Travel Plaza (Europe) B.V. (1)
Eurocenter II Barbara Strozzilaan 384 11th floor, 1083 HN, Amsterdam, Netherlands
Tel.: (31) 20 71 47 700
Web Site: http://www.travelplaza-europe.com
Travel Tour Operator
N.A.I.C.S.: 561520
Jarmaine Maduro Rib *(Asst Mgr-Fin)*

JTB FRANCE S.A.S.

29 Rue du Louvre, 75002, Paris, France
Tel.: (33) 155316666
Web Site: http://www.jtb.fr
Rev.: $37,300,000
Emp.: 49
Travel Services
N.A.I.C.S.: 561520
Isabelle Besnier *(Mgr-Personnel)*

JTC GROUP HOLDINGS LTD.

JTC House 28 Esplanade, PO Box 1075, E9 Castle Street, Saint Helier, Jersey
Tel.: (44) 1534 700 000
Web Site: http://www.jtcgroup.com
Year Founded: 1987
Financial Services
N.A.I.C.S.: 523999
Nigel Anthony Le Quesne *(Chm & CEO)*

Subsidiaries:

JTC (BVI) Limited (1)
80 Main Street, PO Box 3200, Road Town, VG1110, Tortola, Virgin Islands (British)
Tel.: (284) 8525850
Financial Investment Services
N.A.I.C.S.: 523999

JTC (Cayman) Limited (1)
94 Solaris Avenue 2nd Floor, PO Box 30745, Camana Bay, KY1-1203, Cayman Islands
Tel.: (345) 9497212
Financial Investment Services
N.A.I.C.S.: 523999

JTC (Luxembourg) SA (1)
17 Boulevard FW Raiffeisen, L-2411, Luxembourg, Luxembourg
Tel.: (352) 27172807
Financial Investment Services
N.A.I.C.S.: 523999
Joost Mees *(Mng Dir)*

JTC (Malta) Limited (1)
Suite 5 Level 3 Fafner House National Road, Valletta, HMR 9011, Malta
Tel.: (356) 22479000
Financial Investment Services
N.A.I.C.S.: 523999
Nadine Cachia *(Mng Dir)*

JTC (Suisse) SA (1)
Esplanade de Pont-Rouge 9, Case Postale 3023, Grand-Lancy, 1212, Geneva, Switzerland
Tel.: (41) 225963300
Financial Investment Services
N.A.I.C.S.: 523999
Matthias Belz *(Mng Dir)*

JTC (UK) Limited (1)
The Scalpel 18th Floor 52 Lime Street, Mayfair, London, EC3M 7AF, United Kingdom
Tel.: (44) 2074090181
Financial Investment Services
N.A.I.C.S.: 523999
Will Cameron *(Mng Dir)*

JTC Administration (UK) Limited (1)
3500 Parkway, Fareham, Whiteley, PO15 7AL, Hampshire, United Kingdom
Tel.: (44) 1489555910
Financial Investment Services
N.A.I.C.S.: 523999
Will Cameron *(Gen Mgr)*

JTC Fund Managers (Guernsey) Limited
Frances House Sir William Place, PO Box 156, Saint Peter Port, London, GY1 4EU, Guernsey Channel Isl, United Kingdom
Tel.: (44) 1481 702 400
Financial Investment Services
N.A.I.C.S.: 523999
Adam Moorshead *(Grp Dir-Institutional Client Svcs)*

JTC Group (NZ) Limited (1)
400 Lake Road, Takapuna, Auckland, 0622, New Zealand
Tel.: (64) 93370965
Financial Investment Services
N.A.I.C.S.: 523999

JTC PLC

JTC House 28 Esplanade, PO Box 1075, Saint Helier, JE4 2QP, Jersey
Tel.: (44) 1534700000
Web Site: https://www.jtcgroup.com
Year Founded: 1987
JTC—(LSE)
Rev.: $252,505,680
Assets: $853,186,064
Liabilities: $347,989,144
Net Worth: $505,196,920
Earnings: $43,819,742
Emp.: 1,291
Fiscal Year-end: 12/31/22
Financial And Investment Advisor
N.A.I.C.S.: 523940
Nigel Le Quesne *(CEO)*

Subsidiaries:

INDOS Financial (Ireland) Limited (1)
Kelly Building Slaney Place, Enniscorthy, Wexford, Ireland
Tel.: (353) 539276860
Financial Investment Services
N.A.I.C.S.: 523999

INDOS Financial Limited (1)
The Scalpel 18th Floor 52 Lime Street, London, EC3M 7AF, United Kingdom
Tel.: (44) 2038762218
Web Site: https://www.indosgroup.com
Emp.: 50
Investment Fund Services
N.A.I.C.S.: 525910

JTC (Netherlands) B.V. (1)
Locatellikade 1 11th Floor, 1076 AZ, Amsterdam, Netherlands
Tel.: (31) 204212700
Trust & Fiduciary Services
N.A.I.C.S.: 523991
Eke Verbeke *(Mng Dir)*

JTC Corporate Services (DIFC) Limited (1)
Office 18-4 Central Park Towers Dubai International Finance Centre, PO Box 24075, Dubai, United Arab Emirates
Tel.: (97.1) 44471170
Financial Banking Services
N.A.I.C.S.: 523150

JTC Corporate Services (Ireland) Limited (1)
45 Mespil Road Dublin 4, Dublin, D04 W2F1, Ireland
Tel.: (353) 15848480
Fund Asset Services
N.A.I.C.S.: 525910

JTC Fund Solutions (Guernsey) Limited (1)
Ground Floor Dorey Court Admiral Park, Saint Peter Port, GY1 2HT, Guernsey
Tel.: (44) 1481702400
Fund Administration Services
N.A.I.C.S.: 524292
Chris Corcoran *(Dir-Fund Svcs)*

JTC Fund Solutions (Ireland) Limited (1)
45 Mespil Road Dublin 4, Dublin, D04 W2F1, Ireland
Tel.: (353) 15848450
Fund Asset Services
N.A.I.C.S.: 525910

JTC Fund Solutions RSA (Pty) Ltd. (1)
Block B Century Falls Century Boulevard, Century City, Milnerton, 7441, South Africa
Tel.: (27) 215294860
Financial Investment Services
N.A.I.C.S.: 523999
Elize Bland *(Dir-Fund Svcs)*

JTC Trust Company (South Dakota) Ltd. (1)
140 N Phillips Ave Ste 301, Sioux Falls, SD 57104
Tel.: (605) 864-4490
Financial Investment Services
N.A.I.C.S.: 523999

JTC Trustees (Suisse) Sarl (1)
Esplanade de Pont-Rouge 9, Grand-Lancy, 1212, Geneva, Switzerland
Tel.: (41) 225963300
Trust & Fiduciary Services
N.A.I.C.S.: 523991
Matthias Belz *(Mng Dir)*

JTC Trustees (USA) Ltd. (1)
140 N Phillips Ave Ste 301, Sioux Falls, SD 57104
Tel.: (605) 864-4490
Trust & Fiduciary Services
N.A.I.C.S.: 523991
Michelle Le Herissier *(Mng Dir)*

SALI Fund Management, LLC (1)
6850 Austin Ctr Blvd Ste 300, Austin, TX 78731

AND PRIVATE COMPANIES

Tel.: (512) 735-7254
Web Site: https://www.sali.com
Financial Investment Services
N.A.I.C.S.: 523999

TC3 Group Holdings LLC (1)
309 S Phillips Ave Ste 200, Sioux Falls, SD 57104
Tel.: (605) 338-9170
Web Site: http://www.sdtrustco.com
Sales Range: $1-9.9 Million
Emp.: 5
Trust, Fiduciary & Custody Activities
N.A.I.C.S.: 523991
Pierce H. McDowell III *(Owner)*

perFORM Due Diligence Services Limited (1)
The Scalpel 18th Floor 52 Lime Street, London, EC3M 7AF, United Kingdom
Tel.: (44) 2037468974
Web Site: https://performdd.com
Financial Investment Services
N.A.I.C.S.: 523999

JTEC CORPORATION
10F KPP Yaesu Bldg 1-10-7 Kyobashi, Chuo-ku, Tokyo, 104-0031, Japan
Tel.: (81) 362287273
Web Site: https://www.j-tec-cor.co.jp
Year Founded: 1996
2479—(TKS)
Rev.: $21,420,542
Assets: $13,610,832
Liabilities: $5,668,978
Net Worth: $7,941,854
Earnings: $1,076,974
Fiscal Year-end: 03/31/24
Software Development Services
N.A.I.C.S.: 513210
Takashi Tsumura *(Founder & Pres)*

JTEKT CORPORATION
1-1 Asahi-machi, Chuo-ku, Kariya, 448-8652, Aichi, Japan
Tel.: (81) 566257211 JP
Web Site: https://www.jtekt.co.jp
Year Founded: 1935
6473—(NGO)
Rev.: $12,032,306,820
Assets: $10,334,515,350
Liabilities: $5,310,245,400
Net Worth: $5,024,269,950
Earnings: $245,758,920
Emp.: 46,053
Fiscal Year-end: 03/31/23
Ball & Roller Bearings, Steering Systems & Machine Parts Mfr for Automobile Production
N.A.I.C.S.: 332991
Hiroyuki Kaijima *(Exec VP)*

Subsidiaries:

Daibea Co., Ltd. (1)
594 1157 Osaka Prefecture Ayumino 2 chrome 8 No 1, Izumi, 594-1157, Osaka, Japan
Tel.: (81) 725531711
Web Site: http://www.daibea.co.jp
Rev.: $234,165,600
Assets: $218,288,160
Liabilities: $110,387,280
Net Worth: $107,900,880
Earnings: $6,544,560
Emp.: 570
Fiscal Year-end: 03/31/2018
Automotive Bearing Mfr
N.A.I.C.S.: 332991

Dalian Koyo Wazhou Automobile Bearing Co., Ltd. (1)
No 96 Liaohe East Road Double D Port, Dalian, Liaoning, China
Tel.: (86) 41187407272
Automotive Hub Bearing Mfr
N.A.I.C.S.: 336330

Fuji Kiko Co., Ltd. (1)
2028 Washizu, Kosai, 431-0431, Shizuoka, Japan
Tel.: (81) 53 575 2711
Web Site: https://www.fujikiko-group.com
Emp.: 3,015
Seat Belts, Steering Columns & Suspension Parts Mfr
N.A.I.C.S.: 336360
Etsutaka Ogusu *(VP)*

Subsidiary (US):

Douglas Autotech Corporation (2)
300 Albers Rd, Bronson, MI 49028-1239
Tel.: (517) 369-2315
Web Site: http://www.douglasautotech.com
Motor Vehicle Parts Mfr
N.A.I.C.S.: 336390

Subsidiary (Non-US):

Fuji Autotech (Thailand) Co.,Ltd. (2)
300/16 M1 Tasit Pluak-dang, Rayong, 21140, Thailand
Tel.: (66) 33 010 741
Web Site: http://www.fath.co.th
Automobile Steering Parts Mfr
N.A.I.C.S.: 336330

Fuji Autotech AB (2)
Svista, PO Box 534, SE-631 07, Eskilstuna, Sweden
Tel.: (46) 10 602 36 00
Web Site: http://www.fujiautotech.com
Motor Vehicle Parts Mfr
N.A.I.C.S.: 336390
Marten Svensson *(Pres)*

Fuji Autotech France S.A.S. (2)
97 Rue du 17 Novembre-Mandeure, 25708, Valentigney, Cedex, France
Tel.: (33) 381364300
Emp.: 500
Motor Vehicle Parts Mfr
N.A.I.C.S.: 336390

Subsidiary (Domestic):

Fuji Kiko Autotech Tokai Co., Ltd. (2)
26 Hama, Gamagori, 443-0036, Japan
Tel.: (81) 533663262
Web Site: http://www.fujikiko-group.com
Automobile Parts Mfr
N.A.I.C.S.: 336110

Plant (Domestic):

Fuji Kiko Co., Ltd - Honjo Factory (2)
2-7 Imaidai, Honjo, 367-0058, Saitama, Japan
Tel.: (81) 495211461
Web Site: http://www.fujikiko-group.com
Heavy Duty Vehicle Parts Mfr
N.A.I.C.S.: 336390

Fuji Kiko Co., Ltd - Washizu Factory (2)
2028 Washizu, Kosai, 431-0431, Shizuoka, Japan
Tel.: (81) 535752711
Web Site: http://www.fujikiko-group.com
Automobile Parts Mfr
N.A.I.C.S.: 336390

Subsidiary (Non-US):

Fuji Koyo Czech s.r.o. (2)
Podnikatelska 1144/8, 301 00, Plzen, Czech Republic
Tel.: (420) 37 801 1111
Web Site: https://www.fujikoyo.cz
Motor Vehicle Parts Mfr
N.A.I.C.S.: 336390
Miroslav Balin *(VP)*

P.T. Autotech Indonesia (2)
Kawasan Industri Kota Bukit Indah Blok D-3 No 2, Purwakarta, 41181, West Java, Indonesia
Tel.: (62) 264 351015
Web Site: http://www.fujikiko-group.com
Automobile Steering Parts Mfr
N.A.I.C.S.: 336330

Houko Co., Ltd. (1)
1-3 Hishiike Ejiri, Kota-cho, Nukata, 444-0113, Aichi, Japan
Tel.: (81) 56 462 1211
Web Site: https://www.houko.co.jp
Emp.: 290
CNC Grinder Mfr
N.A.I.C.S.: 332721

JTEKT Automotive Tennessee-Vonore, Co. (1)
55 Excellence Way, Vonore, TN 37885
Tel.: (423) 884-9200
Web Site: http://www.jtekt.co.jp
Sales Range: $50-74.9 Million
Emp.: 500
Mfr of Automotive Parts
N.A.I.C.S.: 336330

JTEKT Corporation (1)
1-1 Asahi-machi, Kariya, 448-8652, Aichi, Japan
Tel.: (81) 56 625 7211
Web Site: https://www.jtekt.co.jp
Sales Range: $500-549.9 Million
Emp.: 2,000
Mfr of Machine Tools & Auto Parts
N.A.I.C.S.: 333517
Katsumi Yamamoto *(Sr Exec Dir)*

JTEKT North America, Inc. (1)
47771 Halyard Dr, Plymouth, MI 48170-2479
Tel.: (734) 454-1500
Web Site: https://jtekt-na.com
Sales Range: $25-49.9 Million
Emp.: 125
Mfr of Steering Systems
N.A.I.C.S.: 336330
Koichi Yamanaka *(Pres & CEO)*

Jtekt (China) Co., Ltd. (1)
Web Site: http://www.jtekt.com.cn
Emp.: 242
Machine Tools Mfr
N.A.I.C.S.: 333517
Shuji Tateishi *(Chm)*

Jtekt (Thailand) Co., Ltd. (1)
172/1 Moo 12 Tambol Bangwua, Amphur Bangpakong, Chachoengsao, 24130, Thailand
Tel.: (66) 38531988
Steering Product Mfr & Distr
N.A.I.C.S.: 336330

Jtekt Asia Pacific Co., Ltd. (1)
172/2 Moo 12 Tambol Bangwua, Amphur, Bangkok, 24130, Chachoengsao, Thailand
Tel.: (66) 33051851
Web Site: https://www.jtekt-asia-pacific.com
Emp.: 178
Bearing Mfr & Distr
N.A.I.C.S.: 332991

Jtekt Automotiva Brasil Ltda. (1)
Av Volkswagen Audi1 200 -Campo Largo da Roseira, Sao Jose dos Pinhais, 83090-680, PR, Brazil
Tel.: (55) 4121028100
Web Site: http://www.jtekt.com.br
Automotive Products Mfr
N.A.I.C.S.: 327910

Jtekt Automotive (Thailand) Co., Ltd. (1)
107 Moo 4 Tambol Pluakdaeng Amphur, Pluakdaeng, Rayong, 21140, Thailand
Tel.: (66) 38954320
Power Steering Pump Mfr & Distr
N.A.I.C.S.: 333996

Jtekt Automotive (Tianjin) Co., Ltd. (1)
No 16 2nd XingHua Branch Road, XiQing Economic Development Area, Tianjin, 300385, China
Tel.: (86) 2283989580
Steering Gear Product Mfr
N.A.I.C.S.: 336330

Jtekt Automotive (Wuxi) Co., Ltd. (1)
B6-A, New District, Wuxi, 214028, Jiangsu, China
Tel.: (86) 51085330909
Ball Bearing Mfr & Distr
N.A.I.C.S.: 332991

Jtekt Automotive Argentina S.A. (1)
Avenida de los Inmigrantes 1301, 1625, Escobar, Buenos Aires, Argentina
Tel.: (54) 3484435700
Steering Product Mfr & Distr

Jtekt Automotive Czech Pardubice, s.r.o. (1)
U Panasonicu 273, Stare Civice, 530 06, Pardubice, Czech Republic

JTEKT CORPORATION

Tel.: (420) 723698800
Web Site: http://www.jtekt-pa.com
Car Transmission Mfr
N.A.I.C.S.: 327910

Jtekt Automotive Czech Plzen, s.r.o. (1)
Folmavska 37/1152, 301 00, Plzen, Czech Republic
Tel.: (420) 378011011
Web Site: http://www.jtekt.cz
Car Steering Product Mfr
N.A.I.C.S.: 336330

Jtekt Automotive Dijon Saint-Etienne S.A.S. (1)
Avenue de Strasbourg ZAC Excellence 2000, 21800, Chevigny-Saint-Sauveur, France
Tel.: (33) 380695600
Steering Product Mfr
N.A.I.C.S.: 336330

Jtekt Automotive England Ltd. (1)
Elmhirst Lane, PO Box 101, Dodworth, Barnsley, S75 3TA, South Yorkshire, United Kingdom
Tel.: (44) 1226733200
Power Steering Pump Mfr & Distr
N.A.I.C.S.: 336330

Jtekt Automotive Lyon S.A.S. (1)
ZI Rue du Broteau, CS 70001, 69540, Lyon, France
Tel.: (33) 472394444
Steering Product Mfr
N.A.I.C.S.: 336330

Jtekt Automotive Mexico, S.A. de C.V. (1)
Avendia Montecillo 100, Parque Industrial Colinas de san Luis Villa de Pozos, 78423, San Luis Potosi, Mexico
Tel.: (52) 4448807600
Torque-Sensing Gear Mfr
N.A.I.C.S.: 334519

Jtekt Automotive North America, Inc. (1)
7 Research Dr, Greenville, SC 29607
Tel.: (864) 770-2100
Web Site: http://www.jtekt-na.com
Bearing Mfr
N.A.I.C.S.: 332991
Koichi Yamanaka *(Pres & CEO)*

Jtekt Automotive Science & Technology Center (Dalian) Co., Ltd. (1)
Rm 701-D NO 12 Building No 21 Software Park Road East, Dalian, Liaoning, China
Tel.: (86) 41184755121
Automotive Products Mfr
N.A.I.C.S.: 336390
Koichi Sugiyama *(Chm)*

Jtekt Automotive South Carolina Inc. (1)
1866 Old Grove Rd, Piedmont, SC 29673
Tel.: (864) 277-0400
Automotive Product Mfr & Distr
N.A.I.C.S.: 336390

Jtekt Automotive Tennessee-Morristown, Inc. (1)
5932 Commerce Blvd, Morristown, TN 37814
Tel.: (423) 585-0999
Power Steering Pump Mfr & Distr
N.A.I.C.S.: 333996

Jtekt Automotive Texas, L.P. (1)
4400 Sterilite Dr, Ennis, TX 75119
Tel.: (972) 878-1800
Steering Product Mfr
N.A.I.C.S.: 336330
Mary Durham *(Pres)*

Jtekt Automotive UK Ltd. (1)
Neath Vale Supplier Park Resolven, Neath, SA11 4SP, West Glamorgan, United Kingdom - Wales
Tel.: (44) 1639713100
Power Steering Pump Mfr & Distr
N.A.I.C.S.: 333996

Jtekt Bearings (Dalian) Co., Ltd. (1)
No 2A-2 Dalian Export Processing Zone A, Dalian, 116600, Liaoning, China
Tel.: (86) 41187310972
Small Ball Bearing Mfr & Distr

JTEKT CORPORATION

JTEKT Corporation—(Continued)
N.A.I.C.S.: 332991

Jtekt Bearings Canada Inc. (1)
4 Victoria Street, Bedford, J0J-1A0, QC, Canada
Tel.: (450) 248-3316
Bearing Mfr & Distr
N.A.I.C.S.: 332991

Jtekt Bearings Czech Republic s.r.o. (1)
Pavelkova 253/5, Bystrovany, 77900, Olomouc, Czech Republic
Tel.: (420) 585126501
Bearing Mfr & Distr
N.A.I.C.S.: 332991

Jtekt Bearings Deutschland GmbH (1)
Werkstrasse 5, Halle Westfalen, D-33790, Halle, Germany
Tel.: (49) 52017070
Bearing Mfr & Distr
N.A.I.C.S.: 332216

Jtekt Bearings India Private Limited (1)
Plot No 8 Phase-3 Sector-8 HSIIDC, Bawal, Rewari, 123 501, Haryana, India
Tel.: (91) 1284263100
Bearing Mfr & Distr
N.A.I.C.S.: 332991

Jtekt Bearings Korea Co., Ltd. (1)
37 Hyeongok Sandan-ro Cheongbuk-eup, Pyeongtaek, Gyeonggi-do, Korea (South)
Tel.: (82) 316120800
Water Pump Bearing Mfr & Distr
N.A.I.C.S.: 332991

Jtekt Bearings North America LLC (1)
7 Research Dr, Greenville, SC 29607
Tel.: (864) 770-2100
Bearing Mfr & Distr
N.A.I.C.S.: 332991

Jtekt Bearings(Wuxi) Co., Ltd. (1)
No 32 Xiangge Road, Hudai Town Binhu District, Wuxi, 214161, Jiangsu, China
Tel.: (86) 51068789186
Ball Bearing Mfr & Distr
N.A.I.C.S.: 332991

Jtekt Brasil Ltda. (1)
Av Volkswagen Audi 1 200-Campo Largo da Roseira, Sao Jose dos Pinhais, 83090-680, PR, Brazil
Tel.: (55) 4121028100
Web Site: https://www.jtekt.com.br
Steering Product Mfr & Distr
N.A.I.C.S.: 336330

Jtekt Czech Republic s.r.o. (1)
Folmavska 37/1152, 30100, Plzen, Czech Republic
Tel.: (420) 378011011
Web Site: https://www.jtekt.cz
Emp.: 900
Steering Products Mfr & Distr
N.A.I.C.S.: 336330

Jtekt Dalian Innovation Automotive Co., Ltd. (1)
No 48 Dalian Economic and Technological Development Zone, Dalian, Liaoning, China
Tel.: (86) 41187338553
Automobile Product Distr
N.A.I.C.S.: 441330
Shuji Tateishi (Chm)

Jtekt Europe Bearings B.V. (1)
Markerkant 13-01, 1314 AL, Almere, Netherlands
Tel.: (31) 36 538 3333
Web Site: https://www.koyo.eu
Machine Tools Mfr
N.A.I.C.S.: 333517
Frank Bush (Mng Dir)

Jtekt Hpi S.A.S. (1)
ZI - 26 rue Condorcet, BP 87, 94432, Chennevieres sur Marne, Cedex, France
Tel.: (33) 14 962 2800
Web Site: https://hpi-eu.com
Hydraulic Components Mfr
N.A.I.C.S.: 333996
Alain Brignou (Pres)

Jtekt IT Center Akita Corporation (1)
4-2-7 Nakadori Nihon Seimei Akita Chuodori Building 3F, Akita, 010-0001, Japan
Tel.: (81) 18 827 6767
Web Site: https://www.jtekt-ita.com
Emp.: 59
Electronic Control Equipment Mfr & Distr
N.A.I.C.S.: 336320

Jtekt Korea Co., Ltd. (1)
13F Seong-do Bldg 207 Dosan-daero, Gangnam-gu, Seoul, 06026, Korea (South)
Tel.: (82) 25497922
Bearing Distr
N.A.I.C.S.: 423840

Jtekt Latin America, S.A. (1)
Ave Aquilino de la Guardia and Calle 52 Banco de Pacifico Building, Panama, Panama
Tel.: (507) 2085900
Web Site: https://koyola.com.pa
Automotive Bearings Mfr & Distr
N.A.I.C.S.: 332991

Jtekt Lioho Automotive (Foshan) Co., Ltd. (1)
No 12 Wusha Section Of Shunpan Road Shunde Industrial Park, Daliang Town Shunde, Foshan, Guandong, China
Tel.: (86) 75722802015
Automobile Parts Mfr & Distr
N.A.I.C.S.: 332991

Jtekt Machinery (Dalian) Co., Ltd. (1)
No 2 Fuan Street Dalian Economic and Technological Development Zone, Dalian, 116600, China
Tel.: (86) 41187334601
Bearing Machine Tool Mfr & Distr
N.A.I.C.S.: 332991

Jtekt Machinery (Thailand) Co., Ltd. (1)
313 Debaratna Road Km 1 Kwang Bangna Nuea, Khet Bangna, Bangkok, 10260, Thailand
Tel.: (66) 236182501
Web Site: https://www.jtekt-machinery.co.th
Bearing Mfr & Distr
N.A.I.C.S.: 332991

Jtekt Machinery Americas Corporation (1)
316 W University Dr, Arlington Heights, IL 60004
Tel.: (847) 253-0340
Web Site: https://jtektmachinery.com
Bearing Machine Tool Mfr & Distr
N.A.I.C.S.: 332991

Jtekt Machinery Europe S.A.S. (1)
Office 2 Grande Allee PA des Petits Carreaux, 94380, Bonneuil-sur-Marne, France
Tel.: (33) 149568580
Electronic Component & Process Control Equipment Mfr & Distr
N.A.I.C.S.: 334519

Jtekt Philippines Corporation (1)
Block 15 Lot 1 Main Boulevard Corner Jose P Rizal Avenue, Lima Technology Center Brgy Malvar, Santo Tomas, 4233, Batangas, Philippines
Tel.: (63) 439810088
Steering Product Mfr
N.A.I.C.S.: 336330

Jtekt Research & Development Center (Wuxi) Co., Ltd. (1)
No 1082 Qianhu Road, Hudai Town Binhu District, Wuxi, 214161, Jiangsu, China
Tel.: (86) 51085898615
Steering Product Mfr
N.A.I.C.S.: 336330
Kazuhiro Takai (Pres)

Jtekt Sales Australia Pty. Ltd. (1)
Unit1 /17 Stanton Road, Seven Hills, 2147, NSW, Australia
Tel.: (61) 287195300
Bearing Mfr & Distr
N.A.I.C.S.: 332991

Jtekt Sales Canada Inc. (1)
3800A Unit5 Laird Road, Mississauga, L5L 0B2, ON, Canada
Tel.: (905) 681-1121
Bearing Mfr & Distr

Jtekt Sales Deutschland GmbH (1)
Bischofstrasse 118, 47809, Krefeld, Germany
Tel.: (49) 21515188300
Web Site: https://toyoda-europe.com
Automobile Parts Mfr & Distr
N.A.I.C.S.: 336390

Jtekt Sales France S.A. (1)
1 rue Francois Jacob, 92500, Rueil-Malmaison, France
Tel.: (33) 141398000
Bearing Mfr & Distr
N.A.I.C.S.: 332216

Jtekt Sales Middle East Fzco (1)
6EA 619 Dubai Airport Free Zone, PO Box 54816, Dubai, United Arab Emirates
Tel.: (971) 42993600
Web Site: https://jtekt.ae
Automotive Steering System Mfr & Distr
N.A.I.C.S.: 336330

Jtekt Sales Uk Ltd. (1)
Whitehall Avenue, Kingston, Milton Keynes, MK10 0AX, United Kingdom
Tel.: (44) 1908289300
Automotive Bearings Mfr & Distr
N.A.I.C.S.: 332991

Jtekt Steering Systems (Xiamen) Co., Ltd. (1)
No 90 Xiyuan Road, Xinyang Industrial Area Haicang District, Xiamen, Fujian, China
Tel.: (86) 5926530888
Steering Gear Product Mfr
N.A.I.C.S.: 336330

Jtekt Torsen Europe S.A. (1)
Rue du Grand Peuplier 11, Parc Industriel de Strepy-Bracquegnies, La Louviere, Belgium
Tel.: (32) 64672211
Automotive Product Mfr & Distr
N.A.I.C.S.: 336390

Jtekt Torsen North America, Inc. (1)
2 Jet View Dr, Rochester, NY 14624-4904
Tel.: (585) 464-5000
Web Site: https://torsen.com
Torque-Sensing Gear Mfr & Distr
N.A.I.C.S.: 334519

Jtekt Ventas Mexico S.A. De C.V. (1)
Av Radial Toltecas No 1197, Bodega 30 Fraccionamiento Industrial Tlaxcolpan, 54030, Tlalnepantla, Mexico
Tel.: (52) 5552073860
Web Site: https://www.jtektventas.com.mx
Automotive Bearings Mfr & Distr
N.A.I.C.S.: 332991

Jtekt Wazhou Automotive (Dalian) Co., Ltd. (1)
No 96 Liaohe East Road Double D Port, Dalian, 116600, Liaoning, China
Tel.: (86) 41187407272
Automotive Hub Bearing Mfr & Distr
N.A.I.C.S.: 332991

Kentucky Advanced Forge, LLC (1)
596 Triport Rd, Georgetown, KY 40324
Tel.: (502) 863-3646
Roller Bearing Mfr
N.A.I.C.S.: 332991
Tadashi Futamura (Principal)

Koyo (U.K.) Limited (1)
Whitehall Avenue, Kingston, Milton Keynes, MK10 0AX, United Kingdom
Tel.: (44) 190 828 9311
Web Site: https://www.koyo.co.uk
Roller Bearing Mfr
N.A.I.C.S.: 332991
Carl Mayes (Mng Dir)

Koyo Australia Pty. Ltd. (1)
Unit 1 17 Stanton Road, Seven Hills, Sydney, 2147, NSW, Australia
Tel.: (61) 28 719 5300
Web Site: https://www.koyoaust.com.au
Bearing Mfr
N.A.I.C.S.: 332991

Koyo Automotive Parts (Wuxi) Co., Ltd. (1)
B6-A National Hi-Tech Industrial Development Zone, Wuxi, 214142, Jiangsu, China

INTERNATIONAL PUBLIC

Tel.: (86) 51085330909
Ball Bearing Mfr
N.A.I.C.S.: 332991

Koyo Bearing Dalian Co., Ltd. (1)
IIA-2 A Zone Export Processing Zone, Dalian, Liaoning, China
Tel.: (86) 41187310972
Bearing Mfr
N.A.I.C.S.: 332991
Shuji Tateishi (Chm)

Koyo Bearings (Europe) Ltd. (1)
Elmhirst Lane, PO Box 101, Dodworth, Barnsley, S75 3TA, South Yorkshire, United Kingdom
Tel.: (44) 1226733200
Roller Bearing Mfr
N.A.I.C.S.: 332991
Masatomo Miyagi (Mng Dir)

Koyo Bearings Canada Inc. (1)
4 Victoria Street, Bedford, J0J-1A0, QC, Canada
Tel.: (450) 248-3316
Bearing Mfr & Distr
N.A.I.C.S.: 332991

Koyo Bearings Ceska republika s.r.o. (1)
Pavelkova 253/5, Bystrovany, 779 00, Olomouc, Czech Republic
Tel.: (420) 58 512 6501
Web Site: https://www.koyobearings.cz
Roller Bearing Mfr
N.A.I.C.S.: 332991

Koyo Bearings Deutschland GmbH (1)
Werkstrasse 5, Halle-Westfalen, 33790, Halle, Germany
Tel.: (49) 52017070
Roller Bearing Mfr
N.A.I.C.S.: 332991
Frank Bush (Mng Dir)

Koyo Bearings India Private Ltd. (1)
Plot No 8 Phase-III Sector-8 HSIIDC, Distt-Rewari, Bawal, 123501, Haryana, India
Tel.: (91) 1284263100
Bearing Mfr
N.A.I.C.S.: 332991

Koyo Bearings Vierzon Maromme SAS (1)
7 Rue Ampere, CS 21033, Zone Industrielle de la Maine, 76153, Maromme, France
Tel.: (33) 232823838
Roller Bearing Mfr
N.A.I.C.S.: 332991

Koyo Canada Inc. (1)
3800A Laird Road Units 4 and 5, Mississauga, L7L CB2, ON, Canada
Bearing Mfr
N.A.I.C.S.: 332991

Koyo Corporation of U.S.A. (1)
2850 Magnolia St, Orangeburg, SC 29116 (100%)
Tel.: (803) 536-6200
Web Site: http://www.koyousa.com
Sales Range: $250-299.9 Million
Emp.: 848
Mfr of Automotive Products
N.A.I.C.S.: 332991
Steve Mccullough (VP)

Koyo Corporation of U.S.A. (1)
29570 Clemmons Rd, Westlake, OH 44145-0028 (100%)
Tel.: (440) 835-1000
Web Site: http://www.koyousa.com
Sales Range: $25-49.9 Million
Emp.: 100
Sales of Ball & Roller Bearings
N.A.I.C.S.: 332991
Peter Marciniszyn (Mgr-Application Engrg)

Koyo Deutschland GmbH (1)
Bargkoppelweg 4, Hamburg, 22145, Germany
Tel.: (49) 406790900
Roller Bearing Mfr
N.A.I.C.S.: 332991
Hiroaki Hori (Mng Dir)

Koyo France S.A. (1)
1 rue Francois Jacob, 92500, Rueil-Malmaison, Cedex, France
Tel.: (33) 141398000

AND PRIVATE COMPANIES

Bearing Distr
N.A.I.C.S.: 327910
Frederic Delemasure *(Mng Dir)*

Koyo Iberica, S.L. (1)
Avenida de la Industria 52, 28823, Coslada, Spain
Tel.: (34) 913290818
Bearing Distr
N.A.I.C.S.: 423840

Koyo Italia S.r.l. (1)
Via G Stephenson 43/a, 20157, Milan, Italy
Tel.: (39) 0229510844
Roller Bearing Distr
N.A.I.C.S.: 327910
Luca Pipinato *(Mng Dir)*

Koyo Jico Korea Co., Ltd. (1)
464 Hyeongok-ri, Cheongbuk-myeon, Pyeongtaek, Gyeonggi-do, Korea (South)
Tel.: (82) 316120800
Water Pump Bearing Mfr
N.A.I.C.S.: 332991

Koyo Joint (Thailand) Co., Ltd. (1)
98 MOO1 Tambol Klong Prawet Amphur, Banpho, 24140, Chachoengsao, Thailand
Tel.: (66) 38 086 9115
Web Site: https://www.koyo.co.th
Machine Tools Mfr
N.A.I.C.S.: 333517
Taiichi Maeno *(Exec Dir)*

Koyo Kullager Scandinavia A.B. (1)
Kanalvagen 5A, 194 61, Upplands Vasby, Sweden
Tel.: (46) 859421210
Bearing Distr
N.A.I.C.S.: 423840

Koyo Kyuei Co., Ltd. (1)
5th Floor Jtect Building, Chuo-ku, Tokyo, 104-0061, Japan
Tel.: (81) 355378123
Web Site: http://www.koyo-qa.co.jp
Roller Bearing Distr
N.A.I.C.S.: 423840

Koyo Latin America, S.A. (1)
Ave Aquilino de la Guardia y Calle 52 Edificio Banco de Pacifico PB, Panama, Panama
Tel.: (507) 208 5900
Web Site: https://www.koyola.com.pa
Bearing Distr
N.A.I.C.S.: 327910

Koyo Lioho (Foshan) Automotive Parts Co., Ltd. (1)
No 12 Wushaduan Shunfan Road Daliang Street, Shunde District, Foshan, Guangdong, China
Tel.: (86) 75722802015
Automotive Bearing Mfr
N.A.I.C.S.: 327910

Koyo Machine Industries Co., Ltd. (1)
2-34 Minami Uematsu-Cho, Yao, 581-0091, Osaka, Japan
Tel.: (81) 72 922 7881
Web Site: https://www.koyo-machine.co.jp
Emp.: 3,761
Surface Grinding Machine Mfr
N.A.I.C.S.: 327910
Motoyasu Nakamura *(Chm)*

Koyo Mexicana, S.A. de C.V. (1)
Av Radial Toltecas No 1197 Bodega 30, Fraccionamiento Industrial Tlaxcolpan, 54030, Tlalnepantla, Mexico
Tel.: (52) 555 207 3860
Web Site: https://www.koyo.com.mx
Miniature Bearing Mfr
N.A.I.C.S.: 332991

Koyo Middle East Fzco (1)
6EA 615 Dubai Airport Free Zone, PO Box 54816, Dubai, United Arab Emirates
Tel.: (971) 4 299 3600
Web Site: https://www.koyo.ae
Ball Bearing Mfr
N.A.I.C.S.: 332991

Koyo Needle Bearings (Wuxi) Co., Ltd. (1)
No 32 Xiangge Road, Hudai Town Binhu District, Wuxi, Jiangsu, China
Tel.: (86) 51068789913
Roller Bearing Mfr

N.A.I.C.S.: 332991
Shuji Tateishi *(Chm)*

Koyo Nichijiku Co., Ltd. (1)
1-2-2 Takahama, Kokurakita-ku, Kitakyushu, 802-0021, Japan
Tel.: (81) 935410710
Web Site: http://www.koyo-njk.co.jp
Roller Bearing Mfr
N.A.I.C.S.: 332991

Koyo Rolamentos do Brasil Ltda. (1)
Avenida Piraporinha 251 Shed 04-Bairro, Planalto, Sao Bernardo do Campo, 09891-001, SP, Brazil
Tel.: (55) 113 372 7500
Web Site: https://www.koyo.com.br
Bearing Mfr
N.A.I.C.S.: 332991

Koyo Romania S.A. (1)
Str Dr Lister nr 24 apt 1 sector 5, 050543, Bucharest, Romania
Tel.: (40) 214104182
Bearing Distr
N.A.I.C.S.: 423840
Radu Hutan *(Mng Dir)*

Koyo Singapore Bearings (Pte) Ltd. (1)
24 Penjuru Road 01-01 CWT Commodity Hub, Singapore, 609128, Singapore
Tel.: (65) 6 274 2200
Web Site: https://www.koyo-sin.com.sg
Steering Product Mfr
N.A.I.C.S.: 336330

Koyo-Kowa Co., Ltd. (1)
Minatomachi Renaissance Namba Building 6th floor, Naniwa-ku, Osaka, 556-0017, Japan
Tel.: (81) 66 632 3601
Web Site: https://www.koyo-kowa.co.jp
Roller Bearing Mfr & Distr
N.A.I.C.S.: 332991

Koyometaltec Co., Ltd. (1)
1626 Sanagu-cho, Iga, 518-0001, Mie, Japan
Tel.: (81) 59 523 3285
Web Site: https://www.koyo-mt.com
Automobile Steering Parts Mfr
N.A.I.C.S.: 336330

Mechatronics Systems Wales Ltd. (1)
Penllergaer Business Park, Swansea, SA4 9HL, United Kingdom
Tel.: (44) 1792543000
Electronic Control Unit Power Pack Mfr
N.A.I.C.S.: 335999

Meiwa Shouko Co., Ltd. (1)
7-11-15 Ginza Jtect Building, Chuo-ku, Tokyo, Japan
Tel.: (81) 35 537 5871
Web Site: https://www.meiwa-shouko.co.jp
Roller Bearing Distr
N.A.I.C.S.: 423840

PT. Jtekt Indonesia (1)
Jl Surya Madya Plot I-27b Kawasan Industri Surya Cipta Kutanegara, Ciampel, Karawang, 41363, Jawa Barat, Indonesia
Tel.: (62) 2678610270
Steering Product Mfr
N.A.I.C.S.: 336330

Shizuoka Koyo Co., Ltd. (1)
1-5-12 Fujimi-cho, Iwata, 438-0083, Shizuoka, Japan
Tel.: (81) 538351434
Web Site: http://www.shizukoh.co.jp
Roller Bearing Distr
N.A.I.C.S.: 423840

Taiwan Jtekt Co., Ltd. (1)
No 23 Guangfu North Road, Hukou Township, Hsinchu, 303036, Taiwan
Tel.: (886) 35972453
Automobile Product Distr
N.A.I.C.S.: 441330

Toyoda Koki do Brasil Industria e Comercio de Maquinas, Ltda. (1)
Avenue Victory Rossi Martini 141, Dist Industria Vitoria Martini, Indaiatuba, 13347-613, SP, Brazil
Tel.: (55) 194 042 5450
Web Site: http://www.toyoda.com.br
Machine Tools Mfr

N.A.I.C.S.: 333517

Toyoda Machinery & Engineering Europe SAS (1)
2 Grande Allee PA des Petits Carreaux, 94380, Bonneuil-sur-Marne, France
Tel.: (33) 149568580
Machine Tools Mfr
N.A.I.C.S.: 333517

Toyoda Machinery S.E. Asia Co., Ltd. (1)
313 Bangna-Trad Road, Khet Bangna, Bangkok, 10260, Thailand
Tel.: (66) 2 361 8252
Web Site: http://www.toyoda-tmsea.com
Machine Tools Mfr
N.A.I.C.S.: 333517

Toyoda Machinery USA Corp. (1)
316 W University Dr, Arlington Heights, IL 60004
Tel.: (847) 253-0340
Web Site: http://www.toyodausa.com
Rev.: $107,672,000
Emp.: 150
Mfr of Machine Tools for Automotive Applications
N.A.I.C.S.: 333517
Jeff Biedka *(Controller)*

Toyoda Micromatic Machinery India Pvt.Ltd. (1)
M3M Cosmopolitan C-101-108 and 114-117 First Floor, Golf Course Extension Road Sector-66, Gurgaon, 122002, Haryana, India
Tel.: (91) 1244264602
Machine Tools Mfr
N.A.I.C.S.: 333517

Toyoda Van Moppes Ltd. (1)
1-54 Shiroyama Maigi-cho, Okazaki, 444-3594, Aichi, Japan
Tel.: (81) 56 448 5311
Web Site: https://www.tvmk.co.jp
CBN Tool Mfr
N.A.I.C.S.: 333514
Kazuo Tabuchi *(Pres)*

Toyooki Kogyo Co., Ltd. (1)
45 Kaizan, Hatchi -cho, Okazaki, 444-3592, Aichi, Japan
Tel.: (81) 56 448 2211
Web Site: https://www.toyooki.jp
Emp.: 450
Hydraulic & Pneumatic Equipment Mfr
N.A.I.C.S.: 333995

Utsunomiya Kiki Co., Ltd. (1)
585 Suzumenomiya-machi, Utsunomiya, 321-0121, Tochigi, Japan
Tel.: (81) 28 653 1311
Web Site: https://www.ukk-co.com
Emp.: 298
Roller Bearing Mfr
N.A.I.C.S.: 332991

Wuxi Koyo Bearing Co., Ltd. (1)
No 30 Xiangge Road, Hudai Town Binhu District, Wuxi, Jiangsu, China
Tel.: (86) 51085161901
Miniature Bearing Mfr
N.A.I.C.S.: 332991
Shuji Tateishi *(Chm)*

Yamato Seiko Co., Ltd. (1)
1354-4 Shimokagemori, Chichibu, 369-1871, Saitama, Japan
Tel.: (81) 49 423 6017
Web Site: https://www.yamatoseiko.co.jp
Temporary Staffing Services
N.A.I.C.S.: 561320

Yutaka High-Tech, Ltd. (1)
1-11-11 Yanagibashi Asakusa Bridge Yutaka High-Tech Building, Taito-ku, Tokyo, 111-0052, Japan
Tel.: (81) 33 861 7491
Web Site: https://www.yutaka-ht.co.jp
Machine Tools Mfr
N.A.I.C.S.: 333517

Yutaka Seimitsu Kogyo, Ltd. (1)
3-45 Akatsuki-cho, Seto, 489-8550, Aichi, Japan
Tel.: (81) 56 148 2221
Web Site: http://www.yutaka.co.jp
Machine Tools Mfr
N.A.I.C.S.: 333517

JTL INDUSTRIES LIMITED

JTEKT INDIA LIMITED
38/6 Delhi-Jaipur Road National Highway 48, Adjacent to Golf Course Extension Road, Gurgaon, 122001, Haryana, India
Tel.: (91) 1244685000
Web Site: https://www.jtekt.co.in
520057—(BOM)
Rev.: $218,267,063
Assets: $136,474,625
Liabilities: $46,211,324
Net Worth: $90,263,300
Earnings: $5,612,703
Emp.: 1,719
Fiscal Year-end: 03/31/22
Motor Vehicle Steering & Suspension Components Mfr
N.A.I.C.S.: 336330
Sudhir Chopra *(Vice Chm)*

Subsidiaries:

JTEKT SONA Automotive India Ltd. (1)
Plot No 26 Sector 5 Industrial Estate Phase II, Growth Center Bawal, Rewari, 123501, Haryana, India
Tel.: (91) 1284264114
Power Steering Products Mfr
N.A.I.C.S.: 336330
Rakesh Gaind *(Sr VP)*

SONA BLW Prazisionsschmiede GmbH (1)
Papenberger Strasse 37, 42859, Remscheid, Germany (100%)
Tel.: (49) 2191150
Web Site: http://www.sona-blw.com
Sales Range: $200-249.9 Million
Emp.: 600
Steel Mfrs
N.A.I.C.S.: 331513

JTF INTERNATIONAL HOLDINGS LIMITED
No 35 Yanjiang Road Shazhuang Tujiang Village Shitan Town, Zengcheng District, Guangzhou, Guangdong, China
Tel.: (86) 2082911968 Ky
Web Site: http://www.jtfoil.com
Year Founded: 2014
8479—(HKG)
Rev.: $313,065,790
Assets: $91,375,210
Liabilities: $32,138,249
Net Worth: $59,236,961
Earnings: $5,681,946
Emp.: 40
Fiscal Year-end: 12/31/21
Petroleum Product Distr
N.A.I.C.S.: 424720
Ziming Xu *(Chm)*

JTL INDUSTRIES LIMITED
SCO-18-19 Sector-28C, Chandigarh, 160002, India
Tel.: (91) 1724668000
Web Site: https://www.jtl.one
Year Founded: 1991
534600—(BOM)
Rev.: $212,237,885
Assets: $76,911,826
Liabilities: $21,340,942
Net Worth: $55,570,884
Earnings: $12,302,445
Emp.: 600
Fiscal Year-end: 03/31/23
Steel Pipe & Tube Mfr
N.A.I.C.S.: 331210
Vijay Singla *(Founder)*

Subsidiaries:

JTL INFRA LIMITED - Mohali Works (1)
Gholu Majra Chandigarh-Ambala Highwa, Distt Mohali, Dera Bassi, 140 506, Punjab, India
Tel.: (91) 9811400096
Steel Products Mfr

JTL INDUSTRIES LIMITED

JTL Industries Limited—(Continued)
N.A.I.C.S.: 331210

JTL INFRA LIMITED - Raipur Works (1)
8J34 447 Urla-Sarora Road Opposite CSEB Sub Station, Urla Industrial Complex Birgaon, Raipur, 492003, Chhattisgarh, India
Tel.: (91) 7713051700
Steel Products Mfr
N.A.I.C.S.: 331210
Uday Dhakad *(VP-Intl Bus)*

JTP CO., LTD.
14th floor Gotenyama Trust Tower
4-7-35 Kitashinagawa, Shinagawa-ku, Tokyo, 140-0001, Japan
Tel.: (81) 364082488
Web Site: https://www.jtp.co.jp
Year Founded: 1987
2488—(TKS)
Rev.: $55,726,550
Assets: $36,187,150
Liabilities: $14,012,800
Net Worth: $22,174,350
Earnings: $2,378,250
Emp.: 470
Fiscal Year-end: 03/31/23
Management Consulting Services
N.A.I.C.S.: 541618
Yutaka Mori *(Pres & CEO)*

Subsidiaries:

Huixintong (Tianjin) Information-Enterprise Co., Ltd. (1)
6-7-A Xinmaokejiyuan 15 Rongyuan Road Chanyequ, Huayuan, Tianjin, 300384, China
Tel.: (86) 2224156862
Information Technology Consulting Services
N.A.I.C.S.: 541512

JTP South Korea Co., Ltd. (1)
Jinsung-Bldg 6F 150 Samusung-Dong, Kangnam-Gu, Seoul, 135090, Korea (South)
Tel.: (82) 220883445
Information Technology Consulting Services
N.A.I.C.S.: 541512

Japan Third Party of America, Inc. (1)
3333 Bowers Ave, Santa Clara, CA 95054
Tel.: (408) 844-8812
Information Technology Consulting Services
N.A.I.C.S.: 541512

JU TENG INTERNATIONAL HOLDINGS LIMITED
Suites 3311-3312 Jardine House 1 Connaught Place, Central, China (Hong Kong)
Tel.: (852) 28400115
Web Site: http://www.juteng.com.hk
3336—(HKG)
Rev.: $1,052,633,243
Assets: $1,809,216,075
Liabilities: $860,196,983
Net Worth: $949,019,093
Earnings: $7,408,133
Emp.: 30,000
Fiscal Year-end: 12/31/22
Notebook Computer Casings Sale & Mfr
N.A.I.C.S.: 326121
Kuo-Kuang Huang *(Exec Dir)*

Subsidiaries:

Dynamic Apex Macao Commercial Offshore Limited (1)
Infante D Henrique 60-62 14th Fl Ed Commercial Central, Macau, China (Macau)
Tel.: (853) 28786835
Web Site: http://www.even-wongjuteng-into.com
Emp.: 3
Metals & Minerals Whslr
N.A.I.C.S.: 423520

Gi Li Co., Ltd. (1)
287-1 Min An Rd, Hsinchuang, 24257, Taipei, Taiwan
Tel.: (886) 222068818
Emp.: 50
Computer Casings Whslr
N.A.I.C.S.: 423430
Li Yu Cheng *(Pres)*

JUBILANT BHARTIA GROUP
1A Sector 16A, Noida, 201 301, India
Tel.: (91) 1204361000
Web Site: http://www.jubilantbhartia.com
Sales Range: $1-4.9 Billion
Emp.: 39,000
Holding Company
N.A.I.C.S.: 551112
Shyam S. Bhartia *(Co-Founder & Co-Chm)*

Subsidiaries:

Jubilant Biosys Limited (1)
96 Industrial Suburb 2nd Stage, Yeshwantpur, Bengaluru, 560 022, Karnataka, India
Tel.: (91) 8066628400
Web Site: http://www.jubilantbiosys.com
Pharmaceuticals Product Mfr
N.A.I.C.S.: 325412
Marcel J. Velterop *(Pres)*

Jubilant Chemsys Limited (1)
B-34 Sector-58, Noida, 201301, Uttar Pradesh, India
Tel.: (91) 1204093300
Web Site: http://www.jchemsys.com
Pharmaceuticals Product Mfr
N.A.I.C.S.: 325412
Vikas Shirsath *(Sr VP-Ops-Global)*

Jubilant Clinsys Inc. (1)
1 Crossroads Dr Ste 2A, Bedminster, NJ 07921-2688
Tel.: (908) 947-7777
Web Site: http://www.clinsys.com
Clinical Research Services
N.A.I.C.S.: 541715

Jubilant Clinsys Limited (1)
C-46 Sector 62, Noida, 201307, Uttar Pradesh, India
Tel.: (91) 1204364000
Agriculture Product Distr
N.A.I.C.S.: 424480

Jubilant Discovery Services Inc. (1)
365 Phoenixville Pike, Malvern, PA 19355
Tel.: (610) 240-8690
Clinical Research Services
N.A.I.C.S.: 541715

Jubilant Foodworks Limited (1)
5th Floor Tower D Plot No 5 Logix Techno Park Sector 127, Noida, 201 304, UP, India
Tel.: (91) 1204090500
Web Site: https://www.jubilantfoodworks.com
Rev.: $462,045,539
Assets: $514,165,484
Liabilities: $318,121,768
Net Worth: $196,043,716
Earnings: $31,466,212
Emp.: 36,001
Fiscal Year-end: 03/31/2021
Pizza Restaurant Owner & Operator
N.A.I.C.S.: 722513
Shyam S. Bhartia *(Co-Founder & Co-Chm)*

Subsidiary (Non-US):

DP Eurasia N.V. (2)
Herikerbergweg 238 Luna Arena, 1101 CM, Amsterdam, Netherlands **(54.67%)**
Tel.: (31) 205755600
Web Site: http://www.dpeurasia.com
Rev.: $138,167,928
Assets: $114,124,588
Liabilities: $112,279,887
Net Worth: $1,844,701
Earnings: ($14,585,027)
Emp.: 3
Fiscal Year-end: 12/31/2020
Restaurant Operators
N.A.I.C.S.: 722511
Peter Wodehouse Williams *(Chm)*

Jubilant FoodWorks Lanka (Pvt.) Ltd. (2)
No 164 Galle Road, Dehiwala-Mount Lavinia, 11091, Sri Lanka
Tel.: (94) 117777888
Web Site: http://www.pizaaonlinedominoslk.com
Sales Range: $10-24.9 Million
Emp.: 40
Fast Food Restaurant Operator
N.A.I.C.S.: 722513

Jubilant Industries INC. (1)
4515 Cantrell Rd, Flowery Branch, GA 30542
Tel.: (770) 965-0909
Clinical Research Services
N.A.I.C.S.: 541715

Jubilant Industries Ltd. (1)
1A Sector 16A, Noida, 201 301, Uttar Pradesh, India
Tel.: (91) 1204361000
Web Site: https://www.jubilantindustries.com
Rev.: $85,222,547
Assets: $58,733,630
Liabilities: $47,126,079
Net Worth: $11,607,551
Earnings: ($1,268,904)
Emp.: 4
Fiscal Year-end: 03/31/2021
Agricultural Products Mfr & Sales
N.A.I.C.S.: 111998
Umesh Sharma *(CFO)*

Jubilant Life Sciences (USA) Inc. (1)
790 Township Line Rd Ste 175, Yardley, PA 19067
Tel.: (215) 550-2810
Web Site: http://www.jubl.com
Pharmaceuticals Product Mfr
N.A.I.C.S.: 325412
Hari S. Bhartia *(Chm & Mng Dir)*

Jubilant Pharmaceuticals NV (1)
Guldensporenpark 22 block C, 9820, Merelbeke, Belgium
Tel.: (32) 92331404
Web Site: http://www.jubilant.be
Clinical Research Services
N.A.I.C.S.: 541715

Jubilant Pharmova Ltd. (1)
1A Sector 16A, Noida, 201 301, Uttar Pradesh, India
Tel.: (91) 1204361000
Web Site: https://www.jubilantpharmova.com
Rev.: $834,857,615
Assets: $1,217,322,015
Liabilities: $570,104,945
Net Worth: $647,217,071
Earnings: $114,060,902
Emp.: 36
Fiscal Year-end: 03/31/2021
Pharmaceutical Researcher, Developer & Mfr
N.A.I.C.S.: 325412
Shyam S. Bhartia *(Co-Chm)*

Subsidiary (US):

Cadista Holdings Inc. (2)
207 Kiley Dr, Salisbury, MD 21801 **(100%)**
Tel.: (410) 860-8500
Web Site: http://www.cadista.com
Rev.: $107,661,000
Assets: $138,103,000
Liabilities: $11,696,000
Net Worth: $126,407,000
Earnings: $29,924,000
Emp.: 277
Fiscal Year-end: 03/31/2014
Holding Company; Generic Pharmaceutical Products Developer, Mfr & Distr
N.A.I.C.S.: 551112
Scott B. Delaney *(Pres & CEO)*

Subsidiary (Domestic):

Jubilant Cadista Pharmaceuticals Inc. (3)
207 Kiley Dr, Salisbury, MD 21801 **(100%)**
Tel.: (410) 860-8500
Web Site: http://www.cadista.com
Sales Range: $100-124.9 Million
Emp.: 277
Generic Pharmaceutical Developer, Mfr & Distr
N.A.I.C.S.: 325412
Kamal Mandan *(CFO)*

Subsidiary (US):

Jubilant HollisterStier, LLC (2)
3525 N Regal St, Spokane, WA 99207-5788
Tel.: (509) 489-5656
Web Site: http://jublhs.com
Sales Range: $50-74.9 Million
Emp.: 500
Contract Pharmaceutical Mfr
N.A.I.C.S.: 325412
Mark Sassler *(Dir-Bus Dev-Contract Mfg & Svcs Div)*

Triad Isotopes, Inc. (1)
4205 Vineland Rd, Orlando, FL 32811
Tel.: (407) 455-6700
Web Site: http://www.triadisotopes.com
Radiopharmaceutical Supplier
N.A.I.C.S.: 456110

JUBILANT FLAME INTERNATIONAL, LTD.
Room 508 T1N Vi Par 360 Xin Long Road, Shanghai, 201103, China
Tel.: (86) 2164748888 NV
Year Founded: 2009
JFIL—(OTCQB)
Assets: $12,595
Liabilities: $1,309,508
Net Worth: ($1,296,913)
Earnings: ($67,365)
Emp.: 5
Fiscal Year-end: 02/29/24
Medical Products Marketer
N.A.I.C.S.: 424210
Yan Li *(Pres & CEO)*

JUBILANT INGREVIA LIMITED
1A Sector 16A, Noida, 201301, Uttar Pradesh, India
Tel.: (91) 1204361000
Web Site: https://www.jubilantingrevia.com
543271—(BOM)
Rev.: $582,494,351
Assets: $516,176,135
Liabilities: $193,028,816
Net Worth: $323,147,318
Earnings: $37,268,636
Emp.: 2,293
Fiscal Year-end: 03/31/23
Pharmaceuticals Mfr
N.A.I.C.S.: 325412
Rajesh Srivastava *(CEO & Mng Dir)*

JUBILEE ENTERPRISE PUBLIC COMPANY LIMITED
179 Bangkok City Tower 10 Fl South Sathorn Road Thungmahamek, Sathorn, Bangkok, 10120, Thailand
Tel.: (66) 26251111
Web Site: https://www.jubileediamond.co.th
JUBILE—(THA)
Rev.: $45,521,381
Assets: $62,259,090
Liabilities: $15,233,740
Net Worth: $47,025,350
Earnings: $5,932,378
Fiscal Year-end: 12/31/23
Jewelry & Diamond Distr
N.A.I.C.S.: 423940
Manu Leopairote *(Chm)*

JUBILEE GOLD EXPLORATION LTD.
696 Warden Av, Toronto, M1L 4W4, ON, Canada
Tel.: (416) 364-0042 ON
Year Founded: 2013
JUB—(TSXV)
Sales Range: Less than $1 Million
Gold Exploration Services
N.A.I.C.S.: 212220
Jeffrey J. Becker *(Pres, CEO & Sec)*

JUBILEE METALS GROUP PLC
1st Floor 7/8 Kendrick Mews, South

Kensington, London, SW7 3HG, United Kingdom
Tel.: (44) 2075842155
Web Site: https://www.jubileemetalsgroup.com
JLP—(AIM)
Rev.: $176,248,674
Assets: $372,713,852
Liabilities: $118,567,064
Net Worth: $254,146,788
Earnings: $16,106,146
Emp.: 874
Fiscal Year-end: 06/30/23
Other Metal Ore Mining
N.A.I.C.S.: 212290
Leon Coetzer *(CEO)*

Subsidiaries:

Braemore Resources Plc (1)
4th Fl 2 Cromwell Pl, London, SW7 2JE, United Kingdom
Tel.: (44) 2075842155
Web Site: http://www.jubileeplatinum.com
Sales Range: $25-49.9 Million
Emp.: 2
Metal Smelting & Refining Services
N.A.I.C.S.: 331410
Colin Baird *(Chm)*

Samancor Chrome Ltd. (1)
1st Floor Block A Cullinan Place Cullinan Close off Rivonia Road, Morningside, Sandton, 2196, South Africa
Tel.: (27) 11 245 1000
Web Site: https://samancorcr.com
Mining & Smelting Mfr
N.A.I.C.S.: 331410
Desmond McManus *(CEO)*

JUBILEE METALS GROUP PLC

Waltie van Rensburg 1st Floor 7 8 Kendrick Mews, South Kensington, London, SW7 3HG, United Kingdom
Tel.: (44) 2075842155
Web Site: http://www.jubileemetalsgroup.com
Metal Recovery, Natural Resources Eploration & Exploitation
N.A.I.C.S.: 212290
Leon Coetzer *(CEO)*

Subsidiaries:

Sable Zinc Kabwe Limited (1)
Plot 5066 Old ZCCM Site, PO Box 80012, Kabwe, Central Province, Zambia
Tel.: (260) 5224429
Copper & Cobalt Processing Services
N.A.I.C.S.: 212230
Mary Sakala *(Sec)*

JUBILEE SPINNING & WEAVING MILLS LTD.

503-E, Johar Town, Lahore, Pakistan
Tel.: (92) 4235173434
Web Site: https://www.jsw.com.pk
Year Founded: 1973
Rev.: $474,632
Assets: $5,874,637
Liabilities: $1,012,417
Net Worth: $4,862,220
Earnings: $207,436
Emp.: 4
Fiscal Year-end: 06/30/19
Textile Spinning Services
N.A.I.C.S.: 313110
Shams Rafi *(CEO)*

JUDGES SCIENTIFIC PLC

52C Borough High Street, London, SE1 1XN, United Kingdom
Tel.: (44) 2038296970 UK
Web Site: https://www.judges.uk.com
Year Founded: 2002
JDG—(AIM)
Rev.: $142,903,307
Assets: $234,520,323
Liabilities: $165,778,844
Net Worth: $68,741,479
Earnings: $16,125,978
Emp.: 595
Fiscal Year-end: 12/31/22
Scientific Instruments Designer & Mfr
N.A.I.C.S.: 334516
Alexander Robert Hambro *(Chm)*

Subsidiaries:

CoolLED Limited (1)
26 Focus Way, Andover, SP10 5NY, United Kingdom
Tel.: (44) 1264323040
Web Site: https://www.coolled.com
Lighting Equipment Mfr
N.A.I.C.S.: 335139
Lisa Cairns *(Mgr)*

Deben UK Limited (1)
Brickfields Business Park Old Stowmarket Road, Woolpit, Bury Saint Edmunds, IP30 9QS, Suffolk, United Kingdom
Tel.: (44) 1359244870
Web Site: https://deben.co.uk
Specimen Cooling Microscope Mfr
N.A.I.C.S.: 334516

Dia-Stron Inc. (1)
9 Trenton Lakewood Rd, Clarksburg, NJ 08510
Tel.: (609) 454-6008
Web Site: https://www.diastron.com
Automation Machinery Mfr
N.A.I.C.S.: 333248

Dia-Stron Limited (1)
Hikenield House East Anton Court, Icknield Way, Andover, SP10 5RG, Hampshire, United Kingdom
Tel.: (44) 1264334700
Web Site: https://www.diastron.com
Automation Machinery Mfr
N.A.I.C.S.: 333248

EWB Solutions Limited (1)
Units 18 and 19 Brickfield Industrial Estate Finway Road, Hemel Hempstead, HP2 7QA, Hertfordshire, United Kingdom
Tel.: (44) 144 226 3195
Web Site: https://www.ewbs.co.uk
Welding & Soldering Equipment Mfr
N.A.I.C.S.: 333992

Fire Testing Technology Limited (1)
Unit 19 Charlwoods Road, East Grinstead, RH19 2HL, West Sussex, United Kingdom
Tel.: (44) 134 232 3600
Web Site: https://www.fire-testing.com
Sales Range: $25-49.9 Million
Fire Testing Equipments Mfr
N.A.I.C.S.: 333415

Henniker Scientific Ltd. (1)
3 Berkeley Court Manor Park, Runcorn, WA7 1TQ, Cheshire, United Kingdom
Tel.: (44) 1925830771
Web Site: https://www.henniker-scientific.com
Plasma Treatment Equipment Mfr & Distr
N.A.I.C.S.: 339112

Moorfield Nanotechnology Limited (1)
Unit 1 Wolfe Close Parkgate Industrial Estate, Knutsford, WA16 8XJ, Cheshire, United Kingdom
Tel.: (44) 1565722609
Web Site: https://moorfield.co.uk
Physical & Chemical Deposition Mfr
N.A.I.C.S.: 325998

Oxford Cryosystems Ltd. (1)
25 Hanborough Business Park, Long Hanborough, Oxford, OX29 8LH, United Kingdom
Tel.: (44) 1993883488
Web Site: https://www.oxcryo.com
Scientific Instrument & Software Mfr
N.A.I.C.S.: 334516
Anthony Cooper *(Mng Dir)*

PE.fiberoptics Limited (1)
ROSA House, Mulberry Business Park, Wokingham, RG41 2GY, Berkshire, United Kingdom
Tel.: (44) 118 977 3003
Web Site: https://www.pefiberoptics.com
Emp.: 13
Fiber Optic Testing Equipment Mfr
N.A.I.C.S.: 334515

Sircal Instruments (U.K.) Limited (1)
Unit 19 Charlwoods Road, East Grinstead, RH19 2HL, West Sussex, United Kingdom
Tel.: (44) 1342335309
Web Site: https://sircal.co.uk
Air Purification Equipment Mfr & Distr
N.A.I.C.S.: 333413

Thermal Hazard Technology (1)
9 Trenton Lakewood Rd, Clarksburg, NJ 08510
Tel.: (609) 454-6062
Web Site: https://www.thermalhazardtechnology.com
Specialised Calorimeters Mfr
N.A.I.C.S.: 334516

UHV Design Limited (1)
Judges House Lewes Road, Laughton, Lewes, BN8 6BN, East Sussex, United Kingdom
Tel.: (44) 132 381 1188
Web Site: https://www.uhvdesign.com
Sales Range: $25-49.9 Million
Scientific Instrument Mfr
N.A.I.C.S.: 334511

JUDO CAPITAL HOLDINGS LIMITED

Level 26 Queen and Collins 376-390 Collins Street, Melbourne, 3000, VIC, Australia
Tel.: (61) 135836 AU
Web Site: https://www.judo.bank
Year Founded: 2016
JDO—(ASX)
Rev.: $170,017,561
Assets: $7,213,372,374
Liabilities: $6,137,181,900
Net Worth: $1,076,190,474
Earnings: ($5,899,663)
Emp.: 465
Fiscal Year-end: 06/30/22
Holding Company
N.A.I.C.S.: 551112
Chris Bayliss *(Deputy CEO)*

Subsidiaries:

Judo Bank Pty. Ltd. (1)
Level 4 28 Margaret St, Sydney, 2000, NSW, Australia
Tel.: (61) 1300363992
Financial Services
N.A.I.C.S.: 522220

JUEWEI FOOD CO., LTD.

Room 1608 Evening Newspaper Building No 267 Wanbao Avenue, Furong District, Changsha, 410016, Hunan, China
Tel.: (86) 73189842956
Web Site: http://www.juewei.cn
Year Founded: 2008
603517—(SHG)
Rev.: $929,846,708
Assets: $1,242,437,438
Liabilities: $276,216,530
Net Worth: $966,220,908
Earnings: $32,647,984
Fiscal Year-end: 12/31/22
Snack Food Mfr & Distr
N.A.I.C.S.: 311919
Wenjun Dai *(Chm & Gen Mgr)*

JUFEEL INTERNATIONAL GROUP

85 Jinshui East Road 19 Fl Bld 3, Yabao East international Sq, Zhengzhou, 450003, Henan, China
Tel.: (86) 371 53626656 WY
Year Founded: 2010
CNJG—(OTCIQ)
Sales Range: $10-24.9 Million
Holding Company
N.A.I.C.S.: 551112
Rongxuan Zhang *(Founder, Pres & CEO)*

JUGGERNAUT EXPLORATION LTD.

300 - 1055 West Hastings Street, Vancouver, V6E 2E9, BC, Canada
Tel.: (604) 559-8028 BC
Web Site: https://www.juggernautltd.com
Year Founded: 2006
4JE1—(DEU)
Rev.: $50,825
Assets: $8,754,824
Liabilities: $385,874
Net Worth: $8,368,950
Earnings: ($4,985,685)
Fiscal Year-end: 09/30/23
Mineral Exploration Services
N.A.I.C.S.: 212290
Daniel Stuart *(Pres & CEO)*

JUGOAGENT J.S.C.

Bulevar Mihaila Pupina 165a, 11070, Novi Beograd, Serbia
Tel.: (381) 11 20 18 700
Web Site: http://www.jugoagent.net
Year Founded: 1947
Emp.: 108
Transportation Services
N.A.I.C.S.: 488999
Milan Marjanovic *(Chm)*

JUGOCENTAR A.D.

Palmira Toljatija 7, Belgrade, Serbia
Tel.: (381) 11 2692 200
Year Founded: 1990
Sales Range: Less than $1 Million
Emp.: 16
Grocery Store Operator
N.A.I.C.S.: 445110

JUGODRVO HOLDING A.D.

Omlidinskih brigada 86, Novi Beograd, Serbia
Tel.: (381) 11 205 40 00
Web Site: http://www.jugodrvo.co.rs
Year Founded: 1946
Sales Range: Less than $1 Million
Emp.: 1
Holding Company
N.A.I.C.S.: 551112

JUGOELEKTRO T.A.D.

Knez Mihailova ulica br 33, 11000, Belgrade, Serbia
Tel.: (381) 11 2 638 100
Web Site: http://www.jugoelektro.rs
Year Founded: 1946
Sales Range: Less than $1 Million
Emp.: 23
Electrical Materials Whslr & Distr
N.A.I.C.S.: 423610

JUGOINSPEKT A.D.

Cika Ljubina 8/V, Belgrade, Serbia
Tel.: (381) 3283697
Web Site: https://www.jugoinspekt.com
Year Founded: 1977
JIBG—(BEL)
Rev.: $4,764,353
Assets: $7,176,427
Liabilities: $1,336,024
Net Worth: $5,840,403
Earnings: ($213,094)
Emp.: 139
Fiscal Year-end: 12/31/23
Technical Testing & Analysis Services
N.A.I.C.S.: 541990
Veselin Timotijevic *(Exec Dir)*

JUGOLEK A.D.

Bore Stankovica 2, Belgrade, Serbia
Tel.: (381) 11 355 0653
Year Founded: 2001
Sales Range: Less than $1 Million
Commodity Contracts Dealing Services
N.A.I.C.S.: 523160

JUGOMETAL A.D.

Jugolek a.d.—(Continued)

JUGOMETAL A.D.
Bulevar Mihajla Pupina 117, Belgrade, Serbia
Tel.: (381) 11 20 19 170
Year Founded: 2000
Sales Range: Less than $1 Million
Emp.: 1
Metal Ores Whslr
N.A.I.C.S.: 423520
Aleksandra Joksimovic *(Mng Dir)*

JUGOPREVOZ A.D.
Alekse Santica 2, 11320, Velika Plana, Serbia
Tel.: (381) 26 514 336
Web Site: http://www.jugoprevozvp.rs
Year Founded: 1978
Sales Range: $1-9.9 Million
Passenger Transportation Services
N.A.I.C.S.: 485999
Djordje Savic *(Mgr-Fin)*

JUGOPREVOZ KOVIN A.D.
Nemanjina 108, Kovin, Serbia
Tel.: (381) 13 742 388
Year Founded: 1948
Sales Range: $1-9.9 Million
Emp.: 100
Passenger Transportation Services
N.A.I.C.S.: 485999

JUGOPREVOZ KRUSEVAC A.D.
Jug Bogdanova 45, Krusevac, Serbia
Tel.: (381) 37421555
Web Site: https://www.jugoprevozks.rs
Year Founded: 1945
JGPK—(BEL)
Rev.: $11,155,768
Assets: $4,950,858
Liabilities: $2,687,452
Net Worth: $2,263,406
Earnings: $78,997
Emp.: 415
Fiscal Year-end: 12/31/23
Passenger Transportation Services
N.A.I.C.S.: 485999
Zivota Cvetkovic *(Gen Mgr)*

JUGOPREVOZ UGOPROMET A.D.
Prve pruge 43n, Belgrade, Serbia
Tel.: (381) 112608565
Web Site: http://www.ugopromet.com
Year Founded: 1980
JPUG—(BEL)
Sales Range: Less than $1 Million
Emp.: 12
Office Space Leasing Services
N.A.I.C.S.: 531120
Sladana Jojic *(Exec Dir & Dir)*

JUGOPREVOZ-GACKO A.D.
Gracanica bb, Gacko, Bosnia & Herzegovina
Tel.: (387) 51464171
JGPG—(BANJ)
Sales Range: $1-9.9 Million
Emp.: 58
Passenger Land Transportation Services
N.A.I.C.S.: 485999
Mitar Miljanovic *(Chm)*

JUGOSLOVENSKI FOND ZA ZITA A.D.
Bulevar Despota Stefana 65, Belgrade, Serbia
Tel.: (381) 11 3220 241
Year Founded: 1990
JUFZ—(BEL)
Sales Range: Less than $1 Million
Emp.: 2

Information Support Services
N.A.I.C.S.: 519290
Vukosav Sakovic *(CEO)*

JUGOSPED A.D.
Terazije 10, 11000, Belgrade, Serbia
Tel.: (381) 11 3691 132
Web Site: http://www.jugosped.co.rs
Freight Forwarding & Logistic Services
N.A.I.C.S.: 488510
Djordje Rasic *(Gen Mgr)*

JUGOTERM A.D.
Mramorsko brdo bb, 18251, Merosina, Serbia
Tel.: (381) 18 4694 550
Web Site: http://www.jugoterm.rs
Year Founded: 1999
Sales Range: $1-9.9 Million
Emp.: 111
Boiler & Radiator Mfr
N.A.I.C.S.: 333414

JUGOZAN A.D.
Karadordeva 13, Belgrade, Serbia
Tel.: (381) 11 3032 158
Year Founded: 1952
Sales Range: Less than $1 Million
Emp.: 30
Commodity Contracts Dealing Services
N.A.I.C.S.: 523160

JUHAYNA FOOD INDUSTRIES CO.
Polygon Building No 2 Beverly Hills Sheikh Zayed, Giza, Egypt
Tel.: (20) 238508393
Web Site: https://www.juhayna.com
Year Founded: 1983
JUFO—(EGX)
Rev.: $558,562,947
Assets: $346,311,874
Liabilities: $145,345,572
Net Worth: $200,966,302
Earnings: $33,388,862
Emp.: 4,000
Fiscal Year-end: 12/31/21
Dairy & Juice Products Mfr & Distr
N.A.I.C.S.: 311511
Safwan A. Thabet *(Chm & Co-CEO)*

JUHORTRANS A.D.
Aerodrom 7, Jagodina, Serbia
Tel.: (381) 35224315
Web Site: http://www.juhortrans.ls.rs
Year Founded: 2003
JHRT—(BEL)
Rev.: $468,135
Assets: $1,335,072
Liabilities: $237,303
Net Worth: $1,097,769
Earnings: $57,232
Fiscal Year-end: 12/31/21
Food Transportation Services
N.A.I.C.S.: 484121
Nebojsa Cvetanovic *(Deputy Dir)*

JUI LI ENTERPRISE CO., LTD.
No 22 Gaonan Highway, Renwu Dist, Kaohsiung, 81453, Taiwan
Tel.: (886) 73438301
Web Site: https://www.juili.com.tw
1512—(TAI)
Rev.: $37,472,741
Assets: $70,716,208
Liabilities: $58,629,809
Net Worth: $12,086,399
Earnings: $119,690
Fiscal Year-end: 12/31/23
Automotive Product Mfr
N.A.I.C.S.: 332510
Wei-Hui Lin *(Pres)*

Subsidiaries:

HAINAN JUI LI INDUSTRY CO., LTD. (1)
No 168 Nan Hai Rd Free Trade Zone, Haikou, 570216, Hainan, China
Tel.: (86) 89836383888
Motor Vehicle Stamping Parts Mfr
N.A.I.C.S.: 336370

Hangzhou Jui Li Jiahe Auto Parts Co., Ltd. (1)
No 951 Qingliu North Rd Jiangdong Industrial Zone, Xiaoshan Dist, Hangzhou, 311222, China
Tel.: (86) 57157179668
Automotive Parts Mfr & Distr
N.A.I.C.S.: 336390

JUIC INTERNATIONAL CORP.
3/F No39 365 Lane, Neihu Dist, Taipei, 11491, Taiwan
Tel.: (886) 226577675
Web Site: https://www.juic.com.tw
Year Founded: 1982
6114—(TPE)
Rev.: $50,533,971
Assets: $67,041,334
Liabilities: $25,835,069
Net Worth: $41,206,266
Earnings: $3,621,236
Fiscal Year-end: 12/31/22
Printed Circuit Board Mfr
N.A.I.C.S.: 334418

Subsidiaries:

Suzhou Jiuhong Electron Co., Ltd. (1)
NO 16 BeiHai Road, LiuHe Town, Taicang, JiangSu, China
Tel.: (86) 51253118455
Electronic Products Mfr
N.A.I.C.S.: 334419

JUJIANG CONSTRUCTION GROUP CO., LTD.
No 669 Qingfeng South Road, Tongxiang, 314500, Zhejiang, China
Tel.: (86) 57380890909   CN
Web Site: https://www.jujiang.cn
Year Founded: 1965
1459—(HKG)
Rev.: $1,200,644,078
Assets: $912,065,918
Liabilities: $681,205,496
Net Worth: $230,860,422
Earnings: $7,833,618
Emp.: 1,147
Fiscal Year-end: 12/31/22
Construction Contracting Services
N.A.I.C.S.: 541330
Shuigen Jin *(Sec)*

JUJUBEE SA
ul Ceglana 4, 40-514, Katowice, Poland
Tel.: (48) 322191085
Web Site: https://www.jujubee.pl
Software Development Services
N.A.I.C.S.: 541511
Michal Jakub Stepien *(Chm)*

JUKI CORPORATION
2-11-1 Tsurumaki, Tama, 206-8551, Tokyo, Japan
Tel.: (81) 423572211   JP
Web Site: https://www.juki.co.jp
Year Founded: 1938
6440—(TKS)
Rev.: $671,777,500
Assets: $987,665,360
Liabilities: $758,162,060
Net Worth: $229,503,300
Earnings: $(49,878,150)
Emp.: 4,713
Fiscal Year-end: 12/31/23
Industrial & Consumer Sewing Machines Sales & Mfr
N.A.I.C.S.: 321999

INTERNATIONAL PUBLIC

Akira Kiyohara *(Chm & Pres)*

Subsidiaries:

Alkareem Machinery (1)
12 Thlemaia St 4 Moasasepelzaaho Rd, PO Box 114, Ahmainshams, Cairo, Egypt (100%)
Tel.: (20) 101373838
Sales Range: $25-49.9 Million
Emp.: 30
Sewing Machines
N.A.I.C.S.: 321999

Essegi Automation S.R.L. (1)
Via Della Tecnica 33, Sovizzo, 36050, Vicenza, Italy
Tel.: (39) 0444376380
Web Site: http://www.storagesolutions.it
Automated Warehouse Mfr
N.A.I.C.S.: 332710

JUKI (SHANGHAI) INDUSTRIAL CO., LTD. (1)
435 Xing Ping Road, Jia Ding, Shanghai, 201818, China
Industrial Sewing Machine Mfr
N.A.I.C.S.: 333248

JUKI AIZU CORPORATION (1)
75 Omi Omi Shiokawa-machi, Kitakata, 969-3532, Fukushima, Japan
Tel.: (81) 241273101
Emp.: 257
Lost Wax Casting & Metal Injection Molded Products Mfr
N.A.I.C.S.: 333517

JUKI AMERICA, INC. (1)
8500 NW 17th St Ste 100, Miami, FL 33126-1035
Tel.: (305) 594-0059
Web Site: http://www.juki.com
Industrial Sewing Machine Whslr
N.A.I.C.S.: 423830

Division (Domestic):

Juki America Inc. - Home Sewing Division (2)
8500 NW 17th St Ste 100, Miami, FL 33126.
Tel.: (305) 594-0059
Web Site: http://www.jukihome.com
Emp.: 42
Industrial Sewing Machine Whslr
N.A.I.C.S.: 423830
Minoru Nitta *(Pres)*

JUKI CORPORATION - ELECTRONIC ASSEMBLY SYSTEMS BUSINESS UNIT (1)
2-11-1 Tsurumaki, Tama, 206-8551, Tokyo, Japan
Tel.: (81) 423572254
Web Site: http://www.juki.co.jp
Industrial Machinery Whslr
N.A.I.C.S.: 423830

Unit (Domestic):

JUKI CORPORATION - ELECTRONIC ASSEMBLY SYSTEMS BUSINESS UNIT - NISHI NIHON CENTER (2)
Room A 1F OAK Esaka Bldg 10-28 Hiroshiba, Suita, 564-0052, Osaka, Japan
Tel.: (81) 6 6380 2000
Industrial Sewing Machine Whslr
N.A.I.C.S.: 423830

JUKI CORPORATION - ELECTRONIC ASSEMBLY SYSTEMS BUSINESS UNIT - SMT TRAINING CENTER (2)
2-11-1 Tsurumaki, Tama, 206-8551, Tokyo, Japan
Tel.: (81) 42 357 2298
Industrial Apprenticeship Training Services
N.A.I.C.S.: 611513

JUKI CORPORATION - ELECTRONIC ASSEMBLY SYSTEMS BUSINESS UNIT - CYUBU NIHON CENTER (1)
5th F Meitetsukotu Bldg 2-3-5 Nishihioki, Nakagawa-ku, Nagoya, 454-8515, Aichi, Japan
Tel.: (81) 52 321 3107
Industrial Sewing Machine Mfr

AND PRIVATE COMPANIES

JUKI CORPORATION

N.A.I.C.S.: 333248

JUKI DO BRASIL COMERCIO E SERVICOS DE MAQUINAS LTDA. (1)
Rua Pamplona 1018 Cj 91/92, Jardim Paulista, 01405-001, Sao Paulo, Brazil
Tel.: (55) 11 3266 7821
Web Site: http://www.jukidobrasil.net.br
Industrial Sewing Machine Whslr
N.A.I.C.S.: 423830

JUKI GENERAL SERVICE CORPORATION (1)
2-11-1 Tsurumaki, Tama, 206-8551, Tokyo, Japan
Tel.: (81) 4 2357 2521
Web Site: http://www.jukigs.jp
Home Renovation Services
N.A.I.C.S.: 236118

JUKI HIROSHIMA CORPORATION (1)
306-31 Higashisakeyama-cho, Miyoshi, 728-0023, Hiroshima, Japan
Tel.: (81) 824 62 1191
Web Site: http://www.juki-hs.co.jp
Industrial Machinery Mfr
N.A.I.C.S.: 333248

JUKI MATSUE CORPORATION (1)
2207-1 Sasou Shinji-cho, Matsue, 699-0406, Shimane, Japan
Tel.: (81) 852 66 1121
Web Site: http://www.juki-mt.co.jp
Industrial Sewing Machine Mfr
N.A.I.C.S.: 333248

JUKI METAL CORPORATION (1)
425 Kamimise Odai-cho, Takigun, Taki, 519-2403, Mie, Japan
Tel.: (81) 59 882 1355
Web Site: https://www.jukikinzoku.com
Emp.: 67
Pig Iron & Cast Metal Mfr
N.A.I.C.S.: 331110
Yoshihide Yanagioka *(Chm)*

JUKI OHTAWARA CORPORATION (1)
1863 Kitakanemaru, Otawara, 324-0011, Tochigi, Japan
Tel.: (81) 28 723 5111
Web Site: http://www.sewingcenter.com.ua
Industrial Sewing Machine Whslr
N.A.I.C.S.: 423830

JUKI SALES (JAPAN) CORPORATION (1)
2-11-1 Tsurumaki, Tama, 206-8551, Tokyo, Japan
Tel.: (81) 423572530
Web Site: http://www.jukihanbai.co.jp
Industrial Sewing Machine Whslr
N.A.I.C.S.: 423830

JUKI SMT ASIA CO., LTD. (1)
700/166 Moo 1 Amata Nakorn Industrial Estate Baankao, Phanthong District, Chon Buri, 20160, Thailand
Tel.: (66) 3846 5306
Sales Range: $25-49.9 Million
Emp.: 50
Industrial Sewing Machine Whslr
N.A.I.C.S.: 423830

Juki (China) Co., Ltd - Dongguan (1)
Room 508 Block B Hongxi Center Eco-Business, No 2 Tiyu Road, Dongguan, Guangdong, China
Tel.: (86) 76922420276
Mfr & Sales of Sewing Machines & Other Electric Home Appliances
N.A.I.C.S.: 333248

Juki (China) Co., Ltd. (1)
Room 901-903 Hailiang Building-A No 22 Lane 118 Zhongjiang Road, Putuo District, Shanghai, 200062, China
Tel.: (86) 2162368888
Web Site: http://www.jukichina.com
Industrial Sewing Machine Whslr
N.A.I.C.S.: 423830
Heji Bowen *(Chm & Gen Mgr)*

Subsidiary (Domestic):

Juki Xinxing Industry Co., Ltd. (2)
Guangyang Road 160, Langfang, Hebei, China **(100%)**

Tel.: (86) 3165905137
Industrial Sewing Machine Mfr
N.A.I.C.S.: 333248

Juki (China) Co., Ltd.-Qingdao (1)
Room 1028 New World Building No 9 Fuzhou South Road, Qingdao, Shandong, China
Tel.: (86) 53286071988
Web Site: http://www.jukichina.com
Sewing Machines Mfr & Distr
N.A.I.C.S.: 321999

Juki (Europe) GmbH Turkey (1)
Kocman Caddesi Gamze Sokak No 45, Gunesli, 34600, Istanbul, SP, Turkiye
Tel.: (90) 2126308921
Sales Range: $25-49.9 Million
Emp.: 2
Mfr & Sales of Sewing Machines & Other Electric Home Appliances
N.A.I.C.S.: 333248

Juki (Hong Kong) Ltd. (1)
Flat 5D High Fashion Centre 1- 11 Kwai Hei Street, Kwai Chung, New Territories, China (Hong Kong) **(100%)**
Tel.: (852) 24237888
Web Site: http://www.juki.com.hk
Sewing Machines Distr
N.A.I.C.S.: 423830

Juki (Middle Europe) GmbH Minsk (1)
Charuzaj 25/3 office no 203, 220123, Minsk, Belarus
Tel.: (375) 173344233
Web Site: http://www.juki.at
Sales Range: $25-49.9 Million
Emp.: 5
Representative Office
N.A.I.C.S.: 333248

Juki (Ningbo) Precision Co., Ltd. (1)
Maoshan Industry Zone, Yinzhou, Ningbo, China
Tel.: (86) 57488466299
Industrial Sewing Machine Parts Mfr
N.A.I.C.S.: 333248

Juki (Romania) S.R.L. (1)
Gral Vasile Milea Blvd 2, Sector 6, Bucharest, Romania **(100%)**
Tel.: (40) 214100124
Mfr & Sales of Sewing Machines & Other Electric Home Appliances
N.A.I.C.S.: 333248

Juki (Thailand) Company Limited (1)
1768 Thai Summit Tower 2nd Floor New Phetchaburi Road, Bangkapi Sub District Huai Kwang District, Bangkok, 10310, Thailand
Tel.: (66) 20160140
Lockstitch & Sewing Machine Mfr
N.A.I.C.S.: 333248

Juki (Vietnam) Co., Ltd. (1)
Tan Thuan Export Processing Zone, Tan Thuan Dong Ward District 7, Ho Chi Minh City, Vietnam
Tel.: (84) 2837701441
Industrial Sewing Machine Parts Mfr
N.A.I.C.S.: 333248

Juki (langfang) Industrial Co., Ltd. (1)
No 17 Baihe Road, Langfang Economic and Technical Development Zone, Hebei, China
Tel.: (86) 3165905102
Sewing machines Mfr
N.A.I.C.S.: 321999

Juki Automation Systems AG (1)
Weissenstein Strasse 81, Solothurn, 4500, Switzerland **(100%)**
Tel.: (41) 326262929
Web Site: http://www.jas-smt.com
Sales Range: $10-24.9 Million
Emp.: 25
Sewing Machines
N.A.I.C.S.: 321999

Subsidiary (Non-US):

JUKI AUTOMATION SYSTEMS GMBH (2)
Neuburger Strasse 41, 90451, Nuremberg, Germany
Tel.: (49) 9119362660

Industrial Machinery Whslr
N.A.I.C.S.: 333248
Andreas Polzer *(CTO)*

Juki Automation Systems Corporation (1)
2-11-1 Tsurumaki, Tama-Shi, Tokyo, 206-8551, Japan
Tel.: (81) 423572293
Industrial Sewing Machine Parts Mfr
N.A.I.C.S.: 333248

Juki Automation Systems Inc. (1)
5151 McCrimmon Pkwy Ste 200, Morrisville, NC 27560-8200
Tel.: (919) 460-0111
Web Site: https://jukiamericas.com
Sales Range: $25-49.9 Million
Emp.: 15
Sewing Machines Distr
N.A.I.C.S.: 423620

Juki Automation Systems Ltd (1)
5 Lloyds Court Manor Royal, Crawley, RH10 9QU, West Sussex, United Kingdom
Tel.: (44) 1293 592270
Web Site: http://www.juki.co.jp
Industrial Sewing Machine Whslr
N.A.I.C.S.: 423620

Juki Bangladesh Ltd (1)
Delwar Bhaban 4th Floor 104 Agrabad C/A, Chittagong, 4000, Bangladesh **(100%)**
Tel.: (880) 3 171 1948
Web Site: https://www.jukibangladesh.com
Sales Range: $25-49.9 Million
Sewing Machines Distr
N.A.I.C.S.: 423620

Juki Bangladesh Ltd. (1)
Natore Tower 5th Floor Plot 32-D and 32-E Road 02 Sector 03, Uttara Model Town, Dhaka, 1230, Bangladesh **(25%)**
Tel.: (880) 24 895 4731
Web Site: https://www.juki.com.sg
Sales Range: $25-49.9 Million
Emp.: 35
Industrial & Home Sewing Machine Distr
N.A.I.C.S.: 423620

Juki Central Europe Ltd. (1)
Poleczki 21 Platan Park C, 02 822, Warsaw, Poland
Web Site: http://www.jukieurope.com
Sales Range: $25-49.9 Million
Sewing Machines Distr
N.A.I.C.S.: 423830

Juki Central Europe Sp.Zo.O. Moscow (1)
Leninskaya Sloboda 26 Omega 2 bld A office 410, 115280, Moscow, Russia
Tel.: (7) 4959261798
Web Site: http://www.juki.biz
Industrial & Home Sewing Machine Distr
N.A.I.C.S.: 423830

Juki Corporation - Ohtawara Plant (1)
1863 Kitakanemaru, Otawara, 324-0011, Tochigi, Japan
Tel.: (81) 287 23 5111
Web Site: http://www.juki.co.jp
Sewing machines Mfr
N.A.I.C.S.: 333248

Juki France SA (1)
33 Rue Jean Jaures, F 59814, Lesquin, Cedex, France **(100%)**
Tel.: (33) 320862003
Web Site: http://www.sewingcenter.com.ua
Sales Range: $25-49.9 Million
Emp.: 15
Distribution of Industrial Sewing Machines
N.A.I.C.S.: 423830

Juki Hanoi Service Center (1)
51 Trieu Viet Vuong St, Hai Ba Trung District, Hanoi, Vietnam **(100%)**
Tel.: (84) 49435265
Web Site: http://www.sewingcenter.com.ua
Sales Range: $25-49.9 Million
Emp.: 5
Sewing Machines
N.A.I.C.S.: 321999

Juki India Private Limited (1)
1090/I Ground & First Floor 18th Cross Sector III HSR Layout, Bengaluru, 560102, India

Tel.: (91) 8042511900
Web Site: http://www.jukiindia.com
Sales Range: $25-49.9 Million
Emp.: 29
Mfr & Sales of Sewing Machines & Other Electric Home Appliances
N.A.I.C.S.: 333248

Branch (Domestic):

Juki India Private Limited (2)
B 220 Okhla Industrial Area Phase 1, New Delhi, 110020, India **(100%)**
Tel.: (91) 1126813333
Web Site: http://www.juki.com
Sales Range: $25-49.9 Million
Emp.: 17
Mfr & Sales of Sewing Machines & Other Electric Home Appliances
N.A.I.C.S.: 333248

Juki India Private Limited (2)
AB-1 Prafulla Kanan Krishnapur Tara Maa Apartment Ground Floor, Kolkata, 700101, West Bengal, India
Tel.: (91) 8229934967
Web Site: http://www.jukiindia.com
Mfr & Sales of Sewing Machines & Other Electric Home Appliances
N.A.I.C.S.: 333248

Juki India Private Limited (2)
Sri Muthu Plaza 320 Avinasi Road Pushpa theatre, Tirupur, 641 602, India **(100%)**
Tel.: (91) 421 424 6743
Web Site: https://jukiindia.com
Sales Range: $25-49.9 Million
Sewing Machines
N.A.I.C.S.: 321999

Juki Industrial Equipment Technology Corporation (1)
70 Masuda Ishigaminishi Masuda-machi, Yokote, 019-0793, Akita, Japan
Tel.: (81) 182454341
Web Site: http://www.jdkc.co.jp
Electric Equipment Mfr
N.A.I.C.S.: 334419
Hideya Sudo *(Pres)*

Plant (Domestic):

Juki Industrial Equipment Technology Corporation - Daisen Factory (2)
1-34 Kamiametsu Tsuchikawa, Daisen, 019-2111, Akita, Japan
Tel.: (81) 187 75 0050
Steel Plate Parts Mfr
N.A.I.C.S.: 331110

Juki Industrial Equipment Technology Corporation - Yoshino Factory (2)
26 Murashita Masudamachi Yoshino, Yokote, 019-0703, Akita, Japan
Tel.: (81) 182454351
Industrial Machinery Mfr
N.A.I.C.S.: 333248

Juki Italia S.p.A. (1)
Via Bergamo 4, 20045, Lainate, MI, Italy
Tel.: (39) 02 937 5791
Web Site: https://www.juki.it
Sales Range: $25-49.9 Million
Emp.: 10
Sewing Machines Distr
N.A.I.C.S.: 423830

Juki Lanka Service Centre Pvt. Ltd. (1)
No 34 2nd Floor Hunupitiya Road, Colombo, Sri Lanka
Tel.: (94) 112470354
Lockstitch & Sewing Machine Mfr
N.A.I.C.S.: 333248
Susantha Peeris *(Gen Mgr)*

Juki Machinery Bangladesh Ltd. (1)
Nator Tower 5th Floor Plot 32 D&E Road 02 Sector 03 Uttara, Dhaka, Bangladesh
Tel.: (880) 248954731
Web Site: http://www.juki.com.bd
Industrial Sewing Machine Parts Mfr
N.A.I.C.S.: 333248
Aditta Rahman Robi *(Sr Engr)*

Juki Machinery Vietnam Co., Ltd. (1)
Tel.: (84) 2835178833
Industrial Sewing Machine Parts Mfr
N.A.I.C.S.: 333248

Juki Proserve Corporation (1)

JUKI CORPORATION

Juki Corporation—(Continued)
2-11-1 Tsurumaki, Tama, 206-8551, Tokyo, Japan
Tel.: (81) 423572521
Web Site: https://www.juki-ps.co.jp
Emp.: 100
Real Estate Services
N.A.I.C.S.: 531390

Juki Singapore Pte. Ltd. (1)
20 Bendemeer Road 04-12 Bs Bendemeer Centre, Singapore, 339914, Singapore **(100%)**
Tel.: (65) 65534388
Web Site: https://www.juki.com.sg
Sales Range: $25-49.9 Million
Emp.: 50
Sewing Machines Distr
N.A.I.C.S.: 423830

Juki Technosolutions Corporation (1)
2-11-1 Tsurumaki, Tama, 206-8551, Tokyo, Japan
Tel.: (81) 423572383
Sewing machines Mfr
N.A.I.C.S.: 423830

Juki Union Special, Mexico S.A. de C.V. (1)
#73-APA Col Centro, 06080, Mexico, DF, Mexico
Tel.: (52) 57099215
Mfr & Sales of Sewing Machines & Other Electric Home Appliances
N.A.I.C.S.: 333248

SUZUTAMI Precision Industry Co., Ltd. (1)
1411 Takemori, Teradomari, Nagaoka, 959-0161, Niigata, Japan
Tel.: (81) 256982500
Emp.: 116
Industrial Machinery Mfr
N.A.I.C.S.: 333248
Hiroyuki Watanabe *(Pres)*

Shanghai Juki Sewing Machine Co., Ltd. (1)
No 580 Dong Xue Rd Yu Yang Bang Cun, Dong Jing Town Songjiang, Shanghai, China
Tel.: (86) 2157670950
Industrial Sewing Machine Parts Mfr
N.A.I.C.S.: 333248

Tokyo Juki International Trading (Shanghai) Co. Ltd. (1)
Room 904-905 Building A Hailiang Building No 22 Lane 118, Zhongjiang Road Putuo District, Shanghai, 200336, China **(100%)**
Tel.: (86) 216238202
Web Site: http://www.jukichina.com
Sales Range: $25-49.9 Million
Emp.: 60
Industrial & Home Sewing Machine Distr
N.A.I.C.S.: 423620

JULABO LABORTECHNIK GMBH

Eisenbahnstrasse 45, Seelbach, 77960, Germany
Tel.: (49) 7823510
Web Site: http://www.julabo.com
Year Founded: 1967
Rev.: $34,631,782
Emp.: 330
Liquid Temperature Control System Mfr
N.A.I.C.S.: 334512
Gerhard Juchheim *(Owner & Mng Dir)*

Subsidiaries:

JULABO France SAS (1)
50 Avenue D Alsace, Colmar, France
Tel.: (33) 6 7120 9497
Liquid Temperature Control System Mfr
N.A.I.C.S.: 334512

JULABO Italia SRL (1)
Via M. Prestinari 2, 20158, Milan, Italy
Tel.: (39) 02 3932 5483
Liquid Temperature Control System Mfr
N.A.I.C.S.: 334512

JULABO Japan Co., Ltd. (1)
Via Ritz Ibaraki, 8-18 Sonoda-cho, Osaka, Ibaraki, Japan
Tel.: (81) 726 38 7200
Liquid Temperature Control System Mfr
N.A.I.C.S.: 334512

JULABO Korea Co., Ltd. (1)
#407 New T-Castle, 429-1 Gasan-Dong Geumcheon-Gu, Seoul, 153-803, Korea (South)
Tel.: (82) 2 6277 3700
Liquid Temperature Control System Mfr
N.A.I.C.S.: 334512

JULABO LATIN AMERICA (1)
Tucuman 1424 - 2 D, C1050AAH, Buenos Aires, Argentina
Tel.: (54) 11 4371 1647
Web Site: http://www.julabo-latinamerica.com
Liquid Temperature Control System Mfr
N.A.I.C.S.: 334512
Pablo Joaquin Scarpin *(Mgr-Sls)*

JULABO NEDERLAND B.V. (1)
Expeditieweg 8-06, 6657 KL, West Maas en Waal, Netherlands
Tel.: (31) 487 507060
Web Site: http://www.julabo.com
Emp.: 4
Liquid Temperature Control System Mfr
N.A.I.C.S.: 334512
Hans Diels *(Mgr-Netherlands)*

JULABO Singapore Pte., Ltd. (1)
16 Ayer Rajah Crescent 04-05G, Tempco Technominium, Singapore, 139965, Singapore
Tel.: (65) 6775 1516
Liquid Temperature Control System Mfr
N.A.I.C.S.: 334512

JULABO Technology (Beijing) Co. Ltd. (1)
Room 503C Building 106 Lize Zhongyuan, Wangjing New Industrial Zone, Beijing, 100 102, Chaoyang District, China
Tel.: (86) 10 5165 6060
Liquid Temperature Control System Mfr
N.A.I.C.S.: 334512

JULABO UK Ltd. (1)
34 Thorpe Wood, Thorpe Wood Business Park, Peterborough, PE3 6SR, United Kingdom
Tel.: (44) 1733 265892
Liquid Temperature Control System Mfr
N.A.I.C.S.: 334512

JULABO USA, Inc. (1)
884 Marcon Blvd, Allentown, PA 18109
Tel.: (610) 231-0250
Web Site: http://www.julabo.com
Emp.: 35
Liquid Temperature Control System Mfr
N.A.I.C.S.: 334512
Rory Dietrich *(Asst Controller)*

JULI PLC

19 Kodesoh Street, Ikeja, Lagos, Nigeria
Tel.: (234) 9090550989
Web Site: https://juliplc.ng
JULI—(NIGE)
Sales Range: Less than $1 Million
Pharmaceuticals Mfr
N.A.I.C.S.: 325412
Julius Adelusi-Adeluyi *(Founder & Chm)*

JULI SLING CO., LTD.

Juli Road, Xushui District, Baoding, 072550, Hebei, China
Tel.: (86) 3128999999
Web Site: https://www.julisling.com
002342—(SSE)
Year Founded: 1985
Rev.: $305,034,444
Assets: $628,867,044
Liabilities: $279,859,320
Net Worth: $349,007,724
Earnings: $1,274,832
Emp.: 3,000
Fiscal Year-end: 12/31/22
Synthetic Fiber Webbing, Steel Wire Rope Slings, Steel Tie Rods, Thick Ropes, Metal Clamps, Lifting Tools, Chain Slings, Sling Connecting Components & Sling Equipment Mfr
N.A.I.C.S.: 331222
Qiang Fu *(CFO)*

Subsidiaries:

J&L Juli Holding (Canada) Ltd. (1)
7768 French St, Vancouver, V6P 4V6, BC, Canada
Tel.: (604) 267-2122
Web Site: http://www.jlrigging.ca
Sales Range: $50-74.9 Million
Emp.: 2
Rigging Products Distr
N.A.I.C.S.: 423390

JULIUS BAER GROUP LTD.

Bahnhofstrasse 36, PO Box 8010, 8010, Zurich, Switzerland
Tel.: (41) 588881111 CH
Web Site: https://www.juliusbaer.com
Year Founded: 1896
BAER—(OTCIQ)
Rev.: $2,874,833,703
Assets: $107,301,884,701
Liabilities: $100,469,068,736
Net Worth: $6,832,815,965
Earnings: $502,660,754
Emp.: 7,425
Fiscal Year-end: 12/31/23
Commercial Banking Services
N.A.I.C.S.: 551111
Dieter A. Enkelmann *(CFO & Member-Exec Bd)*

Subsidiaries:

Bank Julius Baer & Co. Ltd. (1)
Bahnhofstrasse 36, PO Box 8010, 8010, Zurich, Switzerland **(100%)**
Tel.: (41) 588881111
Web Site: http://www.juliusbaer.com
Sales Range: $700-749.9 Million
Emp.: 1,500
Private Banking Services
N.A.I.C.S.: 522110

Subsidiary (Domestic):

Bank Julius Baer & Co. Ltd. (2)
Piazzetta San Carlo 1, PO Box 5847, 6901, Lugano, Switzerland
Tel.: (41) 588858111
Private Banking Services
N.A.I.C.S.: 522110
Sergio Leoni *(Head-Market)*

Banque Julius Baer & Cie SA (2)
Rue Pierre Fatio 7, PO Box 3142, CH 1211, Geneva, Switzerland
Tel.: (41) 227083838
Web Site: http://www.juliusbaer.com
Sales Range: $200-249.9 Million
Emp.: 300
Private Banking Services
N.A.I.C.S.: 522110

Subsidiary (Non-US):

Julius Baer Patrimoine Conseil Sarl (2)
17 Cours Edouard VII, 75009, Paris, France
Tel.: (33) 1 5343 9058
Web Site: http://www.juliusbaer.com
Banking Services
N.A.I.C.S.: 522110

Bank Julius Baer Europe AG (1)
An der Welle 1, PO Box 15 02 52, 60062, Frankfurt, Germany
Tel.: (49) 6990743500
Emp.: 150
Banking Services
N.A.I.C.S.: 522110
Alexandre Grewlich *(Branch Mgr)*

Julius Baer (Hong Kong) Ltd. (1)
18/F Two Exchange Square 8 Connaught Place, Central, China (Hong Kong)
Tel.: (852) 28994788
Investment Advisory Services
N.A.I.C.S.: 523940

Julius Baer (Monaco) S.A.M. (1)
La Lestra 13 Avenue de Grande Bretagne,

INTERNATIONAL PUBLIC

98000, Monaco, Monaco
Tel.: (377) 93105000
Web Site: http://www.juliusbaer.com
Sales Range: $50-74.9 Million
Banking Services
N.A.I.C.S.: 522110

Julius Baer (Uruguay) S.A. (1)
Avda Gral Rivera 6329, 11500, Montevideo, Uruguay
Tel.: (598) 26005050
Emp.: 10
Private Banking Services
N.A.I.C.S.: 522180

Julius Baer Advisory S.A.E. Ltd. (1)
City Stars Star Capital Tower 8 El Forsane St, Nasr, 11771, Cairo, Egypt
Tel.: (20) 224801718
Web Site: http://www.juliusbaer.com
Sales Range: $50-74.9 Million
Emp.: 6
Private Banking Services
N.A.I.C.S.: 523150

Julius Baer Consultores (Peru) S.A.C. (1)
Victor Andres Belaunde No 147 Via Principal 123 Torre Real 1 Piso 6, Oficina 601, Lima, L27, Peru
Tel.: (51) 1 442 22 36
Web Site: http://www.juliusbaer.com
Private Banking Services
N.A.I.C.S.: 522180

Julius Baer Consultores S.A. (1)
Torre Edicampo Piso 3 Av Francisco de Miranda Campo Alegre, 1060, Caracas, Venezuela
Tel.: (58) 2122640041
Private Banking Services
N.A.I.C.S.: 522180

Julius Baer Fiduciaria S.r.l. (1)
Corso di Porta Nuova 3, 20122, Milan, Italy
Tel.: (39) 0292871721
Sales Range: $50-74.9 Million
Emp.: 10
Banking Services
N.A.I.C.S.: 522110
Bargella Giampaolo *(Pres)*

Julius Baer Financial Consultancy S.A. (1)
Avenida del Libertador 498 piso 15, C1001ABR, Buenos Aires, Argentina
Tel.: (54) 1152720820
Web Site: http://www.juliusbaer.com
Private Banking Services
N.A.I.C.S.: 522180

Julius Baer International Ltd. (1)
1 St Martin's Le Grand, London, EC1A 4AS, United Kingdom
Tel.: (44) 2034818100
Web Site: http://www.juliusbaer.com
Private Banking Services
N.A.I.C.S.: 522110

Julius Baer Investment Advisory GesmbH (1)
Himmelpfortgasse 13/8, 1010, Vienna, Austria
Tel.: (43) 153572020
Web Site: http://www.juliusbaer.com
Financial Advisory Services
N.A.I.C.S.: 523940

Julius Baer Private Banking (1)
Rue Pierre Fatio 7, 1204, Geneva, Switzerland
Tel.: (41) 227083838
Banking Services
N.A.I.C.S.: 522110

Kairos Investment Management S.p.A. (1)
Via San Prospero 2, 20121, Milan, Italy **(100%)**
Tel.: (39) 02 77718 1
Web Site: http://www.kairospartners.com
Emp.: 140
Holding Company; Wealth & Investment Fund Management Services
N.A.I.C.S.: 551112
Gabriele Zuliani *(CFO)*

Subsidiary (Non-US):

Kairos Asset Management SA (2)

Via Greina 2, 6900, Lugano, Switzerland
Tel.: (41) 91 260 7575
Web Site: http://www.kairospartners.com
Wealth Management & Investment Advisory Services
N.A.I.C.S.: 523940

Kairos Investment Management Limited (2)
10 Portman Square, London, W1H 6AZ, United Kingdom
Tel.: (44) 20 7398 3000
Web Site: http://www.kairospartners.com
Wealth & Investment Fund Management Services
N.A.I.C.S.: 523940

WMPartners Wealth Management Ltd. (1)
Nueschelerstrasse 30, PO Box 2591, 8022, Zurich, Switzerland
Tel.: (41) 58 888 38 38
Web Site: http://www.wmpartners.ch
Sales Range: $50-74.9 Million
Emp.: 40
Investment Consulting, Wealth Management & Wealth Advisory Services
N.A.I.C.S.: 523940

JULIUS MEINL INDUSTRIE-HOLDING GMBH
Julius Meinl Gasse 3-7, 1160, Vienna, Austria
Tel.: (43) 1 48860   AT
Web Site:
    http://www.meinlcoffee.com
Year Founded: 1862
Sales Range: $300-349.9 Million
Emp.: 700
Holding Company; Coffee Products Mfr & Whslr
N.A.I.C.S.: 551112
Herbert Vlasaty *(Mng Dir & Member-Mgmt Bd)*

Subsidiaries:

INCAB S.p.A. (1)
Via Macello 26 A, 39100, Bolzano, Italy   (100%)
Tel.: (39) 0471307211
Web Site: http://www.meinl.it
Sales Range: $25-49.9 Million
Emp.: 15
Coffee Mfr
N.A.I.C.S.: 311812

Julius Meinl Baliarne, a.s. (1)
U Libenskeho pivovaru 63, 180 00, Prague, Czech Republic
Tel.: (420) 296411328
Tea & Coffee Distr
N.A.I.C.S.: 445298

Julius Meinl Coffee Intl., A.S. (1)
Pribinova 25 (Tower 115), 810 11, Bratislava, Slovakia   (99%)
Tel.: (421) 258280801
Web Site: http://www.meinl.sk
Sales Range: $25-49.9 Million
Emp.: 35
Coffee Mfr
N.A.I.C.S.: 311920

Julius Meinl Gida San. ve Tic. Ltd. Sti. (1)
Kemankes Karamustafa Pasa Mah Kara Ali Kaptan Sok No 7, Karakoy Beyoglu, Istanbul, Türkiye
Tel.: (90) 2122436993
Tea & Coffee Distr
N.A.I.C.S.: 445298

Julius Meinl Gourmet GmbH (1)
Julius Meinl Gasse 3 7, 1160, Vienna, Austria
Tel.: (43) 1488600
Web Site: http://www.meinl.com
Sales Range: $25-49.9 Million
Emp.: 150
Bakery Products
N.A.I.C.S.: 311812
Kirisits Josef *(Dir-Sls)*

Julius Meinl Hungary kft. (1)
Budafoki ut 187-189, 1117, Budapest, Hungary
Tel.: (36) 12251336
Web Site: http://www.meinl.hu
Tea & Coffee Distr
N.A.I.C.S.: 445298

Julius Meinl Italia SpA (1)
Via Verona 70, 36077, Altavilla Vicentina, Italy
Tel.: (39) 0444334401
Tea & Coffee Distr
N.A.I.C.S.: 445298
Chiara Zambello *(Mgr-Sls Admin)*

Julius Meinl Nahrungsmittel Produktions Ges.m.b.H. (1)
Julius Meinl Gasse 3-7, 1160, Vienna, Austria
Tel.: (43) 148860
Sales Range: $25-49.9 Million
Emp.: 150
Bakery Products
N.A.I.C.S.: 311812

Julius Meinl Romania srl. (1)
Str Fabricii 1/A 4050, Covasna, Targu Secuiesc, Romania
Tel.: (40) 267360729
Tea & Coffee Distr
N.A.I.C.S.: 445298

Julius Meinl UK Ltd. (1)
Unit 3 Ground Floor Lafone House Leathermarket 11-13 Weston Street, London, SE1 3ER, United Kingdom
Tel.: (44) 2031766444
Tea & Coffee Distr
N.A.I.C.S.: 445298

Meinl Bank AG (1)
Bauernmarkt 2, 1010, Vienna, Austria
Tel.: (43) 15318800
Web Site: http://www.meinlbank.com
Sales Range: $25-49.9 Million
Emp.: 100
Private Banking Services
N.A.I.C.S.: 522110
Julius Meinl *(Mng Dir)*

Meinl Internet Commerce GmbH (1)
Julius Meinl Gasse 3-7, 1160, Vienna, Austria
Tel.: (43) 1 488 60 1311
Web Site: http://www.meinl.com
Coffee Products Online Retailer
N.A.I.C.S.: 455219

JULIUS TALLBERG-KIINTEISTOET OYJ
Suomalaistentie 7, 02270, Espoo, Finland
Tel.: (358) 207420700
Web Site: http://www.tallberg.fi
Sales Range: $10-24.9 Million
Emp.: 7
Real Estate Services
N.A.I.C.S.: 531210
Martin Tallberg *(Pres & COO)*

JULIUS ZORN GMBH
Juliusplatz 1, 86551, Aichach, Germany
Tel.: (49) 82519010
Web Site: http://www.juzo.com
Year Founded: 1912
Rev.: $59,704,735
Emp.: 404
Compression Therapy Aids Mfr & Distr
N.A.I.C.S.: 423450
Annerose Zorn-West *(Mng Dir)*

Subsidiaries:

Julius Zorn, Inc. (1)
3690 Zorn Dr, Cuyahoga Falls, OH 44223
Tel.: (330) 923-4999
Web Site: http://www.juzousa.com
Apparels Mfr
N.A.I.C.S.: 315250
Annerose Zorn *(CEO)*

Juzo Scandinavia AB (1)
Tegelangsgatan 13, 602 28, Norrkoping, Sweden
Tel.: (46) 114422250
Medical Device Mfr
N.A.I.C.S.: 334510
Annerose Zorn *(CEO)*

Juzo UK Ltd. (1)
Unit 1 Edison Place Dryburgh Industrial Estate, Dundee, DD2 3QU, United Kingdom
Tel.: (44) 1382826620
Medical Device Mfr
N.A.I.C.S.: 334510
Annerose Zorn *(CEO)*

JULLUNDUR MOTOR AGENCY (DELHI) LTD.
458-1/16 Sohna Road Opp New Court, Gurgaon, 122 001, Haryana, India
Tel.: (91) 1244233867
Web Site: https://www.jmaindia.com
Year Founded: 1927
JMA—(NSE)
Rev.: $61,023,788
Assets: $35,245,885
Liabilities: $10,428,032
Net Worth: $24,817,853
Earnings: $3,285,271
Emp.: 546
Fiscal Year-end: 03/31/23
Automotive Spare Parts Distr
N.A.I.C.S.: 423120
Virat Sondhi *(Co-Mng Dir)*

JULONG CO., LTD.
308 Qianshan Middle Road, Tiedong District, Anshan, 114044, Liaoning, China
Tel.: (86) 4122538288
Web Site: http://www.julong.cc
Year Founded: 2004
300202—(CHIN)
Rev.: $86,695,411
Assets: $347,613,573
Liabilities: $97,151,993
Net Worth: $250,461,580
Earnings: $7,314,245
Emp.: 1,580
Fiscal Year-end: 12/31/20
Franking Machine Mfr
N.A.I.C.S.: 333310

JUMA AL MAJID GROUP
Juma Al Majid Group Building Salahuddin Street Hor Al Anz Area, PO Box 156, Dubai, United Arab Emirates
Tel.: (971) 42665210
Web Site: http://www.al-majid.com
Year Founded: 1950
Sales Range: $1-4.9 Billion
Emp.: 6,000
Holding Company
N.A.I.C.S.: 551112
Juma Al Majid *(Founder & Chm)*

Subsidiaries:

Al Majid Industries L.L.C (1)
Industrial Al Quez, PO Box 156, Dubai, 156, United Arab Emirates
Tel.: (971) 4 3380908
Web Site: http://www.al-majidindustries.com
Sales Range: $25-49.9 Million
Emp.: 100
Refrigeration & Fire Fighting Equipment Cabinet Mfr
N.A.I.C.S.: 337110
Osama Latayfe *(Mgr-Ops)*

Al Majid Property Co LLC. (1)
Al Muteena Building, Dubai, United Arab Emirates
Tel.: (971) 4 271 5252
Web Site: http://www.almajidproperty.com
Emp.: 90
Real Property Management Services
N.A.I.C.S.: 531312

Al Majid Travel and Tourism (1)
#1020 Al Majid Travel Bulding Near Dubai Clock Tower, PO Box 1020, Dubai, 1020, United Arab Emirates
Tel.: (971) 4 2211176
Web Site: http://wwwalmajidtravel.com

Sales Range: $10-24.9 Million
Emp.: 40
Travel & Tour Operator
N.A.I.C.S.: 561510

Awafi Foodstuff Ind. Co. L.L.C. (1)
Industrial Area 10, Sharjah, United Arab Emirates
Tel.: (971) 6 5343436
Snack Delicacy Mfr
N.A.I.C.S.: 311919

General Navigation And Commerce Company (GENAVCO) L.L.C (1)
Karama, Dubai, 5563, United Arab Emirates
Tel.: (971) 4 3961000
Web Site: http://www.genavco.com
Sales Range: $75-99.9 Million
Emp.: 200
Construction, Industrial & Quarry Equipment Supplier
N.A.I.C.S.: 423810
Walib Ismail *(Pres)*

Juma Al Majid Concrete Products Plants L.L.C. (1)
Opposite Kanoo 3 Road InterChange Al Quoz Industrial Area, PO Box 3762, Dubai, 3762, United Arab Emirates
Tel.: (971) 4 3477555
Concrete Products Mfr
N.A.I.C.S.: 327390
Mohamad Majid *(Gen Mgr)*

Juma Al Majid Electro Mechanical Works L.L.C (1)
Marrakesh Street Umm Ramool, Dubai, 60204, United Arab Emirates
Tel.: (971) 4 2851145
Electromechanical Engineering Services
N.A.I.C.S.: 541330

Subsidiary (Domestic):

Al Arabia Electro Mechanical L.L.C (2)
Juma Al Majid Bldg Marrakesh Street Umm Ramool Al Rashidiya, PO Box 60204, Dubai, United Arab Emirates
Tel.: (971) 4 2851145
Web Site: http://www.al-majid.com
Sales Range: $150-199.9 Million
Emp.: 980
Electromechanical Engineering Services
N.A.I.C.S.: 541330
Saleh Chehade *(CEO)*

Al Arabia For Operation & Maintenance L.L.C (2)
PO Box 60204, Dubai, United Arab Emirates
Tel.: (971) 4 2854249
Electromechanical Engineering Services
N.A.I.C.S.: 541330

Skyline Travel, Tourism & Shipping (1)
Sharjah Clock Tower Opp Alza Ara Hospital Next to Optic Cetnre, Sharjah, United Arab Emirates
Tel.: (971) 6 5636923
Web Site: http://www.skylineuae.com
Sales Range: $1-4.9 Billion
Emp.: 20
Travel & Tour Operator
N.A.I.C.S.: 561510
Samer Ascha *(Gen Mgr)*

JUMBO BAG LTD.
S K Enclave No 4 Nowroji Road, Chetput, Chennai, 600031, India
Tel.: (91) 4426461415
Web Site:
    https://www.jumbobaglimited.com
516078—(BOM)
Rev.: $17,900,337
Assets: $13,805,187
Liabilities: $9,479,352
Net Worth: $4,325,835
Earnings: $144,813
Emp.: 241
Fiscal Year-end: 03/31/22
Polypropylene Bag Mfr
N.A.I.C.S.: 314910
Gupta G. P. N. *(CFO)*

JUMBO ELECTRONICS COMPANY LTD.

Jumbo Bag Ltd.—(Continued)

JUMBO ELECTRONICS COMPANY LTD.
ESAG Building Tariq Bin Ziyad Road, PO Box 3426, Dubai, United Arab Emirates
Tel.: (971) 43367999
Web Site: http://www.jumbocorp.com
Year Founded: 1974
Sales Range: $350-399.9 Million
Emp.: 1,000
Electronic, Communication & Computer Products Distr
N.A.I.C.S.: 423620
Vidya M. Chhabria *(Founder & Chm)*

JUMBO GROUP LIMITED
4 Kaki Bukit Avenue 1 03-08, Kaki Bukit Industrial Estate, Singapore, 417939, Singapore
Tel.: (65) 62658626
Web Site: https://www.jumbogroup.sg
42R—(CAT)
Rev.: $132,460,911
Assets: $97,588,737
Liabilities: $53,147,833
Net Worth: $44,440,904
Earnings: $10,538,718
Emp.: 515
Fiscal Year-end: 09/30/23
Restaurant Chain
N.A.I.C.S.: 722511
Kiam Meng Ang *(Grp CEO)*

JUMBO INTERACTIVE LIMITED
Level 1 601 Coronation Drive, PO Box 824, Toowong, 4066, QLD, Australia
Tel.: (61) 738313705
Web Site:
 https://www.jumbointeractive.com
JIN—(ASX)
Rev.: $106,392,895
Assets: $113,406,116
Liabilities: $36,511,084
Net Worth: $76,895,032
Earnings: $28,945,646
Emp.: 250
Fiscal Year-end: 06/30/24
Online Lottery Services
N.A.I.C.S.: 713290
David Todd *(CFO)*

Subsidiaries:

Gatherwell Limited (1)
Jactin House Urban Village 24 Hood Street Ancoats, Manchester, United Kingdom
Tel.: (44) 1865582482
Web Site: https://www.gatherwell.co.uk
Lottery Management Services
N.A.I.C.S.: 713290

Intellitron Pty. Ltd. (1)
Level 1 601 Coronation Dr, Toowong, 4066, QLD, Australia
Tel.: (61) 733315940
Software Publishing Services
N.A.I.C.S.: 513210

Jumbo Interactive GmbH (1)
Willy-Brandt Platz 3, 81829, Munich, Germany **(100%)**
Tel.: (49) 8912228000
Web Site: http://www.jumbolotto.de
Online Lottery & Gaming Services
N.A.I.C.S.: 713210
Yan Stessen *(Mng Dir)*

Jumbo Interactive North America (1)
3030 Greenmont Circle, Belmont, NC 28012 **(100%)**
Tel.: (760) 521-2929
Web Site: http://www.jumbointeractive.com
Emp.: 1
Online Lottery & Gaming Services
N.A.I.C.S.: 713290
Brian J. Roberts *(Pres-North America)*

Jumbo Interactive Pty. Ltd. (1)
Level 1 601 Coronation Drive, Toowong, 4066, QLD, Australia
Tel.: (61) 738313705
Online Lottery Retail Services
N.A.I.C.S.: 713290

Stride Management Corp. (1)
3950 12 Street NE, Calgary, AB, Canada
Tel.: (61)
Web Site: https://www.stridemgmt.com
Lottery & Raffle Management Services
N.A.I.C.S.: 713290

TMS Global Services Pty. Ltd. (1)
370 St Kilda Road, Melbourne, 3004, VIC, Australia
Tel.: (61) 393212800
Sales Range: $50-74.9 Million
Emp.: 10
Online Lottery Retailer & Whslr
N.A.I.C.S.: 713290

Subsidiary (Non-US):

TMS Fiji Limited (2)
1st Floor Ming Building 81 Amy Street, Suva, 142, Fiji
Tel.: (679) 3315125
Web Site: http://www.tattersalls.com.au
Sales Range: $25-49.9 Million
Emp.: 20
Online Lottery Retail Services
N.A.I.C.S.: 713290
Graeme Brown *(Pres & Exec Dir)*

JUMBO S.A.
9 Kyprou Idras Str, Moschato, 183 46, Athens, Greece
Tel.: (30) 2104805200
Web Site: https://corporate.e-jumbo.gr
Year Founded: 1986
JUMSY—(OTCIQ)
Rev.: $1,024,585,379
Assets: $2,050,046,305
Liabilities: $515,552,983
Net Worth: $1,534,493,322
Earnings: $268,293,758
Emp.: 5,591
Fiscal Year-end: 12/31/22
Toys & Stationery Items Retail Sales
N.A.I.C.S.: 459120
Evangelos Papaevangelou *(Deputy Chm)*

JUMBO SUPERMARKTEN B.V.
Rijksweg 15, Veghel, 5462CE, Netherlands
Tel.: (31) 413380200 Nl
Web Site:
 http://www.jumbosupermarkten.nl
Sales Range: $5-14.9 Billion
Emp.: 13,800
Supermarket Operator
N.A.I.C.S.: 445110
Colette Cloosterman-van Eerd *(Supervisory Bd of Dirs & Chm-Supervisory Bd)*

Subsidiaries:

C1000 (1)
Databankweg 26, Amersfoort, 3821 AL, Netherlands
Tel.: (31) 33 453 3600
Web Site: http://www.c1000.nl
Sales Range: $250-299.9 Million
Emp.: 600
Grocery Stores
N.A.I.C.S.: 424410
T. Heidman *(CEO)*

La Place B.V. (1)
Arendstraat 25, 1223 RE, Hilversum, Netherlands
Tel.: (31) 303000500
Web Site: http://www.laplace.com
Restaurant Operators
N.A.I.C.S.: 722511

Laurus International B.V. (1)
Parallelweg 64, 5223, 's-Hertogenbosch, Netherlands
Tel.: (31) 736 223 622
Web Site: http://www.laurus.nl
Groceries Whslr
N.A.I.C.S.: 424410

Subsidiary (Domestic):

Laurus Nederland B.V. (2)
Parallelweg 64, PO Box 175, 's-Hertogenbosch, 5201 AD, Noord-Brabant, Netherlands
Tel.: (31) 736223622
Web Site: http://www.laurus.com
Rev.: $1,982,324,462
Emp.: 150
Provider of Grocery Services
N.A.I.C.S.: 445110

Subsidiary (Domestic):

Van Der Neut Supermarkten B.V. (3)
Parallelweg 64, 5223, 's-Hertogenbosch, Netherlands
Tel.: (31) 736223622
Groceries Whslr
N.A.I.C.S.: 424410

Super Babylon Nederland B.V. (1)
Herengracht 468, 1017 CA, Amsterdam, Noord Holland, Netherlands
Tel.: (31) 736 403 111
Groceries Whslr
N.A.I.C.S.: 424410

JUMEI INTERNATIONAL HOLDING LIMITED
20th Floor Tower B Zhonghui Plaza 11 Dongzhimen South Road, Dongcheng District, Beijing, 100007, China
Tel.: (86) 10 5676 6999 Ky
Web Site: http://www.jumei.com
Year Founded: 2010
Rev.: $623,558,519
Assets: $747,625,185
Liabilities: $204,190,659
Net Worth: $543,434,526
Earnings: $17,043,924
Emp.: 3,005
Fiscal Year-end: 12/31/18
Online Beauty Products Retailer
N.A.I.C.S.: 456120
Leo Ou Chen *(Founder, Chm, CEO & Acting CFO)*

Subsidiaries:

IT'S HANBUL CO., LTD (1)
311 Hakdong-ro, Gangnam-gu, Seoul, Korea (South)
Tel.: (82) 234500123
Web Site: http://www.itshanbul.com
Cosmetic Product Distr
N.A.I.C.S.: 424210

JUMIA TECHNOLOGIES AG
Skalitzer Strasse 104, 10997, Berlin, Germany
Tel.: (49) 30398203451 De
Web Site: http://group.jumia.com
Year Founded: 2012
JMIA—(NYSE)
Rev.: $186,402,000
Assets: $189,942,000
Liabilities: $121,218,000
Net Worth: $68,724,000
Earnings: ($104,178,000)
Emp.: 2,915
Fiscal Year-end: 12/31/23
Online Shopping Services
N.A.I.C.S.: 459999
Jeremy Hodara *(Co-Founder)*

JUMP WORLD HOLDING LIMITED
12th Floor Tower A Changtai Plaza 2889 Jinke Road, Pudong New District, Shanghai, 201203, China
Tel.: (86) 21 5080 1857 Ky
Year Founded: 2018
Sales Range: $25-49.9 Million
Emp.: 376
Holding Company
N.A.I.C.S.: 551112
Yaxi Wu *(Chm & CEO)*

INTERNATIONAL PUBLIC

JUMPGATE AB
Tel.: (46) 704387000
Web Site: https://jumpgategames.se
Year Founded: 2016
Game Development Services
N.A.I.C.S.: 541512
Don Geyer *(CEO)*

JUNEE LIMITED
3791 Jalan Bukit Merah 09-03 E-Centre at Redhill, Singapore, 159471, Singapore
Tel.: (65) 60221124 VG
Year Founded: 2021
JUNE—(NASDAQ)
Rev.: $2,903,179
Assets: $8,006,374
Liabilities: $1,041,386
Net Worth: $6,964,988
Earnings: ($854,927)
Emp.: 24
Fiscal Year-end: 06/30/24
Management Consulting Services
N.A.I.C.S.: 541618

JUNEYAO AIRLINES CO., LTD.
Lane 2 kangqiao East Road, Pudong, Shanghai, 201210, China
Tel.: (86) 2195520
Web Site:
 https://global.juneyaoair.com
Year Founded: 2006
603885—(SHG)
Rev.: $1,152,732,915
Assets: $6,338,674,068
Liabilities: $4,995,078,992
Net Worth: $1,343,595,076
Earnings: ($582,362,310)
Fiscal Year-end: 12/31/22
Oil Transportation Services
N.A.I.C.S.: 488190
Wang Junjin *(Chm)*

JUNG GUMMITECHNIK GMBH
Robert-Bosch-Strasse 2-6, 64683, Einhausen, Germany
Tel.: (49) 625196340
Web Site: http://www.jung-gt.de
Year Founded: 1982
Sales Range: $10-24.9 Million
Emp.: 64
Fitting Components Mfr
N.A.I.C.S.: 332919
Herr Alexander Kreisz *(Gen Mgr)*

JUNG SHING WIRE CO., LTD.
231 Section 3 Zhongzheng Rd, Jenteh District, T'ainan, 717, Taiwan
Tel.: (886) 62705211
Web Site: http://www.jswire.com.tw
Year Founded: 1971
1617—(TAI)
Rev.: $92,451,973
Assets: $105,808,394
Liabilities: $38,694,364
Net Worth: $67,114,030
Earnings: $258,805
Emp.: 1,000
Fiscal Year-end: 12/31/23
Magnet Wires Mfr
N.A.I.C.S.: 335139
Dong-Ze Wang *(Gen Mgr)*

Subsidiaries:

Dongguan Jung Shing Wire Co., Ltd. (1)
No 125 Huanshi Nan Road Tangxia Town, Dongguan, 523726, Guangdong, China
Tel.: (86) 76987913003
Web Site: http://www.jswire.com.tw
Sales Range: $100-124.9 Million
Emp.: 282
Silo Mfr
N.A.I.C.S.: 332618

Longsun Technologies Co., Ltd. (1)
No 51 Hwan Gong Rd, Yang Kang Ind Dist, Tainan City, 71041, Taiwan

Tel.: (886) 63015408
Web Site: http://www.longsun.tw
Sales Range: $25-49.9 Million
Emp.: 30
Switching Power Converters & Inverters Mfr
N.A.I.C.S.: 335999
Pet Wang *(Pres)*

JUNG TECHNOLOGIES HOLDING AG
Gartenstrasse 4, 6300, Zug, Switzerland   CH
Web Site:
 http://www.jungtechnologies.ch
Holding Services
N.A.I.C.S.: 551112
Thomas W. Jung *(Pres)*

Subsidiaries:

ACUTRONIC Schweiz AG   (1)
Techcenter Schwarz, 8608, Bubikon, Switzerland   (100%)
Tel.: (41) 552532323
Web Site: http://www.acutronic.com
Sales Range: $10-24.9 Million
Emp.: 100
Developer & Mfr of Flight Motion Simulators & Inertial Guidance Test Equipment
N.A.I.C.S.: 334511
Colin Stevens *(VP-Sls)*

Subsidiary (US):

ACUTRONIC USA Inc.   (2)
700 Waterfront Dr, Pittsburgh, PA 15222-4742
Tel.: (412) 926-1200
Web Site: http://www.acutronic.com
Flight Motion Simulators & Inertial Guidance Test Equipment Mfr
N.A.I.C.S.: 334511

JUNG VON MATT
Glashuttenstrasse 38, 20357, Hamburg, Germany
Tel.: (49) 40 43210
Web Site: http://www.jvm.com
Sales Range: $50-74.9 Million
Emp.: 500
Advetising Agency
N.A.I.C.S.: 541810
Jean-Remy von Matt *(Co-Founder)*

Subsidiaries:

Jung von Matt/Donau   (1)
Langenfeldgasse 27/B/3, 1120, Vienna, Austria
Tel.: (43) 1 811 45 0
Web Site: http://www.jvm.com
Emp.: 40
N.A.I.C.S.: 541810
Andreas Putz *(Mng Dir)*

Jung von Matt/Elbe   (1)
Glashuttenstrasse 38, 20357, Hamburg, Germany
Tel.: (49) 40 432 42 0
Web Site: http://www.jvm.com
N.A.I.C.S.: 541810
Jens Pfau *(Dir-Creative)*

Jung von Matt/Limmat   (1)
Wolfbachstrasse 19, 20357, Hamburg, Germany
Tel.: (49) 44 254 66 00
Web Site: http://www.jvm.com
N.A.I.C.S.: 541810

Jung von Matt/Neckar   (1)
Neckarstrasse 155, 70173, Stuttgart, Germany
Tel.: (49) 7112489840
Web Site: http://www.jvm-neckar.de
N.A.I.C.S.: 541810
Peter Waibel *(Owner)*

Jung von Matt/Spree   (1)
Hasenheide 54, Berlin, 10967, Germany
Tel.: (49) 30 789 56 0
Web Site: http://www.jvm.com
Sales Range: $25-49.9 Million
Emp.: 100
N.A.I.C.S.: 541810
Peter Gocht *(Dir-Creative & Copy)*

Jung von Matt/Stroemmen   (1)

Kungsgatan 17 5 tr, 111 43, Stockholm, Sweden
Tel.: (46) 8 410 479 00
Web Site: http://www.jungvonmatt.se
Sales Range: $25-49.9 Million
Emp.: 11
Advertising Agencies Services
N.A.I.C.S.: 541810
Johan Jager *(Creative Dir)*

JvM next GmbH   (1)
Glashuttenstrasse 38, 20357, Hamburg, Germany
Tel.: (49) 40 4321 0
Web Site: http://www.jvm.de
Emp.: 80
Mobile Software Development Services
N.A.I.C.S.: 541511
Peter Figge *(Exec Officer)*

KASPEN/Jung von Matt   (1)
Kralodvorska 16, 11000, Prague, Czech Republic
Tel.: (420) 296 327 000
Web Site: http://www.kaspenjvm.com
N.A.I.C.S.: 541810

JUNGDAWN CO., LTD.
137-17 Dongsu Agricultural and Industrial Complex Road, Naju, Jeollanam-do, Korea (South)
Tel.: (82) 613345289
Web Site: https://jungdawn.com
Year Founded: 2014
208140—(KRS)
Rev.: $140,091,840
Assets: $130,155,891
Liabilities: $58,047,121
Net Worth: $72,108,770
Earnings: $11,750,399
Emp.: 387
Fiscal Year-end: 12/31/22
Financial Investment Management Services
N.A.I.C.S.: 523940

JUNGFRAUBAHN HOLDING AG
Harderstrasse 14, 3800, Interlaken, Switzerland
Tel.: (41) 338287111
Web Site: https://www.jungfrau.ch
Year Founded: 1994
JFN—(SWX)
Rev.: $330,566,914
Assets: $1,060,000,005
Liabilities: $274,913,241
Net Worth: $785,086,764
Earnings: $94,624,436
Emp.: 822
Fiscal Year-end: 12/31/23
Holding Company
N.A.I.C.S.: 551112
Thomas Bieger *(Chm)*

JUNGHANS UHREN GMBH
Geishaldenstrasse 49, 78713, Schramberg, Germany
Tel.: (49) 742218100
Web Site: http://www.junghans.de
Year Founded: 1861
Rev.: $36,000,000
Emp.: 6,000
Watch & Clock Mfr
N.A.I.C.S.: 334519
Matthias Stotz *(Mng Dir)*

JUNGHEINRICH AG
Friedrich Ebert-Damm 129, 22047, Hamburg, Germany
Tel.: (49) 4069480   De
Web Site:
 https://www.jungheinrich.com
Year Founded: 1953
JUN3—(DUS)
Rev.: $6,121,941,594
Assets: $7,627,587,158
Liabilities: $5,174,501,012
Net Worth: $2,453,086,146
Earnings: $330,355,175

Emp.: 21,117
Fiscal Year-end: 12/31/23
Industrial Trucks, Material Handling Equipment & Warehousing Technology Mfr
N.A.I.C.S.: 333924
Hans-George Frey *(Chm-Supervisory Bd)*

Subsidiaries:

Arculus GmbH   (1)
Balanstrasse 73 Haus 10, 81541, Munich, Germany
Tel.: (49) 8921129880
Web Site: https://www.arculus.de
Emp.: 100
Software Development Services
N.A.I.C.S.: 541511

Gebrauchtgerate-Zentrum Dresden GmbH & Co. KG   (1)
Hamburger Ring 3, 1665, Klipphausen, Germany
Tel.: (49) 35204 7945 0
Web Site: http://www.gebrauchtgeraete-zentrum.de
Emp.: 16
Fork Lift Truck Mfr & Distr
N.A.I.C.S.: 333924

ISI Automation GmbH & Co. KG   (1)
Im Langen Kamp 3, Extertal, 32699, Cologne, Germany
Tel.: (49) 526294690
Web Site: https://www.isi-automation.com
Emp.: 35
Computer Training Services
N.A.I.C.S.: 611420

Jungheinrich (CR), S.r.o.   (1)
Modletice 101, 25101, Ricany, Czech Republic
Tel.: (420) 313333111
Web Site: https://www.jungheinrich.cz
Sales Range: $50-74.9 Million
Emp.: 150
Navigational Services to Shipping
N.A.I.C.S.: 488330

Jungheinrich (Portugal) Equipamentos de Transporte, Lda.   (1)
Rua Francisco Lyon de Castro - Mem Martins Business Park Ed 6, Mem Martins, 2729-015, Lisbon, Portugal
Tel.: (351) 219156060
Web Site: https://www.jungheinrich.pt
Sales Range: $25-49.9 Million
Emp.: 50
Navigational Services to Shipping
N.A.I.C.S.: 488330

Jungheinrich Australia Pty. Ltd. (1)
37 White Road, Gepps Cross, Adelaide, 5094, SA, Australia
Tel.: (61) 882431222
Logistic Services
N.A.I.C.S.: 541614

Jungheinrich Austria Vertriebs Ges.m.b.H.   (1)
Slamastrasse 41, 1230, Vienna, Austria
Web Site: https://www.jungheinrich.at
Emp.: 200
Navigational Services to Shipping
N.A.I.C.S.: 488330

Jungheinrich Beteiligungs-GmbH   (1)
Am Stadtrand 35, Hamburg, 22047, Germany
Tel.: (49) 4069481550
Logistics Consulting Servies
N.A.I.C.S.: 541614

Jungheinrich Business Services Romania S.R.L.   (1)
Bd Saturn no 51, 500428, Brasov, Romania
Tel.: (40) 244700701
Logistic Services
N.A.I.C.S.: 541614

Jungheinrich Colombia SAS   (1)
Parque Industrial San Jorge Bodega 57 Calle 2 18-93 Via Mosquera, Mosquera, Cundinamarca, Colombia
Tel.: (57) 1 428 9080
Web Site: https://www.jungheinrich.co
Industrial Machinery Equipment Distr
N.A.I.C.S.: 423830

Jungheinrich Danmark A/S   (1)
Park Alle 350c 1st floor, 2605, Brondby, Denmark
Tel.: (45) 89874800
Web Site: https://www.jungheinrich.dk
Sales Range: $25-49.9 Million
Emp.: 60
Navigational Services to Shipping
N.A.I.C.S.: 488330

Jungheinrich Degempoint AG & Co. KG   (1)
Degernpoint E10, 85368, Moosburg, Germany
Tel.: (49) 8761800
Forklift Mfr & Distr
N.A.I.C.S.: 333924

Jungheinrich Degernpoint AG & Co. KG   (1)
Degernpoint E10, 85368, Moosburg, Germany
Tel.: (49) 8761800
Industrial Machinery Equipment Distr
N.A.I.C.S.: 423830

Jungheinrich Design Center Houston Corporation   (1)
2121 W Sam Houston Pkwy N, Houston, TX 77043-2305
Tel.: (713) 932-2100
Industrial Truck Mfr
N.A.I.C.S.: 333924
Harnisch Carsten *(Mng Dir)*

Jungheinrich Ecuador S.A.   (1)
Av Luis Felipe Pezo Campuzano and 3er Pasaje 32 Bodegas La Carlota 12, Guayaquil, Ecuador
Tel.: (593) 46005072
Web Site: https://www.jungheinrich.ec
Industrial Machinery Equipment Distr
N.A.I.C.S.: 423830

Jungheinrich Export AG & Co. KG   (1)
Am Stadtrand 35, 22047, Hamburg, Germany
Web Site: http://cy.jungheinrich.com
Sales Range: $25-49.9 Million
Emp.: 25
Industrial Lift Truck Distr
N.A.I.C.S.: 423830
Alexander Oezbahadir *(Mgr-Export)*

Jungheinrich Finance AG & Co. KG   (1)
Friedrich-Ebert-Damm 129, 22047, Hamburg, Germany
Tel.: (49) 4069480
Web Site: http://www.jungheinrich.de
Financial Management Services
N.A.I.C.S.: 523999

Jungheinrich Finance S.r.l.   (1)
Via Amburgo 1, Rosate, 20088, Milan, Italy
Tel.: (39) 02908711
Web Site: http://www.jungheinrich.it
Emp.: 150
Financial Management Services
N.A.I.C.S.: 523999

Jungheinrich Financial Services GmbH   (1)
Friedrich-Ebert-Damm 129, 22047, Hamburg, Germany
Tel.: (49) 4069480
Web Site: http://www.jungheinrich.de
Financial Management Services
N.A.I.C.S.: 523999

Jungheinrich Financial Services Ltd.   (1)
Sherbourne House Sherbourne Drive, Tilbrook, Milton Keynes, MK7 8HX, United Kingdom
Tel.: (44) 1908 363 100
Financial Management Services
N.A.I.C.S.: 523999

Jungheinrich Financial Services S.r.l.   (1)
Via Amburgo 1, Rosate, 20081, Milan, Italy
Tel.: (39) 02 908711
Sales Range: $50-74.9 Million
Emp.: 150
Financial Management Services
N.A.I.C.S.: 523999

Jungheinrich Fleet Services S.L. (1)

JUNGHEINRICH AG

Jungheinrich AG—(Continued)
Poligono Industrial El Barcelones C/Hostal del Pi 9, 08639, Abrera, Spain
Web Site: http://www.jungheinrich.es
Industrial Trucking Machinery Rental Services
N.A.I.C.S.: 532490

Jungheinrich France S.A.S. (1)
4 rue des Freres Caudron, CS 60002, 78142, Velizy-Villacoublay, Cedex, France
Tel.: (33) 139456868
Web Site: https://www.jungheinrich.fr
Emp.: 200
Navigational Services to Shipping
N.A.I.C.S.: 488330
Alexander Abe *(Pres)*

Jungheinrich Hellas EPE (1)
Tel.: (30) 2102447800
Web Site: http://www.jungheinrich.gr
Sales Range: $25-49.9 Million
Emp.: 50
Navigational Services to Shipping
N.A.I.C.S.: 488330
Elena Kalloma *(Gen Mgr)*

Jungheinrich Hungaria Kft
Vendel Park Tormasret u 14, 2051, Biatorbagy, Hungary
Tel.: (36) 2 353 1500
Web Site: https://www.jungheinrich.hu
Forklift Truck Distr
N.A.I.C.S.: 423830

Jungheinrich Istif Makinalari San. ve Tic. Ltd. Sti. (1)
Kucukbakkalkoy Mahallesi Defne Sokak Buyukhanli Plaza No 3, Ic Kapi No 33 Atasehir, 34750, Istanbul, Turkiye
Tel.: (90) 2164300800
Web Site: https://www.jungheinrich.com.tr
Sales Range: $25-49.9 Million
Emp.: 15
Navigational Services to Shipping
N.A.I.C.S.: 488330

Jungheinrich Italiana S.r.l. (1)
via Hamburg 1, 20088, Rosate, MI, Italy
Tel.: (39) 0290 8711
Web Site: https://www.jungheinrich.it
Emp.: 300
Industrial Lift Truck Mfr
N.A.I.C.S.: 333924

Jungheinrich Katalog GmbH & Co. KG (1)
Kieler Str 105, 22769, Hamburg, Germany
Tel.: (49) 40 89706 0
Web Site: http://www.jh-profishop.de
Sales Range: $50-74.9 Million
Emp.: 75
Industrial Fork Lift Distr
N.A.I.C.S.: 423830
Stefan Wissler *(Gen Mgr)*

Jungheinrich Landsberg AG & Co. KG (1)
Bitterfelder Strasse 2, 6188, Landsberg, Germany
Tel.: (49) 346027060
Emp.: 15
Battery Powered Truck Mfr
N.A.I.C.S.: 333924

Jungheinrich Lift Truck (Shanghai) Co., Ltd. (1)
4th Floor Building 1 Lane 1588 Shen Chang Road, Minhang District, Shanghai, China
Tel.: (86) 2153295000
Industrial Machinery Equipment Distr
N.A.I.C.S.: 423830

Jungheinrich Lift Truck Comercio de Empilhadeiras Ltda. (1)
Rod Vice Prefeito Hermenegildo Tonolli 2535, 13295-000, Itupeva, 13295-000, Sao Paulo, Brazil
Tel.: (55) 1148390800
Web Site: https://www.jungheinrich.com.br
Sales Range: $25-49.9 Million
Emp.: 50
Industrial Forklift Machinery Distr
N.A.I.C.S.: 423830

Jungheinrich Lift Truck Corp. (1)
5601 Eastport Blvd, Richmond, VA 23231
Tel.: (804) 737-2400

Web Site: http://www.jungheinrich-us.com
Navigational Services to Shipping
N.A.I.C.S.: 488330

Jungheinrich Lift Truck Finance Ltd. (1)
Sherbourne House Sherbourne Drive Tilbrook, Milton Keynes, MK7 8HX, Bucks, United Kingdom
Tel.: (44) 1908 363100
Financial Management Services
N.A.I.C.S.: 523999

Jungheinrich Lift Truck India Private Ltd. (1)
Tel.: (91) 2225727901
Industrial Machinery Equipment Distr
N.A.I.C.S.: 423830

Jungheinrich Lift Truck Limited (1)
J5 Maynooth Business Campus, Maynooth, Ireland
Tel.: (353) 1 651 7100
Web Site: https://www.jungheinrich.ie
Sales Range: $25-49.9 Million
Emp.: 40
Navigational Services to Shipping
N.A.I.C.S.: 488330

Jungheinrich Lift Truck Ltd. (1)
335/3 Moo 9 Bangna-Trad KM 19 Rd, Tambon Bangchalong Amphoe Bangplee, Samut Prakan, 10540, Thailand
Tel.: (66) 20090200
Web Site: https://www.jungheinrich.co.th
Sales Range: $25-49.9 Million
Emp.: 45
Navigational Services to Shipping
N.A.I.C.S.: 488330

Jungheinrich Lift Truck Ltda. (1)
Rua Norivaldo Martins da Silva 150, CEP 13 211-241 Bairro do Retir, Jundiai, Brazil
Tel.: (55) 1148158200
Web Site: http://www.jungheinrich.com.br
Sales Range: $25-49.9 Million
Emp.: 90
Navigational Services to Shipping
N.A.I.C.S.: 488330

Jungheinrich Lift Truck Malaysia Sdn. Bhd. (1)
No 22A Jalan Anggerik Mokara 31/47 Seksyen 31, Kota Kemuning, 40460, Shah Alam, Malaysia
Tel.: (60) 355259888
Industrial Machinery Equipment Distr
N.A.I.C.S.: 423830

Jungheinrich Lift Truck Manufacturing (Shanghai) Co., Ltd. (1)
No 651 Tianyi Rd Qingpu Industry Park, Shanghai, 201712, China
Tel.: (86) 2159228224
Industrial Lift Truck Mfr
N.A.I.C.S.: 333924

Jungheinrich Lift Truck OOO (1)
Tel.: (7) 4957809777
Web Site: https://www.jungheinrich.ru
Navigational Services to Shipping
N.A.I.C.S.: 488330
Stefan Demming *(Mng Dir)*

Jungheinrich Lift Truck Oy (1)
Ahjonkulma 1, 04220, Kerava, Finland
Tel.: (358) 10 616 8585
Web Site: https://www.jungheinrich.fi
Sales Range: $25-49.9 Million
Emp.: 34
Navigational Services to Shipping
N.A.I.C.S.: 488330
Mika Laatikainen *(CEO & Mng Dir)*

Jungheinrich Lift Truck SIA (1)
Ritausmas 23, Riga, 1058, Latvia
Tel.: (371) 67813913
Web Site: https://www.jungheinrich.lv
Sales Range: $25-49.9 Million
Emp.: 15
Navigational Services to Shipping
N.A.I.C.S.: 488330
Lada Kalinina *(Chm-Mgmt Bd)*

Jungheinrich Lift Truck Singapore Pte Ltd. (1)
7 Joo Koon Way, Singapore, 628945, Singapore
Tel.: (65) 65587600
Web Site: https://www.jungheinrich.com.sg

Sales Range: $25-49.9 Million
Emp.: 35
Navigational Services to Shipping
N.A.I.C.S.: 488330

Jungheinrich Lift Truck TOV (1)
V Kachaly Str 5-G, 3126, Kiev, Ukraine
Tel.: (380) 445831583
Web Site: https://www.jungheinrich.ua
Forklift Machinery Distr
N.A.I.C.S.: 423830

Jungheinrich Lift Truck UAB (1)
Servces st 1, 02121, Vilnius, Lithuania
Tel.: (370) 52322242
Web Site: https://www.jungheinrich.lt
Sales Range: $25-49.9 Million
Emp.: 20
Navigational Services to Shipping
N.A.I.C.S.: 488330
Ladar Kalenan *(Gen Mgr)*

Jungheinrich Moosburg AG & Co. KG (1)
Steinbockstrasse 38, 85368, Moosburg, Germany
Tel.: (49) 8761800
Automated Intralogistics System & Maintenance Services
N.A.I.C.S.: 541614

Jungheinrich Moosburg GmbH (1)
Steinbockstrasse 38, 85368, Moosburg, Germany
Tel.: (49) 8761 80 0
Emp.: 100
Battery Powered Truck Mfr
N.A.I.C.S.: 333924
Herbert Peters *(Gen Mgr)*

Jungheinrich Nederland B.V. (1)
H A Lorentzweg 3, 2408 AS, Alphen aan den Rijn, Netherlands
Tel.: (31) 172446789
Web Site: https://www.jungheinrich.nl
Sales Range: $25-49.9 Million
Emp.: 100
Navigational Services to Shipping
N.A.I.C.S.: 488330

Jungheinrich New Zealand Ltd. (1)
10 Offenhauser Drive, East Tamaki, Auckland, 2013, New Zealand
Tel.: (64) 800111193
Web Site: https://www.adaptalift.co.nz
Forklift Equipment Mfr
N.A.I.C.S.: 333924

Jungheinrich Norderstedt AG & Co. KG (1)
Lawaetzstr 9-13, 22844, Norderstedt, Germany
Tel.: (49) 4052690
Web Site: http://www.jungheinrich.de
Emp.: 100
Battery Powered Truck Mfr
N.A.I.C.S.: 333924

Jungheinrich Norge AS (1)
Tel.: (47) 2350
Web Site: https://www.jungheinrich.no
Sales Range: $75-99.9 Million
Emp.: 145
Industrial Forklift Machinery Distr
N.A.I.C.S.: 423830
Arild Dragon Set *(CEO)*

Jungheinrich Peru S.A.C. (1)
Carretera Panamericana Sur Km 29.5 Unidad F-01 Megacentro, Lurin, Peru
Tel.: (51) 12070640
Industrial Machinery Equipment Distr
N.A.I.C.S.: 423830

Jungheinrich Polska Sp. z.o.o. (1)
Bronisze ul Swierkowa 3, Bronisze k Warszawy, 05-850, Ozarow Mazowiecki, Poland
Tel.: (48) 223328800
Web Site: https://www.jungheinrich.pl
Sales Range: $25-49.9 Million
Emp.: 50
Navigational Services to Shipping
N.A.I.C.S.: 488330

Jungheinrich Profishop AG & Co. KG (1)
Tel.: (49) 4 089 7060
Web Site: https://www.jh-profishop.de
Industrial Machinery Equipment Distr
N.A.I.C.S.: 423830

INTERNATIONAL PUBLIC

Jungheinrich Profishop GmbH (1)
Slamastr 41, 1230, Vienna, Austria
Tel.: (43) 800539966
Web Site: https://www.jh-profishop.at
Sales Range: $25-49.9 Million
Emp.: 90
Industrial Fork Lift Truck Machinery Mfr
N.A.I.C.S.: 333241

Jungheinrich Rentalift SpA (1)
Miraflores 9699, Pudahuel, Santiago, Chile
Tel.: (56) 224997100
Industrial Machinery Equipment Distr
N.A.I.C.S.: 423830

Jungheinrich Romania S.R.L. (1)
Str Trandafirilor nr 169, Comuna Barcanesti, Tatarani, Romania
Tel.: (40) 72 355 9990
Web Site: https://www.jungheinrich-shop.ro
Industrial Machinery Equipment Distr
N.A.I.C.S.: 423830

Jungheinrich Service & Parts AG & Co. KG (1)
Maybachstrasse 1-3, 24568, Kaltenkirchen, Germany
Tel.: (49) 4052692000
Industrial Machinery Equipment Distr
N.A.I.C.S.: 423830

Jungheinrich South Africa (Pty) Ltd. (1)
Unit 2 Cheia Crescent, Pomona AH, Kempton Park, 1619, South Africa
Tel.: (27) 105968460
Web Site: https://www.jungheinrich-shop.co.za
Industrial Machinery Equipment Distr
N.A.I.C.S.: 423830

Jungheinrich Svenska AB (1)
Starrvagen 16, 23261, Arlov, Sweden
Tel.: (46) 40 690 4600
Web Site: https://www.jungheinrich.se
Sales Range: $25-49.9 Million
Emp.: 35
Navigational Services to Shipping
N.A.I.C.S.: 488330

Jungheinrich UK Holdings Ltd. (1)
Sherbourne House Sherbourne Drive, Tilbrook, Milton Keynes, MK7 8HX, Bucks, United Kingdom
Tel.: (44) 190 836 3100
Web Site: https://www.jungheinrich.co.uk
Emp.: 750
Investment Management Service
N.A.I.C.S.: 523999

Jungheinrich UK Ltd. (1)
Sherbourne House Sherbourne Drive, Tilbrook, Milton Keynes, MK7 8HX, United Kingdom
Tel.: (44) 1908363100
Web Site: https://www.jungheinrich.co.uk
Sales Range: $125-149.9 Million
Emp.: 300
Navigational Services to Shipping
N.A.I.C.S.: 488330

Jungheinrich Vertrieb Deutschland AG & Co. KG (1)
Friedrich-Jungheinrich Strasse 2, 74343, Sachsenheim, Germany
Tel.: (49) 7142 704.0
Sales Range: $50-74.9 Million
Emp.: 100
Industrial Forklift Machinery Distr
N.A.I.C.S.: 423830
Sven Feldmann *(Gen Mgr)*

Jungheinrich d.o.o. (1)
Korenova cesta 11, 1241, Kamnik, Slovenia
Tel.: (386) 15610480
Web Site: https://www.jungheinrich.si
Emp.: 40
Navigational Services to Shipping
N.A.I.C.S.: 488330

Jungheinrich de Espana S.A.U. (1)
C/Hostal del Pi 9 Poligono Industrial El Barcelones, 08630, Abrera, Barcelona, Spain
Tel.: (34) 937738200
Web Site: http://www.jungheinrich.es
Forklift Trucking Machinery Distr
N.A.I.C.S.: 423830

Jungheinrich n.v./s.a. (1)

Esperantolaan 1, Heverlee, 3001, Leuven, Belgium
Tel.: (32) 1 639 8711
Web Site: https://www.jungheinrich.be
Sales Range: $25-49.9 Million
Emp.: 250
Navigational Services to Shipping
N.A.I.C.S.: 488330

Jungheinrich spol S.r.o. (1)
Dialnicna cesta 17, 903 01, Senec, Slovakia
Tel.: (421) 249205811
Web Site: https://www.jungheinrich.sk
Sales Range: $25-49.9 Million
Emp.: 40
Navigational Services to Shipping
N.A.I.C.S.: 488330

Lifttrucks JH (1)
Koshkunova Street 1, 50010, Almaty, Kazakhstan
Tel.: (7) 7272911955
Web Site: http://www.jungheinrich.cn
Navigational Services to Shipping
N.A.I.C.S.: 488330

MIAS Hungary Kft. (1)
Esze Tamas u 23, 3200, Gyongyos, Hungary
Tel.: (36) 37507121
Emp.: 130
Industrial Machinery Equipment Mfr
N.A.I.C.S.: 333248

MIAS Inc. (1)
14240 S Lakes Dr, Charlotte, NC 28273
Tel.: (704) 665-1098
Industrial Machinery Equipment Mfr
N.A.I.C.S.: 333248

MIAS Maschinenbau, Industrieanlagen & Service GmbH
Waldmeisterstrasse 99, 80935, Munich, Germany
Tel.: (49) 89354960
Emp.: 150
Industrial Machinery Equipment Mfr
N.A.I.C.S.: 333248
Walter Kennerknecht (Head-Sls)

MIAS Materials Handling (Kunshan) Co., Ltd. (1)
No 399 Jian De Rd GIP II, Zhangpu Town, Kunshan, 215321, China
Tel.: (86) 51257293100
Industrial Machinery Equipment Mfr
N.A.I.C.S.: 333248
David Wang (Gen Mgr)

JUNGLE21 SA
c/ Antonio Maura 16 4, 28014, Madrid, Spain
Tel.: (34) 916588770
Web Site: https://wejungle.com
Year Founded: 2021
MLJ21—(EUR)
Rev.: $12,727,540
Assets: $9,184,446
Liabilities: $8,391,935
Net Worth: $792,511
Earnings: $2,697,771
Emp.: 140
Fiscal Year-end: 12/31/21
Digital Marketing Services
N.A.I.C.S.: 541810
Agustin Vivancos (CEO & Founder)

JUNHE PUMPS HOLDING CO., LTD.
QingDian West Yinxian Rd, Haishu District, Ningbo, 315000, Zhejiang, China
Tel.: (86) 13326126851
Web Site: https://www.junhepumps.com
Year Founded: 2003
603617—(SHG)
Rev.: $105,829,308
Assets: $351,241,446
Liabilities: $167,715,873
Net Worth: $183,525,573
Earnings: $7,557,255
Emp.: 1,500
Fiscal Year-end: 12/31/22

Household Water Pump Mfr
N.A.I.C.S.: 333914
Zhang Ahua (Chm)

JUNIOR A.D.
selo Brzece bb, Brus, Serbia
Tel.: (381) 37 823 355
Web Site: http://www.juniorhotel.rs
Year Founded: 1990
Sales Range: Less than $1 Million
Emp.: 70
Home Management Services
N.A.I.C.S.: 721110

JUNIPER DEVELOPMENT GROUP
31 Brisbane Road, Mooloolaba, 4557, QLD, Australia
Tel.: (61) 754448765
Web Site: http://www.juniper.com.au
Sales Range: $25-49.9 Million
Emp.: 75
Development, Property Management & Construction Services
N.A.I.C.S.: 236220
Graeme Juniper (Co-Mng Dir)

JUNMA TYRE CORD COMPANY LIMITED
No 80 Chenghang Hedong Road, Yangshe Town, Zhangjiagang, 215617, Jiangsu, China
Tel.: (86) 512 5829 1688 CN
Year Founded: 1998
Sales Range: $400-449.9 Million
Tyre Cord Mfr
N.A.I.C.S.: 325998
Peixing Yang (Chm)

JUNO MINERALS LIMITED
Level 1 2A 300 Fitzgerald Street, PO Box Z5117, Perth, 6006, WA, Australia
Tel.: (61) 893465599
Web Site: https://www.junominerals.com.au
Year Founded: 2020
JNO—(ASX)
Rev.: $304,766
Assets: $14,983,962
Liabilities: $221,417
Net Worth: $14,762,544
Earnings: ($6,386,306)
Fiscal Year-end: 06/30/23
Mineral Exploration Services
N.A.I.C.S.: 212390
Melissa North (CFO)

JUNO PHARMACEUTICALS, INC.
402-2233 Argentia Road, L5N 2X7, Mississauga, ON, Canada
Tel.: (905) 829-3838
Web Site: https://www.junopharm.ca
Pharmaceutical Manufacturing
N.A.I.C.S.: 325412
Bruce Levins (COO)

Subsidiaries:

Omega Laboratories Limited (1)
11177 Hamon Street, Montreal, H3M 3E4, QC, Canada
Tel.: (514) 335-0310
Web Site: https://www.omegapharma.ca
Health Care Srvices
N.A.I.C.S.: 621610
Bruce W. Levins (Pres & Gen Mgr)

JUNTENDO CO., LTD.
2179-1 Toudacho, Masuda, 699-3676, Shimane, Japan
Tel.: (81) 856242400 JP
Web Site: https://www.juntendo.co.jp
Year Founded: 1977
9835—(TKS)
Sales Range: $350-399.9 Million
Emp.: 638

Household Appliance Store Operator
N.A.I.C.S.: 444110
Izuka Tadashi (Mng Dir)

JUPAI HOLDINGS LIMITED
Room 603 Building B4 Lane 9 Yunjuan North Road, Pudong New District, Shanghai, 201100, China
Tel.: (86) 2152265851 Ky
Web Site: https://www.jpinvestment.cn
Year Founded: 2012
JPPYY—(OTCIQ)
Rev.: $15,811,203
Assets: $145,596,586
Liabilities: $15,412,253
Net Worth: $130,184,333
Earnings: $3,050,627
Emp.: 90
Fiscal Year-end: 12/31/22
Holding Company; Third-Party Wealth Management Services
N.A.I.C.S.: 551112
Jianda Ni (CEO & Chm)

JUPITER BACH A/S
Theilgaards Alle 4, 4600, Koge, Denmark
Tel.: (45) 55 589 3333
Web Site: http://jupiterbach.com
Wind Electric Power Generation
N.A.I.C.S.: 221115
Lars Steen Rasmussen (CEO)

Subsidiaries:

BACH Composite Industry a/s (1)
Erhvervsvej 9, 7760, Hurup, Denmark
Tel.: (45) 96 88 32 00
Web Site: http://www.bach-ci.com
Rev.: $55,656,300
Plastic Composite Mfr
N.A.I.C.S.: 326199
Soren Friis Knudsen (Chm)

JUPITER EMERGING & FRONTIER INCOME TRUST PLC
The Zig Zag Building 70 Victoria Street, London, SW1E 6SQ, United Kingdom
Tel.: (44) 2038171000
JEFI—(LSE)
Rev.: $6,078,512
Assets: $116,698,749
Liabilities: $14,691,888
Net Worth: $102,006,861
Earnings: $4,488,622
Fiscal Year-end: 09/30/20
Investment Management Service
N.A.I.C.S.: 525990
Charles Sunnucks (Mgr-Fund)

JUPITER ENERGY LIMITED
Level 14 333 Collins Street, Melbourne, 3000, VIC, Australia
Tel.: (61) 398639779
Web Site: https://www.jupiterenergy.com
JPR—(ASX)
Rev.: $3,162,025
Assets: $15,788,593
Liabilities: $78,282,113
Net Worth: ($62,493,520)
Earnings: ($8,819,618)
Emp.: 31
Fiscal Year-end: 06/30/22
Crude Petroleum Extraction Services
N.A.I.C.S.: 211120
Geoffrey Gander (Chm & CEO)

Subsidiaries:

Jupiter Energy (Kazakhstan) Pty Ltd (1)
Ground Fl 10 Outram St, West Perth, 005, WA, Australia
Tel.: (61) 8 9322 8222
Web Site: http://www.jupiterenergy.com
Emp.: 1
Oil & Gas Exploration Services

N.A.I.C.S.: 213112
Jeoff Gander (Mng Dir)

JUPITER FUND MANAGEMENT PLC
The Zig Zag Building 70 Victoria Street, London, SW1E 6SQ, United Kingdom
Tel.: (44) 2038171000 UK
Web Site: https://www.jupiteram.com
JUP—(LSE)
Rev.: $679,538,860
Assets: $1,827,219,576
Liabilities: $624,143,884
Net Worth: $1,203,075,692
Earnings: $142,967,916
Emp.: 593
Fiscal Year-end: 12/31/20
Holding Company; Investment Fund Management Services
N.A.I.C.S.: 551112
Edward H. Bonham Carter (Vice Chm)

Subsidiaries:

Jupiter Investment Management Group Limited (1)
1 Grosvenor Place, London, SW1X 7JJ, United Kingdom
Tel.: (44) 207 412 0703
Web Site: http://www.jupiteram.com
Rev.: $51,600,000,000
Investment Holding Company
N.A.I.C.S.: 551112

Subsidiary (Domestic):

Jupiter Asset Management Limited (2)
1 Grosvenor Place, London, SW1X 7JJ, United Kingdom
Tel.: (44) 2038171000
Web Site: http://www.jupiteram.com
Investment Fund Management Services
N.A.I.C.S.: 523940
Despina Constantinides (Head-Media Rels)

Affiliate (Domestic):

European Opportunities Trust PLC (3)
123 Victoria Street, London, SW1E 6DE, United Kingdom (9.93%)
Tel.: (44) 2039850445
Web Site: http://www.europeanopportunitiestrust.com
Rev.: $48,121,040
Assets: $1,260,404,112
Liabilities: $116,224,768
Net Worth: $1,144,179,344
Earnings: $36,084,224
Fiscal Year-end: 05/31/2022
Closed-End Investment Fund
N.A.I.C.S.: 525990

Jupiter Green Investment Trust PLC (3)
The Zig Zag Building 70 Victoria Street, London, SW1E 6SQ, United Kingdom (29.2%)
Tel.: (44) 8005614000
Web Site: http://www.jupiteram.com
Rev.: $642,488
Assets: $76,796,984
Liabilities: $4,169,616
Net Worth: $72,627,368
Earnings: ($708,048)
Fiscal Year-end: 03/31/2022
Closed-End Investment Fund
N.A.I.C.S.: 525990
Abbie Llewellyn-Waters (Mgr)

JUPITER INFOMEDIA LTD.
336 Laxmi Plaza Laxmi Industrial Estate New Link Road, Andheri W, Mumbai, 400053, India
Tel.: (91) 2242661743
Web Site: https://www.jupiterinfomedia.com
534623—(BOM)
Rev.: $757,302
Assets: $2,532,184
Liabilities: $38,943
Net Worth: $2,493,241

JUPITER INFOMEDIA LTD.

Jupiter Infomedia Ltd.—(Continued)
Earnings: $63,513
Emp.: 5
Fiscal Year-end: 03/31/22
Information Retrieval & Web Hosting Services
N.A.I.C.S.: 519290
Umesh Vasantlal Modi *(Founder, Chm, CEO & Mng Dir)*

JUPITER LIFE LINE HOSPITALS LIMITED
Eastern Express Highway Service Road Next To Viviana Mall, Thane, 400601, Maharashtra, India
Tel.: (91) 2262975555
Web Site: https://www.jupiterhospital.com
Year Founded: 2007
543959—(BOM)
Rev.: $108,533,229
Assets: $119,840,934
Liabilities: $75,589,478
Net Worth: $44,251,456
Earnings: $8,865,248
Emp.: 3,183
Fiscal Year-end: 03/31/23
Healthcare Technology Services
N.A.I.C.S.: 541511
Ajay Pratap Thakker *(Mng Dir)*

JUPITER MINES LIMITED
Level 42 108 St Georges Tce, GPO Box Z5117, Perth, 6000, WA, Australia
Tel.: (61) 8 9346 5500
Web Site: http://www.jupitermines.com
Sales Range: $1-9.9 Million
Emp.: 1
Gold Mining & Exploration
N.A.I.C.S.: 212220
Priyank Thapliyal *(CEO)*

JUPITER UK GROWTH INVESTMENT TRUST PLC
The Zig Zag Building 70 Victoria Street, London, SW1E 6SQ, United Kingdom
Tel.: (44) 2038171000
JUKG—(LSE)
Assets: $70,524,732
Liabilities: $5,731,692
Net Worth: $64,793,040
Earnings: ($10,269,828)
Fiscal Year-end: 06/30/19
Investment Management Service
N.A.I.C.S.: 525990
Steve Davies *(Mgr-Fund)*

JUPITER WAGONS LIMITED
48 Vandna Vihar Narmada Road, Gorakhpur, Jabalpur, 482001, Madhya Pradesh, India
Tel.: (91) 7612661336
Web Site: https://jupiterwagons.com
533272—(BOM)
Rev.: $161,308,247
Assets: $146,383,446
Liabilities: $53,171,609
Net Worth: $93,211,837
Earnings: $6,777,894
Emp.: 507
Fiscal Year-end: 03/31/22
Vehicle & Locomotive Bodies Mfr
N.A.I.C.S.: 336211
Abhishek Jaiswal *(CEO)*

Subsidiaries:

BONATRANS India Private Limited (1)
Plot No A - 119 Shendra Five Star Industrial Area Shendra MIDC, Aurangabad, 431 154, Maharashtra, India **(94.2%)**
Tel.: (91) 2407113900
Railway Equipment Distr

N.A.I.C.S.: 423120
Samir Joshi *(Mgr-Maintenance)*

JURA TRUST AG
Stadtle 28, PO Box 838, 9490, Vaduz, Liechtenstein
Tel.: (423) 2377575
Web Site: http://www.juratrust.li
Year Founded: 1978
Sales Range: $50-74.9 Million
Emp.: 20
Investment Management Service
N.A.I.C.S.: 523999
Angelika Nigg *(Officer-Compliance)*

JURA-GUSS GMBH
Industriestrasse 5, 92335, Beilngries, Germany
Tel.: (49) 846164160
Web Site: http://www.aluminium-giesserei.com
Year Founded: 1953
Rev.: $18,621,900
Emp.: 300
Mechanical Processing & Toolmaking Equipments Mfr
N.A.I.C.S.: 333515
Philipp Teschke *(Mng Dir)*

JURGING GMBH & CO.
Dissener Str 5, 33775, Versmold, Germany
Tel.: (49) 542394350
Web Site: http://www.juerging.de
Year Founded: 1923
Rev.: $20,691,000
Emp.: 62
Food Products Mfr
N.A.I.C.S.: 311999
Andreas Jurging *(Gen Mgr)*

JUROKU FINANCIAL GROUP, INC.
8-26 Kanda-cho, Gifu, 500-8833, Japan
Tel.: (81) 582070016
Web Site: https://www.16fg.co.jp
7380—(NGO)
Rev.: $851,245,219
Assets: $49,785,509,681
Liabilities: $46,807,049,993
Net Worth: $2,978,459,688
Earnings: $128,972,544
Emp.: 2,705
Fiscal Year-end: 03/31/24
Commercial Banking Services
N.A.I.C.S.: 522110

JUSHRI TECHNOLOGIES, INC.
Room 601 Bldg 4 999 Jinzhong R, Changning District, Shanghai, 200335, China
Tel.: (86) 2162386622
300762—(SSE)
Rev.: $56,245,644
Assets: $472,659,408
Liabilities: $94,949,712
Net Worth: $377,709,696
Earnings: $12,015,432
Fiscal Year-end: 12/31/22
Communication Equipment Mfr
N.A.I.C.S.: 334220
Shiping Hu *(Pres)*

JUST BRIDGING LOANS PLC
1 Charterhouse Mews Farringdon, London, EC1M 6BB, United Kingdom
Tel.: (44) 2031997114
Web Site: http://www.justbridging.co.uk
Financial Lending Services
N.A.I.C.S.: 522390
John McLellan *(COO)*

JUST CASH FLOW PLC
1 Charterhouse Mews Farringdon, London, EC1M 6BB, United Kingdom

Tel.: (44) 2031997114
Web Site: http://www.just-cashflow.com
JCF21—(CYP)
Rev.: $14,154,210
Assets: $101,992,748
Liabilities: $115,008,916
Net Worth: ($13,016,168)
Earnings: ($4,088,214)
Fiscal Year-end: 12/31/19
Financial Lending Services
N.A.I.C.S.: 522390
John Davies *(Chm)*

JUST DIAL LTD
Palm Court Building-M 501/B 5th Floor Besides Goregaon Sports Complex, New Link Road Malad West, Mumbai, 400 064, India
Tel.: (91) 2228884060
Web Site: https://www.justdial.com
535648—(BOM)
Rev.: $104,983,515
Assets: $550,490,850
Liabilities: $74,624,550
Net Worth: $475,866,300
Earnings: $9,668,295
Emp.: 13,343
Fiscal Year-end: 03/31/22
Search Engine
N.A.I.C.S.: 519290
V. S. S. Mani *(Co-Founder, CEO & Mng Dir)*

JUST EAT TAKEAWAY.COM N.V.
Oosterdoksstraat 80, 1011 DK, Amsterdam, Netherlands
Tel.: (31) 202107007
Web Site: https://www.takeaway.com
Year Founded: 2000
JTKWY—(OTCIQ)
Rev.: $5,929,138,200
Assets: $13,209,151,800
Liabilities: $4,791,502,800
Net Worth: $8,417,649,000
Earnings: ($6,004,838,400)
Fiscal Year-end: 12/31/22
Online Food Ordering Services
N.A.I.C.S.: 492210
Brent Wissink *(CFO & Member-Mgmt Bd)*

Subsidiaries:

GrubHub, Inc. (1)
111 W Washington St Ste 2100, Chicago, IL 60602
Web Site: http://www.grubhub.com
Rev.: $1,819,982,000
Assets: $2,388,919,000
Liabilities: $972,122,000
Net Worth: $1,416,797,000
Earnings: ($155,861,000)
Emp.: 2,841
Fiscal Year-end: 12/31/2020
Online & Mobile Platform for Restaurant Pick-Up & Delivery Orders
N.A.I.C.S.: 722310
Maggie Drucker *(Chief Legal Officer)*

Subsidiary (Domestic):

Eat24, LLC (2)
140 New Montgomery St Ste 900, San Francisco, CA 94105
Tel.: (866) 328-1123
Web Site: http://www.eat24.com
Food Delivery Services
N.A.I.C.S.: 722511

KMLee Investments Inc (2)
12100 W Washington Blvd, Los Angeles, CA 90066
Tel.: (424) 835-3905
Mobile Food Delivery Services
N.A.I.C.S.: 722310

LAbite.com, Inc. (2)
111 W Washington St Ste 2100, Chicago, IL 60602
Tel.: (877) 585-7878

INTERNATIONAL PUBLIC

Local Delivery Services
N.A.I.C.S.: 492210

MealPort USA LLC (2)
1100 SE Taylor St, Portland, OR 97214
Tel.: (503) 239-0100
Web Site: http://www.d-dish.com
Restaurant Management & Catering Services
N.A.I.C.S.: 722511

SCVNGR, Inc. (2)
1 Center Plz Fl 6, Boston, MA 02108-1887
Web Site: http://www.thelevelup.com
Software Development Services
N.A.I.C.S.: 541511
Christina Dorobek *(Chief Sls Officer)*

Subsidiary (Non-US):

Seamless Europe, Ltd. (2)
Henry Wood House 2 Riding House Street West Central, London, W1W 7FA, United Kingdom
Tel.: (44) 20 3318 1875
Food Delivery Services
N.A.I.C.S.: 722511
James Young *(Head-Sls-UK)*

Subsidiary (Domestic):

Seamless North America, LLC (2)
232 Madison Ave Ste 1409, New York, NY 10016
Tel.: (212) 944-7755
Web Site: http://www.seamless.com
Sales Range: $10-24.9 Million
Emp.: 50
Web-Based Ordering for Restaurants, Florists & Gift Shops
N.A.I.C.S.: 541519

Slick City Media, Inc. (2)
75 Varick St 4th Fl, New York, NY 10013
Tel.: (212) 633-2410
Web Site: http://www.menupages.com
Food Delivery Services
N.A.I.C.S.: 722511

Tapingo, Inc. (2)
39 Stillman St, San Francisco, CA 94107
Web Site: http://www.tapingo.com
Mobile Food Ordering Application Developer
N.A.I.C.S.: 541511

Just Eat plc (1)
Fleet Place House 2 Fleet Place, London, EC4M 7RF, United Kingdom
Tel.: (44) 2031143333
Web Site: http://www.justeatplc.com
Rev.: $989,201,090
Assets: $1,565,589,974
Liabilities: $547,962,836
Net Worth: $1,017,627,138
Earnings: $101,394,698
Emp.: 3,290
Fiscal Year-end: 12/31/2018
Online Food Delivery Services
N.A.I.C.S.: 492210
Paul Harrison *(CFO)*

Subsidiary (Domestic):

Just-Eat.co.uk Ltd. (2)
Imperial Place 4 Maxwell Rd, Borehamwood, WD6 1JN, United Kingdom
Tel.: (44) 844 243 7777
Web Site: http://www.just-eat.co.uk
Sales Range: $25-49.9 Million
Emp.: 180
Food Delivery Website Operator
N.A.I.C.S.: 522320
Lucy Milne *(Dir-Mktg)*

Subsidiary (Non-US):

Menulog Pty. Ltd. (2)
Level 23 227 Elizabeth Street, Sydney, 2000, NSW, Australia
Tel.: (61) 292408188
Web Site: http://www.menulog.com.au
Emp.: 130
Online Food Delivery Services
N.A.I.C.S.: 722330
Morten Birk Belling *(Mng Dir)*

JUST ENERGY GROUP INC.
100 King Street West Suite 2630, Toronto, M5X 1E1, ON, Canada
Tel.: (905) 670-4440

Web Site: http://www.justenergy.com
JE.H—(OTCIQ)
Rev.: $2,154,608,000
Assets: $1,623,814,000
Liabilities: $1,429,613,000
Net Worth: $194,201,000
Earnings: $678,527,000
Emp.: 1,125
Fiscal Year-end: 03/31/22
Natural Gas & Electricity Distr
N.A.I.C.S.: 221210
R. Scott Gahn *(Pres & CEO)*

Subsidiaries:

Commerce Energy, Inc. (1)
1 Centerpointe Dr Ste 350, La Palma, CA 90623-2520
Tel.: (714) 259-2500
Web Site: http://www.commerceenergy.com
Sales Range: $450-499.9 Million
Emp.: 200
Electric & Natural Gas Marketing Services
N.A.I.C.S.: 211120

Fulcrum Retail Holdings LLC (1)
3800 Buffalo Speedway Ste 500, Houston, TX 77098
Tel.: (713) 881-8590
Web Site: http://taraenergy.com
Holding Company; Electric Power Distribution Services
N.A.I.C.S.: 551112

Unit (Domestic):

Tara Energy (2)
4201 SW Freeway, Houston, TX 77027
Tel.: (713) 830-1019
Web Site: http://www.taraenergy.com
Electric Power Generation
N.A.I.C.S.: 221122
Khanh Tran *(Mgr-Mktg-East Asia)*

Interactive Energy Group LLC (1)
PO Box 864524, Plano, TX 75086
Web Site:
 http://www.interactiveenergygroup.com
Natural Gas Distribution Services
N.A.I.C.S.: 221210

Just Energy, LLC (1)
5251 Westheimer Rd Ste 1000, Houston, TX 77056-5411
Web Site: http://www.justenergy.com
Holding Company; Electric Power Distr
N.A.I.C.S.: 551112
Patrick McCullough *(Pre & CEO)*

Subsidiary (Domestic):

Just Energy Texas LP (2)
5251 Westheimer Rd Ste 1000, Houston, TX 77056
Tel.: (713) 850-6790
Web Site: http://www.justenergy.com
Electric Power Distr
N.A.I.C.S.: 221122

TerraPass Inc. (1)
5251 Westheimer Rd Ste 1000, Houston, TX 77056
Web Site: http://www.terrapass.com
Environmental Services
N.A.I.C.S.: 541620

JUST JEANS GROUP PTY LIMITED
658 Church Street, Richmond, 3121, Victoria, Australia
Tel.: (61) 3 9420 0200
Web Site:
 http://www.justjeans.com.au
Year Founded: 1970
Emp.: 130
Clothing Apparel Sales
N.A.I.C.S.: 315210

JUST KITCHEN HOLDINGS CORP.
Suite 1430-800 West Pender St, Vancouver, V6C 2V6, BC, Canada
Tel.: (604) 638-8063   BC
Web Site:
 https://www.en.justkitchen.com
Year Founded: 2019
JK—(TSXV)
Rev.: $82,359
Assets: $9,796,567
Liabilities: $4,765,984
Net Worth: $5,030,583
Earnings: ($13,067,899)
Fiscal Year-end: 09/30/22
Holding Company
N.A.I.C.S.: 551112
Jason Chen *(CEO)*

JUST LIFE GROUP LIMITED
103 Hugo Johnston Drive, Penrose, Auckland, 1061, New Zealand
Tel.: (64) 96301300   NZ
Web Site:
 https://www.justlifegroup.co.nz
Year Founded: 1987
JLG—(NZX)
Rev.: $21,947,967
Assets: $32,867,225
Liabilities: $15,906,699
Net Worth: $16,960,526
Earnings: $1,290,072
Fiscal Year-end: 06/30/23
Water Coolers & Bottled Drinking Water Mfr
N.A.I.C.S.: 333415
Anthony Edwin Falkenstein *(Chm & CEO)*

Subsidiaries:

Just Water New Zealand Limited (1)
103 Hugo Johnston Drive, Penrose, Auckland, 1061, New Zealand
Tel.: (64) 80 080 1802
Web Site: https://www.justwater.co.nz
Sales Range: $50-74.9 Million
Emp.: 100
Water Filtration Equipment Sales & Services
N.A.I.C.S.: 445298

JUST ON COSMETICS
9 Schoof Street, Wilsonia, 5206, East London, South Africa
Tel.: (27) 437450022
Web Site: http://www.juston.co.za
Sales Range: $600-649.9 Million
Emp.: 900
Cosmetics & Beauty Supply Store Owner & Operator
N.A.I.C.S.: 456120
Surendra Naidoo *(CEO)*

JUST PLANNING INC.
7-35-1 Nishikamata, Ota-ku, Tokyo, 144-0051, Japan
Tel.: (81) 337301041
Web Site: https://www.justweb.co.jp
Year Founded: 1998
4287—(TKS)
Rev.: $20,395,760
Assets: $34,509,200
Liabilities: $2,652,320
Net Worth: $31,856,880
Earnings: $2,400,640
Fiscal Year-end: 01/31/22
Software Development Services
N.A.I.C.S.: 513210
Nozomi Yamamoto *(Pres)*

JUSTEM CO., LTD.
57 Tapsil-ro 35beon-gil, Giheung-gu, Yongin, Gyeonggi-do, Korea (South)
Tel.: (82) 318312800
Web Site: https://www.justem.co.kr
Year Founded: 2016
417840—(KRS)
Semiconductor Device Mfr & Distr
N.A.I.C.S.: 334413
Youngjin Lim *(CEO)*

JUSTIN ALLEN HOLDINGS LIMITED
31/F Excel Center 483A Castle Peak Road, Kowloon, China (Hong Kong)
Tel.: (852) 31993388   Ky
Web Site:
 https://www.justinallengroup.com
Year Founded: 1983
1425—(HKG)
Rev.: $155,646,900
Assets: $104,913,120
Liabilities: $22,957,905
Net Worth: $81,955,215
Earnings: $22,426,868
Emp.: 1,988
Fiscal Year-end: 12/31/22
Holding Company
N.A.I.C.S.: 551112
Kwok Pui Tam *(Founder, Chm, CEO & Exec Dir)*

JUSTSYSTEMS CORPORATION
108-4 Hiraishi-wakamatsu, Kawauchi-cho, Tokushima, 771-0189, Japan
Tel.: (81) 886661000
Web Site:
 https://www.justsystems.com
Year Founded: 1979
4686—(TKS)
Rev.: $270,910,850
Assets: $721,144,390
Liabilities: $99,784,560
Net Worth: $621,359,830
Earnings: $76,913,960
Emp.: 303
Fiscal Year-end: 03/31/24
Software Developer
N.A.I.C.S.: 513210
Kyotaro Sekinada *(Pres & CEO)*

Subsidiaries:

JustSystems Canada, Inc. (1)
3220-666 Burrard Street, PO Box 207, Vancouver, V6C 2X8, BC, Canada
Tel.: (604) 602-9928
Software Development Services
N.A.I.C.S.: 541511
Patrick Y. Yang *(Controller)*

JUSUNG ENGINEERING CO., LTD.
240 Oporo, Gwangju, Gyeonggi-do, Korea (South)
Tel.: (82) 317607000
Web Site: https://www.jseng.com
Year Founded: 1995
036930—(KRS)
Rev.: $335,898,998
Assets: $638,959,474
Liabilities: $267,264,893
Net Worth: $371,694,581
Earnings: $81,433,380
Emp.: 527
Fiscal Year-end: 12/31/22
Electric Equipment Mfr
N.A.I.C.S.: 334413
Chul Joo Hwang *(CEO)*

JUTAL OFFSHORE OIL SERVICES LIMITED
10th Floor Chiwan Petroleum Building Shekou, Nanshan District, Shenzhen, 518068, China
Tel.: (86) 75526694111
Web Site: http://www.jutal.com
Year Founded: 1995
3303—(OTCIQ)
Rev.: $242,430,079
Assets: $440,222,364
Liabilities: $198,301,811
Net Worth: $241,920,553
Earnings: ($28,831,690)
Emp.: 2,739
Fiscal Year-end: 12/31/22
Engineeering Services
N.A.I.C.S.: 541330
Lishan Wang *(Exec Dir)*

Subsidiaries:

Chengdu Jutal Oil & Gas Engineering Co., Ltd. (1)
Room 1402 14th Floor Unit 1 Building1 No 8 of Jitai No 3 Road, Hi-tech Zone, Chengdu, 610041, China
Tel.: (86) 2885170663
Engineering Services
N.A.I.C.S.: 541330

Jutal Offshore Shipbuilding Services (Dalian) Company Limited (1)
No 1 Haifang Street, Xigang District, Dalian, 116021, China
Tel.: (86) 41184483508
Engineeering Services
N.A.I.C.S.: 541330

Jutal Oilfield Services (Tianjin) Company Limited (1)
4th Floor Building 23 Innovation and Entrepreneurship Park Xinbei Road, Tanggu District, Tianjing, 300457, China
Tel.: (86) 2266282238
Engineering Services
N.A.I.C.S.: 541330

Penglai Jutal Offshore Engineering Heavy Industries Company Limited (1)
No 305 Xianjing East Road, Penglai Economic Development Zone, Shandong, 265609, China
Tel.: (86) 5353455100
Web Site: https://zh.pjoe.com.cn
Engineeering Services
N.A.I.C.S.: 541330

Shenzhen Jutal Machinery Equipment Co., Ltd. (1)
10th Fl Chiwan Petroleum Building Shekou, Nanshan District, Shenzhen, 518068, China
Tel.: (86) 75526694111
Emp.: 50
Oil & Gas Field Machinery Mfr
N.A.I.C.S.: 333132

Shenzhen Marine Diving Engineering Co., Ltd. (1)
10 floor Chiwan Petroleum building, Shekou, Shenzhen, 51806, China
Tel.: (86) 7525308063
Web Site: https://smde.com.cn
Engineeering Services
N.A.I.C.S.: 541330

Zhuhai Jutal Offshore Oil Services Company Limited (1)
Zhuhai Gaolan Port Economic Zone, Zhuhai, 519050, China
Tel.: (86) 7567228999
Engineering Services
N.A.I.C.S.: 541330

JUTE SPINNERS LIMITED
House 71 Road 9/A New, Dhanmondi R/A, Dhaka, 1209, Bangladesh
Tel.: (880) 28129149
Web Site:
 http://www.jsl.shamsbd.com
Year Founded: 1979
JUTESPINN—(DHA)
Sales Range: Less than $1 Million
Jute Yarn & Twine Mfr
N.A.I.C.S.: 314994

JUTEC HOLDINGS CORPORATION
1-3-2 Shibadaimon, Minato-ku, Tokyo, Japan
Tel.: (81) 364359100   JP
Web Site: http://www.jutec-hd.jp
Year Founded: 2009
3157—(TKS)
Rev.: $1,098,916,111
Assets: $503,323,282
Liabilities: $355,176,643
Net Worth: $148,146,638
Earnings: $16,445,321
Emp.: 84
Fiscal Year-end: 03/31/24
Holding Company
N.A.I.C.S.: 551112
Kenichiro Adachi *(Pres)*

Subsidiaries:

Good Houser Co., Ltd. (1)

JUTEC HOLDINGS CORPORATION

JUTEC Holdings Corporation—(Continued)

618 Nishihojuka, Nakano Miyagino-ku, Ka-sukabe, 344-0102, Saitama Prefecture, Japan
Tel.: (81) 487482211
Web Site: https://goodhouser.jp
Emp.: 40
Housing Related Material Retailer
N.A.I.C.S.: 444180

Green Houser Co., Ltd. (1)
18-1 Kamiobukuroda Nakano, Miyagino-Ku, Sendai, 983-0013, Miyagi, Japan (100%)
Tel.: (81) 222544170
Sales Range: $125-149.9 Million
Emp.: 150
Building & Housing Materials Distr; Contract Construction Work Services
N.A.I.C.S.: 423390

Ishimoku Emori Corporation (1)
2-111 Minato, Kanazawa, 920-0211, Ishikawa, Japan
Tel.: (81) 762388770
Web Site: https://ishimoku-emori.jp
Emp.: 52
Residential Building Materials Sales
N.A.I.C.S.: 444180

JUTEC Akita Corporation (1)
Kawajiricho Okawabata 170-42, Akita, Japan
Tel.: (81) 18 862 2662
Residential Building Materials Whslr
N.A.I.C.S.: 444180

JUTEC Butsuryu Corporation (1)
Kita-Kochi 876 Kawamukai-machi, Tsuzuki-ku, Yokohama, Kanagawa, Japan
Tel.: (81) 454711888
General Freight Transport; Vehicle Leasing
N.A.I.C.S.: 484110

JUTEC Corporation (1)
6-3-4 Shimbashi, Minato-ku, Tokyo, 105-0004, Japan
Tel.: (81) 334331300
Emp.: 767
Home Building & Industrial Materials Whslr
N.A.I.C.S.: 423390
Kenichiro Adachi *(Chm)*

Jraifu Support Corporation (1)
Nishi-Shinbashi 3-4-2, Minato-ku, Tokyo, Japan
Tel.: (81) 3 3432 2220
Building Management & Insurance Agency
N.A.I.C.S.: 531311
Katsuhiro Kuriyama *(Pres & CEO)*

Jutec Home Corporation (1)
4-1 Shineicho, Tsuzuki Ward, Yokohama, 224-0035, Kanagawa, Japan (100%)
Tel.: (81) 120206244
Home Planning, Design & Building; Interior Planning, Design & Furnishing
N.A.I.C.S.: 541310

Kunthiro.Hometech Corporation (1)
3rd Heinatsuka Nametsu, Nakajima-mura Nishishirakawa-gun, Fukushima, 961-0102, Japan
Tel.: (81) 248522030
Web Site: http://www.elp-shirakawa.jp
Newly Built House Extension Services
N.A.I.C.S.: 236118

Office Operation Co. Ltd. (1)
6-3-4 Shimbashi, Minato-ku, Tokyo, 105-0004, Japan
Tel.: (81) 345823379
Web Site: https://office-operation.co.jp
Planning, Design, Development, Sales, Leasing & Maintenance of Computer Systems
N.A.I.C.S.: 541512

Senken Corporation (1)
12-36 Sakurao Honmachi, Hatsukaichi, 983-0034, Hiroshima, Japan
Tel.: (81) 82 932 1918
Web Site: https://www.sen-ken.co.jp
Sales Range: $25-49.9 Million
Emp.: 23
Residential Building Material Sales
N.A.I.C.S.: 444180

Welltec Corporation (1)
Togoshi 1-25-20, Shinagawa-ku, Tokyo, 142-0041, Japan
Tel.: (81) 3 5751 8390
Web Site: http://www.welltec-corporation.jp
Sales Range: $25-49.9 Million
Emp.: 8
Apartment Renovation
N.A.I.C.S.: 236118

Welltec Kansai Corporation (1)
Nakasonecho 3043-5, Kita-ku, Sakai, Osaka, Japan
Tel.: (81) 72 257 8815
Residential Building Material Sales & General Construction Contracting
N.A.I.C.S.: 444180

JUTLANDER BANK A/S

Markedsvej 5-7, Aars, 9600, Denmark
Tel.: (45) 9657 5800
Web Site: http://www.jutlander.dk
JUTBK—(OMX)
Rev.: $146,411,101
Assets: $2,932,798,764
Liabilities: $2,435,433,363
Net Worth: $497,365,402
Earnings: $56,283,709
Emp.: 462
Fiscal Year-end: 12/31/19
Banking Services
N.A.I.C.S.: 522110
Per Sonderup *(CEO)*

JUTZE INTELLIGENCE TECHNOLOGY CO., LTD.

Unit 3301 33F No 701 Yunjin Road, Xuhui District, Shanghai, 200232, China
Tel.: (86) 2164969730
Web Site: http://www.jutze.com
Year Founded: 2007
300802—(SSE)
Rev.: $95,970,420
Assets: $196,002,612
Liabilities: $26,002,080
Net Worth: $170,000,532
Earnings: $18,105,984
Fiscal Year-end: 12/31/22
Optical Instrument Mfr
N.A.I.C.S.: 333310
Yong Yang *(Chm & Gen Mgr)*

JUVA LIFE INC.

Suite 1400 885 West Georgia St, Vancouver, V6C 3E8, BC, Canada   BC
Web Site: https://www.juvalife.com
Year Founded: 2018
JUVAF—(OTCQB)
Rev.: $5,763,800
Assets: $20,374,685
Liabilities: $10,630,372
Net Worth: $9,744,313
Earnings: ($10,482,820)
Fiscal Year-end: 12/31/22
Pharmaceutical Product Mfr & Distr
N.A.I.C.S.: 325412
Doug Chloupek *(CEO)*

JV GLOBAL LIMITED

Level 10 182 St Georges Tce, Perth, 6000, WA, Australia
Tel.: (61) 8 63230870
Web Site: http://www.jvglobal.com.au
Rev.: $5,179
Assets: $276,236
Liabilities: $79,086
Net Worth: $197,149
Earnings: ($345,459)
Fiscal Year-end: 06/30/18
Steel Building Products Mfr
N.A.I.C.S.: 331221
Justin Mouchacca *(Sec)*

Subsidiaries:

JV International Pty Ltd (1)
Unit 9 47 Monash Ave, Como, Perth, 6152, Western Australia, Australia
Tel.: (61) 8 9309 1544

Sales Range: $50-74.9 Million
Emp.: 2
Steel Building Products Whslr
N.A.I.C.S.: 423390

JVCKENWOOD CORPORATION

3-12 Moriyacho, Kanagawa-ku, Yokohama, 221-0022, Kanagawa, Japan
Tel.: (81) 454445232
Web Site: https://www.jvckenwood.com
Year Founded: 2008
6632—(TKS)
Rev.: $2,376,023,990
Assets: $2,094,173,590
Liabilities: $1,292,909,390
Net Worth: $801,264,200
Earnings: $86,035,760
Emp.: 15,880
Fiscal Year-end: 03/31/24
Holding Company
N.A.I.C.S.: 551112
Shoichiro Eguchi *(Pres, Pres, CEO & CEO)*

Subsidiaries:

ASK Industries S.p.A. (1)
Via dell Industrial 12, Monte San Vito, 60037, Ancona, Italy
Tel.: (39) 0717 4521
Web Site: http://www.askgroup.it
Automotive Products Whslr
N.A.I.C.S.: 441330
Fanesi Simone *(Product Mgr)*

EF Johnson Technologies, Inc. (1)
1440 Corporate Dr, Irving, TX 75038-2401
Tel.: (972) 819-0700
Web Site: https://www.efjohnson.com
Sales Range: $75-99.9 Million
Emp.: 200
Communications Equipment Designer & Mfr
N.A.I.C.S.: 334220
Karthik Rangarajan *(Sr VP-Strategy & Products)*

JVC America Corp. (1)
705 Enterprise St, Aurora, IL 60504-8149 (100%)
Tel.: (630) 851-7855
Web Site: http://www.jvc.com
Sales Range: $100-124.9 Million
Emp.: 325
Television & Radio Electrical Appliances Mfr
N.A.I.C.S.: 334310

Subsidiary (Domestic):

JVC U.S.A. (2)
1700 Valley Rd, Wayne, NJ 07470
Tel.: (973) 317-5000
Web Site: http://www.jvc.com
Sales Range: $100-124.9 Million
Household Audio & Video Equipment & Blank Media Distr
N.A.I.C.S.: 811310

Division (Domestic):

JVC Industrial America Inc. (3)
2280 Enrico Fermi Dr Bldg D Ste 23, San Diego, CA 92154
Tel.: (619) 661-5300
Web Site: http://www.jvc.com
Sales Range: $25-49.9 Million
Emp.: 15
Audio & Video Equipment Mfr
N.A.I.C.S.: 334310

JVC U.S.A (Professional Video Div.) (3)
1700 Valley Rd, Wayne, NJ 07470 (100%)
Tel.: (973) 317-5000
Web Site: http://www.pro.jvc.com
Sales Range: $25-49.9 Million
Emp.: 200
Audio & Video Equipment Mfr
N.A.I.C.S.: 334310

JVC International (Europe) GmbH (1)
Slamastrasse 43, 1230, Vienna, Austria
Tel.: (43) 1 610 37 0
Web Site: http://www.jvc.at
Electronic Product Mfr & Distr

N.A.I.C.S.: 334419
David Tollovich *(Mgr-Fin)*

JVC Manufacturing (Thailand) Co., Ltd. (1)
Navanakorn Estate Zone 3 107 Moo 18 Tambol Klong Neung, Amphur Klong Luang, Pathumthani, 12120, Thailand
Tel.: (66) 2529 2105 09
Web Site: http://www.jmt.co.th
Audio & Video Equipment Mfr
N.A.I.C.S.: 334310

JVC Manufacturing Malaysia Sdn. Bhd. (1)
Lot 1 Persiaran Jubli Perak Jalan 22/1 Seksyen 22, 40300, Shah Alam, Selangor, Malaysia
Tel.: (60) 3 5548 3330
Web Site: http://my.jvckenwood.com
Audio & Imaging Equipment Mfr
N.A.I.C.S.: 334310
Tek Guan Lim *(Mgr-Factory)*

JVC Networks, Inc. (1)
10-2F Shibuya First Tower 10-2F 1-2-2 Higashi, Shibuya-ku, Tokyo, 150-0011, Japan
Tel.: (81) 3 5467 9160
Web Site: http://www.jvc-networks.jp
Audio Video Equipment Mfr & Distr
N.A.I.C.S.: 334310

JVC Optical Components (Thailand) Co., Ltd. (1)
189 Moo 3 Rachasima-chokchai T Nongbuasala Muang, Nakhon Ratchasima, 30000, Thailand
Tel.: (66) 44212231
Electronic Components Mfr
N.A.I.C.S.: 334419

JVC Polska Sp. Zo. o. (1)
Ul Polczynska 116 A, 01-304, Warsaw, Poland
Tel.: (48) 22 666 11 11
Web Site: http://www.jvc.pl
Electronic Components Distr
N.A.I.C.S.: 423690
Jacek Wojtasinski *(Natl Key Acct Mgr & Product Mgr)*

JVC Taiwan Corp. (1)
5F 101 Fu Hsing N Rd, Taipei, Taiwan
Tel.: (886) 2 22980968
Web Site: http://www.jvc.com.tw
Audio Video Equipment Mfr & Distr
N.A.I.C.S.: 334310

JVCKENWOOD (China) Investment Co., Ltd. (1)
Room 609 610 Zhongqing Building 19 Dongsanhuan North Road, Chaoyang District, Beijing, 100020, China
Tel.: (86) 105 758 1705
Web Site: https://www.pro-jvc.com.cn
Electronic Products Mfr
N.A.I.C.S.: 336390

JVCKENWOOD (Thailand) Co., Ltd. (1)
240/33 240/35 Ayothaya Tower 18th Floor Ratchadaphisek Road Soi 18, Huai Khwang Subdistrict Huai Khwang District, Bangkok, 10310, Thailand
Tel.: (66) 2 274 1770
Web Site: https://th.jvckenwood.com
Audio & Video Equipment Distr
N.A.I.C.S.: 423690

JVCKENWOOD Australia Pty. Ltd. (1)
Suite 4 02 City Views Business Park 65 Epping Road, Macquarie Park, 2113, NSW, Australia
Tel.: (61) 28 879 2222
Web Site: https://au.jvckenwood.com
Electronic Products Mfr
N.A.I.C.S.: 336390

JVCKENWOOD Belgium N.V. (1)
Leuvensesteenweg 248J, 1800, Vilvoorde, Belgium
Tel.: (32) 27579060
Web Site: http://www.be.jvckenwood.com
Electronic Products Mfr
N.A.I.C.S.: 336390
Geert Van Muylem *(Mgr-Svc)*

JVCKENWOOD Creative Media Corporation (1)
58-4 Shinmeicho, Yokosuka, 239-8528, Kanagawa, Japan

AND PRIVATE COMPANIES JVCKENWOOD CORPORATION

Tel.: (81) 46 837 5488
Web Site: https://jkcm.victor.jp
Recorded Optical Disc Mfr & Whslr
N.A.I.C.S.: 334610

JVCKENWOOD Design Corporation (1)
17th Floor Setagaya Business Square Tower 4-10-1 Yoga, Setagaya-ku, Tokyo, Japan
Tel.: (81) 33 708 2801
Web Site: https://design.jvckenwood.com
Professional Design Services
N.A.I.C.S.: 541490

JVCKENWOOD Deutschland GmbH (1)
Konrad-Adenauer-Allee 1-11, 61118, Bad Vilbel, Germany
Tel.: (49) 61 014 9880
Web Site: https://de.jvc.com
Audio Visual Equipment Whslr
N.A.I.C.S.: 459110
Marcel Herrmann *(Mktg Mgr-Healthcare)*

JVCKENWOOD Electronics (Thailand) Co., Ltd. (1)
240 33 240 35 Ayothaya Tower 18th Floor Ratchadaphisek Road Soi 18, Huai Khwang Subdistrict Huai Khwang District, Bangkok, 10310, Thailand
Tel.: (66) 22741770
Web Site: http://th.jvckenwood.com
Electronic Products Mfr
N.A.I.C.S.: 336390
Panida Saithanu *(Asst Mgr)*

JVCKENWOOD Electronics Malaysia Sdn. Bhd. (1)
7F Menara AmFirst No 1 Jalan 19 3, 46300, Petaling Jaya, Selangor, Malaysia
Tel.: (60) 79573330
Web Site: http://my.jvckenwood.com
Electronic Products Mfr
N.A.I.C.S.: 336390

JVCKENWOOD Engineering Corporation (1)
3-12 Moriya-cho, Kanagawa-ku, Yokohama, 221-0022, Kanagawa, Japan
Tel.: (81) 45 450 2964
Web Site: https://jkeg.jvckenwood.com
Emp.: 216
Wireless Communication Equipment Mfr
N.A.I.C.S.: 334290

JVCKENWOOD Gulf Fze (1)
Unit A1SR06 JAFZA Business Plus, Jebel Ali Free Zone South Jebel Ali, Dubai, United Arab Emirates
Tel.: (971) 4 816 5100
Web Site: https://www.ae.jvckenwood.com
Electronic Components Distr
N.A.I.C.S.: 423690

JVCKENWOOD Hong Kong Holdings Limited (1)
Unit A 5 F Garment Centre 576 586 Castle Peak Road, Kowloon, China (Hong Kong)
Tel.: (852) 2 602 1500
Web Site: https://www.shinwa-net.com
Automotive Products Whslr
N.A.I.C.S.: 441330

JVCKENWOOD Hong Kong Ltd. (1)
Unit A 5 F Garment Centre 576 586 Castle Peak Road, Kowloon, China (Hong Kong)
Tel.: (852) 24104567
Electronic Products Mfr
N.A.I.C.S.: 336390

JVCKENWOOD Iberica, S.A. (1)
Avenida Tomas Ribeiro 43 Piso 0 Letra J, Carnaxide, 2790-221, Portugal
Tel.: (351) 214191815
Electronic Components Distr
N.A.I.C.S.: 423690

JVCKENWOOD Latin America, S.A. (1)
Calle 50 Plaza Credicorp Bank Panama Piso 11, Panama, Panama
Tel.: (507) 210 1088
Web Site: https://pa.jvckenwood.com
Consumer Electronics Whslr
N.A.I.C.S.: 423620
Ilicht Cardenas *(Product Mgr)*

JVCKENWOOD Malaysia Sdn. Bhd. (1)
7F Menara AmFIRST No 1 Jalan 19/3, 46300, Petaling Jaya, Selangor, Malaysia
Tel.: (60) 379573330
Web Site: http://my.jvckenwood.com
Audio & Wireless Communication Equipment Mfr
N.A.I.C.S.: 334220

JVCKENWOOD Nagaoka Corporation (1)
1-2-1 Higashi Takami, Nagaoka, 940-0006, Niigata, Japan
Tel.: (81) 2 5824 6611
Electric Equipment Mfr
N.A.I.C.S.: 334419

JVCKENWOOD Singapore Pte. Ltd. (1)
1 Ang Mo Kio Street 63, Singapore, 569110, Singapore
Tel.: (65) 6 496 4500
Web Site: https://sg.jvckenwood.com
Car Stereo Whslr
N.A.I.C.S.: 441330

JVCKENWOOD Technologies Singapore Pte. Ltd. (1)
1 Ang Mo Kio Street 63, Singapore, 569110, Singapore
Tel.: (65) 6 690 1111
Web Site: https://jkts.jvckenwood.com
Electronic Products Mfr
N.A.I.C.S.: 336390

JVCKENWOOD U.K. Limited (1)
First Floor Gleneagles The Belfry Colonial Way, Watford, WD24 4WH, Hertfordshire, United Kingdom
Tel.: (44) 208 208 7500
Web Site: https://uk.jvckenwood.com
Electronic Products Mfr
N.A.I.C.S.: 336390
Scott Bannatyne *(Mng Dir)*

JVCKENWOOD Video Tech Corporation (1)
2-13-19 Jingumae, Shibuya-ku, Tokyo, 150-0001, Japan
Tel.: (81) 33 470 6621
Web Site: https://www.video-tech.co.jp
Emp.: 49
Film & Video Production Services
N.A.I.C.S.: 512110
Kakuro Obata *(Pres)*

JVCKENWOOD Yamagata Corporation (1)
1-15-80 Takarada, Tsuruoka, 997-0011, Yamagata, Japan
Tel.: (81) 23 524 4811
Web Site: https://jky.jvckenwood.com
Electric Equipment Mfr
N.A.I.C.S.: 336390

Kenwood Corporation (1)
2967-3 Ishikawa-Machi, Hachioji City, Tokyo, 192 8525, Japan
Tel.: (81) 426465111
Web Site: http://www.kenwood.co.jp
Sales Range: $1-4.9 Billion
Emp.: 2,383
Wireless Radio Products, Car & Home Electronics Mfr
N.A.I.C.S.: 334310
Shoichiro Eguchi *(Exec VP)*

Subsidiary (Non-US):

JVCKENWOOD Nederland B.V. (2)
Amsterdamseweg 37, 1422 AC, Uithoorn, Netherlands **(100%)**
Tel.: (31) 29 751 9900
Web Site: https://www.kenwood.nl
Sales Range: $25-49.9 Million
Emp.: 25
Electronics Mfr
N.A.I.C.S.: 334310

Subsidiary (Domestic):

Kenwood Design Corporation (2)
3-17-9 Aobadai, Meguro Ku, Tokyo, 153 0042, Japan **(100%)**
Tel.: (81) 354577221
Web Site: http://www.kenwooddesign.com
Sales Range: $25-49.9 Million
Emp.: 50
Audio & Video Equipment Mfr
N.A.I.C.S.: 334310
Mitsutoshi Nakamura *(Pres)*

Kenwood Devices Corporation (2)
1-16-2 Hakusan, Midori-ku, Yokohama, 226-8525, Kanagawa, Japan **(100%)**
Tel.: (81) 459340508
Sales Range: $25-49.9 Million
Emp.: 50
Audio & Video Equipment Mfr
N.A.I.C.S.: 334310

Subsidiary (Non-US):

Kenwood Electronics (Hong Kong) Ltd. (2)
Suite 2504 25/F Tower 2 Nina Tower No 8 Yeung Uk Road, 223 Hing Fong Road, Tsuen Wan, NT, China (Hong Kong) **(100%)**
Tel.: (852) 24104567
Web Site: http://www.kenwoodhk.hk
Sales Range: $25-49.9 Million
Emp.: 30
Audio & Video Equipment Mfr
N.A.I.C.S.: 334310

Kenwood Electronics (Malaysia) Sdn. Bhd. (2)
4 01 Level 4 Wisma Academy, Lot 4A Jalan 19 1, 46300, Petaling Jaya, Selangor Darul Ehsau, Malaysia **(100%)**
Tel.: (60) 379588333
Web Site: http://www.kenwood-electronics.com.my
Sales Range: $10-24.9 Million
Emp.: 20
Audio & Video Equipment Mfr
N.A.I.C.S.: 334310

Kenwood Electronics Australia Pty. Ltd. (2)
16 Giffnock Ave Centre Ct Estate, North Ryde, 2113, NSW, Australia **(100%)**
Tel.: (61) 288792222
Web Site: http://www.kenwood.com.au
Audio & Wireless Communication Equipment Mfr
N.A.I.C.S.: 334220
Shinichi Yoshikoshi *(Mng Dir)*

Kenwood Electronics Belgium N.V. (2)
Leuvensesteenweg 248 J, 1800, Vilvoorde, Belgium **(100%)**
Tel.: (32) 27579060
Web Site: http://www.kenwood.be
Sales Range: $25-49.9 Million
Emp.: 30
Audio & Video Equipment Mfr
N.A.I.C.S.: 334310
Luc Gaudaen *(Mng Dir)*

Kenwood Electronics Brazil Ltda. (2)
Alameda Santos 771 Conjunto 21, Cerqueira Cesar CEP, 01410 001, Sao Paulo, SP, Brazil **(100%)**
Tel.: (55) 11 3066 0280
Audio & Video Equipment Mfr
N.A.I.C.S.: 334310

Kenwood Electronics Bretagne S.A. (2)
Rue Saint Exupery, 35150, Janze, France **(100%)**
Tel.: (33) 299473232
Web Site: http://www.kenwood.fr
Sales Range: $25-49.9 Million
Emp.: 70
Audio & Wireless Communication Equipment Mfr
N.A.I.C.S.: 334220

Kenwood Electronics Canada, Inc. (2)
6070 Kestrel Rd, Mississauga, L5T 1S8, ON, Canada **(100%)**
Tel.: (905) 670-7211
Web Site: http://www.kenwood.ca
Sales Range: $25-49.9 Million
Emp.: 33
Audio & Wireless Communication Equipment Distr
N.A.I.C.S.: 334310
Wilf Mulder *(Mgr-Natl Sls-Comm Div)*

Kenwood Electronics Deutschland GmbH (2)
Rembrucker Strasse 15, 63150, Heusenstamm, Germany **(100%)**
Tel.: (49) 610469010
Web Site: http://www.kenwood.de

Sales Range: $50-74.9 Million
Emp.: 60
Audio & Wireless Communication Equipment Mfr
N.A.I.C.S.: 334220

Kenwood Electronics France S.A. (2)
L Etoile Paris Nord 2 50 Allee des Impressionnistes, BP58416, Villepinte Roissy ch de Gaulle, 95944, Paris, Cedex, France **(100%)**
Tel.: (33) 825 800 109
Web Site: http://www.kenwood-electronics.fr
Sales Range: $25-49.9 Million
Emp.: 30
Audio & Wireless Communication Equipment Mfr
N.A.I.C.S.: 334220

Kenwood Electronics Gulf FZE (2)
PO Box 61318, Jebel Ali, Dubai, United Arab Emirates **(100%)**
Tel.: (971) 48837400
Web Site: http://www.ae.kenwood.com
Sales Range: $25-49.9 Million
Emp.: 15
Audio & Video Equipment Mfr
N.A.I.C.S.: 334310

Kenwood Electronics Italia S.p.A. (2)
Via G Sirtori 7 9, 20129, Milan, Italy **(100%)**
Tel.: (39) 02204821
Audio & Video Equipment Mfr
N.A.I.C.S.: 334310

Kenwood Electronics Latin America S.A. (2)
Paitilla Plaza Credicorp Bank Panama, Piso 11 Oficina 1102 & 1104, Panama, 552791, Panama **(100%)**
Tel.: (507) 2101088
Web Site: http://www.kenwood.com.pa
Sales Range: $25-49.9 Million
Emp.: 13
Audio & Wireless Communication Equipment Mfr
N.A.I.C.S.: 334220

Kenwood Electronics Singapore Pte. Ltd. (2)
1 Amg Mo Kio St 63, Singapore, 569110, Singapore **(100%)**
Tel.: (65) 67413336
Web Site: http://www.kenwoodaudio.com
Sales Range: $25-49.9 Million
Emp.: 30
Audio & Wireless Communication Equipment Mfr
N.A.I.C.S.: 334310

Kenwood Electronics Technologies (S) Pte. Ltd. (2)
No 1 Ang Mo Kio Street 63, Singapore, 569110, Singapore **(100%)**
Tel.: (65) 64823222
Web Site: http://www.kets.kenwood.com
Sales Range: $25-49.9 Million
Emp.: 200
Audio & Wireless Communication Equipment Mfr
N.A.I.C.S.: 334220

Kenwood Electronics U.K. Ltd. (2)
Kenwood House Dwight Road, Watford, WD1 8EB, Herts, United Kingdom **(100%)**
Tel.: (44) 1923816444
Web Site: http://www.kenwood-electronics.co.uk
Sales Range: $50-74.9 Million
Emp.: 40
Audio & Wireless Communication Equipment Mfr
N.A.I.C.S.: 334220

Subsidiary (Domestic):

Kenwood Engineering Corporation (2)
2967 3 Ishikawa-machi, Hachioji, Tokyo, 192-8525, Japan **(100%)**
Tel.: (81) 426469861
Web Site: http://www.kenwood-eng.co.jp
Emp.: 230
Audio & Wireless Communication Equipment Mfr
N.A.I.C.S.: 334310
Chikada Yochitsutu *(Pres)*

JVCKENWOOD CORPORATION

JVCKENWOOD Corporation—(Continued)

Subsidiary (Non-US):

Kenwood Iberica S.A. (2)
Carretera de Rubi 88 Planta 1A, Sant Cugat del Valles, 08174, Barcelona, Spain **(100%)**
Tel.: (34) 93 507 5252
Web Site: https://www.kenwood.es
Sales Range: $25-49.9 Million
Emp.: 40
Car & Home Electronics
N.A.I.C.S.: 334310

Subsidiary (Domestic):

Kenwood Kenex Corporation (2)
2967-3 Ishikawa-machi, Hachioji, Tokyo, 153 0042, Japan
Tel.: (81) 334775471
Web Site: http://www.kenwood.co.jp
Audio & Video Equipment Mfr
N.A.I.C.S.: 334310

Kenwood Nagano Corporation (2)
2676 1 Nishi Minowa, Ina, Nagano, 399 4501, Japan **(100%)**
Tel.: (81) 265764111
Sales Range: $25-49.9 Million
Emp.: 200
Audio & Wireless Communication Equipment Mfr
N.A.I.C.S.: 334220
Moodi Yamoriyama (Mng Dir)

Kenwood Personnel Corporation (2)
2967-3 Ishikawa-machi, Hachioji, Tokyo, 192 8525, Japan
Tel.: (81) 426465210
Audio & Wireless Communication Equipment Mfr
N.A.I.C.S.: 334310

Kenwood Service (Japan) Corporation (2)
1-16-2 Hakusan, Midori-Ku, Yokohama, 226 8525, Kanagawa, Japan **(100%)**
Tel.: (81) 459396234
Web Site: http://www.kenwood-service.com
Sales Range: $25-49.9 Million
Emp.: 198
Audio & Wireless Communication Equipment Mfr
N.A.I.C.S.: 334310

Subsidiary (US):

Kenwood USA Corporation (2)
2201 E Dominguez St, Long Beach, CA 90801
Tel.: (310) 639-9000
Web Site: https://www.kenwood.com
Sales Range: $75-99.9 Million
Emp.: 300
Consumer Audio Electronics Mfr & Distr
N.A.I.C.S.: 541511
Keith Lehmann (Sr VP)

Subsidiary (Domestic):

Kenwood Yamagata Corporation (2)
1-15-80 Takarada, Tsuruoka, 997-0011, Yamagata, Japan **(100%)**
Tel.: (81) 235244811
Web Site: http://yk.kenwood.com
Sales Range: $25-49.9 Million
Emp.: 200
Audio & Wireless Communication Equipment Mfr
N.A.I.C.S.: 334220

Subsidiary (Non-US):

Shanghai Kenwood Electronics Co., Ltd. (2)
2160 Rongle East Road, PO Box 021, Songjiang, Shanghai, 201613, China **(100%)**
Tel.: (86) 2157741800
Web Site: http://www.kenwood.com.cn
Sales Range: $75-99.9 Million
Emp.: 400
Audio & Video Equipment Mfr
N.A.I.C.S.: 334310

Kenwood Electronics Trading (Shanghai) Co., Ltd. (1)
Rm 901 D Cheng Feng Ctr 1088 W Ar Rd, Shanghai, China
Tel.: (86) 21 5882 8701
Electronic Product Distr
N.A.I.C.S.: 423690

Kenwood Geobit Corporation (1)
15-13 Nanpeidaicho, Shibuya-Ku, Tokyo, 150-0036, Japan
Tel.: (81) 3 5457 7246
Mobile Phone Distr
N.A.I.C.S.: 423690

LLC JVCKENWOOD RUS (1)
st Suschevsky Val 31 building 1, 127018, Moscow, Russia
Tel.: (7) 4955892235
Web Site: https://ru.jvckenwood.com
Audio & Video Equipment Distr
N.A.I.C.S.: 423690

P.T. JVC Electronics Indonesia (1)
Jl Surya Lestari Kav I-16B Suryacipta City of Industry Kel Kutamekar, Kec Ciampel, Karawang, 41363, Jawa Barat, Indonesia
Tel.: (62) 26 744 0520
Web Site: https://www.jvc-jein.co.id
Emp.: 2,512
Car Electronic Equipment Mfr
N.A.I.C.S.: 334310

PT. JVCKENWOOD Indonesia (1)
Wisma Keiai 17th Floor Jl Jend Sudirman Kav 3, Jakarta, 10220, Indonesia
Tel.: (62) 21 572 4178
Web Site: https://id.jvckenwood.com
Electronic Products Mfr
N.A.I.C.S.: 336390

Radio Activity S.r.l. (1)
Via Privata Cascia 11, 20128, Milan, Italy
Tel.: (39) 023 651 4205
Web Site: http://www.radioactivity-tlc.com
Radio Device Mfr
N.A.I.C.S.: 334220
Umberto Poggi (Sls Dir)

Rein Medical GmbH (1)
Monforts Quartier 23, 41238, Monchengladbach, Germany
Tel.: (49) 21 616 9840
Web Site: https://reinmedical.com
Emp.: 50
Medical Tehnology Mfr
N.A.I.C.S.: 339112
Dieter Cyganek (Founder & Mng Dir)

Shinwa International Holdings Ltd. (1)
Unit A 5/F Garment Centre, Lai Chi Kok, Hong Kong, China (Hong Kong) **(100%)**
Tel.: (852) 2940 8777
Web Site: http://www.shinwa-net.com
Holding Company
N.A.I.C.S.: 551112
Yoshifumi Naito (Chm)

Subsidiary (Non-US):

Shinwa Industries (China) Ltd. (2)
No 26 Huifeng West No 2 Road Zhongkai High-tech Park, Huizhou, 516006, China
Tel.: (86) 752 260 2373
Electronic Component Mfr & Distr
N.A.I.C.S.: 334419

Shinwa Industries (Chongqing) Ltd. (2)
3/F Block 1 No 108 Jinyu Road, North New, Chongqing, 401122, China
Tel.: (86) 23 6301 6086
Electronic Component Mfr & Distr
N.A.I.C.S.: 334419

Subsidiary (Domestic):

Shinwa Industries (H.K.) Ltd. (2)
1906-1910 CCT Telecom Building 11, Wo Shing Street Fo Tan, Shatin, Hong Kong, China (Hong Kong)
Tel.: (852) 2602 1500
Audio Equipment Mfr
N.A.I.C.S.: 334310

Subsidiary (Non-US):

Shinwa Industries (Hangzhou) Ltd. (2)
Block B Eastern Factory No 5 No 19 Road, Hangzhou Economic & Technological Area, Hangzhou, 310018, China
Tel.: (86) 571 8673 7076
Electronic Component Mfr & Distr
N.A.I.C.S.: 334419

Shinwa Industries (Shenzhen) Ltd. (2)
Unit 2201-01 Reith Building 1002 Yanhe North Road, Lo Wu, Shenzhen, 518001, China
Tel.: (86) 755 2583 3118
Electronic Component Mfr & Distr
N.A.I.C.S.: 334419

Shinwa Industries (Xi'an) Ltd. (2)
3-4/F Building 5 Big Dipper Industrial Park No 4955 Shangyuan Road, Caotan Eco-industrial Park, Xi'an, 710032, China
Tel.: (86) 29 8131 9378
Electronic Component Mfr & Distr
N.A.I.C.S.: 334419

Shinwa Mechatronics (Shenzhen) Ltd. (2)
Block D11 1st Industrial Zone of Fenghuang, Fuyong Baoan, Shenzhen, 518103, Guangdong, China
Tel.: (86) 755 2733 7111
Electronic Component Mfr & Distr
N.A.I.C.S.: 334419

Shinwa Precision (Hungary) Kft (2)
Muhi u 2/a, 3534, Miskolc, Hungary
Tel.: (36) 4 653 0700
Web Site: https: www.shinwa-net.com
Plastic Parts Mfr & Distr
N.A.I.C.S.: 326199

Victor Company of Japan, Ltd. (1)
6F Creative One Akihabara Bldg 5-3-4 Ueno Taito-ku, Tokyo, 110-8605, Japan **(52.43%)**
Tel.: (81) 3 3834 2388
Web Site: http://www.ngo-jvc.net
Sales Range: $1-4.9 Billion
Emp.: 11,611
Audio, Video & Computer Equipment Research, Development & Mfr
N.A.I.C.S.: 334310
Yuta Ito (Pres)

Subsidiary (Non-US):

JVC (U.K.) Ltd. (2)
JVC House JVC Business Pk, 12 Priestley Way, London, NW2 7BA, United Kingdom **(100%)**
Tel.: (44) 2084503282
Web Site: http://www.jvc.co.uk
Sales Range: $200-249.9 Million
Emp.: 50
Audio & Video Equipment Mfr
N.A.I.C.S.: 334310
Scott Bannatyne (Pres)

JVC Canada, Inc. (2)
6070 Kestrel Road, Mississauga, L5T 1S8, ON, Canada **(100%)**
Tel.: (905) 670-7211
Web Site: http://www.jvc.ca
Sales Range: $25-49.9 Million
Emp.: 55
Audio & Video Equipment Mfr
N.A.I.C.S.: 334310

JVC Deutschland GmbH (2)
Gruener Weg 12, 61169, Friedberg, Hessen, Germany **(100%)**
Tel.: (49) 60319390
Web Site: http://www.jvc.de
Sales Range: $25-49.9 Million
Emp.: 40
Audio & Video Equipment Mfr
N.A.I.C.S.: 334310

JVC Professional Europe Limited (2)
12 3 Cy, 16 Priestley Way, London, MW27 BA, United Kingdom **(100%)**
Tel.: (44) 2082086200
Web Site: http://www.jvcpro.co.uk
Sales Range: $25-49.9 Million
Emp.: 30
Audio & Video Equipment Mfr
N.A.I.C.S.: 334310
Yash Patel (Exec Dir-CCTV Europe)

Victor Creative Media Co., Ltd. (1)
1612-1 Shimotsuruma, Yamato, 242-0001, Japan
Tel.: (81) 4 6275 1113
Compact Disc Prerecorded Services
N.A.I.C.S.: 334610

JVK INTERNATIONAL MOVERS LTD.

222 Krungthep Kreetha Road, Bangkok, 10240, Thailand
Tel.: (66) 23794646
Web Site: http://www.jvkmovers.com
Year Founded: 1979
Emp.: 200
Moving & Transportation Services
N.A.I.C.S.: 541614
Nuchjarin Tiapplia (Gen Mgr)

JVL AGRO INDUSTRIES LIMITED

Jhunjhunwala Bhavan, Nati Imli, Varanasi, 221 001, Uttar Pradesh, India
Tel.: (91) 542 2211312
Web Site: http://www.jvlagro.com
Rev.: $566,619,742
Assets: $320,853,104
Liabilities: $232,298,846
Net Worth: $88,554,258
Earnings: $4,758,091
Emp.: 616
Fiscal Year-end: 03/31/17
Hydrogenated Vegetable Oil & Refined Oil Mfr
N.A.I.C.S.: 311225
Adarsh Jhunjhunwala (Exec Dir)

Subsidiaries:

JVL Overseas Pte. Ltd. (1)
1 North Bridge Road 18-07 High Street Centre, Singapore, 179094, Singapore
Tel.: (65) 90304501
Vegetable Margarine Mfr
N.A.I.C.S.: 311225

JVM CO., LTD.

121 Hosandong-ro, Dalseo-gu, Daegu, 42709, Korea (South)
Tel.: (82) 535849999
Web Site: https://www.myjvm.com
Year Founded: 1977
054950—(KRS)
Rev.: $108,896,842
Assets: $177,724,201
Liabilities: $56,445,035
Net Worth: $121,279,166
Earnings: $12,085,232
Emp.: 328
Fiscal Year-end: 12/31/22
Medical Equipment Mfr
N.A.I.C.S.: 334510
Yong-hee Lee (Pres & CEO)

JVM EQUIPMENT LTD.

Mallards House Stall House Lan North Heath Pulborough, North Heath Nr. Pulborough, Horsham, RH20 2HR, West Sussex, United Kingdom
Tel.: (44) 1798 875 992
Web Site: http://www.jvmequipment.com
Sales Range: $300-349.9 Million
Emp.: 500
Construction, Earthmoving & Lifting Equipment Distr
N.A.I.C.S.: 423810
Maxwell Skilman (Mng Dir)

Subsidiaries:

JVM AG (1)
Beethovenstrasse 45, 8002, Zurich, Switzerland
Tel.: (41) 44 280 6464
Construction Equipment Distr
N.A.I.C.S.: 423810

JVM Equipment International Ltd. (1)
77 Sir John Rogerson's Quay, Dublin, 2, Ireland
Tel.: (353) 1 6401857
Emp.: 5
Construction, Earthmoving & Lifting Equipment Distr
N.A.I.C.S.: 423810

JVSPAC ACQUISITION CORP.
G/F Hang Tak Building 1 Electric Street, Wanchai, China (Hong Kong)
Tel.: (852) 92589728   VG
Year Founded: 2021
JVSA—(NASDAQ)
Assets: $394,375
Liabilities: $491,697
Net Worth: ($97,322)
Earnings: ($76,827)
Fiscal Year-end: 12/31/23
Investment Management Service
N.A.I.C.S.: 523999

JW CAYMAN THERAPEUTICS COMPANY LIMITED
4F Bldg 42 No 225 Meisheng Road Pilot Free Trade Zone, Shanghai, China
Tel.: (86) 2150464201   Ky
Web Site:
   http://www.jwtherapeutics.com
Year Founded: 2016
2126—(HKG)
Health Care Srvices
N.A.I.C.S.: 621610
Yiping James Li *(Chm)*

Subsidiaries:

JW Therapeutics (Suzhou) Co., Ltd.   (1)
Building 21 4/F 218 Sangtian Street, Suzhou Industrial Park, Suzhou, 215123, Jiangsu, China
Tel.: (86) 51267998618
Pharmaceutical Product Mfr & Distr
N.A.I.C.S.: 325412

JW HOLDINGS CORPORATION
2477 JW Tower Nambusunhwan-ro, Seocho-dong Seocho-gu, Seoul, 137-864, Korea (South)
Tel.: (82) 28406777
Web Site: https://www.jw-holdings.com
Year Founded: 1945
096760—(KRS)
Rev.: $663,099,442
Assets: $887,863,636
Liabilities: $632,251,089
Net Worth: $255,612,547
Earnings: $16,990,593
Emp.: 138
Fiscal Year-end: 12/31/22
Investment Management Service
N.A.I.C.S.: 551112
Kyung Ha Lee *(Pres & Co-CEO)*

Subsidiaries:

JW Chemitown   (1)
15 Seolgyenamu-gil Daedeok-myeon, Anseong, Gyeonggi-do, Korea (South)
Tel.: (82) 316721284
Pharmaceutical Product Mfr
N.A.I.C.S.: 325412

JW Industrial   (1)
South Beltway 2477, Seocho-gu, Seoul, 137-864, Korea (South)
Tel.: (82) 2 2109 7891
Web Site: http://www.jw-industrial.co.kr
Metal Fabricating Services
N.A.I.C.S.: 332312

JW Life Science   (1)
28 Hanjin 1-gil, Seocho-gu, Seoul, 137-864, Korea (South)
Tel.: (82) 413517600
Web Site: http://www.jw-lifescience.co.kr
Pharmaceuticals Product Mfr
N.A.I.C.S.: 325412

JW Pharmaceutical Corporation   (1)
2477 Nambusunhwan-ro, Seocho-gu, Seoul, 137-864, Korea (South)
Tel.: (82) 2 840 6777
Web Site: http://www.jw-pharma.co.kr
Pharmaceuticals Product Mfr
N.A.I.C.S.: 325412

Subsidiary (Non-US):

Euvipharm Pharmaceuticals Joint Stock Company   (2)
Binh Tien 2 Duc Hoa Ha, Duc Hoa, Vietnam
Tel.: (84) 72843779623
Web Site: http://www.euvipharm.com
Pharmaceuticals Product Mfr
N.A.I.C.S.: 325411
Hau Nguyen *(Mgr-R&D)*

Subsidiary (US):

JW Theriac Pharmaceutical Corp.   (2)
600 Broadway Ste 580, Seattle, WA 98122
Tel.: (206) 436-1400
Web Site: http://www.theriacpharm.com
Pharmaceuticals Product Mfr
N.A.I.C.S.: 325412

Jw ShinYak Corporation   (1)
38 Gwacheon-daero 7-gil, Seocho-gu, Gwacheon, 137-864, Gyeonggi-do, Korea (South)
Tel.: (82) 28406111
Web Site: http://www.jw-shinyak.co.kr
Rev.: $78,778,907
Assets: $72,170,058
Liabilities: $29,454,132
Net Worth: $42,715,926
Earnings: $1,057,243
Emp.: 237
Fiscal Year-end: 12/31/2022
Pharmaceutical Product Mfr & Distr
N.A.I.C.S.: 325412
Seungho Baek *(CEO)*

Subsidiary (Domestic):

JW Creagene, Inc.   (2)
2F 137 Sagimakgol-ro, Jungwon-gu, Seongnam, Gyeonggi-do, Korea (South)   (99.75%)
Tel.: (82) 31 737 3300
Web Site: http://www.creagene.com
Pharmaceuticals Product Mfr
N.A.I.C.S.: 325412

JWH GROUP PTY LTD
Level 1 80 Walters Drive, Osborne, 6017, WA, Australia
Tel.: (61) 894647800
Web Site: http://www.jwh.com.au
Year Founded: 2001
Sales Range: $150-199.9 Million
Emp.: 650
Holding Company
N.A.I.C.S.: 551112
Julian Walter *(Mng Dir)*

Subsidiaries:

Constructive Media Pty Ltd   (1)
366 Scarborough Beach Rd, Osborne Park, 6017, WA, Australia
Tel.: (61) 8 9461 7380
Web Site:
   http://www.constructivemedia.com.au
Animation Designing Services
N.A.I.C.S.: 512191
Mitch Hector *(Project Mgr)*

Oswald Homes Pty ltd   (1)
366 Scarborough Beach Rd, Osborne Park, 6017, WA, Australia
Tel.: (61) 8 9231 4800
Web Site: http://www.oswaldhomes.com.au
Emp.: 20
Building Construction Services
N.A.I.C.S.: 236116
Emma Griffin *(Gen Mgr)*

Plunkett Homes Pty ltd   (1)
34 Burton Street, Cannington, 6979, WA, Australia
Tel.: (61) 8 9366 0000
Web Site: http://www.plunkethomes.com.au
Building Construction Services
N.A.I.C.S.: 236116

Rural Building Company Pty Ltd.   (1)
96-102 Stirling Terrace, Albany, 6330, WA, Australia
Tel.: (61) 8 9842 8400
Web Site: http://www.ruralbuilding.com.au
Building Construction Services
N.A.I.C.S.: 236115

Darren Burr *(Gen Mgr)*

JWIPC TECHNOLOGY CO., LTD.
13/F Haisong Building B Tairan 9th Rd, Futian, Shenzhen, 518042, Guang Dong, China
Tel.: (86) 75523981883
Web Site: https://www.jwipc.com
Year Founded: 2011
001339—(SSE)
Rev.: $425,789,676
Assets: $423,324,252
Liabilities: $163,133,568
Net Worth: $260,190,684
Earnings: $16,718,832
Fiscal Year-end: 12/31/22
Electronic Product Mfr & Distr
N.A.I.C.S.: 334419
Weiwei Yuan *(Chm)*

JWW INVEST SA
Ul Rolna 43b, 40-555, Katowice, Poland
Tel.: (48) 322036048
Web Site: http://www.jwwinvest.pl
Year Founded: 2012
JWW—(WAR)
Rev.: $3,395,579
Assets: $2,235,442
Liabilities: $1,297,612
Net Worth: $937,830
Earnings: $167,505
Fiscal Year-end: 12/31/23
Building Construction Services
N.A.I.C.S.: 236220
Maria Wcislo *(Chm)*

JX ENERGY LTD.
Suite 3600 888-3rd Street S W, Calgary, T2P 5C5, AB, Canada
Tel.: (403) 355-6623   Ca
Web Site: http://www.persta.ca
Year Founded: 2005
3395—(HKG)
Rev.: $10,239,813
Assets: $26,812,376
Liabilities: $30,965,502
Net Worth: ($4,153,126)
Earnings: ($15,967,805)
Emp.: 5
Fiscal Year-end: 12/31/23
Natural Gas Mfr & Distr
N.A.I.C.S.: 211130
Binyou Dai *(COO)*

JX LUXVENTURE LIMITED
Bin Hai Da Dao No 270, Lang Qin Wan Guo Ji Du Jia Cun Zong He Lou, Haikou, 570100, Hainan, China
Tel.: (86) 59588507988   MH
Web Site: http://www.kbsfashion.com
Year Founded: 2012
JXJT—(NASDAQ)
Rev.: $31,840,588
Assets: $21,918,401
Liabilities: $6,763,706
Net Worth: $15,154,695
Earnings: $3,043,779
Emp.: 57
Fiscal Year-end: 12/31/23
Men's Clothing Mfr & Retailer
N.A.I.C.S.: 315250
Keyan Yan *(Chm, Pres & CEO)*

JY GAS LIMITED
3/F Jiaoyun Group Building No 2568 Shi'an Road, Weifang Municipality, Gaomi, Shandong, China   Ky
Web Site: https://www.gmjytrq.com
Year Founded: 2003
1407—(HKG)
Rev.: $72,856,105
Assets: $76,815,511
Liabilities: $32,506,872
Net Worth: $44,308,638
Earnings: $7,963,243
Emp.: 102
Fiscal Year-end: 12/31/22
Natural Gas Distribution Services
N.A.I.C.S.: 221210
Xiaolong Luan *(CEO)*

JY GRANDMARK HOLDINGS LIMITED
Suites 3008-10 30/F Tower One Times Square 1 Matheson Street, Causeway Bay, China (Hong Kong)
Tel.: (852) 39189218   Ky
Web Site:
   http://www.jygrandmark.com
Year Founded: 2013
2231—(HKG)
Rev.: $72,068,724
Assets: $1,753,210,462
Liabilities: $1,231,200,032
Net Worth: $522,010,429
Earnings: ($124,650,630)
Emp.: 873
Fiscal Year-end: 12/31/22
Holding Company
N.A.I.C.S.: 551112
Michael Sze Ming Chan *(Chm)*

JYNWEL CAPITAL LIMITED
19/F 50 Connaught Road, Central, China (Hong Kong)
Tel.: (852) 3911 2000   HK
Web Site:
   http://www.jynwelcapital.com
Year Founded: 2010
Emp.: 30
Investment Firm
N.A.I.C.S.: 523999
Jho Low *(CEO)*

Subsidiaries:

EMI Music Publishing   (1)
75 9th Ave, New York, NY 10011
Tel.: (212) 492-1200
Music Publisher & Distr
N.A.I.C.S.: 512230

Subsidiary (Non-US):

EMI Music Publishing (Belgium) SA NV   (2)
E Plaskylaan 179, 1030, Brussels, Belgium
Tel.: (32) 22450320
Sales Range: $10-24.9 Million
Emp.: 4
Music Publisher & Distr
N.A.I.C.S.: 512250

EMI Music Publishing (Greece) LLC   (2)
259 Messoghion Avenue, N Psychiko, 154 51, Athens, Greece
Tel.: (30) 2106714626
Sales Range: $10-24.9 Million
Emp.: 2
Music Publisher & Distr
N.A.I.C.S.: 512230

EMI Music Publishing (Holland) B.V.   (2)
Groest 91 93, 1211 EB, Hilversum, Netherlands
Tel.: (31) 356462000
Sales Range: $25-49.9 Million
Emp.: 15
Music Publisher & Distr
N.A.I.C.S.: 512250

EMI Music Publishing Canada   (2)
109 Atlantic Ave Ste 301, Toronto, M6K 1X4, ON, Canada
Tel.: (416) 583-5481
Web Site: http://www.emimusicpub.com
Music Publisher & Distr
N.A.I.C.S.: 512230

EMI Music Publishing Ceska Republika, a.s.   (2)
Kovarova 39, Stodulky, 155 00, Prague, Czech Republic
Tel.: (420) 296397115
Web Site: http://www.emi.

JYNWEL CAPITAL LIMITED

Jynwel Capital Limited—(Continued)
Sales Range: $10-24.9 Million
Emp.: 2
Music Publisher & Distr
N.A.I.C.S.: 512230

EMI Music Publishing Chile (2)
Alfredo Barros Errazuriz, Providencia, 1954, Santiago, Chile
Tel.: (56) 22091009
Sales Range: $10-24.9 Million
Emp.: 5
Music Publisher & Distr
N.A.I.C.S.: 512250

EMI Music Publishing Denmark A/S (2)
Bjorns Tradgardsgrand 1, SE 116-21, Stockholm, Sweden
Tel.: (46) 8 441 19 60
Web Site: http://www.sonyatv.com
Emp.: 19
Music Publisher & Distr
N.A.I.C.S.: 512230
Patrik Sventelius (Mng Dir)

EMI Music Publishing Hong Kong (2)
Unit 207 Prosterhui Millenni Plz, 6-8 Harbour Road, North Point, China (Hong Kong)
Tel.: (852) 29565400
Web Site: http://www.sonyatv.com
Sales Range: $25-49.9 Million
Emp.: 13
Music Publisher & Distr
N.A.I.C.S.: 512250

EMI Music Publishing Italia SRL (2)
Via Moremendo 2 27, 20149, Milan, Italy
Tel.: (39) 0248010216
Sales Range: $25-49.9 Million
Emp.: 23
Music Publisher & Distr
N.A.I.C.S.: 512250

EMI Music Publishing Ltd. (2)
30 Golden Sq, London, W1F 9LD, United Kingdom
Tel.: (44) 2030593059
Music Publisher & Distr
N.A.I.C.S.: 512230

EMI Music Publishing Malaysia SDN BHD (2)
Suite 21 7 The Boulevard Lingakaran Syed Putra, Mid Valley City, 59200, Kuala Lumpur, Malaysia
Tel.: (60) 22016888
Music Publishing & Distr
N.A.I.C.S.: 512250

EMI Music Publishing Mexico (2)
Blvd Manuel Avila Camacho 76 Piso 5, Col Lomas de Chapultepec Miguel Hidalgo, Mexico, 11000, Mexico
Tel.: (52) 5555407930
Sales Range: $10-24.9 Million
Emp.: 25
Music Publishing & Distr
N.A.I.C.S.: 512230

EMI Music Publishing Portugal (2)
Praca Nuno Rodriguez dos Santos, Urban Das Laranjeiras 7, 1600 171, Lisbon, Portugal
Tel.: (351) 217217400
Sales Range: $10-24.9 Million
Emp.: 5
Music Publisher & Distributor
N.A.I.C.S.: 512250

EMI Music Publishing Scandinavia AB (2)
Sveavagen 24 26, 103 63, Stockholm, Sweden
Tel.: (46) 858795500
Sales Range: $10-24.9 Million
Emp.: 14
Music Publisher & Distr
N.A.I.C.S.: 512250
Johnny Tennander (Mng Dir)

EMI Music Publishing Spain (2)
Calle Gran Via 39 7a Planta, Madrid, 28013, Spain
Tel.: (34) 915239940
Sales Range: $10-24.9 Million
Emp.: 20
Music Publisher & Distr

N.A.I.C.S.: 512250
Juan Ignacio (Mng Dir)

JYOT INTERNATIONAL MARKETING LIMITED
Room No 1 1 Pandurang Society Judges Bungalow Road Bodakdev, Ahmedabad, 380054, Gujarat, India
Tel.: (91) 9099946908
Web Site: https://www.jyotinternational.co.in
Year Founded: 1989
542544—(BOM)
Rev.: $2,215,196
Assets: $11,211,378
Liabilities: $7,879,031
Net Worth: $3,332,347
Earnings: $1,534,468
Emp.: 2
Fiscal Year-end: 03/31/23
Financial Services
N.A.I.C.S.: 541611
Jayesh Shah (Compliance Officer)

JYOTHY LABORATORIES LTD
Ujala House Ram Krishna Mandir Road Kondivita, Off Andheri Kurla Road Andheri East, Mumbai, 400059, India
Tel.: (91) 2266892800
Web Site: https://www.jyothylabs.com
532926—(BOM)
Rev.: $344,737,316
Assets: $281,423,715
Liabilities: $69,705,581
Net Worth: $211,718,134
Earnings: $32,722,599
Emp.: 2,602
Fiscal Year-end: 03/31/23
Fabric Care, Insecticides, Utensil Cleaners & Fragrances Mfr
N.A.I.C.S.: 325320
M. R. Jyothy (CMO)

Subsidiaries:

Jyothy Consumer Products Ltd. (1)
Ujala House Ram Krishna Mandir Road Kondivita, Off Andheri Kurla Road Andheri East, Mumbai, 400059, India   (83.66%)
Tel.: (91) 22 66892800
Web Site: http://www.jyothylaboratories.com
Sales Range: $75-99.9 Million
Emp.: 100
Household Chemical Products Mfr
N.A.I.C.S.: 325998

Jyothy Fabricare Services Ltd (1)
N904 North block Rear Wing Manipal Center Dickenson Road, Bengaluru, 560 042, KA, India
Tel.: (91) 8040337300
Web Site: https://www.jfsl.in
Sales Range: $700-749.9 Million
Emp.: 250
Laundry Care Services
N.A.I.C.S.: 812310
M. P. Ramachandran (Mng Dir)

JYOTI BIKASH BANK LTD.
R and P Complex Kamal Pokhari, PO Box No 6518, Kathmandu, Nepal
Tel.: (977) 15970306
Web Site: https://www.jbbl.com.np
Year Founded: 2008
JBBL—(NEP)
Rev.: $36,757,932
Assets: $503,582,601
Liabilities: $459,464,968
Net Worth: $44,117,633
Earnings: $5,583,143
Fiscal Year-end: 07/15/21
Banking Services
N.A.I.C.S.: 522110
Hari Prasad Acharya (Chm)

JYOTI LTD.
Nanubhai Amin Marg P O Chemical Industries, Vadodara, 390 003, Gujarat, India

Tel.: (91) 2653054588
Web Site: https://www.jyoti.com
504076—(BOM)
Rev.: $16,445,029
Assets: $49,439,945
Liabilities: $89,428,344
Net Worth: ($39,988,398)
Earnings: ($481,818)
Emp.: 240
Fiscal Year-end: 03/31/21
Hydraulic Engineering Equipment Mfr & Distr
N.A.I.C.S.: 333996
Rahul Nanubhai Amin (Chm & Mng Dir)

Subsidiaries:

Jyoti Ltd. - ELECTRONICS & CONTROL SYSTEMS (RELAY DIVISION) (1)
B/3-15 BIDC Gorwa, Vadodara, 390 016, India
Tel.: (91) 2652280561
Web Site: http://www.jyoti.com
Relay Mfr
N.A.I.C.S.: 334513

Jyoti Ltd. - SWITCHGEAR DIVISION (1)
J/44-59 BIDC Gorwa, Vadodara, 390 016, India
Tel.: (91) 9624184434
Sales Range: $400-449.9 Million
Switchgear Mfr
N.A.I.C.S.: 335313
Milind Kulkarni (Asst Gen Mgr-Switchgear Bus)

JYOTI RESINS & ADHESIVES LTD.
1104-1112 Ellite Nr Shapath Hexa, Opp Kargil Petrol Pump Near Sola Over Bridge S G Highway, Ahmedabad, 380 060, India
Tel.: (91) 9427320474
Web Site: https://www.euro7000.com
Year Founded: 1993
514448—(BOM)
Rev.: $14,703,539
Assets: $19,672,505
Liabilities: $13,674,324
Net Worth: $5,998,180
Earnings: $1,660,531
Fiscal Year-end: 03/31/21
Adhesive Mfr
N.A.I.C.S.: 325520
Jagdish N. Patel (Chm & Mng Dir)

Subsidiaries:

Jyoti Resins & Adhesives Ltd. - Gandhinagar Factory (1)
Survey No 873 Village Santej Tal, Gandhinagar, Kalol, 382721, Gujarat, India
Tel.: (91) 2764 286327
Adhesive Mfr
N.A.I.C.S.: 325520

JYOTI STRUCTURES LTD
6th Floor Valecha Chambers New Link Road, Andheri West, Mumbai, 400053, Maharashtra, India
Tel.: (91) 2240915000
Web Site: https://jyotistructures.in
513250—(BOM)
Rev.: $21,089
Assets: $192,452,374
Liabilities: $1,747,476,153
Net Worth: ($1,555,023,779)
Earnings: ($240,081,483)
Emp.: 1,365
Fiscal Year-end: 03/31/21
Turnkey Solutions Provider
N.A.I.C.S.: 221320
Kanayo R. Thakur (Exec Dir)

JYOTIRGAMYA ENTERPRISES LIMITED
P 37/38 Officer No 3 Gomti Complex

2nd Floor Mayur Vihar Phase I, New Delhi, 110091, India
Tel.: (91) 9205562494
Web Site: http://www.jeltrade.com
539246—(BOM)
Rev.: $5,081
Assets: $533,776
Liabilities: $92,132
Net Worth: $441,644
Earnings: ($7,625)
Emp.: 3
Fiscal Year-end: 03/31/20
Jewellery Product Mfr & Distr
N.A.I.C.S.: 339910
Sahil Minhaj Khan (Mng Dir)

JYP ENTERTAINMENT CO., LTD.
205 Gangdong daero, Gangdong-gu, Seoul, Korea (South)
Tel.: (82) 222258100
Web Site: https://www.jype.com
Year Founded: 1996
035900—(KRS)
Rev.: $265,299,249
Assets: $315,330,812
Liabilities: $81,778,467
Net Worth: $233,552,345
Earnings: $51,760,016
Emp.: 325
Fiscal Year-end: 12/31/22
Audio Production & Distribution Services
N.A.I.C.S.: 512240
Sang-Bong Byeon (CFO & VP)

JYSK-FYNSK KAPITAL A/S
Bakken 38, 8722, Hedensted, Denmark
Tel.: (45) 40 15 14 77
Web Site: http://www.jf-kapital.dk
Emp.: 2,000
Privater Equity Firm
N.A.I.C.S.: 523999
Per Kristensen (CEO)

Subsidiaries:

KE Fibertec AS (1)
Industrivej Vest 21, 6600, Vejen, Denmark   (75%)
Tel.: (45) 75 36 42 00
Web Site: http://www.ke-fibertec.com
Emp.: 120
Air Distribution Equipment Mfr
N.A.I.C.S.: 333413
Carsten Jespersen (Mng Dir)

Subsidiary (US):

KE Fibertec North America Inc. (2)
2107 Emmorton Park Rd Ste 102, Edgewood, MD 21040
Tel.: (443) 299-6435
Web Site: http://www.kefibertec.com
Emp.: 6
Air Distribution Equipment Mfr
N.A.I.C.S.: 333413
Gert S. Jensen (Pres)

JYSKE BANK A/S
Vestergade 8-16, 8600, Silkeborg, Denmark
Tel.: (45) 89898989   DK
Web Site: https://www.jyskebank.dk
Year Founded: 1967
JYSK—(CSE)
Rev.: $1,822,430,583
Assets: $112,814,891,985
Liabilities: $106,175,427,935
Net Worth: $6,639,464,051
Earnings: $854,277,901
Emp.: 3,940
Fiscal Year-end: 12/31/23
Banking Services
N.A.I.C.S.: 522110
Anders Christian Dam (CEO & Mng Dir-Private, Fin, Risk, Legal & Comm)

AND PRIVATE COMPANIES

Subsidiaries:

Berbens Effectenkantoor B.V (1)
Schatbeurderlaan 10, Weert, 6006, Netherlands
Tel.: (31) 495456000
Web Site: http://www.berbens.nl
Sales Range: $50-74.9 Million
Emp.: 14
Trusts Estates & Agency Accounts
N.A.I.C.S.: 525920
Van Derhillen *(Mng Dir)*

Gl. Skovridergaard A/S (1)
Marienlundsvej 36, 8600, Silkeborg, Denmark (100%)
Tel.: (45) 87225500
Web Site: https://www.glskov.dk
Sales Range: $10-24.9 Million
Hotels & Motels
N.A.I.C.S.: 721110

JN Data A/S (1)
Frichsvej 18, 8600, Silkeborg, Denmark (51%)
Tel.: (45) 6 363 6363
Web Site: https://www.jndata.dk
Sales Range: $25-49.9 Million
Emp.: 500
Data Processing Services
N.A.I.C.S.: 518210

Jyske Bank (Schweiz) AG (1)
Wasserwerkstrasse 12, Zurich, 8021, Switzerland
Tel.: (41) 443687373
Web Site: http://www.jyskebank.ch
Sales Range: $50-74.9 Million
Emp.: 50
Commericial Banking
N.A.I.C.S.: 522110
Tim Marshall *(Mng Dir)*

Jyske Finans A/S (1)
Kastaniehojvej 2, 8600, Silkeborg, Denmark
Tel.: (45) 89894210
Web Site: https://jyskefinans.dk
Sales Range: $25-49.9 Million
Emp.: 170
Car Financing Management Services
N.A.I.C.S.: 541611

Jyske Invest Fund Management A/S (1)
Vestergade 8-16, DK-8600, Silkeborg, Denmark
Tel.: (45) 89892500
Web Site: https://jyskeinvest.com
Emp.: 30
Financial Investment Services
N.A.I.C.S.: 523999

Jyske Realkredit, Kgs. (1)
Klampenborgvej 205, 2800, Kongens Lyngby, Denmark
Tel.: (45) 89897777
Web Site: https://jyskerealkredit.com
Property Mortgage Loan Services
N.A.I.C.S.: 522299

Sundbyvesterhus A/S (1)
Vestergade 8-16, Silkeborg, Denmark (100%)
Tel.: (45) 89222222
Real Estate Agency
N.A.I.C.S.: 531210

JZ CAPITAL PARTNERS LIMITED

PO Box 255, Trafalgar Court Les Banques, Saint Peter Port, GY1 3QL, Guernsey
Tel.: (44) 2037271143 GY
Web Site: https://www.jzep.co.uk
JZCLF—(OTCIQ)
Rev.: $23,851,000
Assets: $358,443,000
Liabilities: $43,945,000
Net Worth: $314,498,000
Earnings: $2,646,000
Fiscal Year-end: 02/28/23
Closed-End Investment Fund
N.A.I.C.S.: 525990
David Macfarlane *(Chm)*

Subsidiaries:

Action Products Marketing Corp. (1)
1779 Chessie Ln, Ottawa, IL 61350
Tel.: (515) 276-9610
Web Site: https://www.waterlinerenewal.com
Emp.: 8
Manhole Rehabilitation Services
N.A.I.C.S.: 238990
Keith Walker *(Dir-Global Brands)*

National Inspection & Consultants, LLC (1)
9911 Bavaria Rd, Fort Myers, FL 33913 (37.4%)
Tel.: (239) 939-4313
Web Site: https://www.nicinc.com
Inspection & Consulting Services for Engineering & Construction Industries
N.A.I.C.S.: 541690
Robert A. Vigne *(Pres)*

JZR GOLD INC.

404-1688 152nd Street, Surrey, V4A 4N2, BC, Canada
Tel.: (604) 560-8898
Web Site: https://jzrgold.com
JZRIF—(OTCIQ)
Rev.: $2,551
Assets: $1,136,130
Liabilities: $1,348,960
Net Worth: ($212,829)
Earnings: ($93,209)
Fiscal Year-end: 06/30/19
Mineral Exploration Services
N.A.I.C.S.: 213114
Robert Klenk *(CEO)*

K & P INTERNATIONAL HOLDINGS LIMITED

Units 2304-06 23/F Riley House 88 Lei Muk Road, Kwai Chung, New Territories, China (Hong Kong)
Tel.: (852) 22763000
Web Site: http://www.kpihl.com
0675—(HKG)
Rev.: $53,939,756
Assets: $68,494,813
Liabilities: $17,580,165
Net Worth: $50,914,648
Earnings: $8,164,116
Emp.: 866
Fiscal Year-end: 12/31/21
Precision Parts & Components Sale & Mfr
N.A.I.C.S.: 332721
Yau Wah Chan *(Deputy Chm)*

Subsidiaries:

Hi-Tech Polymer (China) Inc. (1)
Unit 2304-06 23 Fl Riley House 88 Lei Muk Rd, Kwai Chung, NT, China (Hong Kong)
Tel.: (852) 22763838
Web Site: http://www.kpihl.com
Emp.: 50
Polymer Product Mfr
N.A.I.C.S.: 325211

Hi-Tech Precision Industrial Limited (1)
Rm 2304-06 23 F Riley House 88 Lei Muk Rd, Kwai Chung, NT, China (Hong Kong)
Tel.: (852) 24266420
Web Site: http://www.htpil.com
Sales Range: $25-49.9 Million
Emp.: 20
Silicon Rubber Products Mfr
N.A.I.C.S.: 326291

Hideki Electronics Limited (1)
Units 2304-06 23/F Riley House 88 Lei Muk Road, Kwai Chung, New Teritories, China (Hong Kong)
Tel.: (852) 24260138
Web Site: http://www.hidekielectronics.com
Sales Range: $25-49.9 Million
Emp.: 600
Clocks & Watches Whslr
N.A.I.C.S.: 423940

Sun Ngai Plastic Products Factory Limited (1)
Units 2304-06 23/F Riley House 88 Lei Muk Road, Kwai Chung, China (Hong Kong)
Tel.: (852) 24212168
Web Site: http://www.sunngai.com
Plastic Material Distr
N.A.I.C.S.: 424610
Silvia Lee *(Sls Mgr)*

TQL Technology Limited (1)
Rm 2304-06 23 F Riley House 88 Lei Muk Rd, Kwai Chung, NT, China (Hong Kong)
Tel.: (852) 24817833
Web Site: http://www.tql-technology.com
Liquid Crystal Display Mfr
N.A.I.C.S.: 334419

K - MAIL ORDER GMBH & CO. KG

Sachsenstrasse 23, 75177, Pforzheim, Germany
Tel.: (49) 18053200
Web Site: http://www.klingel.de
Sales Range: $350-399.9 Million
Emp.: 2,200
Mail Order & Electronic Shopping Services
N.A.I.C.S.: 423940
Andreas Kohm *(Mng Dir)*

Subsidiaries:

Alba Moda GmbH (1)
Daimlerstrasse 13, 32108, Bad Salzuflen, Germany (100%)
Tel.: (49) 52229200
Web Site: http://www.albamoda.de
Sales Range: $100-124.9 Million
Emp.: 350
Fashion & Lifestyle Products Mail Order
N.A.I.C.S.: 424350
Daniela Angerer *(Mgr)*

K AUCTION INC.

Art Tower 23 Eonju-ro 172-gil, Gangnam-gu, Seoul, Korea (South)
Tel.: (82) 234798888
Web Site: https://www.k-auction.com
Year Founded: 2005
102370—(KRS)
Rev.: $21,258,321
Assets: $166,862,434
Liabilities: $70,083,423
Net Worth: $96,779,011
Earnings: $3,088,863
Emp.: 104
Fiscal Year-end: 12/31/22
Investment Management Service
N.A.I.C.S.: 523999

K CAR CO., LTD.

3F 27 Seonyu-ro 43-gil, Yeongdeungpo-gu, Seoul, 07210, Korea (South)
Tel.: (82) 27540944
Web Site: https://www.kcar.com
Year Founded: 2017
381970—(KRS)
Rev.: $1,669,959,934
Assets: $409,851,582
Liabilities: $221,306,824
Net Worth: $188,544,758
Earnings: $23,288,949
Emp.: 1,147
Fiscal Year-end: 12/31/22
Automotive Retailer
N.A.I.C.S.: 423110

K LASER TECHNOLOGY INC.

No 1 Li Hsin 6th Rd Hsinchu Science Park, Hsin-chu, Taiwan
Tel.: (886) 35770316
Web Site: https://www.klasergroup.com
2461—(TAI)
Rev.: $185,721,828
Assets: $261,291,007
Liabilities: $127,572,185
Net Worth: $133,718,822
Earnings: ($2,723,863)
Emp.: 1,014
Fiscal Year-end: 12/31/23
Paperboard Mfr
N.A.I.C.S.: 322130
Alex Kuo *(Chm)*

K M SUGAR MILLS LIMITED

Subsidiaries:

Amagic Holographics India Pvt. Ltd. (1)
B-74 Ambad MIDC Industrial Area, Ambad, Nasik, 422010, Maharashtra, India
Tel.: (91) 2532381734
Web Site: http://www.amagicindia.com
Sales Range: $25-49.9 Million
Emp.: 28
Hologram Mfr
N.A.I.C.S.: 325992

Amagic Holographics, Inc. (1)
3123 W Macarthur Blv, Santa Ana, CA 92704
Tel.: (714) 897-3978
Web Site: http://www.klaser.usa.com
Sales Range: $25-49.9 Million
Emp.: 10
Hologram Mfr
N.A.I.C.S.: 325992

K Laser Technology (Dong Guan) Co., Ltd. (1)
Dapianmei Village, Dalingshan Town, Dongguan, 523832, Guangdong, China
Tel.: (86) 76985601301
Web Site: http://www.klasergroup.com
Sales Range: $125-149.9 Million
Emp.: 400
Hologram Mfr
N.A.I.C.S.: 325992

K Laser Technology (HK) Co., Ltd. (1)
No 5 1/Floor Trust Centre 912 Cheung Sha Wan Road, Kowloon, China (Hong Kong)
Tel.: (852) 27858768
Web Site: http://www.klaserhk.com
Sales Range: $25-49.9 Million
Optical Product Mfr
N.A.I.C.S.: 333310

K Laser Technology (Korea) Co., Ltd. (1)
19 Hyeongoksandan-ro Cheongbuk-myeon, Cheongbuuk-Myeon, Pyeongtaek, 17812, Gyeonggi-do, Korea (South)
Tel.: (82) 316848969
Web Site: http://www.klaser.co.kr
Emp.: 20
Hologram Mfr
N.A.I.C.S.: 325992

K Laser Technology (Thailand) Co., Ltd. (1)
111/89 Moo 7 Tambon Bang Chalong, Amphoe, Bang Phli, 10540, Samut Prakarn, Thailand
Tel.: (66) 23371211
Web Site: http://www.klasergroup.com
Sales Range: $25-49.9 Million
Emp.: 77
Hologram Mfr
N.A.I.C.S.: 325992

K Laser Technology (USA) Co., Ltd. (1)
3123 W MacArthur Blvd, Santa Ana, CA 92704
Tel.: (714) 897-3978
Web Site: https://klaser-usa.com
Holographic Product Distr
N.A.I.C.S.: 423410

K Laser Technology Japan Co., Ltd. (1)
1-4-44 Atobe Honmachi, Yao, 581-0064, Osaka, Japan
Tel.: (81) 729258888
Web Site: https://klaser-j.com
Sales Range: $25-49.9 Million
Hologram Mfr
N.A.I.C.S.: 325992

Wuxi K Laser Technologies Co., Ltd. (1)
No 23 Changjiang Road New District Zone, Wuxi, 214028, Jiangsu, China
Tel.: (86) 510 85210688
Web Site: http://www.klasergroup.com
Sales Range: $125-149.9 Million
Emp.: 300
Hologram Mfr
N.A.I.C.S.: 325992

K M SUGAR MILLS LIMITED

K M SUGAR MILLS LIMITED

K M Sugar Mills Limited—(Continued)
11 Moti Bhawan Collectorganj,
Kanpur, 224 001, India
Tel.: (91) 5122310762
Web Site: https://www.kmsugar.com
Year Founded: 1950
KMSUGAR—(NSE)
Rev.: $69,239,229
Assets: $85,257,545
Liabilities: $56,123,217
Net Worth: $29,134,328
Earnings: $3,582,060
Emp.: 339
Fiscal Year-end: 03/31/21
Sugar Refining Services
N.A.I.C.S.: 311314
L. K. Jhunjhunwala *(Chm)*

K W NELSON INTERIOR DESIGN AND CONTRACTING GROUP LIMITED
Rm 1703 17/F Technology Plaza 651 King's Road, Quarry Bay, China (Hong Kong)
Tel.: (852) 28569330   Ky
Web Site:
   http://www.kwnelson.com.hk
Year Founded: 2009
8411—(HKG)
Rev.: $5,421,428
Assets: $10,245,773
Liabilities: $1,037,340
Net Worth: $9,208,433
Earnings: ($433,755)
Emp.: 12
Fiscal Year-end: 12/31/22
Interior Design Services
N.A.I.C.S.: 541410
King Wai Lau *(Founder, Chm & CEO)*

K W PETROLEUM SERVICES LTD.
849 56th St E, Saskatoon, S7K 5Y9, SK, Canada
Tel.: (306) 244-4468
Web Site: http://www.kwpetro.com
Year Founded: 1982
Construction Services
N.A.I.C.S.: 237990
Joleen Huchkowski *(Office Mgr)*

K&C GLOBAL CO., LTD.
810 811 Humansky Valley 33 Omokcheon-ro, 132 Beon-Gil Gwonseon-GU, Suwon, 16642, Korea (South)
Tel.: (82) 31 2780797   KR
Year Founded: 1997
Sales Range: $1-9.9 Million
Emp.: 60
Carbon Nano-Materials & Inorganic Nano Fibers Mfr
N.A.I.C.S.: 313110
Simon Lai *(Founder)*

Subsidiaries:

NTPIA Corporation Co., Ltd. - Dongtan Plant   (1)
11-23 SONGDO-DONG, Dongtan-myeon, Hwaseong, 445-812, Gyeonggi, Korea (South)
Tel.: (82) 32 73 11 10
Web Site: http://www.ntpia.co.kr
Nano Fiber Mfr
N.A.I.C.S.: 322219

K&D PRATT GROUP INC.
21 Frazee Avenue Burnside Industrial Park, Dartmouth, B3B 1Z4, NS, Canada
Tel.: (902) 468-1955
Web Site: https://www.kdpratt.com
Rev.: $28,700,000
Emp.: 100
Industrial Products Supplier
N.A.I.C.S.: 423840

Yolanda Daniel *(VP-Fin)*

K&K GROUP AG
Gubelstrasse 19, 6300, Zug, Switzerland
Tel.: (41) 41 72720 00   CH
Web Site:
   http://www.koflerkompanie.com
Holding Company; Catering & Other Hospitality Services
N.A.I.C.S.: 551112
Martin Osbeck *(COO)*

Subsidiaries:

Kofler & Kompanie GmbH   (1)
Linkstrasse 12, 10785, Berlin, Germany
Tel.: (49) 30 259289 0
Web Site: http://www.koflerkompanie.com
Catering & Other Hospitality Services
N.A.I.C.S.: 722320
Oliver Wendel *(Mng Dir)*

Subsidiary (Domestic):

Airport Club fur International Executives GmbH   (2)
Frankfurt Airport Center I Hugo-Eckener-Ring, 60549, Frankfurt am Main, Germany
Tel.: (49) 69 69707 0
Web Site: http://www.airportclub.de
Pub Operator
N.A.I.C.S.: 713910
Roland Ross *(CEO, Mng Dir & Gen Mgr)*

K&K SUPERSTORE SOUTHERN PUBLIC COMPANY LIMITED
9/9 Moo 5 Lopburiramet, Khlong Hae Hatyai, Songkhla, 90110, Thailand
Tel.: (66) 74205288   TH
Web Site: https://www.kandk.co.th
Year Founded: 1993
KK—(THA)
Rev.: $31,172,298
Assets: $13,618,430
Liabilities: $8,710,124
Net Worth: $4,908,306
Earnings: ($130,554)
Fiscal Year-end: 12/31/23
Consumer Products Distr
N.A.I.C.S.: 423620
Kawispong Sirithananonsakul *(Mng Dir)*

K&L INC.
Hakuyo Building 3-10 Nibancho, Chiyoda Ku, Tokyo, 102-0084, Japan
Tel.: (81) 3 3263 2996
Web Site: http://www.klt.co.jp
Year Founded: 1963
Sales Range: $10-24.9 Million
Emp.: 90
Advetising Agency
N.A.I.C.S.: 541810
Sumitaka Kita *(Pres)*

Subsidiaries:

InterStudio Inc.   (1)
Bancho 5th Building 5-5 Nibancho, Chiyoda-ku, Tokyo, 102-0084, Japan
Tel.: (81) 3 5211 8127
Web Site: http://www.klt.co.jp
Emp.: 70
N.A.I.C.S.: 541810
Shinichi Okazaki *(VP)*

K&L Advertising Asia Pte Ltd.   (1)
5 Jalan kileng barat petro center unit no 0707, Singapore, 159349, Singapore
Tel.: (65) 6883 0550
Emp.: 6
N.A.I.C.S.: 541810
Tetsuzo Kita *(Chm & Mng Dir)*

K&L Advertising Hong Kong Ltd.   (1)
Rm 1704 17th Fl Tai Yau Bldg, 181 Johnston Rd, Wanchai, China (Hong Kong)
Tel.: (852) 2833 0065
Emp.: 30
N.A.I.C.S.: 541810
Oga Zaki *(Mng Dir)*

K&L Amsterdam   (1)
Bavinckstaete Bldg Prof JH Bavincklaan 5, 1183 AT, Amstelveen, Netherlands
Tel.: (31) 20 640 59 50
Sales Range: Less than $1 Million
Emp.: 5
N.A.I.C.S.: 541810
Osamu Ishizukae *(Mgr)*

K&L Creative Sevices   (1)
Bancho 5th Building 5-5 Nibancho, Chiyoda-ku, Tokyo, 102-0084, Japan
Tel.: (81) 3 5211 8139
Web Site: http://www.klt.co.jp
N.A.I.C.S.: 541810
Shinichi Okazaki *(VP)*

K&L Interactive Inc.   (1)
Bancho 5th Building 5-5 Nibancho, Chiyoda-ku, Tokyo, 102-0084, Japan
Tel.: (81) 3 5211 8126
Web Site: http://www.klt.co.jp
Emp.: 80
N.A.I.C.S.: 541810
Shinichi Okazaki *(VP)*

K&M HAULIERS LTD.
The Aerodrome Watnall Road, Hucknall, Nottingham, NG15 6EN, United Kingdom
Tel.: (44) 1159 630 630
Web Site:
   http://www.kmhauliers.co.uk
Year Founded: 1948
Sales Range: $25-49.9 Million
Emp.: 21
Warehousing Storage & Transport Services
N.A.I.C.S.: 493110

K&O ENERGY GROUP INC.
661 Mobara, Mobara, 297-0026, Chiba, Japan
Tel.: (81) 475271011   JP
Web Site: https://www.k-and-o-energy.co.jp
Year Founded: 2014
1663—(TKS)
Rev.: $682,752,820
Assets: $790,145,050
Liabilities: $131,278,440
Net Worth: $658,866,610
Earnings: $45,829,760
Fiscal Year-end: 12/31/23
Holding Company
N.A.I.C.S.: 551112
Akio Midorikawa *(Pres & Dir-Rep)*

Subsidiaries:

Boso Computer Service Co., Ltd.   (1)
661 Mobara, Mobara, 297-0026, Chiba, Japan
Tel.: (81) 475244234
Data Processing Services
N.A.I.C.S.: 518210

Kanpatsu Service Co., Ltd.   (1)
661 Mobara, Mobara, 297-0026, Chiba, Japan
Tel.: (81) 475225553
Real Estate Lending Services
N.A.I.C.S.: 531110

Kanto Construction Co., Ltd.   (1)
661 Mobara, Mobara, 297-0026, Chiba, Japan
Tel.: (81) 475 24 2262
Web Site: http://www.kan-ken.co.jp
Sales Range: $100-124.9 Million
Pipeline Laying, Engineering & Construction Services
N.A.I.C.S.: 236220

Kanto Natural Gas Development Co., Ltd.   (1)
661 Mobara, Mobara, 297-8550, Chiba, Japan
Tel.: (81) 475231313
Web Site: https://www.gasukai.co.jp
Emp.: 188
Natural Gas Production Services
N.A.I.C.S.: 211130
T. Mori *(Pres)*

INTERNATIONAL PUBLIC

Kng Welltechno Co., Ltd.   (1)
699 Mobara, Mobara, 297-0026, Chiba, Japan
Tel.: (81) 475362891
Web Site: https://www.kng-wt.co.jp
Emp.: 31
Drilling Services
N.A.I.C.S.: 213111

Nihon Tennen Gas Co., Ltd.   (1)
4-15-11 Nihonbashi Honcho, Chuo-ku, Tokyo, 103-0023, Japan
Tel.: (81) 336636391
Web Site: http://www.ntgas.co.jp
Sales Range: $50-74.9 Million
Emp.: 75
Natural Gas Production Services
N.A.I.C.S.: 211130

Otaki Gas Co., Ltd.   (1)
661 Mobara, Mobara, 297-8567, Chiba, Japan
Tel.: (81) 475240010
Web Site: http://www.otakigas.co.jp
Sales Range: $125-149.9 Million
Natural Gas Distr
N.A.I.C.S.: 221210

Subsidiary (Domestic):

Otaki Sangyo Co., Ltd.   (2)
661 Mobara, Mobara, 297-0026, Chiba, Japan
Tel.: (81) 475240161
Web Site: http://www.gasukai.co.jp
Compressed Natural Gas Mfr
N.A.I.C.S.: 211130

Shinei Engineer Corporation   (2)
1352-3 Gosho, Ichihara, 290-0066, Chiba, Japan
Sales Range: $25-49.9 Million
Gas Construction Services
N.A.I.C.S.: 237120

Techno Earth Corporation   (1)
661 Mobara, Mobara-city, Chiba, 297-0026, Japan
Tel.: (81) 475224115
Web Site: http://www.technoearth.co.jp
Well Drilling Services
N.A.I.C.S.: 213111

Welma Co., Ltd.   (1)
2-3-3 Watanabe-dori, Chuo-ku, Fukuoka, 810-0004, Japan
Tel.: (81) 927912212
Web Site: http://www.welma.co.jp
Emp.: 55
Seismic Well Drilling & Hot Spring Survey Services
N.A.I.C.S.: 541360
Yoshihiro Fujise *(Pres)*

K&S CORPORATION LIMITED
591 Boundary Road, Truganina, 3029, VIC, Australia
Tel.: (61) 387443500   AU
Web Site:
   https://www.ksgroup.com.au
KSC—(ASX)
Rev.: $556,911,854
Assets: $435,616,882
Liabilities: $197,937,500
Net Worth: $237,679,382
Earnings: $20,850,182
Emp.: 1,800
Fiscal Year-end: 06/30/24
Wharf, Local & Interstate Cartage, Warehousing, Logistics & Fuel Distribution
N.A.I.C.S.: 488510
Christopher Bright *(Gen Counsel & Sec)*

Subsidiaries:

Cochrane's Transport Limited   (1)
3847 Cambridge Road, Cambridge, 3434, New Zealand
Tel.: (64) 78233640
Web Site: https://www.aotearoapark.co.nz
Real Estate Services
N.A.I.C.S.: 531390
Libby Cochrane *(Gen Mgr)*

K&S (NZ) Limited   (1)

AND PRIVATE COMPANIES

3847 Te Awamatu Road, Cambridge, 3434, New Zealand
Tel.: (64) 7 827 6002
Web Site: http://www.ksfreighters.co.nz
Emp.: 100
Holding Company; Regional Managing Office; Freight Forwarding Services
N.A.I.C.S.: 551112
Greg Cochrane (Exec Gen Mgr)

Subsidiary (Domestic):

K&S Freighters Limited (2)
3847 Cambridge Road, PO Box 725, Cambridge, 3434, New Zealand
Tel.: (64) 78276002
Web Site: http://www.ksgroup.com.au
Sales Range: $25-49.9 Million
Emp.: 120
Road, Rail & Coastal Freight Forwarding Services
N.A.I.C.S.: 488510
Greg Cochrane (Gen Mgr)

K&S Freighters Pty. Ltd. (1)
30-32 Francis Street, Port Adelaide, 5015, SA, Australia
Tel.: (61) 72245400
Web Site: http://www.ksgroup.com.au
Warehousing & Freight Trucking Services
N.A.I.C.S.: 493110

Subsidiary (Domestic):

Scott Corporation Limited (2)
55 Davies Road, Locked Bag 7, Padstow, 2211, NSW, Australia
Tel.: (61) 297929400
Bulk Materials Transport Services
N.A.I.C.S.: 488510

Subsidiary (Domestic):

Bulktrans Pty Limited (3)
55 Davies Rd, Padstow, 2211, NSW, Australia
Tel.: (61) 297929400
Sales Range: $125-149.9 Million
Emp.: 400
Trucking & Courier Services
N.A.I.C.S.: 484110
Paul Sarant (Mng Dir)

Chemtrans Pty Limited (3)
55 Davies Rd, Padstow, 2211, NSW, Australia
Tel.: (61) 297929400
Web Site: http://www.scottcorp.com.au
Sales Range: $125-149.9 Million
Emp.: 25
Trucking & Courier Services
N.A.I.C.S.: 484110
Bryan Walsh (CFO)

K&S Fuels (1)
141-147 Jubilee Highway West, Mount Gambier, 5290, SA, Australia
Tel.: (61) 887211704
Emp.: 100
Fuel & Petroleum Products Distr
N.A.I.C.S.: 457210
Peter Sims (Gen Mgr)

K&S Group Pty Ltd (1)
141-147 Jubilee Highway West, PO Box 567, Mount Gambier, 5290, SA, Australia
Tel.: (61) 387443500
Web Site: http://www.ksgroup.com.au
Emp.: 60
Logistic Services
N.A.I.C.S.: 541614

K&S Integrated Distribution Pty Ltd (1)
325 Thompson Road, Geelong, 3215, Australia
Tel.: (61) 352785777
Web Site: http://www.ksgroup.com
Sales Range: $25-49.9 Million
Emp.: 100
Warehousing & Transport Services
N.A.I.C.S.: 493110
David Lockett (Branch Mgr)

K&S Transport Management Pty Ltd (1)
141-147 Jubilee Highway West, Mount Gambier, 5290, SA, Australia
Tel.: (61) 887211777
Web Site: http://www.ksgroup.com.au

Emp.: 30
Freight Transportation Services
N.A.I.C.S.: 484110

Kain & Shelton Pty Ltd (1)
46 Margaret St, Mount Gambier, 5290, SA, Australia
Tel.: (61) 887211774
Sales Range: $25-49.9 Million
Emp.: 10
General Warehousing Services
N.A.I.C.S.: 493110
Paul Sarant (Mng Dir)

Subsidiary (Domestic):

Kain & Shelton (Agencies) Pty Ltd (2)
141-147 Jubilee Highway West, PO Box 567, Mount Gambier, 5290, SA, Australia
Tel.: (61) 887211700
Petroleum Product Distr
N.A.I.C.S.: 424720

Regal Transport Group Pty. Ltd. (1)
160 Lakes Road, Hazelmere, Perth, 6055, WA, Australia
Tel.: (61) 893769600
Freight Transportation Services
N.A.I.C.S.: 488510
Bob Young (Branch Mgr)

K'S HOLDINGS CORPORATION

2-7-5 Jonan, Mito, 310-8282, Ibaraki, Japan
Tel.: (81) 292249600
Web Site: https://www.ksdenki.co.jp
Year Founded: 1947
8282—(TKS)
Rev.: $4,748,419,090
Assets: $2,896,495,390
Liabilities: $1,117,361,010
Net Worth: $1,779,134,380
Earnings: $48,781,800
Fiscal Year-end: 03/31/24
Appliance Store Operator
N.A.I.C.S.: 455110
Tadashi Hiramoto (Chm, Pres & Exec Officer)

K+S AKTIENGESELLSCHAFT

Bertha-von-Suttner-Strasse 7, 34131, Kassel, Germany
Tel.: (49) 56193010
Year Founded: 1889
SDF—(MUN)
Rev.: $4,274,846,962
Assets: $10,457,843,606
Liabilities: $3,279,266,609
Net Worth: $7,178,576,997
Earnings: $232,033,474
Emp.: 11,256
Fiscal Year-end: 12/31/23
Holding Company; Potash & Magnesium, Rock Salt, Inorganic Chemicals & Fertilizers Mfr & Distr; Waste Management & Recycling Services
N.A.I.C.S.: 551112
Burkhard Lohr (Chm-Exec Bd)

Subsidiaries:

1. **K+S Verwaltungs GmbH** (1)
Bertha-Von-Suttner-Str 7, Kassel, 34131, Hessen, Germany
Tel.: (49) 56193010
Specialty Fertilizer Distr
N.A.I.C.S.: 424690

1. **K+S Verwaltungs GmbH & Co. Erwerbs KG** (1)
Bertha-von-Suttner-Str 7, 34131, Kassel, Germany
Tel.: (49) 56193010
Web Site: http://www.k-plus-s.com
Fertilizer Distr
N.A.I.C.S.: 424690

3. **K+S Verwaltungs GmbH & Co. Erwerbs KG** (1)
Bertha-von-Suttner-Str 7, 34131, Kassel, Hessen, Germany
Tel.: (49) 56193010

Fertilizer Distr
N.A.I.C.S.: 424910

COMPO Austria GmbH (1)
Hietzinger Hauptstrasse 119, 1130, Vienna, Austria
Tel.: (43) 18 766 3930
Web Site: http://www.compo.at
Sales Range: $50-74.9 Million
Emp.: 13
Fertilizer Mineral Mining Services
N.A.I.C.S.: 212390
Hans-Jurgen Riehl (Gen Mgr)

COMPO Benelux N.V (1)
Filliersdreef 14, Deinze, 9800, Belgium
Tel.: (32) 9 381 83 83
Web Site: http://www.compo.be
Sales Range: $25-49.9 Million
Emp.: 35
Plantation & Seed Distr
N.A.I.C.S.: 424910
Walter Stevens (Gen Mgr)

COMPO Hellas S.A. (1)
54 Egialias, 151 25, Maroussi, Athens, Greece
Tel.: (30) 2111769100
Web Site: http://www.compo-expert.com
Crop Farming Services
N.A.I.C.S.: 111998

COMPO Verwaltungsgesellschaft mbH (1)
Gildenstr 38, Munster, 48157, Germany
Tel.: (49) 25132770
Fertilizer Whslr
N.A.I.C.S.: 424910

Canadian Brine Ltd. (1)
755 Boul St-Jean Bureau 700, Pointe-Claire, H9R 5M9, QC, Canada
Tel.: (514) 630-0900
Emp.: 20
Salt Distr
N.A.I.C.S.: 424690

Canadian Salt Finance Company (1)
755 Boul St-Jean Bureau 700, Pointe-Claire-Dorval, H9R 5M9, QC, Canada
Tel.: (514) 630-0900
Web Site: http://www.mortonsalt.com
Financial Management Services
N.A.I.C.S.: 523999
Mark Roberts (Pres)

Chemische Fabrik Kalk GmbH (1)
Olpenerstrasse 9 13, 51103, Cologne, Germany (100%)
Tel.: (49) 22182961
Web Site: https://www.cfk-gmbh.com
Sales Range: $25-49.9 Million
Emp.: 8
Trading & Sales of Chemicals
N.A.I.C.S.: 325998
Dirk Vogel (Head-Sales)

Chemische Fabrik Kalk GmbH (1)
Olpenerstrasse 9 13, 51103, Cologne, Germany (100%)
Tel.: (49) 22182961
Web Site: https://www.cfk-gmbh.com
Sales Range: $25-49.9 Million
Emp.: 8
Trading & Sales of Chemicals
N.A.I.C.S.: 325998
Dirk Vogel (Head-Sales)

Chemische Fabrik Kalk GmbH (1)
Olpenerstrasse 9 13, 51103, Cologne, Germany (100%)
Tel.: (49) 22182961
Web Site: https://www.cfk-gmbh.com
Sales Range: $25-49.9 Million
Emp.: 8
Trading & Sales of Chemicals
N.A.I.C.S.: 325998
Dirk Vogel (Head-Sales)

Chemische Fabrik Kalk GmbH (1)
Olpenerstrasse 9 13, 51103, Cologne, Germany (100%)
Tel.: (49) 22182961
Web Site: https://www.cfk-gmbh.com
Sales Range: $25-49.9 Million
Emp.: 8
Trading & Sales of Chemicals
N.A.I.C.S.: 325998
Dirk Vogel (Head-Sales)

Compania Minera Punta de Lobos Ltda. (1)

Ruta A-750 km 26 Tarapaca Region, Iquique, Chile
Tel.: (56) 224696200
Mineral Product Mfr & Distr
N.A.I.C.S.: 327999
Luis Fernandez (Mgr-Mine & Production Dept)

Deutscher Strassen-Dienst GmbH (1)
Bertha-von-Suttner-Strasse 7, 34131, Kassel, Germany
Tel.: (49) 56193010
Web Site: https://www.dsd-winterdienst.de
Salt Mfr
N.A.I.C.S.: 311942

Empresa Maritima S.A. (1)
Costanera Sur 2730, Las Condes, 7550000, Chile
Tel.: (56) 2 469 6100
Cargo Handling Services
N.A.I.C.S.: 488390

Erlebnis Bergwerk Merkers (1)
Zufahrtstrasse, Krayenberggemeinde, 36460, Merkers-Kieselbach, Germany
Tel.: (49) 369 561 4101
Web Site: https://www.erlebnisbergwerk.de
Mineral Mining Services
N.A.I.C.S.: 213115

European Salt Company (1)
Karlstrasse 80, D 47495, Rheinberg, Germany (100%)
Tel.: (49) 2803480
Web Site: http://www.esco-salt.com
Sales Range: $400-449.9 Million
Emp.: 1,352
Salt Producer
N.A.I.C.S.: 325998
Hanf Galland (Plant Mgr)

Subsidiary (Non-US):

Salines Cerebos et de Bayonne S.A. (2)
Rte De Ladour, Mouguerre, F 64990, Saint-Pierre d'Irube, France
Tel.: (33) 559528800
Sales Range: $25-49.9 Million
Emp.: 73
Evaporated Salt
N.A.I.C.S.: 325180

Plant (Domestic):

esco - european salt company GmbH & Co. KG - Bernburg Plant (2)
Kustrenaer Weg 7, 06406, Bernburg, Germany
Tel.: (49) 3471 81 0
Web Site: http://www.k-plus-s.com
Fertilizer Mfr
N.A.I.C.S.: 325314

esco - european salt company GmbH & Co. KG - Borth Plant (2)
Karlstr 80, Rheinberg, 47495, Germany
Tel.: (49) 2803 48 2212
Web Site: http://www.k-plus-s.com
Nitrogen Fertilizer Mfr
N.A.I.C.S.: 325311
Heinrich Gerland (Gen Mgr)

esco - european salt company GmbH & Co. KG - Braunschweig-Luneburg plant (2)
Bahnhofstr 15, 38368, Grasleben, Germany
Tel.: (49) 53571820
Fertilizer Mfr
N.A.I.C.S.: 325314

Subsidiary (Non-US):

esco france S.A.S. (2)
49 Ave Georges Pompidou, 92593, Levallois-Perret, France
Tel.: (33) 1 496459 00
Sales Range: $25-49.9 Million
Emp.: 3
Salt Distr
N.A.I.C.S.: 424690

Frisia Zout B.V. (1)
Lange lijnbaan 15, 8861, Harlingen, Netherlands
Tel.: (31) 517492499
Web Site: https://frisiazoutharlingen.nl
Emp.: 135

K+S AKTIENGESELLSCHAFT

K+S Aktiengesellschaft—(Continued)
Salt Mfr
N.A.I.C.S.: 311942

German Bulk Chartering GmbH (1)
Glockengiesserwall 3, Hamburg, 20095, Germany (100%)
Tel.: (49) 40309060
Web Site: http://www.k-plus-s.com
Sales Range: $50-74.9 Million
Emp.: 4
Shipping of Chemical Products & Fertilizers
N.A.I.C.S.: 212390
Hoppe George *(Mng Dir)*

Glendale Salt Development LLC (1)
123 N Wacker Dr, Chicago, IL 60606-1743
Tel.: (312) 807-2000
Spice Manufacturing
N.A.I.C.S.: 311942

Ickenroth GmbH (1)
Auf der Heide 4, 56424, Staudt, Germany
Tel.: (49) 26 029 2770
Web Site: https://www.icko.de
Salt Packaging Services
N.A.I.C.S.: 561910
Rainer Klausch *(Gen Mgr)*

Inagua General Store, Ltd. (1)
Gregory and Kortwright Street, Matthew Town, Great Inagua, Bahamas
Tel.: (242) 339 1866
Web Site: https://www.inaguageneralstore.com
Grocery Products Retailer
N.A.I.C.S.: 445110

International Salt Company LLC (1)
655 Northern Blvd, Clarks Summit, PA 18411
Tel.: (888) 388-4726
Web Site: http://www.internationalsalt.com
Sales Range: $50-74.9 Million
Emp.: 35
Salt Mining Services
N.A.I.C.S.: 212390
Daniel Thompson *(CEO)*

Inversiones K+S Sal de Chile Ltda. (1)
Tajamar 183 piso 6 Las Condes, Santiago, Chile
Tel.: (56) 2 4696200
Financial Investment Services
N.A.I.C.S.: 523940

K Plus S Africa (Pty) Ltd. (1)
19th Bath Avenue Corner Selby Road, Parkwood, Johannesburg, 2193, South Africa
Tel.: (27) 118805200
Mineral Product Mfr & Distr
N.A.I.C.S.: 327999

K Plus S Middle East FZE (1)
Office 410 - Indigo Tower Cluster D Jumeirah Lakes Towers, PO Box 337465, Jebel Ali, Dubai, United Arab Emirates
Tel.: (971) 48814720
Web Site: https://www.ks-middleeast.com
Fertilizer Distr
N.A.I.C.S.: 424910
Herve Cospain *(Mng Dir)*

K plus S Iberia S.L. (1)
Joan d' Austria 39-47, 08005, Barcelona, Spain
Tel.: (34) 932 247 334
Web Site: http://www.kali-gmbh.com
Chemical Products Mfr
N.A.I.C.S.: 325180

K+S AN-Instituts Verwaltungsgesellschaft mbH (1)
Bertha-Von-Suttner-Str 7, Kassel, 34131, Hessen, Germany
Tel.: (49) 56193010
Web Site: http://www.k-plus-s.com
Nitrogen Fertilizer Mfr
N.A.I.C.S.: 325311
Norbert Steiner *(CEO)*

K+S Agricoltura S.p.A. (1)
Via Marconato 8, 20811, Cesano Maderno, Italy
Tel.: (39) 0362 5121
Fertilizer Mfr
N.A.I.C.S.: 325314

K+S Agro Mexico S.A. de C.V (1)
Ave Lopez Mateos Sur 5060 Int 3a Col Miguel de la Madrid Hurtado, 45239, Zapopan, Jalisco, Mexico
Tel.: (52) 33 36123165
Web Site: http://www.k-plus-s.com
Fertilizer Mfr
N.A.I.C.S.: 325314

K+S Aktiengesellschaft - Plant Salzdetfurth (1)
Griesbergstr 8, 31162, Bad Salzdetfurth, Germany
Tel.: (49) 506 3490
Web Site: http://www.k-plus-s.com
Nitrogen Fertilizer Mfr
N.A.I.C.S.: 325311

K+S Baustoffrecycling GmbH (1)
Gluckauf Strasse 50, 31319, Sehnde, Germany
Tel.: (49) 5132501358
Web Site: https://www.ks-baustoff.de
Recycling Material Building Construction Services
N.A.I.C.S.: 236210

K+S Benelux B.V. (1)
Stationsweg 5A, 4811, Breda, Netherlands
Tel.: (31) 76 564 50 40
Chemical Products Mfr
N.A.I.C.S.: 325180
Niels Fanselow *(Gen Mgr)*

K+S Beteiligungs GmbH (1)
Tel.: (49) 56193010
Nitrogen Fertilizer Mfr
N.A.I.C.S.: 325311

K+S Brasileira Fertilizantes e Produtos Industriais Ltda. (1)
Rua Engenheiro Antonio Jovino 220 Conj 23, Sao Paulo, 05727-220, Brazil
Tel.: (55) 1137791588
Web Site: http://www.ksbrasileira.com.br
Fertilizer Distr
N.A.I.C.S.: 424690

K+S CZ a.s. (1)
Novodvorska 1062/12, Lhotka, 142 00, Prague, Czech Republic
Tel.: (420) 21 281 2640
Web Site: https://www.ks-cz.com
Emp.: 11
Salt & Potassium Distr
N.A.I.C.S.: 424690
Jiri Harencak *(Gen Mgr)*

K+S Chile S.A. (1)
Costanera Sur Rio Mapocho 2730-of 601, Las Condes, Santiago, Chile
Tel.: (56) 224696200
Web Site: http://www.ks-latam.com
Salt Mfr & Distr
N.A.I.C.S.: 325998
Walther Meyer Venegas *(VP-Ops & Supply Chain)*

K+S Consulting GmbH (1)
Bertha-von-Suttner-Strasse 7, 34111, Kassel, Germany
Tel.: (49) 561 93010
Web Site: http://www.ks-consult.com
Potash & Rock Salt Mining Services
N.A.I.C.S.: 212390

K+S Entsorgung GmbH (1)
Bertha-von-Suttner-Str 7, 34131, Kassel, Germany
Tel.: (49) 561 9301 1575
Web Site: http://www.ks-entsorgung.com
Waste Disposal Services
N.A.I.C.S.: 562219
Matthias Plomer *(Mng Dir)*

K+S Finance Belgium BVBA (1)
Culliganlaan 2G, 1831, Diegem, Belgium
Tel.: (32) 27110160
Sales Range: $50-74.9 Million
Emp.: 3
Financial Management Services
N.A.I.C.S.: 523999

K+S Gubre ve Endustri Urunleri San. ve Tic. Ltd. Sti. (1)
Buyukdere Caddesi No 7 GIZ 2000 Plaza Kat 9, Maslak, 34398, Istanbul, Turkiye
Tel.: (90) 212290 6180
Fertilizer Distr
N.A.I.C.S.: 424910

Christoth Werwie *(Pres)*

K+S IT-Services GmbH (1)
Ludwig-Erhard-Str 6, Kassel, 34131, Germany
Tel.: (49) 5619301300
Information Technology Consulting Services
N.A.I.C.S.: 541512

K+S Italia S.r.L. (1)
Via Giberti 7, 37122, Verona, Italy
Tel.: (39) 045 597977
Fertilizer Distr
N.A.I.C.S.: 424690

K+S KALI Atlantique S.A.S. (1)
Route De Gesvres, 53140, Pre-en-Pail, France
Tel.: (33) 2 43 30 13 70
Fertilizer Mfr
N.A.I.C.S.: 325314

K+S KALI France S.A.S. (1)
5 rue Gaston Boyer, 51100, Reims, France
Tel.: (33) 326 84 22 35
Web Site: http://www.kali-gmbh.com
Sales Range: $25-49.9 Million
Emp.: 15
Chemical Products Mfr
N.A.I.C.S.: 325180
Knut Clasen *(Gen Mgr)*

K+S KALI GmbH (1)
Bertha-von-Suttner-Str 7, 34131, Kassel, Germany
Tel.: (49) 56193010
Web Site: https://www.kali-gmbh.com
Potassium Mining Services
N.A.I.C.S.: 212390
Steffen Kirchhof *(Chief HR Officer)*

Subsidiary (Non-US):

K+S Asia Pacific Pte. Ltd. (2)
1 Harbourfront Avenue 16-05 Keppel Bay Tower, Singapore, 098632, Singapore
Tel.: (65) 62740100
Web Site: https://www.ks-asiapacific.com
Emp.: 1
Specialty Fertilizer Distr
N.A.I.C.S.: 424690
Charlotte Cheong *(Mgr-Fin & Admin)*

K+S Fertilizers (India) Private Limited (2)
Office No 612 6th Floor Bestech Business Tower Sector 48, Gurgaon, 122018, Haryana, India
Tel.: (91) 1244035167
Web Site: https://kplussindia.com
Sales Range: $25-49.9 Million
Emp.: 2
Specialty Fertilizer Distr
N.A.I.C.S.: 424690

Plant (Domestic):

K+S KALI GmbH - Neuhof-Ellers Plant (2)
Am Kaliwerk 6, 36119, Neuhof, Germany
Tel.: (49) 6655 81 0
Nitrogen Fertilizer Mfr
N.A.I.C.S.: 325311
Martin Ebeling *(Mgr)*

K+S KALI GmbH - Sigmundshall plant (2)
Tienberg 25, 31515, Wunstorf, Germany
Tel.: (49) 5031 104 1
Fertilizer Mfr
N.A.I.C.S.: 325314

K+S KALI GmbH - Werk Bergmannssegen-Hugo Plant (2)
Gluckauf-Str 50, 31319, Sehnde, Germany
Tel.: (49) 5132 5011
Web Site: http://www.k-plus-s.com
Fertilizer Mfr
N.A.I.C.S.: 325314

K+S KALI GmbH - Werra Plant (2)
Nipper Strasse, 36269, Philippsthal, Germany
Tel.: (49) 6620 79 0
Nitrogen Fertilizer Mfr
N.A.I.C.S.: 325311

K+S KALI GmbH - Zielitz Plant (2)
Farsleber Strasse 1, 39326, Zielitz, Germany
Tel.: (49) 39208 40

INTERNATIONAL PUBLIC

Nitrogen Fertilizer Mfr
N.A.I.C.S.: 325311
Wolfgang Kuhn *(Head-Personnel)*

K+S KALI Wittenheim S.A.S. (1)
27 Rue du General de Gaulle, 68270, Wittenheim, France
Tel.: (33) 389626600
Potassium & Magnesium Fertilizer Mfr
N.A.I.C.S.: 325311

K+S KALI du Roure S.A.S. (1)
61 Avenue Paul Langevin, 7400, Le Teil, France
Tel.: (33) 4 7549 1717
Sales Range: $25-49.9 Million
Emp.: 20
Fertilizer Mfr
N.A.I.C.S.: 325314
Campa Philippe *(Gen Mgr)*

K+S Minerals & Agriculture GmbH (1)
Bertha-von-Suttner-Strasse 7, 34131, Kassel, Germany
Tel.: (49) 56193010
Web Site: http://www.ks-minerals-and-agriculture.com
Fertilizer Mfr
N.A.I.C.S.: 325314
Burkhard Lohr *(Chm)*

K+S Mining Argentina S.A. (1)
Edif Laminar Plaza Ing Butty 240 piso 18 ofic 16, C1001 AFB, Buenos Aires, Argentina
Tel.: (54) 11 4342 2220
Fertilizer Mining Services
N.A.I.C.S.: 212390

K+S Montana Holdings LLC (1)
123 N Wacker Dr, Chicago, IL 60606-1743
Tel.: (312) 807-2000
Investment Management Service
N.A.I.C.S.: 523999
Christian Herrmann *(CEO)*

K+S Netherlands Holding B.V. (1)
Lange Lijnbaan 15, Harlingen, 8861 NW, Friesland, Netherlands
Tel.: (31) 517492499
Web Site: http://www.k-plus-s.com
Sales Range: $50-74.9 Million
Emp.: 80
Investment Management Service
N.A.I.C.S.: 523999
Matthias Mohr *(Gen Mgr)*

K+S North America Corporation (1)
3900 Gabrielle Ln 6407, Aurora, IL 60598
Tel.: (212) 697-4994
Web Site: http://www.ks-northamerica.com
Fertilizer Distr
N.A.I.C.S.: 424690

K+S North America Salt Holdings LLC (1)
123 N Wacker Dr, Chicago, IL 60606-1743
Tel.: (312) 807-2000
Emp.: 350
Investment Management Service
N.A.I.C.S.: 523999
Andreas Ruhland *(Dir-Internal Auditing)*

Subsidiary (Non-US):

Ecuatoriana de Sal y Productos Quimicos C.A. (2)
10 de Agosto 103y Malecon, Guayaquil, Ecuador
Tel.: (593) 42325666
Web Site: http://www.ecuasal.com
Sales Range: $25-49.9 Million
Emp.: 30
Consumer & Commercial Salt Producer
N.A.I.C.S.: 212390

Subsidiary (Domestic):

K+S Salt LLC (2)
444 W Lake St Ste 3000, Chicago, IL 60606-0090
Tel.: (312) 807-3000
Mineral Product Mfr & Distr
N.A.I.C.S.: 327999

Morton International, Inc. (2)
444 W lake St, Chicago, IL 60606-1743
Tel.: (312) 807-2000
Web Site: http://www.mortonsalt.com

Sales Range: $125-149.9 Million
Emp.: 375
Industrial & Consumer Salt Producer & Sales
N.A.I.C.S.: 325998
Christian Herrmann *(Pres)*

Subsidiary (Domestic):

Morton Bahamas Ltd. (3)
450 Cargo Rd, Cape Canaveral, FL 32920-4406
Tel.: (242) 339-1300
Web Site: http://www.k-plus-s.com
Nitrogen Fertilizer Mfr
N.A.I.C.S.: 325311

Subsidiary (Non-US):

Morton International Co., Ltd. (3)
10th Floor MCC Kandasudacho Building, 2-2 Kandasuda-cho, 2-chome Chiyoda-ku, Tokyo, 1010041, Japan
Tel.: (81) 3 5296 0700
Sales Range: $25-49.9 Million
Emp.: 8
Specialty Chemicals Mfr
N.A.I.C.S.: 325320

Joint Venture (Domestic):

Toyo-Morton, Ltd. (4)
Kyobashi EDOGRAND Bldg 2-1 Kyobashi 2-chome, Chuo-ku, Tokyo, 104-0031, Japan **(50%)**
Tel.: (81) 332720717
Sales Range: $25-49.9 Million
Emp.: 30
Specialty Chemicals Mfr
N.A.I.C.S.: 325998

Plant (Domestic):

Toyo-Morton, Ltd. - Saitama Plant (5)
25-26 Miyako, Namegawamachi Hikigun, Saitama, 355-0812, Japan
Tel.: (81) 49 356 4361
Web Site: http://www.toyoink.co.jp
Adhesive Mfr
N.A.I.C.S.: 325520

Subsidiary (Domestic):

Morton Salt Inc. (3)
123 N Wacker Dr, Chicago, IL 60606-1743
Tel.: (312) 807-2000
Web Site: http://www.mortonsalt.com
Salt Product Mfr
N.A.I.C.S.: 311942

Plant (Domestic):

Morton Salt Inc - Cincinnati Plant (4)
5336 Ohio River Rd, Cincinnati, OH 45233
Tel.: (513) 941-4930
Web Site: http://www.mortonsalt.com
Emp.: 15
Salt Mfr
N.A.I.C.S.: 311942

Morton Salt Inc - Detroit Plant (4)
10335 Flora St, Detroit, MI 48209
Tel.: (313) 843-6173
Industrial Salt Mfr
N.A.I.C.S.: 325998

Morton Salt Inc - Elston plant (4)
1357 N Elston Ave, Chicago, IL 60622-2478
Tel.: (773) 235-1030
Web Site: http://www.k-plus-s.com
Fertilizer Mfr
N.A.I.C.S.: 325311

Morton Salt Inc - Glendale Plant (4)
13000 W Glendale Ave, Glendale, AZ 85301-2408
Tel.: (623) 247-3000
Salt Mfr
N.A.I.C.S.: 311942

Morton Salt Inc - Grand Saline Plant (4)
801 State Hwy 110, Grand Saline, TX 75140-5145
Tel.: (903) 962-4204
Web Site: http://www.k-plus-s.com
Salt Mfr
N.A.I.C.S.: 311942

Morton Salt Inc - Grantsville Plant (4)
Interstate 80 Exit 84, Grantsville, UT 84029
Tel.: (801) 250-6335
Web Site: http://www.k-plus-s.com
Fertilizer Mfr
N.A.I.C.S.: 325311

Morton Salt Inc - Hutchinson Plant (4)
1000 Morton Rd, South Hutchinson, KS 67505
Tel.: (620) 669-0401
Web Site: http://www.k-plus-s.com
Salt Mfr
N.A.I.C.S.: 311942

Morton Salt Inc - Long Beach Plant (4)
1050 Pier F Ave, Long Beach, CA 90802-6215
Tel.: (562) 437-0071
Web Site: http://www.k-plus-s.com
Salt Mfr
N.A.I.C.S.: 311942

Morton Salt Inc - Manistee Plant (4)
180 6th St, Manistee, MI 49660-3000
Tel.: (231) 723-2561
Web Site: http://www.k-plus-s.com
Nitrogen Fertilizer Mfr
N.A.I.C.S.: 325311

Morton Salt Inc - New Iberia Plant (4)
11217 Morton Rd, New Iberia, LA 70560
Tel.: (337) 867-4241
Web Site: http://www.k-plus-s.com
Fertilizer Mfr
N.A.I.C.S.: 325314

Morton Salt Inc - Newark Plant (4)
7380 Morton Ave, Newark, CA 94560-0305
Tel.: (510) 797-2281
Web Site: http://www.k-plus-s.com
Sales Range: $25-49.9 Million
Emp.: 75
Salt Mfr
N.A.I.C.S.: 311942
Frank Koucky *(Controller-Facility)*

Morton Salt Inc - Painesville Plant (4)
570 Headlands Rd, Painesville, OH 44077
Tel.: (440) 354-9001
Web Site: http://www.k-plus-s.com
Fertilizer Mining Services
N.A.I.C.S.: 212390
Mark Mitchel *(Mgr-Facility)*

Morton Salt Inc - Perth Amboy Plant (4)
920 State St, Perth Amboy, NJ 08862-0909
Tel.: (732) 826-8414
Web Site: http://www.k-plus-s.com
Nitrogen Fertilizer Mfr
N.A.I.C.S.: 325311

Morton Salt Inc - Port Canaveral Plant (4)
450 Cargo Rd, Cape Canaveral, FL 32920-4406
Tel.: (321) 868-7136
Web Site: http://www.k-plus-s.com
Nitrogen Fertilizer Mfr
N.A.I.C.S.: 325311

Morton Salt Inc - Rittman Plant (4)
151 Industrial Ave, Rittman, OH 44270-1593
Tel.: (330) 925-3015
Web Site: http://www.k-plus-s.com
Fertilizer Mfr
N.A.I.C.S.: 325314

Morton Salt Inc - Silver Springs Plant (4)
45 Ribaud Ave E, Silver Springs, NY 14550
Tel.: (585) 493-2511
Web Site: http://www.k-plus-s.com
Nitrogen Fertilizer Mfr
N.A.I.C.S.: 325311

Morton Salt Inc - St. Paul Plant (4)
1111 Childs Rd, Saint Paul, MN 55106
Tel.: (651) 774-8738
Web Site: http://www.k-plus-s.com
Nitrogen Fertilizer Mfr
N.A.I.C.S.: 325311

Subsidiary (Non-US):

The Canadian Salt Co. Ltd. (2)
755 St John Blvd St 700, Pointe-Claire, H9R 5M9, QC, Canada
Tel.: (514) 630-0900
Web Site: http://www.windsorsalt.com
Sales Range: $25-49.9 Million
Emp.: 45
Consumer & Commercial Salt Producer
N.A.I.C.S.: 212390
Guy Leblanc *(Pres)*

Subsidiary (Domestic):

The Canadian Salt Co. Ltd. (3)
30 Prospect Ave, Windsor, N9C 3G3, ON, Canada
Tel.: (519) 255-5400
Web Site: http://www.windsorsalt.com
Sales Range: $50-74.9 Million
Consumer & Commercial Salt Producer
N.A.I.C.S.: 212390
Mike Soave *(Mgr-Facility)*

K+S Peru S.A.C. (1)
Av Elmer Faucett 2864, Callao, Peru
Tel.: (51) 1 718 6633
Web Site: https://www.ks-peru.com
Salt Distr
N.A.I.C.S.: 424690

K+S Polska Sp. z o.o (1)
Wiosny Ludow 2, 61-831, Poznan, Poland
Tel.: (48) 618509366
Sales Range: $50-74.9 Million
Emp.: 14
Fertilizer Mfr
N.A.I.C.S.: 212390

K+S Potash Canada (1)
300-201 1st Street E, Saskatoon, S7K 0B8, SK, Canada
Tel.: (306) 986-5251
Web Site: http://www.ks-potashcanada.com
Sales Range: $100-124.9 Million
Emp.: 200
Potash Mining & Production Services
N.A.I.C.S.: 212390

K+S Salt of the Americas Holding B.V. (1)
Lange Lijnbaan 15, Harlingen, 8861, Friesland, Netherlands
Tel.: (31) 517492499
Web Site: http://www.frisiazout.nl
Sales Range: $50-74.9 Million
Emp.: 80
Investment Management Service
N.A.I.C.S.: 523999
Durk van Duinen *(Gen Mgr)*

K+S Salz GmbH (1)
Landschaftstr 1, Hannover, 30159, Germany
Tel.: (49) 511850300
Web Site: http://www.esco-salt.com
Salt Mining Services
N.A.I.C.S.: 212390
Erich Krug *(Mng Dir)*

K+S Transport GmbH (1)
Glockengiesserwall 3, 20095, Hamburg, Germany
Tel.: (49) 40 30906 0
Web Site: http://www.kalitransport.com
Logistics Consulting Servies
N.A.I.C.S.: 541614

K+S UK & Eire Ltd. (1)
Unit 13 Watermark Way Foxholes Business Park, Hertford, SG13 7TZ, United Kingdom
Tel.: (44) 199 251 7400
Web Site: https://www.ks-ukeire.co.uk
Sales Range: $50-74.9 Million
Emp.: 4
Mineral Fertilizer Distr
N.A.I.C.S.: 424910
Richard Pinner *(Mng Dir)*

K+S Versicherungsvermittlungs GmbH (1)
Bertha-Von-Suttner-Str 7, 34131, Kassel, Germany
Tel.: (49) 56193010
Insurance Agency Services
N.A.I.C.S.: 524210

K+S Windsor Salt Ltd. (1)
755 Boul St-Jean Suite 700, Pointe-Claire-Dorval, H9R 5M9, QC, Canada
Tel.: (514) 630-0900
Web Site: http://www.windsorsalt.com
Emp.: 800
Salt Mfr
N.A.I.C.S.: 311942

Kali AG (1)
Murtenstrasse 116, 3202, Frauenkappelen, Switzerland
Tel.: (41) 31 926 60 00
Web Site: http://www.kali.ch
Potassium Mining Services
N.A.I.C.S.: 212390

Kali-Union Verwaltungsgesellschaft mbH (1)
Bertha-Von-Suttner-Str 7, 34131, Kassel, 34131, Germany
Tel.: (49) 56193010
Nitrogen Fertilizer Mfr
N.A.I.C.S.: 325311

MS "Butes" Schiffahrts GmbH & Co. KG (1)
Industriestr 12-14, 49733, Haren, Germany
Tel.: (49) 59325010
Web Site: http://www.wessels.de
Sales Range: $25-49.9 Million
Emp.: 45
Marine Cargo Handling Services
N.A.I.C.S.: 488320
Simon Frei *(Gen Mgr)*

MSW-Chemie GmbH (1) **(68.5%)**
Tel.: (49) 532691080
Sales Range: $25-49.9 Million
Emp.: 23
Mfr & Sales of Explosives
N.A.I.C.S.: 325920

Salina Diamante Branco Ltda (1)
Av Das Americas 1155 Salas 2101 a 2104, Barra da Tijuca, Rio de Janeiro, 22631-000, Brazil
Tel.: (55) 21 3154 8850
Web Site: http://www.salbrasil.com.br
Emp.: 25
Food Products Mfr
N.A.I.C.S.: 311999
Gabriel Bueno *(Gen Mgr)*

Servicios Portuarios Patillos S.A. (1)
Tajamar 183 Piso 6, Las Condes, 7550000, Santiago, Chile
Tel.: (56) 2 4696200
Web Site: http://www.spl.cl
Salt Mfr & Distr
N.A.I.C.S.: 212390
Matthias Mohr *(Gen Mgr)*

Shenzhen K+S Trading Co. Ltd (1)
Fuhua 3 Road International Chamber of Commerce Room 3010 No 168, Futian District, Shenzhen, 518048, Guangdong, China
Tel.: (86) 75582825901
Web Site: http://www.kali-gmbh.com
Sales Range: $25-49.9 Million
Emp.: 11
Fertilizer Mfr
N.A.I.C.S.: 325311
Yanliang Guo *(Gen Mgr)*

Solne mlyny, a.s (1)
Sladkovskeho c p 234/47, Holice, 779 11, Olomouc, Czech Republic
Tel.: (420) 58 742 1222
Web Site: http://www.solnemlyny.cz
Sales Range: $25-49.9 Million
Emp.: 65
Salt Product Mfr & Distr
N.A.I.C.S.: 311942
Radomir Tichy *(Dir-Fin)*

VATEL Companhia de Produtos Alimentares S.A. (1)
Estrada da Macol n 39 Apartado 211, Sobralinho, 2615-711, Alverca do Ribatejo, Portugal
Tel.: (351) 219518420
Web Site: https://www.vatel.pt
Emp.: 59
Food Products Mfr
N.A.I.C.S.: 311999

Weeks Island Landowner LLC (1)
123 N Wacker Dr, Chicago, IL 60606-1743
Tel.: (312) 807-2000
Salt Mfr

K+S AKTIENGESELLSCHAFT

K+S Aktiengesellschaft—(Continued)
N.A.I.C.S.: 311942

esco Benelux N.V. (1)
Park Lane Culliganlaan 2G Bus 1, 1831,
Diegem, Belgium
Tel.: (32) 27110160
Chemical Products Mfr
N.A.I.C.S.: 325199
Fabrice Boedt (Mng Dir)

esco Holding France S.A.S (1)
1 Rue De La Saline, 54510, Dombasle-sur-Meurthe, France
Tel.: (33) 3 8318 2111
Investment Management Service
N.A.I.C.S.: 523940

esco International GmbH (1)
Landschaftstr 1, Hannover, 30159, Niedersachsen, Germany
Tel.: (49) 511850300
Nitrogen Fertilizer Mfr
N.A.I.C.S.: 325311
Erik Dust (Mgr)

esco Nordic AB (1)
Drakegatan 10, Box 184, Gothenburg, 412 50, Sweden
Tel.: (46) 31 77370 01
Web Site: http://www.kali-gmbh.com
Salt Mfr
N.A.I.C.S.: 311942

esco Spain S.L. (1)
Joan d'Austria 39-47, 8005, Barcelona, Spain
Tel.: (34) 93 22 47 238
Nitrogen Fertilizer Mfr
N.A.I.C.S.: 325311
Jean Michel Devaux (Gen Mgr)

esco Verwaltungs GmbH (1)
Landschaftstr 1, Hannover, 30159, Germany
Tel.: (49) 511850300
Salt Distr
N.A.I.C.S.: 424490

K-BRO LINEN INC.
14903 137 Avenue NW, Edmonton, T5V 1R9, AB, Canada
Tel.: (780) 453-5218 AB
Web Site: https://www.k-brolinen.com
Year Founded: 1954
74R—(DEU)
Rev.: $242,305,926
Assets: $275,404,346
Liabilities: $143,688,009
Net Worth: $131,716,337
Earnings: $13,295,398
Emp.: 2,400
Fiscal Year-end: 12/31/23
Linen Supply Services
N.A.I.C.S.: 812331
Linda J. McCurdy (Pres & CEO)

Subsidiaries:

Fishers Services Ltd. (1)
Edenfields Cupar Trading Estate, Fife, Cupar, KY15 4SX, United Kingdom
Tel.: (44) 133 465 4033
Web Site: https://fisherslaundry.co.uk
Linens & Commercial Service Workwear Rental & Laundry Services
N.A.I.C.S.: 532289
Michael Jones (Grp Mng Dir)

K-Bro Linen Systems Inc (1)
14903 137 Avenue NW, Edmonton, T5V 1R9, AB, Canada
Tel.: (780) 453-5218
Web Site: https://www.k-brolinen.com
Industrial Laundry Services
N.A.I.C.S.: 812320

Division (Domestic):

K-Bro Linen Systems Inc - Buanderie HMR Division (2)
367 boulevard des Chutes, Quebec, G1E 3G1, QC, Canada
Tel.: (418) 661-6163
Web Site: https://www.buanderiehmr.com
Sales Range: $25-49.9 Million
Emp.: 80
Industrial Laundry Services

Subsidiary (Non-US):

N.A.I.C.S.: 812320

K-Bro Linen Systems Inc - Les Buanderies Dextraze Division (2)
599 rue Simonds Sud, Granby, J2J 1C1, QC, Canada
Tel.: (450) 378-3187
Web Site: http://www.dextraze.ca
Sales Range: $25-49.9 Million
Emp.: 100
Industrial Laundry Services
N.A.I.C.S.: 812320

K-D HERMANN GMBH
Hainbrunner Strasse 97, Hirschhorn, 69434, Germany
Tel.: (49) 62729223
Year Founded: 1982
Rev.: $18,858,514
Emp.: 60
Labelling Machines Mfr
N.A.I.C.S.: 333993
Martin Hermann (Mng Dir)

K-DEVELOP OY
Muuntotie 3, 01510, Vantaa, Finland
Tel.: (358) 10 219 2152
Web Site: http://www.k-develop.fi
Emp.: 60
Holding Company
N.A.I.C.S.: 551112
Oloff Sandell (CEO)

Subsidiaries:

IP-Produkter Oy (1)
Muuntotie 3, 01510, Vantaa, Finland
Tel.: (358) 10 219 2100
Web Site: http://www.ip-produkter.fi
Sales Range: $10-24.9 Million
Emp.: 50
Industrial Equipment Import & Marketing & Distribution Services
N.A.I.C.S.: 423830
Vesa Viitala (Mng Dir)

Oy Finn-Gamec Ab (1)
Koskelo Trade Park Koskelontie 23 D 5, 02920, Espoo, Finland
Tel.: (358) 102192250
Web Site: https://www.finn-gamec.fi
Gas Distribution Equipment Mfr
N.A.I.C.S.: 333414

K-ENSOL CO., LTD.
6-23 51-Gil Gwangpyeong-Ro, Gangnam-gu, Seoul, Korea (South)
Tel.: (82) 25779031
Web Site: https://k-ensol.com
Year Founded: 1989
053080—(KRS)
Rev.: $298,216,683
Assets: $245,997,190
Liabilities: $123,865,416
Net Worth: $122,131,774
Earnings: $12,268,154
Emp.: 148
Fiscal Year-end: 12/31/22
Industrial Machinery Mfr
N.A.I.C.S.: 333310
Koo Jakyum (Co-CEO)

K-LINE CONSTRUCTION LTD.
215 Beardsley Rd Suite 1, Woodstock, E7M 4E1, NB, Canada
Tel.: (506) 328-9848
Web Site: https://www.k-lineconstruction.com
Year Founded: 1981
Emp.: 300
Telecommunication & Power Line Construction
N.A.I.C.S.: 423610
Sean Jones (COO)

K-ONE TECHNOLOGY BERHAD
66 and 68 Jalan 22/21 Damansara Jaya, 47400, Petaling Jaya, Selangor, Malaysia
Tel.: (60) 377281111 MY
Web Site: https://store.k-one.com
Year Founded: 2001
K1—(KLS)
Rev.: $22,572,771
Assets: $36,945,108
Liabilities: $8,496,705
Net Worth: $28,448,403
Earnings: ($2,072,366)
Emp.: 309
Fiscal Year-end: 12/31/20
Electronic Product Mfr & Distr
N.A.I.C.S.: 335210
Edwin Beng Fook Lim (Co-Founder & Chm)

Subsidiaries:

Big' Ant (M) Sdn. Bhd. (1)
66 68 Jalan SS22/21, Damansara Jaya, 47400, Petaling Jaya, Selangor, Malaysia
Tel.: (60) 37 728 1111
Web Site: https://www.bigant.com.my
Software Development Services
N.A.I.C.S.: 541511

G-AsiaPacific Sdn. Bhd. (1)
Block I-7-5 SetiaWalk Persiaran Wawasan, Pusat Bandar, 47160, Puchong, Selangor, Malaysia
Tel.: (60) 38 084 2300
Web Site: https://www.g-asiapac.com
Cloud Computing Services
N.A.I.C.S.: 541519

K-One Manufacturing Sdn. Bhd. (1)
5 7 9 Persiaran Rishah 7, Ipoh, 30100, Perak, Malaysia
Tel.: (60) 55269588
Electronic Products Mfr
N.A.I.C.S.: 334419

K-RITE CONSTRUCTION LTD.
12849 148 St NW, Edmonton, T5L 2H9, AB, Canada
Tel.: (780) 452-6291
Web Site: https://www.krite.com
Year Founded: 1989
Rev.: $12,304,990
Emp.: 50
General Building Contractor Services
N.A.I.C.S.: 236220
Jim Kratchkowski (Founder & Pres)

Subsidiaries:

Maxim Excavating Ltd. (1)
12849 148 St NW, Edmonton, T5L 2H9, AB, Canada
Tel.: (780) 455-2170
Building Contracting Services
N.A.I.C.S.: 236210
Aron Reedes (Mgr)

K-STAR SPORTS LIMITED
Level 7 Menara Milenium Jalan Damanlela, Pusat Bandar Damansara Damansara Heights, 50490, Kuala Lumpur, Malaysia
Tel.: (60) 20849000 SG
Web Site: https://www.kstarsports.com
KSTAR—(KLS)
Rev.: $29,010,377
Assets: $24,739,557
Liabilities: $18,851,422
Net Worth: $5,888,136
Earnings: ($1,562,509)
Fiscal Year-end: 12/31/19
Investment Holding Company; Athletic Footwear Mfr & Distr
N.A.I.C.S.: 551112
JianPing Ding (Chm)

K-TECH CONSTRUCTION PUBLIC COMPANY LIMITED
33/4 The 9th Tower Tower B Level 18 Rama 9 Road, Kwang Huaykwang Khet Huaykwang, Bangkok, 10310, Thailand
Tel.: (66) 2018 1688
Web Site: http://www.ktech.co.th
Year Founded: 1997

INTERNATIONAL PUBLIC

KTECH—(THA)
Sales Range: $25-49.9 Million
Emp.: 105
Engineeering Services
N.A.I.C.S.: 541330
Vichien Ratanabirabongse (Chm)

K-TEL INTERNATIONAL INC.
220 Saulteaux Crescent, Winnipeg, R3J 3W3, MB, Canada
Tel.: (204) 889-5430 MB
Web Site: http://www.ktel.com
Direct Music & Consumer Products Marketer & Mail Order Services
N.A.I.C.S.: 459140
Philip Kives (Founder & CEO)

Subsidiaries:

Dominion Entertainment, Inc. (1)
7600 wizata ste 2b, Golden Valley, MN 55426-4908
Tel.: (763) 268-0220
Web Site: http://www.k-tel.com
Sales Range: $1-9.9 Million
Emp.: 3
Music Licensing
N.A.I.C.S.: 512110

K-Tel Direct, Inc. (1)
2655 Cheshire Ln North Ste 100, Plymouth, MN 55447
Tel.: (763) 559-5566
Sales Range: $1-9.9 Million
Emp.: 13
Music Recording & Consumer Products Mail Order Services
N.A.I.C.S.: 512120

K-tel MultiMedia (UK) Limited (1)
Units 1 & 2 Wadsworth Close, Perivale, UB6 7FJ, United Kingdom
Tel.: (44) 2087996358
Music Store Operator
N.A.I.C.S.: 459510

K-TIG LIMITED
Building 5/9 William Street Mile End, Adelaide, 5301, SA, Australia
Tel.: (61) 873246800 AU
Web Site: https://www.k-tig.com
KTG—(ASX)
Rev.: $1,196,449
Assets: $5,552,163
Liabilities: $1,019,909
Net Worth: $4,532,254
Earnings: ($3,434,575)
Fiscal Year-end: 06/30/21
Investment Services
N.A.I.C.S.: 523999
Brett Tucker (Co-Sec)

Subsidiaries:

Keyhole TIG (USA) Inc. (1)
1001 Technology Dr Ste 1049, Mount Pleasant, PA 15666-1782
Tel.: (724) 990-3724
Welding Automation Equipment Mfr
N.A.I.C.S.: 333992

Keyhole TIG Pty. Limited (1)
Building 5 9 William Street, Mile End, SA, Australia
Tel.: (61) 873246800
Welding Automation Equipment Mfr
N.A.I.C.S.: 333992

K-TOP REITS CO., LTD.
19 Miwon Bldg 70 Gukjegeumyungro, Yeongdeungpo-gu, Seoul, Korea (South)
Tel.: (82) 27835858
Web Site: https://www.ktopreits.co.kr
Year Founded: 2010
145270—(KRS)
Rev.: $16,591,769
Assets: $207,280,192
Liabilities: $133,923,377
Net Worth: $73,356,814
Earnings: $7,709,589
Emp.: 13
Fiscal Year-end: 12/31/22

AND PRIVATE COMPANIES

Real Estate Prorperty Leasing Services
N.A.I.C.S.: 531120
Myung-Shik Lee (CEO)

K. ATHIENITIS CONTRACTORS-DEVELOPERS PUBLIC LTD
48 Themistokli Dervi Ave Office 801, 1066, Nicosia, Cyprus
Tel.: (357) 22447855
Web Site: http://www.athienitis.net
Year Founded: 1984
Building Construction Services
N.A.I.C.S.: 237310

K. H. GROUP HOLDINGS LTD.
Unit 01 82/F International Commerce Centre 1 Austin Road West, Kowloon, China (Hong Kong)
Tel.: (852) 3 669 7878
Web Site: http://www.kh-holdings.com
Year Founded: 1985
1557—(HKG)
Rev.: $96,962,908
Assets: $84,871,420
Liabilities: $75,179,733
Net Worth: $9,691,686
Earnings: ($2,366,267)
Emp.: 160
Fiscal Year-end: 03/31/22
Holding Company
N.A.I.C.S.: 551112
Rongsheng Chen (Chm & Exec Dir)

Subsidiaries:

K. H. Foundations Limited (1)
1/F KT336 334-336 Kwun Tong Road, Kwun Tong, Kowloon, China (Hong Kong)
Tel.: (852) 23890868
Web Site: https://www.khfoundations.com
Emp.: 80
Building Contractor Services
N.A.I.C.S.: 238110

K. J. BEAMISH CONSTRUCTION CO., LIMITED
PO Box 250, King City, L7B 1B2, ON, Canada
Tel.: (905) 833-4666
Web Site: http://www.kjbeamish.ca
Year Founded: 1946
Rev.: $74,337,932
Emp.: 500
Highways & Roads Construction & Maintenance Services
N.A.I.C.S.: 237310
Robin Beamish (Pres)

K. KOUIMTZIS S.A
10th km EO, Sindos Thessaloniki, 57400, Athens, Greece
Tel.: (30) 2310796970
Web Site: https://www.kouimtzis.gr
Industrial Machinery Mfr & Distr
N.A.I.C.S.: 333248

K. KYTHREOTIS HOLDINGS PUBLIC LTD.
38 Griva Digheni Str, 3106, Limassol, Cyprus
Tel.: (357) 25212800
Web Site: https://www.kythreotis.com.cy
Year Founded: 1943
KYTH—(CYP)
Rev.: $16,216,230
Assets: $17,793,825
Liabilities: $4,656,109
Net Worth: $13,137,716
Earnings: $718,587
Fiscal Year-end: 12/31/19
Holding Company
N.A.I.C.S.: 551112
Costas P. Kythreotis (Gen Mgr)

K. MIKIMOTO & CO., LTD.
4-5-5 Ginza, Chuo-ku, Tokyo, 104-8145, Japan
Tel.: (81) 335354611
Web Site: http://www.mikimoto.com
Year Founded: 1899
Sales Range: $250-299.9 Million
Emp.: 700
Cultured Pearl Pearl Jewelry & Precious Jewelry Mfr
N.A.I.C.S.: 339910
Kokichi Mikimoto (Founder)

Subsidiaries:

Mikimoto (America) Co. Ltd. (1)
730 5th Ave, New York, NY 10019-5429 (100%)
Tel.: (212) 457-4600
Web Site: http://www.mikimotoamerica.com
Sales Range: $50-74.9 Million
Emp.: 120
Cultured Pearl & Pearl Jewelry Distr
N.A.I.C.S.: 458310
Urvashi Singh (Coord-Mdse)

Mikimoto Jewelry Mfg. Co., Ltd. (1)
3-20-8 Aobadai, Meguro-Ku, Tokyo, 153-0042, Japan
Tel.: (81) 3 3463 9221
Web Site: http://www.mikimoto-jf.co.jp
Emp.: 200
Jewelry Mfr
N.A.I.C.S.: 339910

Mikimoto Pharmaceutical Co., Ltd. (1)
1425 Kurose-cho, Ise, Mie-Ken, Japan
Tel.: (81) 596 22 4145
Web Site: http://www.mikimoto-cosme.com
Emp.: 200
Pharmaceuticals Product Mfr
N.A.I.C.S.: 325412
Kokichi Mikimoto (Founder)

K. S. OILS LIMITED
Jiwajiganj, Morena, 476001, India
Tel.: (91) 7532 300000
Web Site: http://www.ksoils.com
Sales Range: $500-549.9 Million
Edible Oil Processor
N.A.I.C.S.: 111120
Davesh Agarwal (CFO)

Subsidiaries:

PT Mega Artha Persada (1)
Wisma GKBI 38th Floor, Jalan Jendral Sudirman, Jakarta, 10210, Indonesia
Tel.: (62) 2130001723
Palm Oil Mfr
N.A.I.C.S.: 311224

K. SENG SENG CORPORATION BHD
Lot 3707 Jalan 7/5 Taman Industri Selesa Jaya, 43300, Balakong, Selangor Darul Ehsan, Malaysia
Tel.: (60) 389615555
Web Site: https://www.kssc.com.my
Year Founded: 1985
KSSC—(KLS)
Stainless Steel Products Mfr
N.A.I.C.S.: 331110
Seng Lee Koh (Mng Dir)

Subsidiaries:

K. Seng Seng Manufacturing Sdn Bhd (1)
Lot 3707 Jalan 7/5 Taman Industri Selesa Jaya, Balakong, 43300, Selangor, Malaysia
Tel.: (60) 389615555
Steel Industrial Fasteners Mfr
N.A.I.C.S.: 339993

PTM Steel Industry Sdn Bhd (1)
Lot 3707 Jalan 7/5Taman Industri Selesa Jaya, Balakong, 43300, Selangor, Malaysia
Tel.: (60) 389615555
Steel Products Mfr
N.A.I.C.S.: 332996

Three & Three Hardware Sdn Bhd (1)
Lot 3707 Jalan 7/5 Taman Industri Selesa Jaya, Balakong, 43300, Selangor, Malaysia
Tel.: (60) 389615555
Sales Range: $50-74.9 Million
Emp.: 80
Steel Product Distr
N.A.I.C.S.: 423510

K. WAH INTERNATIONAL HOLDINGS LIMITED
29F K Wah Centre 191 Java Road, North Point, China (Hong Kong)
Tel.: (852) 28800178
Web Site: https://www.kwih.com
0173—(HKG)
Rev.: $1,121,198,280
Assets: $9,771,078,398
Liabilities: $3,824,112,345
Net Worth: $5,946,966,053
Earnings: $181,876,583
Emp.: 968
Fiscal Year-end: 12/31/22
Real Estate Investment & Development Services
N.A.I.C.S.: 531390
Che-Woo Lui (Founder, Chm & Mng Dir)

Subsidiaries:

Asahi Kohatsu Corporation (1)
13-1 Nihombashi Kabuto-Cho, Chuo-ku, Tokyo, 103-0026, Japan
Tel.: (81) 356438990
Web Site: http://www.akcjapan.co.jp
Sales Range: $25-49.9 Million
Emp.: 12
Real Estate And Building Maintenance
N.A.I.C.S.: 541350
Sadao Taguma (Pres)

Cresleigh Property Management (Shanghai) Co., Ltd. (1)
18/F 1010 Central Huai hai Road, Shanghai, 200031, China
Tel.: (86) 2161133333
Property Management Services
N.A.I.C.S.: 531390

K. Wah Management Services Limited (1)
29 F K Wah Ctr, 191 Java Rd N Point, Hong Kong, China (Hong Kong)
Tel.: (852) 28800178
Business Management Consulting Services
N.A.I.C.S.: 541618

K. Z. LEASING & FINANCE LTD.
First Floor Deshna Chambers B/h Kadwa Patidar Wadi, Usmanpura, Ahmedabad, 380014, Gujarat, India
Tel.: (91) 7927542298
Web Site: https://www.kzgroup.in
511728—(BOM)
Rev.: $234,291
Assets: $2,950,459
Liabilities: $918,278
Net Worth: $2,032,180
Earnings: $34,350
Fiscal Year-end: 03/31/23
Financial Services
N.A.I.C.S.: 523999
Parvinkumar Keshavlal Patel (Chm & Mng Dir)

K. ZUGHAIBI & B. KABBANI GENERAL PARTNERSHIP
19 Tahlia Street Daralhijaz Bulding 5th-floor, PO Box 15570, Jeddah, 21454, Saudi Arabia
Tel.: (966) 26641264
Web Site: http://www.gulfbase.com
Sales Range: $10-24.9 Million
Emp.: 20
Financial & Business Information Services
N.A.I.C.S.: 513199
Khalid M. Zughaibi (Co-Founder & Mng Partner)

K.C. METALSHEET PUBLIC COMPANY LIMITED
No 567 Village No 2 Liang muang Road, Phra Lap Subdistrict Mueang District, Khon Kaen, 40000, Thailand
Tel.: (66) 43306999
Web Site: https://www.kcmetalsheet.co.th
KCM—(THA)
Rev.: $11,334,366
Assets: $19,414,995
Liabilities: $6,917,329
Net Worth: $12,497,666
Earnings: ($82,321)
Fiscal Year-end: 12/31/23
Steel Products Mfr
N.A.I.C.S.: 332999
Sakchai Jarernsiripornkul (Chm)

K.C. PROPERTY PUBLIC COMPANY LIMITED
410/125-126 Ratchadaphisek Road, Samsen Nok Subdistrict Huai Khwang District, Bangkok, 10310, Thailand
Tel.: (66) 22765924
Web Site: https://www.kcproperty.co.th
KC—(THA)
Rev.: $6,193,952
Assets: $30,642,811
Liabilities: $20,088,746
Net Worth: $10,554,065
Earnings: ($1,921,124)
Fiscal Year-end: 12/31/23
Real Estate Development Services
N.A.I.C.S.: 531390
Kittipat Inthaket (Vice Chm)

K.C.G TEXTILE EGYPT S.A.
Industrial zone South A6, 10th of Ramadan City, Egypt
Tel.: (20) 15 410774
Web Site: http://www.kcgtextile.com
Year Founded: 2007
Textile Products Mfr
N.A.I.C.S.: 314999
Yashar Kojok Jalik (Chm)

K.H.S. MUSICAL INSTRUMENT CO., LTD.
No. 162 Zhongshan 2nd Rd, Luzhou District, Taipei, 247, Taiwan
Tel.: (886) 222825151
Web Site: http://www.khsmusic.com
Year Founded: 1930
Sales Range: $250-299.9 Million
Emp.: 700
Musical Instrument Mfr
N.A.I.C.S.: 339992
Wu Hsieh (Chm, Pres & CEO)

Subsidiaries:

Jupiter Band Instruments, Inc. (1)
12020 Eastgate Blvd, Mount Juliet, TN 37122-3183
Tel.: (512) 288-7400
Web Site: http://www.jupitermusic.com
Sales Range: $25-49.9 Million
Emp.: 35
Musical Instrument Mfr
N.A.I.C.S.: 339992

K.I. ABDULKADIR & PARTNERS CO. LTD.
Mohammed Mahmood Zahid Street, PO Box 9547, Suleimania District, Jeddah, 21423, Saudi Arabia
Tel.: (966) 26405846
Web Site: http://www.kiaksa.com
Year Founded: 1981
Sales Range: $10-24.9 Million
Emp.: 250
Laboratory, Scientific, Environmental & Technical Training Instruments & Equipment Distr
N.A.I.C.S.: 423450

K.I. ABDULKADIR & PARTNERS CO. LTD.

K.I. Abdulkadir & Partners Co. Ltd.—(Continued)
Abdul Ibrahim (Mng Dir)

K.J. BEAMISH CONSTRUCTION CO., LIMITED
3300 King Vaughan Town Line, PO Box 250, King City, L7B 1B2, ON, Canada
Tel.: (905) 833-4666
Web Site: http://www.kjbeamish.ca
Year Founded: 1946
Rev.: $74,337,932
Emp.: 500
Construction & Maintenance Services, Road & Highway Construction
N.A.I.C.S.: 237310
Kingston John Beamish (Founder)

K.K. BIRLA GROUP
9/1 R N Mukherjee Road Birla Building 5th Floor, Kolkata, 700 001, India
Tel.: (91) 3322430497
Web Site: http://www.birla-sugar.com
Sugar Mfr
N.A.I.C.S.: 311314
Chandra Shekhar Nopany (Chm & Mng Dir)

Subsidiaries:

Chambal Fertilisers & Chemicals Ltd. (1)
Corporate One First Floor 5 Commercial Centre, Jasola, New Delhi, 110 025, India
Tel.: (91) 1141697900
Web Site: https://www.chambalfertilisers.com
Rev.: $3,349,987,411
Assets: $1,531,091,661
Liabilities: $685,468,497
Net Worth: $845,623,164
Earnings: $123,948,205
Emp.: 1,050
Fiscal Year-end: 03/31/2023
Fertilizers, Cement, Software, investments & Chemical Engineering Services
N.A.I.C.S.: 325311
Anil Kapoor (Mng Dir)

Subsidiary (Domestic):

Chambal Infrastructure Ventures Limited (2)
Corporate 1 1st Fl, 5 Commercial Center Jasola, New Delhi, 110 025, India
Tel.: (91) 1141697900
Web Site: http://www.chambalfertilisers.in
Sales Range: $25-49.9 Million
Emp.: 15
Infrastructure Managing Services
N.A.I.C.S.: 238190
Abhay Baijal (VP-Fin)

Subsidiary (US):

Dynatek, Inc. (2)
17488 Laurel Dr Ste 206, Livonia, MI 48152
Tel.: (734) 462-2880
Sales Range: $1-9.9 Million
Emp.: 60
Software Services
N.A.I.C.S.: 513210

Subsidiary (Domestic):

Inuva Info Management (Pvt) Ltd. (2)
DC 27 26 Deb Kutir Salt Lk Sector -I, Kolkata, 700064, India
Tel.: (91) 3323589760
Mortgage & Real Estate Financial Services
N.A.I.C.S.: 522299

Subsidiary (US):

Inuva Info Management Inc. (2)
2650 Steeple Chase Rd, Davie, FL 33330-1035
Tel.: (954) 200-8040
Web Site: http://www.inuva.com
Mortgage & Real Estate Financial Services
N.A.I.C.S.: 525990

MortageHub Inc (2)
3220 Tillman Dr Ste 301, Bensalem, PA 19020-2028
Tel.: (610) 834-3800
Industrial Services
N.A.I.C.S.: 541420

Richmond Title Services (2)
2901 Dallas Pkwy Ste 420, Plano, TX 75093-5998
Tel.: (214) 291-8808
Sales Range: $25-49.9 Million
Emp.: 35
Insurance & Financial Services
N.A.I.C.S.: 524210

ISGN Technologies Ltd. (1)
Sucons Oki Info Park E34 IT Highway, Chennai, 603103, India
Tel.: (91) 4439199393
Web Site: http://www.isgn.com
Sales Range: $25-49.9 Million
Emp.: 85
Mortgage Management Software & Services
N.A.I.C.S.: 513210
Krishna Srinivasan (CEO)

Sutlej Textiles & Industries Ltd. (1)
E-wing 5th & 6th Floor Lotus Corporate Park 185/A Graham Firth Steel, Compound Near Jay Coach Off Western Express Highway Goregaon East, Mumbai, 400063, Maharashtra, India
Tel.: (91) 2242198800
Web Site: https://www.sutlejtextiles.com
Rev.: $261,417,975
Assets: $291,920,265
Liabilities: $161,611,905
Net Worth: $130,308,360
Earnings: ($499,590)
Emp.: 18,186
Fiscal Year-end: 03/31/2021
Yarn, Fabric & Apparel Mfr
N.A.I.C.S.: 313110
Suresh Kumar Khandelia (Pres & CEO)

Subsidiary (US):

American Silk Mills, LLC (2)
329 S Wrenn St Ste 401B, High Point, NC 27260
Tel.: (570) 822-7147
Web Site: http://www.americansilk.com
Textile & Fabric Finishing Mills
N.A.I.C.S.: 313310
David R. Corbin (CEO)

Unit (Domestic):

Sutlej Textiles & Industries Ltd - Rajasthan Textile Mills (2)
Pachpahar Rd, Bhawani Mandi, 326502, Rajasthan, India
Tel.: (91) 7433222052
Web Site: http://www.sutlej-textiles.com
Sales Range: $650-699.9 Million
Textile Spinning Yarn Services
N.A.I.C.S.: 313110
S.S. Maheshwari (Pres)

The Oudh Sugar Mills Limited (1)
9/1 RN Mukherjee Road 5th Floor, Kolkata, 700 001, India
Tel.: (91) 332243 0497
Web Site: http://www.birla-sugar.com
Rev.: $173,071,448
Assets: $230,540,218
Liabilities: $236,806,701
Net Worth: ($6,266,483)
Earnings: $1,467,976
Emp.: 2,231
Fiscal Year-end: 03/31/2016
Sugar Mfr
N.A.I.C.S.: 311313

Upper Ganges Sugar Industries Ltd. (1)
Birla Building 5th Floor 9/1 R N Mukherjee Road, Kolkata, 700 001, India
Tel.: (91) 3322430497
Web Site: http://www.birla-sugar.com
Rev.: $129,528,705
Assets: $158,795,194
Liabilities: $148,336,690
Net Worth: $10,458,504
Earnings: $2,174,085
Emp.: 1,782
Fiscal Year-end: 03/31/2016
Sugar Producer
N.A.I.C.S.: 111930

K.K. KINGSTON LTD.
Milfordhaven Rd, PO Box 1104, Lae, 411, Papua New Guinea
Tel.: (675) 4722745
Web Site: http://www.kingston.com.pg
Year Founded: 1972
Sales Range: $150-199.9 Million
Emp.: 340
Cleaning Chemicals, Bleach, Toilet Tissue, Hand Towels, Plastic Bottles & Caps, Food Containers, Water Tanks, Septic Tanks, Rubbish Bins & Cable Pits Mfr
N.A.I.C.S.: 325612
Keith Kingston (Owner & Mng Dir)

K.L. RESOURCES PTE. LTD.
No 19 Sungei Kadut Loop, Singapore, 729462, Singapore
Tel.: (65) 62885935
Web Site: https://www.klresources.com.sg
Year Founded: 2000
Sales Range: $25-49.9 Million
Emp.: 14
Waste Paper & Scrap Whslr
N.A.I.C.S.: 423390
Kim Leong Chan (Mgr)

Subsidiaries:

Asia Recycling Resources Pte. Ltd. (1)
5 Fourth Lok Yang Road, Singapore, 629702, Singapore
Tel.: (65) 62626631
Web Site: https://asia-recycling.com
Sales Range: $25-49.9 Million
Waste Paper & Scrap Whslr
N.A.I.C.S.: 423930

Intrapac (UK) Ltd. (1)
1 Campion Place, London, SE28 8EN, United Kingdom
Tel.: (44) 2083116555
Web Site: http://www.muda.com.my
Packaging Material Distr
N.A.I.C.S.: 423840

K.R.S. CORPORATION
3-50-1 Chofugaoka, Chofu-shi, Chofu-shi, Tokyo, 182-0021, Japan
Tel.: (81) 424410711
Web Site: https://www.krs.co.jp
Year Founded: 1966
9369—(TKS)
Rev.: $1,308,934,530
Assets: $842,816,660
Liabilities: $478,000,710
Net Worth: $364,815,950
Earnings: ($9,458,060)
Emp.: 664
Fiscal Year-end: 11/30/23
Warehousing Services
N.A.I.C.S.: 493110
Hideaki Nishio (Chm & Pres)

K.S. OILS LTD
Jiwaji Ganj, 476001, Morena, Madhya Pradesh, India
Tel.: (91) 7532300000
Web Site: http://www.ksoils.com
Year Founded: 1985
526209—(BOM)
Integrated Edible Oil Company
N.A.I.C.S.: 533110
Ramesh Chand Garg (Chm)

Subsidiaries:

K S Agri Resources Pte. Ltd. (1)
6 Battery Rd, 16-06, Singapore, 049909, Singapore
Tel.: (65) 63233978
Agri Commodity Trading Services
N.A.I.C.S.: 926140

KS Natural Resources Pte. Ltd. (1)
6 Battery Rd, 16-06, Singapore, 049909, Singapore
Tel.: (65) 63233978

INTERNATIONAL PUBLIC

Sales Range: $25-49.9 Million
Emp.: 1
Edible Oil Sales
N.A.I.C.S.: 111219

K.S. TERMINALS INC.
No 8 Zhangbin E 3rd Road Xianxi Township, Chang-Hua, 507, Taiwan
Tel.: (886) 47582765
Web Site: https://ksterminals.com
Year Founded: 1973
3003—(TAI)
Rev.: $136,357,430
Assets: $266,254,119
Liabilities: $59,992,934
Net Worth: $206,261,185
Earnings: $17,956,865
Fiscal Year-end: 12/31/23
Electrical Terminals Mfr
N.A.I.C.S.: 335931
Cheng Ke-Pin (Founder & Chm)

K.W. METAL WORK PCL
300/142 Moo 1, Tasit Subdistrict Pluak Daeng District, Rayong, 21140, Thailand
Tel.: (66) 23814999
Web Site: https://www.kw-metalwork.com
Year Founded: 2009
KWM—(THA)
Rev.: $13,514,423
Assets: $18,375,469
Liabilities: $3,727,231
Net Worth: $14,648,239
Earnings: $677,838
Fiscal Year-end: 12/31/23
Agricultural Machinery Distr
N.A.I.C.S.: 423820
Ekapan Vanagosoom (Chm)

K2 ASSET MANAGEMENT HOLDINGS LTD.
Level 44 101 Collins Street, Melbourne, 3000, VIC, Australia
Tel.: (61) 396916111
Web Site: https://www.k2am.com.au
KAM—(ASX)
Rev.: $3,508,351
Assets: $7,283,657
Liabilities: $1,880,706
Net Worth: $5,402,951
Earnings: ($424,535)
Emp.: 20
Fiscal Year-end: 06/30/24
Asset Management Services
N.A.I.C.S.: 523940
Hollie Anne Wight (CFO)

Subsidiaries:

K2 Asset Management Ltd. (1)
Level 32 101 Collins Street, Melbourne, 3000, VIC, Australia
Tel.: (61) 39 691 6111
Web Site: https://www.k2am.com.au
Sales Range: $50-74.9 Million
Emp.: 23
Fund Management Services
N.A.I.C.S.: 525910

K2 ENERGY LIMITED
Level 2 Kyle House 27 Macquarie Place, Sydney, 2000, NSW, Australia
Tel.: (61) 292513311 AU
Web Site: http://www.k2energy.com.au
KTE—(ASX)
Rev.: $6,822
Assets: $3,300,387
Liabilities: $685,916
Net Worth: $2,614,472
Earnings: ($38,246)
Fiscal Year-end: 06/30/19
Solar Cell Mfr
N.A.I.C.S.: 339999
Terence Flitcroft (Sec)

K2 F&B HOLDINGS LIMITED

51 Ubi Avenue 1 02-17/18 Paya, Ubi Industrial Park, Singapore, 408933, Singapore
Tel.: (65) 64466056 Ky
Web Site: https://www.fuchangroup.com
Year Founded: 2004
2108—(HKG)
Rev.: $42,217,678
Assets: $150,063,622
Liabilities: $84,610,316
Net Worth: $65,453,306
Earnings: $5,536,620
Emp.: 372
Fiscal Year-end: 12/31/23
Holding Company
N.A.I.C.S.: 551112
Chee Keong Chu *(Chm & CEO)*

K2 GOLD CORPORATION
Suite 1020-800 West Pender St, Vancouver, V6C 2V6, BC, Canada
Tel.: (604) 331-5090 BC
Web Site: https://k2gold.com
Year Founded: 2011
KTGDF—(OTCQB)
Rev.: $19,139
Assets: $12,065,837
Liabilities: $279,831
Net Worth: $11,786,006
Earnings: ($1,405,372)
Fiscal Year-end: 12/31/20
Metal Mining Services
N.A.I.C.S.: 212290
John Robins *(Chm)*

K2 GROUP
5200 Finch Avenue East Suite 302, Toronto, M1S 4Z3, ON, Canada
Tel.: (416) 335-7100
Web Site: https://www.k2group.ca
Year Founded: 2017
Emp.: 500
Privater Equity Firm
N.A.I.C.S.: 523940
Kailash Kasal *(Founder & Pres)*

Subsidiaries:

Quality Inn & Suites (1)
2301 E Morthland Dr Quality Bldg, Valparaiso, IN 46383
Tel.: (219) 465-1700
Home Management Services
N.A.I.C.S.: 721110

K2 HOLDING S.A.
Platinium V Building 44A Domaniewska St, 02-672, Warsaw, Poland
Tel.: (48) 224487000
K2I—(WAR)
Sales Range: $1-9.9 Million
Emp.: 300
Internet Marketing Services
N.A.I.C.S.: 513210
Kasia Wisniewska *(Mng Dir-K2 Media)*

K2 KOREA CO. LTD.
901-14 Jagok-ro, Gangnam-gu, Seoul, Korea (South)
Tel.: (82) 1644 7781
Web Site: http://www.k2.co.kr
Outdoor & Sporting Goods Mfr & Whslr
N.A.I.C.S.: 339920
Young Hoon Jeong *(CEO)*

K2 LT AB
Metalistu g3, Kauno Apskritis, 57241, Kedainiai, 57241, Lithuania
Tel.: (370) 63397722
Web Site: https://www.lietuvoskrematoriumas.lt
K2LT—(RSE)
Rev.: $2,510,671

Assets: $5,953,643
Liabilities: $1,714,428
Net Worth: $4,239,215
Earnings: $1,167,421
Emp.: 10
Fiscal Year-end: 12/31/20
Cremation Services
N.A.I.C.S.: 624190
Bernardas Vilkelis *(Dir)*

K2A KNAUST & ANDERSSON FASTIGHETER AB
Nybrogatan 59, 114 40, Stockholm, Sweden
Tel.: (46) 105105510
Web Site: https://www.k2a.se
Year Founded: 2013
K2A.PREF—(OMX)
Rev.: $44,036,771
Assets: $998,491,093
Liabilities: $764,468,812
Net Worth: $234,022,280
Earnings: ($53,298,788)
Emp.: 44
Fiscal Year-end: 12/31/23
Real Estate Manangement Services
N.A.I.C.S.: 531311
Johan Knaust *(CEO & Mng Dir)*

K2FLY LIMITED
Level 4 502 Hay Street, Subiaco, 6008, WA, Australia
Tel.: (61) 863331833
Web Site: https://www.k2fly.com
K2F—(ASX)
Rev.: $7,675,289
Assets: $20,241,029
Liabilities: $9,482,606
Net Worth: $10,758,422
Earnings: ($3,540,625)
Fiscal Year-end: 06/30/22
Miscellaneous Financial Investment Activities
N.A.I.C.S.: 523999
Brian Miller *(CEO)*

K3 BUSINESS TECHNOLOGY GROUP PLC
Baltimore House 50 Kansas Avenue, Manchester, M50 2GL, United Kingdom
Tel.: (44) 1618764498 UK
Web Site: https://www.k3btg.com
Year Founded: 2001
KBT—(AIM)
Rev.: $64,535,147
Assets: $72,086,786
Liabilities: $27,766,732
Net Worth: $44,320,054
Earnings: ($5,401,010)
Emp.: 300
Fiscal Year-end: 11/30/22
Software Developer & Retailer
N.A.I.C.S.: 513210
Robert Price *(CFO)*

Subsidiaries:

K3 Business Solutions (1)
Bartley House Station Road, Hook, RG27 9JF, Hants, United Kingdom
Tel.: (44) 8442252480
Web Site: https://www.k3btg.com
Enterprise Software Solutions
N.A.I.C.S.: 513210
David John Bolton *(CEO)*

K3 Landsteinar Nederland BV (1)
Donau 106-108, Hague, 2491 BC, South Holland, Netherlands
Tel.: (31) 70 301 6070
Web Site: http://www.k3btg.com
Sales Range: $25-49.9 Million
Emp.: 30
Software Solutions Distr
N.A.I.C.S.: 513210

K3 Retail and Business Solutions Limited (1)
Unit F4 Bymac Ctr NW Business Park, Bal-

lycoolin, Dublin, Ireland
Tel.: (353) 18208321
Web Site: http://www.k3btg.com
Sales Range: $25-49.9 Million
Emp.: 4
Software Solutions Services
N.A.I.C.S.: 541511
Russell Edward Dorset *(Mng Dir)*

K3 Supply Chain Solutions Limited (1)
50 Kansas Ave, Manchester, M50 2GL, Lancashire, United Kingdom
Tel.: (44) 1618764498
Web Site: http://www.k3btg.com
Sales Range: $25-49.9 Million
Emp.: 100
Software Solutions Services
N.A.I.C.S.: 541511
Paul Roebuck *(Dir-Sls)*

K7 LUMBER INC.
165 place Jean Juneau, Saint-Augustin-de-Desmaures, G3A 2W1, QC, Canada
Tel.: (418) 878-5181
Web Site: http://www.boisk7.com
Year Founded: 1984
Rev.: $30,479,026
Emp.: 5
Timber Products Distr
N.A.I.C.S.: 423310
Jean Marc Bouchard *(Pres & CEO)*

K9 GOLD CORP.
Tel.: (604) 669-2279 BC
Year Founded: 2005
5GP—(DEU)
Assets: $6,674,688
Liabilities: $159,413
Net Worth: $6,515,275
Earnings: ($1,893,451)
Fiscal Year-end: 12/31/22
Energy & Resource Exploration Services
N.A.I.C.S.: 211120
Brian Morrison *(CEO & CFO)*

K92 MINING INC.
Suite 488-1090 West Georgia Street, Vancouver, V6E 3V7, BC, Canada
Tel.: (604) 416-4445 BC
Web Site: https://www.k92mining.com
Year Founded: 2010
KNTNF—(OTCQX)
Rev.: $101,692,600
Assets: $154,990,122
Liabilities: $30,299,684
Net Worth: $124,690,438
Earnings: $32,542,453
Fiscal Year-end: 12/31/19
Gold Mining Services
N.A.I.C.S.: 212220
John Lewins *(CEO)*

Subsidiaries:

K92 Mining (Australia) Pty Ltd. (1)
Level 4 - 231 Adelaide Terrace, East Perth, Perth, 6004, WA, Australia
Tel.: (61) 737390161
Gold Ore Mining Services
N.A.I.C.S.: 212220

K92 Mining Ltd. (1)
PO Box 1290, Lae, 411, Morobe, Papua New Guinea
Tel.: (675) 71002451
Gold Ore Mining Services
N.A.I.C.S.: 212220

KA SHUI INTERNATIONAL HOLDINGS LIMITED
Room A 29th Floor Tower B Billion Centre 1 Wang Kwong Road, Kowloon Bay, Kowloon, China (Hong Kong)
Tel.: (852) 37598900 Ky
Web Site: http://www.kashui.com
Year Founded: 1980

0822—(HKG)
Rev.: $191,815,973
Assets: $218,109,150
Liabilities: $53,598,960
Net Worth: $164,510,190
Earnings: $8,779,395
Emp.: 3,750
Fiscal Year-end: 12/31/22
Lead & Zinc Ore Mining Services
N.A.I.C.S.: 212230
Yuen Fat Lee *(Chm)*

Subsidiaries:

Alphalite Incorporation (1)
11920 Altamar Pl, Santa Fe Springs, CA 90670
Web Site: https://www.alphalite.com
Lighting Product Mfr
N.A.I.C.S.: 334413

Huizhou Wing Yu Metal & Plastic Manufactory Company Limited (1)
2nd Floor Block 101, Longxi Environmental Electroplating Industrial Park Boluo, Huizhou, Guangdong, China
Tel.: (86) 7523105150
Metal Die Casting Product Mfr & Distr
N.A.I.C.S.: 331523

Ka Shui Metal Manufacturing (Shenzhen) Co., Ltd. (1)
11 Dongshen Road Egongling Pinghu, Longgang District, Shenzhen, China
Tel.: (86) 75528456490
Plastic Injection Product Distr
N.A.I.C.S.: 423830

Ka Shui Plastic Technology Company Limited (1)
Room A 29th Floor Tower B Billion Centre, 1 Wang Kwong Road, Kowloon Bay, China (Hong Kong)
Tel.: (852) 37598900
Plastics Product Mfr
N.A.I.C.S.: 326199

Ka Shui Technology (Huizhou) Company Limited (1)
Ka Shui Technology Park No9 Long Hai 3rd Road, Western Dayawan District, Huizhou, Guangdong, China
Tel.: (86) 7523098666
Metal Die Casting Product Distr
N.A.I.C.S.: 423510

KAAR TECHNOLOGIES INDIA PVT LTD.
Level 8 Shyamala Towers No 136 Arcot Road, Chennai, 600093, India
Tel.: (91) 4440651500 In
Web Site: https://www.kaartech.com
Year Founded: 2006
Emp.: 100
Digital Transformation Consulting & Other Management Consulting Services
N.A.I.C.S.: 518210
Maran Nagarajan *(CEO)*

Subsidiaries:

Dunn Solutions Group, Inc. (1)
5550 Touhy Ave, Skokie, IL 60077
Tel.: (847) 673-0900
Web Site: http://www.dunnsolutions.com
Sales Range: $10-24.9 Million
Emp.: 68
Computer Software Development
N.A.I.C.S.: 541511
William Dunn *(Deputy CEO)*

KAARYA FACILITIES & SERVICES LTD.
Unit 217 Gemstar Commercial Complex Ramchandra Lane Extn Kanchpada, Malad W, Mumbai, 400 064, India
Tel.: (91) 2240030768
Web Site: https://www.kaarya.co.in
Year Founded: 2009
Rev.: $2,495,071
Assets: $2,208,260
Liabilities: $705,882

KAARYA FACILITIES & SERVICES LTD.

Kaarya Facilities & Services Ltd.—(Continued)
Net Worth: $1,502,378
Earnings: $168,094
Emp.: 15
Fiscal Year-end: 03/31/19
Property Management Services
N.A.I.C.S.: 531311
Vineet Pandey (Co-Mng Dir)

KABE GROUP AB
Jonkopingsvagen 21, PO Box 14, Tenhult, Jonkoping, Sweden
Tel.: (46) 36393700
Web Site: https://www.kabe.se
Year Founded: 1957
KABE.B—(OMX)
Rev.: $260,274,560
Assets: $200,089,120
Liabilities: $59,452,960
Net Worth: $140,636,160
Earnings: $8,179,360
Emp.: 879
Fiscal Year-end: 12/31/20
Automobile Mfr
N.A.I.C.S.: 336110
Nils-Erik Danielsson (Chm)

Subsidiaries:

KAMA Fritid AB (1)
Box 23, 551 12, Jonkoping, Sweden
Tel.: (46) 36353700
Web Site: https://www.kamafritid.se
Caravan Distr
N.A.I.C.S.: 423110

S. KAROSSER AB (1)
Timmervagen 11, 917 32, Dorotea, Sweden
Tel.: (46) 94251290
Web Site: https://www.easycampers.se
Caravan Distr
N.A.I.C.S.: 423110

KABELWERK EUPEN AG
Malmedyer Strasse 9, 94700, Eupen, Belgium
Tel.: (32) 87597000
Web Site: http://www.eupen.com
Year Founded: 1747
Cable Products Mfr
N.A.I.C.S.: 335929
Mike Goblet (Comml Dir)

KABELWERK MEISSEN WILHELM BALZER GMBH
Niederauer Strasse 52, 01662, Meissen, Germany
Tel.: (49) 35217230
Web Site: http://www.balzer-kabel.de
Year Founded: 1864
Sales Range: $75-99.9 Million
Emp.: 1,000
Cable & Wire Mfr
N.A.I.C.S.: 332618
Lars Balzer (Mng Dir)

KABILE-LB AD
Obhoden pat Zapad 57, Yambol, 8603, Bulgaria
Tel.: (359) 46661881
KABL—(BUL)
Sales Range: Less than $1 Million
Dairy Products Mfr
N.A.I.C.S.: 311812
Kiril Nikolov Georgiev (Chm)

KABOKO MINING LIMITED
Ground Floor 1 Havelock Street, West Perth, 6005, WA, Australia
Tel.: (61) 8 9488 5220
Web Site: http://www.kabokomining.com
Sales Range: Less than $1 Million
Emp.: 3
Manganese Mining & Exploration Services
N.A.I.C.S.: 212290
Tokkas Van Heerden (CEO)

KABRA COMMERCIAL LIMITED
Govind Bhawan 4th Floor 2 Brabourne Road, Kolkata, 700 001, West Bengal, India
Tel.: (91) 3322254058
Web Site: https://www.kcl.net.in
Year Founded: 1982
539393—(BOM)
Rev.: $1,986,538
Assets: $3,350,148
Liabilities: $1,502,950
Net Worth: $1,847,198
Earnings: $91,568
Emp.: 5
Fiscal Year-end: 03/31/22
Fuel Product Distr
N.A.I.C.S.: 423520
Rajesh Kumar Kabra (Mng Dir)

KABRA DRUGS LIMITED
208 Swadesh Bhavan 2 Press Complex AB Road, Indore, 452011, Madhya Pradesh, India
Tel.: (91) 9884624100
Web Site: https://www.kabradrugs.com
Year Founded: 1989
524322—(BOM)
Rev.: $765
Assets: $84,356
Liabilities: $172,006
Net Worth: ($87,650)
Earnings: ($40,513)
Emp.: 31
Fiscal Year-end: 03/31/23
Pharmaceutical Drug Mfr & Distr
N.A.I.C.S.: 424210

KABRA EXTRUSIONTECHNIK LTD
Fortune Terraces 10th Floor B Wing Opp Citi Mall Link Road, Andheri West, Mumbai, 400 053, Maharashtra, India
Tel.: (91) 2226734822
Web Site: https://www.kolsite.com
KABRAEXTRU—(NSE)
Rev.: $37,825,597
Assets: $54,482,119
Liabilities: $16,517,469
Net Worth: $37,964,649
Earnings: $3,352,686
Emp.: 405
Fiscal Year-end: 03/31/21
Plastic Extrusion Machinery Mfr
N.A.I.C.S.: 333248
Shreevallabh G. Kabra (Chm & Mng Dir)

KABSONS INDUSTRIES LIMITED
Madhuw Vihar 2 Floor Plot No 17 H No 8-2-293/82/C/17, Road No 7 Jubilee Hills, Hyderabad, 500 033, Telangana, India
Tel.: (91) 4023554970
Web Site: https://www.kabsons.co.in
Year Founded: 1992
524675—(BOM)
Rev.: $1,633,206
Assets: $1,735,222
Liabilities: $577,723
Net Worth: $1,157,499
Earnings: $218,514
Emp.: 21
Fiscal Year-end: 03/31/22
Fuel Product Mfr & Distr
N.A.I.C.S.: 324110
Rajiv Kabra (Chm)

KABUSHIKI KAISHA SEIYOKEN
4-58 Ueno Koen, Taito-Ku, Tokyo, 110-8715, Japan
Tel.: (81) 3 38212181
Web Site: http://www.seiyoken.co.jp
Year Founded: 1872
9734—(JAS)
Sales Range: Less than $1 Million
Restaurant Services
N.A.I.C.S.: 722511
Yutaka Sakai (Pres)

KABUTO DECOM, INC.
C 35 Miya Momori 4 Jyo 1 Chome, Chuo Ku, Sapporo, 064 0954, Japan
Tel.: (81) 116212611
Year Founded: 1971
Sales Range: $1-9.9 Million
Emp.: 65
Real Estate Development & Construction
N.A.I.C.S.: 237210

Subsidiaries:

Kabuto International Phoenix Inc. (1)
1 Daniel Burnham Ct Ste 205C, San Francisco, CA 94109-5455 (100%)
Tel.: (415) 776-2120
Real Estate
N.A.I.C.S.: 721110

Subsidiary (Domestic):

Wigwam Resort (2)
300 E Wigwam Blvd, Litchfield Park, AZ 85340
Tel.: (623) 935-3811
Web Site: http://www.wigwamarizona.com
Resort Services
N.A.I.C.S.: 721110
Katy Powers (Mng Dir & Gen Mgr)

KACAREVO A.D.
Kosovska 63, 26212, Kacarevo, Serbia
Tel.: (381) 13 601 210
Web Site: http://www.kacarevoad.rs
Year Founded: 1989
Sales Range: $1-9.9 Million
Emp.: 47
Pig Farming Services
N.A.I.C.S.: 112210

KACHCHH MINERALS LIMITED
22 Mansur Building 1st Floor 98 Princess Street, Mumbai, 400002, Maharashtra, India
Tel.: (91) 2222010028
531778—(BOM)
Rev.: $74,106
Assets: $234,788
Liabilities: $78,271
Net Worth: $156,517
Earnings: ($11,348)
Emp.: 6
Fiscal Year-end: 03/31/23
Mining Services
N.A.I.C.S.: 212323
Ashok Jivrajbhai Bhut (CEO)

KADDY LIMITED
25 Tarlington Place, Smithfield, 2164, NSW, Australia
Tel.: (61) 280021991
DW8—(ASX)
Rev.: $101,696
Assets: $142,866
Liabilities: $1,912,003
Net Worth: ($1,769,137)
Earnings: ($1,535,969)
Fiscal Year-end: 06/30/23
Asset Management Services
N.A.I.C.S.: 523940
Thomas Amos (Chm)

KADER HOLDINGS COMPANY LIMITED
11/F Kader Building 22 Kai Cheung Road, Kowloon, China (Hong Kong)
Tel.: (852) 27981688
Web Site: https://www.kader.com.hk

INTERNATIONAL PUBLIC

Year Founded: 1948
0180—(HKG)
Rev.: $44,875,793
Assets: $376,678,733
Liabilities: $98,843,355
Net Worth: $277,835,378
Earnings: ($10,833,038)
Emp.: 1,009
Fiscal Year-end: 12/31/22
Holding Company; Toys & Plastic Mfr
N.A.I.C.S.: 551112
Ivan Tien-li Ting (Exec Dir)

Subsidiaries:

Bachmann (China) Limited (1)
Rm 5203/TOP The Outstanding Park No 18 Wuwei Road, Putuo District, Shanghai, 200331, China
Tel.: (86) 2162567701
Web Site: http://www.bachmannchina.com.cn
Emp.: 10
Toy Trains Mfr
N.A.I.C.S.: 339930
Rick Li (Gen Mgr)

Bachmann Asia Limited (1)
11/F Kader Bldg 22 Kai Cheung Rd, Kowloon Bay, Kowloon, China (Hong Kong)
Tel.: (852) 27981529
Plastics & Toys Whslr
N.A.I.C.S.: 423920

Bachmann Europe Plc (1)
Moat Way Barwell, Leicester, LE9 8EY, United Kingdom
Tel.: (44) 1455245577
Web Site: https://www.bachmann.co.uk
Sales Range: $25-49.9 Million
Emp.: 40
Model Trains Mfr
N.A.I.C.S.: 336350

Bachmann Industries, Inc. (1)
1400 E Erie Ave, Philadelphia, PA 19124
Tel.: (215) 533-1600
Web Site: https://www.bachmanntrains.com
Sales Range: $50-74.9 Million
Emp.: 55
Scale Model Electrical Train Sets & Accessories Mfr
N.A.I.C.S.: 423920
Michael R. Sellinger (Pres & CEO)

K Cellars (Hong Kong) Limited (1)
4/F Kader Building 22 Kai Cheung Road, Kowloon Bay, China (Hong Kong)
Tel.: (852) 28711099
Web Site: https://www.kcellars.com.hk
Wine Whslr
N.A.I.C.S.: 424820

Kader Industrial Company Limited (1)
11/F Kader Building 22 Kai Cheung Road, Kowloon Bay, Kowloon, China (Hong Kong)
Tel.: (852) 27981688
Web Site: http://www.kader.com.hk
Sales Range: $25-49.9 Million
Emp.: 100
Plastics & Toys Mfr
N.A.I.C.S.: 314910
Kenneth Ting (Mng Dir)

SDK Services Limited (1)
22 Kai Cheung Road 7th Floor Kader Building, Kowloon Bay, Kowloon, China (Hong Kong)
Tel.: (852) 31273800
Office Administrative Services
N.A.I.C.S.: 561110

Sanda Kan Technology (Shenzhen) Company Limited (1)
Song Gang Town Bao An, Xi Tou District, Shenzhen, 518105, Guangdong, China
Tel.: (86) 755 2742 9205
Toy Mfr
N.A.I.C.S.: 339930

Tinco Toys Company Limited (1)
11/F Kader Building 22 Kai Cheung Road, Kowloon Bay, Kowloon, China (Hong Kong)
Tel.: (852) 27981688
Web Site: http://www.tincotoys.com
Emp.: 100
Toy Mfr
N.A.I.C.S.: 339930

AND PRIVATE COMPANIES

Walitoys & Garment Limited (1)
9 Floor Wing Hong Centre 18 Wing Hong Street, Lai Chi Kok, Kowloon, China (Hong Kong)
Tel.: (852) 2548 8233
Web Site: http://www.walitoys.com
Sales Range: $400-449.9 Million
Emp.: 1,250
Stuffed Toys & Doll Clothing Mfr
N.A.I.C.S.: 339930

KADIMASTEM LTD.
Pinchas Sapir 7 Weizmann Science Park, PO Box 4152, Nes Ziyyona, 74140, Israel
Tel.: (972) 737971600
Web Site: https://www.kadimastem.com
Year Founded: 2009
KDST—(TAE)
Assets: $2,311,369
Liabilities: $3,515,955
Net Worth: ($1,204,586)
Earnings: ($3,317,862)
Fiscal Year-end: 12/31/23
Pharmaceutical Preparation Manufacturing
N.A.I.C.S.: 325412
Michel Revel (Founder)

KADINJACA A.D.
Milosa Obrenovica 4, 31000, Uzice, Serbia
Tel.: (381) 31564244
Web Site: https://www.kadinjaca.co.rs
Year Founded: 1945
KDNC—(BEL)
Sales Range: $1-9.9 Million
Emp.: 188
Cloth Product Mfr
N.A.I.C.S.: 315990

KADINJACA A.D.
Milenka Topalovic 78, Bajina Basta, Serbia
Tel.: (381) 31 865 567
Year Founded: 1958
Sales Range: Less than $1 Million
Emp.: 2
Construction Materials Whslr
N.A.I.C.S.: 423390
Dragisa Vasic (Exec Dir)

KADOKAWA CORPORATION
2-13-3 Fujimi, Chiyoda-ku, Tokyo, 102-8177, Japan
Tel.: (81) 332388561   JP
Web Site: https://tp.kadokawa.co.jp
Year Founded: 2014
9468—(TKS)
Rev.: $1,706,100,490
Assets: $2,249,449,100
Liabilities: $844,387,840
Net Worth: $1,405,061,260
Earnings: $75,248,240
Fiscal Year-end: 03/31/24
Holding Company; Entertainment Media Publisher, Licensor & Distr
N.A.I.C.S.: 551112

Subsidiaries:

ATX Inc. (1)
1-chome-12-15 Fujimi, Chiyoda City, Tokyo, 102-0071, Japan
Tel.: (81) 332388480
Web Site: http://www.atx.co.jp
Computer System Design Services
N.A.I.C.S.: 541512

Bookwalker Taiwan Co. Ltd. (1)
5th Floor No 44 Lane 11 Guangfu North Road, Songshan District, Taipei, Taiwan
Tel.: (886) 227473143
Web Site: http://www.bookwalker.com.tw
Magazine Book Publisher
N.A.I.C.S.: 513120
Adline Lee (Ops Mgr)

Choubunsha Publishing Co., Ltd. (1)
1F Fujimi Building 1-6-1 Fujimi, Chiyoda-ku, Tokyo, 102-0071, Japan
Tel.: (81) 368625200
Web Site: http://www.choubunsha.com
Magazine Book Publisher
N.A.I.C.S.: 513120

DWANGO Co., Ltd. (1)
Kabukiza Tower 4-12-15 Ginza, Chuo-ku, Tokyo, 104-0061, Japan
Tel.: (81) 3 35496300
Web Site: http://dwango.co.jp
Sales Range: $350-399.9 Million
Emp.: 928
Holding Company; Network Entertainment Software Publishing & Support Services
N.A.I.C.S.: 551112
Yuriya Komatsu (CFO)

Kadokawa Amarin Company Limited (1)
378 Chaiyaphruk Road, Taling Chan, Bangkok, 10170, Thailand
Tel.: (66) 24340333
Web Site: http://www.phoenixnext.com
Magazine Book Publisher
N.A.I.C.S.: 513120
Taro Iwasaki (Mng Dir)

Kadokawa Ca (Thailand) Co., Ltd. (1)
Tel.: (66) 26576150
Magazine Book Publisher
N.A.I.C.S.: 513120

Kadokawa Contents Academy Co., Ltd. (1)
2-13-3 Fujimi, Chiyoda-ku, Tokyo, 102-8177, Japan
Tel.: (81) 368628755
Web Site: http://www.kadokawa-ca.co.jp
Magazine Book Publisher
N.A.I.C.S.: 513120

Kadokawa Corporation (1)
2-13-3 Fujimi, Chiyoda-ku, Tokyo, 102-8177, Japan
Tel.: (81) 332388401
Web Site: http://www.ir.kadokawa.co.jp
Holding Company; Entertainment Media Publisher, Licensor & Distr
N.A.I.C.S.: 551112
Masaki Matsubara (Pres)

Subsidiary (Domestic):

Building Book Center Co., Ltd. (2)
315-1 Chikumazawa Miyoshimachi, Iruma, 354-0043, Saitama, Japan
Tel.: (81) 492595331
Web Site: http://www.bbc-kadokawa.co.jp
Sales Range: $25-49.9 Million
Emp.: 230
Logistics Consulting Servies
N.A.I.C.S.: 541614

Glovision, Inc. (2)
GS Bldg Minami Motomachi 3, Shinjuku-Ku, Tokyo, 160-0012, Japan
Tel.: (81) 333578201
Web Site: http://www.glovision.co.jp
Sales Range: $25-49.9 Million
Emp.: 70
Movie Dubbing Services
N.A.I.C.S.: 512199
Shunichi Okabe (Pres)

Subsidiary (Non-US):

Kadokawa Media (Taiwan) Co., Ltd. (2)
105 5f No 46 Ln 11 Kuang-fu N Rd, Taipei, Taiwan
Tel.: (886) 227472433
Web Site: http://www.kadokawa.com.tw
Publishing Services
N.A.I.C.S.: 513120

Subsidiary (Domestic):

Kadokawa Media House Inc. (2)
1-12-7 Iidabashi 12 Ctr Bldg 8F, Chiyoda-ku, Tokyo, 102-0072, Japan
Tel.: (81) 332385712
Web Site: http://www.kmh.kadokawa.co.jp
Sales Range: $25-49.9 Million
Emp.: 50
Advertising Agencies
N.A.I.C.S.: 541810
Masahiro Kiba (Pres)

Kadokawa Daiei Studio Co., Ltd. (1)
6-1-1 Tamagawa, Chofu, 182-0025, Tokyo, Japan
Tel.: (81) 424821151
Web Site: http://www.kd-st.co.jp
Magazine Book Publisher
N.A.I.C.S.: 513120

Kadokawa Gempak Starz Sdn. Bhd. (1)
17 19 Jalan 8/146, Bandar Tasik Selatan, 57000, Kuala Lumpur, Selangor, Malaysia
Tel.: (60) 126170045
Web Site: https://www.shop.gempakstarz.com
Magazine Book Publisher
N.A.I.C.S.: 513120

Kadokawa Taiwan Corporation (1)
3F 3rd Floor No 223 Songjiang Rd, Zhongshan District, Taipei, Taiwan
Tel.: (886) 225153000
Web Site: http://www.kadokawa.com.tw
Magazine Book Publisher
N.A.I.C.S.: 513120

KADOYA SESAME MILLS INC.
Osaki Twin Building East 4F 5-1-18 Kitashinagawa, Shinagawa-ku, Tokyo, 141-0001, Japan
Tel.: (81) 367216957
Web Site: https://www.kadoya.com
Year Founded: 1957
2612—(TKS)
Rev.: $235,844,800
Assets: $282,055,310
Liabilities: $54,975,370
Net Worth: $227,079,940
Earnings: $14,905,550
Emp.: 413
Fiscal Year-end: 03/31/24
Sesame Seeds
N.A.I.C.S.: 111120
Atsushi Kume (Pres & CEO)

KAEHLIG ANTRIEBSTECHNIK GMBH
Pappelweg 4, 30179, Hannover, Germany
Tel.: (49) 511674930
Web Site: https://www.kag-hannover.com
Year Founded: 1967
Sales Range: $10-24.9 Million
Emp.: 150
Electrical Drive & Motor Developer & Mfr
N.A.I.C.S.: 335312
Matthias Kaehlig (Chm, CEO & Mng Dir)

KAESSBOHRER GELANDE-FAHRZEUG AG
Kaessbohrerstrasse 11, 88471, Laupheim, Germany
Tel.: (49) 73929000
Web Site: http://www.kaessbohrerag.com
Year Founded: 1969
Sales Range: $200-249.9 Million
Emp.: 448
All Terrain Vehicle Mfr
N.A.I.C.S.: 336110
Alexander Schoellhorn (CFO)

Subsidiaries:

Kassbohrer All Terrain Vehicles, Inc. (1)
8850 Double diamon PKWy, Reno, NV 89521
Tel.: (775) 857-5000
Web Site: http://www.katvpb.com
Sales Range: $25-49.9 Million
Emp.: 39
Provider of All-Terrain Recreation Vehicles
N.A.I.C.S.: 423110
John C. Gilbert (Pres & CEO)

Kassbohrer E.S.E. (1)
455 Route Porte de Tarentaise, 73790, Tours-en-Savoie, France
Tel.: (33) 479104610
Web Site: http://www.pistenbully.fr
Sales Range: $25-49.9 Million
Emp.: 45
Automobile & Motor Vehicle Whslr
N.A.I.C.S.: 423110
Didier Bic (Gen Mgr)

KAF SECURITIES SDN. BHD.
11th-14th Floors Chulan Tower No 3, Jalan Conlay, 50450, Kuala Lumpur, Malaysia
Tel.: (60) 3 2171 0228   MY
Web Site: http://www.kaf.com
Emp.: 300
Holding Company
N.A.I.C.S.: 551112

Subsidiaries:

KAF Investment Bank Berhad (1)
Level 14 Chulan Tower No 3 Jalan Conlay, 50450, Kuala Lumpur, Malaysia   (100%)
Tel.: (60) 3 2171 0228
Web Site: http://www.kaf.com.my
Rev.: $59,775,217
Assets: $1,662,170,025
Liabilities: $1,314,704,394
Net Worth: $347,465,631
Earnings: $19,860,500
Fiscal Year-end: 05/31/2019
Investment Banking
N.A.I.C.S.: 523150
Rohaizad Ismail (CEO)

Subsidiary (Domestic):

KAF-Seagroatt & Campbell Berhad (2)
Level 14 Chulan Tower No 3 Jalan Conlay, 50450, Kuala Lumpur, Malaysia
Tel.: (60) 3 2171 0228
Web Site: http://www.kaf.com.my
Sales Range: $1-9.9 Million
Stockbroking & Financial Services
N.A.I.C.S.: 523940
Ahmad Kadis (Chm)

KAFAA FOR FINANCIAL & ECONOMICAL INVESTMENTS PLC
Wasfi AL-Tal St- PC Plaza Complex Office 404, PO Box 3778, Wasfi Al Tal Street, Amman, 11953, Jordan
Tel.: (962) 65537223
KAFA—(AMM)
Assets: $5,030,766
Liabilities: $745,583
Net Worth: $4,285,183
Earnings: ($32,938)
Emp.: 2
Fiscal Year-end: 12/31/22
Financial Investment Services
N.A.I.C.S.: 523999
Abdallah Alshanti - Acting (Gen Mgr)

KAFEIN YAZILIM HIZMETLERI TICARET AS
YTU Davutpasa Campus Twin Pools District Old London Asphalt Street, Incubation Center A2 Block No 151/1B Interior Door No B01 Esenler, Istanbul, Turkiye
Tel.: (90) 2129242030
Web Site: https://www.kafein.com.tr
Year Founded: 2005
KFEIN—(IST)
Rev.: $12,093,251
Assets: $11,664,226
Liabilities: $3,651,295
Net Worth: $8,012,931
Earnings: $2,133,332
Emp.: 664
Fiscal Year-end: 12/31/22
Software Development Services
N.A.I.C.S.: 541511
Ali Cem Kalyoncu (Chm)

KAFR EL ZAYAT PESTICIDES & CHEMICALS CO.

KAFR EL ZAYAT PESTICIDES & CHEMICALS CO.

Kafr El Zayat Pesticides & Chemicals Co.—(Continued)
El Sharikat St Kafr El Zayat Gharbia, Tanta, Egypt
Tel.: (20) 402542444
Web Site: https://www.kz.com.eg
Year Founded: 1957
KZPC.CA—(EGX)
Rev.: $42,648,792
Assets: $41,298,425
Liabilities: $25,047,819
Net Worth: $16,250,606
Earnings: $4,889,101
Emp.: 700
Fiscal Year-end: 12/31/22
Pesticide Mfr
N.A.I.C.S.: 325320
Essam Albert El Dabe *(Chm)*

KAFRIT INDUSTRIES LTD.
Kfar Gaza D N, Negev, 8514200, Israel
Tel.: (972) 86809845
Web Site: https://kafrit.com
Year Founded: 1993
Plastics Product Mfr
N.A.I.C.S.: 326199
Alon Kessler *(Gen Mgr)*

KAGA ELECTRONICS CO., LTD.
20 Kanda Matsunagacho, Chiyoda-ku, Tokyo, 101-8629, Japan
Tel.: (81) 356570111
Web Site: https://www.taxan.co.jp
Year Founded: 1968
8154—(TKS)
Rev.: $3,587,227,170
Assets: $1,895,695,120
Liabilities: $896,058,210
Net Worth: $999,636,910
Earnings: $134,480,450
Emp.: 8,021
Fiscal Year-end: 03/31/24
Electronic Component Sales
N.A.I.C.S.: 423690
Shintaro Kakei *(Sr Mng Dir)*

Subsidiaries:

AD DEVICE CO., LTD. (1)
Akihabara Bill Realty & Dev 3-12-8 Soto-Kanda, Chiyoda-ku, Tokyo, 101-0021, Japan
Tel.: (81) 344553105
Web Site: http://www.ad-device.co.jp
Rev.: $843,944,000
Emp.: 68
Electronic Parts & Semiconductor Whslr
N.A.I.C.S.: 334413

ADM, Inc. (1)
Sun Mullion NBF Tower Minami Honmachi 2 6 12, Osaka, 541 0054, Chuo Ku, Japan (55.41%)
Tel.: (81) 662442701
Web Site: http://www.adm.co.jp
Sales Range: $150-199.9 Million
Emp.: 85
Electronic Components & Equipment Sales & Marketing
N.A.I.C.S.: 449210

Access Games Inc. (1)
2F and 3F KAGA Building 2-2-6 Minami-Senba, Chuo-ku, Osaka, 542-0081, Japan
Tel.: (81) 661050459
Emp.: 65
Game Software Publisher
N.A.I.C.S.: 513210
Takahiro Urazawa *(Pres)*

Ad Device (H.K.) Limited (1)
Room714 7/F Miramar Tower 132 Nathan Road, Tsim Sha Tsui, Kowloon Bay, Kowloon, China (Hong Kong)
Tel.: (852) 21172995
Web Site: https://www.ad-device.co.jp
Emp.: 7
Electronic Parts Whslr
N.A.I.C.S.: 423690
Kazunari Yamabe *(Pres)*

Ad Device (Shanghai) Co., Ltd. (1)
19F/C International Shipping Financial Building 720 Pu Dong Avenue, Post Code 200120, Shanghai, China
Tel.: (86) 2120250125
Web Site: https://www.taxan.co.jp
Emp.: 3
Electric Equipment Mfr
N.A.I.C.S.: 334419
Kenichi Kishi *(Pres)*

Ad Device (Thailand) Co., Ltd. (1)
24 Prime Building 11th Fl Soi Sukhumvit 21 Asoke Sukhumvit Rd, Klongtoey-Nua Sub-District Wattana District, Bangkok, Thailand
Tel.: (66) 26617102
Web Site: https://www.taxan.co.jp
Emp.: 3
Electric Equipment Mfr
N.A.I.C.S.: 334419

Digital Media Lab Inc. (1)
Web Site: http://www.dml.co.jp
Sales Range: $25-49.9 Million
Emp.: 81
Digital Equipments Mfr
N.A.I.C.S.: 334515

Dreams Corporation (1)
22-7 Minamiooi 6-chome, Shinagawa-ku, Tokyo, 140-0013, Japan
Tel.: (81) 337624140
Emp.: 215
Electronic Services
N.A.I.C.S.: 541360

EXCEL CO., LTD. (1)
9F 20 Kandamatsuga-cho, Chiyoda-ku, Tokyo, 101-0023, Japan
Tel.: (81) 356570160
Web Site: http://www.excelweb.co.jp
Sales Range: $600-649.9 Million
Emp.: 123
Electronic Devices & Integrated Circuit Mfr & Distr
N.A.I.C.S.: 334413
Isaku Tanimura *(Sr Exec Officer)*

Subsidiary (Non-US):

Excel Asian Taiwan Co., Ltd. (2)
11F-3 No 171 Song De Rd, Sin Yi Dist, Taipei, 11085, Taiwan
Tel.: (886) 2 2726 9139
Electronic Components Distr
N.A.I.C.S.: 423690

Excel Electronics (Hong Kong) Ltd. (2)
Units 2008-2009 20/F Chevalier Commercial Centre 8 Wang Hoi Road, Kowloon bay, Kowloon, China (Hong Kong)
Tel.: (852) 2750 1728
Electronic Components Distr
N.A.I.C.S.: 423690

Excel Electronics (Hui Zhou) Ltd. (2)
5FL No 3 Bldg Zhonghai Technology Industrial Area Long Hai 3rd, Xiang Shui He Daya Wan Dist, Huizhou, 516081, China
Tel.: (86) 752 5369 780
Electronic Components Distr
N.A.I.C.S.: 423690

Excel Electronics Trading (Shenzhen) Ltd. (2)
806-07 RM 8/F Modern International Building No 3038 Jintian Road, Futian District, Shenzhen, 518048, China
Tel.: (86) 755 8253 7357
Electronic Components Distr
N.A.I.C.S.: 423690

Excel Electronics Trading (Thailand) Co., Ltd. (2)
Unit 23-13 Interchange 21 Bldg 23rd Fl 399 Sukhumvit Rd, Klongtoey-Nua Wattana, Bangkok, 10110, Thailand
Tel.: (66) 2 611 2670
Electronic Components Distr
N.A.I.C.S.: 423690

Excel International Trading (Shanghai) Co., Ltd. (2)
6F-F Zhao Feng World Trade Building No 369 Jiang Su Road, Shanghai, 200050, China
Tel.: (86) 21 6339 0620
Electronic Components Distr
N.A.I.C.S.: 423690

Excel Singapore Pte. Ltd. (2)
10 Anson Road 28-06B International Plaza, Singapore, 079903, Singapore
Tel.: (65) 6222 3844
Electronic Components Distr
N.A.I.C.S.: 423690

WiseOps Co., Limited (1)
Unit 2001 20/F Chevalier Commercial Centre 8 Wang Hoi Road, Kowloon bay, Kowloon, 852, China (Hong Kong)
Tel.: (852) 31044530
Electronic Components Distr
N.A.I.C.S.: 423690

Fujitsu Devices Inc. (1)
Shin-Yokohama Chuo Bldg 2-100-45 Shin-Yokohama, Kohoku-Ku, Yokohama, 222-8508, Kanagawa, Japan
Tel.: (81) 454738030
Web Site: https://www.kagafei.com
Emp.: 58
Electric Equipment Mfr
N.A.I.C.S.: 334419
Masamitsu Teramoto *(Pres)*

Fujitsu Electronics (Dalian) Software Ltd. (1)
Room 702 Building 22 No 36 Software Park East Road, Dalian, 116023, China
Tel.: (86) 41162284619
Web Site: https://www.kagafei.com
Emp.: 33
Electric Equipment Mfr
N.A.I.C.S.: 334419

Fujitsu Electronics (Shanghai) Co., Ltd. (1)
Rm 302-303 Building T2N EBA center Hongqiao No 377 Songhong Road, Changning District, Shanghai, 200335, China
Tel.: (86) 2161463688
Web Site: https://www.kagafei.com
Emp.: 47
Electronic Parts Whslr
N.A.I.C.S.: 423690

Fujitsu Electronics America, Inc. (1)
1250 E Arques Ave M/S333, Sunnyvale, CA 94085-5401
Tel.: (408) 746-6000
Web Site: https://www.fujitsu.com
Emp.: 23
Electronic Parts Whslr
N.A.I.C.S.: 423690
Toshihisa Hoshino *(Pres)*

Fujitsu Electronics Europe GmbH (1)
Robert Bosch Str 25, 63225, Langen, Germany
Tel.: (49) 6103690222
Web Site: https://kagafeieurope.com
Emp.: 41
Electronic Parts Whslr
N.A.I.C.S.: 423690
Axel Tripkewitz *(Pres)*

Fujitsu Electronics Inc. (1)
Shin-Yokohama Chuo Bldg 2-100-45 Shin-Yokohama, Kohoku-Ku, Yokohama, 222-8508, Kanagawa, Japan (70%)
Tel.: (81) 454738030
Web Site: https://www.kagafei.com
Emp.: 502
Semiconductor Device Mfr & Distr
N.A.I.C.S.: 334413
Junji Ogihara *(Pres)*

Subsidiary (Non-US):

FUJITSU DEVICES (DALIAN) ENGINEERING LIMITED (2)
Room 201-A Building 3 Dalian Software Park International, Dalian, 116023, China
Tel.: (86) 41139707170
Software Development Services
N.A.I.C.S.: 541511

Fujitsu Electronics Korea Ltd. (1)
902 416 Yeongdong-daero, Gangnam-gu, Seoul, 06176, Korea (South)
Tel.: (82) 234847100
Web Site: https://www.kagafei.com
Emp.: 17
Electronic Parts Whslr
N.A.I.C.S.: 423690

Fujitsu Electronics Pacific Asia Ltd. (1)

INTERNATIONAL PUBLIC

Unit 403 on 4th Floor of Magnet Place Tower 1, 77-81 Container Port Road New Territories, Kwai Chung, China (Hong Kong)
Tel.: (852) 27363232
Web Site: https://www.kagafei.com
Emp.: 27
Electronic Parts Whslr
N.A.I.C.S.: 423690

Hubei Kaga Electronics Limited (1)
NO 168Huairen Road Xiaohan Avenue, Xiaonan District, Xiaogan, Hubei, China
Tel.: (86) 7122660066
Web Site: https://www.taxan.co.jp
Emp.: 294
Automobile Equipment Mfr
N.A.I.C.S.: 336110
Haruo Kobayashi *(Pres)*

KAGA AMUSEMENT CO., LTD. (1)
Web Site: http://www.kga.co.jp
Sales Range: $50-74.9 Million
Emp.: 13
Amusement Park Equipments Mfr & Whslr
N.A.I.C.S.: 713990

KAGA EDUCATIONAL MARKETING CO., LTD. (1)
10F Akihabara Fudosan Bldg 3-12-8 Soto-Kanda, Chiyoda-ku, Tokyo, 101-0021, Japan
Tel.: (81) 344553252
Web Site: http://www.kgem.co.jp
Sales Range: $25-49.9 Million
Emp.: 9
Computer Software Support Services
N.A.I.C.S.: 541511

KAGA SPORTS CO., LTD. (1)
4F 20 Kanda matsunagacho, Chiyoda-ku, Tokyo, 101-0023, Japan
Tel.: (81) 356570148
Web Site: http://www.active.gs
Sales Range: $50-74.9 Million
Emp.: 89
Golf Equipments Mfr & Whslr
N.A.I.C.S.: 339920

KGF Co., Ltd. (1)
3F New Suehiro Building 5-1-3 Sotokanda, Chiyoda-ku, Tokyo, 101-0021, Japan
Tel.: (81) 358178156
Web Site: https://www.kgf-taxan.co.jp
Sales Range: $10-24.9 Million
Emp.: 39
Restaurant Management Services
N.A.I.C.S.: 722511

Kaga (Dalian) Co., Ltd. (1)
RM 03 23 F Dalian Tian-An Tower No 88 Zhongshan Rd, Zhongshan Dist, Dalian, 116001, Liaoning, China
Tel.: (86) 411 8887 1233
Web Site: http://www.taxan.co.jp
Sales Range: $50-74.9 Million
Emp.: 7
Semiconductor, Custom Parts & Electronic Parts Whslr
N.A.I.C.S.: 423690
Yoshihito Ohno *(Pres)*

Kaga (Dalian) Electronics Co., Ltd. (1)
Room 03 23/F Dalian Tian-An Tower No88 Zhongshan Road, Zhongshan District, Dalian, 116001, China
Tel.: (86) 41188871233
Emp.: 5
Electronic Parts Whslr
N.A.I.C.S.: 423690
Shuichi Miyai *(Pres)*

Kaga (Europe) Electronics B.V. (1)
3 Forest Court Oaklands Park, Wokingham, RG41 2FD, Berkshire, United Kingdom
Tel.: (44) 1189123330
Web Site: http://www.kagaeuro.com
Sales Range: $50-74.9 Million
Emp.: 9
Electronic Parts & Semiconductor Whslr
N.A.I.C.S.: 423690

Kaga (H.K.) Electronics Ltd. (1)
Rm 3301-05 Manhattan Place 23 Wang Tai Road, Tsim Sha Tsui, Kowloon, China (Hong Kong)
Tel.: (852) 21117900
Web Site: http://www.kaga.com.cn
Sales Range: $50-74.9 Million
Emp.: 80
Electronic Parts Whslr

AND PRIVATE COMPANIES

N.A.I.C.S.: 423690
Motonori Toshinari *(Pres)*

Kaga (Korea) Electronics Co., Ltd. (1)
7 Fl Gangnammirae Tower 174 saimdang-ro Seocho-Dong, Kangnam-Ku, Seoul, 137862, Korea (South)
Tel.: (82) 234862541
Web Site: http://www.taxan.co.jp
Sales Range: $25-49.9 Million
Emp.: 13
Electronic Parts & Semiconductor Whslr
N.A.I.C.S.: 423690
Katsutoshi Suzuki *(Pres)*

Kaga (Shanghai) Electronics Co., Ltd. (1)
19F/D International Shipping and Financial Building, 720 Pu Dong Ave, Shanghai, 200120, China
Tel.: (86) 2150366008
Web Site: https://en.kagash.com.cn
Sales Range: $25-49.9 Million
Emp.: 30
Electronic Components Mfr & Distr
N.A.I.C.S.: 423690

Kaga (Shenzhen) Electronics Ltd. (1)
NO 13 Xin Xin Tian industrial Zone Xin sha Road sha jing Street, baoan District, Shenzhen, China
Tel.: (86) 75526687188
Web Site: https://www.taxan.co.jp
Emp.: 1,180
Electric Equipment Mfr
N.A.I.C.S.: 334419
Takao Okabe *(Pres)*

Kaga (Shenzhen) Trading Ltd. (1)
Rm3302 News Building Shennan Road NO 1002, Shenzhen, Guangdong, China
Tel.: (86) 75525951155
Web Site: https://www.taxan.co.jp
Emp.: 30
Electronic Parts Whslr
N.A.I.C.S.: 423690
Keiji Tsuruta *(Pres)*

Kaga (Singapore) Electronics Pte. Ltd. (1)
5 Harper Road 03-01Diamond Industries Building, Singapore, 369673, Singapore
Tel.: (65) 65331201
Web Site: https://www.taxan.co.jp
Sales Range: $25-49.9 Million
Emp.: 9
Electronic Parts Distr
N.A.I.C.S.: 423690
Takashi Nagamine *(Pres)*

Kaga (Taiwan) Electronics Co., Ltd. (1)
Empire Building 12F No 87 Sung Chiang Road, Taipei, Taiwan
Tel.: (886) 225065641
Web Site: https://www.taxan.co.jp
Emp.: 14
Electric Equipment Mfr
N.A.I.C.S.: 334419
Koji Onaka *(Pres)*

Kaga Amusement Malaysia Sdn. Bhd.
Soho Suite KLCC A2-37-2 Leve137 Jalan Perak, 50450, Kuala Lumpur, Malaysia
Tel.: (60) 321817116
Web Site: https://www.taxan.co.jp
Emp.: 9
Automobile Equipment Mfr
N.A.I.C.S.: 336110
Taketoshi Masuzawa *(Pres)*

Kaga Components (Malaysia) Sdn. Bhd. (1)
1415 Lorong Perusahaan 1, Perai Industrial Estate Kawasan Perusahaan Perai, 13600, Perai, Pulau Pinang, Malaysia
Tel.: (60) 43902344
Web Site: https://www.kgcompo.com.my
Emp.: 775
Electric Equipment Mfr
N.A.I.C.S.: 334419
Kenichi Senoo *(Pres)*

Kaga Components Co., Ltd. (1)
3-18-10 Motoasakusa, Taito-ku, Tokyo, 111-0041, Japan
Tel.: (81) 344553161
Web Site: http://www.kgcompo.co.jp
Sales Range: $50-74.9 Million
Emp.: 250
Power Supplies Design & Mfr
N.A.I.C.S.: 335999
Suguru Moriguchi *(Pres)*

Kaga Create Co., Ltd. (1)
No 12 No 17 Fl 8 Akihabara Realty & Dev Bldg 3-Chome Soto-Kanda, Chiyoda-ku, Tokyo, 101-0021, Japan
Tel.: (81) 344553157
Web Site: http://www.kaga-create.co.jp
Sales Range: $25-49.9 Million
Emp.: 8
Web Designing Services
N.A.I.C.S.: 541511
Katou Tomoyasu *(Pres)*

Kaga Devices (H.K.) Ltd. (1)
Manhattan Place 23 Wang Tai Road 35th Fl 3301-3305, Tsim Sha Tsui, Kowloon, China (Hong Kong)
Tel.: (852) 21117955
Web Site: http://www.kaga.com.cn
Sales Range: $25-49.9 Million
Emp.: 15
Semiconductor & Electronic Parts Whslr
N.A.I.C.S.: 423690
Keiji Tsuruta *(Pres)*

Kaga Devices Co., Ltd. (1)
Tokyo Akihabara Bill Realty & Dev 3-12-8 Soto-Kanda, Chiyoda-ku, Tokyo, 101-0021, Japan
Tel.: (81) 344553150
Web Site: http://www.kgdev.jp
Sales Range: $50-74.9 Million
Emp.: 62
Semiconductor Device Whslr
N.A.I.C.S.: 423610
Atsushi Tsukamoto *(Pres & CEO)*

Kaga Devices India Private Limited
No 18 2nd Floor Chinnaswamy Mudaliar Road Off Queens Road, Tasker Town, Bengaluru, 560 051, India
Tel.: (91) 8041607121
Web Site: https://www.taxan.co.jp
Emp.: 10
Electronic Parts Whslr
N.A.I.C.S.: 423690
Atsushi Tsukamoto *(Pres)*

Kaga Electronics (Thailand) Co., Ltd. (1)
1 85-86 Moo 5 Sub-Dist, U-Thai Dist, Ayutthaya, 13210, Thailand
Tel.: (66) 35227601
Sales Range: $150-199.5 Million
Emp.: 307
Semiconductor & Electronic Parts Whslr
N.A.I.C.S.: 423690
Haruo Kobayashi *(Pres)*

Kaga Electronics (USA) Inc. (1)
2480 N 1st St, San Jose, CA 95131
Tel.: (408) 570-0955
Web Site: http://www.taxan.com
Sales Range: $50-74.9 Million
Emp.: 8
Electronic Parts Whslr
N.A.I.C.S.: 423690
Kaname Yamanaka *(Pres)*

Kaga Electronics (Vietnam) Co., Ltd. (1)
Standard Factory No 10B C Plot H-1 Thang Long Industrial Park II, Di Su Ward My Hao Town, My Hao, Hung Yen, Vietnam
Tel.: (84) 2213589321
Web Site: https://www.taxan.co.jp
Emp.: 122
Electronic Parts Whslr
N.A.I.C.S.: 423690
Kenichi Yoshioka *(Pres)*

Kaga Electronics India Private Limited (1)
No 44 Eros Corporate Park Block-k Sector-2 IMT Manesar, Gurgaon, 122052, Haryana, India
Tel.: (91) 1242291202
Web Site: https://www.taxan.co.jp
Emp.: 7
Automobile Equipment Mfr
N.A.I.C.S.: 336110

Kaga Electronics Indonesia, PT (1)
Kawasan Industri MM2100 Jl Bali Blok O-1-2, Cikarang Barat, Bekasi, 17530, Indonesia
Tel.: (62) 218981285
Web Site: https://www.taxan.co.jp
Emp.: 5
Electric Equipment Mfr
N.A.I.C.S.: 334419
Makoto Sugaya *(Pres)*

Kaga Ems Towada Co., Ltd. (1)
1-15-1 Motomachi Higashi, Towada, 034-0003, Aomori, Japan
Tel.: (81) 176251131
Web Site: https://www.kg-ems-twd.co.jp
Emp.: 313
Electric Equipment Mfr
N.A.I.C.S.: 334419

Kaga Hightech Co., Ltd. (1)
11F Akihabara Fudosan Bldg 3-12-8 Soto-Kanda, Chiyoda-ku, Tokyo, 101-0021, Japan
Tel.: (81) 344553188
Web Site: http://www.kagaht.co.jp
Sales Range: $50-74.9 Million
Emp.: 199
Digital Camera Mfr & Whslr
N.A.I.C.S.: 334118
Seki Shouji *(Pres)*

Kaga Micro Solution Co., Ltd. (1)
Kaga Electronics Building 20 Kanda Matsunagacho, Chiyoda-ku, Tokyo, 101-0023, Japan
Tel.: (81) 356570150
Web Site: http://sc.microsol.co.jp
Emp.: 346
Electric Equipment Mfr
N.A.I.C.S.: 334419

Kaga Solution Network Co., Ltd. (1)
3-27-10 Hatchobori, Chuo-ku, Tokyo, 104-0032, Japan
Tel.: (81) 359310123
Web Site: https://www.solnet.ne.jp
Sales Range: $75-99.9 Million
Emp.: 200
Computer Equipment Whslr
N.A.I.C.S.: 423430

Kaga Taxan (Suzhou) Electronics Co., Ltd. (1)
NO 20 DaTong Road B-11 Export Processing Zone, New& Hi-tech District, Suzhou, China
Tel.: (86) 51268711018
Web Site: https://www.taxan.co.jp
Emp.: 417
Electric Equipment Mfr
N.A.I.C.S.: 334419
Yukio Matsumoto *(Pres)*

Kaga Tech Co., Ltd. (1)
20 Kanda Matsunaga-cho, Chiyoda-ku, Tokyo, 101-0023, Japan
Tel.: (81) 356570140
Web Site: https://www.kagatech.co.jp
Sales Range: $25-49.9 Million
Emp.: 31
Environmental Management System Solutions
N.A.I.C.S.: 541715

Kaga Techno Service Co., Ltd. (1)
4-5-15 KT Bldg Taihei; Sumida-ku, 130-0012, Tokyo, Japan
Tel.: (81) 356194111
Web Site: http://www.kgts.co.jp
Sales Range: $25-49.9 Million
Emp.: 60
Telecommunication Equipment Services
N.A.I.C.S.: 517810
Masaaki Fujii *(Mgr-Sls)*

Kaga Technology (Suzhou) Electronics Co., Ltd. (1)
JinYan Road No 8 Build 22, High&New Technology District, Suzhou, Jiangsu, China
Tel.: (86) 51280801958
Web Site: https://www.taxan.co.jp
Emp.: 127
Electric Equipment Mfr
N.A.I.C.S.: 334419

Kd Tec S.R.O. (1)
Nadrazni 722, Kdyne, 345 06, Plzen, Czech Republic
Tel.: (420) 379432420
Web Site: https://www.kdtec.cz
Emp.: 110
Electric Equipment Mfr
N.A.I.C.S.: 334419
Nobuki Omi *(Pres)*

OTSUKA ELECTRIC CO., LTD. (1)
1-14-7 Yutenji, Meguro-ku, Tokyo, 153-0052, Kanagawa, Japan
Tel.: (81) 337197175
Web Site: https://www.oec-d.com
Sales Range: $25-49.9 Million
Emp.: 30
Electronic Parts Distr & Whslr
N.A.I.C.S.: 423690

SI Electronics Ltd. (1)
12th Fl Akihabara Fudosan Bldg 3-12-8 Soto-Kanda, Chiyoda-ku, Tokyo, 101-0021, Japan
Tel.: (81) 344553270
Web Site: http://www.sie.co.jp
Sales Range: $25-49.9 Million
Emp.: 47
Software Development Services
N.A.I.C.S.: 541511

Sankoh Engineering Corporation (1)
4F 20 Kanda Matsunagacho, Chiyoda-ku, Tokyo, 101-0023, Japan
Tel.: (81) 356570115
Web Site: https://www.taxan.co.jp
Emp.: 49
Engineeering Services
N.A.I.C.S.: 541330

Suzhou Taxan Kaga Trading Co., Ltd. (1)
The 2th Floor No 22 No 8 JinYan Road, Yangshan Tecnology Park Suzhou New District, Suzhou, China
Tel.: (86) 51262828668
Web Site: https://www.taxan.co.jp
Emp.: 1
Electronic Equipment Mfr & Whslr
N.A.I.C.S.: 334419
Takao Okabe *(Pres)*

Taxan Mexico S.A. De C.V. (1)
Av Carrusel Uno 111 Logistik Park, Villa de Reyes, 79526, San Luis Potosi, Mexico
Tel.: (52) 4445007450
Web Site: https://taxanmx.com
Emp.: 324
Electronic Parts Whslr
N.A.I.C.S.: 423690
Takayuki Tsurumi *(Pres)*

Workbit Corporation (1)
1-1-2 Chuo Yamato-shi Kondo Second Bldg 5F, Yamato, 242-0021, Kanagawa, Japan
Tel.: (81) 462613228
Web Site: http://www.workbit.co.jp
Sales Range: $25-49.9 Million
Emp.: 7
Large Scale Integrated Circuits Mfr
N.A.I.C.S.: 334118

KAGARA LTD.
31 Labouchere Road, South Perth, 6151, WA, Australia
Tel.: (61) 8 6436 0700   AU
Web Site: http://www.kagara.com.au
Year Founded: 1981
Sales Range: $150-199.9 Million
Emp.: 440
Mineral Properties Development & Exploration Services
N.A.I.C.S.: 212230
Joseph Allen Treacy *(Exec Gen Mgr-Minerals & Bus Dev)*

Subsidiaries:

Kagara Copper Pty Ltd (1)
L 2 24 Outram St, West Perth, 6005, WA, Australia
Tel.: (61) 8 9481 1211
Copper Ore Mining Services
N.A.I.C.S.: 212230

Mungana Pty Ltd (1)
Second Floor 24 Outram Street, West Perth, 6005, WA, Australia
Tel.: (61) 8 9481 1211
Mineral Exploration Services
N.A.I.C.S.: 213115

Kagara Ltd.—(Continued)

KAGETSUENKANKO CO., LTD.
1-1-1 Sakuragicho, Naka-ku, Yokohama, 231-0062, Kanagawa, Japan
Tel.: (81) 045 2288860   JP
Web Site:
http://www.kagetsuenkanko.co.jp
Year Founded: 1950
Bicycle Race Track Services
N.A.I.C.S.: 711212

KAGISO TISO HOLDINGS PROPRIETARY LIMITED
Kagiso Tiso House 100 West Street, Wierda Valley, Sandton, 2196, South Africa
Tel.: (27) 11 562 2500   ZA
Web Site: http://www.kagiso.com
Year Founded: 1993
Investment Holding Company
N.A.I.C.S.: 551112
Mbonsi Danisa *(Chief Investment Officer & Dir-Investments)*

Subsidiaries:

Kagiso Asset Management (Pty.) Limited   (1)
5th Floor MontClare Place, Cnr Campground & Main Roads, Claremont, 7708, Cape Town, South Africa   (70%)
Tel.: (27) 216736300
Web Site: http://www.kagisoam.com
Sales Range: $50-74.9 Million
Emp.: 40
Investment Management Service
N.A.I.C.S.: 523940
Roland Greaver *(Founder & CEO)*

Kagiso Media Limited   (1)
Kagiso Tiso House 1st Floor 100 West Street Wierda Valley, Sandton, 2196, Johannesburg, South Africa
Tel.: (27) 11 034 9200
Web Site: http://www.kagisomedia.co.za
Broadcasting, Information Publishing, Internet & Audiovisual Content Media Services
N.A.I.C.S.: 519290

Subsidiary (Domestic):

Jacaranda FM Pty Ltd.   (2)
89 14th Road Erands Gardens, Midrand, Midrand, 1685, Gauteng, South Africa   (80%)
Tel.: (27) 110635700
Web Site: http://www.jacarandafm.com
Radio Station Broadcasting Services
N.A.I.C.S.: 516110
Dewald Hattingh *(Mgr-Sls-Polokwane)*

Kagiso Ventures (Pty.) Limited   (1)
Kagiso House 16 Fricker Road, Illovo Boulevard, Illovo, 2196, Gauteng, South Africa   (100%)
Tel.: (27) 11 537 0537
Equity Investment Firm
N.A.I.C.S.: 523999

Servest Group (Pty.) Ltd.   (1)
Corner of Bridal Veil Road and Tugela Lane, Waterfall LogisticsPrecinct, Johannesburg, 2090, South Africa   (51%)
Tel.: (27) 86 022 5584
Web Site: http://www.servest.co.za
Security, Cleaning, Interior & Exterior Landscaping Services
N.A.I.C.S.: 561210
Dennis Zietsman *(Deputy Chm)*

KAGOME CO., LTD.
3-14-15 Nishiki, Naka-ku, Nagoya, 460 0003, Aichi, Japan
Tel.: (81) 529513571
Web Site: https://www.kagome.co.jp
Year Founded: 1899
2811—(NGO)
Rev.: $1,484,836,472
Assets: $1,755,189,957
Liabilities: $853,736,373
Net Worth: $901,453,584
Earnings: $78,044,268
Emp.: 2,921
Fiscal Year-end: 12/31/23

Vegetable-Based Food & Beverage Sales & Mfr
N.A.I.C.S.: 311999
Satoshi Yamaguchi *(Pres)*

Subsidiaries:

Hibikinada Greenfarm Co Ltd   (1)
4 Yanagasakimachi, Wakamatsu-ku, Kitakyushu, 808-0111, Fukuoka, Japan
Tel.: (81) 937426182
Emp.: 50
Tomato Farming Services
N.A.I.C.S.: 111219
Hideyuki Ikari *(Pres)*

Holding da Industria Transformadora do Tomate, SGPS S.A.   (1)
Apart -13 Leziria dos Cortes, 2601-906, Castanheira do Ribatejo, Portugal
Tel.: (351) 263285200
Web Site: https://hit-tomato.com
Food & Beverage Mfr & Whslr
N.A.I.C.S.: 311999

K.H Delica Co Ltd   (1)
3-21-1 Nihombashihamacho, Chuo-ku, Tokyo, 103-0007, Japan
Tel.: (81) 356238505
Food Products Mfr & Distr
N.A.I.C.S.: 311999

Kagome (Hangzhou) Food Co., Ltd.   (1)
No 27 The 4th Avenue Economic Technology Development Zone, Hangzhou, 310018, Zhejiang, China
Tel.: (86) 57186918438
Web Site: http://www.kagome.com.cn
Vegetable Beverage Mfr & Distr
N.A.I.C.S.: 311999

Kagome (Tianjin) Food Industry Co., Ltd.   (1)
12-02 80 Haiyun Road Teda, Tianjin, China
Tel.: (86) 2259861298
Food & Beverage Mfr & Whslr
N.A.I.C.S.: 311999

Kagome Australia Pty Ltd.   (1)
54 Cornelia Creek Road, Echuca, 3564, VIC, Australia
Tel.: (61) 35 482 0700
Web Site: https://www.kagome.com.au
Tomato Processing Mfr
N.A.I.C.S.: 311421
Louise Anderson *(Mgr-Technical)*

Kagome Distribution Service Co Ltd   (1)
Tokyo Kagome Bldg 5f, Chuo-ku, Tokyo, 103-0004, Japan
Tel.: (81) 358232870
Web Site: http://www.kagome-logistics.co.jp
Logistics & Warehousing Services
N.A.I.C.S.: 541614

Kagome Fudosan Co., Ltd.   (1)
3-14-15 Nishiki, Naka-ku, Nagoya, 34350, Japan
Tel.: (81) 529714931
Web Site: http://www.kagome.co.jp
Sales Range: $25-49.9 Million
Emp.: 20
Nonresidential Building Operators
N.A.I.C.S.: 531312

Kagome Labio Co., Ltd.   (1)
8-5 Marunouchi 2-chome, Naka-ku, Nagoya, 460 0002, Japan
Tel.: (81) 522317731
Sales Range: $125-149.9 Million
Emp.: 287
Dairy Products Mfr
N.A.I.C.S.: 311514

Kagome Real Estate Co Ltd   (1)
3-14-15 Nishiki, Nagoya, 460-0003, Aichi, Japan
Tel.: (81) 529714931
Real Estate Development Services
N.A.I.C.S.: 531390

Kagome, Inc.   (1)
333 Johnson Rd, Los Banos, CA 93635-9768   (100%)
Tel.: (209) 826-8850
Web Site: https://kagomeusa.com
Sales Range: $450-499.9 Million
Emp.: 1,942

Canned Tomato Products & Canned Soft Drinks Mfr
N.A.I.C.S.: 311421

Unit (Domestic):

Kagome Foods, Inc.   (2)
710 N Pearl St, Osceola, AR 72370
Tel.: (870) 563-2601
Web Site: http://www.kagomeusa.com
Sauce & Dressing Mfr
N.A.I.C.S.: 311941

Taiwan Kagome Co., Ltd.   (1)
No 394 Xiaoxinying, Shanhua Dist, Tainan City, 741, Taiwan
Tel.: (886) 65837116
Web Site: https://www.kagome.com.tw
Emp.: 130
Canned Food Products Mfr
N.A.I.C.S.: 311421

United Genetics Holding LLC   (1)
8000 Fairview Rd, Hollister, CA 95023
Tel.: (831) 636-4882
Web Site: https://unitedgenetics.com
Vegetable Seed Producer
N.A.I.C.S.: 111211

United Genetics Turkey Tohum Fide A.S.   (1)
Tasdelen Mahallesi Sirri Celik Bulvari No 7, Cekmekoy, 34788, Istanbul, Turkiye
Tel.: (90) 2164308040
Web Site: http://www.kagome.co.jp
Canned Food Product Distr
N.A.I.C.S.: 424490

Vegitalia S.p.A.   (1)
Zona Industriale del Fullone, San Marco Argentano, 87018, Cosenza, Italy
Tel.: (39) 098 451 6111
Web Site: http://www.vegitalia.com
Sales Range: $75-99.9 Million
Emp.: 150
Canned Food Product Distr
N.A.I.C.S.: 424490

KAHIRA PHARMACEUTICALS & CHEMICAL INDUSTRIES COMPANY
4 Abdel-Hamid Eldeeb St Victoria SQ, Shoubra, Cairo, Egypt
Tel.: (20) 222021431
Web Site: http://www.kahira-pharma.com
Year Founded: 1962
Pharmaceuticals Product Mfr
N.A.I.C.S.: 325412
Jamal Hafedh Takal *(Chm & Mng Dir)*

KAI CORPORATION
3-9-5 Iwamoto-cho, Chiyoda-ku, Tokyo, 101-8586, Japan
Tel.: (81) 3 3862 6411   JP
Web Site: http://www.kai-group.com
Year Founded: 1908
Sales Range: $450-499.9 Million
Emp.: 2,600
Cutlery, Kitchen Utensil & Cosmetic Accessories Mfr & Distr
N.A.I.C.S.: 332215
Koji Endo *(Pres & CEO)*

Subsidiaries:

Great Works China Co., Ltd.   (1)
4th Floor Building 43 No 498 North Wu Lu Mu Qi Road, Xuhui District, Shanghai, 200040, China
Tel.: (86) 2163568830
Web Site: http://www.greatworks.cn
Marketing & Advertising Services
N.A.I.C.S.: 541613

Great Works Inc.   (1)
Hiroo AK Building 7F, 5-25-2 Hiroo, Tokyo, 150-0012, Shibuya-ku, Japan
Tel.: (81) 3 6721 9377
Web Site: http://www.greatworks.jp
Sales Range: $25-49.9 Million
Emp.: 20
Marketing & Advertising Services
N.A.I.C.S.: 541810

Kai Cutlery (H.K.) Ltd.   (1)

Unit 1104-1105 11/F Lu Plaza 2 Wing Yip Street, Kwun Tong, Kowloon, China (Hong Kong)
Tel.: (852) 2558 9682
Kitchen Utensil Distr
N.A.I.C.S.: 423220

Kai Europe GmbH   (1)
Kottendorfer Strasse 5, 42697, Solingen, Germany
Tel.: (49) 212 2323 80
Web Site: http://www.kai-europe.com
Kitchen Utensil Distr
Koji Endo *(CEO)*

Kai Industries Co., Ltd.   (1)
1110 Oyana, Seki-shi, Gifu, 501-3992, Japan
Tel.: (81) 575 28 3131
Web Site: http://www.kai-ind.co.jp
Kitchen Knife Distr
N.A.I.C.S.: 423710

Kai Manufacturing India Pvt. Ltd.   (1)
803 Ansal Bhawan 16, K G Marg, New Delhi, 110001, India
Tel.: (91) 11 43049797
Kitchen Utensil Mfr
N.A.I.C.S.: 332215

Kai U.S.A. Ltd.   (1)
18600 SW Teton Ave, Tualatin, OR 97062
Tel.: (503) 682-1966
Web Site: http://www.kaiusaltd.com
Kitchen Knife Mfr
N.A.I.C.S.: 332215
Hiroshi Jack Igarashi *(COO)*

Subsidiary (Domestic):

Universal Razor Industries, LLC   (2)
6031 Malburg Way, Los Angeles, CA 90058
Tel.: (323) 581-9000
Web Site: http://www.universalrazor.com
Kitchen Knife Mfr
N.A.I.C.S.: 332215

Kai Vietnam Co., Ltd.   (1)
Plot I 1&2Thang Long Industrial Park, Dong Anh Dist, Hanoi, Vietnam
Tel.: (84) 43 9550020
Kitchen Knife Distr
N.A.I.C.S.: 423710

Kaijirushi Korea Corporation   (1)
Hangangro 1Ga Yongsan Park XI D-1402 205, Hangang-daero Yongsan-gu, Seoul, 140-752, Korea (South)
Tel.: (82) 2 2071 8717
Kitchen Knife Distr
N.A.I.C.S.: 423710

Shanghai Kai Cutlery Co., Ltd.   (1)
No 155 Fanhua Rd, Industrial Zone Songjiang, Shanghai, China
Tel.: (86) 21 57741465
Web Site: http://www.kai-china.com
Kitchen Knife Distr
N.A.I.C.S.: 423710

Shanghai Kai Trade Co., Ltd.   (1)
1603-2 Huayi Plaza 2020 Zhongshan Road West, Xuhui District, Shanghai, China
Tel.: (86) 21 64326390
Kitchen Knife Distr
N.A.I.C.S.: 423710

kai R&D (Guangzhou) co., ltd.   (1)
Room 1812-1813 18/F Block B China Shine Plaza No 9 Linhexi Road, Tianhe District, 510610, Guangzhou, China
Tel.: (86) 20 8523 6693
Kitchen Utensil Distr
N.A.I.C.S.: 423220

KAI CORPORATION LTD.
17 rue de Monceau, 75008, Paris, France
Tel.: (33) 1 5376 2052   HK
Web Site: http://www.kaicorpltd.com
Year Founded: 2010
Real Estate Consulting & Deal Advisory Services
N.A.I.C.S.: 541618
Anna M. Kalifa *(Founder & Mng Dir)*

KAI YUAN HOLDINGS LIMITED
28/F Chinachem Century Tower 178

AND PRIVATE COMPANIES

Gloucester Road, Wanchai, China
(Hong Kong)
Tel.: (852) 35889900   BM
Web Site:
   https://www.kaiyuanholdings.com
1215—(HKG)
Rev.: $19,573,673
Assets: $461,114,333
Liabilities: $214,956,968
Net Worth: $246,157,365
Earnings: ($5,242,290)
Emp.: 7
Fiscal Year-end: 12/31/22
Investment Management Service
N.A.I.C.S.: 523940
Jian Xue (CEO)

Subsidiaries:

Hotel de EDGE Limited   (1)
94 Connaught Road West, Sheung Wan,
China (Hong Kong)
Tel.: (852) 35599988
Hotel Operator
N.A.I.C.S.: 713210

KAIBO FOODS COMPANY LIMITED
Room 2102 F&G Nan Fung Centre
264-298 Castle Peak Rd, Tsuen Wan,
China (Hong Kong)
Tel.: (852) 2412 2208   NV
Web Site: http://www.hkwaibo.com
Year Founded: 2007
Sales Range: $100-124.9 Million
Emp.: 487
Potato Starch Producer
N.A.I.C.S.: 311999
Joanny Kwok (Chm & CEO)

KAIDI ECOLOGICAL AND ENVIRONMENTAL TECHNOLOGY CO., LTD.
Kaid Building Special No 1 Jiangxia
Road, Donghu New Economic &
Technological Development Zone,
Wuhan, 430223, China
Tel.: (86) 27 67869001
Web Site: http://www.china-kaidi.com
000939—(SSE)
Rev.: $381,017,788
Assets: $4,328,955,478
Liabilities: $4,730,143,139
Net Worth: ($401,187,662)
Earnings: ($547,266,760)
Emp.: 6,041
Fiscal Year-end: 12/31/19
Eletric Power Generation Services
N.A.I.C.S.: 221112
Sun Shouen (Chm, Exec VP & Controller-Interim)

KAIEMEI ELECTRONIC CORP.
13th Floor No 81 Section 1 Xintai 5th
Road, Xizhi Dist, Taipei, 22101, Taiwan
Tel.: (886) 226981010
Web Site: https://jamicon.teapo.com
2375—(TAI)
Rev.: $157,324,400
Assets: $465,586,823
Liabilities: $171,997,018
Net Worth: $293,589,805
Earnings: $8,681,807
Emp.: 2,100
Fiscal Year-end: 12/31/23
Capacitor Mfr
N.A.I.C.S.: 334416

Subsidiaries:

Dongguan Luxon Electronics
Corp.   (1)
89A Qiaojiao West Road, Tangxia, Dongguan, Guangdong, China
Tel.: (86) 769 8791 7888
Electronic Components Mfr
N.A.I.C.S.: 334416

Suzhou Kaimei Electronics Co.,
Ltd.   (1)
Hangqiao Road, Wangting Township Xiangcheng District, Suzhou, China
Tel.: (86) 51265388640
Electric Equipment Mfr
N.A.I.C.S.: 334419

Teapo Dongguan Electronic
Corp.   (1)
No 89A Qiaojiao West Road, Tangxia Town,
Dongguan, Guangdong, China
Tel.: (86) 76987914676
Capacitor Mfr
N.A.I.C.S.: 334416

Teapo Electronics Dongguan Co.,
Ltd.   (1)
No 6A2 6A3 Gaoli 1st Rd, Gaoli Ind Zone
Tangxia Town, Dongguan, Guangdong,
China
Tel.: (86) 76987914676
Electronic Products Mfr
N.A.I.C.S.: 334419

Teapo Suzhou Electronic Corp.   (1)
No 555 JinFeng South Road MuDu Industrial Zone, Suzhou, China
Tel.: (86) 512 6636 6868
Electronic Components Mfr.
N.A.I.C.S.: 334419

KAIHAN CO., LTD.
Nagoya Sogo Ichiba Building 4-15-15
Meieki Nakamura, Nagoya, 450-0002,
Aichi, Japan
Tel.: (81) 525862666
Web Site: https://www.kaihan.co.jp
3133—(TKS)
Rev.: $16,141,620
Assets: $23,901,760
Liabilities: $18,018,860
Net Worth: $5,882,900
Earnings: ($4,706,320)
Emp.: 93
Fiscal Year-end: 03/31/24
Restaurant Operators
N.A.I.C.S.: 722511
Toshiki Hisada (Pres)

KAILASH AUTO FINANCE LIMITED
15 Roland Complex 2nd Floor 37/17
The Mall, Kanpur, 208001, India
Tel.: (91) 7506556362
Web Site: http://www.kailfin.com
Year Founded: 1984
Sales Range: $1-9.9 Million
Financial Services
N.A.I.C.S.: 523999

KAILASH BIKAS BANK LIMITED
Putalisadak New Plaza, Kathmandu,
Nepal
Tel.: (977) 97714443034   NP
Web Site:
   https://bankkosamachar.com
KBBL—(NEP)
Banking Services
N.A.I.C.S.: 522110
Rajendra Giri (Chm)

KAILASH GROUP
SPL-3 RIICO Industrial Area Sitapura
Tonk Road, Jaipur, 302 022, India
Tel.: (91) 141 3911400 500
Web Site:
   http://www.thekailashgroup.com
Holding Company
N.A.I.C.S.: 551112
I. C. Agarwal (Founder & Chm)

Subsidiaries:

Genus Apparels Ltd.   (1)
Singhania Chowk 14/4 Milestone Old Sher
Shah Suri Marg Mathura Road, Village Atmadpur Near Slf Mall, Faridabad, 121003,
Haryana, India
Tel.: (91) 9643309720
Web Site: http://www.genusapparels.com

Emp.: 800
Apparels Mfr
N.A.I.C.S.: 315250
Amit Agarwal (Founder)

Genus Electrotech Ltd.   (1)
Survey No 43 Galpadar Road, Ta Anjar Dist
Kutch, Gandhidham, 370110, Gujarat, India
Tel.: (91) 2836240872
Web Site: http://www.genuselectrotech.co.in
Household Appliances Mfr
N.A.I.C.S.: 335220
P. S. Sudhakar (VP-PCB Div)

Genus Innovation Ltd.   (1)
Ajmer Road Ganpati Enclave B-9 2nd Floor,
Jaipur, 302 006, India
Tel.: (91) 1412220456
Motor & Automatic Control Mfr
N.A.I.C.S.: 335312
Deepak Mishra (Head-HR Ops)

Genus Paper & Boards Limited   (1)
Village Aghwanpur Kanth Road, Moradabad, 244504, India
Tel.: (91) 5912511171
Web Site: https://www.genuspaper.com
Rev.: $86,796,703
Assets: $113,089,803
Liabilities: $55,363,455
Net Worth: $57,726,347
Earnings: ($1,410,467)
Emp.: 1,054
Fiscal Year-end: 03/31/2023
Packaging Paper, Particle Board & Ingot
Mfr
N.A.I.C.S.: 322299
Ishwar Chandra Agarwal (Chm)

Subsidiary (Domestic):

Genus Prime Infra Limited   (2)
D-116 Okhla Industrial Area Phase-1, New
Delhi, 110020, India
Tel.: (91) 1147114800
Web Site: https://www.genusprime.com
Rev.: $32,841
Assets: $9,374,618
Liabilities: $1,767,349
Net Worth: $7,607,269
Earnings: ($4,506)
Fiscal Year-end: 03/31/2021
Real Estate Development Services
N.A.I.C.S.: 531390
Amit Agarwal (CEO)

KAILI RESOURCES LIMITED
Suite 1312 87-89 Liverpool Street,
Sydney, 2000, NSW, Australia
Tel.: (61) 292646288   BM
Web Site:
   https://www.kailigroup.com.au
Year Founded: 1996
KLR—(ASX)
Rev.: $284,062
Assets: $1,414,175
Liabilities: $2,440,011
Net Worth: ($1,025,835)
Earnings: ($23,355)
Fiscal Year-end: 12/31/22
Coal & Mineral Exploration Services
N.A.I.C.S.: 213113
Long Zhao (Sec)

KAILONG HIGH TECHNOLOGY CO., LTD.
No 158 Ouyang Road Miaotangqiao
Qianqiao Supporting Area, Huishan
District, Wuxi, 214153, Jiangsu,
China
Tel.: (86) 15961878397
Web Site: https://www.kailongtec.com
Year Founded: 2001
300912—(SSE)
Rev.: $87,161,724
Assets: $217,973,808
Liabilities: $106,826,148
Net Worth: $111,147,660
Earnings: ($38,499,084)
Emp.: 1,200
Fiscal Year-end: 12/31/22
Pollution Control Product Distr
N.A.I.C.S.: 423830
Zhicheng Zang (Chm & Gen Mgr)

Subsidiaries:

Jiangsu Kailong Baodun Power Technology Co., Ltd.   (1)
No 2 No 228 Lantian Road Airport Industrial
Park, Jiangning Development District, Nanjing, China
Tel.: (86) 15365019333
Pollution Control Product Mfr & Whslr
N.A.I.C.S.: 334512

Kailong Lanfeng New Material Technology Co., Ltd.   (1)
No 78 Jingang Avenue, Dagang New District, Zhenjiang, China
Tel.: (86) 18796010208
Pollution Control Product Mfr & Whslr
N.A.I.C.S.: 334512

KAILUAN ENERGY CHEMICAL CO., LTD.
East Tower No 70 Xinhua East Avenue, Tangshan, 063018, Hebei,
China
Tel.: (86) 3152812013   CN
Web Site: http://www.kkcc.com.cn
Year Founded: 2001
600997—(SHG)
Rev.: $3,424,811,909
Assets: $4,553,503,851
Liabilities: $2,164,975,272
Net Worth: $2,388,528,579
Earnings: $278,125,177
Emp.: 12,661
Fiscal Year-end: 12/31/21
Coal Mining & Distr
N.A.I.C.S.: 212115
Hua Pei (Chm)

KAINANTU RESOURCES LTD.
550 Burrard St 2900, Vancouver,
V6C 0A3, BC, Canada
Tel.: (658) 318-8125
Web Site:
   http://www.kainanturesources.com
Year Founded: 2018
SPMEF—(OTCQB)
Assets: $11,394,000
Liabilities: $3,173,000
Net Worth: $8,221,000
Earnings: ($1,607,000)
Emp.: 7
Fiscal Year-end: 12/31/23
Asset Management Services
N.A.I.C.S.: 523940
Giuseppe Perone (Sec)

KAINOS GROUP PLC
4-6 Upper Crescent, Belfast, BT7
1NT, United Kingdom
Tel.: (44) 2890571100   UK
Web Site: https://www.kainos.com
Year Founded: 1986
KNOS—(LSE)
Rev.: $465,176,691
Assets: $289,920,960
Liabilities: $129,384,675
Net Worth: $160,536,285
Earnings: $51,691,815
Fiscal Year-end: 03/31/23
Digital Solution Development Services
N.A.I.C.S.: 541511
Tom Burnet (Chm)

Subsidiaries:

Formulate Kainos Limited   (1)
21 Farringdon Road Second Floor, London,
EC1M 3HA, United Kingdom
Tel.: (44) 1905888704
Web Site: http://www.formulate.group
Software Development Services
N.A.I.C.S.: 541511

Intuitive Technologies, LLC   (1)
12136 W Bayaud Ave Ste 360, Lakewood,
CO 80228
Tel.: (303) 278-3707
Web Site: http://www.intuitivetek.com
Computer System Design Services

KAINOS GROUP PLC

Kainos Group plc—(Continued)
N.A.I.C.S.: 541512
Brian Storrs *(Founder & Pres)*

Kainos Software Poland Spolka z.o.o (1)
Tryton Business House ul Jana z Kolna 11, 80-864, Gdansk, Poland
Tel.: (48) 588826680
Web Site: http://www.kainos.pl
IT Development Services
N.A.I.C.S.: 541511

Kainos WorkSmart Limited (1)
6-7 St Stephen s Green, Dublin, Ireland
Tel.: (353) 16369000
Software Development Services
N.A.I.C.S.: 541511

Kainos Worksmart ApS (1)
Radhuspladsen 16, 1550, Copenhagen, Denmark
Tel.: (45) 2890571100
Software Development Services
N.A.I.C.S.: 541511

Kainos Worksmart Canada Inc. (1)
Suite 2200 25 King Street West, Commerce Court North, Toronto, M5L 2A1, ON, Canada
Tel.: (647) 931-0589
Software Development Services
N.A.I.C.S.: 541511

KAINOS LABORATORIES, INC.
23818 Hongo, Bunkyo-ku, Tokyo, Japan
Tel.: (81) 338164123
Web Site: https://www.kainos.co.jp
Year Founded: 1975
4556—(TKS)
Sales Range: $1-4.9 Billion
Diagnostic Reagent Mfr
N.A.I.C.S.: 325413
Yukihiro Nagatsu *(Mng Dir)*

KAINOS MEDICINE, INC.
3F Bldg A Korea Bio-Park 700 Daewangpangyo-ro, Bundang-gu, Seongnam, 13488, Gyeonggi-do, Korea (South)
Tel.: (82) 25677419
Web Site: https://www.kainosmedicine.com
Year Founded: 2007
284620—(KRS)
Rev.: $102,719
Assets: $30,796,160
Liabilities: $7,161,870
Net Worth: $23,634,290
Earnings: ($12,572,014)
Emp.: 23
Fiscal Year-end: 12/31/22
Medicine Product Mfr & Distr
N.A.I.C.S.: 325412
Jaemoon Lee *(Chief Bus Officer & VP-Biology)*

KAIRA CAN COMPANY LIMITED
ION House Dr E Moses Road Mahalaxmi, Mumbai, 400 011, Maharashtra, India
Tel.: (91) 2266608711
Web Site: https://www.kairacan.com
Year Founded: 1962
504840—(BOM)
Rev.: $23,098,189
Assets: $13,368,496
Liabilities: $4,125,822
Net Worth: $9,242,674
Earnings: $255,173
Emp.: 213
Fiscal Year-end: 03/31/21
Metal Can Mfr & Whslr
N.A.I.C.S.: 332431
Hiten Vanjara *(Compliance Officer & Sec)*

KAIRIKIYA CO., LTD.
6th floor Kyoto Fukutoku Building 670 Teraimizumachi, Nakagyo Ward, Kyoto, 604-8152, Japan
Tel.: (81) 752113338
Web Site: https://corp.kairikiya.co.jp
Year Founded: 2003
5891—(TKS)
Emp.: 2,678
Restaurant Operators
N.A.I.C.S.: 722511

KAIROS INDUSTRIAL HOLDINGS LTD.
1111 Church Street Hatfield, Pretoria, 83, South Africa
Tel.: (27) 12342 1111
Web Site: http://www.kairos.co.za
Sales Range: $25-49.9 Million
Emp.: 10
Mining Supplier & Bricks Mfr
N.A.I.C.S.: 327331
Warwick A. Lombard *(Dir-Fin)*

KAIROS INDUSTRIES AG
Kurfurstendamm 214, 10719, Berlin, Germany
Tel.: (49) 3088725330
Web Site: http://www.kairos-industries.com
Sales Range: Less than $1 Million
Investment Services
N.A.I.C.S.: 523999

Subsidiaries:

Feldmuehle GmbH (1)
Pinnauallee 3, 25436, Uetersen, Germany
Tel.: (49) 4122 719 0
Web Site: http://www.feldmuehle-uetersen.com
Specialty & Graphic Paper Mill
N.A.I.C.S.: 322120

KAIROS MINERALS LIMITED
Suite 12 Level 1 / 100 Railway Rd, Daglish, 6008, WA, Australia
Tel.: (61) 863801904
Web Site: https://www.kairosminerals.com.au
KAI—(ASX)
Rev.: $312,399
Assets: $22,638,381
Liabilities: $461,897
Net Worth: $22,176,485
Earnings: ($3,177,047)
Fiscal Year-end: 06/30/22
Mining Exploration Services
N.A.I.C.S.: 213114
Adrien Wing *(Sec)*

Subsidiaries:

AMN Nominees Pty. Ltd. (1)
Ste 2 1233 High St, Armadale, 3143, VIC, Australia
Tel.: (61) 398248166
Web Site: http://www.miningprojectsgroup.com.au
Sales Range: $50-74.9 Million
Emp.: 3
Gold & Base Metal Exploration Services
N.A.I.C.S.: 212220

KAIROUS ACQUISITION CORP. LIMITED
Unit 9-3 Oval Tower Damansara No 685 Jalan Damansara, Taman Tun Dr Ismail, 60000, Kuala Lumpur, Malaysia
Tel.: (60) 77339340 Ky
Year Founded: 2021
KACL—(NASDAQ)
Rev.: $1,380,151
Assets: $22,914,408
Liabilities: $26,915,877
Net Worth: ($4,001,469)
Earnings: $451,465
Emp.: 2
Fiscal Year-end: 06/30/23
Investment Services
N.A.I.C.S.: 523999
Joseph Moh Hon Lee *(Chm & CEO)*

KAIRUIDE HOLDING CO., LTD.
Room 201 2nd Floor Building C4-1 No 201 Peigong Avenue, Duodao District Jingmen High-tech Zone, Jingmen, 448124, Hubei, China
Tel.: (86) 16502052227
Web Site: https://002072krd.com
Year Founded: 2000
002072—(SSE)
Rev.: $50,421,852
Assets: $14,160,744
Liabilities: $7,000,344
Net Worth: $7,160,400
Earnings: ($1,457,352)
Fiscal Year-end: 12/31/22
Holding Company
N.A.I.C.S.: 551112
Ji Xiaowen *(Chm & Gen Mgr)*

KAISA GROUP HOLDINGS LIMITED
Renmin South Road Kerry Center 33rd Floor, Luohu, Shenzhen, China
Tel.: (86) 75525181818 HK
Web Site: https://www.kaisagroup.com
Year Founded: 1999
1638—(HKG)
Rev.: $3,564,759,089
Assets: $37,113,877,102
Liabilities: $32,165,484,156
Net Worth: $4,948,392,946
Earnings: ($1,826,874,410)
Emp.: 15,881
Fiscal Year-end: 12/31/22
Property Development Services
N.A.I.C.S.: 531190
Yuenan Sun *(Vice Chm)*

Subsidiaries:

Kaisa Capital Investment Holdings Limited (1)
No 3610 36/F The Center 99 Queens Road, Central, China (Hong Kong) (56%)
Tel.: (852) 36788589
Web Site: http://www.elasialtd.com
Rev.: $25,521,420
Assets: $71,342,115
Liabilities: $53,861,993
Net Worth: $17,480,123
Earnings: $660,323
Emp.: 102
Fiscal Year-end: 12/31/2022
Engineering & Construction Equipment Rental & Maintenance Services
N.A.I.C.S.: 532412
Guo Peineng *(Deputy Chm)*

Subsidiary (Domestic):

Manta Engineering & Equipment Co. Ltd. (2)
Room 3610 36/F The Center 99 Queen's Road Central, Fo Tan, Central, China (Hong Kong)
Tel.: (852) 2 369 6411
Web Site: https://www.manta.com.sg
Equipment Rental & Maintenance Services
N.A.I.C.S.: 811310

Subsidiary (Non-US):

Manta Equipment (S) Pte Ltd (2)
4 Tuas View Circuit, Singapore, 637356, Singapore
Tel.: (65) 62277388
Construction & Infrastructure Sector Services
N.A.I.C.S.: 541310
Hui Pin Lee *(Controller-Fin)*

KAISA HEALTH GROUP HOLDINGS LIMITED
30/F The Center 99 Queens Road, Central, China (Hong Kong)
Tel.: (852) 39690008 BM
Web Site: http://www.megamedicaltech.com

INTERNATIONAL PUBLIC

Year Founded: 1997
0876—(HKG)
Rev.: $24,416,123
Assets: $97,868,745
Liabilities: $37,828,230
Net Worth: $60,040,515
Earnings: ($21,946,830)
Emp.: 940
Fiscal Year-end: 12/31/22
Holding Company; Electronic & Communication Products Mfr
N.A.I.C.S.: 551112
Tianyu Wu *(Vice Chm)*

KAISA JIAYUN TECHNOLOGY INC.
Room 3501 Block B China Resources Land Building, No 9668 Yuehai Street Nanshan District Shenzhen, Shenzhen, 518057, China
Tel.: (86) 75586969363
Web Site: https://www.kaisacloud.com
Year Founded: 2002
300242—(CHIN)
Rev.: $106,292,157
Assets: $78,854,492
Liabilities: $30,502,955
Net Worth: $48,351,537
Earnings: ($13,457,330)
Fiscal Year-end: 12/31/23
Mobile Internet Advertising & Internet Trading
N.A.I.C.S.: 541890

KAISA PROSPERITY HOLDINGS LIMITED
Room 507 Kaisa Center 66 Nan Yuan Road, Futian, Shenzhen, China
Tel.: (86) 75522658123 Ky
Year Founded: 1999
2168—(HKG)
Rev.: $250,457,173
Assets: $315,712,426
Liabilities: $119,607,041
Net Worth: $196,105,385
Earnings: $14,965,938
Emp.: 12,159
Fiscal Year-end: 12/31/22
Holding Company
N.A.I.C.S.: 551112
Liao Chuanqiang *(Chm)*

KAISEN ENERGY CORP.
522 11th Avenue SW Ste 400, Calgary, AB, Canada
Tel.: (587) 350-5760 AB
Web Site: http://www.kaisenenergy.com
Oil & Gas Exploration
N.A.I.C.S.: 213112
Cameron King *(Pres & CEO)*

KAISER (CHINA) CULTURE CO., LTD.
Building A29 Kexing Science Park, Nanshan District, Shenzhen, 518057, China
Tel.: (86) 75586531031 CN
Web Site: https://www.kaiser.com.cn
Year Founded: 1994
002425—(SSE)
Rev.: $86,019,135
Assets: $697,453,617
Liabilities: $75,863,259
Net Worth: $621,590,358
Earnings: ($90,791,357)
Fiscal Year-end: 12/31/22
Internet Entertainment Business; Apparel Designer, Mfr & Distr;Online Games, TV Shows, Comics & Other Intellectual Property Commercial Products Distr
N.A.I.C.S.: 315250
Heming Zheng *(Chm)*

KAISER ARTS & KRAFTS LIMITED
Suit 204 Amber Estate 2nd Floor
Main Shahrah-e-Faisal, Karachi, Pakistan
Tel.: (92) 4390171
Apparel Garment Mfr
N.A.I.C.S.: 315990

KAISER CORPORATION LIMITED
Unit No 283-287 F Wing 2nd Floor Solaris - I Saki Vihar Road, Andheri East, Mumbai, 400 072, India
Tel.: (91) 2222690034
Web Site:
http://www.kaiserpress.com
Year Founded: 1993
531780—(BOM)
Rev.: $4,532,551
Assets: $4,232,619
Liabilities: $2,844,756
Net Worth: $1,387,864
Earnings: $133,565
Fiscal Year-end: 03/31/22
Printing Services
N.A.I.C.S.: 323111
Bhushanlal Desraj Arora *(Chm & Mng Dir)*

Subsidiaries:

Xicon International Limited
283-287 F Wing 2nd Floor Solaris-I Saki Vihar Road, Andheri East, Mumbai, 400072, Maharashtra, India
Tel.: (91) 2228478700
Web Site:
https://www.xiconinternational.com
Fabricated Product Mfr
N.A.I.C.S.: 332999
Ketan R. Kinariwala *(Gen Mgr-Procurement & Logistics)*

KAISER PARTNER PRIVATBANK AG
Pflugstrasse 10/12, Vaduz, 9290, Liechtenstein
Tel.: (423) 2365757
Web Site:
http://www.kaiserpartner.com
Investment Advice
N.A.I.C.S.: 523940
Fritz Kaiser *(Chm)*

KAISER REEF LIMITED
Level 8 London House 216 St Georges Terrace, Perth, 6000, WA, Australia
Tel.: (61) 894810389   AU
Web Site:
https://www.kaiserreef.com.au
Year Founded: 2019
KAU—(ASX)
Rev.: $20,011,884
Assets: $21,057,333
Liabilities: $4,613,881
Net Worth: $16,443,452
Earnings: $763,915
Fiscal Year-end: 06/30/23
Gold Mining Services
N.A.I.C.S.: 212220

KAISHAN GROUP CO., LTD.
No 851 Feidu Road Lingang New Area, China Shanghai Pilot Free Trade Zone, Shanghai, 201306, Zhejiang, China
Tel.: (86) 5703662177
Web Site:
https://www.kaishancomp.com
Year Founded: 2002
300257—(CHIN)
Rev.: $527,096,700
Assets: $1,840,969,728
Liabilities: $1,024,660,260
Net Worth: $816,309,468
Earnings: $57,375,864
Emp.: 4,500
Fiscal Year-end: 12/31/22
Air Compressor Mfr
N.A.I.C.S.: 333912
Kejian Cao *(Board of Directors & Chm)*

KAISUN HOLDINGS LIMITED
11/F Oriental Crystal Commercial Building, 46 Lyndhurst Terrace, Central, China (Hong Kong)
Tel.: (852) 25662862   Ky
Web Site: http://www.kaisun.hk
8203—(HKG)
Rev.: $34,002,338
Assets: $67,795,703
Liabilities: $67,902,930
Net Worth: ($107,228)
Earnings: ($2,535,210)
Emp.: 108
Fiscal Year-end: 12/31/22
Anthracite Mining Services
N.A.I.C.S.: 212115
Joseph Nap Kee Chan *(Chm)*

Subsidiaries:

Anway Enterprises Limited   (1)
Unit A1 10/F Sing Shun Factory Building 495 Castle Peak Road, Lai Chi Kok, Kowloon, China (Hong Kong)
Tel.: (852) 24100628
Web Site: http://www.anway.hk
Investment Holding Services
N.A.I.C.S.: 551112

KAITORI OKOKU CO., LTD.
5-12 Kawanishi-dori, Minato-ku, Nagoya, 455-0073, Aichi, Japan
Tel.: (81) 523047851
Web Site: https://www.okoku.jp
Year Founded: 1999
3181—(TKS)
Sales Range: $1-4.9 Billion
Emp.: 100
Used Merchandise Retailer
N.A.I.C.S.: 459510
Kazuo Hasegawa *(Chm & Pres)*

KAIXIN AUTO HOLDINGS
Room 903 Block A Dongjin International Center Huagong Road, Chaoyang District, Beijing, 100015, China
Tel.: (86) 1067204948   Ky
Web Site: https://ir.kaixin.com
Year Founded: 2016
KXIN—(NASDAQ)
Rev.: $253,840,000
Assets: $74,160,000
Liabilities: $36,081,000
Net Worth: $38,079,000
Earnings: ($196,579,000)
Emp.: 35
Fiscal Year-end: 12/31/21
Business Management Services
N.A.I.C.S.: 561110
Mingjun Lin *(Chm & CEO)*

Subsidiaries:

Morning Star Automotive, Inc.   (1)
1425 E St, Salida, CO 81201
Tel.: (719) 539-2333
Sales Range: $1-9.9 Million
Emp.: 20
New Car Dealers
N.A.I.C.S.: 441110

KAIYUAN EDUCATION TECHNOLOGY GROUP CO., LTD.
No 172 Kaiyuan Road Economic and Technological Development Zone, Changsha, 410000, Hunan, China
Tel.: (86) 73184874926
Web Site: http://www.ckic.net
Year Founded: 1992
300338—(CHIN)
Rev.: $92,495,520
Assets: $121,273,308
Liabilities: $109,698,732
Net Worth: $11,574,576
Earnings: $4,741,308
Emp.: 800
Fiscal Year-end: 12/31/22
Coal Quality Testing & Analysis Instruments & Equipment Mfr
N.A.I.C.S.: 334513
Jianwen Luo *(Chm)*

KAIZEN AUTOMOTIVE GROUP
4620 Blackfoot Trail SE, Calgary, T2G 4G2, AB, Canada
Tel.: (587) 390-3629
Web Site:
https://www.kaizenauto.com
Emp.: 100
Car Dealership
N.A.I.C.S.: 441120
Nate Clark *(CEO)*

Subsidiaries:

Summit Fleet   (1)
1260 Highfield Crescent SE, Calgary, T2G 5M3, AB, Canada
Tel.: (701) 609-5128
Web Site: https://www.summitfleet.com
Motor Vehicles Mfr
N.A.I.C.S.: 336211

Subsidiary (US):

Flex Fleet Rental LLC   (2)
6975 S Union Park Ctr Ste 500, Salt Lake City, UT 84047
Tel.: (801) 899-9399
Web Site: https://flexfleetrental.com
Truck, Utility Trailer & RV Rental & Leasing
N.A.I.C.S.: 532120
Eric Stats *(COO)*

KAIZEN HOLDING LTD
2380 10 Ave NE, Salmon Arm, V1E 2S4, BC, Canada
Tel.: (250) 832-9433
Web Site: http://www.hilltoptoyota.net
Year Founded: 1988
Rev.: $11,476,733
Emp.: 25
New & Used Car Dealers
N.A.I.C.S.: 441110
James MacDonald *(Mgr-Svc)*

KAIZEN PLATFORM, INC.
1-27-6 Shirokane, Minato-Ku, Tokyo, 108-0072, Japan
Tel.: (81) 359091151
Web Site:
https://www.kaizenplatform.com
Year Founded: 2017
4170—(TKS)
Rev.: $30,791,870
Assets: $30,976,210
Liabilities: $8,359,110
Net Worth: $22,617,100
Earnings: ($148,890)
Emp.: 128
Fiscal Year-end: 12/31/23
Software Development Services
N.A.I.C.S.: 541511
Kenji Sudo *(Founder, Chm, Pres & CEO)*

KAJARIA CERAMICS LTD
J1/B1 Extn Mohan Co - op Industrial Estate Mathura Road, Opp Badarpur Thermal Power Station, New Delhi, 110 044, India
Tel.: (91) 1126946409
Web Site:
https://www.kajariaceramics.com
Year Founded: 1985
KAJARIACER—(NSE)
Rev.: $382,500,300
Assets: $344,880,900
Liabilities: $91,953,225
Net Worth: $252,927,675
Earnings: $42,164,850
Emp.: 2,475
Fiscal Year-end: 03/31/21
Ceramic Tile Mfr
N.A.I.C.S.: 327120
Rishi Kajaria *(Co-Mng Dir)*

Subsidiaries:

Cosa Ceramics Private Limited   (1)
Lakhadhirpur Road, Morbi, 363642, Gujarat, India
Tel.: (91) 9825230956
Web Site: https://www.cosaceramics.com
Ceramic Mfr
N.A.I.C.S.: 327110
Parth Tanna *(Asst Mgr)*

Kajaria Plywood Private Limited   (1)
J1/B1 Extn Mohan Co-Opp Badarpur Thermal Power Station Mathura Road, Op Industrial Estate, New Delhi, 110 044, India
Tel.: (91) 1126946409
Web Site: https://www.kajariaply.com
Ceramic Mfr
N.A.I.C.S.: 327110

KAJIMA CORPORATION
3-1 Motoakasaka 1-chome, Minato-ku, Tokyo, 107-8388, Japan
Tel.: (81) 355441111   JP
Web Site: https://www.kajima.co.jp
Year Founded: 1840
1812—(TKS)
Rev.: $17,616,806,750
Assets: $20,723,334,890
Liabilities: $12,634,975,340
Net Worth: $8,088,359,550
Earnings: $760,368,130
Emp.: 8,219
Fiscal Year-end: 03/31/24
Real Estate Manangement Services
N.A.I.C.S.: 551112
Takao Nomura *(Exec VP)*

Subsidiaries:

ARMO Co., Ltd.   (1)
313-16 Hayashima Hayashimacho, Tsukubo-Gun, Okayama, 701-0304, Japan
Tel.: (81) 864760307
Pharmaceuticals Product Mfr
N.A.I.C.S.: 325412

ARTES Corporation   (1)
1-6-1 Higashi-Ohi, Shinagawa-ku, Tokyo, 140-0011, Japan
Tel.: (81) 357834811
Web Site: https://www.artecorp.co.jp
Real Estate Manangement Services
N.A.I.C.S.: 531390

Act Technical Support Inc.   (1)
Akasaka Nakanishi Building 5F 6F 4-1-33 Akasaka, Minato-ku, Tokyo, 107-0052, Japan
Tel.: (81) 355708585
Web Site: https://www.act.co.jp
Temporary Facility & Technical Support Staffing Services
N.A.I.C.S.: 561320
Taku Nagato *(Pres)*

Avant Associates, inc.   (1)
Akasaka Nakagawa Building 3F Floor 3-11-3 Akasaka, Minato-ku, Tokyo, 107-0052, Japan
Tel.: (81) 355448411
Web Site: https://www.avant-a.jp
Urban Planning Development Services
N.A.I.C.S.: 925120

Bang Tao Beach Ltd.   (1)
59/7 Moo 6 Ban Khok Tanod Road, Cherngtalay sub-district Thalang District, Phuket, 83110, Thailand
Tel.: (66) 76510120
Construction Services
N.A.I.C.S.: 236220

Chemical Grouting Co., Ltd.   (1)
Tiger Techno 2-2-5 Kyodo Hall 3F door, Minato-ku, Tokyo, 105-0001, Japan
Tel.: (81) 355750511
Web Site: http://www.chemicalgrout.co.jp
Emp.: 311
Ground Engineering Services
N.A.I.C.S.: 541330
Yuichi Tachiwada *(Pres)*

Clima-Teq Co., Ltd.   (1)

KAJIMA CORPORATION

Kajima Corporation—(Continued)

NMF Shinjuku EAST Building 10-5 Tomihisa-cho, Shinjuku-ku, Tokyo, 162-0067, Japan
Tel.: (81) 353122211
Web Site: https://www.clima-teq.com
Sales Range: $200-249.9 Million
Emp.: 373
Design, Construction & After-Sales Services Related to Electrical, HVAC & Electronic Systems & Devices
N.A.I.C.S.: 238990
Tatsuo Haga (Deputy Gen Mgr)

Cockram Corporation (1)
110 Cubitt Street, Cremorne, 3121, VIC, Australia
Tel.: (61) 388628888
Web Site: http://www.cockram.com
Industrial Building Construction Services
N.A.I.C.S.: 236210
Robert Milne (Gen Mgr-Australia)

Core5 Industrial Partners LLC (1)
1230 Peachtree St NE Ste 3560, Atlanta, GA 30309
Tel.: (404) 262-5405
Web Site: https://www.c5ip.com
Real Estate Services
N.A.I.C.S.: 531390
Timothy J. Gunter (Pres & CEO)

Development Ventures Group, Inc. (1)
350 5th Ave Ste 5340, New York, NY 10118
Tel.: (212) 899-4570
Web Site: https://www.devengroup.us
Real Estate Development Services
N.A.I.C.S.: 531390
Dennis Biggs (Pres & CEO)

East Real Estate Co., Ltd. (1)
6-5-11 Akasaka, Minato-Ku, Tokyo, 107-8348, Japan
Tel.: (81) 355440911
Real Estate Management Services
N.A.I.C.S.: 531390

Engineering & Risk Services Corporation (1)
7F Ginza 6-chome-SQUARE 6-17-1 Ginza, Chuo-ku, Tokyo, 104-0061, Japan
Tel.: (81) 368219091
Web Site: https://www.ers-co.co.jp
Sales Range: $1-9.9 Million
Emp.: 24
Real Estate Evaluation & Risk Assessment Consulting Services; Owned 50% by Kajima Corporation & 50% by OYO Corporation
N.A.I.C.S.: 541620

Flournoy Construction Company (1)
1100 Brookstone Ctr Pkwy, Columbus, GA 31904
Tel.: (706) 689-8830
Web Site: https://flournoycg.com
Construction Services
N.A.I.C.S.: 236220

Global BIM Inc. (1)
K-Front Building 1-3-9 Motoakasaka, Minato-ku, Tokyo, 107-0051, Japan
Tel.: (81) 364382760
Web Site: https://www.global-bim.com
Construction Services
N.A.I.C.S.: 236220
Takashi Nakano (Pres)

Grout Trading Co., Ltd. (1)
2-2-5 Toranomon Kyodotsushinkaikan3f, Minato-ku, Tokyo, 105-0001, Japan
Tel.: (81) 355750505
Construction Engineering Services
N.A.I.C.S.: 541330

Hotel Kajima no Mori Co., Ltd. (1)
1373-6 Karuizawa, Karuizawa Town Kitasaku District, Nagano, 389-0102, Japan
Tel.: (81) 267423535
Web Site: https://kajimanomori.co.jp
Hotel Operator
N.A.I.C.S.: 721110

Icon Co Pty Ltd (1)
110 Cubitt Street, Richmond, 3121, VIC, Australia
Tel.: (61) 394296099
Web Site: http://www.icon.co
Construction Services
N.A.I.C.S.: 236220

Evan Byrne (CEO & Mng Dir)

Icon Developments Autratlia Pty Ltd (1)
Level 2 6 Palmer Parade, Cremorne, 3121, VIC, Australia
Tel.: (61) 385939666
Web Site: http://www.icondev.co
Real Estate Development Services
N.A.I.C.S.: 531390
Matthew Bourke (CEO)

Ilya Corporation (1)
Pair Horse Building 6-5-16 Akasaka, Minato-ku, Tokyo, 107-0052, Japan
Tel.: (81) 355612500
Web Site: https://www.ilya.co.jp
Emp.: 208
Interior Design, Planning & Decoration Services
N.A.I.C.S.: 541410
Ryoichi Tazawa (Pres)

Indochina Kajima Development Ltd. (1)
Suite 901 Indochina Plaza Hanoi 241 Xuan Thuy, Cau Glay District, Hanoi, Vietnam
Tel.: (84) 2439350250
Real Estate Development Services
N.A.I.C.S.: 531390

K-Provision Co., Ltd. (1)
5F Akasaka Building 4-13-13 Akasaka, Minato-ku, Tokyo, 107-0052, Japan
Tel.: (81) 355747210
Web Site: https://www.k-provision.com
Advertising Agency Services
N.A.I.C.S.: 541810

KR Lease Corporation (1)
2-2-10 Koraku Matsuya Bldg 6f, Bunkyo-Ku, Tokyo, 112-0004, Japan
Tel.: (81) 358022310
Financial Lending Services
N.A.I.C.S.: 522220

KRC Co., Ltd. (1)
1-20 Sumiyoshicho, Shinjuku-Ku, Tokyo, 162-0065, Japan
Tel.: (81) 353798771
Construction Engineering Services
N.A.I.C.S.: 541330

Kajima Aquatech Corporation (1)
Arai Building 2F 5-31 Motoakasaka 1-chome, Minato-ku, Tokyo, 107-0051, Japan
Tel.: (81) 357705561
Sales Range: $25-49.9 Million
Emp.: 50
Industrial Plant Water System Engineering & Maintenance Services
N.A.I.C.S.: 238990

Kajima Asia Pacific Holdings Pte. Ltd. (1)
19 Changi Business Park Crescent 06-05 The GEAR, Singapore, 489690, Singapore
Tel.: (65) 63480520
Web Site: http://www.kajima.com.sg
Real Estate Development Services
N.A.I.C.S.: 531390

Kajima Associate, Inc. (1)
3550 Lenox Rd NE Ste 1850, Atlanta, GA 30326
Tel.: (404) 564-3900
Web Site: https://kajimausa.com
Interior Design Services
N.A.I.C.S.: 541410

Kajima Australia Pty Ltd (1)
2/110 Cubitt Street, Cremorne, 3121, VIC, Australia
Tel.: (61) 390772181
Construction Services
N.A.I.C.S.: 236220

Kajima Building & Design Group, Inc. (1)
3490 Piedmont Rd NE Ste 900, Atlanta, GA 30305
Tel.: (404) 812-8600
Web Site: https://www.kbd.group
Emp.: 245
Construction Design Services
N.A.I.C.S.: 541320
Bona Allen (CFO & Sr VP)

Kajima Corporation (China) Co., Ltd. (1)
Lei ShingInternational Plaza 11th Floor No 1319 West Yan'an Road, Changning, Shanghai, 200050, China
Tel.: (86) 2162260997
Web Site: https://www.kajima-china.com
Construction Services
N.A.I.C.S.: 236220
Andrew Neumann (Gen Mgr)

Kajima Czech Design & Construction s.r.o. (1)
Generala Piky 430/26 Telehouse building B 3rd floor, 160 00, Prague, Czech Republic
Tel.: (420) 222241150
Web Site: https://www.kajima.cz
Sales Range: $25-49.9 Million
Emp.: 3
Construction Engineering Services
N.A.I.C.S.: 541330

Kajima Development Pte. Ltd. (1)
Room1604-5 Allied Kajima Building 138 Gloucester Road, Wanchai, China (Hong Kong)
Tel.: (852) 25986767
Construction Services
N.A.I.C.S.: 236220

Kajima Development Pte. Ltd. (1)
19 Changi Business Park Crescent 05-01 The GEAR, Singapore, 489690, Singapore
Tel.: (65) 63457115
Construction Services
N.A.I.C.S.: 236220

Kajima Estates (Europe) Ltd. (1)
10 St Giles Square, London, WC2H 8AP, United Kingdom
Tel.: (44) 2030751800
Real Estate Development Services
N.A.I.C.S.: 531390

Kajima Europe Lou Roucas S.A.R.L. (1)
4300 route de Bagnols en Foret, La Motte en Provence, 83920, Marseille, France
Tel.: (33) 494518200
Real Estate Development Services
N.A.I.C.S.: 531390

Kajima Europe S.A.S. (1)
10 Rue de la Paix, Paris, 75002, France
Tel.: (33) 142612053
Property Development Services
N.A.I.C.S.: 531390

Kajima Europe U.K. Holding Ltd. (1)
Grove House 248a Marylebone Road, London, NW1 6JZ, United Kingdom (100%)
Tel.: (44) 2074650007
Web Site: http://www.kajimaeurope.com
Sales Range: $250-299.9 Million
Emp.: 40
Holding Company; Architectural, Engineering & Construction Management Services & Real Estate Development
N.A.I.C.S.: 551112
Michiya M. Uchida (Pres)

Subsidiary (Non-US):

Kajima France Development S.A.R.L. (2)
10 Rue De La Paix, 75002, Paris, France (100%)
Tel.: (33) 142612053
Web Site: http://www.kajimaeurope.com
Sales Range: $50-74.9 Million
Emp.: 4
Real Estate Acquisition & Development
N.A.I.C.S.: 531390
Kaoru Yamamutu (Gen Mgr)

Kajima Property Holdings Ltd. (2)
(100%)
Tel.: (44) 2074650007
Web Site: http://www.kajima.co.uk
Sales Range: $50-74.9 Million
Holding Company; Property Development Services
N.A.I.C.S.: 551112

Division (Non-US):

Kajima Partnerships Ltd. (3)
Tel.: (44) 2030751800
Web Site: http://www.kajima.co.uk
Public Sector Property Development Services
N.A.I.C.S.: 531390

INTERNATIONAL PUBLIC

Kajima Fit Co., Ltd. (1)
4-1-17 Kamiyacho Prime Place 8th Floor Toranomon, Minato-ku, Tokyo, 105-0001, Japan
Tel.: (81) 363815258
Web Site: http://www.kajima-fit.co.jp
Construction Services
N.A.I.C.S.: 236220

Kajima India Pvt. Ltd. (1)
1103 Tower-A Signature Towers South City-I, Gurgaon, 122001, Haryana, India
Tel.: (91) 1244911450
Web Site: http://www.kajimaindia.com
Emp.: 70
Construction & Project Management Services
N.A.I.C.S.: 236220
Koji Oura (Mng Dir)

Kajima Information Communication Technology Co., Ltd. (1)
YM Building 6-13-7 Akasaka, Minato-ku, Tokyo, 107-0052, Japan
Tel.: (81) 335685240
Web Site: https://www.kajima-ict.co.jp
Emp.: 201
Construction Services
N.A.I.C.S.: 236220

Kajima Institute Publishing Co., Ltd. (1)
2-5-14 Yaesu, Chuo-Ku, Tokyo, 104-0028, Japan
Tel.: (81) 362025200
Web Site: http://www.kajima-publishing.co.jp
Emp.: 20
Books Publishing Services
N.A.I.C.S.: 513130
Sumio Gsubouthi (Gen Mgr)

Kajima Kress Co., Ltd. (1)
1-7-10 Motoakasaka Motoakasaka Bldg 2f, Minato-Ku, 107-0051, Tokyo, Japan
Tel.: (81) 334020081
Highways & Street Construction Services
N.A.I.C.S.: 237310

Kajima Leasing Corporation (1)
1-6-6 Moto-Akasaka Safety building 16th floor, Minato-ku, Tokyo, 107-0051, Japan
Tel.: (81) 354749210
Web Site: https://www.kajima-leasing.co.jp
Emp.: 61
Financial Lending Services
N.A.I.C.S.: 522220

Kajima Mechatro Engineering Co., Ltd. (1)
7F Fujiin Building 1-1-5 Motoakasaka, Minato-ku, Tokyo, 107-0051, Japan
Tel.: (81) 354743720
Web Site: https://www.kme.jp
Sales Range: $50-74.9 Million
Emp.: 209
Civil Engineering, Construction & Cargo Handling Equipment Mfr, Sales & Leasing
N.A.I.C.S.: 333120

Kajima Myanmar Co., Ltd. (1)
B-303 Water Supply Department Compound DUHD Ministry of Construction, Yang Aung Lane-2 Ward No 2 Yankin Township, Yangon, Myanmar
Tel.: (95) 9778864945
Web Site: https://www.kajima-myanmar.com
Emp.: 140
Construction Services
N.A.I.C.S.: 236220

Kajima Myanmar Development & Management Co., Ltd. (1)
B-303 Water Supply Department Compound DUHD Ministry of Construction, Yang Aung Lane-2 Ward No 2 Yankin Township, Yangon, Myanmar
Tel.: (95) 9953533789
Construction Services
N.A.I.C.S.: 236220

Kajima Overseas Asia Pte. Ltd. (1)
19 Changi Business Park Crescent 04-05 The GEAR, Singapore, 489690, Singapore
Tel.: (65) 63398890
Web Site: http://www.kajima.com.sg
Sales Range: $550-599.9 Million
Emp.: 300
Holding Company; Architectural, Engineering & Construction Management Services & Real Estate Development

AND PRIVATE COMPANIES / KAJIMA CORPORATION

N.A.I.C.S.: 551112

Subsidiary (Non-US):

Chung-Lu Construction Co., Ltd. (2)
8F No 223 Songjiang Rd, Zhongshan Dist,
Taipei, 104472, Taiwan
Tel.: (886) 225180812
Web Site: https://www.kajima.com.tw
Sales Range: $50-74.9 Million
Emp.: 349
Commercial Construction Contractor Services
N.A.I.C.S.: 236220
Onodera Toshihiro *(Pres & CFO)*

Kajima (Malaysia) Sdn. Bhd. (2)
Unit 28 1 Level 28 Menara 1 Sentrum No
201 Kuala Lumpur Sentral, Jalan Tun Sambanthan, 50470, Kuala Lumpur, Malaysia
Tel.: (60) 322722525
Web Site: https://www.kajima.com.my
Sales Range: $50-74.9 Million
Emp.: 250
Architectural, Engineering & Construction Management Services
N.A.I.C.S.: 236220

Division (Domestic):

Kajima Design Asia Pte. Ltd. (2)
19 Changi Business Park Crescent 04-05
The GEAR, 06/02 Parkway Parade, Singapore, 489690, Singapore (100%)
Tel.: (65) 63398890
Web Site: http://www.kajima.com.sg
Sales Range: $75-99.9 Million
Emp.: 13
Architectural Design & Engineering Services
N.A.I.C.S.: 541310

Subsidiary (Non-US):

Kajima Philippines Inc. (2)
12th Floor 6788 Building Ayala Avenue,
Makati, Philippines (100%)
Tel.: (63) 288866818
Web Site: https://www.kajima.com.ph
Sales Range: $25-49.9 Million
Emp.: 205
Architectural, Engineering & Construction Management Services
N.A.I.C.S.: 236220
Fusaaki Kato *(Exec VP)*

P.T. Kajima Indonesia (2)
Sentral Senayan II 3rd Floor Jl Asia Afrika
No 8, Jakarta Pusat, 10270,
Indonesia (100%)
Tel.: (62) 215724477
Web Site: http://www.kajima.co.id
Sales Range: $25-49.9 Million
Emp.: 173
Architectural Design, Engineering & Construction Management Services
N.A.I.C.S.: 236220

Thai Kajima Co., Ltd. (2)
19th Fl Ramaland Bldg 952 Rama 4 Road,
Bangrak, Bangkok, 10500,
Thailand (100%)
Tel.: (66) 26329300
Web Site: https://www.kajima.co.th
Sales Range: $25-49.9 Million
Emp.: 500
Architectural Design, Engineering & Construction Management Services
N.A.I.C.S.: 236220
Masanori Hamad *(Pres)*

Kajima Poland sp. z.o.o. (1)
Al Jerozolimskie 65/79 Centrum LIM 12th
floor room 12 13, 00-697, Warsaw, Poland
Tel.: (48) 226307520
Web Site: https://www.kajima.pl
Sales Range: $25-49.9 Million
Emp.: 6
Industrial Building Construction Engineering Services
N.A.I.C.S.: 236210
Maciej Runkiewicz *(Co-Chm-Mgmt Bd)*

Kajima Real Estate Investment Advisors Inc. (1)
6th Floor of Okamura Akasaka Building
2-13-1, Nagatacho Chiyoda-ku, Tokyo, 100-0014, Japan
Tel.: (81) 365508570
Web Site: http://www.kajima-reia.com
Real Estate Advisory Services
N.A.I.C.S.: 531210

Kajima Road Co., Ltd. (1)
7-27 Kouraku 1-chome, Bunkyo-ku, Tokyo,
112-8566, Japan
Tel.: (81) 358028001
Web Site: https://www.kajimaroad.co.jp
Sales Range: $250-299.9 Million
Emp.: 1,329
Road, Bridge & Other Civil Engineering Construction Services
N.A.I.C.S.: 237310
Hidemitsu Yoshihiro *(Pres)*

Subsidiary (Domestic):

Japan Sea Works Co., Ltd. (2)
1-15 Kagurazaka Kagurazakaitchome Bldg
8f, Shinjuku-Ku, Tokyo, 162-0825, Japan
Tel.: (81) 363272571
Marine Engineering Services
N.A.I.C.S.: 541330

Kajima Shenyang Construction Management & Consulting Co., Ltd. (1)
501 Traders Hotel 68 Zhong Hua Road,
Heping District, Shenyang, 110-001, China
Tel.: (86) 2423413641
Web Site: http://www.kajima.co.jp
Construction Management Consulting Services
N.A.I.C.S.: 541618

Kajima Tatemono Sogo Kanri Co., Ltd. (1)
Ginza 6-Chome Square 17-1 Ginza
6-chome, Chuo-ku, Tokyo, 104-0061, Japan
Tel.: (81) 367487111
Web Site: https://www.kajima-tatemono.co.jp
Emp.: 2,850
Real Estate Development Services
N.A.I.C.S.: 531390

Kajima Technical Research Institute (1)
19-1 Tobitakyu 2-chome, Chofu-shi, Tokyo,
182-0036, Japan (100%)
Tel.: (81) 424851111
Web Site: http://www.kajima.co.jp
Sales Range: $125-149.9 Million
Emp.: 290
Engineering Technologies Research & Development; Training & Consultation Services
N.A.I.C.S.: 541715

Kajima Tohoku Kousan Co., Ltd. (1)
1-6-1 Narita Tomiya-machi, Kurokawa-gun,
Miyagi, 981-3341, Japan
Tel.: (81) 22 351 5269
Real Estate Development Services
N.A.I.C.S.: 531390

Kajima U.S.A. Inc. (1)
3550 Lenox Rd NE Ste 1850, Atlanta, GA
30326 (100%)
Tel.: (404) 564-3900
Web Site: https://www.kajimausa.com
Sales Range: $1-4.9 Billion
Holding Company; Architectural, Engineering & Construction Management Services & Real Estate Development
N.A.I.C.S.: 551112
Michiya Uchida *(Pres & CEO)*

Division (Domestic):

Kajima International Inc. (2)
3550 Lenox Rd NE Ste 1850, Atlanta, GA
30326 (100%)
Tel.: (404) 564-3900
Web Site: http://www.kajimausa.com
Holding Company; Architectural Design, Engineering & Construction Management Services
N.A.I.C.S.: 551112

Subsidiary (Domestic):

Batson-Cook Company (3)
817 4th Ave, West Point, GA 31833-1504
Tel.: (770) 955-1951
Web Site: http://www.batson-cook.com
Sales Range: $500-549.9 Million
Emp.: 71
Commercial, Institutional, Industrial & Multifamily Residential Building Construction Contractors
N.A.I.C.S.: 236220
R. Randall Hall *(Pres & CEO)*

Subsidiary (Domestic):

Batson-Cook Development Company (4)
3400 Overton Park Dr Ste 100, Atlanta, GA
30339
Tel.: (770) 953-9600
Web Site: https://www.batsoncookdev.com
Sales Range: $125-149.9 Million
Emp.: 300
Real Estate Development Services
N.A.I.C.S.: 531390
J. Littleton Glover *(Pres & CEO)*

Subsidiary (Domestic):

Hawaiian Dredging Construction Company, Inc. (3)
605 Kapiolani Blvd, Honolulu, HI 96813
Tel.: (808) 735-3211
Web Site: https://www.hdcc.com
Sales Range: $600-649.9 Million
Emp.: 600
Civil, Residential & Commercial Construction Contractors
N.A.I.C.S.: 236220
Paul Silen *(VP-Comml Div)*

KCS West, Inc. (3)
250 E 1st St Ste 700, Los Angeles, CA
90012 (100%)
Tel.: (323) 269-0020
Web Site: https://kcswest.com
Sales Range: $25-49.9 Million
Emp.: 20
Architectural Design, Commercial Construction & Construction Management Services
N.A.I.C.S.: 236220
Elmond K. Wan *(Pres)*

Kajima Building & Design, Inc. (3)
3490 Piedmont Rd NE Ste 900, Atlanta, GA
30305-4804
Tel.: (404) 812-8600
Web Site: http://kbd.group
Sales Range: $50-74.9 Million
Emp.: 180
Holding Company; Architectural Design, Engineering & Construction Services
N.A.I.C.S.: 551112

Subsidiary (Domestic):

KBD Construction Services, Inc. (4)
3490 Piedmont Rd Ne Ste 900, Atlanta, GA
30305-4804
Tel.: (404) 812-8600
Web Site: http://www.kbdgroupusa.com
Sales Range: $25-49.9 Million
Emp.: 50
Architectural Design, Engineering & Construction Services
N.A.I.C.S.: 236220
Shinya Urano *(Pres & CEO)*

Subsidiary (Domestic):

The Austin Company (3)
6095 Parkland Blvd, Cleveland, OH 44124
Tel.: (440) 544-2600
Web Site: https://www.theaustin.com
Sales Range: $75-99.9 Million
Emp.: 565
Architectural Design, Engineering, Construction Management & Consulting Services
N.A.I.C.S.: 541310
Michael G. Pierce *(Pres)*

Division (Domestic):

Kajima Real Estate Development Inc. (2)
3550 Lenox Rd NE Ste 1850, Atlanta, GA
30326 (100%)
Tel.: (404) 564-3900
Web Site: http://www.kajima.co.jp
Holding Company; Real Estate Development Services
N.A.I.C.S.: 551112

Subsidiary (Domestic):

Commercial Developments International, Inc. (3)
1251 Ave of the Americas Ste 910, New
York, NY 10020
Tel.: (212) 899-4570
Web Site: http://www.kajimausa.com

Sales Range: $50-74.9 Million
Emp.: 3
Commercial Real Estate Development Services
N.A.I.C.S.: 531390
Alan T. Kessler *(Pres & CEO)*

Kajima Development Corporation (3)
250 E 1st St Ste 400, Los Angeles, CA
90012 (100%)
Tel.: (323) 262-8484
Web Site: http://www.kajimausa.com
Sales Range: $50-74.9 Million
Emp.: 7
Residential Real Estate Development Services
N.A.I.C.S.: 531390
Hiroaki Iizawa *(Pres)*

Kajima Vietnam Co., Ltd. (1)
14th Floor AB Tower 76A Le Lai Street, District 1, Ho Chi Minh City, Vietnam
Tel.: (84) 2835210720
Web Site: https://www.kajima.com.vn
Emp.: 300
Construction Services
N.A.I.C.S.: 236220

Kajima Yaesu Kaihatsu Co., Ltd. (1)
6-5-11 Akasaka, Minato-Ku, Tokyo, 107-0052, Japan
Tel.: (81) 355441247
Emp.: 6
Real Estate Manangement Services
N.A.I.C.S.: 531390
Yamaguchi Teruaki *(Mgr)*

Katabami Kogyo Co., Ltd. (1)
1-5-8 Motoakasaka Toraya No 2 Building,
Minato-ku, Tokyo, 107-8638, Japan
Tel.: (81) 3 5413 8100
Web Site: http://www.katabami.co.jp
Insurance Services
N.A.I.C.S.: 524113
Junsuke Kajima *(Pres)*

Niigata Bandaijima Building Co., Ltd. (1)
5-1 Bandaijima Building 6th floor, Chuo-ku,
Niigata, 950-0078, Japan
Tel.: (81) 252488661
Web Site: http://www.niigata-bandaijima-building.co.jp
Construction Engineering Services
N.A.I.C.S.: 541330

PT Jimbaran Greenhill (1)
Jl Pura Batu Meguwung, Jimbaran, Bali,
80361, Indonesia
Tel.: (62) 3613705231
Construction Services
N.A.I.C.S.: 236220

PT Senayan Trikarya Sempana (1)
Sentral Senayan I 8th Floor Jl Asia Afrika
No 8 Gelora Bung Karno, Senayan, Jakarta, 10270, Indonesia
Tel.: (62) 215723456
Web Site: https://www.sentralsenayan.com
Real Estate Development Services
N.A.I.C.S.: 531390

RTC Inc. (1)
3948 Kaminokawa Kaminokawamachi,
Kawachi-Gun, Tochigi, 329-0611, Japan
Tel.: (81) 285566699
Construction Engineering Services
N.A.I.C.S.: 541330

Ramaland Development Co., Ltd. (1)
19th Floor Ramaland Building 952 Rama IV
Road, Bangrak, Bangkok, 10500, Thailand
Tel.: (66) 26329777
Web Site: http://www.kajima.com.sg
Emp.: 15
Construction Design Services
N.A.I.C.S.: 541490

Riverside Tower Commercial Center Ltd. (1)
74 Bach Dang, Hai Chau District, Da Nang,
Vietnam
Tel.: (84) 2363840850
Construction Services
N.A.I.C.S.: 236220
Thu Pham *(Mktg Mgr)*

Taiko Trading Co., Ltd. (1)
Toraya Dai-2 Building 4F 1-5-8 Moto-

KAJIMA CORPORATION

Kajima Corporation—(Continued)
Akasaka, Minato-ku, Tokyo, 107-0051, Japan
Tel.: (81) 354131500
Web Site: http://www.taiko.co.jp
Sales Range: $1-4.9 Billion
Emp.: 295
Building Materials, Construction Machinery & Equipment Sales & Leasing Services
N.A.I.C.S.: 423390
Shigemitsu Moriya *(Pres)*

Toshi Kankyo Engineering Co., Ltd. (1)
Second Floor Kiba Chome No 6 No 35 Kiba Okamoto building, Koto-ku, Tokyo, 135-0042, Japan
Tel.: (81) 356390740
Web Site: http://www.tkeng.co.jp
Waste Treatment Services
N.A.I.C.S.: 562998

Yaesu Book Center Co., Ltd. (1)
Daiichi Tokyo Building 7F 1-24-1 Kandasu-dacho, Chiyoda-ku, Tokyo, 104-8456, Japan
Tel.: (81) 335257025
Web Site: https://www.yaesu-book.co.jp
Book Store Operating Services
N.A.I.C.S.: 459210

KAJO NEUKIRCHEN MANAGEMENT UND BETEILIGUNGS GMBH

Frankfurter Strasse 20, Westend Duo, 65760, Eschborn, Germany
Tel.: (49) 6196998950   De
Web Site: http://www.neukirchen-gruppe.de
Investment Management Service
N.A.I.C.S.: 523940
Kajo Neukirchen *(CEO)*

Subsidiaries:

Lahnpaper GmbH (1)
Auf Bruhl 15-27, 56112, Lahnstein, Germany
Tel.: (49) 2621 177 0
Web Site: http://www.lahnpaper.de
Sales Range: $50-74.9 Million
Emp.: 170
Specialty Paper Mfr
N.A.I.C.S.: 322299
Detlef Stoltefaut *(Mng Dir)*

NEUKIRCHEN Immobilien Verwaltungs GmbH (1)
Liebigstrasse 11, 60323, Frankfurt am Main, Germany
Tel.: (49) 69 977 8876 0
Web Site: http://www.kaneco.de
Real Estate Investment & Asset Management
N.A.I.C.S.: 531390

KAKA INDUSTRIES LIMITED

67 Bhagwati Nagar Opp Nilkanth Arcade Kuha-Kanbha Road, Kathwada GIDC, Ahmedabad, 382415, India
Tel.: (91) 8511139999
Web Site:
 https://www.kakaprofile.com
Year Founded: 2019
543939—(BOM)
Emp.: 200
Plastic Material Mfr & Distr
N.A.I.C.S.: 325211
Chintan Bodar *(CFO)*

KAKAKU.COM INC.

Digital Gate Building 6th to 8th floors 3-5-7 Ebisu Minami, Shibuya-ku, Tokyo, 150-0022, Japan
Tel.: (81) 357254554
Web Site: https://help.kakaku.com
Year Founded: 1997
2371—(TKS)
Rev.: $442,394,080
Assets: $550,665,880
Liabilities: $208,988,370
Net Worth: $341,677,510
Earnings: $119,607,950
Emp.: 1,401
Fiscal Year-end: 03/31/24
Electronic Commerce Services
N.A.I.C.S.: 513199
Kaoru Hayashi *(Chm)*

Subsidiaries:

Kakaku.com Insurance, Inc. (1)
9th floor Shinbashi i-mark building 2-6-2 Shinbashi, Minato-ku, Tokyo, 105-0004, Japan
Tel.: (81) 335952855
Emp.: 146
Recruitment Services
N.A.I.C.S.: 541612

Time Design Co., Ltd. (1)
Ebisu First Square 8F 1-18-14 Ebisu Shibuya-ku, Tokyo, 150-0013, Japan
Tel.: (81) 364477799
Web Site: http://www.timedesign.co.jp
Travel Tour Operator
N.A.I.C.S.: 561520
Yuzo Takamatsu *(CEO)*

KAKAO CORPORATION

242 Cheomdan-ro, Jeju, 63309, Jeju-do, Korea (South)
Tel.: (82) 18991326   KR
Web Site:
 https://www.kakaocorp.com
Year Founded: 1995
035720—(KRS)
Rev.: $5,609,163,604
Assets: $18,689,762,139
Liabilities: $8,403,255,285
Net Worth: $10,286,506,854
Earnings: ($751,562,851)
Emp.: 3,880
Fiscal Year-end: 12/31/23
Internet Servies
N.A.I.C.S.: 551112
Brian Kim *(Chm)*

Subsidiaries:

kakao M. (1)
Samsung-dong Jungsuk Building Road 17 Teheran-ro 103, Gangnam-Gu, Seoul, 135-882, Korea (South)   (76.4%)
Tel.: (82) 2 2280 7700
Web Site: http://www.iloen.com
Rev.: $545,512,811
Assets: $510,520,709
Liabilities: $179,093,810
Net Worth: $331,426,899
Earnings: $63,627,129
Emp.: 341
Fiscal Year-end: 12/31/2017
Music Distribution & Streaming Services
N.A.I.C.S.: 512250

KAKAO GAMES CORP.

14th Floor 152 Pangyoyeok-ro, Bundang-Gu, Seongnam, Gyeonggi-do, Korea (South)
Tel.: (82) 15668834
Web Site:
 https://www.kakaogamescorp.com
Year Founded: 2013
293490—(KRS)
Rev.: $880,280,242
Assets: $2,971,313,175
Liabilities: $1,425,890,092
Net Worth: $1,545,423,083
Earnings: ($179,202,796)
Emp.: 436
Fiscal Year-end: 12/31/22
Software Development Services
N.A.I.C.S.: 541511
Leo Cho *(Co-CEO)*

KAKAOBANK CORP.

11th floor 131 Bundangnaegok-ro, Baekhyeon-dong Pangyo Techwon Bundang-gu, Seongnam, Gyeonggi-do, Korea (South)
Tel.: (82) 262886000
Web Site:
 https://www.kakaobank.com
Year Founded: 2016
323410—(KRS)
Rev.: $1,191,901,340
Assets: $29,330,700,088
Liabilities: $25,088,675,534
Net Worth: $4,242,024,554
Earnings: $195,278,565
Fiscal Year-end: 12/31/22
Banking Services
N.A.I.C.S.: 522110
Hoyoung Yun *(CEO)*

KAKAOPAY CORPORATION

Azit B 15F 166 Pangyoyeok-ro, Bundang-Gu, Seongnam, Gyeonggi-do, Korea (South)
Tel.: (82) 16447405
Web Site: https://www.kakaopay.com
Year Founded: 2017
377300—(KRS)
Rev.: $400,121,396
Assets: $2,555,283,401
Liabilities: $1,091,674,883
Net Worth: $1,463,608,518
Earnings: $20,551,799
Emp.: 1,114
Fiscal Year-end: 12/31/22
Financial Services
N.A.I.C.S.: 523999
Simon Shin *(Head-Payment Bus Grp & Corp Dev Office)*

KAKATIYA CEMENT SUGAR & INDUSTRIES LIMITED

1-10-140/1 Gurukrupa Ashok Nagar, Hyderabad, 500 020, Telangana, India
Tel.: (91) 4027637717
Web Site:
 https://www.kakatiyacements.com
Year Founded: 1979
500234—(BOM)
Rev.: $22,405,533
Assets: $42,600,517
Liabilities: $10,426,730
Net Worth: $32,173,787
Earnings: $2,642,927
Emp.: 481
Fiscal Year-end: 03/31/22
Cement Mfr
N.A.I.C.S.: 327310
P. Veeraiah *(Mng Dir & Chm)*

Subsidiaries:

Kakatiya Cement Sugar & Industries Limited - Cement Works (1)
Srinivas Nagar Dondapadu, Kodad Mandal, Nalgonda, India
Tel.: (91) 8654 200014
Cement Mfr
N.A.I.C.S.: 327310

Kakatiya Cement Sugar & Industries Limited - Sugar Works (1)
Peruvancha Village, Kallaru Mandal, Khammam, 507 209, India
Tel.: (91) 8761 287207
Sugar Mfr
N.A.I.C.S.: 311314
Pavan Kumar *(Pres)*

KAKATIYA TEXTILES LIMITED

Plot No 9 & 10 Industrial Estate Tetali West Godavari, Tanuku, 534 218, Andhra Pradesh, India
Tel.: (91) 8819224005   In
Web Site:
 http://www.kakatiyatextiles.com
Year Founded: 1981
521054—(BOM)
Rev.: $902,452
Assets: $2,632,756
Liabilities: $4,167,436
Net Worth: ($1,534,680)
Earnings: $67,238
Emp.: 99
Fiscal Year-end: 03/31/23
Cotton Yarn Mfr & Distr
N.A.I.C.S.: 313110

INTERNATIONAL PUBLIC

KAKEL MAX AB

Dalvagen 4, S-740 46, Ostervala, Sweden
Tel.: (46) 29270370   SE
Web Site: https://kakelmax.se
Year Founded: 1987
KAKEL—(OMX)
Rev.: $16,504,163
Assets: $9,241,620
Liabilities: $3,996,553
Net Worth: $5,245,066
Earnings: $502,028
Emp.: 53
Fiscal Year-end: 12/31/22
Home Improvement Products; Ceramic Tiles, Vowels, Fixes, Natural Stones & Bathroom Fittings
N.A.I.C.S.: 423620
Daniel Kallberg *(CEO)*

Subsidiaries:

Empire Denmark APS (1)
Virkeholm 3 B, 2730, Herlev, Denmark
Tel.: (45) 43 600 609
Web Site: http://www.empiredenmark.dk
Sales Range: $25-49.9 Million
Emp.: 11
Household Appliance Retailer
N.A.I.C.S.: 449210

Empire Sweden AB (1)
Ostermalmsgatan 87A, 114 59, Stockholm, Sweden
Tel.: (46) 858630400
Web Site: http://www.empire.se
Household Product Distr
N.A.I.C.S.: 423620
Ulf Bork *(CEO)*

SIA Empire Baltics (1)
Udens 20/22, Riga, 1007, Latvia
Tel.: (371) 673 21 205
Web Site: http://www.sodastream.lv
Sales Range: $50-74.9 Million
Emp.: 5
Household Appliance Distr
N.A.I.C.S.: 423210

KAKEN PHARMACEUTICAL CO., LTD.

28-8 Honkomagome 2-chome, Bunkyo-ku, Tokyo, 113-8650, Japan
Tel.: (81) 359775001
Web Site: https://www.kaken.co.jp
4521—(TKS)
Rev.: $476,210,840
Assets: $1,134,428,030
Liabilities: $184,207,480
Net Worth: $950,220,550
Earnings: $53,045,250
Emp.: 1,143
Fiscal Year-end: 03/31/24
Pharmaceuticals Mfr
N.A.I.C.S.: 325412
Hiroyuki Horiuchi *(Pres & Pres)*

KAKIYASU HONTEN CO., LTD.

8 Yoshinomaru, Kuwana, 511-8555, Mie, Japan
Tel.: (81) 594235500
Web Site:
 https://www.kakiyasuhonten.co.jp
Year Founded: 1871
2294—(TKS)
Rev.: $244,913,720
Assets: $143,351,070
Liabilities: $26,638,300
Net Worth: $116,712,770
Earnings: $9,254,000
Emp.: 886
Fiscal Year-end: 04/30/24
Meat Food Product Mfr & Distr
N.A.I.C.S.: 311613
Yasumasa Akatsuka *(Chm, Pres & CEO)*

KAKUYASU GROUP CO., LTD.

2-3-1 Toshima, Kita-Ku, Tokyo, 114-0003, Japan

AND PRIVATE COMPANIES

Tel.: (81) 339196110
Web Site: https://www.kakuyasu.co.jp
Year Founded: 1921
7686—(TKS)
Rev.: $855,373,660
Assets: $224,429,330
Liabilities: $197,222,570
Net Worth: $27,206,760
Earnings: $10,542,950
Fiscal Year-end: 03/31/24
Food & Beverage Distr
N.A.I.C.S.: 424820
Maegakiuchi Yoko (Pres & CEO)

KAL ENERGY, INC.
World Trade Center 14th Floor Jl Jenderal Sudirman Kav 29-31, Jl Jenderal Sudirman Kav 29-31, 12920, Jakarta, Indonesia
Tel.: (62) 215211110
Metal Mining Services
N.A.I.C.S.: 213114
William Bloking (Pres)

KAL GROUP LIMITED
1 Westhoven Street, Malmesbury, Paarl, 7646, Western, South Africa
Tel.: (27) 224828000   ZA
Web Site: https://www.kalgroup.co.za
Year Founded: 1912
KAL—(JSE)
Rev.: $1,182,789,108
Assets: $437,780,184
Liabilities: $274,796,470
Net Worth: $162,983,713
Earnings: $25,348,916
Emp.: 7,423
Fiscal Year-end: 09/30/23
Agricultural Product Mfr
N.A.I.C.S.: 325311
George M. Steyn (Chm)

KALAMAZOO RESOURCES LIMITED
16 Douro Place, West Perth, 6005, WA, Australia
Tel.: (61) 894818188   AU
Web Site: https://www.kzr.com.au
Year Founded: 2011
KZR—(ASX)
Rev.: $140,433
Assets: $18,075,290
Liabilities: $3,308,366
Net Worth: $14,766,924
Earnings: ($2,452,843)
Fiscal Year-end: 06/30/24
Gold Exploration Services
N.A.I.C.S.: 212220
Luke Reinehr (Chm & CEO)

KALANEUVOS OY
Hukkasentie 25, Sastamala, 38220, Finland
Tel.: (358) 104 111 400
Web Site: https://kalaneuvos.com
Year Founded: 1975
Emp.: 100
Fresh, Smoked & Marinated Fish Products Whslr
N.A.I.C.S.: 424460
Hanna Peltokangas (Dir-HR)

Subsidiaries:

Heimon Kala OY   (1)
Karajamaentie 6, 14300, Renko, Finland
Tel.: (358) 3644840
Web Site: http://www.heimonkala.fi
Emp.: 100
Fish Farming & Distr
N.A.I.C.S.: 112511
Marko Knuutinen (Product Mgr-ICT)

KALBER DAIRY J.S. CO.
No 26 Second Alley Moffateh St Beheshti St, Tehran, Iran
Tel.: (98) 2188732226

Web Site: https://www.kalber-dairy.com
Year Founded: 1994
KLBR—(THE)
Sales Range: Less than $1 Million
Emp.: 530
Dairy Products Mfr
N.A.I.C.S.: 311514

KALDERA COMPANY D.O.O.
Karadordeva bb, 78250, Laktasi, Bosnia & Herzegovina
Tel.: (387) 51 580 654
Web Site: http://www.kalderacompany.com
Year Founded: 1991
KLDR—(BANJ)
Sales Range: Less than $1 Million
Electric Equipment Mfr
N.A.I.C.S.: 335311

KALE ENVIRONMENTAL TECHNOLOGY (SHANGHAI) CO., LTD.
No 1588 Maixin Road, Xinqiao Town Songjiang District, Shanghai, 201108, China
Tel.: (86) 13655516303
Web Site: https://www.kalefans.net
Year Founded: 2010
301070—(CHIN)
Rev.: $42,673,176
Assets: $134,646,408
Liabilities: $23,608,260
Net Worth: $111,038,148
Earnings: $4,226,040
Fiscal Year-end: 12/31/22
Fan Mfr & Distr
N.A.I.C.S.: 336320
Xiaobo Lu (Chm & Gen Mgr)

KALEKIM KIMYEVI MADDELER SANAYI VE TICARET A.S.
Firuzkoy Neighborhood Firuzkoy Boulevard No 188, Avcilar, 34325, Istanbul, Turkiye
Tel.: (90) 2124230018
Web Site: http://www.kalekim.com
Year Founded: 1973
KLKIM—(IST)
Rev.: $114,450,851
Assets: $95,968,142
Liabilities: $35,644,385
Net Worth: $60,323,757
Earnings: $28,016,492
Fiscal Year-end: 12/31/22
Chemical Products Mfr
N.A.I.C.S.: 325998
Timur Karaoglu (CEO & Gen Mgr)

KALESERAMIK CANAKKALE KALEBODUR SERAMIK SANAYI A.S.
Buyukdere Caddesi Kaleseramik Binasi, Levent, 34330, Istanbul, Turkiye
Tel.: (90) 2123715253
Web Site: http://www.kale.com.tr
Year Founded: 1957
KLSER—(IST)
Rev.: $328,966,018
Assets: $423,346,173
Liabilities: $160,142,905
Net Worth: $263,203,268
Earnings: $9,999,468
Fiscal Year-end: 12/31/23
Granite Mfr & Distr
N.A.I.C.S.: 327991
Cemsit Baylan (Deputy Gen Mgr)

KALGOORLIE GOLD MINING LIMITED
Level 1 1209 Hay Street, West Perth, 6005, WA, Australia
Tel.: (61) 860022700   AU

Web Site: https://www.kalgoldmining.com.au
Year Founded: 2020
KAL—(ASX)
Rev.: $31
Assets: $10,906,855
Liabilities: $237,610
Net Worth: $10,669,245
Earnings: ($625,520)
Fiscal Year-end: 06/30/23
Mining Services
N.A.I.C.S.: 212290
Graeme Smith (Sec)

KALIKA LAGHUBITTA BITTIYA SANSTHA LTD.
Buddhachowk Pokhara-10 Kaski, Pokhara, Nepal
Tel.: (977) 61434412
Web Site: https://www.kalikabank.com.np
KMCDB—(NEP)
Rev.: $4,470,977
Assets: $29,684,261
Liabilities: $25,295,838
Net Worth: $4,388,423
Earnings: $204,460
Fiscal Year-end: 07/16/23
Commercial Banking Services
N.A.I.C.S.: 522110
Krishna Bahadur Khand (Chm)

KALINA POWER LIMITED
Suite 6 795 Glenferrie Road, Hawthorn, 3122, VIC, Australia
Tel.: (61) 392362800   AU
Web Site: https://www.kalinapower.com
Sales Range: Less than $1 Million
Emp.: 10
Energy Industry Equity Investment Firm
N.A.I.C.S.: 523999
Stephen White (Chm)

KALIUM LAKES LIMITED
Unit 1A 146 Balcatta Road, Balcatta, 6021, WA, Australia
Tel.: (61) 892403200   AU
Web Site: http://www.kaliumlakes.com.au
KLL—(ASX)
Rev.: $31,458
Assets: $280,145,140
Liabilities: $155,791,432
Net Worth: $124,353,708
Earnings: ($28,002,500)
Fiscal Year-end: 06/30/22
Potash Exploration Services
N.A.I.C.S.: 212390
Gregory Starr (Chm)

KALLAM TEXTILES LIMITED
Chowdavaram, Guntur, 522019, Andhra Pradesh, India
Tel.: (91) 8632344018
Web Site: https://www.ksml.in
Year Founded: 1994
530201—(BOM)
Rev.: $50,200,604
Assets: $69,260,104
Liabilities: $45,026,757
Net Worth: $24,233,346
Earnings: ($2,580,566)
Emp.: 414
Fiscal Year-end: 03/31/23
Yarn & Garment Mfr
N.A.I.C.S.: 313110
Poluri Venkateswara Reddy (Co-Mng Dir)

KALLEBACK PROPERTY INVEST AB
PO Box 239, 721 06, Vasteras, Sweden
Tel.: (46) 812032200

Web Site: https://www.kallebackproperty.se
KAPIAB—(OMX)
Rev.: $7,120,178
Assets: $113,413,321
Liabilities: $59,236,468
Net Worth: $54,176,852
Earnings: $5,104,574
Fiscal Year-end: 12/31/22
Real Estate Manangement Services
N.A.I.C.S.: 531390
Marrti Nordmark (CEO)

KALLFASS VERPACKUNGS-MASCHINEN GMBH
Siemensstrasse 8, 72622, Nurtingen, Germany
Tel.: (49) 70226070
Web Site: http://www.kallfass.de
Year Founded: 1965
Rev.: $23,725,680
Emp.: 90
Packaging Machinery Mfr
N.A.I.C.S.: 333993
Jens Kallfass (Mng Dir)

Subsidiaries:

Kallfass France SAS   (1)
Rue Erasme Gerber, 67700, Saverne, France
Tel.: (33) 88910402
Packaging Machinery Distr
N.A.I.C.S.: 423830
Alain Mattes (Branch Mgr)

KALLO, INC.
255 Duncan Mill Road Suite 504, North York, M3B 3H9, ON, Canada
Tel.: (416) 246-9997   NV
Web Site: https://www.kalloinc.ca
KALO—(OTCIQ)
Assets: $13,535
Liabilities: $6,509,097
Net Worth: ($6,495,562)
Earnings: ($8,093,468)
Emp.: 4
Fiscal Year-end: 12/31/21
Healtcare Services
N.A.I.C.S.: 541219
Lloyd A. Chiotti (Exec VP)

KALNORTH GOLD MINES LIMITED
Tel.: (61) 890218327
Web Site: https://www.kalnorthgoldmines.com
Rev.: $21,226
Assets: $3,968,847
Liabilities: $932,098
Net Worth: $3,036,749
Earnings: ($577,258)
Emp.: 8
Fiscal Year-end: 06/30/19
Gold Mining Services
N.A.I.C.S.: 212220
Jiajun Hu (Chm & Sec)

KALO GOLD CORP.
Suite 1507 1030 West Georgia Street, Vancouver, V6E 2Y3, BC, Canada
Tel.: (604) 363-0411
Web Site: https://kalogoldcorp.com
Year Founded: 2019
KALO—(TSXV)
Rev.: $21,669
Assets: $887,124
Liabilities: $486,114
Net Worth: $401,009
Earnings: ($2,608,181)
Fiscal Year-end: 08/31/23
Business Consulting Services
N.A.I.C.S.: 522299
Kevin Ma (Interim CFO, Pres-Capital Markets Lead, Sec & Exec VP-Capital Markets)

KALON ACQUISITION CORP.

Kalon Acquisition Corp.—(Continued)

KALON ACQUISITION CORP.
885 W Georgia St 2200, Vancouver, V6C 3E8, BC, Canada
Tel.: (212) 682-2420
Web Site:
https://www.kalonacquisition.com
Year Founded: 2019
KAC.P—(TSXV)
Assets: $104,663
Liabilities: $26,799
Net Worth: $77,864
Earnings: ($70,981)
Fiscal Year-end: 07/31/24
Business Consulting Services
N.A.I.C.S.: 522299
Andrew Benjamin *(CFO & Chief Comml Officer)*

KALORIMETA GMBH
Heidenkampsweg 40, Hamburg, Germany
Tel.: (49) 40237750
Web Site: http://www.kalo.de
Metering Services
N.A.I.C.S.: 541990
Thomas Colell *(Head-Sls-Mgmt)*

Subsidiaries:

QUNDIS GmbH (1)
Sonnentor 2, 99974, Erfurt, Germany
Tel.: (49) 361 26 2800
Web Site: http://www.qundis.com
Metering Device Mfr
N.A.I.C.S.: 334519
Rupert Paris *(Gen Mgr)*

KALPA COMMERCIAL LIMITED
301 Neelkanth Chamber II 14 Local Shopping Complex, Saini Enclave, Delhi, 110 092, India
Tel.: (91) 1165260012
Web Site:
http://www.kalpacommercial.in
Year Founded: 1985
Rev.: $308,337
Assets: $8,213,545
Liabilities: $17,052
Net Worth: $8,196,493
Earnings: $23,075
Fiscal Year-end: 03/31/18
Fabric & Textile Product Distr
N.A.I.C.S.: 424310
Mukul Jindal *(Exec Dir)*

KALPATARU LTD.
101 Kalpataru Synergy Opp Grand Hyatt, Santacruz, Mumbai, India
Tel.: (91) 2230645000
Web Site: http://www.kalpataru.com
Year Founded: 1969
Sales Range: $200-249.9 Million
Emp.: 1,000
Real Estate & Property Developer Services
N.A.I.C.S.: 236117
Mofatraj P. Munot *(Founder & Chm)*

Subsidiaries:

Kalpataru Power Transmission Limited (1)
Kalpataru Synergy 7th Floor Opp Grand Hyatt Santacruz E, Mumbai, 400055, Maharashtra, India
Tel.: (91) 2230645000
Web Site: https://kalpataruprojects.com
Rev.: $1,776,746,790
Assets: $2,095,756,845
Liabilities: $1,569,011,535
Net Worth: $526,745,310
Earnings: $90,368,460
Emp.: 3,296
Fiscal Year-end: 03/31/2021
Engineeering Services
N.A.I.C.S.: 541330
Sanjay Dalmia *(Exec Dir)*

Division (Domestic):

Kalpataru Power Transmission Ltd. - Biomass Energy Division (2)
27BB Tehsil Padampur, Sri Ganganagar, 335041, Rajasthan, India
Tel.: (91) 154 2473725
Electric Power Transmission Services
N.A.I.C.S.: 221122

Plant (Domestic):

Kalpataru Power Transmission Ltd. - Gandhinagar Plant (2)
Plot No A-4/1 A-4/2 A-5 G I D C Electronic Estate Sector-25, Gandhinagar, 382 025, India
Tel.: (91) 79 23214400
Electric Power Transmission Services
N.A.I.C.S.: 221122

Subsidiary (US):

Kalpataru Power Transmission USA INC. (2)
7500 Rialto Blvd Bldg 1 Ste 250, Austin, TX 78735
Tel.: (832) 341-7086
Web Site: http://www.kalpatarupower.us
Electricit Power Transmission Equipment Mfr
N.A.I.C.S.: 335311

Subsidiary (Domestic):

Kalpataru Satpura Transco Private limited. (2)
101 Part III GIDC Estate Sector 28, Gandhinagar, 382028, Gujarat, India
Tel.: (91) 79 232 14000
Electric Power Transmission Services
N.A.I.C.S.: 221122
Manish Mohnot *(Mng Dir)*

Shree Shubham Logistics Limited (2)
Plot No 1A 2A GIDC Electronic Estate Sector No 25, Gandhinagar, 382028, India (100%)
Tel.: (91) 79 2321 4000
Web Site: http://www.ssl.in
Emp.: 6
Logistics Consulting Servies
N.A.I.C.S.: 541614
Vishesh Singhvi *(Gen Mgr)*

Kalpataru Properties (Thane) Pvt. Ltd. (1)
Siddhachal Shopping Complex 1st floor Pokhran Road, No 2 Near Vasant Vihar, Thane, 400 601, India
Tel.: (91) 22 2171 3737
Real Estate Development Services
N.A.I.C.S.: 531210

Property Solutions India Pvt. Ltd. (1)
73 Kalpataru Square Off Andheri Kurla Road, Kondavita Lane Andheri E, Mumbai, 400 059, India
Tel.: (91) 2233277100
Web Site: http://www.psipl.co.in
Real Estate Property Development Services
N.A.I.C.S.: 531390
Deepak Shanbhag *(COO)*

KALRAY SA
180 Avenue de l Europe, 38330, Montbonnot-Saint-Martin, France
Tel.: (33) 476189071
Web Site: https://www.kalrayinc.com
Year Founded: 2008
3FS—(BER)
Rev.: $15,151,569
Assets: $53,158,227
Liabilities: $21,682,121
Net Worth: $31,476,106
Earnings: ($18,564,848)
Emp.: 103
Fiscal Year-end: 12/31/21
Electronic Products Mfr
N.A.I.C.S.: 334111
Eric Baissus *(CEO)*

KALREZ PETROLEUM (SERAM) LIMITED
Jl Jend Gatot Subroto Kav 171-73 Menara Bidakara Lt 5 Pancoran, Jakarta, 12780, Indonesia
Tel.: (62) 21 837 93019
Crude Oil Extraction Services
N.A.I.C.S.: 211120

KALTHOFF LUFTFILTER UND FILTERMEDIEN GMBH
Gutenbergstr 8, D-59379, Selm, Germany
Tel.: (49) 25929650
Web Site: http://www.kalthoff-luftfilter.de
Year Founded: 1963
Rev.: $23,173,920
Emp.: 163
Air Filter Products & Services
N.A.I.C.S.: 333413
Hans-Joachim Badt *(Partner)*

KALUGSK SBYT COMPANY AO
Per Suvorova 8, Kaluga, 248001, Russia
Tel.: (7) 4842701801
Web Site: http://www.ksc.kaluga.ru
KLSB—(MOEX)
Sales Range: Less than $1 Million
Electric Power Distribution Services
N.A.I.C.S.: 221122

KALYAN CAPITALS LTD.
Plaza-3 P-204 Second Floor Central Square 20 Manohar Lal Khurana Marg, Bara Hindu Rao, Delhi, 110006, India
Tel.: (91) 7417823670
Web Site: https://kalyancapitals.com
Year Founded: 1983
538778—(BOM)
Rev.: $563,260
Assets: $6,623,956
Liabilities: $2,345,255
Net Worth: $4,278,700
Earnings: $133,801
Emp.: 3
Fiscal Year-end: 03/31/21
Financial Support Services
N.A.I.C.S.: 541611
Rajesh Gupta *(Chm & Mng Dir)*

KALYAN JEWELLERS INDIA LIMITED
Tc 32 / 204 / 2 Sitaram Mill Road, Punkunnam, Thrissur, 680002, Kerala, India
Tel.: (91) 4872437333
Web Site:
https://www.kalyanjewellers.net
Year Founded: 1908
543278—(BOM)
Rev.: $1,481,874,986
Assets: $1,221,011,474
Liabilities: $792,678,432
Net Worth: $428,333,042
Earnings: $30,604,529
Emp.: 7,803
Fiscal Year-end: 03/31/22
Jewellery Distr
N.A.I.C.S.: 458310
T. S. Kalyanaraman *(Chm & Mng Dir)*

Subsidiaries:

Kalyan Jewellers FZE (1)
Shop No-7 Lootah Building Damascus Street Opp Fortune Grand Hotel, Al Qusais, 113498, Dubai, United Arab Emirates
Tel.: (971) 8000320603
Web Site: https://stores.kalyanjewellers.net
Jewellery Distr
N.A.I.C.S.: 458310

Kalyan Jewellers LLC (1)
Abdul Jaleel Business Center 3rd Floor Unit No 303 Najma Airport Road, Doha, Qatar
Tel.: (974) 40192733
Jewellery Distr
N.A.I.C.S.: 458310

INTERNATIONAL PUBLIC

Kalyan Jewellers for Golden Jewelry Company, W.L.L. (1)
13th Floor Ghunaim Tower Abu Baker Al Siddeeq Al Qibla Maliya, Kuwait, Kuwait
Tel.: (965) 22287633
Jewelry Retailer
N.A.I.C.S.: 458310

KALYANI COMMERCIALS LIMITED
BG-223 Sanjay Gandhi Transport Nagar GT Karnal Road, New Delhi, 110 042, India
Tel.: (91) 1143063223
Web Site:
https://www.kalyanicommercials.com
Year Founded: 1985
Rev.: $78,771,736
Assets: $10,190,247
Liabilities: $9,300,997
Net Worth: $889,250
Earnings: $91,167
Emp.: 161
Fiscal Year-end: 03/31/16
Financial Services
N.A.I.C.S.: 523999
Shankar Lal Agarwal *(Mng Dir)*

KALYANI GROUP
Mundhwa Pune Cantonment, Pune, 411036, India
Tel.: (91) 2026702777
Web Site:
http://www.kalyanigroup.com
Sales Range: $1-4.9 Billion
Emp.: 10,000
Holding Company; Steel Forgings; Automotive Products
N.A.I.C.S.: 551112
B. N. Kalyani *(Chm & Mng Dir)*

Subsidiaries:

Automotive Axles Limited (1)
Hootagalli Industrial Area Off Hunsur Road, Mysore, 570 018, Karnataka, India
Tel.: (91) 8217197500
Web Site: http://www.autoaxle.com
Rev.: $279,194,293
Assets: $138,669,145
Liabilities: $47,628,679
Net Worth: $91,040,465
Earnings: $19,426,773
Emp.: 988
Fiscal Year-end: 03/31/2023
Motor Vehicle Rear Drive Axle Assemblies Mfr; Owned by Kalyani Group & by ArvinMeritor, Inc.
N.A.I.C.S.: 336390
Babasaheb Neelkanth Kalyani *(Chm)*

Bharat Forge Ltd. (1)
Mundhwa, PO Box 57, Pune Cantonment Area, Pune, 411 036, Maharashtra, India
Tel.: (91) 20 67042777
Web Site: http://www.bharatforge.com
Engine & Automotive Parts Mfr
N.A.I.C.S.: 336390
Kishore Saletore *(Exec Dir)*

Subsidiary (US):

Bharat Forge America Inc (2)
2807 S Martin Luther King Jr Blvd, Lansing, MI 48910-2653
Tel.: (517) 393-5300
Web Site: http://www.bharatforge.com
Sales Range: $50-74.9 Million
Emp.: 150
Iron & Steel Forgings
N.A.I.C.S.: 332111

Division (Domestic):

Bharat Forge Limited - Capital Goods Division (2)
CS-8-10 6th Floor Tower A The Corenthum Bldg A-41 Sector 62, Noida, 201301, Uttar Pradesh, India
Tel.: (91) 120 4638000
Automobile Parts Mfr
N.A.I.C.S.: 336390

AND PRIVATE COMPANIES

Subsidiary (Non-US):

CDP Bharat Forge GmbH (2)
Mittelstr 64, 58256, Ennepetal, Germany
Tel.: (49) 2333 796 0
Web Site: http://www.cdp-bharatforge.com
Automobile Parts Mfr
N.A.I.C.S.: 336390
Michael Weis (Chm & Mng Dir)

Kalyani Carpenter Special Steels Ltd. (1)
Mundhwa, Pune Cantonment, Pune, 411 036, Maharashtra, India (83.75%)
Tel.: (91) 20 66215000
Web Site: http://www.kalyanicarpenter.com
Sales Range: $150-199.9 Million
Metal Sales & Services; Owned by Kalyani Group & Carpenter Technology Corporation
N.A.I.C.S.: 331110

Kalyani Forge Limited (1)
1st Floor C Wing Shangrila Gardens Opp Bund Garden, Pune, 411001, India
Tel.: (91) 2137252335
Web Site: https://www.kalyaniforge.co.in
Rev.: $24,879,063
Assets: $24,993,587
Liabilities: $11,317,242
Net Worth: $13,676,345
Earnings: ($240,281)
Emp.: 576
Fiscal Year-end: 03/31/2021
Forged Machine Component Mfr
N.A.I.C.S.: 332111
Rohini Gaurishankar Kalyani (Chm & Mng Dir)

Kalyani Infotech Solutions Ltd. (1)
Industry House Opp Kalyani Steels Carpenter Limited, Mundhwa, Pune, 411036, Maharashtra, India
Tel.: (91) 20 26814971
Web Site: http://www.kalyaniinfotech.com
Computer System Design Services
N.A.I.C.S.: 541512
Abhay Jagdale (Co-CEO-Engg & Trng Svcs)

Kalyani TechnoForge Limited (1)
S No 72-76 Behind Siporex, Mundhawa, Pune, 411036, India
Tel.: (91) 20 66441000
Web Site: http://www.kalyanitechnoforge.com
Steel Forging Services
N.A.I.C.S.: 332111
S. B. Kalyani (Chm)

Plant (Domestic):

Kalyani TechnoForge Limited - Baramati Plant (2)
Survey No A-7 MIDC, Baramati Dist, Pune, 413 102, India
Tel.: (91) 2112 243854
Steel Forging Services
N.A.I.C.S.: 332111

Kalyani TechnoForge Limited - Manesar Plant (2)
Plot No 103 Sector 8 IMT MIDC, Manesar, Gurgaon, 122001, Haryana, India
Tel.: (91) 124 4679500
Steel Forging Services
N.A.I.C.S.: 332111
Amit Kalyani (Mng Dir)

Kalyani TechnoForge Limited - Ranjangaon Plant (2)
Plot No E-84 MIDC Ranjangaon Ind, Village - Karegaon Taluka - Shirur Dist, Pune, India
Tel.: (91) 2138 674000
Steel Forging Services
N.A.I.C.S.: 332111

Kalyani Technologies Ltd. (1)
Office No 602 Level 6 Tower No 15, Cybercity Magarpatta Hadapsar, Pune, 411 013, India
Tel.: (91) 20 64011375
Web Site: http://www.kalyanitechnologies.com
Information Technology Consulting Services
N.A.I.C.S.: 541512
Yogesh Zope (CEO-Tech Svcs SBU)

Synise Technologies Ltd (1)
Omkar Plot No A-8 Shivtirth Nagar Paud Road, Kothrud, Pune, 411038, India
Tel.: (91) 20 30277500
Web Site: http://www.synise.com
Information Technology Consulting Services
N.A.I.C.S.: 541512
Ashok Dani (CEO)

KALYANI INVESTMENT COMPANY LIMITED
Mundhwa, Pune, 411 036, Maharashtra, India
Tel.: (91) 2066215000
Web Site: https://www.kalyani-investment.com
533302—(BOM)
Sales Range: $1-9.9 Million
Emp.: 2
Investment Management Service
N.A.I.C.S.: 523999
Amit B. Kalyani (Chm)

KALYANI STEELS LTD
Corporate Building 2nd Floor Mundhwa, Pune, 411036, Maharashtra, India
Tel.: (91) 2066215000
Web Site: https://www.kalyanisteels.com
Year Founded: 1973
KSL—(NSE)
Rev.: $168,009,387
Assets: $225,287,244
Liabilities: $68,392,643
Net Worth: $156,894,602
Earnings: $25,932,680
Emp.: 63
Fiscal Year-end: 03/31/21
Mfr of Forging & Engineering Carbon & Alloy Steels
N.A.I.C.S.: 332111
Ravindra Kumar Goyal (Mng Dir)

KALYANPUR CEMENTS LIMITED
2&3 Dr Rajendra Prasad Sarani, Kolkata, 700001, West Bengal, India
Tel.: (91) 33 22302977
Web Site: http://www.kalyanpur.com
Year Founded: 1937
502150—(BOM)
Sales Range: $1-9.9 Million
Cement Mfr & Whslr
N.A.I.C.S.: 327310
Shailendra Prakash Sinha (Mng Dir)

KAM & RONSON MEDIA GROUP INC.
30 Wertheim Court Unit 10 East Office, Richmond Hill, L4B 1B9, ON, Canada
Tel.: (905) 886-8882
Year Founded: 2003
Sales Range: $1-9.9 Million
Motion Picture & Video Distribution Services
N.A.I.C.S.: 512120
Kam Chak Man (Co-Founder, Pres & CEO)

KAM HING INTERNATIONAL HOLDINGS LIMITED
Unit A 23rd Floor TML Tower No 3 Hoi Shing Road, Tsuen Wan, New Territories, China (Hong Kong)
Tel.: (852) 24060080
Web Site: http://www.kamhingintl.com
2307—(HKG)
Rev.: $523,536,420
Assets: $519,434,873
Liabilities: $274,934,625
Net Worth: $244,500,248
Earnings: ($6,976,035)
Emp.: 3,919
Fiscal Year-end: 12/31/22
Knitted Fabrics, Dyed Yarn & Garment Product Mfr
N.A.I.C.S.: 424310
Siu Yuk Wong (Exec Dir)

Subsidiaries:

En Ping Kam Hing Textile & Dyeing Co., Ltd. (1)
No 68 Industrial North Road Enzhou, En-ping Shi, Jiangmen, Guangdong, China
Tel.: (86) 7507816688
Garment & Clothing Accessory Mfr
N.A.I.C.S.: 315990

Guangzhou Kam Sing Textile and Dyeing Company Limited (1)
No 32 Li Ye Rd Dong Chong Town, Panyu Dist, Guangzhou, 511453, Guangdong, China
Tel.: (86) 2084903888
Garments Mfr & Sales
N.A.I.C.S.: 313230

Guangzhou Kamhing Textile Dyeing Co., Ltd. (1)
32 Li Ye Roa, Dong Chong Nansha, Guangzhou, Guangdong, China
Tel.: (86) 2084903888
Garment & Clothing Accessory Mfr
N.A.I.C.S.: 315990

Hong Kong Kam Hing Threads Limited (1)
Rm 1-9 8/F Lucida Industrial Building, 43-47 Wang Lung Street, Tsuen Wan, NT, China (Hong Kong)
Tel.: (852) 24060080
Sales Range: $25-49.9 Million
Emp.: 100
Fabrics Processing Services
N.A.I.C.S.: 313240
Daryl Lye (Gen Mgr)

Kam Hing Global Garment Company Limited (1)
Rm 1-3 12/F Lucida Industrial Building, 43-47 Wang Lung St, Tsuen Wan, NT, China (Hong Kong)
Tel.: (852) 24064938
Garments Mfr & Sales
N.A.I.C.S.: 315210

Kam Hing Piece Works (S) Pte Limited (1)
Unit 05-03 5/F HB Centre No 12 Tannery Road, Singapore, 347722, Singapore
Tel.: (65) 68426896
Web Site: http://www.kamhingpieceworks.com
Sales Range: $25-49.9 Million
Emp.: 8
Customer Care Services
N.A.I.C.S.: 541613
Julie Tay (Mgr)

Kam Hing Piece Works Limited (1)
Workshop A on 23rd Floor TML Tower No 3 Hoi Shing Road, Tsuen Wan, New Territories, China (Hong Kong)
Tel.: (852) 24060080
Web Site: https://www.khpieceworks.com
Emp.: 100
Knitted Fabrics & Dyed Yarns Sales
N.A.I.C.S.: 424350

Kam Hing Textile Macao Commercial Offshore Company Limited (1)
Av Do Dr Rodrigo Rodrigues No 576-600J, Edif Commercial First Inter P11-05, Macau, China (Macau)
Tel.: (853) 2 870 0182
Web Site: https://www.kamhingintl.com
Emp.: 7
Garments Mfr & Sales
N.A.I.C.S.: 313210

Kam Wing International Textile Company Limited (1)
8/F Lucida Industrial Building, 43-47 Wang Lung Street, Tsuen Wan, NT, China (Hong Kong)
Tel.: (852) 24060080
Web Site: http://www.kamhingintl.com
Sales Range: $50-74.9 Million
Emp.: 200
Apparel Whslr
N.A.I.C.S.: 424350

Sparkle Logistics Limited (1)
8/F Lucida Ind Bldg 43-47 Wang Lung St, Tsuen Wan, NT, China (Hong Kong)
Tel.: (852) 24064983
Air & Sea Freight Transportation Services
N.A.I.C.S.: 481112

KAMA HOLDINGS LIMITED
Block-C Sector-45, Gurgaon, 122 003, Haryana, India
Tel.: (91) 1244354400
Web Site: https://www.kamaholdings.com
532468—(BOM)
Rev.: $1,160,237,838
Assets: $1,812,828,381
Liabilities: $838,889,756
Net Worth: $973,938,625
Earnings: $163,296,684
Emp.: 3
Fiscal Year-end: 03/31/21
Real Estate & Education Services
N.A.I.C.S.: 531210
Kartik Bharat Ram (Chm)

Subsidiaries:

Shri Educare Limited (1)
Unitech Business Zone Tower- C 1st Floor Nirvana Country Sector 50, South City 2 Gurugram, New Delhi, 122 018, India
Tel.: (91) 1244529900
Web Site: https://www.shrieducare.com
Educational Support Services
N.A.I.C.S.: 611710
Sudha Santhanam (Assoc VP)

KAMA RESOURCES INC.
Suite 1707-B 17th Floor CTS Center 219 Zhong Shan Wu Road, Guangzhou, 510030, China
Tel.: (86) 13808821282 NV
Web Site: http://www.kamaresources.cn
Year Founded: 2009
Emp.: 1
Automotive Financing
N.A.I.C.S.: 522310
Dayong Sun (Pres, CEO, Treas & Sec)

KAMADA LTD.
2 Holzman Street Science Park, PO Box 4081, Rehovot, 7670402, Israel
Tel.: (972) 89406472 II
Web Site: https://www.kamada.com
Year Founded: 1990
KMDA—(NASDAQ)
Rev.: $129,339,000
Assets: $322,379,000
Liabilities: $146,359,000
Net Worth: $176,020,000
Earnings: ($2,321,000)
Emp.: 380
Fiscal Year-end: 12/31/22
Pharmaceuticals Mfr
N.A.I.C.S.: 325412
David Tsur (Founder & Deputy Chm)

KAMADGIRI FASHION LTD.
202 2nd Floor Rajan House Appa Saheb Marathe Marg, Near century bhavan Prabhadevi, Mumbai, 400025, India
Tel.: (91) 66662904
Web Site: https://www.kflindia.com
Year Founded: 1987
514322—(BOM)
Rev.: $38,611,441
Assets: $21,220,891
Liabilities: $16,332,580
Net Worth: $4,888,311
Earnings: $201,433
Emp.: 3,000
Fiscal Year-end: 03/31/23
Textile & Apparels Mfr
N.A.I.C.S.: 315990
Pradip Kumar Narayan Prasad Goenka (Chm & Mng Dir)

KAMAKURA SHINSHO, LTD.

Kamakura Shinsho, Ltd.—(Continued)
Kanematsu Bldg 3rd Floor 2-14-1
Kyobashi, Chuo-ku, Tokyo, 103-0021,
Japan
Tel.: (81) 362623521
Web Site: https://www.kamakura-net.co.jp
Year Founded: 1984
6184—(TKS)
Rev.: $41,540,310
Assets: $28,700,320
Liabilities: $6,352,640
Net Worth: $22,347,680
Earnings: $3,757,700
Emp.: 298
Fiscal Year-end: 01/31/24
Internet Portal for End of Life Planning
N.A.I.C.S.: 519290
Fumio Kobayashi *(Pres & COO)*

KAMANA SEWA BIKAS BANK LTD.

Gyaneshwar Aanand Bhairab Marg,
Kathmandu, Nepal
Tel.: (977) 15970030
Web Site:
https://www.kamanasewabank.com
KSBBL—(NEP)
Rev.: $54,724,287
Assets: $468,973,279
Liabilities: $433,484,667
Net Worth: $35,488,612
Earnings: $2,708,009
Emp.: 1,031
Fiscal Year-end: 07/16/23
Commercial Banking Services
N.A.I.C.S.: 522110
Praben Basnet *(CEO)*

Subsidiaries:

Kamana Bikash Bank Limited (1)
Gyaneshwar Aanand Bhairab Marg, Kathmandu, 30, Nepal
Tel.: (977) 01 4440115
Web Site: http://www.kamanasewabank.com
Banking Services
N.A.I.C.S.: 522110

Sewa Bikas Bank Limited (1)
Pushpa Lal Park Rupandehi, Butwal, 32908, Nepal
Tel.: (977) 71 546993
Web Site: http://www.sewabank.com.np
Banking Services
N.A.I.C.S.: 522110
Bhim Prasad Tulachan *(Chm)*

KAMANWALA HOUSING CONSTRUCTION LIMITED

406 New Udyog Mandir-2 Mogul
Lane, Mahim West, Mumbai, 400
016, Maharashtra, India
Tel.: (91) 2224456029
Web Site:
https://www.kamanwalahousing.com
511131—(BOM)
Rev.: $589,906
Assets: $12,338,705
Liabilities: $1,697,685
Net Worth: $10,641,019
Earnings: ($23,865)
Emp.: 2
Fiscal Year-end: 03/31/21
Construction Engineering Services
N.A.I.C.S.: 541330
Atul Attarsen Jain *(Co-Founder & Mng Dir)*

KAMAT HOTELS INDIA LTD

KHIL House 70-C Nehru Road Vile
Parle East Adjoining Orchid Hotel,
Mumbai, 400 099, India
Tel.: (91) 2226164000
Web Site: https://www.khil.com
526668—(BOM)
Rev.: $19,878,427
Assets: $63,728,915
Liabilities: $88,458,224
Net Worth: ($24,729,309)
Earnings: ($3,094,701)
Emp.: 689
Fiscal Year-end: 03/31/22
Hotel Services
N.A.I.C.S.: 721110
Vithal Venketesh Kamat *(Chm & Mng Dir)*

Subsidiaries:

Orchid Hotels Pune Private Limited
Pune-Banglore Road Near Balewadi Sports Complex, Balewadi, Pune, 411045, India
Tel.: (91) 2067914040
Web Site: https://www.orchidhotel.com
Hotel Services
N.A.I.C.S.: 721110

KAMAX-WERKE RUDOLF KELLERMANN GMBH & CO. KG

Peter Huetter Allee 29, 37520, Osterode am Hartz, Germany
Tel.: (49) 55223150   De
Web Site: http://www.kamax.com
Year Founded: 1935
Sales Range: $600-649.9 Million
Emp.: 340
Fasteners, Bolts & Studs Mfr
N.A.I.C.S.: 332722
Stefan Schulz *(VP-HR)*

Subsidiaries:

KAMAX (Zhenjiang) Automotive Fasteners Trading Co., Ltd. (1)
4th Floor Henghuayuan 12 Dingmaoqiao Road 230, Zhenjiang, 212009, Jiangsu, China
Tel.: (86) 511 85916 608
Web Site: http://www.kamax.com
Emp.: 14
Fastener Mfr
N.A.I.C.S.: 332722
Jiang Dong Liang *(Gen Mgr)*

KAMAX Automotive Fasteners (China) Co., Ltd. (1)
No 25 Changyang Road Wujin Economic Development Zone, Changzhou, 213149, Jiangsu, China
Tel.: (86) 519 8011 6666
Emp.: 60
Fastener Mfr
N.A.I.C.S.: 332722

KAMAX Automotive GmbH (1)
Dr-Rudolf-Kellermann-Str 2, 35315, Homberg (Ohm), Germany
Tel.: (49) 6633 79 0
Web Site: http://www.kamax.com
Emp.: 75
Fastener Mfr
N.A.I.C.S.: 332722

KAMAX GmbH & Co. KG (1)
Am Kreuzweg 4, 36304, Alsfeld, Germany
Tel.: (49) 6631 7766 0
Fastener Mfr
N.A.I.C.S.: 332722

KAMAX K.K. (1)
580-16 Horikawa-chou, Saiwaki-ku, Kawasaki, 212-0013, Kanagawa-ken, Japan
Tel.: (81) 44 542 3680
Fastener Mfr
N.A.I.C.S.: 332722

KAMAX L.P. (1)
1194 Roods Lake Rd, Lapeer, MI 48446
Tel.: (810) 664-7741
Web Site: http://www.kamax.com
Sales Range: $125-149.9 Million
Emp.: 460
Bolt Nut & Screw Mfr
N.A.I.C.S.: 332722
Heather Dinverno *(Dir-HR)*

KAMAX S.A.U. (1)
Calle del Emperador 4 Museros, 46136, Valencia, Comunidad Valenciana, Spain
Tel.: (34) 96 145 20 25
Emp.: 215
Fastener Mfr
N.A.I.C.S.: 332722

KAMAX k.s. (1)
Priemyselna 3752, Bardejov, Slovakia
Tel.: (421) 54 48887 31
Emp.: 150
Fastener Mfr
N.A.I.C.S.: 332722

KAMAX s.r.o. (1)
Nudvojovicka 1474, 511 01, Turnov, Czech Republic
Tel.: (420) 481 353 111
Web Site: http://www.kamax.com
Emp.: 440
Fastener Mfr
N.A.I.C.S.: 332722

KAMAYA KAGAKU KOGYO CO. LTD.

23-6 Asakusabashi 5 chrome, Tokyo, 111-0053, Taitou-ku, Japan
Tel.: (81) 3 3865 8825
Cosmetics Products Mfr
N.A.I.C.S.: 456120

Subsidiaries:

Thai Kamaya Co., Ltd. (1)
314 Moo 1 Tambon Bueng Sriracha, Chon Buri, 20230, Thailand
Tel.: (66) 3848 0510
Web Site: http://www.thaikamaya.com
Emp.: 400
Cosmetics Packaging
N.A.I.C.S.: 561910

KAMAZ PUBLICLY TRADED COMPANY

Avtozavodsky Avenue 2, Naberezhnye Chelny, 423827, Tatarstan, Russia
Tel.: (7) 8005550099
Web Site: https://www.kamaz.ru
Year Founded: 1969
KMAZ—(MOEX)
Rev.: $3,626,635,860
Assets: $3,654,114,660
Liabilities: $2,878,363,890
Net Worth: $775,750,770
Earnings: $62,406,510
Emp.: 31,931
Fiscal Year-end: 12/31/21
Automobile Mfr
N.A.I.C.S.: 336110
Sergey A. Kogogin *(Chm-Mgmt Bd)*

Subsidiaries:

Chelnyvodokanal LLC (1)
Khlebny proezd 27, PO Box 1166, 423800, Naberezhnye Chelny, Russia
Tel.: (7) 8552534450
Web Site: http://www.chelnyvodokanal.ru
Emp.: 1,462
Water Supply & Wastewater Disposal Services
N.A.I.C.S.: 221310

JSC NefAZ (1)
st Yanaulskaya 3, Neftekamsk, 452680, Russia   (50.02%)
Tel.: (7) 3478362074
Web Site: http://www.nefaz.ru
Sales Range: Less than $1 Million
Motor Vehicles Mfr
N.A.I.C.S.: 336120

KAMAZ International Trade Company JSC (1)
2 Pr Avtozavodsky, Naberezhnye Chelny, Russia
Tel.: (7) 8552452277
Automotive Truck & Spare Part Retailer
N.A.I.C.S.: 441330

KAMAZ-Energo LLC (1)
St Promyshlennaya d 73 industrial zone, Industrial and Communal Zone Industrial Zone, Naberezhnye Chelny, Russia
Tel.: (7) 8552372866
Web Site: http://www.kamaz-energo.ru
Electric Power Transmission Services
N.A.I.C.S.: 221121

KAMAZ-Engineering JSC (1)
13 Mir St, 020004, Kokshetau, Kazakhstan
Tel.: (7) 162723723
Automotive Truck & Spare Part Mfr
N.A.I.C.S.: 336211

KAMAZzhilbyt LLC (1)
St Academician Rubanenko Building 6, 423810, Naberezhnye Chelny, Russia
Tel.: (7) 8552396677
Web Site: http://www.kamgb.ru
Hotel & Recreation Resort Services
N.A.I.C.S.: 721110

KIP Master JSC (1)
45 Proizvodstvenny Proezd, 423800, Naberezhnye Chelny, Russia
Tel.: (7) 8552534520
Web Site: http://www.kipmaster.ru
Emp.: 6,900
Lease Non-Residential Premise Services
N.A.I.C.S.: 531120

NPF First Industrial Alliance JSC (1)
St Vishnevsky 2E, 420097, Kazan, Russia
Tel.: (7) 8432644409
Web Site: http://www.ppafond.ru
Pension Fund & Insurance Services
N.A.I.C.S.: 525110

OAO Tuimazinskiy Zavod Avtobetonovozov (1)
Republic of Bashkortostan, 452755, Tuymazy, 452755, Russia   (51.77%)
Tel.: (7) 3478271011
Web Site: https://www.tzacom.ru
Sales Range: Less than $1 Million
Concrete Machinery Mfr
N.A.I.C.S.: 333120

OOO Crane Center KAMAZ (1)
Promyshlenno-kommunalnaya Zona 45 Proizvodstvenny Proezd, Naberezhnye Chelny, Russia
Tel.: (7) 8552915252
Automotive Truck Mfr
N.A.I.C.S.: 336211

KAMBI GROUP PLC

Avenue 77 A4 Triq in-Negozju Zone 3
Central Business District, Birkirkara,
CBD 3010, Malta
Tel.: (356) 27922100
Web Site: https://www.kambi.com
Year Founded: 2010
KAMBI—(OMX)
Rev.: $179,156,054
Assets: $262,128,211
Liabilities: $85,798,619
Net Worth: $176,329,592
Earnings: $28,546,298
Emp.: 1,000
Fiscal Year-end: 12/31/22
Financial Support Services
N.A.I.C.S.: 541611
Kristian Nylen *(CEO)*

Subsidiaries:

Kambi Malta Limited (1)
Avenue 77 A4 Triq in-Negozju Zone 3, Central Business District, Birkirkara, CBD 3010, Malta
Tel.: (356) 27922100
Information Technology Services
N.A.I.C.S.: 541511

Kambi Philippines Inc. (1)
18/F Zuellig Building Makati Ave cor Paseo de Roxas, Makati, 1226, Philippines
Tel.: (63) 28330454
Information Technology Services
N.A.I.C.S.: 541511

Kambi Services Limited (1)
3rd Floor 1 Queen Caroline Street, London, W6 9HQ, United Kingdom
Tel.: (44) 2081429325
Information Technology Services
N.A.I.C.S.: 541511

Kambi Sweden AB (1)
Halsingegatan 38 1, 11343, Stockholm, Sweden
Tel.: (46) 850902209
Information Technology Services
N.A.I.C.S.: 541511

AND PRIVATE COMPANIES

KAMCHATSKENERGO
st Embankment 10, Petropavlovsk-Kamchatsky, 683000, Russia
Tel.: (7) 4152216759
Web Site: http://www.kamenergo.ru
KCHE—(MOEX)
Sales Range: Less than $1 Million
Electric Power Distribution Services
N.A.I.C.S.: 221122
Sergey Vyacheslavovich Vasilev *(Chm)*

KAMDAR GROUP (M) BERHAD
113 Jalan Tuanku Abdul Rahman, 50100, Kuala Lumpur, Malaysia
Tel.: (60) 326020562
Web Site:
   https://www.kamdar.com.my
KAMDAR—(KLS)
Rev.: $14,485,467
Assets: $60,761,394
Liabilities: $13,018,969
Net Worth: $47,742,425
Earnings: ($1,105,387)
Emp.: 1,300
Fiscal Year-end: 06/30/23
Textile & Textile Products Retail Services
N.A.I.C.S.: 313210
Lee Hoon Chia *(Exec Dir)*

Subsidiaries:

Kamdar (Bru) Sdn. Bhd. (1)
Unit 24/25 Ground Floor Block B Regent Square Kg Kiulap, Bandar Seri Begawan, BE1518, Brunei Darussalam
Tel.: (673) 2233018
Clothing Accessories Retailer
N.A.I.C.S.: 458110

Kamdar (South) Sdn. Bhd. (1)
1 Jalan Tun Fatimah Bacang Utama, Melaka, 75350, Malaysia
Tel.: (60) 326938988
Sales Range: $25-49.9 Million
Emp.: 40
Clothing Accessories Retailer
N.A.I.C.S.: 458110
Kamal Kamdar *(Mgr)*

Kamdar Sdn. Berhad (1)
Unit TV 02 & TV 03-GF The Verva No G-3 & 5 Jalan Merbah 1, Bandar Jaya, 47170, Puchong, Selangor, Malaysia
Tel.: (60) 380740045
Textile Product Whslr
N.A.I.C.S.: 424990

Pusat Membeli-belah Kamdar (Penang) Sdn. Bhd. (1)
No 14 Burmah Road, 10050, Penang, Malaysia
Tel.: (60) 42277089
Web Site: http://www.kamdar.com.my
Emp.: 30
Clothing Accessories Retailer
N.A.I.C.S.: 458110

Pusat Membeli-belah Kamdar Sdn. Bhd. (1)
15 Kompleks Seri Temin Jalan Ibrahim, 08000, Sungai Petani, Kedah, Malaysia
Tel.: (60) 44216558
Web Site: http://www.kamdar.com.my
Emp.: 31
Clothing Accessories Retailer
N.A.I.C.S.: 458110

KAMDHENU LTD
2nd Floor Tower-A Building No 9, DLF Cyber City Phase-III, Gurgaon, 122 002, Haryana, India
Tel.: (91) 1244604500
Web Site:
   https://www.kamdhenulimited.com
532741—(BOM)
Rev.: $85,819,611
Assets: $58,849,341
Liabilities: $32,265,638
Net Worth: $26,583,703
Earnings: $2,057,901
Emp.: 859

Fiscal Year-end: 03/31/21
Steel Bar Mfr
N.A.I.C.S.: 331110
Satish Kumar Agarwal *(Chm & Mng Dir)*

KAMEDA SEIKA CO., LTD.
3-1-1 Kameda Industrial Park, Konan-Ku, Niigata, 950 0198, Japan
Tel.: (81) 253822111
Web Site:
   http://www.kamedaseika.co.jp
2220—(TKS)
Rev.: $631,479,740
Assets: $796,571,100
Liabilities: $309,295,120
Net Worth: $487,275,980
Earnings: $14,918,770
Emp.: 4,040
Fiscal Year-end: 03/31/24
Rice Cracker Mfr
N.A.I.C.S.: 311821
Michiyasu Tanaka *(Chm & CEO)*

Subsidiaries:

Kameda USA, Inc. (1)
3868 W Carson St Ste 312, Torrance, CA 90503
Tel.: (310) 944-9639
Web Site: http://www.kamedausa.com
Emp.: 4
Snack Food Mfr & Distr
N.A.I.C.S.: 311919
Taco Yasumaru *(Gen Mgr)*

Maisen Co., Ltd. (1)
Tel.: (81) 120810932
Web Site: http://www.maisen.co.jp
Food Mfr & Distr
N.A.I.C.S.: 311999

N.A.S CO., LTD. (1)
No 79AEo St 288Sangkat Olympic Khan Chamkar Morn, 12312, Phnom Penh, Cambodia
Tel.: (855) 12786971
Automobile Dealers
N.A.I.C.S.: 441110

N.A.S. Co., Ltd. (1)
185-1 Ichinoyama, Agano, 959-2062, Niigata, Japan
Tel.: (81) 250625740
Web Site: https://www.autoforum-nas.jp
Automotive Repair & Maintenance Services
N.A.I.C.S.: 811111

NIIGATA YUSO CO., LTD (1)
No 1 10th 5-chome Sunaoka, Gangnam-gu, Niigata, Japan   (100%)
Tel.: (81) 250674861
Web Site: http://www.niigatayuso.com
Emp.: 452
Logistic & Warehousing Services
N.A.I.C.S.: 493110

Nisshin Seika Co., Ltd. (1)
1312 Shimokokuracho, Utsunomiya, 321-0403, Tochigi, Japan
Tel.: (81) 286741212
Web Site: https://www.nissin-seika.co.jp
Emp.: 180
Rice Cracker Mfr & Distr
N.A.I.C.S.: 311821

Onisi Foods Co., Ltd. (1)
3rd Floor Ichigo Seizaka Building 3-4-2 Mita, Minato- ku, Tokyo, 108-0073, Japan
Tel.: (81) 334523212
Web Site: http://www.onisifoods.co.jp
Food Mfr & Distr
N.A.I.C.S.: 311999

TH Foods, Inc. (1)
2134 Harlem Rd, Loves Park, IL 61111   (45%)
Tel.: (815) 636-9500
Sales Range: $125-149.9 Million
Emp.: 355
Snack Food Mfr
N.A.I.C.S.: 311821

THAI KAMEDA CO., LTD. (1)
118 Moo 9 Soi Watmahawong Puchaosamingphrai Rd, Phra Pradaeng, 10130, Samut Prakan, Thailand
Tel.: (66) 27484265

Rice Cracker Mfr & Distr
N.A.I.C.S.: 311999

Thien Ha Kameda JSC (1)
Km 29-Nation Route 5A Ben Residential Groups, Bach Sam Ward My Hao Town, Hung Yen, Vietnam
Tel.: (84) 2213946789
Web Site: http://www.thienha-kamedafood.com
Rice Cake Mfr
N.A.I.C.S.: 311999

Tianjin Kameda Food Co., Ltd. (1)
No 5 Xintai Street Development Zone, Tianjin, China
Tel.: (86) 2266200458
Rice Crackers Mfr & Sales
N.A.I.C.S.: 311821

Toyosu Co., Ltd. (1)
1-3-11 Sumiyoshi, Ikeda, 563-0033, Osaka, Japan
Tel.: (81) 727624711
Web Site: https://www.toyosu.co.jp
Emp.: 131
Rice Cracker Mfr & Distr
N.A.I.C.S.: 311821

KAMEI CORPORATION
3-1-18 Kokubuncho, Aoba-Ku, Sendai, 980-8583, Miyagi, Japan
Tel.: (81) 222646111   JP
Web Site: https://www.kamei.co.jp
Year Founded: 1903
8037—(TKS)
Rev.: $3,782,460,130
Assets: $2,145,672,100
Liabilities: $1,094,239,230
Net Worth: $1,051,432,870
Earnings: $66,833,710
Emp.: 4,777
Fiscal Year-end: 03/31/24
Holding Company; Gas Stations; Commercial Real Estate
N.A.I.C.S.: 551112
Hiroyuki Takahashi *(Sr Exec Dir & Head-Sls)*

Subsidiaries:

Agri Corporation (1)
6-86-1 Onoe-cho, Naka-ku, Yokohama, 231-0015, Kanagawa, Japan
Tel.: (81) 452125588
Web Site: https://www.ywc.co.jp
Alcoholic Beverages Whslr
N.A.I.C.S.: 424820
Takenori Sato *(CEO)*

Aim Co., Ltd. (1)
6-1-1 Nishinakajima Shin-Osaka Prime Tower 2nd Floor, Yodogawa-ku, Osaka, 532-0011, Japan
Tel.: (81) 668855180
Web Site: http://www.aim-ph.com
Emp.: 27
Pharmaceutical Product Retailer
N.A.I.C.S.: 456110

Central Boeki Calif., Ltd. (1)
19801 S Rancho Way Ste A, Rancho Dominguez, CA 90220
Tel.: (310) 323-1817
Grocery Product Whslr
N.A.I.C.S.: 424490
Hitoshi Endo *(Exec VP)*

H. Cleveland And Co., Ltd. (1)
202 14980 104th Ave, Surrey, V3R 1M9, BC, Canada
Tel.: (778) 395-0047
Sales Range: $25-49.9 Million
Emp.: 3
Building Materials Distr
N.A.I.C.S.: 236210

Ikemitsu Enterprises Co., Ltd. (1)
UD Kamiyacho Building 5F 3-18-19 Toranomon, Minato-ku, Tokyo, 105-0001, Japan
Tel.: (81) 364590480
Web Site: https://www.ikemitsu.co.jp
Emp.: 19
Alcohol Whslr
N.A.I.C.S.: 424820
Makoto Hasebe *(Chm & Exec Dir)*

KC Central Trading Co., Ltd. (1)

2nd Fl KDX Ginza East Bldg 3-7-2 Irifune, Chuo-ku, Tokyo, 104-0042, Japan
Tel.: (81) 352449778
Web Site: https://www.boeki.co.jp
Grocery Product Whslr
N.A.I.C.S.: 424490
Yoshiyuki Takamatsu *(Co-Pres)*

Kamei Auto Hokkaido Corporation (1)
1-18-1-36 Tsukisamuhigashi, Toyohira-ku, Sapporo, 062-0051, Hokkaido, Japan
Tel.: (81) 118557400
Web Site: http://www.volvo-hokkaido.com
Used Car Parts Whslr
N.A.I.C.S.: 423140

Kamei Proact Corporation (1)
5th floor UD Kamiyacho Building 3-18-19 Toranomon, Minato-ku, Tokyo, 105-0001, Japan
Tel.: (81) 364501234
Web Site: https://www.kamei-pro.co.jp
Fashionable Product Distr
N.A.I.C.S.: 424350
Fumiyuki Kamei *(CEO)*

Katagiri & Co., Inc. (1)
224 E 59th St Bet 2nd & 3rd Aves, New York, NY 10022
Tel.: (212) 755-3566
Web Site: https://www.katagiri.com
Grocery Product Whslr
N.A.I.C.S.: 424490

Kodama Co., Ltd. (1)
3-1 Chigasakichuo Center South SKY Building 4F, Tsuzuki-ku, Yokohama, 224-0032, Kanagawa, Japan
Tel.: (81) 459491331
Web Site: http://www.kodamacorp.co.jp
Emp.: 152
Software Development & Design Services
N.A.I.C.S.: 541512
Hiroyuki Kodama *(Pres & CEO)*

MCS Co., Ltd. (1)
102-3 Jimmucho, Yao, 581-0067, Osaka, Japan
Tel.: (81) 729257728
Web Site: https://www.mcs-g.co.jp
Pharmaceutical Product Retailer
N.A.I.C.S.: 456110

Marron Co., Ltd. (1)
2F Minamino Medicine Building 3-1-3 Nishikatakura, Hachioji, 192-0917, Tokyo, Japan
Tel.: (81) 426320225
Web Site: https://www.marron-g.co.jp
Emp.: 159
Pharmaceutical Product Retailer
N.A.I.C.S.: 456110

Mito Pharmacy Co., Ltd. (1)
5-36-7 Takasago Mito Pharmacy Head Office Building 5F, Katsushika-ku, Tokyo, 125-0054, Japan
Tel.: (81) 336072563
Web Site: https://www.mito-ph.com
Emp.: 97
Pharmaceutical Product Retailer
N.A.I.C.S.: 456110

Mitsumoto Shoji Co., Ltd. (1)
4-37-18 Fujimidai, Kunitachi-shi, Tokyo, 186-0003, Japan
Tel.: (81) 425715401
Web Site: http://www.mitumoto.co.jp
Office Supply Retailer
N.A.I.C.S.: 459410

Orix Rent-A-Car Kamei Co., Ltd. (1)
2-11-10 Chuo, Aoba Ward, Sendai, Miyagi Prefecture, Japan
Tel.: (81) 222660543
Web Site: https://www.kamei.co.jp
Rental Car Retailer
N.A.I.C.S.: 532111

Oshimaono Shoji Co., Ltd. (1)
215 Toyo Ohira-cho, Tochigi, 329-4402, Japan
Tel.: (81) 282224188
Web Site: https://www.onoshoji.co.jp
Emp.: 178
Gardening Product Distr
N.A.I.C.S.: 424910

Persol Tempstaff Kamei Corporation (1)

KAMEI CORPORATION

Kamei Corporation—(Continued)
8th floor Kakyoin Square 1-1-20 Kakyoin, Aoba-ku, Sendai, 980-0013, Miyagi, Japan
Tel.: (81) 222663171
Web Site: https://www.persol-tempstaffkamei.co.jp
Emp.: 30,000
Temporary Staffing Services
N.A.I.C.S.: 561320

Sanko Mabis (Beijing) Corp. (1)
Citis Bldg No 19-02 19 Jianguomenwai Ave, Beijing, China
Tel.: (86) 1065018557
Bearing Product Distr
N.A.I.C.S.: 423840

Sanko Progress Mabis Corporation (1)
20-7 Samon-cho, Shinjuku-ku, Tokyo, 160-0017, Japan
Tel.: (81) 363863501
Web Site: https://www.sanko-mabis.com
Emp.: 90
Marine Product Whslr
N.A.I.C.S.: 423860
Katsuhiro Shoji *(Pres & CEO)*

Santouka Kamei Canada Foods Ltd. (1)
1690 Robson St, Vancouver, V6G 1C7, BC, Canada
Tel.: (604) 681-8121
Web Site: https://www.santouka-canada.com
Food Restaurant Services
N.A.I.C.S.: 722511
Hitoshi Hatanaka *(Founder)*

Sendai Toyopet Co., Ltd. (1)
2-8-1 Kutake, Miyagino-ku, Sendai, 983-0036, Japan
Tel.: (81) 222321111
Web Site: https://www.p-sendai.co.jp
Emp.: 502
Car Dealer
N.A.I.C.S.: 441120

Sun-Eight Trading Co., Ltd. (1)
22F Shin-Aoyama Building West Wing 1-1 Minami-Aoyama1-chome, Minato-ku, Tokyo, 107-0062, Japan
Tel.: (81) 354141572
Web Site: https://www.sun-eight.com
Emp.: 51
Bakery Ingredient Whslr
N.A.I.C.S.: 424490
Mitsuo Wakatabi *(Pres)*

Tohoku Gas Corporation (1)
50 Mukaihara Odakura, Nishigo-mura Nishishirakawa-gun, Fukushima, 961-8061, Japan
Tel.: (81) 248271188
Web Site: http://www.tohoku-gas.co.jp
Liquefied Gas Distr
N.A.I.C.S.: 221210

Toyota Sendai Rental & Leasing Co., Ltd. (1)
2-8-1 Kutake, Miyagino-ku, Sendai, Japan
Tel.: (81) 222320100
Web Site: https://www.r-sendai.co.jp
Emp.: 92
Rental Car Retailer
N.A.I.C.S.: 532111

Vintners Inc. (1)
5F UD Kamiyacho Bldg 3-18-19 Toranomon, Minato-ku, Tokyo, 105-0001, Japan
Tel.: (81) 354058368
Web Site: https://www.vintners.co.jp
Wine Whslr
N.A.I.C.S.: 424820

Wing Ace Corporation (1)
UD-Kamiyacho Bldg 5F 3-18-19 Toranomon, Minato-ku, Tokyo, 105-0001, Japan
Tel.: (81) 354044855
Web Site: https://www.wingace.jp
Food Products Distr
N.A.I.C.S.: 424490
Makoto Hasebe *(Pres)*

Yamagata Toyopet Co., Ltd. (1)
5-5-2 Iida Nishi, Yamagata, 990-9588, Japan
Tel.: (81) 120088567
Web Site: https://www.yamagata-toyopet.jp

Emp.: 290
Car Dealer
N.A.I.C.S.: 441120

KAMENI AGREGATI A.D.
Ivana Franje Jukica bb, 78000, Banja Luka, Bosnia & Herzegovina
Tel.: (387) 51218887
KMAG-R-A—(BANJ)
Rev.: $142,706
Assets: $2,537,172
Liabilities: $743,636
Net Worth: $1,793,536
Earnings: ($241,829)
Emp.: 4
Fiscal Year-end: 12/31/12
Limestone Quarrying Services
N.A.I.C.S.: 212312
Dragan Cerovac *(Chm-Mgmt Bd)*

KAMENSK-URALSKY METAL-LURGICAL WORKS J.S.CO
5 Zavodskaya st, 623405, Kamensk-Uralsky, Sverdlovsk, Russia
Tel.: (7) 3439395300
Web Site: http://www.kumz.ru
Year Founded: 1944
Metal Products Mfr & Sales
N.A.I.C.S.: 332999
Aleksey Filippov *(Mng Dir-Rolling Complex)*

KAMEYAMA CO., LTD.
2-9-11 Oyodonaka, Kita-Ku, Osaka, 531-0076, Japan
Tel.: (81) 647989071
Web Site: http://www.kameyama.co.jp
Year Founded: 1927
Sales Range: $75-99.9 Million
Emp.: 500
Candle Mfr
N.A.I.C.S.: 339999
Susumu Tanigawa *(Pres)*

KAMIGUMI CO., LTD.
4-1-11 Hamabe-dori, Chuo-ku, Kobe, 651-0083, Hyogo, Japan
Tel.: (81) 782715110
Web Site: https://www.kamigumi.co.jp
Year Founded: 1867
9364—(TKS)
Rev.: $1,763,448,850
Assets: $3,198,717,810
Liabilities: $638,730,910
Net Worth: $2,559,986,900
Earnings: $165,481,350
Emp.: 4,261
Fiscal Year-end: 03/31/24
Marine Transportation Services
N.A.I.C.S.: 488320
Masami Kubo *(Chm & CEO)*

Subsidiaries:

Iwagawa Jozo Co., Ltd. (1)
6557-6 Iwakawa Osumi-cho, Soo-shi, Kagoshima, 899-8102, Japan
Tel.: (81) 994821151
Brewery Mfr
N.A.I.C.S.: 312120

Japan Port Industry Co., Ltd. (1)
16 Uozakihamacho, Higashinada Ward, Kobe, 658-0024, Hyogo, Japan
Tel.: (81) 784527551
Emp.: 45
Transportation Services
N.A.I.C.S.: 484110

KAMIGUMI GLOBAL SOLUTIONS MALAYSIA SDN. BHD. (1)
No 1 Blok A Konica Minolta Business Technologies SB Jalan Nobat 6, Kawasan Perindustrian Bukit Rambai Tanjung Minyak, 75260, Melaka, Malaysia
Tel.: (60) 63362080
Marine Cargo Handling Services
N.A.I.C.S.: 488320
Norihide Hisasaki *(Pres)*

Kamigumi (Hong Kong) Co., Ltd. (1)
Unit 1306 Tower 1 13/F Ever Gain Plaza 88 Container Port Road, Kwai Chung, NT, China (Hong Kong)
Tel.: (852) 28279063
Marine Cargo Handling Services
N.A.I.C.S.: 488320
Masahiro Nakamura *(Chm)*

Kamigumi (Malaysia) Sdn. Bhd. (1)
Suite 10 04A 10th Floor Wisma Mpl Jalan Raja Chulan, 50200, Kuala Lumpur, Malaysia
Tel.: (60) 321414900
Marine Cargo Handling Services
N.A.I.C.S.: 488320
Toshiyuki Nakai *(Pres)*

Kamigumi (Taiwan) Co., Ltd. (1)
7F No 203 Section 2 Bade Rd, Zhongshan District, Taipei, 10491, Taiwan
Tel.: (886) 225093128
Marine Cargo Handling Services
N.A.I.C.S.: 488320
Taishi Ota *(Pres)*

Kamigumi (Vietnam) Co., Ltd. (1)
Freight Transportation Services
N.A.I.C.S.: 488510
Shunta Suzuki *(Pres)*

Kamigumi Air Service Co., Ltd. (1)
3-7-11 Shibaura Kamigumi Headquarters Building 1st floor, Minato-ku, Tokyo, Japan
Tel.: (81) 334526417
Emp.: 24
Transportation Services
N.A.I.C.S.: 484110
Toshiyuki Higashi *(Pres & CEO)*

Kamigumi Co., Ltd. (1)
Chang Fu Gong Center Room No 508 Jia - 26 Jian Guomen Wai Street, Beijing, 100022, China
Tel.: (86) 1065138581
Transportation Services
N.A.I.C.S.: 484110

Kamigumi Co., Ltd. (1)
Room No 1217 12A Floor Sakura Tower 339 Bogyoke Aung San Road, Kyauktada Township, Yangon, Myanmar
Tel.: (95) 1255026
Transportation Services
N.A.I.C.S.: 484110

Kamigumi Co., Ltd. (1)
House No 548 Ground Floor Road No 13 DOHS Baridhara, Dhaka, 1206, Bangladesh
Tel.: (880) 28416301
Transportation Services
N.A.I.C.S.: 484110

Kamigumi Co., Ltd. - Heavy Cargo & Energy Cargo Transportation Division (1)
7th Floor 4-1-11 Hamabe-dori, Chuo-ku, Kobe, 651-0083, Japan
Tel.: (81) 782715133
Marine Cargo Handling Services
N.A.I.C.S.: 541614

Kamigumi Co., Ltd. - International Logistics Division (1)
6th Floor 4-1-11 Hamabe-dori, Chuo-ku, Kobe, 651-0083, Japan
Tel.: (81) 782715159
Marine Cargo Handling Services
N.A.I.C.S.: 541614

Kamigumi Co., Ltd. - Port Logistics Division (1)
4th Floor 4-1-11 Hamabe-dori, Chuo-ku, Kobe, 651-0083, Japan
Tel.: (81) 782715146
Marine Cargo Handling Services
N.A.I.C.S.: 541614

Kamigumi International Forwading (Shenzhen) Co., Ltd. (1)
Tel.: (86) 75582084375
Freight Transportation Services
N.A.I.C.S.: 488510
Takashi Gozatani *(Chm)*

Kamigumi International Forwarding (Shanghai) Co., Ltd. (1)
Tel.: (86) 2163290200
Freight Transportation Services
N.A.I.C.S.: 488510

INTERNATIONAL PUBLIC

Hiroshi Kawakami *(Pres)*

Kamigumi International Forwarding (Shenzhen) Co., Ltd. (1)
Room 2905-06 29th Floor Shum Yip Centre 5045 Shennan East Road, Shenzhen, 518000, Guangdong, China
Tel.: (86) 75582084375
Transportation Services
N.A.I.C.S.: 484110

Kamigumi Marine Transport Co., Ltd. (1)
Freight Transportation Services
N.A.I.C.S.: 488510

Kamigumi Meixco, S.A. de C.V. (1)
Carretera Estatal 100 KM 3 6 Int 4-B San Ildefonso, Colon, 76295, Queretaro, Mexico
Tel.: (52) 14426029333
Transportation Services
N.A.I.C.S.: 484110

Kamigumi Mexico S.A. de C.V. (1)
Carretera Estatal 100 km 3 6 Col Pedro Escobedo, 76700, Queretaro, Mexico
Tel.: (52) 14426029336
Marine Cargo Handling Services
N.A.I.C.S.: 488320
Mai Takura *(Gen Dir)*

Kamigumi Middle East L.L.C. (1)
Office 7A AD Ports 280 Building Taweelah Kizad, PO Box 137386, Abu Dhabi, United Arab Emirates
Tel.: (971) 25667917
Transportation Services
N.A.I.C.S.: 484110
Mai Takura *(Gen Mgr)*

Kamigumi Singapore Pte. Ltd. (1)
Tel.: (65) 62219322
Freight Transportation Services
N.A.I.C.S.: 488510

Kamigumi USA Inc. (1)
5550 Granite Pkwy Ste 295, Plano, TX 75024
Tel.: (972) 987-5138
Transportation Services
N.A.I.C.S.: 484110

Kamigumi-EFR Logistics (Myanmar) Co., Ltd (1)
Logistics Consulting Servies
N.A.I.C.S.: 541614
Masaki Senju *(Pres)*

Kamitsu Unyu Co., Ltd. (1)
4-5 Seimon-dori, Hirohata-ku, Himeji, 671-1116, Hyogo, Japan
Tel.: (81) 792361438
Marine Cargo Handling Services
N.A.I.C.S.: 488320

Kamix Corp. (1)
4-1-11 Hamabe-dori 4th floor Kamigumi Head Office Building, Chuo-ku, Kobe, 651-0083, Hyogo, Japan
Tel.: (81) 782715204
Web Site: https://kamix.com
Medical Equipment Distr
N.A.I.C.S.: 423450

MB Service Japan Co., Ltd. (1)
880 Owadacho, Hitachi, 319-1234, Ibaraki, Japan
Tel.: (81) 294918801
Web Site: https://www.mbservice-j.co.jp
Emp.: 51
Automobile Parts Mfr
N.A.I.C.S.: 336390

Maruko Marine Transport Co., Ltd. (1)
2-1-27 Chikko, Minato-ku, Osaka, 552-0021, Japan
Tel.: (81) 665764101
Marine Cargo Handling Services
N.A.I.C.S.: 488320

Oita Koun Co., Ltd. (1)
Tel.: (81) 975589611
Freight Transportation Services
N.A.I.C.S.: 488510

PT. KAMIGUMI INDONESIA (1)
Menara 165 7th Floor Unit B Jl TB Simatupang Kav 1 Cilandak Timur, Jakarta Selatan, 12560, Indonesia
Tel.: (62) 2129406390

Marine Cargo Handling Services
N.A.I.C.S.: 488320
Masashi Kajikawa *(Pres)*

PT. KAMIGUMI LOGISTICS INDONESIA (1)
Kawasan Greenland International Industrial Center G I I C Block AE, No 05 Kota Deltamas Desa Nagasari Kecamatan Serang Baru, Bekasi, 17330, Indonesia
Tel.: (62) 212 215 7120
Web Site: https://www.kamigumi.co.jp
Logistics Consulting Servies
N.A.I.C.S.: 541614
Masashi Kajikawa *(Pres)*

Shanghai Kamigumi Logistic Service Co., Ltd. (1)
No 2808 Huancheng West Road, Fengxian, Shanghai, 201401, China
Tel.: (86) 2169135472
Transportation Services
N.A.I.C.S.: 484110

Shanghai Kamigumi Logistics Service Co., Ltd. (1)
No 601 Xin Hua Gong Road Jiangqiao, Jiading, Shanghai, 201812, China
Tel.: (86) 2169135472
Logistics Consulting Servies
N.A.I.C.S.: 541614
Shinichi Asano *(Gen Mgr)*

Sunny Marine Transport Co., Ltd. (1)
1-2-12 Irifune, Minato-ku, Nagoya, 455-0032, Japan
Tel.: (81) 526528881
Marine Cargo Handling Services
N.A.I.C.S.: 488320

TOYOTSU KAMIGUMI LOGISTICS (CHANGSHU) CO., LTD. (1)
Tel.: (86) 51252358555
Logistics Consulting Servies
N.A.I.C.S.: 541614
Tetsuro Kanai *(Deputy Gen Mgr)*

Thai Logistics Service Co., Ltd. (1)
3656/65 GreenTower Bldg Room Unit No L 20th Fl Rama 4 Rd, Klongton Klongtoey, Bangkok, 10110, Thailand
Web Site: https://www.tls.co.th
Emp.: 100
Transportation Services
N.A.I.C.S.: 484110
Wataru Ito *(Pres & CEO)*

Thilawa Global Logistics Co., Ltd. (1)
Lot No B10 Thilawa Special Economic Zone, A Area, Yangon, Myanmar
Tel.: (95) 12309017
Transportation Services
N.A.I.C.S.: 484110
Yee Mon Say Thu *(Mgr-Sls & Mktg)*

KAMMERER GMBH
Romereschstrasse 33, 49090, Osnabruck, Germany
Tel.: (49) 541 604 0 De
Web Site: http://www.kaemmerer-gmbh.de
Year Founded: 2014
Specialty Paper Products Mfr
N.A.I.C.S.: 322299
Jurgen Oess *(CEO)*

KAMPAC INTERNATIONAL PLC
Park Place Suite 203 Sheikh Zayed Road, PO Box 61396, Jebel Ali Free Zone, Dubai, United Arab Emirates
Tel.: (971) 4 329 7371
Web Site: http://www.kampacgroup.com
Year Founded: 1988
Sales Range: $1-4.9 Billion
Emp.: 800
Oil & Gas Exploration Services; Real Estate, Telecommunications & Infrastructure Development
N.A.I.C.S.: 211120
Charles Ampofo *(Founder & Chm)*

Subsidiaries:

KAMPAC TRAVEL & TOURS LLC (1)
Park Place Building Suite 203 Sheikh Zayed Road, Dubai, 61396, United Arab Emirates
Tel.: (971) 43297371
Web Site: http://www.kampacgroup.com
Emp.: 14
Travel & Tour Operating Agencies
N.A.I.C.S.: 561520
Charles Ampofo *(Chm)*

KAMPANI CONSULTANTS LTD
507 Tulsiani Chambers 5th Floor, Nariman Point, Mumbai, 400021, India
Tel.: (91) 22 6630 3030
Web Site: http://www.kampaniconsultants.in
Year Founded: 1981
Sales Range: Less than $1 Million
Financial Management Services
N.A.I.C.S.: 523940
V. Subramoniam *(Chief Compliance Officer)*

KAMUX CORP.
Parolantie 66 A, 13130, Hameenlinna, 13130, Finland
Tel.: (358) 107785500
Web Site: https://www.kamux.com
Year Founded: 2003
KAMUX—(HEL)
Rev.: $1,045,434,923
Assets: $220,807,252
Liabilities: $103,820,419
Net Worth: $116,986,834
Earnings: $11,655,515
Emp.: 918
Fiscal Year-end: 12/31/22
Automotive Retailer
N.A.I.C.S.: 441330
Juha Kalliokoski *(CEO)*

KAN-NANMARU CORPORATION
5F Minamiurawa Shuka Bldg 2-35-11 Minami-Urawa, Minami-ku, Saitama, 336-0017, Saitama, Japan
Tel.: (81) 488819056
Web Site: http://www.kannanmaru.co.jp
Year Founded: 1978
7585—(TKS)
Rev.: $6,437,200
Assets: $17,801,520
Liabilities: $6,475,920
Net Worth: $11,325,600
Earnings: ($77,440)
Emp.: 360
Fiscal Year-end: 06/30/22
Restaurant Operating Services
N.A.I.C.S.: 722511
Takashi Nonomura *(Pres & CEO)*

KANABO GROUP PLC
Churchill House 137-139 Brent Street, London, NW4 4DJ, United Kingdom
Tel.: (44) 7980878561 UK
Web Site: https://www.kanabogroup.com
Year Founded: 2016
KNB—(LSE)
Rev.: $33,943
Assets: $1,075,314
Liabilities: $73,317
Net Worth: $1,001,997
Earnings: ($177,861)
Fiscal Year-end: 12/31/20
Portfolio Management & Investment Advice
N.A.I.C.S.: 523940
Ian Mattioli *(Chm)*

KANADEN CORPORATION
Triton square z 1-8-12 Harumi, Chuo-ku, Tokyo, 104-6215, Japan
Tel.: (81) 367478800
Web Site: https://www.kanaden.co.jp
Year Founded: 1907
8081—(TKS)
Rev.: $768,551,310
Assets: $565,789,560
Liabilities: $247,161,120
Net Worth: $318,628,440
Earnings: $22,963,140
Emp.: 830
Fiscal Year-end: 03/31/24
Electrical & Electronic Component Distr
N.A.I.C.S.: 423610
Hiroshi Ogasawara *(Exec Officer & Sr Gen Mgr-Semiconductor & Device Div)*

Subsidiaries:

KANADEN (THAILAND) CO., LTD. (1)
4345 Bhiraj Tower at BITEC 14th Floor Room No BTB-TWR 14 1407, Sukhumvit Road Bangna Tai Subdistrict, Bangkok, 10260, Thailand
Tel.: (66) 21305644
Electronic Equipment Whlsr
N.A.I.C.S.: 423690

KANADEN CORPORATION (H.K.) LTD. (1)
Unit 07b 10/F CDW Building 388 Castle Peak Road, Tsuen Wan, New Territories, China (Hong Kong)
Tel.: (852) 28610386
Semiconductor Device Whlsr
N.A.I.C.S.: 423690

KANADEN CORPORATION (S.H.) LTD. (1)
1505 Sheng Gao International Tower 137 Xian Xia Rd, Shanghai, 200051, China
Tel.: (86) 2162287711
Electronic Equipment Whlsr
N.A.I.C.S.: 423690

KANADEN CORPORATION SINGAPORE PTE. LTD. (1)
3791 Jalan Bukit Merah 10-10 e-Centre Redhill, Singapore, 159471, Singapore
Tel.: (65) 62764181
Web Site: https://www.kanaden.co.jp
Electronic Equipment Whlsr
N.A.I.C.S.: 423690

KANADEN TECHNO ENGINEERING CORPORATION (1)
201 Shinjuku Koyo Building 5-15-6 Shinjuku, Shinjuku-ku, Tokyo, 160-0022, Japan
Tel.: (81) 333562214
Electronic Equipment Whlsr
N.A.I.C.S.: 423690

KANADEN TELESYS CORPORATION (1)
Electric Equipment Mfr
N.A.I.C.S.: 335999

Kanaden (Vietnam) Co., Ltd. (1)
IDMC My Dinh Building No 15 Pham Hung Street My Dinh 2 Ward, Nam Tu Liem District, Hanoi, Vietnam
Tel.: (84) 2432066695
Factory Automation Equipment Distr
N.A.I.C.S.: 423830
Toshihiro Matsuda *(Gen Dir)*

Kanaden Brain Corporation (1)
Triton Square Z Building 1-8-12 Harumi, Chuo-ku, Tokyo, 104-6215, Japan
Tel.: (81) 335326001
Web Site: http://www.kanadenbrain.co.jp
Software Services
N.A.I.C.S.: 541511

Kanaden Engineering Corporation (1)
16th floor Triton Square Building Z 1-8-12 Harumi, Chuo-ku, Tokyo, 104-6216, Japan
Tel.: (81) 367478890
Web Site: https://www.kanaden-eng.jp
Emp.: 60
Engineeering Services
N.A.I.C.S.: 541330

Kanaden Reinetsu Corporation (1)
Daiwaa Hamamatsucho Building 1-9-10 Hamamatsu-cho, Minato-ku, Tokyo, 105-0013, Japan
Tel.: (81) 3 3459 9321
Electronic Equipment Whlsr
N.A.I.C.S.: 423690

Kanaden Supply Corporation (1)
Kanaden-daimon Annex 2-6-1 Shibadaimon, Minato-ku, Tokyo, 105-0012, Japan
Tel.: (81) 3 3432 5508
Electronic Equipment Whlsr
N.A.I.C.S.: 423690

Kanaden Trading (Thailand) Co., Ltd. (1)
4345 Bhiraj Tower at BITEC 14th Floor Room No BTB-TWR 14 1407, Sukhumvit Road Bangna Tai Subdistrict Bangna District, Bangkok, 10260, Thailand
Tel.: (66) 21305644
Factory Automation Equipment Distr
N.A.I.C.S.: 423830
Jun Minemura *(Mng Dir)*

RYOSHIN ELECTRONIC ENGINEERING CORPORATION (1)
2-6-4 Kuramae, Taito-ku, Tokyo, 111-0051, Japan
Tel.: (81) 338636721
Electric Equipment Mfr
N.A.I.C.S.: 335999

TECHNO-CREATE CORPORATION (1)
Tel.: (81) 335530112
Web Site: http://www.techno-create.co.jp
Emp.: 20
Electric Equipment Mfr
N.A.I.C.S.: 335999

Tohoku Kanaden Telecom Engineering Corporation (1)
Uesugi Building 7F 1-17-7 Uesugi, Aoba-ku, Sendai, 980-0812, Miyagi, Japan
Tel.: (81) 222675971
Industrial Machinery Mfr
N.A.I.C.S.: 333248

KANAI JUYO KOGYO CO.,LTD
1-2-9 Dojima, Kita-ku, Osaka, 530-003, Japan
Tel.: (81) 663463348
Web Site: http://www.kanaijuyo.co.jp
Year Founded: 1894
Rev.: $60,841,200
Emp.: 201
Textile Machinery Mfr & Whlsr
N.A.I.C.S.: 333248
Hiroaki Kanai *(Pres)*

Subsidiaries:

Kanai Juyo Kogyo Co.,Ltd - Non-Woven Factory (1)
1-1 Kanai-cho, Takarazuka, 665-0824, Hyogo, Japan
Tel.: (81) 797872281
Nonwoven Product Mfr
N.A.I.C.S.: 313230

Kanai Juyo Kogyo Co.,Ltd - Textile Machinery Factory (1)
4-1 Okuhata, Itami, 664-025, Hyogo, Japan
Tel.: (81) 727810051
Textile Machinery Product Distr
N.A.I.C.S.: 423830

Tokusen Kogyo Co., Ltd. (1)
1081 Minamiyama Sumiyoshi-cho, Hyogo, Ono, 675-1361, Japan
Tel.: (81) 794 63 1050
Web Site: http://www.tokusen.co.jp
Metal Wire Product Mfr
N.A.I.C.S.: 331420
Hiromi Kanai *(Chm & CEO)*

Subsidiary (Domestic):

JAPAN FINE STEEL CO., LTD (2)
19-1 Ishiide 1-chome, Sanyo Onodashi, Yamaguchi, 756-0063, Japan
Tel.: (81) 836834982
Web Site: http://www.jpfs.co.jp
Emp.: 200
Steel Pole Mfr
N.A.I.C.S.: 331222

KANAI JUYO KOGYO CO., LTD

Kanai Juyo Co.,Ltd—(Continued)
Subsidiary (Non-US):

KANAI TOKUSEN SHANGHAI CO., LTD. (2)
3001 Tingwei Road, Jinshan, 201508, Shanghai, China
Tel.: (86) 2167277070
Steel Tire Cord Mfr
N.A.I.C.S.: 314994

Subsidiary (US):

TOKUSEN U.S.A., Inc. (2)
1500 Amity Rd, Conway, AR 72033
Tel.: (501) 327-6800
Web Site: http://www.tokusenusa.com
Steel Tire Cord Mfr
N.A.I.C.S.: 314994

KANAK KRISHI IMPLEMENTS LIMITED
1/586 Sector-1 Vaishali, Ghaziabad, 201 010, Uttar Pradesh, India
Tel.: (91) 1132318627
Web Site: http://www.kanakkrishi.com
Agricultural Machinery Mfr & Distr
N.A.I.C.S.: 333111
Satyendra Kumar (Officer-Compliance)

KANAKIA GROUP
215-Atrium 10th Floor Next to Courtyard by Marriott Hotel, Opp Divine Child High School Andheri Kurla Road Andheri East, Mumbai, 400 093, India
Tel.: (91) 22 67267777
Web Site: http://www.kanakia.com
Year Founded: 1986
Emp.: 500
Holding Company Services
N.A.I.C.S.: 551112
Rasesh B. Kanakia (Co-Founder)

Subsidiaries:

Cineline India Limited (1)
2nd Floor Vilco Center Subash Rd Vishnu Prasad Society Navpada, Vile Parle East, Mumbai, 400057, India
Tel.: (91) 2267266666
Web Site: https://www.moviemax.co.in
Rev.: $30,473,784
Assets: $69,227,778
Liabilities: $51,306,517
Net Worth: $17,921,261
Earnings: ($544,286)
Emp.: 306
Fiscal Year-end: 03/31/2024
Real Estate Manangement Services
N.A.I.C.S.: 531390
Jatin J. Shah (Officer-Compliance & Sec)

KANAME KOGYO CO., LTD.
Ikebukuro NS Building 2-14-8 Ikebukuro, Toshima-ku, Tokyo, 171-0014, Japan
Tel.: (81) 339865341
Web Site: https://www.kaname-k.co.jp
Year Founded: 1973
6566—(TKS)
Rev.: $89,254,830
Assets: $155,863,800
Liabilities: $33,856,420
Net Worth: $122,007,380
Earnings: $8,493,850
Emp.: 462
Fiscal Year-end: 03/31/24
Industrial Waste Recycling Services
N.A.I.C.S.: 562111
Shuzo Fujii (Chm & Pres)

KANAMIC NETWORK CO., LTD.
31F Ebisu Garden Place Tower 4-20-3 Ebisu, Shibuya-ku, Tokyo, 150-6031, Japan
Tel.: (81) 357983955
Web Site: https://www.kanamic.net
3939—(TKS)
Rev.: $26,559,140
Assets: $40,079,770
Liabilities: $17,576,110
Net Worth: $22,503,660
Earnings: $5,409,670
Fiscal Year-end: 09/30/23
Software Development Services
N.A.I.C.S.: 541511
Takuma Yamamoto (Pres)

KANAMOTO CO., LTD.
1-19 Odori Higashi 3-chome, Chuo-ku, Sapporo, 060-0041, Hokkaido, Japan
Tel.: (81) 112091600
Web Site: https://www.kanamoto.co.jp
9678—(SAP)
Rev.: $1,820,111,040
Assets: $2,955,497,600
Liabilities: $1,594,383,120
Net Worth: $1,361,114,480
Earnings: $80,779,600
Emp.: 3,832
Fiscal Year-end: 10/31/22
Construction Equipment Rental & Sales
N.A.I.C.S.: 238910
Yuichi Asano (Mgr-Credit Mgmt Div)

Subsidiaries:

Comsupply Co., Ltd. (1)
8 3 Koeicho, Ebetsu, 067-0051, Hokkaido, Japan
Tel.: (81) 113916330
Web Site: http://www.com-supply.com
Equipment Rental Services
N.A.I.C.S.: 532420

KG Flowtechno Co., Ltd. (1)
2nd floor K Building Hamamatsucho 1-7-7 Shibadaimon, Minato-ku, Tokyo, 105-0012, Japan
Tel.: (81) 36 402 5480
Web Site: https://www.kgflowtechno.co.jp
Construction Machinery Mfr
N.A.I.C.S.: 333120
Tetsuo Kanamoto (Chm)

Kanamoto & JP Nelson Equipment (M) Sdn. Bhd. (1)
Lot C-43 Kawasan Perindustrian Nilai Nilai, Nilai Industrial Estate, 71800, Negeri Sembilan, Malaysia
Tel.: (60) 67990991
Equipment Rental Services
N.A.I.C.S.: 532420

Kanamoto (HK) Co., Ltd. (1)
No 107 Ng Ka Tsuen Kam Sheung Road, Yuen Long, China (Hong Kong)
Tel.: (852) 35905480
Construction Machinery Mfr
N.A.I.C.S.: 333120

Kanamoto Fecon Hassyu Construction Equipment Rental JSC (1)
3th floor CEO Tower Pham Hung Street, Me Tri ward Nam Tu Liem District, Hanoi, Vietnam
Tel.: (84) 246 265 9168
Web Site: https://kfh.com.vn
Equipment Rental Services
N.A.I.C.S.: 532420
Nguyen Quang Hai (Gen Dir)

Kanatech Co., Ltd. (1)
2 5 8 Kita 1 Johigashi 3rd Floor of Sosei Park Building, Chuo-ku, Sapporo, 060-0031, Hokkaido, Japan
Tel.: (81) 112715121
Web Site: http://www.kanatec.com
Temporary Unit House Mfr & Whslr
N.A.I.C.S.: 321991

Kanki Co., Ltd. (1)
2-9-19 Sotohama-cho, Suma-ku, Kobe, 654-0043, Japan
Tel.: (81) 78 733 2221
Web Site: http://www.kanki-kobe.co.jp
Emp.: 103
Industrial Equipment Whslr
N.A.I.C.S.: 423690

Kyushu Kensan Co., Ltd. (1)
3-21-7 Matsushima, Higashi-ku, Fukuoka, 813-0062, Japan (100%)
Tel.: (81) 92 623 2323
Web Site: http://www.k-kensan.co.jp
Emp.: 140
Civil Engineering & Construction Machinery Leasing & Rental
N.A.I.C.S.: 532412

Machida Kikou Co., Ltd. (1)
1991 Kuba, Nakagusuku-mura Nakagami-gun, Okinawa, 901-2401, Japan
Tel.: (81) 98 895 5803
Web Site: https://www.machida-kiko.com
Emp.: 170
Equipment Rental Services
N.A.I.C.S.: 532420

Nishiken Co., Ltd. (1)
1-9 Wakamatsu Miyanojinmachi, Kurume, 839-0804, Fukuoka, Japan
Tel.: (81) 94 235 5840
Web Site: https://www.r-nishiken.co.jp
Emp.: 525
Industrial Equipment Whsr
N.A.I.C.S.: 423690

PT Kanamoto Indonesia (1)
KEM Tower 15th Floor Jl Ladasan Pacu Barat Blok B10 Kav 2, Kota Baru Bandar Kemayoran, Jakarta Pusat, 10610, Indonesia
Tel.: (62) 2165704012
Construction Machinery Mfr
N.A.I.C.S.: 333120

Porter Excavations Pty. Ltd. (1)
5110 Colac - Ballarat Rd Cambrian Hil, Victoria, 3352, VIC, Australia
Tel.: (61) 1800774473
Web Site: https://porterplant.com.au
Construction Machinery Mfr
N.A.I.C.S.: 333120

Porter Utilities Pty Ltd (1)
5110 Colac Ballarat Rd Cambrian Hill, Victoria, 3352, VIC, Australia
Tel.: (61) 428353625
Web Site: http://utilities.porterplant.com.au
Gas Station Building Services
N.A.I.C.S.: 237120
Phil Higgins (Ops Mgr)

Sanwa Kikai Lease Co., Ltd. (1)
1-4-15 Hoshigauraminami, Kushiro, 084-0913, Hokkaido, Japan
Tel.: (81) 15 451 4101
Web Site: https://www.sanwa-rental.co.jp
Construction Equipment Whslr
N.A.I.C.S.: 423690

Shanghai KG Machinery Co., Ltd. (1)
Bazaar Road 800 No 14 Building Katsudai 14 Tower 52 Rooms A14 F 800, Shang Cheng Road Shanghai Pudong New Area Suncome Cimic Tower Pudong, Shanghai, 200120, China
Tel.: (86) 2122157747
Construction Machinery Mfr
N.A.I.C.S.: 333120

Siam Kanamoto Co., Ltd. (1)
888 8 Moo5 Srinakarin Rd, Samrong Nuea Muang Samuthprakarn, Samut Prakan, 10270, Thailand
Tel.: (66) 23858701
Web Site: http://siamkanamoto.co.th
Equipment Rental Services
N.A.I.C.S.: 532420

Sugakikai Kogyo Co., Ltd. (1)
3-9-27 Minami-Horie, Nishi-ku, Osaka, Japan
Tel.: (81) 66 541 7931
Web Site: https://www.suga-kikai.co.jp
Emp.: 120
Equipment Rental Services
N.A.I.C.S.: 532420

Unite Co., Ltd. (1)
1-14-8 Nihonbashi Ningyocho 4th floor Suitengumae Building, Chuo-ku, Tokyo, 103-0013, Japan
Tel.: (81) 36 667 8471
Web Site: https://www.unitenet.co.jp
Emp.: 626
Industrial Equipment Whsl
N.A.I.C.S.: 423690

KANANI INDUSTRIES LTD.
GE-1080 Bharat Diamond Bourse G-Block, Bandra Kurla Complex Bandra East, Mumbai, 400051, India
Tel.: (91) 2240050222
Web Site: https://www.kananiindustries.com
KANANIIND—(NSE)
Rev.: $32,798,744
Assets: $15,818,273
Liabilities: $8,223,420
Net Worth: $7,594,853
Earnings: $263,368
Emp.: 29
Fiscal Year-end: 03/31/23
Jewelry Product Distr
N.A.I.C.S.: 423940
Premjibhai Devajibhai Kanani (Chm)

Subsidiaries:

Kil International Limited (1)
Room No 1502 15/F Rise Commercial Building No 5-11 Granville Circuit, Tsim Sha Tsui, Kowloon, China (Hong Kong)
Tel.: (852) 27224144
Jewelry Product Distr
N.A.I.C.S.: 423940

KANCELARIA PRAWNA - INKASO WEC SA
Piotrkowska 270, 90-361, Lodz, Poland
Tel.: (48) 426817474
Web Site: https://www.kancelariawec.eu
Year Founded: 1995
Law firm
N.A.I.C.S.: 541199
Sylwia Pastusiak-Brzezinska (Vice Chm)

KANCERA AB
Karolinska Institutet Science Park Nanna Svartz Vag 4, SE-171 65, Solna, Sweden
Tel.: (46) 850126080
Web Site: https://www.kancera.com
Year Founded: 2010
KAN—(OMX)
Rev.: $103,242
Assets: $6,516,171
Liabilities: $1,784,899
Net Worth: $4,731,273
Earnings: ($6,441,718)
Emp.: 5
Fiscal Year-end: 12/31/23
Pharmaceuticals Mfr
N.A.I.C.S.: 325412
Erik Nerpin (Chm)

Subsidiaries:

iNovacia AB (1)
Lindhagensgatan 133, 112 51, Stockholm, Sweden
Tel.: (46) 8 50 10 30 40
Web Site: http://www.inovacia.se
Drug Discovery & Development Services
N.A.I.C.S.: 541715

KANCHAN INTERNATIONAL LTD.
28 A/B Raju Indus Estate Penkar Pada Road, Near Dahisar Check Naka, Thane, 401 104, India
Tel.: (91) 22 67760606
Web Site: http://www.kanchanappliances.com
Cooking Appliance Mfr
N.A.I.C.S.: 335220

KANCHI KARPOORAM LIMITED
No 1 Barnaby Avenue Barnaby Road Kilpauk, Chennai, 600 010, Tamil Nadu, India
Tel.: (91) 4426401914

AND PRIVATE COMPANIES

Web Site:
https://www.kanchikarpooram.com
538896—(BOM)
Rev.: $34,605,316
Assets: $26,472,851
Liabilities: $1,220,105
Net Worth: $25,252,746
Earnings: $4,187,834
Emp.: 104
Fiscal Year-end: 03/31/22
Camphor & Related Product Mfr
N.A.I.C.S.: 325199
Suresh V. Shah *(Mng Dir)*

KANCO ENTERPRISES LTD
Jasmine Tower 3rd Floor 31 Shakespeare Sarani, Kolkata, 700017, India
Tel.: (91) 332281 5217
Web Site: http://www.kanco.in
Rev.: $23,340
Assets: $2,716,776
Liabilities: $13,965,100
Net Worth: ($11,248,324)
Earnings: ($168,048)
Emp.: 7
Fiscal Year-end: 03/31/18
Tea & Textile Products Mfr
N.A.I.C.S.: 316990
Umang Kanoria *(Chm & Mng Dir)*

Subsidiaries:

Kanco Overseas (1)
Dholka-Bagodara Hwy, Walthera Taluka-Dholka, Ahmedabad, 387810, Gujarat, India
Tel.: (91) 2714247404
Web Site: http://www.kanco.in
Cotton Yarn Mfr
N.A.I.C.S.: 111920
M. L. Sabarwal *(Gen Mgr)*

KANCO TEA & INDUSTRIES LIMITED
Jasmine Tower 3rd Floor 31 Shakespeare Sarani, Kolkata, 700 017, India
Tel.: (91) 3322815217   In
Web Site: https://www.kancotea.in
Year Founded: 1983
541005—(BOM)
Rev.: $12,952,463
Assets: $15,448,615
Liabilities: $5,892,589
Net Worth: $9,556,026
Earnings: $519,016
Emp.: 2,426
Fiscal Year-end: 03/31/22
Tea Mfr & Whslr
N.A.I.C.S.: 311920
Anuradha Kanoria *(Exec Dir)*

KANDA HOLDINGS CO., LTD.
2-4 Kanda Misakicho 3-chome, Chiyoda-ku, Tokyo, 101-0061, Japan
Tel.: (81) 363271811
Web Site: https://www.kanda-web.co.jp
Year Founded: 1943
9059—(TKS)
Rev.: $337,923,030
Assets: $308,878,690
Liabilities: $150,073,440
Net Worth: $158,805,250
Earnings: $15,024,530
Emp.: 2,784
Fiscal Year-end: 03/31/24
Investment Management Service
N.A.I.C.S.: 523940
Fujihisa Harashima *(Pres)*

Subsidiaries:

Kanda Core-Techno Co., Ltd. (1)
3-2-4 Kanda-Misakicho, Chiyoda-ku, Tokyo, 279-0024, Chiba, Japan
Tel.: (81) 363271831
General Freight Trucking Services
N.A.I.C.S.: 484110

Subsidiary (Domestic):

JPL Co., Ltd. (2)
Kasuga Tower Building 2nd floor 4-24-8 Hongo, Bunkyo-ku, Tokyo, 113-0033, Japan
Tel.: (81) 358053088
Web Site: https://www.j-jpl.com
Packaging Services
N.A.I.C.S.: 561910

Pegasus Global Express Co., Ltd. (1)
1-8-11 Shinkiba, Koto-ku, Tokyo, 136-0082, Japan
Tel.: (81) 335221555
Web Site: https://www.pegasus-group.com
Emp.: 200
Air Freight & Logistic Services
N.A.I.C.S.: 481112

KANDA TSUSHINKI CO., LTD.
24 Toyamacho Kanda, Chiyoda-Ku, Tokyo, 101-0043, Japan
Tel.: (81) 332527731
Web Site: https://www.kandt.co.jp
Year Founded: 1947
1992—(TKS)
Rev.: $47,274,720
Assets: $62,550,430
Liabilities: $24,417,340
Net Worth: $38,133,090
Earnings: $3,602,450
Emp.: 232
Fiscal Year-end: 03/31/24
Electric Equipment Mfr
N.A.I.C.S.: 334419
Kambe Masato *(Pres & CEO)*

KANDAGIRI SPINNING MILLS LIMITED
Udayapatti PO, P B No 3, Salem, 636 140, Tamilnadu, India
Tel.: (91) 4272244400
Web Site: https://www.kandagirimills.com
Year Founded: 1976
521242—(BOM)
Rev.: $555,009
Assets: $2,132,362
Liabilities: $3,047,171
Net Worth: ($914,809)
Earnings: ($121,239)
Emp.: 5
Fiscal Year-end: 03/31/21
Textile Products Mfr
N.A.I.C.S.: 314999
R. Selvarajan *(Mng Dir)*

KANDENKO CO., LTD.
4-8-33 Shibaura, Minato-ku, Tokyo, 108 8533, Japan
Tel.: (81) 354762111   JP
Web Site: https://www.kandenko.co.jp
Year Founded: 1944
1942—(TKS)
Rev.: $3,955,602,470
Assets: $3,749,687,750
Liabilities: $1,463,949,750
Net Worth: $2,285,738,000
Earnings: $180,750,450
Emp.: 7,619
Fiscal Year-end: 03/31/24
Construction, Telecommunications Infrastructure, Electric Power Infrastructure & Engineering Services
N.A.I.C.S.: 236220
Kiyoshi Goto *(Chm)*

Subsidiaries:

Chiba K Techno Co Ltd (1)
4-20-13 Suehiro, Chuo-ku, Chiba, 260-0843, Japan
Tel.: (81) 432652020
Web Site: https://chiba-k-techno.com
Emp.: 48
Electronic Services
N.A.I.C.S.: 238210

Gunma K-Techno Co., Ltd (1)
120-1 Shokanjimachi, Takasaki, 370-0008, Gunma, Japan
Tel.: (81) 273655610
Web Site: http://www.g-k-techno.jp
Industrial Machinery Equipment Mfr
N.A.I.C.S.: 333248

Handenko Corporation (1)
Nishi Hankyu Building 2-1-18 Shibata, Kita-ku, Osaka, 530-0012, Japan
Tel.: (81) 663771301
Web Site: https://www.handenko.co.jp
Emp.: 102
Electronic Services
N.A.I.C.S.: 238210

Ibaraki K-Techno Co., Ltd (1)
2-7-14 Jonan, Mito, 310-0803, Ibaraki, Japan
Tel.: (81) 292255112
Construction Engineering Services
N.A.I.C.S.: 541330

Japan Facility Solutions, Inc. (1)
17th floor Shin-Osaki Kogyo Building 1-6-4 Osaki, Shinagawa-ku, Tokyo, 141-0032, Japan   (10%)
Tel.: (81) 363712500
Web Site: http://www.j-facility.com
Sales Range: $25-49.9 Million
Emp.: 200
Facilities Environmental Management Consulting Services
N.A.I.C.S.: 541620

Kanagawa K-Techno Co., Ltd (1)
1-8-1 Hiranuma, Nishi-ku, Yokohama, 220-8540, Kanagawa, Japan
Tel.: (81) 456202010
Web Site: http://www.k-k-techno.co.jp
Emp.: 28
Industrial Building Construction Services
N.A.I.C.S.: 236210

Kandenko Engineering (Malaysia) Sdn. Bhd. (1)
Suite A-5-3 Northpoint Offices Midvalley City, No 1Medan Syed Utara, 59200, Kuala Lumpur, Malaysia
Tel.: (60) 3 2283 3848
Sales Range: $25-49.9 Million
Emp.: 20
Construction Services
N.A.I.C.S.: 236220

Kandenko Engineering Consulting (Shanghai) Co., Ltd. (1)
Room 222 2F No 201-211, Chengjiaqiao Zhilu Minhang Di, Shanghai, 201103, China
Tel.: (86) 2164053041
Construction Services
N.A.I.C.S.: 236220

Kanko Facilities Co Ltd (1)
1-6-4 Osaki Shinagawa-ku, Tokyo, 141-0032, Japan
Tel.: (81) 363727830
Sales Range: $50-74.9 Million
Emp.: 200
Electronic Services
N.A.I.C.S.: 238210

Kanko Fudousan Kanri Co., Ltd (1)
4th floor Yushima Natsume Building 2-18-6 Yushima, Bunkyo-ku, Tokyo, 113-0034, Japan
Tel.: (81) 338137531
Web Site: https://k-asset-m.com
Sales Range: $25-49.9 Million
Emp.: 26
Real Estate Brokerage Services
N.A.I.C.S.: 531210

Kanko Power Techno Co Ltd (1)
Kandenko Building 2F 3-5-3 Higashirokugo, Ota-ku, Tokyo, 144-0046, Japan
Tel.: (81) 357138200
Web Site: https://www.kanko-pt.co.jp
Emp.: 254
Heavy Construction Services
N.A.I.C.S.: 237990

Kanko Syoji Co Ltd (1)
NBF Ueno Building 4-24-11 Higashiueno, Taito-ku, Tokyo, 110-8631, Japan
Tel.: (81) 358266300
Web Site: https://www.kankosyoji.co.jp
Sales Range: $125-149.9 Million
Emp.: 158
Electrical Equipment Sales Services

N.A.I.C.S.: 221118

Kawasaki Setsubi Kogyo Co., Ltd. (1)
1-6-47 Osu, Naka-ku, Nagoya, 460-0011, Aichi, Japan   (49.8%)
Tel.: (81) 522217700
Web Site: https://www.kawasaki-sk.co.jp
Emp.: 382
Air Conditioning, Plumbing & Electrical Systems Installation Services
N.A.I.C.S.: 238220

Kei Lease Co Ltd (1)
Kandenkoyushima Bldg Bekkan, 4 1 18 Yushima Bunkyo-Ku, Tokyo, 113 0034, Japan
Tel.: (81) 338137161
Equipment Leasing Services
N.A.I.C.S.: 532490

NetSave Co Ltd (1)
4th floor Akasaka KS Building 1-4-1, Akasaka Minato-ku, Tokyo, 107-0052, Japan
Tel.: (81) 355757721
Web Site: http://www.netsave.co.jp
Sales Range: $100-124.9 Million
Emp.: 449
Electrical Construction Services
N.A.I.C.S.: 335999

Saitama K-Techno Co., Ltd (1)
3-1-17 Harayama, Midori-ku, Saitama, 336-0931, Japan
Tel.: (81) 488812855
Emp.: 44
Industrial Building Construction Services
N.A.I.C.S.: 236210

Shizuoka K-Techno Co., Ltd (1)
8-12 Yoneyamacho, Numazu, 410-0046, Shizuoka, Japan
Tel.: (81) 559297878
Construction Engineering Services
N.A.I.C.S.: 541330

Thai Kandenko Co., Ltd. (1)
Tel.: (66) 26595732
Web Site: http://www.kandenko.co.th
Construction Services
N.A.I.C.S.: 236220

Tokyo Kouji Keibi Co., Ltd (1)
3-14-3 Hongo Kondo Building 3 F, Bunkyo-ku, Tokyo, 113-0033, Japan
Tel.: (81) 338181441
Industrial Building Construction Services
N.A.I.C.S.: 236210

Transmission Line Construction Co., Ltd. (1)
Toshima 6-chome No 9 No 5 KDK Prince building 4F, Kita-ku, Tokyo, 114-0003, Japan
Tel.: (81) 363718900
Web Site: http://www.k-tlc.co.jp
Sales Range: $125-149.9 Million
Emp.: 164
Power Transmission Towers Construction Services
N.A.I.C.S.: 221122

Vietnam Kandenko Co., Ltd. (1)
12th Floor ICON4 Tower 243A De La Thanh street, Lang Thuong ward Dong Da district, Hanoi, Vietnam
Tel.: (84) 2437246606
Electrical & Transmission Line Services
N.A.I.C.S.: 238210

Yamanashi K-Techno Co., Ltd (1)
2-24-6 Myojin-cho, Hachioji, 192-0046, Japan
Tel.: (81) 426569811
Web Site: https://www.tama-kt.co.jp
Emp.: 6
Electric Equipment Mfr
N.A.I.C.S.: 335999

KANDI TECHNOLOGIES GROUP, INC.
Jinhua City Industrial Zone, Jinhua, 321016, Zhejiang, China
Tel.: (86) 57982239856   DE
Web Site: https://www.kandivehicle.com
Year Founded: 2004
KNDI—(NASDAQ)
Rev.: $117,813,049

KANDI TECHNOLOGIES GROUP, INC.

KANDI TECHNOLOGIES GROUP, INC.—(Continued)
Assets: $482,982,276
Liabilities: $85,289,305
Net Worth: $397,692,971
Earnings: ($12,123,663)
Emp.: 971
Fiscal Year-end: 12/31/22
All-Terrain Vehicles & Go-Karts Developer, Mfr & Marketer
N.A.I.C.S.: 336110
Xiaoming Hu (Chm, Pres & CEO)

Subsidiaries:

SC Autosports, LLC (1)
8050 Forest Ln, Dallas, TX 75243
Tel.: (972) 271-0888
Web Site: https://www.kandiamerica.com
All-Terrain Vehicles & Go-Karts Developer, Mfr & Marketer
N.A.I.C.S.: 336110

Zhejiang Kandi Vehicles Co., Ltd. (1)
Jinhua City Industrial Zone, Jinhua, 321016, Zhejiang, China **(100%)**
Tel.: (86) 57982239856
Motor Vehicle Body Mfr
N.A.I.C.S.: 336211

KANDY HOTELS CO. (1938) PLC
No 327 Union Place, 02, Colombo, Sri Lanka
Tel.: (94) 117657900
Year Founded: 1927
KHC.N0000—(COL)
Rev.: $4,071,958
Assets: $44,525,138
Liabilities: $13,984,495
Net Worth: $30,540,643
Earnings: ($398,973)
Fiscal Year-end: 03/31/24
Hotel & Restaurant Operator
N.A.I.C.S.: 721110

KANE BIOTECH INC.
290100 Innovation Drive, Winnipeg, R3T 6A8, MB, Canada
Tel.: (204) 453-1301 **Ca**
Web Site: https://www.kanebiotech.com
Year Founded: 2001
KNBIF—(OTCQB)
Rev.: $1,257,730
Assets: $4,798,735
Liabilities: $6,024,578
Net Worth: ($1,225,844)
Earnings: ($3,793,989)
Emp.: 20
Fiscal Year-end: 12/31/21
Molecular Mechanisms Developer of Biofilm Formation & Methods for Finding Compounds Which Inhibit or Disrupt Biofilms
N.A.I.C.S.: 325414
Philip Renaud (Chm)

KANE CONSTRUCTIONS PTY LTD
28 34 Rooney Street, Melbourne, 3121, VIC, Australia
Tel.: (61) 394298888
Web Site: http://www.kaneconstructions.com
Sales Range: $75-99.9 Million
Emp.: 135
Construction Services
N.A.I.C.S.: 236210
Jonathan Forster (Chm)

KANE HOLDINGS LIMITED
La Plaiderie House La Plaiderie, Saint Peter Port, GY1 1WG, Guernsey
Tel.: (44) 1481730397 **GY**
Web Site: http://www.kane-group.com
Year Founded: 2000
Holding Company; Life Insurance, Pension & Investment Management Services
N.A.I.C.S.: 551112
John Uprichard (CEO)

Subsidiaries:

Kane LPI Solutions Limited (1)
6th Floor Cumberland House 1 Victoria Street, Hamilton, HM 11, Bermuda
Tel.: (441) 295 8448
Web Site: http://www.kane-group.com
Life Insurance, Pension & Investment Asset Management Services
N.A.I.C.S.: 524292
John Uprichard (CEO)

Subsidiary (Non-US):

Kane LPI Solutions (Cayman) Limited (2)
PO Box 10008, Willow House Cricket Square, Georgetown, KY1-1001, Grand Cayman, Cayman Islands
Tel.: (345) 4412958448
Web Site: http://www.kane-group.com
Life Insurance, Pension & Investment Asset Management Services
N.A.I.C.S.: 524292
Simon Hinshelwood (Grp Chm)

Kane LPI Solutions (MENA) Limited (2)
Dubai International Financial Centre The Gate Village 1 2nd Fl Unit 8, PO Box 506732, Dubai, United Arab Emirates
Tel.: (971) 4 434 3642
Web Site: http://www.kane-group.com
Life Insurance, Pension & Investment Asset Management Services
N.A.I.C.S.: 524292

Kane LPI Solutions (Malta) Limited (2)
Central Business Centre Mdina Road, Zebbug, ZBG 9015, Malta
Tel.: (356) 22471900
Web Site: http://www.kane-group.com
Life Insurance, Pension & Investment Asset Management Services
N.A.I.C.S.: 524292
Graziella Vella (Mng Dir)

Subsidiary (US):

Kane LPI Solutions (USA), Inc. (2)
PO Box 161, Greenwich, CT 06836
Tel.: (203) 661-0304
Web Site: http://www.kane-group.com
Life Insurance, Pension & Investment Asset Management Services
N.A.I.C.S.: 524292
Christopher Gorski (Grp Head-Legal, Risk & Compliance)

KANEFUSA CORPORATION
1-1 Nakaoguchi Ohguchi-cho, Niwa, 480-0192, Aichi, Japan
Tel.: (81) 587957221
Web Site: https://www.kanefusa.net
5984—(TKS)
Rev.: $132,728,800
Assets: $229,823,090
Liabilities: $41,894,180
Net Worth: $187,928,910
Earnings: $5,856,460
Emp.: 1,439
Fiscal Year-end: 03/31/24
Industrial Cutting Tool Mfr
N.A.I.C.S.: 333517
Masato Watanabe (Pres)

Subsidiaries:

Kanefusa China Corporation (1)
No 50 Zhuzhu Rd, Lujia Town, Kunshan, Jiangsu, China
Tel.: (86) 51257875072
Sales Range: $50-74.9 Million
Emp.: 200
Cutting Tool Mfr
N.A.I.C.S.: 333515

Kanefusa Europe B.V. (1)
De Witbogt 12, 5652 AG, Eindhoven, Netherlands
Tel.: (31) 402900901
Web Site: http://www.kanefusa.net
Sales Range: $25-49.9 Million
Emp.: 11
Knives Sawblade & Other Cutting Tools Mfr
N.A.I.C.S.: 333515

Kanefusa India Pvt. Ltd. (1)
Plot No 169 Sector-8 IMT Manesar, Gurgaon, 122051, Haryana, India
Tel.: (91) 1244208440
Web Site: http://www.kanefusa.net
Emp.: 10
Knives Sawblade & Other Cutting Tools Mfr
N.A.I.C.S.: 333515

Kanefusa USA Inc. (1)
621 Dolwick Dr, Erlanger, KY 41018
Tel.: (859) 283-1450
Web Site: https://www.kanefusa.net
Sales Range: $25-49.9 Million
Emp.: 15
Metal Cutting Tools Distr
N.A.I.C.S.: 333517
Mikio Kamiya (Pres)

Kunshan Kanefusa Corporation (1)
No 50 Zhuzhu Road, Lujia Town, Kunshan, Jiangsu, China
Tel.: (86) 51257875072
Web Site: http://www.kanefusa.net
Sales Range: $50-74.9 Million
Emp.: 180
Cutting Tool Mfr
N.A.I.C.S.: 333515

P.T. Kanefusa Indonesia (1)
EJIP Industrial Park JI CISOKAN RAYA Plot 8 D South Cikarang, Bekasi, 17530, West Java, Indonesia
Tel.: (62) 218970360
Knives Sawblade & Other Cutting Tools Mfr
N.A.I.C.S.: 332216

KANEKA CORPORATION
2-3-18 Nakanoshima, Kita-ku, Osaka, 530-8288, Japan
Tel.: (81) 662265050 **JP**
Web Site: https://www.kaneka.co.jp
Year Founded: 1949
4118—(TKS)
Rev.: $5,038,816,220
Assets: $5,752,055,050
Liabilities: $2,616,383,420
Net Worth: $3,135,671,630
Earnings: $153,484,200
Emp.: 3,390
Fiscal Year-end: 03/31/24
PVC & Caustic Soda, Specialty Plastics, Plastic Products, Foodstuffs, Pharmaceuticals, Electrical & Electronic Materials & Synthetic Fibers Mfr
N.A.I.C.S.: 325211
Minoru Tanaka (Pres)

Subsidiaries:

Anaspec Inc. (1)
34801 Campus Dr, Fremont, CA 94555
Web Site: http://www.anaspec.com
Biopharmaceutical Product Mfr & Distr
N.A.I.C.S.: 325412
Lieven Janssens (Pres)

Biomaster, Inc. (1)
8th floor Yokohama Excellent III 3-35 Minami-Nakadori, Naka-ku, Yokohama, 231-0006, Kanagawa, Japan
Tel.: (81) 452223363
Web Site: https://www.biomaster.jp
Medical Equipment Distr
N.A.I.C.S.: 423450

CEMEDINE Co., Ltd. (1)
18F Gate City Ohsaki East Tower 1-11-2 Osaki, Shinagawa-ku, Tokyo, 141-8620, Japan **(99.99%)**
Tel.: (81) 364217411
Web Site: http://www.cemedine.co.jp
Rev.: $276,625,360
Assets: $238,921,760
Liabilities: $94,505,840
Net Worth: $144,415,920

INTERNATIONAL PUBLIC

Earnings: $14,316,720
Emp.: 549
Fiscal Year-end: 03/31/2022
Adhesive Mfr
N.A.I.C.S.: 325520

Subsidiary (Non-US):

Asia Cemedine Co., Ltd. (2)
1717-1723 Onnut Road, Suanluang, Bangkok, 10250, Thailand
Tel.: (66) 23317301
Web Site: https://www.asiacemedine.com
Adhesive Mfr & Distr
N.A.I.C.S.: 325520

Plant (Domestic):

CEMEDINE AUTOMOTIVE CO., LTD. - Kinuura Plant (2)
1-11 Suma-cho, Hekinan, 447-0854, Aichi, Japan
Tel.: (81) 566 48 3311
Web Site: http://www.cemedine.co.jp
Adhesive Mfr
N.A.I.C.S.: 325520

Subsidiary (Domestic):

CEMEDINE CHEMICAL CO., LTD. (2)
152-7 Kibi-chuocho-nishi, Kaga-gun, Okayama, 716-1554, Japan
Tel.: (81) 866559855
Web Site: http://www.cemedine.co.jp
Adhesive Mfr
N.A.I.C.S.: 325520

CEMEDINE CHEMICAL INDUSTRIES CO., LTD. (2)
2184 Shimo-ono, Koga, 306-0204, Ibaraki, Japan
Tel.: (81) 280912900
Web Site: http://www.cemedine.co.jp
Adhesive Mfr
N.A.I.C.S.: 325520

Plant (Domestic):

CEMEDINE Co., Ltd. - Mie Plant (2)
142-7 Sekicho-ege, Kameyama, 519-1106, Mie, Japan
Tel.: (81) 595 96 1816
Web Site: http://www.cemedine.co.jp
Adhesive Mfr
N.A.I.C.S.: 325520

Subsidiary (Non-US):

CEMEDINE PHILIPPINES CORP. (2)
Block2 Cavite Economic Zone II, General Trias, 4107, Cavite, Philippines
Tel.: (63) 466830325
Adhesive Distr
N.A.I.C.S.: 424690

Subsidiary (Domestic):

CEMEDINE SALES CO., LTD. (2)
Gate City Osaki East Tower 18th floor 1-11-2 Osaki, Shinagawa-ku, Tokyo, 141-8620, Japan
Tel.: (81) 364217405
Web Site: https://www.cemedine-hanbai.com
Adhesive Mfr
N.A.I.C.S.: 325520

Subsidiary (Non-US):

CEMEDINE THAILAND CO., LTD. (2)
1717/1 Onnut Road, Suanluang, Bangkok, 10250, Thailand
Tel.: (66) 23317301
Web Site: http://www.cemedine.co.jp
Coating Materials & Adhesives Mfr & Distr
N.A.I.C.S.: 325520

Cemedine Shanghai Co., Ltd. (2)
39th Floor Hang Seng Bank Tower 1000 Lujiazui Ring Road, Pudong New District, Shanghai, 200120, China
Tel.: (86) 2160701426
Web Site: http://www.cemedine.co.jp
Adhesive Distr
N.A.I.C.S.: 424690

TAIWAN CEMEDINE CO., LTD. (2)
No 76-3 Hsao Qui Lo Shan, Tanshui, New

AND PRIVATE COMPANIES

Taipei City, 25144, Taiwan
Tel.: (886) 226291425
Web Site: http://www.cemedine.co.jp
Coating Materials & Adhesives Mfr & Distr
N.A.I.C.S.: 325520

Cemedine North America LLC (1)
2142 Western Ave, Cincinnati, OH 45214
Tel.: (513) 618-4652
Chemical Products Mfr
N.A.I.C.S.: 325998

Dia Chemical Co., Ltd. (1)
2-1-3 Johoku, Oyama, 323-0029, Tochigi, Japan
Tel.: (81) 285252785
Web Site: https://www.diac.co.jp
Emp.: 57
Plastic Material Mfr & Distr
N.A.I.C.S.: 325211

GeneFrontier Corporation (1)
273-1 Kashiwa 4th floor Sharp Kashiwa Building, Kashiwa, 277-0005, Chiba, Japan
Tel.: (81) 471376301
Web Site: http://www.genefrontier.com
Biopharmaceutical Research & Development Services
N.A.I.C.S.: 541714
Masanobu Sugawara *(CEO)*

Hane Co., Ltd. (1)
1-17-19-3F Marunouchi, Naka-ku, Nagoya, 460-0002, Aichi, Japan
Tel.: (81) 522215411
Web Site: https://www.hane.co.jp
Emp.: 205
Plastic Material Mfr & Distr
N.A.I.C.S.: 325211

Japan Medical Technology Co., Ltd. (1)
Shinjuku Nomura Building 6F 1-26-2 Nishi-Shinjuku, Shinjuku-ku, Tokyo, 163-0558, Japan
Tel.: (81) 367580089
Web Site: http://www.jmt-eco.co.jp
Emp.: 30
Metal Refining Services
N.A.I.C.S.: 331410
Katsumi Ando *(CEO)*

Kaneka (Malaysia) Sdn. Bhd. (1)
Lot 123-124 Jalan Gebeng 2/3 Gebeng Industrial Estate, 26080, Kuantan, Pahang Darul Makmur, Malaysia
Tel.: (60) 95826000
Web Site: https://www.kaneka.com.my
Chemical Product Mfr & Distr
N.A.I.C.S.: 325998
Akira Iwazawa *(Mng Dir)*

Kaneka Aerospace LLC (1)
6166 Egret Ct, Benicia, CA 94510
Tel.: (707) 747-6738
Web Site: https://www.kaneka-aerospace.com
Sales Range: $1-9.9 Million
All Other Miscellaneous Chemical Product & Preparation Mfr
N.A.I.C.S.: 325998

Kaneka Americas Holding, Inc. (1)
6250 Underwood Rd, Pasadena, TX 77507
Tel.: (281) 474-7084
Web Site: https://www.kaneka.com
Business Development Services
N.A.I.C.S.: 611430

Kaneka Asia Co., Ltd. (1)
Room 011 39th Floor No 1000 Lujiazui Ring Road, Pudong New Area, Shanghai, China
Tel.: (86) 2158770761
Raw Material Distr
N.A.I.C.S.: 424590

Kaneka Belgium N.V. (1)
Nijverheidsstraat 16, Oevel, 2260, Westerlo, Belgium (100%)
Tel.: (32) 14257800
Web Site: https://www.kaneka.be
Emp.: 344
Marketing & Sales of PVC Products
N.A.I.C.S.: 325211
Masaaki Kimura *(Mng Dir)*

Kaneka Creative Consulting Co., Ltd. (1)
Nakanoshima Festival Tower 17F 2-3-18 Nakanoshima, Kita-ku, Osaka, 530-0005, Japan
Tel.: (81) 662265060
Web Site: https://www.kcc-web.net
Emp.: 200
Staffing Services
N.A.I.C.S.: 561320

Kaneka Eurogentec S.A. (1)
LIEGE Science Park 5 rue Bois Saint-Jean, 4102, Seraing, Belgium
Tel.: (32) 43727400
Web Site: https://www.eurogentec.com
Medical Equipment Mfr & Distr
N.A.I.C.S.: 339112
Lieven Janssens *(Pres)*

Kaneka Foam Plastics Co., Ltd. (1)
1-1-7 Koraku Glass City Koraku 3F, Bunkyo-ku, Tokyo, 112-0004, Japan
Tel.: (81) 5031815960
Web Site: https://www.knkfps.jp
Plastic Material Mfr & Distr
N.A.I.C.S.: 325211

Kaneka Foods Corporation (1)
13-1 Nishigokencho Sumitomo Real Estate Iidabashi Building 3, Shinjuku-ku, Tokyo, 162-0812, Japan
Tel.: (81) 352278530
Web Site: https://www.kanekashokuhin.co.jp
Foodstuff Product Distr
N.A.I.C.S.: 424490

Kaneka Hoken Center Co., Ltd. (1)
Comfortable Living Building 1-3-18 Tosabori, Nishi-ku, Osaka, 550-0001, Japan
Tel.: (81) 662256670
Web Site: http://www.kaneka-hoken.co.jp
Emp.: 30
Insurance Services
N.A.I.C.S.: 524113

Kaneka Hokkaido Co., Ltd. (1)
13th floor Sapporo Fukoku Life Koshiyama Building, 1-20 Kita 2-jo Nishi 3-chome Chuo-ku, Sapporo, 060-0002, Japan
Tel.: (81) 112225400
Web Site: https://www.kaneka-hokkaido.co.jp
Emp.: 8
Business Development Services
N.A.I.C.S.: 611430

Kaneka Kentech Co., Ltd. (1)
Glass City Koraku 3F 1-1-7 Koraku, Bunkyo-ku, Tokyo, 112-0004, Japan
Tel.: (81) 363702370
Web Site: https://www.kktc.jp
Emp.: 121
Plastic Material Distr
N.A.I.C.S.: 424610

Kaneka Korea Corporation (1)
15th floor 19 Eulji-ro 5-gil Suha-dong Ferrum Tower, Jung-gu, Seoul, Korea (South)
Tel.: (82) 263538570
Web Site: https://www.kanekakorea.co.kr
Business Development Services
N.A.I.C.S.: 611430

Kaneka Medical Tech Corporation (1)
1-12-32 Akasaka Ark Mori Building, Minato-ku, Tokyo, 107-6028, Japan
Tel.: (81) 5031815840
Web Site: https://www.kanekamedicaltech.co.jp
Medical Equipment Mfr & Distr
N.A.I.C.S.: 339112

Kaneka Nutrients L.P. (1)
6250 Underwood Rd, Pasadena, TX 77507
Tel.: (281) 291-4489
Web Site: https://www.kanekanutrients.com
Sales Range: $25-49.9 Million
Emp.: 70
Dietary Supplements Mfr
N.A.I.C.S.: 812191

Kaneka Solar Marketing Co., Ltd. (1)
Higobashi Center Building 1-9-1 Edobori, Nishi-ku, Osaka, 550-0002, Japan
Tel.: (81) 120173325
Web Site: https://www.kaneka-solar-energy.jp
Solar Cell Distr
N.A.I.C.S.: 423690

Kaneka Solartech Corporation (1)
157-74 Kamidai, Toyooka, Hyogo, Japan
Tel.: (81) 796295500
Web Site: https://www.kst.kaneka.co.jp
Solar Cell Mfr
N.A.I.C.S.: 334413

Kaneka Sun Spice Corporation (1)
1-10-17 Jusohigashi, Yodogawa Ward, Osaka, 532-0023, Japan
Tel.: (81) 663062133
Web Site: https://www.kanekasunspice.co.jp
Emp.: 202
Spice Mfr & Distr
N.A.I.C.S.: 311942

Kaneka Takasago Service Center Co., Ltd. (1)
1-73 Okihama-cho Takasago-cho, Takasago, 676-0026, Hyogo, Japan
Tel.: (81) 794452471
Web Site: https://www.kts-kanekagr.co.jp
Emp.: 130
Food Distr
N.A.I.C.S.: 424420

Kaneka Techno Research Corporation (1)
35F Nakanoshima Festival Tower 2-3-18 Nakanoshima, Kita-ku, Osaka, 530-8288, Japan
Tel.: (81) 662264310
Web Site: http://www.ktr.co.jp
Analysis Services
N.A.I.C.S.: 541990
Migaku Oonari *(CEO)*

Kaneka Texas Corp. (1)
6161 Underwood Rd, Pasadena, TX 77507
Tel.: (510) 351-8648
Web Site: http://www.kanekatexas.com
Emp.: 12
PVC Resin Mfr
N.A.I.C.S.: 325211

Kaneka Trading (Shanghai) Co., Ltd. (1)
Room 031 Floor 39 No 1000 Lujiazui Ring Road, Pudong New Area, Shanghai, China
Tel.: (86) 2158794720
Raw Material Distr
N.A.I.C.S.: 424590

Kaneka Your Health Care Co., Ltd. (1)
1-12-32 Akasaka, Minato-ku, Tokyo, 107-6028, Japan
Tel.: (81) 120438910
Web Site: https://www.kaneka-yhc.co.jp
Health & Personal Care Product Retailer
N.A.I.C.S.: 456199

Kanto Styrene Co., Ltd. (1)
2303-2 Oaza Liang, Oyama, 323-0158, Tochigi, Japan
Tel.: (81) 285492516
Web Site: https://www.kanto-styrene.com
Plastic Material Mfr & Distr
N.A.I.C.S.: 325211

Kochi Styrol Co., Ltd. (1)
Tosayamada Kuzume 25 address 12, Kami, 782-0051, Kochi, Japan
Tel.: (81) 887522030
Web Site: http://www.kochi-styrol.co.jp
Plastic Material Mfr & Distr
N.A.I.C.S.: 325211

Nagashima Shokuhin Co., Ltd. (1)
543 Oshitsuke Nagashima-cho, Kuwana, 511-1113, Mie, Japan
Tel.: (81) 594423011
Web Site: https://www.nagashimashokuhin.co.jp
Frozen Food Mfr & Distr
N.A.I.C.S.: 311412

OLED Aomori Co., Ltd. (1)
1-82 Yaehei, Owase Rokkasho-mura Kamikita-gun, Aomori, 039-3212, Japan
Tel.: (81) 175711560
Web Site: https://www.oled-aomori.jp
Emp.: 79
LED Light Mfr
N.A.I.C.S.: 334413

Osaka Synthetic Chemical Laboratories, Inc. (1)
1-1-2 Nishinomiyahama, Nishinomiya, 662-0934, Hyogo, Japan
Tel.: (81) 798225840
Web Site: http://www.tec-osc.co.jp
Pharmaceuticals Mfr

N.A.I.C.S.: 325412

Sanvic Inc. (1)
Tokyo Sales Ryobi Building 7th Floor 3-33-13 Mukojima, Sumida-ku, Tokyo, 131-0033, Japan
Tel.: (81) 356116535
Web Site: http://www.sanvic.co.jp
Chemical Product Mfr & Distr
N.A.I.C.S.: 325998

Shiga Denshi Corporation (1)
2-1-1 Hieitsuji, Otsu, 520-0104, Shiga, Japan
Tel.: (81) 775772140
Web Site: http://www.shiga-denshi.com
Electronic Products Mfr
N.A.I.C.S.: 334419

Shinka Shokuhin Co., Ltd. (1)
3-5-10 Minato, Chuo-ku, Tokyo, 104-0043, Japan
Tel.: (81) 335376070
Web Site: http://www.shinka-s.co.jp
Emp.: 120
Foodstuff Product Mfr & Distr
N.A.I.C.S.: 311999

Showa Kaseikogyo Co., Ltd. (1)
1-603-29 Komatsudai, Hanyu, 348-0038, Saitama, Japan
Tel.: (81) 485615221
Web Site: https://www.showakvc.co.jp
Emp.: 150
Plastic Materials Mfr
N.A.I.C.S.: 325211
Shunichi Ikemoto *(Pres)*

Taiyo Yushi Corporation (1)
2-7 Moriyacho, Kanagawa-ku, Yokohama, 221-0022, Kanagawa, Japan
Tel.: (81) 454414951
Web Site: https://www.taiyo-yushi.co.jp
Emp.: 220
Fat & Oil Mfr
N.A.I.C.S.: 311225

Tamai Kasei Co., Ltd. (1)
3-524-9 Zenibako, Otaru, 047-0261, Hokkaido, Japan
Tel.: (81) 134621100
Web Site: https://www.tamai-kasei.co.jp
Plastic Material Mfr & Distr
N.A.I.C.S.: 325211
Ikiyoshi Nakamichi *(CEO)*

Tatsuta Chemical Co., Ltd. (1)
3-7-19 Higashinihonbashi Yusen, Higashinihonbashi Ekimae Building 5th floor Chuo-ku, Tokyo, 103-0004, Japan
Tel.: (81) 336616591
Web Site: http://www.tatsutachemical.co.jp
Chemical Product Mfr & Distr
N.A.I.C.S.: 325998
Hiroyuki Taniguchi *(Pres)*

Tobu Chemical Co., Ltd. (1)
1252-1 Konoyama, Joso, 300-2746, Ibaraki, Japan
Tel.: (81) 297437071
Web Site: http://www.tobu-kagaku.co.jp
Emp.: 200
Chemical Product Mfr & Distr
N.A.I.C.S.: 325998
Masashi Goto *(Pres & CEO)*

Tochigi Kaneka Corporation (1)
14 Kinugaoka, Moka, 321-4367, Tochigi, Japan
Tel.: (81) 285821231
Web Site: https://www.tochigi-kaneka.co.jp
Emp.: 227
Electronic Products Mfr
N.A.I.C.S.: 334419

Tokyo Kaneka Foods Manufacturing Corporation (1)
23 Takemasawa, Miyoshi-cho Iruma-gun, Saitama, 354-0043, Japan
Tel.: (81) 492582365
Web Site: https://www.tokyokanekafoods.co.jp
Emp.: 163
Fat & Oil Mfr
N.A.I.C.S.: 311225

KANEKO SEEDS CO., LTD.

KANEKO SEEDS CO., LTD.
1-50-12 Furuichi-machi, Maebashi, 371-8503, Gunma, Japan
Tel.: (81) 272511612

KANEKO SEEDS CO., LTD.

Kaneko Seeds Co., Ltd.—(Continued)

Web Site:
https://www.kanekoseeds.jp
Year Founded: 1895
1376—(TKS)
Rev.: $407,162,780
Assets: $321,788,020
Liabilities: $160,233,010
Net Worth: $161,555,010
Earnings: $7,779,970
Emp.: 701
Fiscal Year-end: 05/31/24
Farm Supplies Whslr
N.A.I.C.S.: 424910
Masahiko Kaneko (Pres)

Subsidiaries:

KANEKO SEEDS (THAILAND) CO., LTD (1)
189 M 7 T Banpen, A Muang, Lamphun, 51000, Thailand
Tel.: (66) 53 520 010
Vegetable Distr
N.A.I.C.S.: 424480

KANEL INDUSTRIES LIMITED
203 2nd Floor Abhijeet - 1 Nr Mithakhali Six Roads Ellisbridge, Ahmedabad, 380 006, India
Tel.: (91) 7926423365
Web Site: https://www.kanel.in
Year Founded: 1992
500236—(BOM)
Rev.: $341
Assets: $634,486
Liabilities: $1,485,387
Net Worth: ($850,901)
Earnings: ($21,375)
Emp.: 1
Fiscal Year-end: 03/31/23
Castor Oil Mfr
N.A.I.C.S.: 311224
Dhiren Kanaiyalal Thakkar (Chm, Mng Dir, CFO & Compliance Officer)

KANEMATSU CORPORATION
7-2 Marunouchi 2-chome, Chiyoda-ku, Tokyo, 100-7017, Japan
Tel.: (81) 354408111 JP
Web Site:
https://www.kanematsu.co.jp
Year Founded: 1889
8020—(TKS)
Rev.: $7,433,881,840
Assets: $6,141,534,080
Liabilities: $4,212,484,320
Net Worth: $1,929,049,760
Earnings: $199,011,120
Emp.: 7,446
Fiscal Year-end: 03/31/22
General Trading Company
N.A.I.C.S.: 522299
Masayuki Shimojima (Chm)

Subsidiaries:

ATAD Steel Structure Corp. (1)
99 Nguyen Thi Minh Khai St, Ben Thanh Dist 1, Ho Chi Minh City, Vietnam
Tel.: (84) 2839260666
Web Site: http://atad.vn
Steel Products Mfr
N.A.I.C.S.: 331110
Phan Hoang Huy (Deputy Dir-Sls Div)

Aries Motor Sp. z o.o. (1)
ul Arkuszowa 11, 01-934, Warsaw, Poland
Tel.: (48) 228395007
Web Site: https://www.honda-ariesmotor.pl
Automobile Whslr
N.A.I.C.S.: 423110

Aries Power Equipment Ltd. (1)
ul Pulawska 467, 02-844, Warsaw, Poland
Tel.: (48) 228940890
Web Site: https://www.mojahonda.pl
New Car Dealer Services
N.A.I.C.S.: 441110

Datatec Co., Ltd. (1)
11th floor Green Place Kamata 7-37-10 Nishi Kamata, Ota-ku, Tokyo, 144-0051, Japan
Tel.: (81) 357037041
Web Site: https://www.datatec.co.jp
Emp.: 70
Automotive Equipment Distr
N.A.I.C.S.: 423120

Eiwa Metal Co., Ltd. (1)
3-3-3 Shonai Takaramachi, Toyonaka, 561-0836, Osaka, Japan
Tel.: (81) 663345031
Web Site: https://www.eiwakinzoku.co.jp
Emp.: 19
Steel Products Mfr
N.A.I.C.S.: 238120
Keiichi Harada (Pres)

Japan Logistics Co., Ltd. (1)
1-1 Honmoku Pier, Naka-ku, Yokohama, 220-0000, Kanagawa, Japan
Tel.: (81) 456240118
Web Site: https://www.jalos.co.jp
Freight Trucking Services
N.A.I.C.S.: 484110

KET Electronics (Malaysia) Sdn. Bhd.
A-3A-32 Ste A IOI Blvd Jalan Kenari 5 Bandar, Puchong Jaya, 47170, Puchong, Selangor Darul Ehsan, Malaysia
Tel.: (60) 3 8076 8392
Web Site: https://www.kanematsu.co.jp
Semiconductor Devices Mfr
N.A.I.C.S.: 334413

KG Agri Products, Inc. (1)
20100 Johnson Rd, Marysville, OH 43040-9140
Tel.: (937) 644-8215
Agricultural Services
N.A.I.C.S.: 115116

KGK Czech s.r.o.
Radlicka 608/2, 150 00, Prague, Czech Republic
Tel.: (420) 560501568
Emp.: 4
Machine Tool Whslr
N.A.I.C.S.: 423830
Jun Nagawa (Gen Mgr)

KGK Engineering (Thai) Co., Ltd. (1)
No 846/3 Summer Lasalle Project Unit no A611-3 Lasalle Rd, Bangna-Tai Sub-District Bangna District, Bangkok, 10260, Thailand
Tel.: (66) 20902960
Web Site: https://www.kgk-j.co.jp
Sales Range: $25-49.9 Million
Emp.: 25
Machine Tool Whslr
N.A.I.C.S.: 423830
Yuji Okamoto (Gen Mgr)

KGK Engineering Corp. (1)
4-5-16 Shirahata, Minami Ward, Saitama, 336-0022, Japan
Tel.: (81) 488728711
Web Site: https://www.kgke.jp
Emp.: 17
Industrial Machinery & Equipment Whslr
N.A.I.C.S.: 423830

KGK International Corp. (1)
1550 Louis Ave, Elk Grove Village, IL 60007
Tel.: (847) 621-2655
Web Site: https://www.kgki.com
Commercial & Industrial Equipment Whslr
N.A.I.C.S.: 423830

Kanematsu (China) Co., Ltd. (1)
18th Floor Raffles City Office Tower 268 Xi Zang Middle Road, Shanghai, 200001, China
Tel.: (86) 2163403456
Electric Equipment Mfr
N.A.I.C.S.: 334419

Kanematsu (Hong Kong) Ltd. (1)
Rooms 1116-1117 11 / F The Metropolis Tower 10 Metropolis Drive, Hung Hom, Kowloon, China (Hong Kong)
Tel.: (852) 28216200
Web Site: http://www.kanematsu.co.jp
Semiconductor Devices Mfr
N.A.I.C.S.: 334413

Kanematsu (Thailand) Ltd. (1)
25F Thaniya Plaza Building 52 Silom Road Suriyawongse, Bangrak, Bangkok, 10500, Thailand
Tel.: (66) 26328060
Web Site: http://www.kanematsu.co.jp
Emp.: 37
Semiconductor Devices Mfr
N.A.I.C.S.: 334413

Kanematsu Advanced Materials Corp. (1)
VPO Higashi Nihonbashi 7th Floor 3-4-13 Higashi Nihonbashi, Chuo-ku, Tokyo, 103-0004, Japan
Tel.: (81) 366616430
Web Site: https://www.kanematsu-am.com
Emp.: 115
Electric Component Whslr
N.A.I.C.S.: 423690
Teppei Asaba (Pres)

Kanematsu Aerospace Corporation (1)
1-12-7Shiba, Minato-ku, Tokyo, 105-0014, Japan
Tel.: (81) 357303481
Web Site: https://www.kac.jp
Sales Range: $25-49.9 Million
Emp.: 35
Aircraft Equipment Mfr
N.A.I.C.S.: 336413

Subsidiary (Non-US):

KG Aircraft Rotables Co., Ltd. (2)
Unit 6 Block C Nutgrove Office Park, Rathfarnham, Dublin, Ireland
Tel.: (353) 12988100
Web Site: https://www.kgar.com
Emp.: 3
Aircraft Rotable Component Supply & Repairing Services
N.A.I.C.S.: 488190
Donal O'Doherty (Mng Dir)

Kanematsu Agritech Co., Ltd. (1)
2-8 Shin-Matsudo Ishii Building 4F, Shinmatsudo, Matsudo, 270-0034, Chiba, Japan
Tel.: (81) 473093281
Web Site: http://www.k-agri.co.jp
Sales Range: $100-124.9 Million
Emp.: 62
Mixed Feed & Fertilizer Mfr & Distr
N.A.I.C.S.: 325314
Nobuyuki Ogawa (Exec Dir)

Kanematsu Australia Ltd. (1)
Suite 15 01 15 Castlereagh Street, Sydney, 2000, NSW, Australia
Tel.: (61) 292833347
Sales Range: $50-74.9 Million
Emp.: 5
Steel Products Whslr
N.A.I.C.S.: 423510
Ichiro Nakane (Mng Dir)

Kanematsu Chemicals Corp. (1)
TT-2 Building 9th and 10th floors 8-1 Nihonbashi-Ningyo-cho 3-Chome, Chuo-ku, Tokyo, 103-0013, Japan
Tel.: (81) 356433011
Web Site: https://www.kccjp.co.jp
Emp.: 70
Chemical Distr
N.A.I.C.S.: 424690
Masana Takahashi (Pres)

Kanematsu Communications Ltd. (1)
Shinjuku Bunka Quint Bldg 3F 3-22-7 Yoyogi, Shibuya-ku, Tokyo, 151-8601, Japan
Tel.: (81) 353081011
Web Site: https://www.kcs.ne.jp
Wireless Communication Equipment Distr
N.A.I.C.S.: 423690

Subsidiary (Non-US):

Kanematsu Granks, Corp. (2)
Tel.: (81) 362331970
Web Site: www.granks.co.jp
Mobile Content Service Provider
N.A.I.C.S.: 517810

Kanematsu Devices Korea Corporation (1)
Room 602 Koreana Building 135 Sejongdaero, Jung-gu, Seoul, Korea (South)
Tel.: (82) 27375795
Web Site: https://www.kanematsu.co.kr
Emp.: 17
Electric Equipment Mfr
N.A.I.C.S.: 334419

INTERNATIONAL PUBLIC

Kanematsu Electronics Ltd. (1)
Kyobashi-MID Bldg 13-10 Kyobashi 2-chome, Chuo-ku, Tokyo, 104-8338, Japan **(100%)**
Tel.: (81) 352506801
Web Site: http://www.kel.co.jp
Rev.: $690,487,623
Assets: $798,085,798
Liabilities: $198,615,421
Net Worth: $599,470,377
Earnings: $85,043,166
Emp.: 1,287
Fiscal Year-end: 03/31/2022
Information Technology Support Services
N.A.I.C.S.: 541513
Katsunori Toda (Sr Mng Dir)

Subsidiary (Domestic):

Nippon Office Systems Ltd. (2)
5-8-40 Kiba, Koto-ku, Tokyo, 135-8568, Japan **(100%)**
Tel.: (81) 343215500
Web Site: http://www.nos.co.jp
Sales Range: $50-74.9 Million
Emp.: 267
Integrated Information Technology Support Services
N.A.I.C.S.: 541513
Katsunori Toda (Pres & CEO)

Kanematsu Europe Plc (1)
160 Euston Road, London, NW1 2DX, United Kingdom
Tel.: (44) 2075298124
Web Site: http://www.kanematsu.co.jp
Sales Range: $25-49.9 Million
Emp.: 3
Liquid Crystal Mfr
N.A.I.C.S.: 339999

Kanematsu Food Corp. (1)
2-14-5 Mita 2-chome, Minato-ku, Tokyo, 108-0073, Japan
Tel.: (81) 354412171
Web Site: http://www.kanematsusyokuhin.co.jp
Frozen Food Whslr
N.A.I.C.S.: 424420
Hiroyasu Hirasawa (Gen Mgr)

Kanematsu Futuretech Solutions Corporation (1)
TMG Hatchobori Building 8F 10-7 Hatchobori 1-Chome, Chuo-ku, Tokyo, 104-0032, Japan
Tel.: (81) 355425930
Web Site: https://kft.kanematsu.co.jp
Electronic Equipment Distr
N.A.I.C.S.: 423690
Eiichi Tamura (Pres)

Kanematsu G.m.b.H (1)
Oststrasse 34, 40211, Dusseldorf, 40211, Germany
Tel.: (49) 21136890
Web Site: https://kanematsugmbh.com
Sales Range: $25-49.9 Million
Emp.: 20
Commercial Goods Distr
N.A.I.C.S.: 423440
Mariko Arai Kato (Pres)

Kanematsu Iran Ltd. (1)
Web Site: http://www.kanematsu.co.jp
Emp.: 11
Electric Equipment Mfr
N.A.I.C.S.: 334419

Kanematsu KGK Corp. (1)
15th floor Museum Tower Kyobashi 1-7-2 Kyobashi, Chuo-ku, Tokyo, 104-8510, Japan
Web Site: http://www.kgk-j.co.jp
Sales Range: $75-99.9 Million
Emp.: 194
Machine Tools & Industrial Machinery Whslr
N.A.I.C.S.: 423830
Yasuo Chiba (Pres & CEO)

Kanematsu KGK Trade & Sales (Shanghai) Co., Ltd. (1)
Room 2618 International Trade Center No 2201 West Yan'an Road, Shanghai, 200001, China
Tel.: (86) 2163404883
Web Site: https://www.kgk-c.com
Machine Tool Distr
N.A.I.C.S.: 423840

AND PRIVATE COMPANIES

Kanematsu Logistics & Insurance Ltd. (1)
5th Floor Sawanotsuru-Ningyocho Bldg 1-3-8 Nihonbashi-Ningyo-cho, Chuo-ku, Tokyo, 103-0013, Japan
Tel.: (81) 342193950
Web Site: https://www.kli.co.jp
Emp.: 67
Logistics & Insurance Services
N.A.I.C.S.: 541614
Mariko Arai *(Pres)*

Kanematsu New Zealand Ltd. (1)
Lavender House 27 Lilburn Street, PO Box 2472, Warkworth, 0910, New Zealand
Tel.: (64) 93025660
Sales Range: $50-74.9 Million
Emp.: 3
Fruit & Vegetables Whslr
N.A.I.C.S.: 424480
John Andrews *(Mgr-Trading)*

Kanematsu PWS Ltd. (1)
925 Nippa-cho, Kohoku-ku, Yokohama, 223-0057, Kanagawa, Japan
Tel.: (81) 455441811
Web Site: https://www.pwsj.co.jp
Semiconductor Equipment Mfr & Distr
N.A.I.C.S.: 334413
Hideto Matsui *(Pres)*

Kanematsu Petroleum Corporation (1)
1-1 Kanda Suda-cho, Chiyoda-ku, Tokyo, 120-0000, Japan
Tel.: (81) 352890471
Web Site: https://www.kanematsu-oilgas.co.jp
Emp.: 145
Petroleum Product Whslr
N.A.I.C.S.: 424720

Kanematsu Semiconductor Singapore Pte., Ltd. (1)
100 Tras Street 12-03 Amara Corporate Tower, Singapore, 079027, Singapore
Tel.: (65) 64384440
Web Site: http://www.sg-kss.com
Sales Range: $50-74.9 Million
Emp.: 9
Semiconductor Device Distr
N.A.I.C.S.: 423690

Kanematsu Semiconductor Taiwan Ltd. (1)
11F No 61 Chung Shan N Rd Sec 2, Taipei, Taiwan
Tel.: (886) 225622025
Web Site: http://www.kst.com.tw
Rev.: $11,444,520
Emp.: 15
Semiconductor Device Distr
N.A.I.C.S.: 423690

Kanematsu Soytech Corp. (1)
4F Awajicho Dai Building 3-1-9 Awajicho, Chuo-ku, Osaka, 101-0047, Japan
Tel.: (81) 662053366
Web Site: https://www.kgsoytech.co.jp
Emp.: 30
Food Product Whslr
N.A.I.C.S.: 424490

Kanematsu Trading Corp. (1)
akebono Nihonbashi Bldg 6F 19-5 Nihonbashi Koami-cho, Chuo-ku, Tokyo, 103-0016, Japan
Tel.: (81) 358602200
Web Site: https://www.e-kgt.com
Emp.: 280
Steel Distr
N.A.I.C.S.: 423510
Tomofusa Emi *(Pres)*

Kanematsu USA Inc. (1)
543 W Algonquin Rd, Arlington Heights, IL 60005
Tel.: (847) 981-5600
Web Site: http://www.kanematsuusa.com
Sales Range: $50-74.9 Million
Emp.: 23
Export & Import of IT Related Products, Electronics, Chemicals, Pharmaceuticals & Textiles
N.A.I.C.S.: 423830

Subsidiary (Domestic):

Kai Enterprises, Inc. (2)
2700 Richards Rd Ste 110, Bellevue, WA 98005
Tel.: (425) 373-0395
Web Site: http://www.kaienterprisesinc.com
Sales Range: $25-49.9 Million
Emp.: 3
Agricultural Commodities Distr
N.A.I.C.S.: 424910
Darren L. James *(Pres)*

Steel Service Oilfield Tubular, Inc. (2)
8138 E 63rd St, Tulsa, OK 74133
Tel.: (918) 286-1500
Web Site: http://www.steelserviceoilfield.com
Premium Tubing Distr
N.A.I.C.S.: 423510
Ron Pederson *(Pres)*

Kanematsu Wellness Corp. (1)
9th floor TT-2 Building 3-8-1 Nihonbashi Ningyocho, Chuo-ku, Tokyo, 103-0013, Japan
Tel.: (81) 336695660
Web Site: https://kwn.kanematsu.co.jp
Health Care Products Mfr
N.A.I.C.S.: 325412

Kanematsu Yuso Co., Ltd. (1)
7th floor Toyo Sudacho Building 1-5-1 Kandasudacho, Chiyoda-ku, Tokyo, 101-0041, Japan
Tel.: (81) 366946295
Web Site: https://www.kanematsu-yuso.com
Emp.: 20
Petroleum Product Distr
N.A.I.C.S.: 424720

Kaneyo Co., Ltd. (1)
13F Osaka Center Bldg 4-1-3 Kyutaromachi, Chuo-ku, Osaka, 541-0056, Japan (100%)
Tel.: (81) 662436500
Web Site: https://www.kaneyo-net.co.jp
Emp.: 63
Home Furnishing Material Distr
N.A.I.C.S.: 423220
Yukinobu Nishino *(Chm)*

Kantatsu Co., Ltd. (1)
Tel.: (81) 368636878
Web Site: http://www.kantatsu.co.jp
Optical Instrument Mfr
N.A.I.C.S.: 333310

Kenkosya Co., Ltd. (1)
1-70 Nagamine Nishi, Higashi-ku, Kumamoto, 861-8037, Japan
Tel.: (81) 963862111
Web Site: https://www.kenkosya.co.jp
Wood Window & Door Mfr
N.A.I.C.S.: 321911

Kyowa Steel Co., Ltd. (1)
2283-1 Hatamachi, Kasai, 675-2365, Hyogo, Japan
Tel.: (81) 790423443
Web Site: https://www.kyowasteel.com
Emp.: 85
Steel Product Distr.
N.A.I.C.S.: 423510

Lumonics K. K. (1)
15th floor Tokyo Front Terrace 2-3-14 Higashi-Shinagawa, Shinagawa-ku, Tokyo, 140-0002, Japan
Tel.: (81) 357156767
Web Site: https://lkk.co.jp
Semiconductor Equipment Mfr & Distr
N.A.I.C.S.: 334413

Miracool Co., Ltd. (1)
4F Kelvin Building 2-8-15 Higashikanda, Chiyoda-ku, Tokyo, 101-0031, Japan
Tel.: (81) 358353521
Web Site: https://www.miracool.jp
Sales Range: $50-74.9 Million
Emp.: 7
Shield Paint Distr
N.A.I.C.S.: 424950

Nagasawashouji Co., Ltd. (1)
Midosuji-Daiwa Building 8th Floor 6-8 Kyutarou-machi 3-Chome, Chuo-ku, Osaka, 541-0056, Japan
Tel.: (81) 6 6282 0256
Web Site: http://www.kccjp.co.jp
Semiconductor Machinery Mfr
N.A.I.C.S.: 333242

P.T. Kanematsu Trading Indonesia (1)
ANZ Tower 15th Floor Jalan Jend Sudirman Kav 33A, Jakarta, 10220, Indonesia
Web Site: http://www.kanematsu.co.jp
Industrial Equipment Mfr
N.A.I.C.S.: 333248

PT. Dunia Express Transindo (1)
Tel.: (62) 216511137
Warehousing & Logistics Services
N.A.I.C.S.: 541614

PT. Kanemory Food Service (1)
Jl Main Modern Industries Block AA No 8 Kawasan, Cikandi Modern Industries, Serang, 42186, Indonesia
Tel.: (62) 2548408042
Web Site: http://kanemory.co.id
Food Mfr
N.A.I.C.S.: 311999

Shintoa Corp. (1)
8th Floor Marunouchi Center Bldg 6-1 Marunouchi 1-chome, Chiyoda-ku, Tokyo, 100-8383, Japan
Tel.: (81) 332860211
Web Site: https://www.shintoa.co.jp
Sales Range: $75-99.9 Million
Emp.: 169
Aircraft Engines Whslr
N.A.I.C.S.: 423860

Summit Food Industries Co., Ltd. (1)
112 North Sathorn Road Silom, Bangrak, Bangkok, 10500, Thailand
Tel.: (66) 2 2665590
Rice Crackers Mfr & Whslr
N.A.I.C.S.: 311230

WATANA INTER - TRADE CO., LTD. (1)
25F Thaniya Plaza Building 52 Silom Road, Suriyawongse Bangrak, Bangkok, 10500, Thailand
Tel.: (66) 26328060
Sales Range: $25-49.9 Million
Emp.: 3
Steel Products Mfr
N.A.I.C.S.: 331110
Tanaka Kazuo *(Pres)*

Watachukikai Corp. (1)
7-56-5 Nishikamata, Ota-ku, Tokyo, 144-0051, Japan
Tel.: (81) 337323601
Web Site: https://www.watachu.co.jp
Cutting Tool Whslr
N.A.I.C.S.: 423840

KANEMATSU ENGINEERING CO., LTD.
3981-7 Nunoshida, Kochi, 781-5101, Japan
Tel.: (81) 888455566
Web Site: https://www.kanematsu-eng.jp
Year Founded: 1971
6402—(TKS)
Sales Range: $50-74.9 Million
Automobile Truck Mfr & Distr
N.A.I.C.S.: 336120
Kinichi Yamamoto *(Pres & Sr Mng Dir)*

KANEMATSU SUSTECH CORPORATION
3-3-2 Nihonbashi-Hamacho Tornare Nihonbashi Hamacho, Chuo-ku, Tokyo, 103-0007, Japan
Tel.: (81) 332658231
Web Site: http://www.ksustech.co.jp
Year Founded: 1934
7961—(TKS)
Rev.: $131,764,160
Assets: $118,928,480
Liabilities: $33,744,480
Net Worth: $85,184,000
Earnings: $7,414,880
Emp.: 227
Fiscal Year-end: 03/31/22
Wood Product & Security Equipment Mfr & Whslr
N.A.I.C.S.: 321211

KANESO CO., LTD.

Subsidiaries:

Kanematsu-NNK Corporation - Match Department Awaji Factory (1)
1575 Ikuho Awaji, Hyogo, 656-2223, Japan
Tel.: (81) 799640019
Wood Preservation Services
N.A.I.C.S.: 321114

Kanematsu-NNK Corporation - Wood Preservation Department Kansai Factory (1)
1-2-55 Hirabayashi-minami Suminoe Ward, Osaka, 559-0025, Osaka, Japan
Tel.: (81) 666863281
Wood Preservation Services
N.A.I.C.S.: 321114

Kanematsu-NNK Corporation - Wood Preservation Department Kanto Factory (1)
3-2-12 Shinkiba Koto ward, Tokyo, 136-8622, Japan
Tel.: (81) 335218301
Wood Preservation Services
N.A.I.C.S.: 321114

Kanematsu-NNK Corporation - Wood Preservation Department Okayama Factory (1)
158-2 Kobe, Tsuyama, 708-0015, Okayama, Japan
Tel.: (81) 868289115
Wood Preservation Services
N.A.I.C.S.: 321114

Kanematsu-NNK Corporation - Wood Preservation Department Tohoku Factory (1)
23-126 Hiraba Ouri-aza Ohira-mura Kurokawa-gun, Miyagi, 981-3601, Japan
Tel.: (81) 223454239
Wood Preservation Services
N.A.I.C.S.: 321114

KANEMITSU CORPORATION
2026 Okurahonmachi, Akashi, 673-0874, Hyogo, Japan
Tel.: (81) 789116645
Web Site: https://www.kanemitsu.co.jp
Year Founded: 1947
7208—(TKS)
Rev.: $73,311,510
Assets: $106,454,050
Liabilities: $33,995,230
Net Worth: $72,458,820
Earnings: $4,177,520
Emp.: 587
Fiscal Year-end: 03/31/24
Sheet Metal Pulley Mfr & Whslr
N.A.I.C.S.: 333613
Toshiaki Kanemitsu *(Pres)*

Subsidiaries:

Kanemitsu Corporation - Kasai Plant (1)
In Kasai Minami Indusrial Park 2001-33 Maruyama Abikicho, Kasai, 675-2113, Hyogo, Japan
Tel.: (81) 790498171
Metal Pulley Mfr
N.A.I.C.S.: 333923

Kanemitsu Corporation - Miki Plant (1)
In Miki Plant Park 48-1 Tomoe Besshocho, Miki, 673-0443, Hyogo, Japan
Tel.: (81) 794831388
Metal Pulley Mfr
N.A.I.C.S.: 333923

KANESO CO., LTD.
81 Nawao Asahi-machi, Mie, 510-8101, Japan
Tel.: (81) 593774747
Web Site: https://www.kaneso.co.jp
Year Founded: 1922
5979—(NGO)
Sales Range: Less than $1 Million
Metal Products Mfr
N.A.I.C.S.: 332313
Satoshi Toyoda *(Pres & CEO)*

Kaneso Co., Ltd.—(Continued)

KANGDA NEW MATERIALS (GROUP) CO., LTD
No 655 Qingda Road, Pudong New Area, Shanghai, China
Tel.: (86) 2168918998
Web Site:
https://www.shkdchem.com
Year Founded: 1988
002669—(SSE)
Rev.: $341,487,843
Assets: $738,336,564
Liabilities: $303,181,159
Net Worth: $435,155,405
Earnings: $6,634,014
Emp.: 370
Fiscal Year-end: 12/31/22
Adhesive & Sealant Mfr
N.A.I.C.S.: 325520

KANGDE XIN COMPOSITE MATERIAL CO., LTD.
No 85 ChenGang Road Zhangjiagang New Material Industrial Park, Zhangjiagang, 215634, Jiangsu, China
Tel.: (86) 51280151666
Web Site: http://www.kangdexin.com
002450—(SSE)
Rev.: $211,712,686
Assets: $3,808,046,879
Liabilities: $2,165,739,080
Net Worth: $1,642,307,799
Earnings: ($978,142,950)
Fiscal Year-end: 12/31/19
Laminated Film Mfr
N.A.I.C.S.: 322220

KANGER INTERNATIONAL BERHAD
1001 3rd Floor Building B1 Nanshan Chi Yuen Academy Road, Nanshan District, Shenzhen, Guangdong, China
Tel.: (86) 75533390005
Web Site: http://www.krbamboo.com
KANGER—(KLS)
Rev.: $16,447,660
Assets: $66,867,159
Liabilities: $4,832,752
Net Worth: $62,034,407
Earnings: ($2,602,033)
Emp.: 117
Fiscal Year-end: 09/30/23
Bamboo Flooring & Related Products Mfr & Distr
N.A.I.C.S.: 321999
Xingmin Leng (Deputy Chm)

KANGJI MEDICAL HOLDINGS LIMITED
No 1668 Chunjiang East Road Tonglu Economic Development Zone, Hangzhou, Zhejiang, China
Tel.: (86) 57169900020 Ky
Web Site:
http://www.kangjimedical.com
Year Founded: 2004
9997—(HKG)
Holding Company
N.A.I.C.S.: 551112
Ming Zhong (Chm)

Subsidiaries:

Hangzhou Kangji Medical Instrument Ltd. (1)
No 1668 Chunjiang East Road Economic Development Zone, Tonglu, Hangzhou, 311501, Zhejiang, China
Tel.: (86) 57169900059
Web Site: http://www.hzkangji.com
Medical Instrument Mfr
N.A.I.C.S.: 339112

KANGLI INTERNATIONAL HOLDINGS LTD.
Wuyi Country Hengshanqiao Town Wuiin District, Changzhou, Jiangsu, China
Tel.: (86) 51988608896 Ky
Web Site: http://www.jnpmm.com
Year Founded: 2003
6890—(HKG)
Rev.: $209,498,562
Assets: $231,123,391
Liabilities: $132,201,202
Net Worth: $98,922,190
Earnings: ($4,387,921)
Emp.: 512
Fiscal Year-end: 12/31/22
Steel Product Mfr & Distr
N.A.I.C.S.: 331221
Ping Liu (Chm)

Subsidiaries:

KangLi (HK) Limited (1)
Suite 812 8/F Ocean Centre Harbour City 5 Canton Road, Tsim Sha Tsui, Kowloon, China (Hong Kong)
Tel.: (852) 21153394
Steel Products Mfr
N.A.I.C.S.: 332312

KANGLIM CO., LTD.
484 Cheongnamro Hyundo, Seowon-gu, Cheongju, Chungbuk, Korea (South)
Tel.: (82) 432709256
Web Site: https://www.kanglim.com
Year Founded: 1979
014200—(KRS)
Rev.: $158,736,379
Assets: $213,290,229
Liabilities: $89,054,045
Net Worth: $124,236,185
Earnings: ($20,540,860)
Emp.: 154
Fiscal Year-end: 12/31/22
Crane & Industrial Truck Mfr
N.A.I.C.S.: 333924

KANGMEI PHARMACEUTICAL CO., LTD.
Taike Road, Xiameilin Futian District, Shenzhen, 518000, Guangdong, China
Tel.: (86) 75533187777
Web Site:
https://www.kangmei.com.cn
Year Founded: 1997
600518—(CHIN)
Rev.: $674,847,156
Assets: $1,977,234,576
Liabilities: $996,888,514
Net Worth: $980,346,062
Earnings: $14,194,894
Fiscal Year-end: 12/31/23
Pharmaceutical Product Mfr & Distr
N.A.I.C.S.: 325412
Lai Zhijian (Chm)

KANGNAM JEVISCO CO., LTD.
639 Jungang-daero, Busanjin-gu, Busan, 47326, Korea (South)
Tel.: (82) 7070963175
Web Site: https://www.jevisco.com
Year Founded: 1952
000860—(KRS)
Rev.: $516,318,467
Assets: $734,625,938
Liabilities: $213,951,223
Net Worth: $520,674,715
Earnings: $4,745,753
Emp.: 656
Fiscal Year-end: 12/31/22
Paint & Coating Mfr
N.A.I.C.S.: 325510
Ik-Jun Hwang (Co-CEO)

Subsidiaries:

Kunsul Chemical Industrial Co., Ltd. - Anyang Factory (1)
284-1 Dangjeong-dong, Gunpo, Gyeonggi-do, Korea (South)
Tel.: (82) 31 451 3611
Paints Mfr
N.A.I.C.S.: 325510

Kunsul Chemical Industrial Co., Ltd. - Haman Factory (1)
631 Gyenae-ri, Chilseo-myeon, Seoul, Gyeongnam, Korea (South)
Tel.: (82) 55 586 4221
Paints Mfr
N.A.I.C.S.: 325510

Kunsul Chemical Industrial Co., Ltd. - Pyeongtaek Factory (1)
679-12 Naegi-ri, Poseung-eup, Pyeongtaek, Gyeonggi-do, Korea (South)
Tel.: (82) 31 684 6186
Paints Mfr
N.A.I.C.S.: 325510

KANGPING TECHNOLOGY (SUZHOU) CO., LTD.
No 18 Huayuan Road, Xiangcheng Economic Development Zone, Suzhou, 215131, Jiangsu, China
Tel.: (86) 51267215532
Web Site:
https://www.chinakangping.com
Year Founded: 2004
300907—(SSE)
Rev.: $139,582,872
Assets: $164,157,084
Liabilities: $59,004,504
Net Worth: $105,152,580
Earnings: $4,231,656
Fiscal Year-end: 12/31/22
Electrical Equipment Mfr & Distr
N.A.I.C.S.: 335999
Jianping Jiang (Chm)

KANGSTEM BIOTECH CO., LTD
17th Floor Sinan Bldg 512 Teheran-ro, Gangnam-gu, Seoul, Korea (South)
Tel.: (82) 28881590
Web Site: https://kangstem.com
Year Founded: 2010
217730—(KRS)
Rev.: $12,502,539
Assets: $61,813,838
Liabilities: $25,565,192
Net Worth: $36,248,646
Earnings: ($15,521,045)
Emp.: 86
Fiscal Year-end: 12/31/22
Pharmaceuticals Product Mfr
N.A.I.C.S.: 325412
Kyung-Sun Kang (Founder)

KANGWAL POLYESTER CO., LTD.
1426/18-20 Krungskasem Rd, Soi Yossae Pomprab, Bangkok, 10100, Thailand
Tel.: (66) 22207000
Web Site: http://www.kangwal.co.th
Year Founded: 1995
Sales Range: $150-199.9 Million
Emp.: 850
Organic Fiber Mfr
N.A.I.C.S.: 325220
Kangwal Wongphanlert (Chm)

Subsidiaries:

Kangwal Polyester Co., Ltd. - Phectchaburi Factory (1)
80 Moo 2 Nongchumpon Sub District, Khaoyoi District, Phetchaburi, 76140, Thailand
Tel.: (66) 3244757789
Emp.: 700
Timber Product Mfr
N.A.I.C.S.: 325220

KANGWON LAND, INC.
265 Haiwon-gil, Sabuk-eup, Jeongseon, Gangwon-do, Korea (South)
Tel.: (82) 15887789
Web Site: http://www.high1.com
Year Founded: 1998
035250—(KRS)
Rev.: $974,616,023
Assets: $3,196,666,298
Liabilities: $577,071,449
Net Worth: $2,619,594,850
Earnings: $88,678,330
Emp.: 4,608
Fiscal Year-end: 12/31/22
Hotel, Casino & Golf Course Owner & Operator
N.A.I.C.S.: 721120

KANGXIN NEW MATERIALS CO., LTD.
Te No 1 Xinhe Industrial Park Road Hanchuan Economic Development Zone, East Lake District, Xiaogan, 431600, Hubei, China
Tel.: (86) 7128102866
Web Site:
http://www.hbkangxin.com.cn
Year Founded: 1993
600076—(SHG)
Rev.: $62,712,608
Assets: $1,001,805,049
Liabilities: $344,058,147
Net Worth: $657,746,903
Earnings: ($27,173,353)
Fiscal Year-end: 12/31/22
Timber Product Mfr & Distr
N.A.I.C.S.: 321999
Jiandong Shao (Chm)

KANGYUE TECHNOLOGY COMPANY LIMITED
No 1 Luoqian Street Shouguang Economic Development Zone, Shouguang, Shandong, China
Tel.: (86) 5365788238
Web Site:
https://www.chinakangyue.com
Year Founded: 1963
300391—(CHIN)
Sales Range: $125-149.9 Million
Emp.: 500
Internal Combustion Engine Turbochargers Mfr
N.A.I.C.S.: 333611
Wang Bo (Chm)

KANIKA HOTELS PUBLIC COMPANY LTD
28th October & Makarios III Ave Kanika Enaerios Complex - Block A, PO Box 53029, Limassol, 3300, Cyprus
Tel.: (357) 25814266
Web Site:
http://www.kanikahotels.com
Year Founded: 1975
Home Management Services
N.A.I.C.S.: 721110
Spyros Th. Karaolis (Chm)

KANIKA INFRASTRUCTURE & POWER LIMITED
Crescent Towers 229 AJC Bose Road, Kolkata, 700020, India
Tel.: (91) 33 2280 5707
Web Site: http://www.kanika.com
Rev.: $73,349
Assets: $2,740,887
Liabilities: $758,449
Net Worth: $1,982,438
Earnings: ($39,675)
Emp.: 2
Fiscal Year-end: 03/31/16
Business Process Outsourcing Services
N.A.I.C.S.: 561499

KANISHK STEEL INDUSTRIES LTD.
Old 4 New 7 Thiru-Vi-Ka 3rd Street

Royapettah High Road Mylapore, Chennai, 600 004, India
Tel.: (91) 42919700
Web Site:
https://www.kanishksteels.in
513456—(BOM)
Rev.: $36,451,155
Assets: $14,098,498
Liabilities: $6,034,999
Net Worth: $8,063,499
Earnings: $775,390
Emp.: 126
Fiscal Year-end: 03/31/21
Steel Products Mfr
N.A.I.C.S.: 331110
Vishal Keyal *(Chm, CEO & Mng Dir)*

KANKAI BIKAS BANK LIMITED
Damak-11, Bhadrapur, Nepal
Tel.: (977) 23 584749
Web Site:
http://www.kankaibank.com.np
KNBL—(NEP)
Sales Range: Less than $1 Million
Commercial Banking Services
N.A.I.C.S.: 522110
Sebak Dahal *(Chm)*

KANMONKAI CO., LTD.
Sekine Building 4F 2-2-1 Kanda Tsukasamach, Chiyoda-ku, Tokyo, 101-0048, Japan
Tel.: (81) 356490029
Web Site:
https://www.kanmonkai.co.jp
Year Founded: 1989
3372—(TKS)
Rev.: $33,149,150
Assets: $30,432,440
Liabilities: $24,417,340
Net Worth: $6,015,100
Earnings: $2,181,300
Fiscal Year-end: 03/31/24
Restaurant Services
N.A.I.C.S.: 722511

KANORIA CHEMICALS & INDUSTRIES LTD
KCI Plaza 6th Floor 23-C Ashutosh Chowdhury Avenue, Kolkata, 700 019, India
Tel.: (91) 3340313200
Web Site:
https://www.kanoriachem.com
Year Founded: 1960
KANORICHEM—(NSE)
Rev.: $151,077,927
Assets: $185,898,668
Liabilities: $104,626,977
Net Worth: $81,271,691
Earnings: $2,182,499
Emp.: 385
Fiscal Year-end: 03/31/21
Chemical Intermediates Mfr
N.A.I.C.S.: 333248
S. V. Kanoria *(Exec Dir)*

Subsidiaries:

Renukoot Chemical Works Division (1)
Renukoot, Sonebhadra District, Robertsganj, 231217, Uttar Pradesh, India
Tel.: (91) 5446252044
Web Site: http://www.adityabrila.com
Sales Range: $200-249.9 Million
Emp.: 1,500
Chemicals Mfr
N.A.I.C.S.: 325199
Ravindra Sitani *(Mgr)*

KANORIA ENERGY & INFRASTRUCTURE LIMITED
Hamirgarh, Bhilwara, 311025, Rajasthan, India
Tel.: (91) 1482286102
Web Site:
http://www.ainfrastructure.com
Year Founded: 1980
539620—(BOM)
Rev.: $39,103,551
Assets: $30,763,469
Liabilities: $20,721,656
Net Worth: $10,041,814
Earnings: $1,691,508
Emp.: 446
Fiscal Year-end: 03/31/22
Pipes Mfr
N.A.I.C.S.: 327332
Sanjay Kumar Kanoria *(Mng Dir)*

KANPUR PLASTIPACK LTD.
D19-20 Panki Industrial Area PO Udyog Nagar, Kanpur, 208022, India
Tel.: (91) 5122691113
Web Site: https://www.kanplas.com
Year Founded: 1971
507779—(BOM)
Rev.: $65,667,284
Assets: $55,542,355
Liabilities: $30,968,315
Net Worth: $24,574,040
Earnings: $496,055
Emp.: 2,000
Fiscal Year-end: 03/31/23
Bags Mfr
N.A.I.C.S.: 314910
Manoj Agarwal *(Chm & Mng Dir)*

KANRO INC.
3-20-2 Nishi-Shinjuku 37th floor Opera City Building, Shinjuku-ku, Tokyo, 163-1437, Japan
Tel.: (81) 333708811
Web Site: https://kanro.jp
Year Founded: 1950
2216—(TKS)
Sales Range: $150-199.9 Million
Emp.: 544
Confectionery Product Mfr & Distr
N.A.I.C.S.: 311351
Kazuyasu Misu *(Pres & CEO)*

KANSAI PAINT CO., LTD.
28th Floor Osaka Umeda TwinTowers South 1-13-1 Umeda, kita-ku, Osaka, 530-0001, Japan
Tel.: (81) 671785531   JP
Web Site: https://www.kansai.com
Year Founded: 1918
KSANF—(OTCIQ)
Rev.: $3,716,650,970
Assets: $4,558,936,830
Liabilities: $2,045,497,550
Net Worth: $2,513,439,280
Earnings: $443,590,490
Emp.: 16,844
Fiscal Year-end: 03/31/24
Paints & Coatings Mfr & Sales
N.A.I.C.S.: 325510
Kunishi Mouri *(Pres)*

Subsidiaries:

Astra Industries Ltd. (1)
14 Burnley Road, Workington, Harare, Zimbabwe
Tel.: (263) 4755800
Paint Mfr & Distr
N.A.I.C.S.: 325510

Chongqing Kansai Paint Co., Ltd. (1)
No 80 Liuxing Road, Maliuzui Town BaNan District, Chongqing, 400060, China
Tel.: (86) 2362838816
Web Site: http://www.ccqkp.com
Paint & Coating Mfr
N.A.I.C.S.: 325510

Cosco Kansai Paint & Chemicals (Tianjin) Co., Ltd. (1)
No 42 Fifth Avenue, Tianjin Economic and Technological Development Zone, Tianjin, 300457, China
Tel.: (86) 2225292009
Paint Mfr & Distr
N.A.I.C.S.: 325510

Cosco Kansai Paint & Chemicals (Zhuhai) Co., Ltd. (1)
No 9019 Zhuhai Avenue, Jinwan District, Zhuhai, 519050, China
Tel.: (86) 7563986270
Paint Mfr & Distr
N.A.I.C.S.: 325510

Cosco Kansai Paint (Shanghai) Co., Ltd. (1)
No 621 Huachuang Road, Jinshan District, Shanghai, 201512, China
Tel.: (86) 2131588588
Paint Mfr & Distr
N.A.I.C.S.: 325510

Guangzhou Kansai Paint Co., Ltd (1)
No 26 Huangge East 2nd Road, Huangge Nansha, Guangzhou, 511455, Guangdong, China
Tel.: (86) 20 3468 4900
Web Site: http://www.alesco-gkp.com
Emp.: 120
Paint & Coating Mfr
N.A.I.C.S.: 325510

Helios Domzale, d.o.o. (1)
Kolicevo 2, 1230, Domzale, Slovenia   (99.5%)
Tel.: (386) 17224000
Web Site: http://www.helios-group.eu
Holding Company
N.A.I.C.S.: 551112

Subsidiary (Domestic):

Belinka Perkemija, d.o.o. (2)
Zasavska Cesta 95, Crnuce, 1231, Ljubljana, Slovenia
Tel.: (386) 15886299
Web Site: https://www.belinka-perkemija.com
Wood Protection & Decoration Coating Mfr
N.A.I.C.S.: 325510
Mirko Yrefk *(Mng Dir)*

Chromcom Inzeniring vzdrzevanje in meritve d.o.o. (2)
Kolicevo 90, 1230, Domzale, Slovenia   (99.59%)
Tel.: (386) 17224700
Web Site: http://www.helios-group.eu
Engineeering Services
N.A.I.C.S.: 541330

Subsidiary (Non-US):

Chromos Boje i lakovi d.d. (2)
Radnicka cesta 173D, 10000, Zagreb, Croatia   (87.64%)
Tel.: (385) 12410666
Web Site: https://www.chromos.eu
Emp.: 150
Painting & Wall Covering Contractors
N.A.I.C.S.: 238320
Nikola Janusic *(Mgr-Key Acct)*

HELIOS Srbija ad (2)
Radovana Grkovica 24, 32300, Gornji Milanovac, Serbia
Tel.: (381) 32771000
Web Site: http://www.helios.rs
Paint Varnish & Supplies Merchant Whslr
N.A.I.C.S.: 424950

Subsidiary (Domestic):

HGtrade, trzenje barv, d.o.o. (2)
Kolicevo 100, 1230, Domzale, Slovenia
Tel.: (386) 17298200
Web Site: http://www.hgtrade.si
Paint Varnish & Supplies Merchant Whslr
N.A.I.C.S.: 424950

Subsidiary (Non-US):

Helakor d.o.o. (2)
Bukinjska do br 17, 75000, Tuzla, Bosnia & Herzegovina
Tel.: (387) 35310660
Web Site: http://www.helios-group.eu
Metal Coating Engraving Mfr
N.A.I.C.S.: 332812

Helios BH d.o.o. (2)
Zgoni Bb, 88300, Capljina, Bosnia & Herzegovina
Tel.: (387) 36 805 939
Web Site: http://www.helios.ba
Paint & Varnish Distr
N.A.I.C.S.: 424950

Helios Coatings Deutschland GmbH (2)
Industriepark Nord 74, Mendt, 53567, Buchholz, Germany
Tel.: (49) 2243 9181 0
Web Site: http://www.helios-coatings.de
Paints Mfr
N.A.I.C.S.: 325510

Subsidiary (US):

Helios Coatings Inc. (2)
1411 Navarre Road SW, Canton, OH 44706   (60%)
Tel.: (330) 430-9990
Web Site: http://www.helioscoatingsinc.com
Metallized & Premium Paint Coatings Mfr
N.A.I.C.S.: 325510

Subsidiary (Non-US):

Helios Coatings Romania S.r.l. (2)
Ana Ipatescu street no 44, 759512, Jilava, Romania
Tel.: (40) 268406318
Web Site: http://www.helios-metalcoatings.com
Metal Coating Engraving Mfr
N.A.I.C.S.: 332812

Helios Italia S.p.A. (2)
Via Vittorio Veneto 87, 34170, Gorizia, Italy
Tel.: (39) 0481594300
Web Site: http://www.heliositalia.it
Paint Varnish & Supplies Merchant Whslr
N.A.I.C.S.: 424950

Subsidiary (Domestic):

Helios Kemostik d.o.o. (2)
Mekinje Molkova Pot 16, 1241, Kamnik, Slovenia
Tel.: (386) 1 830 37 50
Web Site: http://www.kemostik.com
Adhesive Mfr
N.A.I.C.S.: 325520

Subsidiary (Non-US):

Helios Makedonija dooel (2)
Bosna i Hercegovina 55, 1000, Skopje, North Macedonia
Tel.: (389) 2 2521 089
Web Site: http://www.helios-group.eu
Paint & Varnish Whslr
N.A.I.C.S.: 424950

Helios Polska Sp. z.o.o (2)
ul Przesok 43, 63-400, Ostrow Wielkopolski, Poland   (97.65%)
Tel.: (48) 627352966
Web Site: http://www.heliospolska.pl
Paint Varnish & Supplies Merchant Whslr
N.A.I.C.S.: 424950

Helios Slovakia s.r.o (2)
Rosinska 15 / A, 010 08, Zilina, Slovakia
Tel.: (421) 41 5177 100
Web Site: http://www.helios.sk
Paint & Coating Distr
N.A.I.C.S.: 424950
Vojtech Doubrava *(Mng Dir)*

Subsidiary (Domestic):

Helios TBLUS, d.o.o. (2)
Kolicevo 65, 1230, Domzale, Slovenia
Tel.: (386) 17224000
Web Site: http://www.helios-group.eu
Paint Varnish & Supplies Merchant Whslr
N.A.I.C.S.: 424950

Helios Tovarna barv lakov in umetnih smol Kolievo d.o.o. (2)
Kolicevo 65, 1230, Domzale, Slovenia
Tel.: (386) 17224000
Web Site: http://www.helios-deco.com
Synthetic Organic Dye & Pigment Mfr
N.A.I.C.S.: 325130

Subsidiary (Non-US):

Rembrandtin Oberosterreich GmbH & Co KG (2)
Lagerstrasse 7, 4481, Asten, Austria
Tel.: (43) 720 010220 0

KANSAI PAINT CO., LTD.

Kansai Paint Co., Ltd.—(Continued)

Web Site: http://www.rembrandtin.com
Paints Mfr
N.A.I.C.S.: 325510

Rembrandtin s.r.o. (2)
Sokolovska 115, Uherske Hradiste, 686 01, Zlin, Czech Republic **(50.12%)**
Tel.: (420) 572 432 285
Web Site: http://www.rembrandtin.cz
Paint Varnish & Supplies Merchant Whslr
N.A.I.C.S.: 424950

Hong Kong Kansai Paint Co., Ltd. (1)
Unit 1-2 8/F Block B Po Yip Building 62-70 Texaco Road, Tsuen Wan, China (Hong Kong)
Tel.: (852) 28911085
Web Site: http://www.kansai.com.hk
Paint Mfr & Distr
N.A.I.C.S.: 325510

Hunan Xiangjiang Kansai Paint Co., Ltd. (1)
16 Lixiang Road W Changsha Economy & Technology, Changsha, 410100, Hunan, China
Tel.: (86) 73184037050
Automotive Paint & Coating Mfr
N.A.I.C.S.: 325510

KDK Automotive Coatings Co., Ltd. (1)
679-12 Naegi-ri Poseung-eup, Gunpo Shi Gyungi Do, Pyeongtaek, 451,821, Korea (South) **(100%)**
Tel.: (82) 316846186
Web Site: http://kansaimalaysia.com
Sales Range: $25-49.9 Million
Emp.: 80
Automotive Paint & Coatings Manufacturer
N.A.I.C.S.: 325510

KNK Coatings Co., Ltd. (1)
152 Poseunggongdan-ro, Poseung-eup, Pyeongtaek, Gyeonggi, Korea (South)
Tel.: (82) 316846186
Web Site: http://www.knkcoatings.com
Paint Mfr & Distr
N.A.I.C.S.: 325510
Moon Sang Chul (CEO)

Kansai Altan Boya Sanayi ve Ticaret Anonim Sirketi (1)
Ankara Asfalti 25 Km, 35730, Kemalpasa, Izmir, Türkiye
Tel.: (90) 232 870 14 70
Web Site: http://www.kansaialtan.com
Sales Range: $200-249.9 Million
Emp.: 700
Polymer Resin Mfr
N.A.I.C.S.: 325211
Eingin Coruslu (Mgr-Automotive Coatings Grp)

Kansai Helios Coatings GmbH (1)
Ignaz-Kock-Strasse 15, 1210, Vienna, Austria
Tel.: (43) 127702201
Paint Mfr & Distr
N.A.I.C.S.: 325510

Kansai Nerolac Paints Ltd. (1)
NEROLAC HOUSE Ganpatrao Kadam Marg, Lower Pare, Mumbai, 400 013, India
Tel.: (91) 2240602501
Web Site: https://www.nerolac.com
Rev.: $907,464,780
Assets: $756,112,943
Liabilities: $209,333,973
Net Worth: $546,778,970
Earnings: $56,168,095
Emp.: 3,379
Fiscal Year-end: 03/31/2023
Paint & Coating Mfr
N.A.I.C.S.: 325510
Harishchandra Meghraj Bharuka (Vice Chm & Mng Dir)

Kansai Paint (America), Inc. (1)
5455 Corporate Dr Ste-205, Troy, MI 48098-2620 **(100%)**
Tel.: (248) 952-0533
Sales Range: $50-74.9 Million
Emp.: 3
Marketing Trends Liaison Office
N.A.I.C.S.: 424950

Kansai Paint (China) Investment Co., Ltd. (1)
Room 912 Sunny Days City No 425 Yishan Road, Xuhui District, Shanghai, 200235, China
Tel.: (86) 2150939636
Paint Mfr & Distr
N.A.I.C.S.: 325510

Kansai Paint (Shenyang) Co., Ltd. (1)
No 18 Shenxi Four East Road Economic & Technology Development Zone, 110143, Shenyang, China
Tel.: (86) 24 2532 6390
Paint & Coating Mfr
N.A.I.C.S.: 325510

Kansai Paint (Singapore) Pte. Ltd. (1)
No2 Tanjong Penjuru 02 Floor, Singapore, 609017, Singapore **(100%)**
Tel.: (65) 62618621
Web Site: http://www.kansaipaint.com.sg
Sales Range: $25-49.9 Million
Emp.: 14
Paint & Coating Mfr
N.A.I.C.S.: 325510

Kansai Paint Asia Pacific Sdn. Bhd. (1)
4 Solok Waja 2 Kawasan Perindustrian Bukit Raja, PO Box 159, 41710, Klang, Selangor, Malaysia
Tel.: (60) 333622388
Web Site: http://www.kansaimalaysia.com
Paint Mfr & Distr
N.A.I.C.S.: 325510

Kansai Paint Co., Ltd. - Amagasaki Plant (1)
33-1 Kanzaki-cho, Amagasaki, 661-8555, Hyogo, Japan
Tel.: (81) 6 6499 4861
Paint & Coating Mfr
N.A.I.C.S.: 325510

Kansai Paint Co., Ltd. - Hiratsuka Plant (1)
5-4-1 Higashi-Hachiman, Hiratsuka, 254-8589, Kanagawa, Japan
Tel.: (81) 463 23 2111
Web Site: http://www.kansai.co.jp
Paint & Coating Mfr
N.A.I.C.S.: 325510

Kansai Paint Co., Ltd. - Kanuma Plant (1)
7-3 Satsuki-cho, Kanuma, 322-0014, Tochigi, Japan
Tel.: (81) 289 76 3011
Web Site: http://www.kansai.co.jp
Paint & Coating Mfr
N.A.I.C.S.: 325510

Kansai Paint Co., Ltd. - Nagoya Plant (1)
Hirachi 1 Azabu-cho, Miyoshi, 470-0206, Aichi, Japan
Tel.: (81) 561 34 3411
Paint & Coating Mfr
N.A.I.C.S.: 325510

Kansai Paint Co., Ltd. - Ono Plant (1)
3 Takumidai, Ono, 675-1322, Hyogo, Japan
Tel.: (81) 794 63 8111
Paint & Coating Mfr
N.A.I.C.S.: 325510

Kansai Paint Co., Ltd.-Technology & Products Development Laboratory (1)
17-1 Higashi-Yawata 4-Chome, Hiratsuka, 254-8562, Kanagawa, Japan
Tel.: (81) 463232100
Web Site: http://www.kansai.co.jp
Sales Range: $125-149.9 Million
Emp.: 300
Research & Development of Paints & Chemical Products
N.A.I.C.S.: 325510

Kansai Paint Europe Limited (1)
Aurora House 71-75 Uxbridge Road, Ealing, London, W5 5SL, Middlesex, United Kingdom **(100%)**
Tel.: (44) 2039270315
Web Site: http://www.kansaipaint.co.uk
Emp.: 4
N.A.I.C.S.: 325510

Kansai Paint H.K., Ltd. (1)
Unit 5 14th Floor Block B Po Yip Building, 62-70 Texaco Road, Tsuen Wan, New Territories, China (Hong Kong) **(100%)**
Tel.: (852) 28911280
Web Site: http://www.kansaipaint.com.hk
Emp.: 9
Paint & Coating Mfr
N.A.I.C.S.: 325510
Goenty Wong (Acct Mgr)

Kansai Paint Marine (Taiwan) Co., Ltd. (1)
4F-4 No 146 Songjian Rd, Taipei, 104, Taiwan
Tel.: (886) 225681016
Paint Mfr & Distr
N.A.I.C.S.: 325510

Kansai Paint Myanmar Co., Ltd. (1)
No 121/120 Bayint Naung Street Road No 65 Sethmu, Plot Shwe Pyi Thar Industrial Zone 4 Shwe Pyi Thar, Yangon, Myanmar
Tel.: (95) 13618695
Paint Mfr & Distr
N.A.I.C.S.: 325510

Kansai Paint Philippines, Inc. (1)
Unit 8A South Luzon International Business Park, Brgy Batino, Calamba, 4027, Laguna, Philippines
Tel.: (63) 495309876
Web Site: https://www.kansaipaint.com.ph
Sales Range: $25-49.9 Million
Emp.: 15
Automotive Paint Mfr
N.A.I.C.S.: 325510
Akiyoshi Watanabe (Pres)

Kansai Paints Lanka (Private) Limited (1)
No 467 Union Place, Colombo, Sri Lanka
Tel.: (94) 112251055
Web Site: http://www.kansaipaintlanka.com
Paint Mfr & Distr
N.A.I.C.S.: 325510

Kansai Paints Nepal Pvt. Ltd. (1)
PO Box No 38, Adarshanagar, Birgunj, Nepal
Tel.: (977) 51521568
Paint Mfr & Distr
N.A.I.C.S.: 325510

Kansai Plascon Botswana (Proprietary) Ltd. (1)
Plot 14394 New Lobatse Road Gaborone West, PO Box 201949, Gaborone, Botswana
Tel.: (267) 3922764725
Paint Mfr & Distr
N.A.I.C.S.: 325510

Kansai Plascon Kenya Ltd. (1)
Jirore Road off Enterprise Road Industrial Area, PO Box 18011, Nairobi, Kenya
Tel.: (254) 206555711
Paint Mfr & Distr
N.A.I.C.S.: 325510

Kansai Plascon Malawi Ltd. (1)
Corner Maunde and Mcleod Roads Makata Industrial Area Chichiri, PO Box 30662, Blantyre, Malawi
Tel.: (265) 1672220
Paint Mfr & Distr
N.A.I.C.S.: 325510

Kansai Plascon Namibia (Proprietary) Ltd. (1)
Corner Iscor Road and Van der Bijl Street Northern Industrial Area, PO Box 3540, Windhoek, 9000, Namibia
Tel.: (264) 612804200
Paint Mfr & Distr
N.A.I.C.S.: 325510

Kansai Plascon SA (1)
10 Frederick Cooper Drive, Factoria/Luipaardsvlei, 1743, Krugersdorp, South Africa
Tel.: (27) 860204060
Web Site: http://www.kansaiplascon.co.za
Sales Range: $450-499.9 Million
Emp.: 1,900
Decorative, Automotive & Industrial Coatings Mfr
N.A.I.C.S.: 325510

Subsidiary (Non-US):

Freeworld Plascon Namibia (Pty) Limited (2)

Corner Iscor And Van Der Bijl St, Windhoek, Namibia
Tel.: (264) 612804209
Web Site: http://www.plascon.co.za
Sales Range: $25-49.9 Million
Emp.: 80
Paints & Coatings Distr
N.A.I.C.S.: 424950

Freeworld Plascon Zambia Limited (2)
Plot 7174 Mukatasha Road, Private Bag RW79X, Lusaka, 10101, Zambia
Tel.: (260) 211287939
Web Site: http://www.kansaiplascon.co.zm
Paints & Coatings Mfr
N.A.I.C.S.: 325510

Subsidiary (Domestic):

Hamilton Brands (Pty) Limited (2)
Unit 24 28 Dan Jacobs Street Alrode, Alberton, 1451, South Africa
Tel.: (27) 114482998
Web Site: http://www.hamiltonbrush.com
Paints & Coatings Mfr
N.A.I.C.S.: 325510

International Colour Corporation (Pty) Limited (2)
7 Bakstein Rd, Olifantsfontein, 1666, Gauteng, South Africa
Tel.: (27) 115429000
Sales Range: $25-49.9 Million
Emp.: 80
Colourant Systems Distr
N.A.I.C.S.: 424950
Kobie Bisschoff (Dir-Technical)

Kansai Plascon (Pty) Ltd (2)
2-4 Bedford Street, Neave Township, Port Elizabeth, 6001, Eastern Cape, South Africa
Tel.: (27) 414011400
Web Site: http://www.plascon-automotive.co.za
Sales Range: $50-74.9 Million
Emp.: 200
Automotive Paint Mfr
N.A.I.C.S.: 325510

Midas Paints (Pty) Limited (2)
53 Stella Rd Montague Gardens, Cape Town, 7441, Western Cape, South Africa
Tel.: (27) 215515570
Web Site: http://www.midaspaints.co.za
Paints & Coatings Mfr & Whslr
N.A.I.C.S.: 325510

Plascon Cape (Pty) Limited (2)
16 Packer Avenue Epping 2 Industria, Goodwood, Cape Town, 7475, Western Cape, South Africa
Tel.: (27) 215052400
Web Site: http://www.plascon.co.za
Sales Range: $50-74.9 Million
Emp.: 190
Paints & Coatings Mfr
N.A.I.C.S.: 325510

Prostart Investments 93 (Pty) Limited (2)
4 Bezuidenhout St, Johannesburg, 2094, Gauteng, South Africa
Tel.: (27) 112160600
Automotive Refinish Coatings Distr
N.A.I.C.S.: 424950

Kansai Plascon Swaziland Ltd. (1)
Corner Mancishane and Sandlane Streets, PO Box 162, Manzini, M200, Eswatini
Tel.: (268) 5052711234
Paint Mfr & Distr
N.A.I.C.S.: 325510

Kansai Plascon Tanzania Ltd. (1)
Plot No 111/113 Julius K Nyerere Road, PO Box 20775, Dar es Salaam, Tanzania
Tel.: (255) 2228651412
Paint Mfr & Distr
N.A.I.C.S.: 325510

Kansai Plascon Uganda Ltd. (1)
Plot No 28 Kyaggwe Road Block 112, PO Box 4627, Namanve Industrial Buisness Park, Kampala, Uganda
Tel.: (256) 2005298016
Paint Mfr & Distr
N.A.I.C.S.: 325510

Kansai Plascon Zambia Ltd. (1)
Plot No 2715 Nyerere Road, PO Box

AND PRIVATE COMPANIES / KAO CORPORATION

20362, Light Industrial Area, Kitwe, Lusaka, Zambia
Tel.: (260) 212211609
Paint Mfr & Distr
N.A.I.C.S.: 325510

Kansai Plascon Zanzibar Ltd. (1)
Plot No 26 House No 1725 Mukanazini Street, PO Box 4519, Mkoa Mjini Magharibi, Zanzibar, Tanzania
Tel.: (255) 242235000
Paint Mfr & Distr
N.A.I.C.S.: 325510

Kansai Resin (Thailand) Co., Ltd. (1)
34 Moo 4 Eastern Tumbol Pluakdaeng, Amphur Pluakdaeng, Rayong, 21140, Thailand
Tel.: (66) 38954747
Sales Range: $25-49.9 Million
Emp.: 84
N.A.I.C.S.: 325510

Kansai-Alphanam Paint Co., Ltd. (1)
3rd Floor Sakura Building 47 Vu Trong Phung Street, Thanh Xuan District, Hanoi, Vietnam
Tel.: (84) 2439393676
Web Site: http://www.kansaipaint.com.vn
Paint Mfr & Distr
N.A.I.C.S.: 325510

P.T. Kansai Paint Indonesia (1)
Blok DD-7 DD-6 Kawasan Industri MM2100 Danauindah, Cikarang Barat, Bekasi, 17530, Jawa Barat, Indonesia (100%)
Tel.: (62) 189982370
Web Site: http://www.kpid.co.id
Automotive Paint & Coating Product Mfr
N.A.I.C.S.: 325510

PT Kansai Prakarsa Coatings (1)
Sahid Sudirman Center Building 45Th Floor Suite Ef, Jl Jendral Sudirman No 86 Karet Tengsin Tanah Abang, Jakarta Pusat, 10220, Indonesia
Tel.: (62) 212520409
Web Site: http://www.kansaicoatings.co.id
Paint Mfr & Distr
N.A.I.C.S.: 325510

Polisan Kansai Boya Sanayi ve Ticaret A.S. (1)
Hilltown Ofis Aydinevler Mah Siteler Yolu Cad 28 No 1/A, Kucukyali-Maltepe, Istanbul, Turkiye
Tel.: (90) 2165788800
Web Site: http://global.polisan.com.tr
Paint Mfr & Distr
N.A.I.C.S.: 325510

Shanghai Cosco Kansai Paint & Chemicals Co., Ltd. (1)
Room 1706 Baohua Center No 355 West Guangzhong Road, Shanghai, 200072, China (100%)
Tel.: (86) 21331833988
Web Site: http://www.kansai.hk.coscoshipping.com
Sales Range: $125-149.9 Million
Emp.: 500
Coating Chemical Mfr
N.A.I.C.S.: 325510

Sime Kansai Paints Sdn. Bhd. (1)
2 Solok Waja 2 Kawasan Perindustrian Bukit Raja, Peti Surat 159, 41710, Kelang, Selangor D E, Malaysia (60%)
Tel.: (60) 333434833
Sales Range: $10-24.9 Million
Emp.: 150
N.A.I.C.S.: 325510

Suzhou Kansai Paint Co., Ltd. (1)
No 12 FengxiaRoad, Lujia Town, Kunshan, 215331, Jiangsu, China
Tel.: (86) 512 5756 3372
Web Site: http://www.szkansai.com
Paint & Coating Mfr
N.A.I.C.S.: 325510

Taiwan Kansai Paint Co., Ltd. (1)
6 Yungkong 2nd Rd Yung An Industrial District Yu, Kaohsiung, 828, Hsien, Taiwan
Tel.: (886) 76223171
Sales Range: $50-74.9 Million
Emp.: 150
Paints & Varnishes
N.A.I.C.S.: 325510
Takemura Tsutomu (Gen Mgr)

Thai Kansai Paint Co., Ltd. (1)
180 Moo 3 Thaeparak Rd, Thaeparak Amphur Muang, Samut Prakan, 10270, Thailand
Tel.: (66) 27532377
Web Site: http://www.kansai.co.jp
Paint & Coating Mfr
N.A.I.C.S.: 325510

Tianjin Cosco Kansai Paint & Chemicals Co., Ltd. (1)
42 5th Avenue, TEDA, Tianjin, 300457, China
Tel.: (86) 22 2529 2004
Web Site: http://www.kansai.com.cn
Paint & Chemical Mfr
N.A.I.C.S.: 325510

Tianjin Winfield Kansai Paint & Chemicals Co., Ltd. (1)
No 95 Taihua Road TEDA, Tianjin, 300457, China
Tel.: (86) 2266230159
Paint Mfr & Distr
N.A.I.C.S.: 325510

US Paint Corporation (1)
831 S 21st St, Saint Louis, MO 63103-3092
Tel.: (314) 621-0525
Web Site: http://www.uspaint.com
Paint & Coating Mfr
N.A.I.C.S.: 325510

KANSAI SUPERMARKET CO., LTD
5-3-38, Chuo-ku, Itami, 664-0851, Hyogo, Japan
Tel.: (81) 727720341
Web Site: https://www.kansaisuper.co.jp
Year Founded: 1959
9919—(TKS)
Rev.: $3,620,494,240
Assets: $1,411,682,800
Liabilities: $767,198,080
Net Worth: $644,484,720
Earnings: $41,256,160
Emp.: 1,141
Fiscal Year-end: 03/31/23
Supermarket Owner & Operator
N.A.I.C.S.: 445110

KANSEKI CO., LTD.
3-1-1 Nishikawada Honmachi, Utsunomiya, 321-0158, Tochigi, Japan
Tel.: (81) 286588123
Web Site: https://www.kanseki.co.jp
Year Founded: 1975
9903—(TKS)
Rev.: $395,428,000
Assets: $266,703,360
Liabilities: $172,013,600
Net Worth: $94,689,760
Earnings: ($1,713,360)
Fiscal Year-end: 02/28/22
Home Tools & Product Distr
N.A.I.C.S.: 423710
Ichiro Otagaki (Pres & CEO)

KANTO DENKA KOGYO CO., LTD.
Yusen Building 3-2 Marunouchi 2-chome, Chiyoda-ku, Tokyo, 100-0005, Japan
Tel.: (81) 342368801
Web Site: https://www.kantodenka.co.jp
Year Founded: 1938
4047—(TKS)
Rev.: $428,116,480
Assets: $828,246,220
Liabilities: $394,775,640
Net Worth: $433,470,580
Earnings: ($30,472,100)
Emp.: 808
Fiscal Year-end: 03/31/24
Chemical Products Mfr
N.A.I.C.S.: 325199
Jun'ichi Hasegawa (Pres)

Subsidiaries:

Kanto Denka Kogyo (Shanghai) Co., Ltd. (1)
Room3506 The Place Tower B 100 Zunyi Road, Changning District, Shanghai, 200051, China
Tel.: (86) 2162787004
Web Site: http://www.kantodenka.co.jp
Chemical Products Distr
N.A.I.C.S.: 424690

Kanto Denka Kogyo Co., Ltd. - Mizushima Plant (1)
4-8 Matsue 4-chome, Kurashiki, Okayama, 712-8533, Japan
Tel.: (81) 864555231
Chemical Products Mfr
N.A.I.C.S.: 325199

Kanto Denka Kogyo Co., Ltd. - Shibukawa Plant (1)
1497 Shibukawa, Shibukawa, 377-8513, Gunma, Japan
Tel.: (81) 279233211
Chemical Products Mfr
N.A.I.C.S.: 325199

Kanto Denka Korea Co., Ltd. (1)
329 27 Seochojungang-ro 24-gil, Seochogu, Seoul, Korea (South)
Tel.: (82) 234712360
Web Site: https://www.kdkkorea.co.kr
Chemical Products Distr
N.A.I.C.S.: 424690

Taiwan Kanto Denka Co., Ltd. (1)
17F-8 No 118 Ciyun Rd, East Dist, Hsinchu, 30072, Taiwan
Tel.: (886) 35771575
Chemical Products Distr
N.A.I.C.S.: 424690

KANTSU CO., LTD.
1-8-13 Nagata Higashi, Osaka, 577-0015, Japan
Tel.: (81) 643088901
Web Site: https://www.kantsu.com
Year Founded: 1983
9326—(TKS)
Rev.: $84,640,420
Assets: $73,090,810
Liabilities: $51,650,650
Net Worth: $21,440,160
Earnings: $347,410
Emp.: 882
Fiscal Year-end: 02/29/24
Logistics Consulting Servies
N.A.I.C.S.: 541614

KANUNGO FINANCIERS LIMITED
B-7 B wing 5th Floor Ajanta Commercial Center Income Tax, Ahmedabad, 380 009, India
Tel.: (91) 7948002688
Web Site: https://www.kanungofinanciers.com
Year Founded: 1982
540515—(BOM)
Rev.: $35,981
Assets: $1,759,922
Liabilities: $1,026,726
Net Worth: $733,196
Earnings: ($471,976)
Fiscal Year-end: 03/31/22
Investment Management Service
N.A.I.C.S.: 523150
Kanak Sureshkumar Rathi (Sec)

KANZHUN LTD.
GrandyVic Building Taiyanggong Middle Road, Chaoyang District, Beijing, 100020, China
Tel.: (86) 1084150633
Web Site: https://ir.zhipin.com
Year Founded: 2014
BZ—(NASDAQ)
Rev.: $691,139,809
Assets: $2,271,624,293
Liabilities: $488,142,994
Net Worth: $1,783,481,299
Earnings: $16,431,006
Emp.: 5,602
Fiscal Year-end: 12/31/22
Recruiting Services
N.A.I.C.S.: 561311
Peng Zhao (Founder, Chm & CEO)

KAO CORPORATION
1-14-10 Kayabacho Nihonbashi, Chuo-Ku, Tokyo, 103-8210, Japan
Tel.: (81) 336607111
Web Site: https://www.kao.com
Year Founded: 1887
4452—(TKS)
Rev.: $13,733,674,240
Assets: $16,494,787,760
Liabilities: $6,970,858,400
Net Worth: $9,523,929,360
Earnings: $1,078,497,200
Emp.: 33,507
Fiscal Year-end: 12/31/21
Chemical Products Mfr
N.A.I.C.S.: 325611
Masakazu Negoro (Mng Exec Officer)

Subsidiaries:

E'quipe Ltd. (1)
Osaki New City 3 1-6-3 Osaki, Shinagawa-ku, Tokyo, 141-0032, Japan
Tel.: (81) 3 5435 2171
Web Site: http://www.eqp.co.jp
Rev.: $146,880,000
Emp.: 800
Cosmetic Product Mfr & Whslr
N.A.I.C.S.: 325620

Fatty Chemical (Malaysia) Sdn. Bhd. (1) (70%)
Tel.: (60) 43998500
Sales Range: $50-74.9 Million
Emp.: 280
Chemical & Chemical Preparation Mfr
N.A.I.C.S.: 325998
Eiji Shima (Mng Dir)

Goldwell Cosmetics (CZ) s.r.o. (1)
Prazska 675/10, 64200, Brno, Czech Republic
Tel.: (420) 547423270
Chemical & Cosmetic Mfr
N.A.I.C.S.: 325620

Guhl Ikebana Cosmetics B.V. (1)
Berkenweg 7, 3818 LA, Amersfoort, Netherlands
Tel.: (31) 365491317
Chemical & Cosmetic Mfr
N.A.I.C.S.: 325620

Guhl Ikebana GmbH (1)
Pfungstadter Strasse 98, 64297, Darmstadt, Germany (90%)
Tel.: (49) 61 513 9600
Web Site: https://www.guhl.com
Sales Range: $25-49.9 Million
Emp.: 35
Mfr of Household & Chemical Products
N.A.I.C.S.: 325998
Karin Overbeck (Mng Dir)

KAO USA Inc. (1)
2535 Spring Grove Ave, Cincinnati, OH 45214-1773
Tel.: (513) 421-1400
Web Site: http://www.kao.com
Sales Range: $50-74.9 Million
Lotions & Soaps Mfr
N.A.I.C.S.: 325611
Joseph Workman (Pres)

Subsidiary (Domestic):

Oribe Hair Care, LLC (2)
401 West St, New York, NY 10014
Tel.: (212) 687-3282
Web Site: http://www.Oribe.com
Rev.: $1,700,000
Emp.: 20
Drugs & Druggists' Sundries Merchant Whslr
N.A.I.C.S.: 424210

KPSS - Kao Professional Salon Services GmbH (1)
Pfungstaedterstrasse 98-102, 64297, Darm-

KAO CORPORATION

Kao Corporation—(Continued)
stadt, Germany
Tel.: (49) 61515020
Web Site: http://www.kpss-hair.com
Sales Range: $50-74.9 Million
Emp.: 250
Mfr & Sale of Household Products, Cosmetics & Industrial Products
N.A.I.C.S.: 456199

KPSS Nederland B.V. (1)
Laan Van Malkenschoten 60, Apeldoorn, 7333 NP, Gelderland, Netherlands
Tel.: (31) 555399899
Web Site: http://www.kpss-hair.nl
Hairdresser Services
N.A.I.C.S.: 812112

Kanebo Cosmetics Inc. (1)
1-14-10 Kayabacho, Nihonbashi Chuo-ku, Tokyo, 103-8210, Japan
Tel.: (81) 367453111
Web Site: https://www.kanebo-cosmetics.co.jp
Sales Range: $750-799.9 Million
Cosmetics Products Mfr
N.A.I.C.S.: 325620

Subsidiary (Non-US):

Chia Lih Pau Chemical Co. (2)
No 180 Ching Cheng 4th Rd, Chien Chin District, Kaohsiung, Taiwan
Tel.: (886) 72162320
Cosmetics Research & Development
N.A.I.C.S.: 325998

Kanebo Cosmetics (China) Co.,Ltd. (2)
CapitaMall No 268 Hengtong Road, Jing'an District, Shanghai, 200051, Changning District, China
Tel.: (86) 215 228 5050
Web Site: https://www.kanebo-cosmetics.cn
Cosmetics & Toiletries Mfr
N.A.I.C.S.: 325620

Kanebo Cosmetics (Europe) Ltd. (2)
Brandschenkestrasse 150, 8002, Zurich, Switzerland
Tel.: (41) 44 808 7654
Web Site: http://www.sensai-cosmetics.com
Sales Range: $25-49.9 Million
Emp.: 30
Cosmetics Mfr & Distr
N.A.I.C.S.: 456120

Kanebo Cosmetics Deutschland GmbH (2)
Poeseldorfer Weg 20-22, 20148, Hamburg, Germany
Tel.: (49) 4 024 8887
Web Site: http://www.kanebo.de
Sales Range: $25-49.9 Million
Emp.: 25
Sales of Cosmetics
N.A.I.C.S.: 456120
Georg Stolzenburg *(Mng Dir)*

Kanebo Cosmetics Italy SpA (2)
Piazza Sigmund Freud 1 Torre 2 22nd Floor, 20154, Milan, Italy
Tel.: (39) 028631121
Web Site: http://www.kanebo-cosmetics.co.jp
Sales Range: $25-49.9 Million
Cosmetics Mfr & Distr
N.A.I.C.S.: 456120
Otsuka Akiyoshi *(Pres)*

Subsidiary (Domestic):

Kanebo Cosmetics Sales Co., Ltd. (2)
Holland Hills Mori Tower 11-2, Tokyo, 105 8085, Japan
Tel.: (81) 364305111
Web Site: http://www.kanebo-cosmetics.co.jp
Sales Range: $200-249.9 Million
Emp.: 800
Cosmetics & Toiletries Mfr
N.A.I.C.S.: 325620

Subsidiary (Non-US):

Kanebo Cosmetics Thailand Co., Ltd. (2)
1521 Sukhumvit Road, Phra Khanong Nuea Watthana, Bangkok, 10110, Thailand
Tel.: (66) 2 714 4060
Web Site: https://www.kanebo.co.th
Cosmetic Mfr & Distr
N.A.I.C.S.: 456120

Kanebo Cosmetiques France S.A.R.L. (2)
89 91 rue de Faubourg, Saint Honore, FR 75008, Paris, France
Tel.: (33) 140165180
Sales Range: $25-49.9 Million
Emp.: 30
Cosmetics Mfr & Distr
N.A.I.C.S.: 456120

Taiwan Kanebo Cosmetics Co., Ltd. (2)
8F No 88 Sec 6 Zhong Shan N Road, Shilin Dist, Taipei, 11155, Taiwan
Tel.: (886) 228386560
Web Site: http://www.twkanebo.com.tw
Sales Range: $25-49.9 Million
Emp.: 50
Cosmetic Mfr & Distr
N.A.I.C.S.: 456120
Tanaka Junichi *(Gen Mgr)*

Kanebo Cosmetics Korea Co., Ltd. (1)
City Air Tower 4F 87-36 Teheran-ro, Kangnam-gu Samsungdong, Seoul, Korea (South)
Tel.: (82) 220165811
Chemical & Cosmetic Mfr
N.A.I.C.S.: 325620

Kanebo Cosmetics Malaysia Sdn. Bhd. (1)
Suite 8 02 and 8 03 Level 8 Menara AmFirst No 1 Jalan 19/3, 46300, Petaling Jaya, Selangor, Malaysia
Tel.: (60) 379549171
Chemical & Cosmetic Mfr
N.A.I.C.S.: 325620

Kanebo Cosmetics Rus LLC (1)
4th Dobryninskiy pereulok 8 Office C12-01, 119049, Moscow, Russia
Tel.: (7) 4952876560
Chemical & Cosmetic Mfr
N.A.I.C.S.: 325620

Kanebo Cosmillion, Ltd. (1)
1-14-10 Nihonbashi Kayabacho, Chuo-ku, Tokyo, 103-8210, Japan
Tel.: (81) 367453611
Web Site: http://www.kanebo-cosmillion.co.jp
Cosmetic Product Mfr & Whslr
N.A.I.C.S.: 325620

Kao (Hong Kong) Limited (1)
30th Floor Phase 1 Sea Fortune Centre 18 Harcourt Road, Hong Kong, China (Hong Kong) (90%)
Tel.: (852) 2 527 7088
Web Site: http://www.kao.com
Sales Range: $25-49.9 Million
Emp.: 80
Household Goods & Chemical Products Mfr
N.A.I.C.S.: 325998

Kao (Malaysia) Sdn. Bhd. (1)
20th Floor Menara AmFirst No 1 Jalan 19/3, 46300, Petaling Jaya, Selangor, Malaysia
Tel.: (60) 37 957 4488
Web Site: https://www.kao.com
Sales Range: $100-124.9 Million
Emp.: 200
Mfr & Sale of Household Products, Cosmetics & Industrial Products
N.A.I.C.S.: 456199

Kao (Malaysia) Sdn., Bhd. (1)
20th Floor Menara AmFirst No 1 Jalan 19/3, 46300, Petaling Jaya, Selangor, Malaysia (45%)
Tel.: (60) 37 957 4488
Web Site: https://www.kao.com
Sales Range: $50-74.9 Million
Emp.: 200
Mfr of Household Goods & Chemical Products
N.A.I.C.S.: 325998

Kao (Singapore) Pte., Ltd. (1)
83 Clemenceau Avenue 16-08 UE Square, Singapore, 239920, Singapore (100%)
Tel.: (65) 6 471 2811
Web Site: https://www.kao.com
Sales Range: $25-49.9 Million
Emp.: 50
Chemical Products Distr
N.A.I.C.S.: 424690

Kao (Taiwan) Corporation (1)
10 F No 207 Section 3 Pei-Hsin Rd, Hsin-Tien District, New Taipei City, 231 43, Taiwan (90%)
Tel.: (886) 286651900
Sales Range: $50-74.9 Million
Emp.: 60
Chemical & Chemical Preparation Mfr
N.A.I.C.S.: 325998

Kao (UK) Limited (1)
130 Shaftesbury Avenue, London, W1D 5EU, United Kingdom
Tel.: (44) 3301239530
Chemical & Cosmetic Mfr
N.A.I.C.S.: 325620

Kao Australia Pty. Limited (1)
1A The Crescent, Kingsgrove, 2208, NSW, Australia
Tel.: (61) 130 013 5722
Web Site: https://www.kmshair.com
Sales Range: $10-24.9 Million
Household Products, Cosmetics & Industrial Products Mfr
N.A.I.C.S.: 325620

Kao Austria Handelsgesellschaft mbH (1)
Franzosenhausweg 36, 4030, Linz, Austria
Tel.: (43) 7323857210
Chemical & Cosmetic Mfr
N.A.I.C.S.: 325620

Kao Brands Europe Ltd. (1)
130 Shaftesbury Avenue, London, W1D 5EU, United Kingdom
Tel.: (44) 2078519800
Sales Range: $50-74.9 Million
Emp.: 80
Cosmetic Product Whslr
N.A.I.C.S.: 424210
Anke Menkhorst *(Gen Mgr)*

Kao Canada Ltd. (1)
75 Courtneypark Drive West Unit 2, Mississauga, L5W 0E3, ON, Canada
Tel.: (905) 670-7890
Web Site: http://www.kaocareers.com
Cosmetic Product Whslr
N.A.I.C.S.: 424210

Kao Chemical Corporation Shanghai (1)
No 1500 Bei Song Road, Min Hang District, Shanghai, 201111, China
Tel.: (86) 21 64092880
Detergent Chemicals Mfr
N.A.I.C.S.: 325998

Kao Chemicals Europe, S.L. (1)
Puig dels Tudons 10, Barbera del Valles, 08210, Barcelona, Spain
Tel.: (34) 93 739 9300
Web Site: https://www.kaochemicals-eu.com
Sales Range: $1-9.9 Million
Emp.: 200
Mfr & Sale of Household Products, Cosmetics & Industrial Products
N.A.I.C.S.: 456199

Kao Chemicals GmbH (1)
Kupferstrasse 1, 46446, Emmerich am Rhein, Germany
Tel.: (49) 28227110
Web Site: https://www.kaochemicals.de
Sales Range: $150-199.9 Million
Emp.: 240
Mfr & Sale of Household Products, Cosmetics & Industrial Products
N.A.I.C.S.: 456199

Kao Chimigraf, S.L. (1)
Carcassl 6-8 P I Can Jardi, Rubi, 08191, Barcelona, Spain
Tel.: (34) 93 586 2040
Web Site: https://www.kaochimigraf.com
Paint & Coating Mfr
N.A.I.C.S.: 325510

Kao Collins Inc. (1)
1201 Edison Dr, Cincinnati, OH 45216
Tel.: (513) 948-9000
Web Site: https://www.kaocollins.com
Inkjet Inks Mfr

INTERNATIONAL PUBLIC

N.A.I.C.S.: 325910

Kao Commercial (Shanghai) Co., Ltd. (1)
11F Capital Square Shanghai Office Tower 268 Hengtong Road, Jingan District, Shanghai, 200070, China
Tel.: (86) 2163352020
Cosmetic Product Whslr
N.A.I.C.S.: 424210

Kao Consumer Products (Southeast Asia) Co., Ltd (1)
161 Soi Mahadlek Luang 3 Ratchadamri Rd 12 & 14 Fl Nantawan Lumpini, Pathumwan, Bangkok, 10330, Thailand
Tel.: (66) 265181816
Cosmetic Product Whslr
N.A.I.C.S.: 424210

Kao Corporation GmbH (1)
Zernin Strasse 12-18, 64297, Darmstadt, Germany (100%)
Tel.: (49) 615150400
Sales Range: $50-74.9 Million
Emp.: 200
Mfr, Marketing & Sales of Professional Hair Care Products
N.A.I.C.S.: 325620

Kao Corporation S.A. (1)
Puig Dels Tudons 10, Barbera del Valles, 08210, Barcelona, Spain
Tel.: (34) 937399300
Web Site: https://chemical.kao.com
Sales Range: $125-149.9 Million
Emp.: 400
Cosmetics Products Mfr
N.A.I.C.S.: 325620

Kao Corporation Shanghai (1)
No 333 Hua Wang Road, Minhang District, Shanghai, 201111, China
Tel.: (86) 2164091210
Cosmetics Whslr
N.A.I.C.S.: 424210

Kao Cosmetic Products Odawara Co., Ltd. (1)
5-3-28 Kotobukicho, Odawara, 250-0002, Kanagawa, Japan
Tel.: (81) 465346111
Chemical & Cosmetic Mfr
N.A.I.C.S.: 325620

Kao Customer Marketing Co., Ltd. (1)
8-3 Nihonbashi Koamicho, Chuo-ku, Tokyo, 103-0016, Japan
Tel.: (81) 367462500
Web Site: http://www.kao.com
Sales Range: $1-4.9 Billion
Emp.: 7,251
Health & Beauty Products
N.A.I.C.S.: 456199

Kao Denmark A/S (1)
Lyngbyvej 2, 2100, Copenhagen, Denmark
Tel.: (45) 46152111
Chemical & Cosmetic Mfr
N.A.I.C.S.: 325620

Kao France Sarl (1)
11 Rue Philippe, 92200, Neuilly-sur-Seine, France
Tel.: (33) 141438600
Chemical & Cosmetic Mfr
N.A.I.C.S.: 325620

Kao Group Customer Marketing Co., Ltd. (1)
8-3 Nihonbashi Koamicho, Chuo-ku, Tokyo, 103-0016, Japan
Tel.: (81) 367462500
Soap & Detergent Mfr
N.A.I.C.S.: 325611

Kao Holdings (Thailand) Co., Ltd. (1)
Wave Place Building, 55 Wireless Road, Lumpini Pathumwan, Bangkok, 10330, Thailand
Tel.: (66) 26554455
Web Site: http://www.kao.th
Sales Range: $150-199.9 Million
Emp.: 400
Household Goods & Chemical Products Mfr
N.A.I.C.S.: 325998
Saito Kozo *(CEO)*

AND PRIVATE COMPANIES

Kao Huludao Casting Materials Co., Ltd. (1)
No 430 Changjiang Road Economic and Technological Development Zone, Beigang Industrial Area, Huludao, Liaoning, China
Tel.: (86) 4293226222
Chemical & Cosmetic Mfr
N.A.I.C.S.: 325620

Kao Industrial (Thailand) Co., Ltd. (1)
O-NES Tower 14th Floor 6 Soi Sukhumvit 6, Klongtoey District, Bangkok, 10110, Thailand (100%)
Tel.: (66) 26554455
Web Site: https://www.kao.com
Sales Range: $300-349.9 Million
Emp.: 600
Cosmetics, Consumer & Chemical Products Mfr
N.A.I.C.S.: 325998

Kao Italy S.p.a. (1)
Via Leonida Bissolati 76, 00187, Rome, Italy
Tel.: (39) 0642745521
Chemical & Cosmetic Mfr
N.A.I.C.S.: 325620

Kao Netherlands B.V. (1)
Berkenweg 7, 3818 LA, Amersfoort, Netherlands
Tel.: (31) 854864400
Chemical & Cosmetic Mfr
N.A.I.C.S.: 325620

Kao New Zealand Limited (1)
Level 3 3 - 5 High Street, Auckland, New Zealand
Tel.: (64) 93685401
Hair Salon Training Services
N.A.I.C.S.: 812112

Kao Norway AS (1)
Drammensveien 39 2etg V, 0271, Oslo, Norway
Tel.: (47) 22556991
Chemical & Cosmetic Mfr
N.A.I.C.S.: 325620

Kao Oleochemical (Malaysia) Sdn. Bhd. (1)
2510 Lorong Perusahaan Satu Prai Industrial Complex, 13600, Perai, Penang, Malaysia
Tel.: (60) 43998500
Web Site: http://www.kao.com
Sales Range: $50-74.9 Million
Emp.: 300
Mfr & Sale of Household Products, Cosmetics & Industrial Products
N.A.I.C.S.: 456199

Kao Plasticizer (Malaysia) Sdn. Bhd. (1)
2510 Lorong Perusahaan Satu Prai Industrial Complex, 13600, Penang, Malaysia
Tel.: (60) 43998500
Sales Range: $100-124.9 Million
Emp.: 300
Mfr & Sale of Household Products, Cosmetics & Industrial Products
N.A.I.C.S.: 456199
Sakamoto Toru *(Mng Dir)*

Kao Professional Salon Services GmbH (1)
Pfungstadterstrasse 92-100, 64297, Darmstadt, Germany
Tel.: (49) 6151 39 60 0
Web Site: http://www.kpss-hair.com
Hairdresser Services
N.A.I.C.S.: 812112

Kao Professional Services Co., Ltd. (1)
2-1-3 Bunka, Sumida-ku, Tokyo, 131-8501, Japan
Tel.: (81) 356307154
Home Care Product Mfr & Whslr
N.A.I.C.S.: 325620

Kao Salon Japan Co., Ltd. (1)
1-14-10 Nihonbashi Kayabacho, Chuo-ku, Tokyo, Japan
Tel.: (81) 356307013
Hair Salon Services
N.A.I.C.S.: 812112

Kao Sanitary Products Ehime Co., Ltd. (1)
6-3 Hiuchi, Saijo, 793-0003, Ehime, Japan
Tel.: (81) 897 55 1888
Personal Care Products Mfr & Whslr
N.A.I.C.S.: 325620

Kao Soap (Malaysia) Sdn. Bhd. (1)
2637 Lrg Perusahaan Satu Prai Industrial Complex, 13600, Penang, Malaysia
Tel.: (60) 43999706
Web Site: http://www.kao.com
Sales Range: $10-24.9 Million
Emp.: 300
Mfr & Sale of Household Products, Cosmetics & Industrial Products
N.A.I.C.S.: 456199

Kao South Africa Pty. Ltd. (1)
Unit 3 Capital Hill Estate K101 Business Park, Cnr R101 and le Roux Avenue, Midrand, 1685, South Africa
Tel.: (27) 113125070
Hair Care Products Distr
N.A.I.C.S.: 456120

Kao Specialties Americas (1)
243 Woodbine St, High Point, NC 27261 (100%)
Tel.: (336) 884-2214
Web Site: https://chemical.kao.com
Sales Range: $100-124.9 Million
Emp.: 160
Industrial Chemicals Mfr
N.A.I.C.S.: 325199

Kao Sweden AB (1)
Kungsbroplan 3A, 112 27, Stockholm, Sweden
Tel.: (46) 855602070
Chemical & Cosmetic Mfr
N.A.I.C.S.: 325620

Kao Switzerland AG (1)
Ruessenstrasse 12, 6340, Baar, Switzerland
Tel.: (41) 417660606
Chemical & Cosmetic Mfr
N.A.I.C.S.: 325620

Kao Trading Corporation Shanghai (1)
No 1500 Bei Song Road, Min Hang District, Shanghai, 201111, China
Tel.: (86) 216 409 2880
Web Site: https://chemical.kao.com
Chemical Product Whslr
N.A.I.C.S.: 424690

Kao USA, Inc. (1)
100 N Charles St 15th Fl, Baltimore, MD 21201
Tel.: (410) 951-5400
Web Site: http://www.goldwell-northamerica.com
Sales Range: $50-74.9 Million
Emp.: 80
Hair Care Products Distr
N.A.I.C.S.: 424210
Trevor Attenborough *(Pres & Gen Mgr)*

Kao Vietnam Co., Ltd. (1)
No 224A Dien Bien Phu Street, Ho Chi Minh City, Vietnam
Tel.: (84) 89325800
Sales Range: $25-49.9 Million
Emp.: 50
Mfr & Sale of Household Products, Cosmetics & Industrial Products
N.A.I.C.S.: 456199
Keisuke Onuma *(CEO)*

Kao-Quaker, Co., Ltd. (1)
2-1-3 Bunka, Sumida-ku, Tokyo, 131-8501, Japan
Tel.: (81) 35 630 7841
Web Site: https://chemical.kao.com
Resin Mfr & Distr
N.A.I.C.S.: 325211
Shigeaki Takashina *(Pres & CEO)*

Plant (Domestic):

Kao-Quaker Co., Ltd. - Toyohashi Plant (2)
4-51 Akemicho, Toyohashi, Aichi, Japan
Tel.: (81) 532 23 2711
Molding Sand Binder Mfr
N.A.I.C.S.: 323111

Kpss (UK) Limited (1)
130 Shaftesbury Avenue, London, W1D 5EU, United Kingdom
Tel.: (44) 3301239530
Hair Salon Services
N.A.I.C.S.: 812112

Kpss Hong Kong Ltd. (1)
Unit A 30/F Tower A Billion Centre No 1 Wang Kwong Road, Kowloon Bay, Kowloon, China (Hong Kong)
Tel.: (852) 25291018
Hair Salon Services
N.A.I.C.S.: 812112

Lissage Ltd. (1)
2F Nissou No 22 Building 1-11-10 Azabudai, Minato-ku, Tokyo, Japan
Tel.: (81) 3 5575 6211
Web Site: http://www.lissage.co.jp
Cosmetics Mfr & Whslr
N.A.I.C.S.: 325620

Molton Brown Limited (1)
130 Shaftesbury Avenue, London, W1D 5EU, United Kingdom
Tel.: (44) 808 178 1188
Web Site: https://www.moltonbrown.co.uk
Sales Range: $125-149.9 Million
Emp.: 50
Cosmetics, Personal Care & Luxury Products
N.A.I.C.S.: 325620

Nivea-Kao Co. Ltd. (1)
18-1 Shintomi 1-chome, Chuo-ku, Tokyo, 104-0041, Japan
Tel.: (81) 33 297 5350
Web Site: https://nivea-kao.jp
Sales Range: $25-49.9 Million
Emp.: 50
Cosmetics & Pharmaceuticals Mfr; Owned 50% by Beiersdorf Group & 50% by Kao Corporation
N.A.I.C.S.: 325620

P.T. Kao Indonesia (1)
Jl Mt Haryono Kav 39-40, Cikoko Pancoran, Jakarta, 12770, Indonesia
Tel.: (62) 2179191980
Web Site: https://www.kao.com
Cosmetics Products Mfr
N.A.I.C.S.: 424210

Affiliate (Domestic):

P.T. Kao Indonesia Chemicals (2)
Grha Persada 2 - 5th Floor Jl KH Noer Ali No 89A, Kayuringin Jaya Kalimalang, Bekasi, 17144, West Java, Indonesia (50%)
Tel.: (62) 212 928 5454
Web Site: https://chemical.kao.com
Sales Range: $50-74.9 Million
Emp.: 150
Mfr of Household Goods & Chemical Products
N.A.I.C.S.: 325998

Pilipinas Kao, Inc. (1)
Jasaan Misamis Oriental Ecozone, Jasaan, Cagayan de Oro, 9003, Misamis Oriental, Philippines (100%)
Tel.: (63) 88 890 5020
Web Site: https://chemical.kao.com
Sales Range: $50-74.9 Million
Emp.: 22
Chemical Products Distr
N.A.I.C.S.: 424690

QuimiKao S.A. de C.V. (1)
Km 22 5 Carretera Guadalajara, 45680, El Salto, Jalisco, Mexico (100%)
Tel.: (52) 333 284 1000
Web Site: https://chemical.kao.com
Sales Range: $25-49.9 Million
Emp.: 10
Mfr of Chemical Products
N.A.I.C.S.: 325998

KAO HSIUNG CHANG IRON & STEEL CORP.
No 318 Zhonghua 1st Rd, Gushan Dist, Kaohsiung, 804, Taiwan
Tel.: (886) 75556111
Web Site: http://www.khc.com.tw
2008—(TAI)
Rev.: $47,754,830
Assets: $246,450,104
Liabilities: $133,706,068
Net Worth: $112,744,036
Earnings: $14,154,681
Fiscal Year-end: 12/31/23
Steel Pole Mfr
N.A.I.C.S.: 331110
Tai-Jung Lu *(Chm)*

Subsidiaries:

Kao Hsiung Chang Iron & Steel Corp. - Pen Factory (1)
No 2 Yongxiang Road, Fang-liao, 940, Pingtung, Taiwan
Tel.: (886) 88668800
Steel Strips Mfr
N.A.I.C.S.: 331110

Kao Hsiung Chang Iron & Steel Corp. - Yong-an Factory (1)
No 6 Yonggong 1st Road, Yong-an Township, Kaohsiung, 828, Taiwan
Tel.: (886) 76229601
Web Site: http://www.khc.com.tw
Steel Pole Mfr
N.A.I.C.S.: 331210

KAONAVI, INC.
Shibuya Scramble Square 38F 2-24-12 Shibuya, Shibuya-ku, Tokyo, 150-6138, Japan
Tel.: (81) 366332781
Web Site:
https://www.corp.kaonavi.jp
Year Founded: 2008
4435—(TKS)
Rev.: $50,401,250
Assets: $43,255,840
Liabilities: $27,973,520
Net Worth: $15,282,320
Earnings: $4,620,390
Fiscal Year-end: 03/31/24
Software Development Services
N.A.I.C.S.: 541511
Tatsuya Hiramatsu *(Exec Officer)*

KAONMEDIA CO, LTD.
Gaon Media Building 884-3 Seongnam-daero, Bundang-Gu, Seongnam, 463-839, Gyeonggi-do, Korea (South)
Tel.: (82) 317248500
Web Site:
https://www.kaonmedia.co.kr
Year Founded: 2001
078890—(KRS)
Rev.: $468,817,454
Assets: $331,446,415
Liabilities: $187,190,521
Net Worth: $144,255,895
Earnings: $8,459,165
Emp.: 268
Fiscal Year-end: 12/31/22
Video Equipment Mfr
N.A.I.C.S.: 334310
Dong-Yeon Lim *(CEO)*

Subsidiaries:

KAON America Latina LTDA. (1)
Alameda Vicente Pinzon 144 - 4th Floor - Room 41 Vila Olimpia, Sao Paulo, 04547-130, Brazil
Tel.: (55) 11 2478 4438
Digital Television Equipment Mfr
N.A.I.C.S.: 334220
Jeff Kim *(VP)*

KAON Germany (1)
Beta-Strasse 10 c, Unterfohring, 85774, Munich, Germany
Tel.: (49) 89 9233459 0
Digital Television Equipment Mfr
N.A.I.C.S.: 334220
Sunjoong Lee *(VP-Sls)*

KAON Norway (1)
Rødkleivfaret 2, Oslo, Norway
Tel.: (47) 9770 7860
Digital Television Equipment Mfr
N.A.I.C.S.: 334220
Tom Buhl *(Exec VP-Sls)*

KAON Russia (1)
Kosigina 15 4th floor office no 425, Moscow, 119334, Russia

KAONMEDIA CO., LTD.

KAONMEDIA CO, LTD—(Continued)
Tel.: (7) 964 787 5242
Digital Television Equipment Mfr
N.A.I.C.S.: 334220
Alex Park (VP-Sls)

Kaon India PVT Ltd. (1)
A 301 Ansal Chamber I Bhikaji Cama Place,
New Delhi, 110066, India
Tel.: (91) 11 4107 6594
Web Site: http://www.kaonmedia.com
Emp.: 3
Digital Television Equipment Mfr
N.A.I.C.S.: 334220
Rakesh Kosla (Mgr-Sls)

Kaon Middle East FZCO (1)
RA08/Warehouse No DB 01, PO Box
262018, Jebel Ali, Dubai, United Arab Emirates
Tel.: (971) 4 8836577
Web Site: http://www.kaonmedia.com
Emp.: 7
Digital Television Equipment Mfr
N.A.I.C.S.: 334220

KAOPU GROUP, INC.

No 100-11 Sec I Zhongqing Road,
North District, Taichung, 404, Taiwan
Tel.: (886) 852 5805 9452   DE
Year Founded: 2013
LNGB—(OTCIQ)
Sales Range: $1-9.9 Million
Holding Company; Funeral Services
N.A.I.C.S.: 551112
Tsung-Min Chang (Bus Mgr)

KAORI HEAT TREATMENT CO., LTD.

No 5-2 Jilin N Rd, Zhongli Dist,
Taoyuan, 320030, Taiwan
Tel.: (886) 34527005
Web Site: https://www.kaori.com.tw
Year Founded: 1970
8996—(TAI)
Rev.: $141,458,872
Assets: $157,914,053
Liabilities: $69,497,757
Net Worth: $88,416,295
Earnings: $18,853,657
Emp.: 404
Fiscal Year-end: 12/31/23
Metal Heat Treatmenting
N.A.I.C.S.: 332811

Subsidiaries:

Kaori Heat Treatment Co., Ltd. - Ben-Chou Plant (1)
No 3 Ben-Kung 2nd Rd Ben-Chou Industrial
District, Kaohsiong, Taiwan
Tel.: (886) 76243132
Heat Exchanger Mfr
N.A.I.C.S.: 332410

Kaori Technology (Ningbo) Co., Ltd. (1)
No 8 Chuangye 4 Rd Free Trade West
Zone, Ningbo, 315800, China
Tel.: (86) 57486875468
Heat Exchanger Mfr
N.A.I.C.S.: 332410

KAP BETEILIGUNGS-AG

Edelzeller StraSSe 44, Fulda, 36043,
Germany
Tel.: (49) 661 103 0
Web Site: http://www.kap.de
Technical Textiles Mfr
N.A.I.C.S.: 314999
Alexander Riedel (CFO)

Subsidiaries:

BEBUSCH Hungaria KFT (1)
Handler Kalman u 3, Oropszlany, 2840, Hungary
Tel.: (36) 34560402
Web Site: http://www.bebusch.hu
Plastic Product Mfr & Distr
N.A.I.C.S.: 326199
Michael Kastrup (Co-CEO)

Bebusch GmbH (1)
Am Gewerbekanal 1, 77716, Haslach im
Kinzigtal, Germany
Tel.: (49) 78327000
Web Site: http://www.bebusch.de
Plastics Product Mfr
N.A.I.C.S.: 326199
Michael Kastrup (Co-CEO)

CaPlast Kunststoffverarbeitungs GmbH (1)
Magdheide 7, 59394, Nordkirchen, Germany
Tel.: (49) 25999130
Web Site: http://www.caplast.de
Roofing Sheet Mfr
N.A.I.C.S.: 332322
Frederik Schaefer (Mng Dir)

ELBTAL PLASTICS GmbH & Co. KG (1)
Grenzstr 9, 01640, Coswig, Germany
Tel.: (49) 352353300
Web Site: http://www.elbtal-plastics.de
Plastics Product Mfr
N.A.I.C.S.: 326113
Andreas Kiehne (Area Mgr-Sls)

Galvanotechnische Oberflachen GmbH (1)
Kaltes Feld 37, 08468, Heinsdorfergrund,
Unterheinsdorf, Germany
Tel.: (49) 37653804621
Web Site: http://www.gtoberflaechen.de
Electroplating Services
N.A.I.C.S.: 332813

Gear Motion GmbH (1)
Adolffstrasse 57, 89584, Ehingen, Germany
Tel.: (49) 73915830
Web Site: http://www.gear-motion.de
Emp.: 160
Plastics Product Mfr
N.A.I.C.S.: 326199
Michael Kastrup (Co-CEO)

IP OOO MINAVTO (1)
Minskaya Str 2/201, Logoysk, 223141,
Minsk, Belarus
Tel.: (375) 177444371
Web Site: http://www.minavto.by
Emp.: 250
Automotive Components Mfr
N.A.I.C.S.: 336390
Alexander Navitski (Mgr-Production)

KAP Textile Holdings SA Ltd. (1)
Spilo Building Oosterland Road, Paarl,
South Africa
Tel.: (27) 218775200
Holding Company
N.A.I.C.S.: 551112

MEHLER ENGINEERED PRODUCTS INDIA PRIVATE LIMITED (1)
Plot No S-10 to S-15 Integrated Textile Park
KIADB Industrial Area, Doddaballapur, Bengaluru, 561203, Karnataka, India
Tel.: (91) 8040963086
Rubber Product Distr
N.A.I.C.S.: 423840

MEHLER ENGINEERED PRODUCTS Inc. (1)
175 Mehler Ln, Martinsville, VA 24112
Tel.: (706) 938-0122
Web Site: http://www.mehlerinc.com
Rubber Product Distr
N.A.I.C.S.: 423840
Gray Sullivan (Exec VP)

Mehler Engineered Products s.r.o. (1)
Branska 329, 514 01, Jilemnice, Czech
Republic
Tel.: (420) 481562131
Web Site: http://www.mehler-ep.com
Rubber Products Mfr
N.A.I.C.S.: 326220
Jan Komanek (Acct Mgr)

Mehler Engineering cord (Suzhou) Co., Ltd. (1)
Shengze Lixin Road Town Third District No
2-5, Wujiang, 215228, Jiangsu, China
Tel.: (86) 51263551386
Web Site: http://www.m-e-p.cn
Rubber Products Mfr
N.A.I.C.S.: 326220
Wang Shi (Gen Mgr)

OLBO & MEHLER TEX PORTUGAL, LDA. (1)
Apartado 441 Landim, 4760 000, Vila Nova de Famalicao, Portugal
Tel.: (351) 252302722
Fabrics Mfr
N.A.I.C.S.: 314994

Prazisionsteile Dresden GmbH & Co. KG (1)
Enno-Heidebroek-Strasse 7, 01237, Dresden, Germany
Tel.: (49) 351839840
Web Site: http://www.pt-dresden.de
Automobile Parts Mfr & Distr
N.A.I.C.S.: 336390

Riflex Film AB (1)
Ekenasvagen 4, 372 73, Ronneby, Sweden
Tel.: (46) 45774800
Web Site: http://www.riflexfilm.com
Emp.: 44
PVC Films & Foils Mfr
N.A.I.C.S.: 326113
Anders Leidefalk (Mng Dir & Sls Mgr)

Steinweg Kunststofffolien GmbH (1)
Kupferstrasse 1, 44577, Castrop-Rauxel,
Germany
Tel.: (49) 23056488
Plastics Product Mfr
N.A.I.C.S.: 326113

Synteen & Luckenhaus GmbH (1)
Robert-Stehli-Strasse 8, Erzingen, 79771,
Klettgau, Germany
Tel.: (49) 77428510
Web Site: http://www.synteen.de
Textile Products Mfr
N.A.I.C.S.: 315990

KAPA CAPITAL, INC.

725 Granville Street Suite 400, Vancouver, V7Y 1G5, BC, Canada
Tel.: (604) 836-6667
Asset Management Services
N.A.I.C.S.: 523940
Vivian Katsuris (CFO & Sec)

KAPCHORUA TEA KENYA PLC

Karen Office Park The Acacia Block
2nd Floor Langata Road, PO Box
42281, 00100, Nairobi, Kenya
Tel.: (254) 203882522
KUKZ—(NAI)
Rev.: $13,480,727
Assets: $18,812,806
Liabilities: $4,635,028
Net Worth: $14,177,778
Earnings: $2,390,257
Emp.: 379
Fiscal Year-end: 03/31/23
Tea Mfr
N.A.I.C.S.: 311920
Ezekiel N. K. Wanjama (Chm)

KAPE TECHNOLOGIES PLC

LABS Hawley Lock 1 Water Lane,
London, NW1 8NZ, United Kingdom
Tel.: (44) 2034324977   IM
Web Site: http://www.kape.com
KAPE—(AIM)
Rev.: $230,665,000
Assets: $1,687,271,000
Liabilities: $823,826,000
Net Worth: $863,445,000
Earnings: $23,338,000
Emp.: 850
Fiscal Year-end: 12/31/21
Cybersecurity Products Developer
N.A.I.C.S.: 513210
Moran Laufer (CFO)

Subsidiaries:

Neutral Holdings Ltd (1)
520 Pike St, Seattle, WA 98101
Tel.: (206) 538-5445
Web Site: http://www.intego.com
Computer System Design Services
N.A.I.C.S.: 541512
Steve Kelly (VP-Engrg)

INTERNATIONAL PUBLIC

KAPIL COTEX LTD.

Shop No 276 Dreams Mall L B S
Marg Near Bhandup Railway Station,
Bhandup West, Mumbai, 400078,
Maharashtra, India
Tel.: (91) 2221660432
Web Site:
  https://kapilcotexlimited.com
Year Founded: 1983
512036—(BOM)
Rev.: $3,101
Assets: $596,662
Liabilities: $88,945
Net Worth: $507,717
Earnings: $5,166
Fiscal Year-end: 03/31/22
Textile Products Mfr
N.A.I.C.S.: 314999
Prakashchandra Rathi (Chm & CFO)

KAPIL RAJ FINANCE LTD.

23-B First Floor Chirag Delhi Opposite Satrang Bhawan, New Delhi,
110017, India
Tel.: (91) 9920865333
Web Site:
  https://www.kapilrajfinanceltd.com
539679—(BOM)
Rev.: $70,739
Assets: $1,185,042
Liabilities: $40,009
Net Worth: $1,145,033
Earnings: $32,240
Fiscal Year-end: 03/31/23
Financial Support Services
N.A.I.C.S.: 523999
Atul Chimanlal Doshi (Exec Dir)

KAPITAL YATIRIM HOLDING A.S.

Visnezade Mh Suleyman Seba Cd,
Besiktas, 34357, Istanbul, Turkiye
Tel.: (90) 537 289 7502
Web Site:
  http://www.kapitalyatrimholdings.com
Year Founded: 2005
KPHOL—(IST)
Holding Company
N.A.I.C.S.: 551112
Mehmet Gur (Chm)

KAPPA CREATE CO., LTD.

Landmark Tower 12th floor 2-2-1 Minatomirai, Nishi-ku, Yokohama, 330-0854, Kanagawa, Japan
Tel.: (81) 120508900
Web Site: https://www.kappa-create.co.jp
Year Founded: 1973
7421—(TKS)
Rev.: $477,215,560
Assets: $199,562,510
Liabilities: $132,748,630
Net Worth: $66,813,880
Earnings: $9,227,560
Fiscal Year-end: 03/31/24
Restaurant Management Services
N.A.I.C.S.: 722511
Go Yamakaze (Pres & CEO)

KAPPAHL HOLDING AB

Idrottsvagen 14, Box 303, SE-431 24,
Molndal, Sweden
Tel.: (46) 317715500
Web Site: http://www.kappahl.com
Rev.: $556,120,544
Assets: $342,516,048
Liabilities: $111,513,696
Net Worth: $231,002,352
Earnings: $41,141,744
Emp.: 2,715
Fiscal Year-end: 08/31/17
Clothing Stores
N.A.I.C.S.: 458110
Charlotte Hogberg (Head-Corp Comm)

AND PRIVATE COMPANIES

KAPSCH-GROUP BETEILIGUNGS GMBH

Subsidiaries:

KappAhl AS (1)
Storgata 37, Fredrikstad, 1602, Norway
Tel.: (47) 69368700
Web Site: http://www.kappahl.no
Sales Range: $400-449.9 Million
Emp.: 1,200
Clothing Stores
N.A.I.C.S.: 458110

KappAhl Aland Ab (1)
Torggatan 7, 22100, Mariehamn, Finland
Tel.: (358) 18527300
Web Site: http://www.kappahl.fi
Clothing Stores
N.A.I.C.S.: 458110

KappAhl OY (1)
Unikkotie 3C, Vantaa, 01300, Finland
Tel.: (358) 98386300
Web Site: http://www.kappahl.com
Sales Range: $25-49.9 Million
Emp.: 12
Clothing Stores
N.A.I.C.S.: 458110

KappAhl Polska Sp.z.o.o. (1)
Ulica Leszno 12, Warsaw, 1192, Poland
Tel.: (48) 225357300
Web Site: http://www.kappahl.pl
Sales Range: $100-124.9 Million
Emp.: 600
Clothing Stores
N.A.I.C.S.: 458110

KAPSCH-GROUP BETEILIGUNGS GMBH

Am Europlatz 2, 1120, Vienna, Austria
Tel.: (43) 50 8110
Web Site: http://www.kapsch.net
Year Founded: 1892
Rev.: $1,386,160,006
Assets: $1,224,638,033
Liabilities: $909,605,238
Net Worth: $315,032,795
Earnings: $37,993,514
Emp.: 6,896
Fiscal Year-end: 03/31/19
Traffic Telematics & Communications Solutions
N.A.I.C.S.: 488490
Kari Kapsch *(COO & Member-Exec Bd)*

Subsidiaries:

FIPOFIX GmbH (1)
Hauptstrasse 63, 3033, Altlengbach, Austria
Tel.: (43) 2275 41 143
Web Site: http://www.fipofix.com
Timber Product Mfr
N.A.I.C.S.: 321219
Marion Koch *(Co-CEO)*

FUN-AGENT d.o.o (1)
Radnicka 39, 10000, Zagreb, Croatia
Tel.: (385) 1 235 7000
Web Site: http://www.funagent.net
Marketing Consulting Services
N.A.I.C.S.: 541613

Kapsch BusinessCom AG (1)
Wienerbergstrasse 53, 1120, Vienna, Austria
Tel.: (43) 50 8110
Web Site: http://www.kapschbusiness.net
Telecommunication Servicesb
N.A.I.C.S.: 517810

Subsidiary (Domestic):

CALPANA business consulting GmbH (2)
Blumauerstrasse 43, 4020, Linz, Austria
Tel.: (43) 7326012160
Web Site: http://www.calpana.com
Emp.: 15
Business Management Consulting Services
N.A.I.C.S.: 541611
Gunther Angerbauer *(CEO)*

ITM Informationstransport und -management Gesellschaft m.b.H. (2)
Floridusgasse 50, 1210, Vienna, Austria
Tel.: (43) 1 25688600
Computer Peripheral Equipment Distr
N.A.I.C.S.: 423430

Subsidiary (Non-US):

Kapsch BusinessCom Kft. (2)
Bocskai ut 77-79, 1113, Budapest, Hungary
Tel.: (36) 1 372 6400
Information Technology Development Services
N.A.I.C.S.: 541511
Istvan Philip *(CEO)*

Kapsch BusinessCom s.r.o. (2)
Ke Stvanici 656/3, 186 00, Prague, Czech Republic
Tel.: (420) 221 466 311
Emp.: 90
Information Technology Development Services
N.A.I.C.S.: 541511
Karel Feix *(CEO)*

Kapsch S.R.L. (2)
World Trade Center Bucharest E Wing 2nd Floor 10 Montreal Square, 011469, Bucharest, Romania
Tel.: (40) 21 4087373
Web Site: http://www.kapsch.net
Information Technology Development Services
N.A.I.C.S.: 541511

Kapsch s.r.o. (2)
Plynarenska 1, 821 09, Bratislava, Slovakia
Tel.: (421) 2 3366 680
Information Technology Development Services
N.A.I.C.S.: 541511

Kapsch Components GmbH & Co. KG (1)
Gutheil-Schoder-Gasse 17, 1230, Vienna, Austria
Tel.: (43) 508110
Information Technology Consulting Services
N.A.I.C.S.: 518210

Kapsch Partner Solutions GmbH (1)
Johann-Hoffmann-Platz 9, 1120, Vienna, Austria
Tel.: (43) 50 811 0
Information Technology Development Services
N.A.I.C.S.: 541511

Kapsch Smart Energy GmbH (1)
Wienerbergstrasse 53, 1120, Vienna, Austria
Tel.: (43) 50 811 5434
Web Site: http://www.kapschsmartenergy.at
Emp.: 10
Information Technology Development Services
N.A.I.C.S.: 541511
Christian Schober *(Gen Mgr)*

Kapsch Telematik Technologies Bulgaria EAD (1)
XS Tower Sofia Park 5 Panorama Sofia Str, 1766, Sofia, Bulgaria
Tel.: (359) 29590029
Information Technology Consulting Services
N.A.I.C.S.: 518210

Kapsch TrafficCom AG (1)
Am Europlatz 2, 1120, Vienna, Austria (61.9%)
Tel.: (43) 508110
Web Site: https://www.kapsch.net
Rev.: $597,253,642
Assets: $518,158,463
Liabilities: $462,788,393
Net Worth: $55,370,070
Earnings: ($26,160,853)
Emp.: 4,039
Fiscal Year-end: 03/31/2023
Vehicle Telematic Systems
N.A.I.C.S.: 488490
Franz Semmernegg *(Chm-Supervisory Bd)*

Subsidiary (Non-US):

Electronic Toll Collection (Pty) Ltd. (2)
36 Assegaai Wood Rooihuis Kraal, Samrand, Centurion, 0157, South Africa
Tel.: (27) 126617624
Vehicle Telematics Solutions
N.A.I.C.S.: 488490

Subsidiary (Domestic):

Kapsch Components KG (2)
Gutheil-Schoder-Gasse 17, 1230, Vienna, Austria
Tel.: (43) 508110
Web Site: http://www.kapsch.net
Vehicle Telematics Solutions
N.A.I.C.S.: 488490

Kapsch Telematic Services GmbH (2)
Am Europlatz 2, 1120, Vienna, Austria
Tel.: (43) 508110
Vehicle Telematic Services
N.A.I.C.S.: 488490
Franz Semmerneg *(Gen Mgr)*

Subsidiary (Non-US):

Kapsch Telematic Services GmbH (3)
Unter den Linden 16, 10117, Berlin, Germany
Tel.: (49) 30 408 173 273
Telecommunication Servicesb
N.A.I.C.S.: 517112

Subsidiary (Non-US):

Kapsch Telematic Services Kft. (2)
Bocskai ut 77-79, 1113, Budapest, Hungary
Tel.: (36) 13726400
Web Site: http://www.kapsch.net
Sales Range: $25-49.9 Million
Emp.: 1
Vehicle Telematics Solutions
N.A.I.C.S.: 488490
Istvan Fulop *(Mng Dir)*

Kapsch Telematic Services Solutions A/S (2)
Store Kongensgade 49, 1264, Copenhagen, Denmark
Tel.: (45) 7022 0089
Telematic & Communications Services
N.A.I.C.S.: 488490

Kapsch Telematic Services Sp. z o.o. (2)
ul Surowieckiego 1, PL 02-785, Warsaw, Poland
Tel.: (48) 225446000
Vehicle Telematics Solutions
N.A.I.C.S.: 488490

Kapsch Telematic Services spol. s r.o. (2)
Ke Stvanici 656/3, 186 00, Prague, Czech Republic (52%)
Tel.: (420) 225026140
Vehicle Telematics Solutions
N.A.I.C.S.: 488490

Kapsch Telematic Technologies Bulgaria AD (2)
16 Boyanska Legenda str, Boyana District, Sofia, 1606, Bulgaria
Tel.: (359) 2 484 0884
Vehicle Telematics Solutions
N.A.I.C.S.: 488490

Kapsch TrafficCom AB (2)
Bataljonsgatan 10, PO Box 1063, 551 10, Jonkoping, Sweden
Tel.: (46) 362901500
Web Site: http://www.kapsch.net
Sales Range: $50-74.9 Million
Emp.: 150
Vehicle Telematics Solutions
N.A.I.C.S.: 488490
Matttias Larsson *(Pres)*

Kapsch TrafficCom Argentina S.A. (2)
Juana Azurduy 2440, C1429BZJ, Buenos Aires, Argentina
Tel.: (54) 11 4703 5500
Vehicle Telematics Solutions
N.A.I.C.S.: 488490

Kapsch TrafficCom Australia Pty Ltd. (2)
Level 10 636 St Kilda Road, Melbourne, 3004, VIC, Australia
Tel.: (61) 386567900
Vehicle Telematics Solutions
N.A.I.C.S.: 488490

Kapsch TrafficCom Canada Inc. (2)
6020 Ambler Drive, Mississauga, L4W 2P1, ON, Canada (100%)
Tel.: (905) 624-3020
Web Site: http://www.kapsch.net
Emp.: 120
Vehicle Toll System Mfr
N.A.I.C.S.: 488490
Andre F. Laux *(COO & Member-Exec Bd)*

Kapsch TrafficCom Chile S.A. (2)
Avenida del Valle Norte 857 piso 3 Ciudad Empresarial, Huechuraba, 8580702, Santiago, Chile
Tel.: (56) 227951200
Web Site: http://www.kapsch.net
Sales Range: $25-49.9 Million
Emp.: 27
Vehicle Telematics Solutions
N.A.I.C.S.: 488490

Kapsch TrafficCom France SAS (2)
Parc d'Affaires Silic Immeuble Panama, 45 rue de Villeneuve, 94573, Rungis, Cedex, France
Tel.: (33) 603482759
Vehicle Telematics Solutions
N.A.I.C.S.: 488490

Subsidiary (US):

Kapsch TrafficCom IVHS Inc. (2)
8201 Greensboro Dr Ste 1002, McLean, VA 22102
Tel.: (703) 885-1976
Telematics & Communications Services
N.A.I.C.S.: 488490
J. B. Kendrick *(Pres-North America)*

Subsidiary (Domestic):

Streetline, Inc. (3)
393 Vintage Park Dr Ste 140, Foster City, CA 94404
Tel.: (650) 242-3400
Web Site: http://www.streetline.com
Smart Parking Solutions
N.A.I.C.S.: 541519
Kurt Buecheler *(Sr VP-Sls & Bus Dev)*

Subsidiary (Non-US):

Kapsch TrafficCom IVHS, S.A. de C.V. (2)
Lago Nyassa 27 Col Granada Del Miguel Hildago, Mexico, 11520, DF, Mexico
Tel.: (52) 55 8488 5444
Web Site: http://www.kapsch.com
Emp.: 9
Telematics & Telecommunications Services
N.A.I.C.S.: 488490

Kapsch TrafficCom Kazakhstan LLC (2)
33 Dinmukhamed Kunayev St Office 803, Nur-Sultan, 010000, Kazakhstan
Tel.: (7) 7172502018
Sales Range: $25-49.9 Million
Emp.: 2
Vehicle Telematics Solutions
N.A.I.C.S.: 488490

Kapsch TrafficCom Ltd. (2)
Unit 2 Espace 26 St Thomas Place, Ely, CB7 4EX, Cambs, United Kingdom
Tel.: (44) 1353644010
Web Site: http://www.kapsch.net
Sales Range: $25-49.9 Million
Emp.: 3
Vehicle Telematics Solutions
N.A.I.C.S.: 488490

Kapsch TrafficCom Ltd. (2)
Level 8 3 Shortland Street Auckland Central, Auckland, 1010, New Zealand
Tel.: (64) 1 893 4924
Web Site: http://www.kapsch.net
Road Telematics & Telecommunications Services
N.A.I.C.S.: 488490

Kapsch TrafficCom Ltd. (2)
13 O'Connel Street, PO Box 37542, Parnell, Auckland, 1151, New Zealand
Tel.: (64) 3 8656 7900
Telematics & Telecommunications Services
N.A.I.C.S.: 488490

Kapsch TrafficCom Pte. Ltd. (2)
260 Orchard Road 07-01/04 The Heeren, Singapore, 238855, Singapore
Tel.: (65) 6738 6746

KAPSCH-GROUP BETEILIGUNGS GMBH

Kapsch-Group Beteiligungs GmbH—(Continued)
Web Site: http://www.kapsch.net
Telematics & Telecommunications Services
N.A.I.C.S.: 488490

Kapsch TrafficCom Russia OOO (2)
Varshavskoye Hwy 17 4th Floor room 4,
117105, Moscow, Russia
Tel.: (7) 4959337717
Web Site: http://www.kapsch.net
Vehicle Telematics Solutions
N.A.I.C.S.: 488490
Borris Boresov *(CEO)*

Kapsch TrafficCom S.r.l. (2)
Blend Tower Piazza Quattro Novembre 7,
I-20124, Milan, Italy
Tel.: (39) 0289827365
Vehicle Telematics Solutions
N.A.I.C.S.: 488490

Kapsch TrafficCom S.r.l. (2)
Via C Bonazzi 2, 40013, Castel Maggiore,
BO, Italy
Tel.: (39) 051 632 4011
Vehicle Telematics Solutions
N.A.I.C.S.: 488490

Kapsch TrafficCom SA (Pty) Ltd. (2)
Unit 37 Sunnyrock Park 5 Sunrock Close
Sunnyrock, 1 Greenvale Road Wilbart,
1401, Germiston, Gauteng, South Africa
Tel.: (27) 114552280
Web Site: http://www.kapsch.co.za
Sales Range: $25-49.9 Million
Emp.: 30
Vehicle Telematics Solutions
N.A.I.C.S.: 488490

Kapsch TrafficCom d.o.o. (2)
Ribiciceva ulica 33, 1000, Ljubljana, Slovenia
Tel.: (386) 590 34 283
Vehicle Telematics Solutions
N.A.I.C.S.: 488490

TMT Services and Supplies (Pty) Ltd. (2)
Ploulelie Ground Floor Building D Plattekloof Park, Bioulelle Crescent Plattekloof,
Cape Town, 7500, South Africa
Tel.: (27) 21 929 5300
Telematics & Telecommunications Services
N.A.I.C.S.: 488490

Transport Telematic Systems LLC (2)
Al Nasr Street, PO Box 113660, Abu Dhabi,
United Arab Emirates
Tel.: (971) 2 633 2564
Telematics & Communications Services
N.A.I.C.S.: 488490

Kapsch TrafficCom Arce Sistemas S.A.U. (1)
Torre Iberdrola Plaza Euskadi 5 4th Floor,
48009, Bilbao, Spain
Tel.: (34) 944440462
Information Technology Consulting Services
N.A.I.C.S.: 518210

Kapsch TrafficCom Inc. (1)
2855 Premiere Pkwy Ste F, Duluth, GA
30097
Tel.: (678) 473-6400
Web Site: http://www.kapsch.com
Emp.: 80
Information Technology Development Services
N.A.I.C.S.: 541511

Kapsch TrafficCom Saudi Arabia Co. Ltd. (1)
Palestine Street Dallah Tower 7th Floor, PO
Box 4334, Al-Rehab, 23343-6422, Jeddah,
Saudi Arabia
Tel.: (966) 126716407
Information Technology Consulting Services
N.A.I.C.S.: 518210

Kapsch TrafficCom South Africa (Pty) Ltd. (1)
Unit 37 Sunnyrock Park 5 Sunrock Close
Sunnyrock, PO Box 11992, Rynfield, Germiston, 1514, Gauteng, South Africa
Tel.: (27) 114552276
Information Technology Consulting Services
N.A.I.C.S.: 518210

Kapsch TrafficCom Transportation Brasil Ltda. (1)
Rua Julio Gonzalez 132 27 Andar, Barra
Funda, Sao Paulo, 01156-060, SP, Brazil
Tel.: (55) 1139587758
Information Technology Consulting Services
N.A.I.C.S.: 518210

Kapsch TrafficCom Transportation S.A.U. (1)
Calle de Anabel Segura 16 Building 3 3rd
Floor, Alcobendas, 28108, Madrid, Spain
Tel.: (34) 910486751
Information Technology Consulting Services
N.A.I.C.S.: 518210

Tolltickets GmbH (1)
Kaiserstrasse 28, 83022, Rosenheim, Germany
Tel.: (49) 80319414444
Web Site: https://www.tolltickets.com
Toll Product Distr
N.A.I.C.S.: 423840

KAPSTON SERVICES LIMITED
Plot No 75 Kavuri Hills, Madhapur,
Hyderabad, 500034, India
Tel.: (91) 9848778243
Web Site:
 https://kapstonservices.com
Year Founded: 2009
KAPSTON—(NSE)
Rev.: $48,083,065
Assets: $21,534,117
Liabilities: $14,500,677
Net Worth: $7,033,439
Earnings: $607,913
Emp.: 348
Fiscal Year-end: 03/31/23
Health Care Facility Services
N.A.I.C.S.: 621999
Srikanth Kodali *(Founder & Mng Dir)*

KAPTAN DEMIR CELIK ENDUSTRISI VE TICARET A.S.
Fahrettin Kerim Gokay Cad Bestekar
Saadettin Kaynak Sk No 2 Altunizade, Uskudar, Istanbul, Turkiye
Tel.: (90) 2165474900
Web Site:
 http://www.kaptandemir.com.tr
Year Founded: 1968
Sales Range: $75-99.9 Million
Emp.: 1,500
Steel Products Mfr
N.A.I.C.S.: 331110
Yasar Kaptan Cebi *(Founder & Chm)*

Subsidiaries:

Cebi Denizcilik ve Ticaret A.S. (1)
Fahrettin Kerim Gokay Cad Bestekar Saadettin Kaynak Sk No 2, Altunizade Uskudar,
Istanbul, 34662, Turkiye
Tel.: (90) 216 428 50 40
Sales Range: $25-49.9 Million
Emp.: 12
Steel Products Mfr
N.A.I.C.S.: 331110
Engin Ozcelik *(Gen Mgr)*

Cebi Enerji Elektrik Uretimi A.S. (1)
Fahrettin Kerim Gokay Cad Bestekar Saadettin Kaynak Sk No 2, Altunizade Uskudar,
Istanbul, Turkiye
Tel.: (90) 216 547 49 00
Eletric Power Generation Services
N.A.I.C.S.: 221112

Kaptan Demir Celik Endustrisi ve Ticaret A.S. - Kaptan Demir Celik Corlu Haddehane Tesisleri Plant (1)
Misinli Belediye Kavsagi Asfaltalti mevkli-
Corlu, Corlu, Tekirdag, Turkiye
Tel.: (90) 282 675 13 13
Steel Products Mfr
N.A.I.C.S.: 331110

Kaptan Demir Celik Endustrisi ve Ticaret A.S. - Kaptan Demir Celik Karabuk Haddehane Tesisleri Plant (1)
Hurriyet Cad No 29A, Karabuk, Turkiye
Tel.: (90) 370 415 47 00
Steel Products Mfr

N.A.I.C.S.: 331110

Kaptan Demir Celik Endustrisi ve Ticaret A.S. - Kaptan Demir Celik M. Ereglisi Izabe Tesisleri Plant (1)
Eksi Elma mevki Seymen Yolu 4 km Marmara Ereglisi, Tekirdag, Turkiye
Tel.: (90) 282 611 00 00
Steel Product Distr
N.A.I.C.S.: 423390

Kaptan Metal Dis Ticaret ve Nakliyat A.S. (1)
Fahrettin Kerim Gokay Cad Bestekar Saadettin Kaynak Sk No 2, Altunizade Uskudar,
Istanbul, 34662, Turkiye
Tel.: (90) 216 547 49 00
Web Site: http://www.kaptangroup.com.tr
Emp.: 20
Steel Product Distr
N.A.I.C.S.: 423390
Tayfun Cebi *(Gen Mgr)*

Martas Marmara Ereglisi Liman Tesisleri A.S. (1)
Fahrettin Kerim Gokay Cad Bestekar Saadettin Kaynak Sk No 2, Altunizade Uskudar,
Istanbul, Turkiye
Tel.: (90) 216 428 50 40
Steel Product Distr
N.A.I.C.S.: 423390

KARACHI STOCK EXCHANGE (GUARANTEE) LIMITED
Stock Exchange Bldg Stock Exchange Rd, Karachi, 74000, Pakistan
Tel.: (92) 21111001122
Web Site: http://www.kse.com.pk
Year Founded: 1947
Sales Range: $50-74.9 Million
Emp.: 250
Stock Exchange Services
N.A.I.C.S.: 523210
Nadeem Naqvi *(Mng Dir)*

KARADANOTE, INC.
MA Shibaura Building 6F 3-8-10
Shibaura, Minato-Ku, Tokyo, 108-
0023, Japan
Tel.: (81) 344313770
Web Site:
 https://www.corp.karadanote.jp
Year Founded: 2008
4014—(TKS)
Application Development Services
N.A.I.C.S.: 541511
Tatsuya Sato *(Founder & Pres)*

KARAFARIN BANK
N 97 Nahid Bd Vali-Asr Ave, PO Box
1966916461, Tehran, Iran
Tel.: (98) 212 3350
Web Site:
 http://www.karafarinbank.com
Year Founded: 1979
KRAF1—(THE)
Rev.: $1,550,919,420
Assets: $8,521,414,020
Liabilities: $7,359,210,380
Net Worth: $1,162,203,640
Earnings: $289,456,420
Emp.: 1,689
Fiscal Year-end: 03/20/21
Commercial Banking & Investment
Banking Services
N.A.I.C.S.: 523150
Mohamadreza Farzin *(Chm & CEO)*

Subsidiaries:

Abnieh Gostar Karafarin Co. (1)
2nd Floor No 53 Behzadi St Ejazi St, Zaferaniyeh, Tehran, Iran
Tel.: (98) 2122418929
Construction Projects Services
N.A.I.C.S.: 236220

Karafarin Bank Brokerage Co. (1)
No 8 Saba Blvd North Africa Blvd, Tehran,
Iran
Tel.: (98) 22655911021
Web Site: http://www.karafarinbrokerage.ir
Financial Investment Services

INTERNATIONAL PUBLIC

N.A.I.C.S.: 523940

Karafarin Bank Investment Co. (1)
5th Floor No 8 Saba Boulevard Africa Street
North, Tehran, Iran
Tel.: (98) 2122654870
Financial Investment Services
N.A.I.C.S.: 523940

Karafarin Foreign Exchange Co. (1)
No 6 8th Floor Karafarin Bank Building Ahmad Ghasir Street, Tehran, Iran
Tel.: (98) 2188550604
Foreign Currency Exchange Services
N.A.I.C.S.: 523160

Karafarin Leasing Co. (1)
Units 13 And 14 8th Floor No 8 Saba Boulevard, Tehran, Iran
Tel.: (98) 2122654671
Leasing Services
N.A.I.C.S.: 532112

KARAKAS ATLANTIS KIYMETLI MADENLER KUYUMCULUK TELEKOMUNIKASYON SANAYI VE TICARET A.S.
Akcay Caddesi No 283/A, Gaziemir,
Izmir, Turkiye
Tel.: (90) 232 274 22 22
Web Site:
 http://www.karakasatlantis.com
Year Founded: 1968
Jewelry Mfr
N.A.I.C.S.: 339910

KARAM CERAMICS LIMITED
A 31 S M C H S, Karachi, Pakistan
Tel.: (92) 2134555512
Web Site:
 https://www.karamceramics.com
Year Founded: 1979
KCL—(LAH)
Rev.: $10,334,133
Assets: $11,466,251
Liabilities: $6,974,839
Net Worth: $4,491,412
Earnings: $207,344
Emp.: 398
Fiscal Year-end: 06/30/19
Ceramic Tile Mfr
N.A.I.C.S.: 327120
Munawar Ali S. Kassim *(CEO)*

Subsidiaries:

Karam Ceramics Limited - Factory (1)
295/311 Deh Halkani Tappo, Mangopir
Road, Karachi, Sindh, Pakistan
Tel.: (92) 3442192790
Sales Range: $450-499.9 Million
Ceramic Tile Mfr
N.A.I.C.S.: 327120

KARAMOLEGOS BAKERY S.A.
Thesi Tzima, 19400, Koropi, Greece
Tel.: (30) 210 6694200
Web Site: http://www.karamolegos-bkr.gr
Year Founded: 1989
KMOL—(ATH)
Sales Range: $100-124.9 Million
Emp.: 617
Baked Goods Mfr & Distr
N.A.I.C.S.: 311812

KARAOLIS GROUP PUBLIC LTD
1 Anastasiou Sioukri Themis Tower
5th Floor, PO Box 53093, 3300, Limassol, Cyprus
Tel.: (357) 25 871871
Web Site:
 http://www.karaolisgroup.com
Year Founded: 1960
Real Estate Development Services
N.A.I.C.S.: 531390

AND PRIVATE COMPANIES

KARATZIS S.A.
Stelios Kazantzidis & Vosporou 2A Street, 71601, Iraklion, Crete, Greece
Tel.: (30) 2810 382900
Web Site: http://www.karatzis.gr
Year Founded: 1979
Rev.: $208,863,312
Assets: $268,250,279
Liabilities: $152,056,679
Net Worth: $116,193,600
Earnings: $8,429,751
Emp.: 443
Fiscal Year-end: 12/31/18
Netting Material Mfr
N.A.I.C.S.: 326199
Athina Karatzi *(Vice Chm)*

Subsidiaries:

Croppy Solutions SL (1)
C/ Montero Calvo 3 Piso 4, 47001, Valladolid, Spain
Tel.: (34) 983 299 718
Web Site: http://www.croppy.es
Packaging Materials Mfr
N.A.I.C.S.: 326199

Mesh Pack GmbH (1)
A-Rudow-Strasse, 38486, Klotze, Germany
Tel.: (49) 39005 93090
Web Site: http://www.meshpack.com
Emp.: 84
Packaging Materials Mfr
N.A.I.C.S.: 326199

PlusPack S.A. (1)
Industrial Area Building Block 12, Nea Alikarnassos, 71601, Greece
Tel.: (30) 2810 381666
Web Site: http://www.pluspack.gr
Emp.: 25
Packaging Products Mfr
N.A.I.C.S.: 326199
Zacharias Kefalogiannis *(Gen Mgr)*

KARAZHYRA JSC
Ul Bi Boranbaya 93, East Kazakhstan Oblast, 071412, Semey, Kazakhstan
Tel.: (7) 222302207
Web Site: https://karazhyra.kz
Year Founded: 2016
KZHR—(KAZ)
Rev.: $97,496,754
Assets: $56,152,699
Liabilities: $21,538,942
Net Worth: $34,613,758
Earnings: $11,167,532
Fiscal Year-end: 12/31/20
Coal Mining Services
N.A.I.C.S.: 213113

KARBALA HOTELS
Al-Sadoon St Sec 101 St 61 Buld 26, Baghdad, Iraq
Tel.: (964) 1 7183751
Year Founded: 1953
HKAR—(IRAQ)
Sales Range: Less than $1 Million
Home Management Services
N.A.I.C.S.: 721110

KARBOCHEM (PTY) LIMITED
Bunsen Street, Sasolburg, 9570, South Africa
Tel.: (27) 116011660 ZA
Web Site: http://www.latex-sa.co.za
Year Founded: 2005
Sales Range: $200-249.9 Million
Emp.: 400
Synthetic Latices Mfr
N.A.I.C.S.: 325212
Piet Johannes Steenkamp *(Exec Dir)*

Subsidiaries:

The Synthetic Latex Co (Pty) Ltd (1)
Eastgate Office Park S Blvd Rd Block A Ground Floor, South Boulevard, Johannesburg, Bruma, South Africa
Tel.: (27) 116011660
Synthetic Latices Mfr
N.A.I.C.S.: 325212

KARBON-X CORP.
510 5th St SW510 5th St SW, Calgary, T2P 3S2, AB, Canada NV
Web Site: https://karbon-x.com
Year Founded: 2017
KARX—(OTCIQ)
Rev.: $412,057
Assets: $3,970,582
Liabilities: $1,142,325
Net Worth: $2,828,257
Earnings: ($2,744,583)
Emp.: 7
Fiscal Year-end: 05/31/24
Personal Care Product Mfr & Distr
N.A.I.C.S.: 325620
Geoff Norman *(Treas & Sec)*

KARDAN N.V.
Kingsfordweg 151, 1043 GR, Amsterdam, Netherlands
Tel.: (31) 203050010 NI
Web Site: https://kardan.nl
KRNV.M—(TAE)
Rev.: $13,338,117
Assets: $190,281,488
Liabilities: $328,511,977
Net Worth: ($138,230,489)
Earnings: ($94,855,944)
Emp.: 132
Fiscal Year-end: 12/31/23
Miscellaneous Financial Investment Activities
N.A.I.C.S.: 523999
Einat Oz-Gabber *(CFO)*

Subsidiaries:

Durango Switzerland B.V. (1)
Kabelweg 21, Amsterdam, 1014 BA, Netherlands
Tel.: (31) 206828700
Sales Range: $50-74.9 Million
Emp.: 15
Trusts Estates & Agency Accounts
N.A.I.C.S.: 525920

GTC Investment B.V. (1)
Claude Debussylaan 30, Vinoly Building 13th Floor, 1082MD, Amsterdam, Netherlands
Tel.: (31) 203050010
Web Site: http://www.kardan.nl
New Housing Operative Builders
N.A.I.C.S.: 236117

Kardan Financial Services B.V. (1)
Decuserstraat 85 B, Amsterdam, 1081 CN, Netherlands (99.05%)
Tel.: (31) 203050010
Web Site: http://www.kardan.nl
Trusts Estates & Agency Accounts
N.A.I.C.S.: 525920

Kardan Real Estate Enterprise and Development Ltd. (1)
154 Menachem Begin Rd, Tel Aviv, Israel
Tel.: (972) 36083456
Web Site: http://www.kardan.nl
Real Estate Agents & Brokers
N.A.I.C.S.: 531210

Sitahal 'Hagal' (Talia) Partnership (1)
No 5 Arik Einstein Street, Or Yehuda, 6037505, Israel
Tel.: (972) 36924453
Web Site: http://www.kardan.com
Sales Range: $75-99.9 Million
Emp.: 350
Engineeering Services
N.A.I.C.S.: 541330

TMNG Ltd. (1)
7 Hatnufa, Petah Tikva, 4951025, Israel
Tel.: (972) 36924601
Web Site: http://www.tmng.co.il
Natural Gas & Engineering Design Services
N.A.I.C.S.: 541330

Tahal Group B.V. (1)
De Cuserstraat 85B, 1081 CN, Amsterdam, Netherlands
Tel.: (31) 203050010
Web Site: http://www.tahal.com
Sales Range: $50-74.9 Million
Emp.: 1,000
Trusts Estates & Agency Accounts
N.A.I.C.S.: 525920

Subsidiary (Non-US):

Eko-Wark Sp. Z.O.O. (2)
ul Kniewska 4, 70-846, Szczecin, Poland
Tel.: (48) 91 469 08 58
Web Site: http://www.ekowark.pl
Sales Range: $75-99.9 Million
Investment Management Service
N.A.I.C.S.: 523999

Palgey Maim Ltd. (2)
Maaele Hamigdal, Yokneam, 20600, Israel
Tel.: (972) 723201243
Web Site: https://www.palgey-maim.com
Engineeering Services
N.A.I.C.S.: 541330
Meirav Kedem *(CEO)*

Tahal Consulting Engineers Ltd. (2)
154 Menachem Begin Road, Tel Aviv, 64921, Israel
Tel.: (972) 36924434
Web Site: http://www.tahal.co.il
Engineeering Services
N.A.I.C.S.: 541330

Tahal Group International B.V. (1)
Claude Debussylaan 30 Vinoly Building 13th Floor, Amsterdam, 1082 MD, Netherlands
Tel.: (31) 203050010
Web Site: http://www.tahal.com
Engineeering Services
N.A.I.C.S.: 541330

Subsidiary (Domestic):

Tahal Group Assets B.V. (2)
Claude Debussylaan 30 Vinoly Building 13th Floor, Amsterdam, 1082, Netherlands
Tel.: (31) 203050010
Web Site: http://www.tahal.com
Asset Management Services
N.A.I.C.S.: 523940

Subsidiary (Non-US):

Dazhou Tianhe Water Supply and Drainage Co., Ltd. (3)
Natural Gas Energy Chemical Industries Zone, Dazhou, 635022, China
Tel.: (86) 8183561010
Water Supply & Drainage System Construction Services
N.A.I.C.S.: 221310

Subsidiary (Domestic):

Task Water B.V. (3)
Claude Debussylaan 30 Vinolyb 13e, Amsterdam, 1082 MD, Netherlands
Tel.: (31) 203050010
Waste Treatment Services
N.A.I.C.S.: 221310

KARDAN YAZAMUT (2011) LTD.
154 Menachem Begin Road, Tel Aviv, 64921, Israel
Tel.: (972) 3 608 3444
Year Founded: 2011
Rev.: $131,876,510
Assets: $315,653,950
Liabilities: $141,585,880
Net Worth: $174,068,071
Earnings: $26,114,528
Fiscal Year-end: 12/31/17
Real Estate Development Services
N.A.I.C.S.: 531390
Eytan Piotr Rechter *(CEO)*

Subsidiaries:

Kardan Israel Ltd. (1)
154 Menachem Begin Road, 64921, Tel Aviv, Israel
Tel.: (972) 36083444
Investment Services
N.A.I.C.S.: 523999
Eytan P. Rechter *(Mng Dir)*

KARDEMIR KARABUK DEMIR

KARDEX HOLDING AG

CELIK SANAYI VE TICARET A.S.
Fabrika Sahasi, 78170, Karabuk, Turkiye
Tel.: (90) 3704182001
Web Site: http://www.kardemir.com
KRDMA—(IST)
Rev.: $1,748,195,765
Assets: $2,030,789,715
Liabilities: $783,028,711
Net Worth: $1,247,761,004
Earnings: $53,776,772
Fiscal Year-end: 12/31/23
Steel Products Mfr
N.A.I.C.S.: 331110
Furkan Unal *(CFO & Exec VP)*

KARDEX HOLDING AG
Thurgauerstrasse 40, CH-8050, Zurich, Switzerland
Tel.: (41) 444194479
Web Site: https://www.kardex.com
KARN—(SWX)
Rev.: $559,463,320
Assets: $414,899,472
Liabilities: $176,743,736
Net Worth: $238,155,736
Earnings: $53,674,088
Emp.: 1,900
Fiscal Year-end: 12/31/21
Holding Company; Automated Storage Solutions & Materials Handling Systems Mfr
N.A.I.C.S.: 551112
Philipp Buhofer *(Chm)*

Subsidiaries:

KRM Service AG (1)
Thurgauerstrasse 40, 8050, Zurich, Switzerland
Tel.: (41) 444194411
Storage Solutions
N.A.I.C.S.: 337215

Kardex Austria GmbH (1)
Janis-Joplin-Promenade 26 Top 9, 1220, Vienna, Austria
Tel.: (43) 18958748
Web Site: http://www.kardex-remstar.at
Sales Range: $25-49.9 Million
Emp.: 20
Automated Storage Systems Retailer
N.A.I.C.S.: 423830
Manfred Schleicher *(Mng Dir)*

Kardex Danmark A/S (1)
Industrivej 10, 5260, Odense, Denmark
Tel.: (45) 66128224
Web Site: https://www.kardex-remstar.dk
Warehouse Vending Machine Operator
N.A.I.C.S.: 445132

Kardex Far East Private Ltd (1)
20 Collyer Quay 23-01, Singapore, 49319, Singapore
Tel.: (65) 60362064636
Sales Range: $25-49.9 Million
Emp.: 11
Automated Storage Systems Retailer
N.A.I.C.S.: 423830

Kardex Finland OY (1)
Piippukatu 11, 40100, Jyvaskyla, Finland
Tel.: (358) 207558250
Sales Range: $25-49.9 Million
Emp.: 20
Automated Storage Systems Mfr
N.A.I.C.S.: 333998

Kardex France SASU (1)
ZA la fontaine du Vaisseau 12 rue Edmond-Michelet, 93363, Neuilly-Plaisance, Cedex, France
Tel.: (33) 14 944 2626
Web Site: https://www.kardex-remstar.fr
Vending Machine Mfr
N.A.I.C.S.: 333310

Kardex Handling Solutions, LLC (1)
700 E Firmin St Ste 257, Kokomo, IN 46902
Web Site: https://www.kardexhandlingsolutions.com
Industrial Equipment Distr

4079

KARDEX HOLDING AG

Kardex Holding AG—(Continued)
N.A.I.C.S.: 423830

Kardex Hungaria Kft (1)
Szabadag Ut 117/A, 2040, Budaors, Hungary
Tel.: (36) 23507150
Web Site: http://www.kardex-remstar.hu
Sales Range: $50-74.9 Million
Emp.: 11
Automated Storage Systems Retailer
N.A.I.C.S.: 423830

Kardex India Storage Solutions Private Ltd (1)
Brigade Rubix 604 6th Floor HMT Watch Factory Road Peenya 1st Stage, Rajajinagar, Bengaluru, 560 022, Karnataka, India
Tel.: (91) 8029724470
Sales Range: $25-49.9 Million
Emp.: 35
Automated Storage Systems Retailer
N.A.I.C.S.: 423830

Kardex Italia S.p.A. (1)
Via Staffora 6, 20090, Opera, Milan, Italy
Tel.: (39) 0257603341
Web Site: http://www.kardex.com
Sales Range: $25-49.9 Million
Emp.: 30
Automated Storage Systems Retailer
N.A.I.C.S.: 423830

Kardex Logistic System (Beijing) Co. Ltd. (1)
Room B07 B1 Legend Star Plaza No 63 Xidawang Road, Chaoyang District, Beijing, China
Tel.: (86) 4008215388
Web Site: https://www.kardex.com.cn
Industrial Automation Services
N.A.I.C.S.: 541330

Kardex MLOG (1)
Wilhelm Maybach Strasse 2, 74196, Neuenstadt am Kocher, Germany
Tel.: (49) 713948930
Web Site: http://www.kardex-mlog.com
Sales Range: $50-74.9 Million
Emp.: 27
Materials Handling Systems Mfr & Planning & Maintenance Services for Logistics Industry
N.A.I.C.S.: 333248

Kardex Malaysia Sdn Bhd (1)
30-1 Premier Suite Menara 1MK 1 Jalan Kiara, Mont Kiara, 50480, Kuala Lumpur, Malaysia
Tel.: (60) 362064636
Logistic Services
N.A.I.C.S.: 541614

Kardex Norge AS (1)
Roseveien 1, 2007, Kjeller, Norway
Tel.: (47) 63947300
Web Site: https://www.kardex-remstar.no
Vending Machine Mfr
N.A.I.C.S.: 333310

Kardex Polska Sp. z o.o. (1)
Rzymowskiego 30, 02-697, Warsaw, Poland
Tel.: (48) 22 314 6959
Web Site: https://www.kardex-remstar.pl
Vending Machine Mfr
N.A.I.C.S.: 333310

Kardex Portugal, Unipessoal Lda. (1)
Rua Dom Antonio Barroso 11, 4050-060, Porto, Portugal
Tel.: (351) 91 730 5775
Web Site: https://www.kardex-remstar.pt
Vending Machine Mfr
N.A.I.C.S.: 333310

Kardex Produktion Deutschland GmbH (1)
Megamat-Platz 1, 86476, Neuburg an der Kammel, Germany
Tel.: (49) 82839990
Logistic Services
N.A.I.C.S.: 541614

Kardex Remstar Inc (1)
41 Eisenhower Dr, Westbrook, ME 04092-2032
Tel.: (207) 854-1861
Web Site: https://www.kardexremstar.com

Sales Range: $25-49.9 Million
Emp.: 50
Automated Office Storage Systems & Filing Systems Retailer
N.A.I.C.S.: 423830
Jens Fankhanel *(CFO)*

Subsidiary (Domestic):

Kardex Production USA Inc (2)
MCDIC Plz Bldg 35 6395 SR 103 N, Lewistown, PA 17044
Tel.: (717) 248-6000
Sales Range: $25-49.9 Million
Automated Office Storage Systems & Filing Systems Mfr
N.A.I.C.S.: 334112

Kardex Remstar SI d.o.o. (1)
Bleiweisova cesta 30, 1000, Ljubljana, Slovenia
Tel.: (386) 189587480
Logistic Services
N.A.I.C.S.: 541614

Kardex SASU ZA La Fontaine du Vaisseau (1)
ZA la Fontaine du Vaisseau 12 rue Edmond-Michelet, 93363, Neuilly-Plaisance, France
Tel.: (33) 1 49 44 26 26
Web Site: http://www.kardex-remstar.fr
Sales Range: $25-49.9 Million
Emp.: 75
Automated Storage Systems Mfr
N.A.I.C.S.: 334112

Kardex Scandinavia AB (1)
Vreemvagen 10, 168 69, Solna, Sweden
Tel.: (46) 8268565
Web Site: http://www.kardex.se
Sales Range: $50-74.9 Million
Emp.: 9
Automated Office Storage & Material Handling Systems Distr
N.A.I.C.S.: 423830
Ole Sverre Spigseth *(Mgr-Sls)*

Kardex Sistemas S.A (1)
Avda Castilla 1 Plta 1 Of 1, 28830, San Fernando de Henares, Madrid, Spain
Tel.: (34) 916779369
Web Site: http://www.kardex-remstar.es
Sales Range: $25-49.9 Million
Emp.: 28
Office Storage Systems & Filing Systems Distr
N.A.I.C.S.: 423830

Kardex South-America SAS (1)
Calle 110 No 9-25 oficina 702, 110111, Bogota, Colombia
Tel.: (57) 3004344735
Logistic Services
N.A.I.C.S.: 541614

Kardex Storage Systems, LLC (1)
11655 Central Pkwy Ste 313, Jacksonville, FL 32224
Web Site: https://kardexstoragesystems.com
Industrial Equipment Distr
N.A.I.C.S.: 423830

Kardex Sverige AB (1)
Fabriksgatan 7, 412 50, Gothenburg, Sweden
Tel.: (46) 31106600
Web Site: https://www.kardex-remstar.se
Vending Machine Mfr
N.A.I.C.S.: 333310

Kardex System AS (1)
Industriveien 25, Skedsmokorset, 2020, Norway
Tel.: (47) 63947300
Web Site: http://www.kardex.no
Sales Range: $25-49.9 Million
Emp.: 18
Automated Storage Systems Retailer
N.A.I.C.S.: 423830

Kardex Systems (UK) Ltd. (1)
Old London Road, Hertford, SG13 7LA, Hertfordshire, United Kingdom
Tel.: (44) 8449390800
Logistic Services
N.A.I.C.S.: 541614

Kardex Systems AG (1)

Chriesbaumstrasse 2, 8604, Volketswil, Switzerland
Tel.: (41) 449476111
Web Site: http://www.kardex-remstar.ch
Sales Range: $25-49.9 Million
Emp.: 43
Automated Office Storage Systems & Filing Systems Distr
N.A.I.C.S.: 423830

Subsidiary (Non-US):

Kardex Systems AG (2)
Tellikavak Sokak Calli Apt 20/4, Erenkoy, Istanbul, 34736, Turkiye
Tel.: (90) 216 386 8256
Web Site: http://www.kardex.com.tr
Sales Range: $25-49.9 Million
Emp.: 7
Automated Office Storage Systems & Filing Systems Distr
N.A.I.C.S.: 423830

Kardex Systems Ireland Ltd. (1)
Earlsfort Centre Earlsfort Terrace, Dublin, 2, Ireland
Tel.: (353) 99429356
Logistic Services
N.A.I.C.S.: 541614

Kardex Systems Ltd (1)
Iris House 8th Fl John Kennedy St, PO Box 53133, CY-3300, Limassol, Cyprus
Tel.: (357) 25875600
Web Site: http://www.kardex.com
Sales Range: $25-49.9 Million
Emp.: 11
Automated Storage Systems Mfr
N.A.I.C.S.: 333998

Kardex Systems Romania SRL (1)
Hanover Office BuildingBulevardul Cetatii etajul 2 no 5-7-9, Timis County, 30254, Timisoara, Romania
Tel.: (40) 256691198
Web Site: https://www.kardex-remstar.ro
Vending Machine Mfr
N.A.I.C.S.: 333310

Kardex Systems bv (1)
PO Box 250, 3440 AG, Woerden, Netherlands
Tel.: (31) 348494040
Web Site: http://www.kardex.nl
Sales Range: $25-49.9 Million
Emp.: 43
Automated Storage Systems Retailer
N.A.I.C.S.: 423830

Kardex Turkey Depolama Sistemleri Ltd. Sti. (1)
19 Mayis Mah Inonu Cad Seylan is Merkezi No 83/3, Kozyatagi Kadikoy, 34736, Istanbul, Turkiye
Tel.: (90) 2163868256
Web Site: https://www.kardex-remstar.com.tr
Vending Machine Mfr
N.A.I.C.S.: 333310

Kardex VCA Pty Ltd (1)
174 Victoria Cross Parade, PO Box 1082, Wodonga, 3690, VIC, Australia
Tel.: (61) 260561202
Web Site: http://www.kvca.com.au
Sales Range: $25-49.9 Million
Emp.: 19
Automated Storage Systems Mfr & Distr
N.A.I.C.S.: 333998

Kardex s.r.o. (1)
Petrska 1136/12, 11000, Prague, Czech Republic
Tel.: (420) 595701180
Web Site: http://www.kardex-remstar.cz
Sales Range: $25-49.9 Million
Emp.: 25
Automated Storage Systems Mfr
N.A.I.C.S.: 334112

S.A. Kardex nv (1)
155 rue Saint-Denis, 1190, Forest, Belgium
Tel.: (32) 23401080
Web Site: http://www.kardex.be
Sales Range: $25-49.9 Million
Emp.: 17
Automated Storage Systems Mfr
N.A.I.C.S.: 334112

Storage Solution Iberica S.L. (1)
C Solsones 2 Edificio Prima Muntades Local C1 2A Planta Escalera B, 08820, El Prat

INTERNATIONAL PUBLIC

de Llobregat, Barcelona, Spain
Tel.: (34) 934 736 794
Automated Storage Systems Retailer
N.A.I.C.S.: 423830

Stow U.K. Co. Ltd (1)
Unit 7 Copsefarm Lancaster Pl South Marston Indus Estate, Swindon, SN4UQ, Wiltshire, United Kingdom
Tel.: (44) 8452013540
Web Site: http://www.stowuk.com
Sales Range: $25-49.9 Million
Emp.: 8
Racking Systems Mfr
N.A.I.C.S.: 334112

KAREL ELEKTRONIK SANAYI VE TICARET A.S.

Ankara Teknoloji Gelistirme Bolgesi, Cyberplaza B Blok Kat 3, 6800, Ankara, Turkiye
Tel.: (90) 3122650290
Web Site: https://www.karel.com.tr
Year Founded: 1986
KAREL—(IST)
Rev.: $320,310,921
Assets: $280,043,259
Liabilities: $194,212,475
Net Worth: $85,830,783
Earnings: $9,869,319
Fiscal Year-end: 12/31/23
Telecommunication Equipment Mfr & Distr
N.A.I.C.S.: 334220

KARELIA TOBACCO COMPANY INC.

Athinon Street, 241 00, Kalamata, Greece
Tel.: (30) 2721069213
Web Site: https://www.karelia.gr
Year Founded: 1888
KARE—(ATH)
Rev.: $1,365,998,273
Assets: $861,435,355
Liabilities: $150,106,842
Net Worth: $711,328,513
Earnings: $92,123,894
Emp.: 552
Fiscal Year-end: 12/31/22
Cigarette & Other Tobacco Product Mfr & Distr
N.A.I.C.S.: 312230
Andrew G. Karelias *(Mng Dir)*

Subsidiaries:

Karelia Bulgaria EOOD (1)
Bellissimo Business Center 102 Bulgaria Blvd Office 18, 1680, Sofia, Bulgaria
Tel.: (359) 28548023
Tobacco Product Mfr & Distr
N.A.I.C.S.: 312230

Karelia Investment S.A (1)
Athinon Street, 241 00, Kalamata, Greece
Tel.: (30) 2721069213
Sales Range: $100-124.9 Million
Emp.: 500
Cigarette Mfr & Exporter
N.A.I.C.S.: 312230

Karelia Tobacco Company (UK) Ltd. (1)
Parkshot House 5 Kew Rd, Richmond, TW9 2PR, Surrey, United Kingdom
Tel.: (44) 2083348353
Emp.: 4
Cigarette Mfr & Exporters
N.A.I.C.S.: 312230

Karelia Tutun ve Ticaret A.S (1)
Tel.: (90) 2122242777
Sales Range: $25-49.9 Million
Emp.: 1
Cigarette Mfr
N.A.I.C.S.: 312230

Meridian SA (1)
120 Athinon Ave, Athens, 10442, Greece
Tel.: (30) 21051547423
Sales Range: $25-49.9 Million
Emp.: 10
Cigarette Mfr & Exporter

AND PRIVATE COMPANIES

N.A.I.C.S.: 312230
Estapaio Karelias *(Mng Dir)*

KARELIAN DIAMOND RE-SOURCES PLC
3300 Lake Drive Citywest Business Campus, Dublin, D24 TD21, Ireland
Tel.: (353) 14796180
Web Site:
https://www.kareliandiamond.com
Year Founded: 2005
KDR—(AIM)
Assets: $12,368,805
Liabilities: $1,807,534
Net Worth: $10,561,271
Earnings: ($314,555)
Emp.: 2
Fiscal Year-end: 05/31/23
Diamond Exploration Company
N.A.I.C.S.: 212390
Maureen T. A. Jones *(Mng Dir & Sec)*

KAREX BERHAD
Lot 594 Persiaran Raja Lumu, Pandamaran Industrial Estate, 42000, Port Klang, Selangor, Malaysia
Tel.: (60) 331656688
Web Site: https://www.karex.com.my
Year Founded: 1988
KAREX—(KLS)
Rev.: $112,606,561
Assets: $152,746,032
Liabilities: $51,885,291
Net Worth: $100,860,741
Earnings: $2,217,566
Emp.: 3,494
Fiscal Year-end: 06/30/23
Latex Condoms, Lubricants & Medical Devices Mfr
N.A.I.C.S.: 326299
Miah Kiat Goh *(CEO)*

Subsidiaries:

Global Protection Corp. (1)
12 Channel St, Boston, MA 02210 **(70%)**
Tel.: (617) 946-2800
Web Site: http://www.globalprotection.com
Condom Mfr
N.A.I.C.S.: 326299
Davin T. Wedel *(Founder & Pres)*

Innolatex Sdn. Bhd. (1)
Lot 594 Persiaran Raja Lumu, Pandamaran Industrial Estate, 42000, Port Klang, Selangor, Malaysia
Tel.: (60) 331680702
Web Site: https://www.innoltx.com
Latex Condom & Rubber Product Mfr
N.A.I.C.S.: 326299

Medical-Latex (DUA) Sdn. Bhd. (1)
Plo 8 Senai Industrial Estate, 81400, Senai, Johor, Malaysia **(100%)**
Tel.: (60) 75978100
Web Site: https://www.medicallatex.com
Condoms Mfr & Sales
N.A.I.C.S.: 424210

KARIN TECHNOLOGY HOLDINGS LIMITED
9th Floor The Whitney 183 Wai Yip Street Kwun Tong, Kowloon, China (Hong Kong)
Tel.: (852) 27633188
Web Site:
https://investor.karingroup.com
K29—(SES)
Rev.: $257,000,647
Assets: $157,000,518
Liabilities: $102,448,427
Net Worth: $54,552,091
Earnings: $2,413,603
Fiscal Year-end: 06/30/22
Electronic Components Distr
N.A.I.C.S.: 334416
Desmond Yiu chown Leung *(CTO & Gen Mgr-IT Infrastructure Div)*

Subsidiaries:

Compucon Computers Limited (1)
8F The Whitney 183 Wai Yip Street, Kwun Tong, Kowloon, China (Hong Kong)
Tel.: (852) 39969624
Web Site: https://www.compucon.com.hk
Electronic Equipment Distr
N.A.I.C.S.: 423690

Compusmart Limited (1)
1 F Karin Building 166 Wai Yip Street, Kwun Tong, Kowloon, China (Hong Kong)
Tel.: (852) 27633207
Computer Peripheral Equipment Distr
N.A.I.C.S.: 423430

IMI Kabel Pte. Ltd. (1)
No 3 Ang Mo Kio Street 62 01-40 Link AMK, Singapore, 569139, Singapore
Tel.: (65) 64880355
Web Site: http://www.imi-kabel.com
Sales Range: $25-49.9 Million
Emp.: 7
Electrical Cables Mfr
N.A.I.C.S.: 335999

Karga Solutions Limited (1)
6/F Karin Building 166 Wai Yip Street, Kwun Tong, Kowloon, China (Hong Kong)
Tel.: (852) 29960430
Web Site: http://www.karingroup.com
Sales Range: $25-49.9 Million
Emp.: 25
Software Development Consulting Services
N.A.I.C.S.: 541618

Karin Electronic Supplies Company Limited (1)
9/F The Whitney 183 Wai Yip Street, Kwun Tong, Kowloon, China (Hong Kong)
Tel.: (852) 23898252
Web Site: http://www.karin.com.hk
Sales Range: $50-74.9 Million
Emp.: 100
Electronic Product Distr
N.A.I.C.S.: 423690

Karin Electronic Trading (Shenzhen) Co., Ltd. (1)
Unit 604 6/F East Block ShengTang Building 1 TaiRan Ninth Road, Futian District, Shenzhen, 518040, Guangdong, China
Tel.: (86) 75561677888
Electronic Components Distr
N.A.I.C.S.: 423690

Karin International Trading (Shanghai) Co., Ltd. (1)
Unit 2007 20/F Tower 1 Kerry Everbright City 218 Tian Mu Road West, Jing An District, Shanghai, 200070, China
Tel.: (86) 2150101668
Web Site: http://www.karingroup.com
Electronic Components Distr
N.A.I.C.S.: 423690

Kepro Solutions Limited (1)
9/F The Whitney 183 Wai Yip Street, Kwun Tong, Kowloon, China (Hong Kong)
Tel.: (852) 27633180
Web Site: http://www.kepro.com.hk
Sales Range: $25-49.9 Million
Emp.: 100
Software Retailer
N.A.I.C.S.: 449210

New Spirit Electronic Technology Development (Shenzhen) Co., Ltd. (1)
Unit 604 6/F East Block ShengTang Building 1 TaiRan Ninth Road, Futian District, Shenzhen, 518040, Guangdong, China
Tel.: (86) 75561677888
Web Site: http://www.karingroup.com
Integrated Circuit Software Development Services
N.A.I.C.S.: 541511

New Spirit Technology Limited (1)
9/F The Whitney 183 Wai Yip Street, Kwun Tong, Kowloon, China (Hong Kong)
Tel.: (852) 27633211
Web Site: http://www.newspirit.hk
Sales Range: $25-49.9 Million
Emp.: 100
Integrated Circuit Software Development Services
N.A.I.C.S.: 541511

Sen Spirit Technology Limited (1)
9/F The Whitney 183 Wai Yip Street, Kwun Tong, Kowloon, China (Hong Kong)
Tel.: (852) 27633154
Web Site: http://www.sstech.com.hk
Packaged Software Retailer
N.A.I.C.S.: 449210

KARINE
13 Rue Tissier, Paris, 75002, France
Tel.: (33) 145482124
Sales Range: $10-24.9 Million
Emp.: 11
Footwear
N.A.I.C.S.: 458210
Joseph Nakam *(Mng Dir)*

KARINGAL ST LAURENCE LIMITED
21-29 Reynolds Road, Belmont, 3216, VIC, Australia
Tel.: (61) 1300558368
Web Site: https://www.genu.org.au
Emp.: 100
Non Profit Organization
N.A.I.C.S.: 561499

Subsidiaries:

IPA Personnel Services Pty. Ltd. (1)
Level 5 350 Collins Street, Melbourne, 3000, VIC, Australia
Tel.: (61) 392522222
Web Site: http://www.ipa.com.au
Recruitment Consulting Services
N.A.I.C.S.: 541612
Paul Barbaro *(COO)*

KARK AG
Cuxhavener Strasse 60ab, 21149, Hamburg, Germany
Tel.: (49) 4079700440
Web Site: http://www.kark.de
Rev.: $41,382,000
Emp.: 7
Aluminum Component Mfr
N.A.I.C.S.: 331318
Matthias Kark *(CEO)*

KARKOTIS MANUFACTURING AND TRADING PUBLIC LTD.
4 Eleftherias Street, PO Box 24571, Agios Dometios, 2369, Nicosia, Cyprus
Tel.: (357) 22 775557
Web Site: http://www.karkotis.com.cy
Year Founded: 1975
Food Products Mfr & Whslr
N.A.I.C.S.: 311999
Christos Karkotis *(Founder)*

KARL BAISCH GMBH
Lagerhausstr 17A, Plattling, 944447, Germany
Tel.: (49) 9931890070
Web Site: http://www.baisch.de
Year Founded: 1907
Rev.: $22,566,984
Emp.: 130
Dental Furniture Mfr
N.A.I.C.S.: 337127
Achim Bickelmann *(Mng Dir)*

KARL E. BRINKMANN GMBH
Foersterweg 36 - 38, Barntrup, 32683, Germany
Tel.: (49) 52634010
Web Site: http://www.keb.de
Year Founded: 1972
Rev.: $114,490,200
Emp.: 730
Electric Equipment Mfr
N.A.I.C.S.: 334419
Vittorio Tavella *(Mng Dir)*

Subsidiaries:

KEB (UK) Ltd. (1)
Morris Close Park Farm Industrial Estate, Northants, Wellingborough, NN8 6 XF, United Kingdom
Tel.: (44) 1933402220
Web Site: http://www.keb.co.uk
Electronic Products Mfr
N.A.I.C.S.: 333612
Tom Skelton *(CEO)*

KEB Antriebstechnik Austria GmbH (1)
Ritzstrasse 8, 4614, Marchtrenk, Austria
Tel.: (43) 7243535860
Electronic Product Distr
N.A.I.C.S.: 459110

KEB Antriebstechnik GmbH (1)
Getriebemotorenwerk Wildbacher Str 5, 08289, Berlin, Germany
Tel.: (49) 3772670
Emp.: 150
Electronic Products Mfr
N.A.I.C.S.: 333612
A. Bornhoeft *(Mgr-Application Sls)*

KEB Italia S.r.l. (1)
Via Newton 2, Settimo Milanese, 20019, Milan, Italy
Tel.: (39) 023353531
Emp.: 40
Electronic Product Distr
N.A.I.C.S.: 459110
Macro Meneguzzi *(Mgr-Area)*

KEB Japan Ltd. (1)
15 - 16 2-Chome, Takanawa Minato-ku, Tokyo, 108 - 0074, Japan
Tel.: (81) 334458515
Emp.: 40
Electronic Products Mfr
N.A.I.C.S.: 333612

KEB Power Transmission Technology (Shanghai) Co., Ltd. (1)
No 435 QianPu Road Chedun Town, Songjiang, 201611, Shanghai, China
Tel.: (86) 2137746688
Emp.: 80
Electronic Products Mfr
N.A.I.C.S.: 333612
Sammi Cai *(Mgr-HR)*

KEB RUS Ltd. (1)
st Lesnaya 30 building 1, Dzerzhinsky, 140093, Moscow, Russia
Tel.: (7) 4956320217
Web Site: http://keb.ru
Electronic Product Distr
N.A.I.C.S.: 459110

Societe Francaise Keb Sasu (1)
Z I de la Croix St Nicolas 14 rue Gustave Eiffel, 94510, La Queue-en-Brie, France
Tel.: (33) 149620101
Emp.: 42
Electronic Product Distr
N.A.I.C.S.: 459110

KARL GROSS INTERNATIONALE SPEDITION GMBH
Martinistrasse 34, D-28195, Bremen, Germany
Tel.: (49) 42117620
Web Site: http://www.karlgross.de
Year Founded: 1876
Rev.: $41,382,000
Emp.: 91
Freight & Logistics Services
N.A.I.C.S.: 488510
Martin Kollmann *(Co-Mng Dir)*

Subsidiaries:

Karl Gross Egypt (LTD) (1)
Al Mehwar St - Building No 22 A Zone 10th - Area No 1, 6th of October City, Egypt
Tel.: (20) 239123642
Logistics Consulting Servies
N.A.I.C.S.: 541614
Raed Assaad Hanna *(Mng Dir)*

Karl Gross International B.V. (1)
Steenhouwer Straat 50, Hoogvliet, 3194 AG, Rotterdam, Netherlands
Tel.: (31) 102981800
Web Site: http://www.karlgross.nl
Logistics Consulting Servies
N.A.I.C.S.: 541614
Jeroen van der Ploeg *(Supvr-Ops)*

Karl Gross Logistics (Shanghai) Co., Ltd. (1)

KARL GROSS INTERNATIONALE SPEDITION GMBH

INTERNATIONAL PUBLIC

Karl Gross Internationale Spedition GmbH—(Continued)
1701 Gang Tai Plaza 700 East Yan'an Road, 200001, Shanghai, China
Tel.: (86) 2163521037
Web Site: http://www.karlgross.com.cn
Logistics Consulting Servies
N.A.I.C.S.: 541614
Martin Kollmann (Mng Dir)

Karl Gross Logistics Viet Nam Co., Ltd. (1)
Ha Do South Building 10th floor Room 1003 60M Truong Son Street, Ward 2 District, Ho Chi Minh City, Vietnam
Tel.: (84) 835470318
Web Site: http://www.karlgross.vn
Logistics Consulting Servies
N.A.I.C.S.: 541614
Lam Thi Thanh Bong (CEO)

KARL JUNGBLUTH KETTEN-FABRIK GMBH & CO. KG
Alsfelderstrasse 73, D-36251, Bad Hersfeld, Germany
Tel.: (49) 662192940
Web Site: http://www.jungbluth-ketten.de
Emp.: 175
Conveyor Chains & Chain Wheels Mfr
N.A.I.C.S.: 333922
Dietmar Schaefer (Mng Dir)

KARL MAYER TEXTILMASCHI-NENFABRIK GMBH
Bruhlstrasse 25, 63179, Obertshausen, Germany
Tel.: (49) 6104 4020
Web Site: http://www.karlmayer.com
Year Founded: 1937
Rev.: $335,343,200
Emp.: 2,300
Textile Machinery Mfr
N.A.I.C.S.: 333248
Helmut Pressl (Mng Dir)

Subsidiaries:

KARL MAYER (CHINA) LTD. (1)
518 South Changwu Rd, Wujin District, Changzhou, 213 166, Jiangsu, China
Tel.: (86) 51986198888
Textile Machinery Distr
N.A.I.C.S.: 423830

KARL MAYER (H.K.) LTD. (1)
2301 23Fl Metroplaza Tower 2 223 Hing Fong Road, Kwai Chung, China (Hong Kong)
Tel.: (852) 27239262
Textile Machinery Distr
N.A.I.C.S.: 423830

KARL MAYER India Private Limited (1)
Bhagwati House A -19 CTS No 689 Veera Desai Road, Andheri West, Mumbai, 400 053, India
Tel.: (91) 2266766172
Textile Machinery Distr
N.A.I.C.S.: 423830

KARL MAYER LIBA Textilmaschinenfabrik GmbH (1)
Oberklingensporn 1, 95119, Naila, Germany
Tel.: (49) 9282670
Web Site: http://www.liba.de
Textile Machinery Mfr
N.A.I.C.S.: 333248
Karlheinz Liebrandt (Mng Dir)

KARL MAYER Malimo Textilmaschinenfabrik GmbH (1)
Mauersbergerstrasse 2, 09117, Chemnitz, Germany
Tel.: (49) 37181430
Textile Machinery Mfr
N.A.I.C.S.: 333248

KARL MAYER R&D GmbH (1)
Bruehlstrasse 25, 63179, Obertshausen, Germany
Tel.: (49) 61044020
Textile Products Mfr
N.A.I.C.S.: 314999

KARL MAYER ROTAL S.r.l. (1)
Via trento No 117, 38017, Mezzolombardo, Trentino, Italy
Tel.: (39) 0461608611
Textile Machinery Distr
N.A.I.C.S.: 423830

KARL MAYER Textile Machinery India Private Limited (1)
Sarkhej Bavala Road, 382213, Ahmedabad, India
Tel.: (91) 9727754322
Textile Products Mfr
N.A.I.C.S.: 314999
Vishal Bhalla (Mgr)

KARL MAYER Textile Machinery Ltd. (1)
Kings Road, Shepshed, LE12 9HT, Leicestershire, United Kingdom
Tel.: (44) 1509502056
Web Site: http://www.karlmayer.co.uk
Textile Machinery Distr
N.A.I.C.S.: 423830
Tony Hooimeijer (Mng Dir)

KARL MAYER Textilmaschinen AG (1)
Fabrikstrasse, 9240, Uzwil, Switzerland
Tel.: (41) 719558400
Textile Machinery Distr
N.A.I.C.S.: 423830

KM.ON GmbH (1)
Carl-Benz-Strasse 21, 60386, Frankfurt am Main, Germany
Tel.: (49) 6926945504
Web Site: http://www.kmon.net
Textile Products Mfr
N.A.I.C.S.: 314999
Sophia Antonia Gottschalk (Mng Dir)

Mayer Textile Machine Corp. (1)
310 N Chimney Rock Rd, Greensboro, NC 27409
Tel.: (336) 294-1572
Industrial Machinery & Equipment Distr
N.A.I.C.S.: 423830

NIPPON MAYER Ltd. (1)
No 27-33 1-chome Kamikitan, Fukui, 918-8522, Japan
Tel.: (81) 7765455006
Textile Machinery Distr
N.A.I.C.S.: 423830

KARL STORZ GMBH & CO.
Dr Karl Storz Strasse 34, 78532, Tuttlingen, Germany
Tel.: (49) 74617080
Web Site: http://www.karlstorz.com
Year Founded: 1980
Sales Range: $350-399.9 Million
Emp.: 1,800
Medical Equipment Mfr
N.A.I.C.S.: 423450

Subsidiaries:

KARL STORZ Adria Eos d.o.o. (1)
Zadarska 80, 10000, Zagreb, Croatia
Tel.: (385) 1 6406070
Web Site: http://www.karlstorz.com
Emp.: 1
Medical Equipment Mfr
N.A.I.C.S.: 423450

KARL STORZ Endoscopia (1)
Miramar Trade Center, Edificio Jerusalem Oficina 108, Havana, Cuba
Tel.: (53) 72 041097
Web Site: http://www.karlstorz.com
Emp.: 3
Medical Equipment Mfr
N.A.I.C.S.: 423450
Leopoldo Cano (Mgr)

KARL STORZ Endoscopia Argentina S.A. (1)
Zufriategui 627, Vicente Lopez, Buenos Aires, Argentina
Tel.: (54) 11 47180919
Web Site: http://www.karlstorz.com
Medical Equipment Mfr
N.A.I.C.S.: 423450

KARL STORZ Endoscopia Iberica S.A. (1)
Parque Empresarial San Fernando, Edificio Munich, 28830, Madrid, Spain
Tel.: (34) 91 677 1051
Medical Equipment Mfr
N.A.I.C.S.: 423450

KARL STORZ Endoscopia Italia S.r.l. (1)
Via dell' Artigianato 3, 37135, Verona, Italy
Tel.: (39) 045 8222000
Web Site: http://www.karlstorz.com
Emp.: 30
Medical Equipment Mfr
N.A.I.C.S.: 423450

KARL STORZ Endoscopia Mexico S.A. de C.V. (1)
Lago Constanza No 326 Col Chapultepec Morales, Mexico, 11520, Mexico
Tel.: (52) 55 52505607
Medical Equipment Mfr
N.A.I.C.S.: 423450

KARL STORZ Endoscopia ROMANIA srl (1)
Str Prof Dr Anton Colorian Nr 74 Sector 4, 041393, Bucharest, Romania
Tel.: (40) 31 4250800
Web Site: http://www.karlstorz.com
Emp.: 20
Medical Equipment Mfr
N.A.I.C.S.: 423450
Cristian Turcu (Gen Mgr)

KARL STORZ Endoscopie France S.A. (1)
12 Rue Georges Guynemer, Quartier de l'Europe, 78280, Guyancourt, France
Tel.: (33) 1 30484200
Medical Equipment Mfr
N.A.I.C.S.: 423450

KARL STORZ Endoscopija d.o.o. (1)
Verovskova c. 60A, 1000, Ljubljana, Slovenia
Tel.: (386) 1 620 5880
Medical Equipment Mfr
N.A.I.C.S.: 423450

KARL STORZ Endoscopy (Shanghai) Ltd., (1)
Unit 3901-3904 Tower 1 Grand Gateway, No 1 Hong Qiao Road, Shanghai, 200030, China
Tel.: (86) 21 61131188
Web Site: http://www.karlstorz.com.cn
Medical Equipment Mfr
N.A.I.C.S.: 423450

KARL STORZ Endoscopy (South Africa) (Pty) Ltd. (1)
Roggebaai, Cape Town, 8012, South Africa
Tel.: (27) 21 4172600
Medical Equipment Mfr
N.A.I.C.S.: 423450

KARL STORZ Endoscopy (UK) Ltd. (1)
392 Edinburgh Avenue, Slough, SL1 4UF, Berkshire, United Kingdom
Tel.: (44) 1753 503500
Medical Equipment Mfr
N.A.I.C.S.: 423450

KARL STORZ Endoscopy Asia Marketing Pte. Ltd. (1)
8 Commonwealth Lane, 06-11 e-Centre, Singapore, 149555, Singapore
Tel.: (65) 63 761066
Medical Equipment Mfr
N.A.I.C.S.: 423450
Thorsten Molitor (Mng Dir)

KARL STORZ Endoscopy Australia Pty. Ltd. (1)
15 Orion Road, Lane Cove, 2066, NSW, Australia
Tel.: (61) 2 94906700
Medical Equipment Mfr
N.A.I.C.S.: 423450

KARL STORZ Endoscopy Canada Ltd. (1)
7171 Millcreek Dr, Mississauga, L5N 3R3, ON, Canada
Tel.: (905) 816-4500
Medical Equipment Mfr

KARL STORZ Endoscopy China Ltd., (1)
Unit 1601 Chinachem Exchange Square, 1 Hoi Wan Street, Hong Kong, China (Hong Kong)
Tel.: (852) 28 652411
Medical Equipment Mfr
N.A.I.C.S.: 423450

KARL STORZ Endoscopy Gulf & Near East (1)
Villa #7 Mushrif Business Park, Abu Dhabi, United Arab Emirates
Tel.: (971) 2 4477593
Medical Equipment Mfr
N.A.I.C.S.: 423450

KARL STORZ Endoscopy India Private Ltd. (1)
181 Okhla Industrial Area, 110 020, New Delhi, India
Tel.: (91) 11 26815445 49
Medical Equipment Mfr
N.A.I.C.S.: 423450

KARL STORZ Endoscopy Japan K. K. (1)
Stage Building 8/F 2-7-2 Fujimi, Chiyoda-ku, Tokyo, 102-0071, Japan
Tel.: (81) 3 63808622
Medical Equipment Mfr
N.A.I.C.S.: 423450

KARL STORZ Endoscopy Korea Co. Ltd. (1)
Jeljon Tower 1 Suite 905 16 Neuti-ro, Bundang-gu, 463-847, Seongnam, Korea (South)
Tel.: (82) 70 4350 7474
Medical Device Distr
N.A.I.C.S.: 423450
Stephen Namkoo Lee (Country Mgr)

KARL STORZ Endoscopy Singapore Sales Pte. Ltd. (1)
No 8 Commonwealth Lane 03-02, Singapore, 149555, Singapore
Tel.: (65) 69229150
Web Site: http://www.karlstorz.com
Emp.: 20
Medical Device Distr
N.A.I.C.S.: 423450
Ronald Gundran (Engr-Technical Svc)

KARL STORZ Endoscopy Suomi OY (1)
Italahdenkatu 23a, 00210, Helsinki, Finland
Tel.: (358) 896824774
Medical Equipment Mfr
N.A.I.C.S.: 423450

KARL STORZ Endoscopy Taiwan Ltd. (1)
6F-1 No. 10 Sec. 1 Beisin Rd, Sindian, Taipei, Taiwan
Tel.: (886) 933014160
Medical Equipment Mfr
N.A.I.C.S.: 423450

KARL STORZ Endoskop Austria GmbH (1)
Landstrarer Hauptstr 148/1/G1, 1030, Vienna, Austria
Tel.: (43) 1 71560470
Medical Equipment Mfr
N.A.I.C.S.: 423450

KARL STORZ Endoskop Sverige AB (1)
Storsatragrand 14, 12724, Skarholmen, Sweden
Tel.: (46) 8 50564800
Emp.: 30
Medical Equipment Mfr
N.A.I.C.S.: 423450
Christer Volten (CEO)

KARL STORZ Endoskope Berlin GmbH (1)
Scharnhorstrasse 3, Berlin, 10115, Germany
Tel.: (49) 30 306909 0
Medical Equipment Mfr
N.A.I.C.S.: 423450

KARL STORZ Endoskope Greece Ltd. (1)

Patriarchou Gregoriou Strasse 32, 54248, Thessaloniki, Greece
Tel.: (30) 2310 304868
Web Site: http://www.karlstorz.com
Emp.: 6
Medical Equipment Mfr
N.A.I.C.S.: 423450
Turcu Christian *(Gen Mgr)*

KARL STORZ Endoskope Greece M.E.P.E. (1)
Sokratous & Kyprou 2, 15127, Athens, Greece
Tel.: (30) 210 6131 386
Medical Equipment Mfr
N.A.I.C.S.: 423450

KARL STORZ Endoskope, Regional Center for Endoscopy S.A.L. (1)
Soldiere Beirut Souks, Block M 3rd Floor, Beirut, Lebanon
Tel.: (961) 1 999390
Medical Equipment Mfr
N.A.I.C.S.: 423450

KARL STORZ Endoskopi Denmark A/S (1)
Skovlytoften 33, 2840, Holte, Denmark
Tel.: (45) 45 162600
Web Site: http://www.karlstorz.com
Emp.: 18
Medical Equipment Mfr & Distr
N.A.I.C.S.: 334516
Morten Ralbjerg *(Gen Mgr)*

KARL STORZ Endoskopi Norge AS (1)
Stamveien 1, 1481, Hagan, Norway
Tel.: (47) 63805600
Web Site: http://www.karlstorz.com
Emp.: 15
Medical Equipment Mfr
N.A.I.C.S.: 423450
Haakan Bay-Eriksson *(Mgr)*

KARL STORZ Endoszkop Magyarorszag Kft. (1)
Toberek utca 2 fsz 17/b, 1112, Budapest, Hungary
Tel.: (36) 195 096 31
Medical Device Distr
N.A.I.C.S.: 423450

KARL STORZ GmbH & Co. KG (1)
80/33 (44/19) Dang Van Ngu, F 10 - Q Phu Nhuan, Ho Chi Minh City, Vietnam
Tel.: (84) 8 991 8442
Medical Equipment Mfr
N.A.I.C.S.: 423450

KARL STORZ Industrial (1)
Gedik Is Merkezi B Blok, Kat 5 D 38-39
Bagdat, Istanbul, Turkiye
Tel.: (90) 216 442 9500
Medical Equipment Mfr
N.A.I.C.S.: 423450

KARL STORZ Marketing America Do Sul Ltda. (1)
Rua Joaquin Floriano, 20th Floor, Sao Paulo, 04534-011, Brazil
Tel.: (55) 11 3526 4600
Web Site: http://www.karlstorz.com
Emp.: 16
Medical Equipment Mfr
N.A.I.C.S.: 423450
Anton Achen *(Gen Mgr)*

KARL STORZ Video Endoscopy Estonia OU (1)
Akadeemia tee 21A, Tallinn, Estonia
Tel.: (372) 6397018
Web Site: http://www.karlstorz.ee
Medical Device Distr
N.A.I.C.S.: 423450
Silvi Kaldoja *(Mgr-HR)*

Karl Storz Endoscopia Latino America Inc. (1)
815 NW 57th Ave Ste 480, Miami, FL 33126-2042
Tel.: (305) 262-8980
Web Site: http://www.karlstorz.com
Sales Range: $50-74.9 Million
Emp.: 10
Provider of Endoscopic Surgical Instruments
N.A.I.C.S.: 423450
Claudio Armesto *(Mgr-Mktg & Sls-Latin America)*

Karl Storz Endoscopy-America, Inc. (1)
2151 E Grand Ave, El Segundo, CA 90245 (100%)
Tel.: (310) 338-8100
Web Site: http://www.karlstorz.com
Sales Range: $300-349.9 Million
Emp.: 576
Mfr of Endoscopic Surgical Instruments
N.A.I.C.S.: 423450
Diane Theodora Spurlock *(Mgr-Compensation & Benefits)*

Subsidiary (Domestic):

Asensus Surgical, Inc. (2)
1 TW Alexander Dr Ste 160, Durham, NC 27703
Tel.: (919) 765-8400
Web Site: https://www.asensus.com
Rev.: $7,087,000
Assets: $116,053,000
Liabilities: $16,408,000
Net Worth: $99,645,000
Earnings: ($75,561,000)
Emp.: 183
Fiscal Year-end: 12/31/2022
Medical Device Mfr
N.A.I.C.S.: 339112
Kathleen Frost *(VP-Intellectual Property)*

Subsidiary (Non-US):

Asensus Surgical Italia, S.r.l. (2)
Viale dell'Innovazione 3, 20126, Milan, Italy
Tel.: (39) 0266111810
Bio Technology Services
N.A.I.C.S.: 541714

TransEnterix Asia PTE Ltd. (3)
8 Shenton Way Suite 05-02 AXA Tower, Singapore, 068811, Singapore
Tel.: (65) 62237757
Surgical Appliance Distr
N.A.I.C.S.: 423450

TransEnterix Europe Sarl (3)
33 rue du Puits Romain, 8070, Bertrange, Luxembourg
Tel.: (352) 282651
Web Site: http://transenterix.com
Pharmaceutical Product Whslr
N.A.I.C.S.: 424210

Karl Storz Endovision, Inc. (1)
91 Carpenter Hill Rd, Charlton, MA 01507-5256
Tel.: (508) 248-9011
Web Site: http://www.karlstorz.com
Sales Range: $100-124.9 Million
Emp.: 500
Mfr of Endoscopic Surgical Instruments
N.A.I.C.S.: 339112
Rich Thomas *(Dir-Continuous Improvement)*

Karl Storz Veterinary Endoscopy America, Inc. (1)
175 Cremona Dr, Goleta, CA 93117-3084
Tel.: (805) 968-7776
Web Site: http://www.karlstorzvet.com
Sales Range: $75-99.9 Million
Emp.: 300
Mfr of Endoscopic Surgical Instruments
N.A.I.C.S.: 423450
Charles Wilhelm *(CEO)*

OOO KARL STORZ Endoskopy - WOSTOK (1)
Derbenyevskaya Nab 7 Building 4, 115114, Moscow, Russia
Tel.: (7) 4959830240
Medical Equipment Mfr
N.A.I.C.S.: 423450

STORZ Endoskop Produktions GmbH (1)
Zweigniederlassung Schaffhausen, Schneckenackerstr. 1, 8200, Schaffhausen, Switzerland
Tel.: (41) 52 640 162
Medical Equipment Mfr
N.A.I.C.S.: 423450

TOO KARL STORZ ENDOSCOPY Kazakhstan (1)
Saryarka 6, Nur-Sultan, Kazakhstan
Tel.: (7) 7172 55 25 49
Web Site: http://www.karlstorz.com
Medical Equipment Mfr
N.A.I.C.S.: 423450

TOV KARL STORZ Ukraine (1)
Obolonska naberezhna 15, Building 3 Office 3, 4210, Kiev, Ukraine
Tel.: (380) 44 4266819
Medical Equipment Mfr
N.A.I.C.S.: 423450

KARLCHEN'S BACKSTUBE GMBH
Oeynhausener Strasse 85, Lohne, D-32584, Germany
Tel.: (49) 5732 9404 0
Web Site: http://www.karlchens-backstube.de
Bakery Mfr
N.A.I.C.S.: 311812

KARLOVACKA BANKA DD
Ivana Gorana Kovacica 1, 47000, Karlovac, Croatia
Tel.: (385) 47417500
Web Site: http://www.kaba.hr
Year Founded: 1955
Commercial Banking Services
N.A.I.C.S.: 522110
Zeljka Surac *(Co-Pres & Member-Mgmt Bd)*

KARLSBERG BRAUEREI GMBH
Karlsbergstrasse 62, D-66424, Homburg, Germany
Tel.: (49) 68411050 De
Web Site: http://www.karlsberg.de
Year Founded: 1878
Sales Range: $125-149.9 Million
Emp.: 600
Beer Brewer & Whslr
N.A.I.C.S.: 312120
Hans-Georg Eils *(Member-Mgmt Bd-Tech & Logistics)*

KARMARAMA
31 Vernon St, London, W14 0RN, United Kingdom
Tel.: (44) 20 7612 1777
Web Site: http://www.karmarama.com
Rev.: $53,554,959
Emp.: 60
N.A.I.C.S.: 541810
Ben Bilboul *(CEO)*

KARMARTS PUBLIC COMPANY LIMITED
81-81/1 Soi Phetchakasem 54 Yak 3 Phetchakasem Rd Bangduan, Phasicharoen, Bangkok, 10160, Thailand
Tel.: (66) 28052756
Web Site: https://www.karmarts.co.th
Year Founded: 1982
KAMART—(THA)
Rev.: $71,680,861
Assets: $124,063,521
Liabilities: $27,600,113
Net Worth: $96,463,408
Earnings: $19,359,262
Emp.: 900
Fiscal Year-end: 12/31/23
Cosmetic Product Whslr
N.A.I.C.S.: 424210
Suwannee Tharacheevin *(Asst Mng Dir-Acctg)*

KARNALI DEVELOPMENT BANK LTD.
Surkhet Road, Nepalgunj, Banke, Nepal
Tel.: (977) 81415040
Web Site: https://www.kdblnepal.com
KRBL—(NEP)
Rev.: $1,280,075
Assets: $43,986,461
Liabilities: $39,381,669
Net Worth: $4,604,792
Earnings: $15,392
Emp.: 141

Fiscal Year-end: 12/31/21
Banking Services
N.A.I.C.S.: 522110
Rajendra Bir Raya *(Chm)*

KARNALYTE RESOURCES INC.
Suite 1201 409 3rd Avenue S, Saskatoon, S7K 5R5, SK, Canada
Tel.: (639) 398-6478 AB
Web Site: https://www.karnalyte.com
Year Founded: 2007
KRN—(TSX)
Rev.: $50,848
Assets: $8,793,609
Liabilities: $2,590,129
Net Worth: $6,203,480
Earnings: ($2,682,438)
Emp.: 3
Fiscal Year-end: 12/31/20
Potash Exploration Services
N.A.I.C.S.: 212390
Vishvesh D. Nanavaty *(Chm)*

KARNAPHULI INSURANCE COMPANY LIMITED
11/B & D Meghna Life- Karnaphuli Bima Bhaban Toyenbee Circular Road, Dhaka, 1000, Bangladesh
Tel.: (880) 2223389043
Web Site: https://www.kiclbd.com
KARNAPHULI—(DHA)
Rev.: $57,550
Assets: $15,812,604
Liabilities: $5,087,315
Net Worth: $10,725,289
Earnings: $1,037,655
Emp.: 314
Fiscal Year-end: 12/31/22
Insurance Services
N.A.I.C.S.: 524298
Nizam Uddin Ahmed *(Chm)*

KARNAVATI FINANCE LIMITED
Vraj 5th Floor, Near Tin Batti Limda Lane, Jamnagar, 361001, Gujarat, India
Tel.: (91) 2882663042
Web Site: https://www.karnavatifinanceltd.com
538928—(BOM)
Rev.: $341,346
Assets: $3,279,719
Liabilities: $1,652,023
Net Worth: $1,627,696
Earnings: $67,274
Emp.: 20
Fiscal Year-end: 03/31/23
Financial Services
N.A.I.C.S.: 525990
Raman Morzaria *(Exec Dir)*

KARNIKA INDUSTRIES LIMITED
6 Gurgola ghat Road Near Gopal Bhawan, Bandhaghat Salkia, Howrah, 711106, West Bengal, India
Tel.: (91) 3326558101 In
Web Site: https://www.karnikaindustries.com
Year Founded: 2022
KARNIKA—(NSE)
Rev.: $15,278,011
Assets: $11,858,596
Liabilities: $9,685,601
Net Worth: $2,172,995
Earnings: $991,671
Emp.: 221
Fiscal Year-end: 03/31/23
Apparel Product Retailer
N.A.I.C.S.: 424350

KARNIMATA COLD STORAGE LIMITED
Village Chekuasole PO Jogerdanga

KARNIMATA COLD STORAGE LIMITED

Karnimata Cold Storage Limited—(Continued)
PS Goaltore, Dist Paschim Medinpur, Burdwan, 721 121, West Bengal, India
Tel.: (91) 3227218314
Web Site:
https://www.karnimatastorage.com
537784—(BOM)
Rev.: $573,359
Assets: $2,218,214
Liabilities: $1,216,834
Net Worth: $1,001,380
Earnings: $55,704
Emp.: 14
Fiscal Year-end: 03/31/23
Cold Storage
N.A.I.C.S.: 493120
Pradip Lodha (CEO & Mng Dir)

KARNOV GROUP AB
Warfvinges Vag 39, 112 51, Stockholm, Sweden
Tel.: (46) 859819100
Web Site:
https://www.karnovgroup.com
Year Founded: 1867
KAR—(OMX)
Rev.: $94,174,465
Assets: $450,326,629
Liabilities: $261,000,081
Net Worth: $189,326,547
Earnings: $12,208,488
Emp.: 246
Fiscal Year-end: 12/31/20
Information Consulting Services
N.A.I.C.S.: 519290
Flemming Breinholt (Co-Pres & Co-CEO)

Subsidiaries:

Ante ApS (1)
Skt Petri Passage 5 1, 1165, Copenhagen, Denmark
Tel.: (45) 25343173
Web Site: https://ante.dk
Law firm
N.A.I.C.S.: 541199

Echoline S.A.S. (1)
78 Allee Jean Jaures, 31000, Toulouse, France
Tel.: (33) 561141986
Web Site: https://www.echoline.fr
Software Development Services
N.A.I.C.S.: 541511

Forlaget Andersen A/S (1)
Sankt Petri Passage 5, 1165, Copenhagen, Denmark
Tel.: (45) 35113512
Web Site: https://www.forlagetandersen.dk
Business Handbook & Course Services
N.A.I.C.S.: 561410

Karnov Group Denmark A/S (1)
Sankt Petri Passage 5 Living Room, 1165, Copenhagen, Denmark
Tel.: (45) 33740700
Web Site: https://www.karnovgroup.dk
Legal & Accounting Information Services
N.A.I.C.S.: 541219

Lamy Liaisons S.A.S. (1)
7 Rue Emmy Noether, 93400, Saint-Ouen, France
Tel.: (33) 185583000
Web Site: https://www.lamy-liaisons.fr
Software Development Services
N.A.I.C.S.: 541511

Notisum AB (1)
Norra Vallgatan 70, 211 22, Malmo, Sweden
Tel.: (46) 86221400
Web Site: https://www.notisum.com
Publishing Information Services
N.A.I.C.S.: 519290
Mans Fornander (Head-Notisum & Sls)

KAROLINSKA DEVELOPMENT AB
Nanna Svartz vag 2, SE 17165, Solna, Sweden
Tel.: (46) 852486070 SE
Web Site:
https://www.karolinskadev.com
KDEV—(OMX)
Rev.: $215,422
Assets: $117,231,542
Liabilities: $956,101
Net Worth: $116,275,441
Earnings: ($8,253,674)
Emp.: 8
Fiscal Year-end: 12/31/22
Medical Products Development & Investment Services
N.A.I.C.S.: 541715
Ulf Richenberg (Gen Counsel)

Subsidiaries:

Akinion Pharmaceuticals AB (1)
Fogdevreten 2A, 171 65, Solna, Sweden
Tel.: (46) 8 524 87909
Web Site: http://www.akinion.se
Pharmaceutical Products Mfr & Distr
N.A.I.C.S.: 325412
Bruno Lucidi (CEO)

Inhalation Sciences Sweden AB (1)
Halsovagen 7 Novum Floor 6 Elevator E, 141 57, Huddinge, Sweden
Tel.: (46) 70 562 5195
Web Site: https://www.inhalation.se
Pharmaceutical Research & Development Services
N.A.I.C.S.: 325412

Novasaid AB (1)
Karolinska Institutet Science Park Fogdevreten 2A, Solna, Sweden
Tel.: (46) 703029588
Web Site: http://www.novasaid.se
Pharmaceutical Research & Development Services
N.A.I.C.S.: 541715

Pharmanest AB (1)
Nobels Vag 3, 171 65, Solna, Sweden
Tel.: (46) 709749057
Web Site: http://www.pharmanest.se
Pharmaceutical Research & Development Services
N.A.I.C.S.: 541715
Helena Jansson (CEO)

KAROO EXPLORATION CORP.
1483 Homer Street Suite 2206, Vancouver, V6Z 3G7, BC, Canada
Tel.: (604) 683-2402
Web Site:
http://www.karooexploration.com
KE—(TSXV)
Sales Range: Less than $1 Million
Metal Exploration Services
N.A.I.C.S.: 213114
James Walchuk (Chm & Acting CEO)

KAROON ENERGY LTD.
Level 3/6 Riverside Quay, Southbank, 3006, VIC, Australia
Tel.: (61) 396167500
Web Site:
https://www.karoonenergy.com.au
KAR—(ASX)
Rev.: $566,500,000
Assets: $1,190,400,000
Liabilities: $716,800,000
Net Worth: $473,600,000
Earnings: $163,000,000
Emp.: 109
Fiscal Year-end: 06/30/23
Crude Petroleum Extraction Services
N.A.I.C.S.: 211120
Edward Munks (COO)

Subsidiaries:

Karoon Energy International Ltd (1)
34 38 Lochiel Ave, PO Box 469, Mount Martha, 3934, VIC, Australia
Tel.: (61) 359741044
Web Site: http://www.karoongas.com.au
Sales Range: $50-74.9 Million
Oil & Gas Exploration Services
N.A.I.C.S.: 213112

Karoon Gas Pty. Ltd. (1)
Ofc 7A 34 38 Lochiel Ave, Mount Martha, 3934, VIC, Australia
Tel.: (61) 359741044
Web Site: http://www.karoongas.com.au
Sales Range: $50-74.9 Million
Oil & Gas Exploration Services
N.A.I.C.S.: 213112

KAROOOOO LTD.
10 Anson Road 12-14 International Plaza, Singapore, 079903, Singapore
Tel.: (65) 62554151
Web Site: https://www.karooooo.com
KARO—(NASDAQ)
Rev.: $222,093,120
Assets: $227,451,330
Liabilities: $68,891,252
Net Worth: $158,560,078
Earnings: $39,826,993
Emp.: 4,387
Fiscal Year-end: 02/29/24
Mobility Data Analytics Solutions
N.A.I.C.S.: 518210
Isaias Jose Calisto (Founder & CEO)

Subsidiaries:

Cartrack Holdings Ltd. (1)
11 Keyes Avenue, Rosebank, 2196, South Africa (100%)
Tel.: (27) 112503132
Web Site: http://www.cartrack.co.za
Rev.: $138,107,430
Assets: $131,177,497
Liabilities: $44,099,947
Net Worth: $87,077,550
Earnings: $32,460,733
Emp.: 2,500
Fiscal Year-end: 02/29/2020
Vehicle Recovery Services
N.A.I.C.S.: 488410
Harry P. Louw (CEO)

Subsidiary (Non-US):

Cartrack Espana, S.L. (2)
Ctra Villaverde-Vallecas km 3 5 CTM Administrative building of 212-215, 28053, Madrid, Spain
Tel.: (34) 910024504
Web Site: http://www.cartrack.com.es
Automobile Parts Distr
N.A.I.C.S.: 441330

Subsidiary (US):

Cartrack Inc. (2)
12100 Wilshire Blvd Ste 1550, Los Angeles, CA 90025
Tel.: (424) 500-8601
Web Site: https://www.cartrack.us
Software Services
N.A.I.C.S.: 541511

Subsidiary (Non-US):

Cartrack Polska Sp. z o.o. (2)
st captain W Pileckiego 67, 02-781, Warsaw, Poland
Tel.: (48) 666202000
Web Site: https://www.cartrack.pl
Software Services
N.A.I.C.S.: 541511

Cartrack Portugal S.A. (2)
Av D Nuno Alvares Pereira n 51, Estoril, 2765-261, Lisbon, Portugal
Tel.: (351) 808100125
Web Site: https://www.cartrack.pt
Software Services
N.A.I.C.S.: 541511
Tiago Ferreira (Sls Mgr)

Cartrack Technologies Pte. Limited (2)
2 Aljunied Ave 1 06-11 Framework Building 2, Singapore, 389977, Singapore
Tel.: (65) 62554151
Web Site: http://www.cartrack.sg
Software Services
N.A.I.C.S.: 541511

INTERNATIONAL PUBLIC

Subsidiary (Non-US):

Cartrack Engineering Technologies Limited (3)
5A Adekunbi Crescent Balogun Bus-Stop Off Awolowo Way, Ikeja, Lagos, Nigeria
Tel.: (234) 7080602600
Web Site: https://www.cartrack.ng
Software Services
N.A.I.C.S.: 541511

Cartrack Malaysia Sdn. Bhd. (3)
Unit BO1-D-6-1 Level 6 Menara 2 Boutique Office 1 Pillar 11, KL Eco City No 3 Jalan Bangsar, 59200, Kuala Lumpur, Wilayah Persekutuan, Malaysia
Tel.: (60) 73369199
Web Site: http://www.cartrack.com.my
Telecommunication Product Distr
N.A.I.C.S.: 423690

Cartrack New Zealand Limited (3)
Level 4 205 Wairau Road Wairau Valley, Auckland, 0627, New Zealand
Tel.: (64) 94441244
Web Site: https://www.cartrack.co.nz
Security System Distr
N.A.I.C.S.: 423430
Dave Brereton (Sls Mgr)

Cartrack Tanzania Limited (3)
Plot No 289 Chwaku Street Kairuki Hospital Road Regent Estate, Mikocheni A, Dar es Salaam, Tanzania
Tel.: (255) 222772434
Web Site: https://www.cartrack.co.tz
Software Services
N.A.I.C.S.: 541511

Cartrack Technologies (China) Limited (3)
Unit 603 6/F Enterprise Square Tower II No 9 Sheung Yuet Road, Kowloon Bay, China (Hong Kong)
Tel.: (852) 39551050
Web Site: http://www.cartrack.com.hk
Automobile Parts Distr
N.A.I.C.S.: 441330

Cartrack Technologies (Thailand) Company Limited (3)
2556 Room 602-607 6th Floor 66 Tower Sukhumvit Road, Bangna-Nuea Bangna, Bangkok, 10260, Thailand
Tel.: (66) 21362929
Web Site: https://en.cartrack.co.th
Telecommunication Product Distr
N.A.I.C.S.: 423690

Cartrack Technologies LLC (3)
Single Business Tower Office 4203-04 Sheikh Zayed Road, PO Box 392764, Dubai, United Arab Emirates
Tel.: (971) 45815600
Web Site: https://www.cartrackme.com
Telecommunication Product Distr
N.A.I.C.S.: 423690

Subsidiary (Non-US):

Cartrack Limitada (4)
Av de Mocambique N 2600, Maputo, Mozambique
Tel.: (258) 843136793
Web Site: http://www.cartrack.co.mz
Software Services
N.A.I.C.S.: 541511

Subsidiary (Non-US):

Cartrack Technologies Phl Inc. (3)
4th Floor SM Cyber Makati One 373 Sen Gil Puyat Ave, Bel - Air Village, Makati, Philippines
Tel.: (63) 286612651
Web Site: https://www.cartrack.com.ph
Software Services
N.A.I.C.S.: 541511

PT. Cartrack Technologies Indonesia (3)
SOHO Capital Building 16th Floor Suite 06 Podomoro City Jl Letjen, S Parman Kav 28, Jakarta, 11470, Indonesia
Tel.: (62) 2150198989
Web Site: https://www.cartrack.id
Software Services
N.A.I.C.S.: 541511
S. Joko (Fin Mgr)

AND PRIVATE COMPANIES

Retriever Limited (3)
Maksons Plaza 3rd Floor Parklands Road, Westlands, Nairobi, Kenya
Tel.: (254) 730940001
Web Site: http://www.retriever.co.ke
Software Services
N.A.I.C.S.: 541511
Adrian Ogol *(Country Mgr)*

Subsidiary (Domestic):

Drive & Save Proprietary Limited (2)
11 Keyes Avenue, Rosebank, 2196, South Africa
Tel.: (27) 860353382
Web Site: https://www.driveandsave.com
Vehicle Insurance Services
N.A.I.C.S.: 524126
Dominic Vieira *(Mgr-Insurance Sls & Ops)*

KARRIE INTERNATIONAL HOLDINGS LIMITED
9/F Southeast Industrial Building 611-619 Castle Peak Road, Tsuen Wan, NT, China (Hong Kong)
Tel.: (852) 24110913 BM
Web Site: https://www.karrie.com.hk
Year Founded: 1980
1050—(HKG)
Rev.: $517,652,717
Assets: $653,421,193
Liabilities: $434,599,916
Net Worth: $218,821,277
Earnings: $70,823,176
Emp.: 3,700
Fiscal Year-end: 03/31/22
Computer & Server Casing Mfr
N.A.I.C.S.: 334111
Wing Fai Tang *(Sec)*

Subsidiaries:

Castfast Magnetics Moulding Limited (1)
10 F Southeast Indus Bldg 611-619 Castle Peak Rd, Tsuen Wan, New Territories, China (Hong Kong)
Tel.: (852) 24110913
Metal Stamping Dies Mfr
N.A.I.C.S.: 333514

Dongguan Feng Gang Castfast Metal & Plastics Co., Ltd. (1)
9 Xing Yuan Road, Yu Quan Industrial Region Feng Gang, Dongguan, 523696, Guangdong, China
Tel.: (86) 76982072800
Plastic & Metal Product Mfr
N.A.I.C.S.: 332999

Dongguan Feng Gang Caston Metal & Plastics Co., Ltd. (1)
Yu Quan Rd, Yu Quan Ind Region Feng Gang, Dongguan, 523696, Guangdong, China
Tel.: (86) 76982072800
Plastic & Metal Product Mfr
N.A.I.C.S.: 332999

Dongguan KRP Development Company Limited (1)
47 Castfast Road, Da Long Industrial Region Feng Gang, Dongguan, 523709, Guangdong, China
Tel.: (86) 76987777455
Plastic & Metal Product Mfr
N.A.I.C.S.: 332999

Hong Kong Hung Hing Metal Manufacturing Company Limited (1)
Room 36 6/F Phase 2 Metro Centre 21 Lam Hing St, Kowloon Bay, Kln, China (Hong Kong)
Tel.: (852) 27952321
Web Site: https://hunghingmm.com
Sales Range: $50-74.9 Million
Emp.: 200
Fabricated Metal Products Mfr
N.A.I.C.S.: 332313

Jiang Su Castfast Electronic Technologies Company Limited (1)
Wen Zhuan Rd Jiangsu Yixing Econ Dev Zone, Yixing, 214203, Jiangsu, China
Tel.: (86) 510 87129688
Computer & Server Casings Mfr

N.A.I.C.S.: 337126

Karrie Industrial Company Limited (1)
10 F Southeast Indl Bldg 611-619 Castle Peak Rd, Tsuen Wan, New Territories, China (Hong Kong)
Tel.: (852) 24110913
Computer Casings & Office Automation Products Mfr & Sales
N.A.I.C.S.: 334118

Karrie Technologies Company Limited (1)
10 F Southeast Indl Bldg 611-619 Castle Peak Rd, Tsuen Wan, New Territories, China (Hong Kong)
Tel.: (852) 24110913
Plastic Injection Molds & Metal Stamping Dies Mfr & Sales
N.A.I.C.S.: 332119

Karwin Engineering Company Limited (1)
10 F Southeast Indus Bldg 611-619 Castle Peak Rd, Tsuen Wan, New Territories, China (Hong Kong)
Tel.: (852) 24110913
Computer Casings Mfr & Sales
N.A.I.C.S.: 334118

Sagem Karrie Technologies (Hong Kong) Company Limited (1)
9 F Southeast Indus Bldg 611-619 Castle Peak Rd, Tsuen Wan, New Territories, China (Hong Kong)
Tel.: (852) 24110913
Electric Equipment Mfr
N.A.I.C.S.: 334511

Shenzhen Zhetong Electronics Company Limited (1)
Block 13A Zone A, Bao Sheng Industrial Region Bai Ni Keng Ping Hu, Shenzhen, 518111, Guangdong, China
Tel.: (86) 75528855617
Plastic & Metal Product Mfr
N.A.I.C.S.: 332999

KARSTEN ENERGY CORP.
328-20th Avenue West, Vancouver, V5Y 2C6, BC, Canada
Tel.: (604) 687-0888 BC
Year Founded: 2012
KAY.H—(TSXV)
Assets: $75,205
Liabilities: $11,740
Net Worth: $63,466
Earnings: ($69,644)
Fiscal Year-end: 12/31/19
Investment Services
N.A.I.C.S.: 523999

KARSTEN S/A
Rua Johann Karsten 260 Testo Salto, 89074-700, Blumenau, Santa Catarina, Brazil
Tel.: (55) 47 33314000
Web Site: http://www.karsten.com.br
Sales Range: $350-399.9 Million
Emp.: 2,500
Household Furnishings
N.A.I.C.S.: 423220
Carlos Odebrecht *(VP)*

KARSU TEKSTIL AS
Suksun Zafer Mah Sedef Boulevard No 146 Incesu, Kayseri, Turkiye
Tel.: (90) 3526974001
Web Site: https://www.karsu.com.tr
Year Founded: 1973
KRTEK—(IST)
Cotton Yarn Mfr & Distr
N.A.I.C.S.: 313110
Azra Seyok *(Mgr-Fin)*

KARSUSAN KARADENIZ AQUACULTURE INDUSTRY, INC.
Basinkoy Mah Florya Cad No 5 A-Blok D 9, Istanbul, Turkiye
Tel.: (90) 216232 24 19

Web Site: http://www.casaemtia.com
Seafood Product Mfr
N.A.I.C.S.: 311710
Oytun Bacon *(Chm)*

KARTESIA ADVISOR LLP
8 Chesterfield Grdens, London, W1J 5BQ, United Kingdom
Tel.: (44) 2037003330
Web Site: http://www.kartesia.com
Privater Equity Firm
N.A.I.C.S.: 523940
Laurent Bouvier *(Mng Partner)*

KARTIK INVESTMENTS TRUST LIMITED
Parry House 2nd Floor No 43 Moore Street, Parrys, Chennai, 600 001, India
Tel.: (91) 4425307123
Web Site: https://www.kartikinvestments.com
Year Founded: 1978
501151—(BOM)
Rev.: $6,402
Assets: $566,561
Liabilities: $84,240
Net Worth: $482,321
Earnings: ($2,902)
Fiscal Year-end: 03/31/23
Financial Investment Services
N.A.I.C.S.: 523999
P. Nagarajan *(Chm)*

KARTING
727 rue Aristide Berges, CS 90027, 38331, Saint Ismier, Cedex, France
Tel.: (33) 476230118
Web Site: http://www.karting-spirit.com
Rev.: $17,300,000
Emp.: 113
Women's Clothing Mfr
N.A.I.C.S.: 315250
Gerry Motte *(Dir)*

KARTO OY
Kuormaajantie 17, 40320, Jyvaskyla, Finland
Tel.: (358) 447887055
Web Site: http://www.korttikauppa.karto.fi
Sales Range: $25-49.9 Million
Emp.: 150
Greeting Card Publishers
N.A.I.C.S.: 513191
Pekka Ojala *(Mng Dir)*

Subsidiaries:

Putinki Oy (1)
Hameentie 105 B, 00550, Helsinki, Finland
Tel.: (358) 97732874
Web Site: http://www.putinki.fi
Paper & Gift Product Whslr
N.A.I.C.S.: 424120
Laura Hartonen *(Mgr-Store)*

KARTONPACK DOBOZIPARI NYRT.
Galamb u 11, 4030, Debrecen, Hungary
Tel.: (36) 52500147 HU
Web Site: http://www.kartonpack.hu
Year Founded: 1952
Packaging Paper Products Mfr
N.A.I.C.S.: 322220
Erzsebet Nemes *(Mgr-Export)*

KARTONSAN KARTON SANAYI VE TICARET A.S.
Prof Dr Bulent Tarcan Caddesi No 5 Engin Pak is Merkezi Kat 3, Gayrettepe, 34349, Istanbul, Turkiye
Tel.: (90) 2122732000
Web Site: https://www.kartonsan.com.tr
Year Founded: 1991

KARUR VYSYA BANK LTD

KARTN—(IST)
Rev.: $103,916,749
Assets: $55,589,633
Liabilities: $12,089,045
Net Worth: $43,500,588
Earnings: $21,790,142
Emp.: 316
Fiscal Year-end: 12/31/22
Coated Cardboard Mfr
N.A.I.C.S.: 322220
Haluk Iber *(CEO)*

Subsidiaries:

Selka ic ve Dis Ticaret A.S. (1)
Prof Dr Bulent Tarcan Caddesi No 5 Engin Pak is Merkezi Kat 3, Gayrettepe, 34349, Istanbul, Turkiye
Tel.: (90) 2122732000
Web Site: https://www.selkaticaret.com
Coated Cardboards Distr
N.A.I.C.S.: 424130

KARTULI SHALI JSC
4 Peikrebi str, Tbilisi, Georgia
Tel.: (995) 91 02 14
Woolen Yarn Mfr
N.A.I.C.S.: 313110

KARULA CO., LTD.
9-2-9 Narita, Kurokawa-Gun, Miyagi, 981-3341, Japan
Tel.: (81) 223515888
Web Site: https://www.re-marumatu.co.jp
Year Founded: 1979
2789—(TKS)
Rev.: $50,326,320
Assets: $54,401,600
Liabilities: $40,781,840
Net Worth: $13,619,760
Earnings: ($4,336,640)
Fiscal Year-end: 02/28/22
Restaurant Operating Services
N.A.I.C.S.: 722511

KARUR KCP PACKKAGINGS LTD.
330/1 Chinna Andan Koil Road, Karur, 639001, Tamil Nadu, India
Tel.: (91) 4324240063
Year Founded: 1961
Sales Range: $100-124.9 Million
Emp.: 1,477
Paper Products Mfr
N.A.I.C.S.: 322299
K. C. Pallani Shamy *(Founder & Chm)*

Subsidiaries:

Karur KCP Packkagings Ltd. - Manufacturing Unit (1)
Marchinaickenpalayam, Ambarampalayam Post, Pollachi, 642 103, Tamilnadu, India
Tel.: (91) 4259 252000
Sales Range: $200-249.9 Million
Emp.: 100
Packaging Plastic Paper Mfr
N.A.I.C.S.: 322220
C. Karunanidhi *(Gen Mgr)*

Karur KCP Packkagings Ltd. - PP & FIBC Unit (1)
S F No 199-201 Trichy Main Road Mayahur, Krishnarayapuram Tk, Karur, 639 108, India
Tel.: (91) 4323 243330
Packaging Plastic Paper Mfr
N.A.I.C.S.: 322220

KARUR VYSYA BANK LTD
No 20 Erode Road Vadivel Nagar L N S, Karur, 639002, India
Tel.: (91) 4324269000
Web Site: https://www.kvb.co.in
590003—(NSE)
Rev.: $867,693,263
Assets: $10,925,967,384
Liabilities: $9,889,086,180
Net Worth: $1,036,881,204

KARUR VYSYA BANK LTD

Karur Vysya Bank Ltd—(Continued)
Earnings: $97,501,677
Emp.: 6,761
Fiscal Year-end: 03/31/22
Banking Services
N.A.I.C.S.: 522110
Srinivasan V. *(Head-Credit Monitoring-Legal-Recovery & Gen Mgr)*

KARVY FINANCIAL SERVICES LIMITED
Unit No 762 6th Floor Building No 7 Solitaire Corporate Park, Andheri East, Mumbai, 400 093, India
Tel.: (91) 2267875300
Web Site:
http://www.karvyfinance.com
Financial Support Services
N.A.I.C.S.: 523940
Amit Saxena *(CEO & Mng Dir)*

Subsidiaries:

Regaliaa Realty Ltd. (1)
Block A II Floor Ameen Manor 138 Nungambakkam High Road, Nungambakkam, Chennai, 600 034, India
Tel.: (91) 44 2833 1454
Web Site: http://www.regaliaarealty.com
Assets: $1,078,399
Liabilities: $1,441,488
Net Worth: ($363,089)
Earnings: ($24,683)
Fiscal Year-end: 03/31/2019
Property Development & Construction Services
N.A.I.C.S.: 236220
D. Sudhakara Reddy *(Chm & Mng Dir)*

KARYES INVESTMENT PUBLIC COMPANY LIMITED
8 Stasinos Ave Photiades Business Centre, 1056, Nicosia, Cyprus
Tel.: (357) 22751555
KAR—(CYP)
Sales Range: Less than $1 Million
Financial Services
N.A.I.C.S.: 523999

KARYON INDUSTRIES BERHAD
No 1 Jalan Sri Plentong 6 Taman Perindustrian Sri Plentong, Masai, 81750, Johor, Malaysia
Tel.: (60) 73864198 MY
Web Site:
https://www.karyongroup.com.my
Year Founded: 2003
KARYON—(KLS)
Rev.: $39,553,983
Assets: $30,218,406
Liabilities: $5,779,676
Net Worth: $24,438,730
Earnings: $1,271,341
Emp.: 248
Fiscal Year-end: 03/31/23
Chemical Product Mfr & Distr
N.A.I.C.S.: 325998
Loh Chen Yook *(Chm)*

Subsidiaries:

Allbright Industries (M) Sdn Bhd (1)
No 2 Jalan Sri Plentong 4, Taman Perindustrian Sri Plentong, 81750, Masai, Johor, Malaysia
Tel.: (60) 73864198
Web Site: https://www.allbright.com.my
Industrial Chemicals Mfr
N.A.I.C.S.: 325199

Hsing Lung Sdn Bhd (1)
No 1 Jalan Sri Plentong 6, Taman Perindustrian Sri Plentong, 81750, Masai, Johor, Malaysia
Tel.: (60) 73864198
Web Site: https://www.hsinglung.com.my
Thermoplastic Product Mfr
N.A.I.C.S.: 325211
Chua Kee Lam *(Founder)*

KASAI KOGYO CO., LTD.
3316 Miyayama, Samukawa-machi, Koza, 253-0106, Kanagawa, Japan
Tel.: (81) 467751125
Web Site: https://www.kasai.co.jp
Year Founded: 1948
7256—(TKS)
Rev.: $1,416,622,150
Assets: $938,917,450
Liabilities: $790,615,490
Net Worth: $148,301,960
Earnings: ($2,068,930)
Emp.: 8,147
Fiscal Year-end: 03/31/24
Automotive Interior Product Mfr & Distr
N.A.I.C.S.: 336360
Kuniyuki Watanabe *(Pres)*

Subsidiaries:

DONGFENG KASAI (DALIAN) AUTOMOTIVE TRIM SYSTEMS CO., LTD. (1)
NO 4 Nangang lu Dalian Baoshui Zone, Dalian, 116600, Liaoning, China
Tel.: (86) 41139251333
Automotive Interior Parts Mfr & Distr
N.A.I.C.S.: 336360

Dongfeng Kasai (Wuhan) Roof Trim Systems Co., Ltd. (1)
No 48 Yao Hua Road, Wuhan Zhuankou Economic and Technology Development Zone, Wuhan, 430056, Hubei, China
Tel.: (86) 2784857001
Automotive Parts Mfr & Whslr
N.A.I.C.S.: 333618

Dongfeng Kasai (Xiangyang) Automotive Trim Systems Co., Ltd. (1)
NO 15Tian laiRoad Gaoxin Zone, Xiangyang, 441007, Hubei, China
Tel.: (86) 7103318327
Automotive Interior Parts Distr
N.A.I.C.S.: 423120

GUNMA KASAI CO., LTD. (1)
1075 Kamieguro Meiwa-cho, Oura, Gunma, Japan
Tel.: (81) 276 73 7811
Automotive Interior Parts Mfr & Distr
N.A.I.C.S.: 336360

Plant (Domestic):

GUNMA KASAI CO., LTD. - Ota Plant (2)
1534-1 Ichinoi-cho Nitta, Ota-shi, Gunma, Japan
Tel.: (81) 276571812
Automotive Exterior Parts Mfr
N.A.I.C.S.: 336360

Guangdong Kawasawa Automotive Trim Parts Co., Ltd. (1)
Dongye Road Houjie Science and Technology Industrial Park, Houjie Town, Dongguan, 523960, Guangdong, China
Tel.: (86) 76989278888
Automotive Parts Mfr & Whslr
N.A.I.C.S.: 333618

Guangzhou Kasai Automotive Interior Trim Parts Co., Ltd. (1)
No 6 Dongfeng Rd Auto City, Huadu, Guangzhou, 510800, Guangdong, China
Tel.: (86) 2061971666
Automotive Interior Parts Mfr & Distr
N.A.I.C.S.: 336360

Guangzhou S.K Automotive Interior Co., Ltd. (1)
No 3 Lingxi Road Xiuquan Street Auto City, Huadu, Guangzhou, 510800, China
Tel.: (86) 2086709156
Automotive Parts Mfr & Whslr
N.A.I.C.S.: 333618

KASAI INDIA (CHENNAI) PRIVATE LIMITED (1)
No 463/2A to 2E, Ezhichoor Village & Post Singaperumal Koil Via Kancheepuram District, Chennai, 603 204, Tamilnadu, India
Tel.: (91) 4467127301
Automotive Interior Parts Mfr & Distr
N.A.I.C.S.: 336360

KASAI SUPPORT SERVICE CO., LTD. (1)
8-23-20 Fukayakami, Ayase, 252-1108, Kanagawa, Japan
Tel.: (81) 467787361
Automotive Interior Parts Mfr & Distr
N.A.I.C.S.: 336360

KASAI TEC CO., LTD. (1)
4839-24 Kitayama, Fujinomiya, Shizuoka, Japan
Tel.: (81) 544591000
Automotive Interior Parts Mfr & Distr
N.A.I.C.S.: 336360

KASAI TECK SEE (THAILAND) CO., LTD. (1)
136 137 Moo 1 Hi Tech Industrial Estate Tambol Banpo Phanakornsri, Amphur Bangpa-in, Ayutthaya, 13160, Phra Nakhon Si Ayutt, Thailand
Tel.: (66) 353501225
Automotive Interior Parts Mfr & Distr
N.A.I.C.S.: 336360
Solai Malai *(Mgr-Engrg)*

Subsidiary (Domestic):

KASAI TECK SEE (THAILAND) CO., LTD. - Pinthong Plant (2)
150/59 Moo 9 Pinthong Industrial Estate II T Nongkham, Si Racha, 20230, Chonburi, Thailand
Tel.: (66) 38347318
Automotive Exterior Parts Mfr
N.A.I.C.S.: 336360

Subsidiary (Non-US):

PT. KASAI TECK SEE INDONESIA - Karawang 2nd Plant (2)
Karawang International Industrial City Jl Maligi II Lot C 4-B, Karawang, 41361, Jawa Barat, Indonesia
Tel.: (62) 2189115035
Automotive Exterior Parts Mfr
N.A.I.C.S.: 336360

KYUSHU KASAI CO., LTD. (1)
200 Oaza Mikoyamasinden, Usa-shi, Oita, Japan
Tel.: (81) 978382222
Automotive Interior Parts Mfr & Distr
N.A.I.C.S.: 336360

Kaifeng Kasai Automotive Trim Parts Co., Ltd. (1)
East of Liudajie South of Hanxing Road Development Zone, Kaifeng, 475000, Henan, China
Tel.: (86) 37123381957
Automotive Interior Parts Mfr & Distr
N.A.I.C.S.: 336360

Kasai (Germany) GmbH (1)
Lehmkuhlenfeld 9, Hattorf, 38444, Wolfsburg, Germany
Tel.: (49) 530891590
Automobile Parts Mfr
N.A.I.C.S.: 333618
Kuniyuki Watanabe *(Mng Dir)*

Kasai Kogyo Co., Ltd. - Yorii Plant (1)
158 Akahama Oaza, Yorii-machi, Osato, 369-1211, Saitama, Japan
Tel.: (81) 485823355
Automotive Exterior Parts Mfr
N.A.I.C.S.: 336360

Kasai Mexicana S.A de C.V. (1)
Blvd Miguel de cervantes Saavedra Sur 7502, Fideicomiso Ciudad Industrial, 37564, Leon, Guanajuato, Mexico
Tel.: (52) 477 763 5550
Web Site: http://www.kasai.com.mx
Automotive Interior Parts Mfr & Distr
N.A.I.C.S.: 336360

Kasai North America, Inc. (1)
1020 Volunteer Pkwy, Manchester, TN 37355
Tel.: (931) 728-4122
Web Site: http://www.kasai-na.com
Automotive Exterior Parts Mfr
N.A.I.C.S.: 336360

Subsidiary (Domestic):

Kasai North America, Inc. - Madison Plant (2)
435 Church Rd, Madison, MS 39110
Tel.: (601) 407-5000
Automotive Exterior Parts Mfr
N.A.I.C.S.: 336360

Kasai North America, Inc. - Prattville Plant (2)
1098 Doster Rd, Prattville, AL 36067
Tel.: (334) 361-1041
Automotive Exterior Parts Mfr
N.A.I.C.S.: 336360

Kasai North America, Inc. - Talladega Plant (2)
50 Homer Dr, Talladega, AL 35160
Tel.: (256) 480-2800
Automotive Exterior Parts Mfr
N.A.I.C.S.: 336360

Kasai North America, Inc. - Upper Sandusky Plant (2)
1111 N Warpole St, Upper Sandusky, OH 43351
Tel.: (419) 209-0470
Automotive Exterior Parts Mfr
N.A.I.C.S.: 336360

Kasai Slovakia S.R.O. (1)
Ul G Schoellera 2, 934 01, Levice, Slovakia
Tel.: (421) 362901300
Automotive Parts Mfr & Whslr
N.A.I.C.S.: 333618
Michal Hamar *(Mgr-Pur)*

Kasai Teck See Co., Ltd. (1)
136 137 Moo 1 Hi Tech Industrial Estate Tambol Banpo Phanakornsri, Amphur Bangpa-in, Ayutthaya, 13160, Thailand
Tel.: (66) 353501225
Automotive Parts Mfr & Whslr
N.A.I.C.S.: 333618

Kasai UK LTD (1)
Stephenson Road Industrial Estate, Washington, NE37 3HR, Tyne & Wear, United Kingdom
Tel.: (44) 191 415 7000
Web Site: http://www.kasai-uk.com
Automotive Interior Parts Mfr & Distr
N.A.I.C.S.: 336360

Plant (Domestic):

Kasai UK LTD - Merthyr Plant (2)
Unit 1 Triangle Business Park, Pentrebach, Merthyr Tydfil, CF48 4TQ, United Kingdom
Tel.: (44) 1685373159
Automotive Exterior Parts Mfr
N.A.I.C.S.: 336360

Kasaikogyo Morocco S.A.R.L. (1)
Entrepot No2 Lot No140 Zone Franche Logistique de Ksar el, Majaz oued R' mel, Tangiers, Morocco
Tel.: (212) 531006200
Automotive Parts Mfr & Whslr
N.A.I.C.S.: 333618
Daisuke Fujimoto *(Mng Dir)*

MIE KASAI CO., LTD. (1)
2202-23 Shoda-cho, Tsu, Mie, Japan
Tel.: (81) 59 225 3080
Automotive Interior Parts Mfr & Distr
N.A.I.C.S.: 336360

Plant (Domestic):

MIE KASAI CO., LTD. - Shiga Plant (2)
2-8 Gokashouobata-chou, Higashiomi-shi, Shiga, Japan
Tel.: (81) 748486900
Automotive Exterior Parts Mfr
N.A.I.C.S.: 336360

PT. KASAI TECK SEE INDONESIA (1)
Karawang International Industrial City Jl Maligi II Lot C 4-B, Karawang, 41361, Jawa Barat, Indonesia
Tel.: (62) 218904242
Automotive Interior Parts Mfr & Distr
N.A.I.C.S.: 336360

SHINIL-MEXICANA S.A. DE C.V. (1)
Avenida Purina No 1 Fracc Mineral de Pozos Puerto Interior, Silao, 36275, Guanajuato, Mexico
Tel.: (52) 4721350100
Automotive Interior Parts Distr

AND PRIVATE COMPANIES

N.A.I.C.S.: 423120

Y-Teks Co., Ltd. (1)
No 1 Shanping Rd, Zhongli Dist, Taoyuan, 32053, Taiwan
Tel.: (886) 34985666166
Automobile Parts Mfr
N.A.I.C.S.: 333618

KASATI JOIN STOCK COMPANY
270A Ly Thuong Kiet St Ward 14, Dist 10, Ho Chi Minh City, Vietnam
Tel.: (84) 838655343
Web Site: https://www.kasati.com.vn
KST—(HNX)
Rev.: $17,910,300
Assets: $24,974,500
Liabilities: $17,843,700
Net Worth: $7,130,800
Earnings: $556,000
Emp.: 150
Fiscal Year-end: 12/31/23
Telecommunications Equipment Mfr
N.A.I.C.S.: 334290

KASB MODARABA
5th Floor Lakson Square Building Office B Sarwar Shaheed Road, Opposite Press Club, Karachi, Pakistan
Tel.: (92) 2135630621
Web Site: http://www.kasbmodaraba.com
KASBM—(KAR)
Rev.: $117,137
Assets: $1,742,558
Liabilities: $192,398
Net Worth: $1,550,160
Earnings: ($220,503)
Emp.: 17
Fiscal Year-end: 06/30/19
Financial Management Services
N.A.I.C.S.: 523940
Khalid Aziz Mirza (Chm)

Subsidiaries:

Pak Brunei Investment Company Limited (1)
Horizon Vista Plot Commercial No 10 Block No 4, Scheme No 5 Clifton, Karachi, Pakistan
Tel.: (92) 213536121519
Web Site: https://www.pakbrunei.pk
Finance & Advisory Services
N.A.I.C.S.: 522320

KASBAH RESOURCES LIMITED
Level 13 459 Collins Street, Melbourne, 3000, VIC, Australia
Tel.: (61) 0394822223   AU
Web Site: http://www.kasbahresources.com
Year Founded: 2005
KAS—(ASX)
Rev.: $7,147
Assets: $5,857,403
Liabilities: $4,398,401
Net Worth: $1,459,002
Earnings: ($5,043,315)
Emp.: 18
Fiscal Year-end: 06/30/19
Mineral Exploration & Development Services
N.A.I.C.S.: 213115
Evan Spencer (Chm)

KASEN INTERNATIONAL HOLDINGS LIMITED
Unit 1111 11/F COSCO Tower 183 Queens Road Central, Sheung Wan, China (Hong Kong)
Tel.: (852) 23599329
Web Site: http://www.kasen.com.cn
0496—(HKG)
Rev.: $121,225,432
Assets: $817,367,522
Liabilities: $296,201,740
Net Worth: $521,165,783
Earnings: $8,388,900
Emp.: 2,117
Fiscal Year-end: 12/31/22
Furniture & Automotive Leather Mfr
N.A.I.C.S.: 316990
Kasen Zhangjin Zhu (Founder & Chm)

Subsidiaries:

Astana Solar LLP (1)
Turan Avenue, Nur-Sultan, 010000, Kazakhstan
Tel.: (7) 7172 551400
Web Site: http://astanasolar.kz
Solar Module Mfr
N.A.I.C.S.: 334413

Kazakhstan Solar Silicon LLP (1)
st Sogrinskaya 223/6, Ust-Kamenogorsk, Oskemen, East Kazakhstan, Kazakhstan
Tel.: (7) 23 220 4150
Web Site: https://www.kazsolarsilicon.kz
Photovoltaic Silicon Cells Mfr
N.A.I.C.S.: 334413
Baizhumin Daniyar Anuarbekovich (Gen Dir)

MK KazSilicon LLP (1)
Komarova St 1, Karatal District, Bastobe, 041011, Almaty Region, Kazakhstan
Tel.: (7) 283440373
Web Site: http://www.kazsilicon.kz
Metallurgical & Polycrystalline Silicon Mfr & Whslr
N.A.I.C.S.: 331110

KASET THAI INTERNATIONAL SUGAR CORPORATION PUBLIC COMPANY LIMITED
24 Aekphol Bldg Vibhavadi Rangsit Rd Ratchadaphisek, Din Daeng, Bangkok, 10400, Thailand
Tel.: (66) 26920869
Web Site: https://www.ktisgroup.com
Year Founded: 1957
KTIS—(THA)
Rev.: $546,675,697
Assets: $412,424,056
Liabilities: $196,039,250
Net Worth: $216,384,806
Earnings: $53,333,738
Emp.: 3,059
Fiscal Year-end: 09/30/23
Sugar Producer & Distr
N.A.I.C.S.: 311314
Sirivuthi Siamphakdee (CFO-KTIS Group)

Subsidiaries:

KTIS Bio Fertiliser Co., Ltd. (1)
24 Aekphol Bldg Vibhavadi Rangsit Rd Ratchadaphisek, Din Daeng, Bangkok, Thailand
Tel.: (66) 26920869
Fertilizer & Soil Mfr & Distr
N.A.I.C.S.: 325314

Kaset Thai Bio Power Co., Ltd. (1)
24 Aekphol Bldg Vibhavadi Rangsit Rd Ratchadaphisek, Din Daeng, Bangkok, Thailand
Tel.: (66) 26920869
Electricity Power Distr Services
N.A.I.C.S.: 221122

Permsinpattana Co., Ltd. (1)
24 Aekphol Bldg Vibhavadi Rangsit Rd Ratchadaphisek, Din Daeng, Bangkok, Thailand
Tel.: (66) 26920869
Shareholder Engagement Services
N.A.I.C.S.: 541199

Thai Identity Sugar Factory Co., Ltd. (1)
24 Aekphol Bldg Vibhavadi Rangsit Rd Ratchadaphisek, Din Daeng, Bangkok, Thailand
Tel.: (66) 26920869
Sugar Mfr & Distr
N.A.I.C.S.: 311314

Thaiekaluck Power Co., Ltd. (1)
24 Aekphol Bldg Vibhavadi Rangsit Rd Ratchadaphisek, Din Daeng, Bangkok, Thailand
Tel.: (66) 26920869
Electricity Power Distr Services
N.A.I.C.S.: 221122

KASHYAP TELE-MEDICINES LIMITED
UI/8 Upper Floor Suryarath Complex Panchwati 1st Lane Ambawadi, Ahmedabad, 380006, Gujarat, India
Tel.: (91) 6359637788
Web Site: https://www.kashyaptele-medicines.com
Year Founded: 2000
Software Development Services
N.A.I.C.S.: 541511
Amit Agrawal (Mng Dir)

KASIKORNBANK PUBLIC COMPANY LIMITED

KASIKORNBANK PUBLIC COMPANY LIMITED
1 Soi Ratburana 27/1 Ratburana Road, Ratburana Subdistrict Rat Burana District, Bangkok, 10140, Thailand
Tel.: (66) 22220000
Web Site: https://www.kasikornbank.com
Year Founded: 1945
KBANK—(OTCIQ)
Rev.: $7,578,830,255
Assets: $121,911,141,330
Liabilities: $105,541,490,177
Net Worth: $16,369,651,153
Earnings: $1,122,567,227
Emp.: 19,862
Fiscal Year-end: 12/31/20
Banking Services
N.A.I.C.S.: 522110
Surat Leelataviwat (Exec VP)

Subsidiaries:

KASIKORN FACTORY & EQUIPMENT CO., LTD (1)
400/22 7th Floor Phahon Yothin Road, Samsen Nai Sub-district Phayathai District, Bangkok, 10400, Thailand
Tel.: (66) 2 290 2900
Web Site: https://www.kasikornfactory-equipment.com
Equipment Leasing Services
N.A.I.C.S.: 532490
Duangkamol Charoenwatfana (Asst Mng Dir)

KASIKORN RESEARCH CENTER CO., LTD (1)
400/22 Kasikornbank Building Phahon Yothin Rd Samsen Nai, PhayaThai, Bangkok, 10400, Thailand
Tel.: (66) 2273 1144
Web Site: http://www.kasikornresearch.com
Market Research Services
N.A.I.C.S.: 541910
Charl Kengchon (Co-Chm)

Kasikorn Asset Management Co., Ltd. (1)
400/22 Kasikornbank Building 6th and 12th Floor Phaholyothin Road, Samsen Nai Sub-District Phayathai District, Bangkok, 10400, Thailand (100%)
Tel.: (66) 2 673 3999
Web Site: https://www.kasikornasset.com
Sales Range: $50-74.9 Million
Emp.: 100
Financial Services
N.A.I.C.S.: 523999

Kasikorn Factoring Co., Ltd. (1)
252/20 Muang Thai-Phatra Office Tower 1 16th Floor Ratchadaphisek Road, Huaykwang, Bangkok, 10310, Thailand (100%)
Tel.: (66) 22902900
Web Site: http://www.kasikornbankgroup.com
Business Services
N.A.I.C.S.: 522299

Kasikorn Labs Co., Ltd. (1)
46/6 Popular Road, Ban Mai Sub-District Pak Kret District, Nonthaburi, 11120, Thailand
Tel.: (66) 20081100
Commercial Banking Services
N.A.I.C.S.: 522110

Kasikorn Leasing Co., Ltd. (1)
17th Floor 400/22 Phahon Yothin Road, Samsen Nai Sub-District Phayathai District, Bangkok, 10400, Thailand (100%)
Tel.: (66) 2 696 9999
Web Site: https://www.kasikornleasing.com
Leasing Services
N.A.I.C.S.: 532490

Kasikorn Pro Co., Ltd. (1)
46/6 Popular Road, Ban Mai Sub-District Pak Kret District, Nonthaburi, 11120, Thailand
Tel.: (66) 20081500
Commercial Banking Services
N.A.I.C.S.: 522110

Kasikorn Securities PCL (1)
400/22 Floor 1 3 11 and 19 Kasikorn Bank Building Phahonyothin Road, Samsennai Phayathai, Bangkok, 10400, Thailand (99.99%)
Tel.: (66) 2 796 0000
Web Site: https://www.kasikornsecurities.com
Sales Range: $50-74.9 Million
Emp.: 35
Investment Banking & Securities Dealing
N.A.I.C.S.: 523150

Kasikorn Serve Co., Ltd. (1)
46/6 Popular Road, Ban Mai Sub-District Pak Kret District, Nonthaburi, 11120, Thailand
Tel.: (66) 20083700
Commercial Banking Services
N.A.I.C.S.: 522110

Kasikorn Soft Co., Ltd. (1)
46/6 Popular Road, Ban Mai Sub-District Pak Kret District, Nonthaburi, 11120, Thailand
Tel.: (66) 20082000
Commercial Banking Services
N.A.I.C.S.: 522110

Kasikorn Technology Group Secretariat Co., Ltd. (1)
46/6 Popular Road, Ban Mai Sub-District Pak Kret District, Nonthaburi, 11120, Thailand
Tel.: (66) 20081000
Commercial Banking Services
N.A.I.C.S.: 522110

Kasikorn X Co., Ltd. (1)
46/6 Popular Road, Ban Mai Sub-District Pak Kret District, Nonthaburi, 11120, Thailand
Tel.: (66) 22220000
Commercial Banking Services
N.A.I.C.S.: 522110

Kasikornbank (China) Company Limited (1)
Unit 1 59/F Tower A Kingkey 100 Building 5016 Shennan East Road, Guiyuan Sub-District Luohu District, Shenzhen, 518001, China
Tel.: (86) 75582291298
Commercial Banking Services
N.A.I.C.S.: 522110

Kasikornthai Bank Limited (1)
Unit 12 Lane Xang Avenue, Xiangngeun Village Chanthabury District, Vientiane, Lao People's Democratic Republic
Tel.: (856) 21410888
Commercial Banking Services
N.A.I.C.S.: 522110
Piyanoot Sangsana (Branch Mgr)

Khao Kla Venture Capital Management Co., Ltd. (1)
400/22 Paholyothin Rd Samsen Nai, Payathai, Bangkok, 10310, Thailand
Tel.: (66) 24703833
Web Site: http://www.khaokla.com
Commercial Banking Services
N.A.I.C.S.: 522110
Patamaporn Chaiyakool (Mng Dir)

Phethai Asset Management Co. Ltd. (1)
252-6 Muang Thai-Phatra Office Tower 1, Floor 14th Ratchadaphisek Road, 10310,

KASIKORNBANK PUBLIC COMPANY LIMITED

Kasikornbank Public Company Limited—(Continued)
Bangkok, Thailand **(100%)**
Tel.: (66) 26945000
Management Consulting Services
N.A.I.C.S.: 541618

Progress Appraisal Co., Ltd. **(1)**
400/22 Thai Farmers Bank Building Phaholyothin Road Samsen Nai, Phaya Thai District, Bangkok, 10400, Thailand
Tel.: (66) 2270 6900
Asset Management Services
N.A.I.C.S.: 531390

Progress Facilities Management Co., Ltd. **(1)**
Thai Farmers Bank Bulding 17th Floor 400/22 Phahonyothin Rd, Bangkok, 10400, Thailand
Tel.: (66) 2273 3288
Property Management Services
N.A.I.C.S.: 531311

Progress HR Co., Ltd **(1)**
Kasikornbank Building Sanampao Branch 2nd Floor No 1019/15, Phaholyothin Road Phayathai Subdistrict, Bangkok, 10400, Thailand
Tel.: (66) 22701070
Web Site: http://www.progresshr.co.th
Human Resource Consulting Services
N.A.I.C.S.: 541612

Progress Management Co., Ltd. **(1)**
17th Floor Thai Farmers Bank Building 400/22 Phahonyothin Rd, Bangkok, 10400, Thailand
Tel.: (66) 2275 1880
Mutual Fund Management Services
N.A.I.C.S.: 523940

Progress Multi Insurance Broker Co., Ltd. **(1)**
Tahol Yothin Road 400 Flat 22, 10400, Bangkok, Thailand
Tel.: (66) 2273 2701
Mutual Fund Management Services
N.A.I.C.S.: 524292

Progress Services Co., Ltd **(1)**
17th FloorThai Farmers Bank Building 400/22 Phahonyothin Road, Samsen Nai, Bangkok, 10400, Thailand
Tel.: (66) 22733293
Mutual Fund Management Services
N.A.I.C.S.: 524292

Progress Software Co. Ltd. **(1)**
Kasikornbank Suapa Bldg 6-7th Floor 306 Suapa Rd Pomprab, Pomprab Satrupai, Bangkok, 10100, Thailand **(100%)**
Tel.: (66) 222579001
Web Site: http://www.progresssoftware.co.th
Sales Range: $125-149.9 Million
Emp.: 300
Software Reproducing
N.A.I.C.S.: 334610

Thanyathamrongkij Co., Ltd **(1)**
1 Soi Rat Burana 27/1 Rat Burana Road, 10140, Bangkok, Thailand
Tel.: (66) 2470 6330
Mutual Fund Management Services
N.A.I.C.S.: 524292

Thanyathanathavee Co., Ltd. **(1)**
1 Soi Rat Burana 27/1 Rat Burana Road, Bangkok, 10140, Thailand
Tel.: (66) 2470 6330
Mutual Fund Management Services
N.A.I.C.S.: 524292

KASKAD CORP.
Dimitar Petkov 119 ent B Fl 3 ap 92, Sofia, 1309, Bulgaria
Tel.: (359) 1 7472311549 **NV**
Web Site:
http://www.corpkaskad.com
Year Founded: 2015
Sales Range: Less than $1 Million
Emp.: 1
Scratch Poster Printing Services
N.A.I.C.S.: 323113
Piotr Sibov *(Pres, Treas & Sec)*

KASPERSKY LAB ZAO
39A/2 Leningradskoe Shosse, 125212, Moscow, Russia
Tel.: (7) 4957978700
Web Site: http://www.kaspersky.com
Year Founded: 1997
Sales Range: $600-649.9 Million
Emp.: 2,300
Security Software Developer
N.A.I.C.S.: 513210
Eugene Kaspersky *(Chm & CEO)*

Subsidiaries:

Kaspersky Lab Australia Pty Ltd **(1)**
Level 1/82 Lorimer Street, Docklands, '3008, VIC, Australia
Tel.: (61) 1300 930 655
Software Development Services
N.A.I.C.S.: 541511
Andrey Tikhonov *(COO)*

Kaspersky Lab Inc. **(1)**
15 Allstate Parkway 6th Floor, Markham, L3R 5B4, ON, Canada
Tel.: (905) 415-4594
Security Software Publisher
N.A.I.C.S.: 513210

Kaspersky Lab Lda **(1)**
Alameda dos Oceanos n 142 0 B, Lisbon, Sacavem, Portugal
Tel.: (351) 210 027 412
Software Development Services
N.A.I.C.S.: 541511

Kaspersky Lab Polska Sp z.o.o. **(1)**
Ul Trawiasta 35, Warsaw, 04-607, Poland
Tel.: (48) 34 368 18 14
Web Site: http://www.kaspersky.pl
Security Software Developer
N.A.I.C.S.: 513210
Katarzyna Kowalczyk *(Mgr-Admin)*

Kaspersky Lab Sea Sdn Bhd **(1)**
Level 11-02 Block A PJ8 No 23 Jalan Barat Seksyen 8, 46050, Petaling Jaya, Malaysia
Tel.: (60) 3 7962 6788
Web Site: http://www.kaspersky.com.my
Software Development Services
N.A.I.C.S.: 541511

Kaspersky Lab South Africa (Pty) Ltd **(1)**
Building 15 Thornhill Office Park Bekker Road Vorna Valley, Midrand, South Africa
Tel.: (27) 800222555
Web Site: http://www.kaspersky.co.za
Software Development Services
N.A.I.C.S.: 541511

Kaspersky Lab UK Ltd **(1)**
97 Milton Park, Abingdon, OX14 4RY, Oxon, United Kingdom
Tel.: (44) 8717 891631
Web Site: http://www.kaspersky.co.uk
Emp.: 140
Security Software Developer
N.A.I.C.S.: 513210
Malcolm Tuck *(Mng Dir)*

Kaspersky Lab, Inc. **(1)**
500 Unicorn Park Dr 3rd Fl, Woburn, MA 01801
Tel.: (781) 503-1800
Web Site: http://www.kaspersky.com
Sales Range: $25-49.9 Million
Emp.: 75
Security Software Publisher
N.A.I.C.S.: 513210
Randy Drawas *(Sr VP-Mktg)*

Kaspersky Labs Asia Pacific Ltd **(1)**
Rm 508-509 5/F International Plaza 20 Sheung Yuet Road, Kowloon, China (Hong Kong)
Tel.: (852) 3694 0437
Web Site: http://www.kaspersky.com.hk
Emp.: 20
Software Development Services
N.A.I.C.S.: 541511
Maxim Mitrokhin *(Dir-Ops)*

Kaspersky Labs GmbH **(1)**
Wienerbergstrasse 11 12a, A 1100, Vienna, Austria
Tel.: (43) 1 99 460 6400
Web Site: http://www.kaspersky.at
Security Software Developer
N.A.I.C.S.: 513210

Kaspersky Labs India Private Ltd **(1)**
Office No 801 & 808 8th Floor Platinum Techno Park, Plot No 17 & 18 Sector 30A, Mumbai, 400 705, India
Tel.: (91) 22 61992525
Web Site: http://www.kaspersky.co.in
Software Development Services
N.A.I.C.S.: 541511
Dipesh Kaura *(Gen Mgr-South-Asia Ops)*

Kaspersky Labs Japan K.K. **(1)**
Sumitomo Fudosan Akihabara Bldg 7F 3-12-8 Soto-kanda, Chiyoda-ku, Tokyo, 101-0021, Japan
Tel.: (81) 3 3526 8520
Web Site: http://www.kaspersky.co.jp
Software Development Services
N.A.I.C.S.: 541511

KASPI.KZ JSC
154a Nauryzbay Batyr St, 050013, Almaty, Kazakhstan
Tel.: (7) 7273306710
Web Site: https://ir.kaspi.kz
Year Founded: 2008
KSPI—(KAZ)
Rev.: $4,278,632,440
Assets: $15,254,085,238
Liabilities: $12,787,261,303
Net Worth: $2,466,823,935
Earnings: $1,897,880,238
Fiscal Year-end: 12/31/23
Online Payment Platform Services
N.A.I.C.S.: 522320
Mikheil Lomtadze *(CEO)*

KASSEM DARWISH FAKHRO & SONS
PO Box 350, Doha, Qatar
Tel.: (974) 4422739
Web Site: http://www.darwish-group.com
Year Founded: 1971
Sales Range: $25-49.9 Million
Emp.: 3,000
General Trading & Contracting
N.A.I.C.S.: 425120
Hasan Jassem Darwish Fakhro *(Partner)*

Subsidiaries:

Arabesque GRC **(1)**
Salwa Industrial Area Street No 41 Gate No 51, PO Box 4800, Doha, Qatar
Tel.: (974) 4600107
Building Interior & Exterior Design Services
N.A.I.C.S.: 541410

Darwish Contracting Co. W.L.L. **(1)**
3rd Floor Behind Darwish Travel Beureau Opposite Diwan Al Emiri, PO Box 3511, Al-Rayyan Rd, Doha, Qatar
Tel.: (974) 443 0670
Building Equipment Contracting Services
N.A.I.C.S.: 238290
Hazem Abu Ahmed *(Sec)*

Darwish Elevators Co. W.L.L. **(1)**
PO Box 4887, Doha, Qatar
Tel.: (974) 432 8261
Elevator Whslr
N.A.I.C.S.: 423830
Murugan Subian *(Sr Engr-Sls)*

Darwish Mechanical & Electrical Co. W.L.L. **(1)**
PO Box 3898, Doha, Qatar
Tel.: (974) 442 2810
Mechanical & Electrical Contracting Services
N.A.I.C.S.: 238210
Suresh Tharmalingam *(Mgr-Ops)*

Darwish Trading Co. W.L.L. **(1)**
Salwa Road Darwish Building, PO Box 92, Doha, Qatar
Tel.: (974) 4428164
Web Site: http://www.darwish-group.com
Whslr of Office Equipment, Electronic Equipment, Building Materials & Industrial Machinery
N.A.I.C.S.: 423420

Darwish Travel Co. W.L.L. **(1)**
PO Box 737, Doha, Qatar
Tel.: (974) 4433120

INTERNATIONAL PUBLIC

Web Site: http://www.dtco-qatar.com
Travel Agency Services
N.A.I.C.S.: 561510

Gulf Automobiles & Trading Co. W.L.L. **(1)**
PO Box 3899, Doha, Qatar
Tel.: (974) 4654777
Web Site: http://www.gulf-automobiles.com
Sales Range: $25-49.9 Million
Emp.: 23
Motor Vehicle Sales, Distr, Repair & Maintenance Services
N.A.I.C.S.: 441227

Oasis Hotel & Beach Club **(1)**
PO Box 717, Doha, Qatar
Tel.: (974) 4424424
Web Site: http://www.oasishotel-doha.com
Sales Range: $25-49.9 Million
Emp.: 80
Hotel & Resort Operations
N.A.I.C.S.: 721110

KASTNER EXETER
Sigford Road, Matford Park, Exeter, EX2 8NL, Devon, United Kingdom
Tel.: (44) 1392201040
Web Site:
http://volvocarsexeter.co.uk
Year Founded: 1927
Sales Range: $15-24.9 Billion
Emp.: 30,374
New & Used Car Dealer
N.A.I.C.S.: 441110
Mike Lloyd *(Dir-Franchise)*

KASUMIGASEKI CAPITAL CO., LTD.
3-2-1 Kasumigaseki Common Gate West Building 22nd Floor, Chiyoda, Tokyo, 100-0013, Japan
Tel.: (81) 355107651
Web Site:
https://www.kasumigaseki.co.jp
Year Founded: 2011
3498—(TKS)
Rev.: $408,560,700
Assets: $482,354,780
Liabilities: $309,818,200
Net Worth: $172,536,580
Earnings: $31,224,400
Emp.: 256
Fiscal Year-end: 08/31/24
Solar Power Generation Services
N.A.I.C.S.: 221114
Masato Kawaguchi *(Mng Dir)*

KAT EXPLORATION, INC.
1149 Topsail Road, Mount Pearl, A1N 5G2, NL, Canada
Tel.: (709) 368-9223
KATX—(OTCIQ)
Assets: $125
Liabilities: $22,267
Net Worth: ($22,142)
Earnings: ($44,142)
Emp.: 1
Fiscal Year-end: 11/30/22
Metal Mining
N.A.I.C.S.: 212290
Caren Currier *(CEO & CFO)*

KATADYN HOLDING AG
Birkenweg 4, 8304, Wallisellen, Switzerland
Tel.: (41) 44839211
Web Site:
http://www.katadyngroup.com
Sales Range: $25-49.9 Million
Emp.: 100
Water Purification System Mfr
N.A.I.C.S.: 326199
Trix Ammann *(CEO)*

Subsidiaries:

Aquafides Schweiz AG **(1)**
Pfaffikerstrasse 37, 8310, Kemptthal, Switzerland

AND PRIVATE COMPANIES

Tel.: (41) 44 835 22 00
Web Site: http://www.aquafides.com
Water Purification System Distr
N.A.I.C.S.: 423830

KNA Foods Llc. (1)
130 Cyber Ct Ste D, Rocklin, CA 95765
Tel.: (916) 624-6050
Water Purification System Distr
N.A.I.C.S.: 423830

Katadyn France (1)
5 rue Gallice, 38100, Grenoble, France
Tel.: (33) 4 76 96 42 46
Web Site: http://www.katadyn.fr
Emp.: 9
Water Purification System Distr
N.A.I.C.S.: 423830
Steven Le Guellec *(Mng Dir)*

Katadyn Germany GmbH (1)
Hessenring 23, 64546, Morfelden-Walldorf, Germany
Tel.: (49) 61 05 45 67 89
Web Site: http://www.katadyn.de
Water Purification System Distr
N.A.I.C.S.: 423830

Katadyn North America, Inc. (1)
6325 Sandburg Rd, Minneapolis, MN 55427
Tel.: (763) 746-3500
Web Site: http://www.katadyn.com
Sales Range: $25-49.9 Million
Emp.: 12
Water Purification System Mfr
N.A.I.C.S.: 326199

Katadyn Production srl. (1)
str Paris nr 11 Parcul Industrial, 507165, Prejmer, Romania
Tel.: (40) 727 005 006
Web Site: http://www.katadyn.ro
Emp.: 25
Water Purification System Distr
N.A.I.C.S.: 423830
Mike Greub *(Pres)*

Katadyn Singapore (1)
15 Jalan Kilang Barat Frontech Centre 06-01, Singapore, Singapore
Tel.: (65) 6276 1005
Web Site: http://www.katadyn.sg
Water Purification System Distr
N.A.I.C.S.: 423830

KATAKURA & CO-OP AGRI CORPORATION

Sumitomo Real Estate Kudan Building 15F 1-8-10 Kudankita, Chiyoda-ku, Tokyo, 102-0073, Japan
Tel.: (81) 352166611 JP
Web Site: https://www.katakuraco-op.com
Year Founded: 1920
4031—(TKS)
Rev.: $272,550,130
Assets: $321,550,060
Liabilities: $165,864,730
Net Worth: $155,685,330
Earnings: ($4,164,300)
Emp.: 827
Fiscal Year-end: 03/31/24
Agricultural Chemicals, Fertilizer & Animal Feed Additives Mfr & Distr
N.A.I.C.S.: 325320

KATAKURA INDUSTRIES CO., LTD.

6-4 Akashicho, Chuo-ku, Tokyo, 104-8312, Japan
Tel.: (81) 368321873
Web Site: https://www.katakura.co.jp
Year Founded: 1873
3001—(TKS)
Rev.: $283,401,480
Assets: $989,841,990
Liabilities: $356,244,140
Net Worth: $633,597,850
Earnings: $21,589,050
Emp.: 97
Fiscal Year-end: 12/31/23
Apparel & Automotive Parts Mfr
N.A.I.C.S.: 315120

Yoshio Furuta *(Sr Mng Dir-Machinery Div)*

Subsidiaries:

Katakura Career Support K.K. (1)
6-4 Akashicho, Chuo-ku, Tokyo, 104-0044, Japan
Tel.: (81) 362640741
Recruiting Services
N.A.I.C.S.: 561311

Katakura Caron Service Corporation (1)
6th Floor Nichirei Akashicho Building 6-4 Akashicho, Chuo-ku, Tokyo, 104-0044, Japan
Tel.: (81) 335415770
Web Site: https://www.katakura-cs.co.jp
Emp.: 757
Tree Planting Work Services
N.A.I.C.S.: 561730

Katakura Insurance Service K.K. (1)
6-4 Akashicho, Chuo-ku, Tokyo, 104-0044, Japan
Tel.: (81) 362640721
Fire Insurance Services
N.A.I.C.S.: 524128

Katakura Machinery Industries Co., Ltd. (1)
7160 Imai Omachi, Matsumoto, 390-1183, Nagano, Japan
Tel.: (81) 263584711
Web Site: http://www.katakurakiki.co.jp
Agricultural Machinery Mfr
N.A.I.C.S.: 333111

Nihon Kikai Kogyo Co., Ltd. (1)
2-31-1 Nakanomachi, Hachioji, 192-0041, Tokyo, Japan
Tel.: (81) 42 622 7281
Web Site: https://www.nikki-net.co.jp
Emp.: 200
Trucks Mfr
N.A.I.C.S.: 336110

Nitivy Company Limited (1)
Nichirei Akashi-cho Bldg 6F 6-4 Akashi-cho, Chuo-ku, Tokyo, 104-0044, Japan
Tel.: (81) 36 264 0757
Web Site: https://www.nitivy.co.jp
Emp.: 150
Fiber Mfr
N.A.I.C.S.: 325220
Michiaki Sagesaka *(Pres)*

Ogran Japan Co., Ltd. (1)
Minamisenba 1-17-9 Pearl Building the third Floor Yubinbango, Chuo-ku, Osaka, 542-0081, Japan
Tel.: (81) 642563730
Web Site: https://www.ogran-japan.co.jp
Emp.: 108
Underwear Mfr & Whslr
N.A.I.C.S.: 315120
Takaharu Shiraki *(Pres & CEO)*

Sanzen Seiyaku K.K. (1)
2-300 Amanumacho, Omiya-ku, Saitama, 330-0834, Japan
Tel.: (81) 486412691
Food Mfr
N.A.I.C.S.: 311999

Toa Eiyo Ltd. (1)
10-6 Hatchobori 3-chome, Chuo-ku, Tokyo, 104-0032, Japan
Tel.: (81) 355428800
Web Site: https://www.toaeiyo.co.jp
Emp.: 510
Pharmaceuticals Mfr
N.A.I.C.S.: 325412

KATALYSATOR S.A.

Wergelandsveien 27, 167, Oslo, Norway
Tel.: (47) 21 42 00 00
Web Site: http://www.katalysator.no
Holding Company; Investments
N.A.I.C.S.: 551112
Jon Hakon Pran *(Mng Dir)*

Subsidiaries:

Alfa Sko AS (1)
Mohagalia 1, 2770, Oppland, Norway
Tel.: (47) 61336900

Web Site: http://www.alfaoutdoor.com
Sales Range: $1-9.9 Million
Footwear Whslr
N.A.I.C.S.: 424340
Pal Olimb *(CEO)*

Norfolier Norge A/S (1)
Slynga 10, 2005, Lillestrom, Raelingen, Norway
Tel.: (47) 98238300
Web Site: http://www.norfolier.no
Sales Range: $75-99.9 Million
Emp.: 250
Plastics Films Mfr
N.A.I.C.S.: 322220

OneCo AS (1)
Andoyfaret 15, 4623, Kristiansand, Norway (70%)
Tel.: (47) 9100 9100
Web Site: http://www.oneco.no
Emp.: 900
Energy Industry & Infrastructure Electrical Engineering & Automation Services
N.A.I.C.S.: 541330
Marvin Jensen *(CEO)*

Vinestor AS (1)
Vollsveien 13 H, 1366, Lysaker, Norway
Tel.: (47) 66776898
Web Site: http://www.vinestor.no
Sales Range: $10-24.9 Million
Wine Distr
N.A.I.C.S.: 424820
Vidar Hovde *(Mng Dir & CEO)*

Subsidiary (Non-US):

NRG Pizza AB (2)
Master Samuelsgatan 44, Box 7733, 103 95, Stockholm, Sweden
Tel.: (46) 6638895
Web Site: http://www.pizzahut.se
Sales Range: $10-24.9 Million
Food Products Distr
N.A.I.C.S.: 424420
Bjorn Kallstrom *(CEO)*

Norfolier Baltic OU (2)
Peterburi Tee 81, 11415, Tallinn, Estonia
Tel.: (372) 6012175
Web Site: http://www.norfolier.ee
Sales Range: $25-49.9 Million
Emp.: 15
Plastics Product Mfr
N.A.I.C.S.: 326199

Norfolier GreenTec AS (2)
Gronvangsalle 2, 6600, Vejen, Denmark (100%)
Tel.: (45) 61 22 67 68
Web Site: http://www.norfolier.com
Sales Range: $25-49.9 Million
Emp.: 19
Plastics Product Mfr
N.A.I.C.S.: 326199

KATALYST DATA MANAGEMENT LP

540-5th Avenue SW Suite 1490, Calgary, T2P 0M2, AB, Canada
Tel.: (403) 294-5274
Web Site: http://www.katalystdm.com
Year Founded: 1985
Data Management Services
N.A.I.C.S.: 541512
Steven Darnell *(Pres)*

Subsidiaries:

Katalyst Data Management LLC (1)
10311 Westpark Dr, Houston, TX 77042
Tel.: (281) 529-3200
Sales Range: $1-9.9 Million
Emp.: 25
Data Management Services for Oil & Gas Operations
N.A.I.C.S.: 213112
Greg Hess *(VP-HR & IT)*

Katalyst Data Management LP - Denver Facility (1)
1700 Broadway Ste 410, Denver, CO 80290
Tel.: (303) 832-5086
Data Management Services
N.A.I.C.S.: 541513

Katalyst Data Management LP - Oklahoma Facility (1)
Union Plz 3030 NW Expy Ste 1203, Oklahoma City, OK 73112
Tel.: (405) 200-0227
Data Management Services
N.A.I.C.S.: 541513

Katalyst Data Management Limited (1)
Building 6 Unit 6/3 Mill Way, Sittingbourne, ME10 2PD, Kent, United Kingdom
Tel.: (44) 1795592370
Data Management Services
N.A.I.C.S.: 541513
Alan Clarke *(Mgr-Ops)*

Kdm Spectrumdata Pty Ltd (1)
32B Jamaica Drive, Grenada North, Wellington, 5028, New Zealand
Tel.: (64) 42329489
Data Management Services
N.A.I.C.S.: 541513
Anthony Duffy *(Mgr-Ops)*

Kdm Spectrumdata Pty Ltd (1)
357 Oxford Street, Hawthorn, 6016, WA, Australia
Tel.: (61) 861615354
Data Management Services
N.A.I.C.S.: 541513
Guy Holmes *(Sr VP)*

KATANA CAPITAL LIMITED

Tel.: (61) 892209888 AU
Web Site: https://www.katanaasset.com
Year Founded: 2005
KAT—(ASX)
Rev.: $923,259
Assets: $30,380,966
Liabilities: $805,266
Net Worth: $29,575,700
Earnings: ($216,066)
Fiscal Year-end: 06/30/22
Investment Management Service
N.A.I.C.S.: 523999
Gabriel Chiappini *(Sec)*

Subsidiaries:

Katana Asset Management Ltd (1)
Level 9 The Quadrant 1 William Street, Perth, 6000, WA, Australia
Tel.: (61) 89 220 9888
Web Site: https://www.katanaasset.com
Emp.: 2
Investment Management Service
N.A.I.C.S.: 523940
Romano Sala Tenna *(Portfolio Mgr)*

KATARE SPINNING MILLS LIMITED

Ground Floor B Wing 14/30 Ravivar Peth Akkalkot Road, Sholapur, 413005, Maharashtra, India
Tel.: (91) 2172376555
Web Site: https://katarespinningmills.com
Year Founded: 1980
502933—(BOM)
Rev.: $1,443,370
Assets: $4,343,778
Liabilities: $4,213,126
Net Worth: $130,651
Earnings: ($237,105)
Fiscal Year-end: 03/31/21
Cotton Yarn Mfr & Whslr
N.A.I.C.S.: 313110
Kishore T. Katare *(Mng Dir)*

KATEX AD

4 Manio Staynov str, 6100, Kazanlak, Bulgaria
Tel.: (359) 43162390
Web Site: https://www.katex.com
KTEX—(BUL)
Sales Range: Less than $1 Million
Worsted Fabric Mfr
N.A.I.C.S.: 339999
Iliya Dimitrov Vandov *(Chm-Mgmt Bd & CEO)*

KATHIMERINI PUBLISHING SA

Kathimerini Publishing SA—(Continued)

KATHIMERINI PUBLISHING SA
Ethnarhou Makariou Avenue & 2 Falireos Street, Neo Faliro, 185 47, Piraeus, Greece
Tel.: (30) 210 4808000
Web Site:
    http://www.ekathimerini.com
Year Founded: 1988
Emp.: 414
Newspaper Publishers
N.A.I.C.S.: 513110
Alexandros Papachelas *(Exec Editor)*

KATILIM VARLIK KIRALAMA A.S.
Saray Mahallesi Dr Adnan Buyukdeniz Caddesi No 10, Umraniye, 34768, Istanbul, Turkiye
Tel.: (90) 2168005555
Web Site:
    http://www.katilimvarlikkiralama.com
Asset Leasing Services
N.A.I.C.S.: 531390

KATIPULT TECHNOLOGY CORP.
900-903 8th Ave SW, Calgary, T2P 0P7, AB, Canada
Tel.: (403) 457-8008
Web Site: http://www.katipult.com
FUND—(TSXV)
Rev.: $1,376,967
Assets: $1,250,646
Liabilities: $3,793,307
Net Worth: ($2,542,661)
Earnings: ($1,187,856)
Fiscal Year-end: 12/31/22
Financial Advisory Services
N.A.I.C.S.: 523940
Ben Cadieux *(CTO)*

KATITAS CO., LTD.
4-2 Miharacho, Kiryu, 376-0025, Gunma, Japan
Tel.: (81) 277431033
Web Site: https://www.katitas.jp
Year Founded: 1978
8919—(TKS)
Rev.: $837,605,980
Assets: $511,389,260
Liabilities: $244,735,250
Net Worth: $266,654,010
Earnings: $56,165,170
Emp.: 843
Fiscal Year-end: 03/31/24
Real Estate Buying & Selling Services
N.A.I.C.S.: 531210
Katsutoshi Arai *(Pres & CEO)*

KATMERCILER ARAC USTU EKIPMAN SANAYI VE TICARET A.S.
Sokak No 10 A O S B, Cigli, 10032, Izmir, Turkiye
Tel.: (90) 2323767575
Web Site:
    https://www.katmerciler.com.tr
Year Founded: 1985
KATMR—(IST)
Rev.: $25,893,836
Assets: $84,756,607
Liabilities: $53,975,495
Net Worth: $30,781,113
Earnings: $2,552,792
Emp.: 411
Fiscal Year-end: 12/31/22
Trucks Mfr
N.A.I.C.S.: 336120
Mehmet Katmerci *(Pres, Member-Exec Bd, VP & Gen Mgr)*

KATO (HONG KONG) HOLDINGS LIMITED
1st Floor Tung Wai Court No 3 Tsing Ling Path, New Territories, Tuen Mun, China (Hong Kong)
Tel.: (852) 57442189
Web Site: https://www.elderlyhk.com
Year Founded: 1991
2189—(HKG)
Rev.: $52,180,531
Assets: $89,371,094
Liabilities: $41,709,203
Net Worth: $47,661,891
Earnings: $16,075,121
Emp.: 518
Fiscal Year-end: 03/31/23
Holding Company
N.A.I.C.S.: 551112
Chi Kan Kwok *(CFO)*

Subsidiaries:

Health Imaging & Check-Up Centre Limited (1)
1/F 168 Sai Yeung Choi Street South Exit B2 of Mongkok MTR Station, Kowloon, China (Hong Kong)
Tel.: (852) 37096072
Web Site: https://healthcheckuphk.com
Medical Laboratory Services
N.A.I.C.S.: 621511

KATO SANGYO CO., LTD.
9-20 Matsubara-cho, Nishinomiya, 662-8543, Hyogo, Japan
Tel.: (81) 798337650
Web Site:
    https://www.katosangyo.co.jp
Year Founded: 1947
9869—(TKS)
Rev.: $7,794,682,190
Assets: $3,211,528,940
Liabilities: $2,107,552,130
Net Worth: $1,103,976,810
Earnings: $85,094,180
Emp.: 1,127
Fiscal Year-end: 09/30/23
Dried, Canned & Processed Food Products Whslr
N.A.I.C.S.: 445110
Kazuya Kato *(Pres)*

Subsidiaries:

Hyogo Kono Co., Ltd. (1)
305 Jiro Arino-cho, Kita-ku, Kobe, 651-1611, Japan
Tel.: (81) 78 981 5185
Web Site: https://www.hyogo-kouno.co.jp
Emp.: 45
Jam Product Mfr & Distr
N.A.I.C.S.: 311421

K-Teion Foods Co., Ltd. (1)
5-43-1 Kitaitami, Itami, 664-0831, Japan
Tel.: (81) 727736800
Web Site: http://www.k-teionfoods.co.jp
Frozen Food Distr
N.A.I.C.S.: 424420

Lein Hing Holdings Sdn. Bhd. (1)
Lot PT 1756 Jln Persiaran KIP Utama Tmn Perindustrian KIP, Tmn Perindustrian KIP, 52200, Kuala Lumpur, Malaysia
Tel.: (60) 36 286 8686
Web Site: http://www.lhh.com.my
Tobacco Product Distr
N.A.I.C.S.: 424940
Kong Hong Meng *(Founder)*

Manna Unyu Co., Ltd. (1)
50-1 Shintamaki Kumiyama-cho, Kuse-gun, Kyoto, 613-0022, Japan
Tel.: (81) 774461190
Emp.: 570
Freight Car Transportation Services
N.A.I.C.S.: 488490

Mersion (M) Sdn. Bhd. (1)
Plot 2-28 Jalan TTC 8, Kawasan Perindustrian Cheng Mukim Cheng, 75250, Melaka, Malaysia
Tel.: (60) 63356353
Food Distribution Services
N.A.I.C.S.: 541614
Tong Hoe Soon *(Founder)*

Naspac Marketing Pte. Ltd. (1)
13 Senoko South Road, Singapore, 758074, Singapore
Tel.: (65) 65117300
Web Site: https://naspac.com.sg
Food Distr
N.A.I.C.S.: 424490

Subsidiary (Non-US):

Nasmark Sdn. Bhd. (2)
Unit 205 Block A4 Leisure Commerce Square No 9 Jalan PJS 8/9, 46150, Petaling Jaya, Selangor Darul Ehsan, Malaysia
Tel.: (60) 378730272
Food Distr
N.A.I.C.S.: 424490
Violet Ooi *(Bus Mgr)*

Sanyo Bussan Co., Ltd. (1)
1-3 Matsugaeda-cho, Kita-ku, Osaka, 530-0037, Japan
Tel.: (81) 663521121
Emp.: 225
Alcoholic Beverage Distr
N.A.I.C.S.: 424820

Toan Gia Hiep Phuoc Trading & Food Processing Join Stock Company (1)
144 Street 79 Tan Quy Ward District 7, Ho Chi Minh City, Vietnam
Tel.: (84) 837710351
Web Site: http://www.togico.vn
Food Distr
N.A.I.C.S.: 424490

Ueshima Co., Ltd. (1)
Tatsuta 2-chome 2-11 Ikaruga-cho, Ikoma, 636-0193, Nara Prefecture, Japan
Tel.: (81) 745741111
Web Site: http://www.ueshima-net.co.jp
Confectionery Product Whslr
N.A.I.C.S.: 424450

Wakayama Sangyo Co., Ltd. (1)
1-5-26 Kamimachi Minami, Higashine, 999-3765, Yamagata, Japan
Tel.: (81) 237470441
Web Site: https://www.zao-highland.com
Emp.: 130
Food Products Mfr
N.A.I.C.S.: 311421
Hitoshi Ishii *(Pres)*

KATO SANSHO CO., LTD.
KATOIHI Building 21-7 Nihonbashi Kabutocho, Chuo-ku, Tokyo, 103-8228, Japan
Tel.: (81) 3 3668 8898
Web Site:
    http://www.katosansho.com
Year Founded: 1909
Rev.: $273,000,000
Emp.: 112
Synthetic Rubber, Rubber ChemicalsPlastics, Machinery, Automotive ProductsGarage Equipments, Health Care ProductsRubber & Plastic Products Mfr
N.A.I.C.S.: 326299
Tatsuo Kato *(Pres)*

Subsidiaries:

Kasan Corp. (Malaysia) Sdn. Bhd. (1)
Suite C-10-06 Level 10 Block C Plaza Mont Kiara, No2 Jalan Kiara Mont Kiara, 50480, Kuala Lumpur, Malaysia
Tel.: (60) 3(6201)7602
Industrial Supplies Merchant Products Mfr
N.A.I.C.S.: 423440
Jiro Kanazu *(Mng Dir)*

Subsidiary (Domestic):

Saiko Rubber (Malaysia) Sdn. Bhd. (2)
No 49-51 Senawang Industrial Estate, 70450, Seremban, Negeri Sembilan, Malaysia
Tel.: (60) 66759955
Resource Recovery Services
N.A.I.C.S.: 562920

KATO WORKS CO., LTD.
9-37 Higashi-ohi 1-chome, Shinagawa-ku, Tokyo, 140-0011, Japan
Tel.: (81) 334581111
Web Site: https://www.kato-works.co.jp
Year Founded: 1895
6390—(TKS)
Rev.: $380,061,780
Assets: $696,231,300
Liabilities: $355,479,190
Net Worth: $340,752,110
Earnings: $27,993,350
Emp.: 1,009
Fiscal Year-end: 03/31/24
Construction Machinery Mfr
N.A.I.C.S.: 333120
Kimiyasu Kato *(Pres)*

Subsidiaries:

Kato Heavy Industries Construction Machinery Co., Ltd. (1)
3174 Showa-machi, Kanazawa-ku, Yokohama, 236-8611, Kanagawa, Japan
Tel.: (81) 45 771 1351
Web Site: http://www.kato-hicom.co.jp
Emp.: 299
Construction Machinery Mfr & Distr
N.A.I.C.S.: 333120
Yoshiki Inoue *(Pres)*

KATOEN NATIE N.V.
Van Aerdtstraat 33, 2060, Antwerp, Belgium
Tel.: (32) 32216811
Web Site:
    http://www.katoennatie.com
Year Founded: 1855
Sales Range: $50-74.9 Million
Emp.: 8,300
Provider of Stevedoring, Storage, Distribution, Shipping & Transportation Services
N.A.I.C.S.: 493110
Fernand Huts *(Chm & Pres)*

Subsidiaries:

Commodity Terminals International NV (1)
Luithagen Haven 9, 2030, Antwerp, Belgium (100%)
Tel.: (32) 35415194
Web Site: http://www.katoennatie.com
Sales Range: $25-49.9 Million
Emp.: 10
General Warehousing & Storage
N.A.I.C.S.: 493110
Chris Smout *(Mng Dir)*

Costa Oriental S.A. (1)
Ruta 8 Km 17500 S N, Edificio Costa Park, 12200, Montevideo, Uruguay (45%)
Tel.: (598) 25182566
Web Site: http://www.costaoriental.com
Sales Range: $1-9.9 Million
Emp.: 250
Provider of Logistics & Port Services
N.A.I.C.S.: 488310
Daniel Carriquiry *(Pres)*

Indaver N.V. (1)
Dijle 17 a, 2800, Mechelen, Belgium
Tel.: (32) 15 28 80 00
Web Site: http://www.indaver.com
Sales Range: $600-649.9 Million
Emp.: 1,687
Waste Management Solutions
N.A.I.C.S.: 562998
Michel Decorte *(CFO)*

Subsidiary (Non-US):

AVG Abfall-Verwertungs-Gesellschaft mbH (2)
Borsigstrasse 2, 22113, Hamburg, Germany
Tel.: (49) 40733510
Web Site: http://www.avg-hamburg.de
Special Waste & Chemico-Physical Treatment Services
N.A.I.C.S.: 562219
Andreas Ellerkmann *(Chm-Supervisory Bd & Mng Dir)*

Katoen Natie (Thailand) Ltd. (1)

AND PRIVATE COMPANIES

20 Muang Mai Map Ta Phut Ln 6 Rd, Huay Pong Sub District, Rayong, 21150, Thailand **(100%)**
Tel.: (66) 38643200
Web Site: http://www.kns.co.th
Sales Range: $75-99.9 Million
Emp.: 300
N.A.I.C.S.: 493110

Katoen Natie - Teesside Handling & Distribution Ltd. (1)
Northway North - Wilton International site, Redcar, TS10 4YA, United Kingdom
Tel.: (44) 1642 833 975
Emp.: 25
Deep Sea Freight Transportation Services
N.A.I.C.S.: 483111
Nathalia Jackobs *(Gen Mgr)*

Katoen Natie Amsterdam B.V. (1)
Cacaoweg 20, 1047 BM, Amsterdam, Netherlands
Tel.: (31) 205879720
Deep Sea Freight Transportation Services
N.A.I.C.S.: 483111
Eugene Bleekemolen *(Dir-Comml)*

Katoen Natie Automotive Contractors (1)
Van Aerdtstraat 33, 2060, Antwerp, Belgium **(100%)**
Tel.: (32) 32216811
Web Site: http://www.katoennatie.com
Sales Range: $25-49.9 Million
Emp.: 60
N.A.I.C.S.: 493110
Stefan DeVrieze *(Mgr-Bus Dev)*

Katoen Natie Brasil Ltda. (1)
CDM Paulinia Av viena 419, PO Box 920, Centro Industrial Paulinia, Sao Paulo, 13140-971, Brazil
Tel.: (55) 19 2116 1550
Web Site: http://www.katoennatie.com
Emp.: 1,000
Deep Sea Freight Transportation Services
N.A.I.C.S.: 483111
Rogerio Fernandes Pirana *(Mgr-HR)*

Katoen Natie Bulk Terminals Linkeroever (1)
Haandorp Weg Kaai 1227, 9130, Kallo, Belgium **(100%)**
Tel.: (32) 35706662
Web Site: http://www.katoennatie.com
Sales Range: $50-74.9 Million
Emp.: 1,000
Port Operations/Stevedoring
N.A.I.C.S.: 488310

Katoen Natie Bulk Terminals NV (1)
Haerdoupweg 1 Kaai 1227, Kallo, B 9130, Belgium **(100%)**
Tel.: (32) 35706743
Web Site: http://www.katoennatie.com
N.A.I.C.S.: 493110

Katoen Natie Canada (1)
18210 - 109th Avenue, Edmonton, T5S 2K2, AB, Canada
Tel.: (780) 489-9040
Web Site: http://www.katoennatie.com
Emp.: 35
Deep Sea Freight Transportation Services
N.A.I.C.S.: 483111
Roeland Ulenaers *(Mgr-Facility)*

Katoen Natie Cargo Agency NV (1)
Haandorp Weg 1, 9130, Kallo, Belgium **(100%)**
Tel.: (32) 32216811
Web Site: http://www.katoennatie.com
Sales Range: $1-9.9 Million
Emp.: 6
Distribution Terminal Operations
N.A.I.C.S.: 493110

Katoen Natie Chemicals South Africa Pty Ltd. (1)
1181 South Coast Road 4052 Mobeni, Durban, Kwazulu Natal, South Africa
Tel.: (27) 31 462 2954
Deep Sea Freight Transportation Services
N.A.I.C.S.: 483111
Simon Pollet *(Mgr-Terminal)*

Katoen Natie Commodities Antwerp (1)
Luithagen Haven 9 2030, Antwerp, Belgium
Tel.: (32) 3 570 44 00

Deep Sea Freight Transportation Services
N.A.I.C.S.: 483111
Chris Smout *(Mng Dir)*

Katoen Natie Cote d'Ivoire SA (1)
10 Rue des Foreurs Zone 3-16, PO Box 966, Abidjan, Cote d'Ivoire
Tel.: (225) 21 25 86 46
Deep Sea Freight Transportation Services
N.A.I.C.S.: 483111
Martijn Versteeg *(Mng Dir)*

Katoen Natie De Henares S.l. (1)
Avda de la Construction n 7 Poligono Industrial Miralcampo, Azuqueca de Henares, 19200, Guadalajara, Spain
Tel.: (34) 949 27 75 59
Deep Sea Freight Transportation Services
N.A.I.C.S.: 483111

Katoen Natie Deutschland GmbH (1)
Bruhler Strasse 60, Wesseling, 50389, Germany
Tel.: (49) 2236 721 667
Deep Sea Freight Transportation Services
N.A.I.C.S.: 483111

Katoen Natie Eesti AS (1)
Muuga Harbour Klaukse tee 1, Uuskula, Harjumaa, 74114, Estonia
Tel.: (372) 7833 000
Deep Sea Freight Transportation Services
N.A.I.C.S.: 483111
Mart Melles *(Mng Dir)*

Katoen Natie Flanders Container Terminals NV (1)
Van Aerdtstraat 33, 2060, Antwerp, Belgium **(100%)**
Tel.: (32) 32216811
Web Site: http://www.katoennatie.com
Sales Range: $25-49.9 Million
Emp.: 60
N.A.I.C.S.: 493110
Sernanv Huts *(CEO)*

Katoen Natie France (1)
Megazone Moselle Est, Farebersviller, 57450, Metz, France **(100%)**
Tel.: (33) 387297039
Web Site: http://www.katoennatie.com
Sales Range: $10-24.9 Million
Emp.: 17,000
Warehousing & Storage Services
N.A.I.C.S.: 493110
Laurent Beitz *(Gen Mgr)*

Katoen Natie Haventransport NV (1)
Van Aerdtstroat 33, 2060, Antwerp, Belgium **(100%)**
Tel.: (32) 32216811
Web Site: http://www.katoennatie.com
Sales Range: $25-49.9 Million
Emp.: 75
N.A.I.C.S.: 493110

Katoen Natie IOT Ltd. (1)
103 Spectra Hiranandani Business Park Powai, Mumbai, 400076, India
Tel.: (91) 22 66 77 27 00
Deep Sea Freight Transportation Services
N.A.I.C.S.: 483111
Rohan Nagpure *(Mgr-Fin)*

Katoen Natie Iberica S.L. (1)
Avenida de les Puntes s/n Poligono Industrial, 43120, Constanti, Tarragona, Spain **(100%)**
Tel.: (34) 977296850
Stevedoring, Storage, Distribution, Shipping & Transportation Services
N.A.I.C.S.: 493110

Katoen Natie Italia Srl (1)
Via della Conca 3, Cremona, 26100, Italy
Tel.: (39) 0372 4155 21
Deep Sea Freight Transportation Services
N.A.I.C.S.: 483111
Dirk Verwimp *(Pres)*

Katoen Natie Lojistik A.S. (1)
Barsan Antrepo Molla Feneri Yolu uzeri Ayaz Sokak No 36, Gebze, 41400, Turkiye
Tel.: (90) 262 751 23 30
Deep Sea Freight Transportation Services
N.A.I.C.S.: 483111

Katoen Natie Lojiṣtik Anonim Sirketi (1)
Katoen Natie Antrepo Karaduvar Mahallesi

Cumhuriyet Bulvari, Sokak No 7A, Mersin, Turkiye
Tel.: (90) 324 221 35 00
Deep Sea Freight Transportation Services
N.A.I.C.S.: 327910

Katoen Natie Louisiana (1)
2727 Parish Ln, Port Allen, LA 70767
Tel.: (225) 749-6011
Deep Sea Freight Transportation Services
N.A.I.C.S.: 483111

Katoen Natie Mexico (1)
Pical Pantaco Almacen 95, Barrion San Sebastian, 02040, Mexico, DF, Mexico **(100%)**
Tel.: (52) 5553532829
Sales Range: $10-24.9 Million
Emp.: 42
N.A.I.C.S.: 493110

Katoen Natie Midwest Inc. (1)
700 Chase St Ste 600, Gary, IN 46404
Tel.: (219) 949-2620
Web Site: http://www.katoennatie.com
Sales Range: $25-49.9 Million
Emp.: 30
Logistic Services
N.A.I.C.S.: 541614

Katoen Natie Northeast Inc. (1)
8 Greek Ln, Edison, NJ 08817
Tel.: (732) 287-8770
Deep Sea Freight Transportation Services
N.A.I.C.S.: 483111

Katoen Natie Nuth B.V. (1)
Industriezone De Horsel Industriestraat 2, Nuth, 6361 HD, Netherlands
Tel.: (31) 402 310 103
Deep Sea Freight Transportation Services
N.A.I.C.S.: 483111
Roger Driessen *(Mgr-Site)*

Katoen Natie Ruhr Logistik GmbH. (1)
Pawiker Strabe 20, Gelsenkirchen, 45896, Germany
Tel.: (49) 209 604 89 02
Deep Sea Freight Transportation Services
N.A.I.C.S.: 483111

Katoen Natie Services(Thailand) Ltd. (1)
20 Muangmai Maptaphut road Lane 6 Tambol Huaypong Amphur Muang, Rayong, 21150, Thailand
Tel.: (66) 38 643200
Deep Sea Freight Transportation Services
N.A.I.C.S.: 483111

Katoen Natie Singapore (Jurong) Pte Ltd (1)
1 Banyan Place, Jurong, 627841, Singapore
Tel.: (65) 6419 2500
Deep Sea Freight Transportation Services
N.A.I.C.S.: 483111
Wallace Tay *(Sr Mgr-Comml & Transportation)*

Katoen Natie Terminal Genk NV (1)
Vanaererdt Str 33, Antwerp, 2060, Belgium **(100%)**
Tel.: (32) 32216811
Sales Range: $25-49.9 Million
Emp.: 100
N.A.I.C.S.: 493110

Katoen Natie Truck & Trailer Service NV (1)
Haandorp Weg, Kaai 1227, 9130, Kallo, Belgium **(100%)**
Tel.: (32) 35706644
N.A.I.C.S.: 493110

Katoen Natie USA (1)
10925 State Hwy 225, La Porte, TX 77571
Tel.: (281) 941-1011
Web Site: http://www.katoennatie.com
Sales Range: $25-49.9 Million
Emp.: 100
Packaging & Storage Warehouse
N.A.I.C.S.: 493110

Katoen Natie Wesseling Logistik GmbH (1)
Curiesstrasse 8, Wesseling, 50389, Germany
Tel.: (49) 2232 566 420

KATOLEC CORPORATION

Web Site: http://www.katoennatie.com
Deep Sea Freight Transportation Services
N.A.I.C.S.: 483111

Trollhattans Terminal AB (1)
Hamnvagen, Stallbackahamnen, S 461 38, Trollhattan, Sweden
Tel.: (46) 52036070
Web Site: http://www.katoennatie.com
N.A.I.C.S.: 493110

KATOLEC CORPORATION
2-8-7 Edagawa, Koto-ku, Tokyo, 135-0051, Japan
Tel.: (81) 3 5683 7000
Web Site: http://www.katolec.com
Year Founded: 1967
Sales Range: $750-799.9 Million
Emp.: 1,980
Freight Transportation Services
N.A.I.C.S.: 488510
Eisuke Kato *(Pres)*

Subsidiaries:

KATOLEC AUTOMOTIVE SYSTEMS (GUANGZHOU) Co., Ltd. (1)
3 Xingda Road Huangpu, Guangzhou, Guangdong, China
Tel.: (86) 2082253550
Emp.: 445
Electronic Equipment Mfr & Distr
N.A.I.C.S.: 334419

KATOLEC DE BAJA CALIFORNIA, S.A. DE C.V. (1)
Boulevard Insurgentes 19208-5 Colonia Cerro, 22223, Tijuana, Baja California, Mexico
Tel.: (52) 6646259076
Emp.: 208
Electronic Products Mfr
N.A.I.C.S.: 334511
Rodolfo Camacho *(Mgr-Quality)*

KATOLEC DEVELOPMENT INC. (1)
6120 Business Ctr Ct Ste F200, San Diego, CA 92154
Tel.: (619) 710-0075
Electrical Appliance Mfr
N.A.I.C.S.: 335210
Brian Fukushima *(Mgr-Sls & Production Control)*

KATOLEC ENGINEERING (Thailand) Co., Ltd. (1)
Amata Nakorn Industrial Estate 700/811 Moo 1, Tambol, Phan Thong, 20160, Chonburi, Thailand
Tel.: (66) 38079983
Emp.: 30
Steel Products Whslr
N.A.I.C.S.: 423510

Katolec (HK) Co., Ltd. (1)
5/F China Travel Hip Kee Godown 2 1 Cheong Hang Road, Hung Hom, Kowloon, China (Hong Kong)
Tel.: (852) 29562552
Emp.: 12
Logistics Consulting Servies
N.A.I.C.S.: 541614

Katolec (Thailand) Co., Ltd. (1)
Saha Rattana Nakorn Industrial Estate, 115/5 Moo 4 Tambol Bangprakoo, Ayutthaya, 13260, Thailand
Tel.: (66) 35364333
Emp.: 664
Printed Circuit Board Package & Assembly of Electronic Parts
N.A.I.C.S.: 334412

Katolec Philippines Corporation (1)
103 East Main Avenue Special Export Processing Zone Laguna Technopark, Binan, Laguna, Philippines
Tel.: (63) 495410455
Emp.: 641
Electrical Appliance Mfr
N.A.I.C.S.: 335210

Katolec Suzhou Co., Ltd. (1)
Bldg D No 58 Yang Dong Road Suzhou Industrial Park, Suzhou, China
Tel.: (86) 51267262223
Emp.: 285
Electrical Appliance Mfr

KATOLEC CORPORATION

Katolec Corporation—(Continued)
N.A.I.C.S.: 335210

Katolec Vietnam Corporation (1)
Lot 41A-B Quang Minh Industrial Zone, Me Linh, Hanoi, Vietnam
Tel.: (84) 438182742
Emp.: 1,138
Electrical Appliance Mfr
N.A.I.C.S.: 335210
Hiromichi Takanezawa Sr. *(Mgr-Pur)*

Katolec West Co., Ltd. (1)
1-5-34 Higashibefu, Settsu, 566-0042, Japan
Tel.: (81) 663400162
Logistics Consulting Servies
N.A.I.C.S.: 541614

P.T. Katolec Indonesia (1)
Ejip Industrial Park Plot 8f Cikarang Selatan, Bekasi, 17550, West Java, Indonesia
Tel.: (62) 298970093
Emp.: 802
Electronic Products Mfr
N.A.I.C.S.: 334511

katolec malaysia sdn.bhd. (1)
150-C Jalan Kampung Jawa Bayan Lepas Free Industrial Zone Phase III, Bayan Lepas, Penang, Malaysia
Tel.: (60) 46432826
Emp.: 306
Electrical Appliance Mfr
N.A.I.C.S.: 335210

KATOMSK AS
Laki 11e, Tallinn, 12618, Estonia
Tel.: (372) 6775 671   EE
Web Site: http://www.katomsk.ee
Year Founded: 1993
Industrial Equipment Distr
N.A.I.C.S.: 423830

KATRIN FIELD INCORPORATED
Town and Country Southville Commercial Calabozo, Santo Tomas, Binan, 4024, Laguna, Philippines
Tel.: (63) 24636063   PH
Web Site: http://www.katrinfield.com
Laboratory Equipment Distr
N.A.I.C.S.: 423490

KATRINA GROUP LTD.
180B Bencoolen Street 11-01, Singapore, 189648, Singapore
Tel.: (65) 62924748   SG
Web Site:
    https://www.katrinagroup.com
Year Founded: 1995
1A0—(CAT)
Rev.: $44,925,396
Assets: $32,942,513
Liabilities: $37,895,933
Net Worth: ($4,953,420)
Earnings: ($1,020,980)
Emp.: 337
Fiscal Year-end: 12/31/23
Investment Holding Services
N.A.I.C.S.: 551112
Alan Keng Chian Goh *(Co-Founder, Chm & CEO)*

Subsidiaries:

Bayang At The Quay Pte. Ltd. (1)
3A River Valley Road 01-05, Singapore, 179020, Singapore
Tel.: (65) 63370144
Web Site: http://bayang.com.sg
Restaurant Operators
N.A.I.C.S.: 722511

Straits Organization Pte. Ltd. (1)
100 Beach Rd 16-09, Singapore, 189702, Singapore
Tel.: (65) 90589512
Web Site: http://www.stresidences.com
Lodging Services
N.A.I.C.S.: 721110
Gillian Ng *(Mktg Mgr)*

Tomo Izakaya Pte Ltd (1)
8 Raffles Ave 01-09, Singapore, 039802, Singapore
Tel.: (65) 63330012
Web Site: https://www.tomoizakaya.com.sg
Restaurant Services
N.A.I.C.S.: 722511
Ibuki Horie *(Gen Mgr)*

KATSURAGAWA ELECTRIC CO., LTD.
4-21-1 Shimomaruko, Ota-Ku, Tokyo, 146-8585, Japan
Tel.: (81) 337580181
Web Site: https://www.kiphq.co.jp
Year Founded: 1945
6416—(TKS)
Rev.: $52,165,520
Assets: $62,726,400
Liabilities: $19,321,280
Net Worth: $43,405,120
Earnings: ($4,336,640)
Fiscal Year-end: 03/31/22
Electronic Machinery Equipment Mfr & Distr
N.A.I.C.S.: 333310
Masanori Watanabe *(Pres & Dir)*

KATZ GROUP INC.
1702 Bell Tower 10104-103 Avenue, Edmonton, T5J 0H8, AB, Canada
Tel.: (780) 990-0505
Web Site: http://www.katzgroup.ca
Year Founded: 1990
Sales Range: $1-4.9 Billion
Emp.: 12,500
Holding Company; Retail Pharmacies & Drug Stores Owner & Operator
N.A.I.C.S.: 551112
Daryl Katz *(Chm)*

Subsidiaries:

WAM (RE) Development Management LP (1)
12420 - 104 Avenue NW Suite 200, Edmonton, T5N 3Z9, AB, Canada
Tel.: (780) 423-5525
Web Site: http://www.wamdevelopment.com
Real Estate Development Services
N.A.I.C.S.: 531390
Correna Craig *(Dir-Mktg)*

KAUCHUK J.S.CO.
Vitosha Blvd 39 floor 3 apartment 5, 1000, Sofia, Bulgaria
Tel.: (359) 34445109
Web Site: https://www.kauchuk.com
Year Founded: 1930
KAU—(BUL)
Sales Range: Less than $1 Million
Rubber Conveyor Belt Mfr
N.A.I.C.S.: 339999

KAUFMAN & BROAD S.A.
127 avenue Charles De Gaulle, 92220, Neuilly-sur-Seine, France
Tel.: (33) 141434343
Web Site:
    https://www.kaufmanbroad.fr
Year Founded: 1968
KOF—(EUR)
Sales Range: $1-4.9 Billion
Real Estate Business; Home, Apartment & Other Residences Developer
N.A.I.C.S.: 236115
Bruno Coche *(Exec VP-Fin)*

Subsidiaries:

Concerto Development SAS (1)
5 rue Saint-Georges, 75009, Paris, France
Tel.: (33) 155047901
Web Site: http://www.concerto-ed.com
Sales Range: $25-49.9 Million
Emp.: 5
Commercial Property Development Services
N.A.I.C.S.: 236220
Thierry Bruneau *(Gen Mgr)*

KAUFMANN & LINDGENS GMBH
Friedrich-List-Allee 71, 41844, Wildenrath, Germany
Tel.: (49) 243298890   De
Web Site:
    http://www.schweissgitter.de
Year Founded: 1952
Welded & Steel Wire Mfr
N.A.I.C.S.: 331110
Frank Niesten *(Mgr-Ops)*

KAULIN MFG CO., LTD.
11F No 128 Sec 3 MinSheng E Rd, Songshan District, Taipei, Taiwan
Tel.: (886) 227130232
Web Site: https://www.siruba.com
Year Founded: 1965
1531—(TAI)
Rev.: $46,455,474
Assets: $136,292,581
Liabilities: $18,978,383
Net Worth: $117,314,198
Earnings: ($1,615,782)
Emp.: 57
Fiscal Year-end: 12/31/23
Industrial Sewing Machine Mfr & Distr
N.A.I.C.S.: 333248

Subsidiaries:

Siruba Latin America Inc. (1)
11380 NW 36th Terrace, Doral, FL 33178
Tel.: (305) 477-4562
Sewing Machine Mfr & Distr
N.A.I.C.S.: 333248

KAUNO ENERGIJA AB
Raudondvario Pl 84, 47179, Kaunas, Lithuania
Tel.: (370) 37305650
Web Site:
    https://www.kaunoenergija.lt
Year Founded: 1963
KNR1L—(RSE)
Rev.: $68,174,689
Assets: $221,002,136
Liabilities: $110,773,737
Net Worth: $110,228,399
Earnings: $1,228
Emp.: 379
Fiscal Year-end: 12/31/21
Electric Power Distribution Services
N.A.I.C.S.: 221122
Nerijus Mordas *(Chm-Mgmt Bd)*

KAUSHALYA INFRASTRUCTURE DEVELOPMENT CORPORATION LTD
HB - 170 Sector III Salt Lake, Kolkata, 700106, India
Tel.: (91) 3323344148
Web Site: https://www.kaushalya.net
532925—(BOM)
Rev.: $180,054
Assets: $11,824,666
Liabilities: $6,289,710
Net Worth: $5,534,956
Earnings: ($861,098)
Emp.: 6
Fiscal Year-end: 03/31/20
Highway & Bridge Construction; Real Estate Development Services
N.A.I.C.S.: 531210
Sanjay Lal Gupta *(Sec)*

Subsidiaries:

Kaushalya Nirman Pvt. Ltd. (1)
HB 170 Sector III Salt Lk City, Kolkata, 700106, West Bengal, India
Tel.: (91) 3323583694
Sales Range: $25-49.9 Million
Emp.: 50
Roads & Highways Maintenance Services
N.A.I.C.S.: 237310

KAUSHALYA LOGISTICS LIMITED

INTERNATIONAL PUBLIC

19 Community Centre 1st & 2nd Floor East Of Kailash, New Delhi, 110065, India
Tel.: (91) 1141326013
Web Site:
    https://www.kaushalya.co.in
Year Founded: 2007
KLL—(NSE)
Rev.: $76,618,289
Assets: $17,052,670
Liabilities: $14,709,099
Net Worth: $2,343,572
Earnings: $856,908
Emp.: 142
Fiscal Year-end: 03/31/23
Logistic Services
N.A.I.C.S.: 541614

KAVANAGH COMMUNICATIONS
1 Beaufort Pklands, Railton Rd, Guildford, GU2 9JX, Surrey, United Kingdom
Tel.: (44) 1483238840
Web Site:
    http://www.kavanaghcomms.com
Sales Range: $10-24.9 Million
Emp.: 20
Commercial Photography, Communications, Corporate Communications, Event Marketing, Exhibit/Trade Shows, Public Relations, Publicity/Promotions, Strategic Planning/Research
N.A.I.C.S.: 541820
Kate Aldred *(Acct Mgr)*

KAVANGO RESOURCES PLC
Salisbury House Suite 425 London Wall, London, EC2M 5PS, United Kingdom
Tel.: (44) 2036515705   UK
Web Site:
    https://www.kavangoresources.com
Year Founded: 2017
KAV—(LSE)
Assets: $8,090,000
Liabilities: $300,000
Net Worth: $7,790,000
Earnings: ($1,740,000)
Fiscal Year-end: 12/31/21
Mineral Exploration Services
N.A.I.C.S.: 213115
Michael Foster *(CEO)*

KAVEH INDUSTRIAL CORPORATION
No.29 & 31, Kaveh Building, Gharani St, Ferdosi Sq, Tehran, 1581613916, Iran
Tel.: (98) 2152834
Web Site:
    http://www.kavehsafebox.com
Office Furniture Mfr
N.A.I.C.S.: 337214
Sayed Hossein Mousavi Natanzi *(CEO)*

Subsidiaries:

Kaveh Industrial Corporation - Isfahan Factory (1)
4th Street Jey Industrial Town, Isfahan, 81651 77584, Iran
Tel.: (98) 311 5721001 3
Safe Deposit Vault Mfr
N.A.I.C.S.: 332999
Mahmood Shabani *(Factory Mgr)*

Kaveh Industrial Corporation - Tehran Factory (1)
14th Km Ab Ali Road, Tehran, 1659875911, Iran
Tel.: (98) 21 77313079 80
Web Site: http://www.kavehsafebox.com
Safety Box & Door Mfr
N.A.I.C.S.: 332999
Saeid Farzin Tehrani *(Factory Mgr)*

AND PRIVATE COMPANIES

KAVEH PAPER INDUSTRIES COMPANY
No 11 Lotfi St 7-TIR sq, PO Box 158755195, 15898 65948, Tehran, Iran
Tel.: (98) 2188300570
Web Site: https://kavehpaper.com
Year Founded: 1988
KSKA1—(THE)
Sales Range: Less than $1 Million
Emp.: 212
Paper Mfr
N.A.I.C.S.: 322120

KAVERI GAS POWER LTD.
5 Ranganathan Garden Anna Nagar, Chennai, 600 040, Tamil Nadu, India
Tel.: (91) 4442172116
Web Site: http://www.kaveripower.com
Natural Gas Extraction Services
N.A.I.C.S.: 211130
S. Elangovan *(Chm & Mng Dir)*

KAVERI SEED COMPANY LTD.
513 B 5th Floor Minerva Complex SD Road, Secunderabad, 500 003, Telangana, India
Tel.: (91) 4049192337
Web Site: https://www.kaveriseeds.in
Year Founded: 1976
KSCL—(NSE)
Rev.: $153,598,208
Assets: $279,968,134
Liabilities: $93,334,318
Net Worth: $186,633,816
Earnings: $37,202,379
Emp.: 850
Fiscal Year-end: 03/31/23
Seed Farming & Processing Services
N.A.I.C.S.: 111191
Gundavaram VenkataBhaskar Rao *(Founder, Chm & Mng Dir)*

KAVIM RASKA A.D. RASKA
Mislopoljska bb, 36350, Raska, Serbia
Tel.: (381) 36 736 366
Web Site: http://www.kavim-raska.rs
KVIM—(BEL)
Sales Range: Less than $1 Million
Food Transportation Services
N.A.I.C.S.: 488490
Zeev Horen *(Chm-Supervisory Bd)*

KAVITA FABRICS LIMITED
105 Balaji Industrial Society-1, Udhana Magdalla Road, Surat, 395 007, Gujarat, India
Tel.: (91) 261 3018759
Web Site: http://www.kavitafabrics.com
Year Founded: 2005
Synthetic Fabric Mfr
N.A.I.C.S.: 313310
Harish Chandak *(Chm & Mng Dir)*

KAVVERI TELECOM PRODUCTS LTD
Plot No 31 to 36 1st Main 2nd Stage, Arakere Mico Layout Banerghatta Road, Bengaluru, 560076, India
Tel.: (91) 8041215999
Web Site: https://www.kavveritelecoms.com
Year Founded: 1991
KAVVERITEL—(NSE)
Rev.: $706,568
Assets: $38,889,108
Liabilities: $34,972,026
Net Worth: $3,917,082
Earnings: $2,242,858
Fiscal Year-end: 03/31/21
Telecom Products Mfr
N.A.I.C.S.: 238210

Rajpeta Kasturi Hanumenthareddy *(CFO & Dir-Ops, HR & Admin)*

Subsidiaries:

DCI Digital Communications. Inc. (1)
500 Van Buren St, PO Box 550, Kemptville, K0G 1J0, ON, Canada
Tel.: (613) 258-1120
Web Site: http://www.dci.ca
Sales Range: $25-49.9 Million
Emp.: 6
Filter Product Mfr
N.A.I.C.S.: 334419

New England Communications Systems Corp. (1)
427 Hayden Station Rd, Windsor, CT 06095
Tel.: (860) 640-6600
Web Site: http://www.qualitywireless.com
Sales Range: $10-24.9 Million
Emp.: 52
Wireless Infrastructure & Specialty Communications Systems
N.A.I.C.S.: 541330

Quality Communications Systems Inc. (1)
1985 Swarthmore Ave, Lakewood, NJ 08701
Tel.: (732) 730-9000
Web Site: http://www.qualitywireless.com
Turn-Key Solutions For Wireless Voice & Data Systems
N.A.I.C.S.: 541330
Brian Fortier *(Pres)*

Spotwave Wireless, Ltd. (1)
500 Van Buren St, PO Box 550, Kemptville, K0G 1J0, ON, Canada
Tel.: (613) 258-5928
Sales Range: $25-49.9 Million
Emp.: 10
Mobile Phone Signal Boosters Mfr
N.A.I.C.S.: 517112

Trackcom Systems International (TSI) (1)
2459 46th Ave, Lachine, H8T 3C9, QC, Canada
Tel.: (514) 631-8837
Sales Range: $25-49.9 Million
Emp.: 4
Wireless Data System Mfr
N.A.I.C.S.: 517112

KAWADA TECHNOLOGIES INC.
4610 Nojima, Nanto, 939-1593, Toyama, Japan
Tel.: (81) 763228822
Web Site: https://www.kawada.jp
3443—(TKS)
Rev.: $853,529,470
Assets: $1,059,173,180
Liabilities: $514,753,750
Net Worth: $544,419,430
Earnings: $49,846,010
Emp.: 2,447
Fiscal Year-end: 03/31/24
Metal Products
N.A.I.C.S.: 332999
Tadahiro Kawada *(Pres)*

Subsidiaries:

Fujimae Steel Co., Ltd. (1)
1-3-11 Takinogawa Kita-ku, Tokyo, 114-8562, Japan
Tel.: (81) 339155163
Web Site: http://www.fujimae.co.jp
Sales Range: $25-49.9 Million
Emp.: 8
Sales of Steel Materials, Cast Steel Products, Construction-Related Machinery & Tools
N.A.I.C.S.: 331221
Shinichi Kawada *(Pres)*

General Robotix, Inc. (1)
302 1-13-4 Ninomiya, 3050047, Tsukuba, Ibaraki, Japan
Tel.: (81) 298568511
Web Site: http://www.arbot.jp
Sales Range: $25-49.9 Million
Emp.: 7
Automated Control Systems Mfr
N.A.I.C.S.: 811198
Takakatsu Isozumi *(Pres)*

Kawada Construction Co., Ltd. (1)
6-3-1 Takinogawa, Kita-ku, Tokyo, 114-8505, Japan
Tel.: (81) 339155321
Web Site: http://www.kawadaken.co.jp
Sales Range: $100-124.9 Million
Emp.: 400
Bridge Construction Services
N.A.I.C.S.: 237310
Takuya Kawada *(Pres)*

Kawada Industries, Inc. (1)
1-3-11 Takinogawa, Kita-ku, Tokyo, 114-8562, Japan
Tel.: (81) 339154322
Web Site: https://www.kawada.co.jp
Sales Range: $350-399.9 Million
Emp.: 1,086
Electrical & Mechanical Engineering Services
N.A.I.C.S.: 541330
Tadahiro Kawada *(Pres)*

Subsidiary (Domestic):

New Central Air Service Co., Ltd. (2)
3177 Handa-machi, Ryugasaki, 301-0806, Ibaraki, Japan **(100%)**
Tel.: (81) 297621271
Web Site: https://www.central-air.co.jp
Oil Transportation Services
N.A.I.C.S.: 481211
Masami Okabe *(Pres)*

Kawada Robotics Corp. (1)
7th floor JPR Ueno East Building 1-3-5 Matsugaya, Taito-ku, Tokyo, 111-0036, Japan
Tel.: (81) 358303951
Web Site: https://www.kawadarobot.co.jp
Computer Equipment Mfr
N.A.I.C.S.: 334111
Kawada Tadahiro *(Pres)*

Kawada Technosystem Co., Ltd. (1)
1-25 Kanda Sudacho R Kanda Manseibashi Building 13F, Chiyoda-ku, Tokyo, 101-0041, Japan
Tel.: (81) 356571234
Web Site: http://www.kts.co.jp
Engineering Services
N.A.I.C.S.: 541330

Kyouryou Maintenance, Inc. (1)
Takinogawa 6-3-1 AK building, Kita-ku, Tokyo, 114-0023, Japan
Tel.: (81) 339108961
Web Site: http://www.hashi-mente.co.jp
Bridge Maintenance Services
N.A.I.C.S.: 237310

Toho Air Service Co., Ltd. (1)
4-7-51 Shinkiba, Koto-ku, Tokyo, 136-0082, Japan
Tel.: (81) 335223020
Web Site: https://www.tohoair.co.jp
Sales Range: $50-74.9 Million
Emp.: 200
Oil Transportation Services
N.A.I.C.S.: 481211
Masayuki Udagawa *(Pres)*

KAWADEN CORPORATION
225 Koiwazawa, Nanyo, 999-2293, Yamagata, Japan
Tel.: (81) 238492011
Web Site: https://www.kawaden.co.jp
Year Founded: 1940
66480—(TKS)
Sales Range: Less than $1 Million
Power Distribution Control Unit Mfr
N.A.I.C.S.: 335311
Satoshi Nishitani *(Chm)*

KAWAGISHI BRIDGE WORKS CO., LTD.
1-2-13 Higashi-Shimbashi, Minato-ku, Tokyo, 105-0021, Japan
Tel.: (81) 335725401
Web Site: https://www.kawagishi.co.jp
Year Founded: 1947
5921—(TKS)
Sales Range: $125-149.9 Million

Steel Product Mfr & Distr
N.A.I.C.S.: 332312
Ryuichi Kawagishi *(Pres)*

KAWAGUCHI CHEMICAL INDUSTRY CO., LTD.
6-42 Ryouke 4 chome, Kawaguchi, 332-0004, Saitama, Japan
Tel.: (81) 482225171
Web Site: https://www.kawachem.co.jp
Year Founded: 1937
4361—(TKS)
Rev.: $61,044,900
Assets: $59,130,600
Liabilities: $40,427,180
Net Worth: $18,703,420
Earnings: $1,807,950
Emp.: 160
Fiscal Year-end: 11/30/23
Chemical Products Mfr
N.A.I.C.S.: 325199
Hideyuki Yamada *(Pres)*

Subsidiaries:

Kawaguchi Chemical Industry Co., Ltd. - Business Development Division (1)
Yamada Bldg 8-4 Uchikanda 2-chome Chiyodaku, Tokyo, Japan
Tel.: (81) 332548481
Business Development Services
N.A.I.C.S.: 541720

KAWAI MUSICAL INSTRUMENTS MFG. CO., LTD.
200 Terajima-cho, Chuo-ku, Hamamatsu, 430 8665, Shizuoka, Japan
Tel.: (81) 534571213   JP
Web Site: https://www.kawai.co.jp
Year Founded: 1927
7952—(TKS)
Rev.: $530,069,120
Assets: $486,086,180
Liabilities: $200,924,170
Net Worth: $285,162,010
Earnings: $18,389,020
Emp.: 2,895
Fiscal Year-end: 03/31/24
Pianos & Musical Instruments Sales & Mfr; Musical & Gymnastics Schools Operator
N.A.I.C.S.: 339992
Hirotaka Kawai *(Chm, Pres & CEO)*

Subsidiaries:

KAWAI Australia Pty. Ltd. (1)
24A / 6-8 Herbert Street, Saint Leonards, 2065, NSW, Australia
Web Site: http://www.kawai.com.au
Musical Instruments Mfr & Whslr
N.A.I.C.S.: 316990

KAWAI Trading (Shanghai) Co., Ltd. (1)
Resources Times Square 28 Tower C No 500, Pudong New District, Shanghai, 200122, China
Tel.: (86) 2168593338
Web Site: http://www.kawaipiano.cn
Emp.: 15
Musical Instrument Whslr
N.A.I.C.S.: 423990

Kawai America Corporation (1)
2055 E University Dr, Rancho Dominguez, CA 90220-6411 **(100%)**
Tel.: (310) 928-6279
Web Site: http://www.kawaius.com
Sales Range: $25-49.9 Million
Emp.: 30
Musical Instrument Importer & Distr
N.A.I.C.S.: 423990

Subsidiary (Domestic):

Kawai America Manufacturing, Inc. (2)
2055 E University Dr, Compton, CA 90220-6411 **(100%)**
Tel.: (800) 421-2177

KAWAI MUSICAL INSTRUMENTS MFG. CO., LTD.

Kawai Musical Instruments Mfg. Co., Ltd.—(Continued)
Web Site: http://www.kawaius.com
Sales Range: $25-49.9 Million
Emp.: 30
Mfr of Fine Pianos
N.A.I.C.S.: 339992
Brian Chung (Gen Mgr)

Kawai Finishing, Inc. (2)
2001 Kawai Rd, Lincolnton, NC 28092-6976 (100%)
Tel.: (864) 848-9995
Sales Range: $10-24.9 Million
Emp.: 15
Finishing of Pianos & Organs
N.A.I.C.S.: 561990

Midi Music Center Inc. (2)
2055 E University Dr, Rancho Dominguez, CA 90220
Tel.: (708) 352-3388
Web Site: https://www.lowrey.com
Musical Instrument Mfr
N.A.I.C.S.: 339992

Kawai Europa GmbH (1)
Europark Fichtenhain A 15, 47807, Krefeld, Germany
Tel.: (49) 215137300
Web Site: https://www.kawai.de
Musical Instrument Distr
N.A.I.C.S.: 423990

Kawai France SAS (1)
9-11 Allee de l'Arche Tour Egee, 92671, Courbevoie, France
Tel.: (33) 170923500
Web Site: https://www.kawaipiano.fr
Musical Instrument Distr
N.A.I.C.S.: 423990

Kawai Piano (Russia) LLC (1)
St Dubininskaya house 57 building 4 Business Center, Brent, 115054, Moscow, Russia
Tel.: (7) 4959959868
Web Site: http://www.kawai.ru
Musical Instrument Distr
N.A.I.C.S.: 423990

Kawai UK Ltd. (1)
Unit 8 Dunfermline Court Maidstone Road, Kingston, Milton Keynes, MK10 0BY, Bucks, United Kingdom
Tel.: (44) 1908288160
Web Site: https://www.kawai.co.uk
Sales Range: $25-49.9 Million
Emp.: 6
Musical Instrument Mfr
N.A.I.C.S.: 316990

PT KAWAI Indonesia (1)
Jl Maligi Raya Lot J-4a Kawasan Industri KIIC, Karawang, 41361, Jawa Barat, Indonesia
Tel.: (62) 2189108947
Web Site: https://www.kawai-global.com
Sales Range: $25-49.9 Million
Emp.: 100
Musical Instrument Mfr
N.A.I.C.S.: 339992
Hiroshi Ushio (Pres)

PT. Kawai Music School Indonesia (1)
Jl Jalur Sutera Boulevard Ruko Spectra, Blok 23C No 6-7, Alam Sutera, Tangerang, Indonesia
Tel.: (62) 2180821492
Web Site: http://music.kawai.co.id
Music School Services
N.A.I.C.S.: 611610

KAWAKAMI PAINT MANUFACTURING CO., LTD.

Tsukaguchi Honmachi 2-41-1, Amagasaki, 661-0001, Hyogo, Japan
Tel.: (81) 664216325
Web Site: https://www.kawakami-paint.co.jp
Year Founded: 1945
4616—(TKS)
Rev.: $43,546,780
Assets: $59,158,960
Liabilities: $37,499,010
Net Worth: $21,659,950
Earnings: $1,439,270
Emp.: 139
Fiscal Year-end: 11/30/23
Paint & Coating Mfr & Distr
N.A.I.C.S.: 325510
Shigemitsu Nomura (Chm)

KAWAKIN HOLDINGS CO., LTD.

2-2-7 Kawaguchi, Kawaguchi, 332-0015, Saitama, Japan
Tel.: (81) 482591111
Web Site: http://www.kawakinhd.co.jp
Year Founded: 2008
Rev.: $356,954,940
Assets: $345,113,520
Liabilities: $185,548,800
Net Worth: $159,564,720
Earnings: $2,201,580
Emp.: 1,742
Fiscal Year-end: 03/31/19
Holding Company; Construction & Industrial Materials Mfr
N.A.I.C.S.: 551112
Shinkichi Suzuki (Pres & CEO)

Subsidiaries:

Dalian Hayashi Lost-Wax Industries Co., Ltd. (1)
No 7 Penghong Street Dalian Development Zone, Dalian, 116600, China
Tel.: (86) 411 8751 7711
Web Site: http://www.dlhayashi.com
Sales Range: $450-499.9 Million
Emp.: 115
Industrial Casting Machinery Mfr & Distr
N.A.I.C.S.: 333248
Xianggao Yu (Gen Mgr)

Hayashi Lost-Wax Industries Co., Ltd. (1)
445 Kurobe Nishiyamacho, Kashiwazaki, 949-4142, Niigata, Japan
Tel.: (81) 257482331
Web Site: http://www.hlw.co.jp
Precision Casting Steel Mfr
N.A.I.C.S.: 331513

Kawaguchi Metal Industries Co., Ltd. (1)
18-19 Miyacho, Kawaguchi, 332-8502, Saitama, Japan
Tel.: (81) 482591112
Web Site: http://www.kawakinkk.co.jp
Industrial Metal Machinery Mfr
N.A.I.C.S.: 333248

Kawakin Business Management Co., Ltd (1)
2-2-7 Kawaguchi, Kawaguchi, 332-8502, Saitama, Japan
Tel.: (81) 48 259 1114
Web Site: http://www.kawakinct.co.jp
Business Management Consulting Services
N.A.I.C.S.: 541611

Kawakin Core-Tech Co., Ltd. (1)
2-2-7 Kawaguchi, Kawaguchi, 332-0015, Saitama, Japan
Tel.: (81) 48 259 1113
Web Site: http://www.kawakinct.co.jp
Sales Range: $25-49.9 Million
Emp.: 4
Architectural Bearing Mfr
N.A.I.C.S.: 332991
Shinkichi Suzuki (Pres & CEO)

Kawakin Techno Solution Co., Ltd. (1)
18-19 Miya-machi, Kawaguchi, 332-8502, Japan
Tel.: (81) 48 259 1111
Web Site: http://www.kawatec.co.jp
Building Construction Damping Services
N.A.I.C.S.: 238390
Nobuo Suzuki (Pres)

Plant (Domestic):

Kawakin Techno Solution Co., Ltd. - Hyogo Factory (2)
272 Okiotsu Hanjo-cho Aza, Kasai, 675-2101, Hyogo, Japan
Tel.: (81) 790 49 2345
Damping Device Mfr
N.A.I.C.S.: 339999

Koyo Seiki Co., Ltd. (1)
Fronton Building 5th Floor 2-340 Katsushika-cho, Funabashi, 273-0032, Chiba, Japan
Tel.: (81) 47 434 3331
Web Site: http://www.koyo-sk.co.jp
Hydraulic Equipment Mfr & Distr
N.A.I.C.S.: 333998

Matsuda Seisakusho Co., Ltd. (1)
1-1 Kiyoku-cho, Kuki, 346-0035, Saitama, Japan
Tel.: (81) 480 22 2111
Web Site: http://www.mtd.co.jp
Sales Range: $25-49.9 Million
Emp.: 110
Injection Molding Machinery Mfr & Distr
N.A.I.C.S.: 333248

Subsidiary (Non-US):

Matsuda Manufacturing (Thailand) Co., Ltd. (2)
26/4 M 3 Lumlukka Rd T Ladsawai, Lam Luk Ka, Pathumthani, 12150, Thailand
Tel.: (66) 2 533 2977
Injection Molding Machine Mfr
N.A.I.C.S.: 333248

Nonagase Co., Ltd. (1)
5th floor Ichigo Sakurabashi Building 4-8-2 Hatchobori, Chuo-Ku, Tokyo, 104-0032, Japan
Tel.: (81) 335521311
Web Site: http://www.nonagase.co.jp
Emp.: 20
Seismic Vibration Control Devices Mfr
N.A.I.C.S.: 335999

KAWAMOTO CORPORATION

Tanimachi Building 2-6-4 Tanimachi, Chuo-ku, Osaka, Japan
Tel.: (81) 669438991
Web Site: https://www.kawamoto-sangyo.co.jp
Year Founded: 1931
3604—(TKS)
Rev.: $195,860,910
Assets: $129,218,890
Liabilities: $77,991,390
Net Worth: $51,227,500
Earnings: $2,650,610
Emp.: 243
Fiscal Year-end: 03/31/24
Medical & Textile Product Mfr & Whslr
N.A.I.C.S.: 339113
Makoto Fukui (Pres)

KAWAN FOOD BERHAD

Lot 129351 Jalan Sungai Pinang 4/19 Taman Perindustrian Pulau Indah, Selangor Halal Hub Fasa 2C, 42920, Pulau Indah, Selangor Darul Ehsan, Malaysia
Tel.: (60) 330991188
Web Site: https://www.kawanfood.com
Year Founded: 1960
KAWAN—(KLS)
Rev.: $62,059,496
Assets: $97,526,007
Liabilities: $13,532,817
Net Worth: $83,993,190
Earnings: $8,143,437
Emp.: 527
Fiscal Year-end: 12/31/22
Frozen Food Product Mfr
N.A.I.C.S.: 311412
Thiam Chai Gan (Chm)

Subsidiaries:

KG Pastry Marketing Sdn. Bhd. (1)
Lot 20 Jalan Pengapit 15/19, 40200, Shah Alam, Selangor, Malaysia
Tel.: (60) 355118388
Web Site: https://8013-my.all.biz
Sales Range: $75-99.9 Million
Emp.: 200
Baked Goods Distr
N.A.I.C.S.: 424490

Kawan Food Manufacturing Sdn. Bhd. (1)
Lot 20 Jalan Pengapit 15/19 Seksyen 15, Kawasan Perindustrian Miel, 40200, Shah Alam, Selangor, Malaysia
Tel.: (60) 126962752
Sales Range: $100-124.9 Million
Emp.: 300
Frozen Food Product Mfr
N.A.I.C.S.: 311412
Gan Thiam Chai (Chm)

Kayangan Manisan (M) Sdn. Bhd. (1)
Seksyen 15, Shah Alam, 40100, Selangor, Malaysia
Tel.: (60) 3 5511 1288
Web Site: http://www.kmanisan.com
Sales Range: $25-49.9 Million
Emp.: 10
Frozen & Fresh Food Products Mfr & Retailer
N.A.I.C.S.: 311412

KAWANISHI WAREHOUSE CO., LTD.

1-4-16 Shichinomiya-cho, Hyogo-ku, Kobe, 652-0831, Japan
Tel.: (81) 786717931
Web Site: https://www.kawanishi.co.jp
Year Founded: 1918
9322—(TKS)
Rev.: $165,203,730
Assets: $252,092,180
Liabilities: $96,459,730
Net Worth: $155,632,450
Earnings: $5,261,560
Emp.: 423
Fiscal Year-end: 03/31/24
Warehousing Services
N.A.I.C.S.: 493110
Jiro Kawanishi (Pres)

Subsidiaries:

Kawanishi Logistics (S) Pte. Ltd. (1)
10 Anson Road 29-06B International Plaza, Singapore, 79903, Singapore
Tel.: (65) 63234113
Freight Forwarding Services
N.A.I.C.S.: 488510

Thai Kawanishi Ltd. (1)
43 Thai CC Tower Room No 344 34th Floor South Sathorn Road Sathorn, Bangkok, 10120, Thailand
Tel.: (66) 26723122
Freight Forwarding Services
N.A.I.C.S.: 488510

KAWARTHA DAIRY LIMITED

89 Prince St W, PO Box 904, Bobcaygeon, K0M 1A0, ON, Canada
Tel.: (705) 738-5123
Web Site: https://www.kawarthadairy.com
Year Founded: 1937
Rev.: $22,953,467
Emp.: 100
Dairy Products Mfr
N.A.I.C.S.: 311514
Ila Crowe (Co-Founder)

KAWASAKI & CO., LTD.

2-9-10 Shinhama, Tadaoka-cho Senboku-gun, Osaka, 595-0814, Japan
Tel.: (81) 724398011
Web Site: https://www.kawasaki-corp.co.jp
Year Founded: 1971
3045—(TKS)
Rev.: $14,520,000
Assets: $55,137,280
Liabilities: $10,773,840
Net Worth: $44,363,440
Earnings: $4,598,000
Fiscal Year-end: 08/31/21
Apparel Product Mfr
N.A.I.C.S.: 315250
Hisanori Kawasaki (Pres & CEO)

AND PRIVATE COMPANIES

KAWASAKI HEAVY INDUSTRIES, LTD.

KAWASAKI GEOLOGICAL EN-GINEERING CO., LTD.
Mita Kawasaki Building 21115 Mita, Minato-ku, Tokyo, 108-0073, Japan
Tel.: (81) 354452071
Web Site: https://www.kge.co.jp
Year Founded: 1943
4673—(TKS)
Rev.: $65,419,430
Assets: $68,163,260
Liabilities: $38,286,000
Net Worth: $29,877,260
Earnings: $1,113,130
Emp.: 351
Fiscal Year-end: 11/30/23
Geological Survey Services
N.A.I.C.S.: 541360
Tadashi Naito *(Chm)*

KAWASAKI HEAVY INDUS-TRIES, LTD.
1-14-5 Kaigan, Minato-ku, Tokyo, 105-8315, Japan
Tel.: (81) 334352111   JP
Web Site:
  https://global.kawasaki.com
Year Founded: 1878
KHE—(DEU)
Rev.: $12,223,787,070
Assets: $17,715,963,360
Liabilities: $13,389,394,470
Net Worth: $4,326,568,890
Earnings: $167,741,970
Emp.: 39,689
Fiscal Year-end: 03/31/24
Personal & Industrial Machinery Mfr
N.A.I.C.S.: 333998
Katsuya Yamamoto *(Mng Exec Officer & Gen Mgr-Corp Plng Div)*

Subsidiaries:

Akashi Ship Model Basin Co., Ltd. (1)
3-1 Kawasaki-cho, Akashi, 673-0014, Japan
Tel.: (81) 78 922 1200
Web Site: https://www.khi.co.jp
Hydrodynamics Experimental Research Services
N.A.I.C.S.: 541715

Alna Yusoki-Yohin Co., Ltd. (1)
665-2 Sawada Yoro-cho, Yoro-gun, Gifu, 503-1241, Japan
Tel.: (81) 584 32 3332
Car Door & Window Frames Mfr
N.A.I.C.S.: 336390

Anhui Conch Kawasaki Energy Conservation Equipment Manufacturing Co., Ltd. (1)
1F Conch International Conference Center 1007 South Jiuhua Road, Wuhu, 241136, Anhui, China
Tel.: (86) 5538398015
Industrial Equipment Mfr
N.A.I.C.S.: 333248

Anhui Conch Kawasaki Engineering Co., Ltd. (1)
3F Conch International Conference Center 1007 South Jiuhua Road, Wuhu, 241136, Anhui, China
Tel.: (86) 5538398606
Industrial Equipment Mfr
N.A.I.C.S.: 333248

Anhui Conch Kawasaki Equipment Manufacturing Co., Ltd. (1)
Yijiang Zone, Huolongang Town, Wuhu, 241138, Anhui, China
Tel.: (86) 5538399692
Industrial Equipment Mfr
N.A.I.C.S.: 333248

Benic Solution Corporation (1)
1-1 Kawasaki-cho, Kawasaki Heavy Industries Akashi Factory, Akashi, 673-8666, Hyogo, Japan
Tel.: (81) 78 921 8521
Web Site: https://www.benic.co.jp
Emp.: 338
Information Technology Consulting Services
N.A.I.C.S.: 541512

Canadian Kawasaki Motors, Inc. (1)
101 Thermos Road, Toronto, M1L 4W8, ON, Canada (100%)
Tel.: (416) 445-7775
Web Site: https://www.kawasaki.ca
Sales Range: $25-49.9 Million
Emp.: 25
Mfr of Trucks, Marketing & Sales of Motorcycles, Trucks, Jet Skis
N.A.I.C.S.: 336120

Changzhou Kawasaki & Kwang Yang Engine Co., Ltd. (1)
No 10-1 Lvtang Road, Xinbei District, Changzhou, 213132, Jiangsu, China
Tel.: (86) 5196 819 9040
Web Site: https://www.kawasaki-engines.com.cn
Industrial Equipment Mfr
N.A.I.C.S.: 333248

Dalian Cosco KHI Ship Engineering Co., Ltd. (1)
No 20 Haiyun Road Lvshun Development Zone, Dalian, Liaoning, China
Tel.: (86) 41139368217
Industrial Equipment Mfr
N.A.I.C.S.: 333248

EarthTechnica Co., Ltd. (1)
Tokyo Tatemono Jimbocho Bldg 2-4 Kanda-Jimbocho, Chiyoda-ku, Tokyo, 101-0051, Japan
Tel.: (81) 332 307 1519
Web Site: https://www.earthtechnica.co.jp
Sales Range: $125-149.9 Million
Emp.: 325
Steel & Iron Mfr & Distr
N.A.I.C.S.: 331110
Masaki Hamaguchi *(Pres)*

Unit (Domestic):

EarthTechnica Co., Ltd. - Yachiyo Works (2)
1780 Kamikoya, Yachiyo, 276-0022, Chiba, Japan
Tel.: (81) 47 483 1111
Iron & Steel Products Mfr
N.A.I.C.S.: 331110

EarthTechnica M&S Co., Ltd. (1)
1780 Kamikoya, Yachiyo, 276-0022, Chiba, Japan
Tel.: (81) 47 486 3600
Web Site: http://www.khi.co.jp
Industrial Plant Construction Services
N.A.I.C.S.: 236210

Flutek, Co Ltd. (1)
192-11 Shinchon-dong 6 Gongdan-ro 98 beon-gil, Seongsan-gu, Changwon, Gyeongsangnam-do, Korea (South)
Tel.: (82) 55 570 5700
Web Site: https://www.flutek.co.kr
Emp.: 150
Hydraulic Pumps Mfr
N.A.I.C.S.: 333914

Plant (Domestic):

Flutek, Ltd. - Uiryeong Plant (2)
Samga ri 79-2 Bongsu Myeon, Kyungnam, Uiryeong, Kyungnam, Korea (South)
Tel.: (82) 55 574 5744
Steering Gears Mfr
N.A.I.C.S.: 333612

Fukae Powtec Corporation (1)
2-19 Miyahara 4-chome, Yodogawa-ku, Osaka, 532-0003, Japan
Tel.: (81) 6 6394 0401
Web Site: http://www.fukae-powtec.co.jp
Industrial Equipment Mfr & Distr
N.A.I.C.S.: 333248

Gifu Technical Institute (1)
1 Kawasaki Cho Kakamigahara, Gifu, 5048710, Japan (100%)
Tel.: (81) 583825712
Sales Range: $700-749.9 Million
Emp.: 3,000
Engineering Services
N.A.I.C.S.: 541330

Hainan Sundiro-Kawasaki Engine Co., Ltd. (1)
Lingui Dadao No 3 Guilinyang Economic Development Area, Qiongshan, 570125, Hainan, China

Tel.: (86) 898 5711586
Web Site: http://www.khi.co.jp
Fluid Power Pumps & Motors
N.A.I.C.S.: 333996

Hydrogen Engineering Australia Pty Ltd (1)
Level 6 Suite 6 09 2 Queen Street, Melbourne, 3000, VIC, Australia
Tel.: (61) 404809288
Industrial Equipment Mfr
N.A.I.C.S.: 333248
Hirofumi Kawazoe *(Gen Mgr)*

India Kawasaki Motors Pvt. Ltd. (1)
Mumbai Pune Road, Akurdi, Pune, 411035, Maharashtra, India
Tel.: (91) 20 2740 7503
Motorcycle Import & Distr
N.A.I.C.S.: 441227
Shishir Sinha *(Dir-Sls & Mktg)*

K Career Partners Corp. (1)
Mitsui Kobe Bldg 35 Nishi-machi, Chuo-ku, Kobe, 650-0038, Hyogo, Japan
Tel.: (81) 78 322 1100
Web Site: http://www.khi.co.jp
Engineering Services
N.A.I.C.S.: 541330

K-GES Co., Ltd. (1)
1-1 Kawasaki-cho, Akashi, 673-8666, Hyogo, Japan
Tel.: (81) 78 927 2941
Web Site: http://www.khi.co.jp
Automotive Engine Parts Mfr
N.A.I.C.S.: 336390

K-Tec Corp. (1)
1-1 Kawasaki-cho, Chuo-ku, Akashi, 673-0014, Hyogo, Japan
Tel.: (81) 78 921 1438
Web Site: http://www.ktec-kobe.co.jp
Motorcycle Parts Mfr
N.A.I.C.S.: 336991
Koji Ogawa *(Pres)*

KCMA Corporation (1)
2140 Barrett Park Dr Ste 101, Kennesaw, GA 30144-3614
Tel.: (770) 499-7000
Web Site: http://www.kawasakiloaders.com
Emp.: 50
Agricultural Machinery Mfr & Distr
N.A.I.C.S.: 333111
Gary Bell *(Gen Mgr)*

KCMJ Corporation (1)
509-1 Tsuchiyama Hiraoka-cho, Kakogawa, 675-0104, Hyogo, Japan
Tel.: (81) 78 944 1175
Construction Machinery Distr
N.A.I.C.S.: 423810

KEE Environmental Construction Co., Ltd. (1)
1-22 Nishidaimotsu-cho, Amagasaki, 660-0827, Hyogo, Japan
Tel.: (81) 6 6482 5001
Plant Construction Engineering Services
N.A.I.C.S.: 236210

KEE Environmental Service, Ltd. (1)
11-1 Minamisuna 2-chome, Koto-ku, Tokyo, 136-8588, Japan
Tel.: (81) 3 3645 2217
Plant Construction Engineering Services
N.A.I.C.S.: 236210

KHI (Dalian) Computer Technology Co., Ltd. (1)
Room 205 International Software Service Center Dalian Software Park, 18 Software Park Road, Dalian, China
Tel.: (86) 41184748270
Industrial Equipment Mfr
N.A.I.C.S.: 333248

KHI Design & Technical Service, Inc. (1)
Unit 1503-P 15th Flr Five E-com Center Pacific Drive, Mall Of Asia Complex, Pasay, 1300, Metro Manila, Philippines (100%)
Tel.: (63) 2 802 5406
Web Site: https://www.kdt.com.ph
Sales Range: $25-49.9 Million
Emp.: 194
Provider of Software Services
N.A.I.C.S.: 541511
Seitaro Ogiso *(Pres)*

KHI JPS Co., Ltd. (1)
1-1 Higashikawasaki-cho 3-chome, Chuo-ku, Kobe, 650-8670, Hyogo, Japan
Tel.: (81) 78 682 5162
Web Site: https://www.khi.co.jp
Ship Building Services
N.A.I.C.S.: 336611

KHITKAN Co., Ltd. (1)
119/18 Moo4 Pluak Daeng-Wangtaphin Sapansi Road, Tambon Pluak Daeng, Rayong, 21140, Thailand
Tel.: (66) 3 895 5062
Motorcycle Spare Parts Mfr
N.A.I.C.S.: 336991

Kansai Engineering Co., Ltd. (1)
Kikuya Dai 2 Bldg 202-3 Sugawara-dori 4-chome, Nagata-ku, Kobe, 653-0015, Hyogo, Japan
Tel.: (81) 78 578 7680
Engineering Services
N.A.I.C.S.: 541330

Kanto Technical Institute (1)
Goko Nisi 6 12 1, Matsudo, 278 8585, Japan (100%)
Tel.: (81) 473895121
Sales Range: $25-49.9 Million
Emp.: 40
Engineering Services
N.A.I.C.S.: 541330

Kawaju Akashi Engineering Co., Ltd. (1)
1-1 Kawasaki-cho, Akashi, 673-8666, Hyogo, Japan
Tel.: (81) 78 921 1925
Industrial Machinery Mfr
N.A.I.C.S.: 333248

Kawaju Facilitech Co., Ltd. (1)
8 Niijima Harima-cho, Kako-gun, Hyogo, 675-0155, Japan
Tel.: (81) 79 435 2128
Web Site: https://www.khi.co.jp
Plant Construction Engineering Services
N.A.I.C.S.: 236210

Kawaju Gifu Engineering Co., Ltd. (1)
2 Kawasaki-cho, Kakamigahara, 504-0971, Gifu, Japan
Tel.: (81) 58 389 4633
Industrial Engineering Services
N.A.I.C.S.: 541330

Kawaju Gifu Manufacturing Co., Ltd. (1)
1 Kawasaki-cho, Kakamigahara, 504-0971, Gifu, Japan
Tel.: (81) 58 389 3390
Web Site: http://www.khi.co.jp
Aerospace Parts Mfr
N.A.I.C.S.: 336413

Kawaju Gifu Service Co., Ltd. (1)
1 Kawasaki-cho, Kakamigahara, 504-8710, Gifu, Japan
Tel.: (81) 58 389 0048
Web Site: http://www.khi.co.jp
Emp.: 250
Aerospace Engineering Services
N.A.I.C.S.: 541330

Kawaju Kobe Support Co., Ltd. (1)
1-1 Higashikawasaki-cho 3-chome, Chuo-ku, Kobe, 650-8670, Hyogo, Japan
Tel.: (81) 78 682 5450
Web Site: http://global.kawasaki.com
Civil Engineering Construction Services
N.A.I.C.S.: 237990

Kawaju Marine Engineering Co., Ltd. (1)
1-1 Higashikawasaki-cho 3-chome, Chuo-ku, Kobe, 650-0044, Hyogo, Japan
Tel.: (81) 78 682 5401
Web Site: http://www.khi.co.jp
Ship Building Services
N.A.I.C.S.: 336611

Kawaju Service Corp. (1)
1-1 Kawasaki-cho, Akashi, 673-0014, Hyogo, Japan
Tel.: (81) 78 921 0444
Web Site: https://global.kawasaki.com
Ship Building Services
N.A.I.C.S.: 336611

KAWASAKI HEAVY INDUSTRIES, LTD.

Kawasaki Heavy Industries, Ltd.—(Continued)

Kawaju Steel Work & Engineering Co., Ltd. (1)
9-27 Kitaminatomachi, Wakamatsu-ku, Kitakyushu, 808-0027, Fukuoka, Japan
Tel.: (81) 93 771 2368
Steel Products Mfr
N.A.I.C.S.: 331110

Kawaju Support Co., Ltd. (1)
1-1 Higashikawasaki-cho 3-chome, Chuo-ku, Kobe, 650-0044, Hyogo, Japan
Tel.: (81) 786825450
Industrial Equipment Mfr
N.A.I.C.S.: 333248

Kawajyu Shoji Co., Ltd. (1)
8 Kaigandori Chuo-ku, Kobe, 650-0024, Hyogo, Japan
Tel.: (81) 783921131
Sales Range: $100-124.9 Million
Emp.: 300
Construction Equipment Mfr
N.A.I.C.S.: 333248
Keiji Matsumura *(Pres)*

Kawasaki (Chongqing) Robotics Engineering Co., Ltd. (1)
No 301 Yunhan Street, Shuitu Industrial Park Beibei District, Chongqing, China
Tel.: (86) 2363173088
Automobile Mfr
N.A.I.C.S.: 336110

Kawasaki Chunhui Precision Machinery (Zhejiang) Ltd. (1)
No 200 YaSha Road, Shangyu Economic Development Zone, Shangyu, 312300, Zhejiang, China
Tel.: (86) 5758 215 6999
Web Site: http://www.khi.co.jp
Precision Machinery Mfr
N.A.I.C.S.: 333248

Kawasaki Construction Machinery Corp. of America (1)
2140 Barrett Park Dr NW Ste 101, Kennesaw, GA 30144-3673
Tel.: (770) 499-7000
Web Site: http://www.kawasakiloaders.com
Sales Range: $25-49.9 Million
Emp.: 50
Mfr of Wheel Loaders
N.A.I.C.S.: 423810
Garry Bell *(VP)*

Kawasaki Engineering Co., Ltd. (1)
4 Kawanishidori 2-chome, Nagata-ku, Kobe, 653-0834, Hyogo, Japan
Tel.: (81) 786128570
Industrial Equipment Mfr
N.A.I.C.S.: 333248

Kawasaki Environmental Plant Engineering Co., Ltd. (1)
5F SA Building 17-12 Kiba, Koto-ku, Tokyo, 135-0042, Japan
Tel.: (81) 358098360
Industrial Equipment Mfr
N.A.I.C.S.: 333248

Kawasaki Gas Turbine Asia Sdn. Bhd. (1)
No 12A Jalan Tiang U8/92 Seksyen U8, Bukit Jelutong Industrial Park, 40150, Shah Alam, Selangor, Malaysia
Tel.: (60) 37 846 2882
Web Site: https://www.kga.com.my
Sales Range: $25-49.9 Million
Emp.: 29
Gas Turbine Generator Mfr & Distr
N.A.I.C.S.: 333611

Kawasaki Gas Turbine Europe GmbH (1)
Nehringstrasse 15, 61352, Bad Homburg, Germany (100%)
Tel.: (49) 61 727 3630
Web Site: https://www.kawasaki-gasturbine.de
Emp.: 40
Steam, Gas & Hydraulic Turbines & Turbine Generator Set Units
N.A.I.C.S.: 333611
Kimihisa Kitamura *(Mng Dir)*

Kawasaki Heavy Industries (1)
12th Fl Skyline Bldg JL MH Thamrin 9, Jakarta, 10340, Indonesia (100%)
Tel.: (62) 213140737
Sales Range: $50-74.9 Million
Emp.: 2
Motor Vehicle Parts & Accessories
N.A.I.C.S.: 423120

Kawasaki Heavy Industries (Europe) B.V. (1)
7th Fl Rivierstaete Amsteldijk 166, Amsterdam, 1079 LH, Netherlands (100%)
Tel.: (31) 206446869
Rev.: $1,291,280
Emp.: 6
Motor Vehicle Parts & Accessories
N.A.I.C.S.: 336340

Kawasaki Heavy Industries (H.K.) Ltd. (1)
Rooms 3710-14 Sun Hung Kai Centre 30 Harbour Road, Wanchai, China (Hong Kong) (100%)
Tel.: (852) 2 522 3560
Web Site: http://www.khi.com.jp
Sales Range: Less than $1 Million
Emp.: 6
Motor Vehicle Parts & Accessories
N.A.I.C.S.: 336340
Kayoshi Uetani *(CEO)*

Kawasaki Heavy Industries (India) Pvt. Ltd. (1)
Plot No 136 Sector-37 Pace City 1, Gurgaon, 122101, Haryana, India
Tel.: (91) 1244371845
Engineering Equipment Distr
N.A.I.C.S.: 423490

Kawasaki Heavy Industries (Singapore) Pte. Ltd. (1)
6 Battery Rd 23 01 Standard Chartered Bank Bldg, Singapore, 049909, Singapore (100%)
Tel.: (65) 62255133
Sales Range: $25-49.9 Million
Emp.: 18
Motor Vehicle Parts & Accessories
N.A.I.C.S.: 336340
Ryo Yamasaki *(Gen Mgr-Sls)*

Kawasaki Heavy Industries (Thailand) Co., Ltd. (1)
28th FL Sathorn Square Office Tower 98 North Sathorn Road Silom, Bangrak, Bangkok, 10500, Thailand
Tel.: (66) 21632839
Industrial Equipment Mfr
N.A.I.C.S.: 333248

Kawasaki Heavy Industries (U.S.A.), Inc. (1)
60 E 42nd St Ste 2501, New York, NY 10165 (100%)
Tel.: (917) 475-1195
Web Site: http://www.khi.co.jp.com
Sales Range: $10-24.9 Million
Emp.: 3
Sales Promotion & Liaison for Aircraft, Industrial Plants & Shipbuilding
N.A.I.C.S.: 541613

Branch (Domestic):

Kawasaki Heavy Industries USA Inc (2)
333 Clay St Ste 4310, Houston, TX 77002 (100%)
Tel.: (713) 654-8981
Engineering Liaison Office
N.A.I.C.S.: 423110

Kawasaki Heavy Industries (UK) Ltd. (1)
4th Fl 3 St Helens Pl, London, EC3A 6AB, United Kingdom (100%)
Tel.: (44) 2075885222
Rev.: $2,956,420
Emp.: 5
Motorcycles, Bicycles & Parts
N.A.I.C.S.: 336991

Kawasaki Heavy Industries Machinery Trading (Shanghai) Co., Ltd. (1)
808 Room Centro 568 Hengfeng Road, Jingan District, Shanghai, 200070, China
Tel.: (86) 2133663200
Industrial Equipment Mfr
N.A.I.C.S.: 333248

Kawasaki Heavy Industries Management (Shanghai), Ltd. (1)
10F Chong Hing Finance Center 288 Nanjing Road West, Huangpu District, Shanghai, 200003, China
Tel.: (86) 2133663100
Industrial Equipment Mfr
N.A.I.C.S.: 333248

Kawasaki Heavy Industries Middle East FZE (1)
Bldg 6W Block-A Office No 709, PO Box 54878, Dubai Airport Free Zone, Dubai, United Arab Emirates
Tel.: (971) 4 214 6730
Web Site: https://www.khi.co.jp
Emp.: 2
Construction Machinery Mfr
N.A.I.C.S.: 333120

Kawasaki Heavy Industries Russia LLC (1)
Office 1803 18th Floor Entrance 3 Krasnopresnenskaya nab12, 123610, Moscow, Russia
Tel.: (7) 4952582115
Industrial Equipment Mfr
N.A.I.C.S.: 333248

Kawasaki Heavy Industries, Ltd. (1)
15F Fu-key Bldg 99 Jen-Ai Road Section 2, Taipei, Taiwan
Tel.: (886) 223221752
Industrial Equipment Mfr
N.A.I.C.S.: 333248

Kawasaki Heavy Industries, Ltd. (Tokyo) (1)
2-4-1 Hamamatsu Cho Minato Ku, Tokyo, 105 6116, Japan (100%)
Tel.: (81) 334352111
Sales Range: $400-449.9 Million
Emp.: 2,000
Motor Vehicle Parts & Accessories
N.A.I.C.S.: 336340

Kawasaki Heavy Industries, Ltd. - KCM Corporation Main Plant (1)
2680 Oka Inami-cho, Kako-gun, Hyogo, 675-1113, Japan
Tel.: (81) 79 495 1211
Emp.: 500
Construction Machinery Mfr
N.A.I.C.S.: 333120
Thadashi Mikawauthi *(Pres)*

Kawasaki Heavy Industries, Ltd. - Kakogawa Works (1)
170 Yamanoue Mukohara Hiraoka-cho, Kakogawa, 675-0112, Hyogo, Japan
Tel.: (81) 79 427 0292
Cast Aluminum Parts Mfr
N.A.I.C.S.: 331523

Kawasaki Heavy Industries, Ltd. - Nagoya Works 1 (1)
11 Kusunoki 320 3-chome, Yatomi, 498-0066, Aichi, Japan
Tel.: (81) 567 68 5117
Airplane Component Mfr
N.A.I.C.S.: 336413

Kawasaki Heavy Industries, Ltd. - Nagoya Works 2 (1)
7-4 Kanaoka Tobishima-mura, Ama-gun, Nagoya, 490-1445, Japan
Tel.: (81) 567 55 0800
Aircraft Components Mfr
N.A.I.C.S.: 336413

Kawasaki Heavy Industries, Ltd. - Nishi-Kobe Works (1)
234 Matsumoto Hasetani-cho, Nishi-ku, Kobe, 651-2239, Hyogo, Japan
Tel.: (81) 78 991 1133
Web Site: http://www.khi.co.jp
Hydraulic Pumps Mfr
N.A.I.C.S.: 333914

Kawasaki Heavy Industries, Ltd. - Sakaide Works (1)
1 Kawasaki-cho, Sakaide, 762-8507, Kagawa, Japan
Tel.: (81) 87 746 1473
Web Site: https://www.khi.co.jp
Ships & Maritime Application Equipment Mfr
N.A.I.C.S.: 333310

Kawasaki Heavy Industries, Ltd. - Seishin Works (1)
170 Yamanoue Mukohara Hiraoka-cho, Kakogawa, 675-0112, Hyogo, Japan
Tel.: (81) 79 427 0292
Engine & Gas Turbines Mfr
N.A.I.C.S.: 333611
T. Kawai *(Gen Mgr)*

Kawasaki Heavy Industries-Akashi Technical Institute (1)
1 1 Kawasaki Cho Akashi, Hyogo, 673 8666, Japan (100%)
Tel.: (81) 789211611
Web Site: http://www.khi.co.jp
Sales Range: $100-124.9 Million
Emp.: 300
Mfr of Motorcycles, Engines, Jet Engines, Industrial Gas Turbines & Welding Robots
N.A.I.C.S.: 336412

Kawasaki Heavy Industries-Akashi Works (1)
1-1 Kawasaki-cho, Akashi, 673-8666, Hyogo, Japan (100%)
Tel.: (81) 78 921 1301
Web Site: http://www.kawasaki-cp.khi.co.jp
Sales Range: $400-449.9 Million
Emp.: 2,200
Mfr of Technological Products for Aircraft, Jet Engines, Motorcycles, General-Purpose Vehicles, Rolling Stock & Total System Engineering
N.A.I.C.S.: 336510
Kenji Komita *(Pres)*

Kawasaki Heavy Industries-Banshu Works (1)
2680 Oka Inami Cho Kako Gun, Hyogo, 675 1113, Japan (100%)
Tel.: (81) 794951211
Web Site: http://www.khi.co.jp
Sales Range: $100-124.9 Million
Emp.: 500
Mfr of Technological Products for Aircraft, Jet Engines, Motorcycles, General-Purpose Vehicles, Rolling Stock & Total System Engineering
N.A.I.C.S.: 336510

Kawasaki Heavy Industries-Gifu Works (1)
1 Kawasaki-cho Kakamigahara, Gifu, 504 8710, Japan
Tel.: (81) 583825712
Airplane Parts Repair Services & Mfr
N.A.I.C.S.: 336510

Kawasaki Heavy Industries-Harima Works (1)
8 Niijima Harima-cho, Kako-gun, Hyogo, 675-0180, Japan (100%)
Tel.: (81) 79 435 2131
Web Site: http://www.khi.co.jp
Sales Range: $200-249.9 Million
Emp.: 600
Mfr of Technological Products for Aircraft, Jet Engines, Motorcycles, General-Purpose Vehicles, Rolling Stock & Total System Engineering
N.A.I.C.S.: 336510

Kawasaki Heavy Industries-Hyogo Works (1)
1 18 Wadayama Dori 2 Chome, Kobe, 652 0884, Hyogo, Japan (100%)
Tel.: (81) 786823111
Sales Range: $200-249.9 Million
Emp.: 1,000
Mfr of Technological Products for Aircraft, Jet Engines, Motorcycles, General-Purpose Vehicles, Rolling Stock & Total System Engineering
N.A.I.C.S.: 336510
Yoshinori Kanehana *(Pres)*

Kawasaki Heavy Industries-Kobe Works (1)
11 Higashikawasaki Cho Chou Ku 3 Chome, Kobe, 650 8670, Japan (100%)
Tel.: (81) 786825001
Sales Range: $800-899.9 Million
Emp.: 3,000
Mfr of Technological Products for Aircraft, Jet Engines, Motorcycles, General-Purpose Vehicles, Rolling Stock & Total System Engineering
N.A.I.C.S.: 336510
Satoshi Hasegawa *(Pres)*

Kawasaki Heavy Industries-Nagoya Works (1)

KAWASAKI HEAVY INDUSTRIES, LTD.

AND PRIVATE COMPANIES

20-3 Kusunoki 3-chome, Yatomi, 498-0066, Aichi, Japan **(100%)**
Tel.: (81) 56 768 5117
Web Site: https://global.kawasaki.com
Sales Range: $25-49.9 Million
Emp.: 100
Mfr of Technological Products for Aircraft, Jet Engines, Motorcycles, General-Purpose Vehicles, Rolling Stock & Total System Engineering
N.A.I.C.S.: 336991

Kawasaki Hydromechanics Corporation (1)
15-1 Minami-futami Futami-cho, Akashi, 674-0093, Hyogo, Japan
Tel.: (81) 78 941 3311
Web Site: https://www.khm.co.jp
Sales Range: $50-74.9 Million
Emp.: 151
Industrial Machinery Mfr
N.A.I.C.S.: 333248
Teruo Taurs *(Pres)*

Kawasaki Life Corporation (1)
1-1-3 Higashikawasaki-cho Kobe Crystal Tower 11th floor, Chuo-ku, Kobe, 650-0044, Hyogo, Japan
Tel.: (81) 78 360 5400
Web Site: https://www.kawasaki-life.jp
Emp.: 303
Real Estate Manangement Services
N.A.I.C.S.: 531390

Kawasaki Machine Systems Korea, Ltd. (1)
3rd Fl Industrial Complex Support Bldg 637, Kojan Dong Namdong Gu, Incheon, 405 817, Korea (South)
Tel.: (82) 328216941
Web Site: http://www.kawasakirobot.co.kr
Sales Range: $25-49.9 Million
Emp.: 20
Motor Vehicle Parts & Accessories
N.A.I.C.S.: 336340

Kawasaki Machine Systems, Ltd. (1)
Furukawa Osaka Bldg 1-29 Dojimahama 2-chome, Kita-ku, Osaka, 530-0004, Japan
Tel.: (81) 6 6344 1275
Gas Turbine Generators Mfr & Distr
N.A.I.C.S.: 333611

Kawasaki Machinery do Brasil Maquinas e Equipamentos Ltda. (1)
Av Paulista 542-6 andar 61-C, Bela Vista, 00310-000, Brazil
Tel.: (55) 1132663318
Industrial Equipment Mfr
N.A.I.C.S.: 333248

Kawasaki Motor Enterprise Thailand Ltd. (1)
2499 New-Phetchaburi Rd, Bang Kapi Huai Khwang, Bangkok, 10310, Thailand **(100%)**
Tel.: (66) 20184999
Web Site: https://www.kawasaki.co.th
Sales Range: $50-74.9 Million
Emp.: 200
Motorcycle Import/Export
N.A.I.C.S.: 441227

Kawasaki Motores Do Brasil Ltda. (1)
Rua das Arraias 286 Colonia Antonio Aleixo, 69008-448, Manaus, Amazonas, Brazil
Tel.: (55) 92 3305 5800
Web Site: http://kawasakibrasil.com.br
Sales Range: $75-99.9 Million
Emp.: 250
Automobile Parts Distr
N.A.I.C.S.: 423120

Kawasaki Motors (Phils.) Corporation (1)
Km 23 East Service Road Bo Cupang, Alabang, Muntinlupa, 1771, Metro Manila, Philippines
Tel.: (63) 28 842 3140
Web Site: https://www.kawasakileisurebikes.ph
Sales Range: $100-124.9 Million
Emp.: 450
Motorcycles, Bicycles & Parts
N.A.I.C.S.: 336991

Kawasaki Motors (Shanghai), Ltd. (1)
Room 504 Kerry Ever Bright City Enterprise Center, No 1 West Tianmu-Road No128 Jingan District, Shanghai, China
Tel.: (86) 2133663120
Industrial Equipment Mfr
N.A.I.C.S.: 333248

Kawasaki Motors (UK) Ltd. (1)
1 Dukes Meadow Millboard Road, Bourne End, SL8 5XF, Buckinghamshire, United Kingdom **(100%)**
Tel.: (44) 162 885 6750
Web Site: https://www.kawasaki.co.uk
Sales Range: $75-99.9 Million
Emp.: 40
Motor Vehicle Parts & Accessories
N.A.I.C.S.: 336991

Kawasaki Motors Corp., U.S.A. (1)
PO Box 25252, Santa Ana, CA 92799-5252 **(100%)**
Tel.: (949) 770-0400
Web Site: http://www.kawasaki.com
Sales Range: $150-199.9 Million
Emp.: 480
Motorcycles, Parts & Accessories, Jet Ski Watercraft, Generators, All Terrain Vehicles, Engines, Utility Vehicles
N.A.I.C.S.: 423110
Fumihiro Ohno *(Sr VP & Gen Mgr)*

Branch (Domestic):

Kawasaki Motors Finance Corporation (2)
26972 Burbank, Foothill Ranch, CA 92610
Tel.: (949) 770-0400
Sales Range: $200-249.9 Million
Emp.: 400
Motor Vehicle Parts & Accessories
N.A.I.C.S.: 522299
Tod Kuwata *(Mng Dir)*

Kawasaki Motors Corporation Japan (1)
1-1 Kawasakicho, Akashi, 673-8666, Hyogo, Japan
Tel.: (81) 78 921 4102
Web Site: https://www.kawasaki-motors.com
Emp.: 180
Motorcycles, Jet Skis & All Terrain & Utility Vehicles Mfr
N.A.I.C.S.: 336991
Takeshi Teranishi *(Pres)*

Kawasaki Motors Enterprise (Thailand) Co., Ltd. (1)
2499 New-Phetchaburi Rd, Bang Kapi Huai Khwang, Bangkok, 10310, Thailand **(50%)**
Tel.: (66) 2 018 4999
Web Site: https://www.kawasaki.co.th
Sales Range: $200-249.9 Million
Emp.: 1,000
Motorcycles, Bicycles & Parts
N.A.I.C.S.: 336991

Kawasaki Motors Europe N.V. (1)
Max-Planck-Strasse 26, 61381, Friedrichsdorf, Germany **(100%)**
Tel.: (49) 6 172 7340
Web Site: https://www.kawasaki.de
Emp.: 50
Motor Vehicle Parts & Accessories
N.A.I.C.S.: 336340

Kawasaki Motors Europe N.V. (1)
Jacobus Spijkerdreef 1-3, Postbus 532, 2132 PZ, Hoofddorp, Netherlands **(100%)**
Tel.: (31) 23 567 0500
Web Site: https://www.kawasaki.eu
Emp.: 75
Motorcycle Dealers
N.A.I.C.S.: 441227

Kawasaki Motors Europe N.V. (1)
PO Box 532, 2130 AM, Hoofddorp, Netherlands **(100%)**
Tel.: (31) 0347324949
Web Site: http://www.kawasaki.com
Sales Range: $25-49.9 Million
Emp.: 40
Motorcycles, Bicycles & Parts
N.A.I.C.S.: 336991

Kawasaki Motors Holding (Malaysia) Sdn. Bhd. (1)
Lot 6 And 8 Jalan Segambutpusat, Segambut, 51200, Kuala Lumpur, Malaysia
Tel.: (60) 362512591

Web Site: http://www.khi.co.jp
Sales Range: $25-49.9 Million
Emp.: 50
Fluid Power Pumps & Motors
N.A.I.C.S.: 333996

Kawasaki Motors Manufacturing Corp., U.S.A. (1)
6600 NW 27th St, Lincoln, NE 68524-8904 **(100%)**
Tel.: (402) 476-6600
Web Site: http://www.kawasaki.com
Emp.: 744
Mfr of Motorcycles
N.A.I.C.S.: 336999
Joe Tabata *(Pres & CEO)*

Kawasaki Motors Pty. Ltd. (1)
Unit Q 10-16 South Street, Rydalmere, 2116, NSW, Australia **(100%)**
Tel.: (61) 296842585
Web Site: http://www.kawasaki.com.au
Emp.: 30
Motor Vehicle Parts & Accessories
N.A.I.C.S.: 336340
Claude Simaona *(CFO)*

Kawasaki Motors Vietnam Co., Ltd. (1)
Unit 709 7th Floor ZEN Plaza 54-56 Nguyen Trai Street, Ben Thanh Ward District 1, Ho Chi Minh City, Vietnam
Tel.: (84) 283 925 5899
Web Site: https://www.kawasaki-motors.vn
Motor Cycle Distr
N.A.I.C.S.: 441227

Kawasaki Naval Engine Service, Ltd. (1)
1-14-5 Kaigan, Minato-ku, Tokyo, 105-8315, Japan
Tel.: (81) 334352782
Web Site: http://www.khi.co.jp
Marine Equipment Repair Services
N.A.I.C.S.: 488390

Kawasaki Plant Systems, Ltd. (1)
Higashikawasaki-cho 3-1-1chome Hyoken, Chuo-ku, Kobe, 650-8670, Hyogo, Japan
Tel.: (81) 786825200
Web Site: http://www.khi.co.jp
Plant Machinery & Equipment Mfr
N.A.I.C.S.: 333248
Toshiyuki Mimura *(Gen Mgr-Plng & Control-Plant & Infrastructure)*

Kawasaki Precision Machinery (Suzhou) Ltd. (1)
668 JianLin Rd New District, New District, Suzhou, 215151, China
Tel.: (86) 512 6616 0365
Hydraulic Pump & Motor Mfr
N.A.I.C.S.: 333996
Hiro Nogushi *(Gen Mgr)*

Kawasaki Precision Machinery (U.S.A.), Inc. (1)
3838 Broadmoor Ave S E, Grand Rapids, MI 49512
Tel.: (616) 975-3100
Web Site: http://www.kpm-usa.com
Sales Range: $25-49.9 Million
Emp.: 25
Hydraulic Products Repair Services & Distr
N.A.I.C.S.: 811310

Kawasaki Precision Machinery (UK) Ltd. (1)
Ernesettle Lane Ernesettle, Plymouth, PL5 2SA, Devon, United Kingdom **(100%)**
Tel.: (44) 175 236 4394
Web Site: https://www.kawasakihydraulics.com
Sales Range: $100-124.9 Million
Emp.: 270
Hydraulic Equipment, Staffa Motor
N.A.I.C.S.: 336340

Kawasaki Precision Machinery Trading (Shanghai) Co., Ltd. (1)
30th Floor Chong Hing Finance Center 288 Nanjing Roag West, Huangpu District, Shanghai, 200003, China
Tel.: (86) 21 3366 3800
Hydraulic Pumps Mfr
N.A.I.C.S.: 333914

Kawasaki Prime Mover Engineering Co., Ltd. (1)

1-1 Higashikawasaki-cho 3-chome, Chuo-ku, Kobe, 650-8670, Hyogo, Japan
Tel.: (81) 78 682 5471
Gas Turbines & Machinery Mfr
N.A.I.C.S.: 333611

Kawasaki Rail Car, Inc. (1)
29 Wells Ave Bldg 4, Yonkers, NY 10701-2753 **(100%)**
Tel.: (914) 376-4700
Web Site: https://www.kawasakirailcar.com
Electric Rail Cars Mfr
N.A.I.C.S.: 336510
Bonnie Pagliaro *(Mgr-Supply Chain)*

Kawasaki Robot Service, Ltd. (1)
1-1 Kawasaki-cho Akashi Plant 86 of Kawasaki Heavy Industries, Akashi, 673-8666, Hyogo, Japan
Tel.: (81) 78 921 1565
Web Site: https://www.khi.co.jp
Industrial Equipment Mfr
N.A.I.C.S.: 333248
Tatsuo Yano *(Pres)*

Kawasaki Robotics (Kunshan) Co., Ltd. (1)
Building 1 No 888 Jinmao Road, Zhoushi Zhen, Kunshan, 215313, Jiangsu, China
Tel.: (86) 51250362201
Electronic Parts Distr
N.A.I.C.S.: 423690

Kawasaki Robotics (Tianjin) Co., Ltd. (1)
1 2/F Building 6 No 19 Xinhuan Road, TEDA, Tianjin, 300457, China
Tel.: (86) 400 922 2400
Web Site: http://www.kawasakirobatic.cn
Industrial Robot System Distr
N.A.I.C.S.: 423830
Sano Masatoshi *(Gen Mgr)*

Kawasaki Robotics (U.S.A.), Inc. (1)
28140 Lakeview Dr, Wixom, MI 48393
Tel.: (248) 446-4100
Web Site: http://robotics.kawasaki.com
Sales Range: $50-74.9 Million
Emp.: 93
Mfr of Industrial Robots
N.A.I.C.S.: 423830

Kawasaki Robotics (UK) Ltd. (1)
Unit 4 Easter Court Europa Boulevard, Westbrook, Warrington, WA5 7ZB, United Kingdom **(100%)**
Tel.: (44) 192 571 3000
Web Site: https://kawasakirobotics.com
Sales Range: $25-49.9 Million
Emp.: 12
Metalworking Machinery
N.A.I.C.S.: 333519
Dave Pearson *(Sr Mgr)*

Kawasaki Robotics GmbH (1)
Im Taubental 32, 41468, Neuss, Germany
Tel.: (49) 21 313 4260
Web Site: https://www.kawasakirobot.de
Automated Systems Mfr
N.A.I.C.S.: 333248

Kawasaki Robotics Korea, Ltd. (1)
43 Namdong-daero 215beon-gil, Namdonggu, Incheon, 21633, Korea (South)
Tel.: (82) 328216941
Electronic Parts Mfr
N.A.I.C.S.: 334419

Kawasaki Rolling Stock Component Co., Ltd. (1)
12-14 Wadayama-dori 2-chome, Hyogo-ku, Kobe, 652-0884, Hyogo, Japan
Tel.: (81) 78 682 3171
Web Site: http://www.khi.co.jp
Rolling Stock Mfr
N.A.I.C.S.: 336510

Kawasaki Rolling Stock Technology Co., Ltd. (1)
2-1-18 Wadayama-dori 2-chome, Hyogo-ku, Kobe, 652-0884, Hyogo, Japan
Tel.: (81) 78 682 3185
Rolling Stock Mfr
N.A.I.C.S.: 336510

Kawasaki Safety Service Industries, Ltd. (1)
2-16 Takatsukadai 3-Chome, Nishi-ku, Kobe, 651-2271, Japan
Tel.: (81) 789921400

4097

KAWASAKI HEAVY INDUSTRIES, LTD.

Kawasaki Heavy Industries, Ltd.—(Continued)
Sales Range: $75-99.9 Million
Emp.: 308
Medical & Safety Equipment Designer & Mfr
N.A.I.C.S.: 561621
Kimiaki Sakamoto *(Mng Dir)*

Kawasaki Shipbuilding Corporation (1)
1-1 Higashikawasaki-cho 3-chome, Kobe, 650-8670, Hyogo, Japan
Tel.: (81) 786825501
Sales Range: $450-499.9 Million
Emp.: 2,000
Design, Construction, Sales & Repair of Ships & Marine Machinery
N.A.I.C.S.: 336611
Kaoru Kawabe *(VP-Ship & Offshore Structure)*

Branch (Domestic):

Kawasaki Shipbuilding Corporation (2)
1 Kawasaki Cho, Sakaide, 762 8507, Kagawa, Japan **(100%)**
Tel.: (81) 877461473
Web Site: http://www.kawasakizosen.co.jp
Sales Range: $700-749.9 Million
Mfr of Ships & Marine Application Equipment
N.A.I.C.S.: 333618

Kawasaki Subsea (UK) Ltd. (1)
2 Queen's Gardens, Aberdeen, AB15 4YD, United Kingdom
Tel.: (44) 1224629702
Industrial Equipment Mfr
N.A.I.C.S.: 333248

Kawasaki Techno Wave Co., Ltd. (1)
1 Kawasaki-cho, Sakaide, 762-8507, Kagawa, Japan
Tel.: (81) 877 46 1494
Ship Building Services
N.A.I.C.S.: 336611

Kawasaki Technology Co., Ltd. (1)
1 Kawasaki-cho 3-chome, Akashi, 673-0014, Hyogo, Japan
Tel.: (81) 78 921 1661
Construction Machinery Mfr
N.A.I.C.S.: 333120

Kawasaki Thermal Engineering Co., Ltd. (1)
1000 Aoji-cho, Kusatsu, 525-8558, Shiga, Japan **(100%)**
Tel.: (81) 77 563 1111
Web Site: https://www.khi.co.jp
Emp.: 529
Air Conditioning Equipment & Multipurpose Boiler Mfr
N.A.I.C.S.: 333415
Susumu Shinohara *(Pres)*

Kawasaki Trading (Shanghai) Co., Ltd. (1)
10F Chong Hing Finance Center 288 Nanjing Road West, Huangpu District, Shanghai, 200003, China
Tel.: (86) 33663700
Industrial Equipment Mfr
N.A.I.C.S.: 333248

Kawasaki Trading Co., Ltd. (1)
3th Floor 8 Kaigan-dori, Chuo-ku, Kobe, 650-0024, Hyogo, Japan
Tel.: (81) 78 392 1131
Web Site: https://www.kawasakitrading.co.jp
Emp.: 359
Industrial Equipment Mfr & Distr
N.A.I.C.S.: 333248
Hisashi Yamaji *(Pres)*

Kawasaki Trading do Brasil Ltda. (1)
Avenida Paulista 542-7 Andar Cj 71, Bela Vista, 01310 000, Sao Paulo, Brazil
Tel.: (55) 11 3266 2790
Construction Machinery Distr
N.A.I.C.S.: 423810

Kawasaki do Brasil Industria e Comercio Ltda. (1)
Avenida Paulista 542-6 Andar Bela Vista, Sao Paulo, 01310-0000, Brazil
Tel.: (55) 1132892388
Web Site: http://www.khi.co.jp
Industrial Machinery Distr

N.A.I.C.S.: 423830

Kawasaki do Brazil Industria E Comercio Ltda. (1)
Avenida Paulista 542-6 Andar, Bela Vista, Sao Paulo, 1310-000, SP, Brazil **(100%)**
Tel.: (55) 1132892388
Web Site: http://www.kawasakimotors.com.br
Rev.: $48,657,150
Emp.: 8
Motorcycles, Bicycles & Parts
N.A.I.C.S.: 336991
Kenji Watanabe *(Pres)*

MES-KHI Yura Dock Co., Ltd. (1)
193-13 Tsunashiro, Yura-cho Hidaka-gun, Wakayama, Japan
Tel.: (81) 738651111
Industrial Equipment Mfr
N.A.I.C.S.: 333248

Medicaroid Corporation (1)
International Medical Device Alliance 6th Floor 1-6-5 Minatojima, Minami-machi Chuo-ku, Kobe, 650-0047, Japan
Tel.: (81) 78 303 8770
Web Site: https://www.medicaroid.com
Medical Diagnostic Equipment Mfr
N.A.I.C.S.: 339112

NanTong COSCO KHI Ship Engineering Co., Ltd. (1)
901 Changjiang Middle Road, Nantong, 226005, Jiangsu, China
Tel.: (86) 5138 516 8888
Web Site: https://www.nacks.com
Ship Building & Repair
N.A.I.C.S.: 336611

Nichijo Corporation (1)
Akebono 5-1-10 Akebono, Teina-ku, Sapporo, 006-0835, Japan
Tel.: (81) 11 681 3115
Web Site: https://www.nichijo.jp
Landscaping Services
N.A.I.C.S.: 561730

Nichijo Manufacturing Co., Ltd. (1)
4-38 Inaho 3-jo 6-chome, Teine-ku, Sapporo, Japan
Tel.: (81) 11 681 3115
Web Site: http://www.nichijo.jp
Snowplows Mfr
N.A.I.C.S.: 333120

Nippi Corporation (1)
3175 Showa-machi, Kanazawa-ku, Yokohama, 236-8540, Japan
Tel.: (81) 45 773 5100
Web Site: https://www.nippi.co.jp
Sales Range: $200-249.9 Million
Emp.: 1,000
Airplane Parts Mfr
N.A.I.C.S.: 336413
Toshifumi Kojima *(Pres)*

Nippi Kosan Co., Ltd. (1)
3175 Showamachi, Kanazawa-ku, Yokohama, 236-0001, Kanagawa, Japan
Tel.: (81) 45 772 4012
Web Site: https://www.nippi-kosan.co.jp
Sales Range: $25-49.9 Million
Emp.: 29
Civil Construction Engineering Services
N.A.I.C.S.: 237990

Nippi Skill Corporation (1)
3175 Showa-machi, Kanazawa-ku, Yokohama, 236-0001, Kanagawa, Japan
Tel.: (81) 45 771 5750
Aerospace Parts Mfr
N.A.I.C.S.: 336413

Nishi-Kobe Works (1)
234 Matsumoto Hazetani Cho, Kobe, 651 2239, Japan **(100%)**
Tel.: (81) 789911133
Industrial Robots & Hydraulics Mfr
N.A.I.C.S.: 423830
Kazuo Hida *(Pres)*

P.T. Kawasaki Motor Indonesia (1)
Jl Madura Block L11 Industrial Estate MM2100, Cikarang Barat, Bekasi, 17530, Utara, Indonesia
Tel.: (62) 212 957 7888
Web Site: https://www.kawasaki-motor.co.id
Sales Range: $200-249.9 Million
Emp.: 700
Motorcycles, Bicycles & Parts

N.A.I.C.S.: 336991
Y. Tanigawa *(Chm)*

Qingdao Sifang Kawasaki Rolling Stock Technology Co., Ltd. (1)
No 88 Jinhongdong Road, Chengyang District, Qingdao, Shandong, China
Tel.: (86) 53287900880
Industrial Equipment Mfr
N.A.I.C.S.: 333248

Sapporo Kawasaki Rolling Stock Engineering Co., Ltd. (1)
14F JR Tower Office Plaza Sapporo Kita 5-jo Nishi 2- chome, Chuoh-ku, Sapporo, 060-0005, Hokkaido, Japan
Tel.: (81) 11 281 1031
Web Site: http://www.khi.co.jp
Rolling Stock Mfr
N.A.I.C.S.: 336510

Shanghai Cosco Kawasaki Heavy Industries Steel Structure Co., Ltd. (1)
No 3768 Panjing Road, Baoshan District, Shanghai, 201908, China **(100%)**
Tel.: (86) 2131190999
Web Site: http://www.khi.co.jp
Sales Range: $100-124.9 Million
Emp.: 500
Fabricated Structural Metal
N.A.I.C.S.: 332312

Ship Partners Co., Ltd. (1)
World Trade Center Bldg 4-1 Hamamatsucho 2-chome, Minato-ku, Tokyo, 105-6116, Japan
Tel.: (81) 3 3435 2216
Ship Building Services
N.A.I.C.S.: 336611

Technica Co., Ltd. (1)
3-7 Nagaoka, Mizuho-cho Nishitama-gun, Tokyo, 190-1232, Japan
Tel.: (81) 42 557 2200
Web Site: https://www.tch2200.co.jp
Software Development Services
N.A.I.C.S.: 541511
Ryota Hiruma *(Pres)*

Tiesse Robot S.p.A. (1)
Via Isorella 32, 25010, Visano, Brescia, Italy
Tel.: (39) 030 995 8621
Web Site: https://www.tiesserobot.com
Sales Range: $25-49.9 Million
Emp.: 70
Aircraft
N.A.I.C.S.: 336411

Union Precision Die Co., Ltd. (1)
170 Yamanoue Hiraoka-cho, Kakogawa, 675-0112, Hyogo, Japan
Tel.: (81) 79 425 0765
Web Site: https://www.union-seiki.co.jp
Sales Range: $25-49.9 Million
Emp.: 83
Die Casting Products Mfr & Testing Services
N.A.I.C.S.: 333511
Yoshihiro Yamazaki *(Pres)*

Wipro Kawasaki Precision Machinery Private Limited (1)
No 15 Sy No 35 and 37 Kumbalgodu Industrial Area, Kumbalgodu Village Kengeri Hobli, Bengaluru, 560074, India
Tel.: (91) 8904075904
Industrial Equipment Mfr
N.A.I.C.S.: 333248

Wuhan Kawasaki Marine Machinery Co., Ltd. (1)
No 43 Wudong Road, Qingshan, Wuhan, 430084, China **(100%)**
Tel.: (86) 278 646 2449
Web Site: https://www.wkm.net.cn
Sales Range: $50-74.9 Million
Emp.: 180
Motor Vehicle Parts & Accessories; Joint Venture Between Kawasaki Heavy Industries & Wuhan Wuhan Marine Machinery Plant (China).
N.A.I.C.S.: 336340

KAWASAKI KISEN KAISHA, LTD.

Iino Building 1-1 Uchisaiwaicho

INTERNATIONAL PUBLIC

2-Chome, Chiyoda-ku, Tokyo, 100-8540, Japan
Tel.: (81) 335955000   JP
Web Site: http://www.kline.co.jp
Year Founded: 1919
KAKKF—(OTCIQ)
Rev.: $6,360,803,000
Assets: $13,943,345,520
Liabilities: $3,204,739,520
Net Worth: $10,738,606,000
Earnings: $692,569,360
Emp.: 5,629
Fiscal Year-end: 03/31/24
Marine, Land & Air Transportation Services; Insurance Services; Warehousing
N.A.I.C.S.: 483111
Eizo Murakami *(Chm)*

Subsidiaries:

Air Tiger Express Companies, Inc. (1)
149-09 183rd St 2nd Fl, Springfield Gardens, NY 11413 **(51%)**
Tel.: (718) 917-6700
Web Site: https://www.airtiger.com
Sales Range: $10-24.9 Million
Emp.: 60
Freight Forwarding
N.A.I.C.S.: 488510
Richard Chu *(Chm)*

Asahi Kisen Kaisha, Ltd. (1)
Daidoseimei Kasumigaseki Bldg 13f, Chiyoda-Ku, Tokyo, 100-0013, Japan
Tel.: (81) 335925741
Web Site: http://www.kawakin.co.jp
Sales Range: $25-49.9 Million
Emp.: 1
Marine Transportation Services
N.A.I.C.S.: 488390
Tomoi Akihiiko *(Gen Mgr)*

Bangkok Cold Storage Service Ltd. (1)
1377 Moo 7 Theparak Road, T Theparak, Amphur Muang, 10270, Samutprakarn, Thailand
Tel.: (66) 23835641
Web Site: http://www.bangkokcoldstorage.com
Warehouse Services
N.A.I.C.S.: 493190

Century Distribution Systems (Hong Kong) Limited (1)
Unit 2805 28th Floor BEA Tower Millennium City 5 418 Kwun Tong Road, Kwun Tong, Kowloon, China (Hong Kong)
Tel.: (852) 2 862 2400
Web Site: https://www.cds-net.com
Emp.: 5
Logistics Consulting Servies
N.A.I.C.S.: 541614
Yasunori Kawase *(CEO)*

Century Distribution Systems (International) Limited (1)
Unit 3001 30th Floor Citicorp Centre 18 Whitfield Road, Causeway Bay, China (Hong Kong)
Tel.: (852) 28622400
Web Site: https://www.cds-net.com
Logistics Consulting Servies
N.A.I.C.S.: 541614

Century Distribution Systems (Shipping) Limited (1)
Unit A2 32nd Fl United Centre No 95, Queensway, Hong Kong, China (Hong Kong)
Tel.: (852) 28622400
Cargo Handling Services
N.A.I.C.S.: 488320

Century Distribution Systems, Inc. (1)
Woodbridge Corporate Plz 485 E Rt 1 S Ste 100, Iselin, NJ 08830 **(100%)**
Tel.: (732) 602-3140
Web Site: http://www.cds-net.com
Rev.: $5,000,000
Emp.: 20
Freight Consolidation, Supply Chain Management, Warehousing & Distribution Services

AND PRIVATE COMPANIES   KAWASAKI KISEN KAISHA, LTD.

N.A.I.C.S.: 541614
Richard Ferguson *(Pres-Universal Div)*

Connaught Freight Forwarders Limited (1)
unit 10-18 22 Fl Kowloon Commerce centre Tower 2, Queensway, Kwai Chung, China (Hong Kong)
Tel.: (852) 28615511
Sales Range: $25-49.9 Million
Emp.: 10
Freight Forwarding Services
N.A.I.C.S.: 488510

Daito Corporation (1)
Shibaura 2-1-13 Minato-ku, Tokyo, Japan (100%)
Tel.: (81) 334526271
Web Site: http://www.daitocorp.co.jp
Rev.: $229,432,416
Emp.: 420
Transportation, Shipping & Warehousing Services
N.A.I.C.S.: 488510
Kazuhiro Matsukawa *(Pres)*

Escobal Japan Ltd. (1)
6 1 2-chome Nakase, Mihama-ku, Chiba, 261-7111, Japan
Tel.: (81) 432972681
Ship Management Services
N.A.I.C.S.: 541618

Hokkai Transportation Co., Ltd. (1)
101-11 2-chome West Port of Kushiro, Kushiro, 084-0914, Japan
Tel.: (81) 154529161
Emp.: 20
Logistics Consulting Servies
N.A.I.C.S.: 541614
Masanori Sakakura *(Mgr)*

Intermodal Engineering Co., Ltd. (1)
Konanyk Bldg 2-14-12 Konan, Tokyo, 108-0075, Minato-ku, Japan
Tel.: (81) 334583264
Web Site: http://www.iecnt.co.jp
Sales Range: $25-49.9 Million
Emp.: 60
Shipping Container Repair Services
N.A.I.C.S.: 811310
Kunihiro Hino *(Pres)*

International Transportation Service, Inc. (1)
1281 Pier G way, Long Beach, CA 90802 (100%)
Tel.: (562) 435-7781
Web Site: https://www.itslb.com
Emp.: 350
Transportation Services
N.A.I.C.S.: 488510
Philip W. Feldhus *(Sr VP-Ops & Labor Rels)*

Subsidiary (Domestic):

Husky Terminal & Stevedoring, Inc. (2)
1101 Port of Tacoma Rd Terminal Four, Tacoma, WA 98421 (50%)
Tel.: (253) 627-6963
Web Site: https://www.huskyterminal.com
Sales Range: $10-24.9 Million
Emp.: 16
Marine Terminal & Stevedoring Services
N.A.I.C.S.: 488320

The Rail-Bridge Terminals (New Jersey) Corporation (2)
322 3rd St, Elizabeth, NJ 07206-2007 (100%)
Tel.: (908) 558-0950
Rev.: $7,000,000
Emp.: 40
Transportation Services
N.A.I.C.S.: 488510

TransBay Container Terminal, Inc. (2)
1101 Port Of Tacoma Rd, Tacoma, WA 98421-3701 (95%)
Tel.: (510) 839-8228
Web Site: http://www.itslb.com
Rev.: $20,000,000
Emp.: 14
Transportation Services
N.A.I.C.S.: 488510

Japan Express Transportation Co., Ltd. (1)
2-1-1 Yashio, Shinagawa-ku, Tokyo, 140-0003, Japan
Tel.: (81) 33 790 0731
Web Site: https://www.jetkk.co.jp
Emp.: 82
Land Transportation Services
N.A.I.C.S.: 488510

K LINE AIR SERVICE (TAIWAN) LTD (1)
8F No 45 Lane 188 Ruiguang Road, Neihu, Taipei, 11491, Taiwan
Tel.: (886) 287518148
Web Site: http://www.klinelogistics.com
Freight Forwarding Services
N.A.I.C.S.: 488510

K LINE SHIP MANAGEMENT (Singapore) PTE LTD (1)
105 Cecil Street 19-00 The Octagon, Singapore, 069534, Singapore
Tel.: (65) 6 305 1100
Web Site: https://www.klsm.com.sg
Sales Range: $25-49.9 Million
Emp.: 42
Ship Management Services
N.A.I.C.S.: 488390
S. Murad *(Gen Mgr-Crewing)*

K Line (Australia) Pty. Ltd. (1)
Level 2 187 Todd Road, Port Melbourne, Port Melbourne, 3207, VIC, Australia
Tel.: (61) 39 685 6996
Web Site: https://www.kline.com.au
Shipping Services
N.A.I.C.S.: 488510

Joint Venture (Domestic):

K Line Auto Logistics Pty. Ltd. (2)
570 St Kilda Rd, Melbourne, 3004, VIC, Australia
Tel.: (61) 3 9944 3000
Vehicle Transport Services
N.A.I.C.S.: 488510

Joint Venture (Domestic):

PrixCar Services Pty. Ltd. (3)
Gate 3 120-124 Foundation Road, Altona North, Truganina, 3029, VIC, Australia (50%)
Tel.: (61) 1300660616
Automobile Transport, Logistics & Storage Services
N.A.I.C.S.: 541614

Subsidiary (Domestic):

PrixCar Transport Services Pty. Ltd. (4)
810-848 Kororoit Creek Road, Altona North, Melbourne, 3025, VIC, Australia
Tel.: (61) 1300 660 616
Web Site: http://www.prixcartransport.com.au
Automobile Transport Services
N.A.I.C.S.: 541614

K Line (Belgium) NV (1)
Geulincxstraats 20, 2060, Antwerp, Belgium
Tel.: (32) 3 221 2140
Web Site: http://www.kline.be
Sales Range: $25-49.9 Million
Emp.: 35
Logistics Consulting Servies
N.A.I.C.S.: 541614

K Line (China) Ltd. (1)
Rm 2101 K Wah Ctr, 1010 Huaihai Zhong Rd, Shanghai, China (100%)
Tel.: (86) 2154050099
Web Site: http://www.kline.com.cn
Rev.: $6,900,000
Transportation Services
N.A.I.C.S.: 488510

K Line (Deutschland) GmbH (1)
Anckelmannsplatz 1, 20537, Hamburg, Germany
Tel.: (49) 4 036 1240
Web Site: https://www.klineglobalroro.com
Emp.: 130
Marine Transport Services
N.A.I.C.S.: 488390

K Line (Europe) Ltd. (1)
6th Floor 200 Aldersgate Street, London, EC1A 4HD, United Kingdom (100%)
Tel.: (44) 207 382 6500
Web Site: https://www.klineurope.com

K Line (Finland) OY (1)
Tynnyrintekijankatu 2, PO Box 57, 581, Helsinki, Finland
Tel.: (358) 207 459 211
Web Site: http://www.kline.fi
Sales Range: $25-49.9 Million
Emp.: 10
Marine Cargo Handling Services
N.A.I.C.S.: 488320

K Line (Hong Kong) Ltd. (1)
33rd Floor United Centre 95 Queensway, Hong Kong, China (Hong Kong) (100%)
Tel.: (852) 28615511
Web Site: http://www.kline.com.hk
Emp.: 100
Transportation Services
N.A.I.C.S.: 488510

K Line (Korea) Ltd. (1)
1st F Sejongro Daewoo Bldg 1st floor 30 Saemunan-ro 3-gil 30, Jongno-gu, Seoul, 03173, Korea (South)
Tel.: (82) 2 397 8200
Web Site: https://www.kline.co.kr
Emp.: 5
Marine Transport Services
N.A.I.C.S.: 488390
Hiroshi Mikita *(Pres & CEO)*

K Line (Nederland) B.V. (1)
Waalhaven ZZ 10, 3088 HH, Rotterdam, Netherlands
Tel.: (31) 104911711
Web Site: http://www.kline.nl
Emp.: 70
Marine Transport Services
N.A.I.C.S.: 488390
Ser Penters *(Mng Dir)*

K Line (Norway) AS (1)
Vollsveren 138, PO Box 51, Lysaker, 1324, Oslo, Norway
Tel.: (47) 67528890
Web Site: http://www.kline.no
Sales Range: $25-49.9 Million
Emp.: 3
Logistics Consulting Servies
N.A.I.C.S.: 541614
Ulrik Jespersen *(Mng Dir)*

K Line (Portugal)-Agentes de Navagacao, S.A. (1)
Cais do Sodre 28, 1200-450, Lisbon, Portugal
Tel.: (351) 21 3211330
Web Site: http://www.kline.pt
Sales Range: $25-49.9 Million
Emp.: 1
Logistics Consulting Servies
N.A.I.C.S.: 541614
Ricardo Crespo *(Reg Dir)*

K Line (Scandinavia) Holding A/S (1)
Snorresgade 18-20, 2300, Copenhagen, Denmark
Tel.: (45) 32953242
Web Site: http://www.kline.dk
Emp.: 5
Investment Management Service
N.A.I.C.S.: 523999
Ulrik Kamstrup Jespersen *(CEO)*

K Line (Singapore) Pte Ltd (1)
11 keppel road h7 07-00 abi plaza, Singapore, 089057, Singapore (95%)
Tel.: (65) 62218977
Web Site: http://www.kline.com.sg
Rev.: $9,637,968
Emp.: 80
Transportation Services
N.A.I.C.S.: 488510
Dere Wakeling *(Mng Dir)*

K Line (Sweden) AB (1)
Foreningsgatan 23, 411 27, Gothenburg, Sweden
Tel.: (46) 31 778 9100
Web Site: http://www.kline.se
Logistics Consulting Servies
N.A.I.C.S.: 541614

K Line (Taiwan) Ltd. (1)
5F No 66 Songjiang Rd, Zhongshan Dist, Taipei, 104, Taiwan

Tel.: (886) 225239798
Web Site: http://www.kline.com.tw
Emp.: 70
Logistic Services
N.A.I.C.S.: 541614

K Line (Thailand) Ltd. (1)
33/29-31 8th Floor and 33/32-33 M Floor Wall Street Tower Building, 33/29-31 Surawonse Road, Surawongse Road Suriyawongse Bangrak, Bangkok, 10500, Thailand
Tel.: (66) 2 625 0000
Web Site: https://www.kline.co.th
Sales Range: $125-149.9 Million
Emp.: 500
Freight Shipping Services
N.A.I.C.S.: 488510
Vitthya Vejjajiva *(Chm)*

K Line Accounting and Finance Co., Ltd. (1)
Iino Bldg 2-1-1 Uchisaiwai-cho 15th Fl, Minato-Ku, Tokyo, 100-0011, Japan
Tel.: (81) 335955578
Sales Range: $50-74.9 Million
Emp.: 18
Financial Management Services
N.A.I.C.S.: 523999
Matsumoto Seiji *(Gen Mgr)*

K Line America, Inc. (1)
8730 Stony Point Pkwy Ste 400, Richmond, VA 23235 (100%)
Tel.: (804) 560-3600
Web Site: http://www.kline
Rev.: $62,000,000
Emp.: 280
Transportation Services
N.A.I.C.S.: 488510
Chris von Kannewurff *(Sr VP)*

K Line Bulk Shipping (UK) Limited (1)
6th Floor 200 Aldersgate Street, London, EC1A 4HD, United Kingdom
Tel.: (44) 20 7 382 5100
Web Site: http://www.klinebulkuk.com
Sales Range: $25-49.9 Million
Emp.: 19
Marine Transportation Services
N.A.I.C.S.: 488390

K Line Business Systems, Ltd. (1)
Sanbancho UF Building 2F 6-3 Sanbancho, Chiyoda-ku, Tokyo, 102-0075, Japan
Tel.: (81) 367794101
Web Site: http://www.kbs.kline.co.jp
Emp.: 111
Ship Management Services
N.A.I.C.S.: 488320

K Line Canada Ltd. (1)
56 Linwood Crescent Mont-Royal, Montreal, H2P 1J2, QC, Canada
Tel.: (514) 733-0004
Web Site: http://www.kline.com.au
Freight Transportation Services
N.A.I.C.S.: 483111

K Line Container Service (Thailand) Ltd. (1)
33 Moo 9 Km 18 Bangna-Trad Road, Bangchalong, Bang Phli, 10540, Samutprakarn, Thailand
Tel.: (66) 2312720917
Web Site: http://www.kcst.co.th
Container Shipping ervices
N.A.I.C.S.: 488510

K Line European Sea Highway Services GmbH (1)
Otto-Lilienthal-Str 25, 28199, Bremen, Germany
Tel.: (49) 4 215 0090
Web Site: https://www.kess.kline.de
Sales Range: $25-49.9 Million
Emp.: 25
Marine Transportation Services
N.A.I.C.S.: 488390
Nobuyuki Yokoyama *(Mng Dir)*

K Line Holding (Europe) Limited (1)
River Plate House 7-11 Finsbury Circus, EC2M 7EA, London, United Kingdom - England
Tel.: (44) 20 7382 6751
Investment Management Service
N.A.I.C.S.: 523999

KAWASAKI KISEN KAISHA, LTD.

Kawasaki Kisen Kaisha, Ltd.—(Continued)

Subsidiary (Domestic):

James Kemball Limited (2)
Clickett Hill Road, Felixstowe, IP11 4BA, Suffolk, United Kingdom
Tel.: (44) 139 460 1500
Web Site: https://www.kemball.co.uk
Sales Range: $75-99.9 Million
Emp.: 19
Fleet Management Services
N.A.I.C.S.: 532112

K Line LNG Shipping (UK) Limited (1)
200 Aldersgate Street 6th Floor, London, EC1A 4HD, United Kingdom
Tel.: (44) 207 382 6500
Web Site: https://www.klineluk.com
Sales Range: $25-49.9 Million
Emp.: 25
Marine Transportation Services
N.A.I.C.S.: 488390

K Line Logistics (Thailand) Ltd. (1)
33/34 M Floor Wall Street Tower Building Surawongse Road, Suriyawongse, Bangrak, 10500, Bangkok, Thailand
Tel.: (66) 2238068595
Web Site: http://www.th.klinelogistics.com
Railway Transportation Services
N.A.I.C.S.: 488210

K Line Logistics (U.S.A.) Inc. (1)
145 Hook Creek Blvd Bldg C5B, Valley Stream, NY 11581
Tel.: (516) 561-0700
Web Site: http://www.us.klinelogistics.com
Freight Forwarding & Customs Brokerage Services
N.A.I.C.S.: 488510
Antonio Rodriguez *(VP & Mgr-Export Ops)*

K Line Logistics, Ltd. (1)
Harumi Island Triton Square Office Tower X Building 30F 1-8-10 Harumi, Chuo-ku, Tokyo, 104-6030, Japan (90.74%)
Tel.: (81) 36 772 8800
Web Site: https://www.klinelogistics.com
Sales Range: $200-249.9 Million
Emp.: 525
Logistic Services
N.A.I.C.S.: 541614

Subsidiary (Non-US):

K LINE LOGISTICS (AUSTRALIA) PTY. LTD. (2)
Level 2 187 Todd Road, PO Box 5067, Garden City, Port Melbourne, 3207, VIC, Australia
Tel.: (61) 39 944 3000
Web Site: https://www.klinelogistics.com.au
Logistics Consulting Servies
N.A.I.C.S.: 541614

K LINE LOGISTICS (MALAYSIA) SDN BHD (2)
No 12 Jalan Sungai Jeluh 32/192, Novelle Kemuning Industrial Park, 40460, Shah Alam, Selangor, Malaysia
Tel.: (60) 355258090
Web Site: http://my.klinelogistics.com
Sales Range: $25-49.9 Million
Emp.: 88
Steel Sheet & Plate Mfr
N.A.I.C.S.: 331315

K LINE LOGISTICS (MEXICO), S.A. DE C.V (2)
Morelos No 176 Col Penon De Los Banos, Mexico, 15520, Mexico
Tel.: (52) 5557844656
Sales Range: $25-49.9 Million
Emp.: 15
Logistics Consulting Servies
N.A.I.C.S.: 541614
Jafunobu Matsuura *(Mng Dir)*

K LINE LOGISTICS (VIETNAM) CO., LTD. (2)
6th Fl 45 Trieu Viet Vuong Street, Hai Ba Trung Dist, Hanoi, 10524, Vietnam
Tel.: (84) 4 39449770
Sales Range: $25-49.9 Million
Emp.: 1
Logistics Consulting Servies
N.A.I.C.S.: 541614

K LINE LOGISTICS FRANCE S.A.S (2)
Zone Cargo No 8 Sogaris Batiment D 14 Rue De LaBelle Borne, BP 14101, CDG, 95701, Roissy-en-France, France
Tel.: (33) 148620653
Web Site: http://www.fr.klinelogistics.com
Sales Range: $25-49.9 Million
Emp.: 10
Logistics Consulting Servies
N.A.I.C.S.: 541614
Pascal Courgenouil *(Dir-Technical)*

K Line Logistics (China) Ltd. (2)
Room D 15/F Long Feng Bldg 1566 West Yan An Road, Chang Ning Area, Shanghai, China
Tel.: (86) 2152581155
Logistics Consulting Servies
N.A.I.C.S.: 541614

K Line Logistics (Hong Kong) Ltd. (2)
Unit 04-06 17/F No 909 Cheung Sha Wan Road, Cheung Sha Wan, Kowloon, China (Hong Kong)
Tel.: (852) 2 727 9333
Web Site: https://www.hk.klinelogistics.com
Logistics Consulting Servies
N.A.I.C.S.: 541614

Subsidiary (Domestic):

K Line Air Travel Ltd. (3)
Unit 1-2A 18/F Regent Centre 88 Queen's Road, 173 Des Voeux Road, Central, China (Hong Kong)
Tel.: (852) 2 543 7683
Web Site: https://www.klinetravel.com
Emp.: 1
Travel Agencies
N.A.I.C.S.: 561510

Subsidiary (Non-US):

K Line Logistics (Singapore) Pte, Ltd. (2)
9 Tampines Grande 04-17/18, Singapore, 528735, Singapore
Tel.: (65) 6 542 9919
Web Site: http://www.sg.klinelogistics.com
Sales Range: $25-49.9 Million
Emp.: 100
Logistics Consulting Servies
N.A.I.C.S.: 541614

K Line Logistics (U.K.) Ltd. (2)
671 Stur Rd N Seltham Trading Esche, Feltham, TW14 0SL, United Kingdom
Tel.: (44) 208893 1122
Sales Range: $25-49.9 Million
Emp.: 2
Logistics Consulting Servies
N.A.I.C.S.: 541614

K Line Maritime (Malaysia) Sdn Bhd (1)
Level 15-02 Plaza Masalam No 2, Jalan Tengku Ampuan Zabedah E9/E Section 9, 40100, Shah Alam, Selangor, Malaysia (57.5%)
Tel.: (60) 35 510 2400
Web Site: https://www.kline.com.my
Emp.: 100
Maritime Transportation Services
N.A.I.C.S.: 488510

K Line Mexico SA de CV (1)
WTC Montecito No 38 Piso 17 Oficina 19-20 Col Napoles, 03810, Mexico, Mexico
Tel.: (52) 5590000963
Transportation Company Services
N.A.I.C.S.: 485999

K Line Offshore AS (1)
Kystveien 14, 4841, Arendal, Norway
Tel.: (47) 40000568
Web Site: http://www.klineoffshore.no
Vessel Provider Services
N.A.I.C.S.: 488330
Tomoyuki Okawa *(CEO)*

K Line Pte Ltd (1)
1 Wallich Street 07-01 Guoco Tower, Singapore, 078881, Singapore
Tel.: (65) 6 215 6215
Web Site: https://www.klpl.com.sg
Sales Range: $50-74.9 Million
Emp.: 170
Marine Transportation Services

N.A.I.C.S.: 488390
Jiro Asakura *(Chm)*

K Line RORO Services Ltd. (1)
Iino Building 1-1 Uchisaiwaicho 2-Chome, Chiyoda-ku, Tokyo, 100-0011, Japan
Tel.: (81) 335955200
Web Site: http://www.roro.kline.co.jp
Car Shipping Agent Services
N.A.I.C.S.: 488510
Haruhiko Sugimoto *(Pres)*

K Line RoRo & Bulk Agencia Maritima Ltda. (1)
Avenida Paulista 542, 10 Floor Bela Vista, Sao Paulo, 01310-000, Brazil
Tel.: (55) 1123482130
Transportation Company Services
N.A.I.C.S.: 485999

K Line RoRo Bulk Ship Management Co., Ltd. (1)
2-2-3 Kaigan-Dori, Chuo-Ku, Kobe, 650-0024, Japan
Tel.: (81) 783349700
Web Site: http://www.krbs.co.jp
Ship Management Services
N.A.I.C.S.: 488320
Eiji Kadono *(Pres)*

K Line Ship Management Co., Ltd. (1)
15th Floor Iino Bldg 1-1 Uchil-Saiwaicho 2-Chome, Chiyoda-ku, Tokyo, 100-0011, Japan
Tel.: (81) 335955549
Web Site: http://www.klsm.co.jp
Rev.: $143,330,000
Emp.: 64
Marine Transportation Services
N.A.I.C.S.: 488390
Hirofumi Sakurai *(Mng Dir)*

Subsidiary (Non-US):

K LINE SHIP MANAGEMENT (India) Pvt LTD (2)
301 Durolite House Plot No C-1 3rd floor Opp Laxmi Industrial Estate, New Link Road Andheri West, Mumbai, 400 053, India
Tel.: (91) 224 926 9700
Web Site: https://www.klsmindia.com
Emp.: 20
Marine Transportation Services
N.A.I.C.S.: 488390
Sudhir K. Goyal *(CEO & Mng Dir)*

K Line Shipping (South Africa) Pty. Ltd. (1)
Millweed House 169-175 Maydon Road, Maydon Wharf, Durban, 4001, South Africa
Tel.: (27) 315210107
Transportation Company Services
N.A.I.C.S.: 485999

K Line Shipping (South Africa) Pty. Ltd. (1)
Millweed House 169-175 Maydon Road, Maydon Wharf, Durban, 4001, South Africa
Tel.: (27) 315210107
Transportation Company Services
N.A.I.C.S.: 485999

K Line Shipping (South Africa) Pty. Ltd. (1)
Millweed House 169-175 Maydon Road, Maydon Wharf, Durban, 4001, South Africa
Tel.: (27) 315210107
Transportation Company Services
N.A.I.C.S.: 485999

K Line Shipping (South Africa) Pty. Ltd. (1)
Millweed House 169-175 Maydon Road, Maydon Wharf, Durban, 4001, South Africa
Tel.: (27) 315210107
Transportation Company Services
N.A.I.C.S.: 485999

K Line Systems, Ltd. (1)
Toranomon Kotohira Tower 10F 1001 2-8 Toranomon 1-Chome, Minato-ku, Tokyo, 105-0001, Japan
Tel.: (81) 355216170
Web Site: http://www.kls.jp.kline.com
Sales Range: $25-49.9 Million
Emp.: 115
Information Technology Consulting Services
N.A.I.C.S.: 541512

INTERNATIONAL PUBLIC

K Line Travel, Ltd. (1)
Harumi Island Triton Square Office Tower X Building 30th Floor, 1-8-10 Harumi Chuo-ku, Tokyo, 104-6030, Japan
Tel.: (81) 35 144 8520
Web Site: https://www.klinetravel.co.jp
Emp.: 39
Travel Agency Services
N.A.I.C.S.: 561510

KMDS Co., Ltd. (1)
1-3 Honcho Sodori Yokohama Building 3rd floor, Naka-ku, Yokohama, 231-0005, Kanagawa, Japan
Tel.: (81) 45 224 8022
Web Site: https://www.kmds.jp
Sales Range: $10-24.9 Million
Emp.: 30
Business Services
N.A.I.C.S.: 561499
Kunihiro Hino *(Pres)*

Kawaki Kosan Kaisha, Ltd. (1)
Nishishimbashinaka Building 4th Floor 1-12-8 Nishishimbashi, Minato-ku, Tokyo, 105-0003, Japan
Tel.: (81) 335955788
Web Site: http://www.kawakikosan.co.jp
Emp.: 25
Real Estate Services
N.A.I.C.S.: 531390
Seiwa Arai *(Mng Dir)*

Kawasaki Kinkai Kisen Kaisha, Ltd. (1)
3-2-1Kasumigaseki Kasumigaseki Common Gate West Building 25th floor, Chiyoda-ku, Tokyo, 100-0013, Japan
Tel.: (81) 335925800
Web Site: http://www.kawakin.co.jp
Sales Range: $250-299.9 Million
Emp.: 235
Marine Transportation Services
N.A.I.C.S.: 488320

Maizuru Kousoku Yusou Co., Ltd. (1)
20-2 Shimazaki Matsukage, Maizuru, 624-0931, Kyoto, Japan
Tel.: (81) 773750830
Web Site: http://www.kline.co.jp
Sales Range: $25-49.9 Million
Emp.: 18
Land Transportation Services
N.A.I.C.S.: 488510

Marine Radio Service, Ltd. (1)
Gotanda Mark Bldg 8-11-13 Nishi-Gotanda, Shinagawa-ku, Tokyo, 141-0031, Japan (100%)
Tel.: (81) 35 437 8340
Web Site: https://www.mrs.jp.kline.com
Emp.: 10
Marine Radio Sales & Repair
N.A.I.C.S.: 334220

Misuzu Machinery Co., Ltd. (1)
2-22 Sakaemachi-dori 5-chome, Chuo-Ku, Kobe, 650-0023, Japan
Tel.: (81) 783512202
Web Site: http://www.misuzu-mac.co.jp
Emp.: 67
Sea Freight Transportation Services
N.A.I.C.S.: 483111

Multimodal Engineering Corporation (1)
4010 Watson Plz Dr Ste 250, Lakewood, CA 90712 (100%)
Tel.: (562) 425-4023
Web Site: http://www.mec-usa.com
Emp.: 25
Engineering Services
N.A.I.C.S.: 541330

Nitto Total Logistics Ltd. (1)
4-6 Minatojima, Chuo-ku, Kobe, 650-0045, Japan (100%)
Tel.: (81) 78 302 0243
Web Site: https://www.nitto-ntl.co.jp
Emp.: 339
Transportation & Logistics Services
N.A.I.C.S.: 541614
Mitsuru Kochi *(Pres)*

Subsidiary (Domestic):

Nitto Tugboat Co., Ltd. (2)
1-15-30 Minamise, Kurashiki, 712-8055, Okayama, Japan

Tel.: (81) 86 456 6537
Web Site: https://www.nittotug.co.jp
Sales Range: $25-49.9 Million
Emp.: 86
Harbor Transportation Services
N.A.I.C.S.: 488310

Ocean Network Express Holdings, Ltd. (1)
11F W Building, 1-8-15 Kohnan Minato-ku, Tokyo, 108-0075, Japan (31%)
Tel.: (65) 62200196
Web Site: https://holdco.one-line.com
Marine transportation
N.A.I.C.S.: 713930

Subsidiary (Non-US):

Ocean Network Express Pte. Ltd. (2)
7 Straits View, #16-01 Marina One East Tower,, Singapore, 018936, Singapore
Tel.: (65) 62200196
Web Site: https://www.one-line.com
Container Shipping Businesses
N.A.I.C.S.: 488330
Jeremy Nixon (CEO)

Subsidiary (US):

TraPac, LLC (3)
920 West Harry Bridges Blvd, Wilmington, CA 90744
Tel.: (310) 830-2000
Web Site: http://www.trapac.com
Rev.: $7,000,000
Emp.: 50
Freight Transportation Arrangement
N.A.I.C.S.: 488510
Scott Axelson (VP-Bus Dev)

Yusen Terminals, LLC (3)
701 New Dock St, Terminal Island, CA 90731
Tel.: (310) 548-8000
Web Site: http://www.yti.com
Marine Cargo Terminal Operating Services
N.A.I.C.S.: 488310
Alan McCorkle (CEO)

PT K Line Indonesia (1)
41st Floor Sinarmas MSIG Tower Jl Jend Sudirman Kav 21, South Jakarta, 12190, Indonesia (51%)
Tel.: (62) 215214070
Web Site: https://www.kline.co.id
Emp.: 200
Transportation Services
N.A.I.C.S.: 488510
Ivan Karyadi (Deputy Gen Mgr)

SEAGATE CORPORATION (1)
2-22-37 Dejima, Minami-ku, Hiroshima, 734-0013, Japan (100%)
Tel.: (81) 82 254 2421
Web Site: https://www.seagatecorp.com
Sales Range: $50-74.9 Million
Emp.: 288
Transportation Services
N.A.I.C.S.: 488510

Shimizu Kawasaki Transportation Co., Ltd (1)
1-5-1 Minato-cho, Shimizu-ku, Shizuoka, 424-0943, Japan
Tel.: (81) 543 53 2481
Web Site: http://www.kline.co.jp
Sales Range: $25-49.9 Million
Emp.: 16
Shipping Agents
N.A.I.C.S.: 488510

Shinki Corporation (1)
Shinko Building 8th Kaigandori, Chuo-Ku, Kobe, 650-0024, Hyogo, Japan
Tel.: (81) 78 332 8255
Web Site: https://www.e-shinki.co.jp
Sales Range: $125-149.9 Million
Emp.: 370
Marine Transportation Services
N.A.I.C.S.: 488390
Michio Kawai (Pres)

Taiyo Nippon Kisen Co., Ltd. (1)
2-2-3 Kaigandori, Chuo-ku, Kobe, 650-0024, Hyogo, Japan
Tel.: (81) 783349700
Sales Range: $125-149.9 Million
Emp.: 136
Ship Management Services

N.A.I.C.S.: 483111

Tokyo Kokusai Koun Kaisha, Ltd. (1)
Ohi No 1, Tokyo, Japan
Tel.: (81) 3 3790 1231
Web Site: http://www.kline.co.jp
Harbor Terminal Services
N.A.I.C.S.: 488310

KAWASE COMPUTER SUPPLIES CO., LTD.
1-4-8 Kyutaromachi, Chuo-ku, Osaka, 541-0056, Japan
Tel.: (81) 664848812
Web Site: https://www.kc-s.co.jp
Year Founded: 1955
7851—(TKS)
Sales Range: $25-49.9 Million
Emp.: 105
Commercial Printing Services
N.A.I.C.S.: 323113
Keisuke Kawase (Pres, CEO & COO)

KAWATA MFG CO., LTD.
1-15-15 Awaza, Nishi-ku, Osaka, 550-0011, Japan
Tel.: (81) 665318211
Web Site: https://www.kawata.cc
Year Founded: 1935
6292—(TKS)
Rev.: $161,905,340
Assets: $176,758,010
Liabilities: $93,194,390
Net Worth: $83,563,620
Earnings: $6,140,690
Emp.: 809
Fiscal Year-end: 03/31/24
Commercial & Service Industry Machinery Mfr
N.A.I.C.S.: 333310
Takayuki Shiba (Operating Officer)

Subsidiaries:

CONAIR KAWATA SALES & SERVICE CO. (1)
455 Allegheny Blvd, Franklin, PA 16323
Tel.: (814) 432-6368
Grain Processing Machine Mfr
N.A.I.C.S.: 333241

KAWATA (SHANGHAI) CO., LTD. (1)
No 325 Yuandian Road Xinzhuang Industry Zone, Minhang District, Shanghai, 201108, China
Tel.: (86) 2133290099
Grain Processing Machine Mfr
N.A.I.C.S.: 333241

KAWATA MACHINERY (HK) LIMITED (1)
Unit 902 9/F Lucky Commercial Centre No 103 Des Voeux Road West, Central, Hong Kong, China (Hong Kong)
Tel.: (852) 31181326
Grain Processing Machine Mfr
N.A.I.C.S.: 333241

KAWATA MARKETING SDN. BHD. (1)
Lot 3986 F G Jalan Haruan 1 Oakland Industrial Park, Sungai Gadut, 70300, Seremban, Negeri Sembilan, Malaysia
Tel.: (60) 67656628
Grain Processing Machine Mfr
N.A.I.C.S.: 333241

KAWATA MFG CO., LTD. - Osaka Plant (1)
5-2-10 Minamitsumori, Nishinari-ku, Osaka, 557-0063, Japan
Tel.: (81) 666570858
Grain Processing Machine Mfr
N.A.I.C.S.: 333241

KAWATA MFG CO., LTD. - Sanda Plant (1)
501-17 Fukushima, Sanda, 669-1313, Hyogo, Japan
Tel.: (81) 795636941
Web Site: http://www.kawata-mfg.co.jp
Grain Processing Machine Mfr
N.A.I.C.S.: 333241

KAWATA MFG CO., LTD. - Tokyo Plant (1)
5-5-13 Ryoke, Kawaguchi, 332-0004, Saitama, Japan
Tel.: (81) 482244447
Grain Processing Machine Mfr
N.A.I.C.S.: 333241
Tsutomu Yamaguchi (Mgr)

KAWATA PACIFIC PTE. LTD. (1)
8 Kaki Bukit Road 2 02-34 Ruby Warehouse Complex, Singapore, 417841, Singapore
Tel.: (65) 62868817
Grain Processing Machine Mfr
N.A.I.C.S.: 333241

PT. KAWATA INDONESIA (1)
Jababeka Techno Park KIJ III Block E2C Pasir Gombong Cikarang Utara, Bekasi, 17530, Jawa Barat, Indonesia
Tel.: (62) 2189844560
Web Site: http://kawata.co.id
Grain Processing Machine Mfr
N.A.I.C.S.: 333241

REIKEN (THAILAND) CO., LTD (1)
136 Moo 1 Hi-tech Industrial Estate Tambol Bannlane, Amphur Bangpa-in, Ayutthaya, 13160, Thailand
Tel.: (66) 35314300
Grain Processing Machine Mfr
N.A.I.C.S.: 333241

TAIWAN KAWATA CO., LTD. (1)
5F No 37 Minzu Rd, East Dist, Hsinchu, 300, Taiwan
Tel.: (886) 35341847
Web Site: http://www.kawatatw.com.tw
Grain Processing Machine Mfr
N.A.I.C.S.: 333241

KAY & QUE (BANGLADESH) LTD.
10th Floor 108 Bir Uttam C R Datta Road, Dhaka, 1205, Bangladesh
Tel.: (880) 58610012
Web Site: https://www.kayandque.com
KAY&QUE—(CHT)
Rev.: $1,633,728
Assets: $6,322,820
Liabilities: $2,734,016
Net Worth: $3,588,804
Earnings: $15,172
Emp.: 170
Fiscal Year-end: 06/30/23
Dry Cell Battery Components Mfr
N.A.I.C.S.: 335910
Tabith M. Awal (Mng Dir)

KAY CEE ENERGY & INFRA LIMITED
9 Krishna Vihar Near Chungi Naka Nanta Road Kunhadi, Kota, 324008, India
Tel.: (91) 7442372124
Web Site: https://www.kayceeenergy.com
Year Founded: 1996
KCEIL—(NSE)
Rev.: $7,442,662
Assets: $9,810,243
Liabilities: $7,124,088
Net Worth: $2,686,156
Earnings: $700,366
Emp.: 339
Fiscal Year-end: 03/31/23
Engineeering Services
N.A.I.C.S.: 541330

KAY POWER & PAPER LIMITED
Gat No 454/457 Village Borgaon, Satara, 415 519, Maharashtra, India
Tel.: (91) 2162265329
Web Site: https://www.kaypowerandpaper.com
Year Founded: 1991
530255—(BOM)
Rev.: $3,102,060

Assets: $3,094,061
Liabilities: $3,030,737
Net Worth: $63,325
Earnings: $8,325
Emp.: 60
Fiscal Year-end: 03/31/21
Electric Power Generation Services & Paper Mfr
N.A.I.C.S.: 221118
Niraj Chandra (Chm & Mng Dir)

KAYA LIMITED
23/C Mahal Industrial Estate Mahakali Caves Road Near Paper Box Lane, Andheri East, Mumbai, 400 093, India
Tel.: (91) 2266195000
Web Site: https://www.kaya.in
Year Founded: 2003
539276—(BOM)
Rev.: $45,709,694
Assets: $44,356,993
Liabilities: $56,714,825
Net Worth: ($12,357,832)
Earnings: ($13,939,656)
Emp.: 686
Fiscal Year-end: 03/31/23
Skin Care Services
N.A.I.C.S.: 812112
Harshraj C. Mariwala (Chm & Mng Dir)

Subsidiaries:

IRIS Medical Centre LLC (1)
Villa 12-6Th Street, Abu Dhabi, United Arab Emirates (100%)
Tel.: (971) 26665000
Holding Company
N.A.I.C.S.: 551112

Minal Specialised Clinic Dermatology LLC (1)
01-402 4th floor C block Crystal Plaza Tower Buheira Corniche road, PO Box 24680, Opp Gold Souk, Sharjah, United Arab Emirates
Tel.: (971) 65749610
Web Site: http://www.drminal.com
Skin & Hair Treatment Services
N.A.I.C.S.: 621111

KAYAC INC.
Old Bank Complex 11-8 Onarimachi, Kamakura, 248-0012, Kanagawa, Japan
Tel.: (81) 467613399
Web Site: https://www.kayac.com
Year Founded: 1998
3904—(TKS)
Rev.: $123,841,030
Assets: $82,811,200
Liabilities: $40,767,500
Net Worth: $42,043,700
Earnings: $3,622,990
Emp.: 572
Fiscal Year-end: 12/31/23
Digital Content Services
N.A.I.C.S.: 513210
Daisuke Yanasawa (CEO)

Subsidiaries:

Kamakura Jitaku Sougisha Inc. (1)
11-8 Onarimachi, Kamakura, 248-0012, Kanagawa, Japan
Tel.: (81) 467814855
Web Site: http://www.kamakura-jitakusou.com
Funeral Services
N.A.I.C.S.: 812210

Manga Designers Lab. Co., Ltd. (1)
6-10-8 Harajuku NA building 6F Harajuku NA Bldg 6F 6-10-8, Jingumae Shibuya-Ku, Tokyo, 150-0001, Japan
Tel.: (81) 368051571
Web Site: https://www.manga-designers.net
Graphic Design Services
N.A.I.C.S.: 541430

Sanko, Inc. (1)
41-1 Kanda Higashi Matsushita-cho,

KAYAC INC.

KAYAC Inc.—(Continued)
Chiyoda-ku, Tokyo, 101-0042,
Japan **(75%)**
Tel.: (81) 35 860 7565
Web Site: https://www.3ko.co.jp
Advertising, Promotion, Branding Campaign
& Marketing Services
N.A.I.C.S.: 541890

Yameryu Inc. (1)
1916-8 Kukihara Joyomachi, Yame, 834-1103, Fukuoka, Japan
Tel.: (81) 943522222
Web Site: http://www.yameryu.jp
Wood Products Mfr
N.A.I.C.S.: 321113

KAYDAV GROUP LIMITED

105 Bamboesvlei Road, Ottery, 7800,
Cape Town, South Africa
Tel.: (27) 217047060 ZA
Web Site: http://www.kaydav.co.za
Year Founded: 2006
KDV—(JSE)
Rev.: $72,920,514
Assets: $38,222,010
Liabilities: $21,082,027
Net Worth: $17,139,983
Earnings: $1,553,615
Emp.: 619
Fiscal Year-end: 12/31/19
Wood Panel Mfr & Whslr
N.A.I.C.S.: 321211
Gary Davidson (CEO)

KAYMUS RESOURCES INC.

Suite 1530 715 5th Avenue Southwest, Calgary, T2P 2X6, AB, Canada
Tel.: (403) 262-9177 AB
Year Founded: 1983
KYS.H—(TSXV)
Rev.: $836,074
Assets: $1,681,503
Liabilities: $236,632
Net Worth: $1,444,871
Earnings: $799,573
Fiscal Year-end: 07/31/22
Oil & Gas Exploration Services
N.A.I.C.S.: 211120
Gordon A. Bowerman (CEO)

KAYNES TECHNOLOGY INDIA LIMITED

23-25 Belagola Food Industrial Estate
Metagalli PO, Mysore, 570016, Karnataka, India
Tel.: (91) 8212582595 In
Web Site:
https://www.kaynestechnology.co.in
Year Founded: 1988
543664—(BOM)
Rev.: $136,384,150
Assets: $170,101,553
Liabilities: $54,958,696
Net Worth: $115,142,857
Earnings: $11,413,704
Emp.: 1,478
Fiscal Year-end: 03/31/23
Information Technology Services
N.A.I.C.S.: 541512

Subsidiaries:

Digicom Electronics Inc. (1)
7799 Pardee Ln, Oakland, CA 94621
Tel.: (510) 639-7003
Web Site: https://digicom.org
Rev.: $3,948,000
Emp.: 6
Electrical Apparatus & Equipment, Wiring
Supplies & Related Equipment Merchant
Whslr
N.A.I.C.S.: 423610
Mo Ohady (Gen Mgr)

KAYS MEDICAL LTD

3 7 Shaw Street, Liverpool, L6 1HH,
United Kingdom
Tel.: (44) 1514822830

Web Site:
http://www.kaysmedical.com
Year Founded: 1976
Rev.: $16,093,781
Emp.: 52
Medical & Safety Products Whslr
N.A.I.C.S.: 423450
Darren Biddlecombe (Dir-Fin)

KAZAGRO NATIONAL MANAGEMENT HOLDING JSC

13 A Imanova street, Nur-Sultan,
010000, Kazakhstan
Tel.: (7) 172705620
Web Site: http://www.kazagro.kz
Year Founded: 2006
KZAG—(KAZ)
Rev.: $319,645,197
Assets: $3,427,200,988
Liabilities: $3,001,453,114
Net Worth: $425,747,875
Earnings: ($29,349,309)
Fiscal Year-end: 12/31/19
Financial Lending Services
N.A.I.C.S.: 533110
Karashukeyev Yerbol Shyrakpayevich (Co-Chm)

Subsidiaries:

Fund For Financial Support of Agriculture Joint-Stock Company (1)
Ave Sary-Arka Turan 19/1, Nur-Sultan,
010000, Kazakhstan
Tel.: (7) 7172678252
Web Site: http://www.fagri.kz
Agricultural Fund Services
N.A.I.C.S.: 523940
Omarov Zhandar Daniyzrbekovich (Chm)

KAZAKH REPUBLICAN TRADING HOUSE ZANGAR JSC

62 Abylai Khan ave, Almaty, 050004,
Kazakhstan
Tel.: (7) 272731248
ZNGR—(KAZ)
Rev.: $1,514,759
Assets: $25,161,759
Liabilities: $22,214,266
Net Worth: $2,947,493
Earnings: ($331,613)
Fiscal Year-end: 12/31/20
Commercial Premise Leasing Services
N.A.I.C.S.: 531190

KAZAKHALTYN MINING-METALLURGICAL CONCERN JSC

6 The 5th District, Stepnogorsk, Kokshetau, 021500, Akmola, Kazakhstan
Tel.: (7) 164528402
Web Site: http://www.kazakhaltyn.kz
KZAL—(KAZ)
Rev.: $158,296,552
Assets: $449,829,809
Liabilities: $328,807,448
Net Worth: $121,022,362
Earnings: $66,434,841
Fiscal Year-end: 12/31/19
Gold Ore Mining Services
N.A.I.C.S.: 212220
Balamir Mahanov (Gen Dir)

KAZAKHMYS COPPER JSC

Ulytau region Kanysh Satbaev
Square 1, 100600, Zhezqazghan,
Kazakhstan
Tel.: (7) 7015257925
KMCP—(KAZ)
Rev.: $2,976,646,840
Assets: $4,247,513,528
Liabilities: $2,594,579,849
Net Worth: $1,652,933,679
Earnings: $245,067,305
Fiscal Year-end: 12/31/23
Metal & Mining Services
N.A.I.C.S.: 213114

KAZAKHMYS INSURANCE JSC

38 Dostyk ave 7 floor block A, Almaty, 050010, Kazakhstan
Tel.: (7) 727 345 01 25
Web Site: http://www.kmic.kz
Insurance Management Services
N.A.I.C.S.: 524298

KAZAKHSTAN KAGAZY JSC

Abay village, Karasai district, Almaty,
040905, Kazakhstan
Tel.: (7) 7272448787 KZ
Web Site:
http://www.kazakhstankagazy.com
Year Founded: 2001
Paper, Corrugated Board & Packaging Products Mfr
N.A.I.C.S.: 322299
Natalya Kim (CFO)

Subsidiaries:

Kagazy Recycling LLP (1)
Toxan bi 39, 150004, Petropavl, Kazakhstan
Tel.: (7) 7152 335870
Paper Products Mfr
N.A.I.C.S.: 322120
Bolat Utemisov (Gen Dir)

Kazupack Ltd LLP (1)
Bekmakhanova 96v, 050030, Almaty, Kazakhstan
Tel.: (7) 7272515585
Cardboard Mfr
N.A.I.C.S.: 322130

PD Logistics LLP (1)
Krasnogvardeisky Trakt 258 B, Almaty,
050030, Kazakhstan
Tel.: (7) 7273410222
Web Site: http://www.pdl.kz
Sales Range: $50-74.9 Million
Emp.: 150
Logistic Services
N.A.I.C.S.: 484121

KAZAKHSTAN POTASH CORPORATION LIMITED

Level 27 101 Collins Street, Melbourne, 3000, VIC, Australia
Tel.: (61) 3 9653 9020
Web Site:
http://www.kazakhpotash.com
Year Founded: 2010
Rev.: $7,114,215
Assets: $81,818,586
Liabilities: $30,679,225
Net Worth: $51,139,361
Earnings: ($6,312,559)
Emp.: 20
Fiscal Year-end: 12/31/17
Gold, Nickel & Copper Mining Services
N.A.I.C.S.: 212220
Andrew Chan (Sec)

KAZAKHSTAN STOCK EXCHANGE JOINT-STOCK COMPANY

8th Floor Northern Building Almaty
Towers, Almaty, 050040, Kazakhstan
Tel.: (7) 727 237 5300 KZ
Web Site: http://www.kase.kz
Year Founded: 1993
Stock Exchange Services
N.A.I.C.S.: 523210
Idel M. Sabitov (Deputy Chm-Mgmt Bd)

KAZAKHSTAN UTILITY SYSTEMS LLP

7F 14/3 Kunayev Street, BC Nursaya,
Nur-Sultan, 010000, Kazakhstan
Tel.: (7) 172279472
Web Site: http://www.kus.kz
Year Founded: 2008
KSYS—(KAZ)
Rev.: $423,586

INTERNATIONAL PUBLIC

Assets: $845,434
Liabilities: $382,129
Net Worth: $463,304
Earnings: $30,522
Emp.: 8,481
Fiscal Year-end: 12/31/22
Electric Power & Heat Generation Services
N.A.I.C.S.: 221111
Aitzhanov Nabi Yerkinovich (Gen Dir)

Subsidiaries:

Energopotok LLP (1)
Tokayev Street 27, Shymkent, Kazakhstan
Tel.: (7) 7252777333
Web Site: http://www.energopotok.kz
Electric Power Distr
N.A.I.C.S.: 221122

Karagandy Zharyk LLP (1)
St Mukanova 57/3, Karaganda, 100008,
Kazakhstan
Tel.: (7) 7212913555
Web Site: http://www.k-zharyk.kz
Electric Power Distr
N.A.I.C.S.: 221122

KaragandyZhyluSbyt LLP (1)
35a Loboda Street, Karaganda, Kazakhstan
Tel.: (7) 7212980001
Web Site: http://www.kzs.kz
Electric Power Distr
N.A.I.C.S.: 221122

Ontustik Zharyk Tranzit LLP (1)
Energetikov Street 1, Abay district, 160000,
Shymkent, Kazakhstan
Tel.: (7) 7252505711
Web Site: http://www.ojt.kz
Electric Power Distr
N.A.I.C.S.: 221122

Raschetnyi Servisnyi Center LLP (1)
5a Loboda Street, Karaganda, Kazakhstan
Tel.: (7) 7212900152
Electric Power Distr
N.A.I.C.S.: 221122

KAZAKHTELECOM JSC

12 Sauran St, Yessil district, 10000,
Nur-Sultan, Kazakhstan
Tel.: (7) 7172580659
Web Site: https://www.telecom.kz
Year Founded: 1994
KZTK—(KAZ)
Rev.: $1,390,451,192
Assets: $2,877,183,075
Liabilities: $1,243,517,714
Net Worth: $1,633,665,362
Earnings: $287,896,662
Emp.: 19,710
Fiscal Year-end: 12/31/22
Telecommunication Servicesb
N.A.I.C.S.: 517112
Marat Mukhtarovich Abdildabekov (CTO & Member-Mgmt Bd)

Subsidiaries:

Digital Economy Development Center LLP (1)
Mangilik El Ave 33/1 BC iPlaza 4th floor,
Astana, Kazakhstan
Tel.: (7) 88000806565
Web Site: https://digitaleconomy.kz
Communication Service
N.A.I.C.S.: 517410

KT Cloud Lab LLP (1)
Special Economic Zone Park of Innovative
Technologies St Ibragimova, House 9 block
1 Alatau Village, Almaty, Kazakhstan
Tel.: (7) 7272220711
Web Site: http://www.eng.mycloud.kz
Emp.: 1,000
Business Outsourcing Services
N.A.I.C.S.: 561499

Kcell JSC (1)
Tel.: (7) 7272588000
Web Site: https://www.kcell.kz
Mobile Voice Telecommunication Services
N.A.I.C.S.: 517810

KAZAX MINERALS INC.

Room 630 7th Floor Arman Business Center, 6 Saryarka Avenue, Nur-Sultan, 010000, Kazakhstan
Tel.: (7) 717 279 03 95 BC
Web Site:
http://www.kazaxmineralsinc.com
Year Founded: 2005
Iron Mining Services
N.A.I.C.S.: 212210

KAZAZOTE JSC
building No 150, Industrial zone 6, 130000, Aktau, Mangistau, Kazakhstan
Tel.: (7) 292579814
Web Site: https://en.kazazot.kz
Year Founded: 2005
KZAZ—(KAZ)
Rev.: $106,692,246
Assets: $251,901,250
Liabilities: $94,945,165
Net Worth: $156,956,085
Earnings: $39,578,217
Fiscal Year-end: 12/31/19
Mineral Mining Services
N.A.I.C.S.: 212390
Dzhumatova Aynagul Yerbolatovna (Sec)

KAZERA GLOBAL PLC
33 St James Square, London, SW1Y 4JS, United Kingdom
Tel.: (44) 2072361177
Web Site: https://kazeraglobal.com
Year Founded: 2006
KZG—(AIM)
Rev.: $145,276
Assets: $6,344,626
Liabilities: $2,080,027
Net Worth: $4,264,599
Earnings: ($2,743,952)
Emp.: 16
Fiscal Year-end: 06/30/22
Investment Services
N.A.I.C.S.: 523999
Giles Clarke (Chm)

Subsidiaries:

MSS Interiors Limited (1)
Pinden End Farm Canada Farm Rd, Dartford, DA2 8EA, Kent, United Kingdom
Tel.: (44) 1474709708
Sales Range: $25-49.9 Million
Emp.: 20
Interior Refurbishment Services
N.A.I.C.S.: 541410

MSS Projects Limited (1)
Ground Fl Barons Ct Manchester Rd, Wilmslow, SK9 1BQ, Cheshire, United Kingdom
Tel.: (44) 1625546700
Sales Range: $50-74.9 Million
Emp.: 167
Heating & Ventilation & Air Conditioning Systems Installation Services
N.A.I.C.S.: 333415

Status Building Services Ltd. (1)
Ground Fl Parong Ct Manchester Rd, Wilmslow, SK9 1BQ, Cheshire, United Kingdom
Tel.: (44) 1737 765222
Sales Range: $25-49.9 Million
Building Maintenance Services
N.A.I.C.S.: 561790

Status Electrical Services Ltd. (1)
Ground Fl Parong Ct Manchester Rd, Wilmslow, SK9 1BQ, Cheshire, United Kingdom
Tel.: (44) 1737765222
Sales Range: $25-49.9 Million
Emp.: 40
Building Electrical Contracting Services
N.A.I.C.S.: 238210

KAZIA THERAPEUTICS LIMITED
Three International Towers Level 24 300 Barangaroo Avenue, Sydney, 2, NSW, Australia
Tel.: (61) 294724101 AU
Web Site:
https://www.kaziatherapeutics.com
Year Founded: 2000
KZIA—(NASDAQ)
Rev.: $1,541,144
Assets: $14,413,168
Liabilities: $21,101,919
Net Worth: ($6,688,752)
Earnings: ($17,880,742)
Fiscal Year-end: 06/30/24
Pharmaceutical Preparation Manufacturing
N.A.I.C.S.: 325412
James Garner (CEO & Mng Dir)

KAZINVESTBANK JSC
172 Dostyk Ave, 050051, Almaty, Kazakhstan
Tel.: (7) 7272619060
Web Site: http://www.kib.kz
Sales Range: $50-74.9 Million
Emp.: 59
Banking Services
N.A.I.C.S.: 522110

KAZTRANSCOM JSC
69/204a Radostovtsev St Zhambyl St Corner, Almaty, 050009, Kazakhstan
Tel.: (7) 7272377402
Web Site: http://www.kaztranscom.kz
KZTC—(KAZ)
Rev.: $42,272,327,340
Assets: $68,844,920,040
Liabilities: $17,394,564,240
Net Worth: $51,450,355,800
Earnings: $2,583,430,200
Emp.: 1,600
Fiscal Year-end: 12/31/19
Telecommunication Servicesb
N.A.I.C.S.: 517111

KAZTRANSOIL JSC
12 NRB 20 Turan Ave, Essil District, 10000, Nur-Sultan, Kazakhstan
Tel.: (7) 7172555298
Web Site: https://www.kaztransoil.kz
KZTO—(KAZ)
Rev.: $571,591,854
Assets: $2,762,438,979
Liabilities: $722,160,536
Net Worth: $2,040,278,442
Earnings: $44,277,298
Emp.: 6,637
Fiscal Year-end: 12/31/22
Oil Transportation Services
N.A.I.C.S.: 486110
Airat Shmanov (Sec)

Subsidiaries:

Batumi Oil Terminal LLC (1)
Saint Severian Adjareli street No 4g, 6000, Batumi, Georgia
Tel.: (995) 422276006
Web Site: https://www.batumioilterminal.com
Oil Transportation Services
N.A.I.C.S.: 486110

Batumi Sea Port LLC (1)
15 Baku Str, Batumi, 6000, Georgia
Tel.: (995) 422274912
Web Site: https://www.batumiport.com
Cargo Handling Services
N.A.I.C.S.: 488320
Meiramkhan Adylkhanov (Gen Dir)

Main Waterline LLP (1)
Kairgali Smagulov str 12, 060002, Atyrau, Kazakhstan
Tel.: (7) 7122762945
Web Site: https://www.mwl.kz
Water Supply Services
N.A.I.C.S.: 221310
Kultumiev Askar (Deputy Gen Dir-Production)

MunaiTas LLP (1)
26/29 Timiryazev Str, Almaty, A15E0G0, Kazakhstan
Tel.: (7) 7273122212
Web Site: http://www.munaitas.kz
Oil Pipeline Services
N.A.I.C.S.: 237120
Nurabayev Murat Dzhanayevich (Dir-Procurement & Logistics Dept)

North-West Pipeline Company Munai-Tas JSC (1)
Satpaeva 29d, Almaty, 050008, Kazakhstan
Tel.: (7) 7273122212
Web Site: http://www.munaitas.kz
Oil Transportation Services
N.A.I.C.S.: 486110

KB AUTOSYS CO., LTD
528-24 Asanoncheon-ro, Asan, Chungcheongnam-do, Korea (South)
Tel.: (82) 415375345
Web Site: https://www.kbautosys.com
Year Founded: 1985
024120—(KRS)
Rev.: $136,558,129
Assets: $156,787,124
Liabilities: $79,691,689
Net Worth: $77,095,435
Earnings: $844,743
Emp.: 203
Fiscal Year-end: 12/31/22
Automobile Equipment Mfr
N.A.I.C.S.: 336110
Sin Wan Kim (CEO)

KB COMPONENTS AB
Industrigatan, 286 85, Örkelljunga, Sweden
Tel.: (46) 43556000
Web Site:
https://www.kbcomponents.com
Year Founded: 1947
Polymer Industries
N.A.I.C.S.: 326199

Subsidiaries:

KB Components Canada, Inc. (1)
2900 St Etienne Blvd, Windsor, N8W 5E6, ON, Canada
Tel.: (519) 974-6596
Plastic Injection Molding Services
N.A.I.C.S.: 326199
David Ulrich (Pres)

Subsidiary (Domestic):

Post Meridiem Plastics Ltd. (2)
2900 St Etienne Blvd, Windsor, N8W 5E6, ON, Canada
Tel.: (519) 974-6596
Plastics Product Mfr
N.A.I.C.S.: 326199

KB DREAM TOGETHER 3RD SPECIAL PURPOSE ACQUISITION CO.
21 Yeouinaru-ro 4-gil, Yeongdeungpo-gu, Seoul, Korea (South)
Tel.: (82) 261140920
Year Founded: 2015
Financial Investment Management Services
N.A.I.C.S.: 523940
Sim Jae-In (CEO)

KB FINANCIAL GROUP INC.
26 Gukjegeumyung-ro 8-gil, Yeongdeungpo-gu, Seoul, 07331, Korea (South)
Tel.: (82) 220737114 KR
Web Site: https://www.kbfg.com
KB—(NYSE)
Rev.: $13,994,007,760
Assets: $610,784,167,280
Liabilities: $566,353,760,880
Net Worth: $44,430,406,400
Earnings: $4,033,630,520
Emp.: 24,663
Fiscal Year-end: 12/31/21
Bank Holding Company
N.A.I.C.S.: 551111

Jong Hee Yang (Head-Insurance Bus Unit)

Subsidiaries:

KB Asset Management Co., Ltd. (1)
Tel.: (82) 221678200
Web Site: http://www.kbam.co.kr
Asset Management Services
N.A.I.C.S.: 523940

KB Asset Management Singapore PTE. LTD. (1)
3 Church Street 21-01 Samsung Hub, Singapore, Singapore
Tel.: (65) 802660
Finance Services
N.A.I.C.S.: 921130

KB Bank Myanmar Co., Ltd. (1)
University Avenue Street No 104, Kamaryut Township, Yangon, Myanmar
Tel.: (95) 17532900
Banking Services
N.A.I.C.S.: 522110

KB Capital Co., Ltd. (1)
295 Hyowon-ro, Paldal-gu, Suwon, 442835, Kyunggi-do, Korea (South) (79.7%)
Web Site: http://www.kbcapital.co.kr
Sales Financing & Leasing Services
N.A.I.C.S.: 522220
Soo-Nam Hwang (Pres & CEO)

KB Daehan Specialized Bank PLC (1)
Building No 1 7th 20th 21st and 22nd Floor Street No 360 Phum 8, Sangkat Boeng Keng Kang Ti Muoy Khan Boeng Keng Kang, Phnom Penh, Cambodia
Tel.: (855) 23991555
Web Site: https://www.kdsb.com.kh
Banking Services
N.A.I.C.S.: 522110

KB Data Systems Co., Ltd. (1)
121-815 13th/14th floor Jaram Building Police Mutual Aid Association, 78 Mapo-daero Mapo-gu, Seoul, 121-040, Korea (South)
Tel.: (82) 232156000
Web Site: https://www.kds.co.kr
Information Technology Consulting Services
N.A.I.C.S.: 541512

KB FINA Joint Stock Company (1)
17th floor Charmvit Tower 117 Tran Duy Hung, Cau Giay District Trung Hoa ward, Hanoi, Vietnam
Tel.: (84) 2473014628
Web Site: https://www.kbfina.com
Investment Consulting Services
N.A.I.C.S.: 523940

KB Futures Co., Ltd. (1)
36-3 Yeoido-dong, Seoul, Korea (South)
Tel.: (82) 2 3786 0872
Financial Management Services
N.A.I.C.S.: 523999

KB Golden Life Care Co., Ltd. (1)
7 Hyeongchon 8-gil, Seocho-gu, Seoul, Korea (South)
Tel.: (82) 221359838
Web Site: https://www.kbgoldenlifecare.co.kr
Nursing Research & Development Services
N.A.I.C.S.: 541714

KB Investment & Securities Co., Ltd. (1)
21/22 Floor Goodmorning Shinhan Investment Tower 23-2 Yeouido-dong, Youngdungpo-gu, Seoul, 150-877, Korea (South)
Tel.: (82) 237778000
Web Site: http://www.kbsec.co.kr
Investment Management & Securities Brokerage Services
N.A.I.C.S.: 523999

KB Investment Co., Ltd. (1)
9-10F 731 Yeongdong-daero, Gangnam-gu, Seoul, 06072, Korea (South)
Tel.: (82) 25455091
Sales Range: $50-74.9 Million
Emp.: 33
Investment Management Service
N.A.I.C.S.: 523999

KB J Capital Co., Ltd. (1)
89 AIA Capital Center Building 3rd Floor Ratchadaphisek Road, Din Daeng Subdis-

4103

KB FINANCIAL GROUP INC.

KB Financial Group Inc.—(Continued)
trict Din Daeng District, Bangkok, Thailand
Tel.: (66) 21613333
Web Site: https://www.kbjcapital.co.th
Credit Card Services
N.A.I.C.S.: 522210

KB KOLAO Leasing Co., Ltd. (1)
Alounmai Tower 7th Fl 23 Singha Rd, Vientiane, Laos
Tel.: (856) 21417900
Web Site: https://www.kbkolaoleasing.com
Auto Instalment Financing Services
N.A.I.C.S.: 532112

KB Kookmin Card Co., Ltd. (1)
30 Saemunan-ro 3-gil, Jongno-gu, Seoul, 110719, Korea (South)
Tel.: (82) 6936 3030
Web Site: http://www.kbcard.com
Credit Card Management Services
N.A.I.C.S.: 522320
Dong-Cheol Lee (CEO)

KB Life Co., Ltd. (1)
167 Naesu-dong Jongno-gu, 110-070, Seoul, Korea (South) **(100%)**
Tel.: (82) 23986800
Web Site: http://www.kbli.co.kr
Insurance & Wealth Management Services
N.A.I.C.S.: 524298

KB Life Partners Co., Ltd. (1)
5th floor Seowoo Building 314 Gangnam-daero, Gangnam-gu, Seoul, Korea (South)
Tel.: (82) 264464100
Web Site: https://www.kblifepartners.co.kr
Insurance Services
N.A.I.C.S.: 522220

KB Microfinance Myanmar Co., Ltd. (1)
3F University Avenue Street No 104, Kamaryut Township, Yangon, Myanmar
Tel.: (95) 9957263323
Microfinance Services
N.A.I.C.S.: 522291

KB Real Estate Trust Co., Ltd. (1)
23-25 Floor 129 Teheran-Ro, Gangnam-Gu, Seoul, 135784, Korea (South)
Tel.: (82) 221909800
Web Site: https://www.kbret.co.kr
Emp.: 153
Real Estate Management Services
N.A.I.C.S.: 531390

KB Securities Co., Ltd. (1)
50 Yeouinaru-ro, Yeongdeungpo-gu, Seoul, 1588-6611, Korea (South)
Tel.: (82) 261140114
Web Site: https://www.kbsec.com
Sales Range: $1-4.9 Billion
Securities Brokerage Services
N.A.I.C.S.: 523150
Park Jeong-rim (CEO)

Subsidiary (US):

KBFG Securities America Inc. (2)
Ste 1900 1370 Ave of the Americas, New York, NY 10019
Tel.: (212) 265-2333
Securities Brokerage Services
N.A.I.C.S.: 523150

KBFG Insurance(China) Co., Ltd. (1)
27F No 2701-2703 Sunnyworld Center 188 Lushan Road, Nanjing, Jiangsu, China
Tel.: (86) 2587780888
Insurance Services
N.A.I.C.S.: 525190

Kookmin Bank (1)
(100%)
Sales Range: $1-4.9 Billion
Emp.: 8,900
Commercial Bank
N.A.I.C.S.: 522110

Subsidiary (Domestic):

JooEun Industrial Co., Ltd. (2)
216 20 Jangsan Dong 6 GA Yeong Jeung Ko, Seoul, 150 809, Korea (South) **(100%)**
Tel.: (82) 234613250
Sales Range: $50-74.9 Million
Emp.: 7
N.A.I.C.S.: 522110

JooEun Leasing Co., Ltd. (2)
5th Floor, Anyang Branch Building, 389-5 Anyang-dong, Manan-gu, Anyang, 430-015, Korea (South)
Tel.: (82) 2 343 68 4271
N.A.I.C.S.: 522110

KB Credit Information Co., Ltd. (2)
22nd Floor Gateway Tower Building #12 Dongja-Dong, Yongsan-Gu, Seoul, 140 709, Korea (South)
Tel.: (82) 2 2070 1090
Web Site: http://www.kbci.co.kr
Financial Credit Services
N.A.I.C.S.: 522299

Subsidiary (Non-US):

Kookmin Bank Cambodia PLC. (2)
No 55 Street 214 Sangkat Boeung Raing, Khan Daun Penh, Phnom Penh, Cambodia
Tel.: (855) 23999202
Sales Range: $50-74.9 Million
Emp.: 24
Commercial Banking Services
N.A.I.C.S.: 522110

Kookmin Bank Hong Kong Limited (2)
1101-1106 Central Plaza 18 Harbour Road, Wanchai, China (Hong Kong) **(100%)**
Web Site: http://www.kbfng.com
Sales Range: $50-74.9 Million
Emp.: 15
Corporate Banking
N.A.I.C.S.: 522110

P.T. KB Data Systems Indonesia (1)
L Avenue Office 12E Jl Raya Pasar Minggu No Kav 16 RT 7/RW 9, Pancoran Kec Pancoran Kota Daerah Khusus Ibukota Jakarta, Jakarta Selatan, Indonesia
Tel.: (62) 2180667239
Web Site: https://kbdsi.com
Financial Information Technology Services
N.A.I.C.S.: 541512

P.T. KB Valbury Sekuritas (1)
Sahid Sudirman Center Lantai 41 Unit AC Jl Jenderal Sudirman No 86, Kelurahan Karet Tengsin Kec Tanah Abang, Jakarta Pusat, Indonesia
Tel.: (62) 2125098300
Web Site: https://www.kbvalbury.com
Investment & Financial Services
N.A.I.C.S.: 523999

P.T. Sunindo Kookmin Best Finance (1)
Sahid Sudirman Center 50th floor, Jakarta, Indonesia
Tel.: (62) 2122535098
Web Site: https://www.skbf.co.id
Vehicle Financing Services
N.A.I.C.S.: 525990

PRASAC Microfinance Institution Plc (1)
Building No 212 Street 271 Tuol Tumpung 2, Chamkarmon, Phnom Penh, Cambodia
Tel.: (855) 23999911
Microfinance Services
N.A.I.C.S.: 522291

i-Finance Leasing Plc (1)
City Tower Building M Floor Unit M1 and M2B Mao Tse Toung Blvd, Sangkat Phsar Depou Ti Muoy Khan Tuol Kouk, Phnom Penh, Cambodia
Tel.: (855) 81761111
Web Site: https://www.ifinanceleasing.com.kh
Innovation & Technology Financial Services
N.A.I.C.S.: 541512

KB NO.5 SPECIAL PURPOSE ACQUISITION COMPANY
25 Gukjegeumyung-ro 8-gil, Yeongdeungpo-gu, Seoul, Korea (South)
Tel.: (82) 27867551
Year Founded: 2014
208350—(KRS)
Rev.: $25,454,502
Assets: $97,651,791
Liabilities: $37,339,593
Net Worth: $60,312,198
Earnings: $1,808,196
Emp.: 150

Fiscal Year-end: 12/31/22
Financial Investment Management Services
N.A.I.C.S.: 523940
Hyeong Yin Cho (CEO)

KB NO.8 SPECIAL PURPOSE ACQUISITION COMPANY
208 301 Mapo-daero, Mapo-gu, Seoul, Korea (South)
Tel.: (82) 23123380
Year Founded: 2015
Financial Investment Management Services
N.A.I.C.S.: 523940

KB SYNTHETICS CO., LTD.
1 51 Wolam Dong, Talso-gu, Taegu, Korea (South)
Tel.: (82) 53 582 4641
Web Site: http://www.kbsyn.co.kr
Year Founded: 1987
Sales Range: $50-74.9 Million
Emp.: 350
Synthetic Textile Product Mfr & Exporter
N.A.I.C.S.: 314999

Subsidiaries:

KB Synthetics Co., Ltd. - BUSAN FACTORY (1)
Bisan-7Dong Seo-gu, 3137-3, Taegu, Korea (South)
Tel.: (82) 53 354 0581
Textile Products Mfr
N.A.I.C.S.: 314999

KB Synthetics Co., Ltd. - CHUK-JEON FACTORY (1)
1169-7 Joongri-Dong, Seo-gu, Taegu, Korea (South)
Tel.: (82) 53 556 7771 5
Textile Products Mfr
N.A.I.C.S.: 314999

Modine Korea, LLC (1)
121 Maegok-ri Tangjeong-myon, Asan, 336-843, Chungnam, Korea (South)
Tel.: (82) 41 538 3114
Car Air-Conditioning Systems, Condensers, Heaters, Evaporators, Oil Coolers, Intercoolers, Cooling Modules, Bus Air Conditioners & Train Air Conditioners Mfr
N.A.I.C.S.: 333415

KBC CORPORATION LTD.
No 588 yuxingshan road, Yiyang, 413000, Hunan, China
Tel.: (86) 7376202107
Web Site: https://www.kbcarbon.com
Year Founded: 2005
688598—(SHG)
Rev.: $203,598,856
Assets: $959,860,985
Liabilities: $119,156,301
Net Worth: $840,704,684
Earnings: $77,383,734
Fiscal Year-end: 12/31/22
Carbon Product Mfr & Distr
N.A.I.C.S.: 335991
Jiqiao Liao (Chm)

KBC GLOBAL LIMITED
2nd floor Gulmohar Status Mahatma Nagar samarth Nagar, Nashik, 422005, Maharashtra, India
Tel.: (91) 8554997995
Web Site: https://www.kardaconstruction.com
Year Founded: 2007
KBCGLOBAL—(NSE)
Rev.: $15,194,907
Assets: $44,627,870
Liabilities: $25,569,057
Net Worth: $19,058,813
Earnings: $2,355,089
Emp.: 68
Fiscal Year-end: 03/31/22
Building Construction Services

N.A.I.C.S.: 236220

KBC GROUP NV
Havenlaan 2, B-1080, Brussels, Belgium
Tel.: (32) 78353137
Web Site: https://www.kbc.com
Year Founded: 1935
KBC—(OTCIQ)
Rev.: $8,837,186,800
Assets: $393,949,382,320
Liabilities: $367,506,603,360
Net Worth: $26,442,778,960
Earnings: $1,768,665,600
Emp.: 41,000
Fiscal Year-end: 12/31/20
Financial Holding Company
N.A.I.C.S.: 551111
Viviane Huybrecht (Gen Mgr-Corp Comm)

Subsidiaries:

Allbox NV (1)
Industriezone Stasegem Venetielaan 28, 8530, Harelbeke, Belgium
Tel.: (32) 5 623 52 61
Web Site: http://www.allbox.be
Sales Range: $50-74.9 Million
Emp.: 100
Corrugated Packaging Products Distr
N.A.I.C.S.: 423840
Yves Vanquaethem (CEO)

Subsidiary (Domestic):

Verkoopkantoor Allbox en Desouter NV (2)
Venetielaan 28, Harelbeke, 8530, Belgium
Tel.: (32) 56235261
Packaging Paper Materials Mfr
N.A.I.C.S.: 322220

Applied Maths Inc. (1)
11940 Jollyville Rd Ste 115N, Austin, TX 78759
Tel.: (512) 482-9700
Web Site: http://www.applied-maths.com
Sales Range: $25-49.9 Million
Emp.: 3
Mathematical Application Software Development Services
N.A.I.C.S.: 541511

Asia Pacific Trading & Investment Co Limited (1)
Rm 1413 14/F Sea View Estate Block A, 2 Watson Road, North Point, China (Hong Kong)
Tel.: (852) 21106953
Investment Management Service
N.A.I.C.S.: 523999

Descar NV (1)
Venetielaan 26, 8530, Harelbeke, Belgium
Tel.: (32) 56 23 52 61
Web Site: http://www.allbox.be
Packaging Products Mfr
N.A.I.C.S.: 322220

Di Legno Interiors NV (1)
Troisdorflaan 18, 3600, Genk, Belgium
Tel.: (32) 8 962 91 00
Web Site: http://www.dilegno.be
Sales Range: $25-49.9 Million
Emp.: 3
Parquet Flooring Materials Mfr
N.A.I.C.S.: 321918

Dynaco USA Inc. (1)
935 Campus Dr, Mundelein, IL 60060
Tel.: (847) 562-4910
Web Site: http://www.dynacodoor.us
Sales Range: $25-49.9 Million
Emp.: 30
Industrial Roll Up Door Mfr & Distr
N.A.I.C.S.: 332321

Gdynia America Shipping Lines (London) Limited (1)
5 Saint Johns Lane, London, EC1M 4BH, United Kingdom
Tel.: (44) 20 7549 1692
Ship Transportation Services
N.A.I.C.S.: 488390

Gulliver Kereskedelmi es Szolgaltato Kft. (1)

AND PRIVATE COMPANIES — KBC GROUP NV

Ezred Utca 1-3, Budapest, 1044, Hungary
Tel.: (36) 14144070
Online Marketing Services
N.A.I.C.S.: 541613

Interlease E.A.D. (1)
135A Tzarigradsko Shose Blvd, 1040, Sofia,
Bulgaria (100%)
Tel.: (359) 2 971 8282
Web Site: http://www.interlease.bg
Commercial Vehicles & Industrial Equipment Leasing Services
N.A.I.C.S.: 532112

Subsidiary (Domestic):

Interlease Auto E.A.D. (2)
135A Tzarigradsko Shose Blvd, 1040, Sofia,
Bulgaria
Tel.: (359) 2 9718282
Web Site: http://www.interlease.bg
Automobile Leasing Services
N.A.I.C.S.: 532112

K&H Bank Zrt. (1)
Lechner Odon Fasor 9, 1095, Budapest,
Hungary
Tel.: (36) 13289000
Web Site: http://www.kh.hu
Sales Range: $250-299.9 Million
Commercial Banking Services
N.A.I.C.S.: 522110
Attila Gombas *(Head-Fin & Corp-SME Credit Mgmt Div)*

KBC Alpha SFIO (1)
ul Chmielna 85/87, 00-805, Warsaw, Poland
Tel.: (48) 22 581 23 32
Financial Management Services
N.A.I.C.S.: 523999

KBC Bank NV (1)
Havenlaan 2, B-1080, Brussels,
Belgium (100%)
Tel.: (32) 78353137
Web Site: http://www.kbc.com
Banking
N.A.I.C.S.: 551111
Wim Verbraeken *(Chief Credit Officer-Grp & Sr Gen Mgr)*

Subsidiary (Domestic):

Antwerpse Diamantbank N.V. (2)
Pelikaanstraat 54, Antwerp, 2018,
Belgium (100%)
Tel.: (32) 32047204
Web Site: http://www.antwerpdiamondbank.com
Sales Range: $25-49.9 Million
Emp.: 160
Banking
N.A.I.C.S.: 522299

Branch (Non-US):

Antwerp Diamond Bank (3)
23 Rue Ferdinand Hodler, 1207, Geneva,
Switzerland (87.2%)
Tel.: (41) 227006612
Web Site: http://www.antwerpdiamondbank.com
Sales Range: $50-74.9 Million
Emp.: 1
Diamond Mining
N.A.I.C.S.: 212290

Subsidiary (Domestic):

Apicing NV (2)
Havenlaan 12, 1080, Sint-Jans-Molenbeek,
Belgium
Tel.: (32) 2 429 00 34
Web Site: http://www.kbc.com
Emp.: 3,000
Financial Management Services
N.A.I.C.S.: 523999

CBC Banque S.A. (2)
Avenue Albert Ier 60, 5000, Namur,
Belgium (100%)
Tel.: (32) 15632353
Web Site: http://www.cbc.be
Rev.: $376,482,688
Assets: $12,033,939,762
Liabilities: $11,434,895,075
Net Worth: $599,044,687
Earnings: $121,514,687
Emp.: 1,282
Fiscal Year-end: 12/31/2014
Commercial Banking & Financial Services
N.A.I.C.S.: 522110

Subsidiary (Non-US):

CIBANK PLC (2)
2 Slavianska Street, 1000, Sofia,
Bulgaria (77.75%)
Tel.: (359) 29399240
Web Site: http://www.cibank.bg
Sales Range: $100-124.9 Million
Emp.: 450
Investment Banking Services
N.A.I.C.S.: 523150

Ceskoslovenska obchodni banka a.s. (2)
Radlicka 333/150, 150 57, Prague, Czech
Republic
Tel.: (420) 224111111
Web Site: http://www.csob.cz
Rev.: $2,010,948,930
Assets: $71,783,258,670
Liabilities: $67,440,439,890
Net Worth: $4,342,818,780
Earnings: $866,600,910
Emp.: 8,626
Fiscal Year-end: 12/31/2019
Banking Services
N.A.I.C.S.: 522110
Petr Knapp *(Sr Exec Officer-Relationship Svcs)*

Subsidiary (Non-US):

CSOB Leasing a.s. (3)
Zizkova 11, 81510, Bratislava, Slovakia
Tel.: (421) 268202111
Web Site: http://www.csobleasing.sk
Financial Lending Services
N.A.I.C.S.: 522220

CSOB Nadacia (3)
Michalska 18, 815 63, Bratislava, Slovakia
Tel.: (421) 2 59 666 794
Financial Management Services
N.A.I.C.S.: 523999

CSOB Stavebna Sporitelna a.s. (3)
Radlinskeho 10, 813 23, Bratislava, Slovakia
Tel.: (421) 2 5966 6896
Commercial Banking Services
N.A.I.C.S.: 522110

Subsidiary (Non-US):

Dala Beheer BV (2)
De Spinde 11, Heino, Raalte, 8141 HB,
Netherlands
Tel.: (31) 572394143
Financial Management Services
N.A.I.C.S.: 523999

Subsidiary (Domestic):

Julie LH BVBA (2)
Excelsiorlaan 23, Zaventem, 1930, Belgium
Tel.: (32) 2 290 40 20
Real Estate Development Services
N.A.I.C.S.: 531390

Subsidiary (Non-US):

KBC Asset Management SA (2)
Place de la Gare 5, 1616, Luxembourg,
Luxembourg
Tel.: (352) 299881 1
Web Site: http://www.kbc.be
Sales Range: $50-74.9 Million
Emp.: 2
Asset Management Services
N.A.I.C.S.: 523940

KBC Bank France (2)
Synergie Park 6 rue Nicolas Appert Lezennes, BP 40041, 59030, Lille, France
Tel.: (33) 320116111
Web Site: http://www.kbc.be
Sales Range: $50-74.9 Million
Emp.: 60
International Trade
N.A.I.C.S.: 522299

Branch (Non-US):

KBC Bank Hong Kong Branch (2)
39th Floor Central Plaza 18 Harbour Road,
Wanchai, China (Hong Kong) (100%)
Tel.: (852) 28793388
Web Site: http://www.kbc.com.hk
Sales Range: $100-124.9 Million
Emp.: 120
Capital & Trade Financial Services
N.A.I.C.S.: 522299

Subsidiary (Non-US):

KBC Bank Ireland plc (2)
Sandwith Street, Dublin, Ireland (75%)
Tel.: (353) 16646100
Web Site: http://www.kbc.ie
Sales Range: Less than $1 Million
Emp.: 1,000
International Banking
N.A.I.C.S.: 522299
Peter Roebben *(CEO)*

Subsidiary (Domestic):

KBC Homeloans (3)
Sandwith Street, Dublin, Ireland (75%)
Tel.: (353) 16646446
Web Site: http://www.kbcmortgages.ie
Sales Range: $350-399.9 Million
Emp.: 800
Mortgage Services
N.A.I.C.S.: 522310

Subsidiary (Non-US):

KBC Lease (Luxembourg) SA (3)
5 Rue des Merovingiens ZAI Bourmicht,
8070, Bertrange, Luxembourg
Tel.: (352) 310 103 1
Web Site: http://www.kbclease.lu
Sales Range: $50-74.9 Million
Emp.: 15
Automotive Financial Leasing Services
N.A.I.C.S.: 522220

Branch (Non-US):

KBC Bank N.V. Singapore Branch (2)
9 Raffles Place 14-20/21 Republic Plaza 2,
12 01 Prudential Tower, Singapore, 048619,
Singapore (100%)
Tel.: (65) 63952828
Web Site: http://www.kbc.be
Sales Range: $50-74.9 Million
Emp.: 65
N.A.I.C.S.: 522299

KBC Bank NV London Branch (2)
111 Old Broad Street, London, EC2N 1BR,
United Kingdom
Tel.: (44) 2076385812
Web Site: http://www.kbc.com
Sales Range: $75-99.9 Million
Emp.: 100
Banking Services
N.A.I.C.S.: 522210

Subsidiary (Non-US):

KBC Bank Taipei Branch (2)
15 F World Financial Ctr, 99 Fu Hsing North
Rd, Taipei, 105, Taiwan
Tel.: (886) 227129133
Web Site: http://www.kbcbank.com.tw
Sales Range: $50-74.9 Million
Emp.: 52
International Banking
N.A.I.C.S.: 522299

KBC Banka A.D. (2)
Omladinskih Brigada 90v, 11070, Belgrade,
Serbia
Tel.: (381) 11 30 50 300
Web Site: http://www.kbcbanka.rs
Commercial Banking Services
N.A.I.C.S.: 522110
Avram Milenkovic *(CEO)*

Subsidiary (Domestic):

KBC Commercial Finance (2)
Havenlaan 6, 1080, Brussels, Belgium
Tel.: (32) 24215200
Web Site: http://www.kbccomfin.be
Sales Range: $50-74.9 Million
Emp.: 90
Credit & Commercial Finance Management Services
N.A.I.C.S.: 522299

KBC Credit Investments NV (2)
Havenlaan 2, Brussels, 1080, Belgium
Tel.: (32) 2 417 41 98
Emp.: 5
Investment Management Service
N.A.I.C.S.: 523999
Mark Stout *(Mgr-Day to Day)*

Subsidiary (Non-US):

KBC Finance Ireland (2)
KBC House 4 Georges Dock International
Financial Services Centre, Dublin, Ireland
Tel.: (353) 1 670 0888
Web Site: http://www.kbc.ie
Sales Range: $350-399.9 Million
Emp.: 60
Financial Management Services
N.A.I.C.S.: 523999
John Reynolds *(CEO)*

KBC Financial Products UK Limited (2)
111 Old Broad Street, London, EC2N 1BR,
United Kingdom (100%)
Tel.: (44) 2076385812
Web Site: http://www.kbcfp.com
Sales Range: $350-399.9 Million
Emp.: 685
Financial Services
N.A.I.C.S.: 522299

Subsidiary (Non-US):

KBC Financial Products Hong Kong Limited (3)
3901 Central Plaza 18 Harbour Road, Wanchai, China (Hong Kong)
Tel.: (852) 2879 3328
Financial Services
N.A.I.C.S.: 522390

Subsidiary (Domestic):

KBC Investments Limited (3)
111 Old Broad Street, London, EC2N 1FP,
United Kingdom
Tel.: (44) 2076146245
Sales Range: $75-99.9 Million
Emp.: 12
Investment Management Service
N.A.I.C.S.: 523999
Theo Ludo Martin Speelmans *(Gen Mgr)*

Subsidiary (Non-US):

KBC Financial Services (Ireland) Limited (2)
Kbc House 4 Georges Dock, Dublin, Ireland
Tel.: (353) 16700888
Financial Management Services
N.A.I.C.S.: 523999

KBC Fund Management Limited (2)
Joshua Dawson House Dawson Street,
Dublin, Ireland
Tel.: (353) 1 514 8801
Web Site: http://www.kbcfm.com
Sales Range: $50-74.9 Million
Emp.: 35
Asset Management Services
N.A.I.C.S.: 523940

KBC Ifima (2)
Watermanweg 92, 3067 GG, Rotterdam,
Netherlands (100%)
Tel.: (31) 104368310
Web Site: http://www.kbc.be
Sales Range: $10-24.9 Million
Emp.: 35
Banking & Credit Services
N.A.I.C.S.: 522299

KBC International Finance NV (2)
Watermanweg 92, Rotterdam, 3067 GG,
Netherlands
Tel.: (31) 104367146
Web Site: http://www.kbc.com
Sales Range: $50-74.9 Million
Emp.: 3
Financial Management Services
N.A.I.C.S.: 523999

KBC Internationale Financieringsmaatschappij NV (2)
Watermanweg 92, Rotterdam, 3067 GG,
Netherlands
Tel.: (31) 10 436 7146
Sales Range: $50-74.9 Million
Emp.: 3
Financial Management Services
N.A.I.C.S.: 523999

Subsidiary (Domestic):

KBC Lease Holding NV (2)

KBC GROUP NV

INTERNATIONAL PUBLIC

KBC Group NV—(Continued)

Prof R Van Overstraetenplein 5, 3000, Leuven, Belgium
Tel.: (32) 16881600
Web Site: http://www.kbcleasegroup.be
Sales Range: $25-49.9 Million
Holding Company; Customer Finance & Leasing Programs
N.A.I.C.S.: 551112

Subsidiary (Non-US):

KBC Lease (Nederland) BV (3)
Camerastraat 25, Almere, 1322 BB, Netherlands
Tel.: (31) 36 5482800
Financial Lending Services
N.A.I.C.S.: 522220

KBC Lease (UK) Limited (3)
14-15 Quarry St, Guildford, GU1 3UY, United Kingdom
Tel.: (44) 1483 500100
Web Site: http://www.kbclease.co.uk
Financial Lending Services
N.A.I.C.S.: 522220

Subsidiary (Domestic):

KBC Lease Belgium NV (3)
Van Overstraetenplein 5, Leuven, 3000, Belgium
Tel.: (32) 16881111
Web Site: http://www.kbclease.be
Sales Range: $150-199.9 Million
Emp.: 35
Automobile Leasing Services
N.A.I.C.S.: 532112

Subsidiary (Domestic):

Fitraco N.V. (4)
Jordaenskaai 25, 2000, Antwerp, Belgium **(100%)**
Tel.: (32) 32135970
Web Site: http://www.fitraco.be
Sales Range: $25-49.9 Million
Emp.: 5
Leisure Equipment Leasing Company
N.A.I.C.S.: 532490

KBC Autolease NV (4)
Prof R Van Overstraetenplein 5, 3000, Leuven, Belgium
Tel.: (32) 16 88 16 00
Web Site: http://www.kbclease.be
Sales Range: $75-99.9 Million
Emp.: 12
N.A.I.C.S.: 532112

Subsidiary (Non-US):

KBC Lease France SA (3)
55 Avenue Marechal Foch, Lyon, 69006, France
Tel.: (33) 472693440
Web Site: http://www.kbclease.fr
Financial Lending Services
N.A.I.C.S.: 522220

Subsidiary (Domestic):

KBC Securities NV (2)
Havenlaan 2, 1080, Brussels, Belgium
Tel.: (32) 2 429 3705
Web Site: http://www.kbcsecurities.com
Securities Brokerage Services
N.A.I.C.S.: 523150
Frederik Vandepitte (Mng Dir)

Subsidiary (Non-US):

KBC Securities Hungary (3)
Lechner Odon fasor 10, 1095, Budapest, Hungary
Tel.: (36) 14834090
Web Site: http://www.kbcsecurities.hu
Emp.: 65
Securities Brokerage Services
N.A.I.C.S.: 523150

KBC Securities Poland (3)
85/87 Chmielna Street Warta Tower, 00-805, Warsaw, Poland
Tel.: (48) 225810800
Sales Range: $50-74.9 Million
Emp.: 25
Securities Brokerage Services
N.A.I.C.S.: 523150
Arne Martin Gilberg (Mgr-Sls)

KBC Securities Patria (2)
Jungmannova 745/24, 110 00, Prague, Czech Republic
Tel.: (420) 221 424 111
Sales Range: $50-74.9 Million
Emp.: 80
Securities Brokerage Services
N.A.I.C.S.: 523150
Veronika Veliskov (Office Mgr)

KBC Towarzystwo Funduszy Inwestycyjnych a.s. (2)
Ul Chmielna 85/87, 00-805, Warsaw, Poland
Tel.: (48) 225812332
Web Site: http://www.kbctfi.pl
Sales Range: $50-74.9 Million
Emp.: 65
Financial Management Services
N.A.I.C.S.: 523999
Katarzyna Szczepkowska (CEO)

Kredietbank Informatique GIE (2)
Boulevard Royal 43, Luxembourg, 2955, Luxembourg
Tel.: (352) 47973314
Commercial Banking Services
N.A.I.C.S.: 522110

Kredietfinance Corporation (September) Limited (2)
14/15 Quarry St, Guildford, GU1 3UY, United Kingdom
Tel.: (44) 1483 500100
Trade Financing Services
N.A.I.C.S.: 522299

Patria Finance a.s. (2)
Vymolova 353/3, 150 27, Prague, Czech Republic
Tel.: (420) 221424240
Web Site: http://www.finance.patria.cz
Sales Range: $50-74.9 Million
Emp.: 100
Financial Management Services
N.A.I.C.S.: 523999

Subsidiary (Domestic):

Patria Corporate Finance, a.s. (3)
Vymolova 353/3, 150 28, Prague, Czech Republic
Tel.: (420) 221424132
Web Site: http://www.cf-en.patria.cz
Sales Range: $50-74.9 Million
Emp.: 15
Investment Banking Services
N.A.I.C.S.: 523150
Marek Rehberger (Mng Dir)

Subsidiary (Non-US):

Patria Direct, a.s. (3)
Michalska 18, Bratislava, 81103, Slovakia
Tel.: (421) 232 203 111
Web Site: http://www.patria-direct.sk
Emp.: 2
Investment Banking Services
N.A.I.C.S.: 523150

Subsidiary (Domestic):

Patria Finance CF a.s. (3)
Vymolova 353/3, 15027, Prague, Czech Republic
Tel.: (420) 221424332
Web Site: http://www.patria.cz
Sales Range: $50-74.9 Million
Emp.: 10
Financial Management Services
N.A.I.C.S.: 523999

Subsidiary (Non-US):

Romstal Leasing IFN SA (2)
Str Matei Basarab nr 20 Sector 3, Bucharest, Romania
Tel.: (40) 21 323 5325
Web Site: http://www.rsl-leasing.ro
Financial Leasing & Real Estate Services
N.A.I.C.S.: 531190

KBC Insurance NV (1)
Waaistraat 6, 3000, Leuven, Belgium
Tel.: (32) 403 552 563
Web Site: http://www.kbc.be
Insurance
N.A.I.C.S.: 524210

Subsidiary (Domestic):

24+ NV (2)
Pastoor Coplaan 100, 2070, Zwijndrecht, Belgium
Tel.: (32) 3 253 60 33
Automobile Breakdown Recovery Services
N.A.I.C.S.: 562920

ADD NV (2)
Researchpark Haasrode, Industrieweg 1, 3001, Heverlee, Belgium
Tel.: (32) 16431001
Web Site: http://www.add.be
Sales Range: $150-199.9 Million
Emp.: 130
Independent Insurance Brokerage Firm
N.A.I.C.S.: 524298

Almarisk NV (2)
Guldensporenpark 84 I, Gebouw, 9820, Merelbeke, Belgium
Tel.: (32) 9 331 54 00
General Insurance Services
N.A.I.C.S.: 524210

Subsidiary (Non-US):

CSOB Pojistovna a.s. (2)
Masarykovo nam 1458, 532 18, Pardubice, Czech Republic
Tel.: (420) 467007111
Web Site: http://www.csobpoj.cz
Sales Range: $200-249.9 Million
Emp.: 751
Insurance Services
N.A.I.C.S.: 524113
Vladimir Bezdek (Chm)

DZI Insurance plc (2)
Georgi Benkovski st N3, Sofia, 1000, Bulgaria **(90.35%)**
Tel.: (359) 29815799
Web Site: http://www.dzi.bg
Emp.: 3,700
Health & Life Insurance Services
N.A.I.C.S.: 524114
Lucien Heysens (Chm)

Subsidiary (Domestic):

DZI - General Insurance JSC (3)
G Benkovski Street No 3, Sredets Distr, Sofia, 1000, Bulgaria
Tel.: (359) 29027083
Web Site: http://www.dzi.bg
General Insurance Services
N.A.I.C.S.: 524210
Kosta Cholakov (Chm-Mgmt Bd & CEO)

Subsidiary (Domestic):

Depannage 2000 NV (2)
Emiel Vloorsstraat 2, Hoboken, Antwerp, 2660, Belgium
Tel.: (32) 32412000
Sales Range: $25-49.9 Million
Emp.: 25
Automobile Breakdown Recovery Services
N.A.I.C.S.: 562920

Subsidiary (Non-US):

KBC Group Re SA (2)
4 rue du Fort Wallis, 2714, Luxembourg, Luxembourg
Tel.: (352) 299 992 1
Web Site: http://www.kbcgroupre.lu
Insurance Management Services
N.A.I.C.S.: 524298
Hans Verstraete (Chm)

Subsidiary (Domestic):

KBC Financial Indemnity Insurance SA (3)
Place De La Gare 5, Luxembourg, 1616, Luxembourg
Tel.: (352) 2999921
Emp.: 2
Insurance Management Services
N.A.I.C.S.: 524298
Evo Bauwens (Gen Mgr)

Subsidiary (Domestic):

Probemo Dubbele Bedieningen NV (2)
Oostjachtpark 13, 9100, Saint-Nicolas, Belgium
Tel.: (32) 37803022

Insurance Management Services
N.A.I.C.S.: 524298

VAB Rijschool NV (2)
Oostjachtpark 13, 9100, Saint-Nicolas, Belgium
Tel.: (32) 3 780 30 30
Web Site: http://www.vabrijschool.be
Sales Range: $50-74.9 Million
Emp.: 30
Educational Support Services
N.A.I.C.S.: 611710

KBC Rusthuisvastgoed NV (1)
Havenlaan 12, Brussels, 1080, Belgium
Tel.: (32) 24290034
Real Estate Development Services
N.A.I.C.S.: 531390
Kim Creten (Mng Dir)

KBL Monaco Conseil et Courtage en Assurance (1)
8 Av de Grande-Bretagne, 98005, Monaco, Monaco
Tel.: (377) 92165555
Insurance Management Services
N.A.I.C.S.: 524298

NV ACTIEF NV (1)
Bosstraat 67-2, 3560, Lummen, Belgium
Tel.: (32) 13353433
Web Site: http://www.actief.be
Sales Range: $200-249.9 Million
Emp.: 255
Financial Management Services
N.A.I.C.S.: 523999
Mark Maesen (CEO)

Net Fund Administration Sp. z.o.o. (1)
Ul Chmielna 85/87, 00-805, Warsaw, Poland
Tel.: (48) 225828828
Web Site: http://www.netfa.pl
Sales Range: $25-49.9 Million
Emp.: 4
Administrative Management Consulting Services
N.A.I.C.S.: 541611

OTP Banka Slovensko, a.s. (1)
Sturova 5, Bratislava, 813 54, Slovakia **(99.44%)**
Tel.: (421) 259791111
Web Site: http://www.otpbanka.sk
Sales Range: $200-249.9 Million
Emp.: 500
Banking Services
N.A.I.C.S.: 522110
Zita Zemkova (Chm)

Raiffeisenbank (Bulgaria) EAD (1)
55 Nikola Vaptsarov Bvld, EXPO 2000, 1407, Sofia, Bulgaria
Tel.: (359) 070010000
Web Site: http://www.rbb.bg
Rev.: $388,032,885
Assets: $5,139,558,241
Liabilities: $4,617,976,224
Net Worth: $521,582,017
Earnings: $71,431,645
Emp.: 2,784
Fiscal Year-end: 12/31/2019
Retail, Commercial & Investment Banking
N.A.I.C.S.: 522110
Victor Spasov (Head-Factoring)

Subsidiary (Domestic):

Raiffeisen Asset Management (Bulgaria) EAD (2)
55 Nikola Vaptsarov Blvd Business Center, EXPO 2000 Phase II, 1407, Sofia, Bulgaria
Tel.: (359) 29 198 5626
Web Site: https://www.ram.bg
Portfolio Management Services
N.A.I.C.S.: 523940

Raiffeisen Leasing Bulgaria OOD (2)
32A Cherni vrah Blvd floor 6, Sofia, 1407, Bulgaria
Tel.: (359) 24919191
Web Site: http://www.rlbg.bg
Automobile Leasing Services
N.A.I.C.S.: 532112

United Bulgarian Bank A.D. (1)
89B Vitosha Blvd UBB Millennium Center, Sofia, 1463, Bulgaria
Tel.: (359) 24831717

AND PRIVATE COMPANIES

Web Site: http://www.ubb.bg
Rev.: $229,709,362
Assets: $6,967,765,528
Liabilities: $6,178,397,579
Net Worth: $789,367,949
Earnings: $86,408,048
Emp.: 2,801
Fiscal Year-end: 12/31/2019
Commercial & Investment Banking, Insurance Brokerage, Factoring & Asset Management Services
N.A.I.C.S.: 522110
Teodor Marinov *(Member-Mgmt Bd & Exec Dir-Legacy)*

Subsidiary (Domestic):

UBB Asset Management AD (2)
5 Sveta Sofia Street, 1040, Sofia, Bulgaria
Tel.: (359) 2 811 37 78
Web Site: http://www.ubbam.bg
Asset Management Services
N.A.I.C.S.: 523940
Tihomir Nenov *(Head-Risk Mgmt)*

UBB Factoring E.O.O.D. (2)
15 Aleksandar Stamboliyski Blvd Fl 5, Sofia, Bulgaria
Tel.: (359) 2 811 29 60
Web Site: http://factoring.ubb.bg
Factoring Services
N.A.I.C.S.: 522299

UBB Insurance Broker A.D. (2)
7 Sveta Sofia Str 7th Floor, 1301, Sofia, Bulgaria
Tel.: (359) 28118850
Web Site: http://www.ubbib.bg
Insurance Brokerage Services
N.A.I.C.S.: 524210
Juliana Gotseva *(Exec Dir)*

Vermogensverwaltungsgesellschaft Merkur mbH (1)
Wachtstrasse 16, 28195, Bremen, Germany
Tel.: (49) 421 36840
Asset Management Services
N.A.I.C.S.: 523940

Zipp Skutery Sp .z.o.o. (1)
ul Leszno 40, Przasnysz, 06-300, Poland
Tel.: (48) 297 71 20 00
Sales Range: $25-49.9 Million
Emp.: 5
Motor Vehicle Parts Mfr
N.A.I.C.S.: 336390

KBG CORP.
84-19 Daeheungsindeok-road, Seongnam-myeon Dongnam-Gu, Cheonan, 31248, Chungcheongnam-do, Korea (South)
Tel.: (82) 415236201   KR
Web Site: https://kbgtech.co.kr
Year Founded: 2001
318000—(KRS)
Rev.: $18,673,512
Assets: $33,037,878
Liabilities: $6,234,438
Net Worth: $26,803,439
Earnings: $2,494,619
Emp.: 75
Fiscal Year-end: 12/31/22
Synthetic Resin Mfr
N.A.I.C.S.: 325212
Boo Tai-Woong *(CEO)*

KBI GROUP
350 Hangang-daero, Yongsan-gu, Seoul, Korea (South)
Tel.: (82) 23110425
Web Site: http://www.kbigrp.com
Sales Range: $1-4.9 Billion
Holding Company
N.A.I.C.S.: 551112

Subsidiaries:

KB Remicon LLC (1)
New Industrial Area Al Jurf 20, Ajman, United Arab Emirates
Tel.: (971) 506347980
Concrete Mfr
N.A.I.C.S.: 327320

KBI Dongkook Ind. Co., Ltd. (1)
350 Hangang-daero, Yongsan-gu, Seoul, Korea (South)
Tel.: (82) 415403500
Web Site: https://www.kbidongkook.com
Rev.: $482,030,876
Assets: $461,855,798
Liabilities: $316,335,653
Net Worth: $145,520,145
Earnings: $5,993,012
Emp.: 388
Fiscal Year-end: 12/31/2023
Automobile Parts Mfr
N.A.I.C.S.: 336390
Jin-San Kim *(CEO)*

Kabul International Co., Ltd. (1)
Kabul Building 350 Hangang-daero, Yongsan-gu, Seoul, Korea (South)
Tel.: (82) 23110311
Real Estate Investment, Development & Lessor
N.A.I.C.S.: 531390

Subsidiary (Non-US):

KBI Japan Co., Ltd. (2)
3F Sanhiro Building 9-9 Yotsuyasakacho, Shinjuku-ku, Tokyo, 160-0002, Japan
Tel.: (81) 333585007
Web Site: https://www.kbijapan.com
Real Estate Managment Services
N.A.I.C.S.: 531390
Baek Seung-ho *(CEO)*

KBI METAL CO., LTD.
350 Hangang-daero, Yongsan-gu, Seoul, Korea (South)
Tel.: (82) 23110417   KR
Web Site: https://www.kbimetal.co.kr
Year Founded: 1985
024840—(KRS)
Rev.: $544,938,036
Assets: $175,970,688
Liabilities: $94,817,256
Net Worth: $81,153,432
Earnings: $1,274,501
Emp.: 239
Fiscal Year-end: 12/31/22
Copper Rod Mfr
N.A.I.C.S.: 331420
Han Sang Park *(CEO)*

KBIO COMPANY INC.
206 834 Olympic-ro, Gangdong-gu, Seoul, Korea (South)
Tel.: (82) 220290700
Web Site: https://kbiocompany.com
Year Founded: 1997
038530—(KRS)
Rev.: $25,808,088
Assets: $63,256,069
Liabilities: $12,022,090
Net Worth: $51,233,979
Earnings: ($5,879,132)
Emp.: 33
Fiscal Year-end: 12/31/22
Optical Communication Components Mfr
N.A.I.C.S.: 333310
Jung-Young Cho *(Chm & CEO)*

Subsidiaries:

Fira Photonics Co. Ltd. (1)
974-17 WolChul-Dong, Buk-Gu, Gwangju, 500 460, Korea (South)
Tel.: (82) 626000000
Web Site: http://www.fi-ra.com
Emp.: 250
Electronic Components Mfr
N.A.I.C.S.: 334416
Sun-Noh Lee *(CEO)*

KBL EUROPEAN PRIVATE BANKERS S.A.
43 Boulevard Royal, L-2955, Luxembourg, Luxembourg
Tel.: (352) 47971   LU
Web Site: http://www.kbl.lu
Year Founded: 1949
Rev.: $498,113,728
Assets: $8,958,880,000
Liabilities: $7,727,034,000
Net Worth: $1,231,846,000
Earnings: $895,888
Emp.: 1,898
Fiscal Year-end: 12/31/18
Bank Holding Company; Private Banking & Investment Advisory Services
N.A.I.C.S.: 551111
Olivier de Jamblinne de Meux *(CEO-Puilaetco Luxembourg)*

Subsidiaries:

Brown, Shipley & Co. Limited (1)
Founders Court, Lothbury, London, EC2R 7HE, United Kingdom
Tel.: (44) 2076069833
Web Site: http://www.brownshipley.com
Sales Range: $125-149.9 Million
Emp.: 120
Investment Advisory & Management Services
N.A.I.C.S.: 523940
Ian Sackfield *(CEO)*

Subsidiary (Domestic):

Fairmount Pension Trustee Limited (2)
Founders Court Lothbury, London, EC2R 7HE, United Kingdom
Tel.: (44) 20 7606 9833
Web Site: http://www.brownshipley.co.uk
Pension Fund Management Services
N.A.I.C.S.: 525110

The Brown Shipley Pension Portfolio Limited (2)
Founders Court Lothbury, London, EC2R 7HE, United Kingdom
Tel.: (44) 20 7606 9833
Pension Fund Management Services
N.A.I.C.S.: 525110

White Rose Nominee Limited (2)
5TH Floor Valiant Building 14 South Parade, Leeds, LS1 5QS, United Kingdom
Tel.: (44) 1132 945000
Financial Management Services
N.A.I.C.S.: 523999

InsingerGilissen, N.V. (1)
Herengracht 537, 1017 BV, Amsterdam, Netherlands
Tel.: (31) 20 5215 000
Web Site: http://www.insingergilissen.nl
Private, Institutional & Corporate Banking Services
N.A.I.C.S.: 523999
Peter Sieradzki *(CEO)*

Subsidiary (Domestic):

TG Fund Management BV (2)
617 Keizersgracht, 1017 DS, Amsterdam, Netherlands
Tel.: (31) 20 527 60 59
Investment Management Service
N.A.I.C.S.: 523999

Theodoor Gilissen Global Custody BV (2)
Keizersgracht 617, Amsterdam, 1017 DS, Netherlands
Tel.: (31) 20 5276000
Web Site: http://www.gilissen.nl
Sales Range: $75-99.9 Million
Emp.: 20
Investment Banking Services
N.A.I.C.S.: 523150
Tanja Nagel *(CEO)*

KBL European Private Bankers S.A. (1)
57 Calle Serrano sexta planta, Madrid, 28006, Spain
Tel.: (34) 91 423 2200
Web Site: http://www.kblbank.es
Emp.: 25
Banking Services
N.A.I.C.S.: 523150
Rafael Grau *(CEO)*

Kredietrust Luxembourg S.A. (1)
11 Rue Aldringen, L-2960, Luxembourg, Luxembourg   (100%)
Tel.: (352) 468191
Fund Management
N.A.I.C.S.: 525910

Merck Finck & Co. (1)
Pacellistrasse 16, 80333, Munich, Germany
Tel.: (49) 8921040
Web Site: http://www.merckfinck.de
Sales Range: $200-249.9 Million
Emp.: 300
Private Bankers
N.A.I.C.S.: 522110
Thilo Wendenburg *(Mng Dir)*

Puilaetco Dewaay Private Bankers S.A. (1)
Avenue Herrmann Debroux 46, Brussels, 1160, Belgium
Tel.: (32) 26794511
Web Site: http://www.pldw.be
Sales Range: $125-149.9 Million
Emp.: 200
Investment Advisory & Management Services
N.A.I.C.S.: 523940
Thierry Smets *(Exec Dir)*

Subsidiary (Non-US):

Banque Puilaetco Dewaay Luxembourg S.A. (2)
Boulevard Emmanuel Servais 2, 2535, Luxembourg, Luxembourg
Tel.: (352) 4730251
Web Site: http://www.puilaetco.lu
Emp.: 2
Commercial Banking Services
N.A.I.C.S.: 522110
Gary Rowley *(Gen Mgr)*

KBS INDIA LIMITED
502 Commerce House 140 Nagindas Master Road Fort, Mumbai, 400 001, India
Tel.: (91) 2269966996
Web Site: https://www.kbs.co.in
Year Founded: 1935
530357—(BOM)
Rev.: $251,935
Assets: $4,076,381
Liabilities: $113,299
Net Worth: $3,963,082
Earnings: $20,384
Emp.: 11
Fiscal Year-end: 03/31/23
Securities Brokerage Services
N.A.I.C.S.: 523150
Tushar Shah *(Chm & Mng Dir)*

KBS INTERNATIONAL HOLDINGS INC.
Xin Fengge Building Yupu Industrial Park, Shishi, 362700, Fujian, China
Tel.: (86) 595 8889 6198   NV
Sales Range: $25-49.9 Million
Emp.: 607
Sportswear, Apparel & Accessories Mfr & Marketer
N.A.I.C.S.: 315990
Keyan Yan *(Chm & CEO)*

KC CO., LTD.
30 Je2gongdan 3-gil Miyang-myeon, Miyang-myeon, Anseong, Gyeonggi-do, Korea (South)
Tel.: (82) 316708900
Web Site: https://www.kct.co.kr
Year Founded: 1987
029460—(KRS)
Rev.: $658,065,794
Assets: $770,546,540
Liabilities: $164,031,256
Net Worth: $606,515,285
Earnings: $91,131,086
Emp.: 227
Fiscal Year-end: 12/31/22
Semiconductor Devices Mfr
N.A.I.C.S.: 334413
Dong Kyu Choi *(Co-CEO)*

Subsidiaries:

KCEnC Co., Ltd. (1)
5 Teheran-ro 103-gil, Gangnam-Gu Samseong-dong, Seoul, Korea (South)
Tel.: (82) 221033636

KC CO., LTD.

KC CO., LTD.—(Continued)
Web Site: http://www.kcenc.co.kr
Construction Engineering Services
N.A.I.C.S.: 541330
Soon-Woo Hong (Co-CEO)

KCTNS Co., Ltd. (1)
6F 552 Yeoksam-ro Gangnam-gu, Seoul, 6187, Korea (South)
Tel.: (82) 220883460
Web Site: http://www.kctns.com
Gas Mfr & Distr
N.A.I.C.S.: 325120

KCTech Taiwan Co., Ltd. (1)
7f 257 E Sec 1 Kuang Ming 6th Rd, Chu-pei, 30264, Taiwan
Tel.: (886) 36583114
Semiconductor Equipment Distr
N.A.I.C.S.: 423690

KC CO.,LTD.
30 Je2gongdan 3-gil Miyang-myeon, Anseong, Gyeonggi-do, Korea (South)
Tel.: (82) 316708900   KR
Web Site: https://www.kct.co.kr
Emp.: 100
Semiconductor Manufacturing Equipment Mfr & Sales
N.A.I.C.S.: 333242

KC COTTRELL CO., LTD.
12F Digital Cube 34 Sangamsan-ro, Mapo-gu, Seoul, 03909, Korea (South)
Tel.: (82) 23206114   KR
Web Site: https://www.kc-cottrell.com
Year Founded: 1973
119650—(KRS)
Rev.: $323,354,734
Assets: $248,104,344
Liabilities: $204,573,501
Net Worth: $43,530,842
Earnings: ($16,973,820)
Emp.: 283
Fiscal Year-end: 12/31/22
Industrial Machinery Mfr
N.A.I.C.S.: 333310
Jeong-wan Kim (CEO-KC Eco Logistics Co Ltd)

Subsidiaries:

KC Cottrell Co., Ltd. - Anseong
Factory (1)
16-180 Seounsingi-Gil, Seoun-Meyon, Anseong, Gyeonggi-Do, Korea (South)
Tel.: (82) 31 678 7700
Industrial Machinery Mfr
N.A.I.C.S.: 333310

KC FEED CO., LTD.
320 Geumho-ro, Geumho-eup, Yeongcheon, Gyeongsangbuk-do, Korea (South)
Tel.: (82) 543326511
Web Site: https://www.kcfeed.co.kr
Year Founded: 1970
025880—(KRS)
Rev.: $67,862,180
Assets: $74,574,426
Liabilities: $27,792,818
Net Worth: $46,781,608
Earnings: $3,239,729
Emp.: 102
Fiscal Year-end: 12/31/22
Animal Feed Mfr
N.A.I.C.S.: 311119
Han-Sik Jung (Board of Directors & CEO)

KC GREEN HOLDINGS CO., LTD.
12th floor Digital Cube 34 Sangamsan-ro, Mapo-gu, Seoul, Korea (South)
Tel.: (82) 23206351
Web Site: https://www.kcgreenholdings.com

Year Founded: 1973
009440—(KRS)
Rev.: $545,496,736
Assets: $608,124,140
Liabilities: $410,247,470
Net Worth: $197,876,670
Earnings: ($13,067,020)
Emp.: 20
Fiscal Year-end: 12/31/22
Environmental Consulting Services
N.A.I.C.S.: 541620
Tae Young Lee (CEO)

Subsidiaries:

Ansung Glass Co., Ltd. (1)
330 Dorim-ri Ip Jang Myeon Do Rim Ri, Seo Buk Gu, Cheonan, 331-822, Chungcheongnam-do, Korea (South)
Tel.: (82) 41 585 9901
Web Site: http://www.asglass.co.kr
Sales Range: $50-74.9 Million
Emp.: 123
Glass Bottle Mfr
N.A.I.C.S.: 327213
Jeong Wan Kim (Mgr)

KC Energia Co., Ltd. (1)
#401 DMB Bldg 200-3 Dong Gyo Dong, Ma Po Gu, Seoul, 121-837, Korea (South)
Tel.: (82) 2 2613 6779
Web Site: http://www.kcgreenholdings.com
Sales Range: $25-49.9 Million
Emp.: 4
Photovoltaic System Installation Services
N.A.I.C.S.: 237130
Jin Ah Yoon (Mng Dir)

KC Enviro Service Co., Ltd. (1)
310-73 Jindalrae-gil, Yeosu, 59614, Jeollanam-do, Korea (South)
Tel.: (82) 616854148
Web Site: https://www.kc-enviro.com
Emp.: 5
Waste Treatment Services
N.A.I.C.S.: 562211

KC Landfill Services Co., Ltd. (1)
118 Eunsupobuk-gil, Songsan-myeon, Hwaseong, 445-390, Gyeonggi, Korea (South)
Tel.: (82) 312673400
Industrial Waste Treatment & Disposal Services
N.A.I.C.S.: 562211

KC Solar Energy Co., Ltd. (1)
253 Singi-ri Seoun-myeon, Anseong, Gyeonggi-do, Korea (South)
Tel.: (82) 2 320 6301
Solar Power Generation Services
N.A.I.C.S.: 221118

KC INDUSTRY CO., LTD.
465 Ganam-ro Ganam-eup, Yeoju, Gyeonggi-do, Korea (South)
Tel.: (82) 318838684
Web Site: https://www.kccond.co.kr
Year Founded: 1995
Precast Concrete Mfr
N.A.I.C.S.: 327331
Kang-Ju Lee (CEO)

KCB GROUP PLC
Kencom House Moi Avenue, PO Box 48400, 100, Nairobi, Kenya
Tel.: (254) 202287001   KE
Web Site: https://kcbgroup.com
Year Founded: 1970
KCB—(NAI)
Rev.: $873,563,600
Assets: $8,989,071,000
Liabilities: $7,693,021,700
Net Worth: $1,296,049,300
Earnings: $178,396,400
Emp.: 7,525
Fiscal Year-end: 12/31/20
Bank Holding Company; Banking & Financial Services
N.A.I.C.S.: 551111
Joshua N. Oigara (CEO & Mng Dir)

Subsidiaries:

KCB Bank Kenya Limited (1)

Kencom House Moi Avenue, PO Box 48400, 00100, Nairobi, Kenya
Tel.: (254) 711087000
Web Site: https://ke.kcbgroup.com
Emp.: 6,859
Commericial Banking
N.A.I.C.S.: 522110

KCB Bank Uganda Ltd. (1)
Commercial Plaza 7th Floor Plot 7 Kampala Road, PO Box 7399, Kampala, Uganda
Tel.: (256) 417118200
Web Site: http://ug.kcbgroup.com
Commercial Banking Services
N.A.I.C.S.: 522110

Kencom House Ltd. (1)
Kencom House Moi Avenue, PO Box 48400, 00100, Kenya
Tel.: (254) 203270000
Real Estate & Property Management Services
N.A.I.C.S.: 531312
Martin Odieno (CEO)

National Bank of Kenya Limited (1)
National Bank Builiding Harambee Avenue, PO Box 72866, 00200, Nairobi, Kenya
Tel.: (254) 202828000
Web Site: http://www.nationalbank.co.ke
Rev.: $85,610,014
Assets: $1,027,648,698
Liabilities: $958,491,466
Net Worth: $69,157,232
Earnings: ($21,217,915)
Emp.: 1,500
Fiscal Year-end: 12/31/2023
Commercial Banking Services
N.A.I.C.S.: 522110
Cromwell K. Kedemi (Dir-Retail Banking)

Savings & Loan Kenya Ltd. (1)
Lonrho House Standard Street, Nairobi, Kenya
Tel.: (254) 202251328
Savings & Loan Bank
N.A.I.C.S.: 522180

KCC CORPORATION
344 Sapyeong-daero, Seocho-gu, Seoul, 06608, Korea (South)
Tel.: (82) 234805000
Web Site: https://www.kccworld.co.kr
Year Founded: 1958
002380—(KRS)
Rev.: $5,196,266,730
Assets: $10,061,878,998
Liabilities: $5,804,155,764
Net Worth: $4,257,723,234
Earnings: $21,983,491
Emp.: 3,426
Fiscal Year-end: 12/31/22
Chemical Products Mfr
N.A.I.C.S.: 325998
Mong-Jin Chung (Chm & CEO)

Subsidiaries:

KCC (Beijing) Co., Ltd. (1)
No 51 West of Shuntong Road, Renhe-Town Shunyi-District, Beijing, 101300, China
Tel.: (86) 1089498181
Building Materials Mfr
N.A.I.C.S.: 327120

KCC (Chongqing) Co., Ltd. (1)
No 26 Huanan Road Yanjia Economic Development, Changshou District, Chongqing, 401220, China
Tel.: (86) 2340766611
Building Materials Mfr
N.A.I.C.S.: 327120

KCC (Guangzhou) Co., Ltd. (1)
No 9 Doutang street Yonghe Economic Zone, Guangzhou, 511356, China
Tel.: (86) 2032221111
Building Materials Mfr
N.A.I.C.S.: 327120

KCC (Hanoi) Co., Ltd. (1)
Yen Phong Industrial Zone, Dong Phong Ward Yen Phong Dist, Yen Phong, Bac Ninh, Vietnam
Tel.: (84) 2413699388
Building Materials Mfr
N.A.I.C.S.: 327120

KCC (Kunshan) Co., Ltd. (1)
No 1388 Huangpujiang Rd, Qiandeng Town, Kunshan, 215147, Jiangsu, China
Tel.: (86) 51257469000
Building Materials Mfr
N.A.I.C.S.: 327120

KCC (Vietnam Nhon Trach) Co., Ltd. (1)
Nhon Trach 06, IZ Long Tho commune, Nhon Trach, Dong Nai, Vietnam
Tel.: (84) 2513683585
Building Materials Mfr
N.A.I.C.S.: 327120

KCC Basildon Chemical Co., Ltd. (1)
Kimber Road, Abingdon, OX14 1RZ, Oxfordshire, United Kingdom
Tel.: (44) 1235526677
Web Site: http://www.kcc-basildon.com
Chemical Products Mfr
N.A.I.C.S.: 325998

KCC Corporation - Beijing Plant (1)
No 51 Shuntong Rd RenheTown, Shunyi Dist, Beijing, 101300, China
Tel.: (86) 1089498852
Sales Range: $50-74.9 Million
Emp.: 170
Paints Mfr
N.A.I.C.S.: 325510
Sang Kook Han (Mgr)

KCC Corporation - Chennai Plant (1)
Plot No K-20 SIPCOT Indus Park, Mambakkam Sriperumbudur, Kanchipuram, 602105, Tamil Nadu, India
Tel.: (91) 4427142000
Web Site: http://www.kccindia.in
Sales Range: $25-49.9 Million
Emp.: 100
Paints Mfr
N.A.I.C.S.: 325510
Vasantha Kumar (Mgr-HR)

KCC Corporation - Greece Plant (1)
Possidonos Ave 46, Alimos, 17455, Athens, Greece
Tel.: (30) 2104282424
Sales Range: $25-49.9 Million
Emp.: 3
Paints Mfr
N.A.I.C.S.: 325510

KCC Corporation - Hamburg Plant (1)
Osterbek Str 90C, 22083, Hamburg, Germany
Tel.: (49) 4027809267
Web Site: http://www.kccworld.co.kr
Sales Range: $25-49.9 Million
Emp.: 2
Marine Paints Mfr
N.A.I.C.S.: 325510

KCC Corporation - Hong Kong Plant (1)
Rm 1903 19th Fl Goldmark, 502 Hennessy Rd, Causeway Bay, China (Hong Kong)
Tel.: (852) 25770476
Sales Range: $25-49.9 Million
Emp.: 2
Paints Mfr
N.A.I.C.S.: 325510

KCC Corporation - Kocaeli Plant (1)
Gebze Organize Sanayi Bolgesi Tembelova Mevkii 3100 Cad No 3107, 41400, Gebze, Kocaeli, Turkiye
Tel.: (90) 2626450200
Web Site: http://www.kccboya.com.tr
Sales Range: $25-49.9 Million
Emp.: 75
Marine Paints Mfr
N.A.I.C.S.: 325510

KCC Corporation - Malaysia Plant 2 (1)
No 1 Jalan Anggerik Mokara 31 53 Seksyen 31, Kota Kemuning, 40460, Shah Alam, Selangor, Malaysia
Tel.: (60) 351222900
Web Site: http://www.kccpaint.co.my
Emp.: 100
Paints Mfr
N.A.I.C.S.: 325510
Soh Kian Lee (Gen Mgr)

AND PRIVATE COMPANIES

KCC Corporation - Tokyo Plant (1)
Kanda Ekimae Plz 6th 3-7-33 Kandakajicho, Chiyoda-ku, Tokyo, 101-0045, Japan
Tel.: (81) 3 5207 9361
Paints Mfr
N.A.I.C.S.: 325510

KCC Europe GmbH (1)
Hansaring 61, 50670, Cologne, Germany
Tel.: (49) 2216694270
Building Materials Mfr
N.A.I.C.S.: 327120

KCC Japan Co., Ltd. (1)
Yurakucho Denki Bldg South Wing 12F
1-7-1 Yurakucho, Chiyoda-ku, Tokyo, 100-0006, Japan
Building Materials Mfr
N.A.I.C.S.: 327120

KCC Paint (India) Pvt. Ltd. (1)
Plot No K-20 Phase II, Sipcot Industrial Park Mambakkam, Sriperumbudur, 602106, Tamilnadu, India
Tel.: (91) 4427142000
Building Materials Mfr
N.A.I.C.S.: 327120

KCC Paints Sdn. Bhd. (1)
No 1 Jalan Anggerik Mokara 31/55 Seksyen 31, Kota Kemuning, 40460, Shah Alam, Selangor, Malaysia
Tel.: (60) 351222900
Web Site: https://www.kccpaint.com.my
Paint & Coating Mfr & Distr
N.A.I.C.S.: 325510

KCC Singapore Pte. Ltd. (1)
31 Tuas South Link Level 4M PLG, Singapore, 636834, Singapore **(100%)**
Tel.: (65) 68620100
Web Site: http://www.kccpaint.com.sg
Sales Range: $25-49.9 Million
Emp.: 10
Paints Mfr
N.A.I.C.S.: 325510
Justin Kim *(Mgr-Sls)*

KCID PT. KCC Indonesia. (1)
Belleza Permata Hijau Office Tower Lantai 17 Unit 9, Jl Letjen Soepeno 34 Permata Hijau, Jakarta, 12210, Indonesia
Tel.: (62) 2130027185
Building Materials Mfr
N.A.I.C.S.: 327120

KCS KCC (Singapore) Pte. Ltd. (1)
31 Tuas South Link4 Level 2M PLG Building, 636834, Singapore
Tel.: (65) 68620100
Building Materials Mfr
N.A.I.C.S.: 327120

KCV KCC (Vietnam) Co., Ltd. (1)
Road 1, Industrial Zone Long Thanh District, Long Thanh, Dong Nai, Vietnam
Tel.: (84) 613514678
Building Materials Mfr
N.A.I.C.S.: 327120

MPM Holdings Inc. (1)
260 Hudson River Rd, Waterford, NY 12188 **(45%)**
Tel.: (518) 237-3330
Web Site: http://www.momentive.com
Rev.: $2,705,000,000
Assets: $2,830,000,000
Liabilities: $2,234,000,000
Net Worth: $596,000,000
Earnings: $69,000,000
Emp.: 5,200
Fiscal Year-end: 12/31/2018
Holding Company
N.A.I.C.S.: 551112
Suraj Kunchala *(Controller)*

Subsidiary (Domestic):

Momentive Performance Materials Inc. (2)
260 Hudson River Rd, Waterford, NY 12188
Tel.: (518) 233-3330
Web Site: https://www.momentive.com
Sales Range: $1-4.9 Billion
Emp.: 5,199
Thermoplastics, Silicon-Based Products & Fused Quartz & Specialty Ceramics Mfr
N.A.I.C.S.: 325211
Suraj Kunchala *(Controller)*

KCC ENGINEERING & CONSTRUCTION CO., LTD
587 Kangnam Main Street, Seocho-gu, Seoul, Korea (South)
Tel.: (82) 25135500
Web Site: https://www.kccworld.net
Year Founded: 1989
021320—(KRS)
Rev.: $1,451,990,580
Assets: $918,964,554
Liabilities: $573,312,765
Net Worth: $345,651,789
Earnings: $3,404,066
Emp.: 1,223
Fiscal Year-end: 12/31/22
Civil Engineering Services
N.A.I.C.S.: 237990
Kwang Joo Shim *(CEO)*

KCC GLASS CORPORATION
Gangnam-daero 587, Seocho-gu, Seoul, Korea (South)
Tel.: (82) 220158500
Web Site: https://www.kccglass.co.kr
Year Founded: 2020
344820—(KRS)
Rev.: $1,107,303,091
Assets: $1,694,736,191
Liabilities: $588,252,979
Net Worth: $1,106,483,212
Earnings: $72,079,510
Emp.: 1,954
Fiscal Year-end: 12/31/22
Glass Products Mfr
N.A.I.C.S.: 327215
Nae-Hoan Kim *(CEO)*

Subsidiaries:

KOREA AUTOGLASS CORPORATION (1)
134 Sandan-gil, Jeonui-myeon, Sejong, Korea (South) **(100%)**
Tel.: (82) 448605000
Web Site: http://kac.kccworld.co.kr
Rev.: $392,188,906
Assets: $428,186,151
Liabilities: $117,834,261
Net Worth: $310,351,891
Earnings: $28,402,365
Emp.: 628
Fiscal Year-end: 12/31/2019
Automotive Glass Mfr
N.A.I.C.S.: 811122

KCCL PLASTIC LTD.
A/6 Nasib Apartment Ambawadi (Elisbridge), B/h Apollo Hospital Near Parimal Under Bridge, Ahmedabad, 380 001, Gujarat, India
Tel.: (91) 7925506077
Web Site: http://www.kcclplastic.com
Rev.: $241,560
Assets: $935,077
Liabilities: $636,118
Net Worth: $298,959
Earnings: ($205)
Fiscal Year-end: 03/31/18
Plastics Product Mfr
N.A.I.C.S.: 326199

KCD INDUSTRIES INDIA LTD.
501 5th Floor Ruby Crescent Business Boulevard Ashok Chakravati Road, Kandivali East, Mumbai, 400 101, India
Tel.: (91) 7715954966
Web Site: https://kcdindustries.com
Year Founded: 1985
540696—(BOM)
Rev.: $569,604
Assets: $946,470
Liabilities: $340,700
Net Worth: $605,769
Earnings: $195,199
Emp.: 12
Fiscal Year-end: 03/31/23
Textile Product Mfr & Distr
N.A.I.C.S.: 313240
Kavita Iyer *(Chm & Mng Dir)*

KCE ELECTRONICS PUBLIC COMPANY LIMITED
72-72/1-3 Lat Krabang Industrial Estate Soi Chalongkrung 31, Kwang Lumplatew Latkrabang, Bangkok, 10520, Thailand
Tel.: (66) 23260196   TH
Web Site: http://www.kce.co.th
Year Founded: 1982
KCE—(THA)
Rev.: $487,020,174
Assets: $560,290,762
Liabilities: $158,922,114
Net Worth: $401,368,648
Earnings: $51,012,185
Emp.: 2,170
Fiscal Year-end: 12/31/23
Printed Circuit Board Mfr & Distr
N.A.I.C.S.: 334418
Bancha Ongkosit *(Chm)*

Subsidiaries:

Chemtronic Technology (Thailand) Co., Ltd. (1)
1/97 Moo 5 Rojana Industrial Park T Kanham, A U-thai, Ayutthaya, 13210, Thailand
Tel.: (66) 357196746
Web Site: https://www.chemtronic-thai.com
Chemical Products Mfr
N.A.I.C.S.: 325199
Thongchai Sansawat *(Mgr-Sls & Mktg)*

K.C.E. International Co., Ltd. (1)
677 Moo 4 Export Processing Zone Bangpoo Industrial Estate, Sukhumvit Road Kwang Phraksa, Samut Prakan, 10280, Thailand
Tel.: (66) 2 709 3156
Circuit Board Mfr & Distr
N.A.I.C.S.: 334412

KCE (Thailand) Co., Ltd. (1)
117 Mu 1 Hi-Tech Industrial Estate Asia Road, Tambol Ban Lain Bang Pa-in, Ayutthaya, 13160, Thailand
Tel.: (66) 35 351 812
Printed Circuit Board Distr
N.A.I.C.S.: 423690

KCE America Inc. (1)
954 San Rafael Ave, Mountain View, CA 94043-1926 **(70%)**
Tel.: (650) 934-3700
Electronic Parts & Equipment Provider
N.A.I.C.S.: 423690

KCE Singapore Pte., Ltd. (1)
1 Sims Lane 05-11 One Sims Lane, Singapore, 387355, Singapore
Tel.: (65) 67485603
Electronic Parts Mfr
N.A.I.C.S.: 334419

KCE Technology Co., Ltd. (1)
17 118 Moo 1 Hi-Tech Industrial Estate Asia Road, Banlain Bang Pa-In, Ayutthaya, 13160, Thailand
Tel.: (66) 3535181219
Electronic Parts Mfr
N.A.I.C.S.: 334419

Thai Business Solution Co., Ltd. (1)
100/61 21st Floor Vongvanij Building Rama 9 Road Huay, Huay Kwang, Bangkok, 10310, Thailand
Tel.: (66) 2 645 1991
Web Site: http://www.thaibusinesssolution.com
Printed Circuit Board Distr
N.A.I.C.S.: 423690

Thai Laminate Manufacturer Co., Ltd. (1)
70 Soi Chalongkrung 31 Kwang Lumplatew, Lat Krabung, Bangkok, 10520, Thailand
Tel.: (66) 23260693
Web Site: https://www.tlm.co.th
Printed Circuit Board Mfr
N.A.I.C.S.: 334412

KCG CORPORATION PUBLIC COMPANY LIMITED
3059 305913 Sukhumvit Road, Bangchak Prakanong, Bangkok, 10260, Thailand
Tel.: (66) 233280409   TH
Web Site: https://www.kcgcorporation.com
Year Founded: 1958
KCG—(THA)
Rev.: $210,319,299
Assets: $171,415,576
Liabilities: $92,775,210
Net Worth: $78,640,366
Earnings: $8,929,885
Emp.: 1,956
Fiscal Year-end: 12/31/23
Food Product Mfr & Distr
N.A.I.C.S.: 311919
Chaiyawat Wibulswasdi *(Chm)*

KCGI CO., LTD.
Level 28 One IFC 10 Gukjegeumyung-ro, Youngdeungpo-gu, Seoul, 07326, Korea (South)
Tel.: (82) 2 6325 3404
Web Site: http://kcgifund.com
Year Founded: 2018
Privater Equity Firm
N.A.I.C.S.: 523999
Nam Kyu Kim *(Chief Compliance Officer & Chief Strategc Officer)*

KCI LIMITED
221 Daejuk 1-ro Daesan-eup, Seosan, Chungcheongnam-do, Korea (South)
Tel.: (82) 314976411
Web Site: https://www.kciltd.com
Year Founded: 1985
036670—(KRS)
Rev.: $84,067,056
Assets: $94,440,738
Liabilities: $19,131,921
Net Worth: $75,308,817
Earnings: $13,665,110
Emp.: 175
Fiscal Year-end: 12/31/22
Chemical Material Mfr
N.A.I.C.S.: 325998
Lee Jin-Yong *(CEO)*

KCI S.A.
Ul Modrzewiowa 38, 32-082, Krakow, Poland
Tel.: (48) 126334088
Web Site: http://www.kci.pl
Year Founded: 1998
KCI—(WAR)
Rev.: $15,955,030
Assets: $94,616,870
Liabilities: $4,583,587
Net Worth: $90,033,282
Earnings: $5,861,280
Fiscal Year-end: 12/31/23
Real Estate Investment Services
N.A.I.C.S.: 531390
Piotr Lysek *(Chm-Mgmt Bd & CEO)*

KCL INFRA PROJECTS LIMITED
B 3 204 Saket Complex, Thane West, Thane, 400601, Maharashtra, India
Tel.: (91) 2232649501   In
Web Site: https://www.kclinfra.com
Year Founded: 1995
531784—(BOM)
Rev.: $698,311
Assets: $4,821,500
Liabilities: $2,191,893
Net Worth: $2,629,607
Earnings: $13,305
Emp.: 14
Fiscal Year-end: 03/31/21
Construction Engineering Services
N.A.I.C.S.: 237990
Mohan Jhawar *(Chm & Mng Dir)*

KCO CAPITAL INC.

KCO CAPITAL INC.

KCO Capital Inc.—(Continued)

1055 West Hastings Street #300,
Vancouver, V6E 2E9, BC, Canada
Tel.: (778) 997-8715   BC
Year Founded: 2011
Investment Services
N.A.I.C.S.: 523999
Kim Oishi (CEO)

KCP LTD

Ramakrishna Buildings 2 P V Cherian
Crescent Road Egmore, Chennai,
600 008, India
Tel.: (91) 4466772600
Web Site: https://www.kcp.co.in
Year Founded: 1941
590066—(BOM)
Rev.: $293,034,651
Assets: $325,122,552
Liabilities: $132,288,347
Net Worth: $192,834,205
Earnings: $32,643,238
Emp.: 634
Fiscal Year-end: 03/31/22
Cement Mfr
N.A.I.C.S.: 325520
Y. Vijaya Kumar (Officer-Compliance & Sec)

Subsidiaries:

KCP Biotech Unit   (1)
Ramakrishna Bldg 2 Dr PV Cherian
Crecent, Egmore, Chennai, 600008, Tamil
Nadu, India
Tel.: (91) 44 6677 2600
Web Site: http://biotech.kcp.co.in
Sales Range: $25-49.9 Million
Emp.: 60
Natural Color Mfr
N.A.I.C.S.: 325130

KCP Cement Division   (1)
Plot No 116 A A Rd No 12, MLA s Colony
Banjara Hills, Hyderabad, 500034, Andhra
Pradesh, India
Tel.: (91) 4023305945
Sales Range: $25-49.9 Million
Emp.: 10
Cement Mfr
N.A.I.C.S.: 327310

KCP Heavy Engineering Division   (1)
8 Basin Road, Thiruvottriyur, Chennai,
600019, Tamil Nadu, India
Tel.: (91) 4466772880
Web Site: http://he.kcp.co.in
Sales Range: $300-349.9 Million
Emp.: 1,100
Mechanical Equipment Mfr
N.A.I.C.S.: 811114
V. Gandhi (Dir-Tech)

KCP Hydel Power Division   (1)
B No AE-2 N S P Colony, Nekarikallu, Guntur, 522 615, Andhra Pradesh, India
Tel.: (91) 8647241269
Web Site: http://www.kcp.co.in
Sales Range: $50-74.9 Million
Emp.: 30
Power Generation Services
N.A.I.C.S.: 221118

KCP Vietnam Industries Limited   (1)
24/3 Street, Cung Son town Son Hoa district, Cung Son, Phu Yen, Vietnam
Tel.: (84) 2573861613
Web Site: https://kcp.vn
Sales Range: $25-49.9 Million
Emp.: 10
Sugar Refining Equipment Mfr
N.A.I.C.S.: 333241
Velagapudi Lakshmana Indira Dutt (Chm)

KCP SUGAR & INDUSTRIES CORPORATION LTD

Ramakrishna Buildings No 239 Old
No 183, Post Box 727, Anna Salai,
Chennai, 600006, Tamil Nadu, India
Tel.: (91) 4428555171
Web Site: https://www.kcpsugar.com
KCPSUGIND—(NSE)
Rev.: $51,353,887
Assets: $87,794,234
Liabilities: $45,029,633
Net Worth: $42,764,600
Earnings: $3,180,695
Emp.: 466
Fiscal Year-end: 03/31/21
Sugar Mfr
N.A.I.C.S.: 311313
R. Ganesan (CFO)

Subsidiaries:

The Eimco- K.C.P.Ltd   (1)
Ramakrishna Buildings No 239 Anna Salai,
Chennai, 600 006, Tamil Nadu, India
Tel.: (91) 4428555171
Web Site: https://www.ekcp.com
Sales Range: $75-99.9 Million
Emp.: 55
Waste Water Treatment Services
N.A.I.C.S.: 221320

KCR RESIDENTIAL REIT PLC

c/o Azets Gladstone House 77-79
High Street, Egham, TW20 9HY, Surrey, United Kingdom
Tel.: (44) 2037935236
Web Site: https://www.kcrreit.com
KCR—(AIM)
Rev.: $1,738,927
Assets: $37,154,187
Liabilities: $18,586,908
Net Worth: $18,567,279
Earnings: ($464,450)
Emp.: 3
Fiscal Year-end: 06/30/22
Real Estate Investment Services
N.A.I.C.S.: 525990
Dominic White (CEO)

KCTC CO. LTD

16F Hanjin Bldg Main Building 63
Namdaemun-ro, Jung-gu, Seoul, Korea (South)
Tel.: (82) 23100700
Web Site: https://www.kctc.co.kr
Year Founded: 1973
009070—(KRS)
Rev.: $705,953,449
Assets: $483,270,307
Liabilities: $285,079,270
Net Worth: $198,191,037
Earnings: $20,163,911
Emp.: 444
Fiscal Year-end: 12/31/22
Logistic Services
N.A.I.C.S.: 541614
Joo-Hwan Ryu (Pres)

Subsidiaries:

KCTC International Ltd.   (1)
Sunhwa-dong 10th Fl Sunhwa B/D 89
Seosomun-ro, Jung-gu, Seoul, Korea (South)
Tel.: (82) 23110600
Logistics Consulting Servies
N.A.I.C.S.: 541614
Byung Do Moon (CEO)

Korea Engineering Co., Ltd   (1)
Industrial Machinery Mfr
N.A.I.C.S.: 333248

Korea Port Logistics Co., Ltd.   (1)
Tel.: (82) 512208744
Logistics Consulting Servies
N.A.I.C.S.: 541614
Kook-Dong Lee (CEO)

KCW CORPORATION

400-86 Galsan-Dong, Dalseo-Gu,
Daegu, Korea (South)
Tel.: (82) 535832333
Web Site: http://www.kcwiper.co.kr
Year Founded: 1988
Sales Range: $50-74.9 Million
Motor Vehicle Parts Whslr
N.A.I.C.S.: 423120
Il-Ho Son (Pres)

KD CORPORATION

707 I Perion 19 Wiryegwangjang-ro,
Sujeong-gu, Seongnam, Gyeonggi-do, Korea (South)
Tel.: (82) 317068577
Web Site: http://www.dymold.kr
Year Founded: 1976
044180—(KRS)
Rev.: $79,368,802
Assets: $225,236,424
Liabilities: $197,336,599
Net Worth: $27,899,825
Earnings: ($2,192,040)
Emp.: 136
Fiscal Year-end: 12/31/22
Plastic Mold Mfr
N.A.I.C.S.: 333511

KD D.D.

Tel.: (386) 15112799
Web Site: http://www.kd-fd.si
SKDR—(LJU)
Assets: $78,278,214
Liabilities: $48,601,924
Net Worth: $29,676,290
Earnings: ($5,935,258)
Fiscal Year-end: 12/31/19
Investment Management Service
N.A.I.C.S.: 523940
Tomas Butina (Deputy Chm-Mgmt Bd)

KD GROUP DD

Dunajska cesta 63, 1000, Ljubljana,
Slovenia
Tel.: (386) 15826700
Web Site: http://www.kd-group.com
KDHR—(LJU)
Sales Range: $25-49.9 Million
Emp.: 1,279
Financial Investment Services
N.A.I.C.S.: 523999
Matija Senk (Exec Dir)

Subsidiaries:

ABDS d. d.   (1)
Ferhadija 16 4, 71000, Sarajevo, Bosnia & Herzegovina
Tel.: (387) 33251440
Web Site: http://www.abds.com.ba
Emp.: 7
Investment Fund Management Services
N.A.I.C.S.: 523940

Adriatic Slovenica d. d.   (1)
Ljubljanska cesta 3a, 6503, Koper, Slovenia
Tel.: (386) 56643100
Web Site: http://www.adriatic-slovenica.si
Sales Range: $100-124.9 Million
Emp.: 220
Insurance Services
N.A.I.C.S.: 524298
Gabrijel Skof (Gen Mgr)

KD Capital Management S. A.   (1)
Gh Manu 5, 010442, Bucharest, Romania
Tel.: (40) 216500446
Sales Range: $50-74.9 Million
Emp.: 9
Financial Investment Services
N.A.I.C.S.: 523999

KD Financna tocka, premozenjsko svetovanje, d. o. o.   (1)
Celovska Cesta 206, 1000, Ljubljana, Slovenia
Tel.: (386) 15826751
Web Site: http://wwwfinancna-tocka.si
Financial Services
N.A.I.C.S.: 523999

KD Investments EAD   (1)
58 Bulgaria Blvd Entrance C47 Office 24,
Sofia, 1680, Bulgaria
Tel.: (359) 28102651
Web Site: http://www.selectam.bg
Sales Range: $50-74.9 Million
Emp.: 6
Mutual Funds Managing Services
N.A.I.C.S.: 525190
Georgi Biserinski (CEO)

KD Investments a. d., Belgrade   (1)
Zmaj Jovina 13, Belgrade, Serbia

INTERNATIONAL PUBLIC

Tel.: (381) 112635918
Investment Fund Management Services
N.A.I.C.S.: 523999
Dusan Lahe (Pres-Mgmt Bd)

KD Investments d. o. o.   (1)
Miramarska 105, Zagreb, 10000, Croatia
Tel.: (385) 16274555
Web Site: http://www.kd-group.hr
Sales Range: $50-74.9 Million
Emp.: 5
Investment Fund Management Services
N.A.I.C.S.: 523999
Zvonimir Maric (CEO)

KD Kapital d. o. o.   (1)
Celovska cesta 206, 1000, Ljubljana, Slovenia
Tel.: (386) 15826796
Web Site: http://www.kd-group.com
Sales Range: $50-74.9 Million
Emp.: 8
Investment Fund Management Services
N.A.I.C.S.: 523999
Janez Bojc (Deputy CEO)

KD Kvart d. o. o.   (1)
Dunajska 63, Ljubljana, 1000, Slovenia
Tel.: (386) 12445050
Web Site: http://www.kd-group.com
Sales Range: $50-74.9 Million
Emp.: 7
Real Estate Agency Services
N.A.I.C.S.: 531390
Meha Gostesa (Mng Dir)

KD Life Asigurari S. A.   (1)
8D Calea Giulesti 3rd floor, Sector 6, Bucharest, 060274, Romania
Tel.: (40) 21 650 55 07
Web Site: http://www.kd-group.ro
Fire Insurance Services
N.A.I.C.S.: 524113

KD Skladi, d. o. o.   (1)
Levstikova 14, 1000, Ljubljana, Slovenia
Tel.: (386) 1 244 50 50
Investment Fund Management Services
N.A.I.C.S.: 523999

KD Upravljanje imovinom d. o. o.   (1)
Radnicka cesta 39, 10000, Zagreb, Croatia
Tel.: (385) 1 627 44 44
Asset Management Services
N.A.I.C.S.: 531311

KD Zivotno osiguranje d. d.   (1)
Draakoviceva 10, 10000, Zagreb, Croatia
Tel.: (385) 16285101
Web Site: http://www.kd-life.hr
Sales Range: $50-74.9 Million
Emp.: 50
Fire Insurance Services
N.A.I.C.S.: 524113
Neven Tisma (Mng Dir)

SAI KD Investments S. A.   (1)
Gh Manu 5, Bucharest, 010442, Romania
Tel.: (40) 1 650 04 44
Web Site: http://www.kd-group.ro
Sales Range: $50-74.9 Million
Emp.: 7
Investment Fund Management Services
N.A.I.C.S.: 523999

KD LEISURES LIMITED

B-702 Neelkanth Business Park Kirol
Village Near Bus Depot, Vidyavihar
West, Mumbai, 400 086, Maharashtra, India
Tel.: (91) 2225162488   In
Web Site:
http://www.vishvesham.com
Year Founded: 1981
540385—(BOM)
Rev.: $53,528
Assets: $553,606
Liabilities: $65,463
Net Worth: $488,143
Earnings: $2,578
Emp.: 1
Fiscal Year-end: 03/31/20
Investment Management Service
N.A.I.C.S.: 523150
Ajaykumar Kantilal Vora (Mng Dir)

KD PHARMA GROUP

AND PRIVATE COMPANIES

Campagna 30, 6934, Bioggio, Switzerland
Tel.: (41) 916056892
Web Site:
http://www.kdpharmagroup.com
Year Founded: 1988
Pharmaceuticals Mfr
N.A.I.C.S.: 325412
Oscar Groet *(CEO)*

KD TREND WEAR LIMITED
KH - 810 2nd Floor Mahipal Pur Extension, Near Maruti Work Shop, New Delhi, 110 037, India
Tel.: (91) 1132318187   In
Web Site: http://www.kdtrend.com
Textile Product Trading Services
N.A.I.C.S.: 523160
Rajesh Verma *(Officer-Compliance)*

KDA GROUP, INC.
Thetford Mines, Thetford Mines, G6G 0G5, QC, Canada
Tel.: (514) 622-7370
Web Site: https://www.groupekda.ca
KDA—(TSXV)
Rev.: $107,769
Assets: $9,791,942
Liabilities: $1,221,822
Net Worth: $8,570,120
Earnings: ($5,449,339)
Fiscal Year-end: 07/31/24
Management Consulting Services
N.A.I.C.S.: 541611
Isabelle Begin *(Exec VP)*

Subsidiaries:

Campus Elitis Pharma Inc.   (1)
1565 Boulevard Lionel-Boulet, Varennes, J3X 1P7, QC, Canada
Web Site: http://www.campuselitis.ca
Health Care Srvices
N.A.I.C.S.: 621610

Logistik Pharma Inc.   (1)
1351 Rue Notre-Dame Est Suite 300, Thetford Mines, G6G 0G5, QC, Canada
Web Site: http://www.logistikpharma.ca
Pharmacy Consulting Services
N.A.I.C.S.: 541611

KDCHEM CO., LTD
234 Haean-ro, Danwon-gu, Ansan, 15611, Gyeonggi-do, Korea (South)
Tel.: (82) 314936882
Web Site: https://www.kdchem.co.kr
Year Founded: 1986
221980—(KRS)
Rev.: $47,649,531
Assets: $93,747,097
Liabilities: $19,841,279
Net Worth: $73,905,818
Earnings: $6,259,978
Emp.: 49
Fiscal Year-end: 12/31/22
Chemical Products Mfr
N.A.I.C.S.: 325998
Nam Kyu Min *(Chm)*

KDD GROUP N.V.
Zhilyanska Street 59, 01033, Kiev, Ukraine
Tel.: (380) 444958430   NL
Web Site:
http://www.kddgroup.com.ua
Year Founded: 1994
Real Estate Investment & Development Services
N.A.I.C.S.: 531390
Alexander Levin *(Chm)*

KDDI CORPORATION
Garden Air Tower 3-10-10 Iidabashi, Chiyoda-ku, Tokyo, 102-8460, Japan
Tel.: (81) 333470077   JP
Web Site: https://www.kddi.com
Year Founded: 1984

9433—(TKS)
Rev.: $38,034,250,670
Assets: $93,505,456,600
Liabilities: $55,185,792,740
Net Worth: $38,319,663,860
Earnings: $4,216,347,140
Emp.: 61,288
Fiscal Year-end: 03/31/24
Telecommunication Servicesb
N.A.I.C.S.: 517111
Takashi Tanaka *(Chm)*

Subsidiaries:

Au Financial Holdings
Corporation   (1)
17th floor Nihonbashi Dia Building 1-19-1 Nihonbashi, Chuo-ku, Tokyo, 103-0027, Japan
Tel.: (81) 343461990
Web Site: https://www.au-financial.com
Insurance Services
N.A.I.C.S.: 524210

Bracnet Ltd.   (1)
Navana Yusuf Infinity Level-7 16 Mohakhali C/A, Dhaka, 1212, Bangladesh
Tel.: (880) 9677111000
Web Site: http://www.bracnet.net
Sales Range: $50-74.9 Million
Emp.: 25
Internet Operating Services
N.A.I.C.S.: 517810
George Hara *(Co-Chm)*

CABLE TELEVISION TOKYO, LTD.   (1)
1-7-4 Azabudai, Minato-Ku, Tokyo, 106-0041, Japan
Tel.: (81) 3 5563 2031
Web Site: http://www.jcom.co.jp
Emp.: 60
Television Broadcasting Services
N.A.I.C.S.: 516120
Maeda Yasuhiro *(Mgr)*

Chubu Telecommunications Co., Inc.   (1)
MI Terrace Nagoya Fushimi 1-10-1 Nishiki, Naka-ku, Nagoya, 460-0003, Japan   **(80.5%)**
Tel.: (81) 527408011
Web Site: https://www.ctc.co.jp
Sales Range: $200-249.9 Million
Emp.: 882
Fixed Line Telecommunication Services
N.A.I.C.S.: 517111

ENERES Co., Ltd.   (1)
2-5-1 Kanda Surugadai Ochanomizu First Building, Chiyoda-ku, Tokyo, 101-0062, Japan   **(59%)**
Tel.: (81) 3 6657 5453
Web Site: http://www.eneres.co.jp
Energy Resource Management Services
N.A.I.C.S.: 221122
Masahiro Kobayashi *(Pres & CEO)*

Subsidiary (Non-US):

Forest Capital Inc.   (2)
999 Broadway W Ste 830, Vancouver, V5Z 1K5, BC, Canada
Tel.: (604) 731-1710
Security Brokerage Services
N.A.I.C.S.: 523150

Japan Internet Exchange Co. Ltd.   (1)
19F KDDI Otemachi Building 1-8-1 Otemachi, Chiyoda-ku, Tokyo, 100-0004, Japan
Tel.: (81) 332439579
Web Site: http://www.jpix.co.jp
Sales Range: $25-49.9 Million
Emp.: 50
Network Communication Services
N.A.I.C.S.: 517810

Japan Telecommunication Engineering Service Co., Ltd.   (1)
2-3-3 Nishi-Shinjuku KDDI Building Annex 4th Floor, Shinjuku-ku, Tokyo, 160-0023, Japan
Tel.: (81) 333478101
Web Site: http://www.j-tes.co.jp
Telecommunication Servicesb
N.A.I.C.S.: 517810

Jupiter Shop Channel Co., Ltd.   (1)

7-2-18 Toyo, Kotu-ku, Tokyo, 104-0033, Japan
Tel.: (81) 355416885
Web Site: https://www.shopch.jp
Emp.: 994
Television Shopping Channel Broadcasting Services
N.A.I.C.S.: 516120

KDDI America, Inc.   (1)
825 3rd Ave 3rd Fl, New York, NY 10022-7583   **(100%)**
Tel.: (212) 295-1200
Web Site: http://www.kddia.com
Sales Range: $50-74.9 Million
Emp.: 215
Telecommunication Servicesb
N.A.I.C.S.: 517810
Masatoshi Nobuhara *(Pres & CEO)*

Affiliate (Domestic):

Telecomet Technoservice, Inc.   (2)
Turfway Rdg Ofc Park 7300 Turfway Rd Ste 500, Florence, KY 41042
Tel.: (859) 647-9333
Sales Range: $25-49.9 Million
Emp.: 3
Network Consulting Services; Joint Venture between KDDI America, Inc. (55%) & Toyota Tsusho America, Inc. (45%)
N.A.I.C.S.: 541690

KDDI DO BRASIL SOLUCOES EM TECNOLOGIA LTDA   (1)
Alameda Santos 1165 9 andar sala 902, Jardim Paulista, Sao Paulo, 01419-002, Brazil
Tel.: (55) 1131791101
Telecommunication Servicesb
N.A.I.C.S.: 517810

KDDI Deutschland GMBH   (1)
Fritz-Vomfelde-Str 8, 40547, Dusseldorf, Germany
Tel.: (49) 211 93698 0
Web Site: http://www.kddi.de
Sales Range: $25-49.9 Million
Emp.: 20
Information Technology Consulting Services
N.A.I.C.S.: 541512
Bela Waldhauser *(CEO)*

KDDI Engineering Corporation   (1)
Shinjuku Bunka Quint Building 3-22-7 Yoyogi, Shibuya-ku, Tokyo, 151-0053, Japan
Tel.: (81) 363625240
Web Site: http://www.kddi-eng.com
Emp.: 2,318
Engineering & Construction Services
N.A.I.C.S.: 541330

KDDI Europe Ltd.   (1)
6th Floor 3 Thomas More Square, London, E1W 1YW, United Kingdom
Tel.: (44) 2075070001
Web Site: https://www.eu.kddi.com
Sales Range: $50-74.9 Million
Emp.: 130
Telecommunication Servicesb
N.A.I.C.S.: 517810
Ken Sakai *(Pres & CEO)*

KDDI Evolva Inc   (1)
Shinjuku First West 1-23-7, Nishi-Shinjuku Shinjuku-ku, Tokyo, 160-0023, Japan
Tel.: (81) 353266700
Web Site: https://www.k-evolva.com
Emp.: 27,000
Data Processing & Preparation Services
N.A.I.C.S.: 518210
Masami Nakazawa *(Pres)*

KDDI Evolva Okinawa
Corporation   (1)
Telework Center 1-32-7 Chuo, Okinawa, 904-0004, Okinawa, Japan   **(100%)**
Tel.: (81) 989210500
Web Site: http://www.k-evolva.com
Emp.: 654
Telemarketing, Help Desk Operations, Market Research & Consulting Service
N.A.I.C.S.: 561422
Akito Ito *(Pres & CEO)*

KDDI Foundation   (1)
Tel.: (81) 359781031
Communications Services; Grantmaking & Research Services

KDDI CORPORATION

N.A.I.C.S.: 517810

KDDI France SAS   (1)
137 Boulevard Voltaire, 75011, Paris, France
Tel.: (33) 1 5801 2000
Web Site: http://www.fra.kddi.com
Sales Range: $25-49.9 Million
Emp.: 100
Telecommunication Servicesb
N.A.I.C.S.: 517810
Makoto Ota *(Pres)*

KDDI Global, LLC   (1)
197 Route 18 S Ste 104, East Brunswick, NJ 08816
Tel.: (732) 828-9002
Telecommunication Servicesb
N.A.I.C.S.: 517810
Mike Rosario *(Asst Mgr)*

KDDI Guangzhou Corporation   (1)
Room907 Dongbao Tower No 767 Dong Feng East Road, Yue Xiu District, Guangzhou, 510600, China
Tel.: (86) 2087326400
Web Site: https://cn.kddi.com
Sales Range: $25-49.9 Million
Emp.: 15
Telecommunication Servicesb
N.A.I.C.S.: 517810

KDDI Hong Kong Ltd.   (1)
Suites 1101-1103 11/F 1063 King s Road, 979 King's Road, Quarry Bay, China (Hong Kong)
Tel.: (852) 2525 6333
Web Site: http://www.kddi.com
Sales Range: $50-74.9 Million
Emp.: 15
Telecommunication Servicesb
N.A.I.C.S.: 517810
Yasuhiko Shiozaki *(Mng Dir)*

KDDI India Private, Ltd.   (1)
Unit no 1101 1102 1103 11th Floor JMD regent square MG Road, Gurgaon, 122 002, Haryana, India
Tel.: (91) 124 496 4700
Web Site: http://www.in.kddi.com
Emp.: 60
Telecommunication Servicesb
N.A.I.C.S.: 517810
Shinsei Iwashiro *(Pres, CEO & Mng Dir)*

KDDI Korea Corporation   (1)
NIA 4F 14 Cheonggyecheon-ro, Jung-gu, Seoul, 4520, Korea (South)
Tel.: (82) 2 310 0400
Web Site: http://www.kddikorea.co.kr
Sales Range: $25-49.9 Million
Emp.: 70
Telephonic Software Development Services
N.A.I.C.S.: 541511
Jun Kigami *(Pres)*

KDDI Malaysia Sdn.Bhd   (1)
24th Floor UBN Tower Jalan P Ramlee, Letter Box 125, 50250, Kuala Lumpur, Malaysia
Tel.: (60) 3 2070 5455
Web Site: http://www.kddi.com.my
Sales Range: $25-49.9 Million
Emp.: 30
Information Technology Consulting Services
N.A.I.C.S.: 541512
Naoki Wakabayashi *(Mng Dir)*

KDDI Okinawa Co., Ltd.   (1)
KDDI Naha Building 4-1 Higashimachi, Naha, 900-0340, Okinawa, Japan
Tel.: (81) 98 864 0077
Web Site: http://www.kddi-ok.ne.jp
Sales Range: $25-49.9 Million
Emp.: 54
Communications Products Sales & Services
N.A.I.C.S.: 517121

KDDI Philippines Corporation   (1)
Unit 25-C 25-D 25th flr Rufino Pacific Tower 6784 Ayala, Ave Cor VA Rufino, Makati, 1200, Metro Manila, Philippines
Tel.: (63) 28872536
Web Site: https://ph.kddi.com
Sales Range: $25-49.9 Million
Emp.: 110
Information Technology Consulting Services
N.A.I.C.S.: 541512
Benji Garcia *(Mgr-Pres/s & Procurement)*

KDDI R & D Laboratories Inc.   (1)

KDDI CORPORATION

KDDI Corporation—(Continued)
2-1-15 Ohara, Fujimino, 356-8502, Saitama, Japan
Tel.: (81) 492787441
Web Site: http://www.kddilabs.jp
Sales Range: $75-99.9 Million
Emp.: 286
Communication System Development Services
N.A.I.C.S.: 541511
Yasuyuki Nakajima (Pres & CEO)

KDDI Research Institute, Inc. (1)
3-10-10 Iidabashi Garden Air Tower 33F, Chiyoda-ku, Tokyo, 102-8460, Japan
Tel.: (81) 3 6678 1950
Web Site: http://www.kddi-ri.jp
Research & Publications Services
N.A.I.C.S.: 541715
Tsuzuki Toujou (Pres)

KDDI Singapore Pte Ltd. (1)
77 Robinson Road 26-00, Singapore, 68896, Singapore
Tel.: (65) 6220 7001
Web Site: http://www.sg.kddi.com
Sales Range: $25-49.9 Million
Emp.: 110
Telecommunication Services b
N.A.I.C.S.: 517810

Subsidiary (Non-US):

KDDI (Thailand) Ltd. (2)
Room No 902 9/F 208 Wireless Road Building Wireless Road, Lumpini Pathumwan, Bangkok, 10330, Thailand
Tel.: (66) 2 651 4877
Web Site: http://www.th.kddi.com
Emp.: 46
System Integration Services
N.A.I.C.S.: 541512
Shigeo Kozai (Mng Dir)

KDDI Vietnam Corporation (2)
Unit 1501 15th Fl ICON4 Building 243A La Thanh Street, Dong Da District, Hanoi, Vietnam
Tel.: (84) 4 3826 2001
Web Site: http://www.vn.kddi.com
Sales Range: $10-24.9 Million
Emp.: 31
System Integration Services
N.A.I.C.S.: 541512
Masaya Taguchi (Pres & CEO)

KDDI Taiwan Corporation (1)
13F-1 No 129 Sec 2 Zhongshan N Rd, Zhongshan District, Taipei, 104, Taiwan
Tel.: (886) 225627001
Web Site: https://tw.kddi.com
Emp.: 20
Information Technology Consulting Services
N.A.I.C.S.: 541512

KDDI Technology Corporation (1)
5-5-13 Toyosu Toyosu Urban Point 3F, Koto-ku, Tokyo, 135-0061, Japan
Tel.: (81) 367161200
Web Site: https://www.kddi-tech.com
Emp.: 135
Communication Software Development Services
N.A.I.C.S.: 541511

KDDI Web Communications Inc. (1)
Minami Aoyama Bright Square 10f 2-26-1 Minamiaoyama, Minato-ku, Tokyo, 107-0062, Japan
Tel.: (81) 363711900
Web Site: http://www.kddi-webcommunications.co.jp
Emp.: 194
Web Hosting Services
N.A.I.C.S.: 518210
Teppei Takahata (Exec VP)

KKBOX Hong Kong Limited, (1)
Rm 3201-18 32/F Millennium City 1 388 Kung Tomg Rd, Kwun Tong, Kowloon, China (Hong Kong)
Tel.: (852) 39722176
Web Site: http://www.kkbox.com
Sales Range: $25-49.9 Million
Emp.: 2
Music Publishing Services
N.A.I.C.S.: 512230
Alex Wong (Gen Mgr)

Kmn Corporation (1)
Mitakokusai Bldg 24th Floor 1-4-28 Mita, Minato-ku, 108-0073, Tokyo, Japan (100%)
Tel.: (81) 354276100
Web Site: http://www.kmn.co.jp
Rev.: $6,754,540
Internet Service Provider
N.A.I.C.S.: 517810

KnowledgeSuite, Inc. (1)
LOOP-X Building 6th Floor 3-9-15 Coast Minato-ku, Tokyo, 108-0022, Japan
Tel.: (81) 354402081
Web Site: http://www.ksj.co.jp
Rev.: $24,412,960
Assets: $31,663,280
Liabilities: $22,922,240
Net Worth: $8,741,040
Earnings: ($1,055,120)
Fiscal Year-end: 09/30/2021
Business Application Development Services
N.A.I.C.S.: 513210

Kokusai Cable Ship Co., Ltd. (1)
Kawasaki Frontier Bldg 6th Floor 11-2 Ekimae Hon-cho, Kawasaki-ku, Kawasaki, 210-0007, Kanagawa, Japan
Tel.: (81) 445780700
Web Site: https://www.k-kcs.co.jp
Emp.: 69
Submarine Cable Installation Services
N.A.I.C.S.: 238210
Takaaki Anraku (Pres)

Mediba Inc. (1)
Izumi Garden Tower 8F 1-6-1 Roppongi, Minato-ku, Tokyo, 106-6008, Japan
Tel.: (81) 355727560
Web Site: http://www.mediba.jp
Sales Range: $75-99.9 Million
Emp.: 423
Advertising Agency Services
N.A.I.C.S.: 541810
Takeshi Oasa (Pres & CEO)

Mobicom Corporation (1)
1st courtyard UNESCO street - 28 MPM Complex, Post Office 38, Sukhbaatar district, Ulaanbaatar, 15171, Mongolia
Tel.: (976) 75759944
Web Site: https://www.mobicom.mn
Mobile Communications Services
N.A.I.C.S.: 517112

Okinawa Telecommunication Network Co., Inc. (1)
4-1 Higashimachi Kddi Naha Bldg 4f, Naha, 900-0034, Okinawa, Japan
Tel.: (81) 988667727
Telecommunication Services b
N.A.I.C.S.: 517810

PT. KDDI Indonesia (1)
Mid Plaza 2 18th Floor Jl Jend Sudirman Kav 10-11, Jakarta, 10220, Indonesia
Tel.: (62) 215706303
Web Site: https://id.kddi.com
Sales Range: $25-49.9 Million
Emp.: 60
System Integration Services
N.A.I.C.S.: 541512
Mada Kai Buka (Gen Mgr)

TU-KA Cellular Tokyo, Inc. (1)
Shibadaimon Center Bldg 1 10 11, Minato-ku, Tokyo, 105 8504, Japan (100%)
Tel.: (81) 354006100
Sales Range: $100-124.9 Million
Emp.: 300
Provider of Mobile Phones
N.A.I.C.S.: 449210

Telehouse Beijing Co. Ltd. (1)
M5 Building No1 Jiuxianqiao East Road, Chaoyang District, Beijing, 100015, China
Web Site: http://www.telehouse.net.cn
Sales Range: $25-49.9 Million
Emp.: 2
Telecommunication Services b
N.A.I.C.S.: 517810

Telehouse International Corp of America (1)
7 Teleport Dr, Staten Island, NY 10311 (62.8%)
Tel.: (718) 355-2500
Web Site: https://www.telehouse.com
Emp.: 55
Secure IT Data Center Services
N.A.I.C.S.: 518210

Telehouse International Corporation of Europe Ltd. (1)
Coriander Avenue, London, E14 2AA, United Kingdom (84.5%)
Tel.: (44) 2075120080
Web Site: http://www.telehouse.net
Sales Range: $50-74.9 Million
Emp.: 100
Secure IT Data Center Services
N.A.I.C.S.: 518210

UQ Communications Inc. (1)
3-10-10 Garden Air Tower, Iidabashi Chiyoda-ku, Tokyo, 102-8460, Japan
Tel.: (81) 120959001
Web Site: http://www.uqwimax.jp
Sales Range: $100-124.9 Million
Emp.: 511
Mobile Telecommunications Services
N.A.I.C.S.: 517112

Wire & Wireless Co., Ltd. (1)
Daiwa Ginza Building 4F 6-2-1 Ginza, Chuo-ku, Tokyo, Japan
Tel.: (81) 4010001139808
Web Site: https://wi2.co.jp
Wireless Broadband Services
N.A.I.C.S.: 517112

KDDL LIMITED
Kamla Centre SCO 88-89 Sector 8-C, Chandigarh, 160009, India
Tel.: (91) 1722548223
Web Site: https://www.kddl.com
Year Founded: 1983
KDDL—(NSE)
Rev.: $136,533,709
Assets: $139,143,349
Liabilities: $54,957,916
Net Worth: $84,185,433
Earnings: $9,229,674
Emp.: 1,234
Fiscal Year-end: 03/31/23
Watch & Accessories Mfr
N.A.I.C.S.: 334519
Sanjeev Kumar Masown (CFO)

Subsidiaries:

Estima AG (1)
Allerheiligenstrasse 30, 2540, Grenchen, Switzerland
Tel.: (41) 326541054
Web Site: https://www.estima.ch
Watch Mfr & Distr
N.A.I.C.S.: 334519

KDDL Ltd - EIGEN Engineering Unit (1)
No 55-A Hunachur Village Jala Hobli, Yelahanka Taluk Bangalore North Near Kiadb Aerospace Park, Bengaluru, 562149, Karnataka, India
Tel.: (91) 8068476500
Web Site: http://www.eigenengineering.com
Sales Range: $50-74.9 Million
Emp.: 200
Watch Parts Mfr
N.A.I.C.S.: 334519

KDJ HOLIDAYSCAPES & RESORTS LTD.
Ram House 4 Gaiwadi Indl Est S V Road, Goregaon West, Mumbai, 400 062, India
Tel.: (91) 2228744640
Hotel & Restaurant Operator
N.A.I.C.S.: 721110
Surendra Kedia (Chm)

KDK DONGKOOK AUTOMOTIVE SPAIN S.A.
Pol Ind Barbalanca s/n, Borja, 50540, Zaragoza, Spain
Tel.: (34) 976866030
Emp.: 194
Automobile Parts Mfr
N.A.I.C.S.: 336390

KDM SHIPPING PUBLIC LIMITED
5/24 Irininskaya str office 97B, 01001, Kiev, Ukraine
Tel.: (380) 504416728
Web Site: http://kdmshipping.com
KDM—(WAR)
Sales Range: $25-49.9 Million
Emp.: 128
Shipping Services
N.A.I.C.S.: 488510
Badiaieva Kateryna (Head-IR)

KDR INDUSTRIALS LTD.
584 Willies Way, PO Box 280, Vancouver, V0N 1G0, BC, Canada
Tel.: (604) 947-2555
Year Founded: 1988
Sales Range: Less than $1 Million
Skin Care Treatment Product Mfr & Distr
N.A.I.C.S.: 325620
Deborah E. Fortescue-Merrin (Pres & CEO)

KDS ACCESSORIES LTD.
191-192 Baizid Bostami Road Nasirabad 1/A, Chittagong, 4210, Bangladesh
Tel.: (880) 31681701
Web Site: https://www.kdsaccessories.com
KDSALTD—(DHA)
Rev.: $25,490,922
Assets: $39,945,809
Liabilities: $22,978,529
Net Worth: $16,967,279
Earnings: $1,397,907
Emp.: 1,316
Fiscal Year-end: 06/30/23
Apparel Trim & Packaging Product Mfr
N.A.I.C.S.: 315990
Khalilur Rahman (Chm)

KDX REALTY INVESTMENT CORPORATION
2-1-6 Uchisaiwaicho, Chiyoda-ku, Tokyo, 105-0004, Japan
Tel.: (81) 356238979
Web Site: https://www.kdx-reit.com
Year Founded: 2005
8972—(TKS)
Sales Range: $100-124.9 Million
Investment Management Service
N.A.I.C.S.: 523999
Hiroaki Momoi (Exec Dir)

KE HOLDINGS INC.
Oriental Electronic Technology Building No 2 Chuangye Road, Haidian District, Beijing, 100086, China
Tel.: (86) 1058104689
Web Site: https://investors.ke.com
Year Founded: 2018
BEKE—(NYSE)
Rev.: $12,372,081,180
Assets: $15,369,853,307
Liabilities: $5,096,281,225
Net Worth: $10,273,572,083
Earnings: ($80,301,805)
Emp.: 110,082
Fiscal Year-end: 12/31/21
Holding Company
N.A.I.C.S.: 551112
Yongdong Peng (Chm & CEO)

KEANGNAM ENTERPRISES, LTD.
530-17 Dapsimni 5-dong, Dongdaemoon-gu, Seoul, 130805, Korea (South)
Tel.: (82) 222100500
Web Site: http://www.eng.kne.co.kr
Year Founded: 1951
Construction & Engineering Business Services
N.A.I.C.S.: 541330

AND PRIVATE COMPANIES — KECK SENG (MALAYSIA) BERHAD

Woan Jong Sung *(CEO)*

KEBA AG
Gewerbepark Urfahr, Postfach 65,
4041, Linz, Austria
Tel.: (43) 732 70900
Web Site: http://www.keba.com
Year Founded: 1968
Sales Range: $1-4.9 Billion
Industrial Automation Developer & Mfr
N.A.I.C.S.: 334512
Gerhard Luftensteiner *(Chm & CEO)*
Subsidiaries:

Heinz Fiege GmbH (1)
Odenwaldring 9, 63934, Rollbach, Germany
Tel.: (49) 9372 9 48 39 100
Web Site: http://www.fiegekg.de
Emp.: 51
Industrial Machinery Mfr & Distr
N.A.I.C.S.: 333248
Mathias Fiege *(Co-Mng Dir)*

LTI Motion Gmbh (1)
Gewerbestr 5-9, 35633, Lahnau, Germany
Tel.: (49) 6441 966 0
Automation Technology
N.A.I.C.S.: 811114
Marco Walz *(Mgr-Global Industry)*

Subsidiary (Domestic):

LEViTEC GmbH (2)
Georg-Ohm-Strasse 11, 35633, Lahnau, Germany
Tel.: (49) 6441 9665 0
Web Site: http://www.lt-i.com
Machine Tools Mfr
N.A.I.C.S.: 333517

Subsidiary (Non-US):

LTi DRiVE Systems (Shanghai) Co., LTD
Rrm 2-East Bldg 4 No 80 2927 Nong Lai Yang Road, Pudong, 200137, Shanghai, China
Tel.: (86) 21 50 40 00 88
Industrial Equipment Distr
N.A.I.C.S.: 423830
Andreas Beer *(Controller-Bus & Supvr-Fin)*

LTi DRiVES Co., Ltd. (2)
2F No 7 Industry E Rd 4 Science-Based Industrial Park, 30077, Hsin-chu, Taiwan
Tel.: (886) 35 795 188
Web Site: http://www.lt-i.com.tw
Industrial Equipment Distr
N.A.I.C.S.: 423830

Subsidiary (US):

LTi DRiVES USA Ltd. (2)
5020 Ritter Rd Ste 103, Mechanicsburg, PA 17055
Tel.: (717) 620-8702
Industrial Equipment Distr
N.A.I.C.S.: 423830

Subsidiary (Non-US):

LTi Dirve Systems (Shanghai) Co. Ltd. (2)
Rm 2 East Bldg 4 no 80 2927 Nong Lai Yang Road, Pudong New Area, Shanghai, 200137, China
Tel.: (86) 21 5040 0088
Web Site: http://www.lt-i.com.cn
Industrial Machinery Mfr
N.A.I.C.S.: 333248
Yongsan Wang *(Gen Mgr)*

LTi Drive Systems Co., Ltd. (2)
1F No 7 Industry East Road 4, Science-Based Industrial Park, 30077, Hsin-chu, Taiwan
Tel.: (886) 3579 5188
Web Site: http://www.lt-i.com.tw
Industrial Machinery Mfr
N.A.I.C.S.: 333248

Subsidiary (Domestic):

LTi Drives GmbH (2)
Gewerbestrasse 5-9, 35633, Lahnau, Germany
Tel.: (49) 6441 966 0

Web Site: http://www.drives.lt-i.com
Machine Tool Mfr & Distr
N.A.I.C.S.: 333517
Hartmut Brown *(Gen Mgr)*

LTi Electronics GmbH (2)
Gewerbestr 5-29, 35633, Lahnau, Germany
Tel.: (49) 6441 966 40
Web Site: http://www.lti-electronics.com
Emp.: 160
Electronic Components Mfr
N.A.I.C.S.: 335999
Hartmut Braun *(Mng Dir)*

KEBODA TECHNOLOGY CO., LTD.
No 2388 Zuchongzhi Road, Pilot Free Trade Zone, Shanghai, 201203, China
Tel.: (86) 2160978999
Web Site: https://www.keboda.com
Year Founded: 2003
603786—(SHG)
Rev.: $475,102,031
Assets: $743,425,441
Liabilities: $139,213,016
Net Worth: $604,212,425
Earnings: $63,214,538
Fiscal Year-end: 12/31/22
Automobile Parts Mfr
N.A.I.C.S.: 336390
Guihua Ke *(Chm & Pres)*
Subsidiaries:

Jiaxing Kem Electromagnetic Technology Co., Ltd. (1)
Floor 2 Building 4 No 1229 East Changsheng Road, Economic Technological Development Zone, Jiaxing, 314003, Zhejiang, China
Tel.: (86) 57389857888
Electromagnetic Product Mfr & Distr
N.A.I.C.S.: 335999

KSK Automotive Components (Pinghu) Co., Ltd. (1)
No 559 Changsheng Road, Pinghu Economic and Technological Development Zone, Pinghu, 314200, Zhejiang, China
Tel.: (86) 57385624623
Auto Wire Mfr & Distr
N.A.I.C.S.: 336320

Keboda (Chongqing) Automotive Electronics Co., Ltd. (1)
No 2 Xikeyi Road, Xiyong Micro-Electronics Park, Chongqing, 401332, China
Tel.: (86) 2388268688
Electric Equipment Mfr
N.A.I.C.S.: 334419

Keboda (Jiaxing) Industrial Corp. (1)
No 1229 East Changsheng Road, Economic Technological Development Zone, Jiaxing, 314003, Zhejiang, China
Tel.: (86) 57382806677
Electric Equipment Mfr
N.A.I.C.S.: 334419

Keboda Deutschland GmbH & Co. KG (1)
Magirus-Deutz-Str 9, 89077, Ulm, Germany
Tel.: (49) 73193406973
Electric Equipment Mfr
N.A.I.C.S.: 334419

Wenzhou Keboda Auto Parts Co., Ltd. (1)
Tel.: (86) 57728805888
Electric Equipment Mfr
N.A.I.C.S.: 334419

KEBOL B.V.
Rijshornstraat 209, Rijsenhout, 1435 HH, Schiphol-Rijk, Netherlands
Tel.: (31) 252 5241 00   NI
Web Site: http://www.kebol.nl
Year Founded: 1989
Perennial Bulb Distr
N.A.I.C.S.: 424930
Jos van der Drift *(Mng Dir)*
Subsidiaries:

Witteman & Co. B.V. (1)

Veenenburgerlaan 108, 2182 DC, Hillegom, Netherlands
Tel.: (31) 252 535 000
Web Site: http://www.darwinplants.com
Plant Distr
N.A.I.C.S.: 424930
Fred Meiland *(Gen Mgr)*

KEC CORPORATION
5 Mabang-ro 10-gil, Seocho-gu, Seoul, Korea (South)
Tel.: (82) 220255000
Web Site: https://www.kec.co.kr
Year Founded: 1969
092220—(KRS)
Rev.: $196,483,358
Assets: $307,671,705
Liabilities: $74,007,729
Net Worth: $233,663,976
Earnings: $16,770,202
Emp.: 564
Fiscal Year-end: 12/31/22
Semiconductor Mfr
N.A.I.C.S.: 334413
Chang-Sup Hwang *(Pres)*
Subsidiaries:

Kec Thailand Company Limited (1)
60 28 Chiangmai Lampang Rd Banklang, Muang Lamphun, Lamphun, 51000, Lamphun, Thailand
Tel.: (66) 53 581417
Web Site: http://www.kec-t.com
Sales Range: $200-249.9 Million
Semiconductor Components Mfr
N.A.I.C.S.: 334413
J. H. Back *(Mgr)*

KEC HOLDINGS CO., LTD.
5 Mabangro 10-Gil, Seocho-gu, Seoul, Korea (South)
Tel.: (82) 234975545
Web Site: https://www.kecholdings.co.kr
Year Founded: 1969
006200—(KRS)
Rev.: $248,492,575
Assets: $359,799,900
Liabilities: $94,930,316
Net Worth: $264,869,584
Earnings: $12,411,675
Emp.: 49
Fiscal Year-end: 12/31/22
Holding Company; Semiconductors
N.A.I.C.S.: 551112
Subsidiaries:

KEC America Corp (1)
15415 Red Hill Ave Ste B, Tustin, CA 92780
Tel.: (714) 862-1606
Web Site: http://www.kec.co.kr
Emp.: 5
Electronic Components Distr
N.A.I.C.S.: 423690
Ricky Ryu *(Mng Dir)*

KEC DEVICE Co.,Ltd (1)
KEC Building 5 Mabang-ro 10-gil, Seocho-gu, Seoul, 153-803, Korea (South)
Tel.: (82) 234975550
Web Site: http://www.kec-d.com
Electronic Technologies Mfr
N.A.I.C.S.: 334416

KEC JAPAN CO.,LTD. (1)
6F Hata bldg 2-2-3 Higashigotanda, Shinagawa-Ku, Tokyo, 141-0022, Japan
Tel.: (81) 354752691
Semiconductor Equipment Mfr
N.A.I.C.S.: 333242

KEC Shanghai Co., Ltd. (1)
Room 526 Building 27 unit 73 Alley 8633 Zhongchun Road, Minhang District, Shanghai, 201101, China
Tel.: (86) 2154902277
Semiconductor Equipment Mfr
N.A.I.C.S.: 333242
Young-Ho Yoon *(Gen Mgr-Mktg)*

KEC Singapore Pte Ltd (1)
9 Tampines Grande 04-12/13, Singapore, 528735, Singapore

Tel.: (65) 67487372
Semiconductor Equipment Mfr
N.A.I.C.S.: 333242

Subsidiary (Non-US):

Thai KEC Sales Co., Ltd (2)
9th Floor Na Nakorn Building 99/349 Changwattana Road, Tungsonghong Laksi, Bangkok, 10210, Thailand
Tel.: (66) 2 576 1484
Semiconductor Equipment Mfr
N.A.I.C.S.: 333242

TSPS Corp (1)
Jeonju 788 Yongam-R Bongdong-Eup, Yeongam, 565-904, Korea (South)
Tel.: (82) 63 261 0891
Web Site: http://www.tspscorp.com
Semiconductor Equipment Mfr
N.A.I.C.S.: 333242

KEC INTERNATIONAL LIMITED
RPG House 463 Dr Annie Besant Road Worli, Mumbai, 400 030, India
Tel.: (91) 2266670200
Web Site: https://www.kecrpg.com
Year Founded: 1945
532714—(BOM)
Rev.: $1,877,651,685
Assets: $2,230,259,850
Liabilities: $1,736,139,405
Net Worth: $494,120,445
Earnings: $45,328,920
Emp.: 6,038
Fiscal Year-end: 03/31/22
Infrastructure Engineering Services
N.A.I.C.S.: 541330
H. V. Goenka *(Chm)*
Subsidiaries:

Al Sharif Group & KEC Ltd. Co. (1)
Floor 16 King s Road Tower King Abdul Aziz Rd, AL-Shatea, Jeddah, Saudi Arabia
Tel.: (966) 126060350
Web Site: http://alsharifkec.com
Electrical Construction Services
N.A.I.C.S.: 238210
Vimal Kejriwal *(CEO & Mng Dir)*

KEC International Limited - Transmission South Asia Unit (1)
8th Floor Building No 9A DLF Cyber City Phase III, Gurgaon, 122 002, India
Tel.: (91) 1246757555
Electric Power Generation Services
N.A.I.C.S.: 221111

SAE Towers Brazil Torres de Transmission Ltda (1)
R Moacyr G Costa 15 - Jd Piemont Sul, 32669-722, Betim, Minas Gerais, Brazil
Tel.: (55) 3133992700
Tower Construction Services
N.A.I.C.S.: 237130
Geraldo Wagner Vieira *(Gen Mgr)*

SAE Towers Holdings LLC (1)
25700 I45 Ste 4028, The Woodlands, TX 77386
Tel.: (281) 763-2282
Web Site: https://www.saetowers.com
Lattice Tower Mfr
N.A.I.C.S.: 332312

SAE Towers Mexico S de RL de CV (1)
Arco Vial Saltillo-Nuevo Laredo Km 24 1, CP 66050, Escobedo, Nuevo Leon, Mexico
Tel.: (52) 8182456100
Tower Construction Services
N.A.I.C.S.: 237130

KECK SENG (MALAYSIA) BERHAD
Suite 1301 13th Floor City Plaza, Jalan Tebrau, 80300, Johor Bahru, Johor Darul Tazim, Malaysia
Tel.: (60) 73322088   MY
Web Site: https://my.keckseng.com
Year Founded: 1943
KSENG—(KLS)
Rev.: $298,352,636
Assets: $662,815,851

KECK SENG (MALAYSIA) BERHAD

Keck Seng (Malaysia) Berhad—(Continued)
Liabilities: $56,388,986
Net Worth: $606,426,865
Earnings: $56,347,192
Emp.: 1,061
Fiscal Year-end: 12/31/23
Investment Holding Company
N.A.I.C.S.: 551112
Ivan Lui Ming Chan *(Exec Dir)*

Subsidiaries:

HKH Holdings Sdn. Bhd. (1)
Regency Tower No8 Jln Ceylon, 50200, Kuala Lumpur, Federal Territory, Malaysia
Tel.: (60) 320788888
Web Site: http://www.keckseng.com
Emp.: 10
Property Development Services
N.A.I.C.S.: 531311
Pauline Tan *(Gen Mgr)*

KSD Enterprises Ltd. (1)
655 Dixon Rd, Toronto, M9W 1J3, ON, Canada
Tel.: (416) 244-1711
Home Management Services
N.A.I.C.S.: 561110
David Quinn *(Gen Mgr)*

KSG Enterprises Ltd. (1)
1956 Ala Moana Blvd, Honolulu, HI 96815-1829
Tel.: (808) 941-7275
Sales Range: $25-49.9 Million
Emp.: 120
Home Management Services
N.A.I.C.S.: 721110
Michael Wilding *(Gen Mgr)*

Keck Seng (Malaysia) Berhad - Palm Oil Factory (1)
111 North Bridge Road 28-00 Peninsula Plaza, Singapore, 179098, Singapore
Tel.: (65) 63382828
Web Site: http://www.keckseng.com
Palm Products Mfr
N.A.I.C.S.: 311224

Keck Seng Investments Pte. Ltd. (1)
111 North Bridge Road, 28-00 Peninsular Plaza, Singapore, 179098, Singapore **(100%)**
Tel.: (65) 63382828
Web Site: http://www.keckseng.org
Investment Holding Company
N.A.I.C.S.: 551112

Kota Tinggi Oil Palm Plantations Sdn. Bhd. (1)
Mukim Sungai Tiram, PO Box 236, Masai, 81757, Johor, Malaysia
Tel.: (60) 72551111
Emp.: 500
Oil Palm Cultivation Services
N.A.I.C.S.: 115112
Chua Teck Ngin *(Gen Mgr)*

Ragamo Sdn. Bhd. (1)
Kong Kong Road, PO Box 1, 81757, Masai, Johor Darul Ta'zim, Malaysia **(100%)**
Tel.: (60) 72551111
Web Site: http://www.keckseng.com
Emp.: 300
Palm Kernel Processing & Products Mfr
N.A.I.C.S.: 311224

Supervitamins Sdn. Bhd. (1)
PO Box 1, 81757, Masai, Johor, Malaysia
Tel.: (60) 72563319
Web Site: http://www.supervitamins.com.my
Sales Range: $25-49.9 Million
Emp.: 30
Nutritional Product Mfr
N.A.I.C.S.: 325412

Tanjong Puteri Golf Resort Berhad (1)
(100%)
Tel.: (60) 72711888
Emp.: 200
Golf Resort Operator
N.A.I.C.S.: 713910

KECK SENG INVESTMENTS (HONG KONG) LIMITED
Unit 2902 West Tower Shun Tak Centre 200 Connaught Road, Central, China (Hong Kong)
Tel.: (852) 25433345 HK
Web Site: https://www.keckseng.com.hk
0184—(HKG)
Rev.: $249,551,866
Assets: $877,312,658
Liabilities: $315,175,796
Net Worth: $562,136,862
Earnings: $15,964,573
Emp.: 1,931
Fiscal Year-end: 12/31/19
Investment Holding Company
N.A.I.C.S.: 551112
Ivan Lui Ming Chan *(Exec Dir)*

Subsidiaries:

Lam Ho Investments Pte. Limited (1)
371 Beach Rd No 17-04, Singapore, 199597, Singapore **(91.6%)**
Tel.: (65) 63382828
Investment Holding Services
N.A.I.C.S.: 551112

Ocean Incorporation Ltd. (1)
388 Ave dos Jardins Oceano 5th Fl Ocean Tower, Taipa, China (Macau) **(100%)**
Tel.: (853) 28811234
Web Site: https://www.oceangardens.com.mo
Property Investment Holding Company
N.A.I.C.S.: 551112

Subsidiary (Domestic):

Ocean Gardens Management Company Limited (2)
No 388 Avenida Dos Jardins Do Oceano Ocean Tower 4 Andar, Taipa, China (Macau) **(69.9%)**
Tel.: (853) 28811234
Web Site: http://www.oceangardens.mo
Residential Property Management Services
N.A.I.C.S.: 531311

Holding (Non-US):

Sheraton Saigon Hotel & Towers (3)
80 Dong du st District 1, District 1, Ho Chi Minh City, 70000, Vietnam **(64.12%)**
Tel.: (84) 838272828
Sales Range: $25-49.9 Million
Emp.: 250
Luxury Hotel Operator
N.A.I.C.S.: 721110
Scott Hodgetts *(Gen Mgr)*

W San Francisco (1)
181 3rd St, San Francisco, CA 94103
Tel.: (415) 777-5300
Web Site: http://www.wsanfrancisco.com
Hotel Operator
N.A.I.C.S.: 721110
Brett Neller *(Dir-Fin)*

Holding (Domestic):

W San Francisco Hotel (2)
181 3rd St, San Francisco, CA 94103
Tel.: (415) 777-5300
Web Site: http://www.wsanfrancisco.com
Hotel Operator
N.A.I.C.S.: 721110

KEDA COMMUNICATIONS LTD
131 Jinshan Road, New District, Suzhou, 215011, China
Tel.: (86) 51268418188
Web Site: http://www.kedacom.com
Year Founded: 1995
Sales Range: $125-149.9 Million
Emp.: 800
Video Product Mfr
N.A.I.C.S.: 334310
Weidong Chen *(CEO)*

Subsidiaries:

Eutrovision Systems, Inc. (1)
No 33-401 Guiping Road 680, Xuhui District, Shanghai, 200233, China
Tel.: (86) 2164956070
Web Site: http://www.eutrovision.com
Video Surveillance Equipments Mfr

N.A.I.C.S.: 334511
Jin-Yi Pan *(Co-Founder & CEO)*

KEDA INDUSTRIAL GROUP CO., LTD.
No 1 Huanzhen Road Guanglong Industrial Park, Chencun Shunde District, Foshan, 528313, Guangdong, China
Tel.: (86) 75723832929
Web Site: https://www.kedachina.com.cn
Year Founded: 1992
600499—(SHG)
Rev.: $1,566,470,403
Assets: $2,969,800,203
Liabilities: $1,098,020,327
Net Worth: $1,871,779,876
Earnings: $596,830,825
Emp.: 4,922
Fiscal Year-end: 12/31/22
Clean Energy Technology Developer
N.A.I.C.S.: 324199
Cheng Bian *(Chm)*

Subsidiaries:

Anhui KEDA Industrial Co., Ltd. (1)
No 2887 Tianmen Rd, Economic-Technological Development Area, Ma'anshan, Anhui, China
Tel.: (86) 5552113600
Web Site: https://www.keda-suremaker.com.cn
Engineering Equipment Mfr & Distr
N.A.I.C.S.: 333248

Anhui Keda Smart Energy Technology Co., Ltd. (1)
10th Floor Xincheng Building No 2659 Hunannan Road, Maanshan Economic & Technological Development Zone, Ma'anshan, Anhui, China
Tel.: (86) 5558886671
Web Site: https://www.kedasd.com
Power Generation Services
N.A.I.C.S.: 221118

Foshan DLT Technology Co., Ltd. (1)
No 25 8F Zone C Sanshui Technology Industry Zone, Foshan, 528137, Guangdong, China
Tel.: (86) 75787652666
Web Site: https://www.dlttec.com
Ceramic Tile Mfr & Distr
N.A.I.C.S.: 327120

Guangdong Keda Hydraulic Technology Co., Ltd. (1)
No12 Xinglong 10rd Guanglong Industrialzone, Chencun Shunde, Foshan, 528313, Guangdong, China
Tel.: (86) 75723836020
Web Site: https://www.hydraulicpump-motor.com
Hydraulic Spare Parts Mfr & Distr
N.A.I.C.S.: 333996

I.C.F.& Welko S.p.A. (1)
Via Sicilia 10, 41053, Maranello, Italy
Tel.: (39) 0536240811
Web Site: https://www.icf-welko.it
Ceramic Products Mfr
N.A.I.C.S.: 327110

KEDA (AnHui) Industrial Co., Ltd. (1)
Lingxiao Road North 555 Economic & Technology Development Zone, Ma'anshan, Anhui, China
Tel.: (86) 555 2113600
Web Site: http://www.kedasuremaker.com
Construction Machinery Mfr
N.A.I.C.S.: 333120

Kami Colourcera Pvt Ltd. (1)
Survey No-412 P1 4 Kerala Patiya B/s Lamica Paper Mill, NH 8-A Kandla highway Nr Bharatnagar ITI Opp Haripar Nava Saduka, Morbi, India
Tel.: (91) 9081813372
Ceramics & Other Large Integrated Equipment Mfr
N.A.I.C.S.: 327110

Keda Industrial (India) Ltd. (1)
Survey No-412 P1 4 Kerala Patiya B/s Lamica Paper Mill, NH 8-A Kandla highway Nr Bharatnagar ITI Opp Haripar Nava Saduka, Morbi, India
Tel.: (91) 9638756184
Ceramics & Other Large Integrated Equipment Mfr
N.A.I.C.S.: 327110

KEDAUNG INDAH CAN TBK
Raya Rungkut Street 15 - 17, Surabaya, 60293, Jawa Timur, Indonesia
Tel.: (62) 318700006
Web Site: https://www.kedaungindahcan.com
Year Founded: 1974
KICI—(INDO)
Rev.: $4,683,346
Assets: $11,705,249
Liabilities: $4,563,704
Net Worth: $7,141,545
Earnings: ($298,161)
Emp.: 537
Fiscal Year-end: 12/31/23
Metal Tank Mfr
N.A.I.C.S.: 332431

KEDENTRANSSERVICE JSC
18 Dostyk Street, Esil District, Nur-Sultan, 010000, Kazakhstan
Tel.: (7) 7172 550 450
Web Site: http://www.kdts.kz
KDTS—(KAZ)
Sales Range: $150-199.9 Million
Cargo Handling & Transportation Services
N.A.I.C.S.: 488320

KEDGE CONSTRUCTION CO., LTD.
6F No 131 Sec 3 Heping E Rd, Taipei, 106, Taiwan
Tel.: (886) 223786789
Web Site: http://www.kedge.com.tw
2546—(TAI)
Rev.: $467,392,997
Assets: $411,553,502
Liabilities: $254,390,193
Net Worth: $157,163,309
Earnings: $32,386,833
Emp.: 564
Fiscal Year-end: 12/31/23
Construction Engineering Services
N.A.I.C.S.: 237990
Ming-Nai Ma *(Chm & CEO)*

KEDIA CONSTRUCTION COMPANY LIMITED
202 Sanjay Building No 3 Rahul Mittal, Industrial Premises Co-op Soc Ltd Andheri East, Mumbai, 400 059, Maharastra, India
Tel.: (91) 2225985900
Web Site: https://www.kcclindia.in
Year Founded: 1981
508993—(BOM)
Rev.: $38,670
Assets: $441,769
Liabilities: $7,753
Net Worth: $434,015
Earnings: $13,773
Emp.: 3
Fiscal Year-end: 03/31/21
Building Construction Services
N.A.I.C.S.: 236115
Nitin S. Kedia *(Chm)*

KEDING ENTERPRISES CO., LTD.
No 268 Fuhui Road, Taishan Dist, New Taipei City, 24353, Taiwan
Tel.: (886) 222963999
Web Site: https://www.twkd.com
Year Founded: 2002
6655—(TAI)
Rev.: $77,665,944
Assets: $208,661,819

Liabilities: $140,325,185
Net Worth: $68,336,634
Earnings: $8,174,727
Emp.: 1,000
Fiscal Year-end: 12/31/23
Plywood Mfr
N.A.I.C.S.: 321211
Hsien-Chang Tsao *(Founder, Chm & Pres)*

KEDRION S.P.A.
Loc Ai Conti, Barga, 55051, Castelvecchio Pascoli, Lucca, Italy
Tel.: (39) 0583767100
Web Site: http://www.kedrion.com
Year Founded: 2001
Sales Range: $300-349.9 Million
Emp.: 700
Biopharmaceutical Research & Development Services
N.A.I.C.S.: 325412
Paolo Marcucci *(Chm & CEO)*

Subsidiaries:

Haemopharm Inc (1)
400 Kelby St Ste 49, Fort Lee, NJ 07024
Tel.: (201) 461-5558
Medical Product Distr
N.A.I.C.S.: 424210
Lucio Stocco *(Pres)*

Subsidiary (Non-US):

KEDPlasma GMBH (2)
Spinnereistr 5 b, 95445, Bayreuth, Germany
Tel.: (49) 9214040
Web Site: http://www.kedplasma.de
Medical Product Distr
N.A.I.C.S.: 424210

Subsidiary (Domestic):

KEDPlasma LLC (2)
1315 Euclid Ave Ste D-20, Bristol, VA 24201
Tel.: (276) 645-6035
Web Site: http://www.kedplasma.us
Emp.: 400
Medical Product Whslr
N.A.I.C.S.: 424210

KEDPlasma Kft. (1)
1/E Infopark Building E ground floor Neumann Janos u, 1117, Budapest, Hungary
Tel.: (36) 12099243
Medical Product Distr
N.A.I.C.S.: 424210

Kedrion Biopharma Inc. (1)
400 Kelby St 11th Fl, Fort Lee, NJ 07024
Tel.: (201) 242-8900
Medical Product Distr
N.A.I.C.S.: 424210

Kedrion International GmbH (1)
Karntner Ring 5-7 Top 501, 1010, Vienna, Austria
Tel.: (43) 1 513 29 44 0
Medical Product Distr
N.A.I.C.S.: 424210

Subsidiary (Non-US):

Kedrion Portugal - Distribuicao de produtos farmaceuticos Lda (2)
Av Jose Gomes Ferreira 15 5 Q, Miraflores, 1495-139, Alges, Portugal
Tel.: (351) 214107246
Medical Product Distr
N.A.I.C.S.: 424210

Kedrion Swiss Sarl. (2)
Obmoos 4, 6301, Zug, Switzerland
Tel.: (41) 714664630
Medical Product Distr
N.A.I.C.S.: 424210

Kedrion Mexicana SA DE CV (1)
Insurgentes Sur 1196 Piso 9 Col Tlacoquemecatl Del Valle C P, Del Benito Juarez, 03200, Mexico, Mexico
Tel.: (52) 5553403493
Medical Product Distr
N.A.I.C.S.: 424210

Plazmaferis Allomas Nonprofit Kft. (1)
Tancsics M ut 80, 2100, Godollo, Hungary
Tel.: (36) 28532200
Medical Product Distr
N.A.I.C.S.: 424210

KEE SHING INVESTMENT (BVI) LIMITED
3/F Kee Shing Centre 74 76 Kimberley Road, Tsimshatsui, Kowloon, China (Hong Kong)
Tel.: (852) 2366 1211   VG
Web Site: http://www.keeshing.com
Holding Company: Trading, Manufacturing, Property & Financial Investments of Electroplating Metals & Chemicals
N.A.I.C.S.: 551112
Ngan Chui Wan *(Sec)*

Subsidiaries:

EngoTech Limited (1)
Unit A 15 F Wongs Factory Building, 368-370 Sha Tsui Road, Tsuen Wan, NT, China (Hong Kong)
Tel.: (852) 24089896
Electroplating Chemical Mfr
N.A.I.C.S.: 325992
Stanley Chi Lam Leung *(Gen Mgr)*

Kee Shing Hardware Supplies Limited (1)
Ground Fl Siu Fu Factory Bldg 201 Wai Yip St, Kwun Tong, Kowloon, China (Hong Kong)
Tel.: (852) 23687247
Stainless Steel Whslr
N.A.I.C.S.: 423510

Kee Shing Industrial Products Limited (1)
3 F Kee Shing Ctr 74-76 Kimberley Rd, Tsim Sha Tsui, Kowloon, China (Hong Kong)
Tel.: (852) 2366 1211
Web Site: http://www.ksip-hk.com
Electroplating Materials Whslr
N.A.I.C.S.: 332813

Subsidiary (Non-US):

KSIP (Singapore) Pte. Ltd. (2)
10 Anson Rd No 28-10 Intl Plz, Singapore, 079903, Singapore
Tel.: (65) 62203379
Web Site: http://www.ksip.com.sg
Electroplating Materials Whslr
N.A.I.C.S.: 332813
W. L. Kee *(Gen Mgr)*

KEE SONG BIO-TECHNOLOGY HOLDINGS LTD.
No 51 Sung Chiang Road, Taipei, Taiwan
Tel.: (886) 225184933
1258—(TPE)
Rev.: $80,372,010
Assets: $73,224,838
Liabilities: $51,082,763
Net Worth: $22,142,075
Earnings: $2,958,916
Fiscal Year-end: 12/31/22
Poultry Product Distr
N.A.I.C.S.: 424440
Kee Song Ong *(Chm)*

KEE TAI PROPERTIES CO., LTD.
10th Floor No 51 Hengyang Road, Taipei, 100, Taiwan
Tel.: (886) 23830666
Web Site: https://www.keetai.com.tw
Year Founded: 1979
2538—(TAI)
Rev.: $12,304,751
Assets: $639,833,227
Liabilities: $443,137,758
Net Worth: $196,695,470
Earnings: $52,905,521
Fiscal Year-end: 12/31/23

Real Estate Development Services
N.A.I.C.S.: 531390
Shin Ming Chen *(Chm)*

KEEMO FASHION GROUP LIMITED
69 Wanke Boyu Xili Liuxin 1st Rd, Nanshan District, Shenzhen, 518052, Guangdong, China
Tel.: (86) 17612822030   NV
Year Founded: 2022
KMFG—(OTCIQ)
Rev.: $21,522
Assets: $28,474
Liabilities: $77,419
Net Worth: ($48,945)
Earnings: ($42,275)
Emp.: 1
Fiscal Year-end: 07/31/24
Apparel Product Retailer
N.A.I.C.S.: 424350

KEEN OCEAN INTERNATIONAL HOLDING LTD.
Unit 5 34 th Cable TV Tower 9 Hoi Shing Road, Tsuen Wan, NT, China (Hong Kong)
Tel.: (852) 31029700   Ky
Web Site: http://www.keenocean.com.hk
Year Founded: 2000
8070—(HKG)
Rev.: $50,345,543
Assets: $30,373,305
Liabilities: $19,943,168
Net Worth: $10,430,138
Earnings: $2,141,745
Emp.: 598
Fiscal Year-end: 12/31/22
Transformer Mfr & Distr
N.A.I.C.S.: 335999
Larry Chi Hang Chung *(Chm)*

Subsidiaries:

He Yuan Sky Wealth Electronic & Plastic Company Limited (1)
South of Keqi Road east of Xinggong Avenue, High-tech Development Zone, Heyuan, China
Tel.: (86) 7622203101
Web Site: https://www.sky-wealth.com
Emp.: 1,000
Electronic Parts Mfr & Distr
N.A.I.C.S.: 334416

KEENSIGHT CAPITAL SAS
64 rue de Lisbonne, 75008, Paris, France
Tel.: (33) 1 83 79 87 30
Web Site: http://www.keensightcapital.com
Privater Equity Firm
N.A.I.C.S.: 523999
Jean-Michel Beghin *(Mng Partner)*

Subsidiaries:

Symeres BV (1)
Kerkenbos 1013, 6546, Nijmegen, Netherlands
Tel.: (31) 24 372 3300
Web Site: https://symeres.com
Biotechnology Research & Development Services
N.A.I.C.S.: 541714
Eelco Ebbers *(Founder & CEO)*

Subsidiary (US):

Organix Incorporated (2)
240 Salem St, Woburn, MA 01801
Tel.: (781) 932-4142
Web Site: http://www.organixinc.com
Rev.: $4,400,000
Emp.: 36
Research & Development in Biotechnology
N.A.I.C.S.: 541714
Paul Blundell *(VP)*

KEEPDATA CO., LTD.
8th Floor Nihombashi Muromachi Building 3 3 16 Nihobashi, Honishicho Chuo ku, Tokyo, 103-0021, Japan
Tel.: (81) 362613982
Web Site: http://www.keepdata.asia
Year Founded: 2009
Data Integration, Search Engine & Visualization Software Systems
N.A.I.C.S.: 518210
Shinichiro Shibuya *(Pres & CEO)*

KEEPER TECHNICAL LABORATORY
4-17 Yoshikawacho, Obu, 474-0046, Aichi, Japan
Tel.: (81) 562455258
Web Site: https://keepergiken.co.jp
Year Founded: 1985
6036—(TKS)
Sales Range: $25-49.9 Million
Emp.: 335
Car Coating
N.A.I.C.S.: 325510
Yoshimichi Tani *(Chm & CEO)*

KEERTHI INDUSTRIES LIMITED
Plot No 40 IDA Balanagar, Hyderabad, 500 037, India
Tel.: (91) 4023078748
Web Site: https://www.keerthiindustries.com
Year Founded: 1982
518011—(BOM)
Rev.: $29,441,843
Assets: $22,737,532
Liabilities: $13,100,763
Net Worth: $9,636,770
Earnings: ($877,415)
Emp.: 243
Fiscal Year-end: 03/31/23
Cement & Clinker Mfr
N.A.I.C.S.: 327310
Jasti Triveni *(Chm)*

KEESON TECHNOLOGY CORPORATION LIMITED
No 158 Qiumao Road, Wangjiangjing Town Xiuzhou District, Jiaxing, 314016, Zhejiang, China
Tel.: (86) 57382283307
Web Site: http://www.keeson.com
Year Founded: 2005
603610—(SHG)
Rev.: $373,932,557
Assets: $656,312,506
Liabilities: $225,524,520
Net Worth: $430,787,986
Earnings: $3,597,890
Fiscal Year-end: 12/31/22
Household Appliance Mfr & Distr
N.A.I.C.S.: 335220
Guohai Tang *(Chm)*

KEFI GOLD AND COPPER PLC
27/28 Eastcastle Street, London, W1W 8DH, United Kingdom
Tel.: (44) 35722256161   UK
Web Site: http://www.kefi-minerals.com
Year Founded: 2006
KEFI—(AIM)
Assets: $40,600,858
Liabilities: $6,541,277
Net Worth: $34,059,581
Earnings: ($8,021,964)
Emp.: 51
Fiscal Year-end: 12/31/22
Metal Mining Services
N.A.I.C.S.: 212290
Eddy Solbrandt *(Head-Sys)*

Subsidiaries:

KEFI Minerals (Ethiopia) Limited (1)

KEFI GOLD AND COPPER PLC

KEFI Gold and Copper plc—(Continued)
1st Floor Daminarof Building, PO Box 57100, Bole Sub-City Kebele 12/13 H No New, Addis Ababa, 57100, Ethiopia
Tel.: (251) 116479976
Web Site: https://www.kefi-minerals.com
Gold Mining Services
N.A.I.C.S.: 212220

KEHUA DATA CO., LTD.
No 457 Malong Road Torch High-Tech Industrial Zone, Xiamen, 361006, China
Tel.: (86) 5925160516
Web Site: https://www.kehua.com
Year Founded: 1988
002335—(SSE)
Rev.: $793,049,400
Assets: $1,400,877,504
Liabilities: $851,145,516
Net Worth: $549,731,988
Earnings: $34,869,744
Emp.: 4,000
Fiscal Year-end: 12/31/22
Power Systems & Supplies Mfr
N.A.I.C.S.: 335311

Subsidiaries:

Beijing Kehua Hengsheng Technology Co., Ltd. (1)
R1011-1014 A Block Cuiwei Plaza No 29 Fuxing Road, Haidian District, Beijing, 100036, China
Tel.: (86) 1063947981
Uninterruptible Power Supply Product Mfr
N.A.I.C.S.: 335999

Shenzhen Kehua Technology Co., Ltd. (1)
C building No 2 Industrial District Hamlet Liuyue Henggang, Shenkeng Longgang District, Shenzhen, 518100, China
Tel.: (86) 75528638889
Uninterruptible Power Supply Product Mfr
N.A.I.C.S.: 335999

Xiamen Hua Rui Sheng Intelligent Technology Co., Ltd. (1)
North building No 65 Wanghai Road Software Zone II, Siming District, Xiamen, 361008, Fujian, China
Tel.: (86) 5925162165
Uninterruptible Power Supply Product Mfr
N.A.I.C.S.: 335999

Zhangzhou Kehua Technology Co., Ltd. (1)
Beidou Industrial Zone, Jinfeng Industrial District, Zhangzhou, 363000, Fujian, China
Tel.: (86) 5962673217
Uninterruptible Power Supply Product Mfr
N.A.I.C.S.: 335999

Zhangzhou Kehua New Energy Technology Co., Ltd. (1)
Taiwanese Investment Wen Pu Industrial Park, Zhangzhou, 363107, Fujian, China
Tel.: (86) 5966783610
Uninterruptible Power Supply Product Mfr
N.A.I.C.S.: 335999

KEHUA HOLDINGS CO., LTD.
No 63 Yongkang Road, Jiangsu Zhongguancun Science and Technology Industrial Park, Changzhou, 213354, Jiangsu, China
Tel.: (86) 51987260688
Web Site: https://www.khmm.com.cn
Year Founded: 2002
603161—(SHG)
Rev.: $317,641,016
Assets: $536,293,728
Liabilities: $358,017,178
Net Worth: $178,276,550
Earnings: $2,741,591
Fiscal Year-end: 12/31/22
Automobile Parts Mfr & Distr
N.A.I.C.S.: 336390
Chen Hongmin (Chm)

KEI INDUSTRIES LTD
D-90 Okhla Industrial Area Phase-1, New Delhi, 110020, India
Tel.: (91) 1126818840
Web Site: https://www.kei-ind.com
Year Founded: 1968
KEI—(NSE)
Rev.: $573,517,991
Assets: $411,407,178
Liabilities: $168,703,763
Net Worth: $242,703,416
Earnings: $37,320,329
Emp.: 1,819
Fiscal Year-end: 03/31/21
Cable Power
N.A.I.C.S.: 333248
Anil Gupta (Chm & Mng Dir)

Subsidiaries:

KEI Industries Ltd - Unit-1 (1)
SP 919 920 922 RIICO Indust Area, Ph III Bhiwadi Dist, Alwar, 301109, Rajasthan, India
Tel.: (91) 1493220106
Web Site: http://www.kei-ind.com
Sales Range: $800-899.9 Million
Cable Mfr
N.A.I.C.S.: 336320
K C Sharma (VP)

KEI Industries Ltd - Unit-2 (1)
99 2 7 Madhuban Indust Estate, Rakholi, Silvassa, 396230, India
Tel.: (91) 2602644404
Web Site: http://www.kei-ind.com
Sales Range: $200-249.9 Million
Cable Mfr
N.A.I.C.S.: 335929
Dilip Barnwal (VP-Ops-Silvassa)

KEIFUKU ELECTRIC RAILROAD CO., LTD.
3-20 Mibu Kayo Gosho-cho, Nakagyo-Ku, Kyoto, 604-8811, Japan
Tel.: (81) 758419381
Web Site: https://www.keifuku.co.jp
Year Founded: 1942
9049—(TKS)
Rev.: $92,817,620
Assets: $152,043,220
Liabilities: $74,184,030
Net Worth: $77,859,190
Earnings: $13,808,540
Emp.: 109
Fiscal Year-end: 03/31/24
Railway Transportation Services
N.A.I.C.S.: 482111
Norio Ohtsuka (Pres & CEO)

KEIHAN HOLDINGS CO., LTD.
1-7-31 Otemae, Chuo-ku, Osaka, 540-6591, Japan
Tel.: (81) 669454585
Web Site: https://www.keihan-holdings.co.jp
Year Founded: 1949
9045—(TKS)
Rev.: $1,997,191,670
Assets: $5,421,680,640
Liabilities: $3,406,820,440
Net Worth: $2,014,860,200
Earnings: $164,522,900
Emp.: 129
Fiscal Year-end: 03/31/24
Transportation Services
N.A.I.C.S.: 482111
Tatsuya Miura (Sr Exec Officer)

Subsidiaries:

Biostyle Co., Ltd. (1)
5F Keihan Shijokawaramachi Building 338 Tominaga-cho, Kawaramachi-dori Shijo-Sagaru Shimogyo-ku, Kyoto, 600-8023, Japan
Tel.: (81) 753523712
Web Site: http://goodnaturestation.com
Food & Cosmetic Product Distr
N.A.I.C.S.: 456199

Biwako Kisen Steamship Co., Ltd. (1)
5-1-1 Hamaotsu, Otsu, 520-0047, Japan
Tel.: (81) 570052105
Ship Transportation Services
N.A.I.C.S.: 488390

Garden Museum Hiei Co., Ltd. (1)
4 Shimeigatake Shugakuin Shikuragaya, Sakyo-ku, Kyoto, 606-0000, Japan
Tel.: (81) 757077733
Web Site: https://gmhiei.jp
Garden Maintenance Services
N.A.I.C.S.: 561730

Hotel Keihan Co., Ltd. (1)
3rd floor Keihan Tenmabashi Building 1-7-24 Otemae, Chuo-ku, Osaka, 540-0008, Japan
Tel.: (81) 665850215
Hotel Operator
N.A.I.C.S.: 721110

KB Enterprise Co., Ltd. (1)
No 8 Guang Yuan Road, Shi Jing Industrial Dong Cheng District, Dongguan, Guang Dong, China
Tel.: (86) 76923287202
Web Site: https://thekbworld.com
Foam Material Mfr
N.A.I.C.S.: 326150

Keihan Agency Inc. (1)
1-7-24 Otemae Keihan Tenmanbashi Building 4th floor, Chuo-ku, Osaka, 540-0008, Japan
Tel.: (81) 647920810
Emp.: 60
Rail Transportation Services
N.A.I.C.S.: 488210

Keihan Asset Management Co., Ltd. (1)
15th floor OMM Building 1-7-31 Otemae, Chuo-ku, Osaka, Japan
Tel.: (81) 669465188
Real Estate Investment Advisory Services
N.A.I.C.S.: 523940

Keihan Building Techno Service Co., Ltd. (1)
1-3-35 Nishikinya, Hirakata, 573-1192, Osaka, Japan
Tel.: (81) 72 847 1230
Web Site: https://www.keihan-bts.jp
Emp.: 820
Building Maintenance Services
N.A.I.C.S.: 561790

Keihan Bus Co., Ltd. (1)
5 Higashikujo Minamiishida-cho, Minami-ku, Kyoto, 601-8033, Japan
Tel.: (81) 756822310
Bus Transportation Services
N.A.I.C.S.: 485210

Keihan Department Stores Co., Ltd. (1)
8-3 Kawahara-cho, Moriguchi, 570-8558, Japan
Tel.: (81) 669941313
Railway Freight Transportation Services
N.A.I.C.S.: 482111

Keihan Engineering Service Co., Ltd. (1)
1-3-35 Nishikinya, Hirakata, 573-1192, Osaka, Japan
Tel.: (81) 728906900
Emp.: 99
Railway Repair & Maintenance Services
N.A.I.C.S.: 488210

Keihan Gardening Co., Ltd. (1)
1-5 Ikaga Kotobuki-cho, Hirakata, 573-0061, Japan
Tel.: (81) 728441134
Web Site: https://keihan-engei.co.jp
Emp.: 151
Railway Freight Transportation Services
N.A.I.C.S.: 482111

Keihan Hotels & Resorts Co., Ltd. (1)
680 Higashishiokoji-cho Higashinotoin-dori Nanajo-shita, Shimogyo-ku, Kyoto, 600-8216, Japan
Tel.: (81) 753613221
Hotel Operator
N.A.I.C.S.: 721110

Keihan Kind Co., Ltd. (1)

INTERNATIONAL PUBLIC

2nd floor Keihan Tenmabashi Building 1-7-24 Otemae, Chuo-ku, Osaka, 540-0008, Japan
Tel.: (81) 647906003
Emp.: 450
Real Estate Lending Services
N.A.I.C.S.: 531110

Keihan Real Estate Co., Ltd. (1)
1-7-31 Otemae OMM Building 15th Floor, Chuo-ku, Osaka, 540-6591, Japan
Tel.: (81) 669461341
Real Estate Brokerage Services
N.A.I.C.S.: 531110
Yoshihisa Doumoto (Pres)

Keihan Ryutsu Systems Co., Ltd. (1)
15-1 Kuzuhahanazonocho Hirakata, Hirakata, 573-1121, Japan
Tel.: (81) 728663340
Railway Freight Transportation Services
N.A.I.C.S.: 482111

Keihan Tatemono Co., Ltd. (1)
1-7-31 Otemae, Chuo-ku, Osaka, 540-6591, Japan
Tel.: (81) 669432010
Emp.: 58
Real Estate Rental Services
N.A.I.C.S.: 531110

Keihan The Store Co., Ltd. (1)
19-14 Okahigashi-cho, Hirakata, 573-0032, Osaka, Japan
Tel.: (81) 728457866
Web Site: https://www.keihan-the-store.jp
Supermarket & Other Grocery Distr
N.A.I.C.S.: 445110

Kojak Bus Co., Ltd. (1)
6th floor Ewaka Kotsu Building 1-1-62 Mano, Otsu, 520-0232, Shiga, Japan
Tel.: (81) 775732701
Emp.: 180
Bus Transportation Services
N.A.I.C.S.: 485999

Kyoto Bus Co., Ltd. (1)
1-1 Saga Myojo-cho, Ukyo-ku, Kyoto, 616-8337, Japan
Tel.: (81) 758717521
Emp.: 297
Bus Transportation Services
N.A.I.C.S.: 485999

Kyoto Century Hotel Co., Ltd. (1)
680 Higashi Shiokoji-cho Shiokoji Sagaru Higashinotoindori, Shimogyo-ku, Kyoto, 600-8216, Japan
Tel.: (81) 753510111
Hotel Operator
N.A.I.C.S.: 721110

Kyoto Tower Co., Ltd. (1)
Tel.: (81) 753613212
Hotel Operator
N.A.I.C.S.: 721110

KEIHANSHIN BUILDING CO., LTD.
2-14 Kawaramachi 4-chome, Chuo-ku, Osaka, 541-0048, Japan
Tel.: (81) 662027331
Web Site: https://www.keihanshin.co.jp
Year Founded: 1948
8818—(TKS)
Rev.: $127,639,100
Assets: $1,101,331,760
Liabilities: $606,414,620
Net Worth: $494,917,140
Earnings: $25,071,730
Emp.: 65
Fiscal Year-end: 03/31/24
Building Leasing & Maintenance Services
N.A.I.C.S.: 531110
Shinji Yamamoto (Mng Dir & Mng Exec Officer)

KEIJIDOUSHAKAN CO., LTD.
6-2-2 Kita 5-jo Nishi, Chuo-Ku, Sapporo, 060-0005, Japan
Tel.: (81) 117761000
Web Site: http://www.keijidousyakan.com

AND PRIVATE COMPANIES

Year Founded: 1998
7680—(TKS)
Automotive Distr
N.A.I.C.S.: 441110
Shoichi Abe (Pres)

KEIKYU CORPORATION
1-2-8 Takashima, Kanagawa Nishi-ku, Yokohama, Japan
Tel.: (81) 357898686
Web Site: https://www.keikyu.co.jp
Year Founded: 1948
9006—(TKS)
Rev.- $1,854,924,640
Assets: $7,184,422,220
Liabilities: $4,820,045,050
Net Worth: $2,364,377,170
Earnings: $553,587,500
Emp.: 2,906
Fiscal Year-end: 03/31/24
Passenger Rail Services
N.A.I.C.S.: 485112

Subsidiaries:

Kawasaki Tsurumi Rinko Bus Co., Ltd. (1)
3-21-6 Nakase, Kawasaki-ku, Kawasaki, 210-0818, Kanagawa, Japan
Tel.: (81) 442803421
Web Site: https://www.rinkobus.co.jp
Sales Range: $200-249.9 Million
Emp.: 873
Bus Charter Services
N.A.I.C.S.: 485510

Keihin Kyuko Bus Co., Ltd. (1)
2-20-20 Takanawa, Minato-ku, Tokyo, 108-0074, Japan
Tel.: (81) 332809170
Web Site: http://www.hnd-bus.com
Sales Range: $450-499.9 Million
Emp.: 1,083
Bus Charter Services
N.A.I.C.S.: 485510
Kazunori Miyazawa (Pres)

Subsidiary (Domestic):

Haneda Keikyu Bus Co., Ltd. (2)
2-20-20 Takanawa Keihindentetsu Honsha Building, Minato-ku, Tokyo, 108-0074, Japan
Tel.: (81) 337439018
Bus Charter Services
N.A.I.C.S.: 485510

Toyo Kankou Co., Ltd. (2)
7-6-1 Kurihama, Yokosuka, 239-0831, Kanagawa, Japan
Tel.: (81) 468373900
Web Site: https://www.toyokankou.co.jp
Emp.: 204
Bus Charter Services
N.A.I.C.S.: 485510

Yokohama Keikyu Bus Co., Ltd. (2)
2-1-3 Nokendai-dori, Kanazawa-ku, Yokohama, 236-0053, Kanagawa, Japan
Tel.: (81) 457719248
Bus Charter Services
N.A.I.C.S.: 485113

Keikyu Department Store Co., Ltd. (1)
1-6-1 Kamiooka Nishi, Kohan-ku, Yokohama, 233-8556, Kanagawa, Japan
Tel.: (81) 458481111
Web Site: https://www.keikyu-depart.com
Department Stores Operation Services
N.A.I.C.S.: 455110

Keikyu Electric Engineering Co., Ltd. (1)
2-3-2 Ikeda, Kawasaki-ku, Kawasaki, 210-0022, Kanagawa, Japan
Tel.: (81) 443225311
Web Site: http://www.kqee.co.jp
Emp.: 192
Electrical Engineering Services
N.A.I.C.S.: 541330

Keikyu Fine-tec Co., Ltd. (1)
2-1-1 Mutsuurahigashi, Kanazawa-ku, Yokohama, 236-0037, Kanagawa, Japan
Tel.: (81) 457811667
Web Site: http://www.keikyu-ftec.co.jp

Emp.: 68
Locomotive & Rail Car Repair Services
N.A.I.C.S.: 488210

Keikyu Kaihatsu Co., Ltd. (1)
1-1-1 Heiwajima, Ota-ku, Tokyo, 143-8532, Japan
Tel.: (81) 337689013
Web Site: http://www.keikyu-kaihatsu.co.jp
Emp.: 653
Leisure & Residential Building Leasing Services
N.A.I.C.S.: 531110
Katsuo Koyama (Mng Dir)

Keikyu Real Estate Co., Ltd. (1)
1-2-8 Takashima, Nishi-ku, Yokohama, 220-0011, Kanagawa, Japan
Tel.: (81) 570200653
Web Site: https://www.keikyu-sumai.com
Emp.: 178
Property Sales & Rental Management Services
N.A.I.C.S.: 531311

Keikyu Station Commerce Co., Ltd. (1)
1-2-8 Takashima, Nishi-ku, Yokohama, 220-0011, Japan
Tel.: (81) 453053100
Web Site: http://www.keikyu-sc.com
Emp.: 426
Kiosk Management Services
N.A.I.C.S.: 561990

Keikyu Store Co., Ltd. (1)
1-2-8 Takashima, Nishi-ku, Yokohama, 220-0011, Japan
Tel.: (81) 453053100
Web Site: https://www.keikyu-store.co.jp
Supermarkets Operation Services
N.A.I.C.S.: 445110

KEILHAUER INDUSTRIES LTD.
1450 Birchmount Road, Toronto, M1P 2E3, ON, Canada
Tel.: (416) 759-5665
Web Site: http://www.keilhauer.com
Year Founded: 1981
Rev.: $73,000,000
Emp.: 290
Office Furniture Mfr
N.A.I.C.S.: 337214
Mike Keilhauer (Pres)

KEIN HING INTERNATIONAL BERHAD
Lot 1863 Jalan Kolej, 43300, Seri Kembangan, Selangor Darul Ehsan, Malaysia
Tel.: (60) 389424649
Web Site: https://www.keinhing.com
KEINHIN—(KLS)
Rev.: $63,189,549
Assets: $60,444,871
Liabilities: $20,553,693
Net Worth: $39,891,178
Earnings: $3,382,563
Emp.: 550
Fiscal Year-end: 04/30/24
Sheet Metal Forming & Precision Machines Mfr
N.A.I.C.S.: 238220
Yim Kong Ng (Sec)

Subsidiaries:

Kein Hing Appliances Sdn. Bhd. (1)
1592-B Jalan Besar, 43300, Seri Kembangan, Selangor Darul Ehsan, Malaysia
Tel.: (60) 389486279
Sales Range: $50-74.9 Million
Emp.: 5
Consumer Electronics Distr
N.A.I.C.S.: 423620

Kein Hing Industry Sdn. Bhd. (1)
Lot 1863 Jalan Kolej, 43300, Seri Kembangan, Selangor, Malaysia
Tel.: (60) 389424649
Web Site: https://www.keinhing.com
Sales Range: $125-149.9 Million
Emp.: 500
Metal Products Mfr & Distr
N.A.I.C.S.: 332999

Kein Hing International Berhad - Factory UK (1)
Lot 2/4 Jalan Indah 2/16 Taman Universiti Indah, 43300, Seri Kembangan, Selangor Darul Ehsan, Malaysia
Tel.: (60) 389421533
Web Site: http://www.keinhing.com
Metal Products Mfr
N.A.I.C.S.: 332999

Kein Hing Muramoto (Vietnam) Co., Ltd. (1)
Plot C-3 Thang Long Industrial Park, Kim Chung Commune Dong Anh District, Hanoi, Vietnam (51%)
Tel.: (84) 438813299
Automotive Parts & Components Mfr & Distr
N.A.I.C.S.: 336310

Zenne Infinity Sdn Bhd (1)
Lot 1863 Jalan Kolej, 43300, Seri Kembangan, Selangor, Malaysia (100%)
Tel.: (60) 389489088
Web Site: http://www.zenne.com.my
Gas Appliances Mfr
N.A.I.C.S.: 333414

KEIO AGENCY INC.
241 Shinjuku-Ku MS Building 23 Fl, Tokyo, 160-8318, Japan
Tel.: (81) 333488610   JP
Web Site: http://www.keio-ag.co.jp
Year Founded: 1986
Rev.: $106,000,000
Emp.: 170
Advertising Agencies, Transportation
N.A.I.C.S.: 541810
Matsu Zaka (Gen Mgr)

KEIO CORPORATION
1-9-1 Sekido, Tama, 206 8502, Japan
Tel.: (81) 423373106   JP
Web Site: https://www.keio.co.jp
Year Founded: 1948
9008—(TKS)
Rev.: $2,701,467,340
Assets: $7,134,754,680
Liabilities: $4,530,877,380
Net Worth: $2,603,877,300
Earnings: $193,296,230
Emp.: 2,434
Fiscal Year-end: 03/31/24
Transportation & Real Estate Services
N.A.I.C.S.: 482111
Tadashi Nagata (Chm)

Subsidiaries:

Keio Atman Co., Ltd. (1)
4th floor Keio Seiseki Sakuragaoka East Exit Building 2-40-1 Sekido, Tama, 206-0011, Tokyo, Japan
Tel.: (81) 423372540
Web Site: https://www.keio-atman.co.jp
Home Furnishing Whslr
N.A.I.C.S.: 423220

Keio Bus Chuo Co., Ltd. (1)
Keio Fuchu 1chome Bldg 7th Floor, 183-0055, Fuchu, Japan
Tel.: (81) 423523710
Urban Transit Systems
N.A.I.C.S.: 485119

Keio Bus Koganei Co., Ltd. (1)
5-3-31 Honcho, Koganei, 184-0004, Japan
Tel.: (81) 423811881
Interurban & Rural Bus Transportation
N.A.I.C.S.: 485210

Keio Business Support Co., Ltd. (1)
5th floor Keio Chofu Kojimacho Building 1-32-2 Kojimacho, Chofu, 182-0026, Tokyo, Japan
Tel.: (81) 424441265
Web Site: https://www.keio-bs.co.jp
Sales Range: $10-24.9 Million
Emp.: 72
Business Services
N.A.I.C.S.: 561499

Keio Chika Chushajou Co., Ltd. (1)
1-2-2 Hatagaya, Shibuya-Ku, Tokyo, 151-0072, Japan
Tel.: (81) 353338711

Web Site: https://www.keiochika.co.jp
Real Estate Manangement Services
N.A.I.C.S.: 531390

Keio Jidousha Co., Ltd. (1)
2-37-3 Sekido, Tama, 206-0011, Japan
Tel.: (81) 423148035
Web Site: https://www.keiotaxi.co.jp
Automobile Leasing Services
N.A.I.C.S.: 532112

Keio Juuki Seibi Co. Ltd. (1)
1-47-1 Sasazuka, Shibuya-ku, Tokyo, 151-0073, Japan
Tel.: (81) 334661111
Web Site: https://www.keiojuuki.co.jp
Emp.: 266
Railway Vehicle Repair & Maintenance Services
N.A.I.C.S.: 811198

Keio Plaza Hotel Co., Ltd. (1)
2-2-1 Nishi-Shinjuku, Shinjuku-ku, Tokyo, 160-8330, Japan
Tel.: (81) 333440111
Web Site: http://www.keioplaza.com
Sales Range: $200-249.9 Million
Emp.: 1,064
Hotels & Motels
N.A.I.C.S.: 721110

Keio Plaza Hotel Sapporo Co., Ltd. (1)
2-1 North 5 West 7, Chuo-ku Hokkaido, Sapporo, 060-0005, Japan
Tel.: (81) 112710111
Web Site: http://www.keioplaza-sapporo.co.jp
Sales Range: $100-124.9 Million
Emp.: 904
Hotels & Motels
N.A.I.C.S.: 721110

Keio Plaza Hotel Tama (1)
1-43 Ochiai, Tama, 206-0033, Tokyo, Japan
Tel.: (81) 42 374 0111
Web Site: http://www.keioplaza.co.jp
Home Management Services
N.A.I.C.S.: 721110

Keio Presso Inn Co., Ltd. (1)
8th floor Keio Shinjuku 3-chome Building 3-1-24, Shinjuku-ku, Tokyo, 160-0022, Japan
Tel.: (81) 353693401
Web Site: https://www.presso-inn.com
Sales Range: $10-24.9 Million
Emp.: 241
Hotels & Motels
N.A.I.C.S.: 721110

Keio Recreation Co., Ltd. (1)
2985 Renkoji, Tama, 206-0021, Tokyo, Japan
Tel.: (81) 423758814
Web Site: https://www.keio-rec.co.jp
Sales Range: $50-74.9 Million
Emp.: 100
Golf Courses & Country Clubs
N.A.I.C.S.: 713910

Keio Retail Service Co., Ltd. (1)
Keiohatsudai 1chome Building 4th Floor Shibuya-Ku, Tokyo, Japan
Tel.: (81) 353651211
Sales Range: $100-124.9 Million
Emp.: 400
Supermarkets & Grocery Stores
N.A.I.C.S.: 445110

Keio Setsubi Service Co., Ltd. (1)
Shinsen Station Building 4-6 Shinsencho, Shibuya-Ku, Tokyo, 150-0045, Japan
Tel.: (81) 354568710
Web Site: https://www.keio-setsubi.co.jp
Real Estate Agents & Brokers
N.A.I.C.S.: 531210

Keio Shokuhin Co., Ltd. (1)
2-37-3 Sekido, Tama, Japan
Tel.: (81) 423372861
Retail Bakeries
N.A.I.C.S.: 311811

Keio Shoseki Hanbai Co., Ltd. (1)
1-22 Toyogaoka, Tama, 206-0031, Japan
Tel.: (81) 423374811
Web Site: https://www.keibundo.co.jp
Sales Range: $25-49.9 Million
Emp.: 19
Book Stores

KEIO CORPORATION

Keio Corporation—(Continued)
N.A.I.C.S.: 459210

Keio Sincere Staff Co., Ltd. (1)
1-9-1 Sekido, Tama, Japan
Tel.: (81) 423690370
Business Services
N.A.I.C.S.: 561499

Keio Store Co., Ltd. (1)
1-7-4 Sekido, Tama, 206-8522, Tokyo, Japan
Tel.: (81) 423372851
Web Site: http://www.keiostore.co.jp
Emp.: 3,003
Supermarkets & Grocery Stores
N.A.I.C.S.: 445110

ReBITA inc. (1)
1-12-23 Mita, Meguro-ku, Tokyo, 153-0062, Japan
Tel.: (81) 354689225
Web Site: https://www.rebita.co.jp
Sales Range: $50-74.9 Million
Emp.: 204
Real Estate Consulting Service
N.A.I.C.S.: 531390
Yoshitaka Minami *(Pres)*

Tokyo Special Coach Manufacture Co., Ltd. (1)
1304-1 Naganuma-cho, Hachioji, 192-0907, Tokyo, Japan
Tel.: (81) 426443517
Web Site: https://www.toutoku.co.jp
Motor Vehicle Body Mfr
N.A.I.C.S.: 336211

KEIOZU HOLDINGS COMPANY

7th Floor Sen Metropolitan Hall Building 2-chome 2-10, Aoba-ku, Sendai, 980-0021, Miyagi, Japan
Tel.: (81) 22 7220333
Web Site: http://www.keiozu.co.jp
Year Founded: 1993
Emp.: 334
Holding Company
N.A.I.C.S.: 551112
Akihiro Yuze *(Dir)*

KEISEI ELECTRIC RAILWAY CO., LTD.

3-3-1 Yawata, Ichikawa, 272-8510, Chiba, Japan
Tel.: (81) 570081160
Web Site: https://www.keisei.co.jp
Year Founded: 1909
9009—(TKS)
Rev.: $1,959,924,490
Assets: $7,034,375,220
Liabilities: $3,933,247,450
Net Worth: $3,101,127,770
Earnings: $579,412,770
Emp.: 1,907
Fiscal Year-end: 03/31/24
Railway Transportation Services
N.A.I.C.S.: 488210
Toshiya Kobayashi *(Pres & Dir-Rep)*

Subsidiaries:

Shin-Keisei Electric Railway Co., Ltd. (1)
4-1-12 Kunugiyama, Kamagaya, 273-0192, Chiba, Japan
Tel.: (81) 47 389 1111
Web Site: http://www.shinkeisei.co.jp
Rev.: $182,671,280
Assets: $659,295,120
Liabilities: $237,614,960
Net Worth: $421,680,160
Earnings: $5,033,600
Emp.: 460
Fiscal Year-end: 03/31/2022
Transportation Services
N.A.I.C.S.: 482111
Yukihito Mashimo *(Pres & CEO)*

KEITH BAGG STAFFING RESOURCES INC.

372 Bay Street Suite 2100, Toronto, M5H 2C9, ON, Canada
Tel.: (416) 863-1800
Web Site: http://www.bagg.com
Year Founded: 1971
Sales Range: $10-24.9 Million
Emp.: 50
Staffing & Employment Placement Agencies
N.A.I.C.S.: 561311
Geoff Bagg *(Pres & CEO)*

Subsidiaries:

Turn key Staffing Solutions Inc (1)
200 Davis Dr Suite 7, Newmarket, L3Y 2N4, ON, Canada
Tel.: (905) 953-9133
Employee Placement Services
N.A.I.C.S.: 561311

KEITH, BAYLEY, ROGERS & CO. LIMITED

1 Royal Exchange Avenue, London, EC3V 3LT, United Kingdom
Tel.: (44) 2074644090
Web Site: http://www.kbrl.co.uk
Sales Range: $25-49.9 Million
Emp.: 25
Stock Brokerage Services
N.A.I.C.S.: 523150
David Coffman *(Dir-Corp Fin)*

KEIWA INCORPORATED

3F Sumitomo Seimei Kayabacho Building 2 Chome-10-5, Nihonbashi Kayabacho Chuo-ku, Tokyo, 103-0025, Japan
Tel.: (81) 356438700
Web Site: https://www.keiwa.co.jp
Year Founded: 1948
4251—(TKS)
Rev.: $124,571,300
Assets: $207,503,030
Liabilities: $63,171,900
Net Worth: $144,331,130
Earnings: $14,059,470
Fiscal Year-end: 12/31/23
Paper Product Mfr & Distr
N.A.I.C.S.: 322299
Keiichi Osamura *(Chm, Pres, CEO & Dir-Rep)*

Subsidiaries:

KEIWA Incorporated (1)
Regus 6th Fl Ste 607 2033 Gateway Pl, San Jose, CA 95110
Tel.: (408) 573-6000
Coated & Laminated Paper Mfr & Distr
N.A.I.C.S.: 326130

Keiwa (Nanjing) Co., Ltd. (1)
No1 Lanxia Road, Moling Industrial Park Jiangning Economic Development Zone, Nanjing, 211111, China
Tel.: (86) 2552157713
Coated & Laminated Paper Mfr & Distr
N.A.I.C.S.: 326130

Seoul Keiwa Optoronics Co., Ltd. (1)
4F Into Building 2 Gangnam-daero 79-gil Banpo-dong 737-19, Seocho-gu, Seoul, 06541, Korea (South)
Tel.: (82) 27551216
Coated & Laminated Paper Mfr & Distr
N.A.I.C.S.: 326130

Taiwan Keiwa Inc. (1)
33 F No 66 Sec 1 Zhongxiao W Rd, Zhongzheng Dist, Taipei, 10018, Taiwan
Tel.: (886) 223700035
Coated & Laminated Paper Mfr & Distr
N.A.I.C.S.: 326130

KEIYO CO., LTD.

1-28-1 Mitsuwadai, Wakaba-ku, Chiba, 264-0032, Japan
Tel.: (81) 43 2551111
Web Site: http://www.keiyo.co.jp
Year Founded: 1952
8168—(TKS)
Sales Range: $1-4.9 Billion
Emp.: 1,603
Home Center Operator
N.A.I.C.S.: 444110
Sigeo Daigo *(Pres)*

KEIYO GAS CO., LTD.

2-8-8 Ichikawa-minami, Ichikawa, 272-8580, Chiba, Japan
Tel.: (81) 473610211
Web Site: https://www.keiyogas.co.jp
Year Founded: 1927
9539—(TKS)
Rev.: $871,027,770
Assets: $1,142,170,640
Liabilities: $486,104,580
Net Worth: $656,066,060
Earnings: $10,351,400
Emp.: 724
Fiscal Year-end: 12/31/23
Natural Gas Distr
N.A.I.C.S.: 221210
Hiroshi Habu *(Pres)*

KEJA DONIA

Assumburg 2, 1081 GC, Amsterdam, Netherlands
Tel.: (31) 206715141
Web Site: http://www.kejadonia.nl
Year Founded: 1983
Sales Range: $10-24.9 Million
Emp.: 21
N.A.I.C.S.: 541810
Rob Troost *(Mng Dir & Owner)*

KEJURUTERAAN SAMUDRA TIMUR BERHAD

Suite A-21-12 Level 21 Menara UOA Bangsar, No 5 Jalan Bangsar Utama 1, 59000, Kuala Lumpur, Malaysia
Tel.: (60) 32 282 2682
Web Site: http://www.kstb.com.my
7185—(KLS)
Sales Range: $1-9.9 Million
Oil & Gas Mfr
N.A.I.C.S.: 211130
Darmendran Kunaretnam *(Exec Dir)*

KEKROPS S.A.

6 Dafnis Street, Palaio Psychiko, 15452, Athens, Greece
Tel.: (30) 2106712071
Web Site: https://www.kekrops.gr
Year Founded: 1923
KEKR—(ATH)
Rev.: $17,687
Assets: $10,459,193
Liabilities: $6,206,501
Net Worth: $4,252,693
Earnings: $13,847
Emp.: 3
Fiscal Year-end: 12/31/20
Real Estate Development Services
N.A.I.C.S.: 531390
Petros K. Souretis *(CEO & Mng Dir)*

KEL CORPORATION

6-17-7 Nagayama, Tama, 206-0025, Tokyo, Japan
Tel.: (81) 423745801
Web Site: https://www.kel.jp
Year Founded: 1962
6919—(TKS)
Rev.: $80,812,663
Assets: $125,034,653
Liabilities: $23,349,845
Net Worth: $101,684,808
Earnings: $5,629,334
Emp.: 318
Fiscal Year-end: 03/31/24
Electronic Connector Mfr
N.A.I.C.S.: 334417
Etsuro Doi *(Pres)*

Subsidiaries:

KEL Connectors, Inc. (1)
830 Stewart Dr 179, Sunnyvale, CA 94085-4513
Tel.: (408) 720-9044
Web Site: http://www.kel.jp

INTERNATIONAL PUBLIC

Connector Mfr & Distr
N.A.I.C.S.: 334417

KEL Corporation - Minami-Alps Factory (1)
454-1 Miyazawa, Minami-Alps, 400-0415, Yamanashi, Japan
Tel.: (81) 552835121
Connector Mfr
N.A.I.C.S.: 334417

KEL Corporation - Nagano Factory (1)
1400-5 Nakau, Kita-azumi-gun, Ikeda, 399-8603, Nagano, Japan
Tel.: (81) 261626511
Connector Mfr
N.A.I.C.S.: 334417

KEL Corporation - Yamanashi Factory (1)
1-1 Ootsuka Misato-cho, Nishi-Yatsushiro-gun, Ichikawa, 409-3611, Yamanashi, Japan
Tel.: (81) 552255611
Connector Mfr
N.A.I.C.S.: 334417

KEL Shanghai Co., Ltd. (1)
Flat 9 6/F Jing an China Tower 1701 West Beijing Rd, Jing an Dist, Shanghai, 200040, China
Tel.: (86) 2164000051
Connector Mfr & Distr
N.A.I.C.S.: 334417

KEL Taiwan Co., Ltd. (1)
3F No 82-2 Dong-shoenn st, Shu-Lin, Taipei, 238, Taiwan
Tel.: (886) 286869200
Connector Mfr & Distr
N.A.I.C.S.: 334417

KELA INVESTMENT FUND LTD

Ig'Al Alon 98, 6789141, Tel Aviv, Israel
Tel.: (972) 36959763
Year Founded: 1993
Financial Investment Services
N.A.I.C.S.: 523999

KELANI CABLES PLC

Weweldura Road, PO Box 14, Kelaniya, Sri Lanka
Tel.: (94) 112911224
Web Site: https://www.kelanicables.com
Year Founded: 1969
KCAB.N0000—(COL)
Rev.: $38,156,174
Assets: $38,521,951
Liabilities: $7,448,778
Net Worth: $31,073,173
Earnings: $9,276,735
Emp.: 495
Fiscal Year-end: 03/31/23
Fiber Optic Electrical Equipment Mfr
N.A.I.C.S.: 335921
Mahinda Saranapala *(CEO)*

KELANI TYRES PLC

Nungamugoda, PO Box 8, Kelaniya, Sri Lanka
Tel.: (94) 2421418
Year Founded: 1991
TYRE.N0000—(COL)
Assets: $22,123,839
Liabilities: $535,439
Net Worth: $21,588,399
Earnings: $2,924,938
Emp.: 8
Fiscal Year-end: 03/31/24
Real Estate Services
N.A.I.C.S.: 531390
De Silva C. *(Chm)*

KELDON ELECTRIC & DATA LTD.

1909 Bredin Road, Kelowna, V1Y 7S9, BC, Canada
Tel.: (250) 861-4255
Web Site: https://www.keldonelectric.com

AND PRIVATE COMPANIES

Year Founded: 1984
Rev.: $10,626,605
Emp.: 90
Electrical Contractor
N.A.I.C.S.: 238210
Brian Yamaoka (Pres)

KELFRED HOLDINGS LIMITED
Room 1606 16/F Block B New Trade Plaza 6 On Ping St, NT, Sha Tin, China (Hong Kong)
Tel.: (852) 26872382 Ky
Web Site: https://www.kelfred.com.hk
Year Founded: 1986
1134—(HKG)
Rev.: $60,031,161
Assets: $32,489,546
Liabilities: $8,425,490
Net Worth: $24,064,057
Earnings: $1,184,423
Emp.: 1,007
Fiscal Year-end: 12/31/22
Holding Company
N.A.I.C.S.: 551112
Ken Kwok (CEO)

KELI MOTOR GROUP CO., LTD.
5th Floor Building B3 Building 9, Bay Science and Technology Ecological Park Nanshan District, Shenzhen, 518057, Guangdong, China
Tel.: (86) 75581958899
Web Site: https://www.kelimotor.com
Year Founded: 2010
002892—(SSE)
Rev.: $166,153,572
Assets: $251,547,660
Liabilities: $71,370,936
Net Worth: $180,176,724
Earnings: $10,284,300
Fiscal Year-end: 12/31/22
Electrical Machine Product Mfr & Distr
N.A.I.C.S.: 335312
Nie Pengju (Chm & CEO)

Subsidiaries:

Hunan Keli Motor Co., Ltd. - Fairport Branch (1)
6 Bordeaux Way, Fairport, NY 14450
Tel.: (585) 421-9482
Motor Mfr
N.A.I.C.S.: 335312

KELI SENSING TECHNOLOGY NINGBO CO., LTD.
No 199 Changxing Road, Jiangbei District C, Ningbo, 315033, Zhejiang, China
Tel.: (86) 4008874165
Web Site: https://www.kelichina.com
Year Founded: 2002
603662—(SHG)
Rev.: $148,894,509
Assets: $496,887,562
Liabilities: $158,575,342
Net Worth: $338,312,220
Earnings: $36,537,752
Fiscal Year-end: 12/31/22
Weighing Instrument Mfr
N.A.I.C.S.: 333993
Jiandong Ke (Chm & Gen Mgr)

Subsidiaries:

Shenyang Longteng Electronic Co., Ltd.
No 76-16 Shenbei Road, Shenbei New District, Shenyang, 110136, China
Tel.: (86) 2486376663
Web Site: https://en.ltelec.com
Electric Equipment Mfr
N.A.I.C.S.: 334419

Yinhuan Traffic Instrument Co., Ltd. (1)
Rainbow Road on the 1st Industrial Park, Yuyao, 315400, Zhejiang, China
Tel.: (86) 57462689077
Web Site: http://www.yinhuanchina.com
Flow Meter Mfr
N.A.I.C.S.: 334514

Yuyao Pacific Weighing Engineering Co., Ltd. (1)
No 50 Tanjialing East Road, Yuyao, Zhejiang, China
Tel.: (86) 57462730166
Web Site: https://www.cn-cells.com
Weighing Indicator Mfr
N.A.I.C.S.: 333998

KELIN ENVIRONMENTAL PROTECTION EQUIPMENT, INC.
No 425 Gaoxin Rd, Wujiang, 215200, Jiangsu, China
Tel.: (86) 51262512888
Web Site: http://www.kelin-china.com
Year Founded: 1979
002499—(SSE)
Rev.: $6,033,410
Assets: $114,758,886
Liabilities: $105,505,002
Net Worth: $9,253,884
Earnings: $1,498,394
Emp.: 500
Fiscal Year-end: 12/31/20
Environmental Protection Equipment Mfr
N.A.I.C.S.: 333413

KELINGTON GROUP BERHAD
3 Jalan Astaka U8/83 Seksyen U8 Bukit Jelutong Industrial Park, 40150, Shah Alam, Selangor Darul Ehsan, Malaysia
Tel.: (60) 378455696 MY
Web Site: https://www.kelington-group.com
Year Founded: 1999
KGB—(KLS)
Rev.: $97,663,253
Assets: $86,709,893
Liabilities: $45,048,465
Net Worth: $41,661,428
Earnings: $4,353,773
Emp.: 411
Fiscal Year-end: 12/31/20
Engineeering Services
N.A.I.C.S.: 541330
Hung Keng Gan (Founder & Chm)

Subsidiaries:

Kelington Engineering (S) Pte. Ltd. (1)
Tel.: (65) 66341683
Emp.: 12
Engineeering Services
N.A.I.C.S.: 541330

Subsidiary (Non-US):

PT Mitracon Graha Solusindo (2)
Beltway Office Park Tower B 5 Th Floor Jl Letjend Tb Simatupang No 41, Jakarta, 12550, Indonesia
Tel.: (62) 2129857263
Web Site: http://mitracon.co.id
Fabric Structural Steel Whslr
N.A.I.C.S.: 423510

Kelington Engineering (Shanghai) Co., Ltd. (1)
403A Block 5 3000 LongDong Ave, Pudong, Shanghai, 201203, China
Tel.: (86) 21068791988
Engineeering Services
N.A.I.C.S.: 541330

KELLER GROUP PLC
2 Kingdom Street, London, W2 6BD, United Kingdom
Tel.: (44) 2076167575 UK
Web Site: https://www.keller.com
Year Founded: 1860
KLR—(LSE)
Rev.: $3,546,770,700
Assets: $2,049,938,550
Liabilities: $1,451,542,950
Net Worth: $598,395,600
Earnings: $53,841,150
Fiscal Year-end: 12/31/22
Ground Engineering Services
N.A.I.C.S.: 237990
James Hind (Pres-North America)

Subsidiaries:

Anderson Drilling Inc. (1)
5775 Eudora St, Commerce City, CO 80022
Tel.: (303) 321-6680
Web Site: http://www.andersondrilling.com
Drilling Equipment Mfr
N.A.I.C.S.: 333132

Anderson Manufacturing Inc. (1)
3360 Hwy 112 S, Camilla, GA 31730
Tel.: (229) 336-5800
Web Site: https://andersontrailers.com
Truck Body Equipment Mfr
N.A.I.C.S.: 336211

Ansah Asia Sdn. Bhd. (1)
B5-10 Block B Plaza Dwitasik Bandar Sri Permaisuri Off, Jalan Tasik Permaisuri 1, 56000, Kuala Lumpur, Malaysia
Tel.: (60) 391712058
Construction Services
N.A.I.C.S.: 541330

Austral Construction Pty. Ltd. (1)
126 Hallam Valley Road, Dandenong, 3175, VIC, Australia
Tel.: (61) 39 797 2700
Web Site: https://www.australconstruction.com.au
Building Construction Services
N.A.I.C.S.: 541330
Craig Allen (Mng Dir)

Bencor Global, Inc. (1)
6811 Ash St, Frisco, TX 75034
Tel.: (972) 247-6767
Web Site: http://www.bencorconstruction.com
Foundation Contractor
N.A.I.C.S.: 238110
Giancarlo Santarelli (Pres)

Case Foundation Company (1)
1325 W Lake St, Roselle, IL 60172-3369 (100%)
Tel.: (630) 529-2911
Web Site: http://www.casefoundation.com
Sales Range: $25-49.9 Million
Emp.: 75
N.A.I.C.S.: 237310
Daniel P. Bien (Pres)

Subsidiary (Domestic):

Case Atlantic Company (2)
4585 148th Ave N Ste 1012, Clearwater, FL 33762
Tel.: (727) 572-7740
Web Site: http://www.caseatlantic.com
Emp.: 5
Drilled Shaft Construction Services
N.A.I.C.S.: 237990

Cyntech Canada Inc. (1)
235061 Wrangler Link SE, Calgary, T1X 0K3, AB, Canada
Tel.: (403) 228-1767
Web Site: https://www.cyntech.com
Emp.: 15
Oil & Gas Pipeline Construction Services
N.A.I.C.S.: 237120
Robert Hoefler (Office Mgr)

Subsidiary (Domestic):

Cyntech Services Inc. (2)
235061 Wrangler Link S E, Calgary, T1X 0K3, AB, Canada
Tel.: (403) 228-1767
Web Site: https://www.cyntech.com
Emp.: 35
Oil & Gas Pipeline Construction Services
N.A.I.C.S.: 237120
Terry Thomson (Office Mgr)

Subsidiary (US):

Cyntech U.S. Inc. (2)
17807 Hwy 105, Plantersville, TX 77363
Tel.: (936) 894-2181
Web Site: http://www.cyntech.com
Sales Range: $25-49.9 Million
Emp.: 9
Oil & Gas Pipeline Construction Services
N.A.I.C.S.: 237120

Cyntech Construction Ltd. (1)
34 Wrangler Place SE 6, Rocky View, T1X 0L7, AB, Canada
Tel.: (403) 228-1767
Building Construction Services
N.A.I.C.S.: 541330
Terry Thompson (Gen Mgr)

Franki Pacific Holdings Pty. Ltd. (1)
4 Burbank Pl Level 1, Baulkham Hills, Parramatta, 2150, Australia (100%)
Tel.: (61) 88661100
Web Site: http://www.franki.com.au
Sales Range: $25-49.9 Million
Emp.: 22
N.A.I.C.S.: 237310

Frankipile Australia Pty Ltd (1)
Level 1 4 Burbank Place, Baulkham Hills, 2153, NSW, Australia
Tel.: (61) 2 8866 1100
Web Site: http://www.franki.com.au
Sales Range: $25-49.9 Million
Emp.: 100
Construction Engineering Services
N.A.I.C.S.: 541330
Sried Laender (Mng Dir)

Division (Domestic):

Frankipile Australia Pty Ltd - EASTERN DIVISION (2)
Level 1 4 Burbank Place, Baulkham Hills, 2153, NSW, Australia
Tel.: (61) 2 8866 1100
Web Site: http://www.franki.com.au
Sales Range: $10-24.9 Million
Emp.: 27
Ground Engineering Services
N.A.I.C.S.: 541330

Frankipile Australia Pty Ltd - NORTHERN DIVISION (2)
43 Holt Street, Eagle Farm, 4009, QLD, Australia
Tel.: (61) 7 3292 3333
Ground Engineering Services
N.A.I.C.S.: 237990
Bruce Boundy (Gen Mgr)

Frankipile Australia Pty Ltd - SOUTHERN DIVISION (2)
Level 2 Building 4 Brandon Business Park 540 Springvale Road, Glen Waverley, 3150, VIC, Australia
Tel.: (61) 395902700
Web Site: http://www.franki.com.au
Ground Engineering Services
N.A.I.C.S.: 541330
John Fletcher (Gen Mgr)

Frankipile Ghana Limited (1)
C205/21 Didebaa Link Abelemkpe, Accra, Ghana
Tel.: (233) 206059601
Building Construction Services
N.A.I.C.S.: 541330

Frankipile Mocambique Limitada (1)
Bairro da Matola D Estrada Nacional N4, PO Box 4291, Avenida Samora Machel Nr 393 Matola, Maputo, Mozambique
Tel.: (258) 823106320
Building Construction Services
N.A.I.C.S.: 541330

Getec North America, Inc. (1)
24 Celestial Dr, Narragansett, RI 02882
Tel.: (800) 477-2506
Web Site: http://www.geo-instruments.com
Geotechnical & Structural Monitoring Solutions
N.A.I.C.S.: 541690
Pierre Gouvin (Pres)

HJ Foundation, Inc. (1)
8275 NW 80 St, Miami, FL 33166
Tel.: (305) 592-8181
Web Site: http://www.hjfoundation.com
Foundation Engineering Services
N.A.I.C.S.: 541330

Hayward Baker Inc. (1)
7550 Teague Rd Ste 300, Hanover, MD 21076
Tel.: (410) 551-8200

KELLER GROUP PLC   INTERNATIONAL PUBLIC

Keller Group plc—(Continued)
Web Site: http://www.haywardbaker.com
Sales Range: $25-49.9 Million
Emp.: 40
Geo Technical Speciality
N.A.I.C.S.: 238990
Eric Drooff (Sr VP-Northeast Reg)

KGS Keller Gerate & Service GmbH (1)
Schwarzwaldstr 1, 77871, Renchen, Germany
Tel.: (49) 7 843 7090
Web Site: https://www.keller-kgs.com
Building Construction Services
N.A.I.C.S.: 541330

Keller (Malaysia) Sdn. Bhd. (1)
B5-10 Block B Plaza Dwitasik Bandar Sri Permaisuri, Off Jln Tasik Permaisuri 1, 56000, Kuala Lumpur, Malaysia
Tel.: (60) 39 173 3198
Web Site: https://www.kellerasean.com
Emp.: 100
Geotechnical Contractor
N.A.I.C.S.: 237310
Y.W. Yee (Gen Mgr)

Keller Australia Pty Limited (1)
Suite G 01 2 Lyonpark Road, Macquarie Park, 2113, NSW, Australia
Tel.: (61) 28 866 1100
Web Site: https://www.keller.com.au
Building Construction Services
N.A.I.C.S.: 541330
David Lovell (Mgr-State)

Keller Central Asia LLP (1)
21B Satpaeva Street Office 4, 060011, Atyrau, Kazakhstan
Tel.: (7) 7017826887
Building Construction Services
N.A.I.C.S.: 541330
Waldemar Kwiatkowski (Dir-Construction)

Keller Cimentaciones Chile SpA (1)
Av Providencia 1 208-Of 409, Providencia, 7500571, Santiago, Chile
Tel.: (56) 225738519
Building Construction Services
N.A.I.C.S.: 541330

Keller Cimentaciones S.L.U. (1)
c/ Argentina 15 Alcala de Henares, 28806, Madrid, Spain
Tel.: (34) 91 298 9600
Web Site: https://www.keller.com.es
Building Construction Services
N.A.I.C.S.: 541330

Keller Cimentaciones SAC (1)
Avenida Javier Prado Oeste 203 San Isidro, Lima, Peru
Tel.: (51) 952993422
Building Construction Services
N.A.I.C.S.: 541330

Keller Cimentaciones de Latinoamerica SA de CV (1)
Avda Presidente Masaryk 101 Int 402, Col Bosques de Chapultepec Mayor Miguel Hidalgo, 11580, Mexico, Mexico
Tel.: (52) 5552039458
Web Site: https://www.keller.com.mx
Building Construction Services
N.A.I.C.S.: 541330

Keller Egypt Ltd. (1)
Sheraton Buildings Plot 10 Block 1161 Nozha, Maadi Corniche, Cairo, Egypt (100%)
Tel.: (20) 2 252 59342
Web Site: http://www.kellerholding.com
Sales Range: $25-49.9 Million
Emp.: 20
Geotechnical Engineering Operations
N.A.I.C.S.: 541360

Keller Engenharia Geotecnica Ltda (1)
Avenida Queiroz Filho 1560 Village 23G Vila Hamburguesa, Sao Paulo, 05319-000, Brazil
Tel.: (55) 1137237900
Web Site: http://www.tecnogeo.com.br
Emp.: 90
Ground Engineering Services
N.A.I.C.S.: 237990

Keller Fondations Speciales SAS (1)
2 rue Denis Papin, CS 69224, Molsheim, 67129, Duttlenheim, Cedex, France
Tel.: (33) 38 859 9200
Web Site: https://www.keller-france.com
Sales Range: $25-49.9 Million
Emp.: 140
Civil Engineering Services
N.A.I.C.S.: 237990
Thierry Bret (Pres)

Keller Fondazioni S.r.l (1)
Via della Siderurgla 10, 37139, Verona, Italy
Tel.: (39) 045 818 6811
Web Site: https://www.keller-fondazioni.com
Emp.: 21
Ground Engineering Services
N.A.I.C.S.: 237990

Keller Foundations (South East Asia) Pte Ltd (1)
18 Boon Lay Way 04-104 Tradehub 21, Singapore, 609966, Singapore
Tel.: (65) 6 316 8500
Web Site: https://www.kellerasean.com
Emp.: 80
Civil Engineering Services
N.A.I.C.S.: 541330

Keller Foundations LLC (1)
7550 Teague Rd Ste 300, Hanover, MD 21076
Tel.: (410) 551-1938
Web Site: http://www.kellerfoundations.com
Building Construction Services
N.A.I.C.S.: 541330
James Hind (Pres)

Keller Foundations Ltd. (1)
254 Main Street North Unit 1, Acton, L7J 1W9, ON, Canada
Tel.: (647) 417-0115
Web Site: http://www.kellerfoundations.ca
Building Construction Services
N.A.I.C.S.: 541330
Mark Redden (Mgr-Project)

Keller Foundations Vietnam Co., Limited (1)
2nd Flr Van Loi Building 24 Dang Thai Mai Street, Phu Nhuan Dist, Ho Chi Minh City, Vietnam
Tel.: (84) 835515022
Building Construction Services
N.A.I.C.S.: 541330

Keller Funderingstechnieken B.V. (1)
Europaplaan 16, PO Box 757, 2400 AT, Alphen aan den Rijn, Netherlands
Tel.: (31) 172471798
Building Construction Services
N.A.I.C.S.: 541330

Keller Funderingsteknik Danmark ApS (1)
Lottenborgvej 24, 2800, Kongens Lyngby, Denmark
Tel.: (45) 53771220
Building Construction Services
N.A.I.C.S.: 541330

Keller Geotehnica Srl (1)
Str Uruguay Nr 27 Et 1 Ap 2, 011444, Bucharest, Romania
Tel.: (40) 212430350
Building Construction Services
N.A.I.C.S.: 541330

Keller Ground Engineering (1)
Oxford Road, Ryton-on-Dunsmore, Coventry, CV8 3EG, United Kingdom (100%)
Tel.: (44) 247 651 1266
Web Site: https://www.keller.co.uk
Sales Range: $25-49.9 Million
Emp.: 60
N.A.I.C.S.: 237310
Jim De Waele (Mng Dir)

Keller Ground Engineering (1)
Templar House 1 Sandbeck Court. Sandbeck Way, Wetherby, LS22 7BA, Yorkshire, United Kingdom (100%)
Tel.: (44) 937541118
Web Site: http://www.kellerge.co.uk
Sales Range: $25-49.9 Million
Emp.: 40
N.A.I.C.S.: 237310

Keller Ground Engineering India Private Ltd (1)
7th Floor Eastern Wing Centennial Square 6A Dr Ambedkar Road, Kodambakkam, Chennai, 600024, India
Tel.: (91) 442 480 7500
Web Site: https://www.kellerindia.com
Sales Range: $25-49.9 Million
Emp.: 450
Ground Engineering Services
N.A.I.C.S.: 237990

Keller Ground Engineering LLC (1)
Al Khuwair Street 33 Office No 107 Building No 79, PO Box 1618, Muscat, Ruwi, 112, Oman
Tel.: (968) 24488675
Building Construction Services
N.A.I.C.S.: 541330
Ramadas Veluri (Mgr-Geotechnical)

Keller Ground Engineering Pty Ltd (1)
Level 1 4 Burbank Place, Baulkham Hills, 2153, NSW, Australia
Tel.: (61) 2 8866 1155
Web Site: http://www.kellerge.com.au
Sales Range: $25-49.9 Million
Emp.: 20
Ground Engineering Services
N.A.I.C.S.: 237990
Ernst Friedlaender (Mng Dir)

Keller Grundbau GmbH (1)
Kaiserleistrasse 8, 63067, Offenbach, Germany (100%)
Tel.: (49) 69 805 1100
Web Site: https://www.kellergrundbau.de
Sales Range: $25-49.9 Million
Emp.: 50
N.A.I.C.S.: 237310

Branch (Non-US):

Keller Grundbau Ges.mbH (2)
Guglgasse 15 BT4a 3 OG, 1110, Vienna, Austria (100%)
Tel.: (43) 1 892 3526
Web Site: https://www.kellergrundbau.at
Sales Range: $25-49.9 Million
Emp.: 70
Civil Engineering Services
N.A.I.C.S.: 237310

Keller Grundbau GmbH (2)
Estrada do Porto da Areia, Apartado 77 Caseanheira 2600 6, P 2600 675, Cascais, Portugal
Tel.: (351) 263285640
Web Site: http://www.keller.com
Sales Range: $25-49.9 Million
Emp.: 35
N.A.I.C.S.: 237310

Keller Grundbau GmbH (2)
Office No 42 Building 485 Road 1010, PO Box 5452, Sanabia, 0410, Manama, Bahrain (100%)
Tel.: (973) 1 774 1677
Web Site: https://www.kellerme.com
Sales Range: $50-74.9 Million
Construction Company
N.A.I.C.S.: 213111

Keller Grundlaggning AB (1)
Ostra Lindomevagen 50, 437 34, Lindome, Sweden
Tel.: (46) 73 095 9746
Web Site: https://www.kellergrundlaggning.se
Construction Engineering Services
N.A.I.C.S.: 541330
Lars Holmstrom (Mng Dir)

Keller Hellas S.A. (1)
Antheon 102, Neoi Epivates, 57019, Thessaloniki, Greece
Tel.: (30) 2392075475
Building Construction Services
N.A.I.C.S.: 541330

Keller Holding GmbH (1)
Kaiserleistr 8, 63067, Offenbach, Germany
Tel.: (49) 6980510
Web Site: http://www.KellerHolding.com
Building Construction Services
N.A.I.C.S.: 541330
Thorsten Holl (Pres & Mng Dir)

Keller Limited (1)
Oxford Road, Ryton-on-Dunsmore, Coventry, CV8 3EG, United Kingdom
Tel.: (44) 247 651 1266
Web Site: https://www.keller.co.uk

Sales Range: $25-49.9 Million
Emp.: 100
Foundation Engineering Services
N.A.I.C.S.: 541330
Jim De Waele (Mng Dir)

Division (Domestic):

Keller Limited - Colcrete Eurodrill Division (2)
Tower Business Park Derby Road, Clay Cross, S45 9DX, Derbyshire, United Kingdom
Tel.: (44) 1246 868700
Web Site: http://www.colcrete-eurodrill.com
Sales Range: $25-49.9 Million
Emp.: 29
Drilling Equipment Mfr
N.A.I.C.S.: 333131
Mark Rex (Mng Dir)

Keller Limited - Keller Foundations Division (2)
Capital House 25 Chapel Street, London, NW1 5DH, United Kingdom
Tel.: (44) 2076167599
Web Site: http://www.keller-foundations.co.uk
Sales Range: $25-49.9 Million
Emp.: 10
Foundation Engineering Services
N.A.I.C.S.: 541330
Jim DeWaele (Mng Dir)

Keller Limited - Keller Geotechnique Division (2)
Unit 5 Weyside Park Newman Lane, Alton, GU34 2PJ, United Kingdom
Tel.: (44) 1420 590328
Web Site: http://www.keller-geotechnique.co.uk
Geotechnical Engineering Services
N.A.I.C.S.: 541330

Subsidiary (Domestic):

Phi Group - Retaining Structures (2)
Montis Court Bounders Lane, Cheltenham, GL52 5JG, United Kingdom
Tel.: (44) 124 270 7600
Web Site: https://www.phigroup.co.uk
Sales Range: $25-49.9 Million
Emp.: 15
Retaining Wall Construction Services
N.A.I.C.S.: 237990

Keller Melyepito Kft (1)
Csorsz utca 41 - VI Emelet, 1124, Budapest, Hungary
Tel.: (36) 15575862
Building Construction Services
N.A.I.C.S.: 541330

Keller New Zealand Limited (1)
GazeBurt 1 Nelson Street, Auckland, 1010, New Zealand
Tel.: (64) 288661100
Building Construction Services
N.A.I.C.S.: 541330

Keller Polska Sp. z o.o (1)
Poznanska 172, 05-850, Ozarow Mazowiecki, Poland
Tel.: (48) 22 448 9200
Web Site: https://www.keller.com.pl
Sales Range: $25-49.9 Million
Emp.: 300
Ground Engineering Services
N.A.I.C.S.: 541330
Tomasz Michalski (Member-Mgmt Bd & Reg Dir-Middle East)

Keller Pty. Ltd. (1)
2-4 Lyon Park Road, Macquarie Park, 2113, NSW, Australia
Tel.: (61) 288661155
Building Construction Services
N.A.I.C.S.: 541330

Keller Specialne Zakladani spol. s r.o. (1)
Na Pankraci 1618/30, 140 00, Prague, Czech Republic
Tel.: (420) 22 621 1301
Web Site: https://www.keller-cz.com
Construction Management Services
N.A.I.C.S.: 541330

Keller Specialne Zakladanie spol. s.r.o. (1)

AND PRIVATE COMPANIES

Hranicna 18-AB6, 821 05, Bratislava, Slovakia
Tel.: (421) 23 255 3200
Web Site: https://www.keller-slovakia.sk
Construction Management Services
N.A.I.C.S.: 541330

Keller Turki Co. Ltd. (1)
Abdul Rehman Ali Al Turki Building ATCO Building 2nd floor, PO Box 718, King Khalid Street, Dammam, 31421, Saudi Arabia (100%)
Tel.: (966) 13 833 3997
Web Site: http://www.atco.com.sa
Sales Range: $25-49.9 Million
Emp.: 60
N.A.I.C.S.: 237310
Mohammed Ali *(Gen Mgr)*

Keller Ukraine LLC (1)
Office Nr 2 401 Nr 30 Ul Vasylkivska, 03022, Kiev, Ukraine
Tel.: (380) 4449619786
Building Construction Services
N.A.I.C.S.: 541330

Keller Zemin Muhendisligi Limited (1)
Harbiye Mah Tesvikiye Caddesi No 17 D 13 Ikbal Ticaret Merkezi Sisli, 34365, Istanbul, Turkiye
Tel.: (90) 4318923526
Building Construction Services
N.A.I.C.S.: 541330

Keller-MTS AG (1)
Allmendstrasse 5, Ennetbaden, 8105, Regensdorf, Switzerland
Tel.: (41) 43 388 7100
Web Site: https://www.keller-mts.ch
Building Construction Services
N.A.I.C.S.: 541330

McKinney Drilling Company (1)
7550 Teague Rd Ste 300 Annapolis Rd Ste 103, Hannover, MD 21076
Tel.: (410) 874-1235
Web Site: http://www.mckinneydrilling.com
Sales Range: $25-49.9 Million
Emp.: 7
Foundation Engineering Services
N.A.I.C.S.: 541330
Nicole Baldwin *(Controller)*

Moretrench American Corporation (1)
100 Stickle Ave, Rockaway, NJ 07866
Tel.: (973) 627-2100
Web Site: http://www.keller-na.com
Heavy Construction
N.A.I.C.S.: 236210

Subsidiary (Domestic):

Ground/Water Treatment & Technology, LLC (2)
627 Mt Hope Rd, Wharton, NJ 07885
Tel.: (973) 983-0901
Web Site: https://www.gwttllc.com
Groundwater Treatment Services
N.A.I.C.S.: 221310

PT. Keller Franki Indonesia (1)
Pusat Perkantoran Graha Kencana Blok EK Jalan Raya Perjuangan, No 88 Kebon Jeruk, Jakarta Barat, 11530, Indonesia
Tel.: (62) 2153660778
Building Construction Services
N.A.I.C.S.: 541330
Hendy Wiyono *(Mgr-Bus Dev)*

Piling Contractors Pty Ltd (1)
5 Jacque Court, PO Box 346, Lawnton, 4501, QLD, Australia
Tel.: (61) 73 292 3333
Web Site: http://www.pilingcontractors.com.au
Emp.: 100
Ground Engineering Services
N.A.I.C.S.: 541330
Carl Vroight *(Mng Dir)*

Remedial Construction Services, L.P. (1)
9977 W Sam Houston Pkwy N Ste 100, Houston, TX 77064
Tel.: (281) 955-2442
Web Site: https://www.reconservices.com
Rev: $28,638,865
Emp.: 500

Hazardous Waste Collection & Disposal Services
N.A.I.C.S.: 562211
Steve Birdwell *(Founder)*

Resource Piling Pte. Ltd. (1)
18 Boon Lay Way 04-104 Tradehub 21, Singapore, 609966, Singapore
Tel.: (65) 63168500
Web Site: http://www.resource-piling.com.sg
Building Construction Services
N.A.I.C.S.: 541330
Ng Calvin *(Mgr-Safety)*

Sivenmark Maskintjanst AB (1)
Lerbergsvagen 90, 434 95, Kungsbacka, Sweden
Tel.: (46) 708877144
Web Site: http://www.sivenmarkmaskintjanst.com
Building Construction Services
N.A.I.C.S.: 541330

Suncoast Post-Tension Ltd. (1)
509 N Sam Houston Pkwy E Ste 400, Houston, TX 77060
Web Site: https://suncoast-pt.com
Building Construction Services
N.A.I.C.S.: 541330
Russ Price *(Sr VP-Engrg)*

The Concrete Doctor Inc. (1)
19215 S 96th St, Hickman, NE 68372
Tel.: (402) 314-8609
Web Site: https://www.mudjackinglincolnne.com
Building Construction Services
N.A.I.C.S.: 541330

Wannenwetsch GmbH Hochdruckwassertechnik (1)
Wolfsgrube 7, 98617, Meiningen, Germany
Tel.: (49) 36 939 4030
Web Site: https://www.wannenwetsch-hdw.de
Building Construction Services
N.A.I.C.S.: 541330

KELLTON TECH SOLUTIONS LTD.
Plot No 1367 Road No 45 Jubilee Hills, Hyderabad, 500 033, Telangana, India
Tel.: (91) 4044333000
Web Site: https://www.kellton.com
Year Founded: 2009
KELLTONTEC—(NSE)
Rev: $16,955,556
Assets: $28,163,828
Liabilities: $8,901,257
Net Worth: $19,262,571
Earnings: $1,486,465
Emp.: 1,269
Fiscal Year-end: 03/31/22
Software Services
N.A.I.C.S.: 541511
Krishna Reddy Chintam *(Founder & Exec Dir)*

Subsidiaries:

Evantage Technologies, Inc. (1)
190 Middlesex Tpke, Iselin, NJ 08830
Tel.: (732) 283-4010
Web Site: http://www.ievantage.com
Sales Range: $10-24.9 Million
Emp.: 50
Data Processing, Hosting & Related Services
N.A.I.C.S.: 518210
Satya Polavarapu *(Pres)*

Kellton Tech (UK) Limited (1)
30 Stamford Street, London, SE1 9LQ, United Kingdom
Tel.: (44) 203 807 6911
Web Site: https://uk.kelltontech.com
Software Development Services
N.A.I.C.S.: 541511

PlanetPro, Inc. (1)
2603 Camino Ramon Ste 432, San Ramon, CA 94583
Tel.: (925) 277-0727
Web Site: http://www.planetpro.com
Management Consulting Services
N.A.I.C.S.: 541611

Ravi Thota *(Founder & CEO)*

Supremesoft Corporation (1)
8200 Greensboro Dr Ste 900, McLean, VA 22102
Tel.: (703) 300-3400
Web Site: https://supremesoft.com
Sales Range: $1-9.9 Million
Emp.: 100
IT Services
N.A.I.C.S.: 541512

Tivix, Inc. (1)
600 California St, San Francisco, CA 94108
Tel.: (415) 680-1299
Web Site: http://www.tivix.com
Software Publisher
N.A.I.C.S.: 513210
Sumit Chachra *(CEO & CTO)*

Vivos Professionals Services LLC (1)
3 Independence Way Ste 209, Princeton, NJ 08540
Tel.: (703) 592-9159
Web Site: https://www.vivosps.com
Pharmaceutical & Clinical Research Services
N.A.I.C.S.: 541715

KELLVE GROUP AB
Vangavagen, 535 91, Kvanum, Sweden
Tel.: (46) 512 300 200 SE
Web Site: http://www.kellve.com
Sales Range: $25-49.9 Million
Emp.: 90
Bulk Materials Handling, Transport & Storage Products & Services
N.A.I.C.S.: 333922
Jimmy Moss *(Mgr-Pur & Production Plng)*

Subsidiaries:

Kellve Service AB (1)
Vangavagen, S 535 91, Kvanum, Sweden (100%)
Tel.: (46) 512 300 200
Web Site: http://www.kellve.com
Technical Solutions for Materials Handling in Turnkey Systems
N.A.I.C.S.: 333922
Leif Ivansson *(CEO)*

Kellve Sweden AB (1)
Vangavagen, S-535 91, Kvanum, Sweden (100%)
Tel.: (46) 512 300 200
Web Site: http://www.kellve.com
Sales Range: $25-49.9 Million
Emp.: 70
Supplier of Wear-Parts & Spare Parts for Conveyors & Assembly Services of Belt Conveyors
N.A.I.C.S.: 333922
Leif Ivansson *(CEO)*

KELLY PARTNERS GROUP HOLDINGS LIMITED
Level 8 32 Walker Street, North Sydney, 2060, NSW, Australia
Tel.: (61) 299230800 AU
Web Site: https://www.kellypartnersgroup.com
Year Founded: 2006
KPG—(ASX)
Rev: $51,668,695
Assets: $81,708,414
Liabilities: $55,694,192
Net Worth: $26,014,222
Earnings: $10,212,351
Emp.: 400
Fiscal Year-end: 06/30/22
Miscellaneous Intermediation
N.A.I.C.S.: 523910
Brett Kelly *(Founder, Chm & CEO)*

Subsidiaries:

Kelly Property Group Pty. Ltd. (1)
457 Swan Street, Richmond, 3121, VIC, Australia
Tel.: (61) 394288007
Web Site: https://www.kellyproperty.com.au

Industrial Property Agency Services
N.A.I.C.S.: 531210
Donna Venables *(Mgr-Property)*

Super Certain Pty. Ltd. (1)
Level 53 MLC Centre 19 Martin Place, Sydney, 2000, NSW, Australia
Tel.: (61) 292311910
Web Site: https://www.supercertain.com.au
Financial Investment Services
N.A.I.C.S.: 523999

KELLY VENTURES LTD.
Suite 615 800 West Pender St, Vancouver, V6C 2V6, BC, Canada
Tel.: (604) 728-4080
Year Founded: 2016
KKL.P—(TSXV)
Assets: $33,955
Liabilities: $9,345
Net Worth: $24,610
Earnings: ($38,111)
Fiscal Year-end: 12/31/23
Asset Management Services
N.A.I.C.S.: 523940
Paul A. Larkin *(CEO, CFO & Sec)*

KELOWNA FLIGHTCRAFT AIR CHARTER LTD.
5655 Airport Way, Kelowna, V1V 1S1, BC, Canada
Tel.: (250) 491-5500
Web Site: http://www.flightcraft.ca
Year Founded: 1970
Rev: $115,599,718
Emp.: 1,000
Oil Transportation Services
N.A.I.C.S.: 481212
Barry Lapointe *(Co-Founder & Pres)*

KELOWNA FORD LINCOLN SALES LTD
2540 Enterprise Way, Kelowna, V1X 7X5, BC, Canada
Tel.: (250) 868-2330
Web Site: http://www.kelownaford.com
Sales Range: $10-24.9 Million
Emp.: 47
New & Used Car Dealer
N.A.I.C.S.: 441110
Dean Bradshaw *(Gen Mgr)*

KELOWNA MERCEDES-BENZ
2580 Enterprise Way, Kelowna, V1X 7X5, BC, Canada
Tel.: (250) 712-0505
Web Site: http://www.kelowna.mercedes-benz.ca
Year Founded: 1997
New & Used Car Dealers
N.A.I.C.S.: 441110
Lance Bremner *(Mgr-Parts)*

KELSIAN GROUP LIMITED
Level 3 26 Flinders Street, Adelaide, 5000, SA, Australia
Tel.: (61) 882028688
Web Site: https://www.kelsian.com
KLS—(ASX)
Rev: $1,346,705,377
Assets: $1,602,262,162
Liabilities: $983,018,115
Net Worth: $619,244,047
Earnings: $38,732,926
Emp.: 12,500
Fiscal Year-end: 06/30/24
Tourism & Transportation Services
N.A.I.C.S.: 561599
Jeffrey R. Ellison *(Chm)*

Subsidiaries:

All Aboard America! Holdings Inc. (1)
230 S Country Club Dr, Mesa, AZ 85210
Tel.: (480) 962-6202
Web Site: http://www.allaboardamerica.com

KELSIAN GROUP LIMITED

Kelsian Group Limited—(Continued)
Sales Range: $10-24.9 Million
Emp.: 110
Bus & Other Motor Vehicle Transit Systems
N.A.I.C.S.: 485113

Kangaroo Island Sealink Pty Ltd. (1)
440 King William Street, Adelaide, 5000, SA, Australia
Tel.: (61) 8 8202 8688
Web Site: http://www.sealink.com.au
Emp.: 500
Tourism & Transportation Services
N.A.I.C.S.: 488390
Jass Ellison (Mng Dir)

KELSO GROUP HOLDINGS PLC
Eastcastle House 27-28 Eastcastle Street, Radbourne, London, W1W 8DH, United Kingdom
Tel.: (44) 1327317627   UK
Web Site: https://www.kelsoplc.com
Year Founded: 2018
KLSO—(LSE)
Assets: $431,680
Liabilities: $55,791
Net Worth: $375,889
Earnings: ($365,216)
Fiscal Year-end: 12/31/22
Holding Company
N.A.I.C.S.: 551112

KELSO PLACE ASSET MANAGEMENT LLP
3 Barrett Street St Christopher's Place, London, W1U 1AY, United Kingdom
Tel.: (44) 2078360000
Web Site: http://www.kelsoplace.com
Year Founded: 2000
Sales Range: $10-24.9 Million
Emp.: 11
Investment Management Service
N.A.I.C.S.: 523940
Sion Kearsey (Founder & Mng Partner)

Subsidiaries:

MDNX Group Ltd. (1)
St James House Oldbury, Southern Industrial Estate, Bracknell, RG12 8TH, United Kingdom
Tel.: (44) 1344 543 700
Web Site: http://www.mdnx.com
Managed Networks & Cloud Services
N.A.I.C.S.: 541519
Andrew Janes (Mgr-HR)

Branch (Domestic):

MDNX (2)
St James House, Oldbury, Bracknell, RG12 8TH, Berkshire, United Kingdom
Tel.: (44) 8445831111
Web Site: http://www.mdnx.com
Sales Range: $25-49.9 Million
Communication System Consulting & Design Services
N.A.I.C.S.: 517112
Karlton Jarvis (Dir-Sls & Acct Dev)

KELSO TECHNOLOGIES INC.
13966 - 18B Avenue, Surrey, V4A 8J1, BC, Canada
Tel.: (903) 583-9200   BC
Web Site: https://www.kelsotech.com
Year Founded: 1987
KIQ—(NYSEAMEX)
Rev.: $10,931,188
Assets: $12,147,143
Liabilities: $1,365,471
Net Worth: $10,781,672
Earnings: ($1,355,417)
Emp.: 38
Fiscal Year-end: 12/31/22
Pressure Valve Mfr
N.A.I.C.S.: 332919
Richard Lee (CFO)

Subsidiaries:

KIQ X Industries Inc. (1)
1130 Stevens Road, Kelowna, V1Z 1G1, BC, Canada
Tel.: (250) 762-5008
Web Site: https://www.kxiwildertec.com
Vehicle Suspension Mfr
N.A.I.C.S.: 336330

Kelso Technologies (USA) Inc. (1)
1526 Texas Ave, Bonham, TX 75418
Tel.: (903) 583-9200
Railway Equipment Distr
N.A.I.C.S.: 423860
Amanda Smith (VP-Ops)

KELT EXPLORATION LTD.
Suite 300 East Tower 311 Sixth Avenue SW, Calgary, T2P 3H2, AB, Canada
Tel.: (403) 294-0154   AB
Web Site: https://www.keltexploration.com
Year Founded: 2012
KEL—(TSX)
Rev.: $226,351,936
Assets: $714,610,433
Liabilities: $149,237,902
Net Worth: $565,372,531
Earnings: $89,380,184
Emp.: 70
Fiscal Year-end: 12/31/21
Oil & Gas Exploration
N.A.I.C.S.: 211120
David John Wilson (Pres & CEO)

Subsidiaries:

Kelt Exploration (LNG) Ltd. (1)
Suite 300 East Tower 311 Sixth Avenue SW, Calgary, T2P 3H2, AB, Canada   (100%)
Tel.: (403) 294-0154
Web Site: http://www.keltexploration.com
Emp.: 50
Oil & Gas Exploration Services
N.A.I.C.S.: 211120

KELTEC PEOPLE
25 Rubislaw Terrace, Aberdeen, AB10 1XE, United Kingdom
Tel.: (44) 1224636555
Web Site: http://www.keltecpeople.com
Sales Range: $25-49.9 Million
Emp.: 14
Recruitment Services
N.A.I.C.S.: 541612
Julie Jamieson (Mgr-Admin)

KELVIN ELECTRIC TRADING CO., LTD.
Unit G 2/F Superluck Industrial Center Phase 2 57 Sha Tsui Road, Tsuen Wan, China (Hong Kong)
Tel.: (852) 24211210
Web Site: http://www.kelvinelectric.com
Year Founded: 1987
Emp.: 15
Household Appliance Distr
N.A.I.C.S.: 423620
Jack Fung (Mgr-Admin)

KELWAY LIMITED
3rd Floor 10 Fleet Place, London, EC4M 7RB, United Kingdom
Tel.: (44) 207 791 6000
Web Site: http://www.kelway.com
Year Founded: 1990
Sales Range: $10-24.9 Million
Emp.: 70
Information Technology Support Services
N.A.I.C.S.: 518210
Phil Doye (CEO)

Subsidiaries:

Kelway APAC (1)
8 Cross Street 10-00 PwC Building, Singapore, 48424, Singapore
Tel.: (65) 68086091
Information Technology Consulting Services
N.A.I.C.S.: 541512

Kelway Africa (1)
5th Floor Mariendahl House Newlands on Main, Claremont, Cape Town, South Africa
Tel.: (27) 218169000
Information Technology Consulting Services
N.A.I.C.S.: 541512

Kelway Australia Pty Ltd (1)
Level 26 1 Bligh Street, Sydney, 2000, NSW, Australia
Tel.: (61) 282268798
Information Technology Consulting Services
N.A.I.C.S.: 541512

Kelway FZ LLC (1)
1910 Shatha Tower, PO Box 500833, Dubai Media City, Dubai, United Arab Emirates
Tel.: (971) 44348078
Information Technology Consulting Services
N.A.I.C.S.: 541512

Kelway Ireland (1)
Unit F6 Centrepoint Business Park Oak Road, Dublin, Ireland
Tel.: (353) 14608899
Information Technology Consulting Services
N.A.I.C.S.: 541512

KEMETYL AB
Rorvagen 7, 13650, Jordbro, Sweden
Tel.: (46) 850410100   SE
Web Site: http://www.kemetyl.com
Year Founded: 1918
Car Care, Home & Leisure Chemical Products Mfr
N.A.I.C.S.: 325998
Ola Tengroth (Owner & CEO)

Subsidiaries:

Kemetyl Belgium nv (1)
Lochtemanweg 42, 3580, Beringen, Belgium
Tel.: (32) 11 45 08 00
Web Site: http://www.kemetyl.be
Chemical Products Mfr
N.A.I.C.S.: 325180
Jean-Paul Hendricks (Sls Dir-Kemetyl Professional Benelux)

Kemetyl Kimya Sanayi ve Ticaret Limited Sirketii (1)
Atasehir Bulvari Gardenya Konut 7/1 Kat 18 Daire 108, Atasehir, Istanbul, Turkiye
Tel.: (90) 216 4551641
Web Site: http://www.kemetyl.com
Chemical Products Mfr
N.A.I.C.S.: 325180
Suleyman Mahir Durukan (Gen Mgr)

Kemetyl Nederland B.V. (1)
Industrieweg 30, 3762 EK, Soest, Netherlands
Tel.: (31) 35 601 28 90
Web Site: http://www.kemetyl.nl
Chemical Products Mfr
N.A.I.C.S.: 325180

Kemetyl Norway AS (1)
Rosenholmveien 25, 1414, Trollasen, Norway
Tel.: (47) 6498 0800
Web Site: http://www.kemetyl.no
Chemical Products Mfr
N.A.I.C.S.: 325180

Kemetyl Polska Sp.z.o.o. (1)
Jerozolimskie Business Park Al Jerozolimskie 146 Budynek C, 02-305, Warsaw, Poland
Tel.: (48) 22 822 53 90
Web Site: http://www.kemetyl.com
Chemical Products Mfr
N.A.I.C.S.: 325180

Kemetyl UK Limited (1)
Office 401 Index House St Georges Lane, Ascot, SL5 7ET, United Kingdom
Tel.: (44) 1344371048
Web Site: http://www.kemetyl.com
Chemical Products Mfr
N.A.I.C.S.: 325180

INTERNATIONAL PUBLIC

KEMFLO INTERNATIONAL CO. LTD
No 3 Huan East Street Da Zhou Pingtung Export Processing Zone, Ping-tung, 900, Taiwan
Tel.: (886) 8 7524736
Web Site: http://www.kemflo.net
Year Founded: 1981
Plastics Product Mfr
N.A.I.C.S.: 326199

Subsidiaries:

Yakima Products Inc. (1)
15025 SW Koll Pkwy, Beaverton, OR 97006-6056
Tel.: (971) 249-7500
Web Site: http://www.yakima.com
Sales Range: $25-49.9 Million
Emp.: 55
Automotive Sports Equipment Racks & Carrier Systems
N.A.I.C.S.: 336390
Jason McGibbon (Global Sr Dir-SIS)

KEMIMEDI CO., LTD.
5 Saneopdanji 2-gil, Pungsan-eup, Andong, Korea (South)
Tel.: (82) 234439252
Cannabis Product Mfr
N.A.I.C.S.: 325411
Gun-Sub Choi (CEO)

KEMIN RESOURCES PLC
28 Eccleston Square, London, SW1V 1NZ, United Kingdom
Tel.: (44) 207 932 2455
Web Site: http://www.keminresources.com
Assets: $3,397,084
Liabilities: $7,432,302
Net Worth: ($4,035,218)
Earnings: ($652,974)
Emp.: 7
Fiscal Year-end: 12/31/17
Gold Mining & Exploration Services
N.A.I.C.S.: 212220

KEMIRA OYJ
Energiakatu 4, PO Box 330, 00101, Helsinki, Finland
Tel.: (358) 108611   FI
Web Site: https://www.kemira.com
Year Founded: 1920
KEMIRA—(HEL)
Rev.: $2,984,650,872
Assets: $3,237,515,260
Liabilities: $1,858,967,600
Net Worth: $1,378,547,660
Earnings: $130,463,690
Emp.: 5,062
Fiscal Year-end: 12/31/19
Holding Company; Chemical Producer
N.A.I.C.S.: 551112
Jukka Hakkila (Deputy CEO, Member-Mgmt Bd & Gen Counsel)

Subsidiaries:

Kemira (Asia) Co., Ltd. (1)
Chemical Products Mfr
N.A.I.C.S.: 325998

Kemira (Thailand) Co., Ltd. (1)
No 283/61-63 Home Place Office Building 12th Floor Soi Sukhumvit 55, Thonglor Klongtonnur Sub-district Wattana District, Bangkok, 10110, Thailand
Tel.: (66) 27299299
Chemical Products Mfr
N.A.I.C.S.: 325998

Kemira Argentina S.A. (1)
Bernardo de Irigoyen 380 Piso 8, C1072AAF, Buenos Aires, Argentina
Tel.: (54) 1143429211
Chemical Products Distr
N.A.I.C.S.: 424690

Kemira Australia Pty. Ltd. (1)

AND PRIVATE COMPANIES

KEMIRA OYJ

15 Conquest Way, Hallam, 3803, VIC, Australia
Tel.: (61) 397023422
Chemical Products Distr
N.A.I.C.S.: 424690

Kemira Cell sp. z.o.o (1)
ul I Armii Wojska Polskiego 21, 07-401, Ostroleka, Poland
Tel.: (48) 297691094
Web Site: http://www.kemira.com
Sales Range: $25-49.9 Million
Emp.: 13
Chemical Products Mfr
N.A.I.C.S.: 325180

Kemira Chemicals Brasil (1)
Av Alfredo Egidio de Souza Aranha 100 Bloco D - 6 andar, Chacara Santo Antonio, Sao Paulo, 04726-170, SP, Brazil
Tel.: (55) 1121894900
Web Site: http://www.kemira.com
Industrial Chemicals Mfr
N.A.I.C.S.: 424690

Kemira Chemicals Canada Inc. (1)
321 Welland Avenue, Saint Catharines, L2R 2R2, ON, Canada
Tel.: (514) 457-0000
Chemical Products Mfr
N.A.I.C.S.: 325998

Kemira Chemicals Germany GmbH (1)
Main Airport Center 7 OG Unterschweinstiege 2-14, 60549, Frankfurt am Main, Germany
Tel.: (49) 692561280
Chemical Products Mfr
N.A.I.C.S.: 325998

Kemira Chemicals Oy (1)
Tel.: (358) 108611
Web Site: http://www.kemira.com
Sales Range: $450-499.9 Million
Emp.: 1,487
Mfr of Industrial, Water & Specialty Chemicals; Atmospheric Gases
N.A.I.C.S.: 325998

Subsidiary (Non-US):

AS Kemivesi (2)
Gaasi tee 7 Lehmja kula Rae vald, 75306, Harjumaa, Estonia
Tel.: (372) 6014206
Sales Range: $25-49.9 Million
Chemical Distr
N.A.I.C.S.: 424690

Subsidiary (Domestic):

Finnish Chemicals Oy (2)
Harmajantie 3, PO Box 07, FI-32741, Aetsa, Finland
Tel.: (358) 2043111
Web Site: http://www.finnishchemicals.com
Sales Range: $250-299.9 Million
Emp.: 200
Fine Chemicals & Chemical Products for the Forest Products Industry
N.A.I.C.S.: 325998

Subsidiary (US):

Finnchem USA Inc. (3)
191 Wateree Station Rd, Eastover, SC 29044
Tel.: (803) 353-8787
Sales Range: $25-49.9 Million
Sodium Chlorate Producer
N.A.I.C.S.: 325998
Raul C. Aizcorbe Jr. *(VP & Gen Mgr)*

Plant (Domestic):

Finnchem USA, Inc. - Augusta Sodium Chlorate Plant (4)
2360 Doug Barnard Pkwy, Augusta, GA 30906
Tel.: (706) 790-9396
Web Site: http://www.kemira.com
Sodium Chlorate Mfr
N.A.I.C.S.: 325199

Subsidiary (Non-US):

Kemifloc A.S. (2)
Web Site: http://www.kemifloc.cz

Sales Range: $25-49.9 Million
Emp.: 35
Chemicals Mfr
N.A.I.C.S.: 325998

Kemipol Sp. z o.o. (2)
ul Kuznicka 6, 72-010, Police, Poland (51%)
Tel.: (48) 913173220
Web Site: http://www.kemipol.com.pl
Sales Range: $25-49.9 Million
Chemicals
N.A.I.C.S.: 325998

Kemira Chemicals (Shanghai) Co. Ltd. (2)
9F Building A6 Modern Service Parks No 1528 Gu Mei Road, Xu Hui District, Shanghai, 200233, China
Tel.: (86) 2160375999
Web Site: http://www.kemira.com
Sales Range: $25-49.9 Million
Emp.: 30
Chemical Products Distr
N.A.I.C.S.: 424690

Kemira Chemicals (UK) Ltd. (2)
Bowling Park Drive, Bradford, BD4 7TT, West Yorkshire, United Kingdom
Tel.: (44) 1274517200
Web Site: http://www.kemira.com
Dry Polyacrylamide Mfr
N.A.I.C.S.: 325998

Plant (Domestic):

Kemira Chemicals (UK) Ltd - Bradford Dry Polyacrylamide Manufacturing Plant (3)
Bowling Park Drive, Bradford, BD4 7TT, West Yorkshire, United Kingdom
Tel.: (44) 1274733891
Specialty Chemicals Mfr
N.A.I.C.S.: 325998

Kemira Chemicals (UK) Ltd - Ellesmere Port Water Treatment Plant (3)
c/o Innospec Business Park Oil Sites Road, Ellesmere Port, CH65 4EY, Cheshire, United Kingdom
Tel.: (44) 1513485893
Specialty Chemicals Mfr
N.A.I.C.S.: 325998

Subsidiary (Non-US):

Kemira Chemicals (Yanzhou) Co., Ltd (2)
West Side of West Beizhan Rd, Yanzhou, 272117, Shandong, China
Tel.: (86) 537 312 2752
Web Site: http://www.kemira.com
Sales Range: $50-74.9 Million
Chemical Products Mfr
N.A.I.C.S.: 325180

Kemira Chemicals AS (2)
Oraveien 14, 1630, Fredrikstad, Norway
Tel.: (47) 69 358 585
Sales Range: $25-49.9 Million
Emp.: 40
Water Treatment Chemical Mfr
N.A.I.C.S.: 325998

Kemira Chemicals B.V. (2)
Moezelweg 151, PO Box 1015, NL 3180 AA, Rozenburg, Netherlands
Tel.: (31) 181282211
Sales Range: $25-49.9 Million
Emp.: 65
N.A.I.C.S.: 424690

Kemira Chemicals India Private Limited (2)
2nd Floor GHB House Plot No 264/A/2 Road No 10, Jubilee Hills, Hyderabad, 500 033, India
Tel.: (91) 402 355 7082
Emp.: 1
Chemical Products Distr
N.A.I.C.S.: 424690
Kothandaraman Venkatesan *(Gen Mgr)*

Kemira Chemicals Korea Corporation (2)
1631-1 Soryong-dong, Gunsan, 573-400, Jeollabuk-do, Korea (South)
Tel.: (82) 634686363
Chemical Products Mfr
N.A.I.C.S.: 325998

Plant (Domestic):

Kemira Chemicals Oy - Vaasa Paper Chemicals Plant (2)
Kruunantie 36, PO Box 500, 65101, Vaasa, Finland
Tel.: (358) 10 8611
Specialty Chemicals Mfr
N.A.I.C.S.: 325998

Subsidiary (Non-US):

Kemira Chemicals S.A./N.V. (2)
Botlekweg 175, 2630, Rotterdam, Netherlands
Tel.: (31) 3 870 5120
Emp.: 200
Chemical Products Distr
N.A.I.C.S.: 424690

Subsidiary (US):

Kemira Chemicals, Inc. (2)
1000 Parkwood Cir Ste 500, Atlanta, GA 30339
Tel.: (770) 436-1542
Web Site: http://www.kemira.com
Sales Range: $50-74.9 Million
Mfr of Specialty Inorganic Chemicals
N.A.I.C.S.: 325199

Plant (Non-US):

Kemira Chemicals, Inc. - St. Catharines Plant (3)
321 Welland Avenue, PO Box 160, Saint Catharines, L2R 2R2, ON, Canada
Tel.: (514) 457-0000
Web Site: http://www.kemira.com
Sales Range: $25-49.9 Million
Emp.: 20
Specialty Paper Chemicals Mfr
N.A.I.C.S.: 325998

Kemira Chemicals, Inc. - Vancouver Paper Chemicals Plant (3)
1035 Derwent Way, Delta, V3M 5R4, BC, Canada
Tel.: (604) 519-2110
Web Site: http://www.kemira.com
Sales Range: $25-49.9 Million
Emp.: 10
Paper Product Chemicals Mfr
N.A.I.C.S.: 325998

Subsidiary (Non-US):

Kemira Water Solutions, Inc. (3)
Tel.: (863) 533-5990
Web Site: http://www.kemiron.com
Mfr of Water Treatment Chemicals
N.A.I.C.S.: 325998

Plant (Domestic):

Kemira Water Solutions, Inc. - Baltimore Water Treatment Chemicals Plant (4)
3925 Fort Armistead Rd, Baltimore, MD 21226
Tel.: (410) 354-3003
Web Site: http://www.kemira.com
Chemical Products Mfr
N.A.I.C.S.: 325998

Kemira Water Solutions, Inc. - East Chicago Water Treatment Chemicals Plant (4)
3761 Canal St, East Chicago, IN 46312
Tel.: (219) 397-2646
Web Site: http://www.kemira.com
Water Treatment Chemical Mfr
N.A.I.C.S.: 325998

Kemira Water Solutions, Inc. - Fontana Water Treatment Chemicals Plant (4)
14000 E San Bernardino Ave, Fontana, CA 92335
Tel.: (909) 429-4001
Web Site: http://www.kemira.com
Sales Range: $25-49.9 Million
Specialty Chemicals Mfr
N.A.I.C.S.: 325998

Kemira Water Solutions, Inc. - Longview Polymer Plant (4)
850 Third Ave, Longview, WA 98632
Tel.: (360) 425-6532
Web Site: http://www.kemira.com

Specialty Chemicals & Materials Developer, Marketer & Mfr
N.A.I.C.S.: 325998

Kemira Water Solutions, Inc. - Mojave Water Treatment Chemicals Plant (4)
18700 Hwy 14 N, Mojave, CA 93501
Tel.: (661) 824-2466
Web Site: http://www.kemira.com
Sales Range: $25-49.9 Million
Water Treatment Chemical Mfr
N.A.I.C.S.: 325998

Kemira Water Solutions, Inc. - Polymer Plant (4)
1 Cyanamid Rd, Mobile, AL 36610
Tel.: (251) 457-6601
Web Site: http://www.kemira.com
Chemical Products Mfr
N.A.I.C.S.: 325998

Kemira Water Solutions, Inc. - Saint Louis Water Treatment Chemicals Plant (4)
10 Bremen Ave, Saint Louis, MO 63147
Tel.: (314) 241-3951
Web Site: http://www.kemira.com
Chemical Products Mfr
N.A.I.C.S.: 325998

Kemira Water Solutions, Inc. - Savannah Water Treatment Chemicals Plant (4)
2247 Gate 2 E Presidents St, Savannah, GA 31402
Tel.: (912) 234-8605
Web Site: http://www.kemiron.com
Sales Range: $25-49.9 Million
Emp.: 52
Chemicals Mfr
N.A.I.C.S.: 325998

Subsidiary (Non-US):

Kemira Chemie GmbH (2)
Unterschweinstiege 2 - 14, Frankfurt, 60549, Germany
Tel.: (49) 618844900
Web Site: http://www.kemira.de
Sales Range: $25-49.9 Million
Emp.: 24
N.A.I.C.S.: 325998

Kemira Chemie GmbH (2)
Hafenstrasse 77, Krems, 3500, Austria
Tel.: (43) 2732711550
Web Site: http://www.kemira.com
Sales Range: $25-49.9 Million
Emp.: 110
N.A.I.C.S.: 325998

Kemira Chimie S.A. (2)
27 Avenue Franklin Roosevelt, Avon, 77210, Fontainebleau, France
Tel.: (33) 160707300
Web Site: http://www.kemira.com
Sales Range: $50-74.9 Million
Emp.: 10
Sales of Chemicals
N.A.I.C.S.: 424690

Kemira Chimie S.A.S.U. (2)
Route de Mothern Zone Portuaire, 67630, Lauterbourg, France
Tel.: (33) 388549850
Sales Range: $75-99.9 Million
Emp.: 20
Waste Treatment Services
N.A.I.C.S.: 221310

Plant (Domestic):

Kemira Chimie S.A.S.U. - Sausheim Defoaming & Deinking Chemicals Plant (3)
3 Avenue de Suisse, Sausheim, 68393, France
Tel.: (33) 3 8963 61 00
Web Site: http://www.kemira.com
Sales Range: $25-49.9 Million
Specialty Chemicals Mfr
N.A.I.C.S.: 325998

Subsidiary (Non-US):

Kemira Italy SpA (2)
Via E Majorana 8, 33058, San Giorgio di Nogaro, UD, Italy
Tel.: (39) 0431645101

KEMIRA OYJ

Kemira Oyj—(Continued)
Emp.: 16
Chemical Distr
N.A.I.C.S.: 424690

Kemira Kemi AB (2)
Industrigatan 83, PO Box 902, SE 251 09, Helsingborg, Sweden
Tel.: (46) 42171000
Web Site: http://www.kemirakemi.com
Sales Range: $10-24.9 Million
Emp.: 274
Miscellaneous Chemical Product Mfr
N.A.I.C.S.: 325998

Kemira France SAS (1)
Route de Mothern Zone Portuaire, 67630, Lauterbourg, France
Tel.: (33) 3 8854 9850
Chemical Products Distr
N.A.I.C.S.: 424690

Kemira Gdansk Sp. z o.o. (1)
Ul Grunwaldzka 411, 80-309, Gdansk, Poland
Tel.: (48) 587736000
Chemical Products Mfr
N.A.I.C.S.: 325998

Kemira Germany GmbH (1)
Innovationspark Marie-Curie-Strasse 10, 51377, Leverkusen, Germany
Tel.: (49) 214206900
Web Site: http://www.kemira.com
Sales Range: $50-74.9 Million
Emp.: 70
Chemical Products Distr
N.A.I.C.S.: 424690

Plant (Domestic):

Kemira Germany GmbH - Rheinberg Water Treatment Chemicals Plant (2)
Weststrasse 15, 47495, Rheinberg, Germany
Tel.: (49) 28439713107
Web Site: http://www.kemira.com
Sales Range: $25-49.9 Million
Emp.: 20
Specialty Chemicals Mfr
N.A.I.C.S.: 325998

Subsidiary (Domestic):

Kemira Germany Sales GmbH (2)
Innovationspark Marie-Curie-Strasse 10, 51377, Leverkusen, Germany
Tel.: (49) 214 20690 0
Web Site: http://www.kemira.com
Sales Range: $25-49.9 Million
Emp.: 50
Chemical Products Distr
N.A.I.C.S.: 424690

Kemira Iberica S.A. (1)
Gran Via De Les Corts Catalanes 641, Barcelona, 8010, Spain
Tel.: (34) 934123050
Web Site: http://www.kemiraiberica.com
Rev.: $49,015,724
Emp.: 100
Mfr of Chemicals
N.A.I.C.S.: 325998

Subsidiary (Non-US):

Aliada Quimica de Portugal Ltd. (2)
Tel.: (351) 234810300
Web Site: http://www.aqp.pt
N.A.I.C.S.: 424690

Plant (Domestic):

Kemira Iberica S.A. - Dos Hermanas Water Treatment Chemicals Plant (2)
Avda Andalucia 234, 41700, Dos Hermanas, Sevilla, Spain
Tel.: (34) 955 66 64 64
Water Purification Chemicals Mfr
N.A.I.C.S.: 325998

Kemira Iberica S.A. - Zaramillo Water Treatment Chemicals Plant (2)
Ctra Bilbao a Balmaseda Km 10 5, Alonsotegui, 48810, Vizcaya, Spain
Tel.: (34) 944 98 21 03
Web Site: http://www.kemira.com
Water Purification Chemicals Mfr

N.A.I.C.S.: 325998

Subsidiary (Domestic):

Kemira Iberica Sales and Marketing S.L. (2)
Gran Via Corts Catalanes 641, Barcelona, 8010, Spain
Tel.: (34) 934 12 30 50
Web Site: http://www.kemira.com
Emp.: 40
Chemical Products Distr
N.A.I.C.S.: 424690

Kemira International Finance B.V. (1)
Moezelweg 151, LS Europoort, Rotterdam, 3198 LS, Netherlands
Tel.: (31) 181282211
Financial Management Services
N.A.I.C.S.: 523999

Kemira Japan Co., Ltd. (1)
Suidobashi Sotobori-dori Building 2F 1-1-5 Koraku, Bunkyo-ku, Tokyo, 112-0004, Japan
Tel.: (81) 356158222
Chemical Products Mfr
N.A.I.C.S.: 327910

Kemira KTM d.o.o. (1)
Ob Zeleznici 14, 1000, Ljubljana, Slovenia
Tel.: (386) 1 520 5200
Web Site: http://www.kemira-ktm.si
Sales Range: $25-49.9 Million
Emp.: 42
Chemical Products Mfr & Distr
N.A.I.C.S.: 325180

Kemira Korea Corporation (1)
273 Hangangdae-ro, Yongsan-Gu, Seoul, 04321, Korea (South)
Tel.: (82) 269253445
Web Site: http://www.kemira.com
Sales Range: $25-49.9 Million
Chemical Products Distr
N.A.I.C.S.: 424690

Kemira Nederland Holding B.V. (1)
Botlekweg 175, Botlek, Rotterdam, 3197 KA, Netherlands
Tel.: (31) 181295800
Web Site: http://www.kemira.com
Investment Management Service
N.A.I.C.S.: 523999

Subsidiary (Domestic):

Kemira Finance Solutions B.V. (2)
Botlekweg 175, Europoort, Rotterdam, 3198 LS, Netherlands
Tel.: (31) 181282211
Sales Range: $100-124.9 Million
Emp.: 200
Financial Management Services
N.A.I.C.S.: 523999
Willem Koorneef *(Gen Mgr)*

Kemira Oyj - Harjavalta Water Treatment Chemicals Plant (1)
Rikkihappotehtaankatu 6, 29200, Harjavalta, Finland
Tel.: (358) 10 8611
Chemical Products Mfr
N.A.I.C.S.: 325180
Olli Hukari *(Branch Mgr)*

Kemira Pigments Oy (1)
Porkkalankatu 3, PO Box 330, FIN 00101, Helsinki, Finland
Tel.: (358) 0108611
Web Site: http://www.kemira.com
Sales Range: $450-499.9 Million
Emp.: 1,554
Production & Marketing of Decorative Paints & Industrial Coatings
N.A.I.C.S.: 325510

Subsidiary (Non-US):

Kemira Chile Comercial Limitada (2)
San Sebastian 2952, Las Condes, 7550050, Santiago, Region Metropolitana, Chile
Tel.: (56) 22340977
Emp.: 4
Chemical Sales
N.A.I.C.S.: 424690

Kemira Polar A/S (1)
G-Vej 3, 2300, Copenhagen, Denmark
Tel.: (45) 33136711

Sales Range: $25-49.9 Million
Emp.: 15
Chemical Products Mfr
N.A.I.C.S.: 325998

Kemira South Africa (Pty) Ltd. (1)
Tel.: (27) 114702904
Chemical Products Mfr
N.A.I.C.S.: 325998

Kemira Taiwan Corporation (1)
8F No 237 Sung Chiang Road, Taipei, 10483, Taiwan
Tel.: (886) 2 2503 0876
Web Site: http://www.kemira.com
Specialty Chemicals Mfr
N.A.I.C.S.: 325998

Kemira Teesport Limited (1)
Teesport, Middlesbrough, TS6 7SA, Cleveland, United Kingdom
Tel.: (44) 1642 463314
Sales Range: $25-49.9 Million
Emp.: 25
Chemical Products Mfr
N.A.I.C.S.: 325998
Steve Lyons *(Gen Mgr)*

Kemira Uruguay S.A. (1)
Juncal 1305 Of 1103 Plaza Independencia, 11000, Montevideo, Uruguay
Tel.: (598) 2 916 9819
Chemical Products Distr
N.A.I.C.S.: 424690

Kemira Water Danmark A/S (1)
Langebrogade 5, Copenhagen, 1411, Denmark
Tel.: (45) 33136711
Web Site: http://www.kemira.dk
Sales Range: $75-99.9 Million
Emp.: 20
Water Filtration
N.A.I.C.S.: 221310

Kemira Water Solutions Canada Inc (1)
3405 Marie-Victorin Boulevard, Varennes, J3X 1P7, QC, Canada
Tel.: (450) 652-0665
Web Site: http://www.kemirawater.ca
Water Treatment Chemicals Mfr & Distr
N.A.I.C.S.: 325998

Plant (Domestic):

Kemira Water Solutions Canada Inc. - Ottawa Water Treatment Chemicals Plant (2)
626 Oak Park Road, Brantford, N3T 5L8, ON, Canada
Tel.: (519) 759-7570
Web Site: http://www.kemira.com
Sales Range: $25-49.9 Million
Emp.: 11
Water Treatment Chemical Mfr
N.A.I.C.S.: 325998

Kemira-Swiecie sp. z.o.o (1)
ul Bydgoska 1, 86-100, Swiecie, Poland
Tel.: (48) 523330623
Emp.: 54
Pine Oil Mfr
N.A.I.C.S.: 325194

Kemwater Cristal S.A. (1)
Str Muncii Nr 14, Fundulea, 915200, Calarasi, Romania (100%)
Tel.: (40) 213112527
Web Site: http://www.kemwater.ro
Sales Range: $1-9.9 Million
Emp.: 80
N.A.I.C.S.: 424690

Kemwater Phil. Corp. (1)
Chemphil Building 851 Antonio S Arnaiz Avenue, Legaspi Village, 1299, Makati, Metro Manila, Philippines
Tel.: (63) 28174803
Web Site: https://www.chemphil.com.ph
Sales Range: $25-49.9 Million
Emp.: 10
Chemical Products Distr
N.A.I.C.S.: 424690

Kemwater ProChemie s.r.o. (1)
Upravna Vody Bradlec 253, CZ 293 06, Kosmonosy, Czech Republic
Tel.: (420) 326724034
Web Site: http://www.prochemie.cz

Sales Range: $25-49.9 Million
Emp.: 50
N.A.I.C.S.: 325998

Plant (Domestic):

Kemwater ProChemie s.r.o. - Hulice Water Treatment Chemicals Plant (2)
Provozovna Hulice, Trhovy Stepanov, 257 63, Hulice, Czech Republic
Tel.: (420) 326 724 034
Chemical Products Mfr
N.A.I.C.S.: 325998

Kemwater ProChemie s.r.o. - Kolin Water Treatment Chemicals Plant (2)
Prazska 54, 280 24, Kolin, Czech Republic
Tel.: (420) 326724034
Sales Range: $25-49.9 Million
Emp.: 3
Chemical Products Mfr
N.A.I.C.S.: 325998
Vladimir Kloucek *(Gen Mgr)*

PT Kemira Indonesia (1)
Perwata Tower Ji Pluit Selatan Raya - CBD Pluit Suite 7-E, Jakarta Utara, Jakarta, 14440, Indonesia
Tel.: (62) 2166676862
Web Site: http://www.kemira.com
Emp.: 25
Chemical Products Distr
N.A.I.C.S.: 424690

Purton Carbons Ltd. (1)
Riddle Street, Berkeley, GL13 9HN, Gloucestershire, United Kingdom
Tel.: (44) 1453511480
Web Site: http://www.cabotcorp.com
Emp.: 9
Carbon Black Distr
N.A.I.C.S.: 424990

SC Kemcristal SRL (1)
Str Labor No 51, 915200, Fundulea, Calarasi, Romania
Tel.: (40) 242642054
Web Site: http://www.kemcristal.ro
Water Purification Chemical Mfr & Distr
N.A.I.C.S.: 325998

Scandinavian Tanking System A/S (1)
G-Vej 3, Copenhagen, 2300, Denmark
Tel.: (45) 33136711
Storage Metal Tank Mfr & Distr
N.A.I.C.S.: 332420

Spruce Vakuutus Oy (1)
Porkkalankatu 3, 00180, Helsinki, Finland
Tel.: (358) 10 8611
General Insurance Services
N.A.I.C.S.: 524210

ZAO Kemira HIM (1)
Liter A 24 Yakubovicha Str, Saint Petersburg, 190000, Russia
Tel.: (7) 812 449 84 85
Web Site: http://www.kemira.com
Sales Range: $25-49.9 Million
Emp.: 18
Chemical Products Distr
N.A.I.C.S.: 424690

KEMP & COMPANY LIMITED

5th Floor DGP House 88 C Old Prabhadevi Road, Mumbai, 400 025, Maharashtra, India
Tel.: (91) 2266539000
Web Site: https://www.kempnco.com
506530—(BOM)
Rev.: $603,098
Assets: $40,469,315
Liabilities: $3,207,682
Net Worth: $37,261,634
Earnings: $114,797
Emp.: 4
Fiscal Year-end: 03/31/22
Travel Goods & Accessory Distr
N.A.I.C.S.: 424130
Shalini Dilip Piramal *(Mng Dir)*

KEMP & DENNING LIMITED

103 Melville Street, Hobart, 7000, TAS, Australia
Tel.: (61) 62300300
Web Site: http://www.kd.com.au
Year Founded: 1902
Rev.: $19,477,458
Assets: $20,747,503
Liabilities: $3,493,859
Net Worth: $17,253,644
Earnings: $9,721,658
Emp.: 260
Fiscal Year-end: 05/31/19
Fired Clay Bricks & Pavers Mfr & Timber, Building Materials, Hardware & Home-Related Products Sales
N.A.I.C.S.: 444140
Charles A. G. Kemp *(Deputy Chm)*

KEMP & LAURITZEN A/S
Roskildevej 12, 2620, Albertslund, Denmark
Tel.: (45) 4366 8888
Web Site: http://www.kemp-lauritzen.dk
Year Founded: 1882
Sales Range: $300-349.9 Million
Emp.: 2,000
Electricity, Piping, Plumbing, Ventilation & Cooling Technical Solutions
N.A.I.C.S.: 541990
Boris Norgaard Kjeldsen *(Chm)*

Subsidiaries:

Lindpro A/S (1)
Fabriksparken 58, 2600, Glostrup, Hovedstaden, Denmark
Tel.: (45) 70101617
Web Site: http://www.lindpro.dk
Sales Range: $400-449.9 Million
Emp.: 1,200
Electrical Engineering Services
N.A.I.C.S.: 238210

Venair A/S (1)
Stamholmen 110, 2650, Hvidovre, Denmark
Tel.: (45) 96142525
Electrical System Installation Services
N.A.I.C.S.: 238210

KEMPE ENGINEERING PTY. LTD.
50 Gheringhap Street, Geelong, 3220, VIC, Australia
Tel.: (61) 352252900   AU
Web Site: http://www.kempe.com.au
Sales Range: $450-499.9 Million
Emp.: 900
Holding Company; Industrial Equipment & Components Mfr & Engineering Services
N.A.I.C.S.: 551112
Grant Kempe *(Mng Dir)*

Subsidiaries:

Link Weld Engineering Pty Ltd (1)
2 Diamantina Wy, Henderson, 6166, Western Australia, Australia
Tel.: (61) 894379501
Sales Range: $100-124.9 Million
Emp.: 200
Oil & Gas Field Services
N.A.I.C.S.: 213112

KEMPER GMBH
Von Siemens Str 20, 48691, Vreden, Germany
Tel.: (49) 2564680
Web Site: http://www.kemper.de
Year Founded: 1977
Rev.: $74,527,823
Emp.: 80
Metals Mfr
N.A.I.C.S.: 332999
Gerd Kemper *(Founder)*

Subsidiaries:

KEMPER (U.K.) Ltd. (1)
Venture Court 2 Debdale Road, Wellingborough, NN8 5AA, Northamptonshire, United Kingdom
Tel.: (44) 8081782740
Welding Equipment Distr
N.A.I.C.S.: 423830
Marc Crawford *(Mgr-Sls)*

KEMPER B.V. (1)
Grevelingenweg 10, 3249 AE, Amsterdam, Netherlands
Tel.: (31) 256468137
Welding Equipment Distr
N.A.I.C.S.: 423830
Ton Bruggink *(Mgr-Intl Sls)*

KEMPER IBERICA, S.L. (1)
Av Riera Principal 8, Alella, 08328, Barcelona, Spain
Tel.: (34) 902109454
Welding Equipment Distr
N.A.I.C.S.: 423830

KEMPER India Pvt. Ltd. (1)
Plot No 52 Udyog Vihar Phase VI Sector 37, Gurgaon, Haryana, India
Tel.: (91) 1244121600
Welding Equipment Distr
N.A.I.C.S.: 423830
Jochen Kemper *(Mgr-Intl Sls)*

KEMPER sarl (1)
7 Avenue de l Europe, 67300, Schiltigheim, France
Tel.: (33) 800911832
Welding Equipment Distr
N.A.I.C.S.: 423830
Ton Bruggink *(Mgr-Intl Sls)*

KEMPER spol. s r.o. (1)
Pyselska 393, 257 21, Porici nad Sazavou, Czech Republic
Tel.: (420) 317798000
Welding Equipment Distr
N.A.I.C.S.: 423830
Miroslav Havlicek *(Mgr-Sls)*

KEMPOWER OYJ
Ala-Okeroistentie 29, Lahti, Finland
Tel.: (358) 290021900
Web Site: https://www.kempower.com
Year Founded: 2017
KEMPOWR—(HEL)
Rev.: $306,080,617
Assets: $256,560,976
Liabilities: $113,103,928
Net Worth: $143,457,047
Earnings: $36,394,129
Emp.: 737
Fiscal Year-end: 12/31/23
Electrical Product Mfr & Distr
N.A.I.C.S.: 336320
Antti Kemppi *(Chm)*

KEMROCK INDUSTRIES & EXPORTS LTD.
Village Asoj Vadodara-Halol Express Way, Tal Waghodia, Vadodara, 391 510, Gujarat, India
Tel.: (91) 2668666200
Fiberglass Reinforced Polymer Mfr
N.A.I.C.S.: 339999
Arvind Mehta *(Dir-Sls & Mktg)*

Subsidiaries:

Kemrock International FZE (1)
4EA Office No 233, PO Box 293536, Dubai Airport Freezone, Dubai, United Arab Emirates
Tel.: (971) 4 2395877
Composite Materials Mfr
N.A.I.C.S.: 322219

Top Glass S.p.A. (1)
Via dei Soldani 3, 23875, Osnago, LC, Italy
Tel.: (39) 039952231
Web Site: http://www.topglass.it
Composite Materials Mfr
N.A.I.C.S.: 326121
Alfonso Branca *(CEO)*

KEMWELL BIOPHARMA PVT. LTD.
34th KM Tumkur Road T-Begur, Nelamangala, Bengaluru, 562 123, India
Tel.: (91) 8026982400   In
Web Site: http://www.kemwellbiopharma.com
Year Founded: 1980
Biopharmaceutical Research, Development & Mfr
N.A.I.C.S.: 325412
Sanjay Lodha *(VP-Ops)*

KEN HOLDING CO., LTD.
No 5 Xinrong Road, Xinqiao Town Songjiang District, Shanghai, 201612, China
Tel.: (86) 2157681101
Web Site: https://www.ken-tools.com
Year Founded: 2000
300126—(CHIN)
Rev.: $70,591,358
Assets: $189,809,545
Liabilities: $35,966,597
Net Worth: $153,842,948
Earnings: $571,006
Emp.: 1,500
Fiscal Year-end: 12/31/23
Power Tool Mfr
N.A.I.C.S.: 333991
Mingting Wu *(Chm, Pres, Principal-Fin & -Interim & Gen Mgr)*

KEN HOLDINGS BERHAD
Level 12 Menara KEN TTDI No 37 Jalan Burhanuddin Helmi, Taman Tun Dr Ismail, 60000, Kuala Lumpur, Malaysia
Tel.: (60) 377279933
Web Site: https://www.kenholdings.com.my
KEN—(KLS)
Rev.: $4,411,217
Assets: $84,603,810
Liabilities: $11,102,011
Net Worth: $73,501,799
Earnings: $616,085
Fiscal Year-end: 12/31/22
Construction Services
N.A.I.C.S.: 236118
Hwa Moon *(Exec Dir)*

Subsidiaries:

Ken Rimba Sdn. Bhd. (1)
Jalan Sungai Rasau Seksyen 16, 40200, Shah Alam, Selangor, Malaysia
Tel.: (60) 355119233
Property Development Services
N.A.I.C.S.: 531390

KENADYR METALS CORP.
488 1090 West Georgia Street, Vancouver, V6E 3V7, BC, Canada
Tel.: (604) 687-7130   BC
Web Site: http://kenadyr.com
Year Founded: 2010
KNDYF—(OTCEM)
Assets: $979,946
Liabilities: $1,170,146
Net Worth: ($190,200)
Earnings: ($416,412)
Fiscal Year-end: 12/31/23
Investment Services
N.A.I.C.S.: 523999
Kevin Ma *(CFO)*

KENANGA INVESTMENT BANK BERHAD
Level 17 Kenanga Tower 237 Jalan Tun Razak, 50400, Kuala Lumpur, Malaysia
Tel.: (60) 321722888   MY
Web Site: https://www.kenanga.com.my
Year Founded: 1973
6483—(KLS)
Rev.: $153,034,074
Assets: $1,261,874,497
Liabilities: $1,045,403,810
Net Worth: $216,470,688
Earnings: $11,715,132
Emp.: 1,355
Fiscal Year-end: 12/31/22
Investment Banking Services
N.A.I.C.S.: 523150
Wai Leong Chay *(Mng Dir-Grp)*

Subsidiaries:

K&N Kenanga Holdings Berhad (1)
8 Floor Kenanga International Jalan Sultan Ismail, 50250, Kuala Lumpur, Malaysia (100%)
Tel.: (60) 321649080
Web Site: http://www.kenanga.com.my
Financial Investment Holding Company
N.A.I.C.S.: 551111
Bruce Yaw Huat Kho *(Exec Dir)*

Kenanga Capital Islamic Sdn Bhd (1)
Level 11 Kenanga Tower 237 Jalan Tun Razak, 50400, Kuala Lumpur, Malaysia
Tel.: (60) 21722888
Investment Banking Services
N.A.I.C.S.: 523150
Jalia Norhanim *(Asst VP)*

Kenanga Capital Sdn Bhd (1)
Level 11 Kenanga Tower 237 Jalan Tun Razak, 50400, Kuala Lumpur, Malaysia
Tel.: (60) 321722888
Web Site: https://kenangacapital.com.my
Money Lending Services
N.A.I.C.S.: 522390
Azlan Abu Rais *(CEO & CEO)*

Kenanga Funds Berhad (1)
12th Floor Menara ING, PO Box 13198, 84 Jalan Raja Chulan, 580802, Kuala Lumpur, Malaysia
Tel.: (60) 321701888
Investment Fund
N.A.I.C.S.: 524292

Kenanga Futures Sdn Bhd (1)
Level 6 10 11 12 Kenanga Tower 237 Jalan Tun Razak, 50400, Kuala Lumpur, Malaysia
Tel.: (60) 321723888
Web Site: https://www.kenangafutures.com.my
Investment Financing Services
N.A.I.C.S.: 523150
Azila Abdul Aziz *(CEO, Exec Dir & Head-Listed Derivatives)*

Kenanga Investors Berhad (1)
Ground Floor Kenanga Tower 237 Jalan Tun Razak, 50400, Kuala Lumpur, Malaysia
Tel.: (60) 321723124
Web Site: https://www.kenangainvestors.com.my
Investment Management Service
N.A.I.C.S.: 523940
Lee Sook Yee *(Chief Investment Officer)*

Subsidiary (Domestic):

Kenanga Islamic Investors Berhad (2)
Level 14 Kenanga Tower 237 Jalan Tun Razak, Kuala Lumpur, Malaysia
Tel.: (60) 321723000
Investment Banking Services
N.A.I.C.S.: 523150
Zulkifli Ishak *(CEO)*

KENCANA AGRI LIMITED
36 Armenian Street 03-02, Singapore, 179934, Singapore
Tel.: (65) 66368998
Web Site: https://www.kencanaagri.com
BNE—(SES)
Rev.: $136,366,000
Assets: $293,257,000
Liabilities: $262,679,000
Net Worth: $30,578,000
Earnings: ($283,000)
Emp.: 2,808
Fiscal Year-end: 12/31/23
Crude Palm & Kernel Oil Producer
N.A.I.C.S.: 311225
Henry Maknawi *(Chm)*

KENCOA AEROSPACE CORPORATION

KENCOA AEROSPACE CORPORATION

Kencoa Aerospace Corporation—(Continued)

172 Jongpo Sandan-ro Yonghyun-myun, Sacheon, 52537, Gyeongsangnam-do, Korea (South)
Tel.: (82) 558554130
Web Site: https://www.kencoa.com
Year Founded: 2013
274090—(KRS)
Rev.: $58,180,845
Assets: $99,515,263
Liabilities: $70,255,819
Net Worth: $29,259,444
Earnings: $2,488,388
Emp.: 333
Fiscal Year-end: 12/31/22
Aircraft Part Mfr
N.A.I.C.S.: 336413
Kenneth Minkyu Lee *(CEO)*

KENDA RUBBER INDUSTRIAL CO., LTD.
146 Section 1 Zhongshan Rd, Changhua County, Yuanlin, 510, Taiwan
Tel.: (886) 48345171
Web Site: https://www.kendatire.com
Year Founded: 1962
2106—(TAI)
Rev.: $1,126,383,292
Assets: $1,429,942,946
Liabilities: $789,849,409
Net Worth: $640,093,537
Earnings: $28,810,032
Emp.: 10,068
Fiscal Year-end: 12/31/23
Tire Mfr & Distr
N.A.I.C.S.: 326211

Subsidiaries:

American Kenda Rubber Ind. Co., Ltd. (1)
7095 Americana Pkwy, Reynoldsburg, OH 43068
Tel.: (866) 33287
Rubber Tire Distr
N.A.I.C.S.: 423120
Dave Craig *(VP)*

Kenda Rubber (Vietnam 2) Co., Ltd. (1)
Route 8 Giang, Dien Industrial Zone Trang Bom District, Dong Nai, Vietnam
Tel.: (84) 25139831713
Pneumatic Tire Mfr
N.A.I.C.S.: 326211

Kenda Rubber (Vietnam) Co., Ltd. (1)
Cho Chieu Str Ho Nai 3 Commune, Trang Bom, Don Nai Pro, Vietnam
Tel.: (84) 6139831713
Rubber Tire Distr
N.A.I.C.S.: 423120

Kenda Rubber Co., Ltd. (1)
West of Industrial Road Dalang Street Boan County, Shenzhen, 518109, Guangdong, China
Tel.: (86) 280952827
Web Site: http://www.kendatire.com
Rubber Tire Distr
N.A.I.C.S.: 423120

Kenda Rubber Industrial Co. Europe GmbH (1)
Greimelstrasse 28, Ubersee, 83236, Germany
Tel.: (49) 86425971490
Rubber Tire Distr
N.A.I.C.S.: 423120

Kenda Tire Co., Ltd. (1)
Dah Jiang Ind Park No 50 Yan Pyng Rd Tzu Tung Village, Yun-lin, 64741, Taiwan
Tel.: (886) 55845271
Rubber Tire Distr
N.A.I.C.S.: 423120
Sam Jones *(Mgr-Aftermarket Sls-North America)*

Kenda Tyre Inc. Co., Ltd. (1)
No 8 Tai An City Road Tianyu Science and Technology Park, Tianjin, 301609, China
Tel.: (86) 22595266667
Rubber Tire Distr
N.A.I.C.S.: 423120

KENDRICK RESOURCES PLC
7/8 Kendrick Mews, London, SW7 3HG, United Kingdom
Tel.: (44) 2039616086 UK
Web Site: https://www.kendrickresources.com
Year Founded: 1989
KEN—(LSE)
Assets: $1,201,713
Liabilities: $1,522,627
Net Worth: ($320,915)
Earnings: ($441,240)
Emp.: 2
Fiscal Year-end: 12/29/21
Metal Mining Services
N.A.I.C.S.: 212230
Alex Borrelli *(Bd of Dirs, Chm & CEO)*

KENDRION N.V.
Vesta Building - 5th floor Herikerbergweg 213, 1101 CN, Amsterdam, Netherlands
Tel.: (31) 850731500
Web Site: https://www.kendrion.com
Year Founded: 1859
KENDR—(EUR)
Rev.: $560,975,610
Assets: $514,353,551
Liabilities: $325,491,043
Net Worth: $188,862,508
Earnings: ($49,967,624)
Emp.: 2,753
Fiscal Year-end: 12/31/22
Electromagnetic Component Mfr
N.A.I.C.S.: 335314
Henk Ten Hove *(Chm-Supervisory Bd)*

Subsidiaries:

Amalga N.V. (1)
Bredabaan 1263-1277, B-2900, Schoten, Belgium
Tel.: (32) 3 6457788
N.A.I.C.S.: 326199

Intorq (Shanghai) Co., Ltd. (1)
No 600 Xin Yuan Road Building No 6 Zone B, Nan Hui District Lingang, Shanghai, 201306, China
Tel.: (86) 2120363810
Automotive Part Mfr & Distr
N.A.I.C.S.: 336310

Intorq India Pvt. Ltd. (1)
Plot No E-2 7 Phase 3, Chakan Industrial Area Kharabwadi Khed-Taluka, Pune, 410501, Maharashtra, India
Tel.: (91) 2135625500
Automobile Parts Mfr
N.A.I.C.S.: 336310
Aniket Gujrathi *(Mng Dir)*

Intorq US Inc.
300 Lk Rdg Dr SE, Smyrna, GA 30082
Tel.: (678) 309-1155
Automotive Part Mfr & Distr
N.A.I.C.S.: 336310

Kendrion (China) Co., Ltd. (1)
10 Huipu Road, Suzhou Industrial Park, Suzhou, 215021, China
Tel.: (86) 51283981819
Automobile Parts Mfr
N.A.I.C.S.: 336310
Telly Kuo *(Mng Dir)*

Kendrion (Donaueschingen/Engelswies) GmbH (1)
August-Fischbach-Strasse 1, 78166, Donaueschingen, Germany
Tel.: (49) 77180090
Electromagnetic Actuator Mfr
N.A.I.C.S.: 333995
Robert Lewin *(Co-Mng Dir)*

Kendrion (Linz) GmbH (1)
Estermannstrasse 27, 4020, Linz, Austria
Tel.: (43) 732776383

Automotive Part Mfr & Distr
N.A.I.C.S.: 336310
Christian Edelmaier *(Mng Dir)*

Kendrion (Markdorf) GmbH (1)
Riedheimer Str 5, 88677, Markdorf, Germany
Tel.: (49) 75449640
Automobile Parts Mfr
N.A.I.C.S.: 336390
Manfred Schlett *(Co-Mng Dir)*

Kendrion (Prostejov) s.r.o. (1)
Prumyslova 10, 79601, Prostejov, Czech Republic
Tel.: (420) 582300711
Automobile Parts Mfr
N.A.I.C.S.: 336310
Tomas Soldan *(Mng Dir)*

Kendrion (Shelby) Inc. (1)
1100 Airport Rd, Shelby, NC 28150-3639
Tel.: (704) 482-9582
Automobile Parts Mfr
N.A.I.C.S.: 336310
Rhett Cathcart *(Mng Dir)*

Kendrion (Villingen) GmbH (1)
Wilhelm-Binder-Strasse 4-6, 78048, Villingen-Schwenningen, Germany
Tel.: (49) 77218770
Electromagnetic Motor Vehicle Component Mfr
N.A.I.C.S.: 335314

Subsidiary (Non-US):

Kendrion (Eibiswald) GmbH (2)
Dr Wilhelm Binder Strasse 1 269, 8552, Eibiswald, Austria
Tel.: (43) 346 642 32 20
Web Site: http://www.kendrion.com
Sales Range: $25-49.9 Million
Motor Vehicle Electromagnetic Components Mfr
N.A.I.C.S.: 335999

Subsidiary (US):

Kendrion (Shelby) Inc (2)
1100 Airport Rd, Shelby, NC 28150-3699
Tel.: (704) 482-9582
Web Site: http://www.fascontrols.com
Sales Range: $125-149.9 Million
Emp.: 260
Mfr of Switches, Actuating Devices, Sensors & Control Components
N.A.I.C.S.: 335314

Subsidiary (Non-US):

Kendrion (Suzhou) Co., Ltd. (2)
Factory Building No 2 17 Su Hong East Road, Suzhou Industrial Park, Suzhou, 215026, China
Tel.: (86) 51283981819
Web Site: http://www.kendrion.cn
Solenoids & Electromagnetic Components Mfr
N.A.I.C.S.: 334416

Kendrion (Suzhou) Co., Ltd. (2)
Factory Building No 1 58 Yin Sheng Road, 215126 Sheng Pu District Suzhou Industrial Park, Suzhou, China
Tel.: (86) 51289185002
Web Site: http://www.kendrion.cn
Electromagnetic Component Mfr
N.A.I.C.S.: 335999

Kendrion Binder Magnete Vertriebsgesellschaft mbH (2)
Estermannstrasse 27, 4020, Linz, Austria
Tel.: (43) 732776383
Web Site: http://www.kendrion-electromagnetic.com
Electromagnetic Component Mfr
N.A.I.C.S.: 335314

Kendrion Binder Magnete s.r.l (2)
Volovatului 122, 725400, Radauti, Romania
Tel.: (40) 230560545
Sales Range: $25-49.9 Million
Emp.: 19
Motor Vehicle Electromagnetic Components Mfr
N.A.I.C.S.: 335999

Kendrion Binder Magnety s.r.o (2)
Prumyslova 10, 79601, Prostejov, Czech Republic

INTERNATIONAL PUBLIC

Tel.: (420) 582300711
Web Site: http://www.kendrion.com
Electromagnetic Component Mfr
N.A.I.C.S.: 334419

Kendrion UK Ltd. (2)
171 Huddersfield Rd Low Moor, Bradford, BD12 0TQ, West Yorkshire, United Kingdom
Tel.: (44) 1274 601111
Web Site: http://kendrion.co.uk
Electromagnetic Brakes & Clutches Mfr
N.A.I.C.S.: 335314
Peter McShane *(Mng Dir)*

Kendrion (Villingen) GmbH (1)
Wilhelm-Binder-Strasse 4-6, 78048, Villingen-Schwenningen, Germany
Tel.: (49) 77218770
Automotive Part Mfr & Distr
N.A.I.C.S.: 336390
Andreas Laschet *(Mng Dir)*

Kendrion Automotive (Sibiu) S.R.L. (1)
Str Lyon 2, 550018, Sibiu, Romania
Tel.: (40) 269505100
Automobile Parts Mfr
N.A.I.C.S.: 336310
Andra Boboc *(Mng Dir)*

Kendrion Industrial (Sibiu) S.R.L (1)
Str Lyon Nr 2 hala 3 camera 1, 550018, Sibiu, Romania
Tel.: (40) 269505100
Automobile Parts Mfr
N.A.I.C.S.: 336310
Mihai Petculescu *(Mng Dir)*

Kendrion Intorq GmbH (1)
Wulmser Weg 5, 31855, Aerzen, Germany
Tel.: (49) 5154705340
Industrial Brake System Mfr
N.A.I.C.S.: 336340
Lars Knoke *(Mng Dir)*

Kendrion Kuhnke Automation GmbH (1)
Lutjenburger Strasse 101, Malente, 23714, Schleswig, Germany
Tel.: (49) 45234020
Industrial Actuator Mfr & Distr
N.A.I.C.S.: 333995

Kendrion LINNIG GmbH (1)
Riedheimer Str 5, 88677, Markdorf, Germany
Tel.: (49) 7 544 9640
Web Site: https://www.kendrion.com
Sales Range: $50-74.9 Million
Emp.: 160
Commercial Vehicle Electromagnetic Components Mfr
N.A.I.C.S.: 335999

Kendrion Magneta GmbH (1)
Dibbetweg 31, D 31855, Aerzen, Germany
Tel.: (49) 5154953131
Web Site: http://www.magneta.de
Sales Range: $25-49.9 Million
Emp.: 48
Magnetic Clutches, Magnetic Particle Clutches & Electromagnetic Brakes Mfr
N.A.I.C.S.: 336320
Wildfried Niere *(Dir-Sls)*

Kendrion Magnettechnik GmbH (1)
August-Fischbach-Strasse 1, 78166, Donaueschingen, Germany
Tel.: (49) 7 718 0090
Web Site: http://www.kendrion-electromagnetic.com
Electromagnetic Component Mfr
N.A.I.C.S.: 334419

Kendrion Mishawaka LLC (1)
56733 Magnetic Dr, Mishawaka, IN 46545-7481
Tel.: (574) 257-2422
Web Site: http://www.kendrion-mishawaka.com
Electromagnetic Coils, Solenoids, Solenoid Valves & Actuators Mfr
N.A.I.C.S.: 334416
Corey Hurcomb *(Mng Dir)*

Linnig Brasil Acoplamentos Ltda (1)
Rua Silverio Finamore 920 Bairro do Leitao, 13290-000, Louveira, Brazil
Tel.: (55) 19 3878 4896
Web Site: http://www.linnig.com.br

Commercial Vehicle Electromagnetic Components Mfr
N.A.I.C.S.: 335999

Linnig Drive Tech. (Nanjing) Co. Ltd (1)
Qi Xia Economic Development Zone, Nanjing, 210034, China
Tel.: (86) 25 833 18 982
Web Site: http://www.kendrion.com
Commercial Vehicle Electromagnetic Components Mfr
N.A.I.C.S.: 335999

Linnig de Mexico, S.A. de C.V. (1)
Camino a Ocotitlan No 110 Col La Estacion, San Mateo Mexicalcingo, 52180, Mexico
Tel.: (52) 722 263 2735
Web Site: http://www.kendrion.com
Emp.: 40
Commercial Vehicle Electromagnetic Components Mfr
N.A.I.C.S.: 335999

Releplex AS (1)
Mureli 3, EE 0006, Tallinn, Estonia
Tel.: (372) 2531235
N.A.I.C.S.: 326199

Tian Jin Tong De Technology & Trading Co. Ltd. (1)
RM 708 No 7 Building No 251 Hong Qi Nan Road, Gong Yu, Xinyuan, China
Tel.: (86) 2223615578
Electromagnetic Actuator Mfr
N.A.I.C.S.: 333995

KENEDIX RESIDENTIAL NEXT INVESTMENT CORPORATION
2-1-6 Uchisaiwaicho, Chiyoda-ku, Tokyo, Japan
Tel.: (81) 3 5157 6011
Web Site: http://www.kdr-reit.com
Year Founded: 2011
3278—(TKS)
Sales Range: $50-74.9 Million
Real Estate Investment Services
N.A.I.C.S.: 523999
Keisuke Sato (Exec Dir)

KENEDIX RETAIL REIT CORPORATION
2-1-6 Uchisaiwaicho, Chiyoda-ku, Tokyo, Japan
Tel.: (81) 356233868
Web Site: http://www.krr-reit.com
Year Founded: 2014
34530—(TKS)
Rev.: $77,997,540
Assets: $2,140,452,180
Liabilities: $1,085,995,020
Net Worth: $1,054,457,160
Earnings: $29,780,220
Fiscal Year-end: 09/30/19
Real Estate Related Services
N.A.I.C.S.: 531390
Moyuru Watanabe (Exec Dir)

KENGOO GROUP CO., LTD.
World Sannomiya Bldg 5/F 3-2-17 Isobe-dori, Chuo-ku, Kobe, 651-0084, Hyogo, Japan
Tel.: (81) 78 262 6002   JP
Web Site: http://www.kengoois.com
Year Founded: 2001
Investment Holding Company
N.A.I.C.S.: 551112
Jianhao Zheng (Founder & Chm)

Subsidiaries:

M.H. Group Ltd. (1)
1-11-1 Sendagaya, Shibuya-ku, Tokyo, 151-0051, Japan   **(50.8%)**
Tel.: (81) 354117222
Web Site: https://www.mhgroup.co.jp
Rev.: $11,674,940
Assets: $11,550,540
Liabilities: $8,054,900
Net Worth: $3,495,640
Earnings: $74,640
Emp.: 237

Fiscal Year-end: 06/30/2024
Hair Salon Management Services
N.A.I.C.S.: 561110
Katsumi Hanzawa (Pres, Mng Dir & Dir-Res)

KENKO MAYONNAISE CO., LTD.
3-8-13 Takaido-Higashi, Suginami-ku, Tokyo, 168-0072, Japan
Tel.: (81) 359627777
Web Site: https://kenkomayo.com
Year Founded: 1958
2915—(TKS)
Rev.: $586,465,640
Assets: $445,315,700
Liabilities: $187,671,120
Net Worth: $257,644,580
Earnings: $18,078,350
Emp.: 3,075
Fiscal Year-end: 03/31/24
Mayonnaise, Dressings & Sauces Mfr & Distr
N.A.I.C.S.: 311941
Takashi Sumii (Pres)

Subsidiaries:

Aizu Wakamatsu Factory of Kantoh Diet Egg Co., Ltd. (1)
535-3 Aza Funagamori-higashi Oaza Tsuruga, Ikkicho, Aizuwakamatsu, 965-0006, Fukushima, Japan
Tel.: (81) 242222545
Sauce Product Mfr & Distr
N.A.I.C.S.: 311941

Dietcook Shiraoi Co., Ltd. (1)
68-11 Aza Ishiyama, Shiraoi-cho Shiraoi-gun, Hokkaido, 059-0921, Japan
Tel.: (81) 144832111
Sauce Product Mfr & Distr
N.A.I.C.S.: 311941

Dietcook Supply Co., Ltd. (1)
3-23-16 Akebono-cho, Fukuyama, 721-0952, Hiroshima, Japan
Tel.: (81) 849575775
Sauce Product Mfr & Distr
N.A.I.C.S.: 311941

Higashi Murayama Factory of Kantoh Diet Egg Co., Ltd. (1)
2-44-3 Aoba-cho, Higashimurayama, 189-0002, Tokyo, Japan
Tel.: (81) 423953381
Sauce Product Mfr & Distr
N.A.I.C.S.: 311941

Kanagawa Factory of Kantoh Dietcook Co., Ltd. (1)
2880-6 Aza Kantamoe Koudu, Odawara, 256-0812, Kanagawa, Japan
Tel.: (81) 465470050
Sauce Product Mfr & Distr
N.A.I.C.S.: 311941

Kansai Dietcook Co., Ltd. (1)
5 Shiroyama Cho, in Ayabe Industrial park, Ayabe, 623-0003, Kyoto, Japan
Tel.: (81) 773433009
Sauce Product Mfr & Distr
N.A.I.C.S.: 311941

Kyushu Dietcook Co., Ltd. (1)
6-9-6 Takagise-nishi, Saga, 849-0921, Japan
Tel.: (81) 952315561
Sauce Product Mfr & Distr
N.A.I.C.S.: 311941

PT. Intan Kenkomayo Indonesia (1)
Jl Tipar Cakung No 49 RT 3/RW 7 Cakung Bar, Kec Cakung Kota Daerah Khusus Ibukota, Jakarta Timur, 13910, Jakarta, Indonesia
Tel.: (62) 2146823262
Web Site: https://www.intankenkoindonesia.co.id
Sauce Product Mfr & Distr
N.A.I.C.S.: 311941

Tokorozawa Factory of Kantoh Dietcook Co., Ltd. (1)
504-2 Kamitomi, Miyoshimachi Iruma-gun, Saitama, 354-0045, Japan
Tel.: (81) 492571113

Sauce Product Mfr & Distr
N.A.I.C.S.: 311941

KENLY PRECISION INDUSTRIAL CO., LTD.
4 Industrial 5th Road, Pingchen Industrial District Hsien, Taoyuan, Taiwan
Tel.: (886) 34696175
5383—(TPE)
Rev.: $50,641,653
Assets: $61,144,202
Liabilities: $35,466,029
Net Worth: $25,678,173
Earnings: $1,543,633
Fiscal Year-end: 12/31/22
Electronic Product Distr
N.A.I.C.S.: 449210
Yung-Chang Chao (Pres)

Subsidiaries:

Jiaxing Kenly Precision Electronic Co., Ltd. (1)
518 Linjin Road, Lindai Town, Jiaxing, 314202, Zhejiang, China
Tel.: (86) 57385627201
Web Site: https://www.kenly.com.cn
Electronic Equipment Mfr & Distr
N.A.I.C.S.: 335999

KENMARE RESOURCES PLC
4th Floor Styne House Hatch Street Upper, Dublin, 2, Ireland
Tel.: (353) 16710411   IE
Web Site: https://www.kenmareresources.com
Year Founded: 1972
KMR—(ISE)
Rev.: $525,990,000
Assets: $1,248,830,000
Liabilities: $145,300,000
Net Worth: $1,103,530,000
Earnings: $206,030,000
Fiscal Year-end: 12/31/22
Commercial Ores Mining & Exploration Services
N.A.I.C.S.: 212290
Tony McCluskey (Dir-Fin)

KENNEDE ELECTRONICS MANUFACTURING CO., LTD.
No 21Jintong Road Tangxia Town, Pengjiang District, Jiangmen, Guangdong, China
Tel.: (86) 3500285101
Web Site: https://www.kennede.com
002723—(SSE)
Rev.: $242,090,316
Assets: $374,889,060
Liabilities: $200,324,124
Net Worth: $174,564,936
Earnings: $1,406,808
Emp.: 2,000
Fiscal Year-end: 12/31/22
Lighting Products & Fans Mfr
N.A.I.C.S.: 335131

KENNEDY FORD SALES LIMITED
280 South Service Rd W, Oakville, L6K 3X5, ON, Canada
Tel.: (905) 845-1646
Web Site: https://www.kennedyford.ca
Year Founded: 1963
Sales Range: $25-49.9 Million
Emp.: 55
New & Used Car Dealers
N.A.I.C.S.: 441110
Taylor Smith (Mgr-Fin Svcs)

KENNEDYS LAW LLP
25 Fenchurch Avenue, London, C3M 5AD, United Kingdom
Tel.: (44) 20 7667 9667
Web Site: http://www.kennedyslaw.com

Year Founded: 1899
Law firm
N.A.I.C.S.: 541110
Jennifer Boldon (Partner)

Subsidiaries:

Kennedys CMK LLP (1)
120 Mountainview Blvd, Basking Ridge, NJ 07920
Tel.: (908) 848-6300
Web Site: http://www.kennedyslaw.com
Law firm
N.A.I.C.S.: 541110

KENNET PARTNERS LTD
4th Floor 21-22 Warwick St, London, W1B 5NE, United Kingdom
Tel.: (44) 20 7839 8020
Web Site: http://www.kennet.com
Year Founded: 1997
Sales Range: $100-124.9 Million
Emp.: 7
Privater Equity Firm
N.A.I.C.S.: 523999
Michael Elias (Mng Dir-London)

Subsidiaries:

Kennet Partners LLC (1)
950 Tower Ln Ste 1710, Foster City, CA 94404
Tel.: (650) 931-0940
Web Site: http://www.kennet.com
Privater Equity Firm
N.A.I.C.S.: 523999

Nuxeo (1)
181 N 11th St Ste 307, New York, NY 11211
Tel.: (888) 882-0969
Web Site: http://www.nuxeo.com
Sales Range: $10-24.9 Million
Content Management Software
N.A.I.C.S.: 513210

TreeHouse Interactive Holding, Inc. (1)
10713 S Jordan Gateway Ste 120, South Jordan, UT 84095
Tel.: (801) 501-7000
Web Site: http://www.impartner.com
Lead Generation Software
N.A.I.C.S.: 513210
Craig Flynn (Founder & Exec VP-Engrg)

KENON HOLDINGS LTD.
1 Temasek Avenue 37-02B Millenia Tower, Singapore, 039192, Singapore
Tel.: (65) 63511780   SG
Web Site: https://www.kenon-holdings.com
Year Founded: 2014
KEN—(NYSE)
Rev.: $573,957,000
Assets: $3,772,060,000
Liabilities: $1,476,142,000
Net Worth: $2,295,918,000
Earnings: $312,652,000
Emp.: 150
Fiscal Year-end: 12/31/22
Holding Company
N.A.I.C.S.: 551112
Cyril Pierre-Jean Ducau (Chm)

Subsidiaries:

OPC Energy Ltd. (1)
Migdal Azrieli Sharona 121 Menachem Begin Street, Tel Aviv, Israel
Tel.: (972) 732505600
Web Site: https://www.opc-energy.com
Rev.: $705,069,750
Assets: $3,486,116,812
Liabilities: $2,037,850,500
Net Worth: $1,448,266,312
Earnings: $46,691,531
Fiscal Year-end: 12/31/2023
Electric Power Distribution
N.A.I.C.S.: 221122
Giora Almogy (CEO)

KENONGWO GROUP US, INC.
Yangjia Group, Xiaobu Town Yuan-

KENONGWO GROUP US, INC.

Kenongwo Group US, Inc.—(Continued)
zhou District, Yichun, 336000, Jiangxi, China
Tel.: (86) 4009152178
Year Founded: 2018
KNGW—(OTCIQ)
Rev.: $7,639,624
Assets: $4,505,803
Liabilities: $2,748,046
Net Worth: $1,757,757
Earnings: $935,154
Emp.: 54
Fiscal Year-end: 12/31/22
Holding Company
N.A.I.C.S.: 551112
Jianjun Zhong *(Chm, Pres, CEO, Treas & Sec)*

KENORLAND MINERALS LTD.
1570 -1111 West Georgia Street, Vancouver, V6E 4M3, BC, Canada
Tel.: (604) 568-6005
Web Site:
 https://www.kenorlandminerals.com
Year Founded: 2016
KLD—(TSXV)
Rev.: $754,038
Assets: $37,818,099
Liabilities: $5,765,468
Net Worth: $32,052,631
Earnings: ($3,334,123)
Emp.: 14
Fiscal Year-end: 12/31/23
Gold Exploration Services
N.A.I.C.S.: 212220
Enoch Kong *(CFO)*

KENPAL FARM PRODUCTS INC.
RR 1, Centralia, N0M 1K0, ON, Canada
Tel.: (519) 228-6444
Web Site: https://www.kenpal.on.ca
Year Founded: 1976
Rev.: $21,634,210
Emp.: 65
Feed Products Mfr
N.A.I.C.S.: 212390
Meredith Ische *(Mgr-Mktg)*

KENROC BUILDING MATERIALS CO. LTD.
950 Bower Crescent, Regina, S4N 7E4, SK, Canada
Tel.: (306) 525-1415
Web Site: http://www.kenroc.com
Year Founded: 1967
Building Materials Distr
N.A.I.C.S.: 444180
Ken Sexton *(Founder)*

Subsidiaries:

Builders Choice Products Ltd. (1)
950 Bower Crescent, Regina, S4N 7E4, SK, Canada
Tel.: (306) 781-2099
Web Site: https://store.builderschoice.ca
Building Materials Distr
N.A.I.C.S.: 444180

Kenroc Building Materials Co. Ltd. (1)
1205 38th Avenue NE, Calgary, T2E 6M2, AB, Canada
Tel.: (403) 276-2262
Web Site: http://www.kenroc.com
Building Materials Distr
N.A.I.C.S.: 444180

Kenroc Building Materials Co. Ltd. (1)
45840 Rowat Avenue, Chilliwack, V2P 1J3, BC, Canada
Tel.: (604) 792-8637
Web Site: http://www.kenroc.com
Building Materials Distr
N.A.I.C.S.: 444180
Kelly Fisher *(Gen Mgr)*

Kenroc Building Materials Co. Ltd. (1)
16850 109 Ave NW, Edmonton, T5P 4Y8, AB, Canada
Tel.: (780) 452-8930
Web Site: http://www.kenroc.com
Building Materials Distr
N.A.I.C.S.: 444180
Jim Carrothers *(Gen Mgr)*

Kenroc Building Materials Co. Ltd. (1)
270 Maclennan Crescent, Fort McMurray, T9H 4G1, AB, Canada
Tel.: (780) 715-2375
Web Site: http://www.kenroc.com
Building Materials Distr
N.A.I.C.S.: 444180
Joe Glass *(Gen Mgr)*

Kenroc Building Materials Co. Ltd. (1)
1210 Chief Louis Way, Kamloops, v2h 1j8, BC, Canada
Tel.: (250) 374-1006
Web Site: http://www.kenroc.com
Building Materials Distr
N.A.I.C.S.: 444180
Chris Zacharko *(Gen Mgr)*

Kenroc Building Materials Co. Ltd. (1)
860 McCurdy Road, Kelowna, V1X 2P7, BC, Canada
Tel.: (250) 807-2555
Web Site: http://www.kenroc.com
Building Materials Distr
N.A.I.C.S.: 444180
Matt Dobson *(Gen Mgr)*

Kenroc Building Materials Co. Ltd. (1)
1975 Robertson Road, Prince George, V2N 1X7, BC, Canada
Tel.: (250) 562-7145
Web Site: http://www.kenroc.com
Building Materials Distr
N.A.I.C.S.: 444180
Eddie Green *(Gen Mgr)*

Kenroc Building Materials Co. Ltd. (1)
8319 Chiles Industrial Ave, Red Deer, T4P 1H2, AB, Canada
Tel.: (403) 309-4667
Web Site: http://www.kenroc.com
Building Materials Distr
N.A.I.C.S.: 444180
Joey Vansdal *(Gen Mgr)*

Kenroc Building Materials Co. Ltd. (1)
915 60 St E, Saskatoon, S7K 5Z7, SK, Canada
Tel.: (306) 933-1233
Web Site: http://www.kenroc.com
Building Materials Distr
N.A.I.C.S.: 444180
Cliff Omichinski *(Gen Mgr)*

Kenroc Building Materials Co. Ltd. (1)
560 Raymur Ave, Vancouver, V6A 3L2, BC, Canada
Tel.: (604) 215-1152
Web Site: http://www.kenroc.com
Building Materials Distr
N.A.I.C.S.: 444180
Kelly Fisher *(Gen Mgr)*

KENSHOO, LTD.
30 Habarzel St 6th Floor, 6158001, Tel Aviv, Israel
Tel.: (972) 37466500
Web Site: http://www.kenshoo.com
Year Founded: 2006
Sales Range: $75-99.9 Million
Digital Marketing Software
N.A.I.C.S.: 513210
Yoav Izhar-Prato *(Co-Founder, Chm & CEO)*

Subsidiaries:

Kenshoo Americas (1)
22 4th St 14th Fl, San Francisco, CA 94103
Tel.: (877) 536-7562
Digital Marketing Software
N.A.I.C.S.: 513210

Kenshoo Australia (1)
179 Elizabeth St Level 13, Sydney, 2000, Australia
Tel.: (61) 2 8316 8900
Web Site: http://www.kenshoo.com
Digital Marketing Software
N.A.I.C.S.: 513210
Michel Van Woudenberg *(Mng Dir-Asia Pacific)*

Kenshoo France (1)
27 Avenue de l'Opera, 75001, Paris, France
Tel.: (33) 01 70 38 51 69
Digital Marketing Software
N.A.I.C.S.: 513210

Kenshoo Germany (1)
Landsberger Strasse 155, 80687, Munich, Germany
Tel.: (49) 89 57959 199
Digital Marketing Software
N.A.I.C.S.: 513210

Kenshoo Hong Kong (1)
31/F Tower 1 Times Square 1 Matheson Street, Causeway Bay, China (Hong Kong)
Tel.: (852) 2506 0005
Web Site: http://www.kenshoo.com
Emp.: 8
Digital Marketing Software
N.A.I.C.S.: 513210

Kenshoo Japan (1)
1-12-1 Shibuya MarkCity 22F Dogen-zaka, Shibuya-ku, Tokyo, 150-0043, Japan
Tel.: (81) 3 4360 5538
Digital Marketing Software
N.A.I.C.S.: 513210
Yukihiko Imamura *(Mng Dir-Asia Pacific & Japan)*

Kenshoo Singapore Pte. Ltd. (1)
19 Cecil Street The Quadrant - Level 4, Singapore, 049704, Singapore
Tel.: (65) 69088189
Software Publisher
N.A.I.C.S.: 513210
Samantha Cheow *(Acct Mgr-Search & APAC)*

Kenshoo UK (1)
66-68 Margaret Street, London, W1W 8SR, United Kingdom
Tel.: (44) 20 7436 9204
Digital Marketing Software
N.A.I.C.S.: 513210

KENSINGTON AGRICULTURAL SERVICES LTD.
15 Park Rd, PO Box 307, Kensington, C0B 1M0, PE, Canada
Tel.: (902) 836-3212
Web Site:
 http://www.kensingtonag.com
Sales Range: $10-24.9 Million
Emp.: 25
Agricultural & Residential Equipment Supplier
N.A.I.C.S.: 423820

KENSINGTON COURT LIMITED
Kensington Court Fontabelle, Saint Michael, 11000, Barbados
Tel.: (246) 4297208   BB
Web Site:
 http://www.kensingtoncourt.com
Year Founded: 1975
Holding Company; Construction, Food Service & Office Equipment Products Distr
N.A.I.C.S.: 551112
Sharon Christie *(CEO)*

Subsidiaries:

H. Jason Jones & Co. Limited (1)
Kensington Court, Fontabelle, Saint Michael, BB11000, Barbados
Tel.: (246) 4297209
Web Site: http://www.hjasonjones.com
Emp.: 70
Construction & Food Service Products Distr; Aluminum Windows & Storefront Systems Mfr
N.A.I.C.S.: 423310
Sharon Christie *(CEO)*

Regional Business Systems Inc. (1)
Kensington Court, Fontabelle, Saint Michael, BB11000, Barbados
Tel.: (246) 426 1510
Web Site:
 http://www.regionalbusinesssystems.com
Sales Range: $50-74.9 Million
Emp.: 50
Software Publisher
N.A.I.C.S.: 513210
Roger Worme *(Gen Mgr)*

KENSOH CO., LTD.
448 Kamifukagawacho, Asakita Ward, Hiroshima, 739-1792, Japan
Tel.: (81) 828401001
Web Site: https://www.kensoh.co.jp
Year Founded: 1971
79390—(TKS)
Sales Range: Less than $1 Million
Sign Product Mfr
N.A.I.C.S.: 339950
Daiichiro Lin *(Pres & CEO)*

KENT FAKTORING A.S.
Askerocagi Caddesi Suzer Plaza No 6 K 4 Elmadag, Sisli, 34367, Istanbul, Turkiye
Tel.: (90) 4444568568
Web Site:
 http://www.kentfactoring.com.tr
KNTFA—(IST)
Sales Range: Less than $1 Million
Financial Consulting Services
N.A.I.C.S.: 541611
Salih Hakan Ozguz *(Chm)*

KENT INDUSTRIAL CO., LTD.
No 17 Dougong 9th Rd, Yunlin County, Douliu, Taiwan
Tel.: (886) 55575356
Web Site: https://www.kentind.com
Year Founded: 1966
6606—(TAI)
Rev.: $24,714,640
Assets: $70,880,340
Liabilities: $15,484,286
Net Worth: $55,396,054
Earnings: $3,364,793
Emp.: 400
Fiscal Year-end: 12/31/23
Machine Tools Mfr
N.A.I.C.S.: 333517

KENTICO SOFTWARE S.R.O.
Nove Sady 996/25, 602 00, Brno, Czech Republic
Tel.: (420) 770139612
Web Site: http://www.kentico.com
Year Founded: 2004
Sales Range: $1-9.9 Million
Emp.: 140
Software Development Services
N.A.I.C.S.: 513210
Dominik Pinter *(CEO)*

Subsidiaries:

Kentico Software BV (1)
Hogehilweg 19, 1101 CB, Amsterdam, Netherlands
Tel.: (31) 621877477
Software Development Services
N.A.I.C.S.: 541511
Bart Omlo *(Mgr)*

Kentico Software LLC (1)
379 Amherst St #375, Nashua, NH 03063   (100%)
Tel.: (866) 328-8998
Web Site: http://www.kentico.com
Creates Dynamic Websites, Intranets, Community Sites & e-Commerce Solutions
N.A.I.C.S.: 513199
John T. Swanson *(Dir-Global Channels)*

Kentico Software Ltd. (1)
Market House 19/21 Market Place, Woking-

ham, RG40 1AP, Berkshire, United
Kingdom (100%)
Tel.: (44) 118 324 6000
Web Site: http://www.kentico.com
Creates Dynamic Websites, Intranets, Community Sites & e-Commerce Solutions
N.A.I.C.S.: 513199
Petr Palas *(Founder & CEO)*

Kentico Software Pty Ltd. (1)
83 Mount St Level 4, Sydney, 2060, NSW,
Australia (100%)
Tel.: (61) 2 8006 1286
Web Site: http://www.kentico.com
Creates Websites, Intranets, Community
Sites & e-Commerce Solutions
N.A.I.C.S.: 541511
Wayne Jasek *(Mng Dir)*

KENTIMA HOLDING AB
Kastanjevagen 4, 24544, Staffanstorp, Sweden
Tel.: (46) 46253040
Web Site: https://www.kentima.com
KENH—(OMX)
Rev.: $5,935,355
Assets: $4,571,637
Liabilities: $1,657,816
Net Worth: $2,913,822
Earnings: $117,077
Emp.: 27
Fiscal Year-end: 12/31/22
Software Services
N.A.I.C.S.: 513210
Kent Nilsson *(CEO)*

KENTURN NANO TEC CO., LTD.
Tel.: (886) 47910271
Web Site:
    https://www.kenturn.com.tw
Year Founded: 1983
4561—(TPE)
Rev.: $34,868,555
Assets: $74,925,617
Liabilities: $39,213,238
Net Worth: $35,712,378
Earnings: $3,534,002
Fiscal Year-end: 12/31/22
Machine Tool Spindle Mfr
N.A.I.C.S.: 333517
Yeh Heng-Tsan *(Chm & Pres)*

KENTVILLE CHRYSLER DODGE JEEP
800 Park Street, PO Box 365, Kentville, B4N 3X1, NS, Canada
Tel.: (902) 678-2134
Web Site:
    http://www.kentvillechrysler.com
Year Founded: 2005
Sales Range: $10-24.9 Million
Emp.: 30
New & Used Car Dealers
N.A.I.C.S.: 441110
Shawn Baines *(Mgr-Svc & Parts)*

KENTZU STEEL SDN BHD
No 9 Jalan 2/89 B Off Jalan Enam
Jalan Chan Sow Lin, Kuala Lumpur,
55200, Malaysia
Tel.: (60) 3 92228001
Web Site:
    http://www.kentzusteel.com.my
Emp.: 60
Steel Mfrs
N.A.I.C.S.: 331210
Ooihund Hock *(Gen Mgr)*

Subsidiaries:

Kanzen Tetsu Sdn. Bhd. (1)
Lot 6109 Jalan Haji Salleh Off Jalan Meru
5-1/2 Miles Darul Ehsan, 41050, Kelang,
Selangor, Malaysia
Tel.: (60) 333927273
Web Site: http://www.kanzen-tetsu.com
Sales Range: $125-149.9 Million
Emp.: 400
Stainless Steel Pipe Mfr & Whlsr

N.A.I.C.S.: 331210

KENVI JEWELS LTD.
Shop No 121 & 122 Super Mall Complex, Ahmedabad, 380006, Gujarat, India
Tel.: (91) 7778883139
Web Site:
    https://www.kenvijewels.com
Year Founded: 2002
540953—(BOM)
Rev.: $10,584,264
Assets: $1,801,452
Liabilities: $160,041
Net Worth: $1,641,411
Earnings: $64,527
Emp.: 18
Fiscal Year-end: 03/31/23
Gold Jewelry Mfr & Distr
N.A.I.C.S.: 339910
Chirag Champaklal Valani *(Founder)*

KENYA AIRWAYS PLC
Airport North Road Embakasi, PO
Box 19002, 00501, Nairobi, Kenya
Tel.: (254) 202374747
Web Site: https://www.kenya-
    airways.com
KQ—(NAI)
Rev.: $1,356,558,748
Assets: $1,342,248,062
Liabilities: $2,376,660,587
Net Worth: ($1,034,412,525)
Earnings: ($172,495,820)
Emp.: 3,141
Fiscal Year-end: 12/31/23
Oil Transportation Services
N.A.I.C.S.: 481111
Michael Joseph *(Chm)*

Subsidiaries:

Jambojet Limited (1)
Airport North Road, PO Box 19079, 00501,
Nairobi, Kenya
Tel.: (254) 711024501
Web Site: https://www.jambojet.com
Airline Services
N.A.I.C.S.: 481111

KENYA ELECTRICITY GENERATING COMPANY LIMITED
Stima Plaza Phase III Kolobot Road,
PO Box 47936, Parklands, 00100,
Nairobi, Kenya
Tel.: (254) 20 3666000
Web Site: http://www.kengen.co.ke
Rev.: $334,908,633
Assets: $3,564,507,331
Liabilities: $1,833,619,013
Net Worth: $1,730,888,318
Earnings: $85,589,888
Emp.: 2,476
Fiscal Year-end: 06/30/17
Electric Generation & Distribution Services
N.A.I.C.S.: 221118
Rebecca Miano *(CEO & Mng Dir)*

KENYA POWER & LIGHTING COMPANY LIMITED
Colobot Rd Stima Plaza, PO Box
30099, 00100, Nairobi, Kenya
Tel.: (254) 703070707
Web Site: https://www.kplc.co.ke
KPLC—(NAI)
Rev.: $1,451,398,039
Assets: $2,688,290,561
Liabilities: $2,256,288,425
Net Worth: $432,002,136
Earnings: ($24,267,966)
Emp.: 10,018
Fiscal Year-end: 06/30/23
Electric Power Distr
N.A.I.C.S.: 237130
Benson Muriithi *(Gen Mgr-Street lighting)*

KENYA REINSURANCE CORPORATION LIMITED
Reinsurance Plaza along Aga Khan
Walk Taifa Road, PO Box 30271,
00100, Nairobi, Kenya
Tel.: (254) 254703083000
Web Site: https://www.kenyare.co.ke
KRIN—(NAI)
Rev.: $452,259,262
Assets: $484,452,905
Liabilities: $171,437,248
Net Worth: $313,015,658
Earnings: $26,780,590
Emp.: 94
Fiscal Year-end: 12/31/20
Reinsurance Services
N.A.I.C.S.: 524130
Jacqueline Njui *(Gen Mgr-Fin & Investments)*

Subsidiaries:

Kenya Reinsurance Corporation
Ltd. (1)
01 Immeuble Sayegh 3eme Etage Rue des
Jardins en face de Nice Cream, BP 7539,
Cocody Valon, Abidjan, Cote d'Ivoire
Tel.: (225) 7052095
Reinsurance Services
N.A.I.C.S.: 524130
Allou Herve *(Reg Mgr)*

Kenya Reinsurance Corporation
Uganda SMC Limited (1)
Redstone House First Floor Bandali Rise,
PO Box 34988, Bugolobi, Kampala, Uganda
Tel.: (256) 701585817
Reinsurance Services
N.A.I.C.S.: 524130
Tadeo Nsubuga *(Reg Mgr)*

KENYA TEA DEVELOPMENT AGENCY LIMITED
KTDA Farmers Building Moi Avenue,
PO Box 30213, Nairobi, 00100, Kenya
Tel.: (254) 20 3227000
Web Site: http://www.ktdateas.com
Sales Range: $10-24.9 Million
Emp.: 800
Tea Farming, Marketing & Trading
N.A.I.C.S.: 311920
Lerionka Tiampati *(Grp CEO)*

Subsidiaries:

Gatunguru Tea Factory Company
Limited (1)
PO Box 188, 10202, Kangema, Kenya
Tel.: (254) 20 2164011
Tea Mfr
N.A.I.C.S.: 311920

Greenland Fedha Ltd (1)
PO Box 30213, 00100, Nairobi, Kenya
Tel.: (254) 20 32277000
Consumer Lending Services
N.A.I.C.S.: 522291

Imenti Tea Factory Company
Limited (1)
PO Box 1800-60200, 60200, Meru, Kenya
Tel.: (254) 20 2367464
Tea Mfr
N.A.I.C.S.: 311920

Kenya Tea Packers Limited (1)
PO Box 413, Kericho, Kenya
Tel.: (254) 774020531
Web Site: http://www.ketepa.com
Tea Packing Services
N.A.I.C.S.: 561910
Paul Murithi Ringera *(Chm)*

Kimunye Tea Factory Company
Limited (1)
Forest Castle Lodge Rd, Kimunye, Kenya
Tel.: (254) 60 51426
Tea Mfr
N.A.I.C.S.: 311920

Majani Insurance Brokers Ltd. (1)
Chai Hse 5th Flr Koinange St, Nairobi, 100, Kenya
Tel.: (254) 202222925

Insurance Brokerage Services
N.A.I.C.S.: 524210

Makomboki Tea Factory Company
Limited (1)
PO Box 1735, 01000, Thika, Kenya
Tel.: (254) 202164010
Tea Mfr
N.A.I.C.S.: 311920

KEO PLC
1 Franklin Roosevelt Avenue, PO Box
50209, 3602, Lemesos, Cyprus
Tel.: (357) 25020000
Web Site: https://www.keogroup.com
Year Founded: 1927
KEO—(CYP)
Sales Range: Less than $1 Million
Beverage Mfr & Distr
N.A.I.C.S.: 424820
Costas Koutsos *(Exec VP)*

KEON CAPITAL INC.
c/o 1800 - 510 West Georgia Street,
Vancouver, V6B 0M3, BC, Canada
Tel.: (604) 288-7813 BC
Web Site:
    http://www.prosperosilver.com
Year Founded: 2008
KEON.H—(TSXV)
Assets: $17,458
Liabilities: $53,678
Net Worth: ($36,221)
Earnings: ($158,540)
Fiscal Year-end: 12/31/23
Silver Mining Services
N.A.I.C.S.: 212220
Tawn Albinson *(Pres & VP-Exploration)*

KEONG HONG HOLDINGS LIMITED
9 Sungei Kadut Street 2, Singapore,
729230, Singapore
Tel.: (65) 65641479
Web Site:
    https://www.keonghong.com
Year Founded: 1983
5TT—(SES)
Rev.: $130,433,494
Assets: $140,079,289
Liabilities: $92,349,759
Net Worth: $47,729,529
Earnings: ($37,646,536)
Emp.: 527
Fiscal Year-end: 09/30/23
Building Construction Services
N.A.I.C.S.: 236220
Ronald Ting Ping Leo *(Chm & CEO)*

Subsidiaries:

K. H. Land Pte Ltd (1)
9 Sungei Katug St 2, Singapore, 729230, Singapore
Tel.: (65) 6564 1479
Web Site: http://www.keonghong.com
Real Estate Manangement Services
N.A.I.C.S.: 531390

KEPCO PLANT SERVICE & ENGINEERING CO., LTD
211 Munhwa-ro, Naju, 58326,
Jeollanam-do, Korea (South)
Tel.: (82) 613450114
Web Site: https://www.kps.co.kr
Year Founded: 1974
051600—(KRS)
Rev.: $1,096,100,400
Assets: $1,198,071,024
Liabilities: $265,603,644
Net Worth: $932,467,380
Earnings: $76,839,525
Emp.: 6,576
Fiscal Year-end: 12/31/22
Power Maintenance Services
N.A.I.C.S.: 541990
Kim Hongyoun *(Pres & CEO)*

KEPI TECH CENTER INC.

KEPCO Plant Service & Engineering Co.
Ltd.—(Continued)

KEPI TECH CENTER INC.
Unit 2502 Prestige Tower F Ortigas Jr Road, Barangay San Antonio Ortigas Center Metro Manila, Pasig, 1605, Philippines
Tel.: (63) 26355964   PH
Web Site: http://www.kepicenter.com
Power Generating Equipment Mfr
N.A.I.C.S.: 335311

KEPLER CAPITAL MARKETS
112 avenue Kleber, 75116, Paris, France
Tel.: (33) 1 5365 3500
Web Site:
http://www.keplercapitalmarkets.com
Sales Range: $200-249.9 Million
Emp.: 800
Investment Services
N.A.I.C.S.: 523999
Laurent Quirin (CEO)

Subsidiaries:

Kepler Capital Markets, Inc.   (1)
50 California St Ste 1500, San Francisco, CA 94111
Tel.: (415) 439-5253
Investment Management Service
N.A.I.C.S.: 523999

KEPLER WEBER S.A.
Rua Do Rocio n 84 3 Andar Vila Olimpia, Sao Paulo, 04757-020, SP, Brazil
Tel.: (55) 33759800   BR
Web Site: https://www.kepler.com.br
Year Founded: 1925
KEPL3—(BRAZ)
Rev.: $44,405,949
Assets: $167,389,333
Liabilities: $51,674,402
Net Worth: $115,714,931
Earnings: $5,226,166
Fiscal Year-end: 12/30/19
Grain Storage Equipment Mfr & Whslr
N.A.I.C.S.: 332420

KEPPEL CORPORATION LIMITED
1 Harbour Front Avenue 02-01 Keppel Bay Tower, Singapore, 098632, Singapore
Tel.: (65) 62706666
Web Site: https://www.keppel.com
Year Founded: 1968
KPELF—(OTCIQ)
Rev.: $5,162,006,669
Assets: $19,887,293,072
Liabilities: $11,723,854,761
Net Worth: $8,163,438,310
Earnings: $684,585,402
Emp.: 12,245
Fiscal Year-end: 12/31/23
Holding Company; Banking Services; Energy & Engineering; Construction, Property Management, Transportation & Telecommunications
N.A.I.C.S.: 551112
Chin Hua Loh (CEO & Exec Dir)

Subsidiaries:

Acresvale Investment Pte Ltd   (1)
230 Victoria Street 06-09 Bugis Junction Tower, Singapore, 188024, Singapore
Tel.: (65) 63388111
Properties Development & Investment Services
N.A.I.C.S.: 531390

Alpha Investment Partners Japan KK
Fukoku Seimei Building 21F 2-2-2 Uchisaiwaicho, Chiyoda-Ku, Tokyo, 100-0011, Japan
Tel.: (81) 355107551
Web Site: http://www.alphaipartners.com
Emp.: 7
Real Estate Investment Services
N.A.I.C.S.: 531390

Alpha Investment Partners Ltd   (1)
230 Victoria Street 12-08 Bugis Junction Towers, Singapore, 188024, Singapore
Tel.: (65) 6433 7702
Web Site: http://www.alphaipartners.com
Sales Range: $50-74.9 Million
Emp.: 70
Real Estate Development & Investment Services
N.A.I.C.S.: 531390
Chin Hua Loh (Chm)

AsiaPac Technology Pte. Ltd.   (1)
Blk 219 Henderson Road No 05-01/02/03/04, Henderson Industrial Park, Singapore, Singapore
Tel.: (65) 62708281
Web Site: https://www1.asiapac.com.sg
Software Development Services
N.A.I.C.S.: 541511

Beijing Kingsley Property Development Co Ltd   (1)
Unit 701 Level 7 China World Tower 2 No 1 Jian Guo Men Wai Avenue, Beijing, 100004, China
Tel.: (86) 10 6505 0866
Web Site: http://www.keppelland.com
Property Development Services
N.A.I.C.S.: 531390
William Tin Kwang Tan (Gen Mgr-North China)

Bintan Offshore Fabricators Pte Ltd   (1)
50 Gul Road, Singapore, 629351, Singapore
Tel.: (65) 68637729
Offshore Engineering Services
N.A.I.C.S.: 541330
Chris Ong (Chm)

Briny Marine Services Sdn Bhd   (1)
Lot 4084 B Simpang 112 Jalan Jaya Negara, Kuala Belait, 1931, Brunei Darussalam
Tel.: (673) 333 3926
Sales Range: $25-49.9 Million
Emp.: 6
Ship Chartering Services
N.A.I.C.S.: 483212
Shah'rin Shahabuddin (Gen Mgr)

Chengdu Hillstreet Development Co., Ltd.   (1)
Unit 903 New Hope Tower 45 Ren Min Nan Lu Section 4, Chengdu, 610041, Sichuan, China
Tel.: (86) 2887026688
Property Management Services
N.A.I.C.S.: 531311

DL Properties Ltd   (1)
20 Cecil Street 07-01 Equity Plaza Raffles Place, Singapore, 049705, Singapore
Tel.: (65) 6538 1995
Emp.: 8
Real Estate Development Services
N.A.I.C.S.: 531390
Johnson Giam (Mgr)

Deepwater Technology Group Pte Ltd   (1)
31 Shipyard Road Singapore, Singapore, 629351, Singapore
Tel.: (65) 6863 7163
Marine Engineering Services
N.A.I.C.S.: 541330

Dragonland Technology Pte Ltd   (1)
31 Tannery Lane 08-01, Singapore, 347788, Singapore
Tel.: (65) 68413777
Investment Holding Management Services
N.A.I.C.S.: 523999

Estella JV Co Ltd   (1)
Saigon Centre 65 Le Loi St, Dist 1, Ho Chi Minh City, Vietnam
Tel.: (84) 8 38218000
Web Site: http://www.estella.com.vn
Property Development Services
N.A.I.C.S.: 531390

FELS Property Holdings Pte Ltd   (1)
1 Harbour Front Avenue 18-01 Keppel Bay Tower Bukit Merah, Singapore, 98632, Singapore
Tel.: (65) 68637350
Investment Management Service
N.A.I.C.S.: 523999

Garden Development Pte. Ltd.   (1)
1 Serangoon North View, Singapore, 554343, Singapore
Tel.: (65) 61009207
Web Site: http://www.gardenresidences-condo.sg
Property Management Services
N.A.I.C.S.: 531311

Glenville Estate Investment Pte Ltd   (1)
230 Victoria St 14-01/10 Bugis Junction, Singapore, 188024, Singapore
Tel.: (65) 63388111
Investment Management Service
N.A.I.C.S.: 523999

Harvestland Development Pte Ltd   (1)
230 Victoria St 14-01/10 Bugis Junction, Singapore, 188024, Singapore
Tel.: (65) 63388111
Real Estate Development Services
N.A.I.C.S.: 531390

Jiangyin Yangtze International Country Club Co Ltd   (1)
No 155 Gongyuan Road, Jiangyin, 214400, Jiangsu, China
Tel.: (86) 510 8685 5333
Golf Club Operating Services
N.A.I.C.S.: 713910

K-REIT Asia Investment Pte Ltd   (1)
230 Victoria Street 14-01 Bugis Junction Tower, Singapore, 188024, Singapore
Tel.: (65) 64337643
Sales Range: $50-74.9 Million
Emp.: 30
Investment Management Service
N.A.I.C.S.: 523999

KPSI Property Inc   (1)
Unit 3-B Country Space I Building Sen Gil Puyat Avenue, Makati, 1200, Philippines
Tel.: (63) 28921816
Sales Range: $50-74.9 Million
Emp.: 5
Property Management Services
N.A.I.C.S.: 531311

KST Maritime   (1)
23 Gul Road, Singapore, 629356, Singapore
Tel.: (65) 66684254
Web Site: https://www.kstmaritime.com
Ship Building Mfr
N.A.I.C.S.: 336611
Romi Kaushal (Mng Dir)

Kepital Management Ltd   (1)
17th Floor Hua Fu Commercial Building 111 Queens Road West, Admiralty, Hong Kong, China (Hong Kong)
Tel.: (852) 25292092
Investment Management Service
N.A.I.C.S.: 523999

Keppel Bay Pte Ltd   (1)
2 Keppel Bay Vista Marina At Keppel Bay, Singapore, 098382, Singapore
Tel.: (65) 6303 8448
Web Site: http://www.marinakeppelbay.com
Ship Chartering Services
N.A.I.C.S.: 488330

Keppel Capital Holdings Pte Ltd   (1)
1 HarbourFront Ave Level 2 Keppel Bay Tower, Singapore, 098632, Singapore
Tel.: (65) 68031818
Web Site: https://www.kepcapital.com
Asset Management Services
N.A.I.C.S.: 523999
Christina Hua Mui Tan (CEO)

Subsidiary (Domestic):

800 Super Holdings Limited   (2)
17A Senoko Way, Singapore, 758056, Singapore   (48%)
Tel.: (65) 63663800
Web Site: http://www.800super.com.sg
Sales Range: $100-124.9 Million
Waste Management & Recycling Services
N.A.I.C.S.: 562998

INTERNATIONAL PUBLIC

Yong Koh Lee (Chm)

Keppel REIT Management Ltd.   (2)
1 HarbourFront Avenue 18-01 Keppel Bay Tower, Singapore, 098632, Singapore
Tel.: (65) 68031818
Web Site: https://www.keppelreit.com
Property Management Services
N.A.I.C.S.: 531311
Kang Leng Hui (CFO)

Keppel DC Singapore 2 Pte. Ltd.   (1)
30A Kallang Place 12-01, Singapore, 339213, Singapore
Tel.: (65) 67857011
Computer Software Development Services
N.A.I.C.S.: 541511

Keppel DHCS Pte Ltd   (1)
48 Changi Business Park Central 2, Singapore, 486067, Singapore
Tel.: (65) 6260 6700
Web Site: https://www.keppeldhcs.com.sg
Heating & Cooling Equipment Mfr
N.A.I.C.S.: 333415

Keppel Energy Pte. Ltd.   (1)
1 HarbourFront Avenue 05-05 Keppel Bay Tower, Singapore, 98632, Singapore
Tel.: (65) 6278 1800
Web Site: http://www.keppelenergy.com
Sales Range: $100-124.9 Million
Emp.: 6
Electric Power Generation & Distribution Services
N.A.I.C.S.: 221118

Subsidiary (Domestic):

Keppel Electric Pte Ltd   (2)
10-01 Harbourfront Centre 1 Maritime Square, Singapore, 99253, Singapore
Tel.: (65) 62781800
Sales Range: $75-99.9 Million
Emp.: 6
Electric Power Distribution Services
N.A.I.C.S.: 221122

Keppel Sea Scan Pte Ltd   (2)
55 Gol Road, Singapore, 629353, Singapore
Tel.: (65) 6262 6100
Web Site: http://www.keppelseascan.com
Emp.: 100
Marine & Offshore Construction Engineering Services
N.A.I.C.S.: 237990

Pipenet Pte Ltd   (2)
1 HarbourFront Avenue 05-05 Keppel Bay Tower, Singapore, 098632, Singapore
Tel.: (65) 62781800
Web Site: http://www.keppelenergy.com
Sales Range: $25-49.9 Million
Pipeline Construction Engineering Services
N.A.I.C.S.: 237120

Keppel Environmental Technology Centre Pte Ltd   (1)
61 Old Toh Tuck Road, Singapore, 597656, Singapore
Tel.: (65) 64622158
Sales Range: $25-49.9 Million
Emp.: 11
Environmental Consulting Services
N.A.I.C.S.: 541620
Terence Goh (Gen Mgr)

Keppel FELS Engineering Shenzhen Co. Ltd   (1)
3rd Floor Chiwan Petroleum Building Chiwan Road No 5, Shenzhen, 518068, China
Tel.: (86) 755 26851902
Offshore Engineering Services
N.A.I.C.S.: 541330
Jong Heng Ho (Gen Mgr)

Keppel Floatec LLC   (1)
5177 Richmond Ave Ste 900, Houston, TX 77056
Tel.: (832) 699-0546
Web Site: http://www.keppelfloatec.com
Engineeering Services
N.A.I.C.S.: 541330
T. K. Das (Pres)

Keppel Hong Da (Tianjin Eco-City) Property Development Co., Ltd.   (1)
No 2018 Zhong Tian Da Dao RBO Block 13 Level 1 Unit 101 Eco-Business, Park Sino-

AND PRIVATE COMPANIES — KEPPEL CORPORATION LIMITED

Singapore Tianjin Eco-City, Tianjin, 300467, China
Tel.: (86) 2266331088
Property Management Services
N.A.I.C.S.: 531311

Keppel Infrastructure Fund Management Pte. Ltd. (1)
1 HarbourFront Avenue 02-01 Keppel Bay Tower, Singapore, 098632, Singapore
Tel.: (65) 68031818
Web Site: http://www.kepinfratrust.com
Emp.: 30
Facility Management Services
N.A.I.C.S.: 561210
Koh Ban Heng *(Chm)*

Affiliate (Domestic):

Keppel Infrastructure Trust (2)
1 HarbourFront Avenue Level 2 Keppel Bay Tower, Singapore, 098632, Singapore (22.9%)
Tel.: (65) 68031818
Web Site: http://www.kepinfratrust.com
Rev.: $1,487,408,959
Assets: $4,421,383,574
Liabilities: $3,007,227,400
Net Worth: $1,414,156,174
Earnings: ($2,097,704)
Emp.: 16
Fiscal Year-end: 12/31/2022
Infrastructure Real Estate Investment Trust
N.A.I.C.S.: 525990
Daniel Cuthbert Ee Hock Huat *(Chm)*

Subsidiary (Non-US):

IXOM HoldCo. Pty. Ltd. (3)
1 Nicholson Street, Melbourne, 3002, VIC, Australia
Tel.: (61) 3 9906 3000
Web Site: http://www.ixom.com
Industrial, Specialty & Fine Chemicals Distr
N.A.I.C.S.: 325998
Dean Draper *(CEO & Mng Dir)*

Subsidiary (Domestic):

Bronson & Jacobs Pty Ltd (4)
70 Marple Avenue, Villawood, 2163, NSW, Australia
Tel.: (61) 287172929
Web Site: http://www.ixom.com
Chemical Products Distr
N.A.I.C.S.: 424690

Subsidiary (Non-US):

Bronson & Jacobs (S.E. Asia) Pte Limited (5)
78 Shenton Way 07-02A Tower 1, Singapore, 079120, Singapore
Tel.: (65) 68625822
Web Site: https://www.ixom.com
Specialty Chemicals Distr
N.A.I.C.S.: 424690

Bronson and Jacobs (H.K.) Limited (5)
Unit 2803B 28/F Cable TV Tower 9 Hoi Shing Road, Tsuen Wan, New Territories, China (Hong Kong)
Tel.: (852) 3793 1200
Web Site: http://www.ixom.com
Chemical Products Mfr
N.A.I.C.S.: 325998

Subsidiary (Non-US):

IXOM Peru S.A.C. (4)
Av El Derby 254 Off No 1504, Lima, Peru
Tel.: (51) 16113500
Web Site: http://www.ixom.com
Emp.: 35
Chemical Products Mfr
N.A.I.C.S.: 325998
Claudia Marchini *(Gen Mgr)*

Ixom Chile S.A. (4)
Calle Dos N 9463 Loteo Industrial Americo Vespucio, Santiago, 8710031, Chile
Tel.: (56) 2 2384 8100
Web Site: http://www.ixom.com
Emp.: 8
Chemical Products Mfr
N.A.I.C.S.: 325199

Ixom Colombia S.A.S. (4)
Cra 19 N 82-85 of 301 Edificio Country Office, Bogota, Colombia

Tel.: (57) 16464700
Web Site: http://www.ixom.com
Chemical Products Mfr
N.A.I.C.S.: 325199

Subsidiary (Domestic):

Keppel Merlimau Cogen Pte. Ltd. (3)
1 HarbourFront Avenue 05-05 Keppel Bay Tower, Singapore, 098632, Singapore (51%)
Tel.: (65) 6278 1800
Web Site: http://www.kepinfra.com
Electric Power Generation Services
N.A.I.C.S.: 221112

Keppel Infrastructure Holdings Pte. Ltd. (3)
1 Harbour Front Avenue 05-05 Keppel Bay Tower, Singapore, 098632, Singapore
Tel.: (65) 62781800
Web Site: http://www.kepinfra.com
Electrical Power Equipment Mfr
N.A.I.C.S.: 335311

Subsidiary (Domestic):

Keppel Gas Pte. Ltd. (2)
1 HarbourFront Avenue 05-05 Keppel Bay Tower, Singapore, 098632, Singapore
Tel.: (65) 62770668
Web Site: https://www.keppelgas.com
Oil & Gas Services
N.A.I.C.S.: 213112

Keppel International Freight Forwarding (Shenzhen) Ltd (1)
Rm 2102 Ming Wah International Convention Centre 8 Gui Shan Road, Shekou Industrial Zone, Shenzhen, 518067, Guangdong, China
Tel.: (86) 755 2685 8291
Emp.: 8
Freight Forwarding Services
N.A.I.C.S.: 488510
Sun Shinxun *(Branch Mgr)*

Keppel Lakefront (Wuxi) Property Development Co., Ltd. (1)
Keppel Waterfront Residence Sales Gallery Northeast of West Gaolang, Road & Jinshi Road Binhu District, Wuxi, 214121, Jiangsu, China
Tel.: (86) 51085623083
Property Management Services
N.A.I.C.S.: 531311

Keppel Land Limited (1)
230 Victoria Street, 15-05 Bugis Junction Towers, Singapore, 188024, Singapore
Tel.: (65) 6338 8111
Web Site: http://www.keppelland.com
Rev.: $1,328,527,845
Assets: $11,384,300,046
Liabilities: $5,314,165,236
Net Worth: $6,070,134,810
Earnings: $524,663,938
Emp.: 3,222
Fiscal Year-end: 12/31/2017
Property Management Services
N.A.I.C.S.: 531312
Chin Hua Loh *(Chm)*

Subsidiary (Domestic):

Keppel Land (Mayfair) Pte Ltd (2)
230 Victoria Street Unit 15-05 Bugis Junction Tower, Singapore, 188024, Singapore
Tel.: (65) 63388111
Web Site: http://www.keppelland.com
Property Development Services
N.A.I.C.S.: 531390

Subsidiary (Non-US):

Keppel Land (Shanghai) Management Co Ltd (2)
1601 Park Place 36 Rd 3601 room, Shanghai, 200040, China
Tel.: (86) 2162883066
Real Estate Development Services
N.A.I.C.S.: 531390

Subsidiary (Domestic):

Keppel Land (Tower D) Pte Ltd (2)
1 Harbourfront Avenue 18-01 Keppel Bay Tower, Singapore, 098632, Singapore
Tel.: (65) 63388111

Web Site: http://www.keppelland.com
Real Estate Manangement Services
N.A.I.C.S.: 531390

Keppel Land International Ltd (2)
230 Victoria St 15-05 Bugis Junction Towers, Singapore, 188024, Singapore
Tel.: (65) 6338 8111
Web Site: http://www.keppelland.com
Emp.: 450
Property Management Services
N.A.I.C.S.: 531311

Subsidiary (Non-US):

Keppel Land Vietnam Properties Pte Ltd (2)
17 Ngo Quyen Stree Unit 04/04A 7th Floor International Centre, Hanoi, Vietnam
Tel.: (84) 4 824 1125
Property Management Services
N.A.I.C.S.: 531312

Keppel Land Watco I Co., Ltd. (2)
Floor 4 Saigon Centre 65 Le Loi Street, District 1, Ho Chi Minh City, Vietnam
Tel.: (84) 8 3 8232500
Real Estate Manangement Services
N.A.I.C.S.: 531390

Keppel Philippines Holdings, Inc. (2)
Unit 3 B Country Space I Building, 133 Sen Gil Puyat Avenue Salcedo Village Brgy Bel Air, Makati, Philippines
Tel.: (63) 8921816
Web Site: https://www.keppelph.com
Rev.: $7,827,656
Assets: $26,842,516
Liabilities: $101,817
Net Worth: $26,740,699
Earnings: $5,504,374
Fiscal Year-end: 12/31/2021
Holding Company
N.A.I.C.S.: 551112
Lory Anne P. Manuel-McMullin *(Asst Sec)*

Keppel Philippines Properties Inc. (2)
26th Floor The Podium West Tower ADB Avenue Wack Wack Greenhills East, 12 ADB Avenue Ortigas Center, Mandaluyong, 1555, Metro Manila, Philippines
Tel.: (63) 285390460
Web Site: https://www.keppelland.com.ph
Rev.: $29,307
Assets: $51,563,742
Liabilities: $1,606,849
Net Worth: $49,956,893
Earnings: ($1,820,670)
Emp.: 12
Fiscal Year-end: 12/31/2020
Investment Management Service
N.A.I.C.S.: 523999
Lock Soon Oh *(Pres)*

Subsidiary (Domestic):

Ocean & Capital Properties Pte Ltd (2)
230 Victoria Street 14-01 Bugis Junction Towers Rochor, Singapore, 188024, Singapore
Tel.: (65) 63388111
Property Management Services
N.A.I.C.S.: 531312

Subsidiary (Non-US):

PT Kepland Investama (2)
International Financial Centre Tower 2 20th Floor Jln Jend Sudirman, Kav 22-23, Jakarta, 12920, Indonesia
Tel.: (62) 215712238
Property Management Services
N.A.I.C.S.: 531311

PT Keppel Land (2)
Wisma BCA Tower II 5A Floor Jl Jend Sudirman Kav 22-23, Jakarta Selatan, Jakarta, 12920, Indonesia
Tel.: (62) 21 571 2238
Real Estate Development Services
N.A.I.C.S.: 531390
Alex Lee Ee Mal *(Pres)*

PT Sukses Manis Indonesia (2)
International Financial Centre Tower 2 20th Floor Jln Jend Sudirman, Kav 22-23, Jakarta, 12920, Indonesia
Tel.: (62) 215712238
Property Management Services

N.A.I.C.S.: 531311

Keppel Land Vietnam Co. Ltd. (1)
Level 26 Saigon Centre Tower 2 67 Le Loi Boulevard, Ben Nghe Ward District 1, Ho Chi Minh City, Vietnam
Tel.: (84) 2838218000
Web Site: https://www.keppelland.com
Real Estate Services
N.A.I.C.S.: 531210

Keppel Letourneau USA, Inc. (1)
5177 Richmond Ave Ste 950, Houston, TX 77056
Tel.: (903) 399-2619
Web Site: http://www.keppelletourneau.com
Oil & Natural Gas Services
N.A.I.C.S.: 213112
Ron MacInnes *(Pres)*

Keppel Logistics (M) Sdn Bhd (1)
Lot 38279 Jalan SU 8A Lion Industrial Park Seksyen 22, Shah Alam, 40300, Selangor, Malaysia
Tel.: (60) 3 5191 1820
Emp.: 40
Logistics Consulting Servies
N.A.I.C.S.: 541614

Keppel Logistics Pte Ltd (1)
7 Gul Circle, Singapore, 629563, Singapore
Tel.: (65) 6861 1911
Web Site: http://www.keppellog.com
Emp.: 10
Logistics Consulting Servies
N.A.I.C.S.: 541614

Keppel Marine Agencies International LLC (1)
5177 Richmond Ave Ste 1065, Houston, TX 77056
Tel.: (713) 600-8371
Marine Agencies
N.A.I.C.S.: 488330
Michael Holcomb *(Pres)*

Keppel Oil & Gas Services Pte. Ltd. (1)
1 HarbourFront Ave #18-01 Keppel Bay Tower, Singapore, 098632, Singapore
Tel.: (65) 6270 6666
Web Site: http://www.kepcorp.com
Sales Range: $50-74.9 Million
Emp.: 10
Holding Company: Oil & Gas Operations
N.A.I.C.S.: 551112

Keppel Seghers Engineering Singapore Pte Ltd (1)
108 Pasir Panjang Road 02-01 Golden Agri Plaza, Singapore, 118535, Singapore
Tel.: (65) 6267 6800
Web Site: http://www.keppelseghers.com
Environmental Consulting Services
N.A.I.C.S.: 541620
Ong Tiong Guan *(CEO)*

Subsidiary (Non-US):

Keppel Seghers Belgium NV (2)
Hoofd 1, 2830, Willebroek, Belgium
Tel.: (32) 38807700
Emp.: 11
Environmental Consulting Services
N.A.I.C.S.: 541620
Martin Bulir *(Mgr-Bus Dev & Sls)*

Keppel Seghers Do Brasil Sistemas Ambientais LTDA (2)
Rua Jerico 255 - cjs 33/35, Vila Madalena, Sao Paulo, 05435-040, Brazil
Tel.: (55) 11 3037 7416
Web Site: http://www.keppelseghers.com
Waste Water Treatment Services
N.A.I.C.S.: 562219

Keppel Seghers Environmental Engineering Technology (Shanghai) Company Ltd (2)
Unit 3389-3390 City Center of Shanghai Tower B 100 Zunyi Road, Changning District, Shanghai, 200051, China
Tel.: (86) 21 6275 2383
Sales Range: $25-49.9 Million
Emp.: 2
Environmental Consulting Services
N.A.I.C.S.: 541620

Keppel Seghers Gmbh (2)
Elisabeth-Selbert-Strasse 5, 40764, Lan-

KEPPEL CORPORATION LIMITED

Keppel Corporation Limited—(Continued)
genfeld, Germany
Tel.: (49) 2173 39286 0
Sales Range: $10-24.9 Million
Emp.: 35
Solid Waste Treatment Services
N.A.I.C.S.: 562219
Lim Heng Tai *(Gen Mgr)*

Keppel Seghers Hong Kong Ltd (2)
17 Fl Hua Su Comml Bldg 111 Queens Rd west, Admiralty, Hong Kong, China (Hong Kong)
Tel.: (852) 2821 7000
Waste Treatment Services
N.A.I.C.S.: 562211

Subsidiary (US):

Keppel Seghers Inc (2)
1235-F Kennestone Cir, Marietta, GA 30066
Tel.: (770) 421-1181
Web Site:
  http://www.keppelseghersusa.com
Sales Range: $25-49.9 Million
Emp.: 8
Environmental Engineering Services
N.A.I.C.S.: 541330

Subsidiary (Non-US):

Keppel Seghers Netherlands BV (2)
Professor Gerbrandyweg 25, Rotterdam, 3197 KK, South Holland, Netherlands
Tel.: (31) 181234300
Sales Range: $200-249.9 Million
Emp.: 30
Waste Treatment Services
N.A.I.C.S.: 221310

Keppel Seghers UK Ltd (2)
The Heath Business and Technical Park, Runcom, WA7 4QX, Cheshire, United Kingdom
Tel.: (44) 1928288238
Web Site: http://www.keppelseghers.com
Environmental Consulting Services
N.A.I.C.S.: 541620

Keppel Seghers Pte. Ltd. (1)
1 HarbourFront Avenue 05-05 Keppel Bay Tower, Singapore, 098632, Singapore
Tel.: (65) 62781800
Web Site: https://www.keppelseghers.com
Engineering & Construction Services
N.A.I.C.S.: 541330

Keppel Singmarine Brasil Ltda (1)
Rua Prefeito Manoel Evaldor de Muller 3388, Bairro Machados, Navegantes, 88-375-000, Santa Catarina, Brazil
Tel.: (55) 47 3342 6460
Web Site: http://www.keppelom.com
Ship Building Services
N.A.I.C.S.: 336611

Keppel Telecommunications & Transportation, Ltd. (1)
7 Gul Circle, Singapore, 629563, Singapore **(100%)**
Tel.: (65) 6897 7372
Web Site: http://www.keppeltt.com.sg
Rev.: $132,388,794
Assets: $1,149,840,224
Liabilities: $440,573,402
Net Worth: $709,266,822
Earnings: $41,826,475
Emp.: 1,511
Fiscal Year-end: 12/31/2017
Logistic Consulting & Telecommunication Services
N.A.I.C.S.: 541614
Thomas Hwi Pang Thieng *(CEO)*

Subsidiary (Domestic):

UrbanFox Pte. Ltd. (2)
27 Greenwich Drive Annexe Building Level 2M, Singapore, 533912, Singapore
Tel.: (65) 64767472
Logistic Services
N.A.I.C.S.: 541614

Marine Technology Development Pte. Ltd. (1)
5 Benoi Road, Singapore, 629879, Singapore
Tel.: (65) 68638344
Ship Building Mfr
N.A.I.C.S.: 336611

Anis Altaf Hussain *(Gen Mgr)*

Nha Be Real Estate JSC (1)
Ground Floor - PV Gas Tower 673 Nguyen Huu Tho Street, Phuoc Kien Nha Be, Ho Chi Minh City, Vietnam
Tel.: (84) 2873029666
Web Site: https://www.celesta.com.vn
Property Development Services
N.A.I.C.S.: 236117

Nusa Maritime Pte Ltd (1)
15 Benoi Road, Singapore, 629888, Singapore
Tel.: (65) 6861 2996
Sales Range: $25-49.9 Million
Emp.: 15
Marine Logistics Services
N.A.I.C.S.: 488390
How Jat Chor *(Chm-Exec Bd)*

Offshore Technology Development Pte Ltd (1)
50 Gul Road, Singapore, 629351, Singapore
Tel.: (65) 68637409
Emp.: 57
Marine Engineering Services
N.A.I.C.S.: 541330

Okachi Investments Ltd (1)
6/F Euro Trade Center 13-14 Connaught Road, Central, China (Hong Kong)
Tel.: (852) 28680968
Web Site: http://www.okachi.hk
Emp.: 20
Financial Investment Services
N.A.I.C.S.: 523999

PT Harapan Global Niaga (1)
International Financial Centre Tower 2 20th Floor Jln Jend Sudirman, Kav 22-23, Jakarta, 12920, Indonesia
Tel.: (62) 215712238
Property Management Services
N.A.I.C.S.: 531311

PT Nongsa Point Marina (1)
Jalan Hang Lekiu Nongsa, Batam, Riau Islands, Indonesia
Tel.: (62) 778 761333
Web Site:
  http://www.nongsapointmarina.com
Resort Management Services
N.A.I.C.S.: 721110

PT Puri Land Development (1)
International Financial Centre Tower 2 20th Floor Jln Jend Sudirman, Kav 22-23, Jakarta, 12920, Indonesia
Tel.: (62) 215712238
Property Management Services
N.A.I.C.S.: 531311

PT Sukses Manis Tangguh (1)
International Financial Centre Tower 2 20th Floor Jln Jend Sudirman, Kav 22-23, Jakarta, 12920, Indonesia
Tel.: (62) 215712238
Property Management Services
N.A.I.C.S.: 531311

Palmsville Investment Pte Ltd (1)
Keppel Bay Tower 18-01 1 Harbour Front Avenue, Singapore, 98632, Singapore
Tel.: (65) 63388111
Investment Management Service
N.A.I.C.S.: 523999

Petro Tower Ltd (1)
8 Hoang Dieu St Ward 1, Vung Tau, Ba Ria-Vung Tau, Vietnam
Tel.: (84) 64 3850098
Property Management Services
N.A.I.C.S.: 531312
Limsock Sii *(Gen Dir)*

Prime Steelkit Pte Ltd (1)
55a Gul Road, Singapore, 629357, Singapore
Tel.: (65) 68611358
Sales Range: $25-49.9 Million
Emp.: 49
Metal Fabricated Products Mfr
N.A.I.C.S.: 332999
Kee Huat Loh *(Gen Mgr)*

Regency Steel Japan Ltd. (1)
46-59 Nakabaru, Tobata-ku, Kitakyushu, 804-8505, Fukuoka, Japan
Tel.: (81) 938613103

Web Site: http://www.rsj2004.com
Emp.: 72
Steel Products Mfr
N.A.I.C.S.: 331221
Chun Yu Wong *(Pres & CEO)*

Riviera Point LLC (1)
582 Huynh Tan Phat St, District 7, Ho Chi Minh City, 70000, Vietnam
Tel.: (84) 8 377 38 777
Web Site: http://www.theview.rivierapoint.com.vn
Sales Range: $50-74.9 Million
Property Development Services
N.A.I.C.S.: 531390

Shanghai Merryfield Land Co Ltd (1)
No 2001 Park Place 1601 Nanjing West Road, Shanghai, 200040, China
Tel.: (86) 21 6288 3066
Web Site: http://www.keppellandchina.com
Emp.: 100
Real Estate Development Services
N.A.I.C.S.: 531390

Straits Mansfield Property Marketing Pte Ltd (1)
23 Church Street 15-01 Downtown, Singapore, 49481, Singapore
Tel.: (65) 63388111
Property Management Services
N.A.I.C.S.: 531312

Straits-KMP Resort Development Pte Ltd (1)
550 Tanah Merah Ferry Road 01-18 A, Singapore, 498833, Singapore
Tel.: (65) 65467555
Home Management Services
N.A.I.C.S.: 721110

Tianjin Pearl Beach International Country Club Co Ltd (1)
Blk2 21-03 Avenue 3 Tianjin Economic Development Zone, Tianjin, 300457, China
Tel.: (86) 22 6720 1919
Golf Course Management Services
N.A.I.C.S.: 713910

Waterfront Properties Pte Ltd (1)
230 Victoria Street 14-01/10 Bugis Junction Office Tower, Singapore, 188024, Singapore
Tel.: (65) 63388111
Web Site: http://www.waterfronthomes.tv
Property Development Services
N.A.I.C.S.: 531390

KEPPEL DC REIT MANAGEMENT PTE. LTD.
1 HarbourFront Avenue Level 2 Keppel Bay Tower, Singapore, 98632, Singapore
Tel.: (65) 68031818 SG
Web Site:
  https://www.keppeldcreit.com
Year Founded: 2009
AJBU—(SES)
Rev.: $212,987,200
Assets: $3,034,576,231
Liabilities: $1,251,677,648
Net Worth: $1,782,898,583
Earnings: $92,557,752
Emp.: 14
Fiscal Year-end: 12/31/23
Trust Management Services
N.A.I.C.S.: 523940
Liang Huihui *(Mgr-Asst)*

KEPPEL PACIFIC OAK US REIT
1 HarbourFront Avenue No 18-01 Keppel Bay Tower, Singapore, 098632, Singapore
Tel.: (65) 68031818
Web Site: https://www.koreusreit.com
CMOU—(SES)
Rev.: $150,757,000
Assets: $1,393,676,000
Liabilities: $670,472,000
Net Worth: $723,204,000
Earnings: ($67,725,000)
Emp.: 8
Fiscal Year-end: 12/31/23

INTERNATIONAL PUBLIC

Real Estate Investment Management Services
N.A.I.C.S.: 531120
David Snyder *(CEO & Chief Investment Officer)*

KEPPEL REIT
1 HarbourFront Avenue, 18-01 Keppel Bay Tower, Singapore, 98632, Singapore
Tel.: (65) 68031818
Web Site: https://www.keppelreit.com
Year Founded: 2006
KREVF—(OTCIQ)
Rev.: $162,494,257
Assets: $6,581,233,790
Liabilities: $2,234,954,428
Net Worth: $4,346,279,363
Earnings: $332,273,435
Emp.: 23
Fiscal Year-end: 12/31/22
Real Estate Investment Trust
N.A.I.C.S.: 525990
Penny Goh *(Chm)*

Subsidiaries:

Ocean Properties Pte. Ltd. (1)
10 Collyer Quay 17-06 Ocean Financial Centre, Singapore, 49315, Singapore
Tel.: (65) 6538 8755
Sales Range: $50-74.9 Million
Property Management Services
N.A.I.C.S.: 531312
Alan Ng *(Asst Gen Mgr)*

KEPUNI HOLDINGS INC.
No 318 Yongping Road, Science and Technology Industrial Park, Taizhou, 225300, Jiangsu, China
Tel.: (86) 52382988888 Ky
Year Founded: 2020
KPNT—(NASDAQ)
Rev.: $9,366,670
Assets: $11,045,662
Liabilities: $7,700,527
Net Worth: $3,345,135
Earnings: $1,351,217
Emp.: 58
Fiscal Year-end: 12/31/20
Holding Company
N.A.I.C.S.: 551112
Xiaofei Cui *(Chm & CEO)*

KERALA AYURVEDA LTD.
Athani P O, Ernakulam District, Aluva, 683585, Kerala, India
Tel.: (91) 4842476301
Web Site:
  https://www.keralaayurveda.biz
530163—(BOM)
Rev.: $11,015,509
Assets: $15,048,292
Liabilities: $13,964,264
Net Worth: $1,084,028
Earnings: ($8,941)
Emp.: 430
Fiscal Year-end: 03/31/22
Ayurvedic Medicine Mfr
N.A.I.C.S.: 325412
Ramesh Vangal *(Chm)*

Subsidiaries:

Ayurvedagram Heritage Wellness Centre Pvt. Ltd. (1)
XQ7XR39 Hemandanahalli Samethanahalli Post Whitefield, Bengaluru, 560 067, Karnataka, India
Tel.: (91) 9845071990
Web Site: https://www.ayurvedagram.com
Ayurveda Services
N.A.I.C.S.: 456199

KERALTY BUSINESS GROUP
Calle 100 11b - 6, Bogota, Colombia
Tel.: (57) 1 646 6060
Web Site: http://www.keralty.com
Year Founded: 1980
Healthcare Services

AND PRIVATE COMPANIES

N.A.I.C.S.: 621999
Joseba Grajales (Pres)
Subsidiaries:

Westchester General Hospital, Inc. (1)
2500 SW 75th Ave, Miami, FL 33155-2805
Tel.: (305) 263-9086
Web Site:
http://www.westchesterhospital.com
Emp.: 570
Specialty Hospitals
N.A.I.C.S.: 622310
Carlos Siu (Dir-IT)

KERAMIA-ALLATINI SA REAL ESTATE MANAGEMENT & HOLDING CO.
G Gennimata 22, Allatini Nea Elvetia Postfach 100, 54250, Thessaloniki, Greece
Tel.: (30) 2310316361
Web Site: https://ceramics-allatini.gr
Real Estate Development Services
N.A.I.C.S.: 531390
Achilleas Kotsias (Chm)

KERAMIKA - HOLDING A.D.
Bulevar Mihajla Pupina 10V/114, 11070, Novi Beograd, Serbia
Tel.: (381) 11 311 9377
Web Site: http://www.tilezza.com
Brick & Clay Mfr
N.A.I.C.S.: 327120

KERAS RESOURCES PLC
Coveham House Downside Bridge Road, Cobham, KT11 3EP, United Kingdom
Tel.: (44) 2072361177 UK
Web Site: https://www.kerasplc.com
Year Founded: 2010
KRS—(AIM)
Rev.: $1,254,734
Assets: $8,437,263
Liabilities: $3,664,479
Net Worth: $4,772,785
Earnings: ($1,258,521)
Emp.: 6
Fiscal Year-end: 12/31/22
Gold Exploration Services
N.A.I.C.S.: 212220
Russell Lamming (CEO)

KERDOS GROUP S.A.
ul Emilii Plater 53, 00-113, Warsaw, Poland
Tel.: (48) 34 351 50 10
Web Site:
http://www.kerdosgroup.com
Year Founded: 1992
Paper Products Mfr
N.A.I.C.S.: 322120
Lucja Gabriela Latos (CEO)

KERESKEDELMI ES HITEL-BANK RT.
Lechner Odon Fasor 9, 1095, Budapest, Hungary
Tel.: (36) 13289000
Web Site: http://www.kh.hu
Year Founded: 1987
Sales Range: $550-599.9 Million
Emp.: 3,787
Banking Services
N.A.I.C.S.: 522110
Bela Singlovics (Chm)
Subsidiaries:

K & H Eszkozfinanszirozo Penzugyi Lizing Zartkoruen Mukodo Reszvenytarsasag (1)
Dozsa Gyorgy Ut 84-A, Budapest, Hungary (100%)
Tel.: (36) 14687888
Activities Related to Credit Intermediation
N.A.I.C.S.: 522390

K & H Lizinghaz Zartkoruen Mukodo Reszvenytarsasag (1)
Lejto Utca 17-A, 1068, Budapest, Hungary (100%)
Tel.: (36) 12368100
Passenger Car Rental
N.A.I.C.S.: 532111

K&H Autopark Kft. (1)
Lechner Odon Fasor 9, 1095, Budapest, Hungary
Tel.: (36) 703353355
Financial Services
N.A.I.C.S.: 921130

K&H Csoportszolgaltato Kozpont Kft. (1)
Lechner Odon Fasor 9, 1095, Budapest, Hungary
Tel.: (36) 13289000
Financial Services
N.A.I.C.S.: 921130

K&H Factor Ltd. (1)
Lechner Odon Fasor 9, 1095, Budapest, Hungary
Tel.: (36) 13289911
Financial Services
N.A.I.C.S.: 921130

K&H Fund Management Plc (1)
Lechner Odon fasor 9, 1095, Budapest, Hungary
Tel.: (36) 614835000
Commercial Banking Services
N.A.I.C.S.: 522110
Gabor Banhalmi (Mgr-Knowledge)

K&H Lease Group (1)
Dozsa Gyorgy ut 84/a, Liget Center, 1068, Budapest, Hungary
Tel.: (36) 612368900
Commercial Banking Services
N.A.I.C.S.: 522110

K&H Mortgage Bank Ltd. (1)
Lechner Odon Fasor 9, 1095, Budapest, Hungary
Tel.: (36) 13289000
Financial Services
N.A.I.C.S.: 921130

KERING S.A.
40 rue de Sevres, 75007, Paris, France
Tel.: (33) 145646100 FR
Web Site: https://www.kering.com
Year Founded: 1963
KER—(OTCIQ)
Rev.: $16,090,189,648
Assets: $34,397,352,496
Liabilities: $19,615,484,096
Net Worth: $14,781,868,400
Earnings: $2,641,207,296
Emp.: 38,553
Fiscal Year-end: 12/31/20
Holding Company; Department Stores Owner & Operator
N.A.I.C.S.: 551112
Jean-Francois Palus (Mng Dir-Grp)
Subsidiaries:

Alexander McQueen (Hong Kong) Ltd. (1)
Room 1103 Lee Garden One 33 Hysan Avenue, Causeway Bay, China (Hong Kong)
Tel.: (852) 58089136
Apparel & Accessories Distr
N.A.I.C.S.: 424350
Gary Tam (Mgr-Store)

Alexander Mcqueen (Macau) Ltd. (1)
3305B Estrada do Istmo Lote 3 Cotai Strip, Macau, China (Macau)
Tel.: (853) 28770170
Apparel & Accessories Distr
N.A.I.C.S.: 424350

Alexander Mcqueen (Singapore) Pte Ltd (1)
111 Somerset Road 17-02, Singapore, 238163, Singapore
Tel.: (65) 31652822
Apparel & Accessories Distr
N.A.I.C.S.: 424350
Pei Sia (Mgr-HR)

Alexander Mcqueen (Thailand) Ltd. (1)
No 689 Bhiraj Tower EmQuartier Level 30 Sukhumvit Road Soi 35, Klongton Nuea Sub-district Wattana District, Bangkok, Thailand
Tel.: (66) 6531652822
Apparel & Accessories Distr
N.A.I.C.S.: 424350

Alexander Mcqueen (the Netherlands) B.V. (1)
Pc Hoofdstraat 70, 1071 CB, Amsterdam, Netherlands
Tel.: (31) 207038731
Luxury Product Mfr & Distr
N.A.I.C.S.: 315990

Alexander Mcqueen Australia Pty Ltd (1)
1341 Dandenong Rd, Chadstone, 3148, VIC, Australia
Tel.: (61) 395304935
Apparel & Accessories Distr
N.A.I.C.S.: 424350

Alexander Mcqueen France SAS (1)
37 Rue Du Cherche Midi, 75006, Paris, France
Tel.: (33) 184953434
Web Site:
https://www.alexandermcqueen.com
Luxury Goods & Jewelry Distr
N.A.I.C.S.: 458310

Alexander Mcqueen New Zealand Ltd. (1)
Shop S146 Westfield Newmarket 277/309 Broadway, Newmarket, Auckland, 1023, New Zealand
Tel.: (64) 95295182
Fashion Product Distr
N.A.I.C.S.: 424350

Alexander Mcqueen Trading Canada Inc. (1)
3401 Dufferin Street Suite 137, Toronto, M6A 2T9, ON, Canada
Tel.: (416) 782-7160
Luxury Product Mfr & Distr
N.A.I.C.S.: 315990

Autumnpaper Malaysia Sdn Bhd (1)
Lot 6 05 Level 6 KPMG Tower 8 First Avenue, Bandar Utama, 47800, Petaling Jaya, Malaysia
Tel.: (60) 6531652822
Apparel & Accessories Distr
N.A.I.C.S.: 424350

BALENCIAGA UK Ltd (1)
5th Floor Rear Suite Oakfield House 35 Perrymount Road, Haywards Heath, RH16 3BW, West Sussex, United Kingdom
Tel.: (44) 2033186027
Web Site: http://www.balenciaga.co.uk
Sales Range: $25-49.9 Million
Emp.: 1
Handbag & Shoes Retailer
N.A.I.C.S.: 458110

BRANDON AB (1)
Lindholmspiren 3B, 417 56, Gothenburg, Sweden
Tel.: (46) 317644700
Web Site: http://www.brandoncompany.com
Emp.: 40
Advertising Services
N.A.I.C.S.: 541890
Paul Preuveneers (CEO)

BRANDON GERMANY GmbH (1)
Wurzburgerstrabe 13, 91074, Herzogenaurach, Germany
Tel.: (49) 9132813200
Sales Range: $25-49.9 Million
Emp.: 4
Clothing & Apparel Retailer
N.A.I.C.S.: 458110

Balenciaga Austria GmbH (1)
Seitzergasse 1-3, 1010, Vienna, Austria
Tel.: (43) 1395088310
Women Jewellery & Clothing Accessory Distr
N.A.I.C.S.: 424350

Balenciaga Belgium B.V. (1)
30 Boulevard Waterloo, 1000, Brussels, Belgium
Tel.: (32) 28825210
Women Jewellery & Clothing Accessory Distr
N.A.I.C.S.: 424350

Balenciaga Czech Republic S.r.o. (1)
13 Parizska 110 00 Stare Mesto, 110 00, Prague, Czech Republic
Tel.: (420) 228886050
Women Jewellery & Clothing Accessory Distr
N.A.I.C.S.: 424350

Balenciaga Denmark APS (1)
Ostergade 52, 1100, Copenhagen, Denmark
Tel.: (45) 33182830
Women Jewellery & Clothing Accessory Distr
N.A.I.C.S.: 424350

Balenciaga Netherlands B.V. (1)
PC Hoofstraat 99, 1071 AC, Amsterdam, Netherlands
Tel.: (31) 207182620
Luxury Product Mfr & Distr
N.A.I.C.S.: 315990

Balenciaga New Zealand Ltd. (1)
Shop S142 Level 1 Westfield Newmarket 277/309 Broadway, Newmarket, Auckland, 1023, New Zealand
Tel.: (64) 95203181
Women Jewellery & Clothing Accessory Distr
N.A.I.C.S.: 424350

Bottega Veneta Greece S.A. (1)
14 Kolokotroni St, Kifissia, 145 62, Athens, Greece
Tel.: (30) 2108085182
Luxury Product Mfr & Distr
N.A.I.C.S.: 315990

Bottega Veneta Ireland Ltd. (1)
Brown Thomas 88-95 Grafton Street, Dublin, D02 VF65, Ireland
Tel.: (353) 16056666
Luxury Product Mfr & Distr
N.A.I.C.S.: 315990

Bottega Veneta Sweden AB (1)
Birger Jarlsgatan 10, 114 34, Stockholm, Sweden
Tel.: (46) 86116688
Jewellery Mfr & Distr
N.A.I.C.S.: 339910

Boucheron (Suisse) SA (1)
Rue Du Rhone 13, 1204, Geneva, 1204, Switzerland
Tel.: (41) 223117071
Web Site: http://www.boucheron.com
Sales Range: $25-49.9 Million
Emp.: 4
Jewelry Retailer
N.A.I.C.S.: 458310
Jean-Francois Keledjian (Gen Mgr)

Boucheron Russia OOO (1)
Tel.: (7) 4953636242
Jewelry Retailer
N.A.I.C.S.: 458310

Boucheron SAM (1)
Avenue Princesse Alice, One Monte Carlo, Monaco, 98000, Monaco
Tel.: (377) 97974244
Fashion Apparels Retailer
N.A.I.C.S.: 458110
Helene Poulit-Duquesne (CEO)

Boucheron SAS (1)
26 Place Vendome, 75001, Paris, France
Tel.: (33) 142615816
Web Site: http://www.boucheron.com
Luxury Goods & Jewelry Distr
N.A.I.C.S.: 458310
Helene Poulit-Duquesne (CEO)

Boucheron Taiwan Co., Ltd. (1)
9Fl-2 No 77 Sec 2 Tun Hwa South Road, Da-an Dist, Taipei, Taiwan
Tel.: (886) 2 25113123
Jewel & Luxury Goods Distr
N.A.I.C.S.: 458310

Boucheron Timepieces S.A. (1)

KERING S.A.

Kering S.A.—(Continued)
Schwanenplatz 5, 6002, Lucerne, Switzerland
Tel.: (41) 413697700
Luxury Jewellery & Watch Mfr
N.A.I.C.S.: 339910

Brioni Spa (1)
Piazza San Bernardo 101, 00187, Rome, RM, Italy
Tel.: (39) 0694500002
Web Site: https://www.brioni.com
Clothing Whslr
N.A.I.C.S.: 458110
Cyril Buzut (CFO)

C. MENDES SAS (1)
7 Avenue George V, Paris, 75008, France
Tel.: (33) 1 56 62 64 00
Sales Range: $50-74.9 Million
Emp.: 200
Clothing Apparel Accessory Distr
N.A.I.C.S.: 458110

CAPRI GROUP Srl (1)
Via Camerelle 25/27, Capri, 80073, Italy
Tel.: (39) 0818370820
Emp.: 8
Fashion Apparels Retailer
N.A.I.C.S.: 458110
Cettima Kaputo (Mgr)

CARAVEL PELLI PREGIATE SpA (1)
Via Dei Campi Alti 3 5 9, 56022, Castelfranco di Sotto, 56022, Pisa, Italy
Tel.: (39) 057148771
Web Site: https://www.caravelspa.com
Skin Tannery Services
N.A.I.C.S.: 316110

CONCERIA BLU TONIC SpA (1)
Via Dei Conciatori 7/A-7/B Ponte a Egola, San Miniato, 56028, Pisa, Italy
Tel.: (39) 0571 484121
Web Site: http://www.blutonic.it
Footwear & Leather Goods Mfr
N.A.I.C.S.: 316210
Adriano Bosche (Gen Mgr)

CONSEIL ET ASSISTANCE (1)
94 avenue Emile Zola, 75015, Paris, France
Tel.: (33) 9 75 47 97 79
Real Estate Management Services
N.A.I.C.S.: 531390

Chem - Tec S.R.L. (1)
Via A da Giussano 36/O, Corbetta, 20011, Milan, Italy
Tel.: (39) 0292867461
Web Site: https://chemtecitalia.it
Chemical Treatment Distr
N.A.I.C.S.: 424690

Ciiem - Tec Srl (1)
Via A da Giussano 36/O, Corbetta, 22011, Milan, MI, Italy
Tel.: (39) 0292867461
Web Site: http://www.chemtecitalia.it
Chemical Technology Services
N.A.I.C.S.: 325998
Carlo De Alessandri (Mgr-R&D & Mfg)

Conceria 800 Spa (1)
Via del Fontino 6/8, Santa Croce sull'Arno, 56029, Pisa, PI, Italy
Tel.: (39) 0571360867
Web Site: https://www.conceria800.it
Leather Mfr
N.A.I.C.S.: 316990
Claudio Lagreca (Mgr-Chemical)

Costanzo & Rizzetto S.R.L. (1)
Via Galvani 8, 15048, Valenza, Italy
Tel.: (39) 0131952336
Web Site: https://www.costanzoerizzetto.it
Emp.: 65
Luxury Product & Jewellery Mfr
N.A.I.C.S.: 339910

Creed Boutique Beverly Hills, LLC (1)
9533 Brighton Way Ste A-1, Beverly Hills, CA 90210
Tel.: (424) 355-0002
Authentic Perfume Mfr & Distr
N.A.I.C.S.: 339999

Creed Boutique Houston, LLC (1)
5085 Westheimer Rd Ste B2570, Houston, TX 77056
Tel.: (281) 910-3289
Authentic Perfume Mfr & Distr
N.A.I.C.S.: 339999

Creed Boutique LLC (1)
45 W 25th St 7th Fl, New York, NY 10010
Web Site: https://creedboutique.com
Authentic Perfume Mfr & Distr
N.A.I.C.S.: 339999

Creed Boutique Las Vegas Crystals, LLC (1)
3720 S Las Vegas Blvd Ste 205, Las Vegas, NV 89158
Tel.: (702) 483-5436
Authentic Perfume Mfr & Distr
N.A.I.C.S.: 339999

Creed Boutique Las Vegas, LLC (1)
Caesars 3500 Las Vegas Blvd S Ste A09, Las Vegas, NV 89109
Tel.: (702) 366-0574
Perfume Product Distr
N.A.I.C.S.: 424210

Creed Boutique Miami, LLC (1)
151 NE 41st St PP-143, Miami, FL 33137
Tel.: (305) 573-9495
Authentic Perfume Mfr & Distr
N.A.I.C.S.: 339999

Creed Boutique Northpark, LLC (1)
8687 N Central Expy Ste 522, Dallas, TX 75225
Tel.: (214) 506-9280
Authentic Perfume Mfr & Distr
N.A.I.C.S.: 339999

Creed Boutique Valley Fair LLC (1)
2855 Stevens Creek Blvd Ste 1127, Santa Clara, CA 95050
Tel.: (408) 482-5231
Authentic Perfume Mfr & Distr
N.A.I.C.S.: 339999

Cyrillus Suisse S.A. (1)
19 rue de la Croix d'Or, 1204, Geneva, 1204, Switzerland
Tel.: (41) 223113582
Web Site: http://www.cyrillus.ch
Clothing Store Operating Services
N.A.I.C.S.: 458110

Donze Cadrans SA (1)
Rue de l Avenir 36, 2400, Le Locle, Switzerland
Tel.: (41) 329316142
Web Site: https://donze-cadrans.com
Jewelry Retailer
N.A.I.C.S.: 458310

FNAC BELGIUM (1)
Slesbroekstraat 101, 1600, Sint-Pieters-Leeuw, Belgium
Tel.: (32) 27009191
Web Site: https://www.fr.fnac.be
Sales Range: $25-49.9 Million
Emp.: 100
Online Marketing & Advertising Services
N.A.I.C.S.: 541613

FNAC PERIPHERIE (1)
67 Bd Du General Leclerc, 92110, Clichy, France
Tel.: (33) 155215389
Computer Peripheral Distr
N.A.I.C.S.: 423430

FNAC PORTUGAL - ACDLDMPT, Lda (1)
Rua Professor Carlos Alberto Da Mota Pinto 9 6ob Lisboa, Lisbon, 1070-374, Portugal
Tel.: (351) 219404700
Web Site: http://www.fnac.pt
General Merchandise Retailer
N.A.I.C.S.: 455219
Claudia Silva (Gen Mgr)

FORM@HOME (1)
Shop 52 DFO Centre 1 Airport Drive Brisbane Airport, Brisbane, 4007, Australia
Tel.: (61) 7 3115 2577
Web Site: https://www.formhome.net.au
Household Cookings Utensils Mfr
N.A.I.C.S.: 335220
Mathew Kinden (Mgr)

Falco Pellami Spa (1)
Via Martin Luther King 2/4, Ponte a Egola, 56028, San Miniato, PI, Italy
Tel.: (39) 0571499114
Web Site: https://www.falco.it
Leather Mfr
N.A.I.C.S.: 316990
Ilaria Frediani (Ops Mgr)

Futura S.R.L. (1)
Via Tagliamento 16, Sesto Ulteriano, 20098, San Giuliano Milanese, MI, Italy
Tel.: (39) 029881193
Web Site: https://www.futura-italia.it
Electronic Component Mfr & Distr
N.A.I.C.S.: 334419

G COMMERCE EUROPE SpA (1)
Via Don Lorenzo Perosi 6, 50018, Scandicci, Florence, Italy
Tel.: (39) 05575921
Sales Range: $200-249.9 Million
Emp.: 1,000
Fashion Apparel Store Operating Services
N.A.I.C.S.: 458110

G.F. LOGISTICA Srl (1)
Via Giuseppe Belletti 4/C, Novara, 28100, Italy
Tel.: (39) 0321677211
Logistics Consulting Servies
N.A.I.C.S.: 541614

G.F. SERVICES Srl (1)
Via Leonardo da Vinci 15, 20024, Garbagnate Milanese, MI, Italy
Tel.: (39) 03389371859
Web Site: https://gefservices.it
Sales Range: $100-124.9 Million
Emp.: 300
Fashion Apparels Retailer
N.A.I.C.S.: 458110
Klaus Bierbrauer (Gen Mgr)

GGW ITALIA Srl (1)
Via Broletto 5, 20121, Milan, Italy
Tel.: (39) 0288005794
Fashion Apparels Retailer
N.A.I.C.S.: 458110

GT SRL (1)
Via Sardegna 5, 42122, Reggio Emilia, Italy
Tel.: (39) 0522551240
Web Site: https://www.gt-simonazzi.com
Textile Services
N.A.I.C.S.: 313310
Eleonora Focardi (Production Mgr)

Ginori 1735 S.A.S. (1)
69 Rue du Faubourg Saint-Honore, 75008, Paris, France
Tel.: (33) 140060495
Tableware & Houseware Mfr
N.A.I.C.S.: 327212

Gucci (Hong Kong) Ltd. (1)
16/F Lincoln House Taikoo Place 979 King s Road, Quarry Bay, China (Hong Kong)
Tel.: (852) 58062999
Apparel & Accessories Distr
N.A.I.C.S.: 424350

Gucci Australia Pty Ltd (1)
Level 26 201-217 Elizabeth Street, Sydney, 2000, NSW, Australia
Tel.: (61) 1300492212
Apparel & Accessories Distr
N.A.I.C.S.: 424350
Alexandra Abraham (Ops Mgr-Flagship)

Gucci Belgium SA (1)
Boulevard de Waterloo 49, 1000, Brussels, Belgium
Tel.: (32) 25111182
Clothing Whslr
N.A.I.C.S.: 458110

Gucci Garden Srl (1)
Piazza della Signoria 10, 50122, Florence, Italy
Tel.: (39) 05575927010
Fashion Product Whslr
N.A.I.C.S.: 458110
Gori Alessandro (Ops Mgr)

Gucci Hungary Kft (1)
Andrassy 23, 1061, Budapest, Hungary
Tel.: (36) 13220971
Clothing Whslr
N.A.I.C.S.: 458110

Gucci Hungary Retail Ltd. (1)

INTERNATIONAL PUBLIC

23 Andrassy ut, 1061, Budapest, Hungary
Tel.: (36) 14131996
Luxury Product Mfr & Distr
N.A.I.C.S.: 315990

Gucci Osteria Japan G.k. (1)
6-6-12 Ginza, Chuo-ku, Tokyo, 104-0061, Japan
Tel.: (81) 362646606
Contemporary Restaurant Services
N.A.I.C.S.: 722511

Immobiliare Arno S.R.L. (1)
Lungarno Pacinotti 52, Pisa, Italy
Tel.: (39) 03487348161
Web Site: https://www.immobiliarearno.com
Real Estate Brokerage Services
N.A.I.C.S.: 531210

International Cosmetics And Perfumes, Inc. (1)
45 W 25th St 7th Fl, New York, NY 10010
Tel.: (212) 643-0011
Web Site: https://www.icperfumes.com
Fragrance & Skincare Distr
N.A.I.C.S.: 424210

KGS Sourcing Limited (1)
20/F Rykadan Capital Tower 135 Hoi Bun Road, Kwun Tong, Kowloon, China (Hong Kong)
Tel.: (852) 23162628
Web Site: https://www.kgssourcing.com
Emp.: 40
Mail Order Shopping Services
N.A.I.C.S.: 424130
Unice Ho (Gen Mgr)

Kering Eyewear Dach GmbH (1)
Ludwigpalais-Ludwigstrasse 8 4 Stock, 80539, Munich, Germany
Tel.: (49) 8945221900
Eyewear Mfr
N.A.I.C.S.: 339115

Kering Eyewear France SAS (1)
40 Rue de Sevres, 75007, Paris, France
Tel.: (33) 170718100
Eyewear Mfr
N.A.I.C.S.: 339115

Kering Eyewear Japan Ltd. (1)
4-3-1 Ginza, Chuo-ku, Tokyo, 104-0061, Japan
Tel.: (81) 354142570
Eyewear Mfr
N.A.I.C.S.: 339115

Kering Eyewear Shanghai Trading Enterprises Ltd. (1)
Unit 01 21F Garden Square No 968 West Road, Jing'An District, Beijing, 200041, China
Tel.: (86) 2161702333
Eyewear Mfr
N.A.I.C.S.: 339115

Kering Eyewear Spa (1)
Via Altichiero 180, 35135, Padova, Italy
Tel.: (39) 0498653411
Web Site: https://keringeyewear.com
Eyewear Mfr
N.A.I.C.S.: 339115

Subsidiary (US):

Maui Jim, Inc. (2)
1 Aloha Ln, Peoria, IL 61615-1871 (90%)
Tel.: (309) 691-3700
Web Site: http://www.mauijim.com
Sales Range: $25-49.9 Million
Emp.: 340
Sunglass Distr
N.A.I.C.S.: 423990
Walter Hester (CEO)

Kering Eyewear Taiwan Ltd. (1)
9F No 35 LN 11 Guangfu N Rd, Songshan Dist, Taipei, 10560, Taiwan
Tel.: (886) 905092857
Eyewear Mfr
N.A.I.C.S.: 339115

Kering Eyewear UK Ltd. (1)
6th Floor 62 Buckingham Gate, London, SW1E 6AJ, United Kingdom
Tel.: (44) 2078983000
Eyewear Mfr
N.A.I.C.S.: 339115
Harry Heyman (Natl Sls Mgr)

AND PRIVATE COMPANIES

KERING S.A.

Kering Finance (1)
10 avenue Hoche, 75008, Paris, France
Tel.: (33) 1 45 64 61 00
Financial Services
N.A.I.C.S.: 523999

Kering Holland N.V. (1)
Amstelplein 1 The Rembrandt Tower,
1096HA, Amsterdam, Netherlands
Tel.: (31) 204621700
Web Site: https://www.guccigroup.com
Sales Range: $1-4.9 Billion
Emp.: 11,200
Designer & Mfr of Personal Living Accessories & Apparel
N.A.I.C.S.: 458110

Subsidiary (Non-US):

BOTTEGA VENETA Srl (2)
Viale Della Siderurgia 4/6, Vicenza, 36100, Italy
Tel.: (39) 04 44 39 65 11
Leather Goods Mfr
N.A.I.C.S.: 316990
Olivier Monteil *(Dir-Worldwide Comm-Lugano)*

Subsidiary (Non-US):

BOTTEGA VENETA (CHINA) TRADING Ltd (3)
Ste 3202-3203 Henglong Plaza 2 No 1366
Nanjing W Rd, Shanghai, 200040, China
Tel.: (86) 2162882000
Leather Goods & Sporting Goods Distr
N.A.I.C.S.: 458320

BOTTEGA VENETA ESPANA SL (3)
Calle Paseo de Gracia 56 6 modulo B,
08007, Barcelona, Spain
Tel.: (34) 930411966
Web Site: https://www.bottegaveneta.com
Fashion Apparels Retailer
N.A.I.C.S.: 458110

BOTTEGA VENETA France SAS (3)
16 R Du Faubourg Saint Honore, 75008,
Paris, France
Tel.: (33) 142655970
Web Site: https://www.bottegaveneta.com
Sales Range: $25-49.9 Million
Emp.: 3
Consumer Goods Retailer
N.A.I.C.S.: 459999
Christino Guido *(Gen Mgr)*

BOTTEGA VENETA GERMANY GmbH (3)
Prannerstrasse 11, 80333, Munich, Germany
Tel.: (49) 3020921107
Handbag Retailer
N.A.I.C.S.: 458110
Carlo Frederico Baratta *(CEO)*

BOTTEGA VENETA HONG KONG Limited (3)
28/F One Taikoo Place 979 King's Road,
Quarry Bay, Hong Kong, China (Hong Kong)
Tel.: (852) 22610771
Web Site: https://www.bottegaveneta.com
Fashion Clothing Apparel Distr
N.A.I.C.S.: 458110

BOTTEGA VENETA MALAYSIA Sdn Bhd (3)
Suite 600 Johor Premium Outlets Jalan
Premium Outlets Indahpura, Kulai, 81000,
Johor, Malaysia
Tel.: (60) 75970791
Leather Goods Retail Store Operating Services
N.A.I.C.S.: 458320

Subsidiary (Non-US):

Balenciaga SA (2)
40 Rue de Sevres, 75007, Paris, France
Tel.: (33) 184952223
Web Site: http://www.balenciaga.com
Sales Range: $25-49.9 Million
Emp.: 85
Personal Living Accessories & Apparel Designer & Mfr
N.A.I.C.S.: 315990
Demna Gvasalia *(Dir-Artistic)*

GUCCI (CHINA) TRADING Ltd (2)
19 West Rd 1788 18th Eco City, Shanghai,
200040, China
Tel.: (86) 2152285533
Jewelry Retail Stores Operating Services
N.A.I.C.S.: 458310

GUCCI AUSTRIA GmbH (2)
Kohlmarkt 5, 1010, Vienna, 1010, Austria
Tel.: (43) 15324088
Web Site: http://www.gucci.com
Emp.: 12
Luxury Shoes Distr
N.A.I.C.S.: 458210
Daniel Zimmerlin *(Gen Mgr)*

GUCCI FINANZIARIA SpA (2)
Via Don Lorenzo Perosi 6, 50018, Scandicci, Florence, Italy
Tel.: (39) 055759221
Web Site: http://www.gucci.com
Emp.: 100
Financial Management Services
N.A.I.C.S.: 523999

GUCCI GROUP JAPAN HOLDING LIMITED (2)
3-6-7 Kitaaoyama Parashio Tower, Minato-Ku, Tokyo, 107-0061, Japan
Tel.: (81) 354696611
Investment Management Service
N.A.I.C.S.: 523999

GUCCI GROUP JAPAN Limited (2)
3-6-7 Kitaaoyama Palacio Tower 3f, Minato-Ku, Tokyo, 107-0061, Japan
Tel.: (81) 354696611
Handbag Retail Stores Operating Services
N.A.I.C.S.: 458110

GUCCI INDIA PRIVATE Ltd (2)
Galleria, Mumbai, 400021, Maharashtra, India
Tel.: (91) 2230277060
Web Site: http://www.gucci.com
Emp.: 1
Jewelry Retailer
N.A.I.C.S.: 458310

GUCCI IRELAND Limited (2)
88-95 Grafton Street, Dublin, Ireland
Tel.: (353) 1 617 1132
Web Site: http://www.gucci.com
Fashion Apparels Retailer
N.A.I.C.S.: 458110

GUCCI LOGISTICA SpA (2)
Via Don Lorenzo Perosi 6, Scandicci,
50018, Florence, Italy
Tel.: (39) 055759221
Logistics Consulting Servies
N.A.I.C.S.: 541614

GUCCI MEXICO S.A. de C.V. (2)
Ejercito Nacional 676 Piso 6 Colonia Polanco III Seccion, Miguel Hidalgo, 11540,
Mexico, Mexico
Tel.: (52) 8004610560
Web Site: https://www.gucci.com
Fashion Apparels Retailer
N.A.I.C.S.: 458110
Maia Jujnovsky *(Gen Mgr)*

GUCCI NEW ZEALAND Ltd (2)
48 Queen Street, Auckland, 1010, New Zealand
Tel.: (64) 800009000
Handbag Retail Stores Operating Services
N.A.I.C.S.: 458110
Christine Woodley *(Mgr-Relationship Mktg)*

Subsidiary (Domestic):

GUCCI PARTICIPATION BV (2)
Amstelplein 1, 1096 HA, Amsterdam, 1096
HA, Netherlands
Tel.: (31) 204621700
Fashion Apparels Retailer
N.A.I.C.S.: 458110
Fh Pinault *(CEO)*

Subsidiary (Non-US):

GUCCI SAM (2)
135 Avenue De Monte Carlo, 98000, Monaco, 98000, Monaco
Tel.: (377) 97973444
Web Site: http://www.gucci.com
Emp.: 5
Fashion Apparels Retailer
N.A.I.C.S.: 458110

GUCCI SHOPS OF CANADA Inc. (2)
130 Bloor Street West Suite 102, Toronto,
M5S 1N5, ON, Canada
Tel.: (416) 963-5127
Web Site: http://www.gucci.com
Emp.: 15
Handbag Retailer
N.A.I.C.S.: 458110
My Luong *(Mgr)*

GUCCI SINGAPORE Pte Limited (2)
390 Orchard Road 10-01 Palais Renaissance, Singapore, 238871, Singapore
Tel.: (65) 67348880
Web Site: http://www.guccisingapore.com
Leather Goods Distr
N.A.I.C.S.: 458320

GUCCI SWEDEN AB (2)
Birger Jarlsgatan 1, 11145, Stockholm, Sweden
Tel.: (46) 858097520
Handbag Retailer
N.A.I.C.S.: 458110

Subsidiary (US):

Gucci America Inc. (2)
195 Broadway, New York, NY 10007
Tel.: (212) 750-5220
Web Site: https://www.gucci.com
Sales Range: $25-49.9 Million
Emp.: 100
Luxury Shoes & Accessories Marketer & Distr
N.A.I.C.S.: 458110
Marco Bizzarri *(Pres & CEO)*

Subsidiary (Non-US):

Richard Ginori 1735 S.p.A. (2)
Viale Giulio Cesare n 50, Sesto Fiorentino,
50019, Florence, Italy
Tel.: (39) 055420491
Web Site: http://www.richardginori1735.com
Emp.: 230
Porcelain & Bone China Tableware Mfr & Distr
N.A.I.C.S.: 327110
Giovanni Giunchedi *(CEO)*

YVES SAINT LAURENT SPAIN SA (2)
Pasero De Gracia 56 6Ta Planta Modulo B,
8007, Barcelona, Spain
Tel.: (34) 911987850
Web Site: https://www.ysl.com
Sales Range: $25-49.9 Million
Emp.: 5
Handbag Retailer
N.A.I.C.S.: 458110
Angel Angel Noemi *(Gen Mgr)*

YVES SAINT LAURENT UK Ltd (2)
5th Floor Rear Suite Oakfield House 35
Perrymount Road, Haywards Heath, RH16
3BW, West Sussex, United Kingdom
Tel.: (44) 2033185913
Web Site: http://www.ysl.com
Fashion Apparels Retailer
N.A.I.C.S.: 458110

Yves Saint Laurent Beaute S.A. (2)
28-34 Boulevard du Parc, 92521, Neuilly-sur-Seine, Cedex, France
Tel.: (33) 8 20 80 7060
Web Site: http://www.ysl-parfums.com
Sales Range: $400-449.9 Million
Emp.: 1,200
Perfumes & Cosmetics Mfr
N.A.I.C.S.: 325620
Francesca Bellettini *(Pres & CEO)*

Kering Venture S.A.S. (1)
15-17 Rue Monsieur, 75007, Paris, France
Tel.: (33) 145646100
Web Site: https://www.kering-ventures.com
Luxury Product Mfr & Distr
N.A.I.C.S.: 315990

LES BOUTIQUES BOUCHERON SAS (1)
26 Place Vendome, 75001, Paris, France
Tel.: (33) 142444244
Jewelry & Watch Retail Store Operating Services
N.A.I.C.S.: 458310

LUXURY GOODS OPERATIONS SA (1)
Via Industria, 6814, Cadempino, 6814, Ticino, Switzerland
Tel.: (41) 918052525
Web Site: http://www.gucci.com
Emp.: 32
Fashion Apparels Retailer
N.A.I.C.S.: 458110
Andries Boone *(Gen Mgr)*

LUXURY GOODS SPAIN SL (1)
Passeig De Gracia 56 6 th Fl B, Barcelona,
08007, Spain
Tel.: (34) 932956184
Web Site: http://www.gucci.com
Sales Range: $25-49.9 Million
Emp.: 5
Fashion Apparels Retailer
N.A.I.C.S.: 458110
Noemi Garcia Angel *(Dir-Fin)*

LUXURY TIMEPIECES JAPAN LIMITED (1)
3-6-7 Kitaaoyama Pracio Tower 4f, Minato-Ku, Tokyo, 107-0061, Japan
Tel.: (81) 357662030
Luxury Watch Distr
N.A.I.C.S.: 423940

Lindberg AS (1)
Bjarkesvej 30, Aabyhoj, 8230, Aarhus, Denmark
Tel.: (45) 87444000
Web Site: https://lindberg.com
Fashion Product Distr
N.A.I.C.S.: 424350

Manufacture Kering Eyewear SAS (1)
1 Rue Benjamin Franklin, 94370, Sucy-en-Brie, France
Tel.: (33) 172052940
Eyewear Mfr
N.A.I.C.S.: 339115

Marbella Pellami SPA (1)
Via Marco Polo n 91, Bientina, 56031, Pisa, PI, Italy
Tel.: (39) 0587755267
Web Site: https://www.conceriamarbella.it
Leather Mfr
N.A.I.C.S.: 316990
Michela Giusti *(Mgr-Quality Control)*

Maui Jim - Italy S.r.l. (1)
Via Della Scienza 15, Lavagno, 37030, Verona, Italy
Tel.: (39) 0458445800
Sunglass Mfr & Distr
N.A.I.C.S.: 339115

Maui Jim Asia Limited (1)
C/O Omlog Asia Ltd Block B G/F Goodman
Western Plaza, No 3 San On Street & 2 Tin
Hau Road Tuen Mum N T, Hong Kong,
China (Hong Kong)
Tel.: (852) 35115388
Sunglass Mfr & Distr
N.A.I.C.S.: 339115

Maui Jim Australia Pty., Ltd. (1)
Unit 6 25 Frenchs Forest Road, French's
Forest, 2086, NSW, Australia
Tel.: (61) 1800010244
Sunglass Mfr & Distr
N.A.I.C.S.: 339115

Maui Jim Canada ULC (1)
Repair Department 2830 Argentia Road
Unit 3, Mississauga, L5N 8G4, ON, Canada
Sunglass Mfr & Distr
N.A.I.C.S.: 339115

Maui Jim Germany, GmbH (1)
Erzberg 8, 38126, Braunschweig, Germany
Tel.: (49) 531121750
Sunglass Mfr & Distr
N.A.I.C.S.: 339115

Maui Jim Middle East FZE (1)
Dubai Airport Free Zone Warehouse I 16,
PO Box 293633, Dubai, United Arab Emirates
Tel.: (971) 42991207
Sunglass Mfr & Distr
N.A.I.C.S.: 339115

Maui Jim Nordic AB (1)
Finlandsgatan 40, 164 74, Kista, Sweden
Tel.: (46) 859482880
Sunglass Mfr & Distr
N.A.I.C.S.: 339115

KERING S.A.

Kering S.A.—(Continued)

Maui Jim South Africa (pty.) Ltd. (1)
37 Waterford Office Park Cnr Waterford Drive & Witkoppen Road, Fourways, 2191, South Africa
Tel.: (27) 100151500
Sunglass Mfr & Distr
N.A.I.C.S.: 339115

Maui Jim Spain, S.L. (1)
C/ Sepulveda 7A, Alcobendas, 28108, Madrid, Spain
Tel.: (34) 900161606
Sunglass Mfr & Distr
N.A.I.C.S.: 339115

Maui Jim Sun Optics India Private Limited (1)
No 1611 New No 40 G Space Building H Block 5th Street 12th Main Road, Anna Nagar, Chennai, 600040, India
Tel.: (91) 4442968899
Sunglass Mfr & Distr
N.A.I.C.S.: 339115

Maui Jim Sunglasses De Mexico S de R.L. de C.V. (1)
Av Gonzalez Gallo No 1897, Bodega 5 Parque Industrial Periferico Sur Colonia San Sebastianito, 45601, Tlaquepaque, Jalisco, Mexico
Tel.: (52) 18000025642
Sunglass Mfr & Distr
N.A.I.C.S.: 339115

Maui Jim Uk Ltd. (1)
Unit 15 The Pines Business Park Broad Street, Guildford, GU3 3BH, Surrey, United Kingdom
Tel.: (44) 1800928370
Sunglass Mfr & Distr
N.A.I.C.S.: 339115

NOGA LUXE SL (1)
Passeig de Gracia 56 6th Floor Building B, Barcelona, 08007, Spain
Tel.: (34) 932956184
Emp.: 9
Fashion Apparels Retailer
N.A.I.C.S.: 458110
Noemi Garcia *(Mgr)*

PAOLETTI Srl (1)
Via A Saffi 6, 25122, Brescia, Italy
Tel.: (39) 030294964
Web Site: https://www.paolettifur.com
Fur Clothing Retailer
N.A.I.C.S.: 458110

PIGINI s.r.l. (1)
Via Carlo Marx 127, 60022, Castelfidardo, 60022, Ancona, Italy
Tel.: (39) 0717820301
Web Site: https://www.pigini.com
Sales Range: $50-74.9 Million
Emp.: 14
Fashion Apparels Retailer
N.A.I.C.S.: 458110
Pigini Fausto *(Mng Dir)*

Pomellato Switzerland S.A. (1)
Augustinergasse 48, 8001, Zurich, Switzerland
Tel.: (41) 435211484
Apparel & Jewellery Distr
N.A.I.C.S.: 424350

Qeelin Canada Ltd. (1)
Store CRU 75 3401 Dufferin Street, Toronto, M6A 2T9, ON, Canada
Tel.: (437) 293-6800
Fine Jewellery Retailer
N.A.I.C.S.: 423940

Qeelin Japan Limited (1)
5-5-13 Ginza, Chuo City, Tokyo, Japan
Tel.: (81) 362285562
Fine Jewellery Retailer
N.A.I.C.S.: 423940

S.A.M YVES SAINT LAURENT OF MONACO (1)
Tavillons Ve Monte Callo de Casino, 98000, Monaco, Monaco
Tel.: (377) 93 25 01 32
Web Site: http://www.ysl.com
Emp.: 5
Apparel Accessories Retailer
N.A.I.C.S.: 458110

S.A.S. Belter. (1)
3 Rue Victor Duruy, 66000, Perpignan, France
Tel.: (33) 622020825
Web Site: https://drbelter.fr
Cosmetic Product Mfr & Distr
N.A.I.C.S.: 325998

SCI Sam Yves Saint Laurent Of Monaco (1)
5B Avenue Princesse Alice, 98000, Monte Carlo, Monaco
Tel.: (377) 93250132
Luxury Product Mfr & Distr
N.A.I.C.S.: 315990

Saint Laurent Arabia Trading LLC (1)
King Fahd Rd, Al Olaya, Riyadh, 12214, Saudi Arabia
Tel.: (966) 112637114
Clothing Accessory Retailer
N.A.I.C.S.: 458110

Saint Laurent Denmark APS (1)
Ostergade 47, 1100, Copenhagen, Denmark
Tel.: (45) 32759550
Luxury Product Mfr & Distr
N.A.I.C.S.: 315990

Saint Laurent Dominican Republic S.A.S. (1)
Av Winston Churchill 93 Bluemall Norte Local L-08, Santo Domingo, Dominican Republic
Tel.: (809) 18296072122
Clothing Accessory Retailer
N.A.I.C.S.: 458110

Saint Laurent Greece A.E. (1)
Building 1 Nammos Village Psarou Beach, 84600, Mykonos, Greece
Tel.: (30) 2289200885
Luxury Product Mfr & Distr
N.A.I.C.S.: 315990

Saint Laurent New Zealand Ltd. (1)
Shop S143 Westfield Newmarket 277-309 Broadway, Newmarket, Auckland, 1023, New Zealand
Tel.: (64) 94413687
Clothing Accessory Retailer
N.A.I.C.S.: 458110

Saint Laurent Norway As (1)
Nedre Slottsgate 13 15, 0159, Oslo, Norway
Tel.: (47) 23507880
Clothing Accessory Retailer
N.A.I.C.S.: 458110

Saint Laurent Poland Sp. Z o.o (1)
9 Bracka Street, 00-501, Warsaw, Poland
Tel.: (48) 223107314
Luxury Product Mfr & Distr
N.A.I.C.S.: 315990

Saint Laurent Portugal S.L. (1)
180 Avenida Da Liberdade, 1250-146, Lisbon, Portugal
Tel.: (351) 210423250
Luxury Product Mfr & Distr
N.A.I.C.S.: 315990

Saint Laurent Sweden AB (1)
NK 244, 111 47, Stockholm, Sweden
Tel.: (46) 852519355
Clothing Accessory Retailer
N.A.I.C.S.: 458110

Sowind Japan KK (1)
Hirakawacho Kyowa Building 3F 2-2-1 Hirakawacho, Chiyoda-ku, Tokyo, 102-0093, Japan
Tel.: (81) 352111791
Web Site: https://sowind-japan.jp
Apparel & Accessories Distr
N.A.I.C.S.: 424350

Test & Innovation Lab S.R.L. (1)
Via Pantin 1, 50018, Scandicci, Italy
Tel.: (39) 05741770001
Web Site: https://www.labtil.com
Fashion & Cosmetic Mfr
N.A.I.C.S.: 325620

The Orange Square Company Ltd. (1)
16th Floor 200 Aldersgate Street, London, EC1A 4HD, United Kingdom
Tel.: (44) 3300532398
Web Site: https://www.creedfragrances.co.uk
Perfume Product Distr
N.A.I.C.S.: 424210

Ulysse Nardin (Asia Pacific) Ltd. (1)
902 Ocean Centre 5 Canton Road, Tsim Sha Tsui, Kowloon, China (Hong Kong)
Tel.: (852) 29570000
Apparel & Accessories Distr
N.A.I.C.S.: 424350
Regina Wong *(Mktg Mgr)*

Ulysse Nardin Le Locle SA (1)
Rue du Jardin 3, 2400, Le Locle, Switzerland
Tel.: (41) 329307400
Jewelry Retailer
N.A.I.C.S.: 458310

Ulysse Nardin Russia LLC (1)
Kolokolnikov per 9/10 str 2, 107045, Moscow, Russia
Tel.: (7) 4957950630
Jewelry Retailer
N.A.I.C.S.: 458310

Usinage Et Nouvelles Technologies S.A.S. (1)
Z A Les Buclets 13 Rue des Cotes, 39400, Morbier, France
Tel.: (33) 384303851
Web Site: https://www.unt.fr
Cutting & Folding Tool Mfr
N.A.I.C.S.: 333515

Vertbaudet UK Ltd. (1)
Highdown House Yeoman Way, Worthing, BN99 3HH, West Sussex, United Kingdom
Tel.: (44) 8448420000
Web Site: https://www.vertbaudet.co.uk
Mail Ordering Shopping Services
N.A.I.C.S.: 458110

Volcom, Inc. (1)
1740 Monrovia Ave, Costa Mesa, CA 92627
Tel.: (949) 646-2175
Web Site: http://www.volcom.com
Sales Range: $300-349.9 Million
Emp.: 543
Outdoor Gear & Apparel Designer, Marketer & Distr
N.A.I.C.S.: 315990

WORLD CAT Ltd (1)
Rm 77-87 8/f Kitec 1 Trademart Drive Wang Chin St, Kowloon Bay, Kowloon, China (Hong Kong)
Tel.: (852) 27374399
Emp.: 18
Clothing Apparels Whslr
N.A.I.C.S.: 424350

Yves Saint Laurent SAS (1)
37-39 Rue de Bellechasse, 75007, Paris, France
Tel.: (33) 184955600
Web Site: https://www.ysl.com
Fashion Clothing Distr
N.A.I.C.S.: 458110

stichd B.V. (1)
De Waterman 2, 5215 MX, Den Bosch, Netherlands
Tel.: (31) 736889393
Web Site: https://stichd.com
Sales Range: $25-49.9 Million
Emp.: 80
Athletic Goods Mfr & Distr
N.A.I.C.S.: 339920
Nina Nix *(Gen Mgr)*

Subsidiary (Non-US):

DOBOTEX ITALIA Srl (2)
Via Dei Missaglia 97, Milan, 20142, Italy
Tel.: (39) 028261514
Web Site: http://www.dobotex.com
Sales Range: $25-49.9 Million
Emp.: 9
Sporting Goods Whslr
N.A.I.C.S.: 423910
Lorenzo Farini *(Country Mgr)*

DOBOTEX UK Ltd (2)
First Floor Office Suite Lancaster House Fountain Court Concorde Way, Millennium Business Park, Mansfield, NG19 7DW, Nottinghamshire, United Kingdom
Tel.: (44) 1623658481

INTERNATIONAL PUBLIC

Women's Clothing Retailer
N.A.I.C.S.: 458110

stichd germany gmbh (2)
Hans-Bockler-Str 1, 40476, Dusseldorf, Germany
Tel.: (49) 2114371170
Web Site: http://www.dobotex.nl
Emp.: 3
Textile Clothing & Footwear Distr
N.A.I.C.S.: 424340
Nina Nix *(Gen Mgr)*

KERJAYA PROSPEK GROUP BERHAD

Menara Vista Petaling 137 Jalan Puchong, Taman Wangsa Permai, 582000, Kuala Lumpur, Malaysia
Tel.: (60) 386828232 MY
Web Site:
https://www.kerjayagroup.com
KERJAYA—(KLS)
Rev.: $320,588,052
Assets: $355,846,296
Liabilities: $104,722,339
Net Worth: $251,123,957
Earnings: $28,666,978
Emp.: 439
Fiscal Year-end: 12/31/23
Construction, Cabinetry, Lighting & Property Development Services
N.A.I.C.S.: 327910
Eng Ho Tee *(Chm)*

Subsidiaries:

Advance Industries Sdn. Bhd. (1)
17-G Jalan Puteri 4/7A Bandar Puterii, 47100, Puchong, Selangor, Malaysia
Tel.: (60) 3 8061 2790
Light Fitting Mfr
N.A.I.C.S.: 335132

Kerjaya Prospek Group Berhad - Ijok Factory (1)
Lot 1676 Jalan Makmur Batu 28, Batang Berjuntai, Ijok, 45600, Malaysia
Tel.: (60) 332791107
Miscellaneous Construction Related Services
N.A.I.C.S.: 236220

KERJAYA PROSPEK PROPERTY BERHAD

No 1 Jalan Wangsa Permai First Floor Bangunan One Wangsa, Taman Wangsa Permai, 52200, Kuala Lumpur, Malaysia
Tel.: (60) 362772666
Web Site:
https://www.kpproperty.com.my
KPPROP—(KLS)
Rev.: $78,438,942
Assets: $228,310,899
Liabilities: $93,925,079
Net Worth: $134,385,820
Earnings: $19,368,466
Emp.: 154
Fiscal Year-end: 03/31/23
Cassettes Mfr
N.A.I.C.S.: 334610
Shiak Wan Leong *(Co-Sec)*

Subsidiaries:

Banda Industries Sdn. Bhd. (1)
No 27 Jalan SS23/11 Taman Sea, 47400, Petaling Jaya, Selangor, Malaysia
Tel.: (60) 378034381
Sales Range: $25-49.9 Million
Emp.: 30
Property Development Services
N.A.I.C.S.: 531390

GSB Properties Sdn. Bhd. (1)
No 27 Jalan SS 23/11 Taman SEA, 47400, Petaling Jaya, Selangor, Malaysia
Tel.: (60) 378038282
Sales Range: $25-49.9 Million
Emp.: 30
Property Development Services
N.A.I.C.S.: 531390
S. B. Gan *(Gen Mgr)*

AND PRIVATE COMPANIES

GSB Summit CD (M) Sdn. Bhd. (1)
No 9 Jalan 3/91A Taman Shamelin
Perkasa, 56100, Kuala Lumpur, Malaysia
Tel.: (60) 392811188
Web Site: http://www.gsbsummit.com.my
Sales Range: $100-124.9 Million
Emp.: 500
Prerecorded Audio Components Mfr
N.A.I.C.S.: 334610

KERLINK SA
1 rue Jacqueline Auriol, 35235,
Thorigne-Fouillard, France
Tel.: (33) 33299122900 FR
Web Site: https://www.kerlink.fr
Year Founded: 2004
ALKLK—(EUR)
Rev.: $15,129,705
Assets: $31,155,757
Liabilities: $22,492,549
Net Worth: $8,663,208
Earnings: ($5,133,017)
Emp.: 71
Fiscal Year-end: 12/31/23
Communication Equipment Mfr & Distr
N.A.I.C.S.: 334515
William Gouesbet *(CEO)*

KERMAN CEMENT INDUSTRIES GROUP INC.
No 3 Africa Boulevard East Farzan,
PO Box 4577-15875, 1917687711,
Tehran, 19176 87711, Iran
Tel.: (98) 2188879421
Web Site: https://www.kcig.ir
Year Founded: 1967
SKER—(THE)
Sales Range: Less than $1 Million
Emp.: 511
Cement Mfr
N.A.I.C.S.: 327310

KERMANSHAH PETROCHEMICAL INDUSTRIES CO.
km 4 of Harsin road-Chehr bridge - km 3 of Shahid Shafiei belt, Kermanshah, Iran
Tel.: (98) 8331272000
Web Site: https://www.kpic.ir
PKER1—(THE)
Sales Range: Less than $1 Million
Chemical Fertilizers Services
N.A.I.C.S.: 212390

KERMAS LTD
20 Sycamore Lodge Stone Hall Pl,
London, EC4M 7DR, United Kingdom
Tel.: (44) 2079379226
Web Site: http://www.kermas.com
Metal Services
N.A.I.C.S.: 332999
Danko Koncar *(Chm & Gen Dir)*

KERMODE RESOURCES LTD.
Suite 230 470 Granville Street, Vancouver, V6C 1V5, BC, Canada
Tel.: (604) 687-7178
Web Site: http://www.kermode.com
KMDRF—(OTCIQ)
Assets: $216,801
Liabilities: $216,527
Net Worth: $274
Earnings: ($430,426)
Fiscal Year-end: 10/31/22
Mineral Exploration Services
N.A.I.C.S.: 213114
Donald G. Moore *(Chm & CEO)*

KERN PARTNERS LTD.
Centennial Place East 3110 520 3rd
Avenue SW, Calgary, T2P 0R3, AB,
Canada
Tel.: (403) 517-1500
Web Site:
 http://www.kernpartners.com

Year Founded: 2000
Rev.: $1,100,000,000
Emp.: 16
Privater Equity Firm
N.A.I.C.S.: 523999
D. Jeffrey van Steenbergen *(Gen Partner)*
Subsidiaries:

Ember Resources Inc. (1)
Devon Tower 800 400 3rd Ave S W, Calgary, T2P 4H2, AB, Canada
Tel.: (403) 270-0803
Web Site: https://www.emberresources.com
Sales Range: $25-49.9 Million
Gas Production
N.A.I.C.S.: 221210

KERNEL HOLDING S.A.
3 T Shevchenka Lane, 1001, Kiev,
01001, Ukraine
Tel.: (380) 444618801
Web Site: https://www.kernel.ua
Year Founded: 1995
KER—(WAR)
Rev.: $3,455,121,000
Assets: $3,885,169,000
Liabilities: $2,141,174,000
Net Worth: $1,743,995,000
Earnings: $298,774,000
Emp.: 10,647
Fiscal Year-end: 06/30/23
Sunflower Oilseed Processing Services
N.A.I.C.S.: 311224
Andrii Verevskyi *(Founder & Chm)*
Subsidiaries:

Druzhba-Nova ALLC (1)
Tel.: (380) 442470058
Web Site: https://www.dnova.com.ua
Agricultural Production Services
N.A.I.C.S.: 115112

Inerco Trade S.A. (1)
Rue Jules-Gachet 9, 1260, Nyon, Switzerland
Tel.: (41) 223651717
Sunflower Oilseed Processing Services
N.A.I.C.S.: 311224

Kropyvnytskyi OEP PJSC (1)
30 Urozhaina Str, Kropyvnytskyi, 25013, Ukraine
Tel.: (380) 522390122
Agricultural Production Services
N.A.I.C.S.: 115112

KERNEX MICROSYSTEMS INDIA LTD
TECHNOPOLIS Plot Nos 38-41
Hardware Technology Park, TSIIC
Layout RAVIRYAL Maheshwaram
Ranga Reddy, Hyderabad, 501510,
India
Tel.: (91) 8414667600
Web Site: https://www.kernex.in
KERNEX—(NSE)
Rev.: $584,402
Assets: $12,319,047
Liabilities: $2,376,999
Net Worth: $9,942,048
Earnings: ($2,426,460)
Emp.: 164
Fiscal Year-end: 03/31/23
Computer Software & Hardware Developer
N.A.I.C.S.: 541511
Manthena Badari Narayana Raju *(Exec Dir)*

KERRY GROUP LIMITED
25/F Kerry Centre 683 King's Road,
Quarry Bay, China (Hong Kong)
Tel.: (852) 29672200 CK
Sales Range: $1-4.9 Billion
Investment Holding Company
N.A.I.C.S.: 551112

Khoon Chen Kuok *(Deputy Chm & Mng Dir)*
Subsidiaries:

Kerry Properties (North China) Development Co., Ltd. (1)
Unit 2806 North Tower Beijing Kerry Centre 1 Guang Hua Rd, Chao Yang District, Beijing, China (100%)
Tel.: (86) 10 8529 6266
Web Site: http://www.kerryprops.com
Real Estate Developments & Investments
N.A.I.C.S.: 531210
Shaohua Qian *(Co-Mng Dir)*

Holding (Non-US):

Kerry Properties Ltd. (2)
25/F Kerry Centre 683 King s Road, Quarry Bay, China (Hong Kong) (52.16%)
Tel.: (852) 29672200
Web Site: https://www.kerryprops.com
Rev.: $1,873,576,636
Assets: $25,250,307,031
Liabilities: $9,172,132,297
Net Worth: $16,078,174,733
Earnings: $764,639,357
Emp.: 7,800
Fiscal Year-end: 12/31/2020
Holding Company; Real Estate Investment, Development & Property Management; Logistics Network Developer & Operator
N.A.I.C.S.: 551112
Bryan Pallop Gaw *(Exec Dir)*

Subsidiary (Non-US):

Beijing Jia Ao Real Estate Development Co. Ltd. (3)
Unit 2301 N Twr Beijing Kerry Ctr, 1 Guang Hua Road Chao Yang Dis, 100020, Beijing, China
Tel.: (86) 1085298228
Web Site: http://www.beijingkerrycentre.com
Real Estate Investment Services
N.A.I.C.S.: 531110

Subsidiary (US):

Burgo Inc. (3)
1509 Wesley Ave, Springdale, AR 72764-0901 (100%)
Tel.: (479) 756-1779
Fast Food Restaurants
N.A.I.C.S.: 722513
Terry Clark *(Pres)*

Subsidiary (Domestic):

Kerry Cargo Centre Limited (3)
Room 1601 16th Floor Kerry Cargo Center, 55 Wing Kei Road, Kwai Chung, China (Hong Kong) (100%)
Tel.: (852) 24103600
Web Site: http://www.kerrylogistics.com
General Warehousing & Storage
N.A.I.C.S.: 493110

Kerry Project Management (H.K.) Limited (3)
25/F Kerry Centre 683 King's Road, Quarry Bay, China (Hong Kong) (100%)
Tel.: (852) 29672200
Web Site: http://www.kerryprops.com
Emp.: 300
Management Consulting Services
N.A.I.C.S.: 541618
Keng Lam Ang *(Exec Dir)*

Kerry Properties (H.K.) Limited (3)
Kerry Centre 683 Kings Road, Quarry Bay, China (Hong Kong) (100%)
Tel.: (852) 29672200
Web Site: http://www.kerryprops.com
Real Estate Agents & Brokers
N.A.I.C.S.: 531210
Bryan Pallop Gaw *(Deputy Gen Mgr)*

Subsidiary (Non-US):

Kerry Properties (Macau) Limited (3)
Flat A 19th Floor San Kin Yip Commercial Center, 51 Foshan Street, Macau, China (Macau)
Tel.: (853) 28785963
Web Site: http://www.kerryprops.com
Real Estate Property Lessors
N.A.I.C.S.: 531190

KERRY GROUP LIMITED

Kerry Properties (Shenzhen) Co. Ltd. (3)
12th Floor Kerry Plz 1st Jhontsisu Road, 14 District, Shenzhen, China (100%)
Tel.: (86) 75582300222
Web Site: http://www.kerryprop.com
Real Estate Property Lessors
N.A.I.C.S.: 531190

Kerry Properties Development Management (Shanghai) Co .Ltd. (3)
5th Floor Tower 1 Kerry Everbright City, 218 Tian Mu Road West, 200070, Shanghai, China (100%)
Tel.: (86) 2163178008
Sales Range: $150-199.9 Million
Emp.: 400
Real Estate Services
N.A.I.C.S.: 531390

Subsidiary (Domestic):

Kerry Property Management Services Limited (3)
25th Fl Kerry Ctr 683 Kings's Rd, Quarry Bay, China (Hong Kong) (100%)
Tel.: (852) 29672200
Sales Range: $50-74.9 Million
Emp.: 300
Real Estate Agents & Brokers
N.A.I.C.S.: 531210

Kerry Real Estate Agency Limited (3)
25/F Kerry Centre 683 King's Road, Quarry Bay, China (Hong Kong) (100%)
Tel.: (852) 29672200
Web Site: http://www.kerryprops.com
Real Estate Agents & Brokers
N.A.I.C.S.: 531210

Kerry Records Management Services Limited (3)
Room 1601 16th Fl Kerry Cargo Ctr, 55 Wing Kei Rd, Kwai Chung, China (Hong Kong) (100%)
Tel.: (852) 24103600
General Warehousing & Storage
N.A.I.C.S.: 493110

Magnifair Company Limited (3)
25th Kerry Ctr, 683 King's Road, Quarry Bay, China (Hong Kong) (100%)
Tel.: (852) 29672200
Web Site: http://www.kerryprops.com
Emp.: 300
Investment Advice
N.A.I.C.S.: 523940
Keng Lam Ang *(Exec Dir)*

Maple Crest Development Limited (3)
25/F Kerry Centre 683 King's Road, Quarry Bay, China (Hong Kong)
Tel.: (852) 29672200
Web Site: http://www.kerryprops.com
Sales Range: $200-249.9 Million
Emp.: 300
Investment Banking & Securities Dealing
N.A.I.C.S.: 523150
Keng Lam Ang *(Exec Dir)*

MegaBox Development Company Limited (3)
25F Kerry Ctr, 6 H 3King Rd, Quarry Bay, China (Hong Kong) (100%)
Tel.: (852) 29672200
Sales Range: $75-99.9 Million
Emp.: 300
Management Consulting Services
N.A.I.C.S.: 541618

MegaBox Management Services Limited (3)
25th Kerry Ctr, 683 Kings Rd, Quarry Bay, China (Hong Kong) (100%)
Tel.: (852) 29672200
Web Site: http://www.kerryprops.com
Emp.: 300
Management Consulting Services
N.A.I.C.S.: 541618
Keng Lam Ang *(Exec Dir)*

Win House Industries Limited (3)
25/F Kerry Ctr 683 King's Rd, Quarry Bay, China (Hong Kong) (100%)
Tel.: (852) 29672200
Web Site: http://www.kerryprops.com
Specialty Trade Contractors

KERRY GROUP LIMITED / INTERNATIONAL PUBLIC

Kerry Group Limited—(Continued)
N.A.I.C.S.: 236220
Keng Lam Ang *(Exec Dir)*

KERRY GROUP PLC
Prince's Street Tralee, County Kerry,
Tralee, V92 EH11, Ireland
Tel.: (353) 667182000
Web Site: http://www.kerrygroup.com
Year Founded: 1972
KRZ—(ISE)
Rev.: $8,655,622,707
Assets: $12,618,605,653
Liabilities: $5,579,106,411
Net Worth: $7,039,499,245
Earnings: $785,775,955
Emp.: 21,000
Fiscal Year-end: 12/31/23
Food Ingredients, Convenience Consumer Food Products & Flavors Mfr
N.A.I.C.S.: 311999
Gerry Behan *(CEO-Taste & Nutrition)*

Subsidiaries:

ARIAKE U.S.A., Inc. (1)
1711 N Liberty St, Harrisonburg, VA 22802-4518
Tel.: (540) 432-6550
Web Site: https://ariake-usa-inc.edan.io
Processed Meat Mfr
N.A.I.C.S.: 112320
Kineo Okada *(Founder & Pres)*

Afribon Cameroun S.A.R.L. (1)
Immeuble CEDAM 6e etage, Bali, Douala, Cameroon
Tel.: (237) 620631348
Financial Services
N.A.I.C.S.: 523999

Biosearch S.A. (1)
Camino de Purchil 66, 18004, Granada, Spain
Tel.: (34) 95 824 0152
Web Site: https://www.biosearchlife.es
Health Food Products Based On Natural Compounds Mfr, Researcher & Developer
N.A.I.C.S.: 325414

Cereal Innovations Limited (1)
45 Stapledon Road, Peterborough, PE2 6TD, Cambridgeshire, United Kingdom
Tel.: (44) 1733234076
Sales Range: $25-49.9 Million
Emp.: 5
Food Products Mfr
N.A.I.C.S.: 311999
Mark Wilkinson *(Gen Mgr)*

Dairyborn Foods Limited (1)
Eaton Green Road, Luton, LU2 9XF, Hertfordshire, United Kingdom
Tel.: (44) 1582 457 979
Sales Range: $25-49.9 Million
Emp.: 10
Dairy Products Mfr
N.A.I.C.S.: 311514
Steve Miller *(Gen Mgr)*

Dera Food Technology CZ SRO (1)
Marikova 36, 621 00, Brno, Czech Republic
Tel.: (420) 541 423 611
Web Site: http://www.dera.cz
Sales Range: $25-49.9 Million
Emp.: 20
Food Products Mfr
N.A.I.C.S.: 311999
Petr Volf *(Dir)*

Dera Limited (1)
Bud 3 Golosiivsky R-N Prov Chervonoarmisky, Kiev, Ukraine
Tel.: (380) 445360234
Food Products Mfr & Distr
N.A.I.C.S.: 311999

EBI Foods Limited (1)
Tel.: (44) 1235554654
Food Coatings & Flavors Mfr
N.A.I.C.S.: 311520

Enmex, S.A. de C.V. (1)
Rio Lerma 228 Fracc Ind, San Nicolas, Tlalnepantla, Mexico
Tel.: (52) 5555655999
Web Site: https://explore.kerry.com

Enzyme Product Mfr & Distr
N.A.I.C.S.: 325411

Fleischmann's Vinegar Company, Inc. (1)
12604 Hiddencreek Way Ste A, Cerritos, CA 90703-0703
Tel.: (562) 483-4600
Web Site: http://www.fleischmannsvinegar.com
Vinegar Mfr
N.A.I.C.S.: 311999

Freshways Limited (1)
IDA Industrial Park Poppintree, Finglas, Dublin, Ireland
Tel.: (353) 1 4046964
Web Site: http://www.freshways.ie
Prepared Sandwich Food Mfr & Distr
N.A.I.C.S.: 311991
Diarmuid Shanahan *(Owner)*

Golden Cow Dairies Limited (1)
Tel.: (44) 2838338411
Web Site: http://www.kerry.ae
Sales Range: $50-74.9 Million
Emp.: 120
Dairy Products Distr
N.A.I.C.S.: 424430

Henry Denny & Sons (NI) Limited (1)
6 Corcrain Road, Portadown, BT62 3UF, United Kingdom
Tel.: (44) 28 38332411
Sales Range: $25-49.9 Million
Emp.: 25
Dairy Products Distr
N.A.I.C.S.: 424990
Paul Barbour *(Gen Mgr)*

Kerry (Canada) Inc. (1)
615 Jack Ross Ave, PO Box 1673, Woodstock, N4S 0A9, ON, Canada
Tel.: (450) 378-0841
Sales Range: $25-49.9 Million
Emp.: 65
Food Ingredient & Flavour Mfr
N.A.I.C.S.: 311999

Kerry (NL) B.V. (1)
Tel.: (31) 365233100
Sales Range: $25-49.9 Million
Emp.: 3
Food Ingredient Mfr
N.A.I.C.S.: 311999

Kerry (Quebec) Inc. (1)
187 Boul Begin RR 1, Sainte-Claire, G0R 2V0, QC, Canada
Tel.: (418) 883-3301
Web Site: http://www.kerry.com
Emp.: 200
Fluid Milk Mfr
N.A.I.C.S.: 311511

Kerry Agribusiness (1)
Kilmallock Road, Charleville, Cork, P56 E367, Ireland
Tel.: (353) 6335000
Web Site: http://www.kerryagribusiness.ie
Dairy Products Mfr
N.A.I.C.S.: 112120

Kerry Bio-Science B.V. (1)
Lindtsedijk 8, 3336 LE, Zwijndrecht, Netherlands
Tel.: (31) 786109920
Web Site: http://www.kerrygroup.com
Sales Range: $150-199.9 Million
Emp.: 970
Food Ingredient Mfr
N.A.I.C.S.: 311999

Subsidiary (US):

Kerry Bio-Science (2)
2402 7th St NW, Rochester, MN 55901-7536
Tel.: (507) 285-3400
Sales Range: $25-49.9 Million
Emp.: 85
Flavors & Food Ingredients Mfr
N.A.I.C.S.: 311999
George Mathey *(Mgr)*

Kerry Bio-Science (2)
158 State Hwy 320, Norwich, NY 13815
Tel.: (607) 334-9951
Sales Range: $25-49.9 Million
Emp.: 125
Flavors & Food Ingredients Mfr

N.A.I.C.S.: 311999
Subsidiary (Non-US):

Kerry Food Ingredients (Philippines) (2)
Tel.: (63) 323400319
Web Site: http://www.kerryfoods.com
Sales Range: $10-24.9 Million
Emp.: 45
Flavors & Food Ingredients Mfr
N.A.I.C.S.: 311999

Kerry Farm Supplies Limited (1)
Farranfore, Killarney, Ireland
Tel.: (353) 66 9764466
Sales Range: $25-49.9 Million
Emp.: 20
Farm Supplies Distr
N.A.I.C.S.: 424910
Raymond Moynihan *(Gen Mgr)*

Kerry Food Ingredients (Cebu), Inc. (1)
P Suico Street, Tabok, Mandaue, 6014, Philippines
Tel.: (63) 323400319
Sales Range: $25-49.9 Million
Emp.: 45
Food Ingredient Chemicals Mfr
N.A.I.C.S.: 325998
Jose Arturo Evalle *(Gen Mgr)*

Kerry Food Ingredients (Cork) Limited (1)
Tel.: (353) 6335750
Sales Range: $25-49.9 Million
Emp.: 90
Food Ingredient Chemicals Mfr
N.A.I.C.S.: 325998

Kerry Food Ingredients (Hangzhou) Company Limited (1)
Tel.: (86) 57186922888
Food Ingredient Chemicals Mfr
N.A.I.C.S.: 325998

Kerry Foods Limited (1)
Tel.: (44) 1784430777
Web Site: https://www.kerrygroup.com
Sales Range: $50-74.9 Million
Emp.: 200
Food Products Mfr & Distr
N.A.I.C.S.: 311999

Kerry Foods Noon Group (1)
Windmill Lane, Southall, UB2 4NA, Middlesex, United Kingdom
Tel.: (44) 20 8571 1866
Web Site: http://www.kerrygroup.com
Emp.: 1,500
Food Products Distr
N.A.I.C.S.: 424420

Kerry Guatemala, S.A. (1)
23 Avenida 34-61 Zona 12, Colonia Santa Elisa, Guatemala, Guatemala
Tel.: (502) 24793650
Food & Raw Material Whslr
N.A.I.C.S.: 445298

Kerry Holding Co. (1)
3400 Millington Rd, Beloit, WI 53511-9554
Tel.: (608) 363-1200
Food Processors & Mfr
N.A.I.C.S.: 311999

Subsidiary (Non-US):

Ganeden Biotech, Inc. (2)
Tel.: (440) 229-5200
Web Site: http://www.ganedenprobiotics.com
Nutrition & Wellnes Products Mfr
N.A.I.C.S.: 325412

Subsidiary (Domestic):

Guernsey Bel Inc. (2)
4300 S Morgan St, Chicago, IL 60609
Tel.: (773) 927-4000
Flavoring Extracts & Syrups
N.A.I.C.S.: 311930

Insight Beverages, Inc. (2)
635 Oakwood Dr, Lake Zurich, IL 60047
Tel.: (847) 438-1598
Web Site: http://www.insightbeverages.com
Sales Range: $1-9.9 Million
Emp.: 25
Beverages Mfr

N.A.I.C.S.: 312111
Kerry, Inc. (2)
3400 Millington Rd Regional Technology and Innovation Centre, Beloit, WI 53511
Tel.: (608) 363-1200
Web Site: http://www.kerryingredients.com
Emp.: 750
Mfr & Distr of Food Products & Food Ingredients
N.A.I.C.S.: 311999

Unit (Domestic):

Kerry Foodservice (3)
30 Paragon Pkwy, Mansfield, OH 44903
Tel.: (419) 522-2722
Sales Range: $25-49.9 Million
Emp.: 50
Mfr & Marketer of Flavored Syrups, Extracts, Specialty Sugars, Oils, Toppings & Dressings
N.A.I.C.S.: 424490

Plant (Domestic):

Kerry Ingredients (3)
1301 Mark St, Elk Grove Village, IL 60007-6711
Tel.: (847) 595-2390
Sales Range: $50-74.9 Million
Emp.: 145
Production/Sale of Decorative Sugar Products, Garnishes & Almond Paste
N.A.I.C.S.: 311340

Kerry Ingredients (3)
400 Prairie Villlage Dr, New Century, KS 66031
Tel.: (913) 780-1212
Web Site: https://www.kerryingredients.com
Rev.: $80,000,000
Emp.: 170
Mfr of Chocolate & Cocoa Products; Candy & Other Confectionery Products
N.A.I.C.S.: 311999

Kerry Ingredients & Flavors (3)
5200 US Hwy 98 S, Lakeland, FL 33813
Tel.: (863) 619-2222
Web Site: http://www.kerry.com
Sales Range: $25-49.9 Million
Emp.: 75
Flavors & Flavor Ingredients Mfr
N.A.I.C.S.: 311930
Susie Brown *(Plant Mgr)*

Kerry Ingredients & Flavors (3)
1916 Tubeway Ave, Commerce, CA 90041
Tel.: (323) 727-1957
Web Site: http://www.kerry.com
Sales Range: $25-49.9 Million
Emp.: 75
Flavoring Extracts & Syrups
N.A.I.C.S.: 311930

Kerry Ingredients & Flavors (3)
11 W Dr Martin Luther King Jr Blvd, Plant City, FL 33563
Tel.: (877) 999-2654
Web Site: http://www.kerry.com
Rev.: $11,300,000
Emp.: 125
Flavors & Flavor Ingredients Mfr
N.A.I.C.S.: 311423

Kerry Ingredients & Flavors Clark Manufacturing Facility (3)
160 Terminal Ave, Clark, NJ 07066-1319
Tel.: (732) 882-0202
Web Site: http://www.kerry.com
Sales Range: $25-49.9 Million
Emp.: 15
Mfr of Food & Flavor Ingredients
N.A.I.C.S.: 311930

Subsidiary (Domestic):

Kerry Savory, Inc. (3)
21612 88th Ave S, Kent, WA 98031-1918
Tel.: (253) 395-9400
Sales Range: $25-49.9 Million
Emp.: 90
Mfr of Spices & Custom Blended Seasonings & Whole Nuts
N.A.I.C.S.: 311942

Kerry Holdings (Ireland) Limited (1)
Princes St, Tralee, V92 EH11, Co Kerry, Ireland
Tel.: (353) 667122433

AND PRIVATE COMPANIES

Emp.: 15
Investment Management Service
N.A.I.C.S.: 523999

Kerry Hungaria KFT. (1)
FSD Park 2, H-2045, Torokbalint, Hungary
Tel.: (36) 23510820
Web Site: https://www.kerry.hu
Sales Range: $25-49.9 Million
Emp.: 16
Spice Blend Mfr
N.A.I.C.S.: 311942

Kerry Iberia Taste & Nutrition, S.L.U. (1)
Coto de Donana 15, Pinto, 28320, Madrid, Spain
Tel.: (34) 3536335750
Food Product Ingredients Mfr
N.A.I.C.S.: 325199

Kerry Ingredients & Flavours Italia S.p.A. (1)
Via Capitani di Mozzo 12/16, 24030, Mozzo, Bergamo, Italy
Tel.: (39) 035468511
Food Ingredient & Flavor Mfr
N.A.I.C.S.: 311351

Kerry Ingredients & Flavours Limited (1)
Princess Street, Tralee, V92 EH11, Co Kerry, Ireland
Tel.: (353) 6335750
Sales Range: $25-49.9 Million
Emp.: 20
Food Ingredient Mfr
N.A.I.C.S.: 311423

Kerry Ingredients (Ireland) Limited (1)
Tel.: (353) 6335400
Cheese & Dairy Products Distr
N.A.I.C.S.: 424490

Kerry Ingredients (M) Sdn. Bhd. (1)
Tel.: (60) 72332800
Sales Range: $150-199.9 Million
Emp.: 290
Application Specific Ingredient & Flavors Distr
N.A.I.C.S.: 424490

Kerry Ingredients (NZ) Limited (1)
11-13 Bell Avenue, Otahuhu, Auckland, 1060, New Zealand
Tel.: (64) 92760950
Sales Range: $25-49.9 Million
Emp.: 100
Food Ingredients Mfr & Distr
N.A.I.C.S.: 311351

Kerry Ingredients (Thailand) Limited (1)
618 Moo 4 Bangpoo Industrial Estate Soi 8a Thumbol Preaksa, Amphur Muang, Samut Prakan, 10280, Thailand
Tel.: (66) 23246100
Emp.: 16
Food Ingredients Mfr & Distr
N.A.I.C.S.: 311351

Kerry Ingredients (UK) Limited (1)
Tel.: (44) 1454201666
Web Site: http://www.kerry-ingredients.co.uk
Sales Range: $75-99.9 Million
Emp.: 200
Food Ingredients & Flavors Distr
N.A.I.C.S.: 424490

Kerry Ingredients (de Mexico) S.A. de C.V. (1)
Tel.: (52) 4626239900
Web Site: http://www.kerrymexico.com
Sales Range: $100-124.9 Million
Emp.: 500
Food Ingredients & Flavor Mfr
N.A.I.C.S.: 311999

Kerry Ingredients Australia Pty. Limited (1)
Tel.: (61) 297414422
Sales Range: $250-299.9 Million
Emp.: 350
Food Ingredient Chemicals Mfr & Distr
N.A.I.C.S.: 325998

Kerry Ingredients GmbH (1)
Hauptstrasse 22, 63924, Kleinheubach, Germany
Tel.: (49) 937140900
Food Additives Mfr
N.A.I.C.S.: 311999

Kerry Ingredients Holdings (France) S.A. (1)
Tel.: (33) 490763131
Investment Management Service
N.A.I.C.S.: 523999

Kerry Ingredients India Pvt. Limited (1)
Tel.: (91) 1244186420
Web Site: http://kerryingredients.in
Food Product Whslr
N.A.I.C.S.: 424420

Kerry Ingredients Nigeria Limited (1)
1st Floor Japaul House Plot 8 Dr Nurudeen, Olowopopo Avenue CBD Agidingbi, Ikeja, Lagos, Nigeria
Tel.: (234) 8126374426
Nutritional Product Mfr
N.A.I.C.S.: 325411

Kerry Ingredients South Africa (Pty) Limited (1)
Tel.: (27) 119236360
Web Site: http://www.kerry.com
Emp.: 12
Food Ingredient Chemicals Mfr & Distr
N.A.I.C.S.: 325998

Kerry Ingredients Trading (Shanghai) Limited (1)
4/F No 92 Bldg No 1122 Qinzhou North Rd Caohejing Development, Shanghai, 200233, China
Tel.: (86) 2154265359
Sales Range: $50-74.9 Million
Emp.: 100
Food Ingredients & Flavoring Agents Distr
N.A.I.C.S.: 424490
Gerald Lennon *(Gen Mgr)*

Kerry Japan Kabushiki Kaisha (1)
1-7-2 Azabudai Kamiyacho Sankei Bldg 2f, Minato-Ku, Tokyo, 106-0041, Japan
Tel.: (81) 355496500
Sales Range: $25-49.9 Million
Emp.: 1
Food Ingredient Mfr
N.A.I.C.S.: 311351

Kerry Kenya Limited (1)
3rd Floor Crater Automobile Building Mombasa Road, Nairobi, Kenya
Tel.: (254) 708701646
Food & Raw Material Whslr
N.A.I.C.S.: 445298

Kerry MENAT DMCC (1)
Customer Co-Creation Centre AG-GF-01&02 Ground Floor AG Tower Silver, PO Box 625768, Cluster / Plot I1 Jumeriah Lakes Towers, Dubai, United Arab Emirates
Tel.: (971) 43635900
Food Product Ingredients Mfr
N.A.I.C.S.: 325199

Kerry Panama, S.A. (1)
Parque Industrial Costa del Este Via Principal y Calle 3ra lote, 88 Corregimiento Parque Lefevre Apartado, 0819-01869, Panama, Panama
Tel.: (507) 2367640
Food & Raw Material Whslr
N.A.I.C.S.: 445298

Kerry Polska Sp. z.o.o. (1)
Tel.: (48) 713996900
Web Site: http://www.kerrygroup.com
Sales Range: $100-124.9 Million
Emp.: 300
Food Ingredients & Flavors Mfr
N.A.I.C.S.: 311351

Kerry Savoury Ingredients France S.A.S. (1)
Tel.: (33) 134388787
Food Ingredients Mfr & Distr
N.A.I.C.S.: 311999

Kerry Taste & Nutrition (Vietnam) Company Limited (1)
Unit 1405-07 14th Floor Me Linh Point Tower 02 Ngo Duc Ke Street, Ben Nghe Ward District 1, Ho Chi Minh City, Vietnam
Tel.: (84) 2839369600
Nutritional Product Mfr
N.A.I.C.S.: 325411

Kerry Treasury Services Limited (1)
Tel.: (353) 14046900
Sales Range: $50-74.9 Million
Emp.: 80
Treasury Services
N.A.I.C.S.: 921130

Kerry do Brasil Ltda. (1)
Av Mercedes Benz 460, Distrito Industrial, Campinas, 13054-750, Sao Paulo, Brazil
Tel.: (55) 1937655000
Sales Range: $100-124.9 Million
Emp.: 400
Food Ingredient & Flavor Mfr
N.A.I.C.S.: 311351

Lactose (India) Limited (1)
Survey No 5 6 & 7A Village Poicha Rania Taluka Savli, Vadodara, 391780, Gujarat, India
Tel.: (91) 9974093308
Web Site: https://www.lactoseindialimited.com
Rev.: $6,349,912
Assets: $12,315,358
Liabilities: $6,953,010
Net Worth: $5,362,348
Earnings: $334,602
Emp.: 103
Fiscal Year-end: 03/31/2022
Pharmaceuticals Product Mfr
N.A.I.C.S.: 325412
Atul Maheshwari *(Chm & Mng Dir)*

Leckpatrick Dairies Limited (1)
Tel.: (44) 2882246146
Web Site: http://www.leckpatrickfoods.com
Dairy Product Retailer
N.A.I.C.S.: 445298

Lifesource Foods Research Limited (1)
Tel.: (353) 2524411
Food Products Research & Development Services
N.A.I.C.S.: 541715

National Food Ingredients Limited (1)
Prince's Street, Tralee, Ireland
Tel.: (353) 61314498
Emp.: 36
Food Ingredient Distr
N.A.I.C.S.: 424490
Mark Jensen *(Gen Mgr)*

Natreon Inc. (1)
14a Jules Ln, New Brunswick, NJ 08901-3636
Tel.: (732) 296-1080
Web Site: http://www.natreoninc.com
Drugs & Druggists' Sundries Merchant Whslr
N.A.I.C.S.: 424210
Vish Budharaju *(Pres)*

Newmarket Co-op Supervalu Limited (1)
New Street, Newmarket, Cork, Ireland
Tel.: (353) 29 60233
Emp.: 5
Super Market Stores Operating Services
N.A.I.C.S.: 445110
Robert Strobl *(Mgr)*

Newmarket Co-operative Creameries Limited (1)
Tel.: (353) 6335750
Sales Range: $25-49.9 Million
Emp.: 56
Cheddar Cheese Mfr
N.A.I.C.S.: 311513

Niacet Corporation (1)
400 47th St, Niagara Falls, NY 14304
Tel.: (716) 285-1474
Web Site: https://www.niacet.com
Sales Range: $50-74.9 Million
Emp.: 190
Specialty Chemicals Mfr
N.A.I.C.S.: 325998
Kelly A. Brannen *(CEO)*

Subsidiary (Non-US):

Niacet b.v. (2)
Papesteeg 91, 4006 WC, Tiel, Netherlands
Tel.: (31) 344615224
Web Site: https://www.niacet.com

KERRY LOGISTICS NETWORK LIMITED

Sales Range: $50-74.9 Million
Emp.: 106
Specialty Chemicals Mfr
N.A.I.C.S.: 325998

Pevesa Biotech, S.A.U. (1)
Poligono Industrial Polivisa Av Industria n/v, El Viso del Alcor, 41520, Seville, Spain
Tel.: (34) 3536335750
Food Product Ingredients Mfr
N.A.I.C.S.: 325199

Proexcar S.A.S. (1)
Cra 50g Guayabal Medellin Guayabal, Medellin, Antioquia, Colombia
Tel.: (57) 4446752
Web Site: https://proexcar.com.co
Food & Raw Material Whslr
N.A.I.C.S.: 445298

Red Arrow Products Company LLC (1)
633 S 20th St, Manitowoc, WI 54220
Tel.: (920) 769-1100
Web Site: http://www.redarrowusa.com
Emp.: 300
Extracts, Flavoring Mfr
N.A.I.C.S.: 311942

Subsidiary (Domestic):

Red Arrow Equipment Company, Inc. (2)
633 S 20th St, Manitowoc, WI 54220
Tel.: (920) 769-1100
Web Site: http://www.redarrowusa.com
Designer & Implementer of Customized Liquid Smoke Application Equipment
N.A.I.C.S.: 311942

Subsidiary (Non-US):

Red Arrow Handels-GmbH (2)
Hanna-Kunath-Strasse 25, 28199, Bremen, Germany
Tel.: (49) 421596570
Web Site: https://explore.kerry.com
Food Flavoring Mfr & Marketer
N.A.I.C.S.: 311930

Subsidiary (Domestic):

Red Arrow International LLC (2)
633 S 20th St, Manitowoc, WI 54220
Tel.: (920) 769-1100
Web Site: http://www.redarrowinternational.com
Extracts & Flavoring Mfr
N.A.I.C.S.: 311942

Rye Valley Foods Limited (1)
Carrickmacross, Monaghan, Ireland
Tel.: (353) 429690400
Sales Range: $100-124.9 Million
Emp.: 45
Food Products Mfr
N.A.I.C.S.: 311999
John Kieran *(Gen Mgr)*

SpringThyme Oils Limited (1)
Unit 6 ShuttleWorth Mead Business Park, Padiham, BB12 7NG, Lancashire, United Kingdom
Tel.: (44) 1282 682100
Web Site: http://www.springthyme.com
Infused Oil & Fats Mfr
N.A.I.C.S.: 311225

Titusfield Limited (1)
5 Coningsby Road Bretton, Peterborough, PE3 8SB, United Kingdom
Tel.: (44) 1733 269 270
Cereal & Biscuits Mfr
N.A.I.C.S.: 311230

William Blake Limited (1)
Unit 1 Western Business Park Oak Close, Dublin, Ireland
Tel.: (353) 1 450 7177
Web Site: http://www.blakesingredients.com
Food Ingredient Distr
N.A.I.C.S.: 424490

KERRY LOGISTICS NETWORK LIMITED

16/F Kerry Cargo Center 55 Wing Kei Road, Kwai Chung, China (Hong Kong)
Tel.: (852) 24103600

KERRY LOGISTICS NETWORK LIMITED

Kerry Logistics Network Limited—(Continued)

Web Site:
http://www.kerrylogistics.com
0636—(HKG)
Rev.: $11,047,806,533
Assets: $5,780,094,308
Liabilities: $3,070,756,920
Net Worth: $2,709,337,388
Earnings: $487,052,295
Emp.: 43,900
Fiscal Year-end: 12/31/22
Freight Transportation Arrangement
N.A.I.C.S.: 488510
William Wing Kai Ma *(Mng Dir-Grp)*

Subsidiaries:

Apex Maritime Co. Inc. **(1)**
206 Utah Ave, South San Francisco, CA 94080-4080
Tel.: (650) 589-2575
Web Site: http://www.apexshipping.com
General Warehousing & Storage
N.A.I.C.S.: 493110
Kevin Bulger *(COO)*

Kerry Distribution (Thailand) Limited **(1)**
Web Site: http://www.kerrylogistics.com
Sales Range: $50-74.9 Million
Emp.: 200
Freight Transportation Arrangement
N.A.I.C.S.: 488510

Kerry EAS Logistics Limited **(1)**
No 21 Xiaoyun Road North Dongsanhuan Road, Chaoyang District, Beijing, 100027, China
Tel.: (86) 1064618899
Oil Transportation Services
N.A.I.C.S.: 488190

Kerry Facilities Management (Hong Kong) Limited **(1)**
1/F Kerry Cargo Centre, 55 Wing Kei Road, Kwai Chung, China (Hong Kong) **(100%)**
Tel.: (852) 22119800
Web Site: http://www.kerrylogistic.com
Ship Building & Repairing
N.A.I.C.S.: 336611

Kerry Facilities Management Services Limited **(1)**
1/F Kerry Cargo Centre, 55 Wing Kei Road, Kwai Chung, China (Hong Kong) **(100%)**
Tel.: (852) 22119800
Web Site: http://www.kerrylogistics.com
Ship Building & Repairing
N.A.I.C.S.: 336611

Kerry Freight (Australia) Pty Ltd. **(1)**
4 Martin Avenue, Gillman, Adelaide, 5013, SA, Australia **(100%)**
Tel.: (61) 883003000
Web Site: http://www.kerrylogistics.com
Local Freight Trucking Distr
N.A.I.C.S.: 484110
Ian Trimboli *(Mng Dir)*

Kerry Freight (Hong Kong) Limited **(1)**
Unit 301 3rd Floor Kerry Cargo Center, 55 Wing Kei Road, Kwai Chung, China (Hong Kong) **(100%)**
Tel.: (852) 22119300
Web Site: http://www.kerrylogistics.com
Sales Range: $25-49.9 Million
Emp.: 100
Freight Transportation Arrangement
N.A.I.C.S.: 488510

Kerry Freight (Korea) Inc. **(1)**
Unit 901 9th Floor E and C Dream Tower, 46 3-Ka Yangpyeong-Dong, Seoul, 150-103, Korea (South)
Tel.: (82) 236640303
Web Site: http://www.kerrylogistics.com
Sales Range: $25-49.9 Million
Emp.: 50
Freight Transportation Arrangement
N.A.I.C.S.: 488510
Spencer Hong *(Pres)*

Kerry Freight (Taiwan) Limited **(1)**
7th Fl No 57 Fu Shing N Rd, Taipei, Taiwan
Tel.: (886) 227784638
Web Site: http://www.kerrylogistics.com
Marine Cargo Handling
N.A.I.C.S.: 488320

Kerry Freight (Thailand) Limited **(1)**
Room 802 8/F Chao Phya Tower, 89 Soi Wat Suan Plu New Road Bangrak, Bangkok, 10500, Thailand
Tel.: (66) 26868999
Sales Range: $50-74.9 Million
Emp.: 200
Deep Sea Freight Transportation
N.A.I.C.S.: 483111

Kerry Freight International Limited **(1)**
Unit 301 3/F Kerry Cargo Centre, 55 Wing Kei Road, Kwai Chung, China (Hong Kong) **(100%)**
Tel.: (852) 22119300
Web Site: http://www.kerrylogistics.com
Sales Range: $25-49.9 Million
Emp.: 100
Deep Sea Freight Transportation Distr
N.A.I.C.S.: 483111

Kerry Logistics (Australia) Pty Ltd. **(1)**
Martin Avenue Gillman, Adelaide, 5013, SA, Australia **(100%)**
Tel.: (61) 883003000
Web Site: http://www.kerrylogistics.com
Sales Range: $25-49.9 Million
Emp.: 65
Local Freight Trucking
N.A.I.C.S.: 484110
Ian Trimboli *(Gen Mgr)*

Kerry Logistics (Belgium) BvbA **(1)**
Middelmolenlaan 168, Deurne, D-2100, Belgium **(100%)**
Tel.: (32) 36083000
Web Site: http://www.kerrylogistics.com
Sales Range: $25-49.9 Million
Emp.: 3
Air & Sea Freight Services
N.A.I.C.S.: 541614
Daniel Hegwein *(Mng Dir)*

Kerry Logistics (Central Europe) GmbH **(1)**
Schaartor 1 4th Floor, 20459, Hamburg, Germany **(100%)**
Tel.: (49) 403006840
Web Site: http://www.kerrylogistics.com
Sales Range: $25-49.9 Million
Emp.: 10
Deep Sea Freight Transportation
N.A.I.C.S.: 483111
Ronnie Kempf *(Mng Dir)*

Subsidiary (Non-US):

Kerry Logistics GmbH **(2)**
Am Concorde Park 1 A210, Schwechat, 2320, Austria **(100%)**
Tel.: (43) 170610900
Sales Range: $25-49.9 Million
Emp.: 20
Marine Cargo Handling
N.A.I.C.S.: 488320
Johann Endfellner *(Mng Dir)*

Kerry Logistics (Germany) GmbH **(1)**
Johannisbollwerk 16, 20459, Hamburg, Germany **(100%)**
Tel.: (49) 403006840
Web Site: http://www.kerrylogistics.com
Sales Range: $25-49.9 Million
Emp.: 10
Deep Sea Freight Transportation
N.A.I.C.S.: 483111
Thomas Blank *(Mng Dir-Europe)*

Kerry Logistics (Malaysia) Sdn Bhd **(1)**
Lot 844 1st Floor Jalan Subang 7 Taman Perindustrian Subang, Subang Jaya, 47500, Selangor, Malaysia
Tel.: (60) 3 8023 8266
Web Site: http://www.kerrylogistics.com
Freight Transportation, Logistics & Supply Chain Management Services & Operations
N.A.I.C.S.: 488510
Patrick Wong *(Gen Mgr)*

Kerry Logistics (Netherlands) B.V.
AMB Fokker Logistics Ctr 2B, Fokkerweg 300, Oude Meer, NL-1438, Netherlands **(100%)**
Tel.: (31) 205046800
Web Site: http://www.kerrylogistics.com
Sales Range: $25-49.9 Million
Emp.: 10
Deep Sea Freight Transportation
N.A.I.C.S.: 483111
Daniel Hegwein *(Mng Dir)*

Kerry Logistics (Shenzhen Yantian) Ltd. **(1)** **(100%)**
Tel.: (86) 75525281166
Web Site: http://www.kerrylogistics.com
Sales Range: $25-49.9 Million
Emp.: 230
Process Physical Distribution & Logistics Consulting Services
N.A.I.C.S.: 541614

Kerry Logistics (Singapore) Pte. Ltd. **(1)** **(67%)**
Tel.: (65) 62142655
Web Site: http://www.kerrylogistics.com
Sales Range: $25-49.9 Million
Emp.: 40
Freight Transportation Arrangement
N.A.I.C.S.: 488510
Robert Tan *(Mng Dir-South Asia)*

Subsidiary (Non-US):

PT Kerry Logistics (Indonesia) **(2)**
Web Site: http://www.kerrylogistics.com
Sales Range: $25-49.9 Million
Emp.: 25
Process Physical Distribution & Logistics Consulting Services
N.A.I.C.S.: 541614

Kerry Logistics (Switzerland) GmbH **(1)**
Uferstrasse 90, Basel, 4057, Switzerland **(100%)**
Tel.: (41) 616332121
Web Site: http://www.kerrylogistics.com
Sales Range: $25-49.9 Million
Emp.: 15
Deep Sea Freight Transportation
N.A.I.C.S.: 483111
Ronnie Kempf *(Mng Dir)*

Kerry Logistics (Thailand) Limited **(1)** **(100%)**
Tel.: (66) 26868999
Web Site: http://www.kerrylogistics.com
Freight Transportation Arrangement
N.A.I.C.S.: 488510

Kerry Logistics (UK) Limited **(1)**
Broadoak Ind Park Ashburton Road West, Trafford Park, M17 1RW, United Kingdom **(91%)**
Tel.: (44) 1618731481
Web Site: http://www.kerry.com
Sales Range: $25-49.9 Million
Emp.: 100
Process Physical Distribution & Logistics Consulting Services
N.A.I.C.S.: 541614
Dave Gaughan *(Mng Dir)*

Kerry Logistics (Western Europe) Sprl **(1)**
Middel Molen Leen 168, Deurne, 2100, Belgium **(100%)**
Tel.: (32) 36083000
Web Site: http://www.kerrylogistics.com
Sales Range: $25-49.9 Million
Emp.: 3
Transportation Services
N.A.I.C.S.: 488999
Ann Busschots *(Office Mgr)*

Kerry Siam Seaport Limited **(1)**
Room 804 8/F Chao Phya Tower 89 Soi Wat Suan Plu New Road, Bangrak, 10500, Bangkok, Thailand
Tel.: (66) 2 686 8999
Web Site: http://www.kerrylogistics.com
Sales Range: $50-74.9 Million
Emp.: 200
Marine Cargo Handling
N.A.I.C.S.: 488320
Kledchai Benjaathonsirikul *(Exec Dir)*

Kerry TJ Logistics Company Limited **(1)**
23F No 123 Sec 3 TaiChung Kang Rd, Taichung, 40767, Taiwan
Tel.: (886) 423501888
Web Site: http://www.kerrytj.com
Rev.: $393,502,520
Assets: $806,059,324
Liabilities: $379,293,095
Net Worth: $426,766,229
Earnings: $59,919,845
Fiscal Year-end: 12/31/2023
Container Transportation Services
N.A.I.C.S.: 484121

Kerry Warehouse (Chai Wan) Limited **(1)**
50 Ka Yip St, Chai Wan, China (Hong Kong) **(100%)**
Tel.: (852) 25586363
Web Site: http://www.kerrylogistics.com
Sales Range: $150-199.9 Million
Emp.: 1,000
General Warehousing & Storage
N.A.I.C.S.: 493110

Kerry Warehouse (Fanling 1) Limited **(1)**
39 On Lok Mun St, On Lok Tsuen, Fanling, China (Hong Kong) **(100%)**
Tel.: (852) 26763638
Web Site: http://www.kerrylogistics.com
Sales Range: $25-49.9 Million
Emp.: 6
General Warehousing & Storage
N.A.I.C.S.: 493110

Kerry Warehouse (Hong Kong) Limited **(1)**
16/F Kerry Cargo Centre, 55 Wing Kei Road, Kwai Chung, China (Hong Kong) **(100%)**
Tel.: (852) 24103600
Web Site: http://www.kerrylogistics.com
Emp.: 50
General Warehousing & Storage
N.A.I.C.S.: 493110

Kerry Warehouse (Kwai Chung) Limited **(1)**
Rm 1601 16th Floor Kerry Cargo Ctr, 55 Wing Kei Road, Kwai Chung, China (Hong Kong) **(100%)**
Tel.: (852) 24103600
Web Site: http://www.kerrylogistics.com
General Warehousing & Storage
N.A.I.C.S.: 493110

Kerry Warehouse (Sheung Shui) Limited **(1)**
2 San Po St, Sheung Shui, China (Hong Kong) **(100%)**
Tel.: (852) 26735878
Web Site: http://www.kerrylogistics.com
General Warehousing & Storage
N.A.I.C.S.: 493110

Kerry Warehouse (Tsuen Wan) Limited **(1)**
3 Shing Yiu St, Kwai Chung, China (Hong Kong) **(100%)**
Tel.: (852) 29672200
General Warehousing & Storage
N.A.I.C.S.: 493110

KerryFlex Supply Chain Solutions (Macau) Limited **(1)**
A De Venceslau De Morais No 143-173 EDF IND, Keck Seng Bloco II 13 andar em, Macau, China (Macau) **(100%)**
Tel.: (853) 28481081
Web Site: http://www.kerrylogistics.com
Sales Range: $25-49.9 Million
Emp.: 8
General Merchandise Stores
N.A.I.C.S.: 455219

KerryFlex Supply Chain Solutions Limited **(1)**
2/F Block A Kerry TC Warehouse 1, 3 Kin Chuen Street, Kwai Chung, China (Hong Kong) **(100%)**
Tel.: (852) 24104200
Web Site: http://www.kerrylogistics.com
Sales Range: $25-49.9 Million
Emp.: 100
General Merchandise Store Distr
N.A.I.C.S.: 455219

KERSEN TECHNOLOGY CO., LTD

No 155 Xinxing South Road Development Zone, Kunshan City, Suzhou, 215300, Jiangsu, China
Tel.: (86) 51257478666
Web Site:
https://www.kersentech.com
Year Founded: 2003
603626—(SHG)
Rev.: $480,682,018
Assets: $800,146,732
Liabilities: $364,293,465
Net Worth: $435,853,267
Earnings: $12,183,715
Emp.: 1,500
Fiscal Year-end: 12/31/22
Precision Metal Component Mfr & Distr
N.A.I.C.S.: 334519
Peter Xu *(Chm & CEO)*

KERUR HOLDINGS LTD.
8 Ariel Sharon Street Building B 2nd Floor, Or Yehuda, 6037607, Israel
Tel.: (972) 35689200
Web Site: https://kerur-holdings.co.il
Year Founded: 1929
KRUR—(TAE)
Rev.: $270,048,069
Assets: $356,833,926
Liabilities: $91,062,853
Net Worth: $265,801,073
Earnings: $31,562,646
Fiscal Year-end: 12/31/23
Electronic & Precision Equipment Repair & Maintenance
N.A.I.C.S.: 811210
Doron Steiger *(CEO)*

KERVAN GIDA SANAYI VE TICARET A.S.
Yakuplu Mah Beysan Sanayi Sitesi Fuar Cad No 9/1, Beylikduzu, 34524, Istanbul, Turkiye
Tel.: (90) 2128757690
Web Site:
https://www.kervangida.com
Year Founded: 1995
KRVGD—(IST)
Rev.: $149,505,850
Assets: $133,036,970
Liabilities: $79,332,622
Net Worth: $53,704,348
Earnings: $12,607,313
Fiscal Year-end: 12/31/22
Packaged Food Product Mfr & Distr
N.A.I.C.S.: 311991
Mehmet Sukru Basar *(Chm)*

KERVANSARAY YATIRIM HOLDING A.S.
Ayazaga Neighborhood Sogut Street Agaoglu Maslak 1453, Sariyer, Istanbul, Turkiye
Tel.: (90) 2123304001
Web Site:
http://www.kervansarayholding.com
Year Founded: 1950
KERVN—(IST)
Rev.: $27,420
Assets: $183,458,398
Liabilities: $170,541,157
Net Worth: $12,917,241
Earnings: ($13,101,465)
Fiscal Year-end: 12/31/23
Holding Company
N.A.I.C.S.: 551112
Selim Sayilgan *(Chm)*

KERVERUS HOLDING IT (CYPRUS) PLC
Anexartisias & Athinon Nora Court 2nd Floor, Limassol, Cyprus
Tel.: (357) 25025070
Software Development Services
N.A.I.C.S.: 541511

KERZNER INTERNATIONAL LIMITED
Executive Offices Coral Towers, Paradise Island, Bahamas
Tel.: (242) 3636000 BS
Web Site: http://www.kerzner.com
Year Founded: 1993
Sales Range: $700-749.9 Million
Emp.: 8,574
Resort & Casino Developer, Operator & Manager
N.A.I.C.S.: 713990
Ian Connolly *(Chief Dev Officer)*

Subsidiaries:

Trading Cove Associates (1)
914 Hartford Tpke, Waterford, CT 06385-0715
Tel.: (860) 442-1202
Web Site:
http://www.waterfordhotelgroup.com
Sales Range: $75-99.9 Million
Emp.: 1
Casino Investment & Development Company; Owned 50% by Waterford Gaming, LLC & 50% by Kerzner International Limited
N.A.I.C.S.: 523999
Len Wolman *(Mng Partner)*

KESAR ENTERPRISES LIMITED
Oriental House 6th Floor 7 Jamshedji Tata Road Churchgate, Mumbai, 400020, India
Tel.: (91) 2222042396
Web Site:
https://www.kesarindia.com
Year Founded: 1933
507180—(BOM)
Rev.: $89,323,088
Assets: $85,800,515
Liabilities: $67,525,185
Net Worth: $18,275,330
Earnings: $12,261,863
Emp.: 252
Fiscal Year-end: 03/31/21
Sugar & Alcoholic Mfr
N.A.I.C.S.: 311314
H. R. Kilachand *(Chm & Mng Dir)*

Subsidiaries:

Kesar Terminals & Infrastructure Limited (1)
Oriental House 6th Floor 7 Jamshedji Tata Road, Churchgate, Mumbai, 400020, India (37.93%)
Tel.: (91) 222 204 2396
Web Site: http://www.kesarinfra.com
Rev.: $6,219,104
Assets: $32,652,042
Liabilities: $31,906,315
Net Worth: $745,727
Earnings: ($3,205,389)
Emp.: 52
Fiscal Year-end: 03/31/2021
Holding Company; Bulk Liquid Storage Terminal Operator & Logistics Services
N.A.I.C.S.: 551112
V. J. Doshi *(CFO)*

Subsidiary (Domestic):

Kesar Multimodal Logistics Limited (2)
Oriental House 6th Floor 7 Jamshedji Tata Road, Churchgate, Mumbai, 400020, India
Tel.: (91) 2222042396
Web Site: https://www.kesarmultimodal.com
Bulk Liquid Storage & Logistic Services
N.A.I.C.S.: 424710
H. R. Kilachand *(Chm)*

KESAR INDIA LIMITED
F-101 Jagat Plaza Law Collage Sqaure Amravati Road, Nagpur, 440010, India
Tel.: (91) 18001230854
Web Site:
https://www.kesarlands.com
Year Founded: 2003
543542—(BOM)
Rev.: $1,850,417
Assets: $3,783,874
Liabilities: $1,485,486
Net Worth: $2,298,387
Earnings: $93,927
Emp.: 70
Fiscal Year-end: 03/31/23
Real Estate Investment Services
N.A.I.C.S.: 531190

KESAR PETROPRODUCTS LIMITED
D 7/1 MIDC Industrial Area Lote Parshuram Taluka Khed, Ratnagiri, 415 722, Maharashtra, India
Tel.: (91) 2356272339
Web Site:
https://www.kesarpetroproducts.com
Rev.: $22,392,449
Assets: $21,114,793
Liabilities: $4,126,812
Net Worth: $16,987,981
Earnings: ($45,353)
Emp.: 196
Fiscal Year-end: 03/31/19
Petrochemical Mfr
N.A.I.C.S.: 325180
Manila M. More *(CFO)*

KESHUN WATERPROOF TECHNOLOGIES CO., LTD.
No 38-1 Hongqi Zhong Road Industrial Zone, Ronggui Shunde district, Foshan, 528300, Guangdong, China
Tel.: (86) 75728637166 CN
Web Site: https://cks.keshun.com.cn
Year Founded: 1996
300737—(SSE)
Rev.: $955,705,595
Assets: $1,248,414,832
Liabilities: $612,211,839
Net Worth: $636,202,993
Earnings: $136,407,459
Fiscal Year-end: 12/31/20
Asphalt Coating Material Mfr & Distr
N.A.I.C.S.: 324122
Weizhong Chen *(Chm)*

KESKISUOMALAINEN OYJ
Tel.: (358) 14622000
Web Site:
https://keskisuomalainen.com
Year Founded: 1870
KSLAV—(HEL)
Rev.: $238,517,160
Assets: $211,299,374
Liabilities: $121,821,714
Net Worth: $89,477,660
Earnings: $8,061,731
Emp.: 1,583
Fiscal Year-end: 12/31/22
Media Advertising Services
N.A.I.C.S.: 541840
Vesa-Pekka Kangaskorpi *(CEO)*

KESKO CORPORATION
Tyopajankatu 12, 00580, Helsinki, Finland
Tel.: (358) 105311 FI
Web Site: https://www.kesko.fi
Year Founded: 1940
KESKOB—(HEL)
Rev.: $12,717,245,845
Assets: $8,368,551,694
Liabilities: $5,391,646,881
Net Worth: $2,976,904,813
Earnings: $534,858,623
Emp.: 17,702
Fiscal Year-end: 12/31/23
Household Product Distr
N.A.I.C.S.: 445110
Jorma Rauhala *(Deputy CEO, Pres-Building & Technical Trade & Member-Mgmt Bd)*

Subsidiaries:

Agro Trade Latvija SIA (1)
46c Rubenu Cels Street, Jelgava, 3002, Latvia
Tel.: (371) 63001717
Farm Product Distr
N.A.I.C.S.: 424910
Martins Reinfeld *(Gen Mgr)*

Bansemko OOO (1)
Michurinsky Pr House 51, Moscow, 119607, Russia
Tel.: (7) 4956452270
Sales Range: $25-49.9 Million
Emp.: 5
Food Store Operating Services
N.A.I.C.S.: 445298
Klaus Laakso *(Gen Mgr)*

Byggmakker Handel AS (1)
Hogslundveien 49, 2020, Skedsmokorset, Norway
Tel.: (47) 33484000
Web Site: https://www.byggmakker.no
Wood Product Distr
N.A.I.C.S.: 423310
Line Tranberg *(Mgr-Mktg)*

Fiesta Real Estate AS (1)
Parnu Mnt 102c, Tallinn, 11312, Estonia
Tel.: (372) 6257407
Real Estate Manangement Services
N.A.I.C.S.: 531390

Intersport Finland LTD (1)
Kutojantie 4, Espoo, 02630, Finland
Tel.: (358) 1053031
Sporting Goods Retailer
N.A.I.C.S.: 459110

Interstroy OOO (1)
Mostovaya St 14 Str 1, Arkhangelsk, 163061, Russia
Tel.: (7) 8182 23 32 10
Wooden Window & Door Mfr
N.A.I.C.S.: 321911

K Auto Oy (1)
Tikkurilantie 123, 01530, Vantaa, Finland
Tel.: (358) 105332425
Web Site: https://www.k-auto.fi
Automobile Parts Distr
N.A.I.C.S.: 441110

K Auto PC Oy (1)
Tikkurilantie 123, 01530, Vantaa, Finland
Tel.: (358) 105332425
Car Dealership Operator
N.A.I.C.S.: 441110

K rauta SIA (1)
15 Tiraines Street, Riga, 1058, Latvia
Tel.: (371) 67810090
Construction Engineering Services
N.A.I.C.S.: 541330

K-citymarket Oy (1)
Kutojantie 4, Espoo, 02630, Finland
Tel.: (358) 105311
Web Site: http://www.citymarket.fi
Departmental Stores Operating Services
N.A.I.C.S.: 455110

K-maatalous Experimental Farm (1)
Hahkialantie 57, 14700, Hauho, Finland
Tel.: (358) 10 53032
Web Site: http://www.k-koetila.fi
Agricultural Products Research & Development Services
N.A.I.C.S.: 541715
Kimmo Filppula *(Gen Mgr)*

Subsidiary (Non-US):

Byggmakker Norge AS (2)
Snipetjernveien 7, 1405, Langhus, Norway
Tel.: (47) 64 91 40 00
Hardware & Building Materials Retailer
N.A.I.C.S.: 444140

K-rauta AB (2)
Matslingan 1, 187 66, Taby, Sweden
Tel.: (46) 8 58 81 89 00
Building Material Retailer
N.A.I.C.S.: 444180
Staffan Wassberg *(Gen Mgr)*

K-talouspalvelukeskus Oy (1)
Kalevantie 2, PO Box 823, 33101, Tampere, Finland
Tel.: (358) 10 5311

KESKO CORPORATION

Kesko Corporation—(Continued)
Web Site: http://www.kesko.fi
Emp.: 200
Business Management Consulting Services
N.A.I.C.S.: 541611

Kalatukku E. Eriksson Oy (1)
Holkkitie 12 A, 00880, Helsinki, Finland
Tel.: (358) 207639303
Web Site: https://www.kalatukkueriksson.fi
Emp.: 75
Seafood Whslr
N.A.I.C.S.: 424460
Martin Soderstrom *(Mgr-Pur)*

Kesko Finance and Administration (1)
Satamakatu 3, PO Box 135, Kesko, Helsinki, FI-00016, Finland **(100%)**
Tel.: (358) 105311
Web Site: http://www.kesko.fi
Sales Range: $1-4.9 Billion
Emp.: 10,000
Responsible for Group's Financing Operations & Financial Management & Provider of Administrative Services to the Business Units
N.A.I.C.S.: 459110

Subsidiary (Domestic):

K-instituutti Oy (2)
Siikajarventie 88 90, 2860, Espoo, Finland **(50%)**
Tel.: (358) 105337271
Web Site: http://www.k-instituutti.fi
Sales Range: Less than $1 Million
Emp.: 60
Training Center for the Trading Sector
N.A.I.C.S.: 611710

Kesko Food Ltd. (1)
Satamakatu 3, FI 00016, Helsinki, Finland **(100%)**
Tel.: (358) 1053030
Sales Range: $200-249.9 Million
Emp.: 800
Supermarket Services
N.A.I.C.S.: 445110
Petteri Niemi *(VP-Commerce Unit)*

Subsidiary (Domestic):

K-Plus Oy (2)
Tyopajankatu 12, Helsinki, 00016, Finland
Tel.: (358) 1053020
Sales Range: $10-24.9 Million
Emp.: 30
Advertising Services
N.A.I.C.S.: 541810
Ismo Riitala *(Sec)*

Keslog LTD (2)
Jokiniementie 31, PO B 47, Vantaa, 01380, Finland
Tel.: (358) 1053050
Web Site: http://www.keslog.fi
Logistics Consulting Servies
N.A.I.C.S.: 541614

Kespro Ltd. (2)
Sahkotie 1, Vantaa, 1510, Finland **(100%)**
Tel.: (358) 1053040
Web Site: http://www.kespro.com
Sales Range: $25-49.9 Million
Emp.: 200
Whslr of Groceries & Non-Food Products
N.A.I.C.S.: 445110

Subsidiary (Non-US):

SIA Konekesko Latvia (2)
Tiraines iela 15, Riga, 1058, Latvia
Tel.: (371) 67064300
Web Site: http://www.konekesko.com
Trading Company; Marketing & Logistics; Developer of Retail Concepts & Operating Systems
N.A.I.C.S.: 541614

Kesko Onninen International Trading Co., Ltd. (1)
5/F Building A Finance Street, No 780 WanHangDu Road Jing'an District, Shanghai, 200042, China
Tel.: (86) 2161253079
Web Site: https://www.onninen.com
Construction Materials Distr
N.A.I.C.S.: 423320

Kesko Resource Management Division (1)
Satamakatu 3, Kesko, FIN 00016, Helsinki, Finland **(100%)**
Tel.: (358) 105311
Sales Range: $75-99.9 Million
Emp.: 484
Provider of Business Services
N.A.I.C.S.: 561499

Subsidiary (Domestic):

Kesko Information & Logistics Management Division (2)
Satamakatu 3, Kesko, FIN 00016, Helsinki, Finland **(100%)**
Tel.: (358) 105311
Web Site: http://www.kesko.fi
Provider of Business Services
N.A.I.C.S.: 561499

Kesko Real Estate Division (2)
Satamakatu 3, Kesko, FIN 00016, Helsinki, Finland **(100%)**
Tel.: (358) 105311
Web Site: http://www.kesko.fi
N.A.I.C.S.: 459110

Subsidiary (Domestic):

Hameenkylan Kauppa Oy (3)
Satamakatu 3, Kesko, 00016, Helsinki, Finland **(100%)**
Tel.: (358) 105311
Web Site: http://www.kesko.com.fi
Sales Range: $600-649.9 Million
Emp.: 1,100
Management & Leasing of Real Estate
N.A.I.C.S.: 531210

Kesko-Eastern Finland, Kuopio (1)
Tel.: (358) 105311
Web Site: http://www.kesko.com
Food, Building & Home Improvements & Car & Machinery Trades Operations
N.A.I.C.S.: 311412

Kesko-Northern Finland (1)
Aimakuja 2, PO Box 16, FIN 90401, Oulu, Finland **(100%)**
Tel.: (358) 105311
Trading Company; Provider of Marketing & Logistics; Developer of Retail Concepts & Operating Systems
N.A.I.C.S.: 541614
Jari Saarinen *(Mng Dir)*

Kesko-Southeastern Finland (1)
K-Citymarket Lahti Laune Ajokatu 53, PO Box 1, 16, Lahti, Finland **(100%)**
Tel.: (358) 105311
Web Site: http://www.kesko.fi
Sales Range: $50-74.9 Million
Emp.: 3
Sporting Goods Retailer
N.A.I.C.S.: 459110

Kesko-Southwestern Finland (1)
Satamakatu 3, 00016, Helsinki, Finland **(100%)**
Tel.: (358) 105311
N.A.I.C.S.: 459110

Kesko-Western Finland (1)
Jokipohjantie 28, PO Box 330, FIN 33101, Tampere, Finland **(100%)**
Tel.: (358) 105311
Web Site: http://www.kesko.com
Sales Range: $50-74.9 Million
Emp.: 100
N.A.I.C.S.: 459110

Kestra Kiinteistopalvelut Oy (1)
Satamakatu 3, Helsinki, 160, Finland
Tel.: (358) 105311
Real Estate Manangement Services
N.A.I.C.S.: 531390

Kiinteisto Mesta Oy (1)
Satamakatu 3, Helsinki, 00016, Finland
Tel.: (358) 1053 22020
Food Products Distr
N.A.I.C.S.: 424420

Kiinteisto Oy Lahden Karisma (1)
Satamakatu 3, 160, Helsinki, Finland
Tel.: (358) 105311
Real Estate Lending Services
N.A.I.C.S.: 531190

Kiinteisto Oy Valivainion Ostoskeskus (1)
Tyrnavantie 14, 90400, Oulu, Finland
Tel.: (358) 10 228 8400
Real Estate Manangement Services
N.A.I.C.S.: 531390

Konekesko Lietuva UAB (1)
Moletu g 13 Didziosios Rieses, LT-14262, Vilnius, Lithuania
Tel.: (370) 52477400
Web Site: http://www.konekesko.com
Agricultural Machinery Distr
N.A.I.C.S.: 423820

Konekesko Ltd. (2)
Porvoontie 245, PL 145, Vantaa, 1380, Finland **(100%)**
Tel.: (358) 1053034
Web Site: http://www.konekesko.com
Sales Range: $50-74.9 Million
Emp.: 250
Construction, Agricultural & Environmental Machinery Manufacturing
N.A.I.C.S.: 333120

Subsidiary (Non-US):

Konekesko Eesti AS (2)
Porguvalja Tee 3a Pildikula Rae Vald, Harjumaa, 75308, Estonia
Tel.: (372) 6059100
Sales Range: $50-74.9 Million
Emp.: 75
Agricultural Machinery Distr
N.A.I.C.S.: 423820

Konekesko Latvija SIA (2)
15 Tiraines Street, 1058, Riga, Latvia
Tel.: (371) 67064300
Sales Range: $25-49.9 Million
Emp.: 10
Material Handling Machinery Mfr
N.A.I.C.S.: 333248

Konekesko OOO (2)
Rustavele 7 Liter A, Saint Petersburg, 195299, Russia
Tel.: (7) 8123264653
Sales Range: $25-49.9 Million
Emp.: 1
Material Handling Machinery Distr
N.A.I.C.S.: 423830

Kr Fastigheter i Eskilstuna AB (1)
Box 756, 191 27, Kista, Sweden
Tel.: (46) 8 58818900
Sales Range: $50-74.9 Million
Emp.: 90
Property Leasing Services
N.A.I.C.S.: 531190
Jari Lind *(CEO)*

Kr Fastigheter i Uppland AB (1)
Sollentunavagen 27, 191 40, Sollentuna, Sweden
Tel.: (46) 858818949
Real Estate Manangement Services
N.A.I.C.S.: 531390

Loimaan Maatalous- ja Rautakauppa Oy (1)
Aleksis Kivenkatu 9, 32200, Loimaa, Finland
Tel.: (358) 2 7625100
Farm Machinery Distr
N.A.I.C.S.: 423820

Mark & Infra i Sverige AB (1)
Hantverkarvagen 6, 187 66, Taby, Sweden
Tel.: (46) 8194498
Web Site: https://markinfra.se
Plastic Pipe Product Distr
N.A.I.C.S.: 424610

Musta Porssi LTD (1)
Kutojantie 4, Espoo, 2630, Finland
Tel.: (358) 105 3031
Household Appliance Distr
N.A.I.C.S.: 423620

Onninen AB (1)
Esbogatan 11, 164 74, Kista, Sweden
Tel.: (46) 196033000
Electrical Equipment Distr
N.A.I.C.S.: 423610

Onninen AS (1)
Betooni 6/2, 13816, Tallinn, Estonia
Tel.: (372) 6105500
Web Site: https://www.onninen.ee

INTERNATIONAL PUBLIC

Electrical Equipment Distr
N.A.I.C.S.: 423610
Margus Martin *(Mgr-Acct)*

Onninen AS (1)
Hogslundveien 49, 2020, Skedsmokorset, Norway
Tel.: (47) 22396000
Web Site: https://www.onninen.no
Electrical Equipment Distr
N.A.I.C.S.: 423610

Onninen Oy (1)
Tyopajankatu 12, 00580, Helsinki, Finland
Tel.: (358) 204855250
Web Site: https://www.onninen.fi
Emp.: 1,200
Electrical Equipment Distr
N.A.I.C.S.: 423610
Laisi Heikki *(Mgr-Sls)*

Onninen SIA (1)
39 Darzciema Street, Riga, 1082, Latvia
Tel.: (371) 67819600
Web Site: https://www.onninen.lv
Electrical Equipment Distr
N.A.I.C.S.: 423610

Onninen Sp. z o.o. (1)
Ul Emaliowa 28, 02-295, Warsaw, Poland
Tel.: (48) 225679000
Web Site: http://www.onninen.pl
Electrical Equipment Distr
N.A.I.C.S.: 423610

Onninen UAB (1)
Savanoriu pr 274, 02301, Vilnius, Lithuania
Tel.: (370) 869473114
Web Site: https://www.onninen.lt
Electrical Equipment Distr
N.A.I.C.S.: 423610

Ovik Lasteknik AB (1)
Maskingatan 2, 891 38, Ornskoldsvik, Sweden
Tel.: (46) 660296900
Web Site: https://www.lasteknik.com
Security Locks Distr
N.A.I.C.S.: 423710

Oy Autocarrera Ab (1)
Hernepellontie 19-23, 00710, Helsinki, Finland
Tel.: (358) 94391140
Web Site: http://www.porsche.fi
Automotive Car Center Services
N.A.I.C.S.: 811111
Janne Maattanen *(Mgr-After Sls)*

Rautakesko Ltd. (1)
Tikkurilantie 10, PO Box 40, 16, Vantaa, Finland **(100%)**
Tel.: (358) 1053030
Web Site: http://www.kesko.fi
Sales Range: $400-449.9 Million
Emp.: 1,201
K-rauta & Rautia Chains & Industrial & Constractor Sales
N.A.I.C.S.: 236210

Subsidiary (Non-US):

Kesko Svenska AB (2)
Bagarbyvagen 61, S 19134, Sollentuna, Sweden **(100%)**
Tel.: (46) 86256900
Web Site: http://www.k-rauta.se
Sales Range: $25-49.9 Million
Emp.: 150
Engaged in the Shoe Store Business in Sweden
N.A.I.C.S.: 458210
Niclas Laogdberg *(Mgr)*

Raukaesko (2)
Parnu Mnt 102C, Tallinn, 11625, Estonia **(100%)**
Tel.: (372) 6257501
Web Site: http://www.k-rauta.ee
Sales Range: $75-99.9 Million
Emp.: 500
Trading Company; Provider of Marketing & Logistics; Developer of Retail Concepts & Operating Systems
N.A.I.C.S.: 541614
Veiko Eren *(Dir-Fin)*

Rautakesko A/S (2)
Tiraines Street 15, Riga, 1058, Latvia **(100%)**
Tel.: (371) 67810090

AND PRIVATE COMPANIES

Web Site: http://www.k-rauta.lv
Sales Range: $75-99.9 Million
Emp.: 400
Trading Company; Marketing & Logistics; Developer of Retail Concepts & Operating Systems
N.A.I.C.S.: 541614

ZAO Stroymaster (2)
Bolshoi Sampsonievskiy Prospekt 68 lit N, 194100, Saint Petersburg, Russia
Tel.: (7) 8123269231
Web Site: http://www.k-rauta.ru
Sales Range: $25-49.9 Million
Emp.: 26
Engaged in the Wholesale Trade of Hardware & Builders' Supplies in Russia
N.A.I.C.S.: 444180

Reinin Liha Oy (1)
Tyopajankatu 2, 00580, Helsinki, Finland
Tel.: (358) 102792290
Web Site: https://www.reininliha.fi
Meat Product Whslr
N.A.I.C.S.: 424470
Sami Lehtonen *(Dir-Sls)*

Ruokakesko LTD (1)
Satamakatu 3, Helsinki, 16, Finland
Tel.: (358) 105 3030
Emp.: 400
Grocery Store Operating Services
N.A.I.C.S.: 445110

Tampereen Lansikeskus Oy (1)
Tesomankatu 2, 33310, Tampere, Finland
Tel.: (358) 102287512
Real Estate Lending Services
N.A.I.C.S.: 531190

VV-Auto Group Oy (1)
Hitsaajankatu 7 B, PO Box 80, FIN 00811, Helsinki, Finland **(100%)**
Tel.: (358) 975831
Sales Range: $50-74.9 Million
Emp.: 160
Automobiles & Commercial Vehicles Importer
N.A.I.C.S.: 488999
Pekka Lahti *(Pres)*

Subsidiary (Domestic):

Auto-Span Oy (2)
Hitsaajankatu 7 C, 00810, Helsinki, Finland **(100%)**
Tel.: (358) 975831
Web Site: http://www.seat.fi
Sales Range: $25-49.9 Million
Emp.: 8
Importing & Marketing of Car Seats
N.A.I.C.S.: 441330

Turun VV-Auto Oy (2)
Rieskalahteentie 89, Turku, 20300, Finland
Tel.: (358) 233 8881
Web Site: http://www.turunvv-auto.fi
Motor Vehicle Dealers
N.A.I.C.S.: 441110
Sami Kivi *(Mgr)*

VV-Autotalot Oy (2)
Mekinaakatu 10, Vantaa, 880, Finland
Tel.: (358) 105333200
Sales Range: $25-49.9 Million
Emp.: 20
New Car Dealers
N.A.I.C.S.: 441110
Harri Buddas *(Gen Mgr)*

XL-Bygg Bergslagen AB (1)
Hemvarnsgatan 9, 171 54, Solna, Sweden
Tel.: (46) 857851600
Web Site: https://www.xlbygg.se
Information Technology Services
N.A.I.C.S.: 541512

KESLA OYJ
Kuurnankatu 24, 80100, Joensuu, Finland
Tel.: (358) 207862841
Web Site: http://www.kesla.fi
Year Founded: 1960
KELAS—(HEL)
Rev.: $49,492,769
Assets: $43,114,613
Liabilities: $29,851,068
Net Worth: $13,263,544
Earnings: ($1,273,473)
Emp.: 250
Fiscal Year-end: 12/31/22
Forestry Equipment Mfr
N.A.I.C.S.: 321912
Veli-Matti Karkkainen *(Chm)*

Subsidiaries:

Kesla GmbH (1)
Frankenweg 48, 77767, Appenweier, Germany
Tel.: (49) 15112686761
Web Site: https://www.kesla-gmbh.de
Crane Equipment Mfr
N.A.I.C.S.: 333120

KESM INDUSTRIES BERHAD
Lot 4 SS 8/4 Sungei Way Free Trade Industrial Zone, 47300, Petaling Jaya, Selangor Darul Ehsan, Malaysia
Tel.: (60) 378740000
Web Site: https://www.kesmi.com
9334—(KLS)
Rev.: $51,515,633
Assets: $99,417,063
Liabilities: $24,657,763
Net Worth: $74,759,300
Earnings: $39,852
Emp.: 834
Fiscal Year-end: 07/31/24
Semiconductor Mfr
N.A.I.C.S.: 333242
Kenneth Teoh Khoon Tan *(Exec Dir)*

Subsidiaries:

KES Systems & Service (1993) Pte. Ltd. (1)
1093 Lower Delta Road 02-01/08, Singapore, 169204, Singapore
Tel.: (65) 62725842
Web Site: https://www.kes93.com.sg
Semiconductor Mfr
N.A.I.C.S.: 334413

Division (Domestic):

KES Systems & Service (1993) Pte. Ltd. - Product Division (2)
Block 1093 Lower Delta Road #02-01/08, Tiong Bahru Industrial Estate, Singapore, 169204, Singapore
Tel.: (65) 6272 5824
Semiconductor Mfr
N.A.I.C.S.: 334413

KES Systems & Service (Shanghai) Co., Ltd. (1)
Unit A 2nd Floor Factory 5 No 350 Xiya Road, Waigaoqiao Pilot Free Trade Zone, Shanghai, 200131, China
Tel.: (86) 2150461808
Semiconductor Mfr
N.A.I.C.S.: 334413
Luo Wen Yao *(Mgr)*

KES Systems & Service Costa Rica Sociedad Anonima (1)
Ultra Park Building 7B Office 1, La Aurora, Heredia, Costa Rica
Tel.: (506) 2293 9126
Semiconductor Mfr
N.A.I.C.S.: 334413

KESM Industries (Tianjin) Co. Ltd. (1)
A 7-1 Saida International Industrial Park, Tianjin Xiqing Econ Dev Area, Tianjin, China
Tel.: (86) 2258786222
Semiconductor Mfr
N.A.I.C.S.: 334413

KESM Industries Berhad (1)
Lot 4 SS 8/4 Sungei Way Free Industrial Zone, 47300, Petaling Jaya, Selangor Darul Ehsan, Malaysia
Tel.: (60) 378740000
Web Site: https://www.kesmi.com
Semiconductor Mfr
N.A.I.C.S.: 334413

KESM Test (M) Sdn. Bhd. (1)
Lot 4 SS 8/4 Sungei Way Free Industrial Zone, 47300, Petaling Jaya, Selangor Darul Ehsan, Malaysia
Tel.: (60) 378740000

Sales Range: $200-249.9 Million
Semiconductor Testing Services
N.A.I.C.S.: 334515
Samuel Lim *(Mng Dir)*

KESP Sdn. Bhd. (1)
Plot 253 Jalan Kampung Jawa, Bayan Lepas Free Industrial Zone Phase III, 11900, Bayan Lepas, Penang, Malaysia
Tel.: (60) 46435922
Web Site: http://www.kesp.com.my
Sales Range: $200-249.9 Million
Electronic Components Mfr
N.A.I.C.S.: 334413

KEST Systems & Service Ltd. (1)
No 8 Hsinann Road Science-Based Industrial Park, Hsin-chu, Taiwan
Tel.: (886) 35772108
Semiconductor Mfr
N.A.I.C.S.: 334413

KESORAM INDUSTRIES LIMITED
9/1 R N Mukherjee Road, Kolkata, 700001, West Bengal, India
Tel.: (91) 3322435453
Web Site: http://www.kesocorp.com
KESORAMIND—(KOL)
Rev.: $497,197,155
Assets: $468,601,770
Liabilities: $398,903,505
Net Worth: $69,698,265
Earnings: ($10,556,910)
Emp.: 1,856
Fiscal Year-end: 03/31/22
Cement Mfr
N.A.I.C.S.: 327310
Manjushree Khaitan *(Vice Chm)*

Subsidiaries:

Cygnet Industries Limited (1)
Industry House 11th Floor 10 Camac Street, Kolkata, 700017, India **(100%)**
Tel.: (91) 3322824721
Web Site: https://kesoramrayon.in
Rayon & Transparent Paper Mfr
N.A.I.C.S.: 313110

Kesoram Industries Limited - Birla Shakti Cement (1)
Office No 613-616 Block 3 White House 6-3-1192/1/2 Kundanbagh, Begumpet, Hyderabad, 500016, Telangana, India
Tel.: (91) 40 4334 4555
Web Site: http://www.birlashakticement.com
Cement Mfr
N.A.I.C.S.: 327310

KESSEBOHMER OHG
Mindener Strasse 208, Bad Essen, 49152, Germany
Tel.: (49) 5742460
Web Site: http://www.kesseboehmer.de
Year Founded: 1954
Sales Range: $100-124.9 Million
Furniture Fittings Mfr
N.A.I.C.S.: 337126
Oliver Kessebohmer *(Mng Dir)*

KESSELRUN RESOURCES LTD.
102-278 Bay Street, Thunder Bay, P7B 1R8, ON, Canada
Tel.: (807) 285-3323
Web Site: https://www.kesselrunresource.com
Year Founded: 2011
KES—(OTCIQ)
Assets: $7,501,271
Liabilities: $645,832
Net Worth: $6,855,439
Earnings: ($554,416)
Fiscal Year-end: 07/31/21
Mineral Exploration Services
N.A.I.C.S.: 212220
Michael Thompson *(Pres & CEO)*

KESTREL GOLD INC.

KEW MEDIA GROUP INC.

603 7347th Ave S W, Calgary, T2P 3P8, AB, Canada
Tel.: (403) 816-2141
Web Site: https://www.kestrelgold.com
Year Founded: 2007
KSTBF—(OTCIQ)
Rev.: $532
Assets: $1,024,145
Liabilities: $72,273
Net Worth: $951,872
Earnings: ($127,047)
Fiscal Year-end: 09/30/23
Gold Exploration Services
N.A.I.C.S.: 212220
Robert H. Solinger *(Pres, CEO & CFO)*

KETER GROUP SA
Zone Industrielle Hahneboesch, L-4587, Differdange, Luxembourg
Tel.: (352) 584545215
Year Founded: 2021
Emp.: 5,100
Holding Company
N.A.I.C.S.: 551112
Jean-Baptiste Wautier *(Chm)*

KEUM KANG STEEL CO., LTD.
701 19 Seoun-ro, Seocho-Gu, Seoul, Korea (South)
Tel.: (82) 234710001
Web Site: https://www.kksteel.co.kr
Year Founded: 1973
053260—(KRS)
Rev.: $187,317,500
Assets: $122,657,101
Liabilities: $26,992,764
Net Worth: $95,664,337
Earnings: $4,192,290
Emp.: 68
Fiscal Year-end: 12/31/22
Steel Sheet & Coil Mfr
N.A.I.C.S.: 331110
Kwang-Nam Joo *(Chm & CEO)*

KEV GROUP INC.
1167 Caledonia Road Suite 200, North York, M6A 2X1, ON, Canada
Tel.: (866) 891-9138
Web Site: http://kevgroup.com
Year Founded: 1996
Cloud-based Online Payments & Fund Management Software Developer
N.A.I.C.S.: 513210
Bram Belzberg *(Chm & CEO)*

KEW MEDIA GROUP INC.
672 Dupont Street Suite 400, Toronto, M6G 1Z6, ON, Canada
Tel.: (647) 956-1965
Web Site: http://www.kewmedia.com
Year Founded: 2015
Holding Company
N.A.I.C.S.: 551112
Steven Silver *(Co-Founder & CEO)*

Subsidiaries:

Frantic Films Corporation (1)
220 Portage Avenue 1300, Winnipeg, R3C 0A5, MB, Canada
Tel.: (204) 949-0070
Web Site: http://www.franticfilms.com
Visual Effects & Animation for Feature Film, Television & Commercials
N.A.I.C.S.: 512110
Jamie Brown *(CEO & Exec Producer)*

Kew Media Group UK Limited (1)
19 Heddon Street, London, W1B 4BG, United Kingdom
Tel.: (44) 2078516500
Web Site: http://kewmedia.com
Sales Range: $75-99.9 Million
Motion Picture & Home Entertainment Distr
N.A.I.C.S.: 512120
Tom Bairstow *(VP-Sls & Distr)*

4143

KEW MEDIA GROUP INC.

Kew Media Group Inc.—(Continued)
Subsidiary (US):

Collins Avenue LLC (2)
5410 Wilshire Blvd Ste 700, Los Angeles, CA 90036
Tel.: (323) 930-6633
Web Site: http://www.collinsave.com
Television Production Services
N.A.I.C.S.: 512110
Casaundra Alcantar *(Office Mgr)*

Content Media Corporation (2)
225 Arizona Ave Ste 250, Santa Monica, CA 90401
Tel.: (310) 576-1059
Television Production Services
N.A.I.C.S.: 512110

Subsidiary (Domestic):

Kew Media International Limited (2)
19-21 Heddon Street, London, W1B 4BG, United Kingdom
Tel.: (44) 2078516500
Web Site: http://kewmedia.com
Motion Picture & Home Entertainment Distr
N.A.I.C.S.: 512120
Alison Balch *(Head-Distr Ops)*

Branch (US):

ContentFilm International - Los Angeles (3)
225 Arizona Ave Ste 250, Santa Monica, CA 90401
Tel.: (310) 576-1059
Sales Range: $25-49.9 Million
Emp.: 11
Motion Picture & Home Entertainment Distr
N.A.I.C.S.: 512120

KEWAL KIRAN CLOTHING LTD

Kewal Kiran Estate 460/7 I B Patel Road, Goregaon East, Mumbai, 400 063, India
Tel.: (91) 2226814400
Web Site: https://www.kewalkiran.com
532732—(BOM)
Rev.: $43,649,042
Assets: $79,472,539
Liabilities: $20,389,797
Net Worth: $59,082,742
Earnings: $2,702,959
Emp.: 1,777
Fiscal Year-end: 03/31/21
Apparels Mfr
N.A.I.C.S.: 315250
Abhijit B. Warange *(Officer-Compliance, Sec & VP-Legal)*

KEWELL TECHNOLOGY CO., LTD.

No 8 Dalongshan Road High-tech Industrial Development Zone, Hi-Tech Zone, Hefei, 230088, Anhui, China
Tel.: (86) 55165837951
Web Site: https://www.kewell.com.cn
Year Founded: 2011
688551—(SHG)
Rev.: $52,669,895
Assets: $190,916,201
Liabilities: $46,289,375
Net Worth: $144,626,826
Earnings: $8,736,334
Fiscal Year-end: 12/31/22
Electrical Equipment Mfr & Distr
N.A.I.C.S.: 335999
Shitao Fu *(Chm)*

KEWPIE CORPORATION

1-4-13 Shibuya, Shibuya-ku, Tokyo, 150-0002, Japan
Tel.: (81) 334863331
Web Site: https://www.kewpie.com
Year Founded: 1919
KWPCF—(OTCIQ)
Rev.: $4,165,342,720
Assets: $3,904,757,120
Liabilities: $1,052,806,480
Net Worth: $2,851,950,640
Earnings: $155,199,440
Emp.: 10,696
Fiscal Year-end: 11/30/22
Condiments & Processed Foods, Egg Products, Fine Chemicals, Salad & Prepared Foods Mfr & Distr
N.A.I.C.S.: 311941
Osamu Chonan *(Pres & CEO)*

Subsidiaries:

Deria Foods Co., Ltd. (1)
2-5-7 Sengawa-cho, Sengawa Kyuport, Chofu, 182-0002, Tokyo, Japan
Tel.: (81) 353847700
Web Site: https://www.deria-foods.co.jp
Emp.: 278
Food Mfr & Whslr
N.A.I.C.S.: 311999

Green Message Co., Ltd. (1)
2415 Shimotsuruma, Yamato, 242-0001, Kanagawa, Japan
Tel.: (81) 462717510
Web Site: https://www.greenmessage.co.jp
Emp.: 160
Food Service
N.A.I.C.S.: 722310

Hangzhou Kewpie Corporation (1)
No 5 16th Street, Economic Development Zone, Hangzhou, Zhejiang, China
Tel.: (86) 57186840960
Web Site: http://kewpie.com.cn
Salad & Dishes Mfr
N.A.I.C.S.: 311941

Hanshin Delica Co., Ltd. (1)
4-7-1 Minami-cho, Kansai Kyuport premises, Itami, 664-0854, Hyogo, Japan
Tel.: (81) 649612770
Web Site: https://hanshindelica.deria-foods.co.jp
Emp.: 280
Salad & Dishes Mfr
N.A.I.C.S.: 311941

Ishikari Delica Co., Ltd. (1)
1-1-2-1 Nishimiyanosawa, Teine-ku, Sapporo, 006-0001, Japan
Tel.: (81) 116641250
Web Site: https://ishikaridelica.deria-foods.co.jp
Emp.: 180
Salad & Dishes Mfr
N.A.I.C.S.: 311941

K. Tis Corporation (1)
3-50-1 Chofugaoka, Chofu, 182-0021, Tokyo, Japan
Tel.: (81) 424264751
Web Site: http://k-tis.jp
Cargo Transportation Services
N.A.I.C.S.: 488510

Kewpie Jyozo Co., Ltd. (1)
2-5-7 Sengawa-cho, Sengawa Kyuport, Chofu, 182-0002, Tokyo, Japan
Tel.: (81) 353847670
Web Site: http://www.kewpie-jyozo.co.jp
Vinegar Mfr & Distr
N.A.I.C.S.: 311941

Kewso Services Corporation (1)
3-50-1 Chofugaoka, Chofu, 182-0021, Tokyo, Japan
Tel.: (81) 424991767
Web Site: http://www.kewso-services.co.jp
Logistic Services
N.A.I.C.S.: 541614

Kifuki U.S.A. Co., Inc. (1)
15547 1st St, Irwindale, CA 91706-6201
Tel.: (626) 334-8090
N.A.I.C.S.: 311422

Kitakami Delica Co., Ltd. (1)
1-89 Omatsuzawa Aisari-cho, Kitakami, 024-5501, Japan
Tel.: (81) 197673903
Web Site: https://kitakamidelica.deria-foods.co.jp
Emp.: 222
Salad & Dishes Mfr
N.A.I.C.S.: 311941

Mosso Kewpie Poland Sp. z o.o. (1)
Puchaly ul Wirazowa 43, 05-090, Raszyn, Poland
Tel.: (48) 227204242
Web Site: https://mossokewpie.pl
Food Product Whslr
N.A.I.C.S.: 424490

Osaka Sanei Logistics Corporation (1)
2-1-1 Nagaokagumachi, Hirakata, 573-0102, Osaka, Japan
Tel.: (81) 728551899
Web Site: http://osaka-3a.co.jp
Transportation Services
N.A.I.C.S.: 488510

PT Manggala Kiat Ananda (1)
Jl Raya Narogong KM 12 5 Pangkalan 5 no 7, Bantar Gebang, Bekasi, Jawa Barat, Indonesia
Tel.: (62) 8111779825
Web Site: http://kamanggala.com
Transportation Services
N.A.I.C.S.: 488510

Potato Delica Co., Ltd. (1)
2595-1 Hotakakitahotaka, Azumino, 399-8302, Nagano, Japan
Tel.: (81) 263810001
Web Site: https://www.potato-delica.co.jp
Emp.: 330
Food Mfr & Whslr
N.A.I.C.S.: 311999

Q&B Foods, Inc. (1)
15547 1st St, Irwindale, CA 91706-6201
Tel.: (626) 334-8090
Web Site: https://www.qbfoods.com
Sales Range: $25-49.9 Million
Emp.: 85
Salad Dressing & Mayonnaise; Private Label & Co-Packing Mfr
N.A.I.C.S.: 311941

S.Y. Promotion Co., Ltd. (1)
5-5-2 Kiba CN-1 Bldg 5F, Koto-ku, Tokyo, 135-0042, Japan
Tel.: (81) 356211208
Web Site: http://www.sy-pro.co.jp
Transportation Logistics Services
N.A.I.C.S.: 488510

San-ei Logistics Corporation (1)
2F Nihonbashi Sunrise Building, 2-13-10 Nihonbashi, Chofu, 103-0027, Tokyo, Japan
Tel.: (81) 332734867
Web Site: http://www.saneilogi.com
Logistic Services
N.A.I.C.S.: 541614

Seto Delica Co., Ltd. (1)
640 Minamiyamaguchi- cho, Owari Higashi Regional Wholesale Market, Seto, 489-0965, Aichi, Japan
Tel.: (81) 561835831
Web Site: https://setodelica.deria-foods.co.jp
Emp.: 247
Food Mfr & Whslr
N.A.I.C.S.: 311999

Shunsai Deli Co., Ltd. (1)
3927-20 Haijima- cho, Akishima, 196-0002, Tokyo, Japan
Tel.: (81) 425198011
Web Site: https://shunsaideli.deria-foods.co.jp
Emp.: 1,100
Salad & Dishes Mfr
N.A.I.C.S.: 311941

Tosu Delica Co., Ltd. (1)
701 Tashirohokamachi, Tosu, 841-0016, Saga, Japan
Tel.: (81) 942833923
Web Site: https://tosudelica.deria-foods.co.jp
Emp.: 149
Salad & Dishes Mfr
N.A.I.C.S.: 311941

Tou Kewpie Co., Ltd. (1)
Shibuya 1-4-11 Shibuya Dongyou, Shibuya-Ku, Tokyo, 150-0002, Japan
Tel.: (81) 334991750
Web Site: http://www.tou-kewpie.com
Food Service
N.A.I.C.S.: 722310

Zen-noh Kewpie Egg-station Co., Ltd. (1)
403-2 Motokurihashi Motokurihashi Gokacho, Sashima, Ibaraki, 306-0313, Japan
Tel.: (81) 280841611
Web Site: https://www.zk-egg-station.co.jp
Emp.: 287
Food Mfr & Whslr
N.A.I.C.S.: 311999

KEY ALLIANCE GROUP BERHAD

Lot 18 2 18th Floor Menara Lien Hoe 8 Persiaran Tropicana, Tropicana Golf and Country Resort, 47410, Petaling Jaya, Selangor Darul Ehsan, Malaysia
Tel.: (60) 378057725 MY
Web Site: https://ir2.chartnexus.com
Year Founded: 1997
KGROUP—(KLS)
Rev.: $10,629,029
Assets: $31,428,485
Liabilities: $8,520,604
Net Worth: $22,907,881
Earnings: ($4,489,266)
Emp.: 95
Fiscal Year-end: 03/31/23
Investment Holding Services
N.A.I.C.S.: 551112
Roy Yew Kee Ho *(Mng Dir)*

Subsidiaries:

Digital Paper Solutions Sdn. Bhd. (1)
28 Jalan Pemberita U1/49 Temasya Industrial Park Glenmarie, 40150, Shah Alam, Selangor Darul Ehsan, Malaysia
Tel.: (60) 355692002
Web Site: http://www.dpaper.com
Printer Distr
N.A.I.C.S.: 423430

Progenet Innovations Sdn. Bhd. (1)
Lot 18 2 18th Floor Menara Lien Hoe No 8 Persiaran Tropicana, 47410, Petaling Jaya, Selangor Darul Ehsan, Malaysia
Tel.: (60) 378009699
Software Development Services
N.A.I.C.S.: 541511

KEY ASIC BERHAD

6 Floor Unit 3 8 First Avenue, Bandar Utama, 47800, Petaling Jaya, Selangor, Malaysia
Tel.: (60) 376643300 MY
Web Site: https://www.keyasic.com
Year Founded: 2005
KEYASIC—(KLS)
Rev.: $4,405,604
Assets: $8,751,246
Liabilities: $1,750,026
Net Worth: $7,001,220
Earnings: ($1,136,168)
Emp.: 36
Fiscal Year-end: 05/31/23
Fabless Semiconductor Mfr;Process Technology Services
N.A.I.C.S.: 334413
Kah Yee Eg *(Chm & CEO)*

Subsidiaries:

Key ASIC Limited (Singapore) (1)
31 Ubi Road 1 05-02, Singapore, 408694, Singapore
Tel.: (65) 67425919
Web Site: http://www.keyasic.com
Sales Range: $25-49.9 Million
Emp.: 30
Integrated Circuits Mfr
N.A.I.C.S.: 334413

KEY CHEVROLET CADILLAC BUICK & GMC INC.

441 Broadway Street East, Yorkton, S3N 3G3, SK, Canada
Tel.: (306) 782-2268
Web Site: http://www.keychev.com
Year Founded: 1990
Sales Range: $10-24.9 Million
Emp.: 35
New & Used Car Dealer
N.A.I.C.S.: 441110

AND PRIVATE COMPANIES

Joel Martinuk *(Dir-Ops)*

KEY COFFEE INC.
2-34-4 Nishi-Shimbashi, Minato-ku, Tokyo, 105-8705, Japan
Tel.: (81) 334333311
Web Site: https://www.keycoffee.co.jp
Year Founded: 1920
2594—(TKS)
Rev.: $487,818,000
Assets: $362,439,520
Liabilities: $157,721,210
Net Worth: $204,718,310
Earnings: $1,189,800
Emp.: 982
Fiscal Year-end: 03/31/24
Coffee Product Mfr & Whslr
N.A.I.C.S.: 311920
Yutaka Shibata *(Pres)*

Subsidiaries:

Key Associates Co., Ltd. (1)
2-34-7 Nishishimbashi Minato-Ku, Tokyo, 105-0003, Japan
Tel.: (81) 334344463
General Insurance Services
N.A.I.C.S.: 524210

Kyoei Corporation (1)
2-2-8 Tonotsuji Sumiyoshi-Ku, Osaka, 558-0042, Osaka, Japan
Tel.: (81) 666716565
Coffee Mfr
N.A.I.C.S.: 311920

PT Toarco Jaya (1)
Jl Bekasi Timur IV/3A, Jakarta Timur, 13410, Indonesia
Tel.: (62) 218191141
Web Site: http://www.toarco.com
Coffee Product Mfr
N.A.I.C.S.: 322299

Taiwan Key Coffee Inc. (1)
14f 191 Fu Hsing N Rd, Taipei, 10596, Taiwan
Tel.: (886) 227152866
Coffee Distr
N.A.I.C.S.: 424490

Tricolore Co., Ltd. (1)
6-12-5 Shimbashi, Minato-ku, Tokyo, 105-0004, Japan
Tel.: (81) 334372511
Web Site: http://www.tricolore.co.jp
Emp.: 1,286
Hotel Operator
N.A.I.C.S.: 721110

honu KATO COFFEE Inc. (1)
Web Site: http://www.katocoffee.com
Coffee Mfr
N.A.I.C.S.: 311920

KEY CORP LIMITED
16 / 16 - A Civil Lines, Kanpur, 208 001, Uttar Pradesh, India
Tel.: (91) 5122305416
Web Site:
   https://www.keycorpltd.com
Year Founded: 1985
507948—(BOM)
Rev.: $2,440,906
Assets: $6,803,255
Liabilities: $151,381
Net Worth: $6,651,873
Earnings: $2,345,840
Fiscal Year-end: 03/31/22
Consumer Financial Services
N.A.I.C.S.: 522291
G. D. Maheshwari *(Exec Dir)*

KEY FINANCE LIMITED
Annecy Ct Ferry Works, KT7 0QJ, Thames Ditton, Surrey, United Kingdom - England
Tel.: (44) 2083390333
Web Site: http://www.keyfinance.com
Year Founded: 1979
Sales Range: $25-49.9 Million
Emp.: 10
Leasing & Financial Services

N.A.I.C.S.: 532420
John Mounsey *(Chm)*

KEY PERFORMANCE GROUP S.A.S.
92 rue de Rochechouart, 75009, Paris, France
Tel.: (33) 155469180
Web Site: http://www.key-performance-group.com
Year Founded: 1999
Marketing Consulting Services
N.A.I.C.S.: 541613
Yohan Stern *(Founder & CEO)*

Subsidiaries:

Mediastay FRANCE (1)
31 rue des Jeuneurs, 75002, Paris, France
Tel.: (33) 155469200
Web Site: http://www.mediastay.com
Free Online Gaming Website Operator; Lead Generation & Performance Advertising Services
N.A.I.C.S.: 541519
Hannah Socard *(Acct Mgr)*

KEY PETROLEUM LIMITED
Suite 2 3B Macquarie Street, Sydney, 2000, NSW, Australia
Tel.: (61) 292519088 AU
Web Site:
   https://www.keypetroleum.com.au
KEY—(ASX)
Rev.: $5,403
Assets: $1,008,986
Liabilities: $196,801
Net Worth: $812,185
Earnings: ($641,956)
Fiscal Year-end: 06/30/24
Oil & Gas Properties Development & Exploration Services
N.A.I.C.S.: 213112
Kane Marshall *(Mng Dir)*

KEY TRAVEL LIMITED
9th Floor St James Building 61-95 Oxford Street, Manchester, M1 6EJ, United Kingdom
Tel.: (44) 2078439602
Web Site: http://www.keytravel.com
Year Founded: 1980
Travel Agency
N.A.I.C.S.: 561510
Saam Hammad *(CEO)*

Subsidiaries:

Raptim International Travel (1)
145 N 4th St Ste 2, Lewiston, NY 14092-1298
Tel.: (716) 754-9232
Web Site: http://www.raptimusa.com
Travel Agencies
N.A.I.C.S.: 561510
David Lundblad *(Pres)*

KEY WARE ELECTRONICS CO., LTD.
No 32 Singbang Rd 21, Neighborhood Dalin Village Taoyuan Dist, Taoyuan, Taiwan
Tel.: (886) 33660667
Web Site: https://key-ware.com.tw
Year Founded: 1997
5498—(TPE)
Rev.: $45,461,433
Assets: $127,981,365
Liabilities: $61,540,506
Net Worth: $66,440,859
Earnings: $98,990
Fiscal Year-end: 12/31/22
Printed Circuit Board Mfr & Distr
N.A.I.C.S.: 334412

Subsidiaries:

Jia Chi Co., Ltd. (1)
No 8-5 Nongond Rd Sec 1, Luzhu Dist, Taoyuan, Taiwan
Tel.: (886) 32220311

Drilling Equipment Distr
N.A.I.C.S.: 423710

Key De Precise Industris Co., Ltd. (1)
No 31 Keji 2nd Rd Hwaya Technology Park, Guishau Dist, Taoyuan, Taiwan
Tel.: (886) 33961172
Machine Tools Supplier
N.A.I.C.S.: 423710

King Ware(Chongqing) Electronics Co., Ltd. (1)
No 2177 Xing Long Avenue, Yongchuan District, Chongqing, China
Tel.: (86) 2349413888
Precision Cutting Tool Mfr & Distr
N.A.I.C.S.: 333515

Kunshan Key Ware Electronics Co., Ltd. (1)
No 69 Lisheng Road, Huaqiao Town, Kunshan, Jiangsu, China
Tel.: (86) 51257697798
Precision Cutting Tool Mfr & Distr
N.A.I.C.S.: 333515

Kunshan Laserware Laser Technology Co., Ltd. (1)
No 69 Lisheng Road, Huaqiao Town, Kunshan, Jiangsu, China
Tel.: (86) 51236830371
Laser Drilling Services
N.A.I.C.S.: 532282

Wuhan Laserware Laser Technology Co., Ltd. (1)
No 266 Taizi Lake Road Economic & Technological Development Zone, Wuhan, Hubei, China
Tel.: (86) 2784740876
Machine Tools Supplier
N.A.I.C.S.: 423710

KEY-SOFT COMPUTER TECHNOLOGY PLC
Torokvesz utca 30/a, Budapest, HU-1022, Hungary
Tel.: (36) 13365300
KULCSSOFT—(BUD)
Rev.: $8,306,142
Assets: $9,740,213
Liabilities: $6,371,039
Net Worth: $3,369,174
Earnings: $3,125,343
Emp.: 82
Fiscal Year-end: 12/31/23
Software Development Services
N.A.I.C.S.: 541511
Tibor Kulcsar *(Chm-Mgmt Bd)*

KEYBRIDGE CAPITAL LIMITED
Suite 614 Level 6 370 St Kilda Road, Melbourne, 3004, VIC, Australia
Tel.: (61) 396867000 AU
Web Site:
   https://www.keybridge.com.au
Year Founded: 1999
KBC—(ASX)
Rev.: $6,537,177
Assets: $14,184,245
Liabilities: $6,551,674
Net Worth: $7,632,571
Earnings: $4,779,617
Emp.: 17
Fiscal Year-end: 06/30/24
Financial Services
N.A.I.C.S.: 523999
Nicholas Francis John Bolton *(CEO & Mng Dir)*

KEYEAST CO., LTD
Hakdong-ro 11 gil, Gangnam-gu, Seoul, 06042, Korea (South)
Tel.: (82) 234442002
Web Site: http://www.keyeast.co.kr
Year Founded: 1996
054780—(KRS)
Rev.: $47,587,885
Assets: $65,673,125
Liabilities: $20,364,154
Net Worth: $45,308,971

KEYENCE CORPORATION

Earnings: ($1,278,392)
Emp.: 59
Fiscal Year-end: 12/31/22
Entertainment Services
N.A.I.C.S.: 611610
Seong Hye Park *(CEO)*

Subsidiaries:

Stream Media Corporation (1)
21F Roppongi Grand Tower 3-2-1 Roppongi, Minato-ku, Tokyo, 106-6221, Japan (50.1%)
Tel.: (81) 368096118
Web Site: https://www.streammedia.co.jp
Rev.: $63,171,900
Assets: $89,865,750
Liabilities: $38,746,850
Net Worth: $51,118,900
Earnings: $1,850,490
Emp.: 90
Fiscal Year-end: 12/31/2023
Broadcasting Services
N.A.I.C.S.: 516120
Young Min Kim *(Chief Strategy Officer)*

KEYENCE CORPORATION
1-3-14 Higashinakajima, Higashiyodogawa-Ku, Osaka, 533-8555, Japan
Tel.: (81) 663791111
Web Site: https://www.keyence.co.jp
Year Founded: 1974
6861—(TKS)
Rev.: $6,393,773,680
Assets: $19,597,275,120
Liabilities: $1,048,339,390
Net Worth: $18,548,935,730
Earnings: $2,443,333,620
Emp.: 12,286
Fiscal Year-end: 03/31/24
Automobile Parts Mfr
N.A.I.C.S.: 334514

Subsidiaries:

KOREA KEYENCE Co., Ltd. (1)
Tel.: (82) 317894300
Web Site: http://www.keyence.co.kr
Sales Range: $25-49.9 Million
Emp.: 60
FA Sensors & Opto-Electronic Measuring Instruments Supplier
N.A.I.C.S.: 334514

Keyence (China) Co., Ltd. (1)
7th Floor Shanghai World Financial Center 100 Century Avenue, Pudong New Area, Shanghai, 200120, China
Tel.: (86) 2150586228
Web Site: http://www.keyence.com.cn
Automation Sensor Mfr
N.A.I.C.S.: 334519

Keyence (Hong Kong) Co., Limited (1)
Unit 2606-07 26/F The Metropolis Tower 10 Metropolis Drive Hunghom, Kowloon, China (Hong Kong)
Tel.: (852) 31041010
Web Site: http://www.keyence.com.cn
Sensors & Measuring Instruments Mfr
N.A.I.C.S.: 334511

Keyence (Malaysia) Sdn. Bhd. (1)
Lot No B-25-2 Level 25 The Ascent Paradigm No 1 Jalan SS 7/26A, Kelana Jaya, 47301, Petaling Jaya, Selangor, Malaysia
Tel.: (60) 378832211
Web Site: http://www.keyence.com.my
Sales Range: $25-49.9 Million
Emp.: 20
FA Sensors & Opto-Electronic Measuring Instruments Supplier
N.A.I.C.S.: 334514

Keyence (Thailand) Co., Ltd. (1)
2034/140-143 Italthai Tower 33rd Floor New Petchburi Road, Bang Kapi Subdistrict Huai Khwang District, Bangkok, 10310, Thailand
Tel.: (66) 20781090
Web Site: https://www.keyence.co.th
Sensors & Measuring Instruments Mfr
N.A.I.C.S.: 334511

Keyence AG (1)

KEYENCE CORPORATION

Keyence Corporation—(Continued)
Birmensdorferstrasse 24, Urdorf, 8902, Switzerland
Tel.: (41) 434557730
Web Site: http://www.keyence.ch
Photoelectric Sensors & Microscopes Mfr
N.A.I.C.S.: 334419
Keith Pakato *(Gen Mgr)*

Keyence Brasil Comercio De Produtos Eletronicos Ltda. (1)
Av Brigadeiro Faria Lima 4221 7th Floor Cj 71 and 72, Itaim Bibi, Sao Paulo, 04538-133, Brazil
Tel.: (55) 1130454011
Web Site: http://www.keyence.com.br
Industrial Equipment Whsr
N.A.I.C.S.: 423830

Keyence Canada Inc. (1)
6775 Financial Drive Suite 202, Mississauga, L5N 0A4, ON, Canada
Tel.: (905) 366-7655
Web Site: http://www.keyence.ca
Sales Range: $25-49.9 Million
Emp.: 25
FA Sensors & Opto-Electronic Instruments Supplier
N.A.I.C.S.: 333310

Keyence Corporation of America (1)
669 River Dr Ste 403, Elmwood Park, NJ 07407
Tel.: (201) 930-0100
Web Site: https://www.keyence.com
Sales Range: $50-74.9 Million
Emp.: 180
FA Sensors & Opto-Electronic Instruments Supplier
N.A.I.C.S.: 333310

Keyence Deutschland GmbH (1)
Siemenstrasse 1, 63263, Neu-Isenburg, Germany (100%)
Tel.: (49) 610236890
Web Site: http://www.keyence.de
Sales Range: $25-49.9 Million
Emp.: 35
FA Sensors & Opto-Electronic Measuring Instruments Supplier
N.A.I.C.S.: 333310

Keyence France S.A. (1)
1 Place Costes et Bellonte, 92270, Bois-Colombes, France
Tel.: (33) 156377800
Web Site: https://www.keyence.fr
Photoelectric Sensors Mfr
N.A.I.C.S.: 334419

Keyence Hungary Kft. (1)
Zihany 7, Budapest, 1031, Hungary
Tel.: (36) 18027360
Web Site: http://www.keyence.co.eu
Emp.: 50
Sensors & Measuring Instruments Mfr
N.A.I.C.S.: 334511
Tibor Estok *(Office Mgr)*

Keyence International (Belgium) NV/SA (1)
Bedrijvenlaan 5, 2800, Mechelen, Belgium
Tel.: (32) 15281222
Web Site: https://www.keyence.eu
Sensors & Measuring Instruments Mfr & Distr
N.A.I.C.S.: 334511

Keyence Italia S.p.A. (1)
Via della Moscova 3, 20121, Milan, Italy
Tel.: (39) 026682220
Web Site: http://www.keyence.it
Electric Equipment Mfr
N.A.I.C.S.: 334419

Keyence Mexico S.A. de C.V. (1)
Av Paseo de la Reforma 243 P11, Col Cuauhtemoc Del Cuauhtemoc, 06500, Mexico, Nuevo Leo, Mexico
Tel.: (52) 5588500100
Web Site: https://www.keyence.com.mx
Electric Equipment Mfr
N.A.I.C.S.: 334419

Keyence Philippines Inc. (1)
Tel.: (63) 289815000
Web Site: http://www.keyence.com.ph
Automation Sensor Mfr
N.A.I.C.S.: 334519

Keyence Poland Sp. z o.o. (1)
Wyscigowa 56, 53-012, Wroclaw, Poland
Tel.: (48) 713686160
Web Site: http://www.keyence.com.pl
Sensors & Measuring Instruments Mfr
N.A.I.C.S.: 334511

Keyence Singapore Pte. Ltd. (1)
10 Kallang Avenue 07-14/17 Aperia Tower 2, Singapore, 339510, Singapore
Tel.: (65) 63921011
Web Site: https://www.keyence.com.sg
Sales Range: $25-49.9 Million
Emp.: 50
Sensors & Measuring Instruments Mfr
N.A.I.C.S.: 334511

Keyence Slovenia (1)
Trg Republike 3, 1000, Ljubljana, Slovenia
Tel.: (386) 14701666
Web Site: http://www.keyence.si
Sensors & Measuring Instruments Mfr
N.A.I.C.S.: 334511
Sebastian Testen *(Gen Mgr)*

Keyence Taiwan Co., Ltd. (1)
12F No 42 Sec 2 Zhongshan N Rd, Zhongshan Dist, Taipei, 104, Taiwan
Web Site: http://www.keyence.com.tw
Sales Range: $25-49.9 Million
Emp.: 70
FA Sensors & Opto-Electronic Measuring Instruments Supplier
N.A.I.C.S.: 334514

Keyence UK Ltd. (1)
Altius House 1 North Fourth Street, Milton Keynes, MK9 1DG, United Kingdom
Tel.: (44) 1908696900
Web Site: https://www.keyence.co.uk
Sales Range: $25-49.9 Million
Emp.: 30
FA Sensors & Opto-Electronic Instruments Supplier
N.A.I.C.S.: 423430

Keyence Vietnam Co., Ltd. (1)
Tel.: (84) 2437725555
Web Site: http://www.keyence.com.vn
Automation Sensor Mfr
N.A.I.C.S.: 334519

Schalt Eletro Eletronica Ind e Com Ltda (1)
Rua Humberto I 340 Vila Mariana, Sao Paulo, 04018-030, Brazil
Tel.: (55) 11 5082 2500
Web Site: http://www.schalt.com.br
Sensors & Measuring Instruments Mfr
N.A.I.C.S.: 334511

KEYERA CORPORATION

2nd Floor Sun Life Plaza West Tower 144 - 4th Avenue SW, Calgary, T2P 3N4, AB, Canada
Tel.: (403) 205-8300
Web Site: https://www.keyera.com
KEY—(TSX)
Rev.: $3,899,592,266
Assets: $6,360,175,778
Liabilities: $4,281,161,852
Net Worth: $2,079,013,926
Earnings: $253,619,870
Emp.: 1,005
Fiscal Year-end: 12/31/21
Natural Gas Extraction
N.A.I.C.S.: 211130
David G. Smith *(CEO)*

Subsidiaries:

Alberta Diluent Terminal Ltd. (1)
1250 Hayter Rd NW, Edmonton, T6S 1A2, AB, Canada
Tel.: (780) 414-7417
Natural Gas Extraction Services
N.A.I.C.S.: 211130

Alberta Envirofuels, Inc. (1)
9511 17th St NW, Edmonton, T6P 1Y3, AB, Canada
Tel.: (780) 449-7800
Sales Range: $50-74.9 Million
Emp.: 100
Petro Chemical Refinery
N.A.I.C.S.: 211120
Laurie Sparks *(Mgr-Ops)*

Keyera Energy Inc. (1)
10370 Richmond Ave Ste 210, Houston, TX 77042
Tel.: (713) 715-4660
Natural Gas Extraction Services
N.A.I.C.S.: 211130

Keyera Energy Ltd. (1)
1680 102 Avenue NW, Edmonton, T6P 1V7, AB, Canada
Tel.: (780) 464-9150
Natural Gas Extraction Services
N.A.I.C.S.: 211130

KEYHAVEN CAPITAL PARTNERS LTD.

1 Maple Place, London, W1T 4BB, United Kingdom
Tel.: (44) 20 7432 6200
Web Site: http://www.keyhavencapital.com
Year Founded: 2003
Emp.: 21
Privater Equity Firm
N.A.I.C.S.: 523999
Sasha van de Water *(Mng Partner)*

KEYHOLDER, INC.

3-16-3 Higashi, Shibuya-ku, Tokyo, 105-0011, Japan
Tel.: (81) 358438800
Web Site: https://www.keyholder.co.jp
Year Founded: 1964
4712—(TKS)
Rev.: $195,074,260
Assets: $192,954,350
Liabilities: $54,564,640
Net Worth: $138,389,710
Earnings: $14,988,260
Emp.: 1,337
Fiscal Year-end: 12/31/23
Holding Company; Amusement Arcades
N.A.I.C.S.: 551112
Nobuyoshi Fujisawa *(Chm)*

Subsidiaries:

TOKYO ROCK STUDIO Co. Ltd. (1)
3-16-3 Higashi, Shibuya-ku, Tokyo, Japan
Tel.: (81) 345319555
Web Site: https://tokyo-rock.co.jp
Video Production Services
N.A.I.C.S.: 512110

United Productions,Inc. (1)
2F F Nissay Ebisu Building 3-16-3 Higashi, Shibuya-ku, Tokyo, 150-0011, Japan
Tel.: (81) 345319555
Web Site: https://www.united-p.co.jp
Emp.: 338
Video Production Services
N.A.I.C.S.: 512120

Wisenlarge, Inc. (1)
Head Office/6-33-14 Jingumae, Shibuya-ku, Tokyo, 150-0001, Japan
Tel.: (81) 0358438803
Web Site: http://www.wisenlarge.jp
Media Services
N.A.I.C.S.: 541840

KEYMED BIOSCIENCES INC.

Building D2 No 18 Middle Road, Tianfu International Bio-Town, Chengdu, 610219, Sichuan, China
Tel.: (86) 2888610620
Web Site: https://en.keymedbio.com
Year Founded: 2016
2162—(HKG)
Rev.: $49,027,332
Assets: $537,622,120
Liabilities: $124,073,577
Net Worth: $413,548,543
Earnings: ($49,538,242)
Emp.: 897
Fiscal Year-end: 12/31/23
Biotechnology Research & Development Services
N.A.I.C.S.: 541714
Bo Chen *(CEO)*

INTERNATIONAL PUBLIC

KEYNE LTD.

Room 4101 41/F Lee Garden One, 33 Hysan Avenue, Causeway Bay, China (Hong Kong)
Tel.: (852) 25791718 BM
Web Site: http://www.nine-express.com.hk
Year Founded: 2001
0009—(HKG)
Rev.: $2,191,215
Assets: $425,626,238
Liabilities: $538,980,623
Net Worth: ($113,354,385)
Earnings: ($64,508,880)
Emp.: 42
Fiscal Year-end: 12/31/22
Holding Company
N.A.I.C.S.: 551112
Junjie Xiang *(Exec Dir)*

Subsidiaries:

Mandarin Films Limited (1)
Room 4101 41/F Lee Garden One 33 Hysan Avenue, Causeway Bay, China (Hong Kong)
Tel.: (852) 25791718
Film Production Services
N.A.I.C.S.: 512110

KEYNOTE FINANCIAL SERVICES LIMITED

The Ruby 9th floor Senapati Bapat Marg Dadar West, Mumbai, 400 028, Maharashtra, India
Tel.: (91) 30266000
Web Site: https://www.keynoteindia.net
Year Founded: 1993
KEYFINSERV—(NSE)
Rev.: $3,105,211
Assets: $16,466,695
Liabilities: $4,789,147
Net Worth: $11,677,548
Earnings: $1,538,918
Emp.: 19
Fiscal Year-end: 03/31/21
Investment Banking Services
N.A.I.C.S.: 523150
Uday S. Patil *(CFO & Dir-Investment Banking)*

KEYPOINT CARRIERS LIMITED

1018 Parkinson Rd, Woodstock, N4S 7W3, ON, Canada
Tel.: (519) 537-8907
Web Site: http://www.keypointcarriers.com
Year Founded: 2000
Transportation Services
N.A.I.C.S.: 484110
Cherie Krampien *(Pres & Controller)*

Subsidiaries:

Keypoint Carriers Limited Laredo Facility (1)
14216 Distribution Ave, Laredo, TX 78045
Tel.: (956) 724-9700
Freight Transportation Services
N.A.I.C.S.: 481212

KEYRUS SA

155 rue Anatole France, 92593, Levallois-Perret, Cedex, France
Tel.: (33) 141341000
Web Site: https://www.keyrus.com
Year Founded: 1996
KEY—(EUR)
Sales Range: $300-349.9 Million
Emp.: 3,000
Management Consulting Services
N.A.I.C.S.: 541611
Eric Cohen *(Founder & CEO)*

Subsidiaries:

Absys Cyborg SAS (1)
3 Carrefour de Weiden, 92130, Issy-les-

Moulineaux, France
Tel.: (33) 141096060
Web Site: http://www.absyscyborg.com
IT Management Services
N.A.I.C.S.: 541611
Laurent Leclercq (Mgr-IT)

Keyrus (China) Ltd. (1)
Unit 2306 Qiangsheng Building No 145 Pu-Jian Road, Pudong District, Shanghai, 200127, China
Tel.: (86) 2168860353
Data Management Services
N.A.I.C.S.: 541611

Keyrus (Israel) Ltd. (1)
Concorde Towers 21 Bar Kochva Street, Bnei Brak, 5126016, Israel
Tel.: (972) 775250590
Data Management Services
N.A.I.C.S.: 541611

Keyrus Hong Kong Limited (1)
13/F Harbour Commercial Building 122-124 Connaught Road Central, Sheung Wan, China (Hong Kong)
Tel.: (852) 28152881
Data Management Services
N.A.I.C.S.: 541611

Keyrus International SA (1)
Rue d Italie 11, CP 3054, 1211, Geneva, Switzerland
Tel.: (41) 225349215
Data Management Services
N.A.I.C.S.: 541611

Keyrus Luxembourg SA (1)
57 route de Longwy, 8080, Bertrange, Luxembourg
Tel.: (352) 26923781
Data Management Services
N.A.I.C.S.: 541611

Keyrus Management S.A (1)
155 rue Anatole France, 92593, Levallois-Perret, Cedex, France
Tel.: (33) 141341000
Web Site: http://www.keyrusmanagement.fr
Data Management Services
N.A.I.C.S.: 541611
Clement Salome (Sr Mgr)

Keyrus Mauritius Ltd. (1)
5eme Etage-Immeuble Mascareignes Avenue Saint Jean, Quatre Bornes, Mauritius
Tel.: (230) 4271132
Data Management Services
N.A.I.C.S.: 541611
Jessen Soobrayen (Project Mgr)

Keyrus N.V. (1)
Nijverheidslaan 3/2, 1853, Strombeek-Bever, Belgium
Tel.: (32) 27060300
Web Site: http://www.keyrus.be
Emp.: 200
Data Consultancy Services
N.A.I.C.S.: 541611
Koen Dils (Mng Dir)

Keyrus Spain SL (1)
Ctra Pozuelo 34 - 1 D, 28220, Majadahonda, Spain
Tel.: (34) 916369854
Data Analytic Services
N.A.I.C.S.: 541611
Ivan Navareno (Mktg Mgr)

Keyrus Tunisia SARL (1)
14 rue Ahmed Rami, 1002, Tunis, Tunisia
Tel.: (216) 71795200
Data Management Services
N.A.I.C.S.: 541611

Keyrus UK Limited (1)
201 Borough High Street, London, SE1 1JA, United Kingdom
Tel.: (44) 2035534900
Web Site: http://www.keyrus.com
Data Analytic Services
N.A.I.C.S.: 541611
Bruno Dehouck (Mng Dir)

Keyrus US Inc. (1)
252 W 37th St Ste 1400, New York, NY 10018
Tel.: (646) 664-4872
Data Consultancy Services
N.A.I.C.S.: 541611

KEYS EDUCATION & CARE LTD
Laganwood House, 44 New Forge Ln, Belfast, BT9 5NW, United Kingdom
Tel.: (44) 2890386050
Web Site:
http://www.keyschildcare.co.uk
Emp.: 1,500
Residential Childcare & Education Services; Support Services for Children, Including Therapy, Fostering, Education, Training & Development
N.A.I.C.S.: 623990
Peter O'Neill (Dir-Mktg)

KEYSHEEN (CAYMAN) HOLDINGS CO., LIMITED
16F No 95 Minquan Road, Xindian Dist, Taipei, Taiwan
Tel.: (886) 222192640
Web Site: http://www.keysheen.com
8427—(TAI)
Rev.: $115,009,939
Assets: $198,807,382
Liabilities: $65,185,191
Net Worth: $133,622,191
Earnings: $(4,275,194)
Fiscal Year-end: 12/31/20
Holding Company
N.A.I.C.S.: 551112
Chung-Hsin Liu (Chm)

KEYSINO SEPARATION TECHNOLOGY, INC.
F5 Bld 6 1888 Xinjinqiao Rd, Pudong New Area, Shanghai, 201206, China
Tel.: (86) 2161638525
Web Site:
https://www.keysinosep.com
Year Founded: 2011
300899—(SSE)
Rev.: $21,631,428
Assets: $99,543,600
Liabilities: $6,859,944
Net Worth: $92,683,656
Earnings: $3,842,748
Fiscal Year-end: 12/31/22
Waste Management Services
N.A.I.C.S.: 562998
Wenyue Ge (Chm & Gen Mgr)

Subsidiaries:

Keysino Separation Technology (Singapore) Pte. Ltd. (1)
C2-14-2 WaterHub 82 Toh Guan Road East, Singapore, 608576, Singapore
Tel.: (65) 62679029
Waste Management Services
N.A.I.C.S.: 562998

KEYSTONE EXCAVATING LTD.
4860 35th Street SE, Calgary, T2B 3M6, AB, Canada
Tel.: (403) 274-5452
Web Site: http://www.ourlifeisdirt.com
Year Founded: 1981
Rev.: $15,165,845
Emp.: 130
Construction Services
N.A.I.C.S.: 236220
Ken Elias (Co-Owner & Chm)

KEYSTONE INFRA LTD.
Ariel Sharon 4 31st floor Hashahar Tower, Givatayim, Israel
Tel.: (972) 35170122
Web Site:
https://www.keystoneisrael.com
Year Founded: 2019
KSTN—(TAE)
Rev.: $69,549,384
Assets: $863,783,382
Liabilities: $350,422,152
Net Worth: $513,361,230
Earnings: $122,635,998
Fiscal Year-end: 12/31/23
Lessors of Other Real Estate Property
N.A.I.C.S.: 531190

KEYSTONE LAW GROUP PLC
48 Chancery Lane, London, WC2A 1JF, United Kingdom
Tel.: (44) 2033193700
Web Site:
https://www.keystonelaw.com
Year Founded: 2002
KEYS—(AIM)
Rev.: $111,941,045
Assets: $52,577,791
Liabilities: $31,011,985
Net Worth: $21,565,806
Earnings: $9,738,986
Fiscal Year-end: 01/31/24
Human Resource Consulting Services
N.A.I.C.S.: 541612
James Knight (Founder & CEO)

KEYSTONE MICROTECH CORP.
No 431 Zhuangjing N Rd, Hsin Chu County, Zhubei, 302, Taiwan
Tel.: (886) 35509980
Web Site: https://ksmt.com.tw
Year Founded: 2006
6683—(TPE)
Rev.: $47,813,964
Assets: $76,814,839
Liabilities: $12,367,820
Net Worth: $64,447,019
Earnings: $12,708,345
Fiscal Year-end: 12/31/22
Semiconductor Devices Mfr
N.A.I.C.S.: 334413
Chih-Min Li (Chm)

KEYSTONE PARTNERS CO., LTD.
Toyo Property Bldg 8th Fl 1-28 1cho-me Toranomon, Minato-ku, Tokyo, 105-0001, Japan
Tel.: (81) 3 6206 1908
Web Site: http://www.ksg-p.co.jp
Year Founded: 2009
Private Investment Firm
N.A.I.C.S.: 523999
Shigeo Yoshida (Chm)

KEYSTONE REALTORS LIMITED
702 Natraj M V Road Junction Western Express Highway Andheri E, Mumbai, 400069, Maharashtra, India
Tel.: (91) 2266766888
Web Site: https://www.rustomjee.com
Year Founded: 1995
543669—(BOM)
Rev.: $80,446,275
Assets: $350,549,745
Liabilities: $270,287,745
Net Worth: $80,262,000
Earnings: $5,442,255
Fiscal Year-end: 03/31/21
Real Estate Development Services
N.A.I.C.S.: 531390

Subsidiaries:

Crest Property Solutions Private Limited (1)
B 404 Kohinoor Square N C Kelkar Marg Dadar West, Mumbai, 400028, India
Tel.: (91) 2249764349
Web Site: https://www.crestproperty.in
Property Management Services
N.A.I.C.S.: 531311

Intact Builders Private Limited (1)
52 2 Floor 100 Ft Road 4 Block, Koramangala, Bengaluru, 560 034, India
Tel.: (91) 9844044111
Web Site: https://www.intactdevelopers.com
Building Construction Services
N.A.I.C.S.: 236220

KEYSTONE WILDLIFE RESEARCH LTD.
112 9547 152nd St, Surrey, V3R 5Y5, BC, Canada
Tel.: (604) 588-1333
Web Site:
http://www.keystonewildlife.com
Year Founded: 1984
Rev.: $10,000,000
Emp.: 15
Environmental Consulting Services
N.A.I.C.S.: 541690

KEYTREE LTD.
114 St Martin's Lane, London, WC2N 4BE, United Kingdom
Tel.: (44) 20 7036 9780
Web Site: http://www.keytree.co.uk
Year Founded: 2006
Sales Range: $10-24.9 Million
Emp.: 77
Information Technology Consultancy Services
N.A.I.C.S.: 541512
Dan McNamara (CEO)

KEYWARE SOLUTIONS INC.
5-37-18 Kamikitazawa, Setagaya-ku, Tokyo, 156-8588, Japan
Tel.: (81) 332901111   JP
Web Site: https://www.keyware.co.jp
3799—(TKS)
Rev.: $135,577,710
Assets: $82,790,250
Liabilities: $25,686,460
Net Worth: $57,103,790
Earnings: $4,818,690
Emp.: 1,283
Fiscal Year-end: 03/31/24
Advanced Security Systems
N.A.I.C.S.: 541511
Masahiro Mita (Pres & CEO)

KEYWARE TECHNOLOGIES NV
Ikaros Business Park Ikaroslaan 24, B-1930, Zaventem, Belgium
Tel.: (32) 23462523
Web Site: https://www.keyware.com
Year Founded: 1996
KEYW—(EUR)
Sales Range: $10-24.9 Million
Electronic Payment Terminal
N.A.I.C.S.: 334118
Guido Van der Schueren (Chm)

Subsidiaries:

Keyware Smart Card Division N.V. (1)
Ikaroslaan 24, 1930, Zaventem, Belgium
Tel.: (32) 23462523
Web Site: http://www.keyware.be
Emp.: 30
Financial Transaction Services
N.A.I.C.S.: 522320
Stephane Vandervelde (Pres)

KEYYO
92-98 Boulevard Victor Hugo, 92110, Clichy, France
Tel.: (33) 1 72387700
Web Site: http://www.keyyo.com
Rev.: $26,275,640
Earnings: $2,471,848
Emp.: 50
Fiscal Year-end: 12/31/15
Telecommunication Servicesb
N.A.I.C.S.: 517810
Philippe Houdouin (Chm)

KFC LTD.
11th floor 2-4-1 Shibakoen, Minato-ku, Tokyo, 105-0011, Japan
Tel.: (81) 364028250
Web Site: https://www.kfc-net.co.jp
Year Founded: 1965

KFC LTD.

KFC Ltd.—(Continued)
3420—(TKS)
Rev.: $165,712,700
Assets: $195,774,980
Liabilities: $59,503,220
Net Worth: $136,271,760
Earnings: $7,779,970
Emp.: 293
Fiscal Year-end: 03/31/24
Construction Materials Distr
N.A.I.C.S.: 423320

KFIC INVEST K.S.C.P.
Al Arabia Tower Building 21 Block 5
Ahmad Al Jaber St, PO Box 21521,
Safat, 13037, Kuwait, Kuwait
Tel.: (965) 1889000
Web Site: http://www.kfic-kw.com
KFIC—(KUW)
Rev.: $6,597,218
Assets: $135,194,631
Liabilities: $37,490,563
Net Worth: $97,704,068
Earnings: ($36,351,612)
Emp.: 2,541
Fiscal Year-end: 12/31/23
Investment & Financial Services
N.A.I.C.S.: 523150
Reham Fuad Mohammed AlGhanim *(Chm)*

Subsidiaries:

KFIC Financial
Brokerage-K.S.C.C (1)
Ahmed Al-Jaber St Al-Arabiya Tower 26th
Floor Fahad Al-Salem Street, Al-Sharq, Kuwait
Tel.: (965) 22258759
Web Site: http://www.kficbrokerage.com
Brokerage Services
N.A.I.C.S.: 523150
Mohammed Alaiban *(Chm)*

KFM KINGDOM HOLDINGS LIMITED
Workshop C 31/F TML Tower 3 Hoi
Shing Road, Tsuen Wan, NT, China
(Hong Kong)
Tel.: (852) 2 614 7138
Web Site: http://www.kingdom.com.hk
Year Founded: 1987
3816—(HKG)
Rev.: $78,960,266
Assets: $100,152,196
Liabilities: $35,060,762
Net Worth: $65,091,434
Earnings: ($6,193,491)
Emp.: 1,053
Fiscal Year-end: 03/31/22
Precision Metal Engineering
N.A.I.C.S.: 332999
Peter Kwok Wah Sun *(Founder & CEO)*

Subsidiaries:

KFM Kingdom Holdings Limited -
Shanghai Production Plant (1)
No 528-530 Huicheng Road Nanhui Industrial Zone, Pudong, Shanghai, 200003, China
Tel.: (86) 21 6800 9618
Web Site: http://www.kingdom.com.hk
Fabricated Metal Products Mfr
N.A.I.C.S.: 332999

KFM Kingdom Holdings Limited -
Shenzhen Production Plant
(Guanlan) (1)
Block A No 1301 Guanguang Road Dabu
Lane Guanlan Street, Longhua New District, Shenzhen, China
Tel.: (86) 755 2678 6338
Fabricated Metal Products Mfr
N.A.I.C.S.: 332999

KFM Kingdom Holdings Limited -
Shenzhen Production Plant (Xili) (1)
No 8 Mumiankeng Industrial Zone, Xili Dakan Village Nanshan District, Shenzhen, 518000, China
Tel.: (86) 755 2695 1138
Web Site: http://www.kingdom.com.hk
Fabricated Metal Products Mfr
N.A.I.C.S.: 332999

KFM Kingdom Holdings Limited - Suzhou Production Plant (1)
3 HuoJu Road Science & Technology Industrial Park, Suzhou New District, Suzhou, China
Tel.: (86) 512 6808 6338
Fabricated Metal Products Mfr
N.A.I.C.S.: 332999

Kingdom Fine Metal Limited (1)
31st floor TML Tower 3 Hoi Shing Road,
New Territories, Tsuen Wan, Hong Kong,
China (Hong Kong)
Tel.: (852) 2614 7138
Fabricated Metal Products Mfr
N.A.I.C.S.: 332999

KFW GROUP
Palmengartenstrasse 5-9, 60325,
Frankfurt am Main, Germany
Tel.: (49) 6974310
Web Site: http://www.kfw.de
Year Founded: 1948
Rev.: $4,387,611,480
Assets: $566,673,796,920
Liabilities: $531,552,747,600
Net Worth: $35,121,049,320
Earnings: $1,530,848,620
Emp.: 6,705
Fiscal Year-end: 12/31/19
Investment Loan Services
N.A.I.C.S.: 522310
Bernd Loewen *(CFO & Member-Exec Bd)*

Subsidiaries:

Deutsche Energie-Agentur
GmbH (1)
Chausseestrasse 128a, 10115, Berlin,
Germany (26%)
Tel.: (49) 30667770
Web Site: http://www.dena.de
Sales Range: $125-149.9 Million
Emp.: 280
Energy Agency Overseeing Environmentally
Friendly & Renewable Energy Production
Methods
N.A.I.C.S.: 221118

Deutsche Investitions- und Entwicklungsgesellschaft mbH (1)
Kammergasse 22, 50676, Cologne, Germany
Tel.: (49) 22149860
Web Site: http://www.deginvest.de
Emp.: 500
Financial Services
N.A.I.C.S.: 523210
Roland Siller *(Chm)*

KfW Capital GmbH & Co. KG (1)
Bockenheimer Landstrasse 98, 60323,
Frankfurt am Main, Germany
Tel.: (49) 6974318880
Web Site: http://www.kfw-capital.de
Financial Services
N.A.I.C.S.: 523210
Richard Eisenbach *(CFO)*

KfW IPEX-Bank GmbH (1)
PalmengartenstraSSe 5-9, 60325, Frankfurt
am Main, Germany
Tel.: (49) 6 9743 1 0
Web Site: http://www.kfw-ipex-bank.de
Project, Export & Trade Financing Services
N.A.I.C.S.: 522299
Christian K. Murach *(Member-Mgmt Bd)*

KG DENIM LIMITED
Then Thirumalai, Jadayampalayam,
Coimbatore, 641302, Tamil Nadu,
India
Tel.: (91) 4254235401
Web Site: https://www.kgdenim.com
500239—(BOM)
Rev.: $59,811,474
Assets: $62,160,803
Liabilities: $51,733,200
Net Worth: $10,427,604
Earnings: ($900,204)
Emp.: 1,761
Fiscal Year-end: 03/31/21
Textiles
N.A.I.C.S.: 424310
K. G. Baalakrishnan *(Chm)*

Subsidiaries:

Trigger Apparels Limited (1)
No 20 Vetrivel Nagar, Goldwins, Coimbatore, 641014, Tamilnadu, India
Tel.: (91) 18008906840
Web Site: http://www.trigger.in
Men Apparel Whslr
N.A.I.C.S.: 424350

KG ECO SOLUTION CO.,LTD.
59 Chodongnonggongdanji-gil,
Chodong-myeon, Miryang, 429-450,
Gyeongsangnam-do, Korea (South)
Tel.: (82) 553916770
Web Site: https://kgecosolution.co.kr
Year Founded: 1999
151860—(KRS)
Rev.: $3,792,233,043
Assets: $3,905,471,145
Liabilities: $1,919,376,046
Net Worth: $1,986,095,099
Earnings: $694,068,132
Emp.: 30
Fiscal Year-end: 12/31/22
Waste Management Systems
N.A.I.C.S.: 562211

Subsidiaries:

KG Chemical Corporation (1)
322 Dangwol-ro, Onsan-eup Ulju-gun, Ulsan, Korea (South)
Tel.: (82) 522311700
Web Site: https://www.kgchem.co.kr
Rev.: $5,067,841,353
Assets: $5,355,124,184
Liabilities: $2,869,379,586
Net Worth: $2,485,744,598
Earnings: $730,791,596
Emp.: 213
Fiscal Year-end: 12/31/2022
Fertilizer & Chemical Product Mfr & Whslr
N.A.I.C.S.: 325312
Jae-seun Kwak *(Pres & CEO)*

KG Mobility Corp. (1)
455-12 Dongsak-ro, Pyeongtaek, Gyeonggi-do, Korea (South) (61.9%)
Tel.: (82) 316101114
Web Site: https://www.kg-mobility.com
Rev.: $2,704,439,290
Assets: $1,581,506,762
Liabilities: $718,113,296
Net Worth: $863,393,467
Earnings: ($47,505,498)
Emp.: 4,271
Fiscal Year-end: 12/31/2022
Sport Utility Vehicles, Recreational Vehicles
& Specialty Motor Vehicles Mfr; Motor Vehicle Parts Mfr
N.A.I.C.S.: 336110
Pawan Kumar Goenka *(Chm)*

KG INTELLIGENCE CO., LTD.
170-108 Hirata, Kita-ku, Okayama,
700-0952, Japan
Tel.: (81) 2415522
Web Site: https://www.kg-net.co.jp
Year Founded: 1950
2408—(TKS)
Rev.: $18,838,130
Assets: $52,749,600
Liabilities: $10,528,650
Net Worth: $42,220,950
Earnings: $2,630,390
Emp.: 203
Fiscal Year-end: 12/31/23
Publishing Services
N.A.I.C.S.: 513199
Takemi Masuda *(Pres)*

KG MOBILIANS CO., LTD.
KG Tower 16th floor 92 Tongil-ro,
Jung-gu, Seoul, 04517, Korea
(South)
Tel.: (82) 2208182546
Web Site: https://www.mobilians.co.kr
Year Founded: 2000
046440—(KRS)
Rev.: $211,781,618
Assets: $363,702,847
Liabilities: $121,022,196
Net Worth: $242,680,651
Earnings: $21,457,266
Emp.: 172
Fiscal Year-end: 12/31/22
Electronic Payment Services
N.A.I.C.S.: 522320
Su Bok Wi *(CEO)*

KG PETROCHEM LIMITED
C-171 Road No 9 J VKI Area, Jaipur,
302 013, Rajasthan, India
Tel.: (91) 1412331231
Web Site: http://www.kgpetro.in
531609—(BOM)
Rev.: $41,804,681
Assets: $46,465,487
Liabilities: $26,507,440
Net Worth: $19,958,047
Earnings: $2,139,951
Emp.: 1,289
Fiscal Year-end: 03/31/21
Apparel & Accessory Mfr & Distr
N.A.I.C.S.: 315990
Gauri Shanker Kandoi *(Chm)*

KGHM POLSKA MIEDZ S.A.
ul M Sklodowskiej-Curie 48, 59-301,
Lubin, Poland
Tel.: (48) 767478200
Web Site: https://kghm.com
Year Founded: 1961
KGH—(WAR)
Rev.: $8,502,989,499
Assets: $13,426,116,666
Liabilities: $5,350,449,681
Net Worth: $8,075,666,985
Earnings: $1,199,316,686
Emp.: 33,654
Fiscal Year-end: 12/31/22
Silver & Copper Mining & Smelting
Services
N.A.I.C.S.: 212230
Marcin Chludzinski *(Pres, CEO & Member-Mgmt Bd)*

Subsidiaries:

Centrum Badan Jakosci sp. z
o.o. (1)
ul M Sklodowskiej Curie 62, 59-301, Lubin, Poland
Tel.: (48) 767469900
Web Site: http://cbj.com.pl
Physical Engineering & Life Sciences Research & Development
N.A.I.C.S.: 541715

DFM ZANAM - LEGMET Sp. z
o.o. (1)
Ul Kopalniana 7, 59-101, Polkowice, Poland
Tel.: (48) 76 84 70 905
Web Site: http://www.kghmzanam.com
Sales Range: $400-449.9 Million
Emp.: 230
Mining Machinery & Equipment Mfr
N.A.I.C.S.: 333131

Dolnoslaska Fabryka Maszyn ZANAM
- LEGMET Sp. z o.o. (1)
ul Kopalniana 7, 59-101, Polkowice, Poland
Tel.: (48) 768470905
Web Site: http://www.zanam-legmet.pl
Building Equipment & Machinery Installation Contractors
N.A.I.C.S.: 238220

Energetyka Sp. z o.o. (1)
ul M Sklodowskiej Curie 58, 59-301, Lubin, Poland
Tel.: (48) 767469105
Web Site: https://energetyka.lubin.pl
Emp.: 830

AND PRIVATE COMPANIES

Hydronics Plumbing & Heating Equipment & Supplies Whslr
N.A.I.C.S.: 423720

Inova Centrum Innowacji Technicznych Sp. z o.o. (1)
Marii Sklodowskiej - Curie Str 183, 59-301, Lubin, Poland
Tel.: (48) 767464110
Web Site: http://www.inova.pl
Electronic & Precision Equipment Repair & Maintenance
N.A.I.C.S.: 811210

Interferie S.A. (1)
ul M Sklodowskiej Curie 176, 59-301, Lubin, Poland
Tel.: (48) 767495400
Web Site: http://www.inmedicalspa.pl
Sales Range: $25-49.9 Million
Emp.: 100
Tour Operator
N.A.I.C.S.: 561520

KGHM (SHANGHAI) COPPER TRADING CO., LTD. (1)
Unit 1511 Citigroup Tower HuaYuan ShiQiao Road 33, New PuDong District, Shanghai, 200120, China
Tel.: (86) 2161629700
Web Site: http://kghm.com
Copper Product Mfr
N.A.I.C.S.: 331529

KGHM Cuprum Sp. z o.o. (1)
ul gen W Sikorskiego 2-8, 53-659, Wroclaw, Poland
Tel.: (48) 717812201
Web Site: https://kghmcuprum.com
Emp.: 171
Physical Engineering & Life Sciences Research & Development
N.A.I.C.S.: 541715
Wojciech Boczar (Chm-Supervisory Bd)

KGHM International Ltd. (1)
Vaughan Office Suite 400 191 Creditview Road, Vaughan, L4L 9T1, ON, Canada
Tel.: (647) 265-9191
Web Site: http://www.kghminternational.com
Rev.: $701,300,000
Assets: $4,384,000,000
Liabilities: $1,480,700,000
Net Worth: $2,903,300,000
Earnings: $17,100,000
Fiscal Year-end: 12/31/2014
Holding Company; Copper & Platinum Mining
N.A.I.C.S.: 551112
Robert Nowak (Pres & CEO)

Co-Headquarters (Domestic):

KGHM International Ltd. - Toronto (2)
145 King Street West Suite 1500, Toronto, M5H 1J8, ON, Canada
Tel.: (416) 628-5929
Web Site: http://www.kghminternational.com
Sales Range: $50-74.9 Million
Emp.: 20
Copper & Platinum Mining
N.A.I.C.S.: 212230
Catharine E. G. Farrow (COO)

Subsidiary (US):

Carlota Copper Company Ltd. (3)
2624 Forest Service Rd 287, Miami, AZ 85539 **(100%)**
Tel.: (928) 473-3518
Copper Ore & Nickel Ore Mining
N.A.I.C.S.: 212230

Division (Domestic):

DMC Mining Services (3)
191 Creditview Road Suite 400, Vaughan, L4L 9T1, ON, Canada
Tel.: (905) 780-1980
Web Site: https://dmcmining.com
Sales Range: $50-74.9 Million
Mining Contractors
N.A.I.C.S.: 213115
Rob Mundy (VP-Raise Boring)

Subsidiary (US):

DMC Mining Services Corporation (3)

488 E 6400 S Ste 250, Salt Lake City, UT 84107
Tel.: (801) 975-1979
Web Site: http://www.dmcmining.com
Sales Range: $50-74.9 Million
Emp.: 12
Mining Services & Solutions
N.A.I.C.S.: 212290
Terry M. Tilley (Mgr-Health, Safety & Environment)

Robinson Nevada Mining Company (3)
4232 W White Pine County Rd 44, Ruth, NV 89319
Tel.: (775) 289-7000
Metal Mining Services
N.A.I.C.S.: 212290
Robby Ruesch (Mgr-Mine Ops)

KGHM Kupfer AG (1)
Bautzener Str 54, Weisswasser, 2943, Germany
Tel.: (49) 35762129502
Copper Mining Services
N.A.I.C.S.: 212230

KGHM Kupferhandelsges.mbH (1)
Rothenturmstrasse 12-2-18, 1010, Vienna, Austria
Tel.: (43) 15134690
Web Site: http://www.kghm.pl
Sales Range: $25-49.9 Million
Emp.: 3
Secondary Smelting Refining & Alloying Copper
N.A.I.C.S.: 331420

KGHM LETIA - Legnicki Park Technologiczny S.A. (1)
Ul Rycerska 24, 59-220, Legnica, Poland
Tel.: (48) 767235440
Web Site: http://www.letia.pl
Sales Range: $50-74.9 Million
Property Management Services
N.A.I.C.S.: 531312
Krzysztof Sadowski (Chm-Mgmt Bd)

KGHM Metraco S.A. (1)
ul Sw M Kolbe 9, 59-220, Legnica, Poland
Tel.: (48) 768667700
Web Site: https://metraco.pl
Sales Range: $25-49.9 Million
Chemical Product & Preparation Mfr
N.A.I.C.S.: 325998

KGHM Polish Copper Ltd (1)
3rd Fl 6-7 Queen St, EC4NISP, London, United Kingdom
Tel.: (44) 2073292429
Web Site: http://www.polishcopper.com
Sales Range: $25-49.9 Million
Emp.: 2
Secondary Smelting Refining & Alloying Copper
N.A.I.C.S.: 331420

KGHM TFI S.A. (1)
Ul Gen W Sikorskiego 2-8, 53-659, Wroclaw, Poland
Tel.: (48) 717900180
Web Site: http://www.tfi.kghm.pl
Sales Range: $50-74.9 Million
Fund Management Services
N.A.I.C.S.: 523940

Miedziowe Centrum Zdrowia S.A. (1)
ul M Sklodowskiej Curie 54, 59-301, Lubin, Poland
Tel.: (48) 768460300
Web Site: http://www.mcz.pl
General Medical & Surgical Hospitals
N.A.I.C.S.: 622110

NITROERG S.A (1)
Plac Alfreda Nobla 1, 43-150, Bierun, Poland
Tel.: (48) 324661900
Web Site: https://nitroerg.pl
Sales Range: $550-599.9 Million
Emp.: 1,000
Explosive & Fuel Additive Mfr
N.A.I.C.S.: 325920
Slawomir Kwiatkowski (Member-Mgmt Bd & Dir-Production & Comml)

PHP MERCUS sp. z o.o. (1)
Ul Kopalniana 11, 59-101, Polkowice, Poland

Tel.: (48) 76 724 81 10
Web Site: http://www.mercus.com.pl
Sales Range: $200-249.9 Million
Copper & Silver Mfr
N.A.I.C.S.: 331529

Pol-Miedz Trans Sp. z o.o. (1)
ul Marii Sklodowskiej-Curie 190, woj dolnoslaskie, 59-301, Lubin, Poland
Tel.: (48) 768471800
Web Site: https://www.pmtrans.com.pl
Transportation Services
N.A.I.C.S.: 488999

Pol-Miedz Trans sp. z o.o. (1)
ul Marii Sklodowskiej-Curie 190, 59-301, Lubin, Lower Silesia, Poland
Tel.: (48) 768471800
Web Site: http://www.pmtrans.pl
Transportation Services
N.A.I.C.S.: 485999

Polskie Centrum Promocji Miedzi Sp. z o.o. (1)
Sw Mikolaja 8-11 room 408, 50 136, Wroclaw, Poland
Tel.: (48) 717812502
Web Site: http://www.copperalliance.pl
Emp.: 10
Secondary Smelting Refining & Alloying Copper
N.A.I.C.S.: 331420
Michal Ramczykowski (Chm)

Przedsiebiorstwo Budowy Kopaln PeBeKa S.A. (1)
ul Marii Sklodowskiej-Curie 76, 59-301, Lubin, Poland
Tel.: (48) 76 840 54 05
Web Site: http://www.pebeka.com.pl
Sales Range: $400-449.9 Million
Construction Engineering Services
N.A.I.C.S.: 237990
Tomasz Rawecki (Chm-Mgmt Bd)

Towarzystwo Ubezpieczen Wzajemnych CUPRUM Sp. z o.o. (1)
ul M Sklodowskiej Curie 82, 59-301, Lubin, Poland **(98.6%)**
Tel.: (48) 767277400
Web Site: http://tuw-cuprum.pl
Health, Property & Casualty Insurance Products & Services
N.A.I.C.S.: 524298

Walcownia Metali Labedy S.A. (1)
ul Metalowcow 6, 44109, Gliwice, Poland
Tel.: (48) 323004285
Web Site: http://www.walcownia.labedy.pl
Coal Mining Services
N.A.I.C.S.: 213113
Marcin Terebelski (Chm-Mgmt Bd)

Walcownia Metali Niezelaznych Sp. z o.o. (1)
ul Metalowcow 6, 44-109, Gliwice, Poland
Tel.: (48) 323306340
Web Site: http://www.wmn.com.pl
Sales Range: $100-124.9 Million
Nonmetallic Mineral Services
N.A.I.C.S.: 213115
Marcin Terebelski (Chm-Mgmt Bd)

Warszawska Fabryka Platerow Hefra S.A. (1)
ul Zeglarska 8, 59-220, Legnica, Poland
Tel.: (48) 667670013
Web Site: http://hefra.pl
Sales Range: $25-49.9 Million
Silver & Silver-Plated Flatware Mfr
N.A.I.C.S.: 339910

KGI FINANCIAL HOLDING CO., LTD.
No 135 Dunhua N Rd, Songshan Dist, Taipei, 105, Taiwan
Tel.: (886) 227638800
Web Site: https://www.kgi.com
Year Founded: 2001
2883—(TAI)
Rev.: $3,027,004,065
Assets: $114,067,224,869
Liabilities: $105,845,649,783
Net Worth: $8,221,575,087
Emp.: 13,484
Fiscal Year-end: 12/31/23

Holding Company
N.A.I.C.S.: 551112
Winnie Huang (Exec VP & Head-Risk Mgmt)

Subsidiaries:

CDIB Capital Group (1)
No 135 Dunhua N Rd, Songshan Dist, Taipei, 105, Taiwan **(100%)**
Tel.: (886) 227638800
Web Site: https://www.cdibcapitalgroup.com
Investment Banking
N.A.I.C.S.: 523150
Melanie Nan (Sr Exec VP)

Subsidiary (Domestic):

CDC Finance & Leasing Corp. (2)
3F 125 Nanking E Road Section 5, Taipei, 105, Taiwan **(76.04%)**
Tel.: (886) 227611758
Sales Range: $25-49.9 Million
Emp.: 50
Financial Investment Services
N.A.I.C.S.: 523999
Chao Ming Meng (Pres)

CDIB Asset Management Co., Ltd. (2)
125 Nanking East Road Section 5, Taipei, Taiwan
Tel.: (886) 227568968
Financial Management Services
N.A.I.C.S.: 523999

CDIB Capital International Corporation (2)
125 Nanjing East Road Section 5, Taipei, 105, Taiwan
Tel.: (886) 2 2763 8800
Web Site: http://www.cdibcapital.com
Equity Investment Firm
N.A.I.C.S.: 523999
Steven Wu (Mng Dir)

Co-Headquarters (Non-US):

CDIB Capital International (Hong Kong) Corporation Limited (3)
7/F ICBC Tower 3 Garden Road, Central, China (Hong Kong)
Tel.: (852) 2 231 8600
Web Site: http://www.cdibcapital.com
Equity Investment Firm
N.A.I.C.S.: 523999
Stephen Choi (Sr VP)

Subsidiary (Non-US):

CDIB Capital International (Korea) Corporation Ltd. (4)
City Airport Terminal 7/F 22 Teheran-ro 87-gil, Gangnam-gu, Seoul, 06164, Korea (South)
Tel.: (82) 2 551 8700
Web Site: http://www.cdibcapital.com
Sales Range: $50-74.9 Million
Emp.: 6
Equity Investment Firm
N.A.I.C.S.: 523999

Subsidiary (Domestic):

China Venture Management Inc. (2)
12F 125 Nanking E Rd Section 5, Taipei, 10504, Taiwan
Tel.: (886) 227673668
Sales Range: $50-74.9 Million
Emp.: 18
Fund Management Services
N.A.I.C.S.: 524292
Lawrence Liu (Chm)

CDIB Capital Innovation Advisors Corporation (1)
12F No 135 Dunhua N Rd, Songshan Dist, Taipei, 105021, Taiwan
Tel.: (886) 227638800
N.A.I.C.S.: 523940

CDIB Private Equity (China) Corporation (1)
Tel.: (86) 2162895708
Asset Management Services
N.A.I.C.S.: 523940

Subsidiary (Non-US):

CDIB Yida Private Equity (Kunshan) Co., Ltd. (2)

KGI FINANCIAL HOLDING CO., LTD.

KGI Financial Holding Co., Ltd.—(Continued)
Tel.: (86) 2162895708
Asset Management Services
N.A.I.C.S.: 523940

CHINA LIFE INSURANCE COMPANY, LTD. (1)
3 4 5 6 7F No 135 Dunhua N Rd, Songshan Dist, Taipei, Taiwan **(55.95%)**
Tel.: (886) 800098889
Web Site: https://www.kgilife.com.tw
Rev.: $5,134,448,785
Assets: $76,327,199,322
Liabilities: $72,858,618,008
Net Worth: $3,468,581,314
Earnings: $427,931,298
Emp.: 13,426
Fiscal Year-end: 12/31/2022
Fire Insurance Services
N.A.I.C.S.: 524298
Yu-Ling Kuo (Chm)

KGI Asia Limited (1)
41/F Central Plaza 18 Harbour Road, Wanchai, Hong Kong, China (Hong Kong)
Tel.: (852) 28785555
Web Site: https://www.kgi.com.hk
N.A.I.C.S.: 523150

KGI Bank Co. Ltd. (1)
No 193 Maijin Rd, Anle District, Keelung, 204, Taiwan
Tel.: (886) 224336566
Web Site: https://www.kgibank.com.tw
N.A.I.C.S.: 522110
Paul Yang (Chm)

KGI Securities Co., Ltd. (1)
700 Mingshui Road, Zhongshan District, Taipei, 104, Taiwan **(100%)**
Tel.: (886) 22 361 9889
Web Site: https://www.kgi.com.tw
Sales Range: $400-449.9 Million
Emp.: 4,800
Holding Company; Securities & Commodities Brokerage Services
N.A.I.C.S.: 551112
Daw-Yi Hsu (Chm)

Subsidiary (Domestic):

Grand Cathay Securities Corporation (2)
14F No 2 Chongqing South Road, Section 1, Taipei, 100, ROC, Taiwan
Tel.: (886) 223148800
Web Site: http://www.gcsc.com.tw
Securities Trading & Brokerage Services
N.A.I.C.S.: 523150

Subsidiary (Non-US):

KGI Asia (Holdings) Pte. Ltd. (2)
Tokio Marine Centre 20 McCallum Street 20th Floor, Singapore, 069046, Singapore
Tel.: (65) 6671 1818
Holding Company; Futures Commodity Contracts Brokerage Services
N.A.I.C.S.: 551112

Subsidiary (Domestic):

KGI Fraser Securities Pte. Ltd. (3)
4 Shenton Way #13-01 SGX Centre 2, Singapore, 068807, Singapore
Tel.: (65) 6535 9455
Web Site: http://www.amfraser.com.sg
Securities Brokerage
N.A.I.C.S.: 523150

KGI Ong Capital Pte. Ltd. (3)
Tokio Marine Centre 20 McCallum Street 20th Floor, Singapore, 069046, Singapore
Tel.: (65) 6671 1818
Web Site: http://www.kgieworld.sg
Emp.: 100
Futures Commodity Contracts Brokerage Services
N.A.I.C.S.: 523160

Subsidiary (Domestic):

KGI Futures Co. Ltd. (2)
12th and 13th Floor No 2 Section 1 Chongqing South Road, Zhongzheng District, Taipei, 100, Taiwan
Tel.: (886) 22 361 9889
Web Site: https://www.kgif.com.tw
Futures Commodity Brokerage Services
N.A.I.C.S.: 523160

Subsidiary (Non-US):

KGI Hong Kong Limited (2)
41/F Central Plaza 18 Harbour Road, Wanchai, China (Hong Kong)
Tel.: (852) 2 878 6888
Web Site: http://www.kgieworld.com
Sales Range: $300-349.9 Million
Emp.: 700
Securities Brokerage Services
N.A.I.C.S.: 523150

Subsidiary (Domestic):

KGI Securities (Taiwan) Co., Ltd. (2)
No 700 Mingshui Rd, Zhongshan Dist, Taipei, 104, Taiwan
Tel.: (886) 22 389 0088
Web Site: https://www.kgi.com.tw
Securities Brokerage Services
N.A.I.C.S.: 523150

KGI Securities Investment Trust Co., Ltd. (2)
No 698 Mingshui Road, Zhongshan District, Taipei, Taiwan
Tel.: (886) 221815678
Web Site: http://www.kgifund.com.tw
Rev.: $397,243,000
Emp.: 70
Investment Fund
N.A.I.C.S.: 525910

Subsidiary (Non-US):

One Asset Management Limited (2)
989 Siam Piwat Tower Floor 9 24 Rama 1 Road, Pathum Wan, Bangkok, 10330, Thailand
Tel.: (66) 2 659 8888
Web Site: https://www.one-asset.com
Sales Range: $75-99.9 Million
Emp.: 200
Fund Management Services
N.A.I.C.S.: 523150

KGI SECURITIES (THAILAND) PUBLIC COMPANY LIMITED
173 Asia Centre Bldg 8th-11th Fl, South Sathorn Rd Khwaeng, Thungmahamek Khet Satorn, Bangkok, 10120, Thailand
Tel.: (66) 26588888
Web Site: http://www.kgieworld.co.th
Sales Range: $25-49.9 Million
Investment Banking & Brokerage Services
N.A.I.C.S.: 523150
Pisit Leeahtam (Vice Chm)

Subsidiaries:

KGI Securities (Thailand) International Holdings Limited (1)
41/F Central Plaza 18 Harbour Road, Wanchai, China (Hong Kong)
Tel.: (852) 28786888
Wireless Telecommunication Services
N.A.I.C.S.: 517112

KGINICIS CO. LTD.
14th and 15th floors KG Tower 92 Tongil-ro, Jung-gu, Seoul, 04517, Korea (South)
Tel.: (82) 15884954
Web Site: https://www.inicis.com
Year Founded: 1998
035600—(KRS)
Rev.: $903,238,032
Assets: $1,114,435,764
Liabilities: $649,894,764
Net Worth: $464,540,999
Earnings: $53,975,781
Emp.: 216
Fiscal Year-end: 12/31/22
Electronic Payment Services
N.A.I.C.S.: 541511
Seung-Yong Yoo (CEO & VP)

Subsidiaries:

KG Allat Corp (1)
660 Yuseong 1 A Dong 5F Dae Wang Pangyo-ro, Bundang-gu, Seongnam, 13494, Gyeonggi-do, Korea (South)
Tel.: (82) 237839990
Online Payment Services
N.A.I.C.S.: 522299

Subsidiary (Domestic):

SRS Korea Co., Ltd. (2)
6/F Yonkang Bldg 270 Yeonji-dong, Jongno-gu, Seoul, 110739, Korea (South)
Tel.: (82) 236708383
Web Site: http://www.srs-korea.com
Restaurant Management Services
N.A.I.C.S.: 541618

KGL LOGISTICS K.S.C.
PO Box 4135, Safat, 13042, Kuwait, Kuwait
Tel.: (965) 1845455
Web Site: http://www.kgllogistics.com
LOGISTICS—(KUW)
Rev.: $70,946,496
Assets: $524,700,004
Liabilities: $211,359,667
Net Worth: $313,340,337
Earnings: ($17,448,752)
Emp.: 177
Fiscal Year-end: 12/31/20
Cargo Booking & Pick-up Services
N.A.I.C.S.: 488320
Jafar Mohamed Ali (Chm)

KGL RESOURCES LIMITED
Level 5 167 Eagle Street, Brisbane, 4000, QLD, Australia
Tel.: (61) 730719003
Web Site: https://www.kglresources.com.au
KGL—(ASX)
Rev.: $271,762
Assets: $82,006,966
Liabilities: $1,189,918
Net Worth: $80,817,048
Earnings: $1,567,756
Emp.: 21
Fiscal Year-end: 06/30/23
Copper Ore Mining Services
N.A.I.C.S.: 212230
Denis Wood (Chm)

KGL RESOURCES LTD.
100 King Street West Suite 7070, Toronto, M5H 3L5, ON, Canada
Tel.: (416) 360-3406
Year Founded: 2006
KN6—(DEU)
Assets: $10,606
Liabilities: $640,950
Net Worth: ($630,344)
Earnings: ($120,720)
Fiscal Year-end: 09/30/23
Mineral Exploration Services
N.A.I.C.S.: 213114
Simon Finnis (CEO & Mng Dir)

KGN INDUSTRIES LIMITED
B- 15 Hirnen Shopping Centre Co Op Housing Society Limited, Near City Centre SV Road Goregaon (West), Mumbai, 400062, India
Tel.: (91) 22 67256547
Web Site: http://www.kgnindustries.com
Oil & Gas Exploration Services
N.A.I.C.S.: 213112
Arifbhai Ismailbhai Memon (Mng Dir)

KH CONSTRUCTION CO., LTD.
165 Gasan Digital 1-ro, Geumcheon, Seoul, 153-803, Korea (South)
Tel.: (82) 263265571
Web Site: https://khconst.co.kr
Year Founded: 2004
226360—(KRS)
Rev.: $43,015,079
Assets: $153,535,978
Liabilities: $67,240,011
Net Worth: $86,295,967
Earnings: ($41,459,608)

INTERNATIONAL PUBLIC

Emp.: 80
Fiscal Year-end: 12/31/22
Financial Investment Management Services
N.A.I.C.S.: 523940

KHADIM INDIA LIMITED
7th Floor Tower C DLF IT Park 08 Major Arterial Road, Block AF New Town Rajarhat, Kolkata, 700163, India
Tel.: (91) 3340090501
Web Site: https://www.khadims.com
Year Founded: 1981
540775—(BOM)
Rev.: $87,941,081
Assets: $86,054,514
Liabilities: $58,638,489
Net Worth: $27,416,025
Earnings: ($4,496,856)
Emp.: 740
Fiscal Year-end: 03/31/21
Garment Product Mfr & Distr
N.A.I.C.S.: 424340
Siddhartha Roy Burman (Chm & Mng Dir)

KHAIRPUR SUGAR MILLS LIMITED
51 2 4 Street 26th Khyaban-e- Jahbaz, Authority Phase V, Karachi, Pakistan
Tel.: (92) 213525013135
Web Site: https://www.khairpursugar.com.pk
Year Founded: 1989
KPUS—(PSX)
Rev.: $15,936,799
Assets: $31,070,102
Liabilities: $16,845,538
Net Worth: $14,224,564
Earnings: $61,649
Emp.: 638
Fiscal Year-end: 09/30/23
Sugar Products Mfr
N.A.I.C.S.: 311314

KHAITAN (INDIA) LIMITED
46C Jawaharlal Nehru Road, Kolkata, 700071, India
Tel.: (91) 3340505000
Web Site: https://www.khaitan.com
Year Founded: 1936
Rev.: $12,898,679
Assets: $17,773,061
Liabilities: $11,997,569
Net Worth: $5,775,492
Earnings: $257,608
Emp.: 260
Fiscal Year-end: 03/31/18
Sugar Mfr
N.A.I.C.S.: 311314
Sunay Krishna Khaitan (Exec Dir)

KHAITAN CHEMICALS & FERTILIZERS LTD.
A B Road Village Nimrani, Khargone, 451 569, Madhya Pradesh, India
Tel.: (91) 7314753666
Web Site: https://kcfl.co.in
Year Founded: 1982
KHAICHEM—(NSE)
Rev.: $112,617,496
Assets: $77,910,979
Liabilities: $43,478,103
Net Worth: $34,432,876
Earnings: $10,851,231
Emp.: 699
Fiscal Year-end: 03/31/22
Chemical Products Mfr
N.A.I.C.S.: 212390
Jagdishlal Chunilal Jajoo (Exec Dir)

KHAITAN ELECTRICALS LIMITED

46C J L Nehru Road, Kolkata, 700 071, India
Tel.: (91) 33 4050 5000
Web Site: http://www.khaitan.com
Electrical Product Mfr & Whslr
N.A.I.C.S.: 335999

KHALID SIRAJ TEXTILE MILLS LIMITED
135 Upper Mall, Lahore, Pakistan
Tel.: (92) 4235761706   PK
Web Site: http://www.kstml.com
Year Founded: 1988
KSTM—(PSX)
Rev.: $109,364
Assets: $1,253,297
Liabilities: $1,412,296
Net Worth: ($158,999)
Earnings: $1,185
Emp.: 6
Fiscal Year-end: 06/30/23
Textile Mill Operator
N.A.I.C.S.: 314999

KHAN BROTHERS PP WOVEN BAG INDUSTRIES LTD.
KBG Tower 15 Malibagh Chowdhurypara DIT Road, Dhaka, 1219, Bangladesh
Tel.: (880) 1710123456
Web Site: https://kbgbd.com
KBPPWBIL—(CHT)
Rev.: $934,514
Assets: $11,487,781
Liabilities: $708,993
Net Worth: $10,778,788
Earnings: ($58,781)
Fiscal Year-end: 06/30/23
Chemical Products Mfr
N.A.I.C.S.: 325199

KHAN'S SUPA IGA GROUP
6a/100 Argyle Street, Picton, 2571, NSW, Australia
Tel.: (61) 246772252
Web Site:
   http://www.khangroup.com.au
Year Founded: 1981
Emp.: 800
Grocery Product Distr
N.A.I.C.S.: 445110
Norin Khan *(Mgr-HR)*

KHANDELWAL EXTRACTIONS LIMITED
Kesharwani Bhawan 51/47 3rd Floor Naya Ganj, Kanpur, 208001, India
Tel.: (91) 5122313195
Web Site:
   https://www.khandelwalextracts.com
Year Founded: 1981
519064—(BOM)
Rev.: $23,596
Assets: $473,051
Liabilities: $228,845
Net Worth: $244,205
Earnings: ($34,494)
Emp.: 8
Fiscal Year-end: 03/31/21
Edible Oil Mfr
N.A.I.C.S.: 311225
K. N. Khandelwal *(Chm)*

Subsidiaries:

KHANDELWAL EXTRACTIONS LIMITED - Unnao Factory   (1)
Magarwara Kanpur Lucknow Road, Akrampur, Unnao, 209801, India
Tel.: (91) 515 2833748
Rice Bran Oil Mfr
N.A.I.C.S.: 311225
Dinesh Khandelwal *(Dir-Fin & CFO)*

KHANDWALA SECURITIES LIMITED
Vikas Building Ground Floor Green Street Fort, Mumbai, 400 023, India
Tel.: (91) 2240767373
Web Site: https://www.kslindia.com
531892—(BOM)
Rev.: $777,690
Assets: $5,224,446
Liabilities: $1,688,403
Net Worth: $3,536,043
Earnings: $53,141
Emp.: 35
Fiscal Year-end: 03/31/23
Investment Banking Services
N.A.I.C.S.: 523150
Paresh J. Khandwala *(Mng Dir)*

KHANG AN INVESTMENT REAL ESTATE JSC
Ground Floor G-BLK-3 The Manor House 91 Nguyen Huu Canh P 22, Binh Thanh District, Ho Chi Minh City, Vietnam
Tel.: (84) 8 35 144 751
Web Site: http://www.khangan.com
Real Estate Development Services
N.A.I.C.S.: 531390

KHANG DIEN HOUSE TRADING & INVESTMENT JOINT STOCK COMPANY
Rooms 1 and 2 11th Floor of Saigon Centre 67 Le Loi Street, Ben Nghe Ward District 1, Ho Chi Minh City, Vietnam
Tel.: (84) 2838208858
Web Site:
   https://www.khangdien.com.vn
Year Founded: 2001
KDH—(HOSE)
Rev.: $113,790,975
Assets: $529,493,003
Liabilities: $222,918,588
Net Worth: $306,574,414
Earnings: $36,609,314
Emp.: 327
Fiscal Year-end: 12/31/19
Real Estate Development Services
N.A.I.C.S.: 531390
Ly Dien Son *(Chm & Gen Dir)*

Subsidiaries:

Khang Phuc House Trading Investment Co., Ltd.   (1)
550 Kinh Duong Vuong St, An Lac Ward Binhtan District, Ho Chi Minh City, Vietnam
Tel.: (84) 838753021
Web Site:
   https://www.khangphuchouse.com.vn
Real Estate Investment Services
N.A.I.C.S.: 531390

KHANH HOI IMPORT EXPORT JOINT STOCK COMPANY
Floor 6 Khahomex Building 360A Ben Van Don Street, Ward 1 District 4, Ho Chi Minh City, Vietnam
Tel.: (84) 839451027
Web Site:
   http://www.khahomex.com.vn
Real Estate Manangement Services
N.A.I.C.S.: 531390
Than Duc Duong *(Chm-Mgmt Bd)*

KHARAFI NATIONAL
Safat, PO Box 24081, Kuwait, 13101, Kuwait
Tel.: (965) 22259000   KW
Web Site:
   http://www.kharafinational.com
Year Founded: 1976
Sales Range: $350-399.9 Million
Emp.: 9,000
Project Management, Procurement & Construction Services for Oil & Gas Industry
N.A.I.C.S.: 541330

Subsidiaries:

Albanian Airlines MAK   (1)
St Deshmoret e 4 Shkurtit Nr2, Tirana, Albania
Tel.: (355) 4230857
Web Site: http://www.albanianair.com
Sales Range: $50-74.9 Million
Emp.: 130
Oil Transportation Services
N.A.I.C.S.: 481111

Kharafi National Co. L.L.C.   (1)
Abu Dhabi Business Hub, PO Box 26831, Mussafah, Abu Dhabi, United Arab Emirates
Tel.: (971) 25130513
Web Site: http://www.kharafinational-fm.com
Engineeering Services
N.A.I.C.S.: 541330

Kharafi National KSC (Closed)   (1)
MAK Centre 2nd Floor Al Sham Road, PO Box 182, Hazmieh, Beirut, Lebanon
Tel.: (961) 43476662
Engineeering Services
N.A.I.C.S.: 541330
Khaled Salaheldin Ibrahim *(Dir-Bus Dev)*

Kharafi National L.L.C.   (1)
PO Box 25693, Dubai, United Arab Emirates
Tel.: (971) 43476662
Web Site: http://www.kharafinational-fm.com
Engineeering Services
N.A.I.C.S.: 541330
Khaled Salaheldin Ibrahim *(Dir-Bus Dev)*

Kharafi National for Infrastructure Projects Developments Construction and Services S.A.E   (1)
2 Abdul Moneim Riyadh Street Thawra Square Al Mohendessen, Imbaba, Giza, Egypt
Tel.: (20) 33367688
Engineeering Services
N.A.I.C.S.: 541330
Elia Saber *(Mgr-Ops)*

Quality Technical Supplies Co. W.L.L.   (1)
PO Box 6994, Ras Salmiyah, Kuwait
Tel.: (965) 22259127
Web Site: http://www.qtechsupplies.com
Industrial Equipment Distr
N.A.I.C.S.: 423830
Saad Om Hani *(Mgr-Ops)*

Quality Technical Supplies Company   (1)
PO Box 30582, Abu Dhabi, United Arab Emirates
Tel.: (971) 25507130
Industrial Equipment Distr
N.A.I.C.S.: 423830

KHARAZMI INVESTMENT COMPANY
Unit 103 & 104 first Floor No 16 Bozorgmehr St Valiasr Ave, Tehran, 14169 34981, Iran
Tel.: (98) 2166485908
Web Site: http://www.khig.ir
Year Founded: 1997
IKHR1—(THE)
Sales Range: Less than $1 Million
Emp.: 1,013
Financial Services
N.A.I.C.S.: 523999

KHARG PETROCHEMICAL CO.
No 40 Dodjamjou St North Dibaji St, PO Box 19615-317, 1951994511, Tehran, 19519 94511, Iran
Tel.: (98) 2122816103
Web Site:
   https://www.khargpetrochemical.ir
Year Founded: 1967
PKHA1—(THE)
Sales Range: Less than $1 Million
Oil Mining Services
N.A.I.C.S.: 324110

KHARIS CAPITAL GP
Route D'esch 412 F, 2086, Luxembourg, Luxembourg
Tel.: (352) 28809940
Web Site:
   http://www.khariscapital.com
Advisory Services
N.A.I.C.S.: 541618
Laurent Vermer *(Principal)*

Subsidiaries:

KHARIS CAPITAL ADVISORY BELGIUM SPRL   (1)
Avenue Louise 489, 1050, Brussels, Belgium
Tel.: (32) 28809970
Advisory Services
N.A.I.C.S.: 541618
Seta Luleci *(Office Mgr)*

Subsidiary (Non-US):

NORDSEE Holding GmbH   (2)
Herwig Strasse No 16, 27572, Bremerhaven, Germany
Tel.: (49) 471 13 02
Web Site: http://www.nordsee.com
Food Products Distr
N.A.I.C.S.: 424460

KHARKH TOUR AMUZEMENT CITY
Al-Saydiah Qater-El-Nada St, Egnadeen County, Baghdad, Iraq
Tel.: (964) 1 5542091
Year Founded: 1989
SKTA—(IRAQ)
Sales Range: Less than $1 Million
Amusement Park Operator
N.A.I.C.S.: 713110

KHASH CEMENT COMPANY
North Sohrvardi Street - Andishe 2 Martyr Hamid Qods- Plate 69, Tehran, 15696 46611, Iran
Tel.: (98) 2142147777
Web Site: https://khashcement.ir
Year Founded: 1986
SKHS—(THE)
Sales Range: $1-9.9 Million
Emp.: 371
Cement Mfr
N.A.I.C.S.: 327310
Mosatafa Parto Afkanan *(Chm)*

KHATOR FIBRE & FABRICS LTD.
9/ 11 Assembly Lane 38 Dadiseth Agiary Lane Ground Floor, Mumbai, 400 002, India
Tel.: (91) 2222414870   In
Web Site: http://www.khator.com
Year Founded: 1986
Rev.: $10,821,071
Assets: $9,499,047
Liabilities: $7,206,890
Net Worth: $2,292,157
Earnings: $101,387
Emp.: 1,500
Fiscal Year-end: 03/31/18
Weaving & Finishing Fabric Mfr
N.A.I.C.S.: 313310
Kailashkumar S. Khator *(Chm)*

KHAVAR SPRING MFG COMPANY
Unit No 4 3th Floor Pars Fanar Building No 80 Golab St, Sadeghieh, 1451964115, Tehran, Iran
Tel.: (98) 2137643000
Web Site: https://en.khsm.co.ir
Year Founded: 1977
KFAN1—(THE)
Sales Range: Less than $1 Million
Motor Vehicle Parts Mfr
N.A.I.C.S.: 336390
Iraj Ramezani *(CEO)*

KHAZANAH NASIONAL BERHAD

Khavar Spring Mfg Company—(Continued)

KHAZANAH NASIONAL BERHAD
Level 33 Tower 2 Petronas Twin Towers, Kuala Lumpur City Center, Kuala Lumpur, 50088, Malaysia
Tel.: (60) 320340000   MY
Web Site:
http://www.khazanah.com.my
Year Founded: 1994
Sales Range: $1-4.9 Billion
Emp.: 300
Investment Services
N.A.I.C.S.: 523999
Ben Chan *(Co-Head-Investments)*

Subsidiaries:

Acibadem Sigorta (1)
Kucukbakkalkoy Mah Basar Sokak No 20, Atasehir, 34750, Istanbul, Turkiye
Tel.: (90) 216 571 55 55
Web Site:
http://www.acibademsigorta.com.tr
Fire Insurance Services
N.A.I.C.S.: 524113

Arca Biru Sdn Bhd (1)
Kedah Aquaculture Complex, 6150, Kuala Lumpur, Kedah Darul Aman, Malaysia
Tel.: (60) 4 794 3884
Seafood Distr
N.A.I.C.S.: 424460

Biotropics Malaysia Berhad (1)
Lot 21 Jalan U1/19 Section U1 Hicom-Glenmarie Industrial Park, 40150, Shah Alam, Selangor Darul Ehsan, Malaysia
Tel.: (60) 3.5565 5600
Web Site:
http://www.biotropicsmalaysia.com
Emp.: 45
Pharmaceuticals Product Mfr
N.A.I.C.S.: 325412
Tengku Syahrir Tengku Adnan *(CEO)*

Cenergi SEA Sdn Bhd (1)
Unit 33-11 Level 11 The Boulevard, Mid Valley City Lingkaran Syed Putra, 59200, Kuala Lumpur, Malaysia
Tel.: (60) 3 2283 2302
Web Site: http://www.cenergi-sea.com
Biomass Electric Power Generation Services
N.A.I.C.S.: 221117
Eric Wong *(Head-Bioenergy)*

Cenviro Sdn Bhd (1)
13th Floor Mercu UEM Jalan Stesen Sentral 5, Kuala Lumpur Sentral, Kuala Lumpur, Malaysia
Tel.: (60) 3 2727 6100
Web Site: http://www.cenviro.com
Waste Management Services
N.A.I.C.S.: 562211
Azmil Khalili Khalid *(Chm)*

Subsidiary (Domestic):

Kualiti Alam Sdn Bhd. (2)
Ladang Tanah Merah A3 Division, Kampung Bukit Pelandok, 71960, Malaysia
Tel.: (60) 6 666 2000
Web Site: http://www.kualitialam.com
Waste Management Services
N.A.I.C.S.: 562211
Amirul Bahri Malek *(Head-Mktg, Environment Support Svcs & Logistics)*

IHH Healthcare Berhad (1)
Level 11 Block A Pantai Hospital Kuala Lumpur 8 Jalan Bukit Pantai, Taman Bukit Pantai, 59100, Kuala Lumpur, Malaysia (62.1%)
Tel.: (60) 322989898
Web Site: https://www.ihhhealthcare.com
Rev.: $4,547,046,596
Assets: $10,901,737,152
Liabilities: $3,873,488,372
Net Worth: $7,028,298,780
Earnings: $736,515,426
Emp.: 70,000
Fiscal Year-end: 12/31/2023
Healthcare Services
N.A.I.C.S.: 622110
Soon Teck Low *(CFO)*

Subsidiary (Non-US):

Acibadem Saglik Hizmetleri ve Ticaret AS (2)

Tekin Sok No 8 Kadikoy, Istanbul, Turkiye (60%)
Tel.: (90) 216 544 44 44
Web Site: http://www.acibadem.com.tr
Sales Range: $400-449.9 Million
Emp.: 200
Healthcare Services
N.A.I.C.S.: 622110
Asim Gun *(Dir-Fin Affairs)*

Gleneagles Global Hospitals (2)
Lakdi-ka-Pul, Hyderabad, 500 004, India (100%)
Tel.: (91) 4030644444
Web Site:
http://www.globalhospitalsindia.com
Hospital Owner & Operator
N.A.I.C.S.: 622110

Parkway Pantai Limited (2)
TripleOne Somerset 111 Somerset Road 15-01, Singapore, 238164, Singapore
Tel.: (65) 6307 7880
Web Site: http://www.parkwaypantai.com
Emp.: 100
Holding Company; Healthcare Services
N.A.I.C.S.: 551112
Cheok Peng Lim *(Vice Chm)*

Subsidiary (Non-US):

Pantai Holdings Berhad (3)
8 Jalan Bukit Pantai, 59100, Kuala Lumpur, Malaysia
Tel.: (60) 2296 0888
Web Site: http://www.pantai.com.my
General Medical & Surgical Hospitals
N.A.I.C.S.: 622110
Parkway Pantai *(CEO)*

Subsidiary (Domestic):

Cheras Medical Centre Sdn. Bhd (4)
No 1 Jalan 1/96A, Taman Cheras Makmur, 56100, Kuala Lumpur, Malaysia (100%)
Tel.: (60) 91452888
Web Site: http://www.pantai.com.my
General Medical & Surgical Hospitals
N.A.I.C.S.: 622110

Hospital Pantai Ayer Keroh Sdn. Bhd. (4)
No 2418 H 1 KM 8 Lebuh Ayer Keroh, KM 8 Lebuh Ayer Keroh, 75450, Melaka, Malaysia (70%)
Tel.: (60) 62319999
Web Site: http://www.pantai.com.my
General Medical & Surgical Hospitals
N.A.I.C.S.: 622110

Pantai Medivest Sdn. Bhd. (4)
Suite 13 01 Penthouse Wisma E and C No 2 Lorong Dungun Kiri, Damansara Heights, 50490, Kuala Lumpur, Malaysia
Tel.: (60) 320921000
Web Site: http://www.medivest.com.my
Hospital Support Services
N.A.I.C.S.: 561990
Salleh Tahir *(CEO)*

Syarikat Tunas Pantai Sdn. Bhd. (4)
82 Jln Tengah, Bayan Lepas, Malaysia (80.7%)
Tel.: (60) 46433888
Web Site: http://www.pantai.com.my
General Medical & Surgical Hospitals
N.A.I.C.S.: 622110

Unitab Medic Sdn. Bhd. (4)
Lot G1-G10 Level 3 Block G Pusat, Bandar Damansara Damansa, 50490, Kuala Lumpur, Malaysia (100%)
Tel.: (60) 320946188
Web Site: http://www.fomema.com.my
Health Screening Services
N.A.I.C.S.: 621511

Subsidiary (Domestic):

Fomema Sdn. Bhd. (5)
Lot 49 and 51 Jalan Kampung Pandan, 55100, Kuala Lumpur, Malaysia (75%)
Tel.: (60) 327828777
Web Site: http://www.fomema.com.my
Health & Allied Services
N.A.I.C.S.: 621610

Subsidiary (Domestic):

Parkway Holdings Limited (3)
Triple One Somerset 111 Somerset Rd 15-

01, Singapore, 238164, Singapore
Tel.: (65) 63077880
Web Site: http://www.parkwayholdings.com
Sales Range: $800-899.9 Million
Hospital Owner & Operator
N.A.I.C.S.: 622110
See Haw Tan *(CFO)*

Joint Venture (Non-US):

Apollo Gleneagles PET-CT Limited (4)
Apollo Hospital Campus, Jubilee Hills, Hyderabad, 5000096, India
Tel.: (91) 4023607777
Web Site: http://www.apollohealthcity.com
Sales Range: $450-499.9 Million
Health & Allied Services
N.A.I.C.S.: 621610
Prathap Chandra Reddy *(Chm)*

Subsidiary (Domestic):

East Shore Hospital Pte Ltd (4)
321 Joo Chiat Place, 427990, Singapore, Singapore
Tel.: (65) 63447588
Web Site: http://www.eastshore.com.sg
Sales Range: $10-24.9 Million
Emp.: 250
General Medical & Surgical Hospitals
N.A.I.C.S.: 622110

Gleneagles Medical Centre Ltd (4)
6A Napier Rd # 03-00, 258500, Singapore, Singapore (100%)
Tel.: (65) 64737222
Web Site: http://www.parkwayhealth.com
General Medical & Surgical Hospitals
N.A.I.C.S.: 622110
Vincent Chia *(CEO)*

Gleneagles Medical Holdings Limited (4)
6A Napier Rd 03-00, 258510, Singapore (100%)
Tel.: (65) 64737222
Web Site: http://www.parkwayhealth.sg
General Medical & Surgical Hospitals
N.A.I.C.S.: 622110

Gleneagles Pharmacy Pte Ltd (4)
6A Napier Road, Singapore, 258500, Singapore (100%)
Tel.: (65) 64737222
Web Site: http://www.gleneagles.com.sg
Sales Range: $10-24.9 Million
Emp.: 150
General Medical & Surgical Hospitals
N.A.I.C.S.: 622110
Vincent Chia *(CEO)*

Gleneagles Radiology Consultants Pte Ltd (4)
6A Napier Rd Ste 03-00, 258500, Singapore, Singapore (100%)
Tel.: (65) 64737222
Web Site:
http://www.parkwayradiology.com.sg
General Medical & Surgical Hospitals
N.A.I.C.S.: 622110

Mount Elizabeth Medical Holdings Ltd (4)
3 Mount Elizabeth, 228510, Singapore, Singapore (100%)
Tel.: (65) 63077880
Web Site:
http://www.mountelizabeth.com.sg
General Medical & Surgical Hospitals
N.A.I.C.S.: 622110

Nippon Medical Care Pte Ltd (4)
6A Napier Road No 0337-00 Annexe Block Gleneagles Hospital, Singapore, 258500, Singapore (70%)
Tel.: (65) 64747707
Web Site:
http://www.nipponmedicalcare.com.sg
Sales Range: $10-24.9 Million
Emp.: 20
General Medical & Surgical Hospitals
N.A.I.C.S.: 622110

Parkway Group Healthcare Pte Ltd (4)
83 Clemenceau Ave # 10-05-06-07, 239920, Singapore, Singapore (100%)
Tel.: (65) 68546666
Web Site: http://www.parkwayhealth.com

INTERNATIONAL PUBLIC

General Medical & Surgical Hospitals
N.A.I.C.S.: 622110

Subsidiary (Domestic):

Parkway Shenton Pte Ltd (5)
20 Bendemeer Road, 339914, Singapore, Singapore (100%)
Tel.: (65) 62277777
Web Site: http://www.parkwayshenton.com
Sales Range: $25-49.9 Million
Emp.: 80
General Medical & Surgical Hospitals
N.A.I.C.S.: 622110

Unit (Domestic):

Shenton Family Medical Clinic (Bukit Gombak) (6)
Block 372 Bukit Batok Street 31 01-378, 650372, Singapore, Singapore (60%)
Tel.: (65) 65665671
Web Site: http://www.parkwayshenton.com
Emp.: 40
Health & Allied Services
N.A.I.C.S.: 621610
Louis Poey *(Mgr-Ops)*

Shenton Family Medical Clinic (Serangoon) (6)
Blk 304 Serangoon Ave 2 No 01-10, 550304, Singapore, Singapore (50%)
Tel.: (65) 64876580
Health & Allied Services
N.A.I.C.S.: 621610

Shenton Family Medical Clinic (Tampines) (6)
Block 201D Tampines Street 21 # 01-1137, 524201, Singapore, Singapore (50%)
Tel.: (65) 67845291
Health & Allied Services
N.A.I.C.S.: 621610

Affiliate (Domestic):

iXchange Pte Ltd (6)
20 Bendemeer Road, Singapore, Singapore (100%)
Tel.: (65) 62802311
Web Site: http://www.parkwayshenton.com
General Medical & Surgical Hospitals
N.A.I.C.S.: 622110

Subsidiary (Domestic):

Parkway Laboratory Services Ltd (4)
28 Ayer Rajah Cres 03-08, Singapore, 139959, Singapore (100%)
Tel.: (65) 62789188
Web Site: http://www.parkwaylab.com.sg
Sales Range: $10-24.9 Million
Emp.: 200
Medical Laboratories
N.A.I.C.S.: 621511
Rachel Heng *(Mgr-Lab)*

Radiology Consultants Pte Ltd (4)
3 Mount Elizabeth, Singapore, 228510, Singapore (100%)
Tel.: (65) 67372666
General Medical & Surgical Hospitals
N.A.I.C.S.: 622110

Iskandar Investment Berhad (1)
G-12 Block 8, Danga Bay Jalan Skudai, 80200, Johor Bahru, Malaysia
Tel.: (60) 7 233 9000
Web Site:
http://www.iskandarinvestment.com
Real Estate Development Services
N.A.I.C.S.: 531390
Khairil Anwar Ahmad *(Pres & CEO)*

LeapEd Services Sdn. Bhd. (1)
Level 52 Menara TM, Jalan Pantai Baharu, 50672, Kuala Lumpur, Malaysia
Tel.: (60) 3 2282 3456
Web Site: http://www.leapedservices.com
Educational Support Services
N.A.I.C.S.: 611710
Zulhaimi Othman *(Mng Dir)*

Malaysian Agrifood Corporation Berhad (1)
No 3 Jalan Perindustrian Puchong, Bandar Metro Puchong, 47160, Puchong, Selangor, Malaysia
Tel.: (60) 3 5623 5000
Web Site: http://www.mafc.com.my
Food Products Distr

AND PRIVATE COMPANIES

N.A.I.C.S.: 424480

Malaysian Airlines Berhad (1)
Administration Building 1 MAS Complex A, Sultan Abdul Aziz Shah Airport, 47200, Subang Jaya, Selangor Darul Ehsan, Malaysia
Tel.: (60) 300 88 3000
Web Site: http://www.malaysiaairlines.com
Sales Range: $1-4.9 Billion
Emp.: 19,577
Oil Transportation Services
N.A.I.C.S.: 481111
Mohammad Nadziruddin Mohammad Basri *(Chief Restructuring Officer)*

Subsidiary (Domestic):

Abacus Distribution Systems (Malaysia) Sdn. Bhd. (2)
No 47 Jln 5/76B Desa Pandan, 55100, Kuala Lumpur, Malaysia (80%)
Tel.: (60) 392841001
Web Site: http://www.abacus.com.my
Computer System Design Services
N.A.I.C.S.: 541512

MASkargo Logistics Sdn. Bhd. (2)
1M Zone C Advanced Cargo Center, Free Commercial Zone, 64000, Kuala Lumpur, Selangor, Malaysia
Tel.: (60) 387771603
Web Site: http://www.maskargo.com
Freight Transportation Arrangement
N.A.I.C.S.: 488510

Malaysia Airlines Cargo Sdn. Bhd. (2)
1M Zone C Advanced Cargo Center, Free Commercial Zone, 64000, Kuala Lumpur, Selangor, Malaysia
Tel.: (60) 387771717
Web Site: http://www.maskargo.com
Emp.: 800
Scheduled Freight Air Transportation
N.A.I.C.S.: 481112
Shahari Sulaiman *(Mng Dir)*

Malaysian Technology Development Corporation Sdn Bhd (1)
Level 8 & 9 Menara Yayasan Tun Razak, Jalan Bukit Bintang, 55100, Kuala Lumpur, Malaysia
Tel.: (60) 3 2172 6000
Web Site: http://www.mtdc.com.my
Financial Consulting Services
N.A.I.C.S.: 523999

PATI Pave Sdn Bhd (1)
Level 3 Menara John Hancock No 6 Jalan Gelenggang Damansara Height, Kuala Lumpur, 50490, Malaysia
Tel.: (60) 3 2710 6336
Engineeering Services
N.A.I.C.S.: 541330

Penerbangan Malaysia Bhd (1)
Level 39 Menara TM Jalan Pantai Baharu, Kuala Lumpur, 59200, Malaysia
Tel.: (60) 3 2246 1200
Web Site: http://www.pmb.com.my
Aircraft Leasing Services
N.A.I.C.S.: 532411

Sun Life Malaysia Assurance Berhad (1)
Level 11 338 Jalan Tuankku Adbul Rahman, 50100, Kuala Lumpur, Malaysia (49%)
Tel.: (60) 3 2612 3600
Web Site: http://www.sunlifemalaysia.com
Life Insurance & Financial Planning Services
N.A.I.C.S.: 524113

Subsidiary (Domestic):

Sun Life Malaysia Takaful Berhad (2)
Level 11 338 Jalan Tuankku Abdul Rahman, 50100, Kuala Lumpur, Malaysia
Tel.: (60) 3 2612 3600
Web Site: http://www.sunlifemalaysia.com
Insurance Services
N.A.I.C.S.: 524298
Jeffry Azmi Mohd Shah *(CEO)*

Themed Attractions Resorts & Hotels Sdn. Bhd. (1)
Level 9 Menara UAC 12 Jalan PJU 7/5, Mutiara Damansara, 47810, Petaling Jaya, Selangor Darul Ehsan, Malaysia
Tel.: (60) 3 7651 0288
Web Site: http://www.tarh.com.my
Hotel Operator
N.A.I.C.S.: 721110
Amirsham Abdul Aziz *(Chm)*

UEM Group Berhad (1)
17-2 Jalan Stesen Sentral 5, Kuala Lumpur Sentral, Kuala Lumpur, 50470, Malaysia (100%)
Tel.: (60) 327276868
Web Site: http://www.uem.com.my
Sales Range: $300-349.9 Million
Holding Company; Construction & Infrastructure
N.A.I.C.S.: 551112
Izzaddin Idris *(CEO & Grp Mng Dir)*

Subsidiary (Domestic):

PLUS Malaysia Berhad (2)
Menara Korporat Persada PLUS Persimpangan Bertingkat Subang KM 15, Lebuhraya Baru Lembah Klang, Petaling Jaya, 47301, Selangor Darul Ehsan, Malaysia
Tel.: (60) 3 7801 6666
Web Site: http://www.plus.com.my
Sales Range: $1-4.9 Billion
Emp.: 200
Toll Expressway Operator
N.A.I.C.S.: 488999
Noorizah Abd Hamid *(Mng Dir)*

Subsidiary (Domestic):

Konsortium Lebuhraya Butterworth-Kulim Sdn Bhd (3)
KM 6 5 Lebuhraya Butterworth-Kulim Permatang Pauh Seberang Jaya, Bukit Damansara, Penang, 13500, Malaysia
Tel.: (60) 4 397 7807
Sales Range: $50-74.9 Million
Emp.: 200
Highway Construction Services
N.A.I.C.S.: 237310
Pazli Kasim *(Reg Mgr)*

Subsidiary (Non-US):

PT Cimanggis Cibitung Tollways (3)
Wisma Bakrie 1 Lantai 17 Jl HR Rasuna Said Kav B2, Jakarta, 12920, Indonesia
Tel.: (62) 21 529 20266
Toll Road Construction Services
N.A.I.C.S.: 237310

Plus Kalyan (Mauritius) Private Limited (3)
10 Frere Felix de Valois Street, Port Louis, Mauritius (100%)
Tel.: (230) 2029890
Web Site: http://plus.listedcompany.com
Highway Street & Bridge Construction
N.A.I.C.S.: 237310

Subsidiary (Domestic):

Projek Lebuhraya Utara-Selatan Berhad (3)
Menara Korporat Persada PLUS Persimpangan Bertingkat Subang, Lebuhraya Barulembah Klong, 47301, Petaling Jaya, Selangor, Malaysia (100%)
Tel.: (60) 378016666
Web Site: http://www.plus.uemnet.com
Sales Range: $400-449.9 Million
Emp.: 500
Highway & Street Construction
N.A.I.C.S.: 237310
Noorizah Abd Hamid *(Mng Dir)*

Teras Teknologi Sdn Bhd (3)
Annex 3 Persada Plus Persimpangan Bertingkat Subang Km 15, Lebuhraya Baru Lembah Klang, 47301, Petaling Jaya, Selangor, Malaysia
Tel.: (60) 376507500
Web Site: http://www.terasworld.com
Sales Range: $25-49.9 Million
Emp.: 190
Payment Software Development Services
N.A.I.C.S.: 541511
Noorizah Abd Hamid *(Chm)*

Subsidiary (Domestic):

UEM Edgenta Berhad (2)
Level 17 Menara UEM Tower 1 Avenue 7, The Horizon Bangsar South City No 8 Jalan Kerinchi, 59200, Kuala Lumpur, Malaysia (69.14%)
Tel.: (60) 327256688
Web Site: https://www.uemedgenta.com
Rev.: $567,374,445
Assets: $706,629,825
Liabilities: $325,639,463
Net Worth: $380,990,363
Emp.: 22,359
Fiscal Year-end: 12/31/2021
Holding Company; Hotels; Real Estate; Health Care
N.A.I.C.S.: 551112
Catherine Siew Yuen Chiew *(Sec & Head-Secretarial)*

Subsidiary (Domestic):

Edgenta Energy Projects Sdn. Bhd. (3)
Level 3A Menara UEM Tower 1 Avenue 7 The Horizon Bangsar South City, No 8 Jalan Kerinchi, 59200, Kuala Lumpur, Malaysia
Tel.: (60) 27256688
Health Care Management Services
N.A.I.C.S.: 621999
Kevin Hor *(Sr Mgr)*

Edgenta Environmental & Material Testing Sdn Bhd (3)
No 3 Jalan P/8 Kawasan Perindustrian MIEL Seksyen 13 Bandar Baru Bangi, 43650, Kuala Selangor, Malaysia
Tel.: (60) 89259370
Health Care Management Services
N.A.I.C.S.: 621999

Edgenta Facilities Sdn. Bhd. (3)
19th Floor Faber Tower Menara 2 Jalan Desa Bahagia Taman Desa, Kuala Lumpur, 58100, Malaysia
Tel.: (60) 376282888
Web Site: http://www.faberfacilities.com.my
Sales Range: $75-99.9 Million
Emp.: 150
Property Management Services
N.A.I.C.S.: 531311

Edgenta Healthcare Management Sdn Bhd (3)
18 Jalan 4/109E Desa Business Park, Tmn Desa off Jalan Klang Lama, 58100, Kuala Lumpur, Malaysia
Tel.: (60) 379838550
Holding Company; Health Services
N.A.I.C.S.: 551112

Subsidiary (Domestic):

Edgenta Mediserve Sdn. Bhd. (4)
10th Floor Menara 2 Faber Tower, Jalan Desa Bahagia, 58100, Kuala Lumpur, Malaysia
Tel.: (60) 376 215 593
Web Site: http://www.fabergroup.com.my
Hospital Support Services
N.A.I.C.S.: 621999

Subsidiary (Domestic):

Edgenta Healthtronics Sdn. Bhd. (5)
Suite P3-03 Building Information Centre Lot 2 Jalan 51a 243, Petaling Jaya, 46100, Malaysia (100%)
Tel.: (60) 376252525
Web Site: http://www.healthtronics.com.my
Biomedical Engineering Maintenance Services
N.A.I.C.S.: 561990
Salleh Tahir *(CEO)*

Subsidiary (Domestic):

Edgenta PROPEL Berhad (3)
Level 8 Menara UEM Tower 1 Avenue 7 The Horizon Bangsar South City, No 8 Jalan Kerinchi, 59200, Kuala Lumpur, Malaysia
Tel.: (60) 327256688
Health Care Management Services
N.A.I.C.S.: 621999

Edgenta Township Management Services Sdn. Bhd. (3)
Level 2 Menara UEM Tower 1 Avenue 7 The Horizon Bangsar South City, No 8 Jalan Kerinchi, 59200, Kuala Lumpur, Malaysia

KHAZANAH NASIONAL BERHAD

Tel.: (60) 327256688
Health Care Management Services
N.A.I.C.S.: 621999

Faber Development Holdings Sdn Bhd (3)
Level 3 Menara UEM Tower 1 Avenue 7, The Horizon Bangsar South City No 8 Jalan Kerinchi, Kuala Lumpur, 59200, Malaysia (100%)
Tel.: (60) 327256688
Web Site: http://www.fabergroup.com
Sales Range: $50-74.9 Million
Emp.: 120
Holding Company; Property Development Services
N.A.I.C.S.: 551112

Subsidiary (Domestic):

Country View Development Sdn Bhd (4)
168 1st Floor Wisma Cosway, Jalan Raja Chulan, 50200, Kuala Lumpur, Malaysia
Tel.: (60) 321456377
Sales Range: $25-49.9 Million
Emp.: 50
Property Development & Facilities Management Services
N.A.I.C.S.: 237210

Faber Grandview Development (Sabah) Sdn Bhd (4)
20th Floor Menara 2 Faber Tower, Jalan Desa Bahagia Tmn Desa, 58100, Kuala Lumpur, Malaysia
Tel.: (60) 379 838 855
Property Development Services
N.A.I.C.S.: 237210

Faber Heights Management Sdn Bhd (4)
20th Floor Menara 2 Faber Tower, Jalan Desa Bahagia Tmn Desa, 58100, Kuala Lumpur, Malaysia
Tel.: (60) 379838855
Property Development Services
N.A.I.C.S.: 237210

Faber Union Sdn Bhd (4)
20th Fl Menara 2 Faber Tower, Jalan Desa Bahagia Tmn Desa, 58100, Kuala Lumpur, Malaysia
Tel.: (60) 376282888
Web Site: http://www.fabergroup.com
Sales Range: $50-74.9 Million
Property Development Services
N.A.I.C.S.: 237210

Rimbunan Melati Sdn. Bhd. (4)
Lot 112 1st Floor Faber Towers Jln Desa Bahagia Taman Desa, 58100, Kuala Lumpur, Malaysia (55%)
Tel.: (60) 3 7628 2833
Property Development Services
N.A.I.C.S.: 237210

Subsidiary (Non-US):

Faber L.L.C. (3)
208 and 209 2nd Floor Al Nasriyah Building Baghdad Street Al Qusais, PO Box 232283, Dubai, United Arab Emirates
Tel.: (971) 42584561
Health Care Management Services
N.A.I.C.S.: 621999

Faber Sindoori Management Services Private Limited (3)
Prince Tower 7th Floor 25 & 26 College Road, Nungambakkam, Chennai, 600006, India
Tel.: (91) 4442649403
Web Site: http://www.sindoorifaber.com
Integrated Facility Management Services
N.A.I.C.S.: 541519
Siva Kandasamy *(Deputy Mgr)*

Subsidiary (Domestic):

KFM Holdings Sdn. Bhd. (3)
Level 10 Menara UEM Tower 1 Avenue 7 The Horizon Bangsar South City, No 8 Jalan Kerinchi, 59200, Kuala Lumpur, Malaysia
Tel.: (60) 27256688
Health Care Management Services
N.A.I.C.S.: 621999
Razin Mustafa *(Asst Mgr)*

KHAZANAH NASIONAL BERHAD

Khazanah Nasional Berhad—(Continued)

Opus Group Berhad (3)
Level 6 Menara UEM Tower 1 Avenue 7,
The Horizon Bangsar South City No 8 Jalan Kerinchi, 59200, Kuala Lumpur, Malaysia **(100%)**
Tel.: (60) 27256868
Sales Range: $125-149.9 Million
Emp.: 600
Holding Company; Project Management & Facilities Management Services
N.A.I.C.S.: 551112
Nikairina Nikjaffar (Mng Dir)

Opus International (M) Berhad (3)
Level 6 Menara UEM Tower 1 Avenue 7
The Horizon Bangsar South City, No 8
Jalan Kerinchi, 59200, Kuala Lumpur, Malaysia
Tel.: (60) 27256688
Health Care Management Services
N.A.I.C.S.: 621999
Masri Theeran (Gen Mgr)

Subsidiary (Non-US):

UEMS Solutions Pte. Ltd. (3)
No 12 Ang Mo Kio St 64 Blk B 03A-11 UE Bizhub Central, Singapore, 569088, Singapore
Tel.: (65) 68183600
Web Site: http://www.uemsgroup.com
Health Care Management Services
N.A.I.C.S.: 621999

Subsidiary (Domestic):

UEM Sunrise Berhad (2)
Level U6 Block C5 Solaris Dutamas, No 1 Jalan Dutamas 1, 50480, Kuala Lumpur, Malaysia **(66.06%)**
Tel.: (60) 27187788
Web Site: https://www.uemsunrise.com
Rev.: $311,836,614
Assets: $2,762,730,794
Liabilities: $1,307,986,243
Net Worth: $1,454,744,550
Earnings: $17,368,042
Emp.: 855
Fiscal Year-end: 12/31/2022
Real Estate Investment & Development Services
N.A.I.C.S.: 531390
Anwar Syahrin Abdul Ajib (CEO & Mng Dir)

Xeraya Capital Sdn Bhd (1)
26 03 - 26 08 Level 26 G Tower 199 Jalan Tun Razak, 50400, Kuala Lumpur, Malaysia
Tel.: (60) 3 2381 8700
Web Site: http://www.xeraya.com
Financial Investment Services
N.A.I.C.S.: 523999
Aditya Puri (Dir-Investments)

iSHARP Sdn Bhd (1)
Ladang Akuakultur Ternakan Udang Bersepadu Kampung Nyatoh, Bandar Permaisuri, 22100, Terengganu, Terengganu Darul Ima, Malaysia
Tel.: (60) 19 311 6500
Seafood Distr
N.A.I.C.S.: 424460

KHAZAR CEMENT CO.
No 115 Motahari St Suleiman Khater St corner of Gross Alley,
1578713513, Tehran, Iran
Tel.: (98) 2188308939
Web Site:
https://www.khazarcement.ir
Year Founded: 1987
SKAZ—(THE)
Sales Range: Less than $1 Million
Cement Mfr
N.A.I.C.S.: 327310
Ishaq Jamal Omid (Vice Chm & Mng Dir)

KHD HUMBOLDT WEDAG INTERNATIONAL AG
VonderWetternStrabe 4a, 51149, Cologne, Germany
Tel.: (49) 22165040
Web Site: https://www.khd.com
Year Founded: 1856
KHDHF—(OTCEM)
Rev.: $248,015,234
Assets: $262,119,439
Liabilities: $157,282,261
Net Worth: $104,837,179
Earnings: $4,724,583
Emp.: 880
Fiscal Year-end: 12/31/23
Holding Company; Cement, Coal & Minerals Processing Equipment Designer & Mfr
N.A.I.C.S.: 551112
Wolfgang Pajonke (Head-Customer Svc Center-Russia & CIS)

Subsidiaries:

Humboldt Wedag (S.A.) (Pty) Ltd. (1)
36 Wankel Street Jet Park, PO Box 8460, Boksburg, 1459, South Africa
Tel.: (27) 113974660
Web Site: http://www.mcnallydhart.com
Sales Range: $25-49.9 Million
Emp.: 40
Industrial Machinery Mfr
N.A.I.C.S.: 333248
Johannes Kottmann (Mng Dir)

Humboldt Wedag Australia Pty. Ltd. (1)
31 Woodlands Dr, 3195, Braeside, VIC, Australia
Tel.: (61) 395805277
Web Site: http://www.khdhumboldt.com
Mining Machinery & Equipment Mfr
N.A.I.C.S.: 333131

Humboldt Wedag India Pvt. Ltd. (1)
A-36 Mohan Co-op Industrial Estate Mathura Road, New Delhi, 110 044, India
Tel.: (91) 1142101100
Web Site: http://www.hw-india.com
Sales Range: $100-124.9 Million
Emp.: 270
Industrial Machinery Mfr
N.A.I.C.S.: 333248
Christofer Ribbing (Head-Customer Svc Centre)

Humboldt Wedag, Inc. (1)
400 Technology Pkwy, Norcross, GA 30092-3406
Tel.: (770) 810-7300
Web Site: http://www.humboldt-wedag.com
Sales Range: $25-49.9 Million
Emp.: 50
Designer & Mfr of Cement, Coal & Minerals Processing Equipment
N.A.I.C.S.: 333248
Rick Cusick (Head-CSC Americas)

KHD Humboldt Wedag GmbH (1)
Colonia Allee 3, 51067, Cologne, Germany
Tel.: (49) 22165041101
Web Site: http://www.khd.com
Holding Company; Regional Managing Office
N.A.I.C.S.: 551112

Subsidiary (Domestic):

EKOF Flotation Gmbh (2)
Herner Str 299, 44809, Bochum, Germany
Tel.: (49) 23490320
Web Site: http://www.ekof.de
Emp.: 10
Coal Processing System Designer & Mfr
N.A.I.C.S.: 213113

Humboldt Wedag GmbH (2)
Von-der-Wettern-Strasse 4a, 51149, Cologne, Germany
Tel.: (49) 22165040
Emp.: 20
Cement Processing Equipment Mfr
N.A.I.C.S.: 333248

KHD Humboldt Wedag Industrial Services AG (2)
Colonia-allee 3, Cologne, 51067, Germany
Tel.: (49) 22165040
Cement Plant Construction Services
N.A.I.C.S.: 236210

ZAB Industrietechnik & Service GmbH (2)
Brauereistr 13, Sachsen-Anhalt Bundesrepublik, 06847, Dessau, Germany
Tel.: (49) 03405029886
Web Site: http://www.khd.com
Commercial & Service Industry Machinery Mfr
N.A.I.C.S.: 333310

Subsidiary (Domestic):

ZAB Zementanlagenbau GmbH (3)
Brauereistrasse 13, Rosslau, 06847, Dessau, Germany
Tel.: (49) 3405029213
Web Site: http://www.khd.com
Emp.: 65
Construction Machinery Equipment Mfr
N.A.I.C.S.: 333120

KHEE SAN BERHAD
Lot 1819-1824 & 1832 Jalan Kolej Pusat Perdagangan, 43300, Seri Kembangan, Selangor Darul Ehsan, Malaysia
Tel.: (60) 389431390 MY
Web Site: https://kheesanbhd.com
Year Founded: 1976
KHEESAN—(KLS)
Rev.: $11,767,731
Assets: $14,948,564
Liabilities: $31,332,272
Net Worth: ($16,383,709)
Earnings: $365,286
Emp.: 350
Fiscal Year-end: 06/30/23
Holding Company; Confectionery Products Mfr
N.A.I.C.S.: 551112
Edward Juan Peng Tan (CEO)

KHEMANI DISTRIBUTORS & MARKETING LIMITED
Plot No D 91-92 Laxminarayan Industrial Park Near BRC Compound, Bhestan Udhana, Surat, 394 210, Gujarat, India
Tel.: (91) 7818081234
Web Site:
https://www.khemanigroup.net
Year Founded: 2011
539788—(BOM)
Rev.: $9,756,489
Assets: $7,558,946
Liabilities: $1,727,871
Net Worth: $5,831,075
Earnings: $624,192
Emp.: 20
Fiscal Year-end: 03/31/23
Consumer Goods Distr
N.A.I.C.S.: 423620
Vijaykumar Mangturam Khemani (Chm & Mng Dir)

KHEOBA CORP.
Petonal el Cerezo 8 2A Los Realejos, 38410, Tenerife, Spain
Tel.: (995) 9292008366 NV
Web Site:
https://www.visiongroupca.com
Year Founded: 2021
KHOB—(OTCQB)
Rev.: $41,055
Assets: $36,541
Liabilities: $32,408
Net Worth: $4,133
Earnings: ($34,295)
Fiscal Year-end: 10/31/24
Software Development Services
N.A.I.C.S.: 541511
Gaga Gvenetatdze (Pres, CEO, CFO, Chief Acctg Officer, Chm, Treas & Sec)

KHERSONGAZ, PJSC
3 Popovycha str c, Kherson, 73022, Ukraine
Tel.: (380) 552 32 70 72
Natural & Liquefied Gas Distr
N.A.I.C.S.: 221210

INTERNATIONAL PUBLIC

KHFM HOSPITALITY & FACILITY MANAGEMENT SERVICES LTD.
01 Nirma Plaza Makhwana Road Marol Naka Andheri East, Mumbai, 400 059, India
Tel.: (91) 2228511234
Web Site: https://www.khfm.in
Year Founded: 1983
KHFM—(NSE)
Rev.: $15,751,398
Assets: $12,895,737
Liabilities: $7,679,938
Net Worth: $5,215,799
Earnings: $445,325
Emp.: 288
Fiscal Year-end: 03/31/21
Facility Management Services
N.A.I.C.S.: 561210
Rahul Krishna Pathak (Compliance Officer)

KHIMJI RAMDAS SHIPPING LLC
Greater Muttrah, PO Box 19, 100, Muscat, Oman
Tel.: (968) 24 707236
Web Site: http://www.kr.om
Emp.: 200
Freight Transportation Arrangement
N.A.I.C.S.: 488510
Dharmraj Bahadur (Gen Mgr)

KHIND HOLDINGS BERHAD
No 2 Jalan Astaka U8/82 Seksyen U8 Bukit Jelutong, Selangor Darul Ehsan, 40150, Shah Alam, Malaysia
Tel.: (60) 378392000
Web Site: https://www.khind.com.my
Year Founded: 1961
7062—(KLS)
Rev.: $108,565,956
Assets: $74,703,962
Liabilities: $28,438,398
Net Worth: $46,265,564
Earnings: $1,530,692
Emp.: 396
Fiscal Year-end: 12/31/23
Electrical Home Appliance Mfr
N.A.I.C.S.: 335210
Kamil Abdul Rahman (Chm)

Subsidiaries:

Khind Alliances Sdn. Bhd. (1)
No 2 Jalan Astaka U8/82 Seksyen U8 Bukit Jelutong, 40150, Shah Alam, Selangor, Malaysia
Tel.: (60) 378392000
Web Site: http://www.khindalliances.com
Kitchen Appliance Distr
N.A.I.C.S.: 423620
Khoo Hock Heng (Project Mgr)

Khind Customer Service Sdn. Bhd. (1)
No 89 Jln Teratai 10 Taman Johor Jaya, 81100, Johor Bahru, Johor, Malaysia
Tel.: (60) 73558991
Web Site: http://www.khind.com
Commercial Property Rental Services
N.A.I.C.S.: 531120

Khind Electrical (Malaysia) Sdn. Bhd. (1)
No 1-2 & 1-3 Jalan 1/3 Pusat Komersial LGSB off Jalan Hospital, 47000, Sungai Buloh, Selangor, Malaysia
Tel.: (60) 361503988
Web Site: http://www.khindelectrical.com.my
Electrical & Electronic Equipment Distr
N.A.I.C.S.: 423690

Khind Marketing (M) Sdn. Bhd. (1)
No 2 Jalan Astaka U8/82 Seksyen U8, Bukit Jelutong, 40150, Shah Alam, Selangor, Malaysia
Tel.: (60) 378392000
Electrical Product Mfr & Distr
N.A.I.C.S.: 335311

Khind Middle East DMCC (1)

AND PRIVATE COMPANIES

2303 Fortune Executive, PO Box 261569, Jumeirah Lakes Towers, Dubai, United Arab Emirates
Tel.: (971) 45803847
Web Site: https://khind.ae
Electrical & Electronic Mfr
N.A.I.C.S.: 334419

Khind Systems (Singapore) Pte. Ltd. (1)
No 5 Penjuru Close 03-00, Singapore, 608600, Singapore
Tel.: (65) 6 862 3777
Web Site: https://www.khind-systems.com
Electrical & Hygiene Mfr
N.A.I.C.S.: 335999
Philip Tan *(Asst Gen Mgr)*

Subsidiary (Non-US):

Khind Electrical (Hong Kong) Limited (2)
Unit D 5/F World Tech Centre No 95 How Ming Street, Kwun Tong, Kowloon, China (Hong Kong)
Tel.: (852) 28336966
Electrical Home Appliance Mfr & Distr
N.A.I.C.S.: 335220
Raymond Yeung *(Mgr-Project & Sls)*

Khind-Mistral (Borneo) Sdn. Bhd. (1)
Lot 1214 Section 66 Jalan Perbadanan, Office Bintawa Industrial Estate, 93450, Kuching, Sarawak, Malaysia
Tel.: (60) 82338511
Electrical Home Appliances Distr
N.A.I.C.S.: 423620

Khind-Mistral (M) Sdn. Bhd. (1)
No 2 Jalan Astaka U8/82 Bukit Jelutong, 40150, Shah Alam, Selangor Darul Ehsan, Malaysia
Tel.: (60) 37 839 2000
Web Site: https://www.khind.com.my
Sales Range: $50-74.9 Million
Emp.: 100
Electrical Home Appliances Distr
N.A.I.C.S.: 423620

Khind-Mistral (Sabah) Sdn. Bhd. (1)
Lot 3-6 Mogoputi Industrial Park Jalan Penampang KM 8, 89500, Kota Kinabalu, Sabah, Malaysia
Tel.: (60) 88718117
Web Site: http://www.khind.ae
Sales Range: $50-74.9 Million
Property & Motor Vehicles Rental Services
N.A.I.C.S.: 531110

Khind-Mistral Industries Sdn. Bhd. (1)
No 2 Jalan Perusahaan 2, Off Jalan Bernam, 45400, Sekincan, Selangor, Malaysia
Tel.: (60) 332411991
Web Site: https://khindmanufacturing.com
Sales Range: $150-199.9 Million
Emp.: 350
Home Appliance Mfr
N.A.I.C.S.: 335220

Subsidiary (Non-US):

Khind Middle East FZE (2)
PO Box 261569, 2303 Fortune Executive - Jumeirah Lakes Towers, Dubai, United Arab Emirates
Tel.: (971) 4 886 0492
Web Site: https://www.khind.ae
Household Appliance Distr
N.A.I.C.S.: 423620

Mayer Malaysia Sdn. Bhd. (1)
No 2 Jalan Astaka U8/82 Seksyen U8 Bukit Jelutong, 40150, Shah Alam, Selangor, Malaysia
Tel.: (60) 378392000
Web Site: https://www.mayermalaysia.com
Kitchen Appliance Distr
N.A.I.C.S.: 423620

Mayer Marketing Pte. Ltd. (1)
71 Ubi Crescent 06-02 Excalibur Centre, Singapore, 408571, Singapore
Tel.: (65) 65426868
Web Site: https://www.mayer.sg
Kitchen Appliance Distr
N.A.I.C.S.: 423620
Sherene Chia *(Mgr-Mktg)*

Mistral (Singapore) Pte. Ltd. (1)
71 Ubi Crescent Excalibur Centre Unit 06-01, Singapore, 408571, Singapore
Tel.: (65) 63465233
Web Site: http://www.mistral.com.sg
Emp.: 50
Household Electrical Appliances Distr
N.A.I.C.S.: 423620

PT Khind Environmental Solutions (1)
Ruko Kirana Butique Office Jl Boulevard Kelaka Gading Blok B1, No 6 Jakarta Utara 14240, Jakarta, 14240, Indonesia
Tel.: (62) 2129375528
Ventilating & Smart Lighting Services
N.A.I.C.S.: 561990
Nelwan Mandagie *(Mgr-Fin & Acctg)*

KHIRON LIFE SCIENCES CORP.
100 King Street West Suite 1600, Toronto, M5X 1G5, ON, Canada
Tel.: (647) 556-5750 BC
Web Site: http://www.khiron.ca
Year Founded: 2012
KHRN—(TSXV)
Rev.: $10,009,273
Assets: $33,070,105
Liabilities: $6,997,495
Net Worth: $26,072,610
Earnings: ($25,916,154)
Emp.: 310
Fiscal Year-end: 12/31/21
Medical Cannabis Research
N.A.I.C.S.: 621511
Alvaro Torres *(Co-Founder & CEO)*

Subsidiaries:

Ilans S.A.S. (1)
Carrera 19 No 82-14, Bogota, Colombia
Tel.: (57) 13078377
Web Site: http://www.ilans.com.co
Hospital & Hospice Services
N.A.I.C.S.: 621999

KHMELNITSKOBLENERGO, PJSC
11A Khranovskogo str c, Khmelnytsky, 29016, Ukraine
Tel.: (380) 382 70 15 59
Web Site: http://www.hoe.com.ua
Electric Power Distr
N.A.I.C.S.: 221122
Oleg Kozachuk *(CEO-Acting)*

KHMELNYTSKGAZ PJSC
41 Myru ave c, Khmelnytsky, 29019, Ukraine
Tel.: (380) 382 71 04 51
Web Site: http://www.hmgaz.com.ua
Natural & Liquefied Gas Distr
N.A.I.C.S.: 221210

KHODAY INDIA LIMITED
Brewery House 7th Mile Kanakapura Road, Bengaluru, 560 062, India
Tel.: (91) 8022956570
Web Site: http://www.khodayindia.com
Year Founded: 1906
507435—(BOM)
Sales Range: $10-24.9 Million
Emp.: 6,000
Breweries Mfr
N.A.I.C.S.: 312120
K. L. Ramachandra *(Chm)*

KHON KAEN SUGAR INDUSTRY PUBLIC COMPANY LIMITED
No 503 KSL Tower Building 9th Floor Sri Ayutthaya Road, Ratchathewi District Thanon Phaya Thai Subdistrict, Bangkok, 10400, Thailand
Tel.: (66) 26426191
Web Site: https://www.kslgroup.com
Year Founded: 1945
KSL—(THA)
Rev.: $538,558,087
Assets: $1,161,794,488
Liabilities: $531,925,319
Net Worth: $629,869,170
Earnings: $26,864,922
Emp.: 2,859
Fiscal Year-end: 10/31/23
Sugar Mfr
N.A.I.C.S.: 311314
Manu Leopairote *(Chm)*

Subsidiaries:

KSL Chemical Co., Ltd. (1)
503 KSL Tower 17th Floor Sriayudhya Road, Rajathevi, Bangkok, 10400, Thailand
Tel.: (66) 2 642 6191
Chemical Products Distr
N.A.I.C.S.: 424690

KSL Export Trading Co., Ltd. (1)
503 KSL TOWER 21th Floor Sriayudhya Rd, Ratchathewi, Bangkok, 10400, Thailand
Tel.: (66) 264262036
Sugar Whslr
N.A.I.C.S.: 424490
Pichai Kanivichaporn *(Mng Dir)*

KSL Real Estate Co., Ltd. (1)
503 K S L Tower 20th Floor Sriayudhya Rd, Rajathevi District, Bangkok, 10400, Thailand
Tel.: (66) 264262213
Real Estate Development Services
N.A.I.C.S.: 531390

New Krung Thai Sugar Factory Co., Ltd. (1)
503 KSL Tower 21st Floor Sri Ayutthaya Rd Phaya Thai Rd, Ratchathewi, Bangkok, 10400, Thailand
Tel.: (66) 2642622939
Cane Sugar Mfr
N.A.I.C.S.: 311314
Chamroon Chinthammit *(Mng Dir)*

Savannakhet Sugar Corporation (1)
Road No 9 KM 81, Atsapangthong, Lianxay, Savannakhet, Lao People's Democratic Republic
Tel.: (856) 416660023
Cane Sugar Mfr
N.A.I.C.S.: 311314

KHONBURI SUGAR PUBLIC COMPANY LIMITED
5 Soi Sukhumvit 57 Khlongton-Nue, Wattana, Bangkok, 10110, Thailand
Tel.: (66) 27254888
Web Site: https://www.kbs.co.th
KBS—(THA)
Rev.: $372,016,391
Assets: $373,676,273
Liabilities: $248,364,958
Net Worth: $125,311,315
Earnings: $27,867,095
Emp.: 1,083
Fiscal Year-end: 12/31/23
Sugar Mfr
N.A.I.C.S.: 311314
Suthep Wongvorazathe *(Chm)*

Subsidiaries:

KBS Investment Co., Ltd. (1)
5 Soi Sukhumvit 57 Klongton Nue, Bangkok, 10110, Thailand
Tel.: (66) 27254888
Financial Investment Services
N.A.I.C.S.: 523999

Subsidiary (Domestic):

KBS Cane & Sugar Co., Ltd. (2)
5 Soi Sukhumvit 57 Klongton Nue, Wattana, Bangkok, 10110, Thailand
Tel.: (66) 27254888
Sugar Products Mfr
N.A.I.C.S.: 311314

KBS Trading Co., Ltd. (1)
289 Moo 13 Jarakhe-Hin, Khonburi, Nakhon Ratchasima, 30250, Thailand
Tel.: (66) 44448338
Sugar Products Mfr
N.A.I.C.S.: 311314

Khonburi Bio Energy Co., Ltd. (1)
5 Soi Sukhumvit 57 Klongton Nue, Wattana, Bangkok, 10110, Thailand
Tel.: (66) 27254888
Ethanol Mfr & Distr
N.A.I.C.S.: 325193

Khonburi Power Plant Co., Ltd. (1)
18 Moo 13 Jarakhe-Hin, Khonburi, Nakhon Ratchasima, 30250, Thailand
Tel.: (66) 44448652
Electric Power Distr
N.A.I.C.S.: 221122

KHONG GUAN LIMITED
338 Jalan Boon Lay, Singapore, 619526, Singapore
Tel.: (65) 62616888 SG
Web Site: https://www.khongguan.com.sg
Year Founded: 1960
K03—(SES)
Rev.: $53,290,729
Assets: $49,499,441
Liabilities: $6,596,850
Net Worth: $42,902,591
Earnings: ($41,557)
Emp.: 612
Fiscal Year-end: 07/31/23
Wheat Flour Milling & Trading; Investment Services
N.A.I.C.S.: 311211

Subsidiaries:

Khong Guan Food Products (Pte.) Ltd. (1)
85 Playfair Road, Singapore, 368000, Singapore (100%)
Tel.: (65) 62822511
Sales Range: Less than $1 Million
Trading of Corn Products & Investment Holdings
N.A.I.C.S.: 111150
Michael Chew *(Mgr)*

KHOOBSURAT LIMITED
7A Bentinck Street 3rd Floor, Kolkata, 700001, West Bengal, India
Tel.: (91) 913340661067
Web Site: https://www.khoobsuratltd.co.in
Year Founded: 1982
Rev.: $91,786
Assets: $3,702,655
Liabilities: $106,195
Net Worth: $3,596,460
Earnings: $5,030
Fiscal Year-end: 03/31/19
Textile Product Whslr
N.A.I.C.S.: 424990
Amalesh Sadhu *(CFO)*

KHOON GROUP LIMITED
Block 5000 Ang Mo Kio Avenue 5 04-01 Techplace II, Singapore, Singapore
Tel.: (65) 65708770 Ky
Web Site: https://www.khoongroup.com
Year Founded: 2018
0924—(HKG)
Rev.: $37,501,212
Assets: $37,448,164
Liabilities: $10,468,579
Net Worth: $26,979,584
Earnings: ($1,147,645)
Emp.: 207
Fiscal Year-end: 06/30/23
Engineeering Services
N.A.I.C.S.: 541330
Jui Khoon Ang *(Chm)*

KHORASAN PEGAH DAIRY COMPANY
13th Kilometer Of Ghuchan Road, PO Box 91735/395, Mashhad, Razavi Khorasan, Iran
Tel.: (98) 511 5421020
Year Founded: 1964

Khorasan Pegah Dairy Company—(Continued)
Emp.: 322
Dairy Products Mfr
N.A.I.C.S.: 112120

KHOUZESTAN STEEL COMPANY
10th KM of Ahwaz-Bandar Imam Khomeini Road, PO Box 1378, 61788-13111, Ahvaz, 61788-13111, Iran
Tel.: (98) 6132908190
Web Site: https://www.ksc.ir
Year Founded: 1973
FKHZ1—(THE)
Sales Range: Less than $1 Million
Mineral Exploration Services
N.A.I.C.S.: 213114

KHOY SUGAR CO.
No 24 North Side Kish East, 15999 43143, Tehran, Iran
Tel.: (98) 4436450902
Web Site: https://khoysugar.ir
Year Founded: 1966
GHND1—(THE)
Sales Range: Less than $1 Million
Sugar Mfr
N.A.I.C.S.: 311314

KHOY TEXTILE CO.
20km from Khoy in Khoy-Marand Road, Tehran, Iran
Web Site: http://www.khoytextile.net
Textile Products Mfr
N.A.I.C.S.: 314999
Seyed Hassan Sadrolgharavi *(Mng Dir)*

KHRONOS ADVISORY LIMITED
622 Emporium Tower 25/F Sukhumvit Rd Klongton, Klongtoey, Bangkok, 10110, Thailand
Tel.: (66) 2664 9100
Web Site: http://www.khronosadvisory.com
Year Founded: 2009
Financial Advisory Services
N.A.I.C.S.: 523940
Robert Binyon *(Chm)*

KHUDUUGIIN TEEVER JOINT STOCK COMPANY
10th Khoroo Uliastai Town, Bayanzurkh District, Ulaanbaatar, Mongolia
Tel.: (976) 11 302727
HUT—(MONG)
Sales Range: Less than $1 Million
Transportation Services
N.A.I.C.S.: 488999
Auyrzana Ch *(CEO)*

KHULNA POWER COMPANY LIMITED
Landmark 3rd Floor 12-14 Gulshan North C/A Gulshan-2, Dhaka, 1212, Bangladesh
Tel.: (880) 258810932
Web Site: https://www.khulnapower.com
Year Founded: 1997
KPCL—(CHT)
Rev.: $46,148,578
Assets: $94,687,374
Liabilities: $25,110,987
Net Worth: $69,576,388
Earnings: ($6,061,533)
Emp.: 10
Fiscal Year-end: 06/30/23
Power Generation Services
N.A.I.C.S.: 221118
Hasan Mahmood Raja *(Chm)*

Subsidiaries:

Khulna Power Company Unit II Ltd. (1)
Extended premises of KPCL Khalishpur, Goalpara, Khulna, Bangladesh
Tel.: (880) 417635568
Eletric Power Generation Services
N.A.I.C.S.: 221118

KHURSHID SPINNING MILLS LIMITED
133-134 Regency the Mall, Faisalabad, Pakistan
Tel.: (92) 412610030
Web Site: https://www.khurshidgroup.com.pk
Year Founded: 1966
KHSM—(KAR)
Rev.: $6,042,734
Assets: $3,206,850
Liabilities: $3,902,457
Net Worth: ($695,607)
Earnings: $206,247
Emp.: 847
Fiscal Year-end: 06/30/21
Textile Mill Operator
N.A.I.C.S.: 314999
Muhammad Ashraf *(Chm)*

KHVATEC CO., LTD.
53-12 1gongdan-ro 10-gil, Gumi, 730-906, Gyeongsangbuk-do, Korea (South)
Tel.: (82) 544650630
Web Site: https://www.khvatec.com
Year Founded: 1992
060720—(KRS)
Rev.: $279,122,950
Assets: $264,431,505
Liabilities: $88,519,097
Net Worth: $175,912,407
Earnings: $19,183,313
Emp.: 417
Fiscal Year-end: 12/31/22
Electronic Components Mfr
N.A.I.C.S.: 334419
Kwang-Hae Nam *(CEO)*

Subsidiaries:

KHLitec (1)
6F 18 Banpo-daero, Seocho-gu, Seoul, Korea (South)
Tel.: (82) 25838817
Electronic Components Mfr
N.A.I.C.S.: 334419

KHV Huizhou Precision Manufacturing Co., Ltd. (1)
22-03 Three Industrial Park, Huicheng District, Huizhou, Guangdong, China
Tel.: (86) 138 2541 8722
Electronic Components Mfr
N.A.I.C.S.: 334419
Eunbo Shim *(Head-Sls & Sourcing Grp)*

KHV Tiajin Precision Manufacturing Co., Ltd. (1)
No 40 Hangkong Road Tianjin Industrial Park, Tianjin, China
Tel.: (86) 22 2489 6661
Electronic Components Mfr
N.A.I.C.S.: 334419

KHVatec Co., Ltd. (1)
1115 Coastal Building East Block Hai De San Dao, Nanshan District, Shenzhen, China
Tel.: (86) 755 8627 1780
Electronic Components Mfr
N.A.I.C.S.: 334419

KHYATI MULTIMEDIA ENTERTAINMENT LIMITED
100 Chinubhai Tower Opp Handloom House Ashram Road, Ahmedabad, 380 009, Gujarat, India
Tel.: (91) 7926584335
Web Site: https://www.khyatimultimedia.com
Year Founded: 1995

531692—(BOM)
Rev.: $5,683
Assets: $324,213
Liabilities: $93,292
Net Worth: $230,921
Earnings: ($18,200)
Emp.: 2
Fiscal Year-end: 03/31/23
Multimedia Development Services
N.A.I.C.S.: 512199
Kartik Jasubhai Patel *(Chm & Mng Dir)*

KHYBER TEXTILE MILLS LIMITED
Shahra e Resham Baldher, Haripur, Khyber Pakhtunkhwa, Pakistan
Tel.: (92) 995655048
Web Site: https://www.khybertextile.com
Year Founded: 1961
KHYT—(PSX)
Rev.: $97,505
Assets: $3,476,415
Liabilities: $169,742
Net Worth: $3,306,673
Earnings: ($14,084)
Emp.: 9
Fiscal Year-end: 06/30/23
Textile Mill Operator
N.A.I.C.S.: 314999
Adam Jadoon *(CEO)*

KHYBER TOBACCO COMPANY LIMITED
Nowshera Road, Mardan, Pakistan
Tel.: (92) 937844639 **PK**
Web Site: https://www.khybertobacco.com
Year Founded: 1954
KHTC—(PSX)
Rev.: $26,745,816
Assets: $27,772,073
Liabilities: $14,123,358
Net Worth: $13,648,715
Earnings: $7,189,255
Emp.: 598
Fiscal Year-end: 06/30/23
Tobacco Mfr
N.A.I.C.S.: 312230
Waseem Ur Rehman *(CEO)*

KI-STAR REAL ESTATE CO., LTD.
762-1 Nishitomida, Honjo, 367-0035, Saitama, Japan
Tel.: (81) 495272525
Web Site: https://www.ki-group.co.jp
Year Founded: 1990
3465—(TKS)
Rev.: $1,871,185,240
Assets: $1,625,650,180
Liabilities: $1,222,281,540
Net Worth: $403,368,640
Earnings: $45,318,160
Emp.: 2,790
Fiscal Year-end: 03/31/24
Real Estate
N.A.I.C.S.: 531390

KIA CORPORATION
12 Heolleung-ro, Seocho-gu, Seoul, 137-938, Korea (South)
Tel.: (82) 234641114 **KR**
Web Site: https://worldwide.kia.com
Year Founded: 1944
000270—(KRS)
Rev.: $64,273
Assets: $61,502
Liabilities: $29,382
Net Worth: $32,120
Earnings: $4,380
Emp.: 35,508
Fiscal Year-end: 12/31/21
Automobile Parts Mfr
N.A.I.C.S.: 336110

Ho-Sung Song *(CEO)*

Subsidiaries:

Kia America, Inc. (1)
111 Peters Canyon Rd, Irvine, CA 92606
Tel.: (949) 468-4800
Web Site: http://www.kiausa.com
Sales Range: $150-199.9 Million
Emp.: 445
Automotive Distr
N.A.I.C.S.: 423110
Scott McKee *(Dir-PR)*

Subsidiary (Domestic):

Kia Georgia, Inc. (2)
7777 Kia Pkwy, West Point, GA 31833
Tel.: (706) 902-7777
Web Site: http://www.kmmgusa.com
Automobile Mfr
N.A.I.C.S.: 336110
Jang Soo Shin *(Pres & CEO)*

Kia Australia Pty Ltd (1)
350 Parramatta Rd, PO Box 2207, North Ryde, 1670, NSW, Australia
Tel.: (61) 131542
Web Site: http://www.kia.com
Emp.: 97
New Car Dealers
N.A.I.C.S.: 441110
Sang-Hyun Cho *(Pres & CEO)*

Kia Canada, Inc. (1)
180 Foster Crescent, Mississauga, L5R 4J5, ON, Canada
Tel.: (905) 755-6250
Web Site: https://www.kia.ca
Automobile Dealers
N.A.I.C.S.: 441110
Elias El-Achhab *(COO)*

Kia Japan Co., Ltd. (1)
3-2-2 Nishinohara, Inzai, 270-1334, Chiba, Japan
Tel.: (81) 476401400
Automobile Mfr
N.A.I.C.S.: 336390

Kia Motors Europe GmbH (1)
Theodor-Heuss-Allee 11, 60486, Frankfurt, Germany
Tel.: (49) 69850928354
Web Site: https://prod2-press.kia.com
Sales Range: $25-49.9 Million
Emp.: 80
Automobile Mfr & Distr
N.A.I.C.S.: 336110
Yong Kew Park *(Pres)*

Subsidiary (Non-US):

Kia Motors Austria GmbH (2)
Sverigestrasse 5, Vienna, 1220, Austria
Tel.: (43) 17342900
Web Site: http://www.kia.at
Emp.: 40
New Car Dealers
N.A.I.C.S.: 441110
Bernard Pink *(Gen Mgr)*

Kia Motors Czech s.r.o. (2)
Jihlavska 1558/21, Michle, 140 00, Prague, Czech Republic
Tel.: (420) 22299933
Web Site: http://www.kia.com
New Car Dealers
N.A.I.C.S.: 441110

Subsidiary (Domestic):

Kia Motors Deutschland GmbH (2)
Theodor-Heuss-Allee 11, 60486, Frankfurt am Main, Germany
Tel.: (49) 691539200
Web Site: http://www.kia.de
New Car Dealers
N.A.I.C.S.: 441110
Martin van Vugt *(COO)*

Subsidiary (Non-US):

Kia Motors Hungary Kft (2)
Budafoki Ut 56, Budapest, 1117, Hungary
Tel.: (36) 13712000
Web Site: http://www.kiamotors.hu
Automobile Whslr
N.A.I.C.S.: 423110
Norbert Nagy *(Mng Dir)*

AND PRIVATE COMPANIES

Kia Motors Iberia SL (2)
Calle Anabel Segura 16 Ed Vega Norte Ii,
28108, Alcobendas, Madrid, Spain
Tel.: (34) 902283285
Web Site: http://www.kia.com
Automobile Whslr
N.A.I.C.S.: 423110

Kia Motors Nederland BV (2)
De Corridor 25, 3621 ZA, Breukelen, Netherlands
Tel.: (31) 346753800
Web Site: http://www.kia.nl
Sales Range: $25-49.9 Million
Emp.: 60
New Car Dealers
N.A.I.C.S.: 441110
Thomas Dral (Mng Dir)

Kia Motors Polska Sp. z.o.o. (2)
ul Pulawska 366, 02-819, Warsaw, Poland
Tel.: (48) 605542542
Web Site: http://www.kia.com
Sales Range: $25-49.9 Million
New Car Dealers
N.A.I.C.S.: 441110
Wojciech Szyszko (Mng Dir)

Kia Motors Sales Slovensko s.r.o. (2)
Einsteinova 19, 851 01, Bratislava, Slovakia
Tel.: (421) 232421333
Web Site: http://www.kia.com
Sales Range: $25-49.9 Million
New Car Dealers
N.A.I.C.S.: 441110

Kia Motors Slovakia s.r.o. (2)
Sv Jana Nepomuckeho 1282/1, PO Box 2,
013 01, Teplicka nad Vahom, Slovakia
Tel.: (421) 415150111
Web Site: http://www.kia.sk
Sales Range: $800-899.9 Million
Emp.: 3,700
Automobile Mfr
N.A.I.C.S.: 336390
Jeong-Ick Lee (VP-Admin Div)

Kia Motors Sweden AB (2)
Kanalvagen 10, Upplands Vasby, 194 61, Sweden
Tel.: (46) 840044300
Web Site: http://www.kia.se
Sales Range: $25-49.9 Million
Emp.: 60
New Car Dealers
N.A.I.C.S.: 441110
Peter Himmer (Mng Dir)

Kia Motors UK Limited (2)
Walton Green, Brooklands, Walton-on-Thames, KT12 1FJ, Surrey, United Kingdom
Tel.: (44) 3332022990
Web Site: https://www.kia.com
Sales Range: $50-74.9 Million
Emp.: 80
Automotive Distr
N.A.I.C.S.: 423110
Simon Hetherington (Dir-Comml)

Kia Motors New Zealand Ltd. (1)
6 Highbrook Drive, PO Box 204090, Highbrook, Auckland, 2161, New Zealand
Tel.: (64) 95736070
Web Site: https://www.kia.co.nz
Sales Range: $25-49.9 Million
Emp.: 22
New Car Dealers
N.A.I.C.S.: 441110
Todd McDonald (Gen Mgr)

Kia Motors SA (Pty) Limited (1)
5 Herman Road Cnr Dick Kemp Street, Meadowdale, Germiston, 1401, South Africa
Tel.: (27) 11 457 0200
Web Site: http://www.kia.co.za
Emp.: 100
Automobile Mfr
N.A.I.C.S.: 336110
Christo Valentyn (Mgr-PR & Product Mktg)

LLC Kia Russia (1)
Ul Valovaya 26, 115054, Moscow, Russia
Tel.: (7) 4952870900
Web Site: http://www.kia.ru
Automobile Dealers
N.A.I.C.S.: 441110

KIA LIM BERHAD
Wisma Ng Hoo Tee 79 Jalan Muar Parit Sulong, 83500, Batu Pahat, Johor Darul Takzim, Malaysia
Tel.: (60) 74187100
Web Site: https://www.kialim.com.my
KIALIM—(KLS)
Rev.: $6,187,546
Assets: $14,392,125
Liabilities: $4,641,992
Net Worth: $9,750,132
Earnings: ($155,266)
Fiscal Year-end: 12/31/22
Clay Brick Mfr
N.A.I.C.S.: 327120
Siew Foong Leong (Sec)

Subsidiaries:

Kangkar Raya Batu Bata Sdn. Bhd. (1)
Wisma Ng Hoo Tee 79 Jalan Muar, Parit Sulong, 83500, Batu Pahat, Johor Darul Takzim, Malaysia
Tel.: (60) 74187100
Web Site: https://www.kialim.com.my
Sales Range: $50-74.9 Million
Emp.: 100
Bricks & Roofing Tiles Mfr
N.A.I.C.S.: 327120

Syarikat Kia Lim Kilang Batu Bata Sdn. Bhd. (1)
No 79 Jalan Muar Wisma Ng Hoo Tee Parit Sulong, Batu Pahat, 83500, Johor Darul Takzim, Malaysia
Tel.: (60) 74188999
Bricks Mfr
N.A.I.C.S.: 327120
Ah Chai Ng (Mgr-Mktg)

KIAN HO PTE LTD.
5 Changi South Street 3, Singapore, 486117, Singapore
Tel.: (65) 6287 5866
Web Site: http://www.kianho.com.sg
Year Founded: 1956
Sales Range: $50-74.9 Million
Bearing & Seals Mfr
N.A.I.C.S.: 332991
Wee Kiong Yeo (Chm)

KIAN SHEN CORPORATION
No 100 Xinjiang Rd, Yangmei Dist, Taoyuan, 326, Taiwan
Tel.: (886) 34783121
Web Site: https://www.kian-shen.com
Year Founded: 1955
1525—(TAI)
Rev.: $46,908,201
Assets: $175,386,080
Liabilities: $30,940,250
Net Worth: $144,445,831
Earnings: $8,436,294
Emp.: 330
Fiscal Year-end: 12/31/22
Automotive Parts Mfr & Distr
N.A.I.C.S.: 336390

KIANG HUAT SEA GULL TRADING FROZEN FOOD PUBLIC COMPANY LIMITED
4/2 Moo 3 Asia Highway No 43, Namom, Songkhla, 90310, Thailand
Tel.: (66) 74222333
Web Site: https://www.kst-hatyai.com
Year Founded: 1978
CHOTI—(THA)
Rev.: $77,447,172
Assets: $74,673,935
Liabilities: $46,279,490
Net Worth: $28,394,445
Earnings: $3,005,605
Fiscal Year-end: 12/31/23
Frozen Seafood Mfr
N.A.I.C.S.: 311710
Chaiwat Laoteppitak (Mng Dir-Acting)

Subsidiaries:

Teppitak Seafood Co., Ltd. (1)
96/22 Moo8 District Bana Naklua Rd, Amphur Muang, Pattani, 94000, Thailand
Tel.: (66) 73 414758
Web Site: http://www.teppitak.com
Frozen Food Whslr
N.A.I.C.S.: 424470
Chanchai Laoteppitaks (Mng Dir)

KIATNAKIN BANK PUBLIC COMPANY LIMITED
209 KKP Tower Sukhumvit 21 Asoke Khlong Toey Nua, Wattana, Bangkok, 10110, Thailand
Tel.: (66) 21655555 TH
Web Site: http://www.kiatnakin.co.th
Year Founded: 1971
KKP—(THA)
Rev.: $896,702,645
Assets: $15,919,169,920
Liabilities: $14,131,078,561
Net Worth: $1,788,091,360
Earnings: $159,269,900
Emp.: 3,907
Fiscal Year-end: 12/31/23
Banking Services
N.A.I.C.S.: 522110
Aphinant Klewpatinond (Co-CEO)

Subsidiaries:

CMIC Development Company Limited (1)
209 10th Fl CMIC Tower Sukhumvit 21 Rd Klongtoey Nua, Wattana, Bangkok, 10110, Thailand
Tel.: (66) 26641396
Emp.: 50
Property Leasing Services
N.A.I.C.S.: 531110

KKP Tower Company Limited (1)
20th Floor KKP Tower A 209 Sukhumvit 21 Asoke Road, Khlong Toey-Nua Wattana, Bangkok, 10110, Thailand
Tel.: (66) 266413967
Rental & Property Management Services
N.A.I.C.S.: 531311

Phatra Asset Management Company Limited (1)
19th Floor Muang Thai-Phatra Complex Building A 252/25, Huaykwang Ratchadapisek Road, Bangkok, 10310, Thailand
Tel.: (66) 23059800
Asset Management Services
N.A.I.C.S.: 523940

Phatra Capital Public Company Limited (1)
9/F MuangThai-Phatra Office Tower 1, 252/6 Ratchadapisek Road Huaykwang, Bangkok, 10310, Thailand (99.93%)
Tel.: (66) 2305 9000
Web Site: http://www.phatrasecurities.com
Sales Range: $50-74.9 Million
Bank Holding Company; Securities & Investment Banking
N.A.I.C.S.: 551111
Banyong Pongpanich (Chm)

Subsidiary (Domestic):

Phatra Securities Public Company Limited (2)
6 8-11/F Muang Thai Phatra Office Tower 1 252/6 Ratchadapisek Road, Huaykwang, Bangkok, 10310, Thailand (98.51%)
Tel.: (66) 23059000
Web Site: http://www.phatrasecurities.com
Sales Range: $50-74.9 Million
Investment Banking & Financial Services
N.A.I.C.S.: 523150

KIATTANA TRANSPORT PUBLIC COMPANY LIMITED
100 Moo 3 Bangtanai Sub-district, Pakkret District, Nonthaburi, 11120, Thailand
Tel.: (66) 250173308
Web Site: https://www.kiattana.co.th
Year Founded: 1994
KIAT—(THA)
Rev.: $23,926,322
Assets: $39,255,318
Liabilities: $6,217,890
Net Worth: $33,037,428
Earnings: $2,518,683
Fiscal Year-end: 12/31/23
Chemicals & Dangerous Goods Transport Services
N.A.I.C.S.: 488490
Cherdkiat Monsereenusorn (Chm)

KIBO CAPITAL PARTNERS LTD.
5th floor, Ebene Skies Rue de l'Institut, Ebene, Mauritius
Tel.: (230) 4042200
Web Site: https://kibo-capital.com
Private Equity
N.A.I.C.S.: 523940
Thierry Hugnin (Co-Founder & Mng Partner)

KIBO ENERGY PLC
Gray Office Park Galway Retail Park Headford Road, Galway, Ireland
Tel.: (353) 91511463 IE
Web Site: https://kibo.energy
Year Founded: 2008
KBO—(JSE)
Rev.: $1,308,688
Assets: $8,429,618
Liabilities: $6,559,996
Net Worth: $1,869,621
Earnings: ($13,769,912)
Emp.: 17
Fiscal Year-end: 12/31/22
Gold & Nickel Mining Services
N.A.I.C.S.: 212220
Louis Coetzee (CEO)

KIBUN FOODS INC.
5-15-1 Ginza Chuo-ku, Tokyo, 104 8101, Japan
Tel.: (81) 3 6891 2751 JP
Web Site: http://www.kibun.co.jp
Year Founded: 1938
Sales Range: $150-199.9 Million
Emp.: 1,309
Seafood Paste Products Mfr & Distr
N.A.I.C.S.: 311710
Masahito Hoashi (Chm & CEO)

Subsidiaries:

Kibun Foods Singapore Pte., Ltd. (1)
6 Clementi Loop Hoe Leong Building 3rd Floor, Singapore, 129814, Singapore
Tel.: (65) 6466 7887
Web Site: http://www.kibun.com.sg
Emp.: 4
Fresh & Frozen Seafood Distr
N.A.I.C.S.: 424460
Tatsuya Shibazaki (Exec Dir)

Kibun Foods USA, Inc. (1)
2101 4th Ave Ste 1240, Seattle, WA 98121-3297 (100%)
Tel.: (206) 467-6287
Sales Range: $50-74.9 Million
Emp.: 10
Foods & Bulk Seafood Mfr
N.A.I.C.S.: 424460
Hiroyuki Uvda (Pres)

Kibun Fresh System Inc. (1)
6-1-1 Heiwajima, Ota-ku, Tokyo, 143-6591, Japan
Tel.: (81) 3 3767 3211
Web Site: http://www.kibun-fs.com
Emp.: 414
Fresh & Frozen Seafood Mfr
N.A.I.C.S.: 311710

Kibun Trading Inc. (1)
2-1-7 Kaigan, Minato-ku, Tokyo, 105-8603, Japan
Tel.: (81) 3 6891 5171
Web Site: http://www.kibun-ti.co.jp
Emp.: 45
Fresh & Frozen Seafood Mfr
N.A.I.C.S.: 311710
Hideki Enokida (Mng Dir)

Yilin Kibun Corporation. (1)
1F 13 Alley 1 Lane 317 Chung Hsin Rd Sec

KIBUN FOODS INC.

Kibun Foods Inc.—(Continued)
5, Taipei, Taiwan
Tel.: (886) 285121235
Fresh & Frozen Seafood Distr
N.A.I.C.S.: 424460

KIC METALIKS LIMITED
32 J I Nehru Roaad Om Tower 3rd Floor Rooom no 304, Kolkata, 700071, India
Tel.: (91) 3340076552
Web Site: https://www.kicmetaliks.com
Year Founded: 1986
513693—(BOM)
Rev.: $73,477,773
Assets: $53,480,523
Liabilities: $31,731,186
Net Worth: $21,749,337
Earnings: $5,278,946
Emp.: 326
Fiscal Year-end: 03/31/22
Iron & Steel Products Mfr
N.A.I.C.S.: 332111
Radhey Shyam Jalan *(Chm & Mng Dir)*

KICHIRI HOLDINGS & CO., LTD.
12th floor 1-17-2 Shibuya, Shibuya-ku, Tokyo, 150-0002, Japan
Tel.: (81) 662623456
Web Site: https://kichiri.co.jp
Year Founded: 1998
3082—(TKS)
Rev.: $85,506,340
Assets: $46,905,020
Liabilities: $35,466,440
Net Worth: $11,438,580
Earnings: $1,592,320
Emp.: 3,725
Fiscal Year-end: 06/30/24
Restaurant Owner & Operator
N.A.I.C.S.: 722511
Masanori Hirakawa *(Pres)*

KID CASTLE EDUCATIONAL CORPORATION
No 98 Min Chuan Road 8th Floor, Xindian District, Taipei, 23141, Taiwan
Tel.: (886) 222185996   DE
Web Site: https://ft.kidcastle.com
Year Founded: 1985
KDCE—(OTCIQ)
Rev.: $3,866,539
Assets: $3,417,822
Liabilities: $422,379
Net Worth: $2,995,443
Earnings: $767,976
Emp.: 6
Fiscal Year-end: 12/31/22
Educational Support Services
N.A.I.C.S.: 611710
Frank I. Igwealor *(Chm, Pres, CEO, CFO, Treas & Sec)*

KID INTERIOR AS
Gilhusveien 1, 3426, Lier, Norway
Tel.: (47) 94026000
Web Site: https://www.kid.no
Textile Products Retailer
N.A.I.C.S.: 812331
Mueller Reidar Gustav *(Chm)*

KIDCO CONSTRUCTION LTD.
4949 76 Ave SE, Calgary, T2C 3C6, AB, Canada
Tel.: (403) 730-2029
Web Site: http://www.kidco.ca
Year Founded: 1977
Rev.: $23,324,400
Emp.: 175
Heavy Construction Services
N.A.I.C.S.: 423810
Trent Bradley *(VP)*

KIDDIELAND INTERNATIONAL LIMITED
14/F Bank of America Tower 12 Harcourt Road, Central, China (Hong Kong)
Tel.: (852) 21163000   Ky
Web Site: http://www.kiddieland.com.hk
3830—(HKG)
Rev.: $22,469,580
Assets: $9,972,413
Liabilities: $5,108,033
Net Worth: $4,864,380
Earnings: ($6,896,475)
Emp.: 159
Fiscal Year-end: 04/30/23
Plastic Product Mfr & Distr
N.A.I.C.S.: 339930
Kenneth Shiu Kee Lo *(CEO)*

Subsidiaries:

Kiddieland Toys Limited   (1)
14/F Bank of America Tower 12 Harcourt Road, Central, China (Hong Kong)
Tel.: (852) 21163000
Toy Mfr & Distr
N.A.I.C.S.: 339930

KIDO GROUP CORP.
138 - 142 Hai Ba Trung Da Kao Ward District 1, Ho Chi Minh City, Vietnam
Tel.: (84) 283827 0468
Web Site: http://www.kdc.vn
Year Founded: 1993
Rev.: $160,718,126
Assets: $106,291,505
Liabilities: $61,282,073
Net Worth: $45,009,432
Earnings: ($25,866,454)
Emp.: 1,500
Fiscal Year-end: 12/31/22
Infant Product Distr
N.A.I.C.S.: 423920
Ching Yiu Lee *(Founder, Chm & Co-CEO)*

Subsidiaries:

Tuong An Vegetable Oil Joint Stock Company   (1)
10th floor Empress Tower So 138-142 Hai Ba Trung Street, Da Kao Ward District 1, Ho Chi Minh City, Vietnam   (65%)
Tel.: (84) 28 3827 7806
Web Site: http://www.tuongan.com.vn
Sales Range: Less than $1 Million
Vegetable Oil Mfr
N.A.I.C.S.: 311224

KIDOZ INC.
Hansa Bank Building Ground Floor, Landsome Road, AI 2640, The Valley, Anguilla
Tel.: (264) 4612646   AI
Web Site: https://www.kidoz.net
Year Founded: 1987
KIDZ—(TSXV)
Rev.: $15,097,056
Assets: $14,387,083
Liabilities: $5,695,324
Net Worth: $8,691,759
Earnings: ($1,347,113)
Emp.: 16
Fiscal Year-end: 12/31/22
Holding Company; Online Bingo Website Developer & Operator
N.A.I.C.S.: 551112
Henry W. Bromley *(CFO)*

KIDS MEDICAL SYSTEMS LIMITED
C-101 Signor Residency B/HSanjay Tower, Shyamal Char Rasta Satellite, Ahmedabad, India
Tel.: (91) 7948989930   In
Web Site: http://www.thekidsclinic.in
Year Founded: 2012
Rev.: $78,281
Assets: $570,191
Liabilities: $110,010
Net Worth: $460,181
Earnings: ($17,953)
Fiscal Year-end: 03/31/19

Health Care Management Services
N.A.I.C.S.: 622310
Pallavi Anirvan Dam *(Mng Dir)*

KIDS SMILE HOLDINGS, INC.
7th floor Gotanda PLACE 1-3-8 Nishigotanda, Shinagawa-Ku, Tokyo, 141-0031, Japan
Tel.: (81) 364217015
Web Site: https://www.kidssmile-hd.co.jp
Year Founded: 2018
7084—(TKS)
Rev.: $85,050,870
Assets: $93,617,430
Liabilities: $51,835,620
Net Worth: $41,781,810
Earnings: $872,520
Fiscal Year-end: 03/31/24
Holding Company
N.A.I.C.S.: 551112
Masafumi Nakanishi *(Pres & Dir-Rep)*

KIDSLAND INTERNATIONAL HOLDINGS LIMITED
Level 9 One Indigo 20 Jiuxianqiao Road, Chaoyang District, Beijing, China
Tel.: (86) 29602968   Ky
Web Site: http://www.kidslandholdings.com
Year Founded: 2001
2122—(HKG)
Rev.: $160,718,126
Assets: $106,291,505
Liabilities: $61,282,073
Net Worth: $45,009,432
Earnings: ($25,866,454)
Emp.: 1,500
Fiscal Year-end: 12/31/22
Infant Product Distr
N.A.I.C.S.: 423920
Ching Yiu Lee *(Founder, Chm & Co-CEO)*

Subsidiaries:

Kidsland HK Limited   (1)
9/F 16 Wyndham Street, Central, China (Hong Kong)
Tel.: (852) 61122675
Web Site: https://www.kidslandhk.com
Toy & Game Product Mfr & Distr
N.A.I.C.S.: 339930

KIDUJA INDIA LIMITED
127-B Mittal Tower, Nariman Point, Mumbai, 400 021, India
Tel.: (91) 2240022100
Web Site: https://kiduja.com
Year Founded: 1985
507946—(BOM)
Assets: $14,922,553
Liabilities: $21,958,346
Net Worth: ($7,035,793)
Earnings: ($615,492)
Emp.: 4
Fiscal Year-end: 03/31/22
Financial Investment Services
N.A.I.C.S.: 523999
Ashish D. Jaipuria *(Chm & Mng Dir)*

KIDZTECH HOLDINGS LIMITED
Rm 802 8/F Inter-Continental Plaza 94 Granville Road, Tsim Sha Tsui East, Kowloon, China (Hong Kong)
Tel.: (852) 27218868   Ky
Web Site: http://www.kidztech.net
Year Founded: 2001
6918—(HKG)
Rev.: $23,788,112
Assets: $103,436,190
Liabilities: $47,507,850
Net Worth: $55,928,340
Earnings: ($10,762,783)
Emp.: 95
Fiscal Year-end: 12/31/22

Holding Company
N.A.I.C.S.: 551112
Yu Huang *(Chm & CEO)*

KIEN GIANG BRICK TILE JOINT STOCK COMPANY
Group 4 Snake Alley Town, Kien Luong Town, Kien Luong District, Kien Giang, Vietnam
Tel.: (84) 773750650
Web Site: http://www.tuynelkiengiang.com.vn
Sales Range: $50-74.9 Million
Emp.: 130
Clay Bricks, Tiles, Refractory & Pottery Mfr
N.A.I.C.S.: 327120
Lam Duy Khanh *(Dir-Ceramic Tile)*

KIEN HUNG JOINT STOCK COMPANY
B4-B5 Road No 1 Thanh Loc Industrial Park Thanh Loc, Chau Thanh District, Kien Giang, Vietnam
Tel.: (84) 2973912989
Web Site: https://www.kihuseavn.com
Year Founded: 2000
KHS—(HNX)
Rev.: $29,018,149
Assets: $20,234,020
Liabilities: $11,641,884
Net Worth: $8,592,136
Earnings: ($420,734)
Emp.: 453
Fiscal Year-end: 12/31/23
Agriculture Forestry & Fishing Services
N.A.I.C.S.: 115310
Tran Quoc Dung *(Chm, Deputy CEO & Gen Mgr)*

KIEPE ELECTRIC GMBH
Kiepe-Platz 1, 40599, Dusseldorf, Germany
Tel.: (49) 2 117 4970   De
Web Site: https://www.kiepe.knorr-bremse.com
Year Founded: 1906
Sales Range: $150-199.9 Million
Emp.: 550
Electrified Transport Components Mfr
N.A.I.C.S.: 333415
Heiko Asum *(Mng Dir)*

Subsidiaries:

APS electronic AG   (1)
Neumatt 4, CH-4626, Niederbuchsiten, Switzerland
Tel.: (41) 623898888
Web Site: http://www.apsag.com
Power Inverters Mfr
N.A.I.C.S.: 335999
Marcus Thiele *(Mng Dir)*

Kiepe Electric Corporation   (1)
262 SW Marine Dr, Vancouver, V5X 2R5, BC, Canada
Tel.: (604) 324-2454
Web Site: http://www.kiepe.knorr-bremse.com
Electrical Equipment Distr
N.A.I.C.S.: 423610

Kiepe Electric Ges.m.b.H.   (1)
Ignaz Kock Strasse 23, A-1210, Vienna, Austria
Tel.: (43) 1331270
Web Site: http://www.kiepe-electric.at
Emp.: 140
Electrotechnical Products Mfr & Distr
N.A.I.C.S.: 333415
Jorg Branschadel *(Exec Dir & Mng Dir)*

Kiepe Electric LLC   (1)
359 Curie Dr, Alpharetta, GA 30005
Tel.: (770) 754-0918
Web Site: http://www.kiepe.knorr-bremse.com
Electric Equipment Mfr
N.A.I.C.S.: 423610

AND PRIVATE COMPANIES

Kiepe Electric S.r.l. (1)
Via Mazzini 3/A, 20063, Cernusco sul Naviglio, Italy
Tel.: (39) 02 92 14 81 48
Web Site: http://www.kiepe.knorr-bremse.com
Power Converters Distr
N.A.I.C.S.: 423610

KIER GROUP PLC
2nd Floor Optimum House Clippers Quay, Salford, M50 3XP, United Kingdom
Tel.: (44) 7933388746
Web Site: https://www.kier.co.uk
KIE—(LSE)
Rev.: $5,016,936,290
Assets: $4,377,780,579
Liabilities: $3,720,424,665
Net Worth: $657,355,914
Earnings: $64,838,220
Emp.: 10,000
Fiscal Year-end: 06/30/24
Construction, Civil Engineering & Facilities Maintenance Services
N.A.I.C.S.: 236220
Hugh E. E. Raven *(Gen Counsel & Sec)*

Subsidiaries:

2020 Liverpool Limited (1)
Station House Mercury Court Tithebarn Street, Liverpool, L2 2QP, United Kingdom
Tel.: (44) 1512372020
Sales Range: $250-299.9 Million
Emp.: 320
Property Valuation, Surveying, Engineering & Transportation Infrastructure Services
N.A.I.C.S.: 531390
Chris Lavery *(Mng Dir)*

Kier Construction Limited (1)
Tempsford Hall, Sandy, SG19 2BD, Bedfordshire, United Kingdom
Tel.: (44) 1767640111
Civil Engineering Services
N.A.I.C.S.: 541330
Peter Young *(Grp Mng Dir)*

Kier Harlow Limited (1)
Mead Industrial Park River Way, Harlow, CM20 2SE, Essex, United Kingdom
Tel.: (44) 127 944 6900
Web Site: https://www.kier.co.uk
Sales Range: $75-99.9 Million
Emp.: 1,000
Equipment Repair & Maintenance Services
N.A.I.C.S.: 811310
John Philips *(Mng Dir)*

Kier Homes Limited (1)
Lysander House, Sandy, SG19 2BD, Bedfordshire, United Kingdom
Tel.: (44) 1767642500
Web Site: http://www.kierhomes.co.uk
Sales Range: $50-74.9 Million
Emp.: 600
Building Construction Services
N.A.I.C.S.: 236220

Kier Limited (1)
The Old Mill Chapel Lane, Warmley, Bristol, BS15 4WW, Avon, United Kingdom
Tel.: (44) 117 961 8000
Web Site: http://www.kier.co.uk
Sales Range: $25-49.9 Million
Emp.: 50
Building Contractors
N.A.I.C.S.: 236116
David Snell *(Mng Dir)*

Kier Managed Services Limited (1)
Conway House Fortran Rd, St Mellons Business Park, Cardiff, CF3 0EY, South Glamorgan, United Kingdom
Tel.: (44) 2920361616
Sales Range: $25-49.9 Million
Emp.: 75
Facilities Management Services
N.A.I.C.S.: 561170

Kier Partnership Homes Limited (1)
Beecham Business Park, Walsall, Aldridge, WS9 8TZ, West Midlands, United Kingdom
Tel.: (44) 1922747700

Sales Range: $25-49.9 Million
Emp.: 25
House Building Contractor
N.A.I.C.S.: 236118

Kier Plant Limited (1)
Chawston Lane Chawston, Bedford, MK44 3BH, United Kingdom
Tel.: (44) 1480477800
Sales Range: $25-49.9 Million
Emp.: 15
Crane Rental Services
N.A.I.C.S.: 333923

Kier Project Investment Limited (1)
Tempsford Hall, Sandy, SG19 2BD, Bedfordshire, United Kingdom
Tel.: (44) 1767355000
Web Site: http://www.kier.co.uk
Sales Range: $75-99.9 Million
Emp.: 500
Building & Civil Engineering Development
N.A.I.C.S.: 541330

Kier Property Limited (1)
6 Cavendish Pl, London, W1G 9NB, United Kingdom
Tel.: (44) 2074622750
Web Site: http://www.kier.co.uk
Sales Range: $25-49.9 Million
Emp.: 80
Industrial Building Construction
N.A.I.C.S.: 236210

Kier Stoke Limited (1)
Alton House, Cromer Rd, Stoke-on-Trent, ST1 6AY, United Kingdom
Tel.: (44) 1782236235
Web Site: http://www.kier.co.uk
Sales Range: $100-124.9 Million
Emp.: 500
Construction & Building Maintenance Services
N.A.I.C.S.: 236117
David Morrison *(Reg Mng Dir)*

Kier Trade City LLP (1)
6 Cavendish Place, London, W1G 0QA, United Kingdom
Tel.: (44) 2032806000
Web Site: http://www.trade-city.co.uk
Logistic Services
N.A.I.C.S.: 541614

MRBL Limited (1)
Export House Cawsey Way, Woking, GU21 6QX, Surrey, United Kingdom
Tel.: (44) 1483 731 000
Web Site: http://www.mouchel.com
Emp.: 200
Holding Company; Engineering Services
N.A.I.C.S.: 551112
Darren Oldham *(Dir-Ops Dev-Transport Plng)*

Subsidiary (Domestic):

Mouchel Ewan Limited (2)
Canterbury House Stevenson's Way Wyvern Business Park, Derby, DE21 6LY, Derbs, United Kingdom
Tel.: (44) 1522 836 000
Web Site: http://www.mouchel.com
Engineeering Services
N.A.I.C.S.: 541330

Mouchel Limited (2)
Export House Cawsey Way, Woking, GU21 6QX, Surrey, United Kingdom
Tel.: (44) 1483 731 000
Web Site: http://www.mouchel.com
Engineeering Services
N.A.I.C.S.: 541330

Joint Venture (Domestic):

Scotland TranServ (2)
150 Polmadie Road Glasgow, Glasgow, G5 0HD, Scotland, United Kingdom
Tel.: (44) 141 218 3800
Web Site: http://www.scotlandtranserv.co.uk
Emp.: 300
Highway Maintenance, Street Lighting & Other Transportation Infrastructure Support Services
N.A.I.C.S.: 488490

The Impact Partnership (Rochdale Borough) Limited (1)
Floor 11 Municipal Offices Smith Street, PO Box 516, Rochdale, OL16 9BS, Lancs, United Kingdom
Tel.: (44) 1706647474
Engineeering Services
N.A.I.C.S.: 541330

KIESEL BAUCHEMIE GMBH & CO. KG
Wolf Hirth-Strasse 2, D-73730, Esslingen, Germany
Tel.: (49) 711931340
Web Site: http://www.kiesel.com
Year Founded: 1959
Rev.: $46,532,563
Emp.: 125
Adhesive Mfr
N.A.I.C.S.: 325520
Matthias Hirsch *(Mng Dir)*

Subsidiaries:

Kiesel Benelux B. V. (1)
Anne Frankplein 12, 5122 CB, Rijen, Netherlands
Tel.: (31) 161244600
Web Site: http://www.kiesel.nl
Adhesive Mfr
N.A.I.C.S.: 325520

Kiesel Polska Sp.z.o.o. (1)
Ul Stysia 37 a, 53525, Wroclaw, Poland
Tel.: (48) 713366062
Web Site: http://www.kiesel.com.pl
Adhesive Mfr
N.A.I.C.S.: 325520

Kiesel Sarl (1)
200 rue de Pari, 67116, Reichstett, France
Tel.: (33) 389490694
Web Site: http://www.fr.kiesel.com
Adhesive Distr
N.A.I.C.S.: 424690

Kiesel s.r.o. (1)
Chodovska 3/228, 141 00, Prague, Czech Republic
Tel.: (420) 2720193413
Web Site: http://www.kiesel.cz
Adhesive Distr
N.A.I.C.S.: 424690

KIESS GMBH & CO. KG
Wiehagen 25, 45472, Mulheim an der Ruhr, Germany
Tel.: (49) 20849580
Web Site: http://www.kiess.de
Year Founded: 1974
Sales Range: $10-24.9 Million
Emp.: 27
Corrosion Protection Products Mfr
N.A.I.C.S.: 325510
Heike Kiess *(Gen Mgr)*

KIESWETTER MOTORS INC.
4202 King Street East, Kitchener, N2G 2P5, ON, Canada
Tel.: (519) 653-2540
Web Site: http://www.kieswettermazda.com
Year Founded: 1978
Sales Range: $10-24.9 Million
Emp.: 40
New & Used Car Dealers
N.A.I.C.S.: 441110
Robert Kieswetter *(Principal)*

KIFS FINANCIAL SERVICES LTD.
B-81 Pariseema Complex CG Road, Ellisbridge, Ahmedabad, 380 006, Gujarat, India
Tel.: (91) 7926400140
Web Site: https://www.kifsfinance.com
535566—(BOM)
Rev.: $4,465,325
Assets: $40,997,830
Liabilities: $35,555,547
Net Worth: $5,442,282
Earnings: $836,226
Emp.: 7
Fiscal Year-end: 03/31/22

Financial Support Services
N.A.I.C.S.: 523999
Rajesh P. Khandwala *(Chm & Mng Dir)*

KII CORPORATION
13th Floor ARK Hills Front Tower 2-23-1 Akasaka, Minato-ku, Tokyo, 107-0052, Japan
Tel.: (81) 3 4590 6470
Web Site: http://www.kii.com
Emp.: 100
Mobile Application Development Software
N.A.I.C.S.: 513210
Masanari Arai *(Co-Founder & CEO)*

Subsidiaries:

Kii Corporation - San Mateo (1)
1900 S Norfolk St Ste 350, San Mateo, CA 94403
Tel.: (650) 577-2340
Emp.: 30
Software Developer
N.A.I.C.S.: 513210
Waqas Makhdum *(VP-Mktg)*

KIJCHAROEN ENGINEERING ELECTRIC PUBLIC COMPANY LIMITED
61 61/5 Moo 8 Soi Wiroonrat Setthakit Rd, Thamai Kratumban, Samut Sakhon, 74110, Thailand
Tel.: (66) 28085000
Web Site: https://www.kjl.co.th
Year Founded: 1996
KJL—(THA)
Rev.: $31,606,778
Assets: $30,878,464
Liabilities: $12,876,773
Net Worth: $18,001,691
Earnings: $4,450,571
Emp.: 544
Fiscal Year-end: 12/31/23
Electrical Component Mfr
N.A.I.C.S.: 334419
Karoon Sujiwarodom *(Chm)*

KIJKSHOP BV
Elisabethhof 19, 2353EH, Leiderdorp, Netherlands
Tel.: (31) 850043383
Web Site: http://www.kijkshop.nl
Year Founded: 1973
Showroom Retailing
N.A.I.C.S.: 455219
Konrad Van Den Bosch *(CEO)*

KIKINDSKI MLIN A.D
vetozara Miletica 198, 23300, Kikinda, Serbia
Tel.: (381) 230422320
Web Site: http://www.kikindskimlin.rs
KIML—(BEL)
Sales Range: Less than $1 Million
Wheat & Flour Product Mfr
N.A.I.C.S.: 311211

KIKKOMAN CORPORATION
250 Noda, Noda, 278-8601, Chiba, Japan
Tel.: (81) 471235111   JP
Web Site: https://www.kikkoman.com
Year Founded: 1917
KIK—(DEU)
Rev.: $4,437,505,830
Assets: $4,060,980,450
Liabilities: $1,071,312,720
Net Worth: $2,989,667,730
Earnings: $313,565,610
Emp.: 7,775
Fiscal Year-end: 03/31/23
Soy Sauce, Teriyaki Barbecue Sauce & Seasoning Mixes Marketer, Distr & Mfr
N.A.I.C.S.: 311941
Yuzaburo Mogi *(Co-Chm)*

KIKKOMAN CORPORATION

Kikkoman Corporation—(Continued)

Subsidiaries:

Del Monte Asia Pte Ltd. (1)
600 NorthBridge Rd Unit No 16-01
Parkview Sq, Paragon, Singapore, 188778,
Singapore **(100%)**
Tel.: (65) 62351926
Sales Range: $25-49.9 Million
Emp.: 12
N.A.I.C.S.: 311421
Iwao Kawamura (Mng Dir)

Del Monte Foods (Xiamen) Co., Ltd (1)
No 151 Meihe Jiu Road, Light Foods Industrial Park Tong'an District, Xiamen, 361100, China
Tel.: (86) 592 739 5631
Web Site: https://www.kikkoman.com
Emp.: 53
Food Products Mfr
N.A.I.C.S.: 311999

Hokkaido Kikkoman Company (1)
1007-53 Izumisawa, Chitose, 2780037,
Hokkaido, Japan
Tel.: (81) 123 28 3888
Food Products Mfr
N.A.I.C.S.: 311999

International Operations Division (1)
2 1 1 Nishi Shinbashi, Minato Ku, Tokyo,
105 8428, Japan **(100%)**
Tel.: (81) 355215360
Web Site: http://www.kikkoman.co.jp
Sales Range: $200-249.9 Million
Emp.: 750
N.A.I.C.S.: 311421

JFC International (Canada) Inc. (1)
1025 Kamato Road, Mississauga, L4W
0C1, ON, Canada
Tel.: (905) 629-0993
Web Site: https://www.jfc.com
Sales Range: $25-49.9 Million
Emp.: 30
Whslr & Distr of Japanese Food Products
N.A.I.C.S.: 424490

JFC International (Europe) GmbH (1)
Theodorstrasse 293, 40472, Dusseldorf,
Germany **(100%)**
Tel.: (49) 211 537 4160
Web Site: https://www.jfc.eu
Sales Range: $25-49.9 Million
Emp.: 30
Soy Sauce & Oriental Food Products
N.A.I.C.S.: 311999
Kenichi Saito (Chm)

Subsidiary (Non-US):

JFC (UK) Limited (2)
Unit 17 7 Premier Park Road, London,
NW10 7NZ, United Kingdom **(100%)**
Tel.: (44) 208 963 7600
Web Site: http://www.jfc.eu
N.A.I.C.S.: 311421

JFC Austria GmbH (2)
Iz-No-Sud Strasse 16 Objekt 70, 2355, Wiener Neudorf, Austria
Tel.: (43) 22369088000
Web Site: https://www.jfc.eu
Sales Range: $25-49.9 Million
Emp.: 8
Soy Sauce & Oriental Food Products Whslr
N.A.I.C.S.: 424420

Subsidiary (Domestic):

JFC Deutschland GmbH (2)
Theodorstrasse 293, 40472, Dusseldorf,
Germany
Tel.: (49) 211 537 4160
Sales Range: $25-49.9 Million
Emp.: 5
Oriental Food Distr
N.A.I.C.S.: 424420

Subsidiary (Domestic):

JFC Restaurant GmbH (3)
Hansaallee 321 Gebaude 20, 40549, Dusseldorf, Germany
Tel.: (49) 211325054
Web Site: http://www.daitokai.de

Sales Range: $10-24.9 Million
Operator of Japanese Restaurants
N.A.I.C.S.: 722511

Subsidiary (Non-US):

JFC France S.A.R.L. (2)
Peripark Gennevilliers Batiment C 101 Avenue Louis Roche, 92230, Gennevilliers, France
Tel.: (33) 1 40 86 42 00
Sales Range: $25-49.9 Million
Emp.: 3
Soy Sauce & Oriental Food Whslr
N.A.I.C.S.: 424420
Nobuhiro Tanaka (Gen Mgr)

JFC International Inc. (1)
7101 E Slauson Ave, Los Angeles, CA
90040-3622
Tel.: (323) 721-6100
Web Site: http://www.jfc.com
Emp.: 100
Distr of Japanese Food Products
N.A.I.C.S.: 424490

Subsidiary (Non-US):

JFC Hong Kong Limited (2)
5th Floor Ever Gain Center, 43-57 Wang
Wo Tsai Street, Tsuen Wan, China (Hong
Kong) **(100%)**
Tel.: (852) 24286431
Sales Range: $25-49.9 Million
Emp.: 50
Food Products Distr
N.A.I.C.S.: 311421

JFC Japan Inc. (1)
Nihonbashi SOYIC bldg 3-11 Nihonbashi
Koamicho, Chuo-ku, Tokyo, 103-0016, Japan
Tel.: (81) 358470581
Web Site: http://www.jfcjapan.co.jp
Food Service
N.A.I.C.S.: 722310
Kenichi Saito (Chm & CEO)

JFC New Zealand Limited (1)
Unit 1/10 Cryers Road East Tamaki, Auckland, 2013, New Zealand
Tel.: (64) 9 969 2400
Sales Range: $50-74.9 Million
Emp.: 20
Food Product Whslr
N.A.I.C.S.: 424420

JFC Singapore Pte. Ltd (1)
52 Tanjong Penjuru CWT Hub 3 02-01,
Paragon, Singapore, 609034, Singapore
Tel.: (65) 6 567 8200
Web Site: https://www.jfc.com.sg
Soy Sauce & Oriental Food Products Whslr
N.A.I.C.S.: 424420

JFC de Mexico S.A. de C.V. (1)
Av Ano de Juarez No 160-B, Col Granjas
San Antonio Iztapalapa, 9070, Mexico, D F,
Mexico **(100%)**
Tel.: (52) 5556868893
Web Site: http://www.kikkoman.com
Sales Range: $25-49.9 Million
Emp.: 35
Soy Sauce & Oriental Food Products
N.A.I.C.S.: 311224

Japan Food (Hawaii), Inc. (1)
887 N Nimitz Hwy, Honolulu, HI 96817-4517
Tel.: (808) 537-9528
Web Site: http://www.jfc.com
Sales Range: $25-49.9 Million
Emp.: 25
Wholesale of Oriental Foods
N.A.I.C.S.: 424410
Toshiyaki Wada (Branch Mgr)

Japan Food Corp. (Australia) Pty. Ltd. (1)
Lane Cove Business park Building C1 16
Mars Road, PO Box 4044, Lane Cove,
2066, NSW, Australia **(100%)**
Tel.: (61) 294298000
Web Site: http://www.jfcaustralia.com.au
Sales Range: $25-49.9 Million
Emp.: 60
N.A.I.C.S.: 311421

KMS Service Inc. (1)
800 Airport Blvd Suite 568, Burlingame, CA
94010 **(100%)**

Tel.: (650) 581-4500
Sales Range: $25-49.9 Million
Emp.: 20
Software Development & Selling Hardware
N.A.I.C.S.: 541512
Nao Haro (Pres)

Kikkoman (S) Pte. Ltd. (1)
7 Senoko Crescent, Singapore, 758263,
Singapore **(100%)**
Tel.: (65) 6 758 8822
Web Site: http://www.kikkoman.sg
Sales Range: $25-49.9 Million
Emp.: 60
Soy Sauce Mfr
N.A.I.C.S.: 311421

Subsidiary (Domestic):

Kikkoman Singapore R&D Laboratory Pte. Ltd. (2)
11 Biopolis Way 05-01 Helios, 3 Science
Drive 3, Singapore, 138667, Singapore
Tel.: (65) 67746061
Web Site: http://www.kikkoman.com
Laboratory Research & Development Services
N.A.I.C.S.: 541715

Kikkoman Australia Pty. Limited (1)
Level 6 132 Arthur St, 132 Arthur St, Sydney, 2060, NSW, Australia **(100%)**
Tel.: (61) 299232533
Web Site: http://www.kikkoman.com.au
Sales Range: $25-49.9 Million
Emp.: 9
Soy Sauce Marinade Mfr
N.A.I.C.S.: 311421
Shunichi Yoshioka (Mng Dir)

Kikkoman Business Service Company (1)
2-1-1 Nishishimbashi Kowanishishimbashi
Bldg, Minato-Ku, Tokyo, 105-0003, Japan
Tel.: (81) 355215116
Web Site: http://www.kikkoman.com
Food & Beverage Distr
N.A.I.C.S.: 424420

Kikkoman Food Products Co. - Takasago Plant (1)
1-1-1 Niihama Arai-cho, Takasago, 676-8510, Hyogo, Japan
Tel.: (81) 79 442 2131
Food Products Mfr
N.A.I.C.S.: 311999

Plant (Domestic):

Kikkoman Food Products Co. - Noda Plant (2)
110 Noda, Noda, 278-0037, Chiba, Japan
Tel.: (81) 4 7123 5134
Food Products Mfr
N.A.I.C.S.: 311999

Kikkoman Foods Europe B.V. (1)
De Vosholen 100, 9611 TG, Sappemeer,
Netherlands **(100%)**
Tel.: (31) 598399898
Web Site: http://www.kikkoman.com
Sales Range: $25-49.9 Million
Emp.: 50
N.A.I.C.S.: 311421
M. Kasuga (Mng Dir)

Subsidiary (Domestic):

Kikkoman Europe R&D Laboratory B.V. (2)
Bilpartner Center Nieuwe Kanaal 7G, 6709
PA, Wageningen, Netherlands
Tel.: (31) 317 420370
Food Products Research & Development
Services
N.A.I.C.S.: 541720

Kikkoman Foods, Inc. (1)
N1365 Six Corners Rd, Walworth, WI
53184
Tel.: (262) 275-6181
Web Site: https://www.kikkoman.com
Sales Range: $50-74.9 Million
Emp.: 150
Soy Sauce, Teriyaki Barbecue Sauce, Steak
Sauce, Seasoning Mixes
N.A.I.C.S.: 311941

Plant (Domestic):

Kikkoman Foods, Inc. - California Plant (2)

INTERNATIONAL PUBLIC

1000 Glenn Dr, Folsom, CA 95630
Tel.: (916) 355-8078
Web Site: https://www.kikkoman.com
Soy Sauce Mfr
N.A.I.C.S.: 311941

Kikkoman International Inc. (1)
50 California St Ste 3600, San Francisco,
CA 94111
Tel.: (415) 956-7750
Web Site: http://www.kikkomanusa.com
Sales Range: $25-49.9 Million
Emp.: 45
Mfr of Soy, Steak, Sweet & Sour, Stir Fry &
Teriyaki Sauces & Seasoning Mixes
N.A.I.C.S.: 424490
Yoko Komori (Acct Mgr)

Kikkoman L.O. Consultoria. Marketing e Promocoes Ltda. (1)
Al Joaquim Eugenio de Lima 680-Cj 54,
Jardim Paulista, Sao Paulo, 01403-000,
Brazil
Tel.: (55) 11 3284 1301
Web Site: http://www.kikkoman.com
Emp.: 6
Marketing Research Service
N.A.I.C.S.: 541910
Lee Naylor (Office Mgr)

Kikkoman Marketing & Planning, Inc. (1)
675 Tollgate Rd Ste G, Elgin, IL
60123-9352 **(100%)**
Tel.: (847) 622-9540
N.A.I.C.S.: 311421

Kikkoman Marketing Center Company Ltd. (1)
7th Fl Iimori Bldg 2 6 11 Nihonbashi Hama
Cho, Chuo Ku, Tokyo, 103 0007,
Japan **(100%)**
Tel.: (81) 356515551
N.A.I.C.S.: 311421

Kikkoman Restaurant, Inc. (1)
4 13 Koami Cho Nihonbashi, Chuo Ku, Tokyo, 103 0016, Japan **(100%)**
Tel.: (81) 336391887
Sales Range: $25-49.9 Million
Emp.: 2
N.A.I.C.S.: 311421

Kikkoman Sales USA, Inc (1)
50 California St Ste 3600, San Francisco,
CA 94111
Tel.: (415) 956-7750
Web Site: http://www.kikkomanusa.com
Emp.: 77
Food Products Mfr & Distr
N.A.I.C.S.: 311999

Kikkoman Soyfoods Co., Ltd. (1)
2-1-1 Irifune, Chuo-ku, Tokyo, 104-8553,
Japan
Tel.: (81) 3 3206 0778
Web Site: http://www.kikkoman-sf.jp
Emp.: 330
Soy Sauce Mfr
N.A.I.C.S.: 311941
Kasenayama Toshihiko (Pres & CEO)

Kikkoman Trading Asia Pte. Ltd. (1)
600 North Bridge Road 16-01 Parkview
Square, Paragon, Singapore, 188778,
Singapore **(100%)**
Tel.: (65) 6 235 6022
Web Site: http://www.kikkoman.co.jp
Sales Range: $50-74.9 Million
Emp.: 6
Holding Company; Foodstuffs Wholesale
Trade Agencies
N.A.I.C.S.: 551112
Polin Tan (Sr Mgr)

Subsidiary (Domestic):

Kikkoman Trading (S) Pte. Ltd. (2)
290 Orchard Rd, 17 08 Paragon, Singapore, 238859, Singapore **(100%)**
Tel.: (65) 62356022
Web Site: http://www.kikkoman.co.jp
Emp.: 5
Foodstuffs Wholesale Trade Agency
N.A.I.C.S.: 425120
Taku Otsuka (Gen Mgr)

Kikkoman Trading Europe GmbH (1)
Theodorstrasse 180, PO Box 330233,
40472, Dusseldorf, Germany

AND PRIVATE COMPANIES

Tel.: (49) 211 537 5940
Web Site: http://www.kikkoman.de
Sales Range: $25-49.9 Million
Emp.: 15
Soy Sauce Mfr & Distr
N.A.I.C.S.: 445110

Manns Wine Co., Ltd. (1)
2-1-1 Nishi-Shimbashi, Minato-ku, Tokyo,
105-0003, Japan **(100%)**
Tel.: (81) 33 507 7432
Web Site: http://www.manns.co.jp
Sales Range: $25-49.9 Million
Emp.: 100
N.A.I.C.S.: 311421
Nagao Komei *(Dir-Production)*

Manns Wine Pub Co., Ltd. (1)
2 1 1 Nishi Shinbashi, Minato-ku, Tokyo,
105 8428, Japan **(100%)**
Tel.: (81) 355215131
Web Site: http: www.kikkoman.co.jp
Wine Merchant
N.A.I.C.S.: 424820

Nippon Del Monte Corporation (1)
2-1-1 Nishi-Shimbashi, Minato-ku, Tokyo,
105-0003, Japan **(100%)**
Tel.: (81) 35 510 3500
Web Site: https://www.delmonte.co.jp
Sales Range: $25-49.9 Million
Emp.: 81
N.A.I.C.S.: 311421
Yoshihisa Kitakura *(Pres)*

Pacific Trading Co., Ltd. (1)
3 Shibaura Maekawa Bldg 16 20 Shibaura
3 Chome, Minato-ku, Tokyo, 108 0023,
Japan **(100%)**
Tel.: (81) 354429251
Web Site: http://www.ptc.co.jp
Sales Range: $10-24.9 Million
Emp.: 50
N.A.I.C.S.: 311421

President Kikkoman, Inc. (1)
No 7 Daying Daying Village, Hsin Shih
Hsiang, T'ainan, 74443, Taiwan **(100%)**
Tel.: (886) 65997995
Sales Range: $25-49.9 Million
Emp.: 100
Mfr & Distribution of Soy Sauce, Teriyaki
Barbecue Sauce, Steak Sauce, Seasoning
Mixes
N.A.I.C.S.: 311941

Seishin Corporation (1)
1-4-1 Kakigara-cho Nihonbashi, Chuo-ku,
Tokyo, 103-0014, Japan
Tel.: (81) 336692876
N.A.I.C.S.: 311421

**Siam Del Monte Company
Limited** (1)
142 Two Pacific Place 18 Floor 1805
Sukhumvit Rd, Klongtoey, Bangkok, 10400,
Thailand
Tel.: (66) 2 401 3015
Food Products Mfr
N.A.I.C.S.: 311999

Sobu Butsuryu Co., Ltd. (1)
236 Noda, Noda, 278-0037, Chiba, Japan
Tel.: (81) 471255151
General Freight Trucking Services
N.A.I.C.S.: 484110

Sobu Service Center Inc. (1)
61 Nakane, Noda, 278-0031, Chiba, Japan
Tel.: (81) 471230505
Convenience Foods Mfr
N.A.I.C.S.: 311999

KIKUCHI SEISAKUSHO CO., LTD.
2161-21 Miyama-cho Hachioji, Tokyo,
192-0152, Japan
Tel.: (81) 426516093
Web Site:
 https://www.kikuchiseisakusho.co.jp
3444—(TKS)
Rev.: $34,431,490
Assets: $58,293,590
Liabilities: $29,295,520
Net Worth: $28,998,070
Earnings: ($5,406,980)
Emp.: 343
Fiscal Year-end: 04/30/24

Metal & Plastic Products Mfr
N.A.I.C.S.: 332999
Isao Kikuchi *(Pres & CEO)*

Subsidiaries:

**KIKUCHI (HONG KONG) LIMITED -
China Factory** (1)
Yu Liang Wei Area, Qingxi Town, Dong-
guan, Guangdong, China
Tel.: (86) 76987338962
Web Site:
 http://www.kikuchiseisakusho.co.jp
Metal Stamping Product Mfr
N.A.I.C.S.: 332119

Kikuchi (Hong Kong) Limited (1)
Unit B 19th Floor Prosperous Commercial
Building, 54 Jarding's Bazaar, Causeway
Bay, China (Hong Kong)
Tel.: (852) 2653 1412
Metal Stamping Product Mfr
N.A.I.C.S.: 332119

KIKUKAWA ENTERPRISE INC.
3477-36 Asama-cho, Ise, 516-0021,
Mie, Japan
Tel.: (81) 596212110
Web Site: https://www.kikukawa.co.jp
Year Founded: 1897
6346—(TKS)
Sales Range: $25-49.9 Million
Emp.: 230
Sawmill & Woodworking Machinery
Mfr
N.A.I.C.S.: 333243
Kazuhiro Kobayashi *(Mgr)*

Subsidiaries:

**Kunshan New Kikukawa Equipment
Co., Ltd.** (1)
No 27 Bai Lu North Rd, Kunshan, Jiangsu,
China
Tel.: (86) 51257738785
Industrial Machinery Distr
N.A.I.C.S.: 423690

KIKUSUI CHEMICAL INDUS-
TRIES CO., LTD.
AMMNAT Building 15F 1-3-3 Sakae,
Naka-ku, Nagoya, 460-0008, Aichi,
Japan
Tel.: (81) 523002222
Web Site: https://www.kikusui-
 chem.co.jp
7953—(NGO)
Rev.: $147,948,422
Assets: $119,398,711
Liabilities: $55,216,370
Net Worth: $64,182,341
Earnings: $2,484,307
Emp.: 420
Fiscal Year-end: 03/31/24
Coatings & Adhesives Mfr
N.A.I.C.S.: 325510
Hitoshi Yamaguchi *(Pres)*

KIKUSUI HOLDINGS CORPO-
RATION
Southwood 4F 6-1 Chigasakichuo,
Tsuzuki-ku, Yokohama, 224-0032,
Kanagawa, Japan
Tel.: (81) 454826353
Web Site: http://www.kikusui.co.jp
Year Founded: 1951
6912—(TKS)
Rev.: $82,545,680
Assets: $106,473,880
Liabilities: $18,660,030
Net Worth: $87,813,850
Earnings: $8,593,000
Emp.: 190
Fiscal Year-end: 03/31/24
Electrical Equipment & Component
Mfr
N.A.I.C.S.: 335999
K. Kobayashi *(Pres & CEO)*

Subsidiaries:

KIKUSUI AMERICA, INC. (1)
3625 Del Amo Blvd Ste 160, Torrance, CA
90503
Tel.: (310) 214-0000
Electronic Product Distr
N.A.I.C.S.: 423690

KILAND LTD.
Unit 3B Level 3 60 Hindmarsh
Square, Adelaide, 5000, SA, Australia
Tel.: (61) 882272482
Web Site: http://www.kipt.com.au
KIL—(ASX)
Rev.: $1,235,864
Assets: $96,541,472
Liabilities: $3,038,710
Net Worth: $93,502,763
Earnings: ($2,456,405)
Emp.: 4
Fiscal Year-end: 06/30/22
Investment Services for Agricultural
Industry
N.A.I.C.S.: 523999
John Sergeant *(Mng Dir)*

Subsidiaries:

**RuralAus Plantation Management Pty
Ltd** (1)
44 Brisbane St, Perth, 6000, Western Aus-
tralia, Australia
Tel.: (61) 861036900
Plantation Management Services
N.A.I.C.S.: 561730

KILBURN CHEMICALS LTD.
Shantiniketan 16th Floor 8 Camac
Street, Kolkata, 700 017, India
Tel.: (91) 332 282 8501
Web Site:
 http://www.kilburnchemicals.com
Rev.: $171,377
Assets: $38,557,980
Liabilities: $33,657,299
Net Worth: $4,900,681
Earnings: ($7,212,360)
Emp.: 148
Fiscal Year-end: 03/31/19
Chemical Products Mfr
N.A.I.C.S.: 325998
S. K. Jalan *(Mng Dir)*

KILBURN ENGINEERING LTD.
Plot No 6 MIDC - Saravali Kalyan
Bhiwandi Road Taluka, Bhiwandi,
Thane, 421 311, Maharashtra, India
Tel.: (91) 2522283000
Web Site:
 https://www.kilburnengg.com
522101—(BOM)
Rev.: $13,363,896
Assets: $27,472,850
Liabilities: $20,958,933
Net Worth: $6,513,917
Earnings: ($12,516,995)
Emp.: 258
Fiscal Year-end: 03/31/21
Industrial Machinery Equipment Mfr
N.A.I.C.S.: 423830
Arvind Kumar Bajoria *(Compliance
Officer & Sec)*

KILBURN OFFICE AUTOMA-
TION LTD.
Shantiniketan 15th & 16th Floor, 8
Camac Street, Kolkata, 700 017, In-
dia
Tel.: (91) 33 22828501
Web Site: http://www.kilburn.in
Rev.: $578,929
Assets: $1,062,269
Liabilities: $1,360,463
Net Worth: ($298,194)
Earnings: ($49,435)
Emp.: 3
Fiscal Year-end: 03/31/18
Electronic Components Mfr

N.A.I.C.S.: 334419
D. K. Ghosh *(Sec)*

KILCOY PASTORAL COMPANY
LTD.
4830 D'Aguilar Highway, Kilcoy,
4515, QLD, Australia
Tel.: (61) 754971277
Web Site: http://www.kpc.com.au
Meat Product Distr
N.A.I.C.S.: 424470
Dean Goode *(CEO)*

KILER HOLDING A.S.
Emniyet Evleri District Eski Buyuk-
dere Street No 1, Esenyurt, 34415,
Istanbul, Turkiye
Tel.: (90) 2124567000 TR
Web Site:
 http://www.kilerholding.com.tr
Year Founded: 1983
Sales Range: $650-699.9 Million
Emp.: 10,000
Holding Company
N.A.I.C.S.: 551112
Nahit Kiler *(Chm)*

Subsidiaries:

Biskon Yapi A.S. (1)
Zafer District Tonguçbaba Street No 96, Ha-
ramidere, 34513, Esenyurt, Turkiye
Tel.: (90) 212 456 15 00
Web Site: http://www.biskon.com
Large Commercial & Residential Building
Construction & Management Services
N.A.I.C.S.: 236220
Eyyup Demirhan *(Gen Mgr)*

Kiler GYO A.S. (1)
Eski Buyukdere Cad Emniyet Evleri Mah No
1/1 Kat 7, Kagithane, 34415, Istanbul, Tur-
kiye
Tel.: (90) 2124567000
Web Site: https://www.kilergyo.com
Real Estate Construction Services
N.A.I.C.S.: 236115
Gokhan Yildiz *(Gen Mgr)*

**Kiler Gayrimenkul Yatirim Ortakligi
A.S.** (1)
Eski Buyukdere Cad Emniyet Evleri Mah No
1/1 Floor 7, Kagithane, 34415, Istanbul,
Turkiye **(65.16%)**
Tel.: (90) 2124567000
Web Site: https://www.kilergyo.com
Real Estate Investment Services
N.A.I.C.S.: 523999
Tarik Gurdil *(Gen Mgr)*

Turex A.S. (1)
Fatih Mah Adile Nasit Bulvan 139 Sk No 4,
34517, Esenyurt, Turkiye
Tel.: (90) 212 699 20 55
Web Site: http://www.turexturizm.com.tr
Motor Vehicle Transportation Services
N.A.I.C.S.: 485113
Celal Kalkan *(Gen Mgr)*

KILIA FLEISCHEREI-UND-
SPEZIAL-MASCHINEN-FABRIK
GMBH
Christianstrasse 160 164, 24536,
Neumunster, Germany
Tel.: (49) 4321309200
Web Site: http://www.kilia.com
Year Founded: 1932
Rev.: $12,279,704
Emp.: 61
Food Processing Machinery Mfr
N.A.I.C.S.: 333241
Frank Bottcher *(Co-Mng Partner)*

KILIC DENIZ URUNLERI URE-
TIMI IHRACAT ITHALAT VE
TIC. A.S.
Kemikler Koyu Mavkii Milas Bodrum
Karayolu 18 km, Milas, Mugla, 48200,
Turkiye
Tel.: (90) 252 559 0283
Web Site: http://www.kilicdeniz.com.tr
Sales Range: $650-699.9 Million

KILIC DENIZ URUNLERI URETIMI IHRACAT ITHALAT VE TIC. A.S.

Kilic Deniz Urunleri Uretimi Ihracat Ithalat ve Tic. A.S.—(Continued)

Emp.: 2,000
Water Processing Systems Mfr
N.A.I.C.S.: 221310
Orhan Kilic (Chm)

KILITCH DRUGS (INDIA) LTD.
37 Ujagar Industrial Estate Waman Tukaram Patil Marg Deonar, Mumbai, 400 088, India
Tel.: (91) 2261214100   In
Web Site: https://www.kilitch.com
KILITCH—(NSE)
Rev.: $9,717,490
Assets: $27,733,456
Liabilities: $10,059,613
Net Worth: $17,673,843
Earnings: $514,141
Emp.: 123
Fiscal Year-end: 03/31/21
Pharmaceuticals Product Mfr
N.A.I.C.S.: 325412
Mukund P. Mehta (Mng Dir)

Subsidiaries:

EyeKare Kilitch Ltd.   (1)
902-B Godrej Coliseum Behind Everard Nagar Off Eastern, Express Highway Nr Priyadarshani Circle Sion E, Mumbai, 400 022, India
Tel.: (91) 2261372222
Web Site: http://www.eyekarekilitch.com
Sales Range: $25-49.9 Million
Emp.: 50
Ophthalmic Goods Mfr
N.A.I.C.S.: 339115
Paresh P. Mehta (Mng Dir)

KILLAM APARTMENT REAL ESTATE INVESTMENT TRUST
3700 Kempt Road Suite 100, Halifax, B3K 4X8, NS, Canada
Tel.: (902) 453-9000
Web Site: https://killamreit.com
KMP—(TSX)
Rev.: $184,996,005
Assets: $2,586,587,724
Liabilities: $1,360,392,401
Net Worth: $1,226,195,323
Earnings: $216,964,671
Emp.: 600
Fiscal Year-end: 12/31/19
Real Estate Services
N.A.I.C.S.: 531390
Philip D. Fraser (Pres & CEO)

KILLI RESOURCES LIMITED
Level 5 191 St Georges Terrace, Perth, 6000, WA, Australia
Tel.: (61) 893242099   AU
Web Site: https://www.killi.com.au
Year Founded: 2021
KLI—(ASX)
Rev.: $227,766
Assets: $2,267,418
Liabilities: $95,586
Net Worth: $2,171,832
Earnings: ($2,658,183)
Fiscal Year-end: 06/30/23
Exploration & Mining Services
N.A.I.C.S.: 213115

KILMER CAPITAL PARTNERS
Scotia Plaza Suite 2700 40 King Street West, PO Box 127, Toronto, M5H 3Y2, ON, Canada
Tel.: (416) 635-6100
Web Site:
http://www.kilmergroup.com
Sales Range: $25-49.9 Million
Emp.: 50
Privater Equity Firm
N.A.I.C.S.: 523999
Eric Gottesman (VP)

KILPEST INDIA LIMITED
7-C Industrial Area Govindpura, Bhopal, 462 023, India
Tel.: (91) 7552586536
Web Site: https://www.kilpest.com
Year Founded: 1972
532067—(BOM)
Rev.: $31,344,968
Assets: $26,416,012
Liabilities: $6,176,490
Net Worth: $20,239,522
Earnings: $15,543,125
Emp.: 47
Fiscal Year-end: 03/31/21
Agrochemical Product Mfr
N.A.I.C.S.: 325320
R. K. Dubey (Chm & Mng Dir)

Subsidiaries:

3B BlackBio Biotech India Limited   (1)
7-C Industrial Area, Govindpura, Bhopal, 462023, M P, India
Tel.: (91) 7554076518
Web Site: https://www.3bblackbio.com
Molecular Diagnostic Kit Mfr
N.A.I.C.S.: 325413

KIM HENG LIMITED
No 48 Penjuru Road, Singapore, 609152, Singapore
Tel.: (65) 67779990
Web Site:
https://www.kimheng.com.sg
5G2—(CAT)
Rev.: $59,163,394
Assets: $113,719,896
Liabilities: $66,626,158
Net Worth: $47,093,738
Earnings: $6,409,040
Emp.: 618
Fiscal Year-end: 12/31/22
Offshore Rig Services & Supply Chain Management; Vessel Sales & Refurbishing Services
N.A.I.C.S.: 213112
Thomas Keng Siong Tan (Chm & CEO)

Subsidiaries:

Bridgewater Offshore Pte. Ltd.   (1)
No 48 Penjuru Road, Singapore, 609152, Singapore   (51%)
Tel.: (65) 67779990
Oil & Gas Exploration Services
N.A.I.C.S.: 213112

Zale Offshore Response Pte. Ltd.   (1)
Penjuru Yard - 48 Penjuru Road, Singapore, 609152, Singapore
Tel.: (65) 67779990
Web Site: https://www.zaleoffshore.com.sg
Vessel & Cargo Salvaging Services
N.A.I.C.S.: 541330

KIM HIN INDUSTRY BERHAD
4 1/2 Mile Kung Phin Road Off Penrissen Road, 93250, Kuching, Sarawak, Malaysia
Tel.: (60) 82451567
Web Site: https://www.kimhin.com.my
Year Founded: 1973
KIMHIN—(KLS)
Rev.: $67,505,878
Assets: $94,713,758
Liabilities: $27,779,278
Net Worth: $66,934,480
Earnings: ($8,734,654)
Fiscal Year-end: 12/31/23
Ceramic Tile Producer & Distr
N.A.I.C.S.: 327120

Subsidiaries:

Ceramica Indah Sdn. Bhd.   (1)
4 1/2 Mile Kung Phin Road, PO Box 1842, off Penrissen Rd, 93736, Kuching, Sarawak, Malaysia
Tel.: (60) 82451567
Web Site: http://www.kimhin.com.my

Emp.: 100
Ceramic Products Mfr
N.A.I.C.S.: 327120
James Chua (Mgr-Mktg)

Kim Hin Ceramic (Seremban) Sdn. Bhd.   (1)
Lot No 10807 Lot 334 Tuanku Jaafar Industrial Estate, PO Box 171, 70720, Seremban, Negeri Sembilan, Malaysia
Tel.: (60) 66774609
Web Site: http://www.kimhin.com.my
Sales Range: $50-74.9 Million
Emp.: 120
Ceramic Products Mfr
N.A.I.C.S.: 327120
Ahmad Bakhtiar Abu Bakar (Mgr-Fin & Admin)

Kim Hin Ceramics (Shanghai) Co., Ltd.   (1)
No 655 Xianju Road, Zhujing Industrial Development Area Jin Shan District, Shanghai, 201500, China   (79.5%)
Tel.: (86) 215 731 4476
Web Site: https://www.sh-kimhin.com
Sales Range: $125-149.9 Million
Emp.: 350
Ceramic Products Mfr
N.A.I.C.S.: 327120

Kim Hin Properties Sdn. Bhd.   (1)
4 1/2 Mile Kung Phin Road Off Penrissen Road, 93250, Kuching, Sarawak, Malaysia
Tel.: (60) 19 8862328
Property Management Services
N.A.I.C.S.: 531311

Kimgres Australia Pty Ltd.   (1)
26-28 Agosta Drive, Laverton, 3026, VIC, Australia
Tel.: (61) 39 369 0511
Web Site: https://www.kimhin.com.my
Ceramic Product Distr
N.A.I.C.S.: 423320

Kimgres Marketing Sdn. Bhd.   (1)
Lot 5 Jalan Kilang 7 Jalan 217, 46050, Petaling Jaya, Selangor, Malaysia
Tel.: (60) 37 783 9811
Web Site: https://www.kimgres.com
Sales Range: $25-49.9 Million
Emp.: 66
Wall & Floor Tiles Distr
N.A.I.C.S.: 444180

KIM HIN JOO (MALAYSIA) BERHAD
Lot 5205C Jalan Perindustrian Balakong Jaya 1/3 Kawasan Perindustrian, Balakong Jaya, 43300, Seri Kembangan, Selangor, Malaysia
Tel.: (60) 389406638   MY
Web Site: https://www.khj-my.com
Year Founded: 1978
KHJB—(KLS)
Rev.: $22,145,072
Assets: $25,324,978
Liabilities: $8,533,609
Net Worth: $16,791,369
Earnings: $1,023,809
Emp.: 255
Fiscal Year-end: 12/31/22
Baby Product Distr
N.A.I.C.S.: 424350
Ai Ning Tan (Co-Sec)

KIM KANG AQUACULTURE SDN BHD
Lot 1646-1647 Jalan Pt Mohammed Kg Bindu, 83010, Batu Pahat, Johor, Malaysia
Tel.: (60) 7415 2007
Web Site:
http://www.kimkang.com.my
Year Founded: 2002
Sales Range: $25-49.9 Million
Emp.: 40
Aquarium Supplies Retailer
N.A.I.C.S.: 712130
Siak Ngan Goh (Founder)

KIM LOONG RESOURCES BERHAD
Unit No 203 2nd Floor Block C Damansara Intan No 1 Jalan SS 20/27, 47400, Petaling Jaya, Selangor Darul Ehsan, Malaysia
Tel.: (60) 371182688
Web Site:
https://www.kimloong.com.my
Year Founded: 1972
KMLOONG—(KLS)
Rev.: $403,882,119
Assets: $267,430,404
Liabilities: $65,589,136
Net Worth: $201,841,268
Earnings: $42,261,246
Emp.: 1,331
Fiscal Year-end: 01/31/23
Palm Oil & Cocoa Cultivation Services
N.A.I.C.S.: 115112
Fook Sin Chong (Co-Sec)

KIM TECK CHEONG CONSOLIDATED BERHAD
Lot 73 Jalan Kilang SEDCO Light Industrial EstateMile 5 5, Jalan Tuaran, 88450, Kota Kinabalu, Sabah, Malaysia
Tel.: (60) 138110111   MY
Web Site:
https://www.kimteckcheong.com
Year Founded: 1938
KTC—(KLS)
Rev.: $154,368,151
Assets: $73,532,406
Liabilities: $33,578,914
Net Worth: $39,953,492
Earnings: $5,313,432
Emp.: 699
Fiscal Year-end: 06/30/23
Consumer Package Goods Distr
N.A.I.C.S.: 425120
Koh Sing Lau (Mng Dir)

Subsidiaries:

Gardenia Bakeries (East Malaysia) Sdn. Bhd.   (1)
Lot 3 Jalan Pelabur 23/1, 40300, Shah Alam, Selangor, Malaysia
Tel.: (60) 355423228
Web Site: https://www.gardenia.com.my
Bakery Product Mfr & Whslr
N.A.I.C.S.: 311812

KIM VI INOX IMPORT EXPORT PRODUCTION JOINT STOCK COMPANY
117 Vo Van Bich Hamlet 11 Tan Thanh Dong commune, Cu Chi District, Ho Chi Minh City, Vietnam
Tel.: (84) 837979009
Web Site:
https://www.kimvico.com.vn
KVC—(HNX)
Rev.: $8,571,413
Assets: $23,144,553
Liabilities: $4,044,192
Net Worth: $19,100,361
Earnings: ($575,193)
Emp.: 14
Fiscal Year-end: 12/31/23
Metal Production, Import & Export
N.A.I.C.S.: 332999
Hung Do (Chm)

KIMBERLEY DIAMONDS LTD.
Level 39 Australia Square Tower 264-278 George Street, Sydney, 2000, NSW, Australia
Tel.: (61) 2 8243 7500   AU
Web Site: http://www.kdl.com.au
Year Founded: 2011
Sales Range: Less than $1 Million
Emp.: 138
Gold Mining Services
N.A.I.C.S.: 212220
Laila Green (CFO & Sec)

AND PRIVATE COMPANIES

KIMBERLEY FINE DIAMONDS
93 Konkerberry Drive, PO Box 20, Kununurra, 6743, WA, Australia
Tel.: (61) 891691133
Web Site:
http://www.kimberleydiamonds.com
Year Founded: 1991
Diamond Jewelry Designer & Retailer
N.A.I.C.S.: 458310
Frauke Bolten-Boshammer *(Founder & CEO)*

KIMCO STEEL SALES LIMITED
1325 John Counter Blvd, Kingston, K7L 4W1, ON, Canada
Tel.: (613) 544-1822
Web Site: http://www.kimcosteel.com
Year Founded: 1972
Rev.: $22,084,017
Emp.: 100
New Steel, Scrap & Waste Materials Whslr
N.A.I.C.S.: 423930
John Meaney *(Mgr-Industrial Scrap)*

KIMDEC CORPORATION SDN. BHD.
No 43 Jalan Industri 1/1 Taman Perindustrian Temerloh, 28400, Mentekab, Pahang, Malaysia
Tel.: (60) 92771888   MY
Sales Range: Less than $1 Million
Property Development Services
N.A.I.C.S.: 531390

KIMIA BIOSCIENCES PVT LTD.
380 & 974 Aggarwal Millennium Tower II, Netaji Subhash Place Pitampura, New Delhi, 110 034, India
Tel.: (91) 11 4706 3600
Web Site:
http://www.kimiabiosciences.com
Pharmaceutical Drug Mfr
N.A.I.C.S.: 325412
Sameer Goel *(Mng Dir)*

Subsidiaries:

Laurel Organics Ltd.   (1)
Village Bhondsi Tehsil Sohna, Gurgaon, 122102, Haryana, India
Tel.: (91) 124 2267351
Web Site: http://www.laurel.co.in
Sales Range: $1-9.9 Million
Pharmaceuticals Product Mfr
N.A.I.C.S.: 325412
Sanjay Gupta *(CFO)*

KIMLUN CORPORATION BERHAD
Suite 19 06 Level 19 Johor Bahru City Square 106-108, Jalan Wong Ah Fook, 80000, Johor Bahru, Johor, Malaysia
Tel.: (60) 72228080
Web Site: https://www.kimlun.com
KIMLUN—(KLS)
Rev.: $160,028,303
Assets: $275,295,108
Liabilities: $121,794,594
Net Worth: $153,500,514
Earnings: ($1,543,121)
Fiscal Year-end: 12/31/22
Construction & Engineering Services
N.A.I.C.S.: 236220
Yon Tin Pang *(Chm)*

Subsidiaries:

SPC Industries Sdn. Bhd.   (1)
21M/S Jalan Pontian, Ulu Choh, 81150, Johor, Malaysia
Tel.: (60) 76996208
Web Site: https://www.spcind.com
Precast Concrete Mfr
N.A.I.C.S.: 327390
Erica Pek *(Sr Mgr-Sls)*

KIMLY LIMITED
17 Woodlands Link, Singapore, 738725, Singapore
Tel.: (65) 62891605   SG
Web Site: https://www.kimlygroup.sg
Year Founded: 1990
1D0—(CAT)
Rev.: $232,569,100
Assets: $247,373,101
Liabilities: $112,078,548
Net Worth: $135,294,554
Earnings: $29,102,631
Emp.: 2,252
Fiscal Year-end: 09/30/23
Coffeeshop Operator
N.A.I.C.S.: 722515
Hee Liat Lim *(Chm)*

Subsidiaries:

Foodclique (Capeview) Pte. Ltd.   (1)
Blk 308 Anchorvale Rd 01-07, Singapore, 540308, Singapore
Tel.: (65) 63847855
Coffeeshop Operator
N.A.I.C.S.: 722515

Kimly Seafood Pte. Ltd.   (1)
514A Bishan Street 13 01-480, Singapore, 571514, Singapore
Tel.: (65) 62551130
Food Products Distr
N.A.I.C.S.: 424420

Subsidiary (Domestic):

Kimly Seafood West Pte. Ltd.   (2)
Blk 221 Boon Lay Place 01-100, Singapore, 640221, Singapore
Tel.: (65) 62659515
Food Products Distr
N.A.I.C.S.: 424420

PP146 Food House Pte. Ltd.   (1)
Blk 146 Potong Pasir Avenue 1, Singapore, 350146, Singapore
Tel.: (65) 62813938
Coffeeshop Operator
N.A.I.C.S.: 722515

Sengkang 266 Food House Pte. Ltd.   (1)
Blk 266 Compassvale Bow 01-01 Multi Storey Car Park, Singapore, 540266, Singapore
Tel.: (65) 68759718
Coffeeshop Operator
N.A.I.C.S.: 722515

KIMOCE
Parc des Collines 26 rue Victor Schoelcher, BP 2487, 68057, Mulhouse, Cedex, France
Tel.: (33) 389438800
Web Site: http://www.kimoce.com
Year Founded: 1991
Sales Range: $1-9.9 Million
Emp.: 38
Software Development Services
N.A.I.C.S.: 541511
Patrick Hett *(Founder)*

KIMOTO CO., LTD.
450 Kyoganoshinden, Kitaseicho, Inabe, 511-0411, Mie, Japan
Tel.: (81) 5031549000
Web Site: https://www.kimoto.co.jp
Year Founded: 1961
7908—(TKS)
Rev.: $65,505,100
Assets: $149,379,390
Liabilities: $29,368,230
Net Worth: $120,011,160
Earnings: $2,214,350
Emp.: 460
Fiscal Year-end: 03/31/24
Industrial Material Mfr & Whslr
N.A.I.C.S.: 326113
Kazunobu Kimoto *(Chm & Pres)*

Subsidiaries:

Kimoto Co., Ltd. - Ibaraki Plant   (1)
13 Kitatone, Koga, 306-0213, Ibaraki, Japan
Tel.: (81) 5031549000
Emp.: 100
Electronic Display Mfr
N.A.I.C.S.: 339950

Kimoto Co., Ltd. - Mie Plant   (1)
73-5 Kyogano Shinden Hokusei-cho, Inabe, 511-0411, Mie, Japan
Tel.: (81) 5031549000
Emp.: 177
Electronic Display Mfr
N.A.I.C.S.: 339950

Kimoto Innovative Technologies (SHANGHAI) Co., Ltd.   (1)
20F-E Shanghai Shi Ye Building No 18 CAO XI Road, Shanghai, 200030, China
Tel.: (86) 2164276272
Electronic Display Distr
N.A.I.C.S.: 423690

Kimoto Ltd.   (1)
Thurgauerstrasse 117, Opfikon, 8152, Zurich, Switzerland
Tel.: (41) 448179999
Web Site: https://www.kimoto.ch
Film Coating Product Mfr & Distr
N.A.I.C.S.: 325992

Kimoto Tech, Inc.   (1)
601 Canal St, Cedartown, GA 30125
Tel.: (770) 748-2643
Film Coating Product Mfr & Distr
N.A.I.C.S.: 325992
David Williams *(Pres)*

Shenyang Kimoto Industries Co., Ltd.   (1)
35-2 Building A Huaqiang Plaza No 100-4 Sanhao Street, Heping District, Shenyang, 110004, Liaoning, China
Tel.: (86) 2424509797
Web Site: http://www.kimoto.com.cn
Software Development Services
N.A.I.C.S.: 541511

KIMOU ENVIRONMENTAL HOLDING LIMITED
Longqiao Avenue Longxi Street, Boluo County, Huizhou, Guangdong, China
Tel.: (86) 7526158990   Ky
Web Site:
http://www.platingbase.com
Year Founded: 2005
6805—(HKG)
Rev.: $153,849,056
Assets: $613,845,367
Liabilities: $422,135,766
Net Worth: $191,709,601
Earnings: $15,262,182
Emp.: 885
Fiscal Year-end: 12/31/22
Holding Company
N.A.I.C.S.: 551112
Lianghong Zhang *(Chm)*

KIMREE, INC.
Xiagang Section Luotang Village Shuikou Street, Huicheng District, Huizhou, 516005, Guangdong, China
Tel.: (86) 752 575 3388   Ky
Web Site: http://www.kimree.com
Sales Range: $75-99.9 Million
Emp.: 2,310
E-Cigarette Mfr
N.A.I.C.S.: 312230
Andre Qiuming Liu *(Chm)*

KIMURA CHEMICAL PLANTS CO., LTD.
2-1-2 Kuiseterajima, Amagasaki, 660-8567, Hyogo, Japan
Tel.: (81) 664882501
Web Site: https://www.kcpc.co.jp
Year Founded: 1924
6378—(TKS)
Rev.: $163,068,700
Assets: $228,977,010
Liabilities: $113,632,510
Net Worth: $115,344,500
Earnings: $10,258,720

Emp.: 398
Fiscal Year-end: 03/31/24
Industrial Machinery Mfr
N.A.I.C.S.: 333248
Masayuki Fukuda *(Sr Mng Dir)*

KIMURA CO., LTD.
6F De Aune Sapporo 1-7 Kita 6-jo Higashi 4-chome, Higashi-ku, Sapporo, 060-8576, Hokkaido, Japan
Tel.: (81) 117214311
Web Site: https://www.kimuranet.jp
Year Founded: 1951
7461—(TKS)
Rev.: $332,430,560
Assets: $245,281,520
Liabilities: $96,470,880
Net Worth: $148,810,640
Earnings: $11,528,880
Fiscal Year-end: 03/31/22
Construction Materials Distr
N.A.I.C.S.: 423390
Yusuke Kimura *(Pres & CEO)*

KIMURA KOHKI CO., LTD.
Uehonmachi Nishi 5-3-5 Ueroku F Building, Chuo-Ku, Osaka, 542-0062, Japan
Tel.: (81) 5037339400
Web Site: https://www.kimukoh.co.jp
Year Founded: 1947
6231—(TKS)
Air Conditioner Mfr & Distr
N.A.I.C.S.: 333415
Keiichi Kimura *(Pres)*

KIMURA-UNITY CO., LTD.
3-8-32 Nishiki, Naka-ku, Nagoya, 460-0003, Aichi, Japan
Tel.: (81) 529627051
Web Site: https://www.kimura-unity.co.jp
Year Founded: 1973
9368—(NGO)
Rev.: $406,296,550
Assets: $427,558,519
Liabilities: $160,270,850
Net Worth: $267,287,669
Earnings: $20,931,610
Emp.: 2,415
Fiscal Year-end: 03/31/24
Logistic Services
N.A.I.C.S.: 541614
Yukio Kimura *(Chm)*

Subsidiaries:

Business People Co., Ltd.   (1)
2-70 Shiga-cho, Kita-ku, Nagoya, 462-0037, Japan
Tel.: (81) 529101661
Web Site: http://www.bpnet.jp
Human Resource Consulting Services
N.A.I.C.S.: 541612

Kimura, Inc.   (1)
102 Cherry Blossom Dr, Laurens, SC 29360
Tel.: (864) 682-8700
Web Site: http://www.kimurainc.com
Emp.: 270
Steel Container Distr
N.A.I.C.S.: 423840

Kimura-Unity Co., Ltd. - Inazawa Plant   (1)
3-1 Okudaosawa-cho, Inazawa, Aichi-ken, Japan
Tel.: (81) 587 32 1221
Logistics Consulting Servies
N.A.I.C.S.: 541614

Kimura-Unity Co., Ltd. - Inuyama Plant   (1)
10 Funada, Inuyama, Aichi-ken, Japan
Tel.: (81) 568 67 3911
Logistics Consulting Servies
N.A.I.C.S.: 541614

Kimura-Unity Co., Ltd. - Kariya Plant   (1)

KIMURA-UNITY CO., LTD.

Kimura-Unity Co., Ltd.—(Continued)

140 Jiuda Nishizakai-cho, Kariya, Aichi-ken, Japan
Tel.: (81) 566 36 2883
Logistics Consulting Services
N.A.I.C.S.: 541614

Kimura-Unity Co., Ltd. – Meiko Plant (1)
1-5-9 Higashihama, Ama-gun, Tobishima, Aichi-ken, Japan
Tel.: (81) 567 55 1277
Logistics Consulting Services
N.A.I.C.S.: 541614

Kimura-Unity Co., Ltd. - Toyota Plant (1)
12 Minamikokute Masuzukanishi-machi, Toyota, Aichi-ken, Japan
Tel.: (81) 565 21 1231
Logistics Consulting Services
N.A.I.C.S.: 541614

SUPER JUMBO CORPORATION (1)
5-50 Showabashi Dori, Nakagawa-ku, Nagoya, 454-0852, Japan
Tel.: (81) 523518000
Web Site: https://www.superjumbo.co.jp
New & Used Car Dealer
N.A.I.C.S.: 441110

TK Logistica de Mexico S. de R.L. de C.V. (1)
Tecate No 33143, Tijuana, 22025, Mexico
Tel.: (52) 664 969 4206
Logistics Consulting Servies
N.A.I.C.S.: 541614

U-netrans Co., Ltd. (1)
60 Minami Niikeshita Uchigoe-cho, Miyoshi, 470-0213, Aichi, Japan
Tel.: (81) 561328088
Web Site: http://www.u-netrans.jp
Logistics Consulting Services
N.A.I.C.S.: 541614

KIMURATAN CORPORATION

13th floor Sannomiya Century Building 83 Kyomachi, Chuo-ku, Kobe, 650-0034, Japan
Tel.: (81) 788068234
Web Site: https://www.kimuratan.co.jp
Year Founded: 1964
8107—(TKS)
Rev.: $8,487,240
Assets: $54,889,440
Liabilities: $48,801,630
Net Worth: $6,087,810
Earnings: $264,400
Emp.: 11
Fiscal Year-end: 03/31/24
Apparel Product Mfr & Whslr
N.A.I.C.S.: 315250

KIN AND CARTA PLC

The Spitfire Building 71 Collier Street, London, N1 9BE, United Kingdom
Tel.: (44) 207 928 8844   UK
Web Site: http://www.kinandcarta.com
Year Founded: 1964
KCT—(LSE)
Rev.: $217,699,540
Assets: $292,333,409
Liabilities: $179,395,544
Net Worth: $112,937,865
Earnings: $3,660,413
Emp.: 1,367
Fiscal Year-end: 07/31/21
Holding Company; Magazines, Books, Corporate Financial Documents, Direct Mail & Other Commercial Printing Services
N.A.I.C.S.: 551112
J. Schwan (CEO)

Subsidiaries:

Amaze plc (1)
Tel.: (44) 20 7440 0540
Web Site: http://www.amaze.com

Sales Range: $10-24.9 Million
Emp.: 250
Advertising & Online Marketing Agency
N.A.I.C.S.: 541810

Subsidiary (Non-US):

Amaze Technology Limited (2)
Tel.: (44) 161 242 5650
Emp.: 150
Digital Technical Consultancy Services
N.A.I.C.S.: 541690

Edit Agency Limited (1)
20 Manvers Street, Bath, BA1 1JW, United Kingdom
Tel.: (44) 1225480480
Web Site: https://edit.co.uk
Sales Range: $25-49.9 Million
Emp.: 7
Data Marketing Consulting Services
N.A.I.C.S.: 541613

Kin and Carta Colombia S.A.S. (1)
Carrera 7 116-50 6th Floor, 110111, Bogota, Colombia
Tel.: (57) 3242001002
Digital Transformation Services
N.A.I.C.S.: 541330

Kin and Carta Partnerships LLC (1)
7th Fl 111 N Canal St, Chicago, IL 60606
Digital Transformation Services
N.A.I.C.S.: 541330

Occam DM Limited (1)
Manor Farm Church Lane, Chilcompton, BA3 4HP, Somerset, United Kingdom
Tel.: (44) 1761 233 833
Web Site: http://www.occam-dm.com
Sales Range: $25-49.9 Million
Emp.: 114
Marketing Management Software Development Services
N.A.I.C.S.: 541511
Neil Evans (Mng Dir)

St. Ives Blackburn Limited (1)
Greenbank Business Park Challenge Way, Blackburn, BB1 5qu, Lancashire, United Kingdom
Tel.: (44) 1254 278800
Sales Range: $50-74.9 Million
Emp.: 102
Commercial Printing Services
N.A.I.C.S.: 323111

St. Ives Burnley Limited (1)
Widow Hill Rd, Burnley, BB10 2BB, Lancashire, United Kingdom
Tel.: (44) 1282 418700
Sales Range: $25-49.9 Million
Emp.: 86
Commercial Printing Services
N.A.I.C.S.: 323111

St. Ives Direct Leeds Limited (1)
Ring Rd, Seacroft, Leeds, LS14 1NH, Yorkshire, United Kingdom (100%)
Tel.: (44) 113 201 8500
Web Site: http://www.stivesdirect.co.uk
Commercial Printing
N.A.I.C.S.: 323111

St. Ives Westerham Press Ltd. (1)
Fir crost way, Edenbridge, TN8 6EL, Kent, United Kingdom (100%)
Tel.: (44) 1732867234
Commercial Printing
N.A.I.C.S.: 323111

Subsidiary (Domestic):

Sevenoaks Print Finishers Ltd (2)
7 Block The Industrial Est, Edenbridge, TN8 6HF, United Kingdom (100%)
Tel.: (44) 1732866060
Sales Range: $25-49.9 Million
Emp.: 80
Commercial Printing
N.A.I.C.S.: 323111

KIN PANG HOLDINGS LIMITED

No 249-263 Edif China Civil Plaza 17 andar L, Alameda Doutor Carlos do Assumpcaso, Macau, China (Macau)
Tel.: (853) 28435877   Ky
Web Site: http://www.kinpang.com.mo
Year Founded: 2006

1722—(HKG)
Rev.: $72,450,314
Assets: $58,135,695
Liabilities: $35,954,212
Net Worth: $22,181,483
Earnings: ($4,241,042)
Emp.: 598
Fiscal Year-end: 12/31/23
Civil Engineering Services
N.A.I.C.S.: 238110
Fong Lan Choi (Co-Founder)

KIN SHING HOLDINGS LIMITED

Unit D 9/F Billion Plaza 2 10 Cheung Yue Street Cheung Sha Wan, Kowloon, China (Hong Kong)
Tel.: (852) 2 950 9123   Ky
Web Site:
   http://www.kinshingholdings.com.hk
Year Founded: 1994
1630—(HKG)
Rev.: $67,578,942
Assets: $50,447,947
Liabilities: $28,944,273
Net Worth: $21,503,675
Earnings: $339,346
Emp.: 1,198
Fiscal Year-end: 03/31/21
Construction Management Services
N.A.I.C.S.: 238190
Chi Kit Leung (Founder & Chm)

KIN YAT HOLDINGS LIMITED

7F Galaxy Factory Building, 25-27 Luk Hop Street San Po Kong, Kowloon, China (Hong Kong)
Tel.: (852) 23522041
Web Site: https://www.kinyat.hk
0638—(HKG)
Rev.: $298,758,309
Assets: $376,374,345
Liabilities: $171,307,754
Net Worth: $205,066,592
Earnings: $7,333,545
Emp.: 5,600
Fiscal Year-end: 03/31/22
Electronic Toys Mfr & Distr
N.A.I.C.S.: 339930
Chor Kit Cheng (Chm & CEO)

Subsidiaries:

Standard Electric Holdings Limited (1)
10F Block A Galaxy Factory Building 25-27 Luk Hop Street, San Po Kong, Kowloon, China (Hong Kong)
Tel.: (852) 2326 7670
Web Site: http://www.standardmotor.net
Electrical Component Mfr & Distr
N.A.I.C.S.: 334512
Stephen Cheng Tsz Hang (CEO)

Plant (Non-US):

Standard Electric Holdings Limited - Guizhou Plant (2)
Tonggu Road Dushan Avenue, Dushan Economic Development Zone, Guiyang, China
Tel.: (86) 8547052888
Electrical Related Equipment Mfr & Distr
N.A.I.C.S.: 336320

Standard Electric Holdings Limited - Shaoguan Plant (2)
Huanghuayuan Industrial Zone Shantangtou, Taiping Town Shixing County, Shaoguan, Guangdong, China
Tel.: (86) 7513338111
Electrical Related Equipment Mfr & Distr
N.A.I.C.S.: 336320

KINA PETROLEUM LTD.

Suite 9 Level 2 209 Harrington St, Sydney, 2000, NSW, Australia
Tel.: (61) 2 8247 2500   PG
Web Site:
   http://www.kinapetroleum.com

Year Founded: 2009
Rev.: $3,550
Assets: $35,095,148
Liabilities: $539,126
Net Worth: $34,556,022
Earnings: ($2,668,791)
Fiscal Year-end: 12/31/17
Petroleum Exploration
N.A.I.C.S.: 211120
Richard Schroder (Mng Dir)

KINA SECURITIES LIMITED

Level 9 Kina Bank Haus Douglas Street, National Capital District, 121, Port Moresby, Papua New Guinea
Tel.: (675) 3083888   PG
Web Site:
   https://www.kinabank.com.pg
Year Founded: 1985
KSL—(PNGX)
Rev.: $67,117,046
Assets: $1,372,154,400
Liabilities: $1,202,514,439
Net Worth: $169,639,962
Earnings: $27,807,715
Emp.: 718
Fiscal Year-end: 12/31/23
Investment Management Service
N.A.I.C.S.: 523940
Greg Pawson (CEO & Mng Dir)

Subsidiaries:

Kina Asset Management Limited (1)
Level 9 Kina Bank Haus Douglas Street, PO Box 1141, Port Moresby, Papua New Guinea
Tel.: (675) 308 3888
Web Site: http://www.kaml.pg
Rev.: $4,527,151
Assets: $21,474,478
Liabilities: $136,413
Net Worth: $21,338,065
Earnings: $4,127,818
Fiscal Year-end: 12/31/2019
Investment Management Service
N.A.I.C.S.: 523940
Rabbie Namaliu (Chm)

Kina Bank Limited (1)
9th Level Kina House Douglas Street, National Capital District, Port Moresby, Papua New Guinea (100%)
Tel.: (675) 3083888
Web Site: https://www.kinabank.com.pg
Commercial Banking
N.A.I.C.S.: 522110
Greg Pawson (CEO)

Subsidiary (Domestic):

Australia & New Zealand Banking Group (PNG) Limited (2)
Portion 13 Section 44 Allotment 30 Granville Poreporena Freeway, PO Box 1152, National Capital District, Port Moresby, Papua New Guinea (100%)
Tel.: (675) 1801444
Web Site: https://www.anz.com
Banking Services
N.A.I.C.S.: 522299

KINATICO LTD

Level 4 999 Hay Street, Perth, 6000, WA, Australia
Tel.: (61) 893883000   AU
Web Site: https://www.cvcheck.com
Year Founded: 2004
KYP—(ASX)
Rev.: $19,175,411
Assets: $21,909,452
Liabilities: $4,727,634
Net Worth: $17,181,818
Earnings: $521,316
Fiscal Year-end: 06/30/24
Software Development Services
N.A.I.C.S.: 513210

KINAXIS INC.

3199 Palladium Drive, Ottawa, K2T 0N9, ON, Canada
Tel.: (613) 592-5780

Web Site: https://www.kinaxis.com
Year Founded: 1984
KXSCF—(OTCIQ)
Rev.: $191,549,000
Assets: $350,743,000
Liabilities: $120,641,000
Net Worth: $230,102,000
Earnings: $23,331,000
Emp.: 569
Fiscal Year-end: 12/31/19
Supply Chain Management Software
N.A.I.C.S.: 513210
Megan Paterson *(Chief HR Officer)*

Subsidiaries:

Kinaxis China (1)
Level 23 Citigroup Tower 33, Huayuan-shiqiao Road, Shanghai, 200120, China
Tel.: (86) 21 6101 0292
Web Site: http://www.kinaxis.com
Emp.: 10
Supply Chain Management Software
N.A.I.C.S.: 513210

Kinaxis Hong Kong (1)
Level 19 Two International Finance Centre, 8 Finance Street, Central, China (Hong Kong)
Tel.: (852) 2251 1859
Supply Chain Management Software
N.A.I.C.S.: 513210

Kinaxis Japan K. K. (1)
Level 5 Funato Building 1-2-3 Kudankita, Chiyoda-ku, Tokyo, 102-0073, Japan
Tel.: (81) 3 5213 1851
Supply Chain Management Software
N.A.I.C.S.: 513210

Kinaxis Netherlands (1)
Fellenoord 130, Eindhoven, 5611ZP, Netherlands
Tel.: (31) 40 2668 619
Web Site: http://www.kinaxis.com
Supply Chain Management Software
N.A.I.C.S.: 513210

Prana Consulting, Inc. (1)
2975 Bowers Ave Ste 303, Santa Clara, CA 95051-0949
Tel.: (408) 727-6344
Web Site: http://www.pranaglobal.com
Supply Chain Management Software Publisher
N.A.I.C.S.: 513210
Vijay Subramanian *(CEO)*

KINCO AUTOMATION SHANGHAI CO., LTD.
Building No 3 Shenjiang Road No 5709 Qiuyue Road No 26, Shanghai Pilot Free Trade Zone, Shanghai, 201210, China
Tel.: (86) 2168798588
Web Site: http://www.kinco.cn
Year Founded: 2008
688160—(SHG)
Rev.: $75,718,633
Assets: $125,520,296
Liabilities: $23,467,298
Net Worth: $102,052,997
Earnings: $12,784,192
Fiscal Year-end: 12/31/22
Automation Product Mfr
N.A.I.C.S.: 334512
Dong Tang *(Chm & Gen Mgr)*

Subsidiaries:

Kinco Electric (Shenzhen) Ltd. (1)
Building 1 No 6 Langshan 1st Road Hi-tech Park North, Nanshan District, Shenzhen, 518057, China
Tel.: (86) 75526585555
Web Site: https://en.kinco.cn
Industrial Machinery Mfr
N.A.I.C.S.: 333310

KINCORA COPPER LIMITED
400 - 837 West Hastings Street, Vancouver, V6C 3N6, BC, Canada
Tel.: (604) 283-1722 BC

Web Site: https://www.kincoracopper.com
Year Founded: 1983
KCC—(ASX)
Assets: $13,404,063
Liabilities: $187,269
Net Worth: $13,216,794
Earnings: ($1,102,469)
Emp.: 15
Fiscal Year-end: 12/31/23
Copper Mining Services
N.A.I.C.S.: 212230
Jonathan Spring *(Pres & CEO)*

Subsidiaries:

Samsul Mineracao Ltda (1)
Av Carlos Gomes 700 8th floor Ed, Platinum Tower, Porto Alegre, Minas Gerais, Brazil
Tel.: (55) 992600993
Web Site: https://www.samsul.com.br
Diamond Mining Services
N.A.I.C.S.: 212290
Eduardo Freitas *(Mgr)*

KINCROME AUSTRALIA PTY LTD
3 Lakeview Drive, Scoresby, 3179, VIC, Australia
Tel.: (61) 397307100
Web Site: http://www.kincrome.com.au
Year Founded: 1987
Sales Range: $25-49.9 Million
Emp.: 120
Hand Tool & Automotive Accessory Mfr
N.A.I.C.S.: 332216
Ronald Allen Burgoine *(CEO)*

KINDCARD, INC.
Baccuit Sur Bauang, Bauang, La Union, Philippines
Tel.: (63) 7753218238 NV
Web Site: http://www.mwfglobal.com
Year Founded: 2016
Rev.: $368,528
Assets: $159,071
Liabilities: $629,108
Net Worth: ($470,037)
Earnings: ($397,118)
Emp.: 1
Fiscal Year-end: 01/31/22
Online Shopping Services
N.A.I.C.S.: 449210
Michael Rosen *(Pres, Treas & Sec)*

KINDEN CORPORATION
2-1-21 Kudan-Minami, Chiyodaku, Tokyo, 102-8628, Japan
Tel.: (81) 352107272 JP
Web Site: https://www.kinden.co.jp
Year Founded: 1944
1944—(TKS)
Rev.: $4,326,350,760
Assets: $5,393,013,070
Liabilities: $1,598,522,740
Net Worth: $3,794,490,330
Earnings: $221,785,330
Emp.: 8,493
Fiscal Year-end: 03/31/24
Electrical & Mechanical Engineering; Construction Services
N.A.I.C.S.: 541330
Yukikazu Maeda *(Vice Chm)*

Subsidiaries:

Aleph Networks Corporation (1)
6F South Wing Kinden Corp 2-3-23 Honjyo-higashi, Kita-ku, Osaka, 531-0074, Japan (100%)
Tel.: (81) 663756237
Web Site: http://www.alephnet.sv-1.jp
Sales Range: $25-49.9 Million
Emp.: 44
Engineering & Environmental Services
N.A.I.C.S.: 541330

Antelec Ltd. (1)
No73 Jolly Maker Chambers - II, Nariman Point, Mumbai, 400 021, India
Tel.: (91) 2222020563
Web Site: http://www.antelecltd.com
Electrical Contracting Services
N.A.I.C.S.: 238210
Sanjiv Banga *(Mng Dir)*

Bintai Kinden Corporation Berhad (1)
10-01-02 PJX-HM Shah Tower Jalan Persiaran Barat, 46050, Petaling Jaya, Selangor, Malaysia
Tel.: (60) 376620488
Web Site: https://www.bintai.com.my
Rev.: $24,571,429
Assets: $53,477,249
Liabilities: $40,554,921
Net Worth: $12,922,328
Earnings: ($24,235,556)
Emp.: 398
Fiscal Year-end: 03/31/2023
Diversified Engineering & Property Services
N.A.I.C.S.: 541330
Puay Koon Ong *(Vice Chm)*

Subsidiary (Non-US):

Bintai Kindenko Pte. Ltd. (2)
152 Ubi Avenue 4 03-302 Smart Innovation Centre, Singapore, 408826, Singapore (69.82%)
Tel.: (65) 62643818
Web Site: https://www.bintai.com.sg
Sales Range: $10-24.9 Million
Emp.: 40
Engineeering Services
N.A.I.C.S.: 541330
Chua Swee Ann *(CEO & Mng Dir)*

Subsidiary (Domestic):

Kejuruteraan Bintai Kindenko Sdn. Bhd. (2)
3-2-8 Kompleks Kantonmen Prima No 698 Jalan Ipoh, 51200, Kuala Lumpur, Malaysia (100%)
Tel.: (60) 340426233
Web Site: http://www.bintai.com.my
Sales Range: $25-49.9 Million
Emp.: 200
Engineeering Services
N.A.I.C.S.: 541330

International Electro-Mechanical Services Co. (1)
Office 407 R338 Oud Metha Offices Next to City Bank, Opposite Raffles Hotel Dubai Healthcare City, Dubai, United Arab Emirates
Tel.: (971) 43344003
Web Site: http://www.iemsc.com
Mechanical Contracting Service
N.A.I.C.S.: 238220

Kinden (Thailand) Co., Ltd. (1)
Tel.: (66) 264273446
Web Site: http://www.kinden.co.th
Sales Range: $25-49.9 Million
Emp.: 230
Electrical & Mechanical Engineering Services
N.A.I.C.S.: 541330

Kinden Denryoku Service Company, Incorporated (1)
5 6 21 Nishitenma, Kita Ku, Osaka, 530-0047, Japan (100%)
Tel.: (81) 663665277
Web Site: http://www.kinden.co.jp
N.A.I.C.S.: 541330

Kinden Electrical & Mechanical Service Company (1)
5 25 12 Higashi Gotanda, Shinagawa Ku, Tokyo, 1410022, Japan (100%)
Tel.: (81) 334473189
Web Site: http://www.kinden.co.jp
Sales Range: $25-49.9 Million
Emp.: 64
N.A.I.C.S.: 541330

Kinden Himeji Service Company, Inc. (1)
4 133 Yasuda, Himeji, 670 0955, Japan (100%)
Tel.: (81) 792881111
Web Site: http://www.kinden.co.jp
Engineeering Services
N.A.I.C.S.: 541330

Nobuo Hoshijima *(Branch Mgr)*

Kinden Hyogo Service Company, Inc. (1)
5-2-2 Hamazoe-dori, Nagata-ku, Kobe, 653-0024, Japan
Tel.: (81) 786852207
Electrical & Mechanical Engineering; Construction Services
N.A.I.C.S.: 541330

Kinden International, Ltd. (1)
4th Floor 81 Hung Go Road Kuutong, Kowloon, China (Hong Kong) (100%)
Tel.: (852) 23686136
Sales Range: $25-49.9 Million
Emp.: 1
N.A.I.C.S.: 541330

Kinden Kansai Services Company, Incorporated (1)
1-13-13 Higashiobase, Higashinari-ku, Osaka, 537-0024, Japan
Tel.: (81) 669761220
Web Site: https://kinden-kansai.co.jp
Emp.: 114
Engineeering Services
N.A.I.C.S.: 541330

Kinden Kyoto Service Company, Incorporated (1)
14 Kamitobasugata Cho Minami Ku, Kyoto, 601 8102, Japan (100%)
Tel.: (81) 756911521
Sales Range: $150-199.9 Million
Emp.: 1,000
N.A.I.C.S.: 541330

Kinden Nagoya Services Company, Incorporated (1)
1 20 Ooaki Cho, Nakamura Ku, Nagoya, 4530042, Aichi, Japan (100%)
Tel.: (81) 524714211
Designer & Constructor of Electricity Systems; Generator, Trasmittor & Distributor of Electric Energy
N.A.I.C.S.: 335312

Kinden Nara Service Company Incorporated (1)
6-20-8 Daianji, Nara, 630 8133, Japan
Tel.: (81) 742628781
Web Site: http://www.kinden.co.jp
Civil Engineering & Related Services
N.A.I.C.S.: 541330

Kinden Nishinihon Service Company, Inc. (1)
2-13-5 Yokokawa-cho, Nishi-ku, Hiroshima, 733-0011, Japan
Tel.: (81) 822941741
Web Site: https://www.kinden-ns.co.jp
Emp.: 29
Electrical & Mechanical Engineering; Construction Services
N.A.I.C.S.: 541330

Kinden Phils Corporation (1)
5FL ODC International Plaza 219 Salcedo St, Legaspi Village, Makati, Philippines
Tel.: (63) 28126440
Web Site: http://www.kinden.co.jp
Electrical & Mechanical Engineering Services
N.A.I.C.S.: 541330

Kinden Service Company, Incorporated (1)
2 10 Suehiro Cho, Kita Ku, Osaka, 5300047, Japan (100%)
Tel.: (81) 663679200
N.A.I.C.S.: 541330

Kinden Shiga Service Company Incorporated (1)
2 18 Uchidehama, Shiga, 5250055, Japan (100%)
Tel.: (81) 775618701
Sales Range: $1-4.9 Billion
Emp.: 7,000
N.A.I.C.S.: 541330

Kinden Shoji Company, Ltd (1)
3-15-23 Nipponbashi-Higashi, Naniwa-ku, Osaka, 556 0006, Japan (100%)
Tel.: (81) 666334811
Sales Range: $25-49.9 Million
Emp.: 50
Engineeering Services
N.A.I.C.S.: 541330

KINDEN CORPORATION

Kinden Corporation—(Continued)

Kinden Vietnam Co., Ltd. (1)
15th floor CMC Tower Duy Tan Street, Dich Vong Hau Ward Cau Giay District, Hanoi, Vietnam
Tel.: (84) 2439342535
Sales Range: $50-74.9 Million
Emp.: 20
Electrical System Installation Services & Mfr
N.A.I.C.S.: 238210
Yoshita Kakishi (Gen Dir)

Kindenko (Thailand) Co., Ltd. (1)
41 Lertpanya Bldg RM No 1001-3 10th FL Soi Lertpanya, Sri-Ayuthaya Road Kwaeng Thanon-Phayathai Khet Ratchatewee, Bangkok, 10400, Thailand
Tel.: (66) 26427344
Web Site: https://www.kinden.co.th
Sales Range: $75-99.9 Million
Emp.: 300
N.A.I.C.S.: 541330
Osamu Kubokochi (Pres)

Kindenspinet Corporation (1)
Kinden Main Store South Building 8F 2-3-12 Honjo Higashi, Kita-ku, Osaka, 531-0074, Japan
Tel.: (81) 663756237
Web Site: https://www.kinden-spinet.co.jp
Emp.: 55
Electronic Services
N.A.I.C.S.: 238210

Kinki Concrete Sales Company, Limited (1)
5-6-21 Nishitenma Kuta-ku, Osaka, Japan
Tel.: (81) 66 314 2575
N.A.I.C.S.: 541330

Kinki Freight Service Company, Incorporated (1)
5 6 21 Nishitenma Kita Ku, Osaka, 5300047, Japan (100%)
Tel.: (81) 663130621
Web Site: http://www.kinden.co.jp
Provider of Transportation Services
N.A.I.C.S.: 488210

MECS CORPORATION (1)
1-13-13 Higashiobase, Osaka, 537-0024, Japan
Tel.: (81) 669760541
Electrical & Mechanical Engineering; Construction Services
N.A.I.C.S.: 541330

Nishihara Engineering Co., Ltd. (1)
Mita Twin Building East Building 4-2-8 Shibaura, Minato-ku, Tokyo, 108-0023, Japan
Tel.: (81) 354276080
Web Site: https://www.nishihara-eng.co.jp
Engineeering Services
N.A.I.C.S.: 541330

P.T. Kinden Indonesia (1)
Summitmas Tower I 19th floor, Jl Jend Sudirman Kav 61-62, 61-62, Jakarta, 12190, Indonesia
Tel.: (62) 215226781
Web Site: https://kinden.co.id
Corporate Services
N.A.I.C.S.: 561410

P.T. Rakintam Electrical Contractors (1)
GMT Bldg 2F 3F Jalan Wijaya 5, Kebayoran Baru, Jakarta, 12170, Wijaya, Indonesia (100%)
Tel.: (62) 217252042
N.A.I.C.S.: 541330

US Kinden Corporation (1)
1021 Kikowaena Pl Bldg 2, Honolulu, HI 96819-2096
Tel.: (808) 839-2741
Sales Range: $25-49.9 Million
Emp.: 125
Electrical & Mechanical Engineering; Construction Services
N.A.I.C.S.: 541330

Subsidiary (Domestic):

Wasa Electrical Services, Inc. (2)
1021 Kikowaena Pl Bldg 2, Honolulu, HI 96819-2012
Tel.: (808) 839-2741
Web Site: http://www.wasahawaii.com
Sales Range: $25-49.9 Million
Emp.: 100
Electrical & Mechanical Engineering Services
N.A.I.C.S.: 541330
Ron Yee (CEO)

Vina Kinden Corporation (1)
3rd Floor Techno Center Thang Long Industrial Park, Dong Anh District, Hanoi, Vietnam
Tel.: (84) 2438811696
N.A.I.C.S.: 541330

KINDOM CONSTRUCTION CORP.
2F 131 No 3 Sec Heping E Rd, Taipei, 106, Taiwan
Tel.: (886) 223786789
Web Site: https://www.kindom.com.tw
Year Founded: 1979
2520—(TAI)
Rev.: $635,812,167
Assets: $1,882,488,761
Liabilities: $1,119,208,728
Net Worth: $763,280,033
Earnings: $100,311,484
Fiscal Year-end: 12/31/23
Construction Engineering Services
N.A.I.C.S.: 237990
Chang Sean (Deputy Gen Mgr)

KINDRED GROUP PLC
Level 6 The Centre Tigne Point, Sliema, TPO 0001, Malta
Tel.: (356) 2133532 Mt
Web Site: https://www.kindredgroup.com
Year Founded: 1997
KINDSDB—(OMX)
Rev.: $1,349,028,023
Assets: $1,541,529,917
Liabilities: $790,456,955
Net Worth: $751,072,961
Earnings: $151,603,131
Emp.: 1,959
Fiscal Year-end: 12/31/22
On-Line Gambling & Gambling Products, Entertainment & Delivery Services
N.A.I.C.S.: 713290
Anne-Jaap Snijders (Chief Comml Officer-Reg 1)

Subsidiaries:

Maria Services Limited (1)
Fawwara Bldg Msida Rd, Gzira, GZR 1405, Malta
Tel.: (356) 21333532
Online Gambling Services
N.A.I.C.S.: 713290

North Development AB (1)
Ringv 100 A, Stockholm, 11860, Sweden
Tel.: (46) 84622300
Web Site: http://www.unibet.com
Sales Range: $25-49.9 Million
Emp.: 94
Online Gambling Services
N.A.I.C.S.: 713290

Unibet (Holding) Limited (1)
Fawwara Bldg Msida Rd, Gzira, GZR1405, Malta
Tel.: (356) 21333532
Sportsbook & Gaming Services
N.A.I.C.S.: 459210

KINDSTAR GLOBALGENE TECHNOLOGY, INC.
Biolake D2-1 666 Gaoxin Road, East Lake High Tech Zone, Wuhan, China
Tel.: (86) 4007361666 Ky
Web Site: https://www.kindstar.com.cn
Year Founded: 2003
9960—(HKG)
Rev.: $133,925,011
Assets: $508,031,818
Liabilities: $107,198,161
Net Worth: $400,833,656
Earnings: $5,046,383
Emp.: 3,125
Fiscal Year-end: 12/31/23
Information Technology Services
N.A.I.C.S.: 541512

KINDUCT TECHNOLOGIES, INC.
1969 Upper Water Street Suite 1201 Purdy's Wharf Tower 2, Halifax, B3J 3R7, NS, Canada
Tel.: (855) 406-8739
Web Site: http://www.kinduct.com
Year Founded: 2010
Human Performance, Sport Performance, Athlete Management System Platform & Data Science
N.A.I.C.S.: 518210
Kaitlin Webb (Mktg Mgr)

Subsidiaries:

mCube, Inc. (1)
2570 N 1st St Ste 300, San Jose, CA 95131
Tel.: (408) 637-5503
Web Site: http://www.mcube-inc.com
Semiconductor Equipment Mfr
N.A.I.C.S.: 334413
Ben Lee (CEO)

KINDY S.A.
37 rue des bonnetiers, 60220, Moliens, France
Tel.: (33) 34 446 4646 FR
Web Site: http://www.groupekindy.com
ALKDY—(EUR)
Sales Range: $25-49.9 Million
Socks & Children's Shoes Mfr & Distr
N.A.I.C.S.: 315120
Nathalie Crouzet (CEO)

KINEMASTER CORPORATION
Solbon Building 21 Banpo-daero 24-gil, Seocho-gu, Seoul, 06648, Korea (South)
Tel.: (82) 221945300
Web Site: https://kinemastercorp.com
Year Founded: 2002
139670—(KRS)
Rev.: $15,025,526
Assets: $12,521,568
Liabilities: $5,208,506
Net Worth: $7,313,062
Earnings: ($11,770,640)
Emp.: 62
Fiscal Year-end: 12/31/22
Software Publisher
N.A.I.C.S.: 513210
Il-Taek Lim (CEO)

KINEPOLIS GROUP N.V.
Schelde 1 Moutstraat 132-146, B-9000, Gent, Belgium
Tel.: (32) 92410000
Web Site: https://corporate.kinepolis.com
Year Founded: 1997
KIN—(EUR)
Rev.: $216,516,604
Assets: $1,434,805,403
Liabilities: $1,279,437,956
Net Worth: $155,367,447
Earnings: ($84,884,895)
Emp.: 1,777
Fiscal Year-end: 12/31/20
Motion Picture Theater Operator
N.A.I.C.S.: 512131
Philip Ghekiere (Vice Chm)

Subsidiaries:

Brightfish NV (1)
Eeuwfeestlaan 20, 1020, Brussels, Belgium
Tel.: (32) 2 788 44 11
Web Site: http://www.brightfish.be
Emp.: 30

INTERNATIONAL PUBLIC

Theater Operator
N.A.I.C.S.: 512131

Kinepolis Braine SA (1)
Boulevard De France, 1420, Braine-l'Alleud, Belgium
Tel.: (32) 2 389 1717
Web Site: http://www.kinepolis.be
Motion Picture Theater Operator
N.A.I.C.S.: 512131
Erwin Six (Gen Mgr)

Kinepolis Espana SA (1)
Cl Edgar Neville S/N, 28223, Pozuelo de Alarcon, Spain
Tel.: (34) 91 512 7014
Web Site: http://www.kinepolis.es
Motion Picture Theater Operator
N.A.I.C.S.: 512131

Kinepolis Film Distribution (KFD) NV (1)
Eeuwfeestlaan 20, 1020, Brussels, Belgium
Tel.: (32) 24742693
Web Site: http://kfd.be
Motion Picture Distribution Services
N.A.I.C.S.: 512120

Kinepolis Holding BV (1)
Buitenruststraat 6, 4337 EH, Middelburg, Netherlands
Tel.: (31) 620607241
Investment Management Service
N.A.I.C.S.: 523940

Kinepolis Mulhouse SA (1)
175 avenue Robert Schuman, CS 11357, 68070, Mulhouse, France
Tel.: (33) 389367811
Web Site: http://business.kinepolis.fr
Emp.: 30
Motion Picture Theater Operator
N.A.I.C.S.: 512131

Kinepolis Poznan S.p.z. o.o. (1)
ul B Krzywoustego 72, 61-144, Poznan, Poland
Tel.: (48) 61 87 15 616
Web Site: http://kinepolis.pl
Theater Operator
N.A.I.C.S.: 512131

Kinepolis Schweiz AG (1)
Ebnatstrasse 149, 8207, Schaffhausen, Switzerland
Tel.: (41) 52 640 10 00
Web Site: http://kinepolis.ch
Emp.: 40
Motion Picture Theater Operator
N.A.I.C.S.: 512131
Lorenz Koch (Mng Dir & Mgr)

Kinepolis Thionville SA (1)
50 route d'Arlon, 57100, Thionville, France
Tel.: (33) 382395933
Web Site: http://business.kinepolis.fr
Motion Picture Theater Operator
N.A.I.C.S.: 512131

KINERGY ADVANCEMENT BERHAD
18 Jalan Radin Bagus 9 Bandar Baru Sri Petaling, 57000, Kuala Lumpur, Malaysia
Tel.: (60) 390553812 MY
Web Site: https://www.kinergyadvancement.com
Year Founded: 1997
KAB—(KLS)
Rev.: $39,577,251
Assets: $60,723,355
Liabilities: $31,725,015
Net Worth: $28,998,340
Earnings: $582,684
Emp.: 211
Fiscal Year-end: 12/31/22
Construction Services
N.A.I.C.S.: 236220
Lai Keng Onn (Mng Dir)

Subsidiaries:

PT Inpola Mitra Elektrindo (1)
Komp Katamso Vista Jl Brigjend Zein Hamid No D-20, Titi Kuning Medan Johor, Medan, 20217, North Sumatra, Indonesia
Tel.: (62) 614157594

Power Cable & Wire Mfr
N.A.I.C.S.: 335929

KINERGY PTE LTD.
1 Changi North Street 1 Lobby 2,
Singapore, 498789, Singapore
Tel.: (65) 64810211
Web Site: http://www.kinergy.com.sg
Year Founded: 1988
Sales Range: $75-99.9 Million
Emp.: 519
Electronic Management Services
N.A.I.C.S.: 334513
Leslie Kuak Choi Lim *(CEO)*

Subsidiaries:

Kinergy EMS (Nantong) Co., Ltd. (1)
No 62 Zhongyang Road, Nantong, 226009,
Jiangsu, China
Tel.: (86) 51385929251
High Precision Machining Parts Mfr
N.A.I.C.S.: 332216

Kinergy Precision Engineering (Nantong) Co., Ltd. (1)
No 62 Zhong Yang Rd, Nantong, 226009,
Jiangsu, China
Tel.: (86) 51385929251
Web Site: http://www.kinergy-nt.com
Sales Range: $50-74.9 Million
Emp.: 200
Electronic Components Mfr
N.A.I.C.S.: 334416

KINERJAPAY CORP.
Jl Multatuli No 8A Clyde Road,
Medan, 20151, Indonesia
Tel.: (62) 8196016168   DE
Web Site: http://www.kinerjapay.co
Year Founded: 2010
KPAY—(OTCIQ)
Rev.: $2,825,676
Assets: $3,722,998
Liabilities: $8,791,949
Net Worth: ($5,068,951)
Earnings: ($19,947,990)
Emp.: 60
Fiscal Year-end: 12/31/19
Software Development Services
N.A.I.C.S.: 541511
Edwin Witarsa Ng *(Chm & CEO)*

KINESIS INDUSTRY CO., LTD.
147 Ching Nian Road, Tachia, Taichung, 437, Taiwan
Tel.: (886) 4 2681 3325   TW
Web Site: http://www.kinesis.com.tw
Sales Range: $300-349.9 Million
Emp.: 1,550
Mfr of Bicycle Frames, Forks & Components
N.A.I.C.S.: 336991
Tom Jeng *(Pres & CEO)*

KINETIC CONSOLIDATED PTY LTD
60 Kingsford Smith Drive, Albion,
4010, QLD, Australia
Tel.: (61) 736370200   AU
Web Site: http://www.mpckinetic.com
Holding Company
N.A.I.C.S.: 551112
John Smith *(CEO)*

Subsidiaries:

Surtron Technologies Pty Ltd (1)
Unit 2 Chilver Street, Kewdale, 6105, WA,
Australia
Tel.: (61) 8 9452 6800
Web Site: http://www.surtron.com.au
Emp.: 40
Mining & Civil Construction Industry Drilling Services
N.A.I.C.S.: 213114
Brenton Armitage *(Mgr-Wireline Svcs)*

KINETIC CONSTRUCTION LTD.
#201 862 Cloverdale Avenue, Victoria, V8X 2S8, BC, Canada
Tel.: (250) 381-6331
Web Site:
http://www.kineticconstruction.com
Year Founded: 1984
Emp.: 150
Building Construction Services
N.A.I.C.S.: 236220
Chris Chalecki *(VP & Branch Mgr)*

KINETIC DEVELOPMENT GROUP LIMITED
Unit B 20th Floor Two Chinachem
Plaza 68 Connaught Road, Central,
China (Hong Kong)
Tel.: (852) 25450668
Web Site: http://www.kineticme.com
1277—(HKG)
Rev.: $864,278,532
Assets: $1,332,766,796
Liabilities: $445,889,480
Net Worth: $886,877,316
Earnings: $372,946,626
Emp.: 1,370
Fiscal Year-end: 12/31/22
Coal Mining & Related Activities
N.A.I.C.S.: 212115
Li Zhang *(Chm)*

KINETIC ENGINEERING, LTD.
Kinetic Innovation Park D-1 Block
Plot No 18/2 MIDC Chinchwad, Pune,
411 019, India
Tel.: (91) 2066142049
Web Site:
https://www.kineticindia.com
Year Founded: 1972
500240—(BOM)
Rev.: $16,973,775
Assets: $20,432,685
Liabilities: $18,693,675
Net Worth: $1,739,010
Earnings: $185,640
Emp.: 800
Fiscal Year-end: 03/31/22
Automobile Dealers
N.A.I.C.S.: 423110
Arun Hastimal Firodia *(Chm)*

KINETIC GROUP SERVICES PTY LTD.
18/607 Bourke St, Melbourne, 3000,
VIC, Australia
Web Site:
https://www.wearekinetic.com
Emp.: 7,300
Trucks & Buses Transportation Operators
N.A.I.C.S.: 485210
Michael Sewards *(Co-CEO)*

Subsidiaries:

The Go-Ahead Group plc (1)
3rd Floor 41-51 Grey Street, Newcastle
upon Tyne, NE1 6EE, United Kingdom
Tel.: (44) 1912323123
Web Site: http://www.go-ahead.com
Rev.: $5,292,935,648
Assets: $3,082,703,260
Liabilities: $2,718,019,668
Net Worth: $364,683,592
Earnings: ($16,428,412)
Emp.: 30,000
Fiscal Year-end: 06/27/2020
Holding Company; Commuter Bus, Rail & Parking Services
N.A.I.C.S.: 551112
Martin Harris *(Mng Dir-Brighton & Hove Buses)*

Subsidiary (Domestic):

Brighton & Hove Bus & Coach Company Limited (2)
43 Conway Street, Hove, BN3 3LT, East
Sussex, United Kingdom (100%)
Tel.: (44) 127 388 6200
Web Site: https://www.buses.co.uk
Sales Range: $550-599.9 Million
Emp.: 1,050
Urban Bus Transportation Services
N.A.I.C.S.: 485113

City of Oxford Motor Services Limited (2)
Cowley House Watlington Road, Cowley,
Oxford, OX4 6GA, United Kingdom
Tel.: (44) 186 578 5400
Web Site: https://www.oxfordbus.co.uk
Sales Range: $125-149.9 Million
Emp.: 600
Bus Transportation Services
N.A.I.C.S.: 485210

East Yorkshire Motor Services Limited (2)
3rd Floor 41-51 Grey Street, Newcastle
upon Tyne, NE1 6EE, United Kingdom
Tel.: (44) 148 259 2929
Web Site:
https://www.eastyorkshirebuses.co.uk
Travel Management Services
N.A.I.C.S.: 561510

Go North East Limited (2)
3rd Floor 41-51 Grey Street, Newcastle
upon Tyne, NE1 6EE, United
Kingdom (99%)
Tel.: (44) 1914205050
Web Site: http://www.simplygo.com
Sales Range: $550-599.9 Million
Emp.: 2,050
Urban Bus Transportation Services
N.A.I.C.S.: 485113

Go North West Limited (2)
Boyle Street, Manchester, M8 8UT, United
Kingdom
Tel.: (44) 330 123 4121
Web Site: https://www.gonorthwest.co.uk
Truck Transportation Services
N.A.I.C.S.: 484121

Go South Coast Limited (2)
2-8 Parkstone Road, Poole, BH15 2PR,
Dorset, United Kingdom
Tel.: (44) 120 233 8420
Web Site: https://gosouthcoast.co.uk
Emp.: 1,700
Holding Company; Urban Bus Transportation Services
N.A.I.C.S.: 551112

Subsidiary (Domestic):

Solent Blue Line Ltd. (3)
3rd Floor 41-51 Grey Street, Newcastle,
NE1 6EE, United Kingdom
Tel.: (44) 1202338421
Web Site: http://www.bluestarbus.co.uk
Urban Bus Transportation Services
N.A.I.C.S.: 485113

Southern Vectis Omnibus Company Ltd. (3)
Nelson Road, Newport, PO30 1RD, Isle of
Wight, United Kingdom
Tel.: (44) 1983827000
Web Site: http://www.islandbuses.info
Sales Range: $50-74.9 Million
Emp.: 250
Local Bus Transportation Services
N.A.I.C.S.: 485113

Wilts and Dorset Bus Company Ltd. (3)
Third Floor 41-51 Grey Street, Newcastle,
NE1 6EE, United Kingdom
Tel.: (44) 1202338420
Web Site: http://www.morebus.co.uk
Urban Bus Transportation Services
N.A.I.C.S.: 485113

Subsidiary (Domestic):

Go-Ahead Leasing Limited (2)
3rd Floor 41-51 Grey Street, Newcastle
upon Tyne, NE1 6EE, United Kingdom
Tel.: (44) 19 1232 3123
Web Site: http://www.go-ahead.com
Sales Range: $50-74.9 Million
Emp.: 40
Financial Lending Services
N.A.I.C.S.: 522220

Go-Ahead London (2)
No 18 Merton High Street, London, SW19
1DN, United Kingdom (100%)
Tel.: (44) 2085456100
Web Site: http://www.goaheadlondon.com
N.A.I.C.S.: 485113
Holding Company; Urban Bus Transportation Services
N.A.I.C.S.: 551112
Unit (Domestic):

London Central (3)
18 Merton High St, London, SW19 1DN,
United Kingdom (100%)
Tel.: (44) 2085456100
Web Site: http://www.londoncentral.com
Sales Range: $50-74.9 Million
Emp.: 150
Urban Bus Transportation Services
N.A.I.C.S.: 485113

London General (3)
18 Merton High Street, London, SW19 1DN,
United Kingdom (100%)
Tel.: (44) 2086461747
Web Site: http://www.londongeneral.co.uk
Sales Range: $50-74.9 Million
Emp.: 150
Urban Bus Transportation Services
N.A.I.C.S.: 485113

Subsidiary (Non-US):

Go-Ahead Transport Services (Dublin) Limited (2)
Ballymount Road Lower, Dublin, D12 X201,
Ireland
Tel.: (353) 81 880 4071
Web Site: https://www.goaheadireland.ie
Travel Management Services
N.A.I.C.S.: 561510
Andy Edwards *(Mng Dir)*

Subsidiary (Domestic):

Govia Limited (2)
6th Floor 1 Warwick Row, London, SW1E
5ER, United Kingdom (65%)
Tel.: (44) 2078213939
Web Site: http://www.govia.info
Sales Range: $50-74.9 Million
Emp.: 15
Holding Company; Commuter Rail Services & Train Station Operator
N.A.I.C.S.: 551112

Subsidiary (Domestic):

London & South Eastern Railway Limited (3)
Friars Bridge Court 41-45 Blackfriars Road,
PO Box 63428, London, SE1 8PG, United
Kingdom
Tel.: (44) 3453227021
Web Site:
http://www.southeasternrailway.co.uk
Commuter Rail Services
N.A.I.C.S.: 485112

London Midland (3)
102 New Street, PO Box 4323, Birmingham, B2 4JB, W Midlands, United
Kingdom (100%)
Tel.: (44) 1216541278
Web Site: http://www.londonmidland.com
Commuter Rail Services
N.A.I.C.S.: 485112

Southern Railway Limited (3)
Go Ahead House 26-28 Addiscombe Road,
Croydon, CR9 5GA, Surrey, United
Kingdom (100%)
Tel.: (44) 2089298600
Web Site: http://www.southernrailway.com
Commuter Railway Transportation Services
N.A.I.C.S.: 485112
Charles Horton *(CEO)*

Subsidiary (Domestic):

Konectbus Limited (2)
Norwich Bus Station Surrey Street, Norwich, NR1 3NX, United Kingdom
Tel.: (44) 3300539358
Web Site: http://www.konectbus.co.uk
Bus Operating Services
N.A.I.C.S.: 485210

London General Transport Services Limited (2)
No 18 Merton High Street, London, SW19
1DN, United Kingdom
Tel.: (44) 208 545 6100
Web Site: https://www.goaheadlondon.com
Transportation Services
N.A.I.C.S.: 484122

KINETIC GROUP SERVICES PTY LTD.

Kinetic Group Services Pty Ltd.—(Continued)

London and Birmingham Railway Limited (2)
102 New St, PO Box 4323, Birmingham, B24HQ, United Kingdom
Tel.: (44) 1216541318
Web Site: http://www.londonmidland.com
Rail Transportation Services
N.A.I.C.S.: 488210

Metrobus Limited (2)
Wheatstone Close, Crawley, RH10 9UA, West Sussex, United Kingdom
Tel.: (44) 1293449191
Web Site: http://www.metrobus.co.uk
Sales Range: $550-599.9 Million
Emp.: 1,400
Urban Bus Transportation Services
N.A.I.C.S.: 485113

Plymouth CityBus Limited (2)
1 Milehouse Road Milehouse, Plymouth, PL3 4AA, Devon, United Kingdom (100%)
Tel.: (44) 1752662271
Web Site: http://www.plymouthcitybus.co.uk
Sales Range: $150-199.9 Million
Emp.: 500
Urban Bus Transportation Services
N.A.I.C.S.: 485113
Richards Stevens (Mng Dir)

Thames Travel (Wallingford) Limited (2)
Thames Travel Collett Southmead Park, Didcot, OX11 7ET, United Kingdom
Tel.: (44) 1865785400
Web Site: http://www.thames-travel.co.uk
Sales Range: $25-49.9 Million
Emp.: 110
Passenger Bus Transportation Services
N.A.I.C.S.: 485210

The Oxford Bus Company Ltd (2)
Cowley House Watlington Road, Oxford, OX4 6GA, Cowley, United Kingdom (100%)
Tel.: (44) 865785400
Web Site: http://www.oxfordbus.co.uk
Sales Range: $250-299.9 Million
Emp.: 550
Urban Bus Transportation Services
N.A.I.C.S.: 485113

KINETIC TRUST LTD.
44 Community Center 2nd Floor Naraina Industrial Area Phase I Near PVR, New Delhi, 110 028, New Delhi, India
Tel.: (91) 1141410592
Web Site: https://www.ktl.co.in
Year Founded: 1992
531274—(BOM)
Rev.: $35,837
Assets: $665,532
Liabilities: $148,182
Net Worth: $517,350
Earnings: $5,530
Fiscal Year-end: 03/31/22
Financial Support Services
N.A.I.C.S.: 523999
Vinod Bansal (Exec Dir)

KINETIKO ENERGY LTD
283 Rokeby Road, Subiaco, 6008, WA, Australia
Tel.: (61) 8 6315 3500
Web Site: http://www.kinetiko.com.au
Sales Range: Less than $1 Million
Coal Bed Methane Mining
N.A.I.C.S.: 212115
Adam Sierakowski (Chm)

KINETIX SYSTEMS HOLDINGS LTD.
Room 2702 Rykadan Capital Tower 135 Hoi Bun Road, Kwun Tong, Kowloon, China (Hong Kong)
Tel.: (852) 21678080
Web Site: http://www.kinetix.com.hk
Year Founded: 1998
Rev.: $24,710,313
Assets: $20,777,589
Liabilities: $9,697,289
Net Worth: $11,080,300
Earnings: ($1,152,019)
Emp.: 85
Fiscal Year-end: 12/31/18
Information Technology Consulting Services
N.A.I.C.S.: 541618
Pak Lun Larry Yu (Chm)

KING ASIA FOODS LTD.
Middle Bank Doncaster Carr Industrial Estate, Doncaster, DN4 5JJ, Yorkshire, United Kingdom
Tel.: (44) 1302760070
Web Site: http://www.kingasia.co.uk
Year Founded: 1985
Sales Range: $10-24.9 Million
Emp.: 150
Food Mfr
N.A.I.C.S.: 311999
Kin Him Fong (Founder & Mng Dir)

KING CHOU MARINE TECHNOLOGY CO., LTD.
23-2F No 2 Chungshan 2nd Road, Kaohsiung, 806, Taiwan
Tel.: (886) 75352939
Web Site: https://www.king-net.com.tw
Year Founded: 1978
4417—(TPE)
Rev.: $102,305,225
Assets: $151,150,986
Liabilities: $52,224,838
Net Worth: $98,926,148
Earnings: $12,561,611
Fiscal Year-end: 12/31/22
Marine Cargo Handling Services
N.A.I.C.S.: 488320
Chia-Jen Chen (CEO)

Subsidiaries:

King Chou (Vietnam) Marine Technology Co., Ltd. (1)
F-3-CN F-4-CN F-9D-CN F-10-CN NA2 Street, My Phuoc 2 Industrial Zone My Phuoc, Ben Cat, Binh Duong, Vietnam
Fishing Net Mfr
N.A.I.C.S.: 314999

King Tai Technology Vietnam Co. Ltd. (1)
Lo G-2-CN Duong NA1-KCN My Phuoc2, P My Phuoc TX Ben Cat T, Binh Dong, Vietnam
Tel.: (84) 2743557891
Web Site: https://kingtaivn.com
Fishing Net Mfr
N.A.I.C.S.: 313210

Kunshan King Chou Fish Net Mfg. Co. Ltd. (1)
China kunshan factory NO 88 ChangXing Branch Road, ZhouShi Town, Kunshan, China
Tel.: (86) 51257301219
Web Site: https://www.kingchou.com
Fishing Net & Twine Mfr
N.A.I.C.S.: 314999

Kunshan King Chou Net Mfg. Co., Ltd. (1)
No 88 ChangXing Branch Road, ZhouShi Town, Kunshan, China
Tel.: (86) 51257301219
Fishing Net Mfr
N.A.I.C.S.: 314999
Peter Zheng (Sls Mgr)

KING CO., LTD.
2-14-9 Nishigotanda, Shinagawa-ku, Tokyo, 141-0031, Japan
Tel.: (81) 334901371
Web Site: https://www.king-group.co.jp
Year Founded: 1948
8118—(TKS)
Rev.: $56,502,280
Assets: $169,242,440
Liabilities: $24,450,390
Net Worth: $144,792,050
Earnings: $3,523,130
Emp.: 156
Fiscal Year-end: 03/31/24
Apparel Product Whslr
N.A.I.C.S.: 424350

Subsidiaries:

Pawn Co., Ltd. (1)
OZAWA BUILDING 3 4F 1-6-6 Jinnan, Shibuya-ku, Tokyo, 150-0041, Japan
Tel.: (81) 334760260
Web Site: http://www.pawn.co.jp
Textile Product Mfr & Distr
N.A.I.C.S.: 315250

KING CORE ELECTRONICS INC.
No 269 Nanfeng Rd, Pingjhen District, Taoyuan, 324, Taiwan
Tel.: (886) 34698855
Web Site: https://www.kingcore.com
6155—(TAI)
Rev.: $17,809,673
Assets: $69,421,986
Liabilities: $20,119,558
Net Worth: $49,302,428
Earnings: $2,445,992
Emp.: 500
Fiscal Year-end: 12/31/23
Electronic Products Mfr
N.A.I.C.S.: 334513

Subsidiaries:

King Core Electronics (Suzhou) Co., Ltd. (1)
No 868 Jiang Lin West Road, Wujiang, Jiangsu, China
Tel.: (86) 512 82073111
Electronic Components Mfr
N.A.I.C.S.: 334419

KING FOOK HOLDINGS LIMITED
9/F King Fook Building 30-32 Des Voeux Road, Central, China (Hong Kong)
Tel.: (852) 28228524
Web Site: http://www.kingfook.com
0280—(HKG)
Rev.: $82,628,457
Assets: $105,945,333
Liabilities: $20,736,115
Net Worth: $85,209,218
Earnings: $3,690,118
Emp.: 137
Fiscal Year-end: 03/31/21
Diamond & Bullion Merchant Whslr
N.A.I.C.S.: 331410
Ka Shing Yeung (Exec Dir)

Subsidiaries:

Jacqueline Emporium Limited (1)
Rm G1-G2 Ground Fl Hotel Miramar 118-130 Nathan Rd, Tsim Sha Tsui, Kowloon, China (Hong Kong)
Tel.: (852) 28228621
Web Site: http://www.kingfook.com
Sales Range: $50-74.9 Million
Emp.: 5
Watch Retailer
N.A.I.C.S.: 423940

Jewellery Hospital Company Limited (1)
Rm K3 3 Fl Kaiser Estate Phase 2 20-28 Man Lok St, Hung Hom, Kowloon, China (Hong Kong)
Tel.: (852) 23762008
Jewelry Product Mfr
N.A.I.C.S.: 339910

King Fook Investment Company Limited (1)
9 Fl King Fook Bldg 30-32 Des Voeux Rd, Central, China (Hong Kong)
Tel.: (852) 25235111
Investment Holding Services
N.A.I.C.S.: 523999

INTERNATIONAL PUBLIC

King Fook Jewellery Group Limited (1)
100 Ground Fl Nathan Rd, Tsim Sha Tsui, Kowloon, China (Hong Kong)
Tel.: (852) 28228524
Web Site: https://www.kingfook.com
Jewelry Whslr
N.A.I.C.S.: 423940

King Fook Securities Company Limited (1)
Rm 1503 15 F Wheelock House 20 Pedder St, Central, China (Hong Kong)
Tel.: (852) 25248271
Securities Brokerage Services
N.A.I.C.S.: 523150

PTE Engineering Limited (1)
Rm 802 8 F Lai Cheong Factory Bldg 479-479A Castle Peak Rd, Cheung Sha Wan, Kowloon, China (Hong Kong)
Tel.: (852) 27601738
Emp.: 10
Commercial Building Construction Services
N.A.I.C.S.: 236220

Superior Travellers Services Limited (1)
1206A 12 F Tower 2 Cheung Sha Wan Plaza 833 Cheung Sha Wan Rd, Cheung Sha Wan, Kowloon, China (Hong Kong)
Tel.: (852) 25445550
Web Site: http://www.superiortravellers.com
Sales Range: $25-49.9 Million
Emp.: 10
Travel Support Services
N.A.I.C.S.: 561599
Stephen Chik (Exec Dir)

KING FREIGHT LINES LIMITED
131 Harris Road, PO Box 880, Pictou, B0K 1H0, NS, Canada
Tel.: (902) 485-8077
Web Site: https://www.kingfreight.com
Year Founded: 1975
Rev.: $13,602,054
Emp.: 100
General Transportation Services
N.A.I.C.S.: 484121
Roland MacDonald (Pres)

KING GEN PUBLIC COMPANY LIMITED
194 Serithai Road, Kannayao Sub-District Kannayao District, Bangkok, 10230, Thailand
Tel.: (66) 20569445
Web Site: http://www.nbc.co.th
KGEN—(THA)
Rev.: $14,307,568
Assets: $34,502,865
Liabilities: $14,186,422
Net Worth: $20,316,443
Earnings: ($1,084,190)
Fiscal Year-end: 12/31/23
Television, Radio & Other Media Broadcasting Services
N.A.I.C.S.: 516120
Samart Deebhijarn (Chm)

KING GEORGE FINANCIAL CORPORATION
Suite 750 - 510 Burrard Street, Vancouver, V6C 3A8, BC, Canada
Tel.: (604) 687-8882
Year Founded: 1999
KGF—(TSXV)
Rev.: $526,586
Assets: $35,106,699
Liabilities: $5,286,324
Net Worth: $29,820,375
Earnings: ($816,240)
Fiscal Year-end: 11/30/20
Real Estate Development Services
N.A.I.C.S.: 531390

KING GLOBAL VENTURES INC.

AND PRIVATE COMPANIES

KING WAI GROUP (THAILAND) PUBLIC COMPANY LIMITED

200-82 Richmond St E, Toronto, M5C 1P1, ON, Canada
Tel.: (204) 955-4803 ON
Web Site: https://www.kingtsxv.com
Year Founded: 2004
KGLDF—(OTCIQ)
Rev.: $20,253
Assets: $2,286,990
Liabilities: $596,620
Net Worth: $1,690,370
Earnings: ($498,548)
Fiscal Year-end: 12/31/21
Gold Exploration & Mining Services
N.A.I.C.S.: 213114
Robert Dzisiak *(CEO)*

KING HWA SIN INDUSTRIAL CO., LTD.
37 Yonde Road Rende Township, T'ainan, 717, Taiwan
Tel.: (886) 62662745
Web Site: http://www.krico.co.tw
Sales Range: $10-24.9 Million
Emp.: 100
Motorcycle Parts Mfr
N.A.I.C.S.: 336991

KING JAMES GROUP COMPANY
3rd Floor Wembley Square N, McKenzie Street Gardens, Cape Town, South Africa
Tel.: (27) 21 465 9511
Web Site: http://www.kingjames.co.za
Year Founded: 1998
Advetising Agency
N.A.I.C.S.: 541810
James Barty *(Grp Mng Dir)*

Subsidiaries:

34 Degrees Agency (1)
41 Coleridge Road, 7925, Cape Town, Salt River, South Africa
Tel.: (27) 21 480 3400
Web Site: http://34.co.za
Advetising Agency
N.A.I.C.S.: 541810

Mnemonic (1)
Wembley Square North, McKenzie St Gardens, Cape Town, South Africa
Tel.: (27) 21 465 3561
Web Site: http://www.mnemonic.co.za
N.A.I.C.S.: 541810

RSVP (1)
3rd Floor Wembley Square North, McKenzie St Gardents, Cape Town, South Africa
Tel.: (27) 21 465 3511
N.A.I.C.S.: 541810

KING JIM CO., LTD.
2-10-18 Higashi-Kanda, Chiyoda-ku, Tokyo, 101-0031, Japan
Tel.: (81) 338645969
Web Site: https://www.kingjim.co.jp
7962—(TKS)
Rev.: $246,019,660
Assets: $217,855,500
Liabilities: $66,703,280
Net Worth: $151,152,220
Earnings: ($1,977,960)
Emp.: 1,822
Fiscal Year-end: 06/30/24
Stationery Products Mfr & Sales
N.A.I.C.S.: 424120
Naomichi Hagita *(Sr Mng Dir)*

Subsidiaries:

G CLASSER CO., LTD. (1)
Eitai Mk 1-5-9 Saga, Koto-ku, Tokyo, 135 0031, Japan
Tel.: (81) 356465026
Web Site: http://www.g-classer.co.jp
Emp.: 14
Commercial Stationery Product Whslr
N.A.I.C.S.: 424120
Mutsumi Daimond *(Pres)*

KING JIM (MALAYSIA) SDN. BHD. (1)
Lot 151 Plot 1 2 Jalan PKNK 3/1, Kawasan Perusahaan, 08000, Sungai Petani, Kedah Darul Aman, Malaysia
Tel.: (60) 44424952
Sales Range: $50-74.9 Million
Emp.: 171
Metal Mechanism Files Mfr
N.A.I.C.S.: 333515

KING JIM (SHANGHAI) TRADING CO., LTD. (1)
Room412-413 Building A No 151 DongJiangWan Road, HongKou District, Shanghai, 200001, China
Tel.: (86) 2153082770
Web Site: https://s-ssl.cn
Stationery Product Whslr
N.A.I.C.S.: 424120

King Jim (HK) Co., Limited (1)
Room 1408 Beverly House 93-107 Lockhart Road, Wanchai, China (Hong Kong)
Tel.: (852) 28380886
Stationery Product Distr
N.A.I.C.S.: 424120

King Jim (Vietnam) Co., Ltd. (1)
Lot D-4A-CN D-4C-CN, My Phuoc Industrial Park 3 Thoi Hoa Ward, Ben Cat, Binh Duong, Vietnam
Tel.: (84) 2839393922
Web Site: https://kingjim.com.vn
Emp.: 1,000
Stationery Product Mfr & Distr
N.A.I.C.S.: 322230

LADONNA CO., LTD. (1)
EITAI-MK Bldg Saga 1-5-9, Koto-ku, Tokyo, 135-0031, Japan
Tel.: (81) 356202780
Web Site: http://www.ladonna-co.net
Sales Range: $25-49.9 Million
Emp.: 40
Photo Frames Mfr
N.A.I.C.S.: 325992

PT King Jim Indonesia (1)
Jl Rembang Industri II/I Rembang Kav, Pasuruan, 67152, East Java, Indonesia
Tel.: (62) 3437401669
Web Site: https://www.kingjim.co.id
Sales Range: $150-199.9 Million
Emp.: 500
Stationery Product Distr
N.A.I.C.S.: 424120

KING LUN HOLDINGS LIMITED
PO Box 71, Road Town, Tortola, Virgin Islands (British)
Tel.: (284) 494 2233 VG
Holding Company
N.A.I.C.S.: 551112
William Kwok Lun Fung *(CEO)*

Subsidiaries:

Fung Holdings (1937) Limited (1)
33/F Alexandria House 18 Chater Road, Central, China (Hong Kong) (100%)
Tel.: (852) 28441937
Web Site: http://www.lifunggroup.com
Sales Range: $15-24.9 Billion
Investment Holding Company
N.A.I.C.S.: 551112
William Kwok Lun Fung *(Grp Mng Dir)*

Subsidiary (Domestic):

LF Asia Investments, Ltd. (2)
33/F Alexandria House 18 Chater Road, Central, China (Hong Kong)
Tel.: (852) 28441937
Web Site: http://www.lifunggroup.com
Equity Investment Firm
N.A.I.C.S.: 523999

KING POLYTECHNIC ENGINEERING CO., LTD.
5F No 210 Ruiguang Rd, Neihu Dist, Taipei, Taiwan
Tel.: (886) 287510858
Web Site: https://kpec.com.tw
Year Founded: 1982
6122—(TPE)
Rev.: $76,868,837

Assets: $116,257,637
Liabilities: $76,448,676
Net Worth: $39,808,961
Earnings: $4,033,737
Fiscal Year-end: 12/31/22
Engineering & Construction Services
N.A.I.C.S.: 541330

KING POWER INTERNATIONAL GROUP CO., LTD.
8 King Power Complex Rangnam Road, Phayathai Ratchathewi, Bangkok, 10400, Thailand
Tel.: (66) 26778888 NV
Web Site: http://www.kingpower.com
Year Founded: 1990
Sales Range: $150-199.9 Million
Emp.: 3,320
Duty-Free & Tax-Free Retailer
N.A.I.C.S.: 455219
Vichai Srivaddhanaprabha *(Chm)*

Subsidiaries:

King Power International Co., Ltd. (1)
8 King Power Complex Rangnam Road, Phayathai Ratchathewi, Bangkok, 10400, Thailand
Tel.: (66) 2677 8888
Duty Free Retailer
N.A.I.C.S.: 459999

KING PRICE FINANCIAL SERVICES (PROPRIETARY) LIMITED
Menlyn Corporate Park Block A 175 Corobay Avenue, Waterkloof Glen Ext 11, Pretoria, 0081, South Africa
Tel.: (27) 860 50 50 50
Web Site: http://www.kingprice.co.za
Insurance Services
N.A.I.C.S.: 524298
Gideon Galloway *(CEO)*

Subsidiaries:

The Standard General Insurance Company Limited (1)
5916 Halfway House, Private Bank X170, Midrand, 1685, South Africa
Tel.: (27) 112569000
Web Site: http://stangenlife.co.za
Sales Range: $350-399.9 Million
Emp.: 1,000
Credit Life Insurance
N.A.I.C.S.: 524113
William Harris *(Mgr-Insurance)*

KING RIVER RESOURCES LIMITED
254 Adelaide Tce, Perth, 6000, WA, Australia
Tel.: (61) 892218055 AU
Web Site: https://www.kingriverresources.com
KRR—(ASX)
Rev.: $1,858,775
Assets: $18,675,240
Liabilities: $324,353
Net Worth: $18,350,887
Earnings: $1,385,085
Fiscal Year-end: 06/30/24
Copper & Other Metal Mining Services
N.A.I.C.S.: 212230
Anthony Barton *(Chm)*

KING SLIDE WORKS CO., LTD.
No 299 Shun An Rd, Lu Zhu Dist, Kaohsiung, 82150, Taiwan
Tel.: (886) 79599688 CN
Web Site: https://www.kingslide.com
Year Founded: 1986
2059—(TAI)
Rev.: $188,461,715
Assets: $673,041,212
Liabilities: $135,542,328
Net Worth: $537,498,884

Earnings: $88,437,127
Emp.: 1,051
Fiscal Year-end: 12/31/23
Electronic, Industrial Equipment & Appliance Designer & Mfr
N.A.I.C.S.: 334419
Shu-Chen Lin *(Gen Mgr)*

Subsidiaries:

King Slide Technology (China) Co., Ltd. (1)
Building 11 No 509 Renqing Rd, Pudong New Area, Shanghai, 201201, China
Tel.: (86) 2150111899
Electronic Equipment Mfr & Whslr
N.A.I.C.S.: 335999

King Slide Technology Co., Ltd. (1)
No 6 Luke 9th Rd, Kaohsiung Science Park Lu Zhu Dist, Kaohsiung, 82151, Taiwan
Tel.: (886) 79761688
Kitchen & Furniture Mfr
N.A.I.C.S.: 337110

King Slide USA, Inc. (1)
12989 Bellaire Blvd Ste 8, Houston, TX 77072
Tel.: (713) 750-9063
Web Site: https://www.kingslide.com
Electronic Equipment Mfr & Whslr
N.A.I.C.S.: 335999

KING STONE ENERGY GROUP LIMITED
17th Floor V Heun Building No 138 Queen's Road, Central, China (Hong Kong)
Tel.: (852) 28015663 HK
Web Site: http://www.663hk.com
0663—(HKG)
Rev.: $18,836,213
Assets: $69,059,100
Liabilities: $23,740,245
Net Worth: $45,318,855
Earnings: $26,456,888
Emp.: 67
Fiscal Year-end: 12/31/22
Coal Mining
N.A.I.C.S.: 213113
Hao Zong *(CEO)*

KING WAI GROUP (THAILAND) PUBLIC COMPANY LIMITED
43 Thai CC Tower 26th Floor South Sathorn Road, Yannawa Sathorn, Bangkok, 10120, Thailand
Tel.: (66) 21295999 TH
Web Site: https://www.kwiasia.com
KWI—(THA)
Rev.: $46,345,212
Assets: $347,421,072
Liabilities: $294,803,095
Net Worth: $52,617,977
Earnings: ($14,743,875)
Emp.: 260
Fiscal Year-end: 12/31/23
Real Estate Development Services
N.A.I.C.S.: 531390
Antonio Tat Chan Hang *(Vice Chm)*

Subsidiaries:

KWI Asset Management Co., Ltd. (1)
43 Thai CC Tower 26th Floor South Sathorn Road, Yan Nawa Sathorn, Bangkok, 10120, Thailand
Tel.: (66) 28440123
Web Site: https://www.kwiam.com
Mutual Fund Management Services
N.A.I.C.S.: 525190

KWI Insurance PCL (1)
No 43 Thai CC Tower 33rd Floor South Sathorn Road, Yannawa Sathorn, Bangkok, 10120, Thailand
Tel.: (66) 26241000
Web Site: https://www.kwii.com
Fire Insurance Services
N.A.I.C.S.: 524113

KWI Life Insurance PCL (1)

4169

KING WAI GROUP (THAILAND) PUBLIC COMPANY LIMITED

King Wai Group (Thailand) Public Company Limited—(Continued)
43 Thai CC Tower 33rd Floor South Sathorn Road, Yan Nawa Sathorn, Bangkok, 10120, Thailand
Tel.: (66) 20339000
Web Site: https://www.kwilife.com
Fire Insurance Services
N.A.I.C.S.: 524113

King Wai Capital Limited (1)
No 43 Thai CC Tower 26th Floor South Sathorn Road, Yannawa Sub-District Sathorn District, Bangkok, 10120, Thailand
Tel.: (66) 21295999
Real Estate Investment Services
N.A.I.C.S.: 531210

Subsidiary (Domestic):

King Wai Insurance Public Company Limited (2)
968 U Chuliang Building 15th Floor Rama IV Road, Silom Bangrak, Bangkok, 10500, Thailand
Tel.: (66) 26241000
Web Site: http://www.kwgi.co.th
Insurance Brokerage Services
N.A.I.C.S.: 524210
Antonio Hang Tat Chan *(Chm)*

Thai-Kami Company Limited (1)
No 43 Thai CC Tower 26th Floor South Sathorn Road, Yannawa Sub-District Sathorn District, Bangkok, 10120, Thailand
Tel.: (66) 21295999
Real Estate Services
N.A.I.C.S.: 531210

Top Property Company Limited (1)
No 43 Thai CC Tower 26th Floor South Sathorn Road, Yannawa Sub-District Sathorn District, Bangkok, 10120, Thailand
Tel.: (66) 21295999
Real Estate Property Development Services
N.A.I.C.S.: 531190

KING WAN CORPORATION LIMITED
8 Sungei Kadut Loop, Singapore, 729455, Singapore
Tel.: (65) 63684300 SG
Web Site: https://www.kingwan.com
Year Founded: 1977
554—(SES)
Rev.: $68,539,070
Assets: $94,201,643
Liabilities: $48,151,527
Net Worth: $46,050,116
Earnings: ($3,573,289)
Emp.: 300
Fiscal Year-end: 03/31/23
Construction Services
N.A.I.C.S.: 236220
Eng Eng Chua *(Mng Dir)*

Subsidiaries:

K&W Mobile Loo Services Pte Ltd (1)
No 8 Sungei Kadut Loop, Singapore, 729455, Singapore
Web Site: http://www.kwmobileloo.com.sg
Portable Lavatories Rental & Cleaning Services
N.A.I.C.S.: 561990

King Wan Construction Pte Ltd (1)
8 Sungei Kadut Loop, Singapore, 729455, Singapore
Tel.: (65) 63684300
Web Site: https://www.kingwan.com
Mechanical & Electrical Engineering Services
N.A.I.C.S.: 541330
Hai Kuey Chua *(Mng Dir)*

KING YUAN ELECTRONICS CO., LTD.
No 81 Section 2 Gongdaowu Rd, Hsinchu, 300, Taiwan
Tel.: (886) 35751888
Web Site: https://www.kyec.com.tw
2449—(TAI)
Rev.: $1,079,999,534
Assets: $2,417,058,446
Liabilities: $1,108,103,003
Net Worth: $1,308,955,443
Earnings: $196,748,415
Emp.: 9,505
Fiscal Year-end: 12/31/23
Semiconductor Mfr
N.A.I.C.S.: 334515
Chin-Kung Lee *(Chm & CEO)*

Subsidiaries:

KYEC Japan - Aldete Corporation (1)
2-3-8 Momochihama, Sawara-ku, Fukuoka, 814-0001, Japan
Tel.: (81) 928216954
Web Site: http://www.kyecjapan.com
Sales Range: $25-49.9 Million
Emp.: 7
Electronic Product Testing Services
N.A.I.C.S.: 541380
Takaro Suzuki *(Pres)*

KYEC Japan K.K. (1)
5F RKB Broadcasting Hall 2-3-8 Momochihama, Sawara-ku, Fukuoka, 814-0001, Japan
Tel.: (81) 928216954
Web Site: https://www.kyecjapan.com
Semiconductor Mfr
N.A.I.C.S.: 333242

KYEC USA Inc. (1)
1735 Technology Dr 270, San Jose, CA 95110
Tel.: (656) 737-6981
Web Site: http://www.kyec.com.tw
Semiconductor Devices Mfr
N.A.I.C.S.: 334413

King Long Technology (Suzhou) Ltd. (1)
No 183 Fang Zhou Road Suzhou Industrial Park, Suzhou, China
Tel.: (86) 51262535188
Measuring & Testing Electricity Mfr
N.A.I.C.S.: 334515

King Yuan Electronics Co., Ltd. - Chu-Nan Factory (1)
No 118 Chung-Hua Road, Chu-Nan, Miao-li, 850, Taiwan
Tel.: (886) 37 595666
Web Site: http://www.kyec.com.tw
Semiconductor Product Mfr
N.A.I.C.S.: 334413

King Yuan Electronics Co., Ltd. - Suzhou Factory (1)
No 183 Fang Zhou Road, Industrial Park, Suzhou, China
Tel.: (86) 51262535188
Web Site: http://www.kltech.com.cn
Measuring & Testing Electricity Mfr
N.A.I.C.S.: 334515

King Yuan Electronics Co., Ltd. - Tongluo Factory (1)
No 8 Tongke N Rd Tong-Luo, Miao-li, Taiwan
Tel.: (886) 37980188
Measuring & Testing Electricity Mfr
N.A.I.C.S.: 334515

KING'S FLAIR INTERNATIONAL (HOLDINGS) LTD.
12/F Yardley Commercial Building 3 Connaught Road West, Sheung Wan, China (Hong Kong)
Tel.: (852) 28506626 Ky
Web Site: http://www.kingsflair.hk
Year Founded: 1989
6822—(HKG)
Rev.: $167,887,075
Assets: $109,010,414
Liabilities: $19,946,370
Net Worth: $89,064,043
Earnings: $13,639,248
Emp.: 193
Fiscal Year-end: 12/31/21
Kitchenware Product Mfr & Distr
N.A.I.C.S.: 327110
Alex Siu Wah Wong *(Founder, Chm & CEO)*

Subsidiaries:

Gloxis Development Limited (1)
22/F Goodwill Industrial Building 36-44 Pak Tin Par Street, Tsuen Wan, China (Hong Kong)
Tel.: (852) 28052182
Web Site: http://www.gourmetkitchen.hk
Kitchenware Retailer
N.A.I.C.S.: 449129

Wonder Household Limited (1)
12/F Yardley Commercial Building 3 Connaught Road West, Sheung Wan, Hong Kong, China (Hong Kong)
Tel.: (852) 24170803
Web Site: http://www.wonderhousehold.com
Household Product Distr
N.A.I.C.S.: 423990
Tony Hui *(Mktg Mgr)*

KING'S HEAD DEVELOPMENT PLC
Posidonos 77, Paphos, Cyprus
Tel.: (357) 26813060
Building Construction Services
N.A.I.C.S.: 236220

KING'S TOWN BANK
No 506 Sec 1 Ximen Rd, West Central District, T'ainan, 700, Taiwan
Tel.: (886) 62135231
Web Site: https://esg.ktb.com.tw
2809—(TAI)
Rev.: $345,574,499
Assets: $12,569,019,408
Liabilities: $10,930,163,850
Net Worth: $1,638,855,558
Earnings: $202,985,734
Emp.: 972
Fiscal Year-end: 12/31/23
Commercial Banking Services
N.A.I.C.S.: 522110
Chen-Chih Tai *(Chm)*

KING'S TOWN CONSTRUCTION CO., LTD.
16F No 150 Boai 2nd Rd, Zuoying Dist, Kaohsiung, 813, Taiwan
Tel.: (886) 75586368
Web Site: http://www.kingtown.com.tw
2524—(TAI)
Rev.: $83,513,061
Assets: $1,210,935,040
Liabilities: $631,190,303
Net Worth: $579,744,738
Earnings: $14,455,704
Emp.: 41
Fiscal Year-end: 12/31/23
Real Estate Development Services
N.A.I.C.S.: 531390
Tien-Tsan Tsai *(Chm)*

KINGBO STRIKE LIMITED
Room 1011 10/F Wing On Centre, 111 Connaught Road Central, Sheung Wan, China (Hong Kong)
Tel.: (852) 35231121 Ky
Web Site: http://www.kingbostrike.com
Year Founded: 2013
1421—(HKG)
Rev.: $27,292,942
Assets: $39,887,194
Liabilities: $8,147,022
Net Worth: $31,740,172
Earnings: ($6,677,682)
Emp.: 23
Fiscal Year-end: 06/30/22
Electrical Engineering Services
N.A.I.C.S.: 541330
Yancheng Liu *(Chm)*

KINGBOARD HOLDINGS LIMITED

INTERNATIONAL PUBLIC

23/F, Delta House, 3 On Yiu Street, Shek Mun, Sha Tin, NT, China (Hong Kong)
Tel.: (852) 26056493
Web Site: http://www.kingboard.com
0148—(OTCIQ)
Rev.: $6,310,261,224
Assets: $12,434,106,228
Liabilities: $4,165,951,410
Net Worth: $8,268,154,817
Earnings: $535,298,989
Emp.: 35,000
Fiscal Year-end: 12/31/22
Laminates, Plastic Circuit Boards & Chemicals
N.A.I.C.S.: 334412
Wing Yiu Chang *(Mng Dir)*

Subsidiaries:

Elec & Eltek International Holdings Limited (1)
Unit B10 3rd-Floor Merit Industrial Centre, 94 Tokwawan Road Tokwawan, Kowloon, China (Hong Kong) (73.63%)
Tel.: (852) 29543333
Web Site: http://www.eleceltek.com
Sales Range: $1-4.9 Billion
Emp.: 12,000
Basic Inorganic Chemical Mfr
N.A.I.C.S.: 325180

Subsidiary (Non-US):

Elec & Eltek (Guangzhou) Electronic Company Limited (2)
No 3 Lin Jiang Road Guangzhou Economic & Technological, Development District, Guangzhou, 510730, China (69.47%)
Tel.: (86) 2082212222
Web Site: http://www.eleceltek.com
Bare Printed Circuit Board Mfr
N.A.I.C.S.: 334412

Elec & Eltek International Company Limited (2)
80 Raffles Place 33-00 UOB Plaza 1, Singapore, 048624, Singapore (70.89%)
Tel.: (65) 62252626
Web Site: http://www.eleceltek.com
Rev.: $616,508,000
Assets: $753,482,000
Liabilities: $317,912,000
Net Worth: $435,570,000
Earnings: $31,256,000
Emp.: 8,600
Fiscal Year-end: 12/31/2019
Printed Circuit Board Mfr
N.A.I.C.S.: 334412
Wing Yiu Chang *(Exec Dir)*

Subsidiary (Non-US):

Elec & Eltek (Thailand) Limited (3)
34 Moo 2 Nonthaburi-Pathumthani Road, Bang-Khayang Muang, Pathumthani, 12000, Thailand
Tel.: (66) 29753001
Electronic Component Mfr & Distr
N.A.I.C.S.: 334419

Elec & Eltek Company (Macao Commercial Offshore) Limited (3)
Av Da Praia Grande No 599 Edificio Comercial Rodrigues 3rd Andar E, Macau, China (Macau)
Tel.: (853) 28389471
Electronic Component Mfr & Distr
N.A.I.C.S.: 334419

Kaiping Pacic Insulating Material Company Limited (3)
No 318 Siqian West Road, Kaiping, Guangdong, China
Tel.: (86) 7502218428
Web Site: http://www.piclaminate.com.cn
Insulation Material Product Mfr
N.A.I.C.S.: 327993

Subsidiary (Non-US):

Guangzhou Elec & Eltek Company Limited (2)
No 3 Linjiang Road Guangzhou Economic & Technological Development, District, Guangzhou, 510730, China (69.47%)
Tel.: (86) 2082212222
Web Site: http://www.eleceltek.com

AND PRIVATE COMPANIES

Bare Printed Circuit Board Mfr
N.A.I.C.S.: 334412

Guangzhou Elec & Eltek High Density Interconnect Technology No.1 Company Limited (2)
No 3 Linjiang Rd Guangzhou Economic & Tech Dev District, Guangzhou, 510730, PRC, China
Tel.: (86) 2082212222 (69.47%)
Web Site: http://www.eleceltek.com
Sales Range: $700-749.9 Million
Emp.: 4,600
Bare Printed Circuit Board Mfr
N.A.I.C.S.: 334412

Kai Ping Elec & Eltek Company Limited (2)
No 318 Siqian West Road, Kaiping, China
Tel.: (86) 7502218428 (67.35%)
Web Site: http://www.eleceltek.com
Sales Range: $700-749.9 Million
Emp.: 4,500
Bare Printed Circuit Board Mfr
N.A.I.C.S.: 334412

Pacific Insulating Material (Thailand) Limited (1)
1-68 Moo 5 Rojana Industrial Park Rojana Rd, Tambon Khanham Amphur Uthai, 13210, Ayutthaya, Thailand (70.89%)
Tel.: (66) 35330772
Sales Range: $25-49.9 Million
Emp.: 164
Bare Printed Circuit Board Mfr
N.A.I.C.S.: 334412

Golden Concept Development Limited (1)
301 3/F Grandmark 10 Granville Road, Tsim Sha Tsui, Kowloon, China (Hong Kong)
Tel.: (852) 27239707
Web Site: https://www.goldconcept.com.hk
Digital Printing Services
N.A.I.C.S.: 323111

Guangzhou Chung Shun Century Fibre Glass Co., Ltd. (1)
Nansha Economic & Technology Development Zone, Tantou Administration District, Beihai, Guangdong, China (72.5%)
Tel.: (86) 7523500078
Pressed & Blown Glass & Glassware Mfr
N.A.I.C.S.: 327212

Heng Yang Kingboard Chemical Co., Ltd. (1)
Songmu Industry Park, Hengyang, Hunan, China
Tel.: (86) 7348539896
Caustic Soda Mfr & Distr
N.A.I.C.S.: 325180

Huiyang TECHWISE Industrial Technology Co. Ltd (1)
Huiyang Economic Development Zone Lenovo Science & Technology Park, Sun City Huizhou City, Huiyang, Guangdong, China (90%)
Tel.: (86) 7523500078
Web Site: http://www.techwise-Circuits.com
Printed Circuit Board Mfr
N.A.I.C.S.: 334412

Huizhou Chung Shun Chemical Company Limited (1)
No 6 Bin Hai 11 Road Daya Bay Economic and Tech, Develop Zone Petrochemical Industrial Park, Huizhou, Guangdong, China
Tel.: (86) 7523096999
Chemical Product Mfr & Distr
N.A.I.C.S.: 325180

Kaiping Elec & Eltek No. 3 Company Limited (1)
No 318 Siqian West Road, Shagang District, Kaiping, 529325, Guangdong, China
Tel.: (86) 7502261016
Printed Circuit Board Mfr
N.A.I.C.S.: 334412

Kaiping Elec & Eltek No. 5 Company Limited (1)
No 318 Siqian W Rd, Kaiping, 529325, Guangdong, China
Tel.: (86) 7502218428
Printed Circuit Board Mfr
N.A.I.C.S.: 334412

Kingboard (Fogang) Laminates Co. Limited (1)
Kingboard Industrial Area, Shijiao Town Fogang County Qin, Fushun, Guangdong, China (72.5%)
Tel.: (86) 7634270188
Web Site: http://www.kingboard.com
Glass & Glazing Contractors
N.A.I.C.S.: 238150

Kingboard (Fogang) Paper Laminates Co., Ltd. (1)
Kingboard Industrial Area, Shijiao Town Fogang County, Qingyuan, Guangdong, China (75.3%)
Tel.: (86) 7634270188
Web Site: https://www.kingboard.com
Laminate Mfr & Distr
N.A.I.C.S.: 326130

Kingboard (Hebei) Chemical Co. Limited (1)
No 1 Kingboard Road, Dameng Town Neiyou County Xing, Wafangdian, Hebei, China (100%)
Tel.: (86) 3195928012
Web Site: http://www.kingboard.com
Oil & Gas Operations
N.A.I.C.S.: 213112

Kingboard (Hebei) Cokechem Co. Limited (1)
No 1 Kingboard Road, Dameng Town Neiyou County Xing, Wafangdian, Hebei, China (100%)
Tel.: (86) 3195928012
Web Site: http://www.kingboard.com
Oil & Gas Operations
N.A.I.C.S.: 213112

Kingboard (Jiangsu) Chemical Co., Ltd. (1)
No 2 Jiasheng Beilu Shizhuang Park, Jiang Yin Economic Development Area, Jiangsu, Jiangsu, China
Tel.: (86) 51086666148
Chemical Product Mfr & Distr
N.A.I.C.S.: 325998

Kingboard (LianZhou) Fibre Glass Co. Limited (1)
Kingboard Industrial Park Lianzhou Town, North 107 Highway, Beihai, Guangdong, China (72.5%)
Tel.: (86) 7636509000
Glass & Glazing Contractors
N.A.I.C.S.: 238150

Kingboard (Panyu Nansha) Petrochemical Company Limited (1)
Nansha Economic & Technology Development Zone, Tantou Managerial Zone Panyu, Guangzhou, Guangdong, China (72.5%)
Tel.: (86) 20 2865 5555
Web Site: http://www.kingboard.com
Plastics Material & Resin Mfr
N.A.I.C.S.: 325211

Kingboard (TaiCang) Chemical Co., Ltd. (1)
Shihua Industrial Area, Port Development Area Liujia P, Suzhou, Jiangsu, China (100%)
Tel.: (86) 51253647022
Web Site: http://www.kingboard.com
Sales Range: $25-49.9 Million
Emp.: 50
Miscellaneous Chemical Product & Preparation Mfr
N.A.I.C.S.: 325998

Kingboard Copper Foil Holdings Limited (1)
23/F Delta House 3 On Yiu Street Shek Mun, Sha Tin, China (Hong Kong)
Tel.: (852) 26056493
Web Site: http://www.kbcopperfoil.com
Rev.: $74,951,349
Assets: $368,139,719
Liabilities: $14,177,038
Net Worth: $353,962,681
Earnings: $3,502,792
Fiscal Year-end: 12/31/2018
Copper Foil Mfr
N.A.I.C.S.: 331420

Kingboard Electronic Raw Material (Jiang Yin) Co., Ltd. (1)
Shizhuang Park, Jiangyin Economic Development Zone, Jiangyin, Jiangsu, China
Tel.: (86) 51086035000
Laminate Mfr & Distr
N.A.I.C.S.: 326130

Kingboard Investments Limited (1)
12 Science Park East Avenue Phase II, Sha Tin, China (Hong Kong) (100%)
Tel.: (852) 26056493
Sales Range: $25-49.9 Million
Emp.: 20
Metal Service Centers & Offices
N.A.I.C.S.: 423510

Kingboard Laminates (Jiangmen) Co., Ltd. (1)
No 40 Jinou Road Jiangmen High Tech Development Zone, Jiangmen, Guangdong, China (72.5%)
Tel.: (86) 7503869888
Web Site: http://www.kblaminates.com
Coated & Laminated Paper Mfr
N.A.I.C.S.: 322220

Kingboard Laminates (Kunshan) Co., Ltd. (1)
Zhangpu Support Area, Kunshan Economic and Technological Development Zone, Kunshan, 215321, Jiangsu, China (72.5%)
Tel.: (86) 51257441689
Web Site: https://www.kingboard.com
Sales Range: $25-49.9 Million
Emp.: 27
Coated & Laminated Paper Mfr
N.A.I.C.S.: 322220

Kingboard Laminates (Shaoguan) Limited (1)
Baoshi Industrial Area, Taiping Town Shixing County, Shaoguan, Guangdong, China (72.5%)
Tel.: (86) 7513312403
Web Site: http://www.kblaminates.com
Coated & Laminated Paper Mfr
N.A.I.C.S.: 322220

Kingboard Laminates Holdings Limited (1)
2nd floor Harbour View 1 Phase-2, Science Park East Avenue, Sha Tin, NT, China (Hong Kong) (72.5%)
Tel.: (852) 26056493
Web Site: http://www.kblaminates.com
Sales Range: $25-49.9 Million
Emp.: 30
Adhesive Mfr
N.A.I.C.S.: 325520

Kunshan Yattao Chemical Co., Ltd. (1)
No 40 Jinou Road Jiangmen High Tech Development Zone, Jiangmen, Guangdong, China
Tel.: (86) 51257441689
Coated & Laminated Paper Mfr
N.A.I.C.S.: 322220

Shi You Chemical (Yangzhou) Co., Ltd. (1)
88-10 Tai Lian Road, Yangzhou Chemical Industry Park, Yizheng, Jiangsu, China
Tel.: (86) 51483290830
Chemical Products Distr
N.A.I.C.S.: 424690

Techwise Circuits Company Limited (1)
1/F Harbour View 1 No 12 Science Park East Avenue, Phase 2 Hong Kong Science Park, Sha Tin, NT, China (Hong Kong) (57%)
Tel.: (852) 26778928
Web Site: http://www.techwise-circuits.com
Sales Range: $800-899.9 Million
Emp.: 3,500
Printed Circuit Board Mfr
N.A.I.C.S.: 334412

Techwise Shirai (Fogang) Circuits Limited (1)
Kingboard Industry Park, Shi Jiao Town Fogang Country, Fushun, Guangdong, China (63%)
Tel.: (86) 7634296800
Electronic Computer Mfr
N.A.I.C.S.: 334111

KINGCAN HOLDINGS LIMITED

Taiwanese Investment Zone Fengshan Industrial Park, Zhangzhou, Fujian, China
Tel.: (86) 5966795345
Web Site: http://www.tw.kingcan.net
8411—(TAI)
Rev.: $869,006,948
Assets: $1,492,429,539
Liabilities: $749,169,284
Net Worth: $743,260,255
Earnings: ($86,151,924)
Fiscal Year-end: 12/31/19
Holding Company
N.A.I.C.S.: 551112

Subsidiaries:

Shandong Fu-zhen Metal Packaging Co. (1)
No 1075 Industrial Rd Mingshui Economic Development Zone, Zhangqiu, Shandong, China
Tel.: (86) 531 61323235
Web Site: http://www.enkingcanholdings.com
Tinplate Can Mfr
N.A.I.C.S.: 332431

KINGCLEAN ELECTRIC CO., LTD.

No 1 Xiangyang Road, Suzhou New District, Suzhou, 215009, Jiangsu, China
Tel.: (86) 51268253260
Web Site: https://www.kingclean.com
Year Founded: 1994
603355—(SHG)
Rev.: $1,251,010,543
Assets: $1,481,964,527
Liabilities: $947,631,246
Net Worth: $534,333,281
Earnings: $137,996,745
Fiscal Year-end: 12/31/22
Household Health Appliance Mfr & Distr
N.A.I.C.S.: 335220
Ni Zugen (Chm & Gen Mgr)

KINGDEE INTERNATIONAL SOFTWARE GROUP COMPANY LTD.

Suite 1501 15FCentral Plaza 18 Harbor Road, Wanchai, China (Hong Kong)
Tel.: (852) 21579390
Web Site: http://www.kingdee.com.hk
0268—(OTCIQ)
Rev.: $514,240,938
Assets: $1,642,729,724
Liabilities: $423,411,462
Net Worth: $1,219,318,261
Earnings: ($52,351,091)
Emp.: 10,663
Fiscal Year-end: 12/31/20
Software Products Developing & Sales
N.A.I.C.S.: 513210
Shaochun Xu (Chm & CEO)

Subsidiaries:

Kingdee International Software Group (H.K.) Co., Ltd. (1)
Suite 1501 15/F Central Plaza 18 Harbour Road, Wanchai, China (Hong Kong)
Tel.: (852) 21579390
Web Site: https://www.kingdee.com.hk
Packaged Sofware Development & Sales
N.A.I.C.S.: 423430
Shaochun Xu (Founder, Chm & CEO)

Kingdee International Software Group (Singapore) Pte Ltd. (1)
5 Temasek Blvd Suntec Tower 5 Level 17, Singapore, 038985, Singapore
Tel.: (65) 64158612
Web Site: http://www.kingdee.com.sg
Software Publisher
N.A.I.C.S.: 513210

KINGDEE INTERNATIONAL SOFTWARE GROUP COMPANY LTD.

Kingdee International Software Group Company Ltd.—(Continued)

Shenzhen Kingdee Middleware Co., Ltd. (1)
Fl 2 Bldg M-6 Middle Section Shenzhen High-tech Indus Park, Shenzhen, 518057, Guangdong, China
Tel.: (86) 75586028059
Web Site: http://www.apusic.com
Software Development Services
N.A.I.C.S.: 541511

Xiamen Kingdee Software Co., Ltd. (1)
B1-B5 15 F Zhongmin Mansion No 72 Shihubin N Rd, Xiamen, 361012, Fujian, China
Tel.: (86) 5925092599
Sales Range: $25-49.9 Million
Emp.: 100
Software Development Services
N.A.I.C.S.: 541511

KINGDOM HOLDING COMPANY

1 Kingdom Centre 66th Floor, PO Box 1, Riyadh, 11321, Saudi Arabia
Tel.: (966) 112111111
Web Site:
   http://www.kingdom.com.sa
Year Founded: 1980
4280—(SAU)
Rev.: $424,668,444
Assets: $14,424,299,427
Liabilities: $4,659,089,988
Net Worth: $9,765,209,439
Earnings: $263,496,334
Emp.: 19
Fiscal Year-end: 12/31/23
Investment Holding Company
N.A.I.C.S.: 551112
Alwaleed Talal *(Chm)*

Subsidiaries:

Kingdom Agriculture Development Company (1)
37 El-Ahrar St 7th Floor, Mohandessin, Giza, Egypt
Tel.: (20) 2027602811
Agricultural Services
N.A.I.C.S.: 541690

Kingdom Hotel Investments (1)
Dubai International Financial Centre, PO Box 121223, Dubai, United Arab Emirates
Tel.: (971) 43611800
Web Site: http://www.kingdomhotels.com
Emp.: 30
Holding Company; Luxury Hotel & Resort Investment, Development & Operator
N.A.I.C.S.: 551112
Sarmad Zok *(Chm & CEO)*

Medical Services Projects Company Ltd (1)
King Abdul Aziz Road, Riyadh, Saudi Arabia
Tel.: (966) 112750677
Healthcare Services
N.A.I.C.S.: 621498

KINGDOM HOLDINGS LIMITED

Henggang Town, Haiyan, Jiaxing, 314313, Zhejiang, China
Tel.: (86) 57386782999   Ky
Web Site: http://www.kingdom-china.com
Year Founded: 2006
0528—(HKG)
Rev.: $283,756,122
Assets: $407,851,049
Liabilities: $198,937,253
Net Worth: $208,913,796
Earnings: $24,121,843
Emp.: 4,087
Fiscal Year-end: 12/31/22
Yarn Mfr
N.A.I.C.S.: 313110
Weiming Ren *(Chm)*

Subsidiaries:

Heilongjiang Kingdom Enterprise Co, Ltd. (1)
Qinggang County, Suihua, Heilongjiang, China
Tel.: (86) 4553121001
Linen Textile Mfr
N.A.I.C.S.: 314999

Jiangsu Ziwei Flax Co., Ltd. (1)
No 1 Huimin West Road, Rugao Economic Development Area, Rugao, Jiangsu, China
Tel.: (86) 513 87303907
Yarn Mfr
N.A.I.C.S.: 313110

Kingdom Europe S.R.L. (1)
Via Delle fonti N 410 412 414, 59100, Prato, Italy
Tel.: (39) 0574757226
Yarn Distr
N.A.I.C.S.: 424310

Zhaosu Jindi Flax Co., Ltd. (1)
Fourth Agricultural Division Qishiwutuan, Zhaosu, Xinjiang, Ili, China
Tel.: (86) 999 6230910
Yarn Mfr
N.A.I.C.S.: 313110

Zhejiang Kingdom Flax Co., Ltd. (1)
No 513 Jinghai Road, Haiyan Economic Development Area, Haiyan, Zhejiang, China
Tel.: (86) 573 86792999
Yarn Mfr
N.A.I.C.S.: 313110

KINGENTA ECOLOGICAL ENGINEERING GROUP CO., LTD.

No 19 Xingda West Street, Linshu, Linyi, 276700, Shandong, China
Tel.: (86) 5397198777
Web Site: http://www.kingenta.com
Year Founded: 1998
002470—(SSE)
Rev.: $1,400,731,488
Assets: $1,892,861,568
Liabilities: $1,465,662,276
Net Worth: $427,199,292
Earnings: ($137,919,132)
Emp.: 10,000
Fiscal Year-end: 12/31/22
Chemical Fertiliser Mfr
N.A.I.C.S.: 325314
Li Yuxiao *(Chm)*

Subsidiaries:

COMPO GmbH (1)
Gildenstrasse 38, 48157, Munster, Germany
Tel.: (49) 25132770
Web Site: https://www.compo.de
Potting Soil, Fertilizer & Other Plant Products Mfr
N.A.I.C.S.: 325314

Subsidiary (Non-US):

COMPO Austria GmbH (2)
Hietzinger Hauptstrasse 119, 1130, Vienna, Austria
Tel.: (43) 187663930
Web Site: http://www.compo.com
Potting Soil, Fertilizer & Other Plant Products Sales
N.A.I.C.S.: 424690

COMPO Benelux N.V. (2)
Venecolaan 56, 9880, Aalter, Belgium
Tel.: (32) 93110000
Web Site: https://www.compo.be
Potting Soil, Fertilizer & Other Plant Products Sales
N.A.I.C.S.: 424690

COMPO Iberia S.L. (2)
Av/ Diagonal 188 3 B, 08018, Barcelona, Spain
Tel.: (34) 932247220
Web Site: https://www.compo.es
Potting Soil, Fertilizer & Other Plant Products Sales
N.A.I.C.S.: 424690

COMPO do Brasil S.A. (2)
Rua Cristovao Nunes Pires 110 100 Andar, Bairro Centro, Florianopolis, 88010-120, SC, Brazil
Tel.: (55) 4837229500
Web Site: http://www.compo-expert.com
Potting Soil, Fertilizer & Other Plant Products Sales
N.A.I.C.S.: 424690

Ecompany International B.V. (1)
Verloren van Themaatweg 2A, 6121 RG, Born, Netherlands
Tel.: (31) 467271000
Web Site: http://www.ekompany.eu
Fertilizer Mfr
N.A.I.C.S.: 325311
Peter Bali *(Mng Dir)*

Kingenta Australia AG Pty. Ltd. (1)
L2 414 Hunter Street, Newcastle, 2300, NSW, Australia
Tel.: (61) 249294972
Web Site: https://www.kingenta.com.au
Fertilizer Mfr
N.A.I.C.S.: 325311
Shaun Bailey *(Dir-Bus Dev)*

Kingenta Vietnam Company Limited (1)
148 Street 43, Tan Quy Ward District 7, Ho Chi Minh City, Vietnam
Tel.: (84) 837763900
Web Site: http://kingenta.com.vn
Fertilizer Mfr
N.A.I.C.S.: 325311

KINGFA SCI &TECH CO., LTD.

Kingfa-Guangzhou No 33 kefeng Road, Science City, Guangzhou, 510663, China
Tel.: (86) 2066818881
Web Site: https://www.kingfa.com.cn
Year Founded: 1993
600143—(SHG)
Rev.: $5,673,891,300
Assets: $7,782,184,580
Liabilities: $5,214,673,536
Net Worth: $2,567,511,044
Earnings: $279,662,648
Fiscal Year-end: 12/31/22
Plastics Product Mfr
N.A.I.C.S.: 325211
Chen Pingxu *(Chm)*

Subsidiaries:

Chengdu Kingfa Sci & Tech Advanced Materials Co., Ltd. (1)
No 333 Fujia Street, Gongxing Subdistrict Office Shuangliu District, Chengdu, 610213, Sichuan, China
Tel.: (86) 2869591661
Plastic Material Mfr & Whslr
N.A.I.C.S.: 325211
Li Chen *(Gen Mgr)*

Jiangsu Kinfa Sci. & Tech. Advanced Materials Co. Ltd. (1)
No 388 Xijiang Road Economic & Technological Development Zone, Kunshan, 215300, China
Tel.: (86) 51283688888
Plastics Material Mfr & Distr
N.A.I.C.S.: 325211

Jiangsu Kingfa Sci & Tech Advanced Materials Co., Ltd. (1)
No 388 Xijiang Road Economic and Technological Development Zone, Kunshan, 215300, China
Tel.: (86) 51283688888
Plastic Material Mfr & Whslr
N.A.I.C.S.: 325211
Hesheng Huang *(Gen Mgr)*

Kingfa Sci & Tech (USA) Inc. (1)
47440 Michigan Ave Ste 100, Canton, MI 48188
Tel.: (734) 888-4100
Plastics Product Mfr
N.A.I.C.S.: 325211
Richard Nie *(Pres)*

Kingfa Sci. & Tech (Malaysia), Ltd. (1)
No 22 Jalan Kasuarina 10/ks7, Bandar Botanic, 41200, Klang, Selangor, Malaysia
Tel.: (60) 333817604
Home Appliance Mfr & Distr
N.A.I.C.S.: 335220

Liaoning Kingfa Advanced Materials Co. Ltd. (1)
Liaobin Coastal Economic and Technological Development Zone, Panjin, 124000, Liaoning, China
Tel.: (86) 4272395779
Plastic Material Distr
N.A.I.C.S.: 424610

Shanghai Kingfa Sci & Tech Dvpt Co., Ltd. (1)
No 88 Kangyuan Road, Zhujiajiao Industrial Park Qingpu District, Shanghai, 201714, China
Tel.: (86) 2169835666
Plastic Material Mfr & Whslr
N.A.I.C.S.: 325211
Hesheng Huang *(Gen Mgr)*

Sichuan Kingfa Sci & Tech Dvpt Co., Ltd. (1)
Yongan Road Intersection, Yongxing Industrial Park Gaoxin District, Mianyang, 621000, Sichuan, China
Tel.: (86) 8162976118
Plastic Material Mfr & Whslr
N.A.I.C.S.: 325211

Tianjin Kingfa Advanced Materials Co., Ltd. (1)
No 1 Weiqi Road Konggang Economic Zone, Tianjin, 300308, China
Tel.: (86) 2259802222
Plastic Material Mfr & Whslr
N.A.I.C.S.: 325211
Zhonglin Wang *(Gen Mgr)*

Wuhan Kingfa Sci & Tech Co., Ltd. (1)
No 28 Lianhu Road Wuhan Economic and Technological Development Zone, Wuhan, 430056, China
Tel.: (86) 2769907500
Plastic Material Mfr & Whslr
N.A.I.C.S.: 325211
Qisheng Yu *(Gen Mgr)*

KINGFA SCIENCE & TECHNOLOGY (INDIA) LTD.

Dhun Building III Floor 827 Anna Salai, Chennai, 600 002, India
Tel.: (91) 4428521736
Web Site:
   https://www.kingfaindia.com
Year Founded: 1987
524019—(BOM)
Rev.: $143,160,777
Assets: $119,666,970
Liabilities: $67,170,790
Net Worth: $52,496,180
Earnings: $4,181,459
Emp.: 221
Fiscal Year-end: 03/31/22
Plastic Materials Mfr
N.A.I.C.S.: 325211
Bo Jingen *(Mng Dir)*

KINGFIELD HEATH LTD.

Kaye House Sheffield Airport Business Park, Europa Link, Sheffield, S91 XU, United Kingdom
Tel.: (44) 42566000
Web Site:
   http://www.kingfieldheath.co.uk
Year Founded: 1999
Sales Range: $200-249.9 Million
Emp.: 1,000
Office Furniture & Suppliers Whslr
N.A.I.C.S.: 423420
Tony Hunt *(Ops Dir)*

KINGFISH LIMITED

Level 1 67-73 Hurstmere Road, Private Bag 93502, Takapuna, Auckland, 0740, New Zealand
Tel.: (64) 94897094
Web Site: https://www.kingfish.co.nz
KFL—(NZX)
Rev.: $281,699
Assets: $276,451,555
Liabilities: $384,569
Net Worth: $276,066,986
Earnings: ($11,644,139)
Fiscal Year-end: 03/31/23

AND PRIVATE COMPANIES

Investment Management Service
N.A.I.C.S.: 523940
Alistair Ryan *(Chm)*

KINGFISHER METALS CORP.
1710 - 1050 W Pender Street, Vancouver, V6E 3S7, BC, Canada
Tel.: (778) 606-2507
Web Site: https://kingfishermetals.com
KFR—(OTCIQ)
Rev.: $508
Assets: $9,294,483
Liabilities: $581,336
Net Worth: $8,713,147
Earnings: ($2,949,156)
Fiscal Year-end: 12/31/21
Business Consulting Services
N.A.I.C.S.: 541611
Dustin Perry *(Founder)*

KINGFISHER MINING LIMITED
Level 8 London House 216 St Georges Terrace, Perth, 6000, WA, Australia
Tel.: (61) 894810389   AU
Web Site: https://www.kingfishermining.com
Year Founded: 2018
KFM—(ASX)
Rev.: $43,750
Assets: $5,126,296
Liabilities: $184,296
Net Worth: $4,942,000
Earnings: ($1,313,133)
Fiscal Year-end: 06/30/23
Mining Services
N.A.I.C.S.: 212290
Stephen Brockhurst *(Sec)*

KINGFISHER PLC
1 Paddington Square, London, W2 1GG, United Kingdom
Tel.: (44) 2073728008   UK
Web Site: https://www.kingfisher.com
Year Founded: 1982
KGF—(LSE)
Rev.: $15,100,450,800
Assets: $14,836,819,200
Liabilities: $7,226,916,000
Net Worth: $7,609,903,200
Earnings: $10,492,800
Emp.: 79,000
Fiscal Year-end: 01/31/20
Household Product Distr
N.A.I.C.S.: 551112
Nigel Cope *(Head-Media Rels)*

Subsidiaries:

B&Q Limited   (1)
B&Q House Chestnut Avenue Chandler's Ford, Eastleigh, SO53 3LE, Hampshire, United Kingdom
Tel.: (44) 38784555
Web Site: https://www.diy.com
Sales Range: $5-14.9 Billion
Emp.: 38,000
Home Improvement Products Retailer
N.A.I.C.S.: 423390
Euan Sutherland *(CEO)*

B&Q Properties Limited   (1)
Hampshire Corporate Pk Templars Way Chandler's Ford, Eastleigh, SO53 3YX, United Kingdom
Tel.: (44) 2380256256
Property Management Services
N.A.I.C.S.: 531311

BCC Electro-Speciaalzaken B.V.   (1)
Postbus 75513, 1118 ZN, Schiphol, Netherlands   (100%)
Tel.: (31) 203348888
Web Site: http://www.bcc.nl
Sales Range: $25-49.9 Million
Mfr of Various Electronic Devices
N.A.I.C.S.: 334419

Brico Depot Romania   (1)
Calea Giulesti 1-3 sector 6, 060251, Bucharest, 060251, Romania
Tel.: (40) 212043434
Web Site: https://www.bricodepot.ro
Home Improvement Products Mfr
N.A.I.C.S.: 236118

Brico Depot SAS   (1)
30/32 rue de la Tourelle, 91310, Longpont-sur-Orge, France   (100%)
Tel.: (33) 169630500
Web Site: https://www.bricodepot.fr
Sales Range: $100-124.9 Million
Hardware & Home Stores
N.A.I.C.S.: 444110

Castorama France S.A.S   (1)
CS 50101, Templemars, 59687, Wattignies, Cedex, France
Tel.: (33) 974750174
Web Site: https://www.castorama.fr
Hardware Store Operation Services
N.A.I.C.S.: 444140

Castorama Polska Sp. Z o.o   (1)
ul Krakowiakow 78, 02-255, Warsaw, Poland
Tel.: (48) 225753100
Web Site: https://www.castorama.pl
Home Center & Hardware Retailer
N.A.I.C.S.: 444110

Castorama-Dubois Investissements   (1)
Parc D Activities, BP 101, Templemars, 59175, France   (98.8%)
Tel.: (33) 320167272
Web Site: http://www.castorama.fr
Sales Range: $1-9.9 Million
Emp.: 800
Do-It-Yourself Retailer
N.A.I.C.S.: 444140

Euro Depot Espana S.A.U   (1)
C/la Selva 10 Inblau Edificio A 1a, Barcelona, 08820, El Prat de Llobregat, 08820, Spain
Tel.: (34) 935739272
Household Product Retail Store Operating Services
N.A.I.C.S.: 445110

Kingfisher Asia Ltd   (1)
2/F KOHO 73-75 Hung To Road, Kwun Tong Kowloon, Hong Kong, China (Hong Kong)   (100%)
Tel.: (852) 39139000
Sales Range: $50-74.9 Million
Emp.: 140
Department Stores
N.A.I.C.S.: 455110

Kingfisher B.V.
Heereweg 21, 2161 AC, Lisse, Netherlands
Tel.: (31) 702223456
Web Site: http://kingfisher.nl
Fund Management Services
N.A.I.C.S.: 523940

Kingfisher France S.A.S.   (1)
Parc d'Activites BP 24, 59175, Templemars, France
Tel.: (33) 320167272
Household Products Retailer
N.A.I.C.S.: 459999
Jaswinder Singh *(Gen Mgr)*

Koctas Yapi Marketleri Ticaret S.A.   (1)
Tasdelen Mahallesi Sirri Celik Bulvari No 5, Cekmekoy, 34788, Istanbul, Turkiye   (50%)
Tel.: (90) 8502095050
Web Site: https://www.koctas.com.tr
Sales Range: $50-74.9 Million
Emp.: 200
DIY Retailers
N.A.I.C.S.: 444110
Alp Onder Ozpamukcu *(Gen Mgr)*

Promarkt Handdels GmbH   (1)
Kolonnenstrasse 30 F, 10829, Berlin, Germany   (100%)
Tel.: (49) 30787800
Web Site: http://www.promarkt.de
Sales Range: $1-4.9 Billion
Emp.: 3,278
Retail of Electrical Products
N.A.I.C.S.: 423620

Reno-Depot Inc.   (1)
1011 rue du Marche Central, Montreal, H4N 3J6, QC, Canada   (100%)
Tel.: (514) 385-6888
Web Site: http://www.renodepot.ca
Sales Range: $50-74.9 Million
Emp.: 175
Hardware Stores
N.A.I.C.S.: 444140

SFD Limited   (1)
Burwood Lodge 27 Romsey Road, Lyndhurst, SO43 7AA, Hampshire, United Kingdom
Tel.: (44) 2380282445
Web Site: https://www.sfdlimited.co.uk
Engineering & Construction Services
N.A.I.C.S.: 541330

Screwfix Direct Limited   (1)
Trade House Mead Avenue, Yeovil, BA22 8RT, Somerset, United Kingdom   (100%)
Tel.: (44) 3330112112
Web Site: https://www.screwfix.com
Sales Range: $200-249.9 Million
Emp.: 900
Mail Order & E-Commerce Retailer of Building, Plumbing & Electrical Products
N.A.I.C.S.: 444140

Subsidiary (Domestic):

Connect Distribution Services Ltd   (2)
Connect House Small Heath Business Park Small Health, Talbot Way, Birmingham, B10 OHJ, United Kingdom
Tel.: (44) 8445573700
Web Site: http://www.connect-distribution.co.uk
Emp.: 500
Home Appliance Whslr
N.A.I.C.S.: 449210
Andrew Sharp *(Mng Dir)*

Subsidiary (Domestic):

ES Realisations 2023 Limited   (3)
Medco House Bordesley Green Road, London, B9 4UA, United Kingdom
Tel.: (44) 8449777888
Web Site: http://www.espares.co.uk
Electronic Shopping
N.A.I.C.S.: 423610

Vanden Borre   (1)
Blvds Dupuis 433, 1070, Brussels, Anderlecht, Belgium   (100%)
Tel.: (32) 25240014
Web Site: http://www.vandenborre.be
Sales Range: $50-74.9 Million
Emp.: 100
Retail of Electrical Products
N.A.I.C.S.: 423620
Yvan De Graeve *(Gen Mgr)*

KINGFORM HEALTH HOMETEXTILE GROUP LIMITED
Level 12 680 George Street, Sydney, 2000, NSW, Australia
Tel.: (61) 2 8280 7000
Web Site: http://www.kingform.com.au
Sales Range: $1-9.9 Million
Holding Company; Household Textile Products
N.A.I.C.S.: 551112
Xikang Jin *(Chm & CEO)*

Subsidiaries:

Zhejiang Kangbao Household Textiles Co., Ltd.   (1)
80 Guang'an Road 3rd Part Economic Development Zone, Tongxiang, 314500, Zhejiang, China
Tel.: (86) 573 88366176
Household Textile Products
N.A.I.C.S.: 314120

KINGKEY FINANCIAL INTERNATIONAL (HOLDINGS) LIMITED
902 Harbour Centre Tower 2 8 Hok Cheung Street, Hunghom, Kowloon, China (Hong Kong)
Tel.: (852) 2 773 6233
Web Site: http://www.kkgroup.com.hk
1468—(HKG)
Rev.: $16,385,748
Assets: $169,771,215
Liabilities: $67,839,482
Net Worth: $101,931,733
Earnings: ($9,432,178)
Emp.: 69
Fiscal Year-end: 03/31/22
Holding Company; Fur Skins & Coats Trading
N.A.I.C.S.: 551112
Chun Chau Wong *(Chm)*

Subsidiaries:

King Privilege Wealth Management Limited   (1)
17 18/F Konnect 303 Jaffe Road, Wan Chai, Hong Kong, China (Hong Kong)
Tel.: (852) 21195600
Web Site: https://kkwm.com.hk
Financial Services
N.A.I.C.S.: 523940

KINGKEY INTELLIGENCE CULTURE HOLDINGS LIMITED
44/F Office Tower Convention Plaza 1 Harbour Road, Wan Chai, Hong Kong, China (Hong Kong)
Tel.: (852) 38913399   HK
Web Site: http://www.kk-culture.com
Year Founded: 1992
0550—(HKG)
Rev.: $6,904,635
Assets: $26,714,820
Liabilities: $1,708,500
Net Worth: $25,006,320
Earnings: ($1,105,680)
Emp.: 32
Fiscal Year-end: 12/31/22
Media Advertising Services
N.A.I.C.S.: 541890
Hing Bun Tsang *(Sec)*

KINGLAND GROUP HOLDINGS LIMITED
Flat B G/F Fu Hop Factory Bldg 209 and 211 Wai Yip Street, Kwun Tong, China (Hong Kong)
Tel.: (852) 27989202   Ky
Web Site: http://www.kinglandgroup.com.hk
Year Founded: 1985
1751—(HKG)
Rev.: $9,646,905
Assets: $7,752,765
Liabilities: $6,699,233
Net Worth: $1,053,533
Earnings: ($1,151,580)
Emp.: 85
Fiscal Year-end: 12/31/22
Civil Engineering Services
N.A.I.C.S.: 238910
On Shek Cheung *(Chm & CEO)*

Subsidiaries:

Kingland (Sino) Company Limited   (1)
Flat B G/F Fu Hop Factory Bldg 209 211 Wai Yip, Kwun Tong, China (Hong Kong)
Tel.: (852) 27989202
Concrete Demolition Services
N.A.I.C.S.: 238910

KINGLAND TECHNOLOGY CO., LTD.
5F Building No 3 Guotou Fortune Plaza No 9 Guangan Road, Fengtai District, Beijing, 100071, China
Tel.: (86) 1064740711
Web Site: http://www.kinglandgroup.com
Year Founded: 1993
000711—(SSE)
Consulting Services
N.A.I.C.S.: 541618
Ma Liyang *(Chm)*

KINGMAKER FOOTWEAR HOLDINGS LIMITED

Kingmaker Footwear Holdings Limited—(Continued)

KINGMAKER FOOTWEAR HOLDINGS LIMITED
17/F Empress Plaza 17-19 Chatham Road South Tsim Sha Tsui, Kowloon, China (Hong Kong)
Tel.: (852) 27231858   BM
Web Site: https://www.kingmaker-footwear.com
Year Founded: 1980
1170—(HKG)
Rev.: $103,792,786
Assets: $211,966,377
Liabilities: $50,063,974
Net Worth: $161,902,403
Earnings: $10,290,540
Emp.: 7,400
Fiscal Year-end: 03/31/21
Footwear Mfr & Distr
N.A.I.C.S.: 316210
Hei Chiu Wong *(Vice Chm, CFO & Sec)*

Subsidiaries:

Kingmaker (Cambodia) Footwear Co., Ltd. (1)
Manhattan Svay Rieng, Special Economic Zone Bavet Commune Chantrea District, Bavet, Svay Rieng, Cambodia
Footwear Mfr
N.A.I.C.S.: 316210

Kingmaker (Vietnam) Footwear Co., Ltd. (1)
No 12 Street 3 Vietnam, Singapore Industrial Park, Thuan An, Binh Duong, Vietnam
Tel.: (84) 2743757236
Footwear Mfr
N.A.I.C.S.: 316210

Maystar Footwear Company Limited (1)
No 3047 Mingzhu S Rd Cuiwei Indus District, Qianshan, Zhuhai, Guangdong, China
Sales Range: $750-799.9 Million
Emp.: 2,600
Footwear Mfr
N.A.I.C.S.: 316210

Miri International Limited (1)
17 F Empress Plz 17-19 Chatham Rd S, Tsim Sha Tsui, Kowloon, China (Hong Kong)
Tel.: (852) 27231858
Sales Range: $25-49.9 Million
Emp.: 30
Footwear Mfr
N.A.I.C.S.: 316210

Star (1) Limited (1)
17/F Empress Plaza 17-19 Chatham Road South, Tsim Sha Tsui, Kowloon, China (Hong Kong)
Tel.: (852) 27231858
Footwear Mfr
N.A.I.C.S.: 316210

KINGMAN MINERALS LTD.
Suite 2150 - 555 West Hastings Street, Vancouver, V6B 4N6, BC, Canada
Tel.: (604) 685-7720   BC
Web Site: https://kingmanminerals.com
Year Founded: 2007
47A—(DEU)
Assets: $1,396,593
Liabilities: $309,262
Net Worth: $1,087,331
Earnings: ($236,394)
Fiscal Year-end: 09/30/23
Copper & Gold Exploration Services
N.A.I.C.S.: 212230
Arthur Brown *(Pres)*

KINGMAN RIVER RESOURCES INC.
250 King Street West, Dundas, L9H 1V9, ON, Canada
Tel.: (905) 628-6000   NV
Year Founded: 2012

Gold & Other Metal Mining
N.A.I.C.S.: 212220
Braden Klumpp *(Pres, CEO, CFO, Treas & Sec)*

KINGNET NETWORK CO., LTD.
Building 3 Pujiang High-tech Plaza No 2388 Chenhang Highway, Minhang District, Shanghai, 362000, China
Tel.: (86) 2150908789
Web Site: https://kingnet.com
002517—(SSE)
Rev.: $523,064,412
Assets: $811,013,580
Liabilities: $173,274,660
Net Worth: $637,738,920
Earnings: $143,933,868
Emp.: 1,600
Fiscal Year-end: 12/31/22
Sport Shoes Mfr
N.A.I.C.S.: 316210

Subsidiaries:

JINJIANG TAIYA SHOES DEVELOP CO.,LTD. (1)
Xibin Guilin Industrial Area, Chendai, Jinjiang, 362211, Fujian, China
Tel.: (86) 59585180120
Shoes Sole Distr
N.A.I.C.S.: 424340

TAIYA(QUANZHOU) SHOES CO.,LTD. (1)
Qingmeng Scle & Industry Area, Quanzhou, 362000, Fujian, China
Tel.: (86) 59522493000
Sports Shoes Mfr & Sales
N.A.I.C.S.: 316210

KINGOLD JEWELRY, INC.
No 8 Han Huang Road, Jiang an District, Wuhan, 430023, Hubei, China
Tel.: (86) 27 6569 4977   DE
Web Site: http://www.kingoldjewelry.com
Year Founded: 1995
Rev.: $2,475,666,092
Assets: $2,699,813,698
Liabilities: $2,061,478,951
Net Worth: $638,334,747
Earnings: $49,546,714
Emp.: 630
Fiscal Year-end: 12/31/18
Jewelry Mfr & Sales
N.A.I.C.S.: 339910
Zhihong Jia *(Founder, Chm & CEO)*

Subsidiaries:

Wuhan Kingold Jewelry Company Limited (1)
1 Jinhuang Rd Jiang an Economic Dev Area, Jianghan District, Wuhan, 430023, China
Tel.: (86) 2765660302
Jewelry Mfr
N.A.I.C.S.: 339910

KINGPAK TECHNOLOGY, INC.
No 84 Taihe Rd, Zhubei, 30267, Hsinchu, Taiwan
Tel.: (886) 35535888
Web Site: http://www.kingpak.com.tw
Year Founded: 1997
6238—(TPE)
Rev.: $77,662,524
Assets: $98,853,148
Liabilities: $26,850,339
Net Worth: $72,002,809
Earnings: $8,966,461
Fiscal Year-end: 12/31/19
Packaging Product Distr
N.A.I.C.S.: 423690
Joe Liu *(Chm)*

KINGS ARMS YARD VCT PLC
1 Benjamin Street, London, EC1M 5QL, United Kingdom   UK

Year Founded: 1995
KAY—(LSE)
Rev.: $1,362,030
Assets: $132,110,578
Liabilities: $831,861
Net Worth: $131,278,717
Earnings: $916,435
Fiscal Year-end: 12/31/22
Investment Management Service
N.A.I.C.S.: 523999
Fiona Wollocombe *(Chm)*

KINGS ENTERTAINMENT GROUP INC.
Suite 1570-505 Burrard Street, Vancouver, V7X 1M5, BC, Canada
Tel.: (250) 558-8819   BC
Web Site: https://www.kingsentertainment.ca
Year Founded: 2005
JKPT—(CNSX)
Entertainment Industry Services
N.A.I.C.S.: 711410
Steven Budin *(CEO)*

KINGS INFRA VENTURES LIMITED
B10 2nd Floor Triveni Courtt K P Vallon Road, Kadavanthara, Kochi, 682 015, Kerala, India
Tel.: (91) 4844865823
Web Site: https://www.kingsinfra.com
Year Founded: 1987
530215—(BOM)
Rev.: $7,342,581
Assets: $8,545,891
Liabilities: $4,238,931
Net Worth: $4,306,960
Earnings: $686,086
Emp.: 17
Fiscal Year-end: 03/31/23
Real Estate Management Services
N.A.I.C.S.: 531390
Shaji Baby John *(Chm & Co-Mng Dir)*

KINGSCROSS HYUNDAI
1957 Eglinton Ave East, Scarborough, M1L 2M3, ON, Canada
Tel.: (416) 755-3322   Ca
Web Site: http://www.kingscrosshyundai.com
Year Founded: 1992
New & Used Car Dealer
N.A.I.C.S.: 441110
Maria Ho *(Office Mgr)*

KINGSEMI CO., LTD.
No 1 Caiyun Road, Hunnan District, Shenyang, 110169, China
Tel.: (86) 2489628888
Web Site: https://www.kingsemi.com
Year Founded: 2002
688037—(SHG)
Rev.: $194,435,341
Assets: $490,885,251
Liabilities: $195,126,755
Net Worth: $295,758,497
Earnings: $28,102,590
Fiscal Year-end: 12/31/22
Semiconductor Product Mfr
N.A.I.C.S.: 334413
Runfu Zong *(Chm, Pres & Gen Mgr)*

KINGSETT CAPITAL
Scotia Plaza 40 King Street West Suite 3700, PO Box 110, Toronto, M5H 3Y2, ON, Canada
Tel.: (416) 687-6700
Web Site: http://www.kingsettcapital.com
Year Founded: 2002
Sales Range: $25-49.9 Million
Emp.: 40
Private Equity Firm Services
N.A.I.C.S.: 523999

INTERNATIONAL PUBLIC

Andrew Kirkham *(VP-Western Canada)*

Subsidiaries:

Northview Apartment Real Estate Investment Trust (1)
6131 - 6th Street SE Suite 200, Calgary, T2H 1L9, AB, Canada
Tel.: (403) 531-0720
Web Site: http://www.northviewreit.com
Rev.: $300,404,145
Assets: $3,501,154,362
Liabilities: $1,896,566,990
Net Worth: $1,604,587,372
Earnings: $185,162,827
Emp.: 937
Fiscal Year-end: 12/31/2019
Real Estate Investment Trust
N.A.I.C.S.: 525990

Subsidiary (Domestic):

Northern Property R.E.I.T. Holdings Inc. (2)
203 4508 42hd St, Bonnyville, T9N 1K5, AB, Canada
Tel.: (780) 826-3304
Real Estate Property Management Services
N.A.I.C.S.: 531311

KINGSGATE CONSOLIDATED LIMITED
Suite 1207 Level 12 14 Martin Place, Sydney, 2000, NSW, Australia
Tel.: (61) 282564800   AU
Web Site: https://www.kingsgate.com.au
KSKGF—(OTCIQ)
Sales Range: Less than $1 Million
Emp.: 25
Gold Ore Mining Services
N.A.I.C.S.: 212220
Ross Smyth-Kirk *(Chm)*

Subsidiaries:

Akara Mining Limited (1)
No 99 Moo 9 Khao Chet Luk, Thap Khlo, Phichit, 66230, Thailand
Tel.: (66) 56614500
Web Site: http://www.akararesources.com
Sales Range: $100-124.9 Million
Emp.: 300
Gold Mining & Exploration Services
N.A.I.C.S.: 212220
Pakorn Sukhum *(CEO)*

Issara Mining Limited (1)
No 90/37 14th Fl Sathorn Thani Building 1, Khet Bangrak, Bangkok, 10500, Thailand
Tel.: (66) 223394723
Web Site: http://www.issaramining.com
Sales Range: $100-124.9 Million
Emp.: 200
Gold Mining Services
N.A.I.C.S.: 212220

KINGSIGNAL TECHNOLOGY CO., LTD.
Floor 23-27 Unit B Block 10 No 1819 Shahexi Road, Shenzhen Bay Eco-Technology Park Nanshan District, Shenzhen, 518052, Guangdong, China
Tel.: (86) 75586319150
Web Site: https://www.kingsignal.com
Year Founded: 2002
300252—(CHIN)
Rev.: $299,247,156
Assets: $764,361,468
Liabilities: $491,172,552
Net Worth: $273,188,916
Earnings: ($53,038,908)
Fiscal Year-end: 12/31/22
RF Signal Cable Mfr
N.A.I.C.S.: 335921
Huang Changhua *(Chm)*

Subsidiaries:

Changzhou Kingsignal Fengshi Communication Equipment Co., Ltd. (1)
No 29 Long Hui Road, Wujin High-Tech De-

velopment Zone, Changzhou, Jiangsu, China
Tel.: (86) 51986925751
Cable & Connector Mfr & Distr
N.A.I.C.S.: 334417

Changzhou Kingsignal Firnic Co., Ltd. (1)
Long Hui Road No 29 Wujin High-tech Development Zone, Changzhou, 213166, JiangSu, China
Tel.: (86) 51986925786
Electronic Cable Mfr
N.A.I.C.S.: 334417

Changzhou PC Specialties Co., Ltd. (1)
No 23 West Longyu Rd, High-Tech Development Zone, Wujin, China
Tel.: (86) 51986486969
Cable & Connector Mfr & Distr
N.A.I.C.S.: 334417

Ganzhou Kingsignal Cable Technology Co., Ltd. (1)
4th Industry road North of Hong Kong industrial park, Ganzhou, 341000, Jiangxi, China
Tel.: (86) 7978086111
Electronic Cable Mfr
N.A.I.C.S.: 334417

Ganzhou Kingsignal Optical Fiber & Cable Co., Ltd. (1)
Golden Avenue Industry Zone, Ganzhou, Jiangxi, China
Tel.: (86) 7978069622
Electronic Cable Mfr
N.A.I.C.S.: 334417

Kingsignal Cable Technology (Ganzhou) Co.,Ltd. (1)
4th Industry Road, North of Hong Kong Industrial Park, Ganzhou, 341000, China
Tel.: (86) 7978086111
Cable & Connector Mfr & Distr
N.A.I.C.S.: 334417

Kingsignal Optical Fiber & Cable (Ganzhou) Co.,Ltd. (1)
Golden Avenue Industry Zone, Ganzhou, Jiangxi, China
Tel.: (86) 7978069622
Cable & Connector Mfr & Distr
N.A.I.C.S.: 334417

Kingsignal Technologies (India) Pvt. Ltd. (1)
No 117 Citi Tower 5th Floor Sir Thiyagaraya Road T Nagar, Chennai, 600017, India
Tel.: (91) 4442035666
Cable & Connector Mfr & Distr
N.A.I.C.S.: 334417

Kingsignal Technology (Thailand) Co., Ltd. (1)
No Empire Tower Building 47th Floor Unit 4703 4704 4709 4710, South Sathorn Road Yannawa Sub-district Sathorn district, Bangkok, 10120, Thailand
Tel.: (66) 842939428
Cable & Connector Mfr & Distr
N.A.I.C.S.: 334417

KINGSLAKE INTERNATIONAL LIMITED
7 Torriano Mews, London, NW5 2RZ, United Kingdom
Tel.: (44) 20 744425670
Web Site: http://www.kingslake.com
Business Software Distr
N.A.I.C.S.: 423430

Subsidiaries:

KM Enterprise Systems Sdn Bhd (1)
Ste B 12 6 Level 12 Wisma Pantai Plz Pantai, 5 Jalan 4 83A off Jalan Pantai, Kuala Lumpur, 59200, Malaysia
Tel.: (60) 322878580
Web Site: http://www.Kingslake.com
Sales Range: $10-24.9 Million
Emp.: 5
Business Application Software Distr
N.A.I.C.S.: 423430

Kingslake Engineering Systems (PVT) LTD. (1)
S-01 Ground Floor Explorer Building International Tech Park, Whitefield Road, Bengaluru, 560066, India
Tel.: (91) 80 4121 9010
Business Software Distribution & Support Services
N.A.I.C.S.: 423430

Kingslake Engineering Systems (Private) Limited (1)
30 Temple Lane, Colombo, 3, Sri Lanka
Tel.: (94) 11 77 99 200
Business Software Distr
N.A.I.C.S.: 423430

Kingslake Europe bv (1)
Zoutkeetlaan 4, 2343 BE, Oegstgeest, Netherlands
Tel.: (31) 715190067
Software Development Services
N.A.I.C.S.: 522320
Grace Spellmann (Office Mgr & Coord-HR)

KINGSLAND ENERGY CORPORATION
002 2305 Victoria Ave, Regina, S4P 0S7, SK, Canada
Tel.: (306) 352-6132
Web Site: http://www.kingslandenergy.com
Year Founded: 2011
KLE—(TSXV)
Sales Range: Less than $1 Million
Oil & Gas Exploration Servcies
N.A.I.C.S.: 213112
Lionel Kambeitz (Chm & CEO-Acting)

KINGSLAND GLOBAL LTD.
15 Kwong Min Road, Singapore, 628718, Singapore
Tel.: (65) 63628998
Web Site: http://kingslandglobal.sg
KLO—(ASX)
Rev.: $1,336,705
Assets: $34,778,123
Liabilities: $14,367,469
Net Worth: $20,410,654
Earnings: ($1,032,927)
Fiscal Year-end: 03/31/21
Real Estate
N.A.I.C.S.: 531390
Sok Hang Chaw (Chm)

KINGSLAND MINERALS LIMITED
Level 1 43 Ventnor Avenue, West Perth, 6005, WA, Australia
Tel.: (61) 893813820 AU
Web Site: https://www.kingslandminerals.com
Year Founded: 2021
KNG—(ASX)
Rev.: $3,444
Assets: $6,686,866
Liabilities: $743,640
Net Worth: $5,943,226
Earnings: ($1,381,322)
Fiscal Year-end: 06/30/23
Mineral Exploration Services
N.A.I.C.S.: 212390
Bruno Seneque (Sec)

KINGSLEY NAPLEY LLP
20 Bonhill Street, London, EC2A 4DN, United Kingdom
Tel.: (44) 2078141200 UK
Web Site: http://www.kingsleynapley.co.uk
Year Founded: 1937
Sales Range: Less than $1 Million
Emp.: 496
Law firm
N.A.I.C.S.: 541110
Jane Keir (Partner-Family & Divorce)

KINGSMEN CMTI PCL
9/19 Moo 7 Lam Luk Ka Klong 6 Road, Bueng Kham Ploi Sub-District, Pathumthani, 12150, Thailand
Tel.: (66) 20528008
Web Site: https://www.kingsmen-cmti.com
Year Founded: 1989
K—(THA)
Rev.: $21,213,513
Assets: $23,065,743
Liabilities: $13,367,003
Net Worth: $9,698,740
Earnings: $406,936
Fiscal Year-end: 12/31/23
Interior Design Services
N.A.I.C.S.: 541410
Chayawat Pisessith (Chm)

KINGSMEN CREATIVES LTD
The Kingsmen Experience 22 Changi Business Park Central 2, Singapore, 486032, Singapore
Tel.: (65) 68800088
Web Site: https://www.kingsmen-int.com
5MZ—(OTCIQ)
Rev.: $243,318,266
Assets: $197,805,854
Liabilities: $117,221,934
Net Worth: $80,583,920
Earnings: $3,016,673
Emp.: 1,700
Fiscal Year-end: 12/31/22
Retail & Commercial Interiors Design Services
N.A.I.C.S.: 337212
Anthony Siew Ling Chong (Mng Dir-Exhibitions & Thematic)

Subsidiaries:

Hi-Light Electrical Pte Ltd (1)
3 Changi South Lane 04-00, Singapore, 486118, Singapore
Tel.: (65) 424303
Electrical Engineering Services
N.A.I.C.S.: 541330

I-Promo Pte Ltd (1)
22 Changi Business Park Central 2, Singapore, 486032, Singapore
Tel.: (65) 68311397
Web Site: https://www.i-promo.com.sg
Event Organizing & Marketing Services
N.A.I.C.S.: 541613

Kingsmen (Shenzhen) Co Ltd. (1)
14A02 Regalia Place 20 Jiabin Road, Shenzhen, China
Tel.: (86) 75582480848
Interior Design Services
N.A.I.C.S.: 541410

Kingsmen Beijing Co., Ltd. (1)
306 Guo Feng Shi Dai Building Block 7 No 3 Yard Qingnian Road West, Chaoyang District, Beijing, 100123, China
Tel.: (86) 52089399
Interior Design Services
N.A.I.C.S.: 541410

Kingsmen Design Pte Ltd (1)
3 Changi South Lane, Singapore, 486118, Singapore
Tel.: (65) 68800088
Web Site: http://www.kingsmen-int.com
Emp.: 300
Interior Design Services
N.A.I.C.S.: 541410

Kingsmen Exhibits Pte Ltd (1)
3 Changi South Lane Kingsmen Creative Centre, Singapore, 486118, Singapore
Tel.: (65) 68800088
Web Site: http://www.kingsmen-int.com
Sales Range: $150-199.9 Million
Emp.: 300
Exhibition Goods Distr
N.A.I.C.S.: 423990

Subsidiary (Domestic):

Kingsmen Environmental Graphics Pte Ltd (2)
22 Changi Business Park Central 2, Singapore, 486032, Singapore
Tel.: (65) 68800283
Web Site: http://www.kingsmen-int.com

Sales Range: $25-49.9 Million
Emp.: 100
Graphic Design Services
N.A.I.C.S.: 541430
Phyllis Lee (Mgr-HR)

Kingsmen Hong Kong Ltd. (1)
728 Topsail Plaza 11 On Sum Street, Sha Tin, New Territories, China (Hong Kong)
Tel.: (852) 26468828
Interior Design Services
N.A.I.C.S.: 541410

Kingsmen Macau Limited (1)
Deco do Goncalo No 20 Edificio Fok Keng R/C-F, Macau, China (Macau)
Tel.: (853) 26468828
Interior Design Services
N.A.I.C.S.: 541410

Kingsmen Middle East LLC (1)
Warehouse No 2 Al Quoz Industrial Area 1 Sheik Zayed Road, PO Box 37741, Dubai, United Arab Emirates
Tel.: (971) 43389340
Web Site: https://www.kingsmen-me.com
Communication Design Services
N.A.I.C.S.: 541490
Rohan Dodhi (Mgr-Bus Dev)

Kingsmen Ooh-media Pte. Ltd. (1)
Kingsmen Creative Ctr 3 Changi S Lane, Singapore, 486118, Singapore (65%)
Tel.: (65) 68800269
Web Site: http://www.kingsmenoohmedia.com
Sales Range: $25-49.9 Million
Emp.: 17
Outdoor Advertising & Marketing
N.A.I.C.S.: 541850

Kingsmen Projects Pte Ltd (1)
3 Changi South Lane Kingsmen Creative Centre, Singapore, 486118, Singapore
Tel.: (65) 68800088
Web Site: http://www.kingsmen-int.com
Sales Range: $75-99.9 Million
Emp.: 400
Interior Design Services
N.A.I.C.S.: 541410

Kingsmen Projects US (1)
3525 Hyland Ave Ste 225, Costa Mesa, CA 92626
Tel.: (949) 642-2555
Communication Design Services
N.A.I.C.S.: 541490
Stephen Hekman (Exec VP)

Kingsmen Sdn Bhd (1)
5 Jalan 6/2B Taman Industri Jaya, 43300, Seri Kembangan, Selangor Ehsan Darul, Malaysia
Tel.: (60) 386554964
Web Site: https://www.kingsmenmalaysia.com
Emp.: 100
Communication Design Services
N.A.I.C.S.: 541490
Ferry Kosasih (Mgr-Design)

Kingsmen Shanghai Co., Ltd. (1)
Room 1501 Hui Tong Building No 569 Jin Ling Road East, Shanghai, 200021, China
Tel.: (86) 2153869000
Web Site: https://kingsmen-gc.com
Interior Design Services
N.A.I.C.S.: 541410

Kingsmen Taiwan International Co., Limited (1)
12-F No 178-1 Sec 4 Jhongsiao E Road, Taipei, 106, Taiwan
Tel.: (886) 227790279
Interior Design Services
N.A.I.C.S.: 541410

Kingsmen Xperience, Inc. (1)
8383 Wilshire Blvd Ste 800, Beverly Hills, CA 90211
Tel.: (310) 531-8118
Communication Design Services
N.A.I.C.S.: 541490

PT Kingsmen Indonesia (1)
Jl Husein Sastranegara No 20, Pegadungan Kalideres, Jakarta Barat, 11840, Indonesia
Tel.: (62) 2154396898
Web Site: https://www.kingsmenindonesia.co.id

KINGSMEN CREATIVES LTD

Kingsmen Creatives Ltd—(Continued)
Communication Design Services
N.A.I.C.S.: 541490
Fetty Handayanty *(Project Mgr)*

Thinkfarm Pte Ltd (1)
22 Changi Business Park Central 2 The Kingsmen Experience, Singapore, 486032, Singapore
Tel.: (65) 68311299
Web Site: https://www.thinkfarm.sg
Marketing Consulting Services
N.A.I.C.S.: 541613

KINGSMEN RESOURCES LIMITED

1305 - 1090 West Georgia Street, Vancouver, V6E 3Z3, BC, Canada
Tel.: (604) 685-9316
Web Site:
https://www.kingsmenresources.com
Year Founded: 2000
KNG—(OTCIQ)
Rev.: $6,067
Assets: $639,884
Liabilities: $10,860
Net Worth: $629,024
Earnings: ($69,146)
Fiscal Year-end: 12/31/20
Mineral Exploration Services
N.A.I.C.S.: 213114
Harvey Lim *(Sec)*

KINGSOFT CORPORATION LIMITED

Kingsoft Tower No 33 Xiaoying West Road, Haidian District, Beijing, 100085, China
Tel.: (86) 1082325515
Web Site: http://www.kingsoft.com
3888—(OTCIQ)
Rev.: $1,176,033,435
Assets: $3,491,872,251
Liabilities: $1,258,169,830
Net Worth: $2,233,702,421
Earnings: ($298,034,227)
Emp.: 7,589
Fiscal Year-end: 12/31/19
Entertainment, Internet Security & Application Software
N.A.I.C.S.: 513210
Tao Zou *(CEO)*

Subsidiaries:

Cheetah Mobile Inc. (1)
Building No 11 Wandong Science and Technology Cultural Innovation, Park No 7 Sanjianfangnanli Chaoyang District, Beijing, 100024, China (60.8%)
Tel.: (86) 1062927779
Web Site: https://www.cmcm.com
Rev.: $92,698,134
Assets: $779,960,124
Liabilities: $426,258,031
Net Worth: $353,702,093
Earnings: ($82,225,991)
Emp.: 845
Fiscal Year-end: 12/31/2023
Mobile Applications
N.A.I.C.S.: 513210
Sheng Fu *(Chm & CEO)*

Subsidiary (Non-US):

MobPartner S.A.S. (2)
91 avenue Ledru Rollin, 75011, Paris, France
Tel.: (33) 1 5839 3400
Web Site: http://www.cheetahmedialink.com
Sales Range: $10-24.9 Million
Mobile Advertising Products & Services
N.A.I.C.S.: 541890

KINGSPAN GROUP PLC

Kingspan Innovation Centre Dublin Road, Kingscourt, A82 XY31, Co Cavan, Ireland
Tel.: (353) 429698000
Web Site:
https://www.kingspangroup.com
Year Founded: 1965
KRX—(ISE)
Rev.: $8,731,491,474
Assets: $8,635,441,399
Liabilities: $4,374,919,059
Net Worth: $4,260,522,340
Earnings: $705,698,252
Emp.: 22,500
Fiscal Year-end: 12/31/23
Engineeering Services
N.A.I.C.S.: 541330
Russell Shiels *(Pres-Access Floors & Insulated Panels-North America)*

Subsidiaries:

ASM Modular Systems Inc. (1)
9500 Industrial Ctr Dr, Ladson, SC 29456-3938 (100%)
Tel.: (843) 534-1110
Web Site: http://www.asmproducts.com
Sales Range: $25-49.9 Million
Emp.: 13
Lumber Plywood Millwork & Wood Panel Whslr
N.A.I.C.S.: 423310
Jay Collins *(Dir-Sls)*

Albion Water Heater Limited (1)
Shelah Rd, Halesowen, B633PG, W Midlands, United Kingdom (100%)
Tel.: (44) 1215855151
Web Site:
http://www.albionwaterheaters.com
Sales Range: $25-49.9 Million
Emp.: 30
Fabricated Structural Metal Mfr
N.A.I.C.S.: 332312

American Solar & Alternative Power LLC (1)
85 Old Long Ridge Rd Ste A1, Stamford, CT 06903-1641
Tel.: (203) 324-7186
Web Site: http://www.solarasap.com
Emp.: 10
Renewable & Alternative Energy Services
N.A.I.C.S.: 221114
Craig Bogardus *(Mgr-Sls & Bus Dev)*

Banro Sections Limited (1)
Manor Works Pleck Rd, Walsall, WS29ES, W Midlands, United Kingdom (100%)
Tel.: (44) 1922724789
Web Site: http://www.banro.co.uk
Engineeering Services
N.A.I.C.S.: 541330

Coppercraft Limited (1)
Kylemore Park W Ballyfermot, Dublin, Ireland
Tel.: (353) 16265146
Web Site: http://www.coppercraft.ie
Copper Wire Drawing
N.A.I.C.S.: 331420

Ecotherm Insulation (UK) Limited (1)
Harvey Rd, Burnt Mills Industrial Estate, Basildon, SS13 1QJ, Essex, United Kingdom
Tel.: (44) 1268591155
Web Site: https://www.ecotherm.co.uk
Thermal Insulation Product Distr
N.A.I.C.S.: 423330
Guvvi Basra *(Sls Mgr-South)*

IB Roof Systems, Inc. (1)
2877 Chad Dr Unit A, Eugene, OR 97408-7396
Web Site: http://www.ibroof.com
Rubber Products Mfr
N.A.I.C.S.: 326299

Izopoli Yapi Elemanlari Taahhut San. Ve Tic A.S (1)
Ciragan Caddesi No 97, Ortakoy, Istanbul, 34347, Turkiye
Tel.: (90) 212 236 60 32
Web Site: http://www.izopoli.com
Insulated Wall Panels & Panel Roof Mfr
N.A.I.C.S.: 332311

Plant (Domestic):

Izopoli Yapi Elemanlari Taahhut San. Ve Tic A.S - Adana Factory (2)
Adana Yumurtalik Serbest Bolgesi, Ceyhan, 01920, Adana, Turkiye
Tel.: (90) 322 634 20 34
Web Site: http://www.izopoli.com
Sales Range: $25-49.9 Million
Insulated Wall Panel & Panel Roof Mfr
N.A.I.C.S.: 332311

Izopoli Yapi Elemanlari Taahhut San. Ve Tic A.S - Bolu Factory (2)
Bolu Organize Sanayi Bolgesi Dr Akin Cakmakci Bulvari No 59, 14240, Bolu, Turkiye
Tel.: (90) 374 243 84 80
Web Site: http://www.izopoli.com
Insulated Wall Panel & Panel Roof Mfr
N.A.I.C.S.: 332311

Kingspan A.S. (1)
Vazni 465, 500 03, Hradec Kralove, Czech Republic (100%)
Tel.: (420) 495866111
Web Site: http://www.kingspan.com
Sales Range: $50-74.9 Million
Chemical Product & Preparation Mfr
N.A.I.C.S.: 325998

Kingspan Access Floors Holdings Limited (1)
The Guildhall Alfred Gelder Street, Hull, HU9 9SU, Yorkshire, United Kingdom
Tel.: (44) 1482 781 701
Investment Management Service
N.A.I.C.S.: 523940

Kingspan Access Floors Limited (1)
Burma Dr Marfleet, Hull, HU95SG, Yorkshire, United Kingdom (100%)
Tel.: (44) 1482781701
Web Site:
http://www.kingspanaccessfloors.co.uk
Sales Range: $50-74.9 Million
Emp.: 150
Sheet Metal Work Mfg
N.A.I.C.S.: 332322

Kingspan B.V. (1)
Lingewei 8, Postbus 6565, 4000 HN, Tiel, Netherlands
Tel.: (31) 344 675 250
Web Site:
http://www.kingspanstructural.com
Sales Range: $25-49.9 Million
Emp.: 7
Insulated Wall Panels & Panel Roof Mfr
N.A.I.C.S.: 321992
Frank Donkers *(Gen Mgr)*

Kingspan Century Limited (1)
Clones Road, Monaghan, Ireland
Tel.: (353) 47 38430
Web Site: http://www.kingspancentury.com
Sales Range: $25-49.9 Million
Emp.: 80
Engineered Timber Frame System Mfr
N.A.I.C.S.: 321215

Kingspan Door Components S.A. (1)
Zone Industrielle de l Europe 1A, Leuze-en-Hainaut, 7900, Belgium (100%)
Tel.: (32) 69452460
Web Site: http://www.kingspandoor.com
Sales Range: $50-74.9 Million
Emp.: 100
Hardware Merchant Whslr
N.A.I.C.S.: 423710

Kingspan Environment Sp. z o.o. (1)
ul Topolowa 5, 62 090, Rokietnica, Poland
Tel.: (48) 618144400
Web Site: http://www.kingspan.com
Fabricated Structural Metal Mfr
N.A.I.C.S.: 332312

Kingspan Environmental (1)
Lingewei 8, 4004 LL, Tiel, Netherlands
Tel.: (31) 344675299 (100%)
Web Site: http://www.kingspan.com
Sales Range: $50-74.9 Million
Emp.: 13
Environmental Construction Materials Whslr
N.A.I.C.S.: 423390

Kingspan Environmental -Belgiuim (1)
Zwaaikomstraat 5, Roeselare, B-8800, Belgium
Tel.: (32) 51 48 51 42
Web Site:
http://www.environmental.kingspan.com
Metal Container Mfr
N.A.I.C.S.: 332439

Kingspan Environmental Limited (1)

INTERNATIONAL PUBLIC

College Road North Aston Clinton, Aylesbury, HP22 5EW, Bucks, United Kingdom
Tel.: (44) 1296 633000
Sales Range: $25-49.9 Million
Emp.: 170
Environmental Engineering Services
N.A.I.C.S.: 541330
Vincent Dave *(Gen Mgr)*

Kingspan Environmental-France (1)
36 Rue du Louvre, 75001, Paris, France
Tel.: (33) 4 74 99 04 56
Web Site: http://www.kingspan-env.fr
Sales Range: $25-49.9 Million
Emp.: 2
Chemical Products Storage Services
N.A.I.C.S.: 493190
Guillaume Vailhen *(Country Mgr)*

Kingspan Fabrications (1)
Sherburn Malton, York, YO17 8PQ, United Kingdom (100%)
Tel.: (44) 1944712207
Web Site:
http://www.kingspanfabrications.com
Sales Range: $25-49.9 Million
Emp.: 300
Sheet Metal Work Mfg
N.A.I.C.S.: 332322

Kingspan Fabrik Limited (1)
The Brickworks, Grangegeeth Slane, Meath, Ireland (100%)
Tel.: (353) 419884800
Web Site: http://www.kingspanfabrik.com
Glass Products Mfr
N.A.I.C.S.: 327215

Kingspan Finance Ltd. (1)
Dublin Rd, Kingscourt, Cavan, Ireland (100%)
Tel.: (353) 429698000
Web Site: http://www.kingspan.com
Sales Range: $50-74.9 Million
Emp.: 30
Securities & Commodity Exchanges
N.A.I.C.S.: 523210

Kingspan Funding Europe (1)
Dublin Road, Kingscourt, Cavan, Ireland
Tel.: (353) 42 969 8000
Web Site: http://www.kingspan.ie
Emp.: 3
Pension Fund Services
N.A.I.C.S.: 525110

Kingspan Funding UK (1)
Greenfield Business Park No 2, Greenfield, Holywell, CH8 7GJ, Flintshire, United Kingdom
Tel.: (44) 1352710777
Investment Management Service
N.A.I.C.S.: 523999

Kingspan GmbH (1)
Teufenerstrasse 25, 9000, Saint Gallen, Switzerland
Tel.: (41) 714402191
Insulated Wall Panels & Panel Roof Mfr
N.A.I.C.S.: 321992
Sacha Staheli *(Country Mgr)*

Kingspan Group Limited (1)
2-4 Greenfield Business Park 2, Holywell, CH8 7GJ, United Kingdom
Tel.: (44) 1352 716100
Web Site: http://www.kingspanpanels.com
Emp.: 450
Insulated Wall Panels & Panel Roof Mfr
N.A.I.C.S.: 321992

Kingspan Holding Belgium N.V. (1)
Bouwelven 17, 2280, Grobbendonk, Antwerp, Belgium
Tel.: (32) 14232535
Web Site: http://www.kingspanpanels.be
Sales Range: $50-74.9 Million
Emp.: 1
Investment Management Service
N.A.I.C.S.: 523999

Kingspan Holding GmbH (1)
Am Schornacker 2, 46485, Wesel, Germany (100%)
Tel.: (49) 281952500
Web Site: http://www.kingspan.de
Sales Range: $50-74.9 Million
Emp.: 30
Trusts Estates & Agency Accounts
N.A.I.C.S.: 525920

AND PRIVATE COMPANIES

KINGSPAN GROUP PLC

Kingspan Holdings (Insulation) Limited (1)
Greenfield Business Park 2, Greenfield, Holywell, CH8 7GJ, Flintshire, United Kingdom
Tel.: (44) 1352 716100
Web Site: http://www.kingspan.com
Investment Management Service
N.A.I.C.S.: 523940

Kingspan Holdings (Irl) Limited (1)
Carrickmacross Road, Kingscourt, Cavan, A82 E897, Ireland **(100%)**
Tel.: (353) 429698500
Web Site: http://www.kingspan.com
Sales Range: $25-49.9 Million
Emp.: 100
Business Services
N.A.I.C.S.: 561499

Kingspan Holdings (Overseas) Limited (1)
Dublin Rd, Kingscourt, Cavan, Ireland
Tel.: (353) 429698500
Web Site: http://www.kingspan.co.uk
Sales Range: $25-49.9 Million
Emp.: 100
New Single-Family Housing Construction
N.A.I.C.S.: 236115

Kingspan Holdings (Structural and Offsite) Limited (1)
Greenfield Business Park 2 Bagillt Road, Holywell, CH8 7GJ, United Kingdom
Tel.: (44) 1352 716100
Web Site: http://www.kingspan.com
Investment Management Service
N.A.I.C.S.: 523999

Kingspan Holdings Netherlands B.V. (1)
Lingewei 8, Tiel, 4004 LL, Netherlands **(100%)**
Tel.: (31) 344675250
Web Site: http://www.kingspaninsulation.nl
Sales Range: $25-49.9 Million
Emp.: 35
Construction Materials Whslr
N.A.I.C.S.: 423390

Kingspan Holdings Panels US Inc. (1)
103 Foulk Rd, Wilmington, DE 19803-3742
Tel.: (302) 691-6082
Investment Management Service
N.A.I.C.S.: 523999

Kingspan Holdings US Inc. (1)
103 Foulk Rd Ste 202, Wilmington, DE 19803-3742 **(100%)**
Tel.: (302) 691-6082
Holding Company
N.A.I.C.S.: 551112

Kingspan Hot Water Systems Limited (1)
Tadman Street, Ardwick, Wakefield, WS1 5QU, United Kingdom
Tel.: (44) 1924 376026
Web Site: http://www.kingspanhws.com
Emp.: 200
Heating Boiler Mfr
N.A.I.C.S.: 332410

Kingspan India Pvt. Ltd. (1)
1B Saket Apt Near Runwal Paradise Right Bhusari Colony, Kothrud Depot, Pune, 411 001, India
Tel.: (91) 20 4002 4430
Web Site: http://www.kingspan.in
Sales Range: $50-74.9 Million
Emp.: 4
Insulated Wall Panel & Panel Roof Distr
N.A.I.C.S.: 423330

Kingspan Insulated Panels Inc. (1)
726 Summerhill Dr, Deland, FL 32724
Tel.: (386) 626-6789
Web Site: http://www.kingspanpanels.us
Insulated Wall Panels & Panel Roof Mfr
N.A.I.C.S.: 332311

Kingspan Insulated Panels Limited (1)
12557 Coleraine Drive, Caledon, L7E 3B5, ON, Canada
Tel.: (905) 951-5600
Web Site: https://www.kingspan.com
Emp.: 8
Insulated Wall Panel & Panel Roof Mfr
N.A.I.C.S.: 332311

Kingspan Insulated Panels Pty Ltd (1)
38-52 Dunheved Circuit, St Mary, Sydney, 2760, NSW, Australia **(100%)**
Tel.: (61) 1300546477
Web Site: http://www.kingspan.com
Sales Range: $25-49.9 Million
Prefabricated Metal Building & Component Mfr
N.A.I.C.S.: 332311

Kingspan Insulation B.V. (1)
Voorenswei 1, Po Box 13, 6669, Dodewaard, Netherlands **(100%)**
Tel.: (31) 488417520
Web Site: http://www.kingspan.nl
Construction Materials Whslr
N.A.I.C.S.: 423390

Kingspan Insulation Limited (1)
Pembridge, Leominster, HR6 9LA, Herefordshire, United Kingdom **(100%)**
Tel.: (44) 1544388601
Web Site: http://www.kingspan.com
Roofing Siding & Insulation Material Whslr
N.A.I.C.S.: 423330

Kingspan Insulation Limited (1)
Bree Industrial Estate, Castleblayney, Monaghan, Ireland
Tel.: (353) 42 979 5000
Web Site: http://www.kingspaninsulation.ie
Sales Range: $25-49.9 Million
Building Materials Mfr
N.A.I.C.S.: 332311

Kingspan Insulation Pty Ltd (1)
Beringarra Avenue, Malaga, 6090, WA, Australia
Tel.: (61) 862406200
Web Site: http://www.kingspaninsulation.com.au
Sales Range: $25-49.9 Million
Emp.: 26
Insulated Wall Panels & Panel Roof Mfr
N.A.I.C.S.: 332311

Kingspan Insulation Sp. z.o.o (1)
Gdanska 134, Gniezno, 62200, Poland
Tel.: (48) 61 425 56 48
Web Site: http://www.kingspaninsulation.pl
Sales Range: $25-49.9 Million
Emp.: 20
Insulated Wall Panels & Panel Roof Mfr
N.A.I.C.S.: 321992
Piotr Cieslewicz *(Mng Dir)*

Kingspan International Finance Ltd. (1)
Dublin Road, Kingscourt, Cavan, Ireland **(100%)**
Tel.: (353) 429698000
Web Site: http://www.kingspan.com
Sales Range: $25-49.9 Million
Emp.: 30
Business Services
N.A.I.C.S.: 561499

Kingspan Investments Limited (1)
Greenfield Business Park No 2, Greenfield, Holywell, CH8 7GJ, Flintshire, United Kingdom
Tel.: (44) 1352 716100
Emp.: 400
Investment Management Service
N.A.I.C.S.: 523999
Gilbert McCarthy *(Mng Dir)*

Kingspan Kft (1)
Horka Dulo 1, 2367, Ujhartyan, Hungary
Tel.: (36) 29 573 400
Web Site: http://www.kingspan.info
Insulated Wall Panel & Panel Roof Mfr
N.A.I.C.S.: 332311

Kingspan LLC (1)
The Balkana area 5 lit BP offices 10 - 18, 192 281, Saint Petersburg, Russia
Tel.: (7) 8126763965
Web Site: http://www.kingspan.com
Sales Range: $25-49.9 Million
Emp.: 8
Insulated Wall & Panel Roof Mfr
N.A.I.C.S.: 321992

Kingspan Light & Air LLC (1)
28662 North Ballard Dr, Lake Forest, IL 60045
Tel.: (847) 816-1060
Rev.: $10,000,000
Emp.: 55
Sheet Metal Work Mfg
N.A.I.C.S.: 332322
Steve Gaynor *(Plant Mgr)*

Kingspan Limited (1)
Unit 2 Greenfield Business Park, Bagillt Road, Holywell, CH87GJ, United Kingdom
Tel.: (44) 1352716100
Web Site: http://www.kingspanpanels.com
Roofing Siding & Insulation Material Whslr
N.A.I.C.S.: 423330

Kingspan Limited (1)
5202 272nd Street, Langley, V4W 1S3, BC, Canada **(100%)**
Tel.: (604) 607-1101
Web Site: http://www.kingspan.com
Prefabricated Insulated Building Panels Mfr
N.A.I.C.S.: 332311

Kingspan Limited (1)
Carrickmacross Rd, Kingscourt, Cavan, Ireland
Tel.: (353) 42 9698 500
Web Site: http://www.kingspan.com
Sales Range: $25-49.9 Million
Emp.: 10
Insulated Panel & Roof Mfr
N.A.I.C.S.: 321999

Kingspan Lviv TOV (1)
Bud 28 Kv 404 Vul Krimska, L'viv, 79035, Ukraine
Tel.: (380) 44 583 02 33
Sales Range: $50-74.9 Million
Emp.: 10
Insulated Wall Panel & Panel Roof Mfr
N.A.I.C.S.: 423330
Alexander Sirry *(Country Mgr)*

Kingspan Miljo AS (1)
Gjerdrumsvei 10 D, Oslo, 1410, Norway
Tel.: (47) 22 02 19 20
Web Site: http://www.kingspanmiljo.no
Emp.: 20
Metal Container Mfr
N.A.I.C.S.: 332439
Lars Bugge *(Mgr)*

Kingspan N.V. (1)
Bouwelven, 2280, Grobbendonk, Belgium **(100%)**
Tel.: (32) 14232535
Web Site: http://www.kingspan.com
Sales Range: $50-74.9 Million
Paint Varnish & Supplies Whslr
N.A.I.C.S.: 424950

Kingspan OU (1)
Mustamae Tee 55, 10621, Tallinn, Estonia
Tel.: (372) 651 6661
Web Site: http://www.kingspan.ee
Emp.: 2
Insulated Wall Panel & Panel Roof Mfr
N.A.I.C.S.: 332311

Kingspan Off-Site Ltd. (1)
Pitfield Kiln Farm, Milton Keynes, MK113LE, Bucks, United Kingdom **(100%)**
Tel.: (44) 1908266200
Burial Casket Mfr
N.A.I.C.S.: 339995

Kingspan Panels Limited (1)
2-4 Greenfield Business Park 2, Holywell, CH8 7GJ, United Kingdom
Tel.: (44) 1352 716100
Web Site: http://www.kingspanpanels.com
Emp.: 450
Panel Mfr
N.A.I.C.S.: 321999

Kingspan Pte Limited (1)
1 Commonwealth Lane 07 26 27, Singapore, 149544, Singapore
Tel.: (65) 62645942
Web Site: http://www.kingspanpanels.asia
Insulated Wall Panels & Panel Roof Mfr
N.A.I.C.S.: 327390

Kingspan Renewables Limited (1)
Tadman Street, Wakefield, WF1 5QU, West Yorkshire, United Kingdom
Tel.: (44) 1924 376 026
Web Site: http://www.kingspansolar.co.uk
Sales Range: $25-49.9 Million
Emp.: 10
Solar Photovoltaic Mfr
N.A.I.C.S.: 334413
Gerard Whelan *(Gen Mgr)*

Subsidiary (Non-US):

Kingspan Renewables Ltd - Poland (2)
Topolowa 5, 62-090, Rokietnica, Poland
Tel.: (48) 61 814 44 00
Web Site: http://www.kingspansolar.com
Sales Range: $25-49.9 Million
Emp.: 10
Solar Heating Equipment Mfr
N.A.I.C.S.: 333414

Kingspan Renewables Ltd. - Germany (2)
Am Schornacker 2, 46485, Wesel, Germany
Tel.: (49) 30 98315341
Web Site: http://www.kingspansolar.com
Solar Equipment Mfr
N.A.I.C.S.: 333414

Kingspan Renewables Srl (2)
Via Castagnera 31, 23868, Valmadrera, Lecco, Italy
Tel.: (39) 0341 581178
Solar Photovoltaic Mfr
N.A.I.C.S.: 334413

Kingspan S.R.L. (1)
Str Grigore Mora No 22 Et 1 Ap 2, Bucharest, 011887, Romania
Tel.: (40) 21 2315089
Web Site: http://www.kingspan.ro
Sales Range: $25-49.9 Million
Insulated Wall Panels & Panel Roof Mfr
N.A.I.C.S.: 321992

Kingspan SIA (1)
Kronvalda Bulvaris 3-1, Riga, 1010, Latvia
Tel.: (371) 2839 3333
Web Site: http://www.kingspan.lv
Insulated Wall Panels & Panel Roof Mfr
N.A.I.C.S.: 327390
Tonu Sepaste *(Country Mgr-Estonia)*

Kingspan Sarl (1)
3 rue Claude Chappe - Bat 3 Parc d'affaires de Crecy, 69370, Saint-Didier-au-Mont-d'Or, France
Tel.: (33) 472 17 90 40
Sales Range: $25-49.9 Million
Emp.: 1
Insulated Wall Panels & Panel Roof Mfr
N.A.I.C.S.: 332311

Kingspan Solar Inc (1)
7510 Montevideo Rd, Jessup, MD 20794
Tel.: (410) 799-6600
Web Site: http://www.kingspansolar.com
Emp.: 6
Solar Thermal Products Installation Services
N.A.I.C.S.: 238220

Kingspan Sp.z o.o. (1)
Ul Przemyslowa 20, Lipsko, 27300, Radom, Poland **(100%)**
Tel.: (48) 3783100
Web Site: http://www.kingspan.pl
Sales Range: $25-49.9 Million
Emp.: 50
Sheet Metal Work Mfg
N.A.I.C.S.: 332322
Krzysztof Kowalczyk *(Pres)*

Kingspan Suelo Technicos S.L. (1)
Los Guindos 2, S S de Los Reyes, 28700, Madrid, Spain
Tel.: (34) 916639094
Web Site: http://www.kingspan.es
Sales Range: $25-49.9 Million
Emp.: 25
Sheet Metal Work Mfg
N.A.I.C.S.: 332322

Kingspan Tarec Industrial Insulation Ltd. (1)
Glossop Brook Road, Glossop, SK138GP, Derbs, United Kingdom
Tel.: (44) 8707330021
Web Site: http://www.kingspantarec.com
Sales Range: $25-49.9 Million
Emp.: 100
Polystyrene Foam Product Mfr
N.A.I.C.S.: 326140

Kingspan Tek GmbH (1)
Beusterstrasse 1A, Klosterfelde, 16348, Berlin, Germany **(100%)**

KINGSPAN GROUP PLC

Kingspan Group PLC—(Continued)
Tel.: (49) 3339687870
Web Site: http://www.tek.kingspan.com
Sales Range: $25-49.9 Million
Emp.: 20
New Single-Family Housing Construction
N.A.I.C.S.: 236115

Kingspan d.o.o. (1)
Gorjanoviceva 22, 10000, Zagreb, Croatia
Tel.: (385) 1 464 80 51
Sales Range: $25-49.9 Million
Emp.: 5
Insulated Wall Panels & Panel Roof Mfr
N.A.I.C.S.: 332311
Sergej Roth (Country Mgr)

Kingspan d.o.o. (1)
Partizanske Avijacije 18/stan 13, 11070, Novi Beograd, Serbia
Tel.: (381) 11 2129 837
Web Site: http://www.kingspan.com
Insulated Wall Pane & Panel Roof Mfr
N.A.I.C.S.: 332311

Kingspan s.r.o. (1)
Stara Vajnorska 27, Bratislava, 831 04, Slovakia
Tel.: (421) 1905388998
Web Site: http://www.kingspan.info
Insulated Wall Panels & Panel Roof Mfr
N.A.I.C.S.: 321992

LOGSTOR Holding A/S (1)
Danmarksvej 11, 9670, Logstor, Denmark
Tel.: (45) 99661000
Web Site: http://www.logstor.com
Sales Range: $350-399.9 Million
Emp.: 1,251
Holding Company
N.A.I.C.S.: 551112
Martin McCourt (Pres & CEO)

Subsidiary (Domestic):

LOGSTOR A/S (2)
Danmarksvej 11, 9670, Logstor, Denmark **(100%)**
Tel.: (45) 99661000
Web Site: http://www.logstor.com
Plastics Pipe & Pipe Fitting Mfr
N.A.I.C.S.: 326122
Kristian Haldrup Overgaard (Exec VP-Oil & Gas)

Subsidiary (Non-US):

LOGSTOR Austria GmbH (3)
Gallgasse 17, 1130, Vienna, Austria
Tel.: (43) 1662494010
Sales Range: $25-49.9 Million
Emp.: 4
Prefabricated Pipe Systems Mfr
N.A.I.C.S.: 332996

LOGSTOR Deutschland GmbH (3)
Skandinavien-Bogen 6, Handewitt, 24983, Kiel, Germany **(100%)**
Tel.: (49) 461773050
Web Site: http://www.logstor.com
Sales Range: $25-49.9 Million
Emp.: 30
Metals Service Center
N.A.I.C.S.: 423510

LOGSTOR Finland OY (3)
Rajalantie 5 Pl 37, Saarijarvi, Oulu, 91310, Finland **(100%)**
Tel.: (358) 103037500
Web Site: http://www.logstor.com
Sales Range: $25-49.9 Million
Emp.: 70
Plastics Pipe & Pipe Fitting Mfr
N.A.I.C.S.: 326122
Juhani Ruotsalainen (Mgr)

LOGSTOR France SA (3)
Coteaux du Bel Air 45 rue de la Liberte, Saint-Germain-en-Laye, 78100, Paris, France **(100%)**
Tel.: (33) 139046410
Plumbing & Heating Equipment & Supplies Whslr
N.A.I.C.S.: 423720

Subsidiary (Domestic):

LOGSTOR Fredericia A/S (3)
Treldevej 191, 7000, Fredericia, Denmark **(100%)**

Tel.: (45) 76233000
Web Site: http://www.logstor.com
Sales Range: $100-124.9 Million
Complete Pre-Insulated Pipe Systems for District Heating & Industrial Purposes
N.A.I.C.S.: 332996

Subsidiary (Non-US):

LOGSTOR Italia Srl (3)
Corso Venezia 12, Milan, 20121, Italy **(100%)**
Tel.: (39) 0276006401
Plumbing & Heating Equipment & Supplies Whslr
N.A.I.C.S.: 423720
Giorgio Anelli (Mng Dir)

LOGSTOR Nederland BV (3)
Debbemeerstraat 21, 2181 HE, Hoofddorp, Netherlands **(100%)**
Tel.: (31) 235632534
Web Site: http://www.logstor.com
Sales Range: $25-49.9 Million
Emp.: 9
Fabricated Structural Metal Mfr
N.A.I.C.S.: 332312
Jan-Hendrik Kors (Mng Dir)

LOGSTOR Polska Sp. Z.o.o (3)
ul Handlowa 1 Mikulczyce, PL 41-807, Zabrze, Poland **(100%)**
Tel.: (48) 32 37 38 100
Web Site: http://www.logstor.com
District Heating & Cooling Production
N.A.I.C.S.: 333414

LOGSTOR Polska Sp. Zo.o. (3)
ul Malborska 60, 82 300, Elblag, Poland
Tel.: (48) 556195919
Sales Range: $25-49.9 Million
Prefabricated Pipe Systems Mfr
N.A.I.C.S.: 332996

LOGSTOR Polska Sp. z o.o. (3)
ul Legionow 2, 82-300, Elblag, Poland
Tel.: (48) 556195919
Prefabricated Pipe Systems Mfr
N.A.I.C.S.: 332996

LOGSTOR Schweiz AG (3)
Adlikerstrasse 290, 8105, Regensdorf, Switzerland **(100%)**
Tel.: (41) 448426511
Web Site: http://www.logstor.com
Sales Range: $25-49.9 Million
Emp.: 14
Plumbing & Heating Equipment & Supplies Whslr
N.A.I.C.S.: 423720

LOGSTOR Sverige AB (3)
Rorverket, Sodra Porten, 68 821, Storfors, Sweden
Tel.: (46) 19208180
Web Site: http://www.logstor.com
Sales Range: $25-49.9 Million
Emp.: 50
Prefabricated Pipe Systems Mfr
N.A.I.C.S.: 332996
Peter Dorsal (Gen Mgr)

LOGSTOR UAB (3)
Gedimino str 5, 44332, Kaunas, Lithuania **(100%)**
Tel.: (370) 37409440
Emp.: 4
Plumbing & Heating Equipment & Supplies Whslr
N.A.I.C.S.: 423720
Gintautas Barila (Gen Mgr)

Affiliate (Non-US):

LOGSTOR Insulation (Wuxi) Co Ltd. (2)
No 17-4 Changjiang S Rd New Area, Wuxi, 214028, China **(65.67%)**
Tel.: (86) 51085343119
Web Site: http://www.logstor.pl
Basic Inorganic Chemical Mfr
N.A.I.C.S.: 325180

Manchester Coppersmiths Limited (1)
Bennett St, Manchester, M125BW, United Kingdom **(100%)**
Tel.: (44) 1612230303
Web Site: http://www.kingspan-renewable.com

INTERNATIONAL PUBLIC

Sales Range: $25-49.9 Million
Emp.: 40
Fabricated Structural Metal Mfr
N.A.I.C.S.: 332312
Barry Fidebottom (Mng Dir)

Morin Corporation (1)
685 Middle St, Bristol, CT 06010
Tel.: (860) 584-0900
Web Site: https://www.morincorp.com
Rev: $10,200,000
Emp.: 30
Roof Deck & Sheet Metal Mfr
N.A.I.C.S.: 332322

Nordic Waterproofing Holding AB (1)
Ronnowsgatan 12, 252 25, Helsingborg, Sweden **(62.6%)**
Tel.: (46) 42362240
Web Site: https://www.nordicwaterproofing.com
Rev.: $418,050,521
Assets: $340,357,976
Liabilities: $173,948,879
Net Worth: $166,409,096
Earnings: $19,341,182
Emp.: 1,318
Fiscal Year-end: 12/31/2023
Holding Company
N.A.I.C.S.: 551112
Martin Ellis (CEO)

Subsidiary (Non-US):

Annebergs Limtrae A/S (2)
Lundtangvej 16-Lunde, DK-6830, Norre Nebel, Denmark
Tel.: (45) 75282133
Web Site: https://www.annebergs-limtrae.dk
Glulam Beams Distr
N.A.I.C.S.: 423310

Byggpartner AS (2)
Skolmar 24, 3232, Sandefjord, Norway
Tel.: (47) 33420900
Web Site: https://www.tak.as
Emp.: 60
Roofing Construction Services
N.A.I.C.S.: 238160

Distri Pond Invest N.V. (2)
Nikelaan 33, Laakdal, 2430, Vorst, Belgium
Tel.: (32) 13618870
Web Site: https://www.distripond.com
Land Construction Services
N.A.I.C.S.: 236220

EG-Trading Oy (2)
Vastanbyntie 31, FI-10600, Tammisaari, Finland
Tel.: (358) 92989924
Web Site: https://eg-trading.fi
Green Roof Construction Services
N.A.I.C.S.: 238160

Gordon Low Products Ltd. (2)
Rookery Road, Wyboston, MK44 3UG, Bedfordshire, United Kingdom
Tel.: (44) 1480405433
Web Site: https://www.gordonlowproducts.co.uk
Pond Liner Mfr & Distr
N.A.I.C.S.: 332313

Subsidiary (Domestic):

Hagmans Tak Ost AB (2)
Eriksbergsgatan 7, 591 45, Motala, Sweden
Tel.: (46) 141213331
Roofing Construction Services
N.A.I.C.S.: 238160

Subsidiary (Non-US):

Hetag Fyn A/S (2)
Industrievej 2, 5750, Ringe, Denmark
Tel.: (45) 70201422
Roofing Mfr & Distr
N.A.I.C.S.: 326299

Hetag JK Tagentreprise A/S (2)
Hvidsvaermervej 165A, 2610, Rodovre, Denmark
Tel.: (45) 44924701
Roofing Mfr & Distr
N.A.I.C.S.: 326299

Hetag Nordjysk Tag A/S (2)
Hjallerup Erhvervspark 4B, 9320, Hjallerup, Denmark
Tel.: (45) 98284019

Roof Park & Courtyard Construction Services
N.A.I.C.S.: 238160

Hetag Tagmaterialer A/S (2)
Stiftsvej 13, 7100, Vejle, Denmark
Tel.: (45) 76752633
Web Site: https://hetag.dk
Roofing Mfr & Distr
N.A.I.C.S.: 326299

IFA Tagdaekning A/S (2)
Vadebrovej 36, 4891, Toreby L, Denmark
Tel.: (45) 54439791
Roofing Mfr & Distr
N.A.I.C.S.: 326299

KerabitPro Oy (2)
Ralssitie 6, 01510, Vantaa, Finland
Tel.: (358) 108511000
Web Site: https://www.kerabit.fi
Building Construction Services
N.A.I.C.S.: 236220

LA Kattohuolto Oy (2)
Ralssitie 6 B, 01510, Vantaa, Finland
Tel.: (358) 103220240
Web Site: https://la-kattohuolto.fi
Building Construction Services
N.A.I.C.S.: 236220

Nordic Waterproofing AS (2)
Vangsveien 10 Bygg A, 1814, Askim, Norway
Tel.: (47) 69833440
Web Site: https://www.mataki.no
Roofing Construction Services
N.A.I.C.S.: 238160

Nordic Waterproofing Oy (2)
Ralssitie 6, FIN-01510, Vantaa, Finland
Tel.: (358) 108511000
Building Construction Services
N.A.I.C.S.: 236220

Nordic Waterproofing Sp. Z o.o. (2)
ul Szczecinska 61/67, 91-222, Lodz, Poland
Tel.: (48) 427120704
Flat Roofing Services
N.A.I.C.S.: 238160

Playgreen Finland Oy (2)
Ralssitie 6, 01510, Vantaa, Finland
Tel.: (358) 108511700
Bituminous Roofing Mfr & Distr
N.A.I.C.S.: 316210

Pond Technics & Training B.V.B.A. (2)
Nikelaan 33, BE-2430, Laakdal, Belgium
Tel.: (32) 13618870
Web Site: https://pondtechnics.be
Swimming Pond Garden Services
N.A.I.C.S.: 713940

Ringsaker Vegg- og Takelementer AS (2)
Brugsvegen 13, 2390, Moelv, Norway
Tel.: (47) 62332660
Web Site: https://rvt.no
Emp.: 1,100
Wooden Construction Element Mfr & Distr
N.A.I.C.S.: 321992

Ripatti Oy (2)
Yrittajankulma 6, 01800, Klaukkala, Finland
Tel.: (358) 108511500
Building Construction Services
N.A.I.C.S.: 541310

SPT-Painting Oy (2)
Ralssitie 6, 01510, Vantaa, Finland
Tel.: (358) 108511900
Building Construction Services
N.A.I.C.S.: 541310

Subsidiary (Domestic):

SealEco AB (2)
Kavsjovagen 38 Norregards Industriomrade, SE-331 35, Varnamo, Sweden
Tel.: (46) 370510100
Web Site: https://www.sealeco.com
Emp.: 1,200
Flat Roofing Services
N.A.I.C.S.: 238160

Subsidiary (Non-US):

SealEco AG (2)
Eisenbahnstrasse 6, 3360, Herzogenbuchsee, Switzerland

AND PRIVATE COMPANIES

Tel.: (41) 629557050
Building Construction Services
N.A.I.C.S.: 541330

SealEco B.V. (2)
Handelsweg 45, 8152 BN, Lemelerveld, Netherlands
Tel.: (31) 572371027
Flat Roofing Services
N.A.I.C.S.: 238160

SealEco Ltd. (2)
77 Canyon Road Excelsior Park, Wishaw, ML2 0EG, Lanarkshire, United Kingdom
Tel.: (44) 1698802250
Flat Roofing Services
N.A.I.C.S.: 238160

SealEco N.V. (2)
Bethovenstraat 62/2, 2960, Brecht, Belgium
Tel.: (32) 33138666
Web Site: https://www.sealeco.com
Emp.: 1,200
Building Construction Services
N.A.I.C.S.: 236220

Seikat OY (2)
Reinilantie 61, 61400, Ylistaro, Finland
Tel.: (358) 108511200
Building Construction Services
N.A.I.C.S.: 541310

Taasinge Elementer A/S (2)
Bjernemarksvej 54, DK-5700, Svendborg, Denmark
Tel.: (45) 62225455
Web Site: https://taasingeelementer.dk
Wooden Element Mfr & Distr
N.A.I.C.S.: 316210

Subsidiary (Domestic):

Urban Green AB (2)
Fageras 1, 342 52, Vislanda, Sweden
Tel.: (46) 47236300
Web Site: https://urbangreen.se
Green Roof Construction Services
N.A.I.C.S.: 238160

Subsidiary (Non-US):

Veg Tech A/S (2)
Maglebytorv 6 1 floor, 2791, Dragor, Denmark
Tel.: (45) 39626869
Web Site: https://www.vegtech.dk
Green Roof Construction Services
N.A.I.C.S.: 238160

Subsidiary (Domestic):

Veg Tech AB (2)
Fageras 1, 342 52, Vislanda, Sweden
Tel.: (46) 47236300
Web Site: https://www.vegtech.se
Emp.: 15
Roof Park & Courtyard Construction Services
N.A.I.C.S.: 238160

Onduline (1)
Rue du Bac, Yainville, Normandie, 76480, France
Tel.: (33) 2 35 05 90 90
Web Site: http://fr.onduline.com
Emp.: 1,600
Lightweight Roofing, Insulation & Other Building Materials Mfr & Distr
N.A.I.C.S.: 324122
Andre Blazquez (Dir-Publication)

Subsidiary (Non-US):

Onduline Belgique SA/NV (2)
Rue Piretfontaine 18, 4140, Sprimont, Belgium
Tel.: (32) 37801735
Web Site: http://be.onduline.com
Lightweight Roofing, Insulation & Other Building Materials Mfr & Distr
N.A.I.C.S.: 324122

Onduline Building Products Limited (2)
Dawson House 5 Jewry Street, London, EC3N 2EX, United Kingdom
Tel.: (44) 2077270533
Web Site: http://uk.onduline.com
Roofing & Insulation Materials Distr
N.A.I.C.S.: 423330

Onduline GmbH (2)
Ostring 11, D-65205, Wiesbaden, Germany
Tel.: (49) 61229900
Web Site: http://www.onduline.de
Roofing & Insulation Materials Distr
N.A.I.C.S.: 423330

Onduline Italia S.p.A. (2)
Via Sibolla 52/53 Loc Cerbaia, Altopascio, IT-55011, Lucca, Italy
Tel.: (39) 058325611
Web Site: http://it.onduline.com
Lightweight Roofing, Insulation & Other Building Materials Mfr & Distr
N.A.I.C.S.: 324122

Onduline Materiais de Construcao, S.A. (2)
Rua das Lages 524, Canelas Vila Nova de Gaia, PT-4410 272, Porto, Portugal
Tel.: (351) 227151230
Web Site: http://www.onduline.pt
Lightweight Roofing, Insulation & Other Building Materials Distr
N.A.I.C.S.: 423330

Onduline Material de Constructii S.r.l. (2)
Str Navodarinr 30-32 sector 1, Bucharest, 14108, Romania
Tel.: (40) 212331264
Web Site: http://ro.onduline.ro
Lightweight Roofing, Insulation & Other Building Materials Distr
N.A.I.C.S.: 423330

Onduline Materiales de Construccion, S.A. (2)
El Campillo Industrial Park Phase 2 P-12, ES-48500, Gallarta, Vizcaya, Spain
Tel.: (34) 946369444
Web Site: http://es.onduline.com
Lightweight Roofing, Insulation & Other Building Materials Mfr & Distr
N.A.I.C.S.: 324122

Onduline Polska Sp. z o. o. ul. (2)
ul Kolobrzeska 8, 02 923, Warsaw, Poland
Tel.: (48) 226518508
Web Site: http://pl.onduline.com
Lightweight Roofing, Insulation & Other Building Materials Distr
N.A.I.C.S.: 423330

Onduline S.M., s.r.o. (2)
Zakourilova 28/1096, 14900, Prague, Czech Republic
Tel.: (420) 267913949
Web Site: http://cz.onduline.com
Lightweight Roofing, Insulation & Other Building Materials Distr
N.A.I.C.S.: 423330

Polmeric Mouldings Limited (1)
Unit 1 Varney Avenue, Spon Lane Trading Estate, West Bromwich, B706AE, W Midlands, United Kingdom (100%)
Tel.: (44) 1215257887
Web Site: http://www.kingspan.com
Sales Range: $25-49.9 Million
Emp.: 16
Plastics Product Mfr
N.A.I.C.S.: 326199

Potton Limited (1)
Eltisley Rd Great Gransden, Sandy, SG19 3AR, Bedfordshire, United Kingdom (100%)
Tel.: (44) 1767676400
Web Site: http://www.potton.co.uk
Sales Range: $25-49.9 Million
Emp.: 100
Prefabricated Wood Building Mfr
N.A.I.C.S.: 321992

Range Cylinders Limited (1)
Tadman Street, Wakefield, WF1 5QU, W Yorkshire, United Kingdom (100%)
Tel.: (44) 1924376026
Web Site: http://www.range-cylinders.co.uk
Sales Range: $25-49.9 Million
Emp.: 100
Refrigerated Warehousing & Storage
N.A.I.C.S.: 493120
Cameron Holroyd (Mng Dir)

STEICO SE (1)
Otto-Lilienthal-Ring 30, 85622, Feldkirchen, Germany (51%)
Tel.: (49) 899915510
Web Site: https://www.steico.com
Rev.: $403,232,672
Assets: $648,711,283
Liabilities: $302,625,960
Net Worth: $346,085,322
Earnings: $18,633,326
Emp.: 1,911
Fiscal Year-end: 12/31/2023
Insulation Material Mfr
N.A.I.C.S.: 321999
Udo Schramek (CEO)

Sensor Systems Limited (1)
180 Gilford Road, Portadown, BT63 5LE, Co Armagh, United Kingdom (100%)
Tel.: (44) 2838364415
Web Site: http://www.sensor-systems.com
Sales Range: $25-49.9 Million
Emp.: 30
Measuring & Testing Electricity & Electrical Signals Instrument Mfr
N.A.I.C.S.: 334515

Tate Access Floors, Inc. (1)
7510 Montevideo Rd, Jessup, MD 20794-9321
Tel.: (410) 799-4200
Web Site: http://www.tateaccessfloors.com
Sales Range: $50-74.9 Million
Emp.: 200
Mfr of Access Floor Systems
N.A.I.C.S.: 332322
Ed Blazeck (Dir-Ops)

Subsidiary (Non-US):

Tate ASP Access Floors Inc (2)
880 Equestrian Court, Oakville, L6L 6L7, ON, Canada
Tel.: (905) 847-0138
Web Site: http://www.tateinc.com
Insulated Wall Panel & Panel Roof Mfr
N.A.I.C.S.: 332311

Titan Environmental Limited (1)
Dundalk Road, Carrickmacross, Co Monaghan, Ireland (100%)
Tel.: (353) 429690022
Web Site: http://www.titanenv.com
Sales Range: $25-49.9 Million
Emp.: 30
Plastics Product Mfr
N.A.I.C.S.: 326199

Titan Environmental Limited (1)
180 Gilford Rd, Portadown, BT324PH, Co Armagh, United Kingdom (100%)
Tel.: (44) 2838364400
Web Site: http://www.titanenv.com
Plastics Product Mfr
N.A.I.C.S.: 326199

UAB Kingspan (1)
Neries kr 16, LT-48402, Kaunas, Lithuania (100%)
Tel.: (370) 37451883
Web Site: http://www.kingspan.lt
Sales Range: $25-49.9 Million
Emp.: 4
Marketing Consulting Services
N.A.I.C.S.: 541613

Vicwest Inc. (1)
5050 South Service Road Unit 200, Burlington, L7L 5Y7, ON, Canada
Tel.: (905) 825-2252
Web Site: http://vicwest.com
Sales Range: $350-399.9 Million
Construction Product Distr
N.A.I.C.S.: 423390

Subsidiary (US):

All Weather Insulated Panels (2)
929 Aldridge Rd, Vacaville, CA 95688
Web Site: http://www.awipanels.com
Insulated Metal Panel Mfr
N.A.I.C.S.: 332311

Subsidiary (Non-US):

P.T.M. s.r.l. s.u. (2)
Via M Tognato 10, 35042, Este, Italy
Tel.: (39) 0429 600973
Web Site: http://www.ptmtechnology.com
Conveyor Equipment Mfr
N.A.I.C.S.: 333922

KINGSROSE MINING LIMITED

Suite 5 CPC 145 Stirling Hwy, Nedlands, 6009, WA, Australia
Tel.: (61) 893893190

Web Site:
https://www.kingsrosemining.com.au
KRM—(ASX)
Rev.: $1,169,032
Assets: $27,048,418
Liabilities: $2,664,613
Net Worth: $24,383,805
Earnings: ($2,578,001)
Emp.: 22
Fiscal Year-end: 06/30/24
Gold Mining
N.A.I.C.S.: 212220
Ivan Kusnadi (Chm-PT Natarang Mining)

KINGSTATE ELECTRONICS CORPORATION

10F No 69-11 Sec 2 JhongJheng E Rd, Danshui Dist, New Taipei City, 25170, Taiwan
Tel.: (886) 228095651
Web Site:
https://www.kingstate.com.tw
Year Founded: 1977
3206—(TPE)
Rev.: $129,662,508
Assets: $88,048,057
Liabilities: $47,556,296
Net Worth: $40,491,761
Earnings: $6,632,117
Fiscal Year-end: 12/31/22
Electronic Parts Mfr
N.A.I.C.S.: 334419
Yentang Chang (Chm & CEO)

KINGSTON DODGE CHRYSLER (1980) LTD.

1429 Princess Street, Kingston, K7M 3E9, ON, Canada
Tel.: (613) 549-8900
Web Site:
http://www.kingstondodge.com
Year Founded: 1980
Sales Range: $10-24.9 Million
Emp.: 55
New & Used Car Dealers
N.A.I.C.S.: 441110
Mark Hughes (Mgr-Sls)

KINGSTON FINANCIAL GROUP LIMITED

72/F The Center 99 Queens Road Central, Central, China (Hong Kong)
Tel.: (852) 22986200
Web Site:
http://www.kingston.com.hk
1031—(HKG)
Rev.: $256,699,607
Assets: $3,535,961,291
Liabilities: $872,732,207
Net Worth: $2,663,229,084
Earnings: $5,770,823
Emp.: 621
Fiscal Year-end: 03/31/22
Investment Services
N.A.I.C.S.: 523999
Yuet Wah Chu (Founder & CEO)

Subsidiaries:

Casa Real Hotel (1)
Avenida do Dr Rodrigo Rodrigues No 1118, Macau, China (Macau)
Tel.: (853) 28726288
Web Site: http://www.casarealhotel.com.mo
Hotel Services
N.A.I.C.S.: 721110

Grandview Hotel Macau (1)
142 Estrada Governador Albano de Oliveira, Taipa, China (Macau)
Tel.: (853) 28837788
Web Site: http://www.grandview-hotel.com
Sales Range: $25-49.9 Million
Emp.: 250
Hotel Services
N.A.I.C.S.: 721110

KINGSTON PROPERTIES LIMITED

Kingston Properties Limited—(Continued)

KINGSTON PROPERTIES LIMITED
36-38 Red Hills Road Building B 1st Floor, Kingston, 10, Jamaica
Tel.: (876) 7547840   FL
Web Site: https://www.kpreit.com
Year Founded: 2008
KPREIT—(JAM)
Rev.: $3,983,764
Assets: $70,956,389
Liabilities: $23,081,996
Net Worth: $47,874,393
Earnings: $4,647,516
Fiscal Year-end: 12/31/23
Real Estate Investment Services
N.A.I.C.S.: 525990
Garfield Sinclair *(Chm)*

KINGSTON RESOURCES LIMITED
202 / 201 Miller Street, North Sydney, 2060, NSW, Australia
Tel.: (61) 280217492   AU
Web Site:
  https://www.kingstonresources.com
Year Founded: 2000
RZZ—(DEU)
Rev.: $9,120,534
Assets: $67,876,331
Liabilities: $21,039,000
Net Worth: $46,837,330
Earnings: ($1,599,933)
Emp.: 2
Fiscal Year-end: 06/30/22
Security Systems Services (except Locksmiths)
N.A.I.C.S.: 561621
Andrew Corbett *(Mng Dir)*

Subsidiaries:

Data-inCrypt Pty. Ltd.   (1)
PO Box 1288, West Perth, 6872, WA, Australia
Tel.: (61) 894152288
Web Site: http://www.data-incrypt.com
Data Recovery Software Solutions
N.A.I.C.S.: 518210

Synergy Business Solutions Australia Pty. Ltd.   (1)
855 Barrie Lane, Homebush, 4740, QLD, Australia
Tel.: (61) 749597350
Web Site: http://www.synergyaustralia.com
Custom Software Development Services
N.A.I.C.S.: 513210

KINGSTON WHARVES LIMITED
195 Second Street Newport West, Kingston, 13, Jamaica
Tel.: (876) 6181068
Web Site:
  https://kingstonwharves.com
Year Founded: 1945
KW—(JAM)
Rev.: $62,999,521
Assets: $383,301,686
Liabilities: $81,836,559
Net Worth: $301,465,127
Earnings: $20,705,566
Emp.: 651
Fiscal Year-end: 12/31/23
Public Wharves Operations & Port Security Services
N.A.I.C.S.: 488310
Jeffery Hall *(Chm)*

Subsidiaries:

Security Administrators Limited (SAL)   (1)
3rd St Newport W, Kingston, Jamaica
Tel.: (876) 9234883
Web Site:
  http://www.securityadministrators.com.jm

Sales Range: $75-99.9 Million
Emp.: 300
Maritime Security & Services
N.A.I.C.S.: 561612
George Reynolds *(Mng Dir)*

KINGSVIEW MINERALS LTD.
501-580 Hornby St, Vancouver, V6C 3B6, BC, Canada
Tel.: (778) 382-8505   BC
Web Site:
  https://www.kingsviewminerals.ca
Year Founded: 2018
KVM—(CNSX)
Assets: $401,598
Liabilities: $70,538
Net Worth: $331,060
Earnings: ($706,256)
Fiscal Year-end: 12/31/21
Mineral Exploration Services
N.A.I.C.S.: 212220
Wafae Ben Bouazza *(Sec)*

KINGSVILLE STAMPING LTD.
1931 Setterington Dr, Kingsville, N9Y 2E5, ON, Canada
Tel.: (519) 326-6331
Web Site:
  http://www.kingsvillestamping.ca
Year Founded: 1986
Sales Range: $10-24.9 Million
Emp.: 100
Automotive Stamping Mfr
N.A.I.C.S.: 332119
Peter Bartsch *(Gen Mgr-Sls)*

KINGSWAY ARMS MANAGEMENT SERVICES INC.
208 Evans Ave Suite 115, Toronto, M8Z 1J7, ON, Canada
Tel.: (647) 288-2924
Web Site:
  http://www.kingswayarms.com
Year Founded: 1997
Retirement Homes & Assisted Living Facilities Operator
N.A.I.C.S.: 623312

KINGSWOOD HOLDINGS LTD.
10-11 Austin Friars, London, EC2N 2HG, United Kingdom
Tel.: (44) 2072930730
Web Site: https://www.kingswood-group.com
Year Founded: 2004
KWG—(AIM)
Rev.: $184,294,370
Assets: $203,605,150
Liabilities: $110,236,052
Net Worth: $93,369,099
Earnings: ($8,194,900)
Emp.: 396
Fiscal Year-end: 12/31/22
Investment Services
N.A.I.C.S.: 523999

Subsidiaries:

JFP Financial Services Limited   (1)
4th Floor Merchant Exchange Gas Road Waters Green, Macclesfield, SK11 6JX, Cheshire, United Kingdom
Tel.: (44) 1625919196
Web Site:
  https://www.jfpfinancialservices.co.uk
Financial Investment Services
N.A.I.C.S.: 523999

Money Matters (North East) Limited   (1)
Orkney Street Enterprise Centre Unit 1 18-20 Orkney Street, Glasgow, G51 2BX, United Kingdom
Tel.: (44) 1414455221
Web Site:
  https://www.moneymattersweb.co.uk
Financial Investment Services
N.A.I.C.S.: 523999

Sterling Trust Professional (Sheffield) Limited   (1)
40 Little London Rd Woodseats, Sheffield, S8 0UH, United Kingdom
Tel.: (44) 1142758882
Financial Investment Services
N.A.I.C.S.: 523999

Strategic Asset Managers Limited   (1)
Castle Mews 2 Old Glasgow Road, Uddingston, Glasgow, G71 7HF, United Kingdom
Tel.: (44) 1698907003
Web Site:
  https://www.strategicassetmanagers.co.uk
Financial Investment Services
N.A.I.C.S.: 523999

KINGWAYTEK TECHNOLOGY CO., LTD.
3F 100 Section 2 Roosevelt Rd, Chungcheng, Taipei, 10084, Taiwan
Tel.: (886) 223635445
Web Site: http://www.kingwaytek.com
6516—(TPE)
Rev.: $15,042,648
Assets: $37,992,996
Liabilities: $5,880,124
Net Worth: $32,112,872
Earnings: $2,467,780
Fiscal Year-end: 12/31/22
Software Products Mfr
N.A.I.C.S.: 334610

KINGWELL GROUP LIMITED
Tel.: (852) 28821195   Ky
Web Site: http://kingwell.todayir.com
01195—(HKG)
Rev.: $5,246,830
Assets: $28,371,887
Liabilities: $7,243,003
Net Worth: $21,128,885
Earnings: ($1,096,830)
Emp.: 72
Fiscal Year-end: 06/30/21
Holding Company; Printed Circuit Boards Mfr; Gold Ore Mining & Processing
N.A.I.C.S.: 551112
Yan Wai Poon *(Sec)*

KINGWISOFT TECHNOLOGY GROUP COMPANY LIMITED
11/F 8 Queens Road, Central, China (Hong Kong)
Tel.: (852) 25958588   Ky
Web Site:
  http://www.zhongjintechnology.com
Year Founded: 2010
8295—(HKG)
Rev.: $132,629,301
Assets: $241,167,861
Liabilities: $73,976,989
Net Worth: $167,190,872
Earnings: $11,790,276
Emp.: 7,351
Fiscal Year-end: 03/31/22
Holding Company; Corporate Finance Advisory & Other Business Related Services
N.A.I.C.S.: 551112
Zhanbin Niu *(Chm)*

KINGWORLD MEDICINES GROUP LIMITED
8th-9th Floor Block A Chuangxin Building Daxin Road, Nanshan District, Shenzhen, 518016, Guangdong, China
Tel.: (86) 75582292888   Ky
Web Site:
  http://www.kingworld.com.cn
1110—(HKG)
Rev.: $134,461,220
Assets: $177,376,165
Liabilities: $79,908,379
Net Worth: $97,467,786

INTERNATIONAL PUBLIC

Earnings: $6,113,297
Emp.: 1,037
Fiscal Year-end: 12/31/22
Pharmaceutical & Healthcare Products Distr
N.A.I.C.S.: 424210
Li Sheng Zhao *(Co-Founder & Chm)*

Subsidiaries:

Kingworld Medicine Healthcare Limited   (1)
Units 1906-1907 19th Floor Shui On Centre 6-8 Harbour Road, Wanchai, China (Hong Kong)
Tel.: (852) 2877 6488
Pharmaceutical Products Distr
N.A.I.C.S.: 424210
Watson Yao *(Gen Mgr)*

Shenzhen Dong Di Xin Technology Company Limited   (1)
Block A 5th floor Fuhua Technical Building No 9116 Beihuan Road, Nanshan District, Shenzhen, 518057, China
Tel.: (86) 7552 765 2471
Web Site: https://www.e-caretalk.com
Medical Equipment Mfr & Distr
N.A.I.C.S.: 339112

KINH BAC CITY DEVELOPMENT HOLDING CORPORATION
Lot B7 Que Vo Industrial Park Phuong Lieu Ward, Que Vo Dist, Bac Ninh, Vietnam
Tel.: (84) 2223634034
Web Site: https://www.kinhbaccity.vn
Year Founded: 2002
KBC—(HOSE)
Rev.: $241,381,434
Assets: $1,377,489,875
Liabilities: $544,389,920
Net Worth: $833,099,955
Earnings: $92,494,141
Emp.: 213
Fiscal Year-end: 12/31/23
Holding Company
N.A.I.C.S.: 551112
Dang Thanh Tam *(Chm)*

KINIK COMPANY
No 64 Zhongshan Rd, Yingge Dist, Taipei, 239010, Taiwan
Tel.: (886) 226791931
Web Site: https://www.kinik.com.tw
Year Founded: 1964
1560—(TAI)
Rev.: $208,669,471
Assets: $322,540,064
Liabilities: $110,877,984
Net Worth: $211,662,080
Earnings: $28,192,778
Emp.: 985
Fiscal Year-end: 12/31/23
Abrasive, Cutting Tool, Glass Lens Mfr & Distr
N.A.I.C.S.: 327910
Po-Chun Lin *(Chm)*

KINIKSA PHARMACEUTICALS, LTD.
Clarendon House 2 Church Street, Hamilton, HM11, Bermuda
Tel.: (441) 8081896257   BM
Web Site:
  https://www.kiniksapolicies.com
Year Founded: 2015
KNSA—(NASDAQ)
Rev.: $220,180,000
Assets: $459,672,000
Liabilities: $63,523,000
Net Worth: $396,149,000
Earnings: $183,363,000
Emp.: 220
Fiscal Year-end: 12/31/22
Biopharmaceutical Product Mfr
N.A.I.C.S.: 325412
John F. Paolini *(Chief Medical Officer)*

AND PRIVATE COMPANIES

KINNEVIK AB

Subsidiaries:

Kiniksa Pharmaceuticals Corp. (1)
100 Hayden Ave, Lexington, MA 02421
Tel.: (781) 431-9100
Web Site: http://www.kiniksa.com
Pharmaceuticals Product Mfr
N.A.I.C.S.: 325412
Sanj K. Patel *(Chm & CEO)*

KINJIRO CO., LTD.
4-14-1 Sotokanda Akihabara UDX Building South 18th floor, Chiyoda-Ku, Tokyo, 101-0021, Japan
Tel.: (81) 362608980
Web Site: https://www.kinjiro-e.com
Year Founded: 1981
4013—(TKS)
Rev.: $27,814,070
Assets: $90,659,830
Liabilities: $26,885,280
Net Worth: $63,774,550
Earnings: $2,623,300
Emp.: 315
Fiscal Year-end: 12/31/23
Software Development Services
N.A.I.C.S.: 541511
Minoru Kamura *(Founder, Chm & Pres)*

KINKO OPTICAL CO., LTD.
No 91 Lane 562 Section 9 Xiangshang Road, Wuqi District, Taichung, 435, Taiwan
Tel.: (886) 426305679
Web Site: https://www.kinko-optical.com
6209—(TAI)
Rev.: $88,197,289
Assets: $134,371,230
Liabilities: $34,877,725
Net Worth: $99,493,505
Earnings: ($1,628,176)
Emp.: 2,450
Fiscal Year-end: 12/31/23
Optical Lens Mfr
N.A.I.C.S.: 333248
Liang-Cheng Chou *(Vice Chm & Gen Mgr)*

Subsidiaries:

FOSHAN HUAGUO OPTICAL CO., LTD. (1)
No 3 Changhong East Road, Zhangcha Town, Foshan, 528000, Guangdong, China
Tel.: (86) 75782960266
Optical Lens Mfr
N.A.I.C.S.: 327215

KINLY HOLDING B.V.
Radarweg 29 14th Floor, Amsterdam, 1043 NX, Netherlands
Tel.: (31) 20 5800 900
Web Site: http://www.kinly.com
Year Founded: 2017
Holding Company; Video Collaboration Services
N.A.I.C.S.: 551112
Robbert Bakker *(CEO)*

Subsidiaries:

AVM Impact Ltd. (1)
Europe House, 170 Windmill Road, Sunbury-on-Thames, TW16 7HB, Middlesex, United Kingdom
Tel.: (44) 1932 733700
Web Site: http://www.avmimpact.com
Video Conferencing & Audio Visual System Design & Installation Services
N.A.I.C.S.: 541512
Edward Cook *(CEO)*

KINNARPS AB
Industrigatan 1, Kinnarp, 521 88, Sweden
Tel.: (46) 51538000
Web Site: http://www.kinnarps.com
Year Founded: 1942
Sales Range: $600-649.9 Million
Emp.: 2,300
Office Furniture Mfr
N.A.I.C.S.: 337214
Robert Petersson *(CEO)*

Subsidiaries:

KINNARPS SRL (1)
46A Virtutii Street, District 6, Bucharest, Romania
Tel.: (40) 372 147 300
Web Site: http://www.kinnarps.com
Furniture Distr
N.A.I.C.S.: 423210

KINNARPS UKRAINE LLC (1)
Floor 4 Building 8-B 3 Surikova street, 03035, Kiev, Ukraine
Tel.: (380) 44 492 1633
Furniture Distr
N.A.I.C.S.: 423210
Andriy Marchenko *(Mgr-Sls)*

Kinnarps (UK) Ltd (1)
69 Turnmill Street, London, EC1M 5RR, United Kingdom
Tel.: (44) 845 130 1313
Web Site: http://www.kinnarps.com
Furniture Distr
N.A.I.C.S.: 423210
Peter May *(Mgr-Sls)*

Kinnarps A/S (1)
Roskildevej 522, 2605, Brondby, Denmark
Tel.: (45) 701 510 10
Web Site: http://www.kinnarps.com
Furniture Distr
N.A.I.C.S.: 423210
Jeanette Qvarnstrom *(COO & Dir-Ops)*

Kinnarps AS (1)
Grindammen 4, 1359, Baerum, Norway
Tel.: (47) 67167100
Web Site: http://www.kinnarps.com
Emp.: 80
Furniture Distr
N.A.I.C.S.: 423210
Ernst Kjaeras *(Acct Mgr)*

Kinnarps Italia Srl (1)
Via Morimondo 26 Edificio 11/A, 20143, Milan, Italy
Tel.: (39) 02 81834911
Web Site: http://www.kinnarps.it
Emp.: 3
Furniture Distr
N.A.I.C.S.: 423210
Nunzia Ricciardi *(Country Mgr)*

Kinnarps Ltda (1)
Beloura Office Park EEO4, Rua do Centro Empresarial, 2710-444, Sintra, Portugal
Tel.: (351) 969 764 420
Web Site: http://www.kinnarps.com
Furniture Distr
N.A.I.C.S.: 423210
Anthony Shee *(CEO)*

Kinnarps Nederland BV (1)
Litauensestraat 17-21, 7204 CN, Zutphen, Netherlands
Tel.: (31) 575 514 422
Web Site: http://www.kinnarps.com
Furniture Distr
N.A.I.C.S.: 423210
Joost Kuyper *(Gen Mgr)*

Kinnarps Oy (1)
Ralssintie 2, 00720, Helsinki, Finland (100%)
Tel.: (358) 207 561 200
Web Site: http://www.kinnarps.com
Furniture Distr
N.A.I.C.S.: 423210
Henrik Slotte *(Mng Dir)*

Kinnarps Polska Sp. z o. o. (1)
ul Pulawska 354/356, 02-819, Warsaw, Poland
Tel.: (48) 22 314 64 70
Web Site: http://www.kinnarps.com
Furniture Distr
N.A.I.C.S.: 423210
Marysia Lorenc *(Mgr-HR Dev)*

Kinnarps Production AB (1)
Hedenstorpsv 3, 555 93, Jonkoping, Sweden
Tel.: (46) 36 31 14 00
Furniture Product Distr
N.A.I.C.S.: 423210

Pentri Karlsson *(CEO)*

Kinnarps Project Solutions (1)
Andalus St Suhaili business center, PO Box 1281, Jeddah, 21431, Saudi Arabia
Tel.: (966) 2 65 009 05
Web Site: http://www.kinnarps.com
Furniture Distr
N.A.I.C.S.: 423210

Kinnarps Project Solutions LLC (1)
4th Floor Albwardy Building, PO 111727, Dubai, United Arab Emirates
Tel.: (971) 4 3595501
Furniture Distr
N.A.I.C.S.: 423210
Asok Kumar *(Acct Mgr-CRT)*

Kinnarps S.A. (1)
1712 route de Quarante Sous, 78630, Orgeval, France
Tel.: (33) 139 082 700
Web Site: http://www.kinnarps.com
Furniture Distr
N.A.I.C.S.: 423210

Kinnarps S.A. de C.V (1)
Sierra Mojada 626, Col Lomas Barrilaco, 11010, Mexico, Mexico
Tel.: (52) 555 520 86 03
Web Site: http://www.kinnarps.com
Furniture Distr
N.A.I.C.S.: 423210
Lucia Espinosa Bracho *(Mgr-Sls & Project)*

Kinnarps Samas GmbH (1)
Mainzer Strasse 183, 67547, Worms, Germany
Tel.: (49) 624140030
Web Site: http://www.kinnarps.de
Sales Range: $250-299.9 Million
Emp.: 1,000
Office Furniture Mfr & Distr
N.A.I.C.S.: 337214

Kinnarps USA Inc. (1)
4301 W William Cannon Dr Ste B-150 305, Austin, TX 78749
Tel.: (855) 811-9676
Web Site: http://www.kinnarps.com
Furniture Distr
N.A.I.C.S.: 423210

Kinnarps do Brasil Ltda. (1)
Rua Oscar Freire 379 12 andar, 01426-001, Sao Paulo, Brazil
Tel.: (55) 11 3066 2550
Furniture Distr
N.A.I.C.S.: 423210
Borje Jerner *(Mng Dir & Partner)*

Kinnarps of Sweden Co. LLC (1)
Al-Mousa Centre Pepsi Street 16 74067, Al Khobar, 31952, Saudi Arabia
Tel.: (966) 3 896 8796
Web Site: http://www.kpsworld.com
Furniture Distr
N.A.I.C.S.: 423210
Anthony Shee *(CEO)*

Kinnarps, a. s. (1)
Komercni zona Pruhonice-Cestlice Obchodni 124, Cestlice, Czech Republic
Tel.: (420) 227 202 200
Web Site: http://www.kinnarps.com
Furniture Distr
N.A.I.C.S.: 423210

Kinnarps, spol. s r.o. (1)
Mytna 42, 811 05, Bratislava, Slovakia
Tel.: (421) 2 2129 0605
Web Site: http://www.kinnarps.com
Furniture Distr
N.A.I.C.S.: 423210

Materia AB (1)
Bredkarrsgatan 7, 573 92, Tranas, Sweden
Tel.: (46) 140 38 56 00
Web Site: http://www.materia.se
Furniture Distr
N.A.I.C.S.: 423210
Andreas Thorn *(Mgr-Pur)*

Skandiform AB (1)
Dolinvagen 8, SE-288 34, Hassleholm, Sweden
Tel.: (46) 44 855 5
Web Site: http://www.skandiform.com
Furniture Distr
N.A.I.C.S.: 423210
Anki Holgersson *(Mgr-Pur)*

UAB Kinnarps (1)
Pamenkalnio g 23/5-1, 01113, Vilnius, Lithuania
Tel.: (370) 5 2312956
Web Site: http://www.kinnarps.lt
Furniture Distr
N.A.I.C.S.: 423210

ZAO Kinnarps (1)
Sadovaja-Samotechnaja Ulitsa 24/27, 127051, Moscow, Russia
Tel.: (7) 4957834437
Web Site: http://www.kinnarps.com
Furniture Distr
N.A.I.C.S.: 423210
Igor Novikov *(Mgr-Sls)*

KINNEVIK AB
Skeppsbron 18, PO Box 2094, SE-103 13, Stockholm, Sweden
Tel.: (46) 856200000   SE
Web Site: https://www.kinnevik.com
Year Founded: 1936
KINV-B—(OTCIQ)
Rev.: $55,728,830
Assets: $5,012,035,554
Liabilities: $501,184,823
Net Worth: $4,510,850,731
Earnings: ($446,392,612)
Emp.: 46
Fiscal Year-end: 12/31/22
Financial Investment Services
N.A.I.C.S.: 551112
Torun Litzen *(Dir-Corp Comm)*

Subsidiaries:

Global Fashion Group S.A. (1)
5 Heienhaff, 1736, Senningerberg, Luxembourg
Tel.: (352) 691205654
Web Site: https://www.global-fashion-group.com
Rev.: $1,670,037,928
Assets: $1,440,848,344
Liabilities: $680,076,488
Net Worth: $760,771,856
Earnings: ($138,054,176)
Emp.: 13,751
Fiscal Year-end: 12/31/2020
Fashion Apparel & Accessory Retailer
N.A.I.C.S.: 458110
Christoph Barchewitz *(Co-CEO)*

Guider Media Group Europe AB (1)
Ringvagen 52, Stockholm, 118 67, Sweden
Tel.: (46) 856200050
Telecommunication Servicesb
N.A.I.C.S.: 517810

Kinnevik Capital Ltd. (1)
3 Burlington Gardens, London, W1S 3EP, United Kingdom
Tel.: (44) 2075181750
Stamp Promotion & Redemption Services
N.A.I.C.S.: 561499

Kinnevik Online Ventures AB (1)
Skeppbron 18, Box 2094, Stockholm, 10313, Sweden
Tel.: (46) 8 562 000 00
Information Technology Consulting Services
N.A.I.C.S.: 541512

Latsin Sia (1)
Meza lela 4, Jaunjelgava, 5134, Latvia
Tel.: (371) 6 51 52 800
Web Site: http://www.latsin.lv
Sales Range: $50-74.9 Million
Emp.: 150
Pulpwood & Timber Products Mfr
N.A.I.C.S.: 321999
Varis Sipols *(Gen Mgr)*

Metro International S.A. (1)
7 Avenue Jean-Pierre Pescatore, L-2324, Luxembourg, Luxembourg
Tel.: (352) 27 751 350
Web Site: http://www.metro.lu
Sales Range: $25-49.9 Million
Holding Company; Newspaper Publisher
N.A.I.C.S.: 551112
Anders Kronborg *(CEO)*

Subsidiary (Non-US):

Metro International AB (2)
PO Box 11217, 100 61, Stockholm, Sweden

KINNEVIK AB

Kinnevik AB—(Continued)
Tel.: (46) 84022030
Holding Company; Newspaper Publisher
N.A.I.C.S.: 551112

Subsidiary (Domestic):

Metro International Sweden AB (3)
Ringvagen 52, Stockholm, 118 67, Sweden
Tel.: (46) 8 12057000
Sales Range: $10-24.9 Million
Emp.: 27
Newspaper Publishers
N.A.I.C.S.: 513110
Per Mikael Jensen (CEO)

Unit (Domestic):

Metro Goteborg (4)
Drottninggatan 36, PO Box 11275, Gothenburg, 41114, Sweden (100%)
Tel.: (46) 31 743 81 00
Web Site: http://www.metro.se
Sales Range: $10-24.9 Million
Emp.: 15
Newspaper Publishing
N.A.I.C.S.: 513110
Hendrick's Bensen (Gen Mgr)

Metro Malmo (4)
Bergsgatan 20, PO Box 125, SE 201 21, Malmo, Sweden (100%)
Tel.: (46) 406600750
Web Site: http://www.metro.se
Newspaper Publishing
N.A.I.C.S.: 513110

Metro Stockholm (4)
Ringvagen 52, PO Box 45075, 104 30, Stockholm, Sweden (100%)
Tel.: (46) 84022030
Web Site: http://www.metro.se
Newspaper Publishing
N.A.I.C.S.: 513110
Andreas Ohlson (Mng Dir)

Subsidiary (Non-US):

Metro Publishing Hong Kong Limited (3)
25/f 148 Electric Road, North Point, China (Hong Kong)
Tel.: (852) 31961600
Web Site: http://www.metrohk.com.hk
Newspaper Publishing Services
N.A.I.C.S.: 513110

Publimetro S.A. (3)
Avenida Kennedy 5737 Oficina 701 Torre Poniente, Las Condes, Santiago, Chile
Tel.: (56) 24215900
Web Site: http://www.publimetro.cl
Sales Range: $25-49.9 Million
Newspaper Publishing
N.A.I.C.S.: 513110
Pablo Mazzei (Gen Mgr)

Recovia AB (1)
Stora Brannbovagen 46, PO Box 2094, 193 33, Sigtuna, Sweden
Tel.: (46) 86283500
Web Site: https://recovia.se
Renewable Energy Production Services
N.A.I.C.S.: 561990

Relevant Traffic Spain S.L. (1)
Garcia de Paredes 17 Bajo-Interior, 28010, Madrid, Spain
Tel.: (34) 91 702 59 61
Web Site: http://www.relevanttraffic.es
Sales Range: $25-49.9 Million
Emp.: 18
Search Engine Optimization Services
N.A.I.C.S.: 519290
Julian Garcia (CEO)

Relevant Traffic Sweden AB (1)
Ringvagen 52, 118 61, Stockholm, Sweden
Tel.: (46) 8 120 650 00
Web Site: http://www.relevanttraffic.se
Search Engine Optimization Services
N.A.I.C.S.: 519290
Anders Norrbom (CTO)

Rolnyvik Sp. z o.o. (1)
ul Wiosenna 8, Barciany, 11-410, Poland
Tel.: (48) 89 753 1079
Agricultural Farms Operating Services
N.A.I.C.S.: 111998

SAS Relevant Traffic (1)
12 Rue Auber, 75009, Paris, France
Tel.: (33) 158053905
Web Site: http://www.relevanttraffic.fr
Sales Range: $25-49.9 Million
Emp.: 12
Search Engine Optimization Services
N.A.I.C.S.: 519290
Dominique Cerruti (Country Mgr)

Sia Latgran (1)
Meza street 4b, Jaunjelgava, 5134, Latvia
Tel.: (371) 65220200
Web Site: http://www.latgran.com
Sales Range: $25-49.9 Million
Emp.: 15
Industrial Biomass Pellets Mfr
N.A.I.C.S.: 339999
Jarl Wallden (Gen Mgr)

KINO POLSKA TV S.A.
ul Pulawska 435a, 02-801, Warsaw, Poland
Tel.: (48) 223567400
Web Site: https://www.kinopolska.pl
Year Founded: 2003
KPL—(WAR)
Rev.: $74,747,205
Assets: $88,267,784
Liabilities: $26,525,915
Net Worth: $61,741,870
Earnings: $11,647,612
Fiscal Year-end: 12/31/23
Television Broadcasting Services
N.A.I.C.S.: 516120
Boguslaw Kisielewski (Chm-Mgmt Bd)

KINOTON DIGITAL SOLUTIONS GMBH
Industriestrasse 20 a, 82110, Germering, Germany
Tel.: (49) 8989 44460
Web Site: http://www.kinoton.com
Year Founded: 1948
Sales Range: $50-74.9 Million
Emp.: 160
Film Editing Equipment Mfr
N.A.I.C.S.: 333310
Renate Zoller (Co-Mng Dir)

KINOVO PLC
Tel.: (44) 1992703431 UK
Web Site: https://www.kinovoplc.com
Year Founded: 2015
KINO—(AIM)
Rev.: $77,823,606
Assets: $27,268,686
Liabilities: $28,078,340
Net Worth: ($809,654)
Earnings: $4,610,803
Emp.: 235
Fiscal Year-end: 03/31/23
Plumbing, Heating & Air-Conditioning Contractors
N.A.I.C.S.: 238220
David Bullen (CEO)

KINPO ELECTRONICS, INC.
No 99 Sec 5 Nanjing East Rd, Songshan District, Taipei, 105, Taiwan
Tel.: (886) 226622660
Web Site: http://www.kinpo.com.tw
Year Founded: 1973
Electronic Equipment Distr
N.A.I.C.S.: 423690
Yu-Hui Huang (Sr VP)

KINROSS GOLD CORPORATION
25 York Street 17th Floor, Toronto, M5J 2V5, ON, Canada
Tel.: (416) 365-5123 ON
Web Site: https://www.kinross.com
Year Founded: 1993
KGC—(NYSE)
Rev.: $3,455,100,000
Assets: $10,396,400,000
Liabilities: $4,514,200,000
Net Worth: $5,882,200,000
Earnings: ($605,700,000)
Emp.: 6,400
Fiscal Year-end: 12/31/22
Gold & Silver Ore Mining
N.A.I.C.S.: 212220
Geoffrey P. Gold (Chief Legal Officer & Exec VP-Corp Dev & External Rels)

Subsidiaries:

Aurelian Ecuador S.A. (1)
Av Amazonas N37-29 y UNP Edificio Eurocenter Piso 5, Quito, Pichincha, Ecuador
Tel.: (593) 22996400
Gold Mining Services
N.A.I.C.S.: 212220
Ron F. Hochstein (Office Mgr)

Chirano Gold Mines Ltd. (1)
2nd Floor Office 1 of Marvel House No 148 A Giffard Road Cantonments, Accra, PMB 222, Ghana
Tel.: (233) 302786079
Gold Mining Services
N.A.I.C.S.: 212220

Compania Minera Mantos de Oro S.A. (1)
Los Carrera 6651, Copiapo, Chile (100%)
Tel.: (56) 52221043
Web Site: http://www.mdo.cl
Sales Range: $200-249.9 Million
Emp.: 450
Gold Ore Mining
N.A.I.C.S.: 212220

Compania Minera Maricunga (1)
Los Carrera 6651, Copiapo, Chile
Tel.: (56) 52528000
Web Site: http://www.maricunga.cl
Gold Mining Services
N.A.I.C.S.: 212220

Echo Bay Minerals Company (1)
363 Fish Hatchery Rd, Republic, WA 99166-1019 (100%)
Tel.: (509) 775-3157
Sales Range: $100-124.9 Million
Emp.: 117
Gold Mining
N.A.I.C.S.: 212220
Mark Ioli (Gen Mgr)

Joint Venture (Domestic):

Round Mountain Gold Corporation (2)
1 Smoky Valley Rd, Round Mountain, NV 89045-0480
Tel.: (775) 377-2366
Web Site: http://www.kinross.com
Sales Range: $75-99.9 Million
Emp.: 800
Gold Mining; Owned 50% by Barrick Gold Corporation & 50% by Kinross Gold Corporation
N.A.I.C.S.: 212220

Fairbanks Gold Mining, Inc (1)
1 Fort Knox Rd, Fairbanks, AK 99707-3726
Tel.: (907) 488-4653
Gold Mining Services
N.A.I.C.S.: 212220

Great Bear Resources Ltd. (1)
1020-800 West Pender Street, Vancouver, V6C 2V6, BC, Canada
Tel.: (604) 646-8354
Web Site: http://www.greatbearresources.ca
Rev.: $5,371,174
Assets: $67,698,540
Liabilities: $10,880,960
Net Worth: $56,817,580
Earnings: ($7,042,444)
Fiscal Year-end: 12/31/2020
Metal Mining Services
N.A.I.C.S.: 212290
Christopher Taylor (Pres & CEO)

Kinross Brasil Mineracao S.A. (1)
BR040 KM365 S/N - Rural Zone, Postal Box 168, Paracatu, 38609-899, Minas Gerais, Brazil
Tel.: (55) 3836791000
Emp.: 2,000
Gold Mining Services
N.A.I.C.S.: 212220

INTERNATIONAL PUBLIC

KINSUS INTERCONNECT TECHNOLOGY CORP.
No 1245 Zhonghua Rd, Xinwu Dist, Taoyuan, 327, Taiwan
Tel.: (886) 34871919
Web Site: https://www.kinsus.com.tw
Year Founded: 2000
3189—(TAI)
Rev.: $877,471,009
Assets: $2,552,962,361
Liabilities: $1,272,373,574
Net Worth: $1,280,588,787
Earnings: $38,274,697
Emp.: 5,707
Fiscal Year-end: 12/31/23
Plastic Ball Grid Substrates Mfr & Distr
N.A.I.C.S.: 326199
Shirley Hu (COO)

Subsidiaries:

Kinsus Interconnect Technology Corp. - Taoyuan Factory (1)
No 810 Zhonghua Rd Xinwu Dist, Taoyuan, 327, Taiwan
Tel.: (886) 34871988
Electronic Parts Distr
N.A.I.C.S.: 423930

Kinsus Interconnect Technology Corp. - Xing-Feng Factory (1)
No 526 Sec 2 Jianxing Rd Xinfeng Township, Hsinchu, 304, Taiwan
Tel.: (886) 35571799
Electronic Parts Distr
N.A.I.C.S.: 423930

Kinsus Suzhou Corp. (1)
2-10 20 Datong Road, Export Processing Zone Suzhou New and Hi-tech District, Jiangsu, China
Tel.: (86) 51266321512
Electronic Parts Distr
N.A.I.C.S.: 423930

Piotek Computer Corp. (1)
1-30 20 Datong Road, Export Processing Zone Suzhou New and Hi-tech District, Jiangsu, China
Tel.: (86) 51262696700
Electronic Parts Distr
N.A.I.C.S.: 423930

KINTAVAR EXPLORATION INC.
75 boulevard de Mortagne, Boucherville, J4B 6Y4, QC, Canada
Tel.: (450) 641-5119 BC
Web Site: https://kintavar.com
Year Founded: 2011
KTR—(TSXV)
Rev.: $2,738,849
Assets: $6,817,914
Liabilities: $894,379
Net Worth: $5,923,535
Earnings: ($490,258)
Fiscal Year-end: 12/31/23
Mineral Exploration Services
N.A.I.C.S.: 327999
Kiril Mugerman (Pres & CEO)

KINTETSU DEPARTMENT STORE CO., LTD.
1-1-43 Abenosuji, Abeno-ku, Osaka, 545-8545, Japan
Tel.: (81) 666241111
Web Site: https://www.d-kintetsu.co.jp
Year Founded: 1934
8244—(TKS)
Rev.: $950,053,280
Assets: $1,155,637,120
Liabilities: $833,186,640
Net Worth: $322,450,480
Earnings: ($7,502,000)
Fiscal Year-end: 02/28/22
Departmental Store Operator
N.A.I.C.S.: 455110
Keiji Takamatsu (Chm)

KINTETSU GROUP HOLDINGS CO.,LTD.

AND PRIVATE COMPANIES

KINTETSU GROUP HOLDINGS CO., LTD.

6-1-55 Uehonmmachi, Tennoji-ku, Osaka, 543-8585, Japan
Tel.: (81) 667753355
Web Site: http://www.kintetsu-ghd.co.jp
Year Founded: 1910
9041—(TKS)
Rev.: $10,771,186,690
Assets: $16,223,028,760
Liabilities: $12,351,882,260
Net Worth: $3,871,146,500
Earnings: $317,762,530
Emp.: 142
Fiscal Year-end: 03/31/24
Transportation, Construction, Travel & Related Services
N.A.I.C.S.: 482111
Toshihide Ogura (Pres)

Subsidiaries:

Event & Convention House, Inc. (1)
Shuwa-Okachimachi Bld 8F 4-27-5 Taito, Taito-ku, Tokyo, 110-0016, Japan
Tel.: (81) 338312601
Web Site: https://www.ech.co.jp
Consulting Services
N.A.I.C.S.: 541611

Fukuyama Transporting Co., Ltd. (1)
20-1 4-chome Higashi Fukatsu-cho, Fukuyama, Hiroshima, Japan
Tel.: (81) 849222000
Web Site: https://corp.fukutsu.co.jp
Rev.: $1,900,791,430
Assets: $3,327,414,510
Liabilities: $1,368,111,360
Net Worth: $1,959,303,150
Earnings: $51,782,740
Fiscal Year-end: 03/31/2024
Transportation & Trucking
N.A.I.C.S.: 484121
Shigehiro Komaru (Chm, Pres & CEO)

Kin-Ei Corp. (1)
1-5-1 Abenosuji, Abeno-ku, Osaka, 545-0052, Japan
Tel.: (81) 666324551
Web Site: http://www.kin-ei.co.jp
Sales Range: $25-49.9 Million
Movie Theater Management Services
N.A.I.C.S.: 512131
Norihiko Sakuta (Pres & CEO)

Kinki Nippon Railway Co., Ltd. (1)
6 1 55 Ue Honmachi, Tennoji Ku, Osaka, 543 8585, Japan
Tel.: (81) 667753511
Sales Range: $1-4.9 Billion
Emp.: 5,000
N.A.I.C.S.: 482111
Petsuya Kobayashi (Pres)

Affiliate (Domestic):

KNT-CT Holdings Co., Ltd. (2)
39FShinjyuku Sumitomo Bldg 2-6-1 Nishi-Shinjyuku, Shinjyuku-ku, Tokyo, 163-0239, Japan (67.1%)
Tel.: (81) 368919600
Web Site: http://www.kntcthd.co.jp
Rev.: $1,688,372,470
Assets: $873,062,020
Liabilities: $581,085,100
Net Worth: $291,976,920
Earnings: $49,839,400
Emp.: 3,424
Fiscal Year-end: 03/31/2024
Travel Services
N.A.I.C.S.: 561510
Yoshihiro Aoki (Exec Officer)

Subsidiary (Domestic):

Club Tourism International Inc. (3)
Shinjyu Island Wing 6-3-1 Nishi, Shinjyuku, Tokyo, 160-8308, Japan
Tel.: (81) 353236955
Tour business
N.A.I.C.S.: 561520

Kintetsu International Express (U.S.A.), Inc. (1)
270 Madison Ave Ste 300, New York, NY 10016
Tel.: (212) 259-9600
Web Site: http://kintetsu.com
Transportation Services
N.A.I.C.S.: 485999

Kintetsu Miyako Hotels International, Inc. (1)
1-55 Uehommachi 6-chome, Tennoji-ku, Osaka, 543-0001, Japan
Tel.: (81) 667747658
Web Site: http://global.miyakohotels.ne.jp
Hotel Operator
N.A.I.C.S.: 721110
Takashi Nishimura (CEO)

Kintetsu Railcar Engineering Co., Ltd. (1)
Kintetsu Uehommachi Ishigatsuji Building 7F 4-13 Ishigatsujicho, Tennoji-ku, Osaka, 543-0031, Japan
Tel.: (81) 667110553
Web Site: http://www.kre-net.co.jp
Emp.: 340
Car, Rail Maintenance Services
N.A.I.C.S.: 488210
Ichiro Maeda (Pres)

Kintetsu Taxi Company Limited (1)
9-4-17 Uehonmachi, Tennoji-ku, Osaka, 543-0001, Japan
Tel.: (81) 667719031
Web Site: https://www.kintetsu-taxi-osaka.co.jp
Emp.: 700
Transportation Services
N.A.I.C.S.: 485999

Kintetsu World Express, Inc. (1)
6-1 Ohte-machi 1-chome, Tokyo, 100 0004, Japan (92.12%)
Tel.: (81) 332012580
Web Site: http://www.kwe.co.jp
Sales Range: $200-249.9 Million
Emp.: 1,073
International Freight Forwarding
N.A.I.C.S.: 488510
Haruto Nakata (Mng Dir)

Subsidiary (Non-US):

APL Logistics, Ltd. (2)
3 Harbourfront Place 06-01 Harbourfront Tower Two, Singapore, 99254, Singapore
Tel.: (65) 6430 8833
Web Site: http://www.apllogistics.com
Emp.: 7,700
Logistics & Transportation Services
N.A.I.C.S.: 488999
William Villalon (Pres)

Subsidiary (Non-US):

APL Logistics (Hong Kong) Ltd. (3)
No 39 Wang Kwong Road 18th Floor Kowloon Bay Plaza, Kowloon, China (Hong Kong)
Tel.: (852) 23027555
Web Site: http://www.apllogistics.com
Logistics & Transportation Services
N.A.I.C.S.: 488999

APL Logistics Cambodia Pvt. Ltd. (3)
Samdach Monireth Boulevard First Floor Regency Complex C, Suite C1/5 & C1/6 Sang Kat Tomnoubteouk Khan Chamkarmon, Phnom Penh, Cambodia
Tel.: (855) 23218000
Web Site: http://www.apllogistics.com
Logistics & Transportation Services
N.A.I.C.S.: 488999

APL Logistics China, Ltd. (3)
12F Tower 1 No 2188 Gonghexin Road Jing An, Shanghai, 200072, China
Tel.: (86) 2126135000
Web Site: http://www.apllogistics.com
Logistics & Transportation Services
N.A.I.C.S.: 488999

APL Logistics Honduras S, de R.L. (3)
Altia Business Park Km 2 Tower A 7th Floor Office #7C, San Pedro Sula, Cortes, Honduras
Tel.: (504) 2561 8100
Web Site: http://www.apllogistics.com
Logistics & Transportation Services
N.A.I.C.S.: 488999

APL Logistics Ltd. (3)
Level 4 1-9 Chandos Street, Saint Leonards, 2065, NSW, Australia
Tel.: (61) 2 9257 0809
Web Site: http://www.apllogistics.com
Logistics & Transportation Services
N.A.I.C.S.: 488999
Michelle Nicholls (Mgr-HR)

APL Logistics Svcs. Thailand Ltd. (3)
3195/10 Rama 4 Road Klongton Klongtoey, 5th Floor Vibulthani Tower I, Bangkok, 10110, Thailand
Tel.: (66) 2 664 5050
Web Site: http://www.apllogistics.com
Logistics & Transportation Services
N.A.I.C.S.: 488999

Unit (Non-US):

APL Logistics UK (3)
Gredley House 11 Broadway, Stratford, London, E15 4BQ, United Kingdom
Tel.: (44) 20 8221 5500
Web Site: http://www.apllogistics.com
Logistics & Transportation Services
N.A.I.C.S.: 488999

Subsidiary (Non-US):

APL Logistics WMS de Mexico, S.A. de C.V. (3)
Av Fuentes de Satelite #88 3er Piso Cd Satelite, Naucalpan, CP 53100, Mexico
Tel.: (52) 5526207200
Web Site: http://www.apllogistics.com
Logistics & Transportation Services
N.A.I.C.S.: 488999

Subsidiary (US):

APL Logistics, Inc. (3)
17600 N Perimeter Dr Ste 150, Scottsdale, AZ 85255
Tel.: (602) 357-9100
Web Site: http://www.apllogistics.com
Freight Consolidating, Cargo Packing & Crating Services
N.A.I.C.S.: 488510

Joint Venture (Domestic):

Vascor, Ltd. (4)
100 Farmers Bank Dr Ste 300, Georgetown, KY 40324
Tel.: (502) 570-2020
Web Site: http://www.vascorlogistics.com
Logistic Services
N.A.I.C.S.: 541614
Jinny Daugherty (CFO)

Subsidiary (Non-US):

PT APL Logistics Indonesia (3)
Jalan Tanah Abang IV No 23-25 Masterpiece Building 3rd Floor, Jakarta, 10160, Indonesia
Tel.: (62) 213861238
Web Site: http://www.apllogistics.com
Logistics & Transportation Services
N.A.I.C.S.: 488999

Subsidiary (Non-US):

KWE-Kintetsu World Express(S)Pte Ltd. (2)
20 Changi South Avenue 2, 115 Airport Cargo Rd, Singapore, 486547, Singapore
Tel.: (65) 65427778
Web Site: http://www.kwe.com
Sales Range: $200-249.9 Million
Emp.: 300
N.A.I.C.S.: 482111
Yoshikazu Yashiki (Mng Dir)

Subsidiary (US):

Kintetsu Enterprises Company of America (2)
21241 S Western Ave Ste 100, Torrance, CA 90501
Tel.: (310) 782-9300
Web Site: http://www.kintetsu-enterprises.com
Hotel or Motel Management
N.A.I.C.S.: 713950

Subsidiary (Non-US):

Kintetsu Intermodal (Taiwan), Inc. (2)
3rd Fl No 99 Chang An E Rd Sect 2, Taipei, 104, Taiwan
Tel.: (886) 225063151
Web Site: http://www.kwe.com
Sales Range: $50-74.9 Million
Emp.: 310
N.A.I.C.S.: 482111

Kintetsu World Express (Australia) Pty. Ltd. (2)
Unit 15 37-41 O'Riordan Street, PO Box 634, Alexandria, 2015, VIC, Australia
Tel.: (61) 296904311
Web Site: http://www.kwe.com
Sales Range: $25-49.9 Million
Emp.: 30
N.A.I.C.S.: 482111
Steve Staimoto (Mng Dir)

Kintetsu World Express (Benelux) B.V. (2)
Ridderhaven 16 3rd Entrance Ground Floor, Rotterdam, 2984 BT, Ridderkerk, Netherlands
Tel.: (31) 180750620
Web Site: http://www.kwe.com
Sales Range: $400-449.9 Million
N.A.I.C.S.: 482111

Kintetsu World Express (Deutschland) GmbH (2)
Wahlerstrasse 37, PO Box 330150, 40472, Dusseldorf, Germany
Tel.: (49) 21165590
Web Site: https://www.kwe.com
Sales Range: $25-49.9 Million
Emp.: 80
Air & Ocean Freight Forwarding Transport
N.A.I.C.S.: 481212

Kintetsu World Express (France) S.A. (2)
Cargo Terminal Entree D Bureau 01-1703 Aeroport Bale-Mulhouse, 68300, Saint Louis, France
Tel.: (33) 389898915
Web Site: http://www.kwe.com
Sales Range: $25-49.9 Million
Emp.: 2
N.A.I.C.S.: 482111

Kintetsu World Express (H.K.) Ltd. (2)
17/F Rykadan Capital Tower 135 Hoi Bun Road Kwun Tong, Kowloon, China (Hong Kong)
Tel.: (852) 27961176
Web Site: http://www.kwe.com
Sales Range: $25-49.9 Million
Emp.: 100
N.A.I.C.S.: 482111

Kintetsu World Express (Malaysia) Sdn. Bhd. (2)
Ste 1201 12th Fl Wisma Prosper Block B Kelana Centre Point, 3 Jalan SS 7/19 Kelana Jaya, 47301, Petaling Jaya, Selangor, Malaysia
Tel.: (60) 378062466
Web Site: http://www.kwe.com
Domestic & Foreign Freight Forwarding Services
N.A.I.C.S.: 484110

Kintetsu World Express (Taiwan), Inc. (2)
3rd Fl No 99 Chang An East Rd Section 2, Taipei, 104, Taiwan
Tel.: (886) 225063151
Web Site: http://www.kwe.com
Sales Range: $100-124.9 Million
Emp.: 299
N.A.I.C.S.: 482111

Kintetsu World Express (Thailand) Co., Ltd. (2)
99 Soi Ladprao 28, Ratchadaphisek Rd Kwaeng Chankasem Khet Chatuchak, Bangkok, 10900, Thailand
Tel.: (66) 27925999
Web Site: http://www.kwe.co.th
Sales Range: $800-899.9 Million
N.A.I.C.S.: 482111

Subsidiary (US):

Kintetsu World Express (U.S.A.), Inc. (2)
1 Jericho Plz Ste 100, Jericho, NY 11753-1635
Tel.: (516) 933-7100

KINTETSU GROUP HOLDINGS CO., LTD.

Kintetsu Group Holdings Co., Ltd.—(Continued)

Web Site: http://www.kweusa.com
Sales Range: $100-124.9 Million
Emp.: 45
Freight Forwarding
N.A.I.C.S.: 488510
Nobutoshi Torii (Pres)

Okinawa Miyako Hotel (1)
40 Matsugawa, Naha, 902-0062, Okinawa, Japan
Tel.: (81) 988871111
Web Site: http://www.miyakohotels.ne.jp
Sales Range: $10-24.9 Million
Emp.: 104
Hotel & Resort Operator
N.A.I.C.S.: 721110
Masato Imura (Gen Mgr)

Osaka Aquarium Kaiyukan Co., Ltd. (1)
1-1-10 Kaigandori, Minato-ku, Osaka, 552-0022, Japan
Tel.: (81) 665765501
Web Site: https://www.kaiyukan.com
Aquarium Services
N.A.I.C.S.: 712130

The Kinki Sharyo Co., Ltd. (1)
2-2-46 Inada-Uemachi Higashi, Osaka, 577-8511, Japan **(49%)**
Tel.: (81) 667465222
Web Site: http://www.kinkisharyo.co.jp
Rev.: $285,247,940
Assets: $393,671,770
Liabilities: $178,840,160
Net Worth: $214,831,610
Earnings: $28,905,530
Emp.: 1,000
Fiscal Year-end: 03/31/2024
Railroad Rolling Stock Mfr
N.A.I.C.S.: 336510
Shuji Okane (Chm)

KINTOR PHARMACEUTICAL LIMITED

Suite 2007 20th Floor Tower 2 The Gateway, Harbour City, Kowloon, China (Hong Kong)
Tel.: (852) 26338966   Ky
Web Site: http://www.kintor.com.cn
Year Founded: 2009
9939—(HKG)
Pharmaceutical Product Mfr & Distr
N.A.I.C.S.: 325412
Youzhi Tong (Founder, Chm & CEO)

Subsidiaries:

Kintor Pharmaceutical (Beijing) Co., Ltd. (1)
Room 1508 Block B Winterlay Center No 1 Xidawang Road, Chaoyang, Beijing, 100000, China
Tel.: (86) 1085950839
Pharmaceuticals Product Mfr
N.A.I.C.S.: 325412

Kintor Pharmaceuticals Hong Kong Limited
Suite 2007 20th Floor Tower 2 The Gateway Harbour City, Kowloon, China (Hong Kong)
Tel.: (852) 26338966
Pharmaceuticals Product Mfr
N.A.I.C.S.: 325412

Kintor Pharmaceuticals Inc. (1)
1011 S Hamilton Rd, Chapel Hill, NC 27517
Tel.: (984) 208-1255
Drug Research & Development Services
N.A.I.C.S.: 541714

KINX, INC.

7th and 10th floors Doowon Building 636 Gangnam-daero, Gangnam-gu, Seoul, Korea (South)
Tel.: (82) 25260900
Web Site: https://www.kinx.net
Year Founded: 2000
093320—(KRS)
Rev.: $85,082,141
Assets: $151,435,090
Liabilities: $28,989,634
Net Worth: $122,445,455

Earnings: $20,967,525
Emp.: 140
Fiscal Year-end: 12/31/22
VoIP Products & Services
N.A.I.C.S.: 334220

KINYARA SUGAR WORKS LTD.

Plot 31 Block 9 & 10, Kampala, Uganda
Tel.: (256) 362600200
Web Site: http://www.kinyara.co.ug
Year Founded: 1967
Sales Range: $50-74.9 Million
Emp.: 800
Sugar Producer & Distr
N.A.I.C.S.: 311314
Ramadasan Pallpuram (Mng Dir)

KINYOSHA CO., LTD.

6F Art Village Osaki Central Tower 1-2-2 Osaki, Shinagawa-ku, Tokyo, 141 0032, Japan
Tel.: (81) 357456200   JP
Web Site: http://www.kinyo-j.co.jp
Year Founded: 1933
Sales Range: $200-249.9 Million
Emp.: 650
Rubber Rollers, Fluororubber Paint, Rubber Sheeting & Rubber Belts Mfr
N.A.I.C.S.: 326299
Kazuo Nakamura (Chm)

Subsidiaries:

KINYO Europe GmbH (1)
SEGRO Park Dusseldorf-Sud Bonner Strasse 339-341, 40589, Dusseldorf, Germany
Tel.: (49) 211 540012 0
Web Site: http://www.kinyoeu.com
Rubber Roller & Blanket Dist
N.A.I.C.S.: 313310

KINYOSHA (Shenzhen) Co., Ltd. (1)
Tower 1 Huaide Cuihai Industrial Garden Zone 2, Fuyong Town Baoan District, Shenzhen, China
Tel.: (86) 755 27342648
Rubber Roller & Blanket Distr
N.A.I.C.S.: 313310

KINYOSHA (Thailand) Co., Ltd. (1)
30/58 Moo 1 Chetsadavithi Road T KhokKham, A Muangsamutsakorn, Samut Sakhon, 74000, Thailand
Tel.: (66) 34 452 130
Rubber Roller & Blanket Distr
N.A.I.C.S.: 313310

KINYOSHA Vietnam Co., Ltd. (1)
Lot No 5 TS6 Road Tien Son Industrial Zone, Bac Ninh, Vietnam
Tel.: (84) 241 3 714 855
Rubber Roller & Blanket Distr
N.A.I.C.S.: 313310

Kinyo Germany GmbH (1)
Immermannstrasse 65C, D 40210, Dusseldorf, Germany
Tel.: (49) 2115400120
Web Site: http://www.kinyo.de
Emp.: 8
Rubber Printing Blankets & Rollers Distr
N.A.I.C.S.: 423830

Kinyo Supply Co., Ltd. (1)
2715 Ago, Kasama, 319-0206, Ibaraki, Japan
Tel.: (81) 299 37 8850
Rubber Roller & Blanket Distr
N.A.I.C.S.: 313310

Kinyo UK Ltd.
Kinyo House Scala Court, Leathley Road, Leeds, LS10 1JD, United Kingdom
Tel.: (44) 1132005680
Web Site: http://www.kinyo-uk.co.uk
Emp.: 14
Rubber Printing Blankets & Rollers Distr
N.A.I.C.S.: 423830
Jill Barrett (Mgr)

Kinyo Virginia, Inc. (1)
290 Enterprise Dr, Newport News, VA 23603

Tel.: (757) 888-2221
Web Site: http://www.kinyova.com
Sales Range: $50-74.9 Million
Emp.: 110
Rubber Printing Rollers & Blankets Mfr
N.A.I.C.S.: 333248
Kazuo Nakamura (Pres)

Kinyosha (HK) Co., Ltd. (1)
Suites 1610-11 16F World Commerce Centre, Harbour City, Kowloon, China (Hong Kong)
Tel.: (852) 25374540
Web Site: http://www.kinyo-j.co.jp
Sales Range: $50-74.9 Million
Emp.: 3
Rubber Printing Blankets & Rollers Distr
N.A.I.C.S.: 423830
Minoru Taguchi (Gen Mgr)

Kinyosha Co., Ltd. - Iwama Plant (1)
Iwama Industrial Park 2600 28 Ago, Kasama, 319-0295, Ibaraki, Japan
Tel.: (81) 299 45 8711
Rubber Roller & Blanket Distr
N.A.I.C.S.: 313310

Kinyosha Co., Ltd. - Minori Plant (1)
1088-1 Hemuro, Omitama, 319-0132, Ibaraki, Japan
Tel.: (81) 299 48 1171
Rubber Roller & Blanket Distr
N.A.I.C.S.: 313310

Kinyosha Co., Ltd. - Shiga Plant (1)
647 Yoshiji, Yasu, 520-2413, Shiga, Japan
Tel.: (81) 77 589 8600
Rubber Roller & Blanket Distr
N.A.I.C.S.: 313310
Keiji Nakata (Pres)

Kinyosha Co., Ltd. - Takehara Plant (1)
1561 1 Nishino-cho Chikaraishi, Takehara, Hiroshima, 725-0002, Japan
Tel.: (81) 846 29 1011
Web Site: http://www.kinyos-j.co.jp
Rubber Roller & Blanket Distr
N.A.I.C.S.: 313310

Kinyosha France SAS (1)
10 Rue Ampere, 91430, Igny, France
Tel.: (33) 169332000
Sales Range: $25-49.9 Million
Emp.: 16
Rubber Printing Blankets & Rollers Distr
N.A.I.C.S.: 423830
Daniel Sauvage (Gen Mgr)

Kinyosha Iberica S.L. (1)
Penedes 42-44, El Prat de Llobregat, 08820, Barcelona, Spain
Tel.: (34) 934780632
Web Site: http://www.kinyoib.com
Sales Range: $50-74.9 Million
Emp.: 10
Rubber Printing Blankets & Rollers Distr
N.A.I.C.S.: 423830
Beatriz Hernandez (Mgr-Pur)

Kinyosha Kanto Sales Co., Ltd. (1)
8-5 Mizutan 2-chome Fujimi-shi, Saitama, 354-0014, Japan
Tel.: (81) 49 252 2661
Rubber Roller & Blanket Distr
N.A.I.C.S.: 313310

KIOCL LIMITED

Block II Koramangala Sarjapura Road, Bengaluru, 560 034, India
Tel.: (91) 8025531461
Web Site: https://www.kioclltd.in
Year Founded: 1976
540680—(BOM)
Rev.: $194,690,091
Assets: $352,262,490
Liabilities: $112,224,519
Net Worth: $240,037,971
Earnings: $11,709,969
Emp.: 654
Fiscal Year-end: 03/31/23
Iron Ore Mfr & Distr
N.A.I.C.S.: 331511
Vidyananda Naregundy (Dir-Production & Projects)

KIP MCGRATH EDUCATION CENTRES LTD

INTERNATIONAL PUBLIC

7 Bond Street, Newcastle, 2300, NSW, Australia
Tel.: (61) 249296711   AU
Web Site:
https://www.kipmcgrath.com
Year Founded: 1976
KME—(ASX)
Rev.: $21,595,887
Assets: $23,287,260
Liabilities: $7,462,607
Net Worth: $15,824,653
Earnings: $879,407
Emp.: 20
Fiscal Year-end: 06/30/24
Education Centers Specializing in Tutoring Services
N.A.I.C.S.: 923110
Storm McGrath (CEO & Mng Dir)

Subsidiaries:

Tutorfly Holdings Inc. (1)
12954 Rockham Ln, Farmers Branch, TX 75234
Tel.: (916) 445-1254
Web Site: https://www.tutorfly.com
Educational Institution Services
N.A.I.C.S.: 611710

KIP REAL ESTATE INVESTMENT TRUST

Tel.: (60) 362591133
Web Site: https://www.kipreit.com.my
KIPREIT—(KLS)
Rev.: $17,724,868
Assets: $216,590,688
Liabilities: $76,914,286
Net Worth: $139,676,402
Earnings: $12,866,032
Emp.: 94
Fiscal Year-end: 06/30/23
Trust Management Services
N.A.I.C.S.: 523940
Hussan Husman (Chm)

KIPLIN METALS INC.

2200 - 885 W Georgia St, Vancouver, V6C 3T7, BC, Canada
Tel.: (613) 715-2020   Ca
Web Site: https://kiplinmetals.com
Year Founded: 1992
KIP—(OTCIQ)
Assets: $1,345,649
Liabilities: $298,972
Net Worth: $1,046,677
Earnings: $(191,484)
Fiscal Year-end: 12/31/19
Mineral Exploration Services
N.A.I.C.S.: 213114
Peter Born (VP-Exploration)

KIPS CO., LTD.

1-5-1 Marunouchi, Chiyoda-Ku, Tokyo, 100-6590, Japan
Tel.: (81) 363863484
Web Site: http://www.kips.co.jp
Year Founded: 2006
9465—(TKS)
Rev.: $1,287,440
Assets: $14,762,000
Liabilities: $4,791,600
Net Worth: $9,970,400
Earnings: $29,040
Fiscal Year-end: 12/31/20
Investment Management Service
N.A.I.C.S.: 523999
Satoru Takada (Exec Dir)

KIRACA HOLDING A.S.

Acibadem Caddesi Doganc Sok No 3, 34660 Uskudar, Istanbul, Turkiye
Tel.: (90) 2165565400
Web Site: http://www.kiraca.com.tr
Sales Range: $350-399.9 Million
Emp.: 1,300
Holding Company
N.A.I.C.S.: 551112
Inan Kirac (Founder & Chm)

AND PRIVATE COMPANIES

Subsidiaries:

Hexagon Engineering and Design Inc. (1)
1 Cadde 15 Yol No 7 Sekerpinar, Cayirova, Kocaeli, Turkiye
Tel.: (90) 262 673 21 00
Web Site: http://www.hexagonstudio.com.tr
Engineeering Services
N.A.I.C.S.: 541330
Murat Ozkan *(Dir-Engrg)*

Kare Investment Securities Inc. (1)
Kisikli Cad No 4 Ak-Sarkuysan Is Merkezi Altunizade, Istanbul, Turkiye
Tel.: (90) 216 559 60 00
Web Site: http://en.kareyatirim.com.tr
Investment Management Service
N.A.I.C.S.: 523940
Aykut Umit Taftali *(Pres)*

Karland Otomotiv Urunleri Sanayi ve Ticaret A.S (1)
Emek Mah Ordu Cad No 10, 34785, Istanbul, Turkiye
Tel.: (90) 216 528 07 00
Web Site: http://en.karland.com.tr
Automobile Parts Mfr
N.A.I.C.S.: 336390
Muzaffer Arpacioglu *(Gen Mgr)*

Karsan Otomotiv Sanayii ve Ticaret A.S. (1)
Hasanaga Organize Sanayi Bolgesi Sanayi Caddesi, Nilufer, 16225, Bursa, Turkiye **(63.46%)**
Tel.: (90) 2244842170
Web Site: https://www.karsan.com.tr
Rev.: $91,114,052
Assets: $194,625,041
Liabilities: $139,055,428
Net Worth: $55,569,613
Earnings: $4,684,808
Emp.: 1,880
Fiscal Year-end: 12/31/2022
Light Commercial Vehicles Mfr
N.A.I.C.S.: 336211
Inan Kirac *(Chm)*

Kirpart A.S. (1)
Gedelek Koyu, 16800, Bursa, Orhangazi, Turkiye
Tel.: (90) 224 586 5350
Web Site: http://en.kirpart.com.tr
Automobile Parts Mfr
N.A.I.C.S.: 336390
Sahin Saylik *(Gen Dir)*

Sirena Marine Denizcilik Sanayi ve Ticaret A.S. (1)
Abdi Ipekci Cad Ada Apt No 22/18 K 5 Nisantasi, Istanbul, 34367, Turkiye
Tel.: (90) 212 219 74 74
Web Site: http://www.sirenamarine.com.tr
Boat Building Mfr
N.A.I.C.S.: 336612

KIRAN PRINT PACK LTD.
W-166 E TTC Industrial Area, MIDC Pawane, Navi Mumbai, 400709, India
Tel.: (91) 2227626427
Web Site:
   http://www.kiranprintpack.com
531413—(BOM)
Rev.: $177,218
Assets: $427,177
Liabilities: $29,962
Net Worth: $397,215
Earnings: ($63,240)
Fiscal Year-end: 03/31/21
Printing Services
N.A.I.C.S.: 323120
Karan Kamal Mohta *(Mng Dir & Officer-Compliance)*

KIRAN SYNTEX LIMITED
No 1/324 Popat Street, Nanpura, Surat, 395 001, Gujarat, India
Tel.: (91) 9327335306
Web Site:
   https://www.kiransyntex.com
Year Founded: 1986
530443—(BOM)
Rev.: $3
Assets: $348,657
Liabilities: $33,734
Net Worth: $314,923
Earnings: ($8,654)
Emp.: 1
Fiscal Year-end: 03/31/21
Polyster Dyed Yarn Mfr & Whslr
N.A.I.C.S.: 313110
Mahesh M. Godiwala *(Chm & Mng Dir)*

KIRCHHOFF GRUPPE
Stefanstrasse 2, 58638, Iserlohn, Germany
Tel.: (49) 2371 820 00
Web Site: http://www.kirchhoff-gruppe.de
Sales Range: $1-4.9 Billion
Emp.: 700
Holding Company
N.A.I.C.S.: 551112
Arndt G. Kirchhoff *(Chm)*

Subsidiaries:

FAUN Umwelttechnik GmbH & Co. KG (1)
Feldhorst 4, 27711, Osterholz-Scharmbeck, Germany
Tel.: (49) 4795 955 0
Web Site: http://www.faun.com
Sales Range: $200-249.9 Million
Emp.: 500
Waste Disposal Vehicle Mfr
N.A.I.C.S.: 336120
Johannes F. Kirchhoff *(Chm-Mgmt Bd & CEO)*

Subsidiary (Domestic):

FAUN Viatec GmbH (2)
Bahnhofstrasse 5, 04668, Grimma, Germany
Tel.: (49) 3437 92 04 0
Web Site: http://www.faun.com
Emp.: 10
Waste Disposal Vehicle & Equipment Mfr
N.A.I.C.S.: 336120

Subsidiary (Non-US):

FAUN Zoeller (UK) Limited (2)
Bryn Cefni Industrial Estate, Llangefni, LL 77 7XA, United Kingdom
Tel.: (44) 1248 722777
Web Site: http://www.faun-zoeller.co.uk
Waste Disposal Vehicle & Equipment Mfr
N.A.I.C.S.: 336120
Simon Hyde *(CEO)*

J. Ochsner AG (2)
Steinackerstrasse 31, Urdorf, 8902, Switzerland
Tel.: (41) 44 735 42 42
Web Site: http://www.ochsner.ch
Waste Disposal Vehicle Mfr
N.A.I.C.S.: 336120

Subsidiary (Domestic):

Jelschen GmbH (2)
Justus-von-Liebig-Str 7-9, 26160, Bad Zwischenahn, Germany
Tel.: (49) 4403 93890
Web Site: http://www.jelschen.de
Car Dealer
N.A.I.C.S.: 441110

KIRCHHOFF Automotive Deutschland GmbH (1)
Am Eckenbach 10-14, 57439, Attendorn, Germany
Tel.: (49) 2722 696 0
Web Site: http://www.kirchhoff-automotive.com
Emp.: 720
Automobile Parts Distr
N.A.I.C.S.: 423120
Andreas Haase *(CFO)*

KIRCHHOFF Automotive GmbH (1)
Stefanstrasse 2, 58638, Iserlohn, Germany
Tel.: (49) 2371 820 00
Web Site: http://www.kirchhoff-automotive.com
Motor Vehicle Parts Mfr
N.A.I.C.S.: 336390

Subsidiary (Non-US):

KIRCHHOFF Automotive (Chongqing) Co., Ltd. (2)
No 1 Chuangxing Road Konggang Development Zone, 401120, Chongqing, China
Tel.: (86) 23 6035 5020
Automobile Parts Distr
N.A.I.C.S.: 423120

KIRCHHOFF Automotive (Shenyang) Co., Ltd. (2)
No 31 Dagucheng Street, Dadong District, 110000, Shenyang, China
Tel.: (86) 24 3162 1088
Automobile Parts Distr
N.A.I.C.S.: 423120

KIRCHHOFF Automotive (Suzhou) Co., Ltd. (2)
No136 5624 6998 35 Jingdong Road Suzhou Industrial Park, Suzhou, 215121, Jiangsu, China
Tel.: (86) 136 5624 6998
Motor Vehicle Parts Mfr
N.A.I.C.S.: 336390

KIRCHHOFF Automotive Portugal, S.A. (2)
Avenida 16 Maio Zona Industrial Norte de Ovar, 3880-102, Ovar, Portugal
Tel.: (351) 256 579 210
Web Site: http://www.kirchhoff-automotive.pt
Metal Component Mfr
N.A.I.C.S.: 331420

KIRCHHOFF Automotive Romania Srl (2)
Henry Ford Street no 29, 200745, Craiova, Romania
Tel.: (40) 372 368 653
Automobile Parts Mfr
N.A.I.C.S.: 423120
Gabriel Porojan *(Mng Dir)*

KIRCHHOFF Espana, S.L.U. (2)
Ctra Zaragoza a Longrono N-232 km 28 Poligono Industrial No 6, 50639, Figueruelas, Spain
Tel.: (34) 97 665 5330
Web Site: http://www.kirchhoff-automotive.com
Emp.: 38
Motor Vehicle Parts Mfr
N.A.I.C.S.: 336390
Miguel A. Tena *(Mng Dir)*

KIRCHHOFF Hungaria Kft. (2)
Deli iparterulet 20377 22 HRSZ, 2500, Esztergom, Hungary
Tel.: (36) 33 510 920
Web Site: http://www.www.kirchhoff-hungaria.hu
Motor Vehicle Parts Mfr
N.A.I.C.S.: 336390

KIRCHHOFF Ireland Ltd. (2)
Lisnnenan, Letterkenny, F92A970, Co Donegal, Ireland
Tel.: (353) 74 91 22422
Web Site: http://www.kirchhoff.ie
Emp.: 70
Motor Vehicle Parts Mfr
N.A.I.C.S.: 336390
Sean McDermott *(Gen Mgr)*

KIRCHHOFF Polska Sp. z o.o. (2)
ul Wojska Polskiego 3, 39-300, Mielec, Poland
Tel.: (48) 177 885 600
Web Site: http://www.kirchhoff.pl
Motor Vehicle Parts Mfr
N.A.I.C.S.: 336390
Janusz Sobon *(Mng Dir)*

Plant (Domestic):

KIRCHHOFF Polska Sp. zo.o. - Gliwice I Plant (3)
ul Mechanikow 9, 44-109, Gliwice, Poland
Tel.: (48) 32 734 62 26
Automobile Parts Mfr
N.A.I.C.S.: 336390

KIRCHHOFF Polska Sp. zo.o. - Gliwice II Plant (3)
ul Nobla 9, 44-109, Gliwice, Poland
Tel.: (48) 32 338 1600
Automobile Parts Mfr
N.A.I.C.S.: 336390

KIRI INDUSTRIES LTD.

Rafal Lechowski *(Mng Dir)*

Subsidiary (Non-US):

KIRCHHOFF Portugal Gametal Metalurgica da Gandarinha S. A. (2)
Avenida 16 de Maio Zona Industrial Norte de Ovar, 3880 102, Ovar, Portugal
Tel.: (351) 256 579 210
Web Site: http://www.gametal.pt
Emp.: 40
Motor Vehicle Parts Mfr
N.A.I.C.S.: 336390
Paul Van Rooij *(Gen Mgr)*

Van-Rob, Inc. (2)
200 Vandorf Sideroad, Aurora, L4G 0A2, ON, Canada
Tel.: (905) 727-8585
Web Site: http://www.van-rob.com
Sales Range: $125-149.9 Million
Emp.: 1,300
Metal Stamping Mfr
N.A.I.C.S.: 332119
Peter van Schaik *(Founder & CEO)*

Subsidiary (Non-US):

VRK Automotive Systems S.A. de C.V. (3)
Km 117 Autopista Mex Pue No 200 Nave 26 Modulo B, Parque Industrial FINSAII, 72730, Cholula, Puebla, Mexico
Tel.: (52) 222 210 5846
Web Site: http://www.Van-Rob.com
Emp.: 17
Motor Vehicle Parts Mfr
N.A.I.C.S.: 336390
Janet Mannix *(Plant Mgr)*

Subsidiary (US):

Van Rob Waverly Inc. (3)
611 W 2nd St, Waverly, OH 45690-9701
Tel.: (740) 947-7763
Web Site: http://www.van-rob.com
Sales Range: $100-124.9 Million
Emp.: 400
Automotive Stampings
N.A.I.C.S.: 336370
Carrie Bliss *(Coord-Stock Maintenance)*

KIRCHHOFF Witte GmbH (1)
Feldmuhlenstrasse 51, 58093, Hagen, Germany
Tel.: (49) 2331 3607 0
Web Site: http://www.witte-werkzeuge.de
Emp.: 12
Hand Tool Mfr
N.A.I.C.S.: 332216
J. Wolfgang Kirchhoff *(CEO)*

Pruckner Rehatechnik GmbH (1)
Schuster Strasse 1, 2111, Vienna, Austria
Tel.: (43) 2262 71700
Web Site: http://www.rehatechnik.co.at
Passenger Transportation Services
N.A.I.C.S.: 485991

KIRI INDUSTRIES LTD.
Plot No 2991A B Nr Water Tank Phasell GIDC Vatva, Ahmedabad, 382 445, Gujarat, India
Tel.: (91) 7925894477
Web Site:
   https://www.kiriindustries.com
532967—(BOM)
Rev.: $114,946,250
Assets: $387,971,393
Liabilities: $63,244,536
Net Worth: $324,726,857
Earnings: $12,925,350
Emp.: 949
Fiscal Year-end: 03/31/23
Synthetic Organic Dyes & Dyes Intermediates Mfr & Exporter
N.A.I.C.S.: 325130
Suresh S. Gondalia *(Compliance Officer & Sec)*

Subsidiaries:

Kiri Renewable Energy Pvt. Ltd. (1)
27/310 Ridgeways Kiambu Road, PO Box 12135-00400, Nairobi, Kenya
Tel.: (254) 727806611
Web Site: https://www.kirienergy.com

KIRI INDUSTRIES LTD.

Kiri Industries Ltd.—(Continued)
Solar Electric Power Generation Services
N.A.I.C.S.: 221114

Pulcra Chemicals GmbH (1)
Am Trippelsberg 92, 40589, Dusseldorf, Germany
Tel.: (49) 21127190200
Synthetic Organic Dyes & Dyes Intermediates Mfr & Exporter
N.A.I.C.S.: 325130

Subsidiary (Domestic):

DyStar Textilfarben GmbH (2)
Industriepark Hochst Bldg B 598, 65926, Frankfurt, Germany
Tel.: (49) 6921090
Web Site: http://www.dystar.com
Sales Range: $1-4.9 Billion
Textile & Leather Industry Dyes & Processing Chemicals Mfr & Services
N.A.I.C.S.: 325130

Subsidiary (Non-US):

DyStar (Shanghai) Trading Co., Ltd. (3)
5-6F Building No 20 201 Min Yi Road, Shanghai, 201612, China
Tel.: (86) 2137746338
Textile & Leather Industry Dyes & Processing Chemicals Mfr & Services
N.A.I.C.S.: 325130

DyStar Anilinas Texteis Unipessoal, Lda. (3)
Rua Eng Ferreira Dias 728 salas 2-4, 4100-246, Porto, Portugal
Tel.: (351) 226153180
Sales Range: $25-49.9 Million
Emp.: 18
Textile & Leather Industry Dyes & Processing Chemicals Mfr & Services
N.A.I.C.S.: 325130

DyStar Benelux (3)
Louizalaan 200, B132 Avenue Louise, 1050, Brussels, Belgium
Tel.: (32) 26442333
Web Site: http://www.dystar.com
Sales Range: $25-49.9 Million
Emp.: 4
Textile & Leather Industry Dyes & Processing Chemicals Mfr & Services
N.A.I.C.S.: 325130

DyStar Boehme Africa (Pty) Ltd. (3)
27 Sheffield Road Willowton, Pietermaritzburg, 3201, South Africa
Tel.: (27) 333908100
Sales Range: $25-49.9 Million
Emp.: 42
Textile & Leather Industry Dyes & Processing Chemicals Mfr & Services
N.A.I.C.S.: 325130

DyStar China Ldt. (3)
Room 2503 9 Chong Yip Street, Kwun Tong, Kowloon, China (Hong Kong)
Tel.: (852) 29553388
Emp.: 10
Textile & Leather Industry Dyes & Processing Chemicals Mfr & Services
N.A.I.C.S.: 325130

DyStar France s.a.r.l. (3)
15 rue des Entrepreneurs, 59700, Lille, France
Tel.: (33) 320423134
Web Site: http://www.dystar.com
Sales Range: $25-49.9 Million
Emp.: 6
Textile & Leather Industry Dyes & Processing Chemicals Mfr & Services
N.A.I.C.S.: 325130

DyStar Hispania, S.L., Sociedad Unipersonal (3)
Famadas 37-57, 08907, Llobregat, Spain
Tel.: (34) 932640440
Textile & Leather Industry Dyes & Processing Chemicals Mfr & Services
N.A.I.C.S.: 325130

DyStar India Private Limited (3)
Marwah House Ground Floor Krishanlal Marwah Marg, Saki Vihar Road Saki Naka, Andheri East, Mumbai, 400 072, India
Tel.: (91) 22 4034 9000

Textiles & Leather Dyeing Products & Services
N.A.I.C.S.: 325130

DyStar Industria e Comercio de Produtos Quimicos Ltda. (3)
Rua Geraldo Flausino Gomes 78 - 4 andar - cjs 41 / 42 Cidade Monaies, Sao Paulo, 04575-060, Brazil
Tel.: (55) 1155083684
Emp.: 80
Textile & Leather Industry Dyes & Processing Chemicals Mfr & Services
N.A.I.C.S.: 325130

DyStar Italia S.r.l. (3)
Via Lepetit 40, 20020, Lainate, MI, Italy
Tel.: (39) 02994401
Textile & Leather Industry Dyes & Processing Chemicals Mfr & Services
N.A.I.C.S.: 325130

DyStar Japan Ltd. (3)
7-20 Azuchimachi 1-chome, Chuo-ku, Osaka, 541-0052, Japan
Tel.: (81) 662636672
Textile & Leather Industry Dyes & Processing Chemicals Mfr & Services
N.A.I.C.S.: 325130

DyStar Korea Ltd. (3)
Ansan Danwon Kyunggi 756-1 2nd Fl, Ansan, Korea (South)
Tel.: (82) 234527878
Emp.: 7
Textile & Leather Industry Dyes & Processing Chemicals Mfr & Services
N.A.I.C.S.: 325130

Subsidiary (US):

DyStar L.P. (3)
9844-A Southern Pine Blvd, Charlotte, NC 28273
Tel.: (704) 561-3000
Web Site: https://www.dystar.com
Textile & Leather Dye & Pigment Mfr
N.A.I.C.S.: 325130
Steven Hennen (CFO-America)

Subsidiary (Domestic):

DyStar Carolina Chemical (4)
8309 Wilkinson Blvd, Charlotte, NC 28214
Tel.: (704) 393-0089
Web Site: http://www.dystar.com
Chemical Additive Mfr
N.A.I.C.S.: 325998

DyStar Foam Control (4)
311 Cleveland Pl, Cheyenne, WY 82007
Tel.: (307) 634-7699
Web Site: http://www.dystar.com
Chemical Additive Mfr
N.A.I.C.S.: 325998

DyStar Hilton Davis (4)
2235 Langdon Farm Rd, Cincinnati, OH 45237
Web Site: http://www.dystar.com
Food, Drug & Cosmetic Dyes Mfr
N.A.I.C.S.: 325199

Subsidiary (Non-US):

DyStar Pakistan (Pvt.) Ltd. (3)
5th Floor Citi Tower 33-A Block-6 P E C H S Main Shahra-e-Faisal, Housing Society Sirajudulla Rd, Karachi, 75350, Pakistan
Tel.: (92) 2134556996
Textile & Leather Industry Dyes & Processing Chemicals Mfr & Services
N.A.I.C.S.: 325130

DyStar Singapore Pte. Ltd. (3)
1A International Business Park 10-01, The Gatewat East, Singapore, 189721, Singapore
Tel.: (65) 66712800
Web Site: https://www.dystar.com
Textile & Leather Industry Dyes & Processing Chemicals Mfr & Services
N.A.I.C.S.: 325130
Yalin Xu (Mng Dir & Pres-DyStar Grp)

DyStar Taiwan Ltd. (3)
Textile & Leather Industry Dyes & Processing Chemicals Mfr & Services
N.A.I.C.S.: 325130

DyStar Thai Ltd. (3)
193 Lake Rajada Building 17th floor, Ratchadapisek Road, Bangkok, 10110, Thailand
Tel.: (66) 22640470
Textile & Leather Industry Dyes & Processing Chemicals Mfr & Services
N.A.I.C.S.: 325130

DyStar de Mexico S. de R.L. de C.V (3)
Av Insurgentes Sur 1685-504, Col Guadalupe Inn, 01020, Mexico, Mexico
Tel.: (52) 5553225100
Textile & Leather Industry Dyes & Processing Chemicals Mfr & Services
N.A.I.C.S.: 325130

PT DyStar Colours Indonesia (3)
Menara Global Building 22nd Floor, Jln Gatot Subroto Kav 27, Jakarta, 12930, Indonesia
Tel.: (62) 215270550
Textile & Leather Industry Dyes & Processing Chemicals Mfr & Services
N.A.I.C.S.: 325130

Texanlab Laboratories Pvt. Ltd. (3)
W-384 TTC Industrial Area, Rabale PO Ghansoli, Navi Mumbai, 400701, Rabale, India
Tel.: (91) 2261417100
Web Site: https://www.texanlabglobal.com
Sales Range: $25-49.9 Million
Emp.: 100
Textile Industry Testing Services
N.A.I.C.S.: 541380
Vinoth Kumar (Gen Mgr)

Synthesis International Limited (1)
PO Box 3335, Reston, VA 20195
Tel.: (703) 464-4711
Web Site: https://www.synthesisinternational.com
Management Consulting Services
N.A.I.C.S.: 541611
Jorge Pardo (CEO & Founder)

KIRIACOULIS MEDITERRANEAN CRUISES SHIPPING S.A.

7 Alimou Ave Alimos, 174 55, Athens, 174 55, Greece
Tel.: (30) 2109886187
Web Site: https://www.kiriacoulis.com
Year Founded: 1986
KYRI—(ATH)
Rev.: $218,143
Assets: $2,358,126
Liabilities: $2,275,717
Net Worth: $82,410
Earnings: ($101,815)
Emp.: 52
Fiscal Year-end: 12/31/22
Yacht Sales & Charter Services
N.A.I.C.S.: 483112
Stavros Th. Kiriacoulis (Founder)

Subsidiaries:

GOUVIA MARINA S.A. (1)
PO Box 60, Tzavros, 49083, Kerkira, Corfu, Greece
Tel.: (30) 26610 91376
Web Site: http://www.d-marin.gr
Marina Operation Services
N.A.I.C.S.: 713930

K & G MED MARINAS MANAGEMENT S.A (1)
7 Alimou Avenue, Alimos, 174 55, Athens, Greece
Tel.: (30) 2109855327
Web Site: http://www.medmarinas.com
Sales Range: $50-74.9 Million
Emp.: 5
Marinas Development & Management Services
N.A.I.C.S.: 713930
Nikos Koutsodontis (Gen Mgr)

Mediterranean Villages S.A (1)
7 Alimou Avenue, Alimos, 17455, Athens, Greece
Tel.: (30) 2109886187
Web Site: http://www.kiriacoulis.com
Sales Range: $25-49.9 Million
Emp.: 5

Commercial Building Construction & Real Estate Sales & Services
N.A.I.C.S.: 236220
Sanis Kiriacoulis (Mgr)

SARL KIRIACOULIS POINT D' AMURE (1)
Esquillette basin Port, 83230, Bormes-les-Mimosas, France
Tel.: (33) 494004200
Web Site: http://www.point-amure.com
Yacht Charter Services
N.A.I.C.S.: 713930

SARL VENT PORTANT (1)
9 Place Bernard Moitessier, 17000, La Rochelle, France
Tel.: (33) 546447693
Web Site: https://www.ventportant.com
Sales Range: $50-74.9 Million
Yacht Charter Services
N.A.I.C.S.: 713930
Odon Van Gaver (Editor & Mgr)

KIRIN GROUP HOLDINGS LIMITED

23/F Sang Woo Building No 227-228 Gloucester Road, Wanchai, China (Hong Kong)
Tel.: (852) 3 107 0884 **BM**
Web Site: http://www.tricor.com.hk
Rev.: $12,425,386
Assets: $46,810,643
Liabilities: $35,720,511
Net Worth: $11,090,132
Earnings: ($6,288,605)
Emp.: 48
Fiscal Year-end: 06/30/19
Holding Company; Insurance Brokerage Services
N.A.I.C.S.: 551112
Yik Chow (Chm & Officer-Compliance)

KIRIN HOLDINGS COMPANY, LIMITED

Nakano Central Park South 4-10-2 Nakano, Nakano-ku, Tokyo, 164-0001, Japan
Tel.: (81) 368377000 **JP**
Web Site: https://www.kirinholdings.com
Year Founded: 2007
KNBWY—(OTCIQ)
Rev.: $17,903,595,600
Assets: $23,806,633,840
Liabilities: $13,197,944,320
Net Worth: $10,608,689,520
Earnings: $696,330,800
Emp.: 31,151
Fiscal Year-end: 12/31/20
Holding Company
N.A.I.C.S.: 551112
Keisuke Nishimura (Sr Exec VP)

Subsidiaries:

Azuma Kirin Industria E Comercio De Bebidas E Alimentos Ltda (1)
Av Paulista 1274 13 Andar Cj 33, 01310-925, Sao Paulo, Brazil
Tel.: (55) 11 3283 0733
Web Site: http://www.azumakirin.com
Beverages Mfr
N.A.I.C.S.: 312120
Rodrigo Peca (Mgr-Mktg)

Azuma Kirin Industria e Comercio de Bebidas e Alimentos Ltda. (1)
Av Paulista 1274 - 7 Andar, Bela Vista, 01310-925, Sao Paulo, Brazil
Tel.: (55) 1132830733
Web Site: http://azumakirincompany.com.br
Food Product Mfr & Distr
N.A.I.C.S.: 311991

Brasil Kirin Participacoes e Representacoes S.A. (1)
Avenida Primo Schincariol 2.300 Itaim, Itu, 13312 900, Brazil **(50.45%)**
Tel.: (55) 11 2118 9500
Web Site: http://www.schincariol.com.br

AND PRIVATE COMPANIES

KIRIN HOLDINGS COMPANY, LIMITED

Sales Range: $1-4.9 Billion
Emp.: 9,307
Holding Company; Production of Beer, Soft Drinks & Mineral Water & Franchise Bars
N.A.I.C.S.: 551112

Holding (Domestic):

Primo Schincariol Industria de Cervejas e Refrigerantes S.A. (2)
Av Primo Schincariol 2222-2300 Itaim, Itu, 13312-900, Brazil
Tel.: (55) 11 4022 9500
Web Site: http://www.schincariol.com.br
Sales Range: $900-999.9 Million
Emp.: 3,210
Beer, Soft Drinks & Mineral Water Mfr
N.A.I.C.S.: 312120
Adriano Schincariol *(Chm & CEO)*

Subsidiary (Domestic):

Primo Schincariol Industria de Cervejas e Refrigerantes do Nordeste S.A (3)
Rodovia Br 101 Km 110,8, Alagoinhas, 48010 970, Bahia, Brazil
Tel.: (55) 7534 228000
Web Site: http://www.schincariol.com.br
Sales Range: $650-699.9 Million
Emp.: 1,517
Soft Drinks Mfr
N.A.I.C.S.: 312111

Primo Schincariol Industria de Cervejas e Refrigerantes do Norte-Nordeste S.A. (3)
Rodovia BR 316 Km 543.7 3o Distrito, Caxias, 65600 970, Maranhao, Brazil
Tel.: (55) 99 3422 6200
Web Site: http://www.schincariol.com.br
Sales Range: $550-599.9 Million
Emp.: 940
Beer, Soft Drinks & Mineral Water Mfr
N.A.I.C.S.: 312120

Coca-Cola Beverages Northeast, Inc. (1)
1 Executive Park Dr, Bedford, NH 03110
Tel.: (603) 627-7871
Web Site: https://www.cokenortheast.com
Soft Drink Mfr & Retailer
N.A.I.C.S.: 312111

Cosmo Foods Co., Ltd. (1)
7F 12-2 Kodenmacho Nihonbashi, Chuo-ku, Tokyo, 103-0001, Japan (34.07%)
Tel.: (81) 332490390
Web Site: http://www.cosmo-foods.co.jp
Sales Range: $25-49.9 Million
Emp.: 40
Food Seasoning & Additive Mfr
N.A.I.C.S.: 311999
Hiroshi Okada *(Founder)*

Diageo Kirin Co., Ltd. (1)
Kirin Nihonbashi Bldg 2-5 Nihonbashi Koami-cho, Chuo-Ku, Tokyo, 103-0016, Japan
Tel.: (81) 3 5645 3001
Web Site: http://www.kirinholdings.co.jp
Beverage Mfr & Distr
N.A.I.C.S.: 312120

Ei Sho Gen Co., Ltd. (1)
HI Gotanda Building 7F 2-11-17 Nishigotanda, Shinagawa-ku, Tokyo, 141-0031, Japan
Tel.: (81) 3 3491 6337
Liquor Mfr
N.A.I.C.S.: 312140

Eishogen Co., Ltd. (1)
2-11-17 Nishigotanda, Shinagawa-ku, Tokyo, 141-0031, Japan
Tel.: (81) 3 3491 6337
Web Site: http://www.kirinholdings.co.jp
Sales Range: $25-49.9 Million
Emp.: 50
Manufacture & Sales of Chinese Liqueurs
N.A.I.C.S.: 445320

FANCL Corporation (1)
89-1 Yamashita-cho, Naka-ku, Yokohama, 231 8528, Kanagawa, Japan (75.24%)
Tel.: (81) 452261200
Web Site: https://www.fancl.jp
Sales Range: $750-799.9 Million
Emp.: 973
Cosmetics Mfr
N.A.I.C.S.: 325620
Kazuyoshi Miyajima *(Pres & COO)*

Subsidiary (Non-US):

Fancl (Thailand) Co., Ltd. (2)
20th Floor TPI Twr 26/56 Nang-linchee Rd, Thungmahamek Sathorn, 10120, Bangkok, Thailand
Tel.: (66) 26786707
Web Site: http://www.fancl.co.th
Sales Range: $25-49.9 Million
Emp.: 32
Cosmetics Beauty Supplies & Perfume Stores
N.A.I.C.S.: 456120

Fancl Asia Pte Ltd. (2)
313 Somerset Rd 01-19, 238895, Singapore, Singapore
Tel.: (65) 6871 1526
Web Site: http://www.fancl.com.sg
Cosmetics Beauty Supplies & Perfume Stores
N.A.I.C.S.: 456120

Subsidiary (Domestic):

Fancl B&H Co., Ltd. (2)
53 Iijimacho Sakae-Ku, Yokohama, Kanagawa, Japan
Tel.: (81) 458955405
Web Site: http://www.fancl.co.jp
Cosmetics Beauty Supplies & Perfume Stores
N.A.I.C.S.: 456120

Fancl Home Life Co., Ltd. (2)
Tk Kannai Plz 4th Floor, Yokohama, Kanagawa, Japan
Tel.: (81) 120302222
Web Site: http://www.fancl.co.jp
Real Estate Agents & Brokers Offices
N.A.I.C.S.: 531210

Fancl Insurance Service Corp. (2)
Yamashita-cho 89-1 Naka-ku Yubinbango, 231-0023, Yokohama, Kanagawa, Japan
Tel.: (81) 452125200
Web Site: http://www.fancl-hoken.co.jp
Insurance Agencies & Brokerages
N.A.I.C.S.: 524210

Subsidiary (US):

Fancl International, Inc. (2)
14450 Myford Rd, Irvine, CA 92606
Tel.: (949) 476-8167
Web Site: http://www.fancl.com
Sales Range: $25-49.9 Million
Emp.: 20
Cosmetics & Toiletries Sales
N.A.I.C.S.: 456120
Gen Inomata *(Pres)*

Subsidiary (Domestic):

Fancl Smile Co., Ltd. (2)
109-1 Iijimacho Sakae-ku, Yokohama, Kanagawa, Japan
Tel.: (81) 458906870
Food Mfr
N.A.I.C.S.: 311999

Subsidiary (Non-US):

Fancl Taiwan Co., Ltd. (2)
Room C 12th Floor 31, Chung Hsiao E Rd Sec 1, Taipei, Taiwan
Tel.: (886) 223218033
Web Site: http://www.fancl.com.tw
Drugs & Druggists Sundries Whslr
N.A.I.C.S.: 424210

Interfood Shareholding Company (1)
Floor 16-Viettel Complex Building 285 Canh Mang Thang 8, 12 ward District 10, Ho Chi Minh City, Vietnam
Tel.: (84) 2822189189
Web Site: https://www.wonderfarmonline.com
Beverage Mfr & Whslr
N.A.I.C.S.: 312111

Kansai Kirin Beverage Service Co., Ltd. (1)
2-1-1 Edobori Nishi-Ku Edobori Center Bldg 11f, Osaka, 550-0002, Japan
Tel.: (81) 664486750
Beer Mfr
N.A.I.C.S.: 312120

Kirin & Communications Co., Ltd (1)
Nakano Central Park South 4-10-2 Nakano, Nakano-ku, Tokyo, 164-0001, Japan
Tel.: (81) 367349738
Web Site: https://www.kirin-com.co.jp
Sales Range: $150-199.9 Million
Emp.: 316
Theme Park Operating Services
N.A.I.C.S.: 713110

Kirin (China) Investment Co., Ltd. (1)
Room 203-204 Yue Da Huang Pu He Bin Building No 356 Xin Zha Road, Huang Pu District, Shanghai, 200003, China
Tel.: (86) 21 5187 7070
Sales Range: $50-74.9 Million
Emp.: 4
Investment Management Service
N.A.I.C.S.: 523999
Shiro Atsumi *(Pres)*

Kirin Beer Marketing Co., Ltd. (1)
6-26-1 Jingumae, Shibuya-ku, Tokyo, 150-0001, Japan
Tel.: (81) 3 6734 9995
Beverage Product Distr
N.A.I.C.S.: 424820

Kirin Beverage Company, Limited (1)
10-2 Nakano 4-chome, Nakano-ku, Tokyo, 164-0001, Japan (100%)
Tel.: (81) 358214001
Web Site: http://www.beverage.co.jp
Emp.: 3,467
Soft Drinks Developer, Mfr & Whslr
N.A.I.C.S.: 312111
Toru Yoshimura *(Pres)*

Subsidiary (US):

Coca-Cola Bottling Company of Northern New England, Inc. (2)
1 Executive Park Dr Ste 330, Bedford, NH 03110
Tel.: (603) 627-7871
Web Site: http://www.ccnne.com
Sales Range: $150-199.9 Million
Emp.: 3,500
Soft Drink Production & Bottling
N.A.I.C.S.: 312111
Bryan Riddell *(CFO & VP-Fin)*

Kirin Brewery Company, Limited (1)
Nakano Central Park South 4-10-2 Nakano, Nakano-ku, Tokyo, 164-0001, Japan (100%)
Tel.: (81) 36 837 7002
Web Site: https://www.kirinholdings.com
Sales Range: $5-14.9 Billion
Beer Breweries & Whslr; Wineries & Wine Whslr
N.A.I.C.S.: 312120
Takayuki Fuse *(Pres & CEO)*

Subsidiary (US):

Four Roses Distillery, LLC (2)
1224 Bonds Mill Rd, Lawrenceburg, KY 40342 (100%)
Tel.: (502) 839-3436
Web Site: http://fourrosesbourbon.com
Sales Range: $25-49.9 Million
Emp.: 100
Brewery Mfr
N.A.I.C.S.: 312120
Ryan Ashley *(COO & Dir-Ops)*

Kirin Brewery of America, LLC (2)
970 W 190th St Ste 890, Torrance, CA 90502-1057 (100%)
Tel.: (310) 354-2400
Web Site: http://www.kirin.com
Sales Range: $10-24.9 Million
Beer Importer & Whslr
N.A.I.C.S.: 424810

Holding (Domestic):

Mercian Corporation (2)
10-2 Nakano 4-chome Nakano Central Park South, Nakano-ku, Tokyo, 164-0001, Japan (100%)
Tel.: (81) 332313910
Web Site: http://www.mercian.co.jp
Sales Range: $800-899.9 Million
Emp.: 670
Wines & Distilled Alcoholic Beverages Mfr & Whslr; Pharmaceuticals & Chemicals Developer & Mfr; Animal Feed Mfr

N.A.I.C.S.: 312130
Tomosaburo Nakao *(Sr Exec VP)*

Subsidiary (Domestic):

Daiichi Alcohol Co., Ltd. (3)
Nakano Central Park South 4-10-2 Nakano, Nakano-ku, Tokyo, 164-0001, Japan
Tel.: (81) 36 837 7012
Web Site: http://www.kirinholdings.co.jp
Ethyl Alcohol Sales
N.A.I.C.S.: 424820

Japan Synthetic Alcohol Co., Ltd. (3)
10-8 Ukishimacho, Kawasaki-Ku, Kawasaki, 210-0862, Kanagawa, Japan
Tel.: (81) 442666571
Alcoholic Beverage Mfr & Distr
N.A.I.C.S.: 312120

Subsidiary (US):

Markham Vineyards (3)
2812 Saint Helena Hwy N, Saint Helena, CA 94574-9655
Tel.: (707) 963-5292
Web Site: http://www.markhamvineyards.com
Sales Range: $25-49.9 Million
Emp.: 25
Vineyards & Winery
N.A.I.C.S.: 312130
David W. Flanary *(Pres)*

Subsidiary (Domestic):

Mercian Chemical Corporation (3)
1-7-9 Horidome-cho Nihonbashi, Chuo-ku, Tokyo, 103-0012, Japan
Tel.: (81) 356145381
Medicinal Chemicals Mfr
N.A.I.C.S.: 325199

Mercian Cleantec Corporation (3)
5-8 Kyobashi 1-chome, Chuo-ku, Tokyo, 104-8305, Japan (100%)
Tel.: (81) 332318910
Web Site: http://www.m-cleantec.com
Sales Range: Less than $1 Million
Emp.: 100
Pharmaceuticals Developer & Mfr
N.A.I.C.S.: 325412

Nippon Liquor Ltd. (3)
14-5 Mita 2-chome, Minato-ku, Tokyo, 108-0073, Japan (51%)
Tel.: (81) 334532201
Web Site: http://www.nlwine.com
Sales Range: $1-9.9 Million
Emp.: 60
Wine & Distilled Beverages Importer & Whslr
N.A.I.C.S.: 424820

Subsidiary (Non-US):

Taiwan Kirin Co., Ltd. (2)
4F 248 Nanking East Road Section 3, Taipei, 10595, Taiwan (100%)
Tel.: (886) 227737070
Web Site: http://www.kirin.com.tw
Emp.: 80
Beer & Liquor Mfr & Distr
N.A.I.C.S.: 424820
Takashi Ueda *(Gen Mgr)*

Kirin Business System Co., Ltd. (1)
4-10-2 Nakano, Nakano-ku, Tokyo, 164-0001, Japan
Tel.: (81) 367349680
Web Site: https://www.kirinbs.co.jp
Emp.: 259
Information Technology Consulting Services
N.A.I.C.S.: 541512

Kirin City Co., Ltd. (1)
1F Tokyo Dia Building 1 1-28-38 Shinkawa, Chuo-ku, Tokyo, 111-0035, Japan
Tel.: (81) 343327485
Emp.: 160
Bar Management & Operation Services
N.A.I.C.S.: 722410

Kirin Distillery Co., Ltd. (1)
970 Shibanta, Gotemba, 412-0003, Shizuoka, Japan
Tel.: (81) 55 089 3131
Web Site: http://www.kirinholdings.co.jp
Sales Range: $75-99.9 Million
Emp.: 200
Alcoholic Beverage Distr

KIRIN HOLDINGS COMPANY, LIMITED

Kirin Holdings Company, Limited—(Continued)
N.A.I.C.S.: 424820

Kirin Echo Co., Ltd. (1)
Real Estate Property Leasing & General Insurance Services
N.A.I.C.S.: 531190

Kirin Engineering Co., Ltd. (1)
9th floor Techno Wave 100 Building 1-1-25 Shin-Urashima-cho, Kanagawa-ku, Yokohama, 221-8558, Kanagawa, Japan
Tel.: (81) 454517601
Web Site: https://www.kirineng.co.jp
Plant Engineering Consulting Services
N.A.I.C.S.: 541330

Kirin Europe GmbH (1)
Berliner Allee 26, 40212, Dusseldorf, Germany
Tel.: (49) 211353086
Web Site: https://www.kirineurope.com
Emp.: 5
Beer Mfr & Distr
N.A.I.C.S.: 312120

Kirin Foods Australia Holdings Pty Ltd (1)
L 7 68 York St, Sydney, 2000, NSW, Australia
Tel.: (61) 391888000
Investment Management Service
N.A.I.C.S.: 523940

Kirin Group Office Co., Ltd. (1)
2-10-1 Shinkawa, Chuo-ku, Tokyo, 104-8288, Japan
Tel.: (81) 3 6734 9294
Web Site: http://www.kirinholdings.co.jp
Sales Range: $25-49.9 Million
Emp.: 250
Business Management Consulting Services
N.A.I.C.S.: 541611

Kirin Holdings Singapore Pte. Ltd. (1)
18 Cross Street 02-101 Office S2051, Singapore, 048423, Singapore
Tel.: (65) 6 908 5078
Web Site: https://www.kirin-singapore.com.sg
Alcoholic Beverages Mfr
N.A.I.C.S.: 312120

Kirin Logistics Co., Ltd. (1)
2-9-6 Shinkawa, Chuo-ku, Tokyo, 104-0033, Japan
Tel.: (81) 3 6734 9651
Beverage Products Logistics Services
N.A.I.C.S.: 541614

Kirin MC Danone Waters Co., Ltd. (1)
6-26-1 Jingumae, Shibuya-ku, Tokyo, 150-0001, Japan
Tel.: (81) 3 6734 9368
Web Site: http://www.kirinholdings.co.jp
Bottled Water Mfr & Distr
N.A.I.C.S.: 312112

Kirin Merchandising Co., Ltd. (1)
1-11-8 Shibuya, Shibuya-Ku, Tokyo, Japan
Tel.: (81) 367349194
Alcoholic Beverages Whslr
N.A.I.C.S.: 424820

Kirin Techno-System Co., Ltd. (1)
10-10 Ohkawa, Kawasaki-ku, Kawasaki, 210-0858, Kanagawa-ken, Japan.
Tel.: (81) 44 366 6801
Web Site: http://www.kirintechno.co.jp
Sales Range: $50-74.9 Million
Emp.: 166
Soft Drink Bottle Mfr
N.A.I.C.S.: 312111
Hironobu Hosokawa *(Pres)*

Kirin-Tropicana Inc. (1)
Shinjuku L Tower 6th Floor 1-6-1 Nishi-Shinjuku, Shinjuku-ku, Tokyo, 163-1506, Japan
Tel.: (81) 3 6734 9796
Fruit Juice Mfr & Distr
N.A.I.C.S.: 311411
Shigeyuki Aoki *(Pres)*

Koiwai Dairy Products Co., Ltd. (1)
Dairy Products Mfr & Distr
N.A.I.C.S.: 311514

Kyowa Kirin Co. Ltd. (1)
Otemachi Financial City Grand Cube 1-9-2 Otemachi, Chiyoda-ku, Tokyo, 100-0004, Japan **(50.3%)**
Tel.: (81) 352057200
Rev.: $3,135,431,970
Assets: $7,273,928,780
Liabilities: $1,343,725,160
Net Worth: $5,930,203,620
Emp.: 5,974
Fiscal Year-end: 12/31/2023
Pharmaceuticals Mfr
N.A.I.C.S.: 325412
Toshifumi Mikayama *(Sr Mng Exec Officer)*

Subsidiary (Non-US):

Kirin Kunpeng (China) Bio-Pharmaceutical Co., Ltd. (2)
970 Longdong Road, Pudong New Area, Shanghai, 201203, China
Tel.: (86) 2150800909
Web Site: http://ir.kyowa-kirin.co.jp
Pharmaceuticals Mfr
N.A.I.C.S.: 325412

Kyowa Hakko (Malaysia) Sdn Bhd (2)
20 Jalan SS 19 5, Selangor Darul Ehsan, 47500, Subang Jaya, Malaysia
Tel.: (60) 3 5734 0669
Pharmaceutical & Food Additive Developer & Mfr
N.A.I.C.S.: 325412

Subsidiary (Domestic):

Kyowa Hakko Bio Co., Ltd. (2)
4-10-2 Nakano Central Park South, Nakano-ku, Tokyo, 164-0001, Japan
Tel.: (81) 366250480
Web Site: https://www.kyowahakko-bio.co.jp
Sales Range: $800-899.9 Million
Emp.: 1,941
Amino Acid, Nucleic Acid & Related Compound Mfr
N.A.I.C.S.: 325412

Subsidiary (Domestic):

Daiichi Fine Chemical Co., Ltd. (3)
530 Chokeiji Takaoka, Toyama, 933 8511, Japan
Tel.: (81) 766213456
Web Site: http://www.daiichi-fcj.co.jp
Food Additive, Pharmaceutical & Specialty Chemicals Mfr
N.A.I.C.S.: 325998
Eptsuoo Ohhima *(Pres)*

Subsidiary (Non-US):

Daiichi Fine Chemical Europe GmbH (4)
Am Wehrhahn 50, 40211, Dusseldorf, Germany
Tel.: (49) 211175450
Web Site: http://www.daiichi.de
Pharmaceutical, Food Additive & Specialty Chemical Mfr
N.A.I.C.S.: 325998

Subsidiary (Non-US):

Kyowa Hakko (H.K.) Co., Ltd. (3)
Room 1501 68 Yee Wo Street, Causeway Bay, China (Hong Kong)
Tel.: (852) 2 895 6795
Web Site: http://www.kyowahakko-bio.co.jp
Sales Range: $50-74.9 Million
Emp.: 10
Sales of Pharmaceuticals, Feed Additives & Chemicals
N.A.I.C.S.: 424910

Shanghai Kyowa Amino Acid Co., Ltd. (3)
No 158 Xintuan Road, Qingpu Industrial Zone, Shanghai, 201707, China
Tel.: (86) 215 970 1998
Web Site: http://www.kyowahakko-bio.co.jp
Pharmaceutical & Food Additive Developer & Mfr
N.A.I.C.S.: 325412

Subsidiary (Non-US):

Kyowa Hakko Europe GmbH (2)
Am Wehrhahn 50, 40211, Dusseldorf, Germany
Tel.: (49) 21 117 5450
Web Site: https://www.kyowa.eu
Sales Range: $25-49.9 Million
Bio Chemical Product Distr
N.A.I.C.S.: 424210
Hirohito Shimazu *(Pres)*

Kyowa Hakko Kirin (Hong Kong) Co., Ltd. (2)
Unit B 13/F Manulife Tower 169 Electric Road, North Point, China (Hong Kong)
Tel.: (852) 2956 0828
Emp.: 1
Pharmaceuticals Product Mfr
N.A.I.C.S.: 325412
D. Suzuki *(Gen Mgr)*

Kyowa Hakko Kirin (Singapore) Pte. Ltd. (2)
80 Robinson Road Unit No 22-01, Singapore, 068898, Singapore
Tel.: (65) 6836 3991
Web Site: http://www.kyowa-kirin.co.jp
Emp.: 25
Pharmaceuticals Product Mfr
N.A.I.C.S.: 325412
Yamamoto Teruo *(Mgr-Admin)*

Kyowa Hakko Kirin (Taiwan) Co., Ltd. (2)
16F No 44 Sec 2, Chung Shan N Road, Taipei, 10548, Taiwan
Tel.: (886) 225642800
Web Site: http://www.kyowa-kirin.com.tw
Sales Range: $25-49.9 Million
Emp.: 30
Pharmaceuticals Mfr
N.A.I.C.S.: 325412
Philip Yu *(Mgr)*

Kyowa Hakko Kirin (Thailand) Co., Ltd. (2)
323 United Center building 20th floor room 2003b Silom road Silom, Bangrak, Bangkok, 10500, Thailand
Tel.: (66) 2 631 2126
Web Site: https://www.kyowakirin.com
Emp.: 15
Pharmaceuticals Product Mfr
N.A.I.C.S.: 325412

Subsidiary (US):

Kyowa Hakko Kirin America, Inc. (2)
212 Carnegie Ctr Ste 101, Princeton, NJ 08540
Tel.: (609) 580-7400
Web Site: http://www.kyowa-kirin.co.jp
Pharmaceuticals Product Mfr
N.A.I.C.S.: 325412

Plant (Domestic):

Kyowa Hakko Kirin Co., Ltd. - Fuji Plant (2)
1188 Shimotogari Nagaizumi-cho, Suntou-gun, Shizuoka, 411-8731, Japan
Tel.: (81) 55 986 7600
Web Site: http://www.kyowa-kirin.co.jp
Pharmaceuticals Product Mfr
N.A.I.C.S.: 325412

Kyowa Hakko Kirin Co., Ltd. - Sakai Plant (2)
1-1-53 Takasu-cho, Sakai-ku, Sakai, 590-8554, Osaka, Japan
Tel.: (81) 72 223 5554
Pharmaceuticals Product Mfr
N.A.I.C.S.: 325412

Kyowa Hakko Kirin Co., Ltd. - Takasaki Plant (2)
100-1 Hagiwaramachi, Takasaki, 370-0013, Gunma, Japan
Tel.: (81) 27 353 2011
Web Site: http://www.kyowa-kirin.co.jp
Sales Range: $100-124.9 Million
Emp.: 400
Pharmaceuticals Product Mfr
N.A.I.C.S.: 325412

Kyowa Hakko Kirin Co., Ltd. - Ube Plant (2)
2547-3 Fujimagari, Ube, 755-8501, Yamaguchi, Japan
Tel.: (81) 836 22 5508
Pharmaceuticals Product Mfr

INTERNATIONAL PUBLIC

N.A.I.C.S.: 325412

Subsidiary (Non-US):

Kyowa Hakko Kirin Korea Co., Ltd. (2)
5th Poonglim Bldg 124 Teheran-ro Gangnam-gu, 135-784, Seoul, Korea (South)
Tel.: (82) 234714321
Web Site: http://www.kyowa-kirin.com
Sales Range: $25-49.9 Million
Emp.: 60
Development & Marketing of Pharmaceutical Drugs
N.A.I.C.S.: 325412

Kyowa Hakko Kirin Korea Co., Ltd. (2)
5F Poonglim Bldg 124 Teheran-ro, Gangnam-gu, Seoul, 135-784, Korea (South)
Tel.: (82) 2 3471 4321
Web Site: http://www.kyowa-kirin.co.kr
Sales Range: $25-49.9 Million
Emp.: 73
Pharmaceuticals Product Mfr
N.A.I.C.S.: 325412
Hyung-Sik Won *(Gen Mgr)*

Subsidiary (US):

Kyowa Hakko Kirin Pharma, Inc. (2)
212 Carnegie Ctr Ste 101, Princeton, NJ 08540-6232
Tel.: (609) 919-1100
Web Site: http://www.kyowa-kpi.com
Pharmaceutical Developer & Mfr
N.A.I.C.S.: 325412
Takuma Nakamura *(Mgr-Project Mgmt)*

Subsidiary (Domestic):

BioWa, Inc. (3)
212 Carnegie Ctr Ste 400, Princeton, NJ 08540
Tel.: (609) 580-7340
Web Site: http://www.biowa.com
Biopharmaceutical Development Services
N.A.I.C.S.: 541714
Takeshi Masuda *(Pres & CEO)*

Hematech, Inc. (3)
4401 S Technology Dr, Sioux Falls, SD 57106
Tel.: (605) 361-6793
Sales Range: $25-49.9 Million
Emp.: 50
Pharmaceuticals Mfr
N.A.I.C.S.: 325412

Kyowa Kirin Pharmaceutical Research, Inc. (3)
9420 Athena Cir, La Jolla, CA 92037 **(100%)**
Tel.: (858) 952-7000
Web Site: http://www.kirinpharma-usa.com
Sales Range: Less than $1 Million
Emp.: 200
Pharmaceutical Products Research & Development
N.A.I.C.S.: 541715

Subsidiary (Non-US):

Kyowa Hakko Kirin U.K. Ltd. (2)
258 Bath Rd, Slough, SL1 4DX, Berks, United Kingdom
Tel.: (44) 1753566000
Sales Range: $25-49.9 Million
Emp.: 25
Pharmaceutical & Food Additive Developer & Mfr
N.A.I.C.S.: 325412

Subsidiary (US):

Kyowa Hakko U.S.A., Inc. (2)
600 3rd Ave 19th Fl, New York, NY 10016
Tel.: (212) 319-5353
Web Site: http://www.kyowa-usa.com
Sales Range: $25-49.9 Million
Emp.: 16
Pharmaceutical, Food Additive & Chemical Mfr & Distr
N.A.I.C.S.: 325412

Subsidiary (Domestic):

BioKyowa Inc. (3)

AND PRIVATE COMPANIES

5469 Nash Rd, Cape Girardeau, MO
63702-1550
Tel.: (573) 335-4849
Web Site: https://www.biokyowa.com
Sales Range: $25-49.9 Million
Acid Mfr
N.A.I.C.S.: 325194

Subsidiary (Non-US):

Kyowa Italiana Farmaceutici
S.R.L.   (2)
Viale Fulvio Testi 280, 20126, Milan, Italy
Tel.: (39) 026447041
Web Site: http://www.kyowa.it
Sales Range: $25-49.9 Million
Emp.: 20
Pharmaceuticals, Feed Additives & Chemical Developer, Mfr & Sales
N.A.I.C.S.: 325412

Subsidiary (Domestic):

Kyowa Medical Promotion Co.,
Ltd.   (2)
Riverside Yomiuri Building 36-2 Nihonbashi-Hakozaki-cho, Chuo-Ku, Tokyo, 103-0015,
Japan
Tel.: (81) 3 5641 8658
Pharmaceuticals Product Mfr
N.A.I.C.S.: 325412

Subsidiary (Non-US):

Orchard Therapeutics plc   (2)
108 Cannon Street, London, EC4N 6EU,
United Kingdom
Tel.: (44) 2038088286
Web Site: http://www.orchard-tx.com
Rev.: $22,655,000
Assets: $218,907,000
Liabilities: $120,643,000
Net Worth: $98,264,000
Earnings: ($150,660,000)
Emp.: 166
Fiscal Year-end: 12/31/2022
Biotechnology Research & Development
Services
N.A.I.C.S.: 541714
Frank E. Thomas (Pres & COO)

ProStrakan Group plc   (2)
Galabank Business Park, Galashiels, TD1
1QH, United Kingdom
Tel.: (44) 1896664000
Web Site: http://www.prostrakan.com
Sales Range: $150-199.9 Million
Emp.: 259
Specialty Pharmaceutical Products Mfr
N.A.I.C.S.: 325412

Subsidiary (Non-US):

Arzneimittel ProStrakan GmbH   (3)
C/o Thomas Merrifield, Moosst. 7, 82319,
Starnberg, Germany
Tel.: (49) 8151446900
Sales Range: $25-49.9 Million
Emp.: 30
Pharmaceuticals Mfr & Whslr
N.A.I.C.S.: 424210

Kyowa Hakko Kirin China Pharmaceutical Co., Ltd.   (3)
970 LongDong Road, Pudong New Area,
Shanghai, 201203, China
Tel.: (86) 21 5080 0909
Web Site: http://www.kyowa-kirin.com.cn
Emp.: 240
Pharmaceuticals Product Mfr
N.A.I.C.S.: 325412

ProStrakan AB   (3)
Gustavslundsvagen 143, 167 51, Bromma,
Sweden
Tel.: (46) 8 50 90 74 10
Emp.: 2
Pharmaceuticals Product Mfr
N.A.I.C.S.: 325412
Daniel Pintilie (Mng Dir)

ProStrakan Farmaceutica SLU   (3)
Ave de Burgos 17-1 Planta, 28036, Madrid,
Spain
Tel.: (34) 915343710
Sales Range: $25-49.9 Million
Emp.: 18
Pharmaceuticals Mfr & Whslr
N.A.I.C.S.: 424210

Subsidiary (US):

ProStrakan Inc   (3)
135 Rte 202/206 Ste 6, Bedminster, NJ
07921
Tel.: (908) 234-1096
Emp.: 20
Pharmaceuticals Mfr & Whslr
N.A.I.C.S.: 424210
Deborah Braccia (Dir-Medical Affairs-United
States)

Subsidiary (Domestic):

ProStrakan Ltd   (3)
Galabank Business Park, Galashiels, TD1
1QH, United Kingdom
Tel.: (44) 1896664000
Web Site: http://www.prostrakan.com
Sales Range: $25-49.9 Million
Emp.: 80
Pharmaceuticals Mfr & Whslr
N.A.I.C.S.: 424210

Subsidiary (Non-US):

ProStrakan Pharma BV   (3)
Herenweg 103 A4, 2105 ME, Heemstede,
Netherlands
Tel.: (31) 23 5298907
Web Site: http://www.prostrakan.nl
Pharmaceuticals Product Mfr
N.A.I.C.S.: 325412

ProStrakan Pharma GmbH   (3)
Monschauer Str 1, Dusseldorf, 40549, Germany
Tel.: (49) 211 416 119 0
Web Site: http://www.prostrakan.de
Pharmaceuticals Product Mfr
N.A.I.C.S.: 325412

Subsidiary (Domestic):

Strakan International Ltd   (3)
Galabank Business Park, Galashiels, TD1
1QH, United Kingdom
Tel.: (44) 1896664000
Web Site: http://www.prostrakan.com
Sales Range: $25-49.9 Million
Emp.: 100
Pharmaceuticals Mfr & Whslr
N.A.I.C.S.: 424210

Lion Pty. Ltd.   (1)
                                        (100%)
Tel.: (61) 293202200
Web Site: https://www.lionco.com
Sales Range: $1-4.9 Billion
Emp.: 8,000
Holding Company; Food & Beverage Mfr &
Distr
N.A.I.C.S.: 551112
Rob McKenzie (Dir-Tech & Grp Supply
Chain)

Subsidiary (Domestic):

Lion-Beer, Spirits & Wine Pty.
Ltd.   (2)
Level 7 68 York Street, Sydney, 2000,
NSW, Australia
Tel.: (61) 293202200
Web Site: http://www.lionco.com
Sales Range: $1-4.9 Billion
Emp.: 5,500
Holding Company; Breweries, Wineries,
Distilleries & Alcoholic Beverages Distr
N.A.I.C.S.: 551112

Subsidiary (Domestic):

Castlemaine Perkins Pty. Ltd.   (3)
185 Milton Road, Milton, 4064, QLD,
Australia   (100%)
Tel.: (61) 733617400
Web Site: http://www.lionco.com
Emp.: 300
Brewery & Beer Distr
N.A.I.C.S.: 312120

J. Boag & Son Pty. Limited   (3)
69 Esplanade, Launceston, 7250, TAS,
Australia   (100%)
Tel.: (61) 363326332
Web Site: http://www.boags.com.au
Sales Range: $75-99.9 Million
Emp.: 100
Beer Brewer & Whslr
N.A.I.C.S.: 312120
Rob Murray (CEO)

Lion Victoria Pty. Ltd.   (3)
1320 Malvern Road, Malvern, 3144, VIC,
Australia
Tel.: (61) 3 9277 5800
Beer Brewery & Whslr
N.A.I.C.S.: 312120

Little Creatures Brewing Pty Ltd   (3)
40 Mews Rd, Fremantle, 6160, WA, Australia
Tel.: (61) 86 215 1000
Web Site: https://littlecreatures.com.au
Sales Range: $25-49.9 Million
Brewery Services
N.A.I.C.S.: 312120

Subsidiary (US):

New Belgium Brewing Company,
Inc.   (3)
500 Linden, Fort Collins, CO 80524
Tel.: (970) 221-0524
Web Site: http://www.newbelgium.com
Rev.: $96,000,000
Emp.: 635
Brewery
N.A.I.C.S.: 312120
Kim Jordan (Founder & Chm)

Subsidiary (Domestic):

The South Australian Brewing Company Pty. Limited   (3)
107 Port Road, Thebarton, 5031, SA,
Australia   (100%)
Tel.: (61) 883548888
Web Site: http://www.lionco.com
Sales Range: $100-124.9 Million
Emp.: 150
Brewery & Beer Distr
N.A.I.C.S.: 312120

Tooheys Pty. Limited   (3)
29 Nyrang Street, Lidcombe, 2141, NSW,
Australia
Tel.: (61) 2 9647 9647
Beer Brewery & Whslr
N.A.I.C.S.: 312120

Myanmar Brewery Limited   (1)
No 221 12 12A Floor Sule Square Sule Pagoda Road, Yangon, Myanmar
Tel.: (95) 944 476 6640
Web Site: https://myanmar-brewery.com
Beer Mfr & Distr
N.A.I.C.S.: 312120
Hideki Mitsuhashi (Mng Dir)

Shinshu Beverage Co., Ltd.   (1)
6691 Imai Nakamichi, Matsumoto, 390-
1131, Nagano, Japan
Tel.: (81) 26 386 2288
Web Site: http://www.shinshu-
beverage.co.jp
Soft Drinks Mfr
N.A.I.C.S.: 312111

Siam Kirin Beverage Co., Ltd.   (1)
29th Fl Unit 2901 United Center Building
323 Silom Rd Silom, Bangrak, Bangkok,
10500, Thailand
Tel.: (66) 2 635 5310
Soft Drink Distr
N.A.I.C.S.: 424490
Noritsu Kikuchi (Pres)

Tokyo Kirin Beverage Service Co.,
Ltd.   (1)
1 Kandaizumicho Kandaizumicho Bldg 8f,
Chiyoda-Ku, Tokyo, 101-0024, Japan
Tel.: (81) 358211070
Emp.: 3
Alcoholic Beverages Mfr
N.A.I.C.S.: 312120

Vivax Co., Ltd.   (1)
9-7 Hashimotocho Anabuki Hiroshima Bldg
2f, Naka-Ku, Hiroshima, 730-0015, Japan
Tel.: (81) 822272751
Alcoholic Beverages Mfr
N.A.I.C.S.: 312120

KIRK KAPITAL A/S

Fjordenhus Havneoen 1, 7100, Vejle,
Denmark
Tel.: (45) 33 44 50 00
Web Site: http://www.kirkkapital.dk
Year Founded: 2007

Private Equity & Capital Investment
Services
N.A.I.C.S.: 523999
Kim Gulstad (CEO)

Subsidiaries:

Kirk Kapital AG   (1)
Grabenstrasse 19, CH 6340, Zug, Switzerland
Tel.: (41) 41 728 85 85
Private Equities & Fixed Income Products
N.A.I.C.S.: 523999
Soren Vad Sorensen (CEO)

Kirk Property A/S   (1)
Damhaven 5d, 7100, Vejle, Denmark
Tel.: (45) 33 44 50 00
Web Site: http://www.kirkkapital.dk
Emp.: 20
Property Management & Sales
N.A.I.C.S.: 531311
Bjarne Ammitzboll (Mng Dir)

KIRKBI A/S

Koldingvej 2, 7190, Billund, Denmark
Tel.: (45) 75338833
Web Site: http://www.kirkbi.com
Holding Company
N.A.I.C.S.: 551112
Kjeld Kirk Kristiansen (Chm)

Subsidiaries:

Armacell GmbH   (1)
Robert-Bosch-Strasse 10, 48153, Munster,
Germany
Tel.: (49) 25176030
Web Site: https://www.local.armacell.com
Emp.: 715
Engineered Foam Rubber & Technical Insulation Product Mfr
N.A.I.C.S.: 326150

BrainPOP LLC   (1)
71 W 23rd St 17th Fl, New York 10010
Tel.: (212) 574-6000
Child & Youth Services
N.A.I.C.S.: 624110
Avraham Kadar (Founder)

Dacta and Pitsco LLC   (1)
915 E Jefferson St, Pittsburg, KS 66762
Tel.: (800) 362-4308
Toy Distr
N.A.I.C.S.: 423920

Hotel Valbella Inn AG   (1)
Voa Selva 4, 7077, Valbella, Switzerland
Tel.: (41) 81 385 08 08
Hotel Operator
N.A.I.C.S.: 721110

INTERLEGO AG   (1)
Oberneuhofstrasse 3, Baar, 6340, Switzerland
Tel.: (41) 41 769 20 40
Emp.: 1
Toy Mfr
N.A.I.C.S.: 339930

KIRK AG   (1)
Bachtalen 33, 6332, Hagendorn, Switzerland
Tel.: (41) 41 767 44 77
Toy Mfr
N.A.I.C.S.: 339930

KIRK AG   (1)
Hilpertstrasse 1, 64295, Darmstadt, Germany
Tel.: (49) 615117700
Toy Distr
N.A.I.C.S.: 423920

KIRKBI Palac Karlin Property
s.r.o   (1)
Thamova 183/11, Karlin, Prague, 186 00,
Czech Republic
Tel.: (420) 224 041 111
Real Estate Investment Services
N.A.I.C.S.: 531210

KIRKBI Real Estate Investment
s.r.o   (1)
Italska 753/27, Vinohrady, Prague, 120 00,
Czech Republic
Tel.: (420) 221 593 111
Real Estate Investment Services

KIRKBI A/S

Kirkbi A/S—(Continued)
N.A.I.C.S.: 531210

LEGO A/S (1)
Aastvej 1, DK 7190, Billund, Denmark
Tel.: (45) 79506070
Web Site: http://www.lego.com
Rev.: $5,573,281,650
Assets: $4,821,927,750
Liabilities: $1,490,455,800
Net Worth: $3,331,471,950
Earnings: $1,236,839,400
Emp.: 17,385
Fiscal Year-end: 12/31/2018
Toy Building Blocks & Educational Toys Mfr;
Theme Park Owner & Operator
N.A.I.C.S.: 339930
Thomas Kirk Kristiansen *(Chm)*

Subsidiary (Non-US):

LEGO Australia Pty. Ltd. (2)
Level 2 1 Innovation Road, Macquarie Park, 2113, NSW, Australia
Tel.: (61) 2 9428 9666
Emp.: 70
Toy Distr
N.A.I.C.S.: 423920

LEGO Belgium n.v. (2)
Ruiterijschool 5, 2930, Brasschaat, Belgium
Tel.: (32) 3247 6186
Toy Distr
N.A.I.C.S.: 423920

LEGO Brand Retail S.A.S (2)
21 Rue Alsace, 92300, Levallois-Perret, France
Tel.: (33) 967210384
Toy Distr
N.A.I.C.S.: 423920

LEGO Canada Inc. (2)
25 Centurian Drive Suite 102, Markham, L3R 5N8, ON, Canada
Tel.: (905) 764-5346
Toy Distr
N.A.I.C.S.: 423920

LEGO Company Limited (2)
33 Bath Road, Slough, SL1 3UF, Berks, United Kingdom
Tel.: (44) 1753 495 000
Web Site: http://www.lego.com
Toy Distr
N.A.I.C.S.: 423920

LEGO Company Ltd. (2)
Rm 902 9/F Tower 1 The Gateway 25 Canton Road, Tsim Sha Tsui, Kowloon, China (Hong Kong)
Tel.: (852) 22627171
Toy Distr
N.A.I.C.S.: 423920

LEGO Education Europe Ltd. (2)
Longus House Newgate Row Eastgate Street, Chester, CH1 1ER, United Kingdom
Tel.: (44) 800 334 5346
Web Site: http://www.education.lego.com
Educational Support Services
N.A.I.C.S.: 611710
David Gregory *(Territory Mgr)*

LEGO GmbH (2)
Technopark II Werner-von-Siemens-Ring 14, 85630, Grasbrunn, Germany
Tel.: (49) 89 45 34 60
Web Site: http://www.legomen.de
Toy Distr
N.A.I.C.S.: 423920

LEGO Handelsgesells. GmbH (2)
Wintergasse 52 Auf der Schanz 2, 3002, Purkersdorf, Austria
Tel.: (43) 2231 62828
Toy Distr
N.A.I.C.S.: 423920

LEGO Hong Kong Limited (2)
Units 1607-11 16/F Miramar Tower 132 Nathan Road, Tsim Sha Tsui, Kowloon, China (Hong Kong)
Tel.: (852) 2366 1515
Toy Distr
N.A.I.C.S.: 423920
Yvonne Lam *(Mgr-Mktg)*

LEGO Hungaria Kft. (2)
Becsi ut 3-5 1/1, 1023, Budapest, Hungary
Tel.: (36) 1 326 01 02

Toy Distr
N.A.I.C.S.: 423920
Judit Sipos *(Country Mgr)*

LEGO Japan Ltd. (2)
Akasaka Garden City 2F 4-15-1, Akasaka Minato-ku, Tokyo, 107-0052, Japan
Tel.: (81) 3 6234 1806
N.A.I.C.S.: 423920
Ken Millhouse *(VP)*

LEGO Korea Co. Ltd. (2)
3F Youngnam Bldg, Yeoksam-dong Kangnam-ku, Seoul, Korea (South)
Tel.: (82) 2 511 6090
Toy Distr
N.A.I.C.S.: 423920

LEGO Manufacturing Kft. (2)
Debreceni U 342, 4400, Nyiregyhaza, Hungary
Tel.: (36) 42 505 000
Toy Distr
N.A.I.C.S.: 423920
Robert Papp *(Mgr-Moulding Quality)*

LEGO Mexico S.A. de C.V. (2)
Paseo Alexander Von Humboldt No 43 A Planta Baja Torre II, Lomas Verdes 3, Naucalpan, 53125, Estado de Mexico, Mexico
Tel.: (52) 55 5358 4063
Toy Distr
N.A.I.C.S.: 423920
Ana Isabel Garcia Lozano *(Mgr-Procurement)*

LEGO New Zealand Ltd. (2)
Level 5 Suite 2 27 Gillies Avenue, Newmarket, Auckland, 1023, New Zealand
Tel.: (64) 9 573 1501
Toy Distr
N.A.I.C.S.: 423920

LEGO Norge A/S (2)
Vollsveien 19, 1366, Lysaker, Norway
Tel.: (47) 80 03 51 44
Toy Distr
N.A.I.C.S.: 423920

LEGO Operaciones de Mexico S.A. de C.V. (2)
Boulevard Nexxus ADN 2400, Cienega de Flores, 65550, Nuevo Leon, Mexico
Tel.: (52) 81 8047 8000
Toy Distr
N.A.I.C.S.: 423920
Gerardo Moreno *(Coord-Production)*

LEGO Park Holding UK Ltd. (2)
Midsummer Place 15, Milton Keynes, MK9 3GB, United Kingdom
Tel.: (44) 1908234960
Holding Company
N.A.I.C.S.: 551112

Subsidiary (Domestic):

LEGO Lifestyle International Ltd. (3)
Unit L21 Lower Rose Gallery, Greenhithe, DA9 9SH, United Kingdom
Tel.: (44) 132 242 7272
Toy Distr
N.A.I.C.S.: 423920

Subsidiary (Non-US):

LEGO Polska Sp. z.o.o. (2)
Ul Woloska 22A, 02-675, Warsaw, Poland
Tel.: (48) 22 278 86 00
Toy Distr
N.A.I.C.S.: 423920
Sebastian Szwaczka *(Acct Mgr)*

LEGO Production s.r.o. (2)
Billundska 2757 GSC House, 272 01, Kladno, Czech Republic
Tel.: (420) 312 778 111
Toy Distr
N.A.I.C.S.: 423920

LEGO S.A. (2)
Orense 34 - Pta 6, 28020, Madrid, Spain
Tel.: (34) 91 417 5963
Toy Distr
N.A.I.C.S.: 423920

LEGO S.A.S. (2)
15/17 rue Vivienne, 75002, Paris, France
Tel.: (33) 1 56 43 83 00
Toy Distr
N.A.I.C.S.: 423920

LEGO S.p.A. (2)
Viale dell Industria 2, 36100, Vicenza, Italy
Tel.: (39) 0444564622
Web Site: http://www.legogroup.it
Building Brick & Construction Toy Model Distr
N.A.I.C.S.: 423920

LEGO Singapore Pte. Ltd. (2)
38 Beach Road Ste 13-11 South Beach Tower, Singapore, 189767, Singapore
Tel.: (65) 6933 6888
Web Site: http://www.lego.com
Toy Distr
N.A.I.C.S.: 423920

LEGO South Africa (Pty.) Ltd. (2)
Corner 14th Avenue & Hendrik Potgieter Street, Ground Floor Lakeview House Constantia Park, Roodepoort, 1709, Gauteng, South Africa
Tel.: (27) 11 475 5977
Toy Distr
N.A.I.C.S.: 423920

Subsidiary (Domestic):

LEGO Systems A/S (2)
Aastvej 1, DK 7190, Billund, Denmark
Tel.: (45) 79506070
Web Site: http://www.lego.com
Sales Range: $400-449.9 Million
Emp.: 2,300
Distribution/Marketing of Toys & Models
N.A.I.C.S.: 459120
Jorgen Vig Knudstorp *(CEO)*

Subsidiary (Domestic):

LEGO Systems (3)
Klovermarken 29, 7190, Billund, Denmark
Tel.: (45) 79506070
Web Site: http://www.lego.com
Sales Range: $125-149.9 Million
Emp.: 380
Marketing/Distribution of Toys & Models
N.A.I.C.S.: 459120

Subsidiary (US):

LEGO Systems, Inc. (2)
555 Taylor Rd, Enfield, CT 06082
Tel.: (860) 749-2291
Web Site: http://www.lego.com
Sales Range: $100-124.9 Million
Emp.: 500
Children's Building Sets & Scientific Models Mfr
N.A.I.C.S.: 339930
Jorgen Vig Knudstorp *(CEO)*

Subsidiary (Domestic):

LEGO Brand Retail Inc. (3)
2601 Preston Rd Ste 1222, Frisco, TX 75034
Tel.: (972) 668-4648
Toy Distr
N.A.I.C.S.: 423920

Subsidiary (Non-US):

LEGO Toy Co., Ltd. (2)
Floor 45 1010 Middle Huaihai Road, Xuhui District, Shanghai, 200031, China
Tel.: (86) 21 3339 4888
Toy Distr
N.A.I.C.S.: 423920
Yuqing Michelle Sun *(Project Mgr)*

LEGO Toy Manufacturing Co., Ltd. (2)
Floor 27 No 2237 South Zhong Huan Road, 314000, Jiaxing, Zhejiang, China
Tel.: (86) 573 82601200
Toy Distr
N.A.I.C.S.: 423920

LEGO Trading CO Ltd. (2)
Room 1904 Floor 19 Building 3 Block 2 Jianguomenwai Street, Chaoyang District, Beijing, China
Tel.: (86) 10 8588 4700
Web Site: http://www.lego.com
Toy Distr
N.A.I.C.S.: 423920

LEGO Trading s.r.o. (2)
U Nakladoveho nadrazi 10, 130 00, Prague, Czech Republic
Tel.: (420) 246 086 911

INTERNATIONAL PUBLIC

Toy Distr
N.A.I.C.S.: 423920

OOO LEGO (2)
Sadovaya-Somotechnayan Street 24/27, Mosenka Plaza 4th Floor, 127051, Moscow, Russia
Tel.: (7) 495 775 4900
Toy Distr
N.A.I.C.S.: 423920

Oy Suomen LEGO Ab (2)
Italahdenkatu 15-17, 00210, Helsinki, Finland
Tel.: (358) 10 3093 220
Toy Distr
N.A.I.C.S.: 423920

LEGO Company Limited (1)
8-10 New Fetter Lane, London, EC4A 1AZ, United Kingdom
Tel.: (44) 1753495000
Toy Distr
N.A.I.C.S.: 423920

Minimax Viking GmbH (1)
Industriestrasse 10/12, Bad Oldesloe, 23840, Germany
Tel.: (49) 4531 803 0
Sales Range: $1-4.9 Billion
Emp.: 6,000
Fire Protection & Life Safety Systems Equipment Mfr
N.A.I.C.S.: 333310
Klaus Hofmann *(CEO)*

Subsidiary (US):

Consolidated Fire Protection, LLC (2)
153 Technology Dr Ste 200, Irvine, CA 92618
Tel.: (949) 727-3277
Web Site: http://www.cfpfire.com
Fire Protection & Life Safety Systems & Services
N.A.I.C.S.: 561790
Keith Fielding *(Pres)*

Subsidiary (Domestic):

Cosco Fire Protection, LLC (3)
1075 W Lambert Rd Bldg D, Brea, CA 92821-2944
Tel.: (714) 989-1800
Web Site: https://www.coscofire.com
Sales Range: $75-99.9 Million
Emp.: 100
Fire Protection Systems
N.A.I.C.S.: 922160

Firetrol Protection Systems, Inc. (3)
3696 W 900 S Ste A, Salt Lake City, UT 84104
Tel.: (801) 485-6900
Web Site: https://www.firetrol.net
Sales Range: $1-9.9 Million
Emp.: 35
Fire Sprinkler System Installation
N.A.I.C.S.: 922160
John White *(Pres)*

Subsidiary (US):

FLAMEX, Inc. (2)
4365 Federal Dr, Greensboro, NC 27410
Tel.: (336) 299-2933
Web Site: https://www.sparkdetection.com
Sales Range: $25-49.9 Million
Emp.: 15
Fire Prevention Equipment Supplier
N.A.I.C.S.: 423720

Subsidiary (Domestic):

Minimax GmbH & Co, KG (2)
Industriestrasse 10/12, 23840, Bad Oldesloe, Germany
Tel.: (49) 45318030
Web Site: http://www.minimax.com
Sales Range: $1-4.9 Billion
Stationary & Mobile Fire Protection Systems Mfr
N.A.I.C.S.: 333310
Volker Bechtloff *(Chm & Mng Dir)*

Subsidiary (Non-US):

Pefipresa S.A. (3)
C/ San Cesareo 22, Poligono Industrial Villaverde, 28021, Madrid, Spain

AND PRIVATE COMPANIES

Tel.: (34) 917109000
Web Site: http://www.pefipresa.com
Fire Protection Systems Mfr
N.A.I.C.S.: 922160

Subsidiary (US):

Viking Group, Inc. (2)
5150 Beltway Dr SE, Caledonia, MI 49316
Tel.: (269) 945-9501
Web Site: http://www.vikinggroupinc.com
Sales Range: $450-499.9 Million
Emp.: 300
Fire Protection Products Mfr
N.A.I.C.S.: 333310
Jeff Norton (VP-Mktg)

KIRKLAND LAKE DISCOVERIES CORP
25 Adelaide Street East Suite 1400, Toronto, M5C 3A1, ON, Canada
Tel.: (416) 414-7011
Web Site:
  https://kirklandlakediscoveries.com
KLKLF—(OTCIQ)
Rev.: $57
Assets: $9,959,580
Liabilities: $308,221
Net Worth: $9,651,358
Earnings: ($2,803,852)
Fiscal Year-end: 03/31/24
Mineral Exploration Services
N.A.I.C.S.: 213114
Paul A. Carroll (Chm)

KIRLOSKAR BROTHERS LIMITED
Yamuna Survey No 98 3-7 Baner Plot No 3, Pune, 411 045, Maharashtra, India
Tel.: (91) 2067214444 In
Web Site:
  http://www.kirloskarpumps.com
500241—(NSE)
Rev.: $378,142,278
Assets: $370,540,730
Liabilities: $219,402,401
Net Worth: $151,138,328
Earnings: $21,941,747
Emp.: 2,487
Fiscal Year-end: 03/31/21
Pumps
N.A.I.C.S.: 336320
Sandeep A. Phadnis (Compliance Officer & Sec)

Subsidiaries:

Braybar Pumps (Proprietary) Limited (1)
Cnr Horne St and Brine Ave Chloorkop Ext 23, Kempton Park, 1620, Gauteng, South Africa
Tel.: (27) 113937177
Industrial Valve Mfr
N.A.I.C.S.: 332911

Karad Projects & Motors Limited (1)
Plot B-67 and 68 MIDC Karad Industrial Area Taswade, Karad, Satara, 415 109, Maharashtra, India
Tel.: (91) 2164258425
Web Site: https://www.kpml.co.in
Metal Stamping Mfr
N.A.I.C.S.: 336370
K. Taranath (Chm)

Kirloskar Brothers (Thailand) Limited (1)
Amata Nakorn Industrial Estate 700/ 711 Moo 1, Phan Thong, Chon Buri, 20160, Thailand
Tel.: (66) 266182724
Web Site: https://kirloskarthailand.com
Industrial Valve Mfr
N.A.I.C.S.: 332911

Kirloskar Brothers Investments Limited (1)
13/A Karve Road, Kothrud, Pune, 411 038, India
Tel.: (91) 20 25453002
Web Site: http://www.kbil.co.in
Investment Management Service
N.A.I.C.S.: 523999

Kirloskar Brothers Ltd - Kondhapuri Works Manufacturing Plant (1)
Gat No 252/2 254/2 Kondhapuri, Tal Shirur Dist, Pune, 412 208, Maharashtra, India
Tel.: (91) 2137240021
Web Site: http://www.kirloskarpumps.com
Sales Range: $25-49.9 Million
Pump Mfr & Whslr
N.A.I.C.S.: 333914

Kirloskar Brothers Ltd - Shirwal Works Manufacturing Plant (1)
Gat No 117 Shindevadi Tal, Khandala, Satara, 412 801, Maharashtra, India
Tel.: (91) 2169244360
Sales Range: $25-49.9 Million
Pump Mfr & Whslr
N.A.I.C.S.: 333914

Kirloskar Constructions & Engineers Limited (1)
Janpriya Crest 3rd Fl 113 Pantheon Rd, Egmore, Chennai, 600008, Tamil Nadu, India
Tel.: (91) 4428195544
Web Site: http://www.kirloskarcel.com
Sales Range: $25-49.9 Million
Emp.: 70
Engineering & Construction Services
N.A.I.C.S.: 541330

Kirloskar Corrocoat Private Limited (1)
Udyog Bhavan Tilak Road, Pune, 411 002, India
Tel.: (91) 9881231135
Web Site: https://www.kicopl.com
Poly Glass Mfr
N.A.I.C.S.: 327215
Alok Kirloskar (Chm)

Kirloskar Pompen B.V. (1)
Twentepoort Oost 24, PO Box 134, 7609 RG, Almelo, Netherlands
Tel.: (31) 850495900
Industrial Valve Mfr
N.A.I.C.S.: 332911

Rodelta Pumps International B.V. (1)
Twentepoort Oost 24, 7609 RG, Almelo, Netherlands
Tel.: (31) 850495900
Web Site: https://www.rodelta.com
Pumps Mfr
N.A.I.C.S.: 333914

Rotaserve B.V. (1)
Twentepoort Oost 24, 7609 RG, Almelo, Netherlands
Tel.: (31) 850495999
Web Site: https://www.rotaserve.com
Pump Maintaining Services
N.A.I.C.S.: 811310

SPP Pumps (Asia) Co. Limited (1)
50 Sukhumvit 21 Road Asoke GMM Grammy Place Office Building, 18 Floor Unit 1805 Khlongtoey-nua, Bangkok, 10110, Thailand
Tel.: (66) 266182724
Pumps Mfr
N.A.I.C.S.: 333914

SPP Pumps (South Africa) (Pty). Limited (1)
Cnr Brine Avenue and Horn Street Chloorkop Ext 1, Kempton Park, 1619, Gauteng, South Africa
Tel.: (27) 113937177
Industrial Valve Mfr
N.A.I.C.S.: 332911
Richard Hose (Product Mgr-Fire)

SPP Pumps Limited (1)
1420 Lakeview Arlington Business Park, Theale, Reading, RG7 4SA, Berkshire, United Kingdom
Tel.: (44) 1189323123
Pumps Mfr
N.A.I.C.S.: 333914

SPP Pumps MENA LLC (1)
Block 234 Road 36 Industrial Zone 3, Mena Egypt Service Center, 6th of October City, Egypt
Tel.: (20) 238206250
Pumps Mfr
N.A.I.C.S.: 333914

KIRMAC AUTOMOTIVE COLLISION SYSTEMS INC.

Mohamed Hassan (Gen Mgr)

SyncroFlo, Inc. (1)
2905 Pacific Dr, Norcross, GA 30071
Tel.: (770) 447-4443
Web Site: https://www.syncroflo.com
Plumbing System Assembling Services
N.A.I.C.S.: 238220
John Kahren (Pres)

The Kolhapur Steel Limited (1)
Pune Bangalore Highway Shiroli Pulachi, Tal Hatkanangale, Kolhapur, 416 122, Maharashtra, India
Tel.: (91) 2302468061
Web Site: https://www.kolhapursteel.com
Steel Mfrs
N.A.I.C.S.: 331110
Ravindra Samant (Mng Dir)

KIRLOSKAR ELECTRIC COMPANY LTD
No 19 2nd Main Road Peenya 1st Stage Phase-1 Peenya, Bengaluru, 560 058, Karnataka, India
Tel.: (91) 8028397256
Web Site: https://kirloskarelectric.com
533193—(NSE)
Rev.: $59,445,033
Assets: $73,431,365
Liabilities: $62,415,934
Net Worth: $11,015,431
Earnings: $3,725,712
Emp.: 944
Fiscal Year-end: 03/31/23
Motor Generators Mfr
N.A.I.C.S.: 335312
Vijay R. Kirloskar (Chm)

KIRLOSKAR INDUSTRIES LIMITED
Office No 801 8th Floor Cello Platina Fergusson College Road, Shivajinagar, Pune, 411 005, India
Tel.: (91) 2029704374 In
Web Site:
  https://www.kirloskarindustries.com
Year Founded: 1978
KIRLOSIND—(NSE)
Rev.: $284,229,855
Assets: $436,281,300
Liabilities: $131,221,545
Net Worth: $305,059,755
Earnings: $42,512,925
Emp.: 14
Fiscal Year-end: 03/31/21
Wind Power Generation & Investment
N.A.I.C.S.: 221118
Aditi V. Chirmule (Exec Dir)

Subsidiaries:

Kirloskar Ferrous Industries Ltd. (1)
13 Laxmanrao Kirloskar Road Khadki, Pune, 411003, Maharashtra, India
Tel.: (91) 8725060021
Web Site: https://www.kirloskarferrous.com
Rev.: $775,346,802
Assets: $657,215,994
Liabilities: $296,508,603
Net Worth: $360,707,392
Earnings: $52,434,506
Emp.: 1,385
Fiscal Year-end: 03/31/2023
Iron Foundry Operator
N.A.I.C.S.: 331511
Atul Chandrakant Kirloskar (Chm)

KIRLOSKAR OIL ENGINES LIMITED
Laxmanrao Kirloskar Road, Khadki, Pune, 411 003, India
Tel.: (91) 2025810341 In
Web Site:
  https://www.kirloskaroilengines.com
Year Founded: 1946
KIRLOSENG—(NSE)
Rev.: $552,648,915
Assets: $686,650,965
Liabilities: $402,500,280
Net Worth: $284,150,685
Earnings: $23,323,755
Emp.: 2,184
Fiscal Year-end: 03/31/22
Diesel Engine & Engine Components Mfr
N.A.I.C.S.: 336310
Rajendra R. Deshpande (CEO & Co-Mng Dir)

Subsidiaries:

Arka Fincap Limited (1)
2504 One Lodha Place Senapati Bapat Marg, Lower Parel, Mumbai, 400013, Maharashtra, India
Tel.: (91) 2240471000
Web Site: https://www.arkaholdings.com
Financial Services
N.A.I.C.S.: 541611

La-Gajjar Machineries Private Limited (1)
Acidwala Estate Nagarwel Hanuman Road, Amraiwadi, Ahmedabad, 380 026, Gujarat, India
Tel.: (91) 7922777485
Stainless Steel Pump Mfr
N.A.I.C.S.: 333996

Optiqua Pipes and Electricals Private Limited (1)
Sr No 298/P & 375/P-1 Panchratna Ind Estate Tal Sanand, Changodar, Ahmedabad, 382213, Gujarat, India
Tel.: (91) 7935019700
Web Site: https://www.optiquaindia.com
Pipe & Pump Mfr
N.A.I.C.S.: 339992

KIRLOSKAR PNEUMATIC CO. LTD.
Plot No 1 Hadapsar Industrial Estate, Pune, 411 013, Maharastra, India
Tel.: (91) 2026727000
Web Site:
  https://www.kirloskarpneumatic.com
KIRLPNU—(NSE)
Rev.: $151,563,509
Assets: $136,898,430
Liabilities: $40,523,584
Net Worth: $96,374,846
Earnings: $13,160,017
Emp.: 749
Fiscal Year-end: 03/31/23
Air Compressors & Pneumatic Tools Mfrs
N.A.I.C.S.: 333912
Rahul C. Kirloskar (Chm)

Subsidiaries:

Joburg Industrial Trading S.A. (Pty) Ltd. (1)
The Stable Business Park 13 Third Road Linbro, Johannesburg, 2090, South Africa
Industrial Equipment Mfr
N.A.I.C.S.: 333248

Kirloskar DMCC (1)
JBC-5 Cluster W Jumeirah Lake Towers and, PO Box 37745, Dubai, United Arab Emirates
Tel.: (971) 44438591
Industrial Equipment Mfr
N.A.I.C.S.: 333248

Kirloskar South East Asia Co. Ltd. (1)
No 54 Room no 1008 BB Building Sukhumvit 21 Asoke Road, Klongtoey Nuea Wattana, Bangkok, 10110, Thailand
Tel.: (66) 20721008
Industrial Equipment Mfr
N.A.I.C.S.: 333248

KIRMAC AUTOMOTIVE COLLISION SYSTEMS INC.
104-2714 Barnet Highway, Coquitlam, V3B 1B8, BC, Canada
Tel.: (604) 464-6404
Web Site: https://www.kirmac.com
Year Founded: 1973
Emp.: 180

KIRMAC AUTOMOTIVE COLLISION SYSTEMS INC.

Kirmac Automotive Collision Systems Inc.—(Continued)
Automotive Body & Paint Repair Center Operator
N.A.I.C.S.: 811121
Ian McIntosh *(Founder)*

KIRSCH PHARMA GMBH
Erzwasche 2, 38229, Salzgitter, Germany
Tel.: (49) 534187971
Web Site: http://www.kirschpharma.com
Year Founded: 1980
Sales Range: $25-49.9 Million
Emp.: 150
Medical Equipment Mfr
N.A.I.C.S.: 339112
Heinz-Jurgen Kirsch *(Owner & Mng Dir)*

Subsidiaries:

Kirsch Pharma Asia Pacific Pte. Ltd. (1)
3 International Business Park 03-07 Nordic European Centre, Singapore, 609927, Singapore
Tel.: (65) 68906666
Pharmaceutical Products Distr
N.A.I.C.S.: 424210
Esther Low *(Mng Dir)*

Kirsch Pharma Australia Pty. Ltd. (1)
Pacific View Business Park 6/10 Rodborough Road, Frenchs Forest, Sydney, 2086, NSW, Australia
Tel.: (61) 299755999
Pharmaceutical Products Distr
N.A.I.C.S.: 424210
Frank Schlueter *(Mng Dir)*

Kirsch Pharma Espana SL (1)
Via Augusta 59 Despacho 807, 08006, Barcelona, Spain
Tel.: (34) 934157001
Pharmaceutical Products Distr
N.A.I.C.S.: 424210

Kirsch Pharma Shanghai Co., Ltd. (1)
Office 733 Tower 2 88 Keyuan Road, Pudong Dist, Shanghai, China
Tel.: (86) 2128986188
Pharmaceutical Products Distr
N.A.I.C.S.: 424210
Yimei Song *(Gen Mgr)*

Kirsch Pharma South Africa (Pty.) Ltd. (1)
Isando Industrial Park Mini Unit 6 Gewel Street, Isando, Johannesburg, South Africa
Tel.: (27) 113925171
Pharmaceutical Products Distr
N.A.I.C.S.: 424210
Hermann Broschk *(Mng Dir)*

KIRTI INVESTMENTS LIMITED
Prestige Precinct 3rd Floor Almeida Road, Panchpakhadi, Thane, 400601, Maharashtra, India
Tel.: (91) 2225985900   In
KIRTIINV—(NSE)
Financial Services
N.A.I.C.S.: 523999

KIS PARTNERS AS
Solbraveien 15, 1383, Asker, Norway
Tel.: (47) 48999997   NO
Web Site: http://www.kis.no
Year Founded: 2012
Holding Company
N.A.I.C.S.: 551112
Jan Sanne *(Chm)*

Subsidiaries:

Kis AS (1)
Solbraveien 15, 1383, Asker, Norway
Tel.: (47) 48 999997
Web Site: http://www.kis.no
Cranes & Lifting Equipment Inspection & Maintenance Services
N.A.I.C.S.: 811310

Jan Sanne *(Mng Dir)*
Subsidiary (Non-US):

Primoteq B.V. (2)
Parallelweg LS 2a, 7553 LG, Hengelo, Netherlands
Tel.: (31) 74 240 3800
Web Site: http://www.primoteq.com
Sales Range: $25-49.9 Million
Emp.: 100
Production Equipment Mfr
N.A.I.C.S.: 811310
Hans Flef *(Mng Dir)*

KISAN MOULDINGS LTD.
Tex Centre K-Wing 3rd Floor 26 A Chandivali Road Andheri East, Mumbai, 400 072, India
Tel.: (91) 2242009200
Web Site: https://www.kisangroup.com
Year Founded: 1982
530145—(BOM)
Rev.: $42,434,478
Assets: $46,442,241
Liabilities: $47,714,640
Net Worth: ($1,272,398)
Earnings: ($11,614,294)
Emp.: 486
Fiscal Year-end: 03/31/22
Industrial Piping Products Mfr
N.A.I.C.S.: 332919
Sanjeev Amarnath Aggarwal *(Chm & Mng Dir)*

KISAN TELECOM CO., LTD.
11F 111 Ogeum-ro, Songpa-Gu, Seoul, 05548, Korea (South)
Tel.: (82) 234338200
Web Site: https://www.kisantel.co.kr
Year Founded: 1994
035460—(KRS)
Rev.: $52,004,623
Assets: $57,102,106
Liabilities: $26,673,084
Net Worth: $30,429,023
Earnings: $2,324,298
Emp.: 61
Fiscal Year-end: 12/31/22
Telecommunication Servicesb
N.A.I.C.S.: 517111

Subsidiaries:

Kisan Telecom Co., Ltd. - Sungnam Plant (1)
4 5 F Joongang induspia-A 517-13 Sangdaewon 1Dong, Joongwon-gu, Seongnam, 462-121, Kyunggi-Do, Korea (South)
Tel.: (82) 31 740 9855
Communication Equipment Mfr
N.A.I.C.S.: 334210

KISCO HOLDINGS CORP.
12 Gongdan-ro 103beon-gil, Seongsan-gu, Changwon, 642-370, Gyeongsangnam-do, Korea (South)
Tel.: (82) 552600500
Web Site: https://www.kiscoholdings.co.kr
Year Founded: 1957
001940—(KRS)
Rev.: $1,388,740,513
Assets: $1,331,463,340
Liabilities: $183,880,262
Net Worth: $1,147,583,078
Earnings: $61,202,626
Emp.: 37
Fiscal Year-end: 12/31/22
Holding Company
N.A.I.C.S.: 551112
Byungje Lee *(CEO)*

Subsidiaries:

Hwan Young Steel Ind, Co., Ltd. (1)
587 Bodeokpro-ro Seokmun-Myun, Dangjin, Chungcheongnam, Korea (South)
Tel.: (82) 413502500
Web Site: http://www.ehansco.co.kr
Steel Mfrs
N.A.I.C.S.: 331110
Chul Gi-Jung *(CEO)*

KISCO Corp. (1)
572 Gonghang-daero, Seongsan-gu, Changwon, 642-370, Gyeongsangnam-do, Korea (South)
Tel.: (82) 552600500
Web Site: https://www.kisco.co.kr
Rev.: $816,223,383
Assets: $719,947,470
Liabilities: $113,312,919
Net Worth: $606,634,551
Earnings: $61,195,518
Emp.: 353
Fiscal Year-end: 12/31/2022
Steel Products Mfr
N.A.I.C.S.: 331110
Jong In Moon *(Co-CEO)*

KISCO LTD.
3-3-7 Fushimimachi, Chuo-ku, Osaka, 541-8513, Japan
Tel.: (81) 6 6203 5651
Web Site: http://www.kisco-net.com
Year Founded: 1921
Emp.: 273
Industrial Chemicals, Equipment & Processed Goods Mfr
N.A.I.C.S.: 424690
Takekazu Kishimoto *(Pres)*

Subsidiaries:

Specialty Coating Systems, Inc. (1)
7645 Woodland Dr, Indianapolis, IN 46278
Tel.: (317) 451-8549
Web Site: http://www.scscoatings.com
Sales Range: $10-24.9 Million
Emp.: 45
Specialty Coating Services
N.A.I.C.S.: 332812
Terry Bush *(Pres & CEO)*

KISMET ACQUISITION ONE CORP.
9 Building B Lesnaya Street, Moscow, 125196, Russia
Tel.: (7) 4997552134   VG
Year Founded: 2020
KSMTU—(NASDAQ)
Sales Range: Less than $1 Million
Investment Services
N.A.I.C.S.: 523999

KISMET RESOURCES CORP.
460-688 West Hastings Street, Vancouver, V6B 1P1, BC, Canada
Tel.: (604) 220-4691
KSMT.P—(TSXV)
Assets: $111,472
Liabilities: $6,293
Net Worth: $105,178
Earnings: ($33,998)
Fiscal Year-end: 12/31/19
Business Consulting Services
N.A.I.C.S.: 522299

KISOJI CO., LTD.
18-13 Shirokane 3-chome, Showa-ku, Nagoya, 466-8507, Aichi, Japan
Tel.: (81) 528721811   JP
Web Site: https://www.kisoji.co.jp
Year Founded: 1952
8160—(TKS)
Rev.: $350,224,240
Assets: $303,888,140
Liabilities: $121,075,370
Net Worth: $182,812,770
Earnings: $2,881,960
Emp.: 1,305
Fiscal Year-end: 03/31/24
Restaurant Operators
N.A.I.C.S.: 722511
Motoyuki Yoshie *(Pres)*

KISSEI PHARMACEUTICAL CO. LTD.
19-48 Yoshino, Matsumoto, 399-8710, Nagano, Japan
Tel.: (81) 263259081
Web Site: https://www.kissei.co.jp
4547—(TKS)
Rev.: $499,577,190
Assets: $1,724,740,690
Liabilities: $263,031,730
Net Worth: $1,461,708,960
Earnings: $73,767,600
Emp.: 1,333
Fiscal Year-end: 03/31/24
Pharmaceutical Products Mfr & Sales
N.A.I.C.S.: 325412
Yoshio Furihata *(Pres & COO)*

Subsidiaries:

Kissei Comtec Co., Ltd. (1)
Wada 4010-10, Matsumoto, 390-1293, Nagano, Japan
Tel.: (81) 263401122
Web Site: http://www.kicnet.co.jp
Sales Range: $25-49.9 Million
Emp.: 346
System Integration Services
N.A.I.C.S.: 541512

KISTEFOS AS
Dokkveien 1, 0250, Oslo, Norway
Tel.: (47) 23117000   NO
Web Site: http://www.kistefos.no
Investment Holding Company
N.A.I.C.S.: 551112
Christen Sveaas *(Owner & Chm)*

Subsidiaries:

Advanzia Bank S.A. (1)
9 rue Gabriel Lippmann, 5365, Munsbach, Luxembourg (59.5%)
Tel.: (352) 26 387 500
Web Site: http://www.advanzia.com
Banking Services
N.A.I.C.S.: 522210
Eirik Holtedahl *(CFO & Deputy CEO)*

Atex Group Ltd. (1)
100 Longwater Avenue, GreenPark, Reading, RG2 6GP, Berks, United Kingdom (85.3%)
Tel.: (44) 1189450128
Web Site: http://www.atex.com
Sales Range: $100-124.9 Million
Media Company Advertising, Subscription, Print & Digital Content Management Services
N.A.I.C.S.: 561499
Jeremy Wilson *(CFO)*

Subsidiary (US):

Kaango, LLC (2)
5613 DTC Pkwy Ste 950, Greenwood Village, CO 80111
Tel.: (303) 339-3844
Web Site: http://www.kaango.com
Online Classified Ad Services
N.A.I.C.S.: 513199

Bergmoen AS (1)
Vilbergveien 101, 2060, Gardermoen, Norway
Tel.: (47) 995 22 696
Web Site: http://www.bergmoen.no
Industrial Building Construction Services
N.A.I.C.S.: 236210
Rolf Hansteen *(Mng Dir)*

Bulk Invest ASA (1)
Henrik Ibsensgt 100, PO Box 2868, Solli, 0230, Oslo, Norway (60.4%)
Tel.: (47) 2313 3400
Emp.: 118
Freight Transportation
N.A.I.C.S.: 483111
Jens Ismar *(CEO)*

NextGenTel Holding ASA (1)
Harbitzalleen 2A, 0275, Oslo, Norway
Tel.: (47) 21964909
Web Site: http://www.nextgentelholding.com
Rev.: $154,404,546
Assets: $81,196,736
Liabilities: $69,726,631
Net Worth: $11,470,105
Earnings: ($6,994,963)
Emp.: 252

AND PRIVATE COMPANIES

Fiscal Year-end: 12/31/2017
Communication Service
N.A.I.C.S.: 517111
Eirik Lunde (CEO)

Subsidiary (Domestic):

NextGenTel AS (2)
Sandslimarka 31, 5254, Sandsli, Norway
Tel.: (47) 55 52 79 00
Web Site: http://www.nextgentel.no
Sales Range: $100-124.9 Million
Emp.: 300
Broadband Services
N.A.I.C.S.: 517810
Jorn Hodne (COO)

Subsidiary (Non-US):

Telio IP Services BV (2)
Prins Bernhardplein 200, 1097 JB, Amsterdam, Netherlands
Tel.: (31) 205214777
Telecommunication Servicesb
N.A.I.C.S.: 517111

Telio Netherlands BV (2)
Veemkade 540, 1097, Amsterdam, North Holland, Netherlands
Tel.: (31) 320750400
Web Site: http://www.telio.de
Sales Range: $25-49.9 Million
Emp.: 10
Telecommunication Servicesb
N.A.I.C.S.: 517112

Telio SA (2)
Thurgauerstrasse 40, 8050, Zurich, Switzerland
Tel.: (41) 443073626
Web Site: http://www.telioholding.no
Sales Range: $25-49.9 Million
Emp.: 15
Telecommunication Servicesb
N.A.I.C.S.: 517111

Subsidiary (Domestic):

Telio Telecom AS (2)
PO Box 54, Skoyen, 0212, Oslo, Norway
Tel.: (47) 21496565
Web Site: http://www.teliotelecom.no
Telecommunication Servicesb
N.A.I.C.S.: 517112

Subsidiary (Non-US):

Tellio ApS (2)
Vesterbrogade 149, 1620, Copenhagen, Denmark
Tel.: (45) 70807025
Web Site: http://www.tellio.dk
Sales Range: $25-49.9 Million
Emp.: 12
Telecommunication Servicesb
N.A.I.C.S.: 517112

Opplysningen 1881 AS (1)
Sigurd Syrs gate 2, 0273, Oslo, Norway (100%)
Tel.: (47) 81 58 18 81
Web Site: http://www.opplysningen.no
Publishing Services
N.A.I.C.S.: 513199
Jan Erik Sorgaard (CEO)

OstomyCure AS (1)
Gaustadalleen 21, 0349, Oslo, Norway (66.6%)
Tel.: (47) 22 95 85 00
Web Site: http://www.ostomycure.com
Medical Technology Development Services
N.A.I.C.S.: 541715
Benedict Broennimann (CEO)

Viking Supply Ships AB (1)
Idrottsvagen 1, 444 31, Stenungsund, Sweden (70.4%)
Tel.: (46) 38124170
Web Site: https://www.vikingsupply.com
Rev.: $38,075,409
Assets: $225,665,368
Liabilities: $12,002,051
Net Worth: $213,663,317
Earnings: $(14,392,744)
Emp.: 317
Fiscal Year-end: 12/31/2021
Holding Company; Shipping Services
N.A.I.C.S.: 551112
Folke Patriksson (Deputy Chm)

Subsidiary (Domestic):

TransAtlantic AB (2)
Lilla Bommen 4A, Box 11397, 40428, Gothenburg, Sweden
Tel.: (46) 31 763 23 00
Web Site: http://www.transatlantic.se
Ship Management Services
N.A.I.C.S.: 488510

Subsidiary (Domestic):

TransAtlantic Services AB (3)
PO Box 1063, SE 251 10, Helsingborg, Sweden
Tel.: (46) 42172700
Sales Range: $25-49.9 Million
Emp.: 5
Shipping Services
N.A.I.C.S.: 483111

Subsidiary (Non-US):

TransAtlantic UK Ltd. (3)
Transatlantic House No 3 Quay, Hedon Road, Hull, HU9 5 PR, North Humberside, United Kingdom
Tel.: (44) 1405767878
Web Site: http://www.rabt.se
Sales Range: $25-49.9 Million
Emp.: 52
Shipping Services
N.A.I.C.S.: 483111

Viking Supply Ships A/S (2)
Islands Brygge 57, 2300, Copenhagen, Denmark
Tel.: (45) 7231 2013
Web Site: http://www.vikingsupply.com
Freight Transportation Services
N.A.I.C.S.: 488510
Thomas Andersson (Dir-Pur)

KISTOS HOLDINGS PLC
2nd Floor 3 St James Square, London, SW1Y 4JU, United Kingdom
Tel.: (44) 2045312800   UK
Web Site: https://www.kistosplc.com
Year Founded: 2020
KIST—(AIM)
Rev.: $444,109,648
Assets: $662,296,568
Liabilities: $551,448,306
Net Worth: $110,848,262
Earnings: $28,017,483
Emp.: 24
Fiscal Year-end: 12/31/22
Holding Company
N.A.I.C.S.: 551112

KISWIRE LTD
37 Gurak-ro 141beon-gil, Suyeong-gu, Busan, 48212, Korea (South)
Tel.: (82) 517601700
Web Site: https://www.kiswire.com
Year Founded: 1945
002240—(KRS)
Rev.: $1,589,646,021
Assets: $1,942,633,361
Liabilities: $617,623,866
Net Worth: $1,325,009,496
Earnings: $62,150,106
Emp.: 805
Fiscal Year-end: 12/31/22
Steel Wire Mfr & Whslr
N.A.I.C.S.: 331110
Hong Young-Chul (CEO)

Subsidiaries:

HONGDUK INDUSTRIAL CO., LTD. (1)
80 Cheolgangsandan-ro 66beon-gil, Daesong-myeon Nam-gu, Pohang, 37875, Gyeongsangbuk-do, Korea (South)
Tel.: (82) 542719400
Steel Pole Mfr
N.A.I.C.S.: 331222

HONGDUK INDUSTRIAL CO., LTD. - GEOCHANG STEEL CORD FACTORY (1)
84 Seokgang 3-gil, Gajo-myeon, Gajo, 50119, Gyeongsangnam-do, Korea (South)
Tel.: (82) 55 943 7977

Web Site: http://www.kiswire.com
Steel Pole Mfr
N.A.I.C.S.: 331222

HONGDUK INDUSTRIAL CO., LTD. - HAMAN STEEL CORD FACTORY (1)
68 Yunoegongdan-gil, Beopsu, 637-833, Gyeongsangnam-do, Korea (South)
Tel.: (82) 55 583 7733
Steel Pole Mfr
N.A.I.C.S.: 331222

HONGDUK INDUSTRIAL CO., LTD. - MACHINERY MANUFACTURING DIVISION (1)
43 Modeok-ro, Sasang-gu, Busan, 617-826, Korea (South)
Tel.: (82) 51 309 1212
Steel Pole Mfr
N.A.I.C.S.: 331222

HONGDUK INDUSTRIAL CO., LTD. - POHANG BEAD WIRE FACTORY (1)
328 Cheolgang-ro, Nam-gu, Pohang, 790-240, Gyeongsangbuk-do, Korea (South)
Tel.: (82) 54 271 6600
Steel Pole Mfr
N.A.I.C.S.: 331222

HONGDUK INDUSTRIAL CO., LTD. - POHANG SILK WIRE FACTORY (1)
81 Songdeok-ro, Daesong-myeon Nam-gu, Pohang, 790-841, Gyeongsangbuk-do, Korea (South)
Tel.: (82) 54 271 6500
Steel Pole Mfr
N.A.I.C.S.: 331222

HONGDUK INDUSTRIAL CO., LTD. - POHANG SPRING WIRE FACTORY (1)
51 Jangheung-ro 39beon-gil, Nam-gu, Pohang, 790-240, Gyeongsangbuk-do, Korea (South)
Tel.: (82) 54 271 3600
Steel Pole Mfr
N.A.I.C.S.: 331222

HyRope (Thailand) Co., Ltd. (1)
700/766 Moo 1 Amata City Chonburi Industrial Estate Phase 8, Phanthong Sub-District Phanthong District, Chon Buri, 20160, Thailand
Tel.: (66) 38079216
Silo Mfr
N.A.I.C.S.: 335929

Hypore Hong Kong Ltd. (1)
DD129 Lots 3178 Ping Ha Road, Lau Fau Shan, Yuen Long, China (Hong Kong)
Tel.: (852) 26150629
Silo Mfr
N.A.I.C.S.: 335929

K.S.WIRE Co., Ltd. (1)
6-5-1 Higashizuka, Kurashiki, 712-8044, Okayama, Japan
Tel.: (81) 864500511
Silo Mfr
N.A.I.C.S.: 335929

KAT LTD. (1)
223 Techno 2-ro, Yuseong-gu, Daejeon, 34026, Korea (South)
Tel.: (82) 429337760
Web Site: https://www.kiswire-kat.com
Steel Pole Mfr
N.A.I.C.S.: 331222

KISTRON LTD. (1)
37 Sandan-ro 68beon-gil, Danwon-gu, Ansan, 15434, Gyeonggi-do, Korea (South)
Tel.: (82) 314916501
Web Site: https://kistron.com
Emp.: 91
Steel Pole Mfr
N.A.I.C.S.: 331222

KISWIRE (Shanghai) TRADING CO., LTD. (1)
Rm 1003 Block A Oriental Financial Plaza Property Management Center, No 1168 Century Avenue Pudong, Shanghai, 200122, China
Tel.: (86) 2152080929
Steel Pipe Distr
N.A.I.C.S.: 423510

KISWIRE BALARAJA INDONESIA, PT (1)
Jl Raya Serang Km 24 Kp Tegal Murni Rt 003 Rw 003, Kel Balaraja Kec Balaraja Kab, Tangerang, 15610, Banten, Indonesia
Tel.: (62) 2159451241
Steel Pole Mfr
N.A.I.C.S.: 331222

KISWIRE CORD LTD. (1)
15 Yusangongdan 7-gil, Yangsan, 50592, Gyeongsangnam-do, Korea (South)
Tel.: (82) 553803414
Steel Pole Mfr
N.A.I.C.S.: 331222

KISWIRE CORD LTD. - CHANGWON FACTORY (1)
18 Jeongdong-ro, Seongsan-gu, Changwon, Gyeongsangnam-do, Korea (South)
Tel.: (82) 55 268 3900
Web Site: http://www.kiswire.com
Emp.: 200
Steel Pole Mfr
N.A.I.C.S.: 331222
Kisoung Jung (Mgr-Factory)

KISWIRE CORD LTD. - POHANG FACTORY (1)
52 Cheolgangsandan-ro 130beon-gil, Daesong-myeon Nam-gu, Pohang, 790-841, Gyeongsangbuk-do, Korea (South)
Tel.: (82) 54 288 6300
Steel Pole Mfr
N.A.I.C.S.: 331222

KISWIRE CORD QINGDAO LTD. (1)
279 Huashan No 1 Road, Jimo, Qingdao, 266200, Shandong, China
Tel.: (86) 53288590118
Steel Pole Mfr
N.A.I.C.S.: 331222

KISWIRE CORD RONGCHENG CO., LTD. (1)
No 36 Chengshan Avenue West, Rongcheng, 264300, Shandong, China
Tel.: (86) 6317523429
Steel Pole Mfr
N.A.I.C.S.: 331222

KISWIRE CORD SDN. BHD. (1)
Plo 475 Jalan Bakau 3 Kawasan Perindustrian Tanjung Langsat, 81700, Pasir Gudang, Johor, Malaysia
Tel.: (60) 72551475
Steel Pole Mfr
N.A.I.C.S.: 331222
Mohd Yunus (Engr-Production)

KISWIRE CORD VIETNAM LTD. (1)
Tel.: (84) 2743551617
Steel Pole Mfr
N.A.I.C.S.: 331222

KISWIRE CORD YANGTZE LTD. (1)
No 45 Zhongyang Road, Economic Technological Development Zone, Nantong, 226009, Jiangsu, China
Tel.: (86) 51385989012
Steel Pole Mfr
N.A.I.C.S.: 331222

KISWIRE Dies Sdn. Bhd. (1)
Plo 475A Jalan Tengar, PO Box 101, Kawasan Perindustrian Tanjung Langsat, 81700, Pasir Gudang, Johor, Malaysia
Tel.: (60) 72882539
Silo Mfr
N.A.I.C.S.: 335929

KISWIRE INC. - BEAD WIRE DIVISION (1)
257 Mawsons way, Newberry, SC 29108
Tel.: (803) 321-0940
Emp.: 20
Steel Pole Mfr
N.A.I.C.S.: 331222
David Minnick (CEO)

KISWIRE INC. - STEEL CORD DIVISION (1)
90 Twin Springs Rd, Newberry, SC 29108
Tel.: (803) 947-7930
Steel Pole Mfr
N.A.I.C.S.: 331222

KISWIRE INDONESIA, PT (1)

KISWIRE LTD

KISWIRE LTD—(Continued)
Jl Panglima Polim Raya No 86 Lt 2 Gedung Harvia Place, Jakarta, 12160, Indonesia
Tel.: (62) 2129426278
Steel Pole Mfr
N.A.I.C.S.: 331222

KISWIRE INTERNATIONAL S.A. (1)
312 Z A E WolserF, 3290, Bettembourg, Luxembourg
Tel.: (352) 281024
Steel Pipe Distr
N.A.I.C.S.: 423510
Marie-Laurence Jeandrain *(Mgr-Customer Svc)*

KISWIRE JAPAN CO. (1)
Kiswire Bldg 4 5F 4-5 Ohdenma-Cho, Nihonbashi, Chuo, 103-0011, Tokyo, Japan
Tel.: (81) 338082839
Steel Pipe Distr
N.A.I.C.S.: 423510

KISWIRE LTD. - BEAD WIRE FACTORY (1)
1 Eosil-ro, Yangsan, 626-230, Gyeongsangnam-do, Korea (South)
Tel.: (82) 55 389 1405
Steel Pole Mfr
N.A.I.C.S.: 331222

KISWIRE LTD. - EONYANG FACTORY (1)
53 Yangdeungnonggong-gil, Sangbukmyeon, Ulsan, 689-823, Ulju-gun, Korea (South)
Tel.: (82) 52 264 3450
Steel Pole Mfr
N.A.I.C.S.: 331222

KISWIRE LTD. - GEONCHEON BEAD WIRE FACTORY (1)
San269-4 Yongmyeong-ri, Geoncheon-eup, Gyeongju, 780-903, Gyeongsangbuk-do, Korea (South)
Tel.: (82) 70 7444 3500
Steel Pole Mfr
N.A.I.C.S.: 331222

KISWIRE LTD. - GEONCHEON SHAPED WIRE FACTORY (1)
173-91 Yongmyeonggongdan-gil, Geoncheon-eup, Gyeongju, 780-903, Gyeongsangbuk-do, Korea (South)
Tel.: (82) 54 740 9700
Steel Pole Mfr
N.A.I.C.S.: 331222

KISWIRE LTD. - GUNBUK FACTORY (1)
25 Hamansandan 4-gil, Gunbuk, Gyeongsangnam-do, Korea (South)
Tel.: (82) 55 583 0475
Web Site: http://www.kiswire.com
Steel Pole Mfr
N.A.I.C.S.: 331222

KISWIRE LTD. - HYROPE FACTORY (1)
5 Sandan 6-ro, Jeonggwan-myeon, Busan, 619-961, Gijang-gun, Korea (South)
Tel.: (82) 51 727 0015
Steel Pole Mfr
N.A.I.C.S.: 331222

KISWIRE LTD. - SPRING WIRE FACTORY (1)
1314 Yangsan-daero, Sangbuk-myeon, Yangsan, 626-856, Gyeongsangnam-do, Korea (South)
Tel.: (82) 55 375 3500
Steel Pole Mfr
N.A.I.C.S.: 331222

KISWIRE Lotus Co., Ltd. (1)
140 One Pacific Place Bldg 17/F Unit 1701 Sukhumvit Road, Klongtoey, Bangkok, 10110, Thailand
Tel.: (66) 26532820
Silo Mfr
N.A.I.C.S.: 335929

KISWIRE NEPTUNE SDN. BHD. (1)
Plo 475C Jalan Ipil 2 Kawasan Perindustrian, Tanjung Langsat, 81700, Pasir Gudang, Johor, Malaysia
Tel.: (60) 72552013
Emp.: 60

Steel Pole Mfr
N.A.I.C.S.: 331222

KISWIRE PINE BLUFF, INC.
5100 Industrial Dr S, Pine Bluff, AR 71602
Tel.: (870) 247-2444
Web Site: http://www.kiswire.com
Emp.: 300
Steel Pole Mfr
N.A.I.C.S.: 331222

KISWIRE QINGDAO LTD. (1)
No 600 Chuangye Road, Qingdao Development Zone, Qingdao, 266510, China
Tel.: (86) 53286821911
Steel Pole Mfr
N.A.I.C.S.: 331222

KISWIRE R&D Sdn. Bhd. (1)
No 33 Jalan Senyum, Kampung Wadihana, 80300, Johor Bahru, Johor, Malaysia
Tel.: (60) 73404000
Silo Mfr
N.A.I.C.S.: 335929

KISWIRE SDN. BHD. (1)
Plo 475 Jalan Keluli 2, Kawasan Perindustrian Pasir Gudang, 81700, Pasir Gudang, Johor, Malaysia
Tel.: (60) 72549400
Steel Pole Mfr
N.A.I.C.S.: 331222

KISWIRE SDN.BHD. B.K.K (1)
140 One Pacific Place Bldg 18/F Unit 1805 Sukhumvit Road, Bangkok, 10110, Thailand
Tel.: (66) 2 653 2820
Steel Pipe Distr
N.A.I.C.S.: 423510

KISWIRE SINGAPORE LTD. (1)
35 Marsiling Industrial Estate Road 3 Unit 05-05, Singapore, 739257, Singapore
Tel.: (65) 62270939
Steel Pipe Distr
N.A.I.C.S.: 423510

KISWIRE SZENTGOTTHARD LLC (1)
Haris 3, 9970, Szentgotthard, Hungary
Tel.: (36) 94552711
Steel Pole Mfr
N.A.I.C.S.: 331222

KISWIRE TRADING, INC. (1)
460 Bergen Blvd Ste 120, Palisades Park, NJ 07650
Tel.: (201) 461-8895
Steel Pipe Distr
N.A.I.C.S.: 423510

KISWIRE, LLC (1)
3890 Steve Reynolds Blvd, Norcross, GA 30093
Tel.: (470) 447-2500
Steel Pipe Distr
N.A.I.C.S.: 423510

Kiswire Cord Czech s.r.o. (1)
Zapadni 65 Prumyslova zona Triangle, Velemysleves, 438 01, Zatec, Czech Republic
Tel.: (420) 472710120
Web Site: https://www.kiswire.cz
Emp.: 170
Silo Mfr
N.A.I.C.S.: 335929

Kiswire Fine Metal (Qingdao) Ltd. (1)
Qingdao Export Processing Zone, Qingdao, 266113, Shandong, China
Tel.: (86) 53287923260
Steel Pole Mfr
N.A.I.C.S.: 331222

QINGDAO KISWIRE PRECISION METAL LTD. (1)
281 HuaShan No 1 Rd, Jimo, Qingdao, 266200, Shandong, China
Tel.: (86) 532 8756 9511
Steel Pole Mfr
N.A.I.C.S.: 331222

KIT FINANCE JSC
Marata 69-71 Business Center Renaissance Plaza St, 191119, Saint Petersburg, Russia
Tel.: (7) 8126110000
Web Site: http://www.brokerkf.ru

Financial Brokerage Services
N.A.I.C.S.: 523160

KITA KOUDENSHA CORPORATION
2-10 Kita 11-jo Nishi 23 Chome, Chuo-ku, Sapporo, 060-0011, Hokkaido, Japan
Tel.: (81) 116402231 JP
Web Site: https://www.kitakoudensha.co.jp
Year Founded: 1952
Emp.: 221
Electrical Equipments Installation & Services
N.A.I.C.S.: 238210

KITAC CORPORATION
102 Shinkocho, Chuo-ku, Niigata, 950-0965, Japan
Tel.: (81) 252811111
Web Site: https://www.kitac.co.jp
Year Founded: 1973
47070—(TKS)
Sales Range: Less than $1 Million
Emp.: 174
Construction Services
N.A.I.C.S.: 541330
Nakayama Masako *(Pres & CEO)*

KITAGAWA CORPORATION
Motomachi, Fuchu, Hiroshima, Japan
Tel.: (81) 847454560
Web Site: https://www.kiw.co.jp
Year Founded: 1941
6317—(TKS)
Rev.: $406,957,870
Assets: $529,738,620
Liabilities: $265,133,710
Net Worth: $264,604,910
Earnings: $8,374,870
Emp.: 1,364
Fiscal Year-end: 03/31/24
Machine Accessories Mfr & Distr
N.A.I.C.S.: 333515

Subsidiaries:

KEMET Japan Co., Ltd. (1)
No 2103 21ST Floor WBG Maribu West, 6-Banchi Nakase 2-chome, Chiba, 261-7114, Japan
Tel.: (81) 432139911
Web Site: http://www.kemet.jp
Sales Range: $10-24.9 Million
Electronic Capacitor Mfr & Polishing Equipment Services
N.A.I.C.S.: 334416
Keisuke Kitagawa *(Pres & CEO)*

Kitagawa (THAILAND) Co., Ltd. (1)
WHA-Chonburi Industrail Estate 1 39 Moo 8, Bowin Sriracha, Chon Buri, 20230, Thailand
Tel.: (66) 3834552833
Web Site: https://www.kiw.co.th
Emp.: 545
Machine Tool Accessory Distr
N.A.I.C.S.: 423830

Kitagawa Europe GmbH (1)
Borsigstrasse 3, 40880, Ratingen, Germany
Tel.: (49) 21021237800
Web Site: http://www.kitagawa.global
Machine Tool Accessory Distr
N.A.I.C.S.: 423830

Kitagawa Europe Ltd. (1)
Unit 1 The Headlands Downton, Salisbury, SP5 3JJ, Wiltshire, United Kingdom
Tel.: (44) 1725514010
Machine Tool Accessory Distr
N.A.I.C.S.: 423830

Kitagawa India Pvt Ltd. (1)
Plot No 42 2nd Phase, Jigani Industrial Area, Bengaluru, 560 105, India
Tel.: (91) 8029765204
Web Site: http://www.kitagawa.global
Machine Tool Accessory Distr
N.A.I.C.S.: 423830
Nethaji K. M. *(Mng Dir)*

INTERNATIONAL PUBLIC

Kitagawa Iron Works (SHANGHAI) Co., Ltd. (1)
Room 308 Building B Far East International Plaza No 317 Xian xia Road, Chang Ning, Shanghai, 200051, China
Tel.: (86) 2162955772
Web Site: http://www.kiw-sh.com
Machine Tool Accessory Distr
N.A.I.C.S.: 423830

Kitagawa Korea Agent Co., Ltd. (1)
811 Ho A Dong SK Twin Techtower 345-9 Kasan-Dong, Dumchon-Gu, Seoul, Korea (South)
Tel.: (82) 28399911
Web Site: http://www.kitagawa.co.kr
Machine Tool Accessory Distr
N.A.I.C.S.: 423830

KITAGAWA SEIKI CO., LTD.
800-8 Ukai-cho, Fuchu, 726-0002, Hiroshima, Japan
Tel.: (81) 847401200
Web Site: https://www.kitagawaseiki.co.jp
Year Founded: 1957
6327—(TKS)
Rev.: $36,903,260
Assets: $52,434,600
Liabilities: $22,814,960
Net Worth: $29,619,640
Earnings: $3,931,040
Emp.: 154
Fiscal Year-end: 06/30/24
Printed Circuit Board Mfr
N.A.I.C.S.: 334412
Masatoshi Uchida *(Pres)*

Subsidiaries:

HOKUSEI KOGYO CO., LTD (1)
6-8-15 Akebono-cho, Fukuyama, 721-0952, Hiroshima, Japan
Tel.: (81) 849531727
Printing Press Mfr
N.A.I.C.S.: 333248

KITAGAWA ENGINEERING CO., LTD. (1)
10530-297 Motoyama-cho, Fuchu, 726-0001, Japan
Tel.: (81) 847401551
Web Site: https://www.kitagawa-engineering.co.jp
Emp.: 40
Printing Press Mfr
N.A.I.C.S.: 333248
Yoshiyuki Kitagawa *(Chm)*

KITAHAMA CAPITAL PARTNERS CO., LTD.
8th Floor Kitahama Business Center 1-17 Kitahama 2-Chome, Chuo-ku, Osaka, 541-0041, Japan
Tel.: (81) 662267581
Web Site: https://kitahamabank.co.jp
Year Founded: 1997
2134—(TKS)
Rev.: $1,546,085
Assets: $8,034,355
Liabilities: $7,023,454
Net Worth: $1,010,902
Earnings: ($3,230,921)
Fiscal Year-end: 03/31/24
Investment Services
N.A.I.C.S.: 523999
Kenji Maeda *(Pres & CEO)*

KITAKEI CO., LTD.
Ito Building 3-6-14 Minami-Honmachi, Chuo-ku, Osaka, 541-0054, Japan
Tel.: (81) 662511161
Web Site: https://www.kitakei.jp
Year Founded: 1959
9872—(TKS)
Rev.: $520,423,846
Assets: $246,522,225
Liabilities: $130,804,301
Net Worth: $115,717,924
Earnings: $6,374,822
Emp.: 376

AND PRIVATE COMPANIES

Fiscal Year-end: 11/30/20
Construction Materials Whslr
N.A.I.C.S.: 423310
Ryoichi Kitamura (Pres)
Subsidiaries:

Fukuzumi Corporation (1)
2-42-6 Kamiya-cho, Himeji, 670-0836,
Hyogo, Japan
Tel.: (81) 792225052
Web Site: http://www.fukuzumi-co.jp
Housing Material Distr
N.A.I.C.S.: 423220

KITANIHON SPINNING CO., LTD.
201-1 Fukudome-cho, Hakusan, 924-0051, Ishikawa, Japan
Tel.: (81) 762777530
Web Site: https://www.ktbo.co.jp
Year Founded: 1948
3409—(TKS)
Rev.: $8,639,270
Assets: $12,274,770
Liabilities: $6,332,380
Net Worth: $5,942,390
Earnings: ($760,150)
Emp.: 73
Fiscal Year-end: 03/31/24
Fiber Yarn Mfr
N.A.I.C.S.: 313110
Toshiaki Kasuya (Pres & CEO)

KITANO CONSTRUCTION CORP.
524 Agata-machi, Nagano, 380-8524, Japan
Tel.: (81) 262335111   JP
Web Site: https://www.kitano.co.jp
Year Founded: 1946
1866—(TKS)
Rev.: $561,612,040
Assets: $514,449,690
Liabilities: $225,638,960
Net Worth: $288,810,730
Earnings: $25,792,220
Emp.: 560
Fiscal Year-end: 03/31/24
Construction & Real Estate Development Services
N.A.I.C.S.: 541810
Takahiro Kitano (Chm, Pres & Exec Officer)
Subsidiaries:

Asahi Agency Co., Ltd. (1)
1306-1 Toigosho, Nagano, 503-0006, Gifu, Japan
Tel.: (81) 262332222
Web Site: http://www.asahi-agency.co.jp
Advertising Services
N.A.I.C.S.: 541810

KITANOTATSUJIN CORPORATION
Sapporo Sosei Square 25F Kita 1-jo Nishi 1-chome 6, Chuo-ku, Sapporo, 060-0001, Hokkaido, Japan
Tel.: (81) 117575567
Web Site: https://www.kitanotatsujin.com
Year Founded: 2002
2930—(TKS)
Rev.: $103,974,850
Assets: $61,321,410
Liabilities: $11,719,770
Net Worth: $49,601,640
Earnings: $7,047,460
Emp.: 277
Fiscal Year-end: 02/29/24
Food Products Mfr
N.A.I.C.S.: 311999
Katsutoshi Kinoshita (Pres & Dir-Rep)

KITAZAWA SANGYO CO., LTD.
2-23-10 Higashi, Shibuya-Ku, Tokyo, 150-0011, Japan
Tel.: (81) 354855111
Web Site: https://www.kitazawasangyo.co.jp
Year Founded: 1951
9930—(TKS)
Rev.: $108,873,310
Assets: $124,472,910
Liabilities: $56,158,560
Net Worth: $68,314,350
Earnings: $4,395,650
Emp.: 419
Fiscal Year-end: 03/31/24
Kitchen Equipment Distr
N.A.I.C.S.: 423440
Masaki Kitagawa (Pres)

KITCATT NOHR ALEXANDER SHAW, LTD.
48-50 Saint John St, London, EC1 4DG, United Kingdom
Tel.: (44) 207 012 3950
Year Founded: 2002
Sales Range: $25-49.9 Million
Emp.: 60
Advertising Agencies
N.A.I.C.S.: 541810
Paul Kitcatt (Partner-Creative)

KITCHENER AERO AVIONICS LTD.
4881 Fountain Street N Hangar 9, Breslau, N0B 1M0, ON, Canada
Tel.: (519) 648-2921
Web Site: http://www.kitcheneraero.com
Year Founded: 1977
Sales Range: $10-24.9 Million
Emp.: 80
Aviation Services
N.A.I.C.S.: 336411
Barry Aylward (Pres)

KITEX GARMENTS LIMITED
P B No 5 Kizhakkambalam, Alwaye, Kochi, 683 562, Kerala, India
Tel.: (91) 4844142000   In
Web Site: https://www.kitexgarments.com
521248—(BOM)
Rev.: $111,277,407
Assets: $135,628,598
Liabilities: $24,770,082
Net Worth: $110,858,516
Earnings: $17,079,071
Emp.: 5,524
Fiscal Year-end: 03/31/22
Fabrics Mfr
N.A.I.C.S.: 313210
Mithun B. Shenoy (Compliance Officer & Sec)
Subsidiaries:

Kitex Kidswear Limited (1)
PO Box No 5, Kizhakkambalam Ernakulam, Aluva, 683562, Kerala, India
Tel.: (91) 4844142000
Web Site: http://www.kitexchildrenswear.com
Aluminium Products Mfr
N.A.I.C.S.: 331314
Sabu M. Jacob (Mng Dir)

KITOKU SHINRYO CO., LTD.
2-8 Kanda-Ogawamachi, Tokyo, 101-0052, Japan
Tel.: (81) 332335121   JP
Web Site: http://www.kitoku-shinryo.co.jp
Sales Range: $1-4.9 Billion
Emp.: 372
Rice, Processed Rice Products & Animal Feed Mfr
N.A.I.C.S.: 111160
Makoto Hirayama (Pres)
Subsidiaries:

Kitoku America Inc. (1)
216F St PDQ Ste 39, Davis, CA 95616
Tel.: (650) 697-0520
Food Products Distr
N.A.I.C.S.: 424490

KITRON ASA
Olav Brunborgs vei 4, NO-1396, Billingstad, Norway
Tel.: (47) 66100000
Web Site: https://www.kitron.com
0F0J—(LSE)
Rev.: $599,181,046
Assets: $542,644,559
Liabilities: $403,489,655
Net Worth: $139,154,905
Earnings: $26,523,832
Emp.: 2,848
Fiscal Year-end: 12/31/22
Contract Electronic Manufacturer
N.A.I.C.S.: 334220
Mindaugas Sestokas (Mng Dir-Kitron UAB-Lithuania & VP Central Eastern Europe)
Subsidiaries:

Combitech Electronics (1)
Slottsgatan 14, PO Box 1017, S 551 11, Jonkoping, Sweden
Tel.: (46) 36194750
Web Site: http://www.combitech.se
Rev.: $8,676,100
Emp.: 317
Electrical Power, Software Development & System Architecture for Transport & Defence Industries
N.A.I.C.S.: 513210

Kitron AB (1)
Mobelvagen 5, 556 52, Jonkoping, Sweden   (100%)
Tel.: (46) 362902100
Web Site: http://kitron.com
Electronic Components Mfr
N.A.I.C.S.: 334419
Stefan Hansson Mutas (Mng Dir)

Kitron AS (1)
Tangen Alle 39, PO Box 799, 4809, Arendal, Norway
Tel.: (47) 37071300
Sales Range: $100-124.9 Million
Emp.: 500
Electronic Components Mfr
N.A.I.C.S.: 334416
Geir Vedoy (Project Mgr)

Kitron Electromechanical (Ningbo) Co. Ltd. (1)
No 179 DongHui Road, Nordic Industrial Park Zhenhai District, Ningbo, 315221, China
Tel.: (86) 57486308600
Electronic Product Mfr & Distr
N.A.I.C.S.: 334419

Kitron Electronics Manufacturing (Ningbo) Co. Ltd. (1)
No 189 Donghui Road, Zhenhai, Ningbo, 315221, China
Tel.: (86) 57486308600
Electronics Product Mfr & Distr
N.A.I.C.S.: 334419

Kitron GmbH (1)
Carl-Zeiss-Str 3, DE-72555, Metzingen, Germany
Tel.: (49) 71233741220
Electronics Product Mfr & Distr
N.A.I.C.S.: 334419
Roland Lutz (Gen Mgr)

Kitron Inc. (1)
160 Jari Dr 160, Johnstown, PA 15904
Tel.: (814) 619-0523
Web Site: http://www.kitron.com
Emp.: 115
Electronic Circuit Boards Mfr & Distr
N.A.I.C.S.: 335999
Peter Nilsson (Pres & CEO)

Subsidiary (Domestic):

Kitron Technologies Inc. (2)
345 Pomroys Dr, Windber, PA 15963-2425
Tel.: (814) 467-9060
Web Site: http://www.kitron.com
Defense Secure Communication System Provider
N.A.I.C.S.: 517112

Kitron Microelectronics AB (1)
Bataljonsgatan 10, PO Box 1052, 55110, Jonkoping, Sweden   (100%)
Tel.: (46) 362902100
Web Site: http://www.kitron.com
Sales Range: $25-49.9 Million
Emp.: 100
Electronic Components Mfr
N.A.I.C.S.: 334419

Kitron Sourcing AS (1)
Tangen Alle 39, PO Box 799, 4809, Arendal, Norway
Tel.: (47) 66100000
Sales Range: $100-124.9 Million
Emp.: 500
Electronic Components Mfr
N.A.I.C.S.: 334416
Hans Petter Thomassen (Mng Dir)

Kitron Sp. z o.o (1)
ul Droga Kurpiowska 75, 86-300, Grudziadz, Poland
Tel.: (48) 566425880
Electronics Product Mfr & Distr
N.A.I.C.S.: 334419

UAB Kitron (1)
151 Taikos Pr, LT-52119, Kaunas, Lithuania   (100%)
Tel.: (370) 37409330
Web Site: http://www.kitron.com
Sales Range: $100-124.9 Million
Electronic Components Mfr
N.A.I.C.S.: 334419
Mindaugas Sestokas (Mng Dir)

UAB Kitron Real Estate (1)
Taikos pr 151, LT-52119, Kaunas, Lithuania
Tel.: (370) 37409330
Electronics Product Mfr & Distr
N.A.I.C.S.: 334419

UAB Lumen Intellectus (1)
Taikos pr 151, 52119, Kaunas, Lithuania
Tel.: (370) 37409330
Sales Range: $150-199.9 Million
Emp.: 370
Real Estate Property Development Services
N.A.I.C.S.: 531210

KITS EYECARE LTD.
510 Seymour Street Suite 1020, Vancouver, V6B 3J5, BC, Canada   BC
Web Site: https://www.kits.com
Year Founded: 2018
KTYCF—(OTCIQ)
Rev.: $68,362,694
Assets: $70,023,290
Liabilities: $29,956,376
Net Worth: $40,066,914
Earnings: ($3,395,792)
Emp.: 115
Fiscal Year-end: 12/31/22
Health Care Srvices
N.A.I.C.S.: 621610
Arshil Abdulla (CTO)

KITWAVE GROUP PLC
Unit S3 Narvik Way Tyne Tunnel Estate, North Shields, NE29 7XJ, Tyne & Wear, United Kingdom
Tel.: (44) 1912592277   UK
Web Site: https://www.kitwave.co.uk
Year Founded: 1987
KITW—(AIM)
Rev.: $683,052,639
Assets: $243,925,260
Liabilities: $146,322,842
Net Worth: $97,602,418
Earnings: $19,469,705
Emp.: 1,236
Fiscal Year-end: 10/31/22
Soft Drink Manufacturing
N.A.I.C.S.: 312111
Subsidiaries:

Andersons (Wholesale) Limited (1)
4A Stephenson Way, Thetford, IP24 3RH, United Kingdom

KITWAVE GROUP PLC

Kitwave Group Plc—(Continued)
Tel.: (44) 1842824505
Web Site:
https://www.andersonswholesale.co.uk
Toy & Gift Whslr
N.A.I.C.S.: 423920

Automatic Retailing (Northern) Limited (1)
Unit S3 Narvik Way Tyne Tunnel Estate, North Shields, NE29 7XJ, Tyne & Wear, United Kingdom
Tel.: (44) 1912380400
Web Site:
https://www.automaticretailing.com
Drink & Snack Retailer
N.A.I.C.S.: 424450

Central Supplies (Brierley Hill) Ltd. (1)
Unit 2 Saltbrook Rd Cradley Brook Park, Halesowen, B63 2QU, United Kingdom
Tel.: (44) 1384414999
Web Site: https://www.centralsupplies.co.uk
Food & Beverage Whslr
N.A.I.C.S.: 424420

David Miller Frozen Foods Limited (1)
Derwent Valley Estate Common Road, Dunnington, York, YO19 5PD, United Kingdom
Tel.: (44) 1904655368
Web Site:
https://www.millerfoodservice.co.uk
Food & Beverage Distr
N.A.I.C.S.: 424420

Eden Farm Limited (1)
1 Cook Way North West Industrial Estate, Peterlee, SR8 2HY, United Kingdom
Tel.: (44) 1915861111
Web Site: https://www.eden-farm.co.uk
Frozen Food Whslr
N.A.I.C.S.: 424420

HB Clark & Co (Successors) Limited (1)
Unit 1 Headways, Stanley, Wakefield, WF3 4FE, United Kingdom
Tel.: (44) 1924290149
Web Site: https://www.hbclark.co.uk
Food & Beverage Mfr
N.A.I.C.S.: 311421

M&M Value Limited (1)
Unit S3 Narvik Way Tyne Tunnel Estate, North Shields, NE29 7XJ, Tyne and Wear, United Kingdom
Tel.: (44) 1912592277
Web Site: https://www.mandmvalue.co.uk
Groceries & Snacks Whslr
N.A.I.C.S.: 424450

M.J. Baker Foodservice Limited (1)
21 Fairfax Road, Heathfield Newton Abbot, Devon, TQ12 6UD, United Kingdom
Tel.: (44) 1626833366
Web Site: https://mjbakerfoodservice.co.uk
Frozen Food Whslr
N.A.I.C.S.: 424420

Squirrels UK Limited (1)
Unit 9 Butterfield Business Park, Luton, LU2 8EU, United Kingdom
Tel.: (44) 1708344666
Web Site: https://squirrelsstock.com
Food & Beverage Distr
N.A.I.C.S.: 424420

Teatime Tasties Limited (1)
57/59 Ripley Street, Bradford, BD5 7TX, West Yorkshire, United Kingdom
Tel.: (44) 1484514331
Web Site: https://www.teatimetasties.com
Drink & Snack Retailer
N.A.I.C.S.: 424450

Turner & Wrights Limited (1)
Vine House Lynstock Way, Lostock, Bolton, BL6 4TW, United Kingdom
Tel.: (44) 1204673000
Web Site:
https://www.turnerandwrights.co.uk
Alcohol & Tobacco Retailer
N.A.I.C.S.: 424940

Westone Wholesale Limited (1)
Unit C Hortonwood 31, Telford, TF1 7GS, United Kingdom
Tel.: (44) 1952670220
Web Site: https://www.westones.co.uk
Food & Beverage Whslr
N.A.I.C.S.: 424420

KITZ CORPORATION
Tokyo Shiodome Building 1-9-1 Higashi-Shinbashi, Minato-ku, Tokyo, 105-7305, Japan
Tel.: (81) 355689270
Web Site: https://www.kitz.co.jp
6498—(TKS)
Rev.: $1,183,611,690
Assets: $1,181,853,370
Liabilities: $457,205,740
Net Worth: $724,647,630
Earnings: $75,090,190
Emp.: 5,382
Fiscal Year-end: 12/31/23
Valve Mfr
N.A.I.C.S.: 332911
Yasuyuki Hotta *(Pres & CEO)*

Subsidiaries:

Filcore Co., Ltd. (1)
60 Sangidaehak-ro, 1Na-402 Shihwa Industrial Complex 3Ba-211 Shihwa Industrial Complex, Siheung, 15085, Korea (South)
Tel.: (82) 314333988
Web Site: http://www.filcore.co.kr
Hollow Fiber Mfr
N.A.I.C.S.: 325220
Kim Seung-Hyun *(Co-CEO)*

Hokutoh Giken Kogyo Corporation (1)
4601 Wakamiko, Sutamacho, Hokuto, 408-0112, Yamanashi, Japan
Tel.: (81) 551425151
Valves & System Equipment Mfr & Distr
N.A.I.C.S.: 332911

Hotel Beniya Co., Ltd. (1)
2-7-21 Kogandori, Suwa, 392-0027, Nagano, Japan
Tel.: (81) 266571111
Web Site: https://hotel-beniya.co.jp
Sales Range: $25-49.9 Million
Emp.: 100
Home Management Services
N.A.I.C.S.: 541618

KITZ (Thailand) Ltd. (1)
426 Moo 17 Bangplee Industrial Estate, soi 6/2 Debaratana Road Km 23 T Bangsaothong, Bang Sao Thong, 10570, Samut Prakan, Thailand
Tel.: (66) 23153129
Butterfly & Copper Alloy Valves Mfr & Whslr
N.A.I.C.S.: 332911

KITZ Corporation (1)
10th Floor Seoul Finance Center 136 Sejong-daero, Jung-gu, Seoul, 4520, Korea (South)
Tel.: (82) 269592450
Valves & System Equipment Mfr & Distr
N.A.I.C.S.: 332911

KITZ Corporation of America (1)
10750 Corporate Dr, Stafford, TX 77477
Tel.: (281) 491-7333
Web Site: https://kitzus-kca.com
Sales Range: $25-49.9 Million
Emp.: 30
Valve Mfr
N.A.I.C.S.: 332911
Jim Walther *(Pres)*

KITZ Corporation of Asia Pacific Pte. Ltd. (1)
22 Pioneer Crescent 03-06, West Park Biz-Central, Singapore, 628556, Singapore
Tel.: (65) 63390350
Web Site: http://kitzasiapacific.com
Valves Mfr & Distr
N.A.I.C.S.: 332911
Hiroshi Nozawa *(Chm)*

KITZ Corporation of Europe, S.A. (1)
Ramon Vinas 8, 08930, Sant Adria de Besos, Barcelona, Spain
Tel.: (34) 934621408
Web Site: http://www.kitzeurope.com
Industrial Machinery Mfr
N.A.I.C.S.: 333248

KITZ Corporation of Jiangsu Kunshan (1)
No 188 Zhongyang Road B Zone, Kunshan Comprehensive Free Trade Zone, Jiangsu, 215300, China
Tel.: (86) 51257716078
Valve Mfr & Distr
N.A.I.C.S.: 332919

KITZ Corporation of Kunshan (1)
No 15 Taihu South Road Economic and Technology Development Zone, Kunshan, 215300, Jiangsu, China
Tel.: (86) 51257638181
Valve Mfr & Distr
N.A.I.C.S.: 332919

KITZ Corporation of Lianyungang (1)
No 16 Yun Yang Road, Lianyungang Economic and Technical Development Zone, Jiangsu, 222047, China
Tel.: (86) 51882366061
Valve Mfr & Distr
N.A.I.C.S.: 332919

KITZ Corporation of Shanghai (1)
Room 1701-1704 International Corporate City No 3000 North ZhongShan Rd, PuTuo District, Shanghai, 200063, China
Web Site: http://www.kitzchina.com
Industrial Valve Whslr
N.A.I.C.S.: 423840

KITZ Corporation of Taiwan (1)
5-26 East Street N E P Z, Kaohsiung, Taiwan
Tel.: (886) 73611235
Control Valve Mfr & Distr
N.A.I.C.S.: 332919

KITZ Engineering Service Co., Ltd. (1)
1-7-59 Akanehama, Narashino, 275-0024, Chiba, Japan
Tel.: (81) 474520585
Web Site: https://www.kesco.jp
Sales Range: $25-49.9 Million
Emp.: 49
Valves Maintenance Services
N.A.I.C.S.: 332911

KITZ Europe GmbH (1)
Siemensstrasse 1, 61130, Nidderau, Germany
Tel.: (49) 6187928100
Valves & System Equipment Mfr & Whslr
N.A.I.C.S.: 332911

KITZ Hong Kong Company Limited (1)
Unit E 33 Floor Monterey Plaza 15 Chong Yip Street, Kwun Tong, Kowloon, China (Hong Kong)
Tel.: (852) 27282199
Valves & System Equipment Mfr & Distr
N.A.I.C.S.: 332911

KITZ Micro Filter Co., Ltd. (1)
2983 Shiga, Chuo-Ku, Suwa, 392-0012, Nagano, Japan
Web Site: http://www.kitzmf.com
Sales Range: $25-49.9 Million
Emp.: 110
Industrial Filter Mfr
N.A.I.C.S.: 333998

KITZ SCT America Corporation (1)
5201 Great America Pkwy Ste 238, Santa Clara, CA 95054
Tel.: (408) 747-5546
Valves & System Equipment Mfr & Distr
N.A.I.C.S.: 332911

KITZ SCT Co., Ltd. (1)
Omorieki Higashiguchi Bldg 3F 1-5-1 Omorikita, OtaKu, Tokyo, 143-0016, Japan
Tel.: (81) 364042171
Water System Valves Mfr
Hisao Hosokawa *(Co-Pres)*

KITZ SCT Corporation of Kunshan (1)
8-3 No 3 Road Export Processing A Zone, Kunshan, 215300, Jiangsu, China
Tel.: (86) 5125735700
Pipe Mfr & Distr
N.A.I.C.S.: 332919

INTERNATIONAL PUBLIC

KITZ SCT of Kunshan (1)
8-3 No 3 Road Export Processing A Zone, Kunshan, 215300, Jiangsu, China
Tel.: (86) 512 5735 0700
Web Site: https://www.kitz-sct.jp
Semiconductor Production Equipment Fittings Mfr & Sales
N.A.I.C.S.: 334419

KITZ Valve & Actuation (Malaysia) Sdn. Bhd. (1)
No 6 Jalan Teknologi Perintis 1/2, Taman Teknologi Nusajaya, 79200, Iskandar Puteri, Johor, Malaysia
Tel.: (60) 75539731
Web Site: http://kitz-kvm.com
Valves Mfr & Distr
N.A.I.C.S.: 332911
Hiroshi Nozawa *(Mng Dir)*

KITZ Valve & Actuation (Thailand) Co., Ltd. (1)
388 Exchange Tower 17th Floor Unit 1701-1 Sukhumvit Road, Klongtoey Subdistrict Klongtoey District, Bangkok, 10110, Thailand
Tel.: (66) 26634700
Web Site: http://www.kitz-kvt.com
Valves Mfr & Distr
N.A.I.C.S.: 332911
Hiroshi Nozawa *(Mng Dir)*

KITZ Valve & Actuation Singapore Pte. Ltd. (1)
22 Pioneer Crescent 03-06, West Park Biz-Central, Singapore, 628556, Singapore
Tel.: (65) 68611833
Web Site: http://kitz-kvs.com.sg
Valves Mfr & Distr
N.A.I.C.S.: 332911
Hiroshi Nozawa *(Mng Dir)*

KITZ Valve & Actuation Vietnam Co., Ltd. (1)
P1-237 2F The Prince Residence No 17-19-21 Nguyen Van Troi Street, Ward 12 Phu Nhuan District, Ho Chi Minh City, Vietnam
Tel.: (84) 2839956932
Web Site: http://kitz-kvv.com
Valves Distr
N.A.I.C.S.: 423840
Hideyuki Aoyagi *(Gen Dir)*

Kitz Metal Works Corporation (1)
7377 Kobayakawa, Miyagawa, Chino, 391-8555, Nagano, Japan (100%)
Tel.: (81) 266793030
Brass Bar Products Mfr & Distr
N.A.I.C.S.: 332999
Takaoki Nakajima *(Pres)*

Metalurgica Golden Arts Ltda. (1)
Rua Getulio Vargas 496, Bairro Renovacao, Veranopolis, 95330-000, Brazil
Tel.: (55) 5434418900
Web Site: https://www.mga.com.br
Valves Mfr & Distr
N.A.I.C.S.: 332911

Micro Pneumatics Pvt. Ltd. (1)
Plot No 133-134 Vasai Municipal Industrial Area, Umela Phata Papdy Vasai Road West, Palghar, 401 207, Maharashtra, India
Tel.: (91) 2506696000
Web Site: http://www.micropneumatics.in
Valves Mfr & Distr
N.A.I.C.S.: 332911

Miyoshi Valve Co., Ltd. (1)
1-10-1 Nakase, Mihama-ku, Chiba, 261-8577, Japan
Tel.: (81) 432991734
Web Site: http://www.miyoshivalve.com
Valves Mfr & Distr
N.A.I.C.S.: 332911

Perrin GmbH (1)
Siemensstrasse 1, 61130, Nidderau, Germany
Tel.: (49) 6187928250
Web Site: https://www.perrin.de
Valves Mfr & Whslr
N.A.I.C.S.: 332911

Shimizu Alloy Mfg Co., Ltd. (1)
928 Higashinonami-cho, Hikone, 522-0027, Shiga, Japan
Tel.: (81) 749233131
Web Site: http://www.shimizugokin.co.jp

AND PRIVATE COMPANIES — KJK CAPITAL OY

Emp.: 165
Water System Valves Mfr
N.A.I.C.S.: 332919

Toyo Valve Co., Ltd. (1)
5F Tokyo Shiodome Building 1-9-1 Higashi-Shinbashi, Minato-ku, Tokyo, 105-7305, Japan
Tel.: (81) 355689270
Web Site: https://www.toyovalve.co.jp
Emp.: 55
Valves & System Equipment Mfr & Distr
N.A.I.C.S.: 332911
Takashi Taira *(Pres)*

YKV Corporation (1)
5th floor Tokyo Shiodome Building 1-9-1 Higashi-Shinbashi, Minato-ku, Tokyo, 105-7305, Japan
Tel.: (81) 355689241
Web Site: https://www.kitz.co.jp
Control Valve Mfr & Distr
N.A.I.C.S.: 332919

KIU HUNG INTERNATIONAL HOLDINGS LIMITED
25/F Fortis Tower 77-79 Gloucester Road, Wanchai, China (Hong Kong)
Tel.: (852) 39535900
Web Site: http://kiuhung.todayir.com
0381—(HKG)
Rev.: $53,665,260
Assets: $112,192,223
Liabilities: $75,853,703
Net Worth: $36,338,520
Earnings: ($4,908,878)
Emp.: 399
Fiscal Year-end: 12/31/22
Investing Management Services
N.A.I.C.S.: 523940
Ki Yau Hui *(Pres-Toy & Gift Bus)*

Subsidiaries:

Better Sourcing Worldwide Limited (1)
14 Fl Yale Indus Ctr 61-63 Au Pui Wan St, Fotan, Sha Tin, NT, China (Hong Kong)
Tel.: (852) 26930368
Web Site: http://www.bettersourcing.com
Toys Whslr
N.A.I.C.S.: 423920

Kiu Hung Industries Limited (1)
14/F Yale Industrial Centre 61-63 Au Pui Wan St, Fotan, Sha Tin, NT, China (Hong Kong)
Tel.: (852) 2 693 0368
Web Site: https://kiuhung.wixsite.com
Sales Range: $25-49.9 Million
Emp.: 30
Toys Whslr
N.A.I.C.S.: 423920

Kiu Hung Toys Company Limited (1)
14 Fl Yale Indus Ctr 61-63 Au Pui Wan St, Fotan, Sha Tin, NT, China (Hong Kong)
Tel.: (852) 26930368
Stuffed Toys & Dolls Mfr
N.A.I.C.S.: 339930

Toland International Limited (1)
14 Fl Yale Indus Ctr 61-63 Au Pui Wan St, Fotan, Sha Tin, NT, China (Hong Kong)
Tel.: (852) 26930339
Web Site: http://www.kiuhung.com
Sales Range: $25-49.9 Million
Emp.: 31
Flags & Garden Products Whslr
N.A.I.C.S.: 424910

KIVETON PARK STEEL LIMITED
Kiveton Park, Sheffield, S26 6NQ, United Kingdom
Tel.: (44) 1909770252
Web Site: http://www.kpsteel.co.uk
Year Founded: 1922
Sales Range: $25-49.9 Million
Emp.: 118
Steel Bar & Wire Products Mfr
N.A.I.C.S.: 332618
Martin J. Lacey *(Dir-Ops)*

KIWI PROPERTY GROUP LIMITED
Level 7 Vero Centre 48 Shortland Street, Auckland, 1010, New Zealand
Tel.: (64) 93594000
Web Site: https://www.kiwiproperty.com
Year Founded: 1992
KWIPF—(OTCIQ)
Rev.: $154,955,144
Assets: $1,936,855,263
Liabilities: $780,464,713
Net Worth: $1,156,390,550
Earnings: ($136,185,407)
Emp.: 98
Fiscal Year-end: 03/31/23
Real Estate Investment Services
N.A.I.C.S.: 525990
Gavin Parker *(Gen Mgr-Funds Mgmt & Capital Markets)*

KIWOOM NO.3 SPECIAL PURPOSE ACQUISITION COMPANY
18 Yeouinaru-ro 4-gil, Yeongdeungpo-gu, Seoul, Korea (South)
Tel.: (82) 237875053
Year Founded: 2015
Financial Investment Management Services
N.A.I.C.S.: 523940
Tae-Hyeong An *(CEO)*

KIWOOM SECURITIES CO., LTD.
Tel.: (82) 237875236
Year Founded: 2000
039490—(KRS)
Rev.: $7,084,601,339
Assets: $38,631,311,213
Liabilities: $34,991,257,234
Net Worth: $3,640,053,979
Earnings: $323,828,691
Emp.: 899
Fiscal Year-end: 12/31/23
Financial Investment Services
N.A.I.C.S.: 523999
Yik Rae Kim *(Chm)*

KIYO LEARNING CO., LTD.
2-10-1 Nagatacho, Chiyoda-Ku, Tokyo, 100-0014, Japan
Tel.: (81) 364345590
Web Site: https://www.kiyo-learning.com
Year Founded: 2010
7353—(TKS)
Educational Support Services
N.A.I.C.S.: 611710
Kiyoshi Ayabe *(Founder, Chm & Pres)*

KIZUNA CORPORATION
3F MG Atago Bldg 3-13-7 Nishi Shimbashi, Minato-ku, Tokyo, 105-0003, Japan
Tel.: (81) 3 57335904
Web Site: http://www.kizunacorp.jp
Year Founded: 1988
Real Estate Development Services
N.A.I.C.S.: 531120
Kenichi Akiyama *(Pres)*

KIZUNA HOLDINGS CORP.
2-2-12 Hamamatsucho JEI Hamamatsucho Building 2nd Floor, Minato-Ku, Tokyo, 105-0013, Japan
Tel.: (81) 358437092
Web Site: https://www.kizuna-hd.co.jp
Year Founded: 2000
7086—(TKS)
Rev.: $69,606,871
Assets: $186,600,595
Liabilities: $151,873,142
Net Worth: $34,727,453

Earnings: $4,625,041
Fiscal Year-end: 05/31/23
Holding Company
N.A.I.C.S.: 551112
Yasuaki Nakamichi *(Pres & CEO)*

KJ WAJA ENGINEERING (M) SDN. BHD.
ST 492 Jalan Tunas Baru Seksyen 1/9 Kawasan Perindustrian, Miel Masjid Tanah, 78300, Melaka, Malaysia
Tel.: (60) 63841895   MY
Year Founded: 2004
Ship Repair & Maintenance Services
N.A.I.C.S.: 336611
Kamarul Zaman Jantan *(Co-Owner & Mng Dir)*

KJAER GROUP A/S
Groennemosevej 6, DK-5700, Svendborg, Denmark
Tel.: (45) 62221111   DK
Web Site: http://www.kjaergroup.com
Year Founded: 1962
Rev.: $56,402,288
Assets: $34,290,713
Liabilities: $20,399,453
Net Worth: $13,891,260
Earnings: $249,750
Emp.: 275
Fiscal Year-end: 12/31/19
Automotive Vehicles & Parts Exporter
N.A.I.C.S.: 441227
Mads Krarup Kjaer *(CEO)*

Subsidiaries:

Automotive Export Supplies Ltd. (1)
Abbey House Wellington Way, Brooklands Business Park, Weybridge, KT13 0TT, Surrey, United Kingdom (100%)
Tel.: (44) 1932350734
Web Site: http://www.aesltd.co.uk
Export of Automotive Vehicles & Parts
N.A.I.C.S.: 441227

Kjaer Group US Inc. (1)
211 N Union St Ste 100, Alexandria, VA 22314
Tel.: (703) 778-9400
Emp.: 3
Automotive Spare Parts Distr
N.A.I.C.S.: 423120
Lars B. Lauritzen *(Pres)*

KJELL GROUP AB
Tarnogatan 6, 211 24, Malmo, Sweden
Tel.: (46) 724655136
Web Site: https://www.kjellgroup.com
Year Founded: 1988
KJELL—(OMX)
Rev.: $241,113,734
Assets: $226,387,929
Liabilities: $131,864,996
Net Worth: $94,522,933
Earnings: $1,161,782
Emp.: 1,200
Fiscal Year-end: 12/31/23
Electronic Parts Distr
N.A.I.C.S.: 423690
Andreas Rylander *(CEO)*

Subsidiaries:

Kjell & Co Norway AS (1)
Sandviksveien 176, 1337, Sandvika, Norway
Tel.: (47) 69520900
Web Site: https://www.kjell.com
Emp.: 1,200
Home Electronics Accessories Mfr & Distr
N.A.I.C.S.: 335999

KJK CAPITAL OY
Kalevankatu 14 C 4th Fl, 00100, Helsinki, Finland
Tel.: (358) 10 279 0050
Web Site: http://www.kjkcapital.com
Year Founded: 2010

Private Investment Services
N.A.I.C.S.: 523999
Kustaa Aima *(Mng Partner)*

Subsidiaries:

AS Baltika (1)
Valukoja 10, 11415, Tallinn, Estonia (100%)
Tel.: (372) 6302801
Web Site: http://www.baltikagroup.com
Rev.: $14,456,385
Assets: $14,118,619
Liabilities: $13,735,408
Net Worth: $383,211
Earnings: ($3,561,896)
Emp.: 173
Fiscal Year-end: 12/31/2021
Clothing Mfr & Retailer
N.A.I.C.S.: 458110
Jaakko Sakari Mikael Salmelin *(Chm-Supervisory Bd)*

Subsidiary (Non-US):

Baltika Poland Sp.z.o.o. (2)
Nalewki 8/62, 00-158, Warsaw, Poland
Tel.: (48) 228318490
Sales Range: $25-49.9 Million
Emp.: 25
Fashion Apparels Retailer
N.A.I.C.S.: 458110

Baltika Ukraina Ltd (2)
Frunze 1-3 3rd Floor Office 32, 04080, Kiev, Ukraine
Tel.: (380) 445314314
Sales Range: $25-49.9 Million
Emp.: 100
Clothing Retail Stores Operation Services
N.A.I.C.S.: 458110

Subsidiary (Domestic):

OU Baltika Tailor (2)
Kuuli 4, Tallinn, Harju, Estonia
Tel.: (372) 6302700
Clothing Retail Stores Operation Services
N.A.I.C.S.: 458110

OU Baltman (2)
Veerenni 24, Tallinn, 10135, Harju, Estonia
Tel.: (372) 6302806
Web Site: http://www.baltman.ee
Sales Range: $50-74.9 Million
Emp.: 217
Formal Wear Retailer
N.A.I.C.S.: 458110

Subsidiary (Non-US):

OY Baltinia AB (2)
Etelaesalmentie 7, 21620, Kuusisto, Finland
Tel.: (358) 400784505
Clothing Retail Stores Operation Services
N.A.I.C.S.: 458110

SIA Baltika Latvija (2)
12 Udens Street, Riga, LV-1007, Latvia
Tel.: (371) 67807540
Web Site: http://www.baltikagroup.com
Sales Range: $50-74.9 Million
Emp.: 101
Clothing Retail Stores Operation Services
N.A.I.C.S.: 458110
Mara Strode *(Mng Dir)*

Kovinoplastika Loz, d.d. (1)
Cesta 19 Oktobra 57 Stari trg pri, 1386, Loz, Slovenia
Tel.: (386) 17095246
Web Site: http://www.kovinoplastika.si
Sales Range: $300-349.9 Million
Emp.: 1,060
Partitions & Fixtures Mfr
N.A.I.C.S.: 337215
Slavica Cuk *(Member-Mgmt Bd)*

Subsidiary (Non-US):

ALVEUS ROMANIA S.R.L. (2)
Str Petre Liciu nr 10 Sector 4, Bucharest, 40308, Romania
Tel.: (40) 21 330 00 13
Web Site: http://www.alveus.ro
Sales Range: $50-74.9 Million
Emp.: 9
Kitchen Appliance Sales & Installation Services
N.A.I.C.S.: 423620
Radu Ilie *(Mng Dir)*

KJK CAPITAL OY

KJK Capital Oy—(Continued)

Alveus Sp. z o.o. (2)
Ul Sloneczna 155 A, 05-506, Lesznowola, Poland
Tel.: (48) 22 643 95 32
Web Site: http://www.alveus.pl
Sales Range: $50-74.9 Million
Emp.: 20
Kitchen Appliance Sales & Installation Services
N.A.I.C.S.: 423620

Alveus Vertriebs GmbH (2)
Arnulfstrabe 37, Munich, 80636, Germany
Tel.: (49) 89 74 66 22 35
Web Site: http://www.alveus.de
Kitchen Appliance Sales & Installation Services
N.A.I.C.S.: 423620

KOVINOPLASTIKA ZAGREB
d.o.o. (2)
Kovinska 29, 10090, Zagreb, Croatia
Tel.: (385) 1 34 51 599
Kitchen Appliance Sales & Installation Services
N.A.I.C.S.: 423620

LOZ METALPRES d.o.o. (2)
Muhvic Antuna 52, 51303, Plesce, Croatia
Tel.: (385) 51 825 102
Web Site: http://www.loz-metalpres.hr
Sales Range: $50-74.9 Million
Emp.: 150
Metal & Plastic Product Mfr
N.A.I.C.S.: 333517

LOZ d.o.o. (2)
Krnjesevacka Bb, 22310, Simanovci, Serbia
Tel.: (381) 22 480 175
Web Site: http://www.lozbgd.co.rs
Sales Range: $50-74.9 Million
Emp.: 13
Kitchen Appliance Sale & Installation Distr
N.A.I.C.S.: 423620

KJMC CORPORATE ADVISORS (INDIA) LTD.

162 Atlanta 16th Floor Nariman Point, Mumbai, 400021, Maharashtra, India
Tel.: (91) 2240945500
Web Site:
https://www.kjmcfinserv.com
532304—(BOM)
Rev.: $842,922
Assets: $6,036,972
Liabilities: $507,719
Net Worth: $5,529,253
Earnings: $47,038
Emp.: 6
Fiscal Year-end: 03/31/23
Financial Services
N.A.I.C.S.: 523940
Inderchand Mohanlal Jain (Chm)

KJMC FINANCIAL SERVICES LTD.

162 16th Atlanta Floor Nariman Point, Mumbai, 400021, India
Tel.: (91) 2240945500
Web Site:
https://www.kjmcfinserv.com
530235—(BOM)
Rev.: $266,994
Assets: $11,283,145
Liabilities: $1,527,449
Net Worth: $9,755,696
Earnings: ($208,900)
Emp.: 4
Fiscal Year-end: 03/31/21
Financial Services
N.A.I.C.S.: 522320
Rajnesh Inderchand Jain (Exec Dir)

KKALPANA INDUSTRIES (INDIA) LIMITED

16A Shakespeare Sarani 4th Floor Room No 3, BK Market, Kolkata, 700071, West Bengal, India
Tel.: (91) 22823744
Web Site:
https://www.kkalpanagroup.com
526409—(BOM)
Rev.: $6,343,537
Assets: $9,884,306
Liabilities: $5,301,428
Net Worth: $4,582,878
Earnings: $684,561
Emp.: 319
Fiscal Year-end: 03/31/22
Polymer Compound Mfr
N.A.I.C.S.: 325991
Rajesh Kumar Kothari (Exec Dir)

KKB ENGINEERING BERHAD

Lot 865 Section 66 Jalan Kilang Bintawa Industrial Estate, 93450, Kuching, Sarawak, Malaysia
Tel.: (60) 82333877
Web Site: http://www.kkbeb.com.my
KKB—(KLS)
Rev.: $102,520,191
Assets: $139,829,827
Liabilities: $39,949,535
Net Worth: $99,880,292
Earnings: $7,476,206
Emp.: 1,170
Fiscal Year-end: 12/31/23
Liquefied Petroleum Gas Cylinders Mfr
N.A.I.C.S.: 332420
Jan Moi Voon (Sec)

Subsidiaries:

Harum Bidang Sdn. Bhd. (1)
Lot 1382 Block 7, Muara Tebas Land District Sejingkat Industrial Estate, 93050, Kuching, Sarawak, Malaysia
Tel.: (60) 82433008
Steel Pole Mfr
N.A.I.C.S.: 331210

KKB Industries (Sabah) Sdn. Bhd. (1)
No 11-13 Jalan 1G KKIP Selatan Lots 13 14 and 15 IZ4, Kota Kinabalu Industrial Park, 88460, Kota Kinabalu, Sabah, Malaysia
Tel.: (60) 88495240
Steel Pole Mfr
N.A.I.C.S.: 331210
Mohd Erwansyah Abdullah (Sr Mgr)

KKCG GROUP

Vinohradska 230/1511, 100 00, Prague, Czech Republic
Tel.: (420) 225 010 612
Web Site: http://kkcg.com
Investment Services
N.A.I.C.S.: 523999
Karel Komarek (Founder)

Subsidiaries:

Allwyn AG (1)
Weinmarkt 9, 6004, Lucerne, Switzerland
Tel.: (41) 412660943
Web Site:
https://www.allwynentertainment.com
Lottery Operator
N.A.I.C.S.: 713290

Subsidiary (Domestic):

Allwyn Entertainment AG (2)
Weinmarkt 9, 6004, Lucerne, Switzerland
Tel.: (41) 412660943
Web Site:
https://www.allwynentertainment.com
Emp.: 100
Lottery Operator
N.A.I.C.S.: 713290
Robert Chvatal (CEO)

Subsidiary (Non-US):

Allwyn International a.s. (2)
Vinohradska 1511/230, 100 00, Prague, Czech Republic
Tel.: (420) 225010650
Lottery Operator
N.A.I.C.S.: 713290
Karel Komarek (Chm)

Camelot UK Lotteries Limited (2)
Tolpits Lane, Watford, WD18 9RN, Herts, United Kingdom
Tel.: (44) 1923425000
Web Site: http://www.camelotgroup.co.uk
Sales Range: $250-299.9 Million
Lottery Services
N.A.I.C.S.: 713290
Gerry Acher (Deputy Chm)

KKO INTERNATIONAL SA

9 Avenue Bugeaud, FR-75116, Paris, France
Tel.: (33) 153656862
Web Site: https://www.kko-international.com
Year Founded: 2011
ALKKO—(EUR)
Sales Range: Less than $1 Million
Cocoa Farming Services
N.A.I.C.S.: 111199
Jacques-Antoine de Geffrier (Founder)

KKRRAFTON DEVELOPERS LIMITED

707 West Bank Ashram road, Ellisbridge, Ahmedabad, 380009, India
Tel.: (91) 797949229525
Web Site:
https://kkrraftondevelopersltd.com
Year Founded: 1992
Rev.: $21,582
Assets: $848,866
Liabilities: $772,931
Net Worth: $75,935
Earnings: $1,525
Fiscal Year-end: 03/31/18
Information Technology Services
N.A.I.C.S.: 541512
Neha Samir Dadia (Mng Dir)

KKTC TELSIM

Ali Riza Efendi Caddesi No 33A, Ortakoy, Nicosia, Cyprus
Tel.: (357) 444 0542
Web Site: http://www.kktctelsim.com
Year Founded: 1995
Mobile Telecommunications Services
N.A.I.C.S.: 517111
Fevzi Tanpinar (Deputy Dir Gen)

KKV AGRO POWERS LTD.

Vivaaga Building 637 Oppanakara Street, Coimbatore, 641 001, Tamil Nadu, India
Tel.: (91) 4222303880
Web Site:
https://www.kkvagropowers.com
Year Founded: 1956
KKVAPOW—(NSE)
Rev.: $148,373,994
Assets: $5,631,281
Liabilities: $3,046,808
Net Worth: $2,584,473
Earnings: $142,965
Emp.: 12
Fiscal Year-end: 03/31/23
Renewable Power Generation Services
N.A.I.C.S.: 221118
T. K. Chandiran (Chm & Mng Dir)

KL-NET CORP.

Tel.: (82) 25387227
Web Site: http://www.klnet.co.kr
Year Founded: 1994
039420—(KRS)
Rev.: $38,582,042
Assets: $46,607,446
Liabilities: $7,432,901
Net Worth: $39,174,545
Earnings: $5,713,370
Emp.: 180
Fiscal Year-end: 12/31/22
Logistic Services
N.A.I.C.S.: 541614

INTERNATIONAL PUBLIC

Jung Jiwon (Pres)

KLAB INC.

Roppongi Hills Mori Tower 6-10-1 Roppongi, Minato-ku, Tokyo, 106-6122, Japan
Tel.: (81) 357711100
Web Site: https://www.klab.jp
Year Founded: 2000
3656—(TKS)
Rev.: $75,983,530
Assets: $125,875,860
Liabilities: $42,859,050
Net Worth: $83,016,810
Earnings: ($12,896,710)
Emp.: 415
Fiscal Year-end: 12/31/23
Software Publisher
N.A.I.C.S.: 513210
Tetsuya Sanada (Chm)

Subsidiaries:

KLab Ventures Inc. (1)
Roppongi Hills Mori Tower 6-10-1 Roppongi, Minato-ku, Tokyo, Japan
Tel.: (81) 357711107
Web Site: http://www.klabventures.jp
Asset Management Services
N.A.I.C.S.: 523940
Hirokazu Nagano (Pres & CEO)

KLABIN S.A.

3rd 4th and 5th Floors Avenida Brigadeiro Faria Lima 3600, Itaim Bibi, 4538-132, Sao Paulo, SP, Brazil
Tel.: (55) 1130465800
Web Site: http://www.klabin.com.br
Year Founded: 1899
KLBN11—(BRAZ)
Rev.: $3,221,921,046
Assets: $9,909,491,880
Liabilities: $7,454,668,113
Net Worth: $2,454,823,767
Earnings: $508,998,396
Emp.: 25,000
Fiscal Year-end: 12/31/23
Paper Mfr & Whslr
N.A.I.C.S.: 322120
Francisco Cesar Razzolini (Dir-Industrial Tech, Innovation, Sustainability & Projects)

Subsidiaries:

Celucat SA (1)
Av Unitika 320-Jd Luciane, Americana, Sao Paulo, Brazil
Tel.: (55) 1934789400
Web Site: http://www.celucat.com.br
Paper Products Mfr
N.A.I.C.S.: 322120

Klabin Argentina S.A. (1)
Calle del Canal 467, Parque Industrial Pilar, B1629MXA, Buenos Aires, Argentina
Tel.: (54) 2304497100
Paper Product Mfr & Whslr
N.A.I.C.S.: 322120

Klabin Austria GmbH (1)
Albertgasse 35, 1080, Vienna, Austria
Tel.: (43) 171728590
Paper Product Mfr & Whslr
N.A.I.C.S.: 322120

Klabin Forest Products Company (1)
80 SW 8th St-Ste 2900, Miami, FL 33131
Tel.: (786) 871-1617
Paper Product Mfr & Whslr
N.A.I.C.S.: 322120

KLAGER PLASTIK GMBH

Portnerstrasse 84, 86356, Neuss, Germany
Tel.: (49) 821207900
Web Site: http://www.klaeger-plastik.de
Year Founded: 1949
Sales Range: $10-24.9 Million
Emp.: 128
Microinjection Moulding Machines Mfr
N.A.I.C.S.: 333248

AND PRIVATE COMPANIES

Karlheinz Klager (Mng Dir)

KLAIPEDOS NAFTA AB
Buriu st 19, LT-92276, Klaipeda, Lithuania
Tel.: (370) 46391772
Web Site: https://www.kn.lt
Year Founded: 1994
KNF1L—(RSE)
Rev.: $75,918,743
Assets: $702,652,767
Liabilities: $524,910,472
Net Worth: $177,742,295
Earnings: ($78,620,871)
Emp.: 375
Fiscal Year-end: 12/31/21
Petroleum Product Distr
N.A.I.C.S.: 424720
Darius Silenskis (CEO)

KLAKKI EHF.
Sidumuli 28, 108, Reykjavik, Iceland
Tel.: (354) 5508600   IS
Web Site: http://www.klakki.is
Sales Range: $1-4.9 Billion
Emp.: 6
Investment, Insurance & Financial Services
N.A.I.C.S.: 523150
Magnus Scheving Thorsteinsson (CEO)

Subsidiaries:

Lifis Insurance Ltd.   (1)
Armula 3, 108, Reykjavik, Iceland
Tel.: (354) 5605000
Web Site: http://www.vis.is
Sales Range: $100-124.9 Million
Fire Insurance Services
N.A.I.C.S.: 524113

Lysing Ltd.   (1)
Sioumul 24, 108, Reykjavik, Iceland
Tel.: (354) 5401700
Web Site: http://www.lysing.is
Sales Range: $25-49.9 Million
Emp.: 50
Asset Financing Services
N.A.I.C.S.: 921130
Lilja Halldorsdottir (Gen Mgr)

VIS Insurance Ltd.   (1)
Armuli 3, 108, Reykjavik, Iceland
Tel.: (354) 5605000
Web Site: https://www.vis.is
Rev.: $221,101,968
Assets: $470,111,805
Liabilities: $318,374,551
Net Worth: $151,737,254
Earnings: $13,261,741
Emp.: 208
Fiscal Year-end: 12/31/2023
Non-Life Insurance Services
N.A.I.C.S.: 524128
Valdimar Svavarsson (Chm)

KLANICA 8. OKTOBAR A.D.
Solunska 2, Petrovac na Mlavi, Serbia
Tel.: (381) 12 331 149
Year Founded: 1989
KOKT—(BEL)
Sales Range: $1-9.9 Million
Meat Processing Services
N.A.I.C.S.: 311612
Nenad Jovanovic (Exec Dir)

KLANICA SO LADILNIK AD
Kliment Ohridski br 45, Strumica, North Macedonia
Tel.: (389) 34322516
KLST—(MAC)
Rev.: $5,016,528
Assets: $3,172,476
Liabilities: $1,231,904
Net Worth: $1,940,571
Earnings: $9,495
Fiscal Year-end: 12/31/23
Meat Product Distr
N.A.I.C.S.: 424470

KLARABO SVERIGE AB
Hyllie Vattenparksgata 11A, 215 32, Malmo, Sweden   SE
Web Site: https://www.klarabo.se
Year Founded: 2015
KLARA.B—(OMX)
Rev.: $57,299,423
Assets: $918,250,060
Liabilities: $527,488,245
Net Worth: $390,761,815
Earnings: ($37,872,020)
Fiscal Year-end: 12/31/23
Residential Property Management Services
N.A.I.C.S.: 531311
Andreas Morfiadakis (CEO)

KLARIA PHARMA HOLDING AB
Tel.: (46) 084464299
Web Site: https://www.klaria.com
KLAR—(OMX)
Rev.: $549,608
Assets: $11,264,810
Liabilities: $4,138,919
Net Worth: $7,125,891
Earnings: ($5,973,194)
Emp.: 6
Fiscal Year-end: 12/31/22
Pharmaceuticals Mfr
N.A.I.C.S.: 325412
Scott Boyer (Chief Scientific Officer)

Subsidiaries:

Karessa Pharma Holding AB   (1)
Lahallsvagen 48, 183 30, Taby, Sweden
Tel.: (46) 8 768 22 33
Web Site: http://www.karessa.se
Pharmaceuticals Mfr
N.A.I.C.S.: 325412
Jan Berglund (COO)

KLARNA AB
Norra Stationsgatan 61 swevagen 426 1011, 113 43, Stockholm, Sweden
Tel.: (46) 8 120 120 00
Web Site: http://www.klarna.com
Sales Range: $50-74.9 Million
Emp.: 900
Online Payment Processing Services
N.A.I.C.S.: 522320
Michael J. Moritz (Chm)

Subsidiaries:

Klarna Austria GmbH   (1)
Mayerhofgasse 1/20, 1040, Vienna, Austria
Tel.: (43) 720883810
Electronic Shopping Services
N.A.I.C.S.: 522220

Klarna BV   (1)
De Ruyterkade 7, 1013 AA, Amsterdam, Netherlands
Tel.: (31) 203030100
Electronic Shopping Services
N.A.I.C.S.: 522220

Klarna GmbH   (1)
Im MediaPark 8a, 50670, Cologne, Germany
Tel.: (49) 22166950100
Electronic Shopping Services
N.A.I.C.S.: 522220

Klarna Norge AS   (1)
Kronprinsens gate 5, 0251, Oslo, Norway
Tel.: (47) 21018991
Management Consulting Services
N.A.I.C.S.: 541618

Klarna UK Limited   (1)
36 Carnaby Street Soho, London, W1F 7DR, United Kingdom
Tel.: (44) 8081893333
Electronic Shopping Services
N.A.I.C.S.: 522390

KLARSEN SA
1 Cours Xavier Arnozan, 33000, Bordeaux, France
Tel.: (33) 557227660   FR
Web Site: https://www.klarsen.com
Year Founded: 1995
ALKLA—(EUR)
Rev.: $2,256,770
Assets: $6,865,804
Liabilities: $8,696,099
Net Worth: ($1,830,295)
Earnings: $1,881,064
Emp.: 8
Fiscal Year-end: 12/31/21
Data Marketing Agency
N.A.I.C.S.: 541613
Julien Parrou-Duboscq (Chm, CEO & Dir-IR)

KLAS A.D.
Marije Bursac 17, 74400, Derventa, Bosnia & Herzegovina
Tel.: (387) 53333087
Year Founded: 1957
CLASS-RA—(BANJ)
Rev.: $6,573
Assets: $476,782
Liabilities: $337,189
Net Worth: $139,593
Earnings: ($49,214)
Emp.: 1
Fiscal Year-end: 12/31/12
Bakery Products Mfr
N.A.I.C.S.: 311812
Milivoje Novic (Chm)

KLAS D.D.
Paromlinska 43, 71 000, Sarajevo, Bosnia & Herzegovina
Tel.: (387) 33727124
Web Site: http://www.klas.ba
Year Founded: 1902
KLASR—(SARE)
Rev.: $30,755,919
Assets: $47,195,404
Liabilities: $28,170,545
Net Worth: $19,024,860
Earnings: $67,267
Emp.: 503
Fiscal Year-end: 12/31/21
Food Products Distr
N.A.I.C.S.: 445298

KLASS CAPITAL CORP.
MaRS Centre Heritage Building 101 College Street Suite 145, Toronto, M5G 1L7, ON, Canada
Tel.: (647) 494-9881
Web Site: http://www.klass.com
Year Founded: 2013
Emp.: 200
Privater Equity Firm
N.A.I.C.S.: 523999
Daniel Klass (Founder & Mng Dir)

Subsidiaries:

Rightsline Software Inc.   (1)
448 S Hill St 901, Los Angeles, CA 90013
Tel.: (310) 507-1270
Web Site: https://www.rightsline.com
Software Development Services
N.A.I.C.S.: 513210
Kira Baca (Chief Revenue Officer)

Subsidiary (Domestic):

RSG Media Systems, LLC   (2)
450 Lexington Ave 4th Fl, New York, NY 10017
Tel.: (212) 448-9191
Web Site: http://www.rsgmedia.com
Sales Range: $1-9.9 Million
Emp.: 41
Computer System Design Services
N.A.I.C.S.: 541512
Mukesh Sehgal (CEO)

Real Software Systems, LLC   (2)
20931 Burbank Blvd Ste B, Woodland Hills, CA 91367
Tel.: (818) 313-8000
Web Site: http://www.realsoftwaresystems.com
Prepackaged Software Services
N.A.I.C.S.: 513210
Dan Boe (VP)

KLASSIK RADIO AG
Imhofstrasse 12, 86159, Augsburg, Germany
Tel.: (49) 82150700
Web Site: http://www.klassikradioag.de
Year Founded: 2001
KA8—(DEU)
Rev.: $21,889,742
Assets: $21,359,884
Liabilities: $11,568,558
Net Worth: $9,791,327
Earnings: $706,477
Emp.: 53
Fiscal Year-end: 12/31/23
Radio Broadcasting Services
N.A.I.C.S.: 516210

KLAUS UNION GMBH & CO. KG
Blumenfeldstrasse 18, Bochum, 44795, Germany
Tel.: (49) 23445950
Web Site: http://www.klaus-union.com
Year Founded: 1946
Rev.: $48,279,000
Emp.: 240
Industrial Pumps & Valves Mfr
N.A.I.C.S.: 333914
Thomas Eschner (Co-Mng Dir)

KLAUSNER TRADING INTERNATIONAL GMBH
Bahnhofstrasse 13, Oberndorf, Tirol, 6372, Austria
Tel.: (43) 53 52 602 0
Web Site: http://www.klausner-group.com
Year Founded: 1991
Sales Range: $350-399.9 Million
Sawmill Operator; Softwood Products Distr
N.A.I.C.S.: 321113
Michael Almberger (Mng Dir)

Subsidiaries:

Klausner Trading USA, Inc.   (1)
1297 Professional Dr Ste 202, Myrtle Beach, SC 29577
Tel.: (843) 626-9600
Sawmill Operator
N.A.I.C.S.: 321113
Thomas Mende (Pres)

KLAVENESS COMBINATION CARRIERS ASA
Drammensveien 260, NO-0283, Oslo, Norway
Tel.: (47) 22526000
Web Site: https://www.combinationcarriers.com
Year Founded: 2018
KCC—(OSL)
Rev.: $287,166,000
Assets: $628,041,000
Liabilities: $266,343,000
Net Worth: $361,698,000
Earnings: $86,899,000
Emp.: 10
Fiscal Year-end: 12/31/23
Freight Transportation Services
N.A.I.C.S.: 483111
Lasse Kristoffersen (Chm)

Subsidiaries:

Klaveness Combination Carriers Asia Pte. Ltd.   (1)
9 Raffles Place 16-02 Republic Plaza, Singapore, 048619, Singapore
Tel.: (65) 63035560
Web Site: https://www.klaveness.com
Commercial Ship Management Services

KLAVENESS COMBINATION CARRIERS ASA

Klaveness Combination Carriers ASA—(Continued)
N.A.I.C.S.: 488390
Anne Mette Hansen *(Sr Mgr)*

KLAVENESS MARINE HOLDING AS
Harbitzalleen 2A, 0275, Oslo, Norway
Tel.: (47) 22398500   NO
Web Site:
  http://www.klavenessmarine.com
Year Founded: 2011
Investment Holding Company
N.A.I.C.S.: 551112
Henrik Romero Falch *(Head-Fin Investments)*

Subsidiaries:

Norwegian Car Carriers AS   **(1)**
Drammensveien 167, 0277, Oslo, Norway
(47) 23116464
Web Site: http://www.noccasa.no
Sales Range: $75-99.9 Million
Emp.: 11
Freight Transportation Services
N.A.I.C.S.: 483112
Lars Nyflot *(Dir-Comml & Chartering)*

KLEANNARA CO., LTD
4th floor Ilshin Building 98 Hannam-daero, Yongsan-gu, Seoul, Korea (South)
Tel.: (82) 222709200
Web Site:
  https://www.kleannara.co.kr
Year Founded: 1966
004540—(KRS)
Rev: $465,150,021
Assets: $507,023,033
Liabilities: $321,909,407
Net Worth: $185,113,626
Earnings: ($2,230,736)
Emp.: 610
Fiscal Year-end: 12/31/22
Paper Products Mfr
N.A.I.C.S.: 322130
Byung Min Choi *(Chm)*

Subsidiaries:

KleanNara Co., Ltd - Cheongju Factory   **(1)**
64 Taeseong 1-gil Gangnae-myeon, Heungdeok-gu, Cheongju, Chungcheongbuk-do, Korea (South)
Tel.: (82) 432307200
Emp.: 1,100
Toilet Paper & Baby Diaper Mfr
N.A.I.C.S.: 322291

KLEEMANN HELLAS S.A.
Kilkis Industrial Area, PO Box 25, 611 00, Kilkis, Greece
Tel.: (30) 23410 38100
Web Site:
  http://www.kleemannlifts.com
Year Founded: 1983
Sales Range: $100-124.9 Million
Emp.: 1,267
Lift Mfr
N.A.I.C.S.: 335999
Nikolaos K. Koukountzos *(Chm)*

Subsidiaries:

KLEEMANN ASANSOR San. Ve Tic. A.S.   **(1)**
Orta Mahallesi Mesudiye Sokak Sabanci Universitesi yani No 8 Orhanli, Tuzla, 34956, Istanbul, Turkiye
Tel.: (90) 216 4662267
Elevator Distr
N.A.I.C.S.: 423830

KLEEMANN LIFT RO S.R.L.   **(1)**
str Filderman Wilhelm nr 4 bis, 3 district, Bucharest, Romania
Tel.: (40) 314228917
Web Site: http://www.kleemannlifts.ro
Emp.: 4
Elevator Distr
N.A.I.C.S.: 423830

Joiulius Athanasidis *(CEO)*

KLEEMANN LIFTOVI d.o.o.   **(1)**
Golubinacka bb Simanovci, Belgrade, Serbia
Tel.: (381) 22 409000
Web Site: http://www.kleemannlifts.com
Lift & Lifting Devices Mfr
N.A.I.C.S.: 335999

KLEEMANN LIFTS RUS   **(1)**
Plekhanova Street 4a, 111123, Moscow, Russia
Tel.: (7) 499 951 13 99
Web Site: http://www.kleemannlifts.ru
Elevator Distr
N.A.I.C.S.: 423830

KLEEMANN LIFTS U.K. LTD   **(1)**
Unit 8 Arena 14 Charbridge Lane, Bicester, OX26 4ST, Oxfordshire, United Kingdom
Tel.: (44) 1869327070
Elevator Distr
N.A.I.C.S.: 423830

Kunshan HK Elevator Systems Co., Ltd   **(1)**
No 238 Chenfeng Road KSND Kunshan American Industrial Park, Kunshan, 215300, Jiangsu, China
Tel.: (86) 512 36823223
Web Site: http://www.kleemannlifts.com.cn
Emp.: 55
Elevator Distr
N.A.I.C.S.: 423830

KLEER VU DELUXE ALBUMS INC.
4330 Garand, Saint Laurent, H4R 2A3, QC, Canada
Tel.: (514) 353-9250
Web Site: http://www.kvdinc.com
Year Founded: 1896
Rev: $12,000,000
Emp.: 25
Office Supplies
N.A.I.C.S.: 459410
Alfred Gestetner *(Pres)*

KLEINKRAFTWERK BIRSECK AG (KKB)
Weidenstrasse 27, CH 4142, Munchenstein, Switzerland
Tel.: (41) 61 415 41 41
Web Site: http://www.kkbenergy.ch
Holding Company; Renewable Energies Production
N.A.I.C.S.: 551112
Antoine Millioud *(CEO)*

Subsidiaries:

Birseck Hydro AG   **(1)**
EBM Joachim Krebs Weidenstrasse 27, 4142, Bern, Switzerland
Tel.: (41) 61 415 43 85
Web Site: http://www.ebm.ch
Energy Consulting Services
N.A.I.C.S.: 541690
Conrad Ammann *(CEO)*

KKB Deutschland GmbH   **(1)**
Dr-Franken-Str 1, 47551, Bedburg-Hau, Germany
Tel.: (49) 2821977090
Web Site: http://www.kkbgmbh.com
Civil Construction Services
N.A.I.C.S.: 236116
Meinard Schmidlin *(Mgr-Asset)*

KKB Verwaltungs GmbH   **(1)**
Bernhard-Nocht-Str 113, 20359, Hamburg, Germany
Tel.: (49) 2131109286
Civil Construction Services
N.A.I.C.S.: 236116

KLEMKE MINING CORPORATION
11564-149 Street NW, Edmonton, T5M 1W7, AB, Canada
Tel.: (780) 454-0664
Web Site: http://www.kmcmining.com
Year Founded: 1949
Rev: $162,847,891

Emp.: 250
Mining Services
N.A.I.C.S.: 213114
Craig Dirk *(Pres)*

KLEOS SPACE SA
9 avenue des Hauts-Fourneaux, 4362, Esch-sur-Alzette, Luxembourg
Tel.: (352) 20882290
Web Site: http://www.kleos.space
Year Founded: 2017
KSS—(ASX)
Rev: $290,819
Assets: $11,092,811
Liabilities: $5,555,838
Net Worth: $5,536,973
Earnings: ($7,812,243)
Emp.: 23
Fiscal Year-end: 12/31/22
Telecommunication Servicesb
N.A.I.C.S.: 517112
Pete Round *(Dir & Chm)*

KLEPIERRE SA
26 boulevard des Capucines, FR-75009, Paris, France
Tel.: (33) 140675400   FR
Web Site: https://www.klepierre.com
LI—(EUR)
Rev: $1,275,085,550
Assets: $22,179,931,563
Liabilities: $11,119,549,621
Net Worth: $11,060,381,942
Earnings: $192,405,343
Fiscal Year-end: 12/31/23
Offices of Other Holding Companies
N.A.I.C.S.: 551112
Jean-Michel Gault *(CFO & Member-Exec Bd)*

Subsidiaries:

Hoog Catharijne BV   **(1)**
Godebaldkwartier 54, 3511 DX, Utrecht, Netherlands
Tel.: (31) 302346113
Web Site: http://www.hoog-catharijne.klepierre.nl
Online Shopping Services
N.A.I.C.S.: 441110
Colette de Zwart *(Mgr-Back Office)*

Klepierre Athinon Fonciere   **(1)**
3 Str Tompra, Agia Paraskevi, Athens, 15342, Greece
Tel.: (30) 2106062100
Real Estate Manangement Services
N.A.I.C.S.: 531390

Klepierre CZ SRO   **(1)**
Plzenska 16, Prague, 150 00, Czech Republic
Tel.: (420) 251 101 061
Sales Range: $25-49.9 Million
Emp.: 35
Real Estate Lending Services
N.A.I.C.S.: 531190
Pavel Kopriva *(Gen Mgr)*

Klepierre Conseil SNC   **(1)**
26 Blvd Capucines, Cs-20 062, Paris, 75009, France
Tel.: (33) 140675740
Web Site: http://www.klepierre.com
Emp.: 600
Real Estate Management Services
N.A.I.C.S.: 531390

Klepierre Creteil SCI   **(1)**
26 boulevard des Capucines, 75009, Paris, 75009, France
Tel.: (33) 140675740
Web Site: http://www.klepierre.com
Emp.: 300
Financial Management Services
N.A.I.C.S.: 522320

Klepierre Finance SAS   **(1)**
26 Boulevard Capucines, 75009, Paris, France
Tel.: (33) 140675740
Emp.: 400
Investment Management Service
N.A.I.C.S.: 523940
Jean-Marc Jestin *(Pres)*

INTERNATIONAL PUBLIC

Klepierre Larissa Ltd.   **(1)**
3 Str Tompra, Agia Paraskevi, Athens, 15342, Greece
Tel.: (30) 2106062100
Real Estate Prorperty Leasing Services
N.A.I.C.S.: 531190

Klepierre Makedonia Fonciere   **(1)**
3 Stratigou Tompra, Agia Paraskevi, 15342, Athens, Greece
Tel.: (30) 2106062100
Real Estate Management Services
N.A.I.C.S.: 531390

Klepierre Management Italia S.r.l.   **(1)**
Via Gadames 7, 2012451, Milan, Italy
Tel.: (39) 02321131
Emp.: 130
Real Estate Investment Services
N.A.I.C.S.: 531390
Ermanno Niccoli *(Gen Mgr)*

Klepierre NEA Efkarpia Fonciere   **(1)**
3 Str Tompra, Agia Paraskevi, Athens, 15342, Greece
Tel.: (30) 2106062100
Real Estate Manangement Services
N.A.I.C.S.: 531390

Klepierre Nederland B.V.   **(1)**
Stationsplein 97, Duvenborch, 3511 ED, Utrecht, Netherlands
Tel.: (31) 302346464
Web Site: http://www.klepierre.com
Retail Store Development & Property Management Services
N.A.I.C.S.: 531312

Subsidiary (Domestic):

Klepierre Vastgoed Ontwikkeling B.V.   **(2)**
Stationsplein 97, 3511 ED, Utrecht, Netherlands
Tel.: (31) 302346123
Commercial Property Development Services
N.A.I.C.S.: 237210

Klepierre Nordica BV   **(1)**
Reguliersdwarsstraat 90, Amsterdam, 1017 BN, Netherlands
Tel.: (31) 205215645
Investment Management Service
N.A.I.C.S.: 523940

Klepierre Plzen a.s.   **(1)**
Radcicka 2, 301 00, Plzen, Czech Republic   **(100%)**
Tel.: (420) 374809300
Web Site: http://cz.club-onlyou.com
Real Estate Development Services
N.A.I.C.S.: 531390
Patrik Packun *(Dir-OC Plzen Plaza)*

Klepierre Poznan SP z.o.o   **(1)**
Armii Ludowej 26, Warsaw, 00-609, Poland
Tel.: (48) 223566950
Real Estate Development Services
N.A.I.C.S.: 531390

Klepierre Praha SRO   **(1)**
Novodvorska 1800/136, 142 00, Prague, Czech Republic
Tel.: (420) 225437100
Web Site: http://www.plazanovodvorska.cz
Shopping Center Operator
N.A.I.C.S.: 531120
Marketa Nicoletti *(Office Mgr)*

Steen & Strom AS   **(1)**
Dronning Eufemias gate 8, 0191, Oslo, Norway
Tel.: (47) 23213500
Web Site: https://www.steenstrom.com
Real Estate Services
N.A.I.C.S.: 531390

Steen & Strom Danemark A/S   **(1)**
Arne Jacobsens Alle 20 3, 2300, Copenhagen, Denmark
Tel.: (45) 70105505
Real Estate Services
N.A.I.C.S.: 531390

Vinterbro Senter DA   **(1)**
Sjoskogenveien 7, PO Box 92, 1407, Vinterbro, Norway
Tel.: (47) 91660630
Web Site:
  http://www.vinterbro.steenstrom.no

Online Shopping Services
N.A.I.C.S.: 444230
Lars-Erik Bakk (Mgr-Leasing)

KLEPPER FALTBOOTWERFT AG
Kaiserkai 10, 20457, Hamburg, Germany
Tel.: (49) 80312715639
Web Site: https://www.klepper.de
KFW1—(BER)
Sales Range: Less than $1 Million
Boat Building Product Mfr
N.A.I.C.S.: 336612
Michael Muller (CEO)

KLESCH & COMPANY SA
Rue de la Coulouvreniere 25, 1204, Geneva, Switzerland
Tel.: (41) 227372777
Web Site: http://www.klesch.com
Sales Range: $5-14.9 Billion
Emp.: 4,500
Private Equity Services
N.A.I.C.S.: 523999
A. Gary Klesch (Founder)

Subsidiaries:

Klesch & Company Limited (1)
16 Paris Street, London, W1E 5JD, United Kingdom
Tel.: (44) 2074934300
Web Site: http://www.klesch.com
Sales Range: $50-74.9 Million
Emp.: 50
Equity Investment Firm
N.A.I.C.S.: 523999
A. Gary Klesch (Founder & Chm)

Holding (Non-US):

Aluminum Delfzijl B.V. (2)
Oosterhorn 20-22, 9936 HD, Farmsum, Netherlands
Tel.: (31) 596638555
Web Site: http://www.aldel.nl
Sales Range: $100-124.9 Million
Aluminum Foundry
N.A.I.C.S.: 331524

Zeeland Aluminum Company NV (2)
Frankrigkweg 2 Havennummer 5993, 4389 PB, Vlissingen, Netherlands
Tel.: (31) 113615000
Web Site: http://www.zalco.nl
Sales Range: $75-99.9 Million
Primary Aluminum Mfr & Distr
N.A.I.C.S.: 331313

KLEVERS GMBH & CO. KG
Oppelner Strasse 11, Monchengladbach, 41199, Germany
Tel.: (49) 216696870
Web Site: http://www.klevers.de
Rev.: $17,628,732
Emp.: 100
Glass Fabric Mfr
N.A.I.C.S.: 313220
Christian Angermeir (Mng Dir)

KLG CAPITAL SERVICES LIMITED
SKIL House, 209 Bank Street Cross Lane, Mumbai, 400 023, Maharashtra, India
Tel.: (91) 2266199000
Web Site: https://www.klgcapital.com
530771—(BOM)
Rev.: $104,882
Assets: $1,713,990
Liabilities: $682,790
Net Worth: $1,031,200
Earnings: $5,626
Emp.: 2
Fiscal Year-end: 03/31/21
Financial Investment Services
N.A.I.C.S.: 523999
Gayathri Ramachandran (Chm)

KLICK COMMUNICATIONS INC.
175 Bloor St E N Tower 3th Fl, Toronto, M4W 3R8, ON, Canada
Tel.: (416) 214-4977
Web Site: http://wwwklickit.com
Year Founded: 1997
Sales Range: $25-49.9 Million
Emp.: 50
Internet Consulting, Design & Development Services
N.A.I.C.S.: 541690
Peter Cordy (Chm)

KLIKON GROUP HOLDINGS PTY LIMITED
Level 7 477 Pitt Street, Haymarket, Sydney, 2000, NSW, Australia
Tel.: (61) 2 9199 0888   AU
Web Site: http://www.ac3.com.au
Year Founded: 1999
Sales Range: Less than $1 Million
Emp.: 300
ICT Infrastructure & Managed Services
N.A.I.C.S.: 513210
Simon Xistouris (CEO)

KLIL INDUSTRIES LTD.
Industrial Area, PO Box 659, Karmiel, 20100, Israel
Tel.: (972) 49953164
Web Site: http://www.klil.co.il
Year Founded: 1950
Sales Range: $100-124.9 Million
Emp.: 250
Construction Aluminum System Mfr
N.A.I.C.S.: 331314
Arie Richtman (CEO)

Subsidiaries:

Klil (UK) Ltd. (1)
1 Victoria Terr, Walsall, WS4 2DA, United Kingdom
Tel.: (44) 1922611940
Aluminum Systems fro Construction
N.A.I.C.S.: 331318

KLIMASAN KLIMA SANAYI VE TICARET AS
Manisa Organize Sanayi Bolgesi 1 Kisim Kecilikoyosb Mah, Cumhuriyet Cad No 1 Yunusemre, 45030, Manisa, Turkiye
Tel.: (90) 2362362233
Web Site: https://klimasan.com.tr
Year Founded: 1915
KLMSN—(IST)
Rev.: $85,650,291
Assets: $131,284,053
Liabilities: $81,337,802
Net Worth: $49,946,251
Earnings: $4,209,398
Fiscal Year-end: 12/31/22
Refrigerator Mfr
N.A.I.C.S.: 335220
Marcelo Faria De Lima (Chm)

KLIMAVENT D.D.
Boce 16, Hadzici, Sarajevo, Bosnia & Herzegovina
Tel.: (387) 33638870
KLMVRK2—(SARE)
Rev.: $276,834
Assets: $4,241,785
Liabilities: $31,212
Net Worth: $4,210,574
Earnings: $6,152
Emp.: 4
Fiscal Year-end: 12/31/20
Cooling & Ventilation Equipment Mfr
N.A.I.C.S.: 333415

KLINGELNBERG AG
Binzmuhlestrasse 171, 8050, Zurich, Switzerland
Tel.: (41) 442787979   CH
Web Site: https://www.klingelnberg.com
Year Founded: 1863
KLIN—(SWX)
Rev.: $336,471,175
Assets: $328,297,117
Liabilities: $172,252,772
Net Worth: $156,044,346
Earnings: $19,074,279
Emp.: 1,313
Fiscal Year-end: 03/31/24
Gear Component Mfr & Distr
N.A.I.C.S.: 333517
Jan Klingelnberg (CEO)

Subsidiaries:

Hofler Yantai Service Co., Ltd. (1)
Rm 1212 Huaxin Intl No 28 Changjiang Road ETDZ, Yantai, 264006, China
Tel.: (86) 5356103500
Gear Machinery Tool Mfr
N.A.I.C.S.: 333517

Klingelnberg (France) SAS (1)
2a rue Ducastel, 78100, Saint Germain-en-Laye, France
Tel.: (33) 178649696
Gear Machinery Tool Mfr
N.A.I.C.S.: 333517

Klingelnberg (Japan) Ltd. (1)
Klingelnberg Bldg 1-13-12 Shin Yokohama, Kohoku-ku, Yokohama, 222-0033, Japan
Tel.: (81) 454736061
Gear Machinery Tool Mfr
N.A.I.C.S.: 333517

Klingelnberg America Inc. (1)
118 E Michigan Av Ste 200, Saline, MI 48176
Tel.: (734) 470-6278
Gear Machinery Tool Mfr
N.A.I.C.S.: 333517
Fabian Wolf (CEO)

Klingelnberg Imexma SA (1)
C/Laurea Miro 153- Esc N Planta 3A-Puerta 2A, 08950, Esplugues de Llobregat, Spain
Tel.: (34) 934703570
Gear Machinery Tool Mfr
N.A.I.C.S.: 333517

Klingelnberg India Private Ltd. (1)
Om Chambers Office No 501 T29/31 Telco Road Near Toyota Showroom MIDC, Bhosari, Pune, 411026, India
Tel.: (91) 9028002650
Gear Machinery Tool Mfr
N.A.I.C.S.: 333517
Prasad Kizhakel (Mng Dir)

Klingelnberg Italiana Srl. (1)
Via A Ponchielli 2, 20063, Cernusco sul Naviglio, MI, Italy
Tel.: (39) 0289756700
Gear Machinery Tool Mfr
N.A.I.C.S.: 333517
Paolo Montanari (Mgr-Area)

Klingelnberg Mexico S.A. de C.V. (1)
Acceso III N 16B Int 8, Zona Industrial Benito Juarez, 76120, Queretaro, Mexico
Tel.: (52) 4422482750
Gear Machinery Tool Mfr
N.A.I.C.S.: 333517
Harald Sieber (Mgr-Svcs)

Klingelnberg do Brasil (1)
Rua Eduardo Tomanik 312, 13201-835, Jundiai, Sao Paulo, Brazil
Tel.: (55) 1139633777
Gear Machinery Tool Mfr
N.A.I.C.S.: 333517

KLINGELNBERG-KLAUSS ELECTRONICS B.V.
Lagedijk 28 /C, 5705, Helmond, Netherlands
Tel.: (31) 492598484
Web Site: http://www.kke-group.com
Sales Range: Less than $1 Million
Emp.: 12
Electronic Parts & Equipment Merchant Whslr

N.A.I.C.S.: 423690
Jeroen Charmant (Gen Mgr)

KLINIK PYRAMIDE AM SEE AG
Bellerivestrasse 34, 8034, Zurich, Switzerland
Tel.: (41) 443881515
Web Site: http://www.pyramide.ch
Year Founded: 1993
Emp.: 120
Plastic & Breast Cancer Surgery Services
N.A.I.C.S.: 622110
Cedric A. George (Dir-Medical)

KLJUC A.D.
Bukatarevica 11, Loznica, Serbia
Tel.: (381) 19 801 393
Year Founded: 1954
Sales Range: Less than $1 Million
Emp.: 42
Cereal Crop Farming Services
N.A.I.C.S.: 111998
Branko Roganovic (Gen Mgr)

KLOCKNER & CO. SE
Am Silberpalais 1, D-47057, Duisburg, Germany
Tel.: (49) 2033070   De
Web Site: https://www.kloeckner.com
Year Founded: 1906
KCO—(DEU)
Rev.: $7,679,193,081
Assets: $4,268,930,219
Liabilities: $2,339,696,620
Net Worth: $1,929,233,599
Earnings: ($210,386,583)
Emp.: 7,733
Fiscal Year-end: 12/31/23
Steel & Metals Distribution Services
N.A.I.C.S.: 423510
Gisbert Ruhl (Chm-Mgmt Bd & CEO)

Subsidiaries:

Becker Stahl-Service GmbH (1)
Weetfelder Str 57, 59199, Bonen, Germany
Tel.: (49) 23839340
Flat Steel & Rolled Sheet Mfr
N.A.I.C.S.: 331221

Subsidiary (Domestic):

Umformtechnik Stendal GmbH (2)
Akazienweg 29, 39576, Stendal, Germany
Tel.: (49) 393164760
Web Site: https://www.umformtechnik-stendal.de
Sheet Metal Forming Mfr
N.A.I.C.S.: 332322

KDI S.A.S. (1)
173-179 boulevard Felix Faure, 93537, Aubervilliers, Cedex, France
Tel.: (33) 14 839 7777
Web Site: https://www.kloecknermetals.fr
Sales Range: $750-799.9 Million
Emp.: 2,500
Iron & Steel Products
N.A.I.C.S.: 212210
Jean Coeur (CEO & Dir-Fin)

Subsidiary (Domestic):

Adrien Targe S.A.S. (2)
Avenue Berthelot, 42320, La Grand-Croix, Loire, France
Tel.: (33) 477292050
Steel Product Distr
N.A.I.C.S.: 423510
M. Petit Luc (Mng Dir)

KDI Authentic S.A.S. (2)
173-179 Boulevard Felix Faure, 93537, Aubervilliers, France
Tel.: (33) 148397679
Web Site: http://www.kdi.fr
Sales Range: $50-74.9 Million
Emp.: 250
Steel Products Mfr & Distr
N.A.I.C.S.: 331110
Philippe Richard (Mng Dir)

KLOCKNER & CO. SE

Klockner & Co. SE—(Continued)

KDI Export S.A.S. (2)
Immeuble de bureaux Les 3 Fontaines, BP 1034, Cergy-Pontoise, 95003, Val d'Oise, France
Tel.: (33) 130757000
Web Site: http://www.kdi.fr
Sales Range: $25-49.9 Million
Emp.: 25
Steel Product Distr
N.A.I.C.S.: 423510
Camille Vinzent (Dir-Comml)

Klockner & Co Deutschland GmbH (1)
Am Silberpalais 1, 47057, Duisburg, Germany
Tel.: (49) 2033070
Web Site: https://shop.kloeckner.de
Sales Range: $1-4.9 Billion
Seal Products Distr
N.A.I.C.S.: 423510
Sven Koepchen (Chm-Mgmt Bd)

Klockner & Co International GmbH (1)
Am Silberpalais 1, 47057, Duisburg, Nordrhein-Westfalen, Germany
Tel.: (49) 2033070
Web Site: http://www.klockner.de
Steel & Metal Products Distr
N.A.I.C.S.: 423510

Subsidiary (Non-US):

ASD Limited (2)
Valley Farm Road, Stourton, Leeds, LS10 1SD, West Yorkshire, United Kingdom
Tel.: (44) 1132540711
Web Site: https://www.kloecknermetalsuk.com
Emp.: 180
Steel & Metal Products Distr
N.A.I.C.S.: 423510

Subsidiary (Domestic):

ASD Interpipe Ltd. (3)
2nd Floor 14-16 High Street, Ironbridge, TF8 7AD, Shropshire, United Kingdom
Tel.: (44) 8452267007
Iron & Steel Pipes Mfr
N.A.I.C.S.: 332996

ASD Metal Services Ltd. (3)
Valley Farm Road Stourton, Leeds, LS10 1SD, W Yorkshire, United Kingdom
Tel.: (44) 1132540711
Web Site: http://www.asdmetalservices.co.uk
Sales Range: $50-74.9 Million
Emp.: 180
Seal Products Distr
N.A.I.C.S.: 423510

ASD Westok Limited (3)
Valley Farm Way, Stourton, Leeds, LS10 1SE, United Kingdom
Tel.: (44) 1132055270
Web Site: https://www.kloecknermetalsuk.com
Sales Range: $25-49.9 Million
Emp.: 65
Cellular Steel Beam & Ultra Shallow Floor Beam Mfr
N.A.I.C.S.: 327390

Subsidiary (Non-US):

Debrunner Koenig Holding AG (2)
Hinterlauben 8, 9004, Saint Gallen, Switzerland
Tel.: (41) 712272900
Web Site: http://www.dkh.ch
Holding Company; Metals Warehousing & Distr
N.A.I.C.S.: 551112
Heinz Rohrer (CFO & Member-Exec Bd)

Subsidiary (Domestic):

BEWETEC AG (3)
Niedermattstrasse 21, Oberbipp, 4538, Bern, Switzerland
Tel.: (41) 582351400
Web Site: https://bewetec.ch
Emp.: 240
Reinforcing Steel Mfr
N.A.I.C.S.: 332312

Debrunner Acifer AG (3)
Hechtackerstrasse 33, 9014, Saint Gallen, Switzerland
Tel.: (41) 582350300
Web Site: http://www.d-a.ch
Sales Range: $25-49.9 Million
Civil Engineering Services & Construction Materials Distr
N.A.I.C.S.: 541330

Debrunner Acifer AG Wallis (3)
Industrie West, 3930, Visp, Switzerland
Tel.: (41) 582352800
Web Site: http://www.d-a.ch
Civil Engineering Services & Construction Materials Distr
N.A.I.C.S.: 237990

Subsidiary (Domestic):

Molok (Valais) S.A. (4)
Rue du Stade 17, 3960, Sierre, Valais, Switzerland
Tel.: (41) 274551505
Web Site: http://www.molok-vs.ch
Underground Waste Collection System Construction Services
N.A.I.C.S.: 562219

Subsidiary (Domestic):

Debrunner Acifer Bewehrungen AG (3)
Industriestrasse 8, Buchs, Saint Gallen, Switzerland
Tel.: (41) 582351070
Web Site: http://www.bewehrungstechnik.ch
Metal Ware Mfr
N.A.I.C.S.: 332313

Debrunner Acifer S.A. Giubiasco (3)
Via Moderna 15, 6512, Giubiasco, Switzerland
Tel.: (41) 582350800
Web Site: http://www.d-a.ch
Civil Engineering Services & Construction Materials Distr
N.A.I.C.S.: 237990

Debrunner Acifer S.A. Romandie (3)
Boulevard de l Arc-en-Ciel 1, 1023, Crissier, Switzerland
Tel.: (41) 582353000
Web Site: http://www.d-a.ch
Sales Range: $25-49.9 Million
Civil Engineering Services & Construction Materials Distr
N.A.I.C.S.: 541330

Debrunner Koenig (3)
Hechtackerstrasse 33, 9014, Saint Gallen, Switzerland
Tel.: (41) 712743318
Web Site: http://www.d-a.ch
Sales Range: $25-49.9 Million
Emp.: 120
Civil Engineering Services & Construction Materials Distr
N.A.I.C.S.: 541330

Debrunner Koenig Management AG (3)
Hinterlauben 8, 9004, Saint Gallen, Switzerland
Tel.: (41) 712272900
Web Site: http://www.dkh.ch
Emp.: 100
Investment Management Service
N.A.I.C.S.: 523940

Koenig Feinstahl AG (3)
Lagerstrasse 10, 8953, Dietikon, Zurich, Switzerland
Tel.: (41) 447433111
Web Site: http://www.koenigfeinstahl.ch
Sales Range: $25-49.9 Million
Emp.: 70
Steel & Metal Warehousing & Distr
N.A.I.C.S.: 423510
Tschanen Daniel (Mgr-Fin & Admin)

Metall Service Menziken AG (3)
Badstrasse 12, 5737, Menziken, Switzerland
Tel.: (41) 584581818
Web Site: http://www.metallservice.ch
Sales Range: $25-49.9 Million
Emp.: 109
Steel & Metal Products Distr
N.A.I.C.S.: 423510

Roland Wipf (Head-Mktg & Sls)

Subsidiary (Non-US):

Grange Steels Ltd. (2)
Tunstall Road Biddulph, Stoke-on-Trent, ST8 6JZ, Staffs, United Kingdom
Tel.: (44) 1782510210
Sales Range: $50-74.9 Million
Emp.: 2
Steel Product Distr
N.A.I.C.S.: 423510

Klockner Participaciones S.A. (2)
Avenida de Bruselas Arroyo De La Vega 38 - Porta A Pis 3, 28108, Alcobendas, Madrid, Spain
Tel.: (34) 913697415
Sales Range: $150-199.9 Million
Emp.: 500
Investment Management Service
N.A.I.C.S.: 523999
Albert Garreta (Mng Dir)

Subsidiary (Domestic):

Comercial de Laminados S.A. (3)
Paseo del Club Deportivo 1 edificio 15 A planta 1, 28223, Pozuelo de Alarcon, Madrid, Spain
Tel.: (34) 91 369 7410
Web Site: https://www.cdl.es
Steel & Metal Products Distr
N.A.I.C.S.: 423510

Subsidiary (Domestic):

Cortichapa S.A. (4)
Crta De la Estacion s/n, 46540, Puig, Valencia, Spain
Tel.: (34) 961470509
Web Site: http://www.cdl.es
Emp.: 50
Steel Product Distr
N.A.I.C.S.: 423510
Albert Garetta Palau (Pres)

Hierros del Ebro S.A. (4)
Jaimeferran 16, Zaragoza, 500014, Spain
Tel.: (34) 976 47 32 50
Web Site: http://www.cdl.es
Iron & Steel Products Distr
N.A.I.C.S.: 331110
Ramon Martinez (Mng Dir)

Hierros del Turia S.A. (4)
PL Los Vientos C/ Alisio s/n, 46119, Naquera, Valencia, Spain
Tel.: (34) 961609900
Iron & Steel Products Distr
N.A.I.C.S.: 423510

Klockner Aluminio Iberica S.A. (4)
Poligono Industrial Can Vinyals Guifre El Pilos, 08130, Santa Perpetua de Mogoda, Barcelona, Spain
Tel.: (34) 937721609
Web Site: http://www.cdl.es
Structured Aluminum Products Mfr
N.A.I.C.S.: 331313

Materiales Siderurgicos S.A. (4)
Pl La Fraila C/ Diamante 1, 28970, Humanes, Madrid, Spain
Tel.: (34) 91 697 92 11
Web Site: http://www.cdl.es
Iron & Steel Products Distr
N.A.I.C.S.: 423510

Perfiles Aragon S.A. (4)
Av Academia General Militar 14, 50015, Zaragoza, Spain
Tel.: (34) 97 651 4111
Web Site: http://www.cdl.es
Sales Range: $75-99.9 Million
Emp.: 50
Structured Steel Mfr & Distr
N.A.I.C.S.: 423510
Maite Miranda (CEO)

Suministros Loinaz S.A. (4)
Ctra Madrid-Irun km 419 Apdo 113, 20200, Beasain, Guipuzcoa, Spain
Tel.: (34) 943805700
Web Site: http://www.cdl.es
Iron & Steel Products Distr
N.A.I.C.S.: 423510

Subsidiary (Non-US):

Kloeckner Metals Belgium N.V. (2)

INTERNATIONAL PUBLIC

Keizersstraat 50, 8530, Harelbeke, Belgium
Tel.: (32) 56268080
Web Site: https://www.kloecknermetals.be
Emp.: 75
Metal Distr
N.A.I.C.S.: 423510

Organically Coated Steels Ltd. (2)
Edwin Avenue Hoo Farm Industrial Estate, Kidderminster, DY11 7RA, Worcestershire, United Kingdom
Tel.: (44) 1562821400
Web Site: http://www.asdocs.co.uk
Sales Range: $25-49.9 Million
Emp.: 100
Steel Products Processing & Sales
N.A.I.C.S.: 331110
Alan Nutbean (Coord-Transport)

Klockner Distribution Industrielle S.A. (1)
173-179 Blvd Felix Faure, 93537, Aubervilliers, Seine-Saint-Denis, France
Tel.: (33) 148397777
Web Site: http://www.kdi.fr
Seal Products Distr
N.A.I.C.S.: 423510
Marc Frustie (Pres)

Subsidiary (Non-US):

Buysmetal N.V. (2)
Keizersstraat 50, 8530, Harelbeke, West Flanders, Belgium
Tel.: (32) 56268080
Web Site: http://www.buysmetal.be
Sales Range: $25-49.9 Million
Emp.: 70
Steel & Metal Products Distr
N.A.I.C.S.: 423510
Claude Bossu (Mgr-Sls)

Subsidiary (Domestic):

Reynolds European S.A.S. (2)
173-179 Boulevard Felix Faure, 93537, Aubervilliers, Cedex, France
Tel.: (33) 148397777
Web Site: https://www.reynolds-european.fr
Sales Range: $25-49.9 Million
Emp.: 16
Seal Products Distr
N.A.I.C.S.: 423510

Klockner Metalsnab AD (1)
119 Iliyantsi Boulevard, Sofia, 1220, Bulgaria
Tel.: (359) 2 926 98 68
Web Site: http://www.metalsnab.com
Sales Range: $50-74.9 Million
Emp.: 98
Metal Warehousing & Distr
N.A.I.C.S.: 423510

Klockner Stahlhandel CZ, s.r.o. (1)
Kolbenova 159, 190 02, Prague, Czech Republic
Tel.: (420) 266039226
Web Site: http://www.stahlhandel.cz
Sales Range: $25-49.9 Million
Emp.: 18
Steel & Metal Products Distr
N.A.I.C.S.: 423510

Klockner Stal I Metal Polska Sp. Z O.O. (1)
Ul June 28 1956 223-229, 61-485, Poznan, Wielkopolskie, Poland
Tel.: (48) 61 858 8200
Web Site: https://3082-pl.all.biz
Sales Range: $50-74.9 Million
Emp.: 80
Steel & Metal Products Distr
N.A.I.C.S.: 423510

Kloeckner Metals Austria GmbH & Co KG (1)
Percostrasse 12, 1220, Vienna, Austria
Tel.: (43) 125946360
Web Site: https://www.kloecknermetals.at
Emp.: 115
Aluminium & Stainless Steel Mfr
N.A.I.C.S.: 331513
Markus Kerbler (Mng Dir)

Kloeckner Metals Corporation (1)
500 Colonial Ctr Pkwy Ste 500, Roswell, GA 30076-8853
Web Site: https://www.kloecknermetals.com

AND PRIVATE COMPANIES — KMC (KUEI MENG) INTERNATIONAL INC.

Sales Range: $200-249.9 Million
Emp.: 700
Steel & Metal Mfr
N.A.I.C.S.: 423510
John T. Paschal *(Pres-Temtco Steel Div)*

Subsidiary (Domestic):

Industrial Manufacturing Services, LLC (2)
1282 Camp Creek Rd, Lancaster, SC 29720
Tel.: (803) 286-5875
Web Site: http://www.indmfg.com
Sales Range: $1-9.9 Million
Emp.: 35
Miscellaneous Fabricated Metal Product Mfr
N.A.I.C.S.: 332999
David Earl *(Pres)*

Macsteel Service Centers USA, Inc. (2)
888 San Clemente Dr Ste 250, Newport Beach, CA 92660
Tel.: (949) 219-9000
Web Site: http://www.macsteelusa.com
Sales Range: $450-499.9 Million
Processes & Distributes Carbon Flat Rolled, Long & Plate Products
N.A.I.C.S.: 331221

Temtco Steel, LLC (2)
PO Box 887, Louisville, MS 39339
Tel.: (662) 773-4445
Steel Product Distr
N.A.I.C.S.: 423510
John T. Paschal *(Co-Founder)*

Kloeckner Metals France S.A.S. (1)
173 -179 Boulevard Felix Faure, 93537, Aubervilliers, Cedex, France
Tel.: (33) 148397777
Web Site: https://www.klocknermetals.fr
Metal Distr
N.A.I.C.S.: 423510

Kloeckner Metals Germany GmbH (1)
Am Silberpalais 1, D-47057, Duisburg, Germany
Tel.: (49) 2033070
Web Site: https://www.kloeckner.de
Stainless Steel Mfr & Distr
N.A.I.C.S.: 331110

Kloeckner Metals ODS Nederlands B.V. (1)
Donk 6, 2991 LE, Barendrecht, Netherlands
Tel.: (31) 18 064 0911
Web Site: https://www.kloecknermetals.nl
Metal & Engineering Products Distr
N.A.I.C.S.: 331491

Metall- und Service-Center Ges.m.b.H. Nfg. KG (1)
Percostrasse 12, 1220, Vienna, Austria
Tel.: (43) 1259463625
Web Site: http://www.metall-center.at
Sales Range: $50-74.9 Million
Emp.: 60
Steel & Metal Products Distr
N.A.I.C.S.: 423510
Marcus Oberhofer *(Mng Dir)*

PC-Tech S.A. (1)
Ch de l'Islettaz Batiment C1, 1305, Penthalaz, Switzerland
Tel.: (41) 216358302
Web Site: https://www.pc-tech.ch
Drilling Machines Mfr
N.A.I.C.S.: 333131

XOM Materials GmbH (1)
Ackerstr 14-15, 10115, Berlin, Germany
Tel.: (49) 30555797010
Web Site: https://www.xom-materials.com
Emp.: 60
Steel Distr
N.A.I.C.S.: 423510
Tim Milde *(COO)*

KLONDIKE GOLD CORP.
3123 - 595 Burrard St, Vancouver, V7X 1J1, BC, Canada
Tel.: (604) 559-4440
Web Site:
 https://www.klondikegoldcorp.com
KDKGF—(OTCQB)
Rev.: $16,888
Assets: $21,734,101
Liabilities: $379,777
Net Worth: $21,354,324
Earnings: ($760,751)
Fiscal Year-end: 02/28/23
Mineral Exploration Services
N.A.I.C.S.: 213114
Peter Tallman *(Pres & CEO)*

Subsidiaries:

Klondike Silver Corp. (1)
804-750 West Pender Street, Vancouver, V6C 2T7, BC, Canada
Tel.: (604) 682-2928
Web Site: https://www.klondikesilver.com
Assets: $13,733,649
Liabilities: $1,879,641
Net Worth: $11,854,008
Earnings: ($1,898,332)
Fiscal Year-end: 05/31/2021
Mineral Exploration Services
N.A.I.C.S.: 213114
Thomas Kennedy *(CEO)*

KLONDIKE MOTORS LTD
191 Range Road, Whitehorse, Y1A 3E5, YT, Canada
Tel.: (867) 668-3399
Web Site:
 http://www.klondikemotors.ca
Sales Range: $10-24.9 Million
Emp.: 30
New & Used Car Dealers
N.A.I.C.S.: 441110
Tammy Hamilton *(Gen Mgr)*

KLOPOTEK AG
Lorenzweg 5 Aufgang A, 12099, Berlin, Germany
Tel.: (49) 3088453182   De
Web Site: http://www.klopotek.com
Year Founded: 1992
Emp.: 14,000
Software Publisher
N.A.I.C.S.: 513210
Ulrich Klopotek *(Chm-Exec Bd)*

Subsidiaries:

Klopotek & Partner GmbH (1)
Lorenzweg 5 Aufgang A, 12099, Berlin, Germany
Tel.: (49) 30884530
Application Services
N.A.I.C.S.: 541511

Klopotek BV (1)
Oostenburgervoorstraat 120-124, 1018 MR, Amsterdam, Netherlands
Tel.: (31) 205210070
Web Site: http://www.klopotek.nl
Application Services
N.A.I.C.S.: 541511

Klopotek North America, Inc. (1)
2001 Route 46 Ste 203, Parsippany, NJ 07054
Tel.: (973) 331-1010
Web Site: http://www.klopotek.com
Software Publisher
N.A.I.C.S.: 513210
David Hetherington *(Pres & CEO)*

Klopotek SAS (1)
6 rue d'Odessa, 75014, Paris, France
Tel.: (33) 171397032
Web Site: http://www.klopotek.fr
Application Services
N.A.I.C.S.: 541511

Klopotek Software & Technology Services Italia S.r.l. (1)
Via G Fara 26, 20124, Milan, Italy
Tel.: (39) 0809647472
Web Site: http://www.klopotek.it
Application Services
N.A.I.C.S.: 541511

Klopotek UK Ltd. (1)
4th Floor Brownan House 29 Wilson Street, London, EC2M 2SJ, United Kingdom
Tel.: (44) 2030340500
Web Site: http://www.klopotek.co.uk
Software Publisher
N.A.I.C.S.: 513210
John Lawson *(Dir)*

KLOVERN AB
Spelhagsvagen 13, 611 31, Nykoping, Sweden
Tel.: (46) 104827000   SE
Web Site: http://www.klovern.se
Year Founded: 1994
Rev.: $389,884,460
Assets: $6,185,102,210
Liabilities: $4,011,373,100
Net Worth: $2,173,729,110
Earnings: $323,974,910
Emp.: 247
Fiscal Year-end: 12/31/19
Real Estate Manangement Services
N.A.I.C.S.: 531390
Rutger Arnhult *(CEO)*

Subsidiaries:

Tobin Properties AB (1)
Humlegardsgatan 19A, 114 46, Stockholm, Sweden
Tel.: (46) 812050000
Web Site: https://www.tobinproperties.se
Housing Property Developer
N.A.I.C.S.: 236116
Per Alnefelt *(CFO)*

KLUANG RUBBER COMPANY (MALAYA) BERHAD
Suite 9D Level 9 Menara Ansar 65 Jalan Trus, 80000, Johor Bahru, Johor, Malaysia
Tel.: (60) 72241035
Web Site:
 https://www.kluangrubber.com
KLUANG—(KLS)
Rev.: $10,665,932
Assets: $278,391,316
Liabilities: $8,636,624
Net Worth: $269,754,692
Earnings: $9,111,550
Emp.: 48
Fiscal Year-end: 06/30/23
Palm Oil Fruits Mfr & Sales
N.A.I.C.S.: 325998
Justin Chung-Shih Lee *(Deputy Chm)*

KLUH SERVICE MANAGEMENT GMBH
Am Wehrhahn 70, Dusseldorf, 40211, Germany
Tel.: (49) 211 9068 01
Web Site: http://www.klueh.de
Multi Service Provider
N.A.I.C.S.: 561790
Frank Theobald *(Chm-Mgmt Bd)*

KLUTHE FRANCE
73 Grand Rue, 57970, Kuntzig, France
Tel.: (33) 382591747
Web Site: http://www.kluthe.com
Rev.: $14,300,000
Emp.: 12
Cleaners & Degreasers Developer & Producer
N.A.I.C.S.: 325510
Zieten Bertram *(Gen Mgr)*

KLUZ PADOBRANI A.D.
Mite Ruzica 8, 11000, Belgrade, Serbia
Tel.: (381) 112860160
Web Site: http://kluzpadobrani.com
Year Founded: 1947
Parachute Mfr
N.A.I.C.S.: 339999

KM CORP.
147 Hyeopdongdanji-gil, Anseong, 17600, Gyeonggi-do, Korea (South)
Tel.: (82) 316788800
Web Site:
 https://www.kmbizglobal.com
Year Founded: 1989
083550—(KRS)
Rev.: $116,314,406
Assets: $141,715,829
Liabilities: $39,694,991
Net Worth: $102,020,838
Earnings: $5,898,589
Emp.: 263
Fiscal Year-end: 12/31/22
Disposable Product Mfr
N.A.I.C.S.: 339113
Shin Byung Soon *(Pres & CEO)*

Subsidiaries:

KM ACT Corp. (1)
7811 N Shepherd Dr, Houston, TX 77088
Tel.: (281) 405-0888
Web Site: http://www.kmact.com
Textile Products Mfr
N.A.I.C.S.: 314999

KM GOLD JSC
Tel.: (7) 272613141
KMGD—(KAZ)
Rev.: $3,183,102
Assets: $4,994,130
Liabilities: $13,061,561
Net Worth: ($8,067,430)
Earnings: ($1,793,538)
Fiscal Year-end: 12/31/20
Gold Mineral Exploration Services
N.A.I.C.S.: 212220
Rahimov Anvar *(Chm & CEO)*

KM PHARMACEUTICAL CO., LTD.
121 Dogok-ri Pyeongtaekhang-ro 268beon-gil Poseung-eup, Pyeongtaek, Gyeonggi-do, Korea (South)
Tel.: (82) 316821749
Web Site: http://www.kmkmp.com
Year Founded: 2001
Oral Care Product Mfr & Distr
N.A.I.C.S.: 325611
Il-Mo Kang *(CEO)*

KMA GLOBAL SOLUTIONS INTERNATIONAL, INC.
438 Gibraltar Dr Unit 11, Mississauga, L5T 2P2, ON, Canada
Tel.: (647) 478-8783
Year Founded: 2006
Business Management Services
N.A.I.C.S.: 561499
Jeffrey D. Reid *(Chm & CEO)*

KMB CO., LTD.
Room 1311 B-line H business Park 25 Beobwon-ro 11-gi, Songpa-gu, Seoul, Korea (South)
Tel.: (82) 244654013
Web Site: http://www.kmbcc.com
Year Founded: 1985
Sales Range: $25-49.9 Million
Emp.: 25
Construction Materials Mfr
N.A.I.C.S.: 327390
Ji Han Chang *(CEO)*

Subsidiaries:

KMB Co., Ltd. - Pyungtaek Factory (1)
233-3 Sin-Ri Jinwi-Myun, Pyeongtaek, 451-865A, Kyunggi-Do, Korea (South)
Tel.: (82) 31 663 4381
Chemical Product Mfr & Distr
N.A.I.C.S.: 325998

KMC (KUEI MENG) INTERNATIONAL INC.
8F-5 No 425 Jhonghua Rd, Yongkang Dist, Tainan City, 710, Taiwan
Tel.: (886) 63037111
Web Site: https://www.kmc-international.com

4203

KMC (KUEI MENG) INTERNATIONAL INC.

KMC (Kuei Meng) International Inc.—(Continued)
Year Founded: 1977
5306—(TAI)
Rev.: $218,061,280
Assets: $379,186,195
Liabilities: $151,431,556
Net Worth: $227,754,639
Earnings: $53,875,958
Fiscal Year-end: 12/31/20
Chain Mfr
N.A.I.C.S.: 333613
Wu Jui-Chang *(CEO)*

Subsidiaries:

K.M.C Automobile Transmission Co., Ltd. (1)
NO 41 Jhongshan Road, Xinhua Dist,
Tainan City, 712, Taiwan
Tel.: (886) 6 590 0711
Web Site: https://www.kmcautomobile.com
Automobile Parts Distr
N.A.I.C.S.: 441330

KMC Chain American Corporation (1)
1713 Lindbergh Ct, La Verne, CA 91750
Tel.: (909) 392-2045
Web Site: https://www.kmcchain.us
Bicycle Chain Distr
N.A.I.C.S.: 459110

KMC Chain Europe N.V. (1)
Businesspark Friesland West 57, 8447 SL,
Heerenveen, Netherlands
Tel.: (31) 513650690
Web Site: https://www.kmcchain.eu
Bicycle Chain Mfr & Distr
N.A.I.C.S.: 336991

P.T. Kuei Meng Chian Indonesia (1)
Rukan Artha Gading Niaga Blok E No 16
Kawasan Sentra Bisnis, Kelapa Gading,
Jakarta, 14240, Indonesia
Tel.: (62) 21 450 9170
Motorcycle Chain & Component Distr
N.A.I.C.S.: 423120

KMC MANAGEMENT CONSULTANTS GMBH & CO. KG
Ossum 14 Schloss Pesch, 40668,
Meerbusch, Germany
Tel.: (49) 21598160
Web Site: http://www.kmconsultants.com
Year Founded: 1988
Sales Range: $10-24.9 Million
Emp.: 36
Management Services
N.A.I.C.S.: 541618
Christa Schneider *(Partner)*

KMC SPECIALTY HOSPITALS INDIA LTD.
6 Royal Road Cantonment, Tiruchirappalli, 620 001, India
Tel.: (91) 4314077777
Web Site: https://www.kauveryhospital.com
524520—(BOM)
Rev.: $18,866,989
Assets: $17,576,218
Liabilities: $5,727,595
Net Worth: $11,848,623
Earnings: $3,238,572
Emp.: 814
Fiscal Year-end: 03/31/22
Health Care Srvices
N.A.I.C.S.: 621610
Sundararaj Chandrakumar *(Co-Founder & Chm)*

KMD BRANDS LIMITED
223 Tuam Street, Christchurch, 8011, New Zealand
Tel.: (64) 93755999
Web Site: https://www.kathmandu.co.nz
Year Founded: 1987
KMD—(ASX)
Rev.: $366,704,402
Assets: $399,593,126
Liabilities: $102,487,676
Net Worth: $297,105,450
Earnings: $38,734,563
Emp.: 1,144
Fiscal Year-end: 07/31/19
Holding Company; Outdoor Clothing Store Owner, Electronic Shopping & Mail Order Houses
N.A.I.C.S.: 458110
Xavier Simonet *(Mng Dir)*

Subsidiaries:

KMD Brands Managed Services (AU) Pty. Ltd. (1)
Level 3 / 105 York St, South Melbourne, VIC, Australia
Tel.: (61) 386726468
Web Site: https://www.kathmandu.com.au
Travel Accessories Whslr
N.A.I.C.S.: 423110

Kathmandu (U.K.) Limited (1)
11-13 Queens Road, Clifton, BS8 1QE, Bristol, United Kingdom
Tel.: (44) 969394069
Web Site: https://www.kathmandu.co.uk
Apparel Retailer
N.A.I.C.S.: 458110

Kathmandu Pty Limited (1)
Level 3 / 105 York St, PO Box 984, South Melbourne, 3205, VIC, Australia
Tel.: (61) 386726468
Web Site: https://www.kathmandu.com.au
Apparel Retailer
N.A.I.C.S.: 458110

Oboz Footwear, LLC (1)
212 S Wallace Ave Ste 103, Bozeman, MT 59715
Tel.: (406) 522-0319
Web Site: https://www.obozfootwear.com
Footwear Merchant Whslr
N.A.I.C.S.: 424340
John Connelly *(CEO)*

Rip Curl Group Pty Ltd, (1)
101 Surfcoast Hwy, Torquay, 3228, VIC, Australia
Tel.: (61) 352610008
Web Site: http://www.ripcurl.com.au
Surfing Equipment & Clothing Mfr
N.A.I.C.S.: 315250
Brian Singer *(Co-Founder)*

Subsidiary (Non-US):

RC Brazil LTDA (2)
Av Miguel Stefno 4544, Enseada Guaruja, Sao Paulo, 11440-534, Brazil
Tel.: (55) 1321010546
Web Site: https://www.ripcurl.com.br
Apparel & Accessory Distr
N.A.I.C.S.: 424310

Rip Chile S.A. (2)
San Ignacio 1101 3 Piso, Centro Empresarial Buena Ventura Quilicura, Santiago, Chile
Tel.: (56) 23877500
Apparel & Accessory Distr
N.A.I.C.S.: 424310

Rip Curl (Thailand) Co., Ltd (2)
120/1 Soi Sukhumvit 26, Klongtan Klongtoey, Bangkok, 10110, Thailand
Tel.: (66) 21085216
Web Site: http://www.ripcurl.co.th
Apparel & Accessory Distr
N.A.I.C.S.: 424310

Rip Curl Canada Inc. (2)
108-173 Forester St, North Vancouver, V7H 0A6, BC, Canada
Tel.: (604) 987-2875
Web Site: https://ripcurl.ca
Apparel & Accessory Distr
N.A.I.C.S.: 424310

Rip Curl Europe (2)
407 Avenue de la Tuilerie, 40150, Soorts-Hossegor, France
Tel.: (33) 558419971
Web Site: http://www.ripcurl.eu
Apparel & Accessory Distr
N.A.I.C.S.: 424310

Rip Curl Indonesia (2)
Komplek pertokoan Kuta Square Blok D 36 - 37 Badung, Kuta, 80361, Indonesia
Tel.: (62) 361756305
Apparel & Accessory Distr
N.A.I.C.S.: 424310

Rip Curl New Zealand (2)
7/21 Queen Street Level 1 Store 57, Mairangi Bay, Auckland, 1010, New Zealand
Tel.: (64) 98832788
Web Site: http://www.ripcurl.co.nz
Apparel & Accessory Distr
N.A.I.C.S.: 424310

Subsidiary (US):

Rip Curl USA (2)
233 E 17 Th St, Costa Mesa, CA 92627
Tel.: (949) 675-2855
Web Site: https://www.ripcurl.com
Apparel & Accessory Distr
N.A.I.C.S.: 424310

Subsidiary (Non-US):

The Curl S.A.C. (2)
Calle Las oropendolas 329, San Isidro, Lima, Peru
Tel.: (51) 2196400
Apparel & Accessory Distr
N.A.I.C.S.: 424310

KMF BUILDERS AND DEVELOPERS LTD.
Flat No 508 Golf Manor NAL Wind Tunnel Road, Bengaluru, 560 017, India
Tel.: (91) 8041486142
Web Site: https://www.kmfbuilders.com
Year Founded: 1995
531578—(BOM)
Rev.: $631,026
Assets: $2,869,293
Liabilities: $1,288,936
Net Worth: $1,580,357
Earnings: $47,808
Emp.: 12
Fiscal Year-end: 03/31/21
Real Estate Development Services
N.A.I.C.S.: 531390
Pradeep Kumar Malik *(Exec Dir)*

KMG MILK FOOD LIMITED
9th Km Stone Pipli to Ambal G T Road, Village Masana, Kurukshetra, 132118, Haryana, India
Tel.: (91) 1744279453
Web Site: https://www.kmggroup.com
Year Founded: 1992
519415—(BOM)
Rev.: $1,147,589
Assets: $996,661
Liabilities: $1,115,650
Net Worth: ($118,990)
Earnings: $27,425
Emp.: 200
Fiscal Year-end: 03/31/21
Dairy Products Mfr
N.A.I.C.S.: 311514
Basudev Garg *(Chm)*

KMH HI TECH CO., LTD.
330 Yeonam Yulgeum-ro, Asan-si, Chungcheongnam-do, Korea (South)
Tel.: (82) 415396114
Web Site: https://www.kmhhitech.com
Year Founded: 1997
052900—(KRS)
Rev.: $123,564,307
Assets: $147,986,957
Liabilities: $58,018,736
Net Worth: $89,968,222
Earnings: $11,438,809
Fiscal Year-end: 12/31/22
Semiconductor Material Mfr
N.A.I.C.S.: 334413
Sang-Gug Lee *(CEO)*

INTERNATIONAL PUBLIC

KMH SHILLA LEISURE CO., LTD.
84 Silla green-gil Bungnae-myeon, Yeoju, 12612, Korea (South)
Tel.: (82) 318863030
Golf Club Operator
N.A.I.C.S.: 713910
Jun-Hak Yoon *(CEO)*

KMK MUNAY AO
Abilkayir Khan Avenue 42 A, 030019, Aktobe, Kazakhstan
Tel.: (7) 7132768910
Web Site: https://www.kmkmunai.com
Year Founded: 2004
LNPT—(KAZ)
Rev.: $131,381,244
Assets: $219,253,596
Liabilities: $128,656,856
Net Worth: $90,596,740
Earnings: $14,708,935
Fiscal Year-end: 12/31/23
Hydrocarbons Exploration Services
N.A.I.C.S.: 211120

KML TECHNOLOGY GROUP LIMITED
B12 G/F Shatin Industrial Centre Siu Lek Yuen Road N T, Sha Tin, China (Hong Kong)
Tel.: (852) 2 686 7777
Web Site: http://www.kml.com.hk
Year Founded: 1977
8065—(HKG)
Rev.: $28,999,734
Assets: $32,686,499
Liabilities: $7,946,716
Net Worth: $24,739,783
Earnings: $4,126,973
Emp.: 203
Fiscal Year-end: 03/31/21
Electromechanical Engineering Services
N.A.I.C.S.: 541330
Kam Ming Luk *(Chm)*

KMM AD
bul Madara 38, 9700, Shumen, Bulgaria
Tel.: (359) 54892020
Web Site: https://www.kmmbg.com
Year Founded: 1968
KMM—(BUL)
Sales Range: Less than $1 Million
Industrial Machine Building Product Mfr
N.A.I.C.S.: 333248

KMN CAPITAL LTD.
Linkonel Street 20, Tel Aviv, 67134, Israel
Tel.: (972) 35652211
Web Site: http://www.kaman.co.il
KMNK—(TAE)
Assets: $323,098
Liabilities: $547,535
Net Worth: ($224,437)
Earnings: ($252,132)
Fiscal Year-end: 12/31/19
Asset Management Services
N.A.I.C.S.: 523940
Yoel Yogev *(CEO)*

KMP PRINTTECHNIK AG
Postfach 1250, 84302, Eggenfelden, Germany
Tel.: (49) 87217730
Web Site: http://www.kmp.com
Year Founded: 1988
Printer Accessories Mfr & Distr
N.A.I.C.S.: 334118
Heinz G. Sieg *(Founder)*

Subsidiaries:

KMP Burotechnik s.r.o. (1)

Ckyne 297, 384 81, Ckyne, Czech Republic
Tel.: (420) 388301051
Web Site: http://www.kmp.cz
Cartridge Mfr
N.A.I.C.S.: 325992

KMP Crusader Manufacturing Ltd. (1)
Unit 6 Arthur Street, Greenock, PA 15 4RT, Renfrewshire, United Kingdom
Tel.: (44) 1475730099
Web Site: http://www.kmpgreenock.co.uk
Cartridge Mfr
N.A.I.C.S.: 325992
Jennifer Cooke *(Controller-Fin)*

KMP PrintTechnik Polska Sp. z o.o. (1)
Al Krakowska 88 Sekocin Stary, 05-090, Raszyn, Poland
Tel.: (48) 227200909
Web Site: http://www.kmppl.com
Emp.: 500
Cartridge Mfr
N.A.I.C.S.: 325992
Pawel Czuprynski *(Mng Dir)*

KMP PrintTechnik s.r.l. (1)
Gumergasse 9, 39100, Bolzano, Italy
Tel.: (39) 03455904659
Cartridge Mfr
N.A.I.C.S.: 325992
Monica Casalini *(Mgr-Area)*

KMS MEDISURGI LIMITED
May Building Ground Floor 297/301 Princess Street Marine Lines East, Mumbai, 400 002, India
Tel.: (91) 2266107700
Web Site: https://www.kmsgroup.in
Year Founded: 1999
540468—(BOM)
Rev.: $1,415,258
Assets: $1,324,625
Liabilities: $414,331
Net Worth: $910,294
Earnings: $29,374
Emp.: 18
Fiscal Year-end: 03/31/22
Medical Product Mfr & Distr
N.A.I.C.S.: 339112
Gaurang Pratapari Kanakia *(Chm & Mng Dir)*

KMS TOOLS & EQUIPMENT LTD
110 Woolridge Street, Coquitlam, V3K 5V4, BC, Canada
Tel.: (604) 522-5599
Web Site: http://www.kmstools.com
Year Founded: 1986
Sales Range: $10-24.9 Million
Emp.: 90
Hardware Stores
N.A.I.C.S.: 444140
Ryan Hare *(Gen Mgr)*

KMT-HANSA CORP.
The Law Building, 2640, The Valley, Anguilla
Tel.: (264) 4973142 Al
Web Site: http://www.kmthansacorp.com
Year Founded: 1978
KMC.H—(TSXV)
Investment Services
N.A.I.C.S.: 523999

KMW INC.
21 Dongtan-daero 25-gil, Hwaseong, Gyeonggi-do, Korea (South)
Tel.: (82) 313708600
Web Site: https://www.kmw.co.kr
Year Founded: 1991
032500—(KRS)
Rev.: $133,205,454
Assets: $256,716,457
Liabilities: $78,359,920
Net Worth: $178,356,537
Earnings: ($19,807,953)
Emp.: 413
Fiscal Year-end: 12/31/22
Communication Devices Mfr
N.A.I.C.S.: 334220
Duk Yong Kim *(Chm & CEO)*

Subsidiaries:

BMS.K (1)
115 Yeongcheon-ri Dongtan-myeon 183-19 Yeongcheon-ro, Hwaseong, Gyeonggi-do, Korea (South)
Tel.: (82) 31 370 8740
Microwave Component Mfr
N.A.I.C.S.: 334419

KMW Japan Inc (1)
K G Bld 5F 1-3 Yamabuki-cho, Naka-ku, Yokohama, 231-0038, Kanagawa-ken, Japan
Tel.: (81) 452316430
Web Site: http://kmwinc.co.jp
Electronic Components Mfr
N.A.I.C.S.: 334419

KMW U.S.A Inc. (1)
1818 E Orangethorpe Ave, Fullerton, CA 92831
Tel.: (714) 515-1100
Web Site: http://www.kmwcomm.com
Electronic Components Mfr
N.A.I.C.S.: 334419
Vinny Chung *(VP-Sls & Mktg)*

Xi'an Huatian Telecom Inc. (1)
No 38 South Tuanjie Road, Hi-Tech Zone, Xi'an, Shaanxi, China
Tel.: (86) 2988384888
Web Site: http://htctelecom.com
Electronic Components Mfr
N.A.I.C.S.: 334419

KN AGRI RESOURCES LIMITED
B1-506 Marathon Innova Opp Peninsula Corporate Park Lower Parel, Mumbai, 400013, Maharashtra, India
Tel.: (91) 7712293706
Web Site: https://www.knagri.com
Year Founded: 1987
KNAGRI—(NSE)
Rev.: $268,300,462
Assets: $45,624,363
Liabilities: $11,789,461
Net Worth: $33,834,902
Earnings: $3,521,372
Emp.: 248
Fiscal Year-end: 03/31/23
Agricultural Product Processing Services
N.A.I.C.S.: 311224

KNAACK-KRANE TRANSPORTTECHNIK GMBH
Pollhornbogen 17, 21107, Hamburg, Germany
Tel.: (49) 40751261
Web Site: http://www.knaack-krane.de
Year Founded: 1963
Sales Range: $10-24.9 Million
Emp.: 100
Crane & Heavy Transport Rental Services
N.A.I.C.S.: 532490
Matthias Knaack *(Chm)*

KNAFAIM HOLDINGS LIMITED
2 Raoul Wallenberg St, Tel Aviv, 6971901, Israel
Tel.: (972) 36539999
Web Site: https://www.knafaim.co.il
Year Founded: 1980
KNFM—(TAE)
Rev.: $27,844,000
Assets: $181,067,000
Liabilities: $105,644,000
Net Worth: $75,423,000
Earnings: $13,616,000
Emp.: 3,760
Fiscal Year-end: 12/31/23
Offices of Other Holding Companies
N.A.I.C.S.: 551112
Shlomo Hanael *(Chm)*

Subsidiaries:

Global Knafaim Leasing Ltd. (1)
2 Raoul Wallenberg St, Ramat Gan, 5250606, Israel
Tel.: (972) 36539999
Web Site: https://www.gkl-leasing.com
Rev.: $10,073,000
Assets: $143,914,000
Liabilities: $94,166,000
Net Worth: $49,748,000
Earnings: ($2,118,000)
Fiscal Year-end: 12/31/2023
Sales Financing
N.A.I.C.S.: 522220
Asaf Luzon *(Mgr-Lease)*

KNAUF INTERFER SE
Graf Beust Allee 37, 45141, Essen, Germany
Tel.: (49) 20183170 De
Web Site: http://www.knauf-interfer.de
Sales Range: $1-4.9 Billion
Holding Company; Steel Processing, Distribution & Services
N.A.I.C.S.: 551112
Michael Steinkamp *(Member-Mgmt Bd)*

Subsidiaries:

Delta-Stahl GmbH (1)
Reihekamp 4, 30890, Barsinghausen, Germany
Tel.: (49) 5105 5248 0
Steel Product Distr
N.A.I.C.S.: 423510

F.W. Brokelmann Aluminiumwerk GmbH + Co. KG (1)
Oesterweg 14, 59469, Ense, Germany
Tel.: (49) 29 38 808 0
Web Site: http://www.broekelmann.com
Aluminium Products Mfr
N.A.I.C.S.: 331313
Christian Wex *(Head-Sls)*

Subsidiary (Domestic):

Brokelmann Alutec GmbH + Co. KG (2)
Hildebrandstrasse 19, Dortmund, 44319, Wickede, Germany
Tel.: (49) 231 92 73 97 0
Web Site: http://www.brokekelmann.com
Emp.: 100
Aluminium Products Mfr
N.A.I.C.S.: 331313
Michael Schneyder *(Pres)*

Subsidiary (Non-US):

Brokelmann Polska Sp. z.o.o. (2)
ul Glogowska 41, 45-315, Opole, Poland
Tel.: (48) 77 410 66 37
Aluminium Product Distr
N.A.I.C.S.: 423510

Giebel Kaltwalzwerk GmbH (1)
Im Ostfeld 1, 58642, Iserlohn, Germany
Tel.: (49) 2374 56 101
Steel Products Mfr
N.A.I.C.S.: 331110

Interfer Aluminium GmbH (1)
Zur Mersch 15, 59457, Werl, Germany
Tel.: (49) 2922 8709 0
Aluminium Product Distr
N.A.I.C.S.: 423510

Interfer Prazisrohr GmbH (1)
Schiess-Strasse 39, 40549, Dusseldorf, Germany
Tel.: (49) 211 52294 0
Web Site: http://www.knauf-interfer.de
Emp.: 40
Steel Product Distr
N.A.I.C.S.: 423510
Michael Steinig *(Mgr)*

Interfer Rohrunion GmbH (1)
Am Industriepark 2, '46562, Voerde, Germany
Tel.: (49) 281 94230 0
Steel Products Mfr
N.A.I.C.S.: 331110

Interfer Staal (1)
Vestdijk 60, 5611 CE, Eindhoven, Netherlands
Tel.: (31) 40 244 1000
Steel Product Distr
N.A.I.C.S.: 423510
Diego Spetgens *(Mgr-Sls)*

Interfer Stahl GmbH - Dortmund (1)
Bulowstrasse 12, 44147, Dortmund, Germany (100%)
Tel.: (49) 231 8286 0
Web Site: http://www.knauf-interfer.de
Sales Range: $75-99.9 Million
Emp.: 120
Wholesale Trade in Steel Products
N.A.I.C.S.: 423510

Interfer Technik GmbH (1)
Sohler Weg 72, 56564, Neuwied, Germany
Tel.: (49) 2631 8247 0
Steel Product Distr
N.A.I.C.S.: 423510

Knauf Interfer Polska Sp. z o.o. (1)
ul Porcelanowa 19, 40-246, Katowice, Poland
Tel.: (48) 32 201 37 04
Steel Product Distr
N.A.I.C.S.: 423510

Max Baum Stahl Service GmbH (1)
Kiffward 34, 47138, Duisburg, Germany
Tel.: (49) 203 4519 0
Steel Products Mfr
N.A.I.C.S.: 331110

Michael Friess GmbH (1)
Schlachtofstrasse 42, 87700, Memmingen, Germany
Tel.: (49) 83318520
Web Site: http://www.knauf-interfer.de
Sales Range: $25-49.9 Million
Emp.: 65
Steel, HVAC Equipment & Hardware & Plumbing Supplier
N.A.I.C.S.: 331110

Saarlandische Handelsgesellschaft mbH (1)
Bahnhofstr 34-36, 66740, Saarlouis, Germany
Tel.: (49) 6831 446 0
Steel Product Distr
N.A.I.C.S.: 423510

Volkel & Winkler GmbH (1)
Eisenstr 4, 57482, Wenden, Germany
Tel.: (49) 2762 60823 0
Steel Product Distr
N.A.I.C.S.: 423510

Walter Patz GmbH (1)
Bahnhofstrasse 76, 57555, Mudersbach, 57555, Sieg, Germany
Tel.: (49) 2745880
Surface-Treated Strips & Sheets
N.A.I.C.S.: 331221

Willems Stahl GmbH (1)
Konigsberger Str 29, 41460, Neuss, Germany
Tel.: (49) 2131 173 710
Steel Product Distr
N.A.I.C.S.: 423510

KNC LABORATORIES CO., LTD.
7-1-19 Minatojimaminamimachi, Chuo-ku Hyogo, Kobe, 650-0047, Japan
Tel.: (81) 789559900
Web Site: https://www.kncweb.co.jp
6568—(TKS)
Sales Range: Less than $1 Million
Emp.: 301
Chemical Products Mfr
N.A.I.C.S.: 325998
Hitoshi Miyauchi *(Founder & Pres)*

KNEAT.COM, INC.
Suite 2001 1969 Upper Water Street, Halifax, B3J 3R7, NS, Canada
Tel.: (902) 706-9074 Ca
Web Site: https://kneat.com
Year Founded: 2013

KNEAT.COM, INC.

kneat.com, Inc.—(Continued)
KSI—(TSX)
Rev.: $5,806,017
Assets: $26,442,341
Liabilities: $11,411,519
Net Worth: $15,030,822
Earnings: ($4,452,088)
Fiscal Year-end: 12/31/20
Gold Mining
N.A.I.C.S.: 212220
Eddie Ryan *(Co-Founder, CEO & Exec Dir)*
Subsidiaries:

Kneat Solutions Inc. (1)
36 E Main St Ste 201, Norristown, PA 19401
Tel.: (813) 503-6654
Computer Software Development Services
N.A.I.C.S.: 541511

Kneat Solutions Limited (1)
Unit 7 Castletroy Business Park Plassey Park Rd, Limerick, V94 KW28, Ireland
Tel.: (353) 61203826
Computer Software Development Services
N.A.I.C.S.: 541511

KNEIP COMMUNICATION S.A.
33 Rue du Puits Romain, 8070, Bertrange, Luxembourg
Tel.: (352) 2272771
Web Site: http://www.kneip.com
Year Founded: 1993
Sales Range: $25-49.9 Million
Emp.: 170
Asset Management Support Services
N.A.I.C.S.: 561499
Bob Kneip *(Founder & Chm)*
Subsidiaries:

La Cote Bleue S.A.S. (1)
10-12 Place Vendome, 75001, Paris, France
Tel.: (33) 144768585
Web Site: http://www.lacotebleue.fr
Sales Range: $1-9.9 Million
Emp.: 12
Financial Information Services
N.A.I.C.S.: 519290
Tixier Philippe *(Mgr)*

KNEISSL TIROL GMBH
Kaiseraufstieg 17, 6330, Kufstein, Austria
Tel.: (43) 537269900
Web Site: http://www.kneissl.com
Sales Range: $10-24.9 Million
Emp.: 25
Retailer of Hiking Trekking Ski Boot & Skis Mfr
N.A.I.C.S.: 316210
Subsidiaries:

Raichle Boots AG (1)
Walzmuhlstrasse 50, CH 8500, Frauenfeld, Switzerland
Tel.: (41) 527233636
Web Site: http://www.raichle.com
Mfr, Developer & Sales of Ski Boots, Snowboard Boots, Hiking & Tracking Boots
N.A.I.C.S.: 316210

KNEOMEDIA LIMITED
180 Flinders Street 7th Floor, Melbourne, 3000, VIC, Australia
Tel.: (61) 1300155606 AU
Web Site:
  https://www.kneomedia.com
KNM—(ASX)
Rev.: $1,188,615
Assets: $1,020,216
Liabilities: $2,938,086
Net Worth: ($1,917,869)
Earnings: ($1,457,992)
Emp.: 3
Fiscal Year-end: 06/30/24
Online Game Publisher
N.A.I.C.S.: 339930

James Kellett *(Chm & CEO)*
Subsidiaries:

KneoWorld UK Limited (1)
26-28 Mount Row 5th Floor, London, W1K 3SQ, United Kingdom
Tel.: (44) 2074093494
Web Site: https://www.kneoworld.co.uk
Educational Support Services
N.A.I.C.S.: 611710

KNH ENTERPRISE CO., LTD.
27F No 456 Sec 4 Xinyi Road, Xinyi District, Taipei, 110, Taiwan
Tel.: (886) 0223459909
Web Site: https://www.knh.com.tw
Year Founded: 1969
9919—(TAI)
Rev.: $96,087,377
Assets: $257,673,328
Liabilities: $161,768,953
Net Worth: $95,904,375
Earnings: $21,540,435
Emp.: 646
Fiscal Year-end: 12/31/23
Nonwoven Product Mfr
N.A.I.C.S.: 313230
Jung-Chi Tai *(Chm)*
Subsidiaries:

KNH (Shanghai) Co., Ltd. (1)
No 5619 Waiqingsong Highway, Qingpu Industrial Zone Qingpu District, Shanghai, 201707, China
Tel.: (86) 2169211200
Nonwoven Fabric Product Mfr & Distr
N.A.I.C.S.: 313230

Kang Na Hsiung Enterprise Co., Ltd. - Shanghai Plant (1)
No 5619 Wai Qing Song Rd Qing Pu Industrial Zone, Qing Pu Town, Shanghai, 201707, China
Tel.: (86) 21 6921 1200
Web Site: http://www.knh.com.tw
Nonwoven Fabric Mfr
N.A.I.C.S.: 313230

KNICK EXPLORATION INC.
536 3rd Avenue, Val d'Or, J9P 1S4, QC, Canada
Tel.: (819) 874-5252 QC
Web Site: http://www.knick.ca
Year Founded: 2004
KNX—(TSXV)
Gold Exploration Services
N.A.I.C.S.: 212220
Jacques Brunelle *(Pres & CEO)*

KNIGHT FRANK LLP
55 Baker Street, London, W1U 8AN, United Kingdom
Tel.: (44) 2076298171 UK
Web Site:
  http://www.knightfrank.co.uk
Year Founded: 1896
Sales Range: $1-4.9 Billion
Emp.: 6,343
Residential & Commercial Property Brokerage Management & Consultancy Services
N.A.I.C.S.: 531210
Andrew Hay *(Head-Residential-Global)*
Subsidiaries:

KNIGHT FRANK, spol. s r.o. (1)
Vaclavske Namesti 3, 110 00, Prague, Czech Republic
Tel.: (420) 224 217 217
Web Site: http://www.knightfrank.cz
Real Estate Consulting Service
N.A.I.C.S.: 531210
David Sajner *(Head-Sls)*

Knight Frank (Cambodia) Pte Ltd (1)
16B 16th Floor Canadia Tower 315 Ang Duong Street, Sangkat Wat Phnom Khan Daun Penh, Phnom Penh, Cambodia
Tel.: (855) 23 966 878

Web Site: http://www.knightfrank.com.kh
Tour Operator
N.A.I.C.S.: 561520
Ross Wheble *(Head-Country)*

Knight Frank (Gauteng) (Pty) Ltd (1)
50 Old Kilcullen Road, Bryanston, 2191, Gauteng, South Africa
Tel.: (27) 11 783 1195
Web Site: http://www.knightfrank.co.za
Emp.: 80
Real Estate Consulting Service
N.A.I.C.S.: 531210
Gail Cawood *(Mgr-Letting)*

Knight Frank (Malawi) Ltd (1)
Floor Plantation House Victoria Avenue, PO Box 1556, Blantyre, Malawi
Tel.: (265) 1823 577
Web Site: http://www.knightfrank.mw
Real Estate Consulting Service
N.A.I.C.S.: 531210

Knight Frank (Northern Territory) Pty Ltd (1)
Level 2 46 Smith Street Mall, Darwin, 0800, NT, Australia
Tel.: (61) 8 8982 2500
Real Estate Consulting Service
N.A.I.C.S.: 531210

Knight Frank (Shanghai) Property Consultants Co, Ltd (1)
17/F Eco City 1788 West Nanjing Road, Jing'an District, Shanghai, 200040, China
Tel.: (86) 2160321788
Web Site: http://www.knightfrank.com.cn
Real Estate Consulting Service
N.A.I.C.S.: 531210
Ying Shin Lee *(Mng Dir)*

Knight Frank (Thailand) Ltd. (1)
65/192 23rd Floor Chamnan Phenjati Business Center Rama 9 Road, Huaykwang District, Bangkok, 10320, Thailand
Tel.: (66) 2 643 8223
Web Site: http://www.knightfrank.co.th
Real Estate Consulting Service
N.A.I.C.S.: 531210
Risinee Sarikaputra *(Dir-Res & Consultancy)*

Knight Frank (Zambia) Ltd (1)
Ground Floor Mpile Office Park 74 Independence Avenue, PO Box 3, Lusaka, Zambia
Tel.: (260) 211 250683
Web Site: http://zm.knightfrank.com
Real Estate Consulting Service
N.A.I.C.S.: 531210
Tim Ware *(Mng Dir)*

Knight Frank Auckland Ltd (1)
Level 1 381 Great South Road, Ellerslie, Auckland, New Zealand
Tel.: (64) 9 377 3700
Web Site: http://www.knightfrank.co.nz
Emp.: 70
Real Estate Consulting Service
N.A.I.C.S.: 531210
Layne Harwood *(Principal)*

Knight Frank Australia Pty. Ltd. (1)
120 Level 29 Collins Street, Melbourne, 3000, VIC, Australia (100%)
Tel.: (61) 396025722
Web Site: http://www.knightfrank.com
Sales Range: $25-49.9 Million
Emp.: 60
Residential & Commercial Property Brokerage, Management & Consultancy Services
N.A.I.C.S.: 531210
Michael Hanscomb *(Dir-Retail Leasing-Sydney)*

Knight Frank Botswana Ltd (1)
183 Queens Road, PO Box 655, Gaborone, Botswana
Tel.: (267) 3953 950
Web Site: http://www.bw.knightfrank.com
Real Estate Consulting Service
N.A.I.C.S.: 531210
Curtis Matobolo *(Mng Dir)*

Knight Frank Cairns Pty Ltd. (1)
Level 1 32 Sheridan Street, Cairns, 4870, QLD, Australia
Tel.: (61) 7 4046 5300
Real Estate Consulting Service
N.A.I.C.S.: 531210

Knight Frank Espana SA (1)

INTERNATIONAL PUBLIC

Suero de Quinones 34, Madrid, 28002, Spain
Tel.: (34) 9178 80700
Web Site: http://www.knightfrank.es
Real Estate Consulting Service
N.A.I.C.S.: 531210
Humphrey White *(Mng Dir)*

Knight Frank Frankfurt GmbH (1)
Fellnerstrasse 5, 60322, Frankfurt am Main, Germany
Tel.: (49) 69 55 66 330
Real Estate Consulting Service
N.A.I.C.S.: 531210
Annette Gause *(Mgr-Fin)*

Knight Frank GmbH Co KG (1)
Prinzregentenstrasse 22, Munich, 80538, Germany
Tel.: (49) 89 83 93 120
Web Site: http://www.knightfrank.de
Emp.: 15
Real Estate Consulting Service
N.A.I.C.S.: 531210
Christian Babock *(Dir-Rental)*

Knight Frank HSC GmbH (1)
Charlottenstrasse 43, Berlin, 10117, Germany
Tel.: (49) 30 23 25 74350
Web Site: http://www.knightfrank.de
Emp.: 7
Real Estate Consulting Service
N.A.I.C.S.: 531210
Ole Sauer *(Mng Partner-Capital Markets & Asset Mgmt)*

Knight Frank India Pvt Ltd (1)
Paville House Near Twin Towers Off Veer Savarkar Marg, Prabhadevi, Mumbai, 400 025, India
Tel.: (91) 22 67450101
Web Site: http://www.knightfrank.co.in
Real Estate Consulting Service
N.A.I.C.S.: 531210
Aditya Sachdeva *(Dir-Strategic Initiatives-Natl)*

Knight Frank Italia s.r.l (1)
Via Borgonuovo 9, 20121, Milan, Italy
Tel.: (39) 0245377310
Web Site: http://www.knightfrank.it
Real Estate Consulting Service
N.A.I.C.S.: 531210
Alessandro C. Riboni *(CEO)*

Knight Frank Kenya Ltd (1)
Lion Place Ground Floor Waiyaki Way, Nairobi, 00623, Kenya
Tel.: (254) 20 4239000
Web Site: http://www.knightfrank.co.ke
Real Estate Consulting Service
N.A.I.C.S.: 531210
Ben Woodhams *(Mng Dir)*

Knight Frank Korea (1)
7F Sungdo Building 207, Dosan-daero Gangnam-gu, Seoul, 135-747, Korea (South)
Tel.: (82) 2 2175 3901
Web Site: http://www.knightfrank.kr
Real Estate Consulting Service
N.A.I.C.S.: 531210

Knight Frank Malaysia Sdn Bhd (1)
Suite 10 01 Level 10 Centrepoint South, Mid Valley City Lingkaran Syed Putra, Kuala Lumpur, 59200, Malaysia
Tel.: (60) 3 2289 9688
Web Site: http://www.knightfrank.com.my
Emp.: 100
Real Estate Consulting Service
N.A.I.C.S.: 531210
Eric Ooi *(Exec Chm)*

Knight Frank Nigeria Limited (1)
24 Campbell Street, PO Box 221, Lagos, Nigeria
Tel.: (234) 8022241450
Web Site: http://www.knightfrank.com.ng
Real Estate Consulting Service
N.A.I.C.S.: 531210
A. I. Omelime *(Partner-Property Mgmt)*

Knight Frank Phuket Co Ltd (1)
49/29-30 Baandon-Cherngthalay Road, T Cherngtalay A Thalang, Phuket, 83110, Thailand
Tel.: (66) 76 325195
Web Site: http://www.knightfrank.co.th
Real Estate Consulting Service

AND PRIVATE COMPANIES — KNIGHTS GROUP HOLDINGS PLC

N.A.I.C.S.: 531210

Knight Frank Pte Ltd (1)
16 Raffles Quay 30-01, Hong Leong Building, 048 581, Singapore, Singapore
Tel.: (65) 6222 1333
Web Site: http://www.knightfrank.com.sg
Real Estate Consulting Service
N.A.I.C.S.: 531210
Alice Tan *(Dir-Residential Project Mktg)*

Knight Frank SA (1)
Louizalaan 143 Avenue Louise, Brussels, 1050, Belgium
Tel.: (32) 2 548 05 48
Web Site: http://www.knightfrank.be
Emp.: 14
Real Estate Consulting Service
N.A.I.C.S.: 531210
Filip Derijck *(Mng Dir)*

Knight Frank Sp. z.o.o. (1)
Mokotowska Square 4 pietro ul Mokotowska 49, Warsaw, 00-542, Poland
Tel.: (48) 22 596 50 50
Web Site: http://www.knightfrank.com.pl
Emp.: 120
Real Estate Consulting Service
N.A.I.C.S.: 531210
Dorota Koscielniak *(Partner & Reg Dir)*

Knight Frank Tanzania Ltd (1)
3rd Floor International House Garden Avenue, Dar es Salaam, Tanzania
Tel.: (255) 222 113 300
Web Site: http://www.knightfrank.co.tz
Real Estate Consulting Service
N.A.I.C.S.: 531210
Remen Lyimo *(Mgr-Admin)*

Knight Frank Uganda Ltd (1)
Plot 21 Yusuf Lule Road 1st Floor Course View Towers, PO Box 24513, Kampala, Uganda
Tel.: (256) 414 341 382
Web Site: http://www.knightfrank.ug
Emp.: 68
Real Estate Consulting Service
N.A.I.C.S.: 531210
Caroline Nassolo *(Partner-HR Bus)*

Knight Frank ZAO (1)
26 Valovaya str, Moscow, 115-054, Russia
Tel.: (7) 495 981 0000
Web Site: http://www.knightfrank.ru
Emp.: 200
Real Estate Consulting Service
N.A.I.C.S.: 531210
Andrey Solovyev *(Dir-Residential Dept)*

Knight Frank Zimbabwe (1)
73A Robert Mugabe Way, PO Box 384, Bulawayo, Zimbabwe
Tel.: (263) 9 67231
Web Site: http://www.knightfrank.co.zw
Emp.: 100
Real Estate Consulting Service
N.A.I.C.S.: 531210

McGrath Limited (1)
55 Pyrmont Street, Pyrmont, 2009, NSW, Australia
Tel.: (61) 293863333
Web Site: http://www.mcgrath.com.au
Rev.: $21,595,887
Assets: $23,287,260
Liabilities: $7,462,607
Net Worth: $15,824,653
Earnings: $879,407
Emp.: 283
Fiscal Year-end: 06/30/2024
Real Estate Agency
N.A.I.C.S.: 531210
John McGrath *(Founder, CEO & Mng Dir)*

Subsidiary (Domestic):

McGrath Sales Paddington Pty Ltd (2)
195 Given Terrace, Paddington, Brisbane, 4064, QLD, Australia
Tel.: (61) 730881555
Real Estate Prorperty Leasing Services
N.A.I.C.S.: 531110
Charles Higgins *(Sls Mgr)*

KNIGHT THERAPEUTICS INC.

3400 de Maisonneuve W Suite 1055, Montreal, H3Z 3B8, QC, Canada
Tel.: (514) 484-4483 Ca
Web Site: https://knighttx.com
Year Founded: 2013
04K—(DEU)
Rev.: $247,828,287
Assets: $713,956,807
Liabilities: $149,982,632
Net Worth: $563,974,175
Earnings: ($12,712,376)
Emp.: 725
Fiscal Year-end: 12/31/23
Pharmaceuticals Mfr
N.A.I.C.S.: 325412
Samira Sakhia *(Pres)*

Subsidiaries:

NeurAxon Inc. (1)
16-1375 Southdown Road Suite 318, Mississauga, L5J 2Z1, ON, Canada
Tel.: (416) 673-6697
Web Site: http://www.neuraxon.com
Biotechnology Research & Development Services
N.A.I.C.S.: 541714
John S. Andrews *(Pres & Chief Scientific Officer)*

KNIGHTEC AB

Rattarvagen 3, 16968, Solna, Sweden
Tel.: (46) 84555300
Web Site: https://knightec.se
Emp.: 100
IT & Engineering Consulting Services
N.A.I.C.S.: 541330
Dimitris Gioulekas *(Founder, Pres & CEO)*

Subsidiaries:

Semcon AB (1)
Lindholmsallen 2, 417 80, Gothenburg, Sweden
Tel.: (46) 317210000
Web Site: http://www.semcon.com
Rev.: $208,915,504
Assets: $165,442,816
Liabilities: $68,206,096
Net Worth: $97,236,720
Earnings: $16,212,224
Emp.: 2,045
Fiscal Year-end: 12/31/2021
Consultancy Services
N.A.I.C.S.: 541618
Johan Ekener *(Pres-Product Information)*

Affiliate (Domestic):

Compliant Logistics AB (2) (50%)
Theres Svenssons Gata 15, 417 80, Gothenburg, Sweden
Tel.: (46) 31 721 00 00
Web Site: http://www.semcon.com
Sales Range: $25-49.9 Million
Emp.: 30
Custom Computer Programming Services
N.A.I.C.S.: 541511

Subsidiary (Non-US):

Haas-Publikationen GmbH (2)
Poststrasse 67, 53840, Troisdorf, Germany
Tel.: (49) 22 418 8020
Web Site: https://www.haas-publikationen.de
Technical Documentation Services
N.A.I.C.S.: 561410

Subsidiary (Domestic):

Semcon Engineering Services Nordic (2) (100%)
Lindholmsallen 2, 417 80, Gothenburg, Sweden
Tel.: (46) 31 721 00 00
Web Site: http://www.semcon.com
Sales Range: $150-199.9 Million
Emp.: 700
International Technology, Engineering Services, Product Information, Life Sciences & Telecommunications
N.A.I.C.S.: 541618
David Sonden *(Gen Mgr-Product Info)*

Subsidiary (Non-US):

Semcon India Pvt Ltd (2)
RMZ Nxt Campus 1B 1st Floor Unit 102 Sonnenahalli Village Mahadevapura, Hobli, Bengaluru, 560 066, India
Tel.: (91) 80 6713 9000
Web Site: http://www.semcon.com
Sales Range: $25-49.9 Million
Emp.: 127
Engineeering Services
N.A.I.C.S.: 541330

Subsidiary (Domestic):

Semcon Informatic Production AB (2) (100%)
Theres Svenssons Gata 15, Gothenburg, 41755, Sweden
Tel.: (46) 317210000
Web Site: http://www.semcon.com
Sales Range: $25-49.9 Million
Emp.: 100
Management Consulting Services
N.A.I.C.S.: 541618

Subsidiary (Non-US);

Semcon Informatic Production Ltd. (2)
Unit 7 & 8 Brook Business Park Brookhampton Lane, Kineton, CV35 0JA, Warwickshire, United Kingdom
Tel.: (44) 1926 642935
Sales Range: $25-49.9 Million
Emp.: 7
Engineeering Services
N.A.I.C.S.: 541330
Torsten Sundin *(Country Mgr-Product Info)*

Subsidiary (Domestic):

Semcon Informatic SRT AB (2) (100%)
Kungsgatan 57, 461 34, Trollhattan, Sweden
Tel.: (46) 31 721 0000
Web Site: http://www.semcon.com
Sales Range: $25-49.9 Million
Emp.: 25
Engineeering Services
N.A.I.C.S.: 541330

Semcon Informatic Services AB (2)
Theres Svenssons Gata 15, 41780, Gothenburg, Sweden
Tel.: (46) 317210000
Web Site: http://www.semcon.com
Sales Range: $150-199.9 Million
Emp.: 1,000
Engineeering Services
N.A.I.C.S.: 541330

Semcon Informatic Solutions AB (2) (100%)
Patentgatan 8, 112 67, Stockholm, Sweden
Tel.: (46) 856290600
Web Site: http://semcon.com
Sales Range: $25-49.9 Million
Management Consulting Services
N.A.I.C.S.: 541618

Subsidiary (Non-US):

Semcon Informatic UK Ltd (2) (100%)
Semcon House Edgehill Drive, Warwick, CV35 6NH, United Kingdom
Tel.: (44) 1926642935
Web Site: http://semcon.com
Sales Range: $25-49.9 Million
Graphic Design Services
N.A.I.C.S.: 541430

Semcon Information and Consulting Co., Ltd. (2)
Rm 3A01 Zhongchen Building Lize Zhong 2nd Road, Chaoyang District, Beijing, 100102, China
Tel.: (86) 10 64 39 93 12
Information Technology Consulting Services
N.A.I.C.S.: 541512

Subsidiary (Domestic):

Semcon International AB (2) (100%)
Lindeholmsallen 2, 417 80, Gothenburg, Sweden
Tel.: (46) 31 721 0000
Web Site: https://www.semcon.com
Sales Range: $400-449.9 Million
Emp.: 1,150
Information Services
N.A.I.C.S.: 519290
Bjorn Stromberg *(CFO)*

Subsidiary (Domestic):

Semcon Extern Engineering AB (3) (100%)
Theres Svenssons Gata 15, 417 80, Gothenburg, Sweden
Tel.: (46) 31648400
Web Site: http://www.semcon.com
Sales Range: $75-99.9 Million
Emp.: 500
Engineeering Services
N.A.I.C.S.: 541330

Zuite AB (3) (30%)
Theres Svenssons Gata 15, 41780, Gothenburg, Sweden
Tel.: (46) 739849202
Sales Range: $150-199.9 Million
Emp.: 1,000
Custom Computer Programming Services
N.A.I.C.S.: 541511

Subsidiary (Non-US):

Semcon KFT (2) (96.67%)
Info Park Gabor Denes u 2 Building D 2nd floor, 1117, Budapest, Hungary
Tel.: (36) 15050616
Engineeering Services
N.A.I.C.S.: 541330
Maria Pataki *(Reg Mgr)*

Subsidiary (Domestic):

Semcon Project Management AB (2) (100%)
Lindholmsallen 2, 417 80, Gothenburg, Sweden
Tel.: (46) 317210000
Web Site: http://www.semcon.com.se
Sales Range: $350-399.9 Million
Emp.: 2,000
Engineering & Project Management Services
N.A.I.C.S.: 541330
Bjorn Stromberg *(CFO)*

Semcon Sweden AB (2) (70%)
Drottninggatan 54 4 tr, 371 33, Karlskrona, Sweden
Tel.: (46) 317210000
Web Site: http://www.semcon.com
Sales Range: $25-49.9 Million
Emp.: 70
Automotive R&D Services
N.A.I.C.S.: 811198

Subsidiary (Non-US):

Semcon UK Ltd (2)
Semcon House Edgehill Drive, Warwick, CV34 6NH, United Kingdom
Tel.: (44) 192 664 2935
Web Site: http://www.semcon.com
Sales Range: $25-49.9 Million
Emp.: 25
Software Development Services
N.A.I.C.S.: 541511
Torsten Sundin *(Country Mgr-Product Info)*

Semcon do Brasil Ltda. (2)
Ave Nacoes Unidas 179, Sao Bernardo do Campo, 09726110, Sao Paulo, Brazil
Tel.: (55) 1141216840
Sales Range: $25-49.9 Million
Emp.: 30
Automotive Engineering Services
N.A.I.C.S.: 541330
Fabricio Cambos *(Reg Mgr)*

KNIGHTHAWK INC.

Suite 211-1015 Austin Avenue, Coquitlam, V3K 3N9, BC, Canada
Tel.: (604) 559-7922
Year Founded: 1993
KHA—(TSXV)
Assets: $582,056
Liabilities: $120,488
Net Worth: $461,568
Earnings: ($61,403)
Fiscal Year-end: 10/30/19
Transportation Services
N.A.I.C.S.: 482112
Kenneth H. Fitzgerald *(Chm)*

KNIGHTS GROUP HOLDINGS PLC

KNIGHTS GROUP HOLDINGS PLC

Knights Group Holdings PLC—(Continued)

The Brampton, Newcastle-under-Lyme, ST5 0QW, Staffordshire, United Kingdom
Tel.: (44) 1782619225
KGH—(AIM)
Rev.: $189,296,008
Assets: $276,572,121
Liabilities: $150,012,920
Net Worth: $126,559,201
Earnings: $12,433,754
Fiscal Year-end: 04/30/24
Legal & Professional Services
N.A.I.C.S.: 541199

Subsidiaries:

Knights Professional Services Limited (1)
The Brampton, Newcastle-under-Lyme, ST5 0QW, Staffs, United Kingdom
Tel.: (44) 1782 619 225
Web Site: http://www.knightsplc.com
Law firm
N.A.I.C.S.: 541199

Subsidiary (Domestic):

Mundays LLP (2)
78 Portsmouth Rd Cedar House, Cobham, KT11 1AN, United Kingdom
Tel.: (44) 1932 590 500
Web Site: http://www.mundays.co.uk
Law firm
N.A.I.C.S.: 541110
Manzoor Gulamhussein Kassam Ishani *(Atty)*

Langleys Solicitors LLP (1)
Olympic House Doddington Rd, Lincoln, LN6 3SE, United Kingdom
Tel.: (44) 152 288 8555
Web Site: http://www.langleys.com
Emp.: 100
Law firm
N.A.I.C.S.: 541110
Sally Cottam *(Co-Partner & Head-Residential Conveyancing)*

Shulmans LLP (1)
120 Wellington Street, Leeds, LS1 4LT, United Kingdom
Tel.: (44) 113 245 2833
Web Site: http://www.shulmans.co.uk
Emp.: 24
Law firm
N.A.I.C.S.: 541110
Andrew Bradley *(Co-Partner & Head-Corp)*

KNIGHTSBRIDGE CHEMICALS LTD.

9th Floor Office 1B Kendah House, PO Box 34398, Sheikh Zayed Road, Dubai, United Arab Emirates
Tel.: (971) 43329410
International Chemicals Mfr
N.A.I.C.S.: 325998
Tucker Link *(Chm)*

Subsidiaries:

Knightsbridge Chemicals Egypt SAE (1)
Area 27 Building No 151 Fifth Compound, New Cairo, Egypt
Tel.: (20) 225424390
Chemicals Mfr
N.A.I.C.S.: 325998
Ahmed Al-Hassan *(Gen Mgr)*

Knightsbridge Chemicals Ltd. (1)
1 Knightsbridge, London, W1X 7UP, United Kingdom
Tel.: (44) 2070737500
Chemicals Mfr
N.A.I.C.S.: 325998

Knightsbridge Investments Limited (1)
30 Hateley Drive, West Midlands, WV4 6SF, Wolverhampton, United Kingdom England
Tel.: (44) 20 7073 7500
Real Estate Investment Trade Company
N.A.I.C.S.: 525990

KNIGHTSBRIDGE FURNITURE PRODUCTIONS LTD

191 Thornton Road, Bradford, BD1 2JT, W Yorkshire, United Kingdom
Tel.: (44) 1274731900
Web Site: http://www.knightsbridge-furniture.co.uk
Year Founded: 1939
Sales Range: $10-24.9 Million
Emp.: 137
Furniture Mfr
N.A.I.C.S.: 337121
Peter Denham *(COO)*

KNILL HOLDING GMBH

Eisengasse 25, 8160, Weiz, Austria
Tel.: (43) 3172 2505 15
Web Site: http://www.knillgruppe.com
Sales Range: $250-299.9 Million
Emp.: 1,700
Holding Company
N.A.I.C.S.: 551112

Subsidiaries:

Almatec AG (1)
Industriestrasse 12, Schupfheim, 6170, Lucerne, Switzerland
Tel.: (41) 414857777
Web Site: http://www.almatec.ch
Steel Products Mfr
N.A.I.C.S.: 331513
Christian Knill *(Pres)*

Almatec GmbH (1)
Im Lochel 2, 35423, Lich, Eberstadt, Germany
Tel.: (49) 6004808131
Machinery Repair & Maintenance Services
N.A.I.C.S.: 811310

DAMP s.r.l. (1)
Via Leonardo da Vinci 15, Carobbio degli Angeli, 24060, Bergamo, Italy
Tel.: (39) 035959390
Web Site: http://www.damp.it
Electric Power Control Device Mfr
N.A.I.C.S.: 334512

EA Elektroarmaturen AG (1)
Ebnatstrasse 150, 8201, Schaffhausen, Switzerland
Tel.: (41) 525602664
Web Site: http://www.ea-sh.ch
Machinery Repair & Maintenance Services
N.A.I.C.S.: 811310

Elsta Mosdorfer Bosnia d.o.o. (1)
Save Kovacevica 11, 75000, Tuzla, Bosnia & Herzegovina
Tel.: (387) 35317050
Machinery Repair & Maintenance Services
N.A.I.C.S.: 811310

Elsta Mosdorfer GmbH (1)
Bahnstrasse 29, 8430, Hartberg, Austria
Tel.: (43) 3452716600
Machinery Repair & Maintenance Services
N.A.I.C.S.: 811310

Elsta Mosdorfer d.o.o. (1)
Buzinski prilaz 10, 10010, Zagreb, Croatia
Tel.: (385) 16448071
Web Site: http://www.elsta.com
Machinery Repair & Maintenance Services
N.A.I.C.S.: 811310

Graph Solutions Pty Ltd (1)
G 05 171 Union Road Surrey Hills, PO Box 134, Melbourne, 3127, VIC, Australia
Tel.: (61) 398992431
Web Site: http://www.graphsolutions.com.au
Machinery Repair & Maintenance Services
N.A.I.C.S.: 811310

IKEBANA ENGINEERING LTD. (1)
Ratchaburi Industrial Estate 155/47 Moo 4 Phetkasem Road Chetsamian, Photharam, Ratchaburi, 70120, Thailand
Tel.: (66) 32375811
Web Site: http://www.ikebana-heatshrink.com
Heat Distribution Equipment & Control Device Mfr
N.A.I.C.S.: 334515

KNILL Energy Holding GmbH (1)
Eisengasse 25, Weiz, 8160, Austria

Tel.: (43) 3172 2505 15
Web Site: http://www.knillgruppe.com
Electricity Transmission & Distribution Infrastructure Solutions
N.A.I.C.S.: 237130
Christian Knill *(CEO)*

KNILL Technology Holding GmbH (1)
Schachen 57, Pischelsdorf in der Steiermark, Weiz, 8212, Austria
Tel.: (43) 311351000
Web Site: http://www.rosendahlnextrom.com
Emp.: 250
Industrial Machinery Mfr
N.A.I.C.S.: 333248
Georg Knill *(CEO)*

Subsidiary (Non-US):

Nextrom Oy (2)
Ensimmainen savu, PO Box 44, Vantaa, 1510, Finland
Tel.: (358) 9 5025 1
Web Site: http://www.nextrom.com
Emp.: 55
Fiber Optic Equipment Mfr
N.A.I.C.S.: 333248
Timo Id *(Mng Dir)*

Subsidiary (US):

Nextrom USA Inc. (3)
333 Swanson Dr Ste 116, Lawrenceville, GA 30043
Tel.: (828) 464-2543
Web Site: http://www.nextrom.com
Sales Range: $25-49.9 Million
Emp.: 12
Fiber Optic Equipment Mfr
N.A.I.C.S.: 333248

Lorunser Austria GmbH (1)
Bahnhofstrasse 9, Schlins, 6824, Feldkirch, Vorarlberg, Austria
Tel.: (43) 552482910
Web Site: http://www.loruenser-substations.com
Switchgear & Electrical Component Mfr
N.A.I.C.S.: 335313
Thurnher Jurgen *(Mng Dir)*

ML Produktion s.r.o. (1)
Prostredna 1221/12, Myjava, 907 01, Trencin, Slovakia
Tel.: (421) 346909901
Machinery Repair & Maintenance Services
N.A.I.C.S.: 811310

Mosdorfer (Thailand) Co. Ltd. (1)
94 T Shinawatra Bldg 3 Fl Sukhumvit Soi 23 Sukhumvit Rd, Klong Toey Nua Wattana, Bangkok, 10110, Thailand
Tel.: (66) 21828351
Electrical Equipment Whslr
N.A.I.C.S.: 423830
Guntram Haas *(Chm)*

Mosdorfer CCL Systems Limited (1)
Market Overton Industrial Estate Ironstone Lane, Market Overton, Oakham, LE15 7PP, United Kingdom
Tel.: (44) 1572768381
Web Site: http://www.mosdorfer.ccl.com
Emp.: 440
Electrical Equipment Whslr
N.A.I.C.S.: 423830

Mosdorfer GmbH (1)
Mosdorfergasse 1, 8160, Weiz, Austria
Tel.: (43) 317225050
Web Site: http://www.mosdorfer.com
Electrical Equipment Whslr
N.A.I.C.S.: 423830

Mosdorfer India Private Limited (1)
403C Wing B1 Marathon Innova Opp Peninsula Corporate Park Lower Parel, 400 013, Mumbai, India
Tel.: (91) 2224926393
Machinery Repair & Maintenance Services
N.A.I.C.S.: 811310
Guntram Haas *(Chm)*

Mosdorfer NA Inc. (1)
1240 25th St SE, Hickory, NC 28602
Tel.: (704) 677-5805
Machinery Repair & Maintenance Services
N.A.I.C.S.: 811310

RC+E AG (1)

INTERNATIONAL PUBLIC

Seestrasse 91, 6052, Hergiswil, Switzerland
Tel.: (41) 413682200
Machinery Repair & Maintenance Services
N.A.I.C.S.: 811310

Rosendahl Industrial Services s.r.l. (1)
Str Lucian Blaga Nr 35, 440227, Satu-Mare, Romania
Tel.: (40) 361403040
Web Site: http://www.rosendahlindustrial.com
Industrial Building Construction Services
N.A.I.C.S.: 236210

Rosendahl Nextrom Electrical Machinery Trading Co. Ltd. (1)
1 Building No 128 Shenfu Road Xin Zhuang Industrial Zone, 201108, Shanghai, China
Tel.: (86) 2151760200
Machinery Repair & Maintenance Services
N.A.I.C.S.: 811310

Rosendahl Nextrom GmbH (1)
Schachen 57, Pischelsdorf in der Steiermark, 8212, Weiz, Austria
Tel.: (43) 311351000
Machinery Repair & Maintenance Services
N.A.I.C.S.: 811310

Rosendahl Nextrom OOO (1)
Storozhevaya str 4, 111020, Moscow, Russia
Tel.: (7) 4992713450
Machinery Repair & Maintenance Services
N.A.I.C.S.: 811310

Rosendahl Nextrom Oy (1)
Ensimmainen savu, PO Box 44, 01511, Vantaa, Finland
Tel.: (358) 950251
Web Site: http://www.rosendahlnextrom.com
Industry Machinery Design & Maintenance Services
N.A.I.C.S.: 333132
Murali Das *(Mgr-Sls)*

Rosendahl Nextrom SA (1)
Le Tresi 6, CP149, 1028, Preverenges, Switzerland
Tel.: (41) 218110808
Machinery Repair & Maintenance Services
N.A.I.C.S.: 811310

KNITWEAR FACTORY MAXIM C.M. PERTSINIDIS S.A.

18th Km Thessaloniki-Serres Nat Road, PO Box 195 48, 54012, Thessaloniki, Greece
Tel.: (30) 23940 72102
Year Founded: 1987
Emp.: 114
Textile Machinery Mfr & Whslr
N.A.I.C.S.: 333248
Tsikoudis Panagiotis *(IR Officer)*

KNJ CO., LTD.

22 Smart sandan 1-ro, Eumbongmyeon, Asan, Chungcheongnam-do, Korea (South)
Tel.: (82) 415348840
Web Site: https://www.knj.kr
Year Founded: 2005
272110—(KRS)
Rev.: $47,795,148
Assets: $82,910,060
Liabilities: $41,658,672
Net Worth: $41,251,388
Earnings: $7,635,012
Emp.: 178
Fiscal Year-end: 12/31/22
Electronic Components Mfr
N.A.I.C.S.: 334419

KNM GROUP BERHAD

15 Jalan Dagang SB4 1 Taman Sungai Besi Indah, 43300, Seri Kembangan, Selangor Darul Ehsan, Malaysia
Tel.: (60) 389463000
Web Site: https://www.knm-group.com
Year Founded: 1990
KNM—(KLS)
Rev.: $101,316,190

Assets: $651,941,164
Liabilities: $475,802,328
Net Worth: $176,138,836
Earnings: ($182,996,825)
Emp.: 1,654
Fiscal Year-end: 06/30/23
Boiler Mfr
N.A.I.C.S.: 332410
Siew Liat Gan *(Vice Chm)*

Subsidiaries:

Borsig GmbH (1)
Egellsstrasse 21, 13507, Berlin, Germany
Tel.: (49) 3 043 0101
Web Site: https://www.borsig.de
Heat Exchanger Mfr
N.A.I.C.S.: 333248
Jurgen Stegger *(Co-CEO & Co-Mng Dir)*

Subsidiary (Domestic):

Borsig Membrane Technology
GmbH (2)
Bottroper Strasse 279, 45964, Gladbeck,
Germany
Tel.: (49) 2043400601
Equipment Mfr
N.A.I.C.S.: 333248
Jurgen Stegger *(Mng Dir)*

Subsidiary (Domestic):

Gmt Membrantechnik GmbH (3)
Am Rhein 5, 79618, Rheinfelden, Germany
Tel.: (49) 76239660960
Web Site: https://www.gmtmem.com
Module Mfr
N.A.I.C.S.: 333248
Katrin Ebert *(Head-Dev)*

Subsidiary (Domestic):

Borsig Zm Compression GmbH (2)
Seiferitzer Allee 26, 08393, Meerane, Germany
Tel.: (49) 376453900
Equipment Mfr
N.A.I.C.S.: 333248
Oliver Kuhner *(Mng Dir)*

Fbm Hudson Italiana SpA (1)
Via per Valtrighe 5, 24030, Terno d'Isola,
BG, Italy
Tel.: (39) 0354941111
Web Site: https://www.fbmhudson.com
Heat Exchanger Mfr
N.A.I.C.S.: 333248
Giulio Sozzi *(Production Mgr)*

Fbm-Knm Fzco (1)
Plot 47-R-1 Jebel Ali Free Zone, PO Box
17101, Dubai, United Arab Emirates
Tel.: (971) 48835681
Heat Exchanger Mfr
N.A.I.C.S.: 333248
Ramesh Jayaraman *(Project Mgr)*

Impress Ethanol Co., Ltd. (1)
825 Phairojkijja Building 12th Floor Bangha-Trad Road, Khwaeng Bangna Khet Bangna,
Bangkok, 10260, Thailand
Tel.: (66) 2 361 4757
Web Site: https://www.impressethanol.com
Biofuel Ethanol Mfr & Whslr
N.A.I.C.S.: 325193
Santi Somroop *(Mgr-HSE)*

KNM Process Systems Sdn.
Bhd. (1)
15 Jalan Dagang SB 4/1, Taman Sungai
Besi Indah, 43300, Seri Kembangan, Selangor, Malaysia
Tel.: (60) 389463000
Equipment Mfr
N.A.I.C.S.: 333248
P. C. Ting *(Gen Mgr)*

Knm Process Equipment Inc. (1)
6204-46 Ave, Box 420, Tofield, Camrose,
T0B 4J0, AB, Canada
Tel.: (780) 662-3181
Equipment Mfr
N.A.I.C.S.: 333248

Knm Special Process Equipment
(Changshu) Co., Ltd. (1)
No 46 Xinggang Road, Changshu Economic Development Zone, Changshu,
215513, Jiangsu, China
Tel.: (86) 51252291888
Heat Exchanger Mfr
N.A.I.C.S.: 333248

Peterborough Green Energy Ltd. (1)
Ruthlyn House 90 Lincoln Road, Peterborough, PE1 2SP, United Kingdom
Tel.: (44) 60389463000
Recycled Product Recovery Services
N.A.I.C.S.: 562920

Petrosab Petroleum Engineering Sdn.
Bhd. (1)
No E-30-5 Lot 30 5th Floor Block E KK
Times Square Phase 1, Off Coastal Highway, 88100, Kota Kinabalu, Sabah, Malaysia
Tel.: (60) 88485358359
Equipment Mfr
N.A.I.C.S.: 333248

Saudi KNM Ltd. (1)
Jubail Industrial City 1 Dammam Highway,
Jubail, 31961, Saudi Arabia
Tel.: (966) 548827130
Petrochemical Mfr & Distr
N.A.I.C.S.: 325110

KNOCH, KERN & CO. KG
Ferdinand-Jergitsch-StraSSe 15,
9020, Klagenfurt, Austria
Tel.: (43) 463 56676 0
Holding Company
N.A.I.C.S.: 551112
Christina Fromme-Knoch *(Chm)*

Subsidiaries:

Wietersdorfer-Industrie-
Beteiligungs-GmbH (1)
Ferdinand-Jergitsch-Str 15, 9020, Klagenfurt, Austria
Tel.: (43) 664 6124010
Web Site: http://www.wietersdorfer.com
Holding Company
N.A.I.C.S.: 551112
Hannes Gailer *(Mng Dir)*

Subsidiary (Domestic):

HOBAS Engineering GmbH (2)
Pischeldorfer Strasse 128, 9020, Klagenfurt, Austria
Tel.: (43) 463482424
Web Site: http://www.hobas.com
Emp.: 1,000
Pipe Mfr & Distr
N.A.I.C.S.: 326122
Thomas Simoner *(Head-R&D & Quality Mgmt)*

Subsidiary (Non-US):

HOBAS (Malaysia) SDN. BHD. (3)
Suite 2 7 Level 2 Block C Plaza Damansara
45 Jalan Medan Setia 1, Bukit Damansara,
50490, Kuala Lumpur, Malaysia
Tel.: (60) 6224 7060
Web Site: http://www.hobas.my
Pipe Product Distr
N.A.I.C.S.: 424610
Mario Anderwald *(Dir-Sls)*

HOBAS AUSTRALIA PTY. LTD. (3)
Unit 1 27 Metrolink Circuit, Campbellfield,
3061, VIC, Australia
Tel.: (61) 3 9305 0600
Web Site: http://www.hobas.com.au
Pipe Product Mfr & Distr
N.A.I.C.S.: 326122
David Morgan *(CEO)*

HOBAS Benelux B.V. (3)
Marconistraat 11-10, 4004 JM, Tiel, Netherlands
Tel.: (31) 344 820030
Web Site: http://www.hobas.nl
Emp.: 10
Pipe Product Distr
N.A.I.C.S.: 424610
George van Halteren *(Mng Dir)*

HOBAS Bulgaria EOOD (3)
86 Osogovo Str Office 402, 1303, Sofia,
Bulgaria
Tel.: (359) 2 986 98 36
Web Site: http://www.hobas.bg
Emp.: 5
Pipe Product Distr
N.A.I.C.S.: 424610
Kalina Galabova *(Mgr-Sls)*

HOBAS CZ spol. s r. o. (3)
Tr Mars Malinovskeho 306, 686 01, Uherske Hradiste, Czech Republic
Tel.: (420) 572 520 311
Web Site: http://www.hobas.cz
Pipe Product Distr
N.A.I.C.S.: 424610

HOBAS Engineering + Rohre AG (3)
Birsigstrasse 2, 4054, Basel, Switzerland
Tel.: (41) 61 201 31 20
Web Site: http://www.hobas.ch
Pipe Product Distr
N.A.I.C.S.: 424610

HOBAS France SAS (3)
Parc St Christophe 10 avenue de
l'Entreprise, 95865, Cergy-Pontoise, France
Tel.: (33) 1 34356610
Web Site: http://www.hobas.fr
Pipe Product Distr
N.A.I.C.S.: 424610

HOBAS Hungaria Kft. (3)
Rokolya u 1-13, 1131, Budapest, Hungary
Tel.: (36) 1 236 0818
Emp.: 5
Pipe Product Distr
N.A.I.C.S.: 424610
Veszpremi Zsuzsanna *(Dir-Sls)*

HOBAS Pipe Hong Kong Ltd. (3)
Unit B 4/F Wing Hang Fincance Centre 60
Gloucester Road, Wanchai, China (Hong Kong)
Tel.: (852) 9151 6849
Pipe Product Distr
N.A.I.C.S.: 424610
James Lee *(Mgr-Sls)*

HOBAS Pipe Systems SRL (3)
Str Drumul Mare nr 2, Clinceni, Judetul Ilfov, Romania
Tel.: (40) 21 300 12 01
Web Site: http://www.hobas.ro
Pipe Product Distr
N.A.I.C.S.: 424610
Ionela Gheorghe *(Area Mgr-Sls)*

Subsidiary (US):

HOBAS Pipe USA, LP (3)
1413 Richey Rd, Houston, TX 77073-3508
Tel.: (281) 821-2200
Web Site: http://www.hobaspipe.com
Pipe Product Mfr & Distr
N.A.I.C.S.: 326122
Ed Kocurek *(Pres & CEO)*

Subsidiary (Non-US):

HOBAS Quebec Inc. (3)
1080 Cote du Beaver Hall Bureau 1610,
Montreal, H2Z 1S8, QC, Canada
Tel.: (514) 574-0810
Web Site: http://www.hobas.ca
Emp.: 5
Pipe Product Distr
N.A.I.C.S.: 424610
Philippe Fischer *(Gen Mgr)*

Subsidiary (Domestic):

HOBAS Rohre GmbH (3)
Wietersdorf 1, 9373, Klein Sankt Paul, Austria
Tel.: (43) 426428520
Web Site: http://www.hobas.com
Emp.: 140
Pipe Product Distr
N.A.I.C.S.: 424610
Mihaela Tabacaru *(Mgr-Quality)*

Subsidiary (Non-US):

HOBAS Rohre GmbH (3)
Gewerbepark 1, 17039, Trollenhagen, Germany
Tel.: (49) 395 45 28 0
Web Site: http://www.hobas.de
Pipe Product Distr
N.A.I.C.S.: 424610
Rudolph Haux *(Mgr-Sls)*

HOBAS SK spol. s r. o. (3)
Vajnorska 136, 831 04, Bratislava, Slovakia
Tel.: (421) 2 446 311 61
Web Site: http://www.amiblu.com
Pipe Product Distr
N.A.I.C.S.: 424610

HOBAS Scandinavia AB (3)
Engelbrektsgatan 15 3 tr, 211 33, Malmo,
Sweden
Tel.: (46) 40 680 02 50
Pipe Product Distr
N.A.I.C.S.: 424610
Richard Hansson *(Mng Dir)*

HOBAS Singapore Pte. Ltd. (3)
110 Robinson Road 08-00, Singapore,
068901, Singapore
Tel.: (65) 9155 4605
Web Site: http://www.hobas.sg
Pipe Product Distr
N.A.I.C.S.: 424610
Kent Goh *(Mgr-Sls)*

HOBAS System Polska Sp. z o.
o. (3)
Ul Koksownicza 11, 41-300, Dabrowa Gornicza, Poland
Tel.: (48) 32 639 04 50
Web Site: http://www.amiblu.com
Emp.: 100
Pipe Product Distr
N.A.I.C.S.: 424610
Thomas Miswlk *(Gen Mgr)*

HOBAS Tubi S.r.l. (3)
Via Eugenio Montale 4/5, 30030, Pianiga,
Italy
Tel.: (39) 041 5952282
Web Site: http://www.hobas.it
Pipe Product Distr
N.A.I.C.S.: 424610
Massimo Cacaveri *(Mng Dir)*

KNOLL MASCHINENBAU GMBH
Schwarzachstrasse 20, 88348, Saulgau, Germany
Tel.: (49) 7581 2008 0
Web Site: http://www.knoll-mb.de
Year Founded: 1970
Pump, Conveying & Filter Systems
Mfr
N.A.I.C.S.: 333914
Matthias Knoll *(CEO)*

Subsidiaries:

KNOLL America, Inc. (1)
313 W Girard St, Madison Heights, MI
48071
Tel.: (248) 588-1500
Web Site: http://www.knollamerica.com
Sales Range: $25-49.9 Million
Emp.: 10
Pump, Conveying & Filter Systems Mfr
N.A.I.C.S.: 333248
Bill Prudhomme *(Pres)*

KNORR-BREMSE AG
Moosacher Str 80, D-80809, Munich,
Germany
Tel.: (49) 8935470 De
Web Site: https://www.knorr-bremse.com
Year Founded: 1905
KBX—(MUN)
Rev.: $8,748,843,111
Assets: $9,105,337,927
Liabilities: $5,974,884,033
Net Worth: $3,130,453,894
Earnings: $609,921,291
Emp.: 33,319
Fiscal Year-end: 12/31/23
Holding Company; Braking Systems
Mfr
N.A.I.C.S.: 551112
Franz-Josef Birkender *(Deputy Chm-Supervisory Bd)*

Subsidiaries:

Anchor Brake Shoe Company
LLC (1)
1920 Downs Dr, Chicago, IL 60185
Tel.: (630) 818-1950
Web Site: http://www.nyab.com
Brake Shoe Mfr
N.A.I.C.S.: 331511

KNORR-BREMSE AG — INTERNATIONAL PUBLIC

Knorr-Bremse AG—(Continued)

Bendix CVS de Mexico SA de CV (1)
Rio Lerma 108 Ext 2 Fracc Ind Tlaxcolpan, 54030, Tlalnepantla, Edo de Mex, Mexico
Tel.: (52) 5516659040
Mechanical Equipment Mfr
N.A.I.C.S.: 333613

Bendix Commercial Vehicle Systems LLC (1)
901 Cleveland St, Elyria, OH 44035-4109
Tel.: (440) 329-9000
Web Site: http://www.bendix.com
Sales Range: $700-749.9 Million
Emp.: 4,100
Air Brakes, Filtration Systems & Components Supplier
N.A.I.C.S.: 423120
Joseph J. McAleese (Co-Chm-Exec Bd)

Bendix Spicer Foundation Brake LLC (1)
901 Cleveland St, Elyria, OH 44035
Tel.: (440) 329-9709
Web Site: http://www.foundationbrakes.com
Mechanical Equipment Mfr
N.A.I.C.S.: 333613
Aaron Schwass (VP & Gen Mgr)

Bost Iberica S.L. (1)
Parque Empresarial de Edificio Francia Planta 2 Escalera B, 28830, San Fernando de Henares, Spain
Tel.: (34) 902100571
Mechanical Equipment Mfr
N.A.I.C.S.: 333613

Cojali France S.A.R.L. (1)
5 Chem de la Grange, 33650, Martillac, France
Tel.: (33) 557359966
Electronic Components Mfr & Distr
N.A.I.C.S.: 334419

Cojali Italia S.R.L. (1)
Via Raffaello Sanzio 12, 20090, Cesano Boscone, Italy
Tel.: (39) 0245713779
Electronic Components Mfr & Distr
N.A.I.C.S.: 334419

Cojali S.L. (1)
Avenida de la Industria s/n Campo de Criptana, 13610, Ciudad Real, Spain
Tel.: (34) 926589670
Web Site: https://www.cojali.com
Electronic Components Mfr & Distr
N.A.I.C.S.: 334419

Cojali USA Inc. (1)
2200 NW 102nd Ave Ste 4B, Doral, FL 33172
Tel.: (305) 960-7651
Electronic Components Mfr & Distr
N.A.I.C.S.: 334419

Comet Fans S.r.l. (1)
Via Lucania 2, Buccinasco, 20090, Milan, Italy
Tel.: (39) 0296790143
Web Site: https://www.cometfans.com
Mechanical Equipment Mfr
N.A.I.C.S.: 333613

Distribuidora Bendix CVS (de) Mexico SA de CV (1)
Calle Rio Lerma 108, 54030, Tlalnepantla, Mexico
Tel.: (52) 5516659039
Mechanical Equipment Mfr
N.A.I.C.S.: 333613

Dr. techn. Josef Zelisko, Fabrik fur Elektrotechnik und Maschinenbau Ges.mbH (1)
Beethovengasse 43-45, 2340, Modling, Austria
Tel.: (43) 22364090
Web Site: https://www.zelisko.com
Energy Transition Product Distr
N.A.I.C.S.: 423610

EKA d.o.o. (1)
Aleksandar Urdarevski 30-94, 1000, Skopje, North Macedonia
Web Site: https://www.eka-knorr-bremse.com
Mechanical Equipment Mfr

N.A.I.C.S.: 333613
Nino Kuzmanovski (Mng Dir)

GT Emissions Systems Ltd. (1)
Traynor Way Whitehouse Business Park, Peterlee, SR8 2RU, Co Durham, United Kingdom
Tel.: (44) 1915862366
Web Site: https://www.gtesys.co.uk
Gas Control Valve Mfr
N.A.I.C.S.: 332911
Chris Hodge (Production Mgr)

GT Group Ltd. (1)
3 Traynor Way, Peterlee, SR8 2RU, Co Durham, United Kingdom
Tel.: (44) 1915862366
Web Site: http://www.gtgroup.co.uk
Sales Range: $1-9.9 Million
Engineering Product Mfr
N.A.I.C.S.: 333248
Geoff Turnbull (Founder)

Guangdong Knorr-Bremse Guo Tong Railway Vehicle Systems Equipment Co., Ltd. (1)
No 8 Keyun Si Road, Xinhui Town Xinhui District, Jiangmen, 552190, Guangdong, China
Tel.: (86) 7506309398
Railway Transportation Services
N.A.I.C.S.: 237990

Hasse & Wrede CVS Dalian, China Ltd. (1)
Automobile Parts Industrial Park Block No 48, Economic Technological Development Zone, Dalian, 116600, China
Tel.: (86) 41187964386
Web Site: http://www.hassewrede.com
Mechanical Equipment Mfr
N.A.I.C.S.: 333613

Hasse & Wrede GmbH (1)
Georg-Knorr-Strasse 4, 12681, Berlin, Germany
Web Site: https://www.hassewrede.com
Mechanical Equipment Mfr
N.A.I.C.S.: 333613
Bernd Spies (Mng Dir)

Heine Resistors GmbH (1)
Otto-Mohr-Strasse 5, 01237, Dresden, Germany
Tel.: (49) 35131920
Web Site: https://www.heine-resistors.com
Mechanical Equipment Mfr
N.A.I.C.S.: 333613
Patrick Rudolph (Mng Dir)

IFB Institut fur Bahntechnik GmbH (1)
Carnotstrasse 6, 10587, Berlin, Germany
Tel.: (49) 303999240
Web Site: http://www.bahntechnik.de
Engineering Services
N.A.I.C.S.: 541330

IFE North America LLC (1)
1 Arthur Peck Dr, Westminster, MD 21157
Tel.: (410) 875-0900
Mechanical Equipment Mfr
N.A.I.C.S.: 333613
Bill Mutschler (Pres)

IFE Tebel Technologies B.V. (1)
Ceresweg No-19 8938 BG, Leeuwarden, 8938, Netherlands (100%)
Tel.: (31) 582973333
Web Site: http://www.ic-tebel.nl
Sales Range: $25-49.9 Million
Emp.: 25
N.A.I.C.S.: 333310
Frannk Borst (Gen Mgr)

IFE-CR a.s. (1)
Evropska 839, 664 42, Modrice, Czech Republic
Web Site: http://www.ife.cz
Emp.: 860
Automatic Door System Mfr
N.A.I.C.S.: 332321

IFE-Tebel Technologies B.V. (1)
Ceresweg 19, 8938 BG, Leeuwarden, Netherlands
Tel.: (31) 582973333
Automatic Door & Gate Mfr
N.A.I.C.S.: 334512

IFE-VICTALL Railway Vehicle Door Systems (Qingdao) Co., Ltd. (1)

No 2 Xinghaizhi Road Huanhai Economic Technical Developing Zone, Chengyang, Qingdao, 266108, China
Tel.: (86) 53287938512
Automatic Door & Gate Mfr
N.A.I.C.S.: 334512
Felix Zhang (Mgr-Production)

IGE-CZ s.r.o. (1)
Ripska 1178/11a, 627 00, Brno, Czech Republic
Tel.: (420) 54 842 4050
Web Site: http://www.info-brno.cz
Automatic Door & Gate Mfr
N.A.I.C.S.: 334512
Ivana Votapkova (Mng Dir)

Icer Rail S.L. (1)
Pol Industrial Agustinos G s/n, 31013, Pamplona, Spain
Tel.: (34) 948488188
Web Site: http://www.icer-rail.com
Railway Vehicle Brake Pad & Brake Block Mfr
N.A.I.C.S.: 336510
Inigo Arana Remirez (Production Mgr)

Kiepe Electric Schweiz AG (1)
Neumatt 4, 4626, Niederbuchsiten, Switzerland
Tel.: (41) 623898888
Web Site: https://www.apsag.com
Auxiliary Converters Mfr
N.A.I.C.S.: 336350

Knorr Brake Company (1)
1 Arthur Peck Dr, Westminster, MD 21157 (100%)
Tel.: (410) 875-0900
Web Site: https://www.knorr-bremse.us
Sales Range: $75-99.9 Million
Brake Systems & Components for Commercial Vehicles
N.A.I.C.S.: 336340
Gregory Dalpe (VP)

Subsidiary (Non-US):

Knorr Brake Ltd. (2)
675 Development Dr, Kingston, K7M 4W6, ON, Canada (100%)
Tel.: (613) 389-4660
Sales Range: $50-74.9 Million
Emp.: 75
Mfr of Systems & Components for Commercial Vehicles
N.A.I.C.S.: 336340

Knorr-Bremse Asia Pacific (Holding) Ltd. (1)
Suite 2901 29F Central Plaza 18 Harbour Rd, Wanchai, China (Hong Kong) (100%)
Tel.: (852) 3657 9800
Sales Range: $25-49.9 Million
Emp.: 100
Mfr of Systems & Components for Commercial Vehicles & Aftermarket Sales
N.A.I.C.S.: 336340
Kevin Bullock (Gen Mgr)

Subsidiary (Non-US):

Knorr-Bremse Australia Pty. Ltd. (2)
23 - 29 Factory Street, PO Box 180, Granville, 2142, NSW, Australia (100%)
Tel.: (61) 288636500
Web Site: http://www.knorr-bremse.com.au
Sales Range: $25-49.9 Million
Brake Systems, Brake Components, Wheels, Doors, Air-Conditioning Equipment & Light Fittings for Railbound Vehicles Mfr
N.A.I.C.S.: 336340
George Sabbouh (Officer-Fin)

Knorr-Bremse Brake Equipment (Shanghai) Co., Ltd. (1)
Building B Silver Square No 666 Shengxia Road Pudong New Area, Shanghai, 201210, China
Tel.: (86) 2138585800
Mechanical Equipment Mfr
N.A.I.C.S.: 333613
Baoping Xu (Mng Dir)

Knorr-Bremse Commercial Vehicle Systems (Shanghai) Co., Ltd. (1)
Building B Silver Square No 666 Shengxia Road, Pudong New Area, Shanghai, 201210, China
Tel.: (86) 2138585800

Brake System Mfr
N.A.I.C.S.: 336340

Knorr-Bremse Commercial Vehicle Systems Japan Ltd. (1)
6-22-1 Nissai-Hanamizuki, Sakado, 350-0269, Saitama, Japan
Tel.: (81) 492739000
Brake System Mfr
N.A.I.C.S.: 336340
Joachim Baczewski (Pres & Dir-Rep)

Knorr-Bremse DETC Commercial Vehicle Braking Technology Co., Ltd. (1)
No 40 Fang Ma Ping Road Huaguo Avenue, Shiyan, 442003, Hubei, China
Tel.: (86) 7198208818
Brake System Mfr
N.A.I.C.S.: 336340

Knorr-Bremse Iberica S.L. (1)
Parque Empresarial de San Fernando Edificio FRANCIA Planta 2, Escalera B, 28830, San Fernando de Henares, Spain
Tel.: (34) 902100571
Brake System Mfr
N.A.I.C.S.: 336340

Knorr-Bremse Nordic Rail Services AB (1)
Traktorvagen 8, 226 60, Lund, Sweden
Tel.: (46) 4 632 9350
Web Site: https://www.knorr-bremse.se
Emp.: 50
Clutch & Brake System Mfr
N.A.I.C.S.: 336340
Alexander Wagner (Member-Exec Bd)

Knorr-Bremse Pamplona S.L. (1)
Pol Industrial Agustinos, 31013, Pamplona, Spain
Tel.: (34) 948488188
Friction Materials Mfr
N.A.I.C.S.: 324122

Knorr-Bremse Polska SfN Sp. z o.o. (1)
Tel.: (48) 228873870
Web Site: http://www.knorr-bremse.pl
Emp.: 100
Clutch & Brake System Mfr
N.A.I.C.S.: 336340
Beata Struminska (Dir-Fin)

Knorr-Bremse Rail Systems (Burton) Ltd. (1)
Unit 1 Stretton Business Park 1 Brunel Drive, Stretton, Burton, DE13 0BY, Staffordshire, United Kingdom
Tel.: (44) 1283505720
Web Site: http://www.knorr-bremse.co.uk
Mechanical Engineering Services
N.A.I.C.S.: 541330
Nick Fitzwater (Mng Dir-Rail Svcs)

Knorr-Bremse Rail Systems (Machining) Ltd. (1)
Westinghouse Way Hampton Park East, Melksham, SN12 6TL, Wiltshire, United Kingdom
Tel.: (44) 1225898700
Mechanical Engineering Services
N.A.I.C.S.: 541330
Stuart Fletcher (Dir-Sls)

Knorr-Bremse Rail Systems (UK) Ltd. (1)
Industrial Park Unit 1 Hazelbottom Rd Hendham Vale, Manchester, M8 0GF, United Kingdom
Tel.: (44) 1225898700
Rail Systems Operator
N.A.I.C.S.: 485112

Subsidiary (Domestic):

Westcode (UK) Ltd. (2)
Carnegie Road, Calne, SN11 9PS, Wiltshire, United Kingdom
Tel.: (44) 1249822283
Rail Air Conditioning Supplier
N.A.I.C.S.: 221330
Sue Hendon (Co-Sec & Dir-Fin)

Knorr-Bremse Rail Systems CIS Holding OOO (1)
Obraztsova Str 4a, 127055, Moscow, Russia
Tel.: (7) 4952300572

AND PRIVATE COMPANIES

KNORR-BREMSE AG

Brake System Mfr
N.A.I.C.S.: 336340

Knorr-Bremse Rail Systems Schweiz AG (1)
Hertistrasse 31, 8304, Wallisellen, Switzerland
Tel.: (41) 448523111
Emp.: 60
Brake System Mfr
N.A.I.C.S.: 336340

Knorr-Bremse Rail Transportation Equipment (Chengdu) Co., Ltd. (1)
Chuanfeng Road High-Tech Industrial Park, Xindu District, Chengdu, 610500, China
Tel.: (86) 15962212251
Emp.: 25
Railway Transportation Services
N.A.I.C.S.: 237990

Knorr-Bremse Railway Technologies (Shanghai) Co., Ltd. (1)
No 508 Chuan Hong Road, Pudong, Shanghai, 201202, China
Mechanical Equipment Distr
N.A.I.C.S.: 423840

Knorr-Bremse Rayli Sistemler Sanayi ve Ticaret Limited Sirketi (1)
Macun Mah 223 Cad No 10/1, Yenimahalle, 06105, Ankara, Turkiye
Tel.: (90) 3123871030
Web Site: http://www.knorr-bremse.com.tr
Brake System Mfr
N.A.I.C.S.: 336340

Knorr-Bremse S.R.L. (1)
Sos Vitan-Barzesti no 9A Sector 4, Bucharest, Romania
Tel.: (40) 374005155
Web Site: http://www.knorr-bremse.ro
Brake System Mfr
N.A.I.C.S.: 336340
Babos Zoltan (Office Mgr)

Knorr-Bremse Services Europe s.r.o. (1)
nam Nerudovo 120/6, 460 01, Liberec, Czech Republic
Tel.: (420) 485840402
Web Site: https://business-services.knorr-bremse.com
Emp.: 300
Brake System Mfr
N.A.I.C.S.: 336340

Knorr-Bremse Services GmbH (1)
Moosacher Str 80, 80809, Munich, Germany
Tel.: (49) 8935470
Brake System Mfr
N.A.I.C.S.: 336340

Knorr-Bremse Sistemas para Veiculos Comerciais Brasil Ltda. (1)
Av Eng Eusebio Stevaux 873 Bloco B, Jurubatuba, CEP 04696 902, Sao Paulo, Brazil **(100%)**
Tel.: (55) 1156811129
Web Site: http://www.knorr-bremse.com.br
Sales Range: Less than $1 Million
Emp.: 400
Mfr of Air Braking Equipment for Rail Vehicles & Commercial Vehicles
N.A.I.C.S.: 333310

Knorr-Bremse Sistemas para Veiculos Ferroviarios Ltda. (1)
Via Cyrineu Tonolli 1519, Itupeva, Sao Paulo, 13295-970, Brazil
Tel.: (55) 1145934001
Web Site: http://www.knorr-bremse.com.br
Commercial Vehicles Components Mfr
N.A.I.C.S.: 336340

Knorr-Bremse Steering Systems Japan Ltd. (1)
25-10 Miyako, Namegawa-machi Hiki-gun, Saitama, 355-0812, Japan
Tel.: (81) 493565005
Brake System Mfr
N.A.I.C.S.: 336340
Ted Takayuki (Dir-Pur)

Knorr-Bremse Systeme fur Nutzfahrzeuge GmbH (1)
Moosacher Str 80, 80809, Munich, Germany **(60%)**
Tel.: (49) 8935470

Web Site: http://www.knorr-bremsesfn.com
Sales Range: $400-449.9 Million
Mfr of Systems & Components for Commercial Vehicles
N.A.I.C.S.: 336340

Subsidiary (Non-US):

Knorr Bremse Systemes Pour Vehicules Utilitaires France S.A. (1)
70 Chemin de Beaufils, BP 34178, Glos, 14104, Lisieux, Cedex, France **(100%)**
Tel.: (33) 231321200
Web Site: http://www.knorr-bremse.fr
Sales Range: $75-99.9 Million
Emp.: 451
Mfr of Systems for Commercial Vehicles
N.A.I.C.S.: 336110

Knorr-Bremse Benelux B.V.B.A. (2)
Blarenberglaan 4 unit 301, 2800, Mechelen, Belgium **(100%)**
Tel.: (32) 15257900
Web Site: http://www.knorr-bremse.be
Sales Range: $10-24.9 Million
Mfr of Systems & Components for Commercial Vehicles
N.A.I.C.S.: 336340

Knorr-Bremse Fekrendszerek Kft. (2)
Georg Knorr utca 8, 6000, Kecskemet, Hungary **(100%)**
Tel.: (36) 76511100
Web Site: http://www.knorr-bremse.hu
Sales Range: Less than $1 Million
Emp.: 652
System & Component for Commercial Vehicle Mfr
N.A.I.C.S.: 336110

Knorr-Bremse Sistemi Per Autoveicoli Commerciali S.p.A. (2)
Via Alessandro Polini 158, 20862, Arcore, MB, Italy **(100%)**
Tel.: (39) 03960751
Web Site: http://www.knorr-bremse.it
Sales Range: $75-99.9 Million
Mfr of Systems & Components for Commercial Vehicles
N.A.I.C.S.: 336340

Knorr-Bremse Systems For Commercial Vehicles Ltd. (2)
Century House Folly Brook Road Emerald Park East Emersons Green, Bristol, BS15 8NL, United Kingdom **(100%)**
Tel.: (44) 1179846110
Web Site: http://www.knorr-bremse.co.uk
Sales Range: $75-99.9 Million
Emp.: 200
Mfr of Systems & Components for Commercial Vehicles
N.A.I.C.S.: 336340

Knorr-Bremse Systemy pro Uitova Vozidla CR spo (2)
Petra Bezruce 399, 46362, Hejnice, Czech Republic **(100%)**
Tel.: (420) 482363611
Web Site: http://www.knorr-bremse.cz
Sales Range: $25-49.9 Million
Emp.: 400
Mfr of Systems & Components for Commercial Vehicles
N.A.I.C.S.: 336340

Knorr-Bremse Systemy pro uzitkova vozilda CR s.r.o. (2)
Svarovska 700 Industrial zone, 46303, Liberec, Straz nad Nisou, Czech Republic **(100%)**
Tel.: (420) 482363611
Web Site: http://www.knorr-bremse.cz
Sales Range: $75-99.9 Million
Emp.: 400
Systems & Components for Commercial Vehicles Mfr
N.A.I.C.S.: 336110

Knorr-Bremse Systeme fur Schienenfahrzeuge GmbH (1)
Moosacher Str 80, 80809, Munich, Germany **(100%)**
Tel.: (49) 8935470
Systems & Components for Rail Vehicles Mfr
N.A.I.C.S.: 336510

Subsidiary (Non-US):

Freinrail Systemes Ferroviaires S.A. (2)

47 49 Rue Gosset, 51057, Reims, France **(100%)**
Tel.: (33) 326797200
Web Site: http://www.knorr-bremse.com
Sales Range: $50-74.9 Million
Emp.: 120
Vehicle Parts & Accessories
N.A.I.C.S.: 336340
Eric Tassilli (Pres)

Knorr-Bremse Ges.m.b.H. (2)
Beethovengasse 43-45, Modling, 2340, Austria **(100%)**
Tel.: (43) 22364090
Web Site: http://www.knorr-bremse.at
Sales Range: $250-299.9 Million
Emp.: 600
Mfr of Systems & Components for Commercial Vehicles
N.A.I.C.S.: 336340
Oliver Schmidt (Chm-Mgmt Bd)

Subsidiary (Domestic):

Dr. Techn. Josef Zelisko GMBH (3)
Beethovengasse 43-45, 2340, Modling, Austria **(100%)**
Tel.: (43) 2236409290
Web Site: http://www.zelisko.com
Sales Range: $150-199.9 Million
Emp.: 400
Mfr of Systems & Components for Commercial Vehicles
N.A.I.C.S.: 336340

Subsidiary (Non-US):

Knorr-Bremse India Private Ltd. (2)
14-6 Mathura Road, Faridabad, 121 003, Haryana, India **(100%)**
Tel.: (91) 1295276409
Web Site: http://www.knorr-bremse.com
Sales Range: $50-74.9 Million
Emp.: 94
Mfr of Systems & Components for Commercial Vehicles
N.A.I.C.S.: 336340

Knorr-Bremse Rail Systems Italia S.r.l. (2)
Via S Quirico 199/I, 50013, Campi Bisenzio, Florence, Italy
Tel.: (39) 0553 0201
Web Site: https://www.knorr-bremse.it
Sales Range: $10-24.9 Million
Vehicle Parts & Accessories
N.A.I.C.S.: 336340
Simone Mantero (Mng Dir)

Knorr-Bremse Rail Systems Japan Ltd. (2)
139 691132 7F Nittochi Nishishinjuku Bldg 6-10-1 Nishishinjuku, Shinjuku-ku, Tokyo, 160-0023, Japan **(94%)**
Tel.: (81) 333462620
Web Site: https://rail.knorr-bremse.com
Sales Range: $25-49.9 Million
Emp.: 20
Mfr of Systems & Components for Rail Vehicles
N.A.I.C.S.: 336510
Akira Shimizu (Pres)

Knorr-Bremse Rail Systems Korea Ltd. (2)
7F Hanlim Bldg 336 Dongho-ro, Jung-gu, Seoul, 100-400, Korea (South) **(100%)**
Tel.: (82) 222805555
Web Site: https://www.knorr-bremse.co.kr
Mfr of Rail Systems & Components
N.A.I.C.S.: 336510

Knorr-Bremse S.A. (Pty.) Ltd. (2)
3 Derrick Road Spartan, Kempton Park, 1610, South Africa **(100%)**
Tel.: (27) 119617800
Web Site: http://www.knorr-bremse.com
Sales Range: $10-24.9 Million
Emp.: 115
Production & Marketing of Rail Vehicle & Commercial Vehicle Brake Mfr
N.A.I.C.S.: 336360

Sociedad Espanola de Frenos, Calefaccion Y Senales, S.A. (2)
Parque Empresarial La Carpetania, Miguel Faraday 1, Madrid, 28906, Spain **(70%)**
Tel.: (34) 911459400
Web Site: http://www.knorr-bremse.es

Sales Range: $10-24.9 Million
Emp.: 141
Mfr of Systems & Components for Commercial Vehicles
N.A.I.C.S.: 336340
Gustavo Vozalea (Mng Dir)

Knorr-Bremse Systemes Ferroviaires S.A. (1)
9 Route de Champigny, CS 10038, 51430, Tinqueux, France
Tel.: (33) 326899500
Brake System Mfr
N.A.I.C.S.: 336340

Knorr-Bremse Systemes pour Vehicules Utilitaires France S.A. (1)
70 Chemin de Beaufils, BP 34178, Glos, 14104, Lisieux, Cedex, France
Tel.: (33) 231321200
Web Site: http://www.knorr-bremse.fr
Clutch & Brake System Mfr
N.A.I.C.S.: 336340

Knorr-Bremse Systems for Commercial Vehicles India Pvt. Ltd. (1)
Survey No 276, Village Mann Hinjewadi Phase II Taluka Mulshi, Pune, 411 057, India
Tel.: (91) 2066746800
Brake System Mfr
N.A.I.C.S.: 336340

Knorr-Bremse Systems for Rail Vehicles (Suzhou) Co., Ltd. (1)
No 69 Shi Yang Road Xu Guan Development Zone, Suzhou, 215151, China
Tel.: (86) 51266165666
Clutch & Brake System Mfr
N.A.I.C.S.: 336340
Joseph Han (Mng Dir)

Knorr-Bremse Systems for Rail Vehicles Enterprise Management (Beijing) Co., Ltd. (1)
Room 3201 Floor 32 Block C Beijing Yintai Center, No 2 Jianguomenwai Avenue Chao Yang District, Beijing, 100022, China
Brake System Mfr
N.A.I.C.S.: 336340
Jonathan Paddison (Mng Dir)

Knorr-Bremse Systemy Kolejowe Polska Sp. z o.o. (1)
Tel.: (48) 122529600
Web Site: http://www.knorr-bremse.pl
Brake System Mfr
N.A.I.C.S.: 336340
Jacek Bilas (Chm)

Knorr-Bremse Technology Center India Pvt. Ltd. (1)
Survey No 276 Village Mann Survey No 276 Village Mann Hinjewadi, Tal.Mulshi, Pune, 411 057, Maharashtra, India
Tel.: (91) 2039147000
Emp.: 200
Engineering Research & Development Services
N.A.I.C.S.: 541715
Deepak Joseph (Head-Dev Truck)

Knorr-Bremse Vasuti Jarmu Rendszerek Hungaria Kft. (1)
Helsinki Ut 105, 1238, Budapest, Hungary **(100%)**
Tel.: (36) 12894100
Web Site: https://www.knorr-bremse.hu
Sales Range: $300-349.9 Million
Mfr of Systems & Components for Commercial Vehicles
N.A.I.C.S.: 336340
Andres Savos (Mng Dir)

Knorr-Bremse/Nankou Air Supply Unit (Beijing) Co., Ltd. (1)
Daobei, Nankou Town Changping District, Beijing, 102202, China
Tel.: (86) 1052726100
Clutch & Brake System Mfr
N.A.I.C.S.: 336340
Frank Qian (Gen Mgr)

M.S. Resistances (Microelettrica Scientifica) S.A.S. (1)
Rue Du Cret de la Perdrix, ZI du Coin, 42400, Saint-Chamond, France
Tel.: (33) 477293980
Brake System Mfr

KNORR-BREMSE AG

Knorr-Bremse AG—(Continued)
N.A.I.C.S.: 336340

Merak Jinxin Air Conditioning Systems (Wuxi) Co., Ltd. (1)
Bldg 6 Taihu Town Industrial Park 7 Lian He Road, Hudai Town Binhu District, Wuxi, 214161, China
Tel.: (86) 51068880555
Mechanical Equipment Mfr
N.A.I.C.S.: 333613
Eric Bi *(Gen Mgr)*

Merak Knorr Climatizacion S.A. (1)
Barcelona 1284, Haedo, 1706, Buenos Aires, Argentina
Tel.: (54) 1148780991
Mechanical Equipment Mfr
N.A.I.C.S.: 333613
Roberto Piccione *(Dir-Technical)*

Merak Sistemas Integrados de Climatizacion S.A. (1)
Headquarters Calle Miguel Faraday 1 Parque Empresarial La, Carpetania, 28906, Getafe, Spain
Tel.: (34) 911459400
Mechanical Equipment Mfr
N.A.I.C.S.: 333613

Microelettrica Heine (Suzhou) Co., Ltd. (1)
Web Site: http://www.microelettrica.com
Electric & Electronic Component Mfr
N.A.I.C.S.: 336320
Freddy Wang *(Dir-Sls)*

Microelettrica Scientifica (Pty.) Ltd. (1)
100 Yacht Street Laser Park Honeydew, Johannesburg, South Africa
Tel.: (27) 117943330
Electric & Electronic Component Mfr
N.A.I.C.S.: 336320

Microelettrica Scientifica S.p.A. (1)
Via Lucania 2, Buccinasco, 20090, Milan, Italy
Tel.: (39) 02575731
Electric & Electronic Component Mfr
N.A.I.C.S.: 336320
Oscar Ciambarella *(Mgr-Sls)*

Microelettrica-USA LLC (1)
300 International Dr N Ste 2, Mount Olive, NJ 07828
Tel.: (973) 598-0806
Brake System Mfr
N.A.I.C.S.: 336340
Vanessa Giordano *(Fin Mgr)*

New York Air Brake LLC (1)
748 Starbuck Ave, Watertown, NY 13601 (100%)
Tel.: (315) 786-5200
Web Site: http://www.nyab.com
Brakes & Related Train-Control Equipment Mfr
N.A.I.C.S.: 336340

Subsidiary (Domestic):

Snyder Equipment Company, Inc. (2)
1375 W Snyder Blvd, Nixa, MO 65714
Tel.: (417) 725-4067
Web Site: http://www.snyderequip.com
Railroad Equipment Mfr
N.A.I.C.S.: 336510

Selectron Systems (Beijing) Co., Ltd. (1)
Tel.: (86) 1085148965
Brake System Mfr
N.A.I.C.S.: 336340

Selectron Systems AG (1)
Bernstrasse 70, 3250, Lyss, Switzerland
Tel.: (41) 323876161
Web Site: https://www.selectron.ch
Electric & Mechanical Engineering Services
N.A.I.C.S.: 541330

Sigma Air Conditioning Pty. Ltd. (1)
23-29 Factory Street, Granville, 2142, NSW, Australia
Tel.: (61) 1300643643
Web Site: http://www.sigma-hvac.com
Air Conditioner & Radiator Mfr
N.A.I.C.S.: 333415

Sigma Coachair Group (China) Co., Ltd. (1)
No 268 West Hehai Road, Xinbei, Changzhou, 213000, Jiangsu, China
Tel.: (86) 13701923531
Mechanical Equipment Mfr
N.A.I.C.S.: 333613

Sydac Pty. Ltd. (1)
153 Wakefield Street, Adelaide, 5000, SA, Australia
Tel.: (61) 882393600
Web Site: http://www.sydac.com
Mechanical Engineering Services
N.A.I.C.S.: 541330
Dermot Dixon *(CEO)*

Technologies Lanka Inc. (1)
155 Industrial Avenue, La Pocatiere, G0R 1Z0, QC, Canada
Tel.: (418) 856-1334
Web Site: http://www.techlanka.com
Mechanical Engineering Services
N.A.I.C.S.: 541330

Transtechnik GmbH & Co. KG (1)
Ohmstrasse 1, 83607, Holzkirchen, Germany
Tel.: (49) 80249900
Mechanical Equipment Mfr
N.A.I.C.S.: 333613
Lorenzo Stendardi *(Mng Dir)*

Universal Investment Universal-KBAM-Fonds Gmbh (1)
Theodor-Heuss-Allee 70, 60486, Frankfurt am Main, Germany
Tel.: (49) 69710430
Web Site: https://www.universal-investment.com
Investment Management Service
N.A.I.C.S.: 523940

tedrive Steering Systems GmbH (1)
Henry-Ford II Strasse 15, Wulfrath, 42489, Germany
Tel.: (49) 2058 905 0
Web Site: http://www.td-steering.com
Motor Vehicle Steering Systems & Components Mfr & Distr
N.A.I.C.S.: 336330
Thomas Bruese *(Gen Mgr)*

Plant (Domestic):

tedrive Steering Systems GmbH - Plant 2 (2)
Kruppstrasse 47, 42489, Wulfrath, Germany
Tel.: (49) 205 89050
Web Site: http://www.td-steering.com
Automotive Steering Mfr
N.A.I.C.S.: 336330
Frank Grummer *(Mgr-Production)*

Subsidiary (Non-US):

tedrive Yonlendirme Sistemleri SAN.Ve TIC.LTD. STI. (2)
Beylikduzu Mermerciler Sanayi Sitesi 7 Cadde No 4, Beylikduzu, 34520, Istanbul, Turkiye
Tel.: (90) 212 8792005
Web Site: http://www.td-steering.com
Automotive Steering System Mfr & Distr
N.A.I.C.S.: 336330
Huseyin Erdem *(Gen Mgr)*

KNOSYS LIMITED
Level 8 31 Queen Street, Melbourne, 3000, VIC, Australia
Tel.: (61) 2035198529
Web Site: https://www.knosys.co
KNO—(ASX)
Rev.: $6,430,455
Assets: $9,524,820
Liabilities: $4,573,496
Net Worth: $4,951,325
Earnings: $130,333
Emp.: 40
Fiscal Year-end: 06/30/24
Software Development Services
N.A.I.C.S.: 513210
Stephen Kerr *(CFO & Sec)*

Subsidiaries:

Greenorbit Inc. (1)
555 Fayetteville St Ste 300, Raleigh, NC 27601
Intranet Software Distr
N.A.I.C.S.: 423430

Greenorbit Pty. Ltd. (1)
Level 8 31 Queen Street, Melbourne, VIC, Australia
Tel.: (61) 1800977827
Web Site: https://greenorbit.com
Emp.: 50
Intranet Software Distr
N.A.I.C.S.: 423430

Greenorbit Software Limited (1)
The Atrium Curtis Rd, Dorking, United Kingdom
Tel.: (44) 2035198529
Intranet Software Distr
N.A.I.C.S.: 423430

Libero IS GmbH (1)
Amtsgericht Aschaffenburg HRB, 15608, Alzenau, Germany
Tel.: (49) 61733563631
Intranet Software Distr
N.A.I.C.S.: 423430

Libero Systems Pty. Ltd. (1)
Level 8 31 Queen St, Melbourne, VIC, Australia
Tel.: (61) 733563631
Intranet Software Distr
N.A.I.C.S.: 423430

KNOT OFFSHORE PARTNERS LP
2 Queens Cross, Aberdeen, AB15 4YB, Aberdeenshire, United Kingdom
Tel.: (44) 1224618420 MH
Web Site: https://www.knotoffshorepartner.com
Year Founded: 2013
KNOP—(NYSE)
Rev.: $268,585,000
Assets: $1,733,953,000
Liabilities: $1,166,049,000
Net Worth: $567,904,000
Earnings: $58,667,000
Emp.: 695
Fiscal Year-end: 12/31/22
Shuttle Tankers Owner & Operator
N.A.I.C.S.: 488390
Trygve Seglem *(Chm)*

KNOW IT AB
Klarabergsgatan 60, Box 3383, 103 68, Stockholm, Sweden
Tel.: (46) 87006600
Web Site: https://www.knowit.se
Year Founded: 1990
KNOW—(OMX)
Rev.: $640,061,630
Assets: $712,350,539
Liabilities: $318,255,922
Net Worth: $394,094,617
Earnings: $36,061,704
Emp.: 4,410
Fiscal Year-end: 12/31/22
IT Consulting & Other Computer Related Services
N.A.I.C.S.: 541512
Mats Olsson *(Chm)*

Subsidiaries:

Creuna A/S (1)
Vesterbro Torv 3 4 sal, 8000, Aarhus, Denmark
Tel.: (45) 70200042
Web Site: http://www.creuna.com
IT Services
N.A.I.C.S.: 541513
Anne Iversen *(Sr Project Mgr)*

Creuna AB (1)
Sveavagen 20, PO Box 3383, 103 68, Stockholm, Sweden
Tel.: (46) 87006600
Web Site: https://www.knowit.se
Management Consulting Services
N.A.I.C.S.: 541611

Endero Oy (1)
Tehtaankatu 27-29 D 4th Floor, 150, Helsinki, Finland
Tel.: (358) 403 400 600
Web Site: http://www.endero.com
Information Technology Consulting Services
N.A.I.C.S.: 541512
Ville Saermaelae *(CEO)*

Subsidiary (Non-US):

Endero OOO (2)
Ul Afonskaja 2, 197341, Saint Petersburg, Russia
Tel.: (7) 812 495 6238
Information Technology Consulting Services
N.A.I.C.S.: 541512

Know IT A-Kraft AB (1)
Platensgatan 8, S-582 20, Linkoping, Sweden
Tel.: (46) 13210560
Web Site: http://www.knowit.se
Computer Related Services
N.A.I.C.S.: 541519

Know IT Business Consulting AB (1)
Stortorget 9, 211 22, Malmo, Sweden
Tel.: (46) 40 6302400
Web Site: http://www.knowit.se
Software Consulting Services
N.A.I.C.S.: 541512
Bertil Nordlund *(Head-Strategy)*

Know IT Business Consulting AS (1)
Tollbodalmenningen 1b, 5004, Bergen, Norway
Tel.: (47) 553 33 900
Software Consulting Services
N.A.I.C.S.: 541512

Know IT Candeo AB (1)
Stationsgatan 43, 972 33, Lulea, Sweden
Tel.: (46) 92015727
Sales Range: $25-49.9 Million
Emp.: 20
Computer Programming Services
N.A.I.C.S.: 541511

Know IT Candeo AB (1)
Storgatan 12, 852 30, Sundsvall, Sweden
Tel.: (46) 60161680
Web Site: http://www.knowit.se
Sales Range: $25-49.9 Million
Emp.: 50
Computer Programming Services
N.A.I.C.S.: 541511

Know IT Candeo AB (1)
Skolgatan 12, S-903 27, Umea, Sweden
Tel.: (46) 90712180
Web Site: http://www.knowit.se
Sales Range: $25-49.9 Million
Emp.: 150
Computer Programming Services
N.A.I.C.S.: 541511

Know IT Candeo Gavle AB (1)
Nygatan 34, Gavle, 80311, Sweden
Tel.: (46) 26510800
Computer Programming Services
N.A.I.C.S.: 541511
Hans Reinikainen *(Gen Mgr)*

Know IT Consulting i Goteborg AB (1)
Gustav Mattssons Vag 2, Box 612, 451 50, Uddevalla, Sweden
Tel.: (46) 52279730
Web Site: http://www.knowit.se
Sales Range: $25-49.9 Million
Emp.: 2
IT Consulting Services
N.A.I.C.S.: 541690

Know IT Consulting i Sodertalje AB (1)
Lovisingatan 3, 151 73, Sodertalje, Sweden
Tel.: (46) 8 700 66 00
Information Technology Consulting Services
N.A.I.C.S.: 541512

Know IT Create i Lund AB (1)
Skiffervagen 10, S-224 78, Lund, Sweden
Tel.: (46) 465900200
Web Site: http://www.knowit.se
Sales Range: $25-49.9 Million
Emp.: 100
Computer Related Services
N.A.I.C.S.: 541519

Know IT Dalarna AB (1)
Maskinistgatan 8, Box 182, 781 22, Bor-

AND PRIVATE COMPANIES — KNOW IT AB

lange, Sweden
Tel.: (46) 24 321 4440
Web Site: https://www.knowit.eu
Sales Range: $25-49.9 Million
Information Technology Consulting Services
N.A.I.C.S.: 541512

Know IT Dalsys AB (1)
Maskinistgatan 8, PO Box 182, 781 70, Borlange, Sweden
Tel.: (46) 243214440
Web Site: http://www.knowit.eu
Sales Range: $25-49.9 Million
Emp.: 40
Computer Related Services
N.A.I.C.S.: 541519

Know IT Dataunit AB (1)
Tel.: (46) 8 700 6600
Web Site: https://www.knowit.se
Emp.: 40
Information Technology Consulting Services
N.A.I.C.S.: 541512
Ulf Wallenborg *(Mgr-Sls)*

Know IT Gavleborg AB (1)
Vagskrivargatan 5, 803 20, Gavle, Sweden
Tel.: (46) 2 651 0800
Web Site: http://wwwtemp.knowit.se
Information Technology Consulting Services
N.A.I.C.S.: 541512

Know IT Goteborg AB (1)
Ostra Hamngatan 16, 411 09, Gothenburg, Sweden
Tel.: (46) 31 711 27 30
Information Technology Consulting Services
N.A.I.C.S.: 541512
Mathias Kindstroem *(Mgr-Web & Collaboration)*

Subsidiary (Domestic):

Know IT System Development AB (2)
Ostra Hamngatan 16, 411 09, Gothenburg, Sweden
Tel.: (46) 317 112 730
Web Site: http://www.knowit.se
Software Development Services
N.A.I.C.S.: 541511

Know IT HRM AB (1)
Klarabergsgatan 60, S-103 68, Stockholm, Sweden
Tel.: (46) 87006600
Web Site: http://www.knowit.se
Sales Range: $25-49.9 Million
Computer Related Services
N.A.I.C.S.: 541519

Know IT IM Goteborg AB (1)
Ostra Hamngatan 16, 411 09, Gothenburg, Sweden
Tel.: (46) 317 112 730
Web Site: http://www.knowitgroup.com
Software Consulting Services
N.A.I.C.S.: 541512

Know IT IM Helikopter AB (1)
Radmansgatan 49, 113 60, Stockholm, Sweden
Tel.: (46) 8 6430310
Sales Range: $25-49.9 Million
Emp.: 34
Information Technology Consulting Services
N.A.I.C.S.: 541512
Christer Arnqvist *(Gen Mgr)*

Know IT IM Innograte AB (1)
Master Samuelsgatan 9, 111 44, Stockholm, Sweden
Tel.: (46) 8 700 66 00
Information Technology Consulting Services
N.A.I.C.S.: 541512

Know IT IM Linkoping AB (1)
Brigadgatan 2, Linkoping, 587 58, Sweden
Tel.: (46) 134 740 000
Web Site: http://wwwtemp.knowit.se
Sales Range: $25-49.9 Million
Emp.: 16
Software Consulting Services
N.A.I.C.S.: 541512
Christer Holman *(CEO)*

Know IT Information Management Stockholm AB (1)
Klarabergsgatan 60, 103 68, Stockholm, Sweden
Tel.: (46) 87006600

Web Site: http://www.knowit.se
Sales Range: $50-74.9 Million
Business Intelligence, Data Warehousing & Data Analysis
N.A.I.C.S.: 518210

Know IT Informationssynerigi AB (1)
Platens gate, S-58220, Linkoping, Sweden
Tel.: (46) 134740000
Web Site: http://www.knowit.eu
Sales Range: $25-49.9 Million
Emp.: 14
Computer Related Services
N.A.I.C.S.: 541519

Know IT Malardalen AB (1)
Kopparbergsvagen 23, S-722 13, Vasteras, Sweden
Tel.: (46) 21349900
Web Site: http://www.knowit.eu
Sales Range: $25-49.9 Million
Emp.: 40
Computer Programming Services
N.A.I.C.S.: 541511

Know IT Malardalen AB (1)
Jarntorgsgatan 3, PO Box 40, Orebro, S-70140, Sweden
Tel.: (46) 19128800
Web Site: http://www.knowit.eu
Sales Range: $25-49.9 Million
Emp.: 40
Computer Programming Services
N.A.I.C.S.: 541511

Know IT Mobile Syd AB (1)
Stortorget 9, 211 22, Malmo, Sweden
Tel.: (46) 406302400
Information Technology Consulting Services
N.A.I.C.S.: 541512
Axel Holtas *(CEO)*

Know IT Net Result International AB (1)
Klarabergsgatan 60, PO Box 844, Stockholm, 101 36, Sweden
Tel.: (46) 841 037 000
Web Site: http://www.knowitgroup.com
Software Consulting Services
N.A.I.C.S.: 541512

Subsidiary (Non-US):

Know IT Estonia Consulting OU (2)
Kotzebue, 10142, Tallinn, Estonia
Tel.: (372) 6605273
Web Site: http://www.knowit.ee
Sales Range: $25-49.9 Million
Emp.: 20
Software Consulting Services
N.A.I.C.S.: 541512
Andres Aavik *(CEO)*

Subsidiary (Domestic):

Know IT Net Result AB (2)
Klarabergsgatan 60 4tr, Box 844, Stockholm, 101 36, Sweden
Tel.: (46) 8 4103 7000
Web Site: http://wwwtemp.knowit.se
Emp.: 70
Software Consulting Services
N.A.I.C.S.: 541512

Know IT Norrland AB (1)
Skolgatan 49, 903 27, Umea, Sweden
Tel.: (46) 90 71 21 80
Software Consulting Services
N.A.I.C.S.: 541512

Know IT Secure AB (1)
Tel.: (46) 8 700 6600
Web Site: http://www.knowit.se
Emp.: 600
Software Consulting Services
N.A.I.C.S.: 541512
Peter Lindstedt *(CEO)*

Know IT Software Solutions AB (1)
Klarabergsgatam 60, Box 3383, 103 68, Stockholm, Sweden
Tel.: (46) 87006600
Web Site: http://www.knowit.se
Sales Range: $25-49.9 Million
Emp.: 30
Software Solutions
N.A.I.C.S.: 541512

Subsidiary (Non-US):

Know IT Software Solutions AS (2)

Parkveien 55, N-202, Oslo, Norway
Tel.: (47) 22444250
Web Site: http://www.knowit.se
Software Solutions
N.A.I.C.S.: 541512

Subsidiary (Domestic):

Know IT Stockholm AMHS AB (2)
Klarabergsgatan 60, Box 3383, 111 21, Stockholm, Sweden
Tel.: (46) 87006600
Web Site: http://www.knowit.se
Software Consulting Services
N.A.I.C.S.: 541512

Know IT Stavanger AS (1)
Lokkeveien 99, 4008, Stavanger, Rogaland, Norway
Tel.: (47) 9 825 7824
Web Site: http://www.temp.knowit.se
Sales Range: $25-49.9 Million
Emp.: 15
Software Consulting Services
N.A.I.C.S.: 541512
Espen Tjonneland *(Gen Mgr)*

Know IT Stockholm AB (1)
Klarabergcatan 60, Box 3383, S-103 68, Stockholm, Sweden
Tel.: (46) 87006600
Web Site: http://www.knowit.se
Sales Range: $50-74.9 Million
Emp.: 200
IT Consulting Services
N.A.I.C.S.: 541690

Know IT Technology Management AB (1)
Ostra Hamngatan 16, 411 09, Gothenburg, Sweden
Tel.: (46) 317 112 730
Information Technology Consulting Services
N.A.I.C.S.: 541512

Know IT Technology Management i Sthlm AB (1)
Klarabergsgatan 60, Box 3383, 103 68, Stockholm, Sweden
Tel.: (46) 870 06 600
Software Consulting Services
N.A.I.C.S.: 541512

Know IT Technowledge i Stockholm (1)
Klragatan 60, Box 3383, 103 68, Stockholm, Sweden
Tel.: (46) 87006600
Sales Range: $25-49.9 Million
Emp.: 10
Computer Related Services
N.A.I.C.S.: 541519

Know IT Yahm Sweden AB (1)
Stortorget 9, 211 22, Malmo, Sweden
Tel.: (46) 7 05 91 22 56
Web Site: http://www.yahm.se
Sales Range: $25-49.9 Million
Emp.: 40
Information Technology Consulting Services
N.A.I.C.S.: 541512

Know it Karlstad AB (1)
Tullhusgatan 1B, 65226, Stockholm, Sweden
Tel.: (46) 5 469 0750
Web Site: http://www.knowit.se
Computer Related Services
N.A.I.C.S.: 541519

Knowit AS (1)
Universitetsgata 1, 0164, Oslo, Norway
Tel.: (47) 22926666
Web Site: https://www.knowit.no
Management Consulting Services
N.A.I.C.S.: 541611

Knowit Architecture AB (1)
Klarabergsgatan 60, Stockholm, Sweden
Tel.: (46) 87006600
IT Services
N.A.I.C.S.: 541513

Knowit Business Consulting AB (1)
Stortorget 9, 211 22, Malmo, Sweden
Tel.: (46) 406 302 400
Web Site: http://www.knowit.se
Sales Range: $25-49.9 Million
Business & Computer Related Services
N.A.I.C.S.: 541519

Knowit Cloud & Architecture AB (1)
Sveavagen 20, Box 3383, 103 68, Stockholm, Sweden
Tel.: (46) 87006600
Information Technology Consulting Services
N.A.I.C.S.: 541512

Knowit Cloud AB (1)
Ostra Hamngatan 16, 411 09, Gothenburg, Sweden
Tel.: (46) 317112730
IT Services
N.A.I.C.S.: 541513

Knowit Connectivity AB (1)
Sveavagen 20, PO Box 3383, 103 68, Stockholm, Sweden
Tel.: (46) 87006600
Management Consulting Services
N.A.I.C.S.: 541611

Knowit Core AB (1)
Kungsgatan 4, 211 22, Helsingborg, Sweden
Tel.: (46) 406302400
IT Services
N.A.I.C.S.: 541513

Knowit Core Syd AB (1)
Stortorget 9, 211 22, Malmo, Sweden
Tel.: (46) 406302400
Information Technology Consulting Services
N.A.I.C.S.: 541512

Knowit Cybersecurity & Law AB (1)
Sveavagen 20, Box 3383, 103 68, Stockholm, Sweden
Tel.: (46) 87006600
Information Technology Consulting Services
N.A.I.C.S.: 541512

Knowit Decision Helikopter AB (1)
Klarabergsgatan 60, Stockholm, Sweden
Tel.: (46) 706916077
IT Services
N.A.I.C.S.: 541513

Knowit Decision Stockholm AB (1)
Klarabergsgatan 60, Stockholm, Sweden
Tel.: (46) 730746781
IT Services
N.A.I.C.S.: 541513

Knowit Digital Management AB (1)
Sveavagen 20, PO Box 3383, 103 68, Stockholm, Sweden
Tel.: (46) 87006600
Management Consulting Services
N.A.I.C.S.: 541611

Knowit Experience Oy (1)
Tehtaankatu 27-29 4krs, 00150, Helsinki, Finland
Tel.: (358) 403400600
IT Services
N.A.I.C.S.: 541513

Knowit Experience Stockholm AB (1)
Maskinistgatan 8, Box 182, 781 22, Borlange, Sweden
Tel.: (46) 243214440
IT Services
N.A.I.C.S.: 541513

Knowit FLX AB (1)
Stortorget 9, 211 22, Malmo, Sweden
Tel.: (46) 406302400
Information Technology Consulting Services
N.A.I.C.S.: 541512

Knowit Insight Accelerate AB (1)
Sveavagen 20, Box 3383, 103 68, Stockholm, Sweden
Tel.: (46) 87006600
Information Technology Consulting Services
N.A.I.C.S.: 541512

Knowit Insight Syd AB (1)
Stortorget 9, 211 22, Malmo, Sweden
Tel.: (46) 406302400
IT Services
N.A.I.C.S.: 541513

Knowit Invativa AB (1)
Biblioteksgatan 6A, 831 30, Ostersund, Sweden
Tel.: (46) 760497456
IT Services
N.A.I.C.S.: 541513

Knowit Jonkoping AB (1)

KNOW IT AB

Know IT AB—(Continued)

Ostra Storgatan 33A, 553 21, Jonkoping, Sweden
Tel.: (46) 87006600
IT Services
N.A.I.C.S.: 541513

Knowit Orebro AB (1)
Rudbecksgatan 7, 702 11, Orebro, Sweden
Tel.: (46) 702440860
IT Services
N.A.I.C.S.: 541513

Knowit Poland Sp. z o.o. (1)
Hrubieszowska 2, PL-01-209, Warsaw, Poland
Tel.: (48) 223552170
Information Technology Consulting Services
N.A.I.C.S.: 541512

Knowit Solutions CoCreate AB (1)
Vikingsgatan 3, 411 04, Gothenburg, Sweden
Tel.: (46) 317112730
Information Technology Consulting Services
N.A.I.C.S.: 541512

Knowit Solutions Danmark A/S (1)
Vesterbro Torv 3 4 sal, Aarhus, 8000, Denmark
Tel.: (45) 21122121
IT Services
N.A.I.C.S.: 541513

Knowit Solutions Datalytics AB (1)
Sveavagen 20, Box 3383, 103 68, Stockholm, Sweden
Tel.: (46) 730746781
Information Technology Consulting Services
N.A.I.C.S.: 541512

Knowit Sydost AB (1)
Blekingegatan 10, 371 57, Karlskrona, Sweden
Tel.: (46) 455314000
Information Technology Consulting Services
N.A.I.C.S.: 541512

Knowit Uppsala AB (1)
Fyristorg 6, 753 10, Uppsala, Sweden
Tel.: (46) 184721000
IT Services
N.A.I.C.S.: 541513

Knowit Uppsala Solutions AB (1)
Fyristorg 6, 753 10, Uppsala, Sweden
Tel.: (46) 184721000
Management Consulting Services
N.A.I.C.S.: 541611

Reaktor AB (1)
Klaraberqsqatan 60, 103 68, Stockholm, Sweden
Tel.: (46) 870 06 600
Software Consulting Services
N.A.I.C.S.: 541512

Reaktor AS (1)
Nagelgarden 6, Bergen, 5001, Norway
Tel.: (47) 55 33 39 00
Web Site: http://www.knowit.no
Software Consulting Services
N.A.I.C.S.: 541512

Reaktor Emerge AS (1)
Nagelgarden 6, Bergen, 5004, Hordaland, Norway
Tel.: (47) 55333900
Sales Range: $25-49.9 Million
Emp.: 17
Software Consulting Services
N.A.I.C.S.: 541512

KNOWLEDGE ECONOMIC CITY DEVELOPERS CO. LTD.

2nd Floor Tower B5 Salama Center Prince Sultan Street, PO Box 6360, 21442, Jeddah, Saudi Arabia
Tel.: (966) 26165577
Web Site:
http://www.madinahkec.com
Year Founded: 2006
Property Development & Economic Services
N.A.I.C.S.: 237210
Adil Abdulmohsin Al Mandil *(Chm)*

KNOWLEDGE MARINE & ENGINEERING WORKS LTD.

Office No 402 Sai Samarth Business Park Deonar Village Road, Govandi East, Mumbai, 400088, India
Tel.: (91) 2235530988
Web Site: https://www.kmew.in
Year Founded: 2015
543273—(BOM)
Rev.: $24,592,922
Assets: $25,316,704
Liabilities: $8,758,288
Net Worth: $16,558,417
Earnings: $5,720,519
Emp.: 100
Fiscal Year-end: 03/31/23
Ship Building & Repairing Services
N.A.I.C.S.: 336611
Sujay M. Kewalramani *(CEO)*

KNOWLEDGE POWER CORPORATION

215 Kelso Crescent Ste 2, Vaughan, L6A 2E1, ON, Canada
Tel.: (416) 727-7875 NV
Year Founded: 2009
Outsourcing Services
N.A.I.C.S.: 561499
Atul Mehra *(Chm, Pres, CEO, CFO & Sec)*

KNOWLEDGE TOWER TRADING COMPANY

2611 Salah Ad Din Al Ayyubi Rd, PO Box 12851, Al Safa, Riyadh, 11437, Saudi Arabia
Tel.: (966) 595455189
Web Site: https://www.kntbook.com
Year Founded: 2011
9551—(SAU)
Rev.: $7,817,778
Assets: $7,233,391
Liabilities: $770,207
Net Worth: $6,463,184
Earnings: $1,429,776
Emp.: 12
Fiscal Year-end: 03/31/23
Educational Support Services
N.A.I.C.S.: 611710
Manne Salem Ali Alsoqor *(Chm)*

KNOX INVESTMENT PARTNERS LIMITED

West Plaza Building Level 10 1-3 Albert Street, Auckland, 1010, New Zealand
Tel.: (64) 93070554 NZ
Web Site:
http://www.knoxpartners.co.nz
Year Founded: 2004
Investment Management Service
N.A.I.C.S.: 523940
Bret Jackson *(Co-Founder & Mng Dir)*

Subsidiaries:

OPUS Print Group (Australia) Pty. Limited (1)
12 Rachael Close, Silverwater, 2128, NSW, Australia (70%)
Tel.: (61) 2 9584 7680
Web Site: http://www.opusgroup.com.au
Sales Range: $25-49.9 Million
Emp.: 400
Multi-Platform Printing & Communications Services
N.A.I.C.S.: 323111
Cliff Brigstocke *(CEO)*

Subsidiary (Domestic):

McPherson's Printing Pty. Ltd. (2)
76 Nelson Street, Maryborough, 3465, VIC, Australia
Tel.: (61) 3 5461 7100
Web Site:
http://www.mcphersonsprinting.com.au
Sales Range: $50-74.9 Million
Emp.: 250
Printing Services
N.A.I.C.S.: 323117
Robert Huismann *(Mgr-Ops)*

KNR CONSTRUCTIONS LIMITED

KNR House 3rd and 4th Floor Plot No 113 and 114 Phase-1 Kavuri Hills, Jubilee Hills Road No 36, Hyderabad, 500 033, India
Tel.: (91) 4040268759
Web Site: https://www.knrcl.com
Year Founded: 1990
532942—(BOM)
Rev.: $498,320,181
Assets: $719,399,171
Liabilities: $370,074,964
Net Worth: $349,324,207
Earnings: $50,012,617
Emp.: 2,173
Fiscal Year-end: 03/31/22
Infrastructure Construction Services
N.A.I.C.S.: 237310
Kamidi Narasimha Reddy *(Mng Dir)*

Subsidiaries:

KNR Shankarampet Project Private Limited (1)
NH-161 Package Alladurg V M, Medak, 502269, Telangana, India
Tel.: (91) 4040268759
Web Site:
https://www.knrshankarampet.com
Pavement Construction Services
N.A.I.C.S.: 237310

KNR Srirangam Infra Private Limited (1)
NH-227 Ariyalur Road Lalgudi Taluk, Pullambadi Village, Tiruchirappalli, 621711, Tamil Nadu, India
Tel.: (91) 4040268759
Web Site: http://www.knrsrirangam.com
Pavement Construction Services
N.A.I.C.S.: 237310

KNR Tirumala Infra Private Limited (1)
Flat No 205 Tejasree Apartments Raghunath Resorts Thanapalli Road, Tirupati Rural, Chittoor, 517507, Andhra Pradesh, India
Tel.: (91) 4040268759
Web Site: http://www.knrtirumala.com
Pavement Construction Services
N.A.I.C.S.: 237310

KNT HOLDINGS LIMITED

30th Floor EW International Tower No 120 Texaco Road, Tsuen Wan, New Territories, China (Hong Kong)
Tel.: (852) 36559688 Ky
Web Site:
https://www.kntholdings.com
Year Founded: 1993
1025—(HKG)
Rev.: $8,082,661
Assets: $12,388,271
Liabilities: $6,607,516
Net Worth: $5,780,755
Earnings: ($5,770,178)
Emp.: 295
Fiscal Year-end: 03/31/21
Holding Company
N.A.I.C.S.: 551112
Sik Chong *(Co-Founder, Chm & CEO)*

KNUSFORD BERHAD

1st Floor Wisma Ekovest No 118 Jalan Gombak, 53000, Kuala Lumpur, Malaysia
Tel.: (60) 340232525
Web Site:
https://www.knusford.com.my
KNUSFOR—(KLS)
Rev.: $33,770,794
Assets: $93,351,958
Liabilities: $46,929,524
Net Worth: $46,422,434
Earnings: ($494,392)
Emp.: 194

INTERNATIONAL PUBLIC

Fiscal Year-end: 03/31/23
Residential Property Development Services
N.A.I.C.S.: 531311
Thiam Wah Lim *(Co-Sec)*

Subsidiaries:

D-Hill Sdn. Bhd. (1)
1st Floor Wisma Ekovest No 118 Jalan Gombak, 53000, Kuala Lumpur, Malaysia
Tel.: (60) 340232525
Web Site: http://www.d-hill.com.my
Real Estate Services
N.A.I.C.S.: 531390

KNUTSFORD EXPRESS SERVICES LTD.

1222 Providence Drive, Montego Bay, Jamaica
Tel.: (876) 9400064
Web Site:
https://www.knutsfordexpress.com
Year Founded: 2006
KEX—(JAM)
Rev.: $4,372,282
Assets: $8,548,558
Liabilities: $3,927,987
Net Worth: $4,620,572
Earnings: ($666,115)
Emp.: 178
Fiscal Year-end: 05/31/21
Transportation Services
N.A.I.C.S.: 485999
Oliver Townsend *(CEO & Mng Dir)*

KNW CO., LTD.

Munsan HighTech Industrial Complex 51 Donyu 3ro, Munsan-eup, P'aju, 41390, Gyeonggi, Korea (South)
Tel.: (82) 319500200
Web Site: https://www.knwkorea.com
105330—(KRS)
Rev.: $76,379,174
Assets: $109,537,045
Liabilities: $49,353,666
Net Worth: $60,183,379
Earnings: $13,857,167
Emp.: 46
Fiscal Year-end: 12/31/22
Design Oriented Film Mfr
N.A.I.C.S.: 325992
Won Seok Oh *(CEO)*

Subsidiaries:

Solvay Korea Co. Ltd. (1)
Solvay Research & Innovation Center Seoul 150, Bukahyun-Ro Seodaemun-Gu, 03759, Seoul, Korea (South)
Tel.: (82) 221255300
Chemical Products Mfr
N.A.I.C.S.: 325199

KO GOLD INC.

217 Queen Street West Suite 401, Toronto, M5V 0R2, ON, Canada
Tel.: (902) 832-5555 ON
Web Site: https://www.kogoldnz.com
Year Founded: 2020
KOG—(CNSX)
Rev.: $81
Assets: $414,809
Liabilities: $106,874
Net Worth: $307,935
Earnings: ($397,124)
Fiscal Year-end: 03/31/23
Gold Mining Services
N.A.I.C.S.: 212220

KO JA (CAYMAN) CO., LTD.

8th Floor No 168 Liancheng Road, Zhonghe District, New Taipei City, 23553, Taiwan
Tel.: (886) 222436177
Web Site: https://www.koja.com.tw
5215—(TAI)
Rev.: $82,502,826
Assets: $142,138,848
Liabilities: $29,251,152

Net Worth: $112,887,696
Earnings: $6,006,900
Emp.: 2,600
Fiscal Year-end: 12/31/23
Computer Products
N.A.I.C.S.: 334118
Chih-Feng Lin *(Chm & Pres)*

KO YO CHEMICAL (GROUP) LTD.
Rom 02 31/F Sino Plaza Glouester Road, Causeway Bay, China (Hong Kong)
Tel.: (852) 25753777   Ky
Web Site: http://www.koyochem.com
Year Founded: 1996
0827—(HKG)
Rev.: $450,013,730
Assets: $820,711,289
Liabilities: $671,869,598
Net Worth: $148,841,690
Earnings: $28,226,578
Emp.: 802
Fiscal Year-end: 12/31/22
Agricultural Chemical Products & Fertilizers Mfr & Distr
N.A.I.C.S.: 325320
Kangdi Jiao *(VP)*

KOA CORPORATION
2-17-2 Midori-cho Fuchu-shi, Tokyo, 183-0006, Japan
Tel.: (81) 423365755
Web Site: https://www.koaglobal.com
6999—(TKS)
Rev.: $428,377,812
Assets: $856,068,475
Liabilities: $336,920,950
Net Worth: $519,147,526
Earnings: $18,295,337
Emp.: 4,309
Fiscal Year-end: 03/31/24
Electronic Components Development Mfr & Sales
N.A.I.C.S.: 334419
Tadao Hanagata *(Pres)*

Subsidiaries:

Dah Hsing Electric Co.,Ltd.   (1)
11F No 34 Section 1 Nanjing East Road, Zhongshan District, Taipei, 10444, Taiwan
Tel.: (886) 225214166
Web Site: https://www.koadah.com
Sales Range: $25-49.9 Million
Emp.: 50
Electronic Parts & Equipment Whslr
N.A.I.C.S.: 423690

KOA ELECTRONICS (TAICANG) CO., LTD.   (1)
No 77 Luoyang East Road, High-Tech Industrial Developement Zone, Taicang, Jiangsu, China
Tel.: (86) 512 53561111
Web Site: http://www.koaglobal.com
Electronic Components Mfr
N.A.I.C.S.: 334419

KOA KAOHSIUNG CORPORATION   (1)
17-2 Kai-Fa Road NEPZ, Kaohsiung, Taiwan
Tel.: (886) 7 363 4157
Web Site: http://www.koaglobal.com.tw
Electronic Components Mfr
N.A.I.C.S.: 334419

KOA Speer Electronics Inc.   (1)
199 Bolivar Dr, Bradford, PA 16701-0547
Tel.: (814) 362-5536
Web Site: https://www.koaspeer.com
Sales Range: $50-74.9 Million
Emp.: 100
Mfr of Electronic Parts & Equipment
N.A.I.C.S.: 423690
Jeffery Rice *(Pres)*

Koa Denko (Malaysia) Sdn.Bhd.   (1)
Lot 7 8 & 9, batu berendam, 75350, Melaka, Malaysia
Tel.: (60) 62328031
Web Site: http://www.koanet.co.jp

Sales Range: $100-124.9 Million
Emp.: 600
Electronic Resistor Mfr
N.A.I.C.S.: 334416
Teh Ky *(Exec Dir)*

Koa Electronics (H.K.) Ltd.   (1)
Unit 2315 Metropolis Tower 10 Metropolis Drive Hunghom, Kowloon, China (Hong Kong)
Tel.: (852) 24926918
Web Site: http://www.hk.koaglobal.com
Sales Range: $25-49.9 Million
Emp.: 37
Electronic Parts & Equipment Whslr
N.A.I.C.S.: 423690

Koa Europe Gmbh   (1)
Kaddenbusch 6, Dageling, 25578, Itzehoe, Germany
Tel.: (49) 4821 89 89 0
Web Site: http://koaeurope.de
Electronic Components Mfr
N.A.I.C.S.: 334419

Shanghai Koa Electronics Trading Co.,Ltd.   (1)
RM 856 Modern International Finance Center No 136 Chifeng Road, Heping District, Shanghai, 300061, China
Tel.: (86) 2164320101
Web Site: http://www.koanet.co.jp
Sales Range: $25-49.9 Million
Emp.: 45
Electronic Parts & Equipment Whslr
N.A.I.C.S.: 423690

Wuxi Koa Electroceramics Co.,Ltd.   (1)
Heqiao, Yixing, Jiangsu, China
Tel.: (86) 51087871645
Web Site: http://www.wuxkoa.com
Sales Range: $50-74.9 Million
Emp.: 300
Electronic Parts & Equipment Whslr
N.A.I.C.S.: 423690

KOA SHOJI HOLDINGS CO., LTD.
13-15 Hiyoshi 7-chome, Kohoku-ku, Yokohama, 223-0061, Kanagawa, Japan
Tel.: (81) 455606607
Web Site: https://www.koashoji-hd.com
Year Founded: 2015
9273—(TKS)
Rev.: $137,673,480
Assets: $199,064,880
Liabilities: $43,247,660
Net Worth: $155,817,220
Earnings: $18,324,120
Emp.: 289
Fiscal Year-end: 06/30/24
Health Care Srvices
N.A.I.C.S.: 621999
Toshiyuki Shuto *(Chm & Pres)*

Subsidiaries:

Koa Isei Co., Ltd.   (1)
13-45 Wakaba-cho, Yamagata, 990-2495, Yamagata, Japan
Tel.: (81) 236227755
Web Site: http://www.isei-pharm.co.jp
Pharmaceutical Product Mfr & Retailer
N.A.I.C.S.: 325412

Koa Shoji Co., Ltd.   (1)
13-15 Hiyoshi 7-chome, Kohoku-ku, Yokohama, 223-0061, Kanagawa, Japan
Tel.: (81) 455606081
Web Site: https://www.koashoji.com
Emp.: 77
Pharmaceuticals Product Mfr
N.A.I.C.S.: 325412
Toshiyuki Shuto *(Chm & Pres)*

KOAL SOFTWARE CO., LTD.
6th Floor Building 4 Central Times Square Lane, 299 Jiangchang West Road Jing'an District, Shanghai, 200436, China
Tel.: (86) 2162327010
Web Site: https://www.koal.com

603232—(SHG)
Rev.: $92,596,706
Assets: $245,165,385
Liabilities: $52,211,222
Net Worth: $192,954,163
Earnings: ($1,223,235)
Emp.: 900
Fiscal Year-end: 12/31/22
Digital Security Services
N.A.I.C.S.: 561622
Yang Wenshan *(Chm)*

KOALA FINANCIAL GROUP LTD
Units 01-02 13/F Everbright Centre 108 Gloucester Road, Wanchai, China (Hong Kong)
Tel.: (852) 25988933   Ky
Web Site: http://www.koala8226.com.hk
8226—(HKG)
Rev.: $2,996,123
Assets: $60,976,365
Liabilities: $11,633,228
Net Worth: $49,343,138
Earnings: ($7,378,680)
Emp.: 17
Fiscal Year-end: 12/31/22
Straw Fuel Briquette Mfr & Distr
N.A.I.C.S.: 324199
Kar Ching Kwan *(Chm)*

Subsidiaries:

KOALA Capital Management Limited   (1)
Room 1301-02 13/F Everbright Centre 108 Gloucester Road, Wanchai, Hong Kong, China (Hong Kong)
Tel.: (852) 31880310
Web Site: https://www.kcmasia.com
Investment Management Service
N.A.I.C.S.: 523999

KOAN HAO TECHNOLOGY CO., LTD.
No 239 Chenggong 3rd Rd, Nant'ou, 54066, Taiwan
Tel.: (886) 492257851
Web Site: https://www.koanhao.com
Year Founded: 1992
8354—(TPE)
Rev.: $21,174,905
Assets: $135,648,845
Liabilities: $74,243,629
Net Worth: $61,405,215
Earnings: $2,492,449
Fiscal Year-end: 12/31/22
Self Adhesive Labels Mfr
N.A.I.C.S.: 322220

KOAS CO., LTD.
17 Seonyu-ro 52-gil, Yeongdeungpo-gu, Seoul, 7222, Korea (South)
Tel.: (82) 221636000
Web Site: https://www.ikoas.com
Year Founded: 1984
071950—(KRS)
Rev.: $75,078,923
Assets: $58,480,778
Liabilities: $44,774,301
Net Worth: $13,706,477
Earnings: ($1,464,956)
Emp.: 280
Fiscal Year-end: 12/31/22
Office Furniture Mfr & Whslr
N.A.I.C.S.: 337214
Jae Gyun Roh *(Chm & CEO)*

Subsidiaries:

Koas Co., Ltd. - Gimpo Factory   (1)
37-39 Seungga-ro, Gimpo, Gyeonggi-do, Korea (South)
Tel.: (82) 319838211
Office Furniture Mfr
N.A.I.C.S.: 337214

Koas Co., Ltd. - Paju 1 Factory   (1)
493 Bangchon-ro, Beopheung-ri Tanhyeon-myeon, Paju, Gyeonggi-do, Korea (South)
Tel.: (82) 319442360
Office Furniture Mfr
N.A.I.C.S.: 337214

Koas Co., Ltd. - Paju 2 Factory   (1)
43-22 Bangchon-ro 538-gil Chukhyeon-ri, Tanhyeon-myeon, Paju, Gyeonggi-do, Korea (South)
Tel.: (82) 319442360
Office Furniture Mfr
N.A.I.C.S.: 337214

Koas Co., Ltd. - Paju 4 Factory   (1)
541-44 Bangchon-ro Chukhyeon-ri, Tanhyeon-myeon, Paju, Gyeonggi-do, Korea (South)
Tel.: (82) 329442360
Office Furniture Mfr
N.A.I.C.S.: 337214

KOATSU GAS KOGYO CO., LTD.
2-4-12 Nakazakinishi, Kita-ku, Osaka, 530-8411, Japan
Tel.: (81) 677112570
Web Site: https://www.koatsugas.co.jp
Year Founded: 1958
4097—(TKS)
Rev.: $616,547,750
Assets: $794,416,240
Liabilities: $289,075,130
Net Worth: $505,341,110
Earnings: $29,764,830
Emp.: 849
Fiscal Year-end: 03/31/24
Industrial Gas Mfr
N.A.I.C.S.: 325120

Subsidiaries:

Koatsu Gas Kogyo Vietnam Co., Ltd.   (1)
Long Duc Industry, Long Duc Ward, Long Thanh, Dong Nai, Vietnam
Tel.: (84) 2513681261
Web Site: https://koatsugas.vn
Industrial Gas & Chemical Product Mfr
N.A.I.C.S.: 325199

KOATSU KOGYO CO., LTD.
5-17-5 Ishiki, Kagoshima, 890-0008, Japan
Tel.: (81) 992298181
Web Site: https://www.koatsuind.co.jp
Year Founded: 1959
1743—(TKS)
Rev.: $69,793,960
Assets: $84,363,910
Liabilities: $24,822,090
Net Worth: $59,541,820
Earnings: $1,609,430
Emp.: 270
Fiscal Year-end: 09/30/23
Construction Engineering Services
N.A.I.C.S.: 541330

KOBA RESOURCES LIMITED
Suite 25 22 Railway Road, Subiaco, 6008, WA, Australia
Tel.: (61) 892261356   AU
Web Site: https://www.kobaresources.com
Year Founded: 2021
KOB—(ASX)
Rev.: $178
Assets: $8,487,530
Liabilities: $551,666
Net Worth: $7,935,864
Earnings: ($2,023,868)
Fiscal Year-end: 06/30/22
Exploration & Mining Services
N.A.I.C.S.: 213115
Ben Vallerine *(Mng Dir)*

KOBALT BV
Van Heuven Goedhartlaan 937, 1181 LD, Amstelveen, Netherlands
Tel.: (31) 20 799 89 98
Emp.: 140

KOBALT BV

Kobalt BV—(Continued)
N.A.I.C.S.: 541810
Marceline Beijer (CEO)

KOBAY TECHNOLOGY BHD.
Wisma Kobay 42B Jalan Rangoon, 10400, George Town, Penang, Malaysia
Tel.: (60) 43711338
Web Site:
https://www.kobaytech.com
KOBAY—(KLS)
Rev.: $66,390,161
Assets: $119,344,754
Liabilities: $35,950,877
Net Worth: $83,393,877
Earnings: $5,415,863
Emp.: 5
Fiscal Year-end: 06/30/23
Molding Tools Equipment Mfr
N.A.I.C.S.: 333511
Mee Choon Wong (Co-Sec)

Subsidiaries:

Bend Weld Engineering Sdn. Bhd (1)
Lot 3611 Batu 30 Jalan Johor, Pekan Nenas, 81500, Johor, Penang, Malaysia
Tel.: (60) 76996889
Web Site: https://www.bendweld.com
Sales Range: $25-49.9 Million
Emp.: 60
Oil Field Equipment Mfr
N.A.I.C.S.: 333132

Elite Paper Trading Sdn. Bhd. (1)
Plot 2060 & 2061 Jalan Persekutuan Permatang Tinggi Light Industry, Seberang Perai Tengah, 14000, Penang, Malaysia
Tel.: (60) 45873690
Precision Tool Mfr
N.A.I.C.S.: 332216

Kual Technologies Sdn. Bhd. (1)
3016 Tingkat Perusahaan 6 Kawasan Perindustrian Prai, 13600, Perai, Penang, Malaysia
Tel.: (60) 174529325
Web Site: https://www.kual.tech
Aluminum Extrusions Mfr
N.A.I.C.S.: 331318

Lipo Corporation Berhad (1)
Plot 30 Hilir Sungai Kluang Satu, Bayan Lepas Industrial Park, Phase 4, 11900, Penang, Malaysia **(51.49%)**
Tel.: (60) 46411888
Web Site: http://www.lipocorp.com
Sales Range: $10-24.9 Million
Precision Machined Components Mfr
N.A.I.C.S.: 332216

Subsidiary (Domestic):

Micro Surface Treatment Sdn. Bhd. (2)
967 Jalan Perusahaan Kawasan Perusahaan, 13600, Perai, Penang, Malaysia
Tel.: (60) 43976817
Web Site: https://www.mst.net.my
Emp.: 80
Precision Component Mfr
N.A.I.C.S.: 332216

Paradigm Metal Industries Sdn. Bhd (2)
2631 Lot 376 377 Lorong Perusahaan 10 Phase 3, Prai Industrial Estate, 13600, Perai, Penang, Malaysia
Tel.: (60) 43902800
Web Site: https://www.pmi.net.my
Fabricated Metal Products Mfr
N.A.I.C.S.: 332312

Paradigm Precision Components Sdn. Bhd (2)
No 2478 Lorong Perusahaan 10 Kawasan Perusahaan Perai, Industrial Park 3, 13600, Perai, Penang, Malaysia
Tel.: (60) 43842621
Web Site: https://ppc.net.my
Emp.: 150
Precision Component Mfr
N.A.I.C.S.: 332216

Paradigm Precision Machining Sdn. Bhd (2)
Plot 83 Medan Bayan Lepas Bayan Lepas Industrial Park, Phase 4, 11900, Bayan Lepas, Penang, Malaysia
Tel.: (60) 46420270
Precision Tool Mfr
N.A.I.C.S.: 332216
T. O. Chand (CEO)

Maker Technologies Sdn. Bhd (1)
Plot 30 Hilir Sungai Kluang Satu Bayan Lepas, Industrial Park Phase 4, 11900, Bayan Lepas, Penang, Malaysia
Tel.: (60) 46443126
Web Site: http://www.kobaytech.com
Sales Range: $25-49.9 Million
Emp.: 6
Precision Component Mfr
N.A.I.C.S.: 332216
Teong Hock Eu (Gen Mgr)

Polytool Integration Sdn. Bhd. (1)
Plot 30 Hilir Sungai Kluang Satu, Industrial Park Phase 4, 11900, Bayan Lepas, Penang, Malaysia
Tel.: (60) 46429731
Web Site: http://www.polytool.com.my
Sales Range: $25-49.9 Million
Emp.: 6
Precision Component Mfr
N.A.I.C.S.: 332216

Polytool Technologies Sdn. Bhd. (1)
Plot 30 Hilir Sungai Kluang Satu Bayan Lepas Industrial Park Phase 4, 11900, Penang, Malaysia
Tel.: (60) 46445888
Web Site: http://www.tech.polytool.com
Sales Range: $25-49.9 Million
Emp.: 70
Precision Tool Mfr
N.A.I.C.S.: 332216
Ch'ng Kean How (Gen Mgr)

KOBAYASHI PHARMACEUTICAL CO., LTD.
KDX Kobayashi Doshomachi Bldg 4-10 Doshomachi 4-chome, Chuo-ku, Osaka, 541-0045, Japan
Tel.: (81) 662220142
Web Site:
https://www.kobayashi.co.jp
Year Founded: 1885
4967—(TKS)
Rev.: $1,229,795,950
Assets: $1,896,383,570
Liabilities: $444,238,130
Net Worth: $1,452,145,440
Earnings: $144,196,420
Emp.: 3,534
Fiscal Year-end: 12/31/23
Pharmaceutical Mfr, Whslr & Retailer; Medical Equipment Importer & Distr
N.A.I.C.S.: 325412
Satoshi Yamane (Sr Gen Mgr)

Subsidiaries:

Aloe Pharmaceutical Co., Ltd. (1)
290-9 Oyanagi, Shimada, 427-0101, Shizuoka, Japan
Tel.: (81) 547300030
Emp.: 60
Pharmaceuticals Product Mfr
N.A.I.C.S.: 325412

Ehime Kobayashi Pharmaceutical Co., Ltd. (1)
1-7-24 Kuroshima, Niihama, 792-0892, Ehime, Japan
Tel.: (81) 897453777
Emp.: 165
Hygienic & Paper Good Mfr
N.A.I.C.S.: 322291

Juju Cosmetics Co., Ltd. (1)
Toyokawa 1-30-3, Tochigi, 570-0057, Osaka Prefecture, Japan
Tel.: (81) 120801016
Web Site: http://www.juju.co.jp
Cosmetics Products Mfr
N.A.I.C.S.: 325620

Kiribai Chemical Co., Ltd. (1)
New Height 1-10-5, Yodogawa-ku, Osaka, 532-0033, Japan
Tel.: (81) 663920333
Web Site: http://www.kiribai.co.jp
Disposabe Body Warmer Distr
N.A.I.C.S.: 424210

Kobayashi Healthcare (Malaysia) Sdn. Bhd.
50-02-2A Level 2 Wisma UOA Damansara 50 Jalan Dungun Damansara Heights, 50490, Kuala Lumpur, Malaysia
Tel.: (60) 320117702
Web Site: http://www.kobayashi-my.com
Daily Good & Other Product Distr
N.A.I.C.S.: 424990
Lily Yaw (Mgr-Mktg)

Kobayashi Healthcare (Thailand) Co., Ltd.
No 540 Mercury Tower 5th 6th Floor Units 505 607 Ploenchit Road, Lumpini Subdistrict Pathumwan District, Bangkok, 10330, Thailand
Tel.: (66) 26585528
Web Site: http://www.kobayashi-th.com
Daily Good & Other Product Distr
N.A.I.C.S.: 424990
Nichapa Roong-In (Mgr-Product)

Kobayashi Healthcare Europe, Ltd. (1)
Power Road Studios 114 Power Road, Chiswick, London, W4 5PY, United Kingdom
Tel.: (44) 208 987 9976
Web Site:
https://www.kobayashihealthcare.co.uk
Daily Good & Other Product Distr
N.A.I.C.S.: 424990
Takaki Yagi (Mng Dir)

Kobayashi Healthcare LLC (1)
245 Kraft Dr, Dalton, GA 30721
Web Site: https://kobayashiamericas.com
Medical Devices & OTC Personal Care Products Mfr & Distr
N.A.I.C.S.: 423450
Daniel Yim (Pres)

Subsidiary (Domestic):

Heatmax, Inc. (2)
245 Kraft Dr, Dalton, GA 30721
Tel.: (706) 226-1800
Web Site: http://www.heatmax.com
Air Activated Heating Products Mfr
N.A.I.C.S.: 333414

Subsidiary (Domestic):

Grabber, Inc. (3)
365 84th St SW Ste 4, Byron, MI 49315
Tel.: (616) 940-1914
Web Site: http://www.grabberworld.com
Sales Range: $10-24.9 Million
Emp.: 15
Vitreous China Plumbing Fixture & China & Earthenware Bathroom Accessories Mfr
N.A.I.C.S.: 327110

Kobayashi Pharmaceutical (Hong Kong) Co., Ltd. (1)
Room 1113 11/F Phase 2 Cheung Sha Wan Plaza 833 Cheung Sha Wan Road, Kowloon, China (Hong Kong)
Tel.: (852) 25432289
Web Site: https://www.kobayashi.com.hk
Daily Good & Other Product Distr
N.A.I.C.S.: 424990

Kobayashi Pharmaceutical (Singapore) Pte. Ltd. (1)
2 Alexandra Road 04-01D Delta House, Singapore, 159919, Singapore
Tel.: (65) 62708239
Web Site: http://www.kobayashi.com.sg
Daily Good & Other Product Distr
N.A.I.C.S.: 424990
Janice Ong (Mgr-Mktg)

Kobayashi Pharmaceutical (Taiwan) Co., Ltd. (1)
4th Floor 11th Floor No 51 Hengyang Road, Zhongzheng District, Taipei, 10045, Taiwan
Tel.: (886) 223131227
Web Site: http://www.kobayashi-tw.com
Daily Good & Other Product Distr
N.A.I.C.S.: 424990

Kobayashi Pharmaceutical Plax Co., Ltd. (1)
20 Yokodoi, Toyama, 939-2216, Japan
Tel.: (81) 764681323
Emp.: 97
Container & Cap Mfr
N.A.I.C.S.: 326199

Meitanhompo Co., Ltd. (1)
1088-11 Kitaseida, Kinokawa, 649-6402, Wakayama, Japan
Tel.: (81) 736793281
Pharmaceuticals Product Mfr
N.A.I.C.S.: 325412

PT. Kobayashi Pharmaceutical Indonesia (1)
Ruko Excellis No 19 Panunggangan Barat, Karawaci Office Park, Tangerang, 15139, Banten, Indonesia
Tel.: (62) 2125617922
Web Site: https://www.kobayashi-id.com
Daily Good & Other Product Distr
N.A.I.C.S.: 424990
Ronald Djarot (Dir-Sls & Mktg)

SP-Planning, Inc. (1)
1-3-31-1513 Suehiro, Kawaguchi, 332-0006, Saitama, Japan
Tel.: (81) 482239895
Display & Model Mfr
N.A.I.C.S.: 337215

Sendai Kobayashi Pharmaceutical Co., Ltd. (1)
Matsusakadaira 4-3 Yamato-cho, Kurokawa-gun, Matsushima, 981-3408, Miyagi Prefecture, Japan
Tel.: (81) 223444300
Web Site: http://www.sendaikobayashi.co.jp
Pharmaceuticals Product Mfr
N.A.I.C.S.: 325412

Shield Healthcare Centers (1)
27911 Franklin Pkwy, Valencia, CA 91355-3465 **(100%)**
Tel.: (661) 294-4200
Web Site: http://www.shieldhealthcare.com
Sales Range: $150-199.9 Million
Emp.: 400
Distr of Medical Supplies
N.A.I.C.S.: 423450
James Snell (Pres)

Suehiro Sangyo Co., Ltd. (1)
8 Aza Kaizu Tomisaka, Shinshiro, 441-1632, Aichi, Japan
Tel.: (81) 536320506
Web Site: https://www.suehiro.co.jp
Daily Good & Other Product Distr
N.A.I.C.S.: 424990

Toyama Kobayashi Pharmaceutical Co., Ltd. (1)
Tel.: (81) 764682811
Emp.: 407
Pharmaceuticals Product Mfr
N.A.I.C.S.: 325412

KOBAYASHI YOKO CO., LTD.
1030014 1157 Nihonbashi Kakigaracho Kobayashi Yoko Building No 2, Chuo-ku, Tokyo, 103-0014, Japan
Tel.: (81) 336694111
Web Site:
https://www.kobayashiyoko.com
Year Founded: 1949
8742—(TKS)
Rev.: $29,652,460
Assets: $122,086,700
Liabilities: $59,146,280
Net Worth: $62,940,420
Earnings: $2,445,700
Fiscal Year-end: 03/31/24
Investment & Financial Services
N.A.I.C.S.: 523160
Shigemitsu Hosogane (Pres)

KOBE BUSSAN CO., LTD.
125-1 Hirano Kakogawa-cho, Kakogawa-shi, Hyogo, 675-0063, Japan
Tel.: (81) 794575001
Web Site:
https://www.kobebussan.co.jp
Year Founded: 1985

AND PRIVATE COMPANIES   KOBE STEEL, LTD.

3038—(TKS)
Rev.: $3,272,361,140
Assets: $1,502,307,190
Liabilities: $690,849,600
Net Worth: $811,457,590
Earnings: $145,770,400
Fiscal Year-end: 10/31/23
Supermarket Operator
N.A.I.C.S.: 445110
Hirokazu Numata *(Pres & Dir-Rep)*

Subsidiaries:

Asabikiwakadori Co., Ltd. (1)
359-1 Godomachi, Takasaki, 370-3336, Gunma, Japan
Tel.: (81) 27 343 2015
Web Site: https://www.asabikiwakadori.co.jp
Chicken Meat Mfr & Distr
N.A.I.C.S.: 311615

Coffee Mame Koubou Co., Ltd. (1)
545 1 Kamiyobe Yobeku, Himeji, 671-1262, Hyogo Prefecture, Japan
Tel.: (81) 792419240
Web Site: http://www.coffeemame.co.jp
Coffee Mfr & Whslr
N.A.I.C.S.: 311920

Dalian Fresh Foods Co., Ltd. (1)
No 14 An Shan Street Development Zone, Dalian, 116600, Liaoning, China
Tel.: (86) 41187619580
Food Products Mfr
N.A.I.C.S.: 311991

G.Communication Co., Ltd. (1)
5-12-3 Kurokawahondouri Kita-ku, Nagoya, 462-0841, Japan
Tel.: (81) 529120885
Web Site: http://www.g-com.jp
Business Consulting Services
N.A.I.C.S.: 541611

Green Poultry Co., Ltd. (1)
1647 1 Shimobara Kagamino cho, Tomata-gun, Okayama, 708-0341, Japan
Tel.: (81) 868545120
Web Site: http://www.green-poultry.co.jp
Chicken Meat Mfr & Distr
N.A.I.C.S.: 311615

Hata Foods Co., Ltd. (1)
460 Yamazura, Ryuo-cho Gamo-gun, Shiga, 520-2564, Japan
Tel.: (81) 74 858 0252
Web Site: https://www.hatafoods.co.jp
Food Product Mfr & Whslr
N.A.I.C.S.: 311999

Kikukawa Co., Ltd. (1)
1-543 Unuma Nishi-cho, Kakamigahara, 509-0132, Gifu, Japan
Tel.: (81) 58 384 1237
Web Site: https://www.sake-kikukawa.co.jp
Food Product Mfr & Whslr
N.A.I.C.S.: 311999

Kobe Bussan (Anqiu) Foods Co., Ltd. (1)
Wenshui North Road Economic Development Zone, Anqiu, 262123, Shandong, China
Tel.: (86) 5364932678
Food Products Mfr
N.A.I.C.S.: 311991

Kobe Bussan Eco Green Hokkaido Co., Ltd. (1)
302-3 Shiomi Mukawa-cho, Yufutsu-gun, Hokkaido, 054-0015, Japan
Tel.: (81) 14 547 2365
Web Site: https://www.kobebussan-eco-h.co.jp
Agricultural Product Mfr & Whslr
N.A.I.C.S.: 333111

Masuzen Co., Ltd. (1)
2060 Esojimamachi, Utsunomiya, 321-0102, Tochigi, Japan
Tel.: (81) 28 633 3945
Web Site: https://www.masuzen.co.jp
Tokoroten Mfr & Whslr
N.A.I.C.S.: 332999

Miyagiseifun Co., Ltd. (1)
70 Mishima, Shimada, Kakuda, 981-1503, Miyagi, Japan
Tel.: (81) 22 461 2525
Web Site: https://www.miyagiseifun.jp
Food Product Mfr & Whslr
N.A.I.C.S.: 311999

Mugipankoubou Co., Ltd. (1)
1035-1 Jushichijo, Mizuho, Gifu, 501-0313, Gifu Prefecture, Japan
Tel.: (81) 583287011
Web Site: https://www.mugipan.co.jp
Bread Mfr & Whslr
N.A.I.C.S.: 311812

Nikunotaiko Co., Ltd. (1)
Matsue 1 chome 19 17, Edogawa-ku, Tokyo, 132-0025, Japan
Tel.: (81) 336525269
Web Site: http://www.nikunotaiko.co.jp
Meat Sausage Mfr
N.A.I.C.S.: 311612

Ostern Foods Co., Ltd. (1)
1-43 Nagamachi, Hirohataku-ku, Himeji, 671-1125, Hyogo, Japan
Tel.: (81) 79 230 2710
Web Site: https://www.osternfoods.co.jp
Egg, Tofu Product & Noodle Mfr & Whslr
N.A.I.C.S.: 311999

Sekihara Sake Brewery Co., Ltd. (1)
1-1029-1 Sekihara-machi, Nagaoka, 940-2035, Niigata-ken, Japan
Tel.: (81) 25 846 2010
Web Site: https://www.sake-sekihara.co.jp
Alcoholic Beverage Mfr & Distr
N.A.I.C.S.: 312140
Kazuo Asami *(Pres)*

Termeltfoods Co., Ltd. (1)
3 of 4077 Tajima, Hofu, 747-0834, Yamaguchi Prefecture, Japan
Tel.: (81) 835290511
Web Site: http://www.termelt-foods.co.jp
Frozen Food Mfr & Whslr
N.A.I.C.S.: 311412

Toyota Nyugyou Co., Ltd. (1)
788 Nanamagari Hakusan-cho, Toyota, 471-0056, Aichi, Japan
Tel.: (81) 56 531 0478
Web Site: https://www.toyota-nyugyo.co.jp
Dairy Product Mfr & Whslr
N.A.I.C.S.: 311514

KOBE ELECTRIC RAILWAY CO., LTD.
No 1-3-24 Shinkaichi, Hyogo-ku, Kobe, 652-0811, Hyogo, Japan
Tel.: (81) 785768651
Web Site: https://www.shintetsu.co.jp
Year Founded: 1926
9046—(TKS)
Rev.: $147,488,930
Assets: $597,881,110
Liabilities: $446,234,490
Net Worth: $151,646,620
Earnings: $6,768,640
Emp.: 511
Fiscal Year-end: 03/31/24
Transportation Services
N.A.I.C.S.: 484110
Nobuhiko Terada *(Chm)*

KOBE STEEL, LTD.
ON Building 9-12 Kita-Shinagawa 5-chome, Shinagawa-ku, Tokyo, 141-8688, Japan
Tel.: (81) 357396000   JP
Web Site: https://www.kobelco.co.jp
Year Founded: 1905
5406—(NGO)
Rev.: $16,803,047,822
Assets: $19,291,530,773
Liabilities: $11,842,930,282
Net Worth: $7,448,600,491
Earnings: $723,831,974
Emp.: 38,050
Fiscal Year-end: 03/31/24
Plant Engineering Services; Iron & Steel Mfr; Aluminum & Copper Products Supplier
N.A.I.C.S.: 331110
Yoshihiko Katsukawa *(Exec Officer-Corp Plng Dept, Fin & Acctg Plng Dept)*

Subsidiaries:

Alcoa Australia Rolled Products (1)
Point Henry Rd, PO Box 460, Geelong, 3220, VIC, Australia   (50%)
Tel.: (61) 352451777
Sales Range: $200-249.9 Million
Emp.: 700
Mfr & Sale of Aluminum Can Stock, Foil & General Sheet
N.A.I.C.S.: 331318

Ceratechno Co., Ltd. (1)
5-11-70 Kisaki, Akashi, 673-0037, Hyogo, Japan
Tel.: (81) 789238678
Web Site: https://www.ceratechno.com
Industrial Furnace Mfr
N.A.I.C.S.: 333994

Chengdu Kobelco Construction Machinery Financial Leasing Ltd. (1)
No 666 Mortor City Avenue, Chengdu, 610100, Sichuan, China
Tel.: (86) 2882841884
Construction Equipment Leasing Services
N.A.I.C.S.: 532412

Grand Blanc Processing, LLC (1)
10151 Gainey Dr, Holly, MI 48442
Tel.: (810) 694-6000
CHQ Wire Mfr & Distr
N.A.I.C.S.: 331222

Hangzhou Kobelco Construction Machinery Co., Ltd. (1)
No 1 22 Street Hangzhou Economic and Technological Development Zone, Hangzhou, Zhejiang, China
Tel.: (86) 87128896588
Hydraulic Excavator Component Mfr
N.A.I.C.S.: 333120

JKW Co., Ltd. (1)
2-17-4 Kuramae JFE Kuramae Building 3rd Floor, Taito-ku, Tokyo, 111-0051, Japan
Tel.: (81) 338643731
Web Site: http://www.jkw.co.jp
Emp.: 29
Welding Rod Distr
N.A.I.C.S.: 423840

Japan Aeroforge, Ltd. (1)
8264-7 Shinminato Tamashima Otoshima, Kurashiki, 713-8103, Okayama, Japan
Tel.: (81) 865230135
Web Site: https://www.japan-aeroforge.com
Forged Products Mfr
N.A.I.C.S.: 332111

Japan Medical Materials Corporation (1)
Uemura Nissei Building 9th Floor 3-3-31 Miyahara, Yodogawa-ku, Osaka, 532-0003, Japan
Tel.: (81) 663501036
Web Site: http://www.jmmc.jp
Sales Range: $200-249.9 Million
Emp.: 600
Artificial Joints, Dental Implants & Other Medical Equipment Mfr; Owned 77% by Kyocera Corporation & 23% by Kobe Steel, Ltd.
N.A.I.C.S.: 339112

Plant (Domestic):

Japan Medical Materials Corp - Shiga Yohkaichi Plant (2)
1166-6 Hebimizo-cho, Higashi-omi, 527-8555, Shiga, Japan
Tel.: (81) 748221550
Communication Equipment Mfr
N.A.I.C.S.: 334290

Japan Superconductor Technology Inc. (1)
Takatsukadai 1-5-5, Nishi-ku, Kobe, 651-2271, Hyogo, Japan
Tel.: (81) 78 991 9445
Web Site: https://www.jastec-inc.com
Superconducting Magnet Mfr & Distr
N.A.I.C.S.: 332999
Hiroshi Uzukawa *(Pres)*

Jiangyin Sugita Fasten Spring Wire Co., Ltd. (1)
Shizhuang Park of Jiangyin Economic Development Zone, No 685 Huangshi Road, Jiangyin, 214446, Jiangsu, China
Tel.: (86) 51086668585
Oil Tempered Wire Mfr & Distr
N.A.I.C.S.: 331222

KOBE & SHINSHO TUBE SPECIALITIES SDN. BHD. (1)
Lot C/23117 Jalan 3/22A Off Batu 6-1/2 Jalan Kepong, Kuala Lumpur, 52100, Malaysia
Tel.: (60) 362507877
Aluminium Tube Mfr
N.A.I.C.S.: 332919

KOBE ALUMINUM AUTOMOTIVE PRODUCTS, LLC (1)
one kobe Rd, Bowling Green, KY 42101-7534
Tel.: (270) 842-6492
Automotive Aluminium Suspension Products Mfr & Distr
N.A.I.C.S.: 336390
Ron Ausbrooks *(Mgr-Product Dev)*

KOBE ELECTRONICS MATERIAL (THAILAND) CO., LTD. (1)
150 Moo 1 Hi-tech Industrial Estate T Banlen, Amphur Bang-Pa-In, Ayutthaya, 13160, Thailand
Tel.: (66) 35314070
Sales Range: $50-74.9 Million
Emp.: 55
Electronic Material Distr
N.A.I.C.S.: 423690
Takashi Fukutani *(Mng Dir)*

KOBE HEATING AND COOLING SUPPLY CO., LTD. (1)
IHD Centre Building 5-1 Kaigandori 1-chome, Chuo-ku, Kobe, 651-0073, Hyogo, Japan
Tel.: (81) 78 261 6025
Heating & Air Conditioning Equipment Distr
N.A.I.C.S.: 423730
Masato Katayama *(Pres & CEO)*

KOBE SPECIAL STEEL WIRE PRODUCTS (PINGHU) CO., LTD. (1)
No 2357 Xingming Road Pinghu Economic Development Zone, Pinghu, 314200, Zhejiang, China
Tel.: (86) 57385223100
Web Site: http://www.ksp-ph.com
Emp.: 104
Cold Headind Quality Wire Distr
N.A.I.C.S.: 423610

KOBE SPECIAL TUBE CO., LTD. (1)
13-1 Chofuminato-machi, Shimonoseki, 752-0953, Yamaguchi, Japan
Tel.: (81) 83 246 3781
Web Site: http://www.kobest.co.jp
Sales Range: $100-124.9 Million
Emp.: 400
Steel Tubes & Pipes Mfr
N.A.I.C.S.: 331210
Keiichi Wada *(Pres)*

KOBE WELDING OF SHANGHAI CO.,LTD. (1)
Building B 8F No 1010 Kai Xuan Road, Changning District, Shanghai, 200052, China
Tel.: (86) 21 6191 7850
Sales Range: $25-49.9 Million
Emp.: 16
Welding Robot System & Parts Distr
N.A.I.C.S.: 423830
Ahita Tomohiro *(Gen Mgr)*

KOBE WELDING OF TANGSHAN CO., LTD. (1)
196 Huoju Road Tangshan New Hi-Tech Development Zone, Tangshan, 63020, Hebei, China   (52%)
Tel.: (86) 3153852805
Web Site: http://www.tskwt.com
Low-Carbon Steel Core Wire & Flux-Cored Welding Materials Mfr & Distr
N.A.I.C.S.: 333992
Baocheng Liu *(Chm)*

KOBE WING STADIUM CO., LTD. (1)
2-2 Misakicho 1-chome, Kobe, 652-0855, Hyogo, Japan
Tel.: (81) 78 652 5656
Web Site: http://www.homes-stadium.jp

KOBE STEEL, LTD.

Kobe Steel, Ltd.—(Continued)
Emp.: 8
Sports Club Maintenance Services
N.A.I.C.S.: 711211
Hideki Adumi *(Mgr)*

KOBELCO & MATERIALS COPPER TUBE (MALAYSIA) SDN. BHD. (1)
Lot 1 Persiaran Sabak Bernam Section 26 Sector B, HICOM Industrial Estate, 40400, Shah Alam, Selangor Darul Ehsan, Malaysia
Tel.: (60) 351912601
Sales Range: $150-199.9 Million
Emp.: 353
Copper Tube & Tube Parts Distr
N.A.I.C.S.: 423690

KOBELCO & MATERIALS COPPER TUBE (THAILAND) CO., LTD. (1)
Rojana Industrial Park Rayong 169 Moo 2 Tambol Nongbua Amphur, Bankhai, Rayong, 21120, Thailand
Tel.: (66) 38 998 200
Web Site: http://www.kmct.jp
Sales Range: $125-149.9 Million
Emp.: 349
Copper Tube Mfr & Distr
N.A.I.C.S.: 332999

KOBELCO & MATERIALS COPPER TUBE, LTD. (1)
2-7-1 Nishishinjuku, Shinjuku-ku, Tokyo, 163-0704, Japan
Tel.: (81) 353268312
Web Site: http://www.kmct.jp
Sales Range: $100-124.9 Million
Emp.: 300
Copper Pipe & Tube Mfr
N.A.I.C.S.: 332919
Hideo Sumida *(Pres & CEO)*

KOBELCO (CHINA) HOLDING CO., LTD. (1)
Room 3701 Hong Kong New World Tower 300 Huai Hai Zhong Road, Luwan District, Shanghai, 200021, China
Tel.: (86) 21 6415 4977
Metal Products Mfr
N.A.I.C.S.: 332999

KOBELCO ADVANCED COATING (AMERICA), INC. (1)
1007 Commerce Ct, Buffalo Grove, IL 60089
Tel.: (847) 520-6000
Web Site: http://www.kobac-us.com
Industrial Equipment Coating Services
N.A.I.C.S.: 561990
Koichiro Akari *(Pres)*

KOBELCO COMPRESSORS MANUFACTURING INDIANA, INC. (1)
3000 Hammond Ave, Elkhart, IN 46516
Tel.: (574) 295-3145
Web Site: http://www.kobelcocompressors.com
Compressor Mfr & Distr
N.A.I.C.S.: 333912

KOBELCO Career Development Co., Ltd. (1)
1-5-1 WakinohamaKaigan-dori, Chuo-ku, Kobe, 651-0073, Japan
Tel.: (81) 782228800
Web Site: http://www.kobelco-hrd.com
Human Resource Development Services
N.A.I.C.S.: 541612
Tetsuya Yoshikawa *(Pres & CEO)*

KOBELCO FINANCIAL CENTER, LTD. (1)
9-12 Kita-Shinagawa 5-chome, Shinagawa-ku, Tokyo, 141-8688, Japan
Tel.: (81) 3 5739 6098
Financial Management Services
N.A.I.C.S.: 523999

KOBELCO LOGISTICS, LTD. (1)
2-4 Wakinohama-Kaigandori 2-chome, Chuo-Ku, Kobe, 651-0073, Hyogo, Japan
Tel.: (81) 78 262 3800
Web Site: https://www.kobelco-logis.co.jp
Emp.: 1,029
Logistics & Distribution Services
N.A.I.C.S.: 541614
Michihide Iwasa *(Pres & CEO)*

KOBELCO MACHINERY ASIA PTE. LTD. (1)
60 Pandan Road, Jurong, 609294, Singapore
Tel.: (65) 62620586
Industrial Compressor & Machinery Distr
N.A.I.C.S.: 423830

KOBELCO MACHINERY INDIA PRIVATE LIMITED (1)
Infinity Benchmark 6th Floor Plot No G1 EP & GP Block, Sector V, Kolkata, 700091, India
Tel.: (91) 33 4011 5222
Metal Working Machinery Distr
N.A.I.C.S.: 423830

KOBELCO PERSONNEL CO., LTD. (1)
Ido Kobe Building 3F, Chuoku, Kobe, 651-0072, Hyogo, Japan
Tel.: (81) 78 392 8082
Web Site: http://www.kobelcopersonnel.co.jp
Sales Range: Less than $1 Million
Emp.: 50
Human Resource Consulting Services
N.A.I.C.S.: 541612
Yoshifumi Furuya *(Exec Dir)*

KOBELCO RESEARCH INSTITUTE, INC. (1)
1-5-1 Wakihamakaigan-dori Kokusai Kenko Kaihatsu Center 6F, Chuo-ku, Kobe, 651-0073, Hyogo, Japan
Tel.: (81) 78 272 5915
Web Site: http://www.kobelcokaken.co.jp
Sales Range: $450-499.9 Million
Emp.: 1,056
Semiconductor Device Mfr, Research & Testing Services
N.A.I.C.S.: 334515

KOBELCO ROBOTICS SERVICE CO., LTD. (1)
100-1 Miyamae, Fujisawa, 251-8551, Japan
Tel.: (81) 466203318
Industrial Robot Machinery Maintenance Services
N.A.I.C.S.: 811310

KOBELCO SANKI SERVICE CO., LTD. (1)
3-1 Araicho-Shinhama 2-chome, Takasago, 676 8670, Hyogo, Japan
Tel.: (81) 79 445 7611
Industrial Machinery Maintenance Services
N.A.I.C.S.: 811310
Gotoda Masaru *(Mgr-Machine)*

KOBELCO SYSTEMS CORPORATION (1)
11F Shimabun Bldg 4-2-7 Iwayanaka-machi, Nada-ku, Kobe, 657-0845, Hyogo, Japan
Tel.: (81) 78 261 7500
Web Site: https://www.kobelcosys.co.jp
Emp.: 1,735
Enterprise Resource Planning Software Development Services
N.A.I.C.S.: 541511
Yoshio Tano *(Pres & CEO)*

Kobe Aluminum Automotive Products (China) Co., Ltd. (1)
No 155 Hongxi Road, Suzhou New District, Jiangsu, 215151, China
Tel.: (86) 51268787060
Aluminium Forgings Mfr
N.A.I.C.S.: 332112

Kobe CH Wire (Thailand) Co., Ltd. (1)
67/16 Moo 5 Chuam Samphan Road Kokfad, Nongjok, Bangkok, 10530, Thailand
Tel.: (66) 29880576
CHQ Wire Mfr & Distr
N.A.I.C.S.: 331222

Kobe Copper (Malaysia) Sdn. Bhd. (1)
Lot 1 Persiaran Sabak Bernam Section 26 Sector B HICOM Industrial Esta, 40000, Shah Alam, Selangor, Malaysia (55%)
Tel.: (60) 351912601
Web Site: http://www.ac.kobelco.co.jp
Sales Range: $25-49.9 Million
Emp.: 350
Secondary Processing & Sale of Copper Tube Fittings
N.A.I.C.S.: 332912
Uno Koiehro *(Pres)*

Kobe MIG Wire (Thailand) Co., Ltd. (1)
491 Soi 1 Bangpoo Industrial Estate Sukhumvit Rd Praeksa, Samut Prakan, 10280, Thailand (51%)
Tel.: (66) 23240588
Web Site: http://www.thaikobe.com
Sales Range: $50-74.9 Million
Emp.: 233
Mfr & Sale of Solid Wires for Welding
N.A.I.C.S.: 333992

Kobe Medical Care Partners Co., Ltd. (1)
2-1-1 Minamicho Minato Island, Chuo Ward, Kobe, 650-0047, Hyogo, Japan
Tel.: (81) 783030310
Hospital Management Services
N.A.I.C.S.: 561110

Kobe Precision Technology Sdn. Bhd. (1)
Plot 39 Phase IV Bayan Lepas Industrial Estate, 11900, Penang, Malaysia (100%)
Tel.: (60) 4 362 7222
Web Site: https://www.kptec.com.my
Emp.: 2,500
Mfr & Sale of Aluminum Computer Disk Substrates
N.A.I.C.S.: 331318
Hideo Senju *(Mng Dir)*

Kobe Precision, Inc. (1)
31031 Huntwood Ave, Hayward, CA 94544 (100%)
Tel.: (510) 487-3200
Web Site: http://www.kpi.com
Sales Range: $25-49.9 Million
Emp.: 100
Reclaimed Silicon Wafers Mfr & Distr
N.A.I.C.S.: 334413

Kobe Real Estate Co Ltd (1)
Shinko Bldg 10 26 Wakinohamacho 2 Chome Chuo Ku, Kobe, 651 0072, Hyogo, Japan (100%)
Tel.: (81) 782612121
Web Site: http://www.kobelco2103.jp
Sales Range: $75-99.9 Million
Emp.: 200
Real Estate Services
N.A.I.C.S.: 531390
Tatsuki Yoshida *(Pres)*

Kobe Steel Asia Pte. Ltd. (1)
72 Anson Road 11-01A Anson House, Singapore, 079911, Singapore (100%)
Tel.: (65) 62216177
Web Site: http://www.kobelco.co.jp
Sales Range: $25-49.9 Million
Emp.: 4
Steel Operations
N.A.I.C.S.: 331210

Kobe Steel Asia Pte. Ltd. (1)
Rm 1603 4 Massmutual Tower, 38 Gloucester Rd, Wanchai, China (Hong Kong) (100%)
Tel.: (852) 28650040
Web Site: http://www.kobelco.jp
Sales Range: $25-49.9 Million
Emp.: 4
Steel, Aluminum & Copper
N.A.I.C.S.: 332111

Kobe Steel Consulting Co., Ltd. (1)
Room F2 14F Jiushi Fuxing Mason No 918 Huai Hai Zhong Lu, Shanghai, 200021, China
Tel.: (86) 21 6415 4977
Web Site: http://www.kobelco.co.jp
Seal Products Distr
N.A.I.C.S.: 423510
Hotta Manabu *(Gen Mgr)*

Kobe Steel USA Inc. (1)
19575 Victor Pkwy Ste 250, Livonia, MI 48152
Tel.: (734) 462-7757
Web Site: http://www.kobelco.co.jp
Aluminum Extruded Product Mfr
N.A.I.C.S.: 333517

Subsidiary (Domestic):

Kobe Steel International (USA) Inc. (2)
535 Madison Ave Fl 5, New York, NY 10022 (100%)
Tel.: (212) 751-9400

INTERNATIONAL PUBLIC

Web Site: http://www.kobelco.co.jp
Sales Range: $25-49.9 Million
Emp.: 8
Financial Services
N.A.I.C.S.: 541611
Anoush Mets *(Mgr-HR)*

Midrex Technologies Inc. (2)
3735 Glen Lake Dr Ste 400, Charlotte, NC 28208 (100%)
Tel.: (704) 373-1600
Web Site: https://www.midrex.com
Sales Range: $25-49.9 Million
Research, Development & Sales of the Midrex Process & Reduction Process
N.A.I.C.S.: 541330
Stephen Montague *(Pres & CEO)*

Kobe Steel USA, Inc. - New York Office (1)
535 Madison Ave, New York, NY 10022-4212
Tel.: (212) 751-9400
Sales Range: $25-49.9 Million
Emp.: 8
Import of Iron & Steel, Steel Castings & Forgings, Welding Electrodes, Nonferrous Metals, Cutting Tools, Construction Machinery, Industrial & Chemical Machinery, Plant Engineering
N.A.I.C.S.: 541611

Kobe Steel, Ltd. - Beijing (1)
Unit 1005 Bldg A The Lucky Tower No 3 N Dongsanhuan Road, Chaoyang District, Beijing, 100027, China
Tel.: (86) 1064618491
Web Site: http://www.kobelco.co.jp
Sales Range: $25-49.9 Million
Emp.: 5
Steel Mfrs
N.A.I.C.S.: 331318
Hotta Manabu *(Pres)*

Kobe Steel, Ltd. - CHOFU WORKS (1)
14-1 Chofu Minatomachi, Shimonoseki, 752-0953, Yamaguchi, Japan
Tel.: (81) 83 246 1211
Web Site: http://www.kobelco.co.jp
Aluminium & Copper Products Mfr
N.A.I.C.S.: 332999

Kobe Steel, Ltd. - FUJISAWA WORKS (1)
100-1 Miyamae, Fujisawa, 251-8551, Kanagawa, Japan
Tel.: (81) 466 20 3111
Welding Services
N.A.I.C.S.: 331491
Matsushita Yukinobu *(Gen Mgr)*

Kobe Steel, Ltd. - FUKUCHIYAMA PLANT (1)
3-36 Osadanocho, Fukuchiyama, 620-0853, Kyoto, Japan
Tel.: (81) 773 27 2131
Web Site: http://www.kobelco.co.jp
Rolled Steel Mfr
N.A.I.C.S.: 331221

Kobe Steel, Ltd. - HARIMA PLANT (1)
41 Niijima Harimacho, Kako-gun, Hyogo, 675-0155, Japan
Tel.: (81) 79 436 2101
Industrial Machinery Mfr
N.A.I.C.S.: 333248

Kobe Steel, Ltd. - IBARAKI PLANT (1)
2-19 Higashi-Unobecho, Ibaraki, 567-0879, Osaka, Japan
Tel.: (81) 72 621 2111
Rolled Steel Mfr
N.A.I.C.S.: 331221
T. Nakamura *(Mgr-Procurement)*

Kobe Steel, Ltd. - Inabe Plant (1)
1100 Daiancho Umedo, Inabe, Mie, Japan
Tel.: (81) 594 77 0330
Aluminium & Copper Products Mfr
N.A.I.C.S.: 332999

Kobe Steel, Ltd. - KAKOGAWA WORKS (1)
1 Kanazawacho, Kakogawa, 675-0137, Hyogo, Japan
Tel.: (81) 79 436 1111
Rolled Steel Mfr

AND PRIVATE COMPANIES — KOBE STEEL, LTD.

N.A.I.C.S.: 331221

Kobe Steel, Ltd. - KOBE WORKS (1)
2 Nadahama Higashicho, Nada-ku, Kobe, 657-0863, Hyogo, Japan
Tel.: (81) 788828030
Web Site: http://www.kobelco.co.jp
Rolled Steel Mfr
N.A.I.C.S.: 331221

Kobe Steel, Ltd. - MOKA PLANT (1)
15 Kinugaoka, Moka, 321-4367, Tochigi, Japan
Tel.: (81) 285 82 4111
Web Site: http://www.kobelco.co.jp
Aluminium & Copper Products Mfr
N.A.I.C.S.: 332999

Kobe Steel, Ltd. - SAIJO PLANT (1)
6400-1 Saijocho Misonou, Higashi-hiroshima, 739-0024, Hiroshima, Japan
Tel.: (81) 82 423 3311
Emp.: 100
Welding Material Mfr
N.A.I.C.S.: 333992
Hiroshi Ikegami *(Branch Mgr)*

Kobe Steel, Ltd. - TAKASAGO WORKS (1)
3-1 Araicho Shinhama 2 chome, Takasago, 676-8670, Hyogo, Japan
Tel.: (81) 79 445 7111
Industrial Machinery Mfr
N.A.I.C.S.: 333248

Kobe Welding of Korea Co., Ltd. (1)
21 14 Palyong Dong, Changwon, Kyung-nam, Korea (South)
Tel.: (82) 552926886
Web Site: http://www.kobe.co.kr
Mfr & Sale of Flux-Cored Wire for Welding Mild Steels
N.A.I.C.S.: 333992

Kobe Wire Products (Foshan) Co., Ltd. (1)
No 1 Fenghuang Road Core Area Shengtai Road, Danzao Town Nanhai District, Foshan, 528216, Guangdong, China
Tel.: (86) 75785409380
CHQ Wire Mfr & Distr
N.A.I.C.S.: 331222

Kobelco Advanced Lube-system Asia Co., Ltd. (1)
13 Hwajeonsandan 6-ro 90beon-gil, Gangseo-gu, Busan, 46738, Korea (South)
Tel.: (82) 512050794
Industrial Machinery Mfr & Distr
N.A.I.C.S.: 333248

Kobelco Aluminum Products & Extrusions Inc. (1)
18 Kobe Way, Bowling Green, KY 42103
Tel.: (270) 938-6440
Web Site: https://www.kobelcoaluminum.com
Aluminium Product Distr
N.A.I.C.S.: 423510

Kobelco Angang Auto Steel Co., Ltd. (1)
Angang Steel Work, West District, Anshan, 114021, Liaoning, China
Tel.: (86) 4126757686
Automotive Cold-Rolled Mfr & Distr
N.A.I.C.S.: 331221

Kobelco Automotive Aluminum Rolled Products (China) Co., Ltd. (1)
No 17 2nd Shengda Branch Road Tianjin Xiqing Economic Development Area, Tianjin, 300383, China
Tel.: (86) 2283986550
Aluminum Sheet Mfr & Distr
N.A.I.C.S.: 331315

Kobelco Business Partners Co., Ltd. (1)
2-2-4 Wakinohamakaigan-dori, Chuo-ku, Kobe, 651-0073, Hyogo, Japan (100%)
Tel.: (81) 782615555
Web Site: https://www.kobelco-kbp.jp
Human Resource Development Consulting Services
N.A.I.C.S.: 541612
Hiroshi Iwasaki *(Pres)*

Kobelco CH Wire Mexicana, S.A. de C.V. (1)
Circuito Santa Fe No 179 Col Puerto Interior, 36275, Silao, Guanajuato, Mexico
Tel.: (52) 4721352900
CHQ Wire Mfr & Distr
N.A.I.C.S.: 331222

Kobelco Compressors & Machinery Philippines Corporation (1)
19th Floor Panorama Tower 34th Street Corner Lane A, Bonifacio Global City Metro Manila, Taguig, Philippines
Tel.: (63) 288978736
Web Site: http://www.kobelco.com.ph
Compressor Mfr
N.A.I.C.S.: 333912

Kobelco Compressors (Cambodia) Co., Ltd. (1)
G22 St Goody Sangkat Teok Thla, Khan Sen Sok, Phnom Penh, Cambodia
Tel.: (855) 23882521
Engineeering Services
N.A.I.C.S.: 541330

Kobelco Compressors (Shanghai) Corporation (1)
Block B 1st Floor Building A No 1068 Tianshan West Road, Changning District, Shanghai, 200335, China
Tel.: (86) 2139966392
Standard Compressor Mfr
N.A.I.C.S.: 333912

Kobelco Compressors (Thailand) Ltd. (1)
2170 Bangkok tower Room No 1102 11th Floor New Petchburi Road, Bangkapi HuayKwang, Bangkok, 10310, Thailand
Tel.: (66) 230802113
Web Site: https://www.kobelcocompressors.co.th
Emp.: 11
Compressor Mfr
N.A.I.C.S.: 333912

Kobelco Compressors (Vietnam) Ltd. (1)
43-45 Lam Ha Street, Bo De Ward Long Bien District, Hanoi, Vietnam
Tel.: (84) 2439447781
Compressor Mfr
N.A.I.C.S.: 333912

Kobelco Compressors America, Inc. (1)
1415 Louisiana St Ste 4111, Houston, TX 77002
Tel.: (713) 655-0015
Web Site: http://www.kobelcocompressors.com
Emp.: 15
Screw Compressors & Parts Mfr
N.A.I.C.S.: 333912

Kobelco Compressors Corporation (1)
1-6-4 Osaki New Osaki Kogyo Building 16F, Shinagawa-ku, Tokyo, 141-0032, Japan
Tel.: (81) 354960011
Web Site: http://www.kobelco-comp.co.jp
Compressor Parts Distr
N.A.I.C.S.: 423830

Kobelco Compressors India Pvt. Ltd. (1)
249 G 3rd Floor AIHP Tower Udyog Vihar Phase IV, Near India Bulls Building, Gurgaon, 122015, Haryana, India
Tel.: (91) 1244380750
Steel Casting & Forging Mfr
N.A.I.C.S.: 332111

Kobelco Compressors Malaysia Sdn. Bhd. (1)
No 9 Jalan Sepadu 25/123A Seksyen 25, 40400, Shah Alam, Selangor, Malaysia
Tel.: (60) 355252757
Steel Casting & Forging Mfr
N.A.I.C.S.: 332111

Kobelco Compressors Manufacturing (Shanghai) Corporation (1)
1515 Xing Rong Road, Jiading Industrial District, Shanghai, 201815, China
Tel.: (86) 2139966381
Web Site: http://www.kobelco.co.jp
Standard Compressor Mfr & Distr
N.A.I.C.S.: 333912

Kobelco Construction Equipment India Pvt. Ltd. (1)
H-200 Sector 63, Distt Gautam Budh Nagar, Noida, 201307, Uttar Pradesh, India
Tel.: (91) 1204079900
Construction Machinery Mfr & Distr
N.A.I.C.S.: 333120

Kobelco Construction Machinery (China) Co., Ltd. (1)
699 Rd 4 south Economic Development Zone, Longquanyi District, Chengdu, 610100, Sichuan, China
Tel.: (86) 2888412000
Web Site: http://www.kobelco-jianji.com
Construction Equipment Leasing Services
N.A.I.C.S.: 532412

Kobelco Construction Machinery Australia Pty. Ltd. (1)
Unit 1 1-5 Interchange Drive, Eastern Creek, 2766, NSW, Australia
Tel.: (61) 288634900
Construction Machinery Distr
N.A.I.C.S.: 423810

Kobelco Construction Machinery Co., Ltd. (1)
Oval Court Ohsaki Mark West 17-1 Higashi-Gotanda 2 Chome, Shinagawa-ku, Tokyo, 141-8626, Japan
Tel.: (81) 357892111
Web Site: http://www.kobelco-kenki.co.jp
Sales Range: $200-249.9 Million
Emp.: 915
Construction Machinery Mfr & Whslr
N.A.I.C.S.: 333120
Kazuhide Naraki *(Pres & CEO)*

Kobelco Construction Machinery Engineering Co., Ltd. (1)
2-1 Itsukaichikou 2-chome, Saeki-ku, Hiroshima, 731-5161, Japan
Tel.: (81) 829435327
Construction Machinery Mfr
N.A.I.C.S.: 333120

Kobelco Construction Machinery Europe B.V. (1)
Veluwezoom 15, 1327 AE, Almere, Netherlands
Tel.: (31) 36 202 0300
Web Site: https://www.kobelco-europe.com
Crawler Crane Distr
N.A.I.C.S.: 423810
Makato Kato *(Mng Dir & Dir-Sls & Field Mktg)*

Kobelco Construction Machinery International Trading Co., Ltd. (1)
17 Futamatashinmachi, Ichikawa, 272-0002, Chiba, Japan
Tel.: (81) 47 327 5505
Web Site: https://www.kobelco.co.jp
Construction Equipment Distr
N.A.I.C.S.: 423810
Kazuhisa Kakinaga *(Pres)*

Kobelco Construction Machinery Japan Co., Ltd. (1)
17 Futamatashinmachi, Ichikawa, 272-0002, Chiba, Japan
Tel.: (81) 473287111
Construction Machinery Mfr
N.A.I.C.S.: 333120

Kobelco Construction Machinery Malaysia Sdn. Bhd. (1)
Lot pt 556 Persiaran Sabak Bernam Seksyen 26, 40400, Shah Alam, Selangor, Malaysia
Tel.: (60) 351927533
Construction Machinery Distr
N.A.I.C.S.: 423810
Yujiro Suzuki *(Mng Dir)*

Kobelco Construction Machinery Middle East & Africa FZCO. (1)
6WA-724 Dubai Airport Free Zone, PO Box 371682, Dubai, United Arab Emirates
Tel.: (971) 4 298 2020
Web Site: https://www.kobelco-mea.com
Construction Machinery Distr
N.A.I.C.S.: 423810
John Boyd *(Mng Dir)*

Kobelco Construction Machinery Southeast Asia Co., Ltd. (1)
571 RSU Tower 9th Floor Unit 903 Sukhumvit Soi 31 Sukhumvit Road, Bangkok, 10110, Thailand
Tel.: (66) 23995900
Construction Machinery Mfr & Distr
N.A.I.C.S.: 333120

Kobelco Construction Machinery U.S.A. Inc. (1)
22370 Merchants Way, Katy, TX 77449
Tel.: (281) 888-4300
Web Site: http://www.kcmu-cranes.com
Crawler Crane Mfr
N.A.I.C.S.: 333923
Brad Hargrave *(Mgr-District Bus)*

Kobelco Eco-Solutions Co., Ltd. (1)
4-78 1-chome Wakinohama-cho, Chuo-ku, Kobe, 651-0072, Japan (100%)
Tel.: (81) 78 232 8018
Web Site: https://www.kobelco-eco.co.jp
Emp.: 1,366
Industrial Equipment Mfr
N.A.I.C.S.: 221320
Tsuyoshi Kasuya *(Pres)*

Kobelco Eco-solutions Vietnam Co., Ltd. (1)
31st Floor Pearl Plaza 561A Dien Bien Phu Street, Ward 25 Dist Binh Thanh, Ho Chi Minh City, Vietnam
Tel.: (84) 2838991355
Sewage Treatment Services
N.A.I.C.S.: 221320

Kobelco Engineered Construction Materials Co., Ltd. (1)
46 Marushima-cho, Amagasaki, 660-0086, Hyogo, Japan
Tel.: (81) 664182621
Web Site: http://www.shinkokenzai.co.jp
Construction Materials Mfr
N.A.I.C.S.: 333120
Kan Kudo *(Pres)*

Kobelco Europe GmbH (1)
Luitpoldstrasse 3, 80335, Munich, Germany
Tel.: (49) 8954344780
Steel Product Mfr & Distr
N.A.I.C.S.: 332999

Kobelco Industrial Machinery India Pvt. Ltd. (1)
No 121 Paranthur Road, Karai Village, Kanchipuram, 631552, Tami Nadu, India
Tel.: (91) 446 720 2330
Web Site: https://www.kimi.co.in
Industrial Machinery Mfr
N.A.I.C.S.: 333248
Praveen Kumar S. *(Mgr-HR)*

Kobelco International (S) Co., Pte. Ltd. (1)
30 Pioneer Crescent 03-15 West Park Biz-Central, Singapore, 628560, Singapore
Tel.: (65) 6 268 1308
Web Site: https://www.kobelco-cranes.com
Construction Machinery Distr
N.A.I.C.S.: 423810
Shinsuke Izumi *(Mng Dir)*

Kobelco Logistics (Shanghai) Ltd. (1)
Gopher Center Rm 801 757 Mengzi Road, Huangpu, Shanghai, 200023, China
Tel.: (86) 2164730982
Emp.: 9
Shipping Logistics Services
N.A.I.C.S.: 541614
Tatsuo Sota *(Chm)*

Kobelco Logistics India Private Limited (1)
New No 105 Sreela Terrace Unit No 7 Second Floor First Main Road, Gandhi Nagar Adyar, Chennai, 600020, India
Tel.: (91) 4442040700
Logistic Services
N.A.I.C.S.: 541614

Kobelco MIG Wire (Thailand) Co., Ltd. (1)
10th FL Sathorn Thani II building 92/23 North Sathorn Rd, Silom Bangrak, Bangkok, 10500, Thailand
Tel.: (66) 26368650
Solid Wire Mfr
N.A.I.C.S.: 331221

Kobelco Machinery Middle East FZE. (1)
Dubai Airport Free Zone Office No 6EA-605, Dubai, United Arab Emirates

KOBE STEEL, LTD.

Kobe Steel, Ltd.—(Continued)
Tel.: (971) 42384009
Compressor Distr
N.A.I.C.S.: 423830

Kobelco Machinery Philippines Inc. (1)
Unit 1 15th Floor 2251 IT Hub Chino Roces Avenue, Barangay Bangkal, Makati, 1223, Philippines
Tel.: (63) 28161779
Engineeering Services
N.A.I.C.S.: 541330

Kobelco Machinery System Engineering Qingdao Co., Ltd. (1)
Room 615 Jingyuan Office Tower 308 Xingyang Road, Chengyang, Qingdao, China
Tel.: (86) 53289081980
Rubber & Plastic Goods Mfr
N.A.I.C.S.: 326299

Kobelco Machinery do Brazil Serviços Empresariais Ltda. (1)
Regus Top Center Paulista Avenida Paulista 854 10th Andar, Sao Paulo, 01310-100, SP, Brazil
Tel.: (55) 1121860265
Compressor Distr
N.A.I.C.S.: 423830

Kobelco Millcon Steel Co., Ltd. (1)
119 Moo 1 Banlang-Natakhwan Road Banlang, Muang Rayong, Rayong, 21000, Thailand
Tel.: (66) 38016591
Automotive Cold-Rolled Mfr & Distr
N.A.I.C.S.: 331221

Kobelco Power Kobe Inc. (1)
Nadahamahigashicho 2, Nada-ku, Kobe, 657-0845, Hyogo, Japan
Tel.: (81) 788828036
Electricity Supply Services
N.A.I.C.S.: 221122

Kobelco Power Moka Inc. (1)
12-1 Kinugaoka 1-chome, Moka, 321-4367, Tochigi, Japan
Tel.: (81) 285819981
Electricity Supply Services
N.A.I.C.S.: 221122

Kobelco Precision Parts (Suzhou) Co., Ltd. (1)
No 12 Factory Export Procesing Zone No 666 Jianlin Road, Sub-Industrial Park Suzhou Hi-tech New District, Jiangsu, 215151, China
Tel.: (86) 51281878277
Conveying Equipment Mfr
N.A.I.C.S.: 333922

Kobelco Professional Service Co., Ltd. (1)
4-2-7 Iwaya-Nakamachi, Nada-ku, Kobe, 657-0845, Japan
Tel.: (81) 78 261 7300
Web Site: https://www.kobelco-kpsc.com
Emp.: 100
Hazardous Waste Management Services
N.A.I.C.S.: 562211
Michiaki Kanamaru *(Pres)*

Kobelco Shinwa Co., Ltd. (1)
597 Yagi Okubo-cho, Akashi, 674-0063, Japan
Tel.: (81) 789368513
Web Site: http://www.kobelcoshinwa.com
Emp.: 225
Packing & Crating Services
N.A.I.C.S.: 488991

Kobelco South East Asia Ltd. (1)
17th Floor Sathorn Thani Tower II 92/49 North Sathorn Road, Khwaeng Silom Khet Bangrak, Bangkok, 10500, Thailand
Tel.: (66) 26368971
Construction Machinery Mfr
N.A.I.C.S.: 333120

Kobelco Stewart Bolling, Inc. (1)
1600 Terex Rd, Hudson, OH 44236-4070
Tel.: (330) 655-3111
Web Site: http://www.ksbiusa.com
Sales Range: $25-49.9 Million
Emp.: 100
Rubber & Plastic Processing Machinery Mfr & Distr

Kobelco Trading (Shanghai) Co., Ltd. (1)
Suite 802 Gopher Center No 757 Mengzi Road, Huangpu District, Shanghai, 200023, China
Tel.: (86) 2153966464
Web Site: http://www.kobelcotrading.com
Steel Products Whslr
N.A.I.C.S.: 423510
Yoshihisa Okamoto *(Chm & CEO)*

Kobelco Training Services Co., Ltd. (1)
88-11 Nishiminatomachi, Kokurakita-Ku, Kitakyushu, 803-0801, Fukuoka, Japan
Tel.: (81) 120505889
Web Site: http://www.kobelco-kyoshu.com
Construction Safety Training Services
N.A.I.C.S.: 611519

Kobelco Welding (Malaysia) Sdn. Bhd. (1)
Plot 502 Jalan Perusahaan Baru, Kawasan Perusahaan, 13600, Perai, Malaysia
Tel.: (60) 43905792
Covered Electrode Mfr & Distr
N.A.I.C.S.: 333992

Kobelco Welding Asia Pacific Pte. Ltd. (1)
No 20 Pandan Avenue, Jurong, Singapore, 609387, Singapore (62%)
Tel.: (65) 62682711
Web Site: http://www.kobewelding.com
Emp.: 55
Mfr & Sale of Welding Electrodes
N.A.I.C.S.: 333992

Kobelco Welding India Pvt. Ltd. (1)
Sewa Corporate Park Unit No 205 2nd Floor Corporate Suites Mg Road, Gurgaon, 122003, Haryana, India
Tel.: (91) 1244010063
Web Site: http://www.kobelcowelding.in
Welding Product Mfr & Distr
N.A.I.C.S.: 333992

Kobelco Welding Solution Co., Ltd. (1)
5-9-12 North Shinigawa, Shinigawa, Tokyo, 141-8688, Japan
Tel.: (81) 357395315
Web Site: http://www.kobelco.co.jp
Welding Consumables & Equipment Distr
N.A.I.C.S.: 423830

Kobelco Welding TechnoSolutions Co., Ltd. (1)
100-1 Miyamae, Fujisawa, 251-8551, Japan
Tel.: (81) 466203222
Web Site: https://www.kobelco-kwts.co.jp
Emp.: 180
Welding Testing Services
N.A.I.C.S.: 541380

Kobelco Welding of America Inc. (1)
4755 Alpine Ste 250, Stafford, TX 77477 (100%)
Tel.: (281) 240-5600
Web Site: http://www.kobelcowelding.com
Sales Range: $25-49.9 Million
Emp.: 11
Welding Consumables Marketer
N.A.I.C.S.: 423510

Kobelco Welding of Europe B.V. (1)
Eisterweg 8, 6422 PN, Heerlen, Netherlands (49.2%)
Tel.: (31) 45 547 1111
Web Site: https://www.kobelcowelding.nl
Sales Range: $25-49.9 Million
Emp.: 100
Mfr & Sale of Flux-Cored Wire for Stainless Steel
N.A.I.C.S.: 333992
Hirohisa Watanabe *(Mng Dir)*

Kobelco Welding of Korea Co., Ltd. (1)
97 Charyongdanji-ro, Uichang-gu, Changwon, 51399, Gyeongnam, Korea (South)
Tel.: (82) 552926886
Flux-Cored Wire Mfr & Distr
N.A.I.C.S.: 331222

Kobelco Welding of Qingdao Co., Ltd. (1)
No 158 Li Shan Road, Huangdao District, Qingdao, 266426, Shandong, China
Tel.: (86) 53280985005
Flux-Cored Wire Mfr & Distr
N.A.I.C.S.: 331222

Kobelco Welding of Shanghai Co., Ltd. (1)
3F B District Building 7 No 1010 Kai Xuan Road, Shanghai, 200052, China
Tel.: (86) 2161917850
Welding Material Distr
N.A.I.C.S.: 423840

Kobelco Welding of Tangshan Co., Ltd. (1)
196 Huoju Road Tangshan New and Hi-Tech Development Zone, Tangshan, 063020, Hebei, China
Tel.: (86) 3153852805
Welding Wire Mfr & Distr
N.A.I.C.S.: 333992

Mahajak Kyodo Co., Ltd. (1)
67/16 Moo 5 Chuam Samphan Road Nongjak, Kokfad, Bangkok, 10530, Thailand
Tel.: (66) 29881493
Steel Bar Mfr & Distr
N.A.I.C.S.: 331221

Midrex International B.V. (1)
Bahnhof Strasse 94, CH-8001, Zurich, Switzerland (100%)
Tel.: (41) 12103377
Marketer of Direct Reduction Process
N.A.I.C.S.: 541715

Midrex Metallurgy Technology Services (Shanghai) Ltd. (1)
Room 504 Shanghai Centre West Office Tower No 1376 West Nanjing Road, Shanghai, 200040, China
Tel.: (86) 2160101294
Metal Mining Services
N.A.I.C.S.: 213114

Midrex Technologies Gulf Services FZCO (1)
Office No 5EA 804 Building 5EA Dubai Airport Free Zone, Dubai, United Arab Emirates
Tel.: (971) 42556383
Steel Products Mfr
N.A.I.C.S.: 332999

Midrex Technologies India Pvt. Ltd. (1)
Global Foyer Golf Course Road, Gurgaon, 122002, Haryana, India
Tel.: (91) 1244908712
Metal Mining Services
N.A.I.C.S.: 213114

Midrex UK, Ltd. (1)
39 Eastcheap, London, EC3M 1DT, United Kingdom
Tel.: (44) 2070891520
Financial Consulting Services
N.A.I.C.S.: 541611

Nippon Koshuha Steel Co., Ltd. (1)
8F TMM Building 1-10-5 Iwamoto-cho, Chiyoda-ku, Tokyo, 101-0032, Japan (36%)
Tel.: (81) 356876023
Web Site: http://www.koshuha.co.jp
Sales Range: $100-124.9 Million
Emp.: 508
Produces Bearing Steel & Tool Steel
N.A.I.C.S.: 331221
Masahiro Kawase *(Co-Pres)*

PRO-TEC Coating Company, Inc. (1)
5000 PRO-TEC Pkwy, Leipsic, OH 45856 (50%)
Tel.: (419) 943-1100
Web Site: http://www.proteccoating.com
Sales Range: $100-124.9 Million
Emp.: 225
Coating of Steel Coils; Joint Venture Between Kobe Steel & U.S. Steel
N.A.I.C.S.: 332812
Richard E. Veitch *(Pres)*

PT. Daya Kobelco Construction Machinery Indonesia (1)
Jl Halmahera Blok DD-10 MM2100 Danau Indah Kabupaten, Kawasan Industri Cikarang Barat, Bekasi, 17530, Jawa Barat, Indonesia
Tel.: (62) 2122143080
Construction Machinery Distr
N.A.I.C.S.: 423810

PT. Kobelindo Compressors (1)
Jln Raya Tanjung Barat No 85, Kel Tanjung Barat Kec Jagakarsa, Jakarta Selatan, 12530, Indonesia
Tel.: (62) 21 782 7002
Web Site: http://www.kobelindo.co.id
Compressor Mfr
N.A.I.C.S.: 333912
Rahadian Mahendra *(Pres)*

Quintus Technologies Co., Ltd. (1)
12 F Sail Tower 266 Hankou Road, Huangpu, Shanghai, 200001, China
Tel.: (86) 2152340233
Sheet Metal Mfr
N.A.I.C.S.: 332322

Ricon Private Limited (1)
12 Tuas Drive 2, Singapore, 638646, Singapore
Tel.: (65) 6 862 2401
Web Site: https://www.ricon.com.sg
Industrial Equipment Distr
N.A.I.C.S.: 423830
Arun Kumar Dhandapani *(Engr-Svc)*

SUZHOU KOBE COPPER TECHNOLOGY CO., LTD. (1)
No 50 Pingsheng Road 4 District of Suzhou Industrial Park, Suzhou, 215126, Jiangsu, China
Tel.: (86) 512 8717 1555
Sales Range: $25-49.9 Million
Emp.: 30
Copper Sheets Distr
N.A.I.C.S.: 423510

Sakai Steel Sheets Works, Ltd. (1)
15 Ishizu Nishimachi, Nishi-ku, Sakai, 592-8332, Japan
Tel.: (81) 722413464
Web Site: http://www.sakaisteelsheets.co.jp
Steel Sheet Distr
N.A.I.C.S.: 423510

Sanwa Tekko Co., Ltd. (1)
7 Kanaoka, Ama-gun, Tobishima, 490-1445, Aichi, Japan
Tel.: (81) 567551700
Web Site: https://www.sanwatekko.co.jp
Emp.: 72
Steel Products Mfr
N.A.I.C.S.: 332999

Shanghai Shinko Computer Technology Co., Ltd. (1)
Baishu Bldg 22F 1230 Zhongshan Road No 1, Shanghai, 200437, China (51%)
Tel.: (86) 2165447420
Sales Range: $25-49.9 Million
Emp.: 30
Computer Software Products & Systems Developer & Sales
N.A.I.C.S.: 541512

Shanghai Shinsho Trading Co., Ltd. (1)
Room 1821 Tomson International Trade Building No 1 Ji Long Road, Wai Gaoqiao Free Trade Zone, Shanghai, China
Tel.: (86) 2153966464
Steel Product Distr
N.A.I.C.S.: 423510

Shinko Actec Co., Ltd. (1)
11th Floor of Shinanobashi Mitsui Building 1-11-7 Utsubohonmachi, Nishi-ku, Osaka, 550-0004, Japan
Tel.: (81) 642566140
Web Site: http://www.shinko-actec.co.jp
Deodorizing Filter Mfr & Distr
N.A.I.C.S.: 333413

Shinko Airtech, Ltd. (1)
3-16 Haradadori 2-chome, Nada-ku, Kobe, 657-0837, Hyogo, Japan
Tel.: (81) 782616550
Web Site: http://www.shinko-airtech.com
Industrial Gas Distr
N.A.I.C.S.: 457210

Shinko Aluminum Wire Co., Ltd. (1)
2153-1 Hishiki 2-chome, Sakai, 593-8315, Osaka, Japan

AND PRIVATE COMPANIES

Tel.: (81) 722714572
Aluminum Alloy Wire Mfr
N.A.I.C.S.: 331491

Shinko Bolt, Ltd. (1)
17 Futamatashinmachi, Ichikawa, 272-0002, Chiba, Japan
Tel.: (81) 47 328 6521
Web Site: https://www.shinkobolt.co.jp
Emp.: 72
Screw Bolt Mfr & Distr
N.A.I.C.S.: 332722
Hiroyuki Sakata *(Pres & CEO)*

Shinko Engineering & Maintenance Co., Ltd. (1)
4-5-22 Iwaya Kitamachi, Nada-ku, Kobe, Hyogo, Japan
Tel.: (81) 788032901
Web Site: http://www.shinkoen-m.jp
Construction Machinery Mfr
N.A.I.C.S.: 333120

Shinko Engineering Co., Ltd. (1)
1682-2 Motoima-cho, Ogaki, 503-8505, Gifu, Japan
Tel.: (81) 5 8489 3121
Web Site: http://www.shinko-zoki.co.jp
Power Systems, Power Transmission & Testing Equipment Mfr
N.A.I.C.S.: 333613
Takaaki Hayata *(Pres)*

Shinko Industrial Co., Ltd. (1)
5-7-21 Ohzu, Minami-ku, Hiroshima, 732-0802, Japan
Tel.: (81) 825081000
Web Site: https://www.shinkohir.co.jp
Emp.: 506
Pump & Steam Turbine Mfr
N.A.I.C.S.: 333611

Shinko Inspection & Service Co., Ltd. (1)
2-3-1 Shinhama, Arai-cho, Takasago, 676-8670, Hyogo, Japan
Tel.: (81) 794459046
Web Site: http://www.sisco.kobelco.com
Emp.: 350
General Testing & Inspection Services
N.A.I.C.S.: 541380

Shinko Kanmon Sohgo Service, Ltd. (1)
14-1 Choufu Minatomachi, Shimonoseki, 752-0953, Yamaguchi, Japan
Tel.: (81) 832461268
Steel Products Mfr
N.A.I.C.S.: 332999

Shinko Kohan Kako, Ltd. (1)
17 Futamatashinmachi, Ichikawa, 272-0002, Chiba, Japan
Tel.: (81) 7327411
Steel Products Mfr
N.A.I.C.S.: 332999

Shinko Leadmikk Co., Ltd. (1)
2-2-1 Komorie, Moji-ku, Kitakyushu, 800-0007, Fukuoka, Japan
Tel.: (81) 933811337
Web Site: https://www.shinko-leadmikk.co.jp
Emp.: 200
Semiconductor Lead Frame Mfr & Distr
N.A.I.C.S.: 334413

Shinko Metal Products Co., Ltd. (1)
2-1 Komorie 2-chome, Moji-ku, Kitakyushu, 800-0007, Japan
Tel.: (81) 933811331
Web Site: http://www.shinkometal.co.jp
Emp.: 170
Metal Products Mfr
N.A.I.C.S.: 332999

Shinko Moka Sohgo Service Ltd. (1)
15 Kinugaoka, Moka, 321-4367, Tochigi, Japan
Tel.: (81) 285828860
Landscaping Services
N.A.I.C.S.: 561790

Shinko Research Co., Ltd. (1)
5-9-11 Kitashinagawa, Shinagawa-ku, Tokyo, 141-0001, Japan
Tel.: (81) 334408140
Web Site: http://www.src-kobelco.co.jp
Emp.: 78
Research Laboratory Services
N.A.I.C.S.: 541380

Shinko Slag Products Co., Ltd. (1)
1-5-1 Wakinohamakaigan Dori 6th Floor IHD Center, Chuo-ku, Kobe, 651-0073, Hyogo, Japan
Tel.: (81) 782615656
Web Site: http://www.shinko-slag.co.jp
Steel Products Mfr
N.A.I.C.S.: 332999

Shinko Techno Engineering Co., Ltd. (1)
2-3-1 Shinhama Takasago Machinery Office 6th Floor, Arai-cho, Takasago, 676-8670, Hyogo, Japan
Tel.: (81) 794434131
Web Site: http://www.s-techno.co.jp
Engineeering Services
N.A.I.C.S.: 541330

Shinko-North Co., Ltd. (1)
1758-1 Mukaihara, Kasumigaura, 315-8523, Ibaraki, Japan
Tel.: (81) 299594111
Web Site: https://www.shinkonorth.co.jp
Aluminum Product Mfr & Distr
N.A.I.C.S.: 331315

Shinsho Corporation (1)
Yodoyabashi Square 6-18 Kitahama 2-chome, Chuo-ku, Osaka, 541-8557, Japan (41%)
Tel.: (81) 662067010
Web Site: http://www.shinsho.co.jp
Rev.: $3,909,358,910
Assets: $2,620,256,880
Liabilities: $2,042,014,080
Net Worth: $578,242,800
Earnings: $60,223,710
Emp.: 1,443
Fiscal Year-end: 03/31/2024
Steel Trader
N.A.I.C.S.: 331110
Satoshi Muta *(Exec Officer-Gen Affairs Dept, Credit & Legal Dept)*

Subsidiary (Domestic):

Matsubo Corporation (2)
33 Mori Bldg 4F 3-8-21 Toranomon, Minato-ku, Tokyo, 105-0001, Japan
Tel.: (81) 35 472 1711
Web Site: https://www.matsubo.co.jp
Sales Range: $50-74.9 Million
Emp.: 137
Industrial Machinery & Equipment Sales
N.A.I.C.S.: 423830
Shigetaka Takatsu *(Pres & CEO)*

Subsidiary (Non-US):

Matsubo GmbH (3)
Berliner Allee 55, 40212, Dusseldorf, Germany (100%)
Tel.: (49) 211358001
Web Site: http://www.matsubo.co.jp
Sales Range: Less than $1 Million
Emp.: 1
N.A.I.C.S.: 333310

Subsidiary (Domestic):

NI Welding Corporation (2)
4-6-17 Nishinakajima, Yodogawa-ku, Osaka, 532-0011, Japan (80%)
Tel.: (81) 6 6302 7701
Web Site: http://www.niwel.co.jp
Emp.: 47
Welding Material Distr
N.A.I.C.S.: 423830
Kikuya Himukai *(Pres)*

Subsidiary (US):

Shinsho American Corporation (2)
26200 Town Ctr Dr Ste 160, Novi, MI 48375
Tel.: (248) 675-0058
Web Site: http://www.shinsho.com
Sales Range: $150-199.9 Million
Emp.: 20
Importer of Iron & Steel
N.A.I.C.S.: 423510
Shutoku Botha *(Pres)*

Shinsho Osaka Seiko (Nangtong) Corporation (1)
No1 Qing Feng Road, Sutong Science and Technology Industrial Park, Nantong, 226017, Jiangsu, China
Tel.: (86) 51389191055
Steel Product Distr
N.A.I.C.S.: 423510

Singapore Kobe Pte. Ltd. (1)
No 3 Sixth Lok Yang Road, Jurong Industrial Estate, Singapore, 628101, Singapore (100%)
Tel.: (65) 62610788
Web Site: https://www.kobelcoskpl.com
Emp.: 300
Mfr & Sale of Copper Tubes & Brass Coils, Copper Sheet Plating
N.A.I.C.S.: 331420

Sumirin Care Life Co., Ltd. (1)
1-5-1 Wakinohamakaigan-dori 3rd Floor, International Health Development Center Chuo-ku, Kobe, 651-0073, Hyogo, Japan
Tel.: (81) 782616665
Web Site: https://www.s-carelife.co.jp
Emp.: 714
Home Care Services
N.A.I.C.S.: 621610

Suzhou Shinko-Shoji Material Co., Ltd. (1)
No 46 Pingsheng Road, Suzhou Industrial Zone IV, Jiangsu, China
Tel.: (86) 5126 287 1233
Web Site: https://www.shinsho-al.cn
Emp.: 90
Aluminum Sheet Mfr
N.A.I.C.S.: 331315
Noriaki Sunada *(CEO)*

Taseto Co., Ltd. (1)
2-4-15 Shin-yokohama Ota Kosan Building Shin-yokohama 4th Floor, Kohoku-ku, Yokohama, 222-0033, Kanagawa, Japan
Tel.: (81) 45 624 8913
Web Site: https://www.taseto.com
Welding Equipment Mfr
N.A.I.C.S.: 333992
Toshihiko Nakano *(Pres)*

Thai Escorp Ltd. (1)
1126/2 Vanit Bldg II Room 1801-2 18th Floor New Phetchaburi Road, Ratchathewi Makkasan, Bangkok, 10400, Thailand
Tel.: (66) 2 254 7645
Web Site: https://www.thaiescorp.co.th
Emp.: 70
Steel Product Distr
N.A.I.C.S.: 423510
Tetsuya Nakamura *(Pres)*

Thai Kobe Welding Co., Ltd. (1)
10th Fl Sathorn Thani II Building 92/23 North Sathorn Rd, Silom, Bangkok, 10500, Bangrak, Thailand (40%)
Tel.: (66) 2636 8650
Web Site: http://www.thaikobe.com
Emp.: 300
Mfr & Sales of Welding Electrodes
N.A.I.C.S.: 333992
Shunki Takei *(Pres)*

Toyotsu Nonferrous Center Corporation (1)
1Oonawa Ozakichou, Anjou, Aichi, Japan
Tel.: (81) 566963411
Aluminum Sheet Mfr
N.A.I.C.S.: 322220

Transnuclear, Ltd. (1)
18-16 1-Chome Shinbashi, Minato-ku, Tokyo, 105-0004, Japan
Tel.: (81) 335082201
Web Site: http://www.tntokyo.co.jp
Transportation Services
N.A.I.C.S.: 485999

Wuxi Compressor Co., Ltd. (1)
No199 Xixie Road, Jiguangdian Industrial Park New District, Wuxi, China
Tel.: (86) 51085024889
Web Site: http://e.compressor-xy.com
Compressor Mfr
N.A.I.C.S.: 333912

Yiyang Yishen Rubber Machinery Co., Ltd. (1)
No 18 Huanyuan Road, Yiyang, 413000, Hunan, China (19.5%)
Tel.: (86) 7374236842
Web Site: http://www.en.yishen.net.cn
Sales Range: $25-49.9 Million
Emp.: 100
Mfr & Sale of Tire Curing Presses
N.A.I.C.S.: 314994

KOBELCO WIRE CO LTD

KOBELCO WIRE CO LTD

10-1 Nakahama-Cho, Amagasaki, 660-0091, Hyogo, Japan
Tel.: (81) 664111051
Web Site: https://www.shinko-wire.co.jp
Year Founded: 1954
5660—(TKS)
Rev.: $216,318,860
Assets: $285,532,170
Liabilities: $134,619,260
Net Worth: $150,912,910
Earnings: $5,988,660
Emp.: 894
Fiscal Year-end: 03/31/24
Secondary Products of Steel Wires Mfr
N.A.I.C.S.: 331110
Masahiro Kawase *(Pres)*

Subsidiaries:

Cable Tech, Ltd. (1)
4 Mikagehama-Cho Higashinada-Ku, Kobe, Hyogo, Japan
Tel.: (81) 788117001
Steel Wire Mfr & Distr
N.A.I.C.S.: 331110

Kobelco Spring Wire (Foshan) Co., Ltd. (1)
Nanhai National Demonstration Eco-Industrial Park Shengtai Road No 12, Danzao Town Nanhai District, Foshan, 528216, Guangdong, China
Tel.: (86) 75785433186
Steel Wire Mfr & Distr
N.A.I.C.S.: 331110

Kosen Service Co., Ltd. (1)
7-2 Tsurumachi, Amagasaki, Hyogo, Japan
Tel.: (81) 664120016
Machine Repair Services
N.A.I.C.S.: 811310

Onoe Rope Engineering, Ltd. (1)
128 Imafuku Onoe-Cho, Kakogawa, Hyogo, Japan
Tel.: (81) 794275107
Steel Wire Mfr & Distr
N.A.I.C.S.: 331110

Shinko Wire (Guangzhou) Sales Co., Ltd. (1)
Room 2901 Goldlion Digital Network Center 138 Tiyu Road East, Tianhe District, Guangzhou, 510620, Guangdong, China
Tel.: (86) 2022836066
Steel Product Distr
N.A.I.C.S.: 423510

Shinko Wire Stainless Company, Ltd. (1)
4-10-20 Tsuruhara, Izumisano, 598-0071, Osaka, Japan
Tel.: (81) 724623001
Web Site: http://www.shinko-wire.co.jp
Emp.: 60
Stainless Steel Wire Mfr
N.A.I.C.S.: 331110

Tesac Shinko Wirerope Co., Ltd. (1)
13f Yodoyabashi Square 2-6-18 Kitahama Chuo-Ku, Osaka, Japan
Tel.: (81) 662230672
Steel Pipe Distr
N.A.I.C.S.: 423510

Tesac Wirerope Co., Ltd. (1)
11-1 Nishiki Nakamachi, Kaizuka, 597-8501, Osaka, Japan (57.9%)
Tel.: (81) 72 432 9251
Web Site: http://www.tesac-wirerope.co.jp
Emp.: 227
Steel Wire Mfr & Distr
N.A.I.C.S.: 331110
Isao Takagi *(Pres)*

Subsidiary (Domestic):

AICHI TESAC CORPORATION (2)
916 Kinome-Cho, Atsuta-Ku, Nagoya, Aichi, Japan
Tel.: (81) 526837775
Wire Rope Distr
N.A.I.C.S.: 423510

Subsidiary (Non-US):

TESAC SHINKO WIREROPE CONSULTING (SHANGHAI) CO.,

KOBELCO WIRE CO LTD

Kobelco Wire Co Ltd—(Continued)
LTD. (2)
Room 3709 Hong Kong New World Tower 300 Huai Hai Zhong Road, Luwan District, Shanghai, 200021, China
Tel.: (86) 2133130510
Wire Rope Consulting Services
N.A.I.C.S.: 541613

KOBENHAVNS LUFTHAVNE A/S
Lufthavnsboulevarden 6, 2770, Kastrup, Denmark
Tel.: (45) 32313231   DK
Web Site: https://www.cph.dk
Year Founded: 1990
KBHL—(CSE)
Rev.: $584,585,769
Assets: $2,198,859,844
Liabilities: $1,776,560,297
Net Worth: $422,299,547
Earnings: $39,090,842
Emp.: 2,546
Fiscal Year-end: 12/31/23
Airport Operator
N.A.I.C.S.: 488119
Christian Poulsen (CEO)

KOBIOLABS, INC.
7F Bld C Daewangpangyo-ro, Bundang-gu, Seongnam, 13488, Gyeonggi-do, Korea (South)
Tel.: (82) 316282500
Web Site: https://www.kobiolabs.com
Year Founded: 2014
348150—(KRS)
Rev.: $8,901,477
Assets: $95,054,259
Liabilities: $21,840,358
Net Worth: $73,213,901
Earnings: ($16,813,732)
Emp.: 56
Fiscal Year-end: 12/31/22
Research & Experimental Development Services
N.A.I.C.S.: 541715
Cheolwon Park (Co-CEO)

KOBMAND HERMAN SALLINGS FOND
Bjodstrupvej 18, 8270, Hojbjerg, Denmark
Tel.: (45) 89 30 30 30   DK
Web Site: http://www.sallingfondene.dk
Year Founded: 1999
Investment Fund
N.A.I.C.S.: 525990

Subsidiaries:

Salling Group A/S (1)
Rosbjergvej 33, 8220, Brabrand, Denmark (81%)
Tel.: (45) 8778 5000
Web Site: http://www.dansksupermarked.dk
Supermarket Operator
N.A.I.C.S.: 445110
Per Bank (Pres)

Subsidiary (Non-US):

Tesco Polska Sp. z o.o. (2)
ul Kapelanka 56, 30-347, Krakow, Poland
Tel.: (48) 122552100
Web Site: http://www.tesco.pl
Supermarket Chain Operator
N.A.I.C.S.: 445110

KOBO BIOTECH LTD.
Plot No 121A/1 Western Hills Addagutta Society Opp JNTU Kukatpally, Yawapur Village Sadasivpet, Hyderabad, 500072, Telangana, India
Tel.: (91) 2242871210
Web Site: https://www.kobobiotech.com
531541—(BOM)
Rev.: $2,266

Assets: $10,808,780
Liabilities: $27,520,215
Net Worth: ($16,711,436)
Earnings: ($2,078,335)
Fiscal Year-end: 03/31/22
Pharmaceuticals Product Mfr
N.A.I.C.S.: 325412

KOBOLD GROUP LIMITED
Level 3 217 George Street, Brisbane, 4000, QLD, Australia
Tel.: (61) 7 3810 0000   AU
Web Site: http://www.kobold.com.au
Year Founded: 2003
Emp.: 25
Commercial, Government & Defense Business Services
N.A.I.C.S.: 561499
Jeff Bugden (Mng Dir)

KOC FIAT KREDI FINANSMAN A.S.
Buyukdere Caddesi Tofas Han No 145, Sisli, 34394, Istanbul, Turkiye
Tel.: (90) 2123370800
KFKTF—(IST)
Rev.: $65,897,790
Assets: $406,140,737
Liabilities: $381,414,003
Net Worth: $24,726,733
Earnings: $7,913,404
Fiscal Year-end: 12/31/23
Financial Lending Services
N.A.I.C.S.: 522390
Ismail Cenk Cimen (Chm)

KOC HOLDING A.S.
Nakkastepe Azizbey Sokak No 1, Kuzguncuk, 34674, Istanbul, Turkiye
Tel.: (90) 2165310000
Web Site: https://www.koc.com.tr
Year Founded: 1926
KCHOL—(IST)
Rev.: $27,856,156,662
Assets: $48,882,457,414
Liabilities: $41,247,115,875
Net Worth: $7,635,341,539
Earnings: $3,651,526,617
Emp.: 114,677
Fiscal Year-end: 12/31/22
Holding Company: Textile, Automotive & Industrial Mfr
N.A.I.C.S.: 551112
Ali Y. Koc (Vice Chm)

Subsidiaries:

Akpa A.S. (1)
Ahmet Hamdi Tanpinar Cad No14, Osmangazi, 16030, Bursa, Turkiye
Tel.: (90) 2242222400
Web Site: http://www.akpakoc.com.tr
Sales Range: $25-49.9 Million
Emp.: 99
Energy Retailing
N.A.I.C.S.: 459999

Akpa Dayanikli Tuketim LPG ve Akaryakit Urunleri Pazarlama A.S. (1)
Buyukdere Caddesi No 145-1, Zincirlikuyu, 34394, Istanbul, Turkiye
Tel.: (90) 2123541777
Web Site: https://www.akpakoc.com.tr
Sales Range: $25-49.9 Million
Liquefied Petroleum Gas Distr
N.A.I.C.S.: 457210

Arcelik A.S. (1)
Karaagac Caddesi No 2-6 Sutluce, Beyoglu, 34445, Istanbul, Turkiye (56%)
Tel.: (90) 2123143434
Web Site: http://www.arcelikglobal.com
Rev.: $4,136,322,466
Assets: $4,084,652,839
Liabilities: $3,247,424,688
Net Worth: $837,228,151
Earnings: $145,883,677
Emp.: 41,030
Fiscal Year-end: 12/31/2022
Appliances, Electronics & Heating & Air Conditioning Equipment Mfr

N.A.I.C.S.: 335220
Rahmi Mustafa Koc (Chm)

Subsidiary (Domestic):

Arcelik Motor Plants (2)
Organize Sanayi Bolgesi 8 Sok No 2 Cerkezkoy, Topkapi, 59500, Tekirdag, Turkiye (100%)
Tel.: (90) 2827365050
Web Site: http://www.arcelik.com
Sales Range: $150-199.9 Million
Emp.: 800
Mfr of Compressors & Electrical Motors
N.A.I.C.S.: 333912

Subsidiary (Non-US):

Blomberg Werke GmbH (2)
Thomas Edison platz 3, 63263, Neu-Isenburg, Germany
Tel.: (49) 610271820
Web Site: http://www.beko.com
Sales Range: $25-49.9 Million
Emp.: 50
Household Appliances Mfr & Distr
N.A.I.C.S.: 335220

S.C. Arctic S.A. (2)
Ansamblul Green Court Bucuresti Cladirea C Et 6 C02, Str Gara Herastrau nr 4D sector 2, Bucharest, 20331, Romania
Tel.: (40) 245605111
Web Site: http://www.arctic.ro
Mfr of Household Refrigerators
N.A.I.C.S.: 335220

Arcelik Hitachi Home Appliances (Thailand) Ltd. (1)
Sathorn Square Office Tower Units 2506-2510, 25th floor No 98 North Sathorn Road Silom Bangrak, Bangkok, 10500, Thailand
Tel.: (66) 2018270
Web Site: https://www.arcelik-hitachi-homeappliances.com
Emp.: 5,970
Home Appliances Mfr & Distr
N.A.I.C.S.: 335220

Arcelik Hitachi Home Appliances Sales (Singapore) Pte. Ltd. (1)
438A Alexandra Road No 01-01/02/03 Alexandra Technopark, Singapore, 119967, Singapore
Tel.: (65) 65362520
Home Appliance Distr
N.A.I.C.S.: 423620

Arcelik Hitachi Home Appliances Sales Hong Kong Limited (1)
18/F Ever Gain Centre 28 On Muk Street Shatin, Hong Kong, China (Hong Kong)
Tel.: (852) 21138883
Web Site: https://www.hitachi-homeappliances.com.hk
Home Appliance Distr
N.A.I.C.S.: 423620

Arcelik Hitachi Home Appliances Sales Malaysia Sdn. Bhd. (1)
Lot 12 Jalan Kemajuan Bangi Industrial Estate, 43650, Bandar Baru Bangi, Selangor, Malaysia
Tel.: (60) 389112600
Home Appliance Distr
N.A.I.C.S.: 423620

Arcelik Hitachi Home Appliances Sales Middle East Fze (1)
PO Box 18008, Jebel Ali Free Zone, Dubai, United Arab Emirates
Tel.: (971) 48831183
Home Appliance Distr
N.A.I.C.S.: 423620

Arcelik Hitachi Home Appliances Sales Vietnam Co., Ltd. (1)
21st Floor Bitexco Financial Tower 2 Hai Trieu Street, District 1 Ben Nghe Ward, Ho Chi Minh City, Vietnam
Tel.: (84) 2838237977
Home Appliance Distr
N.A.I.C.S.: 423620

Arcwaste Collection S.R.L. (1)
Gara Herastrau Street no 4D Green Court Bucharest Sector 2, Bucharest, Romania
Tel.: (40) 2123143434
Web Site: https://arcwaste.ro
Electronic Equipment Mfr & Distr

INTERNATIONAL PUBLIC

N.A.I.C.S.: 335313

Ark Insaat AS (1)
Seyhli Mah Ankara Cad Vadi Sok No 3 Kurtkoy, Pendik, Istanbul, Turkiye
Tel.: (90) 2165950848
Web Site: http://www.arkinsaat.com.tr
Communication Service
N.A.I.C.S.: 517810

Aygaz A.S. (1)
Buyukdere Caddesi N 145-1, Zincirlikuyu, 34394, Istanbul, Turkiye
Tel.: (90) 2123541515
Web Site: http://www.aygaz.com.tr
Sales Range: $1-4.9 Billion
LPG Sourcing, Storage, Filling & Distribution
N.A.I.C.S.: 457210
Rahmi R. Koc (Chm)

Aygaz Dogal Gaz Toptan Satis A.S. (1)
Buyukdere Caddesi No 145-1 Zincirlikuyu, 34394, Istanbul, Turkiye
Tel.: (90) 2123541610
Sales Range: $50-74.9 Million
Natural Gas Distribution Services
N.A.I.C.S.: 221210

Ayvalik Marina ve Yat Isletmeciligi San. ve Tic. A.S. (1)
Kemalpasamah - Attaturk Blv- 61, Ayvalk, Balikesir, 10400, Turkiye
Tel.: (90) 2663122696
Sales Range: $25-49.9 Million
Emp.: 20
Marine Transportation Services
N.A.I.C.S.: 488390
Umut Tepedelenloglu (Mgr)

Beko A and NZ Pty Ltd. (1)
55 Blanck Street, Ormeau, 4208, QLD, Australia
Tel.: (61) 1300282356
Web Site: https://www.beko.com
Emp.: 3
Household Appliances Mfr
N.A.I.C.S.: 335220

Beko Cesko S.R.O. (1)
Shiran Tower Luzna 716/2, 160 00, Prague, Czech Republic
Tel.: (420) 220105371
Sales Range: $50-74.9 Million
Emp.: 7
Household Appliance Distr
N.A.I.C.S.: 423620

Beko Deutschland GmbH (1)
Thomas-Edison-Platz 3, 63263, Neu-Isenburg, Germany
Tel.: (49) 610271820
Web Site: http://www.beko-hausgeraete.de
Household Appliances Mfr
N.A.I.C.S.: 335220

Beko Electronics Espana S.L. (1)
Calle Provenca 888 - Piso 1 Pta 1, Barcelona, 08025, Spain
Tel.: (34) 933184647
Sales Range: $25-49.9 Million
Emp.: 26
Household Appliances Mfr & Distr
N.A.I.C.S.: 335220
Cem Akant (Gen Mgr)

Beko Italy SRL (1)
5 Via Lazzaroni, 21047, Saronno, Varese, Italy
Tel.: (39) 029628991
Web Site: http://www.beko.com
Household Appliance Whslr
N.A.I.C.S.: 423620

Beko PLC (1)
Unit 16 The Hub Logistics Park, Bracetown Clonee, Meath, Ireland
Tel.: (353) 18623411
Household Appliance Distr
N.A.I.C.S.: 423620

Beko S.A. Czech Republic (1)
Emp.: 12
Household Appliances Mfr
N.A.I.C.S.: 335220
Kantor Zoltan (Mng Dir)

Bilkom Bilisim Hizmetleri A.S. (1)
Altunizade Mh Mahir Iz Cd No 26 Floor 2, Uskudar, 34662, Istanbul, Turkiye

AND PRIVATE COMPANIES

Tel.: (90) 2169092556
Web Site: https://www.bilkom.com.tr
Software Development Services
N.A.I.C.S.: 541511

Birlesik Motor Sanayi ve Ticaret AS (1)
Aydinevler Mah Dumlupinar Cad No 24, Kucukyali, Istanbul, Turkiye
Tel.: (90) 2165879800
Web Site: http://www.birmot.com.tr
Sales Range: $50-74.9 Million
Emp.: 170
Automobile Dealership
N.A.I.C.S.: 441110

Defy Appliances (Proprietary) Limited (1)
135 Teakwood Road Jacobs, 4052, Durban, South Africa
Tel.: (27) 314609711
Web Site: http://www.defy.co.za
Sales Range: $800-899.9 Million
Emp.: 2,600
Household Appliances Mfr
N.A.I.C.S.: 335220

Demir Export A.S. (1)
Izmir Cad Koc Ishani No 25/7, Ankara, 06440, Turkiye
Tel.: (90) 3124154500
Web Site: http://www.demirexport.com
Emp.: 100
Mining & Related Services
N.A.I.C.S.: 212290
Savas Sahin *(Mgr)*

Ditas Deniz Isletmeciligi ve Tankerciligi A.S. (1)
Tel.: (90) 2165546200
Sales Range: $25-49.9 Million
Emp.: 4
Marine Transportation Services
N.A.I.C.S.: 483211

Subsidiary (Domestic):

Beykoz Tankercilik A.S. (2)
Baglarbasi Kisikli Caddesi No 26 Altunizade Is Merkezi, Istanbul, 34662, Turkiye **(100%)**
Tel.: (90) 2165546200
Web Site: http://www.ditasdeniz.com.tr
Crude Oil Shipping Services
N.A.I.C.S.: 213112
Bilge Bayburtlugil *(Gen Mgr)*

Kadikoy Tankercilik A.S. (2)
Kisikli Cad Altunizade Is Merkezi No 26 Baglarbasi, Uskudar, Istanbul, 34662, Turkiye **(100%)**
Tel.: (90) 2165546200
Web Site: http://www.ditasdeniz.com.tr
Tanker Marine Transport of Crude Oil, Oil Products & Other Liquefied Substances
N.A.I.C.S.: 483111
Bilge Bayburtlugil *(Gen Mgr)*

Sariyer Tankercilik A.S. (2)
Baglarbasi Kisilki Cad No 26 Altunizade Is Merkezi Kat 2, Uskudar, 34662, Turkiye
Tel.: (90) 2165546200
Marine Transportation Services
N.A.I.C.S.: 488390

Uskudar Tankercilik A.S. (2)
Kisikli cad Altunizade Is Merkezi No 26 Baglarbasi, Uskudar, 34662, Istanbul, Turkiye
Tel.: (90) 2165546200
Web Site: http://www.ditasdeniz.com.tr
Marine Tankers Transport Services
N.A.I.C.S.: 488320

Divan AS (1)
Saray Mah Dr Fazil Kucuk Cad No 15, Istanbul, 134367, Sisli, Turkiye
Tel.: (90) 2165226300
Web Site: http://www.divan.com.tr
Sales Range: $25-49.9 Million
Emp.: 300
Hotel & Restaurant Management & Services
N.A.I.C.S.: 721110

Divan Turizm Isletmeleri A.S. (1)
Unalan Mahallesi Ayazma Caddesi No 131/A, Uskudar, 34700, Istanbul, Umrniye, Turkiye

Tel.: (90) 2165226300
Web Site: https://www.divan.com.tr
Emp.: 100
Tour Operating Services
N.A.I.C.S.: 561520

Duzey A.S. (1)
Alemdag Sapagi Sirri Celik Bulvari, Tasdelen-Cekmekoy, 34788, Istanbul, Turkiye
Tel.: (90) 216 430 02 00
Web Site: http://www.duzey.com.tr
Distr of Koc Group Brands & Other Product Brands
N.A.I.C.S.: 541614
Tamer Hasimoglu *(Pres)*

Duzey Tuketim Mallari Sanayi Pazarlama A.S. (1)
Tasdelen Mahallesi Sirri Celik Bulvari No7, Cekmekoy, 34788, Istanbul, Turkiye
Tel.: (90) 2164300200
Web Site: https://duzey.com.tr
Sales Range: $250-299.9 Million
Emp.: 1,000
Consumer Goods Distr
N.A.I.C.S.: 424990

Elektra Bregenz AG (1)
Pfarrgasse 77 A, 1230, Vienna, Austria
Tel.: (43) 016153900
Web Site: http://www.elektrabregenz.com
Sales Range: $25-49.9 Million
Emp.: 41
Household Appliances Mfr
N.A.I.C.S.: 335220

Entegart Teknoloji Cozum ve Hizmetleri A.S. (1)
Unalan Mahallesi Cagla Sokak Camlica Is Merkezi B Blok No 11/1, Uskudar, 34700, Istanbul, Turkiye
Tel.: (90) 2162292800
Web Site: https://www.entegart.com.tr
Software Development Services
N.A.I.C.S.: 541511

Ford Otomotiv Sanayi A.S. (1)
Akpinar Mahallesi Hasan Basri Caddesi No 2 Sancaktepe, 34885, Istanbul, Turkiye **(41.04%)**
Tel.: (90) 2165647100
Web Site: https://www.fordotosan.com.tr
Rev.: $12,722,756,189
Assets: $6,702,816,296
Liabilities: $4,447,791,818
Net Worth: $2,255,024,478
Earnings: $1,515,209,618
Emp.: 20,000
Fiscal Year-end: 12/31/2023
Automobile Mfr
N.A.I.C.S.: 336110
Ali Yildirim Koc *(Chm)*

Grundig Intermedia GmbH (1)
Thomas-Edison-Platz 3, Langwasser, 63263, Neu-Isenburg, Germany
Tel.: (49) 91159059729
Web Site: http://www.grundig.de
Household Appliances Mfr
N.A.I.C.S.: 335220

Grundig Multimedia B.V. (1)
Kolenbranderstraat 28, 2984 AT, Ridderkerk, Netherlands
Tel.: (31) 180 487181
Household Appliances Mfr
N.A.I.C.S.: 335220

Grundig Nordic AB. (1)
Esbogatan 18, Kista, 164 74, Sweden
Tel.: (46) 86298530
Web Site: https://www.grundig.com
Sales Range: $50-74.9 Million
Emp.: 4
Household Appliance Distr
N.A.I.C.S.: 423620

Harranova Besi ve Tarim Urunleri A.S. (1)
Maridn Yolu 30 Km PK 98, Camlidere, 63190, Sanliurfa, Turkiye
Tel.: (90) 414 255 88 00
Web Site: http://www.harranova.com.tr
Sales Range: $25-49.9 Million
Emp.: 20
Agricultural Farming Services
N.A.I.C.S.: 111998
Ibrahim Tamer Hasimoglu *(Chm)*

Izocam Tic. San. AS (1)

KOC HOLDING A.S.

Altaycesme Mahallesi Camli Sok Main Office No 21 Floor 4 5, Maltepe, 41455, Istanbul, Turkiye
Tel.: (90) 2164404050
Web Site: http://www.izocam.com.tr
Sales Range: $125-149.9 Million
Emp.: 440
Insulation Solutions Mfr
N.A.I.C.S.: 327215
Hady Nassif *(Chm)*

KaTron Savunma Uzay ve Simulasyon Teknolojileri A.S. (1)
Unalan Mah Ayazma Cad Camlica Is Merkezi A Blok Kat 2, Uskudar, 34700, Istanbul, Turkiye
Tel.: (90) 216 556 0500
Web Site: http://katron.com.tr
Sales Range: $25-49.9 Million
Software Development Services
N.A.I.C.S.: 541511

Kav Danismanlik Paz. Tic. AS (1)
11 Kim Sim Celik Bulvari No 3, Beyoglu, 80050, Istanbul, Turkiye
Tel.: (90) 2164309981
Web Site: http://www.kav.com.tr
Match Mfr
N.A.I.C.S.: 321999

Koc Bilgi Grubu Iletisim ve Teknoloji Sirketleri AS (1)
Unalan Mah Ayazma Cad Camlica Is, Merkezi A Blok Kat3 Uskudar, Istanbul, 81190, Turkiye
Tel.: (90) 2165563400
Information Technology Solutions
N.A.I.C.S.: 519290

Subsidiary (Domestic):

Biletix Bilet Dagitim ve Basim Tic AS
Ayazaga Mahallesi Vadistanbul Bulvar Cendere Caddesi No 109/B, 1B Blok Ofis No 1-2, Istanbul, 34396, Turkiye
Tel.: (90) 8507555555
Web Site: http://www.biletix.com
Entertainment Ticket Sales & Distribution
N.A.I.C.S.: 561920

Bilkom AS (2)
Mahir Iz Caddesi No 26 Kat 2, Altunizade, Istanbul, 34662, Uskudar, Turkiye
Tel.: (90) 2169092556
Web Site: http://www.bilkom.com.tr
Computers, Electronics & Internet Services
N.A.I.C.S.: 519290

Kobiline (2)
Unalan Mah Ayazma Cad Koc Camlica Is Merk B 3 Blok, Uskudar, 81190, Istanbul, Turkiye
Tel.: (90) 2165563000
Web Site: http://www.kobiline.com
E-Business Solutions
N.A.I.C.S.: 517810

Koc Bryce Teknoloji Egitim Hizmetleri AS (2)
Kisikli Cad Akoz is merkezi B Blok No1, Blok No18 Altunizade, Istanbul, 34662, Turkiye
Tel.: (90) 2166513737
Web Site: http://www.kocsicsistem.com.tr
Sales Range: $25-49.9 Million
Emp.: 25
IT Training Solutions
N.A.I.C.S.: 923110

KocSistem Bilgi ve Iletisim Hizm. AS (2)
Unalan Mahallesi Cagla Sokak Camlica Is Merkezi No 11, 34700, Istanbul, Uskudar, Turkiye
Tel.: (90) 2165561100
Web Site: https://kocsistem.com.tr
Sales Range: $75-99.9 Million
Emp.: 100
Outsourcing Solutions to Information Systems
N.A.I.C.S.: 561499

PROMENA Elektronik Ticaret AS (2)
Unalan Mahallesi Ayazma Cad Camlica Is Merkez A3 Blok, Uskudar, 34700, Istanbul, Turkiye
Tel.: (90) 2165563040
Web Site: http://www.promena.net

Sales Range: $10-24.9 Million
Emp.: 25
Commercial Procurement Services
N.A.I.C.S.: 561499

Koc Bilgi ve Savunma Teknolojileri A.S. (1)
Yeni Baglica Mahallesi Doganli Cd, Etimesgut, 06790, Ankara, Turkiye
Tel.: (90) 3122188900
Web Site: https://www.kocsavunma.com.tr
Software Development Services
N.A.I.C.S.: 541511

Koc Sistem Bilgi ve Iletisim Hizmetleri A.S. (1)
Unalan Mah Ayazma Cad Camlica Is Merkezi B3 Blok, Uskudar, 34700, Istanbul, Turkiye
Tel.: (90) 216 556 1100
Web Site: http://www.kocsistem.com.tr
Sales Range: $350-399.9 Million
Emp.: 1,168
Information Technology Consulting Services
N.A.I.C.S.: 541512

Kofisa S.A. (1)
54 Rue De Lausanne, Geneva, 1202, Switzerland **(100%)**
Tel.: (41) 223185959
Web Site: http://www.kofisa.com
Sales Range: $25-49.9 Million
Emp.: 16
Industrial Machinery & Equipment Distr
N.A.I.C.S.: 423830

Koratrade MTMC Ltd. (1)
Harbourmaster 4-1, Harbourmaster Street IFSC, Dublin, 1, Ireland
Tel.: (353) 1829 1822
N.A.I.C.S.: 311423

Mogaz Petrol Gazlari AS (1)
Buyukdere Cad No145/1 Aygaz Han, Zincirlikuyu, Istanbul, 80300, Turkiye
Tel.: (90) 2123540404
Web Site: http://www.mogaz.com.tr
Sales Range: $50-74.9 Million
Emp.: 150
Liquefied Petroleum Gas Distr
N.A.I.C.S.: 457210

Opet A.S. (1)
Bulgurlu kaisikliMah Sarigazi Ca No 65, Istanbul, 34796, Uskudar, Turkiye
Tel.: (90) 2165229000
Web Site: http://www.opet.com.tr
Sales Range: $1-4.9 Billion
Emp.: 900
Fuel Oil & Petroleum Products Distr
N.A.I.C.S.: 457210
Oguz Ozcetin *(Deputy Gen Mgr-Fuel)*

Subsidiary (Domestic):

Opet Fuchs Madeni Yag A.S. (2)
A O S B 10006 Sok No 12, Cigli, Izmir, Turkiye
Tel.: (90) 232 376 78 38
Lubricant Oil Mfr & Distr
N.A.I.C.S.: 324191

TBS Denizcilik ve Petrol Urunleri Dis Ticaret AS (2)
Bulgurlu Mh Alemdag Cd Masaldan Is Mrk C Blok 46/2, Camlica Uskudar, Istanbul, Turkiye
Tel.: (90) 2165229049
Web Site: http://www.tbs.com.tr
Oil Product Distr
N.A.I.C.S.: 213112

Otokar Europe SAS (1)
24-26 Rue Du Noyer BP41 Parc Les Scientifiques De Roissy Lot A-3, BP 41, 95700, Roissy-en-France, France
Tel.: (33) 134387676
Web Site: http://www.otokar.com.tr
Sales Range: $25-49.9 Million
Emp.: 10
Automobile Mfr
N.A.I.C.S.: 336110

Otokar Otobus Karoseri San AS (1)
Aydinevler Mah Dumlupinar Cad, No 24 Block A, Istanbul, 34855, Turkiye
Tel.: (90) 2164892950
Web Site: http://www.otokar.com.tr
Sales Range: $200-249.9 Million
Emp.: 1,500
Motor Vehicles Mfr

KOC HOLDING A.S.

Koc Holding A.S.—(Continued)
N.A.I.C.S.: 336110
Serdar Gorguc (Gen Mgr)

Otokoc Hungary Kft. (1)
Kassak Lajos u 19-25, 1134, Budapest, Hungary
Tel.: (36) 17004859
Web Site: http://www.budget.hu
Car Rental Services
N.A.I.C.S.: 532111

Otokoc Otomotiv Tic. ve San. A.S. (1)
Aydinevler Mah Saygi Cad No 60, Kucukyali, 34854, Istanbul, Turkiye
Tel.: (90) 4443300
Web Site: https://www.otokoc.com.tr
Sales Range: $25-49.9 Million
Emp.: 50
Automobile Rental Services
N.A.I.C.S.: 532111
Gorgun Oezdemir (Gen Mgr)

Otokoc Sigorta Aracilik Hizmetleri A.S. (1)
Aydinevler Mah Dumlupinar Cad No 24, Kucukyali, Istanbul, Turkiye
Tel.: (90) 2165879800
Automobile Mfr
N.A.I.C.S.: 336110

RMK Marine AS (1)
icmeler Mevki Ozel Tersaneler Bolgesi, Istanbul, 81700, Tuzla, Turkiye
Tel.: (90) 2163952865
Web Site: http://www.rmkmarine.com
Sales Range: $25-49.9 Million
Emp.: 100
Yacht & Ship Building
N.A.I.C.S.: 336611

Ram Dis Ticaret AS (1)
Altunizade Mahallesi Kisikli Caddesi No 26 Ic Kapi No 4, Uskudar, 34662, Istanbul, Turkiye
Tel.: (90) 2165381100
Web Site: https://www.ram.com.tr
Sales Range: $25-49.9 Million
Import-Export & General Trading Services
N.A.I.C.S.: 541611

Ram Pacific Ltd. (1)
BC 1st Floor Seascap Square Taizi Rd, Shenzhen, 518054, Shekou, China **(100%)**
Tel.: (86) 26889899
Web Site: http://www.rampacific.com
Sales Range: $25-49.9 Million
Emp.: 20
Machinery & Equipment Distr
N.A.I.C.S.: 423830

Ramerica International Inc (1)
12 E 49th St Fl 17, New York, NY 10017 **(100%)**
Tel.: (212) 759-0300
Web Site: http://www.ramericainternational.com
Sales Range: $25-49.9 Million
Emp.: 2
Food Mfr
N.A.I.C.S.: 311423
Nur Emirgil (Gen Mgr)

Setair Hava Tasimaciligi ve Hizm AS (1)
Kisikli Cad No26, Altunizade, Istanbul, 81190, Turkiye
Tel.: (90) 2165543796
Web Site: http://www.setair.com.tr
Charter Jets & Helicopters
N.A.I.C.S.: 532411

Setur Marinalari Marina ve Yat Isletmeciligi (1)
Munir Nurettin, Selcuk Cad Kalamis, Istanbul, 34726, Turkiye
Tel.: (90) 2163462346
Web Site: http://www.seturmarinas.com
Marine Services
N.A.I.C.S.: 713930

Setur Servis Turistik A.S. (1)
24 Kisikli Caddesi, Istanbul, 34662, Turkiye
Tel.: (90) 2164440738
Web Site: http://www.setur.com.tr
Tour Operating Services
N.A.I.C.S.: 561520

Setur Yalova Marina Isletmeciligi A.S. (1)
Suleymanbey Mahallesi Yali Cad Yat Limani, Yalova, Turkiye
Tel.: (90) 2163462346
Marine Transportation Services
N.A.I.C.S.: 483111

Tani Pazarlama ve Iletisim Hizmetleri A.S. (1)
Unalan Mah Ayazma Cad Camlica Business Centre A Blok Kat 3, 34700, Istanbul, Turkiye
Tel.: (90) 216 556 02 00
Sales Range: $25-49.9 Million
Emp.: 90
Marketing Consulting Services
N.A.I.C.S.: 541613
Cem Alpay (Dir-Product Mgmt & Customer Rels)

Tat Konserve San. AS (1)
Sirri Celik Bulvari Tasdelen, 34788, Istanbul, Turkiye
Tel.: (90) 2164300200
Web Site: http://www.tat.com.tr
Sales Range: $50-74.9 Million
Emp.: 120
Food Processing & Distribution
N.A.I.C.S.: 311999

Tofas Turk Otomobil Fabrikasi A.S. (1)
Buyukdere Cad No 145, Tofas Han Zincirlikuyu, 34394, Istanbul, Turkiye **(37.6%)**
Tel.: (90) 2122753390
Web Site: http://www.tofas.com.tr
Rev.: $2,024,535,652
Assets: $1,247,110,160
Liabilities: $897,659,496
Net Worth: $349,450,665
Earnings: $264,465,136
Emp.: 5,928
Fiscal Year-end: 12/31/2022
Automobile Mfr
N.A.I.C.S.: 336110
Altan Aytac (Dir-Fiat Bus Unit)

Tupras Trading Ltd. (1)
6 Chesterfield Gardens, London, W1J5BQ, United Kingdom
Tel.: (44) 2070042399
Web Site: https://tuprastrading.com
Crude Oil Mfr & Distr
N.A.I.C.S.: 324191

TurkTraktor ve Ziraat Makineleri AS (1)
Gazi Mahallesi Anadolu Bulvari No 52 - 52A, Yenimahalle, Ankara, 06560, Turkiye **(37.5%)**
Tel.: (90) 3122333333
Web Site: http://www.turktraktor.com.tr
Sales Range: $400-449.9 Million
Agricultural Tractor Mfr & Distr
N.A.I.C.S.: 333111

Turkiye Petrol Rafinerileri A.S. (1)
Guney Mahallesi Petrol Caddesi No 25, 41790, Korfez, Kocaeli, Turkiye **(51%)**
Tel.: (90) 2128789000
Web Site: https://www.tupras.com.tr
Rev.: $14,880,531,760
Assets: $5,216,671,094
Liabilities: $3,141,466,943
Net Worth: $2,075,204,151
Earnings: $1,274,437,986
Emp.: 6,108
Fiscal Year-end: 12/31/2022
Petroleum Refiner
N.A.I.C.S.: 324110
Ali Y. Koc (Vice Chm)

Subsidiary (Domestic):

Korfez Ulastirma A.S. (2)
Gulbahar Mah Buyukdere Cad Lalezar Is Merkezi No 101A, Sisli, 34394, Istanbul, Turkiye
Tel.: (90) 2129192001
Web Site: https://www.korfezulastirma.com.tr
Air Carriage & Transportation Services
N.A.I.C.S.: 481111

T Damla Denizcilik A.S. (2)
Altunizade Kisikli Street Nr 26 Flat 1, 34662, Istanbul, Turkiye
Tel.: (90) 2165546200
Petroleum Product Transportation Services
N.A.I.C.S.: 486110

Yapi Kredi Bankasi Nederland N.V. (1)
Amstelplein 1, 1096, Amsterdam, Netherlands
Tel.: (31) 204624444
Web Site: https://www.yapikredi.nl
Banking & Financial Services
N.A.I.C.S.: 522110

Yapi Ve Kredi Bankasi A.S. (1)
Yapi Kredi Plaza D Block, Levent Besiktas, 34330, Istanbul, Turkiye **(67.97%)**
Tel.: (90) 2123397000
Web Site: https://www.yapikredi.com.tr
Rev.: $4,117,277,169
Assets: $36,579,111,180
Liabilities: $32,679,188,738
Net Worth: $3,899,922,441
Earnings: $1,629,154,422
Emp.: 15,256
Fiscal Year-end: 12/31/2022
Commercial Banking Services
N.A.I.C.S.: 522110
Akif Cahit Erdogan (Asst Gen Mgr-Informational Technologies & Ops Mgmt)

Subsidiary (Non-US):

Banque de Commerce et de Placements S.A. (2)
Rue de la Fontaine 1, PO Box 3069, CH-1211, Geneva, Switzerland
Tel.: (41) 22 909 191
Banking Services
N.A.I.C.S.: 522110

Joint Venture (Domestic):

Koctas Yapi Marketleri Ticaret S.A. (2)
Tasdelen Mahallesi Sirri Celik Bulvari No 5, Cekmekoy, 34788, Istanbul, Turkiye **(50%)**
Tel.: (90) 8502095050
Web Site: https://www.koctas.com.tr
Sales Range: $50-74.9 Million
Emp.: 200
DIY Retailers
N.A.I.C.S.: 444110
Alp Onder Ozpamukcu (Gen Mgr)

Subsidiary (Non-US):

Yapi Kredi Bank Azerbaijan JSC (2)
628 District C Mammadguluzade Street 73G, AZ 1078, Baku, Azerbaijan
Tel.: (994) 124977795
Web Site: http://www.yapikredi.com.az
Commercial Banking Services
N.A.I.C.S.: 522110

Joint Venture (Non-US):

Yapi Kredi Bank Nederland N.V. (2)
Amstelplein 1 Rembrandt Tower, 1096 HA, Amsterdam, Netherlands
Tel.: (31) 204624444
Web Site: https://www.yapikredi.nl
Rev.: $144,294,827
Assets: $2,249,426,597
Liabilities: $1,829,025,439
Net Worth: $420,401,158
Earnings: $31,653,244
Emp.: 55
Fiscal Year-end: 12/31/2018
Commercial Banking Services
N.A.I.C.S.: 522110
Semih Ulugol (CEO & Member-Mgmt Bd)

Subsidiary (Domestic):

Yapi Kredi Kultur ve Sanat Yayincilik Tic.ve San.A.S. (2)
Yapi Kredi Kultur Sanat Istiklal Caddesi No 161, Beyoglu, 34433, Istanbul, Turkiye
Tel.: (90) 212 252 47 00
Web Site: http://www.ykykultur.com.tr
Sales Range: $25-49.9 Million
Emp.: 80
Book & Magazine Publishing Services
N.A.I.C.S.: 513130
Tulay Gungen (Gen Mgr)

Yapi Kredi Yatirim Menkul Degerler A.S. (2)
Levent Mah Comert St No 1A A Blok D 21-22-23-24-25-27, Besiktas, 34330, Istanbul, Turkiye
Tel.: (90) 2123198000
Web Site: https://ykyatirim.com.tr

INTERNATIONAL PUBLIC

Sales Range: $100-124.9 Million
Emp.: 150
Brokerage, Equity Research & Corporate Financial Services
N.A.I.C.S.: 523150

Zer Merkezi Hizmetler ve Ticaret A.S. (1)
Unalan Mahallesi Cagla Sokak Koc Grup Apartmani No 11A, Uskudar, 34700, Istanbul, Turkiye
Tel.: (90) 2165560100
Web Site: https://www.koczer.com
Business Process Outsourcing Services
N.A.I.C.S.: 561499

KOCH FORD LINCOLN SALES (2003) LTD.
5121 Gateway Boulevard NW, Edmonton, T6H 5W5, AB, Canada
Tel.: (780) 434-8411
Web Site:
http://www.kochfordlincoln.com
Year Founded: 1965
Sales Range: $50-74.9 Million
Emp.: 100
New & Used Car Dealers
N.A.I.C.S.: 441110
Jordan Koch (Chief Mktg Officer)

KOCH GRUPPE AUTOMOBILE AG
Marzahner Chaussee 219, 12681, Berlin, Germany
Tel.: (49) 3054998813
Web Site:
http://www.autoskauftmanbeikoch.de
Sales Range: $100-124.9 Million
Emp.: 240
Car Dealership Owner & Operator
N.A.I.C.S.: 441110
Thomas Greitzke (Member-Mgmt Bd)

Subsidiaries:

Autocenter Koch GmbH (1)
Persiusstrasse 7-8, 10245, Berlin, Germany
Tel.: (49) 30 29 35 92 0
Web Site: http://www.autocenter-koch.de
Sales Range: $75-99.9 Million
Emp.: 250
Motor Vehicle Distr
N.A.I.C.S.: 423110
Thomas Koch (Gen Mgr)

Autoforum Koch GmbH (1)
Hammerlingstr 134-136, Berlin, 12555, Germany
Tel.: (49) 306507330
Web Site: http://www.autoforum-koch-gmbh.de
Sales Range: $75-99.9 Million
Motor Vehicle Distr
N.A.I.C.S.: 423110
Thomas Koch (Gen Mgr)

Autohaus Koch GmbH (1)
An den Drei Hasen 3, 61440, Oberursel, Germany
Tel.: (49) 6171 5900 0
Web Site: http://www.autohauskoch.com
Car Dealer
N.A.I.C.S.: 441110

Autozentrum Koch GmbH (1)
Marzahner Chaussee 219, Berlin, 12681, Germany
Tel.: (49) 3054998860
Web Site: http://www.autozentrum-koch-gmbh.de
Sales Range: $75-99.9 Million
Emp.: 20
Motor Vehicle Distr
N.A.I.C.S.: 423110
Thomas Koch (Gen Mgr)

KOCH MEDIA GMBH
Lochhamer Strasse 9, Planegg, 82152, Germany
Tel.: (49) 89 24 2450 De
Web Site: http://www.kochmedia.com
Year Founded: 1994
Digital Entertainment Products Publisher & Distr

AND PRIVATE COMPANIES

N.A.I.C.S.: 513210
Klemens Kundratitz *(Mng Dir-Germany & Austraria)*

Subsidiaries:

Deep Silver Austria (1)
Betriebsstatte Rottenmann Technologiepark 4a, 8786, Vienna, Austria
Tel.: (43) 3614 5004 0
Software Development Services
N.A.I.C.S.: 541511

Deep Silver Germany (1)
Lochhamer Str 9, Planegg, 82152, Munich, Germany
Tel.: (49) 89 24245 0
Web Site: http://www.deepsilver.de
Software Development Services
N.A.I.C.S.: 541511

Deep Silver Inc. (1)
900 Larkspur Landing Cir Ste 103, Larkspur, CA 94939
Tel.: (310) 978-7200
Web Site: http://www.deepsilver.com
Software Development Services
N.A.I.C.S.: 541511

KOCH MEDIA, S.L.U. (1)
Calle Jose Echegaray 8 Complejo Alvia - Edificio 3, 28232, Las Rozas, Spain
Tel.: (34) 91 114 26 40
Software Distr
N.A.I.C.S.: 423430

Koch Media AG (1)
Hodlerstrasse 2, 9008, Saint Gallen, Switzerland
Tel.: (41) 71 243 00 50
Web Site: http://www.kochmedia.ch
Software Distr
N.A.I.C.S.: 423430

Koch Media Benelux (1)
Princenhagelaan 1 C4, 4813 DA, Breda, Netherlands
Tel.: (31) 76 5230 080
Software Distr
N.A.I.C.S.: 423430

Koch Media GmbH (1)
Gewerbegebiet 1, Postfach 24, Hofen, Reutte, 43, Austria
Tel.: (43) 5672 606 101
Web Site: http://www.kochmedia.at
Emp.: 170
Digital Entertainment Products Publisher & Distr
N.A.I.C.S.: 513210
Klemens Kundratitz *(Chm-Mgmt Bd & CEO)*

Subsidiary (US):

Deep Silver Volition, LLC (2)
1 Main Plz Ste 300, Champaign, IL 61820
Tel.: (217) 355-0320
Web Site: http://www.volition-inc.com
Video Game Developer
N.A.I.C.S.: 449210
Dan Cermak *(Pres)*

Koch Media Limited (1)
Arstaangsvagen 21, 117 43, Stockholm, Sweden
Tel.: (46) 8 124 471 90
Software Distr
N.A.I.C.S.: 423430

Koch Media Ltd. (1)
The Bull Pens Manor Court Scratchface Lane, London, RG25 2PH, Hampshire, United Kingdom
Tel.: (44) 1256 385 200
Software Distr
N.A.I.C.S.: 423430

Koch Media SAS (1)
Immeuble le cesaree I 60-64 rue du landy, 93210, La Plaine Saint-Denis, France
Tel.: (33) 1 73 30 08 30
Web Site: http://www.kochmedia.com
Emp.: 15
Software Distr
N.A.I.C.S.: 423430
Conte Olivier *(CEO)*

Koch Media srl (1)
Via Ripamonti 89, 20141, Milan, Italy
Tel.: (39) 02 573 742 0
Software Distr
N.A.I.C.S.: 423430

KOCH TIEFKUHLKOST
Kurfurstendamm 177, Berlin, 10808, Germany
Tel.: (49) 30498575990
Web Site: http://www.koch-berlin.com
Rev.: $13,794,000
Emp.: 50
Food Products Mfr
N.A.I.C.S.: 311999
Klaus Dieter Wegmann *(Owner)*

KOCOM CO., LTD.
Kocom Bldg 22 Arayuk-ro, Gochoneup, Gimpo, 10136, Gyeonggi-Do, Korea (South)
Tel.: (82) 266752211
Web Site: https://www.kocom.com
Year Founded: 1989
015710—(KRS)
Rev.: $73,080,355
Assets: $114,698,297
Liabilities: $22,339,598
Net Worth: $92,358,699
Earnings: ($2,029,706)
Emp.: 160
Fiscal Year-end: 12/31/22
Electronic Products Mfr
N.A.I.C.S.: 334419
Seong-wook Go *(CEO)*

KODA LTD.
18 Tagore Lane, Singapore, 539424, Singapore
Tel.: (65) 62829882 SG
Web Site:
 https://www.kodaonline.com
BJZ—(SES)
Rev.: $32,442,386
Assets: $55,013,709
Liabilities: $18,752,130
Net Worth: $36,261,578
Earnings: ($2,148,944)
Emp.: 1,500
Fiscal Year-end: 06/30/23
Furniture Mfr
N.A.I.C.S.: 337121
Shwu Lee Koh *(Exec Dir-Fin & Admin)*

Subsidiaries:

Jatat Furniture Industries Sdn Bhd (1)
Block C D E Lot 9 Mukim Senai-Kulai, PO Box 79, Senai, 81400, Johor, Malaysia
Tel.: (60) 75995028
Web Site: https://www.jatat.com
Sales Range: $100-124.9 Million
Emp.: 500
Household Furniture Mfr
N.A.I.C.S.: 337121

Koda International Ltd. (1)
Lot 1 1A Street Tan Tao Industrial Park, Binh Chanh District, Ho Chi Minh City, Vietnam
Tel.: (84) 8 3750 5793
Household Furniture Whslr
N.A.I.C.S.: 423310

Koda Saigon Co., Ltd. (1)
Lot A4 A5 Thuan Dao Industrial Park, Ben Luc District, Ho Chi Minh City, Long An, Vietnam
Tel.: (84) 2723636333
Household Furniture Mfr
N.A.I.C.S.: 337121

Koda Woodcraft Sdn Bhd (1)
Lot 9 Mukim Senai-Kulai, PO Box 79, Senai, 81400, Johor, Malaysia
Tel.: (60) 75995028
Web Site: http://www.kodaonline.com
Emp.: 100
Furniture Mfr & Whslr
N.A.I.C.S.: 337121

Outdoor Living Pte Ltd (1)
28 Defu Lane 4, Singapore, Singapore
Tel.: (65) 62829882
Sales Range: $25-49.9 Million
Emp.: 40
Wooden Furniture Mfr & Distr
N.A.I.C.S.: 337122

Subsidiary (Non-US):

Devon Lifestyle Ltd. (2)
40 Onehunga Mall Ground Level Rear of building, Auckland, 1061, New Zealand
Tel.: (64) 98018141
Web Site: http://www.devonlifestyle.co.nz
Timber & Furniture Distr
N.A.I.C.S.: 423210

KODACO CO., LTD.
331-29 Dorim-ri, Imjang-myeon Seobuk, Cheonan, Chungnam, Korea (South)
Tel.: (82) 414113100
Web Site: https://www.kodaco.co.kr
Year Founded: 1986
046070—(KRS)
Rev.: $237,569,207
Assets: $348,173,777
Liabilities: $338,166,004
Net Worth: $10,007,773
Earnings: ($13,769,543)
Emp.: 250
Fiscal Year-end: 12/31/22
Automobile Parts Mfr
N.A.I.C.S.: 333618
Gui-Seung Ihn *(CEO)*

Subsidiaries:

KODACO Co., Ltd. - Anseong factory (1)
621-9 Manjeong-ri, Gongdo-eup, Anseong, Gyeonggi-do, Korea (South)
Tel.: (82) 31 615 2000
Automobile Spare Parts Mfr
N.A.I.C.S.: 333618

KODAL MINERALS PLC
35-39 Maddox Street, London, W1S 2PP, United Kingdom
Tel.: (44) 2034700470
Web Site:
 https://www.kodalminerals.com
Year Founded: 2010
KOD—(AIM)
Assets: $19,475,064
Liabilities: $993,449
Net Worth: $18,481,615
Earnings: $1,814,337
Emp.: 45
Fiscal Year-end: 03/31/23
Mineral Mining
N.A.I.C.S.: 212390
Bernard Michael Aylward *(CEO)*

KODANSHA LTD.
12-21 Otawa 2-Chome, Bunkyo-Ku, Tokyo, 112 8001, Japan
Tel.: (81) 353953577
Web Site: http://www.kodansha.co.jp
Year Founded: 1909
Sales Range: $1-4.9 Billion
Emp.: 979
Book & Magazine Publisher; Motion Picture & Animated Feature Producer
N.A.I.C.S.: 513130
Noma Yashinobu *(Pres)*

Subsidiaries:

King Records Co., Ltd. (1)
I-2-3 Otowa, Bunkyo, Tokyo, 112-003, Japan
Tel.: (81) 3 3945 2134
Web Site: http://www.kingrecords.net
Music Publishing Services
N.A.I.C.S.: 512230

Kobunsha Co., Ltd. (1)
1-16-6 Otowa, Bunkyo, Tokyo, 112-8011, Japan
Tel.: (81) 3 5395 8164
Web Site: http://www.kobunsha.com
Music Publishers
N.A.I.C.S.: 512230

KODENSHI CORPORATION

Kodansha America LLC (1)
451 Park Ave S 7th Fl, New York, NY 10016
Tel.: (917) 322-6200
Sales Range: $25-49.9 Million
Emp.: 8
Publisher
N.A.I.C.S.: 513130

Kodansha BC Co., Ltd. (1)
6F Dai 2 Otowa Bldg 1-2-2 Otowa, Bunkyo, Tokyo, 112-0013, Japan
Tel.: (81) 3 39415771
Books Publishing Services
N.A.I.C.S.: 513130

Kodansha Europe Ltd. (1)
40 Stockwell Street, Greenwich, London, SE10 8EY, United Kingdom (100%)
Tel.: (44) 2082930111
Web Site: http://www.kodansha.eu
Sales Range: $25-49.9 Million
Emp.: 2
Import & Retail of Books
N.A.I.C.S.: 459210

Kodansha Ltd (1)
12 21 Otowa 2 Chome, Bunkyo Ku, Tokyo, 112 8001, Japan (100%)
Tel.: (81) 339466201
Web Site:
 http://www.bookclub.kodansha.co.jp
Sales Range: $200-249.9 Million
Publishers of English-Language Books & Periodicals
N.A.I.C.S.: 513130

Kodansha Scientific Ltd. (1)
6th Fl Nobi Bldg 25 14 Kagaraka, Shinjuku Ku, Tokyo, 162 0825, Japan
Tel.: (81) 332353701
Web Site: http://www.kspub.co.jp
Sales Range: $25-49.9 Million
Emp.: 15
Publishers of Scientific Books & Magazines
N.A.I.C.S.: 513130

Kodansha USA Publishing, LLC (1)
451 Park Ave S, New York, NY 10016-7390
Tel.: (917) 322-6200
Web Site: http://www.kodanshacomics.com
Comic Book Publishing Services
N.A.I.C.S.: 513120

KODENSHI CORPORATION
161 Jyuichi Makishima-cho Uji, Kyoto, 611-0041, Japan
Tel.: (81) 774237111
Web Site: http://www.kodenshi.co.jp
Year Founded: 1972
Emp.: 227
Optical Semiconductor Device Mfr
N.A.I.C.S.: 334413
Hirokazu Nakajima *(Chm)*

Subsidiaries:

AUK Corp. (1)
62-8 Yakchon-ro 8-gil, Iksan, 54630, Korea (South)
Tel.: (82) 638391111
Web Site: https://www.kodenshiuk.com
Rev.: $116,738,222
Assets: $190,105,020
Liabilities: $15,520,020
Net Worth: $174,585,001
Earnings: $10,076,544
Emp.: 830
Fiscal Year-end: 12/31/2022
Semiconductor Product Mfr
N.A.I.C.S.: 334413
Hisokaya Nakajima *(Chm & CEO)*

Kodenshi (Hong Kong) Co., Ltd. (1)
Rm 708 Block Be Tonic Industrial Centre, 19 Lam Hing Street Kowloon Bay, Kowloon, China (Hong Kong)
Tel.: (852) 2331 3180
Optical Semiconductor Product Mfr & Sales
N.A.I.C.S.: 334413

Kodenshi (SY) Corp. (1)
No 16 No 4 Street Development Zone B#, Shenyang, China
Tel.: (86) 24 2539 5500
Web Site: http://www.kodenshi.cn
Optical Semiconductor Product Mfr & Sales
N.A.I.C.S.: 334413

KODENSHI CORPORATION

Kodenshi Corporation—(Continued)

Kodenshi (Shanghai) Co., Ltd. (1)
Rm B811 Hi-tech Kingworld, No 666 Beijing Road, Shanghai, China
Tel.: (86) 21 5308 0207
Optical Semiconductor Product Mfr & Sales
N.A.I.C.S.: 334413

Kodenshi DH Corp. (1)
361-1 Toyoda, Suwa, Nagano, Japan
Tel.: (81) 266 58 7531
Optical Semiconductor Products Mfr & Sales
N.A.I.C.S.: 334413

Kodenshi Singapore Pte., Ltd. (1)
7500A Beach Road #14-318 The Plaza, Singapore, 199591, Singapore
Tel.: (65) 6296 8733
Optical Semiconductor Products Mfr & Sales
N.A.I.C.S.: 334413

Kodenshi TK Corp. (1)
Kodenshi TK Shibuya Bldg 3-1, Nanpeida-icho Shibuya-ku, Tokyo, 150-0036, Japan
Tel.: (81) 3 4528 5917
Web Site: http://www.kodenshi-tk.co.jp
Optical Semiconductor Products Mfr & Sales
N.A.I.C.S.: 334413

KODI CO., LTD.
A 3rd Floor 338 Gwanggyojungang-ro, Suji-gu, Yongin, Gyeonggi-do, Korea (South)
Tel.: (82) 313227788
Web Site: https://kodi.co.kr
Year Founded: 1999
080530—(KRS)
Rev.: $42,338,547
Assets: $45,682,035
Liabilities: $27,463,134
Net Worth: $18,218,902
Earnings: ($10,234,515)
Emp.: 153
Fiscal Year-end: 12/31/22
Semiconductor Related Equipment Mfr
N.A.I.C.S.: 334413
Kim Do Yon (CEO)

Subsidiaries:

INNO Costec Corporation (1)
Hoedeok Way Beongil 14-57 68, Gwangju, Gyeonggi, Korea (South)
Tel.: (82) 317666222
Web Site: http://www.innocostec.co.kr
Plastic Container Mfr
N.A.I.C.S.: 326199

Surkorea Corporation (1)
3F Gangnam Main Tower 275 Gangnam-daero, Seocho-gu, Seoul, Korea (South)
Tel.: (82) 25753402
Web Site: http://www.surkorea.co.kr
Cosmetics Products Mfr
N.A.I.C.S.: 325620

KODIAK COPPER CORP. (1)
Suite 1020 - 800 West Pender Street, Vancouver, V6C 2V6, BC, Canada
Tel.: (604) 646-8351 BC
Web Site: https://kodiakcoppercorp.com
Year Founded: 1987
KDK—(OTCIQ)
Rev.: $153,550
Assets: $8,949,656
Liabilities: $960,386
Net Worth: $7,989,269
Earnings: ($1,148,559)
Fiscal Year-end: 09/30/19
Gold, Silver & Copper Exploration Services
N.A.I.C.S.: 212220
Tony Ricci (CFO)

KODIAK ENERGY, INC.
833-4th Avenue S W Suite 1120, Calgary, T2P 3T5, AB, Canada
Tel.: (403) 262-8044

Oil & Gas Exploration Services
N.A.I.C.S.: 213112
William Stewart Tighe (Pres & CEO)

KODY TECHNOLAB LIMITED
2nd floor J block Mondeal Retail park Iscon cross-road, Besides Iscon mall SG Highway, Ahmedabad, 380015, Gujarat, India
Tel.: (91) 9377229944
Web Site: https://www.kodytechnolab.com
Year Founded: 2011
KODYTECH—(NSE)
Rev.: $1,348,678
Assets: $1,765,304
Liabilities: $1,197,274
Net Worth: $568,030
Earnings: $354,938
Emp.: 89
Fiscal Year-end: 03/31/23
Software Development Services
N.A.I.C.S.: 541511
Manav Patel (Founder)

KOEI TECMO HOLDINGS CO., LTD.
1-18-12 Minowa-cho, Kohoku-ku, Yokohama, 223-8503, Kanagawa, Japan
Tel.: (81) 455628111
Web Site: https://www.koeitecmo.co.jp
Year Founded: 2009
3635—(TKS)
Rev.: $559,100,240
Assets: $1,624,751,220
Liabilities: $464,352,500
Net Worth: $1,160,398,720
Earnings: $223,365,120
Emp.: 2,531
Fiscal Year-end: 03/31/24
Holding Company
N.A.I.C.S.: 551112
Keiko Erikawa (Chm)

Subsidiaries:

KOEI TECMO BEIJING SOFTWARE CO., LTD. (1)
RM 701 Beijing Inn No 6 South ZhuGan HuTong Chaoyang men Nei, Dongcheng District, Beijing, China
Tel.: (86) 1065883571
Game Software Development Services
N.A.I.C.S.: 541511

KOEI TECMO SOFTWARE VIETNAM CO., LTD. (1)
17th Floor 36 Hoang Cau street, O Cho Dua ward Dong Da district, Hanoi, Vietnam
Tel.: (84) 432321287
Game Software Development Services
N.A.I.C.S.: 541511

KOEI TECMO Singapore Pte. Ltd. (1)
8 Kallang Avenue 12-01/04 Aperia, Singapore, 339509, Singapore
Tel.: (65) 62207581
Game Software Development Services
N.A.I.C.S.: 541511
Shintaro Kobayashi (Pres & COO)

KOEI TECMO TIANJIN SOFTWARE CO., LTD. (1)
21-22F Global Center No 309 Nanjin Road, Nankai District, Tianjin, China
Tel.: (86) 2283280781
Game Software Development Services
N.A.I.C.S.: 541511

KOEI TECMO WAVE CO., LTD. (1)
KUDANMEIZENDO Bldg 4-1-34 Kudankita Chiyoda-ku, Tokyo, 102-0073, Japan
Tel.: (81) 332228333
Web Site: http://www.wave.koeitecmo.co.jp
Arcade Management Services
N.A.I.C.S.: 713120
Kazuyoshi Sakaguchi (Pres)

KOENIG & BAUER AG
FriedrichKoenigStrasse 4, 97010, Wurzburg, Germany
Tel.: (49) 9319090 GM
Web Site: https://www.koenig-bauer.com
Year Founded: 1817
SKB—(MUN)
Rev.: $1,370,470,192
Assets: $1,582,832,888
Liabilities: $1,130,717,744
Net Worth: $452,115,144
Earnings: $16,826,888
Emp.: 5,397
Fiscal Year-end: 12/31/21
Printing Machinery Mfr
N.A.I.C.S.: 333248
Gottfried Weippert (Deputy Chm-Supervisory Bd)

Subsidiaries:

Albert-Frankenthal GmbH (1)
Lambsheimer Str 18, PO Box 1315, 67227, Frankenthal, Germany
Tel.: (49) 62338730
Printing Machinery Repair & Maintenance Services
N.A.I.C.S.: 811310

Holland Graphic Occasions B.V. (1)
De Stek 10, PO Box 51, 1771 SP, Wieringerwerf, Netherlands (100%)
Tel.: (31) 227602642
Web Site: https://h-g-o.nl
Sales Range: $10-24.9 Million
Emp.: 15
Mfr of Printing Machines
N.A.I.C.S.: 333248

KBA (HK) Company Limited (1)
Room 1805 Tins Enterprise Centre 777 Lai Chi Kok Rd Cheung Sha Wan, Cheung Sha Wah, Kowloon, China (Hong Kong) (51%)
Tel.: (852) 27428368
Web Site: http://www.kba.com.hk
Sales Range: $25-49.9 Million
Emp.: 10
Mfr of Printing Machines
N.A.I.C.S.: 333248

KBA (UK) Ltd. (1)
5 Century Court, Tolpits Lane, Watford, WD18 9PX, Herts, United Kingdom (100%)
Tel.: (44) 1923819922
Web Site: http://www.kba-print.co.uk
Sales Range: $25-49.9 Million
Emp.: 25
Printing Machinery Mfr
N.A.I.C.S.: 333248
Andrew Pang (Mng Dir)

KBA Asia-Pacific Sdn. Bhd. (1)
No 2A Jalan PJU3/40 Sunway Damansara, 47810, Petaling Jaya, Selangor, Malaysia (100%)
Tel.: (60) 378858860
Web Site: http://www.kbaprint.de
Sales Range: $25-49.9 Million
Emp.: 15
Mfr of Printing Machines
N.A.I.C.S.: 333248
Carina Shia (Sls Mgr-Southeast Asia)

KBA Australasia Pty. Ltd. (1)
Se 306 4 Hyde Pde, Campbelltown, 2560, Australia
Tel.: (61) 246264400
Printing Machinery Mfr
N.A.I.C.S.: 333248

KBA NORDIC A/S (1)
Lejrvej 17, 3500, Vaerlose, Denmark
Tel.: (45) 44523266
Emp.: 6
Printing Press Mfr
N.A.I.C.S.: 333248

KBA North America Inc. (1)
2555 Regent Blvd, Dallas, TX 75261 (100%)
Tel.: (469) 532-8000
Web Site: http://us.koenig-bauer.com
Sales Range: $125-149.9 Million
Production & Sale of Newspaper Flexo & Gravure Presses
N.A.I.C.S.: 333248

INTERNATIONAL PUBLIC

Eric Frank (Sr VP-Mktg & Product Mgmt)

KBA Printing Machinery (Shanghai) Co., Ltd. (1)
Unit 803 Air China Plaza No 36 Xiaoyun Road, Chaoyang District, Beijing, China
Tel.: (86) 10 8447 5909
Sales Range: $25-49.9 Million
Emp.: 14
Printing Machinery Mfr
N.A.I.C.S.: 333248

KBA RUS OOO (1)
22 km Kiewskogo Chaussee p Moskowskij Hausbesitz 4 Gebaude 5, Stockwerk 7, 142784, Moscow, Russia
Tel.: (7) 4957821377
Web Site: http://www.kba-print.ru
Sales Range: $25-49.9 Million
Emp.: 3
Printing Press Mfr
N.A.I.C.S.: 333248

KBA-Berlin GmbH (1)
Mertensstrasse 127 131, D 13587, Berlin, Germany (100%)
Tel.: (49) 303360020
Web Site: http://www.kba-print.de
Sales Range: $50-74.9 Million
Emp.: 111
Mfr of Printing Machines
N.A.I.C.S.: 333248

KBA-Brasil Ltda. (1)
Rua Tocandia 136, 03345 050, Sao Paulo, Brazil
Tel.: (55) 11 3624 7259
Sales Range: $25-49.9 Million
Emp.: 30
Printing Machinery Mfr
N.A.I.C.S.: 333248

KBA-France SAS (1)
Ctr D Activites Charles De Gaulle 10 Rue Henri Farman, 93297, Tremblay, France (100%)
Tel.: (33) 148609032
Web Site: http://www.kbaprint.de
Sales Range: $50-74.9 Million
Emp.: 35
Mfr of Printing Machines
N.A.I.C.S.: 333248

KBA-Grafitec s.r.o. (1)
Opocenska 83, 51819, Dobruska, Czech Republic (100%)
Tel.: (420) 494672111
Web Site: http://www.kba-grafitec.cz
Sales Range: $25-49.9 Million
Emp.: 400
Printing Machinery Mfr & Whslr
N.A.I.C.S.: 333248
Lubos Moravec (COO)

KBA-Italia S.p.A. (1)
Via Lecco 2, 20020, Lainate, Italy (100%)
Tel.: (39) 029371961
Web Site: http://www.kbaitalia.it
Sales Range: $25-49.9 Million
Emp.: 40
Mfr of Printing Machines
N.A.I.C.S.: 333248

KBA-MetroPrint AG (1)
Benzstrasse 11, 97209, Veitshochheim, Germany
Tel.: (49) 931 90 85 9
Web Site: http://www.kba-metroprint.com
Sales Range: $50-74.9 Million
Emp.: 20
Printing & Coding Machinery Mfr
N.A.I.C.S.: 333248

KBA-Metronic AG (1)
Benzstrasse 11, 97209, Veitshochheim, Germany
Tel.: (49) 93190850
Web Site: http://www.kba-metronic.com
Sales Range: $100-124.9 Million
Emp.: 366
Development, Design, Production, Marketing & Service of Printing & Coding Systems
N.A.I.C.S.: 333248

KBA-NotaSys SA (1)
Avenue du Grey 55, 1018, Lausanne, Switzerland (100%)
Tel.: (41) 213457000
Web Site: http://www.kba-notasys.com
Sales Range: $50-74.9 Million
Emp.: 200
Mfr of High Security Printing Machines

N.A.I.C.S.: 333248
Gerben Van Wijk *(Mgr-Mktg)*

Subsidiary (Non-US):

KBA NotaSys India Pvt. Ltd. (2)
E-95 9th Floor Himalaya House 23 Kasturba Gandhi Marg, New Delhi, 110 001, India
Tel.: (91) 1123311835
Printing Machinery & Equipment Mfr
N.A.I.C.S.: 333248

Subsidiary (US):

KBA-NotaSys North America, Inc. (2)
1725 I St NW Ste 300, Washington, DC 20006
Tel.: (202) 261-3505
Printing Machinery & Equipment Mfr
N.A.I.C.S.: 333248

KBA-SWISS HOLDING SA (1)
Avenue du Grey 55, 1000, Lausanne, Vaud, Switzerland
Tel.: (41) 213101111
Investment Management Service
N.A.I.C.S.: 523999

Koenig & Bauer (DE) GmbH (1)
Friedrich-List-Str 47, 01445, Radebeul, Germany
Tel.: (49) 3518331100
Printing Machinery Repair & Maintenance Services
N.A.I.C.S.: 811310

Koenig & Bauer (JP) Co., Ltd. (1)
Hakozakicho 20-3 Hakozaki Park Building 6F Nihonbashi, Chuo-ku, Tokyo, 103-0015, Japan
Tel.: (81) 356233004
Web Site: http://www.kba-japan.jp
Printing Machinery & Equipment Mfr
N.A.I.C.S.: 333248

Koenig & Bauer AG (1)
Postfach 60 60, 97010, Wurzburg, Germany (100%)
Tel.: (49) 931 909 0
Web Site: http://www.kba.com
Sales Range: $1-4.9 Billion
Emp.: 2,000
Production of Digital Offset Presses
N.A.I.C.S.: 333248

Koenig & Bauer Banknote Solutions (DE) GmbH (1)
Friedrich-Koenig-Strabe 4, 97080, Wurzburg, Germany
Tel.: (49) 9319090
Web Site: https://banknote-solutions.koenig-bauer.com
Commercial Screen Printing Mfr
N.A.I.C.S.: 323113

Koenig & Bauer Banknote Solutions SA (1)
Ave du Grey 55 1018, Lausanne, Switzerland
Tel.: (41) 213457000
Commercial Screen Printing Mfr
N.A.I.C.S.: 323113

Koenig & Bauer FT Engineering GmbH (1)
Lambsheimer Strasse 16, 67227, Frankenthal, Germany
Tel.: (49) 62338733800
Web Site: http://www.engineering.koenig-bauer.com
Printing Machinery & Equipment Mfr
N.A.I.C.S.: 333248

Koenig & Bauer Flexotecnica S.p.A. (1)
Via L Penagini 1, Tavazzano, 26838, Lodi, Italy
Tel.: (39) 03714431
Web Site: http://www.flexotecnica.koenig-bauer.com
Printing Machinery & Equipment Mfr
N.A.I.C.S.: 333248

Koenig & Bauer Giesserei GmbH (1)
Friedrich-Koenig-Str 4, 97080, Wurzburg, Germany
Web Site: http://giesserei.koenig-bauer.com
Emp.: 130
Casting & Mechanical Graphite Product Mfr
N.A.I.C.S.: 331511

Koenig & Bauer IT S.R.L. (1)
Via Lecco 2, 20020, Lainate, Italy
Tel.: (39) 029371961
Web Site: https://it.koenig-bauer.com
Commercial Screen Printing Mfr
N.A.I.C.S.: 323113

Koenig & Bauer Iberica, S.A. (1)
Pol Ind Cami Ral Passeig del Ferrocarril 383, Gava, 08850, Barcelona, Spain
Tel.: (34) 934792780
Web Site: http://iberica.koenig-bauer.com
Emp.: 70
Printing Machinery & Equipment Mfr
N.A.I.C.S.: 333248
Claus Bolza-Schunemann *(Pres)*

Koenig & Bauer Industrial GmbH (1)
Friedrich-Koenig-Strasse 4, 97080, Wurzburg, Germany
Tel.: (49) 9319090
Web Site: https://giesserei.koenig-bauer.com
Metal Printing Machine Mfr
N.A.I.C.S.: 332812

Koenig & Bauer Kammann GmbH (1)
Bergkirchener Str 228, 32549, Bad Oeynhausen, Germany
Tel.: (49) 573451400
Web Site: http://www.kammann.de
Printing Machinery Repair & Maintenance Services
N.A.I.C.S.: 811310
Matthias Graf *(Mng Dir)*

Koenig & Bauer MetalPrint GmbH (1)
Wernerstr 119-129, 70435, Stuttgart, Germany (100%)
Tel.: (49) 711699710
Web Site: https://metalprint.koenig-bauer.com
Printing Machinery Mfr
N.A.I.C.S.: 333248
Ralf Gumbel *(CEO)*

Koenig & Bauer Sheetfed AG & Co. KG (1)
Friedrich-List-Str 47, 01445, Radebeul, Germany
Tel.: (49) 3518330
Printing Machinery & Equipment Mfr
N.A.I.C.S.: 333248

MABEG Machinery (Shanghai) Co., Ltd. (1)
Building 1 No 128 Chengjian Rd, Shanghai, 201108, China
Tel.: (86) 21 64343900
Web Site: http://www.mabeg.com.cn
Emp.: 58
Printing Machinery Mfr
N.A.I.C.S.: 333248
Chang An Wu *(Gen Mgr)*

Maschinenfabrik KBA-Modling AG (1)
Koenig And Bauer Strasse 2, 2344, Enzersdorf, Austria (100%)
Tel.: (43) 223680900
Web Site: http://www.at.koenig-bauer.com
Sales Range: $200-249.9 Million
Sheetfed Offset Presses
N.A.I.C.S.: 333248
Rudolf Vogl *(CEO)*

Print Assist AG (1)
Grabackerstrasse 5, Hori, Bulach, 8181, Zurich, Switzerland
Tel.: (41) 448723300
Emp.: 15
Commercial Printing Services
N.A.I.C.S.: 323111
K. C. Goh *(Gen Mgr)*

PrintHouseService GmbH (1)
Friedrich-Koenig-Strasse 4, 97080, Wurzburg, Germany
Tel.: (49) 9319096999
Web Site: http://www.printhouseservice.com
Printing Machinery Repair & Maintenance Services
N.A.I.C.S.: 811310
Stefan Hessler *(Mng Dir)*

KOENIG & MEYER GMBH & CO. KG
Kiesweg 2, 97877, Wertheim, Germany
Tel.: (49) 93428060
Web Site: http://www.k-m.de
Year Founded: 1949
Emp.: 270
Musical Instrument Mfr
N.A.I.C.S.: 339992
Martin Konig *(Pres & Mng Dir)*

KOENIGSEGG AUTOMOTIVE AB
Valhall Park, 262 91, Angelholm, Sweden
Tel.: (46) 431454460
Web Site:
  http://www.koenigsegg.com
Year Founded: 1994
Sales Range: $10-24.9 Million
Emp.: 45
Sports Car Mfr
N.A.I.C.S.: 336110
Christian von Koenigsegg *(Founder & CEO)*

KOEPON HOLDINGS B.V.
Postbus 46, Winsum, Groningen, 9950 AA, Netherlands
Tel.: (31) 594620980
Web Site: http://www.koepon.com
Sales Range: $1-4.9 Billion
Emp.: 400
Holding Company
N.A.I.C.S.: 551112
Cornelius J. Hartmans *(CEO)*

Subsidiaries:

Alta Genetics, Inc. (1)
Rural Route 2, Rocky View, T4B 2T3, AB, Canada
Tel.: (403) 226-0666
Web Site: http://www.altagenetics.com
Sales Range: $25-49.9 Million
Emp.: 50
Provider of Cattle Genetics & Reproductive Technology Services
N.A.I.C.S.: 541715
Einko Topper *(Dir-Quality & Production)*

Subsidiary (Non-US):

Alta Agricorp (2)
Unit A328 Zhao Wie Hua Deng Building Jiu Xian Qiao Road, Chaoyang District No 14 C, 100015, Beijing, China
Tel.: (86) 10 64354066
Dairy Products Mfr
N.A.I.C.S.: 311514
Chunsheng Ma *(Dir-Sls)*

Alta Deutschland GmbH (2)
Altes Dorf 1, 29525, Uelzen, Germany
Tel.: (49) 581 97 150
Web Site: http://www.altagenetics.com
Emp.: 30
Dairy Products Mfr
N.A.I.C.S.: 311514
Michael Wenzlau *(VP-Sls-Europe)*

Alta Genetics Australia Pty. Ltd. (2)
Unit 11 85-91 Keilor Park Drive, Tullamarine, 3043, VIC, Australia
Tel.: (61) 3 9330 3444
Web Site: http://www.altagenetics.com
Emp.: 6
Dairy Products Mfr
N.A.I.C.S.: 311514
Guido Jakschik *(Gen Mgr)*

Alta Genetics Russia (2)
Lesnaya Str 43, Moscow, Russia
Tel.: (7) 499 978 84 08
Dairy Products Mfr
N.A.I.C.S.: 311514
Dimitri Posunko *(Gen Mgr)*

Alta Genetics do Brasil Ltda. (2)
BR 050 Km 164, Caixa Postal 4008, 38020-970, Uberaba, Minas Gerais, Brazil
Tel.: (55) 34 3318 7777
Dairy Products Mfr
N.A.I.C.S.: 311514

Alta Polska Sp. z o.o. (2)
Topolowa 36, 99-400, Lowicz, Poland
Tel.: (48) 46 837 39 03
Dairy Products Mfr
N.A.I.C.S.: 311514

Alta UK Ltd. (2)
A1 Ash House Melbourn Science Park Cambridge Road, Hert, Melbourn, SG8 6HB, United Kingdom
Tel.: (44) 1763 260832
Dairy Products Mfr
N.A.I.C.S.: 311514

Paul Pon Polska Sp.Z.o.o. (1)
Jaroslawiec 1, 63-000, Sroda Wielkopolska, Poland
Tel.: (48) 61 285 40 41
Web Site: http://paul-pon.pl
Dairy Products Mfr
N.A.I.C.S.: 311514

Saskatoon Colostrum Company Ltd. (1)
30 Molaro Place, Saskatoon, S7K 6A2, SK, Canada
Tel.: (306) 242-3185
Biotechnology Research & Development Services
N.A.I.C.S.: 541714
Deborah Haines *(Founder & Dir-R&D)*

KOESTLIN D.D.
Slavonska cesta 2a, 43000, Bjelovar, Croatia
Tel.: (385) 43492222
Web Site: http://www.koestlin.hr
Year Founded: 1905
KOES—(ZAG)
Sales Range: Less than $1 Million
Bakery Products Mfr
N.A.I.C.S.: 311812
Kresimir Pajic *(Chm-Mgmt Bd)*

KOFFEE BREAK PICTURES LTD.
374 3rd Floor Powai Plaza Hiranandani Garden, Powai, Mumbai, 400076, India
Tel.: (91) 22 30603365
Movies & Entertainment
N.A.I.C.S.: 323117
Babita Sharma *(CFO & Exec Dir)*

KOFOLA CESKOSLOVENSKO AS
Nad Porubkou 2278/31a, Poruba, 708 00, Ostrava, Czech Republic
Tel.: (420) 595601030
Web Site:
  https://www.company.kofola.cz
Year Founded: 2012
KOFOL—(PRA)
Rev.: $310,840,451
Assets: $338,915,410
Liabilities: $278,165,851
Net Worth: $60,749,560
Earnings: $11,264,598
Emp.: 2,041
Fiscal Year-end: 12/31/21
Carbonated Soft Drinks Mfr
N.A.I.C.S.: 312111
Rene Musila *(COO)*

KOGAN.COM LTD
139 Gladstone St, South Melbourne, 3205, VIC, Australia
Tel.: (61) 362858572 AU
Web Site:
  https://www.kogancorporate.com
Year Founded: 2006
KGN—(ASX)
Rev.: $306,959,801
Assets: $162,546,741
Liabilities: $80,012,687
Net Worth: $82,534,054
Earnings: $55,422
Fiscal Year-end: 06/30/24
Online Shopping Dist
N.A.I.C.S.: 423620

KOGAN.COM LTD

Kogan.com Ltd—(Continued)
Mark Licciardo *(Co-Sec)*
Subsidiaries:

Brosa Design Pty. Ltd. (1)
46 Budd Street, Collingwood, 3066, VIC, Australia
Tel.: (61) 370036943
Web Site: http://www.brosa.com.au
Furniture Whslr
N.A.I.C.S.: 423210

KOGE MICRO TECH CO., LTD.
5F No 6 Jiankang Rd, Zhonghe Dist, New Taipei City, 235, Taiwan
Tel.: (886) 222266860
Web Site: https://www.koge.com
Year Founded: 1978
4568—(TPE)
Rev.: $40,623,456
Assets: $53,477,066
Liabilities: $16,797,986
Net Worth: $36,679,080
Earnings: $4,659,038
Fiscal Year-end: 12/31/22
Micro Pump & Solenoid Valve Mfr
N.A.I.C.S.: 332912
Kunlin Chang *(Founder)*
Subsidiaries:

Koge Europe GmbH (1)
Birkenweg 12-16, Ellingen, 91792, Weissenburg, Germany
Tel.: (49) 91417439930
Web Site: https://www.koge-europe.com
Micro Pump Mfr
N.A.I.C.S.: 326112
Yun Chang *(Founder & Gen Mgr)*

Xiamen Koge Micro Tech Co., Ltd. (1)
No 89 South HouXiang Road, HaiCang Xin-Yang Industrial Zone, Xiamen, 361026, China
Tel.: (86) 5926379788
Micro Pump Mfr
N.A.I.C.S.: 326112
Lee Shen *(Asst Gen Mgr)*

KOGI CORPORATION
4-1 Kambee-cho, Otsu-ku, Himeji, 671-1132, Hyogo, Japan
Tel.: (81) 792363221
Web Site: https://www.kogi.co.jp
Year Founded: 1940
5603—(TKS)
Rev.: $171,615,430
Assets: $232,995,890
Liabilities: $121,663,660
Net Worth: $111,332,230
Earnings: $3,556,180
Emp.: 743
Fiscal Year-end: 03/31/24
Casting Metal Mfr
N.A.I.C.S.: 333511
Mikio Yamamoto *(Pres & Chm)*
Subsidiaries:

Kogi Corporation - Himeji East Factory (1)
3-12 Otsu-ku Kambei-cho, Himeji, Japan
Tel.: (81) 792364927
Carbon Ceramic Mfr
N.A.I.C.S.: 327999

KOH BROTHERS ECO ENGINEERING LTD.
15 Genting Road, Koh Brothers Building, Singapore, 349493, Singapore
Tel.: (65) 62898889
Web Site:
https://www.kohbrotherseco.com
Year Founded: 1975
5HV—(CAT)
Rev.: $134,074,074
Assets: $216,198,591
Liabilities: $113,614,330
Net Worth: $102,584,261
Earnings: ($10,134,818)
Emp.: 317
Fiscal Year-end: 12/31/23
Waste Water Treatment, Hydro-Engineering & Palm Oil Production Services
N.A.I.C.S.: 221310
Keng Siang Koh *(Executives)*
Subsidiaries:

Oiltek Global Energy Sdn. Bhd. (1)
Principal Place of Business Lot 6 Jalan Pasaran 23/5 Kawasan MIEL, Phase 10 Section 23, 40300, Shah Alam, Selangor, Malaysia
Tel.: (60) 355428288
Web Site: https://www.oiltek.com.my
Vegetable Oil Mfr
N.A.I.C.S.: 311225

P.T. Bali Environmental Persada (1)
Sunset Road No 89 Sunset Indah I Lt 3 Kuta Blok 5, Kuta-Badung, Bali, 80361, Indonesia
Tel.: (62) 361 763609
Web Site: http://www.pt-bep.com
Sales Range: $75-99.9 Million
Emp.: 8
Waste Water Treatment Services
N.A.I.C.S.: 221310

KOH BROTHERS GROUP LIMITED
15 Genting Road Koh Brothers Building, Singapore, 349493, Singapore
Tel.: (65) 62898889 SG
Web Site:
https://www.kohbrothers.com
Year Founded: 1994
K75—(SES)
Rev.: $269,824,282
Assets: $547,881,542
Liabilities: $306,425,055
Net Worth: $241,456,487
Earnings: ($20,463,531)
Emp.: 493
Fiscal Year-end: 12/31/23
Real Estate Services
N.A.I.C.S.: 531110
Tiat Meng Koh *(Chm)*
Subsidiaries:

Construction Consortium Pte. Ltd. (1)
Koh Brothers Building 11 Lorong Pendek, Singapore, 348639, Singapore
Tel.: (65) 67425972
Web Site: http://www.kohbrothers.com
Construction Materials Whslr
N.A.I.C.S.: 444180

G & W Concrete Products Pte Ltd (1)
65 Sungei Kadut Drive, Singapore, 729564, Singapore
Tel.: (65) 63653388
Sales Range: $50-74.9 Million
Emp.: 200
Paving Blocks Mfr
N.A.I.C.S.: 324121
Alan Tan *(CEO)*

G & W Industrial Corporation Pte Ltd (1)
65 Sungei Kadut Drive, Singapore, 729564, Singapore
Tel.: (65) 63653388
Web Site: http://www.gw-group.com
Sales Range: $25-49.9 Million
Emp.: 100
Foundation Engineering Services
N.A.I.C.S.: 238910

G & W Industries (M) Sdn. Bhd. (1)
644 Jalan Idaman 3/9 Taman, Perindustrian Senai, 81400, Johor, Malaysia
Tel.: (60) 63653388
Web Site: http://www.gw-group.com
Construction Equipment Rental Services
N.A.I.C.S.: 532412

G & W Industries Pte Ltd (1)
50 Tuas Crescent, Singapore, 638730, Singapore
Tel.: (65) 68985333
Web Site: http://www.gw-group.com
Truck Mounted Cement Pumps Leasing & Rental Services
N.A.I.C.S.: 238910

G & W Precast Pte Ltd (1)
Precast Concrete Products Mfr
N.A.I.C.S.: 327331
Chan Ping Meng *(Exec Dir)*

G & W Ready-Mix Pte Ltd (1)
65 Sungei Kadut Drive, Singapore, 729564, Singapore
Tel.: (65) 63653388
Web Site: http://www.gw-group.com
Sales Range: $50-74.9 Million
Emp.: 250
Ready Mix Concrete Mfr & Distr
N.A.I.C.S.: 327320

Koh Brothers Building & Civil Engineering Contractor (Pte.) Ltd. (1)
Koh Brothers Building 11 Lorong Pendek, Singapore, 348639, Singapore
Tel.: (65) 67422242
Web Site: http://www.kohbrothers.com
Emp.: 60
Construction Engineering Services
N.A.I.C.S.: 237310

Koh Brothers Development Pte Ltd (1)
Koh Brothers Building 11 Lorong Pendek, Singapore, 348639, Singapore
Tel.: (65) 62898889
Sales Range: $100-124.9 Million
Emp.: 500
Commercial Construction Services
N.A.I.C.S.: 237310

Koh Brothers Investment Pte Ltd (1)
11 Lorong Pendek, Singapore, Singapore
Tel.: (65) 62898889
Investment Management Service
N.A.I.C.S.: 523940

Kosland Pte. Ltd. (1)
383 Bt Timah Road, Singapore, 259727, Singapore
Tel.: (65) 62356938
Web Site: http://www.locassia.com.sg
Sales Range: $25-49.9 Million
Emp.: 15
Residential Property Development Services
N.A.I.C.S.: 236116
Kelvin Ho *(Mgr)*

Oiltek Sdn. Bhd. (1)
Lot 6 Jalan Pasaran 23/5 Section 23, 40300, Shah Alam, Selangor, Malaysia
Tel.: (60) 355428288
Web Site: http://www.oiltek.com.my
Engineeering Services
N.A.I.C.S.: 541330

Oxford Hotel Pte Ltd (1)
218 Queen Street, Singapore, 188549, Singapore
Tel.: (65) 63322222
Web Site: http://www.oxfordhotel.com.sg
Sales Range: $10-24.9 Million
Emp.: 46
Home Management Services
N.A.I.C.S.: 721110

PT. Koh Brothers Indonesia (1)
First City Komp Block 1 8207 Batam Centre, Batam, 29400, Riau Islands, Indonesia
Tel.: (62) 778 462 111
Property Investment & Development Services
N.A.I.C.S.: 531311

USL Asia Pacific (M) Sdn. Bhd. (1)
No 13/2 Jalan SP 2/1 Taman Serdang Perdana Section 2, 43300, Seri Kembangan, Selangor, Malaysia
Tel.: (60) 389451161
Asphaltic Products Mfr & Whslr
N.A.I.C.S.: 423320

USL Asia Pacific Pte Ltd (1)
38 Sungei Kadut Street 2, Singapore, 729245, Singapore (100%)
Tel.: (65) 68636363
Sales Range: $25-49.9 Million
Emp.: 10
Asphaltic Products Mfr & Whslr
N.A.I.C.S.: 324110

Wealthplus Pte Ltd (1)
Koh Brothers Building 11 Lorong Pendek, Singapore, Singapore
Tel.: (65) 62898889
Investment Management Service
N.A.I.C.S.: 523940

KOH YOUNG TECHNOLOGY INC.
14F Halla Sigma Valley 53 Gasandigital 2-ro, Geumcheon-gu, Seoul, 08588, Korea (South)
Tel.: (82) 263436000
Web Site: https://www.kohyoung.com
Year Founded: 2002
098460—(KRS)
Rev.: $211,200,803
Assets: $300,423,540
Liabilities: $66,354,384
Net Worth: $234,069,156
Earnings: $30,130,482
Emp.: 450
Fiscal Year-end: 12/31/22
Inspection & Measurement Equipment Mfr
N.A.I.C.S.: 333242
Kwangill Koh *(Founder & CEO)*
Subsidiaries:

Japan Koh Young Co., Ltd. (1)
101 Hanahara Dai7 Bldg 6-8-20 Nishinakajima, Yodogawa-ku, Osaka, 532-0011, Japan
Tel.: (81) 663055186
Measuring Equipment Distr
N.A.I.C.S.: 423830

Koh Young America Inc. (1)
6150 W Chandler Blvd Ste 39, Chandler, AZ 85226
Tel.: (480) 403-5000
Measuring Equipment Distr
N.A.I.C.S.: 423830
Denis Dongchul Kang *(Reg Mgr-Sls)*

Koh Young Europe GmbH (1)
Industriegebiet Sud E4, 63755, Alzenau, Germany
Tel.: (49) 61889935663
Measuring Equipment Distr
N.A.I.C.S.: 423830

Koh Young SE Asia Pte. Ltd. (1)
Measuring Equipment Distr
N.A.I.C.S.: 423830
Peter Shin *(Mng Dir)*

KOHAT CEMENT COMPANY LIMITED
37-P Gulberg II, Lahore, Pakistan
Tel.: (92) 42111115225
Web Site:
https://www.kohatcement.com
KOHC—(KAR)
Rev.: $149,396,305
Assets: $224,099,782
Liabilities: $86,091,603
Net Worth: $138,008,179
Earnings: $21,719,520
Emp.: 696
Fiscal Year-end: 06/30/21
Grey & White Cement Mfr
N.A.I.C.S.: 325520
Nadeem Atta *(CEO)*

KOHINOOR CHEMICAL COMPANY (BANGLADESH) LIMITED
36 Shahid Tajuddin Ahmed Sharani, Tejgaon, Dhaka, 1208, Bangladesh
Tel.: (880) 28891267
Web Site: https://www.kohinoor-bd.com
Year Founded: 1956
KOHINOOR—(CHT)
Rev.: $48,869,346
Assets: $31,185,522
Liabilities: $14,568,840
Net Worth: $16,616,682
Earnings: $3,441,251

Emp.: 2,652
Fiscal Year-end: 06/30/23
Soap, Cosmetics & Toiletries Mfr
N.A.I.C.S.: 325611
Mohammad Obaidul Karim *(Chm)*

KOHINOOR ENERGY LIMITED
Post Office Raja Jang Near Tablighi Ijtima Raiwind Bypass, Lahore, Pakistan
Tel.: (92) 4235392317
Web Site: https://www.kel.com.pk
Year Founded: 1994
KOHE—(PSX)
Rev.: $45,267,886
Assets: $25,666,641
Liabilities: $6,300,946
Net Worth: $19,365,695
Earnings: $5,660,554
Emp.: 139
Fiscal Year-end: 06/30/23
Electrical Power Producers
N.A.I.C.S.: 221122
M. Naseem Saigol *(Chm)*

KOHINOOR FOODS LIMITED
Pinnacle Business Tower 10th Floor Surajkund, Delhi, 121001, India
Tel.: (91) 1294242222
Web Site: https://www.kohinoorfoods.in
Rev.: $86,408,538
Assets: $74,702,796
Liabilities: $124,408,104
Net Worth: ($49,705,308)
Earnings: ($59,855,160)
Emp.: 232
Fiscal Year-end: 03/31/19
Food Products Producer
N.A.I.C.S.: 111160
Kamal Deep Chawla *(CFO)*

Subsidiaries:

Indo European Foods Limited (1)
Kohinoor House Langer Rd, Felixstowe, IP11 2BW, Suffolk, United Kingdom
Tel.: (44) 1394276700
Web Site: https://kohinoor-joy.com
Sales Range: $25-49.9 Million
Emp.: 23
Food Products Mfr
N.A.I.C.S.: 311999
Sanjay Nayyar *(Gen Mgr)*

Kohinoor Foods USA Inc. (1)
40 Northfield Ave, Edison, NJ 08837
Tel.: (732) 868-4400
Web Site: http://www.kohinoorfoods.com
Sales Range: $25-49.9 Million
Emp.: 25
Frozen Food Mfr
N.A.I.C.S.: 311412

S.O.L Inc (1)
41 43 Saifee Jubliee St 3rd Fl Flat No 6, Mumbai, 400 003, Maharashtra, India
Tel.: (91) 9322216552
Web Site: http://www.solinc.in
Food Products Distr
N.A.I.C.S.: 424490

KOHINOOR INDUSTRIES LIMITED
17-Aziz Avenue Canal Bank Gulberg-V, Lahore, Pakistan
Tel.: (92) 4235715029
Web Site: https://www.kil.com.pk
KOIL—(PSX)
Rev.: $281,604
Assets: $3,739,496
Liabilities: $167,503
Net Worth: $3,571,992
Earnings: $156,723
Emp.: 18
Fiscal Year-end: 06/30/23
Textile Products Mfr
N.A.I.C.S.: 313110
M. Naseem Saigol *(Chm)*

KOHINOOR MAPLE LEAF GROUP
42 Lawrence Road, Lahore, Pakistan
Tel.: (92) 4236302261
Web Site: http://www.kmlg.com
Year Founded: 1953
Holding Company
N.A.I.C.S.: 551112
Tariq Sayeed Saigol *(Chm)*

Subsidiaries:

Kohinoor Textile Mills Limited (1)
42 Lawerence Road, Lahore, 54000, Pakistan
Tel.: (92) 4236283096
Web Site: https://www.kmlg.com
Rev.: $374,570,942
Assets: $469,620,449
Liabilities: $232,983,266
Net Worth: $236,637,183
Earnings: $33,056,367
Emp.: 7,666
Fiscal Year-end: 06/30/2023
Textile Products Mfr
N.A.I.C.S.: 313210
Taufique Sayeed Saigol *(CEO)*

Kohinoor Textile Mills Limited - Raiwind Division (1)
8th Km Manga-Raiwind Road, Kasur, 55050, Pakistan
Tel.: (92) 425394133
Textile Products Mfr
N.A.I.C.S.: 313240
Waleed Saigol *(Mng Dir)*

Maple Leaf Capital Limited (1)
6711 The Center 99 Queen's Road, Central, China (Hong Kong)
Tel.: (852) 21693905
Emp.: 2
Asset Management Services
N.A.I.C.S.: 531390
Michael Wexler *(CEO)*

Maple Leaf Cement Factory Limited (1)
42 Lawrence Road, Lahore, 54000, Pakistan
Tel.: (92) 4236302261
Web Site: https://www.kmlg.com
Rev.: $223,315,996
Assets: $322,283,393
Liabilities: $149,894,089
Net Worth: $172,389,304
Earnings: $20,760,340
Emp.: 1,636
Fiscal Year-end: 06/30/2023
Cement Mfr
N.A.I.C.S.: 325520
Sayeed Tariq Saigol *(Co-CEO)*

KOHINOOR MILLS LIMITED
8th K M Manga Raiwind Road, Kasur, Pakistan
Tel.: (92) 4236369340
Web Site: https://www.kohinoormills.com
Year Founded: 1949
KML—(PSX)
Rev.: $82,226,795
Assets: $84,290,476
Liabilities: $52,609,858
Net Worth: $31,680,618
Earnings: $1,662,933
Emp.: 1,856
Fiscal Year-end: 06/30/21
Textile Products Mfr
N.A.I.C.S.: 313110
Ismail Aamir Fayyaz *(COO)*

KOHINOOR TECHNO ENGINEERS LIMITED
Plot No1 Gajera Industrial Estate Opp I C Gandhi Mill A K Road, Surat, 395008, Gujarat, India
Tel.: (91) 261 2542786
Web Site: http://www.kohinoormachineries.com
Sales Range: Less than $1 Million
Diamond Cutting Tool Mfr
N.A.I.C.S.: 333515

Kiritbhai Surajram Bhatt *(Founder, Chm & Mng Dir)*

KOHL & FRISCH LIMITED
7622 Keele Street, Concord, L4K 2R5, ON, Canada
Tel.: (800) 265-2520
Web Site: http://www.kohlandfrisch.com
Year Founded: 1916
Sales Range: $75-99.9 Million
Emp.: 900
Drugs Whslr
N.A.I.C.S.: 424210
Ron Frisch *(Owner, Pres & CEO)*

KOHLTECH INTERNATIONAL LTD.
583 MacElmon Road, PO Box 131, Debert, B0M 1G0, NS, Canada
Tel.: (902) 662-3100
Web Site: https://www.kohltech.com
Year Founded: 1977
Rev.: $39,700,996
Emp.: 450
Windows & Doors Mfr & Distr
N.A.I.C.S.: 321911
Carl Ballard *(Pres)*

KOHNAN SHOJI CO., LTD.
2-2-17 Nishimiyahara, Yodogawa-ku, Osaka, 532-0004, Japan
Tel.: (81) 663971621
Web Site: https://www.hc-kohnan.com
Year Founded: 1978
7516—(TKS)
Rev.: $3,351,123,950
Assets: $3,251,169,130
Liabilities: $2,136,217,000
Net Worth: $1,114,952,130
Earnings: $99,642,860
Emp.: 4,429
Fiscal Year-end: 02/29/24
Home Center Operator
N.A.I.C.S.: 444110
Naotaro Hikida *(Pres)*

Subsidiaries:

Beavertozan Co., Ltd. (1)
24-1 Toda, Atsugi, 243-0023, Kanagawa, Japan
Tel.: (81) 462282233
Web Site: http://www.beavertozan.com
Home Improvement Services
N.A.I.C.S.: 444110

Ken Depot Corporation (1)
4F Kanda 91 Building 1-8-3, Kajicho Chiyoda-ku, Tokyo, 101-0044, Japan
Tel.: (81) 352567690
Web Site: http://www.kendepot.co.jp
Building Materials Whslr
N.A.I.C.S.: 423390

KOHOKU KOGYO CO., LTD.
1623 Takatsuki, Takatsuki-cho, Nagahama, 529-0241, Shiga, Japan
Tel.: (81) 749853211
Web Site: https://www.kohokukogyo.co.jp
Year Founded: 1959
6524—(TKS)
Rev.: $95,516,480
Assets: $177,058,570
Liabilities: $34,840,260
Net Worth: $142,218,310
Earnings: $13,499,360
Emp.: 1,430
Fiscal Year-end: 12/31/23
Electrical Component Mfr & Distr
N.A.I.C.S.: 335999
Futoshi Ishii *(Pres & CEO)*

Subsidiaries:

Dongguan Kohoku Electronics Co., Ltd. (1)
No 1 Xialingbei Duan Liaocheng Zhonglu, Liaobu, Dongguan, 523411, Guangdong, China
Tel.: (86) 76983286000
Capacitor Mfr
N.A.I.C.S.: 336320

EpiPhotonics Corp. (1)
ThreeEf Bldg 301B 1-5-6 Yamatohigashi, Yamato, 242-0017, Kanagawa, Japan
Tel.: (81) 462603140
Web Site: http://www.epiphotonics.com
Industrial Chemicals Mfr
N.A.I.C.S.: 334516
Keiichi Nashimoto *(Founder, Pres & CEO)*

Kohoku Electronics (M) Sdn.Bhd. (1)
Lot 2 Jalan Waja 15 Kawasan Perindustrian C PKNS, Telok Panglima Garang, 42500, Kuala Langat, Selangor, Malaysia
Tel.: (60) 331229475
Capacitor Mfr
N.A.I.C.S.: 336320

Kohoku Electronics (S) Pte.Ltd. (1)
101 Cecil Street 19-09 Tong Eng Building, Singapore, 069533, Singapore
Tel.: (65) 62851922
Optical Component Distr
N.A.I.C.S.: 423460

Kohoku Lanka (Pvt.) Ltd. (1)
Ring Road 3 Phase II EPZ, 11450, Katunayake, Sri Lanka
Tel.: (94) 112253492
Optical Component Mfr
N.A.I.C.S.: 327215

Suzhou Kohoku Opto-Electronics Co., Ltd. (1)
1F 2F Building 1 No 128 Taishan Road, Suzhou New District, Suzhou, Jiangsu, China
Tel.: (86) 51268087781
Capacitor Mfr
N.A.I.C.S.: 336320

KOHSAI CO. LTD
3049 Ryuuchi, Kai, 400-0194, Yamanashi, Japan
Tel.: (81) 551284181
Web Site: https://www.kohsai-qq.co.jp
Year Founded: 1967
78780—(TKS)
Sales Range: Less than $1 Million
Emp.: 111
Jewelry Product Mfr
N.A.I.C.S.: 339910
Eiji Fukasawa *(Pres & CEO)*

KOHSOKU CORPORATION
Ogimachi 7-4-20, Miyagino Ward, Sendai, 983-8555, Miyagi, Japan
Tel.: (81) 222591611
Web Site: https://www.kohsoku.com
Year Founded: 1966
7504—(TKS)
Rev.: $702,087,760
Assets: $406,501,780
Liabilities: $162,592,780
Net Worth: $243,909,000
Earnings: $20,583,540
Emp.: 1,023
Fiscal Year-end: 03/31/24
Food Packaging Material Mfr & Distr
N.A.I.C.S.: 333993
Koki Terashi *(Chm)*

KOIKE SANSO KOGYO CO., LTD.
7F KOIKE Bldg 3-4-8 Taihei, Sumida-ku, Tokyo, 130-0012, Japan
Tel.: (81) 336243111 JP
Web Site: https://www.koike-japan.com
Year Founded: 1918
6137—(TKS)
Rev.: $339,668,070
Assets: $485,676,360
Liabilities: $205,518,120
Net Worth: $280,158,240
Earnings: $20,200,160
Fiscal Year-end: 03/31/24

KOIKE SANSO KOGYO CO., LTD.

Koike Sanso Kogyo Co., Ltd.—(Continued)
Cutting & Welding Equipment & Medical Waste Disposal System Mfr
N.A.I.C.S.: 333992
Hideo Koike *(Chm, Pres & CEO)*

Subsidiaries:

Gunma Koike Co., Ltd. (1)
222-1 Naganuma-cho, Isesaki, 372-0855, Gunma, Japan
Tel.: (81) 270324318
Web Site: https://www.gunmakoike.co.jp
Emp.: 90
Machine Tools Mfr
N.A.I.C.S.: 333517

Hishiko Corporation (1)
3-13-1 Hongo, Bunkyo-ku, Tokyo, 113-0033, Japan
Tel.: (81) 358006655
Web Site: http://www.hishiko.co.jp
Sales Range: $25-49.9 Million
Emp.: 58
Magnet Applied Equipment Mfr & Distr
N.A.I.C.S.: 335999
Kenichi Kijima *(Pres)*

Koike Aronson Ransome (1)
635 W Main St, Arcade, NY 14009-1035 (100%)
Tel.: (585) 492-2400
Web Site: http://www.koike.com
Sales Range: $10-24.9 Million
Emp.: 100
Mfr of Welding & Positioning Equipment
N.A.I.C.S.: 621330

Koike Aronson, Inc. (1)
635 W Main St, Arcade, NY 14009
Tel.: (585) 492-2400
Web Site: http://www.koike.com
Sales Range: $50-74.9 Million
Emp.: 100
Welding, Positioning & Thermal Cutting Equipment Mfr
N.A.I.C.S.: 333519
Shane McMahon *(Product Mgr)*

Koike Engineering Germany GmbH (1)
Pappelweg 8, 61169, Friedberg, Germany
Tel.: (49) 603116157100
Web Site: http://www.koike-engineering.com
Industrial Engineering Services
N.A.I.C.S.: 541330
Tom Asano *(Exec Dir)*

Koike Engineering Tangshan Co., Ltd. (1)
No 3 Xichang Road, High-tech Industrial Development Zone, Tangshan, 063020, Hebei, China
Tel.: (86) 3153173858
Web Site: https://www.koike.cn
Engineeering Services
N.A.I.C.S.: 541330

Koike Medical Co., Ltd. (1)
1-24-8 Matsushima, Edogawa-ku, Tokyo, 132-0031, Japan
Tel.: (81) 356626607
Web Site: https://www.koike-medical.co.jp
Emp.: 180
Medical Dental & Hospital Equipment & Supplies Whslr
N.A.I.C.S.: 423450
Katsunori Morishita *(Pres)*

Koike Tech Co., Ltd. (1)
1-9-3 Ohnodai, Midori-ku, Chiba, 267-0056, Japan
Tel.: (81) 432255558
Web Site: https://www.koiketech.com
Emp.: 53
Industrial Machinery & Equipment Mfr
N.A.I.C.S.: 333248
Norio Onozuka *(Pres & Chief Maintenance Officer)*

Suganuma Sangyo K.K. (1)
2-20-15 Nihonzutsumi, Taito-ku, Tokyo, 111-0021, Japan
Tel.: (81) 338747421
Industrial Machinery & Equipment Mfr
N.A.I.C.S.: 333248

Tokyo Sansho K.K. (1)
1-4 Nauchi, Shiroi, 270-1407, Chiba, Japan
Tel.: (81) 474920211
Industrial Machinery & Equipment Mfr
N.A.I.C.S.: 333248

KOIKE-YA INC.
5-9-7 Narimasu, Itabashi-ku, Tokyo, 175-0094, Japan
Tel.: (81) 339792115
Web Site: http://www.koikeya.co.jp
Year Founded: 1977
2226—(TKS)
Rev.: $362,419,690
Assets: $240,597,390
Liabilities: $125,794,910
Net Worth: $114,802,480
Earnings: $14,594,880
Emp.: 434
Fiscal Year-end: 03/31/24
Snacks & Confectionery Product Mfr & Distr
N.A.I.C.S.: 311352
Takashi Koike *(Chm)*

KOIOS BEVERAGE CORP.
810 - 789 West Pender Street, Vancouver, V6C1H2, BC, Canada
Tel.: (844) 255-6467
Year Founded: 2012
FITSF—(OTCIQ)
Rev.: $1,200,983
Assets: $2,504,506
Liabilities: $1,589,845
Net Worth: $914,661
Earnings: ($21,159,674)
Fiscal Year-end: 05/31/22
Oil & Gas Exploration
N.A.I.C.S.: 211120
Johannes van der Linde *(CFO)*

KOITO MANUFACTURING CO., LTD.
Sumitomo Fudosan Osaki Twin Bldg East 5-1-18 Kitashinagawa, Shinagawa-ku, Tokyo, 141-0001, Japan
Tel.: (81) 334437111
Web Site: https://www.koito.co.jp
Year Founded: 1915
KOTMF—(OTCIQ)
Rev.: $6,200,035,230
Assets: $6,495,367,530
Liabilities: $1,687,839,510
Net Worth: $4,807,528,020
Earnings: $212,662,200
Emp.: 23,488
Fiscal Year-end: 03/31/23
Automotive Lighting Equipment & Aircraft Products Mfr
N.A.I.C.S.: 336340
Koichi Sakakibara *(Exec VP)*

Subsidiaries:

Aoitec Co., Ltd. (1)
162-1 Higashimikata-cho, Kita-ku, Hamamatsu, 433-8104, Shizuoka Prefecture, Japan
Tel.: (81) 534379291
Web Site: http://www.aoitec.co.jp
Emp.: 220
Automotive Electronic & Electrical Component Mfr
N.A.I.C.S.: 336320

BrightWay Vision Ltd. (1)
Hat Nahum 7 St, Tirat Karmel, 3508506, Israel
Tel.: (972) 46469900
Emp.: 20
Monitoring System Mfr
N.A.I.C.S.: 336320

Fujieda Auto Lighting Co., Ltd. (1)
800-18 Yokouchi, Fujieda, Shizuoka Prefecture, Japan
Tel.: (81) 546432135
Emp.: 100
Automotive Lighting Equipment Mfr
N.A.I.C.S.: 335139

Fuzhou Koito Tayih Automotive Lamp Co., Ltd. (1)
South East Motor Zone, Qingkou Minhou, Fuzhou, 350119, Fujian, China
Tel.: (86) 59122765266
Emp.: 300
Automotive Lighting Equipment Mfr
N.A.I.C.S.: 335139

Guangzhou Koito Automotive Lamp Co., Ltd. (1)
No B01 Transnational Industry Park, Yuexi Village Shilou Town Panyu District, Guangzhou, 511447, Guangdong, China
Tel.: (86) 2039307000
Emp.: 1,700
Automotive Lighting Equipment Mfr
N.A.I.C.S.: 335139

Haibara Machine & Tools Co., Ltd. (1)
Hosoe 6248, Makinohara, 421-0421, Shizuoka Prefecture, Japan
Tel.: (81) 548225665
Web Site: http://www.haibara-kouki.co.jp
Emp.: 50
Resin Metal Mold Mfr & Distr
N.A.I.C.S.: 333511

Hubei Koito Automotive Lamp Co., Ltd. (1)
No 1 Wenchang Road, Xiaogan National Hi-Tech Development Zone, Xiaogan, 432100, Hubei, China
Tel.: (86) 7122108700
Emp.: 700
Automotive Lighting Equipment Mfr
N.A.I.C.S.: 335139

India Japan Lighting Private Limited (1)
No 1 Puduchatram Tiruvallur High Road, Thirumazhisai, Chennai, 600124, Tamil Nadu, India (50%)
Tel.: (91) 4439106106
Emp.: 800
Automotive Lighting Equipment Mfr & Distr
N.A.I.C.S.: 335139

KI Holdings Co., Ltd. (1)
100 Maeda-cho, Totsuka-ku, Yokohama, Kanagawa, Japan (100%)
Tel.: (81) 458266850
Web Site: http://www.koito-ind.co.jp
Rev.: $415,477,440
Assets: $450,207,120
Liabilities: $287,259,120
Net Worth: $162,948,000
Earnings: $27,705,600
Emp.: 1,658
Fiscal Year-end: 09/30/2018
Holding Company
N.A.I.C.S.: 551112

Subsidiary (Domestic):

Koito Electric Industries, Ltd. (2)
720 Minami-Isshiki Nagaizumi-cho Suntogun, Shizuoka, Japan
Tel.: (81) 559887101
Rev.: $310,619,600
Emp.: 907
Railroad Car Equipment Mfr & Distr
N.A.I.C.S.: 336510
Tsuneo Yamaguchi *(Pres)*

KPS N.A., Inc. (1)
149 Wheeler Ave, Pleasantville, NY 10570
Tel.: (914) 747-8035
Web Site: https://www.kpsna.com
Railroad Car Seat Mfr
N.A.I.C.S.: 336360

Koito Czech s.r.o. (1)
Na Astre 3001, 438 01, Zatec, Czech Republic
Tel.: (420) 415930111
Web Site: http://www.koito-czech.cz
Emp.: 1,300
Automotive Lighting Equipment Mfr
N.A.I.C.S.: 335139

Koito Europe Limited (1)
Kingswood Rd, Hampton Lovett Ind Est, Droitwich, WR9 0QH, Worcestershire, United Kingdom
Tel.: (44) 1905790800
Web Site: http://www.koito-europe.co.uk
Sales Range: $200-249.9 Million
Emp.: 800
Mfr of Vehicular Lighting Equipment

N.A.I.C.S.: 336320

Koito Insurance Services Co., Ltd. (1)
4-8-3 Takanawa, Minato-ku, Tokyo, Japan
Tel.: (81) 334478841
Emp.: 5
Insurance Agency Services
N.A.I.C.S.: 524210

Koito Kyushu Limited (1)
1580-6 Kamiizumi Kuboizumimachi, Saga, 849-0902, Japan
Tel.: (81) 952718355
Web Site: http://www.koito-kyushu.co.jp
Emp.: 920
Automotive Lighting Equipment Mfr
N.A.I.C.S.: 335139

Koito Malaysia Sdn. Bhd. (1)
PT 12630 Jalan Techvalley 4/2 Kawasan Perindustrian, Sendayan Techvalley Bandar Sri Sendayan, 71950, Seremban, Malaysia
Tel.: (60) 66662800
Emp.: 200
Automotive Lighting Equipment Mfr
N.A.I.C.S.: 335139

Koito Transport Co., Ltd. (1)
873 Kikkawa, Shimizu-ku, Shizuoka, Japan
Tel.: (81) 543453016
Emp.: 70
Transportation & Logistics Services
N.A.I.C.S.: 488510

Minatsu, Ltd. (1)
559-6 Hirado-cho IK Building 2F, Totsuka-ku, Yokohama, 244-0803, Kanagawa, Japan
Tel.: (81) 458242150
Web Site: http://www.minatsu.co.jp
Emp.: 220
Traffic Light Maintenance Services
N.A.I.C.S.: 561990

NAL do Brasil Industria e Comercio de Componentes de Iluminacao Ltda. (1)
Avenida Comendador Camillo Julio n 500 Jardim Ibiti do Paco, Sorocaba, 18086-000, Sao Paulo, Brazil
Tel.: (55) 1531414300
Emp.: 400
Automotive Lighting Equipment Mfr
N.A.I.C.S.: 335139

New Fuji Co., Ltd. (1)
142-62 Hitoana, Fujinomiya, 418-0102, Shizuoka Prefecture, Japan
Tel.: (81) 544520106
Web Site: http://www.new-fuji.co.jp
Emp.: 5
Assembly Machine Mfr
N.A.I.C.S.: 333519

Nissei Industries Co., Ltd. (1)
790 Kikkawa, Shimizu-ku, Shizuoka, 424-0055, Japan
Tel.: (81) 543470311
Web Site: http://www.nissei-polarg.co.jp
Emp.: 160
Automotive Bulb Mfr
N.A.I.C.S.: 335139

North American Lighting Mexico, S.A. de C.V (1)
Av Santiago Poniente No 109 Parque Industrial Colinas de San Luis, Colonia Ciudad Satelite, 78423, San Luis Potosi, Mexico
Tel.: (52) 4448042300
Emp.: 1,200
Automotive Lighting Equipment Mfr
N.A.I.C.S.: 335139

North American Lighting, Inc. (1)
20 Industrial Park, Flora, IL 62839
Tel.: (618) 662-4483
Web Site: https://www.nal.com
Sales Range: $200-249.9 Million
Emp.: 550
Mfr of Motor Vehicle Lighting
N.A.I.C.S.: 336320
Mark Otake *(Chm)*

PT. Indonesia Koito (1)
Kawasan Industri Indotaisei Sektor 1A Blok P-3, Kalihurip-Cikampek, Karawang, 41373, Jawa Barat, Indonesia
Tel.: (62) 2648371088

AND PRIVATE COMPANIES

KOKUYO CO., LTD.

Emp.: 700
Automotive Lighting Equipment Mfr
N.A.I.C.S.: 335139

Shizuoka Wire Harness Co., Ltd. (1)
813-1 Kikkawa, Shimizu-ku, Shizuoka, Japan
Tel.: (81) 543451818
Web Site: http://www.swh.co.jp
Emp.: 130
Wire Harnesses Mfr
N.A.I.C.S.: 335931

Shizuokadenso Co., Ltd. (1)
632 Nagasaki, Shimizu-ku, Shizuoka, 424-0065, Japan
Tel.: (81) 543454131
Web Site: http://www.shizuokadensou.com
Emp.: 250
Automotive Lighting Equipment Mfr
N.A.I.C.S.: 335139

Ta Yih Industrial Co., Ltd. (1)
No 11 Xinxin Rd Zhangnan Vil, South Dist, T'ainan, 70268, Taiwan **(100%)**
Tel.: (886) 62615151
Web Site: https://www.tayih-ind.com.tw
Rev.: $157,526,532
Assets: $109,774,612
Liabilities: $51,786,943
Net Worth: $57,987,669
Earnings: $1,386,899
Emp.: 845
Fiscal Year-end: 12/31/2023
Mfr of Motor Vehicle Parts & Accessories
N.A.I.C.S.: 336340
Watanabe Masami *(Vice Chm)*

Takeda Suntech Co., Ltd. (1)
1-10-53 Kuniyoshida, Suruga-ku, Shizuoka, 422-8004, Japan
Tel.: (81) 542677551
Web Site: http://www.takedasuntec.co.jp
Emp.: 50
Resin Metal Mold Mfr
N.A.I.C.S.: 333511

KOIZUMI LIGHTING TECHNOLOGY CORP.
3-3-7 Bingo-machi, Chuo-ku, Osaka, Japan
Tel.: (81) 6 6266 5750
Web Site: http://www.koizumi-lt.co.jp
Year Founded: 1871
Emp.: 609
Lighting Equipment Mfr
N.A.I.C.S.: 335132
Teruyuki Umeda *(Pres & CEO)*

Subsidiaries:

KOIZUMI LIGHTING TECHNOLOGY (SINGAPORE) CORP PTE. LTD. (1)
10 Anson Road 17-06 International Plaza, Singapore, 079903, Singapore
Tel.: (65) 62210572
Emp.: 2
Lighting Fixture Distr
N.A.I.C.S.: 423610
Seiichi Nakajima *(Pres)*

Koizumi Lighting Technology (Shanghai) Co., Ltd. (1)
Room No 1105-1107 ZhonShanNanEr-lu No 440, XuHui, Shanghai, 200032, China
Tel.: (86) 2154202760
Web Site: http://www.koizumi.com.cn
Emp.: 45
Lighting Fixture Distr
N.A.I.C.S.: 423610
Ken Sugimoto *(Pres)*

MIK Smart Lighting Network Corporation (1)
4106-73 Oaza Miyota Miyota-machi, Kitasaku-gun, Nagano, Japan **(24.5%)**
Tel.: (81) 3 6758 6703
Lighting Equipment Designer & Mfr
N.A.I.C.S.: 335139
Shinichi Yamamura *(Exec Officer & Dir)*

KOJAMO OYJ
Mannerheimintie 168a, PO Box 40, 00301, Helsinki, Finland
Tel.: (358) 205083804
Web Site: https://www.kojamo.fi
Year Founded: 1969

KOJAMO—(HEL)
Rev.: $488,133,348
Assets: $9,005,740,149
Liabilities: $5,003,201,237
Net Worth: $4,002,538,912
Earnings: ($98,244,839)
Emp.: 288
Fiscal Year-end: 12/31/23
Asset Management Services
N.A.I.C.S.: 523940
Jani Nieminen *(CEO)*

KOJIMA CO., LTD.
2-1-8 Hoshigaoka, Utsunomiya, 320-8528, Tochigi, Japan
Tel.: (81) 353960707 JP
Web Site: https://www.kojima.net
Year Founded: 1963
7513—(TKS)
Sales Range: $1-4.9 Billion
Emp.: 4,905
Consumer Electronic & Home Appliance Stores
N.A.I.C.S.: 423620
Yuji Nakazawa *(Pres & Dir-Rep)*

KOJIMA IRON WORKS CO., LTD.
155 Kenzaki-machi Takasaki-shi, Takasaki, 370-0807, Gunma, Japan
Tel.: (81) 273431511
Web Site: https://www.kojimatekko.co.jp
Year Founded: 1809
6112—(TKS)
Hydraulic Machinery Mfr & Distr
N.A.I.C.S.: 333998
Shozo Kodama *(Pres)*

Subsidiaries:

Kojima Iron Works Co., Ltd. - Yahata Plant (1)
155 Kenzaki-machi, Takasaki, 370-0883, Gunma, Japan
Tel.: (81) 27 343 1511
Web Site: http://www.kojimatekko.co.jp
Emp.: 100
Hydraulic Machinery Mfr
N.A.I.C.S.: 333998
Shozo Kodama *(Pres)*

KOKAI SAS
6-10 boulevard Foch, 93807, Paris, France
Tel.: (33) 143525252
Web Site: http://www.kookai.fr
Emp.: 600
Women's Clothing Whslr
N.A.I.C.S.: 458110
Jacques Levy *(Chm & CEO)*

KOKEN BORING MACHINE CO.,LTD.
1st Floor Mejiro Nakano Bldg No 17-22 Takada 2-chome, Toshima-ku, Tokyo, 171-8572, Japan
Tel.: (81) 369077888
Web Site: https://www.koken-boring.co.jp
Year Founded: 1947
6297—(TKS)
Rev.: $79,501,840
Assets: $124,746,160
Liabilities: $79,279,200
Net Worth: $45,466,960
Earnings: $1,790,800
Emp.: 230
Fiscal Year-end: 03/31/23
Boring Machines Mfr
N.A.I.C.S.: 333517
Ryujiro Kiyama *(Pres & CEO)*

Subsidiaries:

KOKEN BORING MACHINE CO., LTD. - Atsugi Factory (1)
3012-2 Uenohara Kamiichi, Atsugi, 243-0801, Kanagawa, Japan

Tel.: (81) 462 85 1331
Drilling & Grouting Machine Mfr
N.A.I.C.S.: 333131

KOKEN BORING MACHINE CO., LTD. - Suwa Factory (1)
10801-3 Haramura, Suwagun, Suwa, 391-0100, Nagano, Japan
Tel.: (81) 266796011
Drilling & Grouting Machine Mfr
N.A.I.C.S.: 333131

KOKEN LTD.
7 Yonbancho, Chiyoda-ku, Tokyo, 102-8459, Japan
Tel.: (81) 352761911
Web Site: https://www.koken-ltd.co.jp
Year Founded: 1943
7963—(TKS)
Rev.: $75,061,830
Assets: $147,592,530
Liabilities: $60,016,850
Net Worth: $87,575,680
Earnings: $4,970,090
Emp.: 287
Fiscal Year-end: 12/31/23
Personal Protective Equipment Mfr
N.A.I.C.S.: 812199
Shinichiro Sakai *(Chm & CEO)*

KOKOPELLI, INC.
4F Nibancho Onuma Building 8-3 Nibancho, Chiyoda-Ku, Tokyo, 102-0084, Japan
Tel.: (81) 362614091
Web Site: https://www.kokopelli-inc.com
Year Founded: 2007
4167—(TKS)
Rev.: $12,036,810
Assets: $14,667,590
Liabilities: $2,987,720
Net Worth: $11,679,870
Earnings: $218,130
Emp.: 89
Fiscal Year-end: 03/31/24
Information Technology Services
N.A.I.C.S.: 541512
Shigeru Kondo *(Pres & CEO)*

KOKUSAI CO., LTD
6-21-1 Nagayama, Tama-shi, Tokyo, 206-0025, Japan
Tel.: (81) 423714211
Web Site: https://www.kokusaikk.co.jp
Year Founded: 1969
7722—(TKS)
Rev.: $67,651,121
Assets: $135,559,922
Liabilities: $62,781,614
Net Worth: $72,778,308
Earnings: ($1,704,658)
Emp.: 287
Fiscal Year-end: 03/31/24
Measuring & Controlling Device Mfr
N.A.I.C.S.: 334513
Hiroshi Matsumoto *(Pres)*

Subsidiaries:

KOREA KOKUSAI CO., LTD. (1)
9 Hosandong Ro 1 Gil Horim-dong, Dalseogu, Daegu, 42-715, Korea (South)
Tel.: (82) 535849955
Measuring Instrument Mfr & Distr
N.A.I.C.S.: 334519

Kokusai (Shanghai) Co., Ltd. (1)
889 Shenfu Road Xinzhuang Industry Park, Shanghai, 201108, China
Tel.: (86) 2154426886
Web Site: http://www.kokusaicn.com
Measuring Instrument Mfr & Distr
N.A.I.C.S.: 334519

Kokusai Europe GmbH (1)
Ludwigstrasse 31, 60327, Frankfurt am Main, Germany
Tel.: (49) 6974227886
Web Site: http://www.kokusai.eu
Measuring Instrument Mfr & Distr
N.A.I.C.S.: 334519

Takashi Takami *(Mng Dir)*

Kokusai Incorporated (1)
5333 W 79th St, Indianapolis, IN 46268
Tel.: (317) 704-9922
Web Site: http://www.kokusaiusa.com
Measuring Instrument Mfr & Distr
N.A.I.C.S.: 334519

PT. KOKUSAI ENGINEERING INDONESIA (1)
Komplek Permata Arcadia G21 Cimanggis, Depok, 16954, Indonesia
Tel.: (62) 2180364050
Measuring Instrument Mfr & Distr
N.A.I.C.S.: 334519
Dhani Parasetyo *(Mng Dir)*

Thai Kokusai Co., Ltd. (1)
66 Q House Asoke Bldg 14th Floor Room 1404 Sukhumvit 21, North Klongtoey Wattana, Bangkok, 10110, Thailand
Tel.: (66) 22594741
Web Site: http://www.kokusaikk.co.jp
Measuring Instrument Mfr & Distr
N.A.I.C.S.: 334519

KOKUYO CO., LTD.
6-1-1 Oimazato Minami, Higashinari-ku, Osaka, 537-8686, Japan
Tel.: (81) 669761221 JP
Web Site: https://www.kokuyo.com
Year Founded: 1905
7984—(TKS)
Rev.: $2,330,858,770
Assets: $2,541,141,080
Liabilities: $744,350,740
Net Worth: $1,796,790,340
Earnings: $135,199,210
Emp.: 6,825
Fiscal Year-end: 12/31/23
Paper Products & Office & Business Furniture Designer & Mfr
N.A.I.C.S.: 322230
Hidekuni Kuroda *(Pres, Pres & CEO)*

Subsidiaries:

Actus Co., Ltd. (1)
2-19-1 Shinjuku Bygs Shinjuku Building 12th floor, Shinjuku, Tokyo, 160-0022, Japan
Tel.: (81) 35 269 3201
Web Site: https://www.actus-interior.com
Emp.: 689
Furniture Retailer
N.A.I.C.S.: 449110

CW Facility Solution Inc. (1)
1-2-70 Konan Season Terrace 18F, Minato-ku Shinagawa, Tokyo, 108-8459, Japan
Tel.: (81) 334746530
Web Site: https://www.cw-facility-s.jp
Real Estate Consulting Service
N.A.I.C.S.: 531390

KOKUYO Hokkaido Sales Co., Ltd. (1)
5-1-1 Higashisapporo, Shiroishi-ku, Sapporo, 003-0005, Hokkaido, Japan
Tel.: (81) 11 815 5940
Web Site: https://www.kokuyo-hokkaido.co.jp
Emp.: 54
Office Equipment Whslr
N.A.I.C.S.: 423420

KOKUYO Hokuriku Niigata Sales Co., Ltd. (1)
2-17-2 Kurose Kitamachi, Toyama, 939-8216, Japan
Tel.: (81) 76 491 5946
Web Site: https://www.kokuyo-h.com
Emp.: 102
Office Supplies Whslr
N.A.I.C.S.: 424120

KOKUYO Kitakanto Sales Co., Ltd. (1)
3172-48 Tonyamachi, Utsunomiya, 321-0911, Tochigi, Japan
Tel.: (81) 28 656 5561
Web Site: https://www.kokuyo-kitakanto.co.jp
Office Supplies Whslr
N.A.I.C.S.: 424120

KOKUYO CO., LTD.

Kokuyo Co., Ltd.—(Continued)

KOKUYO Sanyo Shikoku Sales Co., Ltd. (1)
6F Okayama New City Building 3-10 Togiya-cho, Kita-ku, Okayama, 700-0826, Sumitomo, Japan
Tel.: (81) 86 225 5943
Web Site: http://www.kokuyo-sanyo.co.jp
Emp.: 85
Office Supplies Whslr
N.A.I.C.S.: 424120
Chiharu Shirasagi *(Pres)*

KOKUYO Tohoku Sales Co., Ltd. (1)
2-9-10 Central 10th floor Center Tohoku, Aoba-ku, Sendai, 980-0021, Japan
Tel.: (81) 22 796 6594
Web Site: https://www.kokuyo-touhoku.com
Emp.: 98
Office Supplies Whslr
N.A.I.C.S.: 424120

KOKUYO Tokai Sales Co., Ltd. (1)
Kato Ken Building 1-4-10 Kamimaezu, Naka-ku, Nagoya, 460-0013, Aichi, Japan
Tel.: (81) 52 324 5941
Web Site: https://www.kokuyo-tokai.com
Emp.: 50
Office Supplies Whslr
N.A.I.C.S.: 424120

Kaunet Co., Ltd. (1)
1-2-70 Konan Shinagawa Season Terrace 18th floor, Minato-ku, Tokyo, 108-8459, Japan
Tel.: (81) 12 002 8775
Web Site: https://company.kaunet.com
Emp.: 254
Online Shopping Services
N.A.I.C.S.: 425120

Kokuyo & Partners Co., Ltd. (1)
18F Kasumigaseki Building 3-2-5, Kasumigaseki Chiyoda-ku, Tokyo, 100-6018, Japan
Tel.: (81) 355104552
Property Development Services
N.A.I.C.S.: 531390

Kokuyo (Malaysia) Sdn. Bhd. (1)
Lot 79 83 Senawang Industrial Park, 70400, Seremban, Negeri Sembilan D K, Malaysia
Tel.: (60) 6 679 6096
Web Site: http://www.kokuyo-furniture.com
Sales Range: $25-49.9 Million
Furniture Retailer
N.A.I.C.S.: 449110

Kokuyo (Shanghai) Management Co., Ltd. (1)
Room201 2F TowerB Sim Technology Building Lane 633 Jinzhong Road, Changning District, Shanghai, 200335, China
Tel.: (86) 216 070 2650
Web Site: https://www.kokuyo.com
Office Furniture Distr
N.A.I.C.S.: 423210

Kokuyo Camlin Ltd. (1)
48/2 Hilton House Central Road, MIDC Andheri E, Mumbai, 400 093, Maharashtra, India (50.74%)
Tel.: (91) 2266557000
Web Site: https://www.kokuyocamlin.com
Rev.: $93,162,580
Assets: $53,025,286
Liabilities: $21,543,241
Net Worth: $31,482,045
Earnings: $2,931,155
Emp.: 983
Fiscal Year-end: 03/31/2023
Art Materials & Stationery Products Mfr
N.A.I.C.S.: 339940
Ravindra V. Damle *(Compliance Officer, Sec & VP)*

Kokuyo Chubu Sales Co., Ltd. (1)
Nagoyawakamiya Bldg, Nagoya, Japan
Tel.: (81) 522693850
Furniture Retailer
N.A.I.C.S.: 449110

Kokuyo Co., Ltd. (1)
42 Duxton Road, Singapore, 089506, Singapore
Tel.: (65) 62227535
Stationery Product Mfr
N.A.I.C.S.: 322230

Kokuyo Co., Ltd. (1)
42 Duxton Road, Singapore, 089506, Singapore
Tel.: (65) 62227535
Stationery Product Mfr
N.A.I.C.S.: 322230

Kokuyo Commerce (Shanghai) Co., Ltd. (1)
Room 203 Building B Chenxun Technology Building No 633 Jinzhong Road, Changning District, Shanghai, 200335, China
Tel.: (86) 213 252 3939
Web Site: https://www.kokuyo.com
Office Supplies Distr
N.A.I.C.S.: 424120

Kokuyo Design Consultants (Shanghai) Co., Ltd. (1)
1F Xinjinqiao Square No 7 West Beijing Road, Huangpu District, Shanghai, 200003, China
Tel.: (86) 216 141 3000
Web Site: http://www.kokuyo.com
Sales Range: $50-74.9 Million
Office Furniture Distr
N.A.I.C.S.: 423420

Kokuyo Engineering & Technology Co., Ltd. (1)
6-1-1 Oimazato-Minami Higashinari-ku, Osaka, 537-8686, Japan
Tel.: (81) 669761221
Furniture Retailer
N.A.I.C.S.: 449110

Kokuyo Finance Co., Ltd. (1)
6-1-1 Oimazatominami, Higashinari-ku, Osaka, 537-8686, Japan
Tel.: (81) 66 976 1221
Web Site: http://www.kokuyo.co.jp
Sales Range: $50-74.9 Million
Emp.: 10
Commercial & Industrial Machinery & Equipment Rental & Leasing
N.A.I.C.S.: 532490

Kokuyo Furniture (China) Co., Ltd. (1)
1F Xinjinqiao Square No 7 West Beijing Road, Huangpu District, Shanghai, 200003, China
Tel.: (86) 2161413001
Paper Products Mfr
N.A.I.C.S.: 322230

Kokuyo Furniture Commerce and Trading (Shanghai) Co., Ltd. (1)
5F Cartelo Crocodile Building No 568 West Tianshan Road, Changning District, 200335, Shanghai, China
Tel.: (86) 21 6141 3110
Web Site: http://www.kokuyo.com.hk
Home Furniture Distr
N.A.I.C.S.: 423210

Kokuyo International (Malaysia) Sdn. Bhd. (1)
E-31-08 Menara Suezcap 2 KL Gateway No 2 Jalan Kerinchi, Gerbang Kerinchi Lestari, 59200, Kuala Lumpur, Malaysia
Tel.: (60) 327202820
Paper Products Mfr
N.A.I.C.S.: 322230

Kokuyo International (Thailand) Co., Ltd. (1)
999/9 The Office at Central World 9th Fl Unit912 Rama 1 Rd, Pathumwan, Bangkok, 10330, Thailand
Tel.: (66) 22645100
Paper Products Mfr
N.A.I.C.S.: 322230

Kokuyo International Asia Co., Ltd. (1)
8F The Sun's Group Centre 200 Gloucester Road, Wanchai, China (Hong Kong)
Tel.: (852) 2 522 3292
Web Site: http://www.kokuyo.com.hk
Sales Range: $25-49.9 Million
Emp.: 30
Furniture Retailer
N.A.I.C.S.: 449110

Kokuyo International Co., Ltd. (1)
6-1-1 Oimazato-Minami, Higashinari, Osaka, 537-8686, Japan
Tel.: (81) 669768222
Web Site: http://www.kokuyo.co.jp

Sales Range: $25-49.9 Million
Emp.: 6
Converted Paper Product Mfr
N.A.I.C.S.: 322299

Kokuyo K Heart Co., Ltd. (1)
6-8-10 Oimazatominami, Higashinari-ku, Osaka, 537-0013, Japan
Tel.: (81) 669739322
Web Site: https://www.kokuyo-k-heart.com
Furniture Retailer
N.A.I.C.S.: 449129

Kokuyo Kinki Sales Co., Ltd. (1)
6-1-1 Oimazato-minami, Higashinari-Ku, Osaka, 537-8686, Japan
Tel.: (81) 66976 8200
Web Site: http://www.kokuyo.co.jp
Showroom Sales & Services
N.A.I.C.S.: 423220

Kokuyo Kyushu Sales Co., Ltd. (1)
Daihakata Bldg 3rd Floor, Fukuoka, Japan
Tel.: (81) 924375941
Non-Durable Goods Whslr
N.A.I.C.S.: 424990

Kokuyo Logitem Co., Ltd. (1)
6-1-1 Oimazatominami, Higashinari-ku, Osaka, 537-8686, Japan
Tel.: (81) 66 973 9470
Web Site: https://www.kokuyo-logitem.co.jp
Transportation Services
N.A.I.C.S.: 488999

Kokuyo MVP Co., Ltd. (1)
2-201 Minami Koyama-cho, Tottori, 680-0945, Japan
Tel.: (81) 85 728 0241
Web Site: https://www.kokuyo-mvp.co.jp
Emp.: 240
Stationery Product Mfr
N.A.I.C.S.: 322230

Kokuyo Marketing Co., Ltd. (1)
18F Kasumigaseki Building 3-2-5 Kasumigaseki, Chiyoda-ku, Tokyo, 100-6018, Japan
Tel.: (81) 355103146
Non-Durable Goods Whslr
N.A.I.C.S.: 424990

Kokuyo Nishikanto Sales Co., Ltd. (1)
1-23-15 Shinkoyasu, Kanagawa-Ku, Yokohama, Japan
Tel.: (81) 454357411
Printing & Writing Paper & Whslr
N.A.I.C.S.: 424110

Kokuyo Product Shiga Co., Ltd. (1)
Kamigano 312 Aisyo-cho, Echi-gun, Shiga, 529-1203, Japan
Tel.: (81) 74 937 3611
Web Site: https://www.kokuyo-shiga.co.jp
Emp.: 153
Stationery Product Mfr
N.A.I.C.S.: 322230

Kokuyo Riddhi Paper Products Pvt., Ltd. (1)
4th Floor Casablanca 10 Gulhmor Cross Road Jvpd, Mumbai, 400 049, Maharashtra, India
Tel.: (91) 2266990036
Web Site: https://www.krpaperproducts.com
Office Paper Stationary Product Mfr & Distr
N.A.I.C.S.: 322230

Kokuyo Store Creation (Shanghai) Co., Ltd. (1)
7F Siyuan Building 500 Middle Xizang Road, Huangpu District, Shanghai, 200003, China
Tel.: (86) 21 6141 3001
Sales Range: $25-49.9 Million
Emp.: 150
Office Supplies Distr
N.A.I.C.S.: 424120

Kokuyo Store Creation Co., Ltd. (1)
1-8-35 Konan, Minato-Ku, Tokyo, Japan
Tel.: (81) 334746066
Web Site: http://www.kokuyo.co.jp
Sales Range: $50-74.9 Million
Emp.: 120
Furniture Retailer
N.A.I.C.S.: 449110

Kokuyo Trading (Shanghai) Co., Ltd. (1)
No 568 St W Tian, 4 Fl Cartelo Crocodile Bldg, 200335, Shanghai, China
Tel.: (86) 2161413080
Web Site: http://www.kokuyo.cn
Furniture Retailer
N.A.I.C.S.: 449110

Kokuyo Vietnam Co., Ltd. (1)
Land plot B2-B7 Nomura Haiphong IZ, An Duong Dist, Haiphong, Vietnam
Tel.: (84) 225 374 3257
Web Site: https://www.kokuyo.vn
Sales Range: $150-199.9 Million
Emp.: 500
Stationery Products Mfr & Distr
N.A.I.C.S.: 322230

Kokuyo Vietnam Trading Co., Ltd. (1)
Land plot B2-B7 Nomura Haiphong IZ, An Duong District, Haiphong, Vietnam
Tel.: (84) 2253743422
Paper Products Mfr
N.A.I.C.S.: 322230

Kokuyo-IK (Thailand) Co., Ltd. (1)
529 Moo 4 Bangpoo Industrial Estate Soi 8C T Praksa, A Muang, Samut Prakan, 10280, Thailand
Tel.: (66) 2 709 4675
Web Site: http://www.kokuyo.com
Stationery Products Mfr & Distr
N.A.I.C.S.: 322230

PT. Kokuyo Furniture Indonesia (1)
The Plaza Office Tower 28th Floor JL M H Thamrin Kav28-30, Jakarta, 10350, Indonesia
Tel.: (62) 2129922875
Paper Products Mfr
N.A.I.C.S.: 322230

S&T Logistics (Shanghai) Co., Ltd. (1)
No 333 XingBang Rd, JiaDing District, Shanghai, 201815, China
Tel.: (86) 2152849988
Paper Products Mfr
N.A.I.C.S.: 322230

KOLEKTOR GROUP D.O.O.
Vojkova ulica 10, 5280, Idrija, Slovenia
Tel.: (386) 53750100
Web Site: http://www.kolektorgroup.com
Sales Range: $200-249.9 Million
Emp.: 100
Holding Company; Commutators Mfr
N.A.I.C.S.: 551112
Ludvik Kumar *(Exec Dir-Res)*

Subsidiaries:

Kolektor ATP d.o.o. (1)
Industrijska c 2, 6230, Postojna, Slovenia
Tel.: (386) 5 728 37 00
Thermoplastic Product Mfr
N.A.I.C.S.: 325211
Primoz Vrenk *(Mgr-Technical)*

Kolektor Automotive Nanjing Co., Ltd. (1)
No 99 Guangli Road Dongshanqiao Industrial Zone, Jiangning District, Nanjing, 211153, Jiangsu, China
Tel.: (86) 25 6668 5720
Commutator Whlsr
N.A.I.C.S.: 423120
Bostjan More *(Gen Mgr)*

Kolektor Bosna d.o.o. (1)
Nemanjina 61, 78250, Laktasi, Bosnia & Herzegovina
Tel.: (387) 51 530 900
Commutator Mfr
N.A.I.C.S.: 335312

Kolektor Commutator Wuxi Co., Ltd. (1)
No 2A Workshop 73F Block, Wuxi New District, Wuxi, Jiangsu, China
Tel.: (86) 51088651666
Web Site: http://www.kolektorgroup.com
Motor & Generator Mfr
N.A.I.C.S.: 335312
Igor Eogataj *(Gen Mgr)*

Kolektor Comtrade GmbH (1)

Tassendorferstrasse 62, 9020, Klagenfurt, Austria
Tel.: (43) 46345017
Web Site: http://www.kolektorgroup.com
Metal Coating Engraving & Allied Services to Mfr
N.A.I.C.S.: 332812

Kolektor Febo d.o.o. (1)
Omladinska 66, 78250, Laktasi, Bosnia & Herzegovina
Tel.: (387) 51 530 944
Electronic Components Mfr
N.A.I.C.S.: 334416

Kolektor Kautt & Bux GmbH (1)
Schiessmauer 9, 71083, Herrenberg, Germany
Tel.: (49) 70329356245
Plastics Product Mfr
N.A.I.C.S.: 326199

Kolektor Koling Inzeniring, Instalacije, Proizvodnja D.o.o. (1)
Arkova 43, 5820, Idrija, Slovenia
Tel.: (386) 53734160
Web Site: http://www.kolektor.com
Sales Range: $50-74.9 Million
Emp.: 80
Electronic Parts & Equipment Merchant Whslr
N.A.I.C.S.: 423690

Kolektor Liv Postojna, D.d. (1)
Industrijska C 2, 6230, Postojna, Slovenia
Tel.: (386) 57283702
Web Site: http://www.liv.si
Sales Range: $50-74.9 Million
Emp.: 250
Motor Vehicle Electrical & Electronic Equipment Mfr
N.A.I.C.S.: 336320

Kolektor Magma D.o.o (1)
Stegne 29, 1521, Ljubljana, Slovenia
Tel.: (386) 15833100
Sales Range: $50-74.9 Million
Emp.: 200
Electronic Components Manufacturing
N.A.I.C.S.: 334419

Kolektor Magnet Technology GmbH (1)
Zur Halbinsel 6, 45356, Essen, Germany
Tel.: (49) 201 17897 0
Plastic Bonded Permanent Magnet Whslr
N.A.I.C.S.: 423690

Kolektor Missel Schwab GmbH (1)
Max-Planck-Strasse 23, 70736, Stuttgart, Germany
Tel.: (49) 71153080
Web Site: http://www.missel.de
Supplier of Sound & Fire Prevention Insulation Products & Sanitary Systems
N.A.I.C.S.: 423330
Rado Starc (Mng Dir)

Kolektor Prokos D.o.o. (1)
Lapajnetova Ulica 9, 5280, Idrija, Slovenia
Tel.: (386) 55772331
Sales Range: $25-49.9 Million
Emp.: 4
Law firm
N.A.I.C.S.: 541199

Kolektor Sikom d.o.o. (1)
Vojkova 10, 5280, Idrija, Slovenia
Tel.: (386) 53750100
Web Site: http://www.kolektor.si
Emp.: 3,000
Machinery Mfr
N.A.I.C.S.: 333998
Darja Petric (CFO)

Kolektor Sinabit d.o.o. (1)
Slandrova ulica 10, Crnuce, 1231, Ljubljana, Slovenia
Tel.: (386) 1 563 63 00
Computer System Design Services
N.A.I.C.S.: 541512
Jernej Hrovat (Mng Dir)

Kolektor Sinyung Industrial Co., Ltd. (1)
1 2L 12-2B Gumi No 4 Industrial Complex, Bongsan-li Sandong-myeon Gumi, 730-853, Seoul, Korea (South)
Tel.: (82) 544700600
Web Site: http://www.kolektorsinyung.com

Sales Range: $50-74.9 Million
Emp.: 70
Electronic Parts & Equipment Merchant Whslr
N.A.I.C.S.: 423690

Kolektor Synatec d.o.o. (1)
Vojkova ulica 8b p p 57, 5280, Idrija, Slovenia
Tel.: (386) 5 372 06 50
Emp.: 20
Automotive Part Whslr
N.A.I.C.S.: 423120
Erik Iakner (Program Mgr)

Kolektor TKI Inc. (1)
110 Southchase Blvd, Fountain Inn, SC 29644
Tel.: (864) 409-8784
Commutator Mfr & Whslr
N.A.I.C.S.: 335312
Tiffany Blakley (Mgr-Quality Assurance)

Prokol d.o.o. (1)
Lapajnetova 9, 5280, Idrija, Slovenia
Tel.: (386) 53750227
Web Site: http://www.prokol.si
Sales Range: $25-49.9 Million
Emp.: 34
Electrical Products Mfr
N.A.I.C.S.: 423610

KOLIBRI KAPITAL AS
Oevre Slottsgate 3, Oslo, 0157, Norway
Tel.: (47) 41564194
Asset Management Services
N.A.I.C.S.: 523940
Sindre Ottesen (CEO)

KOLIN INSAAT TURIZM SANAYI VE TICARET A.S.
Horasan Sok No 14, Ankara, 66700, Turkiye
Tel.: (90) 3124471700
Web Site: http://www.kolin.com.tr
Year Founded: 1977
Sales Range: $1-4.9 Billion
Emp.: 3,791
Industrial Building Construction Services
N.A.I.C.S.: 236210
Naci Kologlu (Chm)

KOLING AD
Kronstatska 5, 11000, Belgrade, Serbia
Tel.: (381) 11 3670 935
Web Site: http://www.koling.rs
Year Founded: 1990
KLNG—(BEL)
Sales Range: Less than $1 Million
Emp.: 1,080
Construction Services
N.A.I.C.S.: 237990

KOLINPHARMA S.P.A.
Corso Europa 5, 20020, Lainate, MI, Italy
Tel.: (39) 0294324300
Web Site:
  http://www.kolinpharma.com
KIP—(ITA)
Sales Range: Less than $1 Million
Biotechnology Research & Development Services
N.A.I.C.S.: 541714
Rita Paola Petrelli (Founder, Chm & Co-CEO)

KOLLAKORN CORPORATION LIMITED
Level 9 65 York Street, Sydney, 2000, NSW, Australia
Tel.: (61) 280800033   AU
Web Site: http://www.kollakorn.com
Year Founded: 1993
KKL—(ASX)
Rev.: $251,668
Assets: $2,925,271

Liabilities: $5,145,161
Net Worth: ($2,219,890)
Earnings: ($2,888,339)
Emp.: 2
Fiscal Year-end: 06/30/20
Security Software Development Services
N.A.I.C.S.: 541511
David Matthews (CEO)

Subsidiaries:

Mikoh Corporation (1)
909 W 16th St, Newport Beach, CA 92663
Tel.: (949) 467-9289
Web Site: http://shop.mikoh.com
Women's Clothing Retailer
N.A.I.C.S.: 458110

KOLLMORGEN STEUERUNGSTECHNIK GMBH
Broichstrasse 32, 51109, Cologne, Germany
Tel.: (49) 22189850
Web Site: http://www.kollmorgen.de
Year Founded: 1965
Sales Range: $10-24.9 Million
Emp.: 95
Electrical Component Mfr
N.A.I.C.S.: 335999
Bjorn Kollmorgen (Mng Dir)

KOLMAR DE MEXICO, S.A. DE C.V.
Calle Lateral No 20, Tequesquinahuac Ceylan, Tlalnepantla, 54020, Mexico
Tel.: (52) 5553101009   MX
Web Site: http://www.osghq.com
Sales Range: $25-49.9 Million
Emp.: 80
Mfr of Cosmetics
N.A.I.C.S.: 325620
Louis Rovriguez (Mng Dir)

KOLMARBNH CO., LTD.
Web Site: http://www.kolmarbnh.co.kr
200130—(KRS)
Rev.: $441,717,596
Assets: $473,177,054
Liabilities: $164,315,957
Net Worth: $308,861,097
Earnings: $31,073,343
Emp.: 516
Fiscal Year-end: 12/31/22
Investment Holding Company
N.A.I.C.S.: 551112
Hwayung Jung (CEO)

KOLON CORP.
17F Kolon Tower 11 Kolon-ro, Gwacheon, Gyeonggi-do, Korea (South)
Tel.: (82) 2 3677 3114
Web Site: http://www.kolon.com
Year Founded: 1954
Holding Company
N.A.I.C.S.: 551112
Woong Yeul Lee (Chm)

Subsidiaries:

Kolon Fashion Material, Inc. (1)
Kolon Ro 11, Gwacheon, Gyeonggi-Do, Korea (South)
Tel.: (82) 236774286
Web Site: http://www.kolonmaterials.com
Rev.: $2,741,661
Assets: $60,052,548
Liabilities: $27,180,017
Net Worth: $32,872,531
Earnings: ($11,672,036)
Emp.: 151
Fiscal Year-end: 12/31/2022
Textile Materials Mfr
N.A.I.C.S.: 314999
Chul Soo Kim (CEO)

Kolon Global Corporation (1)
Songdo IT Center 32 Songdogwahak-ro, Yeonsu-gu, Incheon, Korea (South)
Tel.: (82) 324209111

Web Site: http://www.kolonglobal.com
Rev.: $1,995,792,963
Assets: $2,173,791,199
Liabilities: $1,741,655,335
Net Worth: $432,135,864
Earnings: $109,013,816
Emp.: 3,430
Fiscal Year-end: 12/31/2022
Heavy Civil Engineering & Construction Services
N.A.I.C.S.: 237990
Chang Woon Yoon (CEO)

Kolon Plastics Inc. (1)
64 Gongdan 3-gil, Gimcheon, Gyeongsangbuk-do, Korea (South)
Tel.: (82) 544208371
Web Site: http://www.kolonplastics.com
Rev.: $397,364,186
Assets: $296,862,367
Liabilities: $100,714,853
Net Worth: $196,147,515
Earnings: $27,377,903
Emp.: 372
Fiscal Year-end: 12/31/2022
Plastic Mfr
N.A.I.C.S.: 326199
Jong-Moon Kim (Chief Div Officer-Production Div)

KOLON ENVIRONMENTAL SERVICE CO. LTD.
6F 55 Pyeongchon-daero 212 beon-gil, Dongan-gu, Anyang, 14067, Gyeonggi-do, Korea (South)
Tel.: (82) 2 2120 8200
Web Site: http://www.kolon-kesco.com
Year Founded: 2002
Environmental Engineering Services
N.A.I.C.S.: 541330
Yong Chung Kong (Mgr)

KOLON INDUSTRIES, INC.
1-23 Kolon Tower Byeoryang-dong, Gwacheon, Gyeonggi-Do, Korea (South)
Tel.: (82) 236773114
Web Site:
  http://www.kolonindustries.com
Year Founded: 1957
002020—(KRS)
Rev.: $4,341,160,461
Assets: $3,434,235,704
Liabilities: $2,548,386,311
Net Worth: $885,849,394
Earnings: $128,007,157
Emp.: 81
Fiscal Year-end: 12/31/22
Textile & Chemical Mfr
N.A.I.C.S.: 314999
Ok Yun Sok (Mng Dir)

Subsidiaries:

FnC Kolon Beijing Corp. (1)
No 610 Air China Plaza No 36 Xiaoyun Road, Chaoyang District, Beijing, China
Tel.: (86) 10 8447 5684
Tire Cord & Polyester Film Mfr
N.A.I.C.S.: 314994

FnC Kolon Shanghai Corp. (1)
Shanghaishi Wuzhonglu 1079 Hao Canhongdasha 4 Lou a zuo, Shanghai, China
Tel.: (86) 21 5422 3520
Tire Cord & Polyester Film Mfr
N.A.I.C.S.: 314994
Yu Vanilla (Brand Mgr-Mktg)

FnC Kolon USA Corp. (1)
547 S Western Ave Ste B, Los Angeles, CA 90020
Tel.: (213) 382-1240
Tire Cord & Polyester Film Mfr
N.A.I.C.S.: 314994

Kolon EU GmbH (1)
Arabella Center 7A Lyoner Str 44 48, 60528, Frankfurt, Germany
Tire Cord & Polyester Film Mfr
N.A.I.C.S.: 314994
Dong Hoom Lim (Mgr)

Kolon GP Chemical Co., Ltd (1)

KOLON INDUSTRIES, INC.

Kolon Industries, Inc.—(Continued)
56 Qing Qiu Road, Suzhou Industrial Park, Suzhou, 215126, China
Tel.: (86) 512 6283 3311
Web Site: http://www.kolonchemical.cn
Chemical Products Mfr
N.A.I.C.S.: 325998

Kolon Huizhou Co., Ltd. (1)
H2 Dayawan Economic and Technical Development Zone, Huizhou, 516082, Guangdong, China
Tel.: (86) 7525280376
Resin Mfr
N.A.I.C.S.: 325211

Kolon Industries Binh Duong Company Limited (1)
Lot C- 5- Expanded Bau Bang Industrial Park, Lai Uyen commune Bau Bang, 590000, Binh Duong, Vietnam
Tel.: (84) 2742222139
Web Site: https://kolon-industries-binh-duong-co-ltd.business.site
Resin Mfr
N.A.I.C.S.: 325211

Kolon Industries Inc. - Gyeongsan Plant (1)
1298 Daehak-ro, Jillyang-eup, Gyeongsan, Gyeongsangbuk-do, Korea (South)
Tel.: (82) 538502012
Web Site: http://www.kolonindustry.com
Yarn Mfr
N.A.I.C.S.: 313110

Kolon Industries Inc.-Chemical Organization (1)
10th Fl Kolon Tower 1-23 Byolyang-dong, Kwach'on, Korea (South)
Tel.: (82) 236776046
Web Site: http://www.kolonchemical.co.kr
Sales Range: $450-499.9 Million
Emp.: 500
Petrochemical Resin Mfr
N.A.I.C.S.: 325998

Kolon Industries, Inc. - Gimcheon Plant 1 (1)
238 Gongdan ro, Gimcheon, Gyeongsangbuk, Korea (South)
Tel.: (82) 54 429 7331
Nylon & Polyester Film Mfr
N.A.I.C.S.: 326112

Kolon Industries, Inc. - Gimcheon Plant 2 (1)
128 Gongdan ro, Gimcheon, Gyeongsangbuk, Korea (South)
Tel.: (82) 54 420 0257
Nylon & Polyester Film Mfr
N.A.I.C.S.: 326112

Kolon Industries, Inc. - Gumi Plant (1)
48 Suchul daero, Gumi, Gyeongsangbuk, Korea (South)
Tel.: (82) 54 469 3051
Tire Cord & Light Diffuser Film Mfr
N.A.I.C.S.: 314994
Park Han Yong (CEO)

Kolon Industries, Inc. - Incheon Plant (1)
680 Baekbeom ro, Seo gu, Incheon, Korea (South)
Tel.: (82) 32 580 0846
Polyurethane Resin Mfr
N.A.I.C.S.: 325211

Kolon Industries, Inc. - Ulsan Plant (1)
33 Sapyeong ro, Nam gu, Ulsan, 44786, Korea (South)
Tel.: (82) 52 259 8106
Hydrocarbon Resin Mfr
N.A.I.C.S.: 325211

Kolon Industries, Inc. - Yeosu Plant (1)
213 Sandanjungang ro, Yeosu, Jeollanam, Korea (South)
Tel.: (82) 61 690 9800
Hydrocarbon Resin Mfr
N.A.I.C.S.: 325211

Kolon Nanjing Co., Ltd. (1)
Heng Jing Road Nanjing Economic & Technological Development Zone, Qixia District, Nanjing, 210046, Jiangsu, China
Tel.: (86) 2585573500
Web Site: http://www.ikolon.com
Tire Cord Mfr
N.A.I.C.S.: 314994

Kolon USA Inc. (1)
65 Challenger Rd Ste 105, Ridgefield Park, NJ 07660
Tel.: (201) 641-5800
Web Site: http://www.ikolon.com
Plastics Films Mfr
N.A.I.C.S.: 326113

P.T. Kolon Ina (1)
JL Raya KM 80, Serang, 42182, Banten, Indonesia
Tel.: (62) 254 281 234
Web Site: http://kolonina.com
Food Packaging Film Mfr
N.A.I.C.S.: 326111

KOLON LIFE SCIENCE INC.
One & Only Tower 110 Magokdong-ro, Gangseo-gu, Seoul, Korea (South)
Tel.: (82) 236774150
Web Site: https://www.kolonls.co.kr
Year Founded: 2000
102940—(KRS)
Rev.: $147,572,060
Assets: $240,928,420
Liabilities: $112,284,687
Net Worth: $128,643,732
Earnings: $1,636,252
Emp.: 452
Fiscal Year-end: 12/31/22
Pharmaceuticals Product Mfr
N.A.I.C.S.: 325412
Sun Jin Kim (CEO)

KOLOS CEMENT LTD.
Mer Rouge, Port Louis, Mauritius
Tel.: (230) 2178000
Web Site: https://www.koloscement.com
KLOS.I0000—(MAU)
Rev.: $52,602,856
Assets: $30,809,271
Liabilities: $22,370,725
Net Worth: $8,438,546
Earnings: $832,845
Fiscal Year-end: 12/31/22
Cement Product Mfr
N.A.I.C.S.: 327310
Dominique Rene Jacky Billon (Exec Dir)

Subsidiaries:

Kolos Madagascar Ltd. (1)
La City 3000 Alarobia Building Block 3 5th floor, Antananarivo, Madagascar
Tel.: (261) 346288010
Web Site: https://mafonja.com
Cement Mfr & Distr
N.A.I.C.S.: 327310

KOLTE PATIL DEVELOPERS LTD
8th Floor City Bay CTS NO 14 P 17 Boat Club Road, Pune, 411 001, India
Tel.: (91) 2067429200
Web Site: https://www.koltepatil.com
Year Founded: 1970
KOLTEPATIL—(NSE)
Rev.: $1,823,656
Assets: $5,059,853
Liabilities: $3,795,036
Net Worth: $1,264,816
Earnings: $134,093
Emp.: 579
Fiscal Year-end: 03/31/23
Real Estate Developers
N.A.I.C.S.: 531110
Vinod Patil (Compliance Officer & Sec)

KOLTSO URALA CB LLC
Ul Gorkogoa D 7, Ekaterinburg, 620075, Russia
Tel.: (7) 3432293016
Web Site: http://www.kubank.ru
Sales Range: Less than $1 Million
Commercial Banking Services
N.A.I.C.S.: 522110
Sergey Valerevich Grudin (Chm-Mgmt Bd)

KOLUT A.D.
Ekonomija Beli jarak bb, Kolut, Serbia
Tel.: (381) 25811838
Year Founded: 1946
KOLT—(BEL)
Sales Range: $1-9.9 Million
Cereal Crop Farming Services
N.A.I.C.S.: 111998

KOMAIHALTEC INC.
1-19-10 Ueno, Taito-ku, Tokyo, 110-8547, Japan
Tel.: (81) 338335101
Web Site: https://www.komaihaltec.co.jp
Year Founded: 1943
5915—(TKS)
Rev.: $366,088,240
Assets: $507,859,520
Liabilities: $289,240,380
Net Worth: $218,619,140
Earnings: $4,131,250
Emp.: 482
Fiscal Year-end: 03/31/24
Building Steel Structure Mfr
N.A.I.C.S.: 331110
Takatoshi Nakamura (Pres & CEO)

Subsidiaries:

Komaihaltec Inc. - Framework Test Facility (1)
33-10 Shintomi, Futtsu, Chiba, Japan
Tel.: (81) 439877405
Web Site: https://www.komaihaltec.co.jp
Framework Testing Services
N.A.I.C.S.: 541380

Komaihaltec Inc. - Futtsu Plant (1)
33-10 Shintomi, Futtsu, 293 WO11, Chiba, Japan
Tel.: (81) 439877470
Steel Framework Mfr
N.A.I.C.S.: 332312

Komaihaltec Inc. - Osaka Plant (1)
2-5-1 Nakajima Nishi-Yodogawa Ward, Osaka, Japan
Tel.: (81) 664752111
Steel Framework Mfr
N.A.I.C.S.: 332312

Komaihaltec Inc. - Wakayama Works (1)
805-2 Kamiya, Yura-cho Hidaka-gun, Wakayama, 649-1122, Japan
Tel.: (81) 738 65 1234
Web Site: http://www.komaihaltec.co.jp
Numerical Control System Mfr
N.A.I.C.S.: 334511

Komaihaltec Inc. - Wind Tunnel Facility (1)
2-5-1 Nakajima, Nishiyodogawa-ku, Osaka, 555-0041, Japan
Tel.: (81) 6 6475 2111
Web Site: http://www.komaihaltec.co.jp
Wind Tunnel Testing Services
N.A.I.C.S.: 238220

KOMARKCORP BERHAD
Lot 132 Jalan 16/1 Kawasan Perindustrian Cheras Jaya, 43200, Balakong, Selangor, Malaysia
Tel.: (60) 390803333
Web Site: https://www.komark.com.my
KOMARK—(KLS)
Rev.: $6,222,999
Assets: $26,490,938
Liabilities: $5,538,951
Net Worth: $20,951,987

INTERNATIONAL PUBLIC

Earnings: ($8,826,921)
Emp.: 145
Fiscal Year-end: 06/30/24
Printing Label Machines Mfr
N.A.I.C.S.: 333248
Yit Chan Tai (Co-Sec)

Subsidiaries:

General Labels & Labelling (JB) Sdn. Bhd. (1)
No 4 Jalan Bayu 3, Bandar Seri Alam, 81750, Masai, Johor, Malaysia
Tel.: (60) 73881021
Packaging & Labeling Services
N.A.I.C.S.: 561910

General Labels & Labelling Pte. Ltd. (1)
Blk 3015A Ubi Road 1 02-12, Singapore, 408705, Singapore
Tel.: (65) 67477391
Packaging & Labeling Services
N.A.I.C.S.: 561910

Komark (Thailand) Co,. Ltd. (1)
Amata Nakhorn Industrial Estate 700/451 Moo 7 Donhuaror, Muangchonburi District, Chon Buri, 20000, Thailand
Tel.: (66) 38454638
Packaging & Labeling Services
N.A.I.C.S.: 561910

Komark International (M) Sdn. Bhd. (1)
Lot 132 Jalan 16/1, Kawasan Perindustrian Cheras Jaya, 43200, Balakong, Selangor, Malaysia
Tel.: (60) 390803333
Web Site: https://www.komark.com.my
Packaging & Labeling Services
N.A.I.C.S.: 561910
Koh Chie Jooi (COO)

Subsidiary (Non-US):

PT Komark Labels & Labelling Indonesia (2)
Jalan Industri Selatan 1 Blok Kk 5d, Kawasan Industri Jababeka Ii Cikarang Selatan, Bekasi, 17550, Indonesia
Tel.: (62) 2189841153
Packaging & Labeling Services
N.A.I.C.S.: 561910

KOMATSU LTD.
2-3-6 Akasaka, Minato-ku, Tokyo, 107-8414, Japan
Tel.: (81) 355614711 JP
Web Site: https://www.komatsu.jp
Year Founded: 1921
KOM1—(DEU)
Rev.: $25,548,456,420
Assets: $37,258,296,160
Liabilities: $16,116,528,440
Net Worth: $21,141,767,720
Earnings: $2,600,545,860
Emp.: 65,738
Fiscal Year-end: 03/31/24
Construction & Industrial Equipment Sales & Mfr
N.A.I.C.S.: 333120
Yasuo Suzuki (Exec Officer & Plant Mgr-Production Div-Ibaraki)

Subsidiaries:

Atommix Industria e Comercio Ltda. (1)
Avenida Getulio Vargas 256, Aruja, 7400-000, Sao Paulo, Brazil (100%)
Tel.: (55) 1146520220
Web Site: http://www.atommix.com.br
Sales Range: $50-74.9 Million
Emp.: 150
Mfr & Sales of Burning Plates, Sheet Metal Products & Hydraulic Turbines for Construction Equipment
N.A.I.C.S.: 333611

Bangkok Komatsu Co., Ltd. (1)
700/21 Moo 5 Bangna-Trad Road T Klongtamru Amata, A Muang, Chon Buri, 20000, Thailand (75%)
Tel.: (66) 382147806
Web Site: http://www.bkc.co.th

AND PRIVATE COMPANIES

KOMATSU LTD.

Sales Range: $100-124.9 Million
Emp.: 700
Mfr & Sales of Construction Equipment;
Joint Venture of Komatsu Ltd. (74.8%) &
Bangkok Motor Works Co., Ltd (25.2%)
N.A.I.C.S.: 333120

Bangkok Komatsu Forklift Co., Ltd. (1)
28/9 Moo 3 Bangna-Trad Road KM 23,
Bangsaothong, Samut Prakan, 10570, Thailand
Tel.: (66) 26632666
Web Site: http://www.bkforklift.com
Industrial Machinery Distr
N.A.I.C.S.: 423830

Bangkok Komatsu Industries Co., Ltd. (1)
700/25 Moo 5 Amata Nakorn Industrial Estate Sukhumvit Rd, Klungtumru Sub-Dt
Muang Dt, Chon Buri, 20000, Thailand
Tel.: (66) 3821 3055
Emp.: 30
Cast Iron Parts Mfr & Distr
N.A.I.C.S.: 331110
Xiao Wu *(Gen Mgr)*

Bangkok Komatsu Sales Co., Ltd. (1)
28/9 Moo 3 Rd Bangna-Trad Km 23, T
Bangsaothong A Bangsaothong, Samut
Prakan, 10570, Thailand
Tel.: (66) 26632666
Web Site: http://www.bangkokkomatsusales.com
Construction Equipment Distr
N.A.I.C.S.: 423810

Cabtec Thai Co., Ltd. (1)
23/3 Moo 9 Tambol Bangpai Amphur
Muang, Chachoengsao, 24000, Thailand
Tel.: (66) 38584408
Construction Equipment Mfr
N.A.I.C.S.: 333120

Cummins Komatsu Engine Company (1)
800 E 3rd St, Seymour, IN 47274-3906
Tel.: (812) 524-6693
Web Site: http://www.komatsu.com
Sales Range: $25-49.9 Million
Emp.: 52
Mfr of Large Sized Diesel Engines
N.A.I.C.S.: 333611

Daiki Corporation (1)
7633 Adairsville Hwy, Adairsville, GA
30103-2104 (33%)
Tel.: (770) 769-4500
Web Site: http://www.daiki-usa.com
Sales Range: $50-74.9 Million
Emp.: 140
Sheet Metal Processing
N.A.I.C.S.: 332119

Daitex Co., Ltd. (1)
5-44-5 Yunizo Kamata Chome Building 2F,
Ota-ku Kamata, Tokyo, 144-0052,
Japan (49%)
Tel.: (81) 357030345
Web Site: http://www.daitex.co.jp
Sales Range: $50-74.9 Million
Emp.: 145
Drafting, Design, Manufacture & Sales of
Machines & Equipment
N.A.I.C.S.: 333310

Gigaphoton China Inc. (1)
7F Building E Chamtime Plaza No 6 Lane
2889 Jinke Road, Pudong New Area,
Shanghai, 201203, China
Tel.: (86) 2168414567
Semiconductor Machinery Tool Mfr
N.A.I.C.S.: 333242

Gigaphoton, Inc. (1)
400 Yokokurashinden, Oyama, 323-8558,
Tochigi, Japan (100%)
Tel.: (81) 28 528 8410
Web Site: https://www.gigaphoton.com
Emp.: 1,219
Developer of Light Units & Systems
N.A.I.C.S.: 332613
Hideichi Sato *(CIO & Sr Exec Officer)*

Subsidiary (Non-US):

Gigaphoton Europe B.V. (2)
Luchthavenweg 81-142A, 5657 EA, Eindhoven, Netherlands
Tel.: (31) 40 2350004
Web Site: http://www.gigaphoton.com
Sales Range: $25-49.9 Million
Emp.: 7
Electronic Components Distr
N.A.I.C.S.: 423690

Gigaphoton Korea Inc. (2)
Nexscien Leaders Tower 8F 12 Wongomae-Ro, Giheung-Gu, Yongin, 446-901,
Gyeonggi-Do, Korea (South)
Tel.: (82) 312110480
Electronic Components Distr
N.A.I.C.S.: 423690

Gigaphoton Taiwan Inc. (2)
No 29 Keya W Rd, Daya Dist, Taichung,
428, Taiwan
Tel.: (886) 425608615
Web Site: http://www.gigaphoton.com
Sales Range: $25-49.9 Million
Emp.: 30
Electronic Components Distr
N.A.I.C.S.: 423690

Subsidiary (US):

Gigaphoton USA Inc. (2)
15201 NW Greenbrier Pkwy Ste C7, Beaverton, OR 97006
Tel.: (503) 597-7771
Electronic Components Distr
N.A.I.C.S.: 423690

Industrial Power Alliance, Ltd. (1)
400 Yokokura Shinden, Oyama, 323-8558,
Tochigi, Japan (50%)
Tel.: (81) 28 528 8210
Web Site: https://www.ipalliance.co.jp
Emp.: 340
Engine Equipment Mfr
N.A.I.C.S.: 333618
Yasuyuki Onodera *(Pres)*

Joy Global (Peru) S.A.C. (1)
Av Jorge Basadre 592, San Isidro, Lima,
27, Peru (40%)
Tel.: (51) 14406541
Mining Machinery & Equipment Mfr
N.A.I.C.S.: 333131

KELK Ltd. (1)
3-25-1 Shinomiya, Hiratsuka, 254-8543,
Kanagawa, Japan
Tel.: (81) 46 322 8724
Web Site: https://www.kelk.co.jp
Emp.: 250
Micro Module & Temperature Control Equipment Mfr & Distr
N.A.I.C.S.: 334512
Hiroaki Takechi *(Pres)*

KMS Katsushiro Machinery (Shandong) Co., Ltd. (1)
No 66 Huoju Road, Development Zone, Jining, 272023, Shandong, China
Tel.: (86) 5372357777
Web Site: http://www.chinakms.net
Emp.: 460
Construction Equipment Mfr
N.A.I.C.S.: 333120

KRANEKS International Co., Ltd. (1)
m Mineevo, 153007, Ivanovo,
Russia (50%)
Tel.: (7) 4932357169
Web Site: http://www.komatsu.com
Sales Range: $25-49.9 Million
Emp.: 25
Metal Works for Excavators Mfr; Joint Venture of Komatsu Ltd. (50%) & KRANEKS
Machinery Company Limited (50%)
N.A.I.C.S.: 332323

Komatsu (Changzhou) Construction Machinery Corp. (1)
No 398 West Huanghe Rd, Xinbei District,
Changzhou, 213132, Jiangsu,
China (50%)
Tel.: (86) 51985113888
Web Site: http://www.komatsu.com
Sales Range: $100-124.9 Million
Emp.: 423
Mfr of Construction Equipment; Joint Venture of Komatsu Ltd. & Changlin Co., Ltd.
N.A.I.C.S.: 333120

Komatsu (Changzhou) Foundry Corporation (1)
Changzhou South-East Economic Development District, Jiangsu, 213018,
China (95%)
Tel.: (86) 51988259933
Iron Casting Product Mfr & Distr
N.A.I.C.S.: 331511

Komatsu (Changzhou) Rebuild Co., Ltd (1)
No 508-2 West Huanghe Rd, Xinbei District,
Changzhou, 213126, Jiangsu, China
Tel.: (86) 519 81661366
Web Site: http://www.komatsu.com
Emp.: 81
Construction Equipment Distr
N.A.I.C.S.: 423810

Komatsu (Shandong) Construction Machinery Corp. (1)
2199 Chong Wen Da Dao, Jining, 272073,
Shandong, China
Tel.: (86) 537 3166668
Compact Machinery & Forklift Truck Mfr
N.A.I.C.S.: 333924

Komatsu (Shanghai) Ltd. (1)
33/F Hsbc Tower No 1000 Lujiazuihuan
Road, Pudong New Area, Shanghai,
200120, China
Tel.: (86) 2168414567
Construction Equipment Mfr
N.A.I.C.S.: 333120

Komatsu America Corporation (1)
8770 W Bryn Mawr Ave Ste 100, Chicago,
IL 60631 (100%)
Tel.: (847) 437-5800
Web Site: http://www.komatsuamerica.com
Construction Equipment Mfr, Sales, Rental & Service
N.A.I.C.S.: 333120
Rod Schrader *(Chm & CEO)*

Subsidiary (Domestic):

Hensley Industries, Inc. (2)
2108 Joe Field Rd, Dallas, TX
75229-3255 (100%)
Tel.: (972) 241-2321
Web Site: https://www.hensleyind.com
Sales Range: $75-99.9 Million
Mfr & Sales of Buckets, Teeth, Edges &
Adapters for Construction & Mining Equipment
N.A.I.C.S.: 333120
Terry Noto *(Gen Mgr-Sls-Americas)*

Division (Domestic):

Hensley Industries, Inc. - Attachments Division (3)
800 S 5th St, Mansfield, TX 76063
Tel.: (817) 477-3167
Web Site: http://www.hensleyind.com
Emp.: 60
Mining Machinery Mfr
N.A.I.C.S.: 333131

Subsidiary (Non-US):

Hensley Lingfeng Co., Ltd. (3)
Industrial Zone He Hua Bridge, Yunlong
Town, Ningbo, 315135, Zhejiang, China
Tel.: (86) 57488474588
Construction Equipment Mfr
N.A.I.C.S.: 333120

Komatsu KVX LLC (3)
Plogfabrikkveien 9, Stasjon, 4353, Klepp,
Norway
Tel.: (47) 5 178 5080
Web Site: https://www.kvx.no
Ground Engaging Tool Mfr
N.A.I.C.S.: 333120
Carsten Bo Andersen *(Mng Dir)*

Division (Domestic):

Komatsu America Corp. (2)
100 Komatsu Dr, Cartersville, GA 30121
Tel.: (678) 721-3600
Web Site: http://www.komatsuamerica.com
Sales Range: $25-49.9 Million (50%)
Emp.: 60
Construction, Mining & Compact Construction Equipment Mfr & Supplier
N.A.I.C.S.: 333120

Division (Domestic):

Komatsu America Corp. - LSP Division (3)

14095 Farmington Rd, Livonia, MI 48154-5455
Tel.: (734) 458-9556
Web Site: http://www.komatsu.com
Emp.: 10
Construction & Mining Equipment Mfr
N.A.I.C.S.: 333120
Noble Koizumi *(Pres)*

NTC America Corporation (3)
46605 Magellan Dr, Novi, MI 48377
Tel.: (248) 560-1200
Web Site: https://www.ntcamerica.com
Emp.: 785
Sheet Metal Mfr
N.A.I.C.S.: 332322

Subsidiary (Domestic):

Komatsu Equipment Company (2)
1486 S Distribution Dr, Salt Lake City, UT
84104-4751
Tel.: (801) 972-3660
Web Site: http://www.komatsueq.com
Sales Range: $75-99.9 Million
Emp.: 120
Construction Equipment Sales, Rentals & Service
N.A.I.C.S.: 423810
Jim Slade *(Branch Mgr-Salt Lake City & Myton)*

Division (Domestic):

Komatsu Financial Limited Partnership (2)
1701 Golf Rd Ste 1-300, Rolling Meadows,
IL 60008
Tel.: (847) 437-5800
Web Site: http://www.komatsuamerica.com
Financing for Heavy Machinery Services
N.A.I.C.S.: 522220

Subsidiary (Domestic):

Komatsu Mining Corp. (2)
135 So 84th Street, Milwaukee, WI 53214
Tel.: (414) 670-8400
Web Site: http://mining.komatsu
Mining Equipment Mfr
N.A.I.C.S.: 333131

Subsidiary (Non-US):

Joy Global (Baotou) Mining Machinery Co. Lt (3)
No 39 Wan Qing Road, Baotou, 014030,
Inner Mongolia, China
Tel.: (86) 4725185600
Mining Machinery & Equipment Mfr
N.A.I.C.S.: 333131
Jason Zhang *(Gen Mgr)*

Joy Global (Canada) Ltd. (3)
Bay 10 - 2256 29 Street NE, Calgary, T1Y
7G4, AB, Canada
Tel.: (403) 730-9851
Mining Machinery & Equipment Mfr
N.A.I.C.S.: 333131

Joy Global (Chile) S.A. (3)
DEI Fogon 180 Parque Industrial La Negra,
Antofagasta, 1240000, Chile
Tel.: (56) 552432724
Mining Machinery & Equipment Mfr
N.A.I.C.S.: 333131

Joy Global (Tianjin) Mining Machinery Co. Ltd. (3)
No 227 Jingsi Road Tianjin Airport Economic Area, Tianjin, 300308, China
Tel.: (86) 22 6570 8000
Mining Machinery Mfr & Sales
N.A.I.C.S.: 333131

Joy Global (UK) Holdings Co. Limited (3)
Bromyard Road, Worcester, WR2 5EG,
United Kingdom
Tel.: (44) 8702526000
Holding Company; Mining Machinery & Equipment Mfr
N.A.I.C.S.: 551112

Subsidiary (Domestic):

Joy Global Industries Limited (4)
Bromyard Roade, Worcester, WR2 5EG,
United Kingdom
Tel.: (44) 3702521000
Mining Machinery & Equipment Mfr

KOMATSU LTD.

INTERNATIONAL PUBLIC

Komatsu Ltd.—(Continued)
N.A.I.C.S.: 333131

Subsidiary (Domestic):

Joy Global (UK) Limited (5)
Bromyard Road, Worcester, WR2 5EG, United Kingdom
Tel.: (44) 870 252 1000
Mining Machinery & Equipment Mfr
N.A.I.C.S.: 333131

Joy Global (UK) Surface Limited (5)
Bromyard Road, Worcester, WR2 5EG, United Kingdom
Tel.: (44) 370 252 1000
Mining Machinery & Equipment Mfr
N.A.I.C.S.: 333131

Subsidiary (Non-US):

Joy Global Australia Pty. Ltd. (3)
13-15 MCCourt road, Moss Vale, 2577, NSW, Australia **(100%)**
Tel.: (61) 248603800
Mining Equipment, Hosts & Electrical Products
N.A.I.C.S.: 333131

Plant (Domestic):

Joy Global Australia Pty. Ltd. -Murarrie (4)
747 Lytton Road Building 5 Level 3, Murarrie, 4172, QLD, Australia
Tel.: (61) 73240 4600
Mining Machinery & Equipment Mfr
N.A.I.C.S.: 333131

Subsidiary (Non-US):

Joy Global France S.a.r.l. (3)
203 Route de Grenoble, Saint Priest, 69800, France
Tel.: (33) 472229797
Mining Machinery & Equipment Whslr
N.A.I.C.S.: 423810

Joy Global Mexico S.A. de C.V. (3)
Ave Obregon 188 Int, Cananea, Sonora, Mexico
Tel.: (52) 645 332 0443
Mining Machinery & Equipment Mfr
N.A.I.C.S.: 333131
Rigoberto Hernandez Morfin *(Mgr-HHRR)*

Joy Global South Africa Pty Ltd (3)
13 Commercial Road, Wadeville, 1401, South Africa **(100%)**
Tel.: (27) 118724000
Mining Machinery, Drill Bits & Deep Drills
N.A.I.C.S.: 333131

Subsidiary (Domestic):

Joy Global Surface Mining Inc. (3)
4400 W National Ave, Milwaukee, WI 53214-3639 **(100%)**
Tel.: (414) 671-4400
Mfr of Electric Mining Shovels & Draglines, Hydraulic Mining Shovels & Electrical Components
N.A.I.C.S.: 333131

Joy Global Underground Mining LLC (3)
601 Lucerne Road, Homer City, PA 15748-9245
Tel.: (724) 915-2200
Mining Machinery & Equipment Mfr
N.A.I.C.S.: 333131

Subsidiary (Domestic):

Joy Global Longview Operations LLC (4)
2400 S MacArthur St, Longview, TX 75602 **(100%)**
Tel.: (903) 237-7000
Designer & Mfr of Drilling & Mining Equipment
N.A.I.C.S.: 333131

Subsidiary (Non-US):

LeTourneau Technologies (Dalian) Co., Ltd. (5)
Songlan St, Jinzhou, Dalian, 116600, Liaoning, China
Tel.: (86) 41187934279
Mining Machinery & Equipment Mfr

N.A.I.C.S.: 333131

Subsidiary (Domestic):

LeTourneau Technologies America, Inc. (5)
2400 S MacArthur St, Longview, TX 75602
Tel.: (903) 237-7000
Mining Machinery & Earthmoving Equipment Mfr
N.A.I.C.S.: 333131

Unit (Domestic):

Joy Global Underground Mining LLC - Abingdon Service Center (4)
26161 Old Trail Rd Ste 1, Abingdon, VA 24210-7631 **(100%)**
Tel.: (276) 623-2000
Mining Equipment Servicing
N.A.I.C.S.: 811310

Plant (Domestic):

Joy Global Underground Mining LLC - Franklin Plant (4)
120 Liberty St, Franklin, PA 16323-1066
Tel.: (814) 437-5731
Mining Machinery & Equipment
N.A.I.C.S.: 333131

Subsidiary (Non-US):

Joy Manufacturing Company (U.K.) Ltd. (3)
George House 36 North Hanover Street, Glasgow, G1 2AD, United Kingdom
Tel.: (44) 1942610100
Mining Machinery & Earthmoving Equipment Mfr
N.A.I.C.S.: 333131

P&H MinePro do Brasil Comercio e Industria Ltda. (3)
Avenida Portugal 4511, Bairro Itapoa, Belo Horizonte, 31710-400, Brazil
Tel.: (55) 9433273000
Mining Machinery & Equipment Mfr
N.A.I.C.S.: 333131

Wuxi Shendga Machinery Co. Ltd. (3)
Binhu District No. 802, Qian Hu Road, 214161, Wuxi, Jiangsu, China
Tel.: (86) 51085408646
Plastics Pipe & Pipe Fitting Mfr
N.A.I.C.S.: 326122

Komatsu America Industries, LLC (1)
1701 Golf Rd Ste 1-100, Rolling Meadows, IL 60008-4208 **(100%)**
Tel.: (847) 437-3888
Web Site: http://www.komatsupress.com
Sales Range: $50-74.9 Million
Emp.: 20
Industrial Machinery Retailer & Servicer
N.A.I.C.S.: 423830
Kaz Tsuchiyama *(Pres)*

Komatsu Asia & Pacific Pte. Ltd. (1)
1 Gul Ave, Singapore, 629648Hashimoto, Singapore **(100%)**
Tel.: (65) 68612033
Sales Range: $25-49.9 Million
Emp.: 60
Construction Equipment & Product Support
N.A.I.C.S.: 333120

Representative Office (Non-US):

Komatsu Asia & Pacific Pte. Ltd. (2)
UMW Corporation SDN Jalan Utas 15 7, PO Box 7052, 40915, Shah Alam, Selangor Darul Ehsan, Malaysia **(100%)**
Tel.: (60) 351635000
Web Site: http://www.umw.com.my
Sales Range: $50-74.9 Million
Emp.: 5
N.A.I.C.S.: 333120
Kenichi Oshima *(Gen Mgr)*

Subsidiary (Non-US):

Komatsu India Private Limited (2)
Plot No A-1 Sipcot Industrial Park & Growth Centre, Panruthi Village Oragadam Thenneri Post Sriperumbudur Taluk, Kanchipuram, 631 604, Tamil Nadu, India
Tel.: (91) 442 715 5000

Web Site: https://www.komatsuindia.in
Sales Range: $25-49.9 Million
Mining Dump Truck Mfr
N.A.I.C.S.: 333120
Masaaki Kamizono *(Mng Dir)*

Komatsu Australia Corporate Finance Pty. Ltd. (1)
50-60 Fairfield Street, Fairfield, 2165, NSW, Australia
Tel.: (61) 297288000
Web Site: http://www.komatsufinance.com.au
Sales Range: $50-74.9 Million
Emp.: 1
Financial Lending Services
N.A.I.C.S.: 522220

Komatsu Australia Pty Ltd (1)
50-60 Fairfield Street, Fairfield, 2165, NSW, Australia **(100%)**
Tel.: (61) 297958222
Web Site: http://www.komatsu.com.au
Sales Range: $100-124.9 Million
Emp.: 200
Financial Services
N.A.I.C.S.: 522320
Sean Taylor *(Mng Dir)*

Komatsu Australia Pty. Ltd. (1)
50-60 Fairfield Street, Fairfield, 2165, NSW, Australia **(50%)**
Tel.: (61) 130 056 6287
Web Site: https://www.komatsu.com.au
Sales Range: $75-99.9 Million
Emp.: 100
Sales of Construction Equipment
N.A.I.C.S.: 423810
Sean Taylor *(Mng Dir)*

Komatsu Bangkok Leasing Co., (1)
28/9 Moo 3 Bangna-Trad Road Km 23, Bang Sao Thong, 10570, Samut Prakan, Thailand
Tel.: (66) 26632777
Web Site: http://www.komatsu.com
Sales Range: $25-49.9 Million
Emp.: 29
Mining Equipment Rental & Leasing Services
N.A.I.C.S.: 532412

Komatsu Botl Finance CIS, LLC. (1)
St Krasnoproletarskaya 36 Business Center Amber Plaza, 127473, Moscow, Russia
Tel.: (7) 4957757535
Web Site: http://www.komatsufinance.ru
Construction Equipment Distr
N.A.I.C.S.: 423390

Komatsu Brasil International Ltda. (1)
Av Manuel Bandeira 291 Bloco D Terreo cjts 12 e 13, Bairro Vila Leopoldina, Sao Paulo, 05317-020, Brazil **(100%)**
Tel.: (55) 1121058000
Web Site: http://www.komatsu.com.br
Sales Range: $50-74.9 Million
Emp.: 65
Sales of Construction Equipment
N.A.I.C.S.: 423810

Komatsu Business Support Ltd. (1)
2-3-6 Akasaka, Minato Ward, Tokyo, Japan **(100%)**
Tel.: (81) 355612858
Web Site: http://www.komatsu-bs.com
Construction Equipment Retailer
N.A.I.C.S.: 532412

Komatsu CIS LLC (1)
1st Volokolamsky proezd 10, 123060, Moscow, Russia
Tel.: (7) 4959823959
Web Site: http://www.komatsu.ru
Sales Range: $50-74.9 Million
Emp.: 10
Construction & Mining Equipment Distr
N.A.I.C.S.: 423810

Subsidiary (Domestic):

Komatsu Manufacturing Rus, LLC (2)
Industrialnaya street building 1, Nagornyi village Yaroslavl district, 150521, Yaroslavl, Russia
Tel.: (7) 4852588290
Web Site: http://www.komatsu.yar.ru

Construction & Mining Equipment Mfr
N.A.I.C.S.: 333120

Komatsu Cabtec Co., Ltd. (1)
1166 Yakushi Ryuoucho, Gamou-gun, Shiga, 520-2551, Japan
Tel.: (81) 748581154
Web Site: http://www.komatsu.com
Automotive Air Conditioning Equipment Mfr
N.A.I.C.S.: 336390

Komatsu Castex Japan Ltd. (KCX) (1)
1-3 Shimotago, Himi, 935-8501, Toyama, Japan
Tel.: (81) 766 91 1511
Manufacture & Sale of Iron & Steel Castings
N.A.I.C.S.: 331110
Ichirou Sasaki *(Gen Mgr)*

Komatsu Castex Ltd. (1)
1-3 Shimotago, Himi, 935-8501, Toyama, Japan
Tel.: (81) 766911511
Web Site: http://www.komatsu-kcx.co.jp
Sales Range: $350-399.9 Million
Emp.: 1,200
Mfg. & Sales of Castings, Casting Models, Engineering & Environmental Measuring
N.A.I.C.S.: 541330
Ichiro Sasaki *(Pres)*

Komatsu China Ltd. (1)
2F and 3F Building E Chamtime Plaza NO 6 Lane 2889 Jinke Road, Pudong New Area, Shanghai, 201203, China **(100%)**
Tel.: (86) 2168414567
Web Site: http://www.komatsu.com.cn
Sales Range: $125-149.9 Million
Emp.: 300
N.A.I.C.S.: 333120

Komatsu China Mining Limited (1)
15 Ronghua South Road, Daxing DistrictYihanz Busine, Beijing, 100176, China
Tel.: (86) 10 65909878
Emp.: 140
Mining Machinery Sales & Maintenance Services
N.A.I.C.S.: 423810
Quan Wang Thang *(CEO)*

Komatsu Construction Attachment Changzhou Co., Ltd. (1)
No 380 West Huanghe Road New & High-Technology, Industrial Development Zone, Changzhou, Jiangsu, China
Tel.: (86) 519 81661350
Web Site: http://www.komatsu.com
Bucket & Front Attachment Mfr & Distr
N.A.I.C.S.: 333120

Komatsu Construction Equipment Sales & Service Japan Ltd. (1)
2-5-8 Fuchinobe, Sagamihara-shi, Yokohama, 229-0006, Kanagawa, Japan
Tel.: (81) 427527222
Web Site: http://www.komatsu-kenki.co.jp
Sales Range: $400-449.9 Million
Emp.: 2,438
Construction & Industrial Equipment Sales & Mfr
N.A.I.C.S.: 333120

Komatsu Corporate Services Ltd. (1)
2-3-6 Akasaka, Minato-ku, Tokyo, 107-8414, Japan
Tel.: (81) 355614780
Real Estate Services
N.A.I.C.S.: 531390

Komatsu Cummins Chile Arrienda S.A. (1)
Panamericana Norte Kilometer 22 1/2, Lampa, Santiago, Chile
Tel.: (56) 29799200
Web Site: http://www.komatsu.com
Sales Range: $50-74.9 Million
Emp.: 30
Construction Equipment Rental & Leasing Services
N.A.I.C.S.: 532412

Komatsu Cummins Chile Ltda. (1)
Americo Vespucio Avenue 0631 3rd Floor, Quilicura, Santiago, Chile **(100%)**
Tel.: (56) 226557777
Web Site: http://www.komatsulatinoamerica.com

AND PRIVATE COMPANIES

KOMATSU LTD.

Sales Range: $150-199.9 Million
Emp.: 350
Holding Company; Joint Venture of Komatsu Ltd. & Cummins Engine Company, Inc.
N.A.I.C.S.: 551112

Komatsu Cummins Engine Co., Ltd. (1)
400 Yokokurashinden, Oyama, 323-8558, Tochigi, Japan **(50%)**
Tel.: (81) 285288380
Web Site: http://www.komatsu.com
Sales Range: $25-49.9 Million
Emp.: 100
Diesel Engine Mfr
N.A.I.C.S.: 333618

Komatsu Customer Support Japan Ltd. (1)
1-17-3 Shirokane, Minato-ku, Tokyo, Japan
Tel.: (81) 5034864123
Construction Equipment Distr
N.A.I.C.S.: 423810

Komatsu Diesel Co., Ltd. (1)
2-3-6 Akasaka, Minato ku, Tokyo, 107 8414, Japan **(100%)**
Tel.: (81) 355613470
Sales Range: $100-124.9 Million
Emp.: 100
Sales & Service of Industrial & Marine Engines, Generators, Power Units & Transmissions
N.A.I.C.S.: 335312
Takashi Terui *(Mgr-Fin)*

Komatsu Electronics, Inc. (1)
135 A-Akamachi Ko, Komatsu, 923-8642, Ishikawa, Japan **(100%)**
Tel.: (81) 761212000
Web Site: http://www.komatsu-ec.co.jp
Sales Range: $50-74.9 Million
Emp.: 300
Mfr & Sales of Thermoelectric Modules & Temperature Control Equipment
N.A.I.C.S.: 335999

Komatsu Europe Coordination Center N.V. (1)
Mechelsesteenweg 586, 1800, Vilvoorde, Belgium **(100%)**
Tel.: (32) 22552411
Web Site: http://www.komatsueurope.com
Emp.: 250
Construction Machinery
N.A.I.C.S.: 333120

Komatsu Europe International N.V. (1)
Mechelsesteenweg 586, 1800, Vilvoorde, Belgium **(100%)**
Tel.: (32) 22552411
Web Site: http://www.komatsu.eu
Emp.: 250
Supervision of European Subsidiary Operations; Sales of Construction Equipment & Product Support
N.A.I.C.S.: 333120

Subsidiary (Non-US):

Komatsu Espana S.A. (2)
Avda Madrid n 23 Antigua N-II, Alcala de Henares, 28802, Madrid, Spain **(33%)**
Tel.: (34) 918872600
Web Site: http://www.kesa.es
Sales Range: $50-74.9 Million
Emp.: 85
Construction Equipment Sales
N.A.I.C.S.: 423810

Komatsu Far East Ltd. (1)
Kotoni 3 1 Bldg 1 20 Kotoni 3 Jo, Nishi Ku, Sapporo, 063 0813, Hokkaido, Japan
Tel.: (81) 116124999
Web Site: http://www.komatsu.co.jp
Sales Range: $50-74.9 Million
Emp.: 10
Export of Construction, Agricultural, Forestry & Logistics Equipment
N.A.I.C.S.: 532412

Komatsu Finance America Inc. (1)
1701 Golf Rd Ste 1-100, Rolling Meadows, IL 60008
Tel.: (847) 437-5800
Web Site: http://www.komatsu.com
Financial Management Services
N.A.I.C.S.: 523999

Komatsu Finance Chile S.A. (1)
Panamericana Norte Kilometer 22 1/2, Lampa, Santiago, Chile
Tel.: (56) 226557777
Construction Equipment Distr
N.A.I.C.S.: 423390

Komatsu Finance Mexico, S.A. de C.V (1)
Juan Salvador Agraz No 50 Piso 4, Santa Fe Cuajimalpa, 05348, Mexico, Mexico
Tel.: (52) 15591783940
Construction Equipment Distr
N.A.I.C.S.: 423390

Komatsu Financial Europe N.V. (1)
Mechelsesteenweg 586, 1800, Vilvoorde, Belgium
Tel.: (32) 22552411
Construction Equipment Leasing Services
N.A.I.C.S.: 532412

Komatsu Financial Leasing China Ltd. (1)
7th Floor Building E Chamtime Plaza NO 6 Lane 2889 Jinke Road, Pudong New Area, Shanghai, 201203, China
Tel.: (86) 21 6841 4567
Web Site: http://www.komatsu.com.cn
Sales Range: $200-249.9 Million
Emp.: 100
Construction Equipment Financial Leasing Services
N.A.I.C.S.: 522220

Komatsu Forest AB (1)
Tegelbruksvagen 1, 907 42, Umea, Sweden
Tel.: (46) 90 70 93 00
Web Site: http://www.komatsuforest.com
Sales Range: $100-124.9 Million
Emp.: 1,400
Forestry Equipment Mfr
N.A.I.C.S.: 333120
Toshio Miyake *(Pres & CEO)*

Komatsu Forest Oy (1)
Haikanvuori 10, 33960, Pirkkala, Finland
Tel.: (358) 207701300
Web Site: http://www.komatsuforest.fi
Sales Range: $10-24.9 Million
Emp.: 36
Forestry Technology
N.A.I.C.S.: 115310

Subsidiary (Non-US):

Komatsu Forest A/S (2)
Uthusvegen 18, 2335, Stange, Hedmark, Norway
Tel.: (47) 9 017 8800
Web Site: https://www.komatsuforest.no
N.A.I.C.S.: 541330
Tore Aaslund *(CEO)*

Komatsu Forest GmbH (2)
Allmendstr 12, Wittershausen, 72189, Vohringen, Germany
Tel.: (49) 74 549 6020
Web Site: https://www.komatsuforest.de
Emp.: 75
N.A.I.C.S.: 541330
Jurgen Munz *(Mng Dir & Exec Dir)*

Komatsu Forest Limited (2)
Unit 2 Longtown Industrial Estate, Longtown, CA6 5TJ, Cumbria, United Kingdom
Tel.: (44) 122 879 2018
Web Site: https://www.komatsuforest.co.uk
Engineeering Services
N.A.I.C.S.: 541330
Per Annemalm *(Mng Dir)*

Komatsu Forest Ltda. (2)
Rua Alto Parana 226, 83324-380, Pinhais, PR, Brazil
Tel.: (55) 41 2102 2828
Web Site: http://www.komatsuforest.com.br
Sales Range: $10-24.9 Million
Emp.: 50
Distr of Forest Products Handling Machines
N.A.I.C.S.: 115310

Komatsu Forest Pty. Ltd. (2)
11/4 Avenue of Americas, Newington, 2127, NSW, Australia
Tel.: (61) 296473600
Web Site: http://www.komatsuforest.com.au
Sales Range: $10-24.9 Million
Emp.: 35
N.A.I.C.S.: 541330

Komatsu SweLog Skogsmaskiner HB (2)
Box 7124, 90704, Umea, Sweden
Tel.: (46) 90709300
Web Site: http://www.komatsuforest.com
Emp.: 460
N.A.I.C.S.: 541330

Partek Cargotec S.r.l. (2)
Via Jovanie Gentiley 3, Milan, 20157, Italy
Tel.: (39) 0239100848
Crane Mfr
N.A.I.C.S.: 333120
Thierry Aubry *(Gen Mgr)*

Komatsu Forklift Australia Pty Ltd. (1)
50-60 Fairfield Street East, Fairfield, 2165, NSW, Australia
Tel.: (61) 29 728 0900
Web Site: https://www.komatsuforklift.com.au
Sales Range: $75-99.9 Million
Emp.: 40
Warehouse Equipment & Forklift Distr
N.A.I.C.S.: 423830
Frank Filippatos *(CFO & Deputy Mng Dir)*

Komatsu Forklift Co., Ltd. (1)
2-8-1 Minami-Oi, Shinagawa-ku, Tokyo, 140-0013, Japan **(65%)**
Tel.: (81) 3 3764 7770
Web Site: http://www.lift.co.jp
Sales Range: $300-349.9 Million
Emp.: 617
Mfr & Sales of Lift Trucks; Automated & Refrigerated Warehouses
N.A.I.C.S.: 423830
Shinya Isoda *(Pres)*

Komatsu Forklift Japan Ltd. (1)
2-8-1 Minami-Ooi, Shinagawa-ku, Tokyo, 140-0013, Japan
Tel.: (81) 337647770
Web Site: http://www.komatsu.com
Forklift Truck Sales & Repair Services
N.A.I.C.S.: 423830
Shinya Isoda *(Pres)*

Komatsu Forklift U.S.A., LLC (1)
1701 Golf Rd Tower One, Rolling Meadows, IL 60008
Tel.: (847) 437-5800
Web Site: http://www.kfiusa.com
Sales Range: $25-49.9 Million
Emp.: 100
Forklift Truck Mfr
N.A.I.C.S.: 333924

Komatsu France S.A. (1)
21a29 Rue du Clos Reine, 78410, Aubergenville, France **(100%)**
Tel.: (33) 130905100
Web Site: http://www.komatsu.eu
Sales Range: $25-49.9 Million
Emp.: 90
Sales of Construction Equipment
N.A.I.C.S.: 333120

Komatsu General Services Ltd. (1)
2-3-6 Akasaka, Minato-ku, Tokyo, 107-8414, Japan **(100%)**
Tel.: (81) 355614780
Web Site: http://www.kgs.co.jp
Sales Range: $125-149.9 Million
Emp.: 292
Real Estate Business, Insurance Agency, Finance Operation, Temporary Employment Agency, Management of Golf Courses; Publication Services
N.A.I.C.S.: 561499
Kingorou Fudetani *(Mng Dir)*

Komatsu Hanomag GmbH (1)
Hanomag Strasse 9, D 30449, Hannover, Germany **(100%)**
Tel.: (49) 51145090
Web Site: http://www.komatsuhanomag.de
Sales Range: $150-199.9 Million
Emp.: 600
Mfr & Sales of Construction Equipment
N.A.I.C.S.: 333120
Getsel Guner *(Pres)*

Komatsu Holding South America Ltda. (1)
Americo Vespucio 0631, Quilicura, Santiago, Chile
Tel.: (56) 26557777
Construction Equipment Distr

N.A.I.C.S.: 423810

Komatsu Huanan Ltd. (1)
Ste 3507 Tower 2 Lippo Center, 89 Queensway Rd, Hong Kong, China (Hong Kong) **(100%)**
Tel.: (852) 28691003
Sales Range: $25-49.9 Million
Emp.: 9
Sales of Construction Equipment
N.A.I.C.S.: 333120

Komatsu Industries (Shanghai) Ltd. (1)
2F and 3F Building E Chamtime Plaza NO 6 Lane 2889 Jinke Road, Shanghai, 201203, China
Tel.: (86) 2168414567
Web Site: http://www.komatsusanki.com
Metal Sheet Sales & Repair Services
N.A.I.C.S.: 423510

Komatsu Industries (Thailand) Co., Ltd. (1)
54 Moo 2 Bangna-Trad Road KM22, Bangsaothong, Samut Prakan, 10540, Thailand
Tel.: (66) 2 740 1850
Industrial Machinery Sales & Maintenance Services
N.A.I.C.S.: 423830

Komatsu Industries Corporation (1)
1-1 Onomachi-shinmachi, Ishikawa, Kanazawa, 920-0225, Japan
Tel.: (81) 762934201
Web Site: http://www.komatsusanki.co.jp
Sales Range: $100-124.9 Million
Emp.: 300
Mfr & Sales of Industrial Machinery
N.A.I.C.S.: 333248
Yasushi Kitade *(Pres & CEO)*

Komatsu Industries Europe GmbH (1)
Eisenstrasse 3, Russelsheim, 65428, Germany **(100%)**
Tel.: (49) 614282060
Web Site: http://www.komatsu-industries.de
Sales Range: $1-9.9 Million
Emp.: 8
Mfr & Sales of Industrial Machinery
N.A.I.C.S.: 333998
Shin kume *(Mgr)*

Komatsu Industries Mexico S.A. de C.V. (1)
Municipio de Rincon de Romos 102-A, Parque Industrial Valle de Aguascalientes San Francisco de los Romo, Aguascalientes, Mexico
Tel.: (52) 4491535950
Industrial Machinery Distr
N.A.I.C.S.: 423830

Komatsu Italia Manufacturing S.P.A. (1)
Via Atheste 4, 35042, Este, PD, Italy
Tel.: (39) 0429616111
Construction Equipment Mfr
N.A.I.C.S.: 333120

Komatsu Italia S.p.A. (1)
Via Atheste 4, 35042, Este, Padova, Italy
Tel.: (39) 0429 616111
Emp.: 400
Construction Machinery Sales & Maintenance Services
N.A.I.C.S.: 423810
Enrico Prandini *(Mng Dir)*

Komatsu Jakarta Office (1)
Jalan Raya Cakung Cilincing Km 4, Jakarta, 14140, Utara, Indonesia **(100%)**
Tel.: (62) 21 440 0611
Web Site: https://www.komi.co.id
Sales Range: $75-99.9 Million
Emp.: 200
Construction & Mining Equipment Sales
N.A.I.C.S.: 423810

Komatsu Latin America Corp. (1)
9725 NW 117th Ave, Miami, FL 33178 **(100%)**
Tel.: (305) 267-3766
Web Site: http://www.komatsuklc.com
Sales Range: $50-74.9 Million
Emp.: 100
Sales of Construction Equipment
N.A.I.C.S.: 423810

KOMATSU LTD.

Komatsu Ltd.—(Continued)

Komatsu Leasing (Cambodia) Plc (1)
713B Veng Sreng Street Phum Tropang Thloeung Sangkat Chom Chao, Khan Porsenchey, Phnom Penh, Cambodia
Tel.: (855) 85900234
Construction & Mining Equipment Distr
N.A.I.C.S.: 423390

Komatsu Logistics Corp. (1)
8Fl 3-1 Kinko-Cho, Kanagawa-ku, Yokohama, 221-8540, Kanagawa, Japan **(98%)**
Tel.: (81) 454507540
Web Site: http://www.btr-komatsu.co.jp
Sales Range: $200-249.9 Million
Emp.: 609
Logistics, Transportation, Warehousing & Engineering Services
N.A.I.C.S.: 541614

Komatsu Ltd. - Kanazawa Plant (1)
1-1 Onomachi-Shinmachi, Kanazawa, 920-0225, Ishikawa, Japan
Tel.: (81) 76 237 2200
Web Site: http://www.komatsu.com
Construction & Mining Machinery Mfr
N.A.I.C.S.: 333120

Komatsu Ltd. - Koriyama Plant (1)
1-1 Machiikedai, Koriyama, 963-0215, Fukushima, Japan
Tel.: (81) 24 9593955
Construction & Mining Machinery Mfr
N.A.I.C.S.: 333120

Komatsu Ltd. - Osaka Plant (1)
3-1-1 Ueno, Hirakata, 573-1011, Osaka, Japan
Tel.: (81) 728406102
Sales Range: $450-499.9 Million
Emp.: 200
Construction & Mining Machinery Mfr
N.A.I.C.S.: 333120

Komatsu Ltd. - Oyama Plant (1)
400 Yokokura Shinden, Oyama, 323-8558, Tochigi, Japan
Tel.: (81) 285 288111
Emp.: 300
Construction & Mining Machinery Mfr
N.A.I.C.S.: 333120

Komatsu Ltd. - Rokko Plant (1)
4-6 Kouyoucho-nishi, Higashinada-ku, Kobe, 658-0033, Hyogo, Japan
Tel.: (81) 78 855 0127
Construction & Mining Machinery Mfr
N.A.I.C.S.: 333120

Komatsu Ltd. - Tochigi Plant (1)
110 Yokokura Shinden, Oyama, 323-8567, Tochigi, Japan
Tel.: (81) 285 288566
Web Site: http://www.komatsu.com
Emp.: 82
Construction & Mining Machinery Mfr
N.A.I.C.S.: 333120

Komatsu Machinery Corporation (1)
23 Tsu Futsu Machi, Komatsu, 923 0392, Ishikawa, Japan **(100%)**
Tel.: (81) 761431187
Web Site: http://www.komatsu.co.jp
Sales Range: $50-74.9 Million
Emp.: 200
Mfr of Machine Tools & Semiconductor Materials; Manufacture & Sales of Automatic Equipment for Processing
N.A.I.C.S.: 333517

Komatsu Marketing Support Australia Pty Ltd (1)
50-60 Fairfield Street East, Fairfield, 2165, NSW, Australia
Tel.: (61) 297958222
Construction Equipment Distr
N.A.I.C.S.: 423810

Komatsu Mexicana S.A. de C.V. (1)
Corredor Industrial S-N, CP 43990, Mexico, Mexico **(47%)**
Tel.: (52) 7919130611
Sales Range: $50-74.9 Million
Emp.: 200
Mfr & Sales of Construction Equipment, Parts & Small & Medium-Sized Mechanical Presses
N.A.I.C.S.: 333120

Komatsu Middle East FZE (1)
JAFZA South Gate 15 Street S300 Plot S21313, PO Box 61037, Dubai, 61037, United Arab Emirates
Tel.: (971) 4 886 5511
Web Site: http://www.komatsu.ae
Emp.: 36
Construction Equipment Distr
N.A.I.C.S.: 423810
Kouichi Segawa (Gen Mgr)

Komatsu NTC Ltd. (1)
100 Fukuno, Nanto, 939-1595, Toyama, Japan
Tel.: (81) 76 322 2161
Web Site: https://ntc.komatsu
Sales Range: $600-649.9 Million
Emp.: 1,514
Industrial Machinery & Semiconductor Mfr
N.A.I.C.S.: 333248
Takahiro Sugino (Pres & COO)

Plant (Domestic):

Komatsu NTC Ltd. - Awazu Plant (2)
Tsu 23 Futsu-machi, Komatsu, 923-0392, Ishikawa, Japan
Tel.: (81) 76 143 4711
Web Site: http://www.komatsu.com
Sales Range: $75-99.9 Million
Emp.: 30
Machine Tool Machinery Mfr
N.A.I.C.S.: 333517
Akira Ikoma (Gen Mgr)

Komatsu NTC Ltd. - Fukuno Plant (2)
641 Nojiri, Nanto, 939-1502, Toyama, Japan
Tel.: (81) 763222165
Web Site: http://www.komatsu-ntc.com
Laser Cutting Machinery Mfr
N.A.I.C.S.: 333517

Komatsu Pakistan Soft (Pvt) Ltd. (1)
1st Floor Mandeer Square Plot 12-C/1 G-8 Markaz, Islamabad, 44000, Pakistan
Tel.: (92) 5122604413
Software Development Services
N.A.I.C.S.: 541511
Hikaru Nakajima (Pres & CEO)

Komatsu Parts Asia Co., Ltd. (1)
700/21 Moo 5 Bangna-Trad Road, Amatanakorn Industrial Estate T Klongtamru A Muang, Chon Buri, 20000, Thailand
Tel.: (66) 3846 5824
Web Site: http://www.komatsu.com
Industrial Machinery Distr
N.A.I.C.S.: 423830

Komatsu Power Generation Systems (Shanghai) Ltd. (1)
No 39 Dongxing Rd Songjiang Industry Zone, Shanghai, 201613, China
Tel.: (86) 21 6774 2156
Web Site: http://www.kpgs.com.cn
Generator Mfr & Distr
N.A.I.C.S.: 335312

Komatsu Rental Ltd. (1)
6th Floor Iwasawa Bldg 2-16-15 Kanagawa 2-Chome, Kanagawa-ku, Yokohama, 221-0045, Kanagawa, Japan
Tel.: (81) 45 274 3337
Web Site: http://www.komatsu.com
Construction Equipment Rental & Leasing Services
N.A.I.C.S.: 532412
Chikashi Shike (Gen Mgr)

Komatsu Safety Training Center Ltd. (1)
6Fl Vort Shin-Yokohama 3-2-6, Kouhoku-ku Shin-Yokohama, Yokohama, 222-0033, Kanagawa, Japan **(100%)**
Tel.: (81) 454700631
Web Site: http://www.komatsu-kyoshujo.co.jp
Sales Range: $25-49.9 Million
Emp.: 134
Safety Training Center
N.A.I.C.S.: 333120

Komatsu Shantui Construction Machinery Co., Ltd. (1)
No 277 Mengzi avenue High-tech zone, Jining, 272000, Shandong, China **(50%)**
Tel.: (86) 377399168
Web Site: http://www.komatsu.com.cn
Sales Range: $100-124.9 Million
Emp.: 934
Mfg. & Sales of Hydraulic Excavators; Joint Venture of Komatsu Ltd. & Shandong Shantui Construction Machinery Co., Ltd.
N.A.I.C.S.: 333120

Komatsu Shearing Co., Ltd. (1)
25 Hei Yasaki Machi, Komatsu, 923 0301, Ishikawa, Japan **(50%)**
Tel.: (81) 761441100
Web Site: http://www.komatsu.co.jp
Sales Range: $50-74.9 Million
Emp.: 150
Cutting, Processing & Sales of Steel Sheets
N.A.I.C.S.: 333515

Komatsu Silicon America, Inc. (1)
1915 NW Amburg Lane Pkwy Ste 200, Beaverton, OR 97006-5768 **(100%)**
Tel.: (503) 640-7000
Web Site: http://www.komsil.com
Sales Range: $25-49.9 Million
Emp.: 30
Mfr & Sales of Semiconductor Silicon Wafers
N.A.I.C.S.: 541870

Komatsu Southern Africa (Pty) Ltd. (1)
Corner Diesel & Isando Rd 196, Isando, 1600, South Africa **(80%)**
Tel.: (27) 119231000
Web Site: http://www.komatsu.co.za
Sales Range: $200-249.9 Million
Sales of Construction & Mining Equipment
N.A.I.C.S.: 423810
Micheal Blom (Mng Dir)

Komatsu Tokki Corporation (1)
2 3 6 Akasaka, Minato Ku, Tokyo, 107 8414, Japan **(100%)**
Tel.: (81) 335687021
Web Site: http://www.komatsu.co.jp
Sales Range: $50-74.9 Million
Emp.: 68
Field Services for Defense Agency Vehicles & Equipment
N.A.I.C.S.: 213112

Komatsu UK Ltd. (1)
Durham road, Chester-le-Street, Birtley, DH3 2QX, Durham, United Kingdom **(100%)**
Tel.: (44) 191 410 3155
Web Site: https://www.komatsu.eu
Sales Range: $100-124.9 Million
Emp.: 350
Mfr & Sales of Construction Equipment
N.A.I.C.S.: 333120
Paul Blanchard (Mng Dir)

Komatsu Used Equipment Corp. (1)
4F Iwasawa Bldg 16-15 Kanagawa 2-Chome, Kanagawa-ku, Yokohama, 221-0045, Kanagawa, Japan
Tel.: (81) 45 450 5567
Web Site: https://www.kuec.com
Emp.: 61
Sales of Used Construction Equipment
N.A.I.C.S.: 333120
Michitaka Kikuchi (Pres)

Komatsu Utility Europe S.p.A. (1)
Via Atheste 4, I 35042, Este, PD, Italy **(100%)**
Tel.: (39) 0429616111
Web Site: http://www.komatsu.eu
Sales Range: $100-124.9 Million
Emp.: 350
Mfr & Sales of Utility Equipment
N.A.I.C.S.: 333120

Komatsu Zenoah Co. (1)
9 1 Chome Minami Dai, Kawagoe, Saitama, 350 1192, Japan **(100%)**
Tel.: (81) 492431111
Web Site: http://www.zenoah.co.jp
Sales Range: $300-349.9 Million
Emp.: 800
Mfg. & Sales of Agricultural, Forestry, Construction & Hydraulic Equipment & Engines
N.A.I.C.S.: 532412

Komatsu do Brasil Ltda. (1)
Rodovia Indio Tibirica 2000 Gualio, Suzano, 08655-000, Sao Paulo, Brazil
Tel.: (55) 11 4745 7000
Web Site: http://www.komatsu.com.br

INTERNATIONAL PUBLIC

Sales Range: $200-249.9 Million
Emp.: 900
Construction Machinery Mfr
N.A.I.C.S.: 333120

L&T-Komatsu Limited (1)
Bellary Rd, Bengaluru, 560 092, India **(50%)**
Tel.: (91) 8023333301
Web Site: http://www.larsentoubro.com
Sales Range: Less than $1 Million
Emp.: 750
Construction Equipment & Hydraulics Mfr
N.A.I.C.S.: 333120

Lehnhoff Hartstahl GmbH (1)
Rungsstr 10-15, 76534, Baden-Baden, Germany
Tel.: (49) 72239660
Web Site: http://www.lehnhoff.de
Construction Equipment Mfr & Distr
N.A.I.C.S.: 333120

Log Max Inc. (1)
1114 W Fourth Plain Blvd, Vancouver, WA 98660-2021
Tel.: (360) 699-7300
Forest Machinery Distr
N.A.I.C.S.: 423810
Greg Porter (VP)

MineWare Pty Ltd (1)
1 Gardner Close, Milton, 4064, QLD, Australia
Tel.: (61) 735051100
Web Site: http://www.mineware.com
Mining Equipment Mfr
N.A.I.C.S.: 333131
Jason Fisher (CEO)

Modular Mining Systems, Inc. (1)
3289 E Hemisphere Loop, Tucson, AZ 85706-5028 **(100%)**
Tel.: (520) 746-9127
Web Site: http://www.modularmining.com
Sales Range: $75-99.9 Million
Emp.: 160
Development, Manufacture & Marketing of Mining Equipment Management Systems
N.A.I.C.S.: 334118
Jorge Mascena (Pres & CEO)

Subsidiary (Non-US):

Modular Mining System Africa, Pty. Ltd. (2)
48 Grosvenor Road, Johannesburg, 2191, South Africa
Tel.: (27) 110608500
Web Site: http://www.modularmining.com
Sales Range: $25-49.9 Million
Emp.: 30
Marketing of Mining Equipment Management Systems
N.A.I.C.S.: 423430

Modular Mining Systems Canada, Ltd. (2)
810-220 Brew Street, Port Moody, V3H 0H6, BC, Canada
Tel.: (604) 468-8715
Web Site: http://www.modularmining.com
Sales Range: $25-49.9 Million
Emp.: 28
Marketing of Mining Equipment Management Systems
N.A.I.C.S.: 423430

Modular Mining Systems China (2)
Rm 802 Jinglong Building No 5 Tuanjiehu Nanli, Chaoyang District, Beijing, 100026, China
Tel.: (86) 1065063958
Web Site: http://www.modularmining.com
Sales Range: $25-49.9 Million
Emp.: 2
Marketing of Mining Equipment Management Systems
N.A.I.C.S.: 423430

Modular Mining Systems Eurasia (2)
4th Street of 8th of March bld 6A 1st floor, Office IV Room 36-38 44 46-58, 125167, Moscow, Russia
Tel.: (7) 4952878688
Web Site: http://www.mmsi.com
Emp.: 24
Marketing of Mining Equipment Management Systems
N.A.I.C.S.: 423430

AND PRIVATE COMPANIES

Anatoly Makarychev *(Gen Mgr)*

Modular Mining Systems India Pvt. Ltd. (2)
Pentagon Tower 4 Unit 402 4th Floor, Magarpatta City Hadapsar, Pune, India
Tel.: (91) 2066837800
Web Site: http://modularmining.com
Modular Mining Services
N.A.I.C.S.: 213115

Modular Mining Systems Pty. Ltd. (2)
2A Bounty Close, PO Box 3130, Tuggerah, 2259, NSW, Australia
Tel.: (61) 243525711
Web Site: http://www.modularmining.com
Sales Range: $25-49.9 Million
Emp.: 48
Marketing of Mining Equipment Management Systems
N.A.I.C.S.: 423430

Modular Mining Systems SCRL (2)
Calle Antequera 777 Piso 9, San Isidro, Lima, Peru
Tel.: (51) 16557000
Web Site: http://www.modularmining.com
Marketing of Mining Equipment Management Systems
N.A.I.C.S.: 423430

Modular Mining Systems do Brasil Ltda (2)
Av Bernardo Monteiro 971 5 Andar Santa Efigenia, Functionarios, Belo Horizonte, 30150-283, MG, Brazil
Tel.: (55) 3131184300
Web Site: http://www.modularmining.com
Emp.: 60
Marketing of Mining Equipment Management Systems
N.A.I.C.S.: 423430

Modular Mining Systems, Inc. y Cia Ltda. (2)
Avda Andres Bello 2777 Piso 1301-1302, Las Condes, Santiago, Chile
Tel.: (56) 225913000
Web Site: http://www.modularmining.com
Marketing of Mining Equipment Management Systems
N.A.I.C.S.: 423430

PT, Modular Mining Indonesia (2)
Jl Jendral Sudirman Stall Kuda RT 19 Balikpapan Super Block BSB F-27, Block F-29, Balikpapan, Kalimantan Timur, Indonesia
Tel.: (62) 5427213975
Web Site: http://www.modularmining.com
Sales Range: $25-49.9 Million
Emp.: 16
Marketing of Mining Equipment Management Systems
N.A.I.C.S.: 423430

Montabert S.A.S (1)
203 route de Grenoble, 69800, Saint-Priest-en-Jarez, France
Tel.: (33) 472229797
Web Site: http://www.montabert.com
Automotive Parts Mfr & Distr
N.A.I.C.S.: 336390

NTC Shanghai Trading Co., Ltd. (1)
2F Building E Chamtime Plaza No 6 Lane 2889 Jinke Road Pudong New Area, Shanghai, 201203, China
Tel.: (86) 2168414567
Industrial Machinery Distr
N.A.I.C.S.: 423830

Nippei Toyama (Thailand) Co., Ltd. (1)
28/9 Moo 3 Bangna-Trad Road KM 23, Bangsaothong, Samut Prakan, 10570, Thailand
Tel.: (66) 27401150
Industrial Machinery Distr
N.A.I.C.S.: 423830

PT Hanken Indonesia (1)
Kawasan Industri MM2100 Block DD 8, Cikarang Barat, Bekasi, 17520, Jawa Barat, Indonesia (50%)
Tel.: (62) 2189983366
Web Site: http://www.hanken.co.id
Sales Range: $100-124.9 Million
Emp.: 300
Sheet Metal Fabrication

N.A.I.C.S.: 332322

PT Hokuriku United Forging Industry (1)
Jalan Jababeka XI Cikarang Industrial Estate, Bekasi, 17530, West Java, Indonesia (26%)
Tel.: (62) 218934087
Sales Range: $200-249.9 Million
Emp.: 800
Mfg. & Sales of Parts for Construction Equipment
N.A.I.C.S.: 333120

PT Katsushiro Indonesia (1)
Jl Jababeka XII Blok IKawasan Industri Jababeka I, Cikarang, Bekasi, 17530, West Java, Indonesia (30%)
Tel.: (62) 21 893 4953
Web Site: https://www.katsushiro.co.id
Sales Range: $25-49.9 Million
Emp.: 100
Mfg. & Sale of Parts for Construction Equipment & Foundries
N.A.I.C.S.: 333120
Yasushi Miyano *(Pres)*

PT Komatsu Astra Finance (1)
United Tractors Head Office Wing Area 6th Floor, Raya Bekasi Street KM 22, Jakarta, 13910, Indonesia
Tel.: (62) 21 460 5948
Web Site: https://www.kaf.co.id
Construction Equipment Distr
N.A.I.C.S.: 423390
Tomoyasu Hamada *(Pres)*

PT Komatsu Indonesia Tbk (1)
Jl Raya Cakung Cilincing Km 4 Sukapura, Jakarta, 14140, Utara, Indonesia (50%)
Tel.: (62) 214400611
Web Site: http://www.komi.co.id
Sales Range: $200-249.9 Million
Emp.: 800
Construction Equipment
N.A.I.C.S.: 333120

PT Komatsu Marketing & Support Indonesia (1)
PT United Tractors Tbk Jl Raya Bekasi KM 22, Cakung, Jakarta, 13910, Indonesia
Tel.: (62) 214604290
Web Site: http://www.komatsu.com
Emp.: 100
Construction & Mining Equipment Sales & Maintenance Services
N.A.I.C.S.: 423810

PT Komatsu Reman Indonesia (1)
Jl Jawa Blok A-05 KBN Cakung Cilincing Sukapura, Cilincing Jakarta Utara, Jakarta, 14140, Indonesia
Tel.: (62) 21 4483 0707
Web Site: http://www.kri-reman.com
Sales Range: $150-199.9 Million
Emp.: 300
Construction Machinery Distr
N.A.I.C.S.: 423810
Unggul Aribowo *(Sr Mgr-Mktg)*

PT Komatsu Undercarriage Indonesia (1)
Jalan Jababeka XI Blok H-16, Cikarang Industrial Estate, Bekasi, 17530, West Java, Indonesia (100%)
Tel.: (62) 218937575
Sales Range: $50-74.9 Million
Emp.: 150
Mfr & Sale of Construction Equipment
N.A.I.C.S.: 333120

Quadco Inc. (1)
66 Industriel Blvd Suite 113, Saint-Eustache, J7R 5C2, QC, Canada
Tel.: (450) 623-3340
Web Site: https://www.quadco.com
Forestry Machinery Services
N.A.I.C.S.: 532412

Southstar Equipment Ltd. (1)
600 Chilcotin Road, Kamloops, V2H-1G5, BC, Canada
Tel.: (250) 828-7820
Web Site: http://www.southstarequipment.com
Forestry Machinery Mfr
N.A.I.C.S.: 333120
Jeff Rankel *(VP)*

Southstar Equipment Ltd. (1)

Unit F Level 2 31A Bartley Terrace Devenport, Auckland, 0624, New Zealand
Tel.: (64) 212658879
Forestry Machinery Mfr
N.A.I.C.S.: 333120

Takahashi Works U.S.A., Inc. (1)
2030 E Park Dr NE, Conyers, GA 30013-5707 (25%)
Tel.: (770) 785-7516
Sales Range: $25-49.9 Million
Emp.: 63
Mfg. & Sales of Cabs for Construction Equipment
N.A.I.C.S.: 333120

TimberPro, Inc. (1)
1407 Industrial Dr, Shawano, WI 54166
Tel.: (715) 524-7899
Web Site: http://www.timberpro.com
Forest Machinery Mfr
N.A.I.C.S.: 333111
Lee Crawford *(Pres)*

UMW Komatsu Heavy Equipment Sdn Bhd (1)
Lot 16 Jalan Utas 15/7 Seksyen 15, Selangor Darul Ehsan, 40200, Shah Alam, Selangor, Malaysia
Tel.: (60) 351633706
Automobile Part Equipment Mfr & Distr
N.A.I.C.S.: 336390
Billy Yap *(Mng Dir)*

Subsidiary (Domestic):

UMW (East Malaysia) Sdn Bhd (2)
Lot 2478 Section 66 KLTD Jalan Belian, PO Box 1902, Pending Industrial Estate, 93738, Kuching, Sarawak, Malaysia
Tel.: (60) 82489911
Automobile Part Equipment Mfr & Distr
N.A.I.C.S.: 336390

Subsidiary (Non-US):

UMW Engineering Services Limited (2)
No 1944/B Block 6 Bogyoke Street A Sint Myint Quarter Yangon-Pathein, Highway Road Hlaing Thar Yar Township, Yangon, Myanmar
Tel.: (95) 98634714
Automobile Part Equipment Mfr & Distr
N.A.I.C.S.: 336390
Thiha Shein *(Gen Mgr)*

Subsidiary (Domestic):

UMW Equipment Sdn Bhd (2)
Lot 3 Jalan Utas 15/7 Seksyen 15, PO Box 7052, Selangor Darul Ehsan, 40200, Shah Alam, Selangor, Malaysia
Tel.: (60) 351635000
Automobile Part Equipment Mfr & Distr
N.A.I.C.S.: 336390
Mohamad Dom Abd Halim *(Sr Mgr)*

Subsidiary (Non-US):

UMW Niugini Limited (2)
Section 57 Allotment 463 Morea Tobo Road 6 Mile Port Moresby, PO Box 5243, National Capital District, Boroko, Papua New Guinea
Tel.: (675) 3255766
Automobile Part Equipment Mfr & Distr
N.A.I.C.S.: 336390
Darshan Rayat *(Gen Mgr)*

Yida Nippei Machine Tool Corporation (1)
11 Road Software Park Road, Ganjing District, Dalian, 116023, Liaoning, China
Tel.: (86) 41184752375
Web Site: http://www.ync-china.com
Construction Equipment Mfr & Distr
N.A.I.C.S.: 333120

KOMATSU MATERE CO.,LTD.
Nu 167 Hama-machi, Nomi, 929-0124, Ishikawa, Japan
Tel.: (81) 761551111
Web Site: https://www.komatsumatere.co.jp
Year Founded: 1943
3580—(TKS)
Rev.: $242,388,700
Assets: $330,486,780

Liabilities: $79,723,210
Net Worth: $250,763,570
Earnings: $12,182,230
Emp.: 1,117
Fiscal Year-end: 03/31/24
Clothing & Material Fabrics Seller & Mfr; Fabric Dyeing & Printing
N.A.I.C.S.: 313310
Sasaki Hisae *(Pres & COO)*

Subsidiaries:

KOMATSU INTERLINK CO., LTD. (1)
He 49-3 Dourin-Machi, Nomi, Ishikawa, Japan
Tel.: (81) 761555151
Web Site: http://www.komatsu-interlink.co.jp
Fabric Mfr & Distr
N.A.I.C.S.: 315990

Komatsu Seiren (Suzhou) Textile Dyeing Co., Ltd. (1)
Hongfu Road Luzhi Zhen Wuzhong Qu, Suzhou, Jiangsu, China
Tel.: (86) 51265021212
Polyester Fabric Mfr & Distr
N.A.I.C.S.: 313110

Komatsu Seiren Co., Ltd. - Mikawa Factory (1)
1-7-1 Kashima-Machi, Hakusan, 929-0201, Ishikawa, Japan
Tel.: (81) 762783888
Fabrics Mfr
N.A.I.C.S.: 315990

Komaxon Co., LTD. (1)
Nu 168-13 Hama-Machi, Nomi, Ishikawa, Japan
Tel.: (81) 1761552006
Web Site: http://www.komaxon.co.jp
Dyeing Fabric Mfr
N.A.I.C.S.: 313310

Subsidiary (Domestic):

Komaxon Co., LTD. - Hakusan Factory (2)
1-8-4 Kashima-Machi, Hakusan, 929-0201, Ishikawa, Japan
Tel.: (81) 762783666
Automotive Interior Product Mfr
N.A.I.C.S.: 336360

Negami Chemical Industrial Co., Ltd. (1)
Ro22 Dorin-Machi, Nomi, 929-0125, Ishikawa, Japan
Tel.: (81) 761 55 3121
Web Site: http://www.negamikogyo.co.jp
Emp.: 109
Resin Mfr
N.A.I.C.S.: 325211
Syunji Sugano *(Pres)*

Subsidiary (Domestic):

Negami Chemical Industrial Co., Ltd. - Fukui Factory (2)
3-7-5 Technoport Kawajiri-Cho, Fukui, 910-3138, Japan
Tel.: (81) 776851123
Resin Mfr
N.A.I.C.S.: 325211

Pazzo Co., Ltd. (1)
2-28-7 Yoyogint Bld 1F Yoyogi Shibuya-Ku, Tokyo, Japan
Tel.: (81) 353711481
Web Site: http://www.pazzo.co.jp
Casual Wear Mfr & Distr
N.A.I.C.S.: 315250
Shingo Fukuda *(Exec VP)*

TOKEN CO., LTD. (1)
76-1 Ukishirocho, Komatsu, 923-0908, Ishikawa, Japan
Tel.: (81) 761218818
Web Site: https://www.token-web.com
General Construction Services
N.A.I.C.S.: 236220

KOMATSU WALL INDUSTRY CO., LTD.
172 Industrial Park, Komatsu, 923-8643, Ishikawa, Japan
Tel.: (81) 761213131

KOMATSU WALL INDUSTRY CO., LTD.

Komatsu Wall Industry Co., Ltd.—(Continued)

Web Site:
  https://www.komatsuwall.co.jp
Year Founded: 1968
7949—(TKS)
Sales Range: $250-299.9 Million
Partition Mfr & Distr
N.A.I.C.S.: 337215
Yutaka Kano (Pres)

KOMAX HOLDING AG
Industriestrasse 6, 6036, Dierikon, Switzerland
Tel.: (41) 414550455 CH
Web Site:
  https://www.komaxgroup.com
KOMN—(SWX)
Rev.: $672,208,426
Assets: $868,631,929
Liabilities: $406,781,596
Net Worth: $461,850,333
Earnings: $57,398,004
Emp.: 3,390
Fiscal Year-end: 12/31/22
Wire-Processing Systems Mfr & Assembly Automation Equipment Services
N.A.I.C.S.: 332618
Andreas Wolfisberg (CFO)

Subsidiaries:

AAT Aston GmbH
Konradstrasse 7, 90429, Nuremberg, Germany
Tel.: (49) 91132660
Web Site: http://aston.de
Cable Component & Equipment Mfr
N.A.I.C.S.: 335999

AD Contact AB Gammeter (1)
Vehnamyllynkatu 6, 33560, Tampere, Finland
Tel.: (358) 33802211
Fabricated Wire Product Mfr
N.A.I.C.S.: 332618

Adcontact AB (1)
Ursviksvagen 127 A, 174 46, Sundbyberg, Sweden
Tel.: (46) 84453600
Web Site: http://www.adcontact.se
Cable Component & Equipment Mfr
N.A.I.C.S.: 335999

Chain Year Industries Crop. (1)
325 Lane 201 Tung-Shu Str Shijr City Hsien, 221, Taipei, Taiwan
Tel.: (886) 226913568
Fabricated Wire Product Mfr
N.A.I.C.S.: 332618

Cofilimacchine S.R.L. (1)
Via Friuli 5, 20853, Biassono, Italy
Tel.: (39) 0392324125
Fabricated Wire Product Mfr
N.A.I.C.S.: 332618

El Proveedor Tecnologico S.R.L. (1)
Gral C M de Alvear 1315 Florida Partido de V Lopez, 1602, Buenos Aires, Argentina
Tel.: (54) 1147613607
Fabricated Wire Product Mfr
N.A.I.C.S.: 332618

Estanflux S.A. (1)
C Gomis 1, 08023, Barcelona, Spain
Tel.: (34) 933516151
Web Site: http://www.estanflux.com
Cable Component & Equipment Mfr
N.A.I.C.S.: 335999

Evoltec AG (1)
ul Bekasow 63/65, 02-803, Warsaw, Poland
Tel.: (48) 225502740
Fabricated Wire Product Mfr
N.A.I.C.S.: 332618

Exmore Benelux bvba (1)
Ketelaarstraat 8, 2340, Beerse, Belgium
Tel.: (32) 14618666
Web Site: http://www.exmore.com
Electronic Assembly & Component Mfr
N.A.I.C.S.: 334419

FEK Company Ltd. (1)
Pushkina Ave 29B, 220015, Minsk, Belarus

Tel.: (375) 447377270
Fabricated Wire Product Mfr
N.A.I.C.S.: 332618

Gammeter OU (1)
Paldiski MNT 31, 76606, Keila, Estonia
Tel.: (372) 6712251
Cable Component & Equipment Mfr
N.A.I.C.S.: 335999

Hansung Tech Co., Ltd. (1)
411 Renaissance-officetel 10 Jangmi-Ro 48 Beongil, Bundang-gu, Seongnam, 13496, Gyeonggi, Korea (South)
Tel.: (82) 317813971
Fabricated Wire Product Mfr
N.A.I.C.S.: 332618

Ing. Emil Novy (1)
Habrova 1429, Ostrov, 363 01, Czech Republic
Tel.: (420) 604208324
Web Site: http://www.komaxcr.cz
Wire & Cable Machinery Mfr
N.A.I.C.S.: 333248

Kabatec GmbH & Co. KG (1)
Am Grubener Weg 15, Burghaun, 36151, Fulda, Germany
Tel.: (49) 6652793620
Web Site: http://www.kabatec.com
Emp.: 90
Taping Machine & Insulating Equipment Mfr
N.A.I.C.S.: 333517
Markus Reisinger (Gen Mgr)

Kinetic Electronics Ltd. (1)
207 Adams Villas, Offaly, Tullamore, Ireland
Tel.: (353) 579321014
Fabricated Wire Product Mfr
N.A.I.C.S.: 332618

KomTech (Pty) Ltd. (1)
The Crest Unit 14 Dawood Close, Ballito, 4420, South Africa
Tel.: (27) 325863626
Web Site: http://komtech.co.za
Stripping & Crimp Tooling Mfr
N.A.I.C.S.: 333515

Komax AG (1)
Industriestrasse 6, 6036, Dierikon, Switzerland (100%)
Tel.: (41) 414550455
Sales Range: $125-149.9 Million
Emp.: 300
Commercial Screen Printing
N.A.I.C.S.: 323113

Komax Austria GmbH (1)
Perfektastrasse 59, 1230, Vienna, Austria
Tel.: (43) 180428710
Electronic Part Mfr & Distr
N.A.I.C.S.: 334419

Komax Automation India Pvt. Ltd. (1)
D-3 Ground Floor Infocity-II Sector-33, Gurgaon, 122001, Haryana, India
Tel.: (91) 8130420003
Web Site: https://www.komaxgroup.com
Emp.: 20
Wire Processing Systems Whslr
N.A.I.C.S.: 423830

Komax Belgium N.V. (1)
Ketelaarstraat 8, 2340, Beerse, Belgium
Tel.: (32) 14618666
Engineering Services
N.A.I.C.S.: 541330

Komax Bulgaria EOOD (1)
18 Nartsis Str, 8600, Yambol, Bulgaria
Tel.: (359) 886888577
Fabricated Wire Product Mfr
N.A.I.C.S.: 332618

Komax Comercial do Brasil Ltda (1)
 (100%)
Tel.: (55) 1130281112
Sales Range: $25-49.9 Million
Emp.: 20
Non-Durable Goods Whslr
N.A.I.C.S.: 424990

Komax Corp (1)
1100 E Corporate Grove Dr, Buffalo Grove, IL 60089-4507 (100%)
Tel.: (847) 537-6640
Web Site: http://www.komaxusa.com

Sales Range: $25-49.9 Million
Commercial & Service Industry Machinery Mfr
N.A.I.C.S.: 333310

Komax Czech Republic Trading s.r.o. (1)
Hviezdoslavova 1188/5, 62700, Brno, Czech Republic
Tel.: (420) 545243454
Electronic Part Mfr & Distr
N.A.I.C.S.: 334419

Komax Deutschland GmbH (1)
Willstatterstr 95, 90449, Nuremberg, Germany (100%)
Tel.: (49) 911324950
Web Site: http://www.komaxwire.de
Sales Range: $25-49.9 Million
Emp.: 24
Electrical Equipment & Component Mfr
N.A.I.C.S.: 335999

Komax Distribution (Thailand) Co., Ltd. (1)
G Floor Unit GA Pipatanasin Building 6/10 Narathiwas Rachanakarin Road, Tungmahamek Sathorn, Bangkok, 10120, Thailand
Tel.: (66) 20425650
Fabricated Wire Product Mfr
N.A.I.C.S.: 332618

Komax France Sarl. (1)
20 rue de l'Avenir, 93806, Epinay-sur-Seine, France
Tel.: (33) 149401313
Web Site: https://www.komax.fr
Industrial Automated Equipment Mfr
N.A.I.C.S.: 333248

Komax Hungary Kft. (1)
Cserszegi utca 2-6, 2092, Budakeszi, Hungary
Tel.: (36) 23884151
Electronic Part Mfr & Distr
N.A.I.C.S.: 334419

Komax Japan K.K. (1)
Owadamachi 1-12-5, Hachioji-shi, Tokyo, 192-0045, Japan
Tel.: (81) 5034969522
Fabricated Wire Product Mfr
N.A.I.C.S.: 332618

Komax KL (1)
No 4 Lorong Chekor Batu 3 Jalan Kelang Lama, 58000, Kuala Lumpur, Malaysia
Tel.: (60) 379812662
Fabricated Wire Product Mfr
N.A.I.C.S.: 332618

Komax Management AG (1)
Industriestrasse 6, CH-6036, Dierikon, Switzerland (100%)
Tel.: (41) 414550455
Sales Range: $100-124.9 Million
Emp.: 650
Online Information Services
N.A.I.C.S.: 519290

Komax Maroc Sarl. (1)
Tel.: (212) 523305285
Sales Range: $50-74.9 Million
Emp.: 24
Commercial & Industrial Machinery & Equipment Rental & Leasing
N.A.I.C.S.: 532490

Komax Portuguesa S.A. (1)
Rua de S Francisco 786 Parque Doroana Fraccao DC Adroana, Alcabideche, Cascais, 2645-019, Portugal (100%)
Tel.: (351) 214448480
Web Site: http://www.komax.pt
Sales Range: $25-49.9 Million
Electrical Equipment & Component Mfr
N.A.I.C.S.: 335999

Komax Romania Trading S.R.L. (1)
Blvd Preciziei Nr 1C Sector 6, 062202, Bucharest, Romania
Tel.: (40) 213355654
Electronic Part Mfr & Distr
N.A.I.C.S.: 334419

Komax SA (PTY) LTD (1)
49 Worraker Street, PO Box 34715, Newton Park, 6055, Port Elizabeth, South Africa (100%)
Tel.: (27) 413955800

INTERNATIONAL PUBLIC

Sales Range: $25-49.9 Million
Emp.: 5
Machine Tools Mfr
N.A.I.C.S.: 333517

Komax Shanghai Co. Ltd. (1)
Building 5-6 88 Lane 3509 South Hong Mei Road, Minhang District, Shanghai, 201108, China
Tel.: (86) 2124165668
Industrial Machinery Mfr
N.A.I.C.S.: 333248

Komax Singapore Pte Ltd (1)
28 Kaki Bukit Crescent Kaki Bukit, Techpark 1, Singapore, 416259, Singapore
Tel.: (65) 62859713
Web Site: https://www.komaxwire.com
Sales Range: $25-49.9 Million
Machine Shops
N.A.I.C.S.: 332710

Komax Slovakia s.r.o. (1)
Cukrova 14, 811 08, Bratislava, Slovakia
Tel.: (421) 252733664
Electronic Part Mfr & Distr
N.A.I.C.S.: 334419

Komax TSK Maroc Sarl. (1)
1 rue Ibn Zohr, 20800, Mohammedia, Morocco
Tel.: (212) 523305285
Electronic Assembly & Component Mfr
N.A.I.C.S.: 334419

Komax Taping GmbH & Co. KG (1)
Am Grubener Weg 15, 36151, Burghausen, Germany
Tel.: (49) 6652793620
Electronic Part Mfr & Distr
N.A.I.C.S.: 334419

Komax Testing Bulgaria EOOD (1)
18 Nartsis Str, 8600, Yambol, Bulgaria
Tel.: (359) 887622278
Engineeering Services
N.A.I.C.S.: 541330

Komax Testing Germany GmbH (1)
Strengelrott 4, 32457, Porta Westfalica, Germany
Tel.: (49) 57179580
Electronic Part Mfr & Distr
N.A.I.C.S.: 334419

Komax Testing India Pvt. Ltd. (1)
Plot No PAP-SH-105 Near CNH New Holland Ph-II SH Khed, Pune, 410501, Maharashtra, India
Tel.: (91) 2135662222
Wire Processing Product Mfr & Distr
N.A.I.C.S.: 332618

Komax Testing Maroc FT S.a.r.l. (1)
Lot RF No 2 Zone Franche d'exportation de Tanger, 90060, Tangiers, Morocco
Tel.: (212) 539409850
Engineeering Services
N.A.I.C.S.: 541330

Komax Testing Mexico, S de R.L. de C.V. (1)
Ramon Rivera Lara No 6472 Iglesias Party, 32610, Ciudad Juarez, Chihuahua, Mexico
Tel.: (52) 6567380232
Wire Processing Product Mfr & Distr
N.A.I.C.S.: 332618

Komax Testing Romania S.R.L. (1)
Str Principala Nr 134/C Cartier Unirea, Nasaud, 420005, Bistrita, Romania
Tel.: (40) 745535313
Engineeering Services
N.A.I.C.S.: 541330

Komax Testing Tunisia S.a.r.l. (1)
16 Rue de I Energie Solaire, ZI Charguia, 2035, Tunis, Tunisia
Tel.: (216) 71770506
Wire Processing Product Mfr & Distr
N.A.I.C.S.: 332618

Komax Testing Turkiye Test Sistemleri San. Ltd. Sti.
 (1)
Karamehmet Mah Avrupa Serbest Bolgesi 9 Sok No 9, Ergene, 59930, Tekirdag, Turkiye
Tel.: (90) 2826911227190
Electronic Part Mfr & Distr
N.A.I.C.S.: 334419

Laselec SA (1)

AND PRIVATE COMPANIES

15 rue Boudeville, 31100, Toulouse, France
Tel.: (33) 582950555
Web Site: http://www.laselec.com
Laser Machine Mfr
N.A.I.C.S.: 333517
Eric Dupont *(Gen Mgr)*

Subsidiary (Non-US):

Komax SLE GmbH & Co. KG (2)
Technopark 4, DE-94481, Grafenau, Germany
Tel.: (49) 85527230000
Web Site: https://www.komax-grafenau.de
Fabricated Wire Product Mfr
N.A.I.C.S.: 332618

Komax de Mexico S. de R.L. de C.V. (2)
Av Rio San Lorenzo 489 Parque Tecnoindustrial Castro del Rio 5ta Etapa, Irapuato, C P 36814, Guanajuato, Mexico
Tel.: (52) 4623871200
Fabricated Wire Product Mfr
N.A.I.C.S.: 332618

Leadmaker Services Ltd. (1)
Spring Cottage Biddenfield Lane Shedfield, Southampton, SO32 2HP, Hampshire, United Kingdom
Tel.: (44) 1329832621
Web Site: http://leadmaker.co.uk
Cable Component & Equipment Mfr
N.A.I.C.S.: 335999
Chris Tidball *(Dir-Technical)*

Lintech S.A.S. (1)
Courtaboeuf ZA 1 Avenue of Norway, 91140, Villebon-sur-Yvette, France
Tel.: (33) 164867090
Web Site: https://www.lintech.fr
Electronic Part Mfr & Distr
N.A.I.C.S.: 334419

MIKOM Electronic d.o.o. (1)
Laze Kostica 1, 18000, Nis, Serbia
Tel.: (381) 18220820
Web Site: http://www.mikomgroup.com
Fabricated Wire Product Mfr
N.A.I.C.S.: 332618

Subsidiary (Non-US):

Mikom d.o.o. (2)
Ulica Stjepana Radica 1/A, Bistrica, 49247, Zlatar, Croatia
Tel.: (385) 49462034
Fabricated Wire Product Mfr
N.A.I.C.S.: 332618

Malintech S.a.r.l. (1)
Lot 38 - 2nd Floor Ain Zahran Building Office No 31, Logistics Zone Free zone, Tangiers, Morocco
Tel.: (212) 539394261
Wire Processing Product Mfr & Distr
N.A.I.C.S.: 332618

Malintech W.P.S. (1)
Lot 24/A2 - 1st Floor Block 24B Office No 12 Tangier Free Zone, Tangiers, Morocco
Tel.: (212) 539393453
Wire Processing Product Mfr & Distr
N.A.I.C.S.: 332618

Matech Systems A/S (1)
Ankelbovej 6, 7190, Billund, Denmark
Tel.: (45) 75338949
Web Site: http://www.matechsystems.dk
Cable Component & Equipment Mfr
N.A.I.C.S.: 335999

Neuftech Philippines Inc. (1)
Unit B-11 2nd Floor Regalena Building 9049 National Highway Brgy, Turbina, 4027, Calamba, Laguna, Philippines
Tel.: (63) 495454056
Fabricated Wire Product Mfr
N.A.I.C.S.: 332618

SCI Femto S.A.S (1)
15B Avenue des Montboucons, 25030, Besancon, Cedex, France
Tel.: (33) 363082400
Web Site: https://www.femto-st.fr
Information Technology Services
N.A.I.C.S.: 541519

Smans N.V. (1)
Bremheidelaan 8, 2300, Turnhout, Belgium
Tel.: (32) 14424401

Web Site: http://www.smans.com
Fabricated Wire Product Mfr
N.A.I.C.S.: 332618

Suba Engineering Pty. Ltd. (1)
6/150 Canterbury Road, Bankstown, 2200, NSW, Australia
Tel.: (61) 297900900
Web Site: http://www.suba.com.au
Cable Component & Equipment Mfr
N.A.I.C.S.: 335999
Ueli Kneubuhler *(Mgr-Technical Support)*

TSK Innovations Co. (1)
9641 Plaza Cir, El Paso, TX 79927
Tel.: (915) 581-9718
Electronic Assembly & Component Mfr
N.A.I.C.S.: 334419

TSK Prufsysteme GmbH (1)
Strengelrott 4, 32457, Porta Westfalica, Germany
Tel.: (49) 57179580
Web Site: http://www.t-s-k.de
Emp.: 400
Electronic Assembly & Component Mfr
N.A.I.C.S.: 334419
Sven Ratjen *(Head-Market Svcs & Comm)*

TSK Services Ltd. (1)
Vodickova 1498, 349 01, Stribro, Czech Republic
Tel.: (420) 374623896
Fabricated Wire Product Mfr
N.A.I.C.S.: 332618

TSK Sistemás de Testes do Brasil Ltda. (1)
AV Sao Gabriel 433 Regiao Metropolitana de, 83404-000, Curitiba, Brazil
Tel.: (55) 4131258300
Electronic Assembly & Component Mfr
N.A.I.C.S.: 334419

TSK Test Sistemleri San. Ltd. Sti. (1)
Karamehmet Mah Avrupa Serbest Bolgesi 9 Sok No 9, Ergene, 59930, Tekirdag, Turkiye
Tel.: (90) 2826911227
Electronic Assembly & Component Mfr
N.A.I.C.S.: 334419
Yuksel Karaman *(Gen Mgr)*

TSK Test Systems SRL (1)
Str Principala Nr 134/C Cartier Unirea, Bistrita Nasaud, 420005, Bistrita, Romania
Tel.: (40) 263228025
Electronic Assembly & Component Mfr
N.A.I.C.S.: 334419
Adrian Miclea *(Gen Mgr)*

TSK Tunisia s.a.r.l. (1)
16 Rue de l Energie Solaire Ex 8612 ZI Charguia I, 2035, Tunis, Tunisia
Tel.: (216) 71770506
Electronic Assembly & Component Mfr
N.A.I.C.S.: 334419
Mohamed Hadj Ali *(Gen Mgr)*

TSK do Brasil Ltda. (1)
AV Sao Gabriel 433 Regiao Metropolitana de Colombo, Curitiba, 83404, Brazil
Tel.: (55) 4136211794
Fabricated Wire Product Mfr
N.A.I.C.S.: 332618

Tamir Engineering & Development Ltd. (1)
7 Hamifalim St Kiriat Arie, PO Box 7079, 49170, Petach Tikva, Israel
Tel.: (972) 39229422
Fabricated Wire Product Mfr
N.A.I.C.S.: 332618

Tekuni Eood (1)
Ul Akademik Petar Dinekov 23 Bl V2 Ap 16 Dragalevtsi, 1415, Sofia, Bulgaria
Tel.: (359) 897761159
Fabricated Wire Product Mfr
N.A.I.C.S.: 332618

Thonauer Gesellschaft m.b.H. (1)
Perfektastrasse 59, 1230, Vienna, Austria
Tel.: (43) 180428710
Dosing Machine Mfr
N.A.I.C.S.: 333241
Thomas Stummer *(Mgr-Sls)*

Subsidiary (Non-US):

Komax Thonauer Kft. (2)

Cserszegi Street 2-6, 2092, Budakeszi, Hungary
Tel.: (36) 23457003
Cable Processing & Dosing Machine Mfr
N.A.I.C.S.: 333241
Balint Alcsuti *(Mgr-Sls)*

SC Thonauer Automatic s.r.l. (2)
Str Precision No 1C, 062202, Bucharest, Romania
Tel.: (40) 213355654
Cable Processing & Dosing Machine Mfr
N.A.I.C.S.: 333241
Sergiu Czompi *(Mgr-Key Acct)*

Thonauer Spol. s.r.o. (2)
Hviezdoslavova 1188/5, 627 00, Brno, Czech Republic
Tel.: (420) 545243454
Cable Processing & Dosing Machine Mfr
N.A.I.C.S.: 333241

Thonauer s.r.o. (2)
Cukrova 14, 813 39, Bratislava, Slovakia
Tel.: (421) 252733664
Cable Processing & Dosing Machine Mfr
N.A.I.C.S.: 333241

Tulintech S.a.r.l. (1)
B40 ZI Sidi Abdelhamid, 4061, Sousse, Tunisia
Tel.: (216) 73321430
Wire Processing Product Mfr & Distr
N.A.I.C.S.: 332618

Unitek Elektrik Makine Otomasyon San. Ve Tic. A.S. (1)
IMES Sanayi Sitesi B Blok 202 Sok No 8 Y Dudullu-umraniye, 34875, Istanbul, Turkiye
Tel.: (90) 2165189440
Web Site: http://www.unitek-elektrik.com
Electrical & Electronic Tool Machinery Distr
N.A.I.C.S.: 423690

WUSTEC GmbH & Co. KG (1)
Hohenkreuzstr 2, Seedorf, 78655, Dunningen, Germany
Tel.: (49) 7402904600
Web Site: https://wus-tec.de
Electronic Part Mfr & Distr
N.A.I.C.S.: 334419

Windeq Technical Centre LLC (1)
1B Domodedovskoye Shosse building 3 office 69, Selkhoztekhnika Settlement, 142116, Podolsk, Moscow, Russia
Tel.: (7) 4954192411
Web Site: https://windeq.ru
Fabricated Wire Product Mfr
N.A.I.C.S.: 332618

KOMBASSAN HOLDING A.S.
Yenisehir Mah Dr M Hulusi Baybal Cd No 12, Selcuklu, Konya, Turkiye
Tel.: (90) 332 221 20 00
Web Site: http://www.kombassan.com.tr
Holding Company
N.A.I.C.S.: 551112
Hasim Sahin *(Chm)*

KOMBINAT KOKSOCHEM-ICZNY ZABRZE S.A.
Pawliczka 1, 41-800, Zabrze, Poland
Tel.: (48) 322711231   PL
Web Site: http://www.kkzabrze.com.pl
Sales Range: $125-149.9 Million
Emp.: 975
Coal Producer
N.A.I.C.S.: 324199
Zdzislaw Trzepizur *(Pres & Mng Dir)*

KOME ON COMMUNICATION LTD.
Block No 338/Paiky 6/2 Dhamdachi Village, Tal and Dist Valsad, Ahmedabad, 396001, Gujarat, India
Tel.: (91) 7926562049
Web Site: http://www.komeon.in
539910—(BOM)
Assets: $1,975,151
Liabilities: $2,462
Net Worth: $1,972,690
Earnings: ($26,634)

Fiscal Year-end: 03/31/22
Television Program Services
N.A.I.C.S.: 512110
Shekhar Narayan Kadam *(Mng Dir)*

KOMEDA HOLDINGS CO., LTD.
3-12-23 Aoi, Higashi-ku, Nagoya, 461-0004, Aichi, Japan
Tel.: (81) 529368880
Web Site: https://www.komeda-holdings.co.jp
Year Founded: 1968
3543—(TKS)
Rev.: $306,543,240
Assets: $728,653,480
Liabilities: $423,003,580
Net Worth: $305,649,900
Earnings: $42,341,480
Fiscal Year-end: 02/29/24
Coffeeshop Operator
N.A.I.C.S.: 445298
Yuichi Amari *(Pres & Dir-Rep)*

KOMEHYO HOLDINGS CO., LTD.
See-Step Building 4F 3-38-5 Osu, Naka-ku, Nagoya, 460-0011, Aichi, Japan
Tel.: (81) 522495366
Web Site: https://komehyohds.com
Year Founded: 1947
2780—(TKS)
Rev.: $789,623,990
Assets: $423,297,790
Liabilities: $233,128,090
Net Worth: $190,169,700
Earnings: $33,215,250
Emp.: 1,087
Fiscal Year-end: 03/31/24
Outlet Goods Whslr
N.A.I.C.S.: 459510

Subsidiaries:

Auto Parts KOMEHYO KK (1)
1-1-2 Hirokawa-cho, Nakagawa-ku, Nagoya, 454-0027, Aichi, Japan
Tel.: (81) 587817512
Web Site: https://www.autoparts-japan.com
Automobile Parts Distr
N.A.I.C.S.: 423120

KOMELON CORPORATION
73 Jangpyeongro, Saha-gu, Busan, Korea (South)
Tel.: (82) 512903100
Web Site: https://www.komelon.co.kr
Year Founded: 1963
049430—(KRS)
Rev.: $63,438,830
Assets: $159,320,624
Liabilities: $10,127,477
Net Worth: $149,193,146
Earnings: $12,130,641
Emp.: 101
Fiscal Year-end: 12/31/22
Measurement Tool Mfr
N.A.I.C.S.: 334519

Subsidiaries:

Komelon Corporation - Komelon France Division (1)
6 rue Lionel Terray, 92500, Rueil-Malmaison, France
Tel.: (33) 1 41 47 49 89
Web Site: http://www.komeloneurope.com
Measuring Tool Mfr
N.A.I.C.S.: 334519

Komelon Corporation - Komelon Steel Division (1)
602 Aenggogae-ro, Namdong-gu, Incheon, Korea (South)
Tel.: (82) 32 822 3211
Measuring Tool Mfr
N.A.I.C.S.: 334519

Komelon USA Corporation (1)
301 Commerce St, Waukesha, WI 53186

KOMELON CORPORATION

Komelon Corporation—(Continued)
Tel.: (262) 524-8273
Web Site: http://www.komelon.com
Measuring Tool Distr
N.A.I.C.S.: 423830

Qingdao Komelon Tool
Corporation (1)
Qingda Industrial Park, Chengyang,
Qingdao, Shandong, China
Tel.: (86) 532 8790 6980
Measuring Tool Distr
N.A.I.C.S.: 423830

KOMERCIJALNA BANKA A.D. BANJA LUKA
Veselina Maslese 6, 78 000, Banja
Luka, Bosnia & Herzegovina
Tel.: (387) 51 244 763
Web Site: http://www.kombank-bl.com
Year Founded: 2006
KMCB—(BANJ)
Sales Range: $1-9.9 Million
Emp.: 144
Banking Services
N.A.I.C.S.: 522110
Lidija Sklopic (Chm-Supervisory Bd)

KOMERCIJALNA BANKA A.D. SKOPJE
Orce Nikolov Str 3, PO Box 563,
1000, Skopje, North Macedonia
Tel.: (389) 23168168
Web Site: http://www.kb.com.mk
Year Founded: 1955
Sales Range: $25-49.9 Million
Emp.: 1,200
Banking Services
N.A.I.C.S.: 522110
Biljana Mitevska (Mgr-Domestic Payment Ops Dept)

Subsidiaries:

KB Publikum Invest AD (1)
Bul Mito Hadzivasilev Jasmin 50, 1000,
Skopje, North Macedonia
Tel.: (389) 23204490
Web Site: http://www.kbpublikum.com.mk
Investment Fund Management Services
N.A.I.C.S.: 523940
Suzana Moskovska (Pres)

KOMERCIJALNO-INVESTICIONA BANKA D.D.
Tone Hrovata bb, 77 230, Velika Kladusa, Bosnia & Herzegovina
Tel.: (387) 37771654
Web Site: http://www.kib-banka.com.ba
KIBBR—(SARE)
Rev.: $2,086,528
Assets: $73,588,896
Liabilities: $55,115,429
Net Worth: $18,473,468
Earnings: $911,077
Emp.: 78
Fiscal Year-end: 12/31/20
Banking Services
N.A.I.C.S.: 522110
Hadzalic Eveldin (Pres)

KOMERI CO., LTD.
Shimizu 4501-1, Minami-ku, Niigata,
950-1492, Niigata, Japan
Tel.: (81) 253714111
Web Site: https://www.komeri.bit.or.jp
Year Founded: 1952
8218—(TKS)
Rev.: $2,450,670,720
Assets: $2,464,545,110
Liabilities: $902,945,830
Net Worth: $1,561,599,280
Earnings: $90,636,320
Emp.: 9,818
Fiscal Year-end: 03/31/24
Departmental Store Operator
N.A.I.C.S.: 455110

Yuichiro Sasage (Pres & CEO)

Subsidiaries:

Yamaki Co., Ltd. (1)
131 Uemachi, Chuo-ku, Osaka, 540-0005,
Japan
Tel.: (81) 667642211
Web Site: https://www.e-yamaki.co.jp
Rev.: $75,671,280
Assets: $73,919,630
Liabilities: $46,084,920
Net Worth: $27,834,710
Earnings: $1,414,540
Emp.: 2,057
Fiscal Year-end: 03/31/2024
Clothing Apparel Mfr & Distr
N.A.I.C.S.: 315250
Keiji Miyamoto (Chm)

KOMGRAD A.D.
Obilicev venac 18-20, 11000, Belgrade, Serbia
Tel.: (381) 24 415 00 16
Web Site: http://www.komgrad.rs
Year Founded: 1969
Sales Range: Less than $1 Million
Emp.: 48
Road Construction Services
N.A.I.C.S.: 237310

KOMICO LTD
8 Mosan-ro, Anseong, 17567,
Gyeonggi-do, Korea (South)
Tel.: (82) 3180565800   KR
Web Site: https://www.komico.com
Year Founded: 2013
183300—(KRS)
Rev.: $221,184,395
Assets: $297,439,919
Liabilities: $99,809,655
Net Worth: $197,630,264
Earnings: $32,188,521
Emp.: 737
Fiscal Year-end: 12/31/22
Semiconductor Mfr
N.A.I.C.S.: 334413
Sung-Soo Jang (VP)

Subsidiaries:

KoMiCo Hillsboro LLC (1)
6231 NE Croeni Ave, Hillsboro, OR 97124
Tel.: (971) 348-5400
Semiconductor Parts Cleaning & Coating Services
N.A.I.C.S.: 811310

KOMIPHARM INTERNATIONAL CO., LTD.
17 Gyeongje-Ro, Siheung, Gyeonggi-Do, Korea (South)
Tel.: (82) 314986104
Web Site: https://www.komipharm.com
Year Founded: 1972
041960—(KRS)
Rev.: $30,526,997
Assets: $85,712,999
Liabilities: $35,361,735
Net Worth: $50,351,264
Earnings: ($5,736,929)
Emp.: 153
Fiscal Year-end: 12/31/22
Veterinary Pharmaceutical Mfr
N.A.I.C.S.: 325412
Yong-Jin Yang (Chm & CEO)

Subsidiaries:

Komipharm International Co., Ltd. - Osong Plant (1)
291 Osonggarak-Ro Osong-Eup, Cheongwon, Chungcheongbuk-do, Korea (South)
Tel.: (82) 432388800
Veterinary Pharmaceutical Mfr
N.A.I.C.S.: 325412

Komipharm International Co., Ltd. - Yesan Plant (1)
235-24 Chusa-Ro Sinam-Myeon, Yesan, Chungcheongnam, Korea (South)
Tel.: (82) 413334262

Veterinary Pharmaceutical Mfr
N.A.I.C.S.: 325412

KOMMUNAL LANDSPENSJONSKASSE GJENSIDIG FORSIKRINGSSELSKAP
Dronning Eufemias Gate 10, 0191,
Oslo, Norway
Tel.: (47) 55548500
Web Site: http://www.klp.no
Year Founded: 1949
Sales Range: $200-249.9 Million
Emp.: 700
Insurance Services
N.A.I.C.S.: 524113
Sverre Thornes (CEO)

Subsidiaries:

KLP Kommunekreditt (1)
Beddinddin 8, N 7014, Trondheim, Norway
Tel.: (47) 73809580
Web Site: http://www.kommunekreditt.no
Rev.: $55,900,000
Emp.: 14
Municipal Financing Services
N.A.I.C.S.: 523940

Oslofjord Varme AS (1)
Brynsveien 2, 1338, Sandvika,
Norway (15%)
Tel.: (47) 67804960
Web Site: http://www.oslofjordvarme.no
Sales Range: $75-99.9 Million
Emp.: 14
District Heating & Cooling Services
N.A.I.C.S.: 221330

KOMMUNALKREDIT AUSTRIA AG
Tuerkenstrasse 9, 1090, Vienna, Austria
Tel.: (43) 1 31 6 31   AT
Web Site: http://www.kommunalkredit.at
Year Founded: 1958
Rev.: $252,409,501
Assets: $4,821,388,915
Liabilities: $4,437,072,225
Net Worth: $384,316,690
Earnings: $33,153,679
Emp.: 251
Fiscal Year-end: 12/31/19
Banking Services; Miscellaneous Financial Investment Activities
N.A.I.C.S.: 523999
Christian Teichmann (Head-Rating & IR)

KOMO A.D.
Svetosavska Bb, 74480, Modrica,
Bosnia & Herzegovina
Tel.: (387) 53883828
KOMO—(BANJ)
Sales Range: $1-9.9 Million
Emp.: 233
Footwear Mfr
N.A.I.C.S.: 316210
Dragoljub Zrnic (Chm)

KOMOLINE AEROSPACE LIMITED
110 Om Towers Satellite Road,
Ahmedabad, 380 015, Gujarat, India
Tel.: (91) 7926746179
Web Site: http://www.komoline.com
Year Founded: 1990
Sales Range: $25-49.9 Million
Emp.: 75
Automated Weather Monitoring Component Mfr
N.A.I.C.S.: 334519
Sumit Dave (Mgr-R&D)

KOMORI CORPORATION
3-11-1 Azumabashi, Sumida-ku, Tokyo, 130 8666, Japan
Tel.: (81) 356087811
Web Site: https://komori-america.us

INTERNATIONAL PUBLIC

Year Founded: 1923
6349—(TKS)
Rev.: $689,277,580
Assets: $1,107,756,680
Liabilities: $351,129,810
Net Worth: $756,626,870
Earnings: $30,677,010
Emp.: 2,562
Fiscal Year-end: 03/31/24
Printing Press & Equipment Mfr & Retailer
N.A.I.C.S.: 333248
Yoshiharu Komori (Chm)

Subsidiaries:

Komori (Shenzhen) Print Engineering Co., Ltd. (1)
West Tower 16 F/L Block B Wisdom Plaza Qiaoxiang Road, Nanshan District, Shenzhen, 518000, China
Tel.: (86) 75586156188
Commercial Offset Machine Mfr
N.A.I.C.S.: 333248

Komori America Corporation (1)
5520 Meadowbrook Industrial Ct, Rolling Meadows, IL 60008 (100%)
Tel.: (847) 806-9000
Web Site: https://www.komori-america.us
Sales Range: $10-24.9 Million
Printing Equipment Mfr, Retailer, Servicer & Distr
N.A.I.C.S.: 423830
Robert Rath (CFO)

Subsidiary (Domestic):

Komori Leasing Incorporated (2)
5520 Meadowbrook Industrial Ct, Rolling Meadows, IL 60008 (100%)
Tel.: (847) 806-9000
Web Site: http://www.komori.com
Sales Range: $1-9.9 Million
Emp.: 210
Printing Press Sales & Services
N.A.I.C.S.: 423830
Bob Rath (CFO)

Komori Corporation - Tsukuba Plant (1)
203-1 Nakayama, Tsukuba, 300-1268, Ibaraki, Japan
Tel.: (81) 298390070
Web Site: http://www.komori.com
Printing Machinery & Equipment Mfr
N.A.I.C.S.: 333248

Komori Currency Technology UK Ltd (1)
Units 2 & 3 Tillingbourne Court Dorking Business Park Station Road, Dorking, RH4 1HJ, Surrey, United Kingdom
Tel.: (44) 1306876331
Emp.: 10
Printing Machinery & Equipment Mfr
N.A.I.C.S.: 333248
Steven Craig (Gen Mgr)

Komori Electronics Co., Ltd. (1)
2589 15 Oaza Nukanome Takahatamachi, Higashi-Okitama, Yamagata, 2589 40, Japan (100%)
Tel.: (81) 238574111
Web Site: http://www.komori.co.jp
N.A.I.C.S.: 333248

Komori Engineering Co., Ltd. (1)
203-1 Nakayama, Tsukuba, 300-1268, Ibaraki, Japan (100%)
Tel.: (81) 298390210
Web Site: http://www.komori.com
Sales Range: $25-49.9 Million
Distr of Electronic Components
N.A.I.C.S.: 333248

Komori France S.A. (1)
65-67 Avenue Leon Jouhaux, 92167, Antony, Cedex, France (100%)
Tel.: (33) 142371414
Web Site: http://www.komori.eu
Sales Range: $50-74.9 Million
Emp.: 40
Printing Machinery Mfr
N.A.I.C.S.: 333248

Komori Hong Kong Limited (1)
Unit 05 25/F Nanyang Plaza 57 Hung To

Road Kwun Tong, Kowloon, China (Hong Kong) **(100%)**
Tel.: (852) 25644339
Web Site: http://www.komori.com
Sales Range: $25-49.9 Million
Emp.: 20
Distribution Equipment for Electronic, Electrical & Mechanical Devices
N.A.I.C.S.: 333248

Komori India Private Limited (1)
FBD ONE Complex 1st Floor Main Mathura Road, Delhi Badarpur Border, Faridabad, 121 003, Haryana, India
Tel.: (91) 9205596111
Commercial Offset Machine Mfr
N.A.I.C.S.: 333248

Komori International (Europe) B.V. (1)
Reactorweg 151, 3542 AD, Utrecht, Netherlands **(100%)**
Tel.: (31) 88 177 0707
Web Site: https://www.komori.eu
Sales Range: $25-49.9 Million
Emp.: 45
Printing Machinery Mfr
N.A.I.C.S.: 333248

Komori International Netherlands B.V. (1)
Reactorweg 151, 3542 AD, Utrecht, Netherlands
Tel.: (31) 881770707
Web Site: https://www.komori.eu
Sales Range: $25-49.9 Million
Emp.: 5
Printing Machinery & Equipment Mfr
N.A.I.C.S.: 333248
E. Kagita *(Mng Dir)*

Komori Italia S.r.l. (1)
Via Enrico Fermi 44, 20090, Assago, MI, Italy **(100%)**
Tel.: (39) 0248884811
Web Site: http://www.komori.it
Sales Range: $25-49.9 Million
Emp.: 20
Printing Machinery Mfr
N.A.I.C.S.: 333248

Komori Kosan Co Ltd (1)
11 1 Azumabashi 3 Chome, Sumida Ku, Tokyo, 130 8666, Japan **(100%)**
Tel.: (81) 356087835
Web Site: http://www.komari.co.jp
Sales Range: $200-249.9 Million
Emp.: 2
N.A.I.C.S.: 333248
Koichiro Imato *(Mgr-HR)*

Komori Machinery Co., Ltd. (1)
300 Oaza Fukuzawa, Takahata-machi Higashi-Okitama-gun, Yamagata, 999-2174, Japan **(100%)**
Tel.: (81) 238575111
Sales Range: $100-124.9 Million
Emp.: 360
N.A.I.C.S.: 333248
Masanobu Wakatsuki *(Mng Dir)*

Komori Malaysia Sdn. Bhd. (1)
No2J-3 Room 2 Jalan Jubli Perak 22/1 Seksyen 22, 40400, Shah Alam, Selangor, Malaysia
Tel.: (60) 355698033
Commercial Offset Machine Mfr
N.A.I.C.S.: 333248

Komori Precision Co., Ltd. (1)
313-6 Minamihanajima, Matsudo, 271 0065, Chiba, Japan
Tel.: (81) 473034054
Sales Range: $25-49.9 Million
Emp.: 10
N.A.I.C.S.: 333248

Komori Printing Machine (Shenzhen) Co., Ltd. (1)
West Tower 16 F/L Block B Wisdom Plaza Qiaoxiang Road, Nanshan District, Shenzhen, 518000, China
Tel.: (86) 75586156188
Sales Range: $25-49.9 Million
Emp.: 3
Printing Machinery & Equipment Mfr
N.A.I.C.S.: 333248
Craig Chan *(Gen Mgr)*

Komori Realty Co., Ltd. (1)
3-11-1 Azumabashi, Sumida-ku, Tokyo, 130-8666, Japan
Tel.: (81) 356087835
Emp.: 3
Real Estate Leasing & Management Services
N.A.I.C.S.: 531190
Hiroshi Takano *(Gen Mgr)*

Komori Southeast Asia Pte. Ltd. (1)
1 Syed Alwi Road 04-01 Song Lin Building, Singapore, 207628, Singapore
Tel.: (65) 62934228
Commercial Offset Machine Mfr
N.A.I.C.S.: 333248

Komori Taiwan Limited (1)
7F No 51 keelung Rd Sec 2, Taipei, 110, Taiwan
Tel.: (886) 227371200
Web Site: http://www.komori.com
Sales Range: $25-49.9 Million
Printing Machinery & Equipment Mfr
N.A.I.C.S.: 333248

Komori U.K. Limited (1)
Unit 3001 Victoria Business Park Victoria Road, Seacroft, Leeds, LS14 2LA, United Kingdom **(100%)**
Tel.: (44) 1138239200
Web Site: http://www.komori.com
Sales Range: $25-49.9 Million
Emp.: 30
Printing Equipment
N.A.I.C.S.: 333248

Komori-Chambon S.A. (1)
11 avenue Buffon, PO Box 26329, 45063, Orleans, Cedex 2, France
Tel.: (33) 238645500
Web Site: https://www.komori-chambon.com
Sales Range: $50-74.9 Million
Emp.: 77
Sales & Distribution of Printing Machinery
N.A.I.C.S.: 423830

MBO Postpress Solutions GmbH (1)
Grabenstrasse 4-6, 71570, Oppenweiler, Germany
Tel.: (49) 7191460
Web Site: https://www.mbo-pps.com
Folding Machines Mfr
N.A.I.C.S.: 333243
Matthias Rapp *(Head-Customer Center, Products & Tech)*

Seria Engineering Inc. (1)
1357-3 Ichishima Hachiman-cho, Gifu, 501-4202, Japan
Tel.: (81) 575620011
Screen Printing Machinery Mfr
N.A.I.C.S.: 323113
Ichiro Kobayashi *(Mng Dir)*

KOMPAN A/S
CF Tietgens Boulevard 32C, 5220, Odense, Denmark
Tel.: (45) 63 62 12 50 DK
Web Site: http://www.kompan.com
Year Founded: 1970
Sales Range: $200-249.9 Million
Children's Playground Equipment Designer, Mfr & Marketer
N.A.I.C.S.: 339920
Connie Astrup-Larsen *(CEO)*

Subsidiaries:

Corocord Raumnetz GmbH (1)
Holzhauser Strasse 139, 13509, Berlin, Germany
Tel.: (49) 30.408988 0
Web Site: http://www.corocord.com
Emp.: 40
Playground Equipment Mfr
N.A.I.C.S.: 339920
Jesper Egelykke Jensen *(Mng Dir)*

Go Play Ltd. (1)
Galway Technology Centre Mervue Business Park, Galway, Ireland
Tel.: (353) 91 704844
Web Site: http://www.goplay.ie
Playground Equipment Designer & Mfr
N.A.I.C.S.: 339920
Martin Carey *(Mgr-Sls)*

Juegos KOMPAN S.A. (1)
C/ Cami del Mig 79-81, 08302, Mataro, Barcelona, Spain
Tel.: (34) 902 194 573
Web Site: http://www.kompan.es
Sales Range: $25-49.9 Million
Emp.: 20
Playground Equipment Mfr
N.A.I.C.S.: 339920
Eduardo Pages Santacana *(Mgr-Fin & Sls Support)*

KOMPAN B.V. (1)
Langestraat 37 A, Heerewaarden, 6624 AA, Maasdriel, Netherlands
Tel.: (31) 886787468
Web Site: http://www.kompan.nl
Sales Range: $25-49.9 Million
Emp.: 50
Playground Equipment Mfr
N.A.I.C.S.: 339920
Willem Van Veenendaal *(Mng Dir)*

KOMPAN Barnland AB (1)
Fabriksvagen 9, 435 35, Molnlycke, Sweden
Tel.: (46) 31968840
Web Site: http://www.kompan.se
Sales Range: $25-49.9 Million
Emp.: 15
Playground Equipment Mfr
N.A.I.C.S.: 339920
Christian Morton Fincham *(Gen Dir)*

KOMPAN Commercial Systems SA (1)
Rue du Teris 2, 4100, Seraing, Belgium
Tel.: (32) 4 384 05 60
Web Site: http://www.kompan-commercialsystems.com
Playground Equipment Designer, Mfr & Marketer
N.A.I.C.S.: 339920
Salih Mere *(Mgr-Export)*

KOMPAN Dica A/S (1)
CF Tietgens Boulevard 32 C, 5220, Odense, Denmark
Tel.: (45) 63 62 10 11
Web Site: http://www.kompan-dica.dk
Emp.: 100
Playground Equipment Mfr
N.A.I.C.S.: 339920
Connie Astrup-Larsen *(Mng Dir)*

KOMPAN GmbH (1)
Raiffeisenstrasse 11, 24941, Flensburg, Germany
Tel.: (49) 461773060
Web Site: http://www.kompan.de
Sales Range: $25-49.9 Million
Emp.: 40
Playground Equipment Mfr
N.A.I.C.S.: 339920

KOMPAN Italia S.r.l. (1)
Via Torino 2, 20123, Milan, Italy
Tel.: (39) 02 89 76 08 61
Web Site: http://www.kompan.it
Playground Equipment Mfr
N.A.I.C.S.: 339920

KOMPAN Ltd. (1)
21 Roebuck Way, Knowl Hill, Milton Keynes, MK5 8HL, United Kingdom
Tel.: (44) 1908201002
Web Site: http://www.kompan.co.uk
Sales Range: $25-49.9 Million
Emp.: 30
Playground Equipment Mfr & Distr
N.A.I.C.S.: 339920
Anne Qvortrup *(Dir-Fin)*

KOMPAN NV/SA (1)
Bosstraat 15, 8780, Oostrozebeke, Belgium
Tel.: (32) 9 216 66 60
Web Site: http://www.kompan.be
Playground Equipment Designer & Mfr
N.A.I.C.S.: 339920

KOMPAN Norge AS (1)
Romikabygget Kjellstad Kjellstadveien 5, 3400, Lier, Norway
Tel.: (47) 81 50 07 02
Web Site: http://www.KOMPAN.no
Playground Equipment Mfr
N.A.I.C.S.: 339920
Oyvind Hansen *(Mng Dir)*

KOMPAN Playscape Pty. Ltd. (1)
12 Kingtel Pl, Geebung, 4034, QLD, Australia
Tel.: (61) 738652800
Web Site: http://www.kompan.com.au
Sales Range: $25-49.9 Million
Emp.: 10
Playground Equipment Mfr
N.A.I.C.S.: 339920
Peter McEwen *(Mng Dir)*

KOMPAN S.A.S. (1)
363 rue Marc-Seguin, 77198, Dammarie-les-Lys, Cedex, France
Tel.: (33) 164377333
Web Site: http://www.kompan.fr
Sales Range: $25-49.9 Million
Emp.: 40
Playground Equipment Mfr
N.A.I.C.S.: 339920
Christian Peter Dyvig *(Chm)*

KOMPAN Suomi Oy (1)
Melkonkatu 22, 00210, Helsinki, Finland
Tel.: (358) 9 4355 240
Web Site: http://www.kompan.fi
Playground Equipment Mfr
N.A.I.C.S.: 339920

KOMPAN, Inc. (1)
930 Broadway, Tacoma, WA 98402
Tel.: (253) 579-1001
Web Site: http://www.kompan.us
Sales Range: $25-49.9 Million
Emp.: 26
Playground Equipment Mfr
N.A.I.C.S.: 339920
Kerrin Smith *(Pres)*

Kompan Middle East and Africa (1)
Dusseldorf Business Tower Al Barsha, Dubai, United Arab Emirates
Tel.: (971) 501526480
Sporting Goods Distr
N.A.I.C.S.: 423910

Lek & Sakerhet AB (1)
Kangerudsvagen 10, 664 40, Slottsbron, Sweden
Tel.: (46) 20414090
Sporting Goods Distr
N.A.I.C.S.: 423910

Lek & Sikkerhet AS (1)
Kjellstadveien 5, 3400, Lier, Norway
Tel.: (47) 32 24 10 20
Web Site: http://www.lekogsikkerhet.no
Playground Equipment Mfr
N.A.I.C.S.: 339920

OOO KOMPAN (1)
2nd Floor Premises XXI XXII Offices 21-32 4-8 32 Marshal Biryuzov, Street Building 1, 123060, Moscow, Russia
Tel.: (7) 4959950152
Web Site: http://www.kompan-russia.ru
Playground Equipment Distr
N.A.I.C.S.: 423910

The Play Practice Ltd. (1)
Quarrywood Court, Livingston, EH54 6AX, United Kingdom
Tel.: (44) 15 06 44 22 66
Web Site: http://www.theplaypractice.co.uk
Emp.: 10
Playground Equipment Designer & Mfr
N.A.I.C.S.: 339920
Colin Griffin *(Gen Mgr)*

Unique Playgrounds Ltd. (1)
Unit 5 Cookstown Enterprise Centre Derryloran Industrial Estate, Cookstown, United Kingdom
Tel.: (44) 28 8676 6003
Web Site: http://www.uniqueplaygrounds.co.uk
Playground Equipment Designer & Mfr
N.A.I.C.S.: 339920

KOMPANIJA BOBAR D.O.O.
Filipa Visnjica Street 211, 76 300, Bijeljina, Srpska, Bosnia & Herzegovina
Tel.: (387) 55232100 BA
Web Site: http://www.bobar.com
Year Founded: 1998
Sales Range: $900-999.9 Million
Emp.: 1,565
Investment Holding Company
N.A.I.C.S.: 551112
Darko Jeremic *(Mgr-Investments)*

KOMPANIJA BOBAR D.O.O.

Kompanija BOBAR d.o.o.—(Continued)
Subsidiaries:

Bobar Autosemberija (1)
Filipa Visnjica Street 211, 76300, Bijeljina, Srpska, Bosnia & Herzegovina
Tel.: (387) 55210490
Web Site: http://www.autosemberija.com
Vehicle Inspection Services
N.A.I.C.S.: 811111

Bobar Bobex DOO (1)
Filipa Visnjica St 211, 76300, Bijeljina, Srpska, Bosnia & Herzegovina
Tel.: (387) 55232150
Sales Range: $50-74.9 Million
Emp.: 20
Investment Services
N.A.I.C.S.: 523999

Division (Domestic):

Bobar Tours (2)
Ulica Nikole Tesle broj 19, 76300, Bijeljina, Srpska, Bosnia & Herzegovina
Tel.: (387) 55202080
Web Site: http://www.bobartours.com
Travel Agency
N.A.I.C.S.: 561510

Bobar spedicija i transport (2)
Filipa Visnjica Street 211, 76300, Bijeljina, Srpska, Bosnia & Herzegovina
Tel.: (387) 55207452
Web Site: http://www.bobar.com
Shipping Services
N.A.I.C.S.: 488390

Bobar Osiguranje DD (1)
Filipa Visnjica Street 211, 76300, Bijeljina, Srpska, Bosnia & Herzegovina
Tel.: (387) 055209299
Web Site: http://www.bobarosiguranje.com
Sales Range: $100-124.9 Million
Emp.: 200
Insurance Services
N.A.I.C.S.: 524298

Bobar inzenjering DOO (1)
Filipa Visnjica Street 211, 76300, Bijeljina, Srpska, Bosnia & Herzegovina
Tel.: (387) 55232146
Engineeering Services
N.A.I.C.S.: 541330

Bobar radio DOO (1)
Filipa Visnjica Street 211, 76300, Bijeljina, Srpska, Bosnia & Herzegovina
Tel.: (387) 55232111
Web Site: http://www.radiobobar.com
Radio Broadcasting Services
N.A.I.C.S.: 516110

Elvaco a.d. (1)
Sabackih Daka 19, 76300, Bijeljina, Bosnia & Herzegovina
Tel.: (387) 55 209 299
Web Site: http://www.elvaco.net
Sales Range: $1-9.9 Million
Emp.: 157
Structural Metal Product Mfr
N.A.I.C.S.: 332312
Gavrilo Bobar *(Chm-Mgmt Bd)*

Holding Drinatrans AD (1)
Karakaj 40B, 75400, Zvornik, Bosnia & Herzegovina
Tel.: (387) 56 260 077
Web Site: http://www.drinatrans.com
Sales Range: $1-9.9 Million
Emp.: 219
Holding Company
N.A.I.C.S.: 551112
Darko Jeremic *(Chm)*

KOMPANIJA GRADITELJ AD
Put za pristaniste bb, 23300, Kikinda, Serbia
Tel.: (381) 230 426 625
Web Site:
http://www.graditeljkikinda.co.rs
Year Founded: 1989
Sales Range: $1-9.9 Million
Road Construction Services
N.A.I.C.S.: 237310

KOMPANIJA MISIC A.D.

Lole Ribara 33, Pozarevac, Serbia
Tel.: (381) 12 55 66 55
Year Founded: 2003
Sales Range: Less than $1 Million
Emp.: 24
Driving School Operator
N.A.I.C.S.: 611692

KOMPAS A.D.
Obilicev venac 26, Belgrade, Serbia
Tel.: (381) 11 328 17 47
Web Site: http://www.kompas.rs
Year Founded: 1951
Sales Range: $1-9.9 Million
Tour Operating Services
N.A.I.C.S.: 561520
Olivera Velimirovic *(Gen Mgr)*

KOMPAS MEDUGORJE D.D.
23 Mother Teresa Medugorje, 88260, Citluk, Bosnia & Herzegovina
Tel.: (387) 36642053
KPSMR—(SARE)
Rev.: $73,788
Assets: $11,477,647
Liabilities: $9,013,722
Net Worth: $2,463,925
Earnings: ($345,207)
Emp.: 10
Fiscal Year-end: 12/31/20
Catering & Tourism Services
N.A.I.C.S.: 722320

KOMPAS MTS D.D.
Prazakova 4, 1000, Ljubljana, Slovenia
Tel.: (386) 15636450
MTSG—(LJU)
Emp.: 310
Border Tourist Services Including Foreign Currency Exchange, Freight Forwarding, Custom Authorities Payment Transactions, Insurance Brokerage, Sales Taxes & Value Added Taxes Refunding
N.A.I.C.S.: 525990
Aleksander Jereb *(CEO)*

KOMPLETT ASA
Ostre Kullerod 4, 3241, Sandefjord, Norway
Tel.: (47) 33005000
Web Site:
https://www.komplettgroup.com
Year Founded: 1999
KOMPL—(EUR)
Rev.: $1,705,774,420
Assets: $879,025,770
Liabilities: $471,077,530
Net Worth: $407,948,240
Earnings: ($3,734,080)
Emp.: 363
Fiscal Year-end: 12/31/21
Electronic Product Distr
N.A.I.C.S.: 423690
Jaan Ivar Semlitsch *(CEO)*

Subsidiaries:

Ironstone AS (1)
Storgata 1, 0155, Oslo, Norway
Tel.: (47) 23507481
Web Site: https://www.ironstoneit.com
Information Technology Services
N.A.I.C.S.: 541511

Komplett Services Sweden AB (1)
Telegrafgatan 4, 16972, Solna, Sweden
Tel.: (46) 86644600
Web Site: https://www.komplettforetag.se
Electric Component Whslr
N.A.I.C.S.: 423690

Webhallen Sverige AB (1)
Telegrafgatan 4, 16972, Solna, Sweden
Tel.: (46) 86736000
Web Site: https://www.webhallen.com
Emp.: 300
Electric Component Whslr
N.A.I.C.S.: 423690

KOMPLI HOLDINGS PLC
1 Charterhouse Mews, Farringdon, London, EC1M 6BB, United Kingdom
Tel.: (44) 203890 1974
Web Site: http://www.kompli-global.com
KOMP—(VIE)
Sales Range: Less than $1 Million
Financial Consulting Services
N.A.I.C.S.: 541611
Jane Jee *(CEO)*

KOMPRESOR A.D.
Zorza Klemansoa 19, Belgrade, Serbia
Tel.: (381) 113285339
Web Site: http://www.kompresor.rs
Year Founded: 1948
KOMPB—(BEL)
Sales Range: $1-9.9 Million
Motor Vehicle Repair & Maintenance Services
N.A.I.C.S.: 811198

KOMPUTRONIK S.A.
Ul Wolczynska 37, 60-003, Poznan, Poland
Tel.: (48) 616680000
Web Site:
https://www.komputronik.com
KOM—(WAR)
Rev.: $415,470,527
Assets: $121,866,870
Liabilities: $57,625,762
Net Worth: $64,241,108
Earnings: ($1,148,628)
Fiscal Year-end: 12/31/23
Electronic Hardware Distr
N.A.I.C.S.: 423710
Wojciech Buczkowski *(Chm & Chm-Mgmt Bd)*

KOMUNALAC MODRICA A.D.
Trg Jovana Raskovica 12, 74480, Modrica, Bosnia & Herzegovina
Tel.: (387) 53812874
Web Site: https://adkomunalac.ba
Year Founded: 2000
KMMD—(BANJ)
Sales Range: Less than $1 Million
Emp.: 39
Waste Collection & Treatment Services
N.A.I.C.S.: 221320
Dusan Jovanovic *(Pres)*

KOMUNALAC TESLIC A.D.
Kralja Petra prvog bb, 74270, Teslic, Bosnia & Herzegovina
Tel.: (387) 53431498
Year Founded: 2001
KCTS-R-A—(BANJ)
Sales Range: Less than $1 Million
Waste Management Services
N.A.I.C.S.: 562998

KOMUNALNE USLUGE AD
Kozarska br 87, 79 101, Prijedor, Bosnia & Herzegovina
Tel.: (387) 52237177
Web Site:
https://komunalneusluge.org
Year Founded: 1961
KUPR-R-A—(BANJ)
Sales Range: Less than $1 Million
Garbage Collection Services
N.A.I.C.S.: 562111
Milan Vujasinovic *(Pres)*

KOMUNALNO A.D.
Luke Delovica 2, 89000, Trebinje, Bosnia & Herzegovina
Tel.: (387) 59260733
Year Founded: 1952
KMTB—(BANJ)
Sales Range: $1-9.9 Million

Emp.: 74
Sanitation & Remediation Services
N.A.I.C.S.: 562910
Milan Mandrapa *(Dir-VD)*

KON TUM SUGAR JOINT STOCK COMPANY
Km 2 Vinh Quang, Hanoi, Kon Tum, Vietnam
Tel.: (84) 84603864958
Web Site:
https://www.ktsduongkontum.vn
Year Founded: 1995
KTS—(HNX)
Rev.: $54,767,800
Assets: $48,151,200
Liabilities: $27,764,300
Net Worth: $20,386,900
Earnings: $3,819,700
Emp.: 256
Fiscal Year-end: 12/31/23
Sugar Mfr
N.A.I.C.S.: 311314

KONA I CORPORATION
Exconventure Tower 3 Eunhaeng-ro 8th Floor, Yeongdeungpo-gu, Seoul, Korea (South)
Tel.: (82) 221687500
Web Site: https://www.konai.com
Year Founded: 1998
052400—(KRS)
Rev.: $185,754,323
Assets: $306,881,910
Liabilities: $195,197,786
Net Worth: $111,684,124
Earnings: $26,296,602
Emp.: 480
Fiscal Year-end: 12/31/22
Electronic Chip & Software Development Services
N.A.I.C.S.: 541512
Jung-il Cho *(CEO)*

Subsidiaries:

Beijing Xinjie Technology Co., Ltd. (1)
Tel.: (86) 1084475927
Smartcard Mfr
N.A.I.C.S.: 326199

KEB Technology India Private Limited (1)
546A 3rd floor Hanuman Mandir Road, Chirag, New Delhi, 1110017, India
Tel.: (91) 1141834499
Smartcard Mfr
N.A.I.C.S.: 326199

KONA C Co., Ltd. (1)
4-78 Daegotro Daegot-Myeon, Gimpo, 415-853, Gyonggido, Korea (South) (100%)
Tel.: (82) 3 1999 5500
Web Site: http://www.kona-c.com
Sales Range: $10-24.9 Million
Emp.: 120
Smartcard Mfr
N.A.I.C.S.: 326199

KONA M Co., Ltd. (1)
341 Jangsu-ro Iwol-myeon, Jincheon, 365-823, Chungcheongbuk-do, Korea (South)
Tel.: (82) 435309000
Web Site: https://www.kona-m.co.kr
Emp.: 100
Smartcard Mfr
N.A.I.C.S.: 326199

KONAKA CO., LTD.
517-2 Shinno-cho, Totsuka-ku, Yokohama, 244-0801, Kanagawa, Japan
Tel.: (81) 458251111
Web Site: https://www.konaka.co.jp
Year Founded: 1979
7494—(TKS)
Rev.: $466,500,730
Assets: $358,839,080
Liabilities: $221,030,750
Net Worth: $137,808,330
Earnings: ($1,141,490)

AND PRIVATE COMPANIES

Fiscal Year-end: 09/30/23
Apparel Clothing Store Operator
N.A.I.C.S.: 458110
Kensuke Konaka *(Pres & CEO)*

Subsidiaries:

Samantha Thavasa Japan Limited (1)
10th floor Sumitomo Real Estate Azabu-Juban Building 1-4-1 Mita, Minato-ku, Tokyo, 108-0073, Japan **(100%)**
Tel.: (81) 354128193
Web Site: https://www.samantha.co.jp
Rev.: $245,542,880
Assets: $199,156,320
Liabilities: $196,719,864
Net Worth: $2,436,456
Earnings: ($40,191,360)
Fiscal Year-end: 02/28/2022
Handbag & Jewelry Mfr & Whslr
N.A.I.C.S.: 316990
Koji Furuya *(Pres & CEO)*

KONAMI GROUP CORPORATION

1-11-1 Ginza Chuo-ku, Tokyo, 104-0061, Japan   JP
Year Founded: 1969
KNM—(LSE)
Rev.: $2,380,666,661
Assets: $4,002,972,120
Liabilities: $1,179,200,198
Net Worth: $2,823,771,922
Earnings: $390,961,238
Emp.: 9,045
Fiscal Year-end: 03/31/24
Holding Company; Amusement Machines, Gaming Software, Electronic Toys & Health-Entertainment Related Products Distr & Mfr
N.A.I.C.S.: 551112
Kimihiko Higashio *(Pres)*

Subsidiaries:

Biz Share Corporation (1)
2-9-14 Minami-senba, Chuo-ku, Osaka, 542-0081, Japan
Tel.: (81) 6 6243 2871
Web Site: http://www.bizshare.co.jp
Game Machine Distr
N.A.I.C.S.: 423990

DIGITAL GOLF Inc. (1)
9-7-2 Akasaka, Minato-ku, Tokyo, 107-0052, Japan
Tel.: (81) 3 5771 0562
Web Site: http://www.digitalgolf.co.jp
Golf Course Gaming Software Development Services
N.A.I.C.S.: 541511

HUDSON SOFT COMPANY, LIMITED (1)
9-7-2 Akasaka, Minato-ku, Tokyo, 107-0052, Japan
Tel.: (81) 3 6439 4622
Web Site: http://www.hudson.co.jp
Gaming & Entertainment Software Publishing Services
N.A.I.C.S.: 513210

Internet Revolution, Inc. (1)
1-11-1 Ginza, Chuo-ku, Tokyo, 104-0061, Japan
Tel.: (81) 366852573
Web Site: http://www.i-revo.jp
Internet Portal Operating Services
N.A.I.C.S.: 519290

KME Co., Ltd. (1)
9-7-2 Akasaka, Minato-ku, Tokyo, 107-8346, Japan
Tel.: (81) 3 5771 0505
Music Copyright Management Services
N.A.I.C.S.: 512230
Fumiaki Tanaka *(Pres)*

Konami Amusement Co., Ltd. (1)
1 Ikejiri Takata, Ichinomiya, 491-0125, Aichi, Japan
Tel.: (81) 586887707
Emp.: 884
Amusement Machines Mfr
N.A.I.C.S.: 333310
Katsunori Okita *(Pres & COO)*

Konami Amusement of Europe Ltd. (1)
Konami House 54 A Cowley Mill Road, Uxbridge, UB8 2QE, Middx, United Kingdom **(100%)**
Tel.: (44) 1895200573
Web Site: http://www.konami.co.uk
Sales Range: $1-9.9 Million
Emp.: 25
Mfr & Distributor of Amusement Arcade Machines
N.A.I.C.S.: 713120
Shinji Hirano *(Pres)*

Konami Australia Pty Ltd. (1)
28 Lord Street, Botany, 2019, NSW, Australia
Tel.: (61) 2 9666 5731
Web Site: http://www.konami.com
Emp.: 15
Gaming Machinery Mfr
N.A.I.C.S.: 339999

Konami Computer Entertainment Studio, Inc. (1)
5 25 Umeda 2 Chome, Kita Ku, Osaka, 530 0001, Japan **(65%)**
Tel.: (81) 663430573
Web Site: http://www.konamistudio.com
Sales Range: $100-124.9 Million
Emp.: 300
Mfr & Distributor of Computer Games
N.A.I.C.S.: 334610

Konami Computer Entertainment Tokyo, Inc. (1)
Mina To Ku, Tokyo, 104 6041, Japan
Tel.: (81) 351440573
Web Site: http://www.konamityo.com
Sales Range: $100-124.9 Million
Emp.: 300
Mfr & Distributor of Computer Games
N.A.I.C.S.: 334610

Konami Corporation (1)
9-7-2 Akasaka, Minato-ku, Tokyo, 107-8323, Japan
Tel.: (81) 354130573
Web Site: http://www.konami.com
Computer Games
N.A.I.C.S.: 334610

Konami Corporation of America Inc. (1)
2381 Rosecrans Ave Ste 200, El Segundo, CA 90245
Tel.: (310) 220-8100
Web Site: http://www.konami.com
Sales Range: $75-99.9 Million
Emp.: 130
Holding Company
N.A.I.C.S.: 551112

Subsidiary (Domestic):

Konami Digital Entertainment, Inc. (2)
14500 Aviation Blvd, Hawthorne, CA 90250-6655
Tel.: (310) 220-8100
Web Site: http://www.konami.com
Sales Range: $25-49.9 Million
Emp.: 100
Video Game Mfr
N.A.I.C.S.: 339930
Kazumi Kitaue *(Chm)*

Konami Gaming, Inc. (2)
585 Konami Cir, Las Vegas, NV 89119
Tel.: (702) 616-1400
Web Site: http://www.gaming.konami.com
Sales Range: $10-24.9 Million
Emp.: 150
Casino Gaming Machine Mfr
N.A.I.C.S.: 713290
Steve Sutherland *(Pres & CEO)*

Konami Cross Media NY, Inc. (1)
53 W 23rd St 11th Floor, New York, NY 10010
Tel.: (212) 590-2100
Web Site: http://www.konami.com
Polyester Film Distr
N.A.I.C.S.: 512120

Konami Digital Entertainment B.V. (1)
Hamburger Allee 2-4, 60486, Frankfurt, Germany

Tel.: (49) 699855730
Web Site: http://www.konami-europe.com
Video Game Mfr
N.A.I.C.S.: 339930
Martin S. Schneider *(Gen Mgr-EMEA)*

Konami Digital Entertainment B.V. (1)
14-16 Sheet Street, Windsor, SL4 1BG, United Kingdom
Tel.: (44) 1753271888
Game Product Distr
N.A.I.C.S.: 423920

Konami Digital Entertainment Co., Ltd. (1)
1-11-1 Ginza, Chuo-ku, Tokyo, 107-8324, Japan
Tel.: (81) 368670573
Web Site: http://www.konami-digital-entertainment.co.jp
Sales Range: $600-649.9 Million
Emp.: 1,904
Planning, Production & Distribution of Online Games, Computer & Video Games, Amusement Machines, Toys, Card Games, Content for Mobile Phones, Music, Image Software, Books & Magazines
N.A.I.C.S.: 713990
Hideki Hayakawa *(Pres & COO)*

Konami Digital Entertainment Ltd. (1)
Room Nos 611B 612 & 613 6/F Tsim Sha Tsui Centre 66 Mody Road, 6th Floor Room 613, Kowloon, China (Hong Kong) **(100%)**
Tel.: (852) 29560573
Web Site: http://www.konami-asia.com
Sales Range: $25-49.9 Million
Emp.: 7
Mfr & Distributor of Computer Games
N.A.I.C.S.: 334610
Bamba Masafumi *(Gen Mgr)*

Konami Manufacturing and Service, Inc. (1)
5-1-1 Higashihara, Zama, 252-0004, Kanagawa, Japan
Tel.: (81) 46 298 0573
Transportation Equipment Maintenance Services & Mfr
N.A.I.C.S.: 811121

Konami Music Entertainment, Inc. (1)
22nd Fl Shibuya Mark City West Bldg 1 12 1 Dogenzaka, Shibuya-ku, Tokyo, 150-0043, Japan **(100%)**
Tel.: (81) 337800573
Sales Range: $100-124.9 Million
Emp.: 300
Mfr & Distributor of Computer Games
N.A.I.C.S.: 334610

Konami Real Estate, Inc. (1)
9-7-2 Akasaka, Minato-ku, Tokyo, 107-8326, Japan
Tel.: (81) 3 5772 0200
Web Site: http://www.konami.co.jp
Real Estate Manangement Services
N.A.I.C.S.: 531390

Konami Sports & Life Co., Ltd. (1)
4-10-1 Higashi-Shinagawa, Shinagawa-ku, Tokyo, 140 0002, Japan
Tel.: (81) 357720300
Web Site: http://www.konamisportsandlife.com
Sales Range: $650-699.9 Million
Emp.: 1,506
Operation & Management of Sports Clubs; Development, Manufacture & Sales of Health & Fitness Machines & Products
N.A.I.C.S.: 713940

Subsidiary (Domestic):

Combi Wellness Corporation (2)
4-10-1 Higashi-Shinagawa, Shinagawa-ku, Tokyo, 140 0002, Japan
Tel.: (81) 357720300
Web Site: http://www.combiwellness.co.jp
Sales Range: $350-399.9 Million
Emp.: 1,506
Development, Manufacture & Sale of Exercise Machines for Home-Use & Fitness Clubs & Health Maintenance Assistance Literature
N.A.I.C.S.: 456199

The Club At Yebisu Garden Co., Ltd. (2)
1-13-2 Mita, Tokyo, Japan
Tel.: (81) 354241212
Web Site: http://www.tcy.co.jp
Sales Range: $25-49.9 Million
Emp.: 30
Sports Teams & Clubs
N.A.I.C.S.: 711211

TAKASAGO ELECTRIC INDUSTRY CO., LTD. (1)
2-9-14 Minami-senba, Chuo-ku, Osaka, 542-0081, Japan
Tel.: (81) 6 6243 7770
Web Site: http://www.takasago-ei.co.jp
Sales Range: $50-74.9 Million
Emp.: 237
Industrial Machinery Mfr & Distr
N.A.I.C.S.: 333248
Masahiro Hamano *(Chm)*

Plant (Domestic):

TAKASAGO ELECTRIC INDUSTRY CO., LTD. - Mie Factory (2)
2066-32 Kano Tamaki-cho, Watarai-gun, Mie, 519-0431, Japan
Tel.: (81) 596 58 7155
Pachinko Machinery Mfr
N.A.I.C.S.: 339999

KONARK SYNTHETIC LTD.

7 Mittal Estate Andheri Kurla Road Saki Naka Andheri E, Mumbai, 400 059, India
Tel.: (91) 2240896300
Web Site: https://www.konarkgroup.co.in
Rev.: $11,298,881
Assets: $20,953,689
Liabilities: $19,990,450
Net Worth: $963,239
Earnings: ($886,623)
Emp.: 394
Fiscal Year-end: 03/31/19
Textile Products Mfr & Distr
N.A.I.C.S.: 314999
Amitabh Kejriwal *(Mng Dir)*

Subsidiaries:

Konark Infratech Private Limited (1)
Konark Plaza Near Sapna Garden, Ulhasnagar, Thane, 421003, Maharashtra, India
Tel.: (91) 2512560501
Web Site: http://www.konarkindia.com
Emp.: 50
Renewable Energy Project Development Services
N.A.I.C.S.: 541330

Konark Synthetic Ltd. - BENGALURU UNIT (1)
No 62/4 13 14 15 Begur Road 11 Cross Ward No 12, Bommanahalli, Bengaluru, 560 068, Karnataka, India
Tel.: (91) 80 25737700
Textile Products Mfr
N.A.I.C.S.: 314999
Pramod Kakrania *(Mgr)*

KONCAR - DISTRIBUTIVNI I SPECIJALNI TRANSFORMATORI D.D.

Josipa Mokrovica 8, PO Box 100, 10090, Zagreb, Croatia
Tel.: (385) 13783777
Web Site: http://www.koncar-dst.hr
KODT—(ZAG)
Sales Range: Less than $1 Million
Transformers Producer
N.A.I.C.S.: 334416
Petar Vlaic *(Member-Mgmt Bd)*

KONCAR - ELECTRICAL INDUSTRY INC

Fallerovo Setaliste 22, 10000, Zagreb, Croatia
Tel.: (385) 13655555
Web Site: https://www.koncar.hr
Year Founded: 1921

KONCAR - ELECTRICAL INDUSTRY INC

KONCAR - Electrical Industry Inc—(Continued)
KOEI—(ZAG)
Rev.: $1,002,350,149
Assets: $1,125,254,443
Liabilities: $539,126,835
Net Worth: $586,127,608
Earnings: $78,266,917
Emp.: 5,271
Fiscal Year-end: 12/31/23
Other Electric Power Generation
N.A.I.C.S.: 221118
Gordan Kolak *(Chm-Mgmt Bd)*

Subsidiaries:

KONCAR - Distribution and Special Transformers Inc
Josipa Mokrovica 8, 10090, Zagreb, Croatia
Tel.: (385) 13783777
Web Site: http://www.koncar.com
Emp.: 500
Electric Power Distribution Services
N.A.I.C.S.: 221122
Ivan Klapan *(Chm-Mgmt Bd)*

Subsidiary (Non-US):

Power Engineering Transformatory Sp. z o.o. (2)
ul Gdynska 83, Czerwonak, 62-004, Poznan, Poland
Tel.: (48) 618928898
Web Site: https://www.petransformatory.pl
Electric Power Equipment & System Mfr
N.A.I.C.S.: 335999
Lukasz Farulewski *(CEO & Mng Dir)*

KONCAR - Household Appliances Ltd (1)
Zitnjak bb, 10 000, Zagreb, Croatia
Tel.: (385) 1 2484 555
Web Site: http://www.koncar-ka.hr
Household Appliances Mfr
N.A.I.C.S.: 335220

KONCAR - Metalne konstrukcije d.d. (1)
Fallerovo setaliste 22, 10000, Zagreb, Croatia
Tel.: (385) 1 3666 560
Web Site: http://www.koncar-mk.hr
Emp.: 249
Fabricated Structural Metal Mfr
N.A.I.C.S.: 332312

Koncar - Digital Ltd. (1)
Fallerovo Setaliste 22, 10000, Zagreb, Croatia
Tel.: (385) 13655375
Software Development Services
N.A.I.C.S.: 541511

Koncar - Electric Vehicles Inc. (1)
Ulica Ante Babaje 1, 10090, Zagreb, Croatia
Tel.: (385) 13496959
Web Site: http://www.koncar-kev.hr
Electric Locomotive Mfr
N.A.I.C.S.: 336510

Koncar - Electrical Engineering Institute Inc. (1)
Fallerovo Setaliste 22, 10000, Zagreb, Croatia
Tel.: (385) 13667315
Web Site: https://www.koncar-institut.hr
Electric Power Equipment & System Mfr
N.A.I.C.S.: 335999
Darinko Bago *(Pres)*

Koncar - Electronics & Informatics Inc. (1)
Fallerovo Setaliste 22, 10000, Zagreb, Croatia
Tel.: (385) 13655900
Web Site: http://www.koncar-inem.hr
Electric Equipment & Electro-Energetic Plant Mfr
N.A.I.C.S.: 335999

Koncar - Engineering Co. Ltd. (1)
Fallerovo Setaliste 22, 10000, Zagreb, Croatia
Tel.: (385) 13667512
Web Site: https://www.koncar-ket.hr
Emp.: 367
Construction Engineering Services
N.A.I.C.S.: 541330

Koncar - Generators & Motors Inc. (1)
Fallerovo Setaliste 22, 10000, Zagreb, Croatia
Tel.: (385) 13667499
Web Site: http://www.koncar-gim.hr
Electric Generator & Motor Mfr
N.A.I.C.S.: 335312

Koncar - Infrastructure & Services Ltd. (1)
Fallerovo Setaliste 22, 10000, Zagreb, Croatia
Tel.: (385) 13794046
Electric Power Generation & Transmission Services
N.A.I.C.S.: 221122

Koncar - Instrument Transformers Inc. (1)
Ulica Josipa Mokrovica 10, 10000, Zagreb, Croatia
Tel.: (385) 13794074
Web Site: https://www.koncar-mjt.hr
Emp.: 290
Power Voltage Transformer Mfr
N.A.I.C.S.: 335311
Davor Bakovic *(Pres)*

Koncar - Low Voltage Switches & Circuit Brakers Inc. (1)
Borongajska Cesta 81c, 10000, Zagreb, Croatia
Tel.: (385) 12369200
Electric Power Generation & Transmission Services
N.A.I.C.S.: 221122

Koncar - Power Plant & Electric Traction Engineering Inc. (1)
Fallerovo Setaliste 22, 10000, Zagreb, Croatia
Tel.: (385) 13667512
Electric Power Generation & Transmission Services
N.A.I.C.S.: 221122

Koncar - Renewable Energy Sources Ltd. (1)
Fallerovo Setaliste 22, 10000, Zagreb, Croatia
Tel.: (385) 13655348
Electric Power Generation & Transmission Services
N.A.I.C.S.: 221122

Koncar - Small Electrical Machines Inc. (1)
Fallerovo Setaliste 22, 10000, Zagreb, Croatia
Tel.: (385) 13667273
Electric Power Generation & Transmission Services
N.A.I.C.S.: 221122

Koncar - Switchgear Inc. (1)
Borongajska Cesta 81c, 10000, Zagreb, Croatia
Tel.: (385) 12380000
Web Site: https://www.koncar-ap.hr
Emp.: 270
Electric Power Generation & Transmission Services
N.A.I.C.S.: 221122
Gordan Kolak *(Pres)*

KONCAR DISTRIBUTIVNI & SPECIJALNI TRANSFORMATORI DD

Josipa Mokrovica 8, PO Box 100, 10090, Zagreb, Croatia
Tel.: (385) 13783713
Web Site: http://www.koncar-dst.hr
Year Founded: 1921
KODT—(ZAG)
Sales Range: $150-199.9 Million
Electrical Products Mfr
N.A.I.C.S.: 335313
Gordan Kolak *(Chm-Supervisory Bd)*

KONCAR-ELEKTROINDUSTRIJA D.D.

Fallerovo setaliste 22, 10000, Zagreb, Croatia
Tel.: (385) 13655555

Web Site: http://www.koncar.hr
Year Founded: 1974
KOEI—(ZAG)
Rev.: $577,780,180
Assets: $722,953,738
Liabilities: $260,691,295
Net Worth: $462,262,444
Earnings: $34,363,721
Emp.: 3,640
Fiscal Year-end: 12/31/21
Electric Equipment Mfr
N.A.I.C.S.: 334419
Gordan Kolak *(Pres)*

Subsidiaries:

Koncar - Engineering for Plant Installation & Commissioning Inc. (1)
Borongajska Cesta 81c, 10000, Zagreb, Croatia
Tel.: (385) 1 235 5111
Web Site: https://www.koncar-kmi.com
Electric Power Generation & Distribution Services
N.A.I.C.S.: 221118

Koncar - Motors and Electrical Systems Ltd. (1)
Fallerovo setaliste 22, 10000, Zagreb, Croatia
Tel.: (385) 13666563
Web Site: https://koncar-mes.hr
Electric Motor Mfr
N.A.I.C.S.: 336320

KONCERN ENERGETYCZNA ENERGA SA

ul Marynarki Polskiej 130, 80 557, Gdansk, Poland
Tel.: (48) 583473013
Web Site: http://www.energa.pl
Sales Range: $350-399.9 Million
Emp.: 1,500
Electric Power
N.A.I.C.S.: 335311

KONCERNAS ACHEMOS GRUPE

Vykinto Str 14, Vilnius, 08117, Lithuania
Tel.: (370) 5 249 2020
Web Site: http://www.achemosgrupe.lt
Year Founded: 2001
Sales Range: $25-49.9 Million
Emp.: 4,000
Holding Company
N.A.I.C.S.: 551112
Audrius Bendaravicius *(Dir-Fin)*

Subsidiaries:

AB Achema (1)
Jonalaukio k Ruklos sen, 55296, Jonava, Lithuania
Tel.: (370) 34956237
Web Site: http://www.achema.lt
Emp.: 1,300
Nitrogen Fertilizer Mfr
N.A.I.C.S.: 325311
Ramunas Miliauskas *(CEO)*

AB Naujoji ruta (1)
V Bielskio g 15, 76176, Siauliai, Lithuania
Tel.: (370) 41425738
Web Site: http://www.nruta.lt
Chocolate & Confectionery Mfr
N.A.I.C.S.: 311351
Laima Verbosaitiene *(Gen Dir)*

Agrochema Eesti OU (1)
Turu 7A, Jogeva, 48303, Estonia
Tel.: (372) 7769410
Web Site: http://www.agrochemaeesti.ee
Fertilizer & Plant Protection Product Whslr
N.A.I.C.S.: 424910

Central Klaipeda terminal, UAB (1)
Baltijos av 40, 93239, Klaipeda, Lithuania
Tel.: (370) 46313137
Web Site: http://www.ckt.lt
Warehousing & Storage Services
N.A.I.C.S.: 493190
Arvydas Skuodas *(Dir-Comml)*

INTERNATIONAL PUBLIC

Fertigent BVBA (1)
Henri Farmanstraat 610A, Gent, 9000, Belgium
Tel.: (32) 92280651
Web Site: http://www.fertigent.com
Nitrogenous Fertilizer Mfr
N.A.I.C.S.: 325311

Grand SPA Lietuva, JSC (1)
V Kudirkos g 45, 66120, Druskininkai, Lithuania
Tel.: (370) 31351200
Web Site: http://www.grandspa.lt
Healtcare Services
N.A.I.C.S.: 621399
Zivile Jasinaviciute *(Mgr-Sls)*

JSC Klaipeda Ship Repair (1)
Pilies str 4, 91240, Klaipeda, Lithuania
Tel.: (370) 46490990
Web Site: http://www.ports.lt
Ship Repairing Services
N.A.I.C.S.: 336611

JSC Projektu Centras (1)
Vytauto av 23, 44352, Kaunas, Lithuania
Tel.: (370) 37409087
Web Site: http://www.projektucentras.lt
Project Management Services
N.A.I.C.S.: 541618

Klaipeda stevedoring company (1)
Zauerveino str 18, 92122, Klaipeda, Lithuania
Tel.: (370) 46399101
Web Site: http://www.klasco.lt
Marine Cargo Handling Services
N.A.I.C.S.: 488320
Linas Liekis *(Dir-Economics & Fin)*

LITEXIMP (1)
Ul Dworcowa 2, 19-335, Prostki, Poland
Tel.: (48) 876112033
Web Site: http://www.liteximp.pl
Agricultural Commodity Trading Services
N.A.I.C.S.: 926140

Litfert sarl (1)
16a Rue Jouanet, 35700, Rennes, France
Tel.: (33) 299842727
Web Site: http://www.litfert.com
Fertilizer Trade Whslr
N.A.I.C.S.: 425120
Andrew Pikciunas *(Mgr)*

UAB Achemos mokymo centras (1)
Cosmonaut 15, 55141, Jonava, Lithuania
Tel.: (370) 59234
Web Site: http://www.achemamc.lt
Professional Training Services
N.A.I.C.S.: 611430

UAB Kroviniu terminalas (1)
Buriu St 17, 92276, Klaipeda, Lithuania
Tel.: (370) 46391095
Web Site: http://www.terminal.lt
Marine Cargo Handling Services
N.A.I.C.S.: 488320

UAB Palangos Vetra (1)
Daukanto str 35 / S Dariaus ir S Gireno str 17, 00135, Palanga, Lithuania
Tel.: (370) 46053032
Web Site: http://www.palangosvetra.lt
Home Management Services
N.A.I.C.S.: 721110
Laura Sugintiene *(Mgr-Sls)*

UAB RENERGA (1)
Jonalaukio k Ruklos sen, 55296, Jonava, Lithuania
Tel.: (370) 34956627
Web Site: http://www.renerga.lt
Eletric Power Generation Services
N.A.I.C.S.: 221118

UAB Zemaitijos grudai (1)
Salantu g 16, 90112, Plunge, Lithuania
Tel.: (370) 844871816
Web Site: http://www.zemaitijosgrudai.lt
Grain Merchant Whslr
N.A.I.C.S.: 424510

KONDO CHEMICAL INDUSTRY CO., LTD.

2-2-4 Tamakushi-cho Higashi, Higashiosaka, 578-0932, Osaka, Japan
Tel.: (81) 72 965 0121

Web Site: http://www.kondo-kagaku.co.jp
Year Founded: 1959
Sales Range: $75-99.9 Million
Emp.: 170
Plastic Product Mfr & Distr
N.A.I.C.S.: 334419
Tsutomu Kondo *(CEO)*

Subsidiaries:

KONDO Chemical Industry Co., Ltd. - Tokushima Plant **(1)**
80-15 Aza-kitahara Donari Donari-tyou 5, Tokushima, 771-1506, Japan
Tel.: (81) 886954747
Plastics Product Mfr
N.A.I.C.S.: 326130

KONDOTEC INC.
2-90 Sakaigawa 2-chome, Nisi-ku, Osaka, 550-0024, Japan
Tel.: (81) 665829672
Web Site: https://www.kondotec.co.jp
Year Founded: 1947
7438—(TKS)
Rev.: $508,130,530
Assets: $403,044,750
Liabilities: $165,613,550
Net Worth: $237,431,200
Earnings: $21,581,650
Emp.: 1,373
Fiscal Year-end: 03/31/24
Construction Material Mfr & Whslr
N.A.I.C.S.: 333120
Katsuhiko Kondo *(Bd of Dirs & Pres)*

Subsidiaries:

Sanwa Denzai Co., Ltd. **(1)**
180 Sakaidocho, Nishi-ku, Nagoya, 452-0804, Japan
Tel.: (81) 525097550
Web Site: http://www.sanwadenzai.co.jp
Emp.: 146
Electrical Equipment Distr
N.A.I.C.S.: 423610

KONE OYJ
Keilasatama 3, PO Box 7, 02150, Espoo, Finland
Tel.: (358) 204751 **FI**
Web Site: https://www.kone.com
Year Founded: 1910
KNEBV—(OTCIQ)
Rev.: $10,104,591,980
Assets: $8,055,036,080
Liabilities: $5,484,672,480
Net Worth: $2,570,363,600
Earnings: $859,494,160
Emp.: 63,536
Fiscal Year-end: 12/31/23
Elevators & Escalators Maintenance & Production Services
N.A.I.C.S.: 333921
Antti Herlin *(Chm)*

Subsidiaries:

AS KONE **(1)**
Mustamae Tee 18, 10617, Tallinn, Estonia
Tel.: (372) 6200700
Web Site: https://www.kone.ee
Emp.: 50
Elevator & Escalator Installation Services
N.A.I.C.S.: 238290

ATB Aufzugtechnik Berlin GmbH **(1)**
Buchholzer Str 55-61, 13156, Berlin, Germany
Tel.: (49) 3077328120
Web Site: https://www.atb-aufzugtechnik-berlin.de
Elevator Maintenance Services
N.A.I.C.S.: 238290

ATH Aufzugstechnik Heilbronn GmbH & Co. KG **(1)**
Austrasse 103, 74076, Heilbronn, Germany
Tel.: (49) 7131649580
Web Site: https://www.ath-aufzuege.de
Emp.: 40
Elevator Maintenance Services
N.A.I.C.S.: 238290

ATPE-AMIB S.A. **(1)**
43-45 Ave de la Convention, 93190, Livry-Gargan, France
Tel.: (33) 1 41 70 70 00
Web Site: http://www.atpe-amib.com
Sales Range: $25-49.9 Million
Emp.: 45
Automatic Metal Door Mfr & Distr
N.A.I.C.S.: 332321
Bernard Vespini *(Gen Mgr)*

ATS-ATPE S.A.S. **(1)**
58 Rue de Neuilly Parc des Guillaumes Building E2-E3, 93130, Noisy-le-Sec, France
Tel.: (33) 180606500
Web Site: https://www.ats-ascenseurs.com
Elevator Mfr
N.A.I.C.S.: 333921

Acre Lifts Limited **(1)**
Points Lane, Saint Andrews, GY6 8UJ, Guernsey, United Kingdom
Tel.: (44) 1481238827
Web Site: http://acrelifts.net
Elevator Services
N.A.I.C.S.: 238290

Alois Kasper GmbH **(1)**
Kasteler Strasse 11 Gebaude H18, Primstal, 66620, Nonnweiler, Germany
Tel.: (49) 687570070
Web Site: https://www.kasper-aufzuege.com
Engineeering Services
N.A.I.C.S.: 541330
Frank Gabriel *(Mng Dir)*

Arabian Elevator & Escalator Co. Ltd. **(1)**
PO Box 14326, 21424, Jeddah, Saudi Arabia **(100%)**
Tel.: (966) 22630055
Web Site: http://www.areeco.com
Sales Range: $100-124.9 Million
Emp.: 400
Elevator Mfr
N.A.I.C.S.: 333921

Ascenseurs Soulier S.N.C. **(1)**
30 Avenue Roger Hennequin, BP 38, Trappes, 78192, France **(100%)**
Tel.: (33) 130507364
Elevator Repair & Maintenance Services
N.A.I.C.S.: 811310
Jean-Paul Bourgeat *(Gen Mgr)*

Ascenseurs Technologie Serrurerie (S.A) **(1)**
128 B Avenue Jean Jaures, 94200, Ivry-sur-Seine, France
Tel.: (33) 156205610
Elevator & Escalator Installation Services
N.A.I.C.S.: 238290

Ascensores Bidasoa S.L. **(1)**
Primautzar 19, Gipuzkoa, 20305, Irun, Spain
Tel.: (34) 943059053
Web Site: https://www.ascensoresbidasoa.com
Elevator Maintenance Services
N.A.I.C.S.: 238290

Ascensores Muralla, S.A. **(1)**
Rua Rio Eo 36 Bajo, 27003, Lugo, Spain
Tel.: (34) 982803395
Web Site: http://www.ascensoresmuralla.com
Elevator Services
N.A.I.C.S.: 238290

Ascensores R Casado, S.A. **(1)**
Calle Alianto 17, 28029, Madrid, Spain
Tel.: (34) 913152820
Web Site: http://www.ascensorescasado.es
Elevator Mfr
N.A.I.C.S.: 333921

Ben Fung Machineries & Engineering Ltd. **(1)**
11/F Two Harbour Square 180 Wai Yip Street, Kwun Tong, Kowloon, China (Hong Kong)
Tel.: (852) 27866500
Web Site: http://www.benfung.com.hk
Elevator Services
N.A.I.C.S.: 238290

CJSC KONE Lifts **(1)**
Lenejramesea 31, 127006, Moscow, Russia

Tel.: (7) 495 223 9595
Web Site: http://www.kone.ru
Elevator & Escalator Installation Services
N.A.I.C.S.: 238290

CRON.UP S.r.l. **(1)**
Piazza Madre Teresa di Calcutta 22/24, 4020, Villa di Serio, BG, Italy
Tel.: (39) 035664676
Web Site: https://www.cronup.it
Elevator Maintenance Services
N.A.I.C.S.: 238290

Cerqueti Servizi S.r.l. **(1)**
Via A Filarete 209, 00176, Rome, RM, Italy
Tel.: (39) 062415150
Web Site: https://www.cerquetiascensori.com
Elevator Services
N.A.I.C.S.: 238290

Citylift S.A. **(1)**
Pol Ind Mas Xirgu Crta Sta Coloma 99, 17005, Girona, Spain
Tel.: (34) 902225490
Web Site: http://cityliftascensores.com
Elevator Services
N.A.I.C.S.: 238290

Cofam S.r.l. **(1)**
Via Natalia Ginzburg 11, 41123, Modena, MO, Italy
Tel.: (39) 059284148
Web Site: https://www.cofam.it
Elevator Services
N.A.I.C.S.: 238290

Crown Lifts Limited **(1)**
Regency House 33-49 Farwig Lane, Bromley, BR1 3RA, Kent, United Kingdom
Tel.: (44) 20 8464 5000
Web Site: http://www.crownlifts.co.uk
Sales Range: $25-49.9 Million
Emp.: 90
Lift Maintenance & Installation Services
N.A.I.C.S.: 811310

Detroit Elevator Company **(1)**
2121 Burdette St, Ferndale, MI 48220
Tel.: (248) 591-7484
Web Site: http://www.detroitelevator.com
Sales Range: $1-9.9 Million
Emp.: 50
Building Equipment Contractors
N.A.I.C.S.: 238290
Daryl Lovelace *(Controller)*

Downey-Goodlein Elevator Corp. **(1)**
10 Pixley Industrial Pkwy, Rochester, NY 14624 **(100%)**
Tel.: (585) 429-6676
Web Site: http://www.dgelevator.com
Sales Range: $1-9.9 Million
Emp.: 18
Elevator Contract Services
N.A.I.C.S.: 333921
Susan McCorry *(CEO)*

Dresdner Aufzugsdienst GmbH **(1)**
Fetscherstrasse 72, 01307, Dresden, Germany
Tel.: (49) 3514014817
Web Site: http://www.dresdner-aufzugsdienst.de
Elevator Maintenance Services
N.A.I.C.S.: 238290

Elevatori Bari S.r.l. **(1)**
Viale Europa 22C, 70132, Bari, Italy
Tel.: (39) 0805041044
Web Site: https://www.elevatorisrl.it
Elevator Services
N.A.I.C.S.: 238290

Engler & Haring GmbH **(1)**
Pfalzburger Str 21, 10719, Berlin, Germany
Tel.: (49) 30 612 70 50
Web Site: http://www.engler-haring.de
Sales Range: $25-49.9 Million
Emp.: 15
Elevator Repair & Maintenance Services
N.A.I.C.S.: 811198
Renate Junker *(Gen Mgr)*

Euroservice Merano S.r.l. **(1)**
Sinichbachstrasse 66, 39012, Merano, BZ, Italy
Tel.: (39) 0473247172
Web Site: https://www.euroservice.bz
Elevator Maintenance Services
N.A.I.C.S.: 238290

Ferrara Ascensori S.r.l. **(1)**
Via G Ribera 5C, 80128, Naples, Italy
Tel.: (39) 081 560 0623
Web Site: https://www.ascensoriferrara.it
Elevator Services
N.A.I.C.S.: 238290

Fiore Ascensori S.a.s. **(1)**
Via degli Artigiani 32, 76121, Barletta, BT, Italy
Tel.: (39) 088 351 5627
Web Site: https://www.ascensorifiore.it
Elevator Services
N.A.I.C.S.: 238290

Gelco Lifts Ltd. **(1)**
92 Agiou Dimitriou Street, PO Box 29510, Kaimakli Industrial Area, 1720, Nicosia, Cyprus
Tel.: (357) 77772326
Web Site: http://www.gelcolifts.com
Lift & Maintenance Services
N.A.I.C.S.: 238290
Stelios Anastasiades *(Mng Dir)*

Giant Kone Elevator Co., Ltd. **(1)**
8A88 Shanghai World Trade Mall No 2299 Yan'an West Road, Changning District, Shanghai, China
Tel.: (86) 2122209999
Web Site: https://www.giantkone.com
Emp.: 3,200
Elevator Mfr
N.A.I.C.S.: 333921

Inmape Ascensores, S.L. **(1)**
C/ Resina 47-D, 28021, Madrid, Spain
Tel.: (34) 916691056
Web Site: https://inmape.es
Elevator Maintenance Services
N.A.I.C.S.: 238290

KONE (Ireland) Limited **(1)**
G7 Calmount Park Calmount Avenue Ballymount, Dublin, D12 NP64, Ireland
Tel.: (353) 14296200
Web Site: https://www.kone.ie
Sales Range: $25-49.9 Million
Emp.: 200
Elevator & Escalator Installation Services
N.A.I.C.S.: 238290

KONE (NI) Limited **(1)**
Units B2 & B3 19 Heron Road Sydenham Business Park, Belfast, BT3 9LE, United Kingdom
Tel.: (44) 2890735900
Web Site: https://www.kone.ie
Sales Range: $25-49.9 Million
Elevator & Escalator Installation Services
N.A.I.C.S.: 238290

KONE (Schweiz) AG **(1)**
Ruchstuckstrasse 21, 8306, Bruttisellen, Switzerland **(100%)**
Tel.: (41) 448383838
Web Site: https://www.kone.ch
Sales Range: $50-74.9 Million
Emp.: 150
Elevator Mfr
N.A.I.C.S.: 333921

KONE A/S **(1)**
Evropska 423/178, 160 00, Prague, 6, Czech Republic **(100%)**
Tel.: (420) 800566300
Web Site: https://www.kone.cz
Sales Range: $25-49.9 Million
Emp.: 50
Elevator Mfr
N.A.I.C.S.: 333921

KONE A/S **(1)**
Marielundvej 10, 2730, Herlev, Denmark
Tel.: (45) 35 87 80 00
Web Site: http://www.kone.com
Emp.: 200
Elevator & Escalator Mfr
N.A.I.C.S.: 333921

KONE AB **(1)**
Kronborgsgrand 13, 164 46, Kista, Sweden **(100%)**
Tel.: (46) 771500000
Web Site: https://www.kone.se
Sales Range: $25-49.9 Million
Elevators, Elevator Maintenance & Modernization Services
N.A.I.C.S.: 333921

KONE AG **(1)**

KONE OYJ

KONE Oyj—(Continued) **(100%)**
Tel.: (43) 59247000
Web Site: https://www.kone.at
Sales Range: $100-124.9 Million
Emp.: 500
Elevators; Elevator Maintenance & Modernization Services
N.A.I.C.S.: 333921

KONE Aksjeselskap **(1)**
Ryenstubben 10-12, PO Box 163, Kjelsas, 0679, Oslo, Norway
Tel.: (47) 90922909
Web Site: https://www.kone.no
Sales Range: $50-74.9 Million
Emp.: 230
N.A.I.C.S.: 333921

KONE Asansor Sanayi ve Ticaret A.S. **(1)**
Icerenkoy Icerenkoy Mah Degirmenyolu Cad No 28 Asiaofispark B Blok D 3, Kat 2 Atasehir, 34752, Istanbul, Türkiye **(100%)**
Tel.: (90) 4445663
Web Site: https://www.kone.com.tr
Sales Range: $25-49.9 Million
Emp.: 30
Elevator Mfr & Distr
N.A.I.C.S.: 333921

KONE Ascensori S.p.A. **(1)**
Via Figino 41, Pero, Milan, 20016, Italy **(100%)**
Tel.: (39) 02339231
Sales Range: $100-124.9 Million
Emp.: 500
Elevators
N.A.I.C.S.: 333921
Angelo Bosoni (Mng Dir)

KONE Ascensorul S.A. **(1)**
West Business Campus Str Preciziei 3Y, 6th District 1st Floor, 062202, Bucharest, Romania
Tel.: (40) 213114601
Web Site: https://www.kone.com.ro
Sales Range: $25-49.9 Million
Emp.: 30
Elevators Repair & Maintenance Services
N.A.I.C.S.: 811198

KONE Assarain LLC **(1)**
Hatat House B Office 103 1st Floor, PO Box 1475, Wadi Adai Ruwi, 112, Muscat, Oman
Tel.: (968) 24657000
Web Site: https://www.kone.om
Elevator Mfr
N.A.I.C.S.: 333921

KONE B.V. **(1)**
Rijn 10, 2491 BG, Hague, Netherlands **(100%)**
Tel.: (31) 703171000
Sales Range: $50-74.9 Million
Emp.: 1,000
Elevator Mfr
N.A.I.C.S.: 333921

KONE Bahrain W.L.L. **(1)**
Office Number 61 Road Number 3629 Block Number 336, PO Box 21303, Al Ameera Commercial Building 767, Adliya, Bahrain
Tel.: (973) 17749271
Web Site: https://www.kone.bh
Emp.: 44
Elevator Maintenance Services
N.A.I.C.S.: 238290

KONE Belgium S.A. **(1)**
Koning Albert II-laan 4, 1000, Brussels, Belgium **(99.6%)**
Tel.: (32) 27309211
Web Site: https://www.kone.be
Sales Range: $25-49.9 Million
Elevators, Elevator Maintenance & Modernization Services
N.A.I.C.S.: 333921

KONE Business Services, s.r.o. **(1)**
Galvaniho 7/B, 82104, Bratislava, Slovakia
Tel.: (421) 800173174
Web Site: https://www.kone.sk
Elevator Maintenance Services
N.A.I.C.S.: 238290

KONE D O O Ljubljana **(1)**
Brnciceva Ulica 5, Crnuce, SI 1231, Ljubljana, Slovenia **(100%)**
Tel.: (386) 15614190
Web Site: https://www.kone.si
Sales Range: $25-49.9 Million
Emp.: 21
N.A.I.C.S.: 333921

KONE Deursystemen B.V. **(1)**
Accustraat 21, 3903 LX, Veenendaal, Netherlands
Tel.: (31) 318532333
Web Site: https://www.waldoor.com
Automatic Pedestrian Door Mfr
N.A.I.C.S.: 321911

KONE Door AB **(1)**
Bagarbyvagen 61, Sollentuna, 191 34, Sweden
Tel.: (46) 87523500
Automatic Metal Door Mfr
N.A.I.C.S.: 332321

KONE EOOD **(1)**
87 Okolovrasten Pat Str 2nd Floor, 1407, Sofia, Bulgaria
Tel.: (359) 80080800
Web Site: https://www.kone.bg
Elevator Mfr
N.A.I.C.S.: 333921

KONE Elevadores, S.A. **(1)**
Calle Albasanz 15 Edif B1 Pl, 28037, Madrid, Spain **(100%)**
Tel.: (34) 913277050
Web Site: https://www.kone.com
Sales Range: $25-49.9 Million
Emp.: 100
N.A.I.C.S.: 333921

KONE Elevator & Escalator **(1)**
Vahrenwalder Str 317, 30179, Hannover, Germany **(100%)**
Tel.: (49) 51164721324
Web Site: http://www.kone.com
Sales Range: $50-74.9 Million
Elevators, Elevator Maintenance & Modernization Services
N.A.I.C.S.: 333921

KONE Elevator (H.K.) Ltd. **(1)**
11/F Two Harbour Square 180 Wai Yip Street, PO Box 388, Kwun Tong, Kowloon, 852, China (Hong Kong) **(100%)**
Tel.: (852) 27866500
Web Site: https://www.kone.hk
Sales Range: $50-74.9 Million
Emp.: 220
Elevator Mfr
N.A.I.C.S.: 333921

KONE Elevator (M) Sdn. Bhd. **(1)**
3rd Floor Wisma Ali Bawal 2 No 11 Jalan Tandang, 46050, Petaling Jaya, Selangor, Malaysia
Tel.: (60) 374947500
Web Site: https://www.kone.my
Sales Range: $25-49.9 Million
Emp.: 90
Elevators & Escalators
N.A.I.C.S.: 333921

KONE Elevator (Shanghai) Co., Ltd. **(1)**
8A88 Shanghai Mart 2299 Yan An Rd W, Shanghai, 200336, China
Tel.: (86) 2122012220
Web Site: https://www.kone.cn
Building Automation System Installation Services
N.A.I.C.S.: 238210

KONE Elevator A/S **(1)**
Marieluntvej 10, 2730, Herlev, NV, Denmark **(100%)**
Tel.: (45) 35878000
Web Site: http://www.kone.com
Sales Range: $50-74.9 Million
Emp.: 250
Elevators, Elevator Maintenance & Modernization Services
N.A.I.C.S.: 333921

KONE Elevator India Ltd. **(1)**
50 Vanagaram Road Ayanambakkam, Chennai, 600 095, India **(100%)**
Tel.: (91) 4426533901
Sales Range: $50-74.9 Million
Emp.: 500
Elevators
N.A.I.C.S.: 333921

Amit Gossain (Mng Dir)

KONE Elevator Pte. Ltd. **(1)**
30a Kallang Place 14-01, Singapore, 339213, Singapore
Tel.: (65) 64246246
Web Site: http://www.kone.com
Sales Range: $25-49.9 Million
Elevators; Elevator Maintenance Services
N.A.I.C.S.: 333921

KONE Elevators Co., Ltd. **(1)**
8A88 Shanghai Mart 2299 Yan An Rd W, Shanghai, 200336, China
Tel.: (86) 212 201 2222
Web Site: https://www.kone.cn
Sales Range: $800-899.9 Million
Emp.: 3,200
Elevator & Escalator Mfr
N.A.I.C.S.: 333921

Plant (Domestic):

KONE Elevators Co., Ltd. **(2)**
88 Middle Gucheng Rd, Kunshan, 215300, Jiangsu, China **(100%)**
Tel.: (86) 51257794550
Web Site: http://www.kone.com
Sales Range: $150-199.9 Million
Elevator & Escalator Mfr
N.A.I.C.S.: 333921

KONE Elevators Cyprus Limited **(1)**
38 Prodromou Avenue, Strovolos, 2063, Nicosia, Cyprus
Tel.: (357) 22778160
Web Site: https://www.kone.com.cy
Elevator Repair & Maintenance Services
N.A.I.C.S.: 811310

KONE Elevators Employee Benefits Pty Limited **(1)**
205 Euston Rd, Alexandria, 2015, NSW, Australia
Tel.: (61) 295777000
Web Site: https://www.kone.com.au
Emp.: 250
Employee Benefit Administration Services
N.A.I.C.S.: 524292

KONE Elevators Finland **(1)**
Aku Korhonen Tie 8, PO Box 26, 00440, Helsinki, Finland **(100%)**
Tel.: (358) 2047551
Sales Range: $100-124.9 Million
Escalators
N.A.I.C.S.: 333921

KONE Elevators Pty Ltd **(1)**
Level 2A 22 Pollen Street Grey Lynn, PO Box 90500, Victoria St West, Auckland, 1142, New Zealand **(100%)**
Tel.: (64) 93619000
Web Site: http://www.kone.co.nz
Sales Range: $25-49.9 Million
N.A.I.C.S.: 333921

KONE Elevators Pty. Ltd. **(1)**
185 O Riordan St, Mascot Locked Bag 9, Alexandria, 2020, NSW, Australia
Tel.: (61) 295777000
Web Site: https://www.kone.com.au
Sales Range: $50-74.9 Million
Elevators & Escalators
N.A.I.C.S.: 333921

KONE Elevators South Africa (Pty) Ltd. **(1)**
20 Friesland Drive, Longmeadow Business Estate, Edenvale, 1610, South Africa **(100%)**
Tel.: (27) 110351800
Web Site: https://www.kone.co.za
Sales Range: $25-49.9 Million
Elevator Mfr
N.A.I.C.S.: 333921

KONE Elevators Taiwan Co. Ltd. **(1)**
Room B 10th Floor No 68 Section 2 Xianmin Avenue, Banqiao, Taipei, 114, Neihu, Taiwan **(100%)**
Tel.: (886) 229589688
Web Site: https://www.kone.tw
Sales Range: $25-49.9 Million
Emp.: 100
Elevator Mfr
N.A.I.C.S.: 333921

KONE Elevators W.L.L. **(1)**
Office Number 61 Road Number 3629 Block Number 336, PO Box 21303, Al Ameera Commercial Building 767, Adliya, Bahrain
Tel.: (973) 17749271
Web Site: https://www.kone.bh
Elevator & Escalator Mfr
N.A.I.C.S.: 333921

KONE Elevators and Escalators Sarl AU **(1)**
Lot Marjana N6 Sidi Maarouf, 20280, Casablanca, Morocco
Tel.: (212) 522580211
Web Site: https://www.kone.ma
Elevator & Escalator Distr
N.A.I.C.S.: 423830

KONE Felvono Kft **(1)**
Madarasz Viktor Utca 47-49 1st Building 5th Floor, 1138, Budapest, Hungary
Tel.: (36) 12396052
Web Site: https://www.kone.hu
Sales Range: $25-49.9 Million
Elevators, Elevator Maintenance & Modernization Services
N.A.I.C.S.: 333921

KONE Garant Aufzug GmbH **(1)**
Philippstrasse 7, 09130, Chemnitz, Germany
Tel.: (49) 371461770
Web Site: https://kone-garant.de
Sales Range: $25-49.9 Million
Elevator Repair & Maintenance Services
N.A.I.C.S.: 811310
Sascha Seiss (Mng Dir)

KONE GmbH **(1)**
Vahrenwalder Strasse 317, 30179, Hannover, Germany **(100%)**
Tel.: (49) 8008801188
Web Site: https://www.kone.de
Sales Range: $100-124.9 Million
Emp.: 400
Elevators & Escalators
N.A.I.C.S.: 333921
Erik Kahlert (Chm)

Subsidiary (Domestic):

Lodige Aufzuge GmbH **(2)**
Balhorner Feld 1, 33106, Paderborn, Germany
Tel.: (49) 5251 3817 0
Web Site: http://www.loedige-aufzuege.com
Elevators Repair & Maintenance Services
N.A.I.C.S.: 811198

KONE Hissit Oy **(1)**
Aku Korhosen tie 8, PL 26, 00440, Helsinki, Finland
Tel.: (358) 2047551
Web Site: https://www.kone.fi
Elevator & Escalator Mfr
N.A.I.C.S.: 333921

KONE Holding France S.A.S. **(1)**
Aeropole Zac de l'Arenas 455 Promenade des Anglais, 06200, Nice, France
Tel.: (33) 497184700
Investment Management Service
N.A.I.C.S.: 523999

KONE Holding GmbH **(1)**
Vahrenwalder Str 317, Hannover, 30179, Germany
Tel.: (49) 51121480
Investment Management Service
N.A.I.C.S.: 523999

KONE Holland B.V. **(1)**
Rijn 10, 2491BG, Hague, Netherlands
Tel.: (31) 703171000
Web Site: http://www.kone.com
Elevator Repair & Maintenance Services
N.A.I.C.S.: 811310

KONE Inc. **(1)**
1 Kone Ct, Moline, IL 61265
Tel.: (309) 764-6771
Web Site: https://www.kone.us
Sales Range: $125-149.9 Million
Emp.: 325
Elevator, Escalator & Autowalks Mfr, Servicer & Installer
N.A.I.C.S.: 333921

Subsidiary (Domestic):

Advanced Elevator Technologies, Inc. **(2)**

AND PRIVATE COMPANIES — KONE OYJ

407R Mystic Ave Unit 18, Medford, MA 02155
Tel.: (781) 391-1303
Web Site: http://www.advancedelevator.com
Emp.: 40
Elevator Repair & Maintenance Services
N.A.I.C.S.: 238290
Arthur E. Merritt *(Pres)*

Apex Elevator Corp. (2)
2711 Dorr Ave J, Fairfax, VA 22031
Tel.: (703) 560-0993
Web Site: http://www.apex-elevator.com
Sales Range: $25-49.9 Million
Emp.: 15
Elevator Contractor
N.A.I.C.S.: 238290

Capital Elevator Service, Inc. (2)
70 Industrial Park Dr Ste 3J, Waldorf, MD 20602-3740
Tel.: (301) 645-5500
Web Site: http://www.capitalelevatorservice.com
Elevator Maintenance, Repair & Modernization Contractor
N.A.I.C.S.: 238290
James Kina *(Pres)*

City Elevator Co. (2)
1384 Broadway 21st Fl, New York, NY 10018
Tel.: (212) 395-3322
Web Site: http://www.city-elevator.com
Rev.: $6,475,000
Emp.: 35
Elevator Inspection, Maintenance & Repair Services
N.A.I.C.S.: 333921

Elevator Maintenance & Repair, Inc. (2)
903 Washington Ferry Rd, Prattville, AL 36067
Tel.: (334) 365-3634
Sales Range: $10-24.9 Million
Emp.: 30
Elevator Maintenance & Repair Services
N.A.I.C.S.: 333921

Elevators Unlimited, Inc. (2)
565 E 70th Ave 1 E, Denver, CO 80229
Tel.: (303) 487-7528
Web Site: http://www.elevatorsunlimited.com
Sales Range: $1-9.9 Million
Emp.: 19
Elevator Maintenance Services
N.A.I.C.S.: 333921
Chris Grothe *(Mgr-Sls)*

Branch (Domestic):

KONE Inc. (2)
2101 Couch Dr, McKinney, TX 75069-7314
Tel.: (972) 547-1201
Sales Range: $25-49.9 Million
Emp.: 250
Mfr of Elevators
N.A.I.C.S.: 811490

KONE Inc. (2)
47-36 36th St, Long Island City, NY 11101-1824 (100%)
Tel.: (718) 361-7200
Web Site: http://www.kone.com
Sales Range: $25-49.9 Million
Elevator Mfr
N.A.I.C.S.: 333921

Division (Domestic):

KONE Inc. - Elevators North America (2)
1801 River Dr, Moline, IL 61265-1374
Tel.: (309) 797-3232
Web Site: http://www.kone.com
Sales Range: $25-49.9 Million
N.A.I.C.S.: 333921

KONE Inc. - Escalator Division (2)
2266 US Hwy 6, Coal Valley, IL 61240 (100%)
Tel.: (309) 949-2101
Web Site: http://www.us.kone.com
Sales Range: $25-49.9 Million
Emp.: 175
Mfr of Escalators
N.A.I.C.S.: 811490

Unit (Domestic):

KONE Inc. - Service Center (2)
1345 N Hobson St, Gilbert, AZ 85233
Tel.: (480) 927-1600
Web Site: http://www.southwestelevator.com
Sales Range: $25-49.9 Million
Emp.: 12
Elevator Maintenance Services
N.A.I.C.S.: 238290

Division (Domestic):

KONE Inc. - Spares (2)
325 19th St, Moline, IL 61265
Tel.: (309) 764-6771
Web Site: https://www.konespares.com
Sales Range: $10-24.9 Million
Emp.: 50
Warehouse
N.A.I.C.S.: 811490

Subsidiary (Domestic):

Moline Accessories Corporation (2)
430 W 7th St, Kansas City, MO 64105-1490 (100%)
Tel.: (816) 842-3778
Sales Range: $50-74.9 Million
Emp.: 100
Real Estate Investment Trust
N.A.I.C.S.: 525990

Sterling Machinery Co., Inc. (2)
104 Port Arthur Ave, Mena, AR 71953 (100%)
Tel.: (479) 394-4248
Sales Range: $25-49.9 Million
Emp.: 75
Machining Center
N.A.I.C.S.: 332710
Robert Martin *(COO)*

Suburban Elevator Company (2)
130 Prairie Lake Rd Unit D, East Dundee, IL 60118 (100%)
Tel.: (847) 783-6200
Web Site: https://www.suburbanelevator.com
Emp.: 100
Elevator Consulting & Installation Services
N.A.I.C.S.: 333921
Carmen Galante *(Co-Owner)*

KONE Industrial Oy (1)
Kuumolankatu 1, 05830, Hyvinkaa, Finland
Tel.: (358) 204751
Elevator & Escalator Mfr
N.A.I.C.S.: 333921

KONE Industrial S.A. de C.V. (1)
Calle Del Progreso No 1300 Norte Parque Industrial Matamoros, Matamoros, 27440, Mexico
Tel.: (52) 8717590720
Elevator Repair & Maintenance Services
N.A.I.C.S.: 811198

KONE Industrial S.p.A. (1)
Via Figino 41, 20016, Pero, MI, Italy
Tel.: (39) 0800233566
Elevator Repair & Maintenance Services
N.A.I.C.S.: 811310

KONE Industrial Servicios S.A. de C.V. (1)
Calle De Progreso No 1300 Nte, Matamoros, 27440, Mexico
Tel.: (52) 8717590700
Elevator Repair & Maintenance Services
N.A.I.C.S.: 811310

KONE International S.A. (1)
Rue de Bretagne 24, PO Box 7, 1950, Woluwe-Saint-Lambert, Belgium (100%)
Tel.: (32) 26769211
Sales Range: $25-49.9 Million
Emp.: 70
N.A.I.C.S.: 333921
Sandra Swaelens *(Mgr-HR)*

KONE Investistion GmbH (1)
Lembockgasse 61, 1230, Vienna, Austria
Tel.: (43) 1 86367
Web Site: http://www.kone.com
Emp.: 200
Elevator Distr
N.A.I.C.S.: 423830

KONE Japan Co. Ltd. (1)
15F Cerulean Tower 26-1 Sakuragaoka-cho, Shibuya-ku, Tokyo, 150-8512, Japan (100%)
Tel.: (81) 354565191
Web Site: http://www.kone.com
Sales Range: $25-49.9 Million
Emp.: 2
N.A.I.C.S.: 333921

KONE Kenya Limited (1)
Crowne Plaza Annexe 13th Floor Along Kenya Road, PO Box 35174-00100, Nairobi, Kenya
Tel.: (254) 709823000
Elevator Mfr
N.A.I.C.S.: 333921

KONE LLC (1)
Plot no 10 B Mohamed Naguib Axis Fifth Settlement Kone 2nd floor, Silver Palm Building, New Cairo, Egypt
Tel.: (20) 23244300
Web Site: https://www.kone.eg
Elevator Mfr
N.A.I.C.S.: 333921

KONE Lifts LLC (1)
13 Mykola Pymonenko Street FORUM Business Center block 7B, Office 42, 04050, Kiev, Ukraine
Tel.: (380) 443777740
Web Site: https://www.kone.ua
Sales Range: $25-49.9 Million
Emp.: 2
Escalator Repair & Maintenance Services
N.A.I.C.S.: 811310

KONE Lifts s.r.o. (1)
Pekna Cesta 19, 83152, Bratislava, Slovakia (100%)
Tel.: (421) 244873270
Sales Range: $10-24.9 Million
Emp.: 43
N.A.I.C.S.: 333921

KONE Ltd. (1)
5 Hamelacha St, PP Box 8026, Industrial Park Poleg, Netanya, 4250540, Israel
Tel.: (972) 98303030
Web Site: https://www.kone.co.il
Elevator Mfr
N.A.I.C.S.: 333921

KONE Luxembourg s.a.r.l. (1)
Rue du Commerce 18, Foetz, 3895, Luxembourg, Luxembourg (100%)
Tel.: (352) 4551601
Sales Range: $25-49.9 Million
Emp.: 50
N.A.I.C.S.: 333921

KONE Makedonija Dooel (1)
Filip Vtori Makedonski 3 Soravia Centar 7-i Kat, 1000, Skopje, North Macedonia
Tel.: (389) 113591230
Elevator Mfr
N.A.I.C.S.: 333921

KONE Makedonija Dooel Skopje (1)
Filip Vtori Makedonski 3 Soravia Centar 7-i kat, 1000, Skopje, North Macedonia
Tel.: (389) 113591230
Web Site: https://www.kone.mk
Elevator & Escalator Distr
N.A.I.C.S.: 423830

KONE Metro AB (1)
Kronborgsgrand 13, 164 96, Kista, Sweden
Tel.: (46) 771500000
Elevator Mfr
N.A.I.C.S.: 333921

KONE Montage GmbH (1)
Ernst Abbe Str 4, 56070, Koblenz, Germany
Tel.: (49) 26198404
Web Site: https://www.kone.de
Emp.: 4
Escalator Repair & Maintenance Services
N.A.I.C.S.: 811198
Alexander Vitt *(Gen Mgr)*

KONE Nederland Holding B.V. (1)
Rijn 10, Hague, 2490BG, Netherlands
Tel.: (31) 703171000
Sales Range: $100-124.9 Million
Emp.: 150
Investment Management Service
N.A.I.C.S.: 523999
Wim Koster *(Gen Mgr)*

KONE Plc (1)
Global House Fox Ln N, Chertsey, KT16 9HW, Surrey, United Kingdom (100%)
Tel.: (44) 3451999999
Web Site: https://www.kone.co.uk
Sales Range: $200-249.9 Million
Emp.: 600
Elevators; Elevator Maintenance & Modernization Services
N.A.I.C.S.: 333921

Branch (Domestic):

KONE (UK)-Keighley (2)
Worth Bridge Rd, Keighley, BD21 4YA, West Yorkshire, United Kingdom (100%)
Tel.: (44) 1535662841
Web Site: http://www.kone.com
Sales Range: $75-99.9 Million
Emp.: 300
Elevator & Escalator Mfr
N.A.I.C.S.: 333921

KONE Plc-Glasgow (2)
Suite G7/G4 Duart House Finch Way, Strathclyde Business Park, Bellshill, ML4 3PR, United Kingdom (100%)
Tel.: (44) 8451 999 999
Web Site: http://www.kone.com
Sales Range: $25-49.9 Million
Emp.: 60
Elevator Mfr & Distr
N.A.I.C.S.: 333921

KONE Portugal- Elevadores Lda. (1)
Av Infante D Henrique cross Av Marechal Gomes da Costa, Xerox Building North Wing Floor 0, 1950 -421, Lisbon, Portugal
Tel.: (351) 213917800
Web Site: https://www.kone.pt
Sales Range: $25-49.9 Million
Emp.: 3
Elevator & Escalator Installation Services
N.A.I.C.S.: 238290

KONE Pte. Ltd. (1)
30A Kallang Place 14-01, Singapore, 339213, Singapore
Tel.: (65) 64246246
Web Site: https://www.kone.sg
Elevator Repair & Maintenance Services
N.A.I.C.S.: 811310

KONE Public Company Limited (1)
555 Rasa Tower II 26th Fl Phaholyothin Road Chatuchak, Bangkok, 10900, Thailand (92%)
Tel.: (66) 20886500
Web Site: https://www.kone.co.th
Sales Range: $100-124.9 Million
Emp.: 300
Elevator & Escalator Mfr
N.A.I.C.S.: 333921

KONE Quebec, Inc. (1)
1730 Newton Ave, Quebec, G1P 4J4, QC, Canada (100%)
Tel.: (418) 877-2183
Sales Range: $25-49.9 Million
Emp.: 50
Installation & Repair & Maintenance of Elevators
N.A.I.C.S.: 333921
Kelly Laitch *(Pres & CEO)*

KONE Rulletrapper AS (1)
Kjelsasveien 172d, Oslo, 0884, Norway
Tel.: (47) 22587000
Sales Range: $25-49.9 Million
Emp.: 200
Escalator Repair & Maintenance Services
N.A.I.C.S.: 811310

KONE Rulltrappor A.B. (1)
Kronborgsgrand 13, 164 46, Kista, Sollentuna, Sweden (100%)
Tel.: (46) 771500000
Web Site: http://www.kone.com
Sales Range: $25-49.9 Million
Elevator Mfr
N.A.I.C.S.: 333921

KONE S.A (1)
5 Filikon and 1 Deligiorgi Str, Peristeri, 121 31, Athens, Greece
Tel.: (30) 2105793000
Elevator Mfr
N.A.I.C.S.: 333921

KONE S.A. (1)
ZAC de l Arenas Bat Aeropole 455 Promenade des Anglais, BP 3316, 06206, Nice, France

KONE OYJ

INTERNATIONAL PUBLIC

KONE Oyj—(Continued)
Tel.: (33) 970808080
Web Site: https://www.kone.fr
Elevator Installation Services & Mfr
N.A.I.C.S.: 333921

KONE S.p.A. (1)
Via Figino 41, 20016, Milan, Pero,
Italy **(100%)**
Tel.: (39) 02339231
Sales Range: $200-249.9 Million
Emp.: 600
Elevator & Escalator Mfr
N.A.I.C.S.: 333921

KONE SSC s.r.o. (1)
Tomasikova 64, 831 04, Bratislava, Slovakia
Tel.: (421) 259221111
Sales Range: $50-74.9 Million
Emp.: 20
Elevator & Escalator Installation Services
N.A.I.C.S.: 238290
Timea Cerbova *(Mgr-HR)*

KONE Scandinavia AB (1)
Bagarbyvagen 61, 191 34, Sollentuna,
Sweden
Tel.: (46) 8 7523500
Web Site: http://www.kone.com
Emp.: 150
Elevators Repair & Maintenance Services
N.A.I.C.S.: 811198
Mennander Juha *(Gen Mgr)*

KONE Servicezentrale GmbH (1)
Tel.: (49) 51121480
Sales Range: $25-49.9 Million
Emp.: 25
Elevator Repair & Maintenance Services
N.A.I.C.S.: 811198

KONE Sp. z o.o. (1)
ul Poleczki 35, 02-822, Warsaw, Poland
Tel.: (48) 800566300
Web Site: https://www.kone.pl
Sales Range: $50-74.9 Million
Emp.: 200
Elevator Mfr
N.A.I.C.S.: 333921

KONE Uganda Limited (1)
Sixth floor Soliz House Plot 23 Lumumba
Avenue Nakasero, PO Box 10927, Kampala, Uganda
Tel.: (256) 312370855
Web Site: https://www.kone.ug
Elevator Mfr
N.A.I.C.S.: 333921

KONE Vietnam Limited Liability Company (1)
5th Floor Centre Point Building 106 Nguyen
Van Troi Street, Ward 8 Phu Nhuan Dist,
Ho Chi Minh City, Vietnam
Tel.: (84) 2839975373
Web Site: https://www.kone.vn
Sales Range: $25-49.9 Million
Emp.: 2
Elevator Repair & Maintenance Services
N.A.I.C.S.: 811310

KONE d.o.o. (1)
Zagrebacka cesta 145A/III, 10000, Zagreb,
Croatia
Tel.: (385) 13867130
Web Site: https://www.kone.hr
Elevator Mfr
N.A.I.C.S.: 333921

KONE d.o.o. (1)
Moskovska 93, 81000, Podgorica, Montenegro
Tel.: (382) 20339800
Web Site: https://www.kone.me
Elevator Mfr
N.A.I.C.S.: 333921

KONE d.o.o. (1)
Omladinskih Brigada 90 D sprat 6,
Beograd-Novi, 11070, Belgrade, Serbia
Tel.: (381) 113591230
Web Site: https://www.kone.rs
Elevator Mfr
N.A.I.C.S.: 333921

KONE ehf (1)
Lynghals 5, 110, Reykjavik, Iceland
Tel.: (354) 4151160
Web Site: https://www.kone.is
Elevator Sales & Installation Services

N.A.I.C.S.: 423830
Olafur S. Einarsson *(Mng Dir)*

KONE s.r.o. (1)
Galvaniho 7/B, 821 04, Bratislava, Slovakia
Tel.: (421) 800173174
Web Site: https://www.kone.sk
Emp.: 65
Elevators Repair & Maintenance Services
N.A.I.C.S.: 811198

KONE, Inc. (1)
6696 Financial Drive Unit 2, Mississauga,
L5N 7J6, ON, Canada **(100%)**
Tel.: (905) 858-8383
Web Site: https://www.kone.com
Sales Range: $25-49.9 Million
Emp.: 50
Elevators & Conveyers Distr
N.A.I.C.S.: 333921

KPI Elevators, Inc. (1)
BDO Equitable Tower 25th Floor 8751
Paseo de Roxas, De La Rosa St, Makati,
1226, Philippines **(100%)**
Tel.: (63) 288112934
Web Site: https://www.kone.ph
Sales Range: $1-9.9 Million
Emp.: 60
N.A.I.C.S.: 333921

Kone Mexico, S.A. de C.V. (1)
Av Revolucion 756 Piso 6 Santa Maria
Nonoalco, Benito Juarez, 03700, Mexico,
Mexico
Tel.: (52) 5519460100
Web Site: https://www.kone.mx
Sales Range: $50-74.9 Million
Elevator Mfr
N.A.I.C.S.: 333921

Konematic GmbH (1)
Hainbuchenweg 14-18, Klecken, 21224,
Rosengarten, Germany
Tel.: (49) 4105 5551 10
Web Site: http://www.kone.com
Elevators & Automatic Door Mfr
N.A.I.C.S.: 333921

L.A.M. Lombarda Ascensori Montacarichi S.r.l. (1)
12 Via Provinciale Castellanzese, 20027,
Rescaldina, MI, Italy
Tel.: (39) 0331453503
Web Site: https://www.lamascensori.it
Elevator Services
N.A.I.C.S.: 238290

Lift Maintenance Limited (1)
12 Jordanvale Avenue, Partick, Glasgow,
G14 0QP, United Kingdom
Tel.: (44) 141 9593601
Web Site: http://www.lmlifts.co.uk
Sales Range: $25-49.9 Million
Emp.: 70
Elevator Repair & Maintenance Services
N.A.I.C.S.: 811310

Marryat & Scott Egypt S.A.E. (1)
Kilo 28 Cairo - Alex Desert Road, PO Box
104, Abou Rawash Industrial Zone, Cairo,
Egypt **(49%)**
Tel.: (20) 235390040
Web Site: https://marryatscott.com.eg
Sales Range: $50-74.9 Million
Emp.: 200
Elevators & Escalators
N.A.I.C.S.: 333921

Marvi Ascensores S.L. (1)
Partida Bova 7, 25196, Lleida, Spain
Tel.: (34) 973247250
Sales Range: $25-49.9 Million
Emp.: 10
Elevator Installation Services & Distr
N.A.I.C.S.: 238290
Javier Bernal *(Gen Mgr)*

Matthias Schernikau GmbH (1)
Bahnhofstrasse 4, 21493, Mohnsen, Germany
Tel.: (49) 41593759900
Web Site: https://liftfabrik.de
Emp.: 150
Elevator Maintenance Services
N.A.I.C.S.: 238290

Mingot S.r.l. (1)
507/2 Zona Artigianale Dolina, 34018, San
Dorligo della Valle, TS, Italy
Tel.: (39) 0408327127

Web Site: https://www.mingotrieste.it
Elevator & Escalator Installation Services
N.A.I.C.S.: 238290

Motala Hissar A.B. (1)
Laxorgatan 1, Box 4029, 59104, Motala,
Sweden
Tel.: (46) 14 123 7050
Web Site: https://www.motalahissar.se
Sales Range: $25-49.9 Million
Emp.: 55
N.A.I.C.S.: 333921
Stefan Westin *(Mng Dir)*

Nettuno S.r.l. (1)
Viale Industria 16/18, 24060, Castelli, BG,
Italy
Tel.: (39) 035847508
Web Site: https://www.nettuno.net
Hand Cleanser Chemical Product Mfr
N.A.I.C.S.: 325199

Neulift Service Molise S.r.l. (1)
area via del Melograno 30, 86039, Termoli,
CB, Italy
Tel.: (39) 0875714006
Web Site: https://www.neuliftmolise.it
Elevator Services
N.A.I.C.S.: 238290

Neulift Service Triveneto S.r.l. (1)
Viale dell Industria 23/ 4-5, 35129, Padova,
PD, Italy
Tel.: (39) 0498089509
Web Site: https://www.neulifttriveneto.it
Elevator Services
N.A.I.C.S.: 238290

O&K Escalators S.A. (1)
Centre d'Affaires 2 rue Louis Armand,
F-92661, Asnieres, Cedex, France
Tel.: (33) 141321250
Web Site: http://www.kone.com
Escalator Mfr
N.A.I.C.S.: 333921

PACA ASCENSEURS SERVICES SARL (1)
Agavon ZAC 4 Avenue Lamartine, 13170,
Les Pennes-Mirabeau, France
Tel.: (33) 442341370
Web Site: http://www.paca-ascenseurs.fr
Elevator Repair & Maintenance Services
N.A.I.C.S.: 811210
Patrick Mordenti *(Pres)*

PT Kone Indo Elevator (1)
Park Tower 9th floor, MNC Center Complex
Jl Kebon Sirih No 17 - 19, Jarkarta Pusat,
Jakarta, 10340, Indonesia
Tel.: (62) 2130060418
Web Site: https://www.kone.co.id
Emp.: 316
Elevator Repair & Maintenance Services
N.A.I.C.S.: 811310

Prokodis S.N.C. (1)
Zi La Begude, 06340, Cantaron, France
Tel.: (33) 4 93 91 54 35
Web Site: http://www.prokodis.com
Sales Range: $25-49.9 Million
Elevators & Automatic Door Parts Mfr
N.A.I.C.S.: 332322

RUMAN S.r.l. (1)
Vle Europa 72, 20090, Cusago, Milan, Italy
Tel.: (39) 0290390221
Elevator Repair & Maintenance Services
N.A.I.C.S.: 811198

Recolift SA (1)
Sr via Santa Maria 68, 6596, Gordola, Switzerland
Tel.: (41) 91 780 47 30
Web Site: http://www.recolift.ch
Lift Repair & Maintenance Services
N.A.I.C.S.: 811310

Rimma S.r.l. (1)
Via Simone Cuccia n 45, 90144, Palermo,
Italy
Tel.: (39) 091343545
Web Site: https://www.rimma.it
Elevator Services
N.A.I.C.S.: 238290

SGS Vostok Limited (1)
18 Andropova Prospect bldg 7, 115432,
Moscow, Russia
Tel.: (7) 4957754620
Web Site: https://www.sgs.ru

Sales Range: $1-4.9 Billion
Emp.: 330
Inspection & Verification Services
N.A.I.C.S.: 926150
Julia Marskova *(Coord-Environmental Svcs)*

SIA KONE Lifti Latvija Oy (1)
Dzerbenes iela 27a, Riga, 1006,
Latvia **(100%)**
Tel.: (371) 6 755 4268
Web Site: https://www.kone.lv
N.A.I.C.S.: 333921

SK-Fordertechnik GmbH (1)
Jarrestr 8. 22303, Hamburg, Germany
Tel.: (49) 40209112620
Web Site: https://www.sk-foerdertechnik.de
Elevator Services
N.A.I.C.S.: 238290

Sabiem S.p.A. (1)
Via Figino 41, Pero, 20016, Milan, Italy
Tel.: (39) 02339231
Elevator Installation Services
N.A.I.C.S.: 238290

Societe Francaise des Ascenseurs KONE (1)
Centre d'Affaires Objectif 2 2 Rue Louis
Armand, F 92661, Asnieres,
France **(95%)**
Tel.: (33) 141321250
Web Site: http://www.kone.com
Sales Range: $100-124.9 Million
Emp.: 300
Elevators & Escalators Maintenance & Modernization Services
N.A.I.C.S.: 333921

Stel S.r.l. (1)
Via Verginese 24/b, Gambulaga, 44015,
Ferrara, Italy
Tel.: (39) 05 325 5586
Web Site: https://www.stel.it
Telecommunication Servicesb
N.A.I.C.S.: 517810

Suur-Helsingin Hissihuolto Oy (1)
Itakatu 5 C, Helsinki, 930, Finland
Tel.: (358) 20 7983 200
Sales Range: $25-49.9 Million
Emp.: 30
Elevator & Escalator Installation Services
N.A.I.C.S.: 238290
Harri Niemine *(Gen Mgr)*

Tecnicas Autocontrol, S.L.U. (1)
C/ Francisco de Toledo 15, 14011, Cordoba, Spain
Tel.: (34) 957282962
Web Site: https://www.tecnicasautocontrol.com
Elevator Installation Services
N.A.I.C.S.: 238990

Tecnocram S.r.l. (1)
Via degli Orti Gianicolensi 21, 152, Milan,
Italy
Tel.: (39) 06 5815404
Lifting Equipment Installation Services
N.A.I.C.S.: 238290

Tosca Ascensori S.r.l. (1)
Via del Guado SNC, Sesto Pergola district,
26817, San Martino in Strada, Lodi, Italy
Tel.: (39) 0371476084
Web Site: https://www.ascensorilodi.com
Sales Range: $25-49.9 Million
Emp.: 15
Elevator Mfr
N.A.I.C.S.: 333921

UAB KONE (1)
M Slezeviciaus g 13, LT - 06326, Vilnius,
Lithuania
Tel.: (370) 52429796
Web Site: https://www.kone.lt
Elevator Mfr
N.A.I.C.S.: 333921

Unilift S.r.l. (1)
Via Ca Marcello 57, 30172, Venice, Italy
Tel.: (39) 041986091
Web Site: https://www.uniliftascensori.it
Elevator Services
N.A.I.C.S.: 238290

Uppsala Hiss Montage och El AB (1)
Soderforsgatan 23, Uppsala, 752 28, Sweden

AND PRIVATE COMPANIES

Tel.: (46) 18550530
Lifting Installation Services
N.A.I.C.S.: 238290

VITALI Ascensori s.r.l. (1)
Via Arenzano 453, 47522, Cesena, Italy
Tel.: (39) 0547347201
Web Site:
   https://www.ascensorimontacarichivitali.it
Elevator & Escalator Mfr
N.A.I.C.S.: 333921

ZAO KONE Lifts Moscow (1)
Uspensky Per 3 Build 2, 127006, Moscow,
Russia (100%)
Tel.: (7) 4952239595
Web Site: http://www.kone.com
Project Management Services
N.A.I.C.S.: 333921

ZAO KONE Lifts St. Petersburg (1)
41/7 nab Chernoy Rechky off 216 Business
Center, Progress City, Saint Petersburg,
197342, Russia
Tel.: (7) 8123135199
Sales Range: $25-49.9 Million
Emp.: 15
Elevators & Escalators Sales & Service
N.A.I.C.S.: 333921
Diana Olshevskaya *(Mgr-Sls)*

KONECRANES OYJ

Koneenkatu 8, FI-05830, Hyvinkaa,
Finland
Tel.: (358) 0 20 427 11
Web Site:
   http://www.konecranes.com
Lifting Equipment And Services Provider
N.A.I.C.S.: 333924
Christoph Vitzthum *(Chm)*

Subsidiaries:

MHE-Demag (S) Pte. Ltd. (1)
33 Gul Circle, Singapore, 629570,
Singapore (50%)
Tel.: (65) 63053500
Web Site: http://www.mhe-demag.com
Sales Range: $550-599.9 Million
Emp.: 200
Provider of Material Handling Equipment &
System Distr
N.A.I.C.S.: 488320
Bill Chua *(Reg Mgr-Mktg)*

KONECRANES PLC

Koneenkatu 8, PO Box 661, FI-
05801, Hyvinkaa, Finland
Tel.: (358) 2042711
Web Site:
   https://www.konecranes.com
Year Founded: 1994
KNCRY—(OTCIQ)
Rev.: $3,904,452,136
Assets: $4,933,225,960
Liabilities: $3,396,574,896
Net Worth: $1,536,651,064
Earnings: $150,090,928
Emp.: 17,027
Fiscal Year-end: 12/31/20
Process Cranes, Industrial Cranes,
Harbor Cranes, Forklift Trucks &
Reach Stackers Mfr; Crane Maintenance, Repair, Inspection & Operator
Training Services
N.A.I.C.S.: 333923
Mikko Uhari *(Member-Exec Bd & Exec VP-Bus Area Industrial Equipment)*

Subsidiaries:

Bouyer Manutention S.A. (1)
ZA Papillon 170 rue Henry Potez, 37210,
Parcay-Meslay, France
Tel.: (33) 2 47 40 04 00
Electrical Equipment Installation & Maintenance Services
N.A.I.C.S.: 238210

CGP-Konecranes S.A. (1)
1 Rue De Boijny, Boigny-sur-Bionne,
45760, France (100%)
Tel.: (33) 238719400

Web Site: http://www.cgp.konecranes.fr
Sales Range: $10-24.9 Million
Emp.: 65
Mfr of Cranes & Hoists
N.A.I.C.S.: 333120

Cranex Konecranes Sp. z.o.o. (1)
Porcelanwa West St19, 40585, Katowice,
Poland (100%)
Tel.: (48) 322054295
Web Site: http://www.koneecranes.pl
Sales Range: $25-49.9 Million
Emp.: 15
Mfr of Cranes & Hoists
N.A.I.C.S.: 333120
Andreas Lizkoske *(Mgr)*

Dalian Konecranes Company Ltd. (1)
Rm 1808 Pearl River International Building
No 99 Xinkai Road, Xigang District, Dalian,
116011, China
Tel.: (86) 411 83779376
Crane Repair Services & Mfr
N.A.I.C.S.: 811310

Eurofactory GmbH (1)
Liebengrun 167, 7368, Remptendorf, Germany
Tel.: (49) 366402890
Emp.: 15
Hoist Mfr
N.A.I.C.S.: 333923

KCI Cranes Holding (Singapore) Pte Ltd (1)
25 Tuas View Close, Singapore, 637480,
Singapore
Tel.: (65) 68612233
Web Site: http://www.konecranes.com.sg
Sales Range: $50-74.9 Million
Emp.: 30
Investment Management Service
N.A.I.C.S.: 523999

Kaverit Cranes and Service ULC (1)
5300 Main way, Burlington, L7L 6B8, ON,
Canada
Tel.: (905) 332-9494
Web Site: http://www.kaveritcranes.com
Sales Range: $50-74.9 Million
Emp.: 220
Crane Repair Services & Mfr
N.A.I.C.S.: 811310
Sadi Arbid *(Pres)*

Konecranes (France) (1)
Boulevard De Verdun, PO Box 727, 76060,
Le Grand-Quevilly, Cedex, France (100%)
Tel.: (33) 235259514
Web Site: http://www.konecranes.fr
Sales Range: $1-9.9 Million
Emp.: 15
Mfr of Cranes & Hoists
N.A.I.C.S.: 333120

Konecranes (France) S.A. (1)
1 Route de Boigny, 45760, Boigny-sur-
Bionne, France
Tel.: (33) 23 871 9400
Web Site: https://www.konecranes.com
Sales Range: $25-49.9 Million
Emp.: 80
Mfr of Cranes & Hoists
N.A.I.C.S.: 333120
Jean Maxime Guhur *(Mng Dir)*

Konecranes (Shanghai) Co. Ltd. (1)
Building 4 No 100 Lane 2891 South Qilian
shan Road, Shanghai, 200331,
China (100%)
Tel.: (86) 212 606 1000
Web Site: https://www.konecranes.com
Sales Range: $200-249.9 Million
Emp.: 800
Mfr of Cranes & Hoists
N.A.I.C.S.: 333120

Konecranes (Thailand) Ltd. (1)
789/11 Moo 1 Pinthong Industrial Park
Phase II, Tambon Nongkham, Si Racha,
20230, Chonburi, Thailand
Tel.: (66) 3 834 8305
Web Site: https://www.konecranes.com
Crane Machinery Mfr
N.A.I.C.S.: 333923

Konecranes A/S (1)
Baldersbuen 15 A, 2640, Hedehusene,
Denmark (100%)

Tel.: (45) 46591288
Web Site: http://www.konecranes.com
Sales Range: $25-49.9 Million
Emp.: 50
Mfr of Cranes & Hoists
N.A.I.C.S.: 333120
Martin Olsen *(Branch Mgr)*

Konecranes AB (1)
Bjorkhem 19, PO Box 56, S 291 21, Kristi-
anstad, Sweden
Tel.: (46) 44188400
Sales Range: $25-49.9 Million
Emp.: 25
Mfr of Cranes & Hoists
N.A.I.C.S.: 333120
Kari Akman *(Mng Dir)*

Konecranes AG (1)
Walkrastrasse 41, Daniken, 4658, Switzerland
Tel.: (41) 794892575
Crane Component Distr
N.A.I.C.S.: 423830

Konecranes AS (1)
Fredrik Selmers vei 6, PO Box 168, 0663,
Oslo, Norway
Tel.: (47) 22079700
Web Site: https://www.konecranes.com
Sales Range: $25-49.9 Million
Emp.: 65
Mfr of Cranes & Hoists
N.A.I.C.S.: 333120
Pekka Kujala *(Gen Mgr)*

Konecranes BV (1)
Signaal 70, 1446 XA, Purmerend, Netherlands
Tel.: (31) 29 948 8888
Web Site: https://www.konecranes.com
Sales Range: $25-49.9 Million
Emp.: 30
Mfr of Cranes & Hoists
N.A.I.C.S.: 333120

Konecranes Canada, Inc. (1)
5300 Mainway, Burlington, L7L 6A4, ON,
Canada (100%)
Tel.: (905) 332-9494
Web Site: https://www.konecranes.com
Sales Range: $25-49.9 Million
Emp.: 50
Mfr of Cranes
N.A.I.C.S.: 333120

Konecranes Chile. (1)
Manuel Rodriguez No 72 Parque Industrial
Libertadores, Colina, 9361299, Santiago,
Chile
Tel.: (56) 2 952 8900
Web Site: https://www.konecranes.com
Sales Range: $25-49.9 Million
Emp.: 145
Crane Mfr
N.A.I.C.S.: 333923

Konecranes Company Ltd. (1)
8F Shin Osaki Kangyo Building 1-6-4 Osaki,
Shinagawa-ku, Tokyo, 141-0032, Japan
Tel.: (81) 3 5436 6446
Web Site: http://www.konecranes.com
Crane Mfr
N.A.I.C.S.: 333923

Konecranes Finance Oy (1)
Koneenkatu 8, Hyvinkaa, 5830, Finland
Tel.: (358) 204 2711
Financial Management Services
N.A.I.C.S.: 523999
Pekka Lundmark *(Gen Mgr)*

Subsidiary (Non-US):

TBA Leicester Limited (2)
Lancer House, 38 Scudamore Road, Leicester, LE3 1UQ, United Kingdom
Tel.: (44) 1162821800
Construction Machinery Equipment Mfr
N.A.I.C.S.: 333120

Konecranes Finland Oy (1)
Koneenkatu 8, 5801, Hyvinkaa, Finland
Tel.: (358) 20 427 11
Overhead Traveling Crane Mfr
N.A.I.C.S.: 333923
Pekka Lundmark *(CEO)*

Konecranes GmbH (1)
Muhlenfeld 20, 30853, Langenhagen,
Germany (100%)
Tel.: (49) 5 117 7040

KONECRANES PLC

Web Site: https://www.konecranes.com
Sales Range: $50-74.9 Million
Emp.: 80
Mfr of Cranes & Hoists
N.A.I.C.S.: 333120

Plant (Domestic):

Konecranes GmbH - Ansbach (2)
Robert Bosch Strasse 10, 91522, Ansbach,
Germany
Tel.: (49) 981 97196 0
Web Site: http://www.konecranes.de
Mfr of Cranes & Hoists
N.A.I.C.S.: 333120

Konecranes GmbH - Berlin (2)
Engellstrasse 21, Berlin, 13507, Germany
Tel.: (49) 304147197 0
Emp.: 6
Mfr of Cranes & Hoists
N.A.I.C.S.: 333120

Konecranes Hellas Lifting Equipment and Services S.A. (1)
Industrial Area Thebes Position Charaintini,
Athens, 15124, Greece
Tel.: (30) 6942 200 800
Web Site: http://www.konecranes.gr
Sales Range: $25-49.9 Million
Emp.: 8
Lifting Equipment Repair & Maintenance
Service
N.A.I.C.S.: 811310

Konecranes Holding BV (1)
Amperestraat 15, 1446 TP, Purmerend,
Netherlands
Tel.: (31) 29948 88 88
Investment Management Service
N.A.I.C.S.: 523999

Konecranes Holding GmbH (1)
Boehringerstr 4, Mannheim, 68307, Germany
Tel.: (49) 621 78990 0
Investment Management Service
N.A.I.C.S.: 523999

Konecranes India Private Ltd. (1)
19 Level 2 Muttha Towers Don Bosco Road
Yerwada, Pune, 411 006, India
Tel.: (91) 20 40047470
Web Site: http://www.konecranes.in
Sales Range: $100-124.9 Million
Emp.: 36
Material Handling Equipment Mfr
N.A.I.C.S.: 333248

Konecranes Kft. (1)
Kesmark U 14/B, 1158, Budapest, Hungary
Tel.: (36) 1 555 52 70
Sales Range: $25-49.9 Million
Emp.: 71
Overhead Crane Mfr
N.A.I.C.S.: 333923

Konecranes Latvia (1)
Maza Krasta 83, Riga, LV-1003, Latvia
Tel.: (371) 67394491
Web Site: https://www.konecranes.com
Sales Range: $25-49.9 Million
Emp.: 6
Mfr of Cranes & Hoists
N.A.I.C.S.: 333120
Sergejs Veselovs *(Gen Mgr)*

Konecranes Lifting Systems GmbH (1)
Heinrich Hertz Suite 18, Dreieich, 61330,
Germany
Tel.: (49) 51177040
Sales Range: $50-74.9 Million
Emp.: 70
Lifting Equipment Distr
N.A.I.C.S.: 423830

Konecranes Lifting Systems GmbH (1)
Salzburger Str 54, 5303, Thalgau, Austria
Tel.: (43) 6235 20030 0
Web Site: http://www.konecranes.com
Sales Range: $25-49.9 Million
Emp.: 15
Lifting Equipment Mfr
N.A.I.C.S.: 333921

Konecranes Lifttrucks AB (1)
Anders Anderssons Vag 13, Box 103, 285
23, Markaryd, Sweden
Tel.: (46) 43373300

KONECRANES PLC

INTERNATIONAL PUBLIC

Konecranes Plc—(Continued)
Web Site: https://www.kclifttrucks.com
Sales Range: $50-74.9 Million
Emp.: 200
Lift Truck Mfr
N.A.I.C.S.: 333998
Anders Nilsson (Dir-Technical & Quality)

Konecranes Machine Tool Service Ltd. (1)
Unit 5 Bourtree Technopark Minto Drive, Altens, Aberdeen, AB12 3LW, United Kingdom
Tel.: (44) 1224 466847
Machine Tool Repair & Maintenance Services
N.A.I.C.S.: 811310
Jeff Earley (Mgr-Bus Dev)

Konecranes Machine Tool Services Ltd. (1)
1, Farrier Road, Lincoln, G74 5LR, Lincolnshire, United Kingdom
Tel.: (44) 1522 687878
Web Site: https://www.konecranes.com
Sales Range: $25-49.9 Million
Emp.: 12
Machine Tool Repair & Maintenance Services
N.A.I.C.S.: 811310

Konecranes Mexico S.A. de C.V. (1)
Alfredo del Mazo No 10 Colonia Pedregal de Atizapan, Atizapan de Zaragoza, 52948, Mexico, Mexico **(100%)**
Tel.: (52) 5550771670
Web Site: https://www.konecranes.com
Emp.: 80
Process & Industrial Cranes Mfr
N.A.I.C.S.: 333923
Felipe Sanchez (Mng Dir)

Konecranes Norway Holding A/S (1)
Brobekkveien 60, 598, Oslo, Norway
Tel.: (47) 22079700
Web Site: http://www.konecranes.com
Emp.: 50
Investment Management Service
N.A.I.C.S.: 523999

Konecranes Ou (1)
Sepise 8, EE-11415, Tallinn, Estonia
Tel.: (372) 6112795
Web Site: https://www.konecranes.com
Sales Range: $25-49.9 Million
Cranes & Hoists Mfr
N.A.I.C.S.: 333120
Eero Tagapere (Mgr-Maintenance)

Konecranes Peru S.R.L. (1)
Calle German Schreiber N 272 Of 302, San Isidro, Lima, Peru
Tel.: (51) 1 222 2922
Crane Repair & Maintenance Service
N.A.I.C.S.: 811310

Konecranes Pte Ltd. (1)
8 Admiralty St 06-11 Admirax, 757438, Singapore
Tel.: (65) 68612233
Sales Range: $25-49.9 Million
Emp.: 50
Mfr of Cranes & Hoists
N.A.I.C.S.: 333120

Konecranes Pty Ltd (1)
5 Jurie Street, Alberton, 1457, South Africa
Tel.: (27) 11 864 2800
Web Site: http://www.konecranes.com
Sales Range: $50-74.9 Million
Emp.: 13
Crane Mfr
N.A.I.C.S.: 333923

Konecranes Pty Ltd. (1)
14 Heild Rd, Ingleburn, 2565, NSW, Australia **(100%)**
Tel.: (61) 296049355
Web Site: http://www.konecranes.com
Sales Range: $50-74.9 Million
Emp.: 250
Mfr of Cranes & Hoists
N.A.I.C.S.: 333120

Konecranes Pty Ltd. (1)
6D Henserson Pl, Penrose, 1061, New Zealand
Tel.: (64) 96345322
Web Site: http://www.konecranes.com.au
Sales Range: $25-49.9 Million
Emp.: 8
Mfr of Cranes & Hoists
N.A.I.C.S.: 333120

Konecranes S.A. (1)
Str C Brediceanu 21C, 300012, Timisoara, Romania
Tel.: (40) 25 620 3514
Web Site: http://www.konecranes.com
Sales Range: $25-49.9 Million
Emp.: 25
Overhead Traveling Crane Mfr
N.A.I.C.S.: 333923
Christian Breban (Gen Mgr)

Konecranes SA/NV (1)
Bosstraat 75, 3560, Lummen, Belgium **(100%)**
Tel.: (32) 1 353 9660
Web Site: https://www.konecranes.com
Sales Range: $1-9.9 Million
Emp.: 43
Mfr of Cranes & Hoists
N.A.I.C.S.: 333120
Tom Colpaert (Gen Mgr)

Konecranes Sdn. Bhd. (1)
No 12 Jalan SS26 13, Taman Mayang Jaya, Petaling Jaya, 47301, Selangor, Malaysia
Tel.: (60) 378803100
Web Site: http://www.konecranes.com
Sales Range: $25-49.9 Million
Emp.: 22
Mfr of Cranes & Hoists
N.A.I.C.S.: 333120

Konecranes Service Oy (1)
Koneenkatu 8, 5801, Hyvinkaa, Finland
Tel.: (358) 204 2711
Crane & Machine Tools Repair & Maintenance Service
N.A.I.C.S.: 811310
Pekka Lunpnark (CEO)

Konecranes Slovakia s.r.o. (1)
Kyjevske namestie 6, 974 04, Banska Bystrica, Slovakia
Tel.: (421) 91 754 4450
Web Site: https://www.konecranes.com
Overhead Crane Mfr
N.A.I.C.S.: 333923
Robert Hoefler (Gen Mgr)

Konecranes Sp. z o.o. (1)
Al Grunwaldzka 250, 80-314, Gdansk, Poland
Tel.: (48) 58 320 90 86
Lifting Repair & Maintenance Services
N.A.I.C.S.: 811198
Andrzej Leczkowsk (Gen Mgr)

Konecranes Supply Hungary Kft. (1)
Kesmark Utca 14 B Ep, Budapest, 1158, Hungary
Tel.: (36) 1 555 52 70
Crane Component Distr
N.A.I.C.S.: 423830
Csaba Uhelyi (Gen Mgr)

Konecranes Sweden Holding AB (1)
Bjorkhemsvagen 19, Box 56, Kristianstad, 29154, Sweden
Tel.: (46) 44188400
Web Site: http://www.konecranes.com
Emp.: 20
Investment Management Service
N.A.I.C.S.: 523999

Konecranes Talhas, Pontes Rolantes e Servicos Ltda. (1)
Avenida Victor Andrew 2055 - Eden, Sorocaba, 18086-390, Sao Polo, Brazil
Tel.: (55) 15 3325 6101
Crane Repair & Maintenance Service
N.A.I.C.S.: 811310

Konecranes Ticaret Ve Servis Limited Sirketi (1)
Inonu Cad Cetinkaya Town Center No 92 K 6 D 5, Kozyatagi, 34742, Istanbul, Turkiye
Tel.: (90) 2164108067
Web Site: https://www.konecranes.com
Sales Range: $25-49.9 Million
Emp.: 23
Crane Mfr
N.A.I.C.S.: 333923
Sami Korpela (Country Mgr)

Konecranes UK Limited (1)
Lloyds House Albion Road, West Bromwich, B70 8AX, W Midlands, United Kingdom **(100%)**
Tel.: (44) 1215691000
Web Site: http://www.konecranes.co.uk
Sales Range: $25-49.9 Million
Emp.: 40
Mfr of Cranes & Hoists
N.A.I.C.S.: 333120

Division (Domestic):

Konecranes UK Ltd. - Industrial Crane Division (1)
2 Peel Park Place, College Milton, East Kilbride, G74 5LR, Scotland, United Kingdom
Tel.: (44) 1355220591
Web Site: http://www.konecranesukindustrial.com
Sales Range: $25-49.9 Million
Emp.: 80
Mfr of Cranes & Hoists
N.A.I.C.S.: 333120
Gordon Adie (Mng Dir)

Konecranes Vietnam Co.,Ltd (1)
Room 801 8th Fl 60 Nguyen Dinh Chieu, Da Kao Ward District 1, Ho Chi Minh City, Vietnam
Tel.: (84) 8 6296 1948
Sales Range: $25-49.9 Million
Emp.: 13
Industrial Crane Machinery Mfr
N.A.I.C.S.: 333923
Lay Hoang Viet (Country Mgr)

Konecranes YardIT Oy (1)
Taivaltie 5, 1610, Vantaa, Finland
Tel.: (358) 204 2711
Material Handling Software Development Services
N.A.I.C.S.: 541511
Panu Routila (CEO)

Konecranes, Inc. (1)
4401 Gateway Blvd, Springfield, OH 45502-9339
Tel.: (937) 525-5533
Web Site: https://www.konecranes.com
Sales Range: $25-49.9 Million
Emp.: 60
Mfr of Process Cranes, Industrial Cranes, Harbor Cranes, Forklift Trucks & Reach Stackers; Crane Maintenance, Repair, Inspection & Operator Training Services
N.A.I.C.S.: 333923

Subsidiary (Domestic):

KCI Koneports Americas (2)
4220 Steve Reynolds Blvd Ste 1, Norcross, GA 30093
Tel.: (770) 279-9936
Sales Range: $25-49.9 Million
Emp.: 50
Mfr of Cranes & Hoists
N.A.I.C.S.: 424310

Konecranes Nuclear Equipment & Services, LLC (2)
5300 S Emmer Dr, New Berlin, WI 53151
Tel.: (262) 784-1873
Emp.: 150
Material Handling Equipment Repair & Maintenance Services
N.A.I.C.S.: 811310
Cassandra Dale (Coord-Export Compliance)

Konecranes Orley Meyer (2)
S 86 W 22400 Edgewood Ave, Big Bend, WI 53103-0070
Tel.: (713) 466-7541
Web Site: http://www.kciusa.com
Mfr of Hoists & Cranes
N.A.I.C.S.: 333120

Plant (Domestic):

Konecranes, Inc. - Houston Plant (2)
7300 Chippewa Blvd, Houston, TX 77086-3231
Tel.: (281) 445-2225
Web Site: http://www.konecranesamerica.com
Sales Range: $25-49.9 Million
Emp.: 60
Mfr of Process Cranes, Industrial Cranes, Harbor Cranes, Forklift Trucks & Reach Stackers; Crane Maintenance, Repair, Inspection & Operator Training Services
N.A.I.C.S.: 333923
Pekka Lundmark (CEO & Pres)

Subsidiary (Domestic):

MMH Holdings Inc. (2)
315 W Forest Hill Ave, Oak Creek, WI 53154 **(100%)**
Tel.: (414) 764-6200
Web Site: http://www.morriscranes.com
Holding Company
N.A.I.C.S.: 551112

Subsidiary (Domestic):

Morris Material Handling Inc. (3)
315 W Forest Hill Ave, Oak Creek, WI 53154
Tel.: (414) 764-6200
Web Site: http://www.morriscranes.com
Sales Range: $150-199.9 Million
Emp.: 80
Mfr & Installer of Electric Overhead Traveling Cranes, Monorail Hoists, Rail-Mounted Gantries & Woodyard & Portal Cranes
N.A.I.C.S.: 333923

Subsidiary (Domestic):

Merwin, LLC (2)
315 W Forest Hill Ave, Oak Creek, WI 53154-2905
Tel.: (406) 778-3245
Crane Repair & Maintenance Service
N.A.I.C.S.: 811310

R&M Materials Handling Inc. (2)
4501 Gateway Blvd, Springfield, OH 45502-8863
Tel.: (937) 328-5100
Web Site: http://www.rmhoist.com
Sales Range: $25-49.9 Million
Hoists Cranes & Monorails
N.A.I.C.S.: 423830
Jane Vandegrift (Pres)

Shepard Niles (2)
220 N Genesee St, Montour Falls, NY 14865-9647
Tel.: (607) 535-7111
Web Site: http://www.shepard-niles.com
Sales Range: $25-49.9 Million
Emp.: 15
Mfr of Cranes, Hoists & Conveyors
N.A.I.C.S.: 333923

Lloyds Konecranes Pension Trustees Ltd. (1)
Albion Road, West Bromwich, B70 8AX, West Midlands, United Kingdom
Tel.: (44) 121 569 1000
Web Site: http://www.konecranes.com
Emp.: 40
Employee Benefit Services
N.A.I.C.S.: 525110

Nosturiexpertit Oy-Nosturilloyds (1)
Kytajankatu 23A, 05830, Hyvinkaa, Finland **(100%)**
Tel.: (358) 95484144
Web Site: https://www.nosturiexpertit.fi
Sales Range: $1-9.9 Million
Emp.: 5
Mfr of Cranes & Hoists
N.A.I.C.S.: 333120

PT Konecranes (1)
Kompleks Mitra Sunter Blok B-31, Jl Yos Sudarso Kav 89, Sunter Jaya, Jakarta, 14350, Utara, Indonesia
Tel.: (62) 216508022
Sales Range: $25-49.9 Million
Emp.: 100
Cranes & Hoists Mfr
N.A.I.C.S.: 333120

S.C. Konecranes SA Timisoara (1)
str C Brediceanu 21 C ap 35, 300012, Timisoara, Romania **(100%)**
Tel.: (40) 25 620 3514
Web Site: https://www.konecranes.com
Sales Range: $25-49.9 Million
Emp.: 25
Mfr of Cranes & Hoists
N.A.I.C.S.: 333120

SWF Krantechnik Co., Ltd. (1)
Room 6A No 105 Qi Lian Shan Nan Road Lane 2891, Shanghai, 200331, China
Tel.: (86) 213 652 8282
Web Site: https://www.swfkrantechnik.com

Sales Range: $25-49.9 Million
Emp.: 27
Overhead Crane Mfr
N.A.I.C.S.: 333923
Alex Gao *(Engr-Sls)*

SWF Krantechnik GmbH (1)
Boehringerstr 4, 68307, Mannheim, Germany
Tel.: (49) 62 178 9900
Web Site: https://www.swfkrantechnik.com
Lifting Equipment Distr
N.A.I.C.S.: 423830
Iris Steeg *(Controller)*

Saudi Cranes & Steel Works Factory LLC (1)
Jubail Industrial City, PO Box 10043, 31961, Al Jubayl, Saudi Arabia
Tel.: (966) 3 341 0030
Web Site: http://www.saudicranes.com
Sales Range: $25-49.9 Million
Emp.: 100
Overhead Traveling Crane Installation Services Mfr
N.A.I.C.S.: 333923

TBA Doncaster Limited (1)
Unit 4 Railway court Ten Pound Walk, Doncaster, DN4 5FB, United Kingdom
Tel.: (44) 1302330837
Measuring & Controlling Device Mfr
N.A.I.C.S.: 334519

Terex MHPS GmbH (1)
Forststrasse 16, 40597, Dusseldorf, Germany
Tel.: (49) 211 7102 0
Web Site: http://www.demagcranes.com
Compressors, Material Handling Machinery, Air Motors, Cranes, Fork Lifts, Plastic Injection Machines, Hydraulic Excavators & Vacuum Pumps Mfr
N.A.I.C.S.: 333923

Subsidiary (Domestic):

Demag Cranes & Components GmbH (2)
Ruhrstrasse 28, 58300, Wetter, Germany
Tel.: (49) 2335 920
Web Site: http://www.demagcranes.com
Industrial Cranes Mfr
N.A.I.C.S.: 333923

Subsidiary (US):

Demag Cranes & Components Corp. (3)
6675 Parkland Blvd Ste 200, Cleveland, OH 44139
Tel.: (440) 248-2400
Web Site: http://www.demagcranes.us
Overhead Crane & Hoist Mfr
N.A.I.C.S.: 333923

Unit (Domestic):

Demag Cranes & Components Corp. - Houston Region (4)
16430 Aldine Westfield Rd, Houston, TX 77032
Tel.: (281) 443-7331
Web Site: http://www.demagcranes.com
Crane, Hoist & Monorail System Mfr
N.A.I.C.S.: 333923

Subsidiary (Non-US):

Demag Cranes & Components GesmbH (3)
Vilniusstrasse 5, Salzburg, 5020, Austria
Tel.: (43) 662889060
Web Site: http://www.demagcranes.at
Material Handling Equipment Mfr
N.A.I.C.S.: 333120

Demag Cranes & Components Pty. Ltd. (3)
92 Long Street, Smithfield, 2164, NSW, Australia
Tel.: (61) 1300 336 241
Web Site: http://www.demag.com.au
Crane Mfr
N.A.I.C.S.: 333923

Demag Cranes & Components S.A.S. (3)
5 avenue Ampere CS 80539, Chalons-en-Champagne, 51012, France
Tel.: (33) 326667400
Web Site: http://www.demagcranes.fr
Cranes & Components Mfr
N.A.I.C.S.: 333923

Demag Cranes & Components S.A.U (3)
Calle Basauri 17, 28023, Madrid, Spain
Tel.: (34) 91 8873 600
Web Site: http://www.demagcranes.es
Industrial Cranes Mfr
N.A.I.C.S.: 333120

Demag Cranes & Components Srl (3)
Via Archimede 45-47, 20864, Agrate Brianza, Italy
Tel.: (39) 03965531
Web Site: http://www.demagcranes.it
Industrial Cranes Mfr
N.A.I.C.S.: 333923

Subsidiary (Domestic):

Donati Sollevamenti S.r.l. (4)
Via S Quasimodo 17, 20025, Legnano, Italy
Tel.: (39) 0331 14811
Web Site: http://donaticranes.com
Lifting Equipment Mfr
N.A.I.C.S.: 333923

Subsidiary (Non-US):

Demag Cranes & Components Trading (Shanghai) Co. Ltd. (3)
789 Sui De Road, Putuo District, Shanghai, 200331, China
Tel.: (86) 216025 9029
Web Site: http://www.demagcranes.com.cn
Crane Component Distr
N.A.I.C.S.: 423830

Konecranes Demag Brasil Ltda. (3)
Rodovia Raposo Tavares km 31 Jardim Dinorah, Caixa Postal 806 0, Cotia, Sao Paulo, 06703-030, Brazil
Tel.: (55) 1121457920
Web Site: http://www.demagcranes.com.br
Cranes & Components Mfr
N.A.I.C.S.: 333923

Konecranes and Demag (Pty) Ltd. (3)
60 Atlas Road, Boksburg, 1460, South Africa
Tel.: (27) 11 898 3500
Web Site: https://www.demagcranes.com
Industrial Cranes Mfr
N.A.I.C.S.: 333120

Konecranes and Demag AG (3)
Bahnhofstrasse 3, Dietlikon, 8305, Switzerland
Tel.: (41) 44 835 1111
Web Site: http://www.demagcranes.ch
Industrial Cranes Mfr
N.A.I.C.S.: 333120

Konecranes and Demag Private Limited (3)
National Realty Pvt Ltd Level 3 Survey no 75/2/3, Baner, Pune, 411045, Maharashtra, India
Tel.: (91) 20 67191509
Web Site: http://www.demagcranes.com
Crane Component Distr
N.A.I.C.S.: 423830

Konecranes and Demag s.r.o. (3)
Bienerova 1536, Slany, 274 81, Czech Republic
Tel.: (420) 312514111
Web Site: http://www.demagcranes.cz
Crane Mfr
N.A.I.C.S.: 333923

Konecranes and Demag, Lda. (3)
Avenida dos Moinhos 16A Alfragide, Rua Industrial de Urtigueira 43-55, Amadora, 2610-120, Lisbon, Portugal
Tel.: (351) 214362913
Web Site: http://www.demagcranes.pt
Crane Mfr
N.A.I.C.S.: 333923

Subsidiary (Domestic):

Kranservice Rheinberg Gmbh (3)
Vinckeweg 15, 47119, Duisburg, Germany
Tel.: (49) 203860540
Web Site: http://www.ksr-kran.de

Industrial Cranes Mfr
N.A.I.C.S.: 333923

Subsidiary (Non-US):

Konecranes Port Services (Benelux) (2)
Vosseschijnstraat 98, Kaai 198, Antwerp, 2030, Belgium
Tel.: (32) 35464500
Port Services
N.A.I.C.S.: 488310

Port Equipment Southern Africa (Pty) Ltd. (2)
18 Monaco Place, Westmead, Durban, 3610, South Africa
Tel.: (27) 21 9053020
Port Services
N.A.I.C.S.: 488310

UAB Konecranes (1)
Birutes g 9, 91223, Klaipeda, Lithuania
Tel.: (370) 4 626 7004
Web Site: https://www.konecranes.com
Sales Range: $25-49.9 Million
Emp.: 6
Mfr of Cranes & Hoists
N.A.I.C.S.: 333120
Jonas Paulikas *(Mng Dir)*

Verlinde S.A. (1)
2 Boulevard De L Industrie, BP 20059, 28509, Vernouillet, France
Tel.: (33) 237389595
Web Site: http://www.verlinde.com
Lifting Equipment Mfr & Distr
N.A.I.C.S.: 333998

WMI Konecranes India Ltd. (1)
Village Road Bhandup West, Mumbai, 400 078, India
Tel.: (91) 22 25661661
Web Site: http://www.wmicranes.com
Material Handling Equipment Mfr
N.A.I.C.S.: 333248
J. Nandi *(Exec Dir)*

ZAO Konecranes (1)
Lermontovsky Str 44, 198103, Saint Petersburg, Russia
Tel.: (7) 812 327 0288
Web Site: http://www.konecranes.ru
Mfr of Cranes & Hoists
N.A.I.C.S.: 333120

KONEKT LIMITED
Level 3 338 Pitt St, Sydney, 2000, NSW, Australia
Tel.: (61) 29307 4000   AU
Web Site: http://www.konekt.com.au
Rev.: $68,615,998
Assets: $57,842,114
Liabilities: $34,542,926
Net Worth: $23,299,187
Earnings: ($132,683)
Emp.: 800
Fiscal Year-end: 06/30/18
Organizational Health & Risk Management Solutions
N.A.I.C.S.: 561499
Damian Banks *(CEO & Mng Dir)*

Subsidiaries:

Konekt Australia Pty Ltd. (1)
Level 3 11-13 Lucknow Place, West Perth, 6005, WA, Australia
Tel.: (61) 892197222
Web Site: http://www.konekt.com.au
Sales Range: $50-74.9 Million
Emp.: 25
Health Insurance Services
N.A.I.C.S.: 524130
Juleen Shields *(Gen Mgr)*

Konekt Employment Pty Ltd (1)
Level 3 338 Pitt Street, Sydney, 2000, NSW, Australia
Tel.: (61) 296415000
Web Site: http://www.konektemployment.com.au
Human Resource Consulting Services
N.A.I.C.S.: 541612
Anthony Steel *(CEO)*

Konekt Workplace Health Solutions Pty Ltd. (1)
Level 12 234 Sussex St, Sydney, 2001, NSW, Australia
Tel.: (61) 296505111
Web Site: http://www.konekt.com.au
Sales Range: $50-74.9 Million
Emp.: 18
Health Insurance Services
N.A.I.C.S.: 524130

KONFOONG MATERIALS INTERNATIONAL CO., LTD.
198 Anshan Road Mingbang science and Technology Industrial Park, Yuyao, Zhejiang, China
Tel.: (86) 57458127888
Web Site: https://www.kfmic.com
Year Founded: 2005
300666—(CHIN)
Rev.: $366,436,571
Assets: $883,361,494
Liabilities: $301,678,023
Net Worth: $581,683,471
Earnings: $35,983,597
Fiscal Year-end: 12/31/23
Electronic Material Mfr & Distr
N.A.I.C.S.: 334413
Yao Lijun *(Chm & CTO)*

KONFRUT GIDA SANAYI VE TICARET AS
Cevizli Mahallesi Zuhal Caddesi Ritim, AVM A3 Blok Apt No 46C/182 Maltepe, Istanbul, Türkiye
Tel.: (90) 2165456868
Web Site: https://www.konfrut.com.tr
KNFRT—(IST)
Rev.: $145,646,496
Assets: $89,419,485
Liabilities: $51,763,609
Net Worth: $37,655,876
Earnings: $5,254,943
Fiscal Year-end: 12/31/23
Fruit & Vegetable Beverage Mfr
N.A.I.C.S.: 311411
Axel Gillner *(Chm)*

KONG SUN HOLDINGS LIMITED
Unit 803-4 8 F Everbright Centre 108 Gloucester Road, Wanchai, China (Hong Kong)
Tel.: (852) 31888851
Web Site: http://www.kongsun-hldgs.com
0295—(HKG)
Rev.: $78,024,071
Assets: $842,921,446
Liabilities: $360,771,559
Net Worth: $482,149,886
Earnings: $40,760,788
Emp.: 769
Fiscal Year-end: 12/31/22
Property Investment Services
N.A.I.C.S.: 525990
Shaoyuan Wang *(CFO)*

KONGSBERG AUTOMOTIVE ASA
Dyrmyrgata 48, 3611, Kongsberg, Norway
Tel.: (47) 32770500   NO
Web Site:
  https://www.kongsbergauto.com
Year Founded: 1987
0HW0—(LSE)
Rev.: $1,190,533,032
Assets: $1,102,959,520
Liabilities: $801,426,600
Net Worth: $301,532,920
Earnings: ($144,932,320)
Emp.: 11,234
Fiscal Year-end: 12/31/20
Holding Company; Automotive Seating, Control Systems, Fluid Assemblies & Driver Interface Products Mfr & Whslr
N.A.I.C.S.: 551112

KONGSBERG AUTOMOTIVE ASA

INTERNATIONAL PUBLIC

Kongsberg Automotive ASA—(Continued)

Henning E. Jensen *(Pres & CEO)*

Subsidiaries:

Kongsberg Actuation Systems BV (1)
Noord Esmarkerrondweg 419, Enschede, 7533 BL, Netherlands
Tel.: (31) 534861234
Web Site: http://www.kongsbergautomotive.com
Emp.: 12
Automotive Parts Mfr & Distr
N.A.I.C.S.: 336390
Henning Jenssen *(CEO)*

Kongsberg Actuation Systems GmbH (1)
Hoseler Str 40, Heiligenhaus, 42579, Germany
Tel.: (49) 20569130
Sales Range: $50-74.9 Million
Emp.: 70
Automobile Parts Distr
N.A.I.C.S.: 423120
Raimund Langer *(Mng Dir)*

Kongsberg Actuation Systems Ltd (1)
Foxbridge Way, Normanton, WF6 1TN, United Kingdom
Tel.: (44) 192 422 8000
Web Site: https://www.kongsbergautomotive.com
Sales Range: $50-74.9 Million
Emp.: 14
Automobile Parts Mfr
N.A.I.C.S.: 336390

Kongsberg Actuation Systems SL (1)
Avda Tastuena s/n Poligono Ind Valdemuel, Epila, 50290, Zaragoza, Spain
Tel.: (34) 976603265
Fluid Transfer System Mfr
N.A.I.C.S.: 333996

Kongsberg Automotive (1)
Pantheon 2, 7521 PR, Enschede, Netherlands
Tel.: (31) 534861234
Web Site: http://www.kongsbergautomotive.com
Sales Range: $25-49.9 Million
Nylon Hose & Tubing Products for Automobiles
N.A.I.C.S.: 332912

Kongsberg Automotive (India) Private Ltd. (1)
Building No 2 Gat No 312/2, Nanekarwadi Chakan Tal Khed Dist, Pune, 410 501, India
Tel.: (91) 2135667802
Automotive Air Brake Coupling Mfr
N.A.I.C.S.: 336340

Kongsberg Automotive (Shanghai) Co., Ltd. (1)
No 30-32 Xikun Rd, Xinqu, 214028, Wuxi, China
Tel.: (86) 51085285430
Automotive Parts Mfr & Distr
N.A.I.C.S.: 336390

Kongsberg Automotive (Wuxi) Ltd. (1)
No 30 32 Xikun Road, Wuxi Singapore Ind Park, Wuxi, 214028, Jiangsu, China
Tel.: (86) 51085282165
Automotive Components Mfr
N.A.I.C.S.: 336310

Kongsberg Automotive AB (1)
Fabriksgatan 3-4, Box 504, 565 28, Mullsjo, Sweden
Tel.: (46) 3 923 8000
Web Site: https://www.kongsbergautomotive.com
Sales Range: $200-249.9 Million
Emp.: 540
Automotive Components Mfr & Distr
N.A.I.C.S.: 336310

Kongsberg Automotive AS (1)
Dyrmyrgata 48, Box 62, 3611, Kongsberg, Norway (100%)
Tel.: (47) 3 277 0500
Web Site: https://www.kongsbergautomotive.com
Sales Range: $25-49.9 Million
Emp.: 90
Automotive Seating, Control Systems, Fluid Assemblies & Driver Interface Products Mfr & Whslr
N.A.I.C.S.: 336390

Kongsberg Automotive Driveline System India Ltd. (1)
48KM Milestone Delhi-Mathura Road Sector-10, Prithla, Palwal, 121 102, Haryana, India
Tel.: (91) 1275256600
Automotive Gear Shifter Mfr
N.A.I.C.S.: 336350

Kongsberg Automotive GmbH (1)
Heinrich Rockstroh Strasse 10, Marktredwitz, DE-95615, Germany
Tel.: (49) 9231952890
Sales Range: $25-49.9 Million
Emp.: 24
Automotive Components Mfr
N.A.I.C.S.: 336310

Kongsberg Automotive Inc. (1)
27275 Haggerty Rd Ste 610, Novi, MI 48377-3635
Tel.: (248) 468-1300
Web Site: http://www.kongsbergautomotive.com
Emp.: 100
Automotive Components Mfr
N.A.I.C.S.: 336310

Subsidiary (Domestic):

Kongsberg Actuation Systems II Inc (2)
1 Firestone Dr, Suffield, CT 06078-2611
Tel.: (860) 668-1285
Rubber & Plastics Hoses Mfr
N.A.I.C.S.: 326220

Plant (Domestic):

Kongsberg Automotive Inc. - Milan (2)
3000 Kefauver Dr, Milan, TN 38358-3473
Tel.: (731) 686-0805
Sales Range: $25-49.9 Million
Automotive Components Mfr
N.A.I.C.S.: 336310

Kongsberg Automotive Inc. - Suffield (2)
1 Firestone Dr, Suffield, CT 06078-2611
Tel.: (860) 668-1285
Web Site: https://www.kongsbergautomotive.com
Sales Range: $25-49.9 Million
Emp.: 100
Teflon Hose Fittings & Assemblies
N.A.I.C.S.: 326220

Kongsberg Automotive Inc. - Van Wert (2)
1265 Industrial Ave, Van Wert, OH 45891-2432
Tel.: (419) 238-0070
Sales Range: $200-249.9 Million
Mechanical Flexible Cable Control Systems

Kongsberg Automotive Inc. - Willis (2)
300 S Cochran, Willis, TX 77378
Tel.: (936) 856-2971
Sales Range: $50-74.9 Million
Automotive Door, Window, Seating & Release Systems Mfr
N.A.I.C.S.: 336390

Kongsberg Automotive Japan KK (1)
28F Taiyo Life bldg 2-16-2, Konan Minato-ku, Tokyo, 108-0075, Japan
Tel.: (81) 345906626
Automotive Gear Shifter Mfr
N.A.I.C.S.: 336350

Kongsberg Automotive Limited (1)
Foxbridge Way, Normanton, WF6 1TN, West Yorkshire, United Kingdom
Tel.: (44) 192 422 8000
Web Site: http://www.kongsbergautomotive.co.uk
Emp.: 204
Automotive Components Mfr
N.A.I.C.S.: 336310

Subsidiary (Domestic):

Kongsberg Automotive Ltd. - Normanton (2)
Foxbridge Way, Normanton, WF6 1TN, West Yorkshire, United Kingdom
Tel.: (44) 192 422 8000
Web Site: https://www.kongsbergautomotive.com
Emp.: 204
Hose & Hose Assemblies
N.A.I.C.S.: 332912

Kongsberg Automotive Ltd. (1)
160 Eogok-ro, Yangsan, 50591, Gyeongsangnam, Korea (South)
Web Site: https://www.kongsbergautomotive.com
Sales Range: $25-49.9 Million
Automotive Components Mfr
N.A.I.C.S.: 336330

Kongsberg Automotive Ltda. (1)
Av Arquimedes nr 1021 Jd Guanabara, Jundiai, Sao Paulo, 12211-840, Brazil
Tel.: (55) 113 378 2600
Web Site: https://www.kongsbergautomotive.com
Automotive Components Mfr
N.A.I.C.S.: 336310

Kongsberg Automotive SARL (1)
2 Rue Du Centre, 93160, Noisy-le-Grand, France
Tel.: (33) 155858160
Sales Range: $50-74.9 Million
Emp.: 8
Automotive Parts & Accessories Distr
N.A.I.C.S.: 423120
Paul Juerss *(Gen Mgr)*

Kongsberg Automotive SRL de CV (1)
Autopista Puente a Pharr 1500 Parque Industrial Reynosa, Apartado Postal 935, Reynosa, 78500, Mexico
Tel.: (52) 8999581100
Automotive Components Mfr
N.A.I.C.S.: 336310

Kongsberg Automotive Sp. z o.o. (1)
Ul 3 Maja 8, PL-05800, Pruskow, Poland
Tel.: (48) 227383500
Emp.: 100
Automotive Components Mfr
N.A.I.C.S.: 336310

Kongsberg Automotive s.r.o (1)
Hlavna 48, Vrable, 95201, Slovakia
Tel.: (421) 377911542
Emp.: 1,000
Automotive Parts Mfr & Distr
N.A.I.C.S.: 336390
Kazimierz Ponganis *(Mgr-Expedition)*

Kongsberg Automotive, Kft (1)
Bajcsy-Zs u 201/D, Somogy, 8600, Siofok, Hungary
Tel.: (36) 84506595
Web Site: http://www.kongsbergautomotive.com
Sales Range: $75-99.9 Million
Emp.: 350
Automotive Motion Control System Mfr
N.A.I.C.S.: 811114

Kongsberg Driveline Systems GmbH (1)
Am Burgberg 7, Dassel, 37586, Germany
Tel.: (49) 55642010
Automotive Parts & Accessories Distr
N.A.I.C.S.: 423120

Kongsberg Driveline Systems SAS (1)
650 Avenue de la Republique, 74300, Cluses, France
Tel.: (33) 450983011
Automotive Gear Shifter Mfr
N.A.I.C.S.: 336350

Kongsberg Inc (1)
90 28e Rue, Grand-Mere, G9T 5Z8, QC, Canada
Tel.: (819) 533-3201
Sales Range: $100-124.9 Million
Emp.: 30
Electronic Components Mfr
N.A.I.C.S.: 334419
Rob Cowans *(Gen Mgr)*

Kongsberg Interior Systems Kft (1)
Bahjcsy-Zsilinszky Utca 201/D, Siofok, 8600, Hungary
Tel.: (36) 84506595
Sales Range: $100-124.9 Million
Emp.: 400
Automobile Product Distr
N.A.I.C.S.: 441330
Balazs Kallai *(Gen Mgr)*

Kongsberg Interior Systems S. de RL de CV (1)
Poniente 2 S/N, Matamoros, 87348, Mexico
Tel.: (52) 8688108969
Sales Range: $400-449.9 Million
Emp.: 1,300
Automotive Wire & Cable Mfr
N.A.I.C.S.: 335929

Kongsberg Power Products Systems AB (1)
Hestravagen 1, Ljungsarp, SE-514 55, Tranemo, Sweden
Tel.: (46) 321533350
Motor Vehicle Parts Mfr & Distr
N.A.I.C.S.: 336390

Kongsberg Power Products Systems Srl (1)
Via Dante Alighieri 47, Selvazzano Dentro, 35030, Italy
Tel.: (39) 0498731911
Sales Range: $25-49.9 Million
Emp.: 4
Electrical Equipment Mfr & Distr
N.A.I.C.S.: 335999

Kongsberg Raufoss Distribution SAS (1)
54 Route Industrielle de la Hardt, 67120, Molsheim, France
Tel.: (33) 38 847 8747
Web Site: https://www.kongsbergautomotive.com
Emp.: 15
Automotive Components Mfr & Distr
N.A.I.C.S.: 441330

Kongsberg SRL (1)
Via Dante 47, Selvazzano Dentro, Selvazzano Dentro, 35030, Italy
Tel.: (39) 0498731911
Sales Range: $25-49.9 Million
Emp.: 25
Automobile Cable Mfr
N.A.I.C.S.: 336390
Paolo Gottardo *(Gen Mgr)*

Shanghai Kongsberg Automotive Dong Feng Morse Co., Ltd. (1)
1288 Kang Qiao East Road, Shanghai, 201319, China
Tel.: (86) 2158134400
Sales Range: $50-74.9 Million
Emp.: 20
Automotive Parts Mfr & Distr
N.A.I.C.S.: 336390

Shanghai Lone Star Cable Co., Ltd. (1)
2nd Building 777 Yuandong Rd, Nanqiao Town Fengxian District, Shanghai, 201401, China
Tel.: (86) 2167105400
Web Site: http://www.lonestar.com.cn
Automotive Electric Cable Mfr
N.A.I.C.S.: 336320

KONGSBERG DEVOTEK AS

Dyrmyrgate 11, PO Box 384, 3604, Kongsberg, Norway
Tel.: (47) 90770400
Web Site: http://www.semcon.com
Sales Range: $25-49.9 Million
Emp.: 100
Engineeering Services
N.A.I.C.S.: 541330
Per Kleven *(Mng Dir)*

KONGSBERG ESCO AS

Gamle Gormsrudvej 40, PO Box 85, Kongsberg, N-3602, Norway
Tel.: (47) 92645700 NO
Web Site: http://www.esco.no

AND PRIVATE COMPANIES — KONGSBERG GRUPPEN ASA

Year Founded: 1877
Sales Range: Less than $1 Million
Emp.: 90
Mfr of Valves, Hoses & Pipe Fittings for Water Distribution
N.A.I.C.S.: 332919
Jan-Fredrik Ormaasen *(Pres)*

Subsidiaries:

KONGSBERG ESCO AB (1)
Industrigatan 2, 595 41, Mjolby, Sweden
Tel.: (46) 142 828 80
Web Site: http://www.escoab.se
Valve & Pipe Fitting Mfr
N.A.I.C.S.: 332911

Kongsberg Esco mpv AS (1)
Gamle Gomsrudv 40, 3616, Kongsberg, Norway
Tel.: (47) 926 45 700
Web Site: http://www.escompv.com
Industrial Valve Mfr
N.A.I.C.S.: 332911
Per Risvik Syversen *(Pres)*

KONGSBERG GRUPPEN ASA
Kirkegardsveien 45, NO-3616, Kongsberg, Norway
Tel.: (47) 32288200
Web Site: https://www.kongsberg.com
Year Founded: 1814
KOG—(OSL)
Rev.: $3,992,863,121
Assets: $5,232,000,419
Liabilities: $3,613,404,972
Net Worth: $1,618,595,447
Earnings: $365,203,892
Emp.: 13,086
Fiscal Year-end: 12/31/23
Aerospace & Marine Navigation, Positioning, Guidance & Automation System Developer & Mfr
N.A.I.C.S.: 334511
Even Aas *(Exec VP-Pub Affairs, Comm & Sustainability)*

Subsidiaries:

Coach Solutions ApS (1)
Ostbanegade 123 Block 3 1 floor, 2100, Copenhagen, Denmark
Tel.: (45) 33122122
Web Site: https://www.coachsolutions.com
Maritime Transportation Services
N.A.I.C.S.: 483111

GeoAcoustics Asia Pacific Pte Ltd. (1)
30 Loyang Way 07 12, Singapore, 508769, Singapore
Tel.: (65) 65463687
Sales Range: $50-74.9 Million
Emp.: 3
Marine Equipment Distr
N.A.I.C.S.: 423860

GeoAcoustics Ltd (1)
Shuttleworth Close, Gapton Hall Industrial Estate, Great Yarmouth, NR31 0NQ, Norfolk, United Kingdom
Tel.: (44) 1493600666
Emp.: 35
Sonar Seabed Survey Equipment Mfr
N.A.I.C.S.: 334519
Richard Dowdeswell *(Pres)*

GeoAcoustics Ltd. (1)
Shuttleworth Close, Great Yarmouth, NR31 0NQ, United Kingdom
Tel.: (44) 1493 600 666
Sales Range: $25-49.9 Million
Emp.: 35
Sonar Seabed Survey Equipment Mfr
N.A.I.C.S.: 334519

Interconsult Bulgaria Ltd. (1)
7 Indzhe Voivoda Str, 1309, Sofia, Bulgaria
Tel.: (359) 29201120
Web Site: http://www.icb.bg
Software Development & Consultancy Services
N.A.I.C.S.: 541511

KM Mexico S.A. de CV (1)
Av La Marigalante 311-31, Boca Del Rio, 94298, Veracruz, Mexico
Tel.: (52) 229 921 7708
Web Site: http://www.kongsberg.com
Sales Range: $25-49.9 Million
Marine Equipment Distr
N.A.I.C.S.: 327910

KM Tech LLC (1)
Ul Rizhskaya Building 1 Office 407, 195196, Saint Petersburg, Russia
Tel.: (7) 812 495 56 06
Sales Range: $25-49.9 Million
Emp.: 25
Marine Equipment Distr
N.A.I.C.S.: 423860
Andrey Kozhevnikov *(Gen Dir)*

Kongsberg Aviation Maintenance Services AS (1)
Fetveien 80-84, 2007, Kjeller, Norway
Tel.: (47) 91210000
Web Site: https://www.kongsbergams.com
Emp.: 470
Aircraft Mfr
N.A.I.C.S.: 336411

Kongsberg Defence & Aerospace AS (1)
Kirkegardsveien 45, PO Box 1003, NO-3601, Kongsberg, Norway **(100%)**
Tel.: (47) 32288200
Emp.: 4,500
Supplier of Defense & Aerospace-related Systems
N.A.I.C.S.: 334511

Subsidiary (Non-US):

Kongsberg Defence Oy (2)
Tolkkimaentie 8A, FI-13130, Hameenlinna, Finland
Tel.: (358) 401739272
Aircraft Equipment Distr
N.A.I.C.S.: 423860

Subsidiary (Domestic):

Kongsberg Norcontrol IT AS (2)
Bromsveien 17, PO Box 1024, Horten, 3183, Norway
Tel.: (47) 33 08 48 00
Web Site: http://www.kongsberg.com
Sales Range: $25-49.9 Million
Emp.: 60
Maritime Surveillance Software Development Services
N.A.I.C.S.: 541511

Subsidiary (Non-US):

Kongsberg Norcontrol IT Pty. Ltd. (3)
11 Churchill Road, Gillitts, Durban, 3610, South Africa
Tel.: (27) 317678150
Sales Range: $50-74.9 Million
Emp.: 2
Aircraft Equipment Distr
N.A.I.C.S.: 423860

Kongsberg Norcontrol Limited (3)
310 Bristol Business Park The Crescent, Stoke Gifford, Bristol, BS16 1EJ, United Kingdom
Tel.: (44) 1454774466
Web Site: http://www.kongsberg.com
Sales Range: $25-49.9 Million
Emp.: 5
Marine Surveillance Software Development Services
N.A.I.C.S.: 541511

Kongsberg Norcontrol Pte. Ltd (3)
20 Harbour Drive 06-01A, Singapore, 117612, Singapore
Tel.: (65) 67731464
Web Site: http://www.kongsberg.com
Sales Range: $25-49.9 Million
Emp.: 1
Marine Surveillance Software Development Services
N.A.I.C.S.: 541511

Kongsberg Norcontrol Surveillance Pvt. Ltd. (3)
805 Iscon elegance S G Highway Near Shapath IV, Prahladnagar, Ahmedabad, 380015, Gujarat, India
Tel.: (91) 9099916146
Sales Range: $25-49.9 Million
Emp.: 25
Marine Surveillance Services
N.A.I.C.S.: 561621
Cyrus Anklesaria *(Gen Mgr)*

Marine Data Solutions (Pty.) Ltd. (3)
Cnr Borcherds Quarry & Michigan Str Unit 7 Airport Business Park, PO Box 51680, Airport Industria Waterfront, Cape Town, 7490, South Africa
Tel.: (27) 213868517
Web Site: http://www.marinedata.co.za
Sales Range: $25-49.9 Million
Emp.: 15
Maritime Surveillance Software Development Services
N.A.I.C.S.: 541511
David H. Lewis *(Mng Dir-Acting)*

Subsidiary (US):

Kongsberg Protech Systems USA Corporation (2)
210 Industrial Park Rd, Johnstown, PA 15904-1933
Tel.: (814) 269-5700
Web Site: http://www.kongsberg.com
Communications, Surveillance & Weapons Control System Mfr
N.A.I.C.S.: 334511

Subsidiary (Domestic):

Kongsberg Spacetec AS (2)
Prestvannveien 38, PO Box 6244, Tromso, 9292, Norway
Tel.: (47) 77 66 08 00
Web Site: http://www.spacetec.no
Sales Range: $25-49.9 Million
Satellite Ground Station & System Supplier
N.A.I.C.S.: 423850
Hege K. Ingebrigtsen *(Mgr-Dev, Fin & Admin)*

Kongsberg Drilling Managment Solutions AS (1)
Sandslimarka 63, 5254, Sandsli, Norway
Tel.: (47) 55 10 49 90
Web Site: http://www.kdms.no
Sales Range: $25-49.9 Million
Emp.: 16
Oil & Gas Industry Software Development Services
N.A.I.C.S.: 541511

Kongsberg Evotec AS (1)
Storeholvegen 9, 6080, Ulsteinvik, Norway
Tel.: (47) 94 84 10 00
Web Site: http://www.kongsberg.com
Sales Range: $50-74.9 Million
Emp.: 7
Marine Technology Handling System Distr
N.A.I.C.S.: 423860

Kongsberg GeoAcoustics Pte. Ltd. (1)
81 Toh Guan Rd East 04-01 02 Secom Centre, Singapore, 608606, Singapore
Tel.: (65) 64116400
Web Site: http://www.km.kongsberg.com
Marine Equipment Distr
N.A.I.C.S.: 423860

Kongsberg Gruppen ASA Business Development (1)
Kirkegardsveien 45, 3616, Kongsberg, Norway **(100%)**
Tel.: (47) 32288200
Web Site: http://www.kongsberg.com
Sales Range: $25-49.9 Million
Emp.: 50
N.A.I.C.S.: 334511

Kongsberg Integrated Tactical Systems Inc. (1)
10 Pinehurst Dr, Bellport, NY 11713-1573
Tel.: (631) 775-1500
Web Site: https://www.kongsberg.com
Marine Equipments Supplier
N.A.I.C.S.: 423830

Kongsberg Maritime AS (1)
Kirkegardsveien 45, PO Box 483, 3616, Kongsberg, Norway **(100%)**
Tel.: (47) 81573700
Sales Range: $800-899.9 Million
Marine Surveying, Positioning & Navigation System Developer & Mfr
N.A.I.C.S.: 334511

Subsidiary (Non-US):

Kongsberg Maritime Canada Ltd. (2)
Suite 210 238 Brownlow Avenue, Dartmouth, B3B 1Y2, NS, Canada
Tel.: (902) 468-2268
Sales Range: $25-49.9 Million
Emp.: 15
Marine Equipments Whslr
N.A.I.C.S.: 423830

Kongsberg Maritime China (Jiangsu) Ltd. (2)
No 711 Changjiang Road, Zhenjiang, 212000, China
Tel.: (86) 51181983333
Marine Equipment Distr
N.A.I.C.S.: 423860
Havard Johnsen *(Gen Mgr)*

Kongsberg Maritime China Ltd. (2)
20/F No 18 Lane 666 Haiyang West Road, Pudong New District, Shanghai, 201206, China
Tel.: (86) 2131279888
Sales Range: $25-49.9 Million
Marine Positioning, Automation & Navigation System Developer, Mfr & Whslr
N.A.I.C.S.: 334511

Subsidiary (Domestic):

Kongsberg Maritime Engineering AS (2)
Sondre Kullerod 1, 3241, Sandefjord, Norway
Tel.: (47) 33422924
Web Site: http://www.kongsberg.com
Electro Instrumentation & Telecommunication Engineering Services
N.A.I.C.S.: 541330

Subsidiary (Non-US):

Kongsberg Maritime GmbH (2)
Hellgrundweg 109, 22525, Hamburg, Germany
Tel.: (49) 405473460
Web Site: http://www.kongsberg.com
Marine Automation, Positioning & Navigation System Developer, Mfr & Whslr
N.A.I.C.S.: 334511

Kongsberg Maritime Hellas SA (2)
7 Gravias Street, 18545, Piraeus, Greece
Tel.: (30) 210 4117200
Sales Range: $25-49.9 Million
Emp.: 15
Underwater Equipment Distr
N.A.I.C.S.: 423830
Leif Kristian Weum *(Mng Dir)*

Kongsberg Maritime Hoi Tung Holding Ltd. (2)
No 6 Building 401 Chuanqiao Road, 201206, Shanghai, China
Tel.: (86) 21 31279888
Web Site: http://www.kongsberg.com
Sales Range: $200-249.9 Million
Emp.: 30
Investment Management Service
N.A.I.C.S.: 523999

Kongsberg Maritime Holland BV (2)
Edisonweg 10, 3208 KB, Spijkenisse, Netherlands
Tel.: (31) 181623611
Web Site: http://www.kongsberg.com
Sales Range: $25-49.9 Million
Marine Positioning, Automation & Navigation System Developer, Mfr & Whslr
N.A.I.C.S.: 334511

Subsidiary (US):

Kongsberg Maritime Inc. (2)
10777 Westheimer Rd Ste 1200, Houston, TX 77042
Tel.: (713) 329-5580
Sales Range: $25-49.9 Million
Marine Automation System Mfr & Distr
N.A.I.C.S.: 336999

Subsidiary (Domestic):

Kongsberg Discovery US, LLC (3)
19210 33rd Ave W Ste A, Lynnwood, WA 98036-4707
Tel.: (425) 712-1107
Marine Equipment & Machinery Distr

KONGSBERG GRUPPEN ASA   INTERNATIONAL PUBLIC

Kongsberg Gruppen ASA—(Continued)
N.A.I.C.S.: 423830

Kongsberg Maritime Simulation Inc. (3)
115B Leonard Dr, Groton, CT 06340
Tel.: (860) 405-2300
Maritime & Offshore Simulators Mfr
N.A.I.C.S.: 333310

Subsidiary (Non-US):

Kongsberg Maritime India Pvt. Ltd. (2)
EI-145 Ttc Industrial Area Midc Mahape, Navi Mumbai, 400 710, India
Tel.: (91) 2268197200
Web Site: http://www.kongsberg.com
Sales Range: $25-49.9 Million
Marine Equipment Distr
N.A.I.C.S.: 423860
T. N. Sreenivasan *(Gen Mgr-Technical)*

Kongsberg Maritime Korea Ltd. (2)
9-7 Sandan 3-ro Jeonggwan-Eup, Gijang-gun, Busan, 46027, Korea (South)
Tel.: (82) 517498600
Sales Range: $25-49.9 Million
Marine Positioning, Automation & Navigation System Developer, Mfr & Whslr
N.A.I.C.S.: 334511

Kongsberg Maritime Ltd. (2)
Ground Floor Building 1000 Lakeside North Harbour Western Road, Waterlooville, Portsmouth, PO6 3EZ, Hampshire, United Kingdom
Tel.: (44) 2392247800
Web Site: https://www.km.kongsberg.com
Underwater Camera & Imaging Equipment Mfr
N.A.I.C.S.: 334220

Kongsberg Maritime Middle East DMCCO (2)
Plot no SR-15 Community 321 -Madinat Dubai Al Melaheyah, PO Box 361023, Dubai Maritime City, Dubai, United Arab Emirates
Tel.: (971) 48753000
Emp.: 50
Marine Equipment Whslr
N.A.I.C.S.: 423860
Halvard Sagdahl *(Gen Mgr)*

Kongsberg Maritime Poland Sp. z.o.o. (2)
Ulziemowita 10d, 71-717, Szczecin, Poland
Tel.: (48) 91 459 9300
Web Site: http://www.kongsberg.com
Sales Range: $50-74.9 Million
Project Engineering & IT Solutions for the Global Marine Industry
N.A.I.C.S.: 541330
Radoslaw Sochanowski *(Mng Dir)*

Kongsberg Maritime Pte. Ltd. (2)
81 Toh Guan Rd East, 04 01/02 Secom Centre, Singapore, 608606, Singapore
Tel.: (65) 64116400
Marine Positioning, Automation & Navigation System Developer, Mfr & Whslr
N.A.I.C.S.: 334511

Kongsberg Maritime Simulation Ltd. (2)
139 Water Street Suite 902, Saint John's, NF A1C 1B2, NL, Canada
Tel.: (709) 579-4859
Web Site: http://www.km.kongsberg.com
Sales Range: $50-74.9 Million
Emp.: 5
Maritime Offshore Simulator Whslr
N.A.I.C.S.: 423860

Kongsberg Maritime Srl, (2)
Via Cornelia 498 Block 2-first Floor, 00166, Rome, Italy
Tel.: (39) 0661522476
Web Site: http://www.kongsberg.com
Sales Range: $50-74.9 Million
Marine Equipment Distr
N.A.I.C.S.: 423860

Kongsberg Maritime do Brasil S.A. (2)
Av Rio Branco 173 16 Andar Centro, 20040 007, Rio de Janeiro, Brazil
Tel.: (55) 21 2240 9402

Sales Range: $50-74.9 Million
Emp.: 5
Underwater Equipments Whslr
N.A.I.C.S.: 423830
Eduardo Sanchec *(CEO)*

Subsidiary (Domestic):

SeaFlex AS (2)
Solbraveien 45, 1383, Asker, Norway
Tel.: (47) 66761666
Web Site: http://www.seaflex.com
Sales Range: $50-74.9 Million
Emp.: 30
Offshore Platform Riser & Piping System Developer & Mfr
N.A.I.C.S.: 213112

Subsidiary (US):

SeaFlex Riser Technology Inc. (3)
5373 W Sam Houston Pwy N Ste 200, Houston, TX 77041
Tel.: (713) 895-1840
Web Site: http://www.seaflex.com
Sales Range: $1-9.9 Million
Offshore Platform Riser & Piping System Developer & Mfr
N.A.I.C.S.: 213112

Subsidiary (Domestic):

Simrad A/S (2)
Strandpromenaden 50, PO Box 111, 3191, Horten, Norway
Tel.: (47) 81573700
Web Site: http://www.simrad.com
Sonar System & Fish Finder Equipment Developer & Mfr
N.A.I.C.S.: 334511
Olav Vitterso *(VP-Fishery)*

Subsidiary (US):

Simrad Fisheries (3)
19210 33rd Ave W, Lynnwood, WA 98036
Tel.: (425) 712-1136
Web Site: http://www.simrad.com
Fish Finding & Fishery Research Equipment Mfr
N.A.I.C.S.: 334511

Simrad North America Inc. (3)
Ste 101 1010 SE Everett Mall Way, Everett, WA 98208-2855 (100%)
Tel.: (425) 778-8821
Web Site: http://www.simrad.com
Sonar System & Fish Finder Equipment Developer & Mfr
N.A.I.C.S.: 334511

Simrad North America Inc. (3)
19210 33rd Ave W Ste A, Lynnwood, WA 98036-4749
Tel.: (425) 712-1136
Web Site: http://www.kongsberg.com
Electronic Equipment Whslr
N.A.I.C.S.: 423830

Subsidiary (Non-US):

Simrad Spain SL (3)
Poligono Partida Torres 38 Nava 8, 3570, Villajoyosa, Spain
Tel.: (34) 966 810 149
Sales Range: $25-49.9 Million
Emp.: 2
Electronic Components Distr
N.A.I.C.S.: 423690
Agustin Mayans *(Gen Mgr)*

Kongsberg Maritime CM Korea Ltd. (1)
197 Noksansaneopbuk-ro, Gangseo-gu, Busan, Korea (South)
Tel.: (82) 518314100
Marine Logistics Services
N.A.I.C.S.: 541614

Kongsberg Maritime Denmark A/S (1)
Langerak 16B, DK-9220, Aalborg, Denmark
Tel.: (45) 99303600
Maritime Transportation Services
N.A.I.C.S.: 483111

Kongsberg Maritime France S.A.R.L. (1)
23 Rue d'Anjou, 75008, Paris, France
Tel.: (33) 140889266
Marine Logistics Services

N.A.I.C.S.: 541614

Kongsberg Maritime Japan Co. Ltd. (1)
Harborland Dia Nissei Building 9F 1-7-4 Higashi, Kawasaki-cho Chuo-ku, Kobe, 650-0044, Hyogo, Japan
Tel.: (81) 789458332
Marine Logistics Services
N.A.I.C.S.: 541614

Kongsberg Maritime Mexico S.A.de C.V. (1)
Av La Marigalante 311-31, Boca Del Rio, 94298, Veracruz, Mexico
Tel.: (52) 2299217708
Maritime Transportation Services
N.A.I.C.S.: 483111

Kongsberg Maritime Namibia Pty. Ltd. (1)
Old Power Station 2nd Street East, Walvis Bay, Namibia
Tel.: (264) 64275440
Marine Logistics Services
N.A.I.C.S.: 541614

Kongsberg Maritime Netherlands B.V. (1)
Edisonweg 10, 3208 KB, Spijkenisse, Netherlands
Tel.: (31) 181623611
Maritime Transportation Services
N.A.I.C.S.: 483111

Kongsberg Maritime Sweden AB (1)
Batbyggarevagen 1, S-681 95, Kristinehamn, Sweden
Tel.: (46) 55084000
Maritime Transportation Services
N.A.I.C.S.: 483111

Kongsberg Maritime Turkey Denizcilik Sanayi Ve Ticaret Limited (1)
Cevizli Mah Tugay Yolu Cad No 69/A Pi-azza Ofis Kat 13 No 40, Maltepe, 34846, Istanbul, Turkiye
Tel.: (90) 2164469999
Maritime Transportation Services
N.A.I.C.S.: 483111

Kongsberg Mesotech Ltd. (1)
1598 Kebet Way, Port Coquitlam, V3C 5M5, BC, Canada
Tel.: (604) 464-8144
Web Site: http://www.kongsberg-mesotech.com
Sales Range: $25-49.9 Million
Emp.: 60
Underwater Acoustic Equipments Mfr
N.A.I.C.S.: 334511

Kongsberg Naeringseiendom AS (1)
Kirkegardsveien 45 No 3601, 1001, Kongsberg, Norway
Tel.: (47) 32288200
Real Estate Manangement Services
N.A.I.C.S.: 531390

Kongsberg Oil & Gas Technologies AS (1)
Hamangskogen 60, Sandvika, 1338, Norway
Tel.: (47) 67 80 48 00
Web Site: http://www.kongsberg.com
Sales Range: $25-49.9 Million
Emp.: 75
Oil & Gas Industry Software Development Services
N.A.I.C.S.: 541511

Kongsberg Oil & Gas Technologies Inc. (1)
11000 Richmond Ave Ste 400, Houston, TX 77042
Tel.: (713) 808-6800
Web Site: http://www.kongsberg.com
Sales Range: $25-49.9 Million
Emp.: 60
Software Development & Management Services
N.A.I.C.S.: 513210

Kongsberg Oil & Gas Technologies Ltd. (1)
11 The Briars Waterberry Drive, Waterlooville, PO7 7YH, Hants, United Kingdom
Tel.: (44) 2392 247 800
Web Site: http://www.kongsberg.com

Sales Range: $25-49.9 Million
Emp.: 25
Oil & Gas Field Software Development Services
N.A.I.C.S.: 541511

Kongsberg Oil & Gas Technologies PVT Ltd. (1)
4th Floor Plot No 29-32 36-37 Pudhari Bhavan Sector - 30a Vashi, Navi Mumbai, 400 705, India
Tel.: (91) 22 4153 2650
Web Site: http://www.kongsberg.com
Sales Range: $25-49.9 Million
Emp.: 20
Offshore Engineering Services
N.A.I.C.S.: 541330

Kongsberg Process Simulation PVT Ltd. (1)
6th Floor Plot No - 29-32 36-37 Pudhari Bhavan Sector - 30a Vashi, 400 705, Navi Mumbai, India
Tel.: (91) 22 4157 5200
Web Site: http://www.km.kongsberg.com
Marine Equipment Distr
N.A.I.C.S.: 423860

Kongsberg Protech Systems Australia Pty Ltd. (1)
Level 10 5 Queens Road, Melbourne, 3004, Australia
Tel.: (61) 3 9869 1100
Sales Range: $25-49.9 Million
Emp.: 3
Software Development Services
N.A.I.C.S.: 541511

Kongsberg Protech Systems USA Corporation Inc. (1)
1725 Duke St Ste 600, Alexandria, VA 22314
Tel.: (703) 838-8910
Web Site: http://www.kongsberg.com
Weapon Control System Distr
N.A.I.C.S.: 423990

Kongsberg Seatex AS (1)
Pirsenteret, 7462, Trondheim, Norway
Tel.: (47) 73 54 55 00
Sales Range: $25-49.9 Million
Emp.: 2
Precision Positioning & Motion Sensing System Mfr
N.A.I.C.S.: 334290
Gard Ueland *(Pres)*

Kongsberg Teknologipark AS (1)
Kirkegardsveien 45, 3616, Kongsberg, Norway
Tel.: (47) 32288250
Web Site: https://www.kongsberg-teknologipark.no
Emp.: 5,600
Property Management Services
N.A.I.C.S.: 531312

Konsberg Norspace AS (1)
Knudsrodveien 7, 3189, Horten, Norway
Tel.: (47) 3303 2700
Sales Range: $50-74.9 Million
Emp.: 10
Electronic Equipment Distr
N.A.I.C.S.: 423690

Lodic As (1)
Pirsenteret D4 Brattorkaia, PO Box 1248, Pirsenteret, 7462, Trondheim, Norway
Tel.: (47) 73 54 54 88
Web Site: http://www.lodic.no
Sales Range: $50-74.9 Million
Emp.: 7
Loading & Stability Calculations Software Development Services & Distr
N.A.I.C.S.: 423430

NanoAvionics US LLC (1)
5825 University Research Ct Ste 2100, Riverdale, MD 20737
Tel.: (240) 221-1236
Small Satellite Technology Services
N.A.I.C.S.: 517410

Rolls-Royce Commercial Marine Inc (1)
200 James Dr W, Saint Rose, LA 70087
Tel.: (504) 464-4561
Commercial Sales
N.A.I.C.S.: 441222

4256

KONGSKILDE INDUSTRIES A/S

Skaelskorvej 64, 4180, Soro, Denmark
Tel.: (45) 33683500 DK
Web Site: http://www.kongskilde-industries.com
Year Founded: 1952
Sales Range: $50-74.9 Million
Emp.: 300
Soil Preparation Grain Handling Systems Pneumatic Conveying Systems Heaters
N.A.I.C.S.: 115112
Allan H. Carlsen (CFO-Interim)

Subsidiaries:

Howard S.A. (1)
Apartado 246, Granollers, 08400, Barcelona, Spain (100%)
Tel.: (34) 938492622
Sales Range: $25-49.9 Million
Emp.: 50
Mfr & Sales of Agricultural Machinery
N.A.I.C.S.: 333111

Kongskilde Howard France S.A. (1)
12 Avenue Claude Guillemin, 45071, Orleans, Cedex 2, France (100%)
Tel.: (33) 238253333
Web Site: http://www.kongskilde.com
Sales Range: $25-49.9 Million
Emp.: 30
Mfr & Sales of Agricultural Machinery
N.A.I.C.S.: 333111

Kongskilde Iberica, S.A. (1)
Carretera Granollers Girona Km 1 5, 08500, Les Franqueses del Valles, Spain
Tel.: (34) 938617150
Agricultural Machinery & Equipment Distr
N.A.I.C.S.: 423820

Kongskilde Industries Inc. (1)
19500 N 1425 E Rd, Hudson, IL 61748
Tel.: (309) 820-1090
Agricultural Machinery Distr
N.A.I.C.S.: 423820
Hans Rasmussen (Mng Dir & Mgr-Sls)

Kongskilde Industrietechnik GmbH (1)
Burgstrasse 21, Bochum, D-44867, Germany (100%)
Tel.: (49) 232794830
Web Site: http://www.kongskilde.com
Sales Range: $25-49.9 Million
Emp.: 6
Mfr & Sales of Agricultural Machinery
N.A.I.C.S.: 333111
Klaus Jockisch (Mng Dir)

Kongskilde Polska Spolka z o.o. (1)
Ul Metalowa 15, 99-300, Kutno, Poland
Tel.: (48) 243559615
Agricultural Machinery & Equipment Distr
N.A.I.C.S.: 423820

Kongskilde RUS LLC, (1)
Mashinostroitelnaya str 8a, 302008, Oryol, Russia
Tel.: (7) 9092282128
Agricultural Machinery & Equipment Distr
N.A.I.C.S.: 423820
Alexander Yarushevichyus (Mng Dir)

KONGZHONG CORPORATION

35th Floor Tengda Plaza, No 168 Xizhimenwai Street, Beijing, 100044, China
Tel.: (86) 1088576000 Ky
Web Site: http://www.kongzhong.com
Sales Range: $150-199.9 Million
Emp.: 793
Wireless Interactive Entertainment Services
N.A.I.C.S.: 517112
Leilei Wang (Chm & CEO)

Subsidiaries:

Shanghai Dacheng Network Technology Co., Ltd. (1)
21/F Sun Building No 3553 Zhongshan North Road, Shanghai, 200063, China
Tel.: (86) 2160825088
Web Site: http://www.kongzhong.com
Sales Range: $25-49.9 Million
Emp.: 100
Online Game Development Services
N.A.I.C.S.: 541511
Kan Jiang (VP)

Xiamen Xinreli Scientific and Technology Co., Ltd. (1)
16 Haishan Rd Fl 9, Siming District, Xiamen, China
Tel.: (86) 592 5161157
Wireless Telecommunication Services
N.A.I.C.S.: 517810

KONIC GLORY CO., LTD.

Wonyoung Building 3rd-4th floor 155 Hakdong-ro, Gangnam-gu, Seoul, Korea (South)
Tel.: (82) 234797498
Web Site: https://www.kornicglory.co.kr
Year Founded: 2007
094860—(KRS)
Rev.: $28,142,952
Assets: $36,990,560
Liabilities: $7,187,740
Net Worth: $29,802,820
Earnings: ($1,859,954)
Emp.: 56
Fiscal Year-end: 12/31/22
Network Security System Design Services
N.A.I.C.S.: 541512
Myungjae Cho (CEO)

KONICA MINOLTA, INC.

JP Tower 2-7-2 Marunouchi, Chiyoda-ku, Tokyo, 100-7015, Japan
Tel.: (81) 362502111 JP
Web Site: https://kmbs.konicaminolta.us
Year Founded: 1873
KNCAF—(OTCIQ)
Rev.: $7,667,593,390
Assets: $9,175,023,720
Liabilities: $5,517,168,700
Net Worth: $3,657,855,020
Earnings: $29,883,810
Emp.: 40,015
Fiscal Year-end: 03/31/24
Photographic Equipment Mfr & Sales
N.A.I.C.S.: 333310
Shoei Yamana (Exec Officer, CEO, Pres & Exec Chm)

Subsidiaries:

Ambry Genetics Corp. (1)
15 Argonaut, Aliso Viejo, CA 92656 (60%)
Tel.: (949) 900-5500
Web Site: http://www.ambrygen.com
Genetics Testing Laboratory
N.A.I.C.S.: 541380
Aaron Elliott (CEO)

DocPoint Solutions, LLC (1)
11850 W Market Pl Ste P, Fulton, MD 20759
Tel.: (301) 490-7725
Web Site: https://www.docpointsolutions.com
Consulting Services
N.A.I.C.S.: 541611
Ryan Bortz (Acct Exec)

Dots Gesellschaft fur Softwareentwicklung mbh
Schlesische Strasse 27, 10997, Berlin, Germany
Tel.: (49) 3069579930
Web Site: http://www.dots.de
Software Development Services
N.A.I.C.S.: 541511

Ergo Asia Pty. Ltd. (1)
Level 4 503-505 Kent Street, Sydney, 2000, NSW, Australia
Tel.: (61) 282630333
Web Site: http://commerce-dev.ergoasia.com
Marketing Services
N.A.I.C.S.: 541613

Invicro LLC (1)
27 Drydock Ave 7th Fl W, Boston, MA 02210
Tel.: (617) 904-2100
Web Site: http://www.invicro.com
Software Development Services
N.A.I.C.S.: 541511
Jack Hoppin (Co-Founder)

Kinko's Japan Co., Ltd. (1)
27F Hamamatsucho Building 1-1-1, Shibaura Minato-ku, Tokyo, Japan
Tel.: (81) 120001966
Web Site: http://www.kinkos.co.jp
Printing & Photocopying Store Services
N.A.I.C.S.: 561439

Konica Minolta (CHINA) Investment Ltd. (1)
Rm A K 29F Cross Region Plaza No 899 Lingling Road, Shanghai, 200030, China
Tel.: (86) 21 5489 0202
Web Site: http://www.konicaminolta.com.cn
Lighting Equipment Mfr
N.A.I.C.S.: 335139

Konica Minolta Baltia UAB (1)
J Jasinskio g 16A jejimas is Gostauto gatves, 03163, Vilnius, Lithuania
Tel.: (370) 8 5 210 77 00
Web Site: http://www.konicaminolta.lt
Printing Equipment Distr
N.A.I.C.S.: 423420

Konica Minolta Bizcom Co., Ltd. (1)
1-5-4-10f Nihombashihoncho, Chuo-Ku, Tokyo, 103-0023, Japan
Tel.: (81) 352057840
Information Technology Consulting Services
N.A.I.C.S.: 541512

Konica Minolta Business Associates Co., Ltd. (1)
2970 Ishikawamachi, Hachioji, 192-8535, Tokyo, Japan
Tel.: (81) 426609160
Real Estate Manangement Services
N.A.I.C.S.: 531311

Konica Minolta Business Expert, Inc. (1)
2970 Ishikawamachi, Hachioji, 192-0032, Tokyo, Japan
Tel.: (81) 426609102
Business Management Services
N.A.I.C.S.: 561499

Konica Minolta Business Solutions (Belgium) N.V. (1)
Berkenlaan 8A-B, 1831, Diegem, Belgium
Tel.: (32) 27170811
Web Site: https://www.konicaminolta.be
Sales Range: $100-124.9 Million
Emp.: 260
Printing Machinery Mfr
N.A.I.C.S.: 334118
Xavier Biermez (Mng Dir)

Konica Minolta Business Solutions (Canada) Ltd. (1)
5875 Explorer Drive, Mississauga, L4W 0E1, ON, Canada (100%)
Tel.: (905) 890-6600
Web Site: https://www.konicaminolta.ca
Sales Range: $50-74.9 Million
Emp.: 150
Photographic & Office Equipment & Supplies
N.A.I.C.S.: 333310

Konica Minolta Business Solutions (China) Co., Ltd. (1)
18/F Jinzhong Plaza No 98 Huaihai M Rd, Luwan Dist, Shanghai, 200021, China
Tel.: (86) 2123210600
Business Support Services
N.A.I.C.S.: 561499

Konica Minolta Business Solutions (HK) Ltd. (1)
Room 208 2/F Eastern Centre 1065 Kings Road, Quarry Bay, China (Hong Kong) (100%)
Tel.: (852) 25658181
Web Site: http://www.konicaminolta.com.hk
Office & Photographic Equipment & Instruments
N.A.I.C.S.: 333310

Konica Minolta Business Solutions (M) Sdn. Bhd. (1)
Infinite Centre Lot 1 Jalan 13/6, 46200, Petaling Jaya, Selangor Darul Ehsan, Malaysia
Tel.: (60) 378012611
Web Site: http://www.konicaminolta.com.my
Sales Range: $75-99.9 Million
Emp.: 200
Photographic Equipment & Supplies Services
N.A.I.C.S.: 423410

Konica Minolta Business Solutions (S) Pte. Ltd. (1)
10 Teban Gardens Crescent, Singapore, 608923, Singapore
Tel.: (65) 65635533
Web Site: http://www.konicaminolta.sg
Sales Range: $50-74.9 Million
Emp.: 150
Multifunctional Copiers, Printers, Micro Systems, Facsimile Machines & Related Supplies
N.A.I.C.S.: 333248

Konica Minolta Business Solutions (UK) Ltd. (1)
Miles Gray Rd, Basildon, SS14 3AR, Essex, United Kingdom (100%)
Tel.: (44) 1268534444
Web Site: http://www.konicaminolta.co.uk
Sales Range: $75-99.9 Million
Emp.: 150
Office Equipment Sales & Service
N.A.I.C.S.: 423420
Neil Dingley (Mng Dir)

Subsidiary (Domestic):

Konica Minolta Business Solutions East Ltd. (2)
Orchard Way, Calladine Park, Sutton in Ashfield, NG17 1JU, Nottinghamshire, United Kingdom
Tel.: (44) 1623522100
Web Site: http://www.konicaminolta.co.uk
Sales Range: $25-49.9 Million
Emp.: 60
Office Equipment Whslr
N.A.I.C.S.: 333310

Konica Minolta Business Solutions Australia Pty. Ltd. (1)
4 Drake Ave, Macquarie Park, 2113, NSW, Australia
Tel.: (61) 280262222
Web Site: http://www.konicaminolta.com.au
Sales Range: $150-199.9 Million
Emp.: 350
Business & Office Machines Sales & Service
N.A.I.C.S.: 423420

Konica Minolta Business Solutions Deutschland GmbH (1)
Europaallee 17, 30855, Langenhagen, Germany
Tel.: (49) 51174040
Web Site: https://www.konicaminolta.de
Sales Range: $150-199.9 Million
Emp.: 500
Office Equipment Whslr
N.A.I.C.S.: 423420
Johannes Bischof (Pres)

Konica Minolta Business Solutions Europe GmbH (1)
Europa Allee 17, 30855, Langenhagen, Germany (100%)
Tel.: (49) 51174040
Web Site: http://www.konicaminolta.eu
Sales Range: $100-124.9 Million
Emp.: 450
Photographic Equipment & Supplies
N.A.I.C.S.: 333310

Subsidiary (Non-US):

Konica Minolta Business Solutions Austria GmbH (2)
Amalienstrasse 59-61, 1130, Vienna, Austria (100%)
Tel.: (43) 5087880
Web Site: http://www.konicaminolta.at
Emp.: 120
Photographic Equipment & Business Machines
N.A.I.C.S.: 333310

KONICA MINOLTA, INC.

Konica Minolta, Inc.—(Continued)

Konica Minolta Business Solutions Czech spol. s.r.o. (2)
Zarosicka 13, Brno, 62800, Czech Republic (100%)
Tel.: (420) 841777777
Web Site: http://www.konicaminolta.cz
Sales Range: $25-49.9 Million
Emp.: 200
Photographic & Business Equipment
N.A.I.C.S.: 333310

Konica Minolta Business Solutions Denmark a/s (2)
Lautrupvang 2B, 2750, Ballerup, Denmark (100%)
Tel.: (45) 72212121
Web Site: https://www.konicaminolta.dk
Emp.: 225
Office Equipment Whslr
N.A.I.C.S.: 423420
Lars Worzner (Mng Dir)

Konica Minolta Business Solutions Norway AS (2)
Maridalsveien 323, 0872, Oslo, Norway (100%)
Tel.: (47) 22789800
Web Site: http://www.konicaminolta.no
Sales Range: $50-74.9 Million
Emp.: 180
Business Equipment Services
N.A.I.C.S.: 423420

Konica Minolta Business Solutions Polska s.p.z.o.o. (2)
ul Muszkieterow 15, Warsaw, 02 273, Poland (100%)
Tel.: (48) 225603300
Web Site: http://www.konicaminolta.pl
Sales Range: $25-49.9 Million
Emp.: 70
Photographic & Business Equipment
N.A.I.C.S.: 333310

Konica Minolta Business Solutions Portugal Lda. (2)
Rua Prof Henrique de Barros 4 -10 B, 2685-338, Prior Velho, Portugal (100%)
Tel.: (351) 219492000
Web Site: http://www.konicaminolta.pt
Sales Range: $25-49.9 Million
Emp.: 80
Business Equipment
N.A.I.C.S.: 423420

Konica Minolta Business Solutions Romania s.r.l. (2)
Str Copilului Nr 18 - parter Sector 1, Bucharest, 012178, Romania (100%)
Tel.: (40) 212074560
Web Site: https://www.konicaminolta.ro
Sales Range: $50-74.9 Million
Emp.: 115
Business Equipment
N.A.I.C.S.: 423420
Helmut Ignat (Gen Mgr)

Konica Minolta Business Solutions Slovenia d.o.o. (2)
Letaliska cesta 29, 1000, Ljubljana, Slovenia (100%)
Tel.: (386) 15680500
Web Site: http://www.konicaminolta.si
Sales Range: $1-9.9 Million
Emp.: 30
Business Equipment
N.A.I.C.S.: 423420

Konica Minolta Business Solutions Spain S.A. (2)
Calle de la Ribera del Loira 28 Planta 4, 28042, Madrid, Spain
Tel.: (34) 913277300
Web Site: http://www.konicaminolta.es
Sales Range: $50-74.9 Million
Emp.: 150
Business Equipment
N.A.I.C.S.: 423420

Konica Minolta Business Solutions Sweden AB (2)
Solna Stradvag 926, SE 171 09, Solna, Sweden (100%)
Tel.: (46) 86277607
Web Site: http://www.konicaminolta.com
Sales Range: $25-49.9 Million
Emp.: 400
Photographic Equipment & Supplies

N.A.I.C.S.: 333310

Konica Minolta Hungary Business Solutions Ltd. (2)
4 Galvani Street, Budapest, 1117, Hungary (100%)
Tel.: (36) 614649000
Web Site: http://www.konicaminolta.hu
Sales Range: $1-9.9 Million
Emp.: 90
Research & Development of High-Quality Office & Printing Systems, Related Software Applications & Document Management Solutions
N.A.I.C.S.: 423420

Konica Minolta Photo Imaging Austria GmbH (2)
Amalienstrasse 59 61, Vienna, 1130, Austria
Tel.: (43) 1878820
Web Site: http://www.konicaminolta.at
Sales Range: $25-49.9 Million
Emp.: 13
Provider of Photographic Equipment & Supplies
N.A.I.C.S.: 333310
Johannes Bischos (Mng Dir)

Konica Minolta Slovakia spol. s.r.o. (2)
Galvaniho 17/B, Bratislava-Ruzinov, 82104, Bratislava, Slovakia (100%)
Tel.: (421) 850166177
Web Site: http://www.konicaminolta.sk
Sales Range: $25-49.9 Million
Emp.: 100
Business Equipment Solutions
N.A.I.C.S.: 423420

Konica Minolta Business Solutions Finland Oy (1)
Keilaranta 10 E, 02150, Espoo, Finland
Tel.: (358) 10 4429 000
Web Site: http://www.konicaminolta.fi
Sales Range: $25-49.9 Million
Emp.: 100
Printer Mfr
N.A.I.C.S.: 334118

Konica Minolta Business Solutions France S.A.S. (1)
365 route de Saint Germain, 78420, Carrieres-sur-Seine, France (100%)
Tel.: (33) 130866000
Web Site: https://www.konicaminolta.fr
Sales Range: $250-299.9 Million
Emp.: 1,000
Sales & Service of Office Equipment
N.A.I.C.S.: 423420
Jean-Caluge Cornillet (Pres)

Konica Minolta Business Solutions Italia S.p.A (1)
c /o Green Place Viale Certosa 144, 20156, Milan, Italy
Tel.: (39) 02390111
Web Site: http://www.konicaminolta.it
Sales Range: $25-49.9 Million
Emp.: 65
Medical & Hospital Equipment
N.A.I.C.S.: 456199

Konica Minolta Business Solutions Japan Co., Ltd. (1)
1-5-4 Nihombashihoncho, Chuo-Ku, Tokyo, 103-0023, Japan
Tel.: (81) 352057755
Printer Mfr
N.A.I.C.S.: 334118

Konica Minolta Business Solutions Netherlands B.V. (1)
Hoogoorddreef 9, 1101 BA, Amsterdam, Netherlands
Tel.: (31) 206584100
Web Site: http://www.konicaminolta.nl
Emp.: 150
Printer Mfr
N.A.I.C.S.: 334118

Konica Minolta Business Solutions Russia LLC (1)
St Vereyskaya 29 Building 33 6th Floor Office D601, BC Vereyskaya Plaza III, 121357, Moscow, Russia
Tel.: (7) 4995531212
Sales Range: $25-49.9 Million
Emp.: 70
Business Support Services

N.A.I.C.S.: 561499

Konica Minolta Business Solutions USA, Inc. (1)
100 Williams Dr, Ramsey, NJ 07446
Tel.: (201) 825-4000
Web Site: http://www.kmbs.konicaminolta.us
Photographic Cameras, Office Copiers, Microfilm & Office Equipment Whslr
N.A.I.C.S.: 423690
Allan Schwedock (Sr VP-Ops & Supply Chain)

Subsidiary (Domestic):

AMI Entertainment Network, Inc. (2)
155 Rittenhouse Cir, Bristol, PA 19007
Tel.: (800) 393-0201
Web Site: http://www.amientertainment.com
Touch Screen Entertainment Products, Including Jukeboxes Mfr
N.A.I.C.S.: 334310
John Margold (Sr VP-Sls)

AMS Imaging, LLC (2)
2670 Warwick Ave, Warwick, RI 02889
Tel.: (401) 738-5111
Web Site: http://www.amsimaging.com
Sales Range: $1-9.9 Million
Emp.: 55
Office Supplies & Stationery Stores
N.A.I.C.S.: 459410

All Covered, Inc. (2)
1051 E Hillsdale Blvd Ste 510, Foster City, CA 94404
Tel.: (650) 486-5000
Web Site: http://www.allcovered.com
IT Services
N.A.I.C.S.: 541513
Todd Croteau (Pres)

Subsidiary (Domestic):

MWA Intelligence, Inc. (3)
15990 N Greenway Hayden Loop, Scottsdale, AZ 85260
Software Development Services
N.A.I.C.S.: 541511
Michael Stranaglio (Pres)

Techcess Solutions Inc (3)
3100 Timmons Ln Ste 350, Houston, TX 77027
Tel.: (832) 533-9670
Web Site: http://www.techcessgroup.com
Sales Range: $1-9.9 Million
Emp.: 42
IT Services
N.A.I.C.S.: 541512
Herve Chapellat (COO)

United Computer Sales & Services, Inc. (3)
100 Dobbs Ln Ste 208, Cherry Hill, NJ 08034
Tel.: (856) 795-7330
Web Site: http://www.ucss.com
Sales Range: $10-24.9 Million
Emp.: 32
Computer Systems, Technology Components & Business Solutions
N.A.I.C.S.: 541512
Anthony Calabrese (CEO)

Subsidiary (Domestic):

Altuscio Networks (2)
1080 Holcomb Bridge Rd Bldg 100 Ste 135, Roswell, GA 30076 (100%)
Tel.: (770) 605-1905
Web Site: http://www.altuscionetworks.com
Emp.: 50
Information Technology Services
N.A.I.C.S.: 519290
Ben Silliman (CEO)

CopySource Incorporated (2)
4340 NW 120th Ave, Coral Springs, FL 33065
Tel.: (954) 757-2112
Web Site: http://www.mycopysource.com
Sales Range: $10-24.9 Million
Emp.: 75
Document Management Systems & Services
N.A.I.C.S.: 561410
Dustin Hilley (Dir-IT)

Force Security Solutions, LLC (2)

INTERNATIONAL PUBLIC

8516 Virginia Meadows Dr, Manassas, VA 20109
Tel.: (703) 286-7205
Web Site: https://www.forcesecurity.com
Security System Services
N.A.I.C.S.: 561621

HBP of San Diego, Inc. (2)
4350 Executive Dr Ste 310, San Diego, CA 92121
Tel.: (858) 458-4222
Sales Range: $1-9.9 Million
Emp.: 18
Computer & Office Machine Repair & Maintenance
N.A.I.C.S.: 811210
Neal Ficher (Owner)

Division (Domestic):

Konica Minolta Business Solutions (2)
10300 Ormsby Park Pl, Louisville, KY 40223
Tel.: (502) 491-2722
Web Site: http://www.kmbs.konicaminolta.us
Sales Range: $10-24.9 Million
Emp.: 35
Full-Service Business Equipment Distr
N.A.I.C.S.: 423420

Subsidiary (Domestic):

Konica Minolta Graphic Imaging USA, Inc. (2)
71 Charles St, Glen Cove, NY 11542-2842
Tel.: (616) 575-2800
Sales Range: $100-124.9 Million
Emp.: 275
Digital Graphic Art Supplies Mfr & Distr
N.A.I.C.S.: 333310

Konica Minolta Medical Imaging USA, Inc. (2)
411 Newark Pompton Tpke, Wayne, NJ 07470
Tel.: (973) 633-1500
Web Site: http://www.konicaminolta.com
Sales Range: $50-74.9 Million
Emp.: 100
Mfr of Clinical Diagnostic Equipment
N.A.I.C.S.: 423450
David Widmann (Pres & COO)

Konica Minolta Office Products, Inc. (2)
534 Broadhollow Rd Ste 400, Melville, NY 11747
Tel.: (631) 845-4300
Web Site: http://www.konicaminolta.us
Sales Range: $50-74.9 Million
Emp.: 10
Office Equipment Sales
N.A.I.C.S.: 423420

Konica Minolta Printing Solutions USA, Inc. (2)
2070 Schillinger Rd S, Mobile, AL 36695
Tel.: (251) 633-4300
Web Site: http://www.printer.konicaminolta.net
Sales Range: $25-49.9 Million
Emp.: 40
Mfr of Laser Printers & Image Systems; Laser & Color Laser Transfer Print Systems
N.A.I.C.S.: 334118

Holding (Non-US):

Konica Minolta Europe B.V. (3)
Edisonbaan 14 F, 3430 BL, Nieuwegein, Netherlands
Tel.: (31) 302481200
Web Site: http://www.konicaminolta.com
Sales Range: $25-49.9 Million
Emp.: 15
Mfr of Computer & Office Equipment
N.A.I.C.S.: 333310
Tsutomu Tanahashi (Mng Dir)

Subsidiary (Domestic):

Meridian Imaging Solutions, Inc. (2)
5775 General Washington Dr, Alexandria, VA 22312 (100%)
Tel.: (703) 461-8195
Web Site: http://www.whymeridian.com
Emp.: 115
Document Solutions & Managed IT Services

AND PRIVATE COMPANIES

KONICA MINOLTA, INC.

N.A.I.C.S.: 811210
Juliana McKee *(VP-GEM Sls)*

Mohawk Marketing Corporation (2)
2613 Shore Dr, Virginia Beach, VA 23451-1416
Tel.: (757) 499-8901
Sales Range: $25-49.9 Million
Emp.: 45
Electronic Products Marketing Services
N.A.I.C.S.: 423620

Reengineering Consultants, LLC
130 Wetherby Ln, Westerville, OH 43081
Tel.: (614) 899-2950
Web Site: http://www.reeng.com
Sales Range: $1-9.9 Million
Emp.: 31
Enterprise Content Management Solutions
N.A.I.C.S.: 541512
Greg Boyd *(Pres)*

SymQuest Group, Inc. (2)
530 Community Drive Ste 5, South Burlington, VT 05403
Tel.: (802) 658-9890
Web Site: https://www.symquest.com
Computer Networking, Training & IT Services
N.A.I.C.S.: 541519
Meg Fleming *(Pres)*

Konica Minolta Business Solutions de Mexico SA de C.V. (1)
Av Gustavo Baz No 312 esq Mario Colin, Col Tlalnepantla Industrial Center, Mexico, 54030, DF, Mexico
Tel.: (52) 5555578011
Web Site: http://www.kmbsmx.com.mx
Sales Range: $1-9.9 Million
Emp.: 40
Provider of Office Equipment
N.A.I.C.S.: 333310

Konica Minolta Business Solutions do Brasil Ltda. (1)
Alameda Santos 745-13 andar, Paraiso, 01419-001, Sao Paulo, Brazil
Tel.: (55) 1130505300
Web Site: http://www.konicaminolta.com.br
Sales Range: $25-49.9 Million
Emp.: 100
Sales & Service of Office Equipment
N.A.I.C.S.: 333310

Konica Minolta Business Technologies (Dongguan) Co., Ltd. (1)
No 1 Minolta Road New City Center, Shilong Town, Dongguan, 523326, Guangdong, China
Tel.: (86) 76986114300
Printer Mfr & Distr
N.A.I.C.S.: 333248

Konica Minolta Business Technologies (Wuxi) Co., Ltd. (1)
No 2 Changjiang South Road, New District, Wuxi, 214028, Jiangsu, China
Tel.: (86) 51085346688
Printer Mfr & Distr
N.A.I.C.S.: 333248

Konica Minolta Business Technologies Manufacturing (HK) Ltd. (1)
23 Fl Rykadan Capital Tower 135 Hoi Bun Road, Kwun Tong Ko, Kowloon, China (Hong Kong)
Tel.: (852) 29634567
Sales Range: $25-49.9 Million
Emp.: 85
Printer Mfr
N.A.I.C.S.: 334118
Atsuo Okamoto *(Mng Dir)*

Konica Minolta Business Technologies, Inc. (1)
1 6 1 Marunouchi, Chiyoda Ku, Tokyo, 100 0005, Japan (100%)
Tel.: (81) 332181383
Web Site: http://www.konicaminolta.jp
Sales Range: $1-4.9 Billion
Emp.: 22,000
Copiers, Printers, Micro-Systems, Facsimiles & Related Office Supplies Mfr
N.A.I.C.S.: 333310

Konica Minolta Chemical Co., Ltd. (1)
6909-9 Ono, Fukuroi, 437-1112, Shizuoka Prefecture, Japan
Tel.: (81) 538236777
Photographic Chemical Mfr & Distr
N.A.I.C.S.: 325992

Konica Minolta Consulting (SHENZHEN) Co., Ltd. (1)
27/F Suite A World Finance Centre No 4003 Shennan East Road, Shenzhen, 518010, Guangdong, China
Tel.: (86) 75525980889
Web Site: http://www.konicaminolta.com
Business Consulting Services
N.A.I.C.S.: 541618

Konica Minolta Electronics Co., Ltd. (1)
226 Azamiyachi Ono, Tsuru, 402-0024, Yamanashi, Japan
Tel.: (81) 554 43 4361
Web Site: http://www.konicaminolta.jp
Emp.: 125
Electrical Circuit Board Mfr
N.A.I.C.S.: 334418

Konica Minolta Engineering Co., Ltd. (1)
1 Sakura-cho, Hino, 1918511, Tokyo, Japan
Tel.: (81) 425893730
Web Site: http://www.konicaminolta.jp
Emp.: 156
Measuring Equipment Mfr
N.A.I.C.S.: 334513

Konica Minolta Glass Tech. Co., Ltd. (1)
6-300 Imakuma, Osakasayama, 589-0021, Osaka, Japan
Tel.: (81) 723602410
Photographic Equipment Mfr
N.A.I.C.S.: 325992

Konica Minolta Health Care Co., Ltd. (1)
1 Sakuramachi, Hino, 191-0063, Tokyo, Japan
Tel.: (81) 425891430
Medical & Hospital Equipment Whslr
N.A.I.C.S.: 423450

Konica Minolta Health Care System Support Co., Ltd. (1)
1-2-8 Minoshima, Hakata-Ku, Fukuoka, 812-0017, Japan
Tel.: (81) 924414167
Medical & Hospital Equipment Mfr & Whslr
N.A.I.C.S.: 339112

Konica Minolta Healthcare India, Private Ltd. (1)
Office No 515 5th Floor C-Wing 215-Atrium Centre, Andheri East, Mumbai, 400 059, India
Tel.: (91) 22 6191 6969
Sales Range: $25-49.9 Million
Emp.: 25
Medical Device Distr
N.A.I.C.S.: 423450
Jigar Gada *(Mgr-Sls)*

Konica Minolta IJ Technologies, Inc. (1)
1 Sakura-machi, Hino, 191-8511, Tokyo, Japan
Tel.: (81) 425893701
Web Site: http://www.konicaminolta.com
Sales Range: $50-74.9 Million
Emp.: 160
Printer & Display Mfr
N.A.I.C.S.: 334118
Akiyoshi Ohno *(Owner)*

Konica Minolta IJ Textile Europe S.r.l. (1)
Via Milano 83, 22070, Bregnano, CO, Italy
Tel.: (39) 031771070
Web Site: http://inkjet.konicaminolta.it
Inkjet Textile Printer Distr
N.A.I.C.S.: 423840

Konica Minolta Information System Co., Ltd. (1)
2970 Ishikawacho, Hachioji, 192-8505, Tokyo, Japan
Tel.: (81) 426607690
Web Site: http://www.konicaminolta.jp
Emp.: 193
Information Technology Consulting Services
N.A.I.C.S.: 541512

Konica Minolta International Trading (Shanghai) Co., Ltd. (1)
Rm 1201 Rui Jin Bldg, 205 S Mao Ming Rd, 20020, Shanghai, China
Tel.: (86) 216 4660517
Web Site: http://www.konicaminolta.cn
Sales Range: $25-49.9 Million
Emp.: 60
Import, Sales & After-Sales Services
N.A.I.C.S.: 333310

Konica Minolta Japan, Inc. (1)
Hamamatsucho Building 26F 1-1-1, Shibaura Minato-ku, Tokyo, 105-0023, Japan
Tel.: (81) 120805039
Web Site: http://www.konicaminolta.jp
Printer Mfr & Distr
N.A.I.C.S.: 333248

Konica Minolta Logistics Co., Ltd. (1)
Konicaminolta Nihonbashi Bldg 10F 5-4 1-chome Nihonbashi-honcho, Chuo-ku, Tokyo, 103-0023, Japan
Tel.: (81) 3 5205 7830
Web Site: http://www.konicaminolta.jp
Logistics Consulting Servies
N.A.I.C.S.: 541614

Konica Minolta Mechatronics Co., Ltd. (1)
2 Higashiakatsuchi Yawata-cho, Toyokawa, 442-8555, Aichi Prefecture, Japan
Tel.: (81) 533887661
Web Site: http://bmme.konicaminolta.jp
Optical Sensor Instrument Mfr
N.A.I.C.S.: 333310

Konica Minolta Medical & Graphic (Shanghai) Co., Ltd. (1)
Room1602 Tower B Hongwell International Plaza 1602 West Zhongshan Road, Xuhui District, Shanghai, 200235, China
Tel.: (86) 2164222626
Medical Imaging Equipment Distr
N.A.I.C.S.: 423450

Konica Minolta Medical & Graphic Imaging Europe B.V. (1)
Frankfurtstraat 40, Lijnden, 1175 RH, North Holland, Netherlands
Tel.: (31) 206590260
Sales Range: $25-49.9 Million
Emp.: 28
Medical Device Mfr
N.A.I.C.S.: 334510
Yuhei Okamoto *(Mng Dir)*

Konica Minolta Medical & Graphic Imaging Europe GmbH (1)
Werner-Eckert-Strasse 2, 81829, Munich, Germany
Tel.: (49) 892388750
Web Site: http://www.konicaminolta.de
Sales Range: $25-49.9 Million
Emp.: 10
Medical Device Mfr
N.A.I.C.S.: 334510

Konica Minolta Medical & Graphic, Inc. (1)
Shinjuku Nomura Bldg 1 26 2 Nishishinjuku, Shinjuku-Ku, Tokyo, 163 0512, Japan (100%)
Tel.: (81) 333495145
Web Site: http://www.konicaminolta.jp
Sales Range: $25-49.9 Million
Emp.: 100
Mfr & Provider of Film & Processing Equipment for Medical & Graphic Imaging
N.A.I.C.S.: 322220

Konica Minolta Optical Products (SHANGHAI) Co., Ltd. (1)
No 368 Minolta Road Songjiang Industry Zone, Shanghai, 201600, China
Tel.: (86) 2157741620
Optical Instrument Mfr
N.A.I.C.S.: 333310

Konica Minolta Opto (DALIAN) Co., Ltd. (1)
No 20 Dongbei 2 Street Economic Technology Development Zone, Dalian, 116600, Liaoning, China
Tel.: (86) 41187622575
Optical Lens Mfr
N.A.I.C.S.: 333310

Konica Minolta Opto Devices Co., Ltd. (1)
6-300 Imakuma, Osakasayama, 589-0021, Osaka, Japan
Tel.: (81) 723673371
Optical Instrument & Len Mfr
N.A.I.C.S.: 333310

Konica Minolta Opto Products Co., Ltd. (1)
920 Ninomiya Misakacho, Fuefuki, 406-0807, Yamanashi, Japan
Tel.: (81) 552625551
Optical Instrument & Len Mfr
N.A.I.C.S.: 333310

Konica Minolta Photo Imaging (Thailand) Co., Ltd. (1)
11th Floor Sermmit Tower 159 SOI Asoke Road, Sukhumvit 21, Bangkok, 10110, Thailand
Tel.: (66) 22608655
Sales Range: $25-49.9 Million
Emp.: 30
Provider of Photographic Equipment
N.A.I.C.S.: 333310

Konica Minolta Photo Imaging (UK) Ltd. (1)
Plane Tree Crescent, Feltham, TW13 7HD, United Kingdom
Tel.: (44) 2087516121
Web Site: http://www.konicaminolta.co.uk
Sales Range: $25-49.9 Million
Emp.: 50
Provider of Photo Equipment & Supplies
N.A.I.C.S.: 423410

Konica Minolta Photo Imaging Canada, Inc. (1)
1329 Meyerside Dr, Mississauga, L5T 1C9, ON, Canada
Tel.: (905) 670-7722
Web Site: http://www.konicaminolta.ca
Sales Range: $25-49.9 Million
Emp.: 50
Provider of Photographic Equipment & Supplies
N.A.I.C.S.: 333310

Konica Minolta Photo Imaging, Inc. (1)
3-91 Daisen Nishimachi, Sakai, Osaka, 590 8551, Japan (100%)
Tel.: (81) 722419509
Web Site: http://www.konicaminolta.jp
Sales Range: $800-899.9 Million
Emp.: 4,100
Mfr & Developer of Photographic Equipment such as Digital Cameras, Film Cameras & Lenses
N.A.I.C.S.: 333310

Konica Minolta Photo Imaging, Inc. (1)
1 Sakura-machi, Hino, Tokyo, 191-8511, Japan (100%)
Tel.: (81) 42 589 3707
Web Site: http://www.konicaminolta.jp
Sales Range: $800-899.9 Million
Emp.: 3,900
Mfr & Provider of Consumer & Commercial Photographic Materials, ID Photos, Inkjet Media & Related Equipment
N.A.I.C.S.: 333310

Konica Minolta Planetarium Co., Ltd. (1)
2-3-10 Nishihonmachi, Nishi-ku, Osaka, 500-0005, Japan
Tel.: (81) 661100570
Sales Range: $25-49.9 Million
Emp.: 60
Audio & Projection Equipment Mfr & Whslr
N.A.I.C.S.: 333310

Konica Minolta Printing Solutions Japan Co., Ltd. (1)
Sumitomofudosan Nihombashi Bldg 10f, Chuo-Ku, Tokyo, 103-0023, Japan
Tel.: (81) 352057818
Printing Equipment Distr
N.A.I.C.S.: 423830

Konica Minolta Sensing Europe B.V. (1)
Marconibaan 57, Nieuwegein, 3439 MR, Netherlands
Tel.: (31) 302481193
Web Site: http://www5.konicaminolta.eu
Emp.: 100

KONICA MINOLTA, INC.

Konica Minolta, Inc.—(Continued)
Optical Instrument Mfr
N.A.I.C.S.: 333310

Konica Minolta Sensing, Inc. (1)
3 91 Daisennishimachi, Sakai, Osaka, 590-8551, Japan **(100%)**
Tel.: (81) 722419322
Web Site: http://www.konicaminolta.jp
Sales Range: $50-74.9 Million
Emp.: 240
Mfr Instrument Systems for Photographic, Industrial & Medical Industries
N.A.I.C.S.: 333310
Toshihiko Karasaki *(Pres)*

Konica Minolta Software Development (Dalian) Co., Ltd. (1)
5th Floor No 1 Huixian Park High-tech Industrial Park, Dalian, 116025, China
Tel.: (86) 41139776888
Printer Mfr & Distr
N.A.I.C.S.: 333248

Konica Minolta Software Laboratory Co., Ltd. (1)
231-1 Kamiochiai, Atsugi, 243-0025, Kanagawa, Japan
Tel.: (81) 462206770
Software Development Services
N.A.I.C.S.: 541511

Konica Minolta Sogo Service Co., Ltd. (1)
1-2-6 Tamadaira Noguchi Bldg 2f, Hino, 191-0062, Tokyo, Japan
Tel.: (81) 425828377
Web Site: http://www.konicaminolta.jp
Measurement Equipment Mfr
N.A.I.C.S.: 334513

Konica Minolta Supplies Manufacturing France S.A.S. (1)
Zone Industrielle La Plaine, Eloyes, 88510, Vosges, France
Tel.: (33) 329692000
Sales Range: $25-49.9 Million
Emp.: 59
Photographic Film Mfr
N.A.I.C.S.: 325992

Konica Minolta Supplies Manufacturing Kansai Co., Ltd. (1)
11 Besshochotomoe, Miki, 673-0443, Hyogo, Japan **(100%)**
Tel.: (81) 794 83 5050
Web Site: http://www.konicaminolta.jp
Emp.: 80
Printer Mfr & Supplier
N.A.I.C.S.: 325910
Nishiyama Takeshi *(Pres & CEO)*

Konica Minolta Supplies Manufacturing U.S.A., Inc. (1)
51 Hatfield Ln, Goshen, NY 10924-6712
Tel.: (845) 294-8400
Emp.: 90
Photographic Equipment Mfr
N.A.I.C.S.: 325992
Michael Bello *(Mgr-Production)*

Konica Minolta Technology Center, Inc. (1)
1 Sakuramachi, Hino, 191-8511, Tokyo, Japan
Tel.: (81) 425898452
Information Technology Consulting Services
N.A.I.C.S.: 541512

Konica Minolta Technoproducts Co., Ltd. (1)
2-2-1 Hirosedai, Sayama, 350-1328, Saitama, Japan
Tel.: (81) 429541121
Web Site: http://www.konicaminolta.jp
Electric Equipment Mfr
N.A.I.C.S.: 334419

Konica Minolta Technosearch Corporation (1)
2-15-13 Owadamachi, Hachioji, 192-0045, Tokyo, Japan
Tel.: (81) 426426411
Data Processing Services
N.A.I.C.S.: 518210

Konica Minolta Ukraine (1)
12 Glushkova Av, Kiev, 03680, Ukraine
Tel.: (380) 44 230 10 57

Web Site: http://www.konicaminolta.ua
Printer Mfr
N.A.I.C.S.: 334118

MOBOTIX AG (1)
Kaiserstrasse, D-67722, Langmeil, Germany
Tel.: (49) 630298160
Web Site: https://www.mobotix.com
Rev.: $69,729,551
Assets: $89,954,741
Liabilities: $69,879,678
Net Worth: $20,075,063
Earnings: ($5,970,858)
Emp.: 325
Fiscal Year-end: 09/30/2023
Network Cameras & Software Developer
N.A.I.C.S.: 334310
Thomas Lausten *(CEO)*

Subsidiary (US):

MOBOTIX Corp. (2)
80 Broad St Ste 702, New York, NY 10004
Tel.: (212) 385-6126
Web Site: http://www.mobotix.com
Sales Range: $25-49.9 Million
Emp.: 13
Cameras & Accessories Mfr
N.A.I.C.S.: 334310

Radiant Vision Systems, LLC (1)
18640 NE 67th Ct, Redmond, WA 98052
Tel.: (425) 844-0152
Web Site:
    http://www.radiantvisionsystems.com
Scientific Measurement Equipment Mfr
N.A.I.C.S.: 334513
Douglas Kreysar *(CEO)*

office-boerse.de Internet GmbH (1)
Heerdter Landstr 193, 40549, Dusseldorf, Germany
Tel.: (49) 211 5079900
Web Site: http://www.office-material.de
Emp.: 4
Office Supplies Distr
N.A.I.C.S.: 424120

KONINKLIJKE AHOLD DELHAIZE N.V.

Provincialeweg 11, 1506 MA, Zaandam, Netherlands
Tel.: (31) 886599111 **NI**
Web Site:
    https://www.aholddelhaize.com
Year Founded: 1867
AH—(EUR)
Rev.: $95,671,271,314
Assets: $51,609,108,569
Liabilities: $35,685,301,101
Net Worth: $15,923,807,468
Earnings: $2,022,447,658
Emp.: 402,000
Fiscal Year-end: 12/31/23
Food Products Distr
N.A.I.C.S.: 424420
Wouter Kolk *(CEO-Europe & Indonesia & Member-Mgmt Bd)*

Subsidiaries:

Ahold Czech Republic A.S (1)
Radlicka 117, 158 00, Prague, Czech Republic
Tel.: (420) 234004111
Web Site: http://www.ialbert.cz
Sales Range: $100-124.9 Million
Emp.: 400
Supermarkets Operation Services
N.A.I.C.S.: 445110

Ahold USA, Inc. (1)
1149 Harrisburg Pike, Carlisle, PA 17013
Tel.: (717) 249-4000
Web Site: http://www.ahold.com
Sales Range: $200-249.9 Million
Emp.: 900
Supermarket Operator
N.A.I.C.S.: 445110
Kevin Holt *(COO)*

Subsidiary (Domestic):

Ahold Financial Services, LLC (2)
1149 Harrisburg Pike, Carlisle, PA 17013-1607

Tel.: (717) 960-1700
Financial Management Services
N.A.I.C.S.: 523999
Stephanie Nace *(Gen Mgr)*

Ahold Information Services, Inc (2)
1200 Brookfield Blvd, Greenville, SC 29607
Tel.: (864) 987-5600
Web Site: http://aiscareers.aholdusa.com
Information Technology Consulting Services
N.A.I.C.S.: 541512

American Sales Company, LLC (2)
4201 Walden Ave, Lancaster, NY 14086
Tel.: (716) 686-7000
Web Site:
    http://www.americansalescompany.net
Grocery Stores
N.A.I.C.S.: 445110

Delhaize America, LLC (2)
2110 Exec Dr, Salisbury, NC 28147 **(100%)**
Tel.: (704) 633-8250
Web Site: http://www.delhaizeamerica.com
Supermarket Operator
N.A.I.C.S.: 445110

Subsidiary (Domestic):

Food Lion, LLC (3)
2110 Executive Dr, Salisbury, NC 28145-1330
Web Site: https://legacy.foodlion.com
Grocery Store Operator
N.A.I.C.S.: 424410
Meg Ham *(Pres)*

Subsidiary (Domestic):

FreshDirect, LLC (2)
2 St Ann's Ave, Bronx, NY 10454
Tel.: (718) 928-1000
Web Site: https://www.freshdirect.com
Emp.: 500
Internet Grocery Shopping & Delivery Services
N.A.I.C.S.: 445110
Jason Ackerman *(Co-Founder)*

Giant of Maryland LLC (2)
8301 Professional Pl, Landover, MD 20785
Web Site: http://www.giantfood.com
General Merchandise Product Distr
N.A.I.C.S.: 455219

Subsidiary (Non-US):

Hannaford Bros. Co., LLC (2)
Web Site: https://www.hannaford.com
Retail Supermarkets
N.A.I.C.S.: 445110
Brad Wise *(Pres)*

Subsidiary (Domestic):

MAC Risk Management, Inc (2)
45 Dan Rd Ste 2, Canton, MA 02021-2852
Tel.: (781) 298-4902
Management Consulting Services
N.A.I.C.S.: 541618

Retail Business Services LLC (2)
2110 Executive Dr, Salisbury, NC 28147
Tel.: (704) 633-8250
Web Site:
    https://www.retailbusinessservices.com
General Merchandise Product Distr
N.A.I.C.S.: 455219
Marty Wolfe *(CTO)*

The GIANT Company LLC (2)
1149 Harrisburg Pike, Carlisle, PA 17013
Web Site: https://www.giantfoodstores.com
Grocery Store Operator
N.A.I.C.S.: 445110
John Ruane *(Pres)*

The Stop & Shop Supermarket Company (2)
495 Southern Artery, Quincy, MA 02169-5100
Tel.: (617) 773-4510
Web Site: https://www.stopandshop.com
Grocery Store Operator
N.A.I.C.S.: 445110
Jim Dwyer *(Exec VP-Strategy & Bus Dev)*

Subsidiary (Domestic):

Peapod, LLC (3)

9933 Woods Dr Ste 375, Skokie, IL 60077-1057
Tel.: (847) 583-9400
Web Site: http://www.peapod.com
Sales Range: $400-449.9 Million
Online Grocery Shopping Services
N.A.I.C.S.: 445110
Andrew B. Parkinson *(Co-Founder)*

Albert Ceska republika, s.r.o. (1)
Radlicka 520/117, Jinonice, 158 00, Prague, 5, Czech Republic
Tel.: (420) 234004111
Web Site: https://www.albert.cz
Emp.: 800
General Merchandise Product Distr
N.A.I.C.S.: 455219

Albert Heijn B.V. (1)
Provincial road 11, 1506 MA, Zaandam, Netherlands **(100%)**
Tel.: (31) 886599111
Web Site: https://www.ah.nl
Sales Range: $1-4.9 Billion
Emp.: 1,500
Grocery Stores
N.A.I.C.S.: 445110

Alfa-Beta Vassilopoulos S.A. (1)
81 Spaton Ave Gerakas, 153 44, Athens, Greece **(89.56%)**
Tel.: (30) 2106608000
Web Site: http://www.ab.gr
Supermarket
N.A.I.C.S.: 457110
Zeta Cheimonidou *(VP-Mktg & Strategy)*

Bidfood b.v. (1)
Frankeneng 18, 6716 AA, Ede, Netherlands **(100%)**
Tel.: (31) 888008900
Web Site: http://www.bidfood.nl
Foodservice Whslr
N.A.I.C.S.: 445110
Dick Slootwig *(Mng Dir)*

Delhaize "The Lion" Nederland B.V. (1)
Martinus Nijhofflaan 2, Delft, 2624 ES, Netherlands
Tel.: (31) 152624590
Super Market Stores Operating Services
N.A.I.C.S.: 445110

Delhaize Luxembourg S.A. (1)
19 Route de Bastogne, 9638, Luxembourg, Luxembourg **(100%)**
Tel.: (352) 309911
Web Site: https://www.delhaize.lu
Super Market Stores Operating Services
N.A.I.C.S.: 445110
Remacle Christophe *(Mgr-Store)*

Etos B.V. (1)
Provincialeweg 11, 1506 MA, Zaandam, Netherlands **(100%)**
Tel.: (31) 886594245
Web Site: https://www.etos.nl
Sales Range: $250-299.9 Million
Emp.: 5,000
Retail Drug Services
N.A.I.C.S.: 456110

Etos B.V. (1)
Provincialeweg 11, 1506 MA, Zaandam, Netherlands **(100%)**
Tel.: (31) 886594245
Web Site: https://www.etos.nl
Sales Range: $250-299.9 Million
Emp.: 5,000
Retail Drug Services
N.A.I.C.S.: 456110

Etos B.V. (1)
Provincialeweg 11, 1506 MA, Zaandam, Netherlands **(100%)**
Tel.: (31) 886594245
Web Site: https://www.etos.nl
Sales Range: $250-299.9 Million
Emp.: 5,000
Retail Drug Services
N.A.I.C.S.: 456110

Etos B.V. (1)
Provincialeweg 11, 1506 MA, Zaandam, Netherlands **(100%)**
Tel.: (31) 886594245
Web Site: https://www.etos.nl
Sales Range: $250-299.9 Million
Emp.: 5,000
Retail Drug Services

AND PRIVATE COMPANIES

N.A.I.C.S.: 456110

Gall & Gall B.V. (1)
Provincialeweg 11, 1506 MA, Zaandam, Netherlands (100%)
Tel.: (31) 886594200
Web Site: https://www.gall.nl
Beer & Ale Whslr
N.A.I.C.S.: 424810

Gall & Gall B.V. (1)
Provincialeweg 11, 1506 MA, Zaandam, Netherlands (100%)
Tel.: (31) 886594200
Web Site: https://www.gall.nl
Beer & Ale Whslr
N.A.I.C.S.: 424810

Gall & Gall B.V. (1)
Provincialeweg 11, 1506 MA, Zaandam, Netherlands (100%)
Tel.: (31) 886594200
Web Site: https://www.gall.nl
Beer & Ale Whslr
N.A.I.C.S.: 424810

Gall & Gall B.V. (1)
Provincialeweg 11, 1506 MA, Zaandam, Netherlands (100%)
Tel.: (31) 886594200
Web Site: https://www.gall.nl
Beer & Ale Whslr
N.A.I.C.S.: 424810

Huro NV (1)
Sleihagestraat 57, Oostnieuwkerke IDR Zone 6, 8840, Staden, Belgium (100%)
Tel.: (32) 5 122 7284
Web Site: https://www.huro.be
Asphalt Roof Installation Services
N.A.I.C.S.: 238160

Mega Image SRL (1)
Bulevardul Timisoara 26 etaj 2, 061331, Bucharest, Romania (100%)
Tel.: (40) 800410900
Web Site: https://www.mega-image.ro
Emp.: 9,000
Supermarket
N.A.I.C.S.: 445110
Muller Gabriel *(Dir-Expansion)*

P.T. Lion Super Indo (1)
Menara Bidakara 2 Lt 19 Jl Jendral Gatot Soebroto Kav 71 - 73, Jakarta, Indonesia
Tel.: (62) 2129293333
Web Site: http://www.superindo.co.id
General Merchandise Product Distr
N.A.I.C.S.: 455219

Van Moer Group - Zellik (1)
Isidoor Crokaertstraat 25, 1731, Zellik, Belgium (100%)
Tel.: (32) 2 466 9380
Web Site: http://www.vanmoergroup.com
Merchandise Transport Services
N.A.I.C.S.: 484110
Peter Everaerts *(Mgr-Bus Unit)*

bol.com B.V. (1)
Papendorpseweg 100, 3528 BJ, Utrecht, Netherlands
Tel.: (31) 303104995
Web Site: https://www.bol.com
General Merchandise Product Distr
N.A.I.C.S.: 455219

KONINKLIJKE BAM GROEP N.V.
Runnenburg 9, 3981 AZ, Bunnik, Netherlands
Tel.: (31) 306598988
Web Site: https://www.bam.com
BAMNB—(EUR)
Rev.: $6,921,816,979
Assets: $4,340,457,005
Liabilities: $3,323,988,299
Net Worth: $1,016,468,705
Earnings: $193,127,277
Emp.: 13,897
Fiscal Year-end: 12/31/23
Securities Brokerage
N.A.I.C.S.: 523150
S. Beckers *(Gen Counsel & Sec)*

Subsidiaries:

BAM Belgium NV (1)
Meetdistrict Culliganlaan 5, Bus 2, Diegem, 1831, Brussels, Belgium
Tel.: (32) 38206464
Web Site: https://www.bambelgium.be
Emp.: 220
Construction Services
N.A.I.C.S.: 236220

Subsidiary (Domestic):

Galere SA (2)
Rue Joseph Dupont 73, Chaudfontaine, 4053, Liege, Belgium
Tel.: (32) 43666711
Web Site: http://www.galere.be
Civil Engineering Services
N.A.I.C.S.: 541330

Interbuild NV (2)
Borsbeeksebrug 22 bus 7, Berchem, 2600, Antwerp, Belgium
Tel.: (32) 38206464
Web Site: http://www.baminterbuild.be
Construction Services
N.A.I.C.S.: 236220

Kairos NV (2)
Borsbeeksebrug 22 b7, 2600, Wilrijk, Belgium
Tel.: (32) 38206443
Web Site: http://www.kairos.be
Emp.: 20
Construction Services
N.A.I.C.S.: 236220

BAM Bouw en Vastgoed Nederland BV (1)
Runnenburg 13, 3981 AZ, Bunnik, Netherlands
Tel.: (31) 306598181
Civil Engineering Services
N.A.I.C.S.: 541330

Subsidiary (Domestic):

AM BV (2)
Ptolemaeuslaan 80, Postbus 4052, 3502 HB, Utrecht, Netherlands
Tel.: (31) 306097222
Web Site: http://www.am.nl
Construction Services
N.A.I.C.S.: 236220

BAM Bouw en Techniek BV (2)
Regulierenring 6, 3981 LB, Bunnik, Netherlands
Tel.: (31) 306598966
Web Site: https://www.bambouwentechniek.nl
Civil Engineering Services
N.A.I.C.S.: 541330

BAM Wonen BV (2)
Runnenburg 19, 3981 AZ, Bunnik, Netherlands
Tel.: (31) 306598944
Web Site: https://www.bamwonen.nl
Civil Engineering Services
N.A.I.C.S.: 541330

BAM Construction Limited (1)
Fore 2 2 Huskisson Way, Shirley, Solihull, B90 4EN, United Kingdom
Tel.: (44) 1217464000
Construction Services
N.A.I.C.S.: 236220
David Ellis *(Reg Dir)*

BAM Design Limited (1)
Centrium Griffiths Way, Saint Albans, AL1 2RD, Herts, United Kingdom
Tel.: (44) 1727894200
Construction Services
N.A.I.C.S.: 236220
Andrew Pryke *(Mng Dir)*

BAM Facilities Management Limited (1)
Kelvin House Buchanan Gate Business Park Stepps, Glasgow, G33 6FB, United Kingdom
Tel.: (44) 1417798888
Construction Services
N.A.I.C.S.: 236220

BAM Infra Energie & Water BV (1)
Den Hulst 102, Nieuwleusen, 7711 GS, Dalfsen, Netherlands
Tel.: (31) 887123751
Web Site: http://www.baminfra-energiewater.nl

Renewable Energy Services
N.A.I.C.S.: 221116

BAM Infra Rail BV (1)
Stationsplein 8A, 2801 AK, Breda, Netherlands
Tel.: (31) 765734300
Construction Services
N.A.I.C.S.: 236220

BAM Infra Telecom BV (1)
Rhoneweg 34, 1043 AH, Amsterdam, Netherlands
Tel.: (31) 204117123
Construction Services
N.A.I.C.S.: 236220

BAM Infraconsult BV (1)
H J Nederhorststraat 1, 2801 SC, Gouda, Netherlands
Tel.: (31) 182590510
Construction Services
N.A.I.C.S.: 236220

BAM PPP B.V. (1)
Regulierenring 35, 3981 LA, Bunnik, Netherlands
Tel.: (31) 306598900
Web Site: http://www.bamppp.com
Emp.: 100
Civil Engineering Services
N.A.I.C.S.: 541330
Kieron Meade *(Mng Dir)*

Subsidiary (Non-US):

BAM PPP Deutschland GmbH (2)
Eschborner Landstrasse 130, 60489, Frankfurt am Main, Germany
Tel.: (49) 697409300
Construction Services
N.A.I.C.S.: 236220

BAM PPP Ireland Ltd. (2)
Hartwell Lower Cherryville, Kill, Ireland
Tel.: (353) 45886565
Construction Services
N.A.I.C.S.: 236220

Subsidiary (Domestic):

BAM PPP Nederland B.V. (2)
Runnenburg 9, 3981 AZ, Bunnik, Netherlands
Tel.: (31) 306598615
Construction Services
N.A.I.C.S.: 236220

Subsidiary (Non-US):

BAM PPP UK Ltd. (2)
4 Buchanan Gate Stepps, Glasgow, G33 6FB, United Kingdom
Tel.: (44) 1417798600
Construction Services
N.A.I.C.S.: 236220

BAM Properties Limited (1)
Millennium Gate Gifford Court Fox Den Road, Stoke Gifford, Bristol, BS34 8TT, United Kingdom
Tel.: (44) 1179448865
Construction Services
N.A.I.C.S.: 236220
Dougie Peters *(Mng Dir)*

Grosstagebau Kamsdorf GmbH (1)
OT Kamsdorf Am Revierhaus 30, 07333, Unterwellenborn, Germany
Tel.: (49) 36732360
Web Site: http://www.tagebau-kamsdorf.de
Construction Services
N.A.I.C.S.: 236220

Royal Bam Groep N.V. (1)
Runnenburg 9, 3981 AZ, Bunnik, Netherlands (100%)
Tel.: (31) 306598988
Web Site: http://www.bam.nl
Sales Range: $350-399.9 Million
Emp.: 2,081
Provider of International Contracting, Civil Engineering, Dredging & Consulting Engineering
N.A.I.C.S.: 541330

Subsidiary (Non-US):

BAM Construct UK Ltd (2)
Breakspear Park Breakspear Way, Hemel Hempstead, London, HP2 4UL, Hertfordshire, United Kingdom

Tel.: (44) 1442238300
Web Site: https://www.bam.co.uk
Industrial, Public Building Projects & Commercial Construction Services
N.A.I.C.S.: 236220
Neil McGruer *(Fin Dir & Member-Exec Bd)*

BAM Contractors (2)
Hartwell Lower, Kill, Ireland (100%)
Tel.: (353) 45886400
Web Site: http://www.bam.com
Sales Range: $350-399.9 Million
Emp.: 1,500
Building & Civil Engineering Services
N.A.I.C.S.: 237990

BAM Deutschland Standort Gottingen (2)
Maschmuhlenweg 105, 37081, Gottingen, Germany (100%)
Tel.: (49) 5513090
Web Site: http://www.bam.eu
Sales Range: $100-124.9 Million
Emp.: 350
Industrial, Commercial & Public Building Projects & Housing
N.A.I.C.S.: 236220

Subsidiary (Domestic):

BAM International bv (2)
HJ Nederhorststraat 1, 2801 SC, Gouda, Netherlands (100%)
Tel.: (31) 887123500
Web Site: http://www.baminternational.com
Sales Range: $25-49.9 Million
Emp.: 80
General Construction, Civil Engineering, Road & Housing Construction Outside Western Europe
N.A.I.C.S.: 236220

Subsidiary (Non-US):

BAM Nuttall Ltd. (2)
St James House Knoll Road, Camberley, GU15 3XW, Surrey, United Kingdom (100%)
Tel.: (44) 127663484
Web Site: https://www.bamnuttall.co.uk
Emp.: 3,000
Civil Engineering & Road Construction
N.A.I.C.S.: 237990

Subsidiary (Domestic):

Bam Civiel B.V. (2)
HJ Nederhorststraat 1, 2801, Gouda, Netherlands (100%)
Tel.: (31) 182590600
Web Site: http://www.bamciviel.nl
Sales Range: $25-49.9 Million
Emp.: 250
Civil Engineering in Western Europe
N.A.I.C.S.: 541330
Wouter R. Remmelts *(Chm)*

KONINKLIJKE BRILL N.V.
Plantijnstraat 2, 2321 JC, Leiden, Netherlands
Tel.: (31) 715353500
Web Site: http://www.brill.com
Year Founded: 1683
BRILL—(EUR)
Rev.: $51,854,090
Assets: $66,439,672
Liabilities: $45,165,120
Net Worth: $21,274,552
Earnings: ($3,739,478)
Emp.: 196
Fiscal Year-end: 12/31/22
Book Publishers
N.A.I.C.S.: 513130
Robin Hoytema van Konijnenburg *(Chm-Supervisory Bd)*

KONINKLIJKE DELFTSCH AARDEWERKFABRIEK N.V.
Rotterdamseweg 196, 2628 AR, Delft, Netherlands
Tel.: (31) 152512030
Web Site: https://group.royaldelft.com
PORF—(EUR)
Sales Range: $1-9.9 Million
Emp.: 100

KONINKLIJKE DELFTSCH AARDEWERKFABRIEK N.V.

Koninklijke Delftsch Aardewerkfabriek N.V.—(Continued)
Earthenware Producer
N.A.I.C.S.: 327110
Henk Schouten (CEO)

Subsidiaries:

B.V. Koninklijke van Kempen & Begeer (1)
Zilverstraat 40, 2718, Zoetermeer, Netherlands
Tel.: (31) 793680580
Web Site: http://www.kempen-begeer.nl
Sales Range: $25-49.9 Million
Emp.: 70
Crockery Design & Mfr
N.A.I.C.S.: 327110

Subsidiary (Non-US):

Van Kempen & Begeer Hong Kong Ltd (2)
Rm 21A 235 Wing LOK St Trade Ctr, Sheung Wan, China (Hong Kong)
Tel.: (852) 25196998
Household Tableware Mfr
N.A.I.C.S.: 327110

B.V. Leerdam Crystal (1)
Lingedijk 8, Leerdam, 4142 Ld, Netherlands
Tel.: (31) 345671658
Web Site: http://www.royalleerdamcrystal.nl
Sales Range: $25-49.9 Million
Emp.: 20
Glassware Mfr
N.A.I.C.S.: 327215
Henk Schouten (Mng Dir)

B.V. Royal Delft Onroerend Goed (1)
Rotterdamseweg 196, 2628, Delft, Netherlands
Tel.: (31) 402393393
Household Tableware Mfr
N.A.I.C.S.: 327110

KONINKLIJKE DSM N.V.

Het Overloon 1, 6411 TE, Heerlen, Netherlands
Tel.: (31) 455788111
Web Site: https://www.dsm.com
Year Founded: 1902
KDSKF—(OTCEM)
Rev.: $9,054,608,245
Assets: $18,781,567,019
Liabilities: $7,077,487,589
Net Worth: $11,704,079,430
Earnings: $1,850,852,579
Emp.: 20,682
Fiscal Year-end: 12/31/22
Biotechnology Research & Development Services
N.A.I.C.S.: 551112
Marc Silverand (Mgr-IR)

Subsidiaries:

Amyris Brasil Ltda. (1)
Rua John Dalton 301, Campinas, 13069-330, Sao Paulo, Brazil
Tel.: (55) 1937839450
Web Site: http://www.amyris.com
Industrial Gas Mfr
N.A.I.C.S.: 325120

DSM Agro Services BV (1)
Het Overloon 1, 6411 TE, Heerlen, Netherlands
Tel.: (31) 45 578 8111
Web Site: http://www.dsm.com
Farm Management Services
N.A.I.C.S.: 115116
Feike Sijbesma (Gen Mgr)

DSM Belgium NV (1)
Bureau Brussels Rond-Point Schuman 9, 1040, Brussels, Belgium
Tel.: (32) 2 230 9222
Web Site: http://www.dsm.com
Life Sciences & Materials Sciences Active in Health, Nutrition & Materials
N.A.I.C.S.: 541720

DSM Capua SpA (1)
Strada Statale Appia 46/48, 81043, Capua, Italy
Tel.: (39) 0823 628111
Chemical Products Distr
N.A.I.C.S.: 424690

DSM Central Europe sro (1)
Psohlavcu 16, Prague, 147 00, Czech Republic
Tel.: (420) 261 710 783
Web Site: http://www.dsm.com
Sales Range: $50-74.9 Million
Emp.: 7
Chemical Products Distr
N.A.I.C.S.: 424690
Michal Prochazka (Acct Mgr)

DSM Chemical Technology R&D BV (1)
Urmonderbaan 22, Geleen, 6160 ND, Netherlands
Tel.: (31) 46 4763484
Web Site: http://www.dsm.com
Sales Range: $25-49.9 Million
Emp.: 60
Chemical Product Research & Development Services
N.A.I.C.S.: 541715
Jeroen Kluytmans (Mgr-ACES)

DSM Commercial Coordination & Participations BV (1)
Poststraat 1, 6135 KR, Sittard, Limburg, Netherlands
Tel.: (31) 46 4773999
Chemical Products Distr
N.A.I.C.S.: 424690

DSM Corporate Insurances AG (1)
Stettemerstrasse 28, Schaffhausen, 8207, Switzerland
Tel.: (41) 52 644 12 12
Insurance Management Services
N.A.I.C.S.: 524298

DSM Czech Republic (1)
Rybna 14, 11000, Prague, Czech Republic (100%)
Tel.: (420) 261710785
Web Site: http://www.dsm.com
Sales Range: $50-74.9 Million
Emp.: 10
Sales of Chemicals
N.A.I.C.S.: 424690
Selvie Sedlactova (Gen Mgr)

DSM Desotech (China) Holding BV (1)
5 Ceintuurbaan, Zwolle, 8022 AW, Netherlands
Tel.: (31) 38 4569569
Web Site: http://www.dsm.com
Investment Management Service
N.A.I.C.S.: 523940

DSM Desotech BV (1)
Slachthuisweg 30, Hoek van Holland, 3151 XN, Netherlands
Tel.: (31) 174315544
Web Site: http://www.dsm.com
Chemical Products Distr
N.A.I.C.S.: 424690

DSM Deutschland GmbH (1)
Emanuel Leutze Strasse 8/4Th Floor, 40547, Dusseldorf, Germany (100%)
Tel.: (49) 2114557600
Web Site: http://www.dsm.com
Sales Range: $25-49.9 Million
Emp.: 35
Mfr of Low & High Density Polyethylene, Linear Polyethylene, Polypropylene, Polyamide 4/6, Polycarbonate, Thermoplastic Rubber
N.A.I.C.S.: 325211

DSM Dyneema B.V. (1)
Center Court Brightlands Chemelot Campus Urmonderbaan 22, 6167, Geleen, Netherlands (100%)
Tel.: (31) 467506590
Web Site: http://www.dyneema.com
Sales Range: $50-74.9 Million
Emp.: 220
Polyethylene Fiber Mfr
N.A.I.C.S.: 326199
Wilfrid Gambade (Pres)

Subsidiary (US):

DSM Dyneema LLC (2)
1101 Highway 27 S, Stanley, NC 28164
Tel.: (704) 862-5000
Sales Range: $25-49.9 Million
Emp.: 50
Polyethylene Fiber Mfr
N.A.I.C.S.: 326199
Denise Alexander (Mgr-Fin)

Subsidiary (Domestic):

Cubic Tech Corp. (3)
4511 E Ivy St, Mesa, AZ 85205
Tel.: (480) 641-0438
Web Site: http://cubictechnology.com
Sales Range: $1-9.9 Million
Emp.: 10
Non-Woven Fabric Material Mfr
N.A.I.C.S.: 314999

Subsidiary (Domestic):

DSM High Performance Polyethylenes BV (2)
Het Overloon 1, 6411 TE, Heerlen, Netherlands
Tel.: (31) 455788111
Chemical Products Distr
N.A.I.C.S.: 424690

DSM ICD Participations BV (2)
Het Overloon 1, 6411 TE, Heerlen, Netherlands
Tel.: (31) 45 5788111
Chemical Products Distr
N.A.I.C.S.: 424690

Subsidiary (Non-US):

Nippon Dyneema Co., Ltd. (2)
Toyobo Bldg 2-2-8 Dojima Hama, Kita-ku, Osaka, 530-0004, Japan (50%)
Tel.: (81) 663483484
Web Site: http://www.toyodo.co.jp
Sales Range: $25-49.9 Million
Emp.: 3
Mfr of Polyethylene Fiber
N.A.I.C.S.: 325220

DSM Eastern Europe, LLC (1)
ul Dokukina 16/1 2Nd Floor, Moscow, Russia
Tel.: (7) 4959806060
Web Site: http://www.dsm.com
Sales Range: $25-49.9 Million
Emp.: 40
Thermoplastic Product Mfr
N.A.I.C.S.: 325211

DSM Engineering Plastics International BV (1)
Center Court Brightlands Chemelot Campus Urmonderbaan 22, 6167, Geleen, Netherlands
Tel.: (31) 467506590
Web Site: http://www.dsm.com
Chemical Products Distr
N.A.I.C.S.: 424690

Subsidiary (Domestic):

DSM Advanced Polyesters Emmen BV (2)
Het Overloon 1, Heerlen, 6411 TE, Netherlands
Tel.: (31) 59169333
Web Site: http://www.dsm.com
Emp.: 175
Chemical Products Distr
N.A.I.C.S.: 424690
Jan van Leur (Gen Mgr)

DSM DAB BV (2)
Het Overloon 1, 6411 TE, Heerlen, Netherlands
Tel.: (31) 45 578 8111
Chemical Products Distr
N.A.I.C.S.: 424690

DSM Engineering Plastics BV (2)
Postraat 1, 6130 AA, Sittard, Netherlands
Tel.: (31) 464770123
Web Site: http://www.dsmet.com
Sales Range: $100-124.9 Million
Emp.: 350
N.A.I.C.S.: 325194

Subsidiary (Non-US):

DSM Engineering Materials (3)
1002 Michuhol Tower 12 Gaetbeo-Ro, Yeonsu-gu, Incheon, 21999, Korea (South)
Tel.: (82) 322603400

Web Site: http://www.dsm.com
Plastics Product Mfr
N.A.I.C.S.: 326199

Subsidiary (Domestic):

DSM Engineering Plastic Products (3)
Center Court Brightlands Chemelot Campus Urmonderbaan 22, 6167, Geleen, Netherlands (100%)
Tel.: (31) 467506590
Web Site: http://www.dsm.com
Sales Range: $25-49.9 Million
Emp.: 75
Plastic Materials Mfr
N.A.I.C.S.: 325211

Subsidiary (Non-US):

DSM Engineering Plastics (3)
17Th Floor Room 1701 Singha Complex 1788 New Petchaburi Rd Bang Kapi, Huai Khwang, Bangkok, 10310, Thailand
Tel.: (66) 20095900
Web Site: http://www.dsm.com
Plastics Product Mfr
N.A.I.C.S.: 326199

Subsidiary (Domestic):

DSM Engineering Plastics (China) BV (3)
Poststraat 1, 6135 KR, Sittard, Netherlands
Tel.: (31) 464770123
Chemical Distr
N.A.I.C.S.: 424690

DSM Engineering Plastics (Emmen) BV (3)
Eerste Bokslootweg 17, 7821 AT, Emmen, Netherlands
Tel.: (31) 591693311
Web Site: http://www.dsm.com
Emp.: 300
Plastic Materials Mfr
N.A.I.C.S.: 325211

Subsidiary (US):

DSM Engineering Plastics Inc. (3)
2267 W Mill Rd, Evansville, IN 47732-3333 (100%)
Tel.: (812) 435-7500
Web Site: http://www.dsmep.com
Sales Range: $50-74.9 Million
Emp.: 190
N.A.I.C.S.: 325194

Subsidiary (Non-US):

DSM Engineering Plastics Taiwan Pte. Ltd. (3)
Room 7B17/18 No 5 Hsin-Yi Road Sec 5 TWTC Bldg, Taipei, 110, Taiwan
Tel.: (886) 2 8789 0868
Plastics Product Mfr
N.A.I.C.S.: 326199

DSM India Private Limited (3)
401/402 4th Fl NSG IT Park Aundh, Pune, 411 007, India
Tel.: (91) 20 66430 800
Sales Range: $25-49.9 Million
Emp.: 70
Pharmaceutical Ingredient Mfr & Distr
N.A.I.C.S.: 325412

Subsidiary (Domestic):

DSM Nylatron BV (3)
1 Het Overloon, 6411 TE, Heerlen, Netherlands
Tel.: (31) 455788111
Web Site: http://www.dsm.com
Plastics Product Mfr
N.A.I.C.S.: 326199
Feike Sijbesma (Gen Mgr)

Subsidiary (Non-US):

DSM Specialty Compounds N.V. (3)
Paniswijerstraat 92, Genk, 3600, Belgium
Tel.: (32) 89300511
Web Site: http://www.dsm.com
Sales Range: $50-74.9 Million
Emp.: 220
Mfr of Plastics
N.A.I.C.S.: 326199
Jurgen Harnack (Supvr-Production)

AND PRIVATE COMPANIES **KONINKLIJKE DSM N.V.**

Limited Liability Company Volgalon Limited (3)
st Novozavodskaya 6, Togliatti, 445007, Samara region, Russia
Tel.: (7) 8482561101
Web Site: https://www.volgalon.ru
Chemical Products Distr
N.A.I.C.S.: 424690

Limited Liability Company Volgaplast Compounding (3)
6 Novozavodskaya str, 445007, Togliatti, Russia
Tel.: (7) 8482566186
Composite Chemical Distr
N.A.I.C.S.: 424690

Tai-Young Nylon Co. Ltd (3)
No 25 Ta Yeh Street, Ta Liao Hsiang, 831, Kaohsiung, Taiwan
Tel.: (886) 7 7872251
Sales Range: $25-49.9 Million
Emp.: 40
Chemical Products Distr
N.A.I.C.S.: 424690

DSM Espana SA (1)
La Llacuna 161 2nd Fl, Planta 7a Pta 3 4, 8018, Barcelona, Spain (100%)
Tel.: (34) 934703030
Web Site: http://www.dsm.com
Sales of Plastics & Resins
N.A.I.C.S.: 424610

DSM Executive Services BV (1)
6411 TE, 6411 TE, Heerlen, Limburg, Netherlands
Tel.: (31) 45 5788111
Human Resource Consulting Services
N.A.I.C.S.: 541612

DSM Expert Center BV (1)
Het Overloon 1, 6411 TE, Heerlen, Netherlands
Tel.: (31) 455788111
Web Site: http://www.dsm.com
Emp.: 200
Specialty Chemicals Research & Development Services
N.A.I.C.S.: 541715
Feike Sijbesma *(Pres)*

DSM Finance BV (1)
Het Overloon 1, 6411 TE, Heerlen, 6411 TE, Netherlands
Tel.: (31) 455782905
Sales Range: $200-249.9 Million
Emp.: 400
Financial Services
N.A.I.C.S.: 523999
Jos Caris *(Asst Mgr-Corp Cash)*

DSM Food Specialties B.V. (1)
Alexander Fleminglaan 1, 2613 AX, Delft, Netherlands (100%)
Tel.: (31) 152793474
Sales Range: $350-399.9 Million
Emp.: 1,400
Food & Beverage Ingredient Solutions
N.A.I.C.S.: 311999
Patrick Niels *(Pres)*

Subsidiary (Domestic):

DSM China Holding I BV (2)
Het Overloon 1, 6411 TE, Heerlen, Netherlands
Tel.: (31) 455788111
Web Site: http://www.dsm.com
Sales Range: $150-199.9 Million
Emp.: 450
Investment Management Service
N.A.I.C.S.: 523999
F. Sijbesma *(Mng Dir)*

DSM China Holding II BV (2)
1 Het Overloon, Heerlen, Netherlands
Tel.: (31) 45 578 8111
Investment Management Service
N.A.I.C.S.: 523999

DSM Delft BV (2)
Alexander Fleminglaan 1, 2613 AX, Delft, Netherlands
Tel.: (31) 152799111
Web Site: http://www.dsm.com
Biomedical Material Mfr
N.A.I.C.S.: 325414

DSM Delft Permit BV (2)

Alexander Fleminglaan 1, 2613 AX, Delft, Netherlands
Tel.: (31) 152793474
Web Site: http://www.dsm.com
Chemical Distr
N.A.I.C.S.: 424690

Subsidiary (Non-US):

DSM Food Specialties (2)
Gran Via de Les Corts Catalanes, 8018, Barcelona, Spain (100%)
Tel.: (34) 933774884
Sales Range: $25-49.9 Million
Emp.: 3
Sales of Foodstuff Ingredients
N.A.I.C.S.: 325998
Oscar Prims *(Mgr-Sls)*

DSM Food Specialties (Shanghai) Ltd (2)
98 Baisha Road Xinghuo Development Zone, Pudong New Area, Shanghai, 201419, China
Tel.: (86) 21 5750 4888
Food Ingredient Mfr
N.A.I.C.S.: 311999

DSM Food Specialties Australia Pty Ltd. (2)
9 Moorebank Ave, Moorebank, 2170, NSW, Australia
Tel.: (61) 2 8778 9800
Emp.: 45
Organic Chemical Mfr
N.A.I.C.S.: 325199
Neil Hendy *(Mgr-Tech)*

Subsidiary (Domestic):

DSM Food Specialties China Holding 1 BV (2)
1 Alexander Fleminglaan, Delft, 2600 MA, Netherlands
Tel.: (31) 15 2793474
Web Site: http://www.dsm.com
Emp.: 800
Investment Management Service
N.A.I.C.S.: 523999
Ilona Haaijer *(Pres)*

Subsidiary (Non-US):

DSM Food Specialties Germany GmbH (2)
Niederkasseler Lohweg 175, 40547, Dusseldorf, Germany
Tel.: (49) 2114557700
Food Ingredient Mfr
N.A.I.C.S.: 311999

DSM Food Specialties Italy SpA (2)
Via G Di Vittorio, 02009, Segrate, Milano, Italy
Tel.: (39) 02 2164 1
Web Site: http://www.dsm.com
Food Ingredient Mfr
N.A.I.C.S.: 311999

DSM Food Specialties Ltd. Sti. (2)
Hurriyet Cad No 4/1 No 505 Cankaya, Izmir, Turkiye
Tel.: (90) 232 4640740
Food Ingredient Mfr
N.A.I.C.S.: 311999

Subsidiary (Domestic):

DSM Food Specialties Meltagel BV (2)
1 Alexander Fleminglaan, Delft, 2613AX, Netherlands
Tel.: (31) 15 2793474
Web Site: http://www.dsm.com
Food Ingredient Mfr
N.A.I.C.S.: 311999
Patrick Niels *(CEO)*

Subsidiary (Non-US):

DSM Food Specialties Mexicana S.A. de C.V. (2)
Ave De Las Torres 75, 53500, Mexico, Naucalpan, Mexico (100%)
Tel.: (52) 5555769221
Web Site: http://www.dsm.com
Sales Range: $10-24.9 Million
Emp.: 50
Development, Production & Trade of Foodstuff Ingredients

N.A.I.C.S.: 311999

DSM Food Specialties Poland Sp. z o.o. (2)
Tarczynska 113, 96-320, Warsaw, Poland (100%)
Tel.: (48) 468573131
Web Site: http://www.dsm.com
Sales Range: $1-9.9 Million
Emp.: 7
Development, Production & Trade of Foodstuff Ingredients
N.A.I.C.S.: 311119

DSM Food Specialties Superdex SAS (2)
Route Magnas, Saint-Clar, 32380, France
Tel.: (33) 5 62 66 40 15
Sales Range: $25-49.9 Million
Emp.: 10
Food Ingredient Mfr
N.A.I.C.S.: 311999
Patrick Pronk *(Gen Mgr)*

Subsidiary (US):

DSM Food Specialties USA, Inc. (2)
45 Waterview Blvd, Parsippany, NJ 07054
Tel.: (800) 662-4478
Web Site: http://www.dsm.com
Food Ingredient Mfr
N.A.I.C.S.: 311999

Subsidiary (Non-US):

DSM Gist France SAS (2)
15 Rue Des Comtesses, Seclin, 59472, France (100%)
Tel.: (33) 320964545
Web Site: http://www.dsm.com
Sales Range: $50-74.9 Million
Emp.: 180
Mfr & Sales of Chemical, Veterinarial, Biological, Cosmetic & Pharmaceutical Products
N.A.I.C.S.: 325412
Guionneau Immanuel *(Mgr)*

Subsidiary (Domestic):

DSM Gist Services BV (2)
Alexander Fleminglaan 1, PB 1, Delft, 2613 AX, Netherlands
Tel.: (31) 152792053
Emp.: 1,200
Chemical Products Distr
N.A.I.C.S.: 424690
Frank Teeuwisse *(Mgr-Site)*

DSM France S.A. (1)
Tour Nova 71 Boulevard National, 92250, La Garenne-Colombes, France (100%)
Tel.: (33) 146435900
Web Site: http://www.dsm.com
Sales Range: $25-49.9 Million
Emp.: 26
Mfr of Plastic Resins
N.A.I.C.S.: 325211

DSM Holding Company USA, Inc. (1)
45 Waterview Blvd, Parsippany, NJ 07054-7611
Tel.: (973) 257-1063
Web Site: http://www.dsm.com
Investment Management Service
N.A.I.C.S.: 523940

Subsidiary (Domestic):

DSM PS Executive Centers (2)
1991 Crocker Rd Gemini Towers I, Westlake, OH 44145
Tel.: (440) 892-3300
Web Site: http://psoffices.com
Sales Range: $50-74.9 Million
Emp.: 8
Secretarial & Executive Services
N.A.I.C.S.: 531120
Diane VanEeuwen *(Owner)*

DSM Services USA, Inc. (2)
45 Waterview Blvd, Parsippany, NJ 07054-7611
Tel.: (973) 257-8222
Chemical Products Distr
N.A.I.C.S.: 424690

Kensey Nash Corporation (2)
735 Pennsylvania Dr, Exton, PA 19341
Tel.: (484) 713-2100

Web Site: http://www.kenseynash.com
Emp.: 307
Cardiovascular Medical Devices Mfr
N.A.I.C.S.: 339112
John Witkowski *(Pres)*

Subsidiary (Non-US):

Kensey Nash Europe GmbH (3)
Helfmann-Park 10, 65760, Eschborn, Germany
Tel.: (49) 61969994110
Sales Range: $1-9.9 Million
Emp.: 15
Medical Device Mfr
N.A.I.C.S.: 339112

Subsidiary (Domestic):

Kensey Nash Holding Corporation (3)
3411 Silverside Rd Ste 108WB, Wilmington, DE 19810-4891
Tel.: (302) 478-4600
Surgical & Medical Instrument Mfr
N.A.I.C.S.: 339112

DSM IP Assets BV (1)
Het Overloon 1, 6411 TE, Heerlen, Netherlands
Tel.: (31) 455782050
Intellectual Property Holding Company
N.A.I.C.S.: 551112

DSM Idemitsu Corp. Ltd. (1)
1 1 Anegacaki Kaigan, Chiba, 299 0111, Japan (50%)
Tel.: (81) 436601860
Sales Range: $25-49.9 Million
Emp.: 35
Mfr of Polyethylene; Joint Venture of Royal DSM N.V. (50%) & Idemitsu Kosan Co., Ltd. (50%)
N.A.I.C.S.: 325211

DSM Information & Communication Technology (1)
Global Axis Plot No 152 Gopalan Enterprises SEZ EPIP Area, 560 069, Bengaluru, India
Tel.: (91) 80 6725 5000
Information Technology Consulting Services
N.A.I.C.S.: 541512

DSM Innovation Center BV (1)
Mauritslaan 49, 6129 EL, Urmond, Netherlands
Tel.: (31) 46 476 3128
Sales Range: $75-99.9 Million
Emp.: 400
Intellectual Property Licensing Services
N.A.I.C.S.: 813311

Subsidiary (Domestic):

DSM Bio-based Products & Services BV (2)
Alexander Fleminglaan 1, Delft, 2613 AX, Netherlands
Tel.: (31) 15 279 2504
Web Site: http://www.dsm.com
Emp.: 6
Biotechnology Research & Development Services
N.A.I.C.S.: 541714
Atul Thakrar *(Pres)*

DSM Biomedical BV (2)
Center Court Brightlands Chemelot Campus Urmonderbaan 22, 6167 RD, Geleen, Netherlands
Tel.: (31) 467506590
Web Site: http://www.dsm.com
Sales Range: $25-49.9 Million
Emp.: 50
Medical Polymer Mfr
N.A.I.C.S.: 325998

Subsidiary (US):

DSM Biomedical Inc. (2)
2810 7th St, Berkeley, CA 94710
Tel.: (510) 841-8800
Sales Range: $50-74.9 Million
Emp.: 120
Biomedical Material Mfr
N.A.I.C.S.: 325411
Christophe Dardel *(Pres)*

DSM Functional Materials (2)
1122 Saint Charles St, Elgin, IL 60120-8443

KONINKLIJKE DSM N.V.

INTERNATIONAL PUBLIC

Koninklijke DSM N.V.—(Continued)
Tel.: (847) 697-0400
Web Site: http://www.dsmdesotech.com
Supplier of UV-curable Fiber Opticmaterials
N.A.I.C.S.: 325194

DSM Innovation Inc. (2)
45 Waterview Blvd, Parsippany, NJ 07054-7611
Tel.: (973) 257-8300
Chemical Products Distr
N.A.I.C.S.: 424690

Subsidiary (Domestic):

DSM Succinic Acid B.V. (2)
Alexander Fleminglaan 1, Delft, 2613 AX, Netherlands
Tel.: (31) 152792504
Industrial Chemicals Mfr
N.A.I.C.S.: 325998

DSM Venturing BV (2)
Center Court Brightlands Chemelot Campus
Urmonderbaan 22, 6167 RD, Geleen, Netherlands
Tel.: (31) 467506590
Web Site: http://www.dsm.com
Emp.: 8
Venture Capital Funding Services
N.A.I.C.S.: 523910
Pieter Wolters *(Mng Dir-East Coast-US)*

DSM Innovative Synthesis BV (1)
Urmonderbaan 22, 6167 RD, Geleen, Netherlands
Tel.: (31) 464760525
Web Site: http://www.innosyn.com
Sales Range: $50-74.9 Million
Emp.: 40
Chemical Products Distr
N.A.I.C.S.: 424690
David Hyett *(CFO)*

DSM International BV (1)
1 Het Overloon, Heerlen, 6411 TE, Netherlands
Tel.: (31) 45 578 8111
Chemical Products Distr
N.A.I.C.S.: 424690

DSM International Participations BV (1)
1 Het Overloon, Heerlen, 6411 TE, Netherlands
Tel.: (31) 45 578 8111
Web Site: http://www.dsm.nl
Emp.: 1,000
Chemical Products Distr
N.A.I.C.S.: 424690

DSM Italia s.r.l. (1)
Via Silvio Pellico 12, 22100, Como, Italy (100%)
Tel.: (39) 031236111
Web Site: http://www.dsm.com
Sales Range: $25-49.9 Million
Emp.: 14
Sales of Plastics & Resins
N.A.I.C.S.: 424610

DSM Japan KK (1)
7F-11F 2-6-3 Shibakoen, Minato Ku, Tokyo, 105-0011, Japan (100%)
Tel.: (81) 54721811
Web Site: http://www.dsmjapan.com
Sales Range: $25-49.9 Million
Emp.: 29
Mfr & Sales of Chemical Products
N.A.I.C.S.: 325998

DSM Life Science Products International GmbH (1)
St-Peter-Str 25, 4020, Linz, Austria
Tel.: (43) 7326916
Life Science Research & Development Services
N.A.I.C.S.: 541715

DSM Nederland BV (1)
Het Overloon 1, Heerlen, 6411 TE, Netherlands
Tel.: (31) 464 77 33 22
Investment Management Services
N.A.I.C.S.: 523999

Subsidiary (Domestic):

Chemelot Real Estate B.V. (2)
Poststraat 1, 6135 KR, Sittard, Limburg, Netherlands
Tel.: (31) 464770077
Real Estate Management Services
N.A.I.C.S.: 531390

DSM Industrial Services BV (2)
Mijnweg 1, 6167 AC, Geleen, Netherlands
Tel.: (31) 46 476 66 80
Chemical Products Distr
N.A.I.C.S.: 424690

Graetheide BV (2)
Poststraat 1, 6135 KR, Sittard, Netherlands
Tel.: (31) 46 477 01 11
Chemical Products Distr
N.A.I.C.S.: 424690

Hexagon Energy BV (2)
Het Overloon 1, 6411 TE, Heerlen, Netherlands
Tel.: (31) 455788111
Eletric Power Generation Services
N.A.I.C.S.: 221118

Limburg Raffinaderij BV (2)
Het Overloon 1, 6411 TE, Heerlen, Limburg, Netherlands
Tel.: (31) 455788111
Web Site: http://www.dsm.com
Chemical Products Distr
N.A.I.C.S.: 424690

DSM Nutritional Products AG (1)
Wurmisweg 576, Peter Merian-Strasse 80, CH-4303, Kaiseraugst, Switzerland (100%)
Tel.: (41) 618157777
Web Site: http://www.dsmnutritionalproducts.com
Rev.: $2,293,889,024
Emp.: 6,600
Vitamin & Chemical Supplier
N.A.I.C.S.: 325412
Christoph G. Goppelsroeder *(Pres & CEO)*

Subsidiary (Domestic):

DSM China Holding AG (2)
Wurmisweg 576, Kaiseraugst, 4303, Switzerland
Tel.: (41) 61 815 88 88
Investment Management Service
N.A.I.C.S.: 523940

Subsidiary (Non-US):

DSM China Ltd (2)
476 Li Bing Road Zhangjiang Hi-Tech Park, Pudong New Area, Shanghai, 201203, China
Tel.: (86) 2161417653
Web Site: http://www.dsm.com.cn
Sales Range: $25-49.9 Million
Emp.: 100
Mfr & Sales of Chemical Products
N.A.I.C.S.: 325998

Subsidiary (US):

DSM Nutritional Products (2)
60 Westview St, Lexington, MA 02421
Tel.: (781) 259-7600
Web Site: http://www.dsm.com
Biochemicals Product Mfr
N.A.I.C.S.: 541715
Marcus Lovell Smith *(CEO)*

Subsidiary (Non-US):

DSM Nutritional Products A/S (2)
Kirkebjerg Alle 88 1, Brondby, 2605, Denmark
Tel.: (45) 43 20 89 89
Emp.: 12
Specialty Chemicals Distr
N.A.I.C.S.: 424690

Branch (Domestic):

DSM Nutritional Products AG (2)
Hauptstrasse 4, CH 4334, Sisseln, Switzerland
Tel.: (41) 628662111
Sales Range: $200-249.9 Million
Emp.: 1,000
Vitamins A & E & Pharmaceutical Active Ingredients Mfr
N.A.I.C.S.: 325412

DSM Nutritional Products AG (2)
Zweigniederlassung Werk Lalden, Postfach, 3930, Visp, Switzerland
Tel.: (41) 279456100
Web Site: http://www.dsm.com
Sales Range: $50-74.9 Million
Emp.: 160
Mfr of Chemical Intermediates
N.A.I.C.S.: 325998

Subsidiary (Non-US):

DSM Nutritional Products Argentina SA (2)
Av Lavoisier 3925, B1667AQC, Tortuguitas, Argentina
Tel.: (54) 3327 448600
Web Site: http://www.dsm.com
Animal Feed Mfr
N.A.I.C.S.: 311119

DSM Nutritional Products Asia Pacific Pte Ltd. (2)
30 Pasir Panjang Road Mapletree Business City 13-31, Singapore, 117440, Singapore
Tel.: (65) 66326500
Web Site: http://www.dsm.com
Nutritional Food Ingredient Mfr
N.A.I.C.S.: 311999

Subsidiary (Domestic):

DSM Singapore Industrial Pte Ltd. (3)
30 Pasir Panjang Road Mapletree Business City Unit 13-31, Singapore, 117440, Singapore
Tel.: (65) 66326500
Web Site: http://www.dsm.com
Plastic Materials Mfr
N.A.I.C.S.: 325211

Subsidiary (Non-US):

DSM Nutritional Products Australia Pty Ltd. (2)
41 Edison Road, PO Box 2279, Wagga Wagga, 2650, NSW, Australia
Tel.: (61) 269227015
Web Site: https://www.dsm.com
Nutritional Products
N.A.I.C.S.: 325412

DSM Nutritional Products Canada Inc. (2)
395 Waydom Drive, Ayr, N0B 1E0, ON, Canada
Tel.: (519) 622-2200
Web Site: https://www.dsm.com
Sales Range: $25-49.9 Million
Emp.: 25
Nutritional Food Ingredient Mfr
N.A.I.C.S.: 311999

Plant (Domestic):

DSM Nutritional Products Canada Inc - Cambridge Premix Plant (3)
395 Waydom Drive, Ayr, N0B 1E0, ON, Canada
Tel.: (519) 622-2200
Web Site: http://www.dsm.com
Emp.: 25
Nutritional Food Ingredient Mfr
N.A.I.C.S.: 311999
Dave Trussler *(Plant Mgr)*

DSM Nutritional Products Canada Inc. - High River Premix Plant (3)
1007 Twentieth Street, PO Box 5604, High River, T1V 1M7, AB, Canada
Tel.: (403) 652-7272
Web Site: http://www.dsm.com
Animal Feed Mfr
N.A.I.C.S.: 311119

Subsidiary (Non-US):

DSM Nutritional Products Chile SA (2)
Loteo los Cantaros Parcela nr 1 Ruta 5 Sur km 1010, Puerto Varas, Chile
Tel.: (56) 65 385 300
Nutritional Food Retailer
N.A.I.C.S.: 456191

Plant (Domestic):

DSM Nutritional Products Chile SA - Puerto Varas Premix Plant (3)
Loteo los Cantaros Parcela nr 1 Ruta 5 Sur km 1010, Puerto Varas, Chile
Tel.: (56) 65 385 300
Web Site: http://www.dsm.com
Emp.: 45
Animal Feed Mfr
N.A.I.C.S.: 311119
Jorge Planella *(Mng Dir)*

Subsidiary (Non-US):

DSM Nutritional Products China BV (2)
Het Overloon 1, 6411 TE, Heerlen, Netherlands
Tel.: (31) 455788111
Nutritional Food Ingredient Mfr
N.A.I.C.S.: 311999

Subsidiary (Domestic):

DSM Nutritional Products China Holding GmbH (2)
Wurmisweg 576, 4303, Kaiseraugst, Aargau, Switzerland
Tel.: (41) 61 688 33 33
Investment Management Service
N.A.I.C.S.: 523940

Subsidiary (Non-US):

DSM Nutritional Products Colombia SA (2)
Km 2 4 Via Briceno-Zipaquira Costado Derecho Parque Industrial Tibitoc, Lote 41B y 42B, Tocancipa, Cundinamarca, Colombia
Tel.: (57) 1 587 3540
Food Ingredient Mfr
N.A.I.C.S.: 311999

Plant (Domestic):

DSM Nutritional Products Colombia SA - Feed premix plant (3)
Km 2 4 Via Briceno-Zipaquira Costado Derecho Parque, Tocancipa, Cundinamarca, Colombia
Tel.: (57) 1 587 3540
Animal Food Ingredient Mfr
N.A.I.C.S.: 311119

DSM Nutritional Products Colombia SA - Food/pharmaceutical premix plant (3)
Km 2 4 Via Briceno-Zipaquira Costado Derecho Parque, Tocancipa, Cundinamarca, Colombia
Tel.: (57) 1 587 3540
Food Ingredient Mfr
N.A.I.C.S.: 311999

Subsidiary (Non-US):

DSM Nutritional Products Ecuador SA (2)
Via Sangolqui-Amaguana S/N Km 5 1/2, Quito, Sangolqui, Ruminahui, Ecuador
Tel.: (598) 2 2994600
Food Ingredient Mfr
N.A.I.C.S.: 311999

Subsidiary (Domestic):

DSM Nutritional Products Europe AG (2)
Wurmisweg 576, PO Box 2676, CH-4303, Kaiseraugst, Switzerland
Tel.: (41) 618158888
Web Site: https://www.dsm.com
Food Ingredient Mfr
N.A.I.C.S.: 311999

Subsidiary (Non-US):

DSM Nutritional Products France SAS (2)
Tour Nova 71 Boulevard National, 92250, La Garenne-Colombes, France
Tel.: (33) 146435900
Sales Range: $25-49.9 Million
Emp.: 20
Nutritional Supplements Mfr
N.A.I.C.S.: 325998

Plant (Domestic):

DSM Nutritional Products France SAS - Premix plant (3)
1 Boulevard d Alsace, Village-Neuf, France
Tel.: (33) 3 89 69 69 00
Food Ingredient Mfr
N.A.I.C.S.: 311999

AND PRIVATE COMPANIES — KONINKLIJKE DSM N.V.

Subsidiary (Non-US):

DSM Nutritional Products GmbH (2)
Emil-Barell-Str 3, 79639, Grenzach-Wyhlen, Germany
Tel.: (49) 76249090
Web Site: https://www.dsm.com
Sales Range: $150-199.9 Million
Emp.: 600
Nutritional Food Ingredient Mfr
N.A.I.C.S.: 311999

DSM Nutritional Products Hellas Ltd. (2)
14 Paradissou 1 Patroklou str, PO Box 50969, 15125, Maroussi, Greece
Tel.: (30) 210 8774000
Web Site: http://www.dsm.com
Sales Range: $25-49.9 Million
Emp.: 12
Nutritional Food Ingredient Mfr
N.A.I.C.S.: 311999

Plant (Domestic):

DSM Nutritional Products Hellas Ltd. - Premix Plant (3)
Inofita Industrial Zone, 32011, Oinofita, Viotias, Greece
Tel.: (30) 2262 0 31830
Web Site: http://www.dsm.com
Food Ingredient Mfr
N.A.I.C.S.: 311999

Subsidiary (Non-US):

DSM Nutritional Products Hungary Ltd (2)
Japan Fasor 4, PO Box 1, 2367, Ujhartyan, Hungary
Tel.: (36) 29 57 24 00
Web Site: http://www.dsm.com
Emp.: 36
Food Ingredient Mfr
N.A.I.C.S.: 311999

DSM Nutritional Products Iberia SA (2)
C/ Honduras Parcela 26 Pol Ind El Descubrimiento, Alcala de Henares, 28806, Madrid, Spain
Tel.: (34) 911045500
Animal Food Ingredient Mfr
N.A.I.C.S.: 311119

DSM Nutritional Products India Pvt. Ltd. (2)
B-502 Delphi Building Orchard Avenue Hiranandani Business Park, Powai, Mumbai, 400076, India
Tel.: (91) 22 4034 9100
Web Site: http://www.dsm.com
Emp.: 100
Nutritional Food Ingredient Mfr
N.A.I.C.S.: 311999

Plant (Domestic):

DSM Nutritional Products India Pvt. Ltd. - Thane premix plant (3)
Plot No E57 & E5B Additional MIDC Anandnagar, Ambernath E, 421, 501, Thane, Maharashtra, India
Tel.: (91) 251 6484018
Nutritional Food Ingredient Mfr
N.A.I.C.S.: 311999

Subsidiary (US):

DSM Nutritional Products LLC (2)
45 Waterview Blvd, Parsippany, NJ 07054
Emp.: 250
Animal Feed Mfr
N.A.I.C.S.: 311119

Subsidiary (Non-US):

DSM Nutritional Products Mexico SA de CV (2)
Km 22 5 Carretera Guadalajara-El Salto, 45680, El Salto, Jalisco, Mexico
Tel.: (52) 3336686000
Nutritional Food Ingredient Mfr
N.A.I.C.S.: 311999

DSM Nutritional Products NV (2)
Dorpstraat 4, 9800, Deinze, Belgium
Tel.: (32) 9 381 12 20
Web Site: http://www.dsmnutritionalproducts.com
Sales Range: $25-49.9 Million
Emp.: 70
Food Ingredient Mfr
N.A.I.C.S.: 311999

DSM Nutritional Products Nederland BV (2)
Trade Point West Columbusweg 24, 5928 LC, Venlo, Netherlands
Tel.: (31) 773894400
Web Site: http://www.bsm.com
Nutritional Food Ingredient Mfr
N.A.I.C.S.: 311999

DSM Nutritional Products Peru SA (2)
Av Los Frutales 245 Ate, 15012, Lima, Peru
Tel.: (51) 1 618 6700
Web Site: http://www.dsm.com
Sales Range: $10-24.9 Million
Emp.: 27
Nutritional Food Ingredient Mfr
N.A.I.C.S.: 311999

Plant (Domestic):

DSM Nutritional Products Peru SA - Lima Premix Plant (3)
Av Los Frutales 245 Ate, Lima, Peru
Tel.: (51) 1 618 6700
Animal Food Ingredient Mfr
N.A.I.C.S.: 311119
Gabriela Lock (Gen Mgr)

Subsidiary (Non-US):

DSM Nutritional Products Philippines, Inc. (2)
Unit 1803 One Global Place 5Th Avenue, Bonifacio Global City, 1630, Manila, Philippines
Tel.: (63) 2 553 6506
Web Site: http://www.dsm.com
Sales Range: $25-49.9 Million
Emp.: 20
Animal Feed Mfr
N.A.I.C.S.: 311119

DSM Nutritional Products Romania SRL (2)
Soseaua De Centra No 2L, Stefanestii de Jos, 077175, Ilfov, Romania
Tel.: (40) 213 695 792
Web Site: http://www.dsm.com
Sales Range: $10-24.9 Million
Emp.: 33
Nutritional Food Ingredient Mfr
N.A.I.C.S.: 311999

DSM Nutritional Products Rus LLC (2)
Proizvodstvennaya Str 16, Shilnebash Village, Naberezhnye Chelny, 423888, Russia
Tel.: (7) 8552747446
Web Site: http://www.dsm.com
Sales Range: $10-24.9 Million
Emp.: 40
Nutritional Food Ingredient Mfr
N.A.I.C.S.: 311999

DSM Nutritional Products South Africa (Pty) Ltd. (2)
16 Brewery Street, Isando, 1609, Gauteng, South Africa
Tel.: (27) 113986900
Web Site: http://www.dsm.com
Sales Range: $25-49.9 Million
Emp.: 80
Nutritional Food Ingredient Mfr
N.A.I.C.S.: 311999
John Ronald Pankhurst (Mng Dir)

DSM Nutritional Products Sp. z.o.o. (2)
Tarczynska 113, 96320, Mszczonow, Poland
Tel.: (48) 46 857 3131
Web Site: http://www.dsm.com
Food Ingredient Mfr
N.A.I.C.S.: 311999

DSM Nutritional Products Tatarstan Holding BV (2)
Het Overloon 1, Heerlen, Netherlands
Tel.: (31) 45 5788111
Investment Management Service
N.A.I.C.S.: 523940

DSM Nutritional Products U.K. Limited (2)
Delves Road Heanor Gate, Heanor, DE75 7SG, Derbyshire, United Kingdom
Tel.: (44) 1773536500
Web Site: http://www.dsm.com
Sales Range: $25-49.9 Million
Emp.: 48
Sales of Technical-Grade Ammonium Sulphate, Technical-Grade Urea, Melamine, Phenol, Sodium Cyanide Solution, Cyclohexanone, Caprolactam, Nylon-6 Spinning Chips, KA Oil
N.A.I.C.S.: 424690

DSM Nutritional Products Uruguay SA (2)
Jose MA Guerra 3779, 12000, Montevideo, Uruguay
Tel.: (598) 2 511 4556
Animal Food Ingredient Mfr
N.A.I.C.S.: 311119

Plant (Domestic):

DSM Nutritional Products Uruguay SA - Montevideo premix plant (3)
Jose MA Guerra 3779, Montevideo, 1100, Uruguay
Tel.: (598) 2 511 4556
Animal Food Ingredient Mfr
N.A.I.C.S.: 311119

Subsidiary (Non-US):

DSM Nutritional Products Venezuela SA (2)
Calle F Local Galpones Nos 9 Y 10 Zona Industrial San Vicente Ii, Maracay, 2104, Venezuela
Tel.: (58) 2432372677
Web Site: http://www.dsm.com
Animal Feed Mfr
N.A.I.C.S.: 311119

DSM Nutritional Products Vietnam Ltd. (2)
No 9 Street 14 Vietnam-Singapore Industrial Park Ii-A, Thuan An, Binh Duong, Vietnam
Tel.: (84) 6502221301
Web Site: http://www.dsm.com
Nutritional Food Ingredient Mfr
N.A.I.C.S.: 311999

DSM Nutritional products China Holding BV (2)
1 Het Overloon, Heerlen, 6411 TE, Netherlands
Tel.: (31) 45 578 8111
Web Site: http://www.dsm.com
Sales Range: $150-199.9 Million
Emp.: 450
Investment Management Service
N.A.I.C.S.: 523940
F. Sijbesma (CEO)

DSM Services Mexico SA de CV (2)
Km 22 5 Carretera Guadalajara, 45680, El Salto, Mexico
Tel.: (52) 3336686000
Web Site: http://www.dsm.com
Emp.: 100
Business Management Consulting Services
N.A.I.C.S.: 541611
Manuel Perez (Gen Mgr)

DSM Vitamins (Changchun) Ltd. (2)
No 2988 Zhong Shan Ave Changchun, Changchun, 130031, Jilin, China
Tel.: (86) 431 8963 0336
Web Site: http://www.dsm.com
Nutritional Food Ingredient Mfr
N.A.I.C.S.: 311999

DSM Vitamins (Hunan) Ltd. (2)
No 19 Yue Lu Street High-technology Industry Zone, Hengyang, 421001, Hunan, China
Tel.: (86) 734 2881008
Food Ingredient Mfr
N.A.I.C.S.: 311999

DSM Vitamins (Shanghai) Ltd. (2)
118 Bai Sha Road Xinhuo Development Zone, Shanghai, 201419, China
Tel.: (86) 2157504888
Nutritional Food Ingredient Mfr
N.A.I.C.S.: 311999

Subsidiary (US):

Fortitech Inc. (2)
2105 Technology Dr, Schenectady, NY 12308
Tel.: (518) 372-5155
Web Site: http://www.fortitechpremixes.com
Emp.: 250
Vitamins, Nutrients & Hematinic Preparations Mfr
N.A.I.C.S.: 325412
Brian Scutt (Dir-Reg Ops)

I-Health, Inc. (2)
55 Sebethe Dr Ste 102, Cromwell, CT 06416
Tel.: (860) 894-1200
Web Site: https://dsmihealth.com
Emp.: 100
Nutritional Products Mfr & Distr
N.A.I.C.S.: 311999
Wes Parris (CEO)

Subsidiary (Non-US):

Istituto delle Vitamine SpA (2)
Via Giuseppe di Vittorio snc, 20090, Segrate, Italy
Tel.: (39) 0221641
Web Site: https://www.dsm.com
Food Ingredient Mfr
N.A.I.C.S.: 311999

Ocean Nutrition Canada Limited (2)
101 Research Drive, Dartmouth, B2Y 4T6, NS, Canada
Tel.: (902) 480-3200
Web Site: http://www.dsm.com
Sales Range: $150-199.9 Million
Emp.: 150
Fish Oil Nutritional Supplement Mfr & Distr
N.A.I.C.S.: 325412

P.T. DSM Nutritional Products Indonesia (2)
Arkadia Office Park Tower B 10th Floor Jl Let Jend, T B Simatupang Kav 88, Jakarta, 12520, Indonesia
Tel.: (62) 21 78833456
Web Site: http://www.dsm.com
Animal Feed Mfr
N.A.I.C.S.: 311119

Subsidiary (Domestic):

Pentapharm AG (2)
Domacherstrasse 112, 4147, Aesch, Switzerland
Tel.: (41) 617064848
Web Site: http://www.pentapharm.com
Emp.: 120
Pharmaceutical Ingredient Mfr & Distr
N.A.I.C.S.: 325412

Subsidiary (Non-US):

Rovithai Ltd. (2)
17/1 Maleenont Tower 3199 Rama IV Road Klongton, Khlong Toei, Bangkok, 10110, Thailand
Tel.: (66) 22649800
Animal Food Ingredient Mfr
N.A.I.C.S.: 311119

Vitatene S.A.U. (2)
Antibioticos 59, Leon, 24009, Spain
Tel.: (34) 987 34 44 10
Web Site: http://www.vitatene.com
Organic Chemical Mfr & Distr
N.A.I.C.S.: 325199

DSM Pension Services BV (1)
Het Overloon 1, Postbus 6500, Heerlen, 6401 GH, Netherlands
Tel.: (31) 45 5782577
Web Site: http://www.pdnpensioen.nl
Sales Range: $50-74.9 Million
Emp.: 71
Pension Fund Management Services
N.A.I.C.S.: 525110
G. Rutten (Mng Dir)

DSM Plastomers BV (1)
Het Overloon 1, Heerlen, 6411 TE, Netherlands
Tel.: (31) 455 78 81 11
Chemical Products Mfr
N.A.I.C.S.: 325199

DSM Poland Sp. z.o.o. (1)
Ulica Malczewskiego 28, 02 612, Warsaw, Poland
Tel.: (48) 228449885
Web Site: http://www.dsm

KONINKLIJKE DSM N.V.

Koninklijke DSM N.V.—(Continued)
Sales Range: $25-49.9 Million
Emp.: 4
Mfr of Chemicals
N.A.I.C.S.: 325998

DSM Polymers International BV (1)
PO Box 43, 6130 AA, Sittard, Netherlands **(100%)**
Tel.: (31) 464770077
Web Site: http://www.dsm.com
Mfr of Polymers
N.A.I.C.S.: 325211

DSM Scandinavia AB (1)
Blekingegatan 15, 265 31, Astorp, Sweden
Tel.: (46) 4258300
Sales Range: $50-74.9 Million
Emp.: 1
Industrial Chemical Distr
N.A.I.C.S.: 424690

DSM Schadeverzekeringsmij NV (1)
Het Overloon 1, 6411 TE, Heerlen, Netherlands
Tel.: (31) 45 5788111
Chemical Products Distr
N.A.I.C.S.: 424690

DSM Sourcing BV (1)
Het Overloon 1, 6411 TE, Heerlen, Netherlands
Tel.: (31) 455788111
Chemical Products Distr
N.A.I.C.S.: 424690

DSM South America Ltda (1)
Rua Dr Renato Paes De Barr 717 Conjunto 23, Sao Paulo, 04530-001, Brazil
Tel.: (55) 11 3046 3363
Chemical Products Distr
N.A.I.C.S.: 424690

DSM Trading (Shanghai) Co Ltd. (1)
No 476 Li Bing Road Zhangjiang Hi-Tech Park, Pudong New Area, Shanghai, China
Tel.: (86) 21 6141 8188
Chemical Products Distr
N.A.I.C.S.: 424690

DSM Venturing & Business Development (1)
Het Overloon No 1, PO Box 6500, 6401 JH, Heerlen, Netherlands **(100%)**
Tel.: (31) 455783101
Web Site: http://www.dsm.com
Sales Range: $25-49.9 Million
Emp.: 40
Provider of Venture Capital Services & Business Development
N.A.I.C.S.: 523910
Rob Kirschbaum (Sr Innovation Dir)

Distribuidora FGB Mexicanas S.A. de C.V. (1)
Calzada de Las Bombas 128-2 Col Ex Hacienda de Coapa, 14300, Mexico, D.F., Mexico **(100%)**
Tel.: (52) 55 5679 7167
Web Site: http://www.fersinsa.com
Sales Range: $25-49.9 Million
Emp.: 8
Mfr & Sales of Semi-Synthetic Penicillins
N.A.I.C.S.: 325412

Euroresins Benelux B.V. (1)
Verlaat 22, 3901 RG, Veenendaal, Netherlands **(100%)**
Tel.: (31) 495584910
Web Site: http://www.euroresins.com
Sales Range: $10-24.9 Million
Emp.: 12
Distr of Polyester Resins
N.A.I.C.S.: 424690
Peter van As (Mng Dir)

Firmenich SA (1)
Rue de la Bergere 7, PO Box 148, CH-1242, Satigny, Switzerland **(96.1%)**
Tel.: (41) 227802211
Web Site: https://www.firmenich.com
Fragrances & Flavorings Mfr
N.A.I.C.S.: 325620
Gilbert Ghostine (CEO)

First Choice Ingredients, Inc. (1)
N112W19528 Mequon Rd, Germantown, WI 53022
Tel.: (262) 251-4322
Web Site: https://firstchoiceingredients.com

Sales Range: $1-9.9 Million
Emp.: 12
Groceries And Related Products, Nec, Nsk
N.A.I.C.S.: 424490
James Pekar (Pres)

Geleen Utility Leidingen BV (1)
Het Overloon 1, Heerlen, 6411 TE, Limburg, Netherlands
Tel.: (31) 455788111
Energy Consulting Services
N.A.I.C.S.: 541690

Gist-Brocades Beheer BV (1)
Het Overloon 1, 6411 TE, Heerlen, Netherlands
Tel.: (31) 455788111
Nutritional Food Ingredient Mfr
N.A.I.C.S.: 311999

Interferm BV (1)
Het Overloon 1, 6411 TE, Heerlen, Netherlands
Tel.: (31) 455788111
Chemical Products Distr
N.A.I.C.S.: 424690

Limburg Ventures BV (1)
Boschstraat 76, PO Box 1057, Maastricht, 6211AX, Netherlands
Tel.: (31) 43 3280 320
Web Site: http://www.limburgventures.eu
Financial Management Services
N.A.I.C.S.: 523999
Casper Bruens (Founder)

Sitech Manufacturing Services Beheer BV (1)
Poststraat 1, Postbus 43, 6135 KR, Sittard, Netherlands
Tel.: (31) 46 477 01 11
Chemical Products Mfr
N.A.I.C.S.: 325998

Utility Support Group (USG) BV (1)
Kampstraat 101, 6163 HE, Geleen, Netherlands
Tel.: (31) 467021000
Web Site: http://www.usgbv.com
Sales Range: $25-49.9 Million
Emp.: 25
Utilities Management Consulting Services
N.A.I.C.S.: 541618

KONINKLIJKE HASKONINGDHV GROEP B.V.

Laan 1914 no 35, 3818 EX, Amersfoort, Netherlands
Tel.: (31) 88 348 2000   NI
Web Site: http://www.royalhaskoningdhv.com
Year Founded: 1881
Rev.: $727,576,402
Assets: $366,938,927
Liabilities: $190,134,310
Net Worth: $176,804,617
Earnings: $9,874,925
Emp.: 5,150
Fiscal Year-end: 12/31/19
Holding Company; Engineering & Construction Project Management Consultancy Services
N.A.I.C.S.: 551112
Erik Oostwegel (CEO & Member-Exec Bd)

Subsidiaries:

DHV Engineering Consultancy Co. Ltd. (1)
Floor 25 Building 19 No1515 Gumei Road Phoenix Park of Shanghai, Caohejing HI-TECH Park, Shanghai, 200233, China
Tel.: (86) 2160910699
Engineeering Services
N.A.I.C.S.: 541330

DHV Holdings USA Inc. (1)
7200 Wscnsin Ave Ste 1103, Bethesda, MD 20814
Tel.: (301) 941-1400
Engineeering Services
N.A.I.C.S.: 541330

DHV Hydroprojekt Sp. z.o.o. (1)
ul Dzielna 60, 01-029, Warsaw, Poland
Tel.: (48) 225313400

Web Site: http://www.dhvhydroprojekt.com.pl
Engineeering Services
N.A.I.C.S.: 541330
Stawomir Gappa (Member-Mgmt Bd, Controller & Dir-Resident-Bus Unit)

DHV, S.A. (1)
Largo Rafael Bordalo Pinheiro n 16, 1200-369, Lisbon, Portugal
Tel.: (351) 213254105
Web Site: http://www.dhv.pt
Engineeering Services
N.A.I.C.S.: 541330
Maria Teresa Serra (Project Dir-Intl Bus)

ELC Group Consulting and Engineering Inc. (1)
Ruzgarli Bahce Mah Cumhuriyet Cad Energy Plaza No 2 Kat 6, Beykoz, 34805, Istanbul, Turkiye
Tel.: (90) 2164659130
Engineeering Services
N.A.I.C.S.: 541330
Jurriaan de Jong (Mng Dir)

Haskoning Cambodia Ltd. (1)
No 113 Mao Tse Toung Blvd 245 Parkway Square 2nd floor 2FK4, 12308, Phnom Penh, Cambodia
Tel.: (855) 23223581
Engineeering Services
N.A.I.C.S.: 541330

Haskoning Caribbean Ltd. (1)
11-13 Picton St Newtown, Port of Spain, Trinidad & Tobago
Tel.: (868) 8686285767
Engineeering Services
N.A.I.C.S.: 541330
Hans Maas (Mng Dir)

Haskoning International Services B.V. (1)
Jonkerbosplein 52, 6534 AB, Nijmegen, Netherlands
Tel.: (31) 243284284
Engineeering Services
N.A.I.C.S.: 541330

Haskoning Libya JSC (1)
Asaba a Road KM4, PO Box 2279, Tripoli, Libya
Tel.: (218) 214631784
Engineeering Services
N.A.I.C.S.: 541330
Ghazali Abdulhamid (Mng Dir)

Haskoning Philippines Inc. (1)
Level 17 6750 Office Tower Ayala Avenue, Makati, Manila, Philippines
Tel.: (63) 27558466
Engineeering Services
N.A.I.C.S.: 541330

HaskoningDHV (Malaysia) Sdn Bhd. (1)
23A-8 Oval Damansara No685 Jalan Damansara TTDI, 60000, Kuala Lumpur, Malaysia
Tel.: (60) 377337003
Engineeering Services
N.A.I.C.S.: 541330

HaskoningDHV India PvT Ltd. (1)
Green Boulevard Plot B 9A Tower B 4th Floor Sector 62, Noida, 201301, Uttar Pradesh, India
Tel.: (91) 1204016100
Engineeering Services
N.A.I.C.S.: 541330
Pulkit Seth (Asst Mgr-HR)

HaskoningDHV Nederland B.V. (1)
Laan 1914 No 35, 3818 EX, Amersfoort, Netherlands
Tel.: (31) 88 348 2000
Web Site: http://www.rhdhv.com
Emp.: 900
Engineering & Construction Project Management Consultancy Services
N.A.I.C.S.: 541330
Erik Oostwegel (CEO)

Hydroprojekt Sp. z o.o. (1)
ul Grunwaldzka 21, 60-783, Poznan, Poland
Tel.: (48) 8665832
Web Site: http://www.hydroprojekt.poznan.pl
Engineeering Services

INTERNATIONAL PUBLIC

N.A.I.C.S.: 541330
InterVISTAS (1)
1200 West 73rd Avenue Suite 550, Vancouver, V6P 6G5, BC, Canada
Tel.: (604) 717-1800
Web Site: http://www.intervistas.com
Transportation Consulting Services
N.A.I.C.S.: 541611

NACO, Netherlands Airport Consultants B.V. (1)
Schenkkade 49, 2595 AR, Hague, Netherlands
Tel.: (31) 883481300
Web Site: http://www.naco.nl
Engineeering Services
N.A.I.C.S.: 541330
Gerard van der Veer (Dir-Airport Building Design)

PT Mitra Lingkungan Dutaconsult (1)
Jl RA Kartini 26 Ventura Bldg 4th Fl Suite 405 Cilandak Barat, Cilandak, Jakarta, 12430, Indonesia
Tel.: (62) 217504605
Engineeering Services
N.A.I.C.S.: 541330

Prokom Sp. Z.o.o. (1)
Mieszka I 21, 71-007, Szczecin, Poland
Tel.: (48) 914820341
Web Site: http://www.prokom.szczecin.pl
Automobile Body Parts Mfr
N.A.I.C.S.: 336370

Royal HaskoningDHV (Pty) Ltd. (1)
Tel.: (61) 288545000
Engineering Services
N.A.I.C.S.: 541330
Sarah Buddq (Mng Dir)

Turgis Technology Pty Ltd. (1)
299 Pendoring Rd, Blackheath, Randburg, 2195, Gauteng, South Africa
Tel.: (27) 114762279
Engineeering Services
N.A.I.C.S.: 541330

KONINKLIJKE JUMBO BV

Westzijde 184, Zaandam, 1506 EK, Netherlands
Tel.: (31) 756531300
Web Site: http://www.jumbo.eu
Toy Mfr
N.A.I.C.S.: 339930
Stphanie Smit-Arendse (CEO)

Subsidiaries:

James Galt & Company Limited (1)
Sovereign House Stockford Road, Cheadle, SK8 2EA, Cheshire, United Kingdom
Tel.: (44) 614289111
Web Site: https://www.galttoys.com
Toy & Game Mfr
N.A.I.C.S.: 336991

KONINKLIJKE KPN N.V.

KPN B V Wilhelminakade 123, 3072 AP, Rotterdam, Netherlands
Tel.: (31) 703434343   NI
Web Site: https://www.kpn.com
Year Founded: 1881
KPN—(EUR)
Rev.: $6,049,207,600
Assets: $13,525,719,110
Liabilities: $9,594,838,040
Net Worth: $3,930,881,070
Earnings: $931,666,280
Emp.: 9,724
Fiscal Year-end: 12/31/23
Holding Company; Mobile, Data, Internet, Voice & Visual Media Telecommunications Services
N.A.I.C.S.: 551112
Joost F. E. Farwerck (Chm-Mgmt Bd & CEO)

Subsidiaries:

KPN B.V. (1)
Maanplein 55 Building TP5, Hague, 2516 CK, Netherlands **(100%)**
Tel.: (31) 703434343

AND PRIVATE COMPANIES

Web Site: http://www.kpn.com
Emp.: 500
Provider of Communication Services
N.A.I.C.S.: 517111

Subsidiary (Domestic):

British Telecom B.V. (2)
Televisieweg 14, 1322 AL, Almere, Netherlands (80%)
Tel.: (31) 365474720
Web Site: http://www.bt.com
Sales Range: $25-49.9 Million
Emp.: 10
Broadcasting
N.A.I.C.S.: 334220

Call-2 B.V. (2)
Rontgenlaan 75, 2719 DX, Zoetermeer, 2719 DX, Netherlands
Tel.: (31) 886610870
Web Site: http://www.call2.nl
Sales Range: $75-99.9 Million
Emp.: 350
Information Technology Consulting Services
N.A.I.C.S.: 541512
Machteld Jurrema (Gen Mgr)

E-Plus Nederland B.V. (2)
Maanplein 55TP5 6 25, Hague, 2516 CK, Netherlands
Tel.: (31) 703434343
Telecommunication Servicesb
N.A.I.C.S.: 517810

Subsidiary (Non-US):

KPN EuroRings GbmH (2)
Darmstadter Landstrasse 184, 60598, Frankfurt, Germany
Tel.: (49) 6996874270
Emp.: 20
Telecommunication Servicesb
N.A.I.C.S.: 517810

Subsidiary (Non-US):

Bristol Exchange (3)
123 Easy Street, Bristol, United Kingdom
Tel.: (44) 445555555
Telephone Services
N.A.I.C.S.: 561421
Clark Griswold (Mng Dir)

Subsidiary (Domestic):

KPN Mobile International B.V. (2)
PO Box 30000, 2500 GA, Hague, Netherlands
Tel.: (31) 10 428 9571
Web Site: http://www.kpn-international.com
Mobile Network Operating Services
N.A.I.C.S.: 517112

Telematch BV (2)
Regulusweg 11, 2516 AC, Hague, Netherlands (100%)
Tel.: (31) 880022100
Web Site: https://telematch.nl
Sales Range: $25-49.9 Million
Emp.: 40
Telecommunications
N.A.I.C.S.: 517111

Tetraned VOF (2)
Zuidpool 5, 2801 RW, Gouda, Netherlands
Tel.: (31) 182 593900
Sales Range: $25-49.9 Million
Emp.: 70
System Integration & Networking Services
N.A.I.C.S.: 541512
Jaap Boertjes (Dir-Maintenance & Svcs)

XS4ALL Internet B.V. (2)
Eekholt 42, Diemen, 1112 XH, Netherlands
Tel.: (31) 20 398 7654
Web Site: http://www.xs4all.nl
Internet Access Providing Services
N.A.I.C.S.: 517810

KONINKLIJKE LUCHTVAART MAATSCHAPPIJ N.V.

Amsterdamseweg 55, 1182 GP, Amstelveen, Netherlands
Tel.: (31) 206499123
Web Site: http://www.klm.com
Year Founded: 1919
Air Freight Forwarding Services
N.A.I.C.S.: 481212

Pieter Elbers (Pres & CEO)

Subsidiaries:

Airtrade Holland B.V. (1)
Nobelstraat 19, 2011 TX, Haarlem, Netherlands
Tel.: (31) 23 5160 260
Web Site: http://www.airtrade.com
Airline Ticket Commercial Whslr
N.A.I.C.S.: 425120
Jeroen Martron (CEO)

European Pneumatic Component Overhaul & Repair B.V. (1)
Bellsingel 41, 1119 NT, Schiphol-Rijk, Netherlands
Tel.: (31) 203161730
Web Site: http://www.epcor.nl
Pneumatic Component Repair & Maintenance Services
N.A.I.C.S.: 811310
Bernard Kuiken (Dir-Comml)

KLM Flight Academy B.V. (1)
Burg J G Legroweg 43, 9761 TA, Eelde, Netherlands
Tel.: (31) 50309830
Web Site: http://www.pilootworden.nl
Airline Training Services
N.A.I.C.S.: 611512

KONINKLIJKE PHILIPS N.V.

Philips Center Amstelplein 2, 1096 BC, Amsterdam, Netherlands
Tel.: (31) 205977777 NI
Web Site: http://www.philips.com
Year Founded: 1891
PHG—(NYSE)
Rev.: $21,071,685,440
Assets: $38,027,538,640
Liabilities: $20,248,764,640
Net Worth: $17,778,774,000
Earnings: $4,076,528,560
Emp.: 78,189
Fiscal Year-end: 12/31/21
Holding Company; Electronic & Electrical Components, Consumer Electronics & Semiconductors Mfr & Sales
N.A.I.C.S.: 551112
Jeroen van der Veer (Chm-Supervisory Bd)

Subsidiaries:

Avent Holdings Limited (1)
Lower Road, Glemsford, CO10 7QS, United Kingdom
Tel.: (44) 1787267000
Investment Management Service
N.A.I.C.S.: 523940

Avent Limited (1)
Level Rd Glenford, Sussex, CO1 072F, United Kingdom
Tel.: (44) 1787267000
Parenting & Baby Care Services
N.A.I.C.S.: 624190

BioTelemetry, Inc. (1)
1000 Cedar Hollow Rd, Malvern, PA 19355
Tel.: (610) 729-7000
Web Site: http://www.gobio.com
Rev.: $439,107,000
Assets: $685,720,000
Liabilities: $318,803,000
Net Worth: $366,917,000
Earnings: $29,844,000
Emp.: 1,700
Fiscal Year-end: 12/31/2019
Holding Company; Cardiac Monitoring Device Mfr, Monitoring Services & Laboratory Services
N.A.I.C.S.: 551112
Fred Broadway III (Pres-BioTel Heart)

Subsidiary (Domestic):

Braemar Manufacturing, LLC (2)
1285 Corporate Center Dr Ste 150, Eagan, MN 55121
Tel.: (651) 286-8620
Web Site: http://www.braemarllc.com
Medical Instrument Mfr
N.A.I.C.S.: 339112

Subsidiary (Domestic):

Agility Centralized Research Services, Inc. (3)
2275 Half Day Rd Ste 133, Bannockburn, IL 60015 (100%)
Tel.: (847) 374-1260
Web Site: http://www.agilityresearch.org
Electrocardiogram Data & Management Services
N.A.I.C.S.: 518210

Subsidiary (Domestic):

CardioNet, Inc. (2)
227 Washington St, Conshohocken, PA 19428
Tel.: (610) 729-7000
Web Site: http://www.cardionet.com
Rev.: $111,494,000
Assets: $90,010,000
Liabilities: $20,012,000
Net Worth: $69,998,000
Earnings: ($12,202,000)
Fiscal Year-end: 12/31/2012
Cardiac Monitoring Device Mfr, Monitoring Services & Laboratory Services
N.A.I.C.S.: 339112
Kirk E. Gorman (Chm)

Subsidiary (Non-US):

LifeWatch AG (2)
Baarerstrasse 139, CH-6300, Zug, Switzerland
Tel.: (41) 417286777
Web Site: http://www.lifewatch.com
Telehealth Systems & Diagnostic Monitoring Services
N.A.I.C.S.: 621999

Subsidiary (US):

LifeWatch Corp. (3)
10255 W Higgins Rd Ste 100, Rosemont, IL 60018 (100%)
Tel.: (847) 720-2100
Web Site: http://www.lifewatch.com
Holding Company; Health Monitoring Services
N.A.I.C.S.: 551112

Subsidiary (Non-US):

LifeWatch Japan, Ltd (3)
4-12-7 Hatchobori, Bunkyo-ku Chuo-Ku, Tokyo, 104-0032, Japan (100%)
Tel.: (81) 362805172
Web Site: http://www.lifewatch.com
Medical Technology Services
N.A.I.C.S.: 621512

Lifewatch Technologies Ltd. (3)
2 Pekeris Street, Rehovot, 7670202, Israel (100%)
Tel.: (972) 89484000
Web Site: http://www.lifewatch.com
Medical Technology Services
N.A.I.C.S.: 621512

Subsidiary (Domestic):

LifeWatch Services Inc. (2)
O hare International Ctr II 10255 W Higgins Rd, Rosemont, IL 60018
Tel.: (847) 720-2100
Web Site: http://www.lifewatch.com
Medical Instrument Distr
N.A.I.C.S.: 423450

Telcare Medical Supply, LLC (2)
150 Baker Ave Ext Ste 300, Concord, MA 01742
Tel.: (978) 610-2230
Health Care Srvices
N.A.I.C.S.: 622110
David Bjork (Founder)

Universal Medical, Inc. (2)
720 Brooker Creek Blvd Ste 210, Oldsmar, FL 34677
Tel.: (508) 698-6920
Web Site: https://www.universalmedicalinc.com
Medical Equipment Distr
N.A.I.C.S.: 456199

Universal Medical, Inc. (2)
720 Brooker Creek Blvd Ste 210, Oldsmar, FL 34677
Tel.: (508) 698-6920

KONINKLIJKE PHILIPS N.V.

Web Site: http://www.universalmedicalinc.com
Medical Equipment Distr
N.A.I.C.S.: 456199

VirtualScopics, Inc. (2)
500 Linden Oaks, Rochester, NY 14625
Tel.: (585) 249-6231
Web Site: http://www.virtualscopics.com
Sales Range: $10-24.9 Million
Medical Imaging Analysis Tools Mfr
N.A.I.C.S.: 339112
Ronald Way (COO)

Carestream Health (1)
6200 Tennyson Pkwy, Plano, TX 75024-6097
Tel.: (972) 805-1200
Web Site: http://www.carestreamhealth.com
Health Imaging Products & Services
N.A.I.C.S.: 339112

Compagnie Francaise Philips (1)
33 rue de Verdun, 92156, Suresnes, Cedex, France (100%)
Tel.: (33) 147281000
Web Site: http://www.philips.fr
Mfr of Lighting, Household Appliances, Electronics, Data Systems
N.A.I.C.S.: 335139

De Vitrite Fabriek (The Vitrite Works) B.V. (1)
Elektraweg 1, Zeeland, 4338 PK, Middelburg, Netherlands
Tel.: (31) 118680911
Web Site: https://vitrite.com
Emp.: 100
Lighting Accessory Whslr
N.A.I.C.S.: 423990

Discus Dental Austria GmbH (1)
Josef-Schwer-Gasse 9, Salzburg, 5020, Austria
Tel.: (43) 800449980
Dental Equipment Whslr
N.A.I.C.S.: 423450

Discus Dental Europe B.V. (1)
Van Nelleweg 1, Rotterdam, 3044 BC, South Holland, Netherlands
Tel.: (31) 107503762
Medical Equipment Whslr
N.A.I.C.S.: 423450

Discus International, LLC (1)
8550 Higuera St, Culver City, CA 90232-2522
Tel.: (310) 845-8200
Web Site: http://www.dev2.discusdental.com
Dental Equipment Whslr
N.A.I.C.S.: 423450

Dixtal Tecnologia Industria e Comercio Ltda. (1)
Rua Engenheiro Francisco Pitta Brito 703, Santo Amaro, 04753-080, Brazil
Tel.: (55) 11 5548 4155
Electronic Equipment Whslr
N.A.I.C.S.: 423690

E & D GmbH (1)
Tattenbachplatz 10, 84419, Schwindegg, Germany
Tel.: (49) 80829359511
Web Site: https://www.electronic-u-design.de
Electric Equipment Mfr
N.A.I.C.S.: 334419

EBT Technology, Inc. (1)
110-3 Huan Nsn Rd Nantzu Export Processing Zone, 80681, Kaohsiung, Taiwan
Tel.: (886) 7 362 11 50
Electronic Equipment Whslr
N.A.I.C.S.: 423690

Gaggia S.p.A. (1)
Via Torretta 240, 40041, Gaggio Montano, BO, Italy
Tel.: (39) 0534771111
Web Site: https://www.gaggia.com
Coffee Maker Mfr
N.A.I.C.S.: 335210

Grupo Indal S.L. (1)
Ctra Arcas Reales s/n, Valladolid, 47008, Spain
Tel.: (34) 983 45 75 68
Web Site: http://www.philips.com
Emp.: 30

KONINKLIJKE PHILIPS N.V.   INTERNATIONAL PUBLIC

Koninklijke Philips N.V.—(Continued)
Lighting Equipment Mfr
N.A.I.C.S.: 335139

Subsidiary (Non-US):

Indal Belgie S.A. (2)
Rue des Deux Gares 80, 1070, Anderlecht, Belgium
Tel.: (32) 2 452 27 60
Lighting Equipment Mfr
N.A.I.C.S.: 335139

Indal C&EE, S.R.O. (2)
Barrandova 409/1, 143 00, Prague, Czech Republic
Tel.: (420) 241 768800
Lighting Equipment Mfr
N.A.I.C.S.: 335132

High Tech Campus Eindhoven U.A. (1)
High Tech Campus 1-E The Strip, PO Box 80036, 5656 AE, Eindhoven, Netherlands
Tel.: (31) 402305500
Web Site: https://www.hightechcampus.com
High Technology Facility Management Services
N.A.I.C.S.: 561210

Indalux Iluminacion Tecnica, S.L. (1)
Arcas Reales S/N, Valladolid, 47008, Spain
Tel.: (34) 983 45 75 75
Lighting Equipment Mfr
N.A.I.C.S.: 335139
Arturo Gonzalez *(Mng Dir)*

Industriegrundstucks-Verwaltungsgesellschaft m.b.H. (1)
Triesterstrasse 64, 1100, Vienna, Austria
Tel.: (43) 1 60101 0
Industrial Management Services
N.A.I.C.S.: 541618

InterTrust Technologies Corporation (1)
400 N McCarthy Blvd Ste 220, Milpitas, CA 95035
Tel.: (408) 616-1600
Web Site: https://www.intertrust.com
Sales Range: $25-49.9 Million
Emp.: 60
Develops Digital Rights Management (DRM) Solutions for Providers of Music, Movies, Information & other Digital Content
N.A.I.C.S.: 541511
David Lockwood *(Pres & CEO)*

Latin-American Holdings Corporation (1)
199 Bay St Suite 2800, Toronto, M5L 1A9, ON, Canada
Tel.: (416) 863-2544
Investment Management Service
N.A.I.C.S.: 523940

Limited Liability Company Philips Ukraine (1)
str Patrisa Lumumba 4/6 corp In bldg 7, Building N2 Floor 4, 01042, Kiev, Ukraine
Tel.: (380) 444909868
Web Site: https://www.philips.ua
Consumer Electronics Distr
N.A.I.C.S.: 532210

Ljusgruppen Aktiebolag (1)
Stenyxegatan 17, Malmo, 213 76, Skane, Sweden
Tel.: (46) 40 224100
Lighting Equipment & Component Whslr
N.A.I.C.S.: 423610

New Oxford Aluminum LLC (1)
4942 York Rd, New Oxford, PA 17350-9401
Tel.: (717) 624-2177
Sales Range: $25-49.9 Million
Emp.: 35
Aluminum Casting Mfr
N.A.I.C.S.: 331523
David Miller *(Office Mgr)*

PHILIPS INDUSTRIES Hungary Electronical Mechanical Manufacturing and Trading Limited Liability Company (1)
C Holland Fasor 6, 8000, Szekesfehervar, Hungary
Tel.: (36) 22 53 61 00
Electric Appliances Mfr

N.A.I.C.S.: 335220

PITS NV (1)
Interleuvenlaan 80, Heverlee, 3001, Belgium
Tel.: (32) 16 39 06 11
Sales Range: $25-49.9 Million
Emp.: 40
Lighting Equipment Mfr
N.A.I.C.S.: 335139
Didier de Backer *(Plant Mgr)*

PT. Philips Indonesia (1)
Philips Building 1st Floor Jl Buncit Raya Kav 99, Jakarta, 12510, Indonesia
Tel.: (62) 21 794 75 34
Web Site: http://www.philips.co.id
Sales Range: $450-499.9 Million
Emp.: 1,500
Medical Equipment Mfr & Distr
N.A.I.C.S.: 334510

Philips AB (1)
Knarrarnasgatan 7, Kista, 16440, Stockholm, Sweden (100%)
Tel.: (46) 859852000
Web Site: http://www.philips.com
Sales Range: $750-799.9 Million
Emp.: 300
Seller & Servicer of Consumer Electronics, Lighting, Domestic Appliances, Personal Care Products, Medical Systems, Semiconductors & Electronic Components
N.A.I.C.S.: 423690
Douglas Nelsson *(Mng Dir)*

Philips AG (1)
Allmendstr 140, 8027, Zurich, Switzerland (100%)
Tel.: (41) 444882211
Web Site: http://www.philips.ch
Sales Range: $50-74.9 Million
Emp.: 250
Mfr of Consumer Electric Goods
N.A.I.C.S.: 335210

Philips Argentina Sociedad Anonima (1)
Vedia 3892, C1430DAL, Buenos Aires, Argentina
Tel.: (54) 1145467699
Web Site: https://www.philips.com.ar
Emp.: 300
Electrical Appliance Mfr & Whslr
N.A.I.C.S.: 335999

Philips Avent (1)
Lower Rd Glemsford, New Southgate, Sudbury, CO10 7Q, Suffolk, United Kingdom
Tel.: (44) 1787267000
Web Site: http://www.avent.com
Sales Range: $250-299.9 Million
Emp.: 776
Holding Company
N.A.I.C.S.: 551112

Philips Baltic SIA (1)
Malduguni street 2, Marupe, 2167, Latvia
Tel.: (371) 66163264
Web Site: https://www.philips.lv
Sales Range: $25-49.9 Million
Emp.: 25
Electrical Appliance Whslr
N.A.I.C.S.: 423620

Philips Belguim N.V. (1)
Tweestationsstraat 80, Brussels, 1070, Belgium (100%)
Tel.: (32) 25258111
Web Site: http://www.philips.be
Sales Range: $100-124.9 Million
Emp.: 400
Mfr of Data Systems, Mobil Telephone Systems, Electronics, Analytical Equipment
N.A.I.C.S.: 334290

Philips Bulgaria EOOD (1)
ul BusinessPark Sofia Building 4 Mladost 4, Sofia, 1715, Bulgaria
Tel.: (359) 24899996
Web Site: www.philips.bg
Household Electrical Appliance Whslr
N.A.I.C.S.: 423620

Philips Caribbean Panama, Inc. (1)
Edif Evergreen Piso 9, Panama, Panama
Tel.: (507) 2708300
Electronic Equipment Whslr
N.A.I.C.S.: 423690

Philips Ceska republika s.r.o. (1)

Safrankova 1238/1, PO Box 101, 155 00, Prague, Czech Republic
Tel.: (420) 228880896
Web Site: https://www.philips.cz
Consumer Electronic Product Whslr
N.A.I.C.S.: 423620

Philips Chilena S.A. (1)
Avenida Santa Maria, 0760, Santiago, Chile
Tel.: (56) 27302000
Web Site: https://www.philips.cl
Electronic Equipment Whslr
N.A.I.C.S.: 423690

Philips Colombiana S.A.S. (1)
Calle 93 11A 11 Piso 7, Bogota, Colombia
Tel.: (57) 18000111010
Web Site: https://www.philips.com.co
Electronic Equipment Whslr
N.A.I.C.S.: 423690

Philips Consumer Communications B.V. (1)
Groenewoudseweg 1, Eindhoven, 5621 BA, Netherlands
Tel.: (31) 402791111
Electronic Equipment Whslr
N.A.I.C.S.: 423690

Philips Consumer Lifestyle International B.V. (1)
Amstelplein 2, 1096 BC, Amsterdam, Netherlands
Tel.: (31) 205977777
Consumer Electronics Mfr & Whslr
N.A.I.C.S.: 337126

Philips Consumer Products NV (1)
Tweestationsstraat 80, 1070, Brussels, Belgium
Tel.: (32) 22874287
Electrical Appliance Whslr
N.A.I.C.S.: 423620

Philips Consumer Relations B.V. (1)
IJ Tower Piet Heinkade 55, Amsterdam, 1019 GM, North Holland, Netherlands
Tel.: (31) 205978888
Consumer Relations & Support Services
N.A.I.C.S.: 561421

Philips Danmark A/S (1)
Frederikskaj 6, 1780, Copenhagen, Denmark (100%)
Tel.: (45) 33293333
Web Site: http://www.philips.dk
Sales Range: $50-74.9 Million
Emp.: 240
Electric Equipment Mfr
N.A.I.C.S.: 333992

Subsidiary (Domestic):

Philips Lys A/S (2)
Frederikskaj 6, 1780, Copenhagen, Denmark (100%)
Tel.: (45) 33293743
Sales Range: $25-49.9 Million
Emp.: 50
Mfr of Lightbulbs
N.A.I.C.S.: 335139

Philips Digital Mammography Sweden AB (1)
Smidesvagen 5, 17141, Solna, Stockholm, Sweden
Tel.: (46) 86235200
Sales Range: $10-24.9 Million
Emp.: 100
Mammography Equipment Mfr
N.A.I.C.S.: 334510
Linnea Fryxell *(Mgr-Mktg)*

Philips Egypt (Limited Liability Company) (1)
City stars towers star capital 8 12th floor, Nasr city, Cairo, 11771, Egypt
Tel.: (20) 224801450
Electronic Equipment Whslr
N.A.I.C.S.: 423690
Reham Ammar *(Office Mgr)*

Philips Electronic Components (Shanghai) Co., Ltd. (1)
No 358 Yinglun Road Waigaoqiao Traffer Protection District, New Pudong Area, Shanghai, 200131, China
Tel.: (86) 21 50481188
Electronic Equipment Whslr
N.A.I.C.S.: 423690

Philips Electronics (Shenzhen) Co., Ltd. (1)
Floor P1-P8 No 12 Shihua Road Futian Free Trade Zone, Shenzhen, China
Tel.: (86) 755 83511198
Electronic Components Mfr
N.A.I.C.S.: 334419

Philips Electronics (Suzhou) Co., Ltd. (1)
209 Zhuyuan Road Building B - 3rd 19-21 floor, New District, Suzhou, 215011, Jiansu, China
Tel.: (86) 512 68317506
Electric Equipment Mfr
N.A.I.C.S.: 334419
Xiaohong Lu *(Gen Mgr)*

Philips Electronics (Thailand) Ltd. (1)
1768 Thai Summit Tower 28th Floor New Petchburi Road, Khet Huaykhwang, Bangkok, 10310, Thailand (100%)
Tel.: (66) 26143300
Web Site: https://www.philips.co.th
Sales Range: $800-899.9 Million
Emp.: 5,000
Mfr & Marketer of Consumer Electronics, Domestic Appliances, Lighting Products, Medical Equipment, Semiconductors & Electronic Components
N.A.I.C.S.: 334413

Philips Electronics Asia Pacific Pte Ltd. (1)
622 Lorong 1 Toa Payoh Level 4, Singapore, 319763, Singapore
Tel.: (65) 8008523328
Web Site: https://www.signify.com
Emp.: 100
Lighting Equipment Mfr
N.A.I.C.S.: 335139

Philips Electronics Australia Limited (1)
Philips House 65 Epping Rd, North Ryde, 2113, NSW, Australia
Tel.: (61) 299470000
Sales Range: $50-74.9 Million
Emp.: 200
Electronic Lighting Equipment Mfr & Whslr
N.A.I.C.S.: 335139
Micahel Liem *(CFO)*

Philips Electronics Bangladesh Private Limited (1)
Level 9 Office Unit B East Tower 111 Bir Uttam, Monem Business District, Dhaka, 1205, Bangladesh
Tel.: (880) 2963200109
Electric Equipment Mfr
N.A.I.C.S.: 334419

Philips Electronics China B.V. (1)
Groenewoudseweg 1 Gebouw VO, Eindhoven, 5621 BA, North Brabant, Netherlands
Tel.: (31) 402791111
Electronic Equipment Whslr
N.A.I.C.S.: 423690

Philips Electronics Hong Kong Limited (1)
5/F Core Building 1 1 Science Park East Avenue, Hong Kong Science Park, Sha Tin, New Territories, China (Hong Kong)
Tel.: (852) 2821 5888
Web Site: https://www.philips.com.hk
Sales Range: $200-249.9 Million
Emp.: 1,000
Lighting Equipment Mfr
N.A.I.C.S.: 335139

Philips Electronics Ireland Limited (1)
Philips House South County Business Park Leopardstown, Dublin, Ireland
Tel.: (353) 17640000
Web Site: http://www.philips.com
Sales Range: $25-49.9 Million
Emp.: 42
Consumer Electronic & Electrical Product Whslr
N.A.I.C.S.: 423620

Philips Electronics Japan, Ltd. (1)
Philips Building 2-13-37 Konan, Minato-ku, Tokyo, 108-8507, Japan
Tel.: (81) 337403213

AND PRIVATE COMPANIES

Lighting Equipment Distr
N.A.I.C.S.: 423610

Philips Electronics Korea (1)
260 199 Itaewon Dong Yongsan Ku, Seoul, 140200, Korea (South)
Tel.: (82) 27091212
Web Site: http://www.philips.co.kr
Sales Range: $100-124.9 Million
Emp.: 300
Consumer Electronics Mfr & Marketer
N.A.I.C.S.: 334413

Philips Electronics Nederland B.V. (1)
Building WDV-P 021 High Tech Campus 26, Eindhoven, 5656 AE, Netherlands
Tel.: (31) 40 2746762
Sales Range: $25-49.9 Million
Emp.: 50
Electronic Product Research & Development Services
N.A.I.C.S.: 541715

Unit (Domestic):

Evoluon-Philips Competence Centre (2)
Noordbrabantlaan 1 A, 5656 AE, Eindhoven, Netherlands
Tel.: (31) 402504666
Web Site: http://www.evoluon.com
Sales Range: $25-49.9 Million
Emp.: 50
Electronics Equipment
N.A.I.C.S.: 423690

Subsidiary (Domestic):

Philips Consumer Electronic Services B.V. (2)
Boschdijk 525, PO Box 90050, 5600 PB, Eindhoven, Netherlands (100%)
Tel.: (31) 402791111
Mfr of Electronic & Electrical Components, Consumer Electronics, Semiconductors
N.A.I.C.S.: 334413

Philips Electronics North America Corporation (1)
(100%)
Tel.: (978) 659-3000
Web Site: http://www.usa.philips.com
Sales Range: $5-14.9 Billion
Emp.: 3,000
Mfr of Consumer Electrical & Electronic Components
N.A.I.C.S.: 423620

Subsidiary (Non-US):

Andalusia T.V. Inc. (2)
(100%)
Tel.: (215) 639-3800
Web Site: https://www.andalusiatv.com
Electronics Repair
N.A.I.C.S.: 811210

Digital Lifestyle Outfitters (2)
Tel.: (843) 577-7067
Sales Range: $100-124.9 Million
Emp.: 70
Computer & Digital Music Player Accessories
N.A.I.C.S.: 339999

LG Philips Display USA Inc (2)
Tel.: (734) 996-9400
Web Site: http://www.components.philips.com
Sales Range: $50-74.9 Million
Emp.: 200
Mfr of Cathode Ray Tubes
N.A.I.C.S.: 334419

Norelco Consumer Products Company (2)
Tel.: (203) 973-0200
Web Site: http://www.phillips.com
Sales Range: $25-49.9 Million
Emp.: 100
Miscellaneous Product Mfr
N.A.I.C.S.: 339999

Philips Accessories & Computer Peripherals N.A. (2)
Tel.: (973) 804-2100
Web Site: http://www.powersentry.com
Sales Range: $125-149.9 Million
Emp.: 441

Radio & T.V. Communications Equipment Mfr
N.A.I.C.S.: 334220

Philips Consumer Electronics (2)
Tel.: (719) 667-4801
Web Site: http://www.philips.com
Sales Range: $25-49.9 Million
Emp.: 40
Electronic Parts & Equipments
N.A.I.C.S.: 423690

Philips Consumer Electronics (2)
Tel.: (770) 821-2400
Web Site: http://www.phillips.com
Sales Range: $125-149.9 Million
Emp.: 300
Electronic Accessories
N.A.I.C.S.: 423620

Philips Credit Corporation (2)
Tel.: (212) 536-0500
Corporate Financial Services
N.A.I.C.S.: 522299

Philips Dictation Systems (2)
(100%)
Tel.: (770) 821-3680
Web Site: http://www.dictation.philips.com
Sales Range: $50-74.9 Million
Emp.: 6
Marketer of Digital & Analog Dictation Equipment; Pocket Size Recorders & Remote Microphone Dictation Systems
N.A.I.C.S.: 423420

Philips Dunlee (2)
Tel.: (630) 585-2000
Web Site: http://www.dunlee.com
Sales Range: $125-149.9 Million
Emp.: 300
Mfr of X-Ray Apparatus & Tubes
N.A.I.C.S.: 334517

Philips Electronics Ltd. (2)
(100%)
Tel.: (905) 201-4100
Web Site: http://www.philips.ca
Sales Range: $100-124.9 Million
Emp.: 400
Nuclear Medicine Sales
N.A.I.C.S.: 335999

Plant (Non-US):

Philips Electronics North America (2)
Tel.: (865) 521-4316
Web Site: http://www.philips.com
Sales Range: $125-149.9 Million
Emp.: 400
Mfr of Consumer Electronics
N.A.I.C.S.: 423690

Philips Electronics North America (2)
Tel.: (909) 946-5939
Sales Range: $25-49.9 Million
Emp.: 2
Mfr of Lamp Components
N.A.I.C.S.: 484121

Philips Electronics North America (2)
Tel.: (859) 236-3100
Sales Range: $25-49.9 Million
Emp.: 75
Mfr of Pressed & Blown Glass
N.A.I.C.S.: 327212

Philips Electronics North America (2)
(100%)
Tel.: (202) 962-8550
Web Site: http://www.philips.com
Sales Range: $25-49.9 Million
Emp.: 12
Mfr of Electronic Parts & Equipment
N.A.I.C.S.: 423690

Subsidiary (Non-US):

Philips Light On Digital Solutions (2)
Tel.: (765) 864-0116
Web Site: http://www.philips.com
Sales Range: $50-74.9 Million
Emp.: 3
Electrical Apparatus & Equipments
N.A.I.C.S.: 423690

Philips Lighting Electronics (2)
(100%)
Tel.: (847) 390-5000
Sales Range: $125-149.9 Million
Emp.: 270

Ballasts for Fluorescent & Mercury Vapor & Other High Intensity Discharge Lamps, Dimming & Control Systems, Power Units for Microwave Cooking
N.A.I.C.S.: 335311

Philips Research (2)
Tel.: (914) 945-6000
Web Site: http://www.phcna.com
Sales Range: $25-49.9 Million
Emp.: 220
Basic Research & Development in Electrooptics With Related Programs in Solid State Electronics & Instrumentation
N.A.I.C.S.: 541715

Philips Electronics Singapore Pte Ltd (1)
622A Lorong 1 Toa Payoh 622, TP4 Building, Singapore, 319763, Singapore
Tel.: (65) 68823000
Sales Range: $1-4.9 Billion
Emp.: 3,000
Consumer Electronics Mfr & Marketer
N.A.I.C.S.: 423620

Philips Electronics Technology (Shanghai) Co., Ltd. (1)
No 1805 Huyi Highway Malu Town, Jiading Dist, Shanghai, 201801, China
Tel.: (86) 2159158784
Sales Range: $250-299.9 Million
Emp.: 1,000
Lighting Equipment Distr
N.A.I.C.S.: 423610

Philips Electronics Technology Shanghai Holding B.V. (1)
Groenewoudseweg 1, 5621 BA, Eindhoven, North Brabant, Netherlands
Tel.: (31) 402791111
Investment Management Service
N.A.I.C.S.: 523940

Philips Electronics UK Limited (1)
The Philips Centre, Guildford, GU2 8XH, Surrey, United Kingdom (100%)
Tel.: (44) 8706010101
Web Site: http://www.philips.co.uk
Sales Range: $200-249.9 Million
Emp.: 800
Mfr of Consumer Electronics
N.A.I.C.S.: 334310

Subsidiary (Domestic):

Philips Lighting Ltd. (2)
Philips Centre, Guilford Business Park, Guildford, GU28XH, Surrey, United Kingdom (100%)
Tel.: (44) 8456011283
Web Site: https://www.lighting.philips.com
Lamps, Bulbs, Tubes & Other Lighting Equipment Mfr
N.A.I.C.S.: 335139

Philips Electronics Vietnam Limited (1)
12/F A B Tower 76 Le Lai Street, District 1, Ho Chi Minh City, Vietnam
Tel.: (84) 839111508
Electric Lighting Fixture Mfr
N.A.I.C.S.: 335132

Philips Eletronica do Nordeste S.A. (1)
Av Getulio Vargas 3500 Curado, 50730-680, Recife, Pernambuco, Brazil
Tel.: (55) 81 2122 7033
Electronic Equipment Whslr
N.A.I.C.S.: 423690

Philips Entertainment Lighting Asia Limited (1)
Unit C Block C 14/F Roxy Industrial Centre No 41-49 Kwai Cheong Road, Kwai Chung, New Territories, China (Hong Kong)
Tel.: (852) 2796 9786
Electrical Equipment Distr
N.A.I.C.S.: 423610

Philips Export B.V. (1)
Groenewoudseweg 1, 5621 BA, Eindhoven, Netherlands
Tel.: (31) 402791111
Electronic Equipment Whslr
N.A.I.C.S.: 423690

Philips Healthcare Informatics Limited (1)

KONINKLIJKE PHILIPS N.V.

Channel Wharf Old Channel Road, Belfast, BT3 9DE, United Kingdom
Tel.: (44) 28 9046 1200
Web Site: http://www.philips.com
Sales Range: $25-49.9 Million
Emp.: 25
Software Development Services
N.A.I.C.S.: 541511

Philips Hellas S.A. (1)
1 3 Tzavella Strasse, 152 31, Halandri, Greece
Tel.: (30) 210 616 2000
Web Site: http://www.philips.gr
Electrical Appliance Whslr
N.A.I.C.S.: 423610

Philips IPSC Tamasi Kft. (1)
Szabadsag Utca 107, Tamasi, 7090, Hungary
Tel.: (36) 74571000
Sales Range: $50-74.9 Million
Emp.: 200
Lighting Equipment Mfr
N.A.I.C.S.: 335139

Philips India Limited (1)
Unit No 402 4th Floor Tower 3, Worldmark Maidawas Road Sector -65, Gurgaon, 122018, Haryana, India
Tel.: (91) 9840944855
Holding Company
N.A.I.C.S.: 551112
Rohit Sathe (Pres-Health Sys)

Philips Innovative Applications N.V. (1)
Steenweg op Gierle 417, Turnhout, 2300, Belgium
Tel.: (32) 14401393
Electrical Products Distr
N.A.I.C.S.: 423610

Philips International B.V. (1)
Bldg VO, PO Box 218, 5600 MD, Eindhoven, Netherlands (100%)
Tel.: (31) 402791111
Web Site: http://www.philips.nl
International Holding Company; Mfr of Electronic & Electrical Consumer, Commercial & Industrial Goods
N.A.I.C.S.: 551112

Philips Luxembourg SA (1)
19 Rue Eugene Rupper, 2453, Luxembourg, Luxembourg
Tel.: (352) 4040611
Lighting Equipment Whslr
N.A.I.C.S.: 423610

Philips Magyarorszag Kereskedelmi Kft. (1)
Aliz u1, 1117, Budapest, Hungary
Tel.: (36) 13821820
Web Site: https://www.philips.hu
Medical Equipment Mfr & Distr
N.A.I.C.S.: 334510

Philips Medical Systems (1)
595 Miner Rd, Cleveland, OH 44143-2131
Tel.: (440) 483-3000
Web Site: http://www.careers.philips.com
Sales Range: $1-4.9 Billion
Mfr & Retailer of Medical Imaging Equipment; Distributor of Radiologic Supplies & Accessories
N.A.I.C.S.: 334517

Subsidiary (Domestic):

AllParts Medical, LLC (2)
400 Brick Church Park Dr, Nashville, TN 37207
Tel.: (615) 690-5050
Web Site: https://www.allpartsmedical.com
Medical Imaging Equipment Mfr & Whslr
N.A.I.C.S.: 334510

Blue Jay Consulting, LLC (2)
200 S Orange Ave Ste 2160, Orlando, FL 32801
Tel.: (407) 210-6570
Web Site: http://www.usa.philips.com
Emergency Management Consulting Services
N.A.I.C.S.: 541690

Burton Medical Products Corporation (2)
21100 Lassen St, Chatsworth, CA 91311-4250

KONINKLIJKE PHILIPS N.V.

Koninklijke Philips N.V.—(Continued)
Tel.: (818) 701-8700
Web Site: http://www.burtonmedical.com
Sales Range: $50-74.9 Million
Emp.: 60
Medical Lighting Equipment Designer, Mfr & Distr
N.A.I.C.S.: 335139

Unit (Domestic):

Phillips Lifeline (2)
111 Lawrence St, Framingham, MA 01702-8156
Tel.: (508) 988-1000
Web Site: http://www.lifelinesys.com
Sales Range: $150-199.9 Million
Emp.: 829
Personal Response Products & Services Mfr & Distr
N.A.I.C.S.: 339112

Philips Healthcare Informatics (2)
4100 E 3rd Ave, Foster City, CA 94404
Tel.: (650) 293-2300
Cardiology & Radiology Information Management Products Mfr
N.A.I.C.S.: 423450
Matthew Long *(VP-Mktg-North America)*

Subsidiary (Non-US):

Argus Imaging B.V. (3)
Jan Campertstraat 5, Heerlen, 6416 SG, Netherlands
Tel.: (31) 455470156
Web Site: http://www.argus-imaging.com
Emp.: 50
Medical Equipment Whslr
N.A.I.C.S.: 423450

Subsidiary (Domestic):

Philips Healthcare Informatics-RIS (3)
4050 Rio Bravo Ste 200, El Paso, TX 79902
Tel.: (915) 313-7400
Sales Range: $1-9.9 Million
Emp.: 17
Radiology Management Systems Developer
N.A.I.C.S.: 423450

VISICU, Inc. (3)
217 E Redwood St Ste 1900, Baltimore, MD 21202-3315
Tel.: (410) 276-1960
Web Site: http://www.visicu.com
Sales Range: $25-49.9 Million
Emp.: 104
Healthcare Information Technology & Clinical Solutions Services
N.A.I.C.S.: 519290

Subsidiary (Domestic):

Philips Lifeline (3)
111 Lawrence St, Framingham, MA 01702
Tel.: (855) 681-5351
Web Site: http://www.lifeline.philips.com
Medical Alert Services
N.A.I.C.S.: 423450

Unit (Domestic):

Philips Medical Systems (2)
22100 Bothell Everett Hwy, Bothell, WA 98021 (100%)
Tel.: (425) 487-7000
Web Site: http://www.medical.philips.com
Sales Range: $75-99.9 Million
Emp.: 200
Medical Diagnostic Systems Mfr
N.A.I.C.S.: 423450
Gerard J. Kleisterlee *(Pres)*

Philips Medical Systems (2)
3860 N 1st St, San Jose, CA 95134
Tel.: (408) 321-9100
Web Site: http://www.medical.philips.com
Sales Range: $25-49.9 Million
Emp.: 200
Mfr of Medical & Diagnostic Equipment for Radiation Therapy, Nuclear Medicine, Digital Radiography & Healthcare Information Systems
N.A.I.C.S.: 811210

Division (Domestic):

Philips ADAC (3)
3860 N 1st St, San Jose, CA 95134-1702
Tel.: (603) 645-0162
Web Site: http://www.usa.philips.com
Sales Range: $25-49.9 Million
Emp.: 8
Mfr of Nuclear Medical Diagnostic Systems
N.A.I.C.S.: 334519

Unit (Domestic):

Philips Medical Systems (2)
450 Old Niskayuna Rd, Latham, NY 12110
Tel.: (518) 782-1122
Sales Range: $150-199.9 Million
Emp.: 350
Metal Products Mfr
N.A.I.C.S.: 332999

Philips Medical Systems (2)
64 Perimeter Center E, Atlanta, GA 30346 (100%)
Tel.: (678) 924-6000
Web Site: http://www.medical.philips.com
Sales Range: $25-49.9 Million
Emp.: 40
Mfr of Medical Equipment & Supplies
N.A.I.C.S.: 339112

Philips Medical Systems (2)
4100 E Third Ave Ste 301, Foster City, CA 94404
Tel.: (650) 293-2300
Sales Range: $25-49.9 Million
Emp.: 1
Mfr of Medical Ultrasonic Scanning Devices
N.A.I.C.S.: 238990

Philips Medical Systems (2)
100 Summit Lake Dr, Valhalla, NY 10595
Tel.: (518) 782-1122
Web Site: http://www.medical.philips.com
Sales Range: $25-49.9 Million
Emp.: 1
Surgical & Medical Instruments Mfr
N.A.I.C.S.: 339112

Subsidiary (Domestic):

Philips Medical Systems MR, Inc. (2)
450 Old Niskayuna Rd, Latham, NY 12110
Tel.: (518) 782-1122
Electromedical Equipment Mfr
N.A.I.C.S.: 334510

Philips Remote Cardiac Services (2)
535 Rte 38 Ste 500, Cherry Hill, NJ 08002
Tel.: (856) 354-2222
Sales Range: $25-49.9 Million
Emp.: 40
Remote Cardiac Monitoring & Testing Services
N.A.I.C.S.: 334510
Gene Kupniewski *(Dir-Ops)*

Unit (Domestic):

Philips X Ray (2)
1120 Nashua St, Houston, TX 77008-6453
Tel.: (281) 333-2653
Sales Range: $25-49.9 Million
Emp.: 11
Commercial Equipment
N.A.I.C.S.: 335132

Subsidiary (Domestic):

Raytel Cardiac Services, Inc. (2)
7 Waterside Crossing, Windsor, CT 06095-0727
Tel.: (860) 298-6100
Cardiac Diagnostic Testing Pacemaker Mfr
N.A.I.C.S.: 334510

Respironics, Inc. (2)
1010 Murry Ridge Ln, Murrysville, PA 15668-8525
Tel.: (724) 387-5200
Web Site: http://www.respironics.com
Patient Ventilation Products Designer, Mfr & Marketer
N.A.I.C.S.: 339113
David P. White *(Chief Medical Officer)*

Plant (Non-US):

Philips Respironics Hong Kong (3)
Unit 302A 3 F New Bright Building, 11 Sheung Yuet Raod, Kowloon, China (Hong Kong)
Tel.: (852) 31942200
Web Site: http://www.respironics.com

Sales Range: $25-49.9 Million
Emp.: 100
Patient Ventilation Products Designer, Mfr & Marketer
N.A.I.C.S.: 339112

Subsidiary (Domestic):

Respironics International, Inc. (3)
1010 Murry Rdg Dr, Murrysville, PA 15668
Tel.: (724) 387-5200
Medical Equipment Whslr
N.A.I.C.S.: 423450

Subsidiary (Domestic):

Spectrum Dental, LLC (2)
8554 Hayden Pl, Culver City, CA 90232
Tel.: (310) 845-3160
Web Site: http://www.specdent.com
Dental Care Product Mfr
N.A.I.C.S.: 339114

The Spectranetics Corp. (2)
9965 Federal Dr, Colorado Springs, CO 80921
Tel.: (719) 447-2000
Web Site: http://www.spectranetics.com
Medical Appliances & Equipment Mfr
N.A.I.C.S.: 334510

Subsidiary (Non-US):

Spectranetics International B.V. (3)
Plesmanstraat 6, 3833 LA, Leusden, Netherlands
Tel.: (31) 334347050
Medical Instrument Mfr & Marketer
N.A.I.C.S.: 339112

Subsidiary (Non-US):

Spectranetics Deutschland GmbH (4)
Schweinfurter Strasse 7, 97080, Wurzburg, Germany
Tel.: (49) 9314520080
Web Site: http://www.spectranetics.com
Medical Device Mfr & Marketer
N.A.I.C.S.: 334510

Philips Medical Systems DMC GmbH (1)
Roentgenstrasse 24, 22335, Hamburg, Germany
Tel.: (49) 4050780
Sales Range: $200-249.9 Million
Emp.: 800
Medical Instrument Mfr
N.A.I.C.S.: 339112

Philips Medical Systems Nederland B.V. (1)
Veenpluis 4-6, 5684 PC, Best, Netherlands
Tel.: (31) 402791111
Medical Instrument Mfr & Distr
N.A.I.C.S.: 339112

Philips Medizin Systeme Boblingen GmbH (1)
Hewlett-Packard-Strasse 2, 71034, Boblingen, Germany
Tel.: (49) 70314630
Sales Range: $200-249.9 Million
Emp.: 800
Medical Imaging Equipment Mfr
N.A.I.C.S.: 334510
Michael Dreher *(Co-CEO)*

Philips Mexicana, S.A. de C.V. (1)
Web Site: http://www.philips.com.mx
Electrical Equipment Mfr & Whslr
N.A.I.C.S.: 335999

Philips Nederland B.V. (1)
Boschdijk 525, Eindhoven, 5621 JG, Netherlands
Tel.: (31) 402793333
Consumer Electronics Mfr & Distr
N.A.I.C.S.: 335220

Philips Norge AS (1)
Innspurten 15, 0663, Oslo, Norway
Tel.: (47) 22748000
Medical Equipment Whslr
N.A.I.C.S.: 423450

Philips Overseas Holdings Corporation (1)
281 Hillmount Rd, Markham, L6C 2S3, ON, Canada

INTERNATIONAL PUBLIC

Tel.: (905) 201-4100
Household Appliances Mfr
N.A.I.C.S.: 335220

Philips Oy (1)
Linnoitustie 11, Espoo, 02600, Finland
Tel.: (358) 9615800
Web Site: http://www.philips.fi
Electrical Equipment Whslr
N.A.I.C.S.: 423610

Philips Patient Monitoring Systems China Holding B.V. (1)
High Tech Campus 48, 5656 AE, Eindhoven, Netherlands
Tel.: (31) 402791111
Patient Monitoring Equipment Mfr
N.A.I.C.S.: 334510

Philips Peruana S.A. (1)
Avenida Larco No 1301, Miraflores, Lima, Peru
Tel.: (51) 16106200
Web Site: https://www.philips.com.pe
Electronic Equipment Whslr
N.A.I.C.S.: 423690

Philips Properties NV (1)
Tweestationsstraat 80, Anderlecht, 1070, Belgium
Tel.: (32) 2 525 81 72
Real Estate Manangement Services
N.A.I.C.S.: 531390
Hendrik Vermeylen *(Gen Mgr)*

Philips Romania S.R.L. (1)
Soseaua Pipera Nr 46D-46E-48 Oregon Park Building C Floor 2 Sector 2, 020276, Bucharest, Romania
Tel.: (40) 212032060
Web Site: https://www.philips.ro
Sales Range: $25-49.9 Million
Emp.: 15
Household Appliance Whslr
N.A.I.C.S.: 423620

Philips SC Unterstutzungskasse GmbH (1)
Lubeckertordamm 5, 20099, Hamburg, Germany
Tel.: (49) 4028992966
Fund Management Services
N.A.I.C.S.: 523940

Philips Slovakia s.r.o. (1)
Plynarenska 7/B, Bratislava, 82109, Slovakia
Tel.: (421) 2 20 666 101
Web Site: http://www.philips.sk
Sales Range: $25-49.9 Million
Emp.: 30
Household Appliance Whslr
N.A.I.C.S.: 423620

Philips Slovenija trgovina, d.o.o. (1)
June 24 road 2, Crnuce, 1231, Ljubljana, Slovenia
Tel.: (386) 40720333
Lighting Equipment Distr
N.A.I.C.S.: 423610

Philips South Africa (Proprietary) Limited (1)
54 Maxwell Drive Woodmeet N Office Park, Johannesburg, 2191, Gauteng, South Africa
Tel.: (27) 11 471 5000
Electronic Equipment Whslr
N.A.I.C.S.: 423690

Philips Trustee Company Limited (1)
Philips Centre Guildford Business Park, Guildford, GU2 8XH, Surrey, United Kingdom
Tel.: (44) 1483293171
Business Administrative Services
N.A.I.C.S.: 541611

Philips U.K. Limited (1)
Philips Centre Guildford Business Park Guildford, Surrey, GU2 8XH, United Kingdom
Tel.: (44) 1483293171
Investment Management Service
N.A.I.C.S.: 523940
Peter Mascall *(Mng Dir)*

Philips Uruguay S.A. (1)
Rambla O'Higgins 5303, Montevideo, 11400, Uruguay
Tel.: (598) 26196666
Web Site: http://www.philips.com.uy

AND PRIVATE COMPANIES

Medical Equipment Mfr & Distr
N.A.I.C.S.: 334510

Philips Venture Capital Fund B.V. (1)
Groenewoudseweg 1, Eindhoven, 5621 BA, Netherlands
Tel.: (31) 402791111
Investment Management Service
N.A.I.C.S.: 523940

Philips do Brasil-Walita Div. (1)
Ottosargato 250, Varginha, 37066 440, Minasgarais, Brazil (100%)
Tel.: (55) 3532197160
Web Site: http://www.philips.com.br
Sales Range: $50-74.9 Million
Emp.: 360
Mfr of Electric Housewares
N.A.I.C.S.: 335210

Philips do Brazil Ltda. (1)
Rua Verbo Divino 1400 1, Chacara Santo Antonio, 04719 002, Sao Paulo, SP, Brazil
Tel.: (55) 121250241
Web Site: http://www.philips.com.br
Sales Range: $100-124.9 Million
Emp.: 500
Mfr of Consumer Electric Goods
N.A.I.C.S.: 335210

Philips' Radio B.V. (1)
Groenewoudseweg 1, Eindhoven, 5621 BA, Netherlands
Tel.: (31) 402791111
Electronic Equipment Whslr
N.A.I.C.S.: 423690
Frans Van Houten *(Mng Dir)*

Profile Pharma Limited (1)
Bicentennial Building, Southern Gate,, Tangmere, Chichester, P019 8EZ, United Kingdom
Tel.: (44) 800 1300 855
Web Site: http://www.profilepharma.com
Pharmaceutical Products Distr
N.A.I.C.S.: 424210

Quantum Medical Imaging, LLC (1)
2002 Orville Dr N, Ronkonkoma, NY 11779
Tel.: (631) 567-5800
Web Site: http://www.quantummedical.net
Rev.: $64,500,000
Emp.: 75
Irradiation Apparatus Mfr
N.A.I.C.S.: 334517

RCM Manufacturing, Inc. (1)
107 Competence Drive, Calamba, Philippines
Tel.: (63) 495490829
Surgical Appliance Whslr
N.A.I.C.S.: 423450

RI Finance, Inc. (1)
801 NW St, Wilmington, DE 19801
Tel.: (302) 254-4166
Financial Management Services
N.A.I.C.S.: 523999

RIC Investments, LLC (1)
801 NW St 2nd Fl, Wilmington, DE 19801
Tel.: (302) 656-8907
Financial Investment Services
N.A.I.C.S.: 523999

Remediation Services, Inc. (1)
2735 S 10th St, Independence, KS 67301
Tel.: (620) 331-6216
Web Site: https://www.rsi-ks.com
Remedial Cleanup Services
N.A.I.C.S.: 562910

Respiratory Technologies, Inc. (1)
5905 Nathan Ln N Ste 200, Plymouth, MN 55442
Web Site: https://www.respirtech.com
Surgical & Medical Instrument Mfr
N.A.I.C.S.: 339112

Respironics Deutschland GmbH & Co. KG (1)
Gewerbestr 17, 82211, Herrsching am Ammersee, Germany
Tel.: (49) 815293060
Medical Equipment Mfr
N.A.I.C.S.: 339112

Respironics Deutschland Verwaltungsgesellschaft mbH (1)
Prinzregentenplatz 10, Munich, 81675, Germany
Tel.: (49) 815293060
Administrative Management Consulting Services
N.A.I.C.S.: 541611

Respironics Ltd. (1)
Ascent 1 Aerospace Boulevard, Farnborough, GU14 6XW, United Kingdom
Tel.: (44) 8001300840
Medical Equipment Distr
N.A.I.C.S.: 339112

Respironics Respiratory Drug Delivery (UK) Ltd. (1)
Chichester Business Park City Fields Way, Tangmere, Chichester, PO20 2FT, United Kingdom
Tel.: (44) 8001300840
Medical Equipment Whslr
N.A.I.C.S.: 423450

Respironics Sweden AB (1)
Vretenvagen 10, 171 54, Solna, Sweden
Tel.: (46) 8 120 45900
Web Site: http://www.healthcare.philips.com
Household Appliances Mfr
N.A.I.C.S.: 335220

Saeco International Group S.p.A. (1)
Via Torretta 240, Gaggio Montano, 40041, Bologna, Italy
Tel.: (39) 0534771111
Web Site: http://www.saeco.com
Sales Range: $400-449.9 Million
Emp.: 1,400
Holding Company; Coffee Machines Designer, Mfr & Marketer
N.A.I.C.S.: 551112

Subsidiary (Non-US):

Saeco Argentina S.A. (2)
Lavalle 4072, Capital Federal, C1190ABB, Buenos Aires, Argentina (100%)
Tel.: (54) 1148653357
Web Site: http://www.saecoprofessional.com.ar
Coffee Machines Designer, Mfr & Marketer
N.A.I.C.S.: 333241

Saeco Austria AG (2)
Millennium Pk 1, 6890, Lustenau, Austria
Tel.: (43) 557781380
Web Site: http://www.saeco.at
Sales Range: $25-49.9 Million
Emp.: 20
Coffee Machines Designer, Mfr & Marketer
N.A.I.C.S.: 333241

Saeco Canada Ltee. (2)
8145 Boul St Laurent, Montreal, H2P 2M1, QC, Canada (100%)
Tel.: (514) 385-5551
Web Site: http://www.saeco.ca
Sales Range: $25-49.9 Million
Emp.: 30
Coffee Machines Designer, Mfr & Marketer
N.A.I.C.S.: 333241

Saeco Centroamerica SA (2)
Diagonal a Pizza Hut, Pavas, San Jose, Costa Rica
Tel.: (506) 2291 1151
Web Site: http://www.saecocentroamerica.com
Coffee Maker Mfr
N.A.I.C.S.: 335999

Saeco France S.A. (2)
33 rue de Verdun, 92150, Suresnes, France
Web Site: http://www.saecovending.fr
Sales Range: $25-49.9 Million
Emp.: 10
Coffee Dispenser Mfr
N.A.I.C.S.: 335999

Saeco GmbH (2)
Guerickestrasse 25, 80805, Munich, Germany
Tel.: (49) 89 200045 501
Coffee Machines Designer, Mfr & Marketer
N.A.I.C.S.: 333241

Saeco Iberica S.A. (2)
Sant Ferran 34-36, Cornella de Llobregat, Barcelona, 8940, Spain
Tel.: (34) 93 474 00 17
Web Site: http://www.saecovending.es
Emp.: 15

Coffee Maker Mfr335999
N.A.I.C.S.: 335999

Saeco International Group Australia Pty Ltd (2)
256 Darebin Road, Fairfield, 3078, VIC, Australia (100%)
Tel.: (61) 384864999
Web Site: http://www.saeco.com.au
Coffee Machines Designer, Mfr & Marketer
N.A.I.C.S.: 333241

Saeco Polska Sp. z o.o. (2)
Ul Zeganska 30 A-5, 04-713, Warsaw, Poland
Tel.: (48) 228126202
Web Site: http://www.saeco.com.pl
Sales Range: $25-49.9 Million
Emp.: 10
Coffee Machines Designer, Mfr & Marketer
N.A.I.C.S.: 333241

Subsidiary (US):

Saeco USA Inc. (2)
7905 Cochran Rd Ste 100, Cleveland, OH 44139
Tel.: (440) 528-2000
Sales Range: $25-49.9 Million
Emp.: 35
Coffee Machines Designer, Mfr & Marketer
N.A.I.C.S.: 333241

Subsidiary (Domestic):

Saeco Vending S.p.A. (2)
Loc Casona 1066, 40041, Gaggio Montano, Bologna, Italy
Tel.: (39) 0534 7741
Coffee Vending Machine Mfr
N.A.I.C.S.: 333241

Subsidiary (Non-US):

Saeco do Brasil Comercio de equipamentos Ltda (2)
Rua Dr Fonseca do Brasil, CEP 05716-060, Morumbi, Brazil
Tel.: (55) 1138827300
Web Site: http://www.saeco.com.br
Coffee Machines Designer, Mfr & Marketer
N.A.I.C.S.: 333241

Saecopor-Importacao e Comercio de Aparelhos Electricos, Lda (2)
Gemunde Rua Do Castanhal Lote 21 Sector Ii, 4475-122, Maia, Portugal
Tel.: (351) 229 47 93 10
Electrical Appliance Mfr
N.A.I.C.S.: 335999

Shanghai Apex Electronics Technology Co., Ltd. (1)
Room 203 Building 5 3000 Longdong Ave, Pudong, Shanghai, 201203, China
Tel.: (86) 21 68791007
Web Site: http://www.apex-ultrasound.com
Emp.: 300
Ultrasonic Transducer Mfr
N.A.I.C.S.: 334510

Shenzhen Goldway Industrial Inc. (1)
No 2 Tiangong Road, Nanshan District, Shenzhen, 518057, China
Tel.: (86) 755 26055151
Sales Range: $100-124.9 Million
Emp.: 500
Medical Equipment Mfr
N.A.I.C.S.: 339112

Turk Philips Ticaret A.S. (1)
Tel.: (90) 2165221802
Mfr & Wholesaler of Electronic Parts & Equipment; Joint Venture of Philips A.G. (75%) & Sabanci (25%)
N.A.I.C.S.: 449210

Volcano Corporation (1)
3721 Valley Ctr Dr Ste 500, San Diego, CA 92130
Tel.: (800) 228-4728
Web Site: http://www.volcanocorp.com
Intravascular Ultrasound Product Mfr
N.A.I.C.S.: 334510

Subsidiary (Non-US):

Volcano Europe BVBA (2)
Excelsiorlaan 41, 1930, Zaventem, Belgium
Tel.: (32) 26791076

Intravascular Ultrasound Mfr
N.A.I.C.S.: 334510

WMGD Pty. Limited (1)
U 6 691 Gardeners Rd, Mascot, 2020, NSW, Australia
Tel.: (61) 283389899
Sales Range: $50-74.9 Million
Emp.: 126
Electronic Components Mfr
N.A.I.C.S.: 334419
David O'Rourke *(Gen Mgr)*

KONINKLIJKE VOLKERWESSELS N.V.

Podium 9, 3826 PA, Amersfoort, Netherlands
Tel.: (31) 88 186 6186   NI
Web Site:
  http://www.volkerwessels.com
Year Founded: 1831
Rev.: $7,438,110,120
Assets: $4,513,035,800
Liabilities: $3,097,532,760
Net Worth: $1,415,503,040
Earnings: $160,139,980
Emp.: 17,044
Fiscal Year-end: 12/31/19
Construction Services & Property Development; Road Maintenance & Railtrack Renewals
N.A.I.C.S.: 237990
Dick Boers *(Member-Mgmt Bd)*

Subsidiaries:

BBH Security Services bv (1)
Weegschaalstraat 10, 7324 BG, Apeldoorn, Netherlands
Tel.: (31) 88 186 1010
Construction Engineering Services
N.A.I.C.S.: 541330

Bouwontwikkeling Jongen bv (1)
Europalaan 26, 6199 AB, Maastricht, Netherlands
Tel.: (31) 43 387 39 00
Web Site:
  http://www.bouwontwikkelingjongen.nl
Real Estate Development Services
N.A.I.C.S.: 531390

KWS Infra bv (1)
Lange Dreef 9, 4131 NJ, Vianen, Netherlands
Tel.: (31) 347 35 73 00
Web Site: http://www.kws.nl
Emp.: 100
Construction Engineering Services
N.A.I.C.S.: 541330
Jan De-Boer *(Dir)*

Subsidiary (Domestic):

BRUIL infra bv (2)
Pascalstraat 15, 6716 AZ, Ede, Netherlands
Tel.: (31) 8 627700
Web Site: http://www.bruilinfra.nl
Construction Engineering Services
N.A.I.C.S.: 541330

InfralinQ (2)
Bazeldijk 50, 4221 XX, Hoogblokland, Netherlands
Tel.: (31) 183 56 83 62
Web Site: http://www.infralinq.com
Construction Engineering Services
N.A.I.C.S.: 541330

M.J.O. Holding bv (2)
Luienhoeksestraat 10, 4714 TE, Sprundel, Netherlands
Tel.: (31) 165 38 27 66
Web Site: http://www.mjoomen.nl
Management Consulting Services
N.A.I.C.S.: 541611

Wilchem B.V. (2)
Burgemeester Keijzerweg 12, 3352 AR, Papendrecht, Netherlands
Tel.: (31) 78 641 39 88
Web Site: http://www.wilchem.nl
Road Construction Services
N.A.I.C.S.: 237990

Loostad bv (1)
Boogschutterslaan 44, 7324 BA, Apeldoorn, Netherlands

KONINKLIJKE VOLKERWESSELS N.V.

Koninklijke VolkerWessels N.V.—(Continued)
Tel.: (31) 55 368 38 00
Web Site: http://www.loostad.nl
Real Estate Development Services
N.A.I.C.S.: 531390

Mid Mountain Contractors, Inc. (1)
3075 112th Ave NE Ste 210, Bellevue, WA 98004
Tel.: (425) 202-3600
Web Site: http://www.mjdmtn.com
Civil Construction Services
N.A.I.C.S.: 237990

PCH Integrated Facility Management & Services B.V. (1)
Weegschaalstraat 10, 7324 BG, Apeldoorn, Netherlands
Tel.: (31) 88 186 10 10
Web Site: http://www.pch-dienstengroep.nl
Parking Services
N.A.I.C.S.: 812930

SDK Vastgoed bv (1)
Dillenburgstraat 25a, 5605 JB, Eindhoven, Netherlands
Tel.: (31) 40 250 43 80
Web Site: http://www.sdkvastgoed.nl
Civil Construction Services
N.A.I.C.S.: 237990

VWS Pipeline Control b.v. (1)
Rietgorsweg 6, 3356 LJ, Papendrecht, Netherlands
Tel.: (31) 881864021
Web Site: http://www.pipeline-control.com
Pipeline Construction Services
N.A.I.C.S.: 237990

Van Hattum en Blankevoort bv (1)
Lange Dreef 13, 4131 NJ, Vianen, Netherlands
Tel.: (31) 881865100
Web Site: http://www.vhbinfra.nl
Civil Construction Services
N.A.I.C.S.: 237990

Visser & Smit Bouw bv (1)
Waalhaven Zz 11, 3089 JH, Rotterdam, Netherlands
Tel.: (31) 103131000
Web Site: http://www.visserensmitbouw.nl
Construction Engineering Services
N.A.I.C.S.: 541330

Visser & Smit Hanab bv (1)
Rietgorsweg 6, 3356 LJ, Papendrecht, Netherlands
Tel.: (31) 78 641 72 22
Web Site: http://www.vshanab.nl
Construction Engineering Services
N.A.I.C.S.: 541330

Volker Stevin Contracting Ltd (1)
7175 12th St SE, Calgary, T2H 2S6, AB, Canada
Tel.: (403) 571-5800
Web Site: http://www.volkerstevin.ca
Construction Engineering Services
N.A.I.C.S.: 541330
Damien Festa (Mgr-Underground Utilities)

Subsidiary (Domestic):

McNally Contractors Ltd (2)
4155 - 6th Ave N, Lethbridge, T1H 6X1, AB, Canada
Tel.: (403) 328-3924
Web Site: http://mcnallycontractors.com
Emp.: 170
Civil Construction Services
N.A.I.C.S.: 237990
Kevin Bannister (Controller)

Volker Stevin Materieel bv (1)
Donker Duyvisweg 75, 3316 BL, Dordrecht, Netherlands
Tel.: (31) 78 654 63 00
Web Site: http://www.vwml.nl
Construction Equipment Rental Services
N.A.I.C.S.: 532412

Volker Wessels Telecom BV (1)
Modemweg 23, 3821 BS, Amersfoort, Netherlands
Tel.: (31) 881860666
Web Site: http://www.vwtelecom.com
Emp.: 1,800
Telecommunication Infrastructure Maintenance Services

N.A.I.C.S.: 238210

VolkerWessels Bouw & Vastgoedontwikkeling bv (1)
Reggesingel 4, 7461 BA, Rijssen, Netherlands
Tel.: (31) 548 54 02 50
Construction Services
N.A.I.C.S.: 237990

VolkerWessels Bouwmaterieel bv (1)
Enterstraat 202, 7461 PE, Rijssen, Netherlands
Tel.: (31) 88 186 62 66
Web Site: http://www.materieeldienst.nl
Emp.: 200
Construction Services
N.A.I.C.S.: 237990

VolkerWessels Integraal bv (1)
Lange Dreef 11 G, 4131 NJ, Vianen, Netherlands
Tel.: (31) 88 186 9750
Web Site: http://www.volkerwessels.com
Construction Engineering Services
N.A.I.C.S.: 541330

VolkerWessels UK Ltd. (1)
Hertford Road, Hoddesdon, EN11 9BX, Hertfordshire, United Kingdom
Tel.: (44) 1992 305 000
Web Site: http://www.volkerwessels.co.uk
Construction Engineering Services
N.A.I.C.S.: 541330
Alan Robertson (CEO)

Subsidiary (Domestic):

VolkerInfra Ltd. (2)
The Lancashire Hub Preston City Park Bluebell Way, Preston, PR2 5PE, Lancashire, United Kingdom
Tel.: (44) 1772 759 600
Web Site: http://www.volkerinfra.co.uk
Cable Installation Services
N.A.I.C.S.: 238210
Peter Cooke (Dir-Technical Dev)

VolkerLaser Ltd. (2)
The Lodge Blackpole Road, Worcester, WR4 9FH, Worcestershire, United Kingdom
Tel.: (44) 800 022 3292
Web Site: https://www.volkerlaser.co.uk
Construction Services
N.A.I.C.S.: 237990
Andrew Welsh (Dir-Comml)

VolkerRail Ltd. (2)
Eagre House J3 Business Park Carr Hill, Balby, Doncaster, DN4 8DE, Yorkshire, United Kingdom
Tel.: (44) 1302 79 11 00
Web Site: http://www.volkerrail.co.uk
Emp.: 200
Construction Services
N.A.I.C.S.: 237990
Andrew Wilkins (Dir-Fin)

VolkerWessels Vastgoed bv (1)
Ringwade 4, 3439 LM, Nieuwegein, Netherlands
Tel.: (31) 88 186 68 68
Web Site: http://www.vwvastgoed.nl
Property Development Services
N.A.I.C.S.: 236116

VolkerWessels Vastgoedbeheer (1)
Lange Dreef 7, 4131 NJ, Vianen, Netherlands
Tel.: (31) 88 1861600
Web Site: http://www.vwvastgoedbeheer.nl
Property Development Services
N.A.I.C.S.: 236116

KONINKLIJKE VOPAK N.V.

Westerlaan 10, 3016 CK, Rotterdam, Netherlands
Tel.: (31) 104002911 NI
Web Site: https://www.vopak.com
Year Founded: 1999
VOPKY—(OTCIQ)
Rev.: $1,675,571,255
Assets: $7,345,512,751
Liabilities: $3,618,390,551
Net Worth: $3,727,122,199
Earnings: $539,573,904
Emp.: 5,211
Fiscal Year-end: 12/31/23

Petroleum Products & Chemicals Storage Systems
Ben J. Noteboom (Chm-Supervisory Bd)

Subsidiaries:

Engro Vopak Terminal Ltd (1)
Corporate Office Block 4th Floor Office Number 5 Dolmen City, HC 3 Block 4 Scheme 5 Clifton, 74000, Karachi, Pakistan
Tel.: (92) 213 529 3901
Web Site: http://www.vopak.com
Sales Range: $50-74.9 Million
Emp.: 80
Other Chemical & Allied Products Merchant Whslr
N.A.I.C.S.: 424690

Evos Hamburg GmbH (1)
Alter Rethedamm 2, 21107, Hamburg, Germany
Tel.: (49) 4 075 1960
Web Site: https://www.evos.eu
Sales Range: $75-99.9 Million
Emp.: 150
Petroleum & Chemical Terminals Operation Services
N.A.I.C.S.: 424710
Alexander Fokker (Mgr-Comml)

PT Vopak Terminal Merak (1)
Talavera Suite 19th Floor Unit 03 Talavera Office Park JI TB, Simatupang Kav 22-26 Jakarta Terminal JI Raya Merak KM 3-Gerem Grogol, Cilegon, Banten, Indonesia
Tel.: (62) 2175925250
Petroleum Product Mfr
N.A.I.C.S.: 324199
Tri Jayadi (Mgr-Maintenance)

Terminal de Altamira de S. de R.L. de C.V. (1)
Rio Palmas s/n Col, Puerto Industrial, 89603, Altamira, Tamaulipas, Mexico
Tel.: (52) 8332603700
Petroleum Product Mfr
N.A.I.C.S.: 324199

Thai Tank Terminal Limited (1)
19 I-1 Road Map Ta Phut, Chomphon Chatuchak, Muang Rayong, 21150, Rayong, Thailand (49%)
Tel.: (66) 38673500
Web Site: http://www.thaitank.com
Storage & Transport Services for Liquid Chemicals, Oil & Gas
N.A.I.C.S.: 493190

Vopak Agencies Amsterdam B.V. (1)
Capriweg 28, 1044 AL, Amsterdam, Netherlands
Tel.: (31) 204488700
Web Site: http://www.vopakagencies.com
Sales Range: $25-49.9 Million
Tank Storage & Logistics Services
N.A.I.C.S.: 484220
Dennis Schuijt (Dir-Singapore)

Vopak Agencies Antwerpen NV (1)
Indiestraat 28, 2000, Antwerp, Belgium
Tel.: (32) 32214422
Web Site: http://www.vopakagencies.com
Sales Range: $25-49.9 Million
Oil & Chemical Transportation Services
N.A.I.C.S.: 484230
Jan Daverveldt (Gen Mgr)

Vopak Agencies Terneuzen B.V. (1)
Schuttershofweg 1, 4538 AA, Terneuzen, Netherlands
Tel.: (31) 115630000
Web Site: http://www.vopakagencies.com
Sales Range: $25-49.9 Million
Tank Storage & Logistics Services
N.A.I.C.S.: 484220
Arthur Schot (Gen Mgr-Hub Agencies)

Vopak Asia Pte. Ltd. (1)
52 Jurong Gateway Road 15-01, Singapore, 608550, Singapore
Tel.: (65) 62735677
Sales Range: $50-74.9 Million
Chemical & Oil Terminals Operation Services
N.A.I.C.S.: 424710
Ismail Mahmud (Dir-Product-Chemicals)

INTERNATIONAL PUBLIC

Vopak Brasil S.A. (1)
Tel.: (55) 1332951000
Sales Range: $75-99.9 Million
Emp.: 200
Petroleum & Chemical Terminals Operation Services
N.A.I.C.S.: 424710

Vopak Chemical Terminals Belgium NV (1)
Scheldelaan 410, 2040, Antwerp, Belgian, Belgium
Tel.: (32) 35423290
Emp.: 70
Chemical Terminals Operation Services
N.A.I.C.S.: 561990

Vopak Chemicals EMEA B.V. (1)
Wieldrechtseweg 50, 3316 BG, Dordrecht, South Holland, Netherlands
Tel.: (31) 786528310
Tank Storage & Logistics Services
N.A.I.C.S.: 484230

Vopak Chemicals Logistics Finland Oy (1)
Kuusisaarentie 641, Kotka, 48310, Kymenlaakso, Finland
Tel.: (358) 522692200
Sales Range: $25-49.9 Million
Emp.: 50
Chemical Transportation Services
N.A.I.C.S.: 484220

Vopak Chile Limitada (1)
Terminal San Antonio Antonio Nunez de Fonseca 853, San Antonio, Chile
Tel.: (56) 35354151
Web Site: http://www.vopaklatinamerica.com
Sales Range: $25-49.9 Million
Emp.: 20
Petroleum & Chemical Terminals Operation Services
N.A.I.C.S.: 424710

Vopak China Management Company Ltd. (1)
26F Broad Silver International Building No398 HuaiHai Zhong Road, Luwan, Shanghai, 200020, China
Tel.: (86) 2164310000
Sales Range: $50-74.9 Million
Emp.: 50
Investment Management Service
N.A.I.C.S.: 523940

Vopak Colombia S.A. (1)
Barranquilla Terminal Via 40 No 85-174, Barranquilla, Colombia
Tel.: (57) 3850606
Web Site: https://www.vopak.com
Petroleum & Chemical Terminals Operation Services
N.A.I.C.S.: 424710

Vopak EMEA B.V. (1)
Westerlaan 10, 3016 CK, Rotterdam, Netherlands
Tel.: (31) 635250793
Web Site: https://www.vopakemea.nl
Shipping Services
N.A.I.C.S.: 488330

Vopak Global Shared Services B.V. (1)
Westerlaan 10, Rotterdam, 3016 CK, Netherlands
Tel.: (31) 104002700
Petroleum Product Mfr
N.A.I.C.S.: 324199
Patrick Van der Voort (Pres)

Vopak LNG Holding B.V. (1)
Westerlaan 10, 3016 CK, Rotterdam, Netherlands
Tel.: (31) 104002911
Web Site: http://www.vopak.com
Liquefied Natural Gas Terminal Operation Services
N.A.I.C.S.: 486210
Jan Bert Schutrops (Pres-Europe & Africa)

Vopak Logistic Services OSV B.V. (1)
Vondelingenweg 589, 3196 KK, Vondelingenplaat, Zuid-Holland, Netherlands
Tel.: (31) 102956611
Web Site: http://www.myloading.vopak.com
Sales Range: $25-49.9 Million
Emp.: 8
Chemical Terminals Operation Services

AND PRIVATE COMPANIES

N.A.I.C.S.: 488490
Koos Donkers (Mgr-Logistics)

Vopak Mexico-Coatzacoalcos Terminal (1)
Recinto Fiscal Autorizado Frente a Muelle No 5 Col Centro, CP 96400, Coatzacoalcos, DF, Mexico (100%)
Tel.: (52) 921 212 4292
Web Site: http://www.vopak.com
Bulk Liquid Logistics Service Solutions to the Chemical & Oil Industries
N.A.I.C.S.: 424710

Subsidiary (Domestic):

Vopak Mexico, S.A de C.V. (2)
Veracruz Terminal Interior del Recinto Portuario Escollera Norte s/n, Fracc Ind San Juan de Ulua C P, 91700, Veracruz, Mexico (100%)
Tel.: (52) 2299897500
Tank Terminal Operator
N.A.I.C.S.: 424710

Vopak Terminal Altamira (2)
Zona De Terminales Puerto Industrial, 89603, Tamaulipas, Altamira, Mexico (100%)
Tel.: (52) 8332602070
Web Site: http://www.vopak-mexico.com
Sales Range: $25-49.9 Million
Emp.: 32
N.A.I.C.S.: 483111
Carlos A. Rodriguez (Gen Mgr)

Vopak Terminal Veracruz (2)
Interior Del Recinto Portuario Escollera Norte s/n, Fracc Ind San Juan De Ulua C P, 91700, Veracruz, Mexico (100%)
Tel.: (52) 2299897500
Web Site: http://www.vopak.com.mx
Sales Range: $25-49.9 Million
Emp.: 21
Marine Transportation Of Crude Oil & Refined Products, Vessel Operations, Fleet Personnel Management, Freight Forwarding & Dry-Docking
N.A.I.C.S.: 483111

Vopak Nederland B.V. (1)
Westerlaan 10, 3016 CK, Rotterdam, Netherlands
Tel.: (31) 104002911
Web Site: http://www.vopak.nl
Bulk Liquid Storage Services
N.A.I.C.S.: 493190

Vopak Oil EMEA B.V. (1)
Moezelweg 75 Europoort, Rotterdam, 3198 LS, Zuid-Holland, Netherlands
Tel.: (31) 181240263
Sales Range: $150-199.9 Million
Emp.: 350
Petroleum & Oil Terminals Operation Services
N.A.I.C.S.: 424710
Eelco Hoekstra (Pres)

Vopak Terminal Amsterdam B.V. (1)
Petroleumhavenweg 42, 1041 AC, Amsterdam, Noord-Holland, Netherlands
Tel.: (31) 204473226
Web Site: http://www.vopak.nl
Sales Range: $25-49.9 Million
Emp.: 12
Petroleum & Oil Terminals Operation Services
N.A.I.C.S.: 424710

Vopak Terminal Botlek B.V. (1)
Welplaatweg 115 Port no 4110, Botlek, 3197 KS, Rotterdam, Netherlands
Tel.: (31) 104729799
Web Site: http://www.vopak.nl.com
Sales Range: $75-99.9 Million
Chemical & Biofuel Terminals Operation Services
N.A.I.C.S.: 424710

Vopak Terminal Botlek-Noord B.V. (1)
Main Welplaatweg 110, Botlek, 3197 KS, Zuid-Holland, Netherlands
Tel.: (31) 104729788
Web Site: http://www.oilrotterdam.vopak.com
Petroleum & Oil Terminals Operation Services
N.A.I.C.S.: 424710

Vopak Terminal Chemiehaven B.V.
Chemiestraat 10, Botlek, 3197 KB, Rotterdam, Netherlands
Tel.: (31) 104724400
Web Site: http://www.vopak.com
Sales Range: $50-74.9 Million
Petroleum & Chemical Terminals Operation Services
N.A.I.C.S.: 424710

Vopak Terminal Darwin Pty. Ltd. (1)
780 Berrimah Road, East Arm, Darwin, 0828, NT, Australia
Tel.: (61) 889999100
Web Site: https://www.vopak.com
Sales Range: $25-49.9 Million
Petroleum & Chemical Terminals Operation Services
N.A.I.C.S.: 424710

Vopak Terminal Deer Park Inc. (1)
2759 Independence Pkwy S, Deer Park, TX 77536
Tel.: (281) 604-6000
Web Site: http://www.vopakamericas.com
Petroleum & Chemical Terminals Operation Services
N.A.I.C.S.: 424710

Vopak Terminal Durban (Pty) Ltd. (1)
105 Taiwan Road, Island View Bluff, Durban, 4052, Kwazulu-Natal, South Africa
Tel.: (27) 314669200
Web Site: https://www.vopak.com
Sales Range: $50-74.9 Million
Petroleum & Chemical Terminals Operation Services
N.A.I.C.S.: 424710
Marcel van de Kar (Dir-Comml & Bus Dev-Europe & Africa)

Vopak Terminal Europoort B.V. (1)
Moezelweg 75 Port no 5530, Rotterdam, 3198 LS, Europoort, Netherlands
Tel.: (31) 181240911
Web Site: http://www.oilrotterdam.vopak.com
Sales Range: $150-199.9 Million
Petroleum & Crude Oil Terminals Operation Services
N.A.I.C.S.: 424710

Vopak Terminal Eurotank NV (1)
Industrieweg 16, 2030, Antwerp, Belgium
Tel.: (32) 35457300
Sales Range: $75-99.9 Million
Emp.: 150
Petroleum & Chemical Terminals Operation Services
N.A.I.C.S.: 424710
Jean Fauconnier (Mgr-Terminal)

Vopak Terminal Galena Park Inc. (1)
1500 Clinton Dr, Galena Park, TX 77547-3338
Tel.: (713) 654-6000
Web Site: http://www.vopak.com
Petroleum & Chemical Terminals Operation Services
N.A.I.C.S.: 424710

Vopak Terminal Laurenshaven B.V. (1)
Tel.: (31) 181240911
Terminal Storage Services
N.A.I.C.S.: 424710

Vopak Terminal London Limited (1)
Oliver Road West Thurrock, Grays, RM20 3ED, Essex, United Kingdom
Tel.: (44) 1708863399
Web Site: http://www.vopak.co.uk
Sales Range: $50-74.9 Million
Emp.: 90
Chemicals & Petroleum Terminals Operation Services
N.A.I.C.S.: 424710
Ian Cochrane (Mng Dir)

Vopak Terminal Long Beach Inc. (1)
3601 Dock St, San Pedro, CA 90731-7540
Tel.: (310) 549-0961
Web Site: https://www.vopak.com
Petroleum & Chemical Terminals Operation Services
N.A.I.C.S.: 424710

Vopak Terminal Los Angeles Inc. (1)
401 Canal Ave, Wilmington, CA 90744
Tel.: (310) 549-0961
Petroleum & Chemical Terminals Operation Services
N.A.I.C.S.: 424710

Vopak Terminal North Wilmington Inc. (1)
1710 Woodbine St, Wilmington, NC 28401
Tel.: (910) 763-0104
Web Site: http://www.vopak.com
Sales Range: $25-49.9 Million
Emp.: 25
Petroleum & Chemical Terminals Operation Services
N.A.I.C.S.: 424710

Vopak Terminal Savannah Inc. (1)
280 Brampton Rd Turner and Hart St GPA-Gate 2, Savannah, GA 31408-7390
Tel.: (912) 964-1811
Web Site: http://www.vopak.com
Petroleum & Chemical Terminals Operation Services
N.A.I.C.S.: 424710

Vopak Terminal Shandong Lanshan Limited (1)
Tong Hai Road, Lanshan District, Rizhao, 276808, Shandong, China
Tel.: (86) 6332631665
Web Site: http://www.vopak.com
Petroleum & Chemical Terminals Operation Services
N.A.I.C.S.: 424710

Subsidiary (Non-US):

Vopak Terminal Penjuru Pte. Ltd. (2)
59 Penjuru Road, Jurong Town, Singapore, 609142, Singapore
Tel.: (65) 68678200
Sales Range: $25-49.9 Million
Emp.: 200
Chemical Terminals Operation Services
N.A.I.C.S.: 424710

Subsidiary (Domestic):

Vopak Terminals Singapore Pte. Ltd. (3)
3 Sakra Ave, Singapore, 628226, Singapore
Tel.: (65) 62676230
Sales Range: $125-149.9 Million
Chemical & Oil Terminals Operation Services
N.A.I.C.S.: 424710

Vopak Terminal TTR B.V. (1)
Torontostraat 19 Harbour No 4530, Botlek, 3197 KN, Rotterdam, Netherlands
Tel.: (31) 181270800
Tank Storage & Terminal Services
N.A.I.C.S.: 424710

Vopak Terminal Teesside Ltd. (1)
Seal Sands, Middlesbrough, TS2 1UA, Cleveland, United Kingdom
Tel.: (44) 1642546767
Sales Range: $50-74.9 Million
Emp.: 60
Chemicals & Petroleum Terminals Operation Services
N.A.I.C.S.: 424710
David Tritt (Gen Mgr)

Vopak Terminal Vlaardingen B.V. (1)
Kon Wilhelminahaven Zoz 1 Port no 625, 3134 KH, Vlaardingen, Netherlands
Tel.: (31) 104608899
Web Site: http://www.vlaardingen.vopak.com
Sales Range: $75-99.9 Million
Chemical & Oil Terminals Operation Services
N.A.I.C.S.: 424710

Vopak Terminal Vlissingen B.V. (1)
Tel.: (31) 113615800
Terminal Storage Services
N.A.I.C.S.: 424710
Marco Bogaards (Mgr-Technical)

Vopak Terminal Westpoort B.V. (1)
Westpoortweg 480, 1047 HB, Amsterdam, Netherlands
Tel.: (31) 203075700
Web Site: http://www.evos.eu
Sales Range: $25-49.9 Million
Emp.: 50
Terminal Operation Services

KONISHI CO., LTD.

N.A.I.C.S.: 424710

Vopak Terminal Windmill Ltd. (1)
Hayes Road, Barry, CF64 5RZ, Vale of Glamorgan, United Kingdom
Tel.: (44) 1446736677
Sales Range: $25-49.9 Million
Emp.: 12
Pipeline & Liquid Storage Terminal Services
N.A.I.C.S.: 488999
David Tratt (Mgr-Ops)

Vopak Terminal Zhangjiagang Ltd. (1)
No 8 Shenzhen Road East Bonded Logistics Zone, Zhangjiagang, 215635, Jiangsu, China
Tel.: (86) 51256955600
Web Site: http://www.vopakasia.com
Petroleum & Chemical Terminals Operation Services
N.A.I.C.S.: 424710

Vopak Terminals Australia Pty. Ltd. (1)
Gate B47 20 Friendship Road, Port Botany, Sydney, 2036, NSW, Australia
Tel.: (61) 296664455
Web Site: http://www.vopak.com
Sales Range: $25-49.9 Million
Petroleum & Chemical Terminals Operation Services
N.A.I.C.S.: 424710

Vopak Terminals Korea Ltd. (1)
Tel.: (82) 27993700
Petroleum Product Mfr
N.A.I.C.S.: 324199

Vopak Terminals North America Inc. (1)
2759 Battleground Rd, Deer Park, TX 77536
Tel.: (281) 604-6000
Petroleum & Chemical Terminals Operation Services
N.A.I.C.S.: 424710

Vopak Terminals Sydney Pty. Ltd. (1)
Gate B47 20 Friendship Road, Port Botany, Randwick, 2036, NSW, Australia
Tel.: (61) 296664455
Petroleum Product Mfr
N.A.I.C.S.: 324199

Vopak Terminals of Canada Inc. (1)
5378 Notre Dame Street East, Montreal, H1N 2C4, QC, Canada
Tel.: (514) 255-6077
Web Site: http://www.vopak.com
Sales Range: $25-49.9 Million
Petroleum & Chemical Terminals Operation Services
N.A.I.C.S.: 424710

Vopak Terminals of Eastern Canada Inc. (1)
2775 Avenue Georges V, East Montreal, H1L 6J7, QC, Canada
Tel.: (514) 687-3193
Petroleum Product Mfr
N.A.I.C.S.: 324199
Marc-Andre Paquin (Sls Mgr)

Vopak Venezuela S.A. (1)
Avenida Salom Urb La Belisa, Puerto Cabello, Carabobo, Venezuela
Tel.: (58) 2424012186
Sales Range: $75-99.9 Million
Petroleum & Chemical Terminals Operation Services
N.A.I.C.S.: 424710

Vopak Vietnam Co. Ltd. (1)
Ong Keo Industrial Park, Phuoc Khanh Ward, Nhon Trach, Dong Nai, Vietnam
Tel.: (84) 2513570023
Petroleum Product Mfr
N.A.I.C.S.: 324199

KONISHI CO., LTD.
1-7-1 Doshomachi, Chuo-ku, Osaka, 541-0045, Japan
Tel.: (81) 662282811
Web Site: https://www.bond.co.jp
Year Founded: 1925
4956—(TKS)
Rev: $878,925,090

Konishi Co., Ltd.—(Continued)
Assets: $931,018,500
Liabilities: $371,250,650
Net Worth: $559,767,850
Earnings: $48,543,840
Emp.: 1,540
Fiscal Year-end: 03/31/24
Adhesive & Chemical Product Mfr
N.A.I.C.S.: 325520
Takashi Yokota *(Pres)*

KONKA GROUP CO., LTD.
Overseas Chinese Town, Nanshan District, Shenzhen, 518057, Guangdong, China
Tel.: (86) 75526608866
Web Site:
https://www.konkaglobal.com
Year Founded: 1979
200016—(SSE)
Rev.: $7,523,608,397
Assets: $6,109,175,209
Liabilities: $4,546,287,660
Net Worth: $1,562,887,550
Earnings: $138,708,674
Emp.: 17,822
Fiscal Year-end: 12/31/21
Electronics & Telecommunications Products Mfr
N.A.I.C.S.: 334310

Subsidiaries:

Hong Kong Konka Limited (1)
11th Floor Chinabest Intl Ctr, Kwai Chung, China (Hong Kong)
Tel.: (852) 23927128
Web Site: http://www.konka.com.hk
Electrical Appliance Television & Radio Set Whslr
N.A.I.C.S.: 423620

KONNDOR INDUSTRIES LIMITED
201 Avdhesh House Sarkhej Gandhinagar Highway Opp Guru Govind, Gurudwara Thajtej, Ahmedabad, 380054, Gujarat, India
Tel.: (91) 7940392344
Web Site:
https://konndorindustries.com
532397—(BOM)
Rev.: $512,107
Assets: $1,177,330
Liabilities: $48,598
Net Worth: $1,128,731
Earnings: $80,945
Fiscal Year-end: 03/31/22
Packaging Paper Products Distr
N.A.I.C.S.: 423840
Santoshkumar Pandey *(CFO)*

KONOIKE TRANSPORT CO., LTD.
4-3-9 Fushimimachi, Chuo-ku, Osaka, 541-0044, Japan
Tel.: (81) 662274600
Web Site: https://www.konoike.net
Year Founded: 1945
9025—(TKS)
Rev.: $2,082,341,690
Assets: $1,831,340,160
Liabilities: $931,844,750
Net Worth: $899,495,410
Earnings: $75,016,890
Emp.: 24,000
Fiscal Year-end: 03/31/24
Transportation Services
N.A.I.C.S.: 488510
Kazuki Uenoyama *(Exec Officer & Exec Gen Mgr-Intl Gen Headquarters)*

Subsidiaries:

ASR Recycling Kashima Co., Ltd. (1)
3 Hikari, Kashima, 314-0014, Ibaraki, Japan
Tel.: (81) 299842063
Logistic Services
N.A.I.C.S.: 541614

Air Express, Inc. (1)
Naha Airport International Area 1F 150 Kagamizu, Naha, 901-0142, Okinawa, Japan
Tel.: (81) 988520001
Logistic Services
N.A.I.C.S.: 541614

Airport Terminal Service Co., Ltd. (1)
P2021 Terminal 2 Narita International Airport, Narita, 282-0004, Chiba, Japan
Tel.: (81) 476346020
Logistic Services
N.A.I.C.S.: 541614

Anpha-AG Joint Stock Company (1)
Lot E02 Road No 2, Long Hau Industrial Park, Ho Chi Minh City, Long An, Vietnam
Tel.: (84) 2838734395
Web Site: https://www.konoike.net
Emp.: 113
Refrigerated Food Product Storage Services
N.A.I.C.S.: 493120
Tomohiko Murakami *(Pres)*

BEL International Logistics Ltd. (1)
Flat 8A 8/F Mita Centre 552-566 Castle Peak Road, Kwai Chung, China (Hong Kong)
Tel.: (852) 27960118
Web Site: https://www.bel-intl.com
Freight Forwarding Services
N.A.I.C.S.: 488510
George Lim *(Mgr-IT)*

BEL International Logistics Ltd. (1)
Room 1102-1103 11/F Global New Times Plaza 1666 Sichuan Road North, Shanghai, 200080, China
Tel.: (86) 2161225488
Freight Forwarding Services
N.A.I.C.S.: 488510

BEL International Logistics Vietnam Company Ltd. (1)
Tel.: (84) 2838201128
Logistic Services
N.A.I.C.S.: 541614

BEL Supply Chain Solution Ltd. (1)
7F Mita Centre 552-566 Castle Peak Road, Kwai Chung, China (Hong Kong)
Tel.: (852) 34686678
Freight Forwarding Services
N.A.I.C.S.: 488510
Benny Chung *(Gen Mgr)*

Carna Medical Database Pvt. Ltd. (1)
Tel.: (91) 1244309635
Freight Transportation Services
N.A.I.C.S.: 488510

Chiyoda Inspection Industries Co., Ltd (1)
1-1-24 Shimaya, Konohana-ku, Osaka, 554-0024, Japan
Tel.: (81) 6 6465 1275
Web Site: http://www2.odn.ne.jp
Emp.: 42
Product Testing Services
N.A.I.C.S.: 541380
Izumi Satoru *(Pres)*

Eco Innovation Inc. (1)
3 Hikari, Kashima, 314-0014, Ibaraki, Japan
Tel.: (81) 299843911
Waste Collection & Transportation Services
N.A.I.C.S.: 562112

Hokushin Industry Co., Ltd. (1)
7-6-5 Matsuekita, Wakayama, 640-8420, Japan
Tel.: (81) 73 455 2111
Logistics Consulting Services
N.A.I.C.S.: 541614

J Friendly, Inc. (1)
1001-649 Honsanritsuka, Narita, 286-0118, Chiba, Japan
Tel.: (81) 476404322
Logistic Services
N.A.I.C.S.: 541614

JAPAN AIRWAYS CO., LTD (1)
Freight Transportation Services
N.A.I.C.S.: 488510

Japan Airport Service Co., Ltd. (1)
154-4 Furugome Komae, Narita, 282-0004, Chiba, Japan
Logistic Services
N.A.I.C.S.: 541614

Joshi Konoike Transport & Infrastructure Pvt. Ltd. (1)
M-26 Main Market Greater Kailash-II, New Delhi, 110048, India
Tel.: (91) 1149488900
Web Site: https://www.konoike.net
Emp.: 35
Container Train Transportation Services
N.A.I.C.S.: 488210
Hitendra Joshi *(Pres)*

K Ground Expert Co., Ltd. (1)
2-21 Rinkuoraikita, Izumisano, 598-0048, Osaka, Japan
Tel.: (81) 724630155
Logistic Services
N.A.I.C.S.: 541614

K Ground Service Co., Ltd. (1)
2-21 Rinkuoraikita, Izumisano, Izumisano, 598-0048, Osaka, Japan
Tel.: (81) 724638571
Air Cargo Transportation Services
N.A.I.C.S.: 488119

K Sky Co., Ltd. (1)
Tel.: (81) 724553373
Web Site: http://www.ksky.co.jp
Emp.: 500
Logistics Consulting Services
N.A.I.C.S.: 541614

KONOIKE ASIA (INDIA) PVT. LTD. (1)
Freight Transportation Services
N.A.I.C.S.: 488510

KONOIKE ASIA (MYANMAR) CO., LTD (1)
No 608 Room No 10A 10th Floor Bo Son Pat Condominium, Bo Son Pat Street Pabedan Township, Yangon, Myanmar
Tel.: (95) 1 373757
Truck Transportation Services
N.A.I.C.S.: 488510
Tomoyuki Tanaka *(Pres)*

KONOIKE ASIA (THAILAND) CO., LTD. (1)
3656/73 Green Tower 22nd Fl Rama 4 Rd, Klongton Klongtoey, Bangkok, Thailand
N.A.I.C.S.: 488510

KONOIKE ASIA(JIANGSU) CO., LTD. (1)
No 9 Haitian Road Changshu Advanced Material Industrial Park, Suzhou, China
Tel.: (86) 512 5219 5058
Emp.: 6
Logistics Consulting Services
N.A.I.C.S.: 541614
Iwazo Owada *(Pres)*

KONOIKE EXPRESS (THAILAND) CO., LTD. (1)
335/29 Moo 9 Bangna-Trad Rd Km 19 Banglee, Bangchalong, Bang Phli, Samutprakarn, Thailand
Tel.: (66) 23373023
Web Site: https://www.konoike.net
Emp.: 18
Cargo Transportation Services
N.A.I.C.S.: 484110

KONOIKE EXPRESS CO., LTD. (1)
2-1 Sakaedani, Wakayama, 640-8441, Japan
Tel.: (81) 73 451 4151
Web Site: http://www.konoike.net
Emp.: 90
Waste Collection & Transportation Services
N.A.I.C.S.: 562112
Akira Kubo *(Pres)*

KONOIKE LOGISTICS (SHANGHAI) CO., LTD. (1)
Shanghai Bund International Tower Room No 807 No 99, Huangpu Road, Shanghai, 200080, China
Tel.: (86) 21 6309 1118
Web Site: http://www.konoike.net
Emp.: 70
Logistics Consulting Services
N.A.I.C.S.: 541614

Kyo Rai *(Pres)*

KONOIKE MEDICAL CO., LTD. (1)
1-6-4 Yurakucho, Chiyoda-ku, Tokyo, 100-0006, Japan
Tel.: (81) 3 3580 3860
Truck Transportation Services
N.A.I.C.S.: 488510

KONOIKE MEXICO S.A. de C.V (1)
Logistics Consulting Servies
N.A.I.C.S.: 541614

KONOIKE SHIPPING CO., LTD. (1)
Central square 2F 2-3-1 Shinkawa, Chuo-ku, Tokyo, 104-0033, Japan
Tel.: (81) 367382960
Web Site: https://www.konoike-ship.com
Emp.: 43
Truck & Ocean Transportation Services
N.A.I.C.S.: 484110

KONOIKE TRANSPORT & ENGINEERING (H.K.) LTD. (1)
Unit 7-12 7/F Mita Centre 552-566 Castle Peak Road, Kwai Chung, New Territories, China (Hong Kong)
Tel.: (852) 27357313
Web Site: https://www.konoike.net
Emp.: 27
Ocean & Air Cargo Transportation Services
N.A.I.C.S.: 483211
Tanabe Hiroaki *(Mng Dir)*

KONOIKE TRANSPORT & ENGINEERING (S) PTE LTD. (1)
10 Anson Road 20-02 International Plaza, Singapore, Singapore
Tel.: (65) 6220 0010
Freight Transportation Services
N.A.I.C.S.: 488510

KONOIKE TRANSPORT & ENGINEERING (USA), INC. (1)
1420 Coil Ave, Wilmington, CA 90744
Tel.: (310) 513-1500
Logistics Consulting Services
N.A.I.C.S.: 541614

KONOIKE VINATRANS LOGISTICS CO., LTD (1)
18-A Luu Trong Lu, District 7, Ho Chi Minh City, Vietnam
Logistics Consulting Servies
N.A.I.C.S.: 541614

KONOIKE-E STREET, INC. (1)
901 E E St, Wilmington, CA 90744
Tel.: (310) 233-7300
Web Site: https://www.konoike.net
Emp.: 31
Warehouse Management Services
N.A.I.C.S.: 493120

KONOIKE-EURO LOGISTICS (BANGLADESH) LTD. (1)
House No 162 Eastern Road Lane 3, New Dohs Mohakhali, Dhaka, Bangladesh
Tel.: (880) 2 885 0721
Emp.: 7
Logistics Consulting Servies
N.A.I.C.S.: 541614
Mohd Moniruzzaman *(Pres)*

KONOIKE-GENERAL, INC. (1)
9415 Burtis St, South Gate, CA 90280
Tel.: (562) 806-2445
Web Site: https://www.konoike.net
Emp.: 16
Warehouse Management Services
N.A.I.C.S.: 493120

KONOIKE-SOTUS VENTURE CO., LTD (1)
10/66 308 3rd Floor The Trendy Building Soi Sukhumvit 13, Klongtoey Nua Wattana, Bangkok, Thailand
Tel.: (66) 21687260
Web Site: https://www.konoike.net
Emp.: 111
Investment Advisory Services
N.A.I.C.S.: 523940

KPS CO., LTD. (1)
661-1 Kamikawaraya, Izumisano, Osaka, 598-0001, Japan
Tel.: (81) 72 463 4600
Logistics Consulting Servies
N.A.I.C.S.: 541614

Kanriku Co., Ltd. (1)

AND PRIVATE COMPANIES

Freight Transportation Services
N.A.I.C.S.: 488510

Konohana Transport Co., Ltd. (1)
1-24 Kaminomiyacho, Nakamura-ku, Nagoya, 453-0043, Japan
Tel.: (81) 524813221
Truck Transportation Services
N.A.I.C.S.: 484110

Konoike Air Port Service Co., Ltd. (1)
Tel.: (81) 724632580
Truck Transportation Services
N.A.I.C.S.: 488510

Konoike Asia (Cambodia) Co., Ltd. (1)
No 92AB St 289 Sangkat Beoung Kak 2, Khan Toul Kork, Phnom Penh, Cambodia
Tel.: (855) 23987571
Emp.: 25
Freight Forwarding Services
N.A.I.C.S.: 488510
Tomohiko Yasuda (Pres)

Konoike Cool Logistics (Thailand) Co., Ltd. (1)
335/29 Moo 9 Bangna-Trad Rd Km 19 Banglee, Bangchalong, Bang Phli, 10540, Samutprakarn, Thailand
Tel.: (66) 23373013
Web Site: https://www.konoike.net
Emp.: 64
Refrigerated Food Product Storage Services
N.A.I.C.S.: 493120
Kazumi Fujiwara (Pres)

Konoike Cool Logistics Tohoku Co., Ltd. (1)
9-5-2 Narita Tomiyamatch, Kurokawagun, Miyagi, 981-3341, Japan
Tel.: (81) 22 346 9157
Logistics Consulting Servies
N.A.I.C.S.: 541614

Konoike Corporate Service Co., Ltd. (1)
3-10-29 Shimaya, Konohana-ku, Osaka, 554-0024, Japan
Tel.: (81) 664638110
Logistic Services
N.A.I.C.S.: 541614

Konoike Engineering Co., Ltd (1)
1-36-1 Kanseicho, Minato-ku, Nagoya, 6512126, Japan
Tel.: (81) 52 651 7126
Logistics Consulting Servies
N.A.I.C.S.: 541614

Konoike IT Solutions Co., Ltd. (1)
2-3-1 Shinkawa, Chuo-ku, Tokyo, 104-0033, Japan
Tel.: (81) 335510502
Logistic Services
N.A.I.C.S.: 541614

Konoike J.Transport (Thailand) Co., Ltd. (1)
065/1 Sukhumvit Road Tapradu, Muang Rayong, Rayong, Thailand
Tel.: (66) 38611703
Emp.: 165
Cargo Transportation Services
N.A.I.C.S.: 488510
Yoshiyuki Takii (Pres)

Konoike Logistics (Shenzhen) Co., Ltd. (1)
Tel.: (86) 75583599017
Emp.: 13
Freight Transportation Services
N.A.I.C.S.: 488510

Konoike Myanmar Co., Ltd. (1)
Lot No C-20 Thilawa Sez Zone A, Yangon, Myanmar
Tel.: (95) 12309144
Emp.: 53
Freight Forwarding Services
N.A.I.C.S.: 488510
Yasunori Tanaka (Pres)

Konoike Sky Support Co., Ltd. (1)
5-6 Rinkuoraikita, Izumisano, 598-0048, Osaka, Japan
Tel.: (81) 724634600
Web Site: https://www.konoike-kss.net

Emp.: 200
Air Cargo Handling Services
N.A.I.C.S.: 488119

Konoike-Pacific California, Inc. (1)
1420 Coil Ave, Wilmington, CA 90744
Tel.: (310) 518-1000
Web Site: https://www.kpaccoldstorage.com
Cold Storage Transportation Services
N.A.I.C.S.: 493120
Rich Burke (Pres)

Kyushu Sanko Unyu Co., Ltd. (1)
2-20-3 Ryutuudanchi, Minami-Ku, Kumamoto, 862-8635, Japan
Tel.: (81) 963772135
Logistic Services
N.A.I.C.S.: 541614

Maekawa Transport Co., Ltd. (1)
170 Noda Aridagawacho, Arida, Wakayama, 643-0031, Japan
Tel.: (81) 737 52 2500
Truck Transportation Services
N.A.I.C.S.: 488510

NAB Corporation. (1)
1001-1282 Honsanritsuka, Narita, 286-0118, Chiba, Japan
Tel.: (81) 476334911
Logistic Services
N.A.I.C.S.: 541614

NKS Holding Co., Ltd. (1)
7-16-14 Ginza, Chuo-ku, Tokyo, 104-0061, Japan
Logistic Services
N.A.I.C.S.: 541614

Nichiun Corporation (1)
4-23 Kaigandori, Naka-ku, Yokohama, 231-0002, Japan
Tel.: (81) 45 201 8951
Web Site: http://www.konoike.net
Emp.: 46
Truck & Ocean Transportation Services
N.A.I.C.S.: 484110
Seiji Nanyo (Pres)

OTORI TECH CO., LTD. (1)
Logistics Consulting Servies
N.A.I.C.S.: 541614

PKI MANUFACTURING & TECHNOLOGY, INC. (1)
Lot 14 Phase 1-A SSB First Philippines Industrial Park, Santo Tomas, 4234, Batangas, Philippines
Tel.: (63) 43 405 6388
Web Site: http://www.pkimt.com
Emp.: 30
Logistics Consulting Servies
N.A.I.C.S.: 541614
Enrico N. Salvador (Chm)

PT.KONOIKE TRANSPORT INDONESIA (1)
Wisma Nugra Santana 13th Floor, JI Jend Sudirman Kav 7-8, Jakarta, Indonesia
Tel.: (62) 21 578 52350
Web Site: http://www.Konoike.com
Emp.: 21
Ocean & Air Cargo Transportation Services
N.A.I.C.S.: 483211
Tomonobu Tsuno (Pres)

QINGDAO COSCO KONOIKE LOGISTICS CO., LTD. (1)
Tel.: (86) 53288701607
Logistics Consulting Servies
N.A.I.C.S.: 541614

SANO UNYU CO., LTD. (1)
3-1-16 Kaigandori, Chuo-ku, Kobe, 650-0024, Japan
Tel.: (81) 783910092
Ocean & Air Cargo Transportation Services
N.A.I.C.S.: 483211

SHOWA WAREHOUSING CO., LTD. (1)
725 Ouchida, Kita-ku, Okayama, 701-0165, Japan
Tel.: (81) 86 293 5721
Warehouse Management Services
N.A.I.C.S.: 493120

Shimayakousan Co., Ltd. (1)
3-10-29 Shimaya, Konohana-ku, Osaka, 554-0024, Japan
Tel.: (81) 6 6463 8110

Truck Transportation Services
N.A.I.C.S.: 488510

VINAKO FORWARDING CO., LTD. (1)
Unit 02-03-05 Vietnam Airlines Building 49 Truong Son Str, Tan Binh District, Ho Chi Minh City, Vietnam
Tel.: (84) 8 3844 6252
Air Cargo Transportation Services
N.A.I.C.S.: 488119

KONOSHIMA CHEMICAL CO., LTD.
4-4-7 Imabashi 7th floor Keihanshin Yodoyabashi Building, Chuo-ku, Osaka, 541-0042, Japan
Tel.: (81) 662325350
Web Site:
   https://www.konoshima.co.jp
Year Founded: 1917
4026—(TKS)
Sales Range: $150-199.9 Million
Construction Material & Chemical Product Mfr
N.A.I.C.S.: 327999
Kazuo Ikeda (Pres)

Subsidiaries:

Konoshima Chemical Co., Ltd. - Takuma Factory (1)
Koda 80 Takuma Cho, Mitoyo, Kagawa, Japan
Tel.: (81) 875833155
Chemical Products Mfr
N.A.I.C.S.: 325199

KONRAD MERKT GMBH
Max-Planck-Strasse 30, Spaichingen, 78549, Germany
Tel.: (49) 742470080   De
Web Site: http://www.merkt.de
Year Founded: 1952
Rev: $25,048,944
Emp.: 95
Office Furniture Supplier
N.A.I.C.S.: 423420
Konrad Merkt (Co-CEO)

KONRAD REITZ VENTILATOREN GMBH & CO. KG
Konrad-Reitz-Strasse 1, 37671, Hoxter, Germany
Tel.: (49) 5271964000   DK
Web Site: http://www.reitz-ventilatoren.de
Year Founded: 1948
Sales Range: $100-124.9 Million
Emp.: 800
Industrial Fans Mfr
N.A.I.C.S.: 333413
Ulrich Breder (Mng Dir)

Subsidiaries:

REITZ Middle East FZE (1)
Sharjah Airport Free Zone Y-3-210, PO Box 9383, Sharjah, United Arab Emirates
Tel.: (971) 50 1737486
Web Site: http://www.reitzme.ae
Industrial Equipment Whsr
N.A.I.C.S.: 423830
Siva Prasad Koka (Gen Mgr)

Reitz Fans (Suzhou) Ltd. (1)
No 58 Jiangpu Road, 215126, Suzhou, China
Tel.: (86) 512 62 85 61 00
Web Site: http://www.reitz-china.com
Industrial Equipment Whsr
N.A.I.C.S.: 423830
Sam Jiang (Plant Mgr)

Reitz India Limited (1)
VII Floor Block-A Q City Gachibowli, Nanakramguda, Hyderabad, 500 046, India
Tel.: (91) 40 4488 1888
Web Site: http://www.reitzindia.com
Industrial Equipment Whsr
N.A.I.C.S.: 423830

Reitz South East Asia Pte. Ltd. (1)

KONSORTIUM TRANSNASIONAL BERHAD

31 Cantonment Road, Singapore, 089747, Singapore
Tel.: (65) 62244991
Web Site: http://www.reitz.com.sg
N.A.I.C.S.: 423830
Sheikh Abdullah (Area Mgr)

Reitz Umwelttechnik + Ventilatoren GmbH & Co. KG (1)
Gutenbergstrasse 20-24, 37235, Hessisch Lichtenau, Germany
Tel.: (49) 5602 936 60
Web Site: http://www.reitz-umwelttechnik.de
Industrial Equipment Whsr
N.A.I.C.S.: 423830

Reitz Wentylatory Polska Sp. z o.o. (1)
ul Dziadoszanska 10, 61-248, Poznan, Poland
Tel.: (48) 61 62 42 772
Web Site: http://www.reitz-ventilatoren.de
Industrial Equipment Whsr
N.A.I.C.S.: 423830

Reitz do Brasil Ltda. (1)
Rua Sao Bento 470 Sala 902 Centro, 01010-001, Sao Paulo, Brazil
Tel.: (55) 11 3106 2050
Web Site: http://www.reitzbrasil.com
Industrial Equipment Whsr
N.A.I.C.S.: 423830

Stafa Wirz Ventilator AG (1)
Zentweg 11, 3006, Bern, Switzerland
Tel.: (41) 319388585
Web Site: http://www.staefa-wirz.ch
Sales Range: $25-49.9 Million
Emp.: 36
Air Conditioning Systems
N.A.I.C.S.: 238220

KONRAD WITTWER GMBH
Konigstrasse 30, 70173, Stuttgart, Germany
Tel.: (49) 7112507111
Web Site: http://www.wittwer.de
Year Founded: 1867
Books Retailer & Store Franchisor
N.A.I.C.S.: 459210
Konrad Martin Wittwer (Mng Dir)

KONSEPTI OY
Aleksanterinkatu 15 B, 100, Helsinki, Finland
Tel.: (358) 9 622 6080
Year Founded: 1983
Sales Range: $10-24.9 Million
Emp.: 25
N.A.I.C.S.: 541810
Timo Kivi (Owner)

KONSORCJUM STALI S.A.
ul Paderewskiego 120, 42-400, Zawiercie, Poland
Tel.: (48) 32 672 16 92
Web Site:
   http://konsorcjumstali.com.pl
Sales Range: $200-249.9 Million
Steel Mfr & Distr
N.A.I.C.S.: 331110
Janusz Koclega (Deputy Chm-Supervisory Bd)

KONSORTIUM TRANSNASIONAL BERHAD
Unit 303 Block G Phileo Damansara Shopping Center, Jalan 16/11 off Jalan Damansara Selangor, 46350, Petaling Jaya, Malaysia
Tel.: (60) 379323922
Web Site: https://www.ktb.com.my
EPICON—(KLS)
Rev: $32,684,371
Assets: $30,065,303
Liabilities: $15,680,235
Net Worth: $14,385,068
Earnings: $14,848,280
Emp.: 20
Fiscal Year-end: 12/31/23
Bus Transportation Services
N.A.I.C.S.: 488490

KONSORTIUM TRANSNASIONAL BERHAD

Konsortium Transnasional Berhad—(Continued)

Mohd Nadzmi Mohd Salleh *(Chm & Mng Dir)*

KONTAFARMA CHINA HOLD-INGS LIMITED
15th Floor Allied Kajima Building, 138 Gloucester Road, Wanchai, China (Hong Kong)
Tel.: (852) 21119686   Ky
Web Site: http://www.tfkf.com.hk
1312—(HKG)
Rev.: $113,992,905
Assets: $270,356,483
Liabilities: $122,930,655
Net Worth: $147,425,828
Earnings: ($6,732,255)
Emp.: 922
Fiscal Year-end: 12/31/22
Investment Services
N.A.I.C.S.: 523999
Zhong Yu *(Deputy Gen Mgr-Shanghai SAC)*

Subsidiaries:

Chongqing Kangle Pharmaceutical Co., Ltd.   (1)
No 4 Huazhong Road Chongqing Chemical Industrial Park, Changshou, Chongqing, 401221, China
Tel.: (86) 2362503614
Web Site: http://www.cqkl.com.cn
Pharmaceutical Ingredient Mfr
N.A.I.C.S.: 325412
Xiaoqiang Ge *(Mgr-Regulatory Affairs)*

SPF (Beijing) Biotechnology Co., Ltd.   (1)
Unit 101 Building 1 No 23 Xikang Road, Badaling Town Yanqing District, Beijing, 102101, China
Tel.: (86) 1061168109
Cement & Clinker Mfr & Whslr
N.A.I.C.S.: 327310

Shaanxi Unisplendour Life Care Pharmaceutical Co., Ltd.   (1)
No 78 West Zhongshan Road, Jintai District, Baoji, 721001, Shaanxi, China
Tel.: (86) 9173973390
Cement & Clinker Mfr & Whslr
N.A.I.C.S.: 327310

Shandong Allied Wangchao Cement Limited
Dunzhuangcun, Jiantouji Town Taierzhuang Distric, Zaozhuang, 277415, Shandong, China
Tel.: (86) 632 6818 173
Web Site: http://www.tfkf.com.hk
Cement Mfr
N.A.I.C.S.: 327310

Shandong Shanghai Allied Cement Co., Ltd.   (1)
Sunsuzhuang, Jiantouji Town Taierzhuang District, Zaozhuang, 277405, Shandong, China
Tel.: (86) 632 6811 048
Web Site: http://www.alliedcement.com.hk
Cement Mfr
N.A.I.C.S.: 327310

Shanghai Allied Cement Co., Ltd.   (1)
02 Buidling 27 1388 Zhangdong Road, Pudong, Shanghai, 200203, China
Tel.: (86) 21 6879 6801
Cement Mfr
N.A.I.C.S.: 327310

True Yoga Pte. Ltd.   (1)
Scotts Road Level 4 Pacific Plaza, Singapore, 228210, Singapore
Tel.: (65) 67339555
Web Site: http://www.trueyoga.com.sg
Yoga Class Services
N.A.I.C.S.: 713940

KONTASET KFT.
Helsinki Ut 53, 1201, Budapest, Hungary
Tel.: (36) 14213001
Web Site: http://www.kontaset.hu
Sales Range: $10-24.9 Million
Emp.: 120
Computer & Electric Power Equipment Distr
N.A.I.C.S.: 423430
Gyula Dobozi *(Mng Dir)*

KONTIGO CARE AB
Pavel Snickares grand 12, Uppsala, Sweden
Tel.: (46) 184108880
Web Site:
https://www.kontigocare.com
KONT—(OMX)
Rev.: $2,663,744
Assets: $2,940,047
Liabilities: $935,682
Net Worth: $2,004,365
Earnings: $271,620
Emp.: 14
Fiscal Year-end: 12/31/22
Medicinal Product Mfr
N.A.I.C.S.: 339112
Markku Hamalainen *(Head-R&D)*

KONTINENT SPEDITION GMBH
Goschwitzer Str 34, 07745, Jena, Germany
Tel.: (49) 364129180
Web Site: http://www.kontinent-spedition.de
Year Founded: 1992
Rev.: $13,410,293
Emp.: 85
Logistics & Forwarding Services
N.A.I.C.S.: 541614
Liane Kandler *(Mgr-IT)*

Subsidiaries:

Kontinent-Emo-Trans GmbH   (1)
Manfred-von-Ardenne-Ring 20 Haus E, 1099, Dresden, Germany
Tel.: (49) 3518108509
Transport & Logistic Services
N.A.I.C.S.: 541614
Christian Schust *(Mgr-Ops)*

KONTO D.O.O.
SS Kranjcevica 7, 42000, Varazdin, Croatia
Tel.: (385) 42300900   HR
Web Site: http://www.konto.hr
Sales Range: $1-9.9 Million
Emp.: 11
Software Products Distr
N.A.I.C.S.: 423430

KONTOR SPACE LIMITED
Office No A1 & B1 9th Floor Ashar IT Park Road No 16, Wagle Industrial Estate, Thane, 400604, Maharashtra, India
Tel.: (91) 2262790000   In
Web Site: https://www.kontorspace.in
Year Founded: 2018
KONTOR—(NSE)
Rev.: $492,576
Assets: $713,793
Liabilities: $504,565
Net Worth: $209,228
Earnings: $19,851
Fiscal Year-end: 03/31/23
Construction Engineering Services
N.A.I.C.S.: 541330

KONTOUR XIAN MEDICAL TECHNOLOGY CO., LTD.
No 6 Qinling Avenue, West Caotang Science & Technology Industrial Base High-tech Zone, Xi'an, 710065, Shaanxi, China
Tel.: (86) 2968318314
Web Site:
http://www.kontourmedical.com
Year Founded: 2005

688314—(SHG)
Rev.: $33,688,797
Assets: $89,594,252
Liabilities: $13,543,293
Net Worth: $76,050,959
Earnings: $10,628,027
Fiscal Year-end: 12/31/22
Medical Product Mfr & Distr
N.A.I.C.S.: 339112
Liren Hu *(Chm)*

KONTROL TECHNOLOGIES CORP.
180 Jardin Drive Unit 9, Vaughan, L4K 1X8, ON, Canada
Web Site:
http://www.kontrolenergy.com
KNR—(BZX)
Rev.: $66,035,377
Assets: $17,297,725
Liabilities: $34,931,660
Net Worth: ($17,633,935)
Earnings: ($32,900,169)
Emp.: 75
Fiscal Year-end: 12/31/22
Software Development Services
N.A.I.C.S.: 541511
Paul Ghezzi *(CEO)*

Subsidiaries:

CEM Specialties Inc.   (1)
1100 Dearness Drive Unit 11, London, N6E 1N9, ON, Canada
Web Site: https://www.cemsi.ca
Environmental Services
N.A.I.C.S.: 541620
Gary Saunders *(VP-Ops)*

Efficiency Engineering Inc.   (1)
225 Pinebush Road Suite 202, Cambridge, N1T 1B9, ON, Canada
Tel.: (519) 624-9965
Web Site:
https://www.efficiencyengineering.com
Engineeering Services
N.A.I.C.S.: 541330
Scott Martin *(Pres)*

Kontrol Buildings Inc.   (1)
11 Cidermill Avenue Suite 201, Vaughan, L4K 4B6, ON, Canada
Web Site: https://kontrolbuildings.com
Air Conditioner Installation Services
N.A.I.C.S.: 238220

Ortech Consulting Inc.   (1)
804 Southdown Road, Mississauga, L5J 2Y4, ON, Canada
Tel.: (905) 822-4120
Web Site: https://www.ortechconsulting.com
Environmental Services
N.A.I.C.S.: 541620
Hank Van Bakel *(Pres)*

KONTROLMATIK TEKNOLOJI ENERJI VE MUHENDISLIK A.S.
Huzur Mahallesi Ahmet Bayman Street no 2 Sariyer, Esenler, 34204, Istanbul, Turkiye
Tel.: (90) 904441568
Web Site:
https://www.kontrolmatik.com
Year Founded: 2007
KONTR—(IST)
Rev.: $55,324,374
Assets: $135,190,579
Liabilities: $95,071,339
Net Worth: $40,119,240
Earnings: $14,943,165
Emp.: 496
Fiscal Year-end: 12/31/22
Construction Services
N.A.I.C.S.: 236220
Sami Aslanhan *(Chm)*

Subsidiaries:

McFly Robot Technologies A.S.   (1)
Huzur Mah Ahmet Bayman Cad No 2a Sariyar, Istanbul, Turkiye
Tel.: (90) 2122792203
Web Site: https://mcflyrobot.com

INTERNATIONAL PUBLIC

Robotic Research & Development Services
N.A.I.C.S.: 541715

Signumtte A.S.   (1)
Hacettepe Teknokent 5 R&D Building No12 Cankaya, Universiteler District, 06800, Ankara, Turkiye
Tel.: (90) 3124912813
Web Site: https://signumtte.com
Software Development Services
N.A.I.C.S.: 541511

KONTRON AG
Industriezeile 35, A-4021, Linz, Austria
Tel.: (43) 73276640   AT
Web Site: https://group.kontron.com
Year Founded: 2008
KTN—(MUN)
Rev.: $1,353,289,426
Assets: $1,513,030,454
Liabilities: $848,544,869
Net Worth: $664,485,585
Earnings: $85,781,738
Emp.: 4,838
Fiscal Year-end: 12/31/23
IT Services
N.A.I.C.S.: 541512
Michael Jeske *(Member-Exec Bd & COO-Svcs DACH)*

Subsidiaries:

AMIT GmbH   (1)
Industriezeile 35, 4021, Linz, Austria
Tel.: (43) 732 941 670
Web Site: http://www.amit.at
Emp.: 6
Mobile Software Development Services
N.A.I.C.S.: 541511

Amanox Solutions AG   (1)
Dammweg 9, CH-3013, Bern, Switzerland
Tel.: (41) 313201080
Web Site: https://www.amanox.ch
Cloud Data Management Services
N.A.I.C.S.: 518210
Daniel Heinzmann *(COO)*

CITYCOMP Service GmbH   (1)
Elly-Beinhorn-Str 1, Scharnhausen, D-73760, Ostfildern, Germany
Tel.: (49) 7158687990
Web Site: https://www.citycomp.de
Software Development Services
N.A.I.C.S.: 541511

Funworld srl   (1)
Via Mecenate 84, 20138, Milan, Italy
Tel.: (39) 02 5099131
Web Site: http://www.funworld.com
Entertainment Hardware & Software Solutions
N.A.I.C.S.: 513210
Andrea Scampini *(Gen Mgr)*

Hamcos IT Service GmbH   (1)
Marie-Curie-Strasse 16, 72488, Sigmaringen, Germany
Tel.: (49) 757168980
Web Site: https://www.hamcos.de
Information Technology Services
N.A.I.C.S.: 541511

IMG Corporation Ltd.   (1)
9J3 No 728 Yanan West Road, Shanghai, 200050, China
Tel.: (86) 2152370088
Web Site: http://www.snt-world.com
Sales Range: $25-49.9 Million
Emp.: 60
IT Services
N.A.I.C.S.: 541512
Giaxin Yan *(Gen Mgr)*

Kapsch CarrierCom AG   (1)
Lehrbachgasse 11, 1120, Vienna, Austria
Tel.: (43) 50 8110
Web Site: http://www.kapschcarrier.com
Telecommunication Servicesb
N.A.I.C.S.: 517810

Subsidiary (Non-US):

Kapsch (Beijing) Information and Communication Technology Co., Ltd.   (2)
403-18 4/F No 20 Jiu Xian Qiao Road, Cha-

AND PRIVATE COMPANIES   KONTRON AG

oyang District, Beijing, 100016, China
Tel.: (86) 10 84350747
Telecommunication Servicesb
N.A.I.C.S.: 517112

Kapsch CarrierCom - Unipessoal LDA (2)
Rua Sousa Martins 10, 1050-218, Lisbon, Portugal
Tel.: (351) 215 924 128
Telecommunication Servicesb
N.A.I.C.S.: 517112

Kapsch CarrierCom Deutschland GmbH (2)
Main Airport Center Unterschweinstiege 2-14, 60549, Frankfurt am Main, Germany
Tel.: (49) 7545 96 0
Telecommunication Servicesb
N.A.I.C.S.: 517112
Bernd Eder *(Co-Mng Dir)*

Subsidiary (Domestic):

Kapsch Carrier Solution GmbH (3)
Sperberweg 8, 41468, Neuss, Germany
Tel.: (49) 2131 9526 0
Telecommunication Servicesb
N.A.I.C.S.: 517112
Ralf Arweiler *(Co-Mng Dir)*

Subsidiary (Non-US):

Kapsch CarrierCom Espana, S.L.U. (2)
Edificio Duero C/ Basauri 6 Urb La Florida, 28023, Madrid, Spain
Tel.: (34) 676 995 802
Telecommunication Servicesb
N.A.I.C.S.: 517112

Kapsch CarrierCom France SAS (2)
Batiment Themis Batiment 4 1 rue Jean-Pierre Timbaud, 78180, Montigny-le-Bretonneux, France
Tel.: (33) 1 30 23 70 00
Telecommunication Servicesb
N.A.I.C.S.: 517112

Kapsch CarrierCom Taiwan Co., Ltd. (2)
18/F 100 Roosevelt Rd Sec 2, Taipei, Taiwan
Tel.: (886) 2 2363 1212
Telecommunication Servicesb
N.A.I.C.S.: 517112

Kapsch CarrierCom sp. z o.o. (2)
Poleczki Business Park - Building A1 ul Poleczki 35, 02-822, Warsaw, Poland
Tel.: (48) 22 544 6000
Information Technology Development Services
N.A.I.C.S.: 541511

Kapsch EOOD (2)
Business Park Antim Tower 2 Kukush Str 3rd Floor, 1309, Sofia, Bulgaria
Tel.: (359) 2 812 17 25
Telecommunication Servicesb
N.A.I.C.S.: 517112

Kapsch FE (2)
9a Fabrisiusa Str Office 15, 220007, Minsk, Belarus
Tel.: (375) 172 197 546
Telecommunication Servicesb
N.A.I.C.S.: 517112

Kapsch d.o.o. (2)
33 Ribiciceva Ulica Str, 1000, Ljubljana, Slovenia
Tel.: (386) 590 34 283
Information Technology Development Services
N.A.I.C.S.: 541511

OOO Kapsch CarrierCom Russia (2)
Bolshoy Strochenovskiy Lane 7, 115054, Moscow, Russia
Tel.: (7) 495 9566329
Telecommunication Servicesb
N.A.I.C.S.: 517112

Katek SE (1)
Promenadeplatz 12, 80333, Munich, Germany (87.3%)
Tel.: (49) 89 24881 4280
Web Site: http://www.katek-group.de
Electronic Components Mfr
N.A.I.C.S.: 334419

Rainer Koppitz *(CEO, Member-Exec Bd & Mng Dir)*

Subsidiary (US):

Nextek, Inc. (2)
201 Next Technology Dr, Madison, AL 35758-9117
Tel.: (256) 772-0400
Web Site: http://www.nextekinc.com
Rev.: $9,800,000
Emp.: 160
Search, Detection, Navigation, Guidance, Aeronautical & Nautical System & Instrument Mfr
N.A.I.C.S.: 334511
James Harris *(Founder, Treas, Sec & VP-Programs)*

Kontron AIS GmbH (1)
Otto-Mohr-Strasse 6, 01237, Dresden, Germany
Tel.: (49) 35121660
Web Site: http://kontron-ais.com
Sales Range: $10-24.9 Million
Emp.: 8
Automation System Integration Services
N.A.I.C.S.: 541330
Roman Olwig *(Mgr-Sls)*

Subsidiary (Domestic):

Lucom GmbH Elektrokomponenten und Systeme
Flossaustrasse 22A, 90763, Furth, Germany
Tel.: (49) 9119 576 0600
Web Site: https://www.lucom.de
Communication Equipment Mfr
N.A.I.C.S.: 334290
Jens Hilgner *(Mng Dir)*

Kontron Asia Inc. (1)
5F No 415 Ti-Ding Blvd Sec 2, NeiHu District, Taipei, 11493, Taiwan
Tel.: (886) 227992789
Computer Software Services
N.A.I.C.S.: 541511

Kontron Austria GmbH (1)
Wildbichler Strasse 2e, A-6341, Ebbs, Austria
Tel.: (43) 5373431430
Electronic Control System Mfr
N.A.I.C.S.: 334419
Wolfgang Unterlerchner *(Mng Dir)*

Kontron Electronics AG (1)
Riedstrasse 1, 6343, Rotkreuz, Switzerland
Tel.: (41) 417994799
Electronic Products Mfr
N.A.I.C.S.: 334419
Franz Ott *(Mng Dir)*

Kontron Electronics GmbH (1)
Kantstrasse 10, 72663, Grossbettlingen, Germany
Tel.: (49) 7022 4057 0
Web Site: http://www.kontron-electronics.de
Electronic Products Mfr
N.A.I.C.S.: 334419
Holger Wussmann *(Mng Dir)*

Kontron Europe GmbH (1)
Gutenbergstrasse 2, 85737, Ismaning, Germany
Tel.: (49) 893700580
Computer Software Services
N.A.I.C.S.: 541511
Carlos Queiroz *(CEO)*

Kontron S&T AG
Lise-Meitner-Strasse 3-5, 86156, Augsburg, Germany
Tel.: (49) 821 40860
Web Site: http://www.kontron.com
Sales Range: $350-399.9 Million
Computer Systems Mfr
N.A.I.C.S.: 541512
Hannes Niederhauser *(CEO & Chm-Mgmt Bd)*

Subsidiary (US):

Kontron America Inc. (2)
14118 Stowe Dr, Poway, CA 92064-7147
Tel.: (858) 677-0877
Web Site: http://us.kontron.com
Sales Range: $50-74.9 Million
Emp.: 100

Computer Systems Sales & Customer Support
N.A.I.C.S.: 423430

Subsidiary (Domestic):

BSQUARE Corporation (3)
1415 Western Ave Ste 700, Seattle, WA 98101
Tel.: (425) 519-5900
Web Site: https://www.bsquare.com
Rev.: $36,487,000
Assets: $42,171,000
Liabilities: $6,772,000
Net Worth: $35,399,000
Earnings: ($3,858,000)
Emp.: 44
Fiscal Year-end: 12/31/2022
Computer Software Development
N.A.I.C.S.: 541511
Matthew Inglis *(VP-Engrg)*

Subsidiary (Non-US):

BSQUARE EMEA Limited (4)
County Gate County Way, Trowbridge, BA14 7FJ, Wiltshire, United Kingdom
Tel.: (44) 1225710600
Web Site: http://www.bsquare.com
Sales Range: $25-49.9 Million
Emp.: 52
Software Programming Services
N.A.I.C.S.: 541511

BSQUARE KK (4)
3-16-16 STEP 102 Daizawa, Setagaya, Tokyo, 155-0032, Japan
Tel.: (81) 368054030
Web Site: http://www.bsquare.com
Sales Range: $100-124.9 Million
Computer Software Development
N.A.I.C.S.: 541511

BSQUARE Taiwan Corporation (4)
10F No 49 Sec 3 Minsheng E Rd Zhongshan Dist, Taipei, 104, Taiwan
Tel.: (886) 225016022
Sales Range: $10-24.9 Million
Emp.: 25
Mfr of Windows Software Products
N.A.I.C.S.: 513210
Yvonne Chen *(Office Mgr)*

Subsidiary (Non-US):

Kontron Canada (2)
4555 Rue Ambroise-Lafortune, Boisbriand, J7H 0A4, QC, Canada (100%)
Tel.: (450) 437-5682
Web Site: https://www.kontron.com
Sales Range: $50-74.9 Million
Emp.: 150
Industrial & Technological Services
N.A.I.C.S.: 333310
Robert Courteau *(Gen Mgr)*

Subsidiary (Domestic):

Kontron Embedded Computers GmbH (2)
Oskar Von Miller Strasse 1, 85386, Eching, Germany (100%)
Tel.: (49) 8165770
Web Site: http://www.kontron.com
Sales Range: $50-74.9 Million
Emp.: 170
Mfr of Microcomputer Development Systems, Logic Analyzers & Other Digital Instrumentation
N.A.I.C.S.: 334111
Rolf Schwirz *(CEO)*

Subsidiary (Non-US):

Kontron Modular Computers S.A. (3)
150 rue Marcelin Berthelot, BP 244, ZI Toulon-Est, 83078, Toulon, Cedex, France
Tel.: (33) 498163400
Sales Range: $25-49.9 Million
Emp.: 100
Computer Hardware & Software System Services
N.A.I.C.S.: 541512

Kontron Technologies GmbH (1)
Industriezeile 35, 4020, Linz, Austria
Tel.: (43) 732941670
Web Site: http://www.kontron-technologies.com
Information Technology Services
N.A.I.C.S.: 541511

Kontron Transportation GmbH (1)
Lehrbachgasse 11, 1120, Vienna, Austria
Tel.: (43) 12533700
Emp.: 550
Computer Hardware Services
N.A.I.C.S.: 541511

MAXDATA (Schweiz) AG (1)
Haldenstrasse 5, 6340, Baar, Switzerland
Tel.: (41) 41 766 32 32
Web Site: http://www.maxdata.ch
Computer Equipment Mfr
N.A.I.C.S.: 334118

Quanmax Inc. (1)
401 No 142 TianLin Rd, Shanghai, 200233, China
Tel.: (86) 21 5427 2262
Web Site: http://www.quanmax.com.cn
Electronic Equipment Mfr & Distr
N.A.I.C.S.: 334419

Quanmax Inc. (1)
5F No 415 Ti-Ding Blvd Sec 2, NeiHu District, Taipei, 000114, Taiwan
Tel.: (886) 2 2799 2789
Web Site: http://www.quanmax.com
Emp.: 50
Electronic Equipment Mfr & Distr
N.A.I.C.S.: 334419
Kevin Tseng *(Mgr)*

Quanmax USA Inc. (1)
4790 Irvine Blvd Ste 105-318, Irvine, CA 92620
Tel.: (949) 272-2930
Web Site: http://www.quanmax.com
Electronic Equipment Mfr & Distr
N.A.I.C.S.: 334419

S&T Albania Ltd. (1)
Ibrahim Rugova Str No 70 Ap No 1, 1019, Tirana, Albania
Tel.: (355) 4 227 4641
Web Site: https://www.snt.al
Computer Software Services
N.A.I.C.S.: 541511

S&T Albania Sh.p.k. (1)
Str Ibrahim Rugova No 70 Ap 1, Str Deshmoret e 4 Shkurtit No 5, Tirana, Albania
Tel.: (355) 42274641
Web Site: https://www.axians.al
Emp.: 19
IT Services
N.A.I.C.S.: 541512

S&T Austria GmbH (1)
Geiselbergstrasse 17-19, Vienna, 1110, Austria
Tel.: (43) 1801910
Web Site: http://www.snt.at
Sales Range: $25-49.9 Million
Emp.: 100
IT Services
N.A.I.C.S.: 541512
Hannes Niederhauser *(Gen Mgr)*

S&T BH d.o.o (1)
Kulovica 5/1, 71000, Sarajevo, Bosnia & Herzegovina (100%)
Tel.: (387) 33941630
Web Site: http://www.snt.ba
Sales Range: $25-49.9 Million
Emp.: 5
IT Services
N.A.I.C.S.: 541512

S&T Bilisim Cozumleri Anonim Sirketi (1)
2 Tasocagi Caddesi Cemal Sahir Sok No 4 1 Mecidiyekoy, T 34387, Istanbul, Turkiye
Tel.: (90) 212 3564488
Sales Range: $25-49.9 Million
Emp.: 70
IT Services
N.A.I.C.S.: 541512

S&T Bulgaria e.o.o.d. (1)
7 Iskarsko shosse Blvd Trade Center Europe Building 6 Flour 3, 1528, Sofia, Bulgaria
Tel.: (359) 29651710
Web Site: https://www.kontron.bg
Emp.: 33
IT Services
N.A.I.C.S.: 541512

S&T CEE Holding s.r.o. (1)

KONTRON AG

Kontron AG—(Continued)

Platennicka 19013/2, 821 09, Bratislava, Slovakia
Tel.: (421) 258273111
Web Site: https://www.axians.sk
Sales Range: $50-74.9 Million
IT Services
N.A.I.C.S.: 541512

S&T CZ s.r.o. (1)
V park 2316/12, 148 00, Prague, 4, Czech Republic
Tel.: (420) 296538111
Web Site: https://www.axians.cz
IT Services
N.A.I.C.S.: 541512
Miroslav Becka *(CEO & Mng Dir)*

S&T Consulting Hungary Kft. (1)
Puskas Tivadar Str 14, 2040, Budaörs, Hungary
Tel.: (36) 13718000
Web Site: https://kontron.hu
Sales Range: $25-49.9 Million
IT Services
N.A.I.C.S.: 541512

S&T Crna Gora d.o.o. (1)
Bulevar Revolucije 5, 81000, Podgorica, Montenegro
Tel.: (382) 20202150
Web Site: http://www.snt.me
Sales Range: $25-49.9 Million
IT Services
N.A.I.C.S.: 541512
Milan Maric *(Mng Dir)*

S&T Embedded GmbH (1)
Gutenbergstrasse 2 Ismaning, Eching, 85386, Munich, Germany
Tel.: (49) 893700580
Web Site: http://www.snt-embedded.de
Electric Equipment Mfr
N.A.I.C.S.: 334419

S&T Germany GmbH (1)
Am Flugplatz 35, 56743, Mendig, Germany
Tel.: (49) 265 293 5090
Web Site: https://www.sntde.de
Information Technology Services
N.A.I.C.S.: 541511

S&T Hrvatska d.o.o. (1)
Borongajska cesta 81a, 10000, Zagreb, Croatia (100%)
Tel.: (385) 014603000
Web Site: http://www.cnt.hr
Sales Range: $25-49.9 Million
Emp.: 150
IT Services
N.A.I.C.S.: 541512
Bozidar Vidic *(Country Mgr)*

S&T International (1)
Build 4, Zyatsckay Street 35, Moscow, 127015, Russia
Tel.: (7) 4956456923
Web Site: http://www.sntru.com
Sales Range: $25-49.9 Million
Emp.: 100
IT Services
N.A.I.C.S.: 541512

S&T Macedonia dooel (1)
Ankarska 31, 1000, Skopje, North Macedonia
Tel.: (389) 23065396
Web Site: http://www.snt.com.mk
Sales Range: $25-49.9 Million
IT Services
N.A.I.C.S.: 541512
Boro Antovski *(Mng Dir)*

S&T Medtech S.R.L. (1)
Str Gheorghe Polizu no 58-60 floor 11, Bucharest Corporate Center, 11062, Bucharest, Romania
Tel.: (40) 213172102
Web Site: https://www.snt-medtech.ro
Medical Device Distr
N.A.I.C.S.: 423450

S&T Mold SRL (1)
Street. S Lazo 40 of 31, Chisinau, MD2004, Moldova
Tel.: (373) 22218600
Web Site: http://www.snt.md
Sales Range: $25-49.9 Million
Emp.: 30
IT Services

S&T Moldova S.R.L. (1)
8 Calea Iesilor Str Z Tower Business Center 6 Floor, 2069, Chisinau, Moldova
Tel.: (373) 2 283 7960
Web Site: https://www.snt.md
Computer Software Services
N.A.I.C.S.: 541511

S&T POLAND Sp. z o.o. (1)
ul Postepu 21D, 02-676, Warsaw, Poland
Tel.: (48) 225359500
Information Technology Consulting Services
N.A.I.C.S.: 541611

S&T Plus s.r.o. (1)
Novovorska 994, 142 21, Prague, Czech Republic
Tel.: (420) 239047500
Web Site: http://www.snt-plus.cz
Sales Range: $25-49.9 Million
Emp.: 25
IT Services
N.A.I.C.S.: 541512

S&T Romania S.R.L. (1)
58-60 Gheorghe Polizu Bucharest Corporate Center 11-12 Floor, 011062, Bucharest, Romania
Tel.: (40) 212085800
Web Site: http://www.snt.ro
IT Services
N.A.I.C.S.: 541512

S&T Serbia d.o.o. (1)
Dorda Stanojevica 14/IV, 11070, Belgrade, Serbia (100%)
Tel.: (381) 113116221
Web Site: https://www.axians.rs
Sales Range: $25-49.9 Million
IT Services
N.A.I.C.S.: 541512
Rajko Jovanovic *(Mng Dir)*

S&T Services Polska Sp. z o.o. (1)
ul Postepu 21D, 02-676, Warsaw, Poland
Tel.: (48) 225359500
Sales Range: $75-99.9 Million
Emp.: 400
IT Services
N.A.I.C.S.: 541512

S&T Slovakia s.r.o. (1)
Mlynske Nivy 71, 821 05, Bratislava, Slovakia
Tel.: (421) 2 582 73 111
Web Site: http://www.snt.sk
Sales Range: $25-49.9 Million
IT Services
N.A.I.C.S.: 541512
Stefan Klein *(Dir-Sls)*

S&T Slovenija d.d. (1)
Leskoskova Cesta 6, 1000, Ljubljana, Slovenia
Tel.: (386) 15855200
Web Site: http://www.snt.si
Sales Range: $25-49.9 Million
Emp.: 210
IT Services
N.A.I.C.S.: 541512
Saso Berger *(Country Mgr)*

S&T Software Development Sp. z o.o. (1)
Ul Postepu 21D, 02-676, Warsaw, Poland
Tel.: (48) 22 535 95 00
Web Site: http://www.snt.pl
Sales Range: $25-49.9 Million
IT Services
N.A.I.C.S.: 541512

S&T Ukraine (1)
44a Academician Palladin Avenue, Kiev, 03142, Ukraine
Tel.: (380) 442386388
Web Site: http://www.snt.ua
Sales Range: $25-49.9 Million
Emp.: 120
IT Services
N.A.I.C.S.: 541512

S&T Varias s.r.o. (1)
Apollo Business Center, Mlynske nivy 43A, Bratislava, 82108, Slovakia
Tel.: (421) 258273111
Web Site: https://www.snt-varias.com
Sales Range: $25-49.9 Million
Emp.: 50
IT Services

N.A.I.C.S.: 541512
Peder Dovhun *(Gen Mgr)*

SecureGUARD GmbH (1)
Industriezeile 35, A-4020, Linz, Austria (69%)
Tel.: (43) 732601440
Web Site: https://www.secureguard.at
Computer Security Solutions
N.A.I.C.S.: 334118
Helmut Otto *(Mng Dir)*

Sliger Designs Inc. (1)
1575 Linda Way Ste 107, Sparks, NV 89431 (60%)
Tel.: (775) 356-5595
Web Site: http://www.sliger.com
Emp.: 35
Electric Equipment Mfr
N.A.I.C.S.: 334419

Xtro IT Solutions GmbH (1)
Max-von-Eyth-Str 3, 85737, Ismaning, Germany
Tel.: (49) 89 552 779 0
Web Site: http://www.xtro.de
Information Technology Consulting Services
N.A.I.C.S.: 541512

computer betting company gmbh (1)
Fuchselbachstrasse 7, 4060, Leonding, Austria
Tel.: (43) 722975555
Information Technology Consulting Services
N.A.I.C.S.: 541512

KONYA CIMENTO SANAYII AS

Horozluhan Mah Cihan Sk No 15, Selcuklu, 42300, Konya, Turkiye
Tel.: (90) 3323460355
Web Site: http://www.konyacimento.com.tr
KONYA—(IST)
Rev.: $59,048,021
Assets: $51,380,427
Liabilities: $35,182,004
Net Worth: $16,198,423
Earnings: $4,835,455
Fiscal Year-end: 12/31/22
Cement Mfr & Distr
N.A.I.C.S.: 327310
Mehmet Dulger *(Chm)*

KOOK SOON DANG CO LTD

KOOSOONDANG Bldg 110-3 Samsung-dong, Gangnam-gu, Seoul, Korea (South)
Tel.: (82) 25138500
Web Site: http://www.ksdb.co.kr
Year Founded: 1952
043650—(KRS)
Rev.: $57,232,915
Assets: $194,700,059
Liabilities: $14,951,645
Net Worth: $179,748,414
Earnings: ($3,504,458)
Emp.: 309
Fiscal Year-end: 12/31/22
Beverages Mfr
N.A.I.C.S.: 312120
Bae Sangmin *(CEO)*

KOOL2PLAY SA

Al Jana Pawla II 22, 00-133, Warsaw, Poland
Tel.: (48) 223790491
Web Site: https://www.kool2play.com
Year Founded: 2013
K2P—(WAR)
Software Development Services
N.A.I.C.S.: 541511
Marcin Marzecki *(Chm)*

KOOLSEE NEW MEDIA GROUP LTD.

Level 6 10 Spring Street Suite 604, Sydney, 2000, NSW, Australia
Tel.: (61) 282570855
Web Site: http://www.koolsee.com.au
Online Shopping Service Provider
N.A.I.C.S.: 519290

INTERNATIONAL PUBLIC

Tao Cui *(CEO)*

KOON HOLDINGS LIMITED

11 Sixth Lok Yang Road, Singapore, 628109, Singapore
Tel.: (65) 62615788
Web Site: http://www.koon.com.sg
Rev.: $122,343,768
Assets: $207,371,560
Liabilities: $161,006,908
Net Worth: $46,364,652
Earnings: $75,549
Emp.: 223
Fiscal Year-end: 12/31/17
Holding Company; Civil Engineering Services
N.A.I.C.S.: 551112
Keng Lim Oh *(Exec Dir)*

Subsidiaries:

Econ Precast Pte. Ltd. (1)
26 Kranji Way, Singapore, 739436, Singapore
Tel.: (65) 63686677
Precast Component & Concrete Pile Mfr
N.A.I.C.S.: 327332
Ei Mon Soe *(Engr-Precast Design)*

Subsidiary (Domestic):

Contech Precast Pte. Ltd. (2)
11 Sixth Lok Yang Road, Singapore, 628109, Singapore
Tel.: (65) 62615788
Web Site: http://www.contechpl.com.sg
Precast Component Mfr
N.A.I.C.S.: 327332

Subsidiary (Non-US):

Econ Precast Sdn. Bhd. (2)
Lot 1946 Mukim Jeram Batu Bt 23 1/2 Pekan Nenas, Pekan Nenas, 81500, Johor, Malaysia
Tel.: (60) 76996639
Precast Component & Concrete Pile Mfr
N.A.I.C.S.: 327332

Entire Construction Pte. Ltd. (1)
11sixth Young Rd, Koon Bldg, Singapore, 609269, Singapore
Tel.: (65) 62615788
Sales Range: $25-49.9 Million
Emp.: 3
Civil Engineering Services
N.A.I.C.S.: 237990

Entire Engineering Pte Ltd (1)
11 Sixth Lok Yang Road, Singapore, 628109, Singapore
Tel.: (65) 62615788
Web Site: http://www.koon.com.sg
Construction Machinery Rental Services
N.A.I.C.S.: 532412

Gems Marine Pte. Ltd. (1)
11 Sixth Lok Yang Road, No 02-00, Singapore, 628108, Singapore
Tel.: (65) 62615788
Web Site: http://www.koon.com.sg
Sales Range: $25-49.9 Million
Emp.: 40
Marine Transportation Services
N.A.I.C.S.: 483111

Koon Construction & Transport Co. Pte. Ltd. (1)
11 Sixth Lok Yang Road, No 02 00 Koon Bldg, Singapore, 628109, Singapore
Tel.: (65) 62615788
Web Site: http://www.koon.com.sg
Sales Range: $25-49.9 Million
Emp.: 50
Civil Contractor Services
N.A.I.C.S.: 237990

KOONENBERRY GOLD LIMITED

Suite 6 Level 2 72-78 Carrington Street, Adelaide, 5000, SA, Australia
Tel.: (61) 862459869 AU
Web Site: https://www.koonenberrygold.com.au
Year Founded: 2015

KNB—(ASX)
Rev.: $45,624
Assets: $5,897,694
Liabilities: $178,616
Net Worth: $5,719,078
Earnings: ($1,014,740)
Fiscal Year-end: 06/30/23
Gold Exploration Services
N.A.I.C.S.: 212220

KOOPERATIVA FORBUNDET
Englundavagen 4, PO Box 171 88, Solna, Sweden
Tel.: (46) 107400000   SE
Web Site: http://www.kf.se
Year Founded: 1899
Sales Range: $1-4.9 Billion
Emp.: 18,000
Operation of Food Store Department Store/Superstore Bakery Brewery & Processed Meat Factory Mfr
N.A.I.C.S.: 311811
Lars Idermark *(Pres & CEO)*

Subsidiaries:

Coop Sverige AB   (1)
Englundavagen 4, Solna, 171 885, Sweden
Tel.: (46) 87431000
Web Site: http://www.coop.se
Emp.: 5,600
Supermarket Operator
N.A.I.C.S.: 445110
Sonat Burman-Olsson *(Pres)*

Joint Venture (Non-US):

Coop Trading A/S   (2)
Helgeshoj Alle 57, Hoje Taastrup, 2620, Denmark
Tel.: (45) 8853 0000
Web Site: http://www.cooptrading.com
Internordic Procurement of Branded Products
N.A.I.C.S.: 455219
Rene Sandberg *(Mgr-Strategy & Coordination)*

KF Fastigheter AB   (1)
Stadsgarden 10, PO Box 15200, Stockholm, 10465, Sweden   (100%)
Tel.: (46) 87431000
Web Site: http://www.kff.se
Sales Range: $25-49.9 Million
Emp.: 75
N.A.I.C.S.: 311811

OBS Hypermarket   (1)
PO Box 15200, S-104 65, Stockholm, Sweden
Tel.: (46) 87432700
N.A.I.C.S.: 311811

KOOPS FURNESS N.V.
Ceintuurbaan 50, Postbus 614, 8000 AP, Zwolle, Netherlands
Tel.: (31) 38 880 4600
Web Site: http://www.koops-furness.nl
Year Founded: 1905
Sales Range: $650-699.9 Million
Emp.: 1,200
Holding Company: Automotive Products & Services
N.A.I.C.S.: 551112
A. H. de Koning *(CEO)*

KOOTENAY SILVER INC.
Suite 1125-595 Howe Street, Vancouver, V6C 2T5, BC, Canada
Tel.: (604) 601-5650   BC
Web Site: https://www.kootenaysilver.com
KOOYF—(OTCIQ)
Rev.: $74,306
Assets: $73,849,675
Liabilities: $287,044
Net Worth: $73,562,631
Earnings: ($1,590,958)
Fiscal Year-end: 12/31/20
Silver Exploration & Mining
N.A.I.C.S.: 212220

Kenneth E. Berry *(Chm)*

KOOTENAY ZINC CORP.
1199 West Hastings Street Suite 800, Vancouver, V6E 3T5, BC, Canada
Tel.: (604) 306-0068
KYH1—(BER)
Assets: $416,683
Liabilities: $442,443
Net Worth: ($25,760)
Earnings: ($1,368,753)
Fiscal Year-end: 02/28/19
Mineral Exploration Services
N.A.I.C.S.: 213114
Tara Haddad *(CEO & CFO)*

KOOTH PLC
5 Merchant Square, London, W2 1AY, United Kingdom
Tel.: (44) 203398904   UK
Web Site: https://www.koothplc.com
Year Founded: 2001
KOO—(AIM)
Rev.: $25,397,627
Assets: $20,374,905
Liabilities: $7,097,955
Net Worth: $13,276,950
Earnings: ($903,812)
Emp.: 267
Fiscal Year-end: 12/31/22
Health Care Srvices
N.A.I.C.S.: 621610

KOOVS PLC
3rd Floor 77A Sector 18 IFFCO Road, Gurgaon, 122015, India
Tel.: (91) 1246770000
Web Site: http://www.koovs.com
KOOV—(AIM)
Rev.: $8,459,166
Assets: $38,343,726
Liabilities: $19,245,714
Net Worth: $19,098,012
Earnings: ($20,407,254)
Emp.: 159
Fiscal Year-end: 03/31/19
Online Clothing Retailer
N.A.I.C.S.: 424350
Waheed Alli *(Founder & Chm)*

KOOYMAN B.V.
Kaya WFG Mensing 44, Willemstad, Curacao
Tel.: (599) 94613333   CW
Web Site: http://www.kooymanbv.com
Year Founded: 1934
Sales Range: $75-99.9 Million
Emp.: 400
Building Materials & Hardware Stores Owner & Operator
N.A.I.C.S.: 444110
Bastiaan Kooijman *(Chm-Exec Bd)*

KOP LIMITED
316 Tanglin Road 01-01, Singapore, 247978, Singapore
Tel.: (65) 65337337   SG
Web Site: https://koplimited.com
Year Founded: 2004
5I1—(CAT)
Rev.: $35,198,222
Assets: $141,969,618
Liabilities: $85,993,331
Net Worth: $55,976,288
Earnings: ($22,655,798)
Emp.: 70
Fiscal Year-end: 03/31/23
Video Product Mfr & Distr
N.A.I.C.S.: 334310
Chih Ching Ong *(Chm)*

Subsidiaries:

P.T. Montigo Seminyak   (1)
Jalan Petitenget Seminyak, Bali, 80361, Indonesia
Tel.: (62) 3613019888

Hotel Services
N.A.I.C.S.: 721110

Scorpio East Entertainment Pte Ltd   (1)
Leong Huat Building 02-01 6 Harper Road, Singapore, 369674, Singapore
Tel.: (65) 6282 7082
Film Distribution Services
N.A.I.C.S.: 512120

Scorpio East Multimedia Pte Ltd   (1)
25 Tai Seng Avenue Scorpio East Building 06-01, Singapore, 534104, Singapore
Tel.: (65) 62827082
Emp.: 20
Logistics Consulting Servies
N.A.I.C.S.: 541614

KOPAONIK A.D.
Kralja Petra 153, Blace, Serbia
Tel.: (381) 27371561
Year Founded: 1989
KPNK—(BEL)
Sales Range: Less than $1 Million
Emp.: 25
Home Management Services
N.A.I.C.S.: 721110
Ratko Lazovic *(Exec Dir)*

KOPAONIK A.D.
st Zmaj Jovina 3, Stari grad, 11000, Belgrade, Serbia
Tel.: (381) 113282377
Web Site: https://www.adkopaonik.co.rs
Year Founded: 1946
KOPB—(BEL)
Sales Range: $10-24.9 Million
Emp.: 209
Metal Products Mfr
N.A.I.C.S.: 331210
Rade Doder *(Gen Mgr & Dir)*

KOPERASI ANGKATAN TENTERA MALAYSIA BERHAD
No 1 Jalan 2/65C Off Jalan Pahang Barat, Peti Surat 12698, 53000, Kuala Lumpur, Malaysia
Tel.: (60) 340272600
Web Site: http://www.katmb.com.my
Year Founded: 1960
Sales Range: $100-124.9 Million
Emp.: 200
Commercial Investment Services
N.A.I.C.S.: 523999

Subsidiaries:

Malaysia & Nippon Insurance Berhad   (1)
Level 18 Menara Prudential 10 Jalan Sultan Ismail, 50250, Kuala Lumpur, Malaysia
Tel.: (60) 321761000
Web Site: http://www.pacificmas.com.my
Sales Range: $75-99.9 Million
Emp.: 60
Insurance Services
N.A.I.C.S.: 524128

KOPPARBERG BRYGGERI AB
Tel.: (46) 58088600
Web Site: https://www.kopparbergs.se
Year Founded: 1882
Specialty Drink Mfr
N.A.I.C.S.: 312111
Peter Gunnar Bronsman *(CEO)*

KOPPERMANN & CO. GMBH
Schorner Strasse 12, Baierbrunn, 82065, Germany
Tel.: (49) 897447430
Web Site: http://www.koppermann.eu
Year Founded: 1919
Rev.: $27,500,000
Emp.: 26
Textile Fabrics Distr
N.A.I.C.S.: 314999
Peter Koppermann *(Pres & Mng Dir)*

Subsidiaries:

Koppermann Italia   (1)
Via Torelli Viollier 4, 20125, Milan, Italy
Tel.: (39) 026883625
Web Site: http://www.koppermann.it
Fabric Distr
N.A.I.C.S.: 424310

KOPRAN LTD.
Parijat House 1076 Dr E Moses Road Worli, Mumbai, 400 018, Maharashtra, India
Tel.: (91) 2243661111
Web Site: https://www.kopran.com
KOPRAN—(NSE)
Rev.: $66,429,111
Assets: $77,896,877
Liabilities: $25,232,684
Net Worth: $52,664,193
Earnings: $3,265,152
Emp.: 665
Fiscal Year-end: 03/31/23
Pharmaceuticals Product Mfr
N.A.I.C.S.: 325412
Surendra Somani *(Vice Chm)*

Subsidiaries:

Kopran Research Laboratories Ltd.   (1)
Parijat House 1076 Dr E Moses Road, Worli, Mumbai, 400 018, Maharashtra, India
Tel.: (91) 2243661111
Pharmaceutical Ingredient Mfr
N.A.I.C.S.: 325412

KOPRODUKT A.D.
Bulevar Mihajla Pupina 6, 21000, Novi Sad, Serbia
Tel.: (381) 21 420 661
Web Site: http://www.koprodukt.com
Year Founded: 1959
KPRD—(BEL)
Sales Range: Less than $1 Million
Emp.: 8
Livestock Whslr
N.A.I.C.S.: 424520
Violeta Jurkovic *(Mng Dir)*

KOPY GOLDFIELDS AB
Eriksbergsgatan 10, PO Box 7292, 103 90, Stockholm, Sweden
Tel.: (46) 86602159
Web Site: https://www.kopygoldfields.com
Year Founded: 2007
KOPY—(OMX)
Rev.: $115,775,000
Assets: $223,372,000
Liabilities: $139,345,000
Net Worth: $84,027,000
Earnings: ($29,480,000)
Emp.: 705
Fiscal Year-end: 12/31/22
Gold Exploration Services
N.A.I.C.S.: 212220
Mikhail Damrin *(CEO)*

KOR ALTA CONSTRUCTION LTD.
2461 76th Avenue, Edmonton, T6P 1P5, AB, Canada
Tel.: (780) 440-6661
Web Site: https://www.koralta.com
Year Founded: 1991
Rev.: $34,507,341
Emp.: 20
General Construction Services
N.A.I.C.S.: 236220
Tyler Lemmens *(Principal)*

KORAB RESOURCES LTD.
20 Prowse Street, West Perth, 6005, WA, Australia
Tel.: (61) 894746166
KOR—(ASX)
Rev.: $112,322
Assets: $3,128,723

KORAB RESOURCES LTD.

Korab Resources Ltd.—(Continued)
Liabilities: $3,024,760
Net Worth: $103,964
Earnings: ($622,393)
Emp.: 3
Fiscal Year-end: 06/30/24
Gold & Phosphate Rock Mining Services
N.A.I.C.S.: 212220
Andrej K. Karpinski *(Chm & Sec)*

KORADO BULGARIA
Gladstone Street 28, Strazhitsa, 5150, Veliko Tarnovo, Bulgaria
Tel.: (359) 61614245
Web Site: https://www.korado.bg
KBG—(BUL)
Rev.: $21,512,927
Assets: $17,520,267
Liabilities: $3,792,726
Net Worth: $13,727,542
Earnings: $1,954,974
Emp.: 171
Fiscal Year-end: 12/31/23
Radiator & Fitting Product Mfr
N.A.I.C.S.: 332919
Jiri Reznicek *(Chm-Mgmt Bd & Exec Dir)*

KORAMCO ENERGY PLUS REIT CO., LTD.
Golden Tower 511 Samseong-Ro, Gangnam-Gu, Seoul, Korea (South)
Tel.: (82) 27870000
Web Site:
  http://www.koramcoenergyplus.co.kr
Year Founded: 2019
357120—(KRS)
Real Estate Services
N.A.I.C.S.: 531210
Shin Dong-Soo *(CEO)*

KORAMCO THE ONE REIT
511 Golden Tower Samseong-ro, Gangnam-gu, Seoul, 06158, Korea (South)
Tel.: (82) 27870100
Web Site:
  https://www.koramcothe1.com
Year Founded: 2015
417310—(KRS)
Real Estate Manangement Services
N.A.I.C.S.: 531311
Seok Gyun Yu *(Sr Mgr)*

KORAMIC REAL ESTATE NV
Kapel ter Bede 84, 8500, Kortrijk, Belgium
Tel.: (32) 56249690   BE
Web Site:
  http://www.koramicrealestate.be
Investment Holding Company
N.A.I.C.S.: 551112

Subsidiaries:

Koramic2Engage NV   (1)
Kapel ter Bede 84, 8500, Kortrijk, Belgium
Tel.: (32) 56 24 96 90
Digital Automation, Telesales & Managed Outsourcing Services
N.A.I.C.S.: 561499

Division (Domestic):

Call-IT Belgium NV   (2)
Konterdamkaai 1, 8400, Oostende, Belgium
Tel.: (32) 59 569999
Web Site: http://www.call-it.com
Professional IT Support Services
N.A.I.C.S.: 561311

Subsidiary (Non-US):

Call-IT International B.V.   (3)
Schatbeuderlaan 10, 6002 ED, Weert, Netherlands
Tel.: (31) 495547700
Web Site: http://www.call-it.com
Employment Services

N.A.I.C.S.: 561311

KORBER AG
Anckelmannsplatz 1, 20537, Hamburg, Germany
Tel.: (49) 40 211 0701   De
Web Site: http://www.koerber.de
Year Founded: 1946
Rev.: $2,911,358,458
Assets: $4,250,888,672
Liabilities: $1,855,069,537
Net Worth: $2,395,819,135
Earnings: $361,950,058
Emp.: 10,538
Fiscal Year-end: 12/31/18
Holding Company: Automation, Intralogistics, Machine Tools, Pharma Systems, Tissue & Tobacco Mfr & Services
N.A.I.C.S.: 551112
Bernd Kruppa *(Vice Chm-Supervisory Bd)*

Subsidiaries:

BVG Bergedorfer Versicherungsvermittlung GmbH   (1)
Naglesweg 33-35, 20097, Hamburg, Germany
Tel.: (49) 40 21107 06
Business Support Services
N.A.I.C.S.: 561499

Baltic Elektronik GmbH   (1)
Gruner Weg 2, 23936, Grevesmuhlen, Germany
Tel.: (49) 3881 7824 0
Web Site: http://www.balticelektronik.de
Electronic Services
N.A.I.C.S.: 238210

Fargo Automation, Inc.   (1)
969 34th St N, Fargo, ND 58102
Tel.: (701) 232-1780
Web Site: http://www.fargoautomation.com
Rev.: $8,500,000
Emp.: 65
All Other Industrial Machinery Mfr
N.A.I.C.S.: 333248

Hauni Maschinenbau AG   (1)
Kurt A Korber Chaussee 8-32, 21033, Hamburg, Germany
Tel.: (49) 40 7250 01
Web Site: http://www.hauni.com
Metal Products Mfr
N.A.I.C.S.: 332999

Subsidiary (Domestic):

ASL Analytik Service Labor GmbH & Co.   (2)
Schnackenburgallee 15, 22525, Hamburg, Germany
Tel.: (49) 40 8531 38661
Web Site: http://www.asl-analysis.de
Tobacco & Food Product Analytical Services
N.A.I.C.S.: 541380

Borgwaldt Flavor GmbH   (2)
Schnackenburgalee 15, 22525, Hamburg, Germany
Tel.: (49) 40 8531 380
Web Site: http://www.borgwaldt-flavor.com
Emp.: 35
Tobacco Flavoring Services
N.A.I.C.S.: 334519

Borgwaldt KC GmbH   (2)
Schnackenburgallee 15, 22525, Hamburg, Germany
Tel.: (49) 408531380
Web Site: http://www.borgwaldt.com
Emp.: 80
Quality Control Devices & Machines for Tobacco Industry
N.A.I.C.S.: 334519

Subsidiary (US):

Borgwaldt KC, Inc.   (2)
7741 Whitepine Rd, Richmond, VA 23237
Tel.: (804) 271-6471
Industrial Machinery Distr
N.A.I.C.S.: 423830
Michael Connor *(Mgr)*

Subsidiary (Non-US):

Decoufle s.a.r.l.   (2)
2 avenue du President Francois Mitterand, 91385, Chilly-Mazarin, Cedex, France
Tel.: (33) 1 6910 7000
Industrial Machinery Mfr
N.A.I.C.S.: 333248

Hauni Far East Limited   (2)
Room 907-8 Harbour Centre 25 Harbour Road, Wanchai, China (Hong Kong)
Tel.: (852) 2827 4167
Industrial Machinery Mfr
N.A.I.C.S.: 333248
Vivian Hong *(Gen Mgr-Fin & Controlling)*

Hauni Hungaria Gepgyarto Kft.   (2)
Mora Ferenc u 72, 7632, Pecs, Hungary
Tel.: (36) 72 505 200
Industrial Machinery Mfr
N.A.I.C.S.: 333248

Hauni Japan Co., Ltd.   (2)
Shinwa Building 1-8-10 Shinkiba, Koto-ku, Tokyo, 136-0082, Japan
Tel.: (81) 3 5534 1230
Industrial Machinery & Tool Distr
N.A.I.C.S.: 423830

Hauni Malaysia Sdn. Bhd.   (2)
Lot 16 Jalan Api-Api 26/1, Kawasan Perindustrian Hicom Section 26, 40400, Shah Alam, Selangor Darul Ehsan, Malaysia
Tel.: (60) 3 5191 8000
Industrial Machinery Mfr
N.A.I.C.S.: 333248

Subsidiary (Domestic):

Hauni Primary GmbH   (2)
Grabauer Strasse 49, 21493, Schwarzenbek, Germany
Tel.: (49) 4151 860
Engineeering Services
N.A.I.C.S.: 541330

Subsidiary (US):

Hauni Richmond, Inc.   (2)
2800 Charles City Rd, Richmond, VA 23231
Tel.: (804) 222-5259
Web Site: http://www.hauni.com
Emp.: 100
Industrial Machinery Sales
N.A.I.C.S.: 423830
Jean H. Klele *(Mgr-HR)*

Subsidiary (Non-US):

Hauni Singapore Pte. Ltd.   (2)
6 Temasek Boulevard 30-04, Suntec City, Tower 4, Singapore, 038986, Singapore
Tel.: (65) 6836 9011
Web Site: http://www.hauni.com
Industrial Machinery Sales
N.A.I.C.S.: 423840

Hauni Technical Services and Trading Company Ltd.   (2)
Cinlarli Quarter Islam Kerimov Street No 3 Sunucu Plaza B-Blok, Floor 14 Flat 8-9-10 Konak, Izmir, Turkiye
Tel.: (90) 232 413 05 10
Industrial Machinery & Tool Distr
N.A.I.C.S.: 423830

Hauni Trading (Shanghai) Co., Ltd.   (2)
Room 604 Huaxia Banking Building 256 South Pudong Road, Shanghai, 200120, China
Tel.: (86) 21 68866 618
Industrial Machinery & Tool Distr
N.A.I.C.S.: 423830

Hauni do Brasil Ltda.   (2)
Rua Joaquim Floriano 1052-2 andar-conjs 21 e 22, 04534-004, Itaim, Sao Paulo, Brazil
Tel.: (55) 11 3089 5315
Industrial Machinery & Tool Distr
N.A.I.C.S.: 423830
Cintia Goes *(Mgr-Order Processing-After Sls Svc)*

OOO Hauni St. Petersburg   (2)
Renaissance Plaza Business Center 69-71 B Ul Marata, 191119, Saint Petersburg, Russia
Tel.: (7) 8123137000

INTERNATIONAL PUBLIC

Web Site: http://www.hauni.com
Industrial Machinery & Tool Distr
N.A.I.C.S.: 423830
Alina Pamkratova *(Office Mgr)*

Sodim SAS   (2)
4 rue Danton, 45404, Fleury-les-Aubrais, Cedex, France
Tel.: (33) 2 3872 3872
Industrial Machinery Mfr
N.A.I.C.S.: 333248

Subsidiary (Domestic):

Universelle Engineering U.N.L. GmbH   (2)
Grabauer Strasse 49, 21493, Schwarzenbek, Germany
Tel.: (49) 4151 863
Web Site: http://www.universelle.de
Engineeering Services
N.A.I.C.S.: 541330

Korber Medipak Systems GmbH   (1)
Anckelmannsplatz 1, 20537, Hamburg, Germany
Tel.: (49) 402110701
Web Site: http://www.medipak-systems.com
Pharmaceutical Packaging Services
N.A.I.C.S.: 333993

Subsidiary (Non-US):

Dividella AG   (2)
Werdenstrasse 76, 9472, Grabs, Switzerland   (100%)
Tel.: (41) 81 750 3366
Web Site: http://www.dividella.ch
Emp.: 170
Medical & Surgical Apparatus & Equipment Mfr
N.A.I.C.S.: 339112
Marta Berger *(Mgr-Mktg)*

Subsidiary (US):

Korber Medipak Systems North Amercia Inc.   (2)
14501 58th St N, Clearwater, FL 33760
Tel.: (727) 532-6509
Web Site: http://www.kmedipak.com
Industrial Machinery Distr
N.A.I.C.S.: 423830
Mike DeCollibus *(Pres)*

Subsidiary (Domestic):

Mediseal GmbH   (2)
Flurstrasse 65, 33758, Schloss Holte-Stukenbrock, Germany
Tel.: (49) 5207 8880
Web Site: http://www.mediseal.de
Pharmaceutical Packaging Services
N.A.I.C.S.: 561910
Cord Schmidthals *(Mng Dir)*

Subsidiary (Non-US):

Rondo AG   (2)
Gewerbestrasse 11, 4123, Allschwil, Switzerland
Tel.: (41) 61 486 8787
Web Site: http://www.rondodruck.ch
Emp.: 350
Medicinal Packaging Services
N.A.I.C.S.: 333993

Rondo obaly s.r.o.   (2)
Zemska 230, 33701, Ejpovice, Czech Republic
Tel.: (420) 371 515 515
Web Site: http://www.rondo-packaging.com
Emp.: 100
Medicinal Packaging Services
N.A.I.C.S.: 333993

Subsidiary (US):

Rondo-Pak Inc.   (2)
900 Madison Ave, Norristown, PA 19403
Tel.: (610) 666-6116
Web Site: http://www.rondo-pak.com
Medicinal Packaging Services
N.A.I.C.S.: 561910
Victor L. Dixon *(Pres)*

Subsidiary (Domestic):

Seidenader Maschinenbau GmbH   (2)
Lilienthalstrasse 8, 85570, Markt Schwa-

AND PRIVATE COMPANIES

ben, Germany
Tel.: (49) 8121 8020
Web Site: http://www.seidenader.de
Emp.: 300
Pharmaceutical Packaging Machinery Mfr
N.A.I.C.S.: 333993
Jan Rudolph (Mng Dir)

Korber Process Solutions GmbH (1)
Nagelsweg 33-35, 20097, Hamburg, Germany
Tel.: (49) 40 21107 02
Web Site: http://www.asl-analysis.com
Business Support Services
N.A.I.C.S.: 561499

Subsidiary (Domestic):

Aberle GmbH (2)
Daimlerstrasse 40, 74211, Leingarten, Germany
Tel.: (49) 7131 90590
Web Site: http://www.aberle-automation.com
Business Support Services
N.A.I.C.S.: 561499

Subsidiary (Domestic):

Aberle Logistics GmbH (3)
Gropiusstrasse 12, 31137, Hildesheim, Germany
Tel.: (49) 5121 93573 10
Information Technology Consulting Services
N.A.I.C.S.: 541512

Subsidiary (Domestic):

Aberle Software GmbH (2)
Ruppmannstrasse 33a, 70565, Stuttgart, Germany
Tel.: (49) 711 215710
Web Site: http://www.aberle-software.com
Software Developer
N.A.I.C.S.: 513210

Subsidiary (Non-US):

Fabio Perini S.p.A. (2)
PIP Mugnano Sud, 55100, Lucca, Italy
Tel.: (39) 0583 4601
Business Support Services
N.A.I.C.S.: 561499

Subsidiary (Domestic):

Engraving Solutions S.r.l. (3)
Via del Mugnano 815, 55100, Lucca, Italy
Tel.: (39) 0583 460214
Web Site: http://www.engravingsolutions.it
Tissue Product Mfr
N.A.I.C.S.: 322291

Subsidiary (Non-US):

Fabio Perini (Shanghai) Co., Ltd. (3)
500 Mindong Road, Pudong New District, Shanghai, 201209, China
Tel.: (86) 21 5046 2933
Web Site: http://www.fabioperini.com
Industrial Machinery & Tool Distr
N.A.I.C.S.: 423830

Fabio Perini Germany GmbH (3)
Hammer Landstrasse 1 a, 41460, Neuss, Germany
Tel.: (49) 2131 1561 0
Industrial Machinery & Tool Distr
N.A.I.C.S.: 423830

Fabio Perini Japan Co., Ltd. (3)
831-10 Tadehara, Fuji, 416-0931, Shizuoka, Japan
Tel.: (81) 545 649 501
Industrial Machinery & Tool Distr
N.A.I.C.S.: 423830

Fabio Perini Ltda. (3)
AV Santos Dumont 2283 Bom Retiro, 89219-730, Joinville, SC, Brazil
Tel.: (55) 47 2101 0500
Web Site: http://www.fabeoperini.com
Emp.: 300
Business Support Services
N.A.I.C.S.: 561499

Subsidiary (US):

Fabio Perini North America, Inc. (3)
3060 S Ridge Rd, Green Bay, WI 54304
Tel.: (920) 336-5000
Tissue Converting & Packaging Machinery Mfr

N.A.I.C.S.: 333993
Pete Augustine (Pres)

Subsidiary (Domestic):

Fabio Perini Packaging S.p.A. (3)
Via San Vitalino 7, 40012, Calderara di Reno, BO, Italy
Tel.: (39) 051 3174 111
Packaging Services
N.A.I.C.S.: 561910

Subsidiary (Non-US):

Korber Medipak Systems AG (2)
Neuwiesenstrasse 20, 8400, Winterthur, Switzerland
Tel.: (41) 522 600 922
Web Site: http://www.medipak-systems.com
Industrial Machinery Mfr & Distr
N.A.I.C.S.: 333248
Ulf Brodbeck (Mng Dir)

Subsidiary (Domestic):

Langhammer GmbH (2)
Am Junger Lowe Schacht 7, 09599, Freiberg, Germany
Tel.: (49) 373137740
Web Site: http://www.langhammer.de
Emp.: 50
Business Support Services
N.A.I.C.S.: 561499
Enrico Pes (CEO & Mng Dir)

Subsidiary (Domestic):

LTi GmbH (1)
Gewerbestr 5-9, 35633, Lahnau, Germany
Tel.: (49) 6441 966 0
Web Site: http://www.lt-i.com
Emp.: 900
Automation & Sensor Equipment Mfr
N.A.I.C.S.: 334519

Subsidiary (Domestic):

Dressel GmbH (2)
Heinrich-Hertz-Strasse 18, 59423, Unna, Germany
Tel.: (49) 2303 9474 0
Web Site: http://www.dressel.de
Emp.: 20
Electrical Equipment Whslr
N.A.I.C.S.: 423610
Markus Stehlau (Head-Automation)

Subsidiary (Non-US):

LTi AUSTRIA GmbH (2)
Durisolstr 7, 4600, Wels, Austria
Tel.: (43) 7242 360944 0
Industrial Equipment Distr
N.A.I.C.S.: 423830

LTi ITALIA S.r.l. (2)
Via Fratelli Rosselli 3/2, 20019, Settimo Milanese, Milan, Italy
Tel.: (39) 02 33 51 48 96
Web Site: http://www.lti-motion.com
Industrial Equipment Distr
N.A.I.C.S.: 423830

LTi REEEnergy Co., Ltd. (2)
2F No 7 Industry East Road 4, Science-Based Industrial Park, 30077, Hsin-chu, Taiwan
Tel.: (886) 3579 5188
Web Site: http://www.lt-i.com.tw
Industrial Machinery Sales
N.A.I.C.S.: 423830

Subsidiary (Domestic):

SENSiTEC GmbH (2)
Georg-Ohm-Strasse 11, 35633, Lahnau, Germany
Tel.: (49) 644197880
Web Site: http://www.sensitec.com
Semiconductor Equipment Mfr
N.A.I.C.S.: 334413

andron GmbH (2)
Schlatterstrasse 2, 88142, Wasserburg am Bodensee, Germany
Tel.: (49) 8382 9855 0
Web Site: http://www.andron.de
Machine Tools Mfr
N.A.I.C.S.: 333517
Wilhelm J. Bluemlein (Founder)

Riantics A/S (1)
Industrivej 8, 9510, Arden, Denmark
Tel.: (45) 99400000

Web Site: http://www.riantics.com
Logistics & Storage Solutions
N.A.I.C.S.: 541614
Hans-Henrik Jensen (CEO)

inconso AG (1)
In der Hub 2 - 8, 61231, Bad Nauheim, Germany
Tel.: (49) 6032 348 0
Web Site: http://www.inconso.com
Application Software Distr
N.A.I.C.S.: 423430
Bertram Salzinger (CEO & Member-Mgmt Bd)

KORD HOLDINGS, INC.
12/F Centry Ind Building, Shek Pai Tau Road, Tuen Mun, China (Hong Kong)
Tel.: (852) 24634011 VG
Web Site: http://www.kordparty.com
Year Founded: 1972
Sales Range: $800-899.9 Million
Emp.: 3,000
Holding Company; Party Goods Mfr
N.A.I.C.S.: 551112
San Tung Li (Pres)

Subsidiaries:

Kord Party Favour Manufactory Ltd. (1)
12/F Century Ind Building, Shek Pai Tau Rd, Tuen Mun, China (Hong Kong)
Tel.: (852) 24634011
Web Site: http://www.kordparty.com
Party Goods Mfr
N.A.I.C.S.: 322299

KORDELLOS CH. BROS S.A.
50 Loutsas and Peloponnisou Str, 19600, Mandra-Attikis, Greece
Tel.: (30) 2105500901
Web Site: https://www.kordelos.gr
Year Founded: 1952
KORDE—(ATH)
Sales Range: Less than $1 Million
Steel Products Whslr
N.A.I.C.S.: 423510
Kordellou K. Angeliki (Pres)

KORE FOODS LIMITED
Vision House Tivim Industrial Estate, Mapusa, Goa, 403 526, India
Tel.: (91) 8322257347
Web Site: https://www.korefoods.in
500458—(BOM)
Rev.: $206
Assets: $27,137
Liabilities: $429,315
Net Worth: ($402,178)
Earnings: ($48,286)
Fiscal Year-end: 03/31/23
Nut Product Mfr
N.A.I.C.S.: 111335
Sadashiv V. Shet (Chm)

KORE MINING LTD.
2200 - 885 West Georgia Street, Vancouver, V6C 3E8, BC, Canada
Tel.: (604) 449-2273
Web Site: http://www.koremining.com
Year Founded: 1981
KOREF—(OTCQX)
Rev.: $15,286
Assets: $4,861,675
Liabilities: $752,046
Net Worth: $4,109,629
Earnings: $231,059
Fiscal Year-end: 12/31/21
Mineral Exploration Services
N.A.I.C.S.: 213114
Scott Trebilcock (Pres & CEO)

KORE POTASH PLC
45 Gresham Street, London, EC2V 7BG, United Kingdom
Tel.: (44) 2039631776
Web Site: https://www.korepotash.com

Year Founded: 2017
KP2—(AIM)
Rev.: $66,956
Assets: $168,399,774
Liabilities: $749,495
Net Worth: $167,650,279
Earnings: ($1,513,953)
Emp.: 27
Fiscal Year-end: 12/31/22
Mineral Exploration Services
N.A.I.C.S.: 212390
Gavin Chamberlain (COO)

Subsidiaries:

Kore Potash Limited (1)
Level 3 88 William Street, Perth, 6005, WA, Australia
Tel.: (61) 894632463
Web Site: https://www.korepotash.com
Potash Mining Services
N.A.I.C.S.: 212390

KOREA AEROSPACE INDUSTRIES LTD.
78 Gongdanro 1-ro Sanam-myeon, Sacheon, Gyeongsangnam-do, Korea (South)
Tel.: (82) 558511000
Web Site: http://www.koreaaero.com
047810—(KRS)
Rev.: $2,137,543,313
Assets: $5,961,435,934
Liabilities: $4,846,818,628
Net Worth: $1,114,617,305
Earnings: $88,910,177
Emp.: 5,079
Fiscal Year-end: 12/31/22
Aircraft Mfr
N.A.I.C.S.: 336411
Goo-Young Kang (CEO)

Subsidiaries:

Aviosys Technologies Co., Ltd. (1)
B-802 Head Office B-801 R&D B-903 Factory 723 Pangyo-ro, Bundang-gu, Seongnam, Gyeonggi-do, Korea (South)
Tel.: (82) 7048638900
Web Site: http://www.aviosystech.com
Aircraft Mfr
N.A.I.C.S.: 336411
Jeon Sang-Ik (CEO)

Korea Aerospace Industries Ltd. - Sancheong Factory (1)
2436 Chinhwangyeong-ro Geumseo-myeon, Sancheong, Gyeongsangnam-do, Korea (South)
Tel.: (82) 558511349
Emp.: 70
Aircraft Part Mfr
N.A.I.C.S.: 336413

KOREA AIRPORT SERVICE CO., LTD.
13 Yangcheon-ro, Gangseo-gu, Seoul, Korea (South)
Tel.: (82) 226603114
Web Site: http://www.kas.co.kr
Year Founded: 1968
005430—(KRS)
Rev.: $307,199,670
Assets: $322,979,898
Liabilities: $62,754,877
Net Worth: $260,225,021
Earnings: $4,428,954
Emp.: 2,639
Fiscal Year-end: 12/31/22
Aircraft Ground Handling Services
N.A.I.C.S.: 488119
Seung-Bum Lee (Pres)

KOREA ALCOHOL INDUSTRIAL CO., LTD.
14 Tapsil-ro 35beon-gil, Giheung-gu, Yongin, Gyeonggi-do, Korea (South)
Tel.: (82) 318818000
Web Site: https://www.ka.co.kr
Year Founded: 1984

KOREA ALCOHOL INDUSTRIAL CO., LTD.

Korea Alcohol Industrial Co., Ltd.—(Continued)
017890—(KRS)
Rev.: $393,239,423
Assets: $445,655,813
Liabilities: $87,149,601
Net Worth: $358,506,212
Earnings: $23,264,538
Fiscal Year-end: 12/31/22
Ethyl Alcohol Mfr
N.A.I.C.S.: 325193
Yong-Seok Chi (CEO)

Subsidiaries:

ENF Technology Guangzhou Co., Ltd. (1)
No 8 Cuiguang Street, Luogang District, Guangzhou, China
Tel.: (86) 2032033677
Electronic Materials Mfr
N.A.I.C.S.: 334419

FEM Technology Co., Ltd. (1)
123-34 Injusandan-ro Inju-myeon, Asan, Chungcheongnam-do, Korea (South)
Tel.: (82) 415383700
Semiconductor Material Mfr
N.A.I.C.S.: 334413

KOREA ARLICO PHARM CO., LTD.
7-21 Baumoe-ro 27-gil, Seocho-gu, Seoul, Korea (South)
Tel.: (82) 25850004
Web Site: https://www.arlico.co.kr
Year Founded: 1995
260660—(KRS)
Rev.: $128,654,372
Assets: $117,762,231
Liabilities: $49,847,357
Net Worth: $67,914,873
Earnings: $6,162,277
Emp.: 198
Fiscal Year-end: 12/31/22
Pharmaceutical Product Mfr & Distr
N.A.I.C.S.: 325412
Choi Jae-Hee (CEO)

KOREA ASSET IN TRUST CO LTD
306 Teheran-ro, Gangnam-gu, Seoul, 06210, Korea (South)
Tel.: (82) 221126300
Web Site: http://www.kait.com
Year Founded: 2001
123890—(KRS)
Rev.: $184,042,013
Assets: $1,077,397,399
Liabilities: $340,775,575
Net Worth: $736,621,823
Earnings: $85,511,193
Emp.: 208
Fiscal Year-end: 12/31/22
Real Estate Services
N.A.I.C.S.: 531190

KOREA ASSET INVESTMENT SECURITIES CO., LTD.
12th floor 57 Yeouinaru-ro Sinsong Center Building, Yeongduengpo-Gu, Seoul, 7327, Korea (South)
Tel.: (82) 25506200
Web Site: https://www.kasset.co.kr
Year Founded: 2000
190650—(KRS)
Emp.: 213
Investment Banking Services
N.A.I.C.S.: 523150
Kee Dong-Ho (CEO)

KOREA CABLE T.V CHUNG-BUK SYSTEM CO., LTD.
114 Yeseong-ro, Chungju, Chungcheongbuk-do, Korea (South)
Tel.: (82) 438507104
Web Site: http://www.ccstv.co.kr
066790—(KRS)
Rev.: $14,846,008
Assets: $24,614,814
Liabilities: $5,505,570
Net Worth: $19,109,244
Earnings: $628,708
Emp.: 40
Fiscal Year-end: 12/31/22
Cable Television Broadcasting Services
N.A.I.C.S.: 516120
Hyun-Moo Lee (CEO)

KOREA CAST IRON PIPE IND. CO., LTD.
525 eulsukdodaero, Saha-gu, Busan, 604836, Korea (South)
Tel.: (82) 512915491
Web Site: https://www.kcip.co.kr
Year Founded: 1953
000970—(KRS)
Rev.: $469,370,288
Assets: $389,242,756
Liabilities: $70,095,834
Net Worth: $319,146,921
Earnings: $60,466,039
Emp.: 164
Fiscal Year-end: 03/31/21
Iron Pipe Mfr
N.A.I.C.S.: 331210
Kil-Chool Kim (Chm & CEO)

Subsidiaries:

Korea Cast Iron Pipe Ind. Co., Ltd. - Pohang Plant (1)
1-138 Cheongrim-dong, Pohang, Korea (South)
Tel.: (82) 54 292 5780
Iron Pipe Mfr
N.A.I.C.S.: 331210

KOREA CIRCUIT CO LTD
9 Gangchon-ro 139beon-gil, Danwon-gu, Ansan, Gyeonggi-do, Korea (South)
Tel.: (82) 314913061
Web Site: https://www.kcg.co.kr
Year Founded: 1972
007810—(KRS)
Rev.: $1,224,803,242
Assets: $992,075,036
Liabilities: $415,588,154
Net Worth: $576,486,882
Earnings: $65,770,859
Emp.: 1,247
Fiscal Year-end: 12/31/22
Bare Printed Circuit Board Mfr
N.A.I.C.S.: 334412
Se-Jonn Chang (CEO)

Subsidiaries:

Terranix Co., Ltd. (1)
606-4 Seonggok-dong 12 Jangjagol-lo, Danwon-gu, Ansan, 425-83, Gyeonggi-do, Korea (South)
Tel.: (82) 314947441
Web Site: https://www.terranix.co.kr
Emp.: 107
Printed Circuit Board Mfr & Distr
N.A.I.C.S.: 334412
Seo Jung Ho (Co-CEO)

KOREA COMPUTER & SYSTEMS INC
269 Dokmak-ro, Seoul, Gyeongsangbuk-do, Korea (South)
Tel.: (82) 263775221
Web Site: https://www.kcins.co.kr
Year Founded: 2002
115500—(KRS)
Rev.: $31,974,923
Assets: $29,945,608
Liabilities: $15,923,925
Net Worth: $14,021,683
Earnings: $635,869
Emp.: 54
Fiscal Year-end: 12/31/22
Business Management Consulting Services
N.A.I.C.S.: 541611

KOREA COMPUTER INC
24 Imsu-ro, Gumi, Gyeongsangbuk-do, Korea (South)
Tel.: (82) 415893320
Web Site: http://www.kci.co.kr
Year Founded: 1994
054040—(KRS)
Rev.: $324,947,504
Assets: $119,989,423
Liabilities: $22,672,553
Net Worth: $97,316,870
Earnings: $12,860,895
Emp.: 94
Fiscal Year-end: 12/31/22
Electronic Component Mfr & Distr
N.A.I.C.S.: 334419

KOREA COMPUTER TERMINAL INC.
1201 551-17 Yancheon-ro Gangseo-gu, Seoul, 07532, Korea (South)
Tel.: (82) 263775671
Web Site: https://kctinc.co.kr
Year Founded: 1974
089150—(KRS)
Rev.: $11,172,668
Assets: $41,129,491
Liabilities: $14,464,954
Net Worth: $26,664,537
Earnings: $518,071
Emp.: 50
Fiscal Year-end: 12/31/22
ATMs, Banking Terminals & Other Financial-Based Computer Terminals
N.A.I.C.S.: 334118
Hyun Gyu Lee (CEO)

KOREA CREDIT GUARANTEE FUND
7 Cheomdan-ro Dong-gu, Daegu, 41068, Korea (South)
Tel.: (82) 534304164
Web Site: https://www.kodit.co.kr
Year Founded: 1976
Insurance Service Company
N.A.I.C.S.: 524298

KOREA DEPOSIT INSURANCE CORPORATION
Cheonggyecheon-no 30, Jung-gu, Seoul, 04521, Korea (South)
Tel.: (82) 27581130
Web Site: http://www.kdic.or.kr
Year Founded: 1996
Sales Range: $1-9.9 Million
Emp.: 465
Financial Deposit Insurance Services
N.A.I.C.S.: 524128
Seongbak Wi (Chm & Pres)

KOREA DEVELOPMENT BANK
14 Eunhaeng-ro, Yeongdeungpo-gu, Seoul, 07242, Korea (South)
Tel.: (82) 787 4000   KR
Web Site: http://www.kdb.co.kr
Year Founded: 1954
Rev.: $5,229,839,740
Assets: $231,202,111,040
Liabilities: $201,035,836,860
Net Worth: $30,166,274,180
Earnings: $240,066,420
Emp.: 3,410
Fiscal Year-end: 12/31/19
Commericial Banking
N.A.I.C.S.: 522110
Dong Gull Lee (Chm & CEO)

Subsidiaries:

Daewoo Engineering & Construction Co., Ltd. (1)
Daewoo E&C 170 Eulji-ro, Jung-gu, Seoul, 04548, Korea (South)
Tel.: (82) 222883114
Web Site: http://www.daewooenc.com

INTERNATIONAL PUBLIC

Sales Range: $5-14.9 Billion
Civil Engineering, Housing Construction, Power & Industrial Plant Development & Architectural Services
N.A.I.C.S.: 237990
Kim Hyung (Pres & CEO)

Subsidiary (Non-US):

Beijing Lufthansa Center Co. Ltd. (2)
50 Liangmaqiao Rd, Chaoyang District, Beijing, 100016, China
Tel.: (86) 1064651230
Hotel & Shopping Mall Operator
N.A.I.C.S.: 455110

Subsidiary (US):

Daewoo America Development (New York) Inc. (2)
40 Wall St 25th Fl, New York, NY 10005
Tel.: (212) 482-6065
Web Site: http://www.daewooenc.com
Heavy & Civil Engineering Construction Services
N.A.I.C.S.: 237990

Subsidiary (Non-US):

Daewoo Corporation Philippines Inc. (2)
Unit 2506 Prestige Tower F Ortigas Jr Road Ortigas Center, Pasig, Philippines
Tel.: (63) 2 477 7431
Web Site: http://www.daewooenc.com
Civil Construction Services
N.A.I.C.S.: 237310

Daewoo Engineering & Construction (M) Sdn Bhd (2)
Ste 13-11 13th Fl Wisma UOA II No 21, Jalan Pinang, 50450, Kuala Lumpur, Malaysia
Tel.: (60) 321619162
Web Site: http://www.daewooenc.com
Commercial & Institutional Building Construction Services
N.A.I.C.S.: 236220

Daewoo Power India Ltd. (2)
AB-12th Floor Community Centre, Safdarjung Enclave, New Delhi, India
Tel.: (91) 1126182412
Web Site: http://www.daewooenc.com
Power & Communication Line & Structures Construction
N.A.I.C.S.: 237130

Guilin Daewoo Hotel Co. Ltd. (2)
Binjiang Nan Road, Guilin, Guangxi, China
Tel.: (86) 7732825588
Web Site: http://www.daewooenc.com
Hotel Operator
N.A.I.C.S.: 721110

KDB Bank (Magyarorszag) Rt. (1)
Bajcsy Zeilinszky St 42 46, H 1054, Budapest, Hungary
Tel.: (36) 13749700
Web Site: http://www.kdb.hu
Rev.: $17,404,800
Emp.: 200
Loans & Bills Discounted; Leasing; Deposits & Customer Service; International Operation & Trade-Related Service
N.A.I.C.S.: 523910

KDB Bank Uzbekistan (1)
3 Bukhara Street, 10047, Tashkent, Uzbekistan
Tel.: (998) 781208000
Web Site: http://www.kdb.uz
Commercial Banking Services
N.A.I.C.S.: 522110
Saydmakhmud Saydakhmedov (Deputy Chm-Mgmt Bd)

KDB Ireland Ltd. (1)
Ground Floor Russell House Stokes Place St Stephen's Green, Dublin, Ireland
Tel.: (353) 1 4753644
Web Site: http://www.kdb.co.kr
Financial Investment Management Services
N.A.I.C.S.: 523940

PT KDB Tifa Finance Tbk (1)
Equity Tower 39th Floor SCBD Lot 9 Jl Jendral Sudirman Kav 52-53, Jakarta, 12190, Indonesia   (80.65%)
Tel.: (62) 2150941140

Web Site: https://www.kdbtifa.co.id
Rev.: $11,278,795
Assets: $116,981,405
Liabilities: $42,313,931
Net Worth: $74,667,473
Earnings: $3,889,648
Emp.: 82
Fiscal Year-end: 12/31/2023
Financial Services
N.A.I.C.S.: 523999
Bernard Thien Ted Nam (Chm)

Shinbundang Railroad Co., Ltd. (1)
Shinbundang Railroad Building 33 Daewangpanyo-ro 606 beon gil, Bundang-gu, Seongnam, Gyeonggi-do, Korea (South)
Tel.: (82) 31 8018 7500
Web Site: http://www.shinbundang.co.kr
Railroad Construction Services
N.A.I.C.S.: 237990

KOREA DEVELOPMENT FINANCING CORPORATION

88 Seorin-dong, Jongno-gu, Seoul, 110-790, Korea (South)
Tel.: (82) 237000114   KR
Web Site: http://www.kdf.co.kr
Year Founded: 1975
Sales Range: $75-99.9 Million
Emp.: 50
Financial & Leasing Services
N.A.I.C.S.: 522320
Don Hui Jeon (Pres & CEO)

KOREA DISTRICT HEATING CORPORATION

368 Bundang-ro, Bundang-gu, Seongnam, 463-908, Gyeonggi-do, Korea (South)
Tel.: (82) 16882488
Web Site: https://www.kdhc.co.kr
Year Founded: 1985
071320—(KRS)
Rev.: $3,200,711,814
Assets: $5,735,725,618
Liabilities: $4,457,134,239
Net Worth: $1,278,591,379
Earnings: ($141,111,831)
Emp.: 2,172
Fiscal Year-end: 12/31/22
Electric Power Distr
N.A.I.C.S.: 221122

Subsidiaries:

Korea District Heating Engineering Co., Ltd. (1)
752 Suseo-Dong, Kangnam-gu, Seoul, Korea (South)
Tel.: (82) 220400700
Web Site: http://kdhec.en.ec21.com
Emp.: 50
Engineeering Services
N.A.I.C.S.: 541330
Youn-Ho Kim (CEO)

KOREA ELECTRIC POWER CORPORATION

55 Jeollyeok-ro, Naju, 58322, Jeollanam-do, Korea (South)
Tel.: (82) 613454213   KR
Web Site: https://home.kepco.co.kr
Year Founded: 1981
KEP—(NYSE)
Rev.: $55,120,518,440
Assets: $194,220,160,400
Liabilities: $134,133,259,320
Net Worth: $60,086,901,080
Earnings: ($4,810,887,000)
Emp.: 48,809
Fiscal Year-end: 12/31/21
Electrical Power Generator, Transmitter & Distr
N.A.I.C.S.: 221111
Siyung Yang (Sr Mgr-New York)

Subsidiaries:

Amman Asia Electric Power Company (1)
Al Hijaz Tower 3rd Floor Office 306 158 Makkah Street, PO Box 924, Amman, 11821, Jordan
Tel.: (962) 65546700
Eletric Power Generation Services
N.A.I.C.S.: 221111

Columboola Solar Farm Hold Co Pty. Ltd. (1)
Level 25 Governor Macquarie Tower 1 Farrer Place, Sydney, NSW, Australia
Tel.: (61) 291339000
Web Site: https://columboolasolarfarm.com.au
Solar Electric Power Generation Services
N.A.I.C.S.: 221114

Fujeij Wind Power Company (1)
Al Hijaz Tower 4th Floor Office 404 158 Makkah St, PO Box 924, Amman, 11821, Jordan
Tel.: (962) 22003316
Eletric Power Generation Services
N.A.I.C.S.: 221111

KAPES, Inc. (1)
182-14 Samjeon-dong Cafes Building 31 Samhaksa-ro, Songpa-gu, Seoul, 05587, Korea (South)
Tel.: (82) 7046526064
Web Site: https://www.kapes.co.kr
Research & Development Services
N.A.I.C.S.: 541720
Jung In Kim (CEO)

KEPCO Australia Pty Ltd. (1)
201 Miller St Suite 1004, North Sydney, 2060, NSW, Australia
Tel.: (61) 289049508
Electric Power Distr
N.A.I.C.S.: 221122

KEPCO Bylong Australia Pty. Ltd. (1)
355 Upper Bylong Road, Bylong, 2849, NSW, Australia
Tel.: (61) 289049508
Web Site: http://www.bylongproject.com.au
Emp.: 450
Coal Mining Services
N.A.I.C.S.: 212114

KEPCO CSC Co., Ltd. (1)
727 Bitgaram-ro 7th floor, Naju, 58217, Jeollanam-do, Korea (South)
Tel.: (82) 618208114
Web Site: https://www.kepcocsc.co.kr
Facility Maintenance Services
N.A.I.C.S.: 561210

KEPCO E&C Service Co., Ltd. (1)
269 Hyeoksin-ro Yulgok-dong, Gimcheon, Gyeongsangbuk-do, Korea (South)
Tel.: (82) 544213114
Web Site: http://www.kepco-enc.com
Emp.: 2,300
Facility Maintenance Services
N.A.I.C.S.: 561210
Sung-Arm Kim (Pres & CEO)

KEPCO Engineering & Construction Company, Inc. (1)
269 Hyeoksin-ro, Gimcheon, 39660, Gyeongsangbuk, Korea (South)
Tel.: (82) 544213114
Electric Bulk Power Transmission & Control
N.A.I.C.S.: 221121
Bae-Soo Lee (Pres & CEO)

KEPCO FMS Co., Ltd. (1)
5th floor 727 Bitgaram-ro, Naju, 58217, Jeollanam-do, Korea (South)
Tel.: (82) 18338554
Web Site: https://www.kepcofms.co.kr
Security System Services
N.A.I.C.S.: 561621

KEPCO Ilijan Corporation (1)
18th Floor Citibank Tower 8741 Paseo De Roxas Salcedo Village, Makati, 1227, Philippines
Tel.: (63) 28480231
Electric Power Distribution Services
N.A.I.C.S.: 221122
Jeong-Woo Hyeon (Mng Dir)

KEPCO KDN Co., Ltd. (1)
661 Bitgaram-Ro, Naju, 58322, Jeollanam-do, Korea (South)
Tel.: (82) 619317114
Web Site: https://ns.kdn.com
Emp.: 2,901

Eletric Power Generation Services
N.A.I.C.S.: 221118
Kim Jang-Hyun (Pres)

KEPCO KPS Philippines Corp. (1)
18F Pacific Star Building Makati Ave Cor Gil Puyat Ave, Makati, 1209, Philippines
Tel.: (63) 28043479
Web Site: https://www.kpsphils.weebly.com
Power Plant Maintenance Services
N.A.I.C.S.: 811310
Yong Jea Kim (Pres)

KEPCO MCS Co., Ltd. (1)
Room 506 5th floor Yegaram Tower 7 Sangya 1-gil, Naju, 58217, Jeollanam-do, Korea (South)
Tel.: (82) 613459991
Web Site: https://www.kepcomcs.co.kr
Electric Meter Reading Services
N.A.I.C.S.: 561990

KEPCO Nuclear Fuel Co., Ltd. (1)
242 Daedeok-daero 989beon-gil, Yuseong-gu, Daejeon, Korea (South)
Tel.: (82) 428681000
Web Site: https://www.knfc.co.kr
Nuclear Fuel Mfr
N.A.I.C.S.: 325180

KEPCO Philippines Corporation (1) (100%)
Web Site: http://www.kepcophilippines.com
Sales Range: $150-199.9 Million
Emp.: 187
N.A.I.C.S.: 221122

KEPCO Philippines Holdings Inc. (1)
18th Floor BDO Towers Valero 8741 Paseo de Roxas, Salcedo Village, Makati, 1227, Philippines
Tel.: (63) 288480231
Eletric Power Generation Services
N.A.I.C.S.: 221118

KEPCO SPC Power Corporation (1)
Brgy Colon, Naga, 6037, Cebu, Philippines
Tel.: (63) 325054065
Web Site: https://www.kepcospc.com
Electric Power Generation Services
N.A.I.C.S.: 221111
Jong Ryoon Yoon (Pres & CEO)

KEPCO Solar of Alamosa, LLC (1)
5299 DTC Blvd Prentice Point 290, Greenwood Village, CO 80111
Tel.: (719) 378-5020
Web Site: http://www.kepcoalamosa.com
Solar Electric Power Generation Services
N.A.I.C.S.: 221114

KEPCO-UHDE Inc. (1)
2F E5 Bldg 105 Munji-ro, Yuseong-gu, Daejeon, 34056, Korea (South)
Tel.: (82) 7078621803
Web Site: http://www.kepco-uhde.com
Electric Power Generation Services
N.A.I.C.S.: 221111
Jung-Ho Lee (CEO)

KHNP USA LLC (1)
Paker Plz 400 Kelby St 10th Fl, Fort Lee, NJ 07024
Tel.: (201) 613-0500
Electric Power Generation Services
N.A.I.C.S.: 221111

KOAK Power Limited (1)
1st floor 12-A CBC Building G8-Markaz, Islamabad, Pakistan
Tel.: (92) 518735923
Web Site: https://www.koakpower.com
Facility Maintenance Services
N.A.I.C.S.: 561210
Kim Kyungsik (CEO)

KOMIPO Service Co., Ltd. (1)
23 Myeongcheon-ro 4-gil, Boryeong, 33439, Chungcheongnam-do, Korea (South)
Tel.: (82) 419369306
Web Site: https://www.komipo.kr
Facility Maintenance Services
N.A.I.C.S.: 561210

KOSPO Power Services Ltda. (1)
Ruta 1 13 Km Norte de Nro 9500 Manzana 20 Planta Kelar, Mejillones, Chile
Tel.: (56) 552426800
Web Site: https://www.kospo.cl
Emp.: 50
Electric Power Generation Services

N.A.I.C.S.: 221111
Jaeseok Hwang (CEO)

KOWEPO Lao International Co., Ltd. (1)
Vientiane Center 9th Floor Kouvieng Road, PO Box 4864, Nongchan Village Sisattanak District, Vientiane, Lao People's Democratic Republic
Tel.: (856) 305735042
Web Site: http://www.klicpower.com
Utility Plant Maintenance Services
N.A.I.C.S.: 561730

KST Electric Power Company, S.A.P.I. de C.V. (1)
Sierra Candela 101 Oficina 407, Col Lomas de Chapultepec Del Miguel Hidalgo, 11000, Mexico, Mexico
Tel.: (52) 5541608153
Electric Power Generation Services
N.A.I.C.S.: 221111

Korea Atomic Energy Research Institute (1)
111 Daedeok-Daero 989 Beon-Gil, Yuseong-Gu, Daejeon, Korea (South)
Tel.: (82) 428682000
Web Site: http://www.kaeri.re.kr
Energy Research Services
N.A.I.C.S.: 541715
Won-Seok Park (Pres)

Korea East-West Power Co., Ltd. (1)
167 Samseong-dong Gangnam-gu, 135 791, Seoul, Korea (South)
Tel.: (82) 234568411
Web Site: http://www.ewp.co.kr
Sales Range: $1-4.9 Billion
Emp.: 2,000
Electric Power Distr
N.A.I.C.S.: 221122

Subsidiary (US):

EWP Renewable Corporation (2)
600 W Broadway Ste 1600, San Diego, CA 92101
Tel.: (619) 232-6564
Web Site: http://www.ewprc.com
Biomass Electric Power Generation Services
N.A.I.C.S.: 221117

Subsidiary (Domestic):

DG Whitefield LLC (3)
250 Airport Rd, Whitefield, NH 03598
Tel.: (603) 837-2223
Web Site: http://www.whitefieldpower.webexone.com
Other Electric Power Generation
N.A.I.C.S.: 221118

Korea Electric Power Corporation (1)
400 Kelby St 7th Fl, Fort Lee, NJ 07024
Tel.: (201) 613-4002
Web Site: http://www.kepco.co.kr
Sales Range: $75-99.9 Million
Emp.: 4
Electric Power Distr
N.A.I.C.S.: 221122

Korea Electro Technology Research Institute (1)
Sales Range: $100-124.9 Million
Emp.: 473
National Research Institute for Electrical Technology Research & Testing
N.A.I.C.S.: 541715
Gyu-ha Choe (Pres)

Korea Gas Corporation (1)
120 Cheomdan-ro, Dong-gu, Daegu, Korea (South)
Tel.: (82) 536700114
Web Site: https://www.kogas.or.kr
Rev.: $33,071,563,778
Assets: $42,497,117,363
Liabilities: $35,203,767,822
Net Worth: $7,293,349,541
Earnings: ($554,776,831)
Emp.: 4,163
Fiscal Year-end: 12/31/2023
Natural Gas Extraction Services
N.A.I.C.S.: 211130

Korea Hydro And Nuclear Power Co., Ltd. (1)

KOREA ELECTRIC POWER CORPORATION

Korea Electric Power Corporation—(Continued)
167 Samseong-dong Gangnam-gu, 135-791, Seoul, Korea (South)
Tel.: (82) 516862114
Web Site: http://www.khnp.co.kr
Electric Power Generation
N.A.I.C.S.: 221122
Jae-dong Lee *(Exec VP-Safety, Quality & Tech Div)*

Korea Midland Power Co., Ltd. (1)
167 Samseong-dong Kangnam-gu, 135179, Seoul, Korea (South)
Tel.: (82) 234567371
Web Site: http://www.komipo.co.kr
Sales Range: $1-4.9 Billion
Emp.: 2,410
Electric Power Distr
N.A.I.C.S.: 221122

Korea Nuclear Fuel Co., Ltd. (1)
242 Daedeok-daero 989beon-gil, Yuseong-gu, Daejeon, 34057, Korea (South)
Tel.: (82) 428681000
Web Site: https://www.knfc.co.kr
Nuclear Fuel Distr
N.A.I.C.S.: 221113

Korea Plant Service & Engineering (1)
196 Geumgok-dong Bundang-gu, Seongnam Gyeonggi-do, Seoul, Korea (South)
Tel.: (82) 317104114
Web Site: http://www.kps.co.kr
Industrial Plant Maintenance & Engineering Services
N.A.I.C.S.: 541330

Korea Power Exchange (1)
167 Samseong-dong, Gangnam-gu, Seoul, 135-791, Korea (South)
Tel.: (82) 234566525
Web Site: http://www.kpx.co.kr
Sales Range: $25-49.9 Million
Electric Power Distr
N.A.I.C.S.: 221122

Korea South-East Power Co., Ltd. (1)
Tel.: (82) 7088981000
Sales Range: $1-4.9 Billion
Power & Electricity Generation
N.A.I.C.S.: 221122
Robert Hyang-reol Lyu *(Pres & CEO)*

Korea Southern Power Co., Ltd. (1)
33F BIFC B/D 40 Munhyeongeumyung-ro, Nam-gu, Busan, 48400, Korea (South)
Tel.: (82) 7077138000
Web Site: http://www.kospo.co.kr
Eletric Power Generation Services
N.A.I.C.S.: 221111
Seung Woo Lee *(Pres & CEO)*

Korea Western Power Co., Ltd. (1)
285 Jungang-ro, Taean-eup Taean-gun, Seoul, 32140, Chungcheongnam-do, Korea (South)
Tel.: (82) 414001000
Web Site: https://www.westernpower.co.kr
Sales Range: $75-99.9 Million
Emp.: 2,350
Electric Power Distr
N.A.I.C.S.: 221122
Kim Byung Sook *(Pres & CEO-Acting)*

LSG Hydro Power Limited (1)
4th Floor Emirates Tower Jinnah Super F-7, Islamabad, Pakistan
Tel.: (92) 516134782
Web Site: https://lsg-hydro.com
Hydroelectric Power Generation Services
N.A.I.C.S.: 221111

Mira Power Limited (1)
Mezzanine Floor 15-E Rehmat Centre Jinnah Avenue, Blue Area, Islamabad, Pakistan
Tel.: (92) 5121009856
Web Site: https://www.mira-power.com
Hydroelectric Power Generation Services
N.A.I.C.S.: 221111
Kim Dong Woong *(CEO)*

Nepal Water & Energy Development Company Private Limited (1)
Tel.: (977) 14412229
Web Site: http://www.nwedcpl.com
Hydroelectric Power Generation Services
N.A.I.C.S.: 221111
Hee Woong Kang *(CEO)*

Saemangeum Solar Power Co., Ltd. (1)
4F Cheongdam Building 188 Susong-ro, Gunsan, Jeollabuk-do, Korea (South)
Tel.: (82) 637310902
Web Site: http://www.smgsolar.co.kr
Eletric Power Generation Services
N.A.I.C.S.: 221111

KOREA ELECTRIC POWER INDUSTRIAL DEVELOPMENT CO., LTD.
6th Floor Hansan Building 115 Seosomun-ro, Jung-gu, Seoul, Korea (South)
Tel.: (82) 222502700
Web Site: https://www.kepid.co.kr
Year Founded: 1990
130660—(KRS)
Rev.: $265,414,387
Assets: $121,018,361
Liabilities: $47,427,705
Net Worth: $73,590,656
Earnings: $12,472,376
Emp.: 3,230
Fiscal Year-end: 12/31/22
Electricity Generation & Distribution Services
N.A.I.C.S.: 221118
Eung-Tae Kim *(Dir-Power Generation)*

KOREA ELECTRIC TERMINAL CO., LTD.
38 Gaetbeol-ro, Yeonsu-gu, Incheon, 21999, Songdo-dong, Korea (South)
Tel.: (82) 328149981
Web Site: https://www.ket.com
Year Founded: 1973
025540—(KRS)
Rev.: $895,959,528
Assets: $989,258,541
Liabilities: $321,750,532
Net Worth: $667,508,009
Earnings: $37,298,871
Emp.: 1,176
Fiscal Year-end: 12/31/22
Electronics & Telecommunications Connector Mfr & Sales
N.A.I.C.S.: 334417
Chang-Won Lee *(Chm & CEO)*

Subsidiaries:

Back Bone Electronics Co., Ltd. (1)
Rm 408 Hutai Office Building No 1017 Zhongshan North Rd, Shanghai, China
Tel.: (86) 2156087631
Electric Equipment Mfr
N.A.I.C.S.: 335999

Besconn EMEA, s.r.o. (1)
Royova 777, 020 01, Puchov, Slovakia
Tel.: (421) 314255700
Electric Equipment Mfr
N.A.I.C.S.: 335999

Hainan Xianfeng Electric Imp. & Exp. Co., Ltd. (1)
Rm 7D International Huanhai Building 15 Western Jinmao Road, Haikou, Hainan, China
Tel.: (86) 89868570872
Electric Equipment Mfr
N.A.I.C.S.: 335999

Hanurl Automotive Pvt. Ltd. (1)
First Floor- F2 New No 29 Old No 20 Karpagambal Nagar, Mylapore, Chennai, 600 004, Tamil Nadu, India
Tel.: (91) 4442129181
Motor Vehicle Equipment Mfr
N.A.I.C.S.: 336320

KET SOLUTION Co. Ltd. (1)
701-2 Hyangyang-ri, Paju-eup, P'aju, Gyeonggi-do, Korea (South)
Tel.: (82) 31 937 2000
Electronic Components Mfr
N.A.I.C.S.: 334419

Kong Young Industrial Co., Ltd. (1)
94 Jeongseojin-ro, Seo-gu, Incheon, 22850, Korea (South)
Tel.: (82) 328119730
Electric Equipment Mfr
N.A.I.C.S.: 335999

Konxin Trade Co., Ltd. (1)
XinCheng ST Boxue Rd Carnival forte A3B-1035, Changchun, Jilin, China
Tel.: (86) 43187931711
Electric Equipment Mfr
N.A.I.C.S.: 335999

Leimen Enterprise Ltd. (1)
Unit B 11/F Wah Wai Ind Building 1-7 Wo Heung Street, Fotan, Sha Tin, NT, China (Hong Kong)
Tel.: (852) 26093666
Web Site: https://www.leimen.com.hk
Electric Equipment Mfr
N.A.I.C.S.: 335999

SY Global Southeast Vina Co., Ltd. (1)
C2-3406.G Tower C2 D'Capitale Building 119 Tran Duy Hung, Trung Hoa Ward Cau Giay Dist, Hanoi, Vietnam
Tel.: (84) 968318497
Motor Vehicle Equipment Mfr
N.A.I.C.S.: 336320

Seum Electronics Co. Ltd. (1)
NO 50th Jiuhuashan Road, Yancheng City Economic and Technological Development Zone, Jiangsu, China
Tel.: (86) 51580896006
Electric Equipment Mfr
N.A.I.C.S.: 335999

Tianjin Dong Heng Import & Export Co., Ltd. (1)
1-1-1507 No 2 Haitai Innovation Sixth Road, Huayuan High-Tech Industrial Area Binhai New District, Tianjin, China
Tel.: (86) 2223708324
Motor Vehicle Equipment Mfr
N.A.I.C.S.: 336320

Weihai KET Electronics Co., Ltd. (1)
52 Xianggang Road, Weihai, Shandong, China
Tel.: (86) 6313636888
Emp.: 800
Electric Equipment Mfr
N.A.I.C.S.: 335999

Wellfriend (Beijing) Trading Co., Ltd. (1)
Rm 506 4Th Floor Blook 1 Linheibeida Street 21, Shunyi Distric, Beijing, China
Tel.: (86) 1084786906
Electric Equipment Mfr
N.A.I.C.S.: 335999

YDT Technology Co. Ltd. (1)
No 2 Jinyi Branch Road TaiShang Indurstrial Park HuiXing Street, YuBei district, Chongqing, China
Tel.: (86) 2367589312
Electric Equipment Mfr
N.A.I.C.S.: 335999

KOREA ELECTRONIC CERTIFICATION AUTHORITY, INC.
5th Floor 9-22 Seocho-Daero 62-Gil, Seocho-gu, Seoul, 06631, Korea (South)
Tel.: (82) 15660566
Web Site: https://global.crosscert.com
Year Founded: 1999
041460—(KRS)
Rev.: $30,433,008
Assets: $54,288,273
Liabilities: $17,272,975
Net Worth: $37,015,298
Earnings: $2,759,662
Emp.: 94
Fiscal Year-end: 12/31/22
Technology-Based Accredited Certification Services
N.A.I.C.S.: 541519
Hong Sik Shin *(CEO)*

KOREA ENERGY ECONOMICS INSTITUTE
665-1 Naeson 2-Dong, Euiwang-Si Kyonggi-Do, Seoul, 437-713, Korea (South)
Tel.: (82) 314202114
Web Site: http://www.keei.re.kr
Sales Range: $75-99.9 Million
Emp.: 150
Energy Services
N.A.I.C.S.: 221122
Jin Woo Kim *(Pres)*

KOREA ENGINEERING CONSULTANTS CORP.
111-21 Deokpungdong-ro, Gangdong-gu, Hanam, Gyeonggi-do, Korea (South)
Tel.: (82) 317944551
Web Site: http://www.kecc.co.kr
Year Founded: 1963
023350—(KRS)
Rev.: $217,599,830
Assets: $255,177,341
Liabilities: $141,051,337
Net Worth: $114,126,004
Earnings: $2,914,057
Emp.: 1,600
Fiscal Year-end: 12/31/22
Civil Engineering & Construction Services
N.A.I.C.S.: 237990

KOREA EXCHANGE
40 Munhyeongmyung-ro, Nam-gu, Busan, Korea (South)
Tel.: (82) 516622000
Web Site: http://www.krx.co.kr
Year Founded: 2005
Sales Range: $550-599.9 Million
Securities & Commodities Exchange
N.A.I.C.S.: 523210
Kiwon Kang *(Pres-Derivatives Market Div)*

Subsidiaries:

Korea Exchange - Stock Market Division (1)
76 Yeouinaru-ro, Yeongdeungpo-gu, Seoul, Korea (South)
Tel.: (82) 2 3774 9000
Securities & Commodities Exchange
N.A.I.C.S.: 523210

Korea Securities Depository (1)
1328 Paeks34-6 Yoido-dong Youngdeungpo-guok-dong, Ilsan-ku Koyang, 411-770, Seoul, Korea (South) **(70.34%)**
Tel.: (82) 237743430
Web Site: http://www.ksd.or.kr
Sales Range: $200-249.9 Million
Emp.: 450
Securities Depository & Substitute Settlement Services
N.A.I.C.S.: 522320

Koscom Corporation (1)
33 Yeouido-dong, Yeongdeungpo-gu, 150-977, Seoul, Korea (South) **(76.63%)**
Tel.: (82) 27677114
Web Site: http://www.koscom.co.kr
Sales Range: $125-149.9 Million
Emp.: 500
Securities & Commodities Market Information Technology Development & Operation Services
N.A.I.C.S.: 541513

KOREA EXPORT PACKAGING INDUSTRIAL CO., LTD.
4F Leaders Bldg 63 Seochojungang-ro, Seocho-Gu, Seoul, Korea (South)
Tel.: (82) 25252981 KR
Web Site: http://www.keppack.co.kr
Year Founded: 1957
002200—(KRS)
Rev.: $261,869,321
Assets: $265,014,868
Liabilities: $49,551,310
Net Worth: $215,463,557
Earnings: $15,583,268

Emp.: 407
Fiscal Year-end: 12/31/22
Corrugated Cardboard Mfr & Distr
N.A.I.C.S.: 322220

KOREA FUEL-TECH CORPORATION
23 Seombawi-gil Wongok-myeon, Wongok-myeon, Anseong, Gyeonggi-do, Korea (South)
Tel.: (82) 7070931500
Web Site: https://www.kftec.com
Year Founded: 1996
123410—(KRS)
Rev.: $430,320,469
Assets: $302,275,970
Liabilities: $188,095,335
Net Worth: $114,180,635
Earnings: $7,169,769
Emp.: 529
Fiscal Year-end: 12/31/22
Automobile Parts Mfr
N.A.I.C.S.: 336360
Jaesan Kim (Co-CEO)

Subsidiaries:

KOREA FUEL-TECH CORPORATION - Gongdo Factory (1)
122-12 Gieopdanji-ro, Gongdo-eup, Anseong, Gyeonggi-do, Korea (South)
Tel.: (82) 70 7093 1600
Emp.: 40
Automobile Spare Parts Mfr
N.A.I.C.S.: 336360

KOREA FUEL-TECH CORPORATION - Gyeongju Factory (1)
1189-15 Hwasan-ri, Cheonbuk-myeon, Gyeongju, Gyeongsangbuk-do, Korea (South)
Tel.: (82) 70 7093 1700
Emp.: 30
Automobile Spare Parts Mfr
N.A.I.C.S.: 336360

KOREA FURNITURE CO., LTD.
957 Konghang-Dong, Kangsuh-ku, 157-240, Seoul, Korea (South)
Tel.: (82) 26634121
004590—(KRS)
Rev.: $77,390,047
Assets: $162,655,515
Liabilities: $33,280,202
Net Worth: $129,375,314
Earnings: $9,043,001
Emp.: 57
Fiscal Year-end: 12/31/22
Furniture Product Mfr
N.A.I.C.S.: 337127
Hun-Hak Choi (CEO)

KOREA INDUSTRIAL CO., LTD.
21 Saebyeoksijang-ro, Sasang-gu, Busan, Korea (South)
Tel.: (82) 516005069
Web Site: https://www.kicfeed.com
Year Founded: 1957
002140—(KRS)
Rev.: $213,510,539
Assets: $210,697,606
Liabilities: $129,661,375
Net Worth: $81,036,231
Earnings: $320,506
Emp.: 127
Fiscal Year-end: 12/31/22
Animal Feed Mfr
N.A.I.C.S.: 311119
Jang-Yeol Jeon (Chm & CEO)

KOREA INFORMATION & COMMUNICATION
7F Floor KCCI Bldg 39 Sejong-daero, Jung-Gu, Seoul, 100-743, Korea (South)
Tel.: (82) 23680700
Web Site: http://www.kicc.co.kr
025770—(KRS)
Rev.: $456,723,623
Assets: $307,131,652
Liabilities: $116,739,224
Net Worth: $190,392,428
Earnings: $16,748,062
Emp.: 252
Fiscal Year-end: 12/31/22
Electronic Payment Solutions
N.A.I.C.S.: 921130
Myeong Su Lim (CEO)

KOREA INFORMATION CERTIFICATE AUTHORITY, INC.
6F 69 Geumto-ro, Sujeong-gu, Seongnam, 13487, Gyeonggi-do, Korea (South)
Tel.: (82) 23603010
Web Site: http://www.kica.co.kr
Year Founded: 1999
053300—(KRS)
Rev.: $67,362,289
Assets: $215,393,423
Liabilities: $51,442,694
Net Worth: $163,950,729
Earnings: $5,126,974
Emp.: 128
Fiscal Year-end: 12/31/22
Electronic Transaction Authentification Services
N.A.I.C.S.: 541519

KOREA INFORMATION ENGINEERING SERVICES CO., LTD.
7 Hwangsaeul-ro 359beon-gil, Bundang-gu, Seongnam, Gyeonggi-do, Korea (South)
Tel.: (82) 317898600
Web Site: http://www.kies.co.kr
Year Founded: 1990
039740—(KRS)
Rev.: $80,822,805
Assets: $62,377,390
Liabilities: $27,767,546
Net Worth: $34,609,844
Earnings: $2,879,816
Emp.: 53
Fiscal Year-end: 12/31/22
Software Development Services
N.A.I.C.S.: 541511
Se Bok Lee (CEO)

Subsidiaries:

NEMOCommerce Co., Ltd. (1)
3rd Floor Shina S G Building 542 Yeoksam-ro, Gangnam-gu, Seoul, 135-848, Korea (South)
Tel.: (82) 15444211
Web Site: http://www.nemocommerce.com
Online Business Development Services
N.A.I.C.S.: 425120

KOREA INVESTMENT HOLDINGS CO., LTD.
88 Uisadang-Daero, Yeongdeungpo-gu, Seoul, 150-747, Korea (South)
Tel.: (82) 232766400 KR
Web Site: https://www.koreaholdings.com
Year Founded: 2003
071050—(KRS)
Rev.: $9,263,338,933
Assets: $52,259,027,800
Liabilities: $47,930,668,678
Net Worth: $4,328,359,121
Earnings: $728,565,440
Emp.: 62
Fiscal Year-end: 12/31/19
Holding Company
N.A.I.C.S.: 551111
Kang-Haeng Lee (Pres)

Subsidiaries:

Cornerstone Equity Partners Co., Ltd. (1)
27-1 Yeouido-dong, Yeongdeungpo-gu, Seoul, 150-745, Korea (South) (100%)
Tel.: (82) 2 6000 5100
Sales Range: $50-74.9 Million
Emp.: 13
Privater Equity Firm
N.A.I.C.S.: 523999
Nam-goo Kim (CEO)

Kiara Advisors Pte. Ltd. (1)
1 Raffles Place 43-04 OUB Centre, Singapore, 048616, Singapore
Tel.: (65) 65015620
Investment Advisory Services
N.A.I.C.S.: 523940

Kiara Capital Pte. Ltd. (1)
1 Raffles Place 43-04 OUB Centre, Singapore, 048616, Singapore
Tel.: (65) 65015621
Sales Range: $50-74.9 Million
Emp.: 5
Venture Capital Funding Services
N.A.I.C.S.: 523910

Korea Investment & Securities Asia Limited (1)
Suite 3716-19 Jardine House 1 Connaught Place, Central, China (Hong Kong)
Tel.: (852) 2530 8900
Web Site: http://www.koreaholdings.com
Sales Range: $50-74.9 Million
Investment Banking Services
N.A.I.C.S.: 523150

Korea Investment & Securities Co., Ltd. (1)
88 Uisadang-daero, Yeongdeungpo-Gu, Seoul, 150-745, Korea (South) (100%)
Tel.: (82) 15881251
Web Site: http://www.truefriend.com
Sales Range: $900-999.9 Million
Emp.: 2,685
Asset Management, Securities Brokerage & Investment Banking Services
N.A.I.C.S.: 523150
Sang-Ho Ryu (CEO)

Korea Investment & Securities Europe Limited (1)
30 Crown Place 10th Floor, London, EC2A 4EB, United Kingdom
Tel.: (44) 2070652760
Web Site: http://www.koreaholdings.com
Sales Range: $50-74.9 Million
Investment Management Service
N.A.I.C.S.: 523999

Korea Investment & Securities Singapore Pte. Ltd. (1)
1 Raffles Place 43-04 OUB Centre, Singapore, 048616s, Singapore
Tel.: (65) 6501 5616
Investment Management & Securities Brokerage Services
N.A.I.C.S.: 523150

Korea Investment Capital Co., Ltd. (1)
24 Yeoui-daero, Yeongdeungpo-gu, Seoul, Korea (South)
Tel.: (82) 220554510
Web Site: http://www.kicf.co.kr
Investment Management Service
N.A.I.C.S.: 523940

Korea Investment Management Asia Limited (1)
Suite 2230 Jardine House 1 Connaught Place, Central, China (Hong Kong)
Tel.: (852) 2230 1300
Web Site: http://www.koreaholdings.com
Sales Range: $50-74.9 Million
Emp.: 8
Investment Management Service
N.A.I.C.S.: 523999

Korea Investment Mutual Saving Bank Co., Ltd. (1)
27-1 Yeouido-Dong Yeongdeungpo-gu, Seoul, Gyeonggi-Do, Korea (South)
Tel.: (82) 417 81 01720
Web Site: http://www.kibank.co.kr
Sales Range: $100-124.9 Million
Emp.: 200
Commercial Banking Services
N.A.I.C.S.: 522110
Nam Young Woo (CEO)

Korea Investment Mutual Savings Bank (1)
3rd Floor Miraesanup Building 271-1 Seohyeon-dong, Bundang-gu, Seongnam, 463-824, Gyeonggi-do, Korea (South)
Tel.: (82) 317884000
Web Site: http://www.kisb.co.kr
Sales Range: $100-124.9 Million
Emp.: 133
Commercial Banking Services
N.A.I.C.S.: 522110
Yeung Woo Nam (CEO)

Korea Investment Partners Co., Ltd. (1)
26th Floor Gangnam Finance Center 737 Yeoksam-dong, Gangnam-gu, Seoul, 135-925, Korea (South)
Tel.: (82) 5 609 6023
Web Site: http://www.kipvc.com
Venture Capital Funding Services
N.A.I.C.S.: 523910

Korea Investment Private Equity Co. Ltd. (1)
25th Floor 152 Teheran-ro Gangnam Finance Center, Gangnam-gu Yeoksam-dong, Seoul, Korea (South)
Tel.: (82) 221125005
Web Site: http://pe.koreainvestment.com
Investment Management Service
N.A.I.C.S.: 523940

Korea Investment Trust Management Co., Ltd. (1)
27-1 Yeouido-Dong, Yeongdeungpo-gu, Seoul, 150-745, Korea (South)
Tel.: (82) 232764700
Sales Range: $100-124.9 Million
Emp.: 170
Investment Management Service
N.A.I.C.S.: 523999
Hongrae Cho (CEO)

Korea Investment Value Asset Management (1)
17 F Korea Investment Securities Building 27-1 Yoido-dong, Youngdeungpo-gu, Seoul, 150745, Korea (South)
Tel.: (82) 232766000
Asset Management Services
N.A.I.C.S.: 531390
Sanghoon Han (Mgr-SIs)

Korea Value Asset Management Co., Ltd. (1)
70 Yeoui-daero, Yeongdeungpo-gu, Seoul, Korea (South)
Tel.: (82) 269786300
Web Site: http://vam.koreainvestment.com
Emp.: 19
Asset Management Services
N.A.I.C.S.: 523940
Lee Choi Won (CEO)

PT Korea Investment & Sekuritas Indonesia (1)
Equity Tower 9th Floor Suite A SCBD Lot 9 Jl Jend Sudirman Kav 52-53, Jakarta, 12190, Indonesia
Tel.: (62) 2129911888
Web Site: http://www.kisi.co.id
Banking Services
N.A.I.C.S.: 522110

KOREA KOLMAR CO., LTD.
12-11 Deokgogae-gil, Jeonui-myeon, Sejong, Korea (South)
Tel.: (82) 448600532
Web Site: https://www.kolmar.co.kr
Year Founded: 2012
161890—(KRS)
Rev.: $1,431,016,078
Assets: $2,249,848,371
Liabilities: $1,122,762,503
Net Worth: $1,127,085,867
Earnings: ($16,859,664)
Emp.: 1,009
Fiscal Year-end: 12/31/22
Cosmetic Product Mfr & Distr
N.A.I.C.S.: 456120

Subsidiaries:

Process Technologies And Packaging, Inc. (1)
102 Life Science Dr, Olyphant, PA 18447 (51%)
Tel.: (570) 587-8326

KOREA KOLMAR CO., LTD.

Korea Kolmar Co., Ltd.—(Continued)
Web Site: http://www.protechandpack.com
Rev.: $7,500,000
Emp.: 58
Manufactures & Packages Cosmetics
N.A.I.C.S.: 325620
W. M. Godfrey (CEO)

KOREA KOLMAR HOLDINGS CO., LTD

12-11 Deokgogae-gil, Jeonui-myeon, Sejong, Korea (South)
Tel.: (82) 25150150
Web Site: https://www.kolmar.co.kr
Year Founded: 1990
024720—(KRS)
Rev.: $498,457,629
Assets: $973,401,275
Liabilities: $321,192,044
Net Worth: $652,209,231
Earnings: ($4,668,340)
Emp.: 99
Fiscal Year-end: 12/31/22
Cosmetic & Pharmaceutical Product Mfr
N.A.I.C.S.: 325620
Sang-hyun Yoon (Co-CEO)

Subsidiaries:

Kolmar Cosmetics (Wuxi) Co., Ltd. (1)
No 95 Ximei Road, Xinwu Distirct, Wuxi, Jiangsu, China
Tel.: (86) 51066907080
Web Site: https://hkkolmar.ch
Cosmetic Product Mfr & Distr
N.A.I.C.S.: 325620

Kolmar Korea Co., Ltd. - Makeup Factory 1 (1)
404-15 Nonjang-ri, Jeondong, Chungcheongnam-do, Korea (South)
Tel.: (82) 41 862 2777
Cosmetics Products Mfr
N.A.I.C.S.: 325620

Kolmar Korea Co., Ltd. - Makeup Factory 2 (1)
183-5 Dodang-dong, Wonmi-gu, Bucheon, Gyeongi-do, Korea (South)
Tel.: (82) 32 682 3000
Cosmetics Products Mfr
N.A.I.C.S.: 325620

Kolmar Korea Co., Ltd. - Skin care Factory 1 (1)
Jeonui-meyon yeonji-gun, Jeonui, Chungnam, Korea (South)
Tel.: (82) 41 862 1057
Cosmetics Products Mfr
N.A.I.C.S.: 325620

Kolmar Korea Co., Ltd. - Skin care Factory 2 (1)
618-3 Sinjeong-ri, Jeonui, Chungnam, Korea (South)
Tel.: (82) 41 868 7501
Cosmetics Products Mfr
N.A.I.C.S.: 325620

Korea FoodiPharm, Co., Ltd (1)
25-5 Daepung-ri, Daeso-myeon, Eumseong, Chungcheongbuk-do, Korea (South)
Tel.: (82) 43 535 6691
Web Site: http://www.foodipharm.com
Pharmaceuticals Product Mfr
N.A.I.C.S.: 325412
Jung Hwa Yung (CEO)

YONWOO CO., LTD (1)
13 84 beon-gil Gajwo-ro, Seo-gu, Incheon, Korea (South) (55%)
Tel.: (82) 325758811
Web Site: http://www.yonwoo.kr
Rev.: $180,044,004
Assets: $225,220,421
Liabilities: $35,554,004
Net Worth: $189,666,418
Earnings: $284,473
Emp.: 1,271
Fiscal Year-end: 12/31/2022
Plastics Product Mfr
N.A.I.C.S.: 326199

KOREA LINE CORPORATION

SM R & D Center 78 Magokjungang 8-ro, Gangseo-gu, Seoul, 135-878, Korea (South)
Tel.: (82) 237010114
Web Site: https://www.korealines.co.kr
Year Founded: 1968
005880—(KRS)
Rev.: $1,236,415,094
Assets: $3,444,029,506
Liabilities: $2,075,607,926
Net Worth: $1,368,421,579
Earnings: $132,149,722
Emp.: 199
Fiscal Year-end: 12/31/22
Marine Transportation Services
N.A.I.C.S.: 486910
Suhan Han (CEO)

Subsidiaries:

Korea Line (Singapore) Pte Ltd (1)
1 Wallich Street 07-01 Guoco Tower, Singapore, 078881, Singapore
Tel.: (65) 62156215
Web Site: https://www.klpl.com.sg
Emp.: 105
Deep Sea Freight Transportation Services
N.A.I.C.S.: 483111

KOREA MIRACLE PEOPLE CO., LTD.

94-1 Yongjeonggyeongje-Ro 1-Gil, Gunnae-Myeon, Pocheon, Gyeonggi-do, Korea (South)
Tel.: (82) 315446781
Web Site: https://www.shop2.kmpc01.com
Year Founded: 2014
331660—(KRS)
Household Product Mfr & Distr
N.A.I.C.S.: 335220
Lee Hokyung (CEO)

KOREA MOVENEX CO., LTD

2 Mipo 1-gil, Dong-gu, Ulsan, Korea (South)
Tel.: (82) 522335511
Web Site: https://koreamovenex.com
Year Founded: 1974
010100—(KRS)
Rev.: $1,051,828,401
Assets: $613,135,303
Liabilities: $382,080,170
Net Worth: $231,055,132
Earnings: $27,335,686
Emp.: 495
Fiscal Year-end: 12/31/22
Automobile Parts Mfr
N.A.I.C.S.: 336110
Jin Hyun Son (CEO)

Subsidiaries:

KOFCO U.S.A, INC (1)
2500 W Higgins Rd Ste 450, Hoffman Estates, IL 60195
Tel.: (847) 781-1430
Industrial Machinery Mfr
N.A.I.C.S.: 333248
James Gibbons (Mgr-Sls)

Korea Flange Co., Ltd. - NO. 2 Factory (1)
887 Yeochoan-dong, Nam-gu, Ulsan, Korea (South)
Tel.: (82) 52 273 5001
Industrial Machinery Mfr
N.A.I.C.S.: 333248

Korea Flange Co., Ltd. - NO. 3 Factory (1)
167-1 Dongbu-dong, Dong-gu, Ulsan, Korea (South)
Tel.: (82) 52 233 5511
Automobile Parts Mfr
N.A.I.C.S.: 336390

KOREA NATIONAL OIL CORPORATION

305 Jongga-ro, Jung-gu, Ulsan, 44538, Korea (South)
Tel.: (82) 52 216 2114
Web Site: http://www.knoc.co.kr
Year Founded: 1979
Sales Range: $5-14.9 Billion
Emp.: 1,400
Oil & Natural Gas Production Services
N.A.I.C.S.: 211120
Dong-hee Kim (Exec VP-Exploration Grp)

Subsidiaries:

ANKOR E&P Holdings Corp. (1)
1615 Poydras St Ste 2000, New Orleans, LA 70112
Tel.: (504) 587-6508
Petroleum Product Distr
N.A.I.C.S.: 213112

Dana Petroleum plc (1)
King's Close 62 Huntly Street, Aberdeen, AB10 1RS, United Kingdom
Tel.: (44) 1224616000
Web Site: http://www.dana-petroleum.com
Sales Range: $1-4.9 Billion
Emp.: 313
Oil & Gas Exploration Services
N.A.I.C.S.: 211120
Seok Jeong Chang (Chm)

Subsidiary (Domestic):

Dana Petroleum (E&P) Limited (2)
King's Close 62 Huntly St, Aberdeen, AB10 1RS, United Kingdom
Tel.: (44) 1224652400
Web Site: http://www.dana-petroleum.com
Sales Range: $50-74.9 Million
Emp.: 100
Oil & Gas Exploration Services
N.A.I.C.S.: 211120

Subsidiary (Domestic):

Dana Petroleum (Algeria) Limited (3)
Kings Close 62 Huntly St, Aberdeen, AB10 1RS, United Kingdom
Tel.: (44) 1224652400
Sales Range: $50-74.9 Million
Emp.: 50
Oil & Gas Exploration Services
N.A.I.C.S.: 211120
Rebecca Thomson (Office Mgr)

Dana Petroleum (North Sea) Limited (3)
King's Close 62 Huntly Street, Aberdeen, AB10 1RS, United Kingdom
Tel.: (44) 1224616000
Web Site: http://www.dana-petroleum.com
Sales Range: $50-74.9 Million
Emp.: 100
Oil & Gas Exploration Services
N.A.I.C.S.: 211120

Subsidiary (Domestic):

Dana Petroleum (Russia) Limited (2)
17 Carden Pl, Aberdeen, AB10 1UR, United Kingdom
Tel.: (44) 1224652400
Sales Range: $50-74.9 Million
Emp.: 100
Oil & Gas Exploration Services
N.A.I.C.S.: 211120

Subsidiary (Non-US):

Dana Petroleum East Zeit Limited (2)
Zahret Al Maadi Tower Corniche Al Nil Street Maadi Area, 1303, Cairo, Egypt
Tel.: (20) 2 2529 1500
Oil & Gas Field Exploration Services
N.A.I.C.S.: 213112

Dana Petroleum Netherlands B.V. (2)
Binckhorstlaan 410, 2516 BL, Hague, Netherlands
Tel.: (31) 70 371 3000
Oil & Gas Field Exploration Services
N.A.I.C.S.: 213112
Dinesh M. Shivananthan (Engr-Production & Petroleum)

INTERNATIONAL PUBLIC

Dana Petroleum Norway AS (2)
Lilleakerveien 8, 0283, Oslo, Norway
Tel.: (47) 22 51 42 00
Oil & Gas Field Exploration Services
N.A.I.C.S.: 213112
Reidar Hustoft (Mng Dir)

Subsidiary (Domestic):

Korea Captain Company Limited (2)
New Zealand House 80 Haymarket, London, SW1Y 4TE, United Kingdom
Tel.: (44) 20 7747 3010
Oil & Gas Field Exploration Services
N.A.I.C.S.: 213112

EP Energy Corporation (1)
601 Travis St Ste 1400, Houston, TX 77002 (12.4%)
Tel.: (713) 997-1000
Web Site: http://www.epenergy.com
Sales Range: $1-4.9 Billion
Emp.: 372
Holding Company; Oil & Natural Gas Exploration, Development & Production Services
N.A.I.C.S.: 551112
Jace D. Locke (Gen Counsel, Sec & VP)

Subsidiary (Domestic):

EP Energy LLC (2)
1001 Louisiana St, Houston, TX 77002
Tel.: (713) 997-1200
Web Site: http://www.epenergy.com
Rev.: $1,323,999,999
Assets: $4,180,999,999
Liabilities: $4,779,999,999
Net Worth: ($599,000,000)
Earnings: $1,002,999,999
Emp.: 991
Fiscal Year-end: 12/31/2018
Oil & Natural Gas Exploration & Production
N.A.I.C.S.: 211120
Kyle McCuen (CFO, Treas & Sr VP)

Harvest Operations Corp. (1)
1500 700 2nd Street SW, Calgary, T2P 2W1, AB, Canada
Tel.: (403) 265-1178
Web Site: http://www.harvestenergy.ca
Rev.: $287,883,288
Assets: $2,314,162,284
Liabilities: $2,741,089,680
Net Worth: ($426,927,396)
Earnings: $1,989,624
Emp.: 219
Fiscal Year-end: 12/31/2019
Oil & Gas Field Exploration
N.A.I.C.S.: 213112
Grant Ukrainetz (VP-Fin)

KNOC Caspian LLP (1)
9th floor Karasaibatyr st 152a, 050026, Almaty, Kazakhstan
Tel.: (7) 727 244 4235
Petroleum Product Distr
N.A.I.C.S.: 213112

KNOC Eagle Ford Corp. (1)
5555 San Felipe St Ste 1175, Houston, TX 77056
Tel.: (713) 552-9318
Petroleum Product Distr
N.A.I.C.S.: 213112
Kyung Keun Bae (Engr-Production)

KNOC Trading Singapore Pte. Ltd. (1)
1103 Robinson Road 79, 068897, Singapore, Singapore
Tel.: (65) 6227 7792
Emp.: 2
Petroleum Product Distr
N.A.I.C.S.: 213112
Semin Kwon (Gen Mgr)

KOREA NEW NETWORK CO., LTD.

30 Centumseo-ro, Haeundae-gu, Busan, Korea (South)
Tel.: (82) 518509214
Web Site: http://www.knn.co.kr
Year Founded: 2010
058400—(KRS)
Rev.: $50,591,306
Assets: $171,003,442
Liabilities: $11,870,202
Net Worth: $159,133,240

KOREA OCEAN BUSINESS CORPORATION
7th floor Bldg C1 38 Marine City 2-ro, Haeundae-gu, Busan, 48120, Korea (South)
Tel.: (82) 517951500
Web Site: https://www.kobc.or.kr
Year Founded: 2018
Rev.: $295,422,551
Assets: $9,545,864,435
Liabilities: $3,654,567,428
Net Worth: $5,891,297,007
Earnings: $3,256,733
Fiscal Year-end: 12/31/23
Government Relation Services
N.A.I.C.S.: 921190
Kim Yang-soo (CEO)

KOREA PETRO CHEMICAL IND CO
77 Jahamun-ro Yunam Building, Jongno-gu, Seoul, 3035, Korea (South)
Tel.: (82) 221221422
Web Site: https://www.kpic.co.kr
006650—(KRS)
Rev.: $1,704,328,440
Assets: $1,684,203,540
Liabilities: $256,086,038
Net Worth: $1,428,117,501
Earnings: ($114,323,717)
Emp.: 775
Fiscal Year-end: 12/31/22
Petrochemical Industry & Synthetic Resins
N.A.I.C.S.: 325211
Tae Jeong Young (Pres & CEO)

Subsidiaries:

Korea Petro Chemical Ind Co - Onsan Plant (1)
134 Onsan-ro Onsan-eup, Ulsan, Ulju-gun, Korea (South)
Tel.: (82) 522395151
Petrochemical Products Mfr
N.A.I.C.S.: 325110

Korea Petro Chemical Ind Co - Ulsan Plant (1)
260-158 Cheoyong-ro, Nam-gu, Ulsan, Korea (South)
Tel.: (82) 522725151
Petrochemical Products Mfr
N.A.I.C.S.: 325110

KOREA PETROLEUM INDUSTRIAL CO., LTD.
166 Ichon-ro, Yongsan-Gu, Seoul, Korea (South)
Tel.: (82) 27993114
Web Site: https://www.koreapetroleum.com
Year Founded: 1964
004090—(KRS)
Rev.: $573,666,903
Assets: $266,199,257
Liabilities: $140,612,989
Net Worth: $125,586,268
Earnings: $8,536,476
Emp.: 205
Fiscal Year-end: 12/31/22
Chemical & Petroleum Product Mfr
N.A.I.C.S.: 324121

KOREA PHARMA CO., LTD.
8F 14 Teheran-Ro 4-Gil, Gangnam-Gu, Seoul, Korea (South)
Tel.: (82) 5581277
Web Site: https://www.koreapharma.co.kr
Year Founded: 1974
032300—(KRS)
Rev.: $62,149,566
Assets: $100,436,469
Liabilities: $54,558,026
Net Worth: $45,878,442
Earnings: ($858,313)
Emp.: 288
Fiscal Year-end: 12/31/22
Pharmaceuticals Product Mfr
N.A.I.C.S.: 325412
Eunhee Park (CEO)

KOREA RATINGS CORP.
97 Uisadang-daero Yeongdeungpo-gu, Seoul, 07327, Korea (South)
Tel.: (82) 23685500
Web Site: http://www.korearatings.com
Year Founded: 1983
034950—(KRS)
Rev.: $77,908,806
Assets: $123,725,227
Liabilities: $26,137,672
Net Worth: $97,587,555
Earnings: $19,549,550
Emp.: 187
Fiscal Year-end: 12/31/22
Credit Rating Services
N.A.I.C.S.: 561450
Kibum Kim (Pres & CEO)

Subsidiaries:

KR Plus (1)
78 Mapo-daero, Mapo-gu, Seoul, Korea (South)
Tel.: (82) 2 6480 5500
Web Site: http://www.krplus.co.kr
Risk Managemeng Srvices
N.A.I.C.S.: 541611

KOREA REAL ESTATE INVESTMENT & TRUST CO., LTD.
16-19th Fl 137 Teheran-ro, Gangnam-gu, Seoul, 06132, Korea (South)
Tel.: (82) 234511181
Web Site: http://www.koreit.co.kr
Year Founded: 1996
034830—(KRS)
Rev.: $168,158,004
Assets: $1,357,275,818
Liabilities: $547,579,194
Net Worth: $809,696,624
Earnings: $19,216,780
Emp.: 183
Fiscal Year-end: 12/31/22
Real Estate Investment Trust
N.A.I.C.S.: 525990
Jeong-Hoon Cha (Chm & Co-CEO)

KOREA REFRACTORIES CO., LTD.
370 Musudeul-gil Songsan-myeon, Songsan-myeon, Dangjin, Chungcheongnam-do, Korea (South)
Tel.: (82) 413592200
Web Site: https://www.fskrc.co.kr
Year Founded: 1973
010040—(KRS)
Rev.: $275,179,709
Assets: $250,041,111
Liabilities: $81,037,937
Net Worth: $169,003,174
Earnings: $620,665
Emp.: 585
Fiscal Year-end: 12/31/22
Refractories Mfr
N.A.I.C.S.: 327120
Yongmin Kim (Co-CEO)

KOREA ROBOT MANUFACTURING CO., LTD.
10th Floor Anyang Trade Center BiSan-Dong, DongAn-Ku, Anyang, 14048, Geonggi-do, Korea (South)
Tel.: (82) 313806950
Web Site: http://www.tamulm.com
093640—(KRS)
Rev.: $9,879,050
Assets: $48,145,517
Liabilities: $12,493,377
Net Worth: $35,652,141
Earnings: ($6,982,002)
Emp.: 27
Fiscal Year-end: 12/31/22
Semiconductor Devices Mfr
N.A.I.C.S.: 334413
Yoon-Jong Hyun (Dir-Admin & Mgmt Div)

KOREA SEMICONDUCTOR SYSTEM CO., LTD.
62 Saneop-ro, Ojeong-Gu, Bucheon, Gyeonggi-do, Korea (South)
Tel.: (82) 326622224
Web Site: https://www.koses.co.kr
Year Founded: 1990
089890—(KRS)
Rev.: $55,938,354
Assets: $57,155,277
Liabilities: $11,173,654
Net Worth: $45,981,623
Earnings: $6,044,614
Emp.: 202
Fiscal Year-end: 12/31/22
Semiconductor Machinery Mfr
N.A.I.C.S.: 333242

KOREA STEEL CO., LTD
2205 Gwangmyeong Station Xi Tower B 67 Saebit Gongwon-ro, Sasang-Gu, Gwangmyeong, Gyeonggi-do, Korea (South)
Tel.: (82) 232730500
Web Site: https://www.ekosco.com
Year Founded: 1971
007280—(KRS)
Rev.: $610,485,697
Assets: $421,718,386
Liabilities: $267,357,661
Net Worth: $154,360,725
Earnings: $30,849,814
Emp.: 550
Fiscal Year-end: 12/31/22
Steel Products Mfr
N.A.I.C.S.: 331110

Subsidiaries:

Korea Steel Shape Co., Ltd. - Chilseo-Steel Mill (1)
68 Gyenae-ri, Haman-gun, Chilseo, Gyeongsangnam-do, Korea (South)
Tel.: (82) 55 589 1000
Steel Products Mfr
N.A.I.C.S.: 331110

Korea Steel Shape Co., Ltd. - Noksan Plant (1)
1660-1 Songjeong-dong, Gangseo-gu, Busan, Korea (South)
Tel.: (82) 51 831 6811
Steel Products Mfr
N.A.I.C.S.: 331110

KOREA TIMES CO., LTD.
14th Fl Sejong-daero 17, Jung-gu, Seoul, 04512, Korea (South)
Tel.: (82) 27242715
Web Site: http://www.koreatimes.co.kr
Year Founded: 1950
Sales Range: $25-49.9 Million
Emp.: 100
Daily Newspaper Services
N.A.I.C.S.: 513110
Jae-ku Chang (Chm)

Subsidiaries:

Korea Times Los Angeles Inc. (1)
4525 Wilshire Blvd FL 3, Los Angeles, CA 90010
Tel.: (323) 692-2000
Web Site: http://www.koreatimes.com
Newspapers, Publishing & Printing
N.A.I.C.S.: 513110
Jae Min Chang (CEO & Publr)

KOREA UNITED PHARM INC
22 Nonhyeon-ro 121-gil, Gangnam-gu, Seoul, Chungnam, Korea (South)
Tel.: (82) 25129981
Web Site: https://www.kup.co.kr
033270—(KRS)
Rev.: $201,354,391
Assets: $320,522,295
Liabilities: $61,386,370
Net Worth: $259,135,925
Earnings: $34,725,997
Emp.: 885
Fiscal Year-end: 12/31/22
Pharmaceuticals Distr
N.A.I.C.S.: 424210
Duk-Young Kang (Pres & CEO)

KOREA ZINC COMPANY, LTD.
Young Poong B/D 542 Gangnam-Daero, Gangnam-gu, Seoul, Korea (South)
Tel.: (82) 25193416
Web Site: http://www.koreazinc.co.kr
Year Founded: 1974
010130—(KRS)
Rev.: $7,203,154,063
Assets: $8,941,163,036
Liabilities: $1,784,413,137
Net Worth: $7,156,749,899
Earnings: $395,898,853
Emp.: 1,867
Fiscal Year-end: 12/31/23
Zinc Mining
N.A.I.C.S.: 212230
Chang-Keun Choi (Co-Pres)

Subsidiaries:

Alantum Corp. (1)
8f Starwood Plaza 400 Dunchon-daero, Joongwon-Gu, Seongnam, 462-819, Gyonggi-Do, Korea (South)
Tel.: (82) 317370938
Electronic Services
N.A.I.C.S.: 238210

ICM Pachapaqui S.A.C. (1)
AV Camino Real No 456-Torre Real Of 1104, San Isidro, Lima, Peru
Tel.: (51) 14150530
Metal Mining Services
N.A.I.C.S.: 213114
Sanghyun Suh (Mgr-Comml)

KEMCO Co., Ltd. (1)
Tel.: (81) 332263366
Emp.: 103
Construction Equipment Mfr & Distr
N.A.I.C.S.: 333120
Shoji Okuhara (Pres)

KZ Green Tech Co., Ltd. (1)
139 Ijin-ro Onsan-eup, Ulju-gun, Ulsan, 44997, Korea (South)
Tel.: (82) 522316601
Construction Management Services
N.A.I.C.S.: 532412

KZ X Co., Ltd. (1)
461 Deoksin-ro Onsan-eup, Ulju-gun, Ulsan, 44992, Korea (South)
Tel.: (82) 522316411
Cargo & Port Transportation Services
N.A.I.C.S.: 926120

KZ-Pranda Co., Ltd. (1)
75/51 Ocean Tower2 24th Floor Soi Sukhumvit 19 Sukhumvit Road, Klongtoey Nua Wattana, Bangkok, 10110, Thailand
Tel.: (66) 220414412
Nonferrous Metal Product Distr
N.A.I.C.S.: 423510

Pan Pacific Metal Mining Corp. (1)
Suite 4700 Toronto Dominion Bank Tower, Toronto, M5K 1E6, ON, Canada
Tel.: (416) 601-7910
Metal Mining Services
N.A.I.C.S.: 213114

Sorin Corp. (1)
542 Youngpoong Building Gangnam-daero,

KOREA ZINC COMPANY, LTD.

Korea Zinc Company, Ltd.—(Continued)
Gangnam-gu Nonhyeon-dong, Seoul, Korea (South)
Tel.: (82) 25193381
Metal & Chemical Services
N.A.I.C.S.: 424690

Sorin Information Technology Co., Ltd. (1)
8th floor 542 Gangnham-daero Yeongpoong Building, Nonhyeon-dong Gangnam-gu, Seoul, 06110, Korea (South)
Tel.: (82) 25193600
Computer Distr
N.A.I.C.S.: 423430

Sun Metal Corporation Pty Ltd. (1)
1 Zinc RoadStuart, Stuart, Townsville, 4811, QLD, Australia
Tel.: (61) 747266600
Web Site: http://www.sunmetals.com.au
Emp.: 350
Zinc Metal Mfr & Distr
N.A.I.C.S.: 331529

KOREACENTER CO., LTD.
1401 Building A 168 Gasan Digital 1-ro, Geumcheon-gu, Seoul, Korea (South)
Tel.: (82) 2026 2300
Web Site: http://www.koreacenter.com
Internet Shopping Portal
N.A.I.C.S.: 455219
Gi Hun Kim (CEO)

KOREAN AIR LINES CO., LTD.
260 Haneul-gil, Gangseo-gu, Seoul, 07505, Korea (South)
Tel.: (82) 226567114
Web Site: https://www.koreanair.com
Year Founded: 1969
003490—(KRS)
Rev.: $6,997,726,152
Assets: $23,174,856,188
Liabilities: $20,128,070,003
Net Worth: $3,046,786,185
Earnings: ($211,617,144)
Emp.: 18,518
Fiscal Year-end: 12/31/20
Air Transportation & Management Services
N.A.I.C.S.: 481111

Subsidiaries:

Asiana Airlines, Inc. (1)
47 Osae Dong Kangseo Ku, PO Box 98, Asiana Town, Seoul, 157 713, Korea (South) (63.9%)
Tel.: (82) 26693114
Web Site: http://www.flyasiana.com
Rev.: $708,333,000
Air Transportation
N.A.I.C.S.: 481111

Subsidiary (US):

Asiana Airlines (2)
3530 Wilshire Blvd Ste 1700, Los Angeles, CA 90010-2341
Tel.: (213) 365-4500
Web Site: http://www.flyasiana.com
Oil Transportation Services
N.A.I.C.S.: 561110
Ralph Myers (Gen Mgr)

Subsidiary (Domestic):

Asiana IDT, Inc. (2)
5 6 7F Kumho Asiana Main Tower Suite 76 Saemunanro, Jongro-Gu, Seoul, 110-857, Korea (South)
Tel.: (82) 2 6303 0114
Web Site: http://www.asianaidt.com
Computer System Integration Services
N.A.I.C.S.: 541511

HanJin International Corp. (1)
3000 Supply Ave, Los Angeles, CA 90040 (53.7%)
Tel.: (323) 727-5566
Sales Range: $1-9.9 Million
Emp.: 12
General Line Grocery Merchant Whslr

N.A.I.C.S.: 424410

Hanjin Information Systems & Tele-Communication Co., Ltd. (1)
453 Gonghang-daero, Gangseo-gu, Seoul, 07570, Korea (South)
Tel.: (82) 221667114
Web Site: https://www.hist.co.kr
Commercial Services
N.A.I.C.S.: 561499

Korean Air Lines Co., Ltd. - China Division (1)
11 F Tower 2 South Seas Centre 75 Mody Road Tsimshatsui East, Kowloon, China (Hong Kong)
Tel.: (852) 27337111
Web Site: http://www.koreanair.com
Sales Range: $25-49.9 Million
Emp.: 100
Oil Transportation Services
N.A.I.C.S.: 481111

Korean Air Lines Co., Ltd. - France Division (1)
9 Boulevard de la Madeleine, 75001, Paris, France
Tel.: (33) 142973030
Sales Range: $25-49.9 Million
Emp.: 48
Oil Transportation Services
N.A.I.C.S.: 481111

Korean Air Lines Co., Ltd. - US Division (1)
6101 W Imperial Hwy, Los Angeles, CA 90045
Tel.: (310) 417-5200
Oil Transportation Services
N.A.I.C.S.: 481111

Waikiki Resort Hotel, Inc. (1)
2460 Koa Ave, Honolulu, HI 96815
Tel.: (808) 922-4911
Web Site: http://www.waikikiresort.com
Sales Range: $1-9.9 Million
Emp.: 104
Hotels (except Casino Hotels) & Motels
N.A.I.C.S.: 721110
C. H. Cho (Chm)

KOREAN DRUG CO., LTD.
34 Nonhyeonro 28gil, Gangnam-gu, Seoul, 135-270, Korea (South)
Tel.: (82) 25296100
Web Site: https://www.nicepharma.com
Year Founded: 1980
014570—(KRS)
Rev.: $61,347,771
Assets: $72,494,047
Liabilities: $7,519,457
Net Worth: $64,974,590
Earnings: $9,057,381
Emp.: 256
Fiscal Year-end: 12/31/22
Pharmaceutical Mfr & Whslr
N.A.I.C.S.: 325412
Hai-Ryong Park (Chm, Pres & CEO)

KOREAN ENVIRONMENT TECHNOLOGY CO., LTD.
328 Yongjam-ro, Nam-gu, Ulsan, Korea (South)
Tel.: (82) 522287300
Web Site: https://www.koentec.co.kr
Year Founded: 1993
029960—(KRS)
Rev.: $69,249,685
Assets: $159,723,528
Liabilities: $28,939,838
Net Worth: $130,783,690
Earnings: $30,361,912
Emp.: 86
Fiscal Year-end: 12/31/22
Solid Waste Management Services
N.A.I.C.S.: 562213
Lee Min-Seok (CEO)

KOREAN REINSURANCE COMPANY
68 Jongno 5 Gil, Jongno-gu, Seoul, 03151, Korea (South)

Tel.: (82) 237026000
Web Site: https://www.koreanre.co.kr
Year Founded: 1963
003690—(KRS)
Rev.: $9,648,137,486
Assets: $11,488,225,710
Liabilities: $9,325,704,492
Net Worth: $2,162,521,218
Earnings: $121,076,319
Emp.: 433
Fiscal Year-end: 12/31/22
Reinsurance Services
N.A.I.C.S.: 524130
Jong-Gyu Won (Pres, CEO & Member-Mgmt Bd)

Subsidiaries:

Korean Re Underwriting Ltd. (1)
Room No 703 Gallery 7 of Lloyd's 1986 B/D One Lime Street, London, EC3M 7HA, United Kingdom
Tel.: (44) 2072650031
Insurance Services
N.A.I.C.S.: 524210
John B. Kim (CEO)

Korean Reinsurance Switzerland AG (1)
Brandschenkestrasse 47, 8002, Zurich, Switzerland
Tel.: (41) 433362060
Web Site: http://www.koreanre.ch
Insurance Services
N.A.I.C.S.: 524210
Markus A. Eugster (CEO)

Worldwide Insurance Services, Ltd. (1)
Suite 3606 36/F Central Plaza 18 Harbour Road, Wanchai, China (Hong Kong)
Tel.: (852) 2877 3117
Insurance Management Services
N.A.I.C.S.: 524298
Dong-bin Kim (CEO)

KORFEZ GAYRIMENKUL YATIRIM ORTAKLIGI AS
Altunizade Mahallesi Kisikli Caddesi Akoz Is Merkezi Blok, No 14/1 Ic Kapi No 5 Uskudar, Istanbul, Türkiye
Tel.: (90) 2164009000
Web Site: http://www.korfezgyo.com.tr
KRGYO—(IST)
Sales Range: Less than $1 Million
Asset Management Services
N.A.I.C.S.: 523940
Abdullah Tivnikli (Chm)

KORG INC.
4015-2 Yanokuchi, Inagi-shi, Tokyo, 206-0812, Japan
Tel.: (81) 423795771 JP
Web Site: http://www.korg.com
Year Founded: 1963
Sales Range: $75-99.9 Million
Emp.: 290
Electronic Musical Instruments Mfr & Distr
N.A.I.C.S.: 339992
Seiki Kato (Pres)

Subsidiaries:

KORG HK Ltd. (1)
Workshops 10 & 11 12/F New Tech Plaza 34 Tai Yau St Sampokong, Kowloon, China (Hong Kong)
Tel.: (852) 2511 7163
Musical Instrument Mfr & Distr
N.A.I.C.S.: 339992

Korg (UK) Limited (1)
9 New Market Ct, Kingston, Milton Keynes, MK10 0AU, United Kingdom (100%)
Tel.: (44) 1908857100
Web Site: http://www.korg.co.uk
Sales Range: $25-49.9 Million
Emp.: 30
Electronic Musical Instruments Mfr & Distr
N.A.I.C.S.: 339992
Rob Castle (Chm)

INTERNATIONAL PUBLIC

Korg Europe Limited (1)
9 Newmarket Ct, Kingston, Milton Keynes, MK10 0AU, United Kingdom (100%)
Tel.: (44) 1908857100
Web Site: http://www.korg.co.jp
Sales Range: $25-49.9 Million
Emp.: 4
Mfr & Distr of Electronic Musical Instruments
N.A.I.C.S.: 339992

Korg Italy S.p.A. (1)
Via Cagiata 85, Osimo, 60027, Ancona, Italy
Tel.: (39) 071 7231142
Web Site: http://www.korgpa.com
Musical Instrument Distr
N.A.I.C.S.: 423990
Nilo Baldassarri (Mgr-Quality Control)

Korg Middle East (1)
Jebel Ali Free Zone UA O2, PO Box 262124, Dubai, United Arab Emirates
Tel.: (971) 4 8880 786
Web Site: http://www.korgmiddleeast.com
Musical Instrument Distr
N.A.I.C.S.: 423990
Salim Eden (Chm & Mng Dir)

Korg USA, Inc. (1)
316 S Service Rd, Melville, NY 11747
Tel.: (631) 390-6800
Web Site: http://www.korg.com
Sales Range: $100-124.9 Million
Emp.: 115
Musical Instruments; Synthesizers; Sound Modules; Digital Pianos; Tuners; Hyperperformance Processors
N.A.I.C.S.: 512230
Scott Fiesel (Mgr-Digital Mktg)

Korgtech Inc. (1)
120-1 Kitane Hanazono-machi, Fukaya, 369-1242, Saitama, Japan
Tel.: (81) 48 584 5691
Musical Instrument Mfr & Distr
N.A.I.C.S.: 339992

KORI HOLDINGS LIMITED
11 Sims Drive 06-01 SCN Centre, Singapore, 387385, Singapore
Tel.: (65) 68443445
Web Site: https://www.kori.com.sg
Year Founded: 1982
5VC—(SES)
Rev.: $13,535,258
Assets: $56,689,386
Liabilities: $15,248,079
Net Worth: $41,441,307
Earnings: $396,155
Emp.: 174
Fiscal Year-end: 12/31/23
Civil & Structural Engineering & Construction
N.A.I.C.S.: 237990
Yu Koh Hooi (Chm & CEO)

Subsidiaries:

Kori Construction (M) Sdn. Bhd. (1)
69-3A OG Business Park Jalan Taman Tan Yew Lai, 58200, Kuala Lumpur, Malaysia
Tel.: (60) 377855667
Construction Building Services
N.A.I.C.S.: 236220

KORINDO GROUP
Wisma Korindo 12th Fl Jl MT Haryono Kav 62, Jakarta, 12780, Indonesia
Tel.: (62) 21 797 5959
Web Site: http://www.korindo.co.id
Year Founded: 1969
Holding Company
N.A.I.C.S.: 551112
Eun-ho Seung (Chm)

Subsidiaries:

Korindo Group - Balikpapan Division (1)
Jl R E Martadinata RT 37 No 23, PO Box 168, Balikpapan, 76111, Indonesia
Tel.: (62) 542 733 411
Communication Tower Construction Services

AND PRIVATE COMPANIES

N.A.I.C.S.: 237130

Korindo Group - Pangkalan Bun Division (1)
Jl Korindo 77 Pangkalan Bun, 74102, Kalimantan, Indonesia
Tel.: (62) 532 21156
Communication Tower Construction Services
N.A.I.C.S.: 237130

Korindo Wind Tower Division (1)
Jl Raya Anyer KM 122 Desa Gunung Sugih, Ciwandan Cilegon, Banten, 42447, Indonesia
Tel.: (62) 5460 0882
Web Site: http://www.korindo.co.id
Wind Towers Mfr
N.A.I.C.S.: 237130

Kousa International, LLC (1)
6300 Wilshire Blvd Ste 400, Los Angeles, CA 90048
Tel.: (213) 365-5500
Web Site: http://www.korindowind.com
Emp.: 9
Wholesale Trade Agency & Logistics Services; Wind Tower Installation Services
N.A.I.C.S.: 425120
Ricky Seung *(Pres)*

PT Korindo Heavy Industry (1)
Jl Raya Serang Km 31, Balaraja Barat, Tangerang, 15610, Banten, Indonesia
Tel.: (62) 21 5950088
Communication Tower Construction Services
N.A.I.C.S.: 237130

KORLOFF SA
32 Avenue du Marechal Foch, 69006, Lyon, France
Tel.: (33) 478173941
Web Site: http://www.korloff.com
Rev.: $10,700,000
Emp.: 35
Jewelry Retailer
N.A.I.C.S.: 458310
Bernadette Yoneyama *(Dir)*

Subsidiaries:

Korloff PARIS (1)
12 Rue de le Paix, 75002, Paris, France
Tel.: (33) 1 49 27 92 09
Web Site: http://www.korloffparis.net
Jewelry Retailer
N.A.I.C.S.: 458310

KORNIC AUTOMATION CO., LTD.
108 Yeoui-daero, Yeongdeungpo-gu, 07335, Seoul, Korea (South)
Tel.: (82) 02 2229 6498
Year Founded: 2021
Emp.: 100
Software Publisher
N.A.I.C.S.: 513210
Hyuk Kim Hwaseong Na *(CEO)*

KORNIT DIGITAL LTD.
12 Ha Amal Street, Rosh Ha'Ayin, 4824096, Israel
Tel.: (972) 39085800   Il
Web Site: https://www.kornit.com
Year Founded: 2002
KRNT—(NASDAQ)
Rev.: $219,786,000
Assets: $865,580,000
Liabilities: $69,913,000
Net Worth: $795,667,000
Earnings: ($64,351,000)
Emp.: 873
Fiscal Year-end: 12/31/23
Digital Printing Solutions & Equipment Mfr
N.A.I.C.S.: 323113
Ilan Givon *(Exec VP-Ops)*

KORONA INVEST OY
Tekniikantie 12, 02150, Espoo, Finland
Tel.: (358) 50 337 6969   FI

Web Site: http://www.koronainvest.fi
Year Founded: 2006
Private Equity & Alternative Investment Management Firm
N.A.I.C.S.: 523999
Vesa Lehtomaki *(Co-Founder & CEO)*

KORPORACJA BUDOWLANA DOM S.A.
Ul Budowlana Kartoszyno 3, 84-110, Krokowa, Poland
Tel.: (48) 58 670 60 55
Web Site: http://www.kbdom.eu
KBD—(WAR)
Sales Range: Less than $1 Million
Construction Engineering Services
N.A.I.C.S.: 237990
Jan Mateusz Zajaczkowski *(Chm-Mgmt Bd)*

KORPORACJA GOSPODARCZA EFEKT S.A.
ul Opolska 12, 31-323, Krakow, Poland
Tel.: (48) 124203330
Web Site: https://www.efektsa.pl
EFK—(WAR)
Rev.: $15,044,461
Assets: $52,674,797
Liabilities: $23,218,242
Net Worth: $29,456,555
Earnings: $10,142,785
Fiscal Year-end: 12/31/23
Hotel & Tourist Services
N.A.I.C.S.: 561520
Olga Lipinska-Dlugosz *(Member-Mgmt Bd)*

KORPORACJA KGL SA
ul Gen Wladyslawa Sikorskiego 17, Klaudyn, 05-080, Warsaw, Poland
Tel.: (48) 223213000
Web Site: http://www.kgl.pl
Year Founded: 1992
KGL—(WAR)
Rev.: $142,934,197
Assets: $88,856,453
Liabilities: $54,495,681
Net Worth: $34,360,772
Earnings: $4,649,644
Emp.: 750
Fiscal Year-end: 12/31/23
Thermoplastic Raw Material & Food Packaging Plastic Distr
N.A.I.C.S.: 424130
Krzysztof Gromkowski *(Chm-Mgmt Bd & CEO)*

KORPORATA ELEKTROENERGJITIKE SHQIPTARE
Blloku Vasil Shanto, PO Box 259/1, Tirana, Albania
Tel.: (355) 42259729
Web Site: http://www.kesh.com.al
Sales Range: $5-14.9 Billion
Emp.: 7,738
Electric Power Distr & Producer
N.A.I.C.S.: 221122
Artan Hoxha *(Chm-Supervisory Bd)*

KORRES S.A. NATURAL PRODUCTS
3 Drosini & Tatoiou Street Metamorfosi, 144 52, Athens, Greece
Tel.: (30) 213 01 88 800
Web Site: http://www.korres.com
Homeopathic Pharmacy & Herbal Products Services
N.A.I.C.S.: 424210
Giorgos Korres *(Co-Founder)*

KORTEK CORPORATION
26 Venture-ro 24beon-gil Yeonsu-go, Incheon, 406840, Korea (South)
Tel.: (82) 328603000
Web Site: https://www.kortek.co.kr

Year Founded: 1987
052330—(KRS)
Rev.: $328,700,179
Assets: $361,768,124
Liabilities: $99,712,804
Net Worth: $262,055,320
Earnings: $21,650,678
Emp.: 461
Fiscal Year-end: 12/31/22
Industrial Monitors & Related Services
N.A.I.C.S.: 334118
Young-Dal Kim *(CEO)*

Subsidiaries:

Kortek Australia Pty Ltd (1)
43/9 Salisbury Road, Castle Hill, 2154, NSW, Australia
Tel.: (61) 481285825
Display Product Distr
N.A.I.C.S.: 423690

Kortek USA Inc (1)
1312 Capital Blvd Ste 105, Reno, NV 89502
Tel.: (775) 240-3533
Display Product Distr
N.A.I.C.S.: 423690
Y. G. Choi *(Exec VP)*

Kortek Vina Co., Ltd. (1)
Lot CN-02 Dong Van IV IZ, Dai Cuong Commune Kim Bang Dist, Kim Bang, Ha Nam, Vietnam
Tel.: (84) 2262225000
Industrial Display Monitor Mfr
N.A.I.C.S.: 334513

KORTEKS MENSUCAT SANAYI VE TICARET AS
Organize Sanayi Bolgesi Sari Caddesi No 3, Nilufer, 16140, Bursa, Turkiye
Tel.: (90) 2242191100
KORTS—(IST)
Rev.: $359,513,737
Assets: $1,137,672,777
Liabilities: $673,538,077
Net Worth: $464,134,701
Earnings: $56,628,994
Emp.: 5,496
Fiscal Year-end: 12/31/22
Polyester Fiber & Filament Yarn Mfr
N.A.I.C.S.: 325220
Zeki Zorlu *(Chm)*

KORVEST LTD.
580 Prospect Road, Kilburn, 5084, SA, Australia
Tel.: (61) 883604500   AU
Web Site:
   https://www.korvest.com.au
KOV—(ASX)
Rev.: $68,703,258
Assets: $53,114,984
Liabilities: $17,425,881
Net Worth: $35,689,102
Earnings: $7,374,466
Emp.: 246
Fiscal Year-end: 06/30/24
Industrial Products Mfr
N.A.I.C.S.: 333248
Steven John William McGregor *(Sec & Dir-Fin)*

Subsidiaries:

EzyStrut New South Wales (1)
Lot 304 Progress Circuit, Preston, 2170, NSW, Australia
Tel.: (61) 287837555
Web Site: http://www.ezystrut.com.au
Sales Range: $25-49.9 Million
Emp.: 20
Household Audio & Video Equipment
N.A.I.C.S.: 334310

EzyStrut Queensland (1)
25 Machinery Street, Darra, 4076, QLD, Australia
Tel.: (61) 732596844
Web Site: http://www.ezystrut.com.au

Sales Range: $25-49.9 Million
Emp.: 8
Providers of Household Audio & Video Equipment
N.A.I.C.S.: 334310

EzyStrut South Australia (1)
580 Prospect Road, Kilburn, 5084, SA, Australia
Tel.: (61) 883604550
Web Site: http://www.ezystrut.com.au
Sales Range: $100-124.9 Million
Providers of Household Audio & Video Equipment
N.A.I.C.S.: 334310

EzyStrut Victoria (1)
5/131 Calarco Drive, Derrimut, 3026, VIC, Australia
Tel.: (61) 383687555
Web Site: http://www.ezystrut.com.au
Sales Range: $25-49.9 Million
Emp.: 41
Providers of Household Audio & Video Equipment
N.A.I.C.S.: 334310

Korvest Galvanisers (1)
580 Prospect Road, Kilburn, 5084, Australia   (51%)
Tel.: (61) 883604555
Web Site:
   https://www.korvestgalvanisers.com.au
Sales Range: $100-124.9 Million
Emp.: 200
Providers of Household Audio & Video Equipment
N.A.I.C.S.: 334310
Chris Hartwig *(Mng Dir)*

Power Step (Chile) SpA (1)
Badajoz 130 Of 902, Las Condes, Santiago, Chile
Tel.: (56) 99 153 7941
Fabricated Metal Products Mfr
N.A.I.C.S.: 332119

KORYO CREDIT INFORMATION CO., LTD.
353 Seocho-daero, Seocho-gu, Seoul, 137-882, Korea (South)
Tel.: (82) 234509000
Web Site: http://www.koryoinfo.co.kr
Year Founded: 1991
049720—(KRS)
Rev.: $112,570,143
Assets: $66,909,591
Liabilities: $36,772,517
Net Worth: $30,137,075
Earnings: $8,124,323
Emp.: 814
Fiscal Year-end: 12/31/22
Credit Collection & Research Services
N.A.I.C.S.: 561450
Euy-Kook Yoon *(Chm)*

KORYOJYUHAN CO., LTD.
2-4-33 Minamimachi, Mito, 310-0021, Ibaraki, Japan
Tel.: (81) 292212110
Year Founded: 1981
3495—(TKS)
Rev.: $66,107,160
Assets: $100,174,610
Liabilities: $67,262,830
Net Worth: $32,911,780
Earnings: $4,629,770
Fiscal Year-end: 09/30/23
Real Estate Manangement Services
N.A.I.C.S.: 531390
Toshimichi Sugawara *(Mng Dir)*

KOS INTERNATIONAL HOLDINGS LTD.
Suite 610 6/F Ocean Centre 5 Canton Road TST, Kowloon, China (Hong Kong)
Tel.: (852) 31804988   Ky
Web Site: http://www.kos-intl.com
Year Founded: 2009

KOS INTERNATIONAL HOLDINGS LTD.

KOS International Holdings Ltd.—(Continued)
8042—(HKG)
Rev.: $16,060,538
Assets: $11,688,180
Liabilities: $3,297,788
Net Worth: $8,390,393
Earnings: $1,790,993
Emp.: 110
Fiscal Year-end: 12/31/22
Recruitment Consulting Services
N.A.I.C.S.: 541612
Kevin Ka Kin Chan *(Chm)*

Subsidiaries:

KOS International Limited (1)
Avenida Comercial De Macau FIT Centre 5 Andar, Macau, China (Macau)
Tel.: (853) 82964387
HR & Recruitment Consulting Services
N.A.I.C.S.: 541612

KOSAIDO HOLDINGS CO., LTD.
123 Shibaura, Minato-ku, Tokyo, 108-8378, Japan
Tel.: (81) 334530550
Web Site: https://www.kosaido.co.jp
Year Founded: 1964
7868—(TKS)
Rev.: $234,370,770
Assets: $511,706,540
Liabilities: $201,168,740
Net Worth: $310,537,800
Earnings: $28,660,960
Emp.: 1,091
Fiscal Year-end: 03/31/24
Commercial Printing Services
N.A.I.C.S.: 323111

Subsidiaries:

Kinyosha Printing Co., Ltd. (1)
2-8-4 Unoki, Ota-ku, Tokyo, 146-8577, Japan
Tel.: (81) 337502107
Web Site: https://www.kinyosha.co.jp
Emp.: 234
Game Application Development Services
N.A.I.C.S.: 541511

KOSAKI TMI D.D.
Oresko Nabrezje 1, 2000, Maribor, Slovenia
Tel.: (386) 22352200
Web Site: http://www.kosaki.si
Sales Range: $25-49.9 Million
Emp.: 215
Livestock Slaughtering, Fresh Meat Preparing, Meat Products Processing, Meat & Meat Products Wholesaling & Retailing
N.A.I.C.S.: 311611
Marko Zerak *(Pres)*

KOSAYA GORA IRON WORKS PJSC
Orlovskoe shosse 4, Kosaya Gora village, Tula, 300903, Russia
Tel.: (7) 4872243066 RU
Web Site: https://www.kmz-tula.ru
Year Founded: 1897
KMTZ—(MOEX)
Sales Range: Less than $1 Million
Metallurgical Product Mfr & Distr
N.A.I.C.S.: 331110
Pyatigorov Eugeny *(Chm)*

KOSE CORPORATION
3-6-2 Nihonbashi, Chuo-ku, Tokyo, 103-8251, Japan
Tel.: (81) 332731511 JP
Web Site: https://corp.kose.co.jp
Year Founded: 1946
4922—(TKS)
Rev.: $2,129,878,540
Assets: $2,635,048,130
Liabilities: $628,308,710
Net Worth: $2,006,739,420
Earnings: $82,690,670
Emp.: 12,816
Fiscal Year-end: 12/31/23
Personal Care Product Mfr
N.A.I.C.S.: 325620
Kazutoshi Kobayashi *(CEO)*

Subsidiaries:

ADVANCE Co., Ltd. (1)
856-4 Kitairiso, Sayama, Saitama, Japan
Tel.: (81) 429582101
Cosmetics Mfr
N.A.I.C.S.: 325620

Albion Co., Ltd. (1)
1-7-10 Ginza, Chuo-ku, Tokyo, 104-0061, Japan
Tel.: (81) 355241711
Web Site: https://rashisa.albion.co.jp
Emp.: 3,388
Cosmetics Mfr & Sales
N.A.I.C.S.: 424210
Shoichi Kobayashi *(Pres)*

Albion Cosmetics (America) Inc. (1)
28 W 44th St, New York, NY 10036-6600
Tel.: (212) 869-1052
Cosmetics Distr
N.A.I.C.S.: 456120
June Kawakami *(Mgr-HR)*

COSME LABO Co., Ltd. (1)
3-8-68 Atago, Ageo, Saitama, Japan
Tel.: (81) 487759710
Personal Care Product Mfr
N.A.I.C.S.: 456199

Crie Co., Ltd. (1)
7F Choju Building 1-9-4 Kayabacho Nihonbashi, Chuo-ku, Tokyo, 103-0025, Japan
Tel.: (81) 368425860
Web Site: https://www.koseprofessional.co.jp
Cosmetics Mfr
N.A.I.C.S.: 325620

Dr. PHIL COSMETICS INC. (1)
2-20-1 Hatchobori, Chuo-ku, Tokyo, 104-0032, Japan
Tel.: (81) 332062011
Web Site: https://maison.kose.co.jp
Cosmetics Whslr
N.A.I.C.S.: 424210
Hajime Matsuoka *(Pres)*

INTERCOSME INC. (1)
1913 Sakaiiyoku, Isesaki, Gunma, Japan
Tel.: (81) 270764635
Plastic Containers & Cosmetics Mfr
N.A.I.C.S.: 326199
Kazutoshi Kobayashi *(Pres)*

KOSE (HONG KONG) CO., LTD. (1)
Rm 2803-05 28/F Windsor House 311 Gloucester Road, Causeway Bay, China (Hong Kong)
Tel.: (852) 28663998
Web Site: https://www.kose.com.hk
Sales Range: $25-49.9 Million
Emp.: 30
Cosmetics Mfr
N.A.I.C.S.: 325620

KOSE (Malaysia) Sdn. Bhd. (1)
Unit 7-04 Level 7 Nucleus Tower No 10 Jalan PJU 7/6 Mutiara Damansara, 47800, Petaling Jaya, Selangor, Malaysia
Tel.: (60) 377323811
Cosmetic Product Mfr & Distr
N.A.I.C.S.: 325620

KOSE (Thailand) Co., Ltd. (1)
98 Sathorn Square Building 22nd Floor Unit 2208-2211 Sathorn Road, Silom Bang Rak, Bangkok, 10500, Thailand
Tel.: (66) 206837172
Web Site: https://www.kose-th.com
Cosmetics Products Mfr
N.A.I.C.S.: 325620

KOSE America, Inc. (1)
110 Greene St Ste 407/408, New York, NY 10012
Tel.: (212) 682-3795
Cosmetic Product Mfr & Distr
N.A.I.C.S.: 325620

KOSE Brasil Comercio De Cosmeticos Ltda. (1)
Rua Dr Luiz Migliano 1986 - Cj 2703, Morumbi, Sao Paulo, 05711-001, SP, Brazil
Tel.: (55) 1151022836
Web Site: https://www.casakose.com.br
Cosmetics Products Mfr
N.A.I.C.S.: 325620

KOSE COSMENIENCE CO., LTD. (1)
3-6-2 Nihonbashi, Chuo-ku, Tokyo, 103-0027, Japan
Tel.: (81) 332731511
Web Site: http://www.kose.co.jp
Cosmetics Distr
N.A.I.C.S.: 456120

KOSE COSMEPIA CO., LTD. (1)
Tel.: (81) 368925880
Sales Range: $25-49.9 Million
Emp.: 10
Cosmetics Whslr
N.A.I.C.S.: 456120

KOSE COSMEPORT CORP. (1)
Nihonbashi D Square 1-16-11 Nihonbashi, Chuo-ku, Tokyo, 103-0027, Japan
Tel.: (81) 332778570
Web Site: https://www.kosecosmeport.co.jp
Sales Range: $100-124.9 Million
Emp.: 283
Cosmetics Whslr
N.A.I.C.S.: 456120
Takao Kobayashi *(Pres)*

KOSE Corporation India Pvt. Ltd. (1)
318 319 3rd Floor MGF Metropolis Mall MG Road, Gurgaon, 122002, India
Tel.: (91) 1244780888
Web Site: https://www.koseindia.com
Cosmetics Products Mfr
N.A.I.C.S.: 325620

KOSE INSURANCE SERVICE CO., LTD. (1)
2-8-5 Nihonbashi-kayabacho, Chuo-ku, Tokyo, Japan
Tel.: (81) 343462200
Marketing & Insurance Services
N.A.I.C.S.: 524298

KOSE KOREA CO., LTD. (1)
2nd and 3rd floors K-TOWER 158-23 Samseong-dong, Gangnam-gu, Seoul, 135-280, Korea (South)
Tel.: (82) 234663600
Web Site: https://www.kosekorea.co.kr
Sales Range: $50-74.9 Million
Emp.: 110
Cosmetics Mfr
N.A.I.C.S.: 325620

KOSE Maruho Co., Ltd. (1)
3-6-2 Nihonbashi, Chuo-ku, Tokyo, 103-8251, Japan
Tel.: (81) 120008873
Web Site: http://www.carte-beauty.com
Cosmetic Product Whslr
N.A.I.C.S.: 456120

KOSE Provision Co., Ltd. (1)
3-6-2 Nihonbashi, Chuo-ku, Tokyo, 103-8251, Japan
Tel.: (81) 120018755
Web Site: http://www.maihada.jp
Cosmetic Product Whslr
N.A.I.C.S.: 456120

KOSE SALES CO., LTD. (1)
3-6-2 Nihonbashi, Chuo-ku, Tokyo, 103-0027, Japan
Tel.: (81) 332785121
Web Site: http://www.kose.co.jp
Cosmetics Whslr
N.A.I.C.S.: 456120

Kose Industries Co., Ltd. (1)
1913 Sakaiiyoku, Isesaki, Gunma, Japan
Tel.: (81) 270885881
Cosmetic Product Mfr & Distr
N.A.I.C.S.: 325620

Kose Singapore Pte. Ltd. (1)
1 Kim Seng Promenade Great World City West Tower 12-12, Singapore, 237994, Singapore
Tel.: (65) 62260068
Web Site: https://www.kose.com.sg
Sales Range: $25-49.9 Million
Emp.: 10
Cosmetics Mfr
N.A.I.C.S.: 325620

INTERNATIONAL PUBLIC

PT. INDONESIA KOSE (1)
Wisma 46 Kota BNI 24th Floor Unit 24 07 Jl Jend Sudirman Kav 1, Jakarta, 10220, Indonesia
Tel.: (62) 215746557
Cosmetic Product Mfr & Distr
N.A.I.C.S.: 325620

TAIWAN KOSE CO., LTD. (1)
12th Floor No 200 Section 1 Keelung Road, Xinyi District, Taipei, Taiwan
Tel.: (886) 287863668
Web Site: http://www.kose.com.tw
Sales Range: $200-249.9 Million
Emp.: 700
Cosmetics Whslr
N.A.I.C.S.: 456120

TECHNO LABO Co., Ltd. (1)
2-5-4 Kanda Nishikicho 3F Daini Kametani Building, Chiyoda-ku, Tokyo, 101-0054, Japan
Tel.: (81) 352591104
Web Site: http://www.techno-labo.co.jp
Sales Range: $25-49.9 Million
Emp.: 105
Cosmetics Mfr
N.A.I.C.S.: 325620
A. Ooshima *(Co-Founder & CTO)*

Tarte, Inc. (1)
1375 Broadway Ste 800, New York, NY 10018 **(100%)**
Tel.: (646) 971-2676
Web Site: https://www.tartecosmetics.com
Sales Range: $50-74.9 Million
Emp.: 21
Cosmetic Products Mfr & Distr
N.A.I.C.S.: 325620
Maureen Kelly *(Founder & CEO)*

KOSE R.E. CO., LTD.
1-15-30 Akasaka, Chuo-ku, Fukuoka, 810-0042, Japan
Tel.: (81) 927226677
Web Site: https://www.kose-re.jp
Year Founded: 1990
3246—(TKS)
Rev.: $72,048,580
Assets: $104,052,840
Liabilities: $31,103,830
Net Worth: $72,949,010
Earnings: $8,947,580
Emp.: 72
Fiscal Year-end: 01/31/24
Real Estate Services
N.A.I.C.S.: 531390
Toshikazu Morofuji *(Pres)*

KOSEI ALUMINUM CO., LTD.
1236 Kamiikecho 2-chome, Toyota, 910-3133, Aichi, Japan
Tel.: (81) 565 80 4492 JP
Web Site: http://www.koseijp.co.jp
Year Founded: 1950
Aluminum Wheels, Automobile & Motorcycle Parts Mfr & Sales
N.A.I.C.S.: 331110
Tetsushi Kamiya *(Pres)*

Subsidiaries:

Kosei St. Marys Corporation (1)
1100 McKinley Rd, Saint Marys, OH 45885
Tel.: (419) 394-7840
Web Site: https://www.koseina.com
Sales Range: $150-199.9 Million
Emp.: 600
Cast Aluminum Wheel Mfr & Distr
N.A.I.C.S.: 336390
Chris Cottrill *(Gen Mgr)*

KOSHIDAKA HOLDINGS CO., LTD.
Dogenzaka-dori 10F 2-25-12 Dogenzaka, Shibuya-ku, Tokyo, 150-0043, Japan
Tel.: (81) 343307025
Web Site: https://www.koshidakaholdings.co.jp
Year Founded: 1967
2157—(TKS)
Rev.: $393,554,849

Assets: $383,918,599
Liabilities: $195,087,253
Net Worth: $188,831,346
Earnings: $41,899,298
Fiscal Year-end: 08/31/24
Karaoke Operations; Fitness Center Franchise Owner & Operator
N.A.I.C.S.: 713990
Toshiyuki Sasaki *(Operating Officer)*

Subsidiaries:

Curves International Inc. (1)
400 Schroeder Dr, Waco, TX 76710
Tel.: (254) 399-9285
Web Site: https://www.curves.com
Womens Fitness & Weight Loss Center Franchiser Services
N.A.I.C.S.: 812191
Gary Heavin *(Founder)*

KOSHIDAKA INTERNATIONAL PTE. LTD. (1)
1 Paya Lebar Link 04-01 Paya Lebar Quarter, Singapore, 408533, Singapore
Tel.: (65) 62279336
Fitness Facility Services
N.A.I.C.S.: 721110

KOSHIDAKA KOREA Co., Ltd. (1)
Rm 1008 Hyndai HYEL 213-12 Saechang-ro, Yongsan-gu, Seoul, Korea (South)
Tel.: (82) 27553052
Web Site: https://manekineko.co.kr
Fitness Facility Services
N.A.I.C.S.: 721110

KOSKISEN CORP.
Tehdastie 2, Jarvela, 16600, Helsinki, Finland
Tel.: (358) 2055341
Web Site: https://www.koskisen.fi
KOSKI—(HEL)
Rev.: $342,813,512
Assets: $279,097,777
Liabilities: $132,528,599
Net Worth: $146,569,178
Earnings: $49,614,720
Emp.: 841
Fiscal Year-end: 12/31/22
Wood Finish Contractor Services
N.A.I.C.S.: 238350

KOSMAJ A.D.
Kralja Petra I 182, Mladenovac, Serbia
Tel.: (381) 11 8230 195
Year Founded: 1997
KSMM—(BEL)
Sales Range: Less than $1 Million
Emp.: 13
Bar Management Services
N.A.I.C.S.: 722410
Milojevic Dragana *(Exec Dir)*

KOSMAJ MERMER A.D.
Savica mlin 2a, 11400, Mladenovac, Serbia
Tel.: (381) 118230219
Year Founded: 1952
KSMRM—(BEL)
Assets: $341,287
Liabilities: $169,289
Net Worth: $171,998
Earnings: ($8,302)
Fiscal Year-end: 12/31/23
Rock Shaping Services
N.A.I.C.S.: 212311
Nebosa Janjic *(Exec Dir)*

KOSOVOPROJEKT INZENJERING A.D.
Zvecanska 1, Belgrade, Serbia
Tel.: (381) 113691108
Year Founded: 2000
KSVB—(BEL)
Sales Range: Less than $1 Million
Engineering Consulting Services
N.A.I.C.S.: 541330
Ivan Gledovic *(Exec Dir)*

KOSSAN RUBBER INDUSTRIES BHD
Wisma Kossan Lot 782 Jalan Sungai Putus Off Batu 3 3/4 Jalan Kapar, 42100, Kelang, Selangor Darul Ehsan, Malaysia
Tel.: (60) 332912657
Web Site: https://www.kossan.com.my
Year Founded: 1979
KOSSAN—(KLS)
Rev.: $496,034,709
Assets: $915,798,519
Liabilities: $90,839,365
Net Worth: $824,959,153
Earnings: $33,695,661
Emp.: 3,378
Fiscal Year-end: 12/31/22
Rubber Mfr
N.A.I.C.S.: 325212
Yew Ngo Chia *(Co-Sec)*

Subsidiaries:

Cleanera (Malaysia) Sdn. Bhd. (1)
56-4 Setia Avenue Jalan Setia Prima S U13/S, Setia Alam Seksyen U13, 40170, Shah Alam, Selangor, Malaysia
Tel.: (60) 333410360
Rubber Mfr
N.A.I.C.S.: 326299

Dongguan Cleanera Cleanroom Products Company Limited (1)
Tel.: (86) 76938813777
Web Site: https://www.cleanera.net
Clean Room Product Mfr
N.A.I.C.S.: 339113

Doshin Rubber Products (M) Sdn. Bhd. (1)
Lot PT 34252 Jalan Sekolah Rantau Panjang, 42100, Klang, Selangor, Malaysia
Tel.: (60) 332905619
Web Site: https://www.doshinrubber.com
Rubber Mfr
N.A.I.C.S.: 326299

Hibon Corporation Sdn. Bhd. (1)
Block E F G Lot 6539 Jalan Sungai Keramat 3 Taman Klang Utama B, 42100, Klang, Selangor Darul Ehsan, Malaysia
Tel.: (60) 332902878
Web Site: https://www.hibon.com.my
Rubber Mfr
N.A.I.C.S.: 326299

KOSTA ABRAS AD
ul Klenoec no 84, 6000, Ohrid, North Macedonia
Tel.: (389) 46253621
Web Site: https://kostaabras.mk
Year Founded: 1948
ABRS—(MAC)
Sales Range: Less than $1 Million
Printing Services
N.A.I.C.S.: 323111

KOSTEK SYSTEMS, INC.
231 bangkkojigil Seotan-Myeon, Seotan-Myeon, Pyeongtaek, 17704, Gyeonggi-do, Korea (South)
Tel.: (82) 316461500
Web Site: https://kosteke.imweb.me
Year Founded: 2000
169670—(KRS)
Semiconductor Device Mfr & Distr
N.A.I.C.S.: 334413
Jason Bae *(CEO)*

KOSTENETS-HHI JSC
2 Saedinenie Str, 2030, Kostenets, Bulgaria
Tel.: (359) 71422125
Web Site: https://www.hhi-bg.eu
Year Founded: 1902
HHI—(BUL)
Sales Range: Less than $1 Million
Paper Products Mfr
N.A.I.C.S.: 322299

KOSTER BAUCHEMIE AG
Dieselstrasse 3-10, D 26607, Aurich, Germany
Tel.: (49) 40 3095 30900
Web Site: http://www.koester-bauchemie.com
Year Founded: 1982
Waterproofing Materials Mfr
N.A.I.C.S.: 325998
Hubert Looks *(Member-Mgmt Bd)*

Subsidiaries:

Beijing Koster International Chemical Industry Co. Ltd. (1)
Cai Man Jie 1-1-703 No 69 Chaoyang Rd, Chaoyang District, 100025, Beijing, China
Tel.: (86) 10 52059398
Chemical Products Distr
N.A.I.C.S.: 424690

Chowgule Koster (India) Construction Chemicals Pvt. Ltd. (1)
Bakhtawar 4th Floor Namiman Point, Mumbai, 400021, Maharashtra, India
Tel.: (91) 22 66202500
Web Site: http://www.chowgulekoster.com
Waterproofing Products Mfr & Distr
N.A.I.C.S.: 325998

KOSTER AMERICAN CORP. (1)
2585 Aviator Dr, Virginia Beach, VA 23453
Tel.: (757) 425-1206
Web Site: http://www.kosterusa.com
Chemical Products Mfr
N.A.I.C.S.: 325998
Mike Mudrick *(Mgr-Natl Sls)*

KOSTER Afdichtingssystemen BV (1)
Overveld 15, 3848 BT, Harderwijk, Netherlands
Tel.: (31) 341 467090
Web Site: http://www.koster-afdichtingssystemen.nl
Chemical Products Distr
N.A.I.C.S.: 424690

KOSTER Bulgaria Ltd. (1)
Kostinbrod-2230 Industrial zone Umni Breg No 1, PO Box 59, 1330, Sofia, Bulgaria
Tel.: (359) 72 161 004
Web Site: http://www.koster-bg.com
Chemical Products Distr
N.A.I.C.S.: 424690

KOSTER HRVATSKA d.o.o. (1)
Stupnicke Sipkovine 3/1, Donji Stupnik, 10255, Zagreb, Croatia
Tel.: (385) 16414050
Web Site: http://www.koster.hr
Chemical Products Distr
N.A.I.C.S.: 424690

KOSTER IMP, Unipessoal, Lda. (1)
Rua da Boavista no 291 1, 4050-107, Porto, Portugal
Tel.: (351) 222 076 130
Web Site: http://www.koster.pt
Chemical Products Distr
N.A.I.C.S.: 424690

KOSTER Japan Corp. (1)
2916 Kamiyabe-cho, Totsuka-ku, Yokohama, 2450-053, Japan
Tel.: (81) 45 443 5102
Web Site: http://www.koster-japan.com
Chemical Products Distr
N.A.I.C.S.: 424690

KOSTER Polska Sp. z o.o. (1)
Ul Powstancow 127, 31-617, Krakow, Poland
Tel.: (48) 12 411 49 94
Web Site: http://www.koester.pl
Chemical Products Distr
N.A.I.C.S.: 424690

KOSTER Yapikimyasallari Insaat ve Ticaret A.S (1)
Gebkim Kimya Ihtisas OSB Ataturk Bulvari No 6 Demirciler Osb, 41455, Dilovasi, Kocaeli, Turkiye
Tel.: (90) 262 754 20 20
Web Site: http://www.koster.com.tr
Chemical Products Distr
N.A.I.C.S.: 424690

Koster Aquatecnic Ltd. (1)
Unit 211 Heathhall Industrial Estate, Dumfries, DG1 3PH, United Kingdom
Tel.: (44) 8452268283
Web Site: http://www.kosterwaterproofing.co.uk
Waterproofing Products Supplier
N.A.I.C.S.: 424690
Nigel Day *(Owner)*

Koster Belgie Vlaanderen (1)
Toekomstlaan 24, 2900, Schoten, Belgium
Tel.: (32) 36467711
Web Site: http://www.koster-afdichtingssystemen.be
Chemical Products Distr
N.A.I.C.S.: 424690

Taiwan Koster Products Co., Ltd. (1)
9F-3 No 81 Sec 1 Xintai 5th Rd Far East World Center D Building, Xizhi Dist, Taipei, Taiwan
Tel.: (886) 985 156 856
Chemical Products Distr
N.A.I.C.S.: 424690

KOSTROMSKAYA SBYTOVAYA COMPANIA PJSC
pr Mira 37-39/28, Kostroma, 156013, Russia
Tel.: (7) 4942440123
Web Site: http://www.k-sc.ru
KTSB—(MOEX)
Sales Range: Less than $1 Million
Electric Power Transmission Services
N.A.I.C.S.: 221122
Irina Ivanovna Samarina *(Chm)*

KOSUN BIO CO., LTD.
E and C Dream Tower 146 207 Seonyu-ro Yeongdeungpo-gu, Seoul, Korea (South)
Tel.: (82) 2 2628 0550
Web Site: http://www.hsvital.com
Rev.: $8,584,840
Assets: $58,717,412
Liabilities: $10,111,822
Net Worth: $48,605,589
Earnings: ($63,319,773)
Emp.: 80
Fiscal Year-end: 12/31/18
Food Mfr & Distr
N.A.I.C.S.: 311423

KOT ADDU POWER COMPANY LIMITED
5-B/3 Gulberg-III, Lahore, Pakistan
Tel.: (92) 4235772912
Web Site: https://www.kapco.com.pk
Year Founded: 1984
KAPCO—(PSX)
Rev.: $609,083,830
Assets: $999,937,390
Liabilities: $704,400,355
Net Worth: $295,537,035
Earnings: $94,140,857
Emp.: 563
Fiscal Year-end: 06/30/19
Power Generation Services
N.A.I.C.S.: 221118
Aftab Mahmood Butt *(CEO)*

KOTAGALA PLANTATIONS PLC
53 11 Sir Baron Jayatilaka Mawatha, 1, Colombo, Sri Lanka
Tel.: (94) 112381508
Web Site: https://www.lankemplantations.lk
KOTA—(COL)
Rev.: $28,462,569
Assets: $26,483,635
Liabilities: $15,568,933
Net Worth: $10,914,703
Earnings: $5,782,937
Emp.: 8,495
Fiscal Year-end: 03/31/23
Tea & Rubber Mfr
N.A.I.C.S.: 311920
Mahen S. Madugalle *(CEO)*

KOTAK MAHINDRA BANK LIMITED

Kotak Mahindra Bank Limited—(Continued)

KOTAK MAHINDRA BANK LIMITED
27 BKC C 27 G Block Bandra Kurla Complex, Bandra E, Mumbai, 400051, India
Tel.: (91) 2261661615
Web Site: https://www.kotak.com
Year Founded: 1985
500247—(BOM)
Rev.: $8,170,017,049
Assets: $74,387,594,844
Liabilities: $60,921,447,935
Net Worth: $13,466,146,910
Earnings: $8,081,702,776
Emp.: 73,481
Fiscal Year-end: 03/31/23
Financial Investment Services
N.A.I.C.S.: 523999
Bina Chandarana *(Sec & Sr Exec VP)*

Subsidiaries:

Kotak Investment Advisors Limited (1)
27BKC 7th Floor Plot No C-27 G Block Bandra Kurla Complex, Bandra E, Mumbai, 400 051, Maharashtra, India
Tel.: (91) 2243360754
Investment Advisory Services
N.A.I.C.S.: 523940

Kotak Mahindra (International) Limited (1)
33 Edith Cavell St, Edith Cavell Street, 11324, Port Louis, Mauritius
Tel.: (230) 2129800
Sales Range: $100-124.9 Million
Emp.: 150
Financial Management Services
N.A.I.C.S.: 523940

Kotak Mahindra (UK) Limited (1)
55 Baker Street, London, W1U 7EU, United Kingdom
Tel.: (44) 2079776900
Sales Range: $50-74.9 Million
Emp.: 20
Investment Management Service
N.A.I.C.S.: 523940

Kotak Mahindra Asset Management Company Limited (1)
Kotak Infinity Bldg No 216th Floor Zone IV Infinity Park, Off WesternExpress Highway General A K Vaidya MargMalad E, Mumbai, 400 097, Maharashtra, India
Tel.: (91) 2261152100
Web Site: http://assetmanagement.kotak.com
Sales Range: $100-124.9 Million
Emp.: 120
Investment Banking Services
N.A.I.C.S.: 523150

Kotak Mahindra Capital Company Limited (1)
27BKC 1st Floor Plot No C-27 G Block Bandra Kurla Complex, Bandra E, Mumbai, 400 051, Maharashtra, India
Tel.: (91) 2243360000
Web Site: http://www.kmcc.co.in
Investment Banking & Financial Services
N.A.I.C.S.: 523150
Srinivasan Ramesh *(Co-Mng Dir)*

Kotak Mahindra Prime Limited (1)
4th Floor Bldg No 21 Infinity Park Off Western Express Highway, General AK Vaidya Marg Malad E, Mumbai, 400097, Maharashtra, India
Tel.: (91) 2266056825
Web Site: http://www.kmpl.com
Sales Range: $50-74.9 Million
Emp.: 66
Passenger Vehicles Financing Services
N.A.I.C.S.: 525990
Vyomesh Kapasi *(Mng Dir)*

Kotak Mahindra, Inc. (1)
251 Little Falls Dr, Wilmington, DE 19808
Tel.: (914) 997-6120
Sales Range: $50-74.9 Million
Emp.: 10
Investment Banking Services

Kotak Securities Limited (1)
27 BKC C 27 G Block Bandra Kurla Complex, Bandra E, Mumbai, 400 051, Maharashtra, India
Tel.: (91) 2243360000
Web Site: https://www.kotaksecurities.com
Securities Brokerage Services
N.A.I.C.S.: 523150

Sonata Finance Pvt. Ltd. (1)
II Floor CP-1 PG Tower Kursi Road, Vikas Nagar, Lucknow, 226 022, Uttar Pradesh, India
Tel.: (91) 5326540311
Web Site: http://www.sonataindia.com
Financial Support Services
N.A.I.C.S.: 523999
Anup Kumar Singh *(Mng Dir)*

KOTHARI FERMENTATION & BIOCHEM LIMITED
16 Community Centre 1st Floor Saket, New Delhi, 110017, India
Tel.: (91) 1141664840
Web Site: https://www.kothariyeast.in
Year Founded: 1990
507474—(BOM)
Rev.: $13,066,463
Assets: $15,893,064
Liabilities: $7,663,533
Net Worth: $8,229,530
Earnings: $655,937
Emp.: 206
Fiscal Year-end: 03/31/21
Yeast Mfr & Distr
N.A.I.C.S.: 311999
Pramod Kumar Kothari *(Chm & Mng Dir)*

KOTHARI INDUSTRIAL CORPORATION LIMITED
Kothari Buildings 114 Mahathma Gandhi Salai, Nungambakkam, Chennai, 600 034, India
Tel.: (91) 4428334565
Web Site: http://www.kotharis.in
509732—(BOM)
Sales Range: $10-24.9 Million
Fertilizer Mfr
N.A.I.C.S.: 325314
Pradip D. Kothari *(Chm & Mng Dir)*

KOTHARI PETROCHEMICALS, LTD.
Kothari Buildings No 115 Mahatma Gandhi Salai, Nungambakkam, Chennai, 600 034, India
Tel.: (91) 4435225522
Web Site: https://www.kotharipetro.com
Year Founded: 1990
KOTHARIPET—(NSE)
Rev.: $31,773,692
Assets: $23,296,946
Liabilities: $6,490,206
Net Worth: $16,806,740
Earnings: $3,077,201
Emp.: 148
Fiscal Year-end: 03/31/21
Polybutene & Polyisobutene Mfr.
N.A.I.C.S.: 339999
M. Rajavel *(Exec Dir)*

KOTHARI PRODUCTS LIMITED
Pan Parag House 24/19 The Mall, Kanpur, 208 001, UP, India
Tel.: (91) 5122312171
Web Site: https://www.kothariproducts.in
Year Founded: 1983
530299—(BOM)
Rev.: $195,225,030
Assets: $201,950,385
Liabilities: $44,408,910
Net Worth: $157,541,475
Earnings: $708,435
Emp.: 45

Fiscal Year-end: 03/31/22
Real Estate Investment Services
N.A.I.C.S.: 531390
Deepak Kothari *(Chm & Mng Dir)*

Subsidiaries:

Kothari Products Singapore Pte. Limited (1)
101 Cecil Street 11-07 Tong Eng Building, Singapore, 69533, Singapore
Tel.: (65) 62232216
Web Site: http://www.kothariproducts.com
Emp.: 4
Real Estate Investment Services
N.A.I.C.S.: 531390

KOTHARI SUGARS & CHEMICALS LIMITED
Kothari Buildings No 115 Mahatma Gandhi Salai Nungambakkam, Chennai, 600 034, India
Tel.: (91) 4430225500   In
Web Site: https://www.hckotharigroup.com
Year Founded: 1961
KOTARISUG—(NSE)
Rev.: $74,156,394
Assets: $51,775,517
Liabilities: $20,894,862
Net Worth: $30,880,655
Earnings: $5,026,473
Emp.: 521
Fiscal Year-end: 03/31/23
Food Product Mfr & Distr
N.A.I.C.S.: 311314
Nina Bhadrashyam Kothari *(Chm)*

KOTHARI WORLD FINANCE LIMITED
C/121 Mittal Tower Nariman Point 12th Floor, Mumbai, 400 021, India
Tel.: (91) 22 22851620
Web Site: http://www.kothariworld.com
Year Founded: 1968
511138—(BOM)
Rev.: $588,255
Assets: $3,321,488
Liabilities: $110,432
Net Worth: $3,211,056
Earnings: $363,074
Emp.: 8
Fiscal Year-end: 03/31/19
Financial Investment Services
N.A.I.C.S.: 523999
Liza N. Kothari *(Mng Dir)*

KOTIA ENTERPRISES LIMITED
905 New Delhi House 27 Barakhamba Road, New Delhi, 110 001, India
Tel.: (91) 1140045955   In
Web Site: https://www.kotiaenterprises.com
Year Founded: 1980
539599—(BOM)
Rev.: $61,078
Assets: $1,415,094
Liabilities: $268,357
Net Worth: $1,146,738
Earnings: ($29,072)
Emp.: 5
Fiscal Year-end: 03/31/23
Engineering Goods Distr
N.A.I.C.S.: 423830
Ankit Agarwal *(Mng Dir & CFO)*

KOTOBUKI CORPORATION
1 1 12 Yurakucho, Chiyoda Ku, Tokyo, 100 0006, Japan
Tel.: (81) 354015090
Web Site: http://www.kotobuki-seat.com
Year Founded: 1916
Sales Range: $150-199.9 Million
Emp.: 900

INTERNATIONAL PUBLIC

Mfr of Wooden, Stadium & Auditorium Furniture; Plastics
N.A.I.C.S.: 321920

Subsidiaries:

Audience Systems Limited (1)
W Wiltshire Trading Est Washington Rd, Westbury, BA13 4JP, Wilts, United Kingdom (100%)
Tel.: (44) 1373865050
Web Site: http://www.audiencesystems.com
Sales Range: $25-49.9 Million
Emp.: 100
Mfr of Telescopic, Auditorium & Stadium Seating
N.A.I.C.S.: 337127
Nina Parmenter *(Mgr-Mktg)*

Interkal, LLC (1)
5981 E Cork St, Kalamazoo, MI 49048
Tel.: (269) 349-1521
Web Site: http://www.interkal.com
Sales Range: $50-74.9 Million
Emp.: 140
Telescopic Bleacher Mass Seating Movable Stage & Platform V.O.S. Gym Seating & Sculpture Seat Contour Seat Module Stadium Seating Mfr
N.A.I.C.S.: 337127

Town Art Co., LTD. (1)
1 2 1 B1 Kanda Surugadai, Chiyoda ku, Tokyo, Japan
Tel.: (81) 352805741
Web Site: http://www.townart.co.jp
Sales Range: $25-49.9 Million
Emp.: 15
Public Art Projects Planning, Installation & Maintenance
N.A.I.C.S.: 541330
Shigeyuki Fukazawa *(Pres)*

KOTOBUKI SPIRITS CO., LTD.
2028 Hatagasaki, Yonago, 683-0845, Tottori, Japan
Tel.: (81) 859227456
Web Site: https://www.okashinet.co.jp
Year Founded: 2006
2222—(TKS)
Rev.: $423,271,350
Assets: $307,431,100
Liabilities: $74,607,070
Net Worth: $232,824,030
Earnings: $71,592,910
Emp.: 1,512
Fiscal Year-end: 03/31/24
Confectionery Mfr
N.A.I.C.S.: 311352
Seigou Kawagoe *(Pres & CEO)*

KOTOBUKIYA CO., LTD.
Kotobukiya Bldg 4-5 Midoricho, Tachikawa-shi, Tokyo, 190-8542, Japan
Tel.: (81) 425229810
Web Site: https://www.kotobukiya.co.jp
7809—(TKS)
Sales Range: Less than $1 Million
Emp.: 231
Toy & Game Product Mfr
N.A.I.C.S.: 339930
Kazuyuki Shimizu *(Pres & Member-Exec Bd)*

KOTOBUYIKA CO.
Kotobukiya Bldg 4-5 Midori-cho Tachikawa, Tokyo, 190-8542, Japan
Tel.: (81) 425229810
Web Site: http://www.en.kotobukiya.co.jp
Year Founded: 1953
Sales Range: $25-49.9 Million
Emp.: 200
Model Kits, Action Figures, Vinyl & Resin Statues; Products Related to Modeling; Retail Sales; Consumer Shows Planning & Management
N.A.I.C.S.: 423920
Jeffrey Kashida *(Pres & CEO)*

AND PRIVATE COMPANIES

KOWA CO., LTD.

Subsidiaries:

Koto, Inc. (1)
1411 W 190th St Ste 165, Gardena, CA 90248-4356
Tel.: (949) 863-1860
Toys & Games
N.A.I.C.S.: 336991

KOTON MAGAZACILIK TEKSTIL SANAYI VE TICARET AS
Ayazaga Mah Ayazaga Yolu No 3 A-B Blok Maslak, Sariyer, 34485, Istanbul, Turkiye
Tel.: (90) 2123313300
Web Site: http://www.koton.com
KOTON—(IST)
Rev.: $655,871,524
Assets: $624,230,550
Liabilities: $579,707,917
Net Worth: $44,522,633
Earnings: $(28,737,686)
Fiscal Year-end: 12/31/19
Textile Products Mfr
N.A.I.C.S.: 314999
Yilmaz Yilmaz (Chm)

KOTRA INDUSTRIES BERHAD
No 1 2 & 3 Jalan TTC 12 Cheng Industrial Estate, 75250, Melaka, Malaysia
Tel.: (60) 63362222
Web Site: https://www.kotrapharma.com
Year Founded: 1982
KOTRA—(KLS)
Rev.: $51,259,048
Assets: $69,900,952
Liabilities: $12,529,735
Net Worth: $57,371,217
Earnings: $13,806,138
Emp.: 649
Fiscal Year-end: 06/30/23
Pharmaceuticals Product Mfr
N.A.I.C.S.: 325412
Jimmy Teck onn Piong (Mng Dir)

Subsidiaries:

Kotra Pharma (M) Sdn. Bhd. (1)
1 2 & 3 Jalan TTC 12, Cheng Industrial Estate, 75250, Melaka, Malaysia
Tel.: (60) 63362222
Web Site: https://www.kotrapharma.com
Pharmaceuticals Product Mfr
N.A.I.C.S.: 325412
Jimmy Piong Teck Onn (Mng Dir)

KOTTER GMBH & CO. KG
Wilhelm-Beckmann-Strasse 7, 45307, Essen, Germany
Tel.: (49) 201 2788 388   De
Web Site: http://www.koetter.de
Year Founded: 1934
Sales Range: $450-499.9 Million
Emp.: 18,500
Building Security & Cleaning Services
N.A.I.C.S.: 561612
Martina Kotter (Mng Dir)

Subsidiaries:

German Business Protection GmbH (1)
Friedrichstrasse 95, 10117, Berlin, Germany
Tel.: (49) 30 63967027 0
Web Site: http://www.gbp-security.com
Risk Management Consulting Services
N.A.I.C.S.: 541618

OSD SCHAFER GmbH & Co. KG (1)
Greschbachstrasse 1, 76229, Karlsruhe, Germany
Tel.: (49) 721 98597 70
Web Site: http://www.osd-schaefer.com
Sales Range: $50-74.9 Million
Emp.: 900
Corporate Security Consulting Services
N.A.I.C.S.: 541690
Dirk H. Burhaus (CEO)

KOTYARK INDUSTRIES LIMITED
A-3 2nd Floor Shree Ganesh Nagar Housing Society Ramakaka Temp Chhani, Vadodara, 391740, Gujarat, India
Tel.: (91) 9510976154
Web Site: https://www.kotyark.com
Year Founded: 2016
KOTYARK—(NSE)
Rev.: $13,616,678
Assets: $8,798,226
Liabilities: $1,995,744
Net Worth: $6,802,482
Earnings: $1,373,011
Emp.: 45
Fiscal Year-end: 03/31/23
Biodiesel Fuel Mfr
N.A.I.C.S.: 324199

KOUKANDEKIRUKUN, INC.
7F Tokyo Tatemono Higashi Shibuya Building 1-26-20 Higashi, Shibuya-Ku, Tokyo, 150-0011, Japan
Tel.: (81) 364275381
Web Site: https://www.dekirukun.co.jp
Year Founded: 1998
7695—(TKS)
Rev.: $50,004,650
Assets: $21,059,460
Liabilities: $12,611,880
Net Worth: $8,447,580
Earnings: $1,520,300
Emp.: 187
Fiscal Year-end: 03/31/24
Household Equipment Distr
N.A.I.C.S.: 423620
Masaru Kurihara (Founder, Pres & CEO)

KOURAKUEN HOLDINGS CORPORATION
2-1 Kitakawada Kamiyuki-aiji Tamura-cho, Koriyama, 963-0725, Fukushima, Japan
Tel.: (81) 249433351
Web Site: https://www.kourakuen.co.jp
Year Founded: 1970
7554—(TKS)
Rev.: $177,148,000
Assets: $69,186,870
Liabilities: $57,930,040
Net Worth: $11,256,830
Earnings: $621,340
Fiscal Year-end: 03/31/24
Restaurant Operators
N.A.I.C.S.: 722511
Tsutae Niida (Founder & Chm)

KOUT FOOD GROUP K.S.C.C.
Sour Street Al-Humaizi Bldg 4th Floor, PO Box 26671, Safat, Kuwait, 13127, Kuwait
Tel.: (965) 2228 1430
Web Site: http://www.kfg.com.kw
Sales Range: $350-399.9 Million
Emp.: 4,600
Hospitality Services Including Restaurants, Catering & Franchise Operator & Management Services
N.A.I.C.S.: 722511
Fadwa Yacoub Yousef Al-Humaizi (Chm & Mng Dir)

Subsidiaries:

Al Homaizi FoodStuff Co. (1)
Al Homaizi Bldg Al Soor St, Safat, Kuwait, Kuwait
Tel.: (965) 22402220
Insustrial Machinery & Equipment Whslr
N.A.I.C.S.: 423830

KOVAI MEDICAL CENTER & HOSPITAL LIMITED
99 Avanashi Road, PO Box 3209, Coimbatore, 641014, India
Tel.: (91) 4224323800
Web Site: http://www.kmchhospitals.com
KOVAI—(NSE)
Rev.: $125,282,703
Assets: $183,272,681
Liabilities: $100,102,029
Net Worth: $83,170,651
Earnings: $14,231,572
Emp.: 4,678
Fiscal Year-end: 03/31/22
Medical Treatment Services
N.A.I.C.S.: 622110
Nalla G. Palaniswami (Chm & Co-Mng Dir)

KOVALAM INVESTMENT & TRADING CO.LTD.
G T Road Premises Oswal Woollen Mills Ltd Sherpur, Ludhiana, 141 003, Punjab, India
Tel.: (91) 1615066605
Web Site: https://www.owmnahar.com
505585—(BOM)
Rev.: $432,837
Assets: $10,718,428
Liabilities: $178,257
Net Worth: $10,540,171
Earnings: $365,876
Emp.: 3
Fiscal Year-end: 03/31/24
Financial Investment Services
N.A.I.C.S.: 523999
Jyoti Sud (CFO, Compliance Officer & Sec)

KOVDORSKIY GOK JSC
5 Sukhachova St, Kovdor, Murmansk, 184141, Russia
Tel.: (7) 815 35 7 60 01
Web Site: http://www.eurochemgroup.com
Mineral Exploration Services
N.A.I.C.S.: 213115
Nikolay Ganza (Exec Dir)

Subsidiaries:

Berezniki Mechanical Works, JSC (1)
Maxim Gorkiy Street 17 Perm Region, Berezniki, Russia
Tel.: (7) 3424211800
Web Site: http://www.aobmz.ru
Mineral Processing & Chemical Industry Equipment Mfr
N.A.I.C.S.: 333248

Emerger Fertilizantes S.A. (1)
Dardo Rocha 3412 1640 Martinez, Buenos Aires, Argentina
Tel.: (54) 1148361000
Web Site: http://www.emerger.eurochemgroup.com
Fertilizer Mfr
N.A.I.C.S.: 325311

EuroChem Agro Asia Pte. Ltd. (1)
One George Street 23-04, Singapore, 049145, Singapore
Tel.: (65) 68802840
Fertilizer Mfr
N.A.I.C.S.: 325311
Gino Pang (Sls Mgr)

EuroChem Agro Hungary Kft (1)
Kossuth Major, 8130, Enying, Hungary
Tel.: (36) 622575059
Nitrogen & Phosphate Fertilizer Mfr
N.A.I.C.S.: 325311

EuroChem Agro SAS (1)
68 rue de Villiers, Levallois-Perret, France
Tel.: (33) 140874800
Nitrogen & Phosphate Fertilizer Mfr
N.A.I.C.S.: 325311

EuroChem Agro Spa (1)
Via Marconato 8, 20811, Cesano Maderno, MB, Italy
Tel.: (39) 0362607100
Nitrogen & Phosphate Fertilizer Mfr
N.A.I.C.S.: 325311
Massimo Rossini (Mng Dir)

EuroChem Trading RUS, LLC (1)
Dubininskaya Street 53 P 6, 115054, Moscow, Russia
Tel.: (7) 88002010101
Fertilizer Mineral Mining Services
N.A.I.C.S.: 212390
Evgeny Onatskiy (Gen Mgr)

EuroChem-Fertilizers, LLP (1)
17/1 Al-Farabi Avenue, 050059, Almaty, Kazakhstan
Tel.: (7) 7273565657
Fertilizer Mfr
N.A.I.C.S.: 325311

EuroChem-VolgaKaliy, LLC (1)
7 Lenina St, Kotelnikovo, Volgograd, 404350, Russia
Tel.: (7) 8447655010
Fertilizer Mfr
N.A.I.C.S.: 325311

Fertilizantes Tocantins Ltda (1)
Av T-12 Com Rua T-37 Qd 123-26 Andar Ed Connect Park Business, Setor Bueno, Goiania, 74223-080, Brazil
Tel.: (55) 6234146300
Web Site: http://www.fertilizantestocantins.com.br
Fertilizer Mfr
N.A.I.C.S.: 325311
Tales Coelho (Product Mgr)

Tuapse Bulk Terminal, LLC (1)
10-a Gagarina St krai, Tuapse, Krasnodar, 352800, Russia
Tel.: (7) 8616730984
Logistic Services
N.A.I.C.S.: 488510

KOVILPATTI LAKSHMI ROLLER FLOUR MILLS LIMITED
Tel.: (91) 4622486532
Web Site: https://www.klrf.in
507598—(BOM)
Rev.: $40,486,122
Assets: $14,435,789
Liabilities: $7,443,175
Net Worth: $6,992,614
Earnings: $1,234,698
Emp.: 190
Fiscal Year-end: 03/31/23
Flour Milling Services
N.A.I.C.S.: 311211
Suresh Jagannathan (Chm & Mng Dir)

KOWA CO., LTD.
6-29 Nishiki 3-chome, Naka-ku, Nagoya, 4608625, Japan
Tel.: (81) 529633311   JP
Web Site: http://www.kowa.co.jp
Year Founded: 1939
Sales Range: $1-4.9 Billion
Emp.: 1,879
Diversified Holding Company
N.A.I.C.S.: 551112
Yoshihiro Miwa (Pres & CEO)

Subsidiaries:

Emori & Co., Ltd. (1)
1-6-23 Keya, Fukui, 918-8509, Japan
Tel.: (81) 776369963
Web Site: http://www.emori.co.jp
Sales Range: $1-4.9 Billion
Emp.: 786
Fine Chemicals & Textile Whlslr
N.A.I.C.S.: 424690
Tetsuo Ichikawa (Pres & CEO)

Subsidiary (Domestic):

Brain Corporation (2)
3-5-22 ORIX Yodoyabashi Building 4F Kitahama, Chuo-ku, Osaka, 541-0041, Japan   (100%)
Tel.: (81) 66203 3018
Web Site: http://www.kk-brain.jp
Emp.: 44

KOWA CO., LTD.

Kowa Co., Ltd.—(Continued)
Software Development & Sales
N.A.I.C.S.: 513210
Keiji Hirokane (Pres)

Subsidiary (Non-US):

Emori & Co., (Hong Kong) Ltd. (2)
20F Asia Trade Centre Room 2021 79 Lei Muk Rd, Kwai Chung, NT, China (Hong Kong) **(100%)**
Tel.: (852) 2423 7041
Web Site: http://www.emori.com.hk
Emp.: 5
Chemicals Mfr
N.A.I.C.S.: 325998
Hideyuki Nakata (Mng Dir)

Emori (Thailand) Co., Ltd. (2)
10th Fl Boonmitr Bldg 138 Silom Rd, Suriyawongse Bangrak, Bangkok, 10500, Thailand **(100%)**
Tel.: (66) 22382606
Web Site: http://www.emori.co.jp
Sales Range: $25-49.9 Million
Emp.: 20
Chemicals Whslr
N.A.I.C.S.: 424690
Yoshiaki Yamazaki (Mng Dir)

Subsidiary (Domestic):

Emori Information System Bldg. (2)
1-6 Soft Park Fukui Maruoka-cho, Sakai, 910-0347, Fukui, Japan
Tel.: (81) 776 67 7600
Web Site: http://www.emori.co.jp
Information Systems
N.A.I.C.S.: 519290
Yoshihide Chikugo (Mng Dir)

Emori Logistics Co., Ltd. (2)
1-25-20 Hanando Higashi, Fukui, 918-8013, Japan
Tel.: (81) 776368400
Logistics Management Services
N.A.I.C.S.: 541614

Emori Paint Co., Ltd. (2)
1-25-20 Hanando Higashi, Fukui, 918-8013, Japan
Tel.: (81) 776366600
Web Site: http://www.emori.co.jp
Painting Material Mfr
N.A.I.C.S.: 325510

Subsidiary (Non-US):

Emori Poland Sp. z o.o. (2)
ul Krochmalna 32a lok 1a, Masovian, 00-864, Warsaw, Poland
Tel.: (48) 224020768
Web Site: http://www.emori.co.jp
Sales Range: $50-74.9 Million
Emp.: 3
Chemicals Mfr & Supplier
N.A.I.C.S.: 424690
Kiyotaka Emori (Pres)

Subsidiary (Domestic):

Hokuriku Chemical Industrial Co., Ltd. (2)
29 22 17 Koshikidani-cho, Fukui, 910-3613, Japan
Tel.: (81) 776984670
Chemicals Mfr
N.A.I.C.S.: 325998

Hokuriku Color Co., Ltd. (2)
1-25-20 Hanando Higashi, Fukui, 918-8013, Japan
Tel.: (81) 776357415
Sales Range: $125-149.9 Million
Emp.: 11
Chemical Colours Mfr
N.A.I.C.S.: 325130

ITS Corporation (2)
2nd Fl Sumitomo Syoji Bldg, 1 2 2 Shinsenrinishimachi, Toyonaka, 560-0083, Osaka, Japan
Tel.: (81) 661552000
Web Site: http://www.emori.co.jp
Chemicals Mfr & Supplier
N.A.I.C.S.: 325130
Yoshimiru Matiyama (Gen Mgr)

Nichie-Kosan Co., Ltd. (2)
1 6 23 Keya, Fukui, 918-8510, Japan

Tel.: (81) 776366617
Chemicals Mfr & Supplier
N.A.I.C.S.: 325130

Subsidiary (Non-US):

P.T. Emori Indonesia (2)
Permata Plz Bldg 10th Fl No 1006, JL M H Thamrin 57, Jakarta, 10350, Indonesia
Tel.: (62) 213903272
Sales Range: $50-74.9 Million
Emp.: 10
Chemical Distr
N.A.I.C.S.: 424690

Kowa (Shanghai) Co., Ltd. (1)
Rm 3001 & 3008 Raffles City Shanghai Office Tower, 268 Xizang Road Central, Shanghai, 200001, China
Tel.: (86) 21 6340 3801
Web Site: http://www.kowashanghai.com
Chemical Products Distr
N.A.I.C.S.: 424690

Kowa (Shanghai) Optical Instruments International Co., Ltd. (1)
C-102 North Jiangsu-Road, Changning-District, Shanghai, 200042, China
Tel.: (86) 21 62296977
Web Site: http://www.kowa-int.com
Medical Equipment Distr
N.A.I.C.S.: 423450
Kazuaki Kashio (Gen Mgr)

Kowa (Shanghai) Pharma Consulting Co., Ltd. (1)
17/F Verdant Place 128 West Nanjing Road, Shanghai, 200003, China
Tel.: (86) 21 6340 3803
Web Site: http://www.kowashanghai.cn
Medical Equipment Distr
N.A.I.C.S.: 423450

Kowa (Thailand) Co., Ltd. (1)
Floor 17 Sathorn City Tower 75 South Sathorn Road, Thungmahamek Sathorn, 10120, Bangkok, Thailand
Tel.: (66) 2 679 5041
Web Site: http://www.kowa.co.th
Medical Equipment Distr
N.A.I.C.S.: 423450
A. Surangkana (Mgr-Sls Div)

Kowa American Corporation (1)
20001 S Vermont Ave, Torrance, CA 90502
Tel.: (310) 327-1913
Web Site: http://www.kowa-usa.com
Medical Equipment Distr
N.A.I.C.S.: 423450

Kowa Asia Limited (1)
Room 903 Admiralty Centre Tower1 18 Harcourt Road, Hong Kong, China (Hong Kong)
Tel.: (852) 2520 2270
Web Site: http://www.kowa-asia.com.hk
Textile Products Distr
N.A.I.C.S.: 424310

Kowa Asia Pacific Pte., Ltd. (1)
16 Collyer Quay 16-00 Income at Raffles, Singapore, 048318, Singapore
Tel.: (65) 62220025
Textile Products Distr
N.A.I.C.S.: 424310
Thomas Yeo (Asst Mgr-Sls)

Kowa Estate Co., Ltd. (1)
1-10-37 Higashisakura Hisaya Bldg 3f, Higashi-ku, Nagoya, 461-0005, Japan
Tel.: (81) 529633386
Real Estate Investment Services
N.A.I.C.S.: 531210

Kowa Europe GmbH (1)
Immermannstr 43B, 40210, Dusseldorf, Germany
Tel.: (49) 211 179354
Chemical Products Distr
N.A.I.C.S.: 424690
Mutsumi Narita (CEO)

Subsidiary (Non-US):

Kowa Optimed Europe Ltd. (2)
Sandhurst House 297 Yorktown Road, Sandhurst, GU47 0QA, Berkshire, United Kingdom
Tel.: (44) 1276 937021
Pharmaceutical Product Mfr & Distr
N.A.I.C.S.: 325412

Robert Ireland (CEO)

Kowa Eyecon Co., Ltd. (1)
5-1-10 Takamoridai, Kasugai, 487-0032, Aichi, Japan
Tel.: (81) 568918691
Optical Lens Mfr
N.A.I.C.S.: 333248

Kowa Health Care America, Inc. (1)
20001 S Vermont Ave, Torrance, CA 90502
Tel.: (888) 655-9649
Web Site: http://www.kowahealthcare.com
Healthcare Product Distr
N.A.I.C.S.: 424210
Tony Hatori (CEO)

Kowa India Pvt. Ltd. (1)
408 Town Centre-1 Andheri Kurla Rd, Marol Andheri East, Mumbai, 400 059, India
Tel.: (91) 22 2852 4680
Web Site: http://www.kowaindia.com
Emp.: 12
Chemical Products Distr
N.A.I.C.S.: 424690
Jayshree Shetty (Deputy Mgr-Intl Mktg)

Kowa Korea Co., Ltd. (1)
7F Kookmin 1 Bldg 1009-5, Daechi-dong Gangnam-gu, Seoul, 135-280, Korea (South)
Tel.: (82) 2 6930 4800
Web Site: http://www.kowakorea.com
Medical Equipment Distr
N.A.I.C.S.: 423450

Kowa Optical Products Co., Ltd. (1)
2-1-4 Benten, Soka, Saitama, 340-0004, Japan
Tel.: (81) 489349581
Optical Equipment Mfr & Distr
N.A.I.C.S.: 333310

Kowa Pharmaceutical Europe Co. Ltd. (1)
105 Wharfedale Road, Winnersh Triangle, Wokingham, RG41 5RB, Berkshire, United Kingdom
Tel.: (44) 1189229000
Web Site: http://www.kowapharmaceuticals.eu
Pharmaceutical Products Distr
N.A.I.C.S.: 424210

Kowa Research Institute, Inc. (1)
430 Davis Dr Ste 200, Morrisville, NC 27560
Tel.: (919) 433-1600
Web Site: http://www.kowaus.com
Emp.: 13
Pharmaceutical Research & Development Services
N.A.I.C.S.: 541715
Ian J. Mehr (Dir-Bus Dev)

Kowa Taiwan Tsusho Co., Ltd. (1)
8F No 122 Songjiang Road, Zhongshan, Taipei, 10486, Taiwan
Tel.: (886) 2 2523 2860
Web Site: http://www.kowataiwan.com.tw
Textile Products Distr
N.A.I.C.S.: 424310

Nagoya Kanko Hotel Co., Ltd. (1)
1-19-30 Nishiki, Naka-ku, Nagoya, 460-8608, Japan
Tel.: (81) 52 231 7711
Web Site: http://www.nagoyakankohotel.co.jp
Hotel Operator
N.A.I.C.S.: 721110
Motohisa Fujimori (Pres)

Watabe Wedding Corporation (1)
Kyotooikedaiichiseimei Bld 7F 435 Sasayacho Karasuma Higashi-iru, Oike-dori Nakagyo-ku, Kyoto, 604-8540, Japan
Tel.: (81) 75 3524111
Web Site: http://www.watabe-wedding.co.jp
Sales Range: $400-449.9 Million
Emp.: 2,544
Matrimonial Services
N.A.I.C.S.: 812990

Subsidiary (US):

Creative Studio Guam, Inc. (2)
1082 Pale San Vitores Rd, Tumon, GU 96913
Tel.: (671) 647-6699
Web Site: http://www.thecreativestudio.net

Wedding Related Services
N.A.I.C.S.: 812990

Subsidiary (Domestic):

K.K. Meguro Gajoen (2)
1-8-1 Shimomeguro Meguro-ku, Tokyo, 153-0064, Japan
Tel.: (81) 354343837
Web Site: http://www.megurogajoen.co.jp
Wedding Related Services
N.A.I.C.S.: 812990

Mielparque Corporation (2)
2-5-20 Shibakouen Minato-ku, Tokyo, 105-8582, Japan
Tel.: (81) 334337211
Web Site: http://www.mielparque.jp
Home Management Services
N.A.I.C.S.: 721110

Subsidiary (Non-US):

PT. Watabe Bali (2)
Jl By Pass L Gusti Ngurah Rai No 89x Kedonganan, Kuta, 80362, Bali, Indonesia
Tel.: (62) 361703710
Web Site: http://www.watabe.com
Emp.: 24
Wedding Related Services
N.A.I.C.S.: 812990

Subsidiary (Domestic):

Tsudoie Corporation (2)
1 Chome-35-1 Furuichimachi, Maebashi, 371-0844, Gunma-ken, Japan
Tel.: (81) 272511144
Web Site: http://www.racine.tsudoie.co.jp
Wedding Related Services
N.A.I.C.S.: 812990

Subsidiary (Non-US):

Watabe Europe S.A.R.L. (2)
4 Rue De Clichy, Paris, 75009, France
Tel.: (33) 148783311
Wedding Related Services
N.A.I.C.S.: 812990

Watabe Singapore. PTE. LTD. (2)
30 Victoria Street 01-28 Chijmes Hall 02-06 Chijmes, Singapore, 187996, Singapore
Tel.: (65) 63365320
Web Site: http://www.watabe-wedding.com.sg
Wedding Related Services
N.A.I.C.S.: 812990

Watabe Wedding (Shanghai) Co., Ltd. (2)
No 230 Xinjinqiao Road Pudong New District, Shanghai, 201206, China
Tel.: (86) 2158992723
Apparels Mfr
N.A.I.C.S.: 315250

KOWAL CONSTRUCTION LTD.

601 McCool Street, PO Box 788, Crossfield, T0M 0S0, AB, Canada
Tel.: (403) 946-4450
Web Site:
https://www.kowalconstruction.ca
Year Founded: 1997
Emp.: 250
Oilfield Lease Construction
N.A.I.C.S.: 237120

KOWLOON DEVELOPMENT COMPANY LIMITED

23rd Floor Pioneer Centre 750 Nathan Road, Kowloon, China (Hong Kong)
Tel.: (852) 23962112   HK
Web Site: https://www.kdc.com.hk
0034—(HKG)
Rev.: $584,192,888
Assets: $6,090,140,010
Liabilities: $3,726,838,388
Net Worth: $2,363,301,623
Earnings: $154,259,190
Emp.: 2,668
Fiscal Year-end: 12/31/22
Property Investment & Development Services
N.A.I.C.S.: 531390

Pui Kwan Or *(Exec Dir)*
Subsidiaries:

Country House Property Management Limited (1)
9th Floor Pioneer Centre 750 Nathan Road, Kowloon, China (Hong Kong)
Tel.: (852) 23998201
Property Investment & Investment Holding Services
N.A.I.C.S.: 531390
Gary Ng *(Sr Mgr-Property)*

Excel Billion Holdings Limited (1)
Room 801 8/F Seaview Centre 139-141 Hoi Bun Road, Kwun Tong, Kowloon, China (Hong Kong)
Tel.: (852) 27116833
Web Site: https://www.excelbillion.com
Property Development Services
N.A.I.C.S.: 531390

Kowloon Development Finance Limited (1)
23rd Floor Pioneer Centre 750 Nathan Road, Kowloon, China (Hong Kong)
Tel.: (852) 23962112
Property Investment & Investment Holding Services
N.A.I.C.S.: 531390

Polytec Property (Shenyang) High Cheer Company Limited (1)
Polytec Gardenia Sale Office Ma Guan Qiao, Shenhe District, Shenyang, China
Tel.: (86) 2488903333
Property Investment & Investment Holding Services
N.A.I.C.S.: 531390

Polytec Property (Wuxi) Limited (1)
20 F Jinling Hotel No-1 East Xianqian Street, Wuxi, China
Tel.: (86) 51082769518
Property Investment & Investment Holding Services
N.A.I.C.S.: 531390

Zhongshan Changjiang Zhaoye Real Estate Development Ltd. (1)
Galaxy Heights Sales Office 8 Xue Yuan Road, Shiqi District, Zhongshan, China
Tel.: (86) 76088365728
Property Investment & Investment Holding Services
N.A.I.C.S.: 531390

KOYJ CO., LTD.
146 Cheomdansanup-ro, Daesowon-Myeon, Chungju, Chungcheonbuk-Do, Korea (South)
Tel.: (82) 438421987
Web Site: https://www.koyj.co.kr
Year Founded: 2006
121850—(KRS)
Rev.: $7,441,945
Assets: $31,076,240
Liabilities: $16,386,755
Net Worth: $14,689,485
Earnings: ($6,886,677)
Emp.: 70
Fiscal Year-end: 12/31/22
Films & Coatings Mfr
N.A.I.C.S.: 326112
Jae-hyung Cho *(CEO)*

KOYO ELECTRONICS INDUSTRIES CO., LTD.
4-9-1 Tenjin-cho Kodaira-shi, Tokyo, 187-0004, Japan
Tel.: (81) 423413111
Web Site: http://www.koyoele.co.jp
Year Founded: 1959
Sales Range: $400-449.9 Million
Emp.: 380
Electronic Products Mfr
N.A.I.C.S.: 334419
Tsutomu Yuine *(Pres)*

Subsidiaries:

AutomationDirect, Inc. (1)
3505 Hutchinson Rd, Cumming, GA 30040-5860
Tel.: (770) 889-2858
Web Site: http://www.automationdirect.com
Sales Range: $25-49.9 Million
Emp.: 150
Automation Products Online Sales
N.A.I.C.S.: 423830
Tim Hohmann *(Founder)*

Koyo Sealing Techno Co., Ltd. (1)
No 39 Aza Nishino Kasagi Aizumi-cho, Itano, 771-1295, Tokushima, Japan
Tel.: (81) 886922711
Web Site: http://www.koyo-st.co.jp
Oil Seal Mfr
N.A.I.C.S.: 339991

Koyo Thermo Systems Co., Ltd. (1)
229 Kabata-cho, Tenri, 632-0084, Nara, Japan
Tel.: (81) 743640985
Web Site: http://www.koyo-thermos.co.jp
Emp.: 464
Furnace Mfr & Distr
N.A.I.C.S.: 333414
Nobutaka Takeoka *(Pres & CEO)*

Win System Co., Ltd. (1)
1-28-1 Komaba, Meguro-ku, Tokyo, Japan
Tel.: (81) 354781111
Application Software Development Services
N.A.I.C.S.: 541511

KOYO INTERNATIONAL LIMITED
33 Ubi Avenue 3 0216 Vertex, Singapore, 408863, Singapore
Tel.: (65) 67449388
Web Site: https://www.koyotech.com
5OC—(CAT)
Rev.: $30,448,314
Assets: $27,758,429
Liabilities: $14,452,760
Net Worth: $13,305,669
Earnings: ($2,814,376)
Emp.: 457
Fiscal Year-end: 12/31/22
Mechanical & Electrical Engineering Services
N.A.I.C.S.: 541330
Chek Heng Foo *(CEO & Mng Dir)*

Subsidiaries:

Koyo Engineering (S.E. Asia) Pte. Ltd (1)
55 Ubi Ave 3 # 04-01, Singapore, 408864, Singapore
Tel.: (65) 67449388
Engineeering Services
N.A.I.C.S.: 541330

Koyo M&E Pte. Ltd (1)
5 Kaki Bukit Crescent 05 01 Koyotech Building, Singapore, 416238, Singapore
Tel.: (65) 68427977
Mechanical Engineering Services
N.A.I.C.S.: 541330

KOYOSHA INC.
Hirayama Building 2-16-16 Yushima, Bunkyo-ku, Tokyo, 113-0034, Japan
Tel.: (81) 56159061   JP
Web Site: https://www.koyosha-inc.co.jp
Year Founded: 1949
7946—(TKS)
Rev.: $29,705,340
Assets: $23,135,000
Liabilities: $10,199,230
Net Worth: $12,935,770
Earnings: $965,060
Emp.: 210
Fiscal Year-end: 03/31/24
Commercial Printing Services
N.A.I.C.S.: 323111
Misakita Inuyo *(Pres & CEO)*

KOYOU RENTIA CO., LTD.
Ryoshin Onarimon Bldg 6F 6-17-15 Shinbashi, Minato-ku, Tokyo, 105-0004, Japan
Tel.: (81) 367583501
Web Site: https://www.koyou.co.jp
Year Founded: 1970
7081—(TKS)
Rev.: $219,506,400
Assets: $136,574,670
Liabilities: $67,262,830
Net Worth: $69,311,840
Earnings: $11,372,360
Emp.: 860
Fiscal Year-end: 12/31/23
Office Furnishing Mfr & Distr
N.A.I.C.S.: 337127
Koji Umeki *(Pres)*

Subsidiaries:

Koyou Innotex Co., Ltd. (1)
6F Ryoshin Onarimon Building 6-17-15 Shinbashi, Minato-ku, Tokyo, 105-0004, Japan
Tel.: (81) 359313863
Web Site: https://www.koyou-innotex.co.jp
IT Services
N.A.I.C.S.: 541512

Koyou Logi-X Co., Ltd. (1)
2668-5 Hiratsuka, Shiroi, 270-1402, Chiba, Japan
Web Site: http://www.koyou-logi-x.co.jp
Logistic Services
N.A.I.C.S.: 541614

Koyou Service Co., Ltd. (1)
Hirotomo Building 1-4-17 Akasaka, Minato-ku, Tokyo, 107-8433, Japan
Tel.: (81) 335861211
Web Site: http://www.koyou-service.co.jp
Trading Services
N.A.I.C.S.: 425120

ONE Designs Co., Ltd. (1)
Ryoshin Onarimon Bldg 7F 6-17-15 Shinbashi, Minato-ku, Tokyo, 105-0004, Japan
Tel.: (81) 367583535
Web Site: http://www.koyou-onesd.co.jp
Architecture & Interior Design Services
N.A.I.C.S.: 541410

KOZA ALTIN ISLETMELERI AS
Ugur Mumcu Neighborhood Fatih Sultan Mehmet Blvd No 310 Batikent, Ankara, Istanbul, Turkiye
Tel.: (90) 3125871000
Web Site: https://www.kozaaltin.com.tr
KOZAL—(IST)
Rev.: $274,559,292
Assets: $781,452,154
Liabilities: $83,616,734
Net Worth: $698,305,420
Earnings: $13,752,709
Emp.: 2,491
Fiscal Year-end: 12/31/23
Gold & Silver Mining Services
N.A.I.C.S.: 212220
Ismail Guler *(Chm & Chm-Mgmt Bd)*

KOZA ANADOLU METAL MADENCILIK ISLETMELERI AS
Istanbul Yolu 10 km No 310 Batikent, Ankara, Turkiye
Tel.: (90) 3125871000
Web Site: https://www.kozaanadolumetal.com
KOZAA—(IST)
Rev.: $291,139,182
Assets: $917,249,230
Liabilities: $93,477,409
Net Worth: $823,771,821
Earnings: $19,492,718
Fiscal Year-end: 12/31/23
Metal & Mining Services
N.A.I.C.S.: 213114
Ismail Guler *(Chm & Vice Chm)*

KOZARA A.D.
Omladinska 2, Banatsko Veliko Selo, Serbia
Tel.: (381) 230 451 401
Web Site: http://www.kozarabvs.rs
Year Founded: 1990
Sales Range: $10-24.9 Million
Emp.: 6
Cereal Crop Farming Services
N.A.I.C.S.: 111998

KOZARAPREVOZ A.D.
Kralja Petra I Oslobodioca, 79220, Novi Grad, Bosnia & Herzegovina
Tel.: (387) 52752196
KZPR-R-A—(BANJ)
Rev.: $155,574
Assets: $4,958,706
Liabilities: $1,536,906
Net Worth: $3,421,800
Earnings: $2,459
Emp.: 14
Fiscal Year-end: 12/31/12
Freight Transportation Services
N.A.I.C.S.: 484220
Milos Jancic *(Chm)*

KOZO KEIKAKU ENGINEERING INC
4-38-13 Hon-cho Nakano-ku, Tokyo, 164-0012, Japan
Tel.: (81) 353421100
Web Site: http://www.kke.co.jp
4748—(TKS)
Rev.: $142,760,640
Assets: $166,699,280
Liabilities: $88,968,880
Net Worth: $77,730,400
Earnings: $13,155,120
Emp.: 660
Fiscal Year-end: 06/30/22
Software Programming Services
N.A.I.C.S.: 541511
Tamon Watanabe *(Pres & Exec Officer)*

Subsidiaries:

KKE Singapore Pte. Ltd. (1)
600 North Bridge Road 12-04 Parkview Square, Singapore, 188778, Singapore
Tel.: (65) 68831500
Web Site: https://www.kke.com.sg
Engineering Firm Services
N.A.I.C.S.: 541330

KOZOSUSHI CO., LTD.
3-9-9 Tsukiji, Chuo-ku, Tokyo, 104-0045, Japan
Tel.: (81) 362264400
Web Site: http://www.kozosushi.co.jp
Year Founded: 1972
9973—(TKS)
Rev.: $92,552,860
Assets: $39,923,790
Liabilities: $37,853,510
Net Worth: $2,070,280
Earnings: ($2,396,420)
Emp.: 93
Fiscal Year-end: 12/31/23
Restaurant Operators
N.A.I.C.S.: 722511
Tomihiko Ozaki *(Auditor)*

KP ENERGY LIMITED
KP House Opp Ishwar Farm Junction BRTS Near Bliss IVF Circle, Canal Road Bhatar, Surat, 395017, Gujarat, India
Tel.: (91) 2612234757
Web Site: https://www.kpenergy.in
539686—(BOM)
Rev.: $60,385,785
Assets: $47,177,717
Liabilities: $29,787,207
Net Worth: $17,390,510
Earnings: $5,993,469
Emp.: 1,000
Fiscal Year-end: 03/31/23
Wind Electric Power Generation Services
N.A.I.C.S.: 221115
Faruk Gulambhai Patel *(Mng Dir)*

KP KOMUNALAC A.D.

KP KOMUNALAC A.D.

KP KOMUNALAC a.d.—(Continued)
Ul 11 novembar broj 2, 78420, Srbac,
Bosnia & Herzegovina
Tel.: (387) 51740866
KOMS-R-A—(BANJ)
Sales Range: Less than $1 Million
Waste Management Services
N.A.I.C.S.: 562998

KP TISSUE INC.
2 Prologis Blvd Suite 500, Mississauga, L5W 0G8, ON, Canada
Tel.: (905) 812-6900   Ca
Web Site:
https://www.kptissueinc.com
Year Founded: 2012
KPT—(TSX)
Assets: $55,786,734
Liabilities: $3,899,666
Net Worth: $51,887,068
Earnings: ($1,527,793)
Emp.: 2,700
Fiscal Year-end: 12/31/20
Investment Holding Company; Tissue Products Mfr
N.A.I.C.S.: 551112
Dino J. Bianco (CEO)

KP TOPLANA A.D.
Vojvode Misic 64, 78400, Gradiska,
Bosnia & Herzegovina
Tel.: (387) 603604003
KPTG-R-A—(BANJ)
Sales Range: Less than $1 Million
Gas Mfr
N.A.I.C.S.: 325120
Uros Grahovac (Pres)

KPA-BM HOLDINGS LIMITED
27/F The Octagon 6 Sha Tsui Road,
Tsuen Wan, New Territories, China
(Hong Kong)
Tel.: (852) 24012747   Ky
Web Site: https://www.kpa-bm.com.hk
2663—(HKG)
Rev.: $63,738,047
Assets: $51,866,211
Liabilities: $19,961,074
Net Worth: $31,905,138
Earnings: $1,483,915
Emp.: 163
Fiscal Year-end: 03/31/22
Engineeering Services
N.A.I.C.S.: 541330
Pak Hung Yip (Chm)

KPC PHARMACEUTICALS INC.
No 166 Keyi Road High-tech Development Zone, Kunming, 650106,
Yunnan, China
Tel.: (86) 87168319868
Web Site: https://www.kpc.com.cn
Year Founded: 1951
600422—(SHG)
Rev.: $1,162,801,715
Assets: $1,324,246,931
Liabilities: $602,236,842
Net Worth: $722,010,089
Earnings: $53,798,977
Fiscal Year-end: 12/31/22
Pharmaceutical Product Mfr & Distr
N.A.I.C.S.: 325412
Xiang Gang Zhong (Pres)

Subsidiaries:

Kunming Baker Norton Pharmaceutical Co. Ltd. (1)
Tel.: (86) 68181600
Web Site: http://www.kbn.net.cn
Pharmaceuticals Product Mfr
N.A.I.C.S.: 325412

KPF

136 Unjung-ro, Bundang-gu, Seongnam, Gyeonggi, Korea (South)
Tel.: (82) 3180389700
Web Site: https://www.kpf.co.kr
Year Founded: 1963
024880—(KRS)
Rev.: $628,192,666
Assets: $510,657,372
Liabilities: $348,798,381
Net Worth: $161,858,991
Earnings: $16,151,895
Emp.: 486
Fiscal Year-end: 12/31/22
Nuts & Bolts Mfr
N.A.I.C.S.: 326199
Hyung Noh Kim (Co-CEO)

Subsidiaries:

KPF - Chungju Factory (1)
50 Chungjusandan 5-RO, Chungju,
Chungcheongbuk-do, Korea (South)
Tel.: (82) 438491114
Web Site: http://www.kpf.co.kr
Emp.: 400
Bolts & Nuts Mfr
N.A.I.C.S.: 332722

KPF USA (1)
1701 Eastlake Ave, Glenview, IL 60025
Tel.: (661) 607-5742
Web Site: http://www.kpf.co.kr
Emp.: 2
Bolt & Nuts Mfr
N.A.I.C.S.: 332722
Simon Lee (Gen Mgr)

KPI GREEN ENERGY LIMITED
KP House Near KP Circle Opp Ishwar Farm Junction BRTS, Canal
Road Bhatar, Surat, 395017, Gujarat,
India
Tel.: (91) 2612244757
Web Site:
https://www.kpigreenenergy.com
Year Founded: 2008
542323—(BOM)
Rev.: $78,420,606
Assets: $152,102,958
Liabilities: $120,843,551
Net Worth: $31,259,407
Earnings: $13,286,901
Emp.: 238
Fiscal Year-end: 03/31/23
Eletric Power Generation Services
N.A.I.C.S.: 221118

KPIT TECHNOLOGIES LTD
Plot Number 17 Rajiv Gandhi Infotech Park, MIDC-SEZ Phase-III,
Pune, 411 057, India
Tel.: (91) 2067706000
Web Site: https://www.kpit.com
KPITTECH—(NSE)
Rev.: $412,713,876
Assets: $412,149,690
Liabilities: $210,558,457
Net Worth: $201,591,233
Earnings: $46,887,796
Emp.: 9,928
Fiscal Year-end: 03/31/23
Information Technology & Processing Services
N.A.I.C.S.: 541512
Kishor Patil (Co-Founder, CEO & Mng Dir)

Subsidiaries:

Integrated Industrial Information, Inc. (1)
920 Main Campus Dr Ste 400, Raleigh, NC 27606
Tel.: (919) 755-5301
Web Site: http://www.i-cubed.com
Emp.: 25
Software Publisher
N.A.I.C.S.: 513210
Tony Pease (VP-Emerging Markets)

Subsidiary (Domestic):

Akoya, Inc. (2)

3108 State Rte 59 Ste 124-117, Naperville, IL 60564
Tel.: (224) 612-5110
Sales Range: $10-24.9 Million
Emp.: 2
Engineering Component Design & Mfr
N.A.I.C.S.: 335999
Karen Caswelch (CEO)

KPIT (Shanghai) Software Technology Co., Limited (1)
1603-1604 Tower B Central towers 567
Langao Road, Shanghai, 200333, China
Tel.: (86) 2156315785
Software Development Services
N.A.I.C.S.: 541511

KPIT Cummins Global Business Solutions Ltd. (1)
Plot No 35 36 Rajiv Gandhi Infotech Park
Phase 1 MIDC Hinjawadi, Pune, 411057,
Maharashtra, India
Tel.: (91) 2066525000
Sales Range: $700-749.9 Million
Emp.: 4,000
Business Management Consulting Services
N.A.I.C.S.: 541618
Pawan Sharma (Pres)

KPIT Infosystems Central Europe Sp.z o.o. (1)
Wroclaw Technology Park Ul Klecinska 123,
54-413, Wroclaw, Poland
Tel.: (48) 717858900
Sales Range: $25-49.9 Million
Emp.: 5
Business Management Consulting Services
N.A.I.C.S.: 541618

KPIT Infosystems Incorporated (1)
379 Thornall St, Edison, NJ 08837
Tel.: (732) 321-0921
Web Site: http://www.kpit.com
Emp.: 25
Custom Computer Programming Services
N.A.I.C.S.: 541511
Sachin Tikekar (COO)

Division (Domestic):

KPIT Inforsystems Incorporated (2)
1515 S Federal Hwy Ste 200, Boca Raton, FL 33432
Tel.: (561) 988-8611
Web Site: http://www.kpit.com
Sales Range: $25-49.9 Million
Emp.: 50
Business Applications Consulting
N.A.I.C.S.: 541512

KPIT Technologies (UK) Limited (1)
Coventry University Technology Park Puma
Way, Coventry, CV1 2TT, United Kingdom
Tel.: (44) 2476158631
Software Development Services
N.A.I.C.S.: 541511

KPIT Technologies GK (1)
Senikaikan 5F 3-1-11 Honcho Nihonbashi,
Chuo-ku, Tokyo, 103 0023, Japan
Tel.: (81) 369138501
Software Development Services
N.A.I.C.S.: 541511

KPIT Technologies GmbH (1)
Frankfurter Ring 105b, 80807, Munich, Germany
Tel.: (49) 893229966
Software Development Services
N.A.I.C.S.: 541511
Ravi Pandit (Co-Founder & Chm)

KPIT Technologies Inc. (1)
21333 Haggerty Rd Ste 100, Novi, MI 48375
Tel.: (248) 381-1070
Software Development Services
N.A.I.C.S.: 541511

KPIT Technologies Netherlands B.V. (1)
Westerdoksdijk 423, 1013 BX, Amsterdam,
Netherlands
Tel.: (31) 204190779
Software Development Services
N.A.I.C.S.: 541511

MicroFuzzy Industrie-Elektronic GmbH (1)
Tel.: (49) 891890874

INTERNATIONAL PUBLIC

Automobile Parts Mfr
N.A.I.C.S.: 336390
Vijay Prasad Gopal (Dir-Bus Dev)

ThaiGerTec Co., Ltd. (1)
Rungrojthanakul Building 14th Floor 44/1
Ratchadapisek Road, Huay Kwang District,
Bangkok, 10310, Thailand
Tel.: (66) 21539392
Software Development Services
N.A.I.C.S.: 541511

KPJ HEALTHCARE BERHAD
Level 12 Menara KPJ 238 Jalan Tun
Razak, 50400, Kuala Lumpur, Malaysia
Tel.: (60) 326816222   MY
Web Site:
https://www.kpjhealth.com.my
Year Founded: 1981
KPJ—(KLS)
Rev.: $618,128,677
Assets: $1,480,225,608
Liabilities: $981,978,413
Net Worth: $498,247,196
Earnings: $38,656,720
Emp.: 16,127
Fiscal Year-end: 12/31/22
Health Care Srvices
N.A.I.C.S.: 621491
Hana Abdul Rahim (Co-Sec)

Subsidiaries:

Ampang Puteri Specialist Hospital Sdn Bhd (1)
1 Jalan Mamanda 9 Taman Dato Ahmad
Razali, 68000, Ampang, Selangor, Malaysia
Tel.: (60) 342895000
General Hospital Services
N.A.I.C.S.: 622110

Bandar Baru Klang Specialist Hospital Sdn Bhd (1)
No 102 Persiaran Rajawali/KU 1 Bandar
Baru, 41150, Klang, Selangor, Malaysia
Tel.: (60) 333777888
General Hospital Services
N.A.I.C.S.: 622110
Hue Teck Lee (Dir-Medical)

Ipoh Specialist Hospital Sdn Bhd (1)
26 Jalan Raja Dihilir, 30350, Ipoh, Perak,
Malaysia
Tel.: (60) 524087777
General Hospital Services
N.A.I.C.S.: 622110

Subsidiary (Domestic):

Sri Manjung Specialist Centre Sdn Bhd (2)
Lot 14777 Jalan Lumut, 32000, Sitiawan,
Perak, Malaysia
Tel.: (60) 56918153
General Hospital Services
N.A.I.C.S.: 622110

Jeta Gardens (Qld) Pty. Ltd. (1)
27 Clarendon Avenue, Bethania, Logan,
4205, QLD, Australia
Tel.: (61) 404903947
Web Site: https://www.jetagardens.com
Retirement Living Care Services
N.A.I.C.S.: 623312
Choe Lam Tan (Founder)

Johor Specialist Hospital Sdn Bhd (1)
39B Jalan Abdul Samad, 80100, Johor
Bahru, Johor, Malaysia
Tel.: (60) 72253000
General Hospital Services
N.A.I.C.S.: 622110

Subsidiary (Domestic):

Bandar Dato' Onn Specialist Hospital Sdn Bhd (2)
Jalan Bukit Mutiara Bandar Dato Onn,
81100, Johor Bahru, Johor, Malaysia
Tel.: (60) 73011000
General Hospital Services
N.A.I.C.S.: 622110

KPJ HealthShoppe Sdn Bhd (1)
Tel.: (60) 326029962

AND PRIVATE COMPANIES

Web Site: http://www.kpjshoppe.com
Pharmaceuticals Product Mfr
N.A.I.C.S.: 325412

KPJ Healthcare University College Sdn Bhd (1)
Lot PT 17010 Persiaran Seriemas Kota Seriemas, 71800, Nilai, Negeri Sembilan, Malaysia
Tel.: (60) 1300885758
Web Site: https://www.kpjuc.edu.my
Healthcare University & College Services
N.A.I.C.S.: 611310

Kajang Specialist Hospital Sdn Bhd (1)
Jalan Cheras Kampung Sungai Kantan, 43000, Kajang, Selangor, Malaysia
Tel.: (60) 387692999
General Hospital Services
N.A.I.C.S.: 622110

Maharani Specialist Hospital Sdn Bhd (1)
73-1 Jln Stadium, Kampung Baharu, 84000, Muar, Johor, Malaysia
Tel.: (60) 69564500
General Hospital Services
N.A.I.C.S.: 622110

Pahang Specialist Hospital Sdn Bhd (1)
Jalan Tanjung Lumpur, 26060, Kuantan, Pahang, Malaysia
Tel.: (60) 95112692
General Hospital Services
N.A.I.C.S.: 622110

Pasir Gudang Specialist Hospital Sdn Bhd (1)
Persiaran Dahlia 2 Taman Bukit Dahlia, 81700, Pasir Gudang, Johor, Malaysia
Tel.: (60) 72573999
General Hospital Services
N.A.I.C.S.: 622110

Penang Specialist Hospital Sdn Bhd (1)
570 Jln Perda Utama Bandar Baru Perda, 14000, Bukit Mertajam, Pulau Pinang, Malaysia
Tel.: (60) 45486688
General Hospital Services
N.A.I.C.S.: 622110
Zabidi Hj Abdul Razak *(CEO)*

Perdana Specialist Hospital Sdn Bhd (1)
PT 37 600 Dan Lot 684 Seksyen 14 Jalan Bayam, 15200, Kota Baharu, Kelantan, Malaysia
Tel.: (60) 97458000
General Hospital Services
N.A.I.C.S.: 622110
Munirah Khudri *(Exec Dir)*

Perlis Specialist Hospital Sdn Bhd (1)
No 77 Jalan Dato'Wan Ahmad, 01000, Kangar, Perlis, Malaysia
Tel.: (60) 49707777
General Hospital Services
N.A.I.C.S.: 622110
Naharuddin Mohamad Saifi *(Dir-Medical)*

Pharmaserv Alliances Sdn Bhd (1)
Lot 1 Jalan Nilam 1/7, Subang Hi-Tech Industrial Park, 40000, Shah Alam, Selangor, Malaysia
Tel.: (60) 35 632 2692
Web Site: https://www.kpjpharmaserv.com
Pharmaceuticals Product Mfr
N.A.I.C.S.: 325412

Pride Outlet Sdn Bhd (1)
Level 17 Menara KPJ No 238 Jalan Tun Razak, 50400, Kuala Lumpur, Malaysia
Tel.: (60) 326816222
Web Site: https://www.pridebiomed.com
Bio Medical & Imaging Equipment Mfr
N.A.I.C.S.: 339113
Ismail Yahya *(Gen Mgr)*

Pusat Pakar Kluang Utama Sdn Bhd (1)
1 No 1 Jalan Besar Kampung Yap Tau Sah, 86000, Kluang, Johor, Malaysia
Tel.: (60) 77718999
General Hospital Services
N.A.I.C.S.: 622110

Ahmad Farid Daud *(Dir-Medical)*

Rawang Specialist Hospital Sdn Bhd (1)
Jalan Rawang Bandar Baru, 48000, Rawang, Selangor, Malaysia
Tel.: (60) 360998999
General Hospital Services
N.A.I.C.S.: 622110
Hisham Mansor *(Dir-Medical)*

Selangor Specialist Hospital Sdn Bhd (1)
Jalan Singa 20/1 Seksyen 20, 40300, Shah Alam, Selangor, Malaysia
Tel.: (60) 355431111
General Hospital Services
N.A.I.C.S.: 622110

Sibu Medical Centre Corporation Sdn Bhd (1)
No 52A-G Brooke Drive, 96000, Sibu, Sarawak, Malaysia
Tel.: (60) 84329900
General Hospital Services
N.A.I.C.S.: 622110
Wong Wei *(Dir-Medical)*

Sterile Services Sdn Bhd (1)
Lot 19 Jalan Industri 2/1, Rawang Integrated Industrial Park, 48000, Rawang, Selangor, Malaysia
Tel.: (60) 360922692
Web Site: https://www.kpjsterile.com
Sterilization Services
N.A.I.C.S.: 561910

Total Meal Solution Sdn Bhd (1)
15 Jalan Astana 1E Bandar Bukit Raja, 41050, Klang, Selangor, Malaysia
Tel.: (60) 333580871
Web Site: https://www.tmssb.com.my
Food Meal Product Mfr
N.A.I.C.S.: 311991

KPM HOLDING LIMITED
424 Tagore Industrial Avenue Sindo Park, Singapore, 787807, Singapore
Tel.: (65) 64550881   Ky
Web Site: http://www.kpmholding.com
Year Founded: 1997
8027—(HKG)
Rev.: $10,609,821
Assets: $13,962,606
Liabilities: $5,691,645
Net Worth: $8,270,961
Earnings: ($1,727,224)
Emp.: 88
Fiscal Year-end: 12/31/23
Sign Installation Services
N.A.I.C.S.: 237310
Kelvin Thiam Kiat Tan *(Founder, Chm & Compliance Officer)*

KPM TECH CO., LTD
122 Sandan-ro 163beon-gil, Danwon-gu, Ansan, Gyeonggi-do, Korea (South)
Tel.: (82) 314894100
Web Site: https://www.kpmtech.co.kr
Year Founded: 1971
042040—(KRS)
Rev.: $31,666,121
Assets: $98,696,017
Liabilities: $24,028,200
Net Worth: $74,667,817
Earnings: ($9,244,242)
Emp.: 61
Fiscal Year-end: 12/31/22
Chemical Products Mfr
N.A.I.C.S.: 325998
Ji Hoon Kim *(CEO)*

KPMG AFRICA LIMITED
KPMG Crescent 85 Empire Road, Parktown, 2193, South Africa
Tel.: (27) 116477111   Ky
Web Site: http://www.kpmg.co.za
Year Founded: 1987
Holding Company; Audit, Tax & Advisory Services

N.A.I.C.S.: 551112
Kunle Elebute *(Chm & Sr Partner-Natl)*

Subsidiaries:

KPMG Services (Proprietary) Limited (1)
KPMG Crescent 85 Empire Road, Parktown, 2193, South Africa
Tel.: (27) 11 647 7111
Web Site: http://www.kpmg.com
Emp.: 3,000
Audit, Tax & Advisory Services
N.A.I.C.S.: 541211
Moses Kgosana *(Sr Partner)*

KPMG BAGIMSIZ DENETIM VE SERBEST MUHASEBECI MALI MUSAVIRILIK A.S.
Is Kuleleri Kule 3 Kat 1-9, Levent, Istanbul, 34330, Turkiye
Tel.: (90) 2123166000   TR
Web Site: https://kpmg.com
Auditing, Tax & Consultancy Services
N.A.I.C.S.: 541211

KPMG EUROPE LLP
15 Canada Square, London, E14 5GL, United Kingdom
Tel.: (44) 2073111000   UK
Year Founded: 2007
Emp.: 32,000
Holding Company; Audit, Tax & Advisory Services
N.A.I.C.S.: 551112
Klaus Becker *(Chm-Mgmt Bd & CEO)*

Subsidiaries:

KPMG AG/SA (1)
Viaduktstrasse 42, Postfach 3456, 4002, Basel, Switzerland
Tel.: (41) 58 249 91 91
Web Site: http://www.kpmg.com
Tax & Advisory Services
N.A.I.C.S.: 523940
Brad Maxwell *(Co-Partner-Intl Executive Svcs)*

KPMG Advisory BCVBA (1)
Prins Boudewijnlaan 24d, 2550, Kontich, Belgium
Tel.: (32) 3 821 17 00
Web Site: http://www.kpmg.com
Investment Advisory Services
N.A.I.C.S.: 523940

KPMG Europe LLP Niederlassung Deutschland (1)
Marie-Curie-Strasse 30, 60439, Frankfurt am Main, Germany
Tel.: (49) 6995870
Holding Company; Audit, Tax & Advisory Services
N.A.I.C.S.: 551112

Subsidiary (Domestic):

KPMG AG Wirtschaftsprufungsgesellschaft (2)
Klingelhoferstrasse 18, D-10785, Berlin, Germany
Tel.: (49) 3020680
Web Site: http://www.kpmg.com
Sales Range: $400-449.9 Million
Emp.: 8,700
Audit, Tax & Advisory Services
N.A.I.C.S.: 541211
Klaus Becker *(Chm-Mgmt Bd, CEO & Mng Partner)*

KPMG LLP (1)
15 Canada Square Canary Wharf, London, E14 5GL, United Kingdom
Tel.: (44) 2073111000
Web Site: https://kpmg.com
Audit, Tax & Advisory Services
N.A.I.C.S.: 541211
Bina Mehta *(Chm)*

KPMG N.V. (1)
Amperestraat 19, 1817 DE, Alkmaar, Netherlands
Tel.: (31) 72 514 3800
Web Site: http://www.kpmg.com

KPP GROUP HOLDINGS CO., LTD.

Auditing & Advisory Services
N.A.I.C.S.: 523940

KPMG, S.A. (1)
Paseo de la Castellana 95 Edificio Torre Europa, 28046, Madrid, Spain
Tel.: (34) 91 456 34 00
Web Site: http://www.kpmg.com
Investment Advisory Services
N.A.I.C.S.: 523940

KPMG INTERNATIONAL CO-OPERATIVE
Laan van Langerhuize 1, 1186 DS, Amstelveen, Netherlands
Tel.: (31) 20 656 7890   CH
Web Site: http://www.kpmg.com
Year Founded: 1987
Sales Range: $15-24.9 Billion
Emp.: 155,180
Accounting, Audit, Tax Preparation & Advisory Services Organization
N.A.I.C.S.: 813920
Tony Thompson *(CEO-Europe, Middle East, South Asia & Africa)*

KPMG S.P.A.
Via Vittor Pisani 25, 20124, Milan, MI, Italy
Tel.: (39) 02 67 631   IT
Web Site: http://www.kpmg.com
Emp.: 3,000
Audit, Tax & Advisory Services
N.A.I.C.S.: 541211
Domenico Fumagalli *(Sr Partner)*

KPP GROUP HOLDINGS CO., LTD.
6-24 Akashi-cho, Chuo-ku, Tokyo, 104-0044, Japan
Tel.: (81) 335424111
Web Site: https://www.kpp-gr.com
Year Founded: 1924
9274—(TKS)
Rev.: $4,259,715,350
Assets: $2,277,554,820
Liabilities: $1,736,195,820
Net Worth: $541,359,000
Earnings: $70,151,930
Emp.: 5,624
Fiscal Year-end: 03/31/24
Paper Products Mfr
N.A.I.C.S.: 322299
Madoka Tanabe *(Chm & CEO)*

Subsidiaries:

Antalis SA (1)
8 Rue de Seine, 92100, Boulogne-Billancourt, France   (83.7%)
Tel.: (33) 158042100
Web Site: https://www.antalis.com
Fiscal Year-end: 12/31/2018
Paper Product Distr
N.A.I.C.S.: 424130
Antalis Herve Poncin *(CEO)*

Spicers Limited (1)
155 Logis Boulevard, PO Box 4557, Dandenong South, 3175, VIC, Australia
Tel.: (61) 397688300
Web Site: http://www.paperlinx.com
Rev.: $299,742,502
Assets: $183,765,590
Liabilities: $76,893,875
Net Worth: $106,871,715
Earnings: $2,740,300
Emp.: 390
Fiscal Year-end: 06/30/2018
Holding Company; Fine Paper & Packaging Paper Products Mfr & Distr
N.A.I.C.S.: 551112
David Martin *(CEO)*

Subsidiary (Non-US):

Deutsche Papier (2)
Brixenstrabe St 8, 86167, Augsburg, Germany   (100%)
Tel.: (49) 82174040
Web Site: http://www.deutsche-papier.de

KPP GROUP HOLDINGS CO., LTD.

KPP Group Holdings Co., Ltd.—(Continued)
Sales Range: $125-149.9 Million
Emp.: 150
Paper Merchanting
N.A.I.C.S.: 425120
Carlos Mack (CEO)

Finwood Papers (Pty.) Ltd. (2)
14 Mineral Crescent Crown Mines Ext 3,
Johannesburg, South Africa
Tel.: (27) 112487800
Web Site: http://www.finwood.co.za
Sales Range: $25-49.9 Million
Emp.: 87
Paper & Paperboard Mfr
N.A.I.C.S.: 322120
Russell Sansom (Mgr-Comml)

PPM Frohlen-Reddemann GmbH (2)
Hellersbergstrasse 2a, 41460, Neuss, Germany
Tel.: (49) 213116980
Web Site: http://www.papier-und-karton.de
Sales Range: $50-74.9 Million
Emp.: 9
Newsprint Mill
N.A.I.C.S.: 322120
Jurgen Haase (Mng Dir)

PaperlinX (UK) Limited (2)
Huntsman House Mansion Close, Moulton Park, Northampton, NN3 6LA, United Kingdom
Tel.: (44) 1604495333
Web Site: http://www.paperlinx.co.uk
Holding Company; Paper Products Whslr
N.A.I.C.S.: 551112

Subsidiary (Domestic):

Howard Smith Paper Group Limited (3)
Sovereign House Rhosili Road, Brackmills, NN4 7JE, Northants, United Kingdom
Tel.: (44) 8706082374
Holding Company; Paper & Paperboard Products Mfr & Distr
N.A.I.C.S.: 551112

Subsidiary (Domestic):

Howard Smith Paper Limited (4)
Sovereign House Rhosili Road, Brackmills, NN4 7JE, Northants, United Kingdom
Tel.: (44) 8456084608
Paper Merchanting
N.A.I.C.S.: 459410

Precision Publishing Papers Ltd (4)
2nd Floor Saint Stephens House Dogflud Way, Farnham, GU9 7UD, United Kingdom
Tel.: (44) 1252719461
Sales Range: $25-49.9 Million
Emp.: 10
Paper Product Whslr
N.A.I.C.S.: 424110
David Darwood (Gen Mgr)

Subsidiary (Domestic):

Robert Horne Group Limited (3)
Huntsman House Mansion Close, Moulton Park, Northampton, NN3 6LA, United Kingdom (100%)
Tel.: (44) 1604732150
Sales Range: $500-549.9 Million
Emp.: 775
Paper Merchanting
N.A.I.C.S.: 459410
Paul French (Mng Dir)

Subsidiary (Non-US):

Robert Horne Paper (Ireland) Limited (4)
Unit 10 Fonthill Business Park Fonthill Road, Dublin, 22, Ireland (100%)
Tel.: (353) 14508900
Web Site: http://www.roberthorne.ie
Sales Range: $25-49.9 Million
Emp.: 43
N.A.I.C.S.: 322120
Enda Doophy (Dir-Fin)

Subsidiary (Domestic):

Robert Horne Paper (Scotland) Limited (4)
Huntsman House Deerdykes Court S, Woodhead Industrial Park, Cumbernauld,
G68 9HW, United Kingdom (100%)
Tel.: (44) 1236617777
Sales Range: $25-49.9 Million
Emp.: 40
N.A.I.C.S.: 322120

Robert Horne Paper Co. (4)
Kingston House Brooks Rd, Lewes, BN7 2BY, E Sussex, United Kingdom (100%)
Tel.: (44) 1273476141
Sales Range: $25-49.9 Million
Emp.: 40
Paper Merchanting
N.A.I.C.S.: 459410

Subsidiary (Domestic):

PaperlinX Australia Pty. Ltd. (2)
No 7 Dalmore Drive, Scoresby, 3179, VIC, Australia
Tel.: (61) 385402211
Sales Range: $50-74.9 Million
Emp.: 100
Holding Company; Fine Paper & Packaging Paper Products Marketer & Distr
N.A.I.C.S.: 551112
Andrew Price (CEO & Mng Dir)

Subsidiary (Domestic):

Pebmis Pty Ltd (3)
7 Dalmore Drive, Scoresby, 3179, VIC, Australia
Tel.: (61) 397647300
Paper Products Mfr
N.A.I.C.S.: 322299

Spicers Paper Ltd. (3)
155 Logis Boulevard Dandenong South, Scoresby, 3175, VIC, Australia (100%)
Tel.: (61) 397688400
Web Site: http://www.spicers.com.au
Paper Mfr
N.A.I.C.S.: 322120

Subsidiary (US):

Paper Products Marketing Inc (4)
4380 SW Macadam Ste 370, Portland, OR 97239 (100%)
Tel.: (971) 222-3123
Web Site: https://printright.ppm.com
Sales Range: $25-49.9 Million
Emp.: 34
Marketing of Paper Products
N.A.I.C.S.: 424110
Alice Knight (VP-Fin & Admin)

Subsidiary (Non-US):

PaperlinX BV (2)
Duwijckstraat 17, B 2500, Lier, Belgium
Tel.: (32) 34507500
Web Site: http://www.paperlinx.com
Sales Range: $25-49.9 Million
Emp.: 80
Paper Supplier
N.A.I.C.S.: 459410
Mark Verschaeren (Mgr-Mktg & Comm)

PaperlinX Holdings (Asia) Pte Ltd (5)
3 Gul Crescent, Singapore, 629519, Singapore
Tel.: (65) 67380888
Emp.: 30
Investment Management Service
N.A.I.C.S.: 523999
See Soonseng (Gen Mgr)

Subsidiary (Non-US):

Spicers Paper (Hong Kong) Ltd (3)
Rm 5-6 6/F Remington Ctr 23 Hung To Rd, Kwun Tong, Kowloon, China (Hong Kong)
Tel.: (852) 25603100
Web Site: http://www.spicers.com
Paper Products Mfr & Distr
N.A.I.C.S.: 322299
Elvin Shin (Gen Mgr)

Subsidiary (Domestic):

PaperlinX Investments Pty Ltd (2)
7 Dalmore Drive, Scoresby, 3179, VIC, Australia
Tel.: (61) 397647300
Web Site: http://www.spicers.com.au
Sales Range: $75-99.9 Million
Emp.: 150
Converted Paper Products Distr

N.A.I.C.S.: 424130
Andrew Preece (Gen Mgr)

Subsidiary (Non-US):

PaperlinX Ireland Ltd (2)
No 10 Fonthill Business Park Fonthill Rd, Dublin, Ireland
Tel.: (353) 1450 88 88
Packaging Paper Products Distr
N.A.I.C.S.: 424110
Enda Brophy (Gen Mgr)

PaperlinX Netherlands BV (2)
Apollo Bldg Herikerbergweg 25-27 6th Fl, 1101 CN, Amsterdam, Netherlands
Tel.: (31) 205650700
Web Site: http://www.paperlinx.com
Tape Distr
N.A.I.C.S.: 322211
Tom Park (CEO)

Subsidiary (Domestic):

Buhrmann-Ubbens Papier BV (3)
Jutlandsestraat 2, 7202 CV, Zutphen, Netherlands
Tel.: (31) 575757066
Web Site: https://buhrmannubbens.nl
Sales Range: $100-124.9 Million
Emp.: 500
Paper Merchandise Whslr
N.A.I.C.S.: 459410

PaperlinX Diemen (3)
Stammerkamp 1, Diemen, 1112 VE, Netherlands
Tel.: (31) 20 569 00 00
Web Site: http://www.paperlinx.nl
Sales Range: $50-74.9 Million
Emp.: 250
Graphic & Office Paper, Packaging, Sign & Display Materials & Systems
N.A.I.C.S.: 541430

PaperlinX Netherlands Holdings BV (3)
Herikerbergweg 25-27, Amsterdam, 1101 CN, Noord-Holland, Netherlands
Tel.: (31) 205650700
Sales Range: $25-49.9 Million
Emp.: 40
Paper Product Distr
N.A.I.C.S.: 424110

Subsidiary (Non-US):

Ospap AS (4)
K Hrusovu 292/4, 102 23, Prague, Czech Republic
Tel.: (420) 271081111
Web Site: http://www.ospap.cz
Paper Product Whslr
N.A.I.C.S.: 424110
Ivan Hodacak (Mgr-Facility)

Subsidiary (Domestic):

Multiexpo Spol sro (5)
Videnska 121, 619 00, Brno, Czech Republic
Tel.: (420) 547120130
Web Site: https://www.slevove.cz
Paper Product Distr
N.A.I.C.S.: 424110

Subsidiary (Non-US):

PaperlinX Denmark Holdings ApS (4)
Bastrupgardvej 8-10, 7500, Holstebro, Ringkobing, Denmark
Tel.: (45) 97403366
Sales Range: $50-74.9 Million
Paper Product Distr
N.A.I.C.S.: 424130
Aogan Nielsen (Gen Mgr)

Subsidiary (Domestic):

CC & Co AS (5)
Bastrupgaardvej 8-10, 7500, Holstebro, Denmark
Tel.: (45) 75 722100
Web Site: http://www.cc-co.dk
Packaging Material Distr
N.A.I.C.S.: 423840
Susanne Hedegaard (Mgr-Pur)

Subsidiary (Domestic):

Proost en Brandt BV (3)
Chroomstraat 140, 2718 RH, Zoetermeer, Netherlands
Tel.: (31) 793686262
Web Site: http://www.proost.nl
Sales Range: $25-49.9 Million
Emp.: 25
Paper Mfr
N.A.I.C.S.: 325992

Velpa Enveloppen BV (3)
Pollaan 1, 7202 BV, Zutphen, Netherlands
Tel.: (31) 575743230
Web Site: https://www.velpa.nl
Sales Range: $25-49.9 Million
Emp.: 90
Envelope Mfr & Distr
N.A.I.C.S.: 322230

Subsidiary (Domestic):

PaperlinX Services Pty. Ltd. (2)
7 Dalmore Drive, Scoresby, 3179, VIC, Australia
Tel.: (61) 397647300
Sales Range: $75-99.9 Million
Emp.: 15
Printing & Writing Paper Distr
N.A.I.C.S.: 424110
Andrew Preece (Gen Mgr)

Paperlinx SPS Trust (2)
Level 12 123 Pitt Street, Sydney, 2000, NSW, Australia
Tel.: (61) 292992000
Sales Range: Less than $1 Million
Paper & Communication Material Distr
N.A.I.C.S.: 424110
Ruth Gonzalez (Sec)

Subsidiary (Non-US):

Polyedra AG (2)
Industriestrasse 11, 4665, Oftringen, Switzerland
Tel.: (41) 62 788 50 80
Web Site: http://www.polyedra.ch
Printing & Packaging Paper Products Mfr
N.A.I.C.S.: 322299

Union Papelera Merchanting SL (2)
Calle V 30 Parc III 3a-Centro de Carga Aeropto de Barcelona, El Prat de Llobregat, 08820, Barcelona, Spain
Tel.: (34) 933740310
Web Site: http://www.unionpapelera.es
Paper Product Distr
N.A.I.C.S.: 424130

Zing Sp. z.o.o (2)
Al Jerozolimskie 212, 02-486, Warsaw, Poland
Tel.: (48) 225922929
Web Site: https://www.zing.com.pl
Paper Products Mfr & Distr
N.A.I.C.S.: 322299

KPPD-SZCZECINEK S.A.
ul Warynskiego 2, 78-400, Szczecinek, Poland
Tel.: (48) 943749700
Web Site: https://www.kppd.pl
KPD—(WAR)
Rev.: $90,447,154
Assets: $57,859,756
Liabilities: $18,748,984
Net Worth: $39,110,772
Earnings: ($4,595,274)
Fiscal Year-end: 12/31/23
Timber Product Mfr
N.A.I.C.S.: 321212
Michal Raj (Chm-Supervisory Bd)

KPR MILL LIMITED
Shrivari Srimat 1045 Avinashi Road, Coimbatore, 641 018, India
Tel.: (91) 4222207777
Web Site: https://www.kprmilllimited.com
Year Founded: 2003
KPRMILL—(NSE)
Rev.: $749,139,740
Assets: $671,138,421
Liabilities: $226,717,823
Net Worth: $444,420,598
Earnings: $129,987,411
Emp.: 21,819

AND PRIVATE COMPANIES

Fiscal Year-end: 03/31/23
Cotton Milling
N.A.I.C.S.: 313240
K. P. Ramasamy (Chm)

KPS CONSORTIUM BERHAD
Lot 622 Jalan Lapis Dua Kampung Sementa Batu 6 Jalan Kapar, 42200, Kelang, Selangor Darul Ehsan, Malaysia
Tel.: (60) 332915566 MY
Web Site:
https://www.kpsconsortium.com.my
9121—(KLS)
Rev.: $199,639,860
Assets: $119,290,882
Liabilities: $56,457,411
Net Worth: $62,833,471
Earnings: $3,350,144
Emp.: 258
Fiscal Year-end: 12/31/22
Tissue Paper Mfr
N.A.I.C.S.: 322120
M. Chandrasegaran (Co-Sec)

Subsidiaries:

Hai Ming Industries Sdn. Bhd (1)
Lot 765 Jalan Haji Sirat Off Jalan Meru, 42100, Klang, Selangor, Malaysia
Tel.: (60) 332915566
Plywood Mfr
N.A.I.C.S.: 321212

Hai Ming Paper Mills Sdn. Bhd (1)
Lot 292 & 294 1/2 KM Jalan Muara Tuang, Kota Samarahan, 94300, Kuching, Sarawak, Malaysia
Tel.: (60) 82610688
Plywood Mfr
N.A.I.C.S.: 321212

Hai Ming Trading Co. Sdn. Bhd (1)
Lot No 67 SEDCO Industrial Estate Mile 5 1/2, Tuaran Road off Kolombong Road, 88100, Kota Kinabalu, Sabah, Malaysia
Tel.: (60) 88424650
Plywood Mfr
N.A.I.C.S.: 321212

KPS Plywood Sdn. Bhd. (1)
No 3 Jalan Bk 1/10 Bandar Kinrara Industrial Centre, 47100, Puchong, Selangor, Malaysia
Tel.: (60) 380766670
Timber & Lamination Board Mfr
N.A.I.C.S.: 321215

Subsidiary (Domestic):

Akateak Sdn. Bhd. (2)
No 380-2 Jalan Abdul Rahman, 84000, Muar, Johor, Malaysia
Tel.: (60) 69510384
Plywood Mfr
N.A.I.C.S.: 321212

KPS CORP
52 Dongtan-sandan 10-gil Dongtan-myeon, Hwaseong, 18487, Gyeonggi-do, Korea (South)
Tel.: (82) 3180415400
Web Site: http://www.kpscorp.co.kr
Year Founded: 2000
256940—(KRS)
Rev.: $11,211,449
Assets: $65,623,605
Liabilities: $25,534,431
Net Worth: $40,089,174
Earnings: ($9,234,931)
Emp.: 52
Fiscal Year-end: 12/31/22
Precision Equipment Mfr & Distr
N.A.I.C.S.: 333310

KPT INDUSTRIES LTD.
Shirol, 416 103, Kolhapur, 416 103, Maharashtra, India
Tel.: (91) 2312689900
Web Site: https://www.kpt.co.in
Year Founded: 1976
505299—(BOM)
Rev.: $13,990,595
Assets: $10,453,238
Liabilities: $6,204,062
Net Worth: $4,249,177
Earnings: $293,448
Emp.: 261
Fiscal Year-end: 03/31/21
Electric Power Tools Mfr
N.A.I.C.S.: 333517
Prakash Arvind Kulkarni (Chm & Mng Dir)

KPTCC CO., LTD.
18F Jongno Tower 51 Jong-ro, Jongno-gu, Seoul, Korea (South)
Tel.: (82) 02 565 2858
Web Site: http://kptcc.co.kr
Cancer Treatment Center
N.A.I.C.S.: 621399
Kyu-myeon Jo (Pres & CEO)

KPX CHEMICAL CO., LTD.
17F KPX Building 137 Mapo-daero, Mapo-Gu, Seoul, 4143, Korea (South)
Tel.: (82) 220144000
Web Site:
http://www.kpxchemical.com
Year Founded: 1974
025000—(KRS)
Rev.: $754,405,521
Assets: $595,788,816
Liabilities: $139,280,672
Net Worth: $456,508,143
Earnings: $22,678,751
Emp.: 332
Fiscal Year-end: 12/31/22
Basic Chemicals Mfr
N.A.I.C.S.: 325199

Subsidiaries:

KPX Chemical Co., Ltd. - Ulsan Plant (1)
300-2 Yeocheon-Dong, Nam-ku, Ulsan, Korea (South)
Tel.: (82) 52 279 0200
Chemical Products Mfr
N.A.I.C.S.: 325199

KPX HOLDINGS CO., LTD.
19F KPX Building 137 Mapo-daero, Mapo-gu, Seoul, 04143, Korea (South)
Tel.: (82) 220144150
Web Site:
https://www.kpxholdings.com
Year Founded: 2006
092230—(KRS)
Rev.: $951,423,190
Assets: $1,395,858,547
Liabilities: $344,367,968
Net Worth: $1,051,490,578
Earnings: $28,771,177
Emp.: 25
Fiscal Year-end: 12/31/22
Holding Company
N.A.I.C.S.: 551112
Kyu-mo Yang (Pres)

Subsidiaries:

KPX Development Co., Ltd. (1)
19th floor KPX Building 137 Mapo-daero, Mapo-gu, Seoul, Korea (South)
Tel.: (82) 220144125
Chemical Consulting Services
N.A.I.C.S.: 541690
Junyoung Yang (CEO)

KPX Vina Co., Ltd. (1)
Lot 10 Street no 3 Go Dau Industrial Zone Phuoc Thai Commune, Long Thanh District, Dong Nai, Vietnam
Tel.: (84) 903953762
Chemical Consulting Services
N.A.I.C.S.: 541690
Seunghyun Park (Pres)

KR INVESTMENT LTD.
Suite 500 -1080 Mainland Street, Vancouver, V6B 2T4, BC, Canada
Tel.: (604) 689-2454 BC
Web Site:
http://www.krinvestmentltd.com
Year Founded: 2010
KR.H—(TSXV)
Assets: $946
Liabilities: $159,555
Net Worth: ($158,610)
Earnings: ($125,282)
Fiscal Year-end: 08/31/22
Investment Services
N.A.I.C.S.: 523999
S. John Kim (Pres)

KR MOTORS CO., LTD.
28 Wanam-ro, Seongsan-gu, Changwon, 51573, Gyeongsangnam-do, Korea (South)
Tel.: (82) 552827011 KR
Web Site: https://www.krmotors.com
Year Founded: 1978
000040—(KRS)
Rev.: $89,784,054
Assets: $114,425,083
Liabilities: $83,726,664
Net Worth: $30,698,420
Earnings: ($9,971,981)
Emp.: 52
Fiscal Year-end: 12/31/22
Motorcycle Mfr & Whslr
N.A.I.C.S.: 336991

KRAFT BANK ASA
Trim Towers third floor Larsamyra 18, 4313, Sandnes, Norway
Tel.: (47) 45378100
Web Site: https://www.kraftbank.no
Year Founded: 2018
KRAB—(EUR)
Emp.: 40
Commercial Banking Services
N.A.I.C.S.: 522110
Harald Norvik (Chm)

KRAFTON, INC.
Yeoksam Center Field 231 Teheran-Ro, Gangnam-Gu, Seoul, Korea (South)
Tel.: (82) 15663771
Web Site: https://www.krafton.com
Year Founded: 2007
259960—(KRS)
Software Development Services
N.A.I.C.S.: 541511
Hyunjun Kim (Project Mgr)

KRAFTWAY CORPORATION PLC
16 3d Mytishchinskaya str, 129626, Moscow, Russia
Tel.: (7) 4959692400
Web Site: http://www.kraftway.com
Year Founded: 1993
Emp.: 900
Hardware & Software Designer & IT Equipment Mfr
N.A.I.C.S.: 513210
Alexey Kravtsov (Pres)

KRAJINAPETROL A.D.
Ivana Franje Jukica 2, 78000, Banja Luka, Bosnia & Herzegovina
Tel.: (387) 51212910
Web Site:
https://www.krajinapetrol.com
Year Founded: 1991
KRPT—(BANJ)
Sales Range: $10-24.9 Million
Emp.: 144
Petroleum Product Whslr
N.A.I.C.S.: 424720
Velibor Maksimovic (Pres)

KRAKCHEMIA S.A.
ul Powstania Listopadowego 14, 30-298, Krakow, Poland
Tel.: (48) 126522000
Web Site: https://www.krakchemia.pl
KCH—(WAR)
Rev.: $88,489,900
Assets: $26,145,270
Liabilities: $79,070,538
Net Worth: ($52,925,268)
Earnings: ($75,351,584)
Fiscal Year-end: 12/31/23
Farm Supplies Merchant Wholesalers
N.A.I.C.S.: 424910
Andrzej Zdebski (Chm)

KRAKEN ENERGY CORP.
Suite 907 1030 West Georgia Street, Vancouver, V6E 2Y3, BC, Canada
Tel.: (604) 684-6730
Web Site:
https://krakenenergycorp.com
UUSA—(CNSX)
Rev.: $104,924
Assets: $17,668,299
Liabilities: $88,285
Net Worth: $17,580,014
Earnings: ($3,105,141)
Emp.: 1
Fiscal Year-end: 06/30/24
Mineral Exploration Services
N.A.I.C.S.: 213115
Garrett Ainsworth (Chm)

KRAKEN ROBOTICS INC.
189 Glencoe Drive, Mount Pearl, A1N 4P6, NL, Canada
Tel.: (709) 757-5757 Ca
Web Site:
https://www.krakenrobotics.com
Year Founded: 2008
KRKNF—(OTCIQ)
Rev.: $20,049,232
Assets: $51,212,227
Liabilities: $29,619,502
Net Worth: $21,592,725
Earnings: ($2,766,574)
Emp.: 225
Fiscal Year-end: 12/31/21
Investment Services
N.A.I.C.S.: 523999
Greg Reid (Pres & CEO)

Subsidiaries:

Kraken Power GmbH (1)
Alter Hafen Süd 6, 18069, Rostock, Germany
Tel.: (49) 3816 609 8699
Web Site: http://www.krakenpower.de
Electronic Battery Mfr
N.A.I.C.S.: 335910
Carl Thiede (Founder & Mng Dir)

KRAMSKI GMBH
Heilbronner Strasse 10, 75179, Pforzheim, Germany
Tel.: (49) 72 31 15 410 0
Web Site: http://www.kramski.de
Year Founded: 1978
Sales Range: $75-99.9 Million
Emp.: 600
Stamped Metal Part Mfr
N.A.I.C.S.: 332119
Andreas Kramski (Co-CEO)

Subsidiaries:

KRAMSKI North America, Inc. (1)
7300 Bryan Dairy Rd, Largo, FL 33777
Tel.: (727) 828-1500
Web Site: http://www.kramski.com
Sales Range: $1-9.9 Million
Emp.: 12
Plastics Product Mfr
N.A.I.C.S.: 326199
Ron Letty (VP-Sls)

KRANTI INDUSTRIES LTD.
Gat No 267/B/1 At Post Pirangut, Tal Mulshi, Pune, 412115, Maharashtra, India
Tel.: (91) 2066755676

KRANTI INDUSTRIES LTD.

Kranti Industries Ltd.—(Continued)
Web Site:
https://www.krantiindustries.com
Year Founded: 1981
542459—(BOM)
Rev.: $7,730,773
Assets: $8,113,178
Liabilities: $5,499,012
Net Worth: $2,614,166
Earnings: $8,258
Emp.: 150
Fiscal Year-end: 03/31/21
Industrial Machinery Mfr
N.A.I.C.S.: 332710
Indubala Subhash Vora *(Chm)*
Subsidiaries:
Wonder Precision Private
Limited (1)
J 63 Midc, Bhosari, Pune, 411026, Maharashtra, India
Tel.: (91) 2027120808
Lathe Machine Mfr
N.A.I.C.S.: 333517

KRASNOYARSKENERGOSBYT PJSC
Street Dubrovinsky 43, Krasnoyarsk, 660017, Russia
Tel.: (7) 3912120098
Web Site:
http://www.es.krasnoyarsk.ru
KRSB—(RUS)
Sales Range: Less than $1 Million
Electric Power Distr
N.A.I.C.S.: 423610
Oleg Dyachenko *(Exec Dir)*

KRASTSVETMET JSC
1 Transportny Proezd, 660123, Krasnoyarsk, Russia
Tel.: (7) 3912593333
Web Site:
http://www.krastsvetmet.com
Year Founded: 1943
Sales Range: Less than $1 Million
Metal Product Mfr & Distr
N.A.I.C.S.: 331410
Mikhail Dyagilev *(CEO & Dir Gen)*

KRATOS ENERGY & INFRASTRUCTURE LIMITED
317 Maker Chamber V 221, Nariman Point, Mumbai, 400021, Maharashtra, India
Tel.: (91) 2266341941
Web Site: https://kratosenergy.in
Year Founded: 1979
Rev.: $897,279
Assets: $1,077,298
Liabilities: $355,832
Net Worth: $721,466
Earnings: $130,792
Emp.: 10
Fiscal Year-end: 03/31/19
Energy Consulting Services
N.A.I.C.S.: 541690
Muralidharan P. Pisharam *(CFO)*

KRAUSS-MAFFEI WEGMANN GMBH & CO. KG
Krauss-Maffei-Str 11, Munich, 80997, Germany
Tel.: (49) 898140 50
Web Site: http://www.kmweg.com
Year Founded: 1999
Sales Range: $1-4.9 Billion
Emp.: 3,500
Wheeled & Tracked Military Vehicles Mfr
N.A.I.C.S.: 336992
Frank Haun *(Pres & CEO)*
Subsidiaries:
ATM ComputerSysteme GmbH (1)
Max-Stromeyer-Strasse 116, Konstanz, 78467, Germany
Tel.: (49) 7531 808 3
Web Site: http://www.atm-computer.de
Computer Technology for Reconnaissance, Command & Weapons Control Systems
N.A.I.C.S.: 334118
Friedhelm Lachenmaier *(Mng Dir)*

DSL Defence Service Logistics GmbH (1)
Industriegelande, Freisen, 66629, Sankt Wendel, Germany
Tel.: (49) 6855910
Web Site: http://www.defence-sl.de
Logistic Services
N.A.I.C.S.: 488510

Dutch Defense Vehicle Systems B.V. (1)
Varenschut 18, Helmond, 5705 DK, Netherlands
Tel.: (31) 492 502 727
Web Site: http://www.ddvs.nl
Emp.: 80
Assembly, Maintenance & Repair of Military Vehicles
N.A.I.C.S.: 336992
Peter Buitenhuis *(CEO & Mng Dir)*

Hellenic Defence Vehicle Systems S.A. (1)
Road C-6, 1st Industrial area of Volos, Volos, 38500, Greece **(100%)**
Tel.: (30) 24210 78620
Web Site: http://www.hdvs.gr
Emp.: 50
Production, Assembly & Testing for Vehicle Components
N.A.I.C.S.: 336390
Apostolos Domtzidis *(Gen Mgr)*

KMW ASIA PACIFIC PTE. LTD. (1)
25 international Business Park 03-109 German Centre, Singapore, 609916, Singapore
Tel.: (65) 56628558
Motor Vehicles Mfr
N.A.I.C.S.: 336992

KMW DO BRASIL SISTEMAS MILITARES LTDA. (1)
Rua Dr Bozano 1263 14 andar, Rio Grande, Brazil
Tel.: (55) 5530275673
Motor Vehicles Mfr
N.A.I.C.S.: 336992

KMW Savunma Teknolojileri San ve Tic AS (1)
Suleyman Seba Cad 48 Plaza A-91-92, Besiktas, 34357, Istanbul, Turkiye
Tel.: (90) 2122367583
Motor Vehicles Mfr
N.A.I.C.S.: 336992

KMW Schweisstechnik GmbH (1)
Hermann-Blohm-Strasse 3, Hamburg, 20457, Germany
Tel.: (49) 40 302 397 100
Web Site: http://www.kmweg.de
Welding Technologies
N.A.I.C.S.: 336992
Peter Muller *(Gen Mgr)*

KMW do Brasil Sistemas de Defesa Ltda. (1)
Caixa Postal 158, Santa Maria, 97010-970, Rio Grande, Rio Grande do Sul, Brazil
Tel.: (55) 5532901100
Aircraft Part Mfr
N.A.I.C.S.: 336413
Christian Boge *(CEO)*

WFEL Ltd. (1)
Sir Richard Fairey Road, Heaton Chapel, Stockport, SK4 5BD, Cheshire, United Kingdom
Tel.: (44) 161 975 5700
Web Site: http://www.wfel.co.uk
Sales Range: $50-74.9 Million
Emp.: 250
Mfr of Mobile Bridge Systems
N.A.I.C.S.: 237310
Ian Wilson *(CEO)*

Wegmann USA, Inc. (1)
30 Millrace Dr, Lynchburg, VA 24502
Tel.: (434) 385-1580
Web Site: http://www.wegmannusa.com
Sales Range: $25-49.9 Million
Emp.: 45
Mfr of Products & Components for Military
N.A.I.C.S.: 339999
Dan Ashwell *(VP)*

KRBL LIMITED
C-32 5th and 6th Floor, Sector-62, Noida, 201301, UP, India
Tel.: (91) 1204060300
Web Site: https://www.krblrice.com
530813—(BOM)
Rev.: $547,987,440
Assets: $631,698,795
Liabilities: $127,551,060
Net Worth: $504,147,735
Earnings: $76,291,215
Emp.: 2,296
Fiscal Year-end: 03/31/21
Rice Mill
N.A.I.C.S.: 311212
Anil Kumar Mittal *(Chm & Co-Mng Dir)*
Subsidiaries:
KB Exports Private Limited (1)
605 Dev Corpora Cadbury Junction Eastern Express Highway Service Rd, Thane West, Thane, 400601, Maharashtra, India
Tel.: (91) 2241578900
Web Site: https://www.kaybeeexports.com
Fruit & Vegetable Whslr
N.A.I.C.S.: 424480
Prakash Khakhar *(Founder)*

KRBL DMCC Group (1)
Unit No AG-06-K LAG Tower Plot No JLT-PH1-I1A, Jumeirah Lakes Towers, Dubai, United Arab Emirates
Tel.: (971) 44503681
Rice Product Mfr
N.A.I.C.S.: 311212

KRC CAPITAL B.V.
Leidseweg 219, Voorschoten, 2253 AE, Netherlands
Tel.: (31) 715797129 NI
Web Site: http://www.krccapital.com
Sales Range: $50-74.9 Million
Emp.: 80
Private Equity & Real Estate Investment Firm
N.A.I.C.S.: 523999
Rattan Chadha *(Founder & CEO)*
Subsidiaries:
Hotel Victor - South Beach (1)
1144 Ocean Dr, Miami Beach, FL 33139
Tel.: (305) 779-8700
Web Site:
http://www.hotelvictorsouthbeach.com
Hotel Operator
N.A.I.C.S.: 721110

OSIB Operations Holding B.V. (1)
Leidseweg 219, Voorschoten, 2253 AE, Netherlands
Tel.: (31) 208117055
Web Site: http://www.citizenm.com
Sales Range: $25-49.9 Million
Emp.: 40
Holding Company; Hotel Owner & Operator
N.A.I.C.S.: 551112
Rattan Chadha *(Chm-Mgmt Bd)*

Subsidiary (Domestic):

citizenM Amsterdam-Zuid Operations B.V. (2)
Prinses Irenestraat 30, NL-1077 WX, Amsterdam, Netherlands
Tel.: (31) 208117090
Web Site: http://www.citizenm.com
Hotel Operator
N.A.I.C.S.: 721110

Subsidiary (Non-US):

citizenM Glasgow Operations B.V. (2)
60 Renfrew Street, Glasgow, G2 3BW, Scotland, United Kingdom
Tel.: (44) 2035191111
Web Site: http://www.citizenmglasgow.com
Hotel Operator
N.A.I.C.S.: 721110
Amanda Rennie *(Mgr)*

INTERNATIONAL PUBLIC

Subsidiary (Domestic):

citizenM Schiphol Operations B.V. (2)
Jan Plezierweg 2, near Schiphol Intl Airport, 1118 BB, Amsterdam, NETHERLANDS
Tel.: (31) 208117080
Web Site: http://wwwcitizenm.com
Sales Range: $10-24.9 Million
Emp.: 40
Hotel Operator
N.A.I.C.S.: 721110

KREATE GROUP PLC
Haarakaari 42, 04360, Tuusula, Finland
Tel.: (358) 207851480
Web Site: https://www.kreate.fi
Year Founded: 2014
KREATE—(HEL)
Rev.: $345,371,250
Assets: $145,219,081
Liabilities: $98,996,331
Net Worth: $46,222,750
Earnings: $4,188,431
Emp.: 472
Fiscal Year-end: 12/31/23
Construction Engineering Services
N.A.I.C.S.: 541330
Antti Kakko *(VP)*
Subsidiaries:
Kreate Oy (1)
Haarakaari 42, 04360, Tuusula, Finland
Tel.: (358) 207851148
Web Site: https://kreate.fi
Construction & Civil Engineering Services
N.A.I.C.S.: 541330

KREATOPARAGOGIKI KAVALAS S.A.
13 Aminta Street, 65302, Kavala, Greece
Tel.: (30) 2510222270
Web Site: http://www.kreka.gr
Meat Distr
N.A.I.C.S.: 424470

KREBS & RIEDEL SCHLEIFSCHEIBENFABRIK GMBH & CO KG.
Bremer Strasse 44, 34385, Bad Karlshafen, Germany
Tel.: (49) 56721840
Web Site: http://www.krebs-riedel.com
Year Founded: 1895
Rev.: $19,849,566
Emp.: 250
Grinding Wheel Mfr
N.A.I.C.S.: 333248
Jost Riedel *(Co-Mng Dir)*
Subsidiaries:
Krebs & Riedel Shanghai Co., Ltd. (1)
Yuan Ye Road No 151 Build 1 Room 206, Jiading, Shanghai, 201805, China
Tel.: (86) 2159950913
Web Site: http://www.krebs-riedel.cn
Grinding Wheels Distr
N.A.I.C.S.: 423120

Krebs France SARL (1)
16 Rue De Berlin, BP 47, Montevrain, Marne-la-Vallee, Cedex, France
Tel.: (33) 160315071
Web Site: http://www.krebsfrance.fr
Grinding Wheels Distr
N.A.I.C.S.: 423120

KREBS BIOCHEMICALS & INDUSTRIES LTD.
Kothapalli Village Kasimkota Mandal, Visakhapatnam, 531031, Andhra Pradesh, India
Tel.: (91) 4066808040
Web Site:
https://www.krebsbiochem.com

Year Founded: 1991
524518—(BOM)
Rev.: $7,414,912
Assets: $21,733,571
Liabilities: $27,566,612
Net Worth: ($5,833,041)
Earnings: ($3,870,949)
Emp.: 390
Fiscal Year-end: 03/31/21
Pharmaceutical Chemicals Mfr
N.A.I.C.S.: 325412
Taruni Banda *(Compliance Officer & Sec)*

KREDITBANKEN A/S
HP Hanssens Gade 17, 6200, Aabenraa, 6200, Denmark
Tel.: (45) 73331700
Web Site:
https://www.kreditbanken.dk
KRE—(CSE)
Rev.: $50,897,831
Assets: $859,258,295
Liabilities: $720,610,323
Net Worth: $138,647,972
Earnings: $21,252,767
Emp.: 93
Fiscal Year-end: 12/31/23
Commercial Banking Services
N.A.I.C.S.: 522110
Torben Silberbauer *(CFO)*

KREDYT INKASO S.A.
21B Postepu Street, 02-676, Warsaw, Poland
Tel.: (48) 222125700
Web Site: https://www.kredytinkaso.pl
Year Founded: 2001
KRI—(WAR)
Rev.: $60,188,518
Assets: $202,529,401
Liabilities: $120,191,721
Net Worth: $82,337,680
Earnings: $7,950,808
Fiscal Year-end: 03/31/23
Financial & Debt Collection Services
N.A.I.C.S.: 561440
Maciej Jerzy Szymanski *(Chm-Mgmt Bd & VP)*

KREISEL GMBH UND CO. KG
Muhlenstrasse 38, 02957, Krauschwitz, Germany
Tel.: (49) 35771980
Web Site: http://www.kreisel.eu
Year Founded: 1912
Sales Range: $10-24.9 Million
Emp.: 180
Plant Mfr
N.A.I.C.S.: 333248
Wolfram Kreisel *(Mng Dir)*

KREMENCHUKGAZ, PJSC
46 Geroyiv Brestu str c, Kremenchuk, 39602, Poltava, Ukraine
Tel.: (380) 536 77 97 24
Natural & Liquefied Gas Distr
N.A.I.C.S.: 221210

KREON FINNANCIAL SERVICES LIMITED
New No 29 Old No 12 Mookathal Street Purasawalkam, Chennai, 600 007, India
Tel.: (91) 4442696634
Web Site: https://www.kreon.in
Year Founded: 1994
530139—(BOM)
Rev.: $234,329
Assets: $1,355,075
Liabilities: $1,091,858
Net Worth: $263,217
Earnings: ($65,785)
Emp.: 26
Fiscal Year-end: 03/31/21
Financial Services
N.A.I.C.S.: 523999

Nutika Jain *(Officer-Compliance & Sec)*

KREPEZHNI IZDELIA AD
Kuklensko shose 15, 4004, Plovdiv, 4004, Bulgaria
Tel.: (359) 32692250
Web Site: http://www.ki-bg.com
KREP—(BUL)
Sales Range: Less than $1 Million
Real Estate Asset Management Services
N.A.I.C.S.: 531390

KRETAM HOLDINGS BERHAD
Lot 6 Block 44 Leboh Tiga, PO Box 1292, 90714, Sandakan, Sabah, Malaysia
Tel.: (60) 89218999
Web Site: https://www.kretam.com
KRETAM—(KLS)
Rev.: $180,124,868
Assets: $216,899,683
Liabilities: $45,184,974
Net Worth: $171,714,709
Earnings: $22,930,159
Emp.: 2,895
Fiscal Year-end: 12/31/22
Palm Oil Cultivation Services
N.A.I.C.S.: 311225
Len Kee Wong *(Dir-Grp Plantations)*

Subsidiaries:

Green Edible Oil Sdn. Bhd. (1)
Lot 6 Block 44 Leboh Tiga, PO Box 1292, 90714, Sandakan, Sabah, Malaysia
Tel.: (60) 89218999
Web Site:
https://www.greenedibleoil.com.my
Bio-fuel Mfr
N.A.I.C.S.: 324199

KRETTO SYSCON LIMITED
A401 Sankalp Iconic Opp Vikram Nagar Iscontemple Cross Rd SG Highway, Opp Gujarat College, Ahmedabad, 380006, India
Tel.: (91) 7940329745
Web Site:
https://www.krettosyconltd.com
531328—(BOM)
Rev.: $566,626
Assets: $2,447,666
Liabilities: $225,261
Net Worth: $2,222,405
Earnings: $24,377
Fiscal Year-end: 03/31/22
Software Development Services
N.A.I.C.S.: 541511
Tushar Shashikant Shah *(Mng Dir)*

KREZUS SPOLKA AKCYJNA
Ul M Sklodowskiej-curie 73, 87-100, Torun, Poland
Tel.: (48) 56 656 26 62
Web Site: http://www.nfikrezus.pl
Sales Range: Less than $1 Million
Investment Management Service
N.A.I.C.S.: 523940

KRF UK LTD.
6 Bilton Road, Rugby, CV22 7AB, Warwickshire, United Kingdom
Tel.: (44) 1788541551
Web Site: http://www.krfukltd.co.uk
Bearing Component Mfr
N.A.I.C.S.: 332991

KRI KRI MILK INDUSTRY S.A.
3rd km Nat Road Serres-Drama, 62125, Serres, Greece
Tel.: (30) 2321068300
Web Site: https://international.krikri.gr
KRI—(ATH)
Rev.: $185,498,690
Assets: $138,245,029
Liabilities: $53,092,730

Net Worth: $85,152,299
Earnings: $3,426,507
Emp.: 462
Fiscal Year-end: 12/31/22
Dairy Products Mfr & Distr
N.A.I.C.S.: 311514

KRIDHAN INFRA LIMITED
203 Joshi Chambers Ahmedabad Street Carnac Bunder Masjid E, Mumbai, 400 009, India
Tel.: (91) 2240151523
Web Site: https://www.kridhan.com
Year Founded: 2006
533482—(BOM)
Rev.: $2,534,805
Assets: $6,808,620
Liabilities: $49,433,475
Net Worth: ($42,624,855)
Earnings: ($54,400,710)
Emp.: 348
Fiscal Year-end: 03/31/22
Steel Mfrs
N.A.I.C.S.: 331110
Anil Dhanpatlal Agrawal *(Chm & Mng Dir)*

Subsidiaries:

Readymade Steel Singapore Pte Ltd (1)
5 A Sungei Kadut Dr, Singapore, 729572, Singapore
Tel.: (65) 67605850
Web Site: http://www.khfoges.com.sg
Construction Engineering Services
N.A.I.C.S.: 541330

Subsidiary (Domestic):

KH Foges Pte Ltd (2)
58 Sungei Kadut Drive, Singapore, 729572, Singapore (90%)
Tel.: (65) 67605850
Piling, Foundation & Geotechnical Services
N.A.I.C.S.: 238190
Anil Dhanpatlal Agrawal *(Exec Dir)*

Subsidiary (Domestic):

PSL Engineering Pte. Ltd. (3)
58 Sungei Kadut Drive, Singapore, 729572, Singapore
Tel.: (65) 63621822
Mechanical, Construction & Ground Engineering
N.A.I.C.S.: 541330
Lee Yingee *(Gen Mgr)*

KRIEG, SCHLUPP, BURGE WERBEAGENTUR AG
Seestrasse 367, CH-8038, Zurich, Switzerland
Tel.: (41) 433998055
Web Site: http://www.ksbch.ch
Sales Range: $10-24.9 Million
Emp.: 60
N.A.I.C.S.: 541810
Daniel Krieg *(Co-Owner & Mng Dir)*

KRINGLE PHARMA, INC.
207 Saito Bio Incubator 7-7-15 Saitoasagi, Ibaraki, Osaka, 567-0085, Japan
Tel.: (81) 726418739
Web Site: https://www.kringle-pharma.com
Year Founded: 2001
4884—(TKS)
Pharmaceutical Product Mfr & Distr
N.A.I.C.S.: 325412
Kiichi Adachi *(Pres & CEO)*

KRISENERGY LTD.
83 Clemenceau Ave 10-05 UE Square, Singapore, 239920, Singapore
Tel.: (65) 6 838 5430
Web Site: http://www.krisenergy.com
Rev.: $126,531,037
Assets: $573,855,950

Liabilities: $719,752,999
Net Worth: ($145,897,049)
Earnings: ($168,860,466)
Emp.: 451
Fiscal Year-end: 12/31/19
Oil & Gas Exploration Services
N.A.I.C.S.: 211120
Kelvin Tang *(CEO & Pres-Cambodia)*

Subsidiaries:

KrisEnergy (Cambodia) Ltd. (1)
No 28 Street 310 Sangkat Boeung Keng Kang 1, PO Box 1619, Khan Chamcar Monn, Phnom Penh, Cambodia
Tel.: (855) 23726530
Oil & Gas Production Services
N.A.I.C.S.: 213112

KrisEnergy (Gulf of Thailand) Ltd. (1)
Asia Center 16th Floor No 173/16 South Sathorn Road, Tungmahamek, Bangkok, 10120, Sathorn, Thailand
Tel.: (66) 2 670 8448
Holding Company
N.A.I.C.S.: 551112

KrisEnergy Bangladesh Limited (1)
House 17 Road 9 Baridhara, Dhaka, 1212, Bangladesh
Tel.: (880) 29884337
Web Site: http://www.krisenergy.com
Emp.: 45
Oil & Natural Gas Exploration & Production Services
N.A.I.C.S.: 211120
Edwin Bowles *(Gen Mgr)*

KRISHCA STRAPPING SOLUTIONS LIMITED
Building 01B LOGOS Mappedu Industrial Logistics Park, Mappedu, Chennai, 631203, Tamil Nadu, India
Tel.: (91) 9344991199
Web Site:
https://www.krishcastrapping.com
Year Founded: 2017
KRISHCA—(NSE)
Rev.: $8,682,201
Assets: $4,181,068
Liabilities: $2,869,708
Net Worth: $1,311,360
Earnings: $1,120,149
Emp.: 50
Fiscal Year-end: 03/31/23
Strapping Product Mfr & Distr
N.A.I.C.S.: 332999
Diya Venkatesan *(Sec)*

KRISHNA CAPITAL & SECURITIES LTD.
403 Mauryansh Elanza B/h Parekh Hospital Shyamal Cross Road Satellite, Ahmedabad, 380 015, India
Tel.: (91) 7926768572
Web Site: https://www.kcsl.co.in
539384—(BOM)
Rev.: $56,472
Assets: $823,952
Liabilities: $3,623
Net Worth: $820,329
Earnings: $19,332
Emp.: 3
Fiscal Year-end: 03/31/22
Financial Support Services
N.A.I.C.S.: 523999
Ashokkumar B. Agrawal *(Chm & Mng Dir)*

KRISHNA FERRO PRODUCTS LIMITED
Mandiakudar Village PO Chungimatti, 770 034, Sundergarh, Orissa, India
Tel.: (91) 6624 280284
Web Site:
http://www.krishnaferro.co.in
Year Founded: 1985
Sales Range: $1-9.9 Million
Emp.: 62

KRISHNA FERRO PRODUCTS LIMITED

Krishna Ferro Products Limited—(Continued)
Metal Ferroalloy Mfr
N.A.I.C.S.: 331110
Hari Kishan Agarwal (Mng Dir)

KRISHNA FILAMENT INDUSTRIES LIMITED
Betegaon Village Boisar East, Taluka Palghar, Thane, 401501, Maharashtra, India
Tel.: (91) 2525527881
500248—(BOM)
Rev.: $18,056
Assets: $85,510
Liabilities: $424,363
Net Worth: $(338,853)
Earnings: $3,261
Fiscal Year-end: 03/31/23
Textile Products Mfr
N.A.I.C.S.: 314999
Jagdish Zalavadia (CFO & Exec Dir)

KRISHNA INSTITUTE OF MEDICAL SCIENCES LIMITED
1-8-31/1 Minister Rd Krishna Nagar Colony, Begumpet, Secunderabad, 500003, Telangana, India
Tel.: (91) 4044885000
Web Site:
https://www.kimshospitals.com
Year Founded: 2000
543308—(BOM)
Hospital & Health Care Services
N.A.I.C.S.: 622110
B. Bhaskar Rao (Mng Dir)

Subsidiaries:

Arunodaya Hospitals Private Limited (1)
Bus Stop Bagalgunte Near-Bagalgunte Mallasandra Main Rd, Bhuvaneshwari Nagar T Dasarahalli, Bengaluru, 560057, Karnataka, India
Tel.: (91) 802 839 5214
Web Site:
https://www.arunodayahospitals.com
Hospital Services
N.A.I.C.S.: 622110

Iconkrishi Institute Of Medical Sciences Private Limited (1)
32-11-02 Sheela Nagar BHPV Post, Visakhapatnam, 530026, Andhra Pradesh, India
Tel.: (91) 891 710 0100
Hospital & Health Care Services
N.A.I.C.S.: 622110

KIMS Cuddles Private Limited (1)
1-112/86 Survey No 55/EE, Kondapur Serilingampally, Hyderabad, 500 084, Telangana, India
Tel.: (91) 799 588 8556
Web Site: https://www.kimscuddles.com
Child Care Services
N.A.I.C.S.: 624410

Saveera Institute Of Medical Sciences Private Limited (1)
1-1348 Srinagar Colony Extension Opposite to Sakshi Office, Rudrampeta, Anantapur, 515 004, Andhra Pradesh, India
Tel.: (91) 855 423 4234
Hospital & Health Care Services
N.A.I.C.S.: 622110

KRISHNA PHOSCHEM LIMITED
Wing A2 1st Floor Ostwal Heights Urban Forest, Bhilwara, 311001, Rajasthan, India
Tel.: (91) 1482237104
Web Site:
https://www.krishnaphoschem.com
Year Founded: 2004
KRISHANA—(NSE)
Rev.: $39,051,280
Assets: $69,800,779
Liabilities: $38,410,359
Net Worth: $31,390,420
Earnings: $3,205,563
Emp.: 196
Fiscal Year-end: 03/31/23
Fertilizer Mfr
N.A.I.C.S.: 325314
Praveen Ostwal (Mng Dir)

KRISHNA VENTURES LIMITED
7th Floor Corporate Center Opp Hotel VITS Andheri-Kurla Road, Andheri East, Mumbai, 400059, India
Tel.: (91) 2261898000
Web Site:
https://www.krishnaventuresltd.com
Year Founded: 2000
504392—(BOM)
Rev.: $382
Assets: $1,659,253
Liabilities: $4,750
Net Worth: $1,654,503
Earnings: $(21,977)
Emp.: 5
Fiscal Year-end: 03/31/21
Real Estate Development Services
N.A.I.C.S.: 531390
Vijay Srigopal Khetan (Chm)

KRISTAL 1923 AD VELES
18 Alekso Demnievski St, Veles, North Macedonia
Tel.: (389) 43233855
Web Site: https://kristal.mk
Year Founded: 1923
BGOR—(MAC)
Rev.: $10,725,383
Assets: $14,950,447
Liabilities: $6,609,147
Net Worth: $8,341,300
Earnings: $35,398
Fiscal Year-end: 12/31/19
Cooking Oil Mfr
N.A.I.C.S.: 311224

KRISTAL A.D.
Branka Popovica 115, 78000, Banja Luka, Bosnia & Herzegovina
Tel.: (387) 51371397
KRIS-R-A—(BANJ)
Sales Range: Less than $1 Million
Emp.: 8
Painting & Glazing Services
N.A.I.C.S.: 238390
Budimir Stankovic (Chm)

KRISTAL KOLA VE MESRUBAT SANAYI TICARET A.S.
Bahcelievler Mah Fevzi Cakmak 2 Cad Guzelsehir Sitesi No 1, Buyukcekmece, Istanbul, Turkiye
Tel.: (90) 2128680909
Web Site:
https://www.kristalkola.com.tr
Year Founded: 1994
KRSTL—(IST)
Rev.: $56,109,715
Assets: $33,887,224
Liabilities: $8,908,383
Net Worth: $24,978,841
Earnings: $511,885
Fiscal Year-end: 12/31/23
Soft Drink Mfr & Whslr
N.A.I.C.S.: 312111
Mahmut Erdogan (Chm)

KRITI INDUSTRIES INDIA LTD
Brilliant Sapphir 801-80 8th Floor, Plot No 10 Scheme 78-II, Indore, 452010, Madhya Pradesh, India
Tel.: (91) 7312719100
Web Site: https://www.kritiindia.com
KRITIIND—(NSE)
Rev.: $74,541,067
Assets: $55,859,581
Liabilities: $34,819,812
Net Worth: $21,039,769
Earnings: $2,720,759
Emp.: 490
Fiscal Year-end: 03/31/22
Plastic Polymer Piping System Mfr
N.A.I.C.S.: 325211
Purnima Mehta (Exec Dir)

KRITI NUTRIENTS LIMITED
Mehta Chambers 34 Siyaganj, Indore, 452007, Madhya Pradesh, India
Tel.: (91) 7312719100
Web Site: https://kritiindia.com
Year Founded: 1996
533210—(BOM)
Rev.: $103,225,941
Assets: $22,929,338
Liabilities: $7,572,515
Net Worth: $15,356,823
Earnings: $1,679,660
Emp.: 236
Fiscal Year-end: 03/31/22
Vegetable Oil Mfr
N.A.I.C.S.: 311224
Shiv Singh Mehta (Chm & Mng Dir)

KRITIKA WIRES LTD.
1A Bonfield Lane, Kolkata, 700001, India
Tel.: (91) 3322429581
Web Site:
https://www.kritikawires.com
Year Founded: 2004
KRITIKA—(NSE)
Rev.: $34,381,740
Assets: $14,185,097
Liabilities: $5,306,708
Net Worth: $8,878,389
Earnings: $717,679
Emp.: 195
Fiscal Year-end: 03/31/23
Electric Power Distribution Services
N.A.I.C.S.: 221122
Naresh Kumar Agarwal (Founder & Chm)

KRITON ARTOS SA
Thesi Ammos Kallithea N Alikarnassos Crete, 71500, Iraklion, Greece
Tel.: (30) 2810380850
Web Site: http://www.kritonartos.gr
Year Founded: 2004
Grocery Product Distr
N.A.I.C.S.: 445110
Emmanouel G. Damianakis (Chm & CEO)

KRKA, D.D., NOVO MESTO
Smarjeska cesta 6, 8501, Novo Mesto, Slovenia
Tel.: (386) 73312111   SI
Web Site: https://www.krka.biz
Year Founded: 1954
KRK—(WAR)
Rev.: $1,994,029,143
Assets: $3,051,430,622
Liabilities: $643,034,551
Net Worth: $2,408,396,071
Earnings: $346,320,786
Emp.: 11,780
Fiscal Year-end: 12/31/23
Pharmaceutical Preparation Manufacturing
N.A.I.C.S.: 325412
Joze Colaric (Chm-Mgmt Bd & CEO)

Subsidiaries:

DP KRKA Ukraina (1)
Staronavodnitskaya 13 Section V G 3rd Fl, 01015, Kiev, Ukraine
Tel.: (380) 0445692838
Web Site: http://www.ukraine.krka.biz
Sales Range: $125-149.9 Million
Emp.: 500
Pharmaceutical Preparations
N.A.I.C.S.: 325412

Golf Grad Otocec, d. o. o. (1)
Grajska Cesta 2, Otocec, 8222, Slovenia
Tel.: (386) 41304444
Web Site: http://www.golf-otocec.si
Sales Range: $50-74.9 Million
Golf Course Operation Services
N.A.I.C.S.: 713910

Helvetius S.R.L. (1)
Piazza Liberte 3, 84132, Trieste, Italy
Tel.: (39) 040366633
Web Site: http://www.krka.si
Sales Range: $25-49.9 Million
Emp.: 6
Pharmaceutical Preparations
N.A.I.C.S.: 325412

KRKA Aussenhandels GmbH (1)
Ottostrasse 3-5, 80333, Munich, Germany
Tel.: (49) 895490030
Web Site: http://www.krka.si
Pharmaceutical Preparations
N.A.I.C.S.: 325412

KRKA CR, s. r. o. (1)
Sokolovska 192/79, Karlin, 186 00, Prague, 8, Czech Republic (100%)
Tel.: (420) 221115115
Web Site: https://www.krka.cz
Sales Range: $25-49.9 Million
Emp.: 200
Pharmaceutical Preparations
N.A.I.C.S.: 325412

KRKA FARMA, d. o. o. (1)
Ul Dzemala Bijedica 125a, 71000, Sarajevo, Bosnia & Herzegovina
Tel.: (387) 33720550
Pharmaceuticals Product Mfr
N.A.I.C.S.: 325412

KRKA FARMA, d. o. o., Zagreb (1)
Radnicka cesta 48, 10000, Zagreb, Croatia
Tel.: (385) 16312101
Web Site: http://www.krka.si
Sales Range: $25-49.9 Million
Emp.: 50
Pharmaceutical Preparations
N.A.I.C.S.: 325412

KRKA Farmaceutica Unipessoal Lda (1)
Tel.: (351) 214643650
Web Site: https://www.krka.pt
Sales Range: $25-49.9 Million
Pharmaceuticals Product Mfr
N.A.I.C.S.: 325412
Vasco Esteves (Gen Mgr)

KRKA Farmaceutici Milano, S.r.l. (1)
Viale Achille Papa 30, 20149, Milan, Italy
Tel.: (39) 0233008841
Web Site: https://www.krka.it
Pharmaceutical Drug Mfr
N.A.I.C.S.: 325412

KRKA Magyarorszag Kereskedelmi Kepviselet (1)
Dunavirag utca 2-6 Tower 3 6th Floor, 1138, Budapest, Hungary
Tel.: (36) 13558490
Web Site: http://www.krka.co.hu
Emp.: 30
Pharmaceutical Preparations
N.A.I.C.S.: 325412

KRKA Pharma Dublin Limited (1)
1st Floor Unit H Citywest Shopping Centre Fortunes Walk, Saggart, Dublin, D24 TYT9, Ireland (100%)
Tel.: (353) 14133710
Web Site: https://www.krka.ie
Sales Range: $25-49.9 Million
Emp.: 1
Pharmaceutical Preparations
N.A.I.C.S.: 325412

KRKA Pharma GmbH (1)
Wagramerstrasse 4/ Top 7, 1220, Vienna, Austria
Tel.: (43) 16624300
Web Site: http://www.krka.at
Sales Range: $25-49.9 Million
Pharmaceuticals Product Mfr
N.A.I.C.S.: 325412

KRKA Polska Sp. z o.o. (1)
ul Rownolegla 5, 02-235, Warsaw, Poland
Tel.: (48) 225737500
Web Site: https://www.krka-polska.pl
Sales Range: $200-249.9 Million
Emp.: 650
Pharmaceutical Preparations
N.A.I.C.S.: 325412

AND PRIVATE COMPANIES

KRKA Slovensko, s.r.o. (1)
Karadzicova 8, 821 08, Bratislava, Slovakia
Tel.: (421) 257104501
Web Site: https://www.krka.sk
Emp.: 200
Pharmaceutical Drug Mfr
N.A.I.C.S.: 325412

KRKA Sverige AB (1)
Medborgarplatsen 25 Goeta Ark 175, 118 72, Stockholm, Sweden
Tel.: (46) 86436766
Web Site: https://www.krka.se
Sales Range: $25-49.9 Million
Pharmaceuticals Product Mfr
N.A.I.C.S.: 325412
Robert Vidmar (Mng Dir)

KRKA UKRAINE LLC (1)
St Staronavodnytska 13 office 127, PB 42, 01015, Kiev, Ukraine
Tel.: (380) 443542668
Web Site: https://www.krka.ua
Emp.: 300
Pharmaceuticals Product Mfr
N.A.I.C.S.: 325412

KRKA-FARMA DOO (1)
Jurija Gagarina 26/V/II, 11070, Belgrade, Serbia
Tel.: (381) 112288722
Web Site: https://www.krka.rs
Emp.: 95
Pharmaceuticals Product Mfr
N.A.I.C.S.: 325412
Mladen Gelenic (Gen Mgr)

KRKA-Farma d.o.o. Novi sad (1)
Kralja Petra I Br 32, Novi Sad, 21000, Serbia (100%)
Tel.: (381) 21443511
Web Site: http://www.krka.si
Sales Range: $25-49.9 Million
Emp.: 7
Pharmaceutical Preparations
N.A.I.C.S.: 325412
Mladen Jelenic (Mgr)

Krka Belgium, SA (1)
Avenue Louise 221, 1050, Brussels, Belgium
Tel.: (32) 37805317
Web Site: https://www.krka.be
Emp.: 20
Pharmaceutical Drug Mfr
N.A.I.C.S.: 325412

Krka Bulgaria EOOD (1)
Business Park Sofia street 1 building 5 entrance Ah ground floor, 1766, Sofia, Bulgaria
Tel.: (359) 29623450
Web Site: https://www.krka.bg
Emp.: 3
Pharmaceutical Drug Mfr
N.A.I.C.S.: 325412

Krka Farmaceutica, S.L. (1)
c / Anabel Segura 10 Pl Baja Of-1, Alcobendas, 28108, Madrid, Spain
Tel.: (34) 911610380
Web Site: https://www.krka.com.es
Pharmaceutical Drug Mfr
N.A.I.C.S.: 325412

Krka Finland Oy (1)
Tekniikantie 14, 02150, Espoo, Finland
Tel.: (358) 207545330
Web Site: https://www.krka.fi
Pharmaceutical Drug Mfr
N.A.I.C.S.: 325412

Krka France Eurl (1)
12-14 rue de l'Eglise, 75015, Paris, France
Tel.: (33) 157408225
Web Site: https://www.krka.fr
Pharmaceutical Drug Mfn
N.A.I.C.S.: 325412

Krka Hellas E.P.E. (1)
45 Michalakopoulou Street, 115 28, Athens, Greece
Tel.: (30) 2100101613
Pharmaceutical Drug Product Mfr & Distr
N.A.I.C.S.: 325412

Krka Romania S.R.L. (1)
Splaiul Independentei nr 319 Sema Parc etaj 10 Sector 6, 060032, Bucharest, Romania
Tel.: (40) 213106605

Web Site: https://www.krka.ro
Emp.: 170
Pharmaceutical Drug Mfr
N.A.I.C.S.: 325412

Krka UK Ltd. (1)
Thames House Waterside Drive, Langley, London, SL3 6EZ, United Kingdom
Tel.: (44) 2071646156
Web Site: https://www.krka.co.uk
Pharmaceutical Drug Mfr
N.A.I.C.S.: 325412

Krka USA, LLC (1)
4216 Cravens Point Rd, Wilmington, NC 28409
Tel.: (867) 331-7264
Pharmaceutical Drug Product Mfr & Distr
N.A.I.C.S.: 325412

Krka, d.d., Novo Mesto - Ljubljana Facility (1)
Dunajska cesta 65, 1000, Ljubljana, Slovenia
Tel.: (386) 1 475 11 00
Web Site: http://www.krka.biz
Sales Range: $125-149.9 Million
Pharmaceuticals Product Mfr
N.A.I.C.S.: 325412

Krka, d.d., Novo Mesto - Ljutomer Facility (1)
Ulica Rada Pusenjaka 10, 9240, Ljutomer, Slovenia
Tel.: (386) 2 584 93 00
Web Site: http://www.krka.biz
Pharmaceuticals Product Mfr
N.A.I.C.S.: 325412

Krka, d.d., Novo Mesto - Novo mesto Facility (1)
Smarjeska cesta 6, 8501, Novo Mesto, Slovenia
Tel.: (386) 73317861
Web Site: http://www.krka.biz
Pharmaceuticals Product Mfr
N.A.I.C.S.: 325412

LLC Krka Kazakhstan (1)
Koktem Square Microdistrict Koktem 1 building 15A office 601, Business center, 050040, Almaty, Kazakhstan
Tel.: (7) 7273110809
Pharmaceutical Drug Mfr
N.A.I.C.S.: 325412

OOO KRKA Farma (1)
Golovinskoye Shosse 5 Block 1 22nd Floor, BC Vodny, 125212, Moscow, Russia
Tel.: (7) 4959811095
Web Site: http://www.krka.biz
Pharmaceutical Preparations
N.A.I.C.S.: 325412

OOO KRKA-RUS (1)
Golovinskoye Shosse 5 Block 1 22nd Floor, BC Vodny, 125212, Moscow, Russia
Tel.: (7) 4959811086
Web Site: http://www.krka.biz
Pharmaceutical Preparations
N.A.I.C.S.: 325412

SIA KRKA Latvija (1)
Vienibas gatve 109, Riga, LV-1058, Latvia
Tel.: (371) 67338610
Web Site: https://www.krka.lv
Emp.: 40
Pharmaceutical Drug Mfr
N.A.I.C.S.: 325412

TAD Pharma GmbH (1)
Heinz-Lohmann-Strasse 5, 27472, Cuxhaven, Germany
Tel.: (49) 47216060
Web Site: https://www.tad.de
Sales Range: $50-74.9 Million
Emp.: 250
Pharmaceutical Products Distr
N.A.I.C.S.: 424210

TOV KRKA UKRAINA (1)
Bud 13 Kv 125 Ps 42 Vul Staronavodnitska, Kiev, Ukraine
Tel.: (380) 445811120
Pharmaceuticals Product Mfr
N.A.I.C.S.: 325412

Terme Krka, d. o. o. (1)
Novi trg 1, 8000, Novo mesto, Slovenia
Tel.: (386) 82050300
Web Site: http://www.terme-krka.com

Resort & Hotel Management Services
N.A.I.C.S.: 721110
Joze Berus (CEO)

UAB KRKA LIETUVA (1)
Senasis Ukmerges Kelias 4 Vilniaus r Uzubaliu Kaimas, 14302, Vilnius, Lithuania
Tel.: (370) 52362740
Web Site: https://www.krka.lt
Sales Range: $25-49.9 Million
Emp.: 70
Pharmaceuticals Product Mfr
N.A.I.C.S.: 325412

KRM22 PLC
5 Ireland Yard, London, EC4V 5EH, United Kingdom
Tel.: (44) 2037403900 UK
Web Site: https://www.krm22.com
Year Founded: 2018
KRM—(AIM)
Rev.: $5,393,840
Assets: $14,078,516
Liabilities: $10,063,115
Net Worth: $4,015,400
Earnings: ($3,914,416)
Emp.: 49
Fiscal Year-end: 12/31/22
Investment Management Service
N.A.I.C.S.: 523940
Keith Todd (Chm & CEO)

KROEKER FARMS LTD.
777 Circle K Drive, Winkler, R6W 0K7, MB, Canada
Tel.: (204) 325-4333
Web Site:
  https://www.kroekerfarms.com
Year Founded: 1955
Sales Range: $10-24.9 Million
Potato & Onion Farming
N.A.I.C.S.: 111211
Wayne Rempel (Pres & CEO)

KROHNE INTERNATIONAL, INC.
Ludwig Krohne Strasse 5, 47058, Duisburg, Germany
Tel.: (49) 3014403
Web Site: http://www.krohne-mar.com
Year Founded: 1921
Sales Range: $250-299.9 Million
Emp.: 500
Holding Company
N.A.I.C.S.: 551112
Hilde Rademacher Dubbick (CEO)

Subsidiaries:

Inor Process AB (1)
Travbanegatan 10, PO Box 9125, 200 39, Malmo, Sweden
Tel.: (46) 40 312 560
Web Site: http://www.inor.com
Emp.: 56
Transmitter Mfr & Distr
N.A.I.C.S.: 334513
Joakim Lindstrom (Mgr-Sls & Mktg)

Subsidiary (Non-US):

INOR Transmitter GmbH (2)
Am Bocksborn 5, 63571, Gelnhausen, Germany
Tel.: (49) 6051 14807
Web Site: http://www.inor-gmbh.de
Transmitter Mfr
N.A.I.C.S.: 334513

INOR Transmitter Oy (2)
Unikkotie 13, 01300, Vantaa, Finland
Tel.: (358) 10 4217900
Web Site: http://www.inor.fi
Transmitter Distr
N.A.I.C.S.: 423690
Jari Stadig (CEO)

KROHNE (South East Asia) Pte., Ltd. (1)
9 Kaki Bukit Road 1 02-09 Eunos Technolink, Singapore, 415938, Singapore
Tel.: (65) 6748 1073

Web Site: http://www.sg.krohne.com
Emp.: 20
Measuring Instrument Mfr & Distr
N.A.I.C.S.: 334513
Jack Cheng (Mng Dir)

KROHNE DE MEXICO, SA DE CV (1)
Poza Rica 706 Colonia Petrolera, 89110, Tampico, Tamaulipas, Mexico
Tel.: (52) 833 2173830
Web Site: http://www.krohnemexico.com
Measuring Instrument Distr
N.A.I.C.S.: 423830
Hector Obele Trigos (Dir Gen)

KROHNE IBERIA, S.r.l. (1)
Poligono Industrial Nilo Calle Brasil n 5, 28806, Alcala de Henares, Spain
Tel.: (34) 91 8832152
Web Site: http://www.krohne.es
Measuring Instrument Distr
N.A.I.C.S.: 423830

KROHNE Japan KK (1)
Sanbancho KS Bldg 5F 2-4, Chiyoda-ku, Tokyo, 102-0075, Japan
Tel.: (81) 3 5276 8715
Web Site: http://www.krohne.co.jp
Measuring Instrument Distr
N.A.I.C.S.: 423830

KROHNE Kazakhstan LLP (1)
Dostyk ave 290a, 050020, Almaty, Kazakhstan
Tel.: (7) 727 356 27 70
Web Site: http://www.krohne.kz
Emp.: 15
Measuring Instrument Distr
N.A.I.C.S.: 423830
Alexander Morozov (Gen Mgr)

KROHNE Measurement Technology (Shanghai) Co., Ltd. (1)
Minshen Road 555 Industrial Zone, Songjiang, Shanghai, 201612, China
Tel.: (86) 21 6760 0822
Electromagnetic Flowmeter Mfr
N.A.I.C.S.: 334513
Sue Chuen Lyu (Engr-Technical)

KROHNE New Zealand Ltd (1)
Suite C First Floor Building 6 331 Rosedale Road, Albany, Auckland, 0632, New Zealand
Tel.: (64) 9 414 4305
Web Site: http://www.krohne.co.nz
Measuring Instrument Distr
N.A.I.C.S.: 423830

KROHNE Pressure Solutions GmbH (1)
Oberbecksenerstr 76, 32547, Bad Oeynhausen, Germany
Tel.: (49) 5731 300 566 0
Emp.: 18
Pressure Transmitter Mfr
N.A.I.C.S.: 334513

KROHNE Skarpenord A/S (1)
Stromtangveien 21, 3950, Brevik, Norway
Tel.: (47) 35 56 12 20
Web Site: http://www.krohne-skarpenord.com
Control Systems Mfr
N.A.I.C.S.: 334513
Hasse Hogner (Mng Dir)

Kanex Krohne Anlagen Export GmbH (1)
Ludwig-Krohne-Str 5, 47058, Duisburg, Germany
Tel.: (49) 203301211
Web Site: http://www.krohne.com
Sales Range: $50-74.9 Million
Emp.: 55
Industrial Machinery & Equipment Whslr
N.A.I.C.S.: 423830

Kanex Krohne Grodno (1)
17 September House No 49 Office 112, 230023, Grodno, Belarus
Tel.: (375) 172108074
Web Site: http://www.krohne.com
Sales Range: $50-74.9 Million
Emp.: 2
Industrial Machinery & Equipment Whslr
N.A.I.C.S.: 423830

Khrone Skarpenord AS (1)

KROHNE INTERNATIONAL, INC.

Krohne International, Inc.—(Continued)
Saheimsveien 2, PO Box 3, N 3660, Rjukan, Norway **(100%)**
Tel.: (47) 35093200
Web Site: http://www.skarpenord.com
Flow Meter Mfr
N.A.I.C.S.: 334514

Krohne (Malaysia) Sdn. Bhd. (1)
No F-2 Block 46 2nd Floor Mentari Business Park, Jalan PJS 8/2, Bandar Sunway, 46150, Petaling Jaya, Malaysia
Tel.: (60) 3 5636 8286
Web Site: http://my.krohne.com
Sales Range: $25-49.9 Million
Emp.: 5
Industrial Process Instrumentation Mfr & Supplier
N.A.I.C.S.: 334515
Jason Yew *(Mgr-Sls)*

Krohne (Thailand) Co. Ltd. (1)
202 Le Concorde Building, A3 Fl Ratchapisek Rd Huaykwang, 10310, Bangkok, Thailand
Tel.: (66) 26941411
Web Site: http://www.tokyokeiso-krohne.co.th
Sales Range: $50-74.9 Million
Emp.: 10
Industrial Machinery & Equipment Whslr
N.A.I.C.S.: 423830

Krohne AG (1)
Uferstrasse 90, 4019, Basel, Switzerland
Tel.: (41) 616383030
Web Site: http://www.krohne.com
Sales Range: $25-49.9 Million
Emp.: 20
Industrial Machinery & Equipment Whslr
N.A.I.C.S.: 423830
Ruediger Hartmann *(Gen Mgr)*

Krohne Australia Pty. Ltd. (1)
5 Phiney Place, Ingleburn, 2565, NSW, Australia
Tel.: (61) 294261700
Web Site: http://www.krohne-mar.com
Sales Range: $25-49.9 Million
Emp.: 15
Professional Equipment & Supplies Whslr
N.A.I.C.S.: 423490
Louise Matthews *(Dir-Mktg)*

Krohne Belgium NV (1)
Noordkustlaan, 1702, Groot-Bijgaarden, Belgium
Tel.: (32) 24660010
Web Site: http://www.krohne.com
Sales Range: $50-74.9 Million
Emp.: 10
Industrial Machinery & Equipment Whslr
N.A.I.C.S.: 423830
Andre Boer *(Gen Mgr)*

Krohne Canada Inc. (1)
559 Oakwood Avenue, L7P1S5, Toronto, ON, Canada
Tel.: (416) 658-8574
Professional Equipment & Supplies Whslr
N.A.I.C.S.: 423490

Krohne Conaut Instrumentacao Ltda. (1)
Estrada Louis Pasteur 300, CP 56, 06835-080, Embu, Sao Paulo, Brazil
Tel.: (55) 11 4785 2700
Electromagnetic Flowmeter Mfr
N.A.I.C.S.: 334513

Krohne Engineering GmbH (1)
setl Stromilovo Volga Region, Moscow, 443065, Samara, Russia
Tel.: (7) 846 230 0470
Web Site: http://www.krohne.ru
Engineeering Services
N.A.I.C.S.: 237990

Krohne Gesellschaft m.b.H. (1)
Altmannsdorfer Str 76 12 4 Top11A, 1120, Vienna, Austria
Tel.: (43) 1 203 4532 0
Web Site: http://www.krohne.at
Industrial Machinery & Equipment Whslr
N.A.I.C.S.: 423830

Krohne Instrumentation AS (1)
Ekholtveien 114, PO Box 2178, 1526, Moss, Norway
Tel.: (47) 69264860

Oil & Gas Field Machinery & Equipment Mfr
N.A.I.C.S.: 333132
Even Lund *(Mgr)*

Krohne Italia Srl (1)
Via Laboratori Olivetti 113, 20010, Milan, Italy
Tel.: (39) 024300661
Web Site: http://www.krohne.com
Sales Range: $25-49.9 Million
Emp.: 25
Industrial Machinery & Equipment Whslr
N.A.I.C.S.: 423830

Krohne Ltd. (1)
34-38 Rutherford Drive, Park Farm Industrial Estate N, Wellingborough, NN8 6AE, Northants, United Kingdom
Tel.: (44) 1933408500
Web Site: http://www.krohne.com
Sales Range: $75-99.9 Million
Emp.: 140
Holding Company
N.A.I.C.S.: 551112

Subsidiary (Domestic):

KROHNE Oil & Gas (UK) Limited (2)
70 Carwood Road, Sheffield, S4 7SD, United Kingdom
Tel.: (44) 114 243 1332
Web Site: http://www.krohne-oilandgas.com
Oil & Gas Equipment Distr
N.A.I.C.S.: 423830
Julian Hetherington *(Engr-E & I)*

Krohne Marshall Ltd. (1)
A - 34-35 MIDC Industrial Area H Block Pimpri, H-Block Pimpri, 411018, Pune, India
Tel.: (91) 2027442020
Emp.: 164
Analytical Laboratory Instrument Mfr
N.A.I.C.S.: 334516
Ashutosh Khole *(Mgr-Sls)*

Krohne Measurement Instruments (Shanghai) Co. Ltd. (1)
9th Fl Puyuan Science Pk Building A, 396 Guilin Rd, 200233, Shanghai, China
Tel.: (86) 2164705656
Web Site: http://www.krohne.com
Sales Range: $50-74.9 Million
Emp.: 120
Instrument Mfr for Measuring & Testing Electricity & Electrical Signals
N.A.I.C.S.: 334515

Krohne Messtechnik GmbH & Co. KG (1)
Ludwig-Krohne-Strasse, Duisburg, 47058, Germany
Tel.: (49) 2033010
Web Site: http://www.krohne.com
Professional Equipment & Supplies Whslr
N.A.I.C.S.: 423490
Michael Dubeck *(Mng Dir)*

Subsidiary (Non-US):

Krohne CZ, spol. S.r.o. (2)
Opavska 801/8a, 63900, Brno, Czech Republic **(100%)**
Tel.: (420) 545 220 092
Web Site: http://cz.krohne.com
Sales Range: $25-49.9 Million
Emp.: 50
Miscellaneous Nondurable Goods Whslr
N.A.I.C.S.: 327910
Petr Komp *(Gen Mgr)*

Krohne Nederland B.V. (1)
Kerkeplaat 14, PO Box 110, 3313LC, Dordrecht, Netherlands
Tel.: (31) 786306200
Web Site: http://www.krohne.com
Sales Range: $150-199.9 Million
Emp.: 450
Warm Air Heating & Air-Conditioning Equipment & Supplies Whslr
N.A.I.C.S.: 423830
Andre Boer *(Gen Mgr)*

Krohne Oil & Gas B.V. (1)
Minervum 7441, 4817 ZG, Breda, Netherlands
Tel.: (31) 76 7112000
Oil & Gas Equipment Mfr & Distr
N.A.I.C.S.: 333132
Frank Janssens *(Co-Mng Dir)*

Subsidiary (US):

KROHNE Oil & Gas LLC (2)
4100 N Sam Houston Pkwy W Ste 220, Houston, TX 77086
Tel.: (281) 598-0050
Oil & Gas Equipment Distr
N.A.I.C.S.: 423830

Subsidiary (Non-US):

Krohne Oil & Gas Malaysia Sdn Bhd (2)
No F-2 Block 46 2nd Floor Mentari Business Park Jalan PJS 8/2, Bandar Sunway, 46150, Petaling Jaya, Selangor, Malaysia
Tel.: (60) 3 5636 8286
Web Site: http://www.my.krohne.com
Oil & Gas Equipment Mfr & Distr
N.A.I.C.S.: 333132

Krohne Otomasyon Sanayi ve Ticaret Limited Sirketi (1)
Barbaros Mahallesi Mimar Sinan Caddesi Kutluay Sokak No 9, Atasehir, 34746, Istanbul, Turkiye
Tel.: (90) 216 291 2040
Web Site: http://www.krohne.com.tr
Sales Range: $25-49.9 Million
Emp.: 15
Industrial Machinery & Equipment Whslr
N.A.I.C.S.: 423830

Krohne Polska Sp. z o.o. (1)
Ul Sympatyczna 6 lok 1, 80-176, Gdansk, Poland
Tel.: (48) 585209211
Web Site: http://www.pl.krohne.com
Electronic Components Mfr
N.A.I.C.S.: 334419

Krohne Pty. Ltd. (1)
Bushbuck Close Corporate Park South, PO Box 2069, Midrand, 1685, Gauteng, South Africa
Tel.: (27) 829058175
Web Site: http://www.krohne.com
Emp.: 35
Electrical Apparatus & Equipment Wiring Supplies & Construction Material Whslr
N.A.I.C.S.: 423610
John Boxley *(Gen Mgr)*

Krohne S.A.S. (1)
Les Ors, BP 98, 26103, Romans, France
Tel.: (33) 475054400
Web Site: http://www.krohne.com
Sales Range: $50-74.9 Million
Emp.: 170
Industrial Machinery & Equipment Whslr
N.A.I.C.S.: 327910
Jacques Van Den Bosch *(Gen Mgr)*

Krohne, Inc. (1)
7 Dearborn Rd, Peabody, MA 01960
Tel.: (978) 535-6060
Web Site: http://www.krohne.com
Sales Range: $25-49.9 Million
Emp.: 80
Measuring & Controlling Device Mfr
N.A.I.C.S.: 334519
Brian Elliott *(Gen Mgr)*

PT. KROHNE INDONESIA (1)
Wisma Tugu II 4th Floor East Jl HR Rasuna Said Kav C7, Jakarta, 12920, Indonesia
Tel.: (62) 21 5221146
Web Site: http://www.id.krohne.com
Emp.: 12
Measuring Instrument Distr
N.A.I.C.S.: 423830
Iyan Gantina *(Mgr-Sls)*

KROMBACHER BRAUEREI BERNHARD SCHADEBERG GMBH & CO. KG

Hagener Strasse 261, Krombach, 57223, Kreuztal, Germany
Tel.: (49) 2732 880 0
Web Site: http://www.krombacher.de
Sales Range: $650-699.9 Million
Emp.: 790
Beer Mfr
N.A.I.C.S.: 312120
Friedrich Schadeberg *(Mng Dir)*

Subsidiaries:

Trinks GmbH (1)

INTERNATIONAL PUBLIC

Im Schleeke 115-116, 38640, Goslar, Germany
Tel.: (49) 53217550
Web Site: http://www.trinks.de
Sales Range: $550-599.9 Million
Emp.: 1,600
Beer & Beverage Distr
N.A.I.C.S.: 424810
Norbert Badenmuller *(Mng Dir)*

KROMEK GROUP PLC

NETPark Thomas Wright Way, Sedgefield, Durham, TS21 3FD, United Kingdom
Tel.: (44) 1740626060
Web Site: https://www.kromek.com
Year Founded: 2003
KMK—(AIM)
Rev.: $14,055,117
Assets: $95,254,920
Liabilities: $27,294,245
Net Worth: $67,960,675
Earnings: ($7,267,875)
Emp.: 139
Fiscal Year-end: 04/30/21
X-Ray Imaging & Radiation Detection Products Mfr
N.A.I.C.S.: 339112
Arnab Basu *(CEO)*

Subsidiaries:

eV Products Inc. (1)
143 Zehner School Rd, Zelienople, PA 16063
Tel.: (724) 352-5288
Web Site: https://www.kromek.com
Sales Range: $1-9.9 Million
Emp.: 40
X-Ray & Gamma-Ray Radiation Sensors Designer & Mfr
N.A.I.C.S.: 334511
Rick Smith *(VP & Gen Mgr)*

KROMET INTERNATIONAL INC.

200 Sheldon Drive, Cambridge, N1R 7K1, ON, Canada
Tel.: (519) 623-2511
Web Site: https://www.kromet.com
Year Founded: 1967
Rev.: $22,321,200
Emp.: 200
Metal Component Mfr
N.A.I.C.S.: 332510
John Leitch *(VP-New Bus Dev)*

Subsidiaries:

Kromet Asia Ltd. (1)
6th Floor St John's Building 33 Garden Road, Central, China (Hong Kong)
Tel.: (852) 7712240298
Automobile Parts Distr
N.A.I.C.S.: 423120
Solomon Ngan *(Pres)*

Kromet International Inc. - Alumabrite Division (1)
20 Milburn Road, Hamilton, L8E 3L9, ON, Canada
Tel.: (905) 561-7773
Automobile Parts Mfr
N.A.I.C.S.: 332119

KROMI LOGISTIK AG

Tarpenring 11, 22419, Hamburg, Germany
Tel.: (49) 405371510 De
Web Site: http://www.kromi.de
Year Founded: 1964
K1R—(DEU)
Rev.: $98,873,320
Assets: $48,147,008
Liabilities: $19,651,840
Net Worth: $28,495,168
Earnings: $1,351,064
Emp.: 212
Fiscal Year-end: 06/30/22
Logistic Services
N.A.I.C.S.: 541614

AND PRIVATE COMPANIES

KRONES AG

Bernd Paulini *(CEO & Member-Mgmt Bd)*

Subsidiaries:

KROMI CZ s.r.o. (1)
tr Spojencu 22, 779 00, Olomouc, Ruzodol, Czech Republic
Tel.: (420) 602518318
Business Management Software Solutions Services
N.A.I.C.S.: 513210

KROMI Slovakia s.r.o. (1)
Marianska 24, 971 01, Prievidza, Slovakia
Tel.: (421) 465198540
Sales Range: $25-49.9 Million
Emp.: 10
Business Management Consulting Services
N.A.I.C.S.: 541618

Kromi Logistica Do Brasil Ltda. (1)
Rua Dr Joao Colin 1 629, Joinville, 89204-003, Santa Catarina, Brazil
Tel.: (55) 4730272081
Web Site: https://www.kromi.com.br
Integrated Tool Mfr
N.A.I.C.S.: 333517

Kromi Logistik Ag (1)
4 rue du Vieux Faton, 38500, Voiron, France
Tel.: (33) 616792186
Integrated Tool Mfr
N.A.I.C.S.: 333517

Kromi Logistik Ag (1)
Ul Logisticzna 1, 55-040, Kobierzyce, Poland
Tel.: (48) 727408000
Integrated Tool Mfr
N.A.I.C.S.: 333517

Kromi Logistik Spain S.L. (1)
C/ Miren Mtz Saez del Burgo no 2-4 Bajo, 01008, Vitoria-Gasteiz, Spain
Tel.: (34) 945156878
Integrated Tool Mfr
N.A.I.C.S.: 333517

KRON TELEKOMUNIKASYON HIZMETLERI A.S.

ITU Ayazaga Kampusu Koru Yolu ARI 3 Binasi Teknokent No B401, Maslak, 34467, Istanbul, Turkiye
Tel.: (90) 2122865122
Web Site: http://www.kron.com.tr
Sales Range: $10-24.9 Million
Emp.: 60
Telecommunications Equipment Mfr
N.A.I.C.S.: 334220
Lutfi Yenel *(Chm)*

Subsidiaries:

Kron Telecommunication Technologies Private Limited (1)
Street 80 No 2 G-6/4, Islamabad, Pakistan
Tel.: (92) 3365879737
Wireless Telecommunication Services
N.A.I.C.S.: 517112
Lutfi Yenel *(Chm)*

KRONES AG

Bohmerwaldstrasse 5, 93073, Neutraubling, Germany
Tel.: (49) 9401700
Web Site: http://www.krones.de
Sales Range: $1-4.9 Billion
Emp.: 8,865
Automated Packaging
N.A.I.C.S.: 333993
Hans-Juergen Thaus *(Deputy Chm)*

Subsidiaries:

Automata S.A. (1)
Calzada Atanasio Tzul 21 00 Zona 12 Empresarial El Cortijo II, Ofibodega No 504, Guatemala, Guatemala
Tel.: (502) 24154100
Chemical Products Mfr
N.A.I.C.S.: 325998

Dekron GmbH (1)
Siemensstr 21, 65779, Kelkheim, Germany
Tel.: (49) 6195676770
Web Site: http://www.dekron.tech
Packaging Machinery Mfr
N.A.I.C.S.: 333993
Friederike Kalusche *(Mng Dir)*

Ecomac Gebrauchtmaschinen GmbH (1)
Berliner Str 31, 93073, Neutraubling, Germany
Tel.: (49) 940193050
Web Site: http://www.ecomac.de
Beverage Industry Used Machine Whslr
N.A.I.C.S.: 423830
Ludwig Stierstorfer *(Mng Dir)*

Evoguard GmbH (1)
Dr Hermann Kronseder Strässe 1, Nittenau, 93149, Schwandorf, Germany
Tel.: (49) 9436307700
Web Site: http://www.evoguard.com
Valve Mfr
N.A.I.C.S.: 332911
Martin Zierer *(Mng Dir)*

Gernep GmbH (1)
Benzstrasse 6, 93092, Barbing, Germany
Tel.: (49) 940192130
Web Site: http://www.gernep.de
Industrial Machinery Mfr
N.A.I.C.S.: 333248
Martin Hammerschmid *(Mng Dir)*

HST Maschinenbau GmbH (1)
Werkstrasse 23, 23942, Dassow, Germany
Tel.: (49) 3882688780
Web Site: http://www.hst-homogenizers.com
Homogenizer Machine Mfr
N.A.I.C.S.: 333241
Mario Heinzner *(Mgr-Svc)*

IPS Integrated Packaging Systems FZCO (1)
Tower Bldg No 67 Second Floor St 90 Fifth Settlement, New Cairo, Egypt
Tel.: (20) 225371201
Plastics Bottle Mfr
N.A.I.C.S.: 326160
Amir Ahmed *(Reg Dir)*

Integrated Packaging Systems (IPS) FZCO (1)
Dubai Airport Free Zone 4WA Office 219, PO Box 54337, Dubai, United Arab Emirates
Tel.: (971) 42996662
Web Site: http://www.ipsdubai.com
Plastics Product Mfr
N.A.I.C.S.: 326199
Paula Martins *(Controller-Bus & Ops-Mgr)*

Integrated Packaging Systems Inc. (1)
200 Sheffield St, Cambridge, N3C 1C5, ON, Canada
Web Site: http://www.integratedpackaginggroup.com
Plastics Product Mfr
N.A.I.C.S.: 326111

Integrated Plastics Systems AG (1)
Langgasse 51, 6340, Baar, Switzerland
Tel.: (41) 417106848
Web Site: http://www.ipsplastics.com
Plastics Bottle Mfr
N.A.I.C.S.: 326160

Javlyn Process Systems LLC (1)
3136 S Winton Rd Ste 102, Rochester, NY 14623
Tel.: (585) 424-5580
Web Site: http://www.javlyn.com
Engineeering Services
N.A.I.C.S.: 541330
Ron Bielinis *(Mng Dir)*

Konplan S.R.O. (1)
Podebradova 2842 1, 301 00, Plzen, Czech Republic
Tel.: (420) 377918109
Chemical Products Mfr
N.A.I.C.S.: 325998

Kosme Gesellschaft mbH (1)
Gewerbestrasse 3, 2601, Sollenau, Austria
Tel.: (43) 26284110
Chemical Products Mfr
N.A.I.C.S.: 325998
Maria Steiner *(Head-HR)*

Kosme S.R.L. (1)
Via dell Artigianato 4, Roverbella, 46048, Mantua, Italy
Tel.: (39) 0376751011
Chemical Products Mfr
N.A.I.C.S.: 325998
Stefania Gallo *(Mgr-Pur)*

Krones (Thailand) Co. Ltd. (1)
Interlink Tower 39th Floor 1858 138 Bangna Trad Road, Bangna, Bangkok, 10260, Thailand
Tel.: (66) 27636500
Chemical Products Mfr
N.A.I.C.S.: 325998
Jaturapol Yimyong *(Mgr)*

Krones AG (1)
Kapellenweg 5, Buttwil, 5632, Muri, Switzerland
Tel.: (41) 566755040
Chemical Products Mfr
N.A.I.C.S.: 325998
Rene Noest-Luethi *(Mng Dir)*

Krones Andina Ltda. (1)
Calle 80 69 70 Local 30, Bogota, Colombia
Tel.: (57) 13108748
Chemical Products Mfr
N.A.I.C.S.: 325998
Cesar Ortiz *(Engr-Svc)*

Krones Angola - Representacoes, Comercio e Industria, Lda. (1)
Armazem A 07 Gleba GU03 Zona CCB1 Municipio de Belas, Talatona, Luanda, Angola
Tel.: (244) 226435801
Chemical Products Mfr
N.A.I.C.S.: 325998
Thomas Schmidt *(Gen Mgr)*

Krones Asia Ltd. (1)
Unit 1102 11 F The Metropolis Tower 10 Metropolis Drive, Hunghom, Kowloon, China (Hong Kong)
Tel.: (852) 27212618
Chemical Products Mfr
N.A.I.C.S.: 325998

Krones Bangladesh Limited (1)
Level 13 Concord Colosseum Plot 156 Road 12, Block E Banani Kemal Ataturk Avenue, Dhaka, 1212, Bangladesh
Tel.: (880) 1713062283
Chemical Products Mfr
N.A.I.C.S.: 325998

Krones Chile SpA (1)
Berlin 1015 8900198, San Miguel, Santiago, Chile
Tel.: (56) 232658530
Chemical Products Mfr
N.A.I.C.S.: 325998
Juan Enrique Gonzalez *(Mgr)*

Krones Filipinas Inc. (1)
Unit DEF 10th Floor Inoza Tower 40th Street Bonifacio Global City, 1630, Taguig, Philippines
Tel.: (63) 28223265
Chemical Products Mfr
N.A.I.C.S.: 325998
Lemuel Mainot *(Engr-Field Svc)*

Krones Iberica, S.A.U. (1)
Av de Burgos 19, 28036, Madrid, Spain
Tel.: (34) 914561205
Chemical Products Mfr
N.A.I.C.S.: 325998
Tino Knoll *(Mng Dir)*

Krones Inc. (1)
9600 S 58th St, Franklin, WI 53132-6241
Tel.: (414) 409-4000
Web Site: http://www.krones.com
Automated Packaging
N.A.I.C.S.: 333993
Holger Beckmann *(Pres, CEO & CFO)*

Subsidiary (Domestic):

Javlyn Inc. (2)
3136 S Winton Rd Ste 102, Rochester, NY 14623
Tel.: (585) 424-5580
Web Site: http://www.javlyn.com
Sales Range: $1-9.9 Million
Emp.: 26
Process Technology for Food, Dairy & Beverage Industry
N.A.I.C.S.: 541330
Victor Tifone *(Pres)*

Process & Data Automation, LLC (2)
5451 Merwin Ln, Erie, PA 16510
Tel.: (814) 866-9600
Web Site: http://www.processanddata.com
General Purpose Machinery Mfr
N.A.I.C.S.: 333993
Aarohi Limaye *(Engr-Control)*

Trans-Market Sales & Equipment, Inc. (2)
8915 Maislin Dr, Tampa, FL 33637 (80%)
Tel.: (813) 988-6146
Web Site: http://www.transmarket.com
Sales Range: $1-9.9 Million
Emp.: 24
Food Product Machinery Mfr
N.A.I.C.S.: 333241

Krones India Pvt. Ltd. (1)
Prasad Enclave 118 119 3rd Floor 5th Main Industrial Suburb 2nd Stage, Yeshwanthpur, Bengaluru, 560022, India
Tel.: (91) 8066748300
Chemical Products Mfr
N.A.I.C.S.: 325998
Harish Hanagudu *(Mng Dir)*

Krones Japan Co. Ltd. (1)
Gibraltar Seimei Gotanda Building 2F 15 7 Nishi Gotanda 2 Chome, Shinagawa ku, Tokyo, 141-0031, Japan
Tel.: (81) 334912144
Chemical Products Mfr
N.A.I.C.S.: 325998
Kenji Sato *(Head-Fin)*

Krones Kazakhstan Too (1)
Al-Farabi 65, 50040, Almaty, Kazakhstan
Tel.: (7) 7272582568
Chemical Products Mfr
N.A.I.C.S.: 325998

Krones Korea Ltd. (1)
A 8th Floor MSTATE Building 114 Beobwonro, Songpa-gu, Seoul, 05854, Korea (South)
Tel.: (82) 222038920
Chemical Products Mfr
N.A.I.C.S.: 325998
Dongwook Kim *(Head-Svc)*

Krones LCS Center East Africa Limited (1)
Thika Highway and Eastern Bypass, PO Box 63674-00619, Sukari Industrial Estate Ruiru Muthaiga, Nairobi, Kenya
Tel.: (254) 709540000
Chemical Products Mfr
N.A.I.C.S.: 325998
Moses Kasuva *(Mgr-Svc)*

Krones LCS Center West Africa Limited (1)
Acme Road Ogba Industrial Scheme Plot 7A Block C Ogba, Ikeja, Lagos, Nigeria
Tel.: (234) 14631130
Chemical Products Mfr
N.A.I.C.S.: 325998
Moses Kasuva *(Mgr-Svc)*

Krones Machinery (Taicang) Co. Ltd. (1)
No 9 Ning Bo Dong Lu, Taicang, Suzhou, 215400, Jiangsu, China
Tel.: (86) 51253739300
Chemical Products Mfr
N.A.I.C.S.: 325998
Dan Gong *(Supvr-Comml)*

Krones Machinery Co. Ltd. (1)
6285 Northam Drive Suite 108, Mississauga, L4V 1X5, ON, Canada
Tel.: (905) 364-4900
Chemical Products Mfr
N.A.I.C.S.: 325998
Steve Thomson *(Mgr)*

Krones Machinery Malaysia Sdn. Bhd. (1)
K03-07 02 Tower 3 No1 Jalan Pengaturcara U1 51A Seksyen U1, Shah Alam, 40150, Malaysia
Tel.: (60) 355695611
Chemical Products Mfr
N.A.I.C.S.: 325998
T. S. Yong *(Gen Mgr)*

Krones Makina Sanayi ve Tikaret Ltd. (1)

KRONES AG

Krones AG—(Continued)

Mahmutbey Mah Tasocagi Yolu Cad Agaoglu My Office 212 B Block No 3 3 4, Bagcilar, 34218, Istanbul, Türkiye
Tel.: (90) 2124817474
Chemical Products Mfr
N.A.I.C.S.: 325998

Krones Mex S.A. DE C.V. (1)
Av Jaime Balmes No 8 Int 203 Col Polanco I Seccion, Miguel Hidalgo, 11510, Ciudad Delicias, Mexico
Tel.: (52) 5552796800
Chemical Products Mfr
N.A.I.C.S.: 325998

Krones Nederland B.V. (1)
Tolnasingel 1, 2411, Bodegraven, Netherlands
Tel.: (31) 172211514
Chemical Products Mfr
N.A.I.C.S.: 325998
Boudewijn Kortenhorst *(Mng Dir)*

Krones New Zealand Limited (1)
Unit M 218 Marua Road Mount Wellington, 1051, Auckland, New Zealand
Tel.: (64) 95728148
Chemical Products Mfr
N.A.I.C.S.: 325998
Priyanka Hulikoppe *(Coord-Sls)*

Krones Nordic ApS (1)
Skovlytoften 33, 2840, Copenhagen, Denmark
Tel.: (45) 88323300
Chemical Products Mfr
N.A.I.C.S.: 325998
Dirk Cichon *(Mng Dir)*

Krones Pacific Pty Limited (1)
42 Giffard Street Silverwater, Sydney, 2128, NSW, Australia
Tel.: (61) 296470200
Chemical Products Mfr
N.A.I.C.S.: 325998
Steven Karavendzas *(Sls Mgr)*

Krones Portugal Equipamentos Industriais Lda. (1)
Rua Guerra Junqueiro n 6 E F Queluz de Baixo, 2730-092, Barcarena, Portugal
Tel.: (351) 214342509
Chemical Products Mfr
N.A.I.C.S.: 325998

Krones Romania Prod. S.R.L. (1)
Sos Bucuresti Ploiesti Nr 42 44 Baneasa Business and Technology Park, 13696, Bucharest, Romania
Tel.: (40) 213163539
Chemical Products Mfr
N.A.I.C.S.: 325998
Diana Stoica *(Sls Mgr)*

Krones S.A.R.L (1)
Savoie Hexapole Bat Actipole 4 242 rue, Viviers du Lac, Saint Maurice, 73420, France
Tel.: (33) 479618212
Chemical Products Mfr
N.A.I.C.S.: 325998

Krones S.R.O. (1)
Kovaku 456 28, 150 00, Prague, Czech Republic
Tel.: (420) 220305001
Chemical Products Mfr
N.A.I.C.S.: 325998
Johannes Hafner *(Gen Mgr)*

Krones Sales (Beijing) Co. Ltd. (1)
No 24 Jianguomenwai Dajie, Chao Yang, Beijing, China
Tel.: (86) 1065156365
Chemical Product Whslr
N.A.I.C.S.: 424690
Ivy Li *(Fin Dir)*

Krones Service Europe eood (1)
Boul Alex Malinov 23, Mladost, 1729, Sofia, Bulgaria
Tel.: (359) 29746007
Chemical Products Mfr
N.A.I.C.S.: 325998
Yanko Bakalov *(Engr-Svc)*

Krones Service Europe kft. (1)
Szava utca 5-7, 1107, Budapest, Hungary
Tel.: (36) 12491989

Chemical Products Mfr
N.A.I.C.S.: 325998

Krones Southern Africa (Prop) Ltd. (1)
Private Bag X42, Bryanston, 2021, South Africa
Tel.: (27) 110655700
Chemical Products Mfr
N.A.I.C.S.: 325998
Gert Jacobs *(Project Mgr)*

Krones Spolka z.o.o (1)
Pulawska 303, 02-785, Warsaw, Poland
Tel.: (48) 225494250
Chemical Products Mfr
N.A.I.C.S.: 325998
Pawel Szajkowski *(Mgr-Svc)*

Krones Surlatina S.A. (1)
Blas Parera 745 1602 Florida, Buenos Aires, Vicente Lopez, Argentina
Tel.: (54) 1147300848
Chemical Products Mfr
N.A.I.C.S.: 325998
Nestor De La Vina *(Gen Mgr)*

Krones UK Ltd. (1)
Westregen House Great Bank Road Wingates Ind Park, Westhoughton, Bolton, BL5 3XB, United Kingdom
Tel.: (44) 1942845000
Chemical Products Mfr
N.A.I.C.S.: 325998
Andrew Wilson *(Mng Dir)*

Krones Ukraine LLC (1)
Shovkovichna Str 42 44 Office 2A, Kiev, 02000, Ukraine
Tel.: (380) 445023697
Chemical Products Mfr
N.A.I.C.S.: 325998
Toporov Yuriy *(Mng Dir)*

Krones do Brazil Ltda. (1)
Avenida Presidente Juscelino 1140, 09950-810, Sao Paulo, Brazil
Tel.: (55) 1140795500
Chemical Products Mfr
N.A.I.C.S.: 325998
Renato Brandao *(Mgr-Admin)*

Krones o.o.o (1)
2nd Kazachy Pereulok 4/1, 119180, Moscow, Russia
Tel.: (7) 4955806630
Chemical Products Mfr
N.A.I.C.S.: 325998

Krones-Izumi Processing Pte. Ltd. (1)
14 Robinson Road Far East Finance Building 07 01, Singapore, 048545, Singapore
Tel.: (65) 62024740
Chemical Products Mfr
N.A.I.C.S.: 325998
Victor Lai *(Mng Dir)*

MHT Holding AG (1)
Dr Ruben Rausing Strasse 7, 65239, Hochheim, Germany
Tel.: (49) 61469060
Chemical Products Mfr
N.A.I.C.S.: 325998
Christian Wagner *(CEO)*

MHT USA LLC (1)
665 Hwy 74 S Ste 700, Peachtree City, GA 30269
Tel.: (404) 835-1140
Web Site: http://www.usa.mht-ag.com
Packaging Plastic Product Mfr
N.A.I.C.S.: 326112
Andreas Krampe *(CEO)*

Maquinarias Krones de Venezuela S.A. (1)
Torre Mega IV Ofic 1 A Los Dos Caminos, Caracas, Venezuela
Tel.: (58) 2122392257
Chemical Products Mfr
N.A.I.C.S.: 325998
Samuel Rojas *(Mgr-Acctg)*

Milkron GmbH (1)
Wurzburger Strasse 17, 30880, Laatzen, Germany
Tel.: (49) 511898130
Web Site: http://www.milkron.com
Milk Mfr
N.A.I.C.S.: 311511

Hermann Meyer *(Mng Dir)*

PT. Krones Machinery Indonesia (1)
Tower D Blue 6th Floor, Suite DB 6 Jl Lingkar Luar Barat No 88 Puri Kembangan, Jakarta, 11610, Indonesia
Tel.: (62) 2129527262
Chemical Products Mfr
N.A.I.C.S.: 325998
Lusanto Janto *(Sr Mgr-Sls)*

S.A. Krones N.V. (1)
Parc Scientifique Einstein Rue du Bosquet 17, 1348, Louvain-la-Neuve, Belgium
Tel.: (32) 10480700
Chemical Products Mfr
N.A.I.C.S.: 325998
Willy Tits *(Mgr-On Site & Engr-Field Svc)*

Syskron GmbH (1)
Im Gewerbepark D75, 93059, Regensburg, Germany
Tel.: (49) 9431798570
Web Site: http://www.syskron.com
Information Technology Services
N.A.I.C.S.: 541511
Thomas Bernard *(Mng Dir)*

Syskron X GmbH (1)
Maximilianstrasse 29, 93047, Regensburg, Germany
Tel.: (49) 9431798570
Information Technology Services
N.A.I.C.S.: 541511
Jonas Lehmann *(Product Mgr)*

System Logistics Asia Co. Ltd. (1)
193 53 Lake Rajada Office Complex 14th Floor Ratchadaphisek Road, Klongtoey, Bangkok, 10110, Thailand
Tel.: (66) 225826834
Logistic Services
N.A.I.C.S.: 488510
Marco Squarci *(Dir-Ops)*

System Logistics Corporation (1)
115 Vista Blvd, Arden, NC 28704
Tel.: (828) 654-7500
Logistic Services
N.A.I.C.S.: 488510
Stefano Vitale *(Pres & CEO)*

Subsidiary (Domestic):

Vertique, Inc. (2)
115 Vista Blvd, Arden, NC 28704-9457
Tel.: (828) 654-7500
Web Site: http://www.vertique.com
General Purpose Machinery Mfr
N.A.I.C.S.: 333998

System Logistics GmbH (1)
Oskar von Miller Strasse 6b, 92442, Wackersdorf, Germany
Tel.: (49) 943179857
Web Site: http://www.systemlogistics.com
Logistic Services
N.A.I.C.S.: 488510
Luigi Panzetti *(CEO)*

System Logistics S.P.A. (1)
Via Ghiarola Vecchia 73, 41042, Fiorano Modenese, Italy
Tel.: (39) 0536916111
Chemical Products Mfr
N.A.I.C.S.: 325998
Massimo Boldrini *(Head-Industrial & Ops)*

System Northern Europe AB (1)
Jungmansgatan 12, 211 19, Malmo, Sweden
Tel.: (46) 406278595
Logistic Services
N.A.I.C.S.: 488510

Systemlog De Mexico S.A. DE C.V. (1)
Av Cazadores No 218 Parque Industrial Sierra Madre, Nuevo Leon, 66359, Santa Catarina, Mexico
Tel.: (52) 8150006515
Logistic Services
N.A.I.C.S.: 488510
Paolo Azzolini *(Mgr-Software)*

Trans-Market LLC (1)
8915 Maislin Dr, Tampa, FL 33637
Tel.: (813) 988-6146
Web Site: http://www.transmarket.com
Engineeering Services
N.A.I.C.S.: 541330

Keith Santi *(Pres & CEO)*

Triacos Consulting & Engineering GmbH (1)
An den Gaerten 9, 92665, Altenstadt, Germany
Tel.: (49) 9602944550
Web Site: http://www.triacos.de
Consulting Services
N.A.I.C.S.: 541611
Christian Gradt *(Mng Dir)*

KRONOLOGI ASIA BERHAD

Level 28-D Axiata Tower No 9, Jalan Stesen Sentral 5 Kuala Lumpur Sentral, 50470, Kuala Lumpur, Malaysia
Tel.: (60) 327735700
Web Site: https://www.kronologi.asia
KRONO—(KLS)
Rev.: $66,505,480
Assets: $124,302,850
Liabilities: $36,107,112
Net Worth: $88,195,738
Earnings: $5,185,784
Fiscal Year-end: 01/31/23
Enterprise Data Management Software
N.A.I.C.S.: 513210
Chris Chan *(Mgr-Fin Grp)*

Subsidiaries:

Kronicles (Singapore) Pte. Ltd. (1)
51 Changi Business Park Central 2 The Signature 06-06, Singapore, 486066, Singapore
Tel.: (65) 67259027
Web Site: https://www.kronicles.asia
IT Management Services
N.A.I.C.S.: 541519

Quantum Storage (Hong Kong) Limited (1)
Suite 1908 19F Exchange Tower Wang Chiu Road, Kowloon Bay, Kowloon, China (Hong Kong)
Tel.: (852) 39968085
Information Technology Services
N.A.I.C.S.: 541511

Subsidiary (Non-US):

Quantum Taiwan Limited (2)
9F-4 No 57 Sec 1 Chongqing S Rd, Zhongzheng Dist, Taipei, 10045, Taiwan
Tel.: (886) 223316108
Web Site: https://www.qd-taiwan.com
Information Technology Services
N.A.I.C.S.: 541511

Quantum Storage South Asia Sdn. Bhd. (1)
Level 28-D Axiata Tower No 9 Jalan Stesen Sentral 5 KL Sentral, 50470, Kuala Lumpur, Malaysia
Tel.: (60) 322614488
Information Technology Services
N.A.I.C.S.: 541511

Sandz Solutions Philippines, Inc. (1)
6th Floor CYA Land Building 110 Rada St, Legaspi Village, Makati, 1229, Philippines
Tel.: (63) 288885757
Web Site: https://www.sandz.com
IT Management Services
N.A.I.C.S.: 541519

KRONOS PRESS DISTRIBUTION AGENCY PLC LTD

Nisou Industrial Area Nicosia-Limassol Old Road, PO Box 23694, Nisou, 2571, Nicosia, Cyprus
Tel.: (357) 22711111
Web Site:
http://www.kronospublic.com
Year Founded: 1986
Emp.: 200
Newspaper Publishers
N.A.I.C.S.: 513110

Subsidiaries:

Kronos Express Ltd (1)
5 Pangkratiou Strovolos Industrial Zone, Nicosia, 2033, Cyprus
Tel.: (357) 22570073

Web Site: http://www.kronosexpress.com
Emp.: 50
Courier Service
N.A.I.C.S.: 492110
Giorgos Athinis *(Gen Mgr)*

KROPZ PLC
35 Verulam Road, Hitchin, SG5 1QE, United Kingdom
Tel.: (44) 7789768601   UK
Web Site: https://www.kropz.com
Year Founded: 2018
KRPZ—(AIM)
Rev.: $116,000
Assets: $119,490,000
Liabilities: $92,488,000
Net Worth: $27,002,000
Earnings: ($97,824,000)
Emp.: 19
Fiscal Year-end: 12/31/22
Nitrogenous Fertilizer Manufacturing
N.A.I.C.S.: 325311
Mark Summers *(CEO)*

KROSAKI HARIMA CORPORATION
1-1 Higashihama-cho, Yahatahigashi-ku, Kitakyushu, 806-8586, Fukuoka, Japan
Tel.: (81) 936227224   JP
Web Site: https://www.krosaki.co.jp
5352—(FKA)
Rev.: $1,170,161,690
Assets: $1,183,315,590
Liabilities: $570,588,420
Net Worth: $612,727,170
Earnings: $88,719,420
Emp.: 4,904
Fiscal Year-end: 03/31/24
Clay Refractory Mfr
N.A.I.C.S.: 327120
Masakazu Soejima *(Mng Corp Officer)*

Subsidiaries:

K&K Corporation   (1)
1-3 Higashihamamachi, Yahatanishi-ku, Kitakyushu, 806-0002, Fukuoka, Japan
Tel.: (81) 936314411
Web Site: http://www.kk-corporation.com
Business Support Services
N.A.I.C.S.: 561499

KROSAKI HARIMA CORPORATION - Ako Plant
1061 Tenwa, Ako, 678-0256, Hyogo, Japan
Tel.: (81) 791431211
Web Site: http://www.krosaki.co.jp
Refractory Products Mfr
N.A.I.C.S.: 327120

KROSAKI HARIMA CORPORATION - Chiba Plant   (1)
1 Nihamacho, Chuo-ku, Chiba, 260-0130, Japan
Tel.: (81) 432635671
Sales Range: $25-49.9 Million
Emp.: 3
Refractory Products Mfr
N.A.I.C.S.: 327120
Kenji Urata *(Mgr)*

KROSAKI HARIMA CORPORATION - Fine Ceramics Plant   (1)
1-1 Higashihamamachi, Yahatanishi-ku, Kitakyushu, 806-8586, Fukuoka, Japan
Tel.: (81) 936418035
Ceramic Mfr
N.A.I.C.S.: 327120

KROSAKI HARIMA CORPORATION - Furnace Division   (1)
9F Seifun Kaikan Bldg 6-15 Nihonbashi kabutocho, Chuo-ku, Tokyo, 103-0026, Japan
Tel.: (81) 336690614
Sales Range: $50-74.9 Million
Emp.: 130
Furnace Mfr
N.A.I.C.S.: 333994
Hiroshiko Okumura *(Pres)*

KROSAKI HARIMA CORPORATION - Kisarazu Monolithic Plant   (1)
7-1 Tsukiji, Kisarazu, 292-0835, Chiba, Japan
Tel.: (81) 438370121
Web Site: http://www.krosaki.co.jp
Sales Range: $50-74.9 Million
Emp.: 140
Refractory Products Mfr
N.A.I.C.S.: 327120

KROSAKI HARIMA CORPORATION - Nagoya Taphole Clay Plant   (1)
Nippon Steel Corp 5-3 Tokai-machi, Tokai, 476-0015, Aichi, Japan
Tel.: (81) 526032552
Refractory Products Mfr
N.A.I.C.S.: 327120

KROSAKI HARIMA CORPORATION - Oita Taphole Clay Plant   (1)
Oita Works Nippon Steel Corporation 1 Nishinosu, Oita, 870-0992, Japan
Tel.: (81) 975585036
Web Site: http://www.krosaki.co.jp
Refractory Products Mfr
N.A.I.C.S.: 327120

KROSAKI HARIMA CORPORATION - Takasago Monolithic Plant   (1)
1-3-1 Shinhama Araicho, Takasago, 676-8513, Hyogo, Japan
Tel.: (81) 794431400
Web Site: http://www.krosaki.co.jp
Sales Range: $200-249.9 Million
Emp.: 1,000
Refractory Products Mfr
N.A.I.C.S.: 327120
Hamamoto Yasuo *(Pres)*

KROSAKI HARIMA CORPORATION - Takasago Plant   (1)
3-1 Shinhama Araicho, Takasago, 676-8513, Hyogo, Japan
Tel.: (81) 794431405
Ceramics Mfr & Supplier
N.A.I.C.S.: 327110

KROSAKI HARIMA CORPORATION - Yahata Monolithic Plant   (1)
1-1 Higashihamamachi, Yahatanishi-ku, Kitakyushu, 806-8586, Fukuoka, Japan
Tel.: (81) 936227224
Web Site: http://www.krosaki.co.jp
Sales Range: $450-499.9 Million
Emp.: 2,000
Refractory Products Mfr
N.A.I.C.S.: 327120

KROSAKI HARIMA CORPORATION - Yahata Plant   (1)
1-1 Higashihamamachi, Yahatanishi-ku, Kitakyushu, 806-8586, Fukuoka, Japan
Tel.: (81) 936227224
Web Site: http://www.krosaki.co.jp
Sales Range: $450-499.9 Million
Emp.: 1,500
Refractory Products Mfr
N.A.I.C.S.: 327120

Krohari Chikuro Corporation   (1)
1-1 Higashihamamachi, Yahatanishi-ku, Kitakyushu, 806-8586, Fukuoka, Japan
Tel.: (81) 936412143
Construction Equipment Mfr
N.A.I.C.S.: 333248

Krosaki AMR Refractarios S.A.U.   (1)
Poligono Ibaiondo 31, 20120, Hernani, Gipuzkoa, Spain
Tel.: (34) 943557500
Web Site: http://www.krosaki-amr.com
Sales Range: $25-49.9 Million
Emp.: 80
Refractory Products Mfr
N.A.I.C.S.: 327120

Krosaki Harima (Shanghai) Enterprise Management Co., Ltd.
Room 3204 New Town Center No 83 Lou Shan Guan Road, Changning District, Shanghai, China
Tel.: (86) 215 102 8036
Web Site: https://www.krosaki.net
Emp.: 34
Steel Products Mfr
N.A.I.C.S.: 331110

Krosaki Harima (Shanghai) International Trading Co., Ltd.   (1)
Longzhimeng Building No 1018 Room 2201 Changning Road, Changning Dist, Shanghai, 200070, China
Tel.: (86) 2151028036
Sales Range: $25-49.9 Million
Emp.: 20
Refractory Products Supplier
N.A.I.C.S.: 423320
M. Liu *(Mgr)*

Krosaki Harima Europe B.V.   (1)
Rooswijkweg 84, Velsen-Noord, 1951 MJ, Velsen, Netherlands
Tel.: (31) 251228030
Construction Equipment Mfr
N.A.I.C.S.: 333248
Soumen Kundu *(Mgr-Technical Srvs)*

Krosaki USA Inc.   (1)
11065 Broadway Ste E, Crown Point, IN 46307
Tel.: (219) 661-8531
Web Site: http://www.krosakiusa.com
Sales Range: $25-49.9 Million
Emp.: 15
Refractory Products Mfr
N.A.I.C.S.: 327120
Yohsuke Shimazaki *(Sec)*

Refractaria, S.A.   (1)
Buenavista 13, Asturias, 33187, Siero, Spain
Tel.: (34) 98 574 0600
Web Site: https://www.refractaria.com
Steel Products Mfr
N.A.I.C.S.: 331110

SN Refratecture Tokai Co., Ltd.   (1)
1 Minamifuji Ogakie-cho, Kariya, 448-0813, Aichi, Japan
Tel.: (81) 566213626
Web Site: http://www.snrt.co.jp
Emp.: 32
Refractory Products Mfr
N.A.I.C.S.: 327120

TRL Krosaki China Limited   (1)
Metallurgical and Chemical industrial Park Bayuquan, Yingkou, Liaoning, China
Tel.: (86) 4177233808
Construction Equipment Mfr
N.A.I.C.S.: 333248

Wuxi Krosaki Sujia Refractories Co., Ltd.   (1)
No 4 Fu Chuan Rd Qianqiao Town, Huishan Dist, Wuxi, Jiangsu, China
Tel.: (86) 51083234241
Refractory Products Supplier
N.A.I.C.S.: 423320

Yingkou Krosakiharima Refractories Co., Ltd.   (1)
Jinlongind Park, Dashiqiao, Liaoning, China
Tel.: (86) 4175211852
Construction Equipment Mfr
N.A.I.C.S.: 333248

KROSWANG GMBH
Kickendorf 8, 4710, Grieskirchen, Austria
Tel.: (43) 7248 685 94
Web Site: http://www.kroeswang.at
Grocery Stores
N.A.I.C.S.: 445110
Elisabeth Kroeswang *(Mng Dir)*

Subsidiaries:

R&S Gourmet Express Vertriebsges.m.b.H.   (1)
Gourmetstrasse 1-3, 5071, Wals-Siezenheim, Austria
Tel.: (43) 662669110
Web Site: http://www.gourmet-express.at
Groceries Whslr & Distr
N.A.I.C.S.: 424490
Alexander Wallner *(Officer-Authorized)*

KRSNAA DIAGNOSTICS LTD.
S No 243 A-Hissa No 6/6 Cts No 4519 Near Mayur Trade Centre, Chinchwad, Pune, 411019, India
Tel.: (91) 2046954695
Web Site:
   https://www.krsnaadiagnostics.com
Year Founded: 2011
KRSNAA—(NSE)
Rev.: $69,137,523
Assets: $124,200,395
Liabilities: $23,362,931
Net Worth: $100,837,464
Earnings: $8,478,152
Emp.: 1,000
Fiscal Year-end: 03/31/23
Diagnostic Services
N.A.I.C.S.: 621512
Pallavi Jain *(Mng Dir)*

KRUG INC
421 Manitou Drive, Kitchener, N2C 1L5, ON, Canada
Tel.: (519) 748-5100
Web Site: http://www.krug.ca
Year Founded: 1880
Rev.: $93,194,886
Emp.: 685
Office Furniture Mfr
N.A.I.C.S.: 337211
Len Ruby *(Pres)*

KRUGER INC.
3285 Chemin Bedford, Montreal, H3S 1G5, QC, Canada
Tel.: (514) 737-1131   QC
Web Site: http://www.kruger.com
Year Founded: 1921
Sales Range: $1-4.9 Billion
Emp.: 5,000
Publication Paper Mfr
N.A.I.C.S.: 322120
Jean Majeau *(Sr VP-Corp Affairs & Comm)*

Subsidiaries:

Corner Brook Pulp & Paper Limited   (1)
Mill Rd, Corner Brook, A2H 6J4, NL, Canada   (100%)
Tel.: (709) 637-3000
Web Site: http://www.cbppl.com
Sales Range: $200-249.9 Million
Emp.: 600
Pulp, Paper & Newsprint Mill
N.A.I.C.S.: 322120

Kruger - Brampton Mill   (1)
10 Pedigree Court, Brampton, L6T 5T8, ON, Canada   (100%)
Tel.: (905) 759-1012
Web Site: http://www.krupack.com
Sales Range: $50-74.9 Million
Emp.: 215
Packaging Plant
N.A.I.C.S.: 322211
Derek Gracias *(Mgr-Sls)*

Kruger - Bromptonville Mill   (1)
220 Windsor Road, Sherbrooke, J1C 0E6, QC, Canada   (100%)
Tel.: (819) 846-2721
Web Site: http://www.kruger.com
Sales Range: $125-149.9 Million
Emp.: 450
Newsprint Mill Mfr
N.A.I.C.S.: 322120

Kruger - La Salle Mill   (1)
7474 Cordner St, La Salle, H8N 2W3, QC, Canada   (100%)
Tel.: (514) 366-8050
Sales Range: $50-74.9 Million
Emp.: 225
Corrugated & Solid Fiber Boxes
N.A.I.C.S.: 322211

Kruger - Montreal Mill   (1)
5845 Place Turcot, Montreal, H4C 1V9, QC, Canada   (100%)
Tel.: (514) 934-0600
Web Site: http://www.kruger.com
Sales Range: $75-99.9 Million
Emp.: 225
Packaging Mfr
N.A.I.C.S.: 322211

Kruger - Trois Rivieres Mill   (1)
3735 Gene-H Kruger Boulevard, PO Box 188, Trois Rivieres, G9A 6B1, QC, Canada   (100%)
Tel.: (819) 375-1691

KRUGER INC.

Kruger Inc.—(Continued)
Web Site: http://www.kruger.com
Sales Range: $450-499.9 Million
Emp.: 1,250
Newsprint Mill Coated Paper Recycled Fiber Mfr
N.A.I.C.S.: 322120

Kruger Products L.P. (1)
1900 Minnesota Court Suite 200, Mississauga, L5N 5R5, ON, Canada (85.3%)
Tel.: (905) 812-6900
Web Site: http://www.krugerproducts.ca
Sales Range: $400-449.9 Million
Emp.: 125
Household & Commercial Tissue Paper Products Mfr & Marketer
N.A.I.C.S.: 322291
Mario Gosselin (CEO)

Plant (Domestic):

Kruger Products L.P. - Crabtree Mill (2)
100 1re Avenue, Crabtree, J0K 1B0, QC, Canada
Tel.: (450) 754-2855
Sales Range: $25-49.9 Million
Emp.: 20
Wood Products Mfr
N.A.I.C.S.: 321211

Kruger Products L.P. - Gatineau Mill (2)
20 Laurier Street, PO Box 3200, Station B, Gatineau, J8X 4H3, QC, Canada
Tel.: (819) 595-5302
Web Site: http://www.krugerproducts.ca
Sales Range: $400-449.9 Million
Tissue Paper Mill
N.A.I.C.S.: 322120
Pascal Perreault (Gen Mgr)

Plant (US):

Kruger Products L.P. - Memphis Mill (2)
400 Mahannah Ave, Memphis, TN 38107
Tel.: (901) 260-3900
Wood Products Mfr
N.A.I.C.S.: 321211

Plant (Domestic):

Kruger Products L.P. - New Westminster Mill (2)
1625 5th Avenue, New Westminster, V3M 1Z7, BC, Canada
Tel.: (604) 522-5711
Wood Products Mfr
N.A.I.C.S.: 321211

Kruger Products L.P. - Sherbrooke Mill (2)
2888 rue du College, CP 240, Succursale Lennoxville, Sherbrooke, J1M 1Z4, QC, Canada
Tel.: (819) 565-8220
Wood Products Mfr
N.A.I.C.S.: 321211

Subsidiary (Domestic):

Metro Paper Industries Inc (2)
111 Manville Road, Toronto, M1L 4J2, ON, Canada
Tel.: (416) 757-2737
Paper Products Mfr
N.A.I.C.S.: 424130

Kruger Urban Forest Products, Inc. (1)
220 Windsor Rd, PO Box 100, Sherbrooke, J1C 0E6, QC, Canada (100%)
Tel.: (819) 846-2721
Web Site: http://www.br.kruger.com
Sales Range: $125-149.9 Million
Emp.: 400
Newsprint
N.A.I.C.S.: 322120

Subsidiary (Domestic):

Scierie Parent, Inc. (2)
PO Box 100, Parent, La Tuque, G0X 3P0, QC, Canada (100%)
Tel.: (819) 667-2711
Web Site: http://www.kruger.com

Sales Range: $50-74.9 Million
Emp.: 150
Sawmills
N.A.I.C.S.: 321113

Kruger Wayagamack Inc. (1)
Ile-de-la-Potherie, Trois Rivieres, G9A 5E9, QC, Canada
Tel.: (819) 373-9230
Wood Products Mfr
N.A.I.C.S.: 321211

Kruger Wines and Spirits (1)
1250 Nobel Street Suite 275, Boucherville, J4B 5H1, QC, Canada
Tel.: (450) 645-9777
Wood Products Mfr
N.A.I.C.S.: 321211

Plant (Domestic):

Kruger Wines and Spirits - MONTREAL PRODUCTION PLANT (2)
2021 rue des Futailles, Montreal, H1N 3M7, QC, Canada
Tel.: (450) 645-9777
Wood Products Mfr
N.A.I.C.S.: 321211

Papeles Venezolanos, S.A. (1)
Urb El Rosal Avenida Las Mercedes con calles, Guaicaipuro y Carabobo, Edif Forum Piso 8, Caracas, 1060, Venezuela
Tel.: (58) 212 953 8322
Web Site: http://www.paveca.com.ve
Newspaper Operations
N.A.I.C.S.: 322120

KRUK S.A.
st Wolowska 8, 51-116, Wroclaw, Poland
Tel.: (48) 717902800
Web Site: https://pl.kruk.eu
Year Founded: 1998
KRU—(WAR)
Rev.: $437,939,785
Assets: $2,522,486,020
Liabilities: $1,559,373,726
Net Worth: $963,112,294
Earnings: $250,051,066
Emp.: 3,339
Fiscal Year-end: 12/31/23
Collection Agencies
N.A.I.C.S.: 561440
Piotr Krupa (Chm-Mgmt Bd)

Subsidiaries:

AgeCredit S.r.l. (1)
Via Dell'Arrigoni 308, 47522, Cesena, Italy
Tel.: (39) 0547304390
Web Site: https://www.agecredit.it
Financial Services
N.A.I.C.S.: 523999

KRUK Ceska a Slovenska republika s.r.o. (1)
Czechoslovak Army 954/7, 500 03, Hradec Kralove, Czech Republic
Tel.: (420) 498774200
Web Site: https://cz.kruk.eu
Portfolio Management Services
N.A.I.C.S.: 523940

KRUK Deutschland GmbH (1)
Friedrichstrasse 79, 10117, Berlin, Germany
Tel.: (49) 3081875812
Web Site: https://de.kruk.eu
Portfolio Management Services
N.A.I.C.S.: 523940

KRUK Espana S.L. Unipersonal (1)
C de Juan Ignacio Luca de Tena 14, 28027, Madrid, Spain
Tel.: (34) 91 038 9391
Portfolio Management Services
N.A.I.C.S.: 523940

Kancelaria Prawna Raven P.Krupa Sp. k. (1)
Ul Wolowska 8, 51-116, Wroclaw, Poland
Tel.: (48) 71 790 2800
Web Site: https://www.kancelariaraven.pl
Law firm
N.A.I.C.S.: 541110

Rejestr Dluznikow ERIF BIG S.A. (1)
Plac Bankowy 2, 00-095, Warsaw, Poland
Tel.: (48) 22 59 42 530
Web Site: http://www.erif.pl
Credit Investigation Services
N.A.I.C.S.: 561450

KRUNG THAI BANK PUBLIC COMPANY LIMITED
Building 1 35 Sukhumvit Road, Klong Toey Nua Subdistrict Wattana District, Bangkok, 10110, Thailand
Tel.: (66) 21111111 TH
Web Site: https://krungthai.com
Year Founded: 1966
KGTFF—(OTCIQ)
Rev.: $4,190,215,439
Assets: $101,138,092,374
Liabilities: $89,564,616,698
Net Worth: $11,573,475,676
Earnings: $1,108,848,857
Emp.: 16,421
Fiscal Year-end: 12/31/23
Commercial Banking Services
N.A.I.C.S.: 522110
Krairit Euchukanonchai (Chm-Exec Bd & Vice Chm)

Subsidiaries:

Cermas Company Limited (1)
65/224 Chamnan Phenjati Business Center 27Th Floor Rama 9 Road, Huaykwang, Bangkok, 10310, Thailand (10%)
Tel.: (66) 22 487 0603
Web Site: https://www.cermas.com
Sales Range: Less than $1 Million
Mining
N.A.I.C.S.: 212390

K.M.B. International Company Limited (1)
401 Abico Building 2nd Floor Moo 8 Phaholyothin Road, Khookhot, Lumlooka, Pathumthani, 12130, Thailand (10%)
Tel.: (66) 29992575770
Trading Company
N.A.I.C.S.: 522210

KTB Advisory Co., Ltd. (1)
900 Tonson Tower 9B Fl Phloen Chit Rd, Lumpini Pathumwan, Bangkok, 10330, Thailand
Tel.: (66) 2 257 0550
Financial Advisory Services
N.A.I.C.S.: 523940

KTB Computer Services Co., Ltd. (1)
No 22 Sawai Brown 2 Bldg Soi Sukhumvit 1 Sukhumvit Rd, Klong Toey Nua Wattana, Bangkok, 10110, Thailand
Tel.: (66) 2 646 8000
Web Site: http://www.ktbcs.co.th
Information Technology Consulting Services
N.A.I.C.S.: 541512

KTB General Services Co., Ltd. (1)
No 96/12 Soi Ladprao 106 boonudom 1, Phlapphla Subdistrict Wang Thonglang District, Bangkok, 10310, Thailand
Tel.: (66) 2 791 9800
Web Site: http://www.ktbgs.co.th
Business Support Services
N.A.I.C.S.: 561499

KTB General Services and Security Company Limited (1)
No 96 12 Soi Lat Phrao 106 Bun Udom 1, Wangthonglang, Bangkok, 10310, Thailand (100%)
Tel.: (66) 27919800
Web Site: http://www.ktbgs.co.th
Provider of Commercial Banking Services
N.A.I.C.S.: 522110

Krung Thai Asset Management (1)
11 Q House Sathorn Bldg M Fl S Sathorn Rd, Bangkok, 10120, Thailand (100%)
Tel.: (66) 26704900
Web Site: http://www.ktam.co.th
Sales Range: $50-74.9 Million
Emp.: 100
Provider of Fund Management Services
N.A.I.C.S.: 523940

Krung Thai Computer Services Company Limited (1)

INTERNATIONAL PUBLIC

22 Swai Brown Bldg 2 7 Fl Sukhumvit 1 Sukhumvit Rd, Klong Toey Nua Wattana, Bangkok, 10110, Thailand (99%)
Tel.: (66) 2655192140
Web Site: http://www.kcs.co.th
Sales Range: $75-99.9 Million
Emp.: 375
Information Technology Services
N.A.I.C.S.: 541511

Krung Thai IBJ Leasing Company Limited (1)
No 161 18th Floor Nantawan Building 161 Rajdamri Road, Pathumwan, Bangkok, 10330, Thailand (49%)
Tel.: (66) 26518121
Web Site: http://www.ktibj.co.th
Sales Range: $25-49.9 Million
Financial Lending Services
N.A.I.C.S.: 522320

Krungthai Charoensri Company Limited (1)
277 3 Charoensri Complex Building Prajak Rd, Muang, Udon Thani, Thailand (35%)
Tel.: (66) 42249218
Sales Range: $50-74.9 Million
Emp.: 23
Hire Purchase Business
N.A.I.C.S.: 522210

Krungthai Holding Company Limited (1)
191 50 53 C T I Tower 19th Fl, Ratchadapisek Rd Klong Toey, Bangkok, 10110, Thailand (100%)
Tel.: (66) 22041677
Holding Company
N.A.I.C.S.: 551111

Krungthai Panich Insurance Company Limited (1)
1122 KPI Tower New Petchaburi Rd, Makkasan Ratchathewi, Bangkok, 10400, Thailand (45%)
Tel.: (66) 26241111
Web Site: http://www.kpi.co.th
Sales Range: $100-124.9 Million
Emp.: 220
Non-Life Insurance Products & Services
N.A.I.C.S.: 524128

Krungthai Thanakit Public Company Limited (1)
159 Sermmit Tower 15 And 16th Fl, Klong Toey Asoke Rd Sukhumvit, Bangkok, 10110, Thailand (17%)
Tel.: (66) 226173735
Sales Range: $75-99.9 Million
Emp.: 150
Finance & Securities
N.A.I.C.S.: 921130

Krungthai-AXA Life Insurance Co., Ltd. (1)
Pcl 9 G Tower Grand Rama 9 Floor 1 20-27 Rama 9 Road, Bangkok, 10310, Thailand (50%)
Tel.: (66) 27231159
Web Site: http://www.krungthai-axa.co.th
Sales Range: $200-249.9 Million
Emp.: 526
Life Insurance Products & Services
N.A.I.C.S.: 524113

Thai LNG Company Limited (1)
222 Moo 5 Vibhavadi Rangsit Rd, Tungsonghong, Bangkok, 10210, Laksi, Thailand (10%)
Tel.: (66) 29550955
Sales Range: $75-99.9 Million
Emp.: 100
Energy
N.A.I.C.S.: 221118

The Dhipaya Insurance Public Company Limited (1)
1115 Rama 3 Rd Chong Nonsi, Yannawan, Bangkok, 10120, Thailand (13.24%)
Tel.: (66) 22392200
Web Site: http://www.dhipaya.co.th
Sales Range: $350-399.9 Million
Emp.: 700
Provider of Insurance Services
N.A.I.C.S.: 524298

The Vejthani Hospital (1)
1 Ladprao Road 111, Klong-Chan Bangkapi, Bangkok, 10240, Thailand

AND PRIVATE COMPANIES

Tel.: (66) 2 734 0000
Web Site: https://www.vejthani.com
Emp.: 700
Health Care Srvices
N.A.I.C.S.: 622110

KRUNGDHEP SOPHON PUBLIC COMPANY LIMITED
185 Ratburana Road Kwang Bangpakok, Khet Ratburana, Bangkok, 10140, Thailand
Tel.: (66) 28713191
Web Site: https://www.kwc.co.th
Year Founded: 1961
KWC—(THA)
Rev.: $10,004,362
Assets: $26,351,619
Liabilities: $3,043,798
Net Worth: $23,307,821
Earnings: $2,848,240
Emp.: 153
Fiscal Year-end: 12/31/23
Warehousing Services
N.A.I.C.S.: 493110
Chote Sophonpanich *(Chm)*

Subsidiaries:

K.W.C. Warehouse Co., Ltd. (1)
185 Moo 1 Ratburana Rd Kwang Bangpakok, Khet Ratburana, Bangkok, 10140, Thailand
Tel.: (66) 24273374
Web Site: http://www.kwc.co.th
Sales Range: $25-49.9 Million
Emp.: 24
Warehousing Services
N.A.I.C.S.: 493110

KWC Logistics Co., Ltd. (1)
185 Rat Burana Road, Bang Pakok Rat Burana, Bangkok, 10140, Thailand
Tel.: (66) 287131915
Web Site: https://kwclogistics.in.th
Logistic Services
N.A.I.C.S.: 541614

Krungdhep Document Co., Ltd. (1)
185 Ratburana Road Kwang Bangpakok, Khet Ratburana, Bangkok, 10140, Thailand
Tel.: (66) 28714558
Web Site: http://www.kdc.co.th
Sales Range: $25-49.9 Million
Emp.: 109
Document Storage & Management Services
N.A.I.C.S.: 493110
Suparp Tungtriratanakul *(Mng Dir)*

KRUNGTHAI CAR RENT & LEASE PUBLIC COMPANY LIMITED
455/1 Rama 3 Rd Bangkhlo, Bangkholaem, Bangkok, 10120, Thailand
Tel.: (66) 22918888
Web Site: https://www.krungthai.co.th
Year Founded: 1992
KCAR—(THA)
Rev.: $63,406,243
Assets: $171,692,928
Liabilities: $102,174,221
Net Worth: $69,518,707
Earnings: $5,624,998
Emp.: 142
Fiscal Year-end: 12/31/23
Car Rental Services
N.A.I.C.S.: 532111
Pithep Chantarasereekul *(Chm)*

KRUNGTHAI CARD PUBLIC COMPANY LIMITED
591 United Business Center II 14FL Sukhumvit 33 Rd, North Klongton Wattana, Bangkok, 10110, Thailand
Tel.: (66) 28285059
Web Site: https://www.ktc.co.th
Year Founded: 1996
KTC—(THA)
Rev.: $742,014,987
Assets: $3,293,253,666
Liabilities: $2,246,853,419
Net Worth: $1,046,400,247
Earnings: $211,631,011
Emp.: 1,649
Fiscal Year-end: 12/31/23
Manages Credit Card Business
N.A.I.C.S.: 522210

Subsidiaries:

KTB Leasing Co., Ltd. (1)
23 Soi 3 Phatthana, Talat Nuea Subdistrict Mueang Phuket District, Phuket, 83000, Thailand **(75.05%)**
Tel.: (66) 76643120
Web Site: https://www.ktbleasing.co.th
Automotive Financial Leasing Services
N.A.I.C.S.: 522220

KRUPKE HOLDING GMBH
Bahnhofstrasse 7, 48727, Billerbeck, Germany
Tel.: (49) 254393070 De
Web Site: http://www.krupke-holding.de
Year Founded: 2002
Sales Range: $500-549.9 Million
Investment & Consulting
N.A.I.C.S.: 523999
Norbert Krupke *(Owner)*

Subsidiaries:

HUFA Seal GmbH (1)
Linde 13, 51399, Burscheid, Germany **(100%)**
Tel.: (49) 217476280
Web Site: http://www.hufa.de
Sales Range: $25-49.9 Million
Emp.: 30
Metal Seal Mfr
N.A.I.C.S.: 332999
Gerhard Hanke *(Mng Dir)*

KRUSIK-PLASTIKA A.D.
Pere Jovanovica Komiricanca no 35, Osecina, Serbia
Tel.: (381) 143451211
Web Site: https://www.krusik-plastika.co.rs
Year Founded: 1975
KRPL—(BEL)
Rev.: $12,301,205
Assets: $9,873,242
Liabilities: $2,132,998
Net Worth: $7,740,244
Earnings: $1,012,173
Fiscal Year-end: 12/31/22
Plastics Product Mfr
N.A.I.C.S.: 326199

KRYNICA VITAMIN SA
ul Matyldy 35, 03-606, Warsaw, Poland
Tel.: (48) 227438390
Web Site: https://www.krynicavitamin.com
KVT—(WAR)
Rev.: $91,267,784
Assets: $57,824,695
Liabilities: $37,042,175
Net Worth: $20,782,520
Earnings: ($1,697,409)
Emp.: 300
Fiscal Year-end: 12/31/23
Soft Drinks Mfr
N.A.I.C.S.: 312111
Bartosz Strutynski *(Mgr-Legal)*

KRYPTON INDUSTRIES LIMITED
Nadrazni 48, 514 01, Jilemnice, Czech Republic
Tel.: (420) 737262162 CZ
Polyurethane Mfr
N.A.I.C.S.: 326150
Vladimir Valenta *(Sls Mgr-Europe)*

KRYPTON INDUSTRIES LTD.
410 Vardaan Building 25A Camac St Park Street area, Kolkata, 700016, West Bengal, India
Tel.: (91) 8100202973
Web Site: https://www.kryptongroup.com
Year Founded: 1990
523550—(BOM)
Rev.: $6,140,476
Assets: $7,530,158
Liabilities: $3,525,349
Net Worth: $4,004,809
Earnings: $256,918
Emp.: 202
Fiscal Year-end: 03/31/21
Polyurethane Tire Mfr
N.A.I.C.S.: 326211
Jay Singh Bardia *(Mng Dir)*

KRYSTAL INTEGRATED SERVICES PVT. LTD.
15 Krystal House Dr Mankikar Road, Sion East, Mumbai, 400.022, India
Tel.: (91) 2243531234
Web Site: http://www.krystal-group.com
Sales Range: $1-4.9 Billion
Emp.: 10,000
Facility Management Services
N.A.I.C.S.: 531312
Prasad Lad *(Founder)*

Subsidiaries:

Krystal Aviation Services Pvt Ltd (1)
15 Krystal House Dr Mankikar Road, Sion, 400 022, Mumbai, India
Tel.: (91) 2243531234
Emp.: 1,200
Airport Cleaning Services
N.A.I.C.S.: 561720
Shalaka Bhardwaj *(Head-Bus)*

Krystal Gourmet Services Pvt Ltd (1)
19/4/1 Kalina Village Old CST Road Near Geeta Vihar Hotel, Santacruz, Mumbai, 400 029, Maharashtra, India
Tel.: (91) 22 26656801
Web Site: http://www.krystalgourmet.com
Catering Services
N.A.I.C.S.: 722514
Prasad Lad *(Owner)*

KS ENERGY LIMITED
133 New Bridge Road Chinatown Point 21-01, Singapore, 059413, Singapore
Tel.: (65) 6 577 4600
Web Site: http://www.ksenergy.com.sg
Rev.: $23,921,035
Assets: $229,478,437
Liabilities: $282,542,579
Net Worth: ($53,064,142)
Earnings: $77,388,357)
Fiscal Year-end: 12/31/19
Integrated Oil & Gas Services
N.A.I.C.S.: 213112
Diana Leng *(CFO-KS Drilling Pte Ltd)*

Subsidiaries:

Globaltech Systems Engineering Pte. Ltd. (1)
19 Jurong Port Road, Singapore, 619093, Singapore
Tel.: (65) 65451848
Web Site: http://www.gsepl.com
Sales Range: $25-49.9 Million
Emp.: 30
Industrial Engineering Services
N.A.I.C.S.: 541330

KS Distribution Pte Ltd (1)
19 Jurong Port Road, Singapore, 619093, Singapore
Tel.: (65) 65774626
Web Site: http://www.ksdistribution.com.sg
Sales Range: $250-299.9 Million
Emp.: 800
Oil, Gas & Marine Equipments Distr
N.A.I.C.S.: 423830

Subsidiary (Domestic):

Aqua-Terra Logistics Pte. Ltd. (2)
19 Jurang park Rd, Singapore, 619093, Singapore **(55%)**
Tel.: (65) 6536 1003
Web Site: http://www.aquaterra.com.sg
Emp.: 45
Logistic Services
N.A.I.C.S.: 488510

Aqua-Terra Oilfiled Equipment & Services Pte. Ltd. (2)
19 Jurong Port Road, Singapore, 619093, Singapore **(55%)**
Tel.: (65) 6319 4666
Tools & Equipment Sales for Marine, Oil & Gas Industries
N.A.I.C.S.: 213112
Rodney Tan *(Mng Dir)*

Aqua-Terra Supply Co. Ltd. (2)
No 19 Jurong Port Rd, Singapore, 619093, Singapore
Tel.: (65) 63194666
Web Site: http://www.aqua-terra.com
Sales Range: $150-199.9 Million
Oil, Gas, Marine & Mining Integrated Services
N.A.I.C.S.: 561499

Subsidiary (Non-US):

Dalian F.T.Z. Sin Soon Huat International Trade Co. Ltd. (2)
Room 1008 Dalian Chuanbo Uwan Hotel No 8 Minzhu Guangchang, Dalian Zhongshan, Dalian, 116001, China
Tel.: (86) 411 8256 2283
Industrial Materials & General Hardware Distr
N.A.I.C.S.: 423710

Dutco Tennant Aqua-Terra LLC (2)
PO Box 262504 Jebel Ali Free Zone, Dubai, United Arab Emirates
Tel.: (971) 4 886 5185
Industrial Supplies Distr
N.A.I.C.S.: 423840

KS Distribution (Malaysia) Sdn. Bhd. (2)
No 22 Jalan PJS 11/22 Taman Bandar Sunway, 46150, Petaling Jaya, Selangor Darul Ehsan, Malaysia **(55%)**
Tel.: (60) 356335933
Welding Automation & Industrial Equipment Distr
N.A.I.C.S.: 423830

KS Distribution (Shanghai) Ltd. (2)
6E East Hope Plaza No 1777 Century Avenue, Pudong, Shanghai, China **(55%)**
Tel.: (86) 21 2024 6273
Industrial Materials, General Hardware & Welding Machine Distr
N.A.I.C.S.: 423710

KS Equipment (Shanghai) Ltd. (2)
Block 6E No 1777 Century Avenue, Pudong District, Shanghai, 200122, China
Tel.: (86) 2164453185
Web Site: http://www.ks-equipment.com
Sales Range: $25-49.9 Million
Emp.: 30
Industrial Supplies Distr
N.A.I.C.S.: 423840

Subsidiary (Domestic):

KS Flow Control Pte. Ltd. (2)
19 Jurong Port Road, Singapore, Singapore
Tel.: (65) 62616868
Industrial Controls Distr
N.A.I.C.S.: 423830

Oceanic Offshore Engineering Pte. Ltd. (2)
14 Jalan Tukang, Singapore, 619253, Singapore
Tel.: (65) 6262 6662
Web Site: http://www.oceanicoffshore.com.sg
Emp.: 130
Integrated Supplier, Procurement & Engineering Services
N.A.I.C.S.: 488390

Orient Marine Pte. Ltd. (2)
2 Sixth Lok Yang Road, Scott & English Building, Singapore, 628100, Singapore **(55%)**
Tel.: (65) 6266 6168

KS ENERGY LIMITED

KS Energy Limited—(Continued)
Ship Handling Parts Sales & Service
N.A.I.C.S.: 488390

Subsidiary (Domestic):

Fischer Engineering Pte. Ltd. (3)
2 Sixth Lok Yang Road, Singapore, Singapore
Tel.: (65) 68636770
Turbochargers Repair & Maintenance Services
N.A.I.C.S.: 811310

Subsidiary (Non-US):

PT KSD Indonesia (2)
Kompleks Rukan Puri Mutiara Blok A28-29, Jalan Griya Utama Sunter, Jakarta Utara, 14350, Indonesia (55%)
Tel.: (62) 21 6531 4266
Hydraulic Product Instrumentation, Equipment & Valves Distr
N.A.I.C.S.: 423830

Subsidiary (Domestic):

PT AT Oceanic Offshore (3)
Kompleks Rukan Puri Mutiara Blok A28-29, Jalan Griya Utama Sunter, Jakarta Utara, 14350, Indonesia
Tel.: (62) 778 711 707
Marine Equipment Distr
N.A.I.C.S.: 423830

Subsidiary (Non-US):

Raymonds Supply Co., Ltd. (2)
Block A Unit 11 G/F Shatin Industrial Centre, 5-7 Yuen Shun Circuit, Sha Tin, New Territories, China (Hong Kong) (55%)
Tel.: (852) 2637 2828
Web Site: http://www.raymonds.com.hk
Metalware Distr & Transportation Services
N.A.I.C.S.: 423710

Subsidiary (Non-US):

Raymonds Supply (Shanghai) Co., Ltd. (2)
6E East Hope Plaza No 1777 Century Avenue, Pudong, Shanghai, 200122, China (55%)
Tel.: (86) 21 2024 6273
Metalware Distr & Transportation Services
N.A.I.C.S.: 423710

Raymonds Supply (Shenzhen) Co., Ltd. (3)
Room 305 3rd Floor A Building, Hai Bin Garden Xing Hua Road, Shekou Nanshan, Shenzhen, 518067, China (55%)
Tel.: (86) 755 2688 3639
Merchandise Distr for Oil & Gas Industry
N.A.I.C.S.: 213112

Subsidiary (Domestic):

SSH Corporation Ltd. (2)
19 Jurong Port Rd, Singapore, 619093, Singapore
Tel.: (65) 62656088
Web Site: http://www.sshcorp.com
Sales Range: $150-199.9 Million
Welding Equipment Mfr
N.A.I.C.S.: 333992

Subsidiary (Non-US):

Deltametal (Thailand) Limited (3)
20/22-23 Moo 3 Soi Jatuchote Rattanakosin-Sompote Road, Kwaeng Au-Ngeon Khet Saimai, Bangkok, 10220, Thailand
Tel.: (66) 2998 3809
Web Site: http://www.sshcorp.com
Welding Equipment Distr
N.A.I.C.S.: 423830

Subsidiary (Domestic):

Indo Synergy Pte Ltd (3)
19 Jurong Port Road, Singapore, Singapore
Tel.: (65) 6265 6088
Welding Equipment Distr
N.A.I.C.S.: 423830

Subsidiary (Non-US):

PT Suryasarana Hidup Jaya (4)
Jl Jagir Wonokromo 92 A 100 Pert Mangga Dua Bl A 7/8, Surabaya, 60244, Jawa Timur, Indonesia
Tel.: (62) 31 849 5456
Web Site: http://www.suryasarana.co.id
Sales Range: $25-49.9 Million
Emp.: 50
Welding Equipment Distr
N.A.I.C.S.: 423830
Frankie Setiadi (Mng Dir)

Subsidiary (Non-US):

SSH (Vietnam) Company Limited (3)
May Plaza 63d Vo Van Tan Street, Ward 6 District 3, Ho Chi Minh City, Vietnam (55%)
Tel.: (84) 839307212
Web Site: http://www.sshcorp.com
Industrial Materials & Hardware Distr
N.A.I.C.S.: 423830

Subsidiary (Domestic):

SSH Corporation (PNG) Pte. Ltd. (3)
19 Jurong Port Road, Singapore, 619093, Singapore
Tel.: (65) 62656088
Web Site: http://www.ksenergy.com
Sales Range: $50-74.9 Million
Emp.: 200
Industrial Material Distr
N.A.I.C.S.: 423840

Sin Soon Huat International Trading Pte Ltd (3)
19 Jurong Port Rd, Singapore, 619093, Singapore
Tel.: (65) 62656088
Hardware Whslr
N.A.I.C.S.: 423710

Subsidiary (Non-US):

Sure Link Logistics (Shenzhen) Co., Ltd. (2)
Room 305 3rd Floor A Building Hai Bing Garden Xing Hua Road Shekou, Nanshan, Shenzhen, 518067, China (55%)
Tel.: (86) 755 2688 3639
Freight Transportation Arrangement
N.A.I.C.S.: 488510

Sure Link Transportation Co., Ltd. (2)
Block A Unit 11 G/F Shatin Industrial Centre, 5-7 Yuan Shun Circuit, Sha Tin, NT, China (Hong Kong) (55%)
Tel.: (852) 2637 2828
Web Site: http://www.raymonds.com.hk
Emp.: 2
Freight Transportation Arrangement
N.A.I.C.S.: 488510

KS Drilling Pte Ltd (1)
19 Jurong Port Road, Singapore, 619093, Singapore
Tel.: (65) 6577 4600
Oil Drilling Services
N.A.I.C.S.: 213112
Jumeidi Dirwan Alexander (CEO)

Subsidiary (Non-US):

Atlantic Marine Service Egypt S.A.E. (2)
22 Beirut Street 8th Floor Apt 13, Heliopolis, 11341, Cairo, Egypt
Tel.: (20) 22 256 5004
Web Site: http://www.ksdrilling.com
Sales Range: $25-49.9 Million
Emp.: 100
Oil & Gas Field Equipments Distr
N.A.I.C.S.: 423840

Atlantic Marine Services (Cyprus) Group Limited (2)
2 Sophouli Street Chanteclair House, 7th Floor Office/Apt 701, Nicosia, 1096, Cyprus (80%)
Tel.: (357) 22 456 111
Rig Management & Support Services for Oil & Gas Industry
N.A.I.C.S.: 213112

Atlantic Marine Services BV (2)
Ambachtenstraat 93-97, PO Box 82, 1190 AB, Ouderkerk aan den Amstel, North Holland, Netherlands
Tel.: (31) 20 496 9610
Web Site: http://www.ams-gl.com
Oil & Gas Field Equipments Distr
N.A.I.C.S.: 423840

Atlantic Oilfield Services Europe B.V. (2)
Strawinskylaan 1143 WTC Tower C-11, 1077 XX, Amsterdam, Netherlands (80%)
Tel.: (31) 20 5788388
Support Services for Oil & Gas Industry
N.A.I.C.S.: 213112

Atlantic Oilfield Services Ltd. (2)
Waha Community Block F Office No 1003 Nadd Al Hammer Road, PO Box 28717, Dubai, United Arab Emirates (55%)
Tel.: (971) 4 605 9500
Web Site: http://www.ksedrilling.com
Sales Range: $50-74.9 Million
Emp.: 60
Oilfield Exploration Services
N.A.I.C.S.: 213112

Atlantic Onshore Services BV (2)
Hoogoorddreef 09, 1101BA, Amsterdam, North Holland, Netherlands
Tel.: (31) 203120620
Oil & Gas Field Equipments Distr
N.A.I.C.S.: 423840

Affiliate (Non-US):

PT. Petro Papua Energi (2)
World Trade Centre 5 Lantai 11, Jl Jend Sudirman Kav 29-31, Jakarta, 12920, Indonesia (90%)
Tel.: (62) 21 525 6242
Web Site: http://www.ksdrilling.com
Equipment Leasing & Services for Oil & Gas Industry
N.A.I.C.S.: 213112
Sri Rahayu (Mgr-HR)

KS NALOZBE D.D.
Dunajska cesta 9, 1000, Ljubljana, Slovenia
Tel.: (386) 3001402
Web Site: https://www.ks-nalozbe.com
KSFR—(LJU)
Sales Range: $10-24.9 Million
Emp.: 8
Investment Services
N.A.I.C.S.: 523999
Tanja Petrocnik (CEO & Dir)

KSB LIMITED
Office No 601 Runwal R-Square L B S Marg, Mulund West, Mumbai, 400 080, Maharashtra, India
Tel.: (91) 2027101024
Web Site: https://www.ksb.com
Year Founded: 1960
500249—(BOM)
Rev.: $208,979,453
Assets: $219,679,551
Liabilities: $81,700,164
Net Worth: $137,979,387
Earnings: $20,391,599
Emp.: 1,839
Fiscal Year-end: 12/31/21
Pumps & Valves Mfr
N.A.I.C.S.: 333914
G. Swarup (Chm)

Subsidiaries:

KSB Belgium S.A. (1)
Rue de l Industrie 3, 1301, Wavre, Belgium
Tel.: (32) 10435211
Web Site: https://www.ksb.com
Engineering Services
N.A.I.C.S.: 541330

KSB Pumpe i Armature d.o.o. (1)
Ugrinovacki put 36 deo 6, 11080, Belgrade, Serbia
Tel.: (381) 11 314 3196
Engineering Services
N.A.I.C.S.: 541330

TOV KSB Ukraine (1)
Ryzska Street House 8A 3-d Floor Office 309, 04112, Kiev, 04112, Ukraine
Tel.: (380) 504472050
Web Site: https://www.ksb.com
Pumping Equipment Distr

INTERNATIONAL PUBLIC

N.A.I.C.S.: 423840

KSB SE & CO. KGAA
Johann-Klein-Str 9, 67227, Frankenthal, Germany
Tel.: (49) 6233860
Web Site: https://www.ksb.com
Year Founded: 1871
KSB—(DEU)
Rev.: $3,111,809,251
Assets: $2,947,145,381
Liabilities: $1,603,841,484
Net Worth: $1,343,303,897
Earnings: $194,958,605
Emp.: 16,038
Fiscal Year-end: 12/31/23
Pumps & Valves Mfr & Sales
N.A.I.C.S.: 333914
Stephan Bross (Member-Exec Bd)

Subsidiaries:

AMRI Inc. (1)
2045 Silber Rd, Houston, TX 77055 (89.97%)
Tel.: (713) 682-0000
Web Site: http://www.amrivalves.com
Sales Range: $25-49.9 Million
Emp.: 100
Mfr of Butterfly Valves
N.A.I.C.S.: 332919
Keith McElroy (VP-Sls)

AMVI Aplica. Mecanicas Valvulas Industriales, S.A. (1)
Escudo Street, Burgos, Spain
Tel.: (34) 947 298527
Sales Range: $25-49.9 Million
Emp.: 97
Industrial Pump Mfr
N.A.I.C.S.: 333914

Dalian KSB AMRI Valves Co. Ltd. (1)
Xinhui N Rd, Dalian, 116600, Liaoning, China
Tel.: (86) 41187185231
Taps & Valve Mfr
N.A.I.C.S.: 332911

Dynamik Pumpen GmbH (1)
Bergiusstrasse 4, 28816, Stuhr, Germany
Tel.: (49) 421871180
Web Site: http://www.dynamik-pumpen.de
Emp.: 50
Industrial Pump Maintenance Services
N.A.I.C.S.: 811310
Stefan Henning (Mng Dir)

FluidPartner GmbH (1)
Muhlstrasse 54, 90547, Nuremberg, Germany
Tel.: (49) 91159060360
Web Site: http://www.fluidpartner.de
Pump Fitting & Valve Product Mfr
N.A.I.C.S.: 332912

IOOO KSB BEL (1)
3rd Shchorsa Str 9-48 office 607, 220069, Minsk, Belarus
Tel.: (375) 173364257
Web Site: https://www.ksb.com
Pumping Equipment Retailer
N.A.I.C.S.: 423830

KAGEMA Industrieausrustungen GmbH (1)
Adenser Strasse 1, OT Schulenburg, 30982, Pattensen, Germany
Tel.: (49) 5069909321
Sales Range: $25-49.9 Million
Emp.: 89
Diesel Pump Mfr
N.A.I.C.S.: 333914
Lutz Thiede (Mng Dir & Head-Sls)

KSB (Schweiz) AG (1)
Aeschwuhrstrasse 25, 4665, Oftringen, Switzerland
Tel.: (41) 432109933
Web Site: https://www.ksb.com
Emp.: 40
Pumping Equipment Retailer
N.A.I.C.S.: 423830

KSB (Switzerland) Ltd (1)
Aeschwuhrstrasse 25, 4665, Oftringen, Switzerland (100%)

AND PRIVATE COMPANIES

KSB SE & CO. KGAA

Tel.: (41) 432109933
Web Site: https://www.ksb.com
Sales Range: $25-49.9 Million
Emp.: 40
Design, Manufacture & Sales of Pumps & Valves
N.A.I.C.S.: 332919

KSB A/S (1)
Rugmarken 6, 3520, Farum, Denmark (100%)
Tel.: (45) 70211717
Sales Range: $25-49.9 Million
Emp.: 13
Design, Manufacture & Sales of Pumps & Valves
N.A.I.C.S.: 332919

KSB Algerie Eurl (1)
Zone industrielle El-Alia N 49, Bab Ezzouar, 42300, Algiers, Algeria
Tel.: (213) 23830053
Web Site: https://www.ksb.com
Industrial Pump Sales & Maintenance Services
N.A.I.C.S.: 423830
Orjan Lewerentz (Gen Mgr)

KSB Armaturen GmbH (1)
Johann Klein Str 9, 67227, Frankenthal, Germany (100%)
Tel.: (49) 6233860
Sales Range: $400-449.9 Million
Emp.: 2,000
Design, Manufacture & Sales of Pumps & Valves
N.A.I.C.S.: 333914

KSB Artru Services Rhone Alpes S.A.S. (1)
100 Rue Benoit Mulsant, 69400, Villefranche-sur-Saone, France
Tel.: (33) 474657171
Industrial Equipment Mfr
N.A.I.C.S.: 333248

KSB Australia Pty Ltd. (1)
27 Indwe St, Tottenham, 3012, VIC, Australia (100%)
Tel.: (61) 734368600
Web Site: https://www.ksb.com
Sales Range: $75-99.9 Million
Emp.: 130
Design, Manufacture & Sales of Pumps & Valves
N.A.I.C.S.: 332919

KSB Australia Pty. Ltd (1)
13 Hawkins Crescent, Bundamba, 4304, QLD, Australia
Tel.: (61) 734368600
Web Site: https://www.ksb.com
Sales Range: $50-74.9 Million
Emp.: 12
Industrial Pump Mfr
N.A.I.C.S.: 333914
Dave Alexander (Mng Dir)

Subsidiary (Non-US):

KSB New Zealand Limited (2)
2/5 Civil Place, Auckland, 0632, New Zealand
Tel.: (64) 94764047
Web Site: https://www.ksb.com
Emp.: 3
Industrial Machinery & Equipment Whslr
N.A.I.C.S.: 423830

KSB Bombas Hidraulicas S.A. (1)
Rua Jose Rabello Portella 638, Varzea Paulista, Sao Paulo, 13220-540, SP, Brazil (100%)
Tel.: (55) 1145968500
Web Site: https://www.ksb.com
Sales Range: $1-9.9 Million
Emp.: 600
Design, Manufacture & Sales of Pumps & Valves
N.A.I.C.S.: 332919
Edison Jose Borges (Mgr-Comml)

KSB Bombas e Valvulas S.A (1)
Rua Carlos Lopes 5, 2635-206, Rio de Mouro, Portugal
Tel.: (351) 210112300
Web Site: https://www.ksb.pt
Emp.: 16
Industrial Pump & Valve Mfr
N.A.I.C.S.: 333914

Rafael Monroy (Gen Mgr)

KSB Brasil Ltda. (1)
Rua Jose Rabello Portella 638, Varzea, Paulista, 13220-540, SP, Brazil
Tel.: (55) 1145968500
Web Site: https://www.ksb.com
Industrial Valve Mfr
N.A.I.C.S.: 332911

KSB Cerpadla a Armatury (1)
Gagarinova 7/C, 82103, Bratislava, Slovakia (100%)
Tel.: (421) 243333916
Web Site: https://www.ksb.com
Emp.: 26
Design, Manufacture & Sales of Pumps & Valves
N.A.I.C.S.: 333914

KSB Chile S.A. (1)
Av Las Esteras Sur 2851, Quilicura, 8720047, Santiago, Chile (100%)
Tel.: (56) 26778300
Web Site: https://www.ksb.com
Sales Range: $1-9.9 Million
Emp.: 190
Design, Manufacture & Sales of Pumps & Valves
N.A.I.C.S.: 333914

KSB Colombia SAS (1)
Celta Trade Park - Bodega 48-3 Km 7 Autop, Funza, 250027, Medellin, Bogota Cundinamarca, Colombia
Tel.: (57) 3165785697
Pump Fitting & Valve Product Mfr
N.A.I.C.S.: 332912

KSB Compania Sudamericana de Bombas S.A. (1)
Av Ader 3625, Carapachay, 1606, Buenos Aires, Argentina (67%)
Tel.: (54) 1147663021
Web Site: https://www.ksb.com
Sales Range: $50-74.9 Million
Emp.: 120
Design, Manufacture & Sales of Pumps & Valves
N.A.I.C.S.: 333914
Patrice Linnou (Mng Dir)

KSB Controladora S.A. de C.V. (1)
Ave Independencia 1538 Col. Barrio de San Miguel, 37390, Leon, Guanajuato, Mexico
Tel.: (52) 471 20500
Design, Manufacture & Sales of Pumps & Valves
N.A.I.C.S.: 333914

KSB Dubric, Inc. (1)
3737 Laramie Dr NE, Comstock Park, MI 49321
Web Site: http://www.dubric.com
Engineeering Services
N.A.I.C.S.: 541330

KSB Finance Nederland B.V. (1)
Wilgenlaan 68, 1161 JN, Zwanenburg, Noord-Holland, Netherlands
Tel.: (31) 204079800
Web Site: http://www.ksb.com
Sales Range: $50-74.9 Million
Emp.: 80
Financial Management Services
N.A.I.C.S.: 523999
Nicole Gitz (Gen Mgr)

KSB Finland Oy (1)
Savirunninkatu 4, 04260, Kerava, Finland (100%)
Tel.: (358) 10288411
Web Site: https://www.ksb.com
Emp.: 90
Pumps & Valves
N.A.I.C.S.: 333996

Subsidiary (Domestic):

Mantan Pumppauspalvelu Oy (2)
Savirunninkatu 4, Kerava, 04260, Vilppula, Finland
Tel.: (358) 3 4728 500
Web Site: http://www.ksb.com
Emp.: 13
Industrial Pump Mfr
N.A.I.C.S.: 333914
Veijo Jokinen (Gen Mgr)

KSB Fluid Systems GmbH (1)

Johann Klein Str 9, Frankenthal, 67227, Germany (100%)
Tel.: (49) 6233862883
Design, Manufacture & Sales of Pumps & Valves
N.A.I.C.S.: 333914

KSB GIW, Inc. (1)
5000 Wrightsboro Rd, Grovetown, GA 30813-2842 (100%)
Tel.: (706) 863-1011
Web Site: http://www.giwindustries.com
Sales Range: $50-74.9 Million
Emp.: 400
Solids Handling Pumps, Pump Parts Mfr
N.A.I.C.S.: 333914
Dennis Ziegler (Pres)

KSB Hungary Kft. (1)
Budafoki ut 60 Beltex Building A 1st Floor, 1117, Budapest, Hungary
Tel.: (36) 13711736
Web Site: https://www.ksb.com
Emp.: 25
Pumping Equipment Mfr
N.A.I.C.S.: 333914

KSB ITUR Spain S.A. (1)
Camino de Urteta s/n, 20800, Zarautz, Gipuzkoa, Spain
Tel.: (34) 943899899
Web Site: https://www.ksb.com
Air Conditioning Equipment Distr
N.A.I.C.S.: 423730

KSB Inc. (1)
4415 Sarellen Rd, Richmond, VA 23231-4428 (100%)
Tel.: (804) 222-1818
Web Site: https://www.ksbusa.com
Sales Range: $10-24.9 Million
Emp.: 15
Mfr of Submersible Motor Sewage & Wastewater Pumps & High Pressure Boiler Feed-Pumps
N.A.I.C.S.: 423830
Rick Hale (Controller)

KSB Italia S.p.A. (1)
Via Massimo D'Azeglio 32, Concorezzo, 20863, Milan, Monza and Brianza, Italy (50%)
Tel.: (39) 03960481
Web Site: https://www.ksb.com
Sales Range: $75-99.9 Million
Emp.: 200
Design, Manufacture & Sales of Pumps, Valves & Related Systems & Services
N.A.I.C.S.: 332919
Gilberto Chiarelli (Gen Mgr)

Subsidiary (Domestic):

KSB Service Italia S.r.l. (2)
Via Guido Rossa 12/A, Scorze, 30037, Venice, Italy
Tel.: (39) 0415840917
Pumping Equipment Repair & Maintenance Services
N.A.I.C.S.: 811310

KSB Korea Ltd. (1)
Sooyoung Bldg 6F 13 Hannam-daero 20-gil, Yongsan-gu, Seoul, 04419, Korea (South) (100%)
Tel.: (82) 27904351
Web Site: https://www.ksb.com
Sales Range: $25-49.9 Million
Emp.: 15
Design, Manufacture & Sales of Pumps & Valves
N.A.I.C.S.: 333914

KSB Limited (1)
2 Cotton Way, Loughborough, LE11 5TF, Leicestershire, United Kingdom (100%)
Tel.: (44) 150 923 1872
Web Site: https://www.ksb.com
Sales Range: $50-74.9 Million
Emp.: 85
Design, Manufacture & Sales of Pumps & Valves
N.A.I.C.S.: 332919

KSB Limited (1)
1801-1802 The Phoenix 21-25 Luard Rd Wanchai, Hong Kong, China (Hong Kong) (100%)
Tel.: (852) 21471221
Web Site: http://www.ksb.com.cn

Sales Range: $25-49.9 Million
Emp.: 15
Design, Manufacture & Sales of Pumps & Valves
N.A.I.C.S.: 333914
Karl Zhou (Mng Dir)

KSB Ltd. (1)
Moriryu Building 6F 1-3-9 Shibakoen, Tokyo, 105-0011, Japan (100%)
Tel.: (81) 368092471
Web Site: https://www.ksb.com
Sales Range: $1-9.9 Million
Emp.: 15
Design, Manufacture & Sales of Pumps & Valves
N.A.I.C.S.: 332919

KSB MIL Controls Limited (1)
Meladoor, Annamanada Thrissur Dist, Kerala, 680741, India
Tel.: (91) 4802695700
Angle Control Valve Mfr
N.A.I.C.S.: 332911

KSB Malaysia Pumps & Valves Sdn. Bhd. (1)
Lot 2A Jalan Sungai Kayu Ara 32/36 Taman Perusahaan Berjaya Seksyen 32, 40460, Shah Alam, Selangor, Malaysia
Tel.: (60) 383170173
Web Site: https://www.ksb.com
Emp.: 35
Pump & Valve Product Retailer
N.A.I.C.S.: 423830

KSB Mexicana S.A. de C.V. (1)
Av Penuelas No 19 San Pedrito Penuelas, Postal 836, Apartado, 76148, Queretaro, QRO, Mexico (100%)
Tel.: (52) 442 427 5500
Web Site: https://www.ksb.com
Sales Range: $75-99.9 Million
Emp.: 105
Design, Manufacture & Sales of Pumps & Valves
N.A.I.C.S.: 332919

KSB Middle East FZE (1)
Plot No S30202 South Zone, Jebel Ali Free Zone, 202, Dubai, 202, United Arab Emirates
Tel.: (971) 48035000
Web Site: https://www.ksb.com
Sales Range: $25-49.9 Million
Emp.: 35
Pumps & Valves
N.A.I.C.S.: 333996
Tonjes Cerovsky (Mng Dir & VP-Sls-MEA Reg)

KSB Nederland B.V. (1)
Wilgenlaan 68, 1161 JN, Zwanenburg, Netherlands (100%)
Tel.: (31) 204079800
Web Site: https://www.ksb.com
Sales Range: $25-49.9 Million
Emp.: 80
Design, Manufacture & Sales of Pumps & Valves
N.A.I.C.S.: 423830
Nico Gitz (Gen Mgr)

Subsidiary (Domestic):

VRS Valve Reconditioning Services B.V. (2)
Seggelant West 7 c-h, 3237 MJ, Vierpolders, Netherlands
Tel.: (31) 181 417910
Web Site: http://www.vrservices.nl
Industrial Pump Repair & Maintenance Services
N.A.I.C.S.: 811310

KSB Norge AS (1)
Haugenveien 29, 1423, Ski, Norway
Tel.: (47) 96900900
Web Site: https://www.ksb.com
Sales Range: $25-49.9 Million
Emp.: 25
Industrial Pump Mfr
N.A.I.C.S.: 333914

KSB OOO (1)
possession 1035 building 1 Nikolo-Khovanskoye village Sosenskoye settlement, 108802, Moscow, Russia
Tel.: (7) 4959901176
Web Site: https://www.ksb.com
Emp.: 130

KSB SE & CO. KGAA

KSB SE & Co. KGaA—(Continued)
Industrial Pump Mfr.
N.A.I.C.S.: 333914
Jurgen Sand (Mng Dir)

KSB Osterreich Ges.mbH (1)
Industriezentrum NO Sud Strasse 10 45,
Postfach 23, 2355, Wiener Neudorf,
Austria **(100%)**
Tel.: (43) 5910300
Web Site: https://www.ksb.com
Sales Range: $50-74.9 Million
Emp.: 70
Design, Manufacture & Sales of Pumps &
Valves
N.A.I.C.S.: 332919

KSB Peru S.A. (1)
Av Los Eucaliptos N 371 Int 40 Santa
Genoveva, 15823, Lurin, Peru
Tel.: (51) 14228303
Pump Fitting & Valve Product Mfr
N.A.I.C.S.: 332912

KSB Philippines, Inc. (1)
AMON Compound Corporal Cruz St cor E
Rodriguez Jr Avenue, Bagong Ilog, Pasig,
1600, Philippines
Tel.: (63) 288450391
Web Site: https://www.ksb.com
Pump & Valve Product Distr
N.A.I.C.S.: 423830
Prashant Vishnupant Shirgaonkar (Mng Dir)

KSB Polska Sp. z o.o. (1)
ul Swierkowa 1d, Bronisze, 05-850, Ozarow
Mazowiecki, Poland
Tel.: (48) 223112300
Web Site: https://www.ksb.com
Pumping Equipment Mfr
N.A.I.C.S.: 333914

KSB Pompa (1)
Perpa Ticaret Merkezi B Block K, Okmey-
dani, Istanbul, 34383, Turkiye **(100%)**
Tel.: (90) 2122522504
Web Site: http://www.ksb.com.tr
Sales Range: $50-74.9 Million
Emp.: 70
Design, Manufacture & Sales of Pumps &
Valves
N.A.I.C.S.: 332919
Sinan Ozgur (Gen Mgr)

**KSB Pompes Et Robinetteries S.a.r.l.
d'associe Unique** (1)
Boulevard Tahiri Mohamed El Bekay, Ain
Sebaa, 20250, Casablanca, Morocco
Tel.: (212) 522352934
Pumping Equipment Retailer
N.A.I.C.S.: 423830

KSB Pompy i Armatura Sp. zo.o (1)
Bronisze Ul Swierkowa Street 1D, 04 275,
Ozarow Mazowiecki, Poland **(100%)**
Tel.: (48) 225169340
Web Site: http://www.ksb.pl
Sales Range: $25-49.9 Million
Emp.: 50
Design, Manufacture & Sales of Pumps &
Valves
N.A.I.C.S.: 333914
Jacek Dziarmakowski (Gen Mgr)

**KSB Pumpe i Armature d.o.o.
Beograd** (1)
Mala Pruga 32a, 11080, Belgrade, Serbia
Tel.: (381) 113143196
Web Site: http://www.ksb.com
Pump Fitting & Valve Product Distr
N.A.I.C.S.: 423840

KSB Pumps & Valves Ltd. (1)
Dragomelj 136, 1230, Domzale, Slovenia
Tel.: (386) 12528140
Industrial Valve Mfr & Distr
N.A.I.C.S.: 332911

KSB Pumps (S.A.) (Pty.) Ltd. (1)
Cnr North Reef Activia roads, Activia Park,
Germiston, 1401, Gauteng, South
Africa **(100%)**
Tel.: (27) 118765600
Web Site: http://www.ksbpumps.co.za
Sales Range: $100-124.9 Million
Emp.: 500
Design, Manufacture & Sales of Pumps &
Valves
N.A.I.C.S.: 333914
Wolfgang Demmler (Mng Dir)

KSB Pumps Arabia Ltd. (1)
Salah Uddin Street Al Bayt Bldg No 1 Office
23, PO Box 56368, 11476, Riyadh, Saudi
Arabia
Tel.: (966) 11 227 7060
Web Site: https://www.ksb.com
Emp.: 200
Design, Manufacture & Sales of Pumps &
Valves
N.A.I.C.S.: 333914

KSB Pumps Co. Ltd. (1)
57 Moo 14 Suwinthawong road, 10530,
Bangkok, Thailand **(100%)**
Tel.: (66) 2 988 2324
Web Site: https://www.ksb.com
Sales Range: $50-74.9 Million
Emp.: 94
Design, Manufacture & Sales of Pumps &
Valves
N.A.I.C.S.: 332919

KSB Pumps Co. Ltd., Lahore (1)
16/2 Sir Aga Khan Road, 54000, Lahore,
Pakistan **(58.89%)**
Tel.: (92) 42111572786
Web Site: http://www.ksb.com
Sales Range: $50-74.9 Million
Emp.: 350
Design, Manufacture & Sales of Pumps &
Valves
N.A.I.C.S.: 332919

KSB Pumps Limited, Pune (1)
Mumbai-Pune Road, Pimpri, Pune, 411018,
Maharashtra, India **(40.54%)**
Tel.: (91) 20 2710 1152
Web Site: http://www.ksbindia.co.in
Design, Mfr & Sales of Pumps & Valves
N.A.I.C.S.: 332919
Ysgnesh I. Buch (Deputy Gen Mgr-Mktg)

**KSB Pumps and Valves (Pty)
Ltd.** (1)
Cnr North Reef Road & Activia Road Activia
Park, Germiston, 1401, South Africa
Tel.: (27) 118765600
Web Site: https://www.ksb.com
Industrial Pump & Valve Mfr
N.A.I.C.S.: 333914

KSB Pumps, Inc. (1)
5205 Tomken Road, Mississauga, L4W
3N8, ON, Canada **(100%)**
Tel.: (905) 568-9200
Web Site: https://www.ksb.com
Sales Range: $25-49.9 Million
Emp.: 21
Wholesale Pumps & Valves
N.A.I.C.S.: 332919

KSB Pumpy & Armatury s.r.o. (1)
Klicova 2300/6, 149 00, Prague, 4, Chodov,
Czech Republic **(100%)**
Tel.: (420) 241090211
Web Site: https://www.ksb.com
Sales Range: $25-49.9 Million
Emp.: 35
Design, Manufacture & Sales of Pumps &
Valves
N.A.I.C.S.: 332919
Miroslav Zabicky (Mng Dir)

KSB S.A.S (1)
4 Alee Des Barbanniers, 92635, Gennevil-
liers, France **(99.94%)**
Tel.: (33) 969392979
Web Site: https://www.ksb.com
Sales Range: $50-74.9 Million
Design, Manufacture & Sales of Pumps &
Valves
N.A.I.C.S.: 333914

Subsidiary (Domestic):

KSB-Hydraulor Services (2)
17 rue Robert Schuman, 54850, Messein,
France
Tel.: (33) 3 82 85 63 90
Web Site: http://www.pompes-hydraulor-
services.fr
Sales Range: $10-24.9 Million
Emp.: 33
Industrial Pump Repair Services
N.A.I.C.S.: 811310

KSB Seil Co., Ltd. (1)
76 Noksansaneopbuk-ro 313 beon-gil,
Songjeong-dong Gangseo-gu, Busan, Korea (South)

Tel.: (82) 518311858
Valve Remote Control Product Mfr & Distr
N.A.I.C.S.: 332911
Donny Yoo (Mng Dir)

KSB Service EITB-SITELEC (1)
1483 Avenue de l'Amandie, 84000, Avi-
gnon, Vaucluse, France
Tel.: (33) 490876423
Web Site: http://www.ksb.com
Emp.: 47
Industrial Equipment Repair Services
N.A.I.C.S.: 811310
Eric Leblais (Pres)

KSB Service GmbH (1)
Passower Chaussee PCK Site Building H
213, 16303, Schwedt an der Oder, Ger-
many
Tel.: (49) 3332435111
Pump Fitting & Valve Product Mfr
N.A.I.C.S.: 332912

KSB Service Robinetterie (1)
30 Avenue Du 11 Novembre, 88700, Ram-
bervillers, Vosges, France
Tel.: (33) 329651041
Pumps Mfr
N.A.I.C.S.: 333914

KSB Service Suciba S.L.U. (1)
Araba 2, 48 150, Bilbao, Spain
Tel.: (34) 944533962
Web Site: http://www.ksb.com
Sales Range: $25-49.9 Million
Emp.: 15
Industrial Pump Maintenance Services
N.A.I.C.S.: 811310
David Madariaga (Gen Mgr)

KSB Shanghai Pump Co., Ltd. (1)
No 1400 Jiangchuan Road, Minhang Dis-
trict, Shanghai, 200245, China **(51%)**
Tel.: (86) 4000218000
Web Site: https://www.ksb.com
Sales Range: $25-49.9 Million
Emp.: 800
Design, Manufacture & Sales of Pumps &
Valves
N.A.I.C.S.: 333914

**KSB Singapore (Asia Pacific) Pte.
Ltd.** (1)
7 Woodlands Walk KSB Regional Center,
Singapore, 738320, Singapore
Tel.: (65) 60277346
Web Site: https://www.ksb.com
Design, Manufacture & Sales of Pumps &
Valves
N.A.I.C.S.: 332919
Robert Ong (Dir-Sls & Operation)

KSB Sverige AB (1)
Datavagen 23, PO Box 9023, 400 91, Goth-
enburg, Sweden **(55%)**
Tel.: (46) 317202400
Web Site: https://www.ksb.com
Sales Range: $25-49.9 Million
Emp.: 50
Design, Manufacture & Sales of Pumps &
Valves
N.A.I.C.S.: 332919
Bo Gerdin (Publr)

Subsidiary (Non-US):

PUMPHUSET Sverige AB (2)
Tel.: (46) 859496600
Web Site: https://www.pumphuset.se
Sales Range: $25-49.9 Million
Emp.: 40
Pumping Equipment Sales & Maintenance
Services
N.A.I.C.S.: 423830

KSB Szivattyu es Armatura Kft. (1)
Budafoki ut 60 Beltex A building I floor,
Postfach 462, 1117, Budapest, Hungary
Tel.: (36) 13711736
Web Site: https://www.ksb.com
Sales Range: $25-49.9 Million
Emp.: 20
Design, Manufacture & Sales of Pumps &
Valves
N.A.I.C.S.: 332919

KSB TESMA AG (1)
R Melodou Str 3, 15125, Amaroussion,
Greece **(100%)**
Tel.: (30) 2106108071

INTERNATIONAL PUBLIC

Sales Range: $25-49.9 Million
Emp.: 35
Design, Manufacture & Sales of Pumps &
Valves
N.A.I.C.S.: 332919
George Karotieris (Gen Mgr)

KSB Taiwan Co. Ltd. (1)
7F No 132 Sec 3 Xinyi Rd, Da'an Dist, Tai-
pei, 106022, Taiwan **(100%)**
Tel.: (886) 227079188
Web Site: https://www.ksb.com
Sales Range: $1-9.9 Million
Emp.: 20
Pumps & Valves Mfr
N.A.I.C.S.: 333914
Torsten Gabalnaln (Mng Dir)

KSB Tech Pvt. Ltd (1)
42 Bund Garden Road, Pune, 411 001,
India
Tel.: (91) 2026007000
Pump & Valve Distr
N.A.I.C.S.: 423830
Werner Spiegel (Mng Dir)

**KSB Valves (Changzhou) Co.,
Ltd.** (1)
68 Huanbao Four Road, Changzhou,
213034, Jiangsu, China
Tel.: (86) 2164308030
Emp.: 900
Pump Fitting & Valve Product Mfr
N.A.I.C.S.: 332912

KSB Venezolana C.A. (1)
Urb Las Chimeneas Calle 125, Estado
Carabobo, Valencia, Venezuela **(100%)**
Tel.: (58) 2418433498
Web Site: http://www.ksb.com
Production of Pumps & Valves
N.A.I.C.S.: 332919

KSB Vietnam Co., Ltd. (1)
Plot CII II-11 Road No 1, Long Thanh In-
dustrial Zone, Long Thanh, Dong Nai, Viet-
nam
Tel.: (84) 25113514808
Web Site: https://www.ksb.com
Emp.: 26
Pump & Valve Product Retailer
N.A.I.C.S.: 423830
Nguyen Huu Dang (Gen Dir)

KSB Zambia Limited (1)
Musapas Business Estate Kamfinsa Junc-
tion on T3 Kamfinsa, Kitwe, Zambia
Tel.: (260) 968670002
Web Site: http://ksb-zambia-ltd.business.site
Pump Fitting & Valve Product Mfr
N.A.I.C.S.: 332912

KSB de Mexico, S.A. de C.V. (1)
Av Penuelas No 19 Col San Pedrito Penu-
elas, 76148, Queretaro, Mexico
Tel.: (52) 4424275500
Web Site: https://www.ksb.com
Sales Range: $25-49.9 Million
Pump & Pumping Equipment Mfr
N.A.I.C.S.: 333914

KSB-AMVI S.A. (1)
Caleruega 102 104, 28033, Madrid,
Spain **(100%)**
Tel.: (34) 917242210
Design, Manufacture & Sales of Pumps &
Valves
N.A.I.C.S.: 333914

KSB-AMVI, S.A. (1)
Via de los Poblados 9-11, 28033, Madrid,
Spain **(99.8%)**
Tel.: (34) 917242210
Web Site: http://www.ksb.com
Sales Range: $25-49.9 Million
Design, Manufacture & Sales of Pumps &
Valves
N.A.I.C.S.: 332919

**KSB-Pompa, Armatur Sanayi ve Ti-
caret A.S.** (1)
Mahatma Gandhi Cad No 54 GOP, Can-
kaya, 06680, Ankara, Turkiye
Tel.: (90) 3124371175
Web Site: https://www.ksb.com
Industrial Valve Mfr
N.A.I.C.S.: 332911

Ksb Pumps & Valves Limited (1)
Units A2 and B3 Baba Dogo Road, Prab-
haki Industrial Park Ruaraka, 00621, Nai-

robi, Kenya
Tel.: (254) 2349308
Pump Fitting & Valve Product Mfr
N.A.I.C.S.: 332912

MIL Controls Limited (1)
Meladoor, Annamanada, Thrissur, 680741, Kerala, India
Tel.: (91) 4802695700
Web Site: http://www.milcontrols.com
Emp.: 30
Pump & Control Valve Mfr
N.A.I.C.S.: 333914
Jacob Cherian *(Mng Dir)*

Metis Levage S.A.S (1)
100 rue Benoit Mulsant Mulsant, BP 104, 69400, Villefranche-sur-Saone, Cedex, France
Tel.: (33) 4 74 65 71 74
Web Site: http://www.metislevage.com
Industrial Machinery Mfr
N.A.I.C.S.: 333248
Levage Beauchamp *(Gen Mgr)*

Motoren Jacobs GmbH (1)
Hamburger Strasse 59, 25746, Heide, Germany
Tel.: (49) 481 850 150
Web Site: http://www.motoren-jacobs.de
Sales Range: $25-49.9 Million
Emp.: 30
Industrial Engine Parts Mfr
N.A.I.C.S.: 333618
Riener Markson *(Gen Mgr)*

N.V. KSB Belgium S.A. (1)
Zoning Industriel Sud Rue de l'Industrie 3, Bierges, 1301, Wavre, Belgium (100%)
Tel.: (32) 10435211
Web Site: https://www.ksb.com
Sales Range: $25-49.9 Million
Emp.: 43
Design, Manufacture & Sales of Pumps & Valves
N.A.I.C.S.: 332919
Marco Godenschwege *(Gen Mgr)*

Subsidiary (Domestic):

KSB On Site Machining BVBA (2)
Boomsesteenweg 604/606, 2610, Wilrijk, Belgium
Tel.: (32) 3 830 72 70
Web Site: http://www.on-site-machining.be
Machine Tool Repair & Maintenance Services
N.A.I.C.S.: 811310
Dirk Boeykens *(Mng Dir)*

VRS Industries S.A (2)
Parc Industriel de Feluy Zone B, Zenobe Gramme, Feluy, 7181, Belgium
Tel.: (32) 64217560
Web Site: http://www.valves-industry.com
Emp.: 22
Industrial Valve Mfr
N.A.I.C.S.: 332911
Maki Voulismas *(Gen Mgr-Sls & Technical Dept)*

PMS Pumpen- und Motoren Service GmbH (1)
Welserstr 1, Neuss, 41468, Germany
Tel.: (49) 21313666980
Web Site: http://www.pms-neuss.de
Sales Range: $25-49.9 Million
Emp.: 15
Industrial Pump Mfr
N.A.I.C.S.: 333914

PMS-BERCHEM GmbH (1)
Welserstrasse 1, 41468, Neuss, Germany
Tel.: (49) 21313666980
Pump & Motor Repair Services
N.A.I.C.S.: 811310

PT KSB Indonesia (1)
Jalan Raya Tipar No 42 Cakung, 13910, Jakarta, Indonesia (100%)
Tel.: (62) 2146827215
Sales Range: $50-74.9 Million
Emp.: 200
Design, Manufacture & Sales of Pumps & Valves

PT. KSB Sales Indonesia (1)
Jl Timor Blok D2-1, MM2100 Industrial Town Cibitung, Bekasi, 17520, Indonesia
Tel.: (62) 2189983570

Web Site: https://www.ksb.com
Emp.: 300
Pump Product Mfr & Retailer
N.A.I.C.S.: 332911
Philippe Olivier *(Pres)*

Pumpen Service Bentz GmbH (1)
Carl-Zeiss-Strasse 4-6, 21465, Reinbek, Germany
Tel.: (49) 407273750
Web Site: http://www.pumpenbentz.de
Emp.: 30
Industrial Machinery Repair Services
N.A.I.C.S.: 532490
Martin Bentz *(Gen Mgr)*

REEL s.r.l. (1)
Via Riviera Berica 40, Ponte di Nanto, 36024, Vicenza, Italy
Tel.: (39) 0444739711
Electrical Control Panel Distr
N.A.I.C.S.: 423690

SISTO Armaturen S.A. (1)
18 rue Martin Maas, 6468, Echternach, Luxembourg (52.86%)
Tel.: (352) 3250851
Web Site: https://sisto-aseptic.com
Sales Range: $50-74.9 Million
Emp.: 200
Design, Manufacture & Sales of Pumps & Valves
N.A.I.C.S.: 333914
Markus Schneider *(Mgr-Fin)*

SPI Energie S.A.S. (1)
160 rue du Clapet, 73490, La Ravoire, France
Tel.: (33) 479726562
Web Site: http://www.spienergie.fr
Industrial Vacuum Equipment Mfr
N.A.I.C.S.: 333310

Standard Alloys, Inc. (1)
201 W Lake Shore, Port Arthur, TX 77640
Tel.: (409) 983-3201
Web Site: https://www.ksb.com
Emp.: 100
Castings & Replacement Pump Parts Mfr
N.A.I.C.S.: 331513
R. H. Fisher *(VP-Fin)*

TOO KSB Kazakhstan (1)
206 Tchaikovski street office 6 3rd floor, 050000, Almaty, Kazakhstan
Tel.: (7) 7272377709
Web Site: https://www.ksb.com
Pump Fitting & Valve Product Retailer
N.A.I.C.S.: 423840

Uder Elektromechanik GmbH (1)
Robert-Koch-Strasse 5, 66299, Friedrichsthal, Germany
Tel.: (49) 689798000
Web Site: http://www.uder-elektro.de
Sales Range: $25-49.9 Million
Emp.: 70
Vaccum Pump Mfr
N.A.I.C.S.: 335210
Markus Hanuja *(Gen Mgr)*

gear-tec GmbH (1)
Am Rollfeld 16, 24852, Eggebek, Germany
Tel.: (49) 46 09 30 28 0
Web Site: http://www.gear-tec.de
Wind Turbine Repair & Maintenance Services
N.A.I.C.S.: 811310

KSBG KOMMUNALE BETEILIGUNGSGESELLSCHAFT GMBH & CO. KG
Ruttenscheider Strasse 1-3, 45128, Essen, Germany
Tel.: (49) 2018011280
Web Site: https://stadtwerke-konsortium.de
Municipal Administration Services
N.A.I.C.S.: 561110

KSD HAULAGE CONTRACTORS LTD
11 Hammond Close Attleborough Fields Industrial Estate, Nuneaton, CV11 6RY, Warwickshire, United Kingdom
Tel.: (44) 2476344590

Web Site: http://www.ksd.org.uk
Year Founded: 1976
Rev.: $10,175,011
Emp.: 50
Construction Materials Distr
N.A.I.C.S.: 423320
Paul Dosanjh *(Founder, Chm & CEO)*

KSE LIMITED
Solvent Road Irinjalakuda, Thrissur, 680 121, Kerala, India
Tel.: (91) 4802825476
Web Site: https://www.kselimited.com
519421—(BOM)
Rev.: $228,780,893
Assets: $38,307,933
Liabilities: $7,898,463
Net Worth: $30,409,470
Earnings: $896,982
Emp.: 876
Fiscal Year-end: 03/31/22
Cattle Feed Mfr
N.A.I.C.S.: 311119
R. Sankaranarayanan *(Officer-Nodal)*

KSEC INTELLIGENT TECHNOLOGY CO., LTD.
Building 401 Shipbuilding Industrial Zone, Economic Development Zone Kunming Area Pilot Free Trade Zone, Kunming, 650051, Yunnan, China
Tel.: (86) 87163172696
Web Site: https://www.ksecit.com
Year Founded: 1998
301311—(CHIN)
Rev.: $293,786,760
Assets: $683,213,477
Liabilities: $422,344,168
Net Worth: $260,869,309
Earnings: $11,342,718
Emp.: 2,000
Fiscal Year-end: 12/31/23
Information Technology Services
N.A.I.C.S.: 541512
Hongbo Wang *(Chm)*

KSG AGRO S.A.
40B Starokozatska Str, 49000, Dnepropetrovsk, Ukraine
Tel.: (380) 567870731 LU
Web Site: https://www.ksgagro.com
Year Founded: 2010
KSG—(WAR)
Rev.: $18,786,000
Assets: $31,766,000
Liabilities: $32,600,000
Net Worth: ($834,000)
Earnings: ($1,161,000)
Emp.: 189
Fiscal Year-end: 12/31/23
Sunflower, Wheat, Barley, Rapeseed, Soya & Vegetable Farming
N.A.I.C.S.: 111998
Sergiy Kasianov *(Chm)*

KSH HOLDINGS LIMITED
36 Senoko Road, Singapore, 758108, Singapore
Tel.: (65) 67582266 SG
Web Site: https://www.kimsengheng.com
Year Founded: 1979
ER0—(SES)
Rev.: $158,632,086
Assets: $427,867,358
Liabilities: $192,636,532
Net Worth: $235,230,826
Earnings: ($23,862,912)
Fiscal Year-end: 03/31/24
Property Management Services
N.A.I.C.S.: 531312
Ngat Khow Kwok *(Dir-QAQC)*

Subsidiaries:

KSH Property Development Pte Ltd (1)

36 Senoko Road, Singapore, 758108, Singapore
Tel.: (65) 67582266
Sales Range: $75-99.9 Million
Emp.: 200
Property Development Services
N.A.I.C.S.: 531210
Chee Onn Choo *(Mng Dir)*

Kim Seng Heng Engineering Construction (Pte) Ltd (1)
36 Senoko Road, Singapore, Singapore
Tel.: (65) 67582266
Commercial Building Construction Services
N.A.I.C.S.: 236220

Kim Seng Heng Realty Pte Ltd (1)
36 Senoko Rd, Singapore, 758108, Singapore
Tel.: (65) 67582266
Web Site: http://www.kimsengheng.com
Sales Range: $25-49.9 Million
Emp.: 35
Property Development Services
N.A.I.C.S.: 531210
Chee Onn Choo *(Mng Dir)*

Tianjin Tian Xing Property Management Co., Ltd (1)
No 81 Shi Yi Jing Road, Hedong District, Tianjin, 300171, China (69%)
Tel.: (86) 2224109999
Web Site: http://www.kimsengheng.com
Property Development Services
N.A.I.C.S.: 531311

KSHITIJ POLYLINE LTD.
Ankit Survey No 110/1/13 Amli Village 66 K V A Road, Dadra and Nagar Haveli and Daman and Diu, Silvassa, 396230, India
Tel.: (91) 804 876 4000
Web Site: http://www.kshitijpolyline.com
Year Founded: 1998
KSHITIJPOL—(NSE)
Rev.: $3,311,385
Assets: $5,276,770
Liabilities: $2,819,930
Net Worth: $2,456,840
Earnings: $342
Emp.: 150
Fiscal Year-end: 03/31/21
Plastics Product Mfr
N.A.I.C.S.: 326199
Bharat Hemraj Gala *(Mng Dir)*

KSHITIZ INVESTMENTS LIMITED
509 Loha Bhavan 93 P D mello Road, Carnac Bunder, Mumbai, 400 009, India
Tel.: (91) 2223480344
Web Site: http://www.kiltd.in
503626—(BOM)
Rev.: $20,493
Assets: $59,527
Liabilities: $2,273
Net Worth: $57,254
Earnings: $652
Fiscal Year-end: 03/31/22
Steel Product Mfr & Distr
N.A.I.C.S.: 331221
Kshtij Vinaykumar Rajkumar *(CFO)*

KSIGN CO., LTD.
Gwacheon-daero 7na-gil, Gwacheon, Gyeonggi-do, Korea (South)
Tel.: (82) 25640182
Web Site: https://www.ksign.com
Year Founded: 1999
192250—(KRS)
Rev.: $33,124,447
Assets: $106,691,157
Liabilities: $53,292,856
Net Worth: $53,398,300
Earnings: $4,505,434
Emp.: 84
Fiscal Year-end: 12/31/22
Investment Services
N.A.I.C.S.: 523999

Ksign Co., Ltd.—(Continued)
Seung-Rak Choi (CEO)

KSK CO., LTD.
1625-2 Momura, Inagi, Tokyo, 206-0804, Japan
Tel.: (81) 423781100
Web Site: https://www.ksk.co.jp
Year Founded: 1974
9687—(TKS)
Rev.: $143,952,580
Assets: $144,659,850
Liabilities: $38,133,090
Net Worth: $106,526,760
Earnings: $11,250,220
Emp.: 2,461
Fiscal Year-end: 03/31/24
Software Development Services
N.A.I.C.S.: 541512
Kyotani Tadayuki (CEO)

Subsidiaries:

KSK Kyushu Corporation (1)
6-20-45 Chikami, Minami Ward, Kumamoto, 861-4101, Japan
Tel.: (81) 963536920
Web Site: https://www.ksk-kyushu.co.jp
Emp.: 34
Software Development Services
N.A.I.C.S.: 541511

KSK ENERGY VENTURES LIMITED
8-2-293/82/A/431/A Road No 22 Jubilee Hills, Hyderabad, 500 033, India
Tel.: (91) 4023559922
Web Site: http://www.ksk.co.in
532997—(BOM)
Rev.: $31,007,812
Assets: $527,530,025
Liabilities: $460,574,701
Net Worth: $66,955,324
Earnings: ($54,714,413)
Emp.: 3
Fiscal Year-end: 03/31/19
Electric Power Distr & Generation
N.A.I.C.S.: 221122
S. Kishore (Exec Dir)

Subsidiaries:

VS Lignite Power Private Limited (1)
8-2-293 82 A Rd No 22 jubliee hills, Jubilee Hills, Hyderabad, 500033, India
Tel.: (91) 4023559922
Web Site: http://www.ksk.co
Sales Range: $1-4.9 Billion
Emp.: 400
Power Plant Services
N.A.I.C.S.: 221118
R. K. Bajaj (Head-Admin)

Wardha Power Company Limited (1)
8-2-293182 N431 A Rd No 22, Jubilee Hills, Hyderabad, 500033, India
Tel.: (91) 4023559922
Web Site: www.kskenergy.co.in
Sales Range: $500-549.9 Million
Emp.: 1,000
Power Plant Services
N.A.I.C.S.: 221118

KSK POWER VENTUR PLC
First Names House Victoria Road, Douglas, IM2 4DF, Isle of Man
Tel.: (44) 1624 630630 IM
Web Site: http://www.kskplc.co.uk
Year Founded: 1998
Rev.: $591,258,000
Assets: $4,935,297,000
Liabilities: $4,661,041,000
Net Worth: $274,256,000
Earnings: ($158,896,000)
Fiscal Year-end: 03/31/17
Power Generation Services
N.A.I.C.S.: 221118
Sethuraman Kishore (Exec Dir)

Subsidiaries:

KSK Energy Limited (1)

St James Court Suite 308 St Denis Street, Port Louis, Mauritius
Tel.: (230) 211 6242
Power Generation Services
N.A.I.C.S.: 221118

Sai Regency Power Corporation Private Limited (1)
Office No 3 Crown Court 2nd Floor Door No 128 Cathedral Road, Gopalapuram, Chennai, 600 086, India
Tel.: (91) 44 28117461
Web Site: http://www.ksk.co.in
Emp.: 6
Power Generation Services
N.A.I.C.S.: 221118
N. Ramakrishnan (Gen Mgr)

KSL HOLDINGS BERHAD
Wisma KSL 148 Batu 1 1/2 Jalan Buloh Kasap, 85000, Segamat, Johor, Malaysia
Tel.: (60) 79311430
Web Site: https://www.ksl.my
KSL—(KLS)
Rev.: $248,506,238
Assets: $884,569,971
Liabilities: $76,389,265
Net Worth: $808,180,707
Earnings: $90,735,767
Emp.: 566
Fiscal Year-end: 12/31/23
Property Development Services
N.A.I.C.S.: 531312
Chye Tee Lee (Exec Dir)

Subsidiaries:

KSL Development Sdn. Bhd. (1)
Lot 3047 Jalan Mengkibol, 86000, Kluang, Johor, Malaysia
Tel.: (60) 72893111
Property Development Services
N.A.I.C.S.: 531390

KSL Properties Sdn. Bhd. (1)
L1-95 KSL City 3 Jalan Seladang Taman Abad, 80250, Johor Bahru, Malaysia
Tel.: (60) 72882888
Property Development Services
N.A.I.C.S.: 531390

Khoo Soon Lee Realty Sdn. Bhd. (1)
PTD 71045 Jalan Danga Taman Nusa Bestari 2, Johor Bahru, Skudai, 81300, Malaysia
Tel.: (60) 75122888
Property Development Services
N.A.I.C.S.: 531390

KSL HOLDINGS LIMITED
Office A&B 12/F Billion Plaza 2 No 10 Cheung Yue Street, Kowloon, China (Hong Kong)
Tel.: (852) 2308 1281
Web Site: http://www.kslholdings.com
Sales Range: $1-9.9 Million
Emp.: 30
Engineeering Services
N.A.I.C.S.: 541330

KSM PARTNERS
TT Vasumweg 95, Postbus 1407, 1033 SG, Amsterdam, Netherlands
Tel.: (31) 20 517 42 00
Year Founded: 1968
Emp.: 100
N.A.I.C.S.: 541810
Aad Booman (Art Dir)

KSOLVES INDIA LIMITED
icon Noida 2nd Floor Smartworks Tower-D Logix Cyber Park, Noida, 201301, India
Tel.: (91) 9871977038
Web Site: https://www.ksolves.com
Year Founded: 2012
KSOLVES—(NSE)
Rev.: $3,879,949
Assets: $2,349,661
Liabilities: $525,682

Net Worth: $1,823,979
Earnings: $1,220,031
Emp.: 115
Fiscal Year-end: 03/31/21
Software Development Services
N.A.I.C.S.: 541511
Ratan Srivastava (Chm & Mng Dir)

Subsidiaries:

Ksolves LLC (1)
11 N Market St Ste, San Jose, CA 95113
Tel.: (646) 203-1075
Software Development Services
N.A.I.C.S.: 541511

KSP CO., LTD.
147 Noksan Industrial Buk-ro, Gangseo-gu, Busan, 46753, Songjeong-dong, Korea (South)
Tel.: (82) 518316274
Web Site: https://www.kspvalve.co.kr
Year Founded: 1991
073010—(KRS)
Rev.: $48,833,764
Assets: $46,325,173
Liabilities: $20,223,140
Net Worth: $26,102,033
Earnings: $3,040,367
Emp.: 48
Fiscal Year-end: 12/31/22
Ship Engine Valve Mfr
N.A.I.C.S.: 336310
Beom-Ho Lee (CEO)

KSS LIMITED
Unit No 101A/102 1st Floor Plot No B-17Morya Landmark 2, Andheri West, Mumbai, 400053, India
Tel.: (91) 22 42088600
Year Founded: 1995
Rev.: $6,441,544
Assets: $15,578,759
Liabilities: $10,087,063
Net Worth: $5,491,695
Earnings: ($147,502)
Fiscal Year-end: 03/31/20
Motion Picture & Video Production Services
N.A.I.C.S.: 512110
Ashok Dash (COO)

Subsidiaries:

K Kampus Education Private Limited (1)
Unit No 101A/102 1st Floor Morya Landmark 2 New Link Road, Andheri West, Mumbai, 400 053, India
Tel.: (91) 22 40427680
Web Site: http://www.kkampus.co.in
Educational Support Services
N.A.I.C.S.: 611710
B. S. Radhakrishnan (Grp CEO)

K Sera Sera Miniplex Private Limited (1)
Kohinoor City Mall G-1&7 Ground Floor Kirol Road, Kamani Kurla West, Mumbai, 400070, Maharashtra, India
Tel.: (91) 22 40427676
Motion Picture Theater Operator
N.A.I.C.S.: 512131

K Sera Sera Productions FZE (1)
Hamriyah Free Zone Phase 2, Sharjah, United Arab Emirates
Tel.: (971) 4 354 4435
Movie Production & Distribution Services
N.A.I.C.S.: 512110

KSS LINE LTD.
8th Floor Daeil Building No 12 Insadong-gil, Jongno-gu, Seoul, 03163, Korea (South)
Tel.: (82) 237022700
Web Site: https://www.kssline.com
Year Founded: 1969
044450—(KRS)
Rev.: $341,603,231
Assets: $1,272,585,417
Liabilities: $960,968,482

Net Worth: $311,616,935
Earnings: $34,875,894
Emp.: 438
Fiscal Year-end: 12/31/22
Marine Transportation Services
N.A.I.C.S.: 483111
Dae-Sung Lee (Pres)

Subsidiaries:

Ulsan Maritime Agency Co., Ltd (1)
183-2 Changsaengpo-don, Nam-gu, Ulsan, 44780, Korea (South)
Tel.: (82) 52 261 7285
Web Site: http://www.ulmaria.co.kr
Emp.: 17
Marine Transportation Services
N.A.I.C.S.: 483111
Yun Yeong Seok (Pres)

KT CORPORATION
East Gwanghwamun Bldg East 33 Jong-ro 3-gill, Jongno-gu, Seoul, 03155, Korea (South)
Tel.: (82) 317270114 KR
Web Site: https://corp.kt.com
Year Founded: 1981
KT—(NYSE)
Rev.: $23,189,206,280
Assets: $34,186,593,720
Liabilities: $18,944,805,600
Net Worth: $15,241,788,120
Earnings: $1,342,643,400
Emp.: 21,759
Fiscal Year-end: 12/31/21
Telecommunication Servicesb
N.A.I.C.S.: 517111
Dae-You Kim (Chm)

Subsidiaries:

Altimedia Corporation (1)
Altimedia 2nd Floor Park Bldg 16 Banpodaero 27-gil, Seocho-gu, Seoul, Korea (South)
Tel.: (82) 234704010
Web Site: https://www.altimedia.com
Media Technology Services
N.A.I.C.S.: 518210

BC Card Co., Ltd. (1)
Tel.: (82) 25204114
Web Site: http://www.bccard.com
Credit Card Processing Services
N.A.I.C.S.: 522320

Subsidiary (Non-US):

Wirecard (Vietnam) Ltd. (2)
Unit 3F-B2 3rd Floor Mirae Business Center 268 to Hien Thanh, Ward 15 District 10, Ho Chi Minh City, Vietnam
Tel.: (84) 839798030
Online Payment & Processing Services
N.A.I.C.S.: 522320
Thao Nguyen Van (Deputy Gen Dir)

East Telecom, LLC (1)
Afrasiab 28/14, Tashkent, 100015, Uzbekistan
Web Site: http://www.etc.uz
Digital Telecommunication Services
N.A.I.C.S.: 517810

Enswers Inc. (1)
22F Seoul City Tower Bldg Namdaemunno 5-ga, Jung-gu, Seoul, 100741, Korea (South)
Tel.: (82) 2 598 5857
Web Site: http://www.enswer.net
Sales Range: $25-49.9 Million
Emp.: 60
Electronic Content Technology Services
N.A.I.C.S.: 541990

Genie Music Corporation (1)
4th to 9th floors Hanseok Tower 809-10 Yeoksam-dong, Gangnam-gu, Seoul, Korea (South)
Tel.: (82) 232822600
Web Site: https://www.geniemusic.co.kr
Rev.: $219,443,419
Assets: $260,858,763
Liabilities: $121,899,906
Net Worth: $138,958,858
Earnings: $13,455,027
Emp.: 230

AND PRIVATE COMPANIES

Fiscal Year-end: 12/31/2022
Music Downloading Services
N.A.I.C.S.: 519210
Hun Bae Kim *(CEO)*

H&C Network Co. Ltd. (1)
Sedae Building 14th Floor 11-3 Hoehyeon-Dong 3-Ga, Jung-Gu, Seoul, 100-053, Korea (South)
Tel.: (82) 27798900
Web Site: http://www.hncnet.co.kr
Human Resource Consulting Services
N.A.I.C.S.: 541612

INITECH Co., Ltd. (1)
10th to 11th floors Ace High 2nd Building 61 Digital-ro 26-gil, Guro-gu, Seoul, 152-050, Korea (South)
Tel.: (82) 264457200
Web Site: https://www.initech.com
Securities Brokerage Services
N.A.I.C.S.: 523150

KT AMC Co., Ltd. (1)
890-20 Daechi-dong, Gangnam-gu, Seoul, 135 737, Korea (South)
Tel.: (82) 2 564 2102
Telecommunication Servicesb
N.A.I.C.S.: 517810

KT Alpha Co., Ltd. (1)
23 Boramae-ro 5-gil, Dongjak-gu, Seoul, Korea (South)
Tel.: (82) 15885668
Web Site: https://www.ktalpha.com
Data Communication Services
N.A.I.C.S.: 517810

KT Cloud Co., Ltd. (1)
343 Hakdong-ro, Gangnam-gu, Seoul, Korea (South)
Tel.: (82) 802580005
Web Site: http://cloud.kt.com
Cloud Computing & Data Centre Services
N.A.I.C.S.: 518210

KT Edui Co., Ltd. (1)
KT Sinsa Branch Main Building 4FL 603-1 Sinsa-dong, Gangnam-gu, 135893, Korea (South)
Tel.: (82) 2 3448 4500
Online Education Services
N.A.I.C.S.: 611710

KT Linkus (1)
Samgu Building 6-7th Floors Hangang-ro 3-ga, Yongsan-gu, Seoul, Korea (South)
Tel.: (82) 802580101
Web Site: http://www.ktlinkus.co.kr
Telephone Maintenance & Repair Services
N.A.I.C.S.: 811210

KT M Mobile Co., Ltd. (1)
12th floor KT Seolleung Tower 422 Teheran-ro, Gangnam-gu, Seoul, (South)
Tel.: (82) 18995000
Web Site: https://www.ktmmobile.com
Mobile Telecommunications Internet & Data Services
N.A.I.C.S.: 518210

KT MOS Nambu Co., Ltd. (1)
6th Floor KT Goejeong Building 72 Goejeong-ro, Seo-gu, Daejeon, Korea (South)
Tel.: (82) 424838161
Web Site: https://www.ktmos.co.kr
Telecommunication Facility Maintenance Services
N.A.I.C.S.: 517810

KT Networks Corp. (1)
Level 5 Samil Plaza B/D 837-26 Yeoksam-dong, Gangnam-gu, 135-768, Seoul, Korea (South)
Tel.: (82) 222229114
Web Site: http://www.ktn.co.kr
Telecommunication Servicesb
N.A.I.C.S.: 517810

KT Sat Co., Ltd. (1)
13-14F KT Seonleung Tower 422 Teheran-ro, Gangnam-gu, Seoul, Korea (South)
Tel.: (82) 15777726
Web Site: https://www.ktsat.com
Satellite Communication Services
N.A.I.C.S.: 517410

KT Sports Co., Ltd. (1)
893 Gyeongsu-daero, Jangan-gu, Suwon, Korea (South)
Tel.: (82) 312479720
Web Site: https://www.kt-sports.co.kr
Sports Team Management Services
N.A.I.C.S.: 711211

KT Telecop Co., Ltd. (1)
KT Telecop Building 291 Gamasan-ro, Guro-gu, Seoul, 152-704, Korea (South)
Tel.: (82) 15880112
Web Site: https://www.kttelecop.co.kr
Security Consulting Services
N.A.I.C.S.: 561612

KTDS Co., Ltd. (1)
176 Hyoryeong-ro, Seocho-gu, Seoul, Korea (South)
Information Technology Consulting Services
N.A.I.C.S.: 541512

KTmhows Co., Ltd. (1)
195-1 Asem Tower 35F Samsung-Dong, Kangnam-Gu, Seoul, 135-798, Korea (South)
Tel.: (82) 221897000
Web Site: http://www.mhows.co.kr
Mobile Marketing Services
N.A.I.C.S.: 541613

Korea HD Broadcasting Corp. (1)
10th Fl Korea Broadcaster's Center Mokdong, Yangchun-gu, Seoul, 158-715, Korea (South)
Tel.: (82) 2 3219 6070
Web Site: http://www.koreahd.co.kr
Television Broadcasting Services
N.A.I.C.S.: 516120

Korea Telecom America, Inc. (1)
811 Wilshire Blvd Ste 1440, Los Angeles, CA 90017
Tel.: (213) 738-7500
Web Site: http://www.ktamerica.com
Emp.: 10
Telecommunication Servicesb
N.A.I.C.S.: 517810
Jung Sup Jung *(Pres & CEO)*

Korea Telecom Japan Co., Ltd. (1)
Tel.: (81) 354252300
Web Site: http://www.kt.com
Telecommunication Servicesb
N.A.I.C.S.: 517810

Kt alpha Co., Ltd. (1)
23 Boramae-ro 5-gil, Dongjak-gu, Seoul, 07071, Korea (South)
Tel.: (82) 215885668
Web Site: https://www.ktalpha.com
Rev.: $360,163,015
Assets: $312,809,673
Liabilities: $135,518,073
Net Worth: $177,291,600
Earnings: $9,342,779
Emp.: 580
Fiscal Year-end: 12/31/2022
Internet Service & Communication Service Provider
N.A.I.C.S.: 517111
Han Sang Bong *(Mng Dir)*

Lolab Co., Ltd. (1)
8-13 Jukhyeon-ro, Giheung-gu, Yongin, Gyeonggi-do, Korea (South)
Tel.: (82) 25552979
Web Site: https://www.lolab.com
Optimal Matching Service & Carrier Liability Services
N.A.I.C.S.: 561730

NEXR Co., Ltd. (1)
Tel.: (82) 25657650
Web Site: http://www.nexr.co.kr
Emp.: 20
Information Technology Consulting Services
N.A.I.C.S.: 541512

Nasmedia Co., Ltd. (1)
3 4 5F Samil Plaza 14 Dogok-ro 1-gil, Gangnam-gu, Seoul, 06253, Korea (South)
Tel.: (82) 221887300
Web Site: https://www.nasmedia.co.kr
Rev.: $116,885,847
Assets: $397,325,237
Liabilities: $211,372,663
Net Worth: $185,952,574
Earnings: $20,542,769
Emp.: 438
Fiscal Year-end: 12/31/2022
Online Advertising Services

N.A.I.C.S.: 541890
Han Soo Kyoung *(Exec Dir)*

Nasmedia Thailand Co., Ltd. (1)
163 Rajapark Building 17th Fl Sukhumvit 21, Asok, Bangkok, 10110, Thailand
Tel.: (66) 22586188
Web Site: https://nasmedia.co.th
Digital Marketing Services
N.A.I.C.S.: 541810

P.T. Cranium Royal Aditama (1)
Jl Kelapa Hybrida G1 No 3 Kelapa Gading, Jakarta Utara, Indonesia
Tel.: (62) 8121847066
Web Site: https://www.cranium.id
Information Technology Services
N.A.I.C.S.: 541511

Sidus FNH Corporation (1)
247-11 Nonhyeon-dong, Gangnam-gu, Seoul, 135-010, Korea (South)
Tel.: (82) 2 3393 8700
Movie Production & Distribution Services
N.A.I.C.S.: 512110

Smartro Co., Ltd. (1)
14th floor Eulji Twin Tower East Building 170 Eulji-ro, Jung-gu, Seoul, 04548, Korea (South)
Tel.: (82) 16669114
Web Site: https://www.smartro.co.kr
Sales Range: $100-124.9 Million
Emp.: 206
Credit Card Processing Services
N.A.I.C.S.: 522320

Storywiz Co., Ltd. (1)
1st and 2nd Floors Building B MJ Building 5 Bukchon-ro 1-gil, Jongno-gu, Seoul, Korea (South)
Tel.: (82) 27454499
Web Site: https://www.storywiz.co.kr
Content Planning Services
N.A.I.C.S.: 541613

VP Inc. (1)
13th floor East Building Eulji Twin Tower 170 Eulji-ro, Jung-gu, Seoul, 04548, Korea (South)
Tel.: (82) 15773033
Web Site: https://about.vp.co.kr
Sales Range: $25-49.9 Million
Emp.: 50
Electronic Transactions Processing Services
N.A.I.C.S.: 518210
Kim Joon *(CEO)*

KT CS CORP.
Main Building 6F kt Human Resource Development Center Galmaro 160, Seo-gu, Daejeon, 302-716, Korea (South)
Tel.: (82) 426045127
Web Site: https://www.ktcs.co.kr
Year Founded: 2001
058850—(KRS)
Rev.: $789,601,166
Assets: $319,184,044
Liabilities: $172,244,646
Net Worth: $146,939,397
Earnings: $13,105,072
Emp.: 9,220
Fiscal Year-end: 12/31/22
Call Center Services
N.A.I.C.S.: 561422
Sung-Kyu Yang *(CEO)*

KT INVEST A.S.
Priemyselna 267/23, Ladomerska Vieska, Ziar nad Hronom, 965 01, Slovakia
Tel.: (421) 905502591
Web Site: http://www.ktinvest.sk
Real Estate Management Services
N.A.I.C.S.: 531210
Lubomira Chalmovska *(Chm-Mgmt Bd)*

KT KIRA SERTIFIKALARI VARLIK KIRALAMA A.S.
Buyukdere Cad No 129-1 Kat 3 Esentepe, Sisli, 34394, Istanbul, Turkiye

KT&G CORPORATION

Tel.: (90) 2123541111
Web Site: http://www.ktksvks.com.tr
KTKVK—(IST)
Sales Range: Less than $1 Million
Asset Leasing Services
N.A.I.C.S.: 531390
Rusen Ahmet Albayrak *(Chm)*

KT POWERTEL CO. LTD.
19th Floor KT Information Center 924 Mok-Dong, Yangshon-gu, Seoul, 158-714, Korea (South)
Tel.: (82) 221660130
Web Site: http://www.ktp.co.kr
Year Founded: 1985
Emp.: 141
Telecommunication Servicesb
N.A.I.C.S.: 517810
Yun Soo Kim *(CEO)*

KT SKYLIFE CO., LTD.
6F 7F KT Mok-dong Branch Bldg 918-1 Mok-dong, Yangcheon-gu, Seoul, 158-050, Korea (South)
Tel.: (82) 220033000
Web Site: http://www.skylife.co.kr
Year Founded: 2001
053210—(KRS)
Rev.: $793,259,161
Assets: $1,044,115,805
Liabilities: $386,387,134
Net Worth: $657,728,671
Earnings: $17,155,530
Emp.: 379
Fiscal Year-end: 12/31/22
Satellite Broadcasting Services
N.A.I.C.S.: 517410
Kyung Won Lee *(Asst Mgr)*

KT SUBMARINE CORP.
6F kt Tower 42 Songjeonggwangeogol-ro, Haeundae-gu, Busan, 612-040, Korea (South)
Tel.: (82) 517040009   KR
Web Site:
http://www.ktsubmarine.co.kr
Year Founded: 1995
Emp.: 100
Submarine Fiber Optic Cable Installation & Maintenance Services
N.A.I.C.S.: 336611
Hyung Joon Kim *(Pres & CEO)*

KT&G CORPORATION
100 Pyeongchon-dong, Daedeok-gu, Daejeon, Korea (South)
Tel.: (82) 819310399
Web Site: https://www.ktng.com
Year Founded: 1899
033780—(KRS)
Rev.: $4,488,028,684
Assets: $9,435,416,006
Liabilities: $2,257,385,122
Net Worth: $7,178,030,884
Earnings: $771,085,934
Emp.: 4,504
Fiscal Year-end: 12/31/22
Cigarette Mfr & Sales
N.A.I.C.S.: 312230
Kyung-man Bang *(Pres & CEO)*

Subsidiaries:

Cheong Kwan Jang Taiwan Corporation (1)
1F No 601 Ruiguang Road, Neihu District, Taipei, 11492, Taiwan
Tel.: (886) 226585055
Web Site: http://www.ckj.com.tw
Sales Range: $25-49.9 Million
Emp.: 17
Optical Product Mfr
N.A.I.C.S.: 333310

Cosmocos Co., Ltd. (1)
11F Daekyo Tower 23 Boramae-ro 3-gil, Gwanak-gu, Seoul, Korea (South)
Tel.: (82) 221667700
Web Site: http://www.cosmocos.us

KT&G CORPORATION

KT&G Corporation—(Continued)
Cosmetics Products Mfr
N.A.I.C.S.: 325620
Bin An *(CEO)*

KGC Life & Gin Co., Ltd. (1)
12th Floor Daegyo Building 23 Boramae-ro 3-gil, Gwanak-gu, Seoul, 08708, Korea (South)
Tel.: (82) 221667770
Web Site: http://www.kgclifengin.com
Health Functional Food & Cosmetic Whslr
N.A.I.C.S.: 456199

KT&G Tutun Mamulleri Sanayi ve Ticaret A.S. (1)
Turnan Mah Tire Organize Sanayi Bolgesi 1269 Ada 14 Parsel Tire, Izmir, Turkiye
Tel.: (90) 2325135200
Web Site: http://www.ktng.com.tr
Sales Range: $25-49.9 Million
Emp.: 50
Cigarettes Mfr & Distr
N.A.I.C.S.: 312230
Dongwon Lee *(Mng Dir)*

Korea Ginseng (China) Corp. (1)
A 903 Hongqiao Shanghai Cheng No 100 Zunyi Road, Changning District, Shanghai, China
Tel.: (86) 21 62372315
Ginseng Farming Services
N.A.I.C.S.: 111219

Korea Ginseng Corp. (1)
71 Beotkkot-gil, Daedeok-gu, Daejeon, Korea (South) **(100%)**
Tel.: (82) 15882304
Ginseng Supplement Mfr & Distr
N.A.I.C.S.: 325411
Kim Jae Soo *(CEO)*

Korea Red Ginseng Corporation (1)
1787 Yeonjang-ri Jinan-eup, Jinan, 567-807, North Jeolla, Korea (South)
Tel.: (82) 5 950 85 15
Red Ginseng Mfr
N.A.I.C.S.: 111219

Korean Red Ginseng Corp., Inc. (1)
12750 Ctr Ct Dr Ste 100, Cerritos, CA 90703
Tel.: (562) 860-2323
Health Functional Food & Cosmetic Whslr
N.A.I.C.S.: 456199

PT KT&G Indonesia (1)
Noble House Lt 39 No 2 Jalan Dr Ide Anak Agung Gde Agung Kav E 4 2 RT, 5/RW 2 Kuningan Kecamatan Setiabudi Kota Jakarta Selatan DKI, Jakarta, 12950, Indonesia
Tel.: (62) 2157991291
Health Functional Food & Cosmetic Whslr
N.A.I.C.S.: 456199

SangSang Stay Inc. (1)
9 Namdaemun-ro, Jung-gu, Seoul, 04526, Korea (South)
Tel.: (82) 27770148
Web Site: https://www.sangsangstay.com
Hotel Services
N.A.I.C.S.: 721110

Tae-A Industry Co., Ltd. (1)
San 44 Samseong-myeon, Eumseong-gun, Yongseong, 369-834, Chungcheongbuk, Korea (South)
Tel.: (82) 438786410
Reconstituted Tobacco Mfr
N.A.I.C.S.: 312230

Yungjin Pharmaceutical Company Ltd. (1)
13 Olympic-ro 35da-gil, Songpa-gu, Seoul, 056336, Korea (South) **(57.2%)**
Tel.: (82) 220418200
Web Site: https://www.yungjin.co.kr
Sales Range: $75-99.9 Million
Emp.: 600
Pharmaceutical & Related Products Mfr
N.A.I.C.S.: 325412
Sujun Park *(CEO)*

KTB INVESTMENT & SECURITIES CO., LTD.
KTB Building 66 Yeouidaero, Yeongdeungpo-gu, Seoul, 150 790, Korea (South)
Tel.: (82) 221842000
Web Site: http://www.ktbsecurities.com
030210—(KRS)
Rev.: $1,455,151,298
Assets: $7,507,925,983
Liabilities: $6,728,657,404
Net Worth: $779,268,579
Earnings: $75,492,545
Fiscal Year-end: 12/31/22
Financial Services
N.A.I.C.S.: 523150
Chul Byung Lee *(Co-CEO)*

Subsidiaries:

KTB Asia Advisors Pte. Ltd. (1)
16 Collyer Quay 26-01, Singapore, 49318, Singapore
Tel.: (65) 6532 2253
Investment Services
N.A.I.C.S.: 523999

KTB Asset Management Co., Ltd. (1)
28Fl Post Tower 60 Yeouinaru-ro, Yeongdeungpo-gu, 07328, Seoul, Korea (South)
Tel.: (82) 2 788 8400
Web Site: https://www.daolfund.com
Asset Management Services
N.A.I.C.S.: 533110
Kim Tae-woo *(CEO)*

KTB Investment Management Co., Ltd. (1)
Unit 1701B 17th Floor East Towers LG Twin Towers, Chaoyang District, Beijing, 100022, China
Tel.: (86) 10 6568 1391
Web Site: http://www.ktbchina.com
Emp.: 6
Investment Services
N.A.I.C.S.: 523150

KTB Private Equity Co., Ltd. (1)
30Fl Post Tower 60 Yeouinaru-ro, Yeongdeungpo-gu, Seoul, Korea (South)
Tel.: (82) 22 184 4150
Web Site: https://www.daolpe.com
Financial Services
N.A.I.C.S.: 523999

KTB Securities (Thailand) Company Limited (1)
87/2 CRC Tower 18 39th Fl All Seasons Place Wireless Road Lumpini, Pathumwan, Bangkok, 10330, Thailand
Tel.: (66) 2648 1111
Web Site: http://www.ktbst.co.th
Investment Services
N.A.I.C.S.: 523150
Kin Jung Kyu *(CEO)*

KTB SPECIAL PURPOSE ACQUISITION COMPANY 1 CO., LTD
4F 66 Yeoui-daero, Yeongdeungpo-gu, Seoul, Korea (South)
Tel.: (82) 221842894
Year Founded: 2014
204650—(KRS)
Assets: $9,803,386
Liabilities: $1,140,116
Net Worth: $8,663,269
Earnings: ($2,898)
Financial Investment Management Services
N.A.I.C.S.: 523940
Myeong Ho Jung *(CEO)*

KTESIOS REAL ESTATE SOCIMI, S.A.
Calle Sagasta 15 7 Izq, 28004, Madrid, Spain
Tel.: (34) 910638010 ES
Web Site: https://www.ktesios-socimi.es
Year Founded: 2019
MLKTS—(EUR)
Rev.: $631,726
Assets: $15,845,425
Liabilities: $5,129,230
Net Worth: $10,716,195
Earnings: ($84,541)
Fiscal Year-end: 12/31/21
Real Estate Investment Services
N.A.I.C.S.: 531190
Henry Noel Gallego *(Chm & CEO)*

Subsidiaries:

Quid Pro Quo Alquiler Seguro SOCIMI SA (1)
Calle Sagasta 15 7 Izquierda, 28004, Madrid, Spain
Tel.: (34) 910921195
Web Site: https://www.qpqalquilersegurosocimi.es
Investment Management Service
N.A.I.C.S.: 523999
Henry Gallego *(CEO)*

KTG AGRAR SE
Ferdinandstrasse 12, D-20095, Hamburg, Germany
Tel.: (49) 40 303764 7 De
Holding Company; Agricultural Cultivation & Bioenergy Generation Services
N.A.I.C.S.: 551112
Ulf Hammerich *(COO & Member-Exec Bd)*

Subsidiaries:

AK Feldfrucht GmbH (1)
Gorke 6 b, 17391, Postlow, Germany
Tel.: (49) 3971 211090
Crop Farming Services
N.A.I.C.S.: 111998

Agrar GmbH Kohlberg (1)
Hauptstrasse 98, 98593, Struth-Helmershof, Germany
Tel.: (49) 3683 78 86 41
Web Site: http://www.agrar-gmbh-kohlberg.de
Beef Cattle Ranching & Farming Services
N.A.I.C.S.: 112111

Agrar GmbH Landwirtschaftlicher Produktionsbetrieb Altdobern (1)
Am Marstall, 03229, Altdobern, Germany
Tel.: (49) 3 54 34 2 22
Web Site: http://www.agrar-altdoebern.de
Beef Cattle Ranching & Farming Services
N.A.I.C.S.: 112111

Agrargesellschaft Altjessnitz mbH (1)
Gostauer Str6, Starsiedel, 06686, Lützen, Sachsen-Anhalt, Germany
Tel.: (49) 34444 41614
Crop Farming Services
N.A.I.C.S.: 111998

Incofarming Agrarprodukte und Service GmbH (1)
Lindenstr 1, Linthe, 14822, Brandenburg, Germany
Tel.: (49) 33844 51802
Crop Farming Services
N.A.I.C.S.: 111998

Landwirtschaftliche Produktionsgesellschaft mbH (1)
Leutnitz 37, 07426, Konigsee-Rottenbach, Thuringen, Germany
Tel.: (49) 36739 22212
Crop Farming Services
N.A.I.C.S.: 111998

NGH Agrar GmbH & Co. Agrargesellschaft Hohenseefeld KG (1)
Hauptstr 11, 14913, Nonnendorf, Germany
Tel.: (49) 337 446 0629
Crop Farming Services
N.A.I.C.S.: 111998

NOA Naturoel Anklam AG (1)
Am Hafen 1, 17389, Anklam, Germany
Tel.: (49) 3971 242 018
Web Site: http://www.noa.ag
Oilseed Processing Services
N.A.I.C.S.: 311224

INTERNATIONAL PUBLIC

KTIMA KOSTAS LAZARIDIS S.A.
Adriani Drama, PO Box 157, 66100, Drama, Greece
Tel.: (30) 2521082231
Web Site: http://www.domaine-lazaridi.gr
Year Founded: 1992
KTILA—(ATH)
Sales Range: Less than $1 Million
Emp.: 63
Wine Mfr
N.A.I.C.S.: 312130
Ioulia K. Lazaridi *(Chm)*

KTIS CORPORATION
14 Yeoui-daero, Yeongdeungpo-gu, Seoul, 07320, Korea (South)
Tel.: (82) 232152054
Web Site: http://www.ktis.co.kr
Year Founded: 2001
058860—(KRS)
Rev.: $410,945,796
Assets: $303,891,589
Liabilities: $152,789,243
Net Worth: $151,102,346
Earnings: $12,208,050
Emp.: 7,980
Fiscal Year-end: 12/31/22
Corporate Contact Center Operation & Outsourcing Services
N.A.I.C.S.: 561421

KTK GROUP CO., LTD.
No 88 Jinchuang Road Wujin District, Yaoguan Town, Changzhou, 213102, Jiangsu, China
Tel.: (86) 51988375888
Web Site: https://en.ktk.com.cn
Year Founded: 2003
603680—(SHG)
Rev.: $496,201,933
Assets: $1,230,021,164
Liabilities: $563,594,789
Net Worth: $666,426,375
Earnings: $27,859,460
Fiscal Year-end: 12/31/22
Motor Vehicle Parts Mfr & Distr
N.A.I.C.S.: 336360
Yu Jinkun *(Founder & Chm)*

KTK INC.
2-3-3 Izumi, Higashi-ku, Nagoya, 461-0001, Aichi, Japan
Tel.: (81) 529311881
Web Site: https://www.ktk.gr.jp
Year Founded: 1971
3035—(TKS)
Rev.: $112,653,192
Assets: $55,153,967
Liabilities: $28,964,231
Net Worth: $26,189,736
Earnings: $2,146,190
Fiscal Year-end: 08/31/24
Office Goods Distr
N.A.I.C.S.: 459410
Hideo Aoyama *(Chm, Pres & CEO)*

KTL GLOBAL LIMITED
18 Boon Lay Way 10-139 Tradehub 21, Singapore, 609966, Singapore
Tel.: (65) 69837969
Web Site: https://www.ktl.group
EB7—(SES)
Rev.: $1,483,104
Assets: $804,703
Liabilities: $506,721
Net Worth: $297,982
Earnings: ($2,373,269)
Fiscal Year-end: 12/31/20
Offshore Oil, Gas, Marine & Construction Equipment Mfr & Distr
N.A.I.C.S.: 333132
Chin Teck Oon *(Exec Dir)*

AND PRIVATE COMPANIES

Subsidiaries:

Future Synthetics Pte. Ltd. (1)
7 Gul Road, Singapore, 629364, Singapore
Tel.: (65) 65438888
Web Site: https://www.futuresynx.com
Steel Wire Rope Sling Mfr & Distr
N.A.I.C.S.: 314994

KTL Logan Pte. Ltd. (1)
71 Tuas Bay Dr, Singapore,
Singapore (70%)
Tel.: (65) 65438888
Sales Range: $25-49.9 Million
Emp.: 100
Winch Mfr
N.A.I.C.S.: 333923

KTL Offshore Pte. Ltd. (1)
71 Tuas Bay Drive, Singapore, Singapore
Tel.: (65) 65438888
Web Site: http://www.ktlgroup.com
Steel Wire Ropes Whslr
N.A.I.C.S.: 423610

KTMG LIMITED
5 Harper Road 04-03, Singapore,
369673, Singapore
Tel.: (65) 91886489
Web Site: https://www.ktmg.sg
Year Founded: 1988
XCF—(CAT)
Rev.: $67,196,849
Assets: $42,635,765
Liabilities: $27,762,630
Net Worth: $14,873,135
Earnings: ($1,478,452)
Emp.: 2,310
Fiscal Year-end: 12/31/23
Engineeering Services
N.A.I.C.S.: 541330
Choon Lui Ong *(Exec Dir)*

Subsidiaries:

Knit Textile Integrated Industries Sdn. Bhd. (1)
No 2 Jalan Perahu Kawasan Perindustrian Tongkang Pecah, 83000, Batu Pahat, Johor, Malaysia
Tel.: (60) 74156648
Emp.: 110
Knitted Fabric Mfr
N.A.I.C.S.: 313240

KTP KUNSTSTOFF PALETTENTECHNIK GMBH
Saarstrasse 1, 66359, Bous, Germany
Tel.: (49) 683492100
Web Site: http://www.ktp-online.de
Year Founded: 1988
Sales Range: $10-24.9 Million
Plastic Packaging Products Mfr
N.A.I.C.S.: 326112
Andreas Wintrich *(Mng Dir)*

KTR KUPPLUNGSTECHNIK GMBH
Rodder Damm 170, 48432, Rheine, Germany
Tel.: (49) 59717980
Web Site: http://www.ktr.com
Year Founded: 2000
Sales Range: $25-49.9 Million
Emp.: 800
Couplings, Clamping Sets, Torque Limiters, Torque Measuring Systems & Hydraulic Components Mfr
N.A.I.C.S.: 334519
Josef Gerstner *(CEO)*

Subsidiaries:

Haberkorn Fairtool Kft. (1)
Tunderfurt u3, 1106, Budapest, Hungary
Tel.: (36) 1 884 8800
Web Site: http://www.haberkorn.hu
Couplings, Clamping Sets, Torque Limiters, Torque Measuring Systems & Hydraulic Components Mfr
N.A.I.C.S.: 334519

KTR Benelux B.V. (1)
Adam Smithstraat 37, Hengelo, 7559, Netherlands
Tel.: (31) 74 2505526
Couplings, Clamping Sets, Torque Limiters, Torque Measuring Systems & Hydraulic Components Mfr
N.A.I.C.S.: 334519

Branch (Non-US):

KTR Benelux B.V. - Belgium Office (2)
Blancefloerlaan 167/22, 2050, Antwerp, Belgium
Tel.: (32) 32110567
Couplings, Clamping Sets, Torque Limiters, Torque Measuring Systems & Hydraulic Components Mfr
N.A.I.C.S.: 334519
Hans Hagedoorn *(Gen Mgr)*

KTR Brake Systems GmbH (1)
Zur Brinke 14, 33758, Schloss Holte-Stukenbrock, Germany
Tel.: (49) 52 07 99 161 0
Brake System Mfr
N.A.I.C.S.: 336340
Norbert Partmann *(Gen Mgr)*

KTR CR, spol. s r. o. (1)
Olomoucke 226, 569 43, Jevicko, Czech Republic
Tel.: (420) 461325162
Web Site: http://www.spojky-ktr.cz
Sales Range: $25-49.9 Million
Emp.: 5
Couplings, Clamping Sets, Torque Limiters, Torque Measuring Systems & Hydraulic Components Mfr
N.A.I.C.S.: 334519
Kamil Stopka *(Gen Mgr)*

KTR Corporation (1)
122 Anchor Rd, Michigan City, IN 46361
Tel.: (219) 872-9100
Hydraulic Component Mfr & Distr
N.A.I.C.S.: 336340

KTR Couplings (India) Pvt. Ltd. (1)
T 36 37 & 38, MIDC Bhosari, Pune, 411026, India
Tel.: (91) 2027127325
Web Site: http://www.ktr.com
Sales Range: $25-49.9 Million
Emp.: 70
Couplings, Clamping Sets, Torque Limiters, Torque Measuring Systems & Hydraulic Components Mfr
N.A.I.C.S.: 334519
Shivshankar Pikale *(Mng Dir)*

KTR Couplings Ltd. (1)
Robert House, Unit 7 Acorn Business Park, Sheffield, S8 0TB, United Kingdom
Tel.: (44) 1142587757
Web Site: http://www.ktr.com
Sales Range: $25-49.9 Million
Emp.: 8
Couplings, Clamping Sets, Torque Limiters, Torque Measuring Systems & Hydraulic Components Mfr
N.A.I.C.S.: 334519
Jeff Ancliff *(Mng Dir)*

KTR Couplings South Africa (Pty) Ltd. (1)
28 Spartan Road, Kempton Park, Gauteng, South Africa
Tel.: (27) 11 281 3801
Hydraulic Component Distr
N.A.I.C.S.: 423830
Gavin Doran *(Gen Mgr)*

KTR Finland OY (1)
Tiistinniityntie 4, 2230, Espoo, Finland
Tel.: (358) 207414610
Web Site: http://www.ktr.fi
Couplings, Clamping Sets, Torque Limiters, Torque Measuring Systems & Hydraulic Components Mfr
N.A.I.C.S.: 334519

KTR France (1)
46-48 Chemin De La Bruyere, Dardilly, 69570, France
Tel.: (33) 478645466
Web Site: http://www.ktr.com
Sales Range: $25-49.9 Million
Emp.: 14

Couplings, Clamping Sets, Torque Limiters, Torque Measuring Systems & Hydraulic Components Mfr
N.A.I.C.S.: 334519
Pierre Martin *(Gen Mgr)*

KTR Japan Co., Ltd. (1)
3-1-23 Daikaidori Hyogo-ku, Kobe, 652-0803, Japan
Tel.: (81) 7 85740313
Web Site: http://www.ktr.com
Emp.: 10
Couplings, Clamping Sets, Torque Limiters, Torque Measuring Systems & Hydraulic Components Mfr
N.A.I.C.S.: 334519
Dadashige Nishikura *(Mng Dir)*

KTR Korea Ltd. (1)
101 978-10 Topyung-Dong, Gyeonggi-Do, Seoul, 471-060, Guri, Korea (South)
Tel.: (82) 315694510
Couplings, Clamping Sets, Torque Limiters, Torque Measuring Systems & Hydraulic Components Mfr
N.A.I.C.S.: 334519

KTR Kupplungstechnik AG (1)
Bahnstrasse 60, Regensdorf, 8105, Switzerland
Tel.: (41) 433111550
Web Site: http://www.ktr.com
Sales Range: $25-49.9 Million
Emp.: 9
Couplings, Clamping Sets, Torque Limiters, Torque Measuring Systems & Hydraulic Components Mfr
N.A.I.C.S.: 334519

KTR Kupplungstechnik Norge AS (1)
Fjellbovegen 13, 2016, Frogner, Norway
Tel.: (47) 64835490
Web Site: http://www.ktr.com
Sales Range: $25-49.9 Million
Emp.: 3
Couplings, Clamping Sets, Torque Limiters, Torque Measuring Systems & Hydraulic Components Mfr
N.A.I.C.S.: 334519
Arild Andersen *(Gen Mgr)*

KTR Polska SP. Z. O. O. (1)
Czerwone Maki 65, 30 392, Krakow, Poland
Tel.: (48) 122672883
Couplings, Clamping Sets, Torque Limiters, Torque Measuring Systems & Hydraulic Components Mfr
N.A.I.C.S.: 334519

KTR Power Transmission Technology (Shanghai) Co. Ltd. (1)
Floor 1 & 2 Bldg B, 1501 JinSui Road Pudong, 201206, Shanghai, China
Tel.: (86) 21 50 32 08 80
Couplings, Clamping Sets, Torque Limiters, Torque Measuring Systems & Hydraulic Components Mfr
N.A.I.C.S.: 334519

KTR Privodnaya Technika, LLC (1)
Sverdlovskaya Naberezhnaya 60 Litera A, 195027, Saint Petersburg, Russia
Tel.: (7) 8124956272
Web Site: http://www.ktr.ru
Sales Range: $25-49.9 Million
Emp.: 7
Couplings, Clamping Sets, Torque Limiters, Torque Measuring Systems & Hydraulic Components Mfr
N.A.I.C.S.: 334519

KTR Sverige AB (1)
Hammarbacken 4 B, Box 742, 19127, Sollentuna, Sweden
Tel.: (46) 86250290
Sales Range: $25-49.9 Million
Emp.: 6
Couplings, Clamping Sets, Torque Limiters, Torque Measuring Systems & Hydraulic Components Mfr
N.A.I.C.S.: 334519
Leis Hojlund *(Mng Dir)*

KTR Taiwan Ltd. (1)
1 F No 17 Industry 38 Rd, Taichung Industry Zone, Taichung, 407, Taiwan
Tel.: (886) 423593278
Sales Range: $25-49.9 Million
Emp.: 7
Couplings, Clamping Sets, Torque Limiters, Torque Measuring Systems & Hydraulic Components Mfr
N.A.I.C.S.: 334519

KTR Turkey Guc Aktarma Sistemleri San. Tic. Ltd. Sti. (1)
Kayisdagi Cad No 117/2, Atasehir, 34758, Istanbul, Turkiye
Tel.: (90) 216 574 378 0
Hydraulic Component Distr
N.A.I.C.S.: 423830

KTR do Brasil Ltda. (1)
Rua Henrique Coelho Neto 381, 83321-030, Parana, Brazil
Tel.: (55) 4136689926
Sales Range: $25-49.9 Million
Emp.: 11
Couplings, Clamping Sets, Torque Limiters, Torque Measuring Systems & Hydraulic Components Mfr
N.A.I.C.S.: 334519

KU CHI ENTERPRISE LIMITED
6F No 228 Yongzhen Road, Yonghe District, New Taipei City, Taiwan
Tel.: (886) 229291166 TW
Web Site: http://www.kuchi.com.tw
Non-Fuse Switch Mfr
N.A.I.C.S.: 335313

KU HOLDINGS CO., LTD.
8-17-1 Tsuruma, Machida, 194-8555, Tokyo, Japan
Tel.: (81) 427992130
Web Site: https://www.ku-hd.com
Year Founded: 1972
9856—(TKS)
Rev.: $1,021,661,430
Assets: $565,386,350
Liabilities: $148,222,640
Net Worth: $417,163,710
Earnings: $40,796,920
Emp.: 1,383
Fiscal Year-end: 03/31/24
Holding Company
N.A.I.C.S.: 551112
Yoshihiro Inoue *(Pres, CEO, Founder, COO & Chm)*

KUAIJISHAN SHAOXING WINE CO., LTD.
No 2579 Yangshao Road Hutang Street, Keqiao District, Shaoxing, 312032, Zhejiang, China
Tel.: (86) 57581188579
Web Site: http://www.kuaijishanwine.com
Year Founded: 1993
601579—(SHG)
Rev.: $191,544,674
Assets: $686,506,432
Liabilities: $126,226,655
Net Worth: $560,279,777
Earnings: $43,470,273
Fiscal Year-end: 12/31/21
Spirit Product Mfr & Whslr
N.A.I.C.S.: 312140
Fang Chaoyang *(Chm)*

KUAISHOU TECHNOLOGY CO., LTD.
Building 1 No 6 Shangdi West Road, Haidian District, Beijing, China
Tel.: (86) 4001260088 Ky
Year Founded: 2014
1024—(HKG)
Rev.: $14,429,704,196
Assets: $13,682,769,594
Liabilities: $7,579,225,159
Net Worth: $6,103,544,435
Earnings: ($2,097,346,846)
Emp.: 25,445
Fiscal Year-end: 12/31/22
Information Technology Services
N.A.I.C.S.: 541512
Bing Jin *(CFO)*

KUALA LUMPUR KEPONG BERHAD

KUALA LUMPUR KEPONG BERHAD

Kuala Lumpur Kepong Berhad—(Continued)
Bangunan Mayban Trust Ipoh Level 9
No 28 Jalan Tun Sambanthan,
30000, Ipoh, Perak Darul Ridzuan,
Malaysia
Tel.: (60) 52408000
Web Site: http://www.klk.com.my
KLK—(KLS)
Rev.: $5,004,780,106
Assets: $6,375,955,767
Liabilities: $2,959,287,196
Net Worth: $3,416,668,571
Earnings: $209,671,323
Emp.: 48,487
Fiscal Year-end: 09/30/23
Holding Company
N.A.I.C.S.: 551112
Oi Hian Lee *(CEO)*

Subsidiaries:

B.K.B. Europa SARL (1)
Centre D Activities D Aeroport Epinal Mirecourt, 88503, Mirecourt, France
Tel.: (33) 3 2937 8868
Web Site: http://www.bkbhevea.com
Wood Products Mfr
N.A.I.C.S.: 321999

B.K.B. Hevea Products Sdn Bhd (1)
No 4 Lebuh Perusahaan Kelebang 5 Igb
International Industrial Park, Jalan Kuala
Kangsar, 31200, Ipoh, Perak,
Malaysia (100%)
Tel.: (60) 52911599
Web Site: https://www.bkbhevea.com
Sales Range: $100-124.9 Million
Emp.: 370
Flooring Contractors
N.A.I.C.S.: 238330
Pekka Ropa *(Mng Dir)*

Betatechnic Sdn Bhd (1)
Wisma Taiko 1 Jln S P Seenivasagam,
Ipoh, 30000, Perak, Malaysia
Tel.: (60) 52417844
Property Development Services
N.A.I.C.S.: 531390

Centros Life Science Pte Ltd (1)
16 Tuas South Street 5 Tuas, Singapore,
637795, Singapore
Tel.: (65) 65139370
Pharmaceuticals Product Mfr
N.A.I.C.S.: 325412

Davos Life Science Marketing Pte
Ltd (1)
3 Biopolis Drive Unit 04-19 Synapse, Singapore, 138623, Singapore (51%)
Tel.: (65) 65130144
Web Site: http://www.davoslife.com
Emp.: 15
Drilling Oil & Gas Wells
N.A.I.C.S.: 213111

Davos Life Science Pte Ltd (1)
3 Biopolis Drive 04-19 Synapse, Singapore,
138623, Singapore (51%)
Tel.: (65) 67739021
Web Site: https://www.klkoleo.com
Sales Range: $25-49.9 Million
Emp.: 14
Mfr of Nutraceutical, Cosmeceutical & Pharmaceutical Products
N.A.I.C.S.: 325412

Dr. W. Kolb AG (1)
Maienbrunnenstrasse 1, PO Box 64, 8908,
Hedingen, Switzerland
Tel.: (41) 447624646
Web Site: http://www.kolb.ch
Sales Range: $125-149.9 Million
Emp.: 260
Specialty Chemicals Mfr
N.A.I.C.S.: 325199

Dr. W. Kolb Holding AG (1)
Maienbrunnenstrasse 1, Hedingen, 8908,
Switzerland
Tel.: (41) 44 762 46 46
Web Site: http://www.kolb.ch
Emp.: 250
Specialty Chemicals Mfr
N.A.I.C.S.: 325180

Dr. W. Kolb Netherlands BV (1)
Westelijke Randweg 5, Klundert, 4791 RT,
North Brabant, Netherlands
Tel.: (31) 168387080
Specialty Chemicals Mfr
N.A.I.C.S.: 325199
Mark Bramer *(Gen Mgr)*

IJM Plantations Berhad (1)
2nd Floor Wisma IJM Jalan Yong Shook
Lin, 46050, Petaling Jaya, Selangor Darul
Ehsan, Malaysia (90.33%)
Tel.: (60) 37 985 8288
Web Site: https://www.ijmplantations.com
Forest Nurseries & Gathering of Forest
Products
N.A.I.C.S.: 113210
Joseph Tek Choon Yee *(CEO & Mng Dir)*

KL- Kepong Edible Oil Sdn Bhd (1)
Plo 251 Jalan Besi Satu Pasir Gudang Industrial Estate, Pasir Gudang, 81707,
Malaysia (100%)
Tel.: (60) 72511402
Sales Range: $10-24.9 Million
Emp.: 42
Oilseed & Grain Combination Farming
N.A.I.C.S.: 111191
Nang Dran *(Mgr)*

KL-K Holiday Bungalows Sdn
Bhd (1)
1475 Jln Richmond, 49000, Pahang,
Malaysia (100%)
Tel.: (60) 93622232
Sales Range: $25-49.9 Million
Emp.: 5
Oilseed & Grain Combination Farming
N.A.I.C.S.: 111191

KL-Kepong (Sabah) Sdn Bhd (1)
Big No 3 91009 tower, Locked Bag No 3,
Tawau, 91009, Sabah, Malaysia
Tel.: (60) 89975111
Web Site: http://www.klkepong.com
Emp.: 1,000
Palm Oil Refining Services
N.A.I.C.S.: 311225

KL-Kepong Complex Sdn Bhd (1)
Wisma Taiko 1 Jln S P Seenivasagam,
Ipoh, 30000, Perak, Malaysia
Tel.: (60) 52417844
Web Site: http://www.klk.com.my
Emp.: 2,000
Property Management Services
N.A.I.C.S.: 531311

KL-Kepong Country Homes Sdn
Bhd (1)
Suite 1A-1 Level 1 Menara KLK No 1 Jalan
PJU 7/6, Mutiara Damansara, 47810, Petaling Jaya, Selangor, Malaysia
Tel.: (60) 377261868
Property Development Services
N.A.I.C.S.: 531390

KL-Kepong Industrial Holdings Sdn.
Bhd. (1)
Level 8 Menara KLK No 1 Jalan PJU 7/6,
Mutiara Damansara, 47810, Petaling Jaya,
Selangor, Malaysia
Tel.: (60) 378098833
Web Site: https://www.klkoleo.com
Holding Company
N.A.I.C.S.: 551112

Subsidiary (Domestic):

KL-Kepong Rubber Products Sdn
Bhd (2)
Lot 21251 3/4 Mile Off Jalan Bercham Kawasan Perindustrian Bercham, Kawasan
Perindustrian Bercham, 31400, Ipoh, Perak,
Malaysia (100%)
Tel.: (60) 55417337
Web Site: https://klkrp.com.my
Rubber Products Mfr
N.A.I.C.S.: 326291

KL-Kepong International Ltd (1)
Wisma Taiko 1 Jalan S P Seenivasagam,
Perak Darul Ridzuan, 30000, Ipoh,
Malaysia (100%)
Tel.: (60) 52417844
Sales Range: $75-99.9 Million
Emp.: 200
Holding Company
N.A.I.C.S.: 551112

KL-Kepong Plantation Holdings Sdn
Bhd (1)
Wisma Taiko 1 Jln S P Seenivasagam,
Ipoh, 30000, Perak, Malaysia
Tel.: (60) 52417844
Emp.: 100
Processed Palm Oil Mfr
N.A.I.C.S.: 311225

Subsidiary (Non-US):

Astra-KLK Pte. Ltd. (2)
298 Tiong Bahru Road 14-02/03 Central
Plaza, Singapore, 168730, Singapore
Tel.: (65) 65134560
Logistic Services
N.A.I.C.S.: 541614

Subsidiary (Domestic):

Jasachem Sdn Bhd (2)
No 10 Jalan TSB 10 Taman Industri Sungai
Buloh, Kota Damansara, 47000, Petaling
Jaya, Selangor, Malaysia
Tel.: (60) 361446099
Chemical Products Distr
N.A.I.C.S.: 424690

Subsidiary (Non-US):

P.T. Sekarbumi Alamlestari (2)
Komp Taman Anggrek B2 B4 Jl Tuanku
Tambusai, Pekanbaru, Riau,
Indonesia (65%)
Tel.: (62) 761571885
Oil Palm Plantation Services
N.A.I.C.S.: 311225

KL-Kepong Property Development
Sdn. Bhd. (1)
Suite 1A-1 Level 1 Menara KLK No 1 Jalan
PJU 7/6, Mutiara Damansara, 47810, Petaling Jaya, Selangor, Malaysia
Tel.: (60) 377261868
Web Site: https://www.klk.com.my
Sales Range: $50-74.9 Million
Emp.: 18
Real Estate Property Lessors
N.A.I.C.S.: 531190

KL-Kepong Property Management
Sdn Bhd (1)
Suite 1 A-1 Level 1 Menara KLK No1 Jalan,
Pju 76 Mutiara Damansara, Petaling Jaya,
47810, Malaysia (100%)
Tel.: (60) 377261868
Web Site: http://www.klk.com.my
Sales Range: $50-74.9 Million
Emp.: 60
Real Estate Property Lessors
N.A.I.C.S.: 531190
Hoh Chui Lei *(Gen Mgr)*

KLK Assurance (Labuan) Ltd (1)
C/O Brighton Management Limited, Brighton Place Ground Floo, 87014, Labuan,
Malaysia (100%)
Tel.: (60) 87442899
Reinsurance Carriers
N.A.I.C.S.: 524130
Har Wai Ming *(Exec Dir)*

KLK Bioenergy Sdn Bhd (1)
11 Jalan Utas 15/7, Shah Alam, 40200, Selangor, Malaysia
Tel.: (60) 355191388
Emp.: 53
Biodiesel Mfr
N.A.I.C.S.: 324199

KLK Emmerich GmBH (1)
Steintor 9, 46446, Emmerich am Rhein,
Germany
Tel.: (49) 282 2720
Web Site: https://www.klkoleo.com
Emp.: 450
Chemical Products Mfr
N.A.I.C.S.: 325180

KLK OLEO (1)
Level 8 Menara KLK No 1 Jalan PJU 7/6,
Mutiara Damansara, 47810, Petaling Jaya,
Selangor, Malaysia (96%)
Tel.: (60) 378098833
Web Site: https://www.klkoleo.com
Sales Range: $50-74.9 Million
Emp.: 200
Ethyl Alcohol Manufacturing Sales & Marketing
N.A.I.C.S.: 325193

KLK OLEO Emmerich GmBH (1)
Steintor 9, Emmerich am Rhein, D 46446,
Emmerich, Germany
Tel.: (49) 2822720
Sales Range: $125-149.9 Million
Emp.: 265
Oleochemical Mfr
N.A.I.C.S.: 325998

KLK Oleo (Shanghai) Co Ltd (1)
LZY Tower Room 1603-1608 16th Floor No
4711 Jiao Tong Road, Putuo District,
200333, Shanghai, China
Tel.: (86) 2136361130
Chemical Product Whslr
N.A.I.C.S.: 424690

KLK Overseas Investments Ltd (1)
C-O Equity Trust BVI Limited Palm Grave
House, Road Town, Tortola, Virgin Islands
(British) (100%)
Tel.: (284) 4942616
Web Site: http://www.tms-group.com
Holding Company; Property Investments
N.A.I.C.S.: 551112
Nicholas Lane *(Gen Mgr)*

KSP Manufacturing Sdn Bhd (1)
Level 8 Menara KLK No 1 Jalan PJU 7/6,
Mutiara Damansara, 47810, Petaling Jaya,
Selangor Darul Ehsan, Malaysia (96%)
Tel.: (60) 378098833
Web Site: http://www.klkoleo.com
Soap & Other Detergent Mfr
N.A.I.C.S.: 325611

Kolb Distribution AG (1)
Maienbrunnenstrasse 1, 8908, Hedingen,
8908, Switzerland
Tel.: (41) 447624646
Web Site: https://www.kolb.ch
Specialty Chemicals Distr
N.A.I.C.S.: 424690
Uwe Halder *(Pres)*

Kolb Distribution BV (1)
Westelijke Randweg 5 Harbournumber
M431, PO Box 123, 4790 AC, Klundert,
Netherlands
Tel.: (31) 168414300
Web Site: http://www.kolb.ch
Emp.: 75
Specialty Chemical Whslr
N.A.I.C.S.: 424690
Louis Reau *(Mgr)*

Masif Latex Products Sdn Bhd (1)
Lot 21251 3/4 Mile Off Jalan Bercham Kawasan Perindustrian Bercham, 31400, Ipoh,
Perak, Malaysia
Tel.: (60) 55417337
Web Site: http://www.masif.com.my
House Hold Glove Mfr
N.A.I.C.S.: 339113

PT Satu Sembilan Delapan (1)
Puri Mutiara Blok C No 3-5-6-7 JL Griya
Utama Sunter Agung, Jakarta, 14350,
Indonesia (92%)
Tel.: (62) 2165310746
Palm Oil Mfr
N.A.I.C.S.: 311224

Palm-Oleo (Klang) Sdn Bhd (1)
Lot 1 2 Solok Waja 3 Bukit Raja Industrial
Estate, Kelang, 41710, Selangor, Malaysia
Tel.: (60) 333412115
Emp.: 200
Palm Oil Mfr
N.A.I.C.S.: 311225
Kow Tiat Yong *(Gen Mgr)*

Palm-Oleo Sdn Bhd (1)
Lot 1245 Kundang Industrial Estate, Rawang, 48020, Kuala Lumpur, Selangor,
Malaysia (80%)
Tel.: (60) 360344800
Sales Range: $200-249.9 Million
Emp.: 350
Drilling Oil & Gas Wells
N.A.I.C.S.: 213111
Madhev Balasubramaniam *(Mng Dir)*

Palmamide Sdn Bhd (1)
Lot 1245 Kundang Industrial Estate, 48020,
Rawang, Selangor Darul Ehsan,
Malaysia (88%)
Tel.: (60) 360341213
Web Site: http://www.klkoleo.com
Sales Range: $125-149.9 Million
Emp.: 300
Soap & Other Detergent Mfr
N.A.I.C.S.: 325611

AND PRIVATE COMPANIES

Sabah Cocoa Sdn Bhd (1)
Wisma Taiko 1 Jln S P Seenivasagam, Ipoh, 30000, Perak, Malaysia
Tel.: (60) 52417844
Palm Oil Mfr
N.A.I.C.S.: 311225

Sabah Holdings Corporation Sdn Bhd (1)
Wisma Taiko 1 Jln S P Seenivasagam, Ipoh, 30000, Perak, Malaysia
Tel.: (60) 52417844
Rubber Plant Farming Services
N.A.I.C.S.: 111998

Selbourne Food Services Sdn Bhd (1)
Lot 4 Lbh Sultan Mohamed 3 Bdr Sultan Suleiman, 42000, Port Klang, Malaysia (100%)
Tel.: (60) 331765050
Web Site: http://www.barry-callebaut.com
Sales Range: $25-49.9 Million
Emp.: 65
Chocolate & Confectionery Mfr from Cacao Beans
N.A.I.C.S.: 311351

Stolthaven (Westport) Sdn Bhd (1)
6th Floor Campbell Complex 98 Jalan Dang Wangi, Kuala Lumpur, 50100, Malaysia
Tel.: (60) 326981366
Sales Range: $50-74.9 Million
Emp.: 54
Liquid Storage Tank Leasing Services
N.A.I.C.S.: 531130

Taiko Plantations Sdn Bhd (1)
Wisma Taiko No 1, Jalan S P Seenivasagam Ipoh, Perak, 30000, Darul Ridzuan, Malaysia (100%)
Tel.: (60) 52418444
Sales Range: $75-99.9 Million
Emp.: 400
Oilseed & Grain Combination Farming
N.A.I.C.S.: 111191

The Shanghai Kelantan Rubber Estates (1925) Ltd (1)
No 4 Kampung Ladang Pasir Gajah, Kuala Krai, 18000, Kelantan, Malaysia
Tel.: (60) 9 960 9308
Web Site: http://www.klk.com.my
Emp.: 200
Rubber Products Mfr
N.A.I.C.S.: 326299
Mossin Seis *(Sr Mgr)*

KUANG HONG ARTS MANAGEMENT, INC.
6 Fl 267 Lechun 2 Rd, Zhongshan Dist, Taipei, 10462, Taiwan
Tel.: (886) 225326677
6596—(TPE)
Rev.: $1,318,794
Assets: $25,620,642
Liabilities: $8,754,932
Net Worth: $16,865,710
Earnings: $49,589
Fiscal Year-end: 12/31/22
Entertainment Facility Operator
N.A.I.C.S.: 713940
Klaus Lin *(Chm & CEO)*

KUANG PEI SAN FOOD PRODUCTS PUBLIC CO., LTD.
88/9 Moo 4 Kuang Pei San Road, Tumbon Nathamneua Amphur Muang, Trang, 92190, Thailand
Tel.: (66) 7527 6088
Web Site: http://www.smilingfish.com
Year Founded: 1978
Sales Range: $25-49.9 Million
Seafood Product Mfr
N.A.I.C.S.: 445250
Surin Tohtubtiang *(Chm & CEO)*

KUANG-CHI TECHNOLOGIES CO., LTD.
3rd Floor Software Building No 9 Gaoxin Middle 1st Road, Maling Community Yuehai Street Nanshan District, Shenzhen, 518057, Guangdong, China
Tel.: (86) 57164662918
Web Site: http://www.longsheng988.com
Year Founded: 2001
002625—(SSE)
Sales Range: $50-74.9 Million
Automobile Seats & Other Components Mfr
N.A.I.C.S.: 336360
Liu Ruopeng *(Chm)*

KUANGCHI SCIENCE LIMITED
Room 1220 12/F Leighton Centre 77 Leighton Road, Causeway Bay, China (Hong Kong)
Tel.: (852) 22923900
Web Site: http://www.kuangchiscience.com
0439—(HKG)
Rev.: $6,696,683
Assets: $252,410,093
Liabilities: $46,242,975
Net Worth: $206,167,118
Earnings: ($8,658,780)
Emp.: 67
Fiscal Year-end: 12/31/22
Paper Product Services
N.A.I.C.S.: 322220
Lin Luan *(Co-CEO & CTO)*

KUANGDA TECHNOLOGY GROUP CO., LTD.
1 Kuangda Road, Xunyan Town Wujin District, Changzhou, 213179, Jiangsu, China
Tel.: (86) 51986541888
Web Site: https://www.kuangdacn.com
Year Founded: 1993
002516—(SSE)
Rev.: $228,276,772
Assets: $606,858,682
Liabilities: $78,297,971
Net Worth: $528,560,711
Earnings: $32,138,862
Emp.: 2,500
Fiscal Year-end: 12/31/20
Automotive Textile Mfr
N.A.I.C.S.: 336360
Wu Kai *(Chm)*

Subsidiaries:

Changchun Kuangda Automobile Fabric Co., Ltd. (1)
1111 Kuangda Road, Chaoyang Economic Development Zone, Changchun, China
Tel.: (86) 43185038888
Interior Fabric Distr
N.A.I.C.S.: 424310

Guangzhou Kuangda Automobile Fabric Co., Ltd. (1)
44 Dongpeng Avenue, Economic and Technological Development Zone, Guangzhou, China
Tel.: (86) 2082266268825
Interior Fabric Distr
N.A.I.C.S.: 424310

Jiangsu Kuangda Automobile Textile Group, Inc - Changzhou Plant (1)
No 28 Jiangdong Road Wujin Textile Industrial Park, Hutang Town, 213162, Changzhou, Jiangsu, China
Tel.: (86) 519 86702819
Automobile Interior Fabric Mfr
N.A.I.C.S.: 336360
Gong Xudong *(Gen Mgr)*

Jiangsu Kuangda Electric Power Investment Co., Ltd. (1)
1 Kuangda Road, Xunyan Town Wujin District, Changzhou, Jiangsu, China
Tel.: (86) 51986541888
Electric Power Distr
N.A.I.C.S.: 221122

Kuangda Automobile Trim Parts Co., Ltd. (1)
1 Kuangda Road, Xunyan Town Wujin District, Changzhou, Jiangsu, China
Tel.: (86) 51986547329
Interior Fabric Distr
N.A.I.C.S.: 424310

Shanghai Kuangda Pengdian Automobile Trim Parts Co., Ltd. (1)
Room 402 2 Alley 200 Dapu Road, Shanghai, China
Tel.: (86) 2158633665
Interior Fabric Mfr & Distr
N.A.I.C.S.: 314999

Tianjin Kuangda Automobile Fabric Co., Ltd. (1)
6 Chongqing Street, Jinnan Economic and Technological Development Zone Shuanggang, Tianjin, China
Tel.: (86) 2228593488
Automobile Textile Services
N.A.I.C.S.: 811310

Wuhan Kuangda Automobile Fabric Co., Ltd. (1)
204 Checheng Avenue, Hanyang Economic and Technological Development Zone, Wuhan, China
Tel.: (86) 2784237039
Automobile Textile Services
N.A.I.C.S.: 811310

KUANGLI BIO-TECH HOLDINGS CO., LTD.
9F No 66 Sec 2 Jianguo N Rd, Zhongshan Dist, Taipei, 104, Taiwan
Tel.: (886) 225178779
Web Site: http://www.kskl.com.cn
6431—(TAI)
Rev.: $9,593,969
Assets: $34,116,974
Liabilities: $15,871,709
Net Worth: $18,245,266
Earnings: ($3,406,357)
Fiscal Year-end: 12/31/23
Electronic Components Mfr
N.A.I.C.S.: 334419
Kuancong Chen *(Chm)*

KUANTUM PAPERS LTD.
W1A Godrej Eternia 70 Industrial Area Phase I, Chandigarh, 160 002, India
Tel.: (91) 1725172737
Web Site: https://www.kuantumpapers.com
Year Founded: 1979
532937—(BOM)
Rev.: $56,499,793
Assets: $220,356,222
Liabilities: $108,800,929
Net Worth: $111,555,294
Earnings: $1,737,235)
Emp.: 1,351
Fiscal Year-end: 03/31/21
Wood-Free Writing & Printing Paper Mfr & Distr
N.A.I.C.S.: 322120
Jagesh K. Khaitan *(Chm)*

KUB MALAYSIA BERHAD
Suite A-22-1 Level 22 Hampshire Place Office, 157 Hampshire No 1 Jalan Mayang Sari, 50450, Kuala Lumpur, Selangor Darul Ehsan, Malaysia
Tel.: (60) 327219600
Web Site: https://kub.com
KUB—(KLS)
Rev.: $103,468,571
Assets: $137,044,656
Liabilities: $30,737,354
Net Worth: $106,307,302
Earnings: $7,169,312
Emp.: 100
Fiscal Year-end: 06/30/23
Investment Holding Company
N.A.I.C.S.: 551112
Sharina Saidon *(Co-Sec)*

KUB MALAYSIA BERHAD

Subsidiaries:

Bina Alam Bersatu Sdn Bhd (1)
Lot 9139 Lorong Pinang Off Jalan Bandar 4, Taman Melawati, 53000, Kuala Lumpur, Malaysia (55%)
Tel.: (60) 341068688
Web Site: http://www.kub.com
Sales Range: $25-49.9 Million
Emp.: 30
New Housing Operative Builders
N.A.I.C.S.: 236117

Cybertrek (Malaysia) Sdn Bhd (1)
Level 15 Kub Com No 12, Jalan Yap Kwan Seng, 50450, Kuala Lumpur, Malaysia (100%)
Tel.: (60) 327189314
Motor Vehicle Parts Mfr
N.A.I.C.S.: 336390

Empirical Systems (M) Sdn. Bhd. (1)
1 Jalan Selukat 33/27 Shah Alam Technology Park Section 33, 40400, Shah Alam, Selangor, Malaysia
Tel.: (60) 351201598
Web Site: http://www.kub.com
Sales Range: $25-49.9 Million
Software Development Services
N.A.I.C.S.: 541511
Mohd Fadzli Ghazali *(CEO)*

ITTAR Sdn Bhd (1)
Lorong Produktiviti Satu Off Jalan Sultan, Petaling Jaya, 46904, Malaysia (100%)
Tel.: (60) 3 7957 5150
Holding Company
N.A.I.C.S.: 551112

Subsidiary (Domestic):

ITTAR-IPP (PJ) Sdn. Bhd. (2)
Lorong Produktiviti Satu Off Jalan Sultan, Petaling Jaya, 46904, Malaysia
Tel.: (60) 3 7957 5150
Hospitality Education & Training Services
N.A.I.C.S.: 611710

KFT International (Malaysia) Sdn. Bhd. (1)
Level 9 and 10 Unit 1 Capital 3 Oasis Square Ara Damansara, Jalan PJU 1A/7A, 47301, Petaling Jaya, Selangor, Malaysia
Tel.: (60) 376236400
Web Site: http://www.kub.com
Telephone Exchange Services
N.A.I.C.S.: 517810

KUB Agro Holdings Sdn. Bhd. (1)
Suite A-22-1 Level 22 Hampshire Place Office 157 Hampshire, Wilayah Persekutuan, 50450, Kuala Lumpur, Selangor, Malaysia
Tel.: (60) 327219600
Investment Holding Services
N.A.I.C.S.: 551112

Subsidiary (Domestic):

KUB Maju Mill Sdn. Bhd. (2)
Level 3 Unit 1 Capital 3 Oasis Square Jalan PJU1A/7A, Ara Damansara, 47301, Petaling Jaya, Selangor, Malaysia
Tel.: (60) 376109490
Investment Holding Company Services
N.A.I.C.S.: 551112

KUB Ekuiti Sdn. Bhd. (1)
Level 7 & 8 Blok D Kompleks Kelana Centre Point Jalan Ss7/19, Kelana Jaya, Petaling Jaya, 50450, Selangor, Malaysia
Tel.: (60) 376809666
Investment Management Service
N.A.I.C.S.: 523999

Subsidiary (Domestic):

KUB Agrotech Sdn. Bhd. (2)
Level 8 Block D Kompleks Kelana Centre Point Jalan SS 7/19, Kelana Jaya, 47301, Petaling Jaya, Selangor, Malaysia
Tel.: (60) 3 76809666
Oil Palm Plantation Processing Services
N.A.I.C.S.: 311224

KUB Power Sdn. Bhd. (2)
Level 3 Unit 1 Capital 3 Oasis Square Ara Damansara, Jalan PJU 1A/7A, 47301, Petaling Jaya, Selangor Darul Ehsan, Malaysia
Tel.: (60) 376100018
Web Site: https://www.kub-power.com

KUB MALAYSIA BERHAD

KUB Malaysia Berhad—(Continued)
Sales Range: $25-49.9 Million
Power Transmission Construction Engineering Services
N.A.I.C.S.: 237130

KUB Gaz Sdn. Bhd. (1)
Level 3 Unit 1 Capital 3 Oasis Square Jalan PJU1A/7A, Ara Damansara, 47301, Petaling Jaya, Selangor, Malaysia
Tel.: (60) 376109488
Web Site: http://www.kubgaz.com
LP Gas Distr
N.A.I.C.S.: 457210
Hisham Hussin *(Mgr-Project)*

KUB Sepadu Sdn Bhd (1)
Suite A-22-1 Level 22 Hampshire Place Office 157 Hampshire, PO Box 153, Wilayah Persekutuan, 50450, Kuala Lumpur, Malaysia (100%)
Tel.: (60) 327219600
Drilling Oil & Gas Wells
N.A.I.C.S.: 213111

KUB Telekomunikasi Sdn Bhd (1)
Level 9 10 Unit 1 Capital 3 Oasis Square, Ara Damansara Jalan PJU 1A/7A, 47301, Petaling Jaya, Selangor Darul Ehsan, Malaysia (100%)
Tel.: (60) 376236400
Web Site: https://ktl.kubtel.com
Sales Range: $25-49.9 Million
Telecommunication Services Provider
N.A.I.C.S.: 517810

KUB-Fujitsu Telecommunications (Malaysia) Sdn Bhd (1)
No 1 Jalan Selukat 33-27 Shah Alam Technology Park, Section 33, Shah Alam, 40400, Selangor Darul Ehsan, Malaysia (70%)
Tel.: (60) 351235000
Web Site: http://www.kubtel.com
Sales Range: $25-49.9 Million
Emp.: 80
Telephone Apparatus Mfr
N.A.I.C.S.: 334210

Peraharta Sdn Bhd (1)
Lot G02 Bangunan Seri Kinta Jalan Sultan Idris Shah, 30000, Ipoh, Perak, Malaysia (100%)
Tel.: (60) 52556506
Web Site: http://www.kub.com
Real Estate Property Lessors
N.A.I.C.S.: 531190

Solar Gas Sdn Bhd (1)
Lot 55710 Lorong Kenanga 8, Liquid Bulk Terminal Westport Pulau Indah Pelabuhan Klang, 42009, Kuala Lumpur, Selangor, Malaysia (100%)
Tel.: (60) 331011799
Web Site: https://www.solargas.com.my
Sales Range: $25-49.9 Million
Emp.: 20
Petroleum & Coal Products Mfr
N.A.I.C.S.: 324199

KUBALD GMBH
Kubald Allee 2, 31535, Neustadt, Germany
Tel.: (49) 50328960
Web Site: http://www.kubald.com
Year Founded: 1935
Rev.: $39,145,829
Emp.: 145
Project Management Services
N.A.I.C.S.: 541618
Christiane Gaude *(Co-Mng Dir)*

KUBATRONIK-LEITERPLATTEN GMBH
Karl-Benz-Strasse 13, D-73312, Geislingen, Germany
Tel.: (49) 7331 96914 39 De
Web Site: http://www.kubatronik.de
Printed Circuit Board Mfr
N.A.I.C.S.: 334418
Alois Kubat *(Founder & Owner)*

KUBB LAND SDN BHD
Level 3 Wisma Chinese Chamber 258 Jalan Ampang, Kuala Lumpur, 50450, Malaysia
Tel.: (60) 3 42516801
Web Site: http://www.kubbuilders.com
Year Founded: 2001
Commercial Building Construction Services
N.A.I.C.S.: 236220
Abdul Majid Mohd Yusoff *(CEO)*

KUBE-STAHL GMBH & CO. KG
Helmholtzstrasse 10 12, Langenfeld, 40764, Germany
Tel.: (49) 217385000
Web Site: http://www.kube-stahl.de
Year Founded: 1982
Rev.: $94,893,409
Emp.: 57
Stainless Steel Distr
N.A.I.C.S.: 331110

KUBELL CO LTD
WeWork Nogizaka 1-24-3 Minamiaoyama, Minato, Tokyo, 107-0062, Japan
Tel.: (81) 364590514
Web Site: https://go.chatwork.com
Year Founded: 2000
4448—(TKS)
Rev.: $45,978,650
Assets: $44,475,570
Liabilities: $27,303,590
Net Worth: $17,171,980
Earnings: ($4,395,800)
Emp.: 176
Fiscal Year-end: 12/31/23
Application Development Services
N.A.I.C.S.: 541511
Masaki Yamamoto *(Board of Directors & CEO)*

KUBER RESOURCES CORPORATION
Room 1113 Tower 2 Lippo Centre, Admiralty, Hong Kong, Hong Kong)
Tel.: (852) 37036155 NV
Web Site: https://kuberresources.com
Year Founded: 1998
KUBR—(OTCIQ)
Rev.: $2,249,288
Assets: $5,711,371
Liabilities: $1,537,393
Net Worth: $4,173,978
Earnings: $1,217,956
Fiscal Year-end: 12/31/23
Radio Broadcasting Services
N.A.I.C.S.: 516110
Raymond Fu *(Chm & CEO)*

KUBER UDYOG LTD.
Office Number 156 1st Floor Raghuleela Mega Mall, Kandivali West, Mumbai, 400067, India
Tel.: (91) 7506324443
Web Site: https://www.kuberudyog.com
Year Founded: 1982
539408—(BOM)
Rev.: $73,028
Assets: $877,053
Liabilities: $390,636
Net Worth: $486,418
Earnings: ($27,669)
Emp.: 4
Fiscal Year-end: 03/31/22
Financial Support Services
N.A.I.C.S.: 523999
Nikunj Vasant Chheda *(Officer-Compliance & Sec)*

KUBERAN GLOBAL EDU SOLUTIONS LIMITED
No 401 Ges Complex I St Floor 7th Street, Gandhipuram, Coimbatore, 641012, Tamil Nadu, India
Tel.: (91) 9944488001
Web Site: https://www.kgesltd.in
Year Founded: 2013
543289—(BOM)
Rev.: $114,410
Assets: $326,054
Liabilities: $422
Net Worth: $325,632
Earnings: ($1,699)
Emp.: 7
Fiscal Year-end: 03/31/23
Education Services
N.A.I.C.S.: 611519
K. Chandramouleeswaran *(Mng Dir)*

KUBIK INC.
1680 Mattawa Ave, Mississauga, L4X 3A5, ON, Canada
Tel.: (905) 272-2818
Web Site: http://www.thinkkubik.com
Year Founded: 1988
Sales Range: $25-49.9 Million
Emp.: 300
Exhibits, Events & Environments Designer, Installer, Mfr & Manager
N.A.I.C.S.: 337215
Sam Kohn *(Pres)*

Subsidiaries:

Kubik B.V. (1)
Plotterstraat 1-9, 1033 RX, Amsterdam, Netherlands
Tel.: (31) 20 581 3030
Web Site: http://www.kubik.com
Emp.: 17
Exhibits, Events & Environments Designer, Installer, Mfr & Manager
N.A.I.C.S.: 337215
Antoinette Sulmann *(Office Mgr)*

Kubik Inc. - New Jersey Facility (1)
7000 Commerce Pkwy, Mount Laurel, NJ 08054
Tel.: (856) 234-0052
Event Management Services
N.A.I.C.S.: 711310

Kubik Inc. - Savage Facility (1)
8700 Larkin Rd Ste A, Savage, MD 20763
Tel.: (877) 252-2818
Event Management Services
N.A.I.C.S.: 711310

KUBODERA CO., LTD.
4-27-15 Numabukuro, Nakano, 165-0025, Japan
Tel.: (81) 333861164
9261—(TKS)
Sales Range: Less than $1 Million
Building Product Distr
N.A.I.C.S.: 423390
Nobuhiro Kubodera *(Pres & CEO)*

KUBOTA CORPORATION
2-47 Shikitsuhigashi 1-chome, Naniwa-ku, Osaka, 556-8601, Japan
Tel.: (81) 666482111 JP
Web Site: https://www.kubota.com
Year Founded: 1890
KUBTY—(OTCIQ)
Rev.: $17,687,342,256
Assets: $31,483,658,182
Liabilities: $17,592,099,468
Net Worth: $13,891,558,714
Earnings: $1,033,841,798
Emp.: 50,352
Fiscal Year-end: 12/31/22
Holding Company; Farm & Industrial Equipment, Water Supply Equipment & Infrastructure Equipment Mfr
N.A.I.C.S.: 551112
Katsuhiko Yukawa *(Mng Exec Officer & Gen Mgr-Construction Machinery Div)*

Subsidiaries:

Akita Kubota Corporation (1)

INTERNATIONAL PUBLIC

295-38 Terauchi Kamiyashiki, Akita, 011-0901, Japan
Tel.: (81) 188452121
Web Site: http://www.akita-kubota.co.jp
Agricultural Machinery Distr
N.A.I.C.S.: 423820

Anhui Kubota Sanlian Pump Co., Ltd. (1)
He Xian County Economic Development Zone, Chaohu, 238200, Anhui, China
Tel.: (86) 565 5338018
Web Site: http://www.kubota-sanlian.cn
Industrial Pump Mfr & Distr
N.A.I.C.S.: 333914

Great Plains Manufacturing, Incorporated (1)
1525 E North St, Salina, KS 67401 (100%)
Tel.: (785) 823-3276
Web Site: https://www.greatplainsmfg.com
Emp.: 1,500
Mfr of Agricultural Planting, Spraying & Cultivating Equipment & Landscaping Products; Provider of Trucking Services; Provider of Financing Services
N.A.I.C.S.: 333111
Linda Salem *(Pres & CEO)*

Subsidiary (Domestic):

Great Plains Acceptance Corporation (2)
1525 E North St, Salina, KS 67401
Tel.: (785) 823-3276
Financial Management Services
N.A.I.C.S.: 522320
Sheldon Muninger *(Pres)*

Division (Domestic):

Great Plains Ag Division (2)
1525 E North St, Salina, KS 67401
Web Site: https://www.greatplainsag.com
Grain Drill Mfr
N.A.I.C.S.: 333111

Subsidiary (Non-US):

Great Plains Agro (2)
44 Krugovaya St Building 4 Office 201A, 350047, Krasnodar, Russia
Tel.: (7) 8612792041
Web Site: http://www.greatplainsmfg.ru
Sales Range: $10-24.9 Million
Emp.: 9
Agricultural Support Services
N.A.I.C.S.: 311999
Ruslaan Timov *(Pres)*

Division (Domestic):

Great Plains International Division (2)
1525 E N St, Salina, KS 67401
Tel.: (785) 823-3276
Web Site: http://www.greatplainsint.com
Agricultural Support Services
N.A.I.C.S.: 333111
Tom Bryan *(Pres)*

Great Plains Land Pride Division (2)
1525 E North St, Salina, KS 67401
Tel.: (785) 823-3276
Web Site: https://www.landpride.com
Sales Range: $75-99.9 Million
Emp.: 700
Farm, Turf & Landscape Equipment Mfr & Whslr
N.A.I.C.S.: 333112
John Quinley *(Pres)*

Plant (Domestic):

Great Plains Manufacturing, Inc. - Assaria Plant (2)
108 W 2nd St, Assaria, KS 67416
Tel.: (785) 667-7763
Web Site: http://www.greatplainsmfg.com
Sales Range: $50-74.9 Million
Emp.: 48
Agricultural Equipment Engineering, Research & Development
N.A.I.C.S.: 541715
Greg Arnett *(Mgr-Engrg)*

Unit (Domestic):

Great Plains Manufacturing, Inc. - Grain Drills (2)

AND PRIVATE COMPANIES

1621 Dewey, Salina, KS 67401
Tel.: (785) 823-9556
Web Site: http://www.greatplainsmfg.com
Sales Range: $25-49.9 Million
Emp.: 700
Agricultural Drilling Equipment Mfr
N.A.I.C.S.: 333111
Linda Salem *(Pres-Great Plains Div)*

Great Plains Manufacturing, Inc. - Planting Components (2)
1525 ENSt, Salina, KS 67401
Tel.: (785) 823-3276
Web Site: http://www.greatplainsmfg.com
Sales Range: $10-24.9 Million
Emp.: 100
Agricultural Equipment Planting Components Mfr
N.A.I.C.S.: 333111

Subsidiary (Non-US):

Great Plains Simba (2)
Woodbridge Rd, Sleaford, NG347EW, Lincolnshire, United Kingdom
Tel.: (44) 1529304654
Web Site: http://www.greatplainsmfg.co.uk
Emp.: 50
Farm Equipment Mfr
N.A.I.C.S.: 333111
Alan Davids *(Gen Mgr)*

Division (Domestic):

Great Plains Trucking Division (2)
1935 E N St, Salina, KS 67401
Tel.: (785) 823-2261
Web Site: http://www.gptrucking.com
Emp.: 85
General Freight Trucking Services
N.A.I.C.S.: 484230
Brett Weis *(Pres)*

Subsidiary (Non-US):

Great Plains Ukraine (2)
1 Glushkova Prospect, Pavillion Ste167, Kiev, 3680, Ukraine
Tel.: (380) 445969050
Web Site: http://www.greatplainsmfg.com.ua
Sales Range: $10-24.9 Million
Emp.: 8
Farm Equipment Mfr
N.A.I.C.S.: 333111
Andre Vorobyov *(Mng Dir)*

Hokkaido KUBOTA Corporation (1)
Nishi 3-1-44 Kita-3jo, Chuo-ku, Sapporo, 060-0003, Hokkaido, Japan
Tel.: (81) 11 214 3111
Web Site: http://www.hokkaido-kubota.co.jp
Agricultural Equipment Repair & Maintenance Services
N.A.I.C.S.: 811411

Jiangsu Biaoxin Kubota Industrial Co., Ltd. (1)
186 Xinqiao South Avenue, Jingjiang, 214536, Jiangsu, China (27%)
Tel.: (86) 52384331048
Web Site: http://www.biaoxin.com
Sales Range: $50-74.9 Million
Emp.: 200
Provider of Mowers, Tractors & Farm Equipment
N.A.I.C.S.: 333111

KUBOTA Construction Machinery Japan Corporation (1)
1-1-1 Hama, Amagasaki, 661-8567, Japan
Tel.: (81) 6 6470 6200
Web Site: http://www.kubotakenki.co.jp
Construction Equipment Mfr
N.A.I.C.S.: 333120

KUBOTA Engine (Thailand) Co., Ltd. (1)
360 Moo3 T Khao Hin Son, Phanom Sarakarm, Chachoengsao, 24120, Thailand
Tel.: (66) 38855136
Diesel Engine Mfr
N.A.I.C.S.: 333618

KUBOTA LOGISTICS Corporation (1)
1-247 Shikitsuhigashi, Naniwa-ku, Osaka, 556-8601, Japan
Tel.: (81) 666477811
Web Site: http://www.kbs-kubota.jp
Logistic Services

N.A.I.C.S.: 541614

KUBOTA Seiki Co., Ltd. (1)
4-15-5 Mokuzaidori, Mihara-ku, Sakai, 587-0042, Osaka, Japan
Tel.: (81) 723621637
Web Site: http://www.kubota-seiki.co.jp
Hydraulic Equipment Mfr & Distr
N.A.I.C.S.: 333996

Kubota (Deutschland) GmbH (1)
Senefelderstrasse 3-5, 63110, Rodgau, Germany (100%)
Tel.: (49) 61068730
Web Site: https://kdg.kubota-eu.com
Sales Range: $25-49.9 Million
Emp.: 65
Mowers, Tractors & Farm Equipment Mfr
N.A.I.C.S.: 333111

Kubota (UK) Ltd. (1)
Dormer Rd, Thame, OX9 3UN, Oxfordshire, United Kingdom
Tel.: (44) 1844268000
Web Site: https://www.kubota.co.uk
Sales Range: $50-74.9 Million
Emp.: 125
Sales of Mowers, Tractors & Farm Equipment
N.A.I.C.S.: 423820
Adrian Mann *(Mgr-Product)*

Kubota Agricultural Machinery (Suzhou) Co., Ltd. (1)
No 77 Suhong East Road Suzhou Industrial Park, Suzhou Area China Jiangsu Pilot Free Trade Zone, Suzhou, 215026, Jiangsu, China
Tel.: (86) 51267163122
Web Site: https://www.kubota.com.cn
Sales Range: $200-249.9 Million
Emp.: 800
Provider of Mowers, Tractors & Farm Equipment
N.A.I.C.S.: 333111

Kubota Agricultural Machinery India Pvt., Ltd. (1)
No 94 TVH BELICIAA TOWERS- 1 8th floor MRC Nagar, Sholinganallur, Chennai, 600 028, India
Tel.: (91) 4461041500
Web Site: https://www.kubota.co.in
Emp.: 150
Agricultural Machinery Distr
N.A.I.C.S.: 423820

Kubota Agro-Industrial Machinery Philippines, Inc. (1)
155 Panay Ave, S Triangle Homes, Quezon City, 1103, Philippines (15%)
Tel.: (63) 29201071
Web Site: http://www.kpi.com.ph
Sales Range: $25-49.9 Million
Emp.: 50
Provider of Mowers, Tractors & Farm Equipment
N.A.I.C.S.: 333111
Wilfrido G. Tirona *(Pres & Gen Mgr)*

Kubota Air Conditioner, Ltd. (1)
2-1-3 Kyobashi, Chuo-ku, Tokyo, Japan
Tel.: (81) 332453130
Web Site: http://www.kubota-airconditioner.co.jp
Air Conditioner Installation Services
N.A.I.C.S.: 238220

Kubota Baumaschinen GmbH (1)
Steinhauser Strasse 100, 66482, Zweibrucken, Germany (100%)
Tel.: (49) 63324870
Web Site: https://www.kubota-baumaschinen.de
Sales Range: $100-124.9 Million
Emp.: 260
Mfr of Mowers, Tractors & Farm Equipment
N.A.I.C.S.: 333111

Kubota Canada Ltd. (1)
1155 Kubota Drive, Pickering, L1X 0H4, ON, Canada (100%)
Tel.: (905) 294-7477
Web Site: http://www.kubota.ca
Agriculatural & Industrial Equipments Dist
N.A.I.C.S.: 423830
Yannick Montagano *(Pres)*

Subsidiary (US):

AgJunction Inc. (2)

9105 E Del Camino Dr Ste 115, Scottsdale, AZ 85258
Tel.: (480) 348-9919
Web Site: http://www.agjunction.com
Rev: $16,307,000
Assets: $31,339,000
Liabilities: $7,668,000
Net Worth: $23,671,000
Earnings: ($5,305,000)
Emp.: 55
Fiscal Year-end: 12/31/2020
Agricultural Application Software & Equipment Developer, Mfr & Distr
N.A.I.C.S.: 513210
M. Brett McMickell *(Pres & CEO)*

Subsidiary (Domestic):

AgJunction LLC (3)
8444 N 90th St Ste 130, Scottsdale, AZ 85258
Tel.: (480) 348-9919
Web Site: http://www.satloc.com
Sales Range: $25-49.9 Million
Aerial Agricultural Application Products & Services
N.A.I.C.S.: 334511

Kubota China Financial Leasing Ltd. (1)
6F Tower 1 Kerry Everbright City No 128 Tian Mu Road West, Jingan District, Shanghai, 200070, China
Tel.: (86) 2120278558
Financial Lending Services
N.A.I.C.S.: 522220

Kubota China Holdings Co., Ltd. (1)
6F Tower 1 Kerry Everbright City No 128 Tian Mu Road West, Jingan District, Shanghai, 200070, China
Tel.: (86) 2120272399
Web Site: https://www.kubota.com.cn
Construction Machinery Mfr
N.A.I.C.S.: 333120

Kubota Construction Co., Ltd. (1)
1-247 Shikitsuhigashi, Naniwa-ku, Osaka, 556-8601, Japan
Tel.: (81) 643962310
Web Site: http://www.kubota-const.co.jp
Emp.: 260
Water & Sewage System Construction Services
N.A.I.C.S.: 237110

Kubota Construction Machinery (Shanghai) Co., Ltd. (1)
6th Floor Tower 1 Kerry Corporate Center No 128 Tianmu West Road, Jing'an District, Shanghai, 200070, China
Tel.: (86) 2158794630
Web Site: https://www.kubota.com.cn
Construction Machinery Mfr
N.A.I.C.S.: 333120

Kubota Construction Machinery (Wuxi) Co., Ltd. (1)
No 1 Xinyou South Road, New District, Wuxi, 214028, Jiangsu, China
Tel.: (86) 51085210500
Web Site: https://www.kubota.com.cn
Construction Machinery Mfr
N.A.I.C.S.: 333120

Kubota Credit Co., Ltd. (1)
1-2-47 Shikitsuhigashi, Naniwa-ku, Osaka, 556-0012, Japan
Tel.: (81) 666483084
Web Site: http://www.kubota-credit.co.jp
Agricultural Equipment Finance & Leasing Services
N.A.I.C.S.: 522220

Kubota Credit Corporation U.S.A. (1)
1000 Kubota Dr, Grapevine, TX 76051 (100%)
Tel.: (817) 756-1171
Web Site: http://www.kubotacreditusa.com
Sales Range: $50-74.9 Million
Emp.: 50
Tractors
N.A.I.C.S.: 522291

Kubota Engine (SHANGHAI) Co., Ltd. (1)
6th Floor Tower 1 Kerry Enterprise Center No 128 Tianmu West Road, Jing'an District, Shanghai, 200070, China

KUBOTA CORPORATION

Tel.: (86) 2162360606
Web Site: https://www.kubota.com.cn
Engine Parts Mfr & Distr
N.A.I.C.S.: 336310

Kubota Engine America Corporation (1)
505 Schelter Rd, Lincolnshire, IL 60069
Tel.: (847) 955-2500
Web Site: https://www.kubotaengine.com
Emp.: 100
Industrial Engine & Diesel Generator Distr
N.A.I.C.S.: 423830
Tadahisa Omote *(Pres)*

Kubota Engine Japan Corporation (1)
No 47 Shikitsu Higashi 1-chome, Naniwa-ku, Osaka, 556-8601, Japan
Tel.: (81) 666483638
Web Site: http://www.kubota-enginejapan.co.jp
Industrial Engine Distr
N.A.I.C.S.: 423830

Kubota Environmental Service Co., Ltd (1)
1-3-5 Matsugaya, Taito-Ku, Tokyo, 111-0036, Japan
Tel.: (81) 3 384 73800
Web Site: http://www.kubota-ksk.co.jp
Solid Waste Recycling Services
N.A.I.C.S.: 562111

Kubota Espana S.A. (1)
Calle Fernando Alonso numero 15, 28914, Leganes, Madrid, Spain (100%)
Tel.: (34) 915086442
Web Site: https://kes.kubota-eu.com
Sales Range: $25-49.9 Million
Emp.: 50
Mowers, Tractors & Farm Equipment
N.A.I.C.S.: 333111

Kubota Europe S.A. (1)
19-25 Rue Jules Vercruysse, PO Box 88, 95101, Argenteuil, Cedex, France
Tel.: (33) 134263434
Web Site: https://ke.kubota-eu.com
Sales Range: $250-299.9 Million
Emp.: 150
Mfr of Mowers, Tractors & Farm Equipment
N.A.I.C.S.: 333111
Dai Watanabe *(Pres)*

Kubota Farm & Industrial Machinery Service Ltd (1)
1-1-36 Kitamachi Midorigaoka, Sakai-Ku, Sakai, 590-0806, Osaka, Japan
Tel.: (81) 722411126
Agricultural Machinery Distr
N.A.I.C.S.: 423820

Kubota Farm Machinery Europe S.A.S. (1)
Route de Socx, 59380, Bierne, France
Tel.: (33) 374130001
Tractor Mfr
N.A.I.C.S.: 333111

Kubota Industrial Equipment Corporation (1)
1001 Mcclure Industrial Dr Ste D, Jefferson, GA 30549-1700
Tel.: (706) 387-1000
Tractor Mfr
N.A.I.C.S.: 333111
Hironobu Kubota *(Pres)*

Kubota Insurance Corporation (1)
500 Ala Moana Blvd Ste 420, Honolulu, HI 96813
Tel.: (808) 544-3938
Fire Insurance Services
N.A.I.C.S.: 524113

Kubota Korea Co., Ltd. (1)
11th floor Camco Yangjae Tower 262 Gangnam-daero Dogok-dong, Gangnam-gu, Seoul, 135-860, Korea (South)
Tel.: (82) 220581028
Web Site: https://www.kubotakorea.com
Industrial Tractor Mfr
N.A.I.C.S.: 333924

Kubota Machinery Trading Co., Ltd. (1)
2-47 Shikitsuhigashi 1-chome, Naniwa-ku, Osaka, 556-8601, Japan
Tel.: (81) 666482187

KUBOTA CORPORATION

Kubota Corporation—(Continued)
Web Site: http://www.kubotamachinery.com
Emp.: 49
Construction Machinery Mfr & Distr
N.A.I.C.S.: 333120
Ryo Tsujiyama *(Pres & CEO)*

Kubota Manufacturing of America Corporation (1)
Industrial Park North 2715 Ramsey Rd, Gainesville, GA 30501
Tel.: (770) 532-0038
Web Site: https://www.kubota-kma.com
Emp.: 3,500
Lawn Tractors & Utility Vehicles Mfr
N.A.I.C.S.: 333112

Kubota Materials Canada Corporation (1)
25 Commerce Road, Orillia, L3V 0Z2, ON, Canada
Tel.: (705) 325-2781
Web Site: https://www.kubotamaterials.com
Steel Products Mfr
N.A.I.C.S.: 331210

Kubota Membrane Europe Ltd. (1)
3rd Floor No1 Farrier's Yard 77-85 Fulhan Palace Road, London, W6 8AH, United Kingdom
Tel.: (44) 2087415262
Web Site: https://www.kubota-mbr.com
Sales Range: $25-49.9 Million
Emp.: 6
Submerged Membrane Wastewater Treatment Solutions
N.A.I.C.S.: 325998

Kubota Membrane U.S.A. Corporation (1)
19910 N Creek Pkwy Ste100, Bothell, WA 98011
Tel.: (425) 898-2858
Web Site: https://www.kubota-membrane.com
Sales Range: $25-49.9 Million
Emp.: 5
Submerged Membrane Wastewater Treatment Solutions
N.A.I.C.S.: 325998

Kubota Metal Corporation (1)
25 Commerce Rd, Orillia, L3V 6L6, ON, Canada **(100%)**
Tel.: (705) 325-2781
Web Site: https://www.kubotamaterials.com
Sales Range: $25-49.9 Million
Emp.: 300
Casting of Metal Toothing
N.A.I.C.S.: 331513

Kubota Myanmar Co., Ltd. (1)
Lot No BD-1 Zone B, Thilawa Special Economic Zone, Yangon, Myanmar
Tel.: (95) 12309207
Web Site: https://www.kubota.com.mm
Tractor Distr
N.A.I.C.S.: 423820
Kunitomo Sato *(Mng Dir)*

Kubota Saudi Arabia Company, LLC (1)
PO Box 68638, Dammam Second Industrial, Dammam, 31537, Saudi Arabia
Tel.: (966) 138327209
Web Site: https://www.kubota.com.sa
Steel Product Mfr & Distr
N.A.I.C.S.: 331210

Kubota Systems Inc. (1)
1-2-47 Shikitsuhigashi, Naniwa-ku, Osaka, 556-8601, Japan
Tel.: (81) 666483111
Web Site: http://www.ksi.co.jp
Data Processing Services
N.A.I.C.S.: 518210

Kubota Tractor (Australia) Pty. Ltd. (1)
25-29 Permas Way, Truganina, 3029, VIC, Australia **(100%)**
Tel.: (61) 393944400
Web Site: http://www.kubota.com.au
Sales Range: $25-49.9 Million
Emp.: 100
Mfr of Mowers, Tractors & Farm Equipment
N.A.I.C.S.: 333111
Toshi Kawasaki *(Mng Dir)*

Kubota Tractor Corporation (1)
1000 Kubota Dr, Grapevine, TX 76051
Tel.: (817) 756-1171
Web Site: https://www.kubotausa.com
Sales Range: $75-99.9 Million
Emp.: 275
Distr Tractors, Excavators, Lawn & Garden Equipment & Outdoor Power Products
N.A.I.C.S.: 423820
Masato Yoshikawa *(Gen Mgr-Plng, Control Headquarters, Global IT Mgmt)*

Plant (Domestic):

Kubota Tractor Corporation - Atlanta (2)
1025 Northbrook Pkwy, Suwanee, GA 30024-2931
Tel.: (770) 995-8855
Web Site: https://www.kubota.com
Sales Range: $75-99.9 Million
Distribution of Tractors, Lawn Mowers
N.A.I.C.S.: 423820

Kubota Vietnam Co., Ltd. (1)
Lot B-3A2-CN My Phuoc 3 Industrial Park, Thoi Hoa ward, Ben Cat, Binh Duong, Vietnam
Tel.: (84) 2743577501
Web Site: https://www.kubota.vn
Tractor Mfr & Distr
N.A.I.C.S.: 333924
Satoshi Suzuki *(Mng Dir)*

Kubota-C.I. Co., Ltd. (1)
1-2-47 Shikitsuhigashi Kubota No 2 Bldg 2F, Naniwa-Ku, Osaka, 556-8612, Japan
Tel.: (81) 666482375
Web Site: http://www.kubota-ci.co.jp
Emp.: 55
Pipe Fitting Mfr
N.A.I.C.S.: 326122
Sakaye Ayako *(Office Mgr)*

Kverneland ASA (1)
Plogfabrikkvegen 1, Klepp Stasjon, N-4353, Kvernaland, Norway **(100%)**
Tel.: (47) 51429400
Web Site: https://ien.kvernelandgroup.com
Sales Range: $1-9.9 Million
Emp.: 2,482
Holding Company; Agricultural Equipment Mfr & Distr
N.A.I.C.S.: 551112

Subsidiary (Non-US):

Kverneland Group Deutschland GmbH (2)
Coesterweg 25, 59494, Soest, Germany
Tel.: (49) 29 213 6990
Web Site: https://www.kvernelandgroup.de
Agricultural Equipment Mfr & Distr
N.A.I.C.S.: 333111
Thomas Bortz *(Gen Mgr)*

Kverneland Group France S.A.S. (2)
55 Avenue Ampere, BP 70149, 45800, Saint Jean de Braye, Cedex, France
Tel.: (33) 238524300
Web Site: http://www.kvernelandgroup.com
Holding Company; Agricultural Equipment Mfr & Distr
N.A.I.C.S.: 551112

Subsidiary (Domestic):

Kverneland Group Les Landes Genusson S.A.S. (3)
55 Av Ampere, 45800, Saint Jean de Braye, France **(100%)**
Tel.: (33) 238524300
Web Site: http://www.kvernelandgroup.com
Sales Range: $10-24.9 Million
Agricultural Equipment Mfr & Distr
N.A.I.C.S.: 333111

Subsidiary (Domestic):

Kverneland Group Operations Norway AS (2)
Plogfabrikkvegen 1, 4355, Klepp, Norway **(100%)**
Tel.: (47) 51429000
Web Site: http://www.kvernelandgroup.com
Emp.: 500
Agricultural Equipment Mfr
N.A.I.C.S.: 333111
Friedrich Pehle *(CFO)*

Nippon Plastic Industry Co., Ltd (1)
100-1 Nishida Higashitanaka, Komaki, 485-0826, Aichi, Japan
Tel.: (81) 568 72 2011
Web Site: http://www.nipplasi.co.jp
Plastics Product Mfr
N.A.I.C.S.: 326199

P.T. Kubota Indonesia (1)
Taman Industri Bukit Semarang Baru BSB Blok D 1 Kav 8 Mijen, Semarang, Indonesia
Tel.: (62) 247472849
Web Site: https://www.ptkubota.co.id
Provider of Mowers, Tractors & Farm Equipment
N.A.I.C.S.: 333111

SIAM KUBOTA Corporation Co., Ltd. (1)
101/19-24 Village No 20 Navanakorn Industrial Estate, Khlong Nueng Subdistrict Khlong Luang District, Pathumthani, 12120, Thailand **(100%)**
Tel.: (66) 20798199
Web Site: https://www.siamkubota.co.th
Agricultural Diesel Engines, Tractors & Reapers Mfr
N.A.I.C.S.: 333111

Subsidiary (Domestic):

SIAM KUBOTA Metal Technology Co., Ltd. (2)
359 Moo 3 Khao Hin Son, Phanom Sarakham, Chachoengsao, 24120, Thailand
Tel.: (66) 33051777
Web Site: https://www.skmt.co.th
Metal Products Mfr
N.A.I.C.S.: 332999

Shin Taiwan Agricultural Machinery Co., Ltd. (1)
16 Fengping 2nd Rd, Taliao Shiang, Kaohsiung, 83107, Taiwan **(100%)**
Tel.: (886) 77022333
Web Site: http://www.stam.com.tw
Sales Range: $25-49.9 Million
Emp.: 50
Mfr of Mowers, Tractors & Farm Equipment
N.A.I.C.S.: 333111
Fujitani Teruos *(Gen Mgr)*

Siam Kubota Leasing Co., Ltd. (1)
101/19-24 Moo 20 Soi Navanakorn Khlong Nueng, Khlong Luang, Pathumthani, 12120, Thailand
Tel.: (66) 29090300
Web Site: https://www.skl.co.th
Tractor Retailer
N.A.I.C.S.: 423820

Sime Kubota Sdn. Bhd. (1)
No 1 Jalan Puchong Perindustrian, Puchong Utama, 47100, Puchong, Selangor Darul Ehsan, Malaysia **(53%)**
Tel.: (60) 380688558
Web Site: http://www.kubota.co.jp
Sales Range: $25-49.9 Million
Emp.: 100
Mowers, Tractors & Farm Equipment
N.A.I.C.S.: 333111
Jamie Koh *(Gen Mgr)*

KUBOTA PHARMACEUTICAL HOLDINGS CO., LTD.
1-15-37 Minami-Aoyama, Minato-ku, Tokyo, 107-0062, Japan
Tel.: (81) 365508928 JP
Web Site: https://www.kubotaholdings.co.jp
Year Founded: 2015
4596—(TKS)
Rev.: $283,600
Assets: $21,390,530
Liabilities: $2,623,300
Net Worth: $18,767,230
Earnings: ($10,564,100)
Emp.: 45
Fiscal Year-end: 12/31/23
Pharmaceutical Products & Equipments Mfr
N.A.I.C.S.: 325412
Ryo Kubota *(Chm, Pres & CEO)*

Subsidiaries:

Acucela, Inc. (1)

INTERNATIONAL PUBLIC

818 Stewart St Ste 1110, Seattle, WA 98101
Tel.: (206) 805-8300
Web Site: http://www.acucela.com
Biotechnology Pharmaceutical Mfr, Researcher & Developer
N.A.I.C.S.: 325412
Ryo Kubota *(Chm, Pres & CEO)*

KUBOTEK CORPORATION
4 3 36 Nakanoshima, Osaka, 530-0005, Japan
Tel.: (81) 0664431815
Web Site: http://www.kubota.fr
Year Founded: 1985
Sales Range: $25-49.9 Million
Emp.: 74
Computer Systems Mfr
N.A.I.C.S.: 541512
Tesuo Kubo *(Pres & CEO)*

Subsidiaries:

KUBOTEK Corporation - KYOTO 1st FACTORY (1)
56 Nishiakeda-chou Higashikujo, Minami, Kyoto, 601-8045, Japan
Tel.: (81) 756716509
Computer System Mfr
N.A.I.C.S.: 334610

KUBOTEK Corporation - KYOTO 2nd FACTORY (1)
19 Nishikawabe-chou Higashikujo, Minami, Kyoto, 601-8037, Japan
Tel.: (81) 756714548
Computer System Mfr
N.A.I.C.S.: 334610

KUBOTEK Europe srl (1)
Via Altissimo 55, Caldogno, 36030, Vicenza, Italy
Tel.: (39) 0444585556
Web Site: http://www.kubotekeurope.com
Computer System Design Services
N.A.I.C.S.: 541512

KUBOTEK KOREA Co., Ltd. (1)
502 Sa Tower 1026-30 Sanbon-dong, Gunpo, Gyeonggi, Korea (South)
Tel.: (82) 314576560
Computer Software Distr
N.A.I.C.S.: 423430

Kubotek USA, Inc. (1)
2 Mount Royal Ste 500, Marlborough, MA 01752
Tel.: (508) 229-2020
Web Site: http://www.kubotekusa.com
Sales Range: $25-49.9 Million
Emp.: 30
Computer Systems Mfr
N.A.I.C.S.: 541512

KUCUKER TEKSTIL SANAYI VE TICARET A.S.
Ankara Asfalti Uzeri 10 Km, Denizli, 20140, Turkiye
Tel.: (90) 2582671516
Web Site: http://www.kucuker.com
Year Founded: 1930
Sales Range: $50-74.9 Million
Emp.: 800
Yarn Spinning Mills; Towels, Bathrobes, Bed Sets, Woven & Knitted Fabrics Mfr
N.A.I.C.S.: 313110
Nejat Kucuker *(Chm)*

KUDAN, INC.
2-10-15 Shibuya, Shibuya-ku, Tokyo, 150-0002, Japan
Tel.: (81) 362739760
Web Site: https://www.kudan.io
4425—(TKS)
Rev.: $3,238,900
Assets: $15,718,580
Liabilities: $1,903,680
Net Worth: $13,814,900
Earnings: ($456,090)
Fiscal Year-end: 03/31/24
Software Development Services
N.A.I.C.S.: 541511

AND PRIVATE COMPANIES

Tomohiro Ohno *(Mng Dir)*

KUDELSKI S.A.
22-24 Route de Geneve, PO Box 134, 1033, Cheseaux-sur-Lausanne, Switzerland
Tel.: (41) 217320101   **CH**
Web Site: https://www.nagra.com
Year Founded: 1951
KUD—(SWX)
Rev.: $715,878,000
Assets: $964,964,000
Liabilities: $603,391,000
Net Worth: $361,573,000
Earnings: ($16,255,000)
Emp.: 3,233
Fiscal Year-end: 12/31/22
Holding Company; Digital & Interactive Content Security & Convergent Media Products & Services
N.A.I.C.S.: 551112
Mauro Saladini *(CFO & Member-Exec Bd)*

Subsidiaries:

Conax AS   (1)
Lilleakerveien 10, Sentrum, 283, Oslo, Norway
Tel.: (47) 21002670
Web Site: http://www.conax.com
Sales Range: $100-124.9 Million
Emp.: 140
Access Solutions & Protection Technology for Digital Television
N.A.I.C.S.: 541519

E.D.S.I. SAS   (1)
8 Rue du bordage, 35510, Cesson Sevigne, France
Tel.: (33) 25 787 2960
Web Site: https://www.edsisecurity.com
Embedded Security System Services
N.A.I.C.S.: 561621

Kudelski Security   (1)
Route de Geneve 22-24, Case Postale 134, 1033, Cheseaux-sur-Lausanne, Switzerland
Tel.: (41) 21 732 0101
Web Site: https://www.kudelskisecurity.com
Emp.: 400
Cyber & Media Security Solutions
N.A.I.C.S.: 561621
Tom Marsnik *(VP-US Tech Svcs)*

Branch (US):

Kudelski Security - Atlanta   (2)
101 Marietta St NW Ste 800, Atlanta, GA 30303
Tel.: (770) 955-9899
Web Site: https://kudelskisecurity.com
Information Technology Security & Network Solutions
N.A.I.C.S.: 541519

Kudelski Security Inc.   (1)
12400 Whitewater Dr Ste 100, Minneapolis, MN 55343
Hardware & Software Digital Security Services
N.A.I.C.S.: 541990

Leman Consulting SA   (1)
31 Chemin de Precossy, Nyon, 1260, Switzerland   **(100%)**
Tel.: (41) 223637878
Web Site: http://www.lemanconsulting.ch
Sales Range: $25-49.9 Million
Emp.: 10
Management Consulting Services
N.A.I.C.S.: 541618

Lysis SA   (1)
Chemin De La Chapelle 4 6, CH 1003, Cheseaux-sur-Lausanne, Switzerland
Tel.: (41) 217323000
Web Site: http://www.nagravision.com
Sales Range: $50-74.9 Million
Emp.: 150
Developer of Digital TV
N.A.I.C.S.: 334310
Andre Kudelski *(Chm & CEO)*

Nagra France Sarl   (1)
86 Rue Henri Farman, Paris, 92130, Issy-les-Moulineaux, France   **(100%)**
Tel.: (33) 170716000
Web Site: http://www.nagra.fr
Sales Range: $150-199.9 Million
Emp.: 400
Electronic Parts & Equipment Whslr
N.A.I.C.S.: 423690

Nagra Kudelski (GB) Ltd.   (1)
Park Street, Knightway House, Bagshot, GU195AQ, Surrey, United Kingdom
Tel.: (44) 1276455860
Web Site: http://www.nagra.com
Electrical Appliance Television & Radio Set Whslr
N.A.I.C.S.: 423620

Nagra Media (Taiwan) Co., Ltd.   (1)
4F No 268 Ruiguang Road, Neihu District, New Taipei City, 114, Taiwan
Tel.: (886) 226567600
Hardware & Software Digital Security Services
N.A.I.C.S.: 541990

Nagra Media Australia Pty. Ltd.   (1)
Suite 545 Level 5 7 Eden Park drive, Macquarie Park, 2113, NSW, Australia
Tel.: (61) 298888700
Hardware & Software Digital Security Services
N.A.I.C.S.: 541990

Nagra Media Germany GmbH   (1)
Dingolfinger Strasse 15, Munchen, 81673, Munich, Germany
Tel.: (49) 899628960
Electronic Components Mfr
N.A.I.C.S.: 334419

Nagra Media Japan   (1)
W22th Fl Shibuya Mark City 1-12-1 Dogenzaka, Shibuya-ku, Tokyo, 150-0043, Japan
Tel.: (81) 343605778
Web Site: http://www.nagra.com
Security Software Development Services
N.A.I.C.S.: 541511

Nagra Media Korea LLC   (1)
6FL 602Ho DTC Tower 49, Daewangpangyo-ro 644 beon-gil, Anyang, Gyeonggi, Korea (South)
Tel.: (82) 37890900
Web Site: http://www.nagra.com
Sales Range: $25-49.9 Million
Emp.: 6
Security Software Development Services
N.A.I.C.S.: 541511

Nagra Media Private Limited   (1)
1003 Alpha Hiranandani Business Park, Powai, Mumbai, 400 076, India
Tel.: (91) 22 671 57000
Web Site: http://www.nagra.com
Emp.: 17
Security System Software Development Services
N.A.I.C.S.: 541511

Nagra Media UK Ltd   (1)
Machen The Pavillions Llantarnam Business Park, Llantarnam, Cwmbran, NP44 3UW, Gwent, United Kingdom
Tel.: (44) 1633628300
Security Software Development Services
N.A.I.C.S.: 541511

Nagra Trading SA   (1)
Route De Geneve 22-24, CP 134, Cheseaux-sur-Lausanne, 1033, Switzerland   **(100%)**
Tel.: (41) 217320101
Web Site: http://www.reports.nagra.com
Sales Range: $200-249.9 Million
Emp.: 750
Electrical Equipment & Component Mfr
N.A.I.C.S.: 335999
Andre Kudelski *(CEO)*

Nagra Travel Sarl   (1)
Route De Geneve 22-24, Cheseaux-Lausanne, 1033, Cheseaux-sur-Lausanne, Switzerland
Tel.: (41) 217320101
Emp.: 4
Travel Agency Services
N.A.I.C.S.: 561510

Nagra USA, Inc.   (1)
275 Sacramento St, San Francisco, CA 94111
Tel.: (623) 235-2500
Holding Company; Digital Media Technologies & Services
N.A.I.C.S.: 551112

Subsidiary (Domestic):

EmbedICs LLC   (2)
6630 Eli Whitney Dr Ste G, Columbia, MD 21046
Tel.: (410) 290-1124
Web Site: http://www.embedics.com
Embedded Software, Cryptography & Fabless Semiconductor Design Services
N.A.I.C.S.: 334413
Mark Wilson *(Pres & CEO)*

Joint Venture (Domestic):

NagraStar, LLC   (2)
90 Inverness Cir E, Englewood, CO 80112   **(50%)**
Tel.: (303) 706-5700
Web Site: https://www.nagrastar.com
Sales Range: $25-49.9 Million
Emp.: 90
Satellite Television Conditional Access & Smart Card Products Mfr & Whslr
N.A.I.C.S.: 334610
Pascal Lenoir *(CEO)*

Subsidiary (Domestic):

Nagravision STB Solutions Inc.   (2)
938 Peachtree St NE Ste 200, Atlanta, GA 30309-3919
Tel.: (404) 525-0940
Web Site: http://www.nagravision.com
Electronic Components Mfr
N.A.I.C.S.: 334419

OpenTV, Inc.   (2)
275 Sacramento St, San Francisco, CA 94111
Tel.: (415) 962-5000
Web Site: https://www.opentv.com
Sales Range: $50-74.9 Million
Emp.: 120
Digital Television Software & Services
N.A.I.C.S.: 541511

Subsidiary (Non-US):

OpenTV Australia Pty. Ltd.   (3)
100 Chandos Street, Naremburn, Sydney, 2065, NSW, Australia
Tel.: (61) 2 9438 1304
Web Site: http://www.opentv.com
Emp.: 25
Branded Interactive TV Content
N.A.I.C.S.: 516120

Nagracard SA   (1)
22-24 Rte de Geneve, PO Box 134, 1033, Cheseaux-sur-Lausanne, Switzerland   **(100%)**
Tel.: (41) 217320560
Web Site: http://www.nagravision.com
Sales Range: $200-249.9 Million
Emp.: 600
Electronic Components Mfr
N.A.I.C.S.: 334419
Kudelski Andre *(Mng Dir)*

Nagravision AS   (1)
Rebel House Universitetsgata 2 Sentrum, PO Box 425, 0164, Oslo, Norway
Tel.: (47) 22405200
Digital Broadcasting Services
N.A.I.C.S.: 516120

Nagravision Asia Pte. Ltd.   (1)
47 Scotts Road 18-01 Goldbell Towers, 34-02 AXA Tower, Singapore, 228233, Singapore
Tel.: (65) 68290800
Sales Range: $25-49.9 Million
Emp.: 30
Custom Computer Programming Services
N.A.I.C.S.: 541511

Nagravision Iberica S.L.   (1)
Calle del Principe de Vergara 43 4 planta, 28001, Madrid, Spain
Tel.: (34) 915903950
Sales Range: $25-49.9 Million
Emp.: 22
Architectural Services
N.A.I.C.S.: 541310

Nagravision India Pvt. Ltd.   (1)
Tel.: (91) 8049090400

KUDOS INDUSTRIAL COMPANY

Hardware & Software Digital Security Services
N.A.I.C.S.: 541990

Nagravision Italia Srl   (1)
Via Conca Del Naviglio 18, 20123, Milan, Italy
Tel.: (39) 03923014958
Electronic Components Mfr
N.A.I.C.S.: 334419

Nagravision Ltda   (1)
Rua Geraldo Flausino Gomes 61 4 andar, 04575-060, Sao Paulo, Brazil
Tel.: (55) 1155013885
Sales Range: $25-49.9 Million
Emp.: 20
Electronic Components Mfr
N.A.I.C.S.: 334419

Nagravision SA   (1)
Case Postale 134 Route de Geneve 22-24, Cheseaux-Lausanne, 1033, Cheseaux-sur-Lausanne, Switzerland
Tel.: (41) 217320311
Hardware & Software Digital Security Services
N.A.I.C.S.: 541990

SKIDATA Australasia Pty. Ltd.   (1)
97 Cook Street, Port Melbourne, 3207, VIC, Australia
Tel.: (61) 1300367359
Web Site: https://www.skidata.com
Skiing Facility Services
N.A.I.C.S.: 713920

SKIDATA Benelux BV   (1)
Lubeck 2, 2993 LK, Barendrecht, Netherlands
Tel.: (31) 180692100
Skiing Facility Services
N.A.I.C.S.: 713920

Sentry Control Systems LLC   (1)
6611 Odessa Ave, Van Nuys, CA 91406
Tel.: (818) 252-5700
Web Site: http://www.sentrycontrol.com
Emp.: 150
Security Control Services
N.A.I.C.S.: 561612
Robert de Bruine *(VP-Svc Dept)*

SmarDTV SA   (1)
22 Route de Geneve, Cheseaux-sur-Lausanne, 1033, Switzerland
Tel.: (41) 217320404
Web Site: https://www.smardtv.com
Sales Range: $25-49.9 Million
Emp.: 50
Computer Related Services
N.A.I.C.S.: 541519
Pascal Lenoir *(CEO)*

TESC Test Solution Center GmbH   (1)
Betastrasse 5, 85774, Unterfohring, Germany
Tel.: (49) 89 1250 3000
Web Site: http://www.tesc.tv
Digital Television Receiver Testing Services
N.A.I.C.S.: 541380

KUDO CORPORATION
4-33-10 Shin-Ishikawa, Aoba-ku, Yokohama, 225-0003, Kanagawa, Japan
Tel.: (81) 459115300
Web Site: https://www.kudo.co.jp
1764—(TKS)
Sales Range: $150-199.9 Million
Construction Engineering Services
N.A.I.C.S.: 541330
Jiro Kudo *(Chm)*

KUDOS INDUSTRIAL COMPANY
Rm 1110 11th Fl Wah Shing Ctr, Kwun Tong, Kowloon, China (Hong Kong)
Tel.: (852) 27714315
Web Site: http://www.kudos-ind.com
Year Founded: 1981
Sales Range: $100-124.9 Million
Emp.: 500
Plastic Products Mfr & Exporter

4323

KUDOS INDUSTRIAL COMPANY

Kudos Industrial Company—(Continued)
N.A.I.C.S.: 326199

KUDU INDUSTRIES INC.
9112 40th Street SE, Calgary, T2C 2P3, AB, Canada
Tel.: (403) 279-5838
Web Site: http://www.kudupump.com
Sales Range: $25-49.9 Million
Emp.: 200
Oil Pump Mfr, Sales & Service
N.A.I.C.S.: 333914
Robert A. R. Mills *(Co-Founder & Chm)*

KUEHNE + NAGEL INTERNATIONAL AG
Kuehne Nagel House, PO Box 67, CH-8834, Schindellegi, Switzerland
Tel.: (41) 447869511   **CH**
Web Site: http://home.kuehne-nagel.com
Year Founded: 1890
KHNGF—(OTCIQ)
Rev.: $37,146,148,470
Assets: $16,590,685,500
Liabilities: $12,954,324,330
Net Worth: $3,636,361,170
Earnings: $2,440,472,850
Emp.: 78,087
Fiscal Year-end: 12/31/21
Logistic Services
N.A.I.C.S.: 551112
Lothar Alexander Harings *(Chief HR Officer)*

Subsidiaries:

Agencia de Aduanas KN Colombia S.A.S. **(1)**
Web Site: http://www.kn-aduanas.com
Logistic Services
N.A.I.C.S.: 541614

Anchor Risk Services GmbH **(1)**
Am Sandtorkai 68, 20457, Hamburg, Germany
Tel.: (49) 4099999560
Web Site: https://www.anchorrisk.com
Risk Consultancy Services
N.A.I.C.S.: 541618
Ralf Dettmann *(Mng Dir)*

City Zone Express Sdn. Bhd. **(1)**
Plot 118 Jalan Perusahaan, Bukit Tengah Industrial Park, 14000, Bukit Mertajam, Penang, Malaysia
Tel.: (60) 4 502 5800
Web Site: https://www.czone.com.my
Emp.: 100
Warehousing & Transportation Services
N.A.I.C.S.: 484110
S. Pirithivaraj *(Gen Mgr)*

Commodity Forwarders Inc. **(1)**
11101 S La Cienega Blvd, Los Angeles, CA 90045
Tel.: (310) 348-8855
Web Site: http://www.cfiperishables.com
Freight Forwarding
N.A.I.C.S.: 488510

GFH Underwriting Agency Ltd. **(1)**
55 Standish Court, Box 13, Mississauga, L5R 4B2, ON, Canada
Tel.: (905) 507-7129
Web Site: https://www.gfhassure.com
Insurance Services
N.A.I.C.S.: 524210
Darryl Wolfe *(Natl Dir-Ops)*

Gustav. F. Huebener GmbH **(1)**
Am Sandtorkai 68, 20457, Hamburg, Germany
Tel.: (49) 4037690533
Web Site: https://www.gfh-insurance.com
Marine Insurance Services
N.A.I.C.S.: 524126
Andre Brinkmeier *(Mng Dir)*

KN (Mauritius) Limited **(1)**
Freeport Zone 5, Port Louis, Mauritius
Tel.: (230) 2062457
Logistic Services
N.A.I.C.S.: 541614

KN Airlift GmbH **(1)**
Cargo City Sued, 60549, Frankfurt am Main, Germany
Tel.: (49) 6940040
Air Logistic Services
N.A.I.C.S.: 481112

Kuehne & Nagel (Angola) Transitarios Lda. **(1)**
Rua Rainha Ginga 29 16th Floor Elysee Trade Center, Luanda, Angola
Tel.: (244) 222352734
Sea Freight Transportation Services
N.A.I.C.S.: 483111

Kuehne & Nagel (Ireland) Limited **(1)**
Horizon Logistics Park, Harristown, Swords, K67 A5W6, Ireland
Tel.: (353) 18239777
Sea Freight Transportation Services
N.A.I.C.S.: 483111

Kuehne & Nagel (Pty.) Ltd. **(1)**
Reger Street, Windhoek, Namibia
Tel.: (264) 61375900
Logistic Services
N.A.I.C.S.: 541614

Kuehne & Nagel (Pvt.) Ltd. **(1)**
Galle Road No 109 1st Floor Rotunda Tower, 00300, Colombo, Sri Lanka
Tel.: (94) 115400600
Sea Freight Transportation Services
N.A.I.C.S.: 483111

Kuehne & Nagel AB **(1)**
Torshamnsgatan 39, 164 40, Kista, Sweden
Tel.: (46) 406480000
Web Site: https://se.kuehne-nagel.com
Air Freight Transportation Services
N.A.I.C.S.: 481212

Kuehne & Nagel Jordan Ltd. **(1)**
Shmeisani, 11190, Amman, Jordan
Tel.: (962) 62007000
Sea Freight Transportation Services
N.A.I.C.S.: 483111

Kuehne & Nagel Limited **(1)**
Madinah Road, 21452, Jeddah, Saudi Arabia
Tel.: (966) 22296800
Logistic Services
N.A.I.C.S.: 541614

Kuehne & Nagel Ltd. **(1)**
Jiangchang Rd, Shanghai, 200436, China
Tel.: (86) 2126028000
Sea Freight Transportation Services
N.A.I.C.S.: 483111

Kuehne & Nagel Pty. Ltd. **(1)**
St Kilda Rd 484, Melbourne, 3004, VIC, Australia
Tel.: (61) 393943300
Logistic Services
N.A.I.C.S.: 541614

Kuehne & Nagel UAB **(1)**
A Gostauto g 40B, 03163, Vilnius, Lithuania
Tel.: (370) 52375517
Sea Freight Transportation Services
N.A.I.C.S.: 483111

Kuehne + Nagel (Private) Limited **(1)**
Block-6 47-E-3, 75400, Karachi, Pakistan
Tel.: (92) 2134312023
Sea Freight Transportation Services
N.A.I.C.S.: 483111

Kuehne + Nagel A/S **(1)**
Bredebjergvej 1, 2630, Taastrup, Denmark
Tel.: (45) 36993699
Sea Freight Transportation Services
N.A.I.C.S.: 483111

Kuehne + Nagel AE **(1)**
Spata Artemida, 190 04, Athens, Greece
Tel.: (30) 2103542468
Air Freight Transportation Services
N.A.I.C.S.: 481212

Kuehne + Nagel AS **(1)**
Jalgpalli tn 1, 11312, Tallinn, Estonia
Tel.: (372) 6600966
Sea Freight Transportation Services
N.A.I.C.S.: 483111

Kuehne + Nagel AS **(1)**
Brobekkveien 80A, 0582, Oslo, Norway
Tel.: (47) 21635000
Sea Freight Transportation Services
N.A.I.C.S.: 483111

Kuehne + Nagel Company Limited **(1)**
Le Thanh Ton Street 72, 70100, Ho Chi Minh City, Vietnam
Tel.: (84) 2838282200
Sea Freight Transportation Services
N.A.I.C.S.: 483111

Kuehne + Nagel Company W.L.L. **(1)**
Waha Mall, Dasman, 15451, Kuwait, Kuwait
Tel.: (965) 24333733
Sea Freight Transportation Services
N.A.I.C.S.: 483111

Kuehne + Nagel Euroshipping GmbH **(1)**
Linzer Str 13, 93055, Regensburg, Germany
Tel.: (49) 941608050
River Shipping Services
N.A.I.C.S.: 483212

Kuehne + Nagel FPE **(1)**
Lopatina 7A/1, Kopishe, 220125, Minsk, Belarus
Tel.: (375) 172697045
Sea Freight Transportation Services
N.A.I.C.S.: 483111

Kuehne + Nagel Inc. **(1)**
10 Exchange Pl 19th Fl, Jersey City, NJ 07302-3913 **(100%)**
Tel.: (201) 413-5500
Sales Range: $200-249.9 Million
Emp.: 830
International Freight Forwarding Services
N.A.I.C.S.: 488510

Kuehne + Nagel Inc. **(1)**
Harbor Drive, Pasay, 1300, Philippines
Tel.: (63) 287056100
Logistic Services
N.A.I.C.S.: 541614

Kuehne + Nagel Intermodal GmbH **(1)**
Teltower Str 18, 33719, Bielefeld, Germany
Tel.: (49) 52192033301
Food Transportation Services
N.A.I.C.S.: 488490

Kuehne + Nagel Internationale Transport-Gesellschaft m.b.H. **(1)**
Grosser Grasbrook 11-13, 20457, Hamburg, Germany
Tel.: (49) 40303330
Web Site: http://www.kuhne-nagel.com
Sales Range: $1-4.9 Billion
Emp.: 5,000
Holding Company; Regional Managing Office; Supply Chain Solutions & Logistics Services
N.A.I.C.S.: 551112

Subsidiary (Non-US):

Kuehne + Nagel (AG & Co.) KG **(2)**
(100%)
International Forwarding & Transport Warehousing & Distribution
N.A.I.C.S.: 488510
Hansjorg Rodi *(Mng Dir)*

Kuehne + Nagel Eastern Europe AG **(2)**
Leonard Bernstein Strasse 10, A-1220, Vienna, Austria
Tel.: (43) 12630900
Supply Chain Solutions & Logistics Services
N.A.I.C.S.: 488510

Kuehne + Nagel Gesellschaft m.b.H. **(2)**
Warneckestrasse 10, Vienna, 1110, Austria **(100%)**
Tel.: (43) 1906900
Rev.: $112,837,000
Emp.: 300
International Forwarding & Transport Warehousing & Distribution
N.A.I.C.S.: 488510

Kuehne + Nagel Kft **(1)**
Szent Jozsef ut 4, 2071, Paty, Hungary

INTERNATIONAL PUBLIC

Tel.: (36) 23889000
Web Site: https://hu.kuehne-nagel.com
Sea Freight Transportation Services
N.A.I.C.S.: 483111

Kuehne + Nagel L.L.C. **(1)**
Mesammer St D-Ring Road QA, Doha, Qatar
Tel.: (974) 44318974
Sea Freight Transportation Services
N.A.I.C.S.: 483111

Kuehne + Nagel Lda. **(1)**
Rua Santos Dias 1226, 4465-253, Mamede de Infesta, Portugal
Tel.: (351) 229438680
Sea Freight Transportation Services
N.A.I.C.S.: 483111

Kuehne + Nagel Limited **(1)**
New Petchburi Road 2034, 10310, Bangkok, Thailand
Tel.: (66) 20188800
Logistic Services
N.A.I.C.S.: 541614

Kuehne + Nagel Limited **(1)**
Aintree Avenue 30, 2022, Auckland, New Zealand
Tel.: (64) 92572800
Sea Freight Transportation Services
N.A.I.C.S.: 483111

Kuehne + Nagel Limited **(1)**
Freight Road, 00400, Nairobi, Kenya
Tel.: (254) 206600000
Sea Freight Transportation Services
N.A.I.C.S.: 483111

Kuehne + Nagel Limited **(1)**
Mdina Road 71, QRM 9016, Qormi, Malta
Tel.: (356) 25401600
Sea Freight Transportation Services
N.A.I.C.S.: 483111

Kuehne + Nagel Limited **(1)**
Nyerere Road 29c TZ, Dar es Salaam, Tanzania
Tel.: (255) 2228604104
Logistic Services
N.A.I.C.S.: 541614

Kuehne + Nagel Limited **(1)**
Port Bell Road Plot 7, Kampala, Uganda
Tel.: (256) 41223652
Logistic Services
N.A.I.C.S.: 541614

Kuehne + Nagel Limited **(1)**
7 VIP Road, Mohakhali, 1206, Dhaka, Bangladesh
Tel.: (880) 9612884882
Sea Freight Transportation Services
N.A.I.C.S.: 483111

Kuehne + Nagel Limited **(1)**
Street 360 Corner Norodom Blvd, Khan Chamkamon, 120102, Phnom Penh, Cambodia
Tel.: (855) 23986898
Sea Freight Transportation Services
N.A.I.C.S.: 483111

Kuehne + Nagel Logistics B.V. **(1)**
Marshallweg 2, 5466 AJ, Veghel, Netherlands
Tel.: (31) 413315555
Logistic Services
N.A.I.C.S.: 541614

Kuehne + Nagel Logistics Langenau GmbH **(1)**
Magirusstr 2, 89129, Langenau, Germany
Tel.: (49) 734523610
Spare Parts Retailer
N.A.I.C.S.: 441330

Kuehne + Nagel Ltd. **(1)**
1 Roundwood Avenue, Uxbridge, UB11 1FG, Middlesex, United Kingdom
Web Site: http://www.kn-portal.com
Sales Range: $75-99.9 Million
Emp.: 200
Supply Chain Solutions & Logistics Services
N.A.I.C.S.: 488510

Kuehne + Nagel Ltd. **(1)**
Dock Road 1, Port of Spain, Trinidad & Tobago
Tel.: (868) 6234255
Sea Freight Transportation Services
N.A.I.C.S.: 483111

AND PRIVATE COMPANIES — KUEN LING REFRIGERATING MACHINERY CO., LTD.

Kuehne + Nagel Ltd. (1)
East 21 Tower, Tokyo, 135-0016, Japan
Tel.: (81) 356325350
Sea Freight Transportation Services
N.A.I.C.S.: 483111

Kuehne + Nagel Ltd. (1)
Mapo-daero 4da-gil 41, 04177, Seoul, Korea (South)
Tel.: (82) 220788700
Sea Freight Transportation Services
N.A.I.C.S.: 483111

Kuehne + Nagel Ltd. (1)
Strand Road 426, 11161, Yangon, Myanmar
Tel.: (95) 9977460877
Sea Freight Transportation Services
N.A.I.C.S.: 483111

Kuehne + Nagel Ltd. (1)
10F No 246 Sec 1 Neihu Rd, Taipei, 114661, Taiwan
Tel.: (886) 25445000
Sea Freight Transportation Services
N.A.I.C.S.: 483111

Kuehne + Nagel Ltd. (1)
1st Administration Sector 76, 11477, Cairo, Egypt
Tel.: (20) 226145500
Sea Freight Transportation Services
N.A.I.C.S.: 483111

Kuehne + Nagel Ltda. (1)
Av San Martin Edificio Torre Equipetrol Piso 6, Santa Cruz, Bolivia
Tel.: (591) 33443300
Sea Freight Transportation Services
N.A.I.C.S.: 483111

Kuehne + Nagel Management SASU (1)
19 Blvd Paul Vaillant-Couturier Atrium Rive Gauche, Ivry Port, 94200, Ivry-sur-Seine, France
Tel.: (33) 158913939
Web Site: http://www.kn-portal.com
Supply Chain Solutions & Logistics Services
N.A.I.C.S.: 488510

Kuehne + Nagel N.V. (1)
Lloydstraat 35, 3024 EA, Rotterdam, Netherlands (100%)
Tel.: (31) 104789911
Rev: $112,798,496
Emp: 200
International Forwarding & Transport Warehousing, Porthandling
N.A.I.C.S.: 488510
Gereon Meahmaear *(Gen Mgr)*

Kuehne + Nagel NV (1)
Borsbeeksebrug 30/1, 2600, Antwerp, Belgium
Tel.: (32) 32206311
Sea Freight Transportation Services
N.A.I.C.S.: 483111

Kuehne + Nagel Private Limited (1)
Ameer Ahmed Magu, 20125, Male, Maldives
Tel.: (960) 3303945
Sea Freight Transportation Services
N.A.I.C.S.: 483111

Kuehne + Nagel Pvt. Ltd. (1)
13h Floor AIPL Business Club, Gurgaon, 122 002, India
Tel.: (91) 1244595959
Sea Freight Transportation Services
N.A.I.C.S.: 483111

Kuehne + Nagel S. A. (1)
Av Irlanda E10-16 y Republica del Salvador, 170150, Quito, Ecuador
Tel.: (593) 23819800
Sea Freight Transportation Services
N.A.I.C.S.: 483111

Kuehne + Nagel S.A. (1)
Av Leandro N Alem 815 5to piso 1001, Buenos Aires, Argentina
Tel.: (54) 1155566200
Sea Freight Transportation Services
N.A.I.C.S.: 483111

Kuehne + Nagel S.A. (1)
175 Metros Oeste del Megasuper, Flores, 40801, San Jose, Costa Rica
Tel.: (506) 22985300
Sea Freight Transportation Services

Kuehne + Nagel S.A. (1)
Diagonal 6 10-50, 01010, Guatemala, Guatemala
Tel.: (502) 23645060
Sea Freight Transportation Services
N.A.I.C.S.: 483111

Kuehne + Nagel S.A. (1)
Ave Circunvalacion S/n, San Pedro Sula, Honduras
Tel.: (504) 25164040
Sea Freight Transportation Services
N.A.I.C.S.: 483111

Kuehne + Nagel S.A. (1)
Carretera Norte Km 2 5, Managua, Nicaragua
Tel.: (505) 222511074
Sea Freight Transportation Services
N.A.I.C.S.: 483111

Kuehne + Nagel S.A. (1)
Ave Boulevard Costa Del Este Ciudad de, Panama, Panama
Tel.: (507) 4304870
Sea Freight Transportation Services
N.A.I.C.S.: 483111

Kuehne + Nagel S.A. (1)
Calle Las Begonias 441 27, San Isidro, Peru
Tel.: (51) 16120800
Sea Freight Transportation Services
N.A.I.C.S.: 483111

Kuehne + Nagel S.A. (1)
Juncal 1385, 11008, Montevideo, Uruguay
Tel.: (598) 29155252
Sea Freight Transportation Services
N.A.I.C.S.: 483111

Kuehne + Nagel S.A. (1)
Av Tamanaco, 1060, Caracas, Venezuela
Tel.: (58) 2129515090
Sea Freight Transportation Services
N.A.I.C.S.: 483111

Kuehne + Nagel S.A. de C.V. (1)
103 Avenida Norte No 124, 1101, San Salvador, El Salvador
Tel.: (503) 21330106
Sea Freight Transportation Services
N.A.I.C.S.: 483111

Kuehne + Nagel S.A.S. (1)
Calle 113 7-80, 250051, Bogota, Colombia
Tel.: (57) 17437000
Sea Freight Transportation Services
N.A.I.C.S.: 483111

Kuehne + Nagel SE (1)
Harmatna vul 4, 03067, Kiev, Ukraine
Tel.: (380) 444903232
Sea Freight Transportation Services
N.A.I.C.S.: 483111

Kuehne + Nagel Sdn. Bhd. (1)
Perindustrian Bukit Jelutong, 40150, Shah Alam, Malaysia
Tel.: (60) 378411280
Web Site: http://my.kuehne-nagel.com
Sea Freight Transportation Services
N.A.I.C.S.: 483111

Kuehne + Nagel Servicos Logisticos Ltda. (1)
Av das Nacoes Unidas 14 171, Crystal Tower, Sao Paulo, 04794-000, Brazil
Tel.: (55) 1134688000
Freight Transportation & Logistics Services
N.A.I.C.S.: 484121

Kuehne + Nagel SpA (1)
(100%)
Rev: $56,553,300
Emp: 30
International Forwarding & Transport
N.A.I.C.S.: 488510

Kuehne + Nagel Srl (1)
Iuliu Maniu 6 L Et 10, 061103, Bucharest, Romania
Tel.: (40) 214075850
Sea Freight Transportation Services
N.A.I.C.S.: 483111

Kuehne + Nagel WLL (1)
Road 2803 Block 428 Office 21 Building 205, 34306, Seef, Bahrain
Tel.: (973) 17310488

Sea Freight Transportation Services
N.A.I.C.S.: 483111

Kuehne + Nagel d.o.o. (1)
Gospodarska Ulica 2, 10431, Sveta Nedelja, Croatia
Tel.: (385) 13441640
Sea Freight Transportation Services
N.A.I.C.S.: 483111

Kuehne + Nagel d.o.o. (1)
Partizanska 228, Ugrinovci, 11277, Belgrade, Serbia
Tel.: (381) 113715140
Logistic Services
N.A.I.C.S.: 541614

Kuehne + Nagel d.o.o.e.l. (1)
Bul 8-mi Septemvri br 40, 1000, Skopje, North Macedonia
Tel.: (389) 22786000
Web Site: http://mk.kuehne-nagel.com
Sea Freight Transportation Services
N.A.I.C.S.: 483111

Kuehne + Nagel doo (1)
Ulica Tresnje Br 1, 71210, Ilidza, Bosnia & Herzegovina
Tel.: (387) 33764015
Sea Freight Transportation Services
N.A.I.C.S.: 483111

Nacora (Luxembourg) S.a.r.l. (1)
Rue Edmond Reuter 1, 5326, Contern, Luxembourg
Tel.: (352) 3551411
Sea Freight Transportation Services
N.A.I.C.S.: 483111

Nacora Agencies AG (1)
Dorfstrasse 50, 8834, Schindellegi, Switzerland
Tel.: (41) 447869711
Web Site: https://www.nacora.com
Insurance Services
N.A.I.C.S.: 524210
Steffen G. Bergholz *(Mng Dir)*

Nacora Brokins International AE (1)
99 Vouliagmenis Ave and Iliou 1, Attica, 166-74, Glyfada, Greece
Tel.: (30) 2108931622
Insurance Services
N.A.I.C.S.: 524210

Nacora Correduria de Seguros S.A. (1)
Calle del Antartico 13-19, 08040, Barcelona, Spain
Tel.: (34) 935099100
Insurance Services
N.A.I.C.S.: 524210

Nacora Courtage d'Assurances SAS (1)
23 avenue Aristide Briand, 94110, Arcueil, France
Tel.: (33) 149122890
Insurance Services
N.A.I.C.S.: 524210

Nacora Insurance Brokers (Proprietary) Limited (1)
9 Nguni Drive Longmeadow West, Edenvale, 1609, South Africa
Tel.: (27) 115747000
Insurance Services
N.A.I.C.S.: 524210

Nacora Insurance Brokers GmbH (1)
Objekt 645/2 Stock, 1300, Vienna, Austria
Tel.: (43) 5906901187
Insurance Services
N.A.I.C.S.: 524210
Antonella Milosavljevic *(Mng Dir)*

Nacora Insurance Brokers Inc. (1)
10 Exchange Pl 20th Fl, Jersey City, NJ 07302
Tel.: (201) 413-0535
Insurance Services
N.A.I.C.S.: 524210

Nacora Insurance Brokers Limited (1)
4th Floor Hamalworth House 9 St Clare Street, London, EC3N 1LQ, United Kingdom
Tel.: (44) 2079775500
Insurance Services

N.A.I.C.S.: 524210

Nacora Insurance Brokers Ltd. (1)
77 Foster Crescent, Mississauga, L5R 0K1, ON, Canada
Tel.: (905) 507-1551
Insurance Services
N.A.I.C.S.: 524210

Nacora Insurance Brokers Ltd. (1)
Room 2504 25/F Manhattan Place 23 Wang Tai Road, Kowloon, China (Hong Kong)
Tel.: (852) 28237788
Logistic Services
N.A.I.C.S.: 541614

Nacora International Insurance Brokers AB (1)
Torshamnsgatan 39, 164 40, Kista, Sweden
Tel.: (46) 854581185
Insurance Services
N.A.I.C.S.: 524210
Anna MacDonald *(Mng Dir)*

Nacora LTDA Agencia de Seguros (1)
Calle 113 No 7- 80 Piso 5, Bogota, Colombia
Tel.: (57) 17437000
Insurance Services
N.A.I.C.S.: 524210
Andrea Carolina Villamizar *(Reg Dir)*

Nacora Sigorta Brokerligi A.S. (1)
Suleyman Demirel Bulvari Mall of Istanbul Ofis No 7 K4 D 24, Basaksehir, 34490, Istanbul, Turkiye
Tel.: (90) 2124014717
Insurance Services
N.A.I.C.S.: 524210

Nacora Srl (1)
Via Quintiliano 49, 20138, Milan, Italy
Tel.: (39) 0250670409
Insurance Services
N.A.I.C.S.: 524210

Nacora Versicherungsmakler GmbH (1)
Am Sandtorkai 68, 20457, Hamburg, Germany
Tel.: (49) 4037690501
Insurance Services
N.A.I.C.S.: 524210

Nakufreight Limited (1)
75 Athalassas Avenue Chapo building mezzanine floor, Strovolos, 2012, Nicosia, Cyprus
Tel.: (357) 22498111
Web Site: https://www.nakufreight.com.cy
Sea Freight Transportation Services
N.A.I.C.S.: 483111

OOO Kuehne + Nagel (1)
Olimpiyskiy pr-kt 14, 129090, Moscow, Russia
Tel.: (7) 4957952000
Sea Freight Transportation Services
N.A.I.C.S.: 483111

Oy Kuehne + Nagel Ltd. (1)
Karhumaenkuja 2, 01530, Vantaa, Finland
Tel.: (358) 201611611
Web Site: http://ru.kuehne-nagel.com
Sea Freight Transportation Services
N.A.I.C.S.: 483111

Stute Logistics (AG & Co.) KG (1)
Hans-Bockler-Str 48, 28217, Bremen, Germany
Tel.: (49) 42138620
Web Site: http://www.stute.de
Logistic Services
N.A.I.C.S.: 541614
Marco Hamacher *(Chm)*

Zet Farma Lojistik Hizmetleri Sanayi ve Ticaret A.S. (1)
The Office No 7/E Floor 16 Flat No 128, Basaksehir, Istanbul, Turkiye
Tel.: (90) 2128019110
Web Site: http://www.zetfarma.com
Freight Transportation Services
N.A.I.C.S.: 488510

KUEN LING REFRIGERATING MACHINERY CO., LTD.
No 300 Chikan N Rd, Ziguan Dist, Kaohsiung, Taiwan

KUEN LING REFRIGERATING MACHINERY CO., LTD.

Kuen Ling Refrigerating Machinery Co., Ltd.—(Continued)
Tel.: (886) 76192345
4527—(TPE)
Rev.: $94,827,346
Assets: $99,813,526
Liabilities: $48,664,290
Net Worth: $51,149,236
Earnings: $6,446,081
Fiscal Year-end: 12/31/22
Electric Equipment Mfr
N.A.I.C.S.: 333415
Chung-Kuo Tseng *(Chm, Pres & CEO)*

Subsidiaries:

Kuen Ling Machinery Refrigerating (Shanghai) Co., Ltd. (1)
2nd Floor Area B Building 17 No 470 Jiujing Road, Jiuting Town Songjiang District, Shanghai, China
Tel.: (86) 2167696169
Web Site: https://www.kuenling.com
Air Conditioning Equipment Mfr & Distr
N.A.I.C.S.: 333415

Kuen Ling Machinery Refrigerating (Suzhou) Co., Ltd. (1)
No 815 Jiangxing East Road, Economic Development District, Wujiang, Jiangsu, China
Tel.: (86) 51263406188
Air Conditioning Equipment Mfr & Distr
N.A.I.C.S.: 333415

P.T. Kuen Ling Indonesia (1)
Ruko Galeri Niaga Mediterania 1 Blok B 8 A Jl Pantai Indah Utara 2, Pantai Indah Kapuk Muara Penjaringan, Jakarta, 14460, Utara, Indonesia
Tel.: (62) 215880400
Air Conditioning Equipment Mfr & Distr
N.A.I.C.S.: 333415

KUFU COMPANY INC.
Mita Kokusai Bldg 23F 1-4-28 Mita, Minato-ku, Tokyo, 108-0073, Japan
Tel.: (81) 362642323   JP
Web Site: https://kufu.co.jp
Year Founded: 2018
4399—(TKS)
Rev.: $41,200,810
Assets: $53,571,140
Liabilities: $8,803,200
Net Worth: $44,767,940
Earnings: $146,720
Fiscal Year-end: 09/30/20
Holding Company
N.A.I.C.S.: 551112
Yoshiteru Akita *(Chm & CEO)*

Subsidiaries:

Locoguide, Inc. (1)
1-4-28 Mita, Minato-Ku, Tokyo, 108-0073, Japan
Tel.: (81) 363681052
Web Site: http://www.locoguide.co.jp
E Commerce Site Operator
N.A.I.C.S.: 561599
Yoshiteru Akita *(Pres)*

Minnano Wedding Co., Ltd. (1)
1-13-1 Ginza Shochiku Square Ninth Floor, Tsukiji Chuo-ku, Tokyo, 104-0045, Japan (100%)
Tel.: (81) 3 3549 0211
Web Site: http://www.mwed.co.jp
Sales Range: $1-9.9 Million
Emp.: 90
Wedding Management Services
N.A.I.C.S.: 812990
Yosuke Uchida *(Pres & CEO)*

O-uccino Inc. (1)
2-4-1 Higashi Shinbashi, Minato-ku, Tokyo, 105-0021, Japan (100%)
Tel.: (81) 3 5402 6887
Web Site: http://www.o-uccino.jp
Rev.: $11,508,480
Assets: $14,136,960
Liabilities: $3,356,640
Net Worth: $10,780,320
Earnings: ($2,539,680)
Emp.: 76

Fiscal Year-end: 12/31/2017
Housing & Real Estate Website Operator & Internet Advertising Services
N.A.I.C.S.: 531390
Ikuyo Horiguchi *(Pres)*

Branch (US):

Seven Signatures International Corporation - Honolulu Branch (2)
Trump Tower Waikiki Ste 2509 223 Saratoga Rd, Honolulu, HI 96815
Tel.: (808) 683-7888
Residential Property Sales & Leasing Services
N.A.I.C.S.: 531311

KUHN HOLDING GMBH
Gewerbestrasse 7, 5301, Eugendorf, Austria
Tel.: (43) 622582060   AT
Web Site: http://www.kuhn.at
Sales Range: $600-649.9 Million
Emp.: 1,300
Holding Company; Construction & Industrial Loading Equipment Mfr & Distr
N.A.I.C.S.: 551112
Gunter Kuhn *(Founder & Member-Mgmt Bd)*

Subsidiaries:

EMCO Maier Ges.m.b.H. (1)
Salzburger Strasse 80, 5400, Hallein, Austria
Tel.: (43) 6245 8910
Web Site: http://www.emco-world.com
Sales Range: $200-249.9 Million
Emp.: 630
Metal Cutting Machine Tools Mfr & Distr
N.A.I.C.S.: 333517
Stefan Hansch *(CEO & Chm-Mgmt Bd)*

Subsidiary (Non-US):

EMCO Famuo SRL (2)
Via Maniago 53, 33080, San Quirino, PN, Italy
Tel.: (39) 0434 9160
Metal Products Mfr
N.A.I.C.S.: 333517

EMCO Intos spol. s r.o. (2)
Pod nadrazim 853, CZ-268 01, Horovice, Czech Republic
Tel.: (420) 311 535 115
Web Site: http://www.emco-world.cz
Metal Products Mfr
N.A.I.C.S.: 333517

Subsidiary (Domestic):

EMCO Intos S.r.o. (3)
Husova cl 1373 13, 370 05, Ceske Budejovice, Czech Republic
Tel.: (420) 311 156 940
Web Site: http://www.emco-world.cz
Industrial Machinery Distr & Repair Services
N.A.I.C.S.: 811310

Subsidiary (Non-US):

EMCO Italia SRL (2)
Via Magenta 41, 20010, San Giorgio su Legnano, MI, Italy
Tel.: (39) 0331 418 000
Metal Products Mfr
N.A.I.C.S.: 333517

Subsidiary (Domestic):

EMCO MECOF Srl (3)
Via Molino 2, 15070, Belforte Monferrato, Alessandria, Italy
Tel.: (39) 0143 8201
Web Site: http://www.emco-mecof.it
Emp.: 130
Industrial Machinery Mfr
N.A.I.C.S.: 333248
Mauro Salvadori *(CEO)*

Subsidiary (Non-US):

EMCO Magdeburg AG (2)
Groperstrasse 18, 39124, Magdeburg, Germany
Tel.: (49) 391 2440
Web Site: http://www.emco-magdeburg.de

Metal Products Mfr
N.A.I.C.S.: 333517

Subsidiary (US):

EMCO Maier Corporation (2)
2841 Charter St, Columbus, OH 43228
Tel.: (614) 771-5991
Rev.: $4,000,000
Emp.: 20
Metalworking Machines Mfr
N.A.I.C.S.: 333519
Scott Moore *(CEO)*

Subsidiary (Non-US):

EMCO Maier GmbH & Co. KG (2)
Gottlieb-Daimler-Str 15, 74385, Pleidelsheim, Germany
Tel.: (49) 7144 82420
Web Site: http://www.emco-maier.de
Metal Products Mfr
N.A.I.C.S.: 333517

KUHN Baumaschinen GmbH (1)
Gewerbestrasse 7, Eugendorf, 5301, Austria
Tel.: (43) 622582060
Web Site: http://www.kuhn-group.com
Sales Range: $25-49.9 Million
Emp.: 50
Construction Machinery Mfr, Distr & Leasing Services
N.A.I.C.S.: 333120
Kuhn Stephan *(Gen Mgr)*

KUHN Ladetechnik GmbH (1)
Peter-Anich-Strasse 1, A-4840, Vocklabruck, Austria
Tel.: (43) 7672725320
Industrial Crane, Forklift & Other Loading Equipment Mfr & Distr
N.A.I.C.S.: 333923

Kuhn Baumaschinen Deutschland GmbH (1)
Josef-Neumeier-Strasse 6, 85664, Hohenlinden, Germany
Tel.: (49) 8124 4463 0
Web Site: http://www.kuhn-baumaschinen.de
Construction Machinery Distr
N.A.I.C.S.: 423810

Kuhn Foldmunkagep Kft. (1)
Ocsai ut 5, 1239, Budapest, Hungary
Tel.: (36) 1 289 8080
Web Site: http://www.kuhn.hu
Construction Machinery Distr
N.A.I.C.S.: 423810
Laszlo Mohacsi *(Mgr-Technical)*

Kuhn Hrvatska d.o.o. (1)
Rakitnica 4, 10000, Zagreb, Croatia
Tel.: (385) 1 2407522
Web Site: http://www.kuhn.hr
Construction Machinery Distr
N.A.I.C.S.: 423810

Kuhn Polska Sp.z.o.o (1)
Czastkow Mazowiecki 7, 05-152, Czosnow, Poland
Tel.: (48) 22 784 95 34
Web Site: http://www.kuhn-polska.pl
Construction Machinery Distr
N.A.I.C.S.: 423810

Kuhn Schweiz AG (1)
Bernstrasse 125, Postfach 207, 3627, Heimberg, Switzerland
Tel.: (41) 33 439 88 22
Web Site: http://www.kuhn-gruppe.ch
Emp.: 100
Construction Machinery Distr
N.A.I.C.S.: 423810
Franz Kissling *(CEO & Dir-Sls & Mktg)*

Kuhn Slovakia s.r.o. (1)
Dialnicna cesta 16A, 903 01, Senec, Slovakia
Tel.: (421) 2 63 838 509
Web Site: http://www.kuhn.sk
Construction Machinery Distr
N.A.I.C.S.: 423810
Martin Petruska *(Mgr-Parts)*

Kuhn d.o.o. (1)
Blatnica 1 Obrtno industrijska cona, 1236, Trzin, Slovenia
Tel.: (386) 1 5622271
Web Site: http://www.kuhn.si

INTERNATIONAL PUBLIC

Construction Machinery Distr
N.A.I.C.S.: 423810

Kuhn-MT s.r.o. (1)
Okruzni Ul 673, 370 01, Ceske Budejovice, Czech Republic
Tel.: (420) 380 900 400
Web Site: http://www.kuhn-mt.cz
Construction Machinery Distr
N.A.I.C.S.: 423810

KUHNE GMBH
Einsteinstrasse 20, Saint Augustin, 53757, Germany
Tel.: (49) 2241 902 0
Web Site: http://www.kuhne-group.com
Emp.: 200
Industrial Machinery Mfr
N.A.I.C.S.: 333248
Peter Kuhne *(Pres)*

KUK YOUNG G&M CO., LTD.
7F 36 Seocho-Jungang-ro, Seocho-gu, Seoul, Korea (South)
Tel.: (82) 220150320
Web Site: https://www.kukyounggnm.com
Year Founded: 1969
006050—(KRS)
Rev.: $48,780,755
Assets: $50,739,611
Liabilities: $13,916,130
Net Worth: $36,823,481
Earnings: $1,424,799
Emp.: 117
Fiscal Year-end: 12/31/22
Glass Processing Product Mfr
N.A.I.C.S.: 327215

KUK-IL PAPER MFG. CO., LTD.
388 Gangnam-daero, Gangnam-gu, Seoul, Korea (South)
Tel.: (82) 269005500
Web Site: https://www.kukilpaper.co.kr
Year Founded: 1978
078130—(KRS)
Rev.: $86,287,126
Assets: $100,585,741
Liabilities: $60,194,944
Net Worth: $40,390,797
Earnings: ($11,182,555)
Emp.: 193
Fiscal Year-end: 12/31/22
Paper Products Mfr & Whslr
N.A.I.C.S.: 322120
Tae Hyun Kang *(Pres)*

Subsidiaries:

Kuk-Il Paper Mfg. Co., Ltd. - Yong-In Plant (1)
563 Baegok-daero Idong-myeon, Cheoin-gu, Yongin, Gyeonggi, Korea (South)
Tel.: (82) 313399100
Paper Mfr
N.A.I.C.S.: 322120

KUKBO DESIGN CO., LTD
49gil Worldcup ro, Mapo-gu, Seoul, Korea (South)
Tel.: (82) 262201800
Web Site: https://www.ikukbo.com
Year Founded: 1983
066620—(KRS)
Rev.: $290,223,476
Assets: $209,760,262
Liabilities: $97,987,809
Net Worth: $111,772,453
Earnings: $16,005,391
Emp.: 339
Fiscal Year-end: 12/31/22
Building Interior Design Services
N.A.I.C.S.: 541410

Subsidiaries:

Kukbo Vina Co., Ltd. (1)
No 1501 Block B Cantavil Apt ANPHU Ward

KUKBO LOGISTICS CO., LTD.
8th Floor Kukbo Building 42, Gwangnam-ro Suyeong-gu, Busan, Korea (South)
Tel.: (82) 516006805
Web Site: https://www.kukbo.com
Year Founded: 1953
001140—(KRS)
Rev.: $78,429,628
Assets: $84,339,208
Liabilities: $51,290,451
Net Worth: $33,048,757
Earnings: ($18,381,063)
Emp.: 109
Fiscal Year-end: 12/31/22
Food Transportation Services
N.A.I.C.S.: 484110
Park Chan Ha *(CEO)*

KUKDO CHEMICAL CO LTD
61 Gasan digital 2-ro, Geumcheong-gu, Seoul, Korea (South)
Tel.: (82) 232821400
Web Site: https://www.kukdo.com
Year Founded: 1972
007690—(KRS)
Rev.: $1,228,560,794
Assets: $1,149,804,836
Liabilities: $491,574,672
Net Worth: $658,230,164
Earnings: $56,399,369
Emp.: 777
Fiscal Year-end: 12/31/22
Resin Mfr
N.A.I.C.S.: 325211
Si-Chang Lee *(Pres & Co-CEO)*

Subsidiaries:

Kukdo Chemical Co., Ltd. - Siwha Factory (1)
15 Gongdan 2-daero, Siheung, 429-915, Gyeonggi-do, Korea (South)
Tel.: (82) 314985077
Web Site: http://www.kukdo.com
Polyurethane Resin Mfr
N.A.I.C.S.: 325211

KUKDONG CORPORATION
Creas Building 6F/7F 322 Nonhyeon-ro, Gangnam-gu, Seoul, Korea (South)
Tel.: (82) 234077726
Web Site: https://www.kd.co.kr
Year Founded: 1967
005320—(KRS)
Rev.: $253,015,404
Assets: $134,231,263
Liabilities: $50,585,426
Net Worth: $83,645,837
Earnings: $1,066,263
Emp.: 64
Fiscal Year-end: 12/31/22
Apparel Whslr
N.A.I.C.S.: 424310
Jung Gyu Kim *(CEO)*

Subsidiaries:

KUKDONG APPAREL INC. (1)
17100 Pioneer Blvd Ste 230, Artesia, CA 90701
Tel.: (562) 403-0044
Apparels Mfr
N.A.I.C.S.: 315990
Young-Sub Byun *(Gen Mgr)*

KUKDONG TEXTILE S.A. DE. C.V. (1)
Retorno de Continentes 38 Col Rancho Los Soles, Atlixco, Puebla, Mexico
Tel.: (52) 244 446 2607
Apparels Mfr
N.A.I.C.S.: 315990

P.T. KUKDONG INTERNATIONAL (1)
Rukan Graha Cempaka Mas Blok C No 27 JL Letjend Suprapto, Jakarta, Indonesia
Tel.: (62) 21 426 1740
Apparels Mfr
N.A.I.C.S.: 315990
Iim Dahiman *(Mgr-QA)*

KUKDONG OIL & CHEMICAL CO., LTD.
101 Eosil-ro, Yangsan, 50592, Gyeongsangnam-do, Korea (South)
Tel.: (82) 553709900
Web Site: https://www.kdoc.co.kr
Year Founded: 1979
014530—(KRS)
Rev.: $952,978,966
Assets: $270,809,328
Liabilities: $113,331,257
Net Worth: $157,478,071
Earnings: $15,669,996
Emp.: 117
Fiscal Year-end: 12/31/22
Lubricant Mfr
N.A.I.C.S.: 324191
Sun-Woo Chang *(CEO)*

Subsidiaries:

Kukdong Oil & Chemical Co., Ltd. - LPG DIVISION (1)
507-13 Kamjeon-Dong, Sasang-Gu, Pusan, Korea (South)
Tel.: (82) 51 311 1311
Natural Gas Distribution Services
N.A.I.C.S.: 221210

Kukdong Oil & Chemical Co., Ltd. - WATERPROOFING MEMBRANE DIVISION (1)
139-12 Bokjung-Dong, Kyungnam, Yangsan, Korea (South)
Tel.: (82) 55 387 8171
Membrane Product Mfr
N.A.I.C.S.: 326299

Kukdong Oil & Chemicals Co. Ltd. (1)
VFC TOWER 2nd FL 29 Ton Duc Thang Street, District 1, Ho Chi Minh City, Vietnam
Tel.: (84) 2838270700
Oil & Chemical Mfr
N.A.I.C.S.: 325998

Sunjin Motors Co. Ltd. (1)
146 Jung-daero, Songpa-gu, Seoul, Korea (South)
Tel.: (82) 230120077
Web Site: https://www.sunjinmotors.com
New Car Dealer Services
N.A.I.C.S.: 441110

KUKE MUSIC HOLDING LIMITED
Building 96 4 San Jian Fang South Block, Chaoyang District, Beijing, Beijing, China
Tel.: (86) 1065610392
Web Site: http://www.kuke.com
Year Founded: 2017
KUKE—(NYSE)
Rev.: $14,806
Assets: $34,407
Liabilities: $31,146
Net Worth: $3,262
Earnings: ($9,111)
Emp.: 108
Fiscal Year-end: 12/31/23
Holding Company
N.A.I.C.S.: 551112
He Yu *(Chm & CEO)*

KUKIL METAL CO., LTD.
58 Beonnyeong 2-ro Danwon-gu, Ansan, Gyeonggi-do, Korea (South)
Tel.: (82) 314999192
Web Site: http://www.kukilmetal.com
060480—(KRS)
Rev.: $20,619,366
Assets: $40,040,767
Liabilities: $3,264,347
Net Worth: $36,776,420
Earnings: $771,867
Emp.: 49
Fiscal Year-end: 12/31/22
Brass Bars, Coils & Other Metal Products Mfr
N.A.I.C.S.: 332999
Kim Maeng-Nyon *(Mng Dir)*

KUKJE PHARMA CO., LTD.
96-8 Yatap-ro, Bundang-Gu, Seongnam, Gyeonggi-Do, Korea (South)
Tel.: (82) 317819081
Web Site: https://www.kukjepharm.co.kr
Year Founded: 1959
002720—(KRS)
Rev.: $97,089,470
Assets: $104,766,726
Liabilities: $47,947,933
Net Worth: $56,818,792
Earnings: $2,728,475
Emp.: 377
Fiscal Year-end: 12/31/22
Pharmaceutical Preparation Mfr & Whslr
N.A.I.C.S.: 325412
Nam Taehoon *(CEO)*

Subsidiaries:

Hyorim Industries Inc. (1)
Sangwoo Building 2F 96-8 Yatap-ro, Bundang-gu, Seongnam, 13517, Gyeonggi, Korea (South)
Tel.: (82) 317816061
Water Treatment Equipment Mfr
N.A.I.C.S.: 312112
Nam Tae Hoon *(Co-CEO)*

Kukje Pharmaceutical Industrial Company Limited - Ansan Plant (1)
648 Choji-Dong, Ansan, Gyeonggi-Do, Korea (South)
Tel.: (82) 31 491 9411
Pharmaceuticals Product Mfr
N.A.I.C.S.: 325412

KUKJEON PHARMACEUTICAL CO., LTD.
1516 Geumgang Penterium It Tower 282 Hagui-Ro, Dongan-Gu, Anyang, Gyeonggi-do, Korea (South)
Tel.: (82) 234862246
Web Site: https://www.kukjeon.co.kr
Year Founded: 1995
307750—(KRS)
Rev.: $79,546,205
Assets: $150,406,693
Liabilities: $79,594,809
Net Worth: $70,811,884
Earnings: $6,808,771
Emp.: 114
Fiscal Year-end: 12/31/22
Pharmaceuticals Product Mfr
N.A.I.C.S.: 325412
Hong Jongho *(CEO)*

KULCZYK INVESTMENTS S.A.
65 boulevard Grande Duchesse Charlotte, L-1331, Luxembourg, Luxembourg
Tel.: (352) 26 449 1   LU
Web Site: http://www.kulczykinvestments.com
Year Founded: 2007
Investment Holding Company
N.A.I.C.S.: 551112
Sebastian Kulczyk *(Member-Mgmt Bd)*

Subsidiaries:

Avantor Performance Materials Poland S.A. (1)
Ul Sowinskiego 11, 44-101, Gliwice, Poland
Tel.: (48) 32 23 92 305
Web Site: http://www.english.poch.com.pl
Chemical Products Distr
N.A.I.C.S.: 424690
Dorota Panek *(Mgr-Quality Control-Dept)*

KI Chemistry SARL (1)
11 rue Aldringen, 1118, Luxembourg, Luxembourg
Tel.: (352) 27203020
Web Site: https://ki-chemistry.com
Investment Services
N.A.I.C.S.: 523999

Subsidiary (Non-US):

Qemetica S.A. (2)
ul Wspolna 62, 00-684, Warsaw, Poland   (95.45%)
Tel.: (48) 226391100
Web Site: https://qemetica.com
Rev.: $932,827,683
Assets: $1,926,584,530
Liabilities: $1,280,347,963
Net Worth: $646,236,567
Earnings: $78,838,817
Emp.: 3,000
Fiscal Year-end: 12/31/2021
Chemical Products Mfr
N.A.I.C.S.: 325199
Sebastian Kulczyk *(Chm-Supervisory Bd)*

Subsidiary (Domestic):

Agrochem Czluchow Sp. z.o.o. (3)
Mickiewicza 5, 77 300, Czluchow, Poland
Tel.: (48) 598345670
Web Site: http://www.agrochem.com.eu
Sales Range: $25-49.9 Million
Emp.: 80
Agro Chemicals Mfr & Distr
N.A.I.C.S.: 325320

Agrochem Dobre Miasto Sp. z.o.o. (3)
Ul Spichrzowa 13, 11-040, Dobre Miasto, Poland
Tel.: (48) 896151861
Web Site: http://www.agrochem.com.pl
Agro Chemicals Mfr & Distr
N.A.I.C.S.: 325320

Alwernia Fosforany Sp. z.o.o. (3)
Olszewskiego 25, Alwernia, 32566, Poland
Tel.: (48) 122589100
Web Site: http://www.alwernia.com
Sales Range: $125-149.9 Million
Emp.: 300
Chemicals Producer & Distr
N.A.I.C.S.: 325998
Agnieszka Lisowska *(Mgr-Sls)*

Subsidiary (Non-US):

CIECH Soda Romania S.A. (3)
Str Uzinei nr 2, Judetul Valcea, 240050, Ramnicu Valcea, Romania
Tel.: (40) 250731852
Chemical Product Mfr & Whslr
N.A.I.C.S.: 325998
Witold Urbanowski *(CEO)*

Subsidiary (Domestic):

CIECH Vitrosilicon S.A. (3)
Ul Zaganska 27, 68-120, Ilowa, Poland
Tel.: (48) 683600747
Chemical Products Mfr
N.A.I.C.S.: 325998
Zenon Kozak *(Pres)*

Chemia.Com S.A. (3)
182 Pulwaska St, 02 670, Warsaw, Poland
Tel.: (48) 226391196
Application Software Development Services
N.A.I.C.S.: 541511

Ciech Nieruchomosci S.A. (3)
Ul Wspolna 62, 00-684, Warsaw, Poland
Tel.: (48) 226391313
Real Estate Selling Services
N.A.I.C.S.: 531210
Tomasz Maciejczyk *(Chm)*

Ciech Pianki Sp. z o.o. (3)
Ul Wojska Polskiego 65, 85-825, Bydgoszcz, Poland
Tel.: (48) 523775541
Chemical Products Mfr
N.A.I.C.S.: 325998
Michal Budzynski *(Pres)*

Ciech R&D Sp. z o.o. (3)
Ul Wspolna 62, 00-684, Warsaw, Poland
Tel.: (48) 172407111
Chemical Products Distr
N.A.I.C.S.: 424690

KULCZYK INVESTMENTS S.A.

Kulczyk Investments S.A.—(Continued)

Ciech Sarzyna S.A. (3)
Ul Chemikow 1, 37-310, Nowa Sarzyna, Poland
Tel.: (48) 172407503
Chemical Products Mfr
N.A.I.C.S.: 325998

Ciech Service Sp. z.o.o. (3)
ul. Rakowiecka 41 Lok 15, 02 521, Warsaw, Poland
Tel.: (48) 224093617
Web Site: http://www.ciech-service.home.pl
Personal & Property Protection Services
N.A.I.C.S.: 561612

Ciech Serwis i Remonty Sp. z (3)
Ul Wspolna 62, 00-684, Warsaw, Poland
Tel.: (48) 665955087
Industrial Machinery Repair Services
N.A.I.C.S.: 811310
Agnieszka Galewska (Pres)

Ciech Soda Polska S.A. (3)
Ul Fabryczna 4, 88-101, Inowroclaw, Poland
Tel.: (48) 523541500
Emp.: 1,000
Chemical Product Mfr & Whslr
N.A.I.C.S.: 325998
Jaroslaw Ptaszynski (Pres)

Ciech Trading SA (3)
89 Bema Street, 01-233, Warsaw, Poland
Tel.: (48) 222105800
Web Site: http://www.ciechtrading.com
Sales Range: $25-49.9 Million
Emp.: 100
Chemicals Mfr & Distr
N.A.I.C.S.: 325998
Marzanna Baliszewska (Deputy Dir-Sls)

Subsidiary (Non-US):

Daltrade Ltd (3)
94 Haligate Howden, Goole, DN147SZ, East Yorkshire, United Kingdom
Tel.: (44) 1430430041
Web Site: http://www.daltrade.co.uk
Sales Range: $25-49.9 Million
Emp.: 15
Chemical Distr
N.A.I.C.S.: 424690

Subsidiary (Domestic):

GZNF Fosfory Sp z.o.o. (3)
2 Kujawska St, 80 550, Gdansk, Poland
Tel.: (48) 583438235
Web Site: http://fosfory.pl
Agricultural Chemical Product Mfr
N.A.I.C.S.: 325320

Gdanskie Zaklady Nawozow Fosforowych Fosfory Sp. z o.o. (3)
Ul Kujawska 2, 80-550, Gdansk, Poland
Tel.: (48) 583438271
Web Site: http://www.fosfory.pl
Fertilizer Mfr
N.A.I.C.S.: 325311

Subsidiary (Non-US):

Nordiska Unipol AB (3)
Arstaangsvagen 1C, PO Box 47040, S 10074, Stockholm, Sweden
Tel.: (46) 87445575
Web Site: http://www.nordiskaunipol.se
Sales Range: $50-74.9 Million
Emp.: 3
Polish Chemicals Distr
N.A.I.C.S.: 424690
Dariusz Januszewski (Mng Dir)

Polcommerce GmbH (3)
Billroth Str 2-4-44, Vienna, 1190, Austria
Tel.: (43) 14081511
Web Site: http://www.ciech.com
Sales Range: $25-49.9 Million
Emp.: 5
Chemicals Mfr & Distr
N.A.I.C.S.: 325998

Subsidiary (Domestic):

Polfa Sp. z o.o. (3)
69 Prosta St, 00 838, Warsaw, Poland
Tel.: (48) 224441166
Web Site: http://www.polfa.eu
Sales Range: $25-49.9 Million
Emp.: 40
Chemical Distr
N.A.I.C.S.: 424690

Subsidiary (Non-US):

Polsin Private Ltd (3)
20 Bendemeer Rd No 02-01, Cyberhub, Singapore, 339914, Singapore
Tel.: (65) 62238182
Web Site: http://www.polsin.com.sg
Sales Range: $25-49.9 Million
Emp.: 11
Chemicals Producer & Distr
N.A.I.C.S.: 325998

Subsidiary (Non-US):

Polsin Overseas Shipping Ltd (4)
Ul Armii Krajowej 116 16, 81-824, Sopot, Poland
Tel.: (48) 585552791
Web Site: http://www.polsin.com.pl
Sales Range: $25-49.9 Million
Sea Freight Forwarding Services
N.A.I.C.S.: 483111
Andrzej Smejlis (Chm)

Subsidiary (Non-US):

Proplan Plant Protection Company S.L. (3)
Calle Valle del Roncal 12 1 Planta Oficina 7, Las Rozas, Madrid, Spain
Tel.: (34) 916266097
Web Site: http://www.proplanppc.es
Pesticide Product Mfr
N.A.I.C.S.: 325320

S.C. Uzinele Sodice Govora Ciech Chemical Group S.A. (3)
Street Uzinei N 2 Judetul Valcea, 240007, Ramnicu Valcea, Romania (92.91%)
Tel.: (40) 250731852
Web Site: http://www.usg.ro
Emp.: 700
Chemicals Producer & Distr
N.A.I.C.S.: 424690
Artur Janusz Osuchowski (Pres)

SDC GmbH (3)
An der Loderburger Bahn 4a, 39418, Stassfurt, Germany
Tel.: (49) 3925263301
Chemical Product Mfr & Whslr
N.A.I.C.S.: 325998
Frank Pommerenke (Mng Dir)

Subsidiary (Domestic):

Soda Polska Ciech Sp. z.o.o. (3)
4 Fabryczna St, 88 101, Inowroclaw, Poland
Tel.: (48) 523541500
Web Site: http://www.sodapolska.pl
Sales Range: $200-249.9 Million
Emp.: 700
Chemicals Mfr
N.A.I.C.S.: 325998

Subsidiary (Non-US):

Sodawerk Stassfurt GmbH & Co. KG (3)
An der Loderburger Bahn 4a, 39418, Stassfurt, Germany
Tel.: (49) 39252630
Web Site: http://www.ciechgroup.com
Sales Range: $125-149.9 Million
Emp.: 420
Chemicals Producer & Distr
N.A.I.C.S.: 325998

Subsidiary (Domestic):

Transoda Sp. z.o.o. (3)
Ul Fabryczna 4, 88 101, Inowroclaw, Poland
Tel.: (48) 523541474
Web Site: http://www.transoda.com.pl
Railway Transportation Services
N.A.I.C.S.: 488210

Vitrosilicon S.A. (3)
27 Zaganska St, Ilowa, 68120, Poland
Tel.: (48) 683600747
Web Site: http://www.vitrosilicon.com.pl
Emp.: 350
Smelted Glass & Chemical Products Mfr
N.A.I.C.S.: 325998

ZCh Alwernia S.A. (3)
25 K Olszewskiego St, 32 566, Alwernia, Poland
Tel.: (48) 122589100
Web Site: http://www.alwernia.com.pl
Sales Range: $125-149.9 Million
Emp.: 300
Chemicals Producer & Distr
N.A.I.C.S.: 325998
Wieslaw Halucha (Pres & CEO)

ZCh Organika Sarzyna S.A. (3)
1 Chemikow st, Nowa Sarzyna, 37-310, Poland
Tel.: (48) 172407100
Web Site: http://www.zch.sarzyna.pl
Sales Range: $200-249.9 Million
Emp.: 700
Chemicals Producer & Distr
N.A.I.C.S.: 325998

Zachem UCR Sp. z.o.o. (3)
Ul Wojska Polskiego 65, 85 825, Bydgoszcz, Poland
Tel.: (48) 523747676
Web Site: http://www.zachemucr.com.pl
Sales Range: $75-99.9 Million
Emp.: 300
Organization Development Consulting Services
N.A.I.C.S.: 541612

Zaklady Chemiczne Zachem S.A. (3)
65 Wojska Polskiego St, 85 825, Bydgoszcz, Poland
Tel.: (48) 523747100
Web Site: http://www.zachem.com.pl
Chemicals Mfr
N.A.I.C.S.: 325998

Serinus Energy plc (1)
2nd Floor The Le Gallais Building 54 Bath Street, Saint Helier, JE1 1FW, Jersey (48.1%)
Tel.: (44) 4032648877
Web Site: http://www.serinusenergy.com
Rev: $49,280,000
Assets: $90,182,000
Liabilities: $53,382,000
Net Worth: $36,800,000
Earnings: $1,630,000
Fiscal Year-end: 12/31/2022
Gas & Oil Exploration Services
N.A.I.C.S.: 211120
Lukasz Redziniak (Chm)

KULICKE & SOFFA INDUSTRIES, INC.

23A Serangoon North Avenue 5 01-01, Singapore, 554369, Singapore
Tel.: (65) 2157846000 PA
Web Site: https://www.kns.com
Year Founded: 1951
KLIC—(NASDAQ)
Rev.: $742,491,000
Assets: $1,499,777,000
Liabilities: $325,216,000
Net Worth: $1,174,561,000
Earnings: $57,148,000
Emp.: 2,877
Fiscal Year-end: 09/30/23
Semiconductor Wire Bonding Assembly Equipment Mfr
N.A.I.C.S.: 333242
Lisa Lim (VP-Global HR)

Subsidiaries:

Kulicke & Soffa (1)
1225 Old Alpharetta Rd Ste 260, Alpharetta, GA 30005
Tel.: (770) 751-4420
Web Site: http://www.kns.com
Emp.: 40
Electronics Manufacturing Equipment Mfr
N.A.I.C.S.: 333242

Kulicke & Soffa (1)
Hooge Zijde 32, 5626 DC, Eindhoven, Netherlands
Tel.: (31) 402723000
Web Site: http://www.kns.com
Electronics Manufacturing Equipment Mfr
N.A.I.C.S.: 333242

Kulicke & Soffa (Asia) Limited (1)
Unit 1804 18/F Aitken Vanson Centre 61 Hoi Yuen Road, Kwun Tong, China (Hong Kong)
Tel.: (852) 2994 6277
Semiconductor Device Distr
N.A.I.C.S.: 423690

Kulicke & Soffa (Israel) Ltd. (1)
PO Box 90, Yokneam, 20692, Israel (100%)
Tel.: (972) 49939444
Sales Range: $75-99.9 Million
Emp.: 300
Semiconductor Mfr
N.A.I.C.S.: 334413
Hava Rosenberg (Mgr-Admin)

Kulicke & Soffa (Japan) Ltd. (1)
No 5 Kioke Building 1st Floor 1-3-12 Kita-Shinagawa, Shinagawa-Ku, Tokyo, 1400001, Japan (100%)
Tel.: (81) 357696100
Web Site: http://www.ksj.jp
Sales Range: $10-24.9 Million
Emp.: 15
Automatic Wire Bonders Mfr & Distr
N.A.I.C.S.: 334512
Takashi Tsujimura (Pres & Mng Dir)

Kulicke & Soffa (Malaysia) Sdn. Bhd. (1)
Unit 602-604 6th Floor Damansara Uptown 2, Petaling Jaya, Malaysia
Tel.: (60) 3 7718 6688
Semiconductor Equipment Mfr
N.A.I.C.S.: 334413

Kulicke & Soffa (Phils.) Inc. (1)
8th Floor Unit 8C Uninoil Center Condominium, 1222 Acacia Corner Commerce Avenue, Madrigal Bus Park Alabang, Muntinlupa, 1770, Philippines
Tel.: (63) 2 7710522
Semiconductor Equipment Mfr
N.A.I.C.S.: 334413

Kulicke & Soffa (Shanghai) International Trading Co., Ltd. (1)
Building No 6 No 34 Alley 122 Chun Xiao road, Zhang Jiang Hi-Tech Park, Shanghai, 201203, China
Tel.: (86) 21 5080 5400
Semiconductor Product Distr
N.A.I.C.S.: 334413

Kulicke & Soffa (Suzhou) Limited (1)
255 Su Hong Middle Road, Suzhou Industrial Park, Suzhou, 21521, China
Tel.: (86) 51262588588
Web Site: http://www.kands.com
Sales Range: $350-399.9 Million
Emp.: 1,000
Wire Bonding Equipment for the Semiconductor Assembly Market Supplier
N.A.I.C.S.: 335932

Kulicke & Soffa (Switzerland) Management GmbH (1)
Andhauserstrasse 52, 8572, Berg, Switzerland
Tel.: (41) 716376376
Semiconductor Product Distr
N.A.I.C.S.: 423690

Kulicke & Soffa (Thailand) Ltd. (1)
8F Na-nakorn Building 99/349 Chaengwattana Road, Laksi, Bangkok, 10210, Thailand
Tel.: (66) 2 5761559
Semiconductor Devices Mfr
N.A.I.C.S.: 334413

Kulicke & Soffa Asiapac Inc. (1)
5th Floor No 1 Shin Du Road, Chien Chen District, Kaohsiung, 806, Taiwan
Tel.: (886) 7 2200800
Web Site: http://www.kns.com
Emp.: 50
Semiconductor Equipment Mfr
N.A.I.C.S.: 334413

Kulicke & Soffa GmbH (1)
Andhausen 52, Berg, 8572, Thurgau, Switzerland
Tel.: (41) 716376363
Semiconductor Assembly Equipment Mfr
N.A.I.C.S.: 334413

Kulicke & Soffa Holding Company Pte. Ltd. (1)

AND PRIVATE COMPANIES

6 Serangoon North Avenue 5 Ste 03 16,
Singapore, 554910, Singapore
Tel.: (65) 68809600
Financial Investment Services
N.A.I.C.S.: 523999

Kulicke & Soffa Industries (1)
1821 E Dyer RD 200, Santa Ana, CA 92705
Tel.: (949) 660-0440
Web Site: http://www.kns.com
Ultrasonic Wire Bonder Mfr
N.A.I.C.S.: 334419

Kulicke & Soffa Industries Inc. (1)
1005 Virginia Dr, Fort Washington, PA 19034
Tel.: (215) 784-6000
Sales Range: $125-149.9 Million
Emp.: 300
Semiconductor Equipment Mfr
N.A.I.C.S.: 334413
Bruno Guilmart *(Pres & CEO)*

Kulicke & Soffa Korea Inc. (1)
6th Floor Hanmaum Building 4-4 Yangjae-dong, Seocho-ku, Seoul, Korea (South)
Tel.: (82) 59379535
Semiconductor Equipment Mfr
N.A.I.C.S.: 334413

Kulicke & Soffa Liteq B.V. (1)
Esp 314, 5633 AE, Eindhoven, Netherlands
Tel.: (31) 402723000
Semiconductor Product Mfr
N.A.I.C.S.: 334413

Kulicke & Soffa Orthodyne GmbH (1)
Lina-Ammon-Str 15, 90471, Nuremberg, Germany
Tel.: (49) 911 988 130
Web Site: http://www.kns.com
Semiconductor Equipment Mfr
N.A.I.C.S.: 334413

Kulicke & Soffa Technology (M) Sdn. Bhd. (1)
16 Jalan Tp 5 Taman Perindustrian Sime UEP, Subang Jaya, 47600, Selangor, Malaysia
Tel.: (60) 377186788
Semiconductor Devices Mfr
N.A.I.C.S.: 334413

Kulicke and Soffa Die Bonding GmbH (1)
Andhausen 52, Berg, 8572, Thurgau, Switzerland
Tel.: (41) 716376363
Web Site: http://www.kns.com
Emp.: 13
Semiconductor Devices Mfr
N.A.I.C.S.: 334413

Kulicke and Soffa Pte. Ltd. (1)
23A Serangoon North Avenue 5 Unit 01-01, Singapore, 554369, Singapore
Tel.: (65) 6880 9600
Sales Range: $100-124.9 Million
Emp.: 40
Semiconductor Devices Mfr
N.A.I.C.S.: 334413
Jeffrey Amtman *(Gen Mgr)*

Micro-Swiss Limited (1)
17 Hayetzira, Yoqne'am Illit, 2069010, Israel
Tel.: (972) 49939427
Web Site: http://www.micro-swiss.com
Sales Range: $25-49.9 Million
Emp.: 76
Semiconductor Devices Mfr
N.A.I.C.S.: 334413

Uniqarta, Inc. (1)
42 Trowbridge St Unit 1, Cambridge, MA 02138-4115
Tel.: (701) 491-7053
Web Site: http://www.uniqarta.com
Semiconductor & Related Device Mfr
N.A.I.C.S.: 334413
Doug Crane *(VP-Bus Dev)*

KULT TEKSTIL TURIZM YAYIN-CILIK A.S.
Tomtom Mah Nuri Ziya Sok No 15, Beyoglu, 34433, Istanbul, Turkiye
Tel.: (90) 2122930062   TR
Real Estate Development Services
N.A.I.C.S.: 531390

KULTHORN KIRBY PUBLIC CO., LTD.
126 Soi Chalong Krung 31 Chalong Krung Road, Khwaeng Lam Pla Thio Khet Lat Krabang, Bangkok, 10520, Thailand
Tel.: (66) 232608316
Web Site:
  https://compressor.kulthorn.com
Year Founded: 1980
KKC—(THA)
Rev.: $96,259,606
Assets: $149,356,236
Liabilities: $169,094,018
Net Worth: ($19,737,781)
Earnings: ($37,394,761)
Emp.: 901
Fiscal Year-end: 12/31/23
Hermetic Compressors Mfr
N.A.I.C.S.: 333912
Sutee Simakulthorn *(Pres)*

Subsidiaries:

Kulthorn Kirby Foundry Company Limited (1)
Number 1 Village No 22 Suwinthawong Road, Saladaeng Sub-District Bang Nam Priao District, Chachoengsao, 24000, Thailand
Tel.: (66) 385930169
Cast Iron Parts Mfr
N.A.I.C.S.: 331511

Kulthorn Premier Company Limited (1)
No 446/3 Moo 9, Nongki Subdistrict Kabinburi District, Prachin Buri, 25110, Thailand
Tel.: (66) 3720483541
Emp.: 439
Cast Iron Parts Mfr
N.A.I.C.S.: 331511

Kulthorn Research & Development Company Limited (1)
No 126 Soi Chalong Krung 31 Chalong Krung Road, Lam Platew Subdistrict Lat Krabang District, Bangkok, 10520, Thailand
Tel.: (66) 232608316
Motor Compressor Mfr
N.A.I.C.S.: 333618

Kulthorn Steel Company Limited (1)
No 124 Soi Chalong Krung 31 Chalong Krung Road, Lam Platew Subdistrict Lat Krabang District, Bangkok, 10520, Thailand
Tel.: (66) 23260851
Sheet Metal Products Mfr
N.A.I.C.S.: 332322

Suzhou Kulthorn Magnet Wire Company Limited (1)
18 Long Pu Road, Sip, Suzhou, 215126, Jiangsu, China
Tel.: (86) 5126 283 3750
Web Site: https://www.pdmagnetwire.cn
Magnet Wire Product Mfr & Distr
N.A.I.C.S.: 332999

KUM GMBH & CO KG
Essenbacher Str 2, 91054, Erlangen, Germany
Tel.: (49) 913182680
Web Site: http://www.kum.net
Year Founded: 1919
Rev.: $13,035,330
Emp.: 65
Stationery Product Mfr
N.A.I.C.S.: 322230
Fritz Luttgens *(Owner)*

KUMAGAI GUMI CO., LTD.
2-1 Tsukudo-cho, Shinjuku-ku, Tokyo, 162-8557, Japan
Tel.: (81) 332602111
Web Site:
  https://www.kumagaigumi.co.jp
1861—(TKS)
Rev.: $2,929,505,730
Assets: $3,088,403,520
Liabilities: $1,898,510,980
Net Worth: $1,189,892,540
Earnings: $54,968,760
Emp.: 2,635
Fiscal Year-end: 03/31/24
Engineering, Architecture & General Construction; Design, Manufacture & Sale of Construction Machinery & Equipment; Construction-Related Consulting Services
N.A.I.C.S.: 236210
Yasunori Sakurano *(Pres)*

Subsidiaries:

FATEC CO.,LTD. (1)
165 8 LG Palace Building Donggyo-dong, Mapo-gu, Seoul, 121-754, Korea (South)
Tel.: (82) 2 3141 2152
Web Site: http://www.fatec.co.kr
Sales Range: $25-49.9 Million
Emp.: 10
Construction Engineering Services
N.A.I.C.S.: 541330
Kyung Chun Shien *(Gen Mgr)*

FATEC Co., Ltd. (1)
2-1 Tsukudo-cho, Shinjuku-ku, Tokyo, 162-8557, Japan
Tel.: (81) 332356268
Web Site: https://www.fa-tec.co.jp
Construction Materials Distr
N.A.I.C.S.: 423320

GAEART TK Co. Ltd. (1)
2-1 Tsukudo cho, Shinjuku-Ku, Tokyo, 162-8557, Japan
Web Site: http://www.kumagaigumi.co.jp
Sales Range: $25-49.9 Million
Emp.: 70
Construction & Pavement of Roads & Airports & Other Civil Engineering & Architecture Work
N.A.I.C.S.: 237310
Yasushi Higuchi *(Pres)*

Gaeart Co., Ltd. (1)
8-27 Shinogawamachi, Shinjuku-ku, Tokyo, 162-0814, Japan
Tel.: (81) 352619211
Road Construction Services
N.A.I.C.S.: 237310

K&E Co., Ltd. (1)
2-7-2 Fujimi Stage Building 15th floor, Chiyoda-ku, Tokyo, 102-0071, Japan
Tel.: (81) 335122211
Web Site: http://www.k-and-e.co.jp
Emp.: 380
Building Renovation Services
N.A.I.C.S.: 236118

K&E Co.,Ltd. (1)
Suite 1502 15 F Silvercord Tower II 30 Canton Road Tsim Sha Tsui, Kowloon, China (Hong Kong)
Tel.: (852) 2317 7883
Web Site: http://www.kne.com.hk
Textile Machinery Equipments Mfr
N.A.I.C.S.: 333248

Kumagai Gumi Co., Ltd. (1)
Unit A 11/F MG Tower 133 Hoi Bun Road Kwun Tong, 625 King's Road, Kowloon, China (Hong Kong)
Tel.: (852) 22030888
Provider of Real Estate & Financing Services
N.A.I.C.S.: 531210
Ichinose Katsumi *(Gen Mgr)*

Saitama Chiiki Kaihatsu Kohsha Co., Ltd. (1)
Konan, Saitama, Japan
Golf Course Operations
N.A.I.C.S.: 713910

Summa Kumagai, Inc. (1)
17 Fl Philamlife Tower 8767 Paseo De Roxas Ave, Legaspi Village, Makati, Philippines
Tel.: (63) 27283503
Web Site: http://www.skiconstructions.com
Sales Range: $25-49.9 Million
Emp.: 100
Construction Business
N.A.I.C.S.: 813910

Taiwan Kumagai Co., Ltd. (1)
10690 12th Floor No 205 Section 1 Dunhua South Road Room 1408, Da an District, Taipei, Taiwan
Tel.: (886) 227210427
Web Site: http://www.taiwankumagai.com.tw
Sales Range: $25-49.9 Million
Emp.: 100
Construction Business
N.A.I.C.S.: 236220

Technical Support Co.,Ltd. (1)
2-1 Tsukudocho-cho Kumagai Gumi, Shinjuku-ku, Tokyo, 162-8557, Japan
Tel.: (81) 332358131
Civil Engineering Services
N.A.I.C.S.: 237990

Techno-Space Creates Co.,Ltd. (1)
3-12-12 Higashiikebukuro Showa Bldg 9 F, Toshima-ku, Tokyo, 170-0013, Japan
Tel.: (81) 359601070
Construction Engineering Services
N.A.I.C.S.: 541330

Technos Co., Ltd. (1)
Bldg 4th Floor 1-32 Yamanouekita-machi, Hirakata-City, Osaka, 573-0049, Aichi, Japan   (100%)
Tel.: (81) 728040560
Web Site: http://www.technos24.co.jp
Sales Range: $50-74.9 Million
Emp.: 120
Construction Machinery & Materials Mfr
N.A.I.C.S.: 333120
Katsuya Abuku *(Chm)*

KUMAR WIRE CLOTH MANUFACTURING COMPANY LIMITED
29 - A Dr Atmaram Rangnekar Marg Above Brij Mandal Hall, Girgaum Chowpatty, Mumbai, 400007, India
Tel.: (91) 22 6655300
Web Site:
  http://www.kumarwirecloth.com
Rev.: $41,203
Assets: $78,127
Liabilities: $388,455
Net Worth: ($310,329)
Earnings: ($29,533)
Fiscal Year-end: 03/31/18
Wire Product Mfr
N.A.I.C.S.: 332618

KUMARI BANK LIMITED
Tangal, Kathmandu, Nepal
Tel.: (977) 14443077   NP
Web Site:
  https://www.kumaribank.com
Year Founded: 2001
KBL—(NEP)
Rev.: $89,062,570
Assets: $1,290,633,743
Liabilities: $1,144,219,148
Net Worth: $146,414,595
Earnings: $10,019,342
Emp.: 1,781
Fiscal Year-end: 07/15/20
Investment Banking Services
N.A.I.C.S.: 523150
Niraj Rai *(Head-Credit Risk Mgmt)*

Subsidiaries:

Kasthamandap Development Bank Limited (1)
Pako New Road, PO Box 11844, Kathmandu, Nepal
Tel.: (977) 14258400
Web Site: http://www.kdbl.com.np
Banking Services
N.A.I.C.S.: 522110
Jagannath Gyawali *(Chm)*

KUMBI CO., LTD.
25 Muchon-ri, Bubal-eup, Icheon, Gyeonggi-do, Korea (South)
Tel.: (82) 316325280   KR
Web Site: https://www.kumbi.co.kr
Year Founded: 1973
008870—(KRS)
Rev.: $210,294,680
Assets: $310,843,125
Liabilities: $161,922,154
Net Worth: $148,920,971

KUMBI CO., LTD.

Kumbi Co., Ltd.—(Continued)
Earnings: $3,400,168
Emp.: 249
Fiscal Year-end: 09/30/21
Glass Bottle Mfr & Whslr
N.A.I.C.S.: 327213
Byeong Heon Goh *(Chm)*

Subsidiaries:

Samhwa Crown & Closure Co., Ltd. (1)
140 Gangcheon-ro, Danwon-gu, Ansan, Gyeonggi-do, Korea (South)
Tel.: (82) 314908400
Web Site: https://www.samhwacrown.com
Rev.: $118,461,498
Assets: $170,874,988
Liabilities: $79,056,816
Net Worth: $91,818,172
Earnings: ($13,207,080)
Emp.: 215
Fiscal Year-end: 12/31/2022
Bottle Cap Mfr & Whslr
N.A.I.C.S.: 332119
Byung Hyun Ko *(CEO)*

Shinwoo Co., Ltd. (1)
47 Malgennae 1-gil, Uiwang, Gyeonggi-do, Korea (South)
Tel.: (82) 3142321716
Web Site: https://www.shinwookorea.com
Custom Molded Container Mfr
N.A.I.C.S.: 326160

KUMHO ASIANA GROUP
Kumho Asiana Main Tower 115 1-ga Shinmun-no, Jongro-gu, Seoul, 110-857, Korea (South)
Tel.: (82) 263030114
Web Site:
    http://www.kumhoasiana.com
Sales Range: $15-24.9 Billion
Holding Company
N.A.I.C.S.: 551112
Sam-Koo Park *(Chm)*

Subsidiaries:

Air Busan Inc. (1)
N Chamber In Commerce Industry 24 Hwanryeong Daero, Busanjin-Gu, Busan, Korea (South)
Tel.: (82) 51 410 0800
Web Site: http://www.airbusan.com
Oil Transportation Services
N.A.I.C.S.: 481219

Asiana Abacus Inc. (1)
25th Floor Kumho Asian Main Tower 76 Saemunanro, Jongrogu, Seoul, 110857, Korea (South)
Tel.: (82) 2 2127 8900
Web Site: http://www.abacus.co.kr
Emp.: 40
Transportation Arrangement Services
N.A.I.C.S.: 488510
Se-chang Park *(CEO)*

Asiana Airport Inc. (1)
1373 KonghangDong, Kangsseo-Gu, Seoul, Korea (South)
Tel.: (82) 2 2669 8500
Web Site: http://www.asianaairport.com
Emp.: 1,800
Ramp Handling Services
N.A.I.C.S.: 488190

Asiana Development Co Ltd (1)
Incheon International Airport Cargo Terminal B, Unseodong Junggu, Incheon, Korea (South)
Tel.: (82) 32 744 5600
Oil Transportation Services
N.A.I.C.S.: 488190

Kumho Asiana Cultural Foundation Co., Ltd. (1)
3rd Floor 75 Saemuninro Jongrogu, Seoul, Korea (South)
Tel.: (82) 2 6303 7700
Web Site: http://www.kacf.net
Classical Music & Art Support Services
N.A.I.C.S.: 926110

Kumho Petro Chemical Co., Ltd. (1)
East Wing 10-14 Floor Signature Towers 100 Cheonggyecheon-ro, Jung-gu, Seoul, Korea (South)
Tel.: (82) 269611114
Web Site: http://www.kkpc.com
Rev.: $6,117,305,127
Assets: $5,920,681,796
Liabilities: $1,584,512,354
Net Worth: $4,336,169,441
Earnings: $786,518,855
Emp.: 1,453
Fiscal Year-end: 12/31/2022
Synthetic Rubber & Resins Mfr; Heat & Power Plants; Rubber Chemicals & Electronic Materials Mfr
N.A.I.C.S.: 325110
Chan-Koo Park *(Chm & Co-CEO)*

Joint Venture (Domestic):

Kumho Mitsui Chemicals, Inc. (2)
Floor 11th East Bldg Signature Tower 100 Cheonggyecheon-ro, Joong-gu, Seoul, Korea (South)
Tel.: (82) 269613750
Web Site: https://www.kmci.co.kr
Emp.: 248
MDI Mfr & Sales
N.A.I.C.S.: 325998

Affiliate (Domestic):

Kumho P&B Chemicals, Inc. (2)
8F Signature Towers 100 Cheonggyecheon-ro, Jung-gu, Seoul, Korea (South)
Tel.: (82) 2 6961 1114
Web Site: http://www.kpb.co.kr
Petrochemical Based Basic Compounds Mfr
N.A.I.C.S.: 325110
Shin Woo-sung *(CEO)*

Subsidiary (Domestic):

Kumho Resort Inc. (3)
8th Floor Kumho Asiana Main Tower 76 Saemunan-Ro, Jongro-Gu, Seoul, Korea (South)
Tel.: (82) 2 6306 0114
Web Site: http://www.kumhoresort.co.kr
Travel Tour Operator
N.A.I.C.S.: 561520

Joint Venture (Domestic):

Kumho Polychem Co., Ltd. (2)
8F East Wing Signature Tower 100 Cheonggyecheon-ro, Jung-gu, Seoul, Korea (South) (50%)
Tel.: (82) 269613750
Web Site: https://www.polychem.co.kr
Emp.: 226
Rubber Production & Sales
N.A.I.C.S.: 325212
Sungyu Kim *(CEO)*

Kumho Tire Co., Inc. (1)
555 Sochon-Dong, Gwangsan-Gu, Gwangju, 506-711, Korea (South)
Tel.: (82) 263038114
Web Site: http://www.kumhotire.com
Rev.: $2,729,874,540
Assets: $3,601,053,804
Liabilities: $2,646,479,651
Net Worth: $954,574,154
Earnings: ($59,419,272)
Emp.: 5,521
Fiscal Year-end: 12/31/2022
Tiles Mfr
N.A.I.C.S.: 326211
Jeon Dae-jin *(Pres & CEO)*

Subsidiary (Non-US):

Kumho Tire Canada Inc. (2)
Unit B 6430 Kennedy Rd, Mississauga, L5T 2Z5, ON, Canada
Tel.: (905) 564-0882
Web Site: http://www.kumhotire.ca
Rev.: $55,696,998
Emp.: 10
Tire & Tube Whslr
N.A.I.C.S.: 423130

Subsidiary (US):

Kumho Tire U.S.A., Inc. (2)
133 Peachtree St NE Ste 2800, Atlanta, GA 30303
Web Site: http://www.kumhousa.com
Tire & Tube Mfr & Whslr
N.A.I.C.S.: 326211

Brian Buckham *(Mng Dir-Kumho America Technical Center)*

KUMHO BUSLINES CO., LTD.
904 Kyeongbu Line Terminal 194 Shin Bhanporo, Seocho-gu, Seoul, Korea (South)
Tel.: (82) 2 530 6114
Web Site:
    http://www.kumhobuslines.co.kr
Year Founded: 1946
Bus Transportation Services
N.A.I.C.S.: 485510

KUMHO ELECTRIC, INC.
14th Floor Three IFC Building 10 Gukjegeumyung-ro, Yeongdeungpo-gu, Seoul, Korea (South)
Tel.: (82) 15662718
Web Site: https://www.khe.co.kr
Year Founded: 1935
001210—(KRS)
Rev.: $35,293,576
Assets: $47,411,502
Liabilities: $37,563,736
Net Worth: $9,847,766
Earnings: ($12,719,186)
Emp.: 94
Fiscal Year-end: 12/31/22
Electric Appliance Mfr & Whslr
N.A.I.C.S.: 335139
Lee Hong-Min *(CEO)*

Subsidiaries:

Vivozon Pharmaceutical Co., Ltd. (1)
64-1 Bongmu-Ri Namsa-Myun, Cheoin-Gu, Yongin, Gyunggi-Do, Korea (South)
Tel.: (82) 312139200
Web Site: http://www.lumimicro.com
Rev.: $45,304,603
Assets: $143,486,057
Liabilities: $62,308,599
Net Worth: $81,177,458
Earnings: ($30,092,100)
Emp.: 43
Fiscal Year-end: 12/31/2022
Light Emitting Diode Mfr
N.A.I.C.S.: 334413

KUMHO ENGINEERING & CONSTRUCTION CO., LTD.
Centropolis Building A 26 Ujeonggu-ro, Jongno-gu, Seoul, Korea (South)
Tel.: (82) 263030102
Web Site:
    https://www.kumhoenc.com
Year Founded: 1967
002990—(KRS)
Rev.: $1,571,205,003
Assets: $1,297,122,564
Liabilities: $880,383,002
Net Worth: $416,739,562
Earnings: $15,916,488
Emp.: 1,241
Fiscal Year-end: 12/31/22
Residential & Commercial Engineering & Construction Services
N.A.I.C.S.: 236115
Cho Wan-Seok *(CEO)*

KUMHO HT, INC.
717 Young-ro, Gwangsan-gu, Gwangju, 62214, Korea (South)
Tel.: (82) 629582700
Web Site: https://kumhoht.com
214330—(KRS)
Electric Lighting Fixture Mfr
N.A.I.C.S.: 335132

Subsidiaries:

DiNonA, Inc. (1)
11F 88 Olympic-ro 43-gil, Songpa-gu, Seoul, Korea (South)
Tel.: (82) 25780810
Web Site: http://www.dinonainc.com
Biotechnology Research & Development Services
N.A.I.C.S.: 541714

Hyung-Geun Song *(CEO)*

KUMIAI CHEMICAL INDUSTRY CO., LTD.
4-26 Ikenohata 1-chome, Taito-Ku, Tokyo, 110-8782, Japan
Tel.: (81) 338225036   JP
Web Site: https://www.kumiai-chem.co.jp
Year Founded: 1949
4996—(TKS)
Rev.: $1,141,504,180
Assets: $1,608,997,510
Liabilities: $617,496,460
Net Worth: $991,501,050
Earnings: $127,790,160
Emp.: 2,124
Fiscal Year-end: 10/31/23
Pesticide & Other Agricultural Chemical Mfr & Distr
N.A.I.C.S.: 325320
Yoshitomo Koike *(Pres)*

Subsidiaries:

Asada Shoji Co., Ltd. (1)
7th Floor of Honda Building 1-17-10 Misuji, Taito-ku, Tokyo, 111-0055, Japan
Tel.: (81) 35 833 3381
Web Site: https://www.asada-shoji.co.jp
Emp.: 17
Fertilizer Mfr
N.A.I.C.S.: 325314

Ihara Nikkei Chemical Industry Co., Ltd. (1)
5700-1 Kambara, Shimizu-ku, Shizuoka, 421-3203, Japan
Tel.: (81) 54 388 2561
Web Site: https://www.iharanikkei.net
Emp.: 142
Agricultural Chemical Mfr
N.A.I.C.S.: 325320
Satoshi Yamanashi *(Pres & Mng Dir)*

Iharabras S.A. Industrias Quimicas (1)
Av Liberdade 1701, Cajuru do Sul, Sorocaba, 18087-170, Sau Paulo, Brazil
Tel.: (55) 1532357700
Web Site: https://www.ihara.com.br
Sales Range: $250-299.9 Million
Emp.: 600
Pesticide & Agricultural Chemical Mfr
N.A.I.C.S.: 325320

K-I Chemical Industry Co., Ltd. (1)
328 Shioshinden, Iwata, 437-1213, Shizuoka-ken, Japan
Tel.: (81) 53 858 1000
Web Site: https://www.ki-chemical.co.jp
Emp.: 158
Chemical Product Research & Development; Owned 50% by Ihara Chemical Industry Co., Ltd. & 50% by Kumiai Chemical Industry Co., Ltd.
N.A.I.C.S.: 541715
Kenji Itoh *(Mng Dir)*

K-I Chemical U.S.A. Inc. (1)
5425 Page Rd Ste 160, Durham, NC 27703
Tel.: (914) 682-8934
Sales Range: $50-74.9 Million
Emp.: 10
Chemical Distr
N.A.I.C.S.: 424690
Takuro Shinohara *(Pres)*

K-I Chemical do Brasil Ltda. (1)
Edificio Faria Lima Premium Rua Diogo Moreira 132 Conj 1905/1906, Pinheiros, Sao Paulo, 05423-010, SP, Brazil
Tel.: (55) 1138162850
Chemical Distr
N.A.I.C.S.: 424690

Kumika Logistics Co., Ltd. (1)
100 Shibukawa, Shimizu-ku, Shizuoka, 424-0053, Japan
Tel.: (81) 54 345 3696
Web Site: https://www.kumika-br.co.jp
Emp.: 170
Logistic Services
N.A.I.C.S.: 541614

Onomichi Kumika Industry Co., Ltd. (1)

2-160 Chojabara, Onomichi, 722-0221, Hiroshima, Japan
Tel.: (81) 84 848 1213
Web Site: https://www.onokumi.co.jp
Emp.: 50
Chemical Products Mfr
N.A.I.C.S.: 325998

RIKENGREEN CO., LTD. (1)
Higashi Ueno 4-8-9, Taito-Ku, Tokyo, 110-8520, Japan (36.67%)
Tel.: (81) 3 68028301
Web Site: http://www.rikengreen.co.jp
Sales Range: $1-9.9 Million
Emp.: 142
Industrial Chemical & Drug Mfr
N.A.I.C.S.: 325320

T.J.C. Chemical Co., Ltd. (1)
56/19-20 Bisco Tower 15Fl Sap Road Si Phraya, Bang Rak, Bangkok, 10500, Thailand
Tel.: (66) 2 235 2513
Web Site: https://tjcchemical.com
Sales Range: $25-49.9 Million
Emp.: 25
Basic Inorganic Chemical Mfr
N.A.I.C.S.: 325180

KUMKANG KIND
60 Gwacheon-daero 7da-gil Gwacheon-si, Gyeonggi-do, Seoul, Korea (South)
Tel.: (82) 234154167
Web Site:
 https://www.kumkangkind.com
Year Founded: 1979
014280—(KRS)
Rev.: $559,090,843
Assets: $839,712,977
Liabilities: $495,932,601
Net Worth: $343,780,376
Earnings: $40,942,204
Emp.: 380
Fiscal Year-end: 12/31/22
Construction Materials Mfr & Whslr
N.A.I.C.S.: 331210
Jang Yeol Jeon (CEO)

Subsidiaries:

Dong Suh Chemical Co., Ltd. (1)
403 Cheolgang-ro, Nam-gu, Pohang, Gyeongsangbuk-do, Korea (South)
Tel.: (82) 542788631
Web Site: https://www.idongsuh.com
Coal Tar Mfr & Distr
N.A.I.C.S.: 325194

Dong-Suh Chemical Ind. Co., Ltd. (1)
403 Cheolgang-ro, Nam-gu, Pohang, Gyeongsangbuk-do, Korea (South)
Tel.: (82) 542788631
Web Site: https://www.idongsuh.com
Chemical Products Mfr
N.A.I.C.S.: 325998

Kumkang America, Inc. (1)
1215 W Imperial Hwy Ste 216, Brea, CA 92812
Tel.: (714) 278-9089
Steel Pipe Distr
N.A.I.C.S.: 423510

Kumkang Kind (M) Sdn. Bhd. (1)
B-9-01 Block B Oasis Square No 2 Jalan PJU 1A/7A, Ara Damansara, 47301, Petaling Jaya, Selangor, Malaysia
Tel.: (60) 378310488
Building Materials Distr
N.A.I.C.S.: 423390

Kumkang Kind - Changnyeong Factory (1)
149-16 Gwanggyemaeul-gil Gyeseong-myeon, Changnyeong, Korea (South)
Tel.: (82) 556089200
Web Site: https://www.kumkangkind.com
Scaffolding Product Mfr
N.A.I.C.S.: 332323

Kumkang Kind - Eonyang Factory (1)
140-25 Gachon-ri Samanam-myun Uljoogun, Ulsan, Korea (South)
Tel.: (82) 522555300

Steel Pole Mfr
N.A.I.C.S.: 331210

Kumkang Kind - Eumseong 1 Factory (1)
369-804 Yongsan-ri, Eumseong, Eumseong-gun, Korea (South)
Tel.: (82) 438715212
Aluminum Panel Mfr
N.A.I.C.S.: 331315

Kumkang Kind - Eumseong 2 Factory (1)
369-843 Osaeng-ri Saenggeuk-myeon, Eumseong, Chungcheongbuk-do, Korea (South)
Tel.: (82) 438789903
Aluminium Products Mfr
N.A.I.C.S.: 331315

Kumkang Kind - Jincheon 1 Factory (1)
48-1 Nowon-ri Iwol-myun, Jincheon, Chungcheongbuk-do, Korea (South)
Tel.: (82) 435377411
Aluminium Products Mfr
N.A.I.C.S.: 331315

Kumkang Kind - Jincheon 2 Factory (1)
56-4 Mijam-ri Iwol-myeon, Jincheon, Chungcheongbuk-do, Korea (South)
Tel.: (82) 435375560
Aluminium Products Mfr
N.A.I.C.S.: 331315

Kumkang Kind - Modular Factory (1)
345 Daehwa-ri Seongnam-myeon Dognam-gu, Cheonan, Chungcheongbuk-do, Korea (South)
Tel.: (82) 415963511
Modular Building System Design & Installation Services
N.A.I.C.S.: 332311

Kumkang Kind East Africa Limited (1)
Office 5 4th Floor Tower 1 The Mirage Chiromo Rd, Westlands, Nairobi, Kenya
Tel.: (254) 202500882
Steel Pipe Distr
N.A.I.C.S.: 423510

Kumkang Kind India Private Limited (1)
Office no 404 4th floor Sky Vista BLDG, near Town Square Dorabjee Viman Nagar, Pune, 411 014, Maharashtra, India
Tel.: (91) 2066473800
Steel Pipe Distr
N.A.I.C.S.: 423510
Vikas Pandya (Engr-Design)

Kumkang Kind Vietnam Co., Ltd. (1)
9th Beautiful Saigon BLDG 02 Nguyen Khac Vien St, District 7, Ho Chi Minh City, Vietnam
Tel.: (84) 854136508
Steel Pipe Distr
N.A.I.C.S.: 423510

PT Kumkang Kind Indonesia (1)
Gedung Wisma Slipi Unit 801 Jl Let Jend S Parman Kav 12, Jakarta, Indonesia
Tel.: (62) 81297815600
Steel Pipe Distr
N.A.I.C.S.: 423510

KUMMEL FAHRZEUGTEILE GMBH & CO. KG
An der Muhle 6, 99994, Schlotheim, Germany
Tel.: (49) 360219160
Web Site: http://www.kuemmel-fahrzeugteile.de
Year Founded: 1925
Rev.: $19,932,330
Emp.: 107
Automotive Interior Design Services
N.A.I.C.S.: 811121
Joachim Kummel (CEO)

KUMO HI-TECH CO., LTD.
Eunhyeon myeon Peace Road 1889, Yangju, 130-38, Gyeonggi-do, Korea (South)
Tel.: (82) 31 861 5300

Web Site: http://www.kos.co.kr
Year Founded: 2002
Plastic Door & Frame Mfr
N.A.I.C.S.: 326199
Kang-Yeom Lee (CEO)

KUMPULAN DARUL EHSAN BERHAD
11th Floor Bangunan Affin Bank Shah Alam Lot Presint 3 4, Persiaran Perbandaran Seksyen 14, 40000, Shah Alam, Selangor Darul Ehsan, Malaysia
Tel.: (60) 355114344   MY
Web Site: http://www.kdeb.com
Year Founded: 1985
Emp.: 120
Investment Holding Company Services
N.A.I.C.S.: 551112
Suhaimi Kamaralzaman (Pres)

Subsidiaries:

Central Spectrum (M) Sdn Bhd (1)
No 7 Jalan Perigi Nanas 8/6 Indah Point, Pulau Indah, 42920, Port Klang, Selangor, Malaysia
Tel.: (60) 331012020
Web Site: http://www.pulauindah.com.my
Property Development Services
N.A.I.C.S.: 236116
Mahmud Abbas (CEO)

Hebat Abadi Sdn Bhd (1)
Lot 18 Level 1A Plaza Perangsang, Persiaran Perbandaran, 40000, Shah Alam, Malaysia
Tel.: (60) 355113488
Waste Water Treatment Services
N.A.I.C.S.: 221320
Ramli Mohd Tahir (Gen Mgr)

Kumpulan Hartanah Selangor Berhad (1)
Lot 1A Level 1A Plaza Perangsang Persiaran Perbandaran, PO Box 7180, Shah Alam, 40000, Selangor Darul Ehsan, Malaysia (56.57%)
Tel.: (60) 355223888
Web Site: http://www.khsb.com.my
Sales Range: $10-24.9 Million
Property Management Services
N.A.I.C.S.: 531311
Taseandran Rasiah (Gen Mgr-Project)

Kumpulan Perangsang Selangor Berhad (1)
17th Floor Plaza Perangsang Persiaran Perbandaran, 40000, Shah Alam, Selangor Darul Ehsan, Malaysia (61%)
Tel.: (60) 355248400
Web Site: https://kps.com.my
Rev.: $227,713,323
Assets: $460,175,449
Liabilities: $196,246,410
Net Worth: $263,929,040
Earnings: $294,297
Emp.: 3,404
Fiscal Year-end: 12/31/2023
Property Development & Management Services
N.A.I.C.S.: 531311
Ahmad Fariz Hassan (CEO-Grp & Mng Dir)

Subsidiary (Domestic):

Aqua-Flo Sdn. Bhd. (2)
827 8 Floor Block A Damansara Intan No 1 Jalan SS 20/27, 47400, Petaling Jaya, Selangor, Malaysia (51%)
Tel.: (60) 377257278
Chemical Products Distr
N.A.I.C.S.: 424690
Tan Chee Kit (Gen Mgr)

Century Bond Bhd. (2)
PLO 96 97 98 & 99 Jalan Cyber 5, Senai Industrial Estate Phase III, 81400, Senai, Johor, Malaysia
Tel.: (60) 7 598 1185
Web Site: www.centurybond.com
Industrial Packaging Tapes Mfr
N.A.I.C.S.: 322220

Hydrovest Sdn Bhd (2)
Tingkat 15 Plaza Perangsang, Persiaran Perbandaran, 40000, Shah Alam, Selangor, Malaysia
Tel.: (60) 3 55138284
Waste Water Treatment Services
N.A.I.C.S.: 221320

KUMPULAN FIMA BERHAD
Suite 4 1 Level 4 Block C Plaza Damansara No 45 Jalan Medan Setia, 1 Bukit Damansara, 50490, Kuala Lumpur, Malaysia
Tel.: (60) 320921211
Web Site: https://www.fima.com.my
KFIMA—(KLS)
Rev.: $150,210,794
Assets: $342,824,762
Liabilities: $95,555,132
Net Worth: $247,269,630
Earnings: $16,325,714
Emp.: 3,178
Fiscal Year-end: 03/31/23
Commercial Properties & Rental Management Services
N.A.I.C.S.: 531120
Jasmin Hood (Co-Sec & Sr Gen Mgr-Grp Secretarial & Legal)

Subsidiaries:

Fima Bulking Services Berhad (1)
Jalan Parang 2nd Extension North Port, 42000, Port Klang, Selangor, Malaysia
Tel.: (60) 331767211
Liquid Bulking Storage Services
N.A.I.C.S.: 424710

Fima Instanco Sdn. Bhd. (1)
1st Floor Main Building Lot 6 Jalan P/1A Seksyen 13, 43650, Bandar Baru Bangi, Selangor, Malaysia
Tel.: (60) 389275650
Fish Product Distr
N.A.I.C.S.: 445250

International Food Corporation Limited (1)
Suite 4 1 Level 4 Block C Plaza Damansara No 45 Jalan Medan Setia 1, Bukit Damansara, 50490, Kuala Lumpur, Malaysia
Tel.: (60) 320921211
Web Site: http://www.ifc.com.pg
Fish Product Distr
N.A.I.C.S.: 445250

Percetakan Keselamatan Nasional Sdn. Bhd. (1)
No 1 Jalan Chan Sow Lin, 55200, Kuala Lumpur, Malaysia
Tel.: (60) 392222511
Mechanical & Electrical Services
N.A.I.C.S.: 811114

KUMPULAN H & L HIGH-TECH BERHAD
No 6 Jalan TSB 1 Taman Industri Sungai Buloh, 47000, Sungai Buloh, Selangor, Malaysia
Tel.: (60) 361576339
Web Site:
 https://www.hlhightech.com
Year Founded: 1976
HIGHTEC—(KLS)
Rev.: $5,930,069
Assets: $37,625,698
Liabilities: $8,103,271
Net Worth: $29,522,427
Earnings: $2,217,554
Emp.: 149
Fiscal Year-end: 10/31/23
Precision Engineering Molds Mfr & Sales
N.A.I.C.S.: 331511
Sook Yee Tan (Exec Dir)

Subsidiaries:

H & L High-Tech Mould (Thailand) Co., Ltd. (1)
341/1 Moo 2 Tambol Klongjig Amphur, Bangpa-In Industrial Estate Bangpa-In, Ayutthaya, Thailand
Tel.: (66) 35258641
Plastic Injection Molding Products Mfr

KUMPULAN H & L HIGH-TECH BERHAD

Kumpulan H & L High-Tech Berhad—(Continued)
N.A.I.C.S.: 333511

Plastik STC Sdn Bhd (1)
No 7 Jalan TSB 9, Taman Industri Sungai Buloh, 47000, Sungai Buloh, Selangor, Malaysia
Tel.: (60) 361575313
Plastic Injection Molding Products Mfr
N.A.I.C.S.: 333511

KUMPULAN JETSON BERHAD
11th Floor Menara Tokio Marine Life No 189 Jalan Tun Razak, 50400, Kuala Lumpur, Malaysia
Tel.: (60) 321622282
Web Site: https://www.jetson.com.my
JETSON—(KLS)
Rev.: $41,736,807
Assets: $43,889,643
Liabilities: $34,717,068
Net Worth: $9,172,576
Earnings: ($2,206,597)
Emp.: 4
Fiscal Year-end: 12/31/22
Property Development Services
N.A.I.C.S.: 531311
Kian An Teh (Mng Dir-Grp)

Subsidiaries:

GRP Sdn. Bhd. (1)
Lot 9 Solok Sultan Hishamuddin 7 Kawasan Perusahaan 20, Selat Klang Utara, 42000, Port Klang, Selangor, Malaysia
Tel.: (60) 331765146
Web Site: https://www.grp.com.my
Adhesive & Sealant Mfr
N.A.I.C.S.: 325520

Jeb Auto Sdn. Bhd. (1)
Lot 1569 Jalan Kusta Kawasan Perindustrian Kampung Jaya, 47000, Sungai Buloh, Selangor, Malaysia
Tel.: (60) 361401005
Web Site: http://www.jebauto.com
Automotive Products Mfr
N.A.I.C.S.: 336390

KUMPULAN KITACON BERHAD
No 24 Jalan Rengas Taman Selatan, 41200, Klang, Selangor, Malaysia
Tel.: (60) 333724162
Web Site: https://www.kitacon.com.my
KITACON—(KLS)
Rev.: $169,977,253
Assets: $123,007,808
Liabilities: $58,347,472
Net Worth: $64,660,337
Earnings: $7,916,725
Emp.: 1,083
Fiscal Year-end: 12/31/23
Construction Services
N.A.I.C.S.: 236220

KUMULUS VAPE SA
21 rue Marcel Merieux, 69960, Corbas, France
Tel.: (33) 971357320
Web Site: http://www.kumulusvape.fr
ALVAP—(EUR)
Sales Range: $10-24.9 Million
Online Retailer Services
N.A.I.C.S.: 424690

KUMWELL CORPORATION PUBLIC COMPANY LIMITED
358 Liang Mueang Nonthaburi Road, Lat Yao Chatuchak, Bangkok, 11000, Thailand
Tel.: (66) 29543455
Web Site: https://www.kumwell.com
Year Founded: 1999
KUMWEL—(THA)
Rev.: $15,427,664
Assets: $25,810,372
Liabilities: $9,508,408
Net Worth: $16,301,964

Earnings: $1,007,999
Fiscal Year-end: 12/31/23
Electrical Equipment Mfr & Distr
N.A.I.C.S.: 335210
Boonsak Kiatjaroonlert (CEO)

KUMYANG CO., LTD.
77 Nakdong-daero 960beon-gil, Sasang-Gu, Busan, Gamjeon-dong, Korea (South)
Tel.: (82) 513165881 KR
Web Site: https://www.kyc.co.kr
Year Founded: 1955
001570—(KRS)
Rev.: $163,475,134
Assets: $216,891,283
Liabilities: $123,366,129
Net Worth: $93,525,154
Earnings: ($22,343,530)
Emp.: 116
Fiscal Year-end: 12/31/22
Chemical Products Mfr
N.A.I.C.S.: 325613
Kwang Jy Ryu (Pres & CEO)

Subsidiaries:

K&J CHEMICALS CO., LTD (1)
Inside of Juhua Group Corp, Quzhou, 324004, Zhejiang, China
Tel.: (86) 570 361 5657
Chemical Products Mfr
N.A.I.C.S.: 325998

KUMYANG (LIANYUNGANG) CHEMICAL CO., LTD. (1)
Nanhuan Street Industry District, Lianyungang, 222069, Jiangsu, China
Tel.: (86) 136 4513 7231
Chemical Products Mfr
N.A.I.C.S.: 325998

KUMYANG CHEMICAL (SHANGHAI) CO., LTD. (1)
Tel.: (86) 2167295121
Chemical Products Mfr
N.A.I.C.S.: 325998

KUMYANG CORPORATION (1)
1506 Building B Yuan-Dong International No 317 Xianxia Road, Changning District, Shanghai, 200051, China
Tel.: (86) 21 6405 6701
Chemical Products Mfr
N.A.I.C.S.: 325998

KUMYANG NEIMENGGU CHEMICAL CO., LTD. (1)
Tenggeli Industrial Zone Alashanzuoqi Alashan League, Tenggeli Industrial Zone, Alashan Zuoqi, 750314, China
Tel.: (86) 483 869 2301
Chemical Products Mfr
N.A.I.C.S.: 325998
Hyuk Lee (Pres)

KUMYANG USA INC. (1)
224 W 25th St Ste 702, New York, NY 10001
Tel.: (212) 944-8612
Chemical Products Mfr
N.A.I.C.S.: 325998

KUNMING KUMYANG CHEMICAL CO., LTD (1)
No 29 Jilong Road Huangtupo, West Suburb, Kunming, 650101, Yunnan, China
Tel.: (86) 871 833 4699
Chemical Products Mfr
N.A.I.C.S.: 325998

KUMYANG GREEN POWER CO., LTD.
7th Floor Keumyang Bldg 257, Samsanno & Nam-gu, Ulsan, Korea (South)
Tel.: (82) 522601811
Web Site: https://www.kygp.co.kr
Year Founded: 1993
282720—(KRS)
Rev.: $212,150,569
Assets: $108,881,271
Liabilities: $53,075,095
Net Worth: $55,805,367

Earnings: $6,946,050
Fiscal Year-end: 12/31/22
Construction Services
N.A.I.C.S.: 237310
Yeon-Chul Lee (CEO)

KUN PENG INTERNATIONAL LTD.
1F Building 3 No 1001 Huihe South Street Banbidian Village Gaobeidian Town, Chaoyang District, Beijing, 100025, China
Tel.: (86) 1087227012 NV
Year Founded: 2010
KPEA—(OTCQB)
Holding Company
N.A.I.C.S.: 551112
Zhuang Richun (CEO)

KUNDAN EDIFICE LTD.
Kundan House 291 Dattapada Road Borivali East, Mumbai, 400066, India
Tel.: (91) 9175924916
Web Site: https://www.kundanedifice.com
Year Founded: 2014
KEL—(NSE)
Rev.: $73,523,710
Assets: $36,064,692
Liabilities: $26,205,219
Net Worth: $9,859,472
Earnings: $6,192,576
Emp.: 311
Fiscal Year-end: 03/31/23
Electrical Equipment Mfr & Distr
N.A.I.C.S.: 333414
Divyansh Gupta (Mng Dir)

KUNG LONG BATTERIES INDUSTRIAL CO., LTD.
No 6 Zili 3rd Road, Nant'ou, 54067, Taiwan
Tel.: (886) 492254777
Web Site: https://www.klb.com.tw
1537—(TAI)
Rev.: $209,843,578
Assets: $183,961,764
Liabilities: $48,431,634
Net Worth: $135,530,130
Earnings: $19,918,963
Emp.: 3,921
Fiscal Year-end: 12/31/23
Electrical Batteries Mfr
N.A.I.C.S.: 335910
Vincent Huang-Wei Liu (Assoc VP-Fin)

Subsidiaries:

Kung Long Batteries Industrial Co., Ltd. - Ben Luc Factory (1)
40-BA Chanh Thau-Kp2-TT Ben Luc-Huyen, Ben Luc, Long An, Vietnam
Tel.: (84) 2723872213
Lead Acid Battery Mfr
N.A.I.C.S.: 335910

Kung Long Batteries Industrial Co., Ltd. - Duc Hoa Factory (1)
Cum Cong Nghiep Duc My-Xa Duc Hoa Dong-Huyen, Duc Hoa, Long An, Vietnam
Tel.: (84) 2723779666
Lead Acid Battery Mfr
N.A.I.C.S.: 335910

KUNG SING ENGINEERING CORPORATION
8F No 102 Sec 4 Civic Blvd, Taipei, Taiwan
Tel.: (886) 227514188
Web Site: https://www.kseco.com.tw
5521—(TAI)
Rev.: $144,624,144
Assets: $229,031,517
Liabilities: $63,806,585
Net Worth: $165,224,932
Earnings: $336,491
Emp.: 516

Fiscal Year-end: 12/31/22
Civil Engineering & Construction
N.A.I.C.S.: 237990

KUNGSLEDEN AB
Warfvinges vag 31, PO Box 70414, S-107 25, Stockholm, Sweden
Tel.: (46) 850305200
Web Site: http://www.kungsleden.se
KLED—(OMX)
Rev.: $305,322,080
Assets: $5,193,039,040
Liabilities: $2,258,480,000
Net Worth: $2,934,559,040
Earnings: $199,722,880
Emp.: 132
Fiscal Year-end: 12/31/20
Real Estate Services
N.A.I.C.S.: 531390
Jan-Eric Lindquist (Controller-Fin)

Subsidiaries:

Kungsleden Fastighets AB (1)
Vasagatan 7, PO Box 704 14, S-107 25, Stockholm, Sweden (100%)
Tel.: (46) 850305200
Web Site: http://www.kungsleden.se
Sales Range: $50-74.9 Million
Emp.: 70
Real Estate Property Lessors
N.A.I.C.S.: 531190

Kungsleden Friab AB (1)
Warfvinges Vag 31, Stockholm, 11251, Sweden (100%)
Tel.: (46) 850305274
Real Estate Manangement Services
N.A.I.C.S.: 531390

Kungsleden Mattan AB (1)
Vasagatan 7, Stockholm, 111 20, Sweden (100%)
Tel.: (46) 850305200
Property Leasing & Rental Services
N.A.I.C.S.: 531190

Kungsleden Ost B AB (1)
Medborgarplatsen 25, Stockholm, 10725, Sweden (100%)
Tel.: (46) 850305200
Web Site: http://www.kungsleden.se
Sales Range: $50-74.9 Million
Emp.: 70
Real Estate Property Lessors
N.A.I.C.S.: 531190

Kungsleden Ost G AB (1)
Vasagatan 7, Stockholm, 11872, Sweden (100%)
Tel.: (46) 850305200
Web Site: http://www.kungsleden.se
Sales Range: $50-74.9 Million
Emp.: 70
Real Estate Property Lessors
N.A.I.C.S.: 531190

Kungsleden Real Estate BV (1)
Saturnusstraat 25j, Hoofddorp, Netherlands (100%)
Tel.: (31) 235543430
Trusts Estates & Agency Accounts
N.A.I.C.S.: 525920

Kungsleden Service AB (1)
Warfvinges vag 31, 10725, Stockholm, Sweden (100%)
Tel.: (46) 850305200
Web Site: http://www.kungsleden.se
Sales Range: $50-74.9 Million
Emp.: 100
Real Estate Property Lessors
N.A.I.C.S.: 531190

Kungsleden Syd AB (1)
Medborgarplatsen 25, Stockholm, Sweden (100%)
Tel.: (46) 4074855
Web Site: http://www.kungsleden.se
Sales Range: $50-74.9 Million
Emp.: 70
Real Estate Property Lessors
N.A.I.C.S.: 531190

Realia International BV (1)
Evert Van De Beekstraat 36, Schiphol, Netherlands (100%)
Tel.: (31) 204053063
Real Estate Property Lessors

AND PRIVATE COMPANIES

N.A.I.C.S.: 531190

KUNIKO LIMITED
Level 28 AMP Tower 140 St Georges Terrace, Perth, 6000, WA, Australia
Tel.: (61) 863645095 AU
Web Site: https://www.kuniko.eu
Year Founded: 2017
KNI—(ASX)
Rev.: $126,230
Assets: $10,986,843
Liabilities: $406,921
Net Worth: $10,579,922
Earnings: ($3,349,042)
Fiscal Year-end: 12/31/23
Exploration & Mining Services
N.A.I.C.S.: 213115
Antony Heitmann Beckmand *(CEO)*

KUNIMINE INDUSTRIES CO., LTD.
TMM Bldg 3F 1-10-5 Iwamoto-cho, Chiyoda-ku, Tokyo, 101-0032, Japan
Tel.: (81) 338667251
Web Site: https://www.kunimine.co.jp
Year Founded: 1943
5388—(TKS)
Rev.: $147,687,760
Assets: $240,528,640
Liabilities: $37,461,600
Net Worth: $203,067,040
Earnings: $12,593,680
Emp.: 235
Fiscal Year-end: 03/31/22
Clay & Ceramic & Refractory Minerals Mining
N.A.I.C.S.: 212323
Yasuhiko Kunimine *(Pres)*

Subsidiaries:

Kanben Mining Co., Ltd. (1)
1573 Shirosaki Aga-machi, Higashi-Kanbara-gun, Niigata, 959-4622, Japan
Tel.: (81) 254992028
Bentonite Based Product Mining Services & Retailer
N.A.I.C.S.: 212323

Kunimain Co., Ltd. (1)
722-9 Oaza-Tukinuno Oe-machi, Nishi-Murayama-gun, Yamagata, 990-1271, Japan
Tel.: (81) 237642121
Bentonite Based Product Mining Services & Retailer
N.A.I.C.S.: 212323

Kunimine (Thailand) Co., Ltd. (1)
2 Jasmine City Building 12th floor Soi Sukhumvit23 Prasarnmitr, Klongtoey-Nua Wattana, Bangkok, 10110, Thailand
Tel.: (66) 26127302
Bentonite Based Product Retailer
N.A.I.C.S.: 459999

Kunimine Marketing Co., Ltd. (1)
1-1-25 Todaijima Itatoku Building 3rd floor, Urayasu, 279-0001, Chiba, Japan
Tel.: (81) 477111761
Pet Related Product Retailer
N.A.I.C.S.: 459910

KUNLUN TECH CO., LTD.
Block B Mingyang International Center, Dongcheng District, Beijing, 100005, China
Tel.: (86) 1065210329
Web Site: https://www.kunlun.com
Year Founded: 2008
300418—(CHIN)
Rev.: $664,991,964
Assets: $2,465,529,300
Liabilities: $423,676,656
Net Worth: $2,041,852,644
Earnings: $161,811,000
Emp.: 4,000
Fiscal Year-end: 12/31/22
Online Game Developer
N.A.I.C.S.: 513210
Tian Jin *(Sec & VP)*

KUNMING CHUAN JIN NUO CHEMICAL CO., LTD.
Sifangdi Industrial Park, Tongdu Town Dongchuan District, Kunming, 650500, Yunnan, China
Tel.: (86) 87162124601
Web Site: http://en.kmcjn.com
Year Founded: 2005
300505—(CHIN)
Rev.: $381,892,253
Assets: $500,565,773
Liabilities: $156,409,911
Net Worth: $344,155,862
Earnings: ($12,882,071)
Emp.: 2,000
Fiscal Year-end: 12/31/23
Organic Chemical Mfr
N.A.I.C.S.: 325199
Meng Liu *(Chm & Pres)*

KUNMING DIANCHI WATER TREATMENT CO., LTD.
No 7 water purification plant Hubin Road, Dianchi National Tourist Resort, Kunming, 650000, Yunnan, China
Tel.: (86) 87166038810 CN
Web Site: https://www.kmdcwt.com
Year Founded: 1995
3768—(HKG)
Rev.: $290,047,165
Assets: $1,642,989,442
Liabilities: $989,063,665
Net Worth: $653,925,776
Earnings: $45,508,554
Emp.: 1,492
Fiscal Year-end: 12/31/22
Waste Treatment Services
N.A.I.C.S.: 221310
Ming King Chiu *(Co-Sec)*

KUNMING IRON & STEEL GROUP CO., LTD.
Anning, Kunming, 650302, Yunnan, China
Tel.: (86) 8718603283
Web Site: http://www.ynkg.com
Iron & Steel Mfr
N.A.I.C.S.: 331110
Shudong Hao *(Chm)*

KUNMING LONGJIN PHARMACEUTICAL CO., LTD.
NO 789 Lanmao Rd Kunming Hi-Tech Zone, Majinpu Chenggong, Kunming, China
Tel.: (86) 87168520866
Web Site: https://www.longjin.com.cn
Year Founded: 1996
002750—(SSE)
Rev.: $38,919,936
Assets: $128,966,050
Liabilities: $20,997,431
Net Worth: $107,968,619
Earnings: $1,809,410
Emp.: 260
Fiscal Year-end: 12/31/20
Pharmaceuticals Mfr
N.A.I.C.S.: 325412
Xian'e Fan *(Founder, Chm & Pres)*

KUNMING YUNNEI POWER CO., LTD.
No 66 Jingjing Road, Kunming Economic and Technological Development Zone, Kunming, 650217, Yunnan, China
Tel.: (86) 87167163969
Web Site: https://www.yunneidongli.com
Year Founded: 1999
000903—(SSE)
Rev.: $672,548,292
Assets: $1,871,252,604
Liabilities: $1,255,153,536
Net Worth: $616,099,068

Earnings: ($183,353,976)
Fiscal Year-end: 12/31/22
Small Engine Mfr
N.A.I.C.S.: 333618
Xu Shixiong *(Chm)*

KUNSHAN ASIA AROMA CORP., LTD.
No 269 Wenpu Middle Road, Qiandeng Town Kunshan City, Suzhou, 215341, Jiangsu, China
Tel.: (86) 51282620630
Web Site: https://www.asiaaroma.com
Year Founded: 1996
301220—(SSE)
Rev.: $99,038,160
Assets: $242,458,164
Liabilities: $25,606,152
Net Worth: $216,852,012
Earnings: $18,503,316
Fiscal Year-end: 12/31/22
Chemical Products Mfr
N.A.I.C.S.: 325998
Zhou Junxue *(Chm)*

KUNSHAN DONGWEI TECHNOLOGY CO., LTD.
No 505 Dongding Rd, Bacheng, Kunshan, 215300, Jiangsu, China
Tel.: (86) 51257710500
Web Site: https://en.ksdwgroup.com
Year Founded: 2001
KSDW—(SHG)
Emp.: 1,000
Electrical Equipment Mfr & Distr
N.A.I.C.S.: 333414

KUNSHAN HUGUANG AUTO HARNESS CO., LTD.
No 388 Huguang Road, Zhangpu Town, Kunshan, 215326, Jiangsu, China
Tel.: (86) 51250325196
Web Site: https://www.kshg.com
Year Founded: 1997
605333—(SHG)
Rev.: $460,215,826
Assets: $629,674,218
Liabilities: $421,053,745
Net Worth: $208,620,472
Earnings: $5,765,709
Fiscal Year-end: 12/31/22
Automotive Parts Mfr & Distr
N.A.I.C.S.: 336390
Cheng Sanrong *(Chm & CEO)*

KUNSHAN KINGLAI HYGIENIC MATERIALS CO., LTD.
No 22 Lufeng West Road, Lujia Town, Kunshan, 215331, Jiangsu, China
Tel.: (86) 51287881808
Web Site: http://www.kinglai.com.cn
Year Founded: 2000
300260—(CHIN)
Rev.: $367,856,424
Assets: $516,896,640
Liabilities: $291,578,508
Net Worth: $225,318,132
Earnings: $48,408,516
Fiscal Year-end: 12/31/22
Pipes, Fittings, Pumps & Valves Mfr
N.A.I.C.S.: 332996
Li Shuibo *(Chm & Gen Mgr)*

Subsidiaries:

Kinglai Hygienic Materials Co., Ltd (1)
No 22 West Lufeng Road, Lujia, Jiangsu, China
Tel.: (86) 51257871991
Pipeline Material Mfr & Distr
N.A.I.C.S.: 333998

Polaris Stainless Steel Technology (Kunshan) Co., Ltd (1)

West side of Songjiagang Road, Zhoushi Town, Kunshan, Jiangsu, China
Tel.: (86) 51255128188
Web Site: https://www.paloaristube-pipe.com
Pipeline Material Mfr & Distr
N.A.I.C.S.: 333998

KUNSHAN TOPA INTELLIGENT EQUIPMENT CO., LTD.
No 8 Longhua Road, Yushan town, Kunshan, 215316, Jiangsu, China
Tel.: (86) 51233326888
Web Site: https://www.kstopa.com.cn
Year Founded: 2006
300836—(SSE)
Rev.: $70,134,012
Assets: $118,581,840
Liabilities: $42,479,424
Net Worth: $76,102,416
Earnings: ($6,683,040)
Fiscal Year-end: 12/31/22
Industrial Machinery Product Mfr & Distr
N.A.I.C.S.: 333248
Chaopeng Xiao *(Chm & Gen Mgr)*

KUNSTSTOFFE INDUSTRIES LTD.
128 Bhaudaji Road Kiran Matunga, Mumbai, 400 019, India
Tel.: (91) 2224082689
Web Site: https://www.kunststoffeindia.com
Year Founded: 1985
523594—(BOM)
Rev.: $1,546,514
Assets: $1,573,107
Liabilities: $428,476
Net Worth: $1,144,632
Earnings: $164,690
Emp.: 21
Fiscal Year-end: 03/31/23
Pipes Mfr
N.A.I.C.S.: 326122
Soniya Pravin Sheth *(Mng Dir)*

KUNTZ ELECTROPLATING INC.
851 Wilson Avenue, Kitchener, N2C 1J1, ON, Canada
Tel.: (519) 893-7680
Web Site: http://www.kuntz.com
Year Founded: 1948
Rev.: $76,950,000
Emp.: 600
Steel & Aluminum Components Mfr
N.A.I.C.S.: 332813
Dan Pitz *(Mgr-Sls & Mktg)*

KUNWU JIUDING INVESTMENT HOLDINGS CO., LTD.
Office Building A of Zijin City No 1379 North Riverside Avenue, Donghu District, Nanchang, 330077, Jiangxi, China
Tel.: (86) 79188650615 CN
Web Site: https://www.jdcapital.com
Year Founded: 1997
600053—(SHG)
Rev.: $60,666,517
Assets: $487,264,013
Liabilities: $69,391,717
Net Worth: $417,872,295
Earnings: $24,664,573
Fiscal Year-end: 12/31/22
Private Equity Investment & Portfolio Management Firm
N.A.I.C.S.: 523999

Subsidiaries:

FTL Asia Holdings Limited (1)
27/F Wing On Centre 111 Connaught Road, Central, China (Hong Kong) (100%)
Tel.: (852) 2591 8888
Web Site: http://www.ftlife.com.hk

KUNWU JIUDING INVESTMENT HOLDINGS CO., LTD.

Kunwu Jiuding Investment Holdings Co., Ltd.—(Continued)
Holding Company; Insurance Products & Services
N.A.I.C.S.: 551112

KUNYUE DEVELOPMENT CO., LTD.
19F-2 No 402 Shizheng Rd, Taichung, Taiwan
Tel.: (886) 422588809
5206—(TPE)
Rev.: $12,411,156
Assets: $366,687,334
Liabilities: $279,779,852
Net Worth: $86,907,482
Earnings: ($3,261,389)
Fiscal Year-end: 12/31/22
Real Estate Development Services
N.A.I.C.S.: 531390
Chen Pi Yueh *(Chm & CEO)*

KUO TOONG INTERNATIONAL
8F-5 No 91 Dashun 1st Road, Zuoying District, Kaohsiung, 81357, Taiwan
Tel.: (886) 75573755
Web Site: https://www.kti.com.tw
8936—(TPE)
Rev.: $131,904,622
Assets: $450,574,047
Liabilities: $219,716,993
Net Worth: $230,857,054
Earnings: $4,084,325
Fiscal Year-end: 12/31/20
Construction Services
N.A.I.C.S.: 236220
Ching-Cheng Yeh *(Pres)*

KUO YANG CONSTRUCTION
16F No 49 Min Sheng E Rd Sec 3, Taipei, Taiwan
Tel.: (886) 25000808
Web Site: https://www.kycc.com.tw
2505—(TAI)
Rev.: $24,051,113
Assets: $606,582,893
Liabilities: $272,849,429
Net Worth: $333,733,465
Earnings: $9,970,110
Emp.: 77
Fiscal Year-end: 12/31/23
Construction Engineering Services
N.A.I.C.S.: 237990
Zi-Kuan Lin *(Chm)*

KUOBROTHERS CORP.
5/F 19-3 Sanchong Road, Nangang Dist, Taipei, 115, Taiwan
Tel.: (886) 226552939
8477—(TPE)
Rev.: $74,308,132
Assets: $20,327,049
Liabilities: $10,705,218
Net Worth: $9,621,830
Earnings: ($3,713,535)
Fiscal Year-end: 12/31/22
Online Shopping Services
N.A.I.C.S.: 441110
Yue-Chun Lee *(Chm)*

KUOK (SINGAPORE) LIMITED
No 1 Kim Seng Promenade 07-01 Great World City, Singapore, 237994, Singapore
Tel.: (65) 6733 3600   SG
Web Site: http://www.kuokgroup.com.sg
Year Founded: 1952
Investment Holding Company
N.A.I.C.S.: 551112
Khoon Kuan Kuok *(Chm)*
Subsidiaries:

Pacific Carriers Limited   (1)
No 1 Kim Seng Promenade, #07-02 Great World City, Singapore, 237994, Singapore   (100%)
Tel.: (65) 6733 3500
Web Site: http://www.pclsg.com
Emp.: 50
Holding Company; Dry Freight Shipping, Ship Building & Offshore Marine Support Services
N.A.I.C.S.: 551112
Khoon Kuan Kuok *(Mng Dir)*

Subsidiary (Domestic):

DDW-PaxOcean Asia Pte. Ltd.   (2)
33 Tuas Crescent, Singapore, 638722, Singapore   (67%)
Tel.: (65) 6862 1188
Web Site: http://www.ddw-paxocean.com
Ship Building, Repairing & Engineering Services
N.A.I.C.S.: 336611

Unit (Non-US):

DDW-PaxOcean Asia - Graha   (3)
Jalan Brigjen Katamso, Tanjung Uncang, Pulau Batam, Indonesia
Tel.: (62) 778 392 889
Web Site: http://www.ddw-paxocean.com
Ship Building, Repairing & Engineering Services
N.A.I.C.S.: 336611

DDW-PaxOcean Asia - Nanindah   (3)
Jalan Brigjen Katamso, Tanjung Uncang, Pulau Batam, Indonesia
Tel.: (62) 778 391 962
Web Site: http://www.ddw-paxocean.com
Ship Building, Repairing & Engineering Services
N.A.I.C.S.: 336611

Subsidiary (Non-US):

PACC Ship Managers (Beijing) Co Ltd   (2)
Rm 0716 Sanli Dasha No 208 Andingmenwai Dajie, Beijing, 100011, China
Tel.: (86) 10 51236312
Marine Cargo Services
N.A.I.C.S.: 488320

PACC Shipping Phils., Inc   (2)
B & C 9th Floor Ramon Magsaysay Center 1680 Roxas Boulevard, 1680, Manila, Philippines
Tel.: (63) 2 5214422
Marine Cargo Services
N.A.I.C.S.: 488320

Subsidiary (Domestic):

PCL (Shipping) Pte. Ltd.   (2)
No 1 Kim Seng Promenade, 07-02 Great World City, Singapore, 237994, Singapore
Tel.: (65) 6733 3500
Web Site: http://www.pclsg.com
Deep-Sea Freight Shipping Services
N.A.I.C.S.: 483111
Khoon Kuan Kuok *(Mng Dir)*

Subsidiary (Non-US):

PCL SHIPPING PRIVATE LIMITED   (2)
901 A Wing Godrej Coliseum Off Somaiya Road, Behind Everard Nagar Sion East, Mumbai, 400 022, Maharashtra, India
Tel.: (91) 22 2403 1332
Web Site: http://www.pclsg.com
Marine Cargo Services
N.A.I.C.S.: 488320
Prasad Gore *(Gen Mgr)*

Subsidiary (US):

PCL Shipping Inc.   (2)
One Landmark Sq 9th Fl, Stamford, CT 06901
Tel.: (203) 325-9200
Marine Cargo Services
N.A.I.C.S.: 488320

Subsidiary (Non-US):

Paccship (UK) Limited   (2)
50 Southwark Street, London, SE1 1UN, United Kingdom
Tel.: (44) 20 78024870
Marine Cargo Services
N.A.I.C.S.: 488320

Marcus Chew *(Mgr-Transport)*

KUOK BROTHERS SDN. BHD.
15th Floor UBN Tower No 10 Jalan P Ramlee, PO Box 111, 50250, Kuala Lumpur, Malaysia
Tel.: (60) 28232800   MY
Web Site: http://www.kuokgroup.co
Year Founded: 1949
Investment Holding Company
N.A.I.C.S.: 551112
Khoon Chen Kuok *(Chm)*

Subsidiaries:

Jerneh Asia Berhad   (1)
18th Fl Wisma Jerneh 38 Jalan Sultan Ismail, 50250, Kuala Lumpur, Malaysia
Tel.: (60) 321414255
Web Site: http://www.jerneh.com.my
Sales Range: $10-24.9 Million
General & Life Insurance Underwriting Services
N.A.I.C.S.: 524113

Subsidiary (US):

ACE INA International Holding, Ltd   (2)
436 Walnut St, Philadelphia, PA 19106
Tel.: (215) 640-1000
General Insurance Services
N.A.I.C.S.: 524210

PPB Group Berhad   (1)
12th Floor UBN Tower No 10 Jalan P Ramlee, Letter Box No 115, 50250, Kuala Lumpur, Malaysia   (50.81%)
Tel.: (60) 327260088
Web Site: https://www.ppbgroup.com
Rev.: $1,037,195,775
Assets: $6,158,705,355
Liabilities: $330,960,218
Net Worth: $5,827,745,138
Earnings: $337,446,945
Emp.: 4,768
Fiscal Year-end: 12/31/2020
Holding Company
N.A.I.C.S.: 551112
Siew Nam Oh *(Chm)*

Subsidiary (Domestic):

CWM Group Sdn Bhd   (2)
Lot 12 Persiaran Kemajuan 16/16 Darul Ehsan, 40200, Shah Alam, Selangor, Malaysia
Tel.: (60) 355107800
Web Site: http://www.cwm.com.my
Solid Waste Management & Water Engineering Services
N.A.I.C.S.: 924110
Caprice Yeap *(Asst Mgr)*

Chemquest Sdn. Bhd.   (2)
11 F Wisma Jerneh 38 Jalan Sultan Ismail, 50250, Kuala Lumpur, Malaysia   (55%)
Tel.: (60) 321449552
Web Site: http://www.chemquestgroup.com
Sales Range: $10-24.9 Million
Emp.: 10
Waste Management Services
N.A.I.C.S.: 562998

Cinead Sdn Bhd   (2)
No 1 SS 22/19 Damansara Jaya, 47400, Petaling Jaya, Selangor, Malaysia
Tel.: (60) 122100210
Web Site: http://www.cinead.com.my
Cinema Advertising Services
N.A.I.C.S.: 541810
Geraldine Lee *(Sls Mgr-Media Sls)*

Clonal Palms Sdn Bhd   (2)
172 Lot 1829 Ground Fl Lorong Kota Padawan 3 KCLD, 10th Mile Penrissen Road, 93250, Kuching, Sarawak, Malaysia
Tel.: (60) 82614653
Sales Range: $25-49.9 Million
Emp.: 160
Oil Palm Cultivation Services
N.A.I.C.S.: 311224
Stella O. Chernnee *(Mgr-Ops)*

FFM Berhad   (2)
PT 45125 Batu 15 1/2 Sungai Pelong, 47000, Sungai Buloh, Selangor, Malaysia   (100%)
Tel.: (60) 361457888
Web Site: http://www.ffmb.com.my

INTERNATIONAL PUBLIC

Sales Range: $25-49.9 Million
Emp.: 100
Compounded Animal Feed & Palm Oil Refinement
N.A.I.C.S.: 311211

Subsidiary (Domestic):

FFM (Sabah) Sdn Bhd   (3)
5 5 mile Off Jalan Tuaran Kolombong Industrial Estate, 88450, Kota Kinabalu, Sabah, Malaysia
Tel.: (60) 88426310
Web Site: http://www.ffmb.com.my
Sales Range: $25-49.9 Million
Emp.: 53
Animal Feed Mfr
N.A.I.C.S.: 311119

FFM Farms Sdn Bhd   (3)
PT 45125 Batu 15 1/2 Sungai Pelong, 47000, Sungai Buloh, Selangor, Malaysia
Tel.: (60) 361572289
Sales Range: $125-149.9 Million
Livestock Farming Services
N.A.I.C.S.: 424520

FFM Feedmills (Sarawak) Sdn Bhd   (3)
Lot 2231 Jalan Kilang Pending, Industrial Estate, Kuching, 93450, Sarawak, Malaysia
Tel.: (60) 82482751
Sales Range: $10-24.9 Million
Emp.: 47
Animal Feed Manufacturer
N.A.I.C.S.: 311119
Liew Tau Kuek *(Gen Mgr)*

FFM Grains & Mills Sdn. Bhd.   (3)
Lot 505 Block 8 MTLD Sejingkat Industrial Estate, Jalan Bako, 93050, Kuching, Sarawak, Malaysia   (100%)
Tel.: (60) 82439449
Web Site: http://www.ffmb.com.my
Emp.: 35
Flour Milling Services
N.A.I.C.S.: 311211

FFM Marketing Sdn Bhd   (3)
PT 45125 Batu 15 1/2 Sungai Pelong, 47000, Sungai Buloh, Selangor, Malaysia
Tel.: (60) 331613888
Animal Feed Mfr
N.A.I.C.S.: 311119

Tego Multifil Sdn Bhd   (3)
Lot 9 Lorong Bunga Tanjung 1/2 Senawang Industrial Park, 70400, Seremban, Negeri Sembilan, Malaysia
Tel.: (60) 66778721
Polybag Manufacturers
N.A.I.C.S.: 326199

Tego Sdn Bhd   (3)
Lot 5-8 Senewag Industrial Estate, 70450, Seremban, Negeri Sembilan, Malaysia
Tel.: (60) 66778721
Sales Range: $100-124.9 Million
Polybag Manufacturers
N.A.I.C.S.: 326199

Subsidiary (Domestic):

FFM Pulau Indah Sdn Bhd   (2)
Lot 1 Section 6 Jalan 6/3 Persiaran Okid Pulau Indah, 42920, Port Klang, Selangor, Malaysia
Tel.: (60) 331613888
Animal Feed Mfr
N.A.I.C.S.: 311119

Golden Screen Cinemas Sdn. Bhd.   (2)
No 1 Jalan SS22/19 Damansara Jaya, 47400, Petaling Jaya, Selangor, Malaysia   (98.9%)
Tel.: (60) 378068888
Web Site: http://www.gsc.com.my
Sales Range: $25-49.9 Million
Emp.: 50
Distribution & Exhibition of Films
N.A.I.C.S.: 512131

JBFM Flour Mill Sdn Bhd   (2)
2429 MK 1 Tingkat Perusahann Dua Kawasan Perusahaan Prai, Prai Seberang, Perai, 13600, Malaysia
Tel.: (60) 43999018
Web Site: http://www.jbfm.com.my

AND PRIVATE COMPANIES

Sales Range: $25-49.9 Million
Emp.: 80
Animal Feed Manufacturer
N.A.I.C.S.: 311119

Johor Bahru Flour Mill Sdn Bhd (2)
Lot 6 Industrial Zone 1c Jalan 1C Kota Kinabalu Industrial Park, Sepanggar, 88460, Kota Kinabalu, Sabah, Malaysia (100%)
Tel.: (60) 88490390
Web Site: http://www.jbfm.com.my
Sales Range: $25-49.9 Million
Emp.: 150
Flour Milling Services
N.A.I.C.S.: 311211

Kerry Leisure Concepts Sdn Bhd (2)
Lot 237 Level 2 Cheras LeisureMall Jalan Manis 2 Taman Segar, Cheras, 56100, Kuala Lumpur, Malaysia (50%)
Tel.: (60) 391311663
Sales Range: $50-74.9 Million
Emp.: 60
Amusement Center Operator
N.A.I.C.S.: 713990

Lahad Datu Edible Oils Sdn Bhd (2)
Km 2 Jalan Kastam Baru, 91109, Lahad Datu, Sabah, Malaysia
Tel.: (60) 89884352
Edible Oils Refinery
N.A.I.C.S.: 327910
En Azmer Shamsuddin *(Gen Mgr)*

Malayan Adhesive & Chemicals Sdn Bhd (2)
No 9 Jalan Utas 15/7, PO Box 7086, 40200, Shah Alam, Selangor Darul Ehsan, Malaysia
Tel.: (60) 355661188
Web Site: http://www.mac-resins.com
Emp.: 100
Chemical Manufacturer
N.A.I.C.S.: 325180

PPB Hartabina Sdn Bhd (2)
7th Floor Cheras Plaza No 11 Jalan Manis 1, Taman Segar Cheras, 56100, Kuala Lumpur, Malaysia
Tel.: (60) 391305088
Web Site: http://www.megahrise.com.my
Sales Range: $50-74.9 Million
Emp.: 30
Property Owners & Developers Services
N.A.I.C.S.: 524126

Products Manufacturing Sdn Bhd (2)
Lot PT 31-A1 A2 & A3 Industrial Area Mukin Batu, 65 Miles Jalan Kepong, 52000, Kuala Lumpur, Malaysia
Tel.: (60) 362528298
Contract Manufacturer
N.A.I.C.S.: 236220
Raymond Moody *(Gen Mgr)*

Sitamas Environmental Systems Sdn Bhd (2)
Lot 15 Jalan Pahat 16/8A Section 16, 40702, Shah Alam, Selangor, Malaysia
Tel.: (60) 355104008
Web Site: http://www.sitamas.com
Solid Waste Management & Water Engineering Services
N.A.I.C.S.: 924110
Marik Singh *(Mgr-Production)*

South Island Mining Co Berhad (2)
18th Floor Wisma Jerneh, 330 Simco Bungalow, SG Toh Pawang Bedong, 08100, Kedah, Malaysia
Tel.: (60) 444 581 126
Property Owners & Developers Services
N.A.I.C.S.: 524126

Subsidiary (Non-US):

Vietnam Flour Mills Ltd. (2)
My Xuan A / Z, My Xuan Ward, Phu My, Ba Ria - Vung Tau, Vietnam
Tel.: (84) 2543894883
Web Site: http://www.vfmvn.com.vn
Wheat Flour Mfr
N.A.I.C.S.: 311211

KUPELE DUDINCE AS
Kupelna 106, Dudince, 962 71, Banska Bystrica, Slovakia
Tel.: (421) 455504444
Web Site: https://www.kupeledudince.sk
Year Founded: 2003
1HON002E—(BRA)
Sales Range: Less than $1 Million
Healtcare Services
N.A.I.C.S.: 621999

KUPKE + WOLF GMBH
Werkstrasse 226, 19061, Schwerin, Germany
Tel.: (49) 385640140
Web Site: http://www.kuwo.com
Year Founded: 1981
Sales Range: $10-24.9 Million
Modular Systems Mfr
N.A.I.C.S.: 541330
Gerd Drager *(Mng Dir)*

KURA SUSHI, INC.
1-2-2 Fukasaka, Naka-ku, Sakai, 599-8253, Osaka, Japan
Tel.: (81) 120989014
Web Site: https://www.kurasushi.co.jp
Year Founded: 1977
2695—(TKS)
Rev: $1,498,861,450
Assets: $922,543,710
Liabilities: $422,230,770
Net Worth: $500,312,940
Earnings: $6,118,670
Emp.: 1,537
Fiscal Year-end: 10/31/23
Restaurant Operators
N.A.I.C.S.: 722511
Kunihiko Tanaka *(Pres & CEO)*

Subsidiaries:

KURA SUSHI TAIWAN CO, LTD (1)
104-52 6th Floor No 32 Section 3 Zhongshan North Road, Zhongshan District, Taipei, 10489, Taiwan
Tel.: (886) 289788558
Web Site: https://www.kurasushi.tw
Restaurant Operators
N.A.I.C.S.: 722511

Kula Sushi USA, Inc. (1)
1840 W 182nd St, Torrance, CA 90504
Tel.: (424) 221-5731
Web Site: http://www.kulausa.com
Restaurant Operators
N.A.I.C.S.: 722511
Hajime Uba *(Pres)*

Kura Sushi USA, Inc. (1)
17461 Derian Ave Ste 200, Irvine, CA 92614
Tel.: (657) 333-4100
Web Site: https://www.kurasushi.com
Rev: $237,860,000
Assets: $328,522,000
Liabilities: $165,984,000
Net Worth: $162,538,000
Earnings: ($8,804,000)
Emp.: 3,300
Fiscal Year-end: 08/31/2024
Restaurant Operators
N.A.I.C.S.: 722511
Hajime Uba *(Chm, Pres & CEO)*

KURABO INDUSTRIES LTD.
2-4-31 Kyutarocho, Chuo-ku, Osaka, 541-8581, Japan
Tel.: (81) 662665111
Web Site: https://www.kurabo.co.jp
3106—(TKS)
Rev: $1,000,185,540
Assets: $1,274,335,290
Liabilities: $493,866,150
Net Worth: $780,469,140
Earnings: $44,538,180
Emp.: 3,899
Fiscal Year-end: 03/31/24
Holding Company
N.A.I.C.S.: 551112
Haruya Fujita *(Pres)*

Subsidiaries:

Echo Giken Co., Ltd. (1)
8-1-13 Shinmachi, Ome, 198-0024, Japan
Tel.: (81) 428327511
Semiconductor Cleaning Equipment Mfr & Distr
N.A.I.C.S.: 333242

Foshan Kurashiki Textile Manufacturing Co., Ltd. (1)
No 6 Keyuan 3 Rd High-Tech Area Ronggui, Technology Industrial Park Shunde, Foshan, Guangdong, China
Tel.: (86) 75726387726
Synthetic Fabric Distr
N.A.I.C.S.: 424310

GUANGZHOU KURABO CHEMICALS CO., LTD. (1)
Jingguan 1st Road Yonghe Economic Zone, Guangzhou, China
Tel.: (86) 20 8297 0555
Emp.: 60
Urethane Foam Product Mfr & Distr
N.A.I.C.S.: 326150

Guangzhou Kcf Plastics Co., Ltd. (1)
Damenkou Canglian Village Lilian Street, Huangpu, Guangzhou, China
Tel.: (86) 2082269875
Polyurethane Foam Mfr
N.A.I.C.S.: 326150

Japan Jiffy Foods, Inc. (1)
2-4-31 Kyutaromachi 4th Floor Kurabo Headquarters Building, Chuo-ku, Osaka, 541-0056, Japan
Tel.: (81) 662711510
Web Site: http://www.jiffy.co.jp
Vacuum Freeze-dried Food Mfr & Distr
N.A.I.C.S.: 311423

KURABO DRIVING SCHOOL CO., LTD. (1)
6-1 Kitahama-cho, Kurashiki, 710-0812, Okayama, Japan
Tel.: (81) 864223500
Web Site: https://www.kurabo-ds.co.jp
Driving School Operator
N.A.I.C.S.: 611692

KURABO ENGINEERING WORK SERVICE CO., LTD. (1)
14-41 Shimokida-cho, Neyagawa, 572-0823, Osaka, Japan
Tel.: (81) 728201172
Pollution Control Services
N.A.I.C.S.: 924110

KURABO INTERNATIONAL CO., LTD. (1)
Tel.: (81) 661255200
Web Site: http://www.kurabo-inter.co.jp
Textile Product Mfr & Distr
N.A.I.C.S.: 314999

KURABO SHANGHAI CO., LTD. (1)
Room 1101 11 Floor Tower B No 500 Hongbaoshi Road, Changning District, Shanghai, 201103, China
Tel.: (86) 21 3209 6080
Emp.: 20
Textile Products Distr
N.A.I.C.S.: 424310

KURASHIKI DO BRASIL TEXTIL LTDA. (1)
Av Paulista 542 8 Andar, Bela Vista, 01310-000, Sao Paulo, Brazil
Tel.: (55) 1132847644
Web Site: http://www.kurashiki.com.br
Cotton Yarn Mfr & Distr
N.A.I.C.S.: 314999

KURASHIKI IVY SQUARE, LTD. (1)
7-2 Honmachi, Kurashiki, 710-0054, Okayama, Japan
Tel.: (81) 864220011
Web Site: https://www.ivysquare.co.jp
Emp.: 198
Home Management Services
N.A.I.C.S.: 721110

Koei Shoji Co., Ltd. (1)
2-4-31 Kutaro-cho Kurabo Head Office Building 3rd Floor, Chuo-ku, Osaka, 541-0056, Japan
Tel.: (81) 662618219
Web Site: https://www.koei-sh.co.jp
Emp.: 6
Insurance Services
N.A.I.C.S.: 524210

KURABO INDUSTRIES LTD.

Kurabo Chemical Works Co., Ltd. (1)
119 Nominoo Hiroshima, Kurose-cho, Higashi-hiroshima, 739-2622, Japan
Tel.: (81) 823822440
Synthetic Wood Product Mfr & Distr
N.A.I.C.S.: 321999

Kurabo Denim International Ltd. (1)
Workshop A6 on 31st Floor TML Tower 3 Hoi Shing Road, Tsuen Wan N T, Hong Kong, China (Hong Kong)
Tel.: (852) 23414207
Textile Products Distr
N.A.I.C.S.: 424310

Kurabo Industries Ltd. - Anjo Mill (1)
9-13 Daito-cho, Anjo, 446-8641, Aichi, Japan
Tel.: (81) 566 76 2111
Web Site: http://www.kurabo.co.jp
Textile Products Mfr
N.A.I.C.S.: 314999

Kurabo Industries Ltd. - Gunma Plant (1)
1048-1 Higashi-arai, Sakai, 370-0101, Gunma, Japan
Tel.: (81) 270761122
Chemical Products Mfr
N.A.I.C.S.: 325998

Kurabo Industries Ltd. - Hojo Mill (1)
1005 Hojo, Matsuyama, 799-2495, Ehime, Japan
Tel.: (81) 899921211
Textile Products Mfr
N.A.I.C.S.: 314999

Kurabo Industries Ltd. - Kamogata Plant (1)
301 Rokujoin Nishi, Kamogata-cho Asaguchi, Okayama, 719-0251, Japan
Tel.: (81) 865443967
Chemical Products Mfr
N.A.I.C.S.: 325998

Kurabo Industries Ltd. - Marugame Mill (1)
8-1 1-chome Shioya-cho, Marugame, 763-0065, Kagawa, Japan
Tel.: (81) 877233328
Textile Products Mfr
N.A.I.C.S.: 314999

Kurabo Industries Ltd. - Mie Plant (1)
3-76 Edo bashi, Tsu, 514-0001, Mie, Japan
Tel.: (81) 592367710
Chemical Products Mfr
N.A.I.C.S.: 325998

Kurabo Industries Ltd. - Neyagawa Plant (1)
14-5 Shimokida-cho, Neyagawa, 572-0823, Osaka, Japan
Tel.: (81) 72 822 1161
Web Site: http://www.kurabo.co.jp
Chemical Products Mfr
N.A.I.C.S.: 325998

Kurabo Industries Ltd. - Susono Plant (1)
1818 Suyama, Susono, 410-1231, Shizuoka, Japan
Tel.: (81) 559 98 1231
Web Site: http://www.kurabo.co.jp
Chemical Products Mfr
N.A.I.C.S.: 325998

Kurabo Industries Ltd. - Tokushima Plant (1)
1-15 Tatsumi-cho, Anan, 774-0001, Tokushima, Japan
Tel.: (81) 884 22 8800
Web Site: http://www.kurabo.co.jp
Textile Products Mfr
N.A.I.C.S.: 314999

Kurabo Plant System Co., Ltd. (1)
14-41 Shimokida-cho, Neyagawa, 572-0823, Osaka, Japan
Tel.: (81) 728201172
Web Site: http://www.kksa.co.jp
Industrial Equipment Mfr
N.A.I.C.S.: 333248

Kurabo Techno System Ltd. (1)
Kurabo Bldg 14-41 Shimokida-Cho, Neyagawa, 572-0823, Osaka, Japan

KURABO INDUSTRIES LTD.

Kurabo Industries Ltd.—(Continued)
Tel.: (81) 728203500
Web Site: https://www.kts-kurabo.jp
Emp.: 40
Information Equipment Distr
N.A.I.C.S.: 423430

Kurabo Vietnam Co., Ltd. (1)
Unit 5 Level 8 Saigon Centre Tower 1 65 Le Loi Blvd, District 1, Ho Chi Minh City, Vietnam
Tel.: (84) 2838270155
Textile Products Distr
N.A.I.C.S.: 424310

Kuraki Company Ltd. (1)
1-2-1 Jooka, Nagaoka, 940-8603, Niigata, Japan
Tel.: (81) 258353040
Sales Range: $50-74.9 Million
Emp.: 295
Machine Tools Mfr
N.A.I.C.S.: 333519
Hiroshi Yasukawa (Pres)

Subsidiary (US):

Kuraki America Corporation (2)
1300 Remington Rd Unit D, Schaumburg, IL 60173 (100%)
Tel.: (847) 228-0340
Web Site: https://www.kuraki.com
Sales Range: $25-49.9 Million
Emp.: 7
Machine Tools Mfr
N.A.I.C.S.: 333519

Kuraki Shanghai Co., Ltd. (1)
Room 301 Tower D Oriental International Plaza No 85 Loushan Guan Rd, Changning District, Shanghai, China
Tel.: (86) 2162370777
Machine Tool Distr
N.A.I.C.S.: 423830

Kuraki Taiwan Co., Ltd. (1)
No 32 Houke S Rd, Houli Dist, Taichung, 42152, Taiwan
Tel.: (886) 425598666
Web Site: https://www.kuraki.com.tw
Machine Tool Mfr & Distr
N.A.I.C.S.: 333517

Kurashiki Chemical Products do Brasil Ltda. (1)
Av Maximiano Villa Rios 200 Vila Joest, Leme, Rio de Janeiro, 13614-110, SP, Brazil
Tel.: (55) 1935734100
Polyurethane Foam Mfr
N.A.I.C.S.: 326150

Kurashiki Textile Manufacturing Co., Ltd. (1)
4F Kurabo Head Office Building 2-4-31 Kyutaro-machi, Chuo-ku, Osaka, 541-0056, Japan
Tel.: (81) 662616721
Web Site: https://www.kurasen.co.jp
Emp.: 330
Textile Products Mfr
N.A.I.C.S.: 314999
Takaaki Aoyama (Pres)

P.T. Akurabenitama (1)
Jl Kaliabang Tengah No 28 RT 001 RW 015 Kelurahan Kaliabang Tengah, Kecamatan Bekasi Utara, Bekasi, 17125, Jawa Barat, Indonesia
Tel.: (62) 218880806
Textile Product Mfr & Distr
N.A.I.C.S.: 314999

P.T. KURABO MANUNGGAL TEXTILE INDUSTRIES (1)
Menara Cakrawala 7th Floor JL M H Thamrin 9, Jakarta, 10340, Indonesia
Tel.: (62) 2131937293
Emp.: 780
Cotton Yarn Mfr & Distr
N.A.I.C.S.: 314999

SIAM KURABO CO., LTD. (1)
9th Floor Sintorn Tower 2 130-132 Wireless Road, Lumpini Pathumwan, Bangkok, 10330, Thailand
Tel.: (66) 2 256 6839
Emp.: 165
Textile Product Mfr & Distr
N.A.I.C.S.: 314999

Sheedom Co., Ltd. (1)
Kurabo Bldg 8F 4-31 2-chome Kyutaro-machi, Chuo-ku, Osaka, 541-0056, Japan
Tel.: (81) 647055901
Web Site: https://www.sheedom.co.jp
Plastic Product Mfr & Distr
N.A.I.C.S.: 326199
Hidehiko Chiran (Pres)

Taishoboseki Industries Ltd. (1)
453 Kuroda, Hannan, 599-0203, Osaka, Japan
Tel.: (81) 724721001
Web Site: https://www.taishoboseki.com
Spinning Mfr
N.A.I.C.S.: 313110

Thai Textile Development & Finishing Co., Ltd. (1)
525/1 moo 2 Sukhumvit Rd Bangpoomai Muang, Samut Prakan, 10280, Thailand
Tel.: (66) 232325148
Web Site: http://www.ttdf.co.th
Emp.: 320
Synthetic Fabric Mfr
N.A.I.C.S.: 325220

Tomei Kasei Co., Ltd. (1)
Tel.: (81) 561731212
Web Site: http://www.tomeikasei.co.jp
Polypropylene Product Mfr & Distr
N.A.I.C.S.: 326199

Yamabun Electronics Co., Ltd. (1)
2-13 Shinjonishi, Higashiosakai, 578-0964, Osaka, Japan
Tel.: (81) 667453048
Web Site: http://www.yamabun-ele.co.jp
Emp.: 24
Plastic Film Sheet Mfr & Distr
N.A.I.C.S.: 326112
Keiji Fukumura (Pres)

KURAMOTO CO., LTD.

Hanasui-mae 1-1, Wakayagi Takeyar, Kurihara, 989-5508, Miyagi Prefecture, Japan
Tel.: (81) 228325111
Web Site: https://www.kuramoto.co.jp
Year Founded: 1980
5216—(TKS)
Sales Range: $25-49.9 Million
Emp.: 477
Glass Substrate Mfr
N.A.I.C.S.: 327211
Kachio Iwamoto (Auditor)

Subsidiaries:

KURAMOTO CO., LTD. - Hanaizumi Factory (1)
19-1 Aza-uchibettou Yushima Hanaizumi-cho, Ichinoseki, Iwate, Japan
Tel.: (81) 191825110
Thin Film Device Mfr
N.A.I.C.S.: 334413

KURAMOTO CO., LTD. - Mie Factory (1)
5008-2 Moricho, Tsu, Mie, Japan
Tel.: (81) 592540555
Thin Film Device Mfr
N.A.I.C.S.: 334413

KURARAY CO., LTD.

Tokiwabashi Tower 2-6-4 Otemachi, Chiyoda-ku, Tokyo, 100-8115, Japan
Tel.: (81) 367011000 JP
Web Site: https://www.kuraray.co.jp
Year Founded: 1926
3405—(TKS)
Rev.: $5,536,850,420
Assets: $8,894,298,650
Liabilities: $3,674,952,610
Net Worth: $5,219,346,040
Earnings: $300,942,140
Emp.: 11,906
Fiscal Year-end: 12/31/23
Resins, Synthetic Fibers, Medical Products & Man-Made Leather Mfr
N.A.I.C.S.: 325220
Matthias Gutweiler (Mng Exec Officer)

Subsidiaries:

Calgon Carbon Corporation (1)
3000 GSK Dr, Moon Township, PA 15108
Tel.: (412) 787-6700
Web Site: http://www.calgoncarbon.com
Activated Carbons & Related Products & Services
N.A.I.C.S.: 325998
Stevan R. Schott (Pres & CEO)

Subsidiary (Non-US):

Chemviron Carbon S.E. (2)
Zoning Industriel C De, 7181, Feluy, Hainaut, Belgium
Tel.: (32) 0645118111
Web Site: http://www.chemvironcarbon.com
Mfr of Activated Carbon
N.A.I.C.S.: 325998

Chemviron Carbon Ltd. (1)
Edgar House Lockett Road, Ashton-in-Makerfield, WN4 8DE, Lancashire, United Kingdom
Tel.: (44) 1942275400
Carbon Mfr & Distr
N.A.I.C.S.: 332919

Chemviron France SAS (1)
736 rue des Sabres, 40160, Parentis-en-Born, France
Tel.: (33) 558825770
Chemical Product Mfr & Distr
N.A.I.C.S.: 325998

Hikari Shoes Co., Ltd. (1)
313-180 Toyofuta, Kashiwa, 227 082, Japan
Tel.: (81) 471323300 (50%)
Sales Range: Less than $1 Million
Emp.: 50
Mfr & Sales of Shoes
N.A.I.C.S.: 458210

Ibuki Kosan Co., Ltd. (1)
4330 Osa Tarui-cho, Fuwa-gun, Gifu, 503 2122, Japan
Tel.: (81) 584221251
Emp.: 20
Manufacturing, Processing & Packaging of Plastic Products
N.A.I.C.S.: 326199
Yoshimi Takagi (Pres)

Iruma Country Club Co., Ltd. (1)
1159-1 Neoi Ogose-machi, Iruma-gun, Saitama, 350 0413, Japan
Tel.: (81) 49 292 5111
Web Site: http://www.iruma-cc.co.jp
Golf Course Management
N.A.I.C.S.: 713910

Kuraflex Co., Ltd. (1)
Umeda Hankyu Building Office Tower 8-1 Kakudacho, Kita-Ku, Osaka, 530-8611, Japan
Tel.: (81) 676351560
Web Site: http://www.kuraflex.com
Mfr of Non-Woven Fabric Products
N.A.I.C.S.: 332618

Kuraray (Thailand) Co., Ltd. (1)
17th Floor Unit 1709-1710 Sathorn Square Office Tower, 98 North Sathorn Road Silom Bangrak, Bangkok, 10500, Thailand
Tel.: (66) 21082118
Chemical Products Distr
N.A.I.C.S.: 424690

Kuraray Advanced Chemicals (Thailand) Co., Ltd. (1)
555/1 Energy Complex Building A 10th Floor Vibhavadi Rangsit Road, Chatuchak, Bangkok, 10900, Thailand
Tel.: (66) 25509120
Chemicals Mfr
N.A.I.C.S.: 325211

Kuraray America, Inc. (1)
2625 Bay Area Blvd, Houston, TX 77058
Tel.: (713) 495-7311
Web Site: http://www.kurarayus.com
Emp.: 95
Synthetic Resin Mfr
N.A.I.C.S.: 325211
Juan Umana (Mgr-Sls-Latin America)

Subsidiary (Domestic):

Kuraray Holdings U.S.A., Inc. (2)

INTERNATIONAL PUBLIC

2625 Bay Area Blvd Ste 600, Houston, TX 77058-1551
Tel.: (713) 495-7311
Web Site: http://www.kuraray.co.jp
Investment Management Service
N.A.I.C.S.: 523999

Subsidiary (Domestic):

MonoSol, LLC (3)
707 E 80th Pl Ste 301, Merrillville, IN 46410
Tel.: (219) 762-3165
Web Site: https://www.monosol.com
Sales Range: $125-149.9 Million
Emp.: 500
Water Soluble Packaging Systems Mfr
N.A.I.C.S.: 326112

Subsidiary (Domestic):

Aquestive Therapeutics, Inc. (4)
30 Technology Dr, Warren, NJ 07059
Tel.: (908) 941-1900
Web Site: https://www.aquestive.com
Rev.: $47,680,000
Assets: $57,070,000
Liabilities: $175,624,000
Net Worth: ($118,554,000)
Earnings: ($54,410,000)
Emp.: 130
Fiscal Year-end: 12/31/2022
Pharmaceutical Preparation Mfr & Distr
N.A.I.C.S.: 325412
Santo J. Costa (Chm)

Subsidiary (Non-US):

MonoSol AF, Ltd. (4)
Oak Drive Hartlebury Trading Estate, Hartlebury, Kidderminster, DY10 4JB, Worcestershire, United Kingdom
Tel.: (44) 1299 251 335
Water Soluble Packaging Systems Mfr
N.A.I.C.S.: 326112

Kuraray Aqua Co., Ltd. (1)
Tokiwabashi Tower 2-6-4 Otemachi, Chiyoda-ku, Tokyo, 100-0004, Japan
Tel.: (81) 367011550
Web Site: https://www.kuraray-aqua.co.jp
Water Equipment Distr
N.A.I.C.S.: 424490
Atsumi Adachi (Pres)

Kuraray Asia Pacific Pte. Ltd. (1)
10 Sakra Ave, Singapore, 627887, Singapore
Tel.: (65) 68677088
Web Site: http://www.kuraray.com.sg
Sales Range: $50-74.9 Million
Emp.: 90
Synthetic Resin Mfr & Distr
N.A.I.C.S.: 325211

Kuraray Business Services Co., Ltd. (1)
Umeda Hankyu Building Office Tower 8-1 Kakudacho, Kita-ku, Osaka, 530-8611, Japan
Tel.: (81) 676351347
Web Site: http://www.kuraray.co.jp
Accounting, Personnel & Information System Services
N.A.I.C.S.: 561110

Kuraray Chemical Co., Ltd. (1)
Umeda Hankyu Building Office Tower 8-1 Kakudacho, Kita-ku, Osaka, 530-8611, Japan (100%)
Tel.: (81) 676351600
Web Site: http://www.kuraray.com
Sales Range: $150-199.9 Million
Emp.: 222
Activated Carbon Mfr & Sales
N.A.I.C.S.: 325199

Subsidiary (Domestic):

KC Processing Co., Ltd. (2)
Shin Hankyu Bldg 9F 1 12 39 Umeda, Kita Ku, Osaka, 530 8611, Japan (100%)
Tel.: (81) 663489580
Web Site: http://www.kuraraychemical.com
Sales Range: $25-49.9 Million
Emp.: 30
Processing of Activated Carbon
N.A.I.C.S.: 325199

Plant (Domestic):

KURARAY CHEMICAL CO., LTD. - Tsurumi Plant (2)

AND PRIVATE COMPANIES

KURARAY CO., LTD.

4342 Tsurumi, Bizen, 705-0025, Okayama, Japan
Tel.: (81) 869 65 8331
Chemical Products Mfr
N.A.I.C.S.: 325998

KYOSEI CHEMICAL CO., LTD. - Nakajo Plant (2)
4-7 Kyowa-cho, Tainai, 959-2652, Niigata, Japan
Tel.: (81) 254 43 3838
Web Site: http://www.kuraray.co.jp
Emp.: 2
Electronic Components Mfr
N.A.I.C.S.: 334419

Kuraray China Co., Ltd. (1)
Unit 2207 2 Grand Gateway 3 Hongqiao Road, Xuhui District, Shanghai, 200030, China
Tel.: (86) 2161198111
Chemical Products Mfr & Whslr
N.A.I.C.S.: 325998

Kuraray Co., Ltd. - Kashima Plant (1)
36 Towada, Kamisu, 314-0197, Ibaraki, Japan
Tel.: (81) 299 96 1011
Emp.: 5,000
Synthetic Rubber Mfr
N.A.I.C.S.: 325212

Kuraray Co., Ltd. - Kurashiki Plant (Sakazu) (1)
1621 Sakazu, Kurashiki, 710-0801, Okayama, Japan
Tel.: (81) 86 422 0580
Web Site: http://www.kuraray.co.jp
Membrane Mfr
N.A.I.C.S.: 326299

Kuraray Co., Ltd. - Kurashiki Plant (Tamashima) (1)
7471 Tamashimaotoshima, Kurashiki, 713-8550, Okayama, Japan
Tel.: (81) 86 526 5111
Web Site: http://www.kuraray.co.jp
Synthetic Resin Mfr
N.A.I.C.S.: 325211

Kuraray Co., Ltd. - Niigata Plant (1)
2-28 Kurashiki-cho, Tainai, 959-2691, Niigata, Japan
Tel.: (81) 254 43 2521
Web Site: http://www.kuraray.co.jp
Chemical Products Mfr
N.A.I.C.S.: 325998

Kuraray Co., Ltd. - Okayama Plant (1)
Umeda Hankyu Building Office Tower 8-1, Okayama, 530-8611, Japan
Tel.: (81) 676351000
Web Site: http://www.kuraray.co.jp
Vinyl Acetate Mfr
N.A.I.C.S.: 325199

Kuraray Co., Ltd. - Saijo Plant (1)
892 Tsuitachi, Saijo, 793-8585, Ehime, Japan
Tel.: (81) 897 56 1150
Synthetic Resin Mfr
N.A.I.C.S.: 325211

Kuraray Engineering Co., Ltd. (1)
Umeda Hankyu Building Office Tower 8-1 Kakudacho, Kita-ku, Osaka, 533-8611, Japan
Tel.: (81) 676351870
Web Site: http://www.kuraray.co.jp
Provider of Plant Design & Construction Services
N.A.I.C.S.: 541330

Kuraray Europe GmbH (1)
Philipp-Reis-Strasse 4, 65795, Frankfurt am Main, Germany
Tel.: (49) 69 305 85300
Web Site: http://www.kuraray.eu
Emp.: 650
Chemical Products Mfr & Distr
N.A.I.C.S.: 325998

Subsidiary (Non-US):

EVAL Europe N.V. (2)
Haven 1087 - Keetberglaan 1B, 9120, Melsele, Antwerpen, Belgium
Tel.: (32) 32509733

Web Site: http://www.eval.eu
Sales Range: $25-49.9 Million
Emp.: 10
Polymer Resin Mfr
N.A.I.C.S.: 325211

Kuraray Dental Benelux B.V. (2)
Margadanstraat 20, NL-1976 DN, IJmuiden, Netherlands
Tel.: (31) 255 523 701
Web Site: http://www.kuraray-dental.eu
Dental Supplies Distr
N.A.I.C.S.: 423450

Kuraray Dental Italia S.r.l. (2)
Via San Marco 33, 20121, Milan, Italy
Tel.: (39) 0 263 471 228
Sales Range: $50-74.9 Million
Emp.: 4
Medical Equipment Distr
N.A.I.C.S.: 423450
Fabio Regazzoni (Gen Mgr)

Kuraray Nordic Ab Oy (2)
Perintokuja 8, 01510, Vantaa, Finland
Tel.: (358) 20 71 18 431
Web Site: http://www.kuraray.eu
Sales Range: $50-74.9 Million
Emp.: 4
Chemical Products Distr
N.A.I.C.S.: 424690

Kuraray Europe Nordic AB Oy (2)
Kiinteisto Oy Avia Line 1 Perintotie 2D, 01510, Vantaa, Finland
Tel.: (358) 207118431
Chemical Product Mfr & Distr
N.A.I.C.S.: 325998

Kuraray Fastening Co, Ltd. (1)
Ote Center Bldg, 1 1 3 Otemachi Chiyoda Ku, Tokyo, 100-8115, Japan
Tel.: (81) 367011000
Web Site: http://www.kuraray.co.jp
Sales Range: $100-124.9 Million
Emp.: 70
Mfr of Hook & Loop Fasteners
N.A.I.C.S.: 313220

Plant (Domestic):

KURARAY FASTENING CO., LTD. - Maruoka Plant (1)
56 Noue Maruoka-cho, Sakai, 910-0273, Fukui, Japan
Tel.: (81) 776 67 1940
Web Site: http://www.kuraray.co.jp
Chemical Products Mfr
N.A.I.C.S.: 325998

Kuraray Fudosan Co., Ltd. (1)
Shin-Hankyu Bldg 1-12-39 Umeda Kita-Ku, Osaka, 530 8611, Japan
Tel.: (81) 663489940
Web Site: http://www.kuraray.co.jp
Sales & Management of Houses & Housing Lots; Landscaping
N.A.I.C.S.: 561730

Kuraray Hong Kong Co., Ltd. (1)
Tel.: (852) 23773781
Chemical Products Mfr & Distr
N.A.I.C.S.: 325998

Kuraray India Private Limited (1)
Prius Platinum 2nd floor B wing Rear side D3 district centre, Saket, New Delhi, 110 017, India
Tel.: (91) 11 4610 2900
Web Site: http://www.kuraray.co.jp
Emp.: 8
Chemical Products Distr
N.A.I.C.S.: 424690
Hidemasha Oda (Mng Dir)

Kuraray Interior Co., Ltd. (1)
Umeda Hankyu Building Office Tower 8-1 Kakudacho, Kita-ku, Osaka, 532-8611, Japan
Tel.: (81) 676351870
Web Site: http://www.kuraray.co.jp
Sales Range: $25-49.9 Million
Emp.: 100
Mfr & Sales of Luxury Furniture
N.A.I.C.S.: 449110

Kuraray Korea Ltd. (1)
8th Floor Asia Tower Yeoksam-dong 430 Nonhyeon-ro, Gangnam-gu, Seoul, 135-719, Korea (South)
Tel.: (82) 221826500

Chemical Product Mfr & Distr
N.A.I.C.S.: 325998

Kuraray Kuraflex Co., Ltd. (1)
Osaka Umeda Twin Towers North 8-1 Kakudacho, Kita-ku, Osaka, 530-8611, Japan
Tel.: (81) 676351560
Web Site: https://www.kuraflex.com
Fabrics Mfr
N.A.I.C.S.: 313230

Kuraray Living Co., Ltd. (1)
Umeda Hankyu Building Office Tower 8-1 Kakudacho, Kita-ku, Osaka, 530 8611, Japan
Tel.: (81) 676351530
Emp.: 45
Sales of Packaging Materials, OA Equipment, Miscellaneous Goods & Non-Woven Fabrics
N.A.I.C.S.: 423990

Kuraray Magictape (Shanghai) Co., Ltd. (1)
No 180 Hua Shen Road, Wai Gao Qiao Free Trade Zone, Shanghai, 200131, China
Tel.: (86) 21 5868 2507
Web Site: http://www.kuraray.co.jp
Emp.: 25
Packaging Plastic Tape Mfr & Whslr
N.A.I.C.S.: 325211

Kuraray Medical Inc. (1)
Ote Center Building 1-1-3 Otemachi, Chiyoda-Ku, Tokyo, 100-0004, Japan
Tel.: (81) 3 6701 1700
Sales Range: $125-149.9 Million
Emp.: 27
Medical Equipment Mfr & Distr
N.A.I.C.S.: 334510
Sadaaki Matsuyama (Pres)

Kuraray Methacrylate (Zhang Jia Gang) Co., Ltd. (1)
30 Beijing Rd, Jiansu Yangtze International Chemical Industrial Park, Zhangjiagang, 215634, Jiangsu, China
Tel.: (86) 51258937855
Chemical Product Mfr & Distr
N.A.I.C.S.: 325998

Kuraray Noritake Dental Inc. (1)
2-6-4 Otemachi Tokiwabashi Tower, Chiyoda-ku, Tokyo, 100-0004, Japan
Tel.: (81) 367011700
Web Site: https://www.kuraraynoritake.jp
Dental Medical Material Mfr & Distr
N.A.I.C.S.: 339114

Kuraray Okayama Spinning Co., Ltd. (1)
121 Kaigandori, Minami-Ku, Okayama, 702-8601, Japan
Tel.: (81) 862623414
Web Site: http://www.kuraray.co.jp
Sales Range: $50-74.9 Million
Emp.: 120
Mfr of Synthetic Fibers
N.A.I.C.S.: 325220

Kuraray Plastics Co., Ltd. (1)
39F Umeda Hankyu Building Office Tower8-1 Kakuda-cho, Kita ku, Osaka, 530-8611, Japan
Tel.: (81) 676351500
Web Site: https://www.kurarayplastics.co.jp
Sales Range: $450-499.9 Million
Emp.: 218
Rubber & Synthetic Resin Products
N.A.I.C.S.: 326199

Plant (Domestic):

Kuraray Plastics Co., Ltd. - Ibuki Plant (2)
4330 Osa Tarui-cho, Fuwa-gun, Gifu, 503-2122, Japan
Tel.: (81) 584 22 1251
Web Site: http://www.kuraray.co.jp
Plastic Materials Mfr
N.A.I.C.S.: 325211

Kuraray Saijo Co., Ltd. (1)
892 Tsuitachi, Saijo, 793-8585, Ehime, Japan
Tel.: (81) 897561158
Web Site: http://www.kuraray.co.jp
Sales Range: $450-499.9 Million
Emp.: 2,000
Mfr of Machinery Parts

N.A.I.C.S.: 325998

Kuraray South America Ltda. (1)
Av Paulista 1636 Condominio Paulista Corporate sala 405 Bela Vista, Sao Paulo, 01310-200, Brazil
Tel.: (55) 1126153531
Chemical Products Distr
N.A.I.C.S.: 424690

Kuraray South America Representacoes Ltda. (1)
Av Paulista 1636 - sala 405 CEP, Sao Paulo, 1404001, Brazil
Tel.: (55) 11 2615 3531
Web Site: http://www.kuraray.com.br
Sales Range: $50-74.9 Million
Emp.: 7
Chemical Products Distr
N.A.I.C.S.: 424690

Kuraray Tamashima Co., Ltd. (1)
7471 Tamashima Otoshima, Kurashiki, 713-8550, Okayama, Japan
Tel.: (81) 865265111
Synthetic Fiber Mfr
N.A.I.C.S.: 325211

Kuraray Techno Co., Ltd. (1)
Umeda Hankyu Building Office Tower 8-1 Kakudacho, Kita, Ku, Osaka, 530-8611, Japan
Web Site: http://www.kuraray-techno.com
Sales Range: $400-449.9 Million
Emp.: 1,700
Sub-Construction
N.A.I.C.S.: 236220

Kuraray Trading (Shanghai) Co., Ltd. (1)
Unit 2201 2 Grand Gateway 3 Hongqiao Road, Xu Hui District, Shanghai, 200030, China
Tel.: (86) 21 6407 9182
Chemical Products Distr
N.A.I.C.S.: 424690

Kuraray Trading Co., Ltd. (1)
1-1-3 Ote Center Bldg Otemachi, Otemachi Chuyado-Ku, Tokyo, 100-8115, Japan
Tel.: (81) 367011000
Web Site: http://www.kuraray.co.jp
Sales Range: $1-4.9 Billion
Emp.: 7,000
Importer, Exporter & Whslr of Textile Products & Chemicals
N.A.I.C.S.: 424690

Kuraray Trading Vietnam Co., Ltd. (1)
Rm 1501-02 Saigon Tower 29 Le Duan, Dist-1, Ho Chi Minh City, Vietnam
Tel.: (84) 2838243460
Chemical Product Mfr & Distr
N.A.I.C.S.: 325998

Kuraray Travel Service Corp. (1)
Web Site: http://www.kuraray.co.jp
Sales Range: $25-49.9 Million
Emp.: 10
Travel Services
N.A.I.C.S.: 561599

Kurashiki Kokusai Hotel, Ltd. (1)
1-1-44 Chuo, Kurashiki, 710-0046, Okayama, Japan (100%)
Tel.: (81) 864225141
Web Site: https://www.kurashiki-kokusai-hotel.co.jp
Emp.: 100
Manager of Hotels
N.A.I.C.S.: 721110

Kyosei Chemical Co., Ltd. (1)
Ote Center Building 1-1-3 Otemachi, Chiyoda-Ku, Tokyo, 100-8115, Japan (100%)
Tel.: (81) 367011000
Web Site: http://www.kuraray.co.jp
Mfr & Sales of Pigments, Agricultural Materials & Chemical Products
N.A.I.C.S.: 325130

OOO TROSIFOL (1)
24 Bor Ul Kolzowa, 606440, Nizhniy Novgorod, Russia
Tel.: (7) 8315927444
Web Site: http://www.kuraray.ru
Sales Range: $50-74.9 Million
Emp.: 71
Plastic Film Mfr & Distr

KURARAY CO., LTD.

Kuraray Co., Ltd.—(Continued)
N.A.I.C.S.: 326113
Nikolay Burdukhovskih *(Gen Mgr)*

Okayama Rinkoh Co., Ltd. (1)
2-1-16 Kaigan-dori, Minami-ku, Okayama, 702-8045, Japan
Tel.: (81) 862620161
Web Site: http://www.okarin.co.jp
Logistic Services
N.A.I.C.S.: 541614

Plantic Technologies Ltd (1)
51 Burns Road, Altona, 3018, VIC, Australia
Tel.: (61) 393537900
Web Site: http://www.plantic.com.au
Food Products Mfr
N.A.I.C.S.: 311999
Brendan Morris *(CEO)*

Techno Soft Co., Ltd. (1)
2-6-4 Otemachi, Chiyoda-ku, Tokyo, 100-0004, Japan
Tel.: (81) 367012339
Web Site: http://www.techno-soft.co.jp
Consulting & Temporary Staffing Services
N.A.I.C.S.: 561320
Mukai Yoshiaki *(Dir)*

KURAUDIA HOLDINGS CO., LTD.
34 Nishiin Takadacho, Ukyo-ku, Kyoto, 615-0031, Japan
Tel.: (81) 753152345   JP
Web Site:
    https://www.kuraudia.holdings
Year Founded: 1976
3607—(TKS)
Rev.: $82,222,180
Assets: $79,696,860
Liabilities: $55,880,480
Net Worth: $23,816,380
Earnings: $1,194,240
Emp.: 1,258
Fiscal Year-end: 08/31/24
Bridal Apparel Mfr
N.A.I.C.S.: 315210
Shoji Kura *(Chm & Pres)*

KURDISTAN INTERNATIONAL BANK FOR INVESTMENT & DEVELOPMENT
Gulan Street KIB Building, Erbil, Iraq
Tel.: (964) 66 211 2000
Web Site: http://www.kibid.com
BKUI—(IRAQ)
Sales Range: $10-24.9 Million
Banking & Investment Services
N.A.I.C.S.: 523150
Bustam Abood Al-Janabi *(Mng Dir)*

KURE GRINDING WHEEL CO., LTD.
2-1-5 Hamamatsu-cho, Minato-ku, Tokyo, 105 0013, Japan
Tel.: (81) 334324112
Web Site: http://www.kgw.co.jp
Year Founded: 1943
Sales Range: $150-199.9 Million
Emp.: 450
Abrasive Products Mfr & Distr
N.A.I.C.S.: 327910
Susumu Takahashi *(Pres)*

Subsidiaries:

Kure Grinding Wheel (Thailand) Co.,Ltd. (1)
2922/143 4th Fl Charn Issara Tower 2 New Petchburi Rd, Bangkapi Hway Kwang, Bangkok, 10310, Thailand
Tel.: (66) 2 308 2133
Web Site: http://www.kgw.co.jp
Abrasive Product Mfr
N.A.I.C.S.: 327910
Terauchi Hiroaki *(Mgr-Sls)*

Kure Grinding Wheel Co., Ltd. - Chiba Plant (1)
74 Sugaya, Isumi, 298-0106, Chiba-ken, Japan
Tel.: (81) 470 86 3010
Abrasive Product Mfr
N.A.I.C.S.: 327910

Kure Grinding Wheel Co., Ltd. - Eniwa Plant (1)
193-13 Toiso, Eniwa, 061-1405, Hokkaido, Japan
Tel.: (81) 123 33 8400
Web Site: http://www.kgw.co.jp
Sales Range: $125-149.9 Million
Emp.: 40
Abrasive Product Mfr
N.A.I.C.S.: 327910

Kure Grinding Wheel Co., Ltd. - Kokufu Plant (1)
515-4 Kifune Kokufucho Ima, Takayama, 509-4104, Gifu-ken, Japan
Tel.: (81) 577 72 3032
Abrasive Product Mfr
N.A.I.C.S.: 327910

Kure Grinding Wheel Co., Ltd. - Kure Plant (1)
2-3-20 Yoshiura-shinmachi, Kure, 737-8518, Hiroshima-ken, Japan
Tel.: (81) 823 31 7171
Sales Range: $200-249.9 Million
Abrasive Product Mfr
N.A.I.C.S.: 327910

Taiwan Kure Grinding Wheel Co., Ltd. (1)
71043 No 29 Alley 21 Lane 279 Chung Cheng Road, Yung Kang District, T'ainan, Taiwan
Tel.: (886) 6 204 2506
Abrasive Product Mfr
N.A.I.C.S.: 327910

KUREHA CORPORATION
3-3-2 Nihonbashi-Hamacho, Chuo-ku, Tokyo, 103-8552, Japan
Tel.: (81) 332494666   JP
Web Site: https://www.kureha.co.jp
Year Founded: 1944
4023—(TKS)
Rev.: $1,176,401,530
Assets: $2,185,464,300
Liabilities: $710,456,020
Net Worth: $1,475,008,280
Earnings: $64,341,740
Emp.: 4,217
Fiscal Year-end: 03/31/24
Industrial Chemical Mfr & Retailer
N.A.I.C.S.: 325998
Yoshio Noda *(Sr VP, Mng Dir-Internal Control & Auditing & Gen Mgr-Fin & Acctg)*

Subsidiaries:

Himeyuri Total Work Co., Ltd. (1)
Tel.: (81) 246264111
Web Site: http://www.himeyuri-sougyo.com
Emp.: 26
Industrial Waste Management Services
N.A.I.C.S.: 562998

Krehalon Australia Pty. Ltd. (1)
25 Efficient Drive, Truganina, 3029, VIC, Australia
Tel.: (61) 383751893
Food Packaging Product Whslr
N.A.I.C.S.: 424420

Krehalon B.V. (1)
Parklaan 22 - Bus 4, 2300, Turnhout, Belgium
Tel.: (32) 14408530
Food Packaging Products Mfr
N.A.I.C.S.: 322299

Krehalon B.V. (1)
Unit 10 IPark Industrial Estate Innovation Drive, Kingston upon Hull, HU5 1SG, East Yorkshire, United Kingdom
Tel.: (44) 1482865277
Food Packaging Product Whslr
N.A.I.C.S.: 424420

Krehalon B.V. (1)
8/10 Rue de Bois Sauvage, PO 197, 91006, Evry, Cedex, France
Tel.: (33) 169870707
Food Packaging Products Mfr
N.A.I.C.S.: 322299

Krehalon B.V. (1)
Londenstraat 10, 7418 EE, Deventer, Netherlands
Tel.: (31) 630844603
Food Packaging Products Mfr
N.A.I.C.S.: 322299

Krehalon UK Ltd. (1)
Unit 10 Ipark Industrial Estate Innovation Drive, Hull, HU5 1SG, East Yorkshire, United Kingdom
Tel.: (44) 1482865277
Web Site: http://www.krehalonuk.co.uk
Emp.: 30
Packaging Materials Mfr & Sales
N.A.I.C.S.: 326112
Steven Hinsley *(Mng Dir)*

Kureha (Changshu) Fluoropolymers Co., Ltd. (1)
No 2 Haiping Road, Advanced Materials Industrial Park, Changshu, Jiangsu, China
Tel.: (86) 51252327600
Web Site: https://www.kureha-kfpc.com.cn
Carbon Fiber Mfr & Whslr
N.A.I.C.S.: 335991

Kureha (China) Investment Co., Ltd. (1)
Room 2704 Qiantan World Trade Center No 5 Lane 255 Dongyu Road, Pudong, 200126, Shanghai, China
Tel.: (86) 2163527036
Web Site: http://www.kureha.com.cn
Financial Services
N.A.I.C.S.: 522299

Kureha (Shanghai) Carbon Fiber Materials Co., Ltd. (1)
No 1585 Xingrong Road, Jiading, Shanghai, 201815, China
Tel.: (86) 2139963006
Web Site: http://www.kureha.sh
Carbon Fiber Mfr & Whslr
N.A.I.C.S.: 335991

Kureha Advanced Materials, Inc. (1)
10 Acee Dr Highlands Industrial Park, Natrona Heights, PA 15065
Tel.: (724) 295-3352
Web Site: http://www.kamtl.com
Sales Range: $25-49.9 Million
Emp.: 13
Graphite Insulation Materials Mfr
N.A.I.C.S.: 335991
Yoshitsugu Nishibayashi *(Pres)*

Kureha America Inc. (1)
3151 Briarpark Dr Ste 1025, Houston, TX 77042
Tel.: (281) 916-1633
Web Site: http://www.kureha.com
Industrial Chemical Whslr
N.A.I.C.S.: 424690
Fred Daniell *(Pres)*

Kureha Chemicals Shanghai Co., Ltd. (1)
1585 Xing Rong Rd, Jiading, Shanghai, China
Tel.: (86) 2183363060
Web Site: http://www.kureha.sh
Sales Range: $50-74.9 Million
Emp.: 76
Thermal Insulation Materials Mfr & Whslr
N.A.I.C.S.: 326140

Kureha Corporation - Iwaki Factory (1)
16 Ochiai, Nishiki-machi, Iwaki, 974-8686, Fukushima, Japan
Tel.: (81) 246635111
Synthetic Resin Mfr
N.A.I.C.S.: 325211

Kureha Corporation - Plastics Processing Factory (1)
2221 Kamitamari, Omitama, 311-3493, Ibaraki, Japan
Tel.: (81) 299261181
Web Site: http://www.kureha.co.jp
Sales Range: $125-149.9 Million
Emp.: 200
Polyvinyl Chloride Resins Mfr
N.A.I.C.S.: 325211

Kureha Ecology Management Co., Ltd. (1)
30 Shitanda, Nishiki-machi, Iwaki, 974-

INTERNATIONAL PUBLIC

8232, Fukushima, Japan   (100%)
Tel.: (81) 246631231
Web Site: https://www.kurekan.co.jp
Emp.: 364
Industrial Waste Treatment & Disposal Services
N.A.I.C.S.: 562998
Nobuyuki Taniguchi *(Pres)*

Kureha Energy Solutions LLC (1)
3151 Briarpark Dr Ste 1050, Houston, TX 77042
Tel.: (713) 893-0730
Web Site: http://www.kureha-energy-solutions.com
Industrial Machinery & Equipment Whslr
N.A.I.C.S.: 423830

Kureha Engineering Co., Ltd. (1)
135 Ochiai, Nishikicho, Iwaki, 974-8232, Fukushima, Japan
Tel.: (81) 246635150
Web Site: https://www.kureha-eng.co.jp
Sales Range: $75-99.9 Million
Emp.: 45
Waste Water Treatment & Plant Engineering Services
N.A.I.C.S.: 562211

Kureha Europe B.V. (1)
Londenstraat 10, PO Box 414, 7400 AK, Deventer, Netherlands   (100%)
Tel.: (31) 570505315
Sales Range: $25-49.9 Million
Emp.: 3
Holding & Management Company
N.A.I.C.S.: 551112

Subsidiary (Non-US):

Krehalon France S.A.S. (2)
8/10 rue du Bois Sauvage, BP 197, 91006, Evry, Cedex, France
Tel.: (33) 169870707
Web Site: http://www.krehalon.fr
Sales Range: $25-49.9 Million
Packaging Material Distr
N.A.I.C.S.: 423840

Subsidiary (Domestic):

Krehalon Industrie B.V. (2)
Londenstraat 10, 7418 EE, Deventer, Netherlands
Tel.: (31) 570624333
Web Site: http://www.krehalon.nl
Sales Range: $50-74.9 Million
Food Packaging Materials Mfr
N.A.I.C.S.: 326111

Kureha Extech Co., Ltd. (1)
5691 Shishikura, Kasumigaura, 300-0121, Ibaraki, Japan
Tel.: (81) 298311311
Web Site: http://www.kureha-extron.co.jp
Plastic Films & Sheets Mfr
N.A.I.C.S.: 326112

Kureha Extron Co., Ltd (1)
NET Building 5F 1-23-1 Omorikita, Ota-ku, Tokyo, 143-0016, Japan
Tel.: (81) 337642511
Web Site: https://www.kureha-extron.co.jp
Emp.: 66
Resins Mfr & Distr
N.A.I.C.S.: 325211

Kureha GmbH (1)
Liesegangstrasse 17A, 40211, Dusseldorf, Germany
Tel.: (49) 211369710
Web Site: https://kureha.de
Industrial Chemical Distr
N.A.I.C.S.: 424690

Kureha Gohsen Co., Ltd. (1)
1-63 Motomachi Mibu-cho, Shimotsuga-gun, Tochigi, 321-0223, Japan
Tel.: (81) 647958104
Web Site: https://www.kureha-gohsen.jp
Emp.: 123
Plastic Material Whslr
N.A.I.C.S.: 424610

Kureha Gosen Co., Ltd. (1)
1-33 Motomachi Mibu-cho, Shimotsuga-gun, Tochigi, 321-0223, Japan
Tel.: (81) 282822111
Web Site: http://www.kureha-gohsen.jp
Sales Range: $25-49.9 Million
Emp.: 100
Plastic Resin Mfr

N.A.I.C.S.: 325211
Kouji Suyama (Gen Mgr)

Kureha PGA LLC (1)
901 W DuPont Ave, Belle, WV 25015-1598
Tel.: (304) 513-0100
Sales Range: $25-49.9 Million
Emp.: 45
Polymer Resin Mfr
N.A.I.C.S.: 325211

Kureha Plastics Co., Ltd. (1)
2221 Kamitamari, Omitama, 311-3493, Ibaraki, Japan
Tel.: (81) 299261181
Food Packaging Materials Mfr & Distr
N.A.I.C.S.: 322220

Kureha Service Co., Ltd. (1)
3-3-2 Nihonbashi-Hamacho, Chuo-ku, Tokyo, 103-8552, Japan
Tel.: (81) 332494697
Web Site: http://kureha-service.co.jp
Emp.: 68
Real Estate Services
N.A.I.C.S.: 531390

Kureha Shanghai Trading Co., Ltd. (1)
Room 2704B Building B New Bund World Trade Center1 No 5 Lane255, Shanghai, 200126, China
Tel.: (86) 2154662011
Sales Range: $50-74.9 Million
Emp.: 10
Chemicals Whslr
N.A.I.C.S.: 424690
David Chang (Gen Mgr)

Kureha Special Laboratory Co., Ltd. (1)
16 Ochiai, Nishiki-cho, Iwaki, 974-8232, Fukushima, Japan
Tel.: (81) 246636755
Web Site: https://www.kureha-bunseki.co.jp
Emp.: 92
Laboratory Testing Services
N.A.I.C.S.: 621511
Keiichi Yoshimoto (Pres)

Kureha Staff Service Co., Ltd. (1)
135 Ochiai Nishiki-cho, Iwaki, 974-8232, Fukushima, Japan
Tel.: (81) 246631303
Web Site: https://www.kure-sta.co.jp
Temporary Staffing Services
N.A.I.C.S.: 561320

Kureha Trading Co., Ltd. (1)
Nihonbashi Horidomecho First 1-2-10, Nihonbashi Horidome-cho Chuo-ku, Tokyo, 103-0012, Japan
Tel.: (81) 336398731
Web Site: https://www.kureha-trading.co.jp
Emp.: 93
Chemicals & Allied Products Distr
N.A.I.C.S.: 423830
Fumihiko Yamada (Pres & CEO)

Kureha Unyu Co., Ltd. (1)
69 Ochiai Nishikimachi, Iwaki, 974-8232, Fukushima, Japan
Tel.: (81) 246 63 2311
Web Site: http://www.kure-un.co.jp
Emp.: 178
General Freight Trucking Services
N.A.I.C.S.: 484110

Kureha Vietnam Co., Ltd. (1)
Plot 227/3 Road 13 Amata Industrial Park, Long Binh Ward, 71000, Bien Hoa, Dong Nai, Vietnam
Tel.: (84) 2513936804
Packaging Film Mfr & Sales
N.A.I.C.S.: 326112

Kureha-kai Medical Corporation (1)
1-1 Ochiai, Nishiki-machi, Iwaki, 974-8232, Fukushima, Japan
Tel.: (81) 246632181
Web Site: http://www.kureha-hosp.jp
General Medical Services
N.A.I.C.S.: 622110

Kurehanishiki Construction Co., Ltd. (1)
16 Ayanomachi Nishiki-cho, Iwaki, 974-8232, Fukushima, Japan
Tel.: (81) 246648181
Web Site: https://www.kureha-const.co.jp

Construction Engineering Services
N.A.I.C.S.: 541330

Sunshine Kureha Co., Ltd. (1)
135 Ochiai, Nishiki-machi, Iwaki, 974-8686, Fukushima, Japan
Tel.: (81) 246636688
Administrative Services
N.A.I.C.S.: 561110

KURGANSKAYA GENERIRUY-USHCHAYA KOMPANIYA OAO
Constitution Avenue 29A, Kurgan, 640000, Russia
Tel.: (7) 3522635359
Web Site: https://www.kgk-kurgan.ru
Year Founded: 2006
KGKC—(MOEX)
Sales Range: Less than $1 Million
Eletric Power Generation Services
N.A.I.C.S.: 221118
Stanislav Seyranovich Karapetyan (Chm)

KURIBAYASHI STEAMSHIP CO., LTD.
3F Shin-Otemachi Bldg 2-2-1 Otemachi, Chiyoda-ku, Tokyo, 100-0004, Japan
Tel.: (81) 352037981
Web Site:
   https://www.kuribayashishosen.com
Year Founded: 1919
9171—(TKS)
Rev.: $323,129,850
Assets: $515,130,520
Liabilities: $318,178,960
Net Worth: $196,951,560
Earnings: $11,058,530
Emp.: 1,100
Fiscal Year-end: 03/31/24
Marine Transportation Services
N.A.I.C.S.: 483111
Hiroyoshi Kuribayashi (Chm, Pres & CEO)

KURIERVERLAGS GMBH & CO. KG
Friedrich-Engels-Ring 29, 17033, Neubrandenburg, Germany
Tel.: (49) 395 4575 0   De
Web Site: http://www.nordkurier.de
Newspaper Publishers
N.A.I.C.S.: 513110
Lutz Schumacher (Mng Dir)

Subsidiaries:

Eurotape Media Services GmbH (1)
Buckower Chaussee 134, 12277, Berlin,
Germany (100%)
Tel.: (49) 30742070
Web Site: http://www.eurotape.de
Motion Picture & Video Distr
N.A.I.C.S.: 512120

KURIMOTO LTD
1-12-19 Kitahorie, Nishi-ku, Osaka, 550-8580, Japan
Tel.: (81) 665387943
Web Site: https://www.kurimoto.co.jp
5602—(TKS)
Rev.: $832,364,250
Assets: $999,273,360
Liabilities: $452,428,060
Net Worth: $546,845,300
Earnings: $36,156,700
Emp.: 2,121
Fiscal Year-end: 03/31/24
Ductile Iron Pipes Mfr & Sales
N.A.I.C.S.: 326122
Hirobumi Okada (Sr Mng Exec Officer)

Subsidiaries:

Hokkaido Kanzai Co., Ltd. (1)
4-jo 4-1-40 Shinkawa, Kita-ku Sapporo, Hokkaido, 001-0924, Japan (80%)
Tel.: (81) 117697077

Web Site: https://h-kanzai.co.jp
Sales Range: $50-74.9 Million
Cast Iron Pipes & Valves Mfr
N.A.I.C.S.: 332111

Ks-Tech Co., Ltd. (1)
220 Hokonoki Tateyama-machi, Toyama, 930-0276, Japan
Tel.: (81) 764629611
Rev.: $21,434,144
Emp.: 50
Forging Machine Mfr
N.A.I.C.S.: 333517

Kurimoto Business Associates Co., Ltd. (1)
1-chome 12-19 Kitahorie, Nishi-ku, Osaka, 550-8580, Japan
Tel.: (81) 665387312
Insurance Services
N.A.I.C.S.: 524210

Kurimoto Concrete Industries, Ltd. (1)
961 Toendo Aisyo-cho, Echi-gun, Shiga, 529-1383, Japan
Tel.: (81) 749423111
Web Site: http://www.kuricon-soc.co.jp
Emp.: 60
Concrete Pipe Mfr
N.A.I.C.S.: 327332
Toshio Imai (Pres)

Kurimoto Logistics Corporation (1)
15-1 Ishizu Nishimachi, Nishi-ku, Sakai, 592-8332, Osaka, Japan
Tel.: (81) 722807071
Steel Pipe Distr
N.A.I.C.S.: 423510

Kurimoto Ltd - Chita Factory (1)
2-7 Sinkatanaike Daikouji, Chita, 478-0069, Aichi, Japan
Tel.: (81) 562540311
Steel Pipes & Valves Mfr
N.A.I.C.S.: 331210

Kurimoto Ltd - Fukuoka Factory (1)
760-5 Numaguchi, Miyawaka, 822-0152, Fukuoka, Japan
Tel.: (81) 949520677
Web Site: http://www.kurimoto.co.jp
Winding Pipes & Spiral Ducts Mfr
N.A.I.C.S.: 332919

Kurimoto Ltd - Kagaya Factory (1)
1-64 Izumi 2-chome, Suminoe-ku, Osaka, 559-0023, Japan
Tel.: (81) 666861010
Web Site: http://www.kurimoto.co.jp
Sales Range: $100-124.9 Million
Emp.: 300
Ductile Iron Pipes Mfr
N.A.I.C.S.: 331210
Yoshinaga Yasuhaadu (Mgr)

Kurimoto Ltd - Katano Factory (1)
5-13-1 Ikuno, Katano, 576-0054, Osaka, Japan
Tel.: (81) 728911671
Winding Pipes & Spiral Ducts Mfr
N.A.I.C.S.: 332919

Kurimoto Ltd - Koga Factory (1)
10-6 Okazato, Sashima-gun, Koga, 306-0206, Ibaraki, Japan
Tel.: (81) 280971301
Steel Pipes & Valves Mfr
N.A.I.C.S.: 332911

Kurimoto Ltd - Matsudo Factory (1)
720 Kamihongou, Matsudo, 271-0064, Chiba, Japan
Tel.: (81) 47 368 4111
Steel Pipes & Valves Mfr
N.A.I.C.S.: 331210

Kurimoto Ltd - Okayama Factory (1)
53-1 Aza-Nishimukai Kanaya, Yoshinaga-cho, Bizen, 709-0221, Okayama, Japan
Tel.: (81) 869629958
Winding Pipes & Spiral Ducts Mfr
N.A.I.C.S.: 332919

Kurimoto Ltd - Sakai Factory (1)
14-1 Ishizu Nishi-machi, Nishi-ku, Sakai, 592-8332, Osaka, Japan
Tel.: (81) 722410225
Sales Range: $50-74.9 Million
Emp.: 128
Ductile Iron Pipes Mfr

N.A.I.C.S.: 331210
Yasuharu Yoshinaga (Gen Mgr)

Kurimoto Ltd - Sapporo Factory (1)
4 10 12-chome Hassamu 15 Jyo, Nishi-ku, Sapporo, 063-0835, Hokkaido, Japan
Tel.: (81) 116637553
Steel Pipes & Valves Mfr
N.A.I.C.S.: 331210

Kurimoto Ltd - Sendai Factory (1)
3-12 Azaaokisawakitayama Miake, Kurokawa-gun, Osato, 981-3515, Miyagi, Japan
Tel.: (81) 223476201
Sales Range: $25-49.9 Million
Emp.: 15
Winding Pipes & Spiral Ducts Mfr
N.A.I.C.S.: 332919
Eiji Fukata (Mgr)

Kurimoto Ltd - Sumiyoshi Factory (1)
8-45 Shibatani 2-Chome, Suminoe-ku, Osaka, 559-0021, Japan
Tel.: (81) 666863111
Web Site: http://www.kurimoto.co.jp
Sales Range: $400-449.9 Million
Emp.: 1,300
Industrial Machines & Valves Mfr
N.A.I.C.S.: 332911
Higeaki Fukuri (Pres)

Kurimoto Pipe Engineering Co., Ltd. (1)
2-1-164 Izumi Kurimoto Iron Works Kagaya Factory, Suminoe-ku, Osaka, 559-0023, Japan
Tel.: (81) 666861101
Pipeline Maintenance Services
N.A.I.C.S.: 237120

Kurimoto Plastics Co., Ltd. (1)
12-19 Kitahorie 1-Chome, Nishi-ku, Osaka, 550-8580, Japan
Tel.: (81) 665387701
Rev.: $70,413,400
Emp.: 500
Fiber Reinforced Plastic Pipes & Synthetic Resin Products Mfr
N.A.I.C.S.: 326122
Minoru Fukuda (Mng Dir)

Kurimoto Polymers Co., Ltd. (1)
8th Floor NK Tanimachi Building 9-1-22 Tanimachi, Chuo-ku, Osaka, 542-0012, Japan
Web Site: http://www.kuripoly.jp
Polyethylene Pipe Mfr & Distr
N.A.I.C.S.: 326122

Kurimoto Trading Co., Ltd. (1)
2-4-2 Shinmachi, Nishi-ku, Osaka, 550-0013, Japan
Tel.: (81) 661107450
Steel Pipe Distr
N.A.I.C.S.: 423510

Kurimoto USA, Inc. (1)
550 N State St, York, PA 17403
Tel.: (717) 848-2801
Steel Pipe Mfr & Distr
N.A.I.C.S.: 331210

Kuritetsu (Shanghai) Trading Co., Ltd. (1)
Suite 501 Aetna Tower 107 Zunyi Road, Shanghai, China
Tel.: (86) 2162375849
Steel Pipe Distr
N.A.I.C.S.: 423510

Motoyama Eng Works, Ltd. (1)
5-2 Ohira Aza Kameoka, Kurokawa-gun, Ohira, 981-3697, Miyagi, Japan
Tel.: (81) 223444511
Web Site: https://www.motoyama-cp.co.jp
Emp.: 256
Valve Mfr
N.A.I.C.S.: 332911

Nihon Kaiser Co., Ltd. (1)
5th floor NSS-II Building 2-13-34 Konan, Minato-ku, Tokyo, 108-0075, Japan
Tel.: (81) 364351721
Web Site: https://www.nihon-kaiser.co.jp
Precast Product Mfr & Distr
N.A.I.C.S.: 327390

Readco Kurimoto, LLC (1)
550 N State St, York, PA 17403

KURIMOTO LTD

Kurimoto Ltd—(Continued)
Tel.: (717) 848-2801
Dry Powder Blending Equipment Mfr
N.A.I.C.S.: 333241

Riko, Ltd. (1)
1-3 Minquan Road Minsheng Borough,
Danshui Township, Taipei, Taiwan
Tel.: (886) 288097771
Valve Product Mfr & Distr
N.A.I.C.S.: 332911

Sanko Kiko Co., Ltd. (1)
12 Karahashi Kawakubo-cho, Minami-ku,
Kyoto, 601-8451, Japan
Tel.: (81) 756812771
Web Site: https://www.sankomt.co.jp
Cutting, Measuring & Other Industrial
Equipments Mfr
N.A.I.C.S.: 333310
Yukinobu Nishimura (Mng Dir)

Sasebo Metal Co., Ltd. (1)
50/19 Shiratake-cho, Sasebo, 8571164, Nagasaki, Japan
Tel.: (81) 956313101
Rev.: $9,059,688
Emp.: 40
Cast Iron Mfr
N.A.I.C.S.: 332111
Sieg Makino (Pres)

Sunrise Co., Ltd. (1)
Kaiun-cho A-1-14-1, Nagata-ku, Kobe, 653-0052, Hyogo, Japan
Tel.: (81) 8015262653
Web Site: http://www.sunrise-med.com
Medical Equipment Whslr
N.A.I.C.S.: 423450

Yamatogawa Co., Ltd. (1)
Yamada Kitahorie Bldg 1-12-10, Nishi-ku,
Osaka, 550-0014, Japan
Tel.: (81) 665415153
Rev.: $153,292,768
Cast Iron Pipes & Resins Whslr
N.A.I.C.S.: 423510

Yashima Chemical Engineering Co., Ltd. (1)
Mitsuyaminami 3 chome No 22, Yodogawa-ku, Osaka, 532-0035, Japan
Tel.: (81) 663096461
Web Site: http://www.yashima-ce.co.jp
Emp.: 30
Heating Equipment Mfr
N.A.I.C.S.: 333414
Shinichi Sakurai (Pres)

KURITA WATER INDUSTRIES LTD.
Nakano Central Park East General
Reception on 10F 10-1Nakano
4-Chome, Nakano-ku, Tokyo, 164-0001, Japan
Tel.: (81) 367435000
Web Site: https://www.kurita.co.jp
6370—(TKS)
Rev.: $2,543,693,250
Assets: $3,684,460,270
Liabilities: $1,480,613,560
Net Worth: $2,203,846,710
Earnings: $192,939,290
Emp.: 7,981
Fiscal Year-end: 03/31/24
Water & Environmental Management Services
N.A.I.C.S.: 221310
Kiyoshi Itou (Sr Mng Dir & Gen Mgr-Corp Plng & Control Div)

Subsidiaries:

Aoi Industries Co., Ltd. (1)
5-24 Aosaki 1-chome, Oita, 870-0278, Japan
Tel.: (81) 975217926
Web Site: http://www.kurita.co.jp
Tool Cleaning Services
N.A.I.C.S.: 811310

Avista Technologies (UK) Ltd. (1)
13 Nasmyth Square, Houstoun Industrial
Estate, Livingston, EH54 5GG, United Kingdom
Tel.: (44) 1314496677
Water Treatment Chemical Mfr

N.A.I.C.S.: 325998

Fracta, Inc. (1)
2400 Broadway Ste 220, Redwood City, CA 94063
Web Site: http://www.fracta.ai
Software Development Services
N.A.I.C.S.: 541511
Takashi Kato (Co-Founder, Pres & CEO)

Hansu Co., Ltd. (1)
44 Sandan-ro 35bean-gil, Danwaon-gu, Ansan, Gyeonggi-do, Korea (South)
Tel.: (82) 314927800
Web Site: http://www.hansu.co.kr
Waste Treatment Services
N.A.I.C.S.: 221310
Koichi Kato (Pres & CEO)

Hansu Technical Service Ltd. (1)
Room 802 Building C Bundang Techno
Park 744 Pangyo-ro, Bundang-gu, Seongnam, 13510, Gyeonggi, Korea (South)
Tel.: (82) 317891700
Web Site: https://www.hansuts.co.kr
Waste Treatment Services
N.A.I.C.S.: 221320

Kurita (Singapore) Pte. Ltd. (1)
30 Joo Koon Rd, Singapore, 628984, Singapore
Tel.: (65) 6861 2622
Web Site: http://www.kurita.com.sg
Sales Range: $25-49.9 Million
Emp.: 18
Water Treatment Chemicals, Facilities & Sales
N.A.I.C.S.: 221310
Eishi Shimmura (Mng Dir)

Kurita (Taiwan) Co., Ltd. (1)
11F No 156-1 Songjiang Road, Taipei, 10459, Taiwan
Tel.: (886) 225421568
Web Site: https://www.kuritataiwan.com.tw
Emp.: 55
Water Treatment Chemical Mfr & Sales
N.A.I.C.S.: 325998

Kurita America Holdings Inc. (1)
1313 Valwood Pkwy Ste 370, Carrollton, TX 75006
Tel.: (972) 484-4438
Web Site: http://www.kuritaamerica.com
Sales Range: $75-99.9 Million
Emp.: 20
Waste Treatment Services
N.A.I.C.S.: 221320
Masahiko Mitsumi (CEO)

Subsidiary (Domestic):

Avista Technologies, Inc. (2)
140 Bosstick Blvd, San Marcos, CA 92069
Tel.: (760) 744-0536
Web Site: http://www.avistatech.com
Miscellaneous Chemical Product & Preparation Mfr
N.A.I.C.S.: 325998
Dan Comstock (VP-R&D)

Pentagon Technologies Group, Inc. (2)
21031 Alexander Ct, Hayward, CA 94545
Tel.: (510) 783-5050
Web Site: https://www.pen-tec.com
Integrated Defects Reduction Products & Services; Semiconductor Fabrication & Related Manufacturing Equipment Industry
N.A.I.C.S.: 561720
David Christeson (CFO)

Kurita America Inc. (1)
12270 43rd St NE, Saint Michael, MN 55376
Web Site: http://www.kuritaamerica.com
Waste Treatment Services
N.A.I.C.S.: 221310
Masahiko Mitsuta (Chm)

Kurita Analysis Service Co., Ltd. (1)
2-8-14 Takanodai, Tsukuba, 305-8504, Ibaraki, Japan
Tel.: (81) 298367011
Web Site: https://www.kuritabunseki.co.jp
Sales Range: $250-299.9 Million
Emp.: 300
Water Treatment & Testing Services
N.A.I.C.S.: 221310

Kurita BMS Co., Ltd. (1)

2-1-6 Sasazuka, Shibuya-ku, Tokyo, 151-0073, Japan
Tel.: (81) 353025233
Web Site: https://bms.kurita.co.jp
Emp.: 30
Water Treatment Chemicals Sales
N.A.I.C.S.: 424690

Kurita Buil-Tech Co., Ltd. (1)
2-1-6 Sasazuka, Shibuya-ku, Tokyo, 151-0073, Japan (100%)
Tel.: (81) 333751881
Web Site: http://www.kuritabuiltech.com
Water Treatment Chemicals Sales
N.A.I.C.S.: 424690
Akihiro Yokoyama (Pres)

Kurita Chemical Kanto Ltd. (1)
3-15-7 Kyowa, Chuo-ku, Sagamihara, 252-0234, Kanagawa, Japan
Tel.: (81) 427070234
Web Site: http://www.chemical-kantou.co.jp
Water Treatment Chemicals Sales
N.A.I.C.S.: 424690
Keizo Tanaka (Dir)

Kurita Chemical Manufacturing Ltd. (1)
2585-1 Egawa, Gokamachi, Sashima, 306-0303, Ibaraki, Japan
Tel.: (81) 280843010
Web Site: http://www.kurita.co.jp
Water Treatment Chemical Mfr
N.A.I.C.S.: 325998

Kurita Chemicals Hokkaido Ltd. (1)
1-2-12 Gojo Kikusui Motomachi, Shiroishi-ku, Sapporo, 003-0825, Hokkaido, Japan
Tel.: (81) 118718008
Web Site: https://hokkaido.kurita.co.jp
Emp.: 20
Water Treatment Chemicals Sales
N.A.I.C.S.: 424690

Kurita Chemicals Kansai Ltd. (1)
4-1-6 Mizuki-dori, Hyogo-ku, Kobe, 652-0802, Hyogo, Japan
Tel.: (81) 785787011
Web Site: http://kansai.kurita.co.jp
Sales Range: $25-49.9 Million
Emp.: 48
Water Treatment Chemicals Sales
N.A.I.C.S.: 424690

Kurita Chemicals Kumamoto Ltd. (1)
2-18-94 Oyama-machi, Kumamoto, 861-8045, Japan
Tel.: (81) 963893250
Web Site: http://www.kurita.co.jp
Sales Range: $25-49.9 Million
Emp.: 12
Water Treatment Chemicals Supplier
N.A.I.C.S.: 424690
Youichi Ooya (Mng Dir)

Kurita Chemicals Oita Ltd. (1)
15-29 Harushinmachi, Oita, 870-0912, Japan
Tel.: (81) 975521177
Web Site: http://www.kurita-chemical.jp
Water Treatment Chemicals Sales
N.A.I.C.S.: 424690

Kurita Chemicals Sanyo Co. Ltd. (1)
237-126 Nishifurumatsu, Kita-ku, Okayama, 700-0927, Japan
Tel.: (81) 868050051
Web Site: http://sanyo.kurita.co.jp
Emp.: 23
Water Treatment Chemicals Whslr
N.A.I.C.S.: 424690

Kurita Chemicals Tokai Co., Ltd. (1)
7F Nissay Ichinomiya Building 1-2-8 Shinsei, Ichinomiya, 491-0912, Aichi, Japan
Tel.: (81) 586438300
Web Site: https://tokai.kurita.co.jp
Sales Range: $25-49.9 Million
Emp.: 65
Water Treatment Chemicals Sales
N.A.I.C.S.: 424690

Kurita Chemicals West Japan Ltd. (1)
8-1 Asano 3-Chome, Kokura-Kita-ku, Kitakyushu, 802-0001, Fukuoka, Japan
Tel.: (81) 935115900
Web Site: http://kcw.kurita.co.jp
Water Treatment Chemicals Sales
N.A.I.C.S.: 424690

INTERNATIONAL PUBLIC

Kurita Creation Co., Ltd. (1)
46-1 Hon-Machi 2-chome, Nakano-ku, Tokyo, 164-0012, Japan
Tel.: (81) 353081301
Web Site: http://www.kuritac.co.jp
Sales Range: $25-49.9 Million
Emp.: 40
Household Products Mfr & Supplier
N.A.I.C.S.: 335220

Kurita Engineering Co., Ltd. (1)
2-22 Kitahama 2-chome, Chuo-Ku, Osaka, 541-0041, Japan
Tel.: (81) 662284931
Web Site: http://www.kurita-eng.com
Sales Range: $25-49.9 Million
Emp.: 100
Chemical Cleaning & Renewal Solutions
N.A.I.C.S.: 562219

Kurita Europe GmbH (1)
Giulinistr 2, 67065, Ludwigshafen, Germany
Tel.: (49) 62112183000
Web Site: http://www.kurita.eu
Sales Range: $25-49.9 Million
Emp.: 50
Water Treatment Chemicals Mfr & Sales
N.A.I.C.S.: 325180
Shingo Yamaga (Mng Dir)

Kurita France S.A.S. (1)
ZI du Bec d'Ambes, 33810, Ambes, France
Tel.: (33) 478434250
Waste Treatment Services
N.A.I.C.S.: 221310

Kurita Hokkaido Ltd. (1)
1-2-12 Gojo Kikusui Motomachi, Shiroishi-ku, Sapporo, 003-0825, Hokkaido, Japan
Tel.: (81) 118718008
Web Site: https://hokkaido.kurita.co.jp
Emp.: 20
Waste Treatment Services
N.A.I.C.S.: 221310

Kurita Hokuriku Ltd. (1)
1-11-12 Rencho, Toyama, 931-8333, Japan
Tel.: (81) 764383001
Web Site: https://hokuriku.kurita.co.jp
Emp.: 22
Water Treatment Equipment Mfr
N.A.I.C.S.: 333310

Kurita Iberica SL (1)
Av Alcalde Barnils 64-68 Bloque B Planta 2 Local 4, Sant Cugat del Valles, 08174, Barcelona, Spain
Tel.: (34) 936750345
Waste Treatment Services
N.A.I.C.S.: 221310

Kurita Kansai Ltd. (1)
4-1-6 Mizuki-dori, Hyogo-ku, Kobe, 652-0802, Hyogo Prefecture, Japan
Tel.: (81) 785787011
Web Site: http://kansai.kurita.co.jp
Water Treatment Equipment Mfr
N.A.I.C.S.: 333310

Kurita Kanto Ltd. (1)
3-15-7 Kyowa, Chuo-ku, Sagamihara, 252-0234, Kanagawa Prefecture, Japan
Tel.: (81) 427070234
Web Site: http://kanto.kurita.co.jp
Water Treatment Chemical Mfr
N.A.I.C.S.: 325998

Kurita Kitakantou Co., Ltd. (1)
9-15-3 Shinshirooka, Shirakawa, 349-0212, Saitama Prefecture, Japan
Web Site: http://kitakantou.kurita.co.jp
Water Treatment Equipment Mfr
N.A.I.C.S.: 333310

Kurita Kyusyu Ltd. (1)
4F AIM Building 3-8-1 Asano, Kokura Kita Ward, Kitakyushu, 802-0001, Fukuoka, Japan
Tel.: (81) 935115900
Web Site: https://kyusyu.kurita.co.jp
Emp.: 96
Water Treatment Chemical Mfr
N.A.I.C.S.: 325998

Kurita Meiki Ltd. (1)
1-2913 Takagi Chuo, Fukui, 910-0804, Japan
Tel.: (81) 776535355
Web Site: https://www.kuritameiki.co.jp
Emp.: 30
Waste Treatment Services
N.A.I.C.S.: 562211

AND PRIVATE COMPANIES

Kurita Middle East FZE (1)
Street S-1100 Plot S-40801, Jebel Ali - South, Dubai, United Arab Emirates
Tel.: (971) 48807701
Water Treatment Chemical Mfr
N.A.I.C.S.: 325998

Kurita Polska SP.z.o.o. (1)
Uniwersytecka, 1340-007, Katowice, Poland
Tel.: (48) 327002565
Waste Treatment Services
N.A.I.C.S.: 221310

Kurita R&D Asia Pte. Ltd. (1)
1 Cleantech Loop 04-08 CleanTech One, Singapore, 637141, Singapore
Tel.: (65) 67343260
Waste Treatment Services
N.A.I.C.S.: 221310

Kurita Sanyo Ltd. (1)
237-126 Nishifurumatsu, Kita-ku, Okayama, 700-0927, Japan
Tel.: (81) 868050051
Web Site: http://sanyo.kurita.co.jp
Waste Treatment Services
N.A.I.C.S.: 221310

Kurita Sogo Service Co., Ltd. (1)
Nakano Central Park East 10-1 Nakano 4-Chome, Nakano-ku, Tokyo, 164-0001, Japan
Tel.: (81) 367435039
Waste Treatment Services
N.A.I.C.S.: 221310

Kurita Sverige AB (1)
Marieholmsgatan 56, 415 02, Gothenburg, Sweden
Tel.: (46) 317253460
Waste Treatment Services
N.A.I.C.S.: 221310

Kurita Tokai Ltd. (1)
Nissay Ichinomiya Building 7F Shinsei 1-2-8, Ichinomiya, 491-0912, Aichi, Japan
Tel.: (81) 586438300
Web Site: https://tokai.kurita.co.jp
Emp.: 65
Waste Treatment Services
N.A.I.C.S.: 221310

Kurita Turkey Kimya A.S. (1)
Tugayyolu cad Ofisim Istanbul Plazalari No 20 B Blok Kat 4 Daire 23, Maltepe, 34846, Istanbul, Turkiye
Tel.: (90) 2164500862
Waste Treatment Services
N.A.I.C.S.: 221310

Kurita Water (Malaysia) Sdn. Bhd. (1)
No 89B Jalan i-Park 1/10, Kawasan Perindustrian i-Park Bandar Indahpura Kulai, 81000, Johor Bahru, Malaysia
Tel.: (60) 76608809
Web Site: https://www.kurita.com.my
Emp.: 125
Waste Treatment Services
N.A.I.C.S.: 221310
Eishi Shimmura *(Mng Dir)*

Kurita Water Industries (Dalian) Co., Ltd. (1)
33-27 Industrial Group, Dalian Economic and Technological Development Zone, Dalian, 116600, China
Tel.: (86) 41187613520
Web Site: http://www.kurita.cn
Sales Range: $75-99.9 Million
Emp.: 100
Waste Treatment Services
N.A.I.C.S.: 221320

Kurita Water Industries (Jiangyin) Co., Ltd. (1)
No 58 Dongsheng Road, Jiangyin, Jiangsu, China
Tel.: (86) 51086996866
Waste Treatment Services
N.A.I.C.S.: 221310

Kurita Water Industries (Suzhou) Ltd. (1)
25F SND International Commerce Tower No 28 Shishan Road, Suzhou New District, Suzhou, 215011, Jiangsu, China
Tel.: (86) 51285180118
Web Site: http://www.kwisz.com.cn

Sales Range: $75-99.9 Million
Emp.: 13
Waste Treatment Services
N.A.I.C.S.: 221320

Kurita Water Industries Ltd. - Shizuoka Plant (1)
1060 Kawashiri, Yoshidacho Haibara-gun, Shizuoka, 421-0302, Japan
Tel.: (81) 548331211
Web Site: http://www.kurita.co.jp
Waste Treatment Services
N.A.I.C.S.: 562219

Kurita Water Industries Ltd. - Toyoura Plant (1)
3911-2 Yon-nohama Kawatana, Toyouracho, Shimonoseki, 759-6301, Yamaguchi, Japan
Tel.: (81) 837741991
Waste Treatment Services
N.A.I.C.S.: 221320

Kurita Water Industries Ltd. - Tsuruga Plant (1)
1 Wakaizumicho, Tsuruga, 914-0027, Fukui, Japan
Tel.: (81) 770250389
Web Site: http://www.kurita.co.jp
Sales Range: $75-99.9 Million
Emp.: 10
Waste Treatment Services
N.A.I.C.S.: 221320

Kurita Water Industries Ltd. - Yamaguchi Plant (1)
1-1-10 5F-B Ogori miraimachi, Yamaguchi, 754-0032, Japan
Tel.: (81) 839639235
Sales Range: $75-99.9 Million
Emp.: 3
Waste Treatment Services
N.A.I.C.S.: 221320
Daisuke Imura *(Mgr)*

Kurita Water Technology (Taiwan) Co., Ltd. (1)
3rd Floor-1 No 285 Section 2 Guangfu Road, Hsinchu, Taiwan
Tel.: (886) 35751157
Web Site: http://www.kuritataiwan.com.tw
Water Treatment Equipment Mfr
N.A.I.C.S.: 333810

Kurita do Brasil Ltda. (1)
Avenida Virginia 1800 - Nucleo Ayres, Artur Nogueira, Sao Paulo, 13160-500, Brazil
Tel.: (55) 1938278388
Web Site: https://www.kurita.com.br
Water Treatment Chemicals Mfr & Sales
N.A.I.C.S.: 424690

Kurita-GK Chemical Co., Ltd. (1)
460 Moo 17 Bangphli Industrial Estate, Bangsaothong District, Bang Sao Thong, 10570, Samutprakarn, Thailand
Tel.: (66) 23152300
Web Site: https://www.kurita.co.th
Water Treatment Chemical Mfr
N.A.I.C.S.: 325998

Kurita-GK Vietnam Co., Ltd. (1)
Room 305 3rd Floor Technology Center, Thang Long Industrial Park Kim Chung Commune Dong Anh District, Hanoi, Vietnam
Tel.: (84) 2439590352
Web Site: https://kurita.com.vn
Water Treatment Chemical Mfr
N.A.I.C.S.: 325998

Kuritaz Co., Ltd. (1)
11-22 Minami-Ikebukuro 1-chome, Toshima-ku, Tokyo, 171-0022, Japan (100%)
Tel.: (81) 335900301
Web Site: http://www.kuritaz.co.jp
Sales Range: $150-199.9 Million
Emp.: 799
Waste Treatment Services
N.A.I.C.S.: 221310

Kuritec (Shanghai) Co., Ltd. (1)
Part B second floor Building 17 No 33 Xiya Road, Shanghai Free Trade Zone, Shanghai, 200122, China
Tel.: (86) 2158874377
Web Site: http://www.kwisz.com.cn
Sales Range: $10-24.9 Million
Emp.: 30
Waste Treatment Services
N.A.I.C.S.: 562211

Kuritec Service Co. Ltd. (1)
2-2-22 Kitahama, Chuo-ku, Osaka, 541-0041, Japan
Tel.: (81) 662284947
Web Site: http://www.kuritec.jp
Sales Range: $25-49.9 Million
Emp.: 70
Tool Cleaning Services
N.A.I.C.S.: 811310
Atsushi Tsuchino *(Pres)*

Land Management Inc. (1)
SI Building Aoyama 3F 1-3-6 Kita-Aoyama, Minato-ku, Tokyo, 107-0061, Japan
Tel.: (81) 354126740
Web Site: https://www.landmanagement.co.jp
Soil & Groundwater Remediation Services
N.A.I.C.S.: 562910

Land Solution Inc. (1)
3-6 Kita-Aoyama 1-chome, Minato-ku, Tokyo, 107-0061, Japan
Tel.: (81) 3541267000
Web Site: http://www.landsolution.co.jp
Emp.: 60
Soil Remediation Services
N.A.I.C.S.: 562910

Miyoshi Industries Co., Ltd. (1)
Tel.: (81) 668863017
Web Site: http://www.miyoshi-kougyo.co.jp
Sales Range: $25-49.9 Million
Emp.: 44
Chemical Cleaning Services
N.A.I.C.S.: 325998

Nippon Fine Co., Ltd. (1)
3008 Kashikimura, Iga, 518-1403, Mie, Japan
Tel.: (81) 595471024
Web Site: http://www.nippon-fine.co.jp
Chemical & Tool Cleaning Services
N.A.I.C.S.: 811310

P.T. Kurita Indonesia (1)
Jl Jababeka XII A Kav V-6 Kawasan Industri Jababeka, Cikarang, Bekasi, 17530, Jawa Barat, Indonesia
Tel.: (62) 218936245
Web Site: http://kurita.co.id
Water Treatment Chemicals Mfr & Sales
N.A.I.C.S.: 325998

San-ei Industries Co., Ltd. (1)
114-26 Goto 2 Waga-machi, Inside Gotono Industrial Park Waga-cho, Kitakami, Iwate, Japan
Tel.: (81) 197623483
Web Site: https://www.sanei-ind.net
Emp.: 108
Industrial Equipment Cleaning & Maintenance Services
N.A.I.C.S.: 811310

Sun Kako Co., Ltd. (1)
15 1 Kouto 3-chome, Kamigoori-cho Akougun, Hyogo, 678-1205, Japan
Tel.: (81) 791582002
Web Site: http://www.kurita.co.jp
Tool Cleaning Services
N.A.I.C.S.: 811310

With Kurita Ltd. (1)
Nakano Central Park East 10th floor 4-10-1 Nakano, Nakano-ku, Tokyo, 164-0001, Japan
Tel.: (81) 367436654
Web Site: https://kwk.kurita.co.jp
Emp.: 55
Waste Treatment Services
N.A.I.C.S.: 221310

KURIYAMA HOLDINGS CORPORATION

KURIYAMA HOLDINGS CORPORATION
Matsushita IMP Building 25th floor 3-7 Shiromi 1-Chome, Chuo-Ku, Osaka, 540-6325, Japan
Tel.: (81) 669107013
Web Site: https://www.kuriyama-holdings.com
Year Founded: 1940
3355—(TKS)
Rev.: $508,154,480
Assets: $457,567,330
Liabilities: $176,377,930
Net Worth: $281,189,400
Earnings: $26,892,370
Emp.: 1,141
Fiscal Year-end: 12/31/23
Holding Company
N.A.I.C.S.: 551112
Hironobu Nose *(CEO)*

Subsidiaries:

Accuflex Industrial Hose, Ltd. (1)
760 Imperial Road North, Guelph, N1k 1z3, ON, Canada
Tel.: (519) 836-5460
Hose Mfr
N.A.I.C.S.: 326220

Accuflex Industrial Hose, Ltd. (1)
36663 Van Born Rd Ste 300, Romulus, MI 48174
Tel.: (734) 713-4100
Web Site: https://www.accuflex.com
Hose Mfr & Distr
N.A.I.C.S.: 326220

Airmonte Corporation (1)
2F Kuriyama Building 1-12-4 Nishinakajima, Yodogawa-ku, Osaka, 532-0011, Japan
Tel.: (81) 67 662 8990
Logistic Services
N.A.I.C.S.: 541614

Armored Textiles, Inc. (1)
9 Vose Farm Rd, Peterborough, NH 03458
Tel.: (603) 924-2122
Web Site: https://www.atifireproducts.com
Rev.: $2,850,000
Emp.: 6
Hose Distr
N.A.I.C.S.: 423840

Bulma XXI S.L.U. (1)
Avenida Mare De Deu De Montserrat 4, Sant Joan Despi, Barcelona, Spain
Tel.: (34) 934808848
Chemical Products Mfr
N.A.I.C.S.: 325199

IR (Foshan) Building Materials Trading Co., Ltd. (1)
22 Haikou, Chancheng, Foshan, Guangdong, China
Tel.: (86) 75782669362
Web Site: http://www.irtfs.com
Building Materials Distr
N.A.I.C.S.: 444180

Industrias Quilmes S.A. (1)
Condarco 215, CP 1879, Quilmes, Buenos Aires, Argentina
Tel.: (54) 1152639262
Web Site: https://www.inquisa.com.ar
Hose Mfr & Distr
N.A.I.C.S.: 326220

Jingjiang Ohji Rubber Co., Ltd. (1)
Suyuan Thermal Power East Road No 1, Jingjiang, 214521, Jiangsu, China
Tel.: (86) 52384612388
Rubber & Plastic Product Distr
N.A.I.C.S.: 424610

Kuri Tec Corporation (1)
140 Roy Blvd, Brantford, N3R 7K2, ON, Canada
Tel.: (519) 753-6717
Web Site: https://www.kuritec.com
Hose Mfr & Distr
N.A.I.C.S.: 326220

Kuri Tec Manufacturing, Inc. (1)
2600 E Us Hwy 41, Williamsport, IN 47993
Tel.: (765) 764-6000
Hose Mfr
N.A.I.C.S.: 326220

Kuriyama (Shanghai) Corporation (1)
Shenggao International Building Suite 1006 137 Xian Xia Road, Shanghai, 200051, China
Tel.: (86) 2162411707
Web Site: https://www.shanghaikuriyama.com
Emp.: 232
Hose Whslr
N.A.I.C.S.: 423840

Kuriyama (Thailand) Co., Ltd. (1)
369/8 Moo6 T Bowin, Si Racha, 20230, Chonburi, Thailand
Tel.: (66) 38110413
Web Site: http://www.kuriyama.co.jp

KURIYAMA HOLDINGS CORPORATION

Kuriyama Holdings Corporation—(Continued)
Emp.: 6
Hose Distr
N.A.I.C.S.: 423840
Kazuhiro Yoda *(Mgr-Sls)*

Kuriyama Canada, Inc. (1)
140 Roy Boulevard, Brantford, N3r 7k2, ON, Canada
Tel.: (519) 759-5111
Rubber & Plastic Product Mfr & Distr
N.A.I.C.S.: 326299

Kuriyama Europe Cooperatief U.A. (1)
Buitenveldertselaan 106, 1081 AB, Amsterdam, Netherlands
Tel.: (31) 20 723 0505
Web Site: https://www.kuriyama.eu
Rubber & Plastic Product Mfr & Distr
N.A.I.C.S.: 326299

Kuriyama Japan Corporation (1)
1-3-7 Shiromi Matsushita IMP Building 25th Floor, Chuo-ku, Osaka, 540-6325, Japan
Tel.: (81) 669107013
Rubber & Plastic Product Distr
N.A.I.C.S.: 424610

Kuriyama of America, Inc. (1)
360 E State Pkwy, Schaumburg, IL 60173-5335
Tel.: (847) 755-0360
Web Site: https://www.kuriyama.com
Hose Mfr & Distr
N.A.I.C.S.: 326220

Subsidiary (Non-US):

Kuriyama de Mexico, S.de.R.L.de.C.V. (2)
Av Jose Palomo Martinez No 520-20 Bodega 5 Parque Industrial Omolap, Apodaca, 66633, Nuevo Leon, Mexico
Tel.: (52) 8110861870
Web Site: http://www.kuriyama.com
Emp.: 22
Hose Distr
N.A.I.C.S.: 423840

Kuriyama-Ohji (Thailand) Ltd. (1)
1 MD Tower 7th Fl Soi Bangna-Trad 25 Kwang Bangnanua Khet, Bangna, Bangkok, 10260, Thailand
Tel.: (66) 2 361 8324
Web Site: http://www.ohji-rubber.co.jp
Emp.: 42
Rubber Products Mfr
N.A.I.C.S.: 326299
W. Onanong *(Mgr-Sls & Mktg)*

Plant (Domestic):

Kuriyama-Ohji (Thailand) Ltd. - Rayong Factory (2)
Amata City Industrial Estate 7/113 Moo 4 Mabyangporn, Pluakdaeng, Rayong, 21140, Thailand
Tel.: (66) 38956206
Rubber Products Mfr
N.A.I.C.S.: 326299
Morikiyo Odaka *(Mng Dir)*

Ohji Rubber & Chemicals Co., Ltd. (1)
1-6 Katsuma 2-Chome, Hofu, 747-0822, Yamaguchi, Japan
Tel.: (81) 835220056
Web Site: http://www.ohji-rubber.co.jp
Emp.: 200
Rubber Product Mfr & Distr
N.A.I.C.S.: 326220
Yasuyuki Miyamori *(Pres)*

Ooparts, Inc. (1)
2-32-28 Namiki, Noda, 270-0228, Chiba, Japan
Tel.: (81) 471260411
Floor Tile Installation Services
N.A.I.C.S.: 238330

Piranha Hose Products, Inc. (1)
2500 Weigel, Cadillac, MI 49601
Tel.: (231) 779-4390
Web Site: https://www.piranhahose.com
Hose Mfr & Distr
N.A.I.C.S.: 326220

SUN-A Corporation (1)
870-38 Minami-Hatajiki, Miyoshi, 728-0017, Hiroshima, Japan
Tel.: (81) 824635331
Web Site: http://www.sun-awks.co.jp
Emp.: 102
Sensor Mfr & Distr
N.A.I.C.S.: 334516
Kiyoshi Yamagishi *(Pres & CEO)*

Tecnicas e Ingenieria de Proteccion, S.A.U. (1)
Av de Barcelona 20, Sant Joan Despi, 08970, Barcelona, Spain
Tel.: (34) 936021818
Web Site: http://www.tipsa.com
Hose Mfr & Distr
N.A.I.C.S.: 326220

KURODA PRECISION INDUSTRIES LTD.

Kawasaki Tech Center 580-16 Horikawa-cho, Saiwai-ku, Kawasaki, 212-8560, Kanagawa, Japan
Tel.: (81) 445553800 JP
Web Site: https://www.kuroda-precision.co.jp
Year Founded: 1925
7726—(TKS)
Rev.: $122,311,440
Assets: $171,093,240
Liabilities: $93,776,070
Net Worth: $77,317,170
Earnings: $3,291,780
Emp.: 972
Fiscal Year-end: 03/31/24
Gauges, Ball Screws, Actuators, Tool Holders, Tooling Systems, Press Tools, Motor Cores, Machine Tools, Polishing Machines, Measuring Systems, Medical Equipment Mfr
N.A.I.C.S.: 333248
Hiroshi Kuroda *(Pres)*

Subsidiaries:

Jenaer Gewindetechnik GmbH (1)
Goschwizer Str 39, Postfach 100 212, 07702, Jena, Germany
Tel.: (49) 36 416 8980
Web Site: https://www.jena-tec.de
Emp.: 130
Precision Gear Mfr
N.A.I.C.S.: 332721

Kraftmek Oy (1)
Suokalliontie 9, 01740, Vantaa, Finland
Tel.: (358) 1075501
Sales Range: $25-49.9 Million
Emp.: 50
Electronic Parts & Equipment Whslr
N.A.I.C.S.: 423690
Ilpo Pinola *(Mng Dir)*

Kuroda Jena Tec, Inc. (1)
3939 Royal Dr NW Ste 143, Kennesaw, GA 30144
Tel.: (770) 926-6705
Web Site: https://www.kurodajenatec.com
Linear Drive Equipment Mfr
N.A.I.C.S.: 335999

Kuroda Precision Industries (1)
505 West Golf Rd, Arlington Heights, IL 60005
Tel.: (847) 228-6473
Web Site: http://www.kuroda-precision.com
Sales Range: $25-49.9 Million
Emp.: 1
Technical Servicing of Pneumatic Valves & Ball Screws
N.A.I.C.S.: 541330

Kuroda Precision Industries Korea Ltd. (1)
202F 144-110, Dongan-gu, Anyang, 14083, Gyeonggi, Korea (South)
Tel.: (82) 31 451 4920
Linear Drive Equipment Mfr
N.A.I.C.S.: 335999

KUROGANE KOSAKUSHO LTD.

Osaka Yotsubashi Shinmachi Bldg 4-24 Shinmachi 1-Chome, Nishi-ku, Osaka, 550-0013, Japan
Tel.: (81) 665381010
Web Site: https://www.kurogane-kks.co.jp
Year Founded: 1936
7997—(TKS)
Rev.: $50,906,200
Assets: $58,159,270
Liabilities: $27,814,070
Net Worth: $30,345,200
Earnings: $8,607,260
Fiscal Year-end: 11/30/23
Furniture & Cleaning Equipment Mfr & Distr
N.A.I.C.S.: 337211
Tsuneshi Ando *(Mng Exec Officer)*

Subsidiaries:

Accuride Japan Co., Ltd. (1)
44 Minami - Asaji Iwata, Yawata, 614-8265, Kyoto, Japan
Tel.: (81) 75 983 7500
Web Site: https://www.accuride.co.jp
Precision Slide Mfr & Distr
N.A.I.C.S.: 332721

K. S. M. Co., Ltd. (1)
44 Minami-Asaji Iwata, Yawata, 614-8265, Japan
Tel.: (81) 759819981
Furniture Mfr
N.A.I.C.S.: 332510

Kurogane Kosan Co., Ltd. (1)
731-2 Azaichimachida Katadacho, Tsu, 514-0084, Japan
Tel.: (81) 592374121
Furniture Mfr
N.A.I.C.S.: 332510

KUROS BIOSCIENCES AG

Wagistrasse 25, Schlieren, 8952, Zurich, Switzerland
Tel.: (41) 447334747
Web Site: http://www.kurosbio.com
Medical Device Mfr
N.A.I.C.S.: 339112
Joost De Bruijn *(CEO)*

KUROS BIOSCIENCES AG

Wagistrasse 25, 8952, Schlieren, Switzerland
Tel.: (41) 447334747 CH
Web Site: https://www.kurosbio.com
Year Founded: 2016
KURN—(SWX)
Rev.: $39,890,659
Assets: $84,934,633
Liabilities: $17,532,684
Net Worth: $67,401,949
Earnings: $(16,314,476)
Emp.: 80
Fiscal Year-end: 12/31/23
HMO Medical Centers
N.A.I.C.S.: 621491
Joost De Bruijn *(CEO)*

Subsidiaries:

Kuros Biosciences B.V. (1)
Professor Bronkhorstlaan 10 Building 48, 3723 MB, Bilthoven, Netherlands
Tel.: (31) 302297280
Healtcare Services
N.A.I.C.S.: 621999

Kuros Biosciences USA, Inc. (1)
10 Glenlake Pkwy S Tower Ste150, Atlanta, GA 30328
Tel.: (786) 294-0202
Healtcare Services
N.A.I.C.S.: 621999

RevisiOs B.V. (1)
Professor Bronkhorstlaan 10 bldg 48, 3723 MB, Bilthoven, Netherlands
Tel.: (31) 302297280
Web Site: https://www.revisios.com
Medical Equipment Mfr
N.A.I.C.S.: 339112

KUROTANI CORPORATION

12-2 Nagoe Imizu City, Toyama, 934 8501, Toyama, Japan
Tel.: (81) 766840001
Web Site: https://www.kurotani.co.jp
Year Founded: 1985
3168—(TKS)
Rev.: $510,475,400
Assets: $165,520,420
Liabilities: $106,542,380
Net Worth: $58,978,040
Earnings: $3,309,040
Emp.: 130
Fiscal Year-end: 08/31/24
Nonferrous Metal Scraps & Ingots Mfr
N.A.I.C.S.: 332999
Sumihisa Kurotani *(Pres & CEO)*

KURT OBERMEIER GMBH & CO. KG

Berghauser Strasse 70, 57319, Berlenburg, Germany
Tel.: (49) 27515240
Web Site: http://www.obermeier.de
Sales Range: $50-74.9 Million
Emp.: 150
Chemical Products Mfr
N.A.I.C.S.: 325998
Henning Obermeier *(Mng Dir)*

KURTZ HOLDING GMBH & CO. BETEILIGUNGS KG

Frankenstrasse 2, 97892, Kreuzwertheim, Germany
Tel.: (49) 93428070
Web Site: http://www.kurtzersa.de
Year Founded: 1779
Sales Range: $150-199.9 Million
Emp.: 1,000
Industrial Machinery & Equipment Distr
N.A.I.C.S.: 423830
Raeiner Kurtz *(CEO)*

Subsidiaries:

Ersa GmbH (1)
Leonhard-Karl-Str 24, Wertheim, 97877, Germany
Tel.: (49) 93 42 8000
Soldering Systems Mfr
N.A.I.C.S.: 333992
Rainer Kurtz *(Office Mgr)*

Kurtz Ersa S.A.de C.V. (1)
Felipe Angeles No 52 Col Bellavista Tacubaya, 01140, Mexico, Mexico
Tel.: (52) 55 4353 9220
Industrial Supplies Whslr
N.A.I.C.S.: 423840
Jon Golm *(Jr Mgr-Sls-Midwest)*

Kurtz Far East Ltd. (1)
Unit 03-05 8th Fl One Island South, 373 King's Road, Hong Kong, China (Hong Kong)
Tel.: (852) 23312232
Web Site: http://www.en.kurtz.info
Sales Range: $25-49.9 Million
Emp.: 10
Machine Tools Mfr
N.A.I.C.S.: 333517
Michael Chan *(Mng Dir)*

Division (Domestic):

Ersa Asia Pacific (2)
Unit 03-05 8th Fl One Island South No 2 Heung Yip Rd, China Resources Bldg, Hong Kong, China (Hong Kong)
Tel.: (852) 23312232
Web Site: http://www.kurtz.com
Sales Range: $25-49.9 Million
Emp.: 7
Industrial Machinery & Equipment Whslr
N.A.I.C.S.: 423830
Michael Chang *(Mng Dir)*

Kurtz France S.A.R.L. (1)
15 rue de la Sucharde, F 21800, Chevigny-Saint-Sauveur, France
Tel.: (33) 380566610
Sales Range: $50-74.9 Million
Emp.:
Industrial Machinery & Equipment Whslr
N.A.I.C.S.: 423830
Rupert Guring *(Mgr)*

AND PRIVATE COMPANIES

Division (Domestic):

Ersa France (2)
15 rue de la Sucharde, 21800, Chevigny-Saint-Sauveur, France
Tel.: (33) 3 8056 6610
Web Site: http://www.kurtzersa.fr
Emp.: 6
Soldering Equipment Mfr
N.A.I.C.S.: 333992
Robert Dureng (Office Mgr)

Kurtz GmbH (1)
Industriegebiet Wiebelbach, Frankenstrasse 2, Kreuzwertheim, 97892, Germany
Tel.: (49) 9342 8070
Emp.: 400
Foundry Machinery & Casting Mfr
N.A.I.C.S.: 331511
Rainer Kurtz (Mng Dir)

Kurtz Italia Srl (1)
Via Carlo Cassola 59, Travedona Monate, 21028, Varese, Italy
Tel.: (39) 04993428070
Web Site: http://en.kurtz.info
Sales Range: $50-74.9 Million
Emp.: 1
Industrial Machinery & Equipment Whslr
N.A.I.C.S.: 423830

Kurtz North America Inc. (1)
1779 Pilgrim Rd, Plymouth, WI 53073
Tel.: (920) 893-1779
Web Site: http://www.kurtzersa.com
Rev.: $12,000,000
Emp.: 30
Sales of Industrial Machinery & Equipment
N.A.I.C.S.: 423830
Bill Bruggink (Mgr)

Division (Domestic):

Ersa North America (2)
1779 Pilgrim Rd, Plymouth, WI 53073
Tel.: (920) 893-3772
Web Site: http://www.ersanorthamerica.com
Emp.: 20
Industrial Machinery & Equipment Whslr
N.A.I.C.S.: 423830
Albrecht Beck (Pres & COO)

Kurtz Shanghai Ltd. (1)
Room 601 6th Floor Green Land Business Mansion, 1258 Yu Yuan Road, Shanghai, 200336, China
Tel.: (86) 2131260818
Web Site: http://www.kurtzersa.com
Industrial Machinery & Equipment Whslr
N.A.I.C.S.: 423830

Kurtz South East Asia Private Ltd. (1)
25 International Business Park, 02-106 German Centre, 609916, Singapore, Singapore
Tel.: (65) 65629205
Web Site: http://en.kurtz.info
Industrial Machinery & Equipment Whslr
N.A.I.C.S.: 423830

Kurtz Systems Africa (Pty) Ltd. (1)
Zimbali Coastal Estate, Dolphin Coast, 4418, Zimbali, KwaZulu Natal, South Africa
Tel.: (27) 325381200
Web Site: http://www.en.kurtz.info
Industrial Machinery & Equipment Whslr
N.A.I.C.S.: 423830

Kurtz Zhuhai Manufacturing Ltd. (1)
no 122 Hua Rong Road Qin Shi Industrial Zone, Sanzao Town, Zhuhai, 519040, Guangdongi, China
Tel.: (86) 7563 997888
Industrial Machinery Mfr
N.A.I.C.S.: 333248

MBW Metallbearbeitung Wertheim GmbH (1)
Gyula-Horn-Str 21, D-97877, Wertheim, Germany
Tel.: (49) 9342 96360
Web Site: http://www.kurtzersa.de
Emp.: 110
Sheet Metal Processor
N.A.I.C.S.: 332322
Matthias Sacher (Gen Mgr)

Plant (Domestic):

MBW Metallbearbeitung Wertheim GmbH - Baiersdorf Plant (2)
Erlanger-Str 9, 91083, Baiersdorf, Germany
Tel.: (49) 91 33 77 81 0
Sheet Metal Mfr
N.A.I.C.S.: 332322

OOO Kurtz Ost (1)
6 Zhukovskogo St, Dolgoprudny, 141700, Moscow, Russia
Tel.: (7) 4957756099
Web Site: http://www.kurtz.ru
Industrial Machinery Mfr
N.A.I.C.S.: 333248

KURZEMES ATSLEGA 1 A/S
Kalvenes Iela 27, Aizpute, 3456, Latvia
Tel.: (371) 63 448 075
Web Site: http://www.ka1.lv
KA11R—(RSE)
Rev.: $1,882,157
Assets: $1,530,387
Liabilities: $1,247,994
Net Worth: $282,393
Earnings: ($237,658)
Fiscal Year-end: 12/31/19
Windows Hardware Mfr
N.A.I.C.S.: 321911
Peteris Fridenbergs (Chm)

KUSAM ELECTRICAL INDUSTRIES LIMITED
C-325 3rd Floor Antop Hill Warehousing Co Ltd Vidyalankar College Road, Antop Hill Wadala East, Mumbai, 400037, Maharashtra, India
Tel.: (91) 2227754546
Web Site: https://www.kusamelectrical.com
511048—(BOM)
Rev.: $531,952
Assets: $432,652
Liabilities: $403,778
Net Worth: $28,874
Earnings: $2,357
Emp.: 8
Fiscal Year-end: 03/31/21
Electric Equipment Mfr
N.A.I.C.S.: 335999
Chandmal P. Goliya (Exec Dir)

KUSH INDUSTRIES LIMITED
330-A GIDC OPP Atul Products, Bharuch, Ankleshwar, 393002, Gujarat, India
Tel.: (91) 2426224049
Web Site: https://www.kushindustriesltd.com
Year Founded: 1992
514240—(BOM)
Rev.: $104,646
Assets: $346,370
Liabilities: $1,496,217
Net Worth: ($1,149,847)
Earnings: ($14,555)
Emp.: 2
Fiscal Year-end: 03/31/23
Textile Products Mfr & Distr
N.A.I.C.S.: 314999
Mansukh K. Virani (Compliance Officer)

KUSHAL LTD.
No 43 B/S Navneet Prakashan Sukhramnagar, Gomtipur, Ahmedabad, 380023, Gujarat, India
Tel.: (91) 7926408027
Web Site: http://www.kushallimited.com
Year Founded: 2000
536570—(BOM)
Rev.: $24,987,321
Assets: $227,387,870
Liabilities: $60,280,024
Net Worth: $167,107,845
Earnings: $10,976,634
Emp.: 21
Fiscal Year-end: 03/31/20
Paper Supplier

N.A.I.C.S.: 424110
Sandeep Agrawal (Chm & Mng Dir)

KUSHIKATSU TANAKA CO., LTD.
5F Towa Higashi Gotanda Bldg 1-7-6 Higashi Gotanda Shinagawa-Ku, Tokyo, 141-0022, Japan
Tel.: (81) 354496410
Web Site: http://www.kushi-tanaka.co.jp
3547—(TKS)
Rev.: $99,770,480
Assets: $49,693,810
Liabilities: $33,989,460
Net Worth: $15,704,350
Earnings: $2,531,130
Fiscal Year-end: 11/30/23
Restaurant Management Services
N.A.I.C.S.: 722511

KUSTUR KUSADASI TURIZM ENDUSTRISI A.S.
Bayrakli Dede Mahallesi Kustur Tatil Koyu Kusadas, Aydin, 9440, Turkiye
Tel.: (90) 2566181310
KSTUR—(IST)
Sales Range: Less than $1 Million
Hotel Operator
N.A.I.C.S.: 721110
Emine Tunay Kavasoglu (Chm)

KUSURI NO AOKI HOLDINGS CO., LTD.
5180 Yokoe-cho, Hakusan, 924-8510, Japan
Tel.: (81) 762746115
Web Site: https://www.kusuri-aoki-hd.co.jp
3549—(TKS)
Rev.: $2,887,743,750
Assets: $2,005,824,330
Liabilities: $1,229,678,130
Net Worth: $776,146,200
Earnings: $81,349,270
Fiscal Year-end: 05/31/24
Pharmaceutical Retailer
N.A.I.C.S.: 424210
Keisei Aoki (Founder & Chm)

KUSURINOAOKI CO., LTD.
2512 Matsumoto-machi, Hakusan, 924-8510, Ishikawa, Japan
Tel.: (81) 76 2741111
Web Site: http://www.kusuri-aoki.co.jp
Year Founded: 1985
Sales Range: $900-999.9 Million
Pharmaceuticals Producut Sales
N.A.I.C.S.: 456110
Keisei Aoki (Chm)

KUTAHYA PORSELEN SANAYI A.S.
Eskisehir Highway 8 km, 43100, Kutahya, Turkiye
Tel.: (90) 2742250150
Web Site: https://www.kutahyaporselen.com.tr
Year Founded: 1970
KUTPO—(IST)
Rev.: $79,476,665
Assets: $92,490,579
Liabilities: $23,333,228
Net Worth: $69,157,351
Earnings: $1,273,340
Fiscal Year-end: 12/31/23
Tableware Mfr & Whslr
N.A.I.C.S.: 327110
Sema Gural Surmeli (Chm)

KUTCHO COPPER CORP.
1030 West Georgia St Suite 717, Vancouver, V6E 2Y3, BC, Canada
Tel.: (604) 628-5623   BC
Web Site: https://www.kutcho.ca

KUWAIT AIRWAYS CORPORATION

KC—(OTCIQ)
Rev.: $1,407,477
Assets: $40,781,154
Liabilities: $29,114,076
Net Worth: $11,667,077
Earnings: ($2,921,971)
Fiscal Year-end: 04/30/21
Copper & Zinc Exploration Services
N.A.I.C.S.: 213114
Gavin Cooper (CFO)

KUUHUBB INC.
25 Adelaide Street East Suite 1417, Toronto, M5C 3A1, ON, Canada
Tel.: (358) 0-040-4714   Ca
Web Site: https://www.kuuhubb.com
Year Founded: 1990
BCDMF—(OTCEM)
Rev.: $3,831,497
Assets: $711,140
Liabilities: $9,424,716
Net Worth: ($8,713,576)
Earnings: $4,196,799
Fiscal Year-end: 06/30/22
Diamond Mining Services
N.A.I.C.S.: 212311
Jouni Keranen (CEO)

KUWAIT & GULF LINK TRANSPORT CO. KSCC
80 Shuwaikh Industrial, PO Box 24565, Safat, Kuwait, 13106, Kuwait
Tel.: (965) 1888700
Web Site: https://www.kgl.com
Year Founded: 1982
KGL—(KUW)
Rev.: $354,263,661
Assets: $626,937,505
Liabilities: $496,370,093
Net Worth: $130,567,412
Earnings: $5,886,152
Emp.: 341
Fiscal Year-end: 12/31/22
Holding Company; Transportation & Port Services
N.A.I.C.S.: 551112
Maher Abdullah Marafie (Chm)

Subsidiaries:

KGL Car Rental Company W.L.L. (1)
Al Jahra Road And Ghazali Bridge Shuwaikh, PO Box 24565, Safat, Kuwait, 13106, Kuwait
Tel.: (965) 24961522
Web Site: http://www.kglcarrental.com
Car Rental Services
N.A.I.C.S.: 532111

KUWAIT AIRWAYS CORPORATION
Kuwait International Airport, PO Box 29547, Safat, Kuwait, 13156, Kuwait
Tel.: (965) 22248560
Web Site: http://www.kuwait-airways.com
Year Founded: 1954
Sales Range: $700-749.9 Million
Emp.: 7,000
Airline
N.A.I.C.S.: 481111
Adel Boresly (Dir-PR & Info)

Subsidiaries:

Automated Systems Company K.S.C (1)
Free Zone Future Area Plot B28 B29, Shuwaikh, Kuwait, 13132, Kuwait (68.5%)
Tel.: (965) 24943700
Web Site: https://www.asc-me.net
Rev.: $10,363,824
Assets: $41,353,905
Liabilities: $5,152,303
Net Worth: $36,201,602
Earnings: ($1,085,804)
Emp.: 112
Fiscal Year-end: 12/31/2022
IT Services

KUWAIT AIRWAYS CORPORATION

Kuwait Airways Corporation—(Continued)
N.A.I.C.S.: 541519
Hadeel Yaqoub Yousef Al-Ghunaim *(Vice Chm & CEO)*

Kuwait Airways Corporation - Canada Office (1)
77 Bloor Street W Ste 1210, Toronto, M5S 1M2, ON, Canada
Tel.: (416) 926-1275
Web Site: http://www.kuwaitairways.com
Sales Range: $25-49.9 Million
Emp.: 4
Airline Services
N.A.I.C.S.: 481111
Clifford Tellis *(Mgr-Sls)*

Kuwait Airways Corporation - US Office (1)
Parker Plz 400 Kelby St, Fort Lee, NJ 07024
Tel.: (201) 582-9222
Web Site: http://www.kuwaitairways.com
Sales Range: $500-549.9 Million
Emp.: 5,000
Airline Services
N.A.I.C.S.: 481111

Kuwait Aviation Services Co. (1)
Kuwait International Airport, PO Box 24417, Safat, 13105, Kuwait, Kuwait **(100%)**
Tel.: (965) 2434 5555
Web Site: http://www.kasco.com.kw
Sales Range: $10-24.9 Million
Emp.: 3,000
International Catering & Inflight Services
N.A.I.C.S.: 722320

KUWAIT BUSINESS TOWN REAL ESTATE COMPANY KSCC
KBT Tower 5 Al Mirqab Area Block 3 Plot Not 12 At the junction of Two, Street Khaled Bin Al Waleed and Al-Omar Bin Khatab Streets, Kuwait, Kuwait
Tel.: (965) 22916555
Web Site: http://www.kbt.com.kw
KBT—(KUW)
Rev.: $17,552,452
Assets: $267,551,266
Liabilities: $95,894,520
Net Worth: $171,656,745
Earnings: $11,466,473
Emp.: 19
Fiscal Year-end: 12/31/22
Real Estate Services
N.A.I.C.S.: 531390
Salem Khudhur Mohammad Al-Hasawi *(Chm)*

KUWAIT CABLE VISION COMPANY SAK
Emad Tower 5th Floor Ahmed Al-Jaber Street, PO Box 20664, Sharq Safat, Kuwait, 13067, Kuwait
Tel.: (965) 22452630
Web Site: http://www.kvision.tv
Rev.: $22,832
Assets: $4,720,474
Liabilities: $1,496,801
Net Worth: $3,223,673
Earnings: ($275,227)
Emp.: 15
Fiscal Year-end: 12/31/18
Satellite TV Broadcasting Services
N.A.I.C.S.: 517410

KUWAIT CEMENT COMPANY K.S.C.
Cement House Al-Sawaber St, PO Box 20581, Al-Shuhada Street Safat, Kuwait, 13066, Kuwait
Tel.: (965) 22401700   KW
Web Site: https://www.kuwaitcement.com
Year Founded: 1968
KCEM—(KUW)
Rev.: $222,892,362
Assets: $963,259,323
Liabilities: $331,688,700
Net Worth: $631,570,623
Earnings: $11,829,081
Emp.: 916
Fiscal Year-end: 12/31/22
Cement Mfr & Marketer
N.A.I.C.S.: 327310
Rashed Abdulaziz Abdulmohsen Al-Rashed *(Chm)*

Subsidiaries:

Kuwait Cement Ready-Mix Company (1)
Cement House Al-Sawaber Al-Shuhada St Floor 2, Kuwait, Kuwait
Tel.: (965) 24676013
Web Site: https://www.kcrm-kw.com
Ready Mix Cement Mfr
N.A.I.C.S.: 327320
Khalifa Abdullah Al Fadala *(Chm & Mng Dir)*

KUWAIT COMMERCIAL MARKETS COMPLEX CO. (S.A.K.)
Safat, PO Box 23541, Building Commercial Real Estate Company-first round Safat, Kuwait, 13096, Kuwait
Tel.: (965) 22409552
Sales Range: $1-9.9 Million
Emp.: 380
Commercial Center & Complexe, Shopping Malls Owner, Rental & Leasing Operator Services
N.A.I.C.S.: 531390

Subsidiaries:

Gulf Group Co. (W.L.L) (1)
PO Box 144, Kuwait, 13002, Shuwaikh, Kuwait
Tel.: (965) 24844139
Web Site: http://www.gulfgroupco.com
AC Equipment & System Services
N.A.I.C.S.: 334512

KUWAIT FINANCE HOUSE K.S.C.
AlMirqab Area Abdulla Al-Mubarak Street, PO Box 24989, Safat, Kuwait, 13110, Kuwait
Tel.: (965) 22445050   KW
Web Site: https://www.kfh.com
Year Founded: 1977
KFH—(KUW)
Rev.: $7,131,174,234
Assets: $123,533,231,499
Liabilities: $103,502,229,517
Net Worth: $20,031,001,983
Earnings: $2,194,094,706
Emp.: 17,865
Fiscal Year-end: 12/31/23
Banking & Other Financial Services
N.A.I.C.S.: 522110
Hamad Abdul Mohsen Al-Marzouq *(Chm)*

Subsidiaries:

AREF Investment Group K.S.C.C. (1)
PO Box 24100, Safat, Kuwait, 13101, Kuwait **(52%)**
Tel.: (965) 1815555
Web Site: https://www.arefgroup.com
Rev.: $399,000,000
Investment Services
N.A.I.C.S.: 523999
Khalid Yousif Al Shamlan *(Chm)*

Ahli United Bank B.S.C. (1)
Building 2495 Road 2832 Al Seef District 428, PO Box 2424, Manama, Bahrain
Tel.: (973) 17585858
Web Site: http://www.ahliunited.com.kw
Rev.: $1,729,456,000
Assets: $41,560,972,000
Liabilities: $35,731,573,000
Net Worth: $5,829,399,000
Earnings: $546,102,000
Emp.: 4,304
Fiscal Year-end: 12/31/2022
Bank Holding Company
N.A.I.C.S.: 551111
Adel A. El-Labban *(CEO-Grp & Mng Dir)*

Subsidiary (Non-US):

Ahli United Bank (Egypt) S.A.E. (2)
81 Ninety Street City Centre, PO Box 413, The 5th Settlement New Cairo, 11835, Cairo, Egypt
Banking Services
N.A.I.C.S.: 522110

Ahli United Bank (U.K.) PLC (2)
35 Portman Square, London, W1H 6LR, United Kingdom **(100%)**
Tel.: (44) 2074876500
Web Site: http://www.ahliunited.com
Sales Range: $50-74.9 Million
Emp.: 100
Commericial Banking
N.A.I.C.S.: 522110

Ahli United Bank K.S.C.P. (2)
Joint Banking Center - Al Abdul Razzak Square, PO Box 71, Safat, 12168, Kuwait, Kuwait
Tel.: (965) 22459771
Web Site: http://www.ahliunited.com.kw
Rev.: $453,157,820
Assets: $14,309,034,051
Liabilities: $12,661,356,212
Net Worth: $1,647,677,839
Earnings: $97,344,043
Emp.: 824
Fiscal Year-end: 12/31/2020
Commercial Banking Services
N.A.I.C.S.: 522110
Iman Wajeeh Al-Madani *(Head-HR & Dev)*

Al Ahli Bank of Kuwait KSC (2)
Ahmad Al-Jaber Street Safat Square, PO Box 1387, Safat, 13014, Kuwait, 13014, Kuwait
Tel.: (965) 22400900
Web Site: https://abk.eahli.com
Rev.: $875,319,315
Assets: $20,871,981,540
Liabilities: $18,934,996,262
Net Worth: $1,936,985,277
Earnings: $105,229,289
Emp.: 2,374
Fiscal Year-end: 12/31/2022
Banking Services
N.A.I.C.S.: 522110
Salah Ahmed Al Serhan *(Deputy Chm)*

Subsidiary (Domestic):

Kuwait & Middle East Financial Investment Company K.S.C.C. (3)
Block 1 Building No1 Arabian Gulf Street Khalid Tower, PO Box 819, Opposite of Seif Palace Floor2 Safat, Kuwait, 13009, Kuwait **(48%)**
Tel.: (965) 22255555
Web Site: https://kmefic.com
Rev.: $21,372,027
Assets: $251,508,899
Liabilities: $164,734,821
Net Worth: $86,774,078
Earnings: $3,260,493
Emp.: 78
Fiscal Year-end: 12/31/2022
Investment Management Service
N.A.I.C.S.: 523999
Hamad Al-Thekair *(Chm)*

Subsidiary (Domestic):

Al Hilal Life B.S.C. (2)
17th Floor Office 1701/1702 Building 470 Road 1010, PO Box 5832, Sanabis, 410, Manama, Bahrain
Tel.: (973) 17589800
Web Site: https://www.alhilal.life
Fire Insurance Services
N.A.I.C.S.: 524210
Said Hathout *(CEO)*

Subsidiary (Non-US):

Commercial Bank of Iraq P.S.C. (2)
Al Sadoon Street block 102 St 9 bldg 121 near le Meridian hotell, Baghdad, Iraq **(64.71%)**
Tel.: (964) 7833955530
Web Site: https://cbiq.com.iq
Rev.: $18,511,832
Assets: $362,353,987
Liabilities: $139,004,468
Net Worth: $223,349,519
Earnings: $7,988,334

INTERNATIONAL PUBLIC

Emp.: 260
Fiscal Year-end: 12/31/2022
Commercial Banking Services
N.A.I.C.S.: 522110
Nouri Mazaal Saadoun Al-Dabbisi *(CEO)*

United Bank for Commerce & Investment S.A.C. (2)
Al Jumhoriya Str, Tripoli, Libya
Tel.: (218) 217205851
Web Site: http://www.ubci-libya.com
Banking Services
N.A.I.C.S.: 522110

Al-Enma'a Real Estate Company K.S.C.C. (1)
Abdullah Al-Mobarak Street Al-Enmaa Tower, Kuwait, 13160, Kuwait **(51%)**
Tel.: (965) 1866667
Web Site: https://www.enmaa.com
Rev.: $34,186,374
Assets: $213,392,998
Liabilities: $78,859,110
Net Worth: $134,533,888
Earnings: ($6,098,818)
Emp.: 1,079
Fiscal Year-end: 12/31/2021
Real Estate Investment Services
N.A.I.C.S.: 531390
Saleh Turki Al Khamees *(Chm)*

Aviation Lease and Finance Company K.S.C.C. (1)
2nd Floor Chamber of Commerce & Industry Building, PO Box 2255, Abdul Aziz Al-Sager Street Al-Qibla, Kuwait, 13023, Kuwait
Tel.: (965) 22902888
Web Site: https://www.alafco-kw.com
Rev.: $116,679,373
Assets: $2,882,610,740
Liabilities: $2,163,952,254
Net Worth: $718,658,485
Earnings: ($3,742,781)
Emp.: 40
Fiscal Year-end: 09/30/2023
Aircraft Leasing & Financing Services
N.A.I.C.S.: 532411
Imtiaz Abdulla Khot *(Sr VP-Marketing)*

Development Enterprises Holding Company K.S.C. (1)
Tel.: (965) 2 297 9610
Web Site: https://www.deh.com.kw
Sales Range: $25-49.9 Million
Emp.: 15
Industrial Product Distr
N.A.I.C.S.: 423840
Adel Al Banwan *(Deputy Chm)*

Subsidiary (Domestic):

The Energy House Holding Company K.S.C.P. (2)
Al-Enmaa Tower 14th Floor, Abdullah Al-Mubarak Street, Kuwait, Kuwait **(72.6%)**
Tel.: (965) 22979600
Rev.: $1,617
Assets: $15,399,993
Liabilities: $5,911,386
Net Worth: $9,488,608
Earnings: ($4,782,767)
Emp.: 10
Fiscal Year-end: 12/31/2023
Oil & Gas Investment Services
N.A.I.C.S.: 523999
Ahmad Eissa Al-Sumait *(Chm)*

Diyar Al Muharraq Company W.L.L. (1)
Bahrain World Trade Center West Tower 6th Floor, PO Box 75777, Manama, Bahrain
Tel.: (973) 77155555
Web Site: https://www.diyar.bh
Residential Property Services
N.A.I.C.S.: 531311
Ahmed Alammadi *(CEO)*

Human Investment Corporation (1)
Bahbahani Complex Floor 16, Sharq, Kuwait, Kuwait
Tel.: (965) 22411335
Web Site: http://www.hickwt.com
Sales Range: $25-49.9 Million
Emp.: 17
Human Resource Consulting Services
N.A.I.C.S.: 541612
Abdulaziz A. Al-Jaber *(Chm)*

KFH Capital Investments Company K.S.C. (1)

AND PRIVATE COMPANIES — KUWAIT PETROLEUM CORPORATION

Baitek Tower Safat Square Street Floors 23 32 33, PO Box 3946, Safat, Kuwait, 13040, Kuwait
Tel.: (965) 22987000
Web Site: https://www.kfhcapital.com.kw
Investment Banking Services
N.A.I.C.S.: 523150
Shadi A. Zahran *(Deputy Chm)*

Kuwait Finance House B.S.C. (1)
Bahrain World Trade Center West Tower, PO Box 2066, Manama, Bahrain
Tel.: (973) 77777777
Web Site: https://www.kfh.bh
Commericial Banking
N.A.I.C.S.: 522110

Kuwait Turkish Participation Bank Inc. (1)
Buyukdere Cad No 129, 34394 Esentepe Sisli, 34394, Istanbul, Turkiye **(62%)**
Tel.: (90) 2123541111
Web Site: https://www.kuveytturk.com.tr
Sales Range: $350-399.9 Million
Emp.: 800
Commericial Banking
N.A.I.C.S.: 522110
Ufuk Uyan *(CEO)*

Liquidity Management House KSCC (1)
Batek Building Office 23, Kuwait, 40177, Kuwait
Tel.: (965) 22257602
Investment Management Service
N.A.I.C.S.: 523999
Abdul Nasar Albuaih *(Chm)*

Liquidity Management House for Investment Co. K.S.C.C. (1)
Level 23 Baitak Tower Safat Square Ahmed Al Jaber Street, Kuwait, Kuwait
Tel.: (965) 2225 7600
Web Site: http://www.liquidityhouse.com
Investment Management Service
N.A.I.C.S.: 523999
Emad Yousuf Al Monayea *(Vice Chm, Mng Dir & CEO)*

Saudi Kuwaiti Finance House KSCC (1)
Moon Tower 16th floor 7586 King Fahd Branch Rd, PO Box 50051, Riyadh, 11523, Saudi Arabia
Tel.: (966) 114845500
Web Site: https://skfh.com.sa
Financial Management Services
N.A.I.C.S.: 523999

KUWAIT FLOUR MILLS & BAKERIES CO. S.A.K.
Jamal Abdul Nasser St Shuwaik Industrial Area, PO Box 681, Safat, 13007, Kuwait, Kuwait
Tel.: (965) 24841866 KW
Web Site: http://www.kuwaitflourmills.com
Year Founded: 1961
Flour, Bread, Biscuits, Pasta & Edible Oils Mfr & Distr
N.A.I.C.S.: 311211
Salah M. Al Kulaib *(Chm)*

KUWAIT FOUNDRY CO. (S.A.K.P.)
AL Rai Block No 1 Street No 10 Plot No 1880, PO Box 1393, Block 1180 - Plot No 1 Safat, Kuwait, 13014, Kuwait
Tel.: (965) 24766691
Web Site: https://kwfoundry.com
Year Founded: 1973
KFOUC—(KUW)
Rev.: $2,204,718
Assets: $52,784,576
Liabilities: $2,633,800
Net Worth: $50,150,776
Earnings: $19,834,600
Emp.: 86
Fiscal Year-end: 12/31/23
Iron Casting Mfr
N.A.I.C.S.: 331511
Ali Mohammad Abdullatif Al-Shaya *(Chm & Vice Chm)*

KUWAIT GYPSUM MANUFACTURING & TRADING CO. S.A.K.C.
PO Box 10013, Shuaiba, 65451, Kuwait
Tel.: (965) 23260421
Web Site: http://www.kuwaitgypsum.com
Rev.: $6,184,298
Assets: $16,958,856
Liabilities: $1,136,006
Net Worth: $15,822,849
Earnings: $228,882
Emp.: 69
Fiscal Year-end: 12/31/17
Gypsum Mfr, Distr & Sales
N.A.I.C.S.: 327420

KUWAIT INSURANCE COMPANY S.A.K.
Kuwait Insurance Co HouseAbdulla Al Salem Street, PO Box 769, Safat, Kuwait, 13008, Kuwait
Tel.: (965) 1884433
Web Site: https://www.kic-kw.com
KINS—(KUW)
Rev.: $174,917,214
Assets: $737,009,252
Liabilities: $275,477,482
Net Worth: $461,531,769
Earnings: $40,005,587
Emp.: 250
Fiscal Year-end: 12/31/23
Insurance Services
N.A.I.C.S.: 524126
Ali Morad Behbehani *(Chm)*

KUWAIT INTERNATIONAL BANK K.S.C.
Floor -2 West Tower - Joint Banking Center Ahmed Al Jaber Street, PO Box 22822, Safat, Kuwait, 13089, Kuwait
Tel.: (965) 22311448 KW
Web Site: https://www.kib.com.kw
Year Founded: 1973
KIB—(KUW)
Rev.: $368,517,014
Assets: $11,637,459,781
Liabilities: $10,504,205,532
Net Worth: $1,133,254,249
Earnings: $44,531,834
Emp.: 740
Fiscal Year-end: 12/31/22
Retail Banking, Real Estate Lending & Investment Services
N.A.I.C.S.: 522110
Mohammed Jarrah Al-Sabah *(Chm)*

KUWAIT INVEST HOLDING COMPANY K.S.C.C.
Salhiya Commercial Complex Entrance 8 5th Floor, PO Box 1990, Safat, Kuwait, 13020, Kuwait
Tel.: (965) 22461418
Web Site: http://www.univestgroup.com
Emp.: 9
Investment Services
N.A.I.C.S.: 523999
Anas Khalid Al-Saleh *(Chm)*

KUWAIT INVESTMENT AUTHORITY
Ministries Complex AlMurqab, PO Box 64, Safat Z, 13001, Kuwait, Kuwait
Tel.: (965) 2248 5604
Web Site: http://www.kia.gov.kw
Year Founded: 1953
Investment Holding Company
N.A.I.C.S.: 551112
Bader Al-Ajeel *(Exec Dir-Gen Reserves)*

Subsidiaries:

London City Airport Limited (1)
London City Airport City Aviation House, Royal Docks, London, E16 2PB, United Kingdom
Tel.: (44) 20 7646 0088
Web Site: http://www.londoncityairport.com
Airport Operator
N.A.I.C.S.: 488119
Alison FitzGerald *(COO)*

Wren House Infrastructure Management Limited (1)
55-58 Pall Mall, London, SW1Y 5JH, United Kingdom
Tel.: (44) 20 72964882
Private Equity
N.A.I.C.S.: 523940
Hakim Drissi Kaitouni *(CEO)*

Holding (US):

iTV-3, LLC (2)
602 High Point Ln E, Peoria, IL 61611
Tel.: (309) 689-0711
Web Site: http://i3broadband.com
Emp.: 200
Internet Service Provider
N.A.I.C.S.: 517111

KUWAIT INVESTMENT COMPANY (S.A.K.)
Al- Manakh Building 5th Floor Mubarak Al-Kabeer Street, Sharq, Kuwait, Kuwait
Tel.: (965) 22967000
Web Site: https://www.kic.com.kw
Year Founded: 1961
KINV—(KUW)
Rev.: $65,522,909
Assets: $847,585,186
Liabilities: $363,219,679
Net Worth: $484,365,507
Earnings: $11,521,151
Emp.: 122
Fiscal Year-end: 12/31/22
Investment Services
N.A.I.C.S.: 523999
Bader Naser AlSubaiee *(CEO)*

Subsidiaries:

Kuwait International Fair Company K.S.C. (1)
6th Ring Road Motor-highway, Mishref, 13007, Kuwait, Kuwait **(51%)**
Tel.: (965) 25387100
Web Site: http://www.kif.net
Advertising Agencies
N.A.I.C.S.: 541810

KUWAIT NATIONAL CINEMA COMPANY K.S.C.
Web Site: http://www.cinescape.com.kw
Year Founded: 1954
KCIN—(KUW)
Rev.: $76,465,306
Assets: $623,654,123
Liabilities: $363,082,843
Net Worth: $260,571,280
Earnings: $24,798,053
Emp.: 656
Fiscal Year-end: 12/31/22
Motion Picture, Theater & Cultural Event Services
N.A.I.C.S.: 512120
Sami Ali Hindi *(Mgr-Fin)*

KUWAIT PACKING MATERIALS MANUFACTURING COMPANY K.S.C.C.
South of Sabhan Block 8 Street 82, PO Box 26522, Safat, Kuwait, 13126, Kuwait
Tel.: (965) 24721124
Web Site: http://www.kuwaitpack.com
Year Founded: 1986
Sales Range: $25-49.9 Million
Emp.: 130
Extruded Polystyrene Foam Mfr
N.A.I.C.S.: 326140
Abdulaziz Fahad Omar Al-Serri *(Chm & Mng Dir)*

Subsidiaries:

U-PAK FZC. (1)
No 16 & 17 Technology Park, RAK Free Trade Zone, Ras al Khaimah, United Arab Emirates
Tel.: (971) 72447950
Web Site: http://www.upakfzc.com
Sales Range: $25-49.9 Million
Emp.: 40
Packing Materials & Disposables Mfr
N.A.I.C.S.: 424130
Hamid Anwar *(Deputy Gen Mgr)*

KUWAIT PETROLEUM CORPORATION
PO Box 26565, Safat, 13126, Kuwait, Kuwait
Tel.: (965) 1858585
Web Site: http://www.kpc.com.kw
Year Founded: 1980
Sales Range: $450-499.9 Million
Emp.: 22,000
Crude Oil & Natural Gas Production Hydrocarbon Substance Product & Derivative Mfr
N.A.I.C.S.: 213111
Hashem S. Hashem *(Deputy Chm & CEO)*

Subsidiaries:

Gulf Petrochemical Industries Co. (1)
PO Box 26730, Manama, Bahrain **(33%)**
Tel.: (973) 17731777
Web Site: http://www.gpic.com
Sales Range: $150-199.9 Million
Emp.: 500
Mfr of Petrochemical Products, Ammonia & Methanol
N.A.I.C.S.: 325110
Abdulrahman Jawahery *(Pres)*

Kuwait Aviation Fueling Company K.S.C. (1)
PO Box 1654, Safat, 13017, Kuwait, Kuwait **(100%)**
Tel.: (965) 1835000
Web Site: http://www.kafco.com
Sales Range: $50-74.9 Million
Emp.: 80
Provider of Drilling & Oil Services
N.A.I.C.S.: 213111
Abdullah Al Duaijani *(Vice Chm & Gen Mgr)*

Kuwait Drilling Co. (1)
E Ahmadi Ahmadi Block No 8 Plot No 142, PO Box 9066-61001, Ahmadi, Kuwait **(49%)**
Tel.: (965) 3981598
Sales Range: $350-399.9 Million
Emp.: 650
Drilling
N.A.I.C.S.: 213111

Kuwait Foreign Petroleum Exploration Company K.S.C. (1)
PO Box 5291, Safat, Kuwait, 13053, Kuwait **(100%)**
Tel.: (965) 1836000
Web Site: http://www.kufpec.com
Crude Oil & Natural Gas Exploration Services
N.A.I.C.S.: 211120
Mohammed R. Jasem *(Deputy Chm)*

Kuwait Gulf Oil Company K.S.C. (1)
PO Box 9919, 61010, Ahmadi, Kuwait
Tel.: (965) 23984281
Web Site: http://www.kgoc.com
Oil Exploration & Production
N.A.I.C.S.: 211120

Kuwait National Petroleum Company (1)
Safat, PO Box 70, 13001, Kuwait, Kuwait **(100%)**
Tel.: (965) 2398 9900
Web Site: http://www.knpc.com
Petroleum Refineries
N.A.I.C.S.: 324110

KUWAIT PETROLEUM CORPORATION

Kuwait Petroleum Corporation—(Continued)

Abdulla Fahhad Al-Ajmi *(Deputy CEO-Projects)*

Kuwait Oil Company K.S.C. (1)
Al Ahmadi Area The New Bldg, PO Box 9758, Ahmadi, 61008, Kuwait **(100%)**
Tel.: (965) 23989111
Web Site: http://www.kockw.com
Exploration, Products & Processing of Petroleum
N.A.I.C.S.: 325110
Sami Al-Rushaid *(Chm & Mng Dir)*

Kuwait Oil Tanker Company S.A.K. (1)
Shuwaikh Administrative area Gamal Abdel Nasser Street Block No 4, PO Box 810, Safat, Kuwait, CODE SAFAT 1300, Kuwait **(100%)**
Tel.: (965) 24625050
Web Site: http://www.kotc.com.kw
Sales Range: $50-74.9 Million
Emp.: 500
Operation of a Fleet of Crude Oil Tankers & Liquefied Petroleum Gas & Oil Product Carriers
N.A.I.C.S.: 211120
Nabil M. Bourisli *(Chm & Mng Dir)*

Kuwait Petroleum International (1)
KPC House, 54 Pall Mall, London, SW1Y 5JH, United Kingdom
Tel.: (44) 2074514700
Web Site: http://www.qp.com
Sales Range: $50-74.9 Million
Emp.: 50
Oil Exploration Services
N.A.I.C.S.: 213111
Bakheet Al-Rashidi *(Pres)*

Oil Development Company K.S.C. (1)
PO Box 9220, Ahmadi, 61008, Kuwait
Tel.: (965) 23982317
Web Site: http://www.odckw.com
Sales Range: $50-74.9 Million
Emp.: 5
Oil Industry Support Services
N.A.I.C.S.: 213112
Hashim Mustafa El-Rifaai *(Chm & Mng Dir)*

Oil Sector Services Company (1)
PO Box 1679, Safat, Kuwait, 13016, Kuwait
Tel.: (965) 22335555
Web Site: http://www.ossc.com.kw
Support Services for Oil Industry
N.A.I.C.S.: 213112
Ali Ahmad Al-Obaid *(Chm & Mng Dir)*

Petrochemical Industries Company K.S.C. (1)
PO Box 1084, Safat, Kuwait, Kuwait **(100%)**
Tel.: (965) 3211000
Web Site: http://www.pic.com.kw
Liquid Ammonia, Urea Fertilizer, Sulfur & Polypropylene Mfr & Marketer
N.A.I.C.S.: 325311

Joint Venture (Domestic):

EQUATE Petrochemical Company K.S.C.C. (2)
PO Box 4733, Safat, Kuwait, 13048, Kuwait
Tel.: (965) 1898888
Web Site: http://www.equate.com
Petrochemical Products Mfr
N.A.I.C.S.: 325998
Ramesh Ramachandran *(Pres & CEO)*

Joint Venture (Non-US):

MEGlobal Canada Inc. (2)
Hwy 597 & Prentiss Road, Red Deer, T4N 6N1, AB, Canada **(50%)**
Tel.: (403) 885-8536
Web Site: https://www.meglobal.biz
Chemicals Mfr
N.A.I.C.S.: 325998

Petrochemicals Industries Company (1)
PO Box 1084, Safat, Kuwait, 13011, Kuwait
Tel.: (965) 23851000
Web Site: https://www.pic.com.kw
Petrochemical Mfr & Distr
N.A.I.C.S.: 325110
Hamad A. Alturkait *(Chm)*

KUWAIT PIPE INDUSTRIES & OIL SERVICES COMPANY K.S.C.
Safat, PO Box 3416, Kuwait, 13035, Kuwait
Tel.: (965) 2467 5622 **KW**
Web Site: http://www.kpios.com
Year Founded: 1966
Sales Range: $250-299.9 Million
Emp.: 651
Pipe & Pipeline Mfr
N.A.I.C.S.: 331210
Abdul Kareem Abdullah I. Al-Mutawa *(Chm & CEO)*

Subsidiaries:

Kuwait Pipe Industries & Oil Services Company K.S.C.- John Pickle Middle East (1)
PO Box 3416, Safat, Kuwait, Kuwait
Tel.: (965) 24670072
Web Site: http://www.kpios.com
Sales Range: $200-249.9 Million
Heavy Metal Design & Mfr
N.A.I.C.S.: 332420

KUWAIT PORTLAND CEMENT CO. K.S.C.C.
Al ShuwaikhCanada Dry Street Section Number 101 C, PO Box 42191, In Front Of Kotmac Furniture Showroom Showaikh, 70652, Kuwait, 70652, Kuwait
Tel.: (965) 24835917
Web Site: https://www.portlandkw.co
Year Founded: 1976
PCEM—(KUW)
Rev.: $430,561,100
Assets: $322,968,901
Liabilities: $67,825,223
Net Worth: $255,143,677
Earnings: $16,316,751
Emp.: 1,161
Fiscal Year-end: 12/31/22
Cement Mfr
N.A.I.C.S.: 327310
Khaled Abdallah Al Hamad Al Sakr *(Co-Chm)*

KUWAIT PROJECTS COMPANY (HOLDING) K.S.C.P.
KIPCO Tower Khalid Bin Al Waleed Street, PO Box 23982, Sharq, Kuwait, 13100, Kuwait
Tel.: (965) 22943400
Web Site: https://www.kipco.com
Year Founded: 1975
KPROJ—(KUW)
Rev.: $3,453,479,151
Assets: $37,126,087,946
Liabilities: $31,968,643,765
Net Worth: $5,157,444,181
Earnings: $53,898,404
Emp.: 59
Fiscal Year-end: 12/31/22
Holding Company
N.A.I.C.S.: 551112
Hamad Sabah Al Ahmad Al Sabah *(Chm)*

Subsidiaries:

Al Atoun Steel Industries Company (1)
Safiyah Bint Abdul Mutalib Street District Mahmmediah 1, Post Box 5258, Jeddah, 21422, Saudi Arabia
Tel.: (966) 92000 2868
Web Site: http://alatoun.com
Steel Product Mfr & Distr
N.A.I.C.S.: 331110
F. Sayrafi *(Mgr-Fin Consultant & Private Placement Fin Transaction House)*

Al Rayan Holding Company K.S.C (1)
Al Egaila Al Bairaq Complex 12th Floor, PO Box 95, Jaber Al-Ali, Kuwait, 51701, Kuwait
Tel.: (965) 23824246
Web Site: https://www.alrayanholding.com
Educational Institution Services
N.A.I.C.S.: 611710
Lana Othman Al-Ayyar *(CEO)*

Burgan Bank S.A.K. (1)
Sharq - Kuwait - Abdulla Al-Ahmad Street, PO Box 5389, Safat, 12170, Kuwait, Kuwait **(50.1%)**
Tel.: (965) 22988087
Web Site: http://www.burgan.com
Rev.: $1,051,311,385
Assets: $23,289,544,672
Liabilities: $20,210,422,828
Net Worth: $3,079,121,843
Earnings: $190,288,927
Emp.: 3,827
Fiscal Year-end: 12/31/2022
Commercial & Investment Banking Services
N.A.I.C.S.: 522110
Khalid Fahad Al Zouman *(CFO-Grp)*

Subsidiary (Non-US):

Bank of Baghdad (2)
Baghdad - Al-Nidhal Street, PO Box 3192, Dis 902 - St 11 - Bul 25 & 27, Baghdad, Iraq **(49%)**
Tel.: (964) 7828893173
Web Site: https://www.bankofbaghdad.com.iq
Sales Range: $25-49.9 Million
Commercial Banking Services
N.A.I.C.S.: 522110
Usam Ismail Sharif *(Chm)*

Burgan Bank AS (2)
Eski Buyukdere Caddesi St Tekfen Tower 209 4 Levent, Istanbul, 34394, Turkiye **(99.26%)**
Tel.: (90) 2123713737
Web Site: http://www.eurobanktekfen.com
Commercial Banking & Financial Services
N.A.I.C.S.: 522110
Esra Aydin *(Exec VP-Ops & Mgmt Svcs)*

Gulf Bank Algeria (2)
Route de Cheraga, PO Box 26, Algiers, Algeria
Tel.: (213) 21984904
Web Site: http://www.agb.dz
Commercial Banking; Owned 60% by United Gulf Bank B.S.C., 30% by Tunis International Bank & 10% by Jordan Kuwait Bank
N.A.I.C.S.: 522110

Centerstone Investor, Inc. (1)
228 Park Ave S Ste 75938, New York, NY 10003
Tel.: (212) 503-5790
Web Site: https://centerstoneinv.com
Investment Management Service
N.A.I.C.S.: 523940

FIM Bank Group Ltd. (1)
Mercury Tower The Exchange Financial & Business Centre, Elia Zammit Street, Saint Julian's, STJ 3155, Malta
Tel.: (356) 21322100
Web Site: https://www.fimbank.com
Trade Finance Services
N.A.I.C.S.: 522220

First Securities Brokerage Company K.S.C (1)
Hilalli Street, Sharq, Kuwait, 13124, Kuwait
Tel.: (965) 24954444
Web Site: https://www.oulawasata.com.kw
Security Brokerage Services
N.A.I.C.S.: 523150
Fahad Al-Refae *(CEO)*

Gulfsat Communications Company K.S.C. (1)
Free Trade Zone 2nd Phase Area F98 Bldg 5 Ground Floor Gate 5, PO Box 2400, 13025, Kuwait, Kuwait
Tel.: (965) 22917777
Web Site: https://www.gulfsat.com
Satellite Communication Services
N.A.I.C.S.: 517410

Hunter Capital Group, LLC (1)
136 Heber Ave Ste 304, Park City, UT 84060 **(70%)**
Tel.: (435) 647-3835
Web Site: http://www.huntercapital.com
Sales Range: $75-99.9 Million
Emp.: 4

INTERNATIONAL PUBLIC

Investment Banking & Portfolio Management Services
N.A.I.C.S.: 523150
Larry Griffin *(Mng Dir)*

Subsidiary (Domestic):

Prospector Equity Capital, L.P. (2)
1910 Prospector Ave, Park City, UT 84060
Tel.: (435) 647-3835
Web Site: http://www.pecinvestors.com
Sales Range: $50-74.9 Million
Emp.: 3
Equity Investment Company
N.A.I.C.S.: 523999

Insha'a Holding Company K.S.C. (1)
Fahad Al Salem Street Al-Jon Center 19th Floor, Kuwait, Kuwait
Tel.: (965) 22272555
Web Site: https://inshaaholding.com
Construction Materials Supplier
N.A.I.C.S.: 423320

Jassim Transport & Stevedoring Company K.S.C.P. (1)
PO Box 22801, Safat, Kuwait, 13089, Kuwait
Tel.: (965) 22286100
Web Site: https://www.jtckw.com
Cost Management Services
N.A.I.C.S.: 541611

KAMCO Investment Company Saudi W.L.L. (1)
Mazaya Tower Al Ma'ather Street, Riyadh, Saudi Arabia
Tel.: (966) 112994100
Underwriting Services
N.A.I.C.S.: 523210

Kuwait Hotels Company K.S.C.P. (1)
PO Box 833, Safat, Kuwait, 13009, Kuwait
Tel.: (965) 22257070
Web Site: http://www.khc.com.kw
Rev.: $16,220,638
Assets: $22,533,934
Liabilities: $7,034,181
Net Worth: $15,499,753
Earnings: $1,967,607
Emp.: 17
Fiscal Year-end: 12/31/2022
Hotel Owner & Operator
N.A.I.C.S.: 721110
Ahmad Yousef Al Kandari *(Chm)*

Napesco India LLP (1)
No 146/3 Habibullah Road, T Nagar, Chennai, 600 017, Tamil Nadu, India
Tel.: (91) 4428341255
Web Site: https://napescoindia.com
Oil & Gas Industry Construction Services
N.A.I.C.S.: 237120

North Africa Holding Company K.S.C. (1)
Tel.: (965) 22023750
Web Site: https://www.northafricaholding.com
Investment Banking Services
N.A.I.C.S.: 523999
Fuad A. Akbar *(Chm)*

Subsidiary (Non-US):

Egyptian International Medical Center S.A.E (2)
Pharma Plaza Build 4y From Asmaa Fahmy St, Nasr, Cairo, Egypt
Tel.: (20) 2 414 0215
Web Site: https://www.eimc.com.eg
Pharmaceuticals Product Mfr
N.A.I.C.S.: 325412
Adel Tolba *(CEO)*

PKC Advisory (1)
15th Floor Tower-B DLF Cyber Terraces Building No 5 DLF Cyber City, Haryana, Gurgaon, 122 002, India **(100%)**
Tel.: (91) 1244525300
Web Site: http://www.pkcadvisory.com
Financial Investment Activities
N.A.I.C.S.: 523999
Narendra Baliga *(CEO)*

PKC Advisory Services JLT (1)
Office No 28-502 5th Floor 48 Burj Gate Burj Khalifa Area, PO Box 185799, Dubai, United Arab Emirates
Tel.: (971) 505172003

AND PRIVATE COMPANIES — KUWAIT REAL ESTATE HOLDING COMPANY K.P.S.C.

Web Site: http://www.pkcadvisory.com
Business Management Services
N.A.I.C.S.: 541611
Narendra Baliga (CEO)

Qurain Petrochemical Industries Company K.S.C.P. (1)
26 Floor KIPCO Tower Khalid Bin Al-Waleed Street Safat, PO Box 29299, Sharq, Kuwait, 13153, Kuwait
Tel.: (965) 22943232
Web Site: http://www.qpic-kw.com
Rev.: $757,694,600
Assets: $2,486,537,633
Liabilities: $554,341,899
Net Worth: $1,932,195,734
Earnings: $98,191,047
Emp.: 28
Fiscal Year-end: 12/31/2021
Petrochemical Mfr
N.A.I.C.S.: 325110
Mubarak Abdullah Al-Mubarak Al-Sabah (Chm)

Subsidiary (Domestic):

National Petroleum Services Company K.S.C.G. (2)
Shuaiba West Industrial Area Block 3 Plot 76 Integration Road MA10, with M& Mina Abdullah, Kuwait, Kuwait
Tel.: (965) 22251000
Web Site: http://www.napesco.com
Rev.: $120,851,471
Assets: $172,744,041
Liabilities: $35,387,286
Net Worth: $137,356,755
Earnings: $22,178,495
Emp.: 500
Fiscal Year-end: 12/31/2022
Oil & Gas Services
N.A.I.C.S.: 213112
Omran Habib Jawhar Hayat (Chm)

SACEM Energy and Engineering SA (1)
Imm Mak Crown rue Lac Tanganyika Les Berges du Lac, 1053, Tunis, Tunisia
Tel.: (216) 71966986
Web Site: https://www.sacemenergy.com
Engineeering Services
N.A.I.C.S.: 541330

SACEM Industries S.A. (1)
Imm Mak Crown 3rd Floor Rue Du Lac Tanganyika, Les Berges Du Lac, 1053, Tunis, Tunisia
Tel.: (216) 71966986
Web Site: https://www.sacemindustries.com
Industrial Equipment Distr
N.A.I.C.S.: 423830

SACEM Smart SA (1)
Imm Mak Crown 5eme etage Rue du Lac Tanganyika Les Berges du Lac, 1053, Tunis, Tunisia
Tel.: (216) 71966986
Web Site: https://www.sacemsmart.com
Power Distribution Product Mfr
N.A.I.C.S.: 335311

STE SACEM Training SA (1)
Imm Mak Crown rue Lac Tanganyika Les Berges du Lac, 1053, Tunis, Tunisia
Tel.: (216) 71966986
Web Site: https://www.sacemtraining.com
Employee Training Services
N.A.I.C.S.: 611430

Takaud Savings & Pensions B.S.C. (1)
8th Floor UGB Tower Diplomatic Area, Manama, Bahrain
Tel.: (973) 17511611
Financial Banking Services
N.A.I.C.S.: 523999
Samer Khanachet (Chm)

The Egyptian Company for Factoring S.A.E. (1)
Public Free Zone Block H/11, Nasr, Egypt
Tel.: (20) 26720787
Web Site: https://www.egyptfactors.com
Trade Finance Services
N.A.I.C.S.: 522220

United Facilities Management L.L.C. (1)
48D Block B Al Rabat Street 1st Floor Salalah Mall, Salalah, Oman
Tel.: (968) 23381500
Web Site: https://ufm.com.kw
Business Support Services
N.A.I.C.S.: 561499

United Gulf Bank B.S.C. (1)
UGB Tower Diplomatic Area, PO Box 5964, Manama, Bahrain
Tel.: (973) 17533233
Web Site: http://www.ugbbh.com
Rev.: $113,732,000
Assets: $923,223,000
Liabilities: $590,219,000
Net Worth: $333,004,000
Earnings: $11,420,000
Fiscal Year-end: 12/31/2019
Banking Services
N.A.I.C.S.: 522110
Masaud M. J. Hayat (Chm)

Subsidiary (Non-US):

KAMCO Investment Company K.S.C.C. (2)
Al-Shaheed Tower, Khalid Bin Waleed Street Sharq, Kuwait, Kuwait (72%)
Tel.: (965) 22336600
Web Site: https://www.kamcoinvest.com
Rev.: $79,626,631
Assets: $420,705,122
Liabilities: $205,996,383
Net Worth: $214,708,739
Earnings: $17,550,015
Emp.: 182
Fiscal Year-end: 12/31/2022
Asset Management & Financial Services
N.A.I.C.S.: 523940
Entisar Abdul Raheem Al-Suwaidi (Vice Chm)

Subsidiary (Domestic):

Global Investment House K.S.C.C. (3)
Global Tower Shuhada Street Sharq, PO Box 28807, Safat, 13149, Kuwait, Kuwait (100%)
Tel.: (965) 22951000
Web Site: http://www.globalinv.net
Sales Range: $75-99.9 Million
Emp.: 205
Investment Services
N.A.I.C.S.: 523999
Khawla B. Al Roomi (Exec VP-HR, Admin & Mktg)

Subsidiary (Non-US):

Global Investment House Saudi Arabia (4)
Al-Mather Street, PO Box 66930, Riyadh, 11586, Saudi Arabia
Tel.: (966) 12199966
Investment Services
N.A.I.C.S.: 523999

Shurooq Investment Services Company (4)
6th Fl Ruwi Building 1287, PO Box 3758, Ruwi, 3516, Oman (65%)
Tel.: (968) 24726700
Web Site: http://www.samsco.com
Sales Range: $25-49.9 Million
Emp.: 35
Real Estate Agents & Brokers
N.A.I.C.S.: 531210
Mohamaad Ali Sultan (Chm)

Shurooq Securities Company LLC (4)
Sayed Plaza Building 3rd Floor, PO Box 982, Ruwi, Oman (50%)
Tel.: (968) 24818200
Sales Range: $50-74.9 Million
Emp.: 13
Securities Brokerage
N.A.I.C.S.: 523150

Subsidiary (Non-US):

Tunis International Bank (2)
18 Avenue des Etats Unis d Ameriques, PO Box 81, Belvedere, 1002, Tunis, Tunisia (77%)
Tel.: (216) 71782411
Web Site: https://www.tib.com.tn
Sales Range: $25-49.9 Million
Emp.: 100
Private, Commercial & Investment Banking, International Trade Financing & Credit Card Issuing Services

N.A.I.C.S.: 522110

Subsidiary (Domestic):

United Gulf Bank Securities Company B.S.C. (2)
Diplomatic Area UGB Tower, PO Box 5964, Manama, 5964, Bahrain
Tel.: (973) 17533233
Web Site: http://ugbbh.com
Sales Range: $50-74.9 Million
Investment Banking, Securities Trading & Brokerage Services; Owned 70% by United Gulf Bank B.S.C. & 30% by Kipco Asset Management Company
N.A.I.C.S.: 523150

United Gulf Management Ltd. (1)
7 Old Park Lane, London, W1K1QR, United Kingdom (100%)
Tel.: (44) 2074936000
Web Site: http://www.kipco.com
Sales Range: $75-99.9 Million
Emp.: 5
Corporate Financial Advisory Services
N.A.I.C.S.: 523940

United Industries Company K.S.C.C. (1)
PO Box 25821, Safat, 13119, Kuwait, Kuwait
Tel.: (965) 22943236
Web Site: https://www.uickw.com
Sales Range: $10-24.9 Million
Emp.: 30
Investment Services
N.A.I.C.S.: 523999
Khalifa Al Abdullah Al-Jaber Al-Sabah (Chm)

United Oil Projects Company K.S.C. (1)
Plot 4 Street 7 Block 47 West Shuaiba Industrial Area, Mina Abdullah Industrial Area, Safat, 26011, Kuwait
Tel.: (965) 23263297
Web Site: https://www.uopkt.com
Chemical Products Mfr
N.A.I.C.S.: 325211

United Real Estate Company K.S.C.P. (1)
Al Shaheed Tower Khalid Bin Al-Waleed St, Al-Sharq, Kuwait
Tel.: (965) 1805225
Web Site: https://www.urc.com.kw
Construction & Contracting Services
N.A.I.C.S.: 236117

United Real Estate Company S.A.K. (1)
Al Shaheed Tower Khalid Bin AlWaleed St Sharq, PO Box 2232, Safat, 13023, Kuwait, 13023, Kuwait
Tel.: (965) 1805225
Web Site: https://www.urc.com.kw
Rev.: $275,028,330
Assets: $2,170,090,178
Liabilities: $1,557,318,528
Net Worth: $612,771,650
Earnings: $11,965,699
Emp.: 110
Fiscal Year-end: 12/31/2022
Real Estate Services
N.A.I.C.S.: 531390
Bibi Nasser Sabah Al-Ahmed Al-Sabah (Chm)

Subsidiary (Non-US):

Dhiyafa Holding Company S.A.L. (2)
Office 901/902 9th Floor Northern Building Starco, Minet El-Hosn, Beirut, Lebanon
Tel.: (961) 1 365850
Web Site: http://www.urc.com.kw
Emp.: 1
Investment Management Service
N.A.I.C.S.: 523999

Gulf Egypt for Hotels & Tourism S.A.E (2)
Kamal El Din Hussein St Off El Shaheed Sayed Zakareya St Floor 3, Sheraton Bldgs Heliopolis, Cairo, Egypt
Tel.: (20) 222687153
Home Management Services
N.A.I.C.S.: 721110
Mohsen Abou El-Azm (Mng Dir)

Subsidiary (Domestic):

Kuwait United Construction Management Company W.L.L. (2)
Al Salhiya Area Souk Al Mutahida 4th Floor, 27068, Kuwait, Kuwait
Tel.: (965) 2 2418239
Web Site: http://www.kucm.com
Construction Management Services
N.A.I.C.S.: 541618
Edward D. Chester (Dir-Contract Admin)

Kuwait United Facilities Management Company S.A.K. (Closed) (2)
Muthahida Complex, PO Box 1384, Dasman, Kuwait, 15464, Kuwait
Tel.: (965) 22477920
Web Site: http://www.kufmonline.com
Sales Range: $25-49.9 Million
Emp.: 50
Real Estate Investment Services
N.A.I.C.S.: 531390
Ahmed Yousef Al Kandari (CEO)

Subsidiary (Non-US):

United Lebanese Real Estate Company S.A.L (2)
9th Fl Office 901 Starco Building Block A Omar Al Daouk St, Mina Al Hosn, Beirut, 113012, Lebanon
Tel.: (961) 1365850
Web Site: http://www.urc.com.kw
Sales Range: $50-74.9 Million
Emp.: 8
Real Estate Development Services
N.A.I.C.S.: 531390

Subsidiary (Domestic):

United Universal Real Estate Consulting Company (2)
9th floor Madina Tower Khalid Bin Al Waleed Street, Sharq, Kuwait, Kuwait
Tel.: (965) 2241 2802
Web Site: http://www.uurec.com
Real Estate Development Services
N.A.I.C.S.: 531390
Ramzi Al-Shamali (Gen Mgr)

United Universal Real Estate W.L.L (2)
Khalid Bin Waleed Street City Tower 9th Floor, Kuwait, Kuwait
Tel.: (965) 22412802
Web Site: http://www.uurec.com
Sales Range: $50-74.9 Million
Emp.: 5
Real Estate Consulting Service
N.A.I.C.S.: 531390

KUWAIT REAL ESTATE CO. (K.S.C.)
Darwazat Abdul Razak Street Souk Al Kuwait Building 8th Floor Block B, PO Box 1257, Safat, Kuwait, 13013, Kuwait
Tel.: (965) 1828999
Web Site: https://www.aqarat.com.kw
Year Founded: 1972
KRE—(KUW)
Rev.: $89,768,696
Assets: $1,171,737,119
Liabilities: $742,608,489
Net Worth: $429,128,629
Earnings: $24,503,907
Emp.: 93
Fiscal Year-end: 12/31/22
Real Estate Manangement Services
N.A.I.C.S.: 531390
Ibrahim Saleh Abdullah Al-Therban (Chm)

KUWAIT REAL ESTATE HOLDING COMPANY K.P.S.C.
Al-Shaheed Tower 6th Floor Khaled Ben Al Waleed Street, PO Box 25578, Safat, Kuwait, 13116, Kuwait
Tel.: (965) 22009082   KW
Web Site: https://www.alaqaria.com
Year Founded: 1980
ALAQARIA—(KUW)
Rev.: $1,382,684
Assets: $82,662,241
Liabilities: $53,150,648
Net Worth: $29,511,593
Earnings: ($1,912,769)

KUWAIT REAL ESTATE HOLDING COMPANY K.P.S.C.

Kuwait Real Estate Holding Company K.P.S.C.—(Continued)
Emp.: 15
Fiscal Year-end: 12/31/22
Real Estate & Investment Services
N.A.I.C.S.: 531390
Mohammad Barak Abdulmohsen Al-Mutair *(Chm)*

Subsidiaries:

Al Omran Real Estate Development Co. K.S.C. (1)
Behind the Sheraton - Osama Bin Munqeth Street-Al Kharafi Tower, Floor 15 Qibla Safat, Kuwait, 13022, Kuwait (96%)
Tel.: (965) 22323232
Web Site: http://www.alomran.com.kw
Real Estate Development Services
N.A.I.C.S.: 531390

KUWAIT REINSURANCE CO. K.S.C.C.
harq Area AlShuhadaa Street KRe Tower 8 9 13 Floors, PO Box 21929, Safat, 13080, Kuwait, 13080, Kuwait
Tel.: (965) 22299666
Web Site: https://www.kuwaitre.com
Year Founded: 1972
KUWAITRE—(KUW)
Rev.: $230,844,863
Assets: $694,673,441
Liabilities: $468,822,597
Net Worth: $225,850,843
Earnings: $25,904,319
Emp.: 81
Fiscal Year-end: 12/31/22
Reinsurance Services
N.A.I.C.S.: 524130
Mohammad Abdulmohsen Al Saad *(Vice Chm)*

KUWAIT REMAL REAL ESTATE COMPANY K.P.S.C.
AL Qibla - Fahad Al-Salem St Al Nassar Tower Floor-8, Kuwait, Kuwait
Tel.: (965) 2 225 8855 KW
Web Site: http://www.remalkw.com
Year Founded: 2002
REMAL—(KUW)
Rev.: $6,090,347
Assets: $141,625,995
Liabilities: $132,827,694
Net Worth: $8,798,302
Earnings: ($19,300,528)
Emp.: 14
Fiscal Year-end: 12/31/21
Real Estate Manangement Services
N.A.I.C.S.: 531390
Ihab Hakim Hamouda *(Vice Chm & CEO)*

KUWAIT RESORTS COMPANY (K.S.C.)
Al Sharq Jaber Al Mubarak St Al Shorouq Tower 1, PO Box 5601, Safat, Kuwait, 13057, Kuwait
Tel.: (965) 22474647
Web Site: https://muntazahat.com.kw
Year Founded: 2002
MUNTAZAHAT—(KUW)
Rev.: $23,247,197
Assets: $108,083,662
Liabilities: $15,143,453
Net Worth: $92,940,209
Earnings: $3,297,530
Emp.: 24
Fiscal Year-end: 12/31/22
Home Management Services
N.A.I.C.S.: 721110
Ibrahim Mohammad Alghanim *(Vice Chm & CEO)*

KUWAIT STOCK EXCHANGE
PO Box 22235, Kuwait, 13083, Kuwait
Tel.: (965) 2423133
Web Site: http://www.kuwaitse.com
Sales Range: $50-74.9 Million
Emp.: 190
Stock Exchange Services
N.A.I.C.S.: 523210
Abdulaziz Abdulaziz Saad Al-Rashed *(Vice Chm)*

KUWAIT SWEDISH CLEANING SERVICES CO. S.A.K.
Salah El Deen St Al Bahar Building 3rd Floor, PO Box 21225, Safat, Kuwait, 13073, Kuwait
Tel.: (965) 822224 KW
Web Site: http://www.kuwaitswedish.com
Year Founded: 1982
Sales Range: $200-249.9 Million
Emp.: 2,000
Janitorial & Cleaning Services
N.A.I.C.S.: 561720

KUWAIT SYRIAN HOLDING CO. K.S.C.
Jaber Mubarak Street Al Khalijiya Tower Third floor, PO Box 29838, Safat, Kuwait, 13159, Kuwait
Tel.: (965) 22280887
Web Site: https://www.ksh.com.kw
Year Founded: 2002
EMIRATES—(KUW)
Rev.: $789,112
Assets: $80,675,082
Liabilities: $1,212,383
Net Worth: $79,462,699
Earnings: $303,517
Emp.: 70
Fiscal Year-end: 12/31/22
Investment Services
N.A.I.C.S.: 523999
Ahmad Abdulrahman Alsharqawi *(Chm)*

KUWAYAMA CORPORATION
2-23-21 Higashi-Ueno, Taito-ku, Tokyo, 110-0015, Japan
Tel.: (81) 3 3835 7231
Web Site: http://www.kuwayama.co.jp
Rev.: $293,022,240
Assets: $260,583,600
Liabilities: $115,759,680
Net Worth: $144,823,920
Earnings: $5,567,760
Emp.: 1,471
Fiscal Year-end: 03/31/18
Jewelry Mfr
N.A.I.C.S.: 339910
Yukihiro Kuwayama *(Chm)*

Subsidiaries:

Christy Gem Co., Ltd. (1)
47/49 Moo 4 Gemopolis Sukhapibarn 2 Road Khwang Dokmai, Khet Praves, Bangkok, 10250, Thailand
Tel.: (66) 2 727 0390 2
Web Site: http://www.christy-gem.co.th
Emp.: 500
Jewelry Mfr & Distr
N.A.I.C.S.: 339910

Clair Co., Ltd. (1)
Okuya Bldg 3Rd Floor 2-10-12 Higashi-Ueno, Taito-Ku, Tokyo, Japan
Tel.: (81) 3 38332369
Emp.: 10
Jewellery Distr
N.A.I.C.S.: 423940

Kuwayama Europe N.V. (1)
Schupstraat 9-11, 2018, Antwerp, Belgium
Tel.: (32) 3 2252538
Web Site: http://www.flanders-brilliant.be
Jewellery Distr
N.A.I.C.S.: 423940
Marc Paeshuys *(Mng Dir)*

Kuwayama Corporation - Toyama Factory (1)
1288-1 Miyasu, Uozu, 9370853, Toyama, Japan

Tel.: (81) 765 24 2711
Jewelry Mfr
N.A.I.C.S.: 339910

NJ Corporation (1)
2-10-13 Higashi-ueno, Taito-Ku, Tokyo, 110-0015, Japan
Tel.: (81) 3 58177511
Web Site: http://www.nj-co.com
Jewellery Distr
N.A.I.C.S.: 423940

KUWAZAWA HOLDINGS CORP.
7-1-1 Chuo 2-Jo, Shiroishi-Ku, Sapporo, 003-8560, Hokkaido, Japan
Tel.: (81) 118641111
Web Site: https://kuwazawa-hd.co.jp
Year Founded: 1951
8104—(SAP)
Rev.: $609,326,960
Assets: $377,694,240
Liabilities: $239,473,520
Net Worth: $138,220,720
Earnings: $5,411,120
Fiscal Year-end: 03/31/22
Building Materials Distr
N.A.I.C.S.: 444180
Yoshihide Kuwazawa *(Pres & CEO)*

KUWER INDUSTRIES LIMITED
A-71/72 Sector 58, Noida, 201 301, Uttar Pradesh, India
Tel.: (91) 1202580088
Web Site: https://www.kuwer.com
Year Founded: 1993
530421—(BOM)
Rev.: $7,753,241
Assets: $7,554,470
Liabilities: $5,262,198
Net Worth: $2,292,272
Earnings: $53,645
Emp.: 45
Fiscal Year-end: 03/31/21
Holographic Product Mfr
N.A.I.C.S.: 322220
Tarun Aggarwal *(Chm & Mng Dir)*

KUYA SILVER CORPORATION
150 King Street West Suite 200, Toronto, M5H 1J9, ON, Canada
Tel.: (604) 398-4493
Web Site: https://kuyasilver.com
KUYAF—(OTCQB)
Rev.: $12,288
Assets: $21,751,430
Liabilities: $2,263,910
Net Worth: $19,487,520
Earnings: ($3,677,327)
Fiscal Year-end: 12/31/20
Gold Exploration & Mining Services
N.A.I.C.S.: 212220
David Stein *(Pres)*

KUYAS YATIRIM A.S.
Istanbul Vizyonpark Merkez Plaza Kuyumcular Sokak C-1, Blok No 4 Kat 11 Daire 325-326 Yenibosna, 9400, Istanbul, Turkiye
Tel.: (90) 2126033200
KUYAS—(IST)
Rev.: $7,512,471
Assets: $22,085,373
Liabilities: $5,683,861
Net Worth: $16,401,512
Earnings: $7,140,754
Fiscal Year-end: 12/31/22
Real Estate Investment Services
N.A.I.C.S.: 531210

KUZCO LIGHTING, INC.
19054 28th Avenue, Surrey, V3Z 6M3, BC, Canada
Tel.: (604) 538-7162
Web Site: https://kuzcolighting.com
Year Founded: 2006
Lighting Fixture Mfr
N.A.I.C.S.: 335132

INTERNATIONAL PUBLIC

Nathan Yang *(Pres)*

Subsidiaries:

Auroralight, Inc. (1)
2742 Loker Ave W, Carlsbad, CA 92010
Tel.: (760) 931-2910
Web Site: http://www.auroralight.com
Sales Range: $10-24.9 Million
LED & Halogen Landscape Lighting Fixture Mfr
N.A.I.C.S.: 335132
Steve Wood *(Pres)*

KUZE CO., LTD.
2-29-7 Higashi Ikebukuro, Toshima-ku, Tokyo, 170-0013, Japan
Tel.: (81) 339870018
Web Site: https://www.kuze.co.jp
Year Founded: 1934
2708—(TKS)
Rev.: $425,992,613
Assets: $164,274,814
Liabilities: $120,218,004
Net Worth: $44,056,810
Earnings: $13,267,258
Fiscal Year-end: 03/31/24
Food Distr
N.A.I.C.S.: 445298
Kenkichi Kuze *(Pres)*

Subsidiaries:

Asahi Suisan Co., Ltd. (1)
Toyosu 6-6-1 Management Facility Bld 517, Koto-ku, Tokyo, 135-0061, Japan
Tel.: (81) 36 633 4111
Web Site: https://www.asahisuisan.co.jp
Fishery Products Whslr
N.A.I.C.S.: 424460
Tatsunori Murata *(Pres)*

Kisco Foods Co., Ltd. (1)
1-21-11 Higashi-ikebukuro, Toshima-ku, Tokyo, 170-0013, Japan
Tel.: (81) 33 981 5005
Web Site: https://www.kiscofoods.co.jp
Emp.: 183
Sauce & Soup Mfr
N.A.I.C.S.: 311942
Shinji Hayashi *(Pres & CEO)*

Kisco Foods Co., Ltd. - Shimizu Factory (1)
652-1 Shigenoshima, Shimizu-ku, Shizuoka, 424-0405, Japan
Tel.: (81) 543952622
Spice Mfr
N.A.I.C.S.: 311941

Kisco Foods International Limited (1)
6 Vulcan Place Middleton, PO Box 8240, Christchurch, 8024, New Zealand
Tel.: (64) 33381122
Web Site: https://www.kisco-inter.co.nz
Spice Mfr
N.A.I.C.S.: 311941
Tatsumi Hasegawa *(Pres & CEO)*

Kuze (Chengdu) Trading Co., Ltd. (1)
Room 1E Sino-Japanese Hall No 9 Shenglong Street, Wuhou District, Chengdu, 610042, Sichuan, China
Tel.: (86) 2887060984
Web Site: https://www.kuze.net.cn
Rice Mfr
N.A.I.C.S.: 424490

KVANTUM GROUP DD
Zagrebacka do 50, 71000, Sarajevo, Bosnia & Herzegovina
Tel.: (387) 33 557 926
Business Management Consulting Services
N.A.I.C.S.: 541618

KVAZAR-MICRO HUNGARY KFT.
Office Campus Bld B 3rd FL, 6 Gubacsi ut, 1097, Budapest, Hungary
Tel.: (36) 18804400
Web Site: http://www.kvazar-micro.hu
Sales Range: $25-49.9 Million

Emp.: 30
Information Technology Products & Services
N.A.I.C.S.: 541512
Laszlo Meszaros (Mng Dir)

KVC INDUSTRIAL SUPPLIES SDN. BHD.
Wisma KVC Lot 3 Jalan P10/12, Kawasan Perusahaan Bangi, 43650, Bandar Baru Bangi, Selangor Darul Ehsan, Malaysia
Tel.: (60) 389252828
Web Site: http://www.kvc.com.my
Year Founded: 1989
Sales Range: $75-99.9 Million
Emp.: 200
Industrial Electrical & Electronic Products Distr
N.A.I.C.S.: 423610
Vincent Lee (Gen Mgr)

Subsidiaries:

AZ Master (M) Sdn. Bhd. (1)
Wisma KVC Lot 3 Jalan P10/12, Kawasan Perusahaan Bangi, Bandar Baru Bangi, 43650, Selangor Darul Ehsan, Malaysia
Tel.: (60) 389252828
Web Site: http://www.atis.com.my
Capacitor Raw Materials Whslr
N.A.I.C.S.: 423690

Alliance Motors and Drives Sdn Bhd (1)
No 4 Jalan TS 6/4 Taman Industri Subang, 47513, Subang Jaya, Selangor Darul Ehsan, Malaysia
Tel.: (60) 3 5621 6288
Industrial Supplies Mfr
N.A.I.C.S.: 333248

Cable Solutions (SEA) Pte. Ltd. (1)
6 Changi South St 2 Unit 01-01 Xilin Districentre Building D, Singapore, 486349, Singapore
Tel.: (65) 62927727
Web Site: http://www.cablesolutions.com.sg
Sales Range: $25-49.9 Million
Emp.: 15
Electronic Cable Mfr
N.A.I.C.S.: 335921
Amy Tan (Dir-Sls)

Subsidiary (Non-US):

P.T. Cable Solutions Indonesia (2)
Kompleks Pergudangan Duta Indah Kapuk, Jl Kapuk Raya No 89 Blok A-3, Jakarta, 14460, Indonesia
Tel.: (62) 2154376996
Web Site: http://www.cablesolutions.com.sg
Sales Range: $50-74.9 Million
Emp.: 10
Wires & Cables Distr
N.A.I.C.S.: 423610

Cotel Precision Industries Sdn Bhd (1)
Wisma KVC Lot 3 Jalan P10/12 Kawasan Perusahaan Bangi, 43650, Bandar Baru Bangi, Selangor Darul Ehsan, Malaysia
Tel.: (60) 3 8925 2828
Web Site: http//www.cotel.com.my
Industrial Machinery Mfr
N.A.I.C.S.: 333248

Emen Installation Materials Sdn Bhd (1)
Lot 8249 Jalan 222, 46100, Petaling Jaya, Selangor Darul Ehsan, Malaysia
Tel.: (60) 3 7956 2626
Industrial Machinery Mfr
N.A.I.C.S.: 333248

Flexmodus Sdn. Bhd. (1)
No 5 & 7 Jalan P10/18 Taman Industri Selaman, Seksyen 10, 43650, Bandar Baru Bangi, Selangor, Malaysia
Tel.: (60) 389262118
Emp.: 22
Industrial Precision Products Mfr
N.A.I.C.S.: 332721

KVC Connectors Sdn Bhd (1)
Wisma KVC Lot 3 Jalan P10/12 Kawasan Perusahaan Bangi, 43650, Bandar Baru Bangi, Selangor Darul Ehsan, Malaysia
Tel.: (60) 3 8925 2828
Industrial Machinery Mfr
N.A.I.C.S.: 333248

KVC Industrial Supplies (Johor) Sdn. Bhd. (1)
No 26 Jalan Gemilang 1 Taman Perindustrian Cemerlang, 83000, Ulu Tiram, Johor Darul Takzim, Malaysia
Tel.: (60) 78683888
Web Site: http://www.kvc.com.my
Sales Range: $25-49.9 Million
Emp.: 25
Switches & Sockets Mfr
N.A.I.C.S.: 334419
Wong Bing Ming (Branch Mgr)

KVC Industrial Supplies (Kuantan) Sdn. Bhd. (1)
B380 Jalan Air Putih, 25300, Kuantan, Pahang Darul Makmur, Malaysia
Tel.: (60) 95666688
Web Site: http://www.kvc.com.my
Sales Range: $125-149.9 Million
Emp.: 10
Power Cords Distr
N.A.I.C.S.: 423610
Chen Yoon Seong (Mgr)

KVC Industrial Supplies (Melaka) Sdn. Bhd. (1)
No 65 & 67 Jalan PPM8 Plaza, Pandan Malim Business Park Balai Panjang, 75250, Melaka, Malaysia
Tel.: (60) 63345888
Sales Range: $25-49.9 Million
Emp.: 12
Electric Component Whslr
N.A.I.C.S.: 423690
Francis Chee Peng Sa (Mng Dir)

KVC Industrial Supplies (N.S.) Sdn. Bhd. (1)
PT 12175 Jalan BBN 1/1F Putra Point 2B, Bandar Baru Nilai, 71800, Nilai, Negeri Sembilan, Malaysia
Tel.: (60) 67995888
Web Site: http://www.atis.com.my
Emp.: 16
Electric Signals Mfr
N.A.I.C.S.: 334290
Kenny Tan (Gen Mgr)

KVC Industrial Supplies (Penang) Sdn. Bhd. (1)
No 517 Jalan Perusahaan Baru, Prai Industrial Estate, 13600, Prai, Penang, Malaysia
Tel.: (60) 43898888
Electric Component Whslr
N.A.I.C.S.: 423690

KVC Industrial Supplies (Perak) Sdn. Bhd. (1)
No 21B Jalan Pengkalan Putra 3, Pusat Perniagaan Pengkalan Putra, 31650, Ipoh, Perak Darul Ridzuan, Malaysia
Tel.: (60) 53205205
Sales Range: $25-49.9 Million
Emp.: 20
Industrial Electrical & Electronic Products Distr
N.A.I.C.S.: 423610
Chong Koon Yen (Branch Mgr)

KVC Industries Sdn. Bhd. (1)
Lot 3 Jalan P10/12, Kawasan Perusahaan Bangi, 43650, Bandar Baru Bangi, Selangor, Malaysia
Tel.: (60) 389252828
Web Site: http://www.atis.com.my
Sales Range: $25-49.9 Million
Emp.: 400
Industrial Electronic Products Mfr
N.A.I.C.S.: 334419
Francis Chee Peng Sa (Mng Dir)

KVC Installation Material Store Sdn. Bhd. (1)
Lot 3 Jalan P 10/12 Kawasan Perusahaan Bangi, Bandar Baru Bangi, 43650, Selangor, Malaysia
Tel.: (60) 389252828
Sales Range: $25-49.9 Million
Hardware Retailer
N.A.I.C.S.: 444140
Lee Kok Keong (Mgr)

R & R Industrial Products (M) Sdn. Bhd. (1)
Bangi, Selangor Darul Ehsan, Malaysia
Tel.: (60) 3 8925 2828
Industrial Machinery Mfr
N.A.I.C.S.: 333248

Wisma KVC Lot 3 Jalan P10/12, Kawasan Perusahaan Bangi, 43650, Bandar Baru Bangi, Selangor Darul Ehsan, Malaysia
Tel.: (60) 389263333
Web Site: http://www.kbc.com.my
Sales Range: $50-74.9 Million
Industrial Electrical Product Distr
N.A.I.C.S.: 423610
Vincent Lee (Gen Mgr)

See Wide Letrik (Sel) Sdn Bhd (1)
No 89 Jalan 20/7 Paramount Garden, 46300, Petaling Jaya, Selangor Darul Ehsan, Malaysia
Tel.: (60) 3 7875 7200
Industrial Machinery Mfr
N.A.I.C.S.: 333248

Syarikat See Wide Letrik Sdn Bhd (1)
No 27-1&2 Jalan Loke Yew, 55200, Kuala Lumpur, Malaysia
Tel.: (60) 3 9221 4066
Emp.: 100
Industrial Machinery Mfr
N.A.I.C.S.: 333248
Patrick Chong (Gen Mgr)

KVERVA AS
Brattorkaia 15, 7010, Trondheim, Norway NO
Web Site: http://www.kverva.no
Year Founded: 1991
Holding Company; Investments in Marine Industry
N.A.I.C.S.: 551112
Helge Moen (CEO)

Subsidiaries:

Pelagia AS (1)
Bradbenken 1, 5003, Bergen, Norway (50%)
Tel.: (47) 5 784 4400
Web Site: https://www.pelagia.com
Emp.: 709
Pelagic Fish Products Mfr
N.A.I.C.S.: 424460
Egil Magne Haugstad (CEO)

Subsidiary (Non-US):

United Fish Industries (UK) Limited (2)
Gilbey Road, Grimsby, DN31 2SL, Lincs, United Kingdom
Tel.: (44) 1472263450
Sales Range: $50-74.9 Million
Emp.: 35
Animal Aquaculture
N.A.I.C.S.: 112519
Thomas Tynan (COO)

KVIKA BANKI HF
Borgartun 25 6th floor, 105, Reykjavik, Iceland
Tel.: (354) 5403200 IS
Web Site: http://en.kvika.is
Year Founded: 1999
Rev.: $48,887,582
Assets: $756,506,140
Liabilities: $645,353,249
Net Worth: $111,152,891
Earnings: $15,011,846
Emp.: 109
Fiscal Year-end: 12/31/18
Investment & Financial Services
N.A.I.C.S.: 523999
Bjarni Eyvinds (Mng Dir-Capital Markets)

KVK CORPORATION
641 Inari Takahata Tomika-cho Kamo-gun, Gifu, 501-3304, Japan
Tel.: (81) 574551120
Web Site: http://www.kvk.co.jp
Year Founded: 1949
6484—(TKS)
Rev.: $196,887,953
Assets: $227,710,541
Liabilities: $49,250,069
Net Worth: $178,460,472
Earnings: $13,082,256

Fiscal Year-end: 03/31/24
Plumbing Product Mfr & Distr
N.A.I.C.S.: 332913
Masayuki Suematsu (Pres & Dir-Rep)

Subsidiaries:

Dalian Kitamura Valve Co. Ltd. (1)
No 15 Huaihe West Road, Economic and Technological Development Zone, Dalian, 116600, Liaoning, China
Tel.: (86) 41187612904
Web Site: http://www.kvk.com.cn
Kitchen & Bathroom Product Mfr
N.A.I.C.S.: 337110

KVK Philippines Inc. (1)
Bldg R3-C Lot 13 Phase1B, First Philippine Industrial Park-Special Economic Zone, Tanauan, Batangas, Philippines
Tel.: (63) 9171322723
Kitchen & Bathroom Product Mfr
N.A.I.C.S.: 337110

KWALITY CREDIT & LEASING LIMITED
7 Lyons Range 3rd Floor Room No 9 and 10, Kolkata, 700001, West Bengal, India
Tel.: (91) 9681634539
Web Site:
http://www.kwalitycredit.com
Year Founded: 1992
531206—(BOM)
Rev.: $34,218
Assets: $1,432,965
Liabilities: $15,055
Net Worth: $1,417,910
Earnings: ($67,209)
Emp.: 9
Fiscal Year-end: 03/31/21
Financial Lending Services
N.A.I.C.S.: 522220
Bhagwan Das Soni (Mng Dir & Compliance Officer)

KWALITY LIMITED
KDIL House F-82 Shivaji Place Rajouri Garden, New Delhi, 110027, India
Tel.: (91) 1147006500
Web Site: http://www.kwality.com
531882—(BOM)
Rev.: $306,114,474
Assets: $65,213,387
Liabilities: $342,769,923
Net Worth: ($277,556,536)
Earnings: ($461,195,781)
Emp.: 496
Fiscal Year-end: 03/31/19
Dairy Products
N.A.I.C.S.: 112120
Sanjay Dhingra (Mng Dir)

Subsidiaries:

Kwality Dairy Products, FZE (1)
Warehouse No RA08 GA03 Jebel Ali Free Zone, PO Box No 261451, Dubai, United Arab Emirates
Tel.: (971) 48810740
Dairy Products Mfr
N.A.I.C.S.: 311514

KWALITY PHARMACEUTICALS LIMITED
Vill Nag Kalan Majitha Road, Amritsar, 143 601, Punjab, India
Tel.: (91) 8558820861 In
Web Site:
https://www.kwalitypharma.com
Year Founded: 1983
539997—(BOM)
Rev.: $35,981,673
Assets: $22,694,981
Liabilities: $14,525,361
Net Worth: $8,169,621
Earnings: $2,032,144
Emp.: 496
Fiscal Year-end: 03/31/21
Pharmaceutical Product Mfr & Distr

KWALITY PHARMACEUTICALS LIMITED

Kwality Pharmaceuticals Limited—(Continued)
N.A.I.C.S.: 325412
Ramesh Arora *(Mng Dir)*

KWAN ON HOLDINGS LIMITED
Flat 2803 28/F No 118 Connaught Road West, SaiYing Pun, Hong Kong, China (Hong Kong)
Tel.: (852) 2 889 2675
Web Site:
http://www.kwanconstruction.com
1559—(HKG)
Rev.: $69,485,653
Assets: $123,700,204
Liabilities: $56,481,890
Net Worth: $67,218,314
Earnings: ($3,169,941)
Emp.: 242
Fiscal Year-end: 03/31/21
Water, Road & Drainage Engineering Services
N.A.I.C.S.: 237110
Cao Lei *(Exec Dir)*

KWAN YONG HOLDINGS LIMITED
11 Joo Koon Crescent, Singapore, 629022, Singapore
Web Site:
https://www.kwanyong.com.sg
Year Founded: 2018
9998—(HKG)
Rev.: $58,710,997
Assets: $54,237,045
Liabilities: $27,801,770
Net Worth: $26,435,275
Earnings: ($295,193)
Emp.: 355
Fiscal Year-end: 06/30/22
Holding Company
N.A.I.C.S.: 551112
Mei Kam Kwan *(Chm)*

KWANG DONG PHARMACEUTICAL CO., LTD.
Gasan Building 85 Seochojungang-ro Seocho-gu, Seoul, Korea (South)
Tel.: (82) 260067777
Web Site: http://www.ekdp.com
Year Founded: 1963
009290—(KRS)
Rev.: $1,097,995,211
Assets: $714,862,223
Liabilities: $295,277,762
Net Worth: $419,584,461
Earnings: $20,479,436
Emp.: 1,056
Fiscal Year-end: 12/31/22
Pharmaceuticals Mfr
N.A.I.C.S.: 325412
Gasan Soo Boo Choi *(Founder)*

Subsidiaries:

Kwang Dong Household and Healthcare Inc., (1)
Gasan Building 85 Seocho Jungang-ro, Seocho-gu, Seoul, 137 750, Korea (South) **(100%)**
Tel.: (82) 260067777
Scientific Research, Diagnosis & Treatment of Diseases
N.A.I.C.S.: 541720

Kwang Dong Oriental Hospital (1) **(100%)**
Tel.: (82) 22224888
Hospital Treatments & Services
N.A.I.C.S.: 622110

Kwang Dong Pharmaceutical Co., Ltd. - GMP Plant (1)
114 Sandan-ro, Pyeongtaek, Gyeonggi-do, Korea (South)
Tel.: (82) 31 612 1111
Pharmaceuticals Product Mfr
N.A.I.C.S.: 325412

KwangDong Healthbio Co., Ltd. (1)
39 Yangcheongsongdae-gil, Ochang-eup Cheongwon-gu, Cheongju, Chungcheongbuk-do, Korea (South) **(58.74%)**
Tel.: (82) 432111056
Web Site: https://www.kdhealthbio.com
Emp.: 229
Health Care Srvices
N.A.I.C.S.: 621610
Jeong Hwa-Young *(CEO)*

Kwangdong Pharmaceutical Co., Ltd. - Songtan Plant (1)
1081 Gyeonggi-daero, Pyeongtaek, Gyeonggi-do, Korea (South)
Tel.: (82) 3180301777
Web Site: http://eng.ekdp.com
Pharmaceuticals Product Mfr
N.A.I.C.S.: 325412

KWANG JIN IND. CO., LTD.
370-103 Shinpyeong-dong, Saha-gu, Busan, 604-030, Korea (South)
Tel.: (82) 512049101
Web Site: https://www.kjsteel.co.kr
Year Founded: 1976
026910—(KRS)
Rev.: $45,360,375
Assets: $58,507,472
Liabilities: $37,444,235
Net Worth: $21,063,237
Earnings: $878,922
Emp.: 100
Fiscal Year-end: 12/31/22
Steel Mfr & Whslr
N.A.I.C.S.: 331110
Hur Yoo Seok *(Pres & CEO)*

KWANG MING SILK MILL CO., LTD.
7F No 607 Ruiguang Rd, Neihu Dist, Taipei, 114698, Taiwan
Tel.: (886) 226575859
4420—(TPE)
Rev.: $27,905,919
Assets: $84,103,274
Liabilities: $47,806,929
Net Worth: $36,296,345
Earnings: ($136,135)
Fiscal Year-end: 12/31/22
Textile Products Mfr
N.A.I.C.S.: 313310
Cheng-Tien Chan *(Chm)*

KWANG MYUNG ELECTRIC CO., LTD.
B2-15 Banwol National Industrial Complex 389 Moknae-Dong, Danwon-gu, Ansan, Gyeonggi, Korea (South)
Tel.: (82) 314940720
Web Site: http://www.kmec.co.kr
Year Founded: 1955
017040—(KRS)
Rev.: $96,543,074
Assets: $109,109,811
Liabilities: $36,211,462
Net Worth: $72,898,349
Earnings: $7,379,532
Emp.: 183
Fiscal Year-end: 12/31/15
Switchgear Mfr
N.A.I.C.S.: 335313

KWANG YANG MOTOR CO., LTD.
No 35 Wansing Street, Kaohsiung, Taiwan
Tel.: (886) 73822526
Web Site: http://www.kymco.com
Year Founded: 1963
Sales Range: $450-499.9 Million
Emp.: 2,300
Power-Driven Products Mfr & Sales
N.A.I.C.S.: 333991
Allen Ko *(Chm)*

KWANGMU CO.,LTD.
1F/4F Na-dong 2634-27, Nambusunhwan-ro Seocho-gu, Seoul, Korea (South)
Tel.: (82) 234590500
Web Site: https://kwangmu.co.kr
Year Founded: 1972
029480—(KRS)
Rev.: $59,995,813
Assets: $104,290,322
Liabilities: $42,856,858
Net Worth: $61,433,463
Earnings: ($5,650,017)
Emp.: 120
Fiscal Year-end: 12/31/22
Communication Products Mfr
N.A.I.C.S.: 334419
Sang Yen Lee *(Co-CEO)*

KWANTAS CORPORATION BERHAD
K-63-3rd Floor Signature Office KK Times Square Off Coastal Highway, 88100, Kota Kinabalu, Sabah, Malaysia
Tel.: (60) 88486555
Web Site:
http://www.kwantas.com.my
Year Founded: 1973
Rev.: $186,174,746
Assets: $448,319,539
Liabilities: $179,186,319
Net Worth: $269,133,220
Earnings: ($23,979,295)
Emp.: 5,400
Fiscal Year-end: 06/30/19
Holding Company; Oilseed Processing & Refining Services
N.A.I.C.S.: 551112
Chiew Giok Kwan *(Co-Sec)*

Subsidiaries:

Dongma Palm Industires (Zhangjiagang) Co. Ltd. (1)
Beijing Road Yangtze International Chemical Industry Park, Zhangjiagang, 215634, Jiangsu, China
Tel.: (86) 512 58323059
Oleochemicals & Glycerine Mfr
N.A.I.C.S.: 325199

Kwantas Oil Sdn Bhd (1)
I & II FL Lot 1-5 Bangunanfordeco Jalan Singamata PO BOX 6118, PO Box 61118, Lahad Datu, 91120, Malaysia **(100%)**
Tel.: (60) 89881188
Web Site: www.kwantos.com
Sales Range: $100-124.9 Million
Emp.: 300
Oilseed Processing
N.A.I.C.S.: 311224

Kwantas Plantations Sdn. Bhd. (1)
1st-3rd Fl Lot 1-5 Bangunan Fordeco, Jalan Singamata, 91100, Lahad Datu, Sabah, Malaysia
Tel.: (60) 89881188
Oil Palm Plantation Services
N.A.I.C.S.: 115112

KWC CAPITAL PARTNERS PTY. LTD.
Level 12 32 Martin Place, Sydney, 2001, NSW, Australia
Tel.: (61) 2 9238 3999
Web Site: http://www.kwc.com.au
Private Equity & Real Estate Investment Firm
N.A.I.C.S.: 523999

Subsidiaries:

KWC Funds Pty. Ltd. (1)
Level 12 32 Martin Place, Sydney, 2000, NSW, Australia
Tel.: (61) 29238 3988
Web Site: http://www.kwc.com.au
Emp.: 100
Real Estate Fund Manager
N.A.I.C.S.: 531390
David Tanevski *(Dir)*

KWEICHOW MOUTAI CO., LTD.
Maotai Town, Renhuai, 564501, China
Tel.: (86) 8512386002
Web Site:
https://www.moutaichina.com
Year Founded: 1999
600519—(SHG)
Rev.: $17,908,575,900
Assets: $35,712,818,622
Liabilities: $6,935,776,385
Net Worth: $28,777,042,237
Earnings: $8,805,388,695
Emp.: 8,400
Fiscal Year-end: 12/31/22
Alcoholic Beverage Mfr & Sales
N.A.I.C.S.: 424820

KWESST MICRO SYSTEMS INC.
155 Terence Matthews Crescent Unit Ste 1, Ottawa, K2M 2A8, ON, Canada
Tel.: (604) 230-5176
Web Site: https://www.kwesst.com
Year Founded: 2017
KWE—(NASDAQ)
Rev.: $1,112,180
Assets: $4,152,870
Liabilities: $3,141,268
Net Worth: $1,011,602
Earnings: ($5,498,884)
Emp.: 29
Fiscal Year-end: 09/30/24
Holding Company; Military Tactical Equipment Mfr
N.A.I.C.S.: 551112
Jeffrey MacLeod *(Pres & CEO)*

Subsidiaries:

KWESST Inc. (1)
155 Terence Matthews Crescent, Unit 1, Ottawa, K2M 2A8, ON, Canada
Tel.: (613) 319-0537
Web Site: https://www.kwesst.com
Military Tactical Equipment Mfr
N.A.I.C.S.: 334419
Jeffrey MacLeod *(Pres & CEO)*

KWG GROUP HOLDINGS LIMITED
No 8 Huaxia Road KWG International Finance Place Zhujiang New Town, Guangzhou, 510623, China
Tel.: (86) 2085500800
Web Site:
http://www.kwggroupholdings.com
1813—(HKG)
Rev.: $1,888,750,516
Assets: $28,063,725,253
Liabilities: $22,419,744,235
Net Worth: $5,643,981,018
Earnings: ($1,381,853,444)
Emp.: 3,600
Fiscal Year-end: 12/31/22
Property Development & Management Services
N.A.I.C.S.: 561110
Jian Min Kong *(Founder & Chm)*

KWG LIVING GROUP HOLDINGS LIMITED
Units 8503-05A Level 85 1 Austin Road West, International Commerce Centre, Kowloon, China (Hong Kong)
Tel.: (852) 28787090
Web Site:
https://www.kwggroupholdings.com
Year Founded: 2004
3913—(HKG)
Rev.: $616,779,182
Assets: $1,063,996,108
Liabilities: $538,712,712
Net Worth: $525,283,396
Earnings: $9,169,772
Emp.: 18,000
Fiscal Year-end: 12/31/22
Holding Company

N.A.I.C.S.: 551112
Zhongqi Wang *(VP)*

KWG RESOURCES INC.
141 Adelaide Street West Suite 240, Toronto, M5H 3L5, ON, Canada
Tel.: (416) 642-3575 QC
Web Site: https://canadachrome.com
Year Founded: 1937
KWGBF—(OTCIQ)
Rev.: $2,308
Assets: $1,080,719
Liabilities: $20,448,271
Net Worth: ($19,367,553)
Earnings: ($26,054,039)
Emp.: 3
Fiscal Year-end: 12/31/22
Diamond Exploration Services
N.A.I.C.S.: 212311
Frank C. Smeenk *(Pres & CEO)*

KWH CONSTRUCTORS LTD.
2792 Norland Ave, Burnaby, V5B 3A6, BC, Canada
Tel.: (604) 299-7969
Web Site: https://www.kwhconstructors.com
Year Founded: 1989
Sales Range: $50-74.9 Million
Emp.: 100
Specialty Engineering & Contract Construction Services
N.A.I.C.S.: 238120
Peter Saunderson *(Principal)*

Subsidiaries:

KWH Constructors, Inc. (1)
1155 N State St Ste 420, Bellingham, WA 98225
Tel.: (360) 647-1381
Web Site: http://www.kwhconstructors.com
Emp.: 60
Structural Steel Erection
N.A.I.C.S.: 238120
Peter Saunderson *(Dir-Engrg)*

KWH GROUP LTD
Kauppapuistikko 15 6th floor, 65100, Vaasa, Finland
Tel.: (358) 207787900 FI
Web Site: https://www.kwhgroup.com
Year Founded: 1980
Rev.: $687,242,466
Assets: $881,295,881
Liabilities: $137,565,129
Net Worth: $677,563,795
Earnings: $64,214,528
Emp.: 2,524
Fiscal Year-end: 12/31/21
Abrasive Product Mfr
N.A.I.C.S.: 327910
Henrik Hoglund *(Chm)*

KWIZDA HOLDING GMBH
Universitatsring 5, 1010, Vienna, Austria
Tel.: (43) 59977100
Web Site: http://www.kwizda.at
Sales Range: $350-399.9 Million
Emp.: 1,100
Holding Company Services
N.A.I.C.S.: 551112
Richard Kwizda *(CEO)*

Subsidiaries:

Kwizda Agro GmbH (1)
Dr Karl Lueger Ring 6, 1010, Vienna, Austria
Tel.: (43) 5997710
Web Site: http://www.kwizda-agro.at
Sales Range: $50-74.9 Million
Emp.: 200
Crop Protection Product Mfr
N.A.I.C.S.: 325320

Kwizda Pharma GmbH (1)
Effingergasse 21, 1160, Vienna, Austria
Tel.: (43) 59977300
Web Site: http://www.kwizda-pharma.at

Emp.: 150
Pharmaceuticals Mfr
N.A.I.C.S.: 325412
Stephen Sandor *(Gen Mgr)*

KWONG FONG INDUSTRIES CORPORATION
28F No 97 Sec 2 Dunhua S Rd, Daan Dist, Taipei, 106, Taiwan
Tel.: (886) 227048111
Web Site: http://www.kfic.com.tw
Year Founded: 1968
1416—(TAI)
Rev.: $9,675,234
Assets: $150,215,567
Liabilities: $33,686,123
Net Worth: $116,529,444
Earnings: $3,597,240
Emp.: 109
Fiscal Year-end: 12/31/23
Textile Product Mfr & Distr
N.A.I.C.S.: 314999
Wen Ta Chiu *(Chm, Pres & CEO)*

KWONG LUEN ENGINEERING HOLDINGS LTD.
Unit 2909-2910 29/F The Octagon 6 Sha Tsui Road, N T, Tsuen Wan, China (Hong Kong)
Tel.: (852) 27526020 Ky
Web Site: https://www.kwong-luen.com.hk
Year Founded: 1995
1413—(HKG)
Rev.: $43,268,704
Assets: $37,436,245
Liabilities: $5,575,265
Net Worth: $31,860,980
Earnings: $128,021
Emp.: 136
Fiscal Year-end: 03/31/23
Holding Company
N.A.I.C.S.: 551112
Ho Cheung Wong *(Sec)*

KWONG LUNG ENTERPRISE CO., LTD.
16th Fl No 105 Tun-Hwa S Rd Sec 2, Taipei, 10682, Taiwan
Tel.: (886) 227092550
Web Site: https://www.klf-group.com
Year Founded: 1966
8916—(TPE)
Rev.: $322,177,688
Assets: $267,857,518
Liabilities: $93,629,710
Net Worth: $174,227,809
Earnings: $28,686,646
Emp.: 5,257
Fiscal Year-end: 12/31/22
Home Textile Product Mfr
N.A.I.C.S.: 313310
Ho-Po Chan *(Chm & Pres)*

Subsidiaries:

Bo Hsing Enterprise Co., Ltd. (1)
Lot No A2 National Way 1A, Hoa Phu Industrial Zone Hoa Phu Ward Long Ho District, Vinh Long, Vietnam
Tel.: (84) 2703962749
Down Material Mfr
N.A.I.C.S.: 325211

Kwong Lung (Suzhou) Co.,Ltd. (1)
No 2 Sheng Xi E Rd, Kunshan, 215300, China
Tel.: (86) 51257636301
Outdoor Clothing Mfr
N.A.I.C.S.: 327910

Kwong Lung Enterpris Co., Ltd. (1)
Binh Hung Area, Phuoc Thoi Ward O Mon District, Can Tho, Vietnam
Tel.: (84) 2923665548
Down Material Mfr
N.A.I.C.S.: 325211

Kwong Lung Europe Sp. z o.o. (1)
ul Zlota 59, 00-120, Warsaw, Poland
Tel.: (48) 224895305

Down Material Mfr
N.A.I.C.S.: 325211

Kwong Lung Japan Co., Ltd. (1)
6th Fl 4-Chome 2-18 Minam Ihonmachi, Chou-Ku, Osaka, 541-0054, Japan
Tel.: (81) 662822781
Down Material Mfr
N.A.I.C.S.: 325211

Kwong Lung Meko II Co., Ltd. (1)
Lot 2 20C Street No 8, Tra Noc II Industrial Park Phuoc Thoi Ward O Mon District, Can Tho, Vietnam
Tel.: (84) 2923841026
Down Material Mfr
N.A.I.C.S.: 325211

Kwong Lung-Meko Co., Ltd. (1)
Lot 28 Tra Noc 1 Industrial Zone, Tra Noc Ward Binh Thuy District, Can Tho, Vietnam
Tel.: (84) 2926251392
Down Material Mfr
N.A.I.C.S.: 325211

Kwong Lung-O Mon Company Limited (1)
Binh Hung Area, Phuoc Thoi Ward O Mon District, Can Tho, Vietnam
Tel.: (84) 2923665548
Textile Clothing Mfr & Distr
N.A.I.C.S.: 315210

Snowdown Merchandise (Suzhou) Co., Ltd. (1)
Suite GH 5F No 310 TianShan Rd, Shanghai, 200336, China
Tel.: (86) 2162371639
Web Site: http://www.snowdown-merchandisesu-zhoucoltd.imexbb.com
Emp.: 1,800
Down Material Mfr
N.A.I.C.S.: 325211

KWONG MAN KEE GROUP LTD.
21/F The Bedford 91-93 Bedford Road, Tai Kok Tsui, Kowloon, China (Hong Kong)
Tel.: (852) 2 951 0988 Ky
Web Site: http://www.kmk.com.hk
Year Founded: 2002
8023—(HKG)
Rev.: $14,241,459
Assets: $19,321,399
Liabilities: $6,189,115
Net Worth: $13,132,284
Earnings: $957,040
Emp.: 45
Fiscal Year-end: 03/31/22
Car Park Flooring Services
N.A.I.C.S.: 236220
Chi Man Kwong *(Chm & Compliance Officer)*

KWOON CHUNG BUS HOLDINGS LIMITED
3/F 8 Chong Fu Road, Chai Wan, China (Hong Kong)
Tel.: (852) 25781178 BM
Web Site: https://www.kcbh.com.hk
Year Founded: 1948
0306—(HKG)
Rev.: $139,798,713
Assets: $661,263,435
Liabilities: $369,317,979
Net Worth: $291,945,456
Earnings: ($5,642,101)
Emp.: 3,900
Fiscal Year-end: 03/31/21
Bus Operation Services
N.A.I.C.S.: 485113
Matthew Leung Pak Wong *(Chm)*

Subsidiaries:

Good Funds Services Limited (1)
3F No 8 Chong Fu Rd, Chai Wan, China (Hong Kong)
Tel.: (852) 25781178
Web Site: http://www.kcm.com.hk
Automobile Renting & Transportation Services
N.A.I.C.S.: 561599

Kwoon Chung Motors Company, Limited (1)
3/F 8 Chong Fu Road, Chai Wan, China (Hong Kong)
Tel.: (852) 29798798
Web Site: http://www.kcm.com.hk
Bus Operation Services
N.A.I.C.S.: 485113

Subsidiary (Domestic):

Lantau Tours Limited (2)
Shop 7 G/f Mui Wo Centre 3 Ngan Wan Road Silvermine Bay, Lantau Island, Hong Kong, China (Hong Kong)
Tel.: (852) 29848255
Web Site: https://www.lantautours.com.hk
Travel & Tour Operating Agencies
N.A.I.C.S.: 561520

New Lantao Bus Company (1973) Limited (2)
3rd Floor 8 Chong Fu Road, Chai Wan, China (Hong Kong)
Tel.: (852) 29849848
Web Site: https://www.nlb.com.hk
Sales Range: $50-74.9 Million
Bus Operation Services
N.A.I.C.S.: 485510

Tai Fung Coach Company Limited (1)
3rd Floor 8 Chong Fu Road, Chai Wan, China (Hong Kong)
Tel.: (852) 27949229
Web Site: http://www.taifung.com.hk
Bus Operation Services
N.A.I.C.S.: 485510

Trans-Island Limousine Service Limited (1)
3F 8 Chong Fu Rd, Chai Wan, China (Hong Kong)
Tel.: (852) 25409223
Web Site: http://www.trans-island.com.hk
Airport Shuttle Services
N.A.I.C.S.: 485999

Subsidiary (Domestic):

Intercontinental Hire Cars Limited (2)
3 F 8 Chong Fu Rd, Chai Wan, China (Hong Kong)
Tel.: (852) 22623232
Web Site: http://www.trans-island.com.hk
Limousine Rental Services
N.A.I.C.S.: 485320

Vigor Tours Limited (1)
1/F Ocean View Court 43 Mody Road, Tsim Sha Tsui, Kowloon, China (Hong Kong)
Tel.: (852) 27393828
Web Site: https://www.vigorholding.com
Sales Range: $25-49.9 Million
Airport Shuttle & Limousine Services
N.A.I.C.S.: 485320

KWS SAAT SE & CO. KGAA
Grimsehlstr 31, PO Box 1463, 37555, Einbeck, Germany
Tel.: (49) 55613110
Web Site: https://www.kws.com
KWS—(MUN)
Rev.: $1,801,327,570
Assets: $3,173,126,128
Liabilities: $1,670,434,736
Net Worth: $1,502,691,392
Earnings: $140,435,539
Emp.: 4,673
Fiscal Year-end: 06/30/24
Seed Producer & Distr
N.A.I.C.S.: 111998
Felix Buchting *(CEO)*

Subsidiaries:

AgReliant Genetics LLC (1)
1122 E 169th St, Westfield, IN 46074-9601
Tel.: (317) 896-5552
Web Site: https://www.agreliantgenetics.com
Sales Range: $10-24.9 Million
Emp.: 50
Seed Producer & Distr; Joint Venture of Groupe Limagrain (50%) & KWS SAAT AG (50%)
N.A.I.C.S.: 111998

KWS SAAT SE & CO. KGAA

INTERNATIONAL PUBLIC

KWS SAAT SE & Co, KGaA—(Continued)

Peter Lynch *(VP-Res)*

Division (Domestic):

AgReliant Genetics LLC - Lebanon (2)
4640 E State Rd 32, Lebanon, IN 46052-9299
Tel.: (765) 482-9833
Research Into Corn Soybean & Canola Seeds
N.A.I.C.S.: 424910
Craig Newman *(Pres & CEO)*

Subsidiary (Domestic):

LG Seeds (2)
1122 E 169th St, Westfield, IN 46074
Tel.: (317) 896-0662
Web Site: https://www.lgseeds.com
Development of Agricultural Seeds
N.A.I.C.S.: 111998
Kim Robertson *(Mgr-Mktg)*

Beijing KWS Agriculture Technology Co., Ltd. (1)
Room 603 of 5th Floor in 101 between B3 and 25th F Building No A2, Huixindongjie Chaoyang District, Beijing, China
Tel.: (86) 1064957523
Web Site: https://www.kws.com
Seed Production Services
N.A.I.C.S.: 111120

Betaseed, Inc. (1)
1788 Marschall Rd, Shakopee, MN 55379
Tel.: (952) 445-8090
Web Site: http://www.betaseed.com
Sugar Beet Seed Producer & Distr
N.A.I.C.S.: 111998
John Enright *(Pres)*

Subsidiary (Domestic):

ACH SEEDS INC. (2)
Prairie Ctr Dr 135, Eden Prairie, MN 55344
Tel.: (877) 224-7333
Web Site: http://www.achseeds.com
Seed Production & Cultivation Services
N.A.I.C.S.: 115112

Subsidiary (Non-US):

BETASEED FRANCE S.A.R.L. (2)
Rue De L Horlogerie, BP 164, 62 403, Bethune, Cedex, France
Tel.: (33) 321646991
Web Site: https://www.betaseed.fr
Seed Production & Farming Services
N.A.I.C.S.: 115112
Benoit Rose *(Gen Mgr)*

BETASEED GMBH (2)
Friedrich Ebert Anlage 36, 60325, Frankfurt am Main, Germany
Tel.: (49) 69244333150
Web Site: https://www.betaseed.com
Biotechnology Research & Development Services
N.A.I.C.S.: 541714

KWS UKRAINE T.O.W. (2)
19 Druzhby Narodiv Boulevard floor 8, 01042, Kiev, Ukraine
Tel.: (380) 445865213
Web Site: http://www.kws.de
Plant Breeding Services
N.A.I.C.S.: 115112

DYNAGRI S.A.R.L. (1)
119 Boulevard Emile Zola Residence Nafia 5eme Apartment No 9, 20300, Casablanca, Morocco
Tel.: (212) 22448244
Potato Farming Services
N.A.I.C.S.: 111211

Impetus Agriculture Inc. (1)
4340 Duncan Ave, Saint Louis, MO 63110
Tel.: (314) 703-7198
Web Site: https://www.impetusag.com
Agriculture Research & Development Services
N.A.I.C.S.: 541715
Martha Schlicher *(CEO)*

KWS Austria Saat GmbH (1)
Landstrasser Hauptstrasse 71/1/205, A-1030, Vienna, Austria
Tel.: (43) 12633900
Web Site: https://www.kwsaustria.at
Sales Range: $25-49.9 Million
Emp.: 17
Seed Producer & Distr
N.A.I.C.S.: 111998
Mijodrag Lajic *(CEO)*

KWS Benelux B.V. (1)
Hulstbaan 266, PO Box 2, 9112, Sinaai, Belgium
Tel.: (32) 34490220
Web Site: http://www.kws.de
Sales Range: $10-24.9 Million
Emp.: 50
Seed Producer & Distr
N.A.I.C.S.: 111998

KWS Benelux B.V. (1)
Ettenseweg 4, 4706 PB, Roosendaal, Netherlands
Tel.: (31) 765030003
Seed Production Services & Distr
N.A.I.C.S.: 424910

KWS Benelux B.V. (1)
Ettenseweg 4, 4706 PB, Roosendaal, Netherlands
Tel.: (31) 765030003
Seed Production Services & Distr
N.A.I.C.S.: 424910

KWS Benelux B.V. (1)
Ettenseweg 4, 4706 PB, Roosendaal, Netherlands
Tel.: (31) 765030003
Seed Production Services & Distr
N.A.I.C.S.: 424910

KWS Benelux B.V. (1)
Ettenseweg 4, 4706 PB, Roosendaal, Netherlands
Tel.: (31) 765030003
Seed Production Services & Distr
N.A.I.C.S.: 424910

KWS Berlin GmbH (1)
Bulowstrasse 78, 10783, Berlin, Germany
Tel.: (49) 30816914120
Emp.: 350
Seed Production Services & Distr
N.A.I.C.S.: 424910

KWS Bulgaria EOOD. (1)
Bul Christopher Columbus 80 Astral Business Center, 3rd Floor Office 3 2, 1540, Sofia, Bulgaria
Tel.: (359) 29716320
Seed Production Services & Distr
N.A.I.C.S.: 424910

KWS Cereals USA LLC (1)
495 County Rd 1300 N, Champaign, IL 62550
Tel.: (217) 600-3280
Crop Farming Services
N.A.I.C.S.: 111998

KWS Chile Ltda. (1)
Longitudinal 5 Sur Km 79, Casilla 373, Rancagua, Chile
Tel.: (56) 72740040
Web Site: https://www.kws.cl
Seed Producer & Distr
N.A.I.C.S.: 111998

KWS France S.A.R.L (1)
Zone Industrielle Sud, Route de Paris, 80700, Roye, France
Tel.: (33) 322794010
Web Site: http://www.kws.de
Sales Range: $10-24.9 Million
Emp.: 29
Seed Producer & Distr
N.A.I.C.S.: 111998

Subsidiary (Domestic):

RAZES HYBRIDES S.A.R.L. (2)
Ferme de Bonanza, 11170, Alzonne, France
Tel.: (33) 468765900
Bedding Plants & Seeds Distr
N.A.I.C.S.: 424910
Jean Doyard *(Gen Mgr)*

KWS Gateway Research Center LLC (1)
BRDG Park at The Danforth Plant Science Ctr 1005 N Warson Rd Ste 201, Saint Louis, MO 63132
Tel.: (314) 254-5439

Seed Production Services
N.A.I.C.S.: 111120

KWS INTERSAAT GMBH (1)
Tel.: (49) 55613110
Web Site: http://www.kws.com
Emp.: 100
Plant Breeding & Farming Services
N.A.I.C.S.: 115112

KWS Italia S.p.A (1)
Via Secondo Casadei 8, 47122, Forli, Italy
Tel.: (39) 0543474611
Web Site: https://www.kws.com
Sales Range: $25-49.9 Million
Emp.: 40
Seed Producer & Distr
N.A.I.C.S.: 111998

KWS Klostergut Wiebrechtshausen GmbH (1)
Wiebrechtshausen 1, 37154, Northeim, Germany
Tel.: (49) 5551995549
Web Site: http://www.wiebrechtshausen.de
Agricultural Product Mfr & Distr
N.A.I.C.S.: 111199

KWS LOCHOW GMBH (1)
Ferdinand-von-Lochow-Strasse 5, 29303, Bergen, Germany
Tel.: (49) 50514770
Web Site: https://www.kws.com
Plant Breeding & Research Services
N.A.I.C.S.: 541715

KWS LOCHOW POLSKA SP. Z O.O. (1)
Kondratowice ul Slowianska 5, 57-150, Prusy, Poland
Tel.: (48) 713927300
Web Site: http://www.kws-lochow.pl
Plant Breeding & Farming Services
N.A.I.C.S.: 115112

KWS Landwirtschaft GmbH (1)
Grimsehlstrasse 31, 37574, Einbeck, Germany
Tel.: (49) 5561311728
Web Site: http://www.kws.de
Sales Range: $150-199.9 Million
Emp.: 1,000
Plant Genetic & Biotechnology Research Services
N.A.I.C.S.: 541714
Alexander Coenen *(Gen Mgr)*

KWS MAIS GMBH (1)
Grimsehlstr 31, Postfach 1463, 37555, Einbeck, Germany
Tel.: (49) 5561 311 325
Web Site: http://www.kws.de
Corn Seed Production & Distr
N.A.I.C.S.: 424910

Subsidiary (Domestic):

AGROMAIS GMBH (2)
Grothues 6, 48351, Everswinkel, Germany
Tel.: (49) 258266820
Web Site: https://www.agromais.de
Emp.: 160
Seed Production & Farming Services
N.A.I.C.S.: 115112

Subsidiary (Non-US):

KWS Bulgaria E.O.O.D. (2)
Astral business centre floor 3 office 3 2, Bulevard Christopher Columbus 80, 1540, Sofia, Bulgaria
Tel.: (359) 29716320
Web Site: http://www.kws.bg
Emp.: 1
Seed Production & Farming Services
N.A.I.C.S.: 115112

KWS MAGYARORSZAG KFT (2)
Gyori Ipari Park Szolgatato Haz Gesztenyefa U 4, 9027, Gyor, Hungary
Tel.: (36) 96528710
Web Site: https://www.kws.com
Sales Range: $10-24.9 Million
Emp.: 54
Plant Breeding & Cultivating Services
N.A.I.C.S.: 115112

KWS MAIS FRANCE S.A.R.L. (2)
Tel.: (33) 237203160
Web Site: http://www.kws.fr

Sales Range: $10-24.9 Million
Emp.: 30
Corn & Oil Seed Farming Services
N.A.I.C.S.: 111191

KWS SEMENA S.R.O. (2)
Ivanska cesta 30/B, 821 04, Bratislava, Slovakia
Tel.: (421) 232112590
Web Site: https://www.kws.com
Emp.: 19
Corn Production Services
N.A.I.C.S.: 111150

KWS SEMINTE S.R.L. (2)
Str Barajul Arges Nr 6 Sector 1, 014121, Bucharest, Romania
Tel.: (40) 213154280
Web Site: https://www.kws.ro
Emp.: 135
Corn Farming Services
N.A.I.C.S.: 111150

KWS SJEME D.O.O. (2)
Vukovarska 31, 31000, Osijek, Croatia
Tel.: (385) 31628628
Web Site: https://www.kws.hr
Emp.: 19
Corn Farming Services
N.A.I.C.S.: 111150

KWS Momont S.A.S. (1)
7 rue de Martinval, 59246, Mons-en-Pevele, France
Tel.: (33) 320592011
Web Site: https://www.momont.com
Grain Farming Services
N.A.I.C.S.: 111199

KWS OSIVA s.r.o. (1)
Pod Hradbami 2004/5, 594 01, 594 01, Velke Mezirici, Czech Republic
Tel.: (420) 566520754
Web Site: https://www.kws.com
Seed Producer & Distr
N.A.I.C.S.: 111998

KWS Polska Sp. z o.o. (1)
ul Glogowska 151, 60-206, Poznan, Poland
Tel.: (48) 618738800
Web Site: https://www.kws.com
Seed Producer & Distr
N.A.I.C.S.: 111998

KWS R&D China LTD. (1)
No 626 Huangshan Road High tech Zone 5th Floor, Tower C C 5 Keshi Bldg, Hefei, 230001, Anhui, China
Tel.: (86) 551 5334994
Web Site: http://www.kwschina.com
Biotechnical Research & Development Services
N.A.I.C.S.: 541714
Philip Freiherr von dem Bussche *(CEO)*

KWS R&D RUS LLC (1)
Tel.: (7) 4742280310
Grain & Other Product Breeding Services
N.A.I.C.S.: 111199

KWS SERVICES DEUTSCHLAND GMBH (1)
Grimsehlstrasse 31, Postfach 1463, 37555, Einbeck, Germany
Tel.: (49) 5561311622
Web Site: http://www.kws.de
Emp.: 1,200
Administrative Management Services
N.A.I.C.S.: 541611

KWS SERVICES EAST GMBH (1)
Leonard Bernstein Strasse 10, 1220, Vienna, Austria
Tel.: (43) 6649631668
Web Site: http://www.kws.de
Seed Farming Services
N.A.I.C.S.: 111998

KWS SERVICES MEDITERRANEAN S.A.S. (1)
11 Rue de la Pecherie, 80700, Roye, France
Tel.: (33) 3 22 37 50 08
Administrative Services
N.A.I.C.S.: 561110
Marcelo Repetto *(Mng Dir & Head-Svcs)*

KWS SERVICES NORTH B.V. (1)
Charloisse Lagedijk 536, 3084 LG, Rotterdam, Netherlands
Tel.: (31) 10 410 90 90

AND PRIVATE COMPANIES

Emp.: 5
Corporate Management Services
N.A.I.C.S.: 561110
Rob Neijenhof *(Mgr-Legal Affairs)*

KWS SRBIJA D.O.O. (1)
Industrijska 5, 21220, Becej, Serbia
Tel.: (381) 113016965
Web Site: https://www.kws.com
Emp.: 84
Sugar Beet Seed Farming Services
N.A.I.C.S.: 111991

KWS Scandinavia A/S (1)
Lysholt Alle 3, 7100, Vejle, Denmark
Tel.: (45) 54843211
Web Site: https://www.kws.com
Seed Producer & Distr
N.A.I.C.S.: 111998

KWS Seeds Inc. (1)
5705 W Old Shakopee Rd Ste 110, Bloomington, MN 55437
Tel.: (952) 445-8911
Sugar Beet Seed Farming Services
N.A.I.C.S.: 111991

KWS Sementes Ltda. (1)
Rodovia BR 365 km 428 a direita mais 2 0km - Zona Rural, PO Box 2080, Patos de Minas, Gerais, 38700-973, MG, Brazil
Tel.: (55) 3438182009
Web Site: https://www.kws.com
Seed Breeding Services
N.A.I.C.S.: 111191

KWS Semillas Canarias S.L.U. (1)
Lugar Llano Blanco 17, Aguimes, 35269, Las Palmas, Spain
Tel.: (34) 928126035
Grain & Other Product Breeding Services
N.A.I.C.S.: 111199

KWS Semillas Iberica S.L. (1)
Viticultura 13, Zaratan, 47610, Valladolid, Spain
Tel.: (34) 983334916
Web Site: https://www.kws.com
Seed Producer & Distr
N.A.I.C.S.: 111998

KWS Services North America LLC (1)
5705 W Old Shakopee Rd Ste 110, Bloomington, MN 55437
Tel.: (952) 445-8090
Administrative Services
N.A.I.C.S.: 561110

KWS Servicos e Participacoes South America Ltda. (1)
Av Dr Chucri Zaidan 1550 - 23rd floor Offices 2312/2313, Sao Paulo, 04711-130, SP, Brazil
Tel.: (55) 11941650332
Seed Breeding Services
N.A.I.C.S.: 111191

KWS Suisse SA (1)
Birsigstrasse 4, 4054, Basel, Switzerland
Tel.: (41) 612812410
Web Site: https://www.kws.com
Seed Producer & Distr
N.A.I.C.S.: 111998

KWS Turk Tarym Ticaret A.S. (1)
Organize Sanayi Bolgesi, 14 Cadde No 22, 26110, Eskisehir, Turkiye
Tel.: (90) 2222361760
Web Site: http://www.kwsturk.com.tr
Sales Range: $25-49.9 Million
Emp.: 90
Seed Producer & Distr
N.A.I.C.S.: 111998
Veli Girgin *(Gen Mgr)*

KWS UK Ltd. (1)
56 Church Street, Triplow Nr, Royston, SG8 7RE, Herts, United Kingdom
Tel.: (44) 1763207300
Web Site: https://www.kws.com
Sales Range: $25-49.9 Million
Emp.: 55
Seed Producer & Distr
N.A.I.C.S.: 111998

Klein Wanzlebener Saatzucht Maroc S.A.R.L.A.U. (1)
15-17 rue 6 Octobre 3rd floor n 7 Racine, 20 100, Casablanca, Morocco
Tel.: (212) 522448244

Web Site: https://www.kws.com
Seed Breeding Services
N.A.I.C.S.: 111191

Momont SA de Martinval (1)
7 Rue de Martinval, 59246, Mons-en-Pevele, France
Tel.: (33) 3 20592011
Web Site: http://www.momont.com
Sales Range: $25-49.9 Million
Emp.: 90
Plant Breeding & Farm Supplies Distr
N.A.I.C.S.: 111998
Thierry Momont *(Gen Mgr)*

O.O.O. KWS RUS (1)
Peter the Great Square 2 floor 8, Lipetsk, 398008, Russia
Tel.: (7) 4742280310
Web Site: http://www.kws-rus.com
Agricultural Services
N.A.I.C.S.: 115112

PV Tohumculuk Ve Tarim Urunleri Sanayive Ticaret Limited Sirketi (1)
288/4 Sokak No 16 Park Office Kat 5 D 46, Bayrakli, Izmir, Turkiye
Tel.: (90) 2325036667
Web Site: https://www.popvriendseeds.com.tr
Seed Breeding Services
N.A.I.C.S.: 111191

RAGIS KARTOFFELZUCHT- UND HANDELSGESELLSCHAFT MBH (1)
Grimsehlstr 31, Einbeck, 37574, Niedersachsen, Germany
Tel.: (49) 5561311291
Crop Breeding & Whslr
N.A.I.C.S.: 111998

Subsidiary (Non-US):

KWS Potato B.V. (2)
Johannes Postweg 8, 8308 PB, Nagele, Netherlands
Tel.: (31) 527630555
Web Site: http://www.kwsbenelux.nl
Sales Range: $25-49.9 Million
Emp.: 50
Breeding, Production & Marketing of Seed Potatoes
N.A.I.C.S.: 111211
Roland Peerenboom *(Mng Dir)*

VAN RIJN FRANCE S.A.R.L. (1)
6 Allee des Gibessieres, 78580, Bazemont, France
Tel.: (33) 13 47 50 885
Web Site: http://www.vanrijn-kws-france.fr
Potato Farming Services
N.A.I.C.S.: 111211

KWUNG'S HOLDINGS LIMITED
827 Qixiang Road, Ningbo, Zhejiang, China   Ky
Web Site: https://www.kwungs.com
Year Founded: 1973
1925—(HKG)
Rev.: $111,673,543
Assets: $104,428,306
Liabilities: $42,737,594
Net Worth: $61,690,712
Earnings: $8,417,839
Emp.: 567
Fiscal Year-end: 12/31/23
Holding Company
N.A.I.C.S.: 551112
Jianxin Jin *(Founder)*

KX INNOVATION CO LTD
9th FL 90 Godeokbizvalley-ro 6-gil, Gangdong-gu, Seoul, Korea (South)
Tel.: (82) 226471255
Web Site: https://kxgroup.co.kr
Year Founded: 2000
122450—(KRS)
Rev.: $250,246,097
Assets: $674,244,569
Liabilities: $413,766,166
Net Worth: $260,478,203
Earnings: $29,083,126
Emp.: 88
Fiscal Year-end: 12/31/22

Broadcasting Services
N.A.I.C.S.: 516120
Han Chan-Soo *(Co-CEO)*

Subsidiaries:

Paxnet Inc. (1)
803 Nonhyeon-ro, Gangnam-gu, Seoul, Korea (South)
Tel.: (82) 00016885010
Web Site: http://www.paxnet.moneta.co.kr
Rev.: $1,558,837
Assets: $16,516,305
Liabilities: $35,841,365
Net Worth: ($19,325,060)
Earnings: ($1,810,897)
Emp.: 34
Fiscal Year-end: 12/31/2022
Financial Advice Services
N.A.I.C.S.: 541611
Sung-Woong Ko *(CEO)*

KYB CORPORATION
World Trade Center Building South Tower 28F 2-4-1, Hamamatsu-cho Minato-ku, Tokyo, 105-5128, Japan
Tel.: (81) 334353511   JP
Web Site: https://www.kyb.co.jp
Year Founded: 1948
7242—(TKS)
Rev.: $2,926,782,410
Assets: $3,149,863,300
Liabilities: $1,653,306,420
Net Worth: $1,496,556,880
Earnings: $104,556,980
Emp.: 13,634
Fiscal Year-end: 03/31/24
Hydraulic Equipment & Combined Technologies Mfr & Sales
N.A.I.C.S.: 333248
Minoru Tamai *(Exec Officer)*

Subsidiaries:

CHITA KYB Manufacturing (Zhenjiang) Co., Ltd. (1)
No 8 Building-1F No 300 Gangnan Road North Park, New Energy Industrial Park Zhenjiang New District, Jiangsu, 212132, China
Tel.: (86) 51183172570
Hydraulic Shock Absorber Mfr & Distr
N.A.I.C.S.: 336330

Changzhou KYB Leadrun Vibration Reduction Technology Co., Ltd. (1)
No 19 Shunyuan Road, New District, Changzhou, 213125, Jiangsu, China
Tel.: (86) 51985957206
Hydraulic Shock Absorber Mfr & Distr
N.A.I.C.S.: 336330

Chikuyo Seiki Kogyo Co., Ltd. (1)
5-6-22 Wada Sasaguri-cho, Kasuya-gun, Fukuoka, 811-2414, Japan
Tel.: (81) 929475214
Web Site: https://www.chikuyo.jp
Emp.: 37
Hydraulic Equipment Mfr & Distr
N.A.I.C.S.: 333996

Comercial de Autopecas KYB do Brasil Ltda. (1)
Rua Cyro Correia Pereira 2400 Suite 07 - Cidade Industrial, Curitiba, 81460-050, Brazil
Tel.: (55) 4130123620
Hydraulic Shock Absorber Mfr & Distr
N.A.I.C.S.: 336330

KYB (China) Investment Co., Ltd. (1)
No 121 Wei 3 Road, Dingmao Zhenjiang New Zone, Zhenjiang, 212009, Jiangsu, China
Tel.: (86) 51185580300
Hydraulic Shock Absorber Mfr & Distr
N.A.I.C.S.: 336330

KYB Advanced Manufacturing Spain, S.A.U. (1)
Poligono Industrial Perguita Calle B No 15, Los Arcos, 31210, Navarra, Spain
Tel.: (34) 948640336
Hydraulic Shock Absorber Mfr & Distr
N.A.I.C.S.: 336330

KYB CORPORATION

KYB America LLC (1)
180 Meadow Rd, Addison, IL 60101   (100%)
Tel.: (630) 620-5555
Web Site: http://www.kyb.com
Sales Range: $50-74.9 Million
Emp.: 70
Automotive Shock Absorbers, Industrial Hydraulic Motors & Components Mfr
N.A.I.C.S.: 423120
Michael J. Casper *(VP-Fluid Power Div)*

Division (Domestic):

KYB America LLC (2)
5790 Kateila Ave, Cypress, CA 90630   (100%)
Tel.: (562) 799-8494
Web Site: http://www.kyb.com
Sales Range: $25-49.9 Million
Emp.: 20
Warehouse Distribution of Motor Vehicle Parts to West Coast Region
N.A.I.C.S.: 423120

KYB Asian Pacific Corp. Ltd. (1)
4345 Bhiraj Tower at BITEC Unit 1209-1211 12th Floor, Sukhumvit Road Bangnatai Sub-District Bangna District, Bangkok, 10260, Thailand
Tel.: (66) 23009777
Web Site: http://www.kyb.co.th
Hydraulic Shock Absorber Distr
N.A.I.C.S.: 423840

KYB CHITA Manufacturing Europe s.r.o. (1)
Prumyslova 1421, 537 01, Chrudim, Czech Republic
Tel.: (420) 469363302
Web Site: https://www.kcme.cz
Hydraulic Shock Absorber Mfr
N.A.I.C.S.: 336330

KYB Engineering & Service Co., Ltd. (1)
1-6-7 Shibakoen Sumitomo Real Estate Landmark Plaza, Minato-ku, Tokyo, 105-0011, Japan
Tel.: (81) 368951260
Web Site: http://www.kybes.co.jp
Emp.: 93
Engineeering Services
N.A.I.C.S.: 541330

KYB Europe GmbH (1)
Ctra Irurzun S/No, Ororbia, 31171, Navarra, Spain
Tel.: (34) 948421700
Hydraulic Shock Absorber Mfr & Distr
N.A.I.C.S.: 336330

KYB Industrial Machinery (Zhenjiang) Ltd (1)
No 98 Xiyun Road Dingmao Zhenjiang New Zone, New and Hi-Tech Industry Development Park, Zhenjiang, 212009, Jiangsu, China
Tel.: (86) 51188891008
Web Site: http://www.kyb.co.jp
Industrial Valve Mfr
N.A.I.C.S.: 332911

KYB Italy GmbH (1)
Via Monsignor R Colombo 47, Castellanza, 21053, Varese, Italy
Tel.: (39) 0331503180
Hydraulic Shock Absorber Mfr & Distr
N.A.I.C.S.: 336330

KYB Kanayama Co., Ltd. (1)
4350-130 Tobe Kanayama-cho, Gero, 509-1605, Gifu, Japan
Tel.: (81) 576352201
Web Site: http://www.seiryu.ne.jp
Hydraulic Vane Pump Mfr
N.A.I.C.S.: 333914

KYB Logistics Co., Ltd. (1)
2-16 Himegaoka, Kani, 509-0249, Japan
Tel.: (81) 574266427
Hydraulic Shock Absorber Mfr & Distr
N.A.I.C.S.: 336330

KYB Manufacturing North America Inc. (1)
2625 N Morton, Franklin, IN 46131
Tel.: (317) 736-7774
Web Site: http://www.kyb.com
Emp.: 800

KYB CORPORATION

KYB Corporation—(Continued)
Automotive Components Mfr
N.A.I.C.S.: 336330
James Sanders *(Deputy Gen Mgr)*

KYB Manufacturing Vietnam Co., Ltd. (1)
Plot I10-I11-I12 Thang Long Industrial Park, Vong La Dong Anh District, Hanoi, Vietnam
Tel.: (84) 2438812773
Hydraulic Shock Absorber Mfr & Distr
N.A.I.C.S.: 336330

KYB Manufacturing do Brasil Fabricante de Autopecas S.A. (1)
Rua Francisco Ferreira da Cruz 3000, Fazenda Rio Grande, Parana, 83820-293, Brazil
Tel.: (55) 4121028200
Hydraulic Shock Absorber Mfr & Distr
N.A.I.C.S.: 336330

KYB Mexico S.A. de C.V. (1)
Circuito San Roque Norte 300 Santa Fe II Puerto Interior, Silao, 36275, Guanajuato, Mexico
Tel.: (52) 4727485000
Hydraulic Shock Absorber Mfr & Distr
N.A.I.C.S.: 336330

KYB Middle East Fze (1)
Office No 2010 20th Floor Tower A JAFZA One Bldg Jebel Ali Free Zone, PO Box 261819, Dubai, United Arab Emirates
Tel.: (971) 48872448
Web Site: https://www.kybme.com
Sales Range: $50-74.9 Million
Emp.: 15
Shock Absorbers Distr
N.A.I.C.S.: 423120

KYB Motorcycle Suspension Co., Ltd. (1)
505 Tsuchida, Kani, 509-0297, Gifu, Japan
Tel.: (81) 574271170
Web Site: https://kms.kyb.co.jp
Emp.: 569
Motor Vehicle Suspension Mfr
N.A.I.C.S.: 336330

KYB Motorcycle Suspension India Pvt. Ltd. (1)
Pilot No 6 Sipcot Industrial Park, Vallam Vadagal Village Sriperumbudur Taluk Kancheepuram District, Kanchipuram, 631 604, Tamil Nadu, India
Tel.: (91) 4430124301
Hydraulic Shock Absorber Mfr & Distr
N.A.I.C.S.: 336330

KYB Stage Engineering Co., Ltd. (1)
1129 Kumozunagatsunecho, Tsu, 514-0396, Mie Prefecture, Japan
Tel.: (81) 592349260
Hydraulic Shock Absorber Mfr & Distr
N.A.I.C.S.: 336330

KYB Suspensions Europe, S.A. (1)
Ctra Irurzun S/No, Ororbia, 31171, Navarra, Spain **(100%)**
Tel.: (34) 948421700
Web Site: http://www.kyb.co.jp
Sales Range: $200-249.9 Million
Emp.: 800
Mfr & Sale of Automotive Shock Absorbers & Struts
N.A.I.C.S.: 336330

KYB Trondule Co., Ltd. (1)
3909-Ura, Nagaoka, 949-5406, Niigata Prefecture, Japan
Tel.: (81) 258926903
Web Site: https://kyb-nagaoka.jp
Emp.: 71
Electronic Control Device Mfr
N.A.I.C.S.: 335999

KYB Turkey Corporation (1)
Buyukdere Caddesi Kir Gulu Sk Metrocity D Blok No 4/4, Sisli, Istanbul, 34394, Turkiye
Tel.: (90) 2123191804
Hydraulic Shock Absorber Mfr & Distr
N.A.I.C.S.: 336330

KYB UK Ltd. (1)
Unit 1 Taurus Park Europa Boulevard, Warrington, WA5 7ZT, Cheshire, United Kingdom
Tel.: (44) 1925471444
Hydraulic Shock Absorber Mfr & Distr

KYB-Conmat Pvt. Ltd. (1)
702-703 N H No 8, Por, Vadodara, 391243, Gujarat, India
Tel.: (91) 2656132900
Web Site: https://www.conmatindia.com
Concrete Construction Equipment Mfr & Distr
N.A.I.C.S.: 333120

KYB-UMW Malaysia Sdn Bhd (1)
Lot 8 Jalan Waja 16 Telok Panglima Garang, 42500, Kuala Langat, Selangor Darul Ehsan, Malaysia
Tel.: (60) 333220800
Web Site: https://www.kyb.com.my
Sales Range: $25-49.9 Million
Emp.: 750
Power Steering Pumps Mfr
N.A.I.C.S.: 336330
Makoto Kimura *(Mng Dir)*

KYB-YS Co., Ltd. (1)
9165 Sakaki Sakaki-cho, Hanishina-gun, Nagano, 389-0688, Japan
Tel.: (81) 268822850
Web Site: https://www.kyb-ys.co.jp
Hydraulic Vane Pump Mfr
N.A.I.C.S.: 333914

Kayaba Europe GmbH (1)
Margaretha-Ley-Ring 2, Aschheim, 85609, Munich, Germany
Tel.: (49) 8954801880
Web Site: https://kyb-europe.com
Sales Range: $25-49.9 Million
Emp.: 40
Import & Export of Automotive Shocks & Struts
N.A.I.C.S.: 336330
Sato Hajima *(Pres)*

Kayaba Hydraulics Sales (Shanghai) Ltd (1)
B908 Far East International Plaza 317 Xianxia Road, Shanghai, 200051, China
Tel.: (86) 2162351606
Hydraulic Equipment Sales
N.A.I.C.S.: 423830

Kayaba Industry Co., Ltd - Gifu North plant (1)
2548 Dota, Kani, 509-0298, Gifu, Japan
Tel.: (81) 574265111
Web Site: http://www.kyb.co.jp
Hydraulic Equipment Mfr
N.A.I.C.S.: 333998

Kayaba Spain S.A. (1)
Poligono Indistrial De Ipertequi, 2 Orcoyen, Navarra, 51160, Spain **(60%)**
Tel.: (34) 948321004
Web Site: http://www.kayaba.com
Sales Range: $50-74.9 Million
Emp.: 250
Mfr of Vane Pump for Power Steering
N.A.I.C.S.: 336330

Kensiyuu Co., Ltd. (1)
1159 Bijogi, Toda, 335-0031, Saitama, Japan
Tel.: (81) 484999336
Hydraulic Shock Absorber Mfr & Distr
N.A.I.C.S.: 336330

Kyb (Thailand) Co Ltd (1)
700/363 Moo 6 Amata Nakorn Industrial Park2 Bangna-Trad Road KM 57, Tambol Don Hua Roh Amqhur Muang Chonburi, Chon Buri, 20000, Thailand
Tel.: (66) 38469999
Industrial Valve Mfr
N.A.I.C.S.: 332911

Kyb Europe Gmbh (1)
Langfeldstrasse 11, 80939, Munich, Germany
Tel.: (49) 8954801880
Web Site: http://www.kyb-europe.com
Emp.: 50
Hydraulic Equipment Mfr
N.A.I.C.S.: 333998
Yuto Uchida *(Mng Dir & VP)*

Kyb Hydraulics Industry (Zhenjiang) (1)
Jing 12 Lu New Zone New & Hi Tech Industry Development Park, Zhenjiang, 212009, Jiangsu, China

Tel.: (86) 511 8889 7200
Web Site: http://www.kyb.co.jp
Emp.: 400
Hydraulic Equipment Mfr
N.A.I.C.S.: 333248
Geiichi Nagai *(Mgr-Sls)*

Kyb Iberia (1)
Avenida de Ajalvir KM 1 5 Poligono 42, 28806, Alcala de Henares, Madrid, Spain
Tel.: (34) 918774359
Web Site: http://www.kyb.co.jp
Sales Range: $25-49.9 Million
Emp.: 20
Aircraft Devices Mfr
N.A.I.C.S.: 336412

Kyb Latinomerica S.A de C.V (1)
Blvd Manuel Avila Camacho No 32 Int 403 Col Lomas de Chapultepec Del, Miguel Hidalgo, Mexico, 11000, Mexico
Tel.: (52) 5552825770
Web Site: http://www.kybmx.com
Sales Range: $50-74.9 Million
Emp.: 10
Hydraulic Equipment Distr
N.A.I.C.S.: 423830

Kyb Manufacturing Czech S.r.o (1)
U Panasonicu 277 Stare Civice, 530 06, Pardubice, Czech Republic
Tel.: (420) 466812232
Web Site: https://www.kmcz.cz
Sales Range: $100-124.9 Million
Emp.: 700
Hydraulic Shock Absorber Mfr
N.A.I.C.S.: 336330

Kyb Manufacturing Taiwan Co Ltd (1)
No 493 Guangxing Rd, Bade Dist, Taoyuan, 334, Taiwan
Tel.: (886) 33683123
Web Site: https://www.yunghwa.com.tw
Sales Range: $125-149.9 Million
Emp.: 470
Hydraulic Products Mfr & Sales
N.A.I.C.S.: 332912

Kyb Steering (Thailand) Co Ltd (1)
700/829 Moo 6 T Nongtamlueng, Amphur Panthong, Chon Buri, 20160, Thailand
Tel.: (66) 38185559
Web Site: http://www.kyb.co.jp
Vane Pumps Mfr
N.A.I.C.S.: 333914

LLC KYB Eurasia (1)
Odesskaya Street 2 building A, Odessa, 117638, Moscow, Russia
Tel.: (7) 4957716010
Web Site: http://kyb.ru
Motor Vehicle Suspension Mfr
N.A.I.C.S.: 336330

P.T. Kayaba Indonesia (1)
JL Jawa Blok ii No 4 Kawasan Industri MM2100, Cikarang, 17520, Barat, Indonesia
Tel.: (62) 218981456
Sales Range: $400-449.9 Million
Emp.: 1,050
Mfr & Sale of Shock Absorbers & Motorcycle Parts
N.A.I.C.S.: 336330

PT. Chita Indonesia (1)
JL Jawa Blok ii No 4 Kawasan Industri MM2100, Cikarang, 17520, Indonesia
Tel.: (62) 2189983737
Hydraulic Shock Absorber Mfr & Distr
N.A.I.C.S.: 336330

PT. KYB Hydraulics Manufacturing Indonesia (1)
JL Irian X Blok RR2 Kawasan Industri MM2100 Barat, Cikarang, 17520, Indonesia
Tel.: (62) 2128080145
Hydraulic Shock Absorber Mfr & Distr
N.A.I.C.S.: 336330

Siam Kayaba Co., Ltd. (1)
700/363 Moo 6 Amata Nakorn Industrial Park2 Bangna-Trad Road KM 57, Amqhur Muang Chonburi, Chon Buri, 20000, Thailand **(49%)**
Tel.: (66) 38469999
Sales Range: $100-124.9 Million
Emp.: 300
Mfr & Sale of Shock Absorbers

N.A.I.C.S.: 336330

Takako America Co., Inc. (1)
715 Corey Rd, Hutchinson, KS 67504-1642
Tel.: (620) 663-1790
Web Site: https://www.takako-us.com
Precision Machine Parts Mfr & Distr
N.A.I.C.S.: 332721

Takako Industries, Inc. (1)
1-32-1 Hosono-Nishi, Seika-cho Soraku-gun, Kyoto, 619-0240, Japan
Tel.: (81) 774953336
Web Site: https://www.takako-inc.com
Emp.: 268
Technology Services
N.A.I.C.S.: 541519
Yoshitaka Minami *(Pres & CEO)*

Takako Vietnam Co., Ltd. (1)
27 Dai Lo Doc Lap VSIP, Thuan An, Binh Duong, Vietnam
Tel.: (84) 2743782954
Web Site: https://www.takakovietnam.com
Emp.: 1,170
Hydraulic Piston Pump Mfr & Distr
N.A.I.C.S.: 333996

Thai Kabaya Industries Co., Ltd. (1)
700 363 Moo 6 Amata Nakorn Industrial Park, 2 Bangna Trad Road KM 57 Tambo, Don Hua Roh Amqhur Muang, Chon Buri, 20000, Thailand **(100%)**
Tel.: (66) 38469999
Sales Range: $25-49.9 Million
Emp.: 42
Power Steering Pumps Mfr & Sales
N.A.I.C.S.: 336330

Wuxi KYB Top Absorber Co., Ltd. (1)
No 2 Xikun North Road, Singapore Industrial Park Wuxi New District, Wuxi, 214028, China
Tel.: (86) 51085280067
Web Site: https://www.kyb-china.com
Hydraulic Shock Absorber Mfr & Distr
N.A.I.C.S.: 336330

KYCKR LIMITED

Level 12 680 George Street, Sydney, 2000, NSW, Australia
Tel.: (61) 2 8098 1300   AU
Web Site: http://www.kyckr.com
KYK—(ASX)
Rev.: $2,149,374
Assets: $11,780,786
Liabilities: $1,768,201
Net Worth: $10,012,585
Earnings: ($4,247,094)
Fiscal Year-end: 06/30/21
Data Management Services
N.A.I.C.S.: 541513
Benjamin Michael Cronin *(Head-Regulatory Dev)*

Subsidiaries:

Kyckr Ireland Limited (1)
Arclabs Research Centre, Waterford, Ireland
Tel.: (353) 51306282
Data Management Services
N.A.I.C.S.: 541513

KYCOM HOLDINGS CO., LTD.

4-4 Tsukimi 5-chome, Fukui, 918-8011, Japan
Tel.: (81) 776343512
Web Site: https://www.kyd.co.jp
Year Founded: 1968
9685—(TKS)
Rev.: $40,244,455
Assets: $50,987,762
Liabilities: $23,918,064
Net Worth: $27,069,698
Earnings: $2,768,417
Fiscal Year-end: 03/31/24
Software & Computer Programming Services
N.A.I.C.S.: 541511
Masaki Fukuda *(Pres, Pres, CFO, CFO, COO & COO)*

AND PRIVATE COMPANIES

Subsidiaries:

Hokuriku Kyoei Systems Inc. (1)
Exe-Toyama 1104 1-1-19 Jinzu-Honmachi, Toyama, 930-0003, Japan
Tel.: (81) 76 432 9689
Web Site: http://ksh.kyd.co.jp
Information Technology Consulting Services
N.A.I.C.S.: 541512
Shinji Tera (Mng Dir)

Kyodo Computer Co., Ltd. (1)
1-2-7 Kanda-Suda-cho, Chiyoda-ku, Tokyo, 101-0041, Japan
Tel.: (81) 332545491
Web Site: https://www.kyd.co.jp
Emp.: 256
Software Development Services
N.A.I.C.S.: 541511
Genjiro Miwa (Corp Auditor)

Kyoei Data Center Co., Ltd. (1)
5-4-4 Tsukimi, Fukui, 918-8011, Japan
Tel.: (81) 77 636 1720
Web Site: https://kdc.kyd.co.jp
Software Development Services
N.A.I.C.S.: 541511

Kyushu Kyoei Systems Co., Ltd. (1)
2-chome No 4 No 30 Iwaki building 6F, Hakata-ku, Fukuoka, 812-0013, Japan
Tel.: (81) 92 413 0771
Web Site: http://www.kyusyu-kyoei.co.jp
Emp.: 34
Information Technology Consulting Services
N.A.I.C.S.: 541512
Fujio Saito (Pres)

KYE SYSTEMS CORP.
No 492 Sec 5 Chongxin Rd, Sanchong Dist, Taipei, 24160, Taiwan
Tel.: (886) 229956645
Web Site: http://www.geniusnet.com
2365—(TAI)
Rev.: $25,165,930
Assets: $116,276,950
Liabilities: $17,648,418
Net Worth: $98,628,532
Earnings: $2,340,593
Emp.: 2,491
Fiscal Year-end: 12/31/23
Computer Peripheral Product Mfr
N.A.I.C.S.: 334118

Subsidiaries:

Genius Technology (SHENZHEN) CO., Ltd. (1)
Room 2508 Block A World Trade Plz Fuhong Rd, Futian District, Shenzhen, 523000, Guangdong, China
Tel.: (86) 75583296609
Web Site: http://www.geniusnet.com.cn
Computer Peripheral Equipment Distr
N.A.I.C.S.: 423430

KYE Systems America Corporation (1)
1301 NW 84th Ave Ste 127, Miami, FL 33126
Tel.: (305) 468-9250
Computer Peripheral Equipment Whslr
N.A.I.C.S.: 423430

KYE Systems Europe GmbH (1)
Karl-Benz-Strasse 9, 40764, Langenfeld, Nordrhein-Westfalen, Germany
Tel.: (49) 217397430
Web Site: http://www.genius-europe.com
Sales Range: $25-49.9 Million
Emp.: 10
Computer Peripheral Equipment Distr
N.A.I.C.S.: 423430
Chia-Ti Chu (Mng Dir)

KYE Systems H.K. Corp. Ltd. (1)
Room 1701 Aitken Vanson Centre No 61 Hoi Yuen Road, Kwun Tong, Kowloon, China (Hong Kong)
Tel.: (852) 23423813
Web Site: http://www.geniusnet.com.hk
Computer Peripheral Equipment Distr
N.A.I.C.S.: 423430

KYE Systems UK Ltd. (1)
Unit 4 131 Beddington Lane, Croydon, CR0 4TD, Surrey, United Kingdom
Tel.: (44) 2086642727

Web Site: http://www.geniusnet.co.uk
Sales Range: $50-74.9 Million
Emp.: 5
Computer Peripheral Equipment Distr
N.A.I.C.S.: 423430

KYEONG NAM STEEL CO., LTD.
10 Yeondeok-ro 15beon-gil, Seongsan-gu, Changwon, Gyeongsangnam-do, Korea (South)
Tel.: (82) 552979700
Web Site: http://www.ksteel.co.kr
Year Founded: 1990
039240—(KRS)
Rev.: $318,544,906
Assets: $128,949,403
Liabilities: $49,547,342
Net Worth: $79,402,060
Earnings: $7,409,399
Emp.: 106
Fiscal Year-end: 12/31/22
Rolled Steel Mfr
N.A.I.C.S.: 331221
Choi Hyun (Exec Dir)

KYERYONG CONSTRUCTION INDUSTRIAL CO., LTD
48 Munjeong-ro 48beon-gil, Seo-gu, Daejeon, Korea (South)
Tel.: (82) 424807114
Web Site: https://www.kr-ci.com
Year Founded: 1970
013580—(KRS)
Rev.: $2,262,404,752
Assets: $1,963,541,983
Liabilities: $1,347,829,716
Net Worth: $615,712,267
Earnings: $46,387,249
Emp.: 1,649
Fiscal Year-end: 12/31/22
Engineeering Services
N.A.I.C.S.: 541330
Tae-sik Oh (Co-CEO)

Subsidiaries:

Kyeryong-Khabarovsk Co., Ltd. (1)
Leningradskaya St 53, Khabarovskiy kray, Khabarovsk, Russia
Tel.: (7) 4212735775
Engineeering Services
N.A.I.C.S.: 541330

KYLAND TECHNOLOGY CO., LTD.
Xishanhui Building No 2 Shixing Avenue, Shijingshan District, Beijing, 100144, China
Tel.: (86) 1088798888
Web Site: https://www.kyland.com
Year Founded: 2000
300353—(CHIN)
Rev.: $155,102,688
Assets: $387,470,304
Liabilities: $232,366,212
Net Worth: $155,104,092
Earnings: $2,831,868
Emp.: 320
Fiscal Year-end: 12/31/22
Industrial Ethernet Switches Mfr
N.A.I.C.S.: 335313
Li Ping (Chm & Gen Mgr)

Subsidiaries:

Kyland Technology EMEA GmbH (1)
Arbachtalstrasse 6, 72800, Eningen, Germany
Tel.: (49) 71216952805
Ethernet Switch Dist
N.A.I.C.S.: 423690

KYM HOLDINGS BHD.
Level 17 KYM Tower No 8 Jalan PJU 7/6 Mutiara Damansara, 47800, Petaling Jaya, Selangor, Malaysia
Tel.: (60) 387033333 MY
Web Site: https://www.kym.com.my

Year Founded: 1982
KYM—(KLS)
Rev.: $25,477,249
Assets: $37,659,683
Liabilities: $16,914,074
Net Worth: $20,745,608
Earnings: $1,889,312
Emp.: 161
Fiscal Year-end: 01/31/23
Holding Company
N.A.I.C.S.: 551112
Kheng Yew Lim (Exec Dir)

Subsidiaries:

Hasrat Meranti (Chemor) Sdn. Bhd. (1)
Lot 10 Persiaran Perindustrian Kanthan 5, Kanthan Industrial Estate, 31200, Chemor, Perak, Malaysia
Tel.: (60) 52015000
Web Site: https://hmeranti.com
Industrial Paper Bag Mfr
N.A.I.C.S.: 322220
Mok Tuck Meng (Mng Dir)

Hasrat Meranti (Tapah) Sdn. Bhd. (1)
KM 9 Jalan Tapah Tapah Road, Tapah, 35400, Perak, Malaysia
Tel.: (60) 54018888
Industrial Paper Bag Mfr
N.A.I.C.S.: 322220

Hasrat Meranti Sdn. Bhd. (1)
Lot 10 Persiaran Perindustrian Kanthan 5, Kanthan Industrial Estate, 31200, Chemor, Perak, Malaysia
Tel.: (60) 52015000
Web Site: https://www.hmeranti.com
Industrial Paper Bag Mfr
N.A.I.C.S.: 322220

KYM Industries (M) Sdn. Bhd. (1)
Lot 5 Jalan Perusahaan 1, Berangang Industrial Estate, 43700, Berangang, Selangor, Malaysia
Tel.: (60) 387668500
Packaging Equipment Mfr
N.A.I.C.S.: 333993
Lim Michael (Mng Dir)

KYOBO 5 SPECIAL PURPOSE ACQUISITION COMPANY
97 Uisadang-daero, Yeongdeungpo-gu, Seoul, Korea (South)
Tel.: (82) 237719169
Year Founded: 2015
Financial Investment Management Services
N.A.I.C.S.: 523940
Sung-Hoon Joo (CEO)

KYOBO LIFE INSURANCE CO., LTD.
Jongno-1ga, KPO Box 23, Jongno-gu, Seoul, Korea (South)
Tel.: (82) 15881001 KR
Web Site: http://www.kyobo.co.kr
Year Founded: 1958
Sales Range: $5-14.9 Billion
Emp.: 4,300
Fire Insurance Services
N.A.I.C.S.: 524113
Chang-Jae Shin (Chm & CEO)

Subsidiaries:

Kyobo Information & Communication Co., Ltd. (1)
4 Daesagwan-ro, Seongbuk-gu, Seoul, 136823, Korea (South) (100%)
Tel.: (82) 277086700
Web Site: http://www.kico.co.kr
IT & Logistics Consulting Services
N.A.I.C.S.: 519290
Kyo Chun Oh (Pres)

Saengbo Real Estate Trust Co., Ltd. (1)
14th & 16th floors 424 Teheran ro, Seoul, Gangnam, Korea (South)
Tel.: (82) 234043404
Web Site: http://www.sbnet.co.kr

KYOCERA CORPORATION

Real Estate Company
N.A.I.C.S.: 531390
Sunghee Park (Mgr-Bus)

KYOBO SECURITIES CO., LTD.
Kyobo Securities Bldg 97 Euisadang-daero, Yeongdeungpo-gu, Seoul, Korea (South)
Tel.: (82) 237719000
Web Site: https://www.iprovest.com
Year Founded: 1949
030610—(KRS)
Sales Range: Less than $1 Million
Securities Dealing Services
N.A.I.C.S.: 523150
Bongkwon Park (Co-CEO & Exec Dir)

KYOCERA CORPORATION
6 Takeda Tobadono-cho, Fushimi-ku, Kyoto, 612-8501, Japan
Tel.: (81) 756043500 JP
Web Site: https://global.kyocera.com
Year Founded: 1959
6971—(TKS)
Rev.: $13,247,900,810
Assets: $29,516,135,360
Liabilities: $8,014,743,980
Net Worth: $21,501,391,380
Earnings: $668,099,140
Emp.: 79,185
Fiscal Year-end: 03/31/24
Electric Equipment Mfr
N.A.I.C.S.: 334111
Goro Yamaguchi (Chm)

Subsidiaries:

AVX Electronic Components & Interconnect Solutions Corporation (1)
NTT DATA Shinagawa Building 13F Area Shinagawa 9-36 Konan 1-chome, Minato-ku, Tokyo, 108-0075, Japan
Tel.: (81) 755553179
Ceramic & Electronic Mfr
N.A.I.C.S.: 327110

Dongguan Shilong KYOCERA Co., Ltd. (1)
8 Jingci Road, New City District Shilong Town, Dongguan, 523326, Guangdong, China
Tel.: (86) 76986119611
Ceramic & Electronic Mfr
N.A.I.C.S.: 327110

ELCO Europe GmbH (1)
Benjamin Fox Str 1, 57518, Betzdorf, Germany
Tel.: (49) 1276697004
Electronic Component Mfr & Distr
N.A.I.C.S.: 334419

Fastener Holdings, Inc. (1)
10840 Harney St, Omaha, NE 68154-2638
Tel.: (402) 593-5300
Web Site: http://www.southerncarlson.com
Fastening & Packaging Services
N.A.I.C.S.: 561910
Richard Vogt (CFO)

Subsidiary (Domestic):

Manor Hardware, Inc. (2)
21232 68 Ave W, Lynnwood, WA 98036
Tel.: (425) 778-2841
Web Site: http://www.manorhardware.com
Hardware Merchant Whslr
N.A.I.C.S.: 423710
Robert Duncan (Pres)

Hotel Kyocera Co., Ltd (1)
1409-1 Mitsugi Hayato-cho, Kirishima, 899-5117, Kagoshima, Japan
Tel.: (81) 99 543 7111
Web Site: https://www.h-kyocera.co.jp
Sales Range: $25-49.9 Million
Emp.: 200
Home Management Services
N.A.I.C.S.: 721110
Kazuo Inamori (Founder)

Hotel Nikko Princess Kyoto Co., Ltd. (1)
Karasuma Takatsuji Higashi-iru, Shimogyo-ku, Kyoto, 600-8096, Japan
Tel.: (81) 753422111

KYOCERA CORPORATION

INTERNATIONAL PUBLIC

KYOCERA Corporation—(Continued)

Web Site: http://www.princess-kyoto.co.jp
Emp.: 200
Home Management Services
N.A.I.C.S.: 721110
Nobuharu Shino *(Gen Mgr)*

Hotel Princess Kyoto Co., Ltd. (1)
630 Takahashi-cho Karasuma Takatsuji
Higashi-iru, Shimogyo-ku, Kyoto, 600-8096, Japan
Tel.: (81) 753422111
Hotel Operator
N.A.I.C.S.: 721110

International Golf Resort KYOCERA Co., Ltd. (1)
6122 Gumyo Satsuma-cho, Satsuma-gum, Kagoshima, 895-2201, Japan
Tel.: (81) 996 57 1511
Web Site: http://www.igrkc.com
Golf Resort Operation Services
N.A.I.C.S.: 721110

Japan Medical Materials Corporation (1)
Uemura Nissei Building 9th Floor 3-3-31 Miyahara, Yodogawa-ku, Osaka, 532-0003, Japan
Tel.: (81) 663501036
Web Site: http://www.jmmc.jp
Sales Range: $200-249.9 Million
Emp.: 600
Artificial Joints, Dental Implants & Other Medical Equipment Mfr; Owned 77% by Kyocera Corporation & 23% by Kobe Steel, Ltd.
N.A.I.C.S.: 339112

Plant (Domestic):

Japan Medical Materials Corp - Shiga Yohkaichi Plant (2)
1166-6 Hebimizo-cho, Higashi-omi, 527-8555, Shiga, Japan
Tel.: (81) 748221550
Communication Equipment Mfr
N.A.I.C.S.: 334290

KCCS Career Tech Inc. (1)
Mita Nitto Daibiru Bldg 1F 3-11-36 Mita, Minato-ku, Tokyo, 108-0073, Japan
Tel.: (81) 3 3456 6231
Web Site: http://www.kcct.co.jp
Emp.: 45
Human Resource Consulting Services
N.A.I.C.S.: 541612
Hirohai Kanauchi *(Mng Dir)*

KCCS MOBILE ENGINEERING Co., Ltd (1)
3-5-19 Mita Sumitomo Real Estate Tokyo Mita Garden Tower 20F, Minato-ku, Tokyo, 108-0073, Japan
Tel.: (81) 334554110
Web Site: https://www.kcme.jp
Emp.: 346
Telecommunication Engineering Services
N.A.I.C.S.: 541330

KCCS Management Consulting, Inc. (1)
The Itoyama Tower 10F 3-7-18 Mita, Minato-ku, Tokyo, 108-0073, Japan
Tel.: (81) 3 5765 1537
Web Site: http://www.kcmc.co.jp
Sales Range: $25-49.9 Million
Emp.: 150
Management Consulting Services
N.A.I.C.S.: 541618
Eiji Asada *(Pres)*

KYOCERA (China) Sales & Trading Corporation (1)
Unit 1905-1906 Metropolitan Tower 183 Nanjing Road, Heping District, Tianjin, 300074, China
Tel.: (86) 2228459388
Ceramic & Electronic Mfr
N.A.I.C.S.: 327110

KYOCERA (Malaysia) Sdn. Bhd. (1)
Lot 4A Lower Level 3 Hotel Equatorial Penang No 1, Jalan Bukit Jambul, 11900, Penang, Malaysia
Tel.: (60) 46414190
Ceramic & Electronic Mfr
N.A.I.C.S.: 327110

KYOCERA (Thailand) Co., Ltd. (1)
86/1 Moo 4 Tambol Banklang, Amphur Muang, Lamphun, 51000, Thailand
Tel.: (66) 53581530
Ceramic & Electronic Mfr
N.A.I.C.S.: 327110

KYOCERA (Tianjin) Sales & Trading Corporation (1)
Unit 1905-1906 Metropolitan Tower 183 Nanjing Road, Heping District, Tianjin, 300074, China
Tel.: (86) 2228459388
Web Site: http://www.kyocera.com.cn
Emp.: 150
Electronic Component & Equipment Whslr
N.A.I.C.S.: 423690
Goto Yuji *(Mgr)*

KYOCERA (Tianjin) Solar Energy Co., Ltd. (1)
11 XiangAn Rd Tianjin Economic-Technological Development Area, Tianjin, 300457, China
Tel.: (86) 2259856200
Ceramic & Electronic Mfr
N.A.I.C.S.: 327110

KYOCERA (Wuxi) Electronic Materials Co., Ltd. (1)
91 Meiyu Road, New District, Wuxi, 214028, Jiangsu, China
Tel.: (86) 51085212096
Web Site: https://www.kwem.com.cn
Ceramic & Electronic Mfr
N.A.I.C.S.: 327110

KYOCERA Amoeba Management Consulting (Shanghai) Co. Ltd. (1)
Unit 1510 15F Tower 1 Jing An Kerry Centre 1515 Nanjing Road West, Shanghai, 200040, China
Tel.: (86) 2152985511
Ceramic & Electronic Mfr
N.A.I.C.S.: 327110

KYOCERA Asia Pacific (India) Pvt. Ltd. (1)
1004A 1004B 10th Floor JMD Regent Square M G Road, Gurgaon, 122 002, Haryana, India
Tel.: (91) 1244714298
Web Site: https://india.kyocera.com
Emp.: 20
Electronic Component Mfr & Distr
N.A.I.C.S.: 334419
Hideki Kitamura *(Mng Dir)*

KYOCERA Asia Pacific (Thailand) Co., Ltd. (1)
1 Capital Work Place Building 7th Floor Soi Chamchan Sukhumvit 55 Road, Klongton Nua Wattana, Bangkok, 10110, Thailand
Tel.: (66) 20306688
Web Site: https://thailand.kyocera.com
Sales Range: $25-49.9 Million
Emp.: 27
Electronic Components Mfr
N.A.I.C.S.: 334419

KYOCERA Asia Pacific Pte. Ltd. (1)
298 Tiong Bahru Rd 13-03 05 Central Plaza, Singapore, 168730, Singapore
Tel.: (65) 62710500
Web Site: https://asia.kyocera.com
Sales Range: $25-49.9 Million
Emp.: 50
Electronic Components & Semiconductor Parts
N.A.I.C.S.: 334413

Branch (Non-US):

KYOCERA (Hong Kong) Sales & Trading Limited (2)
Rm 801-802 Tower 1 South Season Centre 75 Mody Road, Tsim Sha Tsui East, Kowloon, China (Hong Kong) (100%)
Tel.: (852) 27237183
Web Site: http://global.kyocera.com
Sales Range: $1-9.9 Million
Emp.: 25
Electronic Components & Products Distr
N.A.I.C.S.: 423690

Subsidiary (Non-US):

Yashica Hong Kong Co., Ltd. (2)
14 Fl Piazza Indus Bldg, 133 Hoi Bun Rd Kwun Tong, Kowloon, China (Hong Kong)
Tel.: (852) 23449632
Sales Range: $25-49.9 Million
Emp.: 3
Mfr of Cameras & Lenses
N.A.I.C.S.: 333310

Subsidiary (Domestic):

KYOCERA Hong Kong Logistics Co., Ltd. (3)
6th Floor Niche Centre No 14 Wang Tai Rd, Kowloon Bay, Kowloon, China (Hong Kong)
Tel.: (852) 2343 5151
Web Site: http://global.kyocera.com
Sales Range: $25-49.9 Million
Mfr of Optical & Precision Instruments
N.A.I.C.S.: 333310

KYOCERA Automotive & Industrial Solutions GmbH (1)
Waldstrasse 41, 63128, Dietzenbach, Germany
Tel.: (49) 607448510
Web Site: https://germany.kyocera.com
Automotive Products Mfr
N.A.I.C.S.: 336390
Manfred Sauer *(Mng Dir)*

KYOCERA Bilgitas Document Solutions Turkey A.S. (1)
Altunizade Mah Prof Fahrettin Kerim Gokay Cad No 45, Uskudar, 34662, Istanbul, Turkiye
Tel.: (90) 3390020
Web Site: https://www.kyoceradocument.com.tr
Information Technology Services
N.A.I.C.S.: 541511

KYOCERA CTC Precision Tools Private Limited (1)
M22 Phase-VII, Adityapur Industrial Area PO Gamharia, Jamshedpur, 832109, India
Tel.: (91) 6572200568
Web Site: https://india.kyocera.com
Cutting Tool Mfr
N.A.I.C.S.: 333515

KYOCERA Chemical (Hong Kong) Ltd. (1)
Room No 801-803 Tower 1 South Seas Centre 75 Mody Road, Tsimshatsui East, Kowloon, China (Hong Kong)
Tel.: (852) 26289588
Web Site: http://global.kyocera.com
Sales Range: $50-74.9 Million
Emp.: 6
Chemical Products Distr
N.A.I.C.S.: 424690

KYOCERA Chemical (Wuxi) Co., Ltd. (1)
91 Meiyu Road, Wuxi New District, Wuxi, 214028, Jiangsu, China
Tel.: (86) 51085212096
Web Site: http://www.kyocera-chemi.cn
Chemical Products Mfr & Distr
N.A.I.C.S.: 325998

KYOCERA Chemical Corporation (1)
5-14-25 Ryoke, Kawaguchi, 332-8533, Saitama, Japan
Tel.: (81) 48 225 6834
Web Site: http://www.kyocera-chemi.jp
Sales Range: $200-249.9 Million
Emp.: 890
Printed Circuit Board Mfr
N.A.I.C.S.: 334412

Plant (Domestic):

KYOCERA Chemical Corp - Kawaguchi Works (2)
5-14-25 Ryoke, Kawaguchi, 332-8533, Saitama, Japan
Tel.: (81) 48 225 8103
Chemical Products Mfr
N.A.I.C.S.: 325998

KYOCERA Chemical Corp. - Kawasaki Works (2)
9-2 Chidori, Kawasaki-ku, Kawasaki, 210-0865, Kanagawa, Japan
Tel.: (81) 44 266 1321
Web Site: http://www.kyocera-chemi.jp
Chemical Products Mfr
N.A.I.C.S.: 325998

KYOCERA Chemical Corp. - Koriyama Works (2)
2-17 Machiikedai, Koriyama, 963-0215, Fukushima, Japan
Tel.: (81) 24 959 1530
Web Site: http://www.kyocera-chemi.jp
Sales Range: $25-49.9 Million
Emp.: 100
Chemical Products Mfr
N.A.I.C.S.: 325998
Yukio Mazawa *(Gen Mgr)*

KYOCERA Chemical Corp. - Moka Works (2)
6-2 Matsuyama, Moka, 321-4346, Tochigi, Japan
Tel.: (81) 285 82 4285
Web Site: http://global.kyocera.com
Chemical Products Mfr
N.A.I.C.S.: 325998

KYOCERA Chemical Singapore Pte. Ltd. (1)
43 Tuas Avenue 9, Singapore, 639195, Singapore
Tel.: (65) 6863 0400
Sales Range: $25-49.9 Million
Emp.: 100
Semiconductor Products Mfr & Distr
N.A.I.C.S.: 334413
Hitoshi Yokouchi *(Mng Dir)*

KYOCERA Circuit Design Philippines, Inc. (1)
15th Floor CyberOne Building Eastwood Cyberpark1, Bagumbayan Libis, Quezon City, 1110, Philippines
Tel.: (63) 26876351
Ceramic & Electronic Mfr
N.A.I.C.S.: 327110

KYOCERA Circuit Solutions Inc. (1)
19-26 Shibaura 3-chome, Minato-ku, Tokyo, 108-8536, Japan
Tel.: (81) 354199764
Web Site: http://www.kyocera-cs.co.jp
Sales Range: $200-249.9 Million
Emp.: 1,000
Printed Circuit Boards Mfr & Whslr
N.A.I.C.S.: 334412
Tetsuo Kuba *(Chm)*

KYOCERA Communication Systems (Shanghai) Co., Ltd. (1)
Room 701 Puruan Building No 2 Boyun Road Pudong Software Park, Pudong, Shanghai, 201203, China
Tel.: (86) 2150805660
Ceramic & Electronic Mfr
N.A.I.C.S.: 327110

KYOCERA Communication Systems Co., Ltd. (1)
Kyocera Head Office Bldg 6 Takeda Tobadono-cho, Fushimi-ku, Kyoto, 612-8450, Japan
Tel.: (81) 756230311
Web Site: https://www.kccs.co.jp
Emp.: 4,291
Ceramic & Electronic Mfr
N.A.I.C.S.: 327910

KYOCERA Communication Systems Singapore Pte. Ltd. (1)
298 Tiong Bahru Road 12-05 Central Plaza, Singapore, 168760, Singapore
Tel.: (65) 62761501
Web Site: http://www.kcsg.com.sg
Network Integration Services
N.A.I.C.S.: 541512
Yoshihito Kurose *(Chm)*

KYOCERA Communication Systems Vietnam Co. Ltd. (1)
Room 603 6th Floor Indochina Plaza Hanoi 241 Xuan Thuy Str, Ding Vong Wd Cau Giay Dist, Hanoi, Vietnam
Tel.: (84) 2437954220
Ceramic & Electronic Mfr
N.A.I.C.S.: 327110

KYOCERA Connector Products (Dongguan) Co. Ltd. (1)
8 Jingci Road, New City District Shilong Town, Dongguan, 523326, Guangdong, China
Tel.: (86) 76986184699
Ceramic & Electronic Mfr
N.A.I.C.S.: 327110

AND PRIVATE COMPANIES

KYOCERA CORPORATION

KYOCERA Connector Products Corporation (1)
402-1 Nakayama-cho, Midori-ku, Yokohama, 226-8512, Japan
Tel.: (81) 45 611 1000
Web Site: http://www.kyocera-connector.com
Sales Range: $100-124.9 Million
Emp.: 45
Electronic Connector Components Mfr
N.A.I.C.S.: 334417
Yoji Date *(Pres)*

Subsidiary (Non-US):

KYOCERA Connector Products Hong Kong Ltd. (2)
Room No 801 802 Tower 1 South Seas Centre 75 Mody Road, Tsimshatsui East, Kowloon, China (Hong Kong)
Tel.: (852) 2342 4395
Sales Range: $25-49.9 Million
Emp.: 6
Electronic Equipment Whslr
N.A.I.C.S.: 423690

KYOCERA Connector Products Korea Co., Ltd. (2)
116 Beomjigi-ro, Danwon-gu, Ansan, 15430, Gyeonggi-do, Korea (South)
Tel.: (82) 314942040
Web Site: http://www.kyocera-connector.com
Electronic Connector Mfr
N.A.I.C.S.: 334417

KYOCERA Corp. - Fine Ceramics Group (1)
6 Takeda Tobadono-cho, Fushimi-ku, Kyoto, 612-8501, Japan
Tel.: (81) 756043441
Fine Ceramic Electronic Components Mfr
N.A.I.C.S.: 334419

Subsidiary (Non-US):

KYOCERA Fineceramics GmbH (2)
Hammfelddamm 6, 41460, Neuss, Germany (100%)
Tel.: (49) 213116370
Web Site: http://www.kyocera.eu
Sales Range: $10-24.9 Million
Emp.: 150
Management Company
N.A.I.C.S.: 541611

KYOCERA Fineceramics Limited (2)
Prospect House Archipelago Lyon Way, Frimley, GU16 7ER, Surrey, United Kingdom
Tel.: (44) 127 669 3450
Web Site: http://www.kyocera.co.uk
Emp.: 12
Ceramic Product Distr
N.A.I.C.S.: 423320
Brett Gurney *(Gen Mgr)*

KYOCERA Fineceramics S.A.S. (2)
Parc Tertiaire Silic 21 rue de Villeneuve, BP 90439, 94583, Rungis, Cedex, France
Tel.: (33) 1 4173 7330
Web Site: http://www.kyocera.fr
Sales Range: $25-49.9 Million
Emp.: 25
Electronic Components Distr
N.A.I.C.S.: 423690
Jan Sustronck *(Gen Mgr)*

KYOCERA Crystal Device Philippines, Inc. (1)
New Cebu Township One Special Ecozone, Barangay Cantao-an, Naga, 6037, Cebu, Philippines
Tel.: (63) 322728191
Ceramic & Electronic Mfr
N.A.I.C.S.: 327110

KYOCERA Display (Zhangjiagang) Co. Ltd. (1)
No 8 Beijing Road Zhangjiagang Free Trade Zone, Zhangjiagang, 215634, Jiangsu, China
Tel.: (86) 51258321128
Ceramic & Electronic Mfr
N.A.I.C.S.: 327110

KYOCERA Display Corporation (1)
5-7-18 Higashinippori, Arakawa Ku, Tokyo, 116 0014, Japan
Tel.: (81) 358118760
Web Site: http://www.kyocera-display.co.jp
Sales Range: $1-4.9 Billion
Emp.: 6,000
Liquid Crystal Displays & Optical-Electronic Devices Mfr
N.A.I.C.S.: 334419

Subsidiary (Non-US):

KYOCERA Display Europe GmbH (2)
Waldstrasse 41, 63128, Dietzenbach, Germany (75%)
Tel.: (49) 607448510
Sales Range: $150-199.9 Million
Emp.: 100
Liquid Crystal Display Developer & Mfr
N.A.I.C.S.: 334419
Rheymhold Schlyerkamc *(Gen Mgr)*

KYOCERA Document Solutions (China) Corporation (1)
Floor 8 Chong Hing Financial Center No 288 Nanjing West Road, Huangpu District, Shanghai, 200003, China
Tel.: (86) 2153011777
Web Site: https://www.kyoceradocument.com.cn
Ceramic & Electronic Mfr
N.A.I.C.S.: 327110

KYOCERA Document Solutions Chile SpA (1)
Tel.: (56) 2226701900
Web Site: http://cl.kyoceradocumentsolutions.com
Business Supply & Equipment Mfr
N.A.I.C.S.: 339940

KYOCERA Document Solutions Czech, s.r.o. (1)
Harfa Office Park Ceskomoravska 2420/15, 190 00, Prague, Czech Republic
Tel.: (420) 222562246
Web Site: https://www.kyoceradocumentsolutions.cz
Ceramic & Electronic Mfr
N.A.I.C.S.: 327110

KYOCERA Document Solutions Inc. (1)
1-2-28 Tamatsukuri, Chuo-ku, Osaka, 540-8585, Japan
Tel.: (81) 66 764 3555
Web Site: https://www.kyoceradocument.com
Emp.: 24,337
Mfr & Sale of Image & Information Devices, Supply Products; Maintenance & Rental Services of Copiers, Facsimiles, Printers, Multifunctional Devices, Toner, Photoconductor Drums
N.A.I.C.S.: 334418
Tetsuo Kuba *(Chm)*

Subsidiary (US):

KYOCERA Document Solutions America, Inc. (2)
225 Sand Rd, Fairfield, NJ 07004
Tel.: (973) 808-8444
Web Site: http://www.kyoceradocument.com
Sales Range: $550-599.9 Million
Emp.: 200
Copiers, Printers, Facsimiles & Imaging Products Mfr
N.A.I.C.S.: 333310
Dan Butler *(Dir-Mktg Comm & Trng)*

Subsidiary (Non-US):

KYOCERA Document Solutions Brazil Ltda. (2)
Av Tambore 1180 Mod B-09 CEP, Tambore, Baruen, 06460-000, Sao Paulo, Brazil
Tel.: (55) 11 4195 8496
Web Site: http://www.kyoceradocument.co.br
Emp.: 45
Electronic Components Distr
N.A.I.C.S.: 423690
Joerg Schickedanz *(Gen Mgr)*

KYOCERA Document Solutions Canada, Ltd. (3)
6120 Kestrel Road, Mississauga, L5T 1S8, ON, Canada (100%)
Tel.: (905) 670-4425
Web Site: https://www.kyoceradocumentsolutions.ca
Sales Range: $1-9.9 Million
Emp.: 40
Distr of Printers & Copiers
N.A.I.C.S.: 424120
Louie Panicolopoulos *(Mgr-Sls)*

KYOCERA Document Solutions Mexico, S.A. de C.V. (3)
Calle Arquimedes No 130 4 Piso, Polanco Distrito Federal, 11560, Mexico, DF, Mexico
Tel.: (52) 5553832741
Web Site: https://www.kyoceradocumentsolutions.mx
Electronic Component Mfr & Distr
N.A.I.C.S.: 334419
Yoshida Faka *(Gen Mgr)*

Subsidiary (Domestic):

Nevill Document Solutions, LLC (3)
2825 W Story Rd, Irving, TX 75038
Tel.: (469) 574-0041
Web Site: http://www.nevillsolutions.com
Sales Range: $10-24.9 Million
Office Equipment Whslr
N.A.I.C.S.: 423420
Reed Allan Melnick *(Pres & Gen Mgr)*

Subsidiary (Non-US):

KYOCERA Document Solutions Asia Limited (2)
13/F Mita Centre 552-566 Castle Peak Road, Tsuen Wan, NT, China (Hong Kong)
Tel.: (852) 24965678
Web Site: https://www.kyoceradocument.com
Emp.: 30
Holding Company; Regional Managing Office
N.A.I.C.S.: 551112
Masayuki Higuchi *(Pres)*

Subsidiary (Non-US):

KYOCERA Document Solutions (Thailand) Corp., Ltd. (3)
335 Ratchadapisek Road, Sawang Subdistrict Bang Sue District, Bangkok, 10800, Thailand
Tel.: (66) 25860333
Web Site: https://www.kyoceradocument.com
Photocopying Machines Distr
N.A.I.C.S.: 423410

Subsidiary (Domestic):

KYOCERA Document Solutions Hong Kong Limited (3)
16/F Mita Centre 552-566 Castle Peak Road, Tsuen Wan, NT, China (Hong Kong)
Tel.: (852) 3 582 4000
Web Site: https://www.kyoceradocument.com
Sales Range: $25-49.9 Million
Emp.: 60
Office Equipment Whslr
N.A.I.C.S.: 423420
Cardiff Chen *(Gen Mgr)*

Subsidiary (Non-US):

KYOCERA Document Solutions India Private Limited (3)
2nd Floor Golf Course Road Sector 53, Gurgaon, 122006, Haryana, India
Tel.: (91) 124 4671000
Web Site: http://www.kyoceradocument.co.in
Emp.: 75
Office Electronic Component Whslr
N.A.I.C.S.: 423420
Hemant Rai *(Gen Mgr)*

KYOCERA Document Solutions Singapore Pte. Ltd. (3)
12 Tai Seng Street 04-01A Luxasia Building, Singapore, 534118, Singapore
Tel.: (65) 67418733
Web Site: http://www.kyoceradocument.com.sg
Sales Range: $25-49.9 Million
Emp.: 7
Office Equipment Repair Services & Distr
N.A.I.C.S.: 811210
Fujiyoshi Kohei *(Mng Dir)*

KYOCERA Document Solutions Taiwan Corporation (3)
104 6th Floor No 37 Section 3 Minquan East Road, Zhongshan District, Taipei, 104, Taiwan
Tel.: (886) 225076709
Web Site: https://www.kyoceradocument.com
Sales Range: $25-49.9 Million
Emp.: 70
Coffee Machine & Printer Mfr
N.A.I.C.S.: 333241

KYOCERA Document Technology (Dongguan) Co., Ltd. (3)
3 Fang Zheng East Road, Shilong Town Kyocera Industrial Park, Dongguan, 523326, Guangdong, China
Tel.: (86) 76986112525
Web Site: http://www.kyoceradocument.com.cn
Office Equipment Whslr
N.A.I.C.S.: 423420

Subsidiary (Non-US):

KYOCERA Document Solutions Australia Pty. Ltd. (2)
Level 3 6-10 Talavera Road, North Ryde, 2113, NSW, Australia
Tel.: (61) 298889999
Web Site: http://www.kyoceramita.com.au
Sales Range: $25-49.9 Million
Emp.: 68
Printing Machinery Distr
N.A.I.C.S.: 423830
David Finn *(Mng Dir)*

KYOCERA Document Solutions Europe B.V. (2)
Bloemlaan 4, 2132 NP, Hoofddorp, Netherlands
Tel.: (31) 206540000
Web Site: https://www.kyoceradocumentsolutions.eu
Sales Range: $75-99.9 Million
Emp.: 170
Holding Company; Regional Managing Office
N.A.I.C.S.: 551112
Stefan Dylka *(Sr Acct Mgr-Sls)*

Subsidiary (Non-US):

KYOCERA Document Solutions (U.K.) Ltd. (3)
Eldon Court 75-77 London Road, Reading, RG1 5BS, Berkshire, United Kingdom
Tel.: (44) 3330151855
Web Site: https://www.kyoceradocument.co.uk
Sales Range: $50-74.9 Million
Emp.: 130
Electronic Device & Equipment Distr
N.A.I.C.S.: 423690

Subsidiary (US):

DataBank IMX, LLC (4)
620 Freedom Business Ctr Ste 120, King of Prussia, PA 19406
Tel.: (800) 873-9426
Web Site: http://www.databankimx.com
Microfilm Conversion & Document Storage & Retrieval Services
N.A.I.C.S.: 561499
Chuck Bauer *(CEO)*

Subsidiary (Domestic):

Griffith, Inc. (5)
458 Pike Rd, Huntingdon Valley, PA 19006
Tel.: (215) 322-8100
Web Site: http://www.alpha-sys.com
Data & Document Management Services
N.A.I.C.S.: 561499

eDocument Resources, LLC (5)
6101 Baker Rd Ste 207, Minnetonka, MN 55345
Tel.: (952) 607-3500
Web Site: http://www.edocumentresources.com
Enterprise Content Management Solution Services
N.A.I.C.S.: 518210
Ken Schempp *(Pres)*

Subsidiary (Non-US):

KYOCERA Document Solutions Austria GmbH (3)

KYOCERA CORPORATION

INTERNATIONAL PUBLIC

KYOCERA Corporation—(Continued)

Altmannsdorfer strasse 91 Stiege 1 2 OG
Top 1, 1230, Vienna, Austria
Tel.: (43) 1863380
Web Site:
 http://www.kyoceradocumentsolutions.at
Emp.: 2
Photocopying Machinery Distr
N.A.I.C.S.: 423690
Frank Koch *(Gen Mgr)*

KYOCERA Document Solutions Belgium N.V./S.A. (3)
Sint-Martinusweg 199 - 201, 1930, Zaventem, Belgium
Tel.: (32) 2 720 9270
Web Site:
 https://www.kyoceradocumentsolutions.be
Sales Range: $25-49.9 Million
Emp.: 4
Electronic Device Distr
N.A.I.C.S.: 423690
Thierry Devresse *(Gen Mgr)*

KYOCERA Document Solutions Danmark A/S (3)
Ejby Industrivej 60, DK-2600, Glostrup, Denmark
Tel.: (45) 70223880
Web Site:
 https://www.kyoceradocumentsolutions.dk
Printing Machinery Distr
N.A.I.C.S.: 423830

KYOCERA Document Solutions Deutschland GmbH (3)
Otto-Hahn-Strasse 12, 40670, Meerbusch, Germany **(100%)**
Tel.: (49) 2 159 9180
Web Site:
 https://www.kyoceradocumentsolutions.de
Sales Range: $100-124.9 Million
Emp.: 300
Electronics Equipment
N.A.I.C.S.: 334419
Reinhold Schlierkamp *(Mng Dir)*

KYOCERA Document Solutions Espana, S.A. (3)
Calle Manacor 2, Las Rozas, 28290, Madrid, Spain
Tel.: (34) 902998822
Web Site:
 https://www.kyoceradocumentsolutions.es
Photocopying Machinery Distr
N.A.I.C.S.: 423690

KYOCERA Document Solutions Finland Oy (3)
Plaza Business Park Pilke Ayritie 16, 00370, Vantaa, Finland
Tel.: (358) 947805200
Web Site:
 https://www.kyoceradocumentsolutions.fi
Sales Range: $25-49.9 Million
Emp.: 14
Electronic Device Distr
N.A.I.C.S.: 423690

KYOCERA Document Solutions France S.A.S. (3)
Espace Technologique de Saint Aubin Route de l'Orme, 91195, Gif-sur-Yvette, France
Tel.: (33) 169852600
Web Site:
 https://www.kyoceradocumentsolutions.fr
Photocopying Machinery Distr
N.A.I.C.S.: 423690

KYOCERA Document Solutions Italia S.p.A. (3)
Via Monfalcone 15, 20132, Milan, MI, Italy
Tel.: (39) 02921791
Web Site:
 https://www.kyoceradocumentsolutions.it
Sales Range: $25-49.9 Million
Emp.: 92
Printer Machine Distr
N.A.I.C.S.: 423430

Subsidiary (Domestic):

KYOCERA Document Solutions Nederland B.V. (3)
Beechavenue 25, 1119 RA, Schiphol-Rijk, Netherlands
Tel.: (31) 20 587 72 00
Web Site:
 http://www.kyoceradocumentsolutions.nl
Sales Range: $25-49.9 Million
Emp.: 60
Electronic Printing & Copying Machine Distr
N.A.I.C.S.: 423690
Etienne Hendriks *(Gen Mgr)*

Subsidiary (Non-US):

KYOCERA Document Solutions Nordic AB (3)
Esbogatan 16B, 164 75, Kista, Sweden
Tel.: (46) 854655000
Web Site:
 https://www.kyoceradocumentsolutions.se
Sales Range: $25-49.9 Million
Emp.: 27
Electronic Components Distr
N.A.I.C.S.: 423690
Esbjorn Wickstrom *(CEO)*

KYOCERA Document Solutions Portugal Lda. (3)
Rua do Centro Cultural No 41, 1700-106, Lisbon, Portugal
Tel.: (351) 218436780
Web Site:
 https://www.kyoceradocumentsolutions.pt
Photocopying Machinery Distr
N.A.I.C.S.: 423690

KYOCERA Document Solutions South Africa (Pty) Ltd. (3)
90 Bekker Rd Hertford Office Park, Kyalami Business Park, Midrand, 1685, South Africa
Tel.: (27) 11 540 2600
Web Site:
 http://www.kyoceradocument.co.za
Sales Range: $25-49.9 Million
Emp.: 55
Photocopying Machinery Distr
N.A.I.C.S.: 423690
Wayne Holborn *(Gen Mgr)*

Subsidiary (Non-US):

KYOCERA Document Solutions Japan Inc. (2)
Web Site:
 http://www.kyoceradocument.co.jp
Monochrome Color Printers Mfr & Distr
N.A.I.C.S.: 334419
Makoto Koga *(Pres)*

KYOCERA Document Solutions New Zealand Ltd. (2)
Ground Floor 19 Byron Avenue Takapuna, Auckland, 622, New Zealand
Tel.: (64) 9 415 4517
Web Site:
 http://www.kyoceradocument.co.nz
Sales Range: $25-49.9 Million
Emp.: 20
Photocopy Machine Distr
N.A.I.C.S.: 424120
Chris Tolley *(Gen Mgr)*

TA Triumph-Adler AG (2)
Sudwestpark 23, 90499, Nuremberg, Germany **(93.8%)**
Tel.: (49) 911 68 98 0
Web Site: http://www.triumph-adler.de
Sales Range: $350-399.9 Million
Emp.: 1,285
Office Machines Mfr; Typewriters, Copiers, Calculators; Word Processing Systems, Printers, Fax, Telephones
N.A.I.C.S.: 333310
Christopher Rheidt *(Co-CEO)*

Subsidiary (Domestic):

Triumph-Adler Experts at Output GmbH (3)
Sudwestpark 23, Nuremberg, 90449, Germany
Tel.: (49) 91168980
Web Site: http://www.experts-at-output.com
Sales Range: $10-24.9 Million
Emp.: 45
Imaging Systems Distr & Service
N.A.I.C.S.: 811210
Masasumi Oda *(Gen Mgr)*

UTAX GmbH (3)
Ohechaussee 235, 22848, Norderstedt, Germany
Tel.: (49) 40528490
Web Site: http://www.utax.com

Printing Equipment Whslr
N.A.I.C.S.: 423420
Simone Brett *(Mgr-PR)*

KYOCERA Document Solutions Russia LLC (1)
Building 2 51/4 Schepkina St, 129110, Moscow, Russia
Tel.: (7) 4957410004
Ceramic & Electronic Mfr
N.A.I.C.S.: 327110

KYOCERA Europe GmbH (1)
Fritz-Muller-Strasse 27, 73730, Esslingen, Germany
Tel.: (49) 711939340
Web Site: https://germany.kyocera.com
Ceramic & Electronic Mfr
N.A.I.C.S.: 327110

KYOCERA Fineceramics Italy S.r.l. (1)
Viale delle Industrie 20/5, 20020, Arese, MI, Italy
Tel.: (39) 03281797603
Web Site: http://italy.kyocera.com
Ceramic & Electronic Mfr
N.A.I.C.S.: 327110

KYOCERA Fineceramics Precision GmbH (1)
Lorenz-Hutschenreuther-Strasse 81, 95100, Selb, Germany
Tel.: (49) 9 287 8070
Web Site: https://www.kyocera-precision.com
Emp.: 274
Ceramic Mfr
N.A.I.C.S.: 327110
Thomas Werminghaus *(Sr Mgr-Bus Dev)*

KYOCERA Fineceramics Solutions GmbH (1)
Steinzeugstrasse 92, 68229, Mannheim, Germany
Ceramic Mfr
N.A.I.C.S.: 327110
Armin Kayser *(Mng Dir)*

KYOCERA Industrial Tools Corporation (1)
2-2-54 Matsuhama-cho, Fukuyama, 720-0802, Hiroshima, Japan **(80%)**
Tel.: (81) 84 975 8989
Web Site: https://www.kyocera-industrialtools.co.jp
Emp.: 164
Power-Driven Hand Tools Mfr
N.A.I.C.S.: 333991
Kenjiro Suzuki *(Pres)*

Subsidiary (Domestic):

Kyocera Industrial Tools Sales Corporation (2)
1-145-1 Hisakata, Tempaku-ku, Nagoya, 468-8512, Aichi, Japan
Tel.: (81) 528071627
Web Site: http://global.kyocera.com
Power Tools & Lawn & Garden Equipment Whslr
N.A.I.C.S.: 423710

Subsidiary (Non-US):

Kyocera Ryobi (Dalian) Machinery Co., Ltd. (2)
No 2 Huanghai West 6th Road, Jinzhou District, Dalian, 116600, China **(66.6%)**
Tel.: (86) 41187621111
Web Site: https://www.kyocera-industrialtools.cn
Power Tools, Builder's Hardware & Other Machinery
N.A.I.C.S.: 332510

KYOCERA International Electronics Co., Ltd. (1)
No 8 Kaifa Rd Nan Tze Export Processing Zone, Kaohsiung, 81170, Taiwan
Tel.: (886) 73612604
Ceramic & Electronic Mfr
N.A.I.C.S.: 327110

KYOCERA International, Inc. (1)
8611 Balboa Ave, San Diego, CA 92123-1580
Tel.: (858) 576-2600
Web Site: http://americas.kyocera.com

Sales Range: $1-4.9 Billion
Emp.: 500
Holding Company; Regional Managing Office
N.A.I.C.S.: 551112
John S. Rigby *(Pres)*

Holding (Domestic):

KYOCERA AVX Components Corporation (2)
1 AVX Blvd, Fountain Inn, SC 29644 **(100%)**
Tel.: (864) 967-2150
Web Site: https://www.kyocera-avx.com
Rev.: $1,791,790,000
Assets: $2,813,278,000
Liabilities: $429,098,000
Net Worth: $2,384,180,000
Earnings: $271,813,000
Emp.: 15,100
Fiscal Year-end: 03/31/2019
Multilayer Ceramic Capacitors Mfr
N.A.I.C.S.: 334419
John Lawing *(CTO & Sr VP)*

Subsidiary (Non-US):

AB Mikroelektronik GmbH (3)
Josef Brandstaetter Str 2, 5020, Salzburg, Austria **(100%)**
Tel.: (43) 662 44991 0
Web Site: http://www.abelektronik.com
Resistive Components
N.A.I.C.S.: 334416
Georg Schafrath *(Mng Dir)*

AVX Czech Republic s.r.o. (3)
Tel.: (420) 465358111
Web Site: http://www.avxcorp.com
Emp.: 1,800
Electronic Component & Accessories Mfr & Supplier
N.A.I.C.S.: 334419
Radek Kovar *(Gen Mgr)*

AVX Electronics (Tianjin) Co. Ltd. (3)
No 9 Qingling Av Yixian Technology Industrial Park Wuqing De, Tianjin, 301726, China
Tel.: (86) 2282118358
Electronic Component & Accessories Mfr & Supplier
N.A.I.C.S.: 334419

Subsidiary (Domestic):

AVX Filters Corporation (3)
11144 Penrose St, Sun Valley, CA 91352-2749 **(85%)**
Tel.: (818) 767-6770
Web Site: http://www.avxcorp.com
Sales Range: $50-74.9 Million
Emp.: 120
Mfr of EMI & RFI Ceramic Filters
N.A.I.C.S.: 333998
Donald Dollar *(Plant Mgr)*

Subsidiary (Non-US):

AVX Israel Ltd. (3)
Har Hotzvim, PO Box 45008, 91450, Jerusalem, Israel
Tel.: (972) 2819707
Provider of Research & Development Services
N.A.I.C.S.: 541715

AVX Ltd. (3)
Admiral House Harlington Way, Fleet, GU51 4BB, Hampshire, United Kingdom **(70%)**
Tel.: (44) 01252770000
Web Site: http://www.avxcorp.com
Sales Range: $25-49.9 Million
Emp.: 25
Ceramic Capacitors
N.A.I.C.S.: 327120

Subsidiary (Domestic):

AVX Tantalum Corporation (3)
1 AVX Blvd, Fountain Inn, SC 29644
Tel.: (864) 967-2150
Web Site: http://www.avxcorp.com
Sales Range: $50-74.9 Million
Emp.: 120
Mfr of Tantalum Capacitors
N.A.I.C.S.: 335999

AND PRIVATE COMPANIES — KYOCERA CORPORATION

Subsidiary (Non-US):

AVX/KYOCERA (Shanghai) International Trading Co., Ltd. (3)
Rm 501 Rm 503 88 Guang Xin Rd, Putuo District, Shanghai, 200000, China
Tel.: (86) 2132551933
Electric Component Whslr
N.A.I.C.S.: 423690

AVX/KYOCERA Yuhan Hoesa (3)
15th Floor Taeseok Building 275-5 Yangjae-dong, Seocho-gu, Seoul, Korea (South)
Tel.: (82) 22515124
Electronic Components Distr
N.A.I.C.S.: 423690
Helen Lee *(Gen Mgr)*

AVX/Kyocera Asia Ltd. (3)
Hilder Center 2 Sung Ping Street, Kowloon, China (Hong Kong)
Tel.: (852) 23633303
Electronic Component & Accessories Mfr & Supplier
N.A.I.C.S.: 334419
Catherine Hou *(Mgr-Sls)*

Subsidiary (Domestic):

American Technical Ceramics Corp. (3)
1 Norden Ln, Huntington Station, NY 11746
Tel.: (631) 622-4700
Web Site: http://www.atceramics.com
Sales Range: $75-99.9 Million
Emp.: 782
RF/Microwave/Millimeter Wave Ceramic & Porcelain Capacitors & Thin Film Products Mf., Designer, Developer & Marketer
N.A.I.C.S.: 334416
Harrison Tarver *(VP-Quality Assurance)*

Branch (Non-US):

ATC Europe (4)
Komsomolsky Prospect, 42 Building 3 Office 9, Moscow, 119048, Russia
Tel.: (7) 4952470747
Fiber Optic & Wireless Mfr
N.A.I.C.S.: 335921

ATC Europe - United Kingdom (4)
34 Pewley Way, Guildford, GU1 3QA, Surrey, United Kingdom
Tel.: (44) 1483207402
Web Site: http://www.atceramics.com
Sales Range: $75-99.9 Million
Emp.: 1
Fiber Optic & Wireless Mfr
N.A.I.C.S.: 335921

Subsidiary (Non-US):

American Technical Ceramics (China) Ltd. (4)
Unity 11th Floor Jinyun Century Building, No 6033 Shennan Road, Shenzhen, 518035, Guandong, China
Tel.: (86) 75583664318
Web Site: http://www.atceramics.com
Sales Range: $10-24.9 Million
Emp.: 13
Technical Support Sales
N.A.I.C.S.: 541513
Simon Li Wandong *(Principal)*

Branch (Non-US):

American Technical Ceramics - Hyderabad (5)
Flat No 303 Sai Teja Towers Plot No 18 Engineers Colony, Hyderabad, 500 073, India
Tel.: (91) 4066620064
Web Site: http://www.atceramics.com
Wireless & Fiber Optic Mfr
N.A.I.C.S.: 332618

Subsidiary (Domestic):

American Technical Ceramics (Florida), Inc. (4)
2201 Corporate Sq Blvd, Jacksonville, FL 32216-1921
Tel.: (904) 726-3400
Web Site: http://www.atceramics.com
Sales Range: $25-49.9 Million
Emp.: 216
Mfr of Ceramic Capacitors
N.A.I.C.S.: 334416
Kathleen M. Kelly *(VP-HR)*

Subsidiary (Non-US):

Avio Excelente, S.A. DE C.V. (3)
Av San Lorenzo No 651, Ciudad Juarez, 32310, Mexico
Tel.: (52) 6566270787
Electrical & Electronic Equipment Mfr
N.A.I.C.S.: 334419

Subsidiary (Domestic):

Bliley Technologies Inc. (3)
2545 W Grandview Blvd, Erie, PA 16506
Tel.: (814) 838-3571
Web Site: http://www.bliley.com
Sales Range: $10-24.9 Million
Emp.: 150
Quartz Crystals, For Electronic Application
N.A.I.C.S.: 334419

Elco USA, Inc. (3)
801 17th Ave S, Myrtle Beach, SC 29577-4245
Tel.: (843) 448-9411
Electronic Components Mfr
N.A.I.C.S.: 334419

Ethertronics Inc. (3)
5501 Oberlin Dr Ste 100, San Diego, CA 92121
Tel.: (858) 550-3820
Web Site: http://www.ethertronics.com
Embedded Antennas (for Wireless Devices) Designer & Mfr
N.A.I.C.S.: 334220

Branch (Non-US):

Ethertronics Inc. (4)
102-604 166 Gosan-ro Gunpo-si, Kyongki, 15850, Gyeonggi-do, Korea (South)
Tel.: (82) 314362290
Web Site: http://www.ethertronics.com
Embedded Antennas (for Wireless Devices) Mfr
N.A.I.C.S.: 334220

Ethertronics Inc. (4)
2F-7 No 3 Yuanqu St, Nangang District, Taipei, 115, Taiwan
Tel.: (886) 226557966
Web Site: http://www.ethertronics.com
Embedded Antennas (for Wireless Devices) Designer & Mfr
N.A.I.C.S.: 334220

Subsidiary (Domestic):

Kyocera Electronic Devices, LLC (3)
1 AVX Blvd Fountain Inn, Greenville, SC 29644-9039
Tel.: (864) 967-2150
Web Site: http://www.kyocera-crystal.jp
Electronic Connector Mfr
N.A.I.C.S.: 334417

Subsidiary (Non-US):

TPC (Malaysia) Sdn. Bhd. (3)
Phase 3 Bayan Lepas Free Trade Zone, Bayan Lepas, 11900, Penang, Malaysia
Tel.: (60) 46446700
Electronic Component Mfr & Supplier
N.A.I.C.S.: 334419
Kumar Krishnamani *(Mng Dir)*

Subsidiary (Domestic):

KYOCERA America, Inc. (2)
8611 Balboa Ave, San Diego, CA 92123
Tel.: (858) 576-2600
Web Site: http://www.americas.kyocera.com
Sales Range: $700-749.9 Million
Ceramic Semiconductor Packages, Consumer Ceramic Products & Photovoltaic Solar Systems & Recrystallized Gemstones
N.A.I.C.S.: 334413
Robert Whisler *(Pres)*

KYOCERA Communications, Inc. (2)
8611 Balboa Ave, San Diego, CA 92123-1580
Tel.: (858) 576-2600
Sales Range: $50-74.9 Million
Emp.: 150
Design, Manufacture & Sales of Wireless Phones
N.A.I.C.S.: 423690
John Chier *(Dir-Corp Comm)*

Subsidiary (Non-US):

KYOCERA Mexicana, S.A. de C.V. (2) (100%)
Sales Range: $100-124.9 Million
Emp.: 500
Ceramic Packaging
N.A.I.C.S.: 327120

Subsidiary (Domestic):

KYOCERA SGS Precision Tools, Inc. (2)
55 S Main St, Munroe Falls, OH 44262
Tel.: (330) 688-6667
Web Site: http://www.sgstool.com
Emp.: 350
Machine Tool Accessories & Cutting Tools Mfr
N.A.I.C.S.: 333515
Thomas J. Haag *(Pres)*

KYOCERA Tycom Corporation (2)
3565 Cadillac Ave, Costa Mesa, CA 92626-1401
Tel.: (714) 428-3600
Web Site: http://www.kyoceratycom.com
Sales Range: $25-49.9 Million
Emp.: 240
Mfr of Carbide Cutting Tools
N.A.I.C.S.: 333517

Subsidiary (Non-US):

KYOCERA TYCOM Canada, Ltd. (3)
7490 Pacific Cir 4, Mississauga, ON, Canada
Tel.: (905) 670-5150
Web Site: http://global.kyocera.com
Metal Machine Tools Mfr
N.A.I.C.S.: 333515

Division (Domestic):

Olean Advanced Products Division (2)
1695 Seneca Ave, Olean, NY 14760-9532
Tel.: (716) 372-6611
Web Site: http://www.avxcorp.com
Sales Range: $50-74.9 Million
Emp.: 80
Mfrof Ceramic Components for Filters
N.A.I.C.S.: 334416
John Monahan *(Gen Mgr)*

Subsidiary (Non-US):

KYOCERA Kinseki Corporation (1)
1 8 1 Izumihon Cho, Komae City, Tokyo, 201 8648, Japan
Tel.: (81) 354973110
Web Site: http://www.kyocera-kinseki.co.jp
Rev: $7,600,140,141
Emp.: 600
Mfr of Quartz Crystals; Crystal Filters, Oscillators
N.A.I.C.S.: 334515

Subsidiary (Domestic):

KYOCERA KINSEKI Hokkaido Corp. (2)
219-1 Higashi-Kiyozumi-cho, Mikasa, 068-2104, Hokkaido, Japan
Tel.: (81) 1267 2 4092
Web Site: http://www.kinseki.co.jp
Electronic Components Mfr
N.A.I.C.S.: 334419

Plant (Domestic):

KYOCERA KINSEKI Hokkaido Corp. - Mikasa Plant (3)
219-1 Higashi-Kiyozumi-cho, Mikasa, 068-2104, Hokkaido, Japan
Tel.: (81) 1267 2 4092
Web Site: http://www.kinseki.co.jp
Electronic Components Mfr
N.A.I.C.S.: 334419

Subsidiary (Domestic):

KYOCERA KINSEKI Yamagata Corp. (2)
5850 Higashine-koh Ohaza, Higashine, 999-3701, Yamagata, Japan
Tel.: (81) 237435611
Web Site: http://www.kinseki.co.jp
Quartz Crystal Device Mfr
N.A.I.C.S.: 334419

KYOCERA Kinseki Hertz Corporation (1)
2161-3 Miyama-cho, Hachioji, Tokyo, 192-0152, Japan
Tel.: (81) 426507211
Web Site: http://www.kyocera-kinseki.jp
Sales Range: $1-9.9 Million
Emp.: 15
Electronic Component Crystal Unit Mfr & Marketer
N.A.I.C.S.: 334419

KYOCERA Korea Co., Ltd. (1)
2nd floor Myeongin Tower 267 Hyoryeong-ro, Seocho-gu, Seoul, 06653, Korea (South)
Tel.: (82) 234633538
Web Site: https://korea.kyocera.com
Electronic Device & Component Distr
N.A.I.C.S.: 423690

KYOCERA Mexico Services, S.A. de C.V. (1)
Blvd Buenavista 2055 Interior A Qtay Universidad, Tijuana, Baja California, Mexico
Tel.: (52) 6646820111
Administrative Services
N.A.I.C.S.: 561110

KYOCERA OPTEC Co., Ltd. (1)
3-1778 Osogi, Ome, 198-0003, Tokyo, Japan
Tel.: (81) 428745111
Web Site: http://www.kop.co.jp
Camera Lenses Mfr
N.A.I.C.S.: 333310
Fuminori Yamagiwa *(Pres)*

KYOCERA Optec (Dongguan) Co., Ltd. (1)
8 Jingci Road, New City District Shilong Town, Dongguan, 523326, Guangdong, China
Tel.: (86) 76986186216
Ceramic & Electronic Mfr
N.A.I.C.S.: 327110

KYOCERA Precision Tools (Ganzhou) Co., Ltd. (1)
No 172 Wei Yi Road Ganzhou Economic and Technological Development Zone, Ganzhou, 341000, Jiangxi, China
Tel.: (86) 7978180101
Ceramic & Electronic Mfr
N.A.I.C.S.: 327110

KYOCERA Precision Tools (Zhuhai) Co., Ltd. (1)
1st and 2nd Floor Building B, Xinqing Science and Technology Industrial Park Doumen, Zhuhai, 519000, China
Tel.: (86) 7565110118
Web Site: https://www.kptz.com.cn
Ceramic & Electronic Mfr
N.A.I.C.S.: 327110

KYOCERA Precision Tools Korea Co., Ltd. (1)
11 Namdong-daero 215beon-gil Namdong Industrial Complex, Namdong-gu, Incheon, 21633, Korea (South)
Tel.: (82) 1093332922
Web Site: https://www.kptk.co.kr
Precision Turned Tools Mfr
N.A.I.C.S.: 332721

KYOCERA Realty Development Co., Ltd. (1)
B1F Kyocera Harajuku Building 6-27-8 Jingumae, Shibuya-ku, Tokyo, 150-0001, Japan
Tel.: (81) 334001945
Web Site: https://krd.kyocera.co.jp
Sales Range: $50-74.9 Million
Emp.: 8
Real Estate Manangement Services
N.A.I.C.S.: 531390

KYOCERA SENCO (NZ) Ltd. (1)
3b/89-91 Ellice Rd, Glenfield, Auckland, 0629, New Zealand
Tel.: (64) 98374649
Ceramic & Electronic Mfr
N.A.I.C.S.: 327110

KYOCERA SGS Precision Tools Europe Ltd. (1)
10 Ashville Way, Wokingham, RG41 2PL, Berkshire, United Kingdom
Tel.: (44) 118 979 5200

KYOCERA CORPORATION

KYOCERA Corporation—(Continued)

Web Site: https://www.kyocera-sgstool.co.uk
Cutting Tool Mfr
N.A.I.C.S.: 333515
Tony Theaker *(Sls Mgr)*

KYOCERA SOC Corporation (1)
1-22-1 Hakusan, Midori-ku, Yokohama, 226-0006, Kanagawa, Japan
Tel.: (81) 45 931 6511
Web Site: https://www.ksoc.co.jp
Emp.: 251
Optical Device Mfr & Distr
N.A.I.C.S.: 333310
Minoru Hijikawa *(Pres)*

KYOCERA Senco EMEA B.V. (1)
Pascallaan 88, 8218 NJ, Lelystad, Netherlands
Web Site: http://www.kyocera-senco.nl
Fastener & Accessory Mfr
N.A.I.C.S.: 339993

KYOCERA Senco Industrial Tools, Inc. (1)
8450 Broadwell Rd, Cincinnati, OH 45244
Web Site: https://www.senco.com
Ceramic & Electronic Mfr
N.A.I.C.S.: 327110

KYOCERA Senco Japan Corporation (1)
Bldg 6 Takeda Tobadono-cho, Fushimi-ku, Kyoto, 612-8450, Japan
Tel.: (81) 756043432
Ceramic & Electronic Mfr
N.A.I.C.S.: 327110

KYOCERA Solar Corporation (1)
10F Kyocera Headquarters Bldg 6 Takeda Tobadono-cho, Fushimi-ku, Kyoto, 612-8450, Japan
Tel.: (81) 756043488
Web Site: http://www.kyocera.co.jp
Emp.: 50
Solar Power Generation Systems Distr
N.A.I.C.S.: 221118

Subsidiary (Non-US):

KYOCERA Solar Europe s.r.o. (2)
Na Pankraci 129/1724, 140 00, Prague, Czech Republic
Tel.: (420) 225992282
Web Site: http://www.kyocerasolar.eu
Solar Power Generating Equipment Distr
N.A.I.C.S.: 423730

Subsidiary (US):

KYOCERA Solar Inc. (2)
7812 E Acoma Dr, Scottsdale, AZ 85260 **(100%)**
Tel.: (480) 948-8003
Web Site: http://www.kyocerasolar.com
Sales Range: $25-49.9 Million
Emp.: 80
Mfr of Solar Equipment
N.A.I.C.S.: 334413
Steve Hill *(Pres)*

Subsidiary (Non-US):

KYOCERA Solar do Brasil Ltda. (3)
Av das Americas 20 007 - Bloco 2 Salas 105 a 108, 22790 851, Rio de Janeiro, Brazil
Tel.: (55) 2137243900
Web Site: http://www.kyocerasolar.com.br
Sales Range: $50-74.9 Million
Emp.: 1
Solar Power Generating Equipment Distr
N.A.I.C.S.: 423830
Mirim Fonseca *(Gen Mgr)*

KYOCERA Telecom Equipment (Malaysia) Sdn. Bhd (1)
Lot 7646, Mukim Of Plentong, Johor Bahru, 81750, Bahru, Malaysia
Tel.: (60) 73870266
Sales Range: $25-49.9 Million
Emp.: 100
Mobile Telecommunication Device Mfr
N.A.I.C.S.: 334220
Sim Boon Tong *(Dir-Admin)*

KYOCERA Tikitin Ltd. (1)
Tietotie 3, 02150, Espoo, Finland
Tel.: (358) 408041570
Ceramic & Electronic Mfr
N.A.I.C.S.: 327110

KYOCERA Unimerco Tooling A/S (1)
Drejervej 2, DK 7451, Sunds, Denmark
Tel.: (45) 97141411
Web Site: https://www.kyocera-unimerco.com
Sales Range: $100-124.9 Million
Emp.: 547
Cutting Tool Mfr
N.A.I.C.S.: 333515

Subsidiary (US):

KYOCERA UNIMERCO Tooling Inc. (2)
6620 State Rd, Saline, MI 48176
Tel.: (734) 944-4433
Web Site: http://www.unimerco.com
Sales Range: $25-49.9 Million
Emp.: 44
Cutting Tool & Machine Tool Accessory Mfr
N.A.I.C.S.: 333515
James Stead *(Mgr-Sls-Natl)*

KYOCERA Vietnam Company Limited (1)
Plot No B-1, Thang Long Industrial Park II Lieu Xa Commune, Yen My, Hung Yen, Vietnam
Tel.: (84) 2213589900
Ceramic & Electronic Mfr
N.A.I.C.S.: 327110

KYOCERA do Brasil Componentes Industriais Ltda. (1)
Tel.: (55) 1532273800
Web Site: http://www.kyocera-componentes.com.br
Optical Parts Mfr
N.A.I.C.S.: 333310

KYOCERA-Ube RF TEC Corporation (1)
800 Ichimiyake, Yasu, Shiga, Japan **(100%)**
Tel.: (81) 775073782
Web Site: http://www.kyocera-ube-rt.jp
Dielectric Ceramic Mfr
N.A.I.C.S.: 333994
Takanori Konishi *(Pres)*

Kyocera Corporation - Fukushima Tanagura Plant (1)
88 Nakatoyo Nagare Tanagura-cho, Higashishirakawa-gun, Fukushima, 963-5692, Japan
Tel.: (81) 247 33 3185
Emp.: 300
Electronic Components Mfr
N.A.I.C.S.: 334419
Nishihara Yoshiaki *(Gen Mgr)*

Kyocera Corporation - Hokkaido Kitami Plant (1)
30 Hoji, Kitami, 099-1595, Hokkaido, Japan
Tel.: (81) 157362222
Electronic Components Mfr
N.A.I.C.S.: 334419

Kyocera Corporation - Kagoshima Hayato Plant (1)
999-3 Uchi Hayato-cho, Kirishima, 899-5195, Kagoshima, Japan
Tel.: (81) 995 42 3321
Web Site: http://global.kyocera.com
Electronic Components Mfr
N.A.I.C.S.: 334419

Kyocera Corporation - Kagoshima Kokubu Plant (1)
1-1 Kokubuyamashita-cho, Kagoshima, 899-4396, Kagoshima, Japan
Tel.: (81) 995 46 1100
Web Site: http://global.kyocera.com
Electronic Components Mfr
N.A.I.C.S.: 334419

Kyocera Corporation - Kagoshima Sendai Plant (1)
1810 Taki-cho, Satsumasendai, 895-0292, Kagoshima, Japan
Tel.: (81) 996 23 4121
Web Site: http://global.kyocera.com
Electronic Components Mfr
N.A.I.C.S.: 334419

Kyocera Corporation - Mie Ise Plant (1)
600-10 Shimono-cho, Ise, 516-8510, Mie, Japan
Tel.: (81) 596 36 4871
Solar Electronic Component Mfr
N.A.I.C.S.: 334419

Kyocera Corporation - Nagano Okaya Plant (1)
3-11-1 Kohagi Osachi, Okaya, 394-8550, Nagano, Japan
Tel.: (81) 266272131
Electronic Components Mfr
N.A.I.C.S.: 334419

Kyocera Corporation - Shiga Gamo Plant (1)
10-1 Kawai-cho, Higashi-omi, 529-1595, Shiga, Japan
Tel.: (81) 748551211
Electronic Components Mfr
N.A.I.C.S.: 334419

Kyocera Corporation - Shiga Yasu Plant (1)
800 Ichimiyake, Yasu, 520-2362, Shiga, Japan
Tel.: (81) 77 587 8800
Web Site: http://global.kyocera.com
Emp.: 1,500
Electronic Components Mfr
N.A.I.C.S.: 334419
Takeyoshi Toga *(Plant Mgr)*

Kyocera Corporation - Shiga Yohkaichi Plant (1)
1166-6 Hebimizo-cho, Higashi-omi, 527-8555, Shiga, Japan
Tel.: (81) 748221550
Electronic Components Mfr
N.A.I.C.S.: 334419

Kyoto Purple Sanga Company Limited (1)
87 Kankobokocho Shijodori-Muromachihigashiiru Ke Kosun Kyoto Bldg 8f, Shimogyo-Ku, Kyoto, 600-8009, Japan
Tel.: (81) 752120635
Web Site: http://www.kyoto-purple-sanga.co.jp
Sales Range: $25-49.9 Million
Emp.: 20
Sports Goods Supplier
N.A.I.C.S.: 423910

Motex Inc. (1)
MOTEX Shin-Osaka Building 5-12-12 Nishinakajima, Yodogawa-ku, Osaka, 532-0011, Japan
Tel.: (81) 663088989
Web Site: https://www.motex.co.jp
Emp.: 446
Software Development Services
N.A.I.C.S.: 541511

Propel Network Sdn. Bhd. (1)
84-1 and 84-2 Jalan Sungai Burung AA32/AA Seksyen 32, Bukit Rimau, 40460, Shah Alam, Selangor, Malaysia
Tel.: (60) 358853880
Web Site: https://propelnetwork.com.my
Information Technology Services
N.A.I.C.S.: 541511

Senco Brands, Inc. (1)
8450 Broadwell Rd, Cincinnati, OH 45244
Tel.: (513) 388-2076
Web Site: https://www.senco.com
Industrial Fastener Mfr
N.A.I.C.S.: 333991

Shanghai KYOCERA Electronics Co., Ltd (1)
No 2077 New Jin Qiao Road, Pudong, Shanghai, 201206, China
Tel.: (86) 2158997777
Electronic Components Mfr
N.A.I.C.S.: 334419

Shanghai KYOCERA Sales & Trading Corporation (1)
Floor 9 Dushi Headquarters Building No 168 Middle Xizang Road, Pudong New Area, Shanghai, 200001, China
Tel.: (86) 2158775366
Electronic Component & Equipment Whslr
N.A.I.C.S.: 423690

System Land, Inc. (1)
Mita Nitto Daibiru Bldg 2F 3-11-36 Mita, Minato-ku, Tokyo, 108-0073, Japan

Tel.: (81) 3 3798 5400
Web Site: http://www.sland.co.jp
Software Development Services
N.A.I.C.S.: 541511

TPC SAS (1)
Avenue du Colonel Prat, Saint Apollinaire, France
Tel.: (33) 380 717400
Web Site: http://global.kyocera.com
Electronic Components Mfr
N.A.I.C.S.: 334419

KYOCHON F&B CO., LTD.

13453 Kyochon 1991 Building 15-3 Geumto-ro 80beon-gil, Sujeong-gu, Seongnam, Gyeonggi-do, Korea (South)
Tel.: (82) 313713500
Web Site: https://www.kyochonfnb.com
Year Founded: 1991
339770—(KRS)
Rev: $396,889,870
Assets: $233,914,585
Liabilities: $96,453,777
Net Worth: $137,460,808
Earnings: $3,791,648
Emp.: 342
Fiscal Year-end: 12/31/22
Meat Distr
N.A.I.C.S.: 424470
Hwang Tae-Jin *(Head-Acctg)*

KYODO ADVERTISING CO., LTD.

New Otani Shin-kioi-cho Building 4-1 Kioi-cho, Chiyoda-ku, Tokyo, 102-8551, Japan
Tel.: (81) 335113701
Year Founded: 1946
Rev: $202,752,000
Emp.: 200
N.A.I.C.S.: 541810
Sotaro Murayama *(Chm)*

Subsidiaries:

Kyodo Advertising Co., Ltd. (1)
2-1-7 Dojima, Kita-ku, Osaka, 530-0003, Japan
Tel.: (81) 6 6345 0381
N.A.I.C.S.: 541810

Kyodo Advertising Co., Ltd. (1)
Yomiuri Fukuoka Building 1-12-15 Akasaka, Chuo-ku, Fukuoka, 810-0042, Japan
Tel.: (81) 92 715 1996
N.A.I.C.S.: 541810

Kyodo Advertising Co., Ltd. (1)
Sapporo Central Minamiku 1-chome Nishi 6, Beichen Building 11, Sapporo, 060-0061, Japan
Tel.: (81) 11 241 7125
N.A.I.C.S.: 541810

Kyodo Advertising Co., Ltd. (1)
Tohoku Ohji Fudosan Building 1-6-18 Kokubu-cho, Aoba-ku, Sendai, 980-0803, Japan
Tel.: (81) 22 266 2336
N.A.I.C.S.: 541810

Kyodo Advertising Co., Ltd. (1)
Asahi Seimei Kanazawa Building 1-8 Oyama-cho, Kanazawa, 920-0918, Japan
Tel.: (81) 76 231 2178
N.A.I.C.S.: 541810

Kyodo Advertising Co., Ltd. (1)
4-10 Asahi Seimei, Sakae-ku, Shizuoka, 420, Japan
Tel.: (81) 54 251 1671
N.A.I.C.S.: 541810

Kyodo Advertising Co., Ltd. (1)
3-1-9 Yuaka, Utsunomiya, 321-0953, Japan
Tel.: (81) 28 636 1605
N.A.I.C.S.: 541810

KYODO PAPER HOLDINGS

Sumitomo Real Estate Ueno Building 6F 1-9-12 Kitaueno, Taito-Ku, Tokyo, 110-0014, Japan

Tel.: (81) 358265171
Web Site:
https://www.kyodopaper.com
Year Founded: 1952
9849—(TKS)
Rev.: $110,552,250
Assets: $65,954,580
Liabilities: $39,633,560
Net Worth: $26,321,020
Earnings: $383,380
Fiscal Year-end: 03/31/24
Paper Product Distr
N.A.I.C.S.: 424130
Katsumi Gunji *(Chm & Pres)*

KYODO PRINTING CO. LTD.
4-14-12 Koishikawa, Bunkyo-ku, Tokyo, 112-8501, Japan
Tel.: (81) 338172111
Web Site:
https://www.kyodoprinting.co.jp
Year Founded: 1897
7914—(TKS)
Rev.: $641,117,120
Assets: $871,297,150
Liabilities: $454,073,950
Net Worth: $417,223,200
Earnings: $9,881,950
Emp.: 1,851
Fiscal Year-end: 03/31/24
Printing Products Mfr
N.A.I.C.S.: 513191
Yoshiaki Fujimori *(Pres)*

Subsidiaries:

Cosmo Graphic Co., Ltd. (1)
4-14-12 Koishikawa, Bunkyo-ku, Tokyo, 112-0002, Japan **(100%)**
Tel.: (81) 338138113
Web Site: https://www.cosmo-g.co.jp
Emp.: 334
Plate Making & Graphic Services
N.A.I.C.S.: 323120

Joban Kyodo Printing Co., Ltd. (1)
1564 Isohara Isohara-cho, Isohara Industrial Park, Kitaibaraki, 319-1541, Japan
Tel.: (81) 29 342 4121
Emp.: 70
Plastic Tank Mfr
N.A.I.C.S.: 326122

Kyodo Logistics Co., Ltd (1)
4-301 Shichizacho, Bunkyo-ku, Koshigaya, 343-0851, Saitama, Japan
Web Site: http://www.kyodologistics.co.jp
Emp.: 250
Logistics & Communication Services
N.A.I.C.S.: 541614

Kyodo Printing (Vietnam) Co. Ltd. (1)
Plot No 414 Road 13, Amata Industrial Park Long Binh Ward, Bien Hoa, Dong Nai, Vietnam
Tel.: (84) 251 389 1057
Web Site: https://vietnam.kyodoprinting.com
Laminated Tube Mfr
N.A.I.C.S.: 326130
Fumie Sakai *(Gen Dir)*

Kyodo Printing Co., Ltd - Commercial Printing Division (1)
4-14-12 Koishikawa, Bunkyo-ku, Tokyo, 112-8501, Japan
Tel.: (81) 338172202
Web Site: https://www.kyodoprinting.com
Sales Range: $1-4.9 Billion
Commercial Printing Services
N.A.I.C.S.: 323111
Toshiaki Inagi *(Pres)*

Kyodo Printing Co., Ltd - Fine Art Reproductions Division (1)
4-14-12 Koishikawa, Tokyo, 112-8501, Bunkyo-ku, Japan
Web Site: http://www.kyodoprinting.co.jp
Sales Range: $25-49.9 Million
Emp.: 5
Art Printing Services
N.A.I.C.S.: 323111

Kyodo Printing Co., Ltd - Goka Plant (1)
7514 Moto-Kurihashi, Sashima Dist, Goka, 306-0313, Ibaraki, Japan
Tel.: (81) 280843511
Printing Services
N.A.I.C.S.: 323111

Kyodo Printing Co., Ltd - Kawajima Plant (1)
6-13-2 Hachiman, Kawajimamachi Hiki-gun, Saitama, 350 0151, Japan
Tel.: (81) 492910200
Web Site: http://www.kyodoprinting.com
Printing Services
N.A.I.C.S.: 323111

Kyodo Printing Co., Ltd - Koishikawa Plant (1)
4-14-12 Koishikawa, Bunkyo-ku, Tokyo, 112-8501, Japan
Tel.: (81) 338172111
Web Site: http://www.kyodoprinting.co.jp
Sales Range: $200-249.9 Million
Emp.: 1,000
Printing Services
N.A.I.C.S.: 323111

Kyodo Printing Co., Ltd - Moriya Plant (1)
1932 Tatsuzawa, Moriya, 302-0118, Ibaraki, Japan
Tel.: (81) 297452681
Web Site: http://www.kyodoprinting.com
Sales Range: $50-74.9 Million
Emp.: 200
Printing Services
N.A.I.C.S.: 323111

Kyodo Printing Co., Ltd - Packaging Printing Division (1)
4-14-12 Koishikawa chome, Bunkyo-ku, Tokyo, 112-8501, Japan
Tel.: (81) 338172246
Sales Range: $1-4.9 Billion
Paperware & Packaging Materials Mfr
N.A.I.C.S.: 322220
Toshiaki Inagi *(Chm)*

Kyodo Printing Co., Ltd - Sales Promotion Center (1)
4-14-12 Koishikawa chome, Bunkyo-ku, 112-8501, Tokyo, Japan
Tel.: (81) 338172033
Product Marketing Services
N.A.I.C.S.: 541613

Kyodo Printing Co., Ltd - Smart Card Division (1)
4-14-0 Koishikawa Bunchyo-ku, Tokyo, 112-8501, Japan
Tel.: (81) 338172612
Web Site: http://www.kyodoprinting.co.jp
Printing & Business Development Services
N.A.I.C.S.: 561499
Shouji Kobayashi *(Mgr)*

Kyodo Printing Co., Ltd - Technical Supervisory Division (1)
4-14-12 Koishikawa, Bunkyo-ku, Tokyo, 112-8501, Japan
Tel.: (81) 338172048
Web Site: http://www.kyodoprinting.co.jp
Sales Range: $700-749.9 Million
Research & Technology Development Services
N.A.I.C.S.: 541720
Toshiaki Inagi *(Pres)*

Kyodo Printing Co., Ltd - Tsurugashima Plant (1)
6-2-12 Fujimi, Tsurugashima, Saitama, 350-2201, Japan
Tel.: (81) 492866060
Printing Services
N.A.I.C.S.: 323111

Kyodo Printing Co., Ltd - Wakayama Plant (1)
560-2 Kumai Aridagawa-cho, Arita-gun, Wakayama, 643-0023, Japan
Tel.: (81) 737527211
Web Site: http://www.kyodoprinting.co.jp
Laminating Tubes Mfr
N.A.I.C.S.: 323111

Kyodo Printing Marketing Solutions Co., Ltd. (1)
4-14-12 Koishikawa, Bunkyo-ku, Tokyo, 112-0002, Japan
Tel.: (81) 33 817 2360

Emp.: 37
Book Binding Services
N.A.I.C.S.: 323120

Kyodo Printing Media Product Co., Ltd. (1)
7514 Motokurihashi Goka-cho, Sashima-gun, Ibaraki, 306-0313, Japan
Tel.: (81) 28 084 3511
Book Binding Services
N.A.I.C.S.: 323120

Kyodo Printing Nishinihon Co., Ltd. (1)
2-1-204 Sakae Kumiyamacho, Kuze-gun, Kyoto, 613 0032, Japan
Tel.: (81) 774412521
Web Site: http://www.kyodoprinting.com
Printing Services
N.A.I.C.S.: 323111

PT. Arisu Graphic Prima (1)
Jl Rungkut Industri VIII / No 18, Surabaya, 60291, Indonesia
Tel.: (62) 31 847 5868
Web Site: https://arisu.kyodoprinting.com
Laminated Tube Mfr
N.A.I.C.S.: 326130

TOMOWEL Payment Service Co., Ltd. (1)
4-14-12 Koishikawa, Bunkyo-ku, Tokyo, 112-0002, Japan
Tel.: (81) 33 817 2422
Emp.: 7
Book Binding Services
N.A.I.C.S.: 323120

KYODO PUBLIC RELATIONS CO., LTD.
10F Ginza Shochiku Square 1-13-1 Tsukiji, Chuo-ku, Tokyo, 104-0045, Japan
Tel.: (81) 36260487 JP
Web Site: https://www.kyodo-pr.co.jp
Year Founded: 1964
2436—(TKS)
Rev.: $48,885,550
Assets: $38,484,520
Liabilities: $14,874,820
Net Worth: $23,609,700
Earnings: $3,452,830
Emp.: 25
Fiscal Year-end: 12/31/23
Public Relations Agency
N.A.I.C.S.: 541820

KYODO-ALLIED INDUSTRIES LTD.
8 Pandan Crescent Unit 01-06, Singapore, 128464, Singapore
Tel.: (65) 62651311
Web Site: http://www.kyodo.com.sg
Sales Range: $10-24.9 Million
Emp.: 60
Clean Room Equipment Mfr
N.A.I.C.S.: 333415
Eddie Tan *(Gen Mgr-Cleanroom Sls-Asia & Middle East)*

Subsidiaries:

Kyodo-Allied Technology Pte Ltd (1)
17 Kian Teck Road, Singapore, Singapore
Tel.: (65) 62651311
Web Site: http://www.kyodo.com.sg
Fan Filter Units Mfr
N.A.I.C.S.: 333413

Kyodo-Allied Trading (Shanghai) Co., Ltd. (1)
Room 2509 Zhong Cheng Bldg No 818 Dong Fang Rd, Pudong, Shanghai, 200122, China
Tel.: (86) 2163607138
Web Site: http://www.kyodo.com.sg
Air Control Equipments Distr
N.A.I.C.S.: 423730

KYOEI SANGYO CO., LTD.
Shinagawa Seaside Canal Tower
4-12-6 Higashi Shinagawa,
Shinagawa-ku, Tokyo, 140-0002, Japan
Tel.: (81) 342415511
Web Site: https://www.kyoei.co.jp
Year Founded: 1947
6973—(TKS)
Rev.: $407,698,190
Assets: $279,411,310
Liabilities: $161,792,970
Net Worth: $117,618,340
Earnings: $8,837,570
Emp.: 878
Fiscal Year-end: 03/31/24
Electronic Equipment Mfr & Distr
N.A.I.C.S.: 334419
Jun Hirasawa *(Pres & Pres)*

Subsidiaries:

Fukushima Kyoei Co., Ltd. (1)
305-2 Ikami- no-Kami Yabuki-cho, Nishishirakawa-gun, Fukushima, 969-0287, Japan
Tel.: (81) 248423151
Web Site: https://www.kyoei.co.jp
Printed Circuit Board Mfr
N.A.I.C.S.: 334412

Kyoei Electronics (Thailand) Co., Ltd. (1)
1 VASU1 Building 8th Floor 803/1 Soi Sukhumvit 25 Sukhumvit Rd, Klongtoey Nua Wattana, Bangkok, 10110, Thailand **(100%)**
Tel.: (66) 26112681
Web Site: https://www.kyoei.co.jp
Emp.: 6
Electronic Equipment Distr
N.A.I.C.S.: 423690
Taihei Sugiyama *(Mng Dir)*

Kyoei Electronics Hong Kong Limited (1)
Unit 1709 17/F Apec Plaza No 49 Hoi Yuen Road, Kwun Tong, Kowloon, China (Hong Kong)
Tel.: (852) 2 508 0457
Emp.: 16
Electronic Components Mfr
N.A.I.C.S.: 334419
Kenji Yamakawa *(Mng Dir)*

Kyoei Electronics Shanghai Co., Ltd. (1)
Room 2308 Shanghai Maxdo Center No 8 Xing Yi Road, Chang Ning, Shanghai, 200336, China
Tel.: (86) 2152081780
Web Site: https://www.kyoei.co.jp
Emp.: 11
Semiconductor Device Distr
N.A.I.C.S.: 327910
Masahiko Hatakeyama *(Pres)*

Kyoei Electronics Singapore Pte Ltd. (1)
190 Middle Road 19-02 Fortune Centre, Singapore, 188979, Singapore **(100%)**
Tel.: (65) 64721566
Web Site: https://www.kyoei.co.jp
Emp.: 12
Semiconductor Device Distr
N.A.I.C.S.: 423690
Takehiro Tsutsumi *(Mng Dir)*

Kyoei Marine Technology Co., Ltd. (1)
2-14-30 Minato-cho, Hakodate, 040-0042, Hokkaido, Japan
Tel.: (81) 138837906
Web Site: https://www.kyoei.co.jp
Emp.: 12
Safety Equipment Distr
N.A.I.C.S.: 423910

Kyoei System Co., Ltd. (1)
6th floor Rhodes Building 2-9-14 Higashiikebukuro, Toshima-ku, Tokyo, 170-0013, Japan
Tel.: (81) 359854126
Emp.: 31
Printed Circuit Board Mfr & Distr
N.A.I.C.S.: 334412

KYOEI SECURITY SERVICE CO., LTD.
Chiyoda Kaikan 1617 Kudan Minami, Chiyoda-Ku, Tokyo, 102-0074, Japan

KYOEI SECURITY SERVICE CO., LTD.

Kyoei Security Service Co., Ltd.—(Continued)
Tel.: (81) 335117780
Web Site: https://www.kyoei-ss.co.jp
Year Founded: 1985
7058—(TKS)
Rev.: $61,829,940
Assets: $45,020,710
Liabilities: $13,920,660
Net Worth: $31,100,050
Earnings: $1,639,280
Emp.: 2,928
Fiscal Year-end: 03/31/24
Security System Services
N.A.I.C.S.: 561621
Fumio Azuma *(Founder, Chm & Pres)*

KYOEI STEEL LTD.
Aqua Dojima West 18F 1-4-16 Doji-mahama, Kita-ku, Osaka, 530-0004, Japan
Tel.: (81) 663465221
Web Site: https://www.kyoeisteel.co.jp
Year Founded: 1947
5440—(TKS)
Rev.: $2,121,691,020
Assets: $2,341,374,370
Liabilities: $1,009,922,070
Net Worth: $1,331,452,300
Earnings: $91,389,860
Emp.: 987
Fiscal Year-end: 03/31/24
Concrete Material Mfr & Distr
N.A.I.C.S.: 331110
Kazuyoshi Ota *(Sr Exec Mng Officer & Gen Mgr-Yamaguchi Div)*

Subsidiaries:

AltaSteel, Inc. (1)
9401 34th St, Edmonton, T6B 2X6, AB, Canada
Tel.: (780) 468-1133
Web Site: http://www.altasteel.com
Steel Bar Mfr
N.A.I.C.S.: 332111
Dev Kittur *(Sr VP-Ops)*

Kanto Steel Ltd. (1)
580 Obatake, Tsuchiura, Ibaraki, Japan
Tel.: (81) 298625111
Web Site: http://www.kantosteel.co.jp
Steel Material Mfr & Distr
N.A.I.C.S.: 331110

Kyoei Industrial Co., Ltd. (1)
Keihan Dojima Building 7F 2-chome 1-31 Dojima, Kita-ku, Osaka, 530-0003, Japan
Tel.: (81) 663439221
Web Site: https://www.kyoeisangyo-ltd.co.jp
Emp.: 240
Steel Product Distr
N.A.I.C.S.: 423510

Kyoei Mesona Inc. (1)
6-4-8 Tsukuda, Nishiyodogawa-ku, Osaka, 555-0001, Japan
Tel.: (81) 664774195
Web Site: http://www.kyoei-mesona.co.jp
Waste Management Services
N.A.I.C.S.: 562998

Kyoei Recycling Co., Ltd. (1)
6289 159 Oaza Onodaji-ko, Sanyo-Onoda, 756-0817, Yamaguchi, Japan
Tel.: (81) 836815388
Web Site: http://www.kyoei-recycle.com
Steel Material Mfr & Distr
N.A.I.C.S.: 331110

Kyoei Steel Ltd - Hirakata Division (1)
3-1-1 Nakamiya Oike, Hirakata, 573-0004, Osaka, Japan
Tel.: (81) 728493224
Web Site: https://www.kyoeisteel.co.jp
Concrete Material Mfr
N.A.I.C.S.: 327999

Kyoei Steel Ltd - Nagoya Division (1)
809-1 Shinmasanari-hitsujinokiri, Ama District, Tobishima, 490-1443, Aichi, Japan
Tel.: (81) 567551088
Web Site: https://www.kyoeisteel.co.jp
Steel Products Mfr
N.A.I.C.S.: 332312

Kyoei Steel Ltd Yamaguchi Division (1)
6289-18 Onoda, Sanyo-Onoda, 756-0817, Yamaguchi, Japan
Tel.: (81) 836836171
Web Site: https://www.kyoeisteel.co.jp
Concrete Material Mfr
N.A.I.C.S.: 327999

Kyoei Steel Vietnam Company Limited (1)
Group 04, Nam Son ward Tam Diep town, Ninh Binh, Vietnam
Tel.: (84) 2293864033
Web Site: https://www.ksvc.com.vn
Emp.: 229
Steel Product Mfr & Distr
N.A.I.C.S.: 332999
Fukunishi Hidekazu *(Gen Dir)*

Maple Leaf Metals Inc. (1)
4510 68 Ave, Edmonton, T6B 2P3, AB, Canada
Tel.: (780) 468-3951
Web Site: http://www.mapleleafmetals.com
Metal Scrap Distr
N.A.I.C.S.: 423930

Nakayama Steel Products Co., Ltd. (1)
1-2-133 Nishijima, Nishiyodogawa-ku, Osaka, 555-0042, Japan
Tel.: (81) 664715881
Web Site: http://www.nspweb.co.jp
Steel Material Mfr & Distr
N.A.I.C.S.: 331110

Sakai Recycle Center Inc. (1)
6 Ohama Nishimachi, Sakai-ku, Sakai, 590-0977, Osaka, Japan
Tel.: (81) 722218567
Web Site: http://www.sak-rc.co.jp
Metal Scrap Distr
N.A.I.C.S.: 423930

Thi Vai International Port Company Limited (1)
Quang Phu Quarter, Phu My Ward Phu My Town, Vung Tau, Vietnam
Tel.: (84) 2543895807
Web Site: http://www.thivaiport.vn
Port Operation Services
N.A.I.C.S.: 488310

Vietnam Italy Steel JSC (1)
Pho Noi A Industrial Zone Giai Pham, Yen My, Hung Yen, Vietnam (100%)
Tel.: (84) 3213942427
Web Site: http://www.vis.com.vn
Steel Mfrs
N.A.I.C.S.: 331110

Vina Kyoei Steel Company Limited (1)
Phu My I Industrial Park, Phu My Ward Phu My Town, Vung Tau, Vietnam
Tel.: (84) 3876277283
Web Site: https://www.vinakyoeisteel.com.vn
Steel Material Mfr
N.A.I.C.S.: 331110

Yodoshi Corporation (1)
16-1 Uwahara Nishimachi, Kawachinagano, 586-8528, Osaka, Japan
Tel.: (81) 721533121
Web Site: http://www.yodoshi.co.jp
Industrial Equipment Mfr
N.A.I.C.S.: 333248

KYOEI TANKER CO., LTD.
2-6 Mita 3-chome, Minato-ku, Tokyo, 108-0073, Japan
Tel.: (81) 344777171
Web Site: https://www.kyoeitanker.co.jp
Year Founded: 1937
9130—(TKS)
Rev.: $93,716,580
Assets: $466,190,080
Liabilities: $338,174,210
Net Worth: $128,015,870
Earnings: $965,060
Emp.: 62
Fiscal Year-end: 03/31/24
Shipping Agencies
N.A.I.C.S.: 488390
Yasushi Takada *(Pres)*

KYOGOKU UNYU SHOJI CO., LTD.
1-2-1 Nihonbashi Hamacho Place 4th floor Nihonbashi Hamacho, Chuo-Ku, Tokyo, 103-0007, Japan
Tel.: (81) 358257131
Web Site: https://www.kyogoku.co.jp
Year Founded: 1947
9073—(TKS)
Rev.: $55,592,981
Assets: $53,339,926
Liabilities: $24,605,213
Net Worth: $28,734,713
Earnings: $396,432
Fiscal Year-end: 03/31/24
Truck Transportation Services
N.A.I.C.S.: 488490
Sakai Fumiaki *(Pres & CEO)*

KYOKUTO BOEKI KAISHA, LTD.
7th Floor Shin-Otemachi Building 2-1 Otemachi 2-chome, Chiyoda-ku, Tokyo, 100-0004, Japan
Tel.: (81) 332443511
Web Site: https://www.kbk.co.jp
Year Founded: 1947
8093—(TKS)
Rev.: $288,592,600
Assets: $328,160,060
Liabilities: $158,349,160
Net Worth: $169,810,900
Earnings: $7,641,160
Emp.: 589
Fiscal Year-end: 03/31/24
Metal Product, Industrial Equipment & Machinery Whslr
N.A.I.C.S.: 333519
Nobuki Tomabechi *(Mng Exec Officer)*

Subsidiaries:

Automax Co., Ltd. (1)
4-28-13 Azusawa, Itabashi-ku, Tokyo, 174-0051, Japan
Tel.: (81) 33 960 8200
Web Site: https://www.automax.co.jp
Analytical Instrument Mfr
N.A.I.C.S.: 334516
Zen Sato *(Pres & CEO)*

Eto Precision (Malaysia) Sdn. Bhd. (1)
C-9-0 C-9-1 Jalan BK5A/2B, Bandar Kinrara, 47180, Puchong, Selangor, Malaysia
Tel.: (60) 38 082 4500
Web Site: https://www.etoprecision.com.my
Hardware Product Mfr
N.A.I.C.S.: 332722
Yuta Tanzawa *(Mng Dir)*

KBK Europe GmbH (1)
Immermannstrasse 13, 40210, Dusseldorf, Germany
Tel.: (49) 211350015
Web Site: https://www.kbkeurope.de
Metal Products, Industrial Equipment & Machinery Whslr
N.A.I.C.S.: 423510
Kiyonori Kaizaki *(Mng Dir)*

KBK Inc. (1)
420 Lexington Ave Rm 2853, New York, NY 10170
Tel.: (212) 687-8564
Web Site: http://www.kbk.co.jp
Sales Range: $25-49.9 Million
Emp.: 50
Metal Products, Industrial Equipment & Machinery Whslr
N.A.I.C.S.: 423510

KBK Steel Products Co., Ltd. (1)
7-1-24 Shinomiya, Hiratsuka, 254-0014, Kanagawa, Japan
Tel.: (81) 463520461
Web Site: http://www.kbk-sp.co.jp
Steel Products Mfr & Distr
N.A.I.C.S.: 331110

INTERNATIONAL PUBLIC

Kyokuto Trading (India) Private Limited (1)
No 33 1th Floor Kamarajar Road, TASS Industrial Estate Ambattur, Chennai, 600 098, Tamil Nadu, India
Tel.: (91) 4443561719
Web Site: http://www.kbk.co.jp
Sales Range: $50-74.9 Million
Emp.: 3
Electronic Equipment Distr
N.A.I.C.S.: 423690

Kyokuto Trading (Shanghai) Co., Ltd. (1)
Room 1501A Building B No 1168 Century Avenue, Pudong New District, Shanghai, 200122, China
Tel.: (86) 2168412066
Web Site: https://www.kbk-cn.com
Emp.: 26
Metal Product, Industrial Equipment & Machinery Whslr
N.A.I.C.S.: 423510

Nippon System Industries Corporation (1)
Yasuda Shibaura No 7 Building 6th Floor 3-21-32 Kaigan, Minato-ku, Tokyo, 108-0022, Japan
Tel.: (81) 357656770
Web Site: http://www.nsi-bizjp.com
Sales Range: $25-49.9 Million
Emp.: 20
Industrial Equipment Distr
N.A.I.C.S.: 423830

Plant Maintenance Corporation (1)
Hirose Bldg 8F 3-17 Kanda-Nishiki-cho, Chiyoda-ku, Tokyo, 101-0054, Japan
Tel.: (81) 35 259 1611
Web Site: https://www.pmchq.co.jp
Industrial Machinery Equipment Mfr & Distr
N.A.I.C.S.: 333248
Tomokazu Takahashi *(Pres)*

Siam Eto Co., Ltd. (1)
21F Queens Tower C 2-3-5 Minatomirai, Nishiku, Yokohama, 220-6221, Kanagawa, Japan
Tel.: (81) 45 222 4813
Web Site: https://eto.co.jp
Emp.: 228
Automation Equipment Mfr
N.A.I.C.S.: 333248
Shinji Sakuma *(Pres & COO)*

Sunco Spring Company, Ltd. (1)
5-10-41 Tsunashimahigashi, Kohoku-ku, Yokohama, 223-8540, Japan
Tel.: (81) 45 543 7701
Web Site: https://sunco-spring.co.jp
Emp.: 65
Spring Component Mfr
N.A.I.C.S.: 332613

Vahle Japan Co., Ltd. (1)
4F EST Bldg 1-7-6 Hiranomachi, chuo-ku, Osaka, 541-0046, Japan
Tel.: (81) 66 227 1117
Web Site: https://www.vahle.jp
Data Transmission Services
N.A.I.C.S.: 517810

Z.R.C. Japan Co., Ltd. (1)
7F New Otemachi Bldg 2-1 Otemachi 2-chome, Chiyoda-ku, Tokyo, 100-0004, Japan
Tel.: (81) 33 244 3830
Web Site: https://www.zrc-japan.com
Paint Product Mfr & Distr
N.A.I.C.S.: 325510

KYOKUTO CO., LTD.
28-53 Kinokuma 1-chome, Hakata-ku, Fukuoka, 541-8519, Japan
Tel.: (81) 925030050
Web Site: https://www.k-cleaning.jp
Year Founded: 1980
2300—(TKS)
Sales Range: Less than $1 Million
Emp.: 1,391
Dry Cleaning Services
N.A.I.C.S.: 812320
Toshihiro Makihira *(Chm)*

KYOKUTO KAIHATSU KOGYO CO. LTD.

AND PRIVATE COMPANIES

KYOKUYO CO. LTD.

8-11-6 Minatojima, Nishinomiya, 650-0045, Hyogo, Japan
Tel.: (81) 783046105   JP
Web Site: https://www.kyokuto.com
7226—(TKS)
Rev.: $846,251,860
Assets: $1,126,456,370
Liabilities: $348,505,640
Net Worth: $777,950,730
Earnings: $23,141,610
Emp.: 3,138
Fiscal Year-end: 03/31/24
Automotive Products & Environmental Equipment & Systems Mfr & Supplier
N.A.I.C.S.: 336110
Kazuya Takahashi *(Chm)*

Subsidiaries:

F. E. Tech Co., Ltd. (1)
6-1-45 Koshienguchi, Nishinomiya, 663-8545, Hyogo, Japan
Tel.: (81) 798642512
Automobile Mfr
N.A.I.C.S.: 336110

F.E.E. Co., Ltd. (1)
6-1-45 Koshienguchi, Nishinomiya, 663-8545, Hyogo, Japan
Tel.: (81) 798661130
Automobile Mfr
N.A.I.C.S.: 336110

FE-Auto Co., Ltd. (1)
8-11-6 Minatojima, Chuo-ku, Kobe, 650-0045, Hyogo, Japan
Tel.: (81) 783046105
Web Site: https://www.fe-auto.co.jp
Emp.: 95
Commercial Vehicle Distr
N.A.I.C.S.: 423110

FE-ONE Co., Ltd. (1)
6-1-45 Koshienguchi, Nishinomiya, 663-8545, Hyogo, Japan
Tel.: (81) 798302029
Automobile Mfr
N.A.I.C.S.: 336110

Hokuriku Heavy Industries, Ltd. (1)
7-3-69 Yamakido, Higashi-ku, Niigata, 950-0871, Japan
Tel.: (81) 252743311
Web Site: https://www.hokuju.com
Emp.: 56
Industrial Machinery Mfr & Distr
N.A.I.C.S.: 333248
Masanori Shimotori *(Pres)*

Kyokuto Kaihatsu (Kunshan) Machinery Co., Ltd. (1)
288 Dujuan Road Kunshan Development Zone, Jiangsu, China
Tel.: (86) 51257720788
Automobile Mfr
N.A.I.C.S.: 336110

Kyokuto Kaihatsu Kogyo Co. Ltd. - Fukuoka Plant (1)
428 Igisu, Iizuka, 820-0053, Fukuoka, Japan
Tel.: (81) 948230880
Automobile Mfr
N.A.I.C.S.: 336110

Kyokuto Kaihatsu Kogyo Co. Ltd. - Miki Plant (1)
Miki Industrial Park 2 Tomoe Bessho-cho, Miki, 673-0443, Hyogo, Japan
Tel.: (81) 794821121
Automobile Mfr
N.A.I.C.S.: 336110

Kyokuto Kaihatsu Kogyo Co. Ltd. - Nagoya Plant (1)
1375 Aza Matsumoto Oaza Higashitanaka, Komaki, 485-0826, Aichi, Japan
Tel.: (81) 568712211
Automobile Mfr
N.A.I.C.S.: 336110

Kyokuto Kaihatsu Kogyo Co. Ltd. - Yokohama Plant (1)
4-1-62 Fukaminishi, Yamato, 242-0018, Kanagawa, Japan
Tel.: (81) 462632211
Automobile Mfr
N.A.I.C.S.: 336110

Kyokuto Kaihatsu Parking Co., Ltd. (1)
2-5-11 Awajicho, Chuo-ku, Osaka, 541-8519, Hyogo, Japan
Tel.: (81) 662057822
Web Site: https://www.kyokuto-parking.com
Emp.: 56
Automobile Mfr
N.A.I.C.S.: 336110

Kyokuto Service Engineering Co., Ltd. (1)
3-15-10 Higashi-shinagawa, Shinagawa-ku, Tokyo, 140-0002, Japan
Tel.: (81) 357819833
Automobile Mfr
N.A.I.C.S.: 336110

Kyokuto Service Engineering Hokkaido Co., Ltd. (1)
12-99-6 Kita-Sanjyo-Higashi, Chuo-ku, Sapporo, 060-0033, Hokkaido, Japan
Tel.: (81) 112515380
Automobile Mfr
N.A.I.C.S.: 336110

Kyokuto Special Automobile Trading (Shanghai) Co., Ltd. (1)
1F Building 3 No 66 Lizhi Road, Pudong New Area, Shanghai, China
Tel.: (86) 2158682571
Automotive Distr
N.A.I.C.S.: 423110

Mori Plant Co., Ltd. (1)
2-3-3 Showa-cho, Abeno-ku, Osaka, 545-0011, Japan
Tel.: (81) 666272381
Automobile Mfr
N.A.I.C.S.: 336110

Nippon Trex Co., Ltd. (1)
350 Minamiyama Shinden Ina-cho, Toyokawa, 441-0193, Aichi, Japan
Tel.: (81) 5033677448
Web Site: https://www.trex.co.jp
Emp.: 1,126
Automobile Body Mfr
N.A.I.C.S.: 336211
Mitsuhiko Nakashima *(Pres)*

PT. Kyokuto Indomobil Distributor Indonesia (1)
6th Floor Indomobil Tower MT Haryono Street Kav 11, Jakarta, 13330, Indonesia
Tel.: (62) 2185918441
Web Site: https://kyokuto.id
Automotive Distr
N.A.I.C.S.: 423110

PT. Kyokuto Indomobil Manufacturing Indonesia (1)
Kawasan Industri Kota Bukit Indah Block D III No 1, Purwakarta, 41181, Jawa Barat, Indonesia
Tel.: (62) 2185918441
Web Site: https://kyokuto.id
Automobile Mfr
N.A.I.C.S.: 336110

Satrac Engineering Private Limited (1)
No 127 Somapura Industial Area, Nidavanda Village Dabaspet 3rd Phase Nelmangala, Bengaluru, 562 132, India
Tel.: (91) 7338334567
Web Site: https://www.satrac.com
Truck Body Mfr
N.A.I.C.S.: 336211

Shinko Automobile Co., Ltd. (1)
2-3-17 Shioya, Sumoto, Hyogo, 656-0021, Japan
Tel.: (81) 799221480
Web Site: https://www.k-shinko.com
Automobile Mfr
N.A.I.C.S.: 336110

TTR Thairung Co., Ltd. (1)
10/95 Sukhumvit Soi 13, Khongtoey-Nua Wattana, Bangkok, 10110, Thailand
Tel.: (66) 21687644
Web Site: http://www.ttrthairung.co.th
Truck Body Mfr & Distr
N.A.I.C.S.: 336211
Sompong Phaoenchoke *(Chm)*

Trex Thairung Co., Ltd. (1)
10/73 Sukhumvit Soi 13 Klongtoey-nua Wattana, Bangkok, 10110, Thailand

Tel.: (66) 21687644
Web Site: http://www.trextr.co.th
Automobile Body Mfr & Distr
N.A.I.C.S.: 336211
Sompong Phaoenchoke *(Chm)*

KYOKUTO SANKI CO., LTD.

190 Hikai, Hyogo, Tatsuno, 679-4195, Japan
Tel.: (81) 791621771
Web Site: https://www.klass-corp.co.jp
Year Founded: 1948
6233—(TKS)
Rev.: $70,105,920
Assets: $74,976,750
Liabilities: $54,309,400
Net Worth: $20,667,350
Earnings: $723,180
Emp.: 289
Fiscal Year-end: 09/30/23
Home Furnishing Mfr & Distr
N.A.I.C.S.: 337127
Masaki Koroyasu *(Chm & Pres)*

Subsidiaries:

ROSECC Co., Ltd. (1)
5-406 Kamiyashiro, Meito-ku, Nagoya, 465-0025, Japan
Tel.: (81) 52 704 3800
Web Site: https://www.rosecc.jp
Factory Automation System Mfr
N.A.I.C.S.: 334290
Yoichi Yamoto *(Pres)*

KYOKUTO SECURITIES CO., LTD.

1-4-7 Nihombashi-Kayabacho, Chuo-ku, Tokyo, 103-0025, Japan
Tel.: (81) 336679171
Web Site: https://www.kyokuto-sec.co.jp
Year Founded: 1947
8706—(TKS)
Rev.: $51,095,300
Assets: $552,159,740
Liabilities: $197,367,990
Net Worth: $354,791,750
Earnings: $28,694,010
Emp.: 247
Fiscal Year-end: 03/31/24
Financial & Real Estate Services
N.A.I.C.S.: 523999
Hiroyuki Kikuchi *(Chm)*

Subsidiaries:

FE Investment Co., Ltd. (1)
Kayabacho 1-5-8 Tokyo Stock Hall 3 floor, Chuo-ku Nihonbashi, Tokyo, 103-0025, Japan
Tel.: (81) 336660661
Web Site: http://www.fe-invest.com
Sales Range: $50-74.9 Million
Emp.: 4
Investment Management Service
N.A.I.C.S.: 523999
Makoto Suzuki *(Pres)*

Kyokuto Property Co., Ltd. (1)
1-1-7 Nihombashi-Kayabacho, Chuo-ku, Tokyo, 103-0025, Japan
Tel.: (81) 356409221
Web Site: http://www.kyokuto-sec.co.jp
Sales Range: $150-199.9 Million
Emp.: 300
Property Management Services
N.A.I.C.S.: 531311

KYOKUYO CO. LTD.

Sumitomo Seimei Sanno Bldg 3-5 3-chome Akasaka, Minato-ku, Tokyo, 107-0052, Japan
Tel.: (81) 355450701   JP
Web Site: https://www.kyokuyo.co.jp
Year Founded: 1937
1301—(TKS)
Rev.: $1,729,202,440
Assets: $1,062,359,200
Liabilities: $673,294,600
Net Worth: $389,064,600

Earnings: $39,236,960
Emp.: 2,089
Fiscal Year-end: 03/31/24
Fresh & Frozen Fish Processor, Transporter & Whslr; Shipping & Warehousing Services
N.A.I.C.S.: 311710
Makoto Inoue *(Pres)*

Subsidiaries:

Apex Kyokuyo Co., Ltd. (1)
3246 Nakashima, Shikamaku-ku, Himeji, 672-8035, Hyogo, Japan
Tel.: (81) 792342670
Web Site: http://www.apex-kyokuyo.co.jp
Emp.: 73
Seafood Product Mfr
N.A.I.C.S.: 311710

Ibusuki Shokuhin Co., Ltd. (1)
1-42 Shinei-cho, Yamagawa Ibusuki, Kagoshima, 891-0501, Japan
Tel.: (81) 993352335
Web Site: https://www.ibusukisyokuhin.com
Seafood Product Mfr
N.A.I.C.S.: 311710

Integrated System Services Co., Ltd. (1)
Nihon Building Building 2 1-2-5 Kayabacho Nihonbashi, Chuo-ku, Tokyo, Japan
Tel.: (81) 356528600
Web Site: https://www.iss-tokyo.co.jp
Emp.: 72
System Development Services
N.A.I.C.S.: 541511

Jokki Co., Ltd. (1)
3-28-5 Kamishakujii, Nerima-ku, Tokyo, 177-0044, Japan
Tel.: (81) 339206885
Web Site: http://www.jokki.jp
Emp.: 450
Seafood Product Mfr
N.A.I.C.S.: 311710

K&U Enterprise Co., Ltd. (1)
1289 Wichian Chodok Mahachai, Mueang Samut Sakhon District, Samut Sakhon, 74000, Thailand
Tel.: (66) 34820922
Web Site: http://www.kue.co.th
Emp.: 1,600
Frozen Food Product Mfr
N.A.I.C.S.: 311412

Kaiyo Foods Co., Ltd. (1)
2831-15 Sunayama, Kamisu, 314-0255, Ibaraki, Japan
Tel.: (81) 479463851
Web Site: http://www.kaiyo-foods.co.jp
Emp.: 60
Seafood Product Mfr
N.A.I.C.S.: 311710

Kuroshio Suisan Co., Ltd. (1)
373 Tomariura, Hata-gun, Otsuki, 788-0353, Kochi, Japan
Tel.: (81) 880731105
Seafood Product Mfr
N.A.I.C.S.: 311710

Kyokuyo (Thailand) Co., Ltd. (1)
92/53 Sathorn Thani Tower 2 18th Floor Room No 1816 Sathorn Nua Road, Khwaeng Silom Khet Bangrak, Bangkok, 10500, Thailand
Tel.: (66) 22384604
Frozen Food Product Mfr
N.A.I.C.S.: 311412

Kyokuyo Akitsu Reizo Co., Ltd. (1)
2-6-1 Jonanjima, Ota-ku, Tokyo, 143-0002, Japan
Tel.: (81) 337991701
Web Site: https://www.akitureizou-logi.com
Emp.: 63
Refrigerated Warehousing & Storage Services
N.A.I.C.S.: 493120

Kyokuyo America Corp. (1)
1200 5th Ave Ste 1575, Seattle, WA 98101-3131   (100%)
Tel.: (206) 405-2670
Web Site: https://kamec.us
Sales Range: $50-74.9 Million
Emp.: 5

KYOKUYO CO. LTD.

Kyokuyo Co. Ltd.—(Continued)
Fresh & Frozen Fish, Import of Seafood Products
N.A.I.C.S.: 424460
Makato Ishihara (Pres)

Kyokuyo Europe B.V. (1)
Tower B-7th Floor WTC Schiphol Airport
Schiphol Boulevard 193, 1118 BG, Schiphol, Netherlands
Tel.: (31) 204059060
Web Site: https://www.kyokuyo-eu.com
Frozen Food Product Mfr
N.A.I.C.S.: 311412

Kyokuyo Feed One Marine Co., Ltd. (1)
392-2 Hisayoshi Ainan-cho, Minamiuwa-gun, Yamanashi, 798-4353, Ehime, Japan
Tel.: (81) 895737180
Web Site: https://www.kfmarine.co.jp
Seafood Product Mfr
N.A.I.C.S.: 311710

Kyokuyo Foods Co., Ltd. (1)
830 Nobenomo, Matsuno-cho Kitauwa-gun, Shikokuchuo, 798-2102, Ehime, Japan
Tel.: (81) 895421600
Frozen & Chilled Product Mfr
N.A.I.C.S.: 311412

Kyokuyo Fresh Co., Ltd. (1)
3-3-2 Rinkai-cho, Edogawa-ku, Tokyo, 134-0086, Japan
Tel.: (81) 338784611
Seafood Product Mfr
N.A.I.C.S.: 311710

Kyokuyo Marine Ehime Co., Ltd. (1)
392-2 Kura Ainan Town, Minamiuwa District, Yamanashi, 798-4353, Ehime, Japan
Tel.: (81) 895726661
Web Site: https://www.kyokuyomarine-ehime.co.jp
Emp.: 13
Seafood Product Mfr
N.A.I.C.S.: 311710

Kyokuyo Marine Farm Co., Ltd. (1)
2198-4 Ofukaura, Sukumo, 788-0034, Kochi, Japan
Tel.: (81) 880655617
Web Site: https://www.kyokuyomarine-farm.co.jp
Emp.: 21
Seafood Product Mfr
N.A.I.C.S.: 311710

Kyokuyo Shoji Co., Ltd. (1)
Sumitomo Seimei Akasaka Bldg 3-3-3 Akasaka, Minato-ku, Tokyo, 107-0052, Japan
Tel.: (81) 362344400
Web Site: https://kyokuyo-shoji.com
Emp.: 25
Fishery & Meat Product Mfr
N.A.I.C.S.: 311710

Kyokuyo Shokuhin Co., Ltd. (1)
3-20-1 Niihama -cho cho, Shiogama, 985-0001, Miyagi, Japan
Tel.: (81) 223646111
Web Site: https://www.kyokuyo-shokuhin.co.jp
Emp.: 411
Frozen Food Product Mfr
N.A.I.C.S.: 311412

Kyokuyo Sougou Service Co., Ltd. (1)
Sumitomo Seimei Akasaka Bldg 3-3-3 Akasaka, Minato-ku, Tokyo, 107-0052, Japan
Tel.: (81) 355450770
Insurance Agency Services
N.A.I.C.S.: 524210

Kyokuyo Suisan Co., Ltd. (1)
1441-1 Habuchi, Yaizu, 421-0213, Shizuoka, Japan
Tel.: (81) 546225111
Web Site: https://www.kyokuyo-suisan.co.jp
Emp.: 120
Frozen Food Product Mfr
N.A.I.C.S.: 311412
Hiroyuki Aoki (Pres)

Qingdao Kyokuyo International Co., Ltd. (1)
Room No 1013 Crowne Plaza Qingdao No76 Xiang Gang Zhong Road, Qingdao, 266000, China

Tel.: (86) 53285781350
Web Site: https://www.kyokuyo-qd.com
Sales Range: $50-74.9 Million
Emp.: 3
Nonresidential Buildings Lessors
N.A.I.C.S.: 531120

KYONGBO PHARMACEUTICAL CO., LTD.
174 Sirok-ro, Asan, Chungcheongnam-do, Korea (South)
Tel.: (82) 414200500
Web Site: https://www.kbpharma.co.kr
Year Founded: 1987
214390—(KRS)
Rev.: $150,535,180
Assets: $184,497,971
Liabilities: $74,276,960
Net Worth: $110,221,010
Earnings: $468,323
Emp.: 484
Fiscal Year-end: 12/31/22
Pharmaceuticals Mfr
N.A.I.C.S.: 325412

Subsidiaries:

Bell I&S Co., Ltd. (1)
8th Floor Chonggeundang Building 8 Chungjeong-ro, Seodaemun-gu, Seoul, Korea (South)
Tel.: (82) 226641570
Web Site: https://www.bellins.net
Information Technology Services
N.A.I.C.S.: 541512

Chong Kun Dang Industry Co., Ltd. (1)
8th Floor Chong Kun Dang Building 8 Chungjeong-ro, Seodaemun-gu, Seoul, Korea (South)
Tel.: (82) 23623111
Web Site: https://www.ckdi.co.kr
Real Estate Services
N.A.I.C.S.: 522292

KYORIN HOLDINGS, INC.
6 Kanda Surugadai 4-Chome, Chiyoda-ku, Tokyo, 101-8311, Japan
Tel.: (81) 335254700
Web Site: http://www.kyorin-gr.co.jp
Year Founded: 1958
4569—(TKS)
Rev.: $790,106,520
Assets: $1,174,114,470
Liabilities: $309,956,120
Net Worth: $864,158,350
Earnings: $35,178,420
Emp.: 1,364
Fiscal Year-end: 03/31/24
Drug & Health Care Products Sales
N.A.I.C.S.: 621491
Minoru Hogawa (Chm)

Subsidiaries:

KYORIN Pharmaceutical Co., Ltd. (1)
6 Kanda Surugadai 4-Chome, Chiyoda-ku, Tokyo, 101-8311, Japan
Tel.: (81) 335254711
Web Site: https://www.kyorin-pharm.co.jp
Sales Range: $550-599.9 Million
Emp.: 1,471
Prescription Medicines Mfr & Whslr
N.A.I.C.S.: 325412
Minoru Hogawa (Chm)

Subsidiary (US):

ActivX Biosciences, Inc. (2)
11025 N Torrey Pines Rd Ste 120, La Jolla, CA 92037
Tel.: (858) 558-5558
Web Site: https://www.activx.com
Pharmaceutical Research & Development Services
N.A.I.C.S.: 541714
Lorrie Daggett (COO)

Plant (Domestic):

KYORIN Pharmaceutical - Okaya Plant (2)

14-3 Kohan 1-Chome, Okaya, 394-0034, Nagano, Japan
Tel.: (81) 266223538
Prescription Medicines Mfr
N.A.I.C.S.: 325412

KYORIN Pharmaceutical Co., Ltd. - Noshiro Plant (2)
1 Matsubara, Noshiro, 016-0000, Akita, Japan
Tel.: (81) 185553456
Web Site: http://www.kyorin-pharm.co.jp
Prescription Medicines Mfr
N.A.I.C.S.: 325412

KYORIN Pharmaceutical Group Facilities Co., Ltd. (1)
6 Kanda Surugadai 4-Chome, Chiyoda-ku, Tokyo, 101-8311, Japan
Tel.: (81) 335254751
Web Site: http://www.kyorin-gfc.co.jp
Pharmaceutical Mfr & Distr
N.A.I.C.S.: 325412
Michiro Ohnota (Pres & CEO)

KYORIN Rimedio Co., Ltd. (1)
287-1 Shimocho Morge-machi, Kanazawa, 920-0017, Ishikawa, Japan
Tel.: (81) 762392270
Web Site: https://www.kyorin-rmd.co.jp
Sales Range: $75-99.9 Million
Emp.: 204
Generic Drugs Mfr & Distr
N.A.I.C.S.: 325412
Hiroshi Hashizume (Pres)

Kyobundo Co., Ltd. (1)
Kyorin Nishi-Shinjuku Bldg 25-13 Nishi-Shinjuku 6-chome, Shinjuku-ku, Tokyo, Japan
Tel.: (81) 353238851
Web Site: http://www.kyobundo.co.jp
Sales Range: $10-24.9 Million
Emp.: 50
Business Development Services
N.A.I.C.S.: 561499

KYORITSU AIR TECH INC.
5-7-1 Wada Sasaguri-machi, Kasuya-Gun, Fukuoka, 811-2414, Japan
Tel.: (81) 929476101
Web Site: https://www.kak-net.co.jp
Year Founded: 1973
5997—(TKS)
Rev.: $84,342,640
Assets: $106,045,130
Liabilities: $46,439,500
Net Worth: $59,605,630
Earnings: $3,459,920
Emp.: 322
Fiscal Year-end: 12/31/23
Ventilation Machinery Mfr & Distr
N.A.I.C.S.: 335210
Yukio Kuno (Pres)

KYORITSU COMPUTER & COMMUNICATION CO., LTD.
Hamamatsucho 1-9-10 DaiwaA Hamamatsucho Building, Minato-ku, Tokyo, 105-0013, Japan
Tel.: (81) 334343141
Web Site: https://www.kccnet.co.jp
Year Founded: 1965
3670—(TKS)
Rev.: $36,150,090
Assets: $21,667,580
Liabilities: $8,355,040
Net Worth: $13,312,540
Earnings: $1,705,380
Emp.: 240
Fiscal Year-end: 03/31/24
IT Services & Solutions
N.A.I.C.S.: 541519
Shigenori Sasaki (Chm & CEO)

KYORITSU ELECTRIC CORPORATION
611 Nakata Honmachi, Suruga-ku, Shizuoka, 422-8686, Japan
Tel.: (81) 542888888
Web Site: https://www.kdwan.co.jp
Year Founded: 1959

6874—(TKS)
Rev.: $213,725,420
Assets: $192,471,680
Liabilities: $75,666,300
Net Worth: $116,805,380
Earnings: $10,996,960
Emp.: 684
Fiscal Year-end: 06/30/24
Industrial Machinery Equipment Mfr
N.A.I.C.S.: 334513
Nobuyuki Nishi (Pres & CEO)

Subsidiaries:

APRESTO Co., Ltd. (1)
3-12-27 Ishida, Suruga-ku, Shizuoka, 422-8042, Japan
Tel.: (81) 54 288 6606
Web Site: https://www.apresto.co.jp
Emp.: 89
Electronic Device Distr
N.A.I.C.S.: 423690

Kyoritsu Electric (Malaysia) Sdn., Bhd. (1)
Suite 5 3 5th Floor P J Technoplex No 2A Jalan 243/51A, 46100, Petaling Jaya, Selangor, Malaysia
Tel.: (60) 378730385
Emp.: 20
Testing Equipment Distr
N.A.I.C.S.: 423830
Hoong Thye Goh (Gen Mgr)

Kyoritsu Electric (Shanghai) Co., Ltd. (1)
Suite 409 CIMIC Tower No 800 Shangcheng Road, Pudong, Shanghai, 200120, China
Tel.: (86) 2158350777
Emp.: 9
Panel Mfr
N.A.I.C.S.: 334515

Kyoritsu Electric (Shenzhen) Co., Ltd. (1)
Room 10C Shenmao Commercial Center Xinmen Rd, Futian District, Shenzhen, China
Tel.: (86) 75582925950
Emp.: 7
Testing Equipment Distr
N.A.I.C.S.: 423830

Kyoritsu Electric (Thailand) Co., Ltd. (1)
301/100 Nonthaburi Road Tha Sai Muang, Nonthaburi, 11000, Thailand
Tel.: (66) 29670911
Emp.: 30
Testing Equipment Distr
N.A.I.C.S.: 423830

Kyoritsu Electric (Vietnam) Co., Ltd. (1)
Floor 11-Ladeco Building No 266 Doi Can Street, Ba Dinh District, Hanoi, Vietnam
Tel.: (84) 2439590277
Emp.: 4
Testing Equipment Distr
N.A.I.C.S.: 423830

Kyoritsu Electric India Pvt Ltd. (1)
Unit No 13 90 Feet Road Sativali Vasai-East, Om Industrial Estate, Palghar, 401208, Maharashtra, India
Tel.: (91) 2502024668
Web Site: http://www.kyoritsuelectric.com
Emp.: 20
Testing Equipment Mfr & Distr
N.A.I.C.S.: 334515

Kyoritsu Electric Tech (Philippines), Inc. (1)
Block 16 Phase IV Cavite Economic Zone Rosario, Cavite, Philippines
Tel.: (63) 465056538
Emp.: 1
Testing Equipment Mfr & Distr
N.A.I.C.S.: 334515

Kyoritsu Engineering (Thailand) Co, Ltd. (1)
301/100 Nonthaburi Road, Tha Sai Muang, Nonthaburi, 11000, Thailand
Tel.: (66) 2 967 0201
Electronic Components Mfr
N.A.I.C.S.: 334419

AND PRIVATE COMPANIES

Kyoritsu Machinery Corporation (2)
63-25 Nakadahoncho, Suruga-ku, Shizuoka, 422-8043, Japan
Tel.: (81) 54 203 2800
Web Site: https://www.kdkikai.co.jp
Emp.: 60
Machine Tools Mfr
N.A.I.C.S.: 333517

Kyoritsu Test System Co., Ltd. (1)
4-3-11 Onodai, Minami-ku, Sagamihara, 252-0331, Kanagawa, Japan
Tel.: (81) 42 730 9044
Web Site: https://www.testsystem.co.jp
Testing Equipment Mfr
N.A.I.C.S.: 334515
Koji Miura *(Pres)*

Kyowa Denko Co., Ltd. (1)
1-6-21 Manse-cho, Shimizu-ku, Shizuoka, 424-0826, Japan
Tel.: (81) 543535392
Web Site: http://www.kdkwan.co.jp
Emp.: 50
Electrical Equipment Mfr & Distr
N.A.I.C.S.: 334515

PT. Kyoritsu Electric Indonesia (1)
Gedung Cikarang Technopark LT 2 JL Inti 1 C1 No 7, Lippo Cikarang Cibatu Cikarang Selatan Kab, Bekasi, 17550, Jawa Barat, Indonesia
Tel.: (62) 2129093182
Emp.: 4
Testing Equipment Mfr & Distr
N.A.I.C.S.: 334515

Sanshin Sangyo Co., Ltd. (1)
6-7 Shingai, Oita, 870-0911, Japan
Tel.: (81) 975521015
Web Site: http://www.san-sin.com
Emp.: 155
Scaffold Distr
N.A.I.C.S.: 423810
Ohno Tsuguo *(Chm)*

Shanghai Kyoritsu KeDi Testsystem Co., Ltd. (1)
1-501A 1228 ZhenNan Road PuTuo, Shanghai, China
Tel.: (86) 2158719778
Emp.: 6
Testing Equipment Distr
N.A.I.C.S.: 423830

KYORITSU MAINTENANCE CO., LTD.
2-18-8 Sotokanda, Chiyoda-ku, Tokyo, 101-8621, Japan
Tel.: (81) 352957777
Web Site: http://www.kyoritsugroup.co.jp
Year Founded: 1979
9616—(TKS)
Rev.: $1,349,272,860
Assets: $1,790,787,810
Liabilities: $1,218,335,370
Net Worth: $572,452,440
Earnings: $82,056,540
Emp.: 5,939
Fiscal Year-end: 03/31/24
Dormitory Management Services
N.A.I.C.S.: 721310
Haruhisa Ishizuka *(Chm)*

Subsidiaries:

Builnet Co., Ltd. (1)
5th floor Shin-Kanda Building 2-15-2 Sotokanda, Chiyoda-ku, Tokyo, 101-0021, Japan
Tel.: (81) 352893930
Emp.: 907
Real Estate Manangement Services
N.A.I.C.S.: 531210

Japan Placement Center Co., Ltd. (1)
2-12-10 Tsukiji MF Building No 26 6th floor, Tsukiji Chuo-ku, Tokyo, 104-0045, Japan
Tel.: (81) 335463633
Emp.: 889
System Development & Design Services
N.A.I.C.S.: 541512
Oyama Pesturo *(Pres)*

Kyoritsu Foods Service Co., Ltd. (1)
Tel.: (81) 358166181
Emp.: 335
Hotel Operator
N.A.I.C.S.: 721110

Kyoritsu Trust Co., Ltd. (1)
6th floor Ochanomizu Chuo Building 2-5-4 Kanda Surugadai, Chiyoda-ku, Tokyo, 101-0062, Japan
Tel.: (81) 352957071
Emp.: 8
Photo Studio Operator
N.A.I.C.S.: 541921

KYORITSU PRINTING CO., LTD.
36-1 Shimizu-cho, Itabashi-ku, Tokyo, 174-8860, Japan
Tel.: (81) 352487800
Web Site: http://www.kyoritsu-printing.co.jp
Year Founded: 1980
7838—(TKS)
Rev.: $365,855,600
Assets: $416,269,040
Liabilities: $260,982,480
Net Worth: $155,286,560
Earnings: $8,373,200
Emp.: 882
Fiscal Year-end: 03/31/22
Commercial Printing Services
N.A.I.C.S.: 323111

KYOSAN ELECTRIC MANUFACTURING CO., LTD.
2-29-1 Heian-cho, Tsurumi-ku, Yokohama, 230-0031, Japan
Tel.: (81) 455011261
Web Site: https://www.kyosan.co.jp
Year Founded: 1917
6742—(TKS)
Rev.: $466,170,250
Assets: $856,411,430
Liabilities: $528,244,760
Net Worth: $328,166,670
Earnings: $22,698,740
Emp.: 2,054
Fiscal Year-end: 03/31/24
Signal Systems & Electrical Equipment Mfr
N.A.I.C.S.: 335999
Shigenobu Nishida *(Mng Exec Officer)*

Subsidiaries:

Actes Kyosan inc. (1)
3-15-38 Tsumadakita, Atsugi, 243-0812, Kanagawa, Japan
Tel.: (81) 46 223 0321
Web Site: http://www.actes-kyosan.co.jp
Electric Device Mfr
N.A.I.C.S.: 334419

Kyosan Electrical Construction Co., Ltd. (1)
2-36-20 Minamirokugo, Ota-ku, Tokyo, 144-0045, Japan
Tel.: (81) 3 5744 3111
Web Site: http://www.kyosan-densetu.co.jp
Emp.: 296
Traffic Signal Equipment Mfr & Distr
N.A.I.C.S.: 334290

Kyosan Engineering Service Co., Ltd. (1)
2-29-5 Heian-cho, Tsurumi-ku, Yokohama, 230-0031, Japan
Tel.: (81) 455016304
Web Site: http://www.kyosanes.co.jp
Emp.: 348
Electrical Signal Installation Services
N.A.I.C.S.: 238210

Kyosan India Pvt. Ltd. (1)
No 601 6th Floor EROS Corporate Tower, Nehru Place, New Delhi, 110 019, India
Tel.: (91) 1146563456
Web Site: https://www.kyosan.co.jp
Traffic Signal Equipment Mfr & Distr
N.A.I.C.S.: 334290

Kyosan Kogyo Co., Ltd. (1)
2-29 Heiancho, Tsurumi-ku, Yokohama, 230-0031, Japan
Tel.: (81) 455038187
Web Site: https://www.kyosan-kogyo.co.jp
Emp.: 17
Office Equipment Distr
N.A.I.C.S.: 423420

Kyosan Metal Industry Co., Ltd. (1)
1-40-19 Komatsubara, Zama, 252-0002, Japan
Tel.: (81) 46 253 2611
Industrial Machinery Mfr & Distr
N.A.I.C.S.: 333998

Kyosan Seiki Co., Ltd. (1)
2-29 Heian-cho, Tsurumi-ku, Yokohama, 230-0031, Japan
Tel.: (81) 455039950
Traffic Signal Equipment Mfr & Distr
N.A.I.C.S.: 334290

Kyosan System Co., Ltd. (1)
2-29 Heiancho, Tsurumi-ku, Yokohama, 230-0031, Japan
Tel.: (81) 455039076
Web Site: http://www.kyosansystem.co.jp
Emp.: 76
Computer System Design Services
N.A.I.C.S.: 541512

Kyosan USA Inc. (1)
2151 O'Toole Ave Ste 40, San Jose, CA 95131
Tel.: (408) 432-6267
Web Site: https://kyosan-usa.com
Electrical Equipment Distr
N.A.I.C.S.: 423610

Osaka Rectifier Co., Ltd. (1)
4-10-37 Torikaikami, Settsu, 566-0062, Osaka, Japan
Tel.: (81) 726530221
Sales Range: $25-49.9 Million
Emp.: 31
Semiconductor & Related Device Mfr
N.A.I.C.S.: 334413

Taiwan Kyosan Co., Ltd. (1)
No 3-1 Jianguo Rd, Tanzi Dist, Taichung, 42760, Taiwan
Tel.: (886) 4 2532 1191
Web Site: http://www.kyosan.com.tw
Sales Range: $25-49.9 Million
Emp.: 190
Manufacture & Export of Signal Relays
N.A.I.C.S.: 335314
Bob Wu *(Chm)*

KYOSHA CO., LTD.
300 Morimurahigashi Kumiyama-cho Kuse-gun, Kyoto, 613-0024, Japan
Tel.: (81) 756313191
Web Site: https://www.kyosha.co.jp
Year Founded: 1959
6837—(TKS)
Rev.: $162,473,800
Assets: $154,277,400
Liabilities: $98,350,190
Net Worth: $55,927,210
Earnings: $3,992,440
Emp.: 1,244
Fiscal Year-end: 03/31/24
Electronic Components Mfr
N.A.I.C.S.: 334419
Kazuto Kojima *(Pres & Exec Officer)*

Subsidiaries:

KYOSHA CO., LTD. - Kyushu Plant (1)
595-1 Tamanakokushaku, Tamana, 865-0005, Kumamoto, Japan
Tel.: (81) 968735359
Web Site: https://www.kyosha.co.jp
Printed Wiring Board Mfr
N.A.I.C.S.: 334419

KYOSHA CO., LTD. - Niigata Plant (1)
2130 Koyoshi, Nishikan-ku, Niigata, 950-1325, Japan
Tel.: (81) 253752772
Printed Wiring Board Mfr
N.A.I.C.S.: 334419

Kyosha Hong Kong Co., Ltd. (1)
Blk A1 1/F Kaiser Estate Phase 1 41 Man Yue St, Hunghom, Kowloon, China (Hong Kong)
Tel.: (852) 23567223
Printed Circuit Board Distr
N.A.I.C.S.: 423690
Chris Wu *(Gen Mgr-Intl Procurement)*

Subsidiary (Non-US):

Guangzhou Kyosha Circuit Technology Co., Ltd. (2)
31 Li Ye Road, Dong Chong Town Nansha District, Guangzhou, Guang Dong, China
Tel.: (86) 2084908292
Printed Wiring Board Mfr
N.A.I.C.S.: 334419

Kyosha (Thailand) Co., Ltd. (2)
252/96 Muang Thai-phatra Complex Tower B 18th Floor Rachadapisek Road, Huay Khwang, Bangkok, 10310, Thailand
Tel.: (66) 26943587
Printed Wiring Board Mfr & Distr
N.A.I.C.S.: 334419

Subsidiary (US):

Kyosha North America, Inc. (2)
39500 Orchard Hill Pl Dr Ste 125, Novi, MI, 48375
Tel.: (248) 719-7061
Printed Wiring Board Mfr & Distr
N.A.I.C.S.: 334419

Kyosha Malaysia Circuit Technology Sdn. Bhd. (1)
Suite 1007 Menara PJ Amcorp Trade Center 18, Jaran Pesiaran Barat, 46050, Petaling Jaya, Selangor, Malaysia
Tel.: (60) 37 956 0492
Printed Wiring Board Whslr
N.A.I.C.S.: 423690

PT. Kyosha Indonesia (1)
Jl Palam II Blok DS No 12A Lippo Cikarang, Bekasi, 17530, Indonesia
Tel.: (62) 218972152
Emp.: 426
Printed Wiring Board Mfr & Distr
N.A.I.C.S.: 334419

Sanwa Electron Co., Ltd. (1)
208 Jindai, Tsuyama, 709-4621, Okayama, Japan
Tel.: (81) 868573711
Emp.: 140
Printed Wiring Board Mfr & Distr
N.A.I.C.S.: 334419

KYOSHIN KENKO CO., LTD.
1-30-17 Arita, Sawara-ku, Fukuoka, 814-0033, Japan
Tel.: (81) 928217491
Web Site: http://www.kyoshin-kenko.co.jp
Year Founded: 1984
Waterproofing Solutions & Services
N.A.I.C.S.: 238990

KYOTO FINANCIAL GROUP, INC.
700 Yakushimae-cho Karasuma-dori Matsubara-Agaru, Shimogyo-ku, Kyoto, 600-8652, Kyoto, Japan
Tel.: (81) 753612211
Web Site: https://www.kyoto-fg.co.jp
Year Founded: 2023
5844—(TSX)
Commercial Bank
N.A.I.C.S.: 522110
Nobuhiro Doi *(Pres)*

KYOTO GROUP AS
Fornebuveien 1, 1366, Lysaker, Norway
Web Site: https://www.kyotogroup.no
Year Founded: 2016
KYOTO—(OSL)
Rev.: $53,864
Assets: $15,886,304
Liabilities: $3,312,095
Net Worth: $12,574,209
Earnings: ($7,899,178)
Emp.: 37
Fiscal Year-end: 12/31/23
Battery Mfr

KYOTO GROUP AS

Kyoto Group AS—(Continued)
N.A.I.C.S.: 335910
Eivind Reiten *(Chm)*

KYOTO KIMONO YUZEN HOLDINGS CO., LTD.
Sumitomo Life Insurance Nihonbashi Odenmacho Building 14-1 Nihonbashi, Odenmacho Chuo-ku, Tokyo, 103-0011, Japan
Tel.: (81) 336399191
Web Site: https://www.kyotokimonoyuzen.co.jp
Year Founded: 1971
7615—(TKS)
Rev.: $46,415,420
Assets: $58,921,540
Liabilities: $41,008,440
Net Worth: $17,913,100
Earnings: ($8,870,620)
Emp.: 470
Fiscal Year-end: 03/31/24
Apparel Product Distr
N.A.I.C.S.: 424350
Masachika Hattori *(Pres & CEO)*

KYOTO TOOL CO., LTD.
128 Sayama-Shinkaichi, Kumiyamacho Kuze-gun, Kyoto, 613-0034, Japan
Tel.: (81) 774463700
Web Site: https://www.ktc.co.jp
Year Founded: 1950
5966—(TKS)
Rev.: $55,709,080
Assets: $109,825,150
Liabilities: $27,656,240
Net Worth: $82,168,910
Earnings: $4,263,450
Emp.: 218
Fiscal Year-end: 03/31/24
Precision Tool Mfr & Whlsr
N.A.I.C.S.: 332216
Shigeru Tanaka *(Pres & CEO)*

KYOWA ELECTRONIC INSTRUMENTS CO., LTD.
Chofugaoka 3-5-1, Chofu, 182-8520, Tokyo, Japan
Tel.: (81) 424881111
Web Site: https://www.kyowa-ei.co.jp
Year Founded: 1949
6853—(TKS)
Rev.: $105,648,090
Assets: $174,803,950
Liabilities: $49,608,730
Net Worth: $125,195,220
Earnings: $6,366,820
Emp.: 541
Fiscal Year-end: 12/31/23
Measuring Instrument Mfr & Whlsr
N.A.I.C.S.: 334515
Giichi Tanaka *(Pres, Pres & Co-CEO)*

Subsidiaries:

Kofu Kyowa Dengyo Co., Ltd. (1)
Emp.: 43
Measuring Instruments Mfr
N.A.I.C.S.: 334515
Takuya Igarashi *(Pres)*

Kyowa Americas Inc. (1)
39555 Orchard Hill Pl Ste 159, Novi, MI 48375
Tel.: (248) 348-0348
Web Site: http://www.kyowa-ei.us
Measuring Equipment Distr
N.A.I.C.S.: 423830
Yoshio Saito *(Pres)*

Kyowa Dengyo (Thailand) Co., Ltd. (1)
124/8-9 Soi Sukhumvit 54, Phra Khanong Tai Subdistrict Phra Khanong District, Bangkok, 10260, Thailand
Tel.: (66) 2 117 3760
Web Site: http://www.kyowa-ei.co.th
Measuring Equipment Distr
N.A.I.C.S.: 423830

Kyowa Dengyo Malaysia Sdn. Bhd. (1)
52 Jalan USJ 9-5P, 47620, Subang Jaya, Selangor Darul Ehsan, Malaysia
Tel.: (60) 380245919
Measuring Equipment Distr
N.A.I.C.S.: 423830

Kyowa Electronic (Shanghai) Trading Co., Ltd. (1)
41A-8505 No 808 Hong Qiao Road Jia Hua Business Center, Shanghai, 200030, China
Tel.: (86) 2164477770
Web Site: http://www.kyowa-ei.cn
Measuring Equipment Distr
N.A.I.C.S.: 423830

Kyowa High Tech Co., Ltd. (1)
3-5-1 Chofugaoka Chofu, Tokyo, 182-8520, Japan
Tel.: (81) 424881121
Emp.: 15
Inspection Equipment Mfr
N.A.I.C.S.: 333310
Nobuo Oinuma *(Pres)*

Kyowa Measurement Engineering Co., Ltd. (1)
3-5-1 Chofugaoka Chofu, Tokyo, 182-8520, Japan
Tel.: (81) 424801811
Emp.: 21
Construction Services
N.A.I.C.S.: 236220

Kyowa Service Center Co., Ltd. (1)
3-5-1 Chofugaoka Chofu, Tokyo, 182-8520, Japan
Tel.: (81) 424897247
Emp.: 38
Inspection Equipment Mfr
N.A.I.C.S.: 333310
Yukio Yamaguchi *(Pres)*

New Tech Co., Ltd. (1)
2-9-15 Onaka Harimacho Kakogun, Hyogo, 675-0142, Japan
Tel.: (81) 794366200
Emp.: 30
Measuring Equipment Repair & Maintenance Services
N.A.I.C.S.: 811210
Fumihiko Ishise *(Pres)*

Tamaya Technics Inc. (1)
3-7 Minami-Oi 6-Chome, Shinagawa-ku, Tokyo, 140-0013, Japan
Tel.: (81) 357645561
Web Site: http://tamaya-technics.com
Optical Instrument Mfr
N.A.I.C.S.: 339115

Yamagata Kyowa Dengyo Co., Ltd. (1)
7057-24 Higashineko Higashine, Yamagata, 999-3701, Japan
Tel.: (81) 237411340
Emp.: 219
Strain Gas Distr
N.A.I.C.S.: 486210

KYOWA ENGINEERING CONSULTANTS CO., LTD.
KEC Building 1-62-11 Sasazuka, Shibuya-Ku, Tokyo, 151-0073, Japan
Tel.: (81) 333763171
Web Site: https://www.kyowa-c.co.jp
Year Founded: 1961
9647—(TKS)
Rev.: $54,444,110
Assets: $50,175,930
Liabilities: $25,460,190
Net Worth: $24,715,740
Earnings: $2,850,180
Emp.: 275
Fiscal Year-end: 11/30/23
Construction Engineering Services
N.A.I.C.S.: 237990
Mitsuru Yamamoto *(Pres & CEO)*

KYOWA LEATHER CLOTH CO., LTD.
1876 Higashi-machi, Chuo-ku, Hamamatsu, 430-8510, Shizuoka, Japan
Tel.: (81) 534252121

Web Site: https://www.kyowale.co.jp
Year Founded: 1935
3553—(TKS)
Rev.: $343,964,570
Assets: $400,916,330
Liabilities: $152,552,190
Net Worth: $248,364,140
Earnings: $12,942,380
Emp.: 1,395
Fiscal Year-end: 03/31/24
Leather Material Mfr
N.A.I.C.S.: 313320
Mikio Hanai *(Pres)*

KYOWA MEDICAL CORPORATION
3-18 Kusanagikita Shimizu-ku, Shizuoka-shi, Shizuoka, 424-8688, Japan
Tel.: (81) 543458144
Emp.: 540
Medical Equipment Distr
N.A.I.C.S.: 423450
Yasuhiko Ikeya *(Pres)*

KYOWAKOGYOSYO CO., LTD.
1-57 Kogyodanchi, Komatsu, 923-8620, Ishikawa, Japan
Tel.: (81) 761210531
Web Site: https://www.kyowakogyosyo.co.jp
Year Founded: 1961
5971—(TKS)
Rev.: $72,524,920
Assets: $118,338,830
Liabilities: $15,579,770
Net Worth: $102,759,060
Earnings: $9,538,230
Emp.: 304
Fiscal Year-end: 04/30/24
Bolt Mfr
N.A.I.C.S.: 332722
Masaki Yamaguchi *(Pres)*

Subsidiaries:

Kyowa Machinery (Shandong) Co., Ltd. (1)
No 9 Ruiyuan Road High-tech Zone, Jining, Shandong, China
Tel.: (86) 5372710886
Emp.: 40
Gear Part Mfr
N.A.I.C.S.: 333612

KYOWANISSEI CO., LTD.
3-8-5 Irifune, Chuo-ku, Tokyo, 104-0042, Japan
Tel.: (81) 363285600
Web Site: https://www.kyowa-nissei.co.jp
Year Founded: 1948
1981—(TKS)
Sales Range: $25-49.9 Billion
Construction Engineering Services
N.A.I.C.S.: 237990
Shigeru Kawano *(Pres & Exec Officer)*

KYUDENKO CORPORATION
1-23-35 Nanokawa, Minamiku, Fukuoka, 815-0081, Japan
Tel.: (81) 925330300
Web Site: https://www.kyudenko.co.jp
Year Founded: 1944
1959—(FKA)
Rev.: $3,645,129,840
Assets: $3,662,873,280
Liabilities: $1,328,115,360
Net Worth: $2,334,757,920
Earnings: $253,770,880
Emp.: 6,750
Fiscal Year-end: 03/31/22
Engineeering Services
N.A.I.C.S.: 541330
Matsuji Nishimura *(Pres)*

INTERNATIONAL PUBLIC

Subsidiaries:

Asia Projects Engineering Pte Ltd. (1)
32 Penjuru Road, Singapore, 609136, Singapore (82.1%)
Tel.: (65) 6 268 9511
Web Site: https://www.apeco.com.sg
Sales Range: $50-74.9 Million
Emp.: 350
Plant Engineering & Maintenance Services
N.A.I.C.S.: 541330
Heng Meng Lek *(Mng Dir)*

KYUDENKO VIETNAM CO., LTD. (1)
8Fl Miss Ao Dai Building 21 Nguyen Trung Ngan str, Ben Nghe Ward Dist 1, Ho Chi Minh City, Vietnam
Tel.: (84) 839110460
Construction Engineering Services
N.A.I.C.S.: 541330
Le Quang Hung *(Mgr-Site)*

KYUDENKO-OHSIS (THAILAND) CO., LTD. (1)
Unit 16B Floor 16 Bangnathani Building 1/33 Soi Bangna-Trad 34, Bangna District, Bangkok, Thailand
Tel.: (66) 23984301
Construction Engineering Services
N.A.I.C.S.: 541330

Kyudenko (Thailand) Co., Ltd. (1)
1/33 Bangnathani Building 16th Floor Soi Bangna-Trad 34, Bangna Tai Bangna, Bangkok, 10260, Thailand
Tel.: (66) 23984301
Web Site: http://www.tkyudenko.com
Electrical Engineering Services
N.A.I.C.S.: 541330
Tomofumi Era *(Mng Dir)*

Kyudenko Malaysia SDN. BHD. (1)
Suite A-5-3 Northpoint Offices Mid Valley City No1 Medan Syed, Putra Utara, 59200, Kuala Lumpur, Malaysia
Tel.: (60) 322826588
Construction Engineering Services
N.A.I.C.S.: 541330
Kazunobu Miyagi *(Mgr)*

Kyudenko South East Asia Pte. Ltd. (1)
32 Penjuru Road, Jurong, Singapore, 609136, Singapore
Tel.: (65) 66020613
Business Development Services
N.A.I.C.S.: 541611

Kyulien Environment Improving Co., Ltd. (1)
No 49 Lane 90 Gongwu Road, Longtan District, Taoyuan, 32559, Taiwan
Tel.: (886) 34990016
Web Site: http://kyulien.com.tw
Electrical Engineering Services
N.A.I.C.S.: 541330

KYUNG CHANG INDUSTRIAL CO., LTD.
6 Seonseo-ro 35-gil, Dalseo-gu, Daegu, Korea (South)
Tel.: (82) 535936344
Web Site: https://www.kc.co.kr
Year Founded: 1961
024910—(KRS)
Rev.: $472,149,574
Assets: $389,667,557
Liabilities: $284,499,852
Net Worth: $105,167,705
Earnings: $15,806,348
Emp.: 1,370
Fiscal Year-end: 12/31/22
Motor Vehicle Parts Mfr
N.A.I.C.S.: 336350
Son Il-Ho *(Chm & CEO)*

Subsidiaries:

Kyung Chang Precision Co., Ltd. (1)
149 Gukgasandan-daero 33-gil Guji-myeon, Dalseong-gun, Daegu, 43011, Korea (South)
Tel.: (82) 537211810
Emp.: 110
Automotive Parts Mfr & Distr

AND PRIVATE COMPANIES

KYUSHU ELECTRIC POWER CO., INC.

N.A.I.C.S.: 336390
Son Il-ho *(Co-CEO)*

Kyung Chang Precision Industrial Co., Ltd. (1)
306-56 Jang-Dong, Dalseo-gu, Daegu, 704-190, Korea (South)
Tel.: (82) 53 586 2333
Web Site: http://www.kccaster.co.kr
Industrial Caster Mfr
N.A.I.C.S.: 332510
Deog-Su Son *(Pres)*

KYUNG IN ELECTRONICS CO., LTD
184 Gasan Digital 2-ro Gasan-dong Byeoksan Digital Valley 2nd, Geumcheon-gu, Seoul, 08501, Korea (South)
Tel.: (82) 221132000
Web Site: https://www.kie.co.kr
Year Founded: 1973
009140—(KRS)
Rev.: $15,384,421
Assets: $52,451,318
Liabilities: $3,392,197
Net Worth: $49,059,121
Earnings: $2,076,614
Emp.: 20
Fiscal Year-end: 12/31/22
Electronic Components Mfr
N.A.I.C.S.: 334419
Kim Seong-Eun *(CEO)*

Subsidiaries:

KyungIn America Inc. (1)
3717 Torrey View Ct, San Diego, CA 92130
Tel.: (619) 268-6077
Web Site: https://www.kyunginamerica.com
Electronic Components Mfr
N.A.I.C.S.: 334419

KyungIn Electronics (Shen Zhen) Co., Ltd. (1)
1st Industrial District Xikeng Heng-Gang, Baoan, Shenzhen, Guangdong, China
Tel.: (86) 755 2861 9648
Electronic Components Mfr
N.A.I.C.S.: 334419

KyungIn Electronics(Tian Jin) Co., Ltd. (1)
Tel.: (86) 2263251721
Electronic Components Mfr
N.A.I.C.S.: 334419

KyungIn Mexico, Sa De C.V. (1)
AV Hacienda Del Colorado 22001 Parque Industrial Presidentes, Delegacion Lapresa, 22570, Tijuana, Baja California, Mexico
Electronic Components Mfr
N.A.I.C.S.: 334419
Leonardo Park *(Gen Mgr)*

KyungIn Precision Co., Ltd. (1)
Byuk San/Kyung In Building 2nd Block 1412 1414 481-10, Ga-san Dong Â Geumchon Gu, Seoul, Korea (South)
Tel.: (82) 2 2113 2019
Emp.: 5
Electronic Components Mfr
N.A.I.C.S.: 334419

KYUNG NAM PHARM CO., LTD.
79 Guryong-ro 4nam-gil, Euiryeong-eup, Uiryeong, Gyeongsangnamdo, Korea (South)
Tel.: (82) 234905160
Web Site:
https://www.kyungnampharm.com
Year Founded: 1957
053950—(KRS)
Rev.: $45,253,324
Assets: $110,540,353
Liabilities: $34,129,934
Net Worth: $76,410,419
Earnings: ($5,199,790)
Emp.: 242
Fiscal Year-end: 12/31/22
Pharmaceutical Product Mfr & Whslr
N.A.I.C.S.: 325412

KYUNG-IN SYNTHETIC CORPORATION
572 Gonghang-daero, Yangcheon-Gu, Seoul, 07947, Korea (South)
Tel.: (82) 325717498
Web Site: https://www.kisco.co
Year Founded: 1971
012610—(KRS)
Rev.: $308,822,841
Assets: $420,510,050
Liabilities: $216,369,546
Net Worth: $204,140,504
Earnings: $10,993,993
Emp.: 570
Fiscal Year-end: 12/31/22
Dye Mfr
N.A.I.C.S.: 325130
HeungJoon Kim *(Chm & CEO)*

Subsidiaries:

Daito-KISCO Corporation (1)
223-48 Seongnam-Dong Seo-Gu, Incheon, 404-220, Korea (South)
Tel.: (82) 325844646
Photosensitive Material Mfr
N.A.I.C.S.: 325992

JMC Corporation (1)
71 Ijin-Ro Onsan-Eup Ulju-Gun, Ulsan, 44998, Korea (South)
Tel.: (82) 522315755
Web Site: http://www.jmcfinechem.com
Emp.: 203
Chemical Product Mfr & Distr
N.A.I.C.S.: 325199
Won Sik Jung *(CEO)*

KYUNGDONG CITY GAS CO., LTD.
260-10 Yeompo-Ro, Buk-Gu, Ulsan, 44259, Korea (South)
Tel.: (82) 522195300
Year Founded: 2017
267290—(KRS)
Rev.: $1,767,892,822
Assets: $818,860,730
Liabilities: $515,904,400
Net Worth: $302,956,330
Earnings: $18,548,254
Emp.: 295
Fiscal Year-end: 12/31/22
Gas Mfr & Distr
N.A.I.C.S.: 325120

KYUNGDONG INVEST CO., LTD.
4 Sunae-ro 46beon-gil, Bundang-gu, Seongnam, Gyeonggi-do, Korea (South)
Tel.: (82) 317381288
Web Site: https://www.kdinvest.co.kr
Year Founded: 1977
012320—(KRS)
Rev.: $217,676,254
Assets: $463,582,742
Liabilities: $107,523,108
Net Worth: $356,059,634
Earnings: $7,391,853
Emp.: 12
Fiscal Year-end: 12/31/22
Natural Gas Supply Services
N.A.I.C.S.: 221210
Young-Hoon Park *(Pres & CEO)*

KYUNGDONG NAVIEN CO., LTD.
5 6F 76-gil 22 Gukhoidae-ro new building of Koami Yeouido-dong, Yeongdeungpo-gu, Seoul, Korea (South)
Tel.: (82) 234892200
Year Founded: 1978
009450—(KRS)
Rev.: $890,380,225
Assets: $780,820,902
Liabilities: $383,741,485
Net Worth: $397,079,416
Earnings: $41,097,657
Emp.: 1,492
Fiscal Year-end: 12/31/22
Heating Equipment Mfr & Whslr
N.A.I.C.S.: 333414
Yeon-ho Son *(CEO)*

Subsidiaries:

Beijing KyungDong Navien Heat Energy Equipment Co., LTD (1)
Tel.: (86) 1069400716
Web Site: http://www.kdnavien.com.cn
Heating Equipment Mfr & Whslr
N.A.I.C.S.: 333414

Kyung Dong One Rus LLC (1)
St Profsoyuznaya d 65 building 1 floor 16, 00048, Moscow, Russia
Tel.: (7) 4952586830
Web Site: http://www.navien.ru
Heating Equipment Mfr & Whslr
N.A.I.C.S.: 333414

Navien America., INC (1)
20 Goodyear, Irvine, CA 92618
Tel.: (949) 420-0420
Web Site: http://www.navienamerica.com
Heating Equipment Mfr & Whslr
N.A.I.C.S.: 333414

Navien Ltd. (1)
Building 2 Ground Floor, Guildford Business Park, Guildford, GU2 8XH, United Kingdom
Tel.: (44) 3443322323
Web Site: https://navien.co.uk
Gas Equipment Mfr
N.A.I.C.S.: 333132
Matthew Byung Gu Choi *(Mng Dir)*

Navien Rus LLC (1)
St Profsoyuznaya 65/1 Floor 16, 117342, Moscow, Russia
Tel.: (7) 4952586830
Web Site: https://www.navien.ru
Oil & Chemical Mfr
N.A.I.C.S.: 325998

Shanghai Navien International Trade Co., LTD (1)
No 448 Bohua Road, Pudong Xinqu, Shanghai, China
Tel.: (86) 21 6888 1761
Web Site: http://www.kdnavien.com.cn
Heating Equipment Mfr & Whslr
N.A.I.C.S.: 333414

KYUNGDONG PHARMACEUTICAL CO., LTD.
26 Gwacheon-daero 7-gil, Gwanak-gu, Seoul, Korea (South)
Tel.: (82) 25766121
Web Site:
https://www.kdpharma.co.kr
Year Founded: 1975
011040—(KRS)
Rev.: $140,144,827
Assets: $238,136,556
Liabilities: $40,615,062
Net Worth: $197,521,494
Earnings: $9,327,620
Emp.: 595
Fiscal Year-end: 12/31/22
Pharmaceutical Product Mfr & Distr
N.A.I.C.S.: 325412
Deok-Hee Ryu *(Pres & CEO)*

Subsidiaries:

Kyungdong Pharmaceutical Co., Ltd. - Hwaseong Plant (1)
224-3 Jeyakdanji-ro, Yanggam-myeon, Hwaseong, Gyeonggi, Korea (South)
Tel.: (82) 313520330
Pharmaceutical Product Mfr & Distr
N.A.I.C.S.: 325412

Kyungdong Pharmaceutical Co., Ltd. - Yanggam Plant (1)
224-3 Jeyakdanji-ro Yanggam-myeon, Hwaseong, Gyeonggi-do, Korea (South)
Tel.: (82) 313520330
Pharmaceutical Product Mfr & Distr
N.A.I.C.S.: 325414

KYUNGNONG CORPORATION
28 Hyoryeong-ro 77-gil, Seocho-gu, Seoul, 06627, Korea (South)
Tel.: (82) 234885800
Web Site: http://www.knco.co.kr
Year Founded: 1957
002100—(KRS)
Rev.: $257,863,431
Assets: $332,967,957
Liabilities: $133,702,756
Net Worth: $199,265,201
Earnings: $11,227,416
Emp.: 370
Fiscal Year-end: 12/31/23
Agrochemical Mfr
N.A.I.C.S.: 325320

KYUSHU ELECTRIC POWER CO., INC.
2-1-82 Watanabe-dori, Chuo-ku, Fukuoka, 810-8720, Japan
Tel.: (81) 927613031
Web Site: https://www.kyuden.co.jp
Year Founded: 1951
9508—(TKS)
Rev.: $14,141,744,670
Assets: $37,857,056,400
Liabilities: $31,768,962,170
Net Worth: $6,088,094,230
Earnings: $1,100,194,840
Emp.: 21,180
Fiscal Year-end: 03/31/24
Electric Power Generation & Distribution Services
N.A.I.C.S.: 221122
Ichirou Fujii *(Exec Officer & VP)*

Subsidiaries:

Capital Kyuden Corporation (1)
2-1-82 Watanabe-dori, Chuo-ku, Fukuoka, 810-0004, Japan
Tel.: (81) 927261626
Venture Capital Financing Services
N.A.I.C.S.: 523999

DENKI BLDG. CO., Ltd. (1)
1-1-1 Watanabe-dori, Chuo-ku, Fukuoka, 810-0004, Japan
Tel.: (81) 927810681
Web Site: https://www.denki-b.co.jp
Emp.: 128
Office Space Rental Services
N.A.I.C.S.: 531120

Fukuoka Energy Service Co., Inc. (1)
6F Tenjin River Front Business Center 4-1-32 Tenjin, Chuo-ku, Fukuoka, 810-0001, Japan
Tel.: (81) 924066142
Web Site: https://www.fukuoka-es.co.jp
Emp.: 66
Heat Services
N.A.I.C.S.: 221330

J-Re-Lights Co., Ltd. (1)
17 Kitakyushu Eco Town 1-62 Hibiki-cho, Wakamatsu-ku, Kitakyushu, 808-0021, Fukuoka, Japan
Tel.: (81) 937522386
Web Site: https://www.j-relights.co.jp
Emp.: 22
Fluorescent Bulbs Recycling Services
N.A.I.C.S.: 562920

Kagoshima Hikari Television Co., Inc. (1)
1-10-15 Take, Kagoshima, Japan
Tel.: (81) 992066800
Television Broadcasting Services
N.A.I.C.S.: 516120

Kitakyushu Liquefied Natural Gas Co., Inc. (1)
46-117 Nakahara, Tobata-ku, Kitakyushu, 804-0002, Fukuoka, Japan
Tel.: (81) 938828900
Web Site: https://www.k-lng.co.jp
Emp.: 76
Liquefied Natural Gas Storage & Distr
N.A.I.C.S.: 221210
Kiyoharu Ohtsubo *(Pres)*

Kyuden Business Front Inc. (1)
4th floor Tenjin Building 2-12-1 Tenjin,

KYUSHU ELECTRIC POWER CO., INC.

Kyushu Electric Power Co., Inc.—(Continued)
Chuo-ku, Fukuoka, 810-0001, Japan
Tel.: (81) 927112610
Web Site: https://www.qbfront.co.jp
Temporary Staffing Services
N.A.I.C.S.: 561320

Kyuden Business Solutions Co., Inc. (1)
Electric Building North Building 2-1-82 Watanabedori, Chuo-ku, Fukuoka, 810-0004, Japan
Tel.: (81) 927819671
Web Site: https://www.qdenbs.com
Emp.: 647
Business Management Software Development Services
N.A.I.C.S.: 541511

Kyuden Ecosol Co., Ltd. (1)
8th floor KMG Building 3-2-23 Yakuin, Chuo-ku, Fukuoka, 810-0022, Japan
Tel.: (81) 929810981
Web Site: https://www.q-mirai.co.jp
Sales Range: $25-49.9 Million
Emp.: 219
Solar Power Structure Installation Services
N.A.I.C.S.: 221114
Hiro Minami *(Asst Plant Mgr)*

Kyuden Good Life Fukuoka Josui Company, Inc. (1)
4-13-17 Yakuin, Chuo-ku, Fukuoka, Japan (100%)
Tel.: (81) 925240010
Web Site: http://www.kyuden.co.jp
Paid Nursing Home Management & Nursing Care Services
N.A.I.C.S.: 623110

Kyuden Good Life Higashifukuoka Company, Inc. (1)
3-28-2 Hanamigaoka, Fukutsu, 811-3214, Fukuoka, Japan
Tel.: (81) 940358045
Web Site: https://www.kyuden-goodlife.co.jp
Emp.: 60
Nursing Home Management & Nursing Services
N.A.I.C.S.: 621610
Koichi Arao *(Mgr)*

Kyuden Good Life Kagoshima Company, Inc. (1)
1-55-10 Kamoike, Kagoshima, 890-0063, Japan
Tel.: (81) 992860700
Nursing Home Management & Nursing Services
N.A.I.C.S.: 623110

Kyuden Good Life Kumamoto Company, Inc. (1)
4-7 Jotomachi, Chuo-ku, Kumamoto, 860-0846, Japan
Tel.: (81) 120875588
Web Site: http://www.kyuden-glk.co.jp
Sales Range: $10-24.9 Million
Emp.: 1
Nursing Home Management & Nursing Care Services
N.A.I.C.S.: 623110

Kyuden Home Security Co., Inc. (1)
2-20-37 Toko, Hakata-ku, Fukuoka, 812-0008, Japan
Tel.: (81) 924772635
Home Security & Monitoring Services
N.A.I.C.S.: 561621

Kyuden Infocom Company, Inc. (1)
2-1-82 Watanabedori, Chuo-ku, Fukuoka, 810-0004, Japan
Tel.: (81) 927718510
Sales Range: $25-49.9 Million
Emp.: 45
Information Technology Planning & Consulting Services
N.A.I.C.S.: 519290

Kyuden International Corporation (1)
Tel.: (81) 927261504
Web Site: http://www.kyuden.co.jp
Sales Range: $75-99.9 Million
Emp.: 100
Eletric Power Generation Services
N.A.I.C.S.: 221118

Kyuden Mirai Energy Company, Incorporated (1)

KMG Bld 8F 3-2-23 Yakuin, Chuo-ku, Fukuoka, 810-0022, Japan
Tel.: (81) 929810981
Web Site: https://www.q-mirai.co.jp
Emp.: 213
Renewable Energy Services
N.A.I.C.S.: 221114
Yutaka Mizumachi *(Pres)*

Kyuden Sangyo Co., Inc. (1)
2-1-82 Watanabe Dori Denki Building North Building, Chuo-ku, Fukuoka, 810-0004, Japan
Tel.: (81) 927813061
Web Site: https://www.kyudensangyo.co.jp
Emp.: 1,356
Eletric Power Generation Services
N.A.I.C.S.: 221118

Kyuden Shared Business Co., Ltd. (1)
1-7-11 Takasago, Chuo-ku, Fukuoka, 810-0011, Japan
Tel.: (81) 925221341
Accounting & Personnel Management Services
N.A.I.C.S.: 541219
Shigeru Masuda *(Pres)*

Kyuden Technosystems Corporation (1)
4-19-18 Shimizu, Minami-Ku, Fukuoka, 815-0031, Japan
Tel.: (81) 925511731
Web Site: https://www.q-tecno.co.jp
Emp.: 599
Electrical Measuring Equipment Mfr
N.A.I.C.S.: 334515
Toshiki Ono *(Pres)*

Kyuki Corporation (1)
4-19-18 Shimizu, Minami-ku, Fukuoka, 815-0031, Japan
Tel.: (81) 925511731
Power Supply Equipment Mfr
N.A.I.C.S.: 334416
Kazutami Oyama *(Pres)*

Kyushu Environmental Management Corporation (1)
1-13-8 Yakuin Kyuden Fudosan Building 5F, Chuo-ku, Fukuoka, 810-0022, Japan
Tel.: (81) 927255208
Document Shredding Services
N.A.I.C.S.: 561990

Kyushu Rinsan KK (1)
3-7-20 Noma, Minami-ku, Fukuoka, 815-0041, Japan
Tel.: (81) 925623013
Web Site: https://www.q-rin.co.jp
Sales Range: $25-49.9 Million
Emp.: 108
Forestry Services
N.A.I.C.S.: 115310

Kyushu Telecommunication Network Co., Inc. (1)
Ropponmatsu US Building 1F 1-12-37 Tani, Chuo-ku, Fukuoka, 810-0001, Japan
Tel.: (81) 929852937
Web Site: https://www.qtnet.co.jp
Broadband Telecommunication Services
N.A.I.C.S.: 517111

NISHI NIPPON AIRLINES CO., LTD. (1)
1302-47 Kosenuki Nada, Higashi-ku, Fukuoka, 812-0002, Japan
Tel.: (81) 926262249
Web Site: https://www.nishiku.co.jp
Sales Range: $25-49.9 Million
Emp.: 154
Air Cargo Transportation Services
N.A.I.C.S.: 481112

NISHIDA TECHNO SERVICE Co., Inc. (1)
1974 Matsuyama-cho, Uto, 869-0416, Kumamoto, Japan
Tel.: (81) 964227411
Web Site: https://www.nts-jpn.com
Public Utility Construction & Engineering Services
N.A.I.C.S.: 237310

Nishigi Kogyo, Co., Inc. (1)
2-9-22 Watanabe-dori, Chuo-ku, Fukuoka, 810-0004, Japan
Tel.: (81) 927118811

Sales Range: $125-149.9 Million
Emp.: 107
Hydroelectric Power Generation Services
N.A.I.C.S.: 221111

Nishimu Electronics Industries, Co., Ltd. (1)
1-2-1 Minoshima, Hakata-ku, Fukuoka, 812-8539, Japan
Tel.: (81) 924610246
Web Site: https://www.nishimu.co.jp
Sales Range: $250-299.9 Million
Emp.: 861
Telecommunication Devices Mfr & Support Services
N.A.I.C.S.: 237130

Nishinippon Environmental Energy Co., Ltd. (1)
1-17-8 Shirogane, Chuo-ku, Fukuoka, 810-0012, Japan
Tel.: (81) 925260601
Thermal Energy Distr
N.A.I.C.S.: 561990
Tateshi Matsuo *(Pres)*

Nishinippon Plant Engineering and Construction Co., Ltd. (1)
1-10-1 Takasago, Chuo-ku, Fukuoka, 810-8540, Japan
Web Site: http://www.npc21.jp
Sales Range: $500-549.9 Million
Emp.: 2,148
Power Plant Construction & Maintenance Services
N.A.I.C.S.: 237130

Oita Liquefied Natural Gas Co., Inc. (1)
4-1 Aosaki, Oita, 870-0278, Japan
Tel.: (81) 975221900
Web Site: https://www.oitalng.co.jp
Emp.: 72
Natural Gas Storage & Distr
N.A.I.C.S.: 221210

RKK Computer Service Co., Inc. (1)
1-5-11 Jiupinji, Chuo-ku, Kumamoto, 862-0976, Japan
Tel.: (81) 963645121
Web Site: http://www.rkkcs.co.jp
Financial Software Development Services
N.A.I.C.S.: 541511
Masaaki Takemura *(Pres)*

West Japan Engineering Consultants, Inc.
Denki-Bldg Sunselco Annex 10F ,1-1-1 Watanabe-dori, Chuo-ku, Fukuoka, 810-0004, Japan
Tel.: (81) 927816277
Web Site: http://www.wjec.co.jp
Sales Range: $150-199.9 Million
Emp.: 560
Engineering Consulting Services
N.A.I.C.S.: 541330

KYUSHU FINANCIAL GROUP, INC

6-6 Kinsei-cho, Kagoshima ku, Kagoshima, 892-0828, Japan
Tel.: (81) 963265588
Web Site: https://www.kyushu-fg.co.jp
Year Founded: 2015
7180—(FKA)
Rev.: $1,537,018,560
Assets: $94,511,046,690
Liabilities: $89,834,428,530
Net Worth: $4,676,618,160
Earnings: $176,869,560
Fiscal Year-end: 03/31/23
Bank Holding Company
N.A.I.C.S.: 551111
Yoshihisa Kasahara *(Pres)*

Subsidiaries:

The Higo Bank, Ltd. (1)
1 Renpeicho, Chuo-ku, Kumamoto, 860-8615, Japan
Tel.: (81) 96 325 2111
Web Site: https://www.higobank.co.jp
Emp.: 2,173
Banking Services
N.A.I.C.S.: 522110
Takahiro Kai *(Pres)*

INTERNATIONAL PUBLIC

The Kagoshima Bank, Ltd. (1)
6-6 Kinseicho, Kagoshima, 892-0828, Japan
Tel.: (81) 99 225 3111
Web Site: https://www.kagin.co.jp
Sales Range: $600-649.9 Million
Emp.: 2,257
Banking Services
N.A.I.C.S.: 522110
Motohiro Kamimura *(Pres)*

Subsidiary (Domestic):

Kyushu Economic Research Institute Co., Ltd. (2)
3-3 Izumicho Annex Building 7F Kagoshima Bank Main Store, Kagoshima, 892-0822, Japan
Tel.: (81) 992257491
Web Site: http://www.ker.co.jp
Emp.: 40
Management Consulting Services
N.A.I.C.S.: 541618
Takashi Suenaga *(Exec Officer)*

The Kagin Accounting Service Co., Ltd. (2)
1 10 Yamanokuchi, Kagoshima, 82-0844, Japan
Tel.: (81) 992165080
Web Site: http://www.kagin.co.jp
Accounting Services
N.A.I.C.S.: 541219

The Kagoshima Card Co., Ltd. (2)
3-3 Izumicho, Kagoshima, 892-0822, Japan
Tel.: (81) 992232011
Web Site: http://www.kagoshimacard.co.jp
Emp.: 125,545
Activities Related to Credit Intermediation
N.A.I.C.S.: 522390
Yoichi Eunohara *(Pres)*

The Kagoshima Lease Co., Ltd. (2)
3-3 Izumicho Annex Building 5F Kagoshima Bank Main Store, Kagoshima, 892-0822, Japan
Tel.: (81) 992252455
Web Site: http://www.kagoshimalease.co.jp
Investment Banking & Securities Dealing
N.A.I.C.S.: 523150

KYUSHU LEASING SERVICE CO., LTD.

Sun Life Center Building 3-18 Hakataekimae 4-chome, Hakata-ku, Fukuoka, 812-0011, Japan
Tel.: (81) 924312530
Web Site: https://www.k-lease.co.jp
Year Founded: 1974
8596—(FKA)
Rev.: $221,487,880
Assets: $1,278,360,780
Liabilities: $1,013,022,160
Net Worth: $265,338,620
Earnings: $20,147,280
Emp.: 155
Fiscal Year-end: 03/31/24
Machinery Leasing Services
N.A.I.C.S.: 532490
Seiji Isoyama *(Pres & CEO)*

KYUSHU RAILWAY COMPANY

3-25-21 Hakataekimae, Hakata-ku, Fukuoka, 812-8566, Japan
Tel.: (81) 92 474 2501
Web Site: http://www.jrkyushu.co.jp
Year Founded: 1987
Emp.: 9,600
Passenger Railway Operator
N.A.I.C.S.: 485112
Koji Karaike *(Pres)*

L & A INTERNATIONAL HOLDINGS LIMITED

Unit D 5/F Wing Hong Centre 18 Wing Hong Street, Kowloon, China (Hong Kong)
Tel.: (852) 37939000
Web Site: http://www.lna.com.hk
Year Founded: 2001
8195—(HKG)
Rev.: $30,249,758

AND PRIVATE COMPANIES

Assets: $48,398,745
Liabilities: $16,215,450
Net Worth: $32,183,295
Earnings: $4,410,225
Emp.: 120
Fiscal Year-end: 03/31/23
Cashmere Garments & Other Apparel Mfr
N.A.I.C.S.: 315990
Chun Kavan Lau *(Exec Dir)*

Subsidiaries:

YH Group Limited (1)
15/F 15/F On Nian Building 67-71 Chatham Road South, Tsim Sha Tsui Oriental Centre, Kowloon, China (Hong Kong)
Tel.: (852) 2 111 3134
Web Site: https://www.yhgpltd.com
Investment Education Services
N.A.I.C.S.: 523999

L & F CO., LTD.

136 Seongseo4chacheomdan-ro, Dalseo-gu, Daegu, 42724, Korea (South)
Tel.: (82) 535927300
Web Site: https://www.landf.co.kr
Year Founded: 2000
066970—(KRS)
Rev.: $2,981,554,278
Assets: $2,319,356,592
Liabilities: $1,333,508,190
Net Worth: $985,848,402
Earnings: $207,866,500
Emp.: 1,483
Fiscal Year-end: 12/31/22
Electronic Components Mfr
N.A.I.C.S.: 334419
Choi Su An *(CEO)*

Subsidiaries:

L & F Co., Ltd. - Guji Factory (1)
111 Gukgasandan-daero 40-gil Guji-myeon, Dalseong-gun, Daegu, Korea (South)
Tel.: (82) 536022100
Electronic Components Mfr
N.A.I.C.S.: 334419

L & F Co., Ltd. - Waegwan Factory (1)
135 2 Saneopdanji-1-gil, Chilgok, 39910, Gyeongsangbuk-do, Korea (South)
Tel.: (82) 549777301
Electronic Components Mfr
N.A.I.C.S.: 334419

L & K ENGINEERING CO., LTD.

5F No 17 Lane 120 Sec 1 Neihu Rd, Neihu District, Taipei, 11493, Taiwan
Tel.: (886) 226576697
Web Site: http://www.lkeng.com.tw
Year Founded: 1978
6139—(TAI)
Rev.: $1,860,906,401
Assets: $1,777,617,415
Liabilities: $1,268,651,576
Net Worth: $508,965,840
Earnings: $115,874,975
Fiscal Year-end: 12/31/23
Semiconductor Equipment Mfr
N.A.I.C.S.: 334413

Subsidiaries:

L & K Engineering (Suzhou) Co., Ltd. (1)
No 33 Fangda Street, Industrial District, Suzhou, 215126, Jiangsu, China
Tel.: (86) 51267027000
Web Site: https://www.lkeng.com.cn
Rev.: $426,705,056
Assets: $361,248,035
Liabilities: $194,268,461
Net Worth: $166,979,573
Earnings: $21,135,198
Fiscal Year-end: 12/31/2022
Clean Room Engineering Services
N.A.I.C.S.: 541330
Yao Zuxiang *(Chm)*

L CATTERTON ASIA ACQUISITION CORP.

8 Marina View Asia Square Tower 1 Suite 41-03, Singapore, 018960, Singapore
Tel.: (65) 66727600 Ky
Web Site: http://www.lcaac.com
Year Founded: 2021
LCAA—(NASDAQ)
Rev.: $15,410,565
Assets: $290,741,991
Liabilities: $305,181,706
Net Worth: ($14,439,715)
Earnings: $10,839,708
Emp.: 3
Fiscal Year-end: 12/31/22
Investment Services
N.A.I.C.S.: 523999
Chinta Bhagat *(Co-CEO)*

L SCHERBERICH

162 Rue Du Ladhof, Colmar, 68016, Cedex, France
Tel.: (33) 389208110
Web Site: http://www.scherberich.com
Rev.: $18,800,000
Emp.: 125
Building & Real Estate Construction
N.A.I.C.S.: 236220
Laurence Svec *(Mgr-Pur)*

L&C BIO CO., LTD.

Suntechcity suite 306 307 308 605 606 607 474 Dunchon-daero, Jungwon-Gu, Seongnam, Gyeonggi-do, Korea (South)
Tel.: (82) 317762975
Web Site: https://www.lncbio.co.kr
Year Founded: 2011
290650—(KRS)
Rev.: $40,323,101
Assets: $153,189,200
Liabilities: $70,490,355
Net Worth: $82,698,845
Earnings: $3,485,382
Emp.: 115
Fiscal Year-end: 12/31/22
Pharmaceuticals Product Mfr
N.A.I.C.S.: 325412
Hwan-Cheol Lee *(CEO)*

L&K BIOMED CO., LTD.

201 16-25 Dongbaekjungang-ro 16beon-gil, Giheung-gu, Yongin, 17015, Gyeonggi-do, Korea (South)
Tel.: (82) 216000841
Web Site: https://www.lnkbiomed.com
Year Founded: 2009
156100—(KRS)
Rev.: $15,161,641
Assets: $40,392,777
Liabilities: $32,138,539
Net Worth: $8,254,238
Earnings: ($10,450,510)
Emp.: 64
Fiscal Year-end: 12/31/22
Medical Device Mfr
N.A.I.C.S.: 339112
Keunju Park *(Pres)*

Subsidiaries:

Aegis Orthopaedics Pty. Ltd. (1)
12/136 Keys Road, Cheltenham, 3192, VIC, Australia
Tel.: (61) 395323179
Web Site: https://aegisortho.com.au
Orthopedic Clinic Services
N.A.I.C.S.: 621111
Grace Chae *(Gen Mgr)*

L&K Biomed Co., Ltd. - Yongin-si Factory (1)
201 16-25 Dongbaekjungang-ro 16 beon-gil, Giheung-gu, Yongin, 446-916, Gyeonggi-do, Korea (South)
Tel.: (82) 2 1600 0841

Medical Device Mfr
N.A.I.C.S.: 339112

L&K GMBH

Frankfurter Str 74, Gross-Gerau, 64521, Germany
Tel.: (49) 61529774520
Web Site: http://www.l-u-k.de
Year Founded: 1993
Rev.: $24,686,016
Emp.: 11
Raw Plastics Provider
N.A.I.C.S.: 424610

Subsidiaries:

Lukoplast spol.s r.o. (1)
Jilemnickeho 1607/45, 958 03, Partizanske, Slovakia
Tel.: (421) 3874987145
Web Site: http://www.lukoplast.sk
Plastic Material Distr
N.A.I.C.S.: 424610
Julius Bruska *(Mng Dir)*

L&P GLOBAL BERHAD

1328 Jalan Sungai Baong Furniture Industrial Estate, Sungai Bakap, 14200, Penang, Malaysia
Tel.: (60) 43907980
Web Site: https://www.lpglobalbhd.com
Year Founded: 1984
L&PBHD—(KLS)
Rev.: $36,360,018
Assets: $31,264,002
Liabilities: $9,370,569
Net Worth: $21,893,432
Earnings: $4,502,444
Emp.: 384
Fiscal Year-end: 12/31/23
Software Development Services
N.A.I.C.S.: 541511

L&T VRINDAVAN PROPERTIES LTD.

City 2 Plot No 177 Vidyanagari Marg C S T Road, Kalina Santacruz E, Mumbai, 400 098, India
Tel.: (91) 2266217300
Web Site: http://www.ltvrindavanproperty.com
Real Estate Services
N.A.I.C.S.: 531390
Pradeep Shintre *(Mgr)*

L'AGENCE AUTOMOBILIERE S.A.

Zone Actipolis 1 24A Route Departementale 201, 68390, Sausheim, France
Web Site: https://www.agenceauto.com
Year Founded: 2004
MLAA—(EUR)
Automotive Distr
N.A.I.C.S.: 423110
Christophe Winkelmuller *(CEO)*

L'AIR LIQUIDE S.A.

75 Quai d Orsay, 75321, Paris, Cedex 07, France
Tel.: (33) 140625555 FR
Web Site: https://www.airliquide.com
Year Founded: 1902
AIQUY—(OTCIQ)
Rev.: $25,426,164,712
Assets: $51,557,953,304
Liabilities: $28,215,743,400
Net Worth: $23,342,209,904
Earnings: $2,990,887,224
Emp.: 64,500
Fiscal Year-end: 12/31/20
Industrial & Medical Gas Mfr
N.A.I.C.S.: 325120
Marcelo Fioranelli *(VP)*

Subsidiaries:

AIR LIQUIDE FINLAND OY (1)
Yrttipellontie 1 C, PL 271, 90101, Oulu, Finland
Tel.: (358) 20 779 0580
Web Site: https://fi.airliquide.com
Sales Range: $25-49.9 Million
Emp.: 500
Industrial Gas Mfr
N.A.I.C.S.: 325120

AIR LIQUIDE Holding Co., Ltd. (1)
Building 18 No 1515 Gumei Road, Shanghai, 200233, China
Tel.: (86) 216 090 3688
Web Site: https://industry.airliquide.cn
Emp.: 4,000
Investment Management Service
N.A.I.C.S.: 523999

Subsidiary (Domestic):

Air Liquide China Holding Co., Ltd (2)
Building 18 No 1515 Gumei Road, Shanghai, 200233, China
Tel.: (86) 216 090 3688
Web Site: https://industry.airliquide.cn
Sales Range: $1-4.9 Billion
Emp.: 4,000
Industrial Gas Mfr
N.A.I.C.S.: 325120

AIR LIQUIDE ITALIA SIEGE (1)
Via Calabria 31, 20158, Milan, Italy
Tel.: (39) 0240261
Web Site: http://www.airliquide.com
Industrial Gas Mfr
N.A.I.C.S.: 325120

AL Air Liquide Espana S.A. (1)
C/ Agustin de Foxa n 4 Planta 4, 28036, Madrid, Spain
Tel.: (34) 91 502 9300
Web Site: https://es.airliquide.com
Industrial Gas Mfr
N.A.I.C.S.: 325120

Air Liquide (Homecare) Ltd. (1)
Alpha House Wassage Way, Hampton Lovett, Droitwich, WR9 0NX, Worcestershire, United Kingdom
Tel.: (44) 1905823370
Industrial Gas Mfr
N.A.I.C.S.: 325120

Subsidiary (Non-US):

Air Liquide (Beijing) Co., Ltd (2)
Rm 1101-1103 Central Office Tower China Overseas Plaza No 8, Chaoyang District, Beijing, 100022, China
Tel.: (86) 10 65681255
Industrial Gas Mfr
N.A.I.C.S.: 325120

Air Liquide (Chengdu) Co., Ltd (2)
Rm 603 Building B Gaoxin International Plaza North Tianfu Ave, Chengdu, 610041, China
Tel.: (86) 28 85339190
Web Site: http://www.cn.airliquide.com
Industrial Gas Mfr
N.A.I.C.S.: 325120

Air Liquide (Guangdong) Industrial Gas Co., Ltd. (2)
Rm 2501 Dong Bao Plaza No 767 Dongfeng Dong Road, Yue Xiu District, Guangzhou, 510080, China
Tel.: (86) 20 87679600
Web Site: http://www.cn.airliquide.com
Industrial Gas Mfr
N.A.I.C.S.: 325120

Air Liquide (Wuhan) Co., Ltd. (2)
No 61 Liufang Road East Lake Hi-tech Development Zone, Wuhan, 430205, Hubei, China
Tel.: (86) 27 81309600
Industrial Gas Mfr
N.A.I.C.S.: 325120

Air Liquide Changshu Co., Ltd (2)
No 8 Yehui Road Economic Development Zone, Changshu, 215536, Sichuan, China
Tel.: (86) 51252656623
Industrial Gas Mfr
N.A.I.C.S.: 325120

L'AIR LIQUIDE S.A.

INTERNATIONAL PUBLIC

L'Air Liquide S.A.—(Continued)

Air Liquide Dalian Co., Ltd (2)
Rm 1505 Yoma International Financial Center No 128 Jinma Road, Dalian, 116600, China
Tel.: (86) 411 87921970
Web Site: http://www.cn.airliquide.com
Sales Range: $25-49.9 Million
Emp.: 50
Industrial Gas Mfr
N.A.I.C.S.: 325120
Chant Kein *(Gen Mgr)*

Air Liquide Engineering Services Asia (Shanghai) Company Ltd (2)
6th Floor A3 Building Cao He Jing Modern Service High-tech Park, Shanghai, 200233, China
Tel.: (86) 21 60919000
Web Site: http://www.cn.airliquide.com
Engineeering Services
N.A.I.C.S.: 541330

Air Liquide Hangzhou Co., Ltd (2)
No 1-1 Miaochangqiao Road Gouzhuang Industrial Park, Yuhang District, Hangzhou, 311112, China
Tel.: (86) 571 89019118
Web Site: http://www.cn.airliquide.com
Sales Range: $150-199.9 Million
Emp.: 800
Construction Engineering Services
N.A.I.C.S.: 541330

Air Liquide Healthcare (2)
Building 18 No 1515 Gumei Road, Shanghai, 200233, China
Tel.: (86) 21 60903688
Web Site: http://www.cn.airliquide.com
Health Care Srvices
N.A.I.C.S.: 621999

Air Liquide Shanghai Co., Ltd (2)
Building 18 No 1515 Gumei Road, Shanghai, 200233, China
Tel.: (86) 21 60903688
Emp.: 17
Industrial Gas Mfr
N.A.I.C.S.: 325120
Marcelo Fioranelli *(Pres)*

Air Liquide Shanghai International Trading Co., Ltd (2)
No 18 Bldg No 1515 Gumei Rd, Shanghai, 244023, China
Tel.: (86) 2160903688
Emp.: 1,000
Chemical Product Whslr
N.A.I.C.S.: 424690
Marcelo Fiolonelli *(Pres)*

Air Liquide Shenyang Teisan Co., Ltd (2)
No 26 Xihe Ninth North Street Shenyang Economic and Technical Developme, Shenyang, 110142, China
Tel.: (86) 24 25175856
Web Site: http://www.cn.airliquide.com
Industrial & Medical Gas Mfr
N.A.I.C.S.: 325120

Air Liquide Tianjin Co., Ltd (2)
21F Tianxin Building No 125 Weidi Road, Hexi District, Tianjin, 300074, China
Tel.: (86) 22 28408422
Web Site: http://www.cn.airliquide.com
Emp.: 300
Industrial Gas Mfr
N.A.I.C.S.: 325120

Air Liquide (Pty) Limited (1)
Cnr Vereeniging and Andre Marais streets, PO Box 124200, Gauteng, Alberton, 1451, Gauteng, South Africa
Tel.: (27) 872881100
Web Site: https://www.airliquide.com
Emp.: 600
Industrial Medical Gas Mfr
N.A.I.C.S.: 325120

Subsidiary (Non-US):

Air Liquide Botswana Properietary Limited (2)
Plot 5638 Nakedi Road, PO Box 40431, BroadHurst Industrial Site, Gaborone, Botswana
Tel.: (267) 391 2988
Web Site: https://www.airliquide.com

Emp.: 50
Industrial Gas Mfr
N.A.I.C.S.: 325120

Air Liquide Advanced Materials, Inc. (1)
3121 Route 22 E Ste 200, Branchburg, NJ 08876
Tel.: (908) 231-9060
N.A.I.C.S.: 325998

Air Liquide Advanced Technologies S.A. (1)
2 Rue De Clemenciere, BP 15, 38360, Sassenage, France
Tel.: (33) 47 643 6030
Web Site: https://advancedtech.airliquide.com
Emp.: 1,000
Industrial Gas Mfr
N.A.I.C.S.: 325120

Air Liquide Algerie - SIDAL Spa (1)
02 Boulevard Aissatidir Place 1er Mai, Algiers, Algeria
Tel.: (213) 21 65 06 58
Oil & Gas Exploration Services
N.A.I.C.S.: 213112

Air Liquide America Corporation (1)
9811 Katy Fwy Ste 100, Houston, TX 77024 **(100%)**
Tel.: (713) 624-8000
Web Site: https://industry.airliquide.us
Sales Range: $250-299.9 Million
Emp.: 600
Supplier of Industrial Gases
N.A.I.C.S.: 325120

Subsidiary (Domestic):

American Air Liquide Holdings, Inc. (2)
2700 Post Oak Blvd Ste 1800, Houston, TX 77056
Tel.: (877) 855-9533
Industrial Gas Mfr
N.A.I.C.S.: 325120
Patrick J. Moore *(Chm-North American Review Board)*

Air Liquide Angola Ltda (1)
Rua do Patriota Nr188 Benfica, Luanda, Angola
Tel.: (244) 944259415
Web Site: http://www.airliquide.com
Emp.: 40
Industrial Gas Mfr
N.A.I.C.S.: 325120

Air Liquide Arabia LLC (1)
King Fahd Bin Abdul Aziz Street Tuwairqi Tower 15th Floor, PO Box 2335, 31952, Al Khobar, Saudi Arabia
Tel.: (966) 138366668
Emp.: 400
Industrial Gas Mfr
N.A.I.C.S.: 325120

Air Liquide Asia - Pacific Co., Ltd (1)
1-9-1 Shinonome, Koto-Ku, Tokyo, 135-0062, Japan
Tel.: (81) 355738556
Industrial Gas Mfr
N.A.I.C.S.: 325120
Jean-Marc de Royere *(CEO)*

Air Liquide Australia Ltd. (1)
Level 12 600 St Kilda Road, Melbourne, 3004, VIC, Australia
Tel.: (61) 39 697 9888
Web Site: https://industry.airliquide.com.au
Emp.: 780
Industrial Gas Mfr & Distr
N.A.I.C.S.: 325120

Subsidiary (Domestic):

Air Liquide Healthcare P/L (2)
Unit 5/476 Gardeners Road, Alexandria, 2015, NSW, Australia
Tel.: (61) 2 9364 7474
Web Site: http://www.airliquidehealthcare.com.au
Sales Range: $10-24.9 Million
Emp.: 50
Medical Gas Distribution Services
N.A.I.C.S.: 621999
Yvoine McCort *(Mng Dir)*

Air Liquide Austria GmbH (1)

Sendnergasse 30, 2320, Schwechat, Austria
Tel.: (43) 170 1090
Web Site: https://industrie.airliquide.at
Emp.: 250
Industrial Gas Mfr
N.A.I.C.S.: 325120

Air Liquide B.V. (1)
Strijp T-Gebouw TQ5-5e verd Achtseweg Zuid 151 F, PO Box 7117, 5651 GW, Eindhoven, Netherlands **(100%)**
Tel.: (31) 20 795 6621
Web Site: http://www.airliquide.nl
Sales Range: $10-24.9 Million
Emp.: 400
Mfr of Industrial Gases
N.A.I.C.S.: 325120

Subsidiary (Non-US):

Air Liquide Acetylene B.V. (2)
Tel.: (31) 40 250 3920
Web Site: https://www.chemelot.nl
Sales Range: $25-49.9 Million
Emp.: 75
Acetylene Distr
N.A.I.C.S.: 424690

Subsidiary (Domestic):

Scott Speciality Gases Netherlands B.V. (2)
Takkebijsters 46-48, 4817 BL, Breda, Netherlands
Tel.: (31) 76 5711828
Sales Range: $25-49.9 Million
Emp.: 40
Industrial Gas Mfr
N.A.I.C.S.: 325120

VitalAire B.V. (2)
Strijp T Building TQ Achtseweg Zuid 151 F, 5651 GW, Eindhoven, Netherlands
Tel.: (31) 40 250 3503
Web Site: http://www.airliquide.nl
Medical Gas Mfr
N.A.I.C.S.: 325120

Air Liquide Belge S.A. (1)
Avenue du Bourget 44, 1130, Brussels, Belgium
Tel.: (32) 2 431 7200
Web Site: http://www.airliquide.be
Sales Range: $25-49.9 Million
Emp.: 40
Industrial Gas Mfr
N.A.I.C.S.: 325120

Subsidiary (Domestic):

Air Liquide Belgium S.A. (2)
Parc d affaires Zenobe Gramme Quai des Vennes 8, 4020, Liege, Belgium
Tel.: (32) 4 349 8989
Web Site: http://www.airliquide.be
Industrial Gas Mfr
N.A.I.C.S.: 325120

Air Liquide Benelux S.A. (2)
Siege Social Parc d'affaires Zenobe Gramme Quai des Vennes 8, Liege, 4020, Belgium
Tel.: (32) 43 49 89 89
Industrial Gas Mfr
N.A.I.C.S.: 325120

Air Liquide Medical S.A. (1)
Avenue du Bourget 44, 1130, Brussels, Belgium
Tel.: (32) 2 431 7200
Web Site: http://www.airliquide.be
Industrial Gas Mfr
N.A.I.C.S.: 325120

Air Liquide Bulgaria EOOD (1)
1 Business Park Sofia Street Build 7B Floor 5, 1766, Sofia, Bulgaria
Tel.: (359) 24899782
Web Site: https://www.airliquide.com
Sales Range: $25-49.9 Million
Emp.: 31
Industrial Gas Mfr & Distr
N.A.I.C.S.: 325120
Francis Bucquet *(Gen Mgr)*

Air Liquide Colombia S.A.S (1)
Cra 7 113-43, Bogota, Colombia
Tel.: (57) 17470305
Industrial Gas Mfr
N.A.I.C.S.: 325120

Air Liquide Danmark A.S. (1)
Hoje Taastrup Vej 42, 2630, Taastrup, Denmark
Tel.: (45) 4 355 5050
Web Site: https://dk.airliquide.com
Industrial Gas Mfr
N.A.I.C.S.: 325120

Air Liquide Deutschland GmbH (1)
Luise-Rainer-Strasse 5, 40235, Dusseldorf, Germany **(100%)**
Tel.: (49) 2116 699 3311
Web Site: https://de.airliquide.com
Sales Range: $125-149.9 Million
Emp.: 4,500
Mfr of Industrial Gases
N.A.I.C.S.: 325120

Subsidiary (Domestic):

AST Service GmbH (2)
Alter Flughafen 14a, 30179, Hannover, Germany
Tel.: (49) 511 350 66 26
Web Site: http://www.ast-service.org
Sales Range: $25-49.9 Million
Emp.: 18
Industrial Gas Mfr
N.A.I.C.S.: 325120

Air Liquide Electronics GmbH (2)
Bergener Ring 15, Ottendorf-Okrilla, 01458, Bautzen, Germany
Tel.: (49) 3 520 5610
Web Site: http://www.airliquide.de
Electronic Device & System Mfr
N.A.I.C.S.: 334419

Air Liquide Industriegase GmbH & Co. KG (2)
Luise Rainer Str 5, Dusseldorf, 40235, Germany
Tel.: (49) 211 66990
Web Site: http://www.airliquide.de
Emp.: 200
Industrial Gas Mfr
N.A.I.C.S.: 325120
Jill Gillesvanle *(Gen Mgr)*

Air Liquide Medical GmbH (2)
Luise-Rainer-Strasse 5, 40235, Dusseldorf, Germany
Tel.: (49) 211 669 9101
Web Site: https://www.airliquide-healthcare.de
Medical Gas Mfr
N.A.I.C.S.: 325120

Cryotherm GmbH & Co. KG (2)
Euteneuen 4 Sieg, Sieg, 57548, Kirchen, Germany
Tel.: (49) 27 419 5850
Web Site: https://www.cryotherminc.com
Insulated Container & Transfer Pipe Mfr
N.A.I.C.S.: 213112

EVC Dresden-Wilschdorf GmbH & Co. KG (2)
Rosenstr 32-34, Dresden, 01067, Saxony, Germany
Tel.: (49) 3518399330
Energy Consulting Services
N.A.I.C.S.: 541618
Kai Princkmann *(Gen Mgr)*

INTEGA GmbH (2)
Ammerthalstrasse 22, Kirchheim, 85551, Munich, Germany
Tel.: (49) 89 613 8720
Web Site: https://www.intega.com
Emp.: 170
Engineeering Services
N.A.I.C.S.: 541330

Air Liquide Dominicana (1)
Av Jose F Pena Gomez casi Esquina Carretera Sanchez vieja, Haina, San Cristobal, 91000, Dominican Republic
Tel.: (809) 594 8306
Web Site: https://www.airliquide.com
Oil & Gas Exploration Services
N.A.I.C.S.: 213112

Air Liquide Egypte S.a.e (1)
Polyom Building - 2nd floor Area 22 - 1st Sector Road, 90 Downtown 5th Settlement, 11835, New Cairo, Egypt
Tel.: (20) 22 322 1100
Web Site: https://www.airliquide.com
Emp.: 364

AND PRIVATE COMPANIES

L'AIR LIQUIDE S.A.

Industrial & Medical Gas Mfr & Distr
N.A.I.C.S.: 325120

Air Liquide Electronics Europe (1)
Tour Kupka C 14 Rue Hoche, La Defense, 92800, Paris, France
Tel.: (33) 155915505
Web Site: http://www.airliquide.com
Mfr & Distr of Specialized Gases for the Electronics Industry
N.A.I.C.S.: 325120

Subsidiary (Domestic):

Ales - Air Liquide Electronics Systems (2)
8 rue des Meridiens, 38130, Echirolles, France **(100%)**
Tel.: (33) 43 849 8800
Web Site: https://ales.airliquide.com
Sales Range: $50-74.9 Million
Emp.: 103
Mfr & Distribution of Specialised Gases & Chemicals for the Electronics Industry
N.A.I.C.S.: 325120
Vinod Romain *(CEO)*

Air Liquide Electronics Materials S.A. (1)
6 Rue Cognacq Jay, Paris, 75007, France
Tel.: (33) 1 40 62 55 55
Web Site: http://www.airliquide.com
Industrial Gas Mfr
N.A.I.C.S.: 325120
Werner Schleser *(Dir-Technical)*

Air Liquide Electronics Systems Asia Ltd. (1)
3F No 28 Keya Road, Taya District, Taichung, Taiwan
Tel.: (886) 425681800
Emp.: 40
Industrial Gas Mfr
N.A.I.C.S.: 325120

Air Liquide Electronics Systems S.A. (1)
8 Rue Des Meridiens-Sud Galaxie, 38130, Echirolles, France
Tel.: (33) 438498800
Web Site: http://www.ales.airliquide.com
Gas Distributing Equipment Mfr
N.A.I.C.S.: 333132

Air Liquide Emirates For Industrial Gases LLC (1)
Plot No B34B02A Jebel Ali Free Zone Authority, PO Box 263844, Jebel Ali, Dubai, United Arab Emirates
Tel.: (971) 800253647
Emp.: 100
Industrial Gas Mfr
N.A.I.C.S.: 325120

Air Liquide Engineering Middle East (1)
Salam Tower 11th Floor Corniche Road, PO Box 24471, Doha, Qatar
Tel.: (974) 4 496 1666
Web Site: https://www.airliquide.com
Industrial Gas Mfr & Distr
N.A.I.C.S.: 424690

Air Liquide Engineering S.A. (1)
7 Rue Cognacq Jay, 75007, Paris, France
Tel.: (33) 1 40 62 55 55
Industrial & Medical Gas Mfr
N.A.I.C.S.: 325120

Air Liquide Espana SA (1)
Paseo De La Castellana 35, Madrid, 28046, Spain **(100%)**
Tel.: (34) 915029300
Sales Range: $50-74.9 Million
Emp.: 200
Mfr of Industrial Gases
N.A.I.C.S.: 325120

Air Liquide Far Eastern Ltd. (1)
7F No 399 Ruiguang Road, Neihu District, Taipei, Taiwan
Tel.: (886) 277342988
Emp.: 650
Industrial Gas Mfr
N.A.I.C.S.: 325120

Air Liquide Finance SA (1)
75 quai d Orsay, 75007, Paris, Cedex 07, France
Tel.: (33) 14 062 5555

Web Site: https://www.airliquide.com
Emp.: 600
Financial Management Services
N.A.I.C.S.: 523999

Air Liquide France Industrie S.A. (1)
152 Avenue Aristide Briand CS 80010, 92227, Bagneux, Cedex, France
Tel.: (33) 481680068
Industrial Gas Mfr
N.A.I.C.S.: 325120

Air Liquide Gas A.B. (1)
Lundavagen 151, 212 24, Malmo, Sweden
Tel.: (46) 4 038 1000
Web Site: https://se.airliquide.com
Sales Range: $25-49.9 Million
Emp.: 95
Industrial Gas Mfr
N.A.I.C.S.: 325120

Subsidiary (Domestic):

Aiolos Medical A.B. (2)
Zakrisdalsvagen 26B / Z64, 653 42, Karlstad, Sweden
Tel.: (46) 54 534805
Web Site: http://www.aiolos.se
Sales Range: $25-49.9 Million
Emp.: 13
Medical Device & Equipment Mfr
N.A.I.C.S.: 339112

Subsidiary (Non-US):

Air Liquide Medicinal SL (2)
Paseo de La Castellana 35, 28046, Madrid, Spain **(100%)**
Tel.: (34) 915029300
Web Site: http://www.airliquidemedicinal.es
Mfr & Supply of Medicinal Gases & Equipment
N.A.I.C.S.: 339112

Air Liquide Gaz San. Ve Tic. A.S. (1)
Resitpasa Mah Eski Buyukdere Cad Park Plaza No 14 Kat 2 Daire 8, Maslak Sariyer, 34398, Istanbul, Turkiye
Tel.: (90) 2123451140
Web Site: https://tr.airliquide.com

Air Liquide Global E&C Solutions Canada LP (1)
888-3rd Street S W Suite 4300 Bankers Hall West, Calgary, T2P 5C5, AB, Canada
Tel.: (403) 774-4300
Industrial Gas Mfr
N.A.I.C.S.: 325120

Air Liquide Global E&C Solutions France S.A. (1)
18 Quai Jules Guesde, 94407, Vitry-sur-Seine, France
Tel.: (33) 148826664
Web Site: https://engineering.airliquide.com
N.A.I.C.S.: 221210
Philippe Merino *(VP-Air Liquide, Supervising Engrg, and Construction)*

Air Liquide Global E&C Solutions Germany GmbH (1)
Olof-Palme-Str 35, 60439, Frankfurt am Main, Germany
Tel.: (49) 6958080
Industrial Gas Mfr
N.A.I.C.S.: 325120

Air Liquide Global E&C Solutions Japan K.K (1)
7-1-15 Goko-dori, Chuo-ku, Kobe, 651-0087, Japan
Tel.: (81) 782650201
Industrial Gas Mfr
N.A.I.C.S.: 325120

Air Liquide Global E&C Solutions Singapore Pte. Ltd. (1)
No 2 Venture Drive 22-28 Vision Exchange, Singapore, 608526, Singapore
Tel.: (65) 62760160
Industrial Gas Mfr
N.A.I.C.S.: 325120

Air Liquide Global E&C Solutions US, Inc. (1)
9811 Katy Fwy, Houston, TX 77024
Tel.: (713) 624-8000
Industrial Gas Mfr
N.A.I.C.S.: 325120

Subsidiary (Domestic):

Air Liquide USA LLC (2)
9811 Katy Frwy Ste 100, Houston, TX 77024
Tel.: (713) 624-8000
Web Site: https://industry.airliquide.us
Emp.: 20,000
Industrial Gas Mfr
N.A.I.C.S.: 325120
Michael J. Graff *(Pres & CEO)*

Subsidiary (Domestic):

Air Liquide Advanced Technologies U.S. LLC (3)
200 GBC Dr, Newark, DE 19702-2462
Tel.: (302) 225-1100
Web Site:
http://www.advancedtech.airliquide.com
Cryogenic Equipment Mfr
N.A.I.C.S.: 332420

Air Liquide America L.P. (3)
821 Chesapeake Dr, Cambridge, MD 21613
Tel.: (410) 228-6400
Web Site: http://www.calgaz.com
Sales Range: $25-49.9 Million
Emp.: 60
Gas Calibration & Regulation Equipment Mfr
N.A.I.C.S.: 325120
John Keating *(Gen Mgr)*

Air Liquide America Specialty Gases LLC (3)
6141 Easton Rd, Plumsteadville, PA 18949-0310
Tel.: (215) 766-8861
Web Site: http://www.scottgas.com
Sales Range: $75-99.9 Million
Emp.: 600
Pure Gases, Gas Mixtures, Pure & Mixed Gases In Disposable Containers, Gas Handling Equipment & Services
N.A.I.C.S.: 325120
Christophe Tardieu *(Gen Mgr)*

Subsidiary (Non-US):

Air Liquide Argentina S.A. (3)
Monsenor Magliano 3079, B1642GLA, San Isidro, Buenos Aires, Argentina
Tel.: (54) 114 708 2200
Web Site: https://www.airliquide.com
Sales Range: $125-149.9 Million
Emp.: 415
Industrial & Medical Gas Mfr
N.A.I.C.S.: 325120

Air Liquide Brasil S.A. (3)
Av Morumbi 8234 3 andar, Santo Amaro, Sao Paulo, 04703-901, Brazil **(100%)**
Tel.: (55) 1155098300
Web Site: https://www.airliquide.com.br
Sales Range: $125-149.9 Million
Emp.: 1,200
Mfr & Sale of Industrial Gases
N.A.I.C.S.: 325120

Air Liquide Canada Inc. (3)
1250 boul Rene-Levesque West Suite 1700, Montreal, H3B 5E6, QC, Canada **(100%)**
Tel.: (514) 878-1667
Web Site: https://www.airliquide.ca
Sales Range: $50-74.9 Million
Emp.: 2,500
Mfr of Industrial Gases
N.A.I.C.S.: 325120
Adam Peters *(Pres & CEO)*

Subsidiary (Domestic):

Keops (4)
1155 University St Ste 1100, Montreal, H3B 3A7, QC, Canada **(100%)**
Tel.: (514) 876-2855
Web Site: http://www.keops.com
Sales Range: $25-49.9 Million
Emp.: 70
Information Technology Solutions
N.A.I.C.S.: 541512
Christian Morin *(Pres)*

Subsidiary (Non-US):

Air Liquide Chile S.A. (3)
Avenida Kennedy 5454 Oficina 801, Vitacura, Santiago, Chile

Tel.: (56) 22 465 7600
Web Site: https://www.industrial.airliquide.cl
Industrial Gas Mfr
N.A.I.C.S.: 325120.

Subsidiary (Domestic):

Air Liquide Electronics U.S. LP (3)
9101 LBJ Freeway Ste 800, Dallas, TX 75243
Tel.: (972) 301-5200
Web Site: http://www.airliquide.com
Specialized Gases Distr
N.A.I.C.S.: 423830

Branch (Domestic):

Air Liquide Electronics U.S. LP - California (4)
46409 Landing Pkwy, Fremont, CA 94538
Tel.: (510) 657-0600
Web Site: http://www.airliquide.com
Rev.: $10,000,000
Emp.: 30
Testing Laboratories
N.A.I.C.S.: 541380
Pierre Michel Dufour *(Sr Exec VP)*

Air Liquide Healthcare America Corporation (4)
2700 Post Oak Blvd Ste 1800, Houston, TX 77056
Tel.: (713) 896-2816
Web Site:
http://www.us.airliquidehealthcare.com
Medical Gas Distr
N.A.I.C.S.: 423450
John Welch *(Mgr-Mktg & Medical Gas Svc)*

Air Liquide Helium America, Inc. (4)
9811 Katy Freeway, Houston, TX 77024
Tel.: (713) 624-8000
Web Site: http://www.airliquide.com
Industrial Gas Mfr
N.A.I.C.S.: 325120

Air Liquide Industrial U.S. LP (4)
12800 W Little York Rd, Houston, TX 77041
Tel.: (713) 896-2315
Web Site: http://www.airliquide.com
Emp.: 300
Industrial Gas Distr
N.A.I.C.S.: 221210
Clarke Hayes *(Dir-Logistics Excellence)*

Subsidiary (Domestic):

Air Liquide Large Industries U.S. LP (4)
8000 N County Rd 225 E, Pittsboro, IN 46167
Tel.: (317) 892-5221
Emp.: 7
Industrial Gas Mfr
N.A.I.C.S.: 325120
Cari Carter *(Office Mgr)*

Air Liquide Process & Construction, Inc. (4)
2700 Post Oak Blvd, Houston, TX 77056-5784
Tel.: (713) 624-8800
Engineeering Services
N.A.I.C.S.: 541330

Subsidiary (Non-US):

Air Liquide Mexico (3)
Jose Clemente Orozco 329 Col Valle Oriente, San Pedro Garza Garcia, 66269, Nuevo Leon, Mexico
Tel.: (52) 818 851 0600
Web Site: http://www.airliquide.com
Sales Range: $25-49.9 Million
Emp.: 55
Industrial Gas Mfr
N.A.I.C.S.: 325120

Air Liquide Uruguay SA (3)
Sede Central Ave Burgues 3230, Montevideo, Uruguay
Tel.: (598) 2203 4203
Industrial Gas Mfr
N.A.I.C.S.: 325120

Subsidiary (Domestic):

Airgas, Inc. (3)
259 N Radnor-Chester Rd Ste 100, Radnor, PA 19087-5283
Tel.: (610) 687-5253

L'AIR LIQUIDE S.A.

L'Air Liquide S.A.—(Continued)
Web Site: https://www.airgas.com
Sales Range: $5-14.9 Billion
Emp.: 18,000
Holding Company; Industrial, Specialty & Medical Gases & Equipment Distr; Welding Equipment & Safety Products Distr
N.A.I.C.S.: 551112
Kent Carter *(Pres-Northeast Reg)*

Subsidiary (Non-US):

Airgas Canada Inc. (4)
#1 931 Ellery Street, Victoria, V9A 4R9, BC, Canada **(100%)**
Tel.: (250) 383-2442
Web Site: http://www.airgas.com
Medical, Industrial & Specialty Gases, Welding & Welding Equipment Whslr
N.A.I.C.S.: 423840

Unit (Domestic):

Airgas East (4)
850 Cassatt Rd Ste 100, Berwyn, PA 19312
Tel.: (484) 913-9730
Web Site: http://www.airgas.com
Sales Range: $75-99.9 Million
Emp.: 100
Industrial Gas Distr
N.A.I.C.S.: 424690
Jack Appolonia *(Pres)*

Airgas Great Lakes (4)
5420 Warner Rd, Cleveland, OH 44125 **(100%)**
Tel.: (216) 447-8878
Web Site: http://www.airgas.com
Industrial, Medical & Specialty Gases Distr; Safety & Welding Supplies
N.A.I.C.S.: 423830
Jeff Cass *(Pres)*

Airgas Gulf Coast (4)
201 W Wally Wilkerson, Houston, TX 77380
Tel.: (281) 447-7400
Web Site: http://www.airgas.com
Emp.: 100
Industrial, Medical & Specialty Gases & Welding Equipment Distr
N.A.I.C.S.: 423840
Jason Favre *(Pres)*

Subsidiary (Domestic):

Airgas Merchant Gases, LLC (4)
6055 Rockside Woods Blvd 500, Cleveland, OH 44131-2301
Tel.: (216) 642-6600
Web Site: http://www.airgas.com
Gas Products Mfr & Distr
N.A.I.C.S.: 325120
Thomas R. Stringer *(Pres)*

Unit (Domestic):

Airgas Mid-America (4)
2950 Industrial Dr, Bowling Green, KY 42102-1117 **(100%)**
Tel.: (270) 842-9489
Web Site: http://www.airgas.com
Emp.: 50
Industrial, Medical & Specialty Gases Distr; Safety & Welding Supplies
N.A.I.C.S.: 424690
James Robert Hilliard *(Pres)*

Airgas Mid-South (4)
31 N Peoria Ave, Tulsa, OK 74120 **(100%)**
Tel.: (918) 582-0885
Web Site: http://www.airgas.com
Emp.: 900
Industrial, Medical & Specialty Gases, Safety & Welding Supplies Distr
N.A.I.C.S.: 423840
Bob Bradshaw *(Pres)*

Airgas National Welders (4)
5311 77 Centre Dr, Charlotte, NC 28217
Tel.: (704) 333-5475
Web Site: http://www.airgas.com
Sales Range: $300-349.9 Million
Emp.: 1,000
Cryogenic, Industrial, Medical, Specialty & Refrigerant Gases Mfr & Distr; Welding Supplies & Equipment Distr
N.A.I.C.S.: 325120
Tony Martin *(Controller)*

Airgas North Central (4)
3400 N Executive Dr, Appleton, WI 54911
Tel.: (920) 734-7173
Web Site: http://www.airgas.com
Industrial & Medical Gases, Welding Equipment & Supplies Whslr
N.A.I.C.S.: 423840
Denton Thompson *(Pres)*

Airgas North Pacific (4)
3632 NE Columbia Blvd, Portland, OR 97211 **(100%)**
Tel.: (503) 288-2527
Web Site: http://www.airgas.com
Emp.: 50
Industrial, Medical & Specialty Gases & Safety & Welding Supplies Whslr
N.A.I.C.S.: 423840
William Sanborn *(Pres)*

Airgas Northeast (4)
130 Cross Rd, Waterford, CT 06385
Tel.: (860) 442-0363
Web Site: http://www.airgas.com
Industrial, Medical & Specialty Gases Distr
N.A.I.C.S.: 424690

Airgas Northern California & Nevada (4)
1725 69th St, Sacramento, CA 95819 **(100%)**
Tel.: (916) 379-1069
Web Site: http://www.airgas.com
Sales Range: $250-299.9 Million
Emp.: 450
Industrial, Medical & Specialty Gases; Safety & Welding Supplies
N.A.I.C.S.: 423840
Matthew B. Whitton *(Pres)*

Subsidiary (Domestic):

Airgas Priority Nitrogen, LLC (4)
681 River Highlands Blvd, Covington, LA 70433
Sales Range: $10-24.9 Million
Oilfield Services, Including Nitrogen Pumping Services
N.A.I.C.S.: 213112
Chris Abide *(Pres)*

Airgas Safety, Inc. (4)
2501 Green Ln, Levittown, PA 19057
Tel.: (215) 826-9000
Web Site: http://www.airgas.com
Sales Range: $150-199.9 Million
Emp.: 200
Industrial Safety Products Distr
N.A.I.C.S.: 423990
Donald S. Carlino *(Pres)*

Unit (Domestic):

Airgas Southeast (4)
109 P Rickman Industrial Dr, Holly Springs, GA 30115 **(100%)**
Tel.: (770) 345-0028
Web Site: http://www.airgas.com
Emp.: 4,000
Distr of Industrial, Medical & Specialty Gases & Safety & Welding Supplies
N.A.I.C.S.: 423830
Kevin M. McBride *(Pres)*

Airgas Southwest (4)
2615 Joe Field Rd, Dallas, TX 75229 **(100%)**
Tel.: (972) 620-6215
Web Site: http://www.airgas.com
Emp.: 150
Distr of Industrial, Medical & Specialty Gases, Safety & Welding Supplies
N.A.I.C.S.: 423840
Brent Sparks *(Pres)*

Subsidiary (Domestic):

Airgas Specialty Products, Inc. (4)
2530 Sever Rd Ste 300, Lawrenceville, GA 30043
Web Site: http://www.airgasspecialtyproducts.com
Emp.: 15
Specialty Chemical Whslr
N.A.I.C.S.: 424690
Joseph P. Sullivan *(Pres)*

Unit (Domestic):

Airgas West (4)
8103 Alondra Blvd, Paramount, CA 90723 **(100%)**
Tel.: (562) 633-5171
Web Site: http://www.airgas.com
Industrial, Medical & Specialty Gas; Safety & Welding Supplies Distr
N.A.I.C.S.: 424690
Cory Garner *(Pres)*

Subsidiary (Non-US):

Airgas, S.A. de C.V. (4)
Matamoros No 860, Reynosa, 88780, Mexico
Tel.: (52) 8999268800
Web Site: http://www.airgas.com
Industrial Gas Mfr
N.A.I.C.S.: 325120

Red-D-Arc Limited (4)
667 South Service Road, PO Box 40, Grimsby, L3M 4G1, ON, Canada **(100%)**
Tel.: (905) 643-4212
Web Site: https://www.red-d-arc.com
Sales Range: $10-24.9 Million
Emp.: 80
Welding Equipment Rental, Sales & Service
N.A.I.C.S.: 532490
Steve Featherstone *(VP-Mktg)*

Subsidiary (Non-US):

Red-D-Arc (FR) SAS (5)
Bat 3142 - Quai du Rhin, BP 91362, 76065, Le Havre, Cedex, France
Tel.: (33) 23 272 4606
Web Site: https://www.red-d-arc.fr
Emp.: 10
Industrial Machinery & Equipment Whslr & Rental Services
N.A.I.C.S.: 423830

Red-D-Arc (Netherlands) B.V. (5)
Nijverheidsweg 32 E, 3251 LP, Stellendam, Netherlands
Tel.: (31) 187490277
Web Site: http://www.red-d-arc.nl
Welding Equipment Rentals & Leasing
N.A.I.C.S.: 532490
Rob Quist *(Mgr-Weld Automation)*

Subsidiary (Domestic):

Red-D-Arc B.V. (6)
Nijverheidsweg 32, 3251 LP, Stellendam, Netherlands
Tel.: (31) 18 749 0277
Web Site: https://www.red-d-arc.nl
Emp.: 13
Industrial Machinery & Equipment Sales & Rentals
N.A.I.C.S.: 423830

Subsidiary (Non-US):

Red-D-Arc Ltd. (5)
Unit 9 Station Rd, Industrial Estate Sutton, Saint Helens, WA9 3JG, Merseyside, United Kingdom
Tel.: (44) 174 485 0085
Web Site: https://www.red-d-arc.uk
Industrial Equipment Rental & Leasing
N.A.I.C.S.: 532490

Unit (US):

Red-D-Arc, Inc. (5)
7060 Mableton Pkwy SE, Mableton, GA 30126-4617
Tel.: (678) 460-0120
Web Site: https://www.red-d-arc.com
Emp.: 10
Welding Machines & Tools Sales & Rental Services
N.A.I.C.S.: 532490
Lia Lyons *(Mgr-Collections)*

Subsidiary (Non-US):

Red-D-Arc, S.A. de C.V. (5)
Zona Industrial Bruno Paglia, R/A Anacleto Canabal 2da Seccion, 91697, Veracruz, Tabasco, Mexico
Tel.: (52) 2299812900
Web Site: https://www.red-d-arc.mx
Industrial Machinery & Equipment Whslr & Rental Services
N.A.I.C.S.: 423830

Subsidiary (Domestic):

Tech Air, Incorporated (4)
152 CT-163, Uncasville, CT 06382

INTERNATIONAL PUBLIC

Tel.: (860) 848-1287
Gas (Industrial, Medical, Specialty) Distribution Services
N.A.I.C.S.: 221210

Subsidiary (Domestic):

Scully Welding Supply Corp. (5)
309 Oak Ln, Collingdale, PA 19023
Welding, Industrial & Safety Supplies Mfr
N.A.I.C.S.: 333992

Air Liquide Healthcare Espana SL (1)
Paseo de Castellana 79, 28046, Madrid, Spain
Tel.: (34) 915029300
Emp.: 1,500
Industrial Gas Mfr
N.A.I.C.S.: 325120

Air Liquide Healthcare Ireland Limited (1)
Unit 8a Keypoint business Park, Ballycoolin, Dublin, Ireland
Tel.: (353) 1 809 1800
Web Site: https://www.airliquidehealthcare.ie
Women Healthcare Services
N.A.I.C.S.: 621610

Air Liquide Hellas S.A. (1)
Voriou Ipirou 74 - 76 & Konitsis, 151 25, Maroussi, Greece
Tel.: (30) 210 5582700
Web Site: http://www.airliquide.com
Sales Range: $50-74.9 Million
Emp.: 110
Industrial Gas Mfr & Distr
N.A.I.C.S.: 325120

Air Liquide Hydrogen Energy SA. (1)
1 Chemin de la Porte des Loges, BP 126, 78350, Les Loges-en-Josas, France
Tel.: (33) 1 39 07 64 96
Web Site: http://www.airliquide-hydrogen-energy.com
Sales Range: $50-74.9 Million
Emp.: 35
Hydrogen Filling Station Operator
N.A.I.C.S.: 221111
Armelle Coulombeau *(Dir-Fin)*

Air Liquide India Holding Pvt. Ltd. (1)
A-24/9 Mohan Co-Operative Industrial Estate Mathura Road, Behind American Express, New Delhi, 110044, India
Tel.: (91) 11 40550200
Sales Range: $125-149.9 Million
Emp.: 300
Industrial Gas Mfr
N.A.I.C.S.: 325120

Subsidiary (Domestic):

Pure Helium India Pvt. Ltd. (2)
406 Balarama Bandra-Kurla Complex, Bandra East, Mumbai, 400 051, India
Tel.: (91) 22 2659 1911
Sales Range: $50-74.9 Million
Emp.: 14
Liquid Helium & Diving Gases Distr
N.A.I.C.S.: 221210

Air Liquide Industrie B.V. (1)
Corkstraat 46, 3047 AC, Rotterdam, Netherlands
Tel.: (31) 102622077
Web Site: https://www.airliquide.com
Emp.: 400
Natural Gas Distribution Services
N.A.I.C.S.: 221210

Subsidiary (Domestic):

Maasvlakte Energie B.V. (2)
Corkstraat 46, 3047 AC, Rotterdam, Netherlands
Tel.: (31) 10 2622077
Eletric Power Generation Services
N.A.I.C.S.: 221118

Air Liquide Industries Belgium S.A. (1)
Avenue du Bourget-Bourgetlaan 44, Bruxelles, 1130, Brussels, Belgium
Tel.: (32) 24317200
Industrial Gas Mfr
N.A.I.C.S.: 325120

Air Liquide International S.A. (1)

AND PRIVATE COMPANIES

75 Quai d Orsay, Paris, 75007, France
Tel.: (33) 1 40 62 55 55
Holding Company
N.A.I.C.S.: 551112

Air Liquide Italia Srl (1)
Via Calabria 31, 20158, Milan,
Italy (100%)
Tel.: (39) 0240261
Web Site: https://it.airliquide.com
Sales Range: $125-149.9 Million
Emp.: 1,500
Mfr of Industrial Gases
N.A.I.C.S.: 325120

Subsidiary (Domestic):

Air Liquide Italia Service S.r.l. (2)
Via Calabria 31, Milan, 20158, Italy
Tel.: (39) 024 0261
Industrial Gas Mfr & Distr
N.A.I.C.S.: 325120

Air Liquide Sanita S.p.A (2)
Via Del Bosco Rinnovato 6 Edificio U7
Milanofiori Nord, 20094, Assago, Italy
Tel.: (39) 0240211
Mfr & Supplier of Medical Gases & Infection Control Solutions
N.A.I.C.S.: 339112

Markos-Mefar S.p.A (2)
Via del Prati, 62, Bovezzo, 25073, Brescia, Italy
Tel.: (39) 030 20159
Web Site: http://www.markosmefar.it
Mfr of Aerosol Therapy & Respiratory Equipment
N.A.I.C.S.: 334510

Tecno Gas S.r.l. (2)
Via Giotto 28, 20032, Cormano, MI, Italy
Tel.: (39) 026 630 5380
Web Site: https://www.tecnogas.eu
Plumbing & Heating Equipment Mfr
N.A.I.C.S.: 326191

Air Liquide Japan Ltd. (1)
Grand Park Tower 3-4-1 Shibaura, Minato-ku, Tokyo, 108-8509, Japan (100%)
Tel.: (81) 36 414 6700
Web Site: https://industry.airliquide.jp
Sales Range: $1-4.9 Billion
Emp.: 2,000
Industrial & Medical Gas Mfr & Plant Engineering
N.A.I.C.S.: 325120

Subsidiary (Domestic):

Air Liquide Engineering Japan, Co. (2)
16 Hijima Harima-cho, Hyogo, 675-0181, Japan
Tel.: (81) 794372714
Web Site: http://www.jp.airliquide.com
Sales Range: $50-74.9 Million
Emp.: 100
Gas Plant Engineering & Construction Services
N.A.I.C.S.: 236210
Takao Yamamoto *(VP-Products & Strategic Plng)*

Japan Air Gases, Co. (2)
9 1 Shinonome 1 chome, Koto ku, Tokyo, 135 0062, Japan (100%)
Tel.: (81) 335362330
Industrial & Medical Gas Mfr
N.A.I.C.S.: 325120

Toshiba Nano Analysis K.K. (2)
8 Shinsugita-cho, Isogo-ku, Yokohama, 235-8522, Japan
Tel.: (81) 45 770 3428
Web Site: https://www.nanoanalysis.co.jp
Emp.: 319
Medical Research & Development Services
N.A.I.C.S.: 541715

Subsidiary (Domestic):

Toshiba Nanoanalysis Corporation (3)
8 Shinsugita-cho, Isogo-ku, Yokohama, 212-8583, Kanagawa, Japan (51%)
Tel.: (81) 45 770 3428
Web Site: https://www.nanoanalysis.co.jp
Sales Range: $150-199.5 Million
Emp.: 253

Semiconductor Devices Evaluation & Analysis Services
N.A.I.C.S.: 334413
Masanori Tomatsu *(Pres & CEO)*

Air Liquide Korea Co., Ltd. (1)
11th floor 501 Teheran-ro Samseong-dong Vplex, Gangnam-gu, Seoul, 06168, Korea (South)
Tel.: (82) 23 019 2500
Web Site: https://industry.airliquide.kr
Emp.: 413
Industrial Gas Mfr
N.A.I.C.S.: 325120

Air Liquide Luxembourg S.A. (1)
Zone PE D Grand Duche du Luxembourg, BP 20, Rodange, Luxembourg
Tel.: (352) 50 62 63 1
Industrial Gas Mfr & Distr
N.A.I.C.S.: 325120

Air Liquide Malaysia Sdn Bhd (1)
Level 17 1Powerhouse Persiaran Bandar Utama, Bandar Utama, 47800, Petaling Jaya, Selangor, Malaysia
Tel.: (60) 327123128
Web Site: http://www.airliquide.com
Industrial Gas Mfr
N.A.I.C.S.: 325120

Subsidiary (Domestic):

SIG Gases Berhad (2)
Plo 137 Kawasan Perindustrian Senai III, 81400, Johor Bahru, Johor, Malaysia
Tel.: (60) 75983863
Web Site: http://www.siggases.com
Industrial Gas Mfr
N.A.I.C.S.: 325120

Southern Industrial Gas Sdn. Bhd. (2)
Plot 37 Kawasan Perindustrain Senai III, Senai, 81400, Johor Bahru, Johor, Malaysia
Tel.: (60) 75983863
Liquid Oxygen & Nitrogen Mfr
N.A.I.C.S.: 325120
Peh Lam Hoh *(Founder)*

Air Liquide Maroc S.A. (1)
Lotissement Attaoufik Sidi Maarouf n 16/18 imm Jet Business Class 4 et, 20270, Casablanca, Morocco
Tel.: (212) 52 276 2000
Web Site: http://www.airliquide.com
Sales Range: $125-149.9 Million
Emp.: 250
Industrial Gas Mfr
N.A.I.C.S.: 325120

Air Liquide Medical Systems S.A. (1)
Parc de Haute Technologie 6 Rue Georges Besse, 92182, Antony, Cedex, France
Tel.: (33) 14 096 6600
Web Site: https://www.device.airliquidehealth.com
Emp.: 200
Respiratory Assistance Equipment Mfr & Distr
N.A.I.C.S.: 339113
Jean-Marc Giner *(CEO)*

Air Liquide Medicinal S.A. (1)
Rua Doutor Antonio Loureiro Borges 4-6 Arquiparque-Miraflores, 1495-131, Alges, Portugal
Tel.: (351) 214124500
Industrial Gas Mfr
N.A.I.C.S.: 325120

Air Liquide Middle East & North Africa FZCO (1)
Suite 829 West Wing Block B Dubai Airport Free Zone, PO Box 54638, Dubai, United Arab Emirates
Tel.: (971) 4 299 3444
Sales Range: $25-49.9 Million
Emp.: 60
Industrial Gas Mfr
N.A.I.C.S.: 325120

Subsidiary (Domestic):

Pure Helium Gulf FZE (2)
Near Round About 5 Jebel Ali Free Zone, PO Box 16848, Jebel Ali, United Arab Emirates
Tel.: (971) 4 8816001

L'AIR LIQUIDE S.A.

Web Site: http://www.airliquide.com
Sales Range: $50-74.9 Million
Emp.: 150
Industrial Gas Mfr & Distr
N.A.I.C.S.: 325120
Roderick Percha *(Chief Accountant)*

Air Liquide Mozambique Lda. (1)
Estrada Nacional 2 Km 5 5, Matola, Mozambique
Tel.: (258) 21750440
Emp.: 800
Industrial Gas Mfr
N.A.I.C.S.: 325120

Air Liquide Munay Tech Gases LLP (1)
Office 210 Turan Avenue 1, Nur-Sultan, 010000, Kazakhstan
Tel.: (7) 7172955027
Emp.: 60
Industrial Gas Mfr
N.A.I.C.S.: 325120

Air Liquide Namibia Proprietary Ltd. (1)
Main Gate-Smelter Road, Tsumeb, 9000, Namibia
Tel.: (264) 67222344
Emp.: 20
Industrial Gas Mfr
N.A.I.C.S.: 325120

Air Liquide New Zealand Ltd. (1)
19 Maurice Road, Auckland, 1642, New Zealand
Tel.: (64) 96223880
Industrial Gas Mfr
N.A.I.C.S.: 325120

Air Liquide Nigeria plc (1)
104/106 Lapido Street Matori, 21551, Ikeja, Lagos, Nigeria
Tel.: (234) 818 207 7190
Web Site: http://www.airliquide.com
Emp.: 85
Industrial Gas Mfr & Distr
N.A.I.C.S.: 221210

Air Liquide Norway AS (1)
Drammensveien 64B, 3050, Mjondalen, Norway
Tel.: (47) 3 227 4140
Web Site: https://no.airliquide.com
Sales Range: $25-49.9 Million
Emp.: 33
Industrial Gas Mfr
N.A.I.C.S.: 325120

Subsidiary (Domestic):

Air Liquide Offshore AS (2)
Bleivassveien 71, Agotnes, 5363, Norway
Tel.: (47) 56 33 44 33
Sales Range: $50-74.9 Million
Emp.: 10
Oil & Gas Exploration Services
N.A.I.C.S.: 213112
Dag Bogetvedt *(Gen Mgr)*

Air Liquide Panama S.A. (1)
Av Jose Agustin Arango, Juan Diaz, Panama, Panama
Tel.: (507) 2530483
Medical & Industrial Gas Distr
N.A.I.C.S.: 221210

Air Liquide Philippines Inc. (1)
12F Ecotower 32nd St cor 9th Ave Bonifacio Global City, Taguig, Taguig, 1634, Philippines
Tel.: (63) 2 838 1780
Web Site: https://industry.airliquide.ph
Sales Range: $75-99.9 Million
Emp.: 230
Industrial Gas Mfr & Distr
N.A.I.C.S.: 325120

Plant (Domestic):

Air Liquide Philippines Inc. - Main Plant (2)
Sandoval Avenue Barrio Pinagbuhatan, Pasig, Metro Manila, Philippines
Tel.: (63) 2 642 1274
Industrial Gas Mfr
N.A.I.C.S.: 325120

Air Liquide Polska Sp. z o.o (1)
Ul Jasnogorska 9, 31-358, Krakow, Poland
Tel.: (48) 12 627 9300

Web Site: https://przemysl.air-liquide.pl
Emp.: 800
Industrial Gas Mfr & Distr
N.A.I.C.S.: 213112

Air Liquide Progetti Italia S.p.A. (1)
Via Guglielmo Ciardi 9, 20148, Milan, Italy
Tel.: (39) 02 4021203
Industrial Gas Mfr
N.A.I.C.S.: 325120

Air Liquide Proprietary Ltd. (1)
Cnr Vereeniging and Andre Marais Streets, PO Box 124200, Alrode, 1451, Gauteng, South Africa
Tel.: (27) 872881100
Emp.: 600
Industrial Gas Mfr
N.A.I.C.S.: 325120

Air Liquide Reunion S.A. (1)
8 Rue Charles Darwin, 97420, Le Port, France
Tel.: (33) 262427980
Industrial Gas Mfr
N.A.I.C.S.: 325120

Air Liquide Romania S.r.l (1)
Euro Tower Building 7th Floor Strada Dinu Vintila 11, District 2, 021101, Bucharest, Romania
Tel.: (40) 31 130 4500
Web Site: http://www.airliquide.com
Emp.: 80
Industrial Gas Mfr
N.A.I.C.S.: 325120

Air Liquide Russie S.A. (1)
Kosmodamianskaya emb 52 building 2, 115035, Moscow, Russia
Tel.: (7) 4956412898
Web Site: https://ndustry.airliquide.ru
Emp.: 600
Industrial Gas Mfr
N.A.I.C.S.: 325120

Subsidiary (Domestic):

Air Liquide OOO (2)
Kosmodamianskaya nab 52 Bld 2, 115035, Moscow, Russia
Tel.: (7) 4956412898
Web Site: http://www.airliquide.com
Sales Range: $50-74.9 Million
Emp.: 200
Industrial Gas Mfr & Distr
N.A.I.C.S.: 325120

Air Liquide Sante (1)
28 rue d'Arcueil, 94250, Gentilly, Cedex, France (100%)
Tel.: (33) 14 198 7000
Web Site: http://www.airliquide.com
Sales Range: $25-49.9 Million
Emp.: 100
Mfr & Supplier of Medical Gases & Infection Control Solutions
N.A.I.C.S.: 339112

Subsidiary (Domestic):

Air Liquide Sante (International) (2)
Tour Ariane Paris la Defense 9, 92800, Puteaux, France
Tel.: (33) 1 44 11 00 00
Industrial Gas Mfr & Distr
N.A.I.C.S.: 325120

Air Liquide Sante France S.A. (2)
28 rue d'Arcueil, 94250, Gentilly, France
Tel.: (33) 14 198 7000
Web Site: https://www.airliquidehealthcare.fr
Industrial Gas Mfr
N.A.I.C.S.: 423450

Subsidiary (Domestic):

ADEP Assistance (3)
Le Narval A 1 - 29 rue des Hautes Patures, 92000, Nanterre, France
Tel.: (33) 146971287
Web Site: https://www.adepassistance.fr
Home Respiratory Healthcare Services
N.A.I.C.S.: 621999
Jack Thorel *(CEO)*

Air Liquide Sante Domicile (3)
28 Rue D Arcueil, 94250, Gentilly, France (100%)
Tel.: (33) 149694600
Web Site: http://www.airliquide.com
Supplier of Home-based Medical Care Svcs

L'AIR LIQUIDE S.A.

INTERNATIONAL PUBLIC

L'Air Liquide S.A.—(Continued)
N.A.I.C.S.: 621610
Ines Andres (Mgr-Procurement)

Orkyn (3)
28 Rue d Arcueil, 94250, Gentilly,
France **(100%)**
Tel.: (33) 14 969 8200
Web Site: http://www.orkyn.fr
Provider of Home-based Health Care Svcs
N.A.I.C.S.: 621610

Subsidiary (Domestic):

Air Liquide Sante Services S.A. (2)
75 quai d'Orsay, 75007, Paris, France
Tel.: (33) 1 40 62 55 55
Medical Equipment Mfr
N.A.I.C.S.: 339112

Seppic S.A. (2)
50 boulevard National, PO Box 90020, La
Defense La Garenne Colombes, 92257,
Paris, Cedex, France **(100%)**
Tel.: (33) 14 291 4000
Web Site: https://www.seppic.com
Sales Range: $50-74.9 Million
Mfr of Chemical & Biological Products
N.A.I.C.S.: 325998

Subsidiary (Domestic):

Givaudan-Lavirotte (3)
56 rue Paul Cazeneuve, PO Box 8344,
Lyon, 69008, France
Tel.: (33) 478615500
Web Site: http://www.seppic.com
Sales Range: $25-49.9 Million
Emp.: 70
Mfr of Chemical & Biological Products
N.A.I.C.S.: 325998

SEPIPROD Castres (3)
127 Chemin De La Poudrerie, PO Box
90128, 81105, Castres, CEDEX,
France **(100%)**
Tel.: (33) 563726969
Web Site: http://www.seppic.com
Sales Range: $125-149.9 Million
Emp.: 200
Mfr of Chemical & Biological Products
N.A.I.C.S.: 325998

Subsidiary (Non-US):

Seppic Belgium (3)
Haven 1053 Nieuwe weg 1B, 2070, Zwijn-
drecht, Belgium
Tel.: (32) 3 250 3911
Web Site: http://www.ceca.com
Sales Range: $25-49.9 Million
Emp.: 42
Mfr of Chemical & Biological Products
N.A.I.C.S.: 325998

Seppic China (3)
Room 1508 No 819 Zhongchuang Building
West Nanjing Rd, Shanghai, 200041,
China **(100%)**
Tel.: (86) 2164660149
Web Site: http://www.seppic.com
Sales Range: $25-49.9 Million
Emp.: 40
Mfr of Chemical & Biological Products
N.A.I.C.S.: 325998

Seppic GmbH (3)
Martinstrasse 16-20, 50667, Cologne,
Germany **(100%)**
Tel.: (49) 221 888 8240
Web Site: https://www.seppic.com
Sales Range: $10-24.9 Million
Emp.: 12
Mfr of Chemical & Biological Products
N.A.I.C.S.: 325998

Subsidiary (US):

Seppic Inc. (3)
30 2 Bridges Rd Ste 210, Fairfield, NJ
07004-1530
Tel.: (973) 882-5597
Web Site: https://www.seppic.com
Sales Range: $25-49.9 Million
Emp.: 30
Mfr of Chemical & Biological Products
N.A.I.C.S.: 424690

Subsidiary (Non-US):

Seppic Italia Srl (3)
Via Quarenghi 27, 20151, Milan,
Italy **(100%)**
Tel.: (39) 023 800 9110
Web Site: https://www.seppic.com
Sales Range: $25-49.9 Million
Emp.: 9
Mfr of Chemical & Biological Products
N.A.I.C.S.: 325998

Seppic UK Ltd (3)
50 Salisbury Rd, PO Box 338, Hounslow,
TW4 6SH, Greater London, United
Kingdom **(100%)**
Tel.: (44) 2085778800
Web Site: http://www.seppic.com
Sales Range: $25-49.9 Million
Emp.: 6
Mfr of Chemical & Biological Products
N.A.I.C.S.: 325998

Subsidiary (Domestic):

Taema (3)
6 Rue Georges Besse CE 80, 92182,
Antony, Cedex, France **(100%)**
Tel.: (33) 140966600
Web Site: http://www.taema.com
Sales Range: $50-74.9 Million
Mfr & Supplier of Respirators & Medical
Gases
N.A.I.C.S.: 339112
Lorbert Reigh (Mng Dir)

VitalAire S.A. (3)
10 rue Cognacq-Jay, 75341, Paris, Cedex
07, France **(100%)**
Tel.: (33) 144110550
Supplier of Medical Gas Systems to the
Healthcare Industry
N.A.I.C.S.: 339112

Subsidiary (Domestic):

DinnoSante (4)
1 Rue Raoul Follereau, Bussy Saint
Georges, 77600, Bussy-Saint-Georges,
France
Tel.: (33) 96 939 3394
Web Site: https://www.dinnosante.fr
Medical Equipment Mfr & Distr
N.A.I.C.S.: 339112

Subsidiary (Non-US):

VitalAire Canada, Inc. (4)
6990 Creditview Rd, Mississauga, L5N 8R9,
ON, Canada **(100%)**
Tel.: (905) 855-0440
Web Site: https://www.vitalaire.ca
Sales Range: $25-49.9 Million
Emp.: 1,000
Supplier of Medical Gas Systems to the
Healthcare Industry
N.A.I.C.S.: 339112

VitalAire GmbH (4)
Bornbarch 2, 22848, Norderstedt,
Germany **(100%)**
Tel.: (49) 8002511111
Web Site: https://www.vitalaire.de
Sales Range: $25-49.9 Million
Emp.: 700
Supplier of Medical Gas Systems to the
Healthcare Industry
N.A.I.C.S.: 339112

Subsidiary (Domestic):

**Fabig-Peters Medizintechnik GmbH &
Co. KG** (5)
Prof-Hugo-Jung-Str 3, Thuringia, 99310,
Arnstadt, Germany
Tel.: (49) 36 285 8250
Web Site: https://www.fp-med.de
Surgical & Medical Equipment Mfr & Distr
N.A.I.C.S.: 339112

**Jonas Medizintechnik Handels
GmbH** (5)
Oderstrasse 73, 14513, Teltow, Germany
Tel.: (49) 3328 3375 0
Web Site: http://www.jonasmed.de
Medical Equipment Mfr & Distr
N.A.I.C.S.: 339112

Licher MT GmbH (5)
Langer Acker 18, 30900, Wedemark, Ger-
many
Tel.: (49) 51 305 8330
Web Site: https://www.lichermt.de

Sales Range: $100-124.9 Million
Emp.: 62
Medical Equipment Distr
N.A.I.C.S.: 423450

Nord Service Projects GmbH (5)
Bornbarch 2, 22848, Norderstedt, Germany
Tel.: (49) 408 400 4070
Web Site: https://www.nordservice-
projects.de
Industrial Gas Mfr & Whslr
N.A.I.C.S.: 325120

Subsidiary (Non-US):

VitalAire Italia S.p.A (5)
Via Del Bosco Rinnovato 6, c/o Centro Dir-
ezionale MilanoFiori Edificio U7, 20090, As-
sago, Italy
Tel.: (39) 0240211
Web Site: http://www.vitalaire.it
Emp.: 70
Supplier of Medical Gas Systems to the
Healthcare Industry
N.A.I.C.S.: 339112

Subsidiary (Domestic):

**Zuther & Hautmann GmbH & Co.
KG** (5)
Siegfried-Marcus-Str 31, Muritz, 17192,
Waren, Germany
Tel.: (49) 39 916 4280
Web Site: https://www.z-h.de
Medical & Surgical Equipment Distr
N.A.I.C.S.: 423450
Olaf Zuther (Mng Dir)

Air Liquide Shuaiba Oxygen (1)
Mina Abdullah Area 4 Bl 72 Street MA7, PO
Box 23192, 13092, Kuwait, Kuwait
Tel.: (965) 668 68 254
Industrial Gas Mfr
N.A.I.C.S.: 325120

Air Liquide Singapore Pte. Ltd. (1)
No 2 Venture Drive 22-28 Vision Exchange,
Singapore, 608526, Singapore
Tel.: (65) 62653788
Industrial Gas Mfr
N.A.I.C.S.: 325120

Air Liquide Skagerak AS (1)
Floodelokka 1, 3915, Porsgrunn,
Norway **(51%)**
Tel.: (47) 94 13 13 00
Web Site: http://skagerak.airliquide.com
Natural Gas Mfr
N.A.I.C.S.: 221210
Forde Halvorsen (CEO)

**Air Liquide Sohar Industrial Gases
LLC** (1)
No 731 Al Amal Bldg Road No 7 124, PO
Box No 66, 327, Sohar, Oman
Tel.: (968) 26850200
Web Site: https://www.omzest.com
Sales Range: $100-124.9 Million
Emp.: 10
Industrial Gas Mfr & Distr
N.A.I.C.S.: 221210

Air Liquide Thailand Ltd (1)
Vorawat Building 14th floor Unit 1401-1402
849 Silom Road, Bangrak, Bangkok, 10500,
Thailand
Tel.: (66) 2 635 1600
Web Site: http://www.airliquide.com
Emp.: 230
Industrial Gas Mfr & Distr
N.A.I.C.S.: 221210

**Air Liquide Trinidad and Tobago
Ltd** (1)
Unit 8 Lots 5 6 Point Lisas Business Park,
Trinity Lane and Bagasse Road Point Lisas,
Couva, Trinidad & Tobago
Tel.: (868) 679 1117
Web Site: https://www.airliquide.com
Emp.: 50
Oil & Gas Exploration Services
N.A.I.C.S.: 213112
Jimmy Mphelane (Mng Dir)

Air Liquide Tunisie S.A. (1)
37 Rue Des Entrepreneurs ZI Charguia II-
Ariana Aeroport, BP 177, 2035, Tunis, Tuni-
sia
Tel.: (216) 36464600
Emp.: 230
Industrial Gas Mfr
N.A.I.C.S.: 325120

Air Liquide UK Ltd. (1)
Station Road, Coleshill, Birmingham, B46
1JY, United Kingdom **(100%)**
Tel.: (44) 167 546 2424
Web Site: https://industry.airliquide.co.uk
Sales Range: $25-49.9 Million
Emp.: 1,000
Industrial & Medical Gases Mfr
N.A.I.C.S.: 325120

Subsidiary (Domestic):

Air Liquide Ltd. (2)
Station Road, Coleshill, B46 1JY, Birming-
ham, United Kingdom
Tel.: (44) 167 546 2424
Web Site: http://www.uk.airliquide.com
Sales Range: $75-99.9 Million
Industrial Gas Mfr
N.A.I.C.S.: 325120

Subsidiary (Domestic):

Air Liquide South East Ltd (3)
Enterprise Drive Four Ashes, Wolverhamp-
ton, WV10 7DF, West Midlands, United
Kingdom
Tel.: (44) 1902 798000
Web Site: http://www.airliquide.com
Industrial & Medical Gas Distr
N.A.I.C.S.: 221210

Subsidiary (Domestic):

Calgaz International LLC (2)
Unit 5 Crown Royal Industrial Park,
Shawcross St, Stockport, SK1 3EY, Chesh-
ire, United Kingdom **(100%)**
Tel.: (44) 161 968 5060
Web Site: http://www.calgaz.com
Sales Range: $25-49.9 Million
Emp.: 25
Mfr of Industrial Gases
N.A.I.C.S.: 325120

Air Liquide Ukraine S.A. (1)
8A Ryzka Street Office 301, 04112, Kiev,
Ukraine
Tel.: (380) 442257510
Web Site: http://www.airliquide.com
Industrial Gas Mfr
N.A.I.C.S.: 325120

Air Liquide Vietnam Co., Ltd (1)
11th floor Capital Tower building 109 Tran
Hung Dao street, Cua Nam Ward Hoan
Kiem district, Hanoi, Vietnam
Tel.: (84) 243 936 1940
Web Site: http://www.airliquide.com
Emp.: 130
Industrial Gas Mfr & Distr
N.A.I.C.S.: 325120

Aqua Lung France (1)
1ere Avenue - 14eme Rue, BP 148, 06513,
Carros, Cedex, France **(100%)**
Tel.: (33) 48 358 0601
Web Site: https://fr.aqualung.com
Sales Range: $50-74.9 Million
Emp.: 120
Mfr of Diving Equipment
N.A.I.C.S.: 339920
Matthieu Bazil (CEO)

Subsidiary (Non-US):

Aqua Lung Canada (2)
6820 Kirkpatrick Crescent, Central Saanich,
Saanichton, V8M 1Z9, BC, Canada
Tel.: (250) 652-5881
Web Site: http://www.aqualung.com
Sales Range: $25-49.9 Million
Emp.: 40
Diving Equipment Mfr
N.A.I.C.S.: 339920

Aqua Lung Japan, Ltd (2)
2229-4 Nurumizu, Atsugi, 243-0033, Kanagawa, Japan **(100%)**
Tel.: (81) 462473222
Web Site: http://www.aqualung.com

AND PRIVATE COMPANIES

Sales Range: $25-49.9 Million
Emp.: 30
Mfr of Diving Equipment
N.A.I.C.S.: 339920
Koichi Takeda *(Pres)*

Aqualung Espana (2)
Avenida de la Antigua Peseta 145 Poligono Industrial Las Atalayas, 3114, Alicante, Spain (100%)
Tel.: (34) 965127170
Web Site: http://www.aqualung.com
Mfr of Diving Equipment
N.A.I.C.S.: 339920

Aqualung Tauchsportartikel GmbH (2)
Josef-Schuttler-Str 12, 78224, Singen, Germany
Tel.: (49) 773193450
Web Site: http://www.aqualung.de
Sales Range: $25-49.9 Million
Emp.: 25
Mfr of Diving Equipment
N.A.I.C.S.: 339920

Technisub S.p.A (2)
Via Gualco 42, 16165, Genoa, Italy (100%)
Tel.: (39) 01054451
Web Site: http://www.technisub.com
Sales Range: $25-49.9 Million
Emp.: 30
Mfr of Diving Equipment
N.A.I.C.S.: 339920

Subsidiary (US):

US Divers (2)
2340 Cousteau Ct, Vista, CA 92081
Tel.: (760) 597-5000
Web Site: https://usdivers.com
Sales Range: $25-49.9 Million
Mfr of Diving Equipment
N.A.I.C.S.: 339920
Stephan Murnane *(Pres)*

Subsidiary (Non-US):

US Divers Japan (2)
816-1 Sanda Atsugi, Kanagawa, Atsugi, Japan
Tel.: (81) 462 42 6537
Web Site: http://www.aqualung.com
Mfr of Diving Equipment
N.A.I.C.S.: 339920

Btl S.A. (1)
Pave Des Moulins, 59260, Hellemmes-Lille, France
Tel.: (33) 3 20 67 67 67
Sales Range: $125-149.9 Million
Emp.: 400
Industrial Gas Mfr
N.A.I.C.S.: 325120

Subsidiary (Non-US):

Farmec Nuova S.r.l. (2)
Via W Flemming 7 Zone Industriale, Settimo di Pescantina, 37026, Pescantina, VR, Italy
Tel.: (39) 045 676 7672
Web Site: https://www.farmec.it
Sales Range: $25-49.9 Million
Emp.: 70
Pharmaceuticals Product Mfr
N.A.I.C.S.: 325412

Unident S.A. (2)
Rue Francois Perreard 4, Case Postale 142, Chene-Bourg, Geneva, 1225, Switzerland
Tel.: (41) 22 839 79 00
Web Site: http://www.unident.ch
Sales Range: $25-49.9 Million
Emp.: 15
Dental Hygiene Products Mfr & Whslr
N.A.I.C.S.: 325612
Keith Bruton *(Mgr-Mktg)*

Carbagas S.A. (1)
Hofgut, 3073, Gumligen, Switzerland
Tel.: (41) 31 950 5050
Web Site: https://www.carbagas.ch
Sales Range: $125-149.9 Million
Emp.: 320
Industrial Gas Mfr
N.A.I.C.S.: 325120

Celki International Ltd (1)
21/F Tins Enterprises Centre 777 Lai Chi Kok Road, Cheung Sha Wan, Kowloon, China (Hong Kong)
Tel.: (852) 2332 3366
Web Site: http://www.celki.com
Respiratory Care Products Mfr
N.A.I.C.S.: 339112
Vincent Rouvier *(CEO)*

Cryolor SA (1)
Argancy Z I des Jonquieres, BP 7, 57365, Ennery, France
Tel.: (33) 387708550
Web Site: https://www.cryolor.com
Sales Range: $50-74.9 Million
Emp.: 200
Cryogenic & Hydrocarbon Gas Storage Services
N.A.I.C.S.: 486210

Cryopal (1)
8 Avenue Gutenberg, 77600, Bussy-Saint-Georges, France
Tel.: (33) 16 476 1500
Web Site: https://www.cryopal.com
Sales Range: $50-74.9 Million
Emp.: 100
Cryogenic Vessel Mfr & Distr
N.A.I.C.S.: 332420

Energas Ltd. (1)
Westmorland Street, Hull, HU2 0HX, East Yorkshire, United Kingdom
Tel.: (44) 167 546 2695
Web Site: https://www.energas.co.uk
Industrial Gas Mfr
N.A.I.C.S.: 325120
Claire White *(Area Mgr-Sls)*

Helium Services S.A. (1)
6 Rue Cognacq Jay, 75007, Paris, France
Tel.: (33) 140625555
Industrial Gas Mfr
N.A.I.C.S.: 325120

LVL Medical Groupe S.A. (1)
10 Avenue Aristide Briand, 92220, Bagneux, France
Tel.: (33) 808800300
Web Site: https://www.lvlmedical.com
N.A.I.C.S.: 621610

La Oxigena Paraguaya S.A. (1)
Avenida Eusebio Ayala 3650 Km 4, Asuncion, 1910, Paraguay
Tel.: (595) 21550607
Industrial Gas Mfr
N.A.I.C.S.: 325120

Lurgi AG (1)
Olof Palme Street 35, Frankfurt am Main, 60539, Germany
Tel.: (49) 6958080
Web Site: http://www.airliquide.com
Sales Range: $1-4.9 Billion
Emp.: 1,300
Design, Construction & Consulting of Industrial Chemical & Metallurgical Plants; Contract Processing of Minerals & Ores; Production of Sponge Iron; Project Management Services
N.A.I.C.S.: 541330

Subsidiary (Non-US):

APSA (2)
C/o Aljomaih Holding Co Al-Jomaih Bldg 5th Floor King Abdulaziz, PO Box 132, Old Airport Road, Riyadh, 11411, Saudi Arabia
Tel.: (966) 1478 21 00
Industrial Plant Construction Services
N.A.I.C.S.: 236210

Air Liquide Engineering Services Asia Co., Ltd. (2)
5F Building 18 No 1515 Gu Mei Road, Shanghai, 200233, China
Tel.: (86) 21 60 91 90 00
Engineeering Services
N.A.I.C.S.: 541330

Subsidiary (Domestic):

Air Liquide Forschung und Entwicklung GmbH (2)
Gwinnerstrasse 27-33, 60388, Frankfurt am Main, Germany
Tel.: (49) 69 4011 201
Web Site: http://www.airliquide.com
Sales Range: $25-49.9 Million
Emp.: 55
Industrial Gas Mfr
N.A.I.C.S.: 325120

Subsidiary (Non-US):

Beijing Lurgi Engineering Consulting Co. Ltd. (2)
Unit 0408 Landmark Tower 2 8 North Dongsanhuan Road, Chaoyang District, Beijing, 100004, China
Tel.: (86) 106 590 6797
Web Site: http://www.airliquide.com
Sales Range: $25-49.9 Million
Emp.: 20
Engineeering Services
N.A.I.C.S.: 541330
Xian-ji Guo *(VP)*

EUROTECNICA S.A. (2)
Martin Lezica 3043 - 2 Piso -B, B1642GJA, San Isidro, Buenos Aires, Argentina
Tel.: (54) 11 47 63 38 38
Web Site: http://www.acunis.de
Engineeering Services
N.A.I.C.S.: 541330

Lurgi (Pty) Ltd. (2)
PO Box 98527, Sloane Park, 2152, South Africa
Tel.: (27) 11 2 44 46 00
Web Site: http://www.lurgi.com
Sales Range: $25-49.9 Million
Emp.: 54
Industrial Plant Construction Services
N.A.I.C.S.: 236210
Sherrylynn Smith *(Project Mgr-Procurement)*

Lurgi Caribbean Ltd. (2)
202 Brook Road Goodwood Park, Trincity, Trinidad & Tobago
Tel.: (868) 6 33 67 18
Web Site: http://www.lurgi.com
Sales Range: $25-49.9 Million
Emp.: 5
Construction Engineering Services
N.A.I.C.S.: 237120

Lurgi Sdn. Bhd. (2)
Suite A-9-1 Wisma HB Megan Avenue II 12 Jalan Yap Kwan Seng, 50450, Kuala Lumpur, Malaysia
Tel.: (60) 3 21 64 64 46
Web Site: http://www.lurgiinc.com
Sales Range: $25-49.9 Million
Emp.: 5
Business Management Consulting Services
N.A.I.C.S.: 541618

Lurgi Turkiye (2)
Meclis - I Mebusan Cd 139A Atlanktik Han Kat 4, Findikli, 80040, Istanbul, Turkiye
Tel.: (90) 2 12 2 52 25 00
Industrial Gas Mfr
N.A.I.C.S.: 325120

Lurgi do Brasil Instalacoes Industriais Ltda. (2)
Av Brig Faria Lima 2369-19 Andar, 01462-900, Sao Paulo, Brazil
Tel.: (55) 11 30 38 06 00
Web Site: http://www.lurgi.com
Sales Range: $25-49.9 Million
Emp.: 5
Industrial Plant Construction Services
N.A.I.C.S.: 236210

Lurgi, S.A. (2)
Avda General Peron 29-9, 28046, Madrid, Spain
Tel.: (34) 915981519
Web Site: http://www.lurgi.com
Sales Range: $25-49.9 Million
Emp.: 20
Plant Construction & Engineering Services
N.A.I.C.S.: 541330

Subsidiary (Domestic):

Plauen Stahl Technologie GmbH (2)
Hammerstrasse 88, 08529, Plauen, Germany
Tel.: (49) 3 741 2830
Web Site: https://www.plauen-stahl.de
Sales Range: $50-74.9 Million
Emp.: 200
Steelwork Contractor
N.A.I.C.S.: 238120

Medicasa Italia S.p.A. (1)
Via Del Bosco Rinnovato 6 Edificio U7 Milanofiori Nord, 20094, Assago, MI, Italy

L'AIR LIQUIDE S.A.

Tel.: (39) 0240211
Web Site: https://www.medicasa.it
Home Nursing Care Services
N.A.I.C.S.: 621610

NordicInfu Care A.B (1)
Gustavslundsvagen 12, 167 51, Bromma, Sweden
Tel.: (46) 8 601 2440
Web Site: https://www.infucare.com
Emp.: 70
Cardiology & Chronic Disease Healthcare Services
N.A.I.C.S.: 622310

Oilfield Hire & Services Ltd. (1)
15 Greenbank Road, Coleshill, Aberdeen, AB12 3BQ, United Kingdom
Tel.: (44) 790 122 7944
Web Site: https://www.ohsuk.com
Oilfield & Liquid Gas Equipment Distr
N.A.I.C.S.: 423830
Tony Green *(Gen Mgr)*

Omasa France (1)
2 Rue des Orangers, 94385, Bonneuil-sur-Marne, France
Tel.: (33) 1 56 71 18 50
Web Site: http://www.omasa.fr
Sales Range: $25-49.9 Million
Emp.: 45
Medical & Surgical Equipment Mfr
N.A.I.C.S.: 339112

Oxymaster S.A. (1)
Av de Las Americas 44-23 Piso 2 Edificio Hornitos, Bogota, Colombia
Tel.: (57) 6017424444
Web Site: https://oxymaster.com
N.A.I.C.S.: 621498

P.T. Air Liquide Indonesia (1)
MM 2100 Industrial Town Blok I-1-2 Jalan, Sulawesi Cikarang Barat, Bekasi, 17520, Indonesia
Tel.: (62) 21 898 0071
Web Site: https://www.airliquide.com
Emp.: 170
Industrial Gas Mfr
N.A.I.C.S.: 325120

Plant (Domestic):

P.T. Air Liquide Indonesia - Cilegon Factory (2)
Jl Australia II Kav M1, Cilegon, 42443, Banten, Indonesia
Tel.: (62) 254 393358
Web Site: http://www.id.airliquide.com
Sales Range: $25-49.9 Million
Emp.: 70
Industrial Gas Mfr
N.A.I.C.S.: 325120
Xu Yan *(Pres)*

Respiratory Homecare Solutions Canada Inc. (1)
N260 6815-8 Street NE, Calgary, T2E 7H7, AB, Canada
Tel.: (587) 779-3250
Web Site: https://www.rhscanada.com
Therapy Services
N.A.I.C.S.: 621330

SIEGE AIR LIQUIDO SA (1)
Rua Doctor Antonio Loureiro Borges 4, Arquiparque Miraflores, Alges, 1495-131, Portugal
Tel.: (351) 2141 64900
Web Site: http://www.airliquide.com
Industrial Gas Mfr
N.A.I.C.S.: 325120

SOAL-Industrial Gases (1)
El-Midane, BP 175523/4, Dekwaneh, Beirut, Lebanon
Tel.: (961) 1 692 380
Web Site: http://www.lb.airliquide.com
Industrial Gas Mfr & Distr
N.A.I.C.S.: 325120
Fouad Haddad *(CEO)*

SOBEGI (1)
Pole 4 avenue du lac, BP-58, 64150, Mourenx, France
Tel.: (33) 55 992 2222
Web Site: https://www.sobegi.com
Emp.: 300
Oil & Gas Exploration Services
N.A.I.C.S.: 213112

L'AIR LIQUIDE S.A.

L'Air Liquide S.A.—(Continued)

Singapore Oxygen Air Liquide Pte. Ltd. (1)
16 Jalan Buroh, Jurong, 619475, Singapore
Tel.: (65) 62653788
Web Site: http://www.soxal.com
Sales Range: $125-149.9 Million
Emp.: 500
Industrial, Medical & Scientific Gases Mfr
N.A.I.C.S.: 325120
Claire Wong (CFO)

Sociedade Portuguesa do Ar Liquido Lda. (1)
Rua Doutor Antonio Loureiro Borges 4-2 Arquiparque-Miraflores, 1495-131, Alges, Portugal
Tel.: (351) 214164900
Emp.: 400
Industrial Gas Mfr
N.A.I.C.S.: 325120

Societe Beninoise des Gaz Industriels S.A. (1)
2 7 Zone Industrielle Route De Porto-Novo, BP 674, Cotonou, Benin
Tel.: (229) 21 33 10 75
Industrial Gas Mfr
N.A.I.C.S.: 325120

Societe Burkinabe des Gaz Industriels S.A. (1)
Zone Industrielle de Gounghin 01, BP 623, Ouagadougou, Burkina Faso
Tel.: (226) 50 34 42 43
Industrial Gas Mfr
N.A.I.C.S.: 325120

Societe Guyanaise de L'Air Liquide (1)
Avenue Prefontaine ZI Pariacabo, PO Box 804, 97388, Kourou, Cedex, French Guiana
Tel.: (594) 321009
Web Site: http://www.airliquide.com
Industrial Gas Mfr
N.A.I.C.S.: 325120

Societe Ivoirienne d Oxygene et d Acetylene (1)
131 Blvd de Marseille, BP 1753, Abidjan, Cote d'Ivoire
Tel.: (225) 21 21 04 57
Industrial Gas Mfr
N.A.I.C.S.: 325120
Ano Adou (Gen Mgr)

Societe Martiniquaise de L Air Liquide (1)
Quartier Californie, Lamentin, 97232, Martinique
Tel.: (596) 596500596
Sales Range: $25-49.9 Million
Emp.: 40
Industrial Gas Mfr
N.A.I.C.S.: 325120

Societe Senegalaise d Oxygene et d Acetylene (1)
Km 3 5 Bd Du Centenaire De, BP 45, Dakar, Senegal
Tel.: (221) 338493030
Health Care Srvices
N.A.I.C.S.: 621999

Societe d'Exploitation de Produits pour les Industries Chimiques (1)
Paris La Defense 50 Boulevard National, CS 90020, 92257, La Garenne-Colombes, Cedex, France
Tel.: (33) 14 291 4000
Web Site: https://www.seppic.com
Sales Range: $75-99.9 Million
Emp.: 167
Specialty Chemicals Mfr & Distr
N.A.I.C.S.: 325998

Societe d'Oxygene et d Acetylene d Extreme-Orient SA (1)
75 Quai d'Orsay, Paris, 75007, France
Tel.: (33) 1 40 62 55 41
Industrial Gas Mfr & Distr
N.A.I.C.S.: 325120

Societe des Gaz Industriels de la Guadeloupe (1)
Lauricisque Zone des Petites Industrie, Pointe-a-Pitre, 97110, Guadeloupe
Tel.: (590) 590894740

Industrial Gas Mfr
N.A.I.C.S.: 325120

Sudac Air Services (1)
Zac des Petits Carreaux - 1 avenue de Lys, 94380, Bonneuil-sur-Marne, France
Tel.: (33) 1 41 94 50 50
Web Site: http://www.sudac.fr
Emp.: 120
Compressor Repair & Maintenance Services
N.A.I.C.S.: 811310

Swazi Gases (Pty.) Limited (1)
PO 2444, Mbabane, Eswatini
Tel.: (268) 505 2062
Industrial Gas Mfr
N.A.I.C.S.: 325120

Vital Air Japan K.K. (1)
2-11-13 Omoriminami, Ota-ku, Tokyo, 143-0013, Japan
Tel.: (81) 33 742 4131
Web Site: https://www.vitalaire.co.jp
Home Oxygen Therapy Services
N.A.I.C.S.: 621610

VitalAire Avattvon Singapore Pte. Ltd. (1)
1 Scotts Road 22-12/13 Shaw Centre, Singapore, 228208, Singapore
Tel.: (65) 67331148
Web Site: http://www.vitalaire.com.sg
Women Healthcare Services
N.A.I.C.S.: 621610

VitalAire Korea Inc. (1)
Room S-07 8th floor Garden 5 Tool-dong 10 Chungmin-ro, Songpa-gu, Seoul, Korea (South)
Tel.: (82) 1 566 0202
Web Site: https://www.vitalaire.co.kr
Home Oxygen Therapy Services
N.A.I.C.S.: 621610

Vitalaire Arabia LLC (1)
4063 Prince Fawaz Bin Abdulaziz St, Ar Rabwah, Riyadh, 12813, Saudi Arabia
Tel.: (966) 92 002 3202
Web Site: https://www.vitalaire.com.sa
Women Healthcare Services
N.A.I.C.S.: 621610

L'ARCHE GREEN N.V.

Tweede Weteringplantsoen 5, 1017 ZD, Amsterdam, Netherlands
Tel.: (31) 582868686 **NI**
Holding Company
N.A.I.C.S.: 551112
Charlene Lucille de Carvalho-Heineken (Pres)

Subsidiaries:

Heineken Holding N.V. (1)
Tweede Weteringplantsoen 5, 1017 ZD, Amsterdam, Netherlands **(52.59%)**
Tel.: (31) 858887233
Web Site: https://www.heinekenholding.com
Rev.: $31,992,077,600
Assets: $48,349,775,600
Liabilities: $28,126,383,600
Net Worth: $20,223,392,000
Earnings: $2,803,781,400
Emp.: 86,390
Fiscal Year-end: 12/31/2022
Holding Company
N.A.I.C.S.: 551112
Michel Ray de Carvalho (Exec Dir)

Subsidiary (Non-US):

Distell Group Holdings Limited (2)
Aan-de-Wagenweg, Stellenbosch, 7600, South Africa
Tel.: (27) 218097000
Web Site: http://www.distell.co.za
Rev.: $2,328,932,253
Assets: $2,005,253,431
Liabilities: $902,834,302
Net Worth: $1,102,419,129
Earnings: $166,253,585
Fiscal Year-end: 06/30/2022
Fine Wines, Spirits, Ciders & Ready-to-Drinks (RTDs) Distr
N.A.I.C.S.: 312130
Marius Lambrechts (Dir-Innovations)

Subsidiary (Non-US):

CVH Spirits Limited (3)
8 Milton Road, College Milton North, East Kilbride, G74 5BU, United Kingdom
Tel.: (44) 1355260999
Web Site: http://www.burnstewartdistillers.com
Sales Range: $75-99.9 Million
Emp.: 150
Scotch Whiskey Distiller
N.A.I.C.S.: 424820
Fraser Thornton (Mng Dir)

Distell Namibia Limited (3)
4 Sollingen St, Windhoek, Namibia
Tel.: (264) 61277038
Sales Range: $75-99.9 Million
Emp.: 115
Beverages & Wines Mfr
N.A.I.C.S.: 424820
Leon Souche (Mng Dir)

Distell Swaziland Limited (3)
Cnr 7th St & 1st Ave, 140, Matsapha, 200, Eswatini
Tel.: (268) 5184107518
Web Site: http://www.distell.co.za
Sales Range: $25-49.9 Million
Emp.: 20
Liquor Distr
N.A.I.C.S.: 424820
Michelle Lloyd (Branch Mgr)

Subsidiary (US):

International Beverage Company, Inc. (3)
1651 Mount Vernon Rd Ste 200, Dunwoody, GA 30338 **(100%)**
Tel.: (770) 390-9714
Web Site: http://www.interbevusa.com
Sales Range: $1-9.9 Million
Emp.: 5
Alcoholic Beverages Whslr
N.A.I.C.S.: 424820
Peter Schwartz (Pres)

Subsidiary (Domestic):

Nederburg Wines (Proprietary) Limited (3)
Sonstraal Road Dal Josafat, Paarl, Western Cape, South Africa
Tel.: (27) 218623104
Sales Range: $50-74.9 Million
Emp.: 71
Wine Mfr
N.A.I.C.S.: 424820

South African Distilleries and Wines (SA) Limited (3)
Ann-Den-Wagen Rd, Stellenbosch, 7600, Western Cape, South Africa
Tel.: (27) 218098103
Web Site: http://www.distell.co.za
Sales Range: $1-4.9 Billion
Emp.: 4,000
Alcoholic Beverages & Wines Mfr
N.A.I.C.S.: 424820
Richard Rushton (CEO)

Subsidiary (Domestic):

Heineken N.V. (2)
Tweede Weteringplantsoen 21, 1017 ZD, Amsterdam, Netherlands **(50.05%)**
Tel.: (31) 205239239
Web Site: https://www.theheinekencompany.com
Alcohol Beverage Mfr & Distr
N.A.I.C.S.: 312120
Bram Westenbrink (Chief Comml Officer)

Subsidiary (Non-US):

Al Ahram Beverages Company S.A.E. (3)
Industrial Area Zone A Area 11 to 24 Block 12003, El Obour, Cairo, Egypt **(100%)**
Tel.: (20) 246141000
Web Site: http://www.alahrambeverages.com
Sales Range: $25-49.9 Million
Emp.: 1,000
Alcoholic & Non-Alcoholic Malt Beverage Wine Liquor Soft Drink & Juices Mfr
N.A.I.C.S.: 312120

Athenian Brewery S.A. (3)

INTERNATIONAL PUBLIC

107 Kifissou Ave, Egaleo, 122 41, Athens, Greece **(98.8%)**
Tel.: (30) 2105384911
Web Site: http://www.athenianbrewery.gr
Sales Range: $75-99.9 Million
Emp.: 500
Brewery
N.A.I.C.S.: 312120
Zooullis Minas (Chm & CEO)

Brasseries du Logone S.A. (3)
PO Box 170, Moundou, Chad **(100%)**
Tel.: (235) 691365
Sales Range: Less than $1 Million
Emp.: 130
Producer & Distributor of Beer & Soft Drinks
N.A.I.C.S.: 312120

Brasseries et Limonaderies du Burundi Brarudi S.A. (3)
Blvd Du 1er Novembre, Bujumbura, Burundi **(59.3%)**
Tel.: (257) 225173
Sales Range: $150-199.9 Million
Emp.: 593
Brewery/Importer of Beer & Soft Drinks
N.A.I.C.S.: 312120

Brasseries et Limonaderies du Rwanda Bralirwa S.A. (3)
PO Box 131, Kigali, Rwanda **(70%)**
Tel.: (250) 252 587170
Web Site: http://www.bralirwa.com
Sales Range: $75-99.9 Million
Emp.: 300
Brewery & Importer of Beer & Soft Drinks
N.A.I.C.S.: 312120

Brasseries, Limonaderies et Malteries Bralima S.A.R.L. (3)
912 Avenue du Flambeau, Kinshasa, Congo, Democratic Republic of **(95%)**
Tel.: (243) 1246557
Mfr of Soft Drinks
N.A.I.C.S.: 312111

Joint Venture (Non-US):

Brau Holding International GmbH & Co. KGaA (3)
Denninger Strasse 165, D-81925, Munich, Germany **(49.9%)**
Tel.: (49) 89923808
Web Site: http://www.brauholdinginternational.com
Holding Company; Beer Breweries Owner & Operator
N.A.I.C.S.: 551112

Subsidiary (Domestic):

Furstlich Furstenbergische Brauerei GmbH & Co. KG (4)
Postplatz 1-4, D-78166, Donaueschingen, Germany
Tel.: (49) 771860
Web Site: http://www.fuerstenberg.de
Beer Brewer & Whslr
N.A.I.C.S.: 312120
Dirk Wagenfuhrer (Dir-Sls-Intl Div)

Subsidiary (Domestic):

Privat-Brauerei Schmucker GmbH & Co. KG (5)
Hauptstrasse 89, 64756, Mossautal, Germany
Tel.: (49) 60617020
Web Site: http://www.schmucker-bier.de
Beer Brewer & Whslr
N.A.I.C.S.: 312120
Willy Schmidt (Mng Dir)

Subsidiary (Domestic):

Kulmbacher Brauerei AG (4)
Lichtenfelser Strasse 9, Kulmbach, 95326, Germany
Tel.: (49) 92217050
Web Site: http://www.kulmbacher.de
Sales Range: $75-99.9 Million
Emp.: 500
Beer Brewer & Whslr; Bottled Water Mfr
N.A.I.C.S.: 312120

Holding (Domestic):

Paulaner Brauerei GmbH & Co. KG (4)

Hochstrasse 75, Munich, 81541, Germany **(50%)**
Tel.: (49) 89480050
Web Site: http://www.paulaner.de
Sales Range: $150-199.9 Million
Emp.: 800
Beer Brewer & Whslr
N.A.I.C.S.: 312120
Andreas Steinfatt *(Mng Dir)*

Subsidiary (Domestic):

Privatbrauerei Hoepfner GmbH **(4)**
Haid-und-Neu-Strasse 18, Karlsruhe, 76131, Germany
Tel.: (49) 72161830
Web Site: http://www.hoepfner.de
Emp.: 80
Beer Brewery Mfr
N.A.I.C.S.: 312120
Christian Lorenz *(Mgr-Logistics)*

Subsidiary (Non-US):

Brau Union Osterreich AG **(3)**
Poschacherstrasse 35, A-4021, Linz, Austria **(80%)**
Tel.: (43) 73269790
Web Site: http://www.brauunion.com
Beer Distr & Whslr
N.A.I.C.S.: 424810
Gabriela Maria Straka *(Head-Comm)*

Subsidiary (Domestic):

Brau Union AG **(4)**
Poschacherstrasse 35, 4021, Linz, Austria **(63%)**
Tel.: (43) 73269790
Web Site: http://www.brauunion.com
Sales Range: $200-249.9 Million
Emp.: 300
Beer Distr
N.A.I.C.S.: 312120
Andreas Stieber *(Dir-Mktg)*

Subsidiary (Domestic):

Brau Union Austria GmbH **(5)**
Poschacherstrasse 35, Linz, 04021, Austria **(100%)**
Tel.: (43) 73269790
Web Site: http://www.brauunion.at
Emp.: 2,200
Beer Mfr & Distr
N.A.I.C.S.: 445320
Markus Liebl *(Mng Dir)*

Brau-Union International GmbH **(5)**
Mautner Markhos Strasse 11, Schwechat, 02320, Austria **(100%)**
Tel.: (43) 170140
Sales Range: $700-749.9 Million
Emp.: 12
Exporter of Beer
N.A.I.C.S.: 312120
Rob Kleinjan *(Dir-Fin)*

Gasteiner Mineralwasser GmbH **(5)**
Erlengrundstrasse 14, Badgastein, 5640, Austria **(100%)**
Tel.: (43) 643426250
Web Site: http://www.gasteiner.at
Sales Range: $50-74.9 Million
Emp.: 48
Mineral Water Bottler & Distr
N.A.I.C.S.: 312112
Harald Doppler *(Dir-Gasteiner Mineralwasser)*

Subsidiary (Non-US):

Stobrno A.S. **(5)**
Hlinky 12, Brno, 66147, Czech Republic **(85%)**
Tel.: (420) 543516201
Web Site: http://www.starobrno.cz
Sales Range: $200-249.9 Million
Beer Brewer & Distr
N.A.I.C.S.: 312120

Subsidiary (Non-US):

DB Breweries Limited **(3)**
1 Bairds Rd, Otahuhu, Manukau, 2025, New Zealand **(100%)**
Tel.: (64) 92593000
Web Site: http://www.dbbreweries.co.nz
Breweries
N.A.I.C.S.: 312120
Grant Caunter *(Mgr-Innovations)*

Heineken France S.A. **(3)**
2 Rue des Martinets, F 92565, Rueil-Malmaison, France **(100%)**
Tel.: (33) 147143600
Web Site: http://www.heineken.com
Sales Range: $75-99.9 Million
Emp.: 350
Brewery
N.A.I.C.S.: 312120

Heineken Hungaria Sorgyarak Zrt. **(3)**
Vandor Sandor St 1, 9400, Sopron, Hungary **(74.6%)**
Tel.: (36) 99516100
Web Site: http://www.heinekenhungaria.hu
Sales Range: $200-249.9 Million
Emp.: 871
Beer Brewery Mfr
N.A.I.C.S.: 312120
Oladele Ajayi *(Gen Mgr)*

Heineken Ireland **(3)**
Leitrim St Murphy's Brewery, 58 Leitrim St, Cork, Ireland **(100%)**
Tel.: (353) 214503371
Web Site: http://www.heineken.ie
Sales Range: $25-49.9 Million
Emp.: 200
Brewery
N.A.I.C.S.: 312120
Maarten Schuurman *(Mng Dir)*

Heineken Italia S.p.A. **(3)**
Viale Edison 110 Sesto San Giovanni, Milano, 20099, Italy **(100%)**
Tel.: (39) 02270761
Web Site: http://www.heinekeninternational.com
Brewery
N.A.I.C.S.: 312120

Heineken Malaysia Berhad **(3)**
Sungei Way Brewery Lot 1135 Batu 9 Jalan Klang Lama, 46000, Petaling Jaya, Selangor Darul Ehsan, Malaysia **(100%)**
Tel.: (60) 378614688
Web Site: https://www.heinekenmalaysia.com
Rev.: $604,246,561
Assets: $298,036,190
Liabilities: $194,659,894
Net Worth: $103,376,296
Earnings: $125,820,106
Emp.: 500
Fiscal Year-end: 12/31/2022
Beer Mfr & Sales
N.A.I.C.S.: 312120
Sow Hoong Ng *(Sec)*

Subsidiary (Domestic):

Heineken Nederland BV **(3)**
Stationsweg 43, 2312 AT, Leiden, Netherlands
Tel.: (31) 736209911
Web Site: http://www.heineken.nl
Brewery
N.A.I.C.S.: 312120

Subsidiary (Non-US):

Heineken Switzerland AG **(3)**
Haldenstrasse 69, 8401, Winterthur, Switzerland
Tel.: (41) 522644141
Web Site: http://www.heineken.ch
Sales Range: $150-199.9 Million
Emp.: 700
Brewery Services
N.A.I.C.S.: 312120

Heineken UK Limited **(3)**
2-3 Broadway Park, South Gyle, Edinburgh, EH12 9JZ, United Kingdom
Tel.: (44) 1315281000
Web Site: http://www.heineken.co.uk
Breweries
N.A.I.C.S.: 312120
Stefan Orlowski *(Mng Dir)*

Subsidiary (Domestic):

H.P. Bulmer Limited **(3)**
The Cider Mills, Plough Ln, Hereford, HR4 OLE, United Kingdom
Tel.: (44) 1432352000
Web Site: http://www.bulmer.com
Cider Mfr & Distr
N.A.I.C.S.: 312120

Scottish & Newcastle Pub Company **(4)**
2-4 Broadway Park, South Gyle, Edinburgh, EH12 9JZ, United Kingdom
Tel.: (44) 131 528 2700
Club Management Services
N.A.I.C.S.: 561499
Willie Crawshay *(Mng Dir)*

Subsidiary (US):

Heineken USA Inc. **(3)**
360 Hamilton Ave Ste 1103, White Plains, NY 10601-1811 **(100%)**
Tel.: (914) 681-4100
Web Site: http://www.heinekenusa.com
Sales Range: $50-74.9 Million
Emp.: 150
Importer of European Beer
N.A.I.C.S.: 424810
Julie Kinch *(Chief Legal Officer & Sr VP)*

Joint Venture (Non-US):

Inversiones y Rentas S.A. **(3)**
CCU Corporate Building Vitacura 2670 23rd Fl, PO Box 33, Santiago, Chile **(50%)**
Tel.: (56) 24273000
Holding Company
N.A.I.C.S.: 551112

Holding (Domestic):

Compania Cervecerias Unidas S.A. **(4)**
Bandera 84 Sixth Floor, Santiago, Chile **(61.56%)**
Tel.: (56) 224273000
Web Site: http://www.ccu.cl
Rev.: $3,796,008,927
Assets: $5,033,110,571
Liabilities: $3,022,753,896
Net Worth: $2,010,356,674
Earnings: $189,678,233
Emp.: 9,354
Fiscal Year-end: 12/31/2022
Alcoholic Beverages Producer, Marketer & Distr
N.A.I.C.S.: 312120
Marisol Bravo *(Officer-Corp Affairs)*

Subsidiary (Non-US):

CCU Argentina S.A. **(5)**
Edison 2659, Martinez, 1640, Argentina
Tel.: (54) 1151672300
Web Site: http://www.ccu.com.ar
Sales Range: $350-399.9 Million
Emp.: 543
Producer & Distr of Beer & Mineral Water
N.A.I.C.S.: 312120
Fernando Sanchis *(Mng Dir)*

Subsidiary (Domestic):

CCU Chile Ltda. **(5)**
Av Pdte Eduardo Frei Montalva 8000, Quilicura, Santiago, Chile
Tel.: (56) 24278200
Web Site: http://www.ccu.cl
Sales Range: $75-99.9 Million
Emp.: 1,389
Producer & Distributor of Beer & Other Beverages
N.A.I.C.S.: 312120

Embotelladoras Chilenas Unidas S.A. **(5)**
Av Presidente Eduardo Frei Montalva 1500, Renca, Santiago, Chile
Tel.: (56) 24274000
Web Site: http://www.ccu-sa.com
Sales Range: $150-199.9 Million
Emp.: 100
Producer & Distributor of Soft Drinks, Mineral Water, Juices & Other Beverages
N.A.I.C.S.: 312112

Vina San Pedro S.A. **(5)**
Betacura 4380 Pisso 6, Betacura, Santiago, Chile **(82.01%)**
Tel.: (56) 24775300
Web Site: http://www.sanpedro.cl
Sales Range: $50-74.9 Million
Emp.: 100
Producer & Distributor of Wine
N.A.I.C.S.: 312130
Alejandro Jorquera Rojas *(Comptroller)*

Subsidiary (Non-US):

Finca La Celia S.A. **(6)**
Ave San Martin 972 3F, 5500, Mendoza, Argentina
Tel.: (54) 2614134400
Web Site: http://www.fincalacelia.com.ar
Sales Range: $10-24.9 Million
Vineyards; Winery
N.A.I.C.S.: 312130

Subsidiary (Non-US):

NV Brouwerijen Alken-Maes Brasseries SA **(3)**
Waarloosveld 10, 2550, Waarloos, Antwerp, Belgium
Tel.: (32) 015309011
Web Site: http://www.alkenmaes.be
Sales Range: $150-199.9 Million
Emp.: 841
Beer & Non-Alcoholic Beer Brewery
N.A.I.C.S.: 312120

Nigerian Breweries Plc **(3)**
Iganmu House Abebe Village Road, PO Box 545, Lagos, Nigeria **(54.2%)**
Tel.: (234) 15801340
Web Site: http://www.nbplc.com
Sales Range: $700-749.9 Million
Emp.: 2,900
Brewery
N.A.I.C.S.: 312120
Jordi Borrut Bel *(CEO & Mng Dir)*

PT Multi Bintang Indonesia Tbk **(3)**
Jalan Daan Mogot Km 19, PO Box 151122, Tangerang, Indonesia **(77.2%)**
Tel.: (62) 216190108
Web Site: http://www.multibintang.co.id
Sales Range: $50-74.9 Million
Emp.: 400
Brewery
N.A.I.C.S.: 312120

Pivovarna Lasko d.d. **(3)**
Trubarjeva ulica 28, SI-3270, Lasko, Slovenia
Tel.: (386) 3 734 8000
Web Site: http://www.pivo-lasko.si
Sales Range: $75-99.9 Million
Beer & Soft Drinks Mfr
N.A.I.C.S.: 312120
Mitja Gobec *(Dir-Logistics)*

Sociedade Central de Cervejas e Bebidas S.A. **(3)**
Estrada da Alfarrobeira, 2625 244, Vialonga, Portugal
Tel.: (351) 219528600
Web Site: http://www.centralcervejas.pt
Sales Range: $300-349.9 Million
Emp.: 1,100
Brewery
N.A.I.C.S.: 312120

Subsidiary (US):

The Lagunitas Brewing Company **(3)**
1280 N McDowell Blvd, Petaluma, CA 94954 **(100%)**
Tel.: (707) 769-4495
Web Site: http://www.lagunitas.com
Beer Brewer & Whslr
N.A.I.C.S.: 312120
Katie Brown *(Head-Brand Comm)*

Subsidiary (Non-US):

United Breweries Ltd. **(3)**
Level 3-4/5 UB Towers UB City 24 Vittal Mallya Road, Bengaluru, 560 001, India **(61.5%)**
Tel.: (91) 802 227 2807
Web Site: http://www.unitedbreweries.com
Rev.: $1,397,215,365
Assets: $798,819,840
Liabilities: $309,326,745
Net Worth: $489,493,095
Earnings: $15,537,795
Emp.: 3,070
Fiscal Year-end: 03/31/2021
Brewery Operator & Beer Distr
N.A.I.C.S.: 312120
Rishi Pardal *(Mng Dir)*

L'ARCHEVEQUE & RIVEST LIMITED

L'ARCHEVEQUE & RIVEST LIMITED

L'Archeveque & Rivest Limited—(Continued)

96 blvd Industriel Blvd, Repentigny,
J6A 4X6, QC, Canada
Tel.: (450) 581-4480   QC
Web Site: http://www.lrivest.com
Year Founded: 1958
Construction Services
N.A.I.C.S.: 237990
Francois Pilon *(Project Mgr)*

L'ATTRAIT CO., LTD.

5th Floor Kokusai Hamamatsu-cho
Bldg 1-9-18 Kaigan, Minato-ku, Tokyo, 105-0022, Japan
Tel.: (81) 3 54057300
Web Site: http://www.lattrait.co.jp
Year Founded: 1990
Rev.: $69,943,200
Assets: $152,497,920
Liabilities: $123,533,100
Net Worth: $28,964,820
Earnings: $5,653,440
Fiscal Year-end: 12/31/18
Real Estate Development Services
N.A.I.C.S.: 531390
Eiichi Wakita *(Chm, Pres & CEO)*

Subsidiaries:

L'attrait Asia (Thailand) Co., Ltd. **(1)**
2 Jusmine Building 12th Floor Sukhumvit 23 North Klongtoey Wattana, Bangkok, 10110, Thailand
Tel.: (66) 26127321
Web Site: http://www.lattrait.asia
Real Estate Manangement Services
N.A.I.C.S.: 531210
Masayoshi Itano *(Gen Mgr)*

L'ECLAIRAGE TECHNIQUE S.A.

41 Rue Lafayette, PO Box 69, Maxeville, 54528, Laxou, Cedex, France
Tel.: (33) 3 83 39 38 00
Web Site: http://www.eclatec.com
Year Founded: 1927
Sales Range: $50-74.9 Million
Emp.: 120
Lighting Fixture Mfr
N.A.I.C.S.: 335139
Vincent Carru *(Pres)*

L'OCCITANE GROUPE S.A.

1 rue du Fort Rheinsheim, L 2419, Luxembourg, Luxembourg
Tel.: (352) 269 6333
Web Site: http://group.loccitane.com
Holding Company
N.A.I.C.S.: 551112
Shimon Kalichman *(Dir-Mktg, PR & Comm)*

Subsidiaries:

L'Occitane International S.A. **(1)**
49 Boulevard Prince Henri, L-1724, Luxembourg, Luxembourg **(100%)**
Tel.: (352) 2696333
Web Site: https://group.loccitane.com
Rev.: $2,743,299,153
Assets: $3,361,790,410
Liabilities: $2,378,073,598
Net Worth: $983,716,812
Earnings: $109,888,841
Emp.: 9,255
Fiscal Year-end: 03/31/2024
Designer, Mfr & Marketer of Cosmetics & Toiletries Based on Natural & Organic Ingredients
N.A.I.C.S.: 325620
Reinold Geiger *(Chm & CEO)*

Subsidiary (Non-US):

Elemis Limited **(2)**
Unit D Poplar Way East Cabot Park, Avonmouth, BS11 0DD, Bristol, United Kingdom
Tel.: (44) 1173161888
Web Site: http://www.elemis.com
Personal Care Products Mfr & Distr
N.A.I.C.S.: 325620
Sean Harrington *(Co-Founder & CEO)*

L'Occitane (Korea) Limited **(2)**
3F J&K Building 62-18 Chungdam-dong, Gangnam-gu, Seoul, 135 953, Korea (South) **(100%)**
Tel.: (82) 2 3014 2900
Web Site: http://www.kr.loccitane.com
Natural & Organic Based Cosmetics & Toiletries Distr
N.A.I.C.S.: 424210

L'Occitane (Suisse) SA **(2)**
chemin du Pre-Fleuri 3, 1228, Plan-les-Ouates, Switzerland **(100%)**
Tel.: (41) 228843818
Natural & Organic Based Cosmetics & Toiletries Distr
N.A.I.C.S.: 456120

L'Occitane Australia Pty Ltd **(2)**
Level 5 107 Mount Street, North Sydney, 2060, Australia **(100%)**
Tel.: (61) 89123000
Natural & Organic Based Cosmetics & Toiletries Distr
N.A.I.C.S.: 456120

L'Occitane GmbH **(2)**
Tiroler Str 80, 9500, Villach, Austria **(56.6%)**
Tel.: (43) 4242 51222
Web Site: http://www.loccitane.at
Sales Range: $25-49.9 Million
Emp.: 12
Cosmetics & Toiletries Distr
N.A.I.C.S.: 456120
Elisabeth Hajek *(Mng Dir)*

L'Occitane GmbH **(2)**
Konigsallee 63-65, 40215, Dusseldorf, Germany **(100%)**
Tel.: (49) 211 1597790
Web Site: http://www.de.loccitane.com
Sales Range: $25-49.9 Million
Emp.: 15
Cosmetics & Toiletry Distr
N.A.I.C.S.: 456120
Dejan Loncaric *(Mng Dir)*

Subsidiary (US):

L'Occitane Inc. **(2)**
1430 Broadway 2nd Fl, New York, NY 10018
Tel.: (212) 696-9098
Web Site: http://www.loccitane.com
Sales Range: $50-74.9 Million
Emp.: 70
Cosmetics
N.A.I.C.S.: 424210
Nicole Parker *(Mgr-PR)*

Subsidiary (Non-US):

L'Occitane Japon K.K. **(2)**
16-1 Hirakawa-cho 2-chome, Chiyoda-ku, Tokyo, 102 0093, Japan **(100%)**
Tel.: (81) 3 3234 6941
Sales Range: $150-199.9 Million
Emp.: 535
Natural & Organic Cosmetics & Toiletries Distr
N.A.I.C.S.: 456120

L'Occitane Ltd. **(2)**
21 Bedford Square, London, WC1B 3HH, United Kingdom **(100%)**
Tel.: (44) 20 7907 0329
Sales Range: $25-49.9 Million
Emp.: 228
Natural & Organic Based Cosmetics & Toiletries Distr
N.A.I.C.S.: 456120

L'OREAL S.A.

41 Rue Martre, 92117, Clichy, Cedex, France
Tel.: (33) 147567000   FR
Web Site: https://www.loreal.com
Year Founded: 1909
OR—(OTCIQ)
Rev.: $44,444,744,226
Assets: $55,962,767,106
Liabilities: $24,585,365,854
Net Worth: $31,377,401,252
Earnings: $6,680,876,322
Emp.: 94,605
Fiscal Year-end: 12/31/23
Personal care Product Mfr

N.A.I.C.S.: 325620
Jean-Pierre Meyers *(Vice Chm)*

Subsidiaries:

Avenamite S.A. **(1)**
Josefa Valcarcel 48, 28045, Madrid, Spain
Tel.: (34) 911778000
Cosmetics Products Mfr
N.A.I.C.S.: 325620

Azzaro SAS **(1)**
16 Rue Montrosier, 92201, Neuilly-sur-Seine, France
Tel.: (33) 55622500
Sales Range: $25-49.9 Million
Emp.: 50
Mfr of Perfumes
N.A.I.C.S.: 325620

Banque de Realisations de Gestion et de Financement **(1)**
41 Rue Martre, 92117, Clichy, France
Tel.: (33) 147567000
Financial Management Services
N.A.I.C.S.: 523999

Beaute Createurs SAS **(1)**
Heron Building V 10 Rue De La Paix, Paris, 75002, France
Tel.: (33) 141056900
Web Site: http://www.ccbparis.fr
Cosmetics Products Mfr
N.A.I.C.S.: 325620

Beautycos International Co. Ltd **(1)**
Jinjihu Road - Zi Teng Jie China-Singapore Suzhou Industrial Park, Suzhou, 215021, Jiangsu, China
Tel.: (86) 5127630085
Cosmetics Products Mfr
N.A.I.C.S.: 325620

Cadum International SA **(1)**
Tour Gama B 193 Rue de Bercy Cedex 12, Paris, 75012, France
Tel.: (33) 1 44 75 10 00
Web Site: http://www.cadum.fr
Personal Care Product Mfr
N.A.I.C.S.: 325620

Canan Kozmetik Sanayi Ve Ticaret A.S. **(1)**
Merkez Mahallesi Hurriyet Cd Cihan Sok No 3 Kyrac Buyukcekmece, Istanbul, 34522, Turkiye
Tel.: (90) 212 622 52 00
Web Site: http://www.canan.com
Sales Range: $50-74.9 Million
Emp.: 10
Personal Care Products Mfr & Distr
N.A.I.C.S.: 325620
Ozgur Uysal *(Mgr-Export)*

Canan Tuketim Urunleri Pazarlama A.S. **(1)**
No 3 Kirac Merkez Mah Hurriyet Cad Cihan Sok, Istanbul, 34522, Turkiye
Tel.: (90) 2126225200
Emp.: 50
Cosmetics Products Mfr
N.A.I.C.S.: 325620
Yassine Bakkare *(Dir-Plant)*

Carita International **(1)**
11 rue du Faubourg Saint-Honore, Paris, 75008, France
Tel.: (33) 144941111
Web Site: http://www.carita.com
Skin & Hair Care Products Mfr
N.A.I.C.S.: 325620

Centrex SA **(1)**
Zone Ind De Moimont, Marly-la-Ville, 95670, Val D Oise, France
Tel.: (33) 134721717
General Warehousing & Storage Services
N.A.I.C.S.: 493110

Cobelsa Cosmeticos, S.A. **(1)**
Carretera Daganzo 3 870, Alcala de Henares, 28806, Madrid, Spain
Tel.: (34) 918893000
Web Site: http://www.loreal.sa
Emp.: 2
Cosmetics Products Mfr
N.A.I.C.S.: 325620

Cosbel S.A. de C.V. **(1)**
Avenida Real de Mayorazgo No 130 Torre M Piso 28, Colonia Xoco Benito Juarez,

INTERNATIONAL PUBLIC

03330, Mexico, Mexico
Tel.: (52) 5559995600
Cosmetics Products Mfr
N.A.I.C.S.: 325620

Cosmelor KK **(1)**
430-8 Kamado, Gotemba, 412-0039, Shizuoka, Japan
Tel.: (81) 550831414
Web Site: https://www.cosmelor.co.jp
Emp.: 220
Cosmetics Products Mfr
N.A.I.C.S.: 325620

Cosmetique Active International S.N.C. **(1)**
28 Rue Du President Wilson, 03200, Vichy, 3200, France
Tel.: (33) 470303500
Cosmetics Products Mfr
N.A.I.C.S.: 325620

Cosmetique Active Production S.A.S. **(1)**
Zi De Vichy Rhue, 03300, Creuzier-le-Vieux, 3300, France
Tel.: (33) 470303500
Cosmetics Products Mfr
N.A.I.C.S.: 325620
Jean Grenier *(Pres)*

Cosmeurop S.A. **(1)**
43 Rue Des Comtes, PO Box 44, Strasbourg, 67200, France
Tel.: (33) 388308686
Sales Range: $50-74.9 Million
Emp.: 200
Mfr of Perfumes
N.A.I.C.S.: 325620

EPISKIN SNC **(1)**
4 rue Alexander Fleming, 69366, Lyon, Cedex, France
Tel.: (33) 43 728 7200
Web Site: https://www.episkin.com
Sales Range: $25-49.9 Million
Emp.: 55
Cosmetics Products Mfr
N.A.I.C.S.: 325620
Jacques Leclaire *(Mng Dir)*

Elebelle (Proprietary) Ltd **(1)**
153 Katherine Street, Johannesburg, 2196, Gauteng, South Africa
Tel.: (27) 112860700
Investment Management Service
N.A.I.C.S.: 523999

Faprogi S.N.C. **(1)**
Le Bois De La Droue Rue De L Etang D Or, Rambouillet, 78120, Yvelines, France
Tel.: (33) 134842800
Cosmetics Products Mfr
N.A.I.C.S.: 325620

Gemey Maybelline Garnier S.N.C. **(1)**
16 Place Vendome, 75001, Paris, France
Tel.: (33) 142600410
Web Site: http://www.gemey-maybelline.com
Cosmetics Products Mfr
N.A.I.C.S.: 325620

Gemey Paris-Maybelline New York **(1)**
20 rue du Paradis, Ormes, 45140, France
Tel.: (33) 238657600
Web Site: http://www.loreal.com
Emp.: 400
Cosmetics Products Mfr
N.A.I.C.S.: 325620
Sofie Cabooter *(Gen Mgr)*

Holdial SA **(1)**
Du 4 Au 6 4 Rue Bertrand Sincholle, 92585, Clichy, Hauts-de-Seine, France
Tel.: (33) 1 40 20 64 74
Cosmetics Products Mfr
N.A.I.C.S.: 325620

L'Oreal (UK) Limited **(1)**
255 Hammersmith Road, London, W6 8AZ, United Kingdom **(100%)**
Tel.: (44) 208 762 4000
Web Site: https://www.loreal.com
Sales Range: $200-249.9 Million
Emp.: 700
Mfr & Distributor of Perfumes & Cosmetics
N.A.I.C.S.: 325620

AND PRIVATE COMPANIES — L'OREAL S.A.

Alan Richardson *(Gen Mgr)*

L'Oreal Adria d.o.o. (1)
Slavonska avenija 1C, Zagreb, 10000, Croatia
Tel.: (385) 16064920
Beauty Product Whslr
N.A.I.C.S.: 456120
Natasa Brekalo *(Product Mgr)*

L'Oreal Argentina SA (1)
Juramento 1775, C1428DNA, Buenos Aires, Argentina
Tel.: (54) 11 4124 0333
Web Site: http://www.lorealparis-ar.com.ar
Emp.: 30
Cosmetics Products Mfr
N.A.I.C.S.: 325620
Anne-Brigitte Spitzbarth *(Gen Mgr)*

L'Oreal Australia Pty Ltd (1)
Level 13 564 St Kilda Road, Melbourne, 3004, VIC, Australia
Tel.: (61) 38 680 0000
Web Site: https://www.loreal.com
Emp.: 900
Cosmetics Products Mfr
N.A.I.C.S.: 325620
Laurent Attal *(Exec VP-Res-Innovation)*

L'Oreal Balkan d.o.o. (1)
Bulevar Zorana Dindica 64 A, Belgrade, 11070, Serbia
Tel.: (381) 112205900
Web Site: http://www.loreal.com
Sales Range: $25-49.9 Million
Emp.: 60
Cosmetics Products Mfr
N.A.I.C.S.: 325620
Brigitte Streller *(Mng Dir)*

L'Oreal Belgilux SA (1)
Avenue Charles-Quint 584, 1082, Brussels, Belgium (100%)
Tel.: (32) 22100511
Web Site: https://www.loreal.com
Emp.: 800
Mfr of Perfume, Cosmetics & Toiletries
N.A.I.C.S.: 325620
Jean-Marc Auverlau *(Gen Mgr)*

Division (Domestic):

L'Oreal Parfums (2)
Ave Charles Quint 584, 1082, Brussels, Belgium (100%)
Tel.: (32) 22100511
Web Site: https://www.loreal.com
Sales Range: $100-124.9 Million
Emp.: 800
Cosmetics Mfr
N.A.I.C.S.: 325620
Gean Mart Auzerlan *(Gen Mgr)*

L'Oreal S.A. - Gemey Division (2)
Avenue Charles-Quint 584, 1082, Brussels, Belgium (100%)
Tel.: (32) 22100511
Web Site: http://www.loreal.com
Emp.: 800
Perfumes
N.A.I.C.S.: 325620
Nicolas Hieronimus *(Pres-Selective Divisions)*

L'Oreal S.A. - Laboratory Division (2)
Ave Charles Quint 584, Brussels, 1082, Belgium (100%)
Tel.: (32) 22100511
Web Site: http://www.loreal.com
Perfumes
N.A.I.C.S.: 325620
Jean-Marc Auverlau *(Gen Mgr)*

L'Oreal Bulgaria EOOD (1)
55 Nikola Vaptzarov Blvd, 1407, Sofia, Bulgaria
Tel.: (359) 28190610
Web Site: http://www.lorealparisbulgaria.com
Emp.: 5
Cosmetics Products Mfr
N.A.I.C.S.: 325620
Jan Cupa *(Gen Mgr)*

L'Oreal Ceska Republika s.r.o (1)
Plzenska 11, 150 00, Prague, Czech Republic
Tel.: (420) 222771111
Web Site: https://www.loreal.com

Cosmetics Products Mfr
N.A.I.C.S.: 325620

L'Oreal Chile S.A. (1)
Av Apoquindo 3885 piso 2, Las Condes, Santiago, Chile
Tel.: (56) 224406000
Web Site: https://www.loreal.com
Cosmetics Products Mfr
N.A.I.C.S.: 325620

L'Oreal China Co Ltd (1)
25F Park Place 1601 West Nanjing Road, JingAn District, Shanghai, 200040, China
Tel.: (86) 215 200 8999
Web Site: https://www.loreal.com
Emp.: 3,500
Personal Care Products Mfr & Distr
N.A.I.C.S.: 325620
Alexis Perakis-Valat *(CEO & Exec VP-Asia Pacific)*

L'Oreal Colombia S.A. (1)
Street 90 11-13, Cundinamarca, Bogota, Colombia
Tel.: (57) 1651300
Web Site: https://www.loreal.com
Beauty Product Whslr
N.A.I.C.S.: 456120
Carolina Mora *(Gen Mgr-FMCG Bus Unit)*

L'Oreal Denmark A/S (1)
Havneholmen 25, 1561, Copenhagen, Denmark
Tel.: (45) 43246484
Web Site: https://www.loreal.com
Sales Range: $125-149.9 Million
Emp.: 30
Cosmetic Product Distr
N.A.I.C.S.: 325620
Mark Jeremy Prestwich *(Mng Dir)*

L'Oreal Deutschland Gmbh (1)
Johannstrasse 1, 40476, Dusseldorf, Germany
Tel.: (49) 21 143 7801
Web Site: https://www.loreal.com
Emp.: 700
Cosmetics Products Mfr
N.A.I.C.S.: 325620

L'Oreal Espana S.A. (1)
Josefa Valcarcel 48, 28045, Madrid, Spain
Tel.: (34) 91 177 8000
Web Site: https://www.loreal.com
Emp.: 2,500
Cosmetics Products Mfr
N.A.I.C.S.: 325620

L'Oreal Finland Oy (1)
Niittykatu 6 B, 2201, Espoo, Finland
Tel.: (358) 9452631
Web Site: http://www.loreal.fi
Emp.: 15
Cosmetics Products Mfr
N.A.I.C.S.: 325620
Pekka Huttunen *(Mgr)*

L'Oreal Hellas S.A. (1)
39A Ethnikis Antistaseos Avenue, Nea Ionia, 14234, Athens, Greece
Tel.: (30) 210 618 8500
Web Site: https://www.loreal.com
Emp.: 720
Cosmetics Products Mfr
N.A.I.C.S.: 325620

L'Oreal Hong-Kong Ltd (1)
35/F Sun Hung Kai Centre 30 Harbour Road, Causeway Bay, Wanchai, China (Hong Kong)
Tel.: (852) 2 828 1300
Web Site: https://www.loreal.com
Emp.: 300
Cosmetics Products Mfr
N.A.I.C.S.: 325620

L'Oreal India Private Ltd (1)
A - Wing 8th Floor Marathon Futurex N M Joshi Marg Lower Parel, Mumbai, 400 013, India
Tel.: (91) 22 67003000
Web Site: http://www.loreal.co.in
Sales Range: $250-299.9 Million
Emp.: 100
Cosmetic Products Mfr & Distr
N.A.I.C.S.: 325620
Pierre-Yves Arzel *(Mng Dir-South Asia Pacific)*

L'Oreal Israel Ltd (1)
Ha'Zoran 4a St 1st floor, Netanya, 42504, Israel
Tel.: (972) 98928202
Web Site: https://www.loreal.com
Emp.: 1,100
Cosmetics Products Mfr
N.A.I.C.S.: 325620

L'Oreal Italia Spa (1)
Via Primaticcio 155, 20147, Milan, Italy
Tel.: (39) 0297066111
Web Site: https://www.loreal.com
Emp.: 2,000
Beauty Product Whslr
N.A.I.C.S.: 456120
Claudio Buongiorno *(Mgr-BI)*

L'Oreal Japan Ltd. (1)
Shinjuku Park Tower 3-7-1, Nishi Shinjuku Shinjuku-ku, Tokyo, 163-1071, Japan (100%)
Tel.: (81) 353886021
Web Site: http://www.nihon-loreal.co.jp
Emp.: 2,700
Marketing & Sale of Cosmetics
N.A.I.C.S.: 456120

L'Oreal Kazakhstan Llp (1)
77 Kunaev Street, Medeu District, Almaty, 050000, Kazakhstan
Tel.: (7) 7272321500
Cosmetics Products Mfr
N.A.I.C.S.: 325620

L'Oreal Korea Ltd. (1)
31st Floor ASEM Tower 517 Yeongdongdaero, Gangnam-gu, Seoul, Korea (South)
Tel.: (82) 234979500
Web Site: https://www.loreal.com
Emp.: 1,800
Beauty Product Whslr
N.A.I.C.S.: 456120
Jorn Zempel *(Gen Mgr-Active Cosmetics & Consumer Div)*

L'Oreal Liban SAL (1)
Immeuble Holdal Face Galerie Georges Matta, BP 175 740, Dekwaneh, Beirut, Lebanon
Tel.: (961) 1 511 420
Web Site: http://www.loreal.com
Sales Range: $50-74.9 Million
Emp.: 17
Cosmetics Products Mfr
N.A.I.C.S.: 325620

L'Oreal Magyarorszag Kosmetikai Kft (1)
Arpad Fejedelem Utja 26-28 Obuda Gate, 1023, Budapest, Hungary
Tel.: (36) 1 438 21 00
Web Site: http://www.loreal.hu
Sales Range: $25-49.9 Million
Emp.: 7
Cosmetics Products Mfr
N.A.I.C.S.: 325620
Thomas Hruska *(Mng Dir)*

L'Oreal Malaysia Sdn Bhd (1)
Crown Penthouse 1 powerhouse No 1 Persiaran Bandar Utama, Bandar Utama, 47800, Petaling Jaya, Selangor Darul Ehsan, Malaysia
Tel.: (60) 376518000
Web Site: https://www.loreal.com
Emp.: 800
Beauty Product Whslr
N.A.I.C.S.: 456120
Andrea Wong *(Mktg Mgr)*

L'Oreal Manufacturing Midrand (Pty) Ltd. (1)
427 15th Road, Halfway House, Midrand, 1685, Gauteng, South Africa
Tel.: (27) 112375300
Emp.: 50
Cosmetics Products Mfr
N.A.I.C.S.: 325620

L'Oreal Maroc SA (1)
17 Rue D Aman Ex Caporal Beaux, 20000, Casablanca, Morocco
Tel.: (212) 52 244 0240
Web Site: https://www.loreal.com
Cosmetics Products Mfr
N.A.I.C.S.: 325620

L'Oreal Mexico S. A de C. V (1)
Avenida Real de Mayorazgo No 130 Torre M Piso 28, Colonia Xoco Benito Juarez, 03330, Mexico, Mexico
Tel.: (52) 5559995600
Web Site: https://www.loreal.com
Emp.: 3,200
Cosmetics Products Mfr

L'Oreal Mexico Servicios S.A. de C.V. (1)
Avenida Real de Mayorazgo No 130 Torre M Piso 28, Colonia Xoco Benito Juarez, 03330, Mexico, Mexico
Tel.: (52) 5559995600
Cosmetics Products Mfr
N.A.I.C.S.: 325620

L'Oreal Middle East FZE (1)
Jebel Ali Free Zone, PO Box 16924, Dubai, United Arab Emirates
Tel.: (971) 48064700
Cosmetics Products Mfr
N.A.I.C.S.: 325620

L'Oreal Nederland B.V. (1)
Scorpius 1, Postbus 505, 2132 LR, Hoofddorp, Netherlands
Tel.: (31) 23 549 9499
Web Site: https://www.loreal.com
Sales Range: $125-149.9 Million
Emp.: 470
Cosmetics Products Mfr
N.A.I.C.S.: 325620
U. Springer *(Principal)*

L'Oreal New Zealand Ltd. (1)
600 Great South Road Building B Level 2, Ellerslie, Auckland, 2024, New Zealand
Tel.: (64) 95834000
Web Site: https://www.loreal.com
Beauty Product Whslr
N.A.I.C.S.: 456120
Juliana Tupuola *(Partner-HR Bus)*

L'Oreal Osterreich Gmbh (1)
Wiedner Gurtel 9 ICON Turm 9, 1100, Vienna, Austria
Tel.: (43) 153 6510
Web Site: https://www.loreal.com
Emp.: 230
Cosmetics Products Mfr
N.A.I.C.S.: 325620
Daniel Robinson *(Gen Mgr)*

L'Oreal Panama S.A. (1)
Calle Villanueva PH PDC piso 11, Costa del Este, Panama, Panama
Tel.: (507) 3022828
Cosmetics Products Mfr
N.A.I.C.S.: 325620

L'Oreal Peru S.A. (1)
Avenida La Floresta 497 Of 303 San Borja, Lima, Peru
Tel.: (51) 1 372 7500
Sales Range: $50-74.9 Million
Emp.: 11
Cosmetics Products Mfr
N.A.I.C.S.: 325620

L'Oreal Philippines, Inc. (1)
23F Robinsons Equitable Tower ADB Avenue, Ortigas Cente, Pasig, 1605, Philippines
Tel.: (63) 282732732
Beauty Product Whslr
N.A.I.C.S.: 456120

L'Oreal Polska Sp. Z.O.O. (1)
62 Grzybowska St, 00-844, Warsaw, Poland
Tel.: (48) 22 676 0100
Web Site: https://www.loreal.com
Cosmetics Products Mfr
N.A.I.C.S.: 325620

L'Oreal Portugal Lda (1)
Rua Doutor Antonio Loureiro Borges 7 Arquiparque, Miraflores, Linda-a-Velha, 1495-131, Portugal
Tel.: (351) 21 412 8500
Web Site: https://www.loreal.com
Emp.: 400
Cosmetics Products Mfr
N.A.I.C.S.: 325620
Artur Justino dos Santos *(Mgr-Supply Chain)*

L'Oreal Produits De Luxe International S.N.C. (1)
106 Rue Danton, 92300, Levallois-Perret, Hauts De Seine, France

L'OREAL S.A.

INTERNATIONAL PUBLIC

L'Oreal S.A.—(Continued)
Tel.: (33) 149646500
Web Site: http://www.loreal.com
Emp.: 130
Cosmetics Products Mfr
N.A.I.C.S.: 325620

L'Oreal Produits de Luxe France S.N.C. (1)
29 R Du Faubourg Saint Honore, Paris, 75008, France
Tel.: (33) 149646650
Cosmetics Products Mfr
N.A.I.C.S.: 325620

L'Oreal Romania SRL (1)
C Floreasca 169 A Corp A Et 6 Sector 1, Bucharest, 14459, Romania
Tel.: (40) 21 2040000
Web Site: http://www.lorealparis.ro
Sales Range: $25-49.9 Million
Emp.: 10
Cosmetics Products Mfr
N.A.I.C.S.: 325620
Gilles Antoine *(Country Mgr)*

L'Oreal Russia (1)
1/8 4eme Goloutvinski Per Bat 1-2, 119180, Moscow, Russia
Tel.: (7) 4952583191
Web Site: http://www.loreal-paris.ru
Cosmetics Products Mfr
N.A.I.C.S.: 325620

L'Oreal Saipo Industriale S.p.A. (1)
Strada Cebrosa 52/56, 10036, Settimo Torinese, Torino, Italy
Tel.: (39) 0118167111
Web Site: https://www.loreal.com
Emp.: 2,000
Cosmetics Products Mfr
N.A.I.C.S.: 325620

L'Oreal Singapore Pte Ltd (1)
1 Raffles Quay 47-01 North Tower, Singapore, 048583, Singapore (51%)
Tel.: (65) 66019200
Web Site: http://www.loreal.com.sg
Sales Range: $50-74.9 Million
Emp.: 550
Marketing & Sale of Cosmetics
N.A.I.C.S.: 325620
Christopher Neo *(Mng Dir)*

L'Oreal Slovenija Kosmetika d.o.o. (1)
Letaliska cesta 29 C, Ljubljana, 1000, Slovenia
Tel.: (386) 15800910
Beauty Product Whslr
N.A.I.C.S.: 456120
Tina Petric *(Mgr-Retail Education & Svcs)*

L'Oreal Slovensko s.r.o. (1)
Namestie 1 maja 18, 811 06, Bratislava, Slovakia
Tel.: (421) 233336111
Beauty Product Whslr
N.A.I.C.S.: 456120

L'Oreal South Africa Holdings Pty Ltd (1)
153 Katherine Street, Johannesburg, 2196, Gauteng, South Africa
Tel.: (27) 112860700
Investment Management Service
N.A.I.C.S.: 523940

L'Oreal Suisse S.A. (1)
Chemin de Blandonnet 10, Case Postale 100, 1214, Vernier, 1214, Geneva, Switzerland
Tel.: (41) 581051010
Cosmetics Products Mfr
N.A.I.C.S.: 325620

L'Oreal Sverige AB (1)
Gustavslundsvagen 22, Box 15 222, 167 15, Bromma, Sweden
Tel.: (46) 8 58 61 52 00
Web Site: http://www.loreal-paris.se
Cosmetics Products Mfr
N.A.I.C.S.: 325620

L'Oreal Thailand Ltd (1)
179 Bangkok City Tower 6th 8th 9th and 21th FL South Sathorn Rd, Tungmahamek Sathorn, Bangkok, 10120, Thailand
Tel.: (66) 2 684 3000
Web Site: https://www.loreal.com
Emp.: 630
Cosmetics Products Mfr
N.A.I.C.S.: 325620
Ines Caldeira *(Mng Dir)*

L'Oreal Turkiye Kozmetik Sanayi Ve Ticaret Anonim Sirketi (1)
Dr Adnan Buyukdeniz Street Saray Mahallesi Akkom 2 Blok K 14-15-16, Umraniye, 34768, Istanbul, Turkiye
Tel.: (90) 8502213200
Emp.: 1,100
Beauty Product Whslr
N.A.I.C.S.: 456120

L'Oreal USA, Inc. (1)
10 Hudson Yards, New York, NY 10001
Tel.: (212) 984-4414
Web Site: https://www.loreal.com
Sales Range: $1-4.9 Billion
Emp.: 1,000
Hair Preparations, Cosmetics & Fragrances Mfr
N.A.I.C.S.: 325620
David Greenberg *(CEO)*

Subsidiary (Domestic):

Essie Cosmetics, Ltd. (2)
575 5th Ave, New York, NY 10017
Tel.: (212) 818-1500
Web Site: http://www.essie.com
Sales Range: $25-49.9 Million
Emp.: 35
Nail Polish, Treatments, Accessories, Spa Products & Lip Glosses Mfr & Marketer
N.A.I.C.S.: 325620

Kiehl's Since 1851 LLC
435 Hudson St 5th Fl, New York, NY 10014 (100%)
Tel.: (917) 606-2740
Web Site: https://www.kiehls.com
Sales Range: $50-74.9 Million
Emp.: 70
Natural Hair & Skin Products Mfr & Retailer
N.A.I.C.S.: 325620
Chris Salgardo *(Pres)*

Subsidiary (Non-US):

L'Oreal Canada (2)
1500 Boul Robert-Bourassa Suite 600, Montreal, H3A 3S7, QC, Canada (100%)
Tel.: (514) 287-4800
Web Site: http://www.loreal.ca
Sales Range: $100-124.9 Million
Emp.: 1,450
Fragrances & Cosmetics Distr
N.A.I.C.S.: 325620
Stephanie Binette *(CMO)*

Division (Domestic):

L'Oreal USA, Inc. - Designer Fragrance Division (2)
575 5th Ave, New York, NY 10017-2422
Tel.: (212) 984-4000
Web Site: http://www.loreal.com
Mfr of Frangrances
N.A.I.C.S.: 456120
Mikki Wosencroft *(Dir-HR)*

Plant (Domestic):

L'Oreal USA, Inc. - Savannah (2)
64 Ross Rd, Savannah, GA 31405
Tel.: (912) 651-3400
Sales Range: $450-499.9 Million
Mfr of Cosmetic, Toilet, Shaving & Hair Coloring Preparations Hair Dressing for the Trade
N.A.I.C.S.: 325620

Subsidiary (Domestic):

Matrix Essentials, Inc. (2)
575 5th Ave, New York, NY 10017-2422
Tel.: (212) 818-1500
Web Site: http://www.matrix.com
Sales Range: $200-249.9 Million
Emp.: 1,000
Hair Care Products Mfr
N.A.I.C.S.: 325620

Maybelline, Inc. (2)
575 5th Ave, New York, NY 10017
Tel.: (212) 818-1500
Sales Range: $400-449.9 Million
Cosmetics & Cosmetic Accessories Mfr
N.A.I.C.S.: 456120

Stephanie Rinaldi *(VP-Customer Mktg, Sls Ops, and Garnier)*

Division (Domestic):

Maybelline Products Co. Inc. (3)
222 Terminal Ave, Clark, NJ 07066-1320
Tel.: (732) 499-2838
Web Site: http://www.lorealusa.com
Rev.: $167,000,000
Emp.: 100
Distr of Cosmetics
N.A.I.C.S.: 424210
Jean-Paul Agon *(Pres & CEO)*

Subsidiary (Domestic):

Pacific Bioscience Laboratories, Inc. (2)
17275 67th Ct, Redmond, WA 98052
Tel.: (425) 285-4000
Web Site: http://www.clarisonic.com
Sales Range: $100-124.9 Million
Emp.: 300
Sonic Skin Care Cleansing System Mfr
N.A.I.C.S.: 335999
Robb Akridge *(VP-Clinical Affairs)*

Redken Laboratories LLC (2)
575 5th Ave, New York, NY 10017-2422
Tel.: (212) 818-1500
Web Site: http://www.redken.com
Sales Range: $1-4.9 Billion
Hair Care Products Mfr & Distr
N.A.I.C.S.: 325620
Pat Parenty *(Pres)*

SalonCentric, Inc. (2)
8878 Ulmerton Rd, Largo, FL 33771
Tel.: (727) 532-8184
Web Site: https://stores.saloncentric.com
Sales Range: $700-749.9 Million
Emp.: 3,000
Beauty Salon Supplies Distr
N.A.I.C.S.: 456120

Subsidiary (Domestic):

Beauty Alliance, Inc. (3)
1901 Ulmerton Rd Ste 225, Clearwater, FL 33762
Tel.: (727) 561-0622
Web Site: http://www.baistore.com
Sales Range: $350-399.9 Million
Emp.: 50
Beauty Parlor Equipment & Cosmetic Supplies Distr
N.A.I.C.S.: 423850

Subsidiary (Domestic):

Ace Beauty Co. (4)
8031 114th Ave Ste 4000, Largo, FL 33773-5006
Tel.: (727) 544-8861
Web Site: http://www.acebeautyco.com
Sales Range: $100-124.9 Million
Beauty Services & Supplies
N.A.I.C.S.: 423850

Subsidiary (Domestic):

Maly's West, Inc. (3)
28145 W Harrison Pkwy, Valencia, CA 91355
Tel.: (661) 295-8317
Web Site: http://www.malys.com
Sales Range: $150-199.9 Million
Emp.: 190
Hair Salon Equipment & Beauty Products Distr
N.A.I.C.S.: 423850

SalonCentric, Inc. (3)
4555 Danvers Dr SE, Grand Rapids, MI 49512-4040
Tel.: (616) 942-0060
Web Site: http://www.saloncentric.com
Sales Range: $75-99.9 Million
Emp.: 200
Hair Salon Equipment & Beauty Products Distr
N.A.I.C.S.: 423850

Subsidiary (Domestic):

Soft Sheen/Carson Products, Inc. (2)
575 Fifth Ave 19th Fl, New York, NY 10017
Tel.: (212) 818-1500
Web Site: http://www.softsheen-carson.com

Sales Range: $50-74.9 Million
Emp.: 150
Hair Care Products Mfr
N.A.I.C.S.: 325620

L'Oreal Ukraine (1)
4 Mykoly Grinchenka Str, Kiev, 3680, Ukraine
Tel.: (380) 443905515
Cosmetics Products Mfr
N.A.I.C.S.: 325620

L'Oreal Uruguay (1)
Av Italia 4273, 11400, Montevideo, Uruguay
Tel.: (598) 26133469
Rev.: $4,000,000
Emp.: 170
Mfr of Perfumes
N.A.I.C.S.: 456120

L'Oreal Verwaltungs GmbH (1)
Hertzstr 175, 76187, Karlsruhe, Germany
Tel.: (49) 721 97270
Investment Management Service
N.A.I.C.S.: 523999

L'Oreal Vietnam Co., Ltd. (1)
10th Floor Vincom Center 45A Ly Tu Trong St, Ben Nghe Ward Dist, Ho Chi Minh City, Vietnam
Tel.: (84) 2839369142
Emp.: 258
Beauty Product Whslr
N.A.I.C.S.: 456120

La Institut Lancome (1)
29 Rue De Faubourg St Honore, F 75008, Paris, France (100%)
Tel.: (33) 149646500
Web Site: http://www.lancome.com
Sales Range: $25-49.9 Million
Emp.: 11
Perfumes
N.A.I.C.S.: 325620

La Roche-Posay Laboratoire Pharmaceutique (1)
327 Ave Saint Anne, BP 124, 86270, La Roche-Posay, France
Tel.: (33) 1 46 88 68 00
Web Site: http://www.laroche-posay.com
Cosmetics Products Mfr
N.A.I.C.S.: 325620
Brigitte Lemarie *(Pres)*

LaScad S.N.C. (1)
7 Rue Touzet Gaillard, Saint-Ouen, 93400, Seine-Saint-Denis, France
Tel.: (33) 158618500
Cosmetics Products Mfr
N.A.I.C.S.: 325620

Laboratoire Sanoflore SA (1)
Sortie Beaufort, 26400, Gigors-et-Lozeron, Drome, France
Tel.: (33) 4 75 76 46 60
Web Site: http://www.sanoflore.net
Sales Range: $25-49.9 Million
Emp.: 25
Cosmetics Products Mfr
N.A.I.C.S.: 325620

Laboratoires Decleor S.A.S. (1)
31 Rue Henri Rochefor, 75017, Paris, France
Tel.: (33) 1 78 46 73 73
Web Site: http://www.decleor.com
Cosmetics & Skin Care Products Mfr
N.A.I.C.S.: 325620
Elisabeth Crouzet *(Mgr-Editorial)*

Laboratoires Garnier Paris (1)
41 Rue Martre, 92117, Clichy, Cedex, France (100%)
Tel.: (33) 1 47 56 7000
Web Site: http://www.loreal.com
Mfr of Skin-Care Products
N.A.I.C.S.: 325620

Lancome Parfums et Beaute (1)
106 Rue Gangom, 92691, Levallois-Perret, France (100%)
Tel.: (33) 149648000
Web Site: http://www.lancome.com
Emp.: 2,000
Perfumes & Cosmetics
N.A.I.C.S.: 325620

Lehoux et Jacque (1)
4 Rue Bertrand Sincholle, 92110, Clichy, France

AND PRIVATE COMPANIES

Tel.: (33) 147564321
Sales Range: $25-49.9 Million
Emp.: 1
Personal Care Product Mfr
N.A.I.C.S.: 325620
Eric Poulner *(Mng Dir)*

Matrix Distribution GmbH (1)
Hertzstr 175, 76187, Karlsruhe, 76187, Germany
Tel.: (49) 72197270
Cosmetics Products Mfr
N.A.I.C.S.: 325620

Nihon L'Oreal KK (1)
Shinjuku Park Tower 3-7-1 Nishi Shinjuku, Shinjuku-ku, Tokyo, 163-1071, Japan
Tel.: (81) 353710138
Web Site: https://www.loreal.com
Emp.: 2,700
Cosmetics Products Mfr
N.A.I.C.S.: 325620

Noveal SASU (1)
16 Rue Maurice Berteaux, 95500, Le Thillay, France
Tel.: (33) 134047400
Web Site: https://www.noveal.com
Emp.: 20
Industrial Inorganic Chemical Mfr
N.A.I.C.S.: 325180

P.T. L'Oreal Indonesia (1)
DBS Bank Tower 29th floor Ciputra World 1 Kuningan Jl Prof DR Satrio, No Kav 3-5 RT 18/RW 4 Kuningan Karet Kuningan Setiabudi, South Jakarta, 12940, Jakarta, Indonesia
Tel.: (62) 212 988 6666
Web Site: https://www.loreal.com
Sales Range: $150-199.9 Million
Emp.: 300
Cosmetic Product Distr
N.A.I.C.S.: 424210
Vismay Sharma *(Pres)*

P.T. Yasulor Indonesia (1)
Jl Raya Bogor Km 26 4, Ciracas, Jakarta, 13740, Indonesia
Tel.: (62) 2129981900
Sales Range: $125-149.9 Million
Emp.: 50
Cosmetics Products Mfr
N.A.I.C.S.: 325620
David Quitan *(Gen Mgr)*

Parfums Cacharel & Cie SNC (1)
16 Place Vendome, Paris, 75008, France
Tel.: (33) 1 40 20 60 00
Web Site: http://www.cacharel.com
Perfume Mfr & Distr
N.A.I.C.S.: 325620

Parfums Cachrel & Cie (1)
41 Rue Martre, 92217, Clichy, France (100%)
Tel.: (33) 147567000
Perfumes
N.A.I.C.S.: 325620

Parfums et Beaute France & Cie. (1)
41 Rue Martre, 92117, Clichy, France (100%)
Tel.: (33) 149646500
Sales Range: $125-149.9 Million
Emp.: 400
Perfumes
N.A.I.C.S.: 325620

Prestige & Collections international SNC (1)
16 Place Vendome, 75001, Paris, France
Tel.: (33) 149646500
Cosmetics Products Mfr
N.A.I.C.S.: 325620

Prestige et Collections Inter. & Cie. (1)
41 Rue Martre, 92117, Clichy, France (100%)
Tel.: (33) 147567000
Web Site: http://www.loreal.com
Sales Range: $1-4.9 Billion
Emp.: 3,000
Perfumes
N.A.I.C.S.: 325620

Productos Capilares L'Oreal S.A. (1)
Josefa Valcarcel 48, 28045, Madrid, Spain

Tel.: (34) 911778000
Sales Range: $200-249.9 Million
Emp.: 800
Cosmetics Products Mfr
N.A.I.C.S.: 325620

Redken France (1)
14 Rue Royale, Paris, 75008, France
Tel.: (33) 1 47 56 70 00
Web Site: http://www.redken.fr
Cosmetics Products Mfr
N.A.I.C.S.: 325620

Seda Plastik Ve Boya San. Ith. Tic. Ldt. Sti (1)
Istiklal Mahallesi 3 Hurriyet Caddesi 382 Sokak, Istanbul, 34522, Turkiye
Tel.: (90) 2126225200
Sales Range: $25-49.9 Million
Emp.: 21
Plastics Product Mfr
N.A.I.C.S.: 326199

Sicos & Cie (1)
Avenue Henri Lefebvre, 59540, Caudry, France
Tel.: (33) 327756666
Cosmetics Products Mfr
N.A.I.C.S.: 456120

Soprocos S.A.S. (1)
Route de Chauny, 02430, Gauchy, France
Tel.: (33) 323513500
Cosmetics Products Mfr
N.A.I.C.S.: 325620

Soproreal S.N.C. (1)
137 Rue Jacques Duclos, 93600, Aulnaysous-Bois, 93600, France
Tel.: (33) 148795000
Cosmetics Products Mfr
N.A.I.C.S.: 325620

Thierry Mugler Parfums (1)
16 Rue Montrosier, 92200, Neuilly-sur-Seine, France
Tel.: (33) 1 55 62 25 38
Web Site: http://www.thierrymugler.com
Sales Range: $25-49.9 Million
Emp.: 100
Mfr of Perfumes
N.A.I.C.S.: 325620

Zao L'Oreal (1)
1/8 Str 1-2 Golutvinski 4-I Per, Moscow, 119180, Russia
Tel.: (7) 4957256389
Web Site: http://www.loreal.com.ru
Cosmetics Products Mfr
N.A.I.C.S.: 325620

L-ACOUSTICS SAS
13 rue Levacher-Cintrat, 91460, Marcoussis, France
Tel.: (33) 1 69 63 69 63   FR
Web Site: http://www.l-acoustics.com
Year Founded: 1984
Emp.: 400
Audio & Video Equipment Mfr
N.A.I.C.S.: 334310

Subsidiaries:

H.G.P. SASU (1)
Zone Industrielle la Boitardiere, 37400, Amboise, Indre et Loire, France
Tel.: (33) 247 30 56 40
Web Site: http://www.hgp.fr
Emp.: 50
Precision Sheet Metal Mfr
N.A.I.C.S.: 332322
Bertrand Bounoure *(Pres & Comml Dir)*

L-Acoustics, Inc. (1)
2201 Celsius Ave Ste E, Oxnard, CA 93030
Tel.: (805) 604-0577
Web Site: http://www.l-acoustics.com
Sales Range: $1-9.9 Million
Emp.: 10
Audio & Video Equipment Mfr
N.A.I.C.S.: 334310
Florent Bernard *(Head-Trng)*

L-GAM ADVISERS LLP
20 Saint James Street, London, SW1A 1ES, United Kingdom
Tel.: (44) 20 7024 4777
Web Site: http://www.l-gam.com

Private Investment Firm
N.A.I.C.S.: 523999
Tito Soso *(Partner)*

L-KONZEPT HOLDING AG
Delitzscher Strasse 13, 4105, Leipzig, Germany
Tel.: (49) 341269840
Web Site: https://www.l-konzept.ag
Year Founded: 1995
LKB—(DEU)
Rev.: $121,426
Assets: $4,095,358
Liabilities: $2,163,585
Net Worth: $1,931,772
Earnings: ($496,741)
Emp.: 1
Fiscal Year-end: 12/30/23
Holding Company
N.A.I.C.S.: 551112
Helmut Ulbricht *(Member-Mgmt Bd)*

Subsidiaries:

L-Konzept Sachsen GmbH (1)
Delitzscher Strasse 13, 04105, Leipzig, Germany
Tel.: (49) 341269840
Web Site: http://www.l-konzept.de
Property Management Services
N.A.I.C.S.: 531311

L. B. FINANCE PLC
No 27575 Prof Stanley Wijesundera Mawatha, 7, Colombo, Sri Lanka
Tel.: (94) 112200000
Web Site: https://www.lbfinance.com
Year Founded: 1971
LFIN—(COL)
Rev.: $306,769,873
Assets: $878,216,434
Liabilities: $700,863,003
Net Worth: $177,353,431
Earnings: $45,092,485
Emp.: 3,804
Fiscal Year-end: 03/31/22
Leasing & Financial Services
N.A.I.C.S.: 522220
Ravindra Yatawara *(Exec Dir)*

L. BILODEAU & FILS LTD
230 de l'Eglise, Honfleur, G0R 1N0, QC, Canada
Tel.: (418) 885-4495
Web Site: http://www.lbilodeau-fils.com
Year Founded: 1963
Rev.: $15,470,405
Emp.: 130
Freight Trucking Services
N.A.I.C.S.: 484110
Isabelle Bilodeau *(Pres)*

L. E. LUNDBERGFORETAGEN AB
Hovslagargatan 5B, Box 14048, SE 104 40, Stockholm, Sweden
Tel.: (46) 8 463 0600   SE
Web Site:
   http://www.lundbergforetagen.se
Year Founded: 1944
LUND.B—(OMX)
Rev.: $3,207,652,000
Assets: $24,723,397,440
Liabilities: $6,757,494,240
Net Worth: $17,965,903,200
Earnings: $1,821,921,920
Emp.: 4,073
Fiscal Year-end: 12/31/21
Investment Management Service
N.A.I.C.S.: 523999
Fredrik Lundberg *(Pres & CEO)*

Subsidiaries:

Fastighets L E Lundberg AB (1)
Olai Kyrkogata 40, 601 85, Norrkoping, Sweden
Tel.: (46) 11216500

L. POSSEHL & CO. MBH

Web Site:
   https://www.lundbergsfastigheter.se
Emp.: 180
Finance Investment Services
N.A.I.C.S.: 523999

Hufvudstaden AB (1)
Regeringsgatan 38, 111 77, Stockholm, Sweden
Tel.: (46) 87629000
Web Site: http://www.hufvudstaden.se
Rev.: $257,176,843
Assets: $4,798,804,874
Liabilities: $1,870,746,579
Net Worth: $2,928,058,295
Earnings: $67,623,891
Emp.: 230
Fiscal Year-end: 12/31/2022
Office & Retail Real Estate Services; Owned 45.2% by L E Lundbergforetagen AB
N.A.I.C.S.: 531390
Fredrik Lundberg *(Chm)*

Subsidiary (Domestic):

Nordiska Kompaniet AB (2)
Hamngatan 18-20, 111 47, Stockholm, Sweden (100%)
Tel.: (46) 87628000
Web Site: http://www.nk.se
Real Estate Property Lessors
N.A.I.C.S.: 531190

Parkaden AB (2)
Regeringsgatan 47-55 NK 100, 111 77, Stockholm, Sweden
Tel.: (46) 8 762 9200
Web Site: https://www.parkaden.se
Sales Range: $25-49.9 Million
Emp.: 5
Parking Operations
N.A.I.C.S.: 812930

LE Lundberg Fastighets AB (1)
Olai Kyrkogata 40, 601 85, Norrkoping, Sweden (100%)
Tel.: (46) 11216500
Web Site: http://www.lundbergs.se
Sales Range: $125-149.9 Million
Emp.: 155
Real Estate Agents & Brokers
N.A.I.C.S.: 531210
Fredrik Lundberg *(Chm)*

L. POSSEHL & CO. MBH
Beckergrube 38-52, 23552, Lubeck, Germany
Tel.: (49) 4511480   De
Web Site: http://www.possehl.de
Year Founded: 1847
Rev.: $4,636,772,491
Assets: $2,075,965,112
Liabilities: $435,803,598
Net Worth: $1,640,161,514
Earnings: $104,395,589
Emp.: 13,331
Fiscal Year-end: 12/31/19
Holding Company
N.A.I.C.S.: 551112
Mario Schreiber *(Vice Chm-Exec Bd)*

Subsidiaries:

Auer Formenbau GmbH (1)
Am Alten Sportplatz 3, 90587, Veitsbronn, Germany
Tel.: (49) 9119732893
Web Site: http://www.afg.tps-group.de
Precision Tool Mfr
N.A.I.C.S.: 333517

BDO Spencer Steward (Johannesburg) Inc (1)
22 Wellington Rd, Parktown, 2193, Johannesburg, South Africa (100%)
Tel.: (27) 114881700
Web Site: http://www.bdo.co.za
Sales Range: $75-99.9 Million
Emp.: 200
Special Industry Machinery Mfr
N.A.I.C.S.: 333310

Baustoff-Handels-Union GmbH & Co. KG (1)
Marktstrasse 24 - Citypassage, 66822, Lubeck, Germany (60%)
Tel.: (49) 45189060

L. POSSEHL & CO. MBH

L. Possehl & Co. mbH—(Continued)
Special Industry Machinery
N.A.I.C.S.: 333310

Bennert GmbH Betrieb fur Bauwerksicherung
Meckfelder Strasse 2, 99102, Klettbach, Germany
Tel.: (49) 362094800
Web Site: http://www.bennert.de
Building Maintenance Services
N.A.I.C.S.: 561790

Bowe Systec (IR) Ltd. (1)
1-3 Burton Hall Park Burton Hall Road, Sandyford, Dublin, D18 W860, Ireland
Tel.: (353) 12903551
Sophisticated Hardware & Software Solution Services
N.A.I.C.S.: 541512
Lisa Banton *(Mng Dir)*

Bowe Systec (Schweiz) AG (1)
Chriesbaumstrasse 2, 8604, Volketswil, Switzerland
Tel.: (41) 433994888
Sophisticated Hardware & Software Solution Services
N.A.I.C.S.: 541512
Daniel Waldmeier *(Mng Dir)*

Bowe Systec AB (1)
Stenorsvagen 44, Box 63, 26122, Landskrona, Sweden
Tel.: (46) 707703300
Sophisticated Hardware & Software Solution Services
N.A.I.C.S.: 541512
Staffan Emtemark *(Sls Mgr-Nordic)*

Bowe Systec Austria GmbH (1)
Carlbergergasse 66 B, 1230, Vienna, Austria
Tel.: (43) 18934320
Sophisticated Hardware & Software Solution Services
N.A.I.C.S.: 541512
Tomas Veigl *(Mng Dir)*

Bowe Systec Comercio De Equipamentos Para Escritorio S.A. (1)
Granja Park 5, 2710-142, Sintra, Portugal
Tel.: (351) 219106610
Sophisticated Hardware & Software Solution Services
N.A.I.C.S.: 541512

Bowe Systec Japan Ltd. (1)
1F Nishi-Shinjuku KF Building 8-14-24, Nishi-shinjuku Shinjuku-ku, Tokyo, 160-0023, Japan
Tel.: (81) 359256280
Web Site: http://www.boewe-systec-japan.jp
Industrial Equipment Distr
N.A.I.C.S.: 423830
Masahiro Koizumi *(CEO)*

Bowe Systec Ltd. (1)
Unit 7 Kings Grove, Industrial Estate Kings Grove, Maidenhead, SL6 4DP, Berkshire, United Kingdom
Tel.: (44) 1628581270
Sophisticated Hardware & Software Solution Services
N.A.I.C.S.: 541512
Lisa Banton *(Mng Dir)*

Bowe Systec Nederland B.V. (1)
Wilmersdorf 44L, 7327 AC, Apeldoorn, Netherlands
Tel.: (31) 555385200
Sophisticated Hardware & Software Solution Services
N.A.I.C.S.: 541512
Hans Put *(Mng Dir)*

Bowe Systec North-America Inc. (1)
8480 Honeycutt Rd Ste 200, Raleigh, NC 27615
Tel.: (919) 714-7277
Sophisticated Hardware & Software Solution Services
N.A.I.C.S.: 541512
John Lombard *(CEO)*

Bowe Systec S.A. (1)
Cl Julian Camarillo 12, 28037, Madrid, Spain
Tel.: (34) 913757270

Sophisticated Hardware & Software Solution Services
N.A.I.C.S.: 541512
Alfredo Calvao *(Mng Dir)*

Bowe Systec S.A.S. (1)
Parc des Guillaumes 58 rue de Neuilly Bat A 1, 93133, Noisy-le-Sec, Cedex, France
Tel.: (33) 156631960
Sophisticated Hardware & Software Solution Services
N.A.I.C.S.: 541512
Loic Busnel *(Mng Dir)*

Bowe Systec S.P.A. (1)
Via del Caucaso 49, 00144, Rome, Italy
Tel.: (39) 0665006201
Sophisticated Hardware & Software Solution Services
N.A.I.C.S.: 541512
Francesco Orsini *(Project Mgr)*

Cookson Drijfhout B.V. (1)
Keienbergweg 12, 1101 GB, Amsterdam, Netherlands
Tel.: (31) 205648520
Web Site: http://www.shop.drijfhoutnl.com
Jewellery Distr
N.A.I.C.S.: 423940

Cookson Metaux Precieux S.A. (1)
58 Rue Beaubourg, Paris, 75003, France
Tel.: (33) 825385385
Jewellery Distr
N.A.I.C.S.: 423940

DFT Deutsche Flachen-Technik Industrieboden GmbH (1)
Allerkai 4, 28309, Bremen, Germany
Tel.: (49) 42145830
Web Site: http://www.dft-bremen.de
Floor Contractor
N.A.I.C.S.: 238330

DMA Maschinen und Anlagenbau GmbH & Co. KG (1)
Eugen-Diesel-Str 8, 37671, Hoxter, Germany
Tel.: (49) 527197060
Web Site: http://www.dma.de
Emp.: 80
Container Glass Mfr
N.A.I.C.S.: 327213

During Schweisstechnik GmbH (1)
Guldenstrasse 11, 86343, Konigsbrunn, Germany
Tel.: (49) 8231 96060
Web Site: http://www.during-welding.com
Welding Machine Mfr & Distr
N.A.I.C.S.: 333992
Peter Kunzmann *(Mng Dir)*

Subsidiary (Non-US):

During MX S.A. (2)
Calle 2 Sur 1706 Cof El Carmen, Puebla, 72000, Mexico
Tel.: (52) 2228937100
Winding Machinery Distr
N.A.I.C.S.: 423830

During do Brasil Ltda. (2)
Rua Jose Fumachi 180 Jd Virginia, Itatiba, 13257-450, Brazil
Tel.: (55) 1144876130
Web Site: http://www.duringdobrasil.com.br
Industrial Machinery Distr
N.A.I.C.S.: 423830

EUROQUARZ GmbH (1)
Sudwall 15, 46282, Dorsten, Germany
Tel.: (49) 236220050
Web Site: http://www.euroquarz.com
Sand Distr
N.A.I.C.S.: 423320

Eidos S.r.l. (1)
Piazza della Chiesa n 1, Cavenago d'Adda, 26824, Lodi, LO, Italy
Tel.: (39) 0371709070
Web Site: http://www.eidos.it
Safety Engineering Services
N.A.I.C.S.: 541330
Carlo Bello *(Pres)*

Entsorgungsgesellschaft mbH fur Mecklenburg-Vorpommern (1)
Am Fischereihafen 113, 18069, Rostock, Germany (50%)
Tel.: (49) 3818113121

Special Industry Machinery
N.A.I.C.S.: 333310

Etipack America, Industria, Comercio e Representacoes Ltda. (1)
R Espartaco 39-Vila Romana, Sao Paulo, 05045-000, Brazil
Tel.: (55) 1138655379
Web Site: http://www.etipackamerica.com
Label Coding Machine Mfr
N.A.I.C.S.: 333993

Etipack B.V. (1)
Weidehek 125-D, 4824 AT, Breda, Netherlands
Tel.: (31) 765422660
Web Site: http://www.etipack.nl
Adhesive Label Mfr
N.A.I.C.S.: 325520
Filip Ysenbaardt *(Mgr-Technical & Comml)*

Etipack S.p.A (1)
Via Aquileia 55/61, 20092, Cinisello Balsamo, MI, Italy
Tel.: (39) 02660621
Web Site: http://www.etipack.it
Adhesive Label Mfr
N.A.I.C.S.: 325520
Marco Parretti *(Sls Dir)*

GWS Printing Systems B.V. (1)
Industrieweg 6, 5145 PV, Waalwijk, Netherlands
Tel.: (31) 884977777
Web Site: http://www.gws.nl
Printing Machinery & Equipment Mfr & Distr
N.A.I.C.S.: 333248

Gabler Maschinenbau GmbH (1)
Niels-Bohr-Ring 5a, 23568, Lubeck, Germany
Tel.: (49) 45131090
Web Site: http://www.gabler-maschinenbau.de
Marine Component Mfr
N.A.I.C.S.: 334290
David Schirm *(CEO)*

Gecko Trading Limited (1)
Gecko Distribution Centre Eastways, Witham, CM8 3GQ, United Kingdom
Tel.: (44) 1376532000
Web Site: http://www.geckojewellery.com
Jewelry Product Mfr
N.A.I.C.S.: 339910
Ruth Johnson *(Gen Mgr)*

Gesellschaft fur das Recycling Kontaminierter Industriebrachen mbH (1)
Einsiedelstrasse 47, D 23554, Lubeck, Germany (100%)
Tel.: (49) 4514088531
Web Site: http://www.possehl-umweltschutz.de
Sales Range: $25-49.9 Million
Emp.: 14
Special Industry Machinery
N.A.I.C.S.: 333310

HF Mixing Group Services (S.E.A.) Sdn. Bhd. (1)
B1-2-3 A Solaris Dutamas No 1 Jalan Dutamas 1, 50480, Kuala Lumpur, Malaysia
Tel.: (60) 362055508
Machinery Equipment Mfr
N.A.I.C.S.: 333248

HIRTLER SEIFEN GmbH (1)
Beiersdorfstrasse 1, 79423, Heitersheim, Germany (100%)
Tel.: (49) 76345100035
Web Site: http://www.hirtler.com
Sales Range: $25-49.9 Million
Emp.: 100
Soap Mfr
N.A.I.C.S.: 325611

Hako Australia Pty. Ltd. (1)
90 Wetherill Street N, Silverwater, 2128, NSW, Australia
Tel.: (61) 287564700
Web Site: http://www.hakoaustralia.com.au
Cleaning Machine Distr
N.A.I.C.S.: 423620

Hako B.V. (1)
Industrieweg 7, 6673 DE, Andelst, Netherlands
Tel.: (31) 488473333

INTERNATIONAL PUBLIC

Web Site: http://www.hako.nl
Cleaning Machinery Mfr
N.A.I.C.S.: 333310

Hako Cleaning System (Shanghai) Co., Ltd. (1)
504 Mingnan Road, Songjiang, Shanghai, 201613, China
Tel.: (86) 2167755050
Web Site: http://www.hako.cn
Cleaning Machine Distr
N.A.I.C.S.: 423810

Hako Espana S.A. (1)
Avenida de Castilla 24, San Fernando De Henares, 28830, Madrid, Spain
Tel.: (34) 900920000
Web Site: http://www.hako.es
Cleaning Machine Distr
N.A.I.C.S.: 423810

Hako GmbH (1)
Hamburger Strasse 209-239, 23843, Bad Oldesloe, Germany
Tel.: (49) 4531 806 0
Web Site: http://www.hako.com
Cleaning Machinery Mfr
N.A.I.C.S.: 333310

Subsidiary (Domestic):

von Oertzen GmbH (2)
Ferdinand Harten Strasse 10, Ammersbek, 22949, Germany
Tel.: (49) 40604110
Web Site: http://www.oertzen-gmbh.com
High Pressure Cleaning System Mfr
N.A.I.C.S.: 333998
Patrick Graef *(Mng Dir)*

Hako Ground & Garden A/S (1)
Lindebergveien 5, 2016, Frogner, Norway
Tel.: (47) 22907760
Web Site: http://www.hako.no
Cleaning Machine Distr
N.A.I.C.S.: 423810

Hako Ground & Garden AB (1)
Skallebackavagen 10, 302 41, Halmstad, Sweden
Tel.: (46) 35100000
Web Site: http://www.hako.se
Cleaning Machine Distr
N.A.I.C.S.: 423810

Hako Group East Asia Ltd. (1)
70 Soi Yeaksoisantisuk Klongtoey, Prakanong Sub-district, Bangkok, 10110, Thailand
Tel.: (66) 27135091
Web Site: http://www.hako.com
Emp.: 8
Cleaning Machine Distr
N.A.I.C.S.: 423810
Teerasak Aksornpattananan *(Mgr-Svc)*

Hako Machines Ltd. (1)
Eldon Close, Crick, NN6 7UD, Northampton, United Kingdom
Tel.: (44) 1788825600
Web Site: http://www.hako.co.uk
Cleaning Machine Mfr & Distr
N.A.I.C.S.: 333310
Joanne Veasey *(Dir-Bus Dev)*

Hako Polska Sp. z o.o. (1)
ul Czerwone Maki 63, 30-392, Krakow, Poland
Tel.: (48) 126221600
Web Site: http://www.hako.pl
Cleaning Machine Mfr & Distr
N.A.I.C.S.: 333310

Hako Schweiz AG (1)
Zeughausstrasse 21, 6210, Sursee, Switzerland
Tel.: (41) 9252626
Web Site: http://www.hako.ch
Cleaning Machine Distr
N.A.I.C.S.: 423810

Hako Technology Sp. z o.o. (1)
Chalupy 30, 76-024, Swieszyno, Poland
Tel.: (48) 943470404
Web Site: http://www.hakotech.pl
Industrial Machinery Mfr
N.A.I.C.S.: 333248
Anna Kudelska *(Sec)*

Hako-Werke GmbH (1)
Hamburger Strasse 209 239, Postfach

AND PRIVATE COMPANIES

1444, 23843, Bad Oldesloe, Germany
Tel.: (49) 45318060
Web Site: http://www.hako.com
Sales Range: $500-549.9 Million
Emp.: 2,431
Indoor & Outdoor Cleaning & Grounds Maintenance Equipment Mfr
N.A.I.C.S.: 333998
Michael Bentin *(Head-Adv Dept)*

Subsidiary (US):

Minuteman International, Inc. (2)
14N845 US Route 20, Pingree Grove, IL 60140
Tel.: (847) 264-5400
Web Site: http://www.minutemanintl.com
Sales Range: $50-74.9 Million
Mfr & Distr Commercial Industrial Floor & Carpet Care Equipment & Cleaning Products
N.A.I.C.S.: 333310

Subsidiary (Non-US):

Minuteman Canada, Inc. (3)
2210 Drew Road, Mississauga, L5S 1B1, ON, Canada
Tel.: (905) 673-3222
Web Site: http://www.minutemanintl.com
Sales Range: $50-74.9 Million
Emp.: 6
Industrial Cleaning Equipment Distr
N.A.I.C.S.: 423830

Subsidiary (Domestic):

Minuteman Powerboss Inc. (3)
175 Anderson St, Aberdeen, NC 28315
Tel.: (910) 944-2105
Web Site: http://www.powerboss.com
Sales Range: $25-49.9 Million
Emp.: 100
Sweeper & Scrubber Designer Mfr & Distr
N.A.I.C.S.: 333310

Division (Domestic):

Multi-Clean, Inc. (3)
600 Cardigan Rd, Shoreview, MN 55126-3964
Tel.: (651) 481-1900
Web Site: http://www.multi-clean.com
Sales Range: $25-49.9 Million
Chemical Cleaning & Coating Product Mfr
N.A.I.C.S.: 325612
Curt Starken *(Dir-Ops)*

Subsidiary (Domestic):

Multiclean, Inc. (3)
600 Cardigan Rd, Shoreview, MN 55126-3964
Tel.: (651) 481-1900
Web Site: http://www.multi-clean.com
Cleaning Product Mfr & Distr
N.A.I.C.S.: 325918
Curt Starken *(Dir-Ops)*

Harburg-Freudenberger Maschinenbau GmbH (1)
Schlachthofstrasse 22, Kautschuktechnik Speiseoltechn, 21079, Hamburg, Germany
Tel.: (49) 40771790
Web Site: http://www.hf-group.com
Sales Range: $150-199.9 Million
Rubber Processing Machinery & Equipment Mfr, Installer & Servicer
N.A.I.C.S.: 333248
Jorn Seevers *(Mng Dir)*

Subsidiary (Non-US):

HF NaJUS, a.s. (2)
Areal ZTS c 924, 8141, Dubnica nad Vahom, Slovakia
Tel.: (421) 424485601
Web Site: http://www.najus.sk
Industrial Machinery Mfr
N.A.I.C.S.: 333248
Hajdik Dusan *(CEO)*

Subsidiary (US):

HF Rubber Machinery Inc. (2)
1701 N Topeka Blvd, Topeka, KS 66608-0220
Tel.: (785) 235-2336
Sales Range: $25-49.9 Million
Emp.: 150
Rubber Processing Equipment Mfr

N.A.I.C.S.: 333248
Paul White *(VP)*

Subsidiary (Non-US):

Harburg-Freudenberger (France) S.A.R.L. (2)
8ter Boulevard Voltaire, 78800, Houilles, France
Tel.: (33) 130866990
Industrial Machinery Distr
N.A.I.C.S.: 423830

Harburg-Freudenberger Belisce d.o.o. (2)
Radnicka 5, 31551, Belisce, Croatia
Tel.: (385) 31516800
Web Site: http://www.hf-group.com
Sales Range: $75-99.9 Million
Machines, Equipment & Systems Development & Mfr
N.A.I.C.S.: 333248

Harburg-Freudenberger Machinery (China) Co., Ltd. (2)
120 Zhuzhou Road Hi-Tech Park, 266101, Qingdao, China
Tel.: (86) 53288706236
Industrial Machinery Distr
N.A.I.C.S.: 423830
Fu Qiang *(Mng Dir)*

Subsidiary (Domestic):

Harburg-Freudenberger Maschinenbau GmbH (2)
Asdorfer Strasse 60, 57258, Freudenberg, Germany
Tel.: (49) 27344910
Web Site: http://www.hf-group.com
Sales Range: $50-74.9 Million
Rubber Mfr
N.A.I.C.S.: 325212

Subsidiary (Non-US):

Pomini Rubber & Plastics S.r.l. (2)
Via Bonvesin de la Riva 43, 20027, Rescaldina, Milan, Italy
Tel.: (39) 0331743111
Industrial Machinery Distr
N.A.I.C.S.: 423830
Jonatan Quintana *(Mgr-Field Svc)*

Hebold Systems GmbH (1)
Peter-Henlein-Strasse 12, 27472, Cuxhaven, Germany
Tel.: (49) 4721601838
Web Site: http://www.hebold-systems.de
Homogenization & Dispersion System Mfr
N.A.I.C.S.: 333241

Heimerle + Meule GmbH (1)
Dennig Strasse 16, 75179, Pforzheim, Germany (90%)
Tel.: (49) 72319400
Web Site: http://www.heimerle-meule.com
Sales Range: $50-74.9 Million
Emp.: 250
Gold & Silver Refinery
N.A.I.C.S.: 331410
Peter Dorner *(Mng Dir)*

Subsidiary (Non-US):

Cookson Precious Metals Limited (2)
59-83 Vittoria Street, Birmingham, B1 3NZ, United Kingdom
Tel.: (44) 1212002120
Web Site: http://www.cooksongold.com
Jewellery Distr
N.A.I.C.S.: 423940

Holsteiner Humus und Erden GmbH (1)
Raabrede 57, D 23560, Lubeck, Germany (33.3%)
Tel.: (49) 451581292
Web Site: http://www.hhe-online.de
Special Industry Machinery
N.A.I.C.S.: 333310

I & B Cleaning Equipment Ltd. (1)
Room 6 11/F Wah Wai Industrial Centre 38-40 Au Pui Wan Street, Fo Tan, Sha Tin, New Territories, China (Hong Kong)
Tel.: (852) 24137370
Web Site: http://www.hako.cn
Cleaning Machine Distr

N.A.I.C.S.: 423810

IRS Stahlhandel GmbH (1)
Bischofstrasse 88, 47809, Krefeld, Germany (100%)
Tel.: (49) 2151507550
Web Site: http://www.irsstahlhandel.de
Sales Range: $25-49.9 Million
Emp.: 9
Steel Ingots & Bars Mfr
N.A.I.C.S.: 332111

Innobit GmbH (1)
Zschockestrasse 1, 67657, Kaiserslautern, Germany
Tel.: (49) 63131069817
Web Site: http://www.innophalt.de
Asphalt Surface Construction Product Mfr
N.A.I.C.S.: 333120

Jacbo Pfahlgrundungen GmbH (1)
Nordring 62, 48465, Schuttorf, Germany
Tel.: (49) 592396970
Web Site: http://www.jacbo.de
Construction Services
N.A.I.C.S.: 236220

Jost Bauunternehmen GmbH (1)
Rodelheimer Landstr 41, 60487, Frankfurt am Main, Germany
Tel.: (49) 699705060
Web Site: http://www.joest-bau.de
Road & Asphalt Construction Services
N.A.I.C.S.: 237310

KWV GmbH (1)
Am Krebsgraben 3/1, 78048, Villingen-Schwenningen, Germany
Tel.: (49) 7721206170
Web Site: http://www.kwv-vs.eu
Wire & Cable Mfr
N.A.I.C.S.: 335929
Rudolf Aprill *(Mng Dir)*

Subsidiary (Non-US):

Kleine Wolke AG (2)
Feldstrasse 2, 5506, Magenwil, Switzerland
Tel.: (41) 566484121
Web Site: http://www.kleinewolke.com
Shower Curtains & Bath Mats Mfr
N.A.I.C.S.: 314110

Kleine Wolke Textilgesellschaft mbH & Co. KG (1)
Fritz-Tecklenborg-Str 3, 28759, Bremen, Germany
Tel.: (49) 42162610
Web Site: http://www.kleinewolke.com
Sales Range: $25-49.9 Million
Emp.: 120
Bathroom Textile Product Mfr & Supplier
N.A.I.C.S.: 314110

Koutadly - Consultadoria Economica e Participacoes, S.A. (1)
R Visconde Bobeda 34-r/c, Porto, 4000-108, Portugal
Tel.: (351) 225106580
Jewelry Mfr & Distr
N.A.I.C.S.: 339910

LOGOPAK Systeme GmbH & Co. KG (1)
Dorfstrasse 40-42, 24628, Hartenholm, Germany
Tel.: (49) 4195 99750
Web Site: http://www.logopak.com
Labelling Machinery Mfr
N.A.I.C.S.: 333998

Subsidiary (Non-US):

LOGOPAK B.V. (2)
Madridstraat 21-25, 1175 RK, Lijnden, Netherlands
Tel.: (31) 235555080
Web Site: http://www.logopak.nl
Labelling Machine Distr
N.A.I.C.S.: 423830

LOGOPAK International Ltd. (2)
Enterprise House George Cayley Drive, Clifton Moor Industrial Estate, York, YO30 4XE, United Kingdom
Tel.: (44) 1904 69 23 33
Web Site: http://www.logopak.co.uk
Labelling Machine Distr
N.A.I.C.S.: 423830

LSS Etikettering A/S (2)

L. POSSEHL & CO. MBH

Normansvej 8, 8920, Randers, Denmark
Tel.: (45) 70202500
Web Site: http://www.lss-dk.com
Emp.: 30
Labelling Machine Mfr & Distr
N.A.I.C.S.: 333998

LOGOPAK Systems AB (1)
Norra Hamngatan 18 4 van, 411 06, Gothenburg, Sweden
Tel.: (46) 317001230
Labelling Machine Distr
N.A.I.C.S.: 423830

Labor Hako S.A.S. (1)
90 Avenue de Dreux, 78370, Plaisir, France
Tel.: (33) 130817777
Web Site: http://www.labor-hako.com
Cleaning Machine Distr
N.A.I.C.S.: 423810

Logopak Sistemas S.L. (1)
Besalu 21 - Pol Ind Pla de la Bruguera, Castellar del Valles, 08211, Barcelona, Spain
Tel.: (34) 931842373
Web Site: http://www.logopak.es
Industrial Equipment Distr
N.A.I.C.S.: 423830

Logopak Vertriebsgesellschaft Sud mbH (1)
Monsheimer Strasse 20, 71299, Wimsheim, Germany
Tel.: (49) 7044954470
Industrial Equipment Distr
N.A.I.C.S.: 423830

Logopak Vertriebsgesellschaft West mbH (1)
Lintorfer Waldstrasse 10, 40489, Dusseldorf, Germany
Tel.: (49) 203742230
Industrial Equipment Distr
N.A.I.C.S.: 423830

Lubeca Versicherungskontor GmbH (1)
Beckergrube 38-52, 23552, Lubeck, Germany (100%)
Tel.: (49) 451148260
Web Site: http://lubeca.eu
Sales Range: $50-74.9 Million
Emp.: 15
Risk Insurance
N.A.I.C.S.: 524126

MAF Magnesite BV (1)
Nieuwe Uitleg 10, 2514 BP, Hague, Netherlands (100%)
Tel.: (31) 703105900
Web Site: http://www.magnesiumoxide.com
Sales Range: $50-74.9 Million
Emp.: 10
Special Industry Machinery
N.A.I.C.S.: 333130

MGG Micro-Gluhlampen-Gesellschaft Menzel GmbH (1)
Hamburger Landstrasse 1, 21465, Wentorf bei Hamburg, Germany
Tel.: (49) 407200020
Web Site: https://www.mgg-lamps.de
Lamp Mfr
N.A.I.C.S.: 335139

Mesabi Control Engineering, Ltd. (1)
7800 3rd St N Ste 900, Oakdale, MN 55128
Tel.: (651) 771-1890
Web Site: http://www.mesabicontrol.com
Mechanical Engineering Services
N.A.I.C.S.: 541330

Mickan Generalbaugesellschaft Amberg mbH & Co. KG (1)
Wernher-von-Braun-Str 24, 92224, Amberg, Germany
Tel.: (49) 96213040
Web Site: http://www.mickan-bau.de
Emp.: 330
Construction Engineering Services
N.A.I.C.S.: 541330
Gunther Hofbeck *(Exec Dir)*

N.V. Bowe Systec S.A. (1)
Mechelsesteenweg 311, 1800, Vilvoorde, Belgium
Tel.: (32) 24560670
Sophisticated Hardware & Software Solution Services

L. POSSEHL & CO. MBH

L. Possehl & Co. mbH—(Continued)
N.A.I.C.S.: 541512
Geert Donkers (Mgr-Customer Svc)

N.V. Hako Belgium S.A. (1)
Industrieweg 27, 9420, Erpe-Mere, Belgium
Tel.: (32) 53802040
Web Site: http://www.hako.be
Cleaning Machine Distr
N.A.I.C.S.: 423810

Nordrohr GmbH (1)
Grootkoppel 24, 23858, Reinfeld, Germany
Tel.: (49) 45332070050
Web Site: http://www.nordrohr.de
Pipe & Sewer Cleaning Services
N.A.I.C.S.: 562991

Nordstahl GmbH (1)
Graf Adolf Platz 1, D 40213, Dusseldorf, Germany (100%)
Tel.: (49) 211380800
Web Site: http://www.nordstahl.de
Sales Range: $25-49.9 Million
Emp.: 45
Special Industry Machinery
N.A.I.C.S.: 333310

Nordvalls Etikett AB (1)
Planteringsgatan 46, 275 39, Sjobo, Sweden
Tel.: (46) 101691700
Web Site: http://www.nordvalls.se
Adhesive Label Mfr
N.A.I.C.S.: 325520
Camilla Goland (Ops Mgr)

Novexx Solutions B.V. (1)
Maarssenbroeksedijk 15, 3542 DL, Utrecht, Netherlands
Tel.: (31) 307609010
Industrial Equipment Distr
N.A.I.C.S.: 423830

Novexx Solutions GmbH (1)
Ohmstrasse 3, 85386, Eching, Germany
Tel.: (49) 81659250
Web Site: http://www.novexx.com
Industrial Equipment Distr
N.A.I.C.S.: 423830
Dietrich Barsch (Mng Dir)

Novexx Solutions S.A.S. (1)
18 rue de l Esterel, 90559, Rungis, Cedex, France
Tel.: (33) 825826152
Industrial Equipment Distr
N.A.I.C.S.: 423830

Nuthen Restaurierungen GmbH + Co. KG (1)
Anton-Lucius-Strasse 14, 99085, Erfurt, Germany
Tel.: (49) 361654710
Web Site: http://www.nuethen.de
Building Maintenance Services
N.A.I.C.S.: 561790

OY Hako Ground & Garden AB (1)
Vanha Porvoontie 256 C, 01380, Vantaa, Finland
Tel.: (358) 98700733
Web Site: http://www.hako.fi
Cleaning Machine Mfr & Distr
N.A.I.C.S.: 333310

Optimus Sorter Technology B.V. (1)
Platinawerf 18, 6641 TL, Beuningen, Netherlands
Tel.: (31) 243451760
Web Site: http://www.optimussorters.com
Peripheral Sorter Mfr
N.A.I.C.S.: 334118

P+S Pflaster- und Strassenbau GmbH (1)
Neudorfer Strasse 1, Wulknitz, 01609, Meissen, Germany
Tel.: (49) 3526554542
Web Site: http://www.punds-bau.de
Road Construction Services
N.A.I.C.S.: 237310

PAGEL Spezial-Beton GmbH & Co. KG (1)
Wolfsbankring 9, 45355, Essen, Germany
Tel.: (49) 201 68504 0
Web Site: http://www.pagel.com
Mortars Mfr
N.A.I.C.S.: 327120

Subsidiary (Non-US):

PAGEL S.A.S. (2)
22 rue Gustave Eiffel, BP 10058, 78306, Poissy, Cedex, France
Tel.: (33) 139223900
Construction Materials Distr
N.A.I.C.S.: 423320

Subsidiary (Domestic):

PAGEL Technische Mortel GmbH & Co. KG (2)
Witteringstr 6, Essen, 45130, Nordrhein-Westfalen, Germany
Tel.: (49) 2017221781
Construction Materials Mfr
N.A.I.C.S.: 327331

PK Rohstoffe GmbH (1)
Krabbenkamp 5, 47138, Duisburg, Germany
Tel.: (49) 2036000330
Web Site: http://www.pk-rohstoffe.de
Waste Management Services
N.A.I.C.S.: 562998
Wolfgang Brast (Gen Mgr)

PlasTec Technology GmbH (1)
Arndtstrasse 9-11, Trappenkamp, 24610, Pinneberg, Germany
Tel.: (49) 432391260
Web Site: http://www.plastec-technology.com
Plastics Product Mfr
N.A.I.C.S.: 326199

Possehl (HK) Holdings Ltd. (1)
Unit D 19th Floor Room 211 Jonhnston Road, Wanchai, Hong Kong, China (Hong Kong) (100%)
Tel.: (852) 28932841
Sales Range: $50-74.9 Million
Emp.: 100
Special Industry Machinery
N.A.I.C.S.: 333310

Possehl Electronics Czech Republic s.r.o (1)
Dysina 297, 330 02, Dysina, Czech Republic
Tel.: (420) 373731124
Electronic Components Mfr
N.A.I.C.S.: 334419
Ludek Bejvi (Mng Dir)

Possehl Electronics Deutschland GmbH (1)
Enztalstrasse 6, 75223, Niefern-Oschelbronn, Germany
Tel.: (49) 7233 69 0
Web Site: http://www.possehlelectronics.de
Emp.: 450
Commercial & Service Industry Machinery Mfr
N.A.I.C.S.: 333310

Possehl Electronics Netherlands B.V. (1)
De Beverspijken 3, 5221 EE, 's-Hertogenbosch, Netherlands (100%)
Tel.: (31) 736393939
Web Site: http://www.possehlelectronics.de
Emp.: 55
Semiconductor Mfr
N.A.I.C.S.: 334413
Peter Pennings (Mng Dir)

Subsidiary (US):

Possehl Connector Services (2)
1521 Morse Ave, Elk Grove Village, IL 60007-5723 (100%)
Tel.: (847) 758-0208
Web Site: http://www.possehlconnector.com
Sales Range: $25-49.9 Million
Emp.: 21
Holding Company
N.A.I.C.S.: 335931

Possehl Connector Services SC, Inc (2)
445 Bryant Blvd, Rock Hill, SC 29732-8210 (100%)
Tel.: (803) 366-8316
Web Site: http://www.possehlconnector.com
Sales Range: $25-49.9 Million
Emp.: 52
Metal Plating & Polishing
N.A.I.C.S.: 332813

Rob Boyer (Mng Dir)

Subsidiary (Non-US):

Possehl Electronics Hong Kong Ltd. (2)
3/F 4/F 5/F Tsuen Wan Industrial Centre Texaco Road, 220248, Tsuen Wan, New Territories, China (Hong Kong) (100%)
Tel.: (852) 26978233
Web Site: http://www.possehlelectronics.com
Sales Range: $50-74.9 Million
Emp.: 200
Electronics Components Mfr & Sales
N.A.I.C.S.: 334413

Possehl Electronics Malaysia Sdn Bhd (2)
Lot 33 Phase IIIA, Batu Berendam Free Trade Zn, 75350, Melaka, Malaysia (100%)
Tel.: (60) 62835979
Electronic Components Mfr & Sales
N.A.I.C.S.: 334419
S. W. Chin (Head-Fin)

Possehl Electronics N.V. (2)
5 rue Pre de la Treille, F 38320, Eybens, France (99%)
Tel.: (33) 675377429
Web Site: http://www.possehlelectronics.com
Sales Range: $25-49.9 Million
Emp.: 35
Semiconductor Mfr
N.A.I.C.S.: 334413
Jens Helbig (Mng Dir)

Subsidiary (Non-US):

Dongguan Possehl Electronics Co. Ltd. (3)
Dawei Xinji Village, Machong Town, Dongguan, China
Tel.: (86) 76939001228
Connector Mfr
N.A.I.C.S.: 335931

Possehl (Malaysia) Sdn. Bhd. (3)
Lot 9 Phase 3a Batu Berendam Free Trade Zone, Melaka, 75350, Malaysia
Tel.: (60) 62832799
Connector Mfr
N.A.I.C.S.: 335931

Subsidiary (Domestic):

Possehl Electronics France S.A.S. (3)
ZI du Buisson - Boulevard, BP 50021, Sagnat, 42230, Roche-la-Moliere, France
Tel.: (33) 477905087
Web Site: http://www.possehlelectronics.com
Emp.: 44
Connector Mfr
N.A.I.C.S.: 335931
Jens Helbig (Mng Dir)

Subsidiary (Non-US):

Possehl Electronics Singapore Pte. Ltd. (2)
No 11Tuas Avenue 4, Jurong, 639366, Singapore (100%)
Tel.: (65) 68615216
Web Site: http://www.possehlelectronics.de
Sales Range: $25-49.9 Million
Semiconductor Mfr
N.A.I.C.S.: 334413

Shenzhen Possehl SEG Electronics Co., Ltd. (2)
No 1 Hong Lliu Road, Futian Free Trade Zone, Shenzhen, 518038, Guangdong, China (100%)
Tel.: (86) 75583591906
Web Site: http://www.possehlelectronics.com
Electronic Components Mfr & Sales
N.A.I.C.S.: 334413

Possehl Electronics Puebla S. de R.L. de C.V. (1)
Calle Tule 39, Parque Industrial Finsa Cuautlancingo, Puebla, 72710, Mexico
Tel.: (52) 2222105633
Electronic Components Mfr
N.A.I.C.S.: 334419

Miguel Prado (Mng Dir)

Possehl Electronics Wackersdorf GmbH (1)
Karl-Rapp-Strasse 1, 92442, Wackersdorf, Germany
Tel.: (49) 9431798590
Electronic Components Mfr
N.A.I.C.S.: 334419
Michael Kerber (Plant Mgr)

Possehl Erzkontor GmbH (1)
Beckergrube 38-52, 23552, Lubeck, Germany (100%)
Tel.: (49) 4511480
Web Site: http://www.erzkontor.com
Sales Range: $25-49.9 Million
Emp.: 34
Mineral Ore Metal Plastic Raw Material & Chemical Mfr
N.A.I.C.S.: 327999

Subsidiary (Domestic):

Mineralmahlwerk C. Welsch GmbH (2)
Am Lippeglacis 11, 46483, Wesel, Germany (100%)
Tel.: (49) 2811649360
Web Site: http://www.erzkontor.com
Sales Range: $1-9.9 Million
Emp.: 25
Mineral Grinding Mills
N.A.I.C.S.: 321918

Subsidiary (Non-US):

Possehl Erzkontor Hong Kong Limited (2)
Unit 901-903 9th Floor Tai Yip Building 141 Thomson Road, Wanchai, China (Hong Kong) (100%)
Tel.: (852) 28275841
Web Site: http://www.erzkontor.hk
Sales Range: $25-49.9 Million
Emp.: 4
Special Industry Machinery
N.A.I.C.S.: 333310

Possehl Inc. (1)
1 Maynard Dr, Park Ridge, NJ 07656-1878 (100%)
Tel.: (201) 307-1500
Special Industry Machinery
N.A.I.C.S.: 333310

Possehl Laminates Limited (1)
Possehl Building 18 Ma Kok Street, Tsuen Wan, China (Hong Kong)
Tel.: (852) 26978233
Web Site: http://www.possehlelectronics.com
Emp.: 200
Semiconductor Components Mfr
N.A.I.C.S.: 333242

Possehl Mittelstandsbeteiligungen GmbH (1)
Beckergrube 38, Lubeck, 23552, Germany
Tel.: (49) 4511480
Industrial Machinery Mfr
N.A.I.C.S.: 333998
Tobias Krauss (Mng Dir)

Possehl Precision Toolings (Shenzhen) Co. Ltd. (1)
No 1 Hong Lui Rd, Futian Free Trade Zone, Shenzhen, China (80%)
Tel.: (86) 7553591906
Special Industry Machinery
N.A.I.C.S.: 333310

Possehl Spezialbau GmbH (1)
Gau-Bickelheimer Strasse 72, 55576, Sprendlingen, Germany (100%)
Tel.: (49) 6701204490
Web Site: http://www.possehl-spezialbau.de
Sales Range: $25-49.9 Million
Emp.: 50
Industrial Flooring, Concrete Maintenance & Preservation & Construction Services
N.A.I.C.S.: 238330
Jorg Henschel (Chm-Mgmt Bd)

Subsidiary (Non-US):

Possehl Aannemingsmaatschappij BV (2)
Zeilmakerijweg 9, 4906 CW, Oosterhout, Netherlands (100%)

AND PRIVATE COMPANIES

Tel.: (31) 162456544
Web Site: http://www.possehl.nl
Sales Range: $25-49.9 Million
Emp.: 50
Concrete Epoxy Systems & Flooring Materials
N.A.I.C.S.: 238330
H. Sehillakans (Mng Dir)

Possehl Posebne Gradnje d.o.o. (2)
Pocehovska Ulica 25, 2000, Maribor,
Slovenia (100%)
Tel.: (386) 22296390
Web Site: http://www.possehl.si
Sales Range: $25-49.9 Million
Emp.: 25
Road Construction & Maintenance
N.A.I.C.S.: 237310
Slobodan Miljatovic (Dir)

Possehl Spezialbau GESMBH (2)
Alte Haupstrasse 31, 9112, Griffen,
Austria (100%)
Tel.: (43) 423321070
Web Site: http://www.possehl-spezialbau.at
Sales Range: $25-49.9 Million
Emp.: 12
Road Maintenance & Construction
N.A.I.C.S.: 237310

Possehl Umweltschutz GmbH (1)
Beckergrube 38-52, 23552, Lubeck,
Germany (100%)
Tel.: (49) 451401011
Web Site: http://www.possehl-umweltschutz.de
Sales Range: $25-49.9 Million
Emp.: 45
Environmental Protection Services
N.A.I.C.S.: 541620

Red Ledge Ltd. (1)
Underbank Mill Dunford Road, Holmfirth,
HD9 2AR, United Kingdom
Tel.: (44) 1484556996
Web Site: http://www.redledge.co.uk
Computer Software Services
N.A.I.C.S.: 541511
Paul Makinson (Engr-Sls)

SAVO-TECHNIK ROTATIONSGUSS GmbH (1)
Am Heisterbusch 18, 19246, Luttow-Valluhn, Germany
Tel.: (49) 3885132800
Web Site: http://www.rotationsguss.com
Emp.: 62
Engineeering Services
N.A.I.C.S.: 541330
Ingolf Rasch (Mng Dir)

SCI L'Hermitage (1)
61 Avenue Jules Quentin, 92000, Nanterre,
France
Tel.: (33) 146957000
Road Construction Services
N.A.I.C.S.: 237310

SGA Conveyor System AB (1)
Ehns gata 10, 511 56, Kinna, Sweden
Tel.: (46) 32512300
Web Site: http://www.sga-conveyor.se
Material Handling Equipment Distr
N.A.I.C.S.: 423830

Sadimato S.A.S. (1)
Sainte Apolline - 90 Avenue de Dreux, BP
48, 78371, Plaisir, Cedex, France
Tel.: (33) 130817730
Web Site: http://www.sadimato.com
Emp.: 100
Sprinkler Installation Services
N.A.I.C.S.: 238220
Eric Hanot (Gen Mgr)

Schwarte Group A/S (1)
Lindholmvej 26, 6710, Esbjerg, Denmark
Tel.: (45) 70102060
Business Management Consulting Services
N.A.I.C.S.: 541618
Kristian Lovstrom Olsen (CEO)

Schwarte Group GmbH (1)
Taubenstrasse 33-43, 48282, Emsdetten,
Germany
Tel.: (49) 25729603000
Business Management Consulting Services
N.A.I.C.S.: 541618
Stephan Hoffman (Plant Mgr)

Schwarte Group GmbH (1)
Neuhofenstrasse 35, 4810, Gmunden, Austria
Tel.: (43) 7612745230
Business Management Consulting Services
N.A.I.C.S.: 541618

Schwarte Group Sp. z o.o (1)
Al Obroncow Tobruku 3A, 10-092, Olsztyn,
Poland
Tel.: (48) 895221802
Business Management Consulting Services
N.A.I.C.S.: 541618
Paulina Jarota (Project Mgr)

Sempsa Joyeria Plateria, S.A. (1)
Avda de la Democracia 13, 28031, Madrid,
Spain
Tel.: (34) 913829220
Web Site: http://www.sempsajp.com
Metal Distr
N.A.I.C.S.: 423940

Technical Plastic Systems GmbH (1)
Karl-Rapp-Str 1, 92442, Wackersdorf, Bayern, Germany
Tel.: (49) 9431798590
Web Site: http://www.tps-group.de
Emp.: 212
Injection Molded Plastic Products Mfr
N.A.I.C.S.: 326199

Technical Plastic Systems S. de R.L. de C.V. (1)
Autopista Mexico Puebla km 117 Nave 21
D Parque Industrial Finsa, Cuautlancingo,
72710, Puebla, Mexico
Tel.: (52) 2222100666
Emp.: 25
Injection Molded Plastic Product Distr
N.A.I.C.S.: 424610

Technicke plastove systemy s.r.o. (1)
Dysina 297, 330 02, Dysina, Czech Republic
Tel.: (420) 373731124
Emp.: 613
Injection Molded Plastic Product Distr
N.A.I.C.S.: 424610

Teutonia Fracht- und Assekuranzkontor GmbH (1)
Possehl Haus Beckergrube 38 52, Lubeck,
20459, Germany (100%)
Tel.: (49) 4511480
Web Site: http://www.lubeca-teutonia.de
Sales Range: $25-49.9 Million
Emp.: 30
Special Industry Machinery
N.A.I.C.S.: 333310
Uwe Luders (Chm & CEO)

Thiendorfer Frasdienst GmbH & Co. KG (1)
Am Fiebig 11, Thiendorf, 01561, Meissen,
Germany
Tel.: (49) 3524888050
Web Site: http://www.thiendorfer.de
Road Construction Services
N.A.I.C.S.: 237310

Tianjin Huade Mineral Product Co., Ltd. (1)
No 10 1 Yuzhuangzi Road, Tanggu,
300454, Tianjin, China (30%)
Tel.: (86) 22 530 1564
Special Industry Machinery
N.A.I.C.S.: 333310

WST Quarz GmbH (1)
Lise Meitner Str 5, 46569, Hunxe, Germany
Tel.: (49) 2819440310
Web Site: http://www.wst-quarz.de
Floor Covering Mfr & Distr
N.A.I.C.S.: 326199

Weston Beamor Holdings Limited (1)
3 - 8 Vyse Street, Birmingham, B18 6LT,
United Kingdom
Tel.: (44) 1216784131
Web Site: http://www.westonbeamor.com
Jewelry Product Mfr
N.A.I.C.S.: 339910
Andrew Morton (Mng Dir)

datakamp System GmbH & Co. KG (1)
Brillenburgsweg 29, 21614, Buxtehude,
Germany
Tel.: (49) 416150070
Web Site: http://www.datakamp.de
Electronic System Component Mfr
N.A.I.C.S.: 334419
Wolfgang Kamp (CEO)

manroland Goss web systems (India) Pvt. Ltd. (1)
D-41 Ground Floor Sector 59, Noida,
201301, Uttar Pradesh, India
Tel.: (91) 1204858200
Web Site: http://www.manrolandgossindia.com
Printing Machinery & Equipment Mfr
N.A.I.C.S.: 333248
Sudeep Bhattacharjee (Mng Dir)

manroland Goss web systems Americas LLC (1)
121 Technology Dr, Durham, NH 38240
Tel.: (603) 750-6600
Printing Machinery & Equipment Mfr & Distr
N.A.I.C.S.: 333248

manroland Goss web systems Australasia Pty. Ltd. (1)
Unit V5 391 Park Rd, Regents Park, 2143,
NSW, Australia
Tel.: (61) 296457900
Web Site: http://www.manrolandgoss-australasia.com
Printing Machinery & Equipment Mfr
N.A.I.C.S.: 333248
Dennis Wickham (Mng Dir)

manroland Goss web systems France S.A.S. (1)
181 rue Henry Bessemer-Batiment B,
60100, Creil, France
Tel.: (33) 344281137
Printing Machinery & Equipment Mfr & Distr
N.A.I.C.S.: 333248

manroland Goss web systems Japan Corp (1)
3-7-4 Hirosedai, Sayama, 350-1328, Saitama, Japan
Tel.: (81) 429541141
Printing Machinery & Equipment Mfr & Distr
N.A.I.C.S.: 333248

manroland Goss web systems Singapore Pte. Ltd. (1)
2 Toh Tuck Link 05-01, Singapore, 596225,
Singapore
Tel.: (65) 122191336
Printing Machinery & Equipment Mfr & Distr
N.A.I.C.S.: 333248

manroland Goss web systems UK Ltd. (1)
Beach House The Oaks Business Park
Longridge Road, Preston, PR2 5BQ, Lancashire, United Kingdom
Tel.: (44) 1772257571
Printing Machinery & Equipment Mfr & Distr
N.A.I.C.S.: 333248

manroland web systems Canada Inc. (1)
2 Robert Speck Parkway 7th Floor - office
number 38, Mississauga, L4Z 1H8, ON,
Canada
Tel.: (630) 920-5852
Commercial Printing Services
N.A.I.C.S.: 323111
Greg Blue (Mng Dir)

manroland web systems France S.A.S. (1)
58 rue de Neuilly-Bat A1 Parc des Guillaumes, Noisy-le-Sec, 93133, France
Tel.: (33) 156631978
Commercial Printing Services
N.A.I.C.S.: 323111
Antoine Chevalier (Mng Dir)

manroland web systems Inc. (1)
2150 Western Ct Ste 420, Lisle, IL 60532
Tel.: (630) 920-5850
Commercial Printing Services
N.A.I.C.S.: 323111
Greg Blue (Mng Dir)

manroland web systems Southern Africa Pty., Ltd. (1)
15 Manhattan Street, Airport Industria,
7490, Cape Town, South Africa
Tel.: (27) 213807751

Printing Machinery & Equipment Mfr & Distr
N.A.I.C.S.: 333248

L. STROETMANN GMBH & CO. KG
Harkortstrasse 30, 48163, Munster,
Germany
Tel.: (49) 25171820
Web Site: http://www.stroetmann.de
Sales Range: $350-399.9 Million
Emp.: 1,000
Grocery Store Operator
N.A.I.C.S.: 445110
Max Stroetmann (Mng Dir)

Subsidiaries:

L. Stroetmann Grossmarkte GmbH & Co. KG (1)
Harkortstrasse 30, Munster, 48163, Germany
Tel.: (49) 2517182426
Web Site: http://www.stroetmann.de
Emp.: 130
Grocery Store Operator
N.A.I.C.S.: 445110

L. Stroetmann Grossverbraucher GmbH & Co. KG (1)
Capeller Strasse 145, 59368, Werne, Germany
Tel.: (49) 238940714
Web Site: http://www.stroetmann.de
Grocery Store Operator
N.A.I.C.S.: 445110

L. Stroetmann Lebensmittel GmbH & Co. KG (1)
Harkortstr 30, 48163, Munster, Germany
Tel.: (49) 25171820
Web Site: http://www.stroetmann.de
Grocery Store Operator
N.A.I.C.S.: 445110

L. Stroetmann Saat GmbH & Co. KG (1)
Harkortstrasse 30, 48163, Munster, Germany
Tel.: (49) 25171820
Web Site: http://www.saatgutprofi.com
Seed Producer Services
N.A.I.C.S.: 115112
Lutz Stroetmann (Mng Dir)

L.A. MAZDA
6217 50th Street, Leduc, T9E 7A9,
AB, Canada
Tel.: (780) 986-9665
Web Site: http://www.lamazda.ca
Sales Range: $25-49.9 Million
Emp.: 85
New & Used Car Dealer
N.A.I.C.S.: 441110
Gilbert Varrence (Gen Mgr)

L.B. BOHLE MASCHINEN + VERFAHREN GMBH
Industriestrasse 18, 59320, Ennigerloh, Germany
Tel.: (49) 252493230
Web Site: http://www.lbbohle.de
Year Founded: 1981
Rev: $25,533,189
Emp.: 201
Pharmaceutical Machine Distr
N.A.I.C.S.: 423450
Martin Hack (VP & Gen Mgr-United States of America)

Subsidiaries:

LB Bohle LLC (1)
700 Veterans Circe Ste 100, Warminster,
PA 18974
Tel.: (215) 957-1240
Pharmaceutical Equipment Distr
N.A.I.C.S.: 423450

L.E.K. CONSULTING GROUP LIMITED
Nova South 160 Victoria Street, London, SW1E 5LB, United Kingdom
Tel.: (44) 2073897200 UK

L.E.K. CONSULTING GROUP LIMITED

L.E.K. Consulting Group Limited—(Continued)

Web Site: https://www.lek.com
Year Founded: 2017
Consulting Services Organization
N.A.I.C.S.: 813910
Stuart Jackson *(Vice Chm)*

Subsidiaries:

L.E.K. Consulting (International) Limited (1)
Nova South 160 Victoria Street, London, SW1E 5LB, United Kingdom
Tel.: (44) 2073897200
Web Site: http://www.lek.com
Management Consulting Services
N.A.I.C.S.: 541611
Vassilis Economides *(Partner-London)*

Affiliate (Non-US):

L.E.K. Consulting (Shanghai) Co., Ltd. (2)
Fl 34 Citic Sq 1168 Nanjing Rd W, Shanghai, 200041, China
Tel.: (86) 2162728200
N.A.I.C.S.: 541611
Helen Chen *(Mng Partner & Head-Healthcare)*

L.E.K. Consulting (Singapore) Pte. Ltd. (2)
50 Raffles Place, Singapore Land Tower #32-01, Singapore, 048623, Singapore
Tel.: (65) 92413847
Web Site: http://www.lek.com
Management Consulting Services
N.A.I.C.S.: 541611
Stephen Charles Sunderland *(Partner & Grp Head-APAC Reg)*

L.E.K. Consulting Australia Pty. Ltd. (2)
Level 32 8 Exhibition Street, 2 Southbank Boulevard, Melbourne, 3000, VIC, Australia
Tel.: (61) 392708300
Web Site: http://www.lek.com
Sales Range: $10-24.9 Million
Emp.: 40
Management Consulting Services
N.A.I.C.S.: 541611
Mark Charles Streeting *(Partner)*

L.E.K. Consulting GmbH (2)
Brienner Str 14, 80333, Munich, Germany
Tel.: (49) 899220050
Web Site: http://www.lek.de
Sales Range: $10-24.9 Million
Emp.: 65
Management Consulting Services
N.A.I.C.S.: 541611
Karin Ann von Kienlin *(Sr Partner)*

Affiliate (US):

L.E.K. Consulting LLC (2)
75 State St 19th Fl, Boston, MA 02109
Tel.: (617) 951-9500
Web Site: http://www.lek.com
Management Strategy Consulting Services
N.A.I.C.S.: 541611
Emanuele Robert Picciola *(Partner, Mng Dir & Grp Head-Americas)*

Affiliate (Non-US):

L.E.K. Consulting S.A.R.L. (2)
3 Rue Paul Cezanne, 75008, Paris, France
Tel.: (33) 147031950
Web Site: http://www.lek.com
Sales Range: $10-24.9 Million
Emp.: 30
Management Consulting Services
N.A.I.C.S.: 541611
Stephane Claquin *(Partner)*

Affiliate (Domestic):

L.E.K. Consulting UK Limited (2)
Nova South 160 Victoria Street, London, SW1E 5LB, United Kingdom
Tel.: (44) 2073897200
Web Site: http://www.lek.com
Consultancy Services
N.A.I.C.S.: 541611
Vassilis Economides *(Partner)*

L.G. BALAKRISHNAN & BROS. LTD.

6/16/13 Krisnarayapuram Road Ganapathy, Coimbatore, 641 006, India
Tel.: (91) 4222532325 In
Web Site: https://www.lgb.co.in
Year Founded: 1937
500250—(BOM)
Rev.: $269,736,466
Assets: $227,014,048
Liabilities: $61,248,420
Net Worth: $165,765,628
Earnings: $30,582,154
Emp.: 2,478
Fiscal Year-end: 03/31/23
Automobile Parts Mfr
N.A.I.C.S.: 336110
B. Vijayakumar *(Chm & Mng Dir)*

Subsidiaries:

BCW V Tech India Private Limited (1)
K Palayam Plant Pillaiyar Kovil Road Kottaipalayam Post, Coimbatore, 641 110, Tamil Nadu, India
Tel.: (91) 422 2653076
Timing Chain Mfr & Distr
N.A.I.C.S.: 333613

GFM Corporation (1)
29685 Calahan Rd, Roseville, MI 48066
Tel.: (586) 777-4542
Web Site: https://gfmcorp.com
Metal Stamping Mfr
N.A.I.C.S.: 332119

LGB Forge Limited (1)
Krisnarayapuram Road Ganapathy, Coimbatore, 641006, India
Tel.: (91) 4222532325
Web Site: https://www.lgbforge.com
Rev.: $12,676,100
Assets: $10,970,287
Liabilities: $6,092,923
Net Worth: $4,877,363
Earnings: $468,673
Emp.: 235
Fiscal Year-end: 03/31/2021
Electrical Component Mfr
N.A.I.C.S.: 336320
B. Vijayakumar *(Chm)*

L.K. TECHNOLOGY HOLDINGS LIMITED

Unit A 8 Floor Mai Wah Industrial Building 1-7 Wah Sing Street, Kwai Chung, New Territories, China (Hong Kong)
Tel.: (852) 3 412 5500
Web Site: http://www.lktechnology.com
0558—(HKG)
Rev.: $518,655,150
Assets: $706,600,936
Liabilities: $389,146,074
Net Worth: $317,454,863
Earnings: $44,326,170
Emp.: 4,000
Fiscal Year-end: 03/31/21
Die Casting Machines & Plastic Injection Moulding Machines Mfr
N.A.I.C.S.: 238290
Kin Ming Wong *(Sec)*

Subsidiaries:

Chongqing L.K. Machinery Co., Ltd. (1)
Industrial Machinery Distr
N.A.I.C.S.: 423830

Fuxin Lida Steel Casting Co. Ltd. (1)
Steel Casting Industry District Moggol, Fuxin Town, Fuxin, 123000, Liaoning, China
Tel.: (86) 4188313888
Web Site: https://www.lklida.cn
Industrial Machinery Mfr
N.A.I.C.S.: 333248
Zhang Weijun *(Gen Mgr)*

L.K. Japan Co., Ltd. (1)
3-2 Mitsuoka 1-chome, Nishi-ku, Kobe, 651-2228, Japan
Tel.: (81) 789983733
Web Site: http://www.lk-j.co.jp
Industrial Machinery Mfr
N.A.I.C.S.: 333248
Norimitsu Ishimoto *(Pres)*

L.K. Machinery Corp. (1)
No 30 Keyuan Rd, Xitun Dist, Taichung, 407, Taiwan
Tel.: (886) 424619797
Web Site: http://www.lkmachinery.com.tw
Industrial Machinery Mfr
N.A.I.C.S.: 333248

L.K. Machinery India Pvt. Ltd. (1)
Tel.: (91) 8888718587
Industrial Machinery Distr
N.A.I.C.S.: 423830

L.K. Machinery International Limited (1)
Unit A 8/F Mai Wah Industrial Building 1-7 Wah Sing Street, Hong Kong, China (Hong Kong)
Tel.: (852) 34125500
Industrial Machinery Mfr
N.A.I.C.S.: 333248
Chong Siw Yin *(Chm)*

L.K. Machinery, Inc. (1)
600 S Kyle St, Edinburgh, IN 46124
Web Site: http://www.lkadvantage.com
Industrial Machinery Mfr & Distr
N.A.I.C.S.: 333248
Bill Damian *(Pres)*

L.K. Precision Machinery (Kunshan) Co., Ltd. (1)
No 188 Xinhong Road, Qiandeng Town, Kunshan, Jiangsu, China
Industrial Machinery Distr
N.A.I.C.S.: 423830

L.K. Tech (Tianjin) Co. Ltd. (1)
Jingyuan Road, Yixingbu Industrial Area Beichen Sci-Tech Park, Tianjin, China
Tel.: (86) 2286996861
Industrial Machinery Distr
N.A.I.C.S.: 423830

LK Machinery Rus Ltd. (1)
Volgogradsky Prospect 46B Bulding 1 Office 504, 109316, Moscow, Russia
Tel.: (7) 4955586178
Industrial Machinery Mfr
N.A.I.C.S.: 333248

LK Systems, Inc. (1)
999 Corporate Dr Ste 100, Ladera Ranch, CA 92694
Tel.: (815) 355-5585
Industrial Machinery Distr
N.A.I.C.S.: 423830

Ningbo L.K. Technology Co., Ltd. (1)
No 18 Yanshanhe North Road, Beilun District, Ningbo, 315806, Zhejiang, China
Industrial Machinery Distr
N.A.I.C.S.: 423830

Shanghai Atech Machinery Co. Ltd. (1)
42 Min Yi Road Xin, Qiao Development Area Song Jiang Industry Zone, Shanghai, China
Tel.: (86) 234125500
Industrial Machinery Distr
N.A.I.C.S.: 423830

Shenzhen Leadwell Technology Co. Ltd. (1)
No 43 Longguan East Road Tsinghua Community Longhua Street, LK High-tech Industrial Park Longhua District, Shenzhen, China
Tel.: (86) 234125500
Industrial Machinery Distr
N.A.I.C.S.: 423830

Thai Prex Engineering Co., Ltd. (1)
99/10 Moo 2 T Bankao A, Phan Thong, 20160, Chonburi, Thailand
Tel.: (66) 57486116566
Industrial Machinery Distr
N.A.I.C.S.: 423830

L.P. TRANSBETON PUBLIC LTD.

Kouriou 9b Office 102 2220 Latsia, Nicosia, Cyprus
Tel.: (357) 22485923
Concrete Products Mfr
N.A.I.C.S.: 327320

L.P.N. DEVELOPMENT PUBLIC COMPANY LIMITED

1168/109 36th Floor Lumpini Tower RAMA 4 Road Tungmahamek subdistrict, Sathorn, Bangkok, 10120, Thailand
Web Site: http://www.lpn.co.th
LPN—(THA)
Rev.: $216,210,533
Assets: $775,509,777
Liabilities: $426,406,188
Net Worth: $349,103,588
Earnings: $10,556,926
Emp.: 6,133
Fiscal Year-end: 12/31/23
Real Estate Manangement Services
N.A.I.C.S.: 531390
Vudhiphol Suriyabhivadh *(Vice Chm)*

L.V. TECHNOLOGY PUBLIC COMPANY LIMITED

719 KPN Tower 9th & 24th Floor Rama IX Road Bangkapi Huaykwang, Bangkok, 10310, Thailand
Tel.: (66) 2 717 0835
Web Site: http://www.lv-technology.com
Sales Range: $25-49.9 Million
Engineeering Services
N.A.I.C.S.: 541330
Phathanuth Meeboonkhurd *(Deputy Mng Dir-Plant Engrg & Project Mgmt)*

L1 LONG SHORT FUND LTD.

Level 51 101 Collins St, Melbourne, 3000, VIC, Australia
Tel.: (61) 392867000
LSF—(ASX)
Rev.: $294,527,242
Assets: $2,989,937,221
Liabilities: $1,706,619,250
Net Worth: $1,283,317,970
Earnings: $113,708,600
Fiscal Year-end: 06/30/24
Investment Management Service
N.A.I.C.S.: 525990
Raphael Lamm *(Mgr-Fund)*

LA ANONIMA

Ituzaingo 147 6070 Lincoln, Buenos Aires, Argentina
Tel.: (54) 2355424800
Web Site: http://www.laanonima.com.ar
Information Technology Services
N.A.I.C.S.: 541519
Federico Braun *(Mgr-Bus Process)*

LA BANQUE CENTRALE DE MADAGASCAR

PO Box 550, Antananarivo, 101, Madagascar
Tel.: (261) 202223465
Web Site: http://www.banque-centrale.mg
Sales Range: $25-49.9 Million
Emp.: 6
Central Bank
N.A.I.C.S.: 521110
M. Frederic Rasamoely *(Pres)*

LA BANQUE DE FRANCE

31 rue Croix des Petits Champs, 75049, Paris, Cedex 01, France
Tel.: (33) 142924292 FR
Web Site: http://www.banque-france.fr
Year Founded: 1800
Rev.: $303,952,401,200
Net Worth: $16,997,235,080

Earnings: $4,306,981,560
Emp.: 98,575
Fiscal Year-end: 12/31/19
Banking Services
N.A.I.C.S.: 522110
Herve Gonsard *(Dir Gen-HR & Gen Mgr)*

LA BRAYER INDUSTRIES LTD.
3811 93 Street, Edmonton, T6E 5K5, AB, Canada
Tel.: (780) 462-4812
Web Site: https://www.labrayer.com
Year Founded: 1965
Emp.: 200
Metal Fabrication & Installation Services
N.A.I.C.S.: 332999

LA BUVETTE S.A.S.
Rue Maurice Perin, Tournes, 08090, Ardennes, France
Tel.: (33) 324523723   FR
Web Site: http://www.labuvette.fr
Year Founded: 1852
Emp.: 166
Animal Hydration Solutions & Breeding Equipment Mfr
N.A.I.C.S.: 333111
Jean-Philippe Bousquet *(Chm)*

LA CAPITALE CIVIL SERVICE MUTUAL
625 Jacques-Parizeau St, Quebec, G1K 9E2, QC, Canada
Tel.: (418) 747-7600   QC
Web Site: http://www.lacapitale.com
Year Founded: 1940
Rev.: $2,638,627,105
Assets: $6,701,519,663
Liabilities: $5,786,506,890
Net Worth: $915,012,773
Earnings: $96,309,280
Emp.: 2,818
Fiscal Year-end: 12/31/19
Holding Company; Financial Services
N.A.I.C.S.: 551112
Pierre Marc Bellavance *(Sec & Exec VP)*

Subsidiaries:

La Capitale Financial Group Inc.   (1)
Delta 3 Building, 2875 Laurier Blvd Suite 400, Quebec, G1V 2M2, QC, Canada
Tel.: (418) 266-9760
Web Site: http://www.lacapitale.com
Financial Services Holding Company
N.A.I.C.S.: 551112
Eric Champagne *(VP-Mktg & Comm)*

Subsidiary (Domestic):

La Capitale Civil Service Insurer Inc.   (2)
625 Rue Saint Amable Street, Quebec, G1K 7X8, QC, Canada
Tel.: (418) 643-3884
Web Site: http://www.lacatatale.com
Sales Range: $100-124.9 Million
Emp.: 150
Life & Health Insurance Services
N.A.I.C.S.: 524113
Eric Marcoux *(Principal-Architecture)*

Subsidiary (Domestic):

La Capitale Financial Security Insurance Company   (3)
7150 Derrycrest Drive, Mississauga, L5W 0E5, ON, Canada
Web Site: http://www.lacapitalefs.com
Life & Health Insurance Services
N.A.I.C.S.: 524113

PennCorp Life Insurance Company   (3)
55 Superior Boulevard, Mississauga, L5T 2X9, ON, Canada
Tel.: (905) 795-2385
Web Site: http://www.penncorp.ca

Sales Range: $50-74.9 Million
Emp.: 78
Specialty Disability Insurance Services
N.A.I.C.S.: 524128

SecuriGlobe inc.   (3)
5005 Lapiniere Boulevard Suite 2070, Brossard, J4Z 0N5, QC, Canada
Tel.: (514) 370-2525
Web Site: http://www.securiglobe.com
Travel Insurance Services
N.A.I.C.S.: 524113

Subsidiary (Domestic):

La Capitale General Insurance Inc.   (2)
625 Saint-Amable St, PO Box 17, Quebec, G1R 2G5, QC, Canada
Tel.: (418) 266-9525
Sales Range: $350-399.9 Million
Emp.: 700
General Insurance Services
N.A.I.C.S.: 524126

Subsidiary (Domestic):

L'Unique, Compagnie d'assurances generales   (3)
625 Jacques-Parizeau St, PO Box 17050, Quebec, G1K 0E1, QC, Canada
Tel.: (418) 683-2711
Web Site: https://www.lunique.qc.ca
Sales Range: $50-74.9 Million
Emp.: 100
Fire Marine & Casualty Insurance
N.A.I.C.S.: 524126

Unica Insurance Inc.   (3)
7150 Derrycrest Drive, Mississauga, L5W 0E5, ON, Canada
Tel.: (905) 677-9777
Web Site: http://www.unicainsurance.com
Sales Range: $75-99.9 Million
Emp.: 150
Property & Casualty Insurance Services
N.A.I.C.S.: 524126
Guy Lecours *(COO)*

Subsidiary (Domestic):

SSQ, Life Insurance Company Inc.   (2)
2525 Laurier Boulevard, Quebec, G1V 2L2, QC, Canada
Tel.: (418) 650-3457
Web Site: http://www.ssq.ca
Rev.: $1,968,044,232
Assets: $10,269,214,704
Liabilities: $9,457,448,112
Net Worth: $811,766,592
Earnings: $77,901,432
Emp.: 2,031
Fiscal Year-end: 12/31/2019
Automobile, Property & Business Insurance Services; Property & Real Estate Asset Management Services
N.A.I.C.S.: 524126
Pierre Marc Bellavance *(Sec)*

Subsidiary (Domestic):

SSQ General Insurance Company Inc.   (3)
2515 Blvd Laurier, PO Box 10530, Sainte-Foy, G1V 0A5, QC, Canada
Tel.: (418) 683-0554
Web Site: http://www.ssqgenerale.com
Sales Range: $100-124.9 Million
Emp.: 250
Automotive, Home & Business Insurance Services
N.A.I.C.S.: 524126

SSQ Realty Inc.   (3)
SSQ Tower 2525 Laurier Boulevard, Sainte-Foy, G1V 2L2, QC, Canada
Tel.: (418) 682-1245
Web Site: http://www.ssqimmobilier.ca
Sales Range: $50-74.9 Million
Emp.: 25
Real Estate & Property Management Services
N.A.I.C.S.: 531390

LA CHAUSSERIA SA
68 rue de Passy, 75016, Paris, France
Tel.: (33) 468741999   FR

Web Site:
   https://www.lachausseria.com
Year Founded: 1966
CHSR—(EUR)
Sales Range: $1-9.9 Million
Footwear Mfr & Distr
N.A.I.C.S.: 316210
Janie Philip *(Chm & CEO)*

LA COOPERATIVE ARTERRIS SCA
Loudes, 11451, Castelnaudary, Cedex, France
Tel.: (33) 4 68 94 44 22
Web Site: http://www.arterris.fr
Grain Farming Services
N.A.I.C.S.: 111199

Subsidiaries:

Dufour Sisteron   (1)
Parc D"activites 1 Allee Des Chenes, 4200, Sisteron, Alpes De Haute Prove, France
Tel.: (33) 492612078
Rev.: $44,300,000
Emp.: 47
N.A.I.C.S.: 311611

LA COOPERATIVE WELCOOP SA
7 Allee de Vincennes, 54500, Nancy, France
Tel.: (33) 820 90 80 90   FR
Web Site:
   http://www.lacooperative.com
Holding Company
N.A.I.C.S.: 551112
Thierry Chapusot *(CEO)*

Subsidiaries:

Pharmagest Interactive SA   (1)
5 Allee De Saint Cloud, Villers les Nancy, 54601, Cedex, France
Tel.: (33) 33383259595
Web Site: http://www.pharmagest.com
Custom Computer Programming Services
N.A.I.C.S.: 541511

Subsidiary (Domestic):

Malta Informatique SASU   (2)
Building Le France 9 rue Montgolfier, 33700, Merignac, France   **(100%)**
Tel.: (33) 5 57 35 19 25
Web Site: http://www.malta-informatique.fr
Software Publisher
N.A.I.C.S.: 513210
Gregoire de Rotalier *(Chm)*

Subsidiary (Non-US):

ICT Group N.V.   (3)
Kopenhagen 9, 2993 LL, Barendrecht, Netherlands   **(70%)**
Tel.: (31) 889082000
Web Site: http://www.ict.eu
Rev.: $174,103,514
Assets: $139,321,783
Liabilities: $78,241,259
Net Worth: $61,080,524
Earnings: $2,991,146
Emp.: 1,413
Fiscal Year-end: 12/31/2019
IT Services & Solutions
N.A.I.C.S.: 541511
Th. J. van der Raadt *(Chm-Supervisory Bd)*

Subsidiary (Domestic):

Procos Engineers & Consultants B.V.   (4)
Klaina Langtong 15, 4201 HL, Gorinchem, Netherlands
Tel.: (31) 183697333
Web Site: http://www.ictprocos.nl
Sales Range: $150-199.9 Million
Business Management Services
N.A.I.C.S.: 561110

RDS IT-Support   (4)
PO Box 121, 2990 AC, Barendrecht, Netherlands
Tel.: (31) 102992222
Web Site: http://www.rds-its.nl

Sales Range: $25-49.9 Million
Emp.: 20
Information Management Services
N.A.I.C.S.: 519290

Rijnmond Distributie Services B.V.   (4)
PO Box 121, 2990 AC, Barendrecht, Netherlands
Tel.: (31) 10 2992222
Computer Software Programming Services
N.A.I.C.S.: 541511

LA CORTEZ ENERGY, INC.
Calle 67 7-35 Oficina 409, Bogota, Colombia
Tel.: (57) 14852020   NV
Web Site:
   http://www.lacortezenergy.com
Year Founded: 2006
Sales Range: $1-9.9 Million
Emp.: 14
Oil & Gas Exploration & Production Services
N.A.I.C.S.: 211120

Subsidiaries:

La Cortez Energy Colombia E.U.   (1)
Calle 67 No 7-35 Oficina 409, Bogota, Colombia
Tel.: (57) 14852020
Web Site: http://www.lacortezenergy.com
Oil & Gas Exploration Services
N.A.I.C.S.: 213112

La Cortez Energy Colombia, Inc.   (1)
Calle 67 No 7-35 Ofc 409, Bogota, Colombia
Tel.: (57) 14852020
Oil & Gas Exploration Services
N.A.I.C.S.: 213112

LA CROSSE TECHNOLOGY
6 Rue Du Commerce, 67118, Geispolsheim, Bas Rhin, France
Tel.: (33) 388555240
Web Site:
   http://www.lacrossetechnology.fr
Rev.: $10,800,000
Emp.: 16
Development of High Precision Engineering Instruments & Consumer Electronics Incorporating Liquid Crystal Display (LCD) & Microprocessor Technology
N.A.I.C.S.: 423690
Daibilian Sebastian *(Pres)*

LA FINANCIERE ATALIAN SAS
11-113, quai Jules Guesde, Vitry-sur-Seine, 94400, France
Tel.: (33) 1 55 53 03 00
Web Site: http://www.atalian.com
Private Investment Firm
N.A.I.C.S.: 523999

Subsidiaries:

Atalian Servest Food Co. Limited   (1)
Servest House Heath Farm Business Centre, Tut Hill Fornham All Saints, Bury Saint Edmunds, IP28 6LG, United Kingdom
Tel.: (44) 800614678
Web Site: http://www.atalianservest.co.uk
Contract Catering Services
N.A.I.C.S.: 722320
Henry Watts *(Mng Dir)*

LA FINANCIERE PATRIMONIALE D'INVESTISSEMENT S.A.S.
24 26 rue Ballu, 75009, Paris, France
Tel.: (33) 158364482
Web Site: http://www.lfpi.fr
Privater Equity Firm
N.A.I.C.S.: 523999

Subsidiaries:

Matebat SAS   (1)
2 route de Lacourtensourt, BP 55124, 31151, Fenouillet, France

LA FINANCIERE PATRIMONIALE D'INVESTISSEMENT S.A.S.

La Financiere Patrimoniale d'Investissement S.A.S.—(Continued)
Tel.: (33) 5 61 70 40 50
Web Site: http://www.matebat.fr
Sales Range: $50-74.9 Million
Emp.: 155
Crane & Construction Machinery Rental Services
N.A.I.C.S.: 532412

LA FONCIERE VERTE SA
7 rue du Docteur Lancereaux, 75008, Paris, France
Tel.: (33) 145633606   FR
Web Site:
  http://www.lafonciereverte.com
Year Founded: 1931
Sales Range: $10-24.9 Million
Real Estate Support Services
N.A.I.C.S.: 531390
Jean-Christophe Elie (CEO)

LA FRANCAISE DE L ENERGIE SA
1 Avenue Saint-Remy Espace Pierrard, 57600, Forbach, France
Tel.: (33) 387043211   FR
Web Site:
  https://www.francaisedelenergie.fr
Year Founded: 2009
FDE—(EUR)
Rev.: $42,334,111
Assets: $176,092,749
Liabilities: $96,581,609
Net Worth: $79,511,140
Earnings: $12,767,382
Emp.: 32
Fiscal Year-end: 06/30/23
Gas Exploration Services
N.A.I.C.S.: 211130
Julien Moulin (Chm)

LA FRANCAISE DES JEUX SA
3-7 Quai du Point du Jour, 92100, Boulogne-Billancourt, France
Tel.: (33) 141103500
Web Site: https://www.groupefdj.com
Year Founded: 1933
LFDJF—(OTCIQ)
Rev.: $2,723,148,251
Assets: $3,831,543,737
Liabilities: $2,528,755,934
Net Worth: $1,302,792,803
Earnings: $438,238,216
Emp.: 2,881
Fiscal Year-end: 12/31/23
Sports Betting & Gaming Services
N.A.I.C.S.: 713290
Stephane Pallez (Chm & CEO)

LA HIPOTECARIA (HOLDING), INC.
Via Espana Plaza Regency 195 Piso No 4, Apdo Postal 0823-04422, Zona 7, Panama, Panama
Tel.: (507) 3008500   Pa
Web Site:
  http://www.lahipotecaria.com
Year Founded: 1997
Sales Range: $25-49.9 Million
Mortgage Loan Services
N.A.I.C.S.: 522310
Alfredo de la Guardia (Pres)

LA IMPERIAL RESOURCES INC.
Suite 600 666 Burrard Street, Vancouver, V6C 2X8, BC, Canada
Tel.: (604) 689-9600   BC
Year Founded: 2004
LAI—(CNSX)
Assets: $3,458
Liabilities: $1,532,027
Net Worth: ($1,528,570)
Earnings: ($35,949)
Fiscal Year-end: 08/31/23
Gold, Silver & Other Metals Mining & Exploration Services
N.A.I.C.S.: 212220
Marilyn Miller (CEO)

LA INTERNATIONAL COMPUTER CONSULTANTS LTD.
International House Festival Way, Stoke-on-Trent, ST1 5UB, Staffordshire, United Kingdom
Tel.: (44) 1782 203040
Web Site:
  http://www.lainternational.co.uk
Year Founded: 1982
Sales Range: $200-249.9 Million
Emp.: 92
Employment Services
N.A.I.C.S.: 561311
Paul Lukic (Chm & CEO)

LA LATINOAMERICANA, SEGUROS, S.A.
Eje Central Lazaro Cardenas No 2 Piso 8, Del Cuauhtemoc, 06007, Mexico, DF, Mexico
Tel.: (52) 51302800
Web Site:
  https://www.latinoseguros.com.mx
Year Founded: 1906
LASEG—(MEX)
Rev.: $80,603
Assets: $84,846
Liabilities: $73,238
Net Worth: $11,607
Earnings: ($1,591)
Emp.: 261
Fiscal Year-end: 12/31/23
Insurance Agency Services
N.A.I.C.S.: 524210
Jose Ernesto Hernandez (Dir-Fin)

LA MANCHA RESOURCES INC.
2001 University Street, Montreal, H3A 2A6, QC, Canada
Tel.: (514) 987-5115
Web Site: http://www.lamancha.ca
Year Founded: 1996
Sales Range: $150-199.9 Million
Emp.: 1,250
Gold Production & Exploration Services
N.A.I.C.S.: 212220
Naguib Onssy Naguib Sawiris (Chm)

LA OPALA RG LIMITED
Eco Centre 8th Floor EM 4 Sector V, Kolkata, 700 091, West Bengal, India
Tel.: (91) 7604088814
Web Site: https://www.laopala.in
Year Founded: 1987
526947—(BOM)
Rev.: $57,461,671
Assets: $108,706,607
Liabilities: $14,783,176
Net Worth: $93,923,431
Earnings: $14,905,285
Emp.: 1,184
Fiscal Year-end: 03/31/23
Tableware Mfr
N.A.I.C.S.: 327212
Sushil Jhunjhunwala (Vice Chm & Co-Mng Dir)

LA POSITIVA SEGUROS
Calle Francisco Masias 370 Piso 3, San Isidro, Peru
Tel.: (51) 2110212
Web Site:
  http://www.lapositiva.com.pe
POSITVC1—(LIM)
Rev.: $750,272,312
Assets: $2,368,172,616
Liabilities: $2,050,116,859
Net Worth: $318,055,758
Earnings: $72,976,817
Fiscal Year-end: 12/31/23
Insurance Agency Services
N.A.I.C.S.: 524210
Juan Manuel Pena Henderson (CEO)

LA POSTE S.A.
44 Boulevard de Vaugirard, 75757, Paris, Cedex 15, France
Tel.: (33) 155440000   FR
Web Site: http://www.laposte.fr
Year Founded: 1991
Sales Range: $25-49.9 Billion
Emp.: 191,897
Postal Service
N.A.I.C.S.: 491110
Paul-Marie Chavanne (Chm-GeoPost & Exec VP)

Subsidiaries:

Asendia Management SAS   (1)
9 rue du Colonel Pierre Avia, 75757, Paris, Cedex, France
Tel.: (33) 810 821 821
Web Site: http://www.asendia.com
Emp.: 1,500
International Postal Services
N.A.I.C.S.: 491110
Marc Pontet (CEO)

Subsidiary (US):

Asendia USA   (2)
701 C Ashland Ave Bldg 24 Ste 3, Folcroft, PA 19032
Tel.: (610) 461-3661
Web Site: http://www.asendiausa.com
International Postal Services
N.A.I.C.S.: 491110
Michael J. Hastings (Chm)

Banque Privee Europeenne   (1)
62 rue du Louvre, 75002, Paris, France
Tel.: (33) 1 44 88 30 00
Web Site: http://www.bpe.fr
Investment Banking Services
N.A.I.C.S.: 523150

Certinomis SA   (1)
10-12 avenue Charles de Gaulle, 94 673, Charenton-le-Pont, Cedex, France
Tel.: (33) 826 826 626
Web Site: http://www.certinomis.fr
Emp.: 12
Computer Data Management Services
N.A.I.C.S.: 541513
Francois Chassery (Dir-Comml & Mktg)

DOCAPOST   (1)
10-12 avenue Charles de Gaulle, 94 220, Charenton-le-Pont, France
Tel.: (33) 1 56 29 70 01
Web Site: http://www.docapost.com
Sales Range: $450-499.9 Million
Emp.: 4,500
Digital Document Management & IT Services
N.A.I.C.S.: 561410
Eric Benolaut (Gen Mgr)

Subsidiary (Domestic):

Seres SA   (2)
10 Avenue Charles de Gaulle, 94220, Charenton-le-Pont, France
Tel.: (33) 1 56 29 79 00
Web Site: http://www.seres.fr
Emp.: 161
Electronic Data Services
N.A.I.C.S.: 518210

Geopost SA   (1)
2 T Rue Louis Armand, 75015, Paris, France   (100%)
Tel.: (33) 155443100
Sales Range: $25-49.9 Million
Emp.: 100
Order & Delivery Logistics Services
N.A.I.C.S.: 541614

Subsidiary (Non-US):

DPDgroup UK Ltd.   (2)
Roebuck Ln, Smethwick, B66 1BY, United Kingdom   (100%)
Tel.: (44) 1215002500
Web Site: http://www.dpdgroup.co.uk
Parcel Delivery Services

INTERNATIONAL PUBLIC

N.A.I.C.S.: 492110
Dwain McDonald (CEO)

Subsidiary (Domestic):

Interlink Express & Interlink Ireland   (3)
Roebuck Ln, Smethwick, B66 1BY, West Midland, United Kingdom   (100%)
Tel.: (44) 1216983922
Web Site: http://www.geoposteuk.com
Sales Range: $250-299.9 Million
Emp.: 1,500
Parcel Delivery Services
N.A.I.C.S.: 492110
Dwain McDonald (CEO)

La Banque Postale   (1)
115 rue de Sevres, 75275, Paris, Cedex 06, France
Tel.: (33) 157756000
Web Site: http://www.labanquepostale.fr
Financial Services
N.A.I.C.S.: 921130
Yves Brassart (Vice Chm-Supervisory Bd)

Subsidiary (Domestic):

Poste Immo S.A.   (2)
35 39 boulevard Romain Rolland, 75618, Paris, Cedex, France
Tel.: (33) 1 55 44 52 00
Web Site: http://www.poste-immo.fr
Real Estate Development Services
N.A.I.C.S.: 531390
Vincent Revol (Dir-Sls & Mktg)

SOGERCO   (2)
83 Boulevard du Montparnasse, 75006, Paris, France   (100%)
Tel.: (33) 153638950
Sales Range: $50-74.9 Million
Emp.: 10
Insurance Services
N.A.I.C.S.: 524298

MEDIAPOST Group   (1)
19 Rue de la Villette, 69425, Lyon, France
Tel.: (33) 825123123
Web Site: http://www.mediapost.fr
Customer Service Solutions
N.A.I.C.S.: 541890

Subsidiary (Domestic):

Adverline S.A.   (2)
5 Rue de la Terrasse, 75017, Paris, France
Tel.: (33) 1 44920722
Web Site: http://www.adverline.com
Sales Range: $25-49.9 Million
Emp.: 66
Online Advertising Services
N.A.I.C.S.: 541890

Subsidiary (Domestic):

Societe SAS   (3)
5 Rue de la Terrasse, F-75017, Paris, France
Tel.: (33) 1 44 92 3550
Web Site: http://www.societe.com
Legal & Financial Information Services
N.A.I.C.S.: 523999

Sefas Innovation Inc   (1)
20 Mall Rd Ste 210, Burlington, MA 01803
Tel.: (781) 425-5060
Management Consulting Services
N.A.I.C.S.: 541611
Herve Collin (Sr VP-Ops)

Subsidiary (Non-US):

Sefas Innovacion S.A.   (2)
Paseo de las Doce Estrellas 2 Campo de las Naciones, 28042, Madrid, Spain
Tel.: (34) 91 178 25 92
Management Consulting Services
N.A.I.C.S.: 541611

Sefas Innovation Ltd   (2)
Whitefriars Lewins Mead, Bristol, BS1 2NT, United Kingdom
Tel.: (44) 117 906 9920
Management Consulting Services
N.A.I.C.S.: 541611
Charles Hayward (Mgr-Bus Dev)

LA RATIONNELLE NETTOYAGE INDUSTRIEL

AND PRIVATE COMPANIES

20 Allee Des Sablieres Espace Claude Monet, Croissy-sur-Seine, 78290, Yvelines, France
Tel.: (33) 139765969
Web Site: http://www.la-rationnelle.com
Sales Range: $10-24.9 Million
Emp.: 1,000
Professional Cleaning Services
N.A.I.C.S.: 561790
Noureddine Bourimech *(Chm & CEO)*

LA SAVONNERIE DE NYONS S.A.
70 Rue Felix Maurent-ZA Les Laurons II, 26110, Nyons, France
Tel.: (33) 475268534
Web Site: https://www.lasavonneriedenyons-bourse.com
MLSDN—(EUR)
Sales Range: $1-9.9 Million
Soap Product Mfr & Distr
N.A.I.C.S.: 325611
Erwan Allee *(Chm & CEO)*

LA SEDA DE BARCELONA, S.A.
Avenida Remolar 2, 08820, Barcelona, Spain
Tel.: (34) 934017500   ES
Web Site: http://www.laseda.es
Sales Range: $1-4.9 Billion
Emp.: 1,665
Holding Company; Polyethylene Terephthalate Materials & Plastic Packaging Products Mfr & Distr
N.A.I.C.S.: 551112
Carlos Antonio Rocha Moreira da Silva *(Chm & CEO)*

Subsidiaries:

Artenius Italia S.p.A.   (1)
Via Enrico Fermi 46, 33058, San Giorgio di Nogaro, UD, Italy
Tel.: (39) 0431 626695
Web Site: http://www.artenius.com
Polyethylene Terephthalate Mfr
N.A.I.C.S.: 325211

Artenius TurkPET, A.S.   (1)
Yolgecen Mahalles Turhan Cemal Beriker Bulvari No 559, 01355, Adana, Turkiye
Tel.: (90) 3224410253
Web Site: http://www.artenius.com
Sales Range: $75-99.9 Million
Emp.: 160
Polyethylene Terephthalate Mfr
N.A.I.C.S.: 325211

Erreplast, s.r.l.   (1)
Zona Industriale Aversa Nord, 81030, Gricignano d'Aversa, CE, Italy
Tel.: (39) 081 502 6411
Web Site: http://www.erreplast.com
Sales Range: $25-49.9 Million
Emp.: 25
Recycled Polyethylene Terephfthalate Flakes Mfr
N.A.I.C.S.: 325211
Gary Salter *(CEO)*

LA SIA S.P.A.
Luigi Schiavonetti Avenue 286, 00173, Rome, Italy
Tel.: (39) 0645441972
Web Site: https://www.lasia.it
Year Founded: 2004
LASIA—(EUR)
Construction Engineering Services
N.A.I.C.S.: 541330
Maurizio Ciardi *(Pres)*

LA SOCIETE NOUVELLE D'HLM DE MARSEILLE
11 rue d'Armeny, 13006, Marseilles, Cedex 6, France
Tel.: (33) 4 9113 9113
Web Site: http://www.nouvellehlm.fr
Sales Range: $25-49.9 Million
Emp.: 62
Apartment Building Operator
N.A.I.C.S.: 531110
Bernard Bultel *(Dir Gen)*

LA TIM METAL & INDUSTRIES LIMITED
201 Navkar Plaza 2nd Floor Bajaj Road, Vile Parle West, Mumbai, 400056, India
Tel.: (91) 2226203399
Web Site: https://www.latimmetal.com
Year Founded: 1975
505693—(BOM)
Rev.: $77,801,205
Assets: $21,584,895
Liabilities: $16,782,334
Net Worth: $4,802,561
Earnings: $2,454,775
Emp.: 8
Fiscal Year-end: 03/31/22
Tungsten Carbide Product Mfr
N.A.I.C.S.: 331492
Kartik Maganlal Timbadia *(Chm)*

LA-SER EUROPE LIMITED
International House Paddington Street, 66 Chiltern Street, London, W1U 4JT, United Kingdom
Tel.: (44) 20 3137 5800
Web Site: http://www.la-ser.com
Sales Range: $25-49.9 Million
Emp.: 150
Medical Products Consulting, Research & Development
N.A.I.C.S.: 541715
Lucien Abenhaim *(Chm)*

LAAN & SPAR BANK A/S
Hoejbro Plads 9-11, PO Box 2117, 1200, Copenhagen, 1200, Denmark
Tel.: (45) 33782000
Web Site: https://www.lsb.dk
LASP—(CSE)
Rev.: $156,846,233
Assets: $4,344,068,238
Liabilities: $3,993,682,626
Net Worth: $350,385,612
Earnings: $29,377,378
Emp.: 521
Fiscal Year-end: 12/31/22
Banking Services
N.A.I.C.S.: 522110
Anders Bondo Christensen *(Chm)*

LABAT AFRICA LTD
23 Kroton Avenue Weltevreden Park, Johannesburg, 1709, South Africa
Tel.: (27) 116756841
Web Site: https://www.labat.co.za
Year Founded: 1994
LAO—(DEU)
Rev.: $1,216,901
Assets: $10,964,469
Liabilities: $6,398,937
Net Worth: $4,565,532
Earnings: ($1,952,386)
Emp.: 26
Fiscal Year-end: 05/31/22
Financial Investment Services
N.A.I.C.S.: 523999
Rowena Majiedt *(Chm)*

Subsidiaries:

Force Fuel Proprietary Limited   (1)
33 Flamink Street Bracken Gardens, PO Box 145331, Alrode, 1452, South Africa
Tel.: (27) 1190864416
Web Site: http://www.forcefuel.co.za
Bulk Fuel Distr
N.A.I.C.S.: 424710

Reinhardt Transport Group (Pty) Ltd.   (1)
29 Station Avenue Pretoriusstad, Nigel, South Africa
Tel.: (27) 113639300
Web Site: http://reinhardt.co.za
Transportation Services
N.A.I.C.S.: 488490
Derick Reinhardt *(Founder, Chm & CEO)*

South African Micro-Electronic Systems (Pty) Ltd   (1)
Unit 4 Persequor Close 49 De Havilland Crescent Persequor Technopark, Lynnwood, Pretoria, 0081, South Africa
Tel.: (27) 123336021
Web Site: http://www.sames.co.za
Integrate Circuit Mfr & Distr
N.A.I.C.S.: 334413

LABEGE AUTO SPORT S.A.S.
2 Rue Max Planck, 31670, Labege, France
Tel.: (33) 562884545
Web Site: http://www.honda-toulouse.com
Sales Range: $10-24.9 Million
Emp.: 15
Auto Dealership
N.A.I.C.S.: 441110
Pierre Bresson *(Mng Partner)*

LABELKRAFT TECHNOLOGIES LIMITED
No 14/11 Next To SBI Bank GNT Tyre Compound J C Road, Bengaluru, 560 002, India
Tel.: (91) 8040927665
Web Site: https://www.labelkraft.com
Year Founded: 1997
543830—(BOM)
Software Development Services
N.A.I.C.S.: 541511
Mritunjay Kumar *(Officer)*

LABFORWARD GMBH
Elsenstrasse 106, 12435, Berlin, Germany
Tel.: (49) 3016639672
Web Site: https://www.labtwin.com
Year Founded: 2018
Software Devolopement
N.A.I.C.S.: 513210

LABGENOMICS CO., LTD.
700 Daewangpangyo-ro Korea Bio Park, Sampyeong-dong Bundang-gu, Seongnam, 463400, Gyeonggi-do, Korea (South)
Tel.: (82) 316280702
Web Site: https://www.labgenomics.com
Year Founded: 2001
084650—(KRS)
Rev.: $111,040,696
Assets: $192,250,634
Liabilities: $30,789,204
Net Worth: $161,461,430
Earnings: $36,759,211
Emp.: 266
Fiscal Year-end: 12/31/22
In-Vitro Diagnostic Services
N.A.I.C.S.: 325413
Seo Dong-Hee *(Dir)*

LABIANA HEALTH SA
Av Europa 34 D 1st floor, Pozuelo de Alarcon, 28023, Madrid, Spain
Tel.: (34) 919912628
Web Site: https://www.labiana.com
Year Founded: 1958
8RK—(DEU)
Rev.: $61,678,020
Assets: $64,802,826
Liabilities: $57,438,954
Net Worth: $7,363,871
Earnings: $9,713,952
Emp.: 449
Fiscal Year-end: 12/31/22
Pharmaceutical Product Mfr & Distr
N.A.I.C.S.: 325412
Manuel Ramos Ortega *(Pres)*

LABOMAR S.P.A.

LABIANA LIFE SCIENCES, S.A.
C/ Venus 26, 08228, Terrassa, Spain
Tel.: (34) 937369700
Web Site: http://www.labiana.com
Year Founded: 1958
Emp.: 320
Pharmacological Products Mfr
N.A.I.C.S.: 325412
Manuel Ramos Ortega *(CEO)*

Subsidiaries:

Veterinarski zavod Subotica A.D.   (1)
Beogradski put 123, 24106, Subotica, Serbia   (52.83%)
Tel.: (381) 24 624 100
Web Site: http://www.vetzavod.com
Livestock Feed Pharmaceutical & Other Biological Preparation Mfr
N.A.I.C.S.: 311119
Igor Rados *(Gen Mgr)*

LABIXIAOXIN SNACKS GROUP LIMITED
7th Floor AT Tower 180 Electric Road, North Point, China (Hong Kong)
Tel.: (852) 25369669
Web Site: http://www.lbxxgroup.com
1262—(HKG)
Rev.: $96,070,525
Assets: $137,214,464
Liabilities: $91,259,860
Net Worth: $45,954,605
Earnings: ($10,576,051)
Emp.: 1,300
Fiscal Year-end: 12/31/22
Snack Food Mfr
N.A.I.C.S.: 311919
Yu Long Zheng *(Exec Dir)*

Subsidiaries:

Labixiaoxin (Fujian) Food Stuff Industry Co., Ltd   (1)
Wuli Industry Area, Jinjiang, Fujian, China
Tel.: (86) 59588160061
Web Site: http://www.lbxx.cn
Emp.: 1,000
Confectionery Product Mfr & Distr
N.A.I.C.S.: 311340

LABO PRINT S.A.
Ul Szczawnicka 1, 60-471, Poznan, Poland
Tel.: (48) 618411889
Web Site: http://www.laboprint.eu
Year Founded: 2015
LAB—(WAR)
Rev.: $38,083,587
Assets: $31,647,612
Liabilities: $19,006,352
Net Worth: $12,641,260
Earnings: $3,062,500
Fiscal Year-end: 12/31/23
Digital Printing Product Mfr
N.A.I.C.S.: 323113
Krzysztof Fryc *(Chm & CEO)*

LABOM MESS- UND REGELTECHNIK GMBH
Im Gewerbepark 13, 27798, Hude, Germany
Tel.: (49) 44088040
Web Site: http://www.labom.com
Rev.: $25,146,462
Emp.: 160
Measuring Instruments Mfr
N.A.I.C.S.: 334513
Frank Labohm *(Mng Dir)*

LABOMAR S.P.A.
Via N Sauro 35/I, Istrana, 31036, Treviso, TV, Italy
Tel.: (39) 04227312
Web Site: https://www.labomar.com
Year Founded: 1998

LABOMAR S.P.A.

Labomar S.p.A.—(Continued)
LBM—(EUR)
Rev.: $112,782,440
Assets: $168,934,586
Liabilities: $106,365,843
Net Worth: $62,568,743
Earnings: $7,384,732
Emp.: 300
Fiscal Year-end: 12/31/22
Food Supplement Distr
N.A.I.C.S.: 456191
Walter Bertin (Chm)

LABORATOIRE OPHTALMIC B&T
Paris Nord II Bat Le Rousseau, BP 55306, 22 Avenue des nations Roissy, 95 940, Villepinte, CDG Cedex, France
Tel.: (33) 820777500
Web Site: http://www.ophtalmic.fr
Rev.: $44,400,000
Emp.: 137
Opthalmic Laboratory & Testing Center
N.A.I.C.S.: 541380
Arlette Zennou (Personnel Mgr)

LABORATOIRES EXPANSCIENCE
1 Place des Saisons, 92048, Paris, Cedex, France
Tel.: (33) 143346000
Web Site:
   http://www.expanscience.com
Year Founded: 1950
Sales Range: $125-149.9 Million
Emp.: 154
Medicinal & Botanical Products Mfr
N.A.I.C.S.: 325411
Jean-Paul Berthome (CEO)

Subsidiaries:

EXPANSCIENCE BELGIUM (1)
Sphere Business Park Z3 Doornveld 124 2Cl, 1731, Zellik, Belgium
Tel.: (32) 2 466 38 26
Web Site: http://www.expanscience.com
Sales Range: $25-49.9 Million
Emp.: 22
Pharmaceutical Product Mfr & Whslr
N.A.I.C.S.: 325412
Hilde Weckx (Gen Mgr)

EXPANSCIENCE BRAZIL (1)
Rua Manoel da Nobrega 354, 04001-001, Sao Paulo, Brazil
Tel.: (55) 11 3141 1032
Sales Range: $50-74.9 Million
Emp.: 8
Pharmaceutical Product Mfr & Whslr
N.A.I.C.S.: 325412

EXPANSCIENCE FRANCE (1)
10 avenue de l'Arche, 92400, Courbevoie, France
Tel.: (33) 1 43 34 60 00
Pharmaceutical Product Mfr & Whslr
N.A.I.C.S.: 325412
Sophie Vernhes (Mgr-Regulatory Affairs)

EXPANSCIENCE ITALY (1)
Via Moncucco 20/22, 20142, Milan, Italy
Tel.: (39) 02 84 74 72
Pharmaceutical Product Mfr & Whslr
N.A.I.C.S.: 325412

EXPANSCIENCE MEXICO (1)
Amsterdam n 229 Piso 1 Col Hipodromo Condesa, Col Hipodromo Condesa, Mexico, 06100, Mexico
Tel.: (52) 55 55 84 3190
Sales Range: $50-74.9 Million
Emp.: 100
Pharmaceutical Product Mfr & Whslr
N.A.I.C.S.: 325412

EXPANSCIENCE PORTUGAL (1)
Rua Pinheiro Chaga n 17 5 andar, 1050-174, Lisbon, Portugal
Tel.: (351) 219379520
Pharmaceutical Product Mfr & Whslr
N.A.I.C.S.: 325412

EXPANSCIENCE SPAIN (1)
C/ Marie Curie n 7 Edificio ss1a planta-oficina 1 6, Rivas-Vaciamadrid, 28521, Madrid, Spain
Tel.: (34) 91 601 10 70
Pharmaceutical Product Mfr & Whslr
N.A.I.C.S.: 325412

EXPANSCIENCE SWITZERLAND (1)
8 rue Jacques Grosselin, Geneva, CP 1035, Switzerland
Tel.: (41) 22 308 44 00
Web Site:
   http://www.www.expanscience.com
Pharmaceutical Product Mfr & Whslr
N.A.I.C.S.: 325412
Nestle Robert (Mng Dir)

EXPANSCIENCE USA (1)
60 E 56th St 6th Fl, New York, NY 10022
Tel.: (800) 422-2987
Web Site: http://www.mustelausa.com
Sales Range: $25-49.9 Million
Emp.: 13
Pharmaceutical Product Mfr & Whslr
N.A.I.C.S.: 325412

LABORATORIO FARMACEUTICO ERFO S.P.A.
Viale Geki Russo 9, 98049, Villafranca di Verona, ME, Italy
Tel.: (39) 0909146125
Web Site: https://www.erfo.it
Year Founded: 2010
ERFO—(ITA)
Pharmaceutical Product Mfr & Distr
N.A.I.C.S.: 325412
Alessandro Cute (CEO)

LABORATORIO REIG JOFRE, S.A.
Gran Capità 10, 8970, Sant Joan Despi, Spain
Tel.: (34) 934806710   ES
Web Site: https://www.reigjofre.com
RJF—(MAD)
Rev.: $279,246,882
Assets: $384,926,169
Liabilities: $161,025,220
Net Worth: $223,900,949
Earnings: $6,876,824
Emp.: 1,029
Fiscal Year-end: 12/31/20
Pharmaceutical & Nutritional Supplement Mfr & Whslr
N.A.I.C.S.: 325412
Adolf Rousaud Vinas (Sec)

LABORATORIOS BETA S.A.
Ave San Juan 2266, 1232, Buenos Aires, Argentina
Tel.: (54) 1159216399
Web Site: http://www.betalab.com.ar
Sales Range: $500-549.9 Million
Emp.: 650
Pharmaceuticals
N.A.I.C.S.: 325412
George Perez (Mgr-Foreign Affairs)

LABORATORIOS DEL DR. ESTEVE, S.A.
Passeig de la Zona Franca 109 4 Planta, 08038, Barcelona, Spain
Tel.: (34) 93 4466000
Web Site: http://www.esteve.com
Sales Range: $500-549.9 Million
Emp.: 1,500
Pharmaceuticals Mfr
N.A.I.C.S.: 325412
Albert Esteve (CEO)

Subsidiaries:

Esteve FARMA Lda. (1)
Av do Forte 3 Edificio Suecia IV, Piso 0 - Escritorio 0.0.4, 2790-073, Carnaxide, Portugal
Tel.: (351) 21 424 60 10
Web Site: http://www.esteve.pt
Pharmaceutical Products Distr

N.A.I.C.S.: 424210

Esteve Huayi Pharmaceutical Co., Ltd. (1)
Linhai Rd Shaoxing Paojiang, Industrial Zone, 312071, Shaoxing, Zhejiang, China
Tel.: (86) 575 8822 5288
Pharmaceutical Products Distr
N.A.I.C.S.: 424210
Mireia Garcia Vilaseca (Asst Mgr-Quality)

Esteve S.p.A. (1)
Via Ippolito Rosellini 12, 1 piano, 20124, Milan, Italy
Tel.: (39) 0269964201
Web Site: http://www.esteve.it
Veterinary Services
N.A.I.C.S.: 541940

Euracon Pharma GmBh (1)
Max-Planck-Strasse 11, 85716, Unterschleissheim, Germany
Tel.: (49) 89 32141964
Web Site: http://www.epharmapedia.com
Pharmaceutical Products Distr
N.A.I.C.S.: 424210

ISDIN, SA (1)
Provencals 33, 08019, Barcelona, Spain
Tel.: (34) 93 240 20 20
Web Site: http://www.isdin.com
Pharmaceuticals Research & Development for Dermatology Conditions
N.A.I.C.S.: 325412
Antonio Esteve Cruella (CEO)

Subsidiary (Non-US):

Auriga International S.A. (2)
Avenue Victor Hugo 32, B-1420, Braine-l'Alleud, Belgium
Tel.: (32) 23845377
Web Site: http://www.auriga-int.com
Sales Range: $350-399.9 Million
Emp.: 50
Cosmetics & Beauty Products Mfr
N.A.I.C.S.: 325620
Alfred Marchal (CEO)

LABORATORIOS FARMACEUTICOS ROVI S.A.
Calle Jose Isbert 2, Pozuelo de Alarcon, 28223, Madrid, Spain
Tel.: (34) 910213000
Web Site: https://rovi.es
ROVI—(BIL)
Rev.: $915,673,916
Assets: $882,971,631
Liabilities: $283,022,409
Net Worth: $599,949,222
Earnings: $187,988,741
Emp.: 1,862
Fiscal Year-end: 12/31/23
Pharmaceuticals Mfr, Marketer & Distr
N.A.I.C.S.: 325412
Ivan Lopez-Belmonte Encina (Second VP)

LABOSPORT SAS
Technoparc du circuit des 24 Heures, Chemin aux Boeufs, 72100, Le Mans, France
Tel.: (33) 2 43 47 08 40   FR
Web Site: http://www.labosport.com
Year Founded: 1993
Emp.: 130
Analysis, Testing & Technical Inspections Services
N.A.I.C.S.: 541380

Subsidiaries:

Thomas Turf Services, Inc. (1)
11183 State Hwy 30, College Station, TX 77845-7891
Tel.: (979) 774-1600
Web Site: http://www.thomasturf.com
Soil & Tissue Testing Services
N.A.I.C.S.: 541380
James Thomas (Founder & General Manager)

LABOUESSE

INTERNATIONAL PUBLIC

28 Quai De Verdun, 03100, Montluçon, Allier, France
Tel.: (33) 470081800
Web Site: http://www.labouesse.com
Rev.: $12,400,000
Emp.: 48
Building Supplies
N.A.I.C.S.: 423710
Bernard Giraud (Pres)

LABRADOR GOLD CORP.
The Canadian Venture Building 82 Richmond Street East, Toronto, M5C 1P1, ON, Canada
Tel.: (416) 704-8291   BC
Web Site:
   https://www.labradorgold.com
Year Founded: 1987
LAB—(TSXV)
Rev.: $426
Assets: $10,803,478
Liabilities: $188,383
Net Worth: $10,615,094
Earnings: ($1,602,820)
Fiscal Year-end: 09/30/20
Mineral Exploration Services
N.A.I.C.S.: 213114
Roger Moss (Pres & CEO)

LABRADOR IRON MINES HOLDINGS LIMITED
-, PO Box 1178, Stn Toronto Dominion, Toronto, M5K 1P2, ON, Canada
Tel.: (647) 728-4117
Web Site:
   http://www.labradorironmines.ca
Year Founded: 2007
Sales Range: Less than $1 Million
Emp.: 33
Mineral Exploration & Development Services
N.A.I.C.S.: 327999
John F. Kearney (Chm & CEO)

LABRADOR IRON ORE ROYALTY CORPORATION
31 Adelaide St E, PO Box 957, Toronto, M5C 2K3, ON, Canada
Tel.: (416) 362-0066   Ca
Web Site:
   https://www.labradorironore.com
LIF—(TSX)
Sales Range: $150-199.9 Million
Iron Ore Mining Services
N.A.I.C.S.: 212210
Alan R. Thomas (CFO)

Subsidiaries:

Hollinger-Hanna Limited (1)
Scotia Plaza 26th Floor, 40 King St W, Toronto, M5W 2X6, ON, Canada
Tel.: (416) 863-7133
Web Site: http://www.labradoriron.com
Sales Range: $50-74.9 Million
Emp.: 1
Iron Ore Marketing
N.A.I.C.S.: 213114

LABRADOR RESOURCES INC.
3400 350 7th Av SW, Calgary, T2P 3N9, AB, Canada
Tel.: (403) 818-1091   AB
Year Founded: 1981
LTX—(TSXV)
Assets: $881,354
Liabilities: $814,009
Net Worth: $67,345
Earnings: ($104,923)
Fiscal Year-end: 10/31/23
Software & Computer Related Services
N.A.I.C.S.: 541519
Jeffrey A. Howe (Interim CFO)

LABX MEDIA GROUP
478 Bay Street Suite A213, PO Box 216, Midland, L4R 1K9, ON, Canada

AND PRIVATE COMPANIES   **LACTO JAPAN CO., LTD.**

Tel.: (705) 528-6888
Web Site: http://www.labx.com
Year Founded: 1995
Sales Range: $25-49.9 Million
Emp.: 50
Holding Company; Scientific Electronic Market Operator & Periodical Publisher
N.A.I.C.S.: 551112
Bob Kafato (Founder)

Subsidiaries:

Lab Manager   (1)
478 Bay Street, PO Box 216, Midland, L4R 1K9, ON, Canada
Web Site: http://www.labmanager.com
Laboratory Professional Trade Magazine Publisher
N.A.I.C.S.: 513120
Bob Kafato (Pres)

LabX   (1)
334 King Street, PO Box 216, Midland, L4R 3M8, ON, Canada
Tel.: (705) 528-6888
Web Site: http://www.labx.com
Emp.: 50
Online Scientific Equipment Marketplace Operator
N.A.I.C.S.: 425120

LABYRINTH RESOURCES LIMITED
Tel.: (61) 861491573   AU
Web Site:
   https://labyrinthresources.com
LRL—(ASX)
Rev.: $391,571
Assets: $7,560,119
Liabilities: $1,625,742
Net Worth: $5,934,378
Earnings: ($3,119,498)
Emp.: 280
Fiscal Year-end: 06/30/21
Gold & Uranium Mining
N.A.I.C.S.: 212220
Eddie Milne (CFO)

Subsidiaries:

Mintails SA (Pty) Ltd   (1)
1st Fl N Wing Lord Charles Ofc Park, PO Box 36355, 337 Brooklyn Rd Brooklyn, Pretoria, Gauteng, South Africa
Tel.: (27) 123464406
Sales Range: $100-124.9 Million
Emp.: 200
Gold Exploration & Mining Services
N.A.I.C.S.: 212220
Anthony Ehlers (CEO)

Mogale Gold (Pty) Ltd   (1)
14 Tweeplies Rd, PO Box 803, Krugersdorp, 1740, Gauteng, South Africa
Tel.: (27) 116609638
Web Site: http://www.mintailssa.co.za
Emp.: 400
Gold Exploration & Mining Services
N.A.I.C.S.: 212220
Eddie Milner (CEO)

LAC CO., LTD.
Hirakawacho Mori Tower 2-16-1 Hirakawacho, Chiyoda-ku, Tokyo, 102-0093, Japan
Tel.: (81) 367570100
Web Site: https://www.lac.co.jp
Year Founded: 2007
3857—(TKS)
Rev.: $327,042,970
Assets: $157,119,700
Liabilities: $55,299,260
Net Worth: $101,820,440
Earnings: $9,115,190
Emp.: 2,192
Fiscal Year-end: 03/31/24
System Integration Services
N.A.I.C.S.: 541512
Teruhiko Takanashi (Chm)

Subsidiaries:

Asian Link Co., Ltd.   (1)
Emp.: 174
Information Security Services
N.A.I.C.S.: 561621

Cyber Security LAC Co., Ltd.   (1)
8F Samsung Building 942-5 Daechi-dong, Gangnam-gu, Seoul, 135-847, Korea (South)
Tel.: (82) 27613666
Web Site: http://www.cslac.co.kr
Security Solution Services
N.A.I.C.S.: 561612

I Net Rely Corporation   (1)
1-13 Nihonbashi Hakozaki-cho Tokyo Earl Building WEST 4F, Chuo-ku, Tokyo, 103-0015, Japan
Tel.: (81) 368920311
Web Site: https://www.inetrely.co.jp
Emp.: 92
Network Services
N.A.I.C.S.: 517810

LAC LA BICHE TRANSPORT LTD.
66569 RR143, Lac La Biche, T0A 2C0, AB, Canada
Tel.: (780) 623-4711
Web Site:
   http://www.laclabichetransport.ca
Year Founded: 1953
Sales Range: $10-24.9 Million
Truck Transportation Services
N.A.I.C.S.: 484110
Gerald Wowk (Pres)

LACHLAN STAR LIMITED
Level 1 33 Ord Street, West Perth, 6005, WA, Australia
Tel.: (61) 894209300
Web Site:
   http://www.lachlanstar.com.au
Sales Range: $75-99.9 Million
Emp.: 428
Gold & Copper Mineral Developer
N.A.I.C.S.: 212230

Subsidiaries:

Ord Investments Pty. Ltd.   (1)
Lower Ground Fl 57 HaveLock St, West Perth, 6005, Australia
Tel.: (61) 894810051
Copper Exploration & Mining Services
N.A.I.C.S.: 212230

LACOMBE FORD SALES LTD
5610 Highway 2A, Lacombe, T4L 1A3, AB, Canada
Tel.: (403) 782-6811
Web Site:
   http://www.lacombeford.com
Sales Range: $25-49.9 Million
New & Used Car Dealers
N.A.I.C.S.: 441110
Darren Gagnon (CEO)

LACROIX S.A.
7 rue Oceane, PO Box 30004, 44800, Saint-Herblain, Cedex, France
Tel.: (33) 272255959   FR
Web Site: https://fr.lacroix-group.com
Year Founded: 1948
LACR—(EUR)
Rev.: $652,979,376
Assets: $545,661,621
Liabilities: $366,783,320
Net Worth: $178,878,301
Earnings: $10,821,175
Emp.: 5,318
Fiscal Year-end: 12/31/22
Holding Company; Signaling Products, Electronics Components, Remote Monitoring & Control Products Mfr & Technical Support Services
N.A.I.C.S.: 551112
Vincent Bedouin (CEO)

Subsidiaries:

LACROIX Electronics   (1)
21 rue du Bon Air, BP 11502, 49115, Saint-Pierre-Montlimart, France   (100%)
Tel.: (33) 241754000
Web Site: https://www.lacroix-electronics.com
Electronics Components Mfr & Technical Support Services
N.A.I.C.S.: 334419
Frank Weiss (Gen Mgr)

LACROIX Signalisation   (1)
8 impasse du Bourrelier, BP 4, 44801, Saint-Herblain, Cedex, France   (100%)
Tel.: (33) 240923730
Web Site: http://www.lacroix-signalisation.fr
Sign & Signaling Products Mfr
N.A.I.C.S.: 339950

LACROIX Sofrel   (1)
2 rue du Plessis, 35770, Vern-sur-Seiche, France   (100%)
Tel.: (33) 299048900
Web Site: http://www.sofrel.com
Remote Monitoring & Control Products Mfr
N.A.I.C.S.: 334513

LACROIX Trafic   (1)
Z I 1ere avenue 11eme Rue, 06516, Carros, France
Tel.: (33) 492084300
Web Site: http://www.lacroix-trafic.fr
Emp.: 100
Traffic Signal Equipment Mfr
N.A.I.C.S.: 334290

Lacroix Electronics France   (1)
21 Avenue de Bon Air, CS 11502, Montrevault-sur-Evre, 49115, Saint-Pierre-Montlimart, Cedex, France
Tel.: (33) 241754000
Electrical & Electronic Mfr
N.A.I.C.S.: 336320

Lacroix Electronics Zoo   (1)
Ul Lotnicza 2, 82-500, Kwidzyn, Poland
Tel.: (48) 552622100
Web Site: https://www.lacroixkwidzyn.pl
Electrical & Electronic Mfr
N.A.I.C.S.: 336320

Lacroix Singapore Pte. Ltd.   (1)
25 Bukit Batok Crescent 08-06 The Elitist 0, Singapore, 658066, Singapore
Tel.: (65) 92381072
Industrial Component Mfr
N.A.I.C.S.: 336390
Eric Woo (Mgr-Bus Dev)

Lacroix Sofrel Espana S.L.U.   (1)
Francisco Gervas 12, 28108, Alcobendas, Madrid, Spain
Tel.: (34) 915100800
Industrial Component Mfr
N.A.I.C.S.: 336390
Javier Pino Coronel (Sls Dir)

Lacroix Sofrel Srl   (1)
Via Bombrini n 11 interno 7, 16149, Genoa, Italy
Tel.: (39) 010601911
Industrial Component Mfr
N.A.I.C.S.: 336390

Sae It Systems GmbH & Co Kg   (1)
Im Gewerbegebiet Pesch 14, 50767, Cologne, Germany
Tel.: (49) 221598080
Web Site: https://www.sae-it.com
Emp.: 100
Industrial Component Mfr
N.A.I.C.S.: 336390
Oliver Callegari (Mng Dir-Sls)

LACROIX S.A.
397 Avenue du Grand Verger, BP 601, 73000, Chambery, France
Tel.: (33) 479690236   FR
Web Site: http://www.lacroix-charcuterie.com
Year Founded: 1977
Sales Range: $10-24.9 Million
Meats Processor
N.A.I.C.S.: 311611
Jacques Lacroix (Mng Dir)

LACTEAS GARCIA BAQUERO, SA
Calle Syrah Alcazar de San Juan, 13600, Ciudad Real, Spain
Tel.: (34) 926588149
Web Site:
   http://www.garciabaquero.com
Cheese Mfr
N.A.I.C.S.: 311513

Subsidiaries:

Lacteos Caprinos S.A.   (1)
C/Herradores 11-13 Poligono Industrial, 23130, Campillo de Arenas, Jaen, Spain   (80%)
Tel.: (34) 953307237
Web Site: http://www.lacteoscaprinos.com
Dairy Products Distr
N.A.I.C.S.: 424430

LACTEC GMBH
Otto-Hahn-Strasse 6-8, 63110, Rodgau, Germany
Tel.: (49) 610684470
Web Site: http://www.lactec.com
Year Founded: 1986
Rev.: $29,103,295
Emp.: 110
Electrostatic Painting Systems
N.A.I.C.S.: 811121
Udo Klein (Mng Dir-Engrg)

Subsidiaries:

LacTec Automatic Painting Systems (Changchun) Ltd.   (1)
GuiGu Street Nr 3355, 130000, Changchun, China
Tel.: (86) 43181917868
Automotive Parts Painting Services
N.A.I.C.S.: 811121

LacTec ServiCZ s.r.o.   (1)
Horni Lochov 17, 50601, Jicin, Czech Republic
Tel.: (420) 493525903
Automotive Parts Painting Services
N.A.I.C.S.: 811121

Lactec USA LLC   (1)
1163 S Main St Ste 327, Chelsea, MI 48118
Tel.: (313) 300-2398
Automotive Parts Painting Services
N.A.I.C.S.: 811121

LACTINA
107 Rue Du Rhin Napoleon, 67100, Strasbourg, Bas Rhin, France
Tel.: (33) 388405760
Rev.: $14,500,000
Emp.: 35
Feed Mfr
N.A.I.C.S.: 311119
Denis Gohn (DP Mgr)

LACTO JAPAN CO., LTD.
22nd Floor Taiyo Life Nihonbashi Building, 2-11-2 Nihonbashi Chuo-ku, Tokyo, 103-0027, Japan
Tel.: (81) 3 62819701
Web Site: http://www.lactojapan.com
Rev.: $1,071,000,980
Assets: $441,388,780
Liabilities: $294,998,900
Net Worth: $146,389,880
Earnings: $18,000,710
Emp.: 285
Fiscal Year-end: 11/30/19
Dairy Products & Processed Meat
N.A.I.C.S.: 112120
Motohisa Miura (Pres)

Subsidiaries:

Foodtech Products (Thailand) Co., Ltd.   (1)
196 Moo 1, Hi-tech Industrial Estate Tambon Baanlane Amphur Bangpa-In, Ayutthaya, 13160, Thailand
Tel.: (66) 353515102
Web Site: http://www.foodtechthailand.co.th
Cheese Mfr & Retailer
N.A.I.C.S.: 311513
Shin Kojima (Mng Dir)

Lacto Asia (M) Sdn. Bhd.   (1)
No 33 Jalan PJU 3/42 Sunway Damansara

LACTO JAPAN CO., LTD.

Lacto Japan Co., Ltd.—(Continued)

Technology Park, 47810, Petaling Jaya, Selangor, Malaysia
Tel.: (60) 378859925
Web Site: http://www.ftcheese.com.my
Cheese Mfr & Distr
N.A.I.C.S.: 311513

Lacto Asia Pte. Ltd. (1)
8 Eu Tong Sen Street 13-89 Office Tower 1 The Central, Singapore, 059818, Singapore
Tel.: (65) 62241998
Web Site: http://www.lacto.com.sg
Cheese Mfr & Distr
N.A.I.C.S.: 311513
Shin Kojima (Mng Dir)

LADAM AFFORDABLE HOUSING LIMITED

Ladam House C-33 Opp ITI Wagle Industrial Estate, Thane, 400 604, India
Tel.: (91) 2271191000
Web Site:
    https://www.ladamhousing.com
540026—(BOM)
Rev.: $761,257
Assets: $7,231,176
Liabilities: $2,534,074
Net Worth: $4,697,103
Earnings: $76,299
Emp.: 7
Fiscal Year-end: 03/31/22
Real Estate Manangement Services
N.A.I.C.S.: 236116
Sumesh Agarwal (CEO)

LADCO COMPANY LIMITED

200-40 Lakewood Boulevard, Winnipeg, R2J 2M6, MB, Canada
Tel.: (204) 982-5900
Web Site: https://www.ladco.mb.ca
Year Founded: 1919
Sales Range: $50-74.9 Million
Land Development Services
N.A.I.C.S.: 236220
Alan Andrew Borger (Pres)

LADDERUP FINANCE LTD

102-A 1st Floor Hallmark Business Plaza Gurunanak Hospital Road, Bandra - East, Mumbai, 400 051, Maharastra, India
Tel.: (91) 2242466363
Web Site: https://www.ladderup.com
530577—(BOM)
Rev.: $1,354,786
Assets: $9,671,918
Liabilities: $825,481
Net Worth: $8,846,436
Earnings: ($158,893)
Fiscal Year-end: 03/31/23
Investments & Funding Services
N.A.I.C.S.: 525120
Manoj Singrodia (Co-Founder)

Subsidiaries:

Ladderup Corporate Advisory Private Limited (1)
102-A 1st Floor Hallmark Business Plaza Gurunanak Hospital Road Bandra, Mumbai, 400051, Maharashtra, India
Tel.: (91) 2242466363
Sales Range: $50-74.9 Million
Emp.: 37
Financial Advisory Services
N.A.I.C.S.: 523999
Sunil Goyal (Mng Dir)

Ladderup Wealth Management Private Limited (1)
102-A 1st Floor Hallmark Business Plaza Gurunanak Hospital Road, Bandra East, Mumbai, 400 051, Maharashtra, India
Tel.: (91) 2242466363
Web Site: http://www.ladderup.com
Sales Range: $50-74.9 Million
Emp.: 15
Financial Planning Solutions Services
N.A.I.C.S.: 523999

Raghvendra Nath (Co-Founder)

LADPRAO GENERAL HOSPITAL PUBLIC COMPANY LIMITED

2699 Ladprao Rd Khlong Chaokhun Sing, Wang Thong Lang, Bangkok, 10310, Thailand
Tel.: (66) 25302244 TH
Web Site:
    http://www.ladpraohospital.com
Year Founded: 1990
LPH—(THA)
Rev.: $66,021,678
Assets: $88,608,783
Liabilities: $26,912,010
Net Worth: $61,696,773
Earnings: $1,941,422
Emp.: 838
Fiscal Year-end: 12/31/23
Hospital
N.A.I.C.S.: 622110
Somsak Lolekha (Chm)

Subsidiaries:

Asia Medical & Agricultural Laboratory & Research Center Company Limited (1)
361 Soi Ladprao 122 Ladprao Road, Phlabphla Wangthonglang, Bangkok, 10310, Thailand
Tel.: (66) 25162422
Web Site: https://www.amarc.co.th
Pharmaceuticals Product Mfr
N.A.I.C.S.: 325412
Virat Vongsangnak (Founder)

LADUN INVESTMENT COMPANY

Sultan Center - Al Amir Sultan Ibn Abdul Aziz st Building No 2751, Unit No 1 Additional No 6769 North Mathar Dist, Riyadh, 12312, Saudi Arabia
Tel.: (966) 920011560
Web Site: https://www.ladun.sa
Year Founded: 1968
9535—(SAU)
Rev.: $382,928,195
Assets: $738,002,732
Liabilities: $579,165,898
Net Worth: $158,836,834
Earnings: $29,156,823
Emp.: 1,896
Fiscal Year-end: 12/31/23
Financial Investment Services
N.A.I.C.S.: 523999
Suliman Albatli (CEO)

LADY DRUG STORE CO., LTD.

4-3-37 Minamiedo, Matsuyama, 790-8556, Ehime, Japan
Tel.: (81) 89 9178000
Web Site: http://www.lady-drug.co.jp
Year Founded: 1968
Emp.: 786
Retail Store Operator
N.A.I.C.S.: 459999
Kazuro Fujita (Mng Exec Officer)

LAEBON DEVELOPMENTS LTD.

289 Burnt Park Drive, Red Deer, T4S 2L4, AB, Canada
Tel.: (403) 346-7273
Web Site: http://www.laebon.com
Year Founded: 1976
Sales Range: $10-24.9 Million
Construction Services
N.A.I.C.S.: 236115
W. G. Bontje (Partner-Founding)

LAEP INVESTMENTS, LTD.

R Gomes de Carvalho N 1504 1st Floor, Vila Olimpia, Sao Paulo, 04547-005, Brazil
Tel.: (55) 11 3030 6000

Web Site: http://www.laep.com.br
Year Founded: 1994
Sales Range: $75-99.9 Million
Emp.: 2,088
Financial Investment Services
N.A.I.C.S.: 523999
Antonio Romildo Da Silva (Dir-IR)

LAFANG CHINA CO LTD

Lafang Industrial City Xinqing Road Section National Highway, Chaonan District, Shantou, 515041, Guangdong, China
Tel.: (86) 754489833339
Web Site: http://www.laf.cn
Year Founded: 2001
603630—(SHG)
Rev.: $124,552,266
Assets: $303,523,712
Liabilities: $28,064,739
Net Worth: $275,458,973
Earnings: $8,316,411
Fiscal Year-end: 12/31/22
Consumer Product Mfr & Distr
N.A.I.C.S.: 325620
Wu Guiqian (Chm & Gen Mgr)

LAFAYETTE MITTELSTAND CAPITAL

Bleichstrasse 64-66, 60313, Frankfurt, Germany
Tel.: (49) 69870058520
Web Site:
    http://www.lafayettemittelstand.com
Investment Firm
N.A.I.C.S.: 523999
Christian Sydlik (Partner)

Subsidiaries:

Heinz Kettler GmbH & Co.KG (1)
Hauptstrasse 28, 59463, Niederense, Germany
Tel.: (49) 2938810
Web Site: http://intl.kettler.net
Sales Range: $700-749.9 Million
Emp.: 3,500
Outdoor Furniture, Exercise Equipment, Bicycle & Children's Vehicle Mfr
N.A.I.C.S.: 337126
Karin Kettler (Mng Dir)

Plant (Domestic):

Heinz Kettler GmbH & Co.KG - Hanweiler Factory (2)
Heinz-Kettler-Strasse 1, 66271, Kleinblittersdorf, Germany
Tel.: (49) 6805 6008 0
Fitness Equipment Mfr
N.A.I.C.S.: 339920

Heinz Kettler GmbH & Co.KG - Kamen I Factory (2)
Henry-Everling-Strasse 3, 59174, Kamen, Germany
Tel.: (49) 2307 974 0
Fitness Equipment Mfr
N.A.I.C.S.: 339920

Heinz Kettler GmbH & Co.KG - Mersch Factory (2)
Kunststoffverarbeitung Zur Mersch 1, 59457, Werl, Germany
Tel.: (49) 2922 8707 50
Fitness Equipment Mfr
N.A.I.C.S.: 339920

Subsidiary (Non-US):

Kettler (GB) Limited (2)
Merse Road, North Moons Moat, Redditch, B98 9HL, United Kingdom
Tel.: (44) 1527591901
Web Site: http://www.kettler.co.uk
Sales Range: $25-49.9 Million
Emp.: 30
Outdoor Furniture, Exercise Equipment, Bicycle & Children's Vehicle Mfr
N.A.I.C.S.: 337126
Paul Bevington (Mng Dir)

Kettler Austria GmbH (2)
Ginzkeyplatz 10, 5020, Salzburg, Austria
Tel.: (43) 662 620501 0

INTERNATIONAL PUBLIC

Web Site: http://at.kettler.net
Fitness Equipment Distr
N.A.I.C.S.: 423910

Kettler Benelux B.V. (2)
Indumastraat 18, 5753 RJ, Deurne, Netherlands
Tel.: (31) 493 310345
Web Site: http://nl.kettler.net
Fitness Equipment Distr
N.A.I.C.S.: 423910

Kettler International Inc. (2)
101 Applewood Drive, Brighton, K0K 1H0, ON, Canada
Tel.: (613) 475-3300
Web Site: http://www.kettlercanada.com
Fitness Equipment Mfr
N.A.I.C.S.: 339920

Subsidiary (US):

Kettler International, Inc. (2)
1355 London Bridge Rd, Virginia Beach, VA 23453
Tel.: (757) 427-2400
Web Site: http://www.kettlerusa.com
Sales Range: $25-49.9 Million
Emp.: 30
Outdoor Furniture, Exercise Equipment, Bicycle & Children's Vehicle Mfr
N.A.I.C.S.: 337126
Gabe Harrell (Mgr-Credit & Accts Receivable)

Subsidiary (Non-US):

Kettler Israel Ltd. (2)
19 Shahar Hayam St NOF-YAM, Herzliya Pituach, 46606, Israel
Tel.: (972) 9 9545444
Web Site: http://www.kettler.co.il
Fitness Equipment Distr
N.A.I.C.S.: 423910
Elon Delman (Mng Dir)

Kettler Polska Sp. z o.o. (2)
ul Potrzebowicka 5, 64-730, Wielen, Poland
Tel.: (48) 801 430 450
Web Site: http://pl.kettler.net
Fitness Equipment Distr
N.A.I.C.S.: 423910

Kettler S.a.r.l. (2)
5 Rue du Chateau, Lutzelhouse, 67133, Orsay, France
Tel.: (33) 388475580
Web Site: http://www.kettler.fr
Rev.: $21,500,000
Emp.: 183
Outdoor Furniture, Exercise Equipment, Bicycle & Children's Vehicle Mfr
N.A.I.C.S.: 337126

Jurchen Technology GmbH (1)
Prinz-Ludwig-Strasse 5, 97264, Helmstedt, Germany
Tel.: (49) 9369982296600
Web Site: http://www.jurchen-technology.com
Information Technology Services
N.A.I.C.S.: 541511

Subsidiary (Non-US):

Jurchen Technology India Private Limited (2)
Regd Office Unit No 601 602 F Wing Sixth Floor Lotus Corporate Park, Gram Path Compound Off Western Express Highway Goregaon East, Mumbai, 400063, Maharashtra, India
Tel.: (91) 2268156099
Web Site: http://www.jurchen-technology.com
Photovoltaic System Component Mfr
N.A.I.C.S.: 335999

LAFE CORPORATION LIMITED

119 Emerald Hill Road 12-01 Residences at Emerald Hill, Singapore, 229401, Singapore
Tel.: (65) 6509 5235
Web Site:
    http://www.lafecorporation.com
Rev.: $14,587,000
Assets: $55,405,000
Liabilities: $12,102,000
Net Worth: $43,303,000
Earnings: ($10,849,000)
Emp.: 180

AND PRIVATE COMPANIES

Fiscal Year-end: 12/31/18
Compute Magnetic Heads Mfr
N.A.I.C.S.: 334610
Linda Longworth *(Asst Sec)*
Subsidiaries:

Vigers Investment Consultants (Shenzhen) Ltd. (1)
Suite 2101 21/F Greater China International Trade Square Jintian Road, Futian District, Shenzhen, 518034, China
Tel.: (86) 75533393191
Real Estate Development Services
N.A.I.C.S.: 531390

Vigers Macao Company Limited (1)
Level 20 AIA Tower 251A-301 Avenida Comercial de Macau, Macau, China (Macau)
Tel.: (853) 82942488
Real Estate Development Services
N.A.I.C.S.: 531390

Vigers Property Consultants (Beijing) Ltd. (1)
Unit E 7/F Oriental Kenzo Office Building 48 Dongzhimenwai Street, Dong Cheng District, Beijing, 100027, China
Tel.: (86) 1084549722
Real Estate Development Services
N.A.I.C.S.: 531390

Vigers Property Consultants (Shanghai) Ltd. (1)
Unit 804 8/F International Capital Plaza 1318 Sichuan Road North, Hongkou District, Shanghai, 200080, China
Tel.: (86) 2160932188
Real Estate Development Services
N.A.I.C.S.: 531390

Vigers Property Management Services (Hong Kong) Limited (1)
10/F The Grande Building 398 Kwun Tong Road, Kowloon, China (Hong Kong)
Tel.: (852) 23422000
Real Estate Development Services
N.A.I.C.S.: 531390

LAFITTE
455 Route De Bearn, Montaut, 40500, Saint-Sever, France
Tel.: (33) 558764040
Web Site: http://www.lafitte.fr
Year Founded: 1920
Meat & Poultry Whslr
N.A.I.C.S.: 424470
Fabien Chevalier *(Mng Dir)*

LAFLEUR MINERALS INC.
1050 - 1055 W. Georgia St., Vancouver, V6E 3P3, BC, Canada
Tel.: (604) 805-4602 BC
Year Founded: 2017
LFLR—(CNSX)
Assets: $3,302,546
Liabilities: $3,715,768
Net Worth: ($413,222)
Earnings: ($2,337,988)
Emp.: 3
Fiscal Year-end: 03/31/24
Mining services
N.A.I.C.S.: 213111
Paul Teniere *(CEO)*

LAFORO IRON FOUNDRY
170 boulevard Gagnon, Sainte-Claire, G0R 2V0, QC, Canada
Tel.: (418) 883-2255
Web Site: http://www.laforo.com
Year Founded: 1975
Sales Range: $10-24.9 Million
Iron Foundry Mfr
N.A.I.C.S.: 331511
Yvon Fortier *(Founder & Pres)*

LAGAN HOLDINGS LTD.
19 Clarendon Rd, Belfast, BT1 3BG, United Kingdom
Tel.: (44) 2890261000
Web Site: http://www.lagan-group.com

Sales Range: $400-449.9 Million
Emp.: 1,062
Holding Company; Construction & Quarrying Operations
N.A.I.C.S.: 551112
C.G. Jenkins *(Sec)*
Subsidiaries:

Alpha Resource Management Ltd (1)
11 Sheepwalk Road, Lisburn, BT28 3RDG, Antrim, United Kingdom
Tel.: (44) 28 92 661 222
Waste Management Services
N.A.I.C.S.: 562219
Gary Flaherty *(Mgr-Landfill)*

Lagan Asphalt Ltd (1)
Rosemount Business Park, Ballycoolin Road, Dublin, 11, Ireland (100%)
Tel.: (353) 18859999
Web Site: http://www.laganasphaltgroup.com
Sales Range: $25-49.9 Million
Emp.: 50
Asphalt Paving Mixture & Block Mfr
N.A.I.C.S.: 324121
Terry Lagan *(Mng Dir)*

Lagan Bitumen Ltd (1)
Airport Road West Belfast Harbour Estate, Belfast, BT3 9ED, United Kingdom
Tel.: (44) 28 9045 1502
Asphalt Distr
N.A.I.C.S.: 423320

Lagan Brick Ltd. (1)
The Swan, Athy, Kildare, Ireland (100%)
Tel.: (353) 598635513
Web Site: http://www.laganbrick.com
Emp.: 12
Clay Products Mfr
N.A.I.C.S.: 327120
Ray Deegan *(Gen Mgr)*

Lagan Cement B.V. (1)
Postbus 454, 4530 AL, Terneuzen, Netherlands
Tel.: (31) 32 492 68 49 52
Cement Mfr & Distr
N.A.I.C.S.: 327310

Lagan Cement Ltd (1)
Lansdown Cement Works, Killaskillen, Kinnegad, N91 D510, West Meath, Ireland
Tel.: (353) 449379200
Web Site: http://www.lagancement.com
Emp.: 100
Cement Mfr.
N.A.I.C.S.: 327310
Vinnie Glennon *(Bus Dir)*

Lagan Concrete Limited (1)
Milebush, Midleton, Cork, Ireland
Tel.: (353) 21 4883123
Web Site: http://www.laganconcrete.ie
Ready Mix Concrete Distr
N.A.I.C.S.: 423320
Jude Lagan *(Mng Dir)*

Lagan Homes (1)
Lagan House 19 Clarendon Rd, Belfast, BT1 3BG, United Kingdom
Tel.: (44) 2890261026
Web Site: http://www.lagan-homes.co.uk
New Home Building & Sales
N.A.I.C.S.: 236115
Conor Mulligan *(Mng Dir)*

Welsh Slate (1)
Penrhyn Quarry, Bethesda, Bangor, LL57 4YG, Gwynedd, United Kingdom
Tel.: (44) 1248600656
Web Site: https://www.welshslate.com
Sales Range: $100-124.9 Million
Emp.: 200
Natural Slate Whslr for Architectural & Roofing Materials
N.A.I.C.S.: 212311
Chris Allwood *(Mng Dir)*

LAGARRIGUE
Place de la Republique, 12300, Firminy, France
Tel.: (33) 5 6563 4318 FR
Web Site: http://www.lagarriguebtp.fr
Year Founded: 1940

Sales Range: $10-24.9 Million
Emp.: 100
Commercial, Institutional & Civil Engineering & Construction Services
N.A.I.C.S.: 541330
Pascal Carlos *(Dir Gen)*

LAGENDA PROPERTIES BERHAD
Level 4 No 131 Persiaran PM2 1 Pusat Bandar Seri Manjung Seksyen 2, 32040, Seri Manjung, Perak, Malaysia
Tel.: (60) 56887179
Web Site: https://www.agendaproperties.com
Year Founded: 2001
DBE—(KLS)
Rev.: $183,479,372
Assets: $375,985,313
Liabilities: $160,925,551
Net Worth: $215,059,763
Earnings: $37,719,840
Emp.: 374
Fiscal Year-end: 12/31/22
Poultry Broiler Farm & Farm Products Producer
N.A.I.C.S.: 112320
Jimmy Doh Jee Ming *(Mng Dir)*
Subsidiaries:

D.B.E. Poultry Sdn. Bhd. (1)
Plot 138 Kawasan Perindustrian, 32000, Setiawan, Perak, Malaysia
Tel.: (60) 56922822
Web Site: https://www.dbegurney.com
Sales Range: $25-49.9 Million
Emp.: 450
Poultry Rearing Services
N.A.I.C.S.: 112340

LAGERCRANTZ GROUP AB
Torsgatan 2, PO Box 3508, 103 69, Stockholm, Sweden
Tel.: (46) 87006670
Web Site: http://www.lagercrantz.com
LAGR.B—(OMX)
Rev.: $678,674,122
Assets: $752,386,037
Liabilities: $470,557,382
Net Worth: $281,828,655
Earnings: $70,995,720
Emp.: 2,425
Fiscal Year-end: 03/31/23
Electronics & Communications Products & Solutions
N.A.I.C.S.: 334220
Per Ikov *(VP-Bus Dev)*
Subsidiaries:

AC Antennas A/S (1)
Fabriksparken 40, DK-2600, Glostrup, Denmark
Tel.: (45) 45810413
Web Site: https://acantennas.com
Marine Antenna Mfr & Distr
N.A.I.C.S.: 334220

ACTE A/S (1)
Vallensbaekvej 41, 2605, Brondby, Denmark (100%)
Tel.: (45) 4 690 0400
Web Site: https://www.acte.biz
Sales Range: $50-74.9 Million
Emp.: 60
Electronic Components & Modules Distr
N.A.I.C.S.: 423690
Peter Bjornskov *(CEO)*

Subsidiary (Non-US):

Acte UK Limited (2)
Unit 1 West Lancashire Investment Centre White Moss Business Park, Maple View, Skelmersdale, WN8 9TG, Lancs, United Kingdom
Tel.: (44) 1256 845888
Web Site: http://www.acte-uk.com
Emp.: 6
Electronic Components Distr
N.A.I.C.S.: 423690

Lee Nye *(Gen Mgr)*

ACTE AS (1)
Instituttveien 8, PO Box 190, 2007, Kjeller, Norway (100%)
Tel.: (47) 63898900
Web Site: http://www.acte.no
Sales Range: $25-49.9 Million
Emp.: 23
Computer & Computer Peripheral Equipment & Software Whslr
N.A.I.C.S.: 423430

ACTE Oy (1)
Larin Kyostin tie 4, PO Box 36, Helsingfors, 00650, Finland (100%)
Tel.: (358) 9752761
Web Site: http://www.acte.fi
Sales Range: $50-74.9 Million
Emp.: 8
Electrical Apparatus & Equipment Wiring Supplies & Construction Material Whslr
N.A.I.C.S.: 423610
Martus Kald *(Mng Dir)*

ACTE Solutions AB (1)
Karlsbodavagen 39 2nd floor, Bromma, Sweden (100%)
Tel.: (46) 84452828
Web Site: http://www.actesolutions.se
Electrical Apparatus & Equipment Wiring Supplies & Construction Material Whslr
N.A.I.C.S.: 423610

ACTE Sp. z o.o. (1)
ul Krancowa 49, 02-493, Warsaw, Poland (100%)
Tel.: (48) 668330200
Web Site: https://www.acte.pl
Sales Range: $25-49.9 Million
Emp.: 20
Computer & Computer Peripheral Equipment & Software Whslr
N.A.I.C.S.: 423430

Aras Security A/S (1)
Mose Alle 10B, 2610, Rodovre, Denmark
Tel.: (45) 70274090
Web Site: https://www.aras.dk
Emp.: 100
Integrated Security System Mfr & Distr
N.A.I.C.S.: 334511

Aras Security AB (1)
Norra Bulltoftavagen 65 G, 212 43, Malmo, Sweden
Tel.: (46) 105518330
Web Site: https://www.arassecurity.se
Emp.: 100
Integrated Security System Mfr & Distr
N.A.I.C.S.: 334511

Asept International AB (1)
Traktorvagen 17, 226 60, Lund, Sweden
Tel.: (46) 4 632 9700
Web Site: https://www.asept.com
Flexible Packaging Products Mfr
N.A.I.C.S.: 326112
Rikard Malmback *(CEO)*

Betech Data A/S (1)
Stationparkem 37, 2600, Glostrup, Denmark (100%)
Tel.: (45) 43487470
Web Site: http://www.betechdata.dk
Sales Range: $25-49.9 Million
Emp.: 25
Computer Programming Services
N.A.I.C.S.: 541511
Alexander Steen *(Mng Dir)*

Subsidiary (Domestic):

CAD-Kompagniet A/S (2)
Lyskaer 8A, 2730, Herlev, Denmark
Tel.: (45) 70 22 22 17
Web Site: http://www.cadkompagniet.dk
Sales Range: $25-49.9 Million
Emp.: 2
Computer Aided Design Application Services
N.A.I.C.S.: 541512

Bjurenwall Laurea AB (1)
Sodra Vasterasvagen 17, 73451, Kolback, Sweden
Tel.: (46) 22040490
Web Site: https://bjurenwall.se
Steel Product Mfr & Distr
N.A.I.C.S.: 331110

LAGERCRANTZ GROUP AB

Lagercrantz Group AB—(Continued)

COBS AB (1)
Norra Langebergsgatan 4, 421 32, Vastra Frolunda, Sweden
Tel.: (46) 313333840
Communication Equipment Mfr & Distr
N.A.I.C.S.: 334220

CW Lundberg AB (1)
Landsvagen 52, 792 95, Mora, Sweden
Tel.: (46) 25 055 3500
Web Site: https://www.cwlundberg.com
Roofing Product Distr
N.A.I.C.S.: 423330

Came Danmark A/S (1)
Toldbogade 96, 8930, Randers, Denmark
Tel.: (45) 70232919
Web Site: https://www.came-danmark.dk
Integrated Security System Mfr & Distr
N.A.I.C.S.: 334511

Cue Dee AB (1)
Sikea 58, 915 93, Robertsfors, Sweden
Tel.: (46) 93415310
Web Site: https://cuedee.com
Telecommunications Equipment Mfr
N.A.I.C.S.: 334220

Direktronik AB (1)
Konsul Johnsons vag 15, 149 45, Nynashamn, Sweden (100%)
Tel.: (46) 852400700
Emp.: 20
Electrical Apparatus & Equipment Wiring Supplies & Construction Material Whslr
N.A.I.C.S.: 423610
Mats Ryden *(CEO)*

EFC Finland OY (1)
Ahmantie 6, 65520, Vaasa, Helsingby, Finland (100%)
Tel.: (358) 63226222
Web Site: https://www.efc.fi
Sales Range: $50-74.9 Million
Emp.: 60
Electrical Apparatus & Equipment Wiring Supplies & Construction Material Whslr
N.A.I.C.S.: 423610
Kristian Makela *(Mng Dir)*

ElefantRiste A/S (1)
Norgesvej 5, DK-7480, Vildbjerg, Denmark
Tel.: (45) 97426133
Web Site: https://www.elefantriste.dk
Steel Product Mfr & Distr
N.A.I.C.S.: 331110

Elfac A/S (1)
Priorsvej 23, 8600, Silkeborg, Denmark (100%)
Tel.: (45) 86801555
Sales Range: $50-74.9 Million
Emp.: 100
Electrical Apparatus & Equipment Wiring Supplies & Construction Material Whslr
N.A.I.C.S.: 423610
Lars Hartvig Andersen *(Mng Dir & Gen Mgr Sls)*

Elkapsling AB (1)
Industrivagen 1, 841 44, Alby, Sweden
Tel.: (46) 690763000
Web Site: https://www.elkapsling.se
Emp.: 95
Electronic Equipment Mfr & Distr
N.A.I.C.S.: 334419

Elpress AB (1)
Industrivagen 15, 872 32, Kramfors, Sweden (100%)
Tel.: (46) 612717100
Web Site: https://www.elpress.net
Sales Range: $75-99.9 Million
Emp.: 160
Electronic Parts & Equipment Whslr
N.A.I.C.S.: 423690

Subsidiary (Non-US):

Elpress (Beijing) Electrical Components Co. Ltd (2)
Diyang Mansion No Xin 2 Dongsanhuan N Rd Rm 1605, Chaoyang Dist, Beijing, 100027, China
Tel.: (86) 1065005642
Electronic Components Mfr
N.A.I.C.S.: 334419
Johnson Wang *(Gen Mgr)*

Elpress A/S (2)
Randersvej 16, 8600, Silkeborg, Denmark (100%)
Tel.: (45) 86816111
Web Site: https://www.elpress.net
Sales Range: $25-49.9 Million
Emp.: 7
Electronic Parts & Equipment Whslr
N.A.I.C.S.: 423690

Elpress GmbH (2)
Krankelsweg 24, 41748, Viersen, Germany
Tel.: (49) 216293190
Web Site: https://www.elpress.net
Sales Range: $25-49.9 Million
Emp.: 7
Electronic & Mechanical Component Distr
N.A.I.C.S.: 423690

Enkom Active Oy (1)
Upseerinkatu 1-3, 02600, Espoo, Finland
Tel.: (358) 102040000
Electrical & Communication Product Distr
N.A.I.C.S.: 423610

Enkom Oy (1)
Nyakersvagen 6, PO Box 16, Korsholm, 65610, Vaasa, Finland (100%)
Tel.: (358) 63189900
Web Site: http://www.enkom.fi
Sales Range: $50-74.9 Million
Emp.: 60
Electrical Apparatus & Equipment Wiring Supplies & Construction Material Whslr
N.A.I.C.S.: 423610

Excidor AB (1)
Industrigatan 7, 821 41, Bollnas, Sweden
Tel.: (46) 27813670
Emp.: 30
Electronic Products Mfr
N.A.I.C.S.: 334111

Exilight Oy (1)
Autokeskuksentie 16, 33960, Pirkkala, Finland
Tel.: (358) 10 773 5400
Web Site: https://www.exilight.fi
Electrical Equipment Distr
N.A.I.C.S.: 423610
Palle Rokman *(Sls Mgr)*

Frictape Net Oy (1)
PO Box 130, 01801, Klaukkala, Finland
Tel.: (358) 50 347 0594
Electronic Products Mfr
N.A.I.C.S.: 334111

G9 Landskab, Park & Byrum A/S (1)
Toldbodgade 96, 8930, Randers, Denmark
Tel.: (45) 70232999
Home Furnishing Mfr
N.A.I.C.S.: 337121

GasiQ AB (1)
Taljstensvagen 5, 443 61, Stenkullen, Sweden
Tel.: (46) 30224680
Gas Equipment Mfr
N.A.I.C.S.: 333132

Geonor AS (1)
Grini Naeringspark 10, 1361, Osteras, Norway
Tel.: (47) 6715928080
Web Site: https://www.geonor.no
Geotechnical Monitoring Equipment Mfr & Distr
N.A.I.C.S.: 334290

Heath Comm AS (1)
Skuteviksbodene 1/2, 5035, Bergen, Norway (100%)
Tel.: (47) 55304600
Web Site: http://www.heathcomm.no
Sales Range: $25-49.9 Million
Emp.: 14
Computer & Computer Peripheral Equipment & Software Whslr
N.A.I.C.S.: 423430

ISG Nordic AB (1)
Karlsbodavagen 39, 168 67, Bromma, Sweden
Tel.: (46) 8272727
Web Site: https://www.isgnordic.se
Emp.: 1,500
Security & Investigation Services
N.A.I.C.S.: 561611

ISG Systems AB (1)
Sporthallsvagen 10, 26334, Hoganas, Sweden (100%)
Tel.: (46) 42362140
Web Site: http://www.isg.se
Sales Range: $50-74.9 Million
Emp.: 10
Electronic Parts & Equipment Whslr
N.A.I.C.S.: 423690
Thomas Lilja *(Mng Dir)*

ISIC A/S (1)
Edwin Rahrs Vej 54, 8220, Brabrand, Denmark (100%)
Tel.: (45) 70207077
Web Site: http://isic-systems.com
Sales Range: $25-49.9 Million
Emp.: 35
Computer & Computer Peripheral Equipment & Software Whslr
N.A.I.C.S.: 423430

Idesco Oy (1)
Teknologiantie, 90590, Oulu, Finland
Tel.: (358) 44 763 7502
Web Site: https://www.idesco.fi
Security System Services
N.A.I.C.S.: 561621

K & K Active Oy (1)
Italahdenkatu 22 B, 00210, Helsingfors, Finland (100%)
Tel.: (358) 968550550
Web Site: http://www.kandk.fi
Sales Range: $25-49.9 Million
Emp.: 12
Electronic Parts & Equipment Whslr
N.A.I.C.S.: 423690

Kablageproduktion i Vasteras AB (1)
Omformargatan 12, 721 37, Vasteras, Sweden (100%)
Tel.: (46) 21815151
Web Site: http://kpro.se
Sales Range: $25-49.9 Million
Emp.: 50
Steel Wire Drawing
N.A.I.C.S.: 331222

Kondator AB (1)
Energivagen 8, PO Box 121, 135 49, Tyreso, Sweden
Tel.: (46) 855659500
Web Site: https://www.formingfunction.se
Electronic Products Mfr
N.A.I.C.S.: 334111

Lagercrantz A/S (1)
Vallensaekvej 41, 2605, Brondby, Denmark
Tel.: (45) 46900400
Web Site: http://www.lagercrantz.com
Emp.: 3
Electronic Components Distr
N.A.I.C.S.: 423690

Subsidiary (Domestic):

Vanpee & Westerberg A/S (2)
Gammelager 15, 2060, Brondby, Denmark
Tel.: (45) 44 85 90 00
Web Site: http://www.vanpee.dk
Sales Range: $25-49.9 Million
Emp.: 1
Electronic Components Distr
N.A.I.C.S.: 423690

Lagercrantz Asia Ltd (1)
Rm 4020 40/F Jardine Hse 1 Connaught Place, Central, Hong Kong, China (Hong Kong)
Tel.: (852) 28588782
Electronic Equipment Distr
N.A.I.C.S.: 423690

Lagercrantz Communication AB (1)
Korta Gatan 9, PO Box 6004, 17106, Solna, Sweden (100%)
Tel.: (46) 86264100
Web Site: http://www.lagercrantz.se
Sales Range: $25-49.9 Million
Emp.: 20
Electronic Parts & Equipment Whslr
N.A.I.C.S.: 423690
Mats Ryden *(Gen Mgr)*

Leteng AS (1)
Enebakkveien 117 B, 0680, Oslo, Norway
Tel.: (47) 62482450
Web Site: https://www.leteng.no
Network Communication Equipment Distr
N.A.I.C.S.: 423690

Load Indicator AB (1)
Arods Industrivag 58, 422 43, Hisings Backa, Sweden
Tel.: (46) 31220730
Web Site: https://loadindicator.se
Electronic Products Mfr
N.A.I.C.S.: 334111

Logistikcenter Norrkoping (1)
Kiselgatan 33, 602 23, Norrkoping, Sweden (100%)
Tel.: (46) 8 445 2800
Web Site: http://www.elmek.vanpee.se
Sales Range: $25-49.9 Million
Emp.: 18
Electrical Apparatus & Equipment Wiring Supplies & Construction Materials Whslr
N.A.I.C.S.: 423610

Nexlan AS (1)
Kokstadflaten 19B, 5257, Kokstad, Norway
Tel.: (47) 55509150
Web Site: https://www.nexlan.no
Electronic Switch Mfr & Distr
N.A.I.C.S.: 334419

Nikodan Conveyor Systems A/S (1)
Faellesvej 9, 8766, Norre Snede, Denmark
Tel.: (45) 39304316
Web Site: https://nikodan.eu
Automation Conveyor System Mfr & Distr
N.A.I.C.S.: 333922

Nikodan Process Equipment A/S (1)
Faellesvej 9, 8766, Norre Snede, Denmark
Tel.: (45) 3 930 4316
Electronic Products Mfr
N.A.I.C.S.: 334111

Nordic Alarm AB (1)
Karlsbodavagen 39, 168 67, Solna, Sweden (100%)
Tel.: (46) 8272727
Web Site: http://www.nordicalarm.se
Sales Range: $25-49.9 Million
Emp.: 60
Industrial Machinery Mfr
N.A.I.C.S.: 333248

Norwesco AB (1)
Tel.: (46) 87922700
Electro Mechanical Products Mfr & Distr
N.A.I.C.S.: 334419

PcP Nederland B.V. (1)
Havendijk 21, 4731 TA, Oudenbosch, Netherlands
Tel.: (31) 165315300
Grid Grate Mfr & Distr
N.A.I.C.S.: 332323

PcP. Danmark A/S (1)
Sverigesvej 2-4, 7480, Vildbjerg, Denmark
Tel.: (45) 97131200
Web Site: https://www.pcp-corp.com
Steel Product Mfr & Distr
N.A.I.C.S.: 331110

PcP. Norge AS (1)
Kanalvegen 8, 4033, Stavanger, Norway
Tel.: (47) 51950050
Grid Grate Mfr & Distr
N.A.I.C.S.: 332323

PcP. Sverige AB (1)
J A Gahms gata 6, 42131, Vastra Frolunda, Sweden
Tel.: (46) 31535960
Grid Grate Mfr & Distr
N.A.I.C.S.: 332323

Plat & Spiralteknik i Torsas AB (1)
Ramsagsgatan 8, 385 34, Torsas, Sweden
Tel.: (46) 4 864 5650
Web Site: https://www.pst.se
Conveying Equipment Mfr
N.A.I.C.S.: 333922
Magnus Nilsson *(Mng Dir)*

Precimeter Control AB (1)
Ruskvadersgatan 22, 418 34, Gothenburg, Sweden
Tel.: (46) 31 764 5520
Web Site: https://www.precimeter.com
Molten Metal Product Mfr
N.A.I.C.S.: 423510

Precimeter GmbH (1)
Fritz-Kotz-Strasse 1, 51674, Wiehl, Germany

AND PRIVATE COMPANIES

LAHMEYER HOLDING GMBH

Tel.: (49) 9466088
Metal Control Sensor Mfr & Distr
N.A.I.C.S.: 334516

Precimeter Inc. (1)
2215 S 48 th St Ste C, Tempe, AZ 85282-1004
Tel.: (480) 829-1923
Metal Control Sensor Mfr & Distr
N.A.I.C.S.: 334516

Proagria Miljo A/S (1)
Aggershusvej 7, 5450, Otterup, Denmark
Tel.: (45) 64824000
Web Site: https://wapro.com
Electronic Products Mfr
N.A.I.C.S.: 334111

Profsafe AB (1)
Tel.: (46) 371523290
Coin Handling Equipment Mfr
N.A.I.C.S.: 333310

Radonova Laboratories AB (1)
Rapsgatan 25, 754 50, Uppsala, Sweden **(100%)**
Tel.: (46) 18 56 88 00
Web Site:
 http://www.radonovalaboratories.com
Sales Range: $1-9.9 Million
Emp.: 25
Radon Detectors Mfr & Whslr; Radiation Measurement & Analysis Testing Laboratory
N.A.I.C.S.: 541380
Tryggve Ronnqvist (Dir-Technical)

Subsidiary (US):

Radonova, Inc. (2)
900 Oakmont Ln Ste 207, Westmont, IL 60559 **(100%)**
Tel.: (331) 814-2200
Web Site: https://radonova.com
Sales Range: $50-74.9 Million
Emp.: 300
Radon Testing & Protection Plan Services
N.A.I.C.S.: 334519
Bill Rounds (Pres)

SECOS GmbH (1)
Zugerstrasse 74, 6341, Baar, Switzerland **(60%)**
Tel.: (41) 417693538
Electrical Apparatus & Equipment Wiring Supplies & Construction Material Whslr
N.A.I.C.S.: 423610

STV Sv Tele & Video Konsult AB (1)
Anderstorpsvagen 12 2 Tr, Box 6062, Solna, 171 06, Sweden
Tel.: (46) 856844100
Motion Picture & Video Production Services
N.A.I.C.S.: 512110

STV Video Data AB (1)
Karlsbodavagen 39, 168 67, Bromma, Sweden **(100%)**
Tel.: (46) 856844100
Web Site: http://stv.se
Sales Range: $25-49.9 Million
Emp.: 30
Telecommunications
N.A.I.C.S.: 517810

Saja GmbH (1)
Topferstrasse 37, D-49170, Hagen, Germany
Tel.: (49) 5405616790
Web Site: https://www.sajas-group.com
Roller Brush Mfr & Distr
N.A.I.C.S.: 332999

Sajakorpi Oy (1)
Kolsopintie 5, 33470, Ylojarvi, Finland
Tel.: (358) 3 347 7700
Web Site: https://www.sajakorpi.fi
Industrial Brushes Mfr & Distr
N.A.I.C.S.: 339994

Schmitztechnik GmbH (1)
Am Ringofen 24, 41189, Monchengladbach, Germany
Tel.: (49) 216662020
Plastic Fabrication Mfr
N.A.I.C.S.: 326199

Skandex i Bromma AB (1)
Gotgatan 12, Box 140, SE-334 23, Anderstorp, Sweden
Tel.: (46) 8252535
Web Site: https://www.skandex.se

Fireproof Cabinet Mfr & Distr
N.A.I.C.S.: 337214

Skomo A/S (1)
Julius Kajus Vej 1, 8400, Ebeltoft, Denmark
Tel.: (45) 86343444
Graphic Design Services
N.A.I.C.S.: 541430

Steelo AB (1)
Industrivagen 31, 333 72, Bredaryd, Sweden
Tel.: (46) 370374100
Web Site: https://steelo.se
Emp.: 25
Sheet Metal Mfr & Distr
N.A.I.C.S.: 332322

Supply Plus Limited (1)
1 Stirling Way Papworth Business Park, Papworth Everard, Cambridge, CB23 3GY, Cambridgeshire, United Kingdom **(80%)**
Tel.: (44) 1480832200
Web Site: https://www.supplyplus.com
Emp.: 80
Safety & Security Equipment Mfr
N.A.I.C.S.: 561621
Derek Gotts (Mng Dir)

Svensk Stalinredning AB (1)
Industrivagen 31, Bredaryd, 330 10, Varnamo, Sweden
Tel.: (46) 370 37 41 00
Web Site: http://www.stalinredning.se
Emp.: 3
Storage Systems Mfr
N.A.I.C.S.: 332311
Hakan Soderberg (Gen Mgr)

Svenska Industriborstar i Vasteras AB (1)
Odhumlagatan 4, 723 55, Vasteras, Sweden
Tel.: (46) 2120376
Steel & Plastic Brush Mfr
N.A.I.C.S.: 339994

Swedwire AB (1)
Birger Svenssons v 16 D, 432 40, Varberg, Sweden
Tel.: (46) 34 064 5430
Web Site: https://www.swedwire.se
Metal Products Mfr
N.A.I.C.S.: 332999
Jesper Swedenborg (Sls Mgr)

Truxor Wetland Equipment AB (1)
Ostra Polarvagen 10, 917 32, Dorotea, Sweden
Tel.: (46) 94225880
Web Site: https://truxor.com
Emp.: 40
Truxor Machine Mfr & Distr
N.A.I.C.S.: 333111

Unitronic AG (1)
Mundelheimer Weg 9, 40472, Dusseldorf, Germany **(100%)**
Tel.: (49) 21195110
Web Site: http://www.unitronic.de
Sales Range: $25-49.9 Million
Emp.: 30
Electronic Parts & Equipment Whslr
N.A.I.C.S.: 423690

VP metall AS (1)
Raufoss Industripark Bygn 53, 2830, Raufoss, Norway
Tel.: (47) 61151787
Emp.: 22
Metal Products Mfr
N.A.I.C.S.: 332999
Stian Myrland (Project Coord)

Vanpee A/S (1)
Gammelager 15, 2605, Brondby, Denmark
Tel.: (45) 44859000
Electronic Product Distr
N.A.I.C.S.: 423620

Vendig AB (1)
Smedstorpsgatan 10, 532 21, Skara, Sweden
Tel.: (46) 51117360
Web Site: https://vendig.se
Conveyor Component Mfr & Distr
N.A.I.C.S.: 333922
Marten Jilderbo (Sls Mgr)

Wapro AB (1)

Munkahusvagen 103, 37431, Karlshamn, Sweden
Tel.: (46) 45418510
Industrial Machinery Mfr
N.A.I.C.S.: 333248

Waterproof Diving International AB (1)
Industrivagen 39, S-433 61, Partille, Sweden
Tel.: (46) 313368270
Web Site: https://waterproof.eu
Waterproofing Apparel Mfr & Distr
N.A.I.C.S.: 339113

Westmatic Corporation (1)
999 Harlem Rd, Buffalo, NY 14224
Web Site: https://www.westmatic.com
Vehicle Wash System Mfr & Distr
N.A.I.C.S.: 336419

Westmatic Inc. (1)
2700 Dufferin Street Unit 83, Toronto, M6B 4J3, ON, Canada
Web Site: https://www.westmatic.ca
Vehicle Wash System Mfr & Distr
N.A.I.C.S.: 336419

Westmatic i Arvika AB (1)
Fallebergsvagen 28, 671 34, Arvika, Sweden
Tel.: (46) 570727600
Web Site: https://www.westmatic.se
Vehicle Washing Equipment Mfr & Distr
N.A.I.C.S.: 336419

LAGNAM SPINTEX LIMITED
A 51- 53 Riico Growth Centre Hamirgarh, Bhilwara, 311001, Rajasthan, India
Tel.: (91) 1482289210
Web Site:
 https://www.lagnamspintex.com
Year Founded: 2010
LAGNAM—(NSE)
Cotton Yarn Mfr
N.A.I.C.S.: 313110
Shubh Mangal (Exec Dir)

LAGUELLE SA
Les Houches 27 Route de Herisson, 03430, Cosne-d'Allier, France
Tel.: (33) 470070900
Web Site: http://www.laguelle.com
Rev.: $10,300,000
Emp.: 35
Coat Hanger Mfr
N.A.I.C.S.: 326199
Patrice Laguelle (Dir-Pur)

LAGUNA BAY GROUP PTY LTD
Level 1 69 Robertson Street, Fortitude Valley, 4006, QLD, Australia
Tel.: (61) 7 3062 2514
Web Site:
 https://www.lagunabay.com.au
Emp.: 100
Investment Services
N.A.I.C.S.: 523999
Tim McGavin (Founder & Mng Dir)

LAHAV L R REAL ESTATE LTD.
Italy building second floor, Europark, Yakum, 609720, Israel
Tel.: (972) 99527700
Web Site:
 https://www.lahavgroup.co.il
Year Founded: 1963
LAHAV—(TAE)
Rev.: $107,149,605
Assets: $589,845,550
Liabilities: $282,361,924
Net Worth: $307,483,626
Earnings: $28,211,078
Emp.: 2,000
Fiscal Year-end: 12/31/23
Other Activities Related to Real Estate
N.A.I.C.S.: 531390

Shlomo Fedida (CFO)

LAHAYE ATLANTIQUE
Parc d'activites Bois Soeuvre 2 Rue De La Clairiere, 35770, Vern-sur-Seiche, Ille Et Vilaine, France
Tel.: (33) 299004466
Web Site: http://www.lahaye-sa.fr
Rev.: $17,000,000
Emp.: 1,000
Logistics & Transportation
N.A.I.C.S.: 484121
Patrick Lahaye (Pres)

LAHMEYER HOLDING GMBH
Friedberger Strasse 173, 61118, Bad Vilbel, Germany
Tel.: (49) 6101 55 0
Web Site: http://www.lahmeyer.com
Emp.: 1,500
Holding Company; Engineering Services
N.A.I.C.S.: 551112
Bernd Kordes (Pres & CEO)

Subsidiaries:

Consulting Engineers Lahmeyer Nigeria Ltd. (1)
Afri Investment House Plot 2669 Aguiyi Ironsi Street, Maitama, Abuja, Nigeria
Tel.: (234) 8050250799
Engineering Consulting Services
N.A.I.C.S.: 541330

Hidro Dizayn Muhendislik Musavirlik Insaat ve Ticaret A.S. (1)
Ceyhun Atif Kansu Cd No 91 Balgat, Ehlibeyt Mahallesi cankaya, Ankara, Turkiye
Tel.: (90) 3124734100
Web Site: http://www.hidrodizayn.com
Emp.: 190
Engineering Consulting Services
N.A.I.C.S.: 541330
Aldonat Koksal (Mng Dir)

Hidrolin Hidrodizayn & Linerji Enerji Muhendislik ve Musavirlik Ltd. Sti. (1)
Vazha Pshavela Avenue Suite 159, 0189, Tbilisi, Georgia
Tel.: (995) 557612978
Engineering Consulting Services
N.A.I.C.S.: 541330

Lahmeyer Agua y Energia S.A. (1)
Avenida Canaval y Moreyra 452 4 Piso, San Isidro, Lima, Peru
Tel.: (51) 12222286
Web Site: http://www.liperu.com
Engineering Consulting Services
N.A.I.C.S.: 541330

Lahmeyer Berlin GmbH (1)
Ingenieurgesellschaft Sachsendamm 3, 10829, Berlin, Germany
Tel.: (49) 307879130
Web Site: http://www.lahmeyer-berlin.de
Commercial Real Estate Consulting Services
N.A.I.C.S.: 531210
Michael Bergmann (Mng Dir & Exec Dir)

Lahmeyer Consulting Engineers (T) Limited (1)
Mikocheni Off Mwai Kibaki Road ABC Kwanza Nursery Street Plot No 294, Dar es Salaam, Tanzania
Tel.: (255) 784351869
Engineering Consulting Services
N.A.I.C.S.: 541330

Lahmeyer GKW Consult GmbH (1)
Augustaanlage 67, D-68165, Mannheim, Germany
Tel.: (49) 621 41077 0
Web Site: http://www.lahmeyer-gkw.com
Sales Range: $50-74.9 Million
Emp.: 150
Environmental Consulting & Engineering Services
N.A.I.C.S.: 541620
Ralf Bufler (Mng Dir)

Lahmeyer Hydroprojekt GmbH (1)

LAHMEYER HOLDING GMBH

Lahmeyer Holding GmbH—(Continued)
Riessnerstrasse 18, 99427, Weimar, Germany
Tel.: (49) 3643746400
Web Site: http://www.hydroprojekt.de
Emp.: 100
Engineering Consulting Services
N.A.I.C.S.: 541330
Michael Heiland (Mng Dir)

Lahmeyer IDP Consult Inc. (1)
Suite 1610 Tektite East Tower Philippine Stock Exchange Centre, Ortigas Centre, Pasig, Philippines
Tel.: (63) 26875876
Web Site: http://www.idp.com.ph
Business Consulting Services
N.A.I.C.S.: 541611
Evelyn A. Orda (Pres)

Lahmeyer International (India) Pvt. Ltd. (1)
Intec House 37 Institutional Area Sector 44, Gurgaon, 122002, India
Tel.: (91) 1244698500
Web Site: http://www.lahmeyer.in
Construction Engineering Services
N.A.I.C.S.: 541330
Bansi Dhar Banerjee (VP-Bus Dev & Contracts)

Lahmeyer International Qatar LLC (1)
12th Floor Office 23 24 18 Al Meena Street Al Meena Building, PO Box 10822, Old Salata Area, Doha, Qatar
Tel.: (974) 44860645
Engineering Consulting Services
N.A.I.C.S.: 541330
Bernd Kordes (Pres & CEO)

Lahmeyer Munchen Ingenieurgesellschaft mbH (1)
Akademiestrasse 7, 80799, Munich, Germany
Tel.: (49) 893816070
Web Site: http://www.lahmeyer-muenchen.de
Engineering Consulting Services
N.A.I.C.S.: 541330

OOO Lahmeyer International RUS (1)
1st Yamskogo Polya Street House 9/13 Office 507, 125124, Moscow, Russia
Tel.: (7) 4959264367
Web Site: http://www.lirussia.ru
Engineering Consulting Services
N.A.I.C.S.: 541330
Viktor Istomin (Gen Dir)

LAHORE STOCK EXCHANGE (GUARANTEE) LTD.
19 Khayaban-e-Aiwan-e-Iqbal, PO Box 1315, Lahore, 54000, Pakistan
Tel.: (92) 426368000
Web Site: http://www.lse.com.pk
Sales Range: $50-74.9 Million
Emp.: 150
Stock Exchange Services
N.A.I.C.S.: 523210
Aftab Ahmad Chaudhry (CEO & Mng Dir)

LAHOTI OVERSEAS LIMITED
307 Arun Chambers Tardeo, Mumbai, 400 034, India
Tel.: (91) 2240500100
Web Site: https://www.lahotioverseas.com
Year Founded: 1990
531842—(BOM)
Rev.: $122,961,903
Assets: $33,832,631
Liabilities: $11,838,822
Net Worth: $21,993,808
Earnings: $3,232,730
Emp.: 41
Fiscal Year-end: 03/31/22
Cotton Yarn Distr
N.A.I.C.S.: 424990
Umesh Rambilas Lahoti (Mng Dir)

LAI GROUP HOLDING COMPANY LIMITED
19th Floor Kings Wing Plaza Phase 1 No 3 On Kwan Street Shimen, Sha Tin, China (Hong Kong)
Tel.: (852) 2 634 1328 Ky
Web Site: http://www.dic.hk
Year Founded: 1996
8455—(HKG)
Rev.: $17,841,416
Assets: $9,655,443
Liabilities: $4,676,557
Net Worth: $4,978,886
Earnings: ($466,005)
Emp.: 38
Fiscal Year-end: 03/31/22
Interior Design Services
N.A.I.C.S.: 541410
Lai Sin Chan (Founder, Chm & Compliance Officer)

LAI SI ENTERPRISE HOLDING LIMITED
Lai Enterprise Center No 54 Seaside Street, Macau, China (Macau)
Tel.: (853) 28555557 Ky
Web Site: https://www.lai-si.com
Year Founded: 1987
2266—(HKG)
Rev.: $10,960,737
Assets: $22,409,798
Liabilities: $9,366,634
Net Worth: $13,043,164
Earnings: ($2,305,149)
Emp.: 140
Fiscal Year-end: 12/31/23
Building Contract Services
N.A.I.C.S.: 238390
Ieng Man Lai (Chm)

LAI SUN GARMENT (INTERNATIONAL) LIMITED
11F Lai Sun Commercial Centre, 680 Cheung Sha Wan Road, Kowloon, China (Hong Kong)
Tel.: (852) 27410391
Web Site: https://www.laisun.com
0191—(HKG)
Rev.: $785,460,469
Assets: $11,544,923,831
Liabilities: $5,636,151,531
Net Worth: $5,908,772,300
Earnings: ($355,887,936)
Emp.: 4,400
Fiscal Year-end: 07/31/21
Holding Company
N.A.I.C.S.: 551112
U. Po Chu (Exec Dir)

Subsidiaries:

Joy Mind Limited (1)
11 Fl Lai Sun Comml Ctr 680 Cheung Sha Wan Rd, Cheung Sha Wan, Kowloon, China (Hong Kong)
Tel.: (852) 27410391
Investment Management Service
N.A.I.C.S.: 523999

LAI SUN GROUP
19/F AIA Central 1 Connaught Road, Central, China (Hong Kong)
Tel.: (852) 2854 0668
Web Site: http://www.laisun.com
Year Founded: 1947
Holding Company
N.A.I.C.S.: 551112

Subsidiaries:

Lai Sun Development Company Limited (1)
11F Lai Sun Commercial Centre 680 Cheung Sha Wan Road, Kowloon, China (Hong Kong)
Tel.: (852) 27410391
Web Site: https://www.laisun.com
Rev.: $772,171,273
Assets: $10,710,253,880
Liabilities: $5,166,086,887
Net Worth: $5,544,166,993
Earnings: ($342,723,721)
Emp.: 4,400
Fiscal Year-end: 07/31/2022
Property Development Services
N.A.I.C.S.: 531390
Peter Kin Ngok Lam (Chm)

Subsidiary (Domestic):

Lai Fung Holdings Limited (2)
19/F AIA Central 1 Connaught Road Central, Central, China (Hong Kong) (54.56%)
Tel.: (852) 28540668
Web Site: https://www.laifung.com
Rev.: $324,484,144
Assets: $4,357,559,506
Liabilities: $2,492,111,576
Net Worth: $1,865,447,929
Earnings: ($36,615,358)
Emp.: 1,736
Fiscal Year-end: 07/31/2022
Property Development & Investment Services
N.A.I.C.S.: 531312
Shin How Cheng (Exec Dir)

eSun Holdings Limited (2)
11/F Lai Sun Commercial Centre 680 Cheung Sha Wan Road, Kowloon, China (Hong Kong) (77.94%)
Tel.: (852) 27410391
Web Site: https://www.laisun.com
Rev.: $107,083,968
Assets: $408,954,822
Liabilities: $279,667,592
Net Worth: $129,287,230
Earnings: ($47,702,737)
Emp.: 560
Fiscal Year-end: 07/31/2022
Holding Company
N.A.I.C.S.: 551112
Chee Keong Low (Chm)

Subsidiary (Domestic):

Kadokawa Intercontinental Publishing (Asia) Ltd. (3)
Unit 1 20/F Wyler Center Phase 2 200 Tai Lin Pai Road, Kwai Chung, NT, China (Hong Kong)
Tel.: (852) 36532888
Web Site: http://www.hongkongwalker.com
Sales Range: $25-49.9 Million
Emp.: 40
Entertainment Services
N.A.I.C.S.: 512110

Media Asia Group Holdings Limited (3)
20/F Wyler Centre Phase II No 200 Tai Lin Pai Road, Kwai Chung, New Territories, China (Hong Kong) (100%)
Tel.: (852) 23144288
Web Site: http://www.mediaasia.com
Rev.: $45,786,094
Assets: $100,553,969
Liabilities: $59,283,851
Net Worth: $41,270,118
Earnings: ($22,117,619)
Emp.: 143
Fiscal Year-end: 07/31/2021
Holding Company
N.A.I.C.S.: 551112
Peter Kin Ngok Lam (Chm)

LAING O'ROURKE PLC
Bridge Place Anchor Boulevard, Admirals Park Crossways, Dartford, A2 6SN, Kent, United Kingdom
Tel.: (44) 1322296200 UK
Web Site: http://www.laingorourke.com
Year Founded: 1978
Sales Range: $5-14.9 Billion
Emp.: 19,668
Construction & Engineering Services
N.A.I.C.S.: 237310
Ray O'Rourke (Co-Founder & CEO)

Subsidiaries:

Crown House Technologies Limited (1)
Units 18-19 Webner Industrial Estate Ettingshall Road, Wolverhampton, WV2 2LD, United Kingdom (100%)
Tel.: (44) 1902405403

INTERNATIONAL PUBLIC

Web Site: http://www.crownhouse.com
Sales Range: $400-449.9 Million
Emp.: 1,300
Mechanical & Electrical Services
N.A.I.C.S.: 238210

Expanded Limited (1)
Bridge Place 1 and 2 Anchor Boulevard, Crossways, Dartford, DA2 6SN, Kent, United Kingdom
Tel.: (44) 132 229 6200
Web Site: https://www.expandedltd.com
Emp.: 400
Construction Services
N.A.I.C.S.: 236220
Martin Durkan (Dir-Operations)

Expanded Piling Limited (1)
Cheapside Reach, Waltham, Grimsby, DN37 0JD, United Kingdom (100%)
Tel.: (44) 1472822552
Web Site: http://www.laingorourke.com
Construction & Engineering Serivces
N.A.I.C.S.: 237990

Explore Living Plc (1)
Bridge Place Anchor Boulevard, Admirals Park, Dartford, DA2 6SN, Kent, United Kingdom (100%)
Tel.: (44) 1322296200
Web Site: http://www.exploreliving.co.uk
Sales Range: $200-249.9 Million
Emp.: 600
Residential Developer
N.A.I.C.S.: 236116
Anna Stewart (CEO)

Glass Reinforced Concrete UK Limited (1)
Unit B1 Bryans Close, Harworth, DN11 8RY, DoncasterA , United Kingdom
Tel.: (44) 1909 566911
Web Site: http://www.grcuk.com
Emp.: 70
Concrete Product Mfr & Distr
N.A.I.C.S.: 327390

Laing O'Rourke Australia Pty Limited (1)
Level 10 100 Eagle St, Brisbane, 4000, QLD, Australia (100%)
Tel.: (61) 733377100
Web Site: http://www.laingorourke.com.au
Property Development & Project Management Services
N.A.I.C.S.: 237990

Laing O'Rourke Technical Services (India) Private Limited (1)
Vatika Triangle 3rd Floor, Sushant Lok-I block-A, Mehrauli-Gurgaon Road, Gurgaon, 122022, India (100%)
Tel.: (91) 1245017470
Offshore IT Enabled Services
N.A.I.C.S.: 541519

Mailing Products Limited (1)
Fiddlers Reach Wouldham Road, Chelmsford, RM20 4YB, Essex, United Kingdom (100%)
Tel.: (44) 1375391313
Precast Concrete Mfr
N.A.I.C.S.: 327390

Naturstein Vetter GmbH (1)
Industriestrasse 16, 97483, Eltmann, Germany (100%)
Tel.: (49) 95227290
Web Site: http://www.stein-vetter.de
Sales Range: $25-49.9 Million
Emp.: 75
Finished Stone Products Mfr
N.A.I.C.S.: 327991

Select Plant Hire Company Limited (1)
Bridge Place 1 Achnor Boulevard, Admirals Park, Dartford, DA2 6SN, Kent, United Kingdom (100%)
Tel.: (44) 1322296200
Sales Range: $150-199.9 Million
Emp.: 800
Employment Services
N.A.I.C.S.: 561311

Vetter UK Limited (1)
3 Archway Birley Fields, Manchester, M15 5QJ, United Kingdom (100%)
Tel.: (44) 1612276400
Web Site: http://www.vetteruk.com

AND PRIVATE COMPANIES

Sales Range: $25-49.9 Million
Emp.: 100
Finished Stone Products
N.A.I.C.S.: 327991
Alan Sharpley (Mgr-Ops)

LAIQON AG
An der Alster 42, 20099, Hamburg, Germany
Tel.: (49) 403256780
Web Site: https://www.laiqon.ag
Year Founded: 1995
LQAG—(DUS)
Rev.: $33,181,524
Assets: $156,084,610
Liabilities: $97,076,408
Net Worth: $59,008,202
Earnings: ($13,893,805)
Emp.: 195
Fiscal Year-end: 12/31/23
Asset Management Services
N.A.I.C.S.: 523999
Benjamin Kassen (Mng Dir)

LAIRD TECHNOLOGIES GMBH
Ausere Oberaustr 22, Rosenheim, 83026, Germany
Tel.: (49) 803124600
Web Site: http://www.lairdtech.com
Sales Range: $25-49.9 Million
Emp.: 22
Industrial Supplies Mfr
N.A.I.C.S.: 333248
Albert Ashzhl (Gen Mgr)

LAIRD TECHNOLOGIES GOTHENBURG AB
Kryptongatan 20, Molndal, 431 53, Sweden
Tel.: (46) 31 420530
Web Site: http://www.lairdtech.com
Emp.: 100
Thermoelectrical Cooling System Mfr
N.A.I.C.S.: 334512

LAIRD TECHNOLOGIES, INDIA PRIVATE LIMITED
Unit 3 4th Floor Navigator Bldg Information Technology Park Ltd, Whitefield Road, Bengaluru, 560 066, Karnataka, India
Tel.: (91) 80 40740400
Sales Range: $25-49.9 Million
Emp.: 25
Telecommunications Equipment Mfr
N.A.I.C.S.: 334220

LAIWU STEEL GROUP, LTD.
Shandong Province, Zichuan District, Zibo, 255167, China
Tel.: (86) 5335060242
Web Site: http://www.chinaccm.com
Sales Range: $250-299.9 Million
Emp.: 1,640
Provider of Iron & Steel
N.A.I.C.S.: 332111

LAIX INC.
3/F Building B No 1687 Changyang Road, Yangpu District, Shanghai, 200090, China
Tel.: (86) 213 511 7188   Ky
Web Site: http://www.liulishuo.com
Year Founded: 2012
LAIX—(NYSE)
Rev.: $104,937,819
Assets: $25,103,459
Liabilities: $121,930,034
Net Worth: ($96,826,576)
Earnings: $9,178,352
Emp.: 736
Fiscal Year-end: 12/31/21
Information Technology Consulting Services
N.A.I.C.S.: 541512
Yi Wang (Co-Founder, Chm & CEO)

LAJAVI INVERSIONES SL
Paseo San Francisco de Sales 8Madrid, Madrid, 28003, Spain
Tel.: (34) 91 319 48 02
Sales Range: $100-124.9 Million
Ship Building Services
N.A.I.C.S.: 336611

LAJIN ENTERTAINMENT NETWORK GROUP LIMITED
Unit 3903A Far East Finance Centre, 16 Harcourt Road Admiralty, Hong Kong, China (Hong Kong)
Tel.: (852) 29836201   Ky
Year Founded: 2001
8172—(HKG)
Rev.: $1,342,958
Assets: $28,624,515
Liabilities: $8,979,698
Net Worth: $19,644,818
Earnings: ($13,093,358)
Emp.: 69
Fiscal Year-end: 12/31/22
Holding Company
N.A.I.C.S.: 551112
Li Wu (Compliance Officer)

LAKALA PAYMENT CO., LTD.
606 Floor 6 Block D1 No 1 Zhongguancun Beiqing Road, Haidian District, Beijing, 100094, China
Tel.: (86) 1056710773
Web Site: http://www.lakala.com
Year Founded: 2005
300773—(SSE)
Rev.: $757,344,276
Assets: $1,466,191,584
Liabilities: $995,801,040
Net Worth: $470,390,544
Earnings: ($201,771,648)
Fiscal Year-end: 12/31/22
Payment Services
N.A.I.C.S.: 522320
Taoran Sun (Chm)

LAKE CITY FORD SALES LTD.
800 Broadway Avenue North, Williams Lake, V2G 3P4, BC, Canada
Tel.: (250) 392-4455
Web Site: https://www.lakecityford.ca
Rev.: $18,519,274
Emp.: 40
New & Used Car Dealers
N.A.I.C.S.: 441110
Colin Smith (Mgr-Parts)

LAKE MATERIALS CO., LTD.
22-144 Sandan-gil Jeonui-myeon, Yeongdeungpo-gu, Sejong, Korea (South)
Tel.: (82) 444149400
Web Site: https://lakematerials.co.kr
Year Founded: 2010
281740—(KRS)
Rev.: $100,865,651
Assets: $163,762,275
Liabilities: $97,199,997
Net Worth: $66,562,278
Earnings: $20,831,585
Emp.: 4
Fiscal Year-end: 12/31/22
Asset Management Services
N.A.I.C.S.: 523940
Jin-Dong Kim (CEO)

LAKE RESOURCES N.L.
Level 5 126 Phillip Street, Sydney, 2000, NSW, Australia
Tel.: (61) 292999690
Web Site: https://www.lakeresources.com.au
LLKKF—(OTCQB)
Assets: $171,538,664
Liabilities: $3,871,422
Net Worth: $167,667,243
Earnings: ($4,354,331)
Fiscal Year-end: 06/30/22
Copper, Nickel, Lead & Zinc Mining
N.A.I.C.S.: 212230
Stephen Promnitz (Mng Dir)

LAKE VICTORIA MINING COMPANY, INC.
675 West Hastings Street Suite 810, Vancouver, V6B 1N2, BC, Canada
Tel.: (951) 907-9911
Year Founded: 2007
Metal Mining Services
N.A.I.C.S.: 213114
Bradley J. Yourist (CEO)

LAKE WINN RESOURCES CORP.
1400 - 1111 West Georgia Sreet, Vancouver, V6E 4M3, BC, Canada
Tel.: (604) 218-8772   BC
Web Site:
    https://equitorialexploration.com
Year Founded: 2010
EQTXF—(OTCIQ)
Assets: $454,800
Liabilities: $778,552
Net Worth: ($323,753)
Earnings: ($1,078,537)
Fiscal Year-end: 12/31/23
Metal Mining Services
N.A.I.C.S.: 212290
Binny Jassal (CFO)

LAKEEL, INC.
Atago Green Hills MORI Tower 33F 2-5-1 Atago, Minato-ku, Tokyo, 105-0002, Japan
Tel.: (81) 364413850
Web Site: https://www.lakeel.com
Year Founded: 2005
4074—(TKS)
Rev.: $54,259,770
Assets: $45,432,720
Liabilities: $18,320,560
Net Worth: $27,112,160
Earnings: $3,821,510
Emp.: 456
Fiscal Year-end: 12/31/23
Software Development Services
N.A.I.C.S.: 541511
Kubo Tsutomu (CEO)

LAKELAND DAIRIES CO-OPERATIVE SOCIETY LTD.
Head Office, Killeshandra, Cavan, Ireland
Tel.: (353) 494364200
Web Site: http://www.lakeland.ie
Year Founded: 1965
Sales Range: $50-74.9 Million
Emp.: 500
Dairy Processing Cooperative
N.A.I.C.S.: 311514
Michael G. Hanley (CEO)

Subsidiaries:

Lakeland Dairies Agribusiness   (1)
Farm Service Head Office, Killeshandra, Co-Cavan, Ireland
Tel.: (353) 494364200
Web Site: http://www.lakeland.ie
Sales Range: $25-49.9 Million
Emp.: 100
Animal Feed & Fertilizer
N.A.I.C.S.: 325314
Pat Shiels (Gen Mgr)

Lakeland Dairies Food Ingredients   (1)
Head Office Bailieboro, Cavan, Ireland
Tel.: (353) 42 969 4200
Web Site: http://www.lakeland.ie
Dairy Products
N.A.I.C.S.: 311514

Pritchitts   (1)
Foodservice Head Ofc, Killeshandra, H12V273, Cavan, Ireland
Tel.: (353) 494364200

LAKESIDE PROCESS CONTROLS LTD.

Web Site: http://www.lakelands.ie
Sales Range: $100-124.9 Million
Emp.: 450
Dairy Products
N.A.I.C.S.: 311514

LAKELAND LIMITED
Alexandra Buildings, Windermere, LA23 1BQ, Cumbria, United Kingdom
Tel.: (44) 15394 88100
Web Site: http://www.lakeland.co.uk
Year Founded: 1963
Sales Range: $200-249.9 Million
Emp.: 1,500
Housewares & Home Furnishings Retailer
N.A.I.C.S.: 449210
Sam Ryan (Mng Dir)

LAKES BLUE ENERGY NL
Tel.: (61) 396291566
Web Site:
    https://www.lakesoil.com.au
Rev.: $15,873
Assets: $10,976,790
Liabilities: $670,633
Net Worth: $10,306,157
Earnings: ($1,592,301)
Emp.: 7
Fiscal Year-end: 06/30/18
Oil & Gas Exploration Services
N.A.I.C.S.: 211120
Richard D. Ash (Chm)

Subsidiaries:

Rawson Oil & Gas Limited   (1)
McCullough Robertson Level 32 MLC Centre 19 Martin Place, Sydney, 2000, NSW, Australia
Tel.: (61) 290954226
Web Site: http://www.rawsonresources.com
Oil & Gas Exploration
N.A.I.C.S.: 211120
Sarah Potter (CFO & Co-Sec)

Subsidiary (Domestic):

Otway Energy Limited   (2)
95 Pitt Street, Sydney, 2000, NSW, Australia   (100%)
Tel.: (61) 2 8249 8370
Web Site: http://www.otwayenergy.com
Oil & Gas Exploration
N.A.I.C.S.: 211120

LAKESHORE ACQUISITION I CORP.
Suite A-2F 555 Shihui Road, Songjiang District, Shanghai, 201100, China
Tel.: (86) 13816100700   Ky
Year Founded: 2021
LAAA—(NASDAQ)
N.A.I.C.S.:
Bill Chen (Chm & CEO)

LAKESHORE BIOPHARMA CO., LTD.
Building No 2 38 Yongda Road Daxing Biomedical Industry Park, Daxing District, Beijing, 102629, China
Tel.: (86) 1089202086   Ky
Web Site:
    https://www.lakeshorebio.com
Year Founded: 2020
LSB—(NASDAQ)
Rev.: $79,394,419
Assets: $209,490,938
Liabilities: $128,464,368
Net Worth: $81,026,570
Earnings: ($60,016,735)
Emp.: 758
Fiscal Year-end: 03/31/24
Biotechnology Research & Development Services
N.A.I.C.S.: 541714
Chunyuan Wu (CFO)

LAKESIDE PROCESS CONTROLS LTD.

LAKESIDE PROCESS CONTROLS LTD.

Lakeside Process Controls Ltd.—(Continued)
2475 Hogan Drive, Mississauga, L5N 0E9, ON, Canada
Tel.: (905) 629-9340
Web Site:
http://www.lakesidecontrols.com
Year Founded: 1952
Rev.: $33,592,600
Emp.: 140
Automation Solutions Provider
N.A.I.C.S.: 333248
Scott James (VP)

LAKHANI INDIA LIMITED
Plot No 131 Sector 24, Faridabad, 121005, Haryana, India
Tel.: (91) 129 2232793
Sales Range: $50-74.9 Million
Shoe Mfr & Whslr
N.A.I.C.S.: 316210
Arun Virmani (Sec)

LAKHOTIA POLYESTER (INDIA) LIMITED
293 Somwar Ward Bhavsar Lane, Malagaon District, Nasik, Maharashtra, India
Tel.: (91) 2554220500
Web Site: https://www.lakhotiapoly.in
535387—(BOM)
Rev.: $2,230,710
Assets: $2,339,815
Liabilities: $1,314,222
Net Worth: $1,025,593
Earnings: ($65,943)
Emp.: 45
Fiscal Year-end: 03/31/21
Polyester Films, Coated Films, Transfer Foils & Yarns
N.A.I.C.S.: 326112
Madhusudan Shamsundar Lakhotia (Mng Dir)

LAKSHMI AUTOMATIC LOOM WORKS LIMITED
686 Avinashi Road Pappanaickenpalayam, Coimbatore, 641037, India
Tel.: (91) 4222245484
Web Site:
https://www.lakshmiautomatic.com
505302—(BOM)
Rev.: $1,707,955
Assets: $3,816,690
Liabilities: $1,414,280
Net Worth: $2,402,410
Earnings: $255,105
Emp.: 115
Fiscal Year-end: 03/31/23
Textile Machinery Mfr
N.A.I.C.S.: 333248
S. Pathy (Chm)

Subsidiaries:
Lakshmi Automatic Loom Works Ltd. - Unit 1 (1)
Hosur Industrial Complex, Krishnagiri, Hosur, 635126, India
Tel.: (91) 4344 276926
Weaving Machinery Mfr
N.A.I.C.S.: 333248

Lakshmi Automatic Loom Works Ltd. - Unit 2 (1)
Singarampalayam Kinathukadavu Post, Coimbatore, Pollachi, 642109, India
Tel.: (91) 425924 2130
Engineeering Services
N.A.I.C.S.: 541330

LAKSHMI ELECTRICAL CONTROL SYSTEMS LIMITED
Arasur, Coimbatore, 641 407, Tamil Nadu, India
Tel.: (91) 4226616500
Web Site: http://www.lecsindia.com
Year Founded: 1981

504258—(BOM)
Rev.: $35,368,870
Assets: $37,743,656
Liabilities: $8,672,705
Net Worth: $29,070,951
Earnings: $2,114,016
Emp.: 176
Fiscal Year-end: 03/31/22
Textile Machinery Mfr
N.A.I.C.S.: 333248
Nethra Jayavarthanavelu Senthil Kumar (Chm & Mng Dir)

LAKSHMI FINANCE & INDUSTRIAL CORPORATION LIMITED
1st Floor Suryodaya 1-10-60/3 Begumpet, Hyderabad, 500016, Telangana, India
Tel.: (91) 4027760301
Web Site:
https://www.lakshmifinance.org.in
LFIC—(NSE)
Rev.: $431,665
Assets: $5,873,365
Liabilities: $276,494
Net Worth: $5,596,871
Earnings: $66,003
Emp.: 9
Fiscal Year-end: 03/31/23
Investment Management Service
N.A.I.C.S.: 523999

LAKSHMI MACHINE WORKS LTD.
SRK Vidyalaya Post Perianaickenpalayam, Perianaickenpalayam, Coimbatore, 641 020, Tamil Nadu, India
Tel.: (91) 4227192255
Web Site: https://www.lmwglobal.com
Year Founded: 1962
LAXMIMACH—(NSE)
Rev.: $442,163,303
Assets: $497,687,873
Liabilities: $226,028,425
Net Worth: $271,659,447
Earnings: $24,713,311
Emp.: 3,143
Fiscal Year-end: 03/31/22
Textile Machinery & Industrial Tools Mfr
N.A.I.C.S.: 333248
Sanjay Jayavarthanavelu (Chm & Mng Dir)

Subsidiaries:
Lakshmi Machine Works Limited Machine Tool Division (1)
Arasur Unit 1 Periyanayakan Palayam, Coimbatore, 641020, Tamil Nadu, India
Tel.: (91) 4223021300
Sales Range: $750-799.9 Million
Emp.: 3,300
Textile Industry
N.A.I.C.S.: 313310

Lakshmi Machine Works Limited Machine Tool Division & Foundry Division (1)
Arasur, Coimbatore, 641 407, Tamil Nadu, India
Tel.: (91) 4223022511
Sales Range: $750-799.9 Million
Textile Industry
N.A.I.C.S.: 313310
Sanjay Jayavarthanavelu (Mng Dir)

Lakshmi Machine Works Limited Unit 2 (1)
Kaniyur, Coimbatore, 641 659, Tamil Nadu, India
Tel.: (91) 4213983000
Web Site: http://www.lakshmimach.com
Sales Range: $350-399.9 Million
Textile Industry
N.A.I.C.S.: 313310
Sanjai Jayavarthanvelu (Chm & Mng Dir)

LAKSHMI PRECISION SCREWS LTD.
46/1 Mile Stone Northern Bye Pass Hissar Road, Rohtak, 124 001, Haryana, India
Tel.: (91) 1262248288
Web Site: http://www.lpsindia.com
Year Founded: 1972
LAKPRE—(NSE)
Sales Range: $25-49.9 Million
Emp.: 954
Tensile Mfr
N.A.I.C.S.: 339999
Lalit Kumar Jain (Chm, CEO & Mng Dir)

LAKSON GROUP OF COMPANIES
Lakson Square Building 2 Sarwar Shaheed Road, Karachi, 74200, Pakistan
Tel.: (92) 21 569 8000
Web Site: http://www.lakson.com.pk
Sales Range: $500-549.9 Million
Emp.: 700
Manages Businesses Centering on Consumer Package Goods
N.A.I.C.S.: 551112
Zulvulfiqar Lakhani (Mng Dir)

Subsidiaries:
Accuray Surgicals Ltd. (1)
Lakson Square-Bldg 2 Sarwar Shaheed Road, 74200, Karachi, Pakistan
Tel.: (92) 215681419
Web Site: http://www.accuray.com.pk
Sales Range: $25-49.9 Million
Emp.: 8
Surgical, Dental & Veterinary Instrument Mfr
N.A.I.C.S.: 339112

Century Insurance Company Limited (1)
Lakson Square Building No 3 11th Fl, Sarwar Shaheed Road, 74200, Karachi, Pakistan
Tel.: (92) 21111111717
Web Site: http://www.cicl.com.pk
Sales Range: $1-9.9 Million
Emp.: 55
Insurance Services
N.A.I.C.S.: 524298
Afzal Ur-Rahman (Sr Exec VP-Ops)

Lakson Business Solutions Limited (1)
Lakson Square Building 2 Sarwar Shaheed Road, Karachi, 74200, Pakistan
Tel.: (92) 21 3569 8690
Web Site: http://www.laksol.com
Emp.: 64
Information Technology Solutions Services
N.A.I.C.S.: 541511
Safi ur Rehman (Deputy Mgr-Project)

Princeton Travels (Pvt) Ltd. (1)
8 & 9 Ground Floor Lakson Square Building No 2 Sarwar Shaheed Road, Karachi, 74200, Pakistan
Tel.: (92) 21 569 8475 89
Web Site: http://www.princetontravels.com
Tour Operator
N.A.I.C.S.: 561520

LALBHAI GROUP
Naroda Road, Ahmedabad, 380025, India
Tel.: (91) 7968268000
Web Site: http://www.arvind.com
Sales Range: $10-24.9 Million
Emp.: 8,000
Holding Company
N.A.I.C.S.: 551112

Subsidiaries:
Adient Arvind Automotive Fabrics India Private Limited (1)
Arvind Ltd Premises PO Khatraj, Santej / Khatraj Industrial Complex Dist- Gandhinagar, Kalol, 382 721, Gujarat, India
Tel.: (91) 7011156814
Apparel Mfr & Distr
N.A.I.C.S.: 315250

INTERNATIONAL PUBLIC

Amol Dicalite Ltd. (1)
301 Akshay 53 Shrimali Society Navranpura, Ahmedabad, 380009, Gujarat, India
Tel.: (91) 7940246246
Web Site: http://www.amoldicalite.com
Emp.: 30
Filteraids & Filler Products Mfr
N.A.I.C.S.: 325510
Shreyas Chinubhai Sheth (Mng Dir)

Arvind Limited (1)
Naroda Road, Ahmedabad, 380025, Gujarat, India
Tel.: (91) 7968268000
Web Site: https://www.arvind.com
Rev.: $699,503,805
Assets: $917,378,280
Liabilities: $539,734,650
Net Worth: $377,643,630
Earnings: ($3,738,735)
Emp.: 24,774
Fiscal Year-end: 03/31/2021
Fabric & Garment Mfr
N.A.I.C.S.: 313310
Jayesh K. Shah (CFO)

Subsidiary (Domestic):
Anup Engineering Limited (2)
Behind 66 KV Elec Sub Sta Odhav Rd, 382 415, Ahmedabad, Gujarat, India
Tel.: (91) 7922870622
Web Site: http://www.anupengg.com
Rev.: $666,300,000
Emp.: 500
Heat Exchanger Mfr
N.A.I.C.S.: 332410
Rishi Roop Kapoor (CEO)

Arvind Accel Limited (2)
Naroda Rd, Ahmedabad, 380025, Gujarat, India
Tel.: (91) 7922203030
Textile Fabric Mfr
N.A.I.C.S.: 313210

Arvind Infracon LLP (2)
1208 2nd Floor 41st Cross 26th Main 9th Block Jayanagar III Block, Bengaluru, 560011, Karnataka, India
Tel.: (91) 80 22440063
Fabric Product Mfr
N.A.I.C.S.: 313320

Arvind Lifestyle Brands Limited (2)
8th Floor Du Parc Trinity 17 MG Road, Bengaluru, 560 001, India
Tel.: (91) 80 4155 0650
Web Site: http://www.arvindbrands.com
Textile Mfr
N.A.I.C.S.: 314999
J. Suresh (Mng Dir)

Division (Domestic):
Arvind Limited - Denim Division (2)
Naroda Rd, Ahmedabad, 380025, Gujarat, India
Tel.: (91) 79 3013 8000
Web Site: http://www.arvindmills.com
Textile Fabric Mfr
N.A.I.C.S.: 313210
Subir Mukherjee (Head-Mktg)

Arvind Limited - Khakhi Division (2)
Santej Rd Near Khatrej, Gandhinagar Dist, Kalol, 382721, Gujarat, India
Tel.: (91) 2764281100
Khakhi Fabrics Mfr
N.A.I.C.S.: 313230
Pranav Dave (Mgr)

Arvind Limited - Knits Division (2)
PO Khatraj Taluka, Gandhinagar, Kalol, 382721, Gujarat, India
Tel.: (91) 2764675000
Web Site: http://www.arvind.com
Textile & Fabric Distr
N.A.I.C.S.: 424310

Arvind Limited - Shirting Division (2)
Khatrej Taluka Kalol Dist Gandhinagar, Gandhinagar Dist, Kalol, 382721, Gujarat, India
Tel.: (91) 2764281100
Textile Fabric Whslr
N.A.I.C.S.: 424310

Subsidiary (Domestic):
Arvind Retail Limited (2)

5th Floor Du Parc Trinity 17 MG Road, Bengaluru, 560 001, India
Tel.: (91) 80 4048 8775
Textile Mfr
N.A.I.C.S.: 314999
J. Suresh (Mng Dir)

Arvind SmartSpaces Limited
24 Government Servant Society Behind Citibank CG Road, Ahmedabad, 380009, Gujarat, India
Tel.: (91) 7968264023
Web Site:
https://www.arvindsmartspaces.com
Emp.: 120
Real Estate Development Services
N.A.I.C.S.: 531390
Amit Mall (Sr Mgr)

Subsidiary (US):

Arvind Worldwide Inc. (2)
130 W 42nd St Ste 603, New York, NY 10036
Tel.: (212) 768-4815
Web Site: http://www.arvind.com
Emp.: 2
Textile Sales
N.A.I.C.S.: 314999
Viresh Verma (Exec Dir)

Subsidiary (Domestic):

Syntel Telecom Limited (2)
Survey No 33/1 Kondhwa Pisoli Road Pisoli, Pune, 411060, India
Tel.: (91) 20 7101 1234
Web Site: http://www.synteltelecom.com
Telecommunication Servicesb
N.A.I.C.S.: 517112
Dhairyasheel Jadhav (Deputy Gen Mgr-R&D)

Atul Ltd. (1)
Atul, Ahmedabad, 396020, Gujarat, India
Tel.: (91) 2632230000
Web Site: https://www.atul.co.in
Rev.: $703,915,485
Assets: $778,916,775
Liabilities: $170,148,615
Net Worth: $608,768,160
Earnings: $82,547,010
Emp.: 3,034
Fiscal Year-end: 03/31/2022
Chemicals Mfr
N.A.I.C.S.: 325998
Gopi Kannan Thirukonda (CFO)

LALIN PROPERTY PUBLIC COMPANY LIMITED
222/2 Srinakarint Road, Bangkapi, Bangkok, 10240, Thailand
Tel.: (66) 273210415
Web Site:
http://www.lalinproperty.com
Year Founded: 1988
LALIN—(THA)
Rev.: $139,891,715
Assets: $475,652,792
Liabilities: $206,796,207
Net Worth: $268,856,584
Earnings: $24,356,028
Fiscal Year-end: 12/31/23
Property Development Services
N.A.I.C.S.: 531390
Taveesak Watcharakawong (Chm)

LALIQUE GROUP S.A.
Grubenstrasse 18, CH 8045, Zurich, Switzerland
Tel.: (41) 434994500   CH
Web Site: https://www.lalique-group.com
Year Founded: 2000
LLQ—(SWX)
Rev.: $156,842,923
Assets: $330,100,744
Liabilities: $148,635,473
Net Worth: $181,465,271
Earnings: $8,895,709
Emp.: 770
Fiscal Year-end: 12/31/22
Perfumes & Cosmetic Products Developer & Distr

N.A.I.C.S.: 456120
Silvio Denz (Chm)

Subsidiaries:

Chateau Hochberg SAS (1)
2 rue du Chateau Teutsch, 67290, Wingen-sur-Moder, France
Tel.: (33) 388006767
Web Site: https://chateauhochberg.com
Hotel & Motel Operator
N.A.I.C.S.: 721110

Chateau Lafauriepeyraguey Hotel & Restaurant Lalique S.A.S. (1)
Peyraguey 1707 Route des Gourgues, 33210, Bommes, France
Tel.: (33) 524228011
Web Site:
https://www.lafauriepeyrageylalique.com
Hotel & Restaurant Operator
N.A.I.C.S.: 722511

Lalique (Shanghai) Limited (1)
Room 9232 No 567 Weihai Road, Jing'an District, Shanghai, China
Tel.: (86) 2150342504
Beauty Product Distr
N.A.I.C.S.: 456120

Lalique Asia Limited (1)
Room 205 2/F Baskerville House No 13 Duddell Street, Central, China (Hong Kong)
Tel.: (852) 2 127 6168
Beauty Product Distr
N.A.I.C.S.: 456120

Lalique Beauty Distribution SASU (1)
Chemin de Mont A Grillons, Ury, 77760, Paris, France
Tel.: (33) 164691444
Beauty Product Distr
N.A.I.C.S.: 456120

Lalique S.A. (1)
11 Rue Royale, 75008, Paris, France   (99.3%)
Tel.: (33) 153051212
Sales Range: $75-99.9 Million
Crystal Mfr
N.A.I.C.S.: 327212

Subsidiary (Non-US):

Lalique Asia Ltd. (2)
Room 205 2/F Baskerville House, No 13 Duddell Street, Central, China (Hong Kong)
Tel.: (852) 2127 6168
Cosmetic & Perfume Distr
N.A.I.C.S.: 424210

Lalique Crystal Singapore Ltd. (2)
56 Kallang Pudding 03-01, HH Kallang, Singapore, 349328, Singapore
Tel.: (65) 61002123
Emp.: 10
Cosmetic & Perfume Distr
N.A.I.C.S.: 424210

Lalique GmbH (2)
Goethestrasse 32, 60313, Frankfurt am Main, Germany
Tel.: (49) 69289291
Cosmetic & Perfume Distr
N.A.I.C.S.: 424210

Lalique Ltd. (2)
47 Conduit Street, London, W1S 2YP, United Kingdom
Tel.: (44) 2072920444
Cosmetic & Perfume Distr
N.A.I.C.S.: 424210

Affiliate (US):

Lalique North America Inc. (2)
133 5th Ave 3, New York, NY 10003
Tel.: (201) 515-7794
Sales Range: $50-74.9 Million
Emp.: 60
French Crystal Distr
N.A.I.C.S.: 423220

Parfums Gres SA (1)
Grubenstrasse 18, CH-8045, Zurich, Switzerland
Tel.: (41) 434994500
Web Site: https://www.parfumsgres.com
Perfume Whslr
N.A.I.C.S.: 456120

Ultrason (UK) Ltd. (1)
26 West Street, Reigate, RH2 9BX, Surrey, United Kingdom
Tel.: (44) 1737 24 54 99
Web Site: http://www.ultrasun.co.uk
Emp.: 320
Cosmetics Products Mfr
N.A.I.C.S.: 325620

Ultrasun AG (1)
Grubenstrasse 18, CH-8045, Zurich, Switzerland
Tel.: (41) 449461000
Web Site: https://www.ultrasun.com
Skin Care Products Distr
N.A.I.C.S.: 456199

Ultrasun Germany GmbH (1)
Josef-Bosch-Str 4, 78315, Radolfzell, Germany
Tel.: (49) 7732 99 50 51
Cosmetic Product Mfr & Distr
N.A.I.C.S.: 325620

Villa Rene Lalique SAS (1)
18 rue Bellevue, Bas Rhin, 67290, Wingen-sur-Moder, France
Tel.: (33) 388719898
Web Site: https://villarenelalique.com
Emp.: 240
Cosmetic & Perfume Distr
N.A.I.C.S.: 424210

LALIT POLYMERS & ELECTRONICS LTD.
A-9A GreenPark Main, New Delhi, 110016, India
Tel.: (91) 1126968149
Plastics Product Mfr
N.A.I.C.S.: 326199
Dinesh Chand (CFO)

LALLEMAND, INC.
1620 Rue Prefontaine, Montreal, H1W 2N8, QC, Canada
Tel.: (514) 522-2133   Ca
Web Site: http://www.lallemand.com
Year Founded: 1915
Rev.: $20,000,000
Emp.: 3,000
Developer, Producer & Marketer of Yeast & Bacteria
N.A.I.C.S.: 325414
Jean Chagnon (Pres & CEO)

Subsidiaries:

AB Vickers Limited (1)
Dallow Street, Burton-on-Trent, DE14 2PQ, United Kingdom
Tel.: (44) 1283 563268
Web Site: http://www.abvickers.com
Brewing Product Mfr
N.A.I.C.S.: 312120

American Yeast Sales Inc (1)
319 Commerce Way, Pembroke, NH 03275
Tel.: (603) 228-8454
Yeast Whslr
N.A.I.C.S.: 424490

Anchor Yeast (Pty) Ltd. (1)
22 Bunsen Street Industria, PO Box 43143, Johannesburg, 2042, South Africa
Tel.: (27) 112488200
Web Site: http://www.anchor.co.za
Sales Range: $100-124.9 Million
Emp.: 400
Yeast & Baking Ingredient Mfr
N.A.I.C.S.: 311812
Vanda Evans (Mgr-Mktg)

DANSTAR LALLEMAND (1)
Vincenta iz Kastva 17, 10 000, Zagreb, Croatia
Tel.: (385) 1 38 40 613
Web Site: http://www.danstaryeast.com
Yeast Mfr
N.A.I.C.S.: 311999

Danstar Ferment AG (1)
Poststrasse 30,, 6300, Zug, Switzerland
Tel.: (41) 417272030
Food Ingredient Mfr
N.A.I.C.S.: 311999

Subsidiary (US):

BASF Enzymes LLC (2)
3550 John Hopkins Ct, San Diego, CA 92121
Tel.: (858) 431-8500
Web Site: http://www.basf.com
Enzymes & Biologically Active Compounds Developer & Researcher
N.A.I.C.S.: 541714
David Weiner (VP-Tech & Product Dev)

Subsidiary (Domestic):

Evolva SA (2)
Duggingerstrasse 23, 4153, Reinach, Basel-Country, Switzerland
Tel.: (41) 614852000
Web Site: http://www.evolva.com
Sales Range: $25-49.9 Million
Emp.: 70
Drug Mfr
N.A.I.C.S.: 325412

F.X. Wieninger GmbH & Co KG (1)
Alte Poststrasse 81, 94036, Passau, Germany
Tel.: (49) 8518447
Web Site: http://www.wieningerhefe.de
Food Mfr
N.A.I.C.S.: 311999

Hagold Hefe GmbH (1)
Ottakringerstrasse 89, 1160, Vienna, Austria
Tel.: (43) 1491002334
Web Site: http://www.lallemand.com
Sales Range: $25-49.9 Million
Emp.: 50
Food Mfr
N.A.I.C.S.: 311999
Rudolph Kreuz (Gen Mgr)

Hefefabrik Gielgold (1)
Farberstrasse 22-24, Schwarzenbach a d Saale, 95126, Zwickau, Germany
Tel.: (49) 9284949090
Web Site: http://www.giegoldhefe.de
Sales Range: $25-49.9 Million
Emp.: 50
Food Mfr
N.A.I.C.S.: 311999

LALLEMAND / AMERICAN YEAST CORPORATION (1)
2405 N 2nd St, Memphis, TN 38127
Tel.: (901) 353-3480
Yeast Mfr
N.A.I.C.S.: 311999
Jean-Francois Lejeune (Dir-Ops)

LALLEMAND AUSTRALIA PTY LTD (1)
149 Holbrooks Road, Underdale, Adelaide, 5032, SA, Australia
Tel.: (61) 8 8352 7300
Yeast Mfr
N.A.I.C.S.: 311999
Jason Amos (Mng Dir)

LALLEMAND CHILE Y CIA. LTDA. (1)
Av Ricardo Lyon 400 Depto 68, Santiago, Chile
Tel.: (56) 2 2315 832
Yeast Mfr
N.A.I.C.S.: 311999

LALLEMAND HUMAN NUTRITION A/S (1)
Toftebakken 9B, 3460, Birkerod, Denmark
Tel.: (45) 45 95 08 50
Yeast Mfr & Distr
N.A.I.C.S.: 311999

LALLEMAND SA (1)
19 rue des Briquetiers, BP 59, Midi-Pyrenees, 31702, Blagnac, France
Tel.: (33) 562745555
Yeast Mfr
N.A.I.C.S.: 311999

Lallemand Baking Solutions Ltd. (1)
9175 Boul Des Sciences, H1J 2Z6, Anjou, QC, Canada
Tel.: (514) 251-3620
Web Site: http://www.lallemand.com
Commercial Bakeries
N.A.I.C.S.: 311812

Lallemand Bio-Ingredients Inc (1)

LALLEMAND, INC.

Lallemand, Inc.—(Continued)
1620 rue Prefontaine, Montreal, H1W 2N8, QC, Canada
Tel.: (514) 251-3611
Web Site: http://www.bio-lallemand.com
Emp.: 400
Yeast Product Mfr & Distr
N.A.I.C.S.: 311999
Lucie Boucher (Area Mgr-Sls)

Lallemand Mexico S.A. de C.V. (1)
Fundidores s/n Manzana 1 Lote 13 Fraccionamiento Industrial Xhala, 54714, Cuautitlan Izcalli, Mexico
Tel.: (52) 55 2620 5300
Bakery Products Mfr
N.A.I.C.S.: 311812
Carlos Aguirre (Gen Mgr)

Lallemand Sp. z.o.o (1)
ul Kunickiego 28, 20-412, Lublin, Poland
Tel.: (48) 691735545
Web Site: http://www.lallemand.com
Grocery & Related Products Whslr
N.A.I.C.S.: 424490

Lallemand Specialties Inc. (1)
1815 Satellite Blvd Ste 200, Duluth, GA 30097-5237
Tel.: (678) 474-4590
Web Site: http://www.biotaltechnologies.com
Chemicals Mfr
N.A.I.C.S.: 325414
Kevin Dailey (Mgr)

Salutaguse Parmitehas A.S. (1)
Kohila Vald, Salutaguse Raplamaa, 79702, Kohila, Estonia
Tel.: (372) 4892270
Web Site: http://www.lallemand.com
Food Mfr
N.A.I.C.S.: 311999
Prit Piirsalu Prit (Mgr-Logistics)

Siebel Institute of Technology (1)
1777 N Clybourn Ave Ste 2F, Chicago, IL 60614
Tel.: (312) 255-0705
Web Site: http://www.siebelinstitute.com
Rev.: $2,000,000
Emp.: 7
Educational School & Laboratory Service for Brewing
N.A.I.C.S.: 611410
Lyn Kruger (COO)

Suomen Hiiva Oy (1)
Niemenkatu 18 PL 22, 15141, Lahti, Finland
Tel.: (358) 386414
Web Site: http://www.suomenhiiva.fi
Sales Range: $25-49.9 Million
Emp.: 30
Food Mfr
N.A.I.C.S.: 311999

VERDERA OY (1)
Kurjenkellontie 5 B, PO Box 5, 02271, Espoo, Finland
Tel.: (358) 10 217 3700
Web Site: http://www.verdera.com
Emp.: 9
Plant Protection Product Mfr & Distr
N.A.I.C.S.: 325320
Nils-Johan Gronholm (Mng Dir)

LALPIR POWER LTD.

Nishat House 53/A Lawrence Road, Lahore, Pakistan
Tel.: (92) 42111113333
Web Site: https://www.lalpir.com
LPL—(LAH)
Rev.: $82,862,653
Assets: $190,347,099
Liabilities: $94,859,036
Net Worth: $95,488,063
Earnings: $13,161,943
Emp.: 96
Fiscal Year-end: 12/31/19
Thermal Power Production
N.A.I.C.S.: 221116
Hassan Mansha (Chm)

LAM DONG INVESTMENT HYDRAULIC CONSTRUCTION JOINT STOCK COMPANY

No 87 Phu Dong Thien Vuong Street Ward 8, Da Lat, Lam Dong, Vietnam
Tel.: (84) 633821854
Web Site: https://www.lhc.com.vn
Year Founded: 1977
LHC—(HNX)
Rev.: $141,650,900
Assets: $103,089,000
Liabilities: $41,824,700
Net Worth: $61,264,300
Earnings: $7,437,000
Emp.: 250
Fiscal Year-end: 12/31/22
Irrigation Systems, Water Sewage Lines & Other Water-Related Structures
N.A.I.C.S.: 221310
Le Dinh Hien (Chm-Mgmt Bd)

LAM DONG MINERALS & BUILDING MATERIALS JOIN STOCK COMPANY

87 Phu Dong Thien Vuong, Da Lat, Lam Dong, Vietnam
Tel.: (84) 2633554022
Web Site: https://www.lbm-vn.vn
Year Founded: 1994
LBM—(HOSE)
Rev.: $37,151,029
Assets: $31,718,891
Liabilities: $6,975,531
Net Worth: $24,743,360
Earnings: $5,159,929
Fiscal Year-end: 12/31/23
Building Material Mfr & Dealer
N.A.I.C.S.: 444180
Nguyen Ngoc (Mgr-Mktg & Plng Dept)

LAM SON SUGAR JOINT STOCK CORPORATION

Lam Son Town, Tho Xuan District, Sao Vang, Thanh Hoa, Vietnam
Tel.: (84) 378996667
Web Site: https://lasuco.vn
LSS—(HOSE)
Rev.: $110,932,236
Assets: $122,520,107
Liabilities: $49,585,024
Net Worth: $72,935,083
Earnings: $5,089,683
Fiscal Year-end: 12/31/23
Sugar Mfr
N.A.I.C.S.: 311314
Le Van Tam (Chm)

LAM SOON (HONG KONG) LIMITED

Lam Soon Building 21 Dai Fu Street Tai Po Industrial Estate, Tai Po, New Territories, China (Hong Kong)
Tel.: (852) 26803388
Web Site: https://www.lamsoon.com
Year Founded: 1972
0411—(HKG)
Rev.: $743,085,767
Assets: $474,071,407
Liabilities: $102,523,235
Net Worth: $371,548,172
Earnings: $46,135,888
Emp.: 1,690
Fiscal Year-end: 06/30/21
Cleaning & Household Products Mfr
N.A.I.C.S.: 325612
Joseph Leung (Mng Dir-Grp)

Subsidiaries:

Hong Kong Flour Mills Limited (1)
Nam Shun Building 21 Tai Fu Street Tai Po Industrial Estate, Tai Po, Hong Kong, New Territories, China (Hong Kong)
Tel.: (852) 26803888
Flour Milling Operator
N.A.I.C.S.: 311211

Lam Soon Products Supply (Hong Kong) Company Limited (1)
Lam Soon Building 21 Dai Fu Street Tai Po Industrial Building, Hong Kong, New Territories, China (Hong Kong)
Tel.: (852) 26803388
Web Site: http://www.lamsoonoil.com
Edible Oil Product Distr
N.A.I.C.S.: 424990

LAM SOON (THAILAND) PUBLIC COMPANY LIMITED

64 Soi Bangna-Trad 25 Khwaeng Bangna Nuea, Khet Bangn, Bangkok, 10260, Thailand
Tel.: (66) 23618959
Web Site: https://www.lamsoon.co.th
Year Founded: 1974
LST—(THA)
Rev.: $318,297,687
Assets: $206,165,563
Liabilities: $48,949,993
Net Worth: $157,215,570
Earnings: $16,829,907
Emp.: 453
Fiscal Year-end: 12/31/23
Edible Oils, Soap & Detergents Mfr
N.A.I.C.S.: 311225
Shang Ying Whang (Exec Dir)

Subsidiaries:

Lam Soon Edible Oils Sdn. Bhd. (1)
Wisma DLS No 6 Jalan Jurunilai U1/20, PO Box 7478, Hicom Glenmarie Industrial Pk, 40716, Shah Alam, Selangor, Malaysia
Tel.: (60) 37 882 2399
Web Site: https://www.lamsoon.com.my
Sales Range: $25-49.9 Million
Emp.: 100
Oilseed Processing
N.A.I.C.S.: 311224

Lam Soon Singapore Pte Ltd (1)
3000 Marsiling Road, Singapore, 739108, Singapore
Tel.: (65) 6 763 3989
Web Site: https://www.lamsoongroup.com.sg
Soap & Detergent Mfr
N.A.I.C.S.: 325611

Union Frost Company Limited (1)
60 6th Fl Soi Bangna-Trad 25, Bangna, Bangkok, 10260, Thailand
Tel.: (66) 2 361 8950
Web Site: https://www.unionfrost.co.th
Frozen Vegetable Mfr & Distr
N.A.I.C.S.: 311411
Francis Foo (Mng Dir)

Universal Food Public Company Limited (1)
60 Soi Bangna-Trad 25, Khwaeng Bangna Nuea Khet Bangna, Bangkok, 10260, Thailand
Tel.: (66) 23988555
Web Site: https://ufcrefreshcoco.com
Processed Fruit & Vegetable Mfr & Distr
N.A.I.C.S.: 311411
Foo Say Suan Francis (Pres)

LAM THAO FERTILIZERS & CHEMICALS JOINT STOCK COMPANY

Lam Thao Town, Lam Thao District, Viet Tri, Phu Tho, Vietnam
Tel.: (84) 2103825139
Web Site: http://www.supelamthao.vn
LAS—(HNX)
Rev.: $141,740,030
Assets: $97,252,188
Liabilities: $38,677,777
Net Worth: $58,574,411
Earnings: $6,119,766
Emp.: 1,745
Fiscal Year-end: 12/31/23
Fertilizer & Nitrogen Compounds Mfr
N.A.I.C.S.: 325311

LAMAR HOLDING CORP.

Office 152 Bldg 398 Road 2806 Block 428, PO Box 18614, Millennium Tower AlSeef, Manama, Bahrain
Tel.: (973) 9145767312
Web Site: http://www.lamar-holding.com
Holding Company
N.A.I.C.S.: 551112
Lawrence Samsky (Chm)

Subsidiaries:

Human Dimensions Company (W.L.L) (1)
Sharq Al Khaleej Tower 4th Floor, PO Box 29273, Safat, Kuwait, 13152, Kuwait
Tel.: (965) 22243903
Web Site: http://www.hdmena.com
HR Development & Recruitment Services
N.A.I.C.S.: 561311

LAMBDA GENERAL CONTRACTORS INC.

4700 de la Savane Suite 211, Montreal, H4P 1T7, QC, Canada
Tel.: (514) 343-4666
Web Site: http://www.lambdaconstruction.com
Rev.: $12,740,333
Emp.: 8
Construction Services
N.A.I.C.S.: 236220
Mehrdad Amiri (Pres)

LAMBDA THERAPEUTIC RESEARCH LTD.

Lambda House Plot No 38 Survey no 388 Near Silver Oak Club SG Highway, Gota, Ahmedabad, 382481, Gujarat, India
Tel.: (91) 7940202020
Web Site: http://www.lambda-cro.com
Year Founded: 1999
Sales Range: $10-24.9 Million
Emp.: 750
Pharmaceutical Research Services
N.A.I.C.S.: 541715
Bindi Chudgar (Mng Dir)

Subsidiaries:

Lambda Therapeutic Research Sp.z o.o. (1)
Marynarska Office Park Building C VIII Floor, Tasmowa Street 7, 02-677, Warsaw, Poland
Tel.: (48) 225772800
Pharmaceutical Research Services
N.A.I.C.S.: 541715

Lambda Therapeutic Research, Inc. (1)
460 Comstock Road, Toronto, M1L 4S4, ON, Canada
Tel.: (416) 752-3636
Web Site: http://www.lambdacanada-cro.com
Pharmaceutical Preparation Mfr
N.A.I.C.S.: 325412

Novum Pharmaceutical Research Services, Inc. (1)
225 W Station Sq Dr Ste 200, Pittsburgh, PA 15219
Tel.: (412) 363-3300
Web Site: http://www.novumprs.com
Pharmaceutical Research Services
N.A.I.C.S.: 541714
Alan K. Copa (VP-Ops)

LAMBO GROUP BERHAD

Lot 11 1 11 Floor Menara Lien Hoe No 8 Persiaran Tropicana, 47410, Petaling Jaya, Selangor, Malaysia
Tel.: (60) 379875300
Web Site: https://www.lambogroup.my
Year Founded: 2000
LAMBO—(KLS)
Rev.: $3,510,098
Assets: $37,012,279
Liabilities: $2,650,792
Net Worth: $34,361,488
Earnings: ($15,932,407)
Fiscal Year-end: 09/30/22
Information Technology Services

LAMBODHARA TEXTILES LIMITED
3 A 3rd Floor B Block Pioneer Apartments 1075 B Avinashi Road, Coimbatore, 641018, Tamil Nadu, India
Tel.: (91) 4222249038
Web Site: https://www.lambodharatextiles.com
LAMBODHARA—(NSE)
Rev.: $16,344,032
Assets: $18,981,635
Liabilities: $8,596,128
Net Worth: $10,385,507
Earnings: $1,445,235
Emp.: 369
Fiscal Year-end: 03/31/21
Synthetic Yarn Mfr
N.A.I.C.S.: 313110
Guilia Bosco *(Exec Dir)*

LAMBRAKIS PRESS S.A.
80 Michalakopoulou Street, 11528, Athens, Greece
Tel.: (30) 2113659484
Web Site: http://www.dol.gr
Year Founded: 1970
Sales Range: $250-299.9 Million
Emp.: 1,038
Newspaper & Magazine Publishing Services
N.A.I.C.S.: 513110
Stavros P. Psycharis *(Chm)*

LAMDA DEVELOPMENT SA
Kifisias Avenue 37A, 151 23, Maroussi, Greece
Tel.: (30) 2107450600
Web Site: https://www.lamdadev.com
LAMDA—(ATH)
Rev.: $497,418,037
Assets: $4,585,492,881
Liabilities: $3,270,934,982
Net Worth: $1,314,557,898
Earnings: $29,951,430
Emp.: 687
Fiscal Year-end: 12/31/23
Holding Company; Real Estate & Construction Services
N.A.I.C.S.: 551112
Evangelos Chronis *(Vice Chm)*

Subsidiaries:

Designer Outlet Athens S.M. LLC (1)
Building block E71, 190 04, Spata, Greece
Tel.: (30) 2106630830
Web Site: https://designeroutletathens.gr
Restaurant & Cafe Operator
N.A.I.C.S.: 722511

ECE-Lamda Hellas S.A. (1)
37a Kifissias Ave, 15123, Maroussi, Greece (100%)
Tel.: (30) 2107450600
Sales Range: $25-49.9 Million
Emp.: 70
All Other Business Support Services
N.A.I.C.S.: 561499
Kambanis Nikos *(Mng Dir)*

Lamda Estate Development S.A. (1)
37 A Kisisias Ave, Maroussi, 15123, Athens, Greece (100%)
Tel.: (30) 2107450600
Web Site: http://www.lamdadev.com
Emp.: 100
Other Real Estate Property Lessors
N.A.I.C.S.: 531190

Lamda Flisvos Marina A.E. (1)
Paleo Faliro, 17561, Athens, Greece
Tel.: (30) 21098710002
Web Site: http://www.flisvosmarina.com
Marine Cargo Handling
N.A.I.C.S.: 488320

Lamda Olympia Village S.A. (1)
37A Kifissias Avenue Marousi, 151 23, Athens, Greece
Tel.: (30) 2107450600
Web Site: http://www.lamda.com
Sales Range: $50-74.9 Million
Emp.: 100
Nonresidential Buildings Lessors
N.A.I.C.S.: 531120
Odyseas Athamasiou *(Gen Mgr)*

Lamda Prima Properties S.A. (1)
16 Laodikeias And Nymfaiou, 11525, Athens, Greece (100%)
Tel.: (30) 2107450700
Other Real Estate Property Lessors
N.A.I.C.S.: 531190

LAMDONG FOODSTUFFS JOINT STOCK COMPANY
4B Bui Thi Xuan Street, Da Lat, Lam Dong, Vietnam
Tel.: (84) 633827003
Web Site: http://www.vietaz.com
VDL—(HNX)
Rev.: $18,728,800
Assets: $21,031,100
Liabilities: $1,963,600
Net Worth: $19,067,500
Earnings: ($1,628,700)
Emp.: 946
Fiscal Year-end: 03/31/22
Alcoholic Beverages Mfr
N.A.I.C.S.: 312130
Pham Van Anh *(Deputy CEO & Member-Mgmt Bd)*

LAMDONG PHARMACEUTICAL JSC
18 Ngo Quyen Street Ward 6, Da Lat, Lam Dong, Vietnam
Tel.: (84) 639999999
Web Site: https://ladophar.com
LDP—(HNX)
Rev.: $18,741,500
Assets: $22,839,100
Liabilities: $11,592,100
Net Worth: $11,247,000
Earnings: ($3,890,900)
Emp.: 300
Fiscal Year-end: 12/31/22
Pharmaceutical Mfr & Distr
N.A.I.C.S.: 325412
Vo Duy Dao *(Gen Mgr)*

LAMELEE IRON ORE LTD.
1155 University Suite 812, Montreal, H3B 3A7, QC, Canada
Tel.: (514) 393-3777   Ca
Web Site: http://www.lameleeiron.com
Year Founded: 2011
LIR—(TSXV)
Sales Range: Less than $1 Million
Natural Resource Mining
N.A.I.C.S.: 212390
Marc Duchesne *(CFO)*

LAMEX FOODS UK LIMITED
Turnford Place Great Cambridge Road, Turnford, Broxbourne, EN10 6NH, Herts, United Kingdom
Tel.: (44) 1992 473 888   UK
Web Site: http://www.lamexfoods.eu
Year Founded: 1966
Sales Range: $1-4.9 Billion
Emp.: 150
Food Products Wholesale Trade Distr
N.A.I.C.S.: 425120
Phillip O. Wallace *(CEO)*

Subsidiaries:

Lamex B.V. (1)
Koopmanslaan 31-04, 7005 BK, Doetinchem, Netherlands
Tel.: (31) 314 369 180
Emp.: 22
Frozen Food Distr
N.A.I.C.S.: 424420
Henny Wisselink *(Mng Dir)*

Lamex Foods A.B. (1)
Berga Alle 3, 25452, Helsingborg, Sweden
Tel.: (46) 4215 8801
Food Distr
N.A.I.C.S.: 424490

Lamex Foods B.V. (1)
ul Cicha 13-5, 30-129, Krakow, Poland
Tel.: (48) 126384613
Food Products Distr
N.A.I.C.S.: 424490

Lamex Foods Europe AG (1)
Bahnhofstrasse 28 B, 8808, Pfaffikon, Zurich, Switzerland
Tel.: (41) 55 5110 540
Food Distr
N.A.I.C.S.: 424490

Lamex Foods Inc. (1)
8500 Normandale Lk Blvd Ste 1150, Bloomington, MN 55437
Tel.: (952) 844-0585
Web Site: http://www.lamexfoods.eu
Food Products Wholesale Trade Distr
N.A.I.C.S.: 425120
Steven Anderson *(Pres)*

Mondi Lamex d.o.o. (1)
Vrdila, 36000, Kraljevo, Serbia
Tel.: (381) 36 823 020
Web Site: http://www.mondiserbia.rs
Sales Range: $25-49.9 Million
Emp.: 160
Canned Fruit Mfr
N.A.I.C.S.: 311421
Goran Krunic *(Mng Dir)*

LAMILUX HEINRICH STRUNZ HOLDING GMBH & CO. KG
Zehstrasse 2, Postfach 1540, 95111, Rehau, Germany
Tel.: (49) 9283 595 0
Web Site: http://www.lamilux.com
Year Founded: 1955
Rev.: $29,069,214
Emp.: 66
Reinforced Plastic Flatsheets & Composites Mfr
N.A.I.C.S.: 326199

LAMKO TOOL & MOLD INC.
105 Towerline Pl, London, N6E 2T3, ON, Canada
Tel.: (519) 686-2643
Web Site: https://www.lamko.com
Year Founded: 1978
Sales Range: $10-24.9 Million
Molds & Specialty Dyes Mfr
N.A.I.C.S.: 333511
Tony Palmieri *(Mgr-Engrg)*

LAMMHULTS DESIGN GROUP AB
Lammengatan 2, Box 75, 363 45, Lammhult, Sweden
Tel.: (46) 472269670
Web Site: https://www.lammhultsdesign.com
Year Founded: 1945
LAMM.B—(OMX)
Rev.: $99,898,064
Assets: $97,444,256
Liabilities: $39,895,744
Net Worth: $57,548,512
Earnings: ($1,355,088)
Emp.: 308
Fiscal Year-end: 12/31/20
Interior Design & Decoration Services
N.A.I.C.S.: 541410

LAMOR CORPORATION PLC
Rihkamatori 2, 06100, Porvoo, Finland
Tel.: (358) 207650100
Web Site: https://www.lamor.com
Year Founded: 1982
LAMOR—(HEL)
Rev.: $132,225,340
Assets: $176,505,504
Liabilities: $105,356,141
Net Worth: $71,149,363
Earnings: $2,891,215
Emp.: 296
Fiscal Year-end: 12/31/23
Cleaning Equipment Mfr
N.A.I.C.S.: 335999
Fred Larsen *(Vice Chm)*

Subsidiaries:

Lamor Beijing Co., Ltd. (1)
Room 1715 Huasheng International Plaza No 12 Yabaolu Road, Chaoyang, Beijing, 100020, China
Tel.: (86) 1084467400
Environmental Services
N.A.I.C.S.: 813312

Lamor Colombia S.A.S. (1)
Lamor Corporation Sucursal Colombia Carrera 13 96-67 Oficina 303, Bogota, Colombia
Tel.: (57) 18059209
Environmental Services
N.A.I.C.S.: 813312

Lamor Corporation UK Ltd. (1)
3 Medina Court Arctic Road, Cowes, PO31 7XD, Isle of Wight, United Kingdom
Tel.: (44) 1983280185
Environmental Services
N.A.I.C.S.: 813312

Lamor Environmental Solutions Spain S.L. (1)
Calle Joaquin Costa no 4 3 izq, 50001, Zaragoza, Spain
Tel.: (34) 647686719
Environmental Services
N.A.I.C.S.: 813312

Lamor India Private Ltd. (1)
D-178/4 TTC Industrial Area MIDC Nerul East, Navi Mumbai, 400 076, Maharashtra, India
Tel.: (91) 8800891867
Environmental Protection Services
N.A.I.C.S.: 813312

Lamor Middle East LLC (1)
Suite 223 Hatat House Seeb Airport, PO Box 2986, 111, Muscat, Oman
Tel.: (968) 24565111
Environmental Services
N.A.I.C.S.: 813312

Lamor Peru S.A.C. (1)
Calle Amador Merino Reyna 496 Off 303, San Isidro, Lima, Peru
Tel.: (51) 6061716
Environmental Services
N.A.I.C.S.: 813312

Lamor USA Corporation (1)
2 Enterprise Dr Ste 404, Shelton, CT 06484
Tel.: (203) 888-7700
Environmental Services
N.A.I.C.S.: 813312

Lamor Vostok LLC (1)
2 General Dorokhov Str, Moscow, 121357, Russia
Tel.: (7) 4994003500
Environmental Services
N.A.I.C.S.: 813312

LAMPERD LESS LETHAL, INC.
1200 Michener Road, Sarnia, N7S 4B1, ON, Canada
Tel.: (519) 344-4445
Web Site: https://www.lamperdlesslethal.com
Year Founded: 1969
LLLI—(OTCIQ)
Rev.: $126,000
Assets: $236,000
Liabilities: $1,402,000
Net Worth: ($1,166,000)
Earnings: ($334,000)
Fiscal Year-end: 12/31/19
Lethal Weapon Mfr
N.A.I.C.S.: 332992

LAMPRECHT TRANSPORT AG
Peter Merian-Strasse 48 Postfach, Basel, 4002, Switzerland

LAMPRECHT TRANSPORT AG

Lamprecht Transport AG—(Continued)
Tel.: (41) 61 284 74 74
Web Site: http://www.lamprecht.ch
Sales Range: $100-124.9 Million
Emp.: 300
Transport & Logistics Services
N.A.I.C.S.: 488510
Thomas Lamprecht *(CEO)*

Subsidiaries:

American Lamprecht Transport, Inc. (1)
700 Rockaway Tpke 303A, Lawrence, NY 11559
Tel.: (516) 239-6200
Web Site: http://www.american-lamprecht.com
Sales Range: $10-24.9 Million
Emp.: 25
Freight Transportation Arrangement
N.A.I.C.S.: 488510
Alain P. Tiercy *(Exec VP)*

Expo-Cargo Ltd. (1)
Schonaustrasse 33, 4058, Basel, Switzerland
Tel.: (41) 616666030
Web Site: http://www.expo-cargo.ch
Logistics Consulting Servies
N.A.I.C.S.: 541614

FEAG International Freight Forwarders Ltd. (1)
Oberstrasse 149, 9001, Saint Gallen, Switzerland
Tel.: (41) 712233552
Web Site: http://www.feagint.ch
Logistics Consulting Servies
N.A.I.C.S.: 541614

Lamprecht Pharma Logistics Ltd. (1)
Durrenhubelstrasse 7, 4133, Pratteln, Switzerland
Tel.: (41) 612847777
Web Site: http://www.lamprecht-pharma.ch
Logistics Consulting Servies
N.A.I.C.S.: 541614
Urs Suter *(Mng Dir & Mgr-Ops)*

Lamprecht Transport Ltd. (1)
PO Box 17041, Dubai, United Arab Emirates
Tel.: (971) 48059745
Logistics Consulting Servies
N.A.I.C.S.: 541614

LAMPRELL PLC

First Names House Victoria Road, Douglas, IM2 4DF, Isle of Man
Tel.: (44) 7852618046 IM
Web Site: http://www.lamprell.com
Year Founded: 2006
LAM—(LSE)
Rev.: $388,808,000
Assets: $444,738,000
Liabilities: $315,896,000
Net Worth: $128,842,000
Earnings: ($60,048,000)
Emp.: 1,337
Fiscal Year-end: 12/31/21
Holding Company; Oil & Gas Industry Engineering Services
N.A.I.C.S.: 551112
Alex Ridout *(Gen Counsel & Sec)*

Subsidiaries:

Lamprell Energy Limited (1)
PO Box 33455, Dubai, United Arab Emirates (100%)
Tel.: (971) 65282323
Holding Company; Corporate Office
N.A.I.C.S.: 551112

Unit (Domestic):

Lamprell - Sunbelt H2S Safety Services (2)
Oilfields Supply Center Compound Jebel Ali Free Port Zone, PO Box 11791, Dubai, United Arab Emirates
Tel.: (971) 48836182
Sales Range: $50-74.9 Million
Emp.: 125

Oil & Gas Industry Safety Equipment Installation & Consulting Services
N.A.I.C.S.: 238290

Unit (Non-US):

Lamprell - Sunbelt H2S Safety Services, Bautino Hydrotest Facility (3)
Dostyk Hotel, Tupkaragan District, Bautino, 130502, Mangystau, Kazakhstan
Tel.: (7) 7292200128
Web Site: http://www.lamprell.com
Sales Range: $25-49.9 Million
Emp.: 2
Hydrostatic Testing Services
N.A.I.C.S.: 541380

Subsidiary (Domestic):

Lamprell Dubai LLC (2)
Jebel Ali Freezone, PO Box 42149, Dubai, 33455, United Arab Emirates
Tel.: (971) 4 887 2323
Web Site: http://www.lamprell.com
Sales Range: $350-399.9 Million
Offshore Oil & Gas Platform Operational Services
N.A.I.C.S.: 336611

Lamprell Energy FZCo. (1)
PO Box No 261224, Jebel Ali, United Arab Emirates
Tel.: (971) 48814949
Oil & Gas Field Refurbishment & Development Services
N.A.I.C.S.: 213112

Lamprell Sharjah WLL (2)
Plot No HD 23 Inside Hamriyah Phase 1 & 2, PO Box 33455, Sharjah, United Arab Emirates
Tel.: (971) 65285345
Web Site: http://www.lamprell.com
Emp.: 3,000
Oil & Gas Field Refurbishment & Development Services
N.A.I.C.S.: 213112

Rig Metals LLC (2)
Dubai Investment Park, PO Box 115 404, Dubai, United Arab Emirates
Tel.: (971) 48851442
Web Site: http://www.rigmetals.com
Sales Range: $25-49.9 Million
Emp.: 60
Oil & Gas Field Engineering Services
N.A.I.C.S.: 333132
Hani El Kurd *(Gen Mgr)*

LAMPSA HELLENIC HOTELS S.A.

297 Kifisias Avenue, Kifisia, 145 61, Athens, Greece
Tel.: (30) 2106195525
Web Site: https://www.lampsa.gr
Year Founded: 1919
LAMPS—(ATH)
Rev.: $120,565
Assets: $271,953
Liabilities: $165,513
Net Worth: $106,439
Earnings: $17,005
Emp.: 1,196
Fiscal Year-end: 12/31/23
Home Management Services
N.A.I.C.S.: 721110
Georgios Galanakis *(Chm)*

Subsidiaries:

GRAND BRETAGNE Ltd. (1)
Syntagma Square, Athens, 10564, Greece
Tel.: (30) 210 3330000
Web Site: http://www.grandebretagne.gr
Hotel Operator
N.A.I.C.S.: 713210
Stefanos Mavroeidis *(Mgr-Banquet)*

LAMTEX HOLDINGS LIMITED

Room 1814-1815 18/F Star House 3 Salisbury Road, Tsim Sha Tsui, Kowloon, China (Hong Kong)
Tel.: (852) 2840 1133 BM
Web Site: http://www.lamtex.com.hk
Rev.: $21,622,258
Assets: $84,262,759

Liabilities: $6,627,877
Net Worth: $77,634,882
Earnings: ($7,640,970)
Emp.: 900
Fiscal Year-end: 12/31/18
Investment Management Service
N.A.I.C.S.: 523940
Huang Bin *(Chm & Exec Dir)*

LAN FA TEXTILE CO., LTD.

5F-5 No 73 Sec 1 Huanhe N Rd, Datong District, Taipei, 103, Taiwan
Tel.: (886) 225521255
Web Site: https://www.lanfa.com.tw
Year Founded: 1972
1459—(TAI)
Rev.: $39,365,674
Assets: $150,105,590
Liabilities: $58,789,428
Net Worth: $91,316,161
Earnings: $769,646
Fiscal Year-end: 12/31/23
Textile Product Mfr & Distr
N.A.I.C.S.: 314999

Subsidiaries:

Lan Fa Textile Co., Ltd. - Tao Yuan Factory (1)
No 311 Sec 1 Shanlin Rd, Lujhu Township, Taoyuan, 338, Taiwan
Tel.: (886) 33241136
Polyester Processing Silk Mfr
N.A.I.C.S.: 313110

Lan Fa Textile Co., Ltd. - Zu Bay Factory (1)
No 291 Su Shing Rd Shin Zu, Zhubei, Taiwan
Tel.: (886) 35503311
Polyester Processing Silk Mfr
N.A.I.C.S.: 313110

LANAKAM S.A.

2-4 Mesogeion Avenue Athens Tower Building A, 11527, Athens, Greece
Tel.: (30) 2107771033
Web Site: https://www.lanakam.eu
LANAC—(ATH)
Sales Range: Less than $1 Million
Emp.: 19
Fashion Apparel, Heating & Cooling Equipment Distr
N.A.I.C.S.: 424350
Damigos Ioannis *(Chm, Pres, CEO & Gen Mgr)*

LANCASHIRE HOLDINGS LIMITED

Power House 7 Par-la-Ville Road, Hamilton, HM 11, Bermuda
Tel.: (441) 2788950
Web Site: https://www.lancashiregroup.com
LCSHF—(OTCIQ)
Rev.: $1,519,900,000
Assets: $3,901,700,000
Liabilities: $2,393,800,000
Net Worth: $1,507,900,000
Earnings: $321,500,000
Emp.: 393
Fiscal Year-end: 12/31/23
Property Insurance & Reinsurance Products Provider
N.A.I.C.S.: 524126
Alex Maloney *(CEO-Grp)*

Subsidiaries:

Lancashire Insurance Company (UK) Limited (1)
Level 29 20 Fenchurch Street, London, EC3M 3BY, United Kingdom
Tel.: (44) 2072644000
Sales Range: $50-74.9 Million
Emp.: 70
Speciality Insurance Carriers
N.A.I.C.S.: 524113
Adam Williams *(Head-Downstream-Energy)*

INTERNATIONAL PUBLIC

Lancashire Insurance Marketing Services Limited (1)
Level 11 Vitro 60 Fenchurch St, London, EC3M 4AD, United Kingdom
Tel.: (44) 2072644000
Web Site: http://www.lancashiregroup.com
Sales Range: $50-74.9 Million
Emp.: 77
Speciality Insurance Carriers
N.A.I.C.S.: 524113

Lancashire Syndicates Limited (1)
Level 29 20 Fenchurch Street, London, EC3M 3BY, United Kingdom
Tel.: (44) 2071709000
Insurance Agency Services
N.A.I.C.S.: 524210
John Spence *(CEO)*

LANCE BISSETT LTD

63 Fawcett Road, Coquitlam, V3K 6V2, BC, Canada
Tel.: (604) 540-0200
Web Site: http://www.lancebissett.ca
Year Founded: 1929
Rev.: $18,164,099
Emp.: 60
Automated Construction Power Tools Whslr
N.A.I.C.S.: 423810
David Couling *(VP)*

LANCER CONTAINER LINES LIMITED

Unit No H02-2 H02-3 and H02-4 Plot No 60 Sector-11 CBD Belapur, Navi Mumbai, 400 614, India
Tel.: (91) 2227566940
Web Site: https://www.lancerline.com
Year Founded: 2011
539841—(BOM)
Rev.: $87,810,846
Assets: $27,515,656
Liabilities: $17,517,864
Net Worth: $9,997,792
Earnings: $3,952,057
Emp.: 197
Fiscal Year-end: 03/31/22
Logistics Management Services
N.A.I.C.S.: 541614
Abdul Khalik Chataiwala *(Chm & Mng Dir)*

LANCERS, INC.

3-10-13 Shibuya, Shibuya-Ku, Tokyo, 150-0002, Japan
Tel.: (81) 357746086
Web Site: https://www.lancers.co.jp
Year Founded: 2008
4484—(TKS)
Rev.: $30,227,530
Assets: $23,247,370
Liabilities: $15,440,960
Net Worth: $7,806,410
Earnings: $733,710
Fiscal Year-end: 03/31/24
Digital Marketing Services
N.A.I.C.S.: 541870
Yosuke Akiyoshi *(Founder, Pres & CEO)*

LANCO CONSTRUCTION & ENGINEERING PTE LTD

50 Tuas Basin Link, Singapore, 638773, Singapore
Tel.: (65) 6863 6613
Web Site: http://www.lanco.sg
Year Founded: 1994
Engineering & Machining Services
N.A.I.C.S.: 541330

Subsidiaries:

Asian Sealand Engineering Pte Ltd (1)
55 Shipyard Rd, Singapore, 628141, Singapore
Tel.: (65) 62660010
Web Site: http://www.bkmgroup.com.sg
Marine Engineering Services

LANCOR HOLDINGS LTD.
VTN Square 2nd Floor 58 G N Chetty road T Nagar, Chennai, 600 017, India
Tel.: (91) 8144787405
Web Site: https://www.lancor.in
509048—(BOM)
Rev.: $7,225,600
Assets: $51,062,698
Liabilities: $30,848,509
Net Worth: $20,214,189
Earnings: ($1,579,551)
Emp.: 98
Fiscal Year-end: 03/31/21
Property Management Services
N.A.I.C.S.: 531311
Shekar Viswanath Rajaman *(Chm & Mng Dir)*

Subsidiaries:

Lancor Guduvanchery Developments Limited (1)
VTN Square 2nd Floor 58 GN Chetty Road, T Nagar, Chennai, 600 017, India
Tel.: (91) 44 2834884
Property Development Services
N.A.I.C.S.: 531390

Lancor Maintenance & Services Ltd. (1)
VTN Square 2nd Floor No 58 G N Chetty Road, T Nagar, Chennai, 600 017, Tamil Nadu, India
Tel.: (91) 4428345880
Web Site: http://www.lancor.in
Sales Range: $50-74.9 Million
Emp.: 25
Property Maintenance Services
N.A.I.C.S.: 531390

LANCY CO., LTD.
Building 1 No 3 Dajiaoting South Street No 27 Xidawang Road, Chaoyang District, Beijing, 100022, China
Tel.: (86) 1053518800
Web Site: https://www.lancygroup.com
Year Founded: 2006
002612—(SSE)
Rev.: $544,510,512
Assets: $998,279,100
Liabilities: $490,331,556
Net Worth: $507,947,544
Earnings: $2,257,632
Fiscal Year-end: 12/31/22
Women's Clothing Mfr
N.A.I.C.S.: 315250
Dong Ri Shen *(Chm)*

LAND & GENERAL BERHAD
8trium Level 21 Menara 1 Jalan Cempaka SD 12/5, Bandar Sri Damansara, 52200, Kuala Lumpur, Malaysia
Tel.: (60) 362798000
Web Site: https://www.land-general.com
L&G—(KLS)
Rev.: $52,736,296
Assets: $351,875,132
Liabilities: $94,481,058
Net Worth: $257,394,074
Earnings: $5,609,524
Fiscal Year-end: 03/31/23
Property Development & Management Services
N.A.I.C.S.: 531390
Gay Teck Low *(Mng Dir)*

LAND & HOMES GROUP LIMITED
Level 3A 148 Elizabeth Street, Sydney, 2000, NSW, Australia
Tel.: (61) 739055658
Web Site: http://www.landnhomesgroup.com
Year Founded: 1991
LHM—(ASX)
Rev.: $55,377
Assets: $21,860,714
Liabilities: $22,128,782
Net Worth: ($268,068)
Earnings: ($755,835)
Fiscal Year-end: 06/30/23
Real Estate Support Services
N.A.I.C.S.: 531190
Choon Keng Kho *(Chm)*

LAND & HOUSES PUBLIC COMPANY LIMITED
Q House Lumpini Building 37-38 Floor No 1 South Satorn Road, Kwaeng Tungmahamek Khet Satorn, Bangkok, 10120, Thailand
Tel.: (66) 23438900
Web Site: https://www.lh.co.th
Year Founded: 1983
LDHOF—(OTCIQ)
Rev.: $1,010,138,087
Assets: $3,408,650,596
Liabilities: $1,970,794,638
Net Worth: $1,437,855,957
Earnings: $228,771,839
Emp.: 758
Fiscal Year-end: 12/31/22
Real Estate Development Services
N.A.I.C.S.: 531390
Wit Tantiworawong *(CFO & Exec VP)*

Subsidiaries:

Asia Asset Advisory Co., Ltd. (1)
15th Floor Q House Lumpini Building 1 South Sathon Road, Thungmahamek Sathon, Bangkok, 10120, Thailand
Tel.: (66) 2343 8899
Investment Services
N.A.I.C.S.: 523940

Atlantic Real Estate Co., Ltd. (1)
37-38 Floor Q House Lumpini Building 1 South Sathon Road, Thungmahamek Sathon, Bangkok, 10120, Thailand
Tel.: (66) 2343 8900
Property Development Services
N.A.I.C.S.: 531390

Bankok Chain Hospital PLC (1)
950 Prachachuen Road, Bangsue, Bangkok, 10800, Thailand
Tel.: (66) 2910 1600
Web Site: http://kasemrad.co.th
Hospital Services
N.A.I.C.S.: 622110

Double Three Co., Ltd. (1)
9/17 Moo 6 Thepkrasadtree, Tumbonratsada Amphoe Muang, Phuket, 83000, Thailand
Tel.: (66) 76 381 150
Property Development Services
N.A.I.C.S.: 531390

Home Product Center PLC (1)
96/27 Moo 9 Bangkhen Amphoe, Muang, Nonthaburi, 11000, Thailand
Tel.: (66) 2832 1000
Web Site: http://www.homepro.co.th
Construction Materials Sales
N.A.I.C.S.: 423390

L&H Management Co., Ltd. (1)
15th Floor Q House Lumpini Building 1 South Sathon Road, Thungmahamek Sathon, Bangkok, 10120, Thailand
Tel.: (66) 2343 8899
Property Development Services
N.A.I.C.S.: 531390

L&H Property Co., Ltd. (1)
15th Floor Q House Lumpini Building 1 South Sathon Road, Thungmahamek Sathon, Bangkok, 10120, Thailand
Tel.: (66) 2343 8899
Property Development Services
N.A.I.C.S.: 531390

L&H Retail Management Co., Ltd. (1)
15th Floor Q House Lumpini Building 1 South Sathon Road, Thungmahamek Sathon, Bangkok, 10120, Thailand
Tel.: (66) 2343 8899
Property Development Services
N.A.I.C.S.: 531390

L&H Sathon Co., Ltd. (1)
15th Floor Q House Lumpini Building 1 South Sathon Road, Thungmahamek Sathon, Bangkok, 10120, Thailand
Tel.: (66) 2343 8899
Property Development Services
N.A.I.C.S.: 531390

LH Asset Co., Ltd. (1)
37-38th Floor Q House Lumpini Building 1 South Sathon Road, Thungmahamek Sathon, Bangkok, 10120, Thailand
Tel.: (66) 2343 8900
Property Development Services
N.A.I.C.S.: 531390

LH Financial Group PLC (1)
5th Floor Q House Lumpini Building 1 South Sathorn Road, Thungmahamek Sathorn, Bangkok, 10120, Thailand
Tel.: (66) 23590000
Financial Services
N.A.I.C.S.: 523999

LH Mall & Hotel Co., Ltd. (1)
Q House Lumpini Building 15th Floor 1 South Sathon Road, Thungmahamek Sathon, Bangkok, 10120, Thailand
Tel.: (66) 2 343 8899
Web Site: https://www.lhmh.co.th
Real Estate Development Services
N.A.I.C.S.: 531390
Khun Kitti Worrabanpott *(Mng Dir)*

LH Muang Mai Co., Ltd. (1)
9/9 Moo 6 Thepkrasadtree, Tumbornatsada Amphoe Muang, Phuket, 83000, Thailand
Tel.: (66) 894745321
Property Development Services
N.A.I.C.S.: 531390

LH Real Estate Co., Ltd. (1)
37-38th Floor Q House Lumpini Building 1 South Sathon Road, Thungmahamek Sathon, Bangkok, 10120, Thailand
Tel.: (66) 2343 8900
Property Development Services
N.A.I.C.S.: 531390

Land and Houses Fund Management Co., Ltd. (1)
11 Q House Sathon BuildingFl 10 14 South Sathon Rd, Thungmahamek Sathon, Bangkok, 10120, Thailand
Tel.: (66) 22863484
Web Site: https://www.lhfund.co.th
Fund Management Services
N.A.I.C.S.: 523940
Nawarat Puangphairoite *(VP-Compliance & Internal Audit)*

Land and Houses North Co., Ltd. (1)
319 Moo 4 ThumbonnongJam, Amphoe Sansang, Chiang Mai, 50210, Thailand
Tel.: (66) 53 498 911 3
Property Development Services
N.A.I.C.S.: 531390

Land and Houses North-East Co., Ltd. (1)
114/39 Ratchasima-Pakthongchai Road, Tumbonhnongjabok Amphoe Muang, Nakhon Ratchasima, Thailand
Tel.: (66) 44 349 343
Property Development Services
N.A.I.C.S.: 531390

Land and Houses Property Fund 1 (1)
16th Sathorn Thani Building 90/42-43 North Sathorn Road, Silom Bangrak, Bangkok, 10500, Thailand
Tel.: (66) 2636 8248
Property Development Services
N.A.I.C.S.: 531390

Land and Houses Property Fund 2 (1)
130-132 Wireless Road 15th, 17th Floor Sindhorn Building Tower III, Bangkok, 10500, Thailand
Tel.: (66) 2688 7777
Property Development Services
N.A.I.C.S.: 531390

Land and Houses Retail Bank PLC (1)
1 Q House Lumpini Building G 1st 5th 6th and 32nd Floor, South Sathon Rd Thungmahomek Sathon, Bangkok, 10120, Thailand
Tel.: (66) 1327
Web Site: https://www.lhbank.co.th
Banking Services
N.A.I.C.S.: 522110

PT Anekagriya Buminusa Co., Ltd. (1)
Management Office Ruko Sentra Eropa Blok F No 23-24, Kota Wisata Jl Transyogi Km 6 Cibubur, Bogor, 16968, Indonesia
Tel.: (62) 21 8493 4848
Property Development Services
N.A.I.C.S.: 531390

PT Kanaka Grahaasri Co., Ltd. (1)
Management Office Ruko Sentra Eropa Blok F No 23-24, Kota Wisata Jl Transyogi Km 6 Cibubur, Bogor, 16968, Indonesia
Tel.: (62) 21 8493 4848
Property Development Services
N.A.I.C.S.: 531390

PT Mekanusa Cipta Co., Ltd. (1)
Management Office Ruko Sentra Eropa Blok F No 23-24, Kota Wisata Jl Transyogi Km 6 Cibubur, Bogor, 16968, Indonesia
Tel.: (62) 21 8493 4848
Property Development Services
N.A.I.C.S.: 531390

PT Prima Sheati Co., Ltd. (1)
Management Office Ruko Sentra Eropa Blok F No 23-24, Kota Wisata Jl Transyogi Km 6 Cibubur, Bogor, 16968, Indonesia
Tel.: (62) 21 8493 4848
Property Development Services
N.A.I.C.S.: 531390

PT Putra Prabukarya Co., Ltd. (1)
Management Office Ruko Sentra Eropa Blok F No 23-24, Kota Wisata Jl Transyogi Km 6 Cibubur, Bogor, 16968, Indonesia
Tel.: (62) 21 8493 48
Property Development Services
N.A.I.C.S.: 531390

Pacific Real Estate Co., Ltd. (1)
Q House Lumpini Building 15th Floor 1 South Sathon Road, Thungmahamek Sathon, Bangkok, 10120, Thailand
Tel.: (66) 23438899
Web Site: https://www.lhmh.co.th
Property Development Services
N.A.I.C.S.: 531390

Phuket Future Plan Co., Ltd. (1)
9/17 Moo 6 Thepkrasadtree, Tumbonratsada Amphoe Muang, Phuket, 83000, Thailand
Tel.: (66) 76 381 150
Property Development Services
N.A.I.C.S.: 531390

Polar Property Holdings Corp. (1)
South Super Highway Alabang, Mother Earth Subdivision, Muntinlupa, Philippines
Tel.: (63) 7711349
Web Site: https://www.starmalls.com.ph
Property Development Services
N.A.I.C.S.: 531390

Quality Construction Products PLC (1)
144 Moo 16 Bangpa-in Industrial Estate Udomsorayuth Rd, Tambol Bangkrasan Amphor Bang Pa-In Phra Nakhon Si, Ayutthaya, 13160, Thailand
Tel.: (66) 35258999
Web Site: https://qcon.co.th
Building Materials Sales
N.A.I.C.S.: 423390

Quality House PLC (1)
Q House Lumpini Building No 1 South Sathorn Road, Thung Maha Mek Sathon, Bangkok, 10120, Thailand
Tel.: (66) 2 677 7000
Web Site: https://www.qh.co.th
Property Development Services
N.A.I.C.S.: 531390

Siam Tanee Property Co., Ltd. (1)

LAND & HOUSES PUBLIC COMPANY LIMITED

Land & Houses Public Company Limited—(Continued)
37-38th Floor Q House Lumpini Building 1 South Sathon Road, Thungmahamek Sathon, Bangkok, 10120, Thailand
Tel.: (66) 2343 8900
Property Development Services
N.A.I.C.S.: 531390

Siam Tanee Real Estate Co., Ltd. (1)
37-38th Floor Q House Lumpini Building 1 South Sathon Road, Thungmahamek Sathon, Bangkok, 10120, Thailand
Tel.: (66) 2343 8900
Property Development Services
N.A.I.C.S.: 531390

LAND AND HOUSES FREE-HOLD & LEASEHOLD PROPERTY FUND
11 Q House Sathorn Building 14th Floor Sathorn Tai Road, Thung Maha Mek Subdistrict Sathorn District, Bangkok, 10120, Thailand
Tel.: (66) 22863484
LHPF—(THA)
Rev.: $9,248,059
Assets: $114,480,355
Liabilities: $4,974,042
Net Worth: $109,506,313
Earnings: $3,744,462
Emp.: 92
Fiscal Year-end: 12/31/23
Real Estate Investment Trust Services
N.A.I.C.S.: 531190

LAND BUSINESS CO., LTD.
Kasumigaseki Building 30F 325 Kasumigaseki, Chiyoda-ku, Tokyo, 100-6030, Japan
Tel.: (81) 335951371
Web Site: https://www.lbca.co.jp
Year Founded: 1985
8944—(TKS)
Rev.: $31,834,100
Assets: $381,987,930
Liabilities: $249,277,310
Net Worth: $132,710,620
Earnings: $2,474,410
Fiscal Year-end: 09/30/23
Real Estate Manangement Services
N.A.I.C.S.: 531390
Masamichi Kamei *(Chm)*

LAND CO., LTD.
7F Tobu Yokohama 3rd Building 2-8-2-9 Kitasaiwai, Nishi-ku, Yokohama, 220-0004, Kanagawa, Japan
Tel.: (81) 453457778
Web Site: https://www.land.jp
Year Founded: 1996
8918—(TKS)
Rev.: $14,896,090
Assets: $69,815,230
Liabilities: $16,115,570
Net Worth: $53,699,660
Earnings: $1,701,600
Fiscal Year-end: 02/29/24
Real Estate Manangement Services
N.A.I.C.S.: 531390
Hirofumi Wakamatsu *(Chm)*

LAND SECURITIES GROUP PLC
100 Victoria Street, London, SW1E 5JL, United Kingdom
Tel.: (44) 207 413 9000 UK
Web Site: http://www.landsec.com
Year Founded: 1955
LAND—(OTCIQ)
Rev.: $862,152,200
Assets: $14,921,342,800
Liabilities: $5,129,466,160
Net Worth: $9,791,876,640
Earnings: ($1,891,303,960)
Emp.: 530
Fiscal Year-end: 03/31/21
Property Investment & Development
N.A.I.C.S.: 531120
Martin F. Greenslade *(CFO)*

Subsidiaries:

Land Securities Plc (1)
100 Victoria Street, London, SW1E 5JL, United Kingdom (100%)
Tel.: (44) 2074139000
Sales Range: $200-249.9 Million
Property Investment & Development
N.A.I.C.S.: 523940
Martin Greenslide *(Dir-Fin)*

Subsidiary (Domestic):

Land Securities Properties Limited (2)
100 Victoria Street, London, SW1E 5JL, United Kingdom (100%)
Tel.: (44) 2074139000
Sales Range: $150-199.9 Million
N.A.I.C.S.: 531120
Francis Salway *(CEO)*

Subsidiary (Domestic):

Ravenseft Industrial Estates Limited (3)
100 Victoria Street, London, SW1E 5JL, United Kingdom (100%)
Tel.: (44) 207 413 9000
Web Site: https://www.landsecurities.com
Sales Range: $200-249.9 Million
Emp.: 500
N.A.I.C.S.: 531120
Robert Noel *(CEO)*

Ravenseft Properties Limited (3)
100 Victoria Street, London, SW1E 5JL, United Kingdom (100%)
Tel.: (44) 2074139000
Sales Range: $200-249.9 Million
Emp.: 200
N.A.I.C.S.: 531120
Robert Noel *(CEO)*

Ravenside Investments Limited (3)
100 Victoria Street, London, SW1E 5JL, United Kingdom (100%)
Tel.: (44) 207 413 9000
Web Site: https://www.landsecurities.com
Sales Range: $200-249.9 Million
Emp.: 500
N.A.I.C.S.: 531120
Robert Noel *(CEO)*

The City of London Real Property Company Limited (3)
100 Victoria Street, London, SW1E 5JL, United Kingdom (100%)
Tel.: (44) 2074139000
Sales Range: $200-249.9 Million
N.A.I.C.S.: 531120
Martin Greenslide *(Dir-Fin)*

LAND TRANSPORT AUTHORITY OF SINGAPORE
1 Hampshire Road, Singapore, 219428, Singapore
Tel.: (65) 62255 582
Web Site: http://www.lta.gov.sg
Year Founded: 1995
Land Transportation Infrastructure & Systems Regulator & Administrator
N.A.I.C.S.: 926120
Chong Kheng Chua *(Deputy CEO-Infrastructure & Dev)*

Subsidiaries:

EZ-Link Pte Ltd Co. (1)
438B Alexandra Road Blk B Alexandra Technopark 06-08/09, Singapore, 119968, Singapore
Tel.: (65) 64968300
Web Site: http://www.ezlink.com.sg
Transportation Services
N.A.I.C.S.: 488510
Nicholas Lee *(CEO)*

Transit Link Pte. Ltd. (1)
9 Maxwell Rd No 03-02 Annexe A, MND Complex, Singapore, 069112, Singapore
Tel.: (65) 6236 6666
Web Site: http://www.transitlink.com.sg
Sales Range: $75-99.9 Million
Emp.: 300
Integrated Transportation Support & Ticket Solution Services
N.A.I.C.S.: 561499

LANDAI TECHNOLOGY GROUP CORP., LTD.
No 100 Jianshan Road Biquan Street, Bishan District, Chongqing, 402760, China
Tel.: (86) 13883501198
Web Site: https://www.cqld.com
Year Founded: 1996
002765—(SSE)
Rev.: $403,436,592
Assets: $665,911,584
Liabilities: $343,940,688
Net Worth: $321,970,896
Earnings: $26,055,432
Fiscal Year-end: 12/31/22
Passenger Car Component & Accessory Mfr
N.A.I.C.S.: 336999
Tangfu Zhu *(Chm)*

LANDALE LIMITED
57 Hatton Garden, London, EC1N 8HP, United Kingdom
Tel.: (44) 20 7242 4284
Web Site: http://www.landalemetals.co.uk
Sales Range: $1-9.9 Million
Precious Metal Recovery Services
N.A.I.C.S.: 423510
Yossi Meshulam *(Mng Dir)*

LANDBAY INC
Room 3501 EFC Building, Yuhang District, Hangzhou, Zhejiang, China
Tel.: (86) 18621851468 NY
Year Founded: 2016
LNBY—(OTCIQ)
Rev.: $18,188
Assets: $15,599
Liabilities: $99,854
Net Worth: ($84,255)
Earnings: ($37,667)
Fiscal Year-end: 03/31/23
Holding Company
N.A.I.C.S.: 551112
Xiaowei Jin *(Pres, CEO, CFO & Sec)*

LANDER SPORTS DEVELOPMENT CO., LTD.
5F Building 10 No 399 West Section of Fucheng Avenue, Chengdu Hightech Zone Pilot Free Trade Zone, Sichuan, 610041, Zhejiang, China
Tel.: (86) 2886026033
Web Site: http://www.lander.com.cn
Year Founded: 1998
000558—(SSE)
Rev.: $16,738,488
Assets: $257,367,240
Liabilities: $106,117,128
Net Worth: $151,250,112
Earnings: ($5,076,864)
Fiscal Year-end: 12/31/22
Real Estate Development Services
N.A.I.C.S.: 531311
Juwei Qin *(Chm)*

LANDESBANK BADEN-WURTTEMBERG
Am Hauptbahnhof 2, 70173, Stuttgart, Germany
Tel.: (49) 7111270 De
Web Site: http://www.lbbw.de
Year Founded: 1999
Rev.: $15,735,152,860
Assets: $287,389,671,800
Liabilities: $271,797,861,020
Net Worth: $15,591,810,780
Earnings: $497,217,840
Emp.: 10,005
Fiscal Year-end: 12/31/19

INTERNATIONAL PUBLIC

Commercial Banking Services
N.A.I.C.S.: 522110
Alexander Braun *(Officer-Press)*

Subsidiaries:

ALVG Anlagenvermietung GmbH (1)
Pariser Platz 7, 70173, Stuttgart, Germany
Tel.: (49) 7111217970
Web Site: http://www.alvg.de
Financial Consulting Services
N.A.I.C.S.: 541611
Rene Maisch *(Sr Acct Mgr)*

BW Capital Markets Inc (1)
Hanover Road 25B, Florham Park, NJ 07932
Tel.: (212) 218-1800
Commercial Banking Services
N.A.I.C.S.: 522110

Baden Württembergische Bank AG (1)
Kleiner Schlossplatz 11, 70173, Stuttgart, Germany
Tel.: (49) 71112444005
Web Site: http://www.bw-bank.de
Sales Range: $700-749.9 Million
Emp.: 2,361
Commercial & Online Banking Services
N.A.I.C.S.: 522110
Rainer Neske *(CEO)*

Baden-Wurttemberg L-Finance N.V. (1)
Boslaan 2D, 2132 DX, Hoofddorp, Netherlands (100%)
Tel.: (31) 235626372
Web Site: http://www.l-finance.nl
Sales Range: $50-74.9 Million
Emp.: 10
Investment Banking
N.A.I.C.S.: 523150

Baden-Wurttembergische Equity Gesellschaft mit beschränkter Haftung (1)
Kleiner Schlossplatz 11, Stuttgart, 70173, Baden-Wurttemberg, Germany
Tel.: (49) 71112442572
Financial Management Services
N.A.I.C.S.: 523999

Bahnhofplatz-Gesellschaft Stuttgart Aktiengesellschaft (1)
Fritz-Elsas-Strasse 31, 70174, Stuttgart, Germany
Tel.: (49) 71121774256
Web Site: http://www.bahnhofplatzgesellschaften.de
Commercial Property Rental Services
N.A.I.C.S.: 531120

Centro Aleman de Industria y Comercio de Mexico S.de R.L.de C.V. (1)
Camino a Santa Fe 170 Alvaro Obregon, 01210, Mexico, Mexico
Tel.: (52) 55 9172 9210
Financial Management Services
N.A.I.C.S.: 523999

DBW Automotive Components Shanghai Co., Ltd. (1)
Lane 3029 No 58 Building A Hua Xu Road, Qingpu District, 201705, Shanghai, China
Tel.: (86) 21 39873579
Automotive Components Mfr
N.A.I.C.S.: 336390

DBW Fiber Corporation (1)
McQueen Park 101 Innovation Dr, Summerville, SC 29483
Tel.: (843) 285-2280
Timber Product Mfr
N.A.I.C.S.: 314999

DBW Japan Ltd. (1)
East Tower 4F Otemachi First Square 1-5-1 Otemachi, Chiyoda-ku, Tokyo, 100-0004, Japan
Tel.: (81) 3 5219 1521
Timber Product Mfr
N.A.I.C.S.: 314999

DBW Kaliningrad O.O.O. (1)
Alleja Smelych 31A, 236004, Kaliningrad, Russia
Tel.: (7) 4012 971324
Timber Product Mfr
N.A.I.C.S.: 314999

AND PRIVATE COMPANIES

LANDESBANK BADEN-WURTTEMBERG

DBW Polska Sp.z. o.o. (1)
Gorzykowo 1A, 66-131, Cigacice, Poland
Tel.: (48) 68 45 66 800
Web Site: http://www.dbw.pl
Emp.: 250
Timber Product Mfr
N.A.I.C.S.: 314999

DBW-Fiber-Neuhaus GmbH (1)
Thomas-Mann-Strasse 44, 98724, Neuhaus, Germany
Tel.: (49) 3679 727 0
Timber Product Mfr
N.A.I.C.S.: 314999

DEBTVISION GmbH (1)
Fritz-Elsas-Strasse 31, 70174, Stuttgart, Germany
Tel.: (49) 71112773400
Web Site: http://www.debtvision.de
Digital Financial Services
N.A.I.C.S.: 522320
Christoph Steinbrich (Mng Dir)

Entwicklungsgesellschaft Uhlandstrasse 187 GmbH & Co. KG (1)
Katharinenstr 20, 70182, Stuttgart, Germany
Tel.: (49) 30 780 9920
Commercial Banking Services
N.A.I.C.S.: 522110

FRONTWORX Informationstechnologie AG (1)
Lassallestrabe 7, 1020, Vienna, 1020, Austria
Tel.: (43) 1 218 51 24 0
Web Site: http://www.frontworx.com
Information Technology Consulting Services
N.A.I.C.S.: 541512

German Centre for Industry & Trade Beijing Co., Ltd. (1)
11th Floor Unit 1111 Landmark Tower 2, 8 North Dongsanhuan Road Chaoyang District, Beijing, 100004, China
Tel.: (86) 1065906920
Real Estate Services
N.A.I.C.S.: 531390

German Centre for Industry & Trade GmbH (1)
Am Hauptbahnhof 2, 70173, Stuttgart, Germany
Tel.: (49) 71112779183
Web Site: http://www.germancentre.com
Real Estate Services
N.A.I.C.S.: 531390
Gabriele Greiner (Mng Dir)

German Centre for Industry and Trade Pte. Ltd. (1)
25 International Business Park 01-78 German Centre, Singapore, 609916, Singapore
Tel.: (65) 6562 8020
Web Site: http://www.germancentre.sg
Emp.: 60
Residential Building Rental Services
N.A.I.C.S.: 531110
Katharina Ravens (Mng Dir)

Gmeinder Lokomotivenfabrik GmbH i.l. (1)
Anton-Gmeinder-Str 5, 74821, Mosbach, Germany
Tel.: (49) 6261 6747 211
Web Site: http://www.gmeinder-lokomotiven.de
Locomotive Mfr
N.A.I.C.S.: 333618

Huco electronic GmbH (1)
Eugen-Gerstenmaier-Str 8, 32339, Espelkamp, Germany
Tel.: (49) 5772 567 0
Web Site: http://www.hueco.com
Automobile Parts Mfr
N.A.I.C.S.: 336320
Patrick Freier (Mgr-Sls-Export)

Immobilienvermittlung BW GmbH (1)
Fritz-Elsas-Strasse 31, 70174, Stuttgart, Germany
Tel.: (49) 71112442081
Real Estate Services
N.A.I.C.S.: 531390

L-Immobilien GmbH (1)
Heugarten 1, 58093, Hagen, Germany (100%)
Tel.: (49) 23313733140
Web Site: http://www.L-IB.de
Sales Range: $1-4.9 Billion
Emp.: 12,000
Investment Banking
N.A.I.C.S.: 523150

LBBW (Schweiz) AG (1)
Splugenstrasse 10, 8027, Zurich, Switzerland
Tel.: (41) 44 286 26 86
Web Site: http://www.lbbw-schweiz.ch
Emp.: 10
Commercial Banking Services
N.A.I.C.S.: 522110

LBBW Asset Management GmbH (1)
Fritz-Elsas-Strasse 31, 70174, Stuttgart, Germany
Tel.: (49) 711229103000
Web Site: http://www.lbbw-am.de
Sales Range: $50-74.9 Million
Emp.: 100
Commericial Banking
N.A.I.C.S.: 522110
Frank Hagenstein (Chm & Mng Dir)

LBBW Corporate Real Estate Management GmbH (1)
Am Hauptbahnhof 11, 70173, Stuttgart, Germany
Tel.: (49) 71112733623
Real Estate Services
N.A.I.C.S.: 531390

LBBW Dublin Management GmbH (1)
Rheinallee 86, 55120, Mainz, Germany
Tel.: (49) 6131 64 0
Web Site: http://www.lbbw-dm.de
Commercial Banking Services
N.A.I.C.S.: 522110

LBBW GVZ Entwicklungsgesellschaft Leipzig mbH (1)
Humboldtstrasse 25, 04105, Leipzig, Germany
Tel.: (49) 71 6454 2145
Web Site: http://www.gvzleipzig.de
Freight Forwarding Services
N.A.I.C.S.: 488510

LBBW Immobilien Asset Management GmbH (1)
Fritz-Elsas-Str 31, 70174, Stuttgart, Germany
Tel.: (49) 71121770
Real Estate Services
N.A.I.C.S.: 531390

LBBW Immobilien Capital GmbH (1)
Rosental 5, 80331, Munich, Germany
Tel.: (49) 898896990
Real Estate Services
N.A.I.C.S.: 531390

LBBW Immobilien Kommunalentwicklung GmbH (1)
Fritz-Elsas-Strasse 31, 70174, Stuttgart, Germany
Tel.: (49) 71164540
Real Estate Services
N.A.I.C.S.: 531390

LBBW Immobilien Romania S.R.L. (1)
Str Constantin Coanda Nr 5 Et 1 Ap 6 Sect 1, Bucharest, Romania
Tel.: (40) 73 300 3816
Commercial Banking Services
N.A.I.C.S.: 522110

LBBW Leasing GmbH (1)
Pariser Platz 7, Stuttgart, D 70173, Germany
Tel.: (49) 71112717770
Web Site: http://www.lbbw-leasing.de
Sales Range: $50-74.9 Million
Emp.: 4
Commericial Banking
N.A.I.C.S.: 522110
Martin Starck (Mng Dir)

LBBW Luxemburg S.A. (1)
10-12 Boulevard Franklin Delano Roosevelt, 2450, Luxembourg, Luxembourg
Tel.: (352) 475 921 1
Commercial Banking Services
N.A.I.C.S.: 522110

LBBW Mexico S.A. de C.V. (1)
Av Santa Fe No 170/01 02 08 A Col Lomas de Santa Fe, 01219, Mexico, Mexico
Tel.: (52) 5584211040
Web Site: http://www.lbbw.de
Emp.: 8
Financial Management Services
N.A.I.C.S.: 523999

LBBW Trust GmbH (1)
Friedrichstrasse 24, D 70174, Stuttgart, Germany (100%)
Tel.: (49) 7111249801
Web Site: http://www.lbbw.de
Banking Services
N.A.I.C.S.: 522110

LBBW US Real Estate Investment LLC (1)
280 Park Ave, New York, NY 10017
Tel.: (212) 584-1703
Real Estate Consulting Service
N.A.I.C.S.: 531390

LBBW Venture Capital GmbH (1)
Konigstrasse 10 C, 70173, Stuttgart, Germany
Tel.: (49) 711305892020
Web Site: http://www.lbbwvc.de
Sales Range: $50-74.9 Million
Emp.: 5
Commericial Banking
N.A.I.C.S.: 522110
Andreas von Richter (Mng Dir)

LEG Baden-Wurttemberg Verwaltungs-GmbH (1)
Fritz-Elsas-Str 31, Stuttgart, 70174, Baden-Wurttemberg, Germany
Tel.: (49) 71121770
Commercial Banking Services
N.A.I.C.S.: 522110

LIVIDA MOLARIS Grundstucks-Vermietungsgesellschaft mbH & Co. (1)
Thomaseck 1, Ballstedt, 99084, Erfurt, Germany
Tel.: (49) 36167870
Commercial Banking Services
N.A.I.C.S.: 522110

LLC German Centre for Industry and Trade (1)
Prospekt Andropova 18 Korpus 6 Office 10-02, 115432, Moscow, Russia
Tel.: (7) 4996830202
Web Site: http://www.germancentre.ru
Emp.: 20
Business Support Services
N.A.I.C.S.: 541611
Stephan Weiss (Mng Dir)

LOOP GmbH (1)
Am Nordturm 5, 46562, Voerde, Germany
Tel.: (49) 281 83135
Web Site: http://www.loop-gmbh.de
Chemical Products Mfr
N.A.I.C.S.: 325998

Landesbank Baden-Wurttemberg (1)
7th Floor 201 Bishopsgate, London, EC2M 3UN, United Kingdom (100%)
Tel.: (44) 2078268000
Web Site: http://www.lbb.de
Sales Range: $50-74.9 Million
Emp.: 40
Banking Services
N.A.I.C.S.: 522110

Landesbank Baden-Wurttemberg Capital Markets Plc (1)
7th Floor 201 Bishopsgate, London, EC2M 3UN, United Kingdom
Tel.: (44) 2078268000
Financial Banking Services
N.A.I.C.S.: 522110
Nadim Zaman (Mng Dir)

MMV Bank GmbH (1)
Ferdinand-Sauerbruch-Strasse 7, 56073, Koblenz, Germany
Tel.: (49) 26194330
Web Site: http://www.mmv-bank.de
Financial Lending Services
N.A.I.C.S.: 522220

MMV Leasing GmbH (1)
Ferdinand Sauerbruch Strasse 7, 56073, Koblenz, Germany (100%)
Tel.: (49) 26194330
Web Site: http://www.mmv-leasing.de
Sales Range: $200-249.9 Million
Emp.: 430
Investment Banking
N.A.I.C.S.: 523150

Subsidiary (Domestic):

MKB Mittelrheinische Bank GmbH (2)
Ferdinand Sauerbruch Strasse 7, PO Box 22, 56073, Koblenz, Germany (100%)
Tel.: (49) 26194330
Web Site: http://www.mkb-bank.de
Sales Range: $150-199.9 Million
Emp.: 400
Investment Banking
N.A.I.C.S.: 523150

Rheinland-Pfalz Bank (1)
Grosse Bleiche 54-56, D-55068, Mainz, Germany
Tel.: (49) 61316435250
Web Site: http://www.rlp-bank.de
Sales Range: $700-749.9 Million
Emp.: 2,000
Financial & Banking Services
N.A.I.C.S.: 522110
Christina Eistert (Head-Comm & Mktg)

Subsidiary (Non-US):

Landesbank Rheinland-Pfalz International S.A. (2)
10 12 Boulevard Roosevelt, L-2450, Luxembourg, Luxembourg
Tel.: (352) 4759211
Web Site: http://www.lbbw.lu
Sales Range: $75-99.9 Million
Emp.: 170
Banking Services
N.A.I.C.S.: 522110

Rhin-Neckar S.A. (1)
Rue Gabriel Lippmann 1 C, 5365, Munsbach, Luxembourg
Tel.: (352) 228791
Commercial Banking Services
N.A.I.C.S.: 522110

SG Management GmbH (1)
Am Weichselgarten 19, 91058, Erlangen, Germany
Tel.: (49) 91319279977
Web Site: http://www.sgm-immobilien.de
Real Estate Services
N.A.I.C.S.: 531390

SHS Gesellschaft fur Beteiligungen mbH & Co. Mittelstand KG (1)
Bismarckstrasse 12, 72072, Tubingen, Germany (75.02%)
Tel.: (49) 707191690
Web Site: http://www.shs-capital.eu
Life Science & Medical Technology Services
N.A.I.C.S.: 541714
Andre Zimmermann (Partner)

SL Financial Services Corporation (1)
50 Washington St 7th Fl, Norwalk, CT 06854
Tel.: (203) 227-5225
Commercial Banking Services
N.A.I.C.S.: 522110

SL Operating Services GmbH i.l. (1)
Augustaanlage 33, 68165, Mannheim, Germany
Tel.: (49) 6214280
Commercial Banking Services
N.A.I.C.S.: 522110

SUDRENTING ESPANA, S.A. (1)
Avda Diagonal 468 8 C, 08006, Barcelona, 08006, Spain
Tel.: (34) 93 238 93 70
Automobile Finance & Leasing Services
N.A.I.C.S.: 522220
Alejo Lopez (Mng Dir)

Sachsen Bank (1)
Humboldtstrasse 25, 04105, Leipzig, Germany
Tel.: (49) 3419790
Web Site: http://www.sachsenlb.de
Sales Range: $100-124.9 Million
Emp.: 610
Banking Services

LANDESBANK BADEN-WURTTEMBERG

Landesbank Baden-Wurttemberg—(Continued)
N.A.I.C.S.: 522110

SachsenFonds International Equity Holding I GmbH (1)
Max-Planck-Str 3 Aschheim, 85609, Dornach, Germany
Tel.: (49) 89 456660
Commercial Banking Services
N.A.I.C.S.: 522110

Stadtische Pfandleihanstalt Stuttgart Aktiengesellschaf (1)
Gerberstr 3, 70178, Stuttgart, Germany
Tel.: (49) 711 24 56 39
Web Site: http://www.staedtische-pfandleihe.de
Commercial Banking Services
N.A.I.C.S.: 522110

Sud Beteiligungen GmbH (1)
Konigstrasse 10c, 70173, Stuttgart, Germany
Tel.: (49) 711892007200
Web Site: http://www.suedbg.de
Asset Management Services
N.A.I.C.S.: 523940
Michael Flach (Dir-Investments)

SudFactoring GmbH (1)
Pariser Platz 7, 70173, Stuttgart, Germany
Tel.: (49) 711 1271 0
Web Site: http://www.suedfactoring.de
Commercial Banking Services
N.A.I.C.S.: 522110

SudLeasing Suisse AG (1)
Zurcherstr 42, 8103, Unterengstringen, Switzerland
Tel.: (41) 44 864 80 60
Web Site: http://www.suedleasing.de
Automobile Finance & Leasing Services
N.A.I.C.S.: 522220

Sued Factoring GmbH (1)
Pariser Platz 7, 70173, Stuttgart, Germany (100%)
Tel.: (49) 71112710
Web Site: http://www.suedfactoring.de
Sales Range: $50-74.9 Million
Investment Banking
N.A.I.C.S.: 523150

Sued-Kapitalbeteiligungs-Gesellschaft mbH (1)
Friedrichstr 24, 70174, Stuttgart, Germany (100%)
Tel.: (49) 7111277067
Web Site: http://www.suedkb.de
Sales Range: $10-24.9 Million
Emp.: 10
Investment Banking
N.A.I.C.S.: 523150

SuedBau Projektentwicklung und Baumanagement GmbH (1)
Obere Waldplaetze 13, 70569, Stuttgart, Germany
Tel.: (49) 111317253
Web Site: http://www.lbbw.de
Investment Banking
N.A.I.C.S.: 523150

SuedLeasing BerlinDresdenLeipzig GmbH (1)
Wallstrasse 58 59, 10179, Berlin, Germany (100%)
Tel.: (49) 30247542301
Web Site: http://www.suedleasing.de
Sales Range: $50-74.9 Million
Emp.: 400
Investment Banking
N.A.I.C.S.: 523150

SuedLeasing GmbH (1)
Pariser Platz 7, 70173, Stuttgart, Germany (100%)
Tel.: (49) 71112710
Web Site: http://www.suedleasing.de
Financing & Leasing Services
N.A.I.C.S.: 523999
Stefan Lechner (Member-Mgmt Bd)

SuedWert-Wohnungsprivatisierungsgesellschaft mbH (1)
Berliner Strasse 19, 74321, Bietigheim-Bissingen, Germany
Tel.: (49) 7142989190

Web Site: http://www.suedwert.de
Investment Commercial & Residential Housing Mortgage Services
N.A.I.C.S.: 522310
Dieter Schwahn (Mng Dir)

cellent Mittelstandsberatung GmbH (1)
Max-Eyth-Strasse 38, 71088, Holzgerlingen, Germany
Tel.: (49) 7031 62345 0
Web Site: http://www.cellent-mittelstandsberatung.com
Software Development Services
N.A.I.C.S.: 541511

targens GmbH (1)
Calwer Strasse 33, 70173, Stuttgart, Germany
Tel.: (49) 711222992900
Web Site: http://www.targens.de
Emp.: 250
Bank Consulting Services
N.A.I.C.S.: 541618
Lars A. Ludwig (Mng Dir)

LANDESBANK SAAR
Ursulinenstrasse 2, 66111, Saarbrucken, Germany
Tel.: (49) 68138301
Web Site: http://www.saarlb.de
Sales Range: $550-599.9 Million
Emp.: 540
Credit Institution
N.A.I.C.S.: 522299
Frank Eloy (Member-Mgmt Bd)

Subsidiaries:

LBS Saar GmbH (1)
Bahnhofstr 111, 66111, Sarrebruck, Germany (100%)
Tel.: (49) 68138303
Web Site: http://www.lbs.de
Commericial Banking
N.A.I.C.S.: 522110

TEGES Grundstucks-Vermietungsgesellschaft mbH (1)
Bundesrepublik, 10117, Berlin, Germany (50%)
Tel.: (49) 302015393
Nondepository Credit Intermediation
N.A.I.C.S.: 522299

LANDESKRANKENANSTALTEN-BETRIEBSGESELLSCHAFT
Saint Veiter Strasse 34, Klagenfurt, 9020, Austria
Tel.: (43) 463552120
Web Site: http://www.kabeg.at
Sales Range: $500-549.9 Million
Emp.: 7,500
Hospitals & Clinics Operator
N.A.I.C.S.: 622110
Dieter Errath (Head-Personnel & Trng)

LANDI RENZO S.P.A.
Via Nobel 2 Corte Tegge, 42025, Cavriago, RE, Italy
Tel.: (39) 05229433   IT
Web Site:
  https://www.landirenzo.com
Year Founded: 1954
LNDR—(ITA)
Rev.: $331,993,280
Assets: $440,743,551
Liabilities: $325,976,588
Net Worth: $114,766,963
Earnings: ($15,479,081)
Emp.: 913
Fiscal Year-end: 12/31/22
Natural Gas Exploration Service
N.A.I.C.S.: 221210
Stefano Landi (Chm)

Subsidiaries:

Beijing Landi Renzo Autogas System Co. Ltd. (1)
BDA Building n 5 Jing Yuan Bei Jie n 2, Econ-Techno Development Area, Beijing, 100176, China
Tel.: (86) 1067856675
Natural Gas Distribution Services
N.A.I.C.S.: 221210

Krishna Landi Renzo India Private Ltd. (1)
Plot 34 sector 33 Near Infocity-II, Gurgaon, 122001, Haryana, India
Tel.: (91) 1244725017
Natural Gas Distribution Services
N.A.I.C.S.: 221210

L.R. Pak (Pvt) Limited (1)
C-11 SITE Industrial Area, Karachi, 75700, Pakistan
Tel.: (92) 5122529943
Industrial Gas Distribution Services
N.A.I.C.S.: 221210

Landi Renzo Pars Private Joint Stock Company (1)
Unit 1 No 15 Beginning of GolAra Alley Northern Motahari St Darya Blvd, Saadat Abad, 1998874653, Tehran, Iran
Tel.: (98) 218 856 0822
Natural Gas Distribution Services
N.A.I.C.S.: 221210

Landi Renzo Polska Sp. z o.o. (1)
ul Graniczna 79a, Jozefow, 05-410, Otwock, Poland
Tel.: (22) 742800
Web Site: https://www.landi.pl
Industrial Gas Mfr
N.A.I.C.S.: 325120

Landi Renzo Ro S.r.l. (1)
MIOVENI - Bd Dacia Bl P22 Sc D Parter Jud, Arges, Romania
Tel.: (40) 758834450
Natural Gas Distribution Services
N.A.I.C.S.: 221210

Landi Renzo USA Corporation (1)
23535 Telo Ave, Torrance, CA 90505
Tel.: (310) 257-9481
Web Site: https://landiusa.com
Natural Gas Distribution Services
N.A.I.C.S.: 221210

Landi Renzo VE C.A. (1)
n las Parc Intergr n 6 7 8 AV Este-Oest, 2006, San Diego, Carabobo, Venezuela
Tel.: (58) 241 417 6908
Natural Gas Distribution Services
N.A.I.C.S.: 221210

Metatron Control System (Shanghai) Co. Ltd. (1)
Suite 1108 Silver Tower 933 Zhongshan w Rd, Changning District, Shanghai, 200051, China
Tel.: (86) 2151113835
Vehicle Component Mfr & Distr
N.A.I.C.S.: 336390

Metatron S.p.A. (1)
Via Angelelli 61, 40013, Castel Maggiore, BO, Italy
Tel.: (39) 0514171911
Web Site: https://www.metatron.it
Automotive Component Mfr & Distr
N.A.I.C.S.: 336390

OOO Landi Renzo RUS (1)
Elektrozavodskaya Str 27 c 1A, Moscow, 107023, Russia
Tel.: (7) 4951362920
Vehicle Component Mfr & Distr
N.A.I.C.S.: 336390

Officine Lovato Private Ltd. (1)
Unit No 101 1st Floor Kamla Executive Park, MIDC Cross Lane B off Andheri Kurla Road Andheri East, Mumbai, 400 059, Maharashtra, India
Tel.: (91) 2261202222
Natural Gas Distribution Services
N.A.I.C.S.: 221210

SAFE&CEC S.r.l. (1)
Via Ferruccio Lamborghini 18, San Giovanni in Persiceto, Bologna, Italy (51%)
Tel.: (39) 0516878211
Web Site: https://safegas.it
Petroleum & Fuel Industries
N.A.I.C.S.: 324199
Mario Pirraglia (Pres)

Subsidiary (Non-US):

IMW Industries Ltd. (2)

Unit 610 - 44688 South Sumas Road, Chilliwack, V2R 5M3, BC, Canada
Tel.: (604) 795-9491
Web Site: https://imw.ca
Sales Range: $50-74.9 Million
Emp.: 300
Natural Gas Equipment Mfr
N.A.I.C.S.: 333912

Safe S.p.A. (1)
Via Ferruccio Lamborghini 18, 40017, San Giovanni in Persiceto, BO, Italy
Tel.: (39) 0516878211
Web Site: https://safegas.it
Natural Gas Mfr & Distr
N.A.I.C.S.: 325120

LANDIS TAIPEI HOTEL CO., LTD.
41 Sec 2 Min-Chuan East Road, Taipei, 104, Taiwan
Tel.: (886) 225971234
Web Site:
  https://www.taipei.landishotels.com
5703—(TPE)
Rev.: $7,900,322
Assets: $29,635,369
Liabilities: $15,811,306
Net Worth: $13,824,063
Earnings: ($2,670,012)
Fiscal Year-end: 12/31/22
Restaurant Operators
N.A.I.C.S.: 722511

LANDIX, INC.
3-22-2 Shinmachi, Setagaya-Ku, Tokyo, 154-0014, Japan
Tel.: (81) 334277711
Web Site: https://www.landix.jp
Year Founded: 2001
2981—(TKS)
Rev.: $112,641,010
Assets: $101,033,850
Liabilities: $53,798,790
Net Worth: $47,235,060
Earnings: $5,221,900
Emp.: 122
Fiscal Year-end: 03/31/24
Real Estate Development Services
N.A.I.C.S.: 531311
Kazuya Okada (Pres)

LANDLUST GMBH
Emil-Schwate-Strasse 24, Munich, 84364, Germany
Tel.: (49) 8563 2930
Butcher Stores
N.A.I.C.S.: 311613

LANDMARC LEISURE CORPORATION LIMITED
303 Raaj Chamber 115 R K Paramhans Marg Old Nagardas Road, Near Andheri Station Subway Andheri - East, Mumbai, 400069, Maharashtra, India
Tel.: (91) 2261669190
Web Site: https://www.llcl.co.in
Year Founded: 1991
Rev.: $702,814
Assets: $6,787,926
Liabilities: $1,511,265
Net Worth: $5,276,661
Earnings: $16,525
Emp.: 8
Fiscal Year-end: 03/31/18
Fitness Center Operator
N.A.I.C.S.: 713940
Deepak Rajendra Nangalia (CFO)

LANDMARK CARS LIMITED
Landmark House Opp AEC S G Highway Thaltej, Near Gurudwara, Ahmedabad, 380059, Gujarat, India
Tel.: (91) 7069102222
Web Site:
  https://www.grouplandmark.in
Year Founded: 1998

543714—(BOM)
Rev.: $94,142,207
Assets: $73,669,814
Liabilities: $34,655,152
Net Worth: $39,014,662
Earnings: $4,776,517
Emp.: 3,000
Fiscal Year-end: 03/31/22
Automotive Retailer
N.A.I.C.S.: 441330

LANDMARK OPTOELECTRONICS CORPORATION
No 12 Nanke 9th Rd, Shanhua Dist, Tainan City, 741-014, Taiwan
Tel.: (886) 65058999
Web Site: https://www.lmoc.com.tw
Year Founded: 1997
3081—(TPE)
Rev.: $74,442,204
Assets: $160,004,440
Liabilities: $23,790,232
Net Worth: $136,214,208
Earnings: $10,303,474
Emp.: 348
Fiscal Year-end: 12/31/22
Semiconductor Devices Mfr
N.A.I.C.S.: 334413
Roger Lo *(Pres)*

LANDMARK RETAIL HOLDINGS 1 LIMITED
Landmark Group Landmark Tower, Dubai, United Arab Emirates
Tel.: (971) 45174000   AE
Web Site:
    http://www.landmarkgroup.com
Sales Range: $1-4.9 Billion
Emp.: 31,000
Holding Company; Retail & Hospitality Facilities Owner & Operator
N.A.I.C.S.: 551112
Mukesh Jagtiani *(Founder & Chm)*

Subsidiaries:

Al Rashid Group B.S.C. (c)   (1)
PO Box 1088, Manama, Bahrain
Tel.: (973) 17 564005
Web Site: http://www.landmarkgroup.com.bh
Logistics Consulting Servies
N.A.I.C.S.: 541614
Vikas Attri *(COO)*

Citymax Hospitality India Pvt. Ltd.   (1)
1st Floor B Block E 77 Town Centre Building No 3, Yemalur, Bengaluru, 560 037, India
Tel.: (91) 80 42599000
Web Site: http://www.citymaxindia.com
Emp.: 100
Logistics Consulting Servies
N.A.I.C.S.: 541614
Bishal Kapoor *(Pres)*

Home Centre LLC   (1)
PO Box 23003, Doha, Qatar
Tel.: (974) 44289111
Logistics Consulting Servies
N.A.I.C.S.: 541614

Landmark Central Market Co. LLC   (1)
PO Box 49336, Kuwait, 85154, Kuwait
Tel.: (965) 22909909
Logistics Consulting Servies
N.A.I.C.S.: 541614

Landmark Jordan PSC Limited   (1)
PO Box 3671, Amman, 11827, Jordan
Tel.: (962) 65541550
Logistics Consulting Servies
N.A.I.C.S.: 541614

Landmark Retail Holdings 1 Limited   (1)
PO Box 49336, Al Omariya, Kuwait, 85154, Kuwait
Tel.: (965) 22909909
Logistics Consulting Servies
N.A.I.C.S.: 541614

Landmark Retail Lebanon SARL   (1)
Dar Assayad Building Said Freiha Street, Hazmieh, 1038, Lebanon
Tel.: (961) 5 956436
Logistics Consulting Servies
N.A.I.C.S.: 541614

Lifestyle International Pvt. Ltd.   (1)
5th Floor 77 Town Centre Building No 3 Off Old Airport Road, Landmark Group Yemlur PO, Bengaluru, 560 037, India
Tel.: (91) 80 4179 6565
Web Site: http://www.lifestylestores.com
Logistics Consulting Servies
N.A.I.C.S.: 541614
Addepalli Venkata Sitaramkumar *(VP & Head-Bus)*

Max Fashions   (1)
Arifa a Sok No 25 Kat 3 Yenibosna, Istanbul, Turkiye
Tel.: (90) 212 452 78 03
Logistics Consulting Servies
N.A.I.C.S.: 541614

Max Hypermarkets India Pvt. Ltd   (1)
No 39/3 & 44 Bannerghatta Road, Bengaluru, 560 029, India
Tel.: (91) 80 41811600
Logistics Consulting Servies
N.A.I.C.S.: 541614

Orient International Trading   (1)
Block 67 Road 90th 5th Settlement New Cairo, Cairo, Egypt
Tel.: (20) 10 26099900
Logistics Consulting Servies
N.A.I.C.S.: 541614

The Baby Shop LLC   (1)
PO Box 754, PC 133 Al-Khuwair, Muscat, Oman
Tel.: (968) 22086000
Logistics Consulting Servies
N.A.I.C.S.: 541614

LANDMARKS BERHAD
20th Floor Menara Haw Par Jalan Sultan Ismail, 50250, Kuala Lumpur, Malaysia
Tel.: (60) 320260088
Web Site:
    https://www.landmarks.com.my
LANDMRK—(KLS)
Rev.: $5,140,106
Assets: $477,297,143
Liabilities: $91,722,751
Net Worth: $385,574,392
Earnings: ($9,160,423)
Emp.: 623
Fiscal Year-end: 12/31/22
Property Development & Management Services
N.A.I.C.S.: 531311
Eng Kiong Chew *(Gen Mgr-Risk Mgmt & Internal Audit)*

LANDMART HOMES
1005 Skyview Drive Suite 301, Burlington, L7P 5B1, ON, Canada
Tel.: (905) 304-6459
Web Site:
    http://www.landmarthomes.com
Rev.: $16,650,160
Emp.: 15
Building Construction
N.A.I.C.S.: 236115
Rae Fisker *(Mgr-Landmart Homes Decor Boutique)*

LANDOIN EMBALLAGES
Z I Nord Rue De Tamas, 01100, Arbent, Ain, France
Tel.: (33) 474819470
Web Site: http://www.landoin.com
Rev.: $18,900,000
Emp.: 29
Industrial Equipment Whsr
N.A.I.C.S.: 423830
Andre Thibaudier *(Pres)*

LANDOR CARTONS HOLDINGS LTD.
45 Devon Street, Birmingham, B7 4SL, United Kingdom
Tel.: (44) 1213598511
Web Site:
    http://www.landorcartons.co.uk
Year Founded: 1967
Sales Range: $25-49.9 Million
Emp.: 42
Holding Company
N.A.I.C.S.: 551112
Philip Morley *(Mng Dir)*

Subsidiaries:

Landor Cartons Ltd.   (1)
45 Devon Street, Birmingham, B7 4SL, United Kingdom   (100%)
Tel.: (44) 1213598511
Web Site: http://www.landorcartons.co.uk
Sales Range: $25-49.9 Million
Mfr of Cartons
N.A.I.C.S.: 322212
Russell McHardy *(Gen Mgr)*

LANDORE RESOURCES LTD
La Tonnelle House Les Banques, PO Box 141, Saint Peter Port, GY1 3HS, Guernsey
Tel.: (44) 1481721374
Web Site: https://www.landore.com
Year Founded: 2005
LND—(AIM)
Rev.: $1,830,537
Assets: $1,249,245
Liabilities: $410,190
Net Worth: $839,055
Earnings: ($1,466,885)
Emp.: 2
Fiscal Year-end: 12/31/22
Mineral Explorer
N.A.I.C.S.: 213115
William H. Humphries *(CEO)*

Subsidiaries:

Landore Resources Canada Inc.   (1)
555 Central Avenue Suite 1, Thunder Bay, P7B 5R5, ON, Canada
Tel.: (807) 623-3770
Web Site: https://www.landore.com
Mineral Exploration & Development Services
N.A.I.C.S.: 213115

LANDRICH HOLDING LIMITED
Unit 2808 28/F The Octagon 6 Sha Tsui Road, Tsuen Wan, New Territories, China (Hong Kong)
Tel.: (852) 24300018   Ky
Web Site: http://www.landrich.com.hk
Year Founded: 1993
2132—(HKG)
Holding Company
N.A.I.C.S.: 551112
Kai Kwong Tsui *(Chm)*

LANDS END RESOURCES LTD.
340 12th Avenue Southwest Suite 240, Calgary, T2P 3E6, AB, Canada
Tel.: (403) 532-8755   AB
Year Founded: 2006
Sales Range: $1-9.9 Million
Oil & Gas Exploration Services
N.A.I.C.S.: 211120
David W. Harrison *(Pres & CEO)*

LANDSBANKINN HF.
Austurstaeti 11, 155, Reykjavik, Iceland
Tel.: (354) 410 4000   IS
Web Site: http://www.landsbanki.is
Year Founded: 2008
Rev.: $594,569,460
Assets: $11,364,171,370
Liabilities: $9,310,713,670
Net Worth: $2,053,457,700
Earnings: $165,058,200
Emp.: 1,012
Fiscal Year-end: 12/31/18

Retail, Commercial & Investment Banking
N.A.I.C.S.: 522110
Arni Thor Thorbjornsson *(Mng Dir-Corp Banking)*

Subsidiaries:

Landsvaki hf.   (1)
5 Hafnarstraeti, Reykjavik, Iceland   (100%)
Tel.: (354) 5352000
Mutual Fund Management Services
N.A.I.C.S.: 523940

Span ehf.   (1)
Hafnarstraeti 26, 101, Reykjavik, Iceland   (100%)
Tel.: (354) 410 2900
Sales Range: $25-49.9 Million
Emp.: 1
Data Transmission Services
N.A.I.C.S.: 518210

LANDSEA GREEN LIFE SERVICE COMPANY LIMITED
The 10th floor of Hongxin Mansion No 98 Jianye Road, Qinhuai District, Nanjing, 210004, Jiangsu, China
Tel.: (86) 4008009770   Ky
Web Site: https://en.landseawy.com
Year Founded: 2005
1965—(HKG)
Rev.: $128,942,595
Assets: $150,618,492
Liabilities: $113,913,242
Net Worth: $36,705,250
Earnings: ($18,728,124)
Emp.: 3,346
Fiscal Year-end: 12/31/23
Property Management Services
N.A.I.C.S.: 531311
Chao Liu *(VP)*

LANDSEA GREEN MANAGEMENT LIMITED
Room 5103 Level 51 The Center 99 Queens Road, Central, China (Hong Kong)
Tel.: (852) 28796800   BM
Web Site: http://www.landsea.hk
0106—(HKG)
Rev.: $1,237,334,685
Assets: $4,272,008,513
Liabilities: $3,416,903,362
Net Worth: $855,105,151
Earnings: ($106,663,423)
Emp.: 1,891
Fiscal Year-end: 12/31/21
Property Development Services
N.A.I.C.S.: 531390
Ming Tian *(Founder & Chm)*

Subsidiaries:

Landsea Homes of Arizona, LLC   (1)
7600 E Doubletree Ranch Rd Ste 240, Scottsdale, AZ 85258
Tel.: (480) 629-4111
Real Estate Services
N.A.I.C.S.: 531390

Shanghai Kunhong Industrial Co., Ltd.   (1)
RM2982 29F Calderon Dream Plaza No 6088 Humin Rd, Shanghai, 201199, China
Tel.: (86) 216 049 8851
Web Site: https://www.kunhonggroup.com
Industrial Equipment Distr
N.A.I.C.S.: 423830

LANDSON EMISSION TECHNOLOGIES A/S
Kuopiovej 13, 5700, Svendborg, Denmark
Tel.: (45) 70238989   DK
Web Site: http://www.landson.dk
Year Founded: 2016
Diesel Particulate Filters Mfr
N.A.I.C.S.: 336390

LANDSVIRKJUN - THE NATIONAL POWER CO.
(CONTINUED)

Haaleitisbraut 68, 103, Reykjavik, Iceland
Tel.: (354) 5159000
Web Site: http://www.landsvirkjun.com
Year Founded: 1965
Sales Range: $150-199.9 Million
Emp.: 300
Produces, Distributes & Sells Wholesale Electricity to Utilities & Power-Intensive Industries by Special Agreement
N.A.I.C.S.: 221122
Gunnar G. Tomasson *(Member-Exec Bd & Exec VP-Project Plng & Construction)*

Subsidiaries:

Landsnet hf. (1)
Gylfaflot 9, 112, Reykjavik, Iceland
Tel.: (354) 563 9300
Web Site: http://www.landsnet.is
Sales Range: $75-99.9 Million
Emp.: 93
Electricity Transmission System Operator
N.A.I.C.S.: 221121
Guolaug Siguroardottir *(CFO)*

Landsvirkjun Power ehf. (1)
Haaleitisbraut 68, 103, Reykjavik, Iceland
Tel.: (354) 515 8900
Web Site: http://www.lvpower.com
Sales Range: $75-99.9 Million
Emp.: 5
Eletric Power Generation Services
N.A.I.C.S.: 221118
Rikardur Rikardsson *(Mng Dir)*

Orkufjarskipti hf. (1)
Krokhalsi 5c, 110, Reykjavik, Iceland
Tel.: (354) 515 9700
Web Site: http://www.orkufjarskipti.is
Sales Range: $25-49.9 Million
Emp.: 10
Telecommunication Servicesb
N.A.I.C.S.: 517810
Gudmundur Danielsson *(COO)*

LANDTRAN SYSTEMS INC.

9011 50 St, Edmonton, T6B 2Y2, AB, Canada
Tel.: (780) 468-4300   Ca
Web Site: https://www.landtran.com
Year Founded: 1948
Sales Range: $1-9.9 Million
Emp.: 600
Transportation Services
N.A.I.C.S.: 488999
John Assman *(Pres & CEO)*

Subsidiaries:

Continental Cartage Inc. (1)
25245 111 Ave, Acheson, T7X 6C8, AB, Canada (100%)
Tel.: (780) 452-9414
Web Site: http://www.landtrantl.com
Trucking & Contract Hauling Services
N.A.I.C.S.: 484121

Custom Landtran Carriers Inc. (1)
25245 111 Ave, Acheson, T7X 6C8, AB, Canada
Tel.: (780) 452-9414
Web Site: https://www.landtrantl.com
Heavy Haul Transportation Services
N.A.I.C.S.: 488190
Charity Olsson *(Mgr-Branch)*

Landtran Express Inc. (1)
15103 128 Avenue, Edmonton, T5V 1A5, AB, Canada
Tel.: (780) 468-0775
Web Site: http://www.landtranexpress.com
Heavy Haul Transportation Services
N.A.I.C.S.: 488160
Dave Pekar *(Dir-Ops)*

Landtran Logistics Inc. (1)
4819 90A Avenue, Edmonton, T6B 2Y3, AB, Canada
Web Site: http://www.landtranlogistics.com

Logistics Management Services
N.A.I.C.S.: 541614

Monarch Transport (1975) Ltd. (1)
25245 111 Ave, Acheson, T7X 6C8, AB, Canada (100%)
Tel.: (780) 440-6528
Web Site: https://www.monarchtransport.com
Sales Range: $1-9.9 Million
Emp.: 22
Van Truckload Transportation Services
N.A.I.C.S.: 484122
Rod Boychuck *(Gen Mgr)*

Tli Cho Landtran Transport Ltd. (1)
13120 Yellowhead Trail NW, Edmonton, T5L 3C1, AB, Canada (100%)
Tel.: (780) 452-9414
Web Site: http://www.tlicholandtran.com
Sales Range: $1-9.9 Million
Emp.: 22
Scheduled Freight Transportation Services
N.A.I.C.S.: 481112

Valley Roadways Ltd. (1)
1115 Chief Louis Way, Kamloops, V2H 1J8, BC, Canada
Tel.: (250) 374-3467
Web Site: http://www.valleyroadways.com
Food Transportation Services
N.A.I.C.S.: 488490
Rick Angeli *(Mgr-Branch)*

LANDVELAR HF

Smidjuvegur 66, 200, Kopavogur, Iceland
Tel.: (354) 5805800
Web Site: http://www.landvelar.is
Year Founded: 1967
Emp.: 30
Commercial & Service Industry Machinery Mfr
N.A.I.C.S.: 333310
Ingvar Bjarnason *(Mng Dir)*

LANEBURY GROWTH CAPITAL LTD.

789 West Pender Street Suite 1080, Vancouver, V6C 1H2, BC, Canada
Tel.: (604) 428-7050
L01—(DEU)
Rev.: $195,887
Assets: $3,943,035
Liabilities: $651,761
Net Worth: $3,291,273
Earnings: $29,513
Fiscal Year-end: 06/30/22
Investment Services
N.A.I.C.S.: 523940
Lance Tracey *(CEO)*

LANESBOROUGH REAL ESTATE INVESTMENT TRUST

c/o Shelter Canadian Properties Limited 2600 Seven Evergreen Place, Winnipeg, R3L 2T3, MB, Canada
Tel.: (204) 475-9090   MB
Web Site: https://www.lreit.com
LRT.UN—(TSX)
Rev.: $5,762,900
Assets: $100,803,274
Liabilities: $245,236,076
Net Worth: $(144,432,802)
Earnings: $(15,122,267)
Emp.: 275
Fiscal Year-end: 12/31/21
Real Estate Investment Trust
N.A.I.C.S.: 525990
Arni C. Thorsteinson *(Vice Chm & Pres)*

Subsidiaries:

Riverside Terrace Inc. (1)
915 Saskatchewan Crescent West, Saskatoon, S7M 0M7, SK, Canada
Tel.: (306) 664-1250
Web Site: https://www.riversideterrace.ca
Sales Range: $25-49.9 Million
Emp.: 30
Building Operator
N.A.I.C.S.: 236220

LANETRO ZED S.A.

Compleja Europa Empresarial Edificio Bruselas C/Rosabella 4 Planta 1, La Rozas, Madrid, 28230, Spain
Tel.: (34) 916404800   ES
Web Site: http://www.zed.com
Year Founded: 1996
Sales Range: $350-399.9 Million
Emp.: 1,200
Mobile Telephone Content
N.A.I.C.S.: 517112
Oscar Aguado Delicado *(CFO)*

Subsidiaries:

Monstermob Group PLC (1)
Office 3-2-4 Story House, White Cross Quarry Road, Lancaster, LA1 4XQ, Lancashire, United Kingdom (52%)
Tel.: (44) 1524846379
Web Site: http://www.monstermobgroup.plc.uk
Sales Range: $200-249.9 Million
Emp.: 57
Mobile Phone Entertainment Services
N.A.I.C.S.: 517112

Subsidiary (US):

9 Squared Inc. (2)
1999 Broadway Ste 1250, Denver, CO 80202
Tel.: (720) 889-0014
Web Site: http://www.9squared.com
Sales Range: $25-49.9 Million
Mobile Phone Entertainment Content Developer
N.A.I.C.S.: 517810
Ted Suh *(CMO)*

Subsidiary (Non-US):

Information Gateway Inc. (2)
3rd-Floor Mobile Entertainment Ctr, 104 Rada St Legaspi Vig, 1229, Manila, Philippines
Tel.: (63) 28929932
Web Site: http://www.informationgateway.net
Cellular & Wireless Telecommunications
N.A.I.C.S.: 517112

LANFRANCHI S.R.L.

Via Scodoncello 41, 43044, Collecchio, Italy
Tel.: (39) 0521 541011
Web Site: http://www.lanfranchigroup.com
Year Founded: 1980
Emp.: 110
Container Handling Equipment Mfr
N.A.I.C.S.: 333248
Mario Lanfranchi *(Pres)*

Subsidiaries:

LANFRANCHI North Europe S.a.s (1)
109 bis Av Jean Lebas, 59100, Roubaix, France
Tel.: (33) 320689620
Industrial Machinery & Equipment Distr
N.A.I.C.S.: 423830

Lanfranchi North America, Inc. (1)
7808 Woodland Center Blvd Ste 900, Tampa, FL 33614
Tel.: (813) 901-5333
Web Site: http://www.lanfranchigroup.com
Sales Range: $1-9.9 Million
Emp.: 3
Container Handling Equipment Mfr
N.A.I.C.S.: 333248
Mario Lanfranchi *(Pres)*

LANG & SCHWARZ AKTIENGESELLSCHAFT

Breite Strasse 34, 40213, Dusseldorf, Germany
Tel.: (49) 211138400
Web Site: https://www.ls-d.de
Year Founded: 1996
LUS1—(DEU)
Rev.: $523,721,131
Assets: $780,563,350

Liabilities: $734,610,404
Net Worth: $45,952,946
Earnings: $8,202,029
Emp.: 76
Fiscal Year-end: 12/31/23
Holding Company; Financial Support Services
N.A.I.C.S.: 551112
Michael Schwartzkopf *(Chm-Supervisory Bd)*

LANG GMBH & CO. KG

Dillstrasse 4, Huttenberg, 35625, Germany
Tel.: (49) 640370090
Web Site: http://www.lang.de
Year Founded: 1972
Rev.: $16,275,098
Emp.: 75
Industrial Machinery Mfr
N.A.I.C.S.: 333248
Richard Lang *(Founder)*

LANG INC

4th Floor No 506 Section 5 Zhongshan North Road, Shilin District, Taipei, 105, Taiwan
Tel.: (886) 27310868
Web Site: https://langinc.com.tw
6165—(TAI)
Rev.: $88,640,534
Assets: $66,766,406
Liabilities: $36,500,211
Net Worth: $30,266,195
Earnings: $503,941
Fiscal Year-end: 12/31/23
Network Analyzer Mfr
N.A.I.C.S.: 334515

Subsidiaries:

JT US, Inc. (1)
14528 Garfield Ave, Paramount, CA 14528
Tel.: (310) 775-9188
Sales Range: $50-74.9 Million
Emp.: 2
Electronic Components Distr
N.A.I.C.S.: 423690

Jye Tai Precision Industrial (M) Sdn. Bhd. (1)
Plot 7 Zone Perdagangan Bebas Kawasan Perusahaan Jelapang II, Jalan Jelapang, 30020, Ipoh, Perak, Malaysia
Tel.: (60) 55261968
Web Site: http://www.jyetai.com.my
Sales Range: $50-74.9 Million
Emp.: 300
Electronic Components Mfr
N.A.I.C.S.: 335999

Jye Tai Precision Industrial Co., Ltd. - Dong Guan JT (1)
Qishih Town, Dongguan, 523508, Guangdong, China
Tel.: (86) 769 8666 4668
Web Site: http://www.jyetai.com
Emp.: 200
Earphone Jack, Phone Jack & Connectors Mfr
N.A.I.C.S.: 334210

Jye Tai Precision Industrial Co., Ltd. - Suzhou JT Factory (1)
No 333 Ku Loong Rd, Song Ling Town, Wujiang, 215200, Jiangsu, China
Tel.: (86) 51263456418
Web Site: http://www.jyetai.com
Sales Range: $200-249.9 Million
Electronic Components Mfr
N.A.I.C.S.: 335931

LANGENSCHEIDT KOMMANDITGESELLSCHAFT

Mies Van Der Rohe Str 1, D 80807, Munich, Germany
Tel.: (49) 89360960
Web Site: http://www.langenscheidt.de
Sales Range: $25-49.9 Million
Emp.: 250

AND PRIVATE COMPANIES

Book Publishing & Printing; Maps, Atlases, Dictionaries & Encyclopedias
N.A.I.C.S.: 513130
Andreas Langenscheidt *(Mng Dir)*

Subsidiaries:

Hagstrom Map Company (1)
3636 33rd St, Long Island City, NY 11106
Tel.: (718) 784-0055
Web Site: http://www.hagstrommap.com
Sales Range: $25-49.9 Million
Emp.: 50
Whslr of Bilingual Maps, Atlases, Dictionaries & Encyclopedias
N.A.I.C.S.: 513199

Subsidiary (Domestic):

ADC The Map People (2)
6440 General Green Way, Alexandria, VA 22312-2413
Tel.: (703) 750-0510
Web Site: http://www.adcmap.com
Sales Range: $25-49.9 Million
Maps & Atlases Publishers
N.A.I.C.S.: 513199

Arrow Maps (2)
3636 33rd St Ste 401, Astoria, NY 11106-2329
Tel.: (508) 230-2112
Web Site: http://www.arrowmap.com
Sales Range: $25-49.9 Million
Emp.: 18
Mfr of Maps & Atlases
N.A.I.C.S.: 513199

LANGFANG DEVELOPMENT CO., LTD.

22F Block B Langfang Development Building No 3 Yongfeng Road, Guangyang District, Langfang, 065000, Hebei, China
Tel.: (86) 3162766166
600149—(SHG)
Rev.: $29,973,842
Assets: $92,344,899
Liabilities: $57,609,125
Net Worth: $34,735,774
Earnings: ($1,176,833)
Fiscal Year-end: 12/31/22
Management Consulting Services
N.A.I.C.S.: 541611
Mei Cao *(Vice Chm & Gen Mgr)*

LANGHAM HOSPITALITY INVESTMENTS LIMITED

Suite 2702 27th Floor Great Eagle Centre 23 Harbour Road Wanchai, Wanchai, China (Hong Kong)
Tel.: (852) 21862500
Web Site:
 https://www.langhamhospitality.com
1270—(HKG)
Rev.: $42,343,515
Assets: $1,915,385,453
Liabilities: $874,863,945
Net Worth: $1,040,521,508
Earnings: $53,494,028
Emp.: 1,148
Fiscal Year-end: 12/31/22
Hotel Owner & Operator
N.A.I.C.S.: 721110
Ka Shui Lo *(Chm)*

Subsidiaries:

Langham Place Hotel (HK) Limited (1)
8 Peking Road Tsim Sha Tsui, Mongkok, Kowloon, China (Hong Kong)
Tel.: (852) 23751133
Web Site:
 http://hongkong.langhamplacehotels.com
Hotel Operator
N.A.I.C.S.: 721110

LANGHOLM CAPITAL LLP

2nd Floor 17 Waterloo Place, 5-11 Regent Street, London, SW1Y 4AR, United Kingdom
Tel.: (44) 2074848850 UK
Web Site: http://www.langholm.com
Sales Range: $25-49.9 Million
Emp.: 13
Investment Management Service
N.A.I.C.S.: 523940
Bert Wiegman *(Founder & Partner)*

Subsidiaries:

LUMENE Oy (1)
Lasikuja 2, 2780, Espoo, Finland (79%)
Tel.: (358) 204 877 100
Web Site: http://www.lumene.com
Sales Range: $100-124.9 Million
Emp.: 530
Cosmetics & Toiletries Mfr & Distr
N.A.I.C.S.: 325620
Tiina Isohanni *(VP-Innovation & Dev)*

Subsidiary (US):

LUMENE North America LLC (2)
201 Boston Post Rd W Ste 405, Marlborough, MA 01752
Tel.: (508) 460-0404
Web Site: http://www.lumene.com
Emp.: 4
Cosmetics Distr
N.A.I.C.S.: 424210
Joe Pastorkovich *(Gen Mgr)*

Subsidiary (Non-US):

LUMENE Russia (2)
Vsevoloda Vishnevskogo Street 12A, Saint Petersburg, 197022, Russia
Tel.: (7) 4959873451
Web Site: http://www.lumene.com
Cosmetics Mfr & Distr
N.A.I.C.S.: 325620

LANGLEY HOLDINGS PLC

Enterprise Way, Retford, DN22 7HH, Nottinghamshire, United Kingdom
Tel.: (44) 1777 700 039 UK
Web Site:
 http://www.langleyholdings.com
Year Founded: 1975
Rev.: $1,075,766,450
Assets: $1,297,509,481
Liabilities: $369,691,511
Net Worth: $927,817,970
Earnings: $54,737,003
Emp.: 4,918
Fiscal Year-end: 12/31/19
Holding Company
N.A.I.C.S.: 551112
Anthony J. Langley *(Founder, Chm & CEO)*

Subsidiaries:

ARO Welding Technologies SAS (1)
1 Avenue de Tours, BP 40161, Montval-Sur-Loir, 72500, Chateau-du-Loir, France
Tel.: (33) 2 43 44 74 00
Web Site: http://www.arotechnologies.com
Emp.: 500
Industrial Welding Equipment Mfr
N.A.I.C.S.: 333992
Jeanyves David *(Pres)*

Subsidiary (Non-US):

ARO Welding Technologies (Wuhan) Co. Ltd. (2)
81 CheChengNan Road Economic & Technology Developing Zone M Bldg-West, 430056, Wuhan, China
Tel.: (86) 27 8447 1353
Industrial Welding Equipment Distr
N.A.I.C.S.: 423830

ARO Welding Technologies AB (2)
Timotejvagen 7, 439 71, Kungsbacka, Sweden
Tel.: (46) 300 543 988
Industrial Welding Equipment Distr
N.A.I.C.S.: 423830

ARO Welding Technologies GmbH (2)
Blucherstrasse 135b, 86165, Augsburg, Germany
Tel.: (49) 821 797 1980
Industrial Welding Equipment Distr
N.A.I.C.S.: 423830

Subsidiary (US):

ARO Welding Technologies Inc (2)
48500 Structural Dr Chesterfield Township, New Baltimore, MI 48051
Tel.: (586) 949-9353
Industrial Welding Equipment Distr
N.A.I.C.S.: 423830

Subsidiary (Non-US):

ARO Welding Technologies S.A. de C.V. (2)
43B Sur 4720 Estrella del Sur, 72190, Puebla, Mexico
Tel.: (52) 222 230 00 37
Web Site: http://www.arotechnologies.com
Industrial Welding Equipment Distr
N.A.I.C.S.: 423830

ARO Welding Technologies S.A.U (2)
C/ Cuzco 26-28 nave 2, 08030, Barcelona, Spain
Tel.: (34) 93 421 2111
Industrial Welding Equipment Distr
N.A.I.C.S.: 423830

ARO Welding Technologies SA-NV (2)
Riverside Business Park 55/15 Bd Internationalelaan, 1070, Brussels, Belgium
Tel.: (32) 2 555 0750
Industrial Welding Equipment Distr
N.A.I.C.S.: 423830

ARO Welding Technologies s.r.o. (2)
Karloveska 63, 84104, Bratislava, Slovakia
Tel.: (421) 265 440 585
Web Site: http://www.arotechnologies.com
Industrial Welding Equipment Distr
N.A.I.C.S.: 423830

Bradman Lake Ltd (1)
Common Lane North, Suffolk, Beccles, NR34 9BP, United Kingdom
Tel.: (44) 1502 470 500
Web Site: http://www.bradmanlake.com
Industrial Machinery Distr
N.A.I.C.S.: 423830

Subsidiary (Non-US):

Bradman Lake China (2)
No 1111 Zheng Nan Road Room 1105 Building No 5, Shanghai Packaging City, Shanghai, 200331, China
Tel.: (86) 21 6608 1980
Industrial Machinery Distr
N.A.I.C.S.: 423830

Subsidiary (US):

Bradman Lake Inc (2)
3050 Southcross Blvd, Rock Hill, SC 29730
Tel.: (704) 588-3301
Web Site: http://www.bradmanlake.com
Industrial Machinery Distr
N.A.I.C.S.: 423830
Gary Pickett *(Pres)*

Subsidiary (Non-US):

Bradman Lake Russia (2)
100 Schelkovskoe highway Building 2 office 13, Business center East Gate, 105523, Moscow, Russia
Tel.: (7) 495 287 4768
Web Site: http://www.bradmanlake.com
Industrial Machinery Distr
N.A.I.C.S.: 423830

Claudius Peters (Asia Pacific) Pte Ltd. (2)
25 International Business Park 01-65/66 German Centre, Singapore, 609916, Singapore
Tel.: (65) 65629100
Cement Mfr
N.A.I.C.S.: 327310

Claudius Peters (Iberica) SA (1)
Paseo de la Habana 202 Bis, 28036, Madrid, Spain
Tel.: (34) 914133616
Cement Mfr
N.A.I.C.S.: 327310

Claudius Peters Automation Srl (1)
Str Oituz Nr 25C Et 2, Sibiu, Romania
Tel.: (40) 369407036

LANGLEY HOLDINGS PLC

Cement Mfr
N.A.I.C.S.: 327310

Claudius Peters Group GmbH (1)
Schanzenstrasse 40, 21614, Buxtehude, Germany (100%)
Tel.: (49) 41617060
Web Site: http://www.claudiuspeters.com
Sales Range: $300-349.9 Million
Emp.: 80
Engineering Holding Company
N.A.I.C.S.: 551112
Reiner Fruehling *(Mng Dir)*

Subsidiary (US):

Claudius Peters (Americas) Inc. (2)
445 W Bush Tpke, Richardson, TX 75080
Tel.: (972) 386-4451
Aircraft Parts Distr
N.A.I.C.S.: 423860

Subsidiary (Non-US):

Claudius Peters (China) Ltd. (2)
Unit 1705-1706 17/F Laws Commercial Plaza 788 Cheung Sha Wan Road, Lai Chi Kok, Kowloon, China (Hong Kong)
Tel.: (852) 2544 1848
Web Site: http://www.claudiuspeters.com
Aircraft Parts Distr
N.A.I.C.S.: 423860

Claudius Peters (India) Pvt. Ltd (2)
Peninsula Plaza A/16 Fun Republic Lane Off Link Road Unit 408 4th Floo, Andheri West, Mumbai, 400 053, India
Tel.: (91) 22 2674 0045
Aircraft Parts Distr
N.A.I.C.S.: 423860

Claudius Peters (Italiana) s.r.l. (2)
Via Verdi 2 1, 24121, Bergamo, Italy
Tel.: (39) 0 35 237 196
Web Site: http://www.claudiuspeters.com
Aircraft Parts Distr
N.A.I.C.S.: 423860

Claudius Peters (UK) Ltd. (2)
Unit 10 Thatcham Business Village Colthrop Way, Berkshire, Thatcham, RG19 4LW, United Kingdom
Tel.: (44) 1635 872139
Aircraft Parts Distr
N.A.I.C.S.: 423860

Claudius Peters Machinery Service Co. Ltd. (2)
Room 2010 The Exchange Beijing B-118 Jianguo Road, Chaoyang District, Beijing, 100022, China
Tel.: (86) 10 6501 3831
Web Site: http://www.claudiuspeters.com
Aircraft Parts Distr
N.A.I.C.S.: 423860

Claudius Peters Romania S.R.L. (2)
Str Oituz Nr 25C et 2, 550337, Sibiu, Romania
Tel.: (40) 369 407 036
Emp.: 10
Aircraft Parts Distr
N.A.I.C.S.: 423860

Subsidiary (Domestic):

Claudius Peters Technologies GmbH (2)
Schanzenstrasse 40, 21614, Buxtehude, Germany (100%)
Tel.: (49) 41617060
Web Site: http://www.claudiuspeters.com
Sales Range: $75-99.9 Million
Materials Processing Technologies & Engineered Systems
N.A.I.C.S.: 541330
Reiner Fruehling *(Gen Mgr)*

Subsidiary (Non-US):

Claudius Peters Technologies S.A. (2)
34 Avenue de Suisse, 68316, Illzach, France (100%)
Tel.: (33) 389313300
Web Site: http://www.claudiuspeters.com
Sales Range: $25-49.9 Million
Wholesale of Industrial Machinery
N.A.I.C.S.: 423830
Remy Coursaux *(Pres)*

LANGLEY HOLDINGS PLC

Langley Holdings Plc—(Continued)

Claudius Peters do Brasil Ltda. (1)
Rua das Figueiras 474 - 3 Andar, Bairro Jardim, Santo Andre, 09080-300, SP, Brazil
Tel.: (55) 1149039230
Cement Mfr
N.A.I.C.S.: 327310

Marelli Motori Central Europe GmbH (1)
Heilswannenweg 50, 31008, Elze, Germany
Tel.: (49) 5068462440
Motor & Generator Distr
N.A.I.C.S.: 423610

Marelli Motori South Africa Ltd. (Pty) (1)
Unit 2 Corner Director and Megawatt Road Spartan Ext 23, Kempton Park, 1619, Gauteng, South Africa
Tel.: (27) 113921920
Motor & Generator Distr
N.A.I.C.S.: 423610

Oakdale Homes Limited (1)
Building 2 Enterprise Way, Retford, DN22 7HH, Nottinghamshire, United Kingdom
Tel.: (44) 1777710943
Web Site: https://www.oakdalehomes.co.uk
Property Management Services
N.A.I.C.S.: 531311

Piller Germany GmbH & Co KG (1)
Abgunst 24, 37520, Osterode am Hartz, Germany
Tel.: (49) 55223110
Power Supply Equipment Mfr
N.A.I.C.S.: 335999

Piller Group GmbH (1)
Abgunst 24, 37520, Osterode am Hartz, Germany
Tel.: (49) 5522 311 0
Web Site: http://www.piller.com
Uninterruptible Power Supply Mfr
N.A.I.C.S.: 335999
Detlev Seidel *(Member-Mgmt Bd)*

Subsidiary (Non-US):

PILLER (Thailand) Co. Ltd (2)
75 Moo 3 Petchkasem Road, Banmai, Sam Phran, 73110, Nakorn Pathom, Thailand
Tel.: (66) 2 805 81 69
Web Site: http://www.piller.co.th
Uninterruptible Power Supply Distr
N.A.I.C.S.: 423690

Piller Australia Pty Ltd (2)
2/3 Salisbury Road, Castle Hill, Sydney, 2154, NSW, Australia
Tel.: (61) 2 9894 1888
Uninterruptible Power Supply Distr
N.A.I.C.S.: 423690

Piller Denmark A/S (2)
Vintapperbuen 3, 4070, Kirke Hyllinge, Denmark
Tel.: (45) 4640 3214
Uninterruptible Power Supply Distr
N.A.I.C.S.: 423690

Piller France SAS (2)
107-111 Av Georges, PO Box 908, Clemenceau, 92009, Nanterre, Cedex, France
Tel.: (33) 1 47 21 22 55
Uninterruptible Power Supply Distr
N.A.I.C.S.: 423690

Piller Iberica S.L.U (2)
Paseo de la Habana 202 Bis Bj, 28036, Madrid, Spain
Tel.: (34) 91 345 86 58
Uninterruptible Power Supply Distr
N.A.I.C.S.: 423690

Piller Italia S.r.l. (2)
Centro Direzionale Colleoni Palazzo Pegaso 3 Viale Colleoni 25, 20041, Agrate Brianza, MB, Italy
Tel.: (39) 039 6892735
Uninterruptible Power Supply Distr
N.A.I.C.S.: 423690

Piller Power Singapore Pte. Ltd. (2)
25 International Business Park 04-27/29 German Centre, Singapore, 609916, Singapore
Tel.: (65) 6562 9100
Web Site: http://www.piller.com
Uninterruptible Power Supply Distr
N.A.I.C.S.: 423690

Piller UK Limited (2)
Phoenix Way, Westgate, Cirencester, GL7 1RY, Gloucestershire, United Kingdom
Tel.: (44) 1285 657 721
Web Site: http://www.piller.com
Emp.: 40
Uninterruptible Power Supply Distr
N.A.I.C.S.: 423690

Subsidiary (US):

Piller USA Inc (2)
45 W Turner Dr, Middletown, NY 10941-2047
Tel.: (800) 597-6937
Uninterruptible Power Supply Distr
N.A.I.C.S.: 423690

Division (Domestic):

Active Power (3)
2128 W Braker Ln, Austin, TX 78758
Tel.: (512) 836-6464
Web Site: http://www.activepower.com
Flywheel Power Supply & Modular Infrastructure Technologies Designer, Mfr & Whslr
N.A.I.C.S.: 335999

Subsidiary (Non-US):

Active Power (Germany) GmbH (4)
An der Leege 22, 37520, Osterode am Hartz, Germany
Tel.: (49) 5522507700
Web Site: http://www.activepower.com
Energy Storage Products Mfr
N.A.I.C.S.: 335999

Active Power Solutions Ltd. (4)
Westgate Phoenix Way, Cirencester, GL7 1RY, Glos, United Kingdom
Tel.: (44) 1285 657 721
Web Site: http://www.activepower.com
Energy Storage Products Mfr
N.A.I.C.S.: 335999

Piller Power Beijing Co. Ltd. (1)
Rm 803-2 Chaoyangmen Soho No 1 Nan Zhu Gan Hutong, Dongcheng District, Beijing, 100010, China
Tel.: (86) 1065283700
Power Supply Equipment Mfr
N.A.I.C.S.: 335999

Power India Pvt Ltd. (1)
Unit No 207 02nd Floor ABW Tower MG Road, Gurgaon, 122001, Haryana, India
Tel.: (91) 1244290262
Power Supply Equipment Mfr
N.A.I.C.S.: 335999

Pressure Engineering International Ltd (1)
Retford Road, Manton, Worksop, S80 2PU, Nottinghamshire, United Kingdom
Tel.: (44) 1909 535 400
Industrial Machinery Distr
N.A.I.C.S.: 423830

Reader Cement Products Limited (1)
Kirkby Lane, Pinxton, NG16 6HX, Nottinghamshire, United Kingdom
Tel.: (44) 1623518360
Web Site: https://www.reader.co.uk
Cement Product Mfr
N.A.I.C.S.: 327310

Reader Grout & Equipment Ltd (1)
Nunn Brook Road, County Estate, Sutton in Ashfield, NG17 2HW, Nottinghamshire, United Kingdom
Tel.: (44) 1623 518 350
Web Site: http://www.langleyholdings.co.uk
Emp.: 10
Industrial Machinery Distr
N.A.I.C.S.: 423830
Mike Smith *(Bus Dir)*

The Clarke Chapman Group Limited (1)
Saltmeadows Road, PO Box 9, Gateshead, NE8 1SW, Tyne & Wear, United Kingdom
Tel.: (44) 191 477 2271
Web Site: http://www.clarkechapman.co.uk
Emp.: 80
Material Handling Equipment Mfr
N.A.I.C.S.: 333248
Maureen Judd *(Mgr-HR)*

Subsidiary (Domestic):

Clarke Chapman Facilities Management Ltd. (2)
Office 106 Golborne Enterprise Park Kid Glove Road, Golborne, Warrington, WA3 3GR, Cheshire, United Kingdom **(100%)**
Tel.: (44) 1942 715 666
Web Site: http://www.clarkechapman.co.uk
Facilities Management Services
N.A.I.C.S.: 561210

Clarke Chapman Manufacturing Ltd (2)
Saltmeadows Road, Gateshead, NE8 1SW, Tyne and Wear, United Kingdom **(100%)**
Tel.: (44) 1914772271
Web Site: http://www.clarkechapman.co.uk
Emp.: 80
Handling Equipment Mfr
N.A.I.C.S.: 423830

Clarke Chapman Services Ltd. (2)
Unit 15 Planetary Industrial Estate Planetary Road, Willenhall, Wolverhampton, WV13 3XA, United Kingdom **(100%)**
Tel.: (44) 1902 728 844
Web Site: http://www.clarkechapman.co.uk
Emp.: 30
Equipment Support, Installation, Repair & Refurbishment Services
N.A.I.C.S.: 811310
Colin Pagett *(Bus Mgr)*

Stothert & Pitt Ltd (2)
1-9 Yelverton Road, Brislington, Bristol, BS4 5HP, United Kingdom
Tel.: (44) 117 9718601
Emp.: 10
Engineering Consulting Services
N.A.I.C.S.: 541330
Nick Hancock *(Gen Mgr)*

Wellman Booth Ltd (2)
Unit 2 Kirkfield Industrial & Commercial Centre Kirk Lane, Yeadon, Leeds, LS19 7LX, United Kingdom
Tel.: (44) 113 387 9730
Overhead Traveling Crane Mfr
N.A.I.C.S.: 333923
Sukhraj Nahal *(Project Mgr)*

manroland sheetfed GmbH (1)
Muhlheimer Strasse 341, D 63075, Offenbach, Germany
Tel.: (49) 6983050
Web Site: http://www.manrolandsheetfed.com
Sales Range: $300-349.9 Million
Emp.: 1,600
Printing Machinery Mfr
N.A.I.C.S.: 333248
Rafael Penuela-Torres *(Grp CEO)*

Subsidiary (Non-US):

Manroland Australasia Pty. Ltd. (2)
V5 391 Park Road, Regents Park, 2143, NSW, Australia
Tel.: (61) 2 9645 7900
Offset Printing Press Mfr
N.A.I.C.S.: 333248

Manroland Bulgaria EOOD (2)
251 Okolovrasten pat Street Delta center floor 2 office 203, 1766, Sofia, Bulgaria
Tel.: (359) 2 95 594 61
Web Site: http://www.manrolandsheetfed.com
Offset Printing Press Distr
N.A.I.C.S.: 423830

Manroland India Pvt. Ltd. (2)
153 Ground Floor Okhla Industrial Estate Phase-III, New Delhi, 110 020, India
Tel.: (91) 11 47 00 29 00
Web Site: http://www.manroland.com
Offset Printing Press Distr
N.A.I.C.S.: 423830

Manroland Indonesia P.T. (2)
Management Building 2nd Floor Jl Buncit Raya Kav 100, 12510, Jakarta, Indonesia
Tel.: (62) 2179199818
Offset Printing Press Distr
N.A.I.C.S.: 423830

Manroland Italia S.p.A. (2)

INTERNATIONAL PUBLIC

Via Lambretta 2, 20090, Segrate, MI, Italy
Tel.: (39) 02 21 307 1
Offset Printing Press Distr
N.A.I.C.S.: 423830

Manroland Korea Ltd. (2)
2F Gaya Building 570-1, Yeonnam-dong Mapo Gu, Seoul, 121-869, Korea (South)
Tel.: (82) 2 777 5271
Offset Printing Press Distr
N.A.I.C.S.: 423830

Manroland Malaysia Sdn Bhd (2)
Unit 315 Laman Seri Industrial Park, Persiaran Sukan Seksyen 13, 40000, Shah Alam, Selangor, Malaysia
Tel.: (60) 5518 3899
Offset Printing Press Distr
N.A.I.C.S.: 423830

Manroland Osterreich GmbH (2)
IZ No-Sud Strasse 16 Objekt 70/1, Wiener Neudorf, 2355, Austria
Tel.: (43) 22 36 81 21 0
Offset Printing Press Distr
N.A.I.C.S.: 423830

Manroland Printing Equipment (Shenzhen) Co. Ltd. (2)
Room 101-106 Blk C Huahan Chuangxin Park Keyuan Road, Hi-Tech Zone North District, Shenzhen, 518057, China
Tel.: (86) 755 8886 6767
Offset Printing Press Distr
N.A.I.C.S.: 423830

Manroland Sheetfed (UK) Ltd (2)
110-112 Morden Road, Mitcham, CR4 4XB, Surrey, United Kingdom
Tel.: (44) 20 8648 7090
Offset Printing Press Distr
N.A.I.C.S.: 423830

Manroland Southern Africa (PTY) Ltd. (2)
15 Manhattan Street Airport Industria, Cape Town, 7490, South Africa
Tel.: (27) 21 385 05 00
Web Site: http://www.manrolandsheetfed.com
Offset Printing Press Distr
N.A.I.C.S.: 423830

Manroland czech s.r.o. (2)
Prumyslova 10/1428, Prague, 102 00, Czech Republic
Tel.: (420) 272 011 831
Offset Printing Press Distr
N.A.I.C.S.: 423830

Manroland do Brasil Servicos Ltda (2)
Rua das Figueiras 474-3 andar Edificio Eiffel Bairro Jardim, Santo Andre, 09080-300, Sao Paulo, Brazil
Tel.: (55) 11 4903 9200
Offset Printing Press Distr
N.A.I.C.S.: 423830

Manroland latina S.A. (2)
Av Regimiento de Patricios 1052 Floor 3 Office 371, C1265AEP, Buenos Aires, Argentina
Tel.: (54) 1145178807
Web Site: http://www.manrolandsheetfed.com
Offset Printing Press
N.A.I.C.S.: 333248

Manroland latina S.A.C. (2)
Los Geranios No 328, Lince, Lima, Peru
Tel.: (51) 1 421 8442
Offset Printing Press Distr
N.A.I.C.S.: 423830

Manroland latina S.A.S (2)
Carrera 8 Nro 67-63, Bogota, Colombia
Tel.: (57) 12550510
Offset Printing Press Distr
N.A.I.C.S.: 423830

Manroland latina SA de CV (2)
Darwin No 31, Nueva Anzures, Colonia, 11590, Mexico
Tel.: (52) 55 5998 4100
Offset Printing Press Distr
N.A.I.C.S.: 423830

manroland (China) Ltd. (2)
7/F Capella HTR 47 Hung To Road, Kwun Tong, Kowloon, China (Hong Kong)

AND PRIVATE COMPANIES — LANKA GRAPHITE LIMITED

Tel.: (852) 28973398
Web Site: http://www.manroland.cn
Printing Machinery Distr
N.A.I.C.S.: 333248

Subsidiary (Non-US):

manroland (Taiwan) Ltd. (3)
17F-9 No 738 Chung Cheng Road, Chung-Ho District, Taipei, 23511, Taiwan
Tel.: (886) 282262068
Web Site: http://www.manroland.cn
Sales Range: $10-24.9 Million
Printing Machinery Distr
N.A.I.C.S.: 333248

Subsidiary (Non-US):

manroland Adriatic d.o.o. (2)
Kovinska 4A, 10000, Zagreb, Croatia
Tel.: (385) 1 3370 557
Offset Printing Press Distr
N.A.I.C.S.: 423830

manroland Benelux N.V. (2)
Koningin Astridlaan 61, 1780, Wemmel, Belgium
Tel.: (32) 2 456 85 00
Web Site: http://bx.manrolandsheetfed.com
Commercial Printing Services
N.A.I.C.S.: 323111

manroland France SAS (2)
Bat M1 Les Aralias Paris Nord II 66 rue des Vanesses CS 53290, Villepinte, 95958, Roissy-en-France, Cedex, France
Tel.: (33) 1 49 38 40 00
Web Site: http://www.man-roland.fr
Printing Machinery Distr
N.A.I.C.S.: 423830

Subsidiary (Domestic):

manroland Heusenstamm GmbH (2)
Industriestrasse 25, 63150, Heusenstamm, Germany
Tel.: (49) 69 83050
Printing Machinery Mfr
N.A.I.C.S.: 333248

Subsidiary (Non-US):

manroland Iberica Sistemas S.A. (2)
Rua Casal Queimado Edif Man Roland Nr 205-205-A, Cascais, 2750-492, Portugal
Tel.: (351) 214879540
Printing Equipment Mfr
N.A.I.C.S.: 333248

manroland Iberica Sistemas S.L. (2)
C/ San Severo 30 Parque empresarial Barajas Park, 28042, Madrid, Spain
Tel.: (34) 91 329 22 44
Web Site: http://www.man-roland-es.com
Printing Machinery Distr
N.A.I.C.S.: 423830

Subsidiary (US):

manroland Inc. (2)
800 E Oakhill Dr, Westmont, IL 60559 **(100%)**
Tel.: (630) 920-2000
Web Site: http://www.manrolandsheetfed.com
Printing Machinery Mfr
N.A.I.C.S.: 333248

Subsidiary (Non-US):

manroland Canada Inc. (3)
9131 Keele Street Suite A4, Vaughan, L4K 0G7, ON, Canada **(100%)**
Tel.: (905) 265-6300
Web Site: http://www.manrolandsheetfed.com
Sales Range: $25-49.9 Million
Emp.: 17
Printing Machinery Distr
N.A.I.C.S.: 333248
Gina Gigliozzi (Mgr-Sls Admin & Toronto Office)

Subsidiary (Non-US):

manroland Ireland Ltd. (2)
Unit N2 North Ring Business Park, Santry, Dublin, Ireland
Tel.: (353) 1 832 1355
Web Site: http://www.manrolandsheetfed.com
Printing Machinery Mfr

N.A.I.C.S.: 333248

manroland Japan Co., Ltd. (2)
2-3-4 Niizo-Minami, Toda, 335-0026, Saitama, Japan
Tel.: (81) 50 2018 7305
Web Site: http://www.manroland.co.jp
Offset Printing Press Distr
N.A.I.C.S.: 423830
Sascha Bansemer (Mng Dir)

manroland Magyarorszag Kft. (2)
Tablas u 36-38, 1097, Budapest, Hungary
Tel.: (36) 1 326 0907
Web Site: http://www.manrolandsheetfed.com
Sales Range: $50-74.9 Million
Printing Equipment Distr
N.A.I.C.S.: 423830

manroland Nordic Danmark A/S (2)
Lautruphoj 1-3, 2750, Ballerup, Denmark
Tel.: (45) 44 35 55 55
Web Site: http://www.manrolandsheetfed.com
Commercial Printing Services
N.A.I.C.S.: 323113

manroland Nordic Finland Oy (2)
Tammiston Kauppatie 22, 01510, Vantaa, Finland
Tel.: (358) 9 725 66 500
Web Site: http://www.manrolandsheetfed.com
Printing Machinery Distr
N.A.I.C.S.: 423830
Lauri Vanhala (Mng Dir)

manroland Nordic Norge AS (2)
Solheimveien 50, 1473, Lorenskog, Norway
Tel.: (47) 67 92 11 80
Web Site: http://www.manroland.no
Printing Machinery Mfr
N.A.I.C.S.: 333248
Bjorn Gustafsson (Mng Dir)

manroland Nordic Sverige AB (2)
Nohabgatan 12H Byggnad 33, 461 53, Trollhattan, Sweden
Tel.: (46) 52 08 93 00
Web Site: http://www.manrolandsheetfed.com
Printing Machinery Mfr
N.A.I.C.S.: 333248
Bjorn Gustafsson (Mng Dir)

manroland Poland Sp. z o.o. (2)
Wolica Aleja Katowicka 11, 05 830, Nadarzyn, Poland
Tel.: (48) 22 738 00 00
Web Site: http://www.manrolandsheetfed.com
Offset Printing Presses & Related Technologies Mfr
N.A.I.C.S.: 333248

manroland Printing Equipment (Shanghai) Ltd. (2)
Room 901 Bld A HongKou Plaza No 388 West Jiang Wan Rd, Hong Kou, Shanghai, 200083, China
Tel.: (86) 21 3636 3000
Emp.: 50
Printing Machinery Distr
N.A.I.C.S.: 423830
Kurt Herman (Gen Mgr)

manroland Romania S.R.L. (2)
Str Ziduri Intre Vii 19 Corp C Parter Spatiu C-5 Sector 2, Bucharest, 023321, Romania
Tel.: (40) 21 242 0098
Web Site: http://www.manrolandsheetfed.com
Printing Machinery Mfr
N.A.I.C.S.: 333248
Narcisa Vraciu (Mng Dir)

manroland Swiss AG (2)
Schoneich 1, 6265, Roggliswil, Switzerland
Tel.: (41) 34 447 71 11
Web Site: http://www.manrolandsheetfed.com
Printing Machinery Distr
N.A.I.C.S.: 423830

manroland Thailand Ltd. (2)
22/6 Ladprao Soi 21 Jomphol Jatujak, Bangkok, 10900, Thailand
Tel.: (66) 2 513 8629
Web Site: http://www.manrolandsheetfed.com

Printing Machinery Mfr
N.A.I.C.S.: 333248

Subsidiary (Domestic):

manroland Vertrieb und Service GmbH (2)
Borsigstrasse 19, 63165, Muhlheim, Germany
Tel.: (49) 69 83 05 00
Web Site: http://www.manrolandsheetfed.com
Printing Machinery Mfr
N.A.I.C.S.: 333248
Rafael Torres Penuela (Gen Mgr)

Subsidiary (Non-US):

manroland Western Europe Group B.V. (2)
Kuiperbergweg 50, 1101 AG, Amsterdam, Netherlands
Tel.: (31) 205872501
Investment Management Service
N.A.I.C.S.: 523999

manroland d.o.o. (2)
Tolstojeva 9A, 1000, Ljubljana, Slovenia
Tel.: (386) 1 565 92 30
Printing Machinery Distr
N.A.I.C.S.: 423830

LANGLEY TOYOTATOWN
20622 Langley Bypass, Langley, V3A 6K8, BC, Canada
Tel.: (604) 530-3156
Web Site: http://www.toyotatown.ca
Year Founded: 1991
Rev.: $41,522,834
Emp.: 60
New & Used Car Dealers
N.A.I.C.S.: 441110
Scott Kemp (Gen Mgr)

LANGLOIS SOBRETI
23 Rue De La Frebardiere ZI Sud Est, CS 13629, 35063, Rennes, Ille Et Vilaine, France
Tel.: (33) 299268740
Web Site: http://www.langloissobreti.fr
Rev.: $22,800,000
Emp.: 131
Plastering, Drywall & Insulation
N.A.I.C.S.: 238310
Jean-Yves Rottier (Mgr)

LANGOLD REAL ESTATE CO., LTD.
No 3 Jianghan North Road, Jiangan District, Wuhan, 430060, Hubei, China
Tel.: (86) 2783988055
Web Site: http://www.langold.com.cn
Year Founded: 1998
002305—(SSE)
Rev.: $1,378,589,004
Assets: $4,087,584,540
Liabilities: $3,511,569,672
Net Worth: $576,014,868
Earnings: ($121,712,760)
Fiscal Year-end: 12/31/22
Real Estate Development Services
N.A.I.C.S.: 531311
Mingxuan Li (Chm)

LANHAI MEDICAL INVESTMENT CO., LTD.
201 Century Avenue 20th Floor, Pudong New Area, Shanghai, 200120, China
Tel.: (86) 2150292926
Web Site: http://www.lanhaimedical.com
600896—(SHG)
Rev.: $11,397,292
Assets: $442,467,416
Liabilities: $96,782,757
Net Worth: $345,684,659
Earnings: $9,388,709
Emp.: 144

Fiscal Year-end: 12/31/20
Investment Services
N.A.I.C.S.: 523999
Jing He (Sec & VP)

LANIFICIO ANGELICO SRL
Ronco Biellese, Rome, 13845, Italy
Tel.: (39) 015846111
Web Site: http://www.angelico.it
Textile Mfr
N.A.I.C.S.: 314999

Subsidiaries:

Marling & Evans Ltd. (1)
Filkins, Lechlade, GL7 3JJ, Gloucestershire, United Kingdom **(65%)**
Tel.: (44) 1367860660
Web Site: http://www.marlingandevans.co.uk
Sales Range: $25-49.9 Million
Emp.: 20
Woollen Weaving
N.A.I.C.S.: 313210

LANITIS GOLF PUBLIC CO., LTD.
21 Archbishop Kyprianou Street, PO Box 50336, Limassol, Cyprus
Tel.: (357) 25820920
Assets: $86,731,728
Liabilities: $16,771,873
Net Worth: $69,959,855
Earnings: ($323,290)
Golf Resort Management Services
N.A.I.C.S.: 713910

LANKA ALUMINIUM INDUSTRIES PLC
1st Floor Lakshmans Building 321 Galle Road, 3, Colombo, Sri Lanka
Tel.: (94) 112565951
Web Site: https://www.aluminium.lk
Year Founded: 1986
LALU—(COL)
Rev.: $8,759,575
Assets: $11,327,699
Liabilities: $3,481,422
Net Worth: $7,846,277
Earnings: $731,647
Emp.: 279
Fiscal Year-end: 03/31/23
Aluminum Extrusions Mfr
N.A.I.C.S.: 331314
Ranjeevan Seevaratnam (Exec Dir)

LANKA ASHOK LEYLAND PLC
No 41 Edward Lane R A De Mel Mawatha, 3, Colombo, 03, Sri Lanka
Tel.: (94) 112502532
Web Site: https://www.lal.lk
ASHO—(COL)
Rev.: $36,500,323
Assets: $40,659,854
Liabilities: $20,993,705
Net Worth: $19,666,150
Earnings: $1,824,627
Emp.: 239
Fiscal Year-end: 03/31/22
Commercial Vehicles Assembling Services
N.A.I.C.S.: 336211
Umesh Gautam (CEO)

LANKA CEMENT PLC
328 Galle Road, Colombo, 03, Sri Lanka
Tel.: (94) 112573598
Web Site: http://renukahotel.com
Year Founded: 1981
Cement Mfr
N.A.I.C.S.: 327310
Salley M. R. S. (Mng Dir)

LANKA GRAPHITE LIMITED
Suite 32 Level 18 101 Collins Street, Melbourne, 3000, VIC, Australia
Tel.: (61) 392216394   AU

LANKA GRAPHITE LIMITED

Lanka Graphite Limited—(Continued)
Web Site:
http://www.lankagraphite.com.au
Rev.: $13
Assets: $37,351
Liabilities: $1,964,584
Net Worth: ($1,927,233)
Earnings: ($3,998,883)
Fiscal Year-end: 06/30/18
Graphite Exploration Services
N.A.I.C.S.: 213115
Justyn Peter Stedwell *(Sec)*

LANKA MILK FOODS (CWE) PLC
579/1 Welisara, Ragama, Sri Lanka
Tel.: (94) 112956263
Web Site: https://www.lmfgroup.lk
Year Founded: 1981
LMF—(COL)
Rev.: $47,173,866
Assets: $70,325,435
Liabilities: $21,378,200
Net Worth: $48,947,235
Earnings: $3,958,607
Emp.: 724
Fiscal Year-end: 03/31/23
Dairy Products & Beverages Mfr
N.A.I.C.S.: 311514
Don Harold Stassen Jayawardena *(Chm)*

LANKA SUGAR COMPANY (PVT.) LIMITED
No 27 Melbourne Ave, 4, Colombo, Sri Lanka
Tel.: (94) 11 2584184
Web Site: http://www.lankasugar.lk
Sugar & Sugar Products Mfr
N.A.I.C.S.: 311314
Janaka Nimalachandra *(Chm)*

LANKA TILES PLC
Tel.: (94) 112808001
Web Site: https://www.lankatiles.com
Year Founded: 1984
TILE—(COL)
Rev.: $62,195,140
Assets: $62,003,925
Liabilities: $18,955,481
Net Worth: $43,048,444
Earnings: $12,275,896
Emp.: 744
Fiscal Year-end: 03/31/23
Tiles Mfr
N.A.I.C.S.: 327120
Tyrell Roche *(Gen Mgr-Fin)*

LANKA VENTURES PLC
Tel.: (94) 112439201
Web Site: https://www.acuity.lk
Year Founded: 1992
LVEN.N0000—(COL)
Rev.: $951,304
Assets: $30,826,570
Liabilities: $11,419,249
Net Worth: $19,407,321
Earnings: ($1,019)
Fiscal Year-end: 12/31/23
Investment Services
N.A.I.C.S.: 525910
Sumith Arangala *(CEO)*

LANKA WALLTILE PLC
215 Nawala Road Narahenpita, 5, Colombo, 05, Sri Lanka
Tel.: (94) 114526700
Web Site: https://www.lankatiles.com
LWL—(COL)
Rev.: $212,041,974
Assets: $231,598,608
Liabilities: $106,840,799
Net Worth: $124,757,809
Earnings: $36,612,676
Emp.: 6,518
Fiscal Year-end: 03/31/22

Ceramic Tile Mfr
N.A.I.C.S.: 327120
Jayasekera Arachchige Panduka Mahendra Jayasekera *(Mng Dir)*

Subsidiaries:

Horana Plantations Plc (1)
No 400 Deans Road, 10, Colombo, Sri Lanka
Tel.: (94) 112627318
Web Site:
https://www.horanaplantations.com
Emp.: 3,857
Agricultural Organization Services
N.A.I.C.S.: 115116
Ajith Nissanka *(Gen Mgr-Fin)*

Swisstek Aluminium Ltd. (1)
No 23 Nawala Road, Nawala, Colombo, Sri Lanka
Tel.: (94) 117807000
Web Site:
https://www.swisstekaluminium.com
Emp.: 600
Window Mfr
N.A.I.C.S.: 332321
J. A. P. M. Jayasekera *(Mng Dir)*

Uni-Dil Packaging Ltd. (1)
Narampola Road, Moragala Dekatana, Colombo, Sri Lanka
Tel.: (94) 11 540 0000
Web Site: https://www.unidil.com
Packaging Materials Mfr
N.A.I.C.S.: 333993
Bannet Gamalath *(CEO)*

LANKABANGLA FINANCE LTD.
Safura Tower Level 11 20 Kemal Ataturk Avenue Banani, Dhaka, 1213, Bangladesh
Tel.: (880) 29883701
Web Site:
https://www.lankabangla.com
Year Founded: 1997
LANKABAFIN—(DHA)
Rev.: $79,946,828
Assets: $1,031,551,453
Liabilities: $905,412,807
Net Worth: $126,138,646
Earnings: $15,148,353
Emp.: 1,331
Fiscal Year-end: 12/31/21
Financial Services
N.A.I.C.S.: 525990
Quamrul Islam *(Head-Treasury & Fin Institutions)*

Subsidiaries:

LankaBangla Asset Management Company Limited (1)
Praasad Trade Centre 4th Floor 6 Kemal Ataturk Avenue Banani C/A, Dhaka, 1213, Bangladesh
Tel.: (880) 222227421921
Web Site: https://www.lbamcl.com
Portfolio Management Services
N.A.I.C.S.: 523940
Masum Ali *(CEO)*

LankaBangla Investments Limited (1)
Assurance Nazir Tower Level-08 65/B Kemal Ataturk Avenue, Banani, Dhaka, 1213, Bangladesh
Tel.: (880) 2550348535
Web Site: https://www.lankabangla-investments.com
Portfolio Management Services
N.A.I.C.S.: 523940
Iftekhar Alam *(CEO)*

LankaBangla Securities Limited (1)
City Centre 13th Floor 90/1 Motijheel, Dhaka, 1000, Bangladesh
Tel.: (880) 9611016325
Web Site: https://www.lbsbd.com
Financial Investment Market Services
N.A.I.C.S.: 327910
Mohammed Nasir Uddin Chowdhury *(Mng Dir)*

Subsidiary (Domestic):

LankaBangla Information System Limited (2)

A A Bhaban Level 6 23 Motijheel C/A, Dhaka, 1000, Bangladesh
Tel.: (880) 247120278
Web Site: https://www.lbis.info
IT Management Outsourcing & Consulting Services
N.A.I.C.S.: 541511

LANKEM CEYLON PLC
98 Sri Sangaraja Mawatha, PO Box 919, 1000, Colombo, 10, Sri Lanka
Tel.: (94) 115566000
Web Site: https://www.lankem.lk
Year Founded: 1964
LCEY.N0000—(COL)
Rev.: $111,852,793
Assets: $96,559,143
Liabilities: $72,969,873
Net Worth: $23,589,270
Earnings: ($2,208,373)
Fiscal Year-end: 03/31/24
Agro Chemical Product Distr
N.A.I.C.S.: 424690
S. D. R. Arudpragasam *(Chm)*

Subsidiaries:

Colombo Fort Hotels Ltd. (1)
8-2/1 York Arcade Building Leyden Bastian Road, 01, Colombo, Sri Lanka
Tel.: (94) 112326927
Hotel Operator
N.A.I.C.S.: 721110

Galle Fort Hotel (Pvt) Ltd. (1)
No 28 Church Street Galle Fort, Galle Fort, Galle, Sri Lanka
Tel.: (94) 912232870
Boutique Hotel Operator
N.A.I.C.S.: 721110

Sigiriya Village Hotels PLC (1)
PO Box 1, Sigiriya, Matale, 21120, Sri Lanka
Tel.: (94) 662286803
Hotel Operator
N.A.I.C.S.: 721110

LANKOM ELECTRONICS LIMITED
7F No 5 Ln 345 Yang Guang St Neihu, 114, Taipei, Taiwan
Tel.: (886) 266069777
Sales Range: $10-24.9 Million
Emp.: 837
Electromagnetic Component Mfr
N.A.I.C.S.: 335314
Randolph Lu Chun Liu *(CFO)*

Subsidiaries:

LANKom Electronics Co Ltd (1)
7F No 5 Lane 345 Yang Guang Street Neihu, Taipei, 114, Taiwan
Tel.: (886) 2 6606 9777
Electromagnetic Components Distr
N.A.I.C.S.: 334515

LANKom Sales Ltd (1)
Workshop 1805 International Trade Centre 11-19 Sha Tsui Road, Tsuen Wan, New Territories, China (Hong Kong)
Tel.: (852) 24127466
Electric Equipment Mfr
N.A.I.C.S.: 334515
David Ho *(Mgr)*

LANKWITZER LACKFABRIK GMBH
Haynauer Strasse 61-63, 12249, Berlin, Germany
Tel.: (49) 30768887100
Web Site: http://www.lankwitzer.com
Year Founded: 1952
Rev.: $71,261,638
Emp.: 213
Coating System Mfr & Distr
N.A.I.C.S.: 325510
Leo Rokeach *(Mng Dir)*

Subsidiaries:

Lankwitzer Coating Ltd. (1)
Room 821 No 5 Haiying Road, Fengtai District, 100070, Beijing, China
Tel.: (86) 13910876781
Web Site: http://www.lankwitzer.com.cn
Paints Mfr
N.A.I.C.S.: 325510
Zhu Lukezhu *(Gen Mgr)*

Lankwitzer Georgia Ltd. (1)
Tsotne Dadiani 32, 0180, Tbilisi, Georgia
Tel.: (995) 95191116
Paint Distr
N.A.I.C.S.: 424950

Lankwitzer Lackfabrik Bel (1)
Ul Puschkina 8, 225021, Damachava, Belarus
Tel.: (375) 162961265
Web Site: http://www.lankwitzer.by
Paint Mfr & Distr
N.A.I.C.S.: 325510

Lankwitzer Lackfabrik CR, spol s.r.o. (1)
Prumyslova 4393/1a, 79601, Prostejov, Czech Republic
Tel.: (420) 582330605
Web Site: http://www.lankwitzer.cz
Paint Distr
N.A.I.C.S.: 424950

Lankwitzer Lackfabrik GmbH - Leipzig Plant (1)
Zschortauer Str 73 -77, 04129, Leipzig, Germany
Tel.: (49) 30768887200
Paints Mfr
N.A.I.C.S.: 325510

Lankwitzer Lackfabrik GmbH - Osterwieck Plant (1)
Hoppenstedter Str 2, 38835, Osterwieck, Germany
Tel.: (49) 307688870
Paints Mfr
N.A.I.C.S.: 325510

Lankwitzer Polska Sp. z.o.o. (1)
ul Kepska 2, 45-129, Opole, Poland
Tel.: (48) 774547605
Web Site: http://www.lankwitzer.com.pl
Paint Distr
N.A.I.C.S.: 424950

Lankwitzer Slovensko, s.r.o. (1)
Mlynske Nivy 77, 82105, Bratislava, Slovakia
Tel.: (421) 253635934
Web Site: http://www.lankwitzer.sk
Paint Distr
N.A.I.C.S.: 424950

Lankwitzer do Brasil LTDA (1)
Rua Ecapora 209 Cumbica, 07224-090, Guarulhos, Sao Paulo, Brazil
Tel.: (55) 2122248955
Paints Mfr
N.A.I.C.S.: 325510

LANNA RESOURCES PCL
888/99 Mahathun Plaza Bldg 9th Floor Ploenchit Road, Lumpini Pathumwan, Bangkok, 10330, Thailand
Tel.: (66) 22538080
Web Site: https://www.lannar.com
Year Founded: 1985
LANNA—(THA)
Rev.: $670,780,335
Assets: $432,975,498
Liabilities: $121,499,184
Net Worth: $311,476,315
Earnings: $98,475,849
Emp.: 838
Fiscal Year-end: 12/31/23
Lignite Mining
N.A.I.C.S.: 212290
Somkiart Limsong *(Chm)*

Subsidiaries:

Lanna (Singapore) Pte Ltd (1)
7 Temasek Blvd No 16 01 Suntec Tower One, Singapore, 038987, Singapore
Tel.: (65) 63057368
Sales Range: $50-74.9 Million
Emp.: 2
Investment in Coal Mining Service
N.A.I.C.S.: 213113

AND PRIVATE COMPANIES

PT. Lanna Mining Services (1)
Kawasan Bisnis Granadha 8th Fl Jl Jend, Sudirman Kav 50, Jakarta, 12930, Indonesia
Tel.: (62) 2125539313
Web Site: http://www.lannar.com
Coal Trading
N.A.I.C.S.: 212114

Thai Agro Energy Public Co., Ltd. (1)
888/114 Mahatun Plazz Bldg 11th Floor Ploenchit Road, Lumphini Subdistrict Pathumwan District, Bangkok, 10330, Thailand
Tel.: (66) 26273890
Web Site: https://www.thaiagroenergy.com
Rev.: $78,210,327
Assets: $90,259,822
Liabilities: $41,985,217
Net Worth: $48,274,605
Earnings: $883,909
Emp.: 251
Fiscal Year-end: 12/31/2023
Fuel Production & Distribution
N.A.I.C.S.: 457210
Kraisi Sirirungsi (Vice Chm)

LANNEBO & PARTNERS AB
Kungsgatan 5, PO Box 7854, Stockholm, 103 99, Sweden
Tel.: (46) 8 5622 5200   SE
Web Site:
   http://www.lannebofonder.se
Year Founded: 2000
Sales Range: $10-24.9 Million
Emp.: 27
Holding Company; Fund Management Services
N.A.I.C.S.: 551112
Goran Espelund (CEO)

Subsidiaries:

Lannebo Fonder AB (1)
Kungsgatan 5, 111 43, Stockholm, Sweden
Tel.: (46) 8 5622 5200
Web Site: http://www.lannebofonder.se
Sales Range: $10-24.9 Million
Fund Management Services
N.A.I.C.S.: 523940
Goran Espelund (Chm)

LANPEC TECHNOLOGIES LIMITED
8 Lanke St, Anning District, Lanzhou, 730070, Gansu, China
Tel.: (86) 2131021798
Web Site: http://www.lanpec.com
Year Founded: 2001
601798—(SHG)
Rev.: $122,139,099
Assets: $400,218,736
Liabilities: $198,491,441
Net Worth: $201,727,296
Earnings: ($25,859,391)
Fiscal Year-end: 12/31/22
Petrochemical Equipment Mfr
N.A.I.C.S.: 423830
Wang Jian (Chm)

LANSDOWNE OIL & GAS PLC
Paramount Court Corrig Road Sandyford Business Park, Dublin, 18, Ireland
Tel.: (353) 19631760
Web Site:
   https://www.lansdowneoilgas.com
LOGP—(AIM)
Assets: $20,663,974
Liabilities: $2,044,938
Net Worth: $18,619,036
Earnings: ($459,480)
Emp.: 1
Fiscal Year-end: 12/31/22
Holding Company; Oil & Gas Services
N.A.I.C.S.: 551112
Stephen Adrian Renwick Boldy (CEO)

LANSDOWNE PARTNERS LIMITED
15 Davies Street, London, W1K 3AG, United Kingdom
Tel.: (44) 20 7290 5500   UK
Web Site:
   http://www.lansdownepartners.com
Year Founded: 1998
Investment Fund Management Services
N.A.I.C.S.: 523940
Suzanna Lynn Nutton (COO)

Subsidiaries:

Lansdowne Partners (UK) LLP (1)
15 Davies Street, London, W1K 3AG, United Kingdom
Tel.: (44) 20 7290 5500
Web Site:
   http://www.lansdownepartners.com
Investment Fund
N.A.I.C.S.: 525990

LANSDOWNE SECURITY, INC.
27 Chicora Avenue, Toronto, M5R 1T7, ON, Canada
Tel.: (595) 851-8673   TX
Web Site: http://www.lansdowne.com
Investment Services
N.A.I.C.S.: 523999
Chris Davis (Pres & Principal)

LANSEN PHARMACEUTICAL HOLDINGS CO., LTD.
Suites 1203-4 12/F Li Po Chun Chambers 189 Des Voeux Road, Central, 315100, China (Hong Kong)
Tel.: (852) 28289289   Ky
Web Site: http://www.lansen.com.cn
503—(HKG)
Rev.: $54,386,000
Assets: $252,778,000
Liabilities: $55,496,000
Net Worth: $197,282,000
Earnings: $88,205,000
Emp.: 661
Fiscal Year-end: 12/31/20
Pharmaceutical Mfr & Distr
N.A.I.C.S.: 325412
Zhou Hong (Gen Mgr-Ningbo Liwah Pharmaceutical Co., Ltd)

LANSON-BCC
66 rue de Courlancy, 51100, Reims, France
Tel.: (33) 326785000
Web Site: https://www.lanson-bcc.com
Year Founded: 1991
ALLAN—(EUR)
Sales Range: $250-299.9 Million
Wine Mfr
N.A.I.C.S.: 312130
Bruno Paillard (Chm & CEO)

Subsidiaries:

Champagne Boizel SA (1)
46 avenue de Champagne, 51200, Epernay, France
Tel.: (33) 326552151
Web Site: http://www.boizel.com
Wine Mfr
N.A.I.C.S.: 312130

Champagne Chanoine Freres SA (1)
Allee du Vignoble, 51100, Reims, France
Tel.: (33) 326366160
Web Site: http://www.chanoine-freres.fr
Wine & Spirit Whslr
N.A.I.C.S.: 424820

Champagne Lanson S.A.S. (1)
66 rue de Courlancy, CS 20017, 51726, Reims, Cedex, France
Tel.: (33) 326785050
Web Site: http://www.lanson.com
Wine & Spirit Whslr
N.A.I.C.S.: 424820
Francois Van Aal (Pres)

Champagne Philipponnat SA (1)
13 rue du Pont-Mareuil-sur-Ay, CS 60002, 51160, Champagney, France
Tel.: (33) 326569300
Web Site: http://www.philipponnat.com
Wine & Spirit Mfr
N.A.I.C.S.: 312140
Charles Philipponnat (Chm)

Champagne de Venoge SA (1)
33 avenue de Champagne, 51 200, Epernay, France
Tel.: (33) 26533434
Web Site: http://champagnedevenoge.com
Wine & Spirit Mfr
N.A.I.C.S.: 312140

LANTA-BANK JSC
Novokuznetskaya Ul 9, 115184, Moscow, Russia
Tel.: (7) 4959570000
Web Site: http://www.lanta.ru
Year Founded: 1992
Emp.: 100
Commercial Banking Services
N.A.I.C.S.: 522110
Sergei Vladimirovich Dokuchayev (Chm & CEO)

LANTERN HOTEL GROUP LIMITED
Level 8.1 York St, Sydney, 2000, NSW, Australia
Tel.: (61) 2 8223 3602
Web Site:
   http://www.lanternhotels.com.au
Rev.: $26,187,600
Assets: $17,457,940
Liabilities: $22,999,749
Net Worth: ($5,541,809)
Earnings: $320,994
Emp.: 268
Fiscal Year-end: 06/30/16
Home Management Services
N.A.I.C.S.: 721110
Graeme John Campbell (Chm)

LANTHANEIN RESOURCES LIMITED
Level 8 99 St Georges Terrace, Perth, 6000, WA, Australia
Tel.: (61) 894864036   AU
Web Site: https://lanthanein.com
LNR—(ASX)
Rev.: $1,041,948
Assets: $11,024,095
Liabilities: $110,311
Net Worth: $10,913,784
Earnings: $443,593
Fiscal Year-end: 06/30/24
Exploration & Evaluation Of Gold Silver & Other Base Metal Projects
N.A.I.C.S.: 213114
Matthew Foy (Sec)

LANTMANNEN EK FOR
St Goransgatan 160 A, Box 301 92, SE-104 25, Stockholm, Sweden
Tel.: (46) 105560000   SE
Web Site:
   http://www.lantmannen.com
Year Founded: 1880
Rev.: $4,891,651,740
Assets: $4,127,560,650
Liabilities: $2,344,236,360
Net Worth: $1,783,324,290
Earnings: $131,521,140
Emp.: 9,940
Fiscal Year-end: 12/31/18
Holding Company; Food, Energy, Agriculture & Machinery Products & Services
N.A.I.C.S.: 551112
Hans Wallemyr (Vice Chm)

Subsidiaries:

Agro Bizz A/S (1)
Emmelevgyden 25, 5450, Otterup, Denmark
Tel.: (45) 70 20 49 03
Web Site: http://www.agrobizz.com
Agriculture Product Distr
N.A.I.C.S.: 424910

Agro Oil AB (1)
St Goransgatan 160 A, 104 35, Stockholm, Sweden
Tel.: (46) 105560000
Web Site: http://www.agrol.se
Sales Range: $125-149.9 Million
Emp.: 17
Oil Dealers
N.A.I.C.S.: 457210

Agroetanol AB (1)
Hanholmsvagenn 69, Box 932, 601 19, Norrkoping, Sweden   (91%)
Tel.: (46) 105560150
Web Site:
   http://www.lantmannenagroetanol.se
Sales Range: $50-74.9 Million
Emp.: 500
Grain-Based Ethanol Plant Operator
N.A.I.C.S.: 325998
Peter Nimrodsson (Production Mgr)

BioAgri AB (1)
Dag Hammarsskjolds Vag 180, Box 914, Uppsala, SE-751 09, Sweden
Tel.: (46) 18674900
Web Site: http://www.bioagri.se
Sales Range: $25-49.9 Million
Emp.: 5
Non-Chemical Plant Protection Products Developer & Sales
N.A.I.C.S.: 325414
Christian Thaning (Mgr-Dev)

Cardinal Foods AS (1)
Brynsveien 5, 0667, Oslo, Norway   (48%)
Tel.: (47) 22 72 88 60
Web Site: http://www.cardinalfoods.no
Sales Range: $200-249.9 Million
Emp.: 300
Poultry Products & Eggs Producer & Distr
N.A.I.C.S.: 112390
Torfinn Prytz Higdem (CEO)

K-maatalouskaupat Oy (1)
Tikkurilantie 10, 01380, Vantaa, Finland
Tel.: (358) 10 53 032
Agriculture & Forestry Machinery Distr
N.A.I.C.S.: 423820

Klaeckeribolaget AB (1)
Ostragardstanga 2, SE-240 32, Flyinge, Sweden
Tel.: (46) 46 64770
Chicken Producer
N.A.I.C.S.: 112390

Krafft Haestfoder AB (1)
Sanddynevagen 2, SE-311 32, Falkenberg, Sweden
Tel.: (46) 20304040
Web Site: http://www.krafft.nu
Sales Range: $10-24.9 Million
Emp.: 17
Grain & Field Beans Distr
N.A.I.C.S.: 424510

Lantmannen AS-Faktor AB (1)
Goransgatan 160 A, 104 25, Stockholm, Sweden
Tel.: (46) 8 657 42 70
Web Site: http://www.as-faktor.se
Agriculture Product Distr
N.A.I.C.S.: 424910

Lantmannen Agroenergi AB (1)
Fordonsvagen 1, 553 02, Jonkoping, Sweden
Tel.: (46) 10 556 01 30
Web Site: http://www.agroenergi.se
Wood Products Mfr
N.A.I.C.S.: 321999

Lantmannen Aspen AB (1)
Iberovagen 2, 438 54, Hindas, Sweden
Tel.: (46) 301 23 00 00
Web Site: http://www.aspen.se
Fuel Distr
N.A.I.C.S.: 424720

Unit (Domestic):

Cerealia Foods & Bread (2)
Jarna, SE-153 81, Jarna, Sweden
Tel.: (46) 851978700
Web Site: http://www.cerealiafoodservice.se
Flour, Breakfast Foods, Mixes, Pasta, Bread & Ready-Made Meals Developer, Mfr & Marketer

LANTMANNEN EK FOR

Lantmannen ek for—(Continued)
N.A.I.C.S.: 311211

Subsidiary (Non-US):

Lantmannen Unibake International (2)
Oensvej 28 Hatting, 8700, Horsens, Denmark
Tel.: (45) 76285000
Web Site: http://www.lantmannen-unibake.com
Sales Range: $50-74.9 Million
Emp.: 6,000
Bakery Products Mfr & Sales
N.A.I.C.S.: 311811
Werner Devinck (CEO)

Lantmannen BioAgri AB (1)
Fagelbacksvagen 3, 756 51, Uppsala, Sweden
Tel.: (46) 18 67 49 00
Web Site: http://www.bioagri.se
Agriculture Product Distr
N.A.I.C.S.: 424910
Kenneth Alness (CEO)

Lantmannen Bygglant AB (1)
Stangjarnsgatan 7 Norra entren, Orebro, Sweden
Tel.: (46) 10 556 20 00
Web Site: http://www.lantmannenbygglant.se
Wood Products Mfr
N.A.I.C.S.: 321999

Lantmannen Cerealia AB (1)
St Goransgatan, SE-104 92, Stockholm, Sweden
Tel.: (46) 86574200
Web Site: http://www.lantmaennen.com
Sales Range: $250-299.9 Million
Emp.: 20,000
Flour, Flour Mixes, Breakfast Cereals & Pasta Developer, Mfr & Marketer
N.A.I.C.S.: 311211

Subsidiary (Non-US):

Lantmannen Cerealia A/S (2)
Mollegade 12, 7100, Vejle, Denmark
Tel.: (45) 79 41 54 15
Food Product Mfr & Distr
N.A.I.C.S.: 311999

Lantmannen Energi AB (1)
St Goransgatan 160 A, 104 25, Stockholm, Sweden
Tel.: (46) 86574200
Web Site: http://www.lea.se
Bioenergy Developer & Marketer
N.A.I.C.S.: 325414

Lantmannen Invest AB (1)
Box 30192, SE-104 25, Stockholm, Sweden
Tel.: (46) 86574200
Web Site: http://www.lantmannen.com
Sales Range: $350-399.9 Million
Emp.: 853
Investment Services
N.A.I.C.S.: 523999

Lantmannen Lantbruk (1)
von Troils vag 1, 213 73, Malmo, Sweden
Tel.: (46) 10 556 56 00
Web Site: http://www.lantmannenlantbruk.se
Agriculture Product Distr
N.A.I.C.S.: 424910

Lantmannen Maskin AB (1)
Falkenberg 51, SE-311 83, Falkenberg, Sweden
Tel.: (46) 34685005
Web Site: http://www.lantmannenmaskin.se
Sales Range: $200-249.9 Million
Emp.: 600
Farm Equipment Sales
N.A.I.C.S.: 423820

Subsidiary (Non-US):

Akerhus Traktor AS (2)
Industriveien 16, 2069, Jessheim, Norway
Tel.: (47) 63 94 85 80
Web Site: http://www.akershustraktor.no
Farm Equipment Distr
N.A.I.C.S.: 423820

Lantmannen Maskinimport AB (1)
Box 174, SE-201 21, Malmo, Sweden
Tel.: (46) 40386400
Web Site: http://www.lantmaennen.com
Sales Range: $150-199.9 Million
Tractors & Farm Equipment Importer, Marketer & Distr
N.A.I.C.S.: 423820
Hakan Pettersson (Mng Dir)

Lantmannen Schulstad A/S (1)
Hammerholmen 21A, 2650, Hvidovre, Denmark
Tel.: (45) 3639 7100
Web Site: http://www.lantmannen-unibake.com
Food Products Mfr
N.A.I.C.S.: 311999

Lantmannen Solanum AB (1)
Bintjevagen 2, 244 21, Kavlinge, Sweden
Tel.: (46) 46 72 21 00
Agriculture Product Distr
N.A.I.C.S.: 424910

Subsidiary (Domestic):

Lantmannen Unibake Sweden AB (2)
Sliparevagen 1 5, 703 75, Orebro, Sweden
Tel.: (46) 10 556 50 00
Bakery Food Products Mfr
N.A.I.C.S.: 311813
Jonas Lindell (Mng Dir)

Lantmannen Unibake GmbH & Co KG (1)
Justus Von Liebig Str 6, 27283, Verden, Germany
Tel.: (49) 4231 66 3 0
Web Site: http://www.lantmannen-unibake.de
Bakery Products Mfr
N.A.I.C.S.: 311813

Lantmannen Unibake Russia LLC (1)
per Degtyarny d 4 building 1 6 floor, 125009, Moscow, Russia
Tel.: (7) 4957630724
Web Site: http://www.lantmannen-unibake.com
Emp.: 120
Bakery Food Products Mfr
N.A.I.C.S.: 311813

Lantmannen Unibake UK Ltd (1)
3 Tanners Yard London Road, Bagshot, GU19 5HD, Surrey, United Kingdom
Tel.: (44) 1276 850500
Web Site: http://www.lantmannen-unibake.com
Emp.: 750
Bakery Food Product Mfr & Distr
N.A.I.C.S.: 311813
Tim Robinson (Mng Dir)

Lantmannen Unibake USA, Inc (1)
5007 Lincoln Ave Ste 300, Lisle, IL 60532
Tel.: (630) 963-4781
Web Site: http://www.unibakeusa.com
Emp.: 10
Bakery Food Products Mfr
N.A.I.C.S.: 311813
Scott Kolinski (CEO)

NotCenter Viken AB (1)
Vikens Egendom, 521 91, Falkoping, Sweden
Tel.: (46) 515 77 70 80
Agriculture Product Distr
N.A.I.C.S.: 424910

Reppe AB (1)
Jungmansgatan 8, 531 40, Lidkoping, Sweden
Tel.: (46) 105561540
Web Site: http://www.lantmannenreppe.se
Sales Range: $10-24.9 Million
Emp.: 80
Alcohol, Gluten & Glucose Based Grain Mfr
N.A.I.C.S.: 111199

Solanum AB (1)
PO Box 56, SE-244 21, Kavlinge, Sweden
Tel.: (46) 46722100
Web Site: http://www.solanum.se
Sales Range: $10-24.9 Million
Emp.: 40
Potato Farming
N.A.I.C.S.: 111211

Svaloef Weibull AB (1)
von Troils vag 1, 213 37, Malmo, Sweden (60%)
Tel.: (46) 10 556 5600
Web Site: http://www.swseed.com
Sales Range: $125-149.9 Million
Agricultural Seed Production & Whslr
N.A.I.C.S.: 424910

Swe-Chick AB (1)
Stalgatan 3, SE-265 38, Astorp, Sweden
Tel.: (46) 42225190
Chicken Producer
N.A.I.C.S.: 112390

Swecon Anlaeggningsmaskiner AB (1)
Bolindervagen 104B, 635 10, Eskilstuna, Sweden
Tel.: (46) 105560850
Web Site: http://www.sweconkontakt.se
Sales Range: $350-399.9 Million
Emp.: 20
Construction Equipment Dealer
N.A.I.C.S.: 423810

Vaasan Oy (1)
PL 315 Salmisaarenaukio 1, PO Box 315, 00181, Helsinki, Finland
Tel.: (358) 20446111
Web Site: http://www.vaasan.fi
Emp.: 2,950
Bakery Products, Bake-Off Products, Crisp Bread, Thin Crisp & Fresh Bread Producer & Distr
N.A.I.C.S.: 311812
Thomas Isaksson (Mng Dir)

Subsidiary (Non-US):

A/S Hanzas Maiznicas (2)
Brivibas iela 171, Riga, LV 1012, Latvia
Tel.: (371) 6 7805 815
Web Site: http://www.hm.lv
Emp.: 215
Commercial Bakeries
N.A.I.C.S.: 311812

Leibur AS (2)
Leiva 1, Tallinn, 12618, Estonia
Tel.: (372) 6 504 777
Web Site: http://www.leibur.ee
Emp.: 30
Commercial Bakeries
N.A.I.C.S.: 311812
Asso Lankots (Mng Dir)

UAB Vilniaus Duona (2)
Perknkiemio str 7, LT 12131, Vilnius, Lithuania
Tel.: (370) 5 233 0700
Web Site: http://www.vilniausduona.lt
Emp.: 400
Commercial Bakeries
N.A.I.C.S.: 311812

Vaasan Norge AS (2)
Skysstasjonen 11B, PO Box 215, 1383, Asker, Norway
Tel.: (47) 66 98 70 00
Web Site: http://www.vaasan.no
Bakery Products Mfr & Distr
N.A.I.C.S.: 311812

Vaasan Sverige AB (2)
St Goransgatan 160 A, PO Box 30125, 112 17, Stockholm, Sweden
Tel.: (46) 10 556 50 00
Web Site: http://www.vaasan.se
Bakeries
N.A.I.C.S.: 311812

Valtra Traktor AB (1)
Hjalmarvagen 85, PO Box 6016, S 702 20, Orebro, Sweden
Tel.: (46) 34685000
Web Site: http://www.valtra.se
Sales Range: $75-99.9 Million
Emp.: 50
Tractor Mfr
N.A.I.C.S.: 333924

LANXESS AG

Kennedyplatz 1, 50569, Cologne, Germany
Tel.: (49) 22188850 De
Web Site: https://www.lanxess.com
LNXSF—(OTCIQ)
Rev.: $7,411,383,180
Assets: $10,668,903,550
Liabilities: $5,693,761,460
Net Worth: $4,975,142,090
Earnings: $489,014,410
Emp.: 12,849
Fiscal Year-end: 12/31/23
Holding Company; Chemicals & Compounds Mfr & Whslr
N.A.I.C.S.: 551112
Michael Pontzen (CFO & Member-Mgmt Bd)

Subsidiaries:

Aliseca GmbH (1)
Chempark, 51369, Leverkusen, Germany
Tel.: (49) 214 30 1
Web Site: http://www.aliseca.com
Logistics Consulting Servies
N.A.I.C.S.: 541614

Antec International Ltd. (1)
Windham Road Chilton Industrial Estate, Sudbury, CO10 2XD, Suffolk, United Kingdom
Tel.: (44) 1787377305
Biosecurity Products Mfr
N.A.I.C.S.: 325411

Bayer Industry Services GmbH & Co. OHG (1)
Chemiepark Gebaude Q26, Kaiser-Wilhelm-Allee, D-51368, Leverkusen, Germany (40%)
Tel.: (49) 214301
Web Site: http://www.bayerindustry.com
Sales Range: $1-4.9 Billion
Emp.: 5,500
Chemical Industry Utility Supply, Waste Management, Infrastructure, Safety, Security & Technical Services
N.A.I.C.S.: 561210
Joachim Waldi (Dir-Labor)

Bond-Laminates GmbH (1)
Am Patbergschen Dorn 11, 59929, Brilon, Germany
Tel.: (49) 2961966280
Web Site: http://www.bond-laminates.com
Plastic Fabrication Mfr
N.A.I.C.S.: 326199

Emerald Performance Materials, LLC (1)
2020 Front St Ste 100, Cuyahoga Falls, OH 44221
Tel.: (330) 916-6700
Web Site: http://www.emeraldmaterials.com
Sales Range: $400-449.9 Million
Emp.: 750
Chemical Additives & Polymer Mfr
N.A.I.C.S.: 325998
Edward T. Gotch (Pres-Emerald Kalama Chemicals)

Subsidiary (Domestic):

Emerald Kalama Chemical, LLC (2)
1499 SE Tech Ctr Pl Ste 300, Vancouver, WA 98683
Tel.: (360) 954-7100
Web Site: http://www.emeraldmaterials.com
Food Additives Mfr
N.A.I.C.S.: 325998
Edward T. Gotch (CEO)

Subsidiary (Non-US):

Emerald Kalama Chemical B.V. (3)
Mijnweg 1, 6167 AP, Geleen, Netherlands
Tel.: (31) 888880500
Web Site: http://www.emeraldmaterials.com
Sales Range: $10-24.9 Million
Emp.: 130
Food Additives Mfr
N.A.I.C.S.: 325998
Antonella Dall'Osto (Mgr-Sls-EMEA)

Emerald Kalama Chemical Limited (3)
Dans Road, Widnes, WA8 0RF, Cheshire, United Kingdom
Tel.: (44) 151 423 8100
Web Site: http://www.kalama.emeraldmaterials.com
Aroma Chemical Mfr
N.A.I.C.S.: 325199
David Nicholls (Dir)

Europigments S.L. (1)

AND PRIVATE COMPANIES — LANXESS AG

Architecture 27, Vilassar de Mar, 08340, Barcelona, Spain
Tel.: (34) 937540770
Web Site: http://europigments.es
Sales Range: $25-49.9 Million
Mft. of Dyes
N.A.I.C.S.: 325998

IAB Ionenaustauscher GmbH (1)
Salegaster Chaussee 1, 06803, Bitterfeld-Wolfen, Germany
Tel.: (49) 3493358500
Petrochemical Mfr
N.A.I.C.S.: 325110

LANXESS (Changzhou) Co., Ltd. (1)
No 8 Huanghai Road Xinbei Industrial Park, Changzhou, 213127, China
Tel.: (86) 51988021888
Petrochemical Mfr
N.A.I.C.S.: 325110

LANXESS (Liyang) Polyols Co., Ltd. (1)
Qiang Bu No 36 Li Qiang Road, Nan Du Town, Liyang, 213364, Jiangsu, China
Tel.: (86) 51987695653
Web Site: http://www.lanxess.cn
Chemical Products Mfr
N.A.I.C.S.: 325998

LANXESS (Ningbo) Pigments Co., Ltd. (1)
No 1 Haixiang Road, Ningbo, 315204, China
Tel.: (86) 57455843600
Petrochemical Mfr
N.A.I.C.S.: 325110

LANXESS (Pty) Ltd. (1)
Emerald Boulevard Unit 15 Greenstone Hill Office Park, Boulevard Building 15, 1609, Modderfontein, Gauteng, South Africa
Tel.: (27) 114574000
Web Site: http://www.lanxess.com
Sales Range: $25-49.9 Million
Emp.: 40
Chemicals & Compounds Mfr
N.A.I.C.S.: 325998

Subsidiary (Domestic):

LANXESS (Pty) Ltd. (2)
57 Tomango Road, Merebank, 4059, Kwazulu-Natal, South Africa
Tel.: (27) 314626343
Web Site: http://www.lanxessleather.com
Sales Range: $25-49.9 Million
Chemicals & Compounds Mfr
N.A.I.C.S.: 325998

LANXESS (Pty) Ltd. (2)
35 Blue Street, Isithebe, 4490, Kwazulu-Natal, South Africa
Tel.: (27) 343701118
Web Site: http://www.lanxess.com
Sales Range: $25-49.9 Million
Chemicals & Compounds Mfr
N.A.I.C.S.: 325998
Ben Marais *(Mng Dir & CFO)*

LANXESS Mining (Pty) Ltd. (2)
Rietfontein Farm 338 JQ Bleskop, Rustenburg, 0292, South Africa
Tel.: (27) 145360600
Web Site: http://www.lanxess.co.za
Chrome Mining Operations
N.A.I.C.S.: 212390

LANXESS (Wuxi) High Performance Composite Materials Company Limited (1)
Hi and New Tech Industrial Development Zone No 9 Zhu Jiang Road, Wuxi, 214028, Jiangsu, China
Tel.: (86) 51088668228
Petrochemical Mfr
N.A.I.C.S.: 325110

LANXESS Accounting GmbH (1)
Lxs-Lip Geb K 10, Leverkusen, 51373, Germany
Tel.: (49) 2143010
General Accounting Services
N.A.I.C.S.: 541219

LANXESS Buna GmbH (1)
Paul-Baumann-Str 1, Marl, 45772, Germany
Tel.: (49) 23654909
Web Site: http://www.lanxess.de

Emp.: 120
Rubber Products Mfr
N.A.I.C.S.: 325212

LANXESS Butyl Pte. Ltd. (1)
1 Tembusu Road, Singapore, 627595, Singapore
Tel.: (65) 6725 4988
Specialty Chemicals Mfr
N.A.I.C.S.: 325998

LANXESS CISA (Pty) Ltd. (1)
Karbochem Road, 2940, Newcastle, South Africa
Tel.: (27) 343707000
Petrochemical Mfr
N.A.I.C.S.: 325110
Gerhardus Strydom *(Mng Dir)*

LANXESS Central Eastern Europe s.r.o. (1)
Stetinova 4, 811 09, Bratislava, Slovakia
Tel.: (421) 2 32 15 16 26
Web Site: http://www.lanxess.sk
Emp.: 2
Chemical Products Distr
N.A.I.C.S.: 424690
Antonin Humplik *(Country Mgr-Sls)*

LANXESS Chemical (China) Co., Ltd. (1)
34/F Jing Guang Center Hu Jia Lou, Chaoyang District, Beijing, 100020, China
Tel.: (86) 10 6597 3262
Web Site: http://www.lanxess.cn
Emp.: 15
Chemical Products Distr
N.A.I.C.S.: 424690

LANXESS Chemical (Shanghai) Co., Ltd. (1)
29th Floor Ocean Towers, No 550 Yan An Road East, Shanghai, China
Tel.: (86) 21 3318 4888
Chemicals & Compounds Mfr
N.A.I.C.S.: 325998
Yongli Wang *(Ops Mgr)*

LANXESS Chemicals, S.L. (1)
WTC Edifici Nord Planta 7a Moll De Barcelona s/n World Trade Center, 08039, Barcelona, Spain
Tel.: (34) 93 341 52 00
Web Site: http://www.lanxess.com
Chemical Products Distr
N.A.I.C.S.: 424690

LANXESS Chrome Mining (Pty) Ltd. (1)
Rietfontein Farm 338 JQ Bleskop, 0292, Rustenburg, South Africa
Tel.: (27) 145360600
Petrochemical Mfr
N.A.I.C.S.: 325110
Sarel Ferreira *(CEO)*

LANXESS Corporation (1)
111 RIDC Park W Dr, Pittsburgh, PA 15275-1112
Tel.: (412) 809-1000
Web Site: http://lanxess.us
Chemicals & Compounds Mfr
N.A.I.C.S.: 325998
Antonis Papadourakis *(Pres & CEO)*

Subsidiary (Domestic):

LANXESS Solutions US Inc. (2)
2 Armstrong Rd, Shelton, CT 06484
Tel.: (203) 573-2000
Web Site: http://lanxess.us
Chemical Additive Mfr
N.A.I.C.S.: 424690
Albert Nitowski *(Sr Mgr)*

Subsidiary (Non-US):

Anderol B.V. (3)
Groot Egtenrayseweg 23, 5928 PA, Venlo, Netherlands
Tel.: (31) 773960340
Web Site: http://anderol-europe.com
Oil & Petroleum Lubricants Mfr
N.A.I.C.S.: 324191

Certis Europe B.V. (3)
Stadsplateau 16, Post box 607, 3500 AP, Utrecht, Netherlands
Tel.: (31) 107118195
Web Site: http://www.certiseurope.nl
Chemical Product Mfr & Distr

N.A.I.C.S.: 325199

Chemtura SIngapore Pte. Ltd. (3)
73 Science Park Dr 04 01 Cintech III, Singapore, 118256, Singapore (100%)
Tel.: (65) 67744800
Chemical Products Mfr
N.A.I.C.S.: 325998

Great Lakes Chemical (Far East) Ltd. (3)
3 Xing Jian Road Nanjing Economic & Technological Development Zone, 555 Hennessy Road, Nanjing, 210046, China
Tel.: (86) 2552376666
Web Site: http://www.greatlakes.com
Sales Range: $150-199.9 Million
Chemical Products Mfr
N.A.I.C.S.: 325998

LANXESS Canada Company (3)
25 Erb Street, Elmira, N3B 2J3, ON, Canada (100%)
Tel.: (519) 669-1671
Web Site: http://lanxess.ca
Agricultural & Industrial Chemicals Mfr
N.A.I.C.S.: 325320

LANXESS Industria de Chemicals e Plasticos Ltda (3)
Bl B - 2nd Floor, Av Maria Coelho Aguiar 215, Sao Luis, 05804-902, Sao Paulo, Brazil (100%)
Tel.: (55) 1137412500
Web Site: http://lanxess.com.br
Industrial Organic Chemicals Mfr
N.A.I.C.S.: 325199

LANXESS Solutions K.K. (3)
23rd Floor Of Marunouchi Kitaguchi Building 1-6-5 Marunouchi, Chiyoda, Tokyo, 100-8215, Japan (100%)
Tel.: (81) 352938000
Web Site: http://lanxess.co.jp
Emp.: 100
Oil & Petroleum Lubricants Mfr
N.A.I.C.S.: 324191
Hitomi Hirowatari *(Dir)*

LANXESS Switzerland GmbH (3)
Bahnhofplatz 65, Frauenfeld, 8500, Switzerland
Tel.: (41) 527234400
Web Site: http://www.lanxess.com
Chemical & Plastic Products Mfr
N.A.I.C.S.: 325998
Ulrich Stewen *(Dir-Global MKtg)*

Subsidiary (Non-US):

Addivant France SAS (4)
2 Chemin Du Trou Bluet, 60840, Catenoy, France (100%)
Tel.: (33) 344775220
Web Site: http://www.addivant.com
Specialty Chemical Solutions, Specialized Services & Manufacturing
N.A.I.C.S.: 325998

BAYROL Deutschland GmbH (4)
Robert-Koch-Strasse 4, Steinkirchen, 82152, Planegg, Germany (100%)
Tel.: (49) 89857010
Web Site: http://www.bayrol.de
Pool Water Treatment Products Mfr
N.A.I.C.S.: 325998

BAYROL France S.A.S. (4)
Chemin des Hirondelles, PO Box 52, 69572, Dardilly, Cedex, France (100%)
Tel.: (33) 472532360
Web Site: http://www.bayrol.fr
Water Treatment Chemical Mfr
N.A.I.C.S.: 424690

BAYROL Iberica S.L.U. (4)
Av Diagonal 453 bis Planta Entresuelo, 08036, Barcelona, Spain
Tel.: (34) 932724848
Web Site: http://www.bayrol.es
Water Treatment Chemicals
N.A.I.C.S.: 325998

LANXESS Solutions UK Ltd. (4)
Tenax Road, Trafford Park, Manchester, M17 1WT, United Kingdom
Tel.: (44) 1618753453
Web Site: http://lanxess.co.uk
Industrial Inorganic Chemical Mfr
N.A.I.C.S.: 325998

Subsidiary (Non-US):

LANXESS Taiwan Ltd. (3)
Tun Hwa North Road Bank Tower Suite 704, Taipei, 105, Taiwan (100%)
Tel.: (886) 227131790
Chemical Products Mfr
N.A.I.C.S.: 325110

Subsidiary (Domestic):

LANXESS Additives Taiwan Ltd. (4)
No. 3-1 Hsing Kung Rd, Kaohsiung, 81567, Taiwan (100%)
Tel.: (886) 73514121
Industrial Organic Chemicals Mfr
N.A.I.C.S.: 325199

Subsidiary (Domestic):

NPC Services, Inc. (3)
2401 Brooklawn Dr, Baton Rouge, LA 70807-1069
Tel.: (225) 778-4973
Chemical Product Whslr
N.A.I.C.S.: 424690

Subsidiary (Non-US):

Witco Specialties (Thailand) Ltd. (3)
127 25 20th Floor Panjathani Tower Non See Road Chong Non See, Yannawa, Bangkok, 10120, Thailand
Tel.: (66) 26811004
Chemical Products Mfr
N.A.I.C.S.: 325613

Subsidiary (Domestic):

LANXESS Sybron Chemicals, Inc. (2)
200 Birmingham Rd, Birmingham, NJ 08011
Tel.: (609) 893-1100
Web Site: http://www.lanxess.com
Sales Range: $25-49.9 Million
Emp.: 15
Specialty Chemicals Sales & Support
N.A.I.C.S.: 424690
Firuza Mir *(Pres & CEO)*

LANXESS Deutschland GmbH (1)
Building K10, 51369, Leverkusen, Germany
Tel.: (49) 143033333
Web Site: http://corporate.lanxess.com
Chemicals & Compounds Mfr
N.A.I.C.S.: 325199

LANXESS Distribution GmbH (1)
Kaiser-Wilhelm-Allee 40, 51369, Leverkusen, Germany
Tel.: (49) 22188855212
Web Site: http://www.lanxess-distribution.com
Chemicals Whslr
N.A.I.C.S.: 424690
Siegbert Arnold *(Mng Dir)*

LANXESS Finance B.V. (1)
Herengracht 450, 1017 CA, Amsterdam, Netherlands
Tel.: (31) 20 625 9410
Financial Management Services
N.A.I.C.S.: 523999

LANXESS Holding Hispania, SL (1)
Moll de Barcelona, WTC Edifici Nord planta 7a, E - 08039, Barcelona, Spain
Tel.: (34) 933415200
Sales Range: $50-74.9 Million
Emp.: 37
Chemicals & Compounds Mfr
N.A.I.C.S.: 325998

LANXESS Hong Kong Limited (1)
Cambridge House TaiKoo Place 36/Fl 979 King's Road Island East, Hong Kong, China (Hong Kong)
Tel.: (852) 3526 8888
Web Site: http://www.lanxess.cn
Sales Range: $50-74.9 Million
Emp.: 60
Chemical Products Distr
N.A.I.C.S.: 424690

LANXESS India Private Limited (1)
Kolshet Road, Thane, 400 607, Maharashtra, India
Tel.: (91) 2225311271
Chemicals & Compounds Mfr
N.A.I.C.S.: 325998

LANXESS AG

INTERNATIONAL PUBLIC

LANXESS AG—(Continued)

LANXESS International Holding GmbH (1)
Kaicer-wiloelmuallee 40, Leverkusen, 51369, Germany
Tel.: (49) 2143033333
Web Site: http://www.lanxess.com
Investment Management Service
N.A.I.C.S.: 523999

LANXESS International SA (1)
Chamblioux-Parc 12, Granges-Paccot, 1763, Fribourg, Switzerland
Tel.: (41) 264228300
Web Site: http://www.lanxess.com
Emp.: 45
Rubber Product Distr
N.A.I.C.S.: 423840

LANXESS K.K. (1)
23rd floor of Marunouchi Kitaguchi Building 1-6-5 Marunouchi, Chiyoda-ku, Tokyo, 100-8215, Japan
Tel.: (81) 352938001
Web Site: http://www.lanxess.co.jp
Sales Range: $100-124.9 Million
Chemicals & Compounds Mfr
N.A.I.C.S.: 325998

Subsidiary (Domestic):

Rhein Chemie Japan Ltd (2)
3-54 Akemi-cho, Chiyoda-Ku, Toyohashi, 441-8074, Japan
Tel.: (81) 532 23 3390
Emp.: 19
Rubber Products Mfr
N.A.I.C.S.: 326299
Hideo Tsuji (CEO)

LANXESS Korea Limited (1)
395-62 Shindaebang-dong, Dongjak-gu, Seoul, 156-712, Korea (South)
Tel.: (82) 28296683
Web Site: http://www.lanxess.co.kr
Sales Range: $50-74.9 Million
Emp.: 30
Chemicals & Compounds Mfr
N.A.I.C.S.: 325998

LANXESS Limited (1)
Oxford House 12-20 Oxford Street, Newbury, RG14 1JB, United Kingdom
Tel.: (44) 1618753248
Web Site: http://www.lanxess.co.uk
Chemical Products Mfr & Distr
N.A.I.C.S.: 325998
Jacques Perez (Mng Dir)

LANXESS Middle East GmbH (1)
Jebel Ali Freezone View 18 Unit 1806, PO Box 263271, Dubai, United Arab Emirates
Tel.: (971) 4 8847578
Web Site: http://www.lanxess.ae
Sales Range: $50-74.9 Million
Emp.: 3
Chemical Products Distr
N.A.I.C.S.: 424690

LANXESS NV (1)
Scheldelaan 420 Haven 507, 2040, Antwerp, Belgium
Tel.: (32) 32127011
Web Site: http://www.lanxess.be
Sales Range: $200-249.9 Million
Emp.: 900
Chemicals & Compounds Mfr
N.A.I.C.S.: 325998

LANXESS Pte. Ltd. (1)
3A International Business Pk Unit 07-10 Bldg ICON@IBP Tower B, Singapore, 609935, Singapore
Tel.: (65) 67255800
Web Site: http://www.lanxess.com
Sales Range: $75-99.9 Million
Emp.: 80
Chemicals & Compounds Mfr
N.A.I.C.S.: 325998

LANXESS Pty. Ltd. (1)
Unit 1 31 Hill Road, Homebush Bay, 2127, NSW, Australia
Tel.: (61) 287483925
Web Site: http://www.lanxess.com
Sales Range: $50-74.9 Million
Emp.: 30
Chemicals & Compounds Mfr
N.A.I.C.S.: 325998

LANXESS S.A. (1)
Planta Baja Oficina A Cazadores De Coquimbo 2860, Vicente Lopez, B1605DXP, Munro, Buenos Aires, Argentina
Tel.: (54) 11 5550 1300
Web Site: http://www.lanxess.com.ar
Sales Range: $50-74.9 Million
Chemical Products Distr
N.A.I.C.S.: 424690

LANXESS S.A. de C.V. (1)
Ejercito Nacional 579 Piso 3 Colonia Granada, Mexico, 11520, Mexico
Tel.: (52) 5552624376
Web Site: http://www.lanxess.mx
Chemical Products Distr
N.A.I.C.S.: 424690

LANXESS S.A.S. (1)
Le Doublon Batiment A 11 Avenue Dubonnet, 92407, Courbevoie, Cedex, France
Tel.: (33) 1 80 46 3000
Web Site: http://www.lanxess.fr
Sales Range: $25-49.9 Million
Emp.: 43
Specialty Chemicals Distr
N.A.I.C.S.: 424690

LANXESS S.r.l. (1)
Via San Bovio 1/3, Segrate, 20090, Milan, Italy
Tel.: (39) 02 3072 1
Web Site: http://www.lanxess.it
Chemical Products Mfr & Distr
N.A.I.C.S.: 325998

OOO LANXESS (1)
BC Bolshevik building 12 Leningradsky Avenue 15, 125040, Moscow, Russia
Tel.: (7) 4951397200
Petrochemical Mfr
N.A.I.C.S.: 325110

Rhein Chemie (Qingdao) Ltd. (1)
Licang District 43 Siliubei Road, 266043, Qingdao, China
Tel.: (86) 532 848216670
Emp.: 180
Specialty Chemicals Mfr
N.A.I.C.S.: 325998
Emily Fang (Gen Mgr)

Rhein Chemie Rheinau GmbH (1)
Duesseldorfer Strasse 23 27, 68219, Mannheim, Germany
Tel.: (49) 62189070
Web Site: http://www.rheinchemie.com
Sales Range: $400-449.9 Million
Emp.: 970
Industrial Chemicals & Specialty Products Mfr
N.A.I.C.S.: 325998
Anno Borkowsky (Pres & CEO)

Division (Non-US):

LANXESS Industria de Produtos Quimicos e Plasticos Ltda. (2)
Ave Maria Coelho Aguiar 215 Bl B-2nd floor, Jardim Sao Luis, Sao Paulo, 05804-902, Brazil
Tel.: (55) 1137412500
Web Site: http://www.lanxess.com.br
Sales Range: $25-49.9 Million
Plastics Product Mfr
N.A.I.C.S.: 326199

Subsidiary (US):

Rhein Chemie Corporation (2)
145 Parker Ct, Chardon, OH 44024
Tel.: (501) 570-7544
Web Site: http://www.rheinchemie.com
Lubricants & Additives Mfr
N.A.I.C.S.: 324191

Tire Curing Bladders LLC (2)
5701 Murray St, Little Rock, AR 72209-2540
Tel.: (501) 562-5410
Sales Range: $10-24.9 Million
Emp.: 100
Tire Curing Bladders Mfr
N.A.I.C.S.: 326299
Wes Morrison (Gen Mgr)

Saltigo GmbH (1)
Katzbergstr 1, 40764, Langenfeld, Germany
Tel.: (49) 2173 2033 0
Web Site: http://www.saltigo.com
Specialty Chemicals Mfr & Distr

N.A.I.C.S.: 325998
Torsten Derr (Mng Dir)

LANYON INVESTMENT COMPANY LIMITED
Level 12 225 George Street, Sydney, 2000, NSW, Australia
Tel.: (61) 292909600
Web Site: http://www.8ec.com.au
LAN—(ASX)
Rev.: $7,662
Assets: $737,279
Liabilities: $92,232
Net Worth: $645,047
Earnings: ($462,834)
Fiscal Year-end: 06/30/21
Investment Services
N.A.I.C.S.: 523999
Kerry Series (Principal)

LANZHOU FOCI PHARMACEUTICAL CO., LTD.
No 2289 Huashan Road, Lanzhou New District, Lanzhou, 730000, Gansu, China
Tel.: (86) 9318362318
Web Site: http://www.fczy.com
Year Founded: 1929
002644—(SSE)
Rev.: $143,092,872
Assets: $363,154,428
Liabilities: $119,705,040
Net Worth: $243,449,388
Earnings: $14,875,380
Emp.: 1,400
Fiscal Year-end: 12/31/22
Pharmaceuticals Mfr
N.A.I.C.S.: 325412
Shan Xiaodong (Chm & Sec-Party Committee)

LANZHOU GREATWALL ELECTRICAL CO., LTD.
No 215 Nongmin lane, Chengguan District, Lanzhou, 730000, Gansu, China
Tel.: (86) 9382236982
Web Site: https://enchinagwe.geec.group
Year Founded: 1998
600192—(SHG)
Rev.: $303,407,320
Assets: $691,500,340
Liabilities: $469,171,942
Net Worth: $222,328,398
Earnings: ($16,817,309)
Fiscal Year-end: 12/31/22
Electrical Equipment Mfr & Distr
N.A.I.C.S.: 335999

Subsidiaries:

Lanzhou Great Wall Electrical Power Equipment Co., Ltd. (1)
No 215 Farmers Lane, Chengguan District, Lanzhou, 730000, Gansu, China
Tel.: (86) 931 510 2504
Web Site: https://www.lzepe.com
Construction Services
N.A.I.C.S.: 236220

Tianshui Changcheng Switchgear Co., Ltd. (1)
No 6 Changkai Road, Qinzhou District, Tianshui, 741018, Gansu Province, China
Tel.: (86) 938 838 8142
Web Site: https://www.chinatcs.com
Emp.: 1,400
Electrical Component Mfr
N.A.I.C.S.: 335999
David J. Zhang (Mgr)

Tianshui Electric Drive Research Institute Co., Ltd. (1)
No 22 Nianpu Industrial Park, National-Level Economic and Technological Development Zone, Tianshui, 741020, China
Tel.: (86) 9388383490
Web Site: http://www.en.tedri.com
Electrical Equipment & Component Mfr
N.A.I.C.S.: 335999

Zhang Feng (Mgr)

Tianshui Great Wall Control Electrical Co., Ltd. (1)
Great Wall Electric Industrial Park Shetang Industrial Park, Maiji District, Tianshui, 741024, Gansu Province, China
Tel.: (86) 938 208 6118
Web Site: https://www.tschk.com
Electrical Component Mfr
N.A.I.C.S.: 335999

Tianshui Greatwall Fruit Juice & Beverage Group Co., Ltd. (1)
Xiaquwan High-tech Industrial Park, Maiji District, Tianshui, 741024, China
Tel.: (86) 938 269 0503
Web Site: https://www.greatwall-juice.com
Fruit Juices Mfr
N.A.I.C.S.: 311411

LANZHOU HUANGHE ENTERPRISE CO., LTD.
22F Jinyun Building No 219 Qingyang Road, Lanzhou, 730030, Gansu, China
Tel.: (86) 9318449054
Web Site: http://www.yellowriver.net.cn
Year Founded: 1993
000929—(SSE)
Rev.: $37,415,196
Assets: $173,627,064
Liabilities: $30,226,716
Net Worth: $143,400,348
Earnings: ($4,105,296)
Fiscal Year-end: 12/31/22
Beer Mfr
N.A.I.C.S.: 445320
Shijiang Yang (Chm)

LANZHOU LISHANG GUOCHAO INDUSTRIAL GROUP CO., LTD.
No 120 Zhongshan Road, Chengguan District, Lanzhou, 730030, Gansu, China
Tel.: (86) 57188230930
Web Site: http://www.lzminbai.com
Year Founded: 1996
600738—(SHG)
Rev.: $98,463,471
Assets: $538,451,949
Liabilities: $256,255,982
Net Worth: $282,195,967
Earnings: $23,719,972
Fiscal Year-end: 12/31/21
Departmental Store Operator
N.A.I.C.S.: 455110
Hong Yidan (Chm, Pres & Dir)

LANZHOU LS HEAVY EQUIPMENT CO., LTD.
No 528 Huanghe Avenue West Section, Lanzhou New District, Lanzhou, 730314, Gansu, China
Tel.: (86) 9312905396
Web Site: http://www.lshec.com
Year Founded: 2001
603169—(SHG)
Rev.: $699,238,458
Assets: $1,643,540,385
Liabilities: $1,173,886,323
Net Worth: $469,654,062
Earnings: $24,701,021
Emp.: 3,800
Fiscal Year-end: 12/31/22
Petrochemical Equipment Mfr & Distr
N.A.I.C.S.: 332420
Fuyong Guo (Chm)

LANZHOU ZHUANGYUAN PASTURE CO LTD
Units 3306-12 33/F Shui On Centre Nos 6-8 Harbour Road, Wanchai, Hong Kong, China (Hong Kong)
Tel.: (852) 9318753001   CN

Web Site:
http://www.lzzhuangyuan.com
Year Founded: 2000
1533—(HKG)
Rev.: $113,347,975
Assets: $471,972,291
Liabilities: $228,087,404
Net Worth: $243,884,887
Earnings: $1,601,504
Emp.: 1,268
Fiscal Year-end: 12/31/20
Dairy Product Mfr & Distr
N.A.I.C.S.: 311514
Guofu Wang *(Deputy Chm & Controller-Fin)*

LAO AIRLINES
2 Pangkham Street, PO Box 6441, Vientiane, Lao People's Democratic Republic
Tel.: (856) 21212057
Web Site: http://www.laoairlines.com
Sales Range: $25-49.9 Million
Emp.: 250
Oil Transportation Services
N.A.I.C.S.: 481111
S. Duangdara *(Mng Dir)*

LAO CAI MINERAL EXPLOITATION & PROCESSING JOINT STOCK COMPANY
28B Phan Dinh Giot Street, Lao Cai Ward, Lao Cai, Vietnam
Tel.: (84) 3830036
LCM—(HOSE)
Rev.: $2,115,744
Assets: $5,768,742
Liabilities: $729,817
Net Worth: $5,038,925
Earnings: $133,694
Fiscal Year-end: 12/31/23
Mining Services
N.A.I.C.S.: 212323
Nguyen Duc Thang *(Gen Dir)*

LAO FENG XIANG CO., LTD.
4th and 5th Floor No 190 Nanjing West Road, Huangpu District, Shanghai, 200235, China
Tel.: (86) 2154480605
Web Site:
http://www.laofengxiang.com
Year Founded: 1992
600612—(SHG)
Rev.: $8,846,624,246
Assets: $3,651,079,578
Liabilities: $1,968,881,050
Net Worth: $1,682,198,528
Earnings: $238,728,157
Fiscal Year-end: 12/31/22
Jewelry Mfr & Distr
N.A.I.C.S.: 339910
Yang Yi *(Chm)*

Subsidiaries:

China First Pencil Co., Ltd. (1)
No 120 Wenbing Road, Xinbang Town Songjing District, Shanghai, 201605, China
Tel.: (86) 21 57892888
Web Site: http://www.chinafirstpencil.cn
Pencil Mfr
N.A.I.C.S.: 321999

LAO HOLDING STATE ENTERPRISE
Lane Xang Avenue Hatsadytai Village Chanthabouly District, Vientiane, Lao People's Democratic Republic
Tel.: (856) 21 263805 06
Web Site: http://www.laoholding.com
Holding Company
N.A.I.C.S.: 551112
Somboune Manolom *(Gen Mgr)*

LAOBAIXING PHARMACY CHAIN JOINT STOCK COMPANY
No 808 Qingzhuhu Road, Kaifu District, Changsha, 410100, Hunan, China
Tel.: (86) 73184035189
Web Site: http://www.lbxdrugs.com
Year Founded: 2001
603883—(SHG)
Rev.: $2,832,642,910
Assets: $3,004,185,539
Liabilities: $2,007,665,174
Net Worth: $996,520,365
Earnings: $110,208,595
Fiscal Year-end: 12/31/22
Pharmaceuticals Product Mfr
N.A.I.C.S.: 325412
Zilong Xie *(Founder & Chm)*

LAON PEOPLE INC.
5F/6F Gwacheon-Urban-Hub 60 Gwacheon-daero 7na-gil, Bundang-gu, Gwacheon, 13840, Gyeonggi-do, Korea (South)
Tel.: (82) 18993058
Web Site:
https://www.laonpeople.com
Year Founded: 2010
300120—(KRS)
Rev.: $20,317,469
Assets: $67,544,665
Liabilities: $25,530,376
Net Worth: $42,014,288
Earnings: ($388,929)
Emp.: 98
Fiscal Year-end: 12/31/22
Electronic Appliance Mfr & Distr
N.A.I.C.S.: 334419
Suk Joong Lee *(CEO)*

Subsidiaries:

Laon Medi Inc. (1)
404 Park B 723 Pangyo-ro, Bundang-gu, Seongnam, 13511, Korea (South)
Tel.: (82) 3180177145
Web Site: https://laon-medi.com
Software Solutions Services
N.A.I.C.S.: 541511

LAOX CO., LTD.
Sumitomo Shibakoen Building, 15/F 2-7-17 Shiba Minato-Ku, Tokyo, 105-0014, Japan
Tel.: (81) 3 68528880
Web Site: http://www.laox.co.jp
Year Founded: 1930
Emp.: 2,014
Household Appliance Retailer
N.A.I.C.S.: 449210
Masaji Taniguchi *(Founder)*

Subsidiaries:

Laox Media Solutions Co., Ltd. (1)
8F Unizo Koishikawa Urban Building 5-3-13 Otsuka, Bunkyo-ku, Tokyo, 112-0012, Japan
Tel.: (81) 369029995
Web Site: http://www.laox-mediasoln.co.jp
Event Organizing Services
N.A.I.C.S.: 561920

Laox Real Estate Co., Ltd. (1)
2-11-1 Shibakoen Sumitomo Fudosan Shibakoen Tower 14th Floor, Minato-ku, Tokyo, Japan
Tel.: (81) 354058851
Web Site: http://www.laox-realestate.co.jp
Real Estate Brokerage Services
N.A.I.C.S.: 531210

LAP KEI ENGINEERING (HOLDINGS) LIMITED
Unit 6 6th Floor Block B Tonic Industrial Centre 19 Lam Hing Street, Kowloon Bay, China (Hong Kong)
Tel.: (852) 27988210   Ky
Web Site: http://www.lapkeieng.com
Year Founded: 1997

1690—(HKG)
Rev.: $51,245,055
Assets: $37,592,228
Liabilities: $18,957,465
Net Worth: $18,634,763
Earnings: $1,465,995
Emp.: 132
Fiscal Year-end: 12/31/22
Building Engineering Services
N.A.I.C.S.: 541330
Nui Ho So *(Founder)*

LAPCO HOLDINGS LIMITED
Unit No 301A 3/F Tower III Enterprise Square, 9 Sheung Yuet Road Kowloon Bay, Kowloon, China (Hong Kong)
Tel.: (852) 27588999   Ky
Web Site: http://www.lapco.com.hk
Year Founded: 1990
8472—(HKG)
Rev.: $123,201,720
Assets: $41,052,578
Liabilities: $30,940,680
Net Worth: $10,111,898
Earnings: $2,591,565
Emp.: 3,853
Fiscal Year-end: 12/31/22
Janitorial Services
N.A.I.C.S.: 561720
Pak Ling Lam *(Founder, Chm, CEO & Compliance Officer)*

Subsidiaries:

Shiny Glory Services Limited (1)
Room 301A Tower 3 Enterprise Plaza Phase 1 9 Sheung Yuet Road, Kowloon Bay, China (Hong Kong)
Tel.: (852) 2 753 7878
Web Site: https://www.shinyglory.com.hk
Recycling Services
N.A.I.C.S.: 562920

LAPIDOTH CAPITAL LTD.
19 Brodetsky St, Tel Aviv, 6905130, Israel
Tel.: (972) 36417241
Web Site: https://www.lapidoth.co.il
Year Founded: 1959
LAPD—(TAE)
Rev.: $1,987,862,105
Assets: $2,109,541,893
Liabilities: $1,262,474,355
Net Worth: $847,067,538
Earnings: $105,339,410
Fiscal Year-end: 12/31/23
Support Activities for Oil & Gas Operations
N.A.I.C.S.: 213112
Jacob Luxembourg *(Chm)*

Subsidiaries:

Lapidoth Heletz LP (1)
19 Brodetsky St, Tel Aviv, 6905130, Israel
Tel.: (972) 36417241
Web Site: https://www.lapidoth.co.il
Rev.: $19,793
Assets: $36,115,992
Liabilities: $1,511,306
Net Worth: $34,604,685
Earnings: $317,770
Fiscal Year-end: 12/31/2022
Oil & Gas Exploration Services
N.A.I.C.S.: 213112
Jacob Luxenburg *(Chm)*

LAPINE CO., LTD.
1-7-31 Otemae Omm Bldg 18F, Chuo-Ku, Osaka, 540-0008, Japan
Tel.: (81) 669463600
Web Site: https://www.lapine.co.jp
Year Founded: 1950
8143—(TKS)
Rev.: $16,604,780
Assets: $24,361,240
Liabilities: $17,852,620
Net Worth: $6,508,620
Earnings: ($2,275,890)
Emp.: 66

Fiscal Year-end: 02/29/24
Apparel Product Mfr & Distr
N.A.I.C.S.: 315250
Yasuhiro Aoi *(Pres)*

LAPLANTE CHEVROLET PONTIAC BUICK GMC LTD
632 Principale St, Casselman, K0A 1M0, ON, Canada
Tel.: (613) 764-2846
Web Site:
http://www.laplantechevrolet.com
Year Founded: 1954
Sales Range: $25-49.9 Million
New & Used Car Dealers
N.A.I.C.S.: 441110
Eric Vivarais *(Mgr-Svc)*

LAPPLAND GOLDMINERS AB
Storgatan 36, 921 31, Lycksele, Sweden
Tel.: (46) 95027500
Web Site:
http://www.lapplandgoldminers.com
Sales Range: $25-49.9 Million
Emp.: 8
Gold Mining & Exploration
N.A.I.C.S.: 212220
Torsten Boerjemalm *(Chm)*

Subsidiaries:

Lappland Goldminers OY (1)
Pahtavaaran Kaivos, Sodankyla, 99600, Finland
Tel.: (358) 405365730
Gold Ore Mining Services
N.A.I.C.S.: 212220

LAR ESPANA REAL ESTATE SOCIMI, S.A.
C/ Rosario Pino 14-16 8th Floor, 28020, Madrid, Spain
Tel.: (34) 914360437
Web Site: http://www.larespana.com
LRE—(BIL)
Rev.: $98,062,473
Assets: $1,704,741,306
Liabilities: $754,174,539
Net Worth: $950,566,767
Earnings: $39,490,125
Emp.: 460
Fiscal Year-end: 12/31/23
Real Estate Investment Services
N.A.I.C.S.: 523999
Jose Luis Del Valle Doblado *(Chm)*

LARA EXPLORATION LTD.
Suite 501 543 Granville Street, Vancouver, V6C 1X8, BC, Canada
Tel.: (604) 669-8777   Ca
Web Site:
https://www.laraexploration.com
Year Founded: 2006
LEW—(DEU)
Rev.: $80,974
Assets: $4,678,387
Liabilities: $157,254
Net Worth: $4,521,133
Earnings: ($2,278,997)
Fiscal Year-end: 12/31/23
Precious & Base Metal Exploration & Mining Services
N.A.I.C.S.: 212230
Miles F. Thompson *(Chm, Pres & CEO)*

LARAMIDE RESOURCES LTD.
The Exchange Tower 130 King Street West Suite 3680, PO Box 99, Toronto, M5X 1B1, ON, Canada
Tel.: (416) 599-7363   Ca
Web Site: https://www.laramide.com
Year Founded: 1996
LMRXF—(OTCQX)
Assets: $74,522,387
Liabilities: $9,503,517
Net Worth: $65,018,870

LARAMIDE RESOURCES LTD.

Laramide Resources Ltd.—(Continued)
Earnings: ($459,389)
Emp.: 9
Fiscal Year-end: 12/31/22
Uranium, Gold & Base Metals Mining & Exploration Services
N.A.I.C.S.: 212290
John Booth (Chm)

Subsidiaries:

Hydro Resources, Inc. (1)
1 Sugar Creek Center Blvd Ste 400, Sugar Land, TX 77478
Tel.: (844) 937-6420
Construction Engineering Services
N.A.I.C.S.: 541330
Alton Cherry (CEO)

Lagoon Creek Resources Pty. Ltd. (1)
Level 4 67 St Pauls Ter, PO Box 103, Spring Hill, 4004, QLD, Australia
Tel.: (61) 738313407
Web Site: http://www.laramide.com
Sales Range: $50-74.9 Million
Emp.: 5
Uranium Mining Exploration & Development Services
N.A.I.C.S.: 212290
Marc Henderson (Pres & CEO)

LAREAU INSURANCE BROKERS

353 St Jacques, Napierville, J0J 1L0, QC, Canada
Tel.: (450) 245-3322
Web Site: http://www.lareau.ca
Year Founded: 1955
Rev.: $23,985,824
Emp.: 50
Insurance Agency Services
N.A.I.C.S.: 524210
Marc-Andre Page (Dir-Bus Dev & Corp Svcs)

LARGAN PRECISION CO., LTD.

No 11 Jingke Rd, Nantun Dist, Taichung, 40852, Taiwan
Tel.: (886) 436002345 CN
Web Site: https://www.largan.com.tw
Year Founded: 1987
3008—(TAI)
Rev.: $1,527,131,507
Assets: $6,101,297,814
Liabilities: $926,348,591
Net Worth: $5,174,949,223
Earnings: $559,744,927
Emp.: 7,900
Fiscal Year-end: 12/31/23
Optical Product Mfr
N.A.I.C.S.: 334610
En-Chou Lin (Chm)

Subsidiaries:

Largan (Dongguan) Optronic Co. (1)
No 5 Tutang Industrial Road, Changping Town, Dongguan, Guangdong, China
Tel.: (86) 76983395446
Plastic Aspherical Lens Mfr
N.A.I.C.S.: 333310

Largan Health AI-Tech Co., Ltd. (1)
5F No 2 Ln 53 Sec 2 Heping E Rd, Daan Dist, Taipei, 106024, Taiwan
Tel.: (886) 227008528
Web Site: https://www.largan-health.com
Medical Equipment Distr
N.A.I.C.S.: 423450

Largan Industrial Optics Co., Ltd. (1)
No 11 Jingke Rd, Nantun Dist, Taichung, 40852, Taiwan
Tel.: (886) 436002345
Web Site: https://www.larganindustrialoptics.com
Optical Component Mfr
N.A.I.C.S.: 327212

Largan Medical Co., Ltd. (1)
No 11 Jingke Rd Nantun Dist, Taichung, 40852, Taiwan
Tel.: (886) 436002345
Mobile Phone Len Mfr
N.A.I.C.S.: 449210

Photonicore Technologies Co., Ltd. (1)
4F No 12 Ln 31 Sec 1 Huangdong Rd, Southern Taiwan Science Park Xinshi Dist, Tainan City, 744092, Taiwan
Tel.: (886) 67035112
Web Site: https://www.photonicore.com.tw
Laser Product Mfr
N.A.I.C.S.: 334419

Suzhou Largan Co., Ltd. (1)
No 588-1,Shanhu West Road Wujiang Economic Development Zone, Wujiang, Jiangsu, China
Tel.: (86) 51263493988
Plastic Aspherical Lens Mfr
N.A.I.C.S.: 333310

LARGO INC.

First Canadian Place 100 King Street West Suite 1600, Toronto, M5X 1C7, ON, Canada
Tel.: (416) 861-9797
Web Site: https://largoinc.com
LGO—(NASDAQ)
Rev.: $229,251,000
Assets: $355,750,000
Liabilities: $81,196,000
Net Worth: $274,554,000
Earnings: ($2,226,000)
Emp.: 479
Fiscal Year-end: 12/31/22
Metal Exploration Services
N.A.I.C.S.: 213114
Alberto Arias (Chm)

LARGO SA

4 Rue Jean Mermoz, 44980, Sainte-Luce-sur-Loire, France
Tel.: (33) 228225601
Web Site: https://www.largo.fr
Year Founded: 2016
ALLGO—(EUR)
Communication Equipment Retailer
N.A.I.C.S.: 423690
Christophe Brunot (CEO)

LARK DISTILLING CO., LTD.

Level 1 91-93 Macquarie, Hobart, 7000, TAS, Australia
Tel.: (61) 362319088 AU
Web Site: https://www.larkdistillery.com
LRK—(ASX)
Rev.: $11,171,714
Assets: $73,869,743
Liabilities: $6,186,165
Net Worth: $67,683,579
Earnings: ($3,050,157)
Fiscal Year-end: 06/30/24
Alcoholic Beverage Mfr & Distr
N.A.I.C.S.: 312130
David Dearie (Bd of Dirs & Chm)

LARK.PL S.A.

Square No 4, 02-495, Warsaw, Poland
Tel.: (48) 224831100
Web Site: http://www.mitsa.pl
Year Founded: 1996
Media & Telecommunication Services
N.A.I.C.S.: 517121
Andrzej Jerzy Piechocki (Chm-Mgmt Bd)

LARQ SA

Ul Tamka 16 lok U4, 00-349, Warsaw, Poland
Tel.: (48) 228280885
Web Site: https://www.larq.pl
LRQ—(WAR)
Rev.: $96,799
Assets: $16,220,274
Liabilities: $2,499,238
Net Worth: $13,721,037
Earnings: $3,215,701
Fiscal Year-end: 12/31/23
Advertising Services
N.A.I.C.S.: 541810
Wojciech Byj (Chm-Mgmt Bd)

LARRAIN VIAL SPA

Avenida El Bosque Norte 0177 1st Floor, Las Condes, Santiago, Chile
Tel.: (56) 223398500 CL
Web Site: https://english.larrainvial.com
Year Founded: 1934
Emp.: 800
Financial Services
N.A.I.C.S.: 523999
Fernando Larrain (Chm & CEO)

Subsidiaries:

Larrain Vial S.A. Corredora de Bolsa (1)
Av El Bosque Norte 0177, Santiago, 7550100, Chile
Tel.: (56) 223398500
Web Site: https://chile.larrainvial.com
Investment Management Service
N.A.I.C.S.: 523940
Fernando Larrain Cruzat (Mng Dir)

LARRY HUDSON CHEVROLET BUICK GMC INC.

1000 Wallace Avenue North, Listowel, N4W 1M5, ON, Canada
Tel.: (866) 230-7036
Web Site: http://www.larryhudson.com
Year Founded: 1984
New & Used Car Dealer
N.A.I.C.S.: 441110
Tom Pollard (Mgr-Sls)

LARRY JEWELRY INTERNATIONAL COMPANY LIMITED

13/F Pacific House 20 Queens Road, Central, China (Hong Kong)
Tel.: (852) 3151 0321 BM
Web Site: http://www.larryjewelryltd.com
Year Founded: 1967
Rev.: $49,115,575
Assets: $80,733,790
Liabilities: $54,636,380
Net Worth: $26,097,410
Earnings: $32,157,322
Emp.: 399
Fiscal Year-end: 12/31/18
Jewelry Mfr & Whslr
N.A.I.C.S.: 339910
Eric Yam Sheng Tay (Dir-Retail-Singapore)

LARRY MACDONALD CHEVROLET BUICK GMC LTD.

28380 Centre Road, Strathroy, N7G 3C4, ON, Canada
Tel.: (519) 245-0410
Web Site: http://www.larrymacdonaldchev.ca
Year Founded: 1980
Rev.: $13,347,016
Emp.: 30
New & Used Car Dealers
N.A.I.C.S.: 441110
Scott Cowen (Gen Mgr)

LARRY RENAUD FORD & R.V. SALES

2560 County Road 20, Harrow, N0R 1G0, ON, Canada
Tel.: (519) 738-6222
Web Site: http://www.renaudrvsales.com
Year Founded: 1974
Sales Range: $10-24.9 Million
New & Used Car Dealers
N.A.I.C.S.: 441110
L.V. Renaud (Pres & CEO)

INTERNATIONAL PUBLIC

LARS LARSEN GROUP

Sodalsparken 18, 8220, Brabrand, Denmark
Tel.: (45) 88183580
Web Site: https://larslarsengroup.com
Emp.: 100
Financial Services
N.A.I.C.S.: 523999
Jacob Brunsborg (Chm-Mgmt Bd)

LARSEN & SHAW LIMITED

575 Durham St West, Walkerton, N0G 2V0, ON, Canada
Tel.: (519) 881-1320
Web Site: http://www.larsenhinge.com
Year Founded: 1919
Rev.: $12,732,677
Emp.: 105
Architectural Product Mfr
N.A.I.C.S.: 332323
Diane Laird (Mgr-Fin & Admin)

LARSEN & TOUBRO LIMITED

L T House Ballard Estate, PO Box 278, Mumbai, 400 001, India
Tel.: (91) 2267525656
Web Site: https://www.larsentoubro.com
Year Founded: 1938
LT—(NSE)
Rev.: $22,333,177,867
Assets: $39,608,214,136
Liabilities: $27,190,826,689
Net Worth: $12,417,387,447
Earnings: $1,502,382,351
Emp.: 49,039
Fiscal Year-end: 03/31/23
Technology, Engineering, Construction & Manufacturing Services
N.A.I.C.S.: 541330
Anilkumar Manibhai Naik (Chm)

Subsidiaries:

Audco India Ltd. (1)
Mount Poonamallee Rd Manapakkam, 600 089, Chennai, India
Tel.: (91) 4422492323
Web Site: http://www.ailvalves.com
Industrial Valves Mfr; Owned 50% by Flowserve Corporation & 50% by Larsen & Toubro Limited
N.A.I.C.S.: 332911

Graphene Solutions Pte. Ltd. (1)
28 Genting Lane 08-08 Platinum 28, Singapore, 349585, Singapore
Tel.: (65) 6 908 0081
Web Site: https://graphenesvc.com
Information Technology Services
N.A.I.C.S.: 541519

Kudgi Transmission Limited (1)
38 Cubbon Road 1st Floor Shivaji Nagar, Bengaluru, 560 001, Karnataka, India
Tel.: (91) 802 502 0120
Power Transmission Services
N.A.I.C.S.: 221121

L&T - MHI Power Boilers Private Limited (1)
12/4 Delhi Mathura Road Near Sarai Khwaja Chowk, Faridabad, 121003, Haryana, India
Tel.: (91) 129 429 1000
Web Site: https://www.lntmhipower.com
Boiler Mfr & Distr
N.A.I.C.S.: 332410
Derek M. Shah (Chm)

L&T - MHI Power Turbine Generators Private Limited (1)
Hazira Manufacturing Complex West Gate No 8 Surat Hazira Road, Bhatha Dist, Surat, 394 510, Gujarat, India
Tel.: (91) 261 280 8000
Web Site: https://www.lmtg.in
Turbines & Generator Mfr
N.A.I.C.S.: 333611
Aloke Sarkar (CEO)

L&T EmSyS Private Limited (1)
Mysore Complex KIADB Industrial Area

AND PRIVATE COMPANIES

LARSEN & TOUBRO LIMITED

Hebbal-Hootagalli, Mysore, 570018, India
Tel.: (91) 821 2405000
Web Site: http://www.lntemsys.com
Software Support Services
N.A.I.C.S.: 541511

L&T Finance Holdings Limited (1)
Brindavan Plot No 177 CST Road Kalina
Santacruz East, Mumbai, 400 098, Maharashtra, India
Tel.: (91) 2262125000
Web Site: https://www.ltfs.com
Rev.: $1,682,164,575
Assets: $14,592,147,570
Liabilities: $11,869,286,520
Net Worth: $2,722,861,050
Earnings: $146,070,015
Emp.: 1
Fiscal Year-end: 03/31/2022
Financial Management Services
N.A.I.C.S.: 523999
Dinanath Dubhashi *(CEO & Mng Dir)*

Subsidiary (Domestic):

L&T Finance Limited (2)
Spanco House BS Deoshi Marg Deonar, Mumbai, 400 088, India (100%)
Tel.: (91) 2242491300
Web Site: http://www.ltfinance.com
Financial & Investment Services
N.A.I.C.S.: 523999

L&T MBDA Missile Systems Limited (1)
L and T-Gate No 1 North Block 1 2nd Floor
Saki Vihar Road, Powai, Mumbai, 400 072, India
Tel.: (91) 226 705 4986
Web Site: https://www.lntmbda.com
Engineeering Services
N.A.I.C.S.: 541330
J. D. Patil *(Chm & Sr Exec VP)*

L&T Mutual Fund Trustee Limited (1)
Brindavan Plot No 177 CST Road, Kalina
Santacruz East, Mumbai, 400098, Maharashtra, India
Tel.: (91) 226 212 5000
Financial Investment Services
N.A.I.C.S.: 523999

L&T Special Steels & Heavy Forgings Private Limited (1)
Gate No 10 Hazira Manufacturing Complex, Bhata, Surat, 394 510, Gujarat, India
Tel.: (91) 261 220 3200
Web Site: https://www.ltshf.com
Iron & Steel Product Mfr
N.A.I.C.S.: 331110

L&T Technology Services Limited (1)
L and T Knowledge City Special Economic Zone IT/ITES, West Block -11 No 8 Village Ankhol, Vadodara, 390019, Gujarat, India
Tel.: (91) 2656705000
Web Site: https://www.ltts.com
Rev.: $764,864,100
Assets: $692,450,850
Liabilities: $216,994,050
Net Worth: $475,456,800
Earnings: $90,977,250
Emp.: 15,953
Fiscal Year-end: 03/31/2021
Engineering Services
N.A.I.C.S.: 541330
Amit Chadha *(CEO & Mng Dir)*

L&T Valves Arabia Manufacturing LLC (1)
Building No 6883 King Abdulaziz Riad Shamalia, Al Khobar, 34428-2492, Saudi Arabia
Tel.: (966) 13 511 5600
Pressure Valve Mfr
N.A.I.C.S.: 332911

L&T-Chiyoda Limited (1)
5th Floor West Block 1 L T Knowledge City
Gate no 1, Ajwa-Waghodia Crossing NH 8, Vadodara, 390 019, Gujarat, India (50%)
Tel.: (91) 2652442000
Web Site: https://www.lntchiyoda.com
Sales Range: $200-249.9 Million
Emp.: 600
Engineering Consulting Services; Owned 50% by Larsen & Toubro Limited & 50% by Chiyoda Corporation
N.A.I.C.S.: 541690

Anand C. Ghaisas *(CEO)*

L&T-Komatsu Limited (1)
Bellary Rd, Bengaluru, 560 092, India (50%)
Tel.: (91) 8023333301
Web Site: http://www.larsentoubro.com
Sales Range: Less than $1 Million
Construction Equipment & Hydraulics Mfr
N.A.I.C.S.: 333120

L&T-Ramboll Consulting Engineers Limited (1)
339 340 Ana Salai Nandanam, Chennai, 600 035, India (100%)
Tel.: (91) 4424331181
Web Site: http://www.ltramboll.com
Sales Range: $50-74.9 Million
Emp.: 200
Engineering Consulting Services; Owned 50% by Larsen & Toubro Limited & 50% by Ramboll
N.A.I.C.S.: 541690

LTIMindtree Limited (1)
Saki Vihar Road Powai, Mumbai, 400072, India (68.73%)
Tel.: (91) 2267525656
Web Site: https://www.ltimindtree.com
Sales Range: $1-4.9 Billion
Emp.: 7,200
Offshore Outsourcing IT Services
N.A.I.C.S.: 541519
Sudhir Chaturvedi *(Pres-Sls)*

Subsidiary (Domestic):

MindTree Ltd. (3)
Global Village RVCE Post Mysore Road, Bengaluru, 560 059, Karnataka, India
Tel.: (91) 8067064000
Web Site: http://www.mindtree.com
Rev.: $1,097,586,000
Assets: $721,924,000
Liabilities: $279,972,000
Net Worth: $441,952,000
Earnings: $88,326,000
Emp.: 21,991
Fiscal Year-end: 03/31/2020
Computer Software Developer
N.A.I.C.S.: 513210
Krishnakumar Natarajan *(Co-Founder)*

Subsidiary (Non-US):

Bluefin Solutions Ltd. (3)
Building 4 Chiswick Park 566 Chiswick High Road, London, W4 5YE, United Kingdom
Tel.: (44) 8702330404
Web Site: http://www.bluefinsolutions.com
IT Consulting Services
N.A.I.C.S.: 541690
Mike Curl *(Founder, Head-Fin Svcs, Media & Life Sciences)*

Subsidiary (US):

Discoverture Solutions LLC (3)
16100 N 71st St Ste 250, Scottsdale, AZ 85254
Tel.: (480) 269-8100
Web Site: http://www.discoverture.com
Information Technology Services
N.A.I.C.S.: 513210
Sanjay Kanungo *(Sr VP & Head-Mktg & Health Care)*

Magnet 360, LLC (3)
5757 Wayzata Blvd, Minneapolis, MN 55416 (100%)
Tel.: (612) 230-2500
Web Site: http://www.magnet360.com
Emp.: 120
Management Consulting Services
N.A.I.C.S.: 541611
Matt Meents *(Founder & CEO)*

Branch (US):

MindTree Ltd. (3)
25 Independence Blvd Ste 401, Warren, NJ 07059
Tel.: (908) 604-8080
Web Site: http://www.mindtree.com
Sales Range: $200-249.9 Million
Computer Software Developer
N.A.I.C.S.: 513210

Branch (Non-US):

MindTree Ltd. (3)

288 Bishopsgate, London, EC2M 4QP, United Kingdom
Tel.: (44) 20 3178 8643
Computer Software Developer
N.A.I.C.S.: 513210
Venu Lambu *(Pres-Markets-Global)*

MindTree Ltd. (3)
Svetsarvagen 15 2tr, 171 41, Solna, Sweden
Tel.: (46) 8 578 77020
Computer Software Developer
N.A.I.C.S.: 513210

MindTree Ltd. (3)
3rd Floor Hopfenstrasse 6, 80335, Munich, Germany
Tel.: (49) 8938038690
Web Site: http://www.mindtree.com
Computer Software Developer
N.A.I.C.S.: 513210

MindTree Ltd. (3)
11 Cours Valmy Tour Pacafic, 92977, Paris, la Defense, France
Tel.: (33) 1 73 29 45 24
Computer Software Developer
N.A.I.C.S.: 513210

MindTree Ltd. (3)
Pegasuslaan 5, 1831, Diegem, Belgium
Tel.: (32) 2 709 2055
Web Site: http://www.mindtree.com
Computer Software Developer
N.A.I.C.S.: 513210

MindTree Ltd. (3)
248 Block B 5W DAFZA, PO Box 293858, Dubai, United Arab Emirates
Tel.: (971) 4260 2400
Web Site: http://www.mindtree.com
Computer Software Developer
N.A.I.C.S.: 513210

MindTree Ltd. (3)
2-21-7-703 Kiba, Koto-ku, Tokyo, 135-0042, Japan
Tel.: (81) 3 5809 8444
Computer Software Developer
N.A.I.C.S.: 513210

MindTree Ltd. (3)
17 Changi Business Park Central 1 05-03 Honeywell Building, Changi Business Park, Singapore, 486073, Singapore
Tel.: (65) 6323 8135
Web Site: http://www.mindtree.com
Computer Software Developer
N.A.I.C.S.: 513210

MindTree Ltd. (3)
Level 26 44 Market St, Sydney, 2000, NSW, Australia
Tel.: (61) 2 9089 8970
Computer Software Developer
N.A.I.C.S.: 513210

Subsidiary (Non-US):

MindTree Software Co. Ltd. (3)
Room 1503I Level 15 Tower 2 Kerry Plaza, 1 Zhong Xin Si Road, Futian District, Shenzhen, 518048, China
Tel.: (86) 755 3304 3162
Computer Software Developer
N.A.I.C.S.: 513210

Larsen & Toubro (East Asia) Sdn Bhd (1)
Sub Lot 24 Lot 16505 Jalan Keluli 1 Kawasan Perindustrian Bukit Raja, Seksyen 7, 40000, Shah Alam, Malaysia
Tel.: (60) 3 3344 2349
Construction Engineering Services
N.A.I.C.S.: 237990

Larsen & Toubro (Qingdao) Rubber Machinery Company Limited (1)
No 388 Lingang 14th Road Lingang Economic Development Zone, Qingdao, 266400, Shandong, China
Tel.: (86) 532 87197902
Web Site: http://www.ltqchina.com
Construction Engineering Services
N.A.I.C.S.: 541330

Larsen & Toubro (Wuxi) Electric Company Limited (1)
90 XiMei Road Wuxi National High-Tech Industrial Development Zone, Wuxi, 214028, China

Tel.: (86) 510 85371100
Construction Engineering Services
N.A.I.C.S.: 541330

Larsen & Toubro Electromech LLC (1)
PO Box 1999, Rue, 112, Ruwi, Oman (100%)
Tel.: (968) 24590577
Sales Range: $700-749.9 Million
Emp.: 3,000
Engineeering Services
N.A.I.C.S.: 541330

Larsen & Toubro Infotech Canada Limited (1)
701 Evans Avenue Suite 308, Toronto, M9C 1A3, ON, Canada
Tel.: (416) 968-2364
Information Technology Consulting Services
N.A.I.C.S.: 541512

Larsen & Toubro International FZE (1)
United Arab Bank Building Al Quassimia Street Hamriyah Free Zone, Near Central Post Office, Sharjah, United Arab Emirates
Tel.: (971) 65731549
Construction Engineering Services
N.A.I.C.S.: 541330

Larsen & Toubro Kuwait Construction General Contracting Company WLL (1)
Block-8 Building-42, East Ahmadi, Kuwait, Kuwait
Tel.: (965) 2 397 0072
Web Site: https://www.larsentoubro.com
Building Construction Services
N.A.I.C.S.: 236220

Nabha Power Limited (1)
Shed No T-2 Punjab, Patiala, 147001, India
Tel.: (91) 1752301171
Thermal Power Plant Operation Services
N.A.I.C.S.: 237130

Nielsen+Partner Pte. Ltd. (1)
11 Collyer Quay 09-09 The Arcade, Singapore, 049317, Singapore
Tel.: (65) 6 908 0879
Business Consultancy Services
N.A.I.C.S.: 541618

Nielsen+Partner Unternehmensberater AG (1)
Obstgartenstrasse 7, 8006, Zurich, Switzerland
Tel.: (41) 44 714 7234
Business Consultancy Services
N.A.I.C.S.: 541618

Nielsen+Partner Unternehmensberater GmbH (1)
Grosser Burstah 45, 20457, Hamburg, Germany
Tel.: (49) 40 369 8350
Web Site: https://nundp.com
Information Technology Consulting Services
N.A.I.C.S.: 541618

Qingdao Larsen & Toubro Trading Company Limited (1)
No 388 Lingang No 14 Road Lingang Economic Development Zone Jiaonan, Qingdao, 266400, Shandong, China
Tel.: (86) 53287197903
Web Site: http://www.larsentoubro.com
Construction Engineering Services
N.A.I.C.S.: 541330

Syncordis France SARL (1)
1 Terrasse Bellini-Tour Initiale, La Defense, 92800, Paris, France
Tel.: (33) 15 317 6349
Business Consultancy Services
N.A.I.C.S.: 541618

Syncordis Limited (1)
10th Floor 6 Bevis Marks, London, EC3A 7BA, United Kingdom
Tel.: (44) 207 266 7777
Business Consultancy Services
N.A.I.C.S.: 541618
Hemal Jayasinghe *(Chief Bus Officer)*

Syncordis Software Services India Private Limited (1)
Block 4 10th Floor A-Wing DLF IT Park-SEZ Campus 1/124 Shivaji Gardens, Mana-

LARSEN & TOUBRO LIMITED

Larsen & Toubro Limited—(Continued)
pakkam, Chennai, 600 089, Tamil Nadu, India
Tel.: (91) 446 620 9600
Business Consultancy Services
N.A.I.C.S.: 541618
Jignesh Jariwala *(Chief Strategy Officer & Head)*

Tractor Engineers Limited (1)
Krislon House 4th Floor, Krishnalal Marwah Marg, Off Saki Vihar Road Saki Naka, Mumbai, 400 072, Maharashtra, India
Tel.: (91) 2267701605
Sales Range: $50-74.9 Million
Emp.: 225
Tractor Mfr
N.A.I.C.S.: 333924

LARUS ENERGY LIMITED
65 York Street Level 8, Sydney, 2000, NSW, Australia
Tel.: (61) 2 8215 1519
Web Site: http://www.newportenergyltd.com
Sales Range: $25-49.9 Million
Emp.: 5
Oil & Gas Exploration Services
N.A.I.C.S.: 211120
Michael Swift *(Mgr-Exploration)*

LARVOTTO RESOURCES LIMITED
Suite 1 88 Broadway, Nedlands, 6009, WA, Australia
Tel.: (61) 863730112   AU
Web Site: https://www.larvottoresources.com
Year Founded: 2020
LRV—(ASX)
Rev.: $44,281
Assets: $11,195,502
Liabilities: $3,811,460
Net Worth: $7,384,042
Earnings: ($4,187,245)
Fiscal Year-end: 12/31/23
Exploration & Mining Services
N.A.I.C.S.: 213115

Subsidiaries:

Hillgrove Mines Pty Ltd. (1)
647 Minesite St, 51 Bracken St Hillgrove Armida, 2350, Sydney, NSW, Australia
Tel.: (61) 267781154
Gold Ore Mining
N.A.I.C.S.: 212220

LASA SUPERGENERICS LIMITED
Plot no C-4 C-4/1 MIDC Lote Parshuram Industrial Area Tal -Khed, Mulund West, Ratnagiri, 415722, Maharashtra, India
Tel.: (91) 2249701092   In
Web Site: https://www.lasalabs.com
LASA—(NSE)
Rev.: $27,632,664
Assets: $28,372,958
Liabilities: $6,680,774
Net Worth: $21,692,184
Earnings: $3,109,156
Emp.: 194
Fiscal Year-end: 03/31/21
Pharmaceutical Preparation Mfr & Distr
N.A.I.C.S.: 325412
Shivanand G. Hegde *(Exec Dir)*

LASACO ASSURANCE PLC
LASACO House Plot 16 Acme Road Ogba, PO Box 3724, Ikeja, Lagos, Nigeria
Tel.: (234) 7000527226
Web Site: https://www.lasacoassurance.com
Year Founded: 1979
LASACO—(NIGE)
Rev.: $31,015,901
Assets: $58,207,525
Liabilities: $29,244,200
Net Worth: $28,963,325
Earnings: $3,297,934
Emp.: 159
Fiscal Year-end: 12/31/22
All Other Insurance Related Activities
N.A.I.C.S.: 524298
Olumide Jayeola *(Gen Mgr-LASACO Properties)*

Subsidiaries:

LASACO Properties Ltd. (1)
16 Acme Rd Ogba, 101233, Ikeja, Lagos, Nigeria
Tel.: (234) 8033006589
Web Site: https://lasacopropertiesltd.com
Real Estate Services
N.A.I.C.S.: 531210

LASACO Trading and Investment Ltd. (1)
Lasaco Assurance Plc House Plot 16 Acme Road Ogba, PO Box 3724, Ikeja, Lagos, Nigeria
Tel.: (234) 7000527226
Web Site: https://ltil.netlify.app
Financial Services
N.A.I.C.S.: 921130

LASALLE LOGIPORT REIT
Pacific Century Place Marunouchi 14th floor 1-11-1 Marunouchi, Chiyoda-ku, Tokyo, Japan
Tel.: (81) 363675600
Web Site: https://www.lasalle-logiport.com
Year Founded: 2015
3466—(TKS)
Rev.: $102,512,439
Assets: $3,729,203,379
Liabilities: $1,653,947,800
Net Worth: $2,075,255,580
Earnings: $50,084,417
Fiscal Year-end: 02/28/22
Real Estate Investment Services
N.A.I.C.S.: 531210
Toshimitsu Fujiwara *(Exec Dir)*

LASCO MANUFACTURING LIMITED
27 Red Hills Road, Kingston, 10, Jamaica
Tel.: (876) 96036623
Web Site: https://manufacturing.lasco.com
Year Founded: 1994
Frozen Dessert & Beverage Product Mfr
N.A.I.C.S.: 311520
Lascelles Chin *(Founder & Chm)*

LASCOM SA
Energy Park 3-Immeuble l'Etendard 36, Avenue de l'Europe, Velizy-Villacoublay, 78140, France
Tel.: (33) 169 35 12 20
Web Site: http://www.lascom.com
Year Founded: 1989
Computer Software Services
N.A.I.C.S.: 541512
Charles Henriot *(CEO)*

Subsidiaries:

Lascom Solutions, Inc. (1)
8304 Clairemont Mesa Blvd, San Diego, CA 92111
Tel.: (858) 452-1300
Web Site: http://www.lascom.com
Sales Range: $1-9.9 Million
Emp.: 21
Custom Computer Programming Services
N.A.I.C.S.: 541511
Jean-Louis Henriot *(Pres)*

LASER SALES INC.
1717 Oxford Street, London, N5V 2Z5, ON, Canada
Tel.: (519) 452-1006
Web Site: http://www.lasersales.org
Year Founded: 1956
Rev.: $11,087,769
Emp.: 55
Industrial Equipment Distr & Mfr
N.A.I.C.S.: 335999
Andy Bethel *(Pres)*

LASER TEK TAIWAN CO., LTD.
No 24839 Xinsheng Rd, Qianzhen Dist, Kaohsiung, Taiwan
Tel.: (886) 78159877
Web Site: https://www.lasertek.com.tw
Year Founded: 1988
6207—(TPE)
Rev.: $38,517,151
Assets: $131,245,621
Liabilities: $72,220,704
Net Worth: $59,024,917
Earnings: $4,741,195
Emp.: 276
Fiscal Year-end: 12/31/24
Electronic Components Mfr
N.A.I.C.S.: 334419
Gary Cheng *(Pres)*

Subsidiaries:

Guochang Electronics (DongGuan) Ltd. (1)
59 7-1 Gaoli Road, Gaoli ind Zone Tangxia Town, Dongguan, Guangdong, China
Tel.: (86) 7698 772 0275
Paper Products Mfr
N.A.I.C.S.: 322299

Laser Tek (Kunshan) Co., Ltd. (1)
No 66 Gaoge Rd, Bacheng east Industry Zone, Kunshan, Jiangsu, China
Tel.: (86) 5125 778 9775
Paper Products Mfr
N.A.I.C.S.: 322299

LaserTek Singapore Pte. Ltd. (1)
Ubi Ave 3 02-42/43 Vertex, Singapore, 408838, Singapore
Tel.: (65) 6 742 8260
Web Site: https://www.lasertek.com.sg
Laser Trimmer Spare Parts Distr
N.A.I.C.S.: 423830

Weikecorp Semiconductor Co., Ltd. (1)
1F No 29 Dong Sec 2 Guangming 6th Rd, Hsinchu County, Zhubei, 302, Taiwan
Tel.: (886) 3 667 3980
Paper Products Mfr
N.A.I.C.S.: 322299

LASERBOND LIMITED
2/57 Anderson Road, Smeaton Grange, Sydney, 2567, NSW, Australia
Tel.: (61) 246314500
Web Site: https://www.laserbond.com.au
LBL—(ASX)
Rev.: $28,033,914
Assets: $40,508,833
Liabilities: $14,844,125
Net Worth: $25,664,707
Earnings: $2,352,268
Emp.: 147
Fiscal Year-end: 06/30/24
Industrial Components Reclamation & Surface Engineering Services
N.A.I.C.S.: 541330
Gregory John Hooper *(Founder & CTO)*

LASERLINE SAFETY AND SECURITY SYSTEMS S.R.L.
Via Don Locatelli 51, 20877, Roncello, MB, Italy
Tel.: (39) 039 682561   IT
Web Site: http://www.laserline.it
Year Founded: 1987
Sales Range: $125-149.9 Million
Safety & Security Systems
N.A.I.C.S.: 561621

Veronica Basile *(Mgr-Mktg & Comml-Automotive Div)*

LASERSSEL CO., LTD.
9-9 Dongtansandan 4-gil, Hwaseong, 18487, Gyeonggi-do, Korea (South)
Tel.: (82) 313730080
Web Site: https://www.laserssel.com
Year Founded: 2015
412350—(KRS)
Semiconductor Device Mfr & Distr
N.A.I.C.S.: 334413
Kenny Kang *(CFO)*

LASERTEC CORPORATION
2-10-1 Shin-yokohama, Kohoku-ku, Yokohama, 222-8552, Japan
Tel.: (81) 454787111
Web Site: https://www.lasertec.co.jp
Year Founded: 1960
6920—(TKS)
Rev.: $1,328,007,320
Assets: $1,687,411,360
Liabilities: $746,232,060
Net Worth: $941,179,300
Earnings: $367,452,720
Emp.: 859
Fiscal Year-end: 06/30/24
Semiconductor Devices Mfr
N.A.I.C.S.: 334413
Haruhiko Kusunose *(Exec VP)*

Subsidiaries:

Lasertec Korea Corporation (1)
1002 Dongtanbanseok-ro 134, Hwaseong, 18455, Gyeonggi-do, Korea (South)
Tel.: (82) 3180150540
Web Site: http://www.lasertec.co.jp
Emp.: 35
Electric Device Mfr
N.A.I.C.S.: 334413
Choon Gablim *(Mgr)*

Lasertec Taiwan Inc. (1)
9F-3 No 8 Ziqiang S Rd, Zhubei, 302, Hsinchu, Taiwan
Tel.: (886) 36579120
Electric Device Mfr
N.A.I.C.S.: 334413

Lasertec U.S.A., Inc. (1)
2107 N 1 St Ste 210, San Jose, CA 95131
Tel.: (408) 437-1441
Electric Device Mfr
N.A.I.C.S.: 334413
Masashi Sunako *(Pres)*

LASSELSBERGER GMBH
Worth 1, 3380, Pochlarn, Austria
Tel.: (43) 275775010
Web Site: http://www.lasselsberger.com
Sales Range: $900-999.9 Million
Emp.: 13,000
Raw Material Building Material & Ceramic Product Mfr
N.A.I.C.S.: 327120
Josef Lasselsberger *(Mng Dir)*

Subsidiaries:

LASSELSBERGER HUNGARIA Kft. (1)
Grassalkovich ut 255, 1239, Budapest, Hungary
Tel.: (36) 1 286 1377
Web Site: http://www.lasselsberger.hu
Building Materials Mfr
N.A.I.C.S.: 327120

LASSELSBERGER ITALY s.r.l. (1)
Via Circonvallazione San Giovanni Evangelista 1, Spezzano di Fiorano, 41040, Modena, Italy
Tel.: (39) 0536 921840
Building Materials Mfr
N.A.I.C.S.: 327120

LASSELSBERGER a.s. (1)
Goncharnaya 17, 109 240, Moscow, Russia
Tel.: (7) 4952210143
Building Materials Mfr
N.A.I.C.S.: 327120

AND PRIVATE COMPANIES

LASSELSBERGER-KNAUF (1)
d.o.o.
P Preradovica 64, 48350, Durdevac, Croatia
Tel.: (385) 48 279 900
Web Site: http://www.lb-knauf.hr
Building Materials Mfr
N.A.I.C.S.: 327120

LASSELSBERGER-KNAUF s.r.l. (1)
str Infratirii 47, 550117, Sibiu, Romania
Tel.: (40) 269 206 017
Web Site: http://www.lbk.ro
Building Materials Mfr
N.A.I.C.S.: 327120

Lasselsberger, s.r.o. (1)
Dmytryevska str No 56A off No 1, 010 54, Kiev, Ukraine
Tel.: (380) 44 593 10 17
Building Materials Mfr
N.A.I.C.S.: 327120

OOO LASSELSBERGER (1)
ul Elektrozavodskaya d 8, 450520, Ufa, Russia
Tel.: (7) 3472936310
Web Site: http://lb-ceramics.ru
Building Materials Mfr
N.A.I.C.S.: 327120

SC LASSELSBERGER SA (1)
Str Zarii nr 12 sector 5, 050461, Bucharest, Romania
Tel.: (40) 21 3183 832
Building Materials Mfr
N.A.I.C.S.: 327120
Andreea Catanoiu (CFO)

Zalakeramia Rt. (1)
Rakoczei 44, 8946, Zalaegerszeg, Tofej, Hungary
Tel.: (36) 92313640
Web Site: http://www.zalakeramia.hu
Sales Range: $75-99.9 Million
Emp.: 3,000
Floor & Wall Tile Mfr
N.A.I.C.S.: 327120

LASSERVICE AS
Sandbrekkeveien 96, Nesttun, 5225, Bergen, Norway
Tel.: (47) 970 55 300 NO
Web Site: http://www.laasservice.no
Year Founded: 1981
Sales Range: $10-24.9 Million
Security Systems & Locksmith Services
N.A.I.C.S.: 561621
Stale Raa (Mng Dir)

Subsidiaries:

Eiendomssikring AS (1)
Stromsveien 266, PB 51, Alnabru, 0614, Oslo, Norway
Tel.: (47) 2328 8100
Web Site: http://www.eiendomssikring.no
Sales Range: $1-9.9 Million
Emp.: 17
Security Systems & Locksmith Services
N.A.I.C.S.: 561621
Knut Kildahl (Gen Mgr)

LASSETERS INTERNATIONAL HOLDINGS LIMITED
SGX Centre 2 17-01 4 Shenton Way, Singapore, 068807, Singapore
Tel.: (65) 63619883 SG
Web Site: http://www.lasseters-intl.com
Year Founded: 2004
5EL—(CAT)
Rev.: $31,852,350
Assets: $103,974,593
Liabilities: $70,623,681
Net Worth: $33,350,912
Earnings: ($3,801,607)
Fiscal Year-end: 06/30/19
Holding Company
N.A.I.C.S.: 551112
Jaya J. B. Tan (Chm)

Subsidiaries:

Cypress Lakes Golf & Country Club Pty Limited (1)
Cnr McDonalds and Thompsons Rd, Pokolbin, 2320, NSW, Australia
Tel.: (61) 249931555
Web Site: http://www.cypresslakes.com.au
Golf Course Club Services
N.A.I.C.S.: 713910

Lasseters Health Club Pty. Ltd. (1)
93 Barrett Drive, Alice Springs, 0870, NT, Australia
Tel.: (61) 889507706
Web Site: http://www.lassetershealthclub.com.au
Sport & Fitness Club Services
N.A.I.C.S.: 713940
Matthew Straight (Gen Mgr)

The Golden Door Health Retreat - Elysia Pty Limited (1)
165 Thompsons Rd, Pokolbin, 2320, NSW, Australia
Tel.: (61) 249938500
Web Site: http://www.elysiaretreat.com.au
Spa & Wellness Centre Services
N.A.I.C.S.: 812199

LASSILA & TIKANOJA PLC
Valimotie 27, FIN- 00380, Helsinki, Finland
Tel.: (358) 10636111 FI
Web Site: https://www.lt.fi
LAT1V—(HEL)
Rev.: $910,964,818
Assets: $712,821,066
Liabilities: $474,962,227
Net Worth: $237,858,839
Earnings: $33,995,251
Emp.: 8,371
Fiscal Year-end: 12/31/22
Environmental Management, Property, Plant Maintenance & Industrial Services
N.A.I.C.S.: 561790
Eero Hautaniemi (Pres, CEO & Member-Exec Bd)

Subsidiaries:

Kiinteisto Oy (1)
Tietokatu 3, 94600, Kemi, Finland
Tel.: (358) 407006429
Web Site: https://www.kiinteistoitatuuli.fi
Property Management Services
N.A.I.C.S.: 531312

L&T Biowatti Oy (1)
Sentnerikuja 1, 00440, Helsinki, Finland
Tel.: (358) 10 4608
Web Site: http://www.biowatti.fi
Sales Range: $25-49.9 Million
Emp.: 100
Construction Engineering Services
N.A.I.C.S.: 541330

L&T Hankinta Ky (1)
Sentnerikuja 1, 00440, Helsinki, Finland (100%)
Tel.: (358) 10636111
Web Site: http://www.lassila-tikanoja.com
Sales Range: $25-49.9 Million
Emp.: 200
Waste Management Services
N.A.I.C.S.: 562998

L&T Kalusto Oy (1)
Valimotie 27, PO Box 28, Helsinki, 00380, Finland (100%)
Tel.: (358) 10636111
Web Site: http://www.lassila-tikanoja.com
Sales Range: $1-4.9 Billion
Emp.: 400
Waste Management Services
N.A.I.C.S.: 562998

L&T Muoviportti Oy (1)
Harjuntie 40, PO Box 22, Merikarvia, 29900, Finland (66.7%)
Tel.: (358) 10636172
Web Site: http://www.muoviportti.fi
Emp.: 33
Plastics Product Mfr
N.A.I.C.S.: 326199
Jani Kuusisto (Supvr-Production)

L&T Toimi Oy (1)
Hopeatie 2, Helsinki, Finland (100%)
Tel.: (358) 10636111
Waste Management Services
N.A.I.C.S.: 562998

L&T Ymparistohuolto Oy (1)
Valimotie 27, Helsinki, 00380, Finland (100%)
Tel.: (358) 10636111
Web Site: http://www.lassila-tikanoja.fi
Sales Range: $1-4.9 Billion
Emp.: 400
Waste Management Services
N.A.I.C.S.: 562998

Lassila & Tikanoja Service AB (1)
Armegatan 40, 17171, Solna, Sweden (100%)
Tel.: (46) 856410340
Web Site: http://www.lt.sc
Sales Range: $25-49.9 Million
Emp.: 127
Waste Management Services
N.A.I.C.S.: 562998
Tapio Keranen (Gen Mgr)

Pussihukka Oy (1)
Hyllilankatu 14, Tampere, 33730, Finland
Tel.: (358) 33640330
Environmental Consulting Services
N.A.I.C.S.: 541620

Suomen Keraystuote Oy (1)
Teollisuustie 9, 33330, Tampere, Finland (100%)
Tel.: (358) 331425300
Web Site: http://www.suomenkeraystuote.fi
Sales Range: $25-49.9 Million
Emp.: 6
Waste Management Services
N.A.I.C.S.: 562998

LASSONDE INDUSTRIES, INC.
755 Principale Street, Rougemont, J0L 1M0, QC, Canada
Tel.: (450) 469-4926
Web Site: https://www.lassonde.com
Year Founded: 1918
OOO—(DEU)
Rev.: $1,748,064,289
Assets: $1,257,806,404
Liabilities: $505,780,886
Net Worth: $752,025,518
Earnings: $66,646,136
Emp.: 3,000
Fiscal Year-end: 12/31/23
Fruit & Vegetable Juice, Wine & Sauce Mfr
N.A.I.C.S.: 311411
Pierre-Paul Lassonde (Chm)

Subsidiaries:

A. Lassonde, Inc. (1)
170 5th Avenue, Rougemont, J0L 1M0, QC, Canada
Tel.: (866) 552-7643
Web Site: http://www.alassonde.com
Pure Fruit Juice & Fruit Drink Processing & Packaging
N.A.I.C.S.: 311421

Division (Domestic):

Arista Wines (2)
705 Principale Street, Rougemont, J0L 1M0, QC, Canada
Tel.: (450) 469-4926
Web Site: http://www.lassonde.com
Sales Range: $75-99.9 Million
Emp.: 400
Wine Producer
N.A.I.C.S.: 312130

Entrepot A.C. L'Ange-Gardien (2)
135 St-Hubert Street, L'Ange-Gardien, J0E 1E0, QC, Canada
Tel.: (450) 293-1770
Apple Warehousing Services
N.A.I.C.S.: 493120

Entrepot Frigo Farnham (2)
250 St-Gregoire Street West, Farnham, J2N 1R1, QC, Canada
Tel.: (450) 293-6210
Emp.: 8
Fresh Apple Refrigeration, Freezing & Storage Services
N.A.I.C.S.: 493120
Vincent Giasson (Mgr)

LASSONDE INDUSTRIES, INC.

Golden Town Apple Products (2)
Box 303, Thornbury, N0H 2P0, ON, Canada
Tel.: (519) 599-6300
Sales Range: $10-24.9 Million
Emp.: 32
Apple Processing & Juice Production
N.A.I.C.S.: 311421
Jay Johnson (Gen Mgr)

Lassonde Beverages Canada (2)
95 Vulcan Street, Toronto, M9W 1L4, ON, Canada
Tel.: (416) 244-4224
Web Site: http://www.lassonde.com
Sales Range: $25-49.9 Million
Emp.: 130
Fruit Juice & Fruit Drink Production & Sales
N.A.I.C.S.: 311421

Lassonde Western Canada (2)
7419 30th Street SE, Calgary, T2C 1N6, AB, Canada
Tel.: (403) 296-9350
Web Site: http://www.lassonde.com
Sales Range: $10-24.9 Million
Emp.: 50
Fruit Juice & Fruit Drink Production & Sales
N.A.I.C.S.: 311421

Orange Maison (2)
9420 Boul Langelier, Montreal, H1P 3H8, QC, Canada (100%)
Tel.: (514) 351-4010
Web Site: http://www.lassonde.com
Sales Range: $10-24.9 Million
Emp.: 30
Orange Juice & Spring Water Distr
N.A.I.C.S.: 311411

Apple & Eve LLC (1)
2 Seaview Blvd, Port Washington, NY 11050
Tel.: (516) 621-1122
Web Site: http://www.appleandeve.com
Sales Range: $150-199.9 Million
Emp.: 75
Fruit Juices Mfr
N.A.I.C.S.: 311421

Lassonde Pappas & Co., Inc. (1)
1 Collins Dr Ste 200, Carneys Point, NJ 08069
Tel.: (856) 455-1000
Web Site: https://www.lassondepappas.com
Canned, Bottled Juices & Cocktail Mixers Mfr & Distr
N.A.I.C.S.: 311411
Jean Gattuso (Chm)

Lassonde Specialities Inc. (1)
200 St-Joseph Street, Saint-Damase-de-L'Islet, J0H 1J0, QC, Canada (100%)
Tel.: (450) 797-3303
Web Site: http://www.lassonde.com
Sales Range: $25-49.9 Million
Emp.: 60
Producer & Exporter of Canned Corn, Sauces, Fondues & Baked Beans
N.A.I.C.S.: 111150

Division (Domestic):

Entreposage Supervision (2)
225 Principale Street, Saint-Damase-de-L'Islet, QC, Canada
Tel.: (450) 797-3303
Warehousing Services
N.A.I.C.S.: 493130

Mondiv (2)
3810 Alfred Laliberte, Boisbriand, J7H 1P8, QC, Canada
Tel.: (450) 979-0717
Web Site: http://www.mondiv.com
Emp.: 10
Long-Shelf-Life Specialty Foods Mfr
N.A.I.C.S.: 311999

Northland Products, LLC (1)
1000 Raindbow Dr, Waterloo, IA 50704
Tel.: (319) 234-5585
Web Site: https://northlandproducts.com
Lubricant & Motor Oil Mfr
N.A.I.C.S.: 324191

Old Orchard Brands, LLC (1)
1991 12 Mile Rd, Sparta, MI 49345
Tel.: (616) 887-1745
Web Site: https://www.oldorchard.com
Frozen Fruit, Juice & Vegetable Mfr
N.A.I.C.S.: 311411

LASSONDE INDUSTRIES, INC.

Lassonde Industries, Inc.—(Continued)
Kevin Miller (VP-Mktg)

Sun-Rype Products Ltd. (1)
1165 Ethel Street, Kelowna, V1Y 2W4, BC, Canada **(100%)**
Tel.: (250) 470-6426
Web Site: http://www.sunrype.com
Sales Range: $150-199.9 Million
Emp.: 350
Food & Beverage Products Mfr & Marketer
N.A.I.C.S.: 311411
Lesli Bradley (Pres)

LAST MILE ENTERPRISES LTD.
4th Floor Vaghela Avenue, Navrangpura, Ahmedabad, 380009, India
Tel.: (91) 7926402089
Web Site: https://lastmilent.com
Year Founded: 1994
526961—(BOM)
Rev.: $682,213
Assets: $11,493,232
Liabilities: $10,973,795
Net Worth: $519,437
Earnings: $502,402
Emp.: 19
Fiscal Year-end: 03/31/21
Securities Brokerage Services
N.A.I.C.S.: 523150
Dhananjay Hasmukhlal Trivedi (Compliance Officer & Sec)

LASTA A.D.
Autoput Beograd-Nis 4, 11050, Belgrade, Serbia
Tel.: (381) 113402300
Web Site: https://www.lasta.rs
Year Founded: 1947
LSTA—(BEL)
Sales Range: $100-124.9 Million
Passenger Transportation Services
N.A.I.C.S.: 485999
Milan Urosevic (CFO)

LASTER TECH CO., LTD.
Building F No 4 Minxiang St Zhonghe Dist, New Taipei City, 23545, Taiwan
Tel.: (886) 222226112
Web Site: https://www.lastertech.com
Year Founded: 1999
3346—(TAI)
Rev.: $277,085,964
Assets: $311,675,681
Liabilities: $204,309,715
Net Worth: $107,365,966
Earnings: $10,163,838
Fiscal Year-end: 12/31/23
Light Emitting Diode Mfr & Distr
N.A.I.C.S.: 334413

Subsidiaries:

Laster Tech (Thailand) Co., Ltd. (1)
16th floor 65/134 Chamnan Phenjati Business Center building Rama9 road, HuayKwang, Bangkok, 10310, Thailand
Tel.: (66) 22486810
Light Emitting Diode Chip Mfr
N.A.I.C.S.: 334413

Laster Tech Automotive (Shanghai) Co., Ltd. (1)
No 666 East Huiwang Rd Jiading Dist, Shanghai, 201807, China
Tel.: (86) 2159548681
Light Emitting Diode Chip Mfr
N.A.I.C.S.: 334413

Laster Tech Electronics (Dongguan) Co., Ltd. (1)
No 7 Ming Zhu 1 Rd Yong Sheng IZ, She Bei Vil Huang Jiang Town, Dongguan, Guangdong, China
Tel.: (86) 76986968566
Light Emitting Diode Chip Mfr
N.A.I.C.S.: 334413

Laster Tech Opto (Jiayuguan) Co., Ltd. (1)
Rm 203 Unit 2 Building Jia 40 Liming Residential Dist, Jiayuguan, 735100, China
Tel.: (86) 13909477999
Light Emitting Diode Chip Mfr
N.A.I.C.S.: 334413

Laster Tech Opto (Shenzhen) Co., Ltd. (1)
Room 1901 Floor 19 Building 1 HeGuShanHuiCheng No 35 Guangtian Road, Luotian Community Yanluo Street Baoan District, Shenzhen, 518105, Guangdong, China
Tel.: (86) 75529108058
Light Emitting Diode Chip Mfr
N.A.I.C.S.: 334413

Li San (Shanghai) International Trade Ltd. (1)
No 666 East Huiwang Rd, Jiading Dist, Shanghai, 201807, China
Tel.: (86) 2159548681
Light Emitting Diode Chip Mfr
N.A.I.C.S.: 334413

LAT CO., LTD.
3 Gajangsaneopseobuk-Ro, Osan, Gyeonggi-do, Korea (South)
Tel.: (82) 313240269
Web Site: https://www.lat7.com
Year Founded: 2017
311060—(KRS)
Electronic Components Mfr
N.A.I.C.S.: 334419
Heung-Hwan Kim (Pres & CEO)

LATAM AIRLINES GROUP S.A.
Presidente Riesco 5711 20th Floor Las Condes, Santiago, Chile
Tel.: (56) 6005262000   CL
Web Site: https://www.latamairlinesgroup.net
Year Founded: 1929
LTM—(SGO)
Rev.: $11,640,541,000
Assets: $14,667,315,000
Liabilities: $14,229,040,000
Net Worth: $438,275,000
Earnings: $581,550,000
Emp.: 35,568
Fiscal Year-end: 12/31/23
Domestic & International Passenger & Cargo Airline Services
N.A.I.C.S.: 481111
Ignacio Cueto Plaza (Chm)

Subsidiaries:

Blue Express INTL S.A. (1)
Av El Retiro 9800, Los Maitenes Industrial Park Pudahuel, Santiago, Chile
Tel.: (56) 26992104
Web Site: https://www.blue.cl
Courier Service
N.A.I.C.S.: 492110

Contecon Guayaquil, S.A. (1)
Av De la Marina Puerto Libertador, Simon Bolivar, Guayaquil, Ecuador
Tel.: (593) 46006300
Web Site: https://www.cgsa.com.ec
Port Operation Services
N.A.I.C.S.: 488310

ICTSI Rio Brasil Terminal 1 S.A. (1)
Rua General Gurjao 105 Cashew, Rio de Janeiro, RJ, Brazil
Tel.: (55) 2130902525
Web Site: https://www.riobrasilterminal.com
Port Operation Services
N.A.I.C.S.: 488310

Lan Cargo S.A. (1)
Avenida Presidente Riesco 5711 piso 20, Las Condes, Santiago, Chile **(99.89%)**
Tel.: (56) 6003005000
Web Site: https://www.latamcargo.com
Sales Range: $650-699.9 Million
Air Cargo Services
N.A.I.C.S.: 481112

Subsidiary (US):

Connecta Corporation (2)
6500 NW 22nd St, Miami, FL 33122
Tel.: (786) 265-6000
Cargo Handling Services
N.A.I.C.S.: 488320

Lan Peru S.A. (1)
Av Jose Pardo 513 Of 3, Lima, Peru
Tel.: (51) 12138300
Oil Transportation Services
N.A.I.C.S.: 488190

Laser Cargo S.R.L. (1)
Corrientes Av 327 3, 1043, Buenos Aires, Argentina
Tel.: (54) 1143433394
Cargo Handling Services
N.A.I.C.S.: 488320

Manila Harbor Center Port Services, Inc. (1)
Mel Lopez Blvd Vitas Tondo, Manila, 1013, Philippines
Tel.: (63) 285167888
Web Site: https://www.mhcpsi.com
Port Services
N.A.I.C.S.: 488310

Prime Airport Services Inc. (1)
6450 NW 22nd St Bldg 710, Miami, FL 33122
Tel.: (786) 265-3500
Web Site: http://www.primeairportservices.com
Cargo Handling Services
N.A.I.C.S.: 488490

TAM S.A. (1)
Av Jurandir 856 Lote 4 1 andar, Sao Paulo, 04072-000, SP, Brazil
Tel.: (55) 11 5582 8817
Web Site: http://www.tam.br
Sales Range: $1-4.9 Billion
Holding Company; Commercial Airline Owner & Operator
N.A.I.C.S.: 551112

Subsidiary (Domestic):

Multiplus S.A. (2)
R Ministro Jesuino Cardoso 454 - 1 E 2 And, 4544051, Sao Paulo, Brazil **(97.2%)**
Tel.: (55) 11 5105 1847
Web Site: http://www.multiplusfidelidade.com.br
Advertising Services
N.A.I.C.S.: 541890

TAM Linhas Aereas S.A. (2)
Rua Atica n 673 6th floor room 62, Sao Paulo, 04634-042, Brazil **(100%)**
Tel.: (55) 1128204816
Web Site: https://www.latamairlines.com
Sales Range: $5-14.9 Billion
Emp.: 28,821
Commercial Airline Operator
N.A.I.C.S.: 481111

Subsidiary (Non-US):

TAM Mercosur S.A. (2)
Avenida Vitacura 2943 Edificio Millenium, Santiago, Chile **(94.98%)**
Tel.: (56) 24990100
Web Site: http://www.tam.com.py
Support Activities for Air Transportation
N.A.I.C.S.: 488190

Transporte Aereo S.A. (1)
Av Americo Vespucio 901, Santiago, Chile
Tel.: (56) 25652525
Oil Transportation Services
N.A.I.C.S.: 488190

LATAM AUTOS LIMITED
Level 4 100 Albert Road South, Melbourne, 3205, VIC, Australia
Tel.: (61) 396927222
Web Site: http://www.latamautos.com
Rev.: $5,305,092
Assets: $24,587,384
Liabilities: $9,790,932
Net Worth: $14,796,452
Earnings: ($9,235,388)
Fiscal Year-end: 12/31/18
Online Auto Sales
N.A.I.C.S.: 441110
Timothy Handley (Co-Founder)

LATENT LIGHT FINANCE LIMITED
120 Local Shopping Centre Aurbindo Place Hauz Khas, New Delhi, 110016, India
Tel.: (91) 114 107 4949
Web Site: http://www.galaxycommercial.in
Year Founded: 1984
539909—(BOM)
Rev.: $396,652,620
Assets: $2,726,651,655
Liabilities: $331,778,265
Net Worth: $2,394,873,390
Earnings: $315,106,155
Fiscal Year-end: 03/31/20
Consumer Lending Services
N.A.I.C.S.: 522291
Dharmender Singhal (CFO)

LATENT VIEW ANALYTICS LIMITED
5th Floor Neville Tower Block A3 Ramanujan It City Sez, Rajiv Gandhi Salai Omr Taramani, Chennai, 600113, India
Tel.: (91) 4443441700
Web Site: https://www.latentview.com
Year Founded: 2006
543398—(BOM)
Rev.: $44,595,642
Assets: $70,870,664
Liabilities: $11,113,011
Net Worth: $59,757,653
Earnings: $12,484,700
Fiscal Year-end: 03/31/21
Management Consulting Services
N.A.I.C.S.: 541611
Venkat Viswanathan (Chm)

Subsidiaries:

Latent View Analytics B.V. (1)
Zuidplein 36, 1077 XV, Amsterdam, Netherlands
Tel.: (31) 20 799 7611
Business Consulting Services
N.A.I.C.S.: 541611

Latent View Analytics Corporation (1)
2540 N 1st St Ste 108, San Jose, CA 95131
Tel.: (408) 493-6653
Business Consulting Services
N.A.I.C.S.: 541611

Latent View Analytics GmbH (1)
Josephsspitalstr 15, 80331, Munich, Germany
Tel.: (49) 8920 704 0270
Business Consulting Services
N.A.I.C.S.: 541611

Latent View Analytics Pte. Ltd. (1)
5 Tampines Central 6 03-38, Singapore, 529482, Singapore
Tel.: (65) 6 591 8704
Business Consulting Services
N.A.I.C.S.: 541611

Latent View Analytics UK Limited (1)
37th Floor 1 Canada Square Canary Wharf, London, E14 5AA, United Kingdom
Tel.: (44) 207 979 7701
Business Consulting Services
N.A.I.C.S.: 541611

LATI INDUSTRIA TERMOPLASTICI S.P.A.
Via F Baracca 7, 21040, Vedano Olona, Varese, Italy
Tel.: (39) 0332409111   IT
Web Site: http://www.lati.com
Year Founded: 1945
Sales Range: $125-149.9 Million
Emp.: 350
Compounder of Engineering Thermoplastics
N.A.I.C.S.: 325211
Francesco Conterno (Chm)

Subsidiaries:

Lati France S.A.S. (1)

AND PRIVATE COMPANIES

Zone Industrielle Des Ebizoires 4 Rue Des Freres Lumiere, Plaisir, 78370, France **(100%)**
Tel.: (33) 130791819
Sales Range: $50-74.9 Million
Emp.: 4
Sales of Thermoplastics
N.A.I.C.S.: 424610

Lati Iberica, S.L. Unipersonal (1)
Via Augusta 59, 08006, Barcelona, Spain **(100%)**
Tel.: (34) 932097377
Sales Range: $50-74.9 Million
Emp.: 3
Sales of Thermoplastics
N.A.I.C.S.: 424610
Marta Clogeg *(Mng Dir)*

Lati Industria Termoplastici Deutschland GmbH (1)
Otto-von-Guericke-Ring 7, 65205, Wiesbaden, Nordenstadt, Germany **(100%)**
Tel.: (49) 6122 90820
Sales Range: $50-74.9 Million
Emp.: 10
Sales of Thermoplastics
N.A.I.C.S.: 424610

Lati Thermoplastics Do Brasil Ltda (1)
Av Prof Gioia Martins 206, 05632 020, Sao Paulo, SP, Brazil **(99%)**
Tel.: (55) 1135024700
Web Site: http://www.lati.com
Sales Range: $50-74.9 Million
Emp.: 1
Sales of Thermoplastics
N.A.I.C.S.: 424610

Lati U.S.A., Inc. (1)
2036 Ewall St # D, Mount Pleasant, SC 29464-3076 **(100%)**
Tel.: (843) 285-2200
Web Site: http://www.lati.com
Sales Range: $25-49.9 Million
Emp.: 6
Compounder Engineering Thermoplastics
N.A.I.C.S.: 325991

Lati UK Limited (1)
Crewe Hall Weston Road The Quadrangle, Crewe, CW1 6UA, Cheshire, United Kingdom **(95%)**
Tel.: (44) 1270501713
Web Site: http://www.lati.com
Sales Range: $1-9.9 Million
Emp.: 2
Sales of Thermoplastics
N.A.I.C.S.: 424610
Andrew Donkin *(Mgr-Sls-UK & Ireland)*

Scandilati Termoplastici AB (1)
Skeppsbroplatsen 1, S 41118, Gothenburg, Sweden **(100%)**
Tel.: (46) 317740236
Web Site: http://www.lati.com
Sales Range: $50-74.9 Million
Emp.: 2
Sales of Thermoplastics
N.A.I.C.S.: 424610

LATIN METALS INC.
890999 West Hastings Street, Vancouver, V6C 2W2, BC, Canada
Tel.: (604) 638-3456 **BC**
Web Site: https://www.latin-metals.com
Year Founded: 2006
LMSQF—(OTCQB)
Assets: $4,955,174
Liabilities: $666,239
Net Worth: $4,288,936
Earnings: ($812,059)
Fiscal Year-end: 10/31/23
Mineral Exploration Services
N.A.I.C.S.: 213114
Keith Henderson *(Pres & CEO)*

LATIN RESOURCES LIMITED
Unit 3 32 Harrogate Street, West Leederville, 6007, WA, Australia
Tel.: (61) 861174798 **AU**
Web Site: https://www.latinresources.com.au

XL5—(DEU)
Rev.: $230,964
Assets: $37,371,831
Liabilities: $3,610,112
Net Worth: $33,761,719
Earnings: ($4,850,248)
Fiscal Year-end: 12/31/22
Iron Ore Mining
N.A.I.C.S.: 212210
Christopher Gale *(Exec Dir)*

Subsidiaries:

Peruvian Latin Resources SAC (1)
Calle Cura Bejar 190 Oficina 303, San Isidro, Lima, Peru
Tel.: (51) 14212009
Mineral Exploration Services
N.A.I.C.S.: 213114

LATINEX HOLDINGS, INC.
Ave Federico Boyd & Calle 49 LATINEX building, Box 0823-00963, Panama, Panama
Tel.: (507) 2691966
Web Site: https://www.latinexholdings.com
Year Founded: 2010
LTXH—(PAN)
Rev.: $9,330,017
Assets: $15,639,597
Liabilities: $14,492,568
Net Worth: $1,147,029
Earnings: $3,409,308
Fiscal Year-end: 12/31/23
Holding Company
N.A.I.C.S.: 551112
Roberto P. Brenes *(VP)*

LATITUDE GROUP HOLDINGS LIMITED
Level 18 130 Lonsdale St, Melbourne, 3000, VIC, Australia
Tel.: (61) 390581564 **AU**
Web Site: https://www.latitudefinancial.com.au
Year Founded: 2015
LFS—(ASX)
Rev.: $625,741,670
Assets: $4,790,245,811
Liabilities: $3,985,264,393
Net Worth: $804,981,417
Earnings: ($89,913,282)
Emp.: 800
Fiscal Year-end: 12/31/23
Holding Company
N.A.I.C.S.: 551112
Bob Belan *(CEO & Mng Dir)*

Subsidiaries:

LatitudePay Australia Pty. Ltd. (1)
800 Collins Street, Docklands, 3008, VIC, Australia
Tel.: (61) 1300557787
Web Site: https://www.latitudepay.com
Financial Services
N.A.I.C.S.: 921130

LatitudePay Malaysia Sdn. Bhd. (1)
Wisma Golden Eagle Realty 11th Floor South Block No 142A Jalan Ampang, Wilayah Persekutuan, 50450, Kuala Lumpur, Malaysia
Tel.: (60) 192185518
Web Site: https://my.latitudepay.com
Financial Services
N.A.I.C.S.: 921130

Latitudepay Singapore Pte. Ltd. (1)
150 Beach Road Level 35 Gateway West, Singapore, 189720, Singapore
Tel.: (65) 90462548
Web Site: https://sg.latitudepay.com
Financial Services
N.A.I.C.S.: 921130

Symple Canada Financial Group Limited (1)
161 Bay Street Suite 2700, Toronto, M5J 2S1, ON, Canada
Web Site: https://sympleloans.ca
Personal Loan Services

N.A.I.C.S.: 522291

LATOUR CAPITAL MANAGEMENT SAS
104 Avenue des Champs Elysees, 75008, Paris, France
Tel.: (33) 14062300
Web Site: https://www.latour-capital.co.uk
Privater Equity Firm
N.A.I.C.S.: 523999

Subsidiaries:

Gutor Electronic GmbH (1)
Hardstrasse 72-74, 5430, Wettingen, Switzerland
Tel.: (41) 564373434
Web Site: http://www.gutor.com
Sales Range: $100-124.9 Million
Emp.: 500
Uninterruptible Power Supply System Mfr
N.A.I.C.S.: 335999

Subsidiary (Non-US):

GUTOR Electronic LLC (2)
Schneider Electric Building 6 EastWangjing Rd, Chaoyang District, Beijing, 100102, China
Tel.: (86) 21 6065 7872
Inverter Mfr
N.A.I.C.S.: 335999

LATROBE MAGNESIUM LIMITED
Suite 4 Level 5 80 Clarence Street, Sydney, 2000, NSW, Australia
Tel.: (61) 292792033 **AU**
Web Site: https://www.latrobemagnesium.com
LMG—(ASX)
Rev.: $4,396,627
Assets: $63,704,535
Liabilities: $35,908,306
Net Worth: $27,796,229
Earnings: ($3,166,792)
Fiscal Year-end: 06/30/24
Magnesium Metal Mfr
N.A.I.C.S.: 332999
David Paterson *(CEO)*

LATTEYS INDUSTRIES LTD.
Plot No 16 Phase 1/2 GIDC Estate Naroda, Ahmedabad, 382330, Gujarat, India
Tel.: (91) 6355455212
Web Site: https://www.latteysindustries.com
Year Founded: 2004
LATTEYS—(NSE)
Rev.: $6,433,187
Assets: $5,291,026
Liabilities: $3,271,950
Net Worth: $2,019,076
Earnings: $156,873
Emp.: 118
Fiscal Year-end: 03/31/23
Pumping Equipment Mfr
N.A.I.C.S.: 333996
Kapoor Chand Garg *(Chm & Mng Dir)*

LATTY INTERNATIONAL S. A.
57 bis rue de Versailles, 91400, Orsay, France
Tel.: (33) 169861112
Web Site: http://www.latty.com
Year Founded: 1920
Nonmetallic Mineral Product Mfr
N.A.I.C.S.: 327999
Christian Xavier *(Dir-Publ)*

Subsidiaries:

LATTY 2RS GmbH (1)
Broeltalstrasse 6-10, 53819, Neunkirchen, Germany
Tel.: (49) 2247 8701 02
Bearing Product Distr
N.A.I.C.S.: 423840

LATTY DICHTUNGSTECHNIK AG (1)
Henzmannstrasse 39, 4800, Zofingen, Switzerland
Tel.: (41) 62 752 20 84
Bearing Product Distr
N.A.I.C.S.: 423840

LATTY IBERICA S.L. (1)
Pedro IV 29-35 4-6A, 08018, Barcelona, Spain
Tel.: (34) 93 356 99 90
Web Site: http://www.latty.es
Bearing Product Distr
N.A.I.C.S.: 423830

LATTY MAROC TECHNISEALS SARL (1)
51 rue Hadj Ahmed Balafrej Roches Noires, 20290, Casablanca, Morocco
Tel.: (212) 522 24 80 90
Bearing Product Distr
N.A.I.C.S.: 423830

LATTY SOUTH AFRICA Ltd (1)
108 Billingham Road Founders View South, Modderfontein, 1610, Edenvale, South Africa
Tel.: (27) 11 452 9755
Emp.: 30
Bearing Product Distr
N.A.I.C.S.: 423830
Chris Muller *(CEO)*

Latty Argentina S.A. (1)
Nstra Sra de la Merced 5334, Caseros, Buenos Aires, Argentina
Tel.: (54) 11 4734 8481
Web Site: http://www.latty.com.ar
Bearing Product Distr
N.A.I.C.S.: 423830

LATVIAN FOREST CO AB
Ringvagen 22 SE, Enebyberg, 128 46, Stockholm, Sweden
Tel.: (46) 37129203972
Web Site: https://www.latvianforest.lv
Financial Management Services
N.A.I.C.S.: 523999
Aleksandrs Tralmaks *(CEO)*

LATVIAN NEWS SERVICE SIA
Audeju iela 15, 1050, Riga, Latvia
Tel.: (371) 67088600 **LV**
Web Site: http://www.latviannewsservice.lv
News Syndicates
N.A.I.C.S.: 516210
Arno Magi *(Owner)*

LATVIJAS ENERGOCELT-NIEKS SIA
43 Lubanas Street, 1073, Riga, Latvia
Tel.: (371) 7241260
Web Site: http://www.lec.lv
Sales Range: $50-74.9 Million
Emp.: 400
Construction, Electric Power, Supply & Communications
N.A.I.C.S.: 238210
Janis Kols *(Chm)*

LATVIJAS JURAS MEDICINAS CENTRS
29 Patversmes st, 1005, Riga, Latvia
Tel.: (371) 67889000
Web Site: https://ljmc.lv
LJM1R—(RSE)
Sales Range: Less than $1 Million
Health Care Srvices
N.A.I.C.S.: 621999
Janis Birks *(Chm & Chm-Mgmt Bd)*

LATVIJAS VALSTS RADIO UN TELEVIZIJAS CENTRS
Str Erglu 7, LV-1012, Riga, Latvia
Tel.: (371) 7108704
Web Site: http://www.lvrtc.lv
Year Founded: 1924
Sales Range: $1-9.9 Million

LATVIJAS VALSTS RADIO UN TELEVIZIJAS CENTRS

Latvijas Valsts radio un televizijas centrs—(Continued)
Emp.: 305
Radio & Television Broadcasting Services
N.A.I.C.S.: 334220

LAUCEL
3 B Rue De Labergement, 21130, Auxonne, Cote D Or, France
Tel.: (33) 380481700
Rev: $21,300,000
Emp.: 66
Grocery Stores
N.A.I.C.S.: 445110
Guy Jacquemin *(Pres)*

LAUDA DR. R. WOBSER GMBH & CO. KG
Pfarrstrasse 41/43, 97922, Lauda-Konigshofen, Germany
Tel.: (49) 93435030 De
Web Site: http://www.lauda.de
Year Founded: 1956
Sales Range: $50-74.9 Million
Emp.: 430
Thermostatic Equipment Mfr
N.A.I.C.S.: 334513
Gunther Wobser *(Pres & CEO)*

Subsidiaries:

LAUDA America Latina C.A. (1)
Ave Las Americas Urb El Rosario, Residencias Agua Santa Apt, A5101, Caracas, Venezuela
Tel.: (58) 274 4164466
Electromechanical Thermostat Mfr
N.A.I.C.S.: 334512

LAUDA China Co., Ltd. (1)
2nd floor Building 6 No 201 MinYi Road, Shanghai, 201612, China
Tel.: (86) 21 64401098
Web Site: http://www.lauda.cn
Electromechanical Thermostat Mfr
N.A.I.C.S.: 334512
Michael Lin *(Gen Mgr)*

LAUDA France S.A.R.L. (1)
69 rue de la Belle Etoile, BP 81050, Roissy Charles de Gaull, 95933, Roissy-en-France, Cedex, France
Tel.: (33) 1 48638009
Web Site: http://www.lauda.fr
Electromechanical Thermostat Mfr
N.A.I.C.S.: 334512

LAUDA Italia S.r.l. (1)
Via Diaz 7/3 Locate Triulzi, 20085, Milan, Italy
Tel.: (39) 02 9079194
Web Site: http://www.lauda-italia.it
Electromechanical Thermostat Mfr
N.A.I.C.S.: 334512

LAUDA Production China Co., Ltd. (1)
Room A 2nd Floor Building 6 No 201 MinYi Road, Shanghai, 201612, China
Tel.: (86) 10 57306210
Electromechanical Thermostat Mfr
N.A.I.C.S.: 334512
Bob Gong *(Gen Mgr)*

LAUDA Singapore Pte. Ltd. (1)
25 International Business Park 04-103M, German Centre, 609916, Singapore, Singapore
Tel.: (65) 6563 0241
Electromechanical Thermostat Mfr
N.A.I.C.S.: 334512
Teck Chia Lee *(Reg Mgr-Sls)*

LAUDA Technology Ltd. (1)
4200 Waterside Solihull Parkway, Birmingham Business Park, Birmingham, B37 7YN, United Kingdom
Tel.: (44) 121 717 4789
Web Site: http://www.lauda-technology.co.uk
Electromechanical Thermostat Mfr
N.A.I.C.S.: 334512

LAUDA Ultracool S.L. (1)
C/ Colom 606, Terrassa, 08228, Barcelona, Spain
Tel.: (34) 93 7854866
Web Site: http://www.lauda.es
Electromechanical Thermostat Mfr
N.A.I.C.S.: 334512
Alexis Daza *(Engr-Product)*

LAUDA-Brinkmann, LP (1)
1819 Underwood Blvd, Delran, NJ 08075
Tel.: (856) 764-7300
Web Site: http://www.lauda-brinkmann.com
Emp.: 30
Electromechanical Thermostat Mfr
N.A.I.C.S.: 334512
Dan Corona *(Mgr-Distribution Center)*

LAUDA-Noah, LP (1)
2501 SE Columbia Way Ste 140, Vancouver, WA 98661
Tel.: (360) 993-1395
Web Site: http://www.lauda-noah.com
Sales Range: $1-9.9 Million
Emp.: 10
Semiconductor Devices Mfr
N.A.I.C.S.: 334413
Pete Adams *(CEO)*

OOO LAUDA Wostok (1)
Malaja Pirogowskaja Str 5, 119435, Moscow, Russia
Tel.: (7) 4959376562
Web Site: http://www.lauda.ru
Electromechanical Thermostat Mfr
N.A.I.C.S.: 334512

LAUNCH PAD MARKETING CORPORATION
600 Alden Rd Ste 606, Markham, L3R OE7, ON, Canada
Tel.: (416) 481-5657
Web Site: http://www.advantex.com
Sales Range: $25-49.9 Million
Emp.: 50
Consumer Marketing Services
N.A.I.C.S.: 541613
Todd Blair *(Pres)*

LAUNCH TECH COMPANY LIMITED
Launch Industrial Park North of Wuhe Avenue Banxuegang, Longgang, Shenzhen, China
Tel.: (86) 75584557891
Web Site: https://www.cnlaunch.com
Year Founded: 1992
2488—(HKG)
Rev: $165,263,664
Assets: $278,920,671
Liabilities: $128,418,366
Net Worth: $150,502,305
Earnings: $46,055,780
Emp.: 843
Fiscal Year-end: 12/31/22
Electronic Automotive Products Mfr
N.A.I.C.S.: 336320
Louis Xin Liu *(Co-Founder & Chm)*

Subsidiaries:

Launch Europe GmbH (1)
Heinrich-Hertz-Strasse 10, 50170, Kerpen, Germany
Tel.: (49) 227398750
Web Site: https://launch-europe.eu
Automotive Electrical Equipment Distr
N.A.I.C.S.: 423120

Launch Iberica S.L. (1)
c/Templer Guido 45 Palau Solita i Plegamans, 08184, Barcelona, Spain
Tel.: (34) 938639818
Automotive Electrical Equipment Distr
N.A.I.C.S.: 423120

Launch Italy GmbH (1)
Via Cimarosa Domenico 73, 40033, Casalecchio di Reno, BO, Italy
Tel.: (39) 0510083151
Web Site: https://www.launch-italy.com
Automobile Maintenance Services
N.A.I.C.S.: 811111

Launch Tech (M) SDN. BHD. (1)
No 7-G Jalan Bandar Sembilan Belas Pusat Bandar Puchong, 47160, Puchong, Selangor, Malaysia
Tel.: (60) 380750551
Emp.: 5
Automotive Electrical Equipment Distr
N.A.I.C.S.: 423120
Yong Chia *(Mgr)*

Launch Tech (USA) Inc (1)
1820 S Milliken Ave, Ontario, CA 91761
Tel.: (562) 463-1580
Web Site: https://www.launchtechusa.com
Emp.: 800
Automotive Electrical Equipment Distr
N.A.I.C.S.: 423120

Launch Tech Company Limited - Shanghai Factory (1)
Bai'an Jiading District city Anting Town Road No 661, Shanghai, 201814, China
Tel.: (86) 2169573368
Automotive Electrical Equipment Mfr
N.A.I.C.S.: 336320

Launch Tech International Co., Ltd. (1)
Citypoint Building-9th Floor 1 Ropemaker Street, London, EC2Y 9HT, United Kingdom
Tel.: (44) 2079976239
Automotive Electrical Equipment Distr
N.A.I.C.S.: 423120

Launch Tech Japan Inc (1)
84-4 Sano, Susono, 410-1118, Shizuoka, Japan
Tel.: (81) 559951320
Automotive Electrical Equipment Distr
N.A.I.C.S.: 423120

Launch Tech Pty. Ltd (1)
4/39 Eddie Rd, Minchinbury, Sydney, 2770, NSW, Australia
Tel.: (61) 1300369788
Web Site: https://www.launchtech.com.au
Automotive Electrical Equipment Distr
N.A.I.C.S.: 423120

Launch Tech UK Limited (1)
Huxley Close, Newnham Industrial Estate, Plymouth, PL7 4JN, Devon, United Kingdom
Tel.: (44) 1752344989
Automotive Diagnostic Tool Distr
N.A.I.C.S.: 423690

Launch Tech USA (Canada) Inc. (1)
2460 Anson Drive Unit 14, Mississauga, L5S 1G7, ON, Canada
Tel.: (905) 677-6667
Web Site: http://www.launchtechusa.com
Emp.: 800
Automobile Product Distr
N.A.I.C.S.: 423120

Launch Technologies SA (PTY) LTD (1)
23 Boeing West Road, Bedfordview, Johannesburg, 2008, South Africa
Tel.: (27) 113973073
Web Site: https://launchsa.co.za
Automotive Electrical Equipment Distr
N.A.I.C.S.: 423120

LAURENS SPETHMANN HOLDING AKTIENGESELL-SCHAFT & CO. KG
Bosteler Feld 6, 21218, Seevetal, Germany
Tel.: (49) 41055040
Web Site: http://www.lsh-ag.de
Sales Range: $700-749.9 Million
Emp.: 1,500
Health Food Mfr & Distr
N.A.I.C.S.: 311230

Subsidiaries:

Krauterhaus Wild GmbH & Co. KG (1)
Mebmerstrasse 29, 97508, Grettstadt, Germany
Tel.: (49) 9729 9110 0
Tea Whslr
N.A.I.C.S.: 424490

MEDIN GmbH & Co. KG (1)
Triebweg 5, 97906, Faulbach, Germany
Tel.: (49) 9392 809 0
Sales Range: $75-99.9 Million
Emp.: 180
Tea Whslr

INTERNATIONAL PUBLIC

N.A.I.C.S.: 424490

Milford Tea GmbH & Co. KG (1)
Meilsener Strasse 4, 21244, Buchholz, Germany
Tel.: (49) 4181 213 0
Web Site: http://www.milford.de
Sales Range: $75-99.9 Million
Emp.: 130
Tea Whslr
N.A.I.C.S.: 424490

OnnO Behrends GmbH & Co. KG (1)
Am Fridericussiel 5-7, 26506, Norden, Germany
Tel.: (49) 4931 1895 0
Web Site: http://www.onnobehrends.de
Sales Range: $25-49.9 Million
Emp.: 80
Tea Mfr & Whslr
N.A.I.C.S.: 311920
Johannes Niclassen *(Mng Dir)*

Ostfriesische Tee Gesellschaft Laurens Spethmann GmbH & Co. KG (1)
Am Bauhof 13-15, Seevetal, 21218, Germany
Tel.: (49) 4105 504 0
Web Site: http://www.otg.de
Sales Range: $50-74.9 Million
Emp.: 230
Tea Mfr & Whslr
N.A.I.C.S.: 311920
Annemarie Leniger *(Exec Dir)*

Subsidiary (Non-US):

Milford Tee Austria Gesellschaft m.b.H. (2)
Schloglstrasse 53, 6060, Hall in Tirol, Austria
Tel.: (43) 5223 5800
Web Site: http://www.milford.at
Tea Mfr & Whslr
N.A.I.C.S.: 311920

PAGES S.A.S. (2)
Route des Estreys, BP 36, Le Puy-en-Velay, Espaly-Saint-Marcel, 43001, France
Tel.: (33) 4 71 09 93 40
Web Site: http://www.pages.fr
Tea Mfr & Whslr
N.A.I.C.S.: 311920
Michael Spethmann *(Chm)*

ZAO Milford Moscow (1)
Ussatscheva Street 62/1 Office 23, Moscow, 119048, Russia
Tel.: (7) 495 7817461
Web Site: http://www.milford.ru
Sales Range: $25-49.9 Million
Emp.: 15
Tea Mfr & Whslr
N.A.I.C.S.: 311920
Ilya Blinov *(Gen Mgr)*

LAURENT LAUGIER SA
84 Boulevard De Plombieres, 13014, Marseilles, Bouches Du Rhone, France
Tel.: (33) 491 63 24 24
Rev: $22,300,000
Emp.: 25
Electrical Appliances, Television & Radio
N.A.I.C.S.: 423620
Richard Philippe *(Dir)*

LAURENT LEBLANC LTD.
3000 Navan Road, Ottawa, K1C 7G4, ON, Canada
Tel.: (613) 830-0066
Web Site:
http://www.laurentleblanc.ca
Year Founded: 1951
Rev: $10,000,000
Emp.: 30
General Contracting Services
N.A.I.C.S.: 238190
Laurent Leblanc *(Pres)*

LAURENT PELLIET SA
Zac De Costardais, Pleudihen Sur

Rance, 22690, Paris, France
Tel.: (33) 299580958
Sales Range: $10-24.9 Million
Emp.: 21
Freight Transportation Arrangement
N.A.I.C.S.: 488510
Philippe Tumoine *(Pres)*

LAURENTIAN BANK OF CANADA
1360 Rene-Levesque Blvd W Suite 600, Montreal, H3G 0E5, QC, Canada
Tel.: (514) 284-7192
Web Site:
https://www.laurentianbank.ca
LT7—(DEU)
Rev.: $1,716,493,996
Assets: $37,675,340,165
Liabilities: $35,516,599,699
Net Worth: $2,158,740,466
Earnings: $136,741,675
Emp.: 3,000
Fiscal Year-end: 10/31/23
Banking Services
N.A.I.C.S.: 522110
Francois Laurin *(CFO & Exec VP-Fin & Treasury)*

Subsidiaries:

B2B Bank (1)
199 Bay Street Suite 600, PO Box 279, STN Commerce Court, Toronto, M5L 0A2, ON, Canada (100%)
Tel.: (514) 284-4500
Web Site: https://www.b2bbank.com
Sales Range: $200-249.9 Million
Emp.: 350
Banking Services
N.A.I.C.S.: 522110

LBC Capital Ltd. (1)
5035 S Service Road, Burlington, L7L 6M9, ON, Canada (100%)
Web Site: https://www.lbccapital.ca
Commercial Financing & Lending Services
N.A.I.C.S.: 522220
Thierry Langevin *(Pres)*

LBC Financial Services Inc. (1)
1981 Av Mcgill College Bureau 1355, Montreal, H3A 3K3, QC, Canada
Tel.: (514) 284-4500
Commericial Banking
N.A.I.C.S.: 522110

LBC Trust Inc. (1)
290 Rue Chabnel W S520, Montreal, H2N 1G5, QC, Canada
Tel.: (514) 522-1846
Web Site: http://www.laurentianbank.com
Sales Range: $50-74.9 Million
Emp.: 10
Commericial Banking
N.A.I.C.S.: 522110

Laurentian Bank Securities Inc. (1)
1360 Rene-Levesque Boulevard West Suite 620, Montreal, H3G 0E8, QC, Canada
Tel.: (514) 350-2800
Sales Range: $100-124.9 Million
Emp.: 120
Investment Banking & Securities Dealing
N.A.I.C.S.: 523150
Kelsey Gunderson *(Pres, CEO & Exec VP-Capital Markets)*

Northpoint Commercial Finance Canada Inc. (1)
5035 South Service Road Suite 500, Burlington, L7L 6M9, ON, Canada
Commercial Financing Services
N.A.I.C.S.: 522220
Chris Cook *(Exec VP & Gen Mgr)*

Northpoint Commercial Finance LLC (1)
1105 Lakewood Pkwy Ste 210, Alpharetta, GA 30009
Web Site: https://northpointcf.com
Commercial Financing Services
N.A.I.C.S.: 522220
Dan Radley *(CEO)*

LAURENTIAN MOTORS SUDBURY LTD.
1221 Kingsway, Sudbury, P3B 2E9, ON, Canada
Tel.: (705) 566-8400
Web Site: http://www.laurentianchrysler.ca
Rev.: $20,035,177
Emp.: 46
New & Used Car Dealers
N.A.I.C.S.: 441110
Doug Wainman *(Mgr-New Car)*

LAURENTIDE CONTROLS LTD.
18000 Trans Canada Hwy, Kirkland, H9J 4A1, QC, Canada
Tel.: (514) 697-9230
Web Site: http://www.laurentide.com
Year Founded: 1968
Rev.: $28,700,000
Emp.: 100
Process Control Equipment Supplier
N.A.I.C.S.: 423830
Steve Dustin *(Pres)*

LAURION MINERAL EXPLORATION INC.
Scotia Tower 40 King Street West Suite 5800, Toronto, M5H 3S1, ON, Canada
Tel.: (705) 788-9186 ON
Web Site: https://www.laurion.ca
Year Founded: 1945
LME—(OTCIQ)
Assets: $1,584,866
Liabilities: $144,796
Net Worth: $1,440,071
Earnings: ($1,725,335)
Fiscal Year-end: 12/31/19
Gold & Other Metals Mining Services
N.A.I.C.S.: 212220
Cynthia E. Le Sueur-Aquin *(Pres & CEO)*

LAVA THERAPEUTICS NV
Yalelaan 62, 3584 CM, Utrecht, Netherlands
Tel.: (31) 850163100 NI
Web Site:
https://www.lavatherapeutics.com
Year Founded: 2016
LVTX—(NASDAQ)
Rev.: $6,769,000
Assets: $101,710,000
Liabilities: $50,532,000
Net Worth: $51,178,000
Earnings: ($41,974,000)
Emp.: 35
Fiscal Year-end: 12/31/23
Biotechnology Research & Development Services
N.A.I.C.S.: 541714
Stephen Hurly *(Pres & CEO)*

LAVATEC LAUNDRY TECHNOLOGY GMBH
Wannenackerstrasse 53, 74078, Heilbronn, Germany
Tel.: (49) 71312980
Web Site: http://www.lavatec.com
Year Founded: 1986
Rev.: $61,259,154
Emp.: 140
Laundry Machinery Mfr
N.A.I.C.S.: 333310

Subsidiaries:

LAVATEC Laundry Technology Inc. (1)
49 Lancaster Dr, Beacon Falls, CT 06403
Tel.: (203) 632-4777
Web Site: http://www.lltusa.com
Laundry Machine Distr
N.A.I.C.S.: 423850
Mark Thrasher *(Pres & Mng Partner)*

LAVATEC Nederland BV (1)
Zuidzijdseweg 204, 3415 PV, Polsbroek, Netherlands
Tel.: (31) 653693546
Laundry Machine Distr
N.A.I.C.S.: 423850

Lavatec Asia Pacific Co Ltd (1)
1111/41 Ladprao 94, 10310, Bangkok, Thailand
Tel.: (66) 29323386
Laundry Machine Distr
N.A.I.C.S.: 423850
Oliver Zaiser *(Mng Dir)*

LAVENA AD
Industrial area, PO Box 114, 9700, Shumen, Bulgaria
Tel.: (359) 54850144 BG
Web Site: https://www.lavena.bg
4L4—(BUL)
Sales Range: $1-9.9 Million
Cosmetics & Liquid Herbal Mfr
N.A.I.C.S.: 339999

LAVERANA GMBH & CO. KG
Am Weingarten 4, D-30974, Wennigsen, Germany
Tel.: (49) 510393910
Web Site: http://www.laverana.de
Year Founded: 1987
Rev.: $49,010,082
Emp.: 240
Cosmetics Distr
N.A.I.C.S.: 456120
Thomas Haase *(Founder)*

LAVIPHARM S.A.
Lavipharm 12 Agias Marinas Street, PO Box 59, GR-19002, Peania, Attica, Greece
Tel.: (30) 2106691000
Web Site: https://lavipharm.com
Year Founded: 1975
LAVI—(ATH)
Sales Range: $25-49.9 Million
Pharmaceutical Products Mfr & Distr
N.A.I.C.S.: 325412
Athanase Lavidas *(Chm & CEO)*

Subsidiaries:

Lavipharm Hellas S.A. (1)
Agias Marinas Street, PO Box 59, Paiania, 190 02, Athens, Attica, Greece
Tel.: (30) 2106691301
Pharmaceutical Device Mfr & Distr
N.A.I.C.S.: 339112

LAVO.TV AS
Akersgata 73, Oslo, 0180, Norway
Tel.: (47) 97168426
Advertising Agency Services
N.A.I.C.S.: 541810
Lars Christian Beitnes *(CEO)*

LAVORO LIMITED
Av Dr Cardoso de Melo 1450 4th Floor Office 401, Vila Olimpia, Sao Paulo, 04548-005, SP, Brazil
Tel.: (55) 1142800709 Ky
Web Site:
https://www.lavoroagro.com
Year Founded: 2023
LVRO—(NASDAQ)
Rev.: $1,902,198,546
Assets: $1,531,130,744
Liabilities: $1,101,673,095
Net Worth: $429,457,650
Earnings: ($44,501,787)
Emp.: 3,778
Fiscal Year-end: 06/30/23
Agriculture Product Distr
N.A.I.C.S.: 424910
Marcos Haaland *(Chm)*

LAVORWASH S.P.A.
Via JF Kennedy 12, 46020, Pegognaga, Mantova, Italy
Tel.: (39) 037655431 IT
Web Site: http://www.lavorwash.it
Year Founded: 1975
High-Pressure Cleaning Systems Mfr
N.A.I.C.S.: 333310
Giancarlo Lanfredi *(Owner)*

Subsidiaries:

Lavorwash GB Ltd (1)
 (100%)
Tel.: (44) 1744738079
Web Site: http://www.lavorwash.co.uk
Sales Range: $50-74.9 Million
Emp.: 5
Service Establishment Equipment & Supplies Whslr
N.A.I.C.S.: 423850

LAW UNION & ROCK INS. PLC
Law Union House 14 Hughes Avenue, Alagomeji Yaba, Lagos, Nigeria
Tel.: (234) 14540071
Web Site:
http://www.lawunioninsurance.com
Year Founded: 1951
LAWUNION—(NIGE)
Rev.: $13,491,902
Assets: $33,289,507
Liabilities: $13,685,557
Net Worth: $19,603,949
Earnings: $2,199,606
Fiscal Year-end: 12/31/19
Life & Non Life Insurance Services
N.A.I.C.S.: 524298
Remi Babalola *(Chm)*

LAWECO MASCHINEN- UND APPARATEBAU GMBH
In der Tutenbeke 23, 32339, Espelkamp, Germany
Tel.: (49) 57722020
Web Site: http://www.laweco.de
Year Founded: 1979
Emp.: 110
Lift Platform Mfr
N.A.I.C.S.: 333248
Dietmar Lagemann *(Mng Partner)*

LAWFINANCE LTD.
Suite 2 Level 16 56 Pitt Street, Sydney, 2000, NSW, Australia
Tel.: (61) 296960220 AU
Web Site:
http://www.lawfinance.com.au
LAW—(ASX)
Rev.: $444,000
Assets: $19,887,000
Liabilities: $55,141,000
Net Worth: ($35,254,000)
Earnings: ($31,077,000)
Fiscal Year-end: 12/31/22
Financial Management Services
N.A.I.C.S.: 522299
Daniel Kleiin *(CEO & Exec Dir)*

Subsidiaries:

Medical Financial Group, LLC (1)
700 E Sonterra Blvd Ste 1210, San Antonio, TX 78258
Tel.: (210) 290-9896
Web Site: https://www.medicalfgtx.com
Medical Financial Services
N.A.I.C.S.: 524114

National Health Finance DM, LLC (1)
1347 N Alma School Rd Ste 120, Chandler, AZ 85224
Tel.: (602) 347-8503
Web Site: https://nationalhealthfinance.com
Health Fund Services
N.A.I.C.S.: 525120
Marialena Ziska *(Chief Revenue Officer)*

LAWN TENNIS ASSOCIATION OF AUSTRALIA LIMITED
Entrance D Olympic Boulevard, Melbourne, 3000, VIC, Australia
Tel.: (61) 399144000
Web Site: http://www.tennis.com.au
Sales Range: $50-74.9 Million
Emp.: 270
Tennis Association

Lawn Tennis Association of Australia Limited—(Continued)
N.A.I.C.S.: 711211
Darren Pearce (Mgr-Media)

LAWO AG
Am Oberwald 8, 76437, Rastatt, Germany
Tel.: (49) 722210020
Web Site: http://www.lawo.de
Year Founded: 1970
Sales Range: $25-49.9 Million
Emp.: 300
Broadcasting Systems Network & Control Technologies Mfr
N.A.I.C.S.: 334419
Philipp Lawo (CEO)

Subsidiaries:

Lawo Group USA Inc. (1)
99 Hudson St 5th Fl, New York, NY 10013
Tel.: (888) 810-4468
Broadcasting Equipment Distr
N.A.I.C.S.: 423690

Lawo International GmbH (1)
Wehntalerstrasse 58, 8157, Dielsdorf, Switzerland
Tel.: (41) 433886800
Broadcasting Equipment Distr
N.A.I.C.S.: 423690
Klaus-Joerg Jasper (Project Mgr & Mgr-Intl Sls)

Lawo North America Corp. (1)
39 Advance Road, Toronto, M8Z 2S6, ON, Canada
Tel.: (416) 292-0078
Broadcasting Equipment Distr
N.A.I.C.S.: 423690
Sandra Gama (Accountant)

LAWRENCE HARVEY SEARCH & SELECTION LTD.
150 Leadenhall Street 4th Floor, London, EC3V 4TE, United Kingdom
Tel.: (44) 203 327 3070
Web Site: http://lawrenceharvey.com
Year Founded: 2002
Sales Range: $10-24.9 Million
Emp.: 90
Recruitment Consultancy Services
N.A.I.C.S.: 561311

LAWSON, INC.
East Tower Gate City Ohsaki 11-2 Osaki 1-chome, Shinagawa-ku, Tokyo, 141-8643, Japan
Tel.: (81) 354766800
Web Site: https://www.lawson.co.jp
Year Founded: 1975
2651—(TKS)
Rev.: $10,691,608,400
Assets: $12,944,531,600
Liabilities: $10,248,912,960
Net Worth: $2,695,618,640
Earnings: $173,272,000
Emp.: 10,385
Fiscal Year-end: 02/28/22
Convenience Stores Owner & Operator
N.A.I.C.S.: 445131
Sadanobu Takemasu (Chm, Pres & CEO)

Subsidiaries:

Eisai Seikaken Co., Ltd. (1)
Toriko Industrial Park 312-4 Toriko Nishihara-mura, Aso District, Kumamoto, 861 2401, Japan (70%)
Tel.: (81) 962793133
Web Site: http://www.eisaiseikaken.co.jp
Fertilizer Mfr & Distr; Farming Method Research & Development Services
N.A.I.C.S.: 424910
Yutaka Kusaki (Pres)

LAWSON ATM Networks Inc. (1)
East Tower Gate City Osaki 11-2 Osaki 1 chome Shinagawa-ku, 141 0032, Tokyo, Japan

Tel.: (81) 120073963
Web Site: http://www.lawson.jp
ATM Networking & Operational Management Services
N.A.I.C.S.: 522180
Kouichi Shiomi (Pres)

Lawson Philippines, Inc. (1)
11th Floor Times Plaza Building U N Avenue corner Taft Avenue, Ermita, Manila, Philippines
Tel.: (63) 285279682
Web Site: https://www.lawson-philippines.com
Snack & Beverage Retailer
N.A.I.C.S.: 424820

Lawson Store100, Inc. (1)
3F East Tower Gate City Osaki 1-11-2 Osaki, Shinagawa-Ku, Tokyo, 141-8613, Japan
Tel.: (81) 343346799
Web Site: http://store100.lawson.co.jp
General Stores Operator
N.A.I.C.S.: 455219
Shigeaki Kawahara (Pres & CEO)

Tokyu Station Retail Service Co., Ltd. (1)
6 Chome Himonya, Meguro-ku, Tokyo, 1520003, Japan
Tel.: (81) 357687830
Web Site: http://www.e-toks.co.jp
Rev.: $955,792,000
Emp.: 435
General Stores
N.A.I.C.S.: 455219

LAWTON DEVELOPMENT CO., LTD.
North 12F No 68 Renmin Avenue, Haikou, 570208, Hainan, China
Tel.: (86) 898 66258868
Web Site: http://www.lawtonfz.com.cn
600209—(SHG)
Rev.: $8,333,092
Assets: $72,531,146
Liabilities: $10,815,094
Net Worth: $61,716,052
Earnings: ($11,841,601)
Fiscal Year-end: 12/31/20
Hotel Operator
N.A.I.C.S.: 721110
Song Gao (Chm)

LAXEY PARTNERS LTD.
Derby House 64 Athol St, Douglas, IM1 1JD, Isle of Man
Tel.: (44) 1624690900
Web Site: http://www.laxeypartners.com
Sales Range: $25-49.9 Million
Emp.: 10
Private Equity Firm
N.A.I.C.S.: 523999
Andrew Pegge (Mng Dir)

Subsidiaries:

Bulgarian Land Development EAD (1)
47A Tsarigradsko Shose Blvd, 1124, Sofia, Bulgaria
Tel.: (359) 2 805 1910
Web Site: http://www.bld.bg
Sales Range: $25-49.9 Million
Commercial & Residential Real Estate Development & Construction Management Services
N.A.I.C.S.: 237210
Dimitar Safov (Gen Mgr)

Laxey Partners (UK) Limited (1)
Princes House 38 Jermyn Street, London, SW1Y 6DN, United Kingdom
Tel.: (44) 207 4946380
Financial Investment Services
N.A.I.C.S.: 523999

LAXMI BANK LIMITED
Hattisar, PO Box 19593, Kathmandu, Nepal
Tel.: (977) 14444684 NP

Web Site: http://www.laxmi.laxmibank.com
Year Founded: 2002
LBL—(NEP)
Rev.: $81,418,142
Assets: $946,638,894
Liabilities: $833,742,389
Net Worth: $112,896,505
Earnings: $14,989,852
Emp.: 1,018
Fiscal Year-end: 07/16/19
Banking Services
N.A.I.C.S.: 522110
Sumed Bhattarai (Deputy CEO)

Subsidiaries:

Laxmi Capital Market Limited (1)
Web Site: http://www.laxmicapital.com.np
Emp.: 9
Commercial Banking Services
N.A.I.C.S.: 522110
Sandeep Pradhan (Sec & Head-Investment Banking)

Laxmi Sunrise Bank Limited (1)
P89H 442, Gairidhara Sadak, Kathmandu, Nepal
Tel.: (977) 14004560
Rev.: $84,441,994
Assets: $980,010,752
Liabilities: $866,538,052
Net Worth: $113,472,700
Earnings: $11,242,919
Emp.: 1,353
Fiscal Year-end: 07/15/2020
Banking Services
N.A.I.C.S.: 522110

Subsidiary (Domestic):

Sonamai Commercial Complex Pvt. Ltd. (2)
25 No Bahadurgunj VDC Ward No 3, Mahottari, Bardibas, Nepal
Tel.: (977) 44550563
Web Site: http://www.sunrisebank.com.np
Sales Range: $200-249.9 Million
Emp.: 400
Banking Services
N.A.I.C.S.: 522110

LAXMI COTSPIN LIMITED.
Gut No 399 Samangaon-Kajla Road Opp Meenatai Thakare Vridhashram, Samangaon Jalna, 431 203, Mumbai, 431 203, Maharashtra, India
Tel.: (91) 9765999633
Web Site: https://www.laxmicotspin.com
Year Founded: 2005
LAXMICOT—(NSE)
Rev.: $17,351,550
Assets: $11,791,331
Liabilities: $6,066,399
Net Worth: $5,724,933
Earnings: ($702,464)
Emp.: 450
Fiscal Year-end: 03/31/23
Textile Products Mfr
N.A.I.C.S.: 314999
Sanjay K. Rathi (Mng Dir)

LAXMI GOLDORNA HOUSE LIMITED
Laxmi House Opp Bandharano Khancho M G Haveli Road, Manekchowk, Ahmedabad, 380001, India
Tel.: (91) 9898985001
Web Site: https://www.laxmilifestyle.co.in
Year Founded: 2010
LGHL—(NSE)
Rev.: $7,180,070
Assets: $13,436,507
Liabilities: $9,665,147
Net Worth: $3,771,360
Earnings: $15,099
Emp.: 25
Fiscal Year-end: 03/31/22
Real Estate Services
N.A.I.C.S.: 531210

INTERNATIONAL PUBLIC

Jayesh Chinubhai Shah (Chm & Mng Dir)

Subsidiaries:

Laxmi Developers Private Limited (1)
Millenium Textile Market 2 Nr Anjana Railway Flyover, Behind Raghukul market Anjana, Surat, 395002, Gujarat, India
Tel.: (91) 9978600222
Web Site: https://laxmideveloper.com
Residential Property Services
N.A.I.C.S.: 531110

LAXMI LAGHUBITTA BITTIYA SANSTHA LTD.
Kathmandu- 03 Kapan Marg, Maharajgunj, Kathmandu, Nepal
Tel.: (977) 14373682
Web Site: https://laxmilaghu.com.np
Year Founded: 2010
LLBS—(NEP)
Sales Range: Less than $1 Million
Financial Banking Services
N.A.I.C.S.: 522110
Jiwan Prakash Limbu (Chm)

LAXMI ORGANIC INDUSTRIES LIMITED
Chandermukhi Building 2Nd & 3Rd Floor, Nariman Point, Mumbai, 400021, India
Tel.: (91) 2249104444
Web Site: https://www.laxmi.com
Year Founded: 1989
543277—(BOM)
Rev.: $242,022,827
Assets: $250,799,367
Liabilities: $109,515,998
Net Worth: $141,283,370
Earnings: $17,344,236
Emp.: 684
Fiscal Year-end: 03/31/21
Chemicals Mfr
N.A.I.C.S.: 325199
Satej Nabar (CEO)

Subsidiaries:

Laxmi Italy S.R.L. (1)
Via Fior di Loto 1, 37021, Bosco Chiesanuova, VR, Italy
Tel.: (39) 0456780077
Web Site: https://lakshmi.it
Perfumes & Cosmetic Distr
N.A.I.C.S.: 456120

Laxmi Lifesciences Private Ltd. (1)
34-A Kamaraj Road, Coimbatore, 641018, Tamil Nadu, India
Tel.: (91) 7094606088
Web Site: https://www.lakshmilife.com
Plastics Product Mfr
N.A.I.C.S.: 326199

Laxmi Organic Industries (Europe) BV (1)
Schipholweg 55, 2316 ZL, Leiden, Netherlands
Tel.: (31) 888225800
Organic Chemical Mfr
N.A.I.C.S.: 325199

Laxmi Petrochem Middle East FZE (1)
PO Box 52700, Hamriya Free Zone, Sharjah, United Arab Emirates
Tel.: (971) 65264207
Organic Chemical Mfr
N.A.I.C.S.: 325199

LAXMIPATI ENGINEERING WORKS LIMITED
Office Block 1st Floor Plot No 237/2 & 3 Sub Plot No A/25, Central Park Society GIDC Pandesara, Surat, 394 221, Gujarat, India
Tel.: (91) 261289441516
Web Site: https://www.laxmipatiengineering.com
Year Founded: 2012

AND PRIVATE COMPANIES

537669—(BOM)
Rev.: $2,921,470
Assets: $3,905,339
Liabilities: $2,159,604
Net Worth: $1,745,735
Earnings: $237,535
Fiscal Year-end: 03/31/20
Ship Building & Repar Services
N.A.I.C.S.: 336611
Manojkumar Govind Prasad Sarawagi *(Exec Dir)*

LAY HONG BERHAD
No 2 Level 10-12 Wisma Lay Hong Jalan Empayar Off Persiaran, Sultan Ibrahim / KU1, 41150, Kelang, Selangor, Malaysia
Tel.: (60) 333434888
Web Site: https://www.layhong.com.my
LAYHONG—(KLS)
Rev.: $226,416,417
Assets: $201,523,843
Liabilities: $101,064,554
Net Worth: $100,459,289
Earnings: $5,977,045
Emp.: 2,356
Fiscal Year-end: 03/31/23
Livestock Farming Services
N.A.I.C.S.: 115210
Weng Hong Yeap *(Exec Dir)*

Subsidiaries:

G-Mart Borneo Retail Sdn Bhd (1)
Frankfurter Mfr
N.A.I.C.S.: 311612

STF Agriculture Sdn Bhd (1)
No 3 Lorong 1H KKIP Selatan Industrial Zone 2, Kota Kinabalu Industrial Park, 88460, Kota Kinabalu, Sabah, Malaysia
Tel.: (60) 8849973567
Frankfurter Mfr
N.A.I.C.S.: 311612

LAY-OUT PLANNING CONSULTANTS CO., LTD.
Floors 6-8 11&14 front desk to 8 of Tower A Tianjian Innovation Center, Nanshan, Shenzhen, 518049, Guangdong, China
Tel.: (86) 75583949689
Web Site: https://www.lay-out.com.cn
Year Founded: 2008
300989—(SSE)
Rev.: $62,065,224
Assets: $165,634,092
Liabilities: $24,349,572
Net Worth: $141,284,520
Earnings: $4,307,472
Fiscal Year-end: 12/31/22
Engineeering Services
N.A.I.C.S.: 541330
Fuhai Wang *(Chm)*

LAYLA TEXTILE & TRADERS LIMITED
801 Crystal Plaza Opp Solitaire Corporate Park, Andheri-Ghatkoper Link Road Chakala Andheri E, Mumbai, 400 099, Madhya Pradesh, India
Tel.: (91) 2267426891
Year Founded: 1983
Rev.: $926,707
Assets: $4,132,982
Liabilities: $212,145
Net Worth: $3,920,837
Earnings: $6,650
Fiscal Year-end: 03/31/17
Textile Products Distr
N.A.I.C.S.: 424310

LAYSTER INVESTMENTS PLC
Poseidonos 77, Paphos, Cyprus
Tel.: (357) 26813060
Investment Services
N.A.I.C.S.: 523940

LAZADA GROUP
Bestway Building, 079212, Singapore, Singapore
Tel.: (65) 3158 7424
Web Site: http://Www.lazada.sg
Year Founded: 2012
Emp.: 2,000
Electronic Shopping
N.A.I.C.S.: 449210
Pierre Poignant *(CEO)*

LAZAR NESIC A.D.
Korzo 1, Subotica, Serbia
Tel.: (381) 24557932
Year Founded: 1960
LNSU—(BEL)
Sales Range: Less than $1 Million
Emp.: 1
Beauty Salon Operator
N.A.I.C.S.: 812112
Natalija Leontijevic *(Exec Dir)*

LAZARD LTD.
Clarendon House 2 Church Street, Hamilton, HM11, Bermuda
Tel.: (441) 2951422 BM
Web Site: http://www.lazard.com
LAZ—(NYSE)
Rev.: $2,593,162,000
Assets: $4,635,781,000
Liabilities: $4,065,919,000
Net Worth: $569,862,000
Earnings: ($75,479,000)
Emp.: 3,291
Fiscal Year-end: 12/31/23
Financial Advisory & Asset Management
N.A.I.C.S.: 523999
Evan L. Russo *(Mng Dir)*

Subsidiaries:

Lazard Group LLC (1)
30 Rockefeller Plz, New York, NY 10112
Tel.: (212) 632-6000
Web Site: https://www.lazard.com
Rev.: $2,844,653,000
Assets: $5,461,799,000
Liabilities: $4,995,286,000
Net Worth: $466,513,000
Earnings: $404,182,000
Emp.: 3,389
Fiscal Year-end: 12/31/2022
Financial Advisory & Asset Management Services
N.A.I.C.S.: 523940
Kenneth Marc Jacobs *(Chm & CEO)*

Subsidiary (Non-US):

Compagnie Financiere Lazard Freres SAS (2)
121 Boulevard Haussmann, 75382, Paris, Cedex 08, France
Tel.: (33) 144130111
Sales Range: $150-199.9 Million
Emp.: 500
Investment Banking Services
N.A.I.C.S.: 523150
Bruno Max Roger *(Mng Dir)*

LLtd 1 Sarl (2)
68 Boulevard de la Petrusse, 2320, Luxembourg, Luxembourg
Tel.: (352) 26483007
Holding Company
N.A.I.C.S.: 551112

Lazard & Co., Holdings Limited (2)
50 Stratton Street, London, W1J 8LL, United Kingdom
Tel.: (44) 2071872000
Sales Range: $150-199.9 Million
Emp.: 300
Investment Management Service
N.A.I.C.S.: 523940

Lazard & Co., Ltd. (2)
50 Stratton St, London, W1J 8LL, United Kingdom
Tel.: (44) 2071872000
Web Site: http://www.lazard.com

Sales Range: $1-4.9 Billion
Emp.: 3,000
Investment Banking
N.A.I.C.S.: 523150

Lazard AB (2)
Sturegatan 24, 114 36, Stockholm, Sweden
Tel.: (46) 84425400
Web Site: http://www.lazard.com
Emp.: 15
Financial Management Services
N.A.I.C.S.: 523999

Subsidiary (Non-US):

Lazard Freres Gestion (3)
11 rue d Argenson, 75008, Paris, France **(100%)**
Tel.: (33) 144130179
Web Site: http://www.lazardfreresgestion.fr
Sales Range: $75-99.9 Million
Investment Management & Advisory Services
N.A.I.C.S.: 523940

Subsidiary (Domestic):

Lazard Alternative Investments LLC (2)
30 Rockefeller Plz, New York, NY 10020
Tel.: (212) 632-6000
Merchant Banking Services, Real Estate & Venture Capital Investments
N.A.I.C.S.: 523999
Russell Planitzer *(Principal)*

Subsidiary (Domestic):

Lazard Alternative Management LLC (3)
30 Rockefeller Plz 48th Fl, New York, NY 10020
Tel.: (212) 632-6000
Venture Capital Firm
N.A.I.C.S.: 523999

Lazard Real Estate Partners LLC (3)
30 Rockefeller Plz, New York, NY 10020
Tel.: (212) 632-6000
Real Estate Investment
N.A.I.C.S.: 531390
Matthew J. Lustig *(CEO & Mng Principal)*

Subsidiary (Non-US):

Lazard Argentina S.A. (2)
Av Del Libertador 350 Floor 8, Buenos Aires, B1638BEP, Argentina
Tel.: (54) 1143195900
Asset Management Services
N.A.I.C.S.: 523150

Lazard Asia (HK) Limited (2)
Suites 2901-02 2916 Two International Finance Centre 8 Finance Street, Central, China (Hong Kong)
Tel.: (852) 25228187
Web Site: http://www.lazard.com
Asset Management Services
N.A.I.C.S.: 523940

Lazard Asia (Hong Kong) Limited (2)
Two International Finance Centre 8 Finance Street, Suites 2901-02 and 2916, Central, China (Hong Kong)
Tel.: (852) 25228187
Asset Management Services
N.A.I.C.S.: 523150

Lazard Asia Limited (2)
1 Raffles Place 29-63 Tower 2, Singapore, 048616, Singapore
Tel.: (65) 65342011
Asset Management Services
N.A.I.C.S.: 523150

Lazard Asset Management (Canada), Inc. (2)
130 King Street West Suite 1800, Toronto, M5X 1E3, ON, Canada
Tel.: (416) 945-6627
Web Site: http://www.lazard.com
Asset Management Services
N.A.I.C.S.: 523940

Lazard Asset Management (Deutschland) GmbH (2)
Neue Mainzer Strasse 75, 60311, Frankfurt am Main, Germany
Tel.: (49) 69506060
Web Site: http://www.lazardnet.com

LAZARD LTD.

Emp.: 100
Investment Management Service
N.A.I.C.S.: 523940

Lazard Asset Management (HK) Limited (2)
Suite 1101 Level 11 Chater House 8 Connaught Road, Central, China (Hong Kong)
Tel.: (852) 22972385
Asset Management Services
N.A.I.C.S.: 523150

Lazard Asset Management (Singapore) Pte. Ltd. (2)
Unit 15-03 Republic Plaza 9 Raffles Place, Singapore, 048619, Singapore
Tel.: (65) 65390500
Asset Management Services
N.A.I.C.S.: 523150

Subsidiary (Domestic):

Lazard Asset Management LLC (2)
30 Rockefeller Plz, New York, NY 10112
Tel.: (212) 632-6024
Web Site: http://www.lazardassetmanagement.com
Asset Management Services
N.A.I.C.S.: 523940
Evan L. Russo *(CEO)*

Subsidiary (Non-US):

Lazard Asset Management Pacific Co. (3)
Level 12 Gateway 1 Macquarie Place, Sydney, 2000, NSW, Australia
Tel.: (61) 282741400
Web Site: http://www.lazardassetmanagement.com
Sales Range: $50-74.9 Million
Emp.: 45
Investment Management Service
N.A.I.C.S.: 523940
Ben Granbery *(Dir & Mgr-Retail-Natl)*

Subsidiary (Non-US):

Lazard Asset Management Limited (2)
50 Stratton Street, London, W1J 8LL, United Kingdom
Tel.: (44) 2075882721
Web Site: http://www.lazardassetmanagement.co.uk
Sales Range: $75-99.9 Million
Emp.: 200
Investment Management Service
N.A.I.C.S.: 523940
Mike Wariebi *(Mng Dir & Head-Alternative Investments Distr-Global)*

Lazard Asset Management Schweiz AG (2)
Uraniastrasse 12, 8001, Zurich, Switzerland
Tel.: (41) 438886480
Asset Management Services
N.A.I.C.S.: 523150

Lazard Australia Private Equity Pty Ltd (2)
Level 44 Gateway 1 Macquarie Place, Sydney, 2000, NSW, Australia
Tel.: (61) 292569992
Web Site: http://www.lazard.com.au
Sales Range: $25-49.9 Million
Emp.: 30
Investment Management Service
N.A.I.C.S.: 523940

Lazard Australia Pty Ltd (2)
Level 16 Gateway Building 1 Macquarie Place, Sydney, 2000, NSW, Australia
Tel.: (61) 292569900
Asset Management Services
N.A.I.C.S.: 523150

Lazard BV (2)
Mondriaan Tower 28th floor Amstelplein 58, 1096 BC, Amsterdam, Netherlands
Tel.: (31) 205611160
Web Site: http://www.lazard.com
Investment Management Service
N.A.I.C.S.: 523940

Lazard BV/SRL (2)
Blue Tower Louise Avenue Louise 326 9th Floor, 1050, Brussels, Belgium
Tel.: (32) 26271382
Asset Management Services

LAZARD LTD.

Lazard Ltd.—(Continued)
N.A.I.C.S.: 523150

Lazard Business Consulting (Beijing) Co., Ltd. (2)
Room 3701 37/F China World Tower 3 No 1 Jianguomenwai Avenue, Chaoyang District, Beijing, 100004, China
Tel.: (86) 1057069288
Asset Management Services
N.A.I.C.S.: 523150

Lazard Canada Inc. (2)
161 Bay Street 45th Floor, Toronto, M5J 2S1, ON, Canada
Tel.: (416) 687-6649
Asset Management Services
N.A.I.C.S.: 523150

Lazard Carnegie Wylie Pty. Ltd. (2)
Level 33 No 101 Collins St, Melbourne, 3000, VIC, Australia
Tel.: (61) 396578400
Web Site: http://www.lazard.com
Sales Range: $50-74.9 Million
Emp.: 22
Private Equity Firm; Financial Advisory Services
N.A.I.C.S.: 523999

Subsidiary (Domestic):

Lazard Carnegie Wylie Investment Management Pty. Ltd. (3)
Level 45 Citigroup Centre, 2 Park Street, Sydney, 2000, NSW, Australia
Tel.: (61) 2 9283 2622
Investment & Management Services
N.A.I.C.S.: 523999

Subsidiary (Non-US):

Lazard Chile S.P.A. (2)
Aurelio Gonzalez 3390, Piso 4 Oficina 401, Santiago, Chile
Tel.: (56) 222463300
Asset Management Services
N.A.I.C.S.: 523150

Lazard China Limited (2)
Room 1804 Tower E1 the Towers Oriental Plaza, No 1 East Chang An Avenue Dong Cheng District, Beijing, 100004, China
Tel.: (86) 1085150880
Web Site: http://www.lazard.com
Investment Management Service
N.A.I.C.S.: 523940

Lazard Colombia S.A.S. (2)
Calle 77 No 7-44-Oficina 1002 Torre Siete 77, Bogota, Colombia
Tel.: (57) 13123048
Asset Management Services
N.A.I.C.S.: 523150

Subsidiary (Domestic):

Lazard Freres & Co., LLC (2)
30 Rockefeller Plz, New York, NY 10020-5900
Tel.: (212) 632-6000
Web Site: http://www.lazard.com
Sales Range: $600-649.9 Million
Emp.: 1,300
Financial Advisory Services
N.A.I.C.S.: 523150

Division (Domestic):

Lazard Middle Market LLC (3)
80 S 8th St Ste 2700, Minneapolis, MN 55402 **(100%)**
Tel.: (612) 339-0500
Web Site: http://www.lazardmm.com
Sales Range: $25-49.9 Million
Emp.: 80
Investment Banking Services
N.A.I.C.S.: 523150
David G. Iverson *(Mng Dir & Head-Consumer, Food & Retail Grp)*

Subsidiary (Non-US):

Lazard Freres Banque SA (2)
121 Boulevard Haussmann Cedex 08, 75008, Paris, France
Tel.: (33) 144130111
Web Site: http://www.lazardfreresgestion.fr
Sales Range: $100-124.9 Million
Emp.: 148

Financial Advisory & Asset Management Services
N.A.I.C.S.: 523999
Bruno Roger *(Chm & CEO)*

Lazard Freres K.K. (2)
Sanno Park Tower 25th Floor 11-1 Nagatacho 2-chome, Chiyoda-ku, Tokyo, 100-6125, Japan
Tel.: (81) 355116011
Web Site: http://www.lazard.com
Investment Management Service
N.A.I.C.S.: 523940

Lazard Freres SAS (2)
175 Boulevard Haussmann, 75008, Paris, France
Tel.: (33) 144130111
Asset Management Services
N.A.I.C.S.: 523150

Lazard Fund Managers (Ireland) Limited (2)
4th Floor Lumen Building Upper Baggot Street, Dublin, Ireland
Tel.: (353) 12468550
Asset Management Services
N.A.I.C.S.: 523150

Lazard Gulf Limited (2)
Level 10 West Unit 1008 Index Tower DIFC, PO Box 506644, Dubai, United Arab Emirates
Tel.: (971) 43728222
Asset Management Services
N.A.I.C.S.: 523150

Lazard India Private Limited (2)
Level 7 The IL & FS Financial Centre Bandra Kurla Complex, Bandra East, Mumbai, 400 051, India
Tel.: (91) 22 6752 6000
Web Site: http://www.lazard.com
Emp.: 25
Financial Management Services
N.A.I.C.S.: 523999

Lazard Japan Asset Management K.K. (2)
ATT Annex 7th Floor 2-11-7, Akasaka Minato-ku, Tokyo, 107-0052, Japan
Tel.: (81) 345502700
Web Site: http://www.lazardnet.com
Emp.: 28
Investment Advisory Services
N.A.I.C.S.: 523940

Lazard Korea Asset Management Co., Ltd. (2)
10F Seoul Finance Center 136 Sejongdaero, Jung-gu, Seoul, 100-768, Korea (South)
Tel.: (82) 262201600
Web Site: http://www.lkam.co.kr
Investment Management Service
N.A.I.C.S.: 523999

Lazard Korea Limited (2)
8F Hanwha Building 109 Sogong-ro, Jung-gu, Seoul, 04525, Korea (South)
Tel.: (82) 27710991
Asset Management Services
N.A.I.C.S.: 523150

Lazard Panama S.A. (2)
Bloc Office Hub 10-D, Santa Maria Business District, Panama, Panama
Tel.: (507) 3219350
Asset Management Services
N.A.I.C.S.: 523150

Lazard Pty Ltd (2)
Level 38 Gateway 1 Macquarie Place, Sydney, 2000, NSW, Australia
Tel.: (61) 2 9256 9900
Web Site: http://www.lazard.com.au
Emp.: 15
Financial Management Services
N.A.I.C.S.: 523999

Lazard Saudi Arabia Limited (2)
15th Floor Nakheel Tower King Fahad Road, Nakheel District, Riyadh, 12381, Saudi Arabia
Tel.: (966) 14347300
Asset Management Services
N.A.I.C.S.: 523150

Lazard sprl (2)
Blue Tower Louise Avenue Louise 326 9th Floor, 1050, Brussels, Belgium

Tel.: (32) 26271382
Web Site: http://www.lazard.com
Investment Management Service
N.A.I.C.S.: 523999

MBA Lazard Argentina (2)
Avenue Alicia Moreau de Justo 140 4th Floor, Buenos Aires, C1107AAD, Argentina
Tel.: (54) 1143195800
Web Site: http://www.mba-lazard.com
Investment Banking & Asset Management Services
N.A.I.C.S.: 523150
Alejandro F. Reynal *(Founder)*

MBA Lazard Chile S.A. (2)
Calle Alcantara 200, 7550000, Las Condes, Chile
Tel.: (56) 222450627
Web Site: http://www.mba-lazard.com
Investment Banking & Asset Management Services
N.A.I.C.S.: 523940

MBA Lazard Colombia S.A.S. (2)
Carrera 7 71 21 Torre B of 1010, Bogota, Colombia
Tel.: (57) 1 312 3048
Web Site: http://www.mba-lazard.com
Sales Range: $50-74.9 Million
Emp.: 8
Investment Banking & Asset Management Services
N.A.I.C.S.: 523150

MBA Lazard Panama S.A. (2)
Edificio World Trade Center 9th Floor - Oficina 901, Panama, Panama
Tel.: (507) 265 0200
Web Site: http://www.lazard.com
Emp.: 10
Investment Banking & Asset Management Services
N.A.I.C.S.: 523150

MBA Lazard Peru S.A.C. (2)
Cal Miguel Dasso Nro 104 Int 1001 Edificio Punta del Este, San Isidro, Peru
Tel.: (51) 1 637 0800
Web Site: http://www.mba-lazard.com
Investment Banking & Asset Management Services
N.A.I.C.S.: 523940

MBA Lazard Uruguay (2)
Ruta 8 Km 17 500 Of 110A Zonamerica Business & Technology Park, 91600, Montevideo, Uruguay
Tel.: (598) 2 518 5533
Investment Banking & Asset Management Services
N.A.I.C.S.: 523150

Maison Lazard S.A.S (2)
12 Avenue Percier, 75008, Paris, France
Tel.: (33) 892976186
Management Consulting Services
N.A.I.C.S.: 541611

LAZURDE COMPANY FOR JEWELRY
Olaya Main Street and Prince Nayef St Intersection, PO Box 41270, Riyadh, 11521, Saudi Arabia
Tel.: (966) 112651119
Year Founded: 2006
4011—(SAU)
Rev.: $533,162,757
Assets: $448,535,633
Liabilities: $344,695,840
Net Worth: $103,839,793
Earnings: $9,108,617
Emp.: 774
Fiscal Year-end: 12/31/22
Jewelry Mfr
N.A.I.C.S.: 339910

LAZURITON NANO BIOTECHNOLOGY (U.S.A.) INC.
341 Sec 2 Wanshou Road 10th Floor, Guishan District, Taoyuan, 333, Taiwan
Tel.: (886) 3 3295585   NV
Web Site: http://lazuriton.com
Year Founded: 2015
Rev.: $1

INTERNATIONAL PUBLIC

Assets: $1,348
Liabilities: $321,125
Net Worth: ($319,777)
Earnings: ($51,241)
Fiscal Year-end: 12/31/20
Nano Fertilizer Product Distr
N.A.I.C.S.: 424910
Chih-Yuan Hsiao *(Chm, Pres & CEO)*

LB ALUMINIUM BERHAD
Lot 11 Jalan Perusahaan, 1 Kawasan Perusahaan Beranang Semenyih, 43700, Beranang, Selangor Darul Ehsan, Malaysia
Tel.: (60) 387258822
Web Site: http://www.lbalum.com
LBALUM—(KLS)
Rev.: $164,608,889
Assets: $164,295,873
Liabilities: $81,986,243
Net Worth: $82,309,630
Earnings: $7,827,725
Emp.: 879
Fiscal Year-end: 04/30/23
Aluminum Extrusions Mfr
N.A.I.C.S.: 331314
Bee Lian Ng *(Co-Sec)*

Subsidiaries:

ALBE Marketing Sdn. Bhd. (1)
53 and 55 Jalan PBS 14/10 Taman Perindustrian Bukit Serdang, 43300, Seri Kembangan, Selangor Darul Ehsan, Malaysia
Tel.: (60) 38 945 4919
Web Site: https://www.lbalum.com
Aluminum Products Sales
N.A.I.C.S.: 331313

ALBE Metal Sdn. Bhd. (1)
Godown No 23 Lot 7574 Jalan 1/113A, 4 1/2 Miles Jalan Keland Lama, 58000, Kuala Lumpur, Malaysia
Tel.: (60) 3 7981 3988
Aluminium Products Mfr
N.A.I.C.S.: 331313

LB Aluminium (Sarawak) Sdn. Bhd. (1)
Lot 846 & 847 Block 7 MTLD, Sejingkat Industrial Park, 93050, Kuching, Sarawak, Malaysia
Tel.: (60) 82 439 633
Aluminium Products Mfr
N.A.I.C.S.: 331313

LB Aluminium (Singapore) Pte Ltd. (1)
No 11 Kaki Bukit Road 1, #03-07 Eunos Technolink, Singapore, 415939, Singapore
Aluminium Products Mfr
N.A.I.C.S.: 331313

Rank Metal Sdn. Bhd. (1)
Lot 2-33 Jalan Perindustrian Mahkota 7 Taman Perindustrian Mahkota, 43700, Beranang, Selangor, Malaysia
Tel.: (60) 387244662
Web Site: https://www.arank.com.my
Aluminum Billets Mfr
N.A.I.C.S.: 331314

Sems Sdn. Bhd. (1)
56 Jalan Taming 7 Taman Taming Jaya, 43300, Balakong, Selangor, Malaysia
Tel.: (60) 183861493
Web Site: https://www.sems.com.my
Motor Vehicle Metal Stamping Mfr
N.A.I.C.S.: 336370

LB SEMICON CO., LTD.
138 Cheongbuksandan-ro, Cheongbuk-myeon, Pyeongtaek, Gyeonggi, Korea (South)
Tel.: (82) 316801600
Web Site: https://www.lbsemicon.com
Year Founded: 2000
061970—(KRS)
Rev.: $402,372,291
Assets: $588,361,221
Liabilities: $296,020,288
Net Worth: $292,340,933
Earnings: $30,839,773
Emp.: 644

AND PRIVATE COMPANIES

Fiscal Year-end: 12/31/22
Semiconductor Devices Mfr
N.A.I.C.S.: 334413
Nick Kim (CEO)

Subsidiaries:

LB Hunet (1)
Web Site: http://www.lbhunet.com
Electronic Components Mfr
N.A.I.C.S.: 334419

LB Investment Inc. (1)
Shinan Building 13th Floor Teheran-ro 512,
Gangnam-gu, Seoul, Korea (South)
Tel.: (82) 234670500
Web Site: https://lbinvestment.com
Capital Investment Services
N.A.I.C.S.: 523150
Park Ki-Ho (CEO)

LB Private Equity Inc. (1)
44F Trade Tower 511 Yeongdong-Daero,
Gangnam-gu, Seoul, Korea (South)
Tel.: (82) 262032635
Venture Capital Firm Services
N.A.I.C.S.: 523910
Brian Bonchun Koo (CEO)

LB-SHELL PLC
Charnwood Building Holywell Park
Ashby Road, Loughborough, LE11
3GB, Leicestershire, United Kingdom
Tel.: (44) 150 927 1271   UK
Web Site: http://www.lb-shell.com
LBP—(LSE)
Sales Range: $100-124.9 Million
Holding Company; Power Technology
Research & Development
N.A.I.C.S.: 551112
John Maguire (CFO & Co-Sec)

Subsidiaries:

Intelligent Energy Limited (1)
Charnwood Building Holywell Park Ashby
Road, Loughborough, LE11 3GB, Leics,
United Kingdom
Tel.: (44) 1509 271271
Web Site: http://www.intelligent-energy.com
Sales Range: $25-49.9 Million
Power Technology Research & Development
N.A.I.C.S.: 541715
Chris Dudfield (CTO)

Subsidiary (US):

Intelligent Energy, Inc. (2)
1731 Technology Dr Ste 755, San Jose, CA
95110
Tel.: (562) 997-3600
Web Site: http://www.intelligent-energy.com
Power Technology Research & Development
N.A.I.C.S.: 541715

LBC EXPRESS HOLDINGS, INC.
LBC Hangar General Aviation Center
Domestic Airport Road, Pasay, 1300,
Metro Manila, Philippines
Tel.: (63) 288568510   PH
Web Site:
 https://www.lbcexpressholdings.com
Year Founded: 1993
LBC—(PHI)
Rev.: $262,050,929
Assets: $277,598,055
Liabilities: $242,821,855
Net Worth: $34,776,200
Earnings: $3,036,653
Emp.: 8,950
Fiscal Year-end: 12/31/23
Holding Company; Private Investment Firm
N.A.I.C.S.: 551112
Miguel Angel A. Camahort (Chm, Pres & CEO)

Subsidiaries:

LBC Express, Inc. (1)
10th Floor Tower B Two Ecom Center Bayshore Ave, corner Harbor Drive Mall of Asia
Complex, Pasay, Metro Manila,
Philippines   (100%)
Tel.: (63) 288585999
Web Site: https://www.lbcexpress.com
Air Courier Services
N.A.I.C.S.: 492110

Subsidiary (US):

LBC Mabuhay USA Corp. (2)
362 East Grand Ave, South San Francisco,
CA 94080
Tel.: (650) 873-0750
Web Site: http://www.teamlbc.com
Rev.: $12,983,208
Emp.: 165
Air Courier Services
N.A.I.C.S.: 492110

LBG MEDIA PLC
20 Dale Street, Manchester, M1 1EZ,
United Kingdom   UK
Web Site:
 https://www.lbgmedia.co.uk
Year Founded: 2012
LBG—(AIM)
Rev.: $79,284,272
Assets: $88,781,873
Liabilities: $11,495,834
Net Worth: $77,286,039
Earnings: $6,749,558
Emp.: 470
Fiscal Year-end: 12/31/22
Digital Marketing Services
N.A.I.C.S.: 541810

Subsidiaries:

LADbible Group Limited (1)
1st & 3rd Floor 20 Dale Street, Manchester,
M1 1EZ, United Kingdom
Tel.: (44) 1612287637
Web Site: https://www.ladbiblegroup.com
Online Social Media Services
N.A.I.C.S.: 541511

LADbible Ireland Limited (1)
The Academy 42 Pearse St, Dublin, D02
YX88, Ireland
Tel.: (353) 2035829504
Online Media Publishing Services
N.A.I.C.S.: 512110

Unilad Group Limited (1)
20 Dale Street, Manchester, M1 1EZ,
United Kingdom
Tel.: (44) 1612287637
Web Site: https://www.unilad.com
Online Media Publishing Services
N.A.I.C.S.: 512110

LBI BELGIUM
Voorstlaan 191 Bd du Souverain,
B-1160, Brussels, Belgium
Tel.: (32) 2 706 05 40
Year Founded: 1994
Emp.: 110
N.A.I.C.S.: 541810
Stanislas Van Oost (CEO)

LBI CAPITAL BERHAD
Lot 1282 Jalan Bukit Kemuning
Seksyen 32, 40460, Shah Alam, Selangor Darul Ehsan, Malaysia
Tel.: (60) 51225128
Web Site: https://www.lbi-capital.com.my
LBICAP—(KLS)
Rev.: $5,570,573
Assets: $33,825,670
Liabilities: $3,350,630
Net Worth: $30,475,040
Earnings: $24,396
Fiscal Year-end: 12/31/22
Property Investment Services
N.A.I.C.S.: 523940
Sau Kian Kong (Exec Dir)

LBI HF.
Alfheimar 74 2nd Floor, 104, Reykjavik, Iceland
Tel.: (354) 410 3900   IS
Web Site: http://www.lbi.is

Financial Holding Company
N.A.I.C.S.: 551111
Halldor H. Backman (Member-Winding-up Bd)

LBL COMMUNICATION GROUP
32 Third Yamskogo Polya St, 125124,
Moscow, Russia
Tel.: (7) 4957894542
Web Site: http://www.lbl.ru
Year Founded: 1992
Sales Range: $25-49.9 Million
Emp.: 200
Communications Strategy Media &
Creative Solution Services
N.A.I.C.S.: 541810
Maria Dobrovidova (Dir-Bus Dev)

LBLUSEM CO. LTD.
9 4gongdan-ro 7-gil, Gupo-dong,
Gumi, 730 400, Gyeongsangbuk-do,
Korea (South)
Tel.: (82) 544700900
Web Site: https://www.lblusem.com
Year Founded: 2004
376190—(KRS)
Semiconductor Production
N.A.I.C.S.: 334413

LBO FRANCE S.A.R.L.
148 rue de l'Universite, Paris, 75007,
France
Tel.: (33) 1 40 62 77 67   FR
Web Site: http://www.lbofrance.com
Year Founded: 1985
Investment Management Service
N.A.I.C.S.: 523940
Robert Daussun (CEO)

Subsidiaries:

CMR France SAS (1)
Technopole de Chateau Gombert 7 rue
John Maynard Keynes, BP 85, 13381, Marseille, France
Tel.: (33) 4 91 11 37 00
Electronic Equipment Distr
N.A.I.C.S.: 423690
Patrice Flot (Mng Dir)

Subsidiary (Non-US):

CMR (Far East) Pte Ltd (2)
9 Tuas View Crescent, Singapore, 637612,
Singapore
Tel.: (65) 6268 8311
Web Site: http://www.cmrfe.com
Emp.: 700
Electric Equipment Mfr
N.A.I.C.S.: 334419
K. H. Choo (Mng Dir)

CMR Autronic GmbH (2)
Grutzmuhlenweg 44, 22339, Hamburg, Germany
Tel.: (49) 40 4840 2331
Web Site: http://www.cmr-autronic-gmbh.de
Electronic Equipment Mfr & Distr
N.A.I.C.S.: 334512

CMR Control Systems India Pvt Ltd (2)
21-24 Saraswati Industrial Estate Survey
No 30/8 & 30/9, Near Prabhat Press Dhayari, Pune, 411 041, India
Tel.: (91) 78750 88891
Sensor Mfr
N.A.I.C.S.: 334512
Mahesh Shinde (Mgr-Ops)

CMR Group Korea LLC (2)
1206 Centum T-Tower 66 Centum
Joongang-ro Central Street, Haeundae-gu,
Busan, 612-020, Korea (South)
Tel.: (82) 51 743 3902
Electronic Equipment Distr
N.A.I.C.S.: 423690

CMR Suzhou Electrical Devices Co., Ltd. (2)
Workshop A5 No 9 Weixin Road Suzhou
Industrial Park, Suzhou, 215122, China
Tel.: (86) 512 6289 0311

LBO FRANCE S.A.R.L.

Sensor Mfr
N.A.I.C.S.: 334512

Subsidiary (US):

CMR USA, LLC (2)
940 Riverside Pl, Leetsdale, PA 15056
Tel.: (724) 452-2200
Electronic Engine Component Mfr
N.A.I.C.S.: 333618
John Gatto (Pres)

Subsidiary (Non-US):

Controle Mesure Regulation Tunisie Sarl (2)
Chemical Street 33 Industrial Aera, Sidi
Rezig, Megrine, 2033, Tunisia
Tel.: (216) 71 426 978
Electronic Equipment Distr
N.A.I.C.S.: 423690
Bernard Dumas (Gen Mgr)

Crouzet Automatismes SAS (1)
12 rue Jean Jullien-Davin, 26902, Valence,
Cedex 9, France   (100%)
Tel.: (33) 475448844
Web Site: http://www.crouzet.com
Design & Production of Automation Components
N.A.I.C.S.: 238210
Benoit Secher (Dir-Edition)

Subsidiary (Non-US):

Crouzet GmbH (2)
Otto-Hahn-Str 3, Hilden, 40721, Germany
Tel.: (49) 21 03 9 80111
Web Site: http://www.crouzet.de
Sales Range: $25-49.9 Million
Emp.: 40
Automatic Control Equipment Mfr
N.A.I.C.S.: 334513

Gravograph Industrie International S.A. (1)
56 Avenue Jean Jaures, 10600, La
Chapelle, France
Tel.: (33) 325416565
Web Site: http://www.gravograph.com
Sales Range: $100-124.9 Million
Emp.: 500
Engraving
N.A.I.C.S.: 333248
Gerard Guyard (Chm)

Subsidiary (US):

Gravograph-New Hermes (2)
2200 Northmont Pkwy, Duluth, GA 30096-5895
Tel.: (770) 623-9697
Web Site: http://www.gravograph.com
Sales Range: $25-49.9 Million
Engraving Technology Services
N.A.I.C.S.: 333248
Gerard Guyard (Dir-Publication)

Innovation Capital SAS (1)
148 rue de l'Universite, 75007, Paris,
France
Tel.: (33) 1 80 06 99 15
Web Site: http://www.innovationcapital.fr
Privater Equity Firm
N.A.I.C.S.: 523999
Chantal Parpex (Pres & Mng Partner)

Laboratoires Dr. N.G. Payot (1)
6/8 Boulevard du Parc, 92200, Neuilly-sur-Seine, Cedex, France   (80%)
Tel.: (33) 1 55 62 54 54
Web Site: http://www.payot.com
Sales Range: $25-49.9 Million
Toiletries Mfr
N.A.I.C.S.: 325620
Herve Lesieur (Dir-Publication)

Serapid, Inc. (1)
34100 Mound Rd, Sterling Heights, MI
48310-6612
Tel.: (586) 274-0774
Web Site: http://www.serapid.com
Sales Range: $1-9.9 Million
Relay & Industrial Control Mfr
N.A.I.C.S.: 335314
William R. Koons (Mgr-Sls)

Terreal S.A (1)
15 Rue Pages, 92150, Suresnes, France
Tel.: (33) 149972030
Web Site: http://www.terreal.com

LBO FRANCE S.A.R.L.

LBO France S.a.r.l.—(Continued)
Sales Range: $600-649.9 Million
Emp.: 2,400
Terracotta Product Mfr
N.A.I.C.S.: 327120
Laurent Musy (CEO)

Subsidiary (Domestic):

Lahera Production (2)
RN 112 - La Roubinarie, 81200, Mazamet, Tarn, France
Tel.: (33) 563616638
Web Site: http://www.terreal.com
Sales Range: $10-24.9 Million
Emp.: 51
Roofing Products Mfr & Whslr
N.A.I.C.S.: 423330
Pascal Assemat (Dir-Site)

Subsidiary (US):

Ludowici Roof Tile Inc. (2)
4757 Tile Plant Rd, New Lexington, OH 43764 (100%)
Tel.: (740) 342-1995
Web Site: http://www.ludowici.com
Sales Range: $100-124.9 Million
Terracotta Roofing Tile Mfr
N.A.I.C.S.: 327120
Tab Colbert (CEO)

Tiama S.A. (1)
ZA Des Plattes, 1 Chemin des Plattes Vour-les, Paris, 69390, France (70%)
Tel.: (33) 437201500
Sales Range: $100-124.9 Million
Mfr of Inspection Systems for Glass Container Industry
N.A.I.C.S.: 333248
Ursula Zukowski (Mgr-Mktg)

Subsidiary (Domestic):

SGCC S.A. (2)
Parc Actiwest Entree 7, 27/41 Blvd Louise Michel, 92230, Gennevilliers, France
Tel.: (33) 1 4613 84 00
Sales Range: $50-74.9 Million
Glass Container Industry Automated Inspection Systems Mfr
N.A.I.C.S.: 333248

LBP COMMUNICATIONS

49 rue Saint Roch, 75001, Paris, France
Tel.: (33) 142618059
Web Site: http://www.lbp-communication.com
Year Founded: 1974
Sales Range: $25-49.9 Million
Emp.: 7
Business-To-Business, Public Relations, Transportation, Travel & Tourism
N.A.I.C.S.: 541820
Lucien Boghen (Assoc Dir)

LBS BINA GROUP BERHAD

Plaza Seri Setia Level 1-4 No 1 Jalan SS9 2, 47300, Petaling Jaya, Selangor Darul Ehsan, Malaysia
Tel.: (60) 378777333
Web Site: https://www.lbs.com.my
LBS—(KLS)
Rev.: $364,837,543
Assets: $881,551,308
Liabilities: $510,159,741
Net Worth: $371,391,567
Earnings: $29,103,601
Emp.: 1,001
Fiscal Year-end: 12/31/22
Property Development Services
N.A.I.C.S.: 531311
Doris Ching Ching Lee (Sec & Gen Mgr-Secretarial & Corp Affairs Dept)

Subsidiaries:

MGB Berhad (1)
H-G Sunway PJ51A Jalan SS9A/19 Seksyen 51A, 47300, Petaling Jaya, Selangor Darul Ehsan, Malaysia
Tel.: (60) 378745888
Web Site: https://www.mgbgroup.com.my
Rev.: $129,693,379
Assets: $194,022,643
Liabilities: $86,787,503
Net Worth: $107,235,139
Earnings: $3,007,750
Emp.: 512
Fiscal Year-end: 12/31/2022
Construction & Property Development
N.A.I.C.S.: 236220
Hock San Lim (Mng Dir)

Zhuhai International Circuit Limited (1)
200 Hagongda Road, Jinding, Zhuhai, 519085, Guangdong, China
Tel.: (86) 7563383228
Web Site: https://www.zic.com.cn
Racetrack Operator
N.A.I.C.S.: 711212

LBT INNOVATIONS LTD.

16 Anster St, Adelaide, 5000, SA, Australia
Tel.: (61) 882271555 AU
Web Site: https://www.lbtinnovations.com
LBT—(ASX)
Rev.: $1,141,159
Assets: $5,295,807
Liabilities: $3,677,885
Net Worth: $1,617,922
Earnings: ($2,497,329)
Emp.: 30
Fiscal Year-end: 06/30/24
Laboratory Equipment Mfr
N.A.I.C.S.: 334516
Raymond Ridge (CFO & Sec)

LC AUTOMATION LTD.

Duttons Way Shadsworth Business Park, Blackburn, BB1 2QR, Lancs, United Kingdom
Tel.: (44) 1254685900
Web Site: http://www.lcautomation.com
Sales Range: $10-24.9 Million
Emp.: 33
Automation, Control & Safety Products Distr
N.A.I.C.S.: 423840
Malcolm Chadwick (Mng Dir)

LC PACKAGING INTERNATIONAL BV

Hoogeveenenweg 150, 2913 LV, Nieuwerkerk, Netherlands
Tel.: (31) 180 39 38 37 NI
Web Site: http://lcpackaging.com
Year Founded: 1923
Sales Range: $200-249.9 Million
Emp.: 1,132
Packaging Products Mfr & Distr
N.A.I.C.S.: 326112
Lucas Lammers (CEO)

Subsidiaries:

LC Packaging UK Ltd (1)
Bridge Road Long Sutton Spalding, Lincolnshire, Spalding, PE12 9EF, United Kingdom
Tel.: (44) 1406 36 2511
Web Site: http://lcpackaging.co.uk
Pacakaging Products Mfr & Distr
N.A.I.C.S.: 322211

Unit (Domestic):

LC Packaging UK Ltd - Scotland (2)
Union Street, Friockheim, Angus, DD114TD, Scotland, United Kingdom
Tel.: (44) 1241828681
Web Site: http://lcpackaging.co.uk
Packaging Product Distr
N.A.I.C.S.: 423840

LC-TEC HOLDING AB

Tunavagen 281, 781 73, Borlange, Sweden
Tel.: (46) 243794070
Web Site: https://www.lc-tec.se
Year Founded: 1988
Display Equipment Mfr
N.A.I.C.S.: 334419
Jesper Osterman (Mng Dir)

LCI EDUCATION NETWORK

1400 Rue du Fort, Montreal, QC, Canada
Tel.: (514) 939-4400
Web Site: http://www.lcieducation.com
Education Services
N.A.I.C.S.: 611710
Sam Rizk (VP)

LCL RESOURCES LIMITED

Tel.: (61) 862459879
Web Site: https://www.loscerros.com.au
LCL—(ASX)
Rev.: $103,266
Assets: $12,144,324
Liabilities: $567,257
Net Worth: $11,577,067
Earnings: ($21,291,869)
Emp.: 64
Fiscal Year-end: 12/31/23
Copper, Gold, Molybdenum & Zinc Exploration Services
N.A.I.C.S.: 212230
Jason Stirbinskis (Mng Dir)

Subsidiaries:

Miraflores Compania Minera SAS (1)
Cra 36 2 Sur-60 Oficina 1301, Medellin, Colombia
Tel.: (57) 43121196
Web Site: https://www.miraflores.co
Gold Mining Services
N.A.I.C.S.: 212220

LCS IMOBILIAR SA

Strada Luncii nr 19 Etaj 2, Cluj-Napoca, Romania
Tel.: (40) 364808371
LCSI—(BUC)
Rev.: $362,091
Assets: $7,911,225
Liabilities: $1,180,355
Net Worth: $6,730,870
Earnings: $234,661
Emp.: 1
Fiscal Year-end: 12/31/23
Building Construction Services
N.A.I.C.S.: 236220
Angela-Simona Rotaru (Pres)

LDC DENTAL PUBLIC COMPANY LIMITED

Level 2 LDC Building 395-395/1 Moo 5 Srinagarindra Road, Samrong Nuea Sub-District, Samut Prakan, 10270, Thailand
Tel.: (66) 27438730
Web Site: https://www.ldcdental.com
Year Founded: 1992
LDC—(THA)
Rev.: $12,412,718
Assets: $16,403,844
Liabilities: $8,996,381
Net Worth: $7,407,462
Earnings: $499,475
Emp.: 400
Fiscal Year-end: 12/31/23
Dental Services
N.A.I.C.S.: 621210
Chaiwat Maneenut (Chm)

LDC SA

2 rue des Erables, FR-69578, Limon-est, Cedex, France
Tel.: (33) 243627000 FR
Web Site: http://www.ldc.fr
Year Founded: 1968
LOUP—(EUR)
Sales Range: $1-4.9 Billion
Emp.: 22,000

INTERNATIONAL PUBLIC

Holding Company; Food Processing; Poultry Production & Processing
N.A.I.C.S.: 551112
Denis Lambert (Chm-Exec Bd)

Subsidiaries:

Ardevol (1)
Zone Industrielle de Flacher, 07340, Felines, Ardeche, France (100%)
Tel.: (33) 475348255
Web Site: http://www.ldc.fr
Rev.: $15,362,846
Emp.: 16
Poultry Production
N.A.I.C.S.: 311615

Arrive (1)
Rue du Stade, BP 1, 85250, Saint-Fulgent, France (100%)
Tel.: (33) 2 51 44 24 24
Web Site: http://www.arrive.fr
Sales Range: $750-799.9 Million
Emp.: 2,975
Mfr & Distr of Animal Feed, Pet Food & Processed Poultry Products for Supermarkets; Vitamin & Mineral Premixes for Animals
N.A.I.C.S.: 311119

Atlantic Traiteur Innovation (1)
ZI du Clos du Poivre Route d'Asserac, 44410, Herbignac, France (100%)
Tel.: (33) 2 51 75 74 00
Web Site: http://www.ldc.fr
Sales Range: $25-49.9 Million
Emp.: 193
Meat & Exotic Product Processing
N.A.I.C.S.: 311999
Bertrand Quinquis (Gen Mgr)

Avilaves Gredos (1)
Pol Ind Las Hervencias parc 42-43, 05004, Madrid, Spain
Tel.: (34) 920351047
Sales Range: $10-24.9 Million
Emp.: 44
Poultry Farming & Processing
N.A.I.C.S.: 311615

Bresdi S.A.S. (1)
Le Bourg, F 71470, Romenay, France (100%)
Tel.: (33) 385408750
Web Site: http://www.ldc.fr
Poultry Slaughtering & Processing
N.A.I.C.S.: 311615

Celtys S.A.S. (1)
Z.I. de Restavy, 56240, Plouay, France
Tel.: (33) 2 97 02 20 20
Web Site: http://www.ldc.fr
Duck & Turkey Based Products & Related Frozen & Convenience Foods Production
N.A.I.C.S.: 311615

Celvia (1)
ZI de Saint Jean Brevelay, 56660, Saint Jean Brevelay, France (100%)
Tel.: (33) 297603388
Web Site: http://www.celvia.com
Emp.: 700
Poultry Processing
N.A.I.C.S.: 311615
Christian Perrot (Chm & Mng Dir)

Daniel Loiseau Gamme (1)
6 rue du Moulin a Cailloux, BP 509, 94577, Orly, France (100%)
Tel.: (33) 1 45 12 09 00
Web Site: http://www.ldc.fr
Sales Range: $25-49.9 Million
Emp.: 49
Creation, Development & Marketing of Processed Meat, Deli & Fish Products for Catering Market
N.A.I.C.S.: 311999
Francis Loiseau (Mgr)

Drosed S.A. (1)
ul Sokolowska 154, Siedlce, 08-110, Poland
Tel.: (48) 256400000
Web Site: http://www.drosed.com.pl
Sales Range: $200-249.9 Million
Emp.: 700
Poultry Farming & Processing
N.A.I.C.S.: 311615
Jacek Lewicki (Gen Mgr)

Branch (Domestic):

Drosed (2)

AND PRIVATE COMPANIES — LE PUBLIC SYSTEME

ul Poznanska 290/292, 87 100, Torun, Poland
Tel.: (48) 48 56 657 45 00
Web Site: http://www.ldc.fr
Sales Range: $200-249.9 Million
Emp.: 666
Poultry Farming & Processing
N.A.I.C.S.: 311615

Subsidiary (Domestic):

Indykpol S.A. (2)
Jesienna 3, 10-370, Olsztyn, Poland
Tel.: (48) 895262222
Web Site: http://www.indykpol.pl
Sales Range: $250-299.9 Million
Meat Processing Services
N.A.I.C.S.: 311612
Piotr Kulikowski *(CEO & Gen Mgr)*

Drosed Surowiec (1)
Reguly Al Powstancow Warszawy 43, 05-816, Warsaw, Poland
Tel.: (48) 22 723 69 56
Web Site: http://www.ldc.fr
Sales Range: $25-49.9 Million
Emp.: 100
Poultry Feed Mfr
N.A.I.C.S.: 311119

Entr'Acte SAS (1)
9 rue Jean Mermoz, 91080, Courcouronnes, France **(100%)**
Tel.: (33) 1 69 87 00 10
Web Site: http://www.ldc.fr
Sales Range: $25-49.9 Million
Emp.: 170
Sandwiches Mfr
N.A.I.C.S.: 311999
Philippe Clavel *(Gen Mgr)*

Europeenne de Plats Cuisines (1)
ZI Beaufreu, BP 18, 72210, Roeze-sur-Sarthe, France **(100%)**
Tel.: (33) 2 43 39 59 50
Web Site: http://www.ldc.fr
Sales Range: $50-74.9 Million
Emp.: 265
Mfr of Prepared Meals
N.A.I.C.S.: 311999

Guillot Cobreda S.A.S. (1)
BP 20, 71290, Cuisery, France
Tel.: (33) 85 27 06 06
Poultry Processing
N.A.I.C.S.: 311615

La Toque Angevine S.A.S. (1)
Zone Industrielle d'Etriche, rue Robert Schumann, 49504, Segre, France
Tel.: (33) 241947100
Web Site: http://www.ldc.fr
Sales Range: $100-124.9 Million
Emp.: 600
Pizzas & Sandwiches Mfr
N.A.I.C.S.: 311999
Nicolas Eymoud *(Gen Mgr)*

Les Charmilles (1)
ZA de la Gare, 49360, Maulevrier, France **(100%)**
Tel.: (33) 241490055
Poultry Breeding, Processing & Catering Products
N.A.I.C.S.: 112390
Dominique Chacun *(Mng Dir)*

Marie SAS (1)
13-15 rue du Pont des Halles, 94526, Rungis, France **(100%)**
Tel.: (33) 1 56 70 90 00
Web Site: http://www.ldc.fr
Sales Range: $50-74.9 Million
Emp.: 220
Chilled & Frozen Foods Mfr
N.A.I.C.S.: 311999

Procanar (1)
La Haie, 56190, Lauzach, France
Tel.: (33) 297487800
Web Site: http://www.procanar.fr
Sales Range: $100-124.9 Million
Emp.: 45
Duck & Processed Poultry Products
N.A.I.C.S.: 311615
Yvan Le Neve *(Gen Mgr)*

Regalette (1)
Z A de Kerboulard, F 56250, Saint Nolff, Bretagne, France **(100%)**
Tel.: (33) 297455890

Web Site: http://www.regalette.com
Sales Range: $10-24.9 Million
Emp.: 100
Pancakes & Crepes Mfr
N.A.I.C.S.: 311999

Servais S.A.S. (1)
Leiu-Dit Le Trianon, 41270, Droue, France
Tel.: (33) 254894040
Web Site: http://www.ldc.fr
Poultry Slaughtering & Processing
N.A.I.C.S.: 311615

LDK SOLAR CO., LTD.
Hi-Tech Industrial Park, Xinyu, 338032, Jiangxi, China
Tel.: (86) 7906860171 Ky
Web Site: http://www.ldksolar.com
Year Founded: 2005
Sales Range: $1-9.9 Million
Emp.: 8,529
Photovoltaic Products Mfr & Supplier
N.A.I.C.S.: 334413
Jack Lai *(CFO, Sec & Exec VP)*

Subsidiaries:

Jiangxi LDK Solar Hi-Tech Co., Ltd. (1)
No 1950 SaiWei Avenue High-Tech Industrial Development Zone, Xinyu, 338032, Jiangxi, China
Tel.: (86) 7906860911
Web Site: http://www.saiweisolar.com
Solar Wafer Mfr
N.A.I.C.S.: 334413

Subsidiary (Domestic):

LDK Solar Hi-Tech (Nanchang) Co., Ltd. (2)
No 999 Torch Boulevard, Nanchang, 330096, Jiangxi, China
Tel.: (86) 791 8105313
Electronic Components Distr
N.A.I.C.S.: 423690

LDK Solar Power Technology (Xinyu) Engineering Co., Ltd. (2)
Road Development Zone, Xinyu, 338000, Jiangxi, China
Tel.: (86) 790 6861781
Solar Wafer Mfr
N.A.I.C.S.: 334413

LDK Solar Canada Inc. (1)
1100 Burloak Dr Ste 300, Burlington, ON, Canada
Tel.: (905) 336-8923
Solar Wafer Mfr
N.A.I.C.S.: 334413

LDK Solar International Company Limited (1)
Unit 23-01 Swd Financial Center, Sheung Wan, China (Hong Kong)
Tel.: (852) 22916020
Web Site: http://www.ldksolar.com
Emp.: 5
Solar Electrical Equipment Distr
N.A.I.C.S.: 423610
Jessica Chan *(Sec)*

LDK Solar Italia S.r.l. (1)
Via San Martino 25, 31020, San Zenone degli Ezzelini, Treviso, Italy
Tel.: (39) 0423 948833
Web Site: http://www.ldksolar.com
Emp.: 2
Solar Power Transmission Equipment Mfr
N.A.I.C.S.: 333613

LDK Solar Spain, S.L. (1)
Avenida de les Garrigues n 46 Parc Empresarial Mas Blau II, 08820, El Prat de Llobregat, Barcelona, Spain
Tel.: (34) 93 222 27 70
Solar Power Transmission Equipment Mfr
N.A.I.C.S.: 333613

LDK Solar USA Inc. (1)
1290 Oakmead Pkwy Ste 306, Sunnyvale, CA 94085
Tel.: (408) 245-0858
Web Site: http://www.ldksolar.com
Multicrystalline Wafers for Solar Sales
N.A.I.C.S.: 334413
Jack Lai *(CFO)*

Subsidiary (Domestic):

LDK Solar Tech USA, Inc. (2)
1290 Oakmead Pkwy Ste 306, Sunnyvale, CA 94085
Tel.: (408) 245-0858
Photo Voltaic Solar Panels Distr
N.A.I.C.S.: 423690

LDK Trading Service Germany GmbH (1)
Sonnenstr 19, 80331, Munich, Germany
Tel.: (49) 89 8563 472 0
Electronic Components Distr
N.A.I.C.S.: 423690

LDLC.COM SA
2 Rue des Erables, 69578, Limonest, Cedex, France
Tel.: (33) 472523777
Web Site: http://www.ldlc.com
ALLDL—(EUR)
Sales Range: $550-599.9 Million
Electronic Components, Network Equipment, Software, Connections, Portable Computers, Digital Cameras, DVDs, Videos & Peripherals Sales & Distr
N.A.I.C.S.: 423620
Laurent Villemonte de la Clergerie *(Chm-Mgmt Bd)*

LDT INC.
126-33 Handeul 1-ro, Seobuk-gu, Cheonan, 31092, Chunggnam, Korea (South)
Tel.: (82) 415207300
Web Site: https://www.ldt.co.kr
Year Founded: 1997
096870—(KRS)
Rev: $8,997,149
Assets: $13,179,097
Liabilities: $1,356,259
Net Worth: $11,822,838
Earnings: $1,498,865
Emp.: 40
Fiscal Year-end: 12/31/22
Semiconductor Product Mfr
N.A.I.C.S.: 334413
Jae-Cheun Jung *(Pres & CEO)*

LE BELIER SA
Plantier de la Reine, BP 103, 33240, Verac, France
Tel.: (33) 557550300 FR
Web Site: http://www.lebelier.com
Year Founded: 1961
Rev: $412,077,798
Assets: $451,568,292
Liabilities: $264,519,738
Net Worth: $187,048,554
Earnings: $31,056,186
Emp.: 4,044
Fiscal Year-end: 12/31/18
Automotive Cast Aluminum Parts Mfr
N.A.I.C.S.: 331315
Philippe Galland *(Chm)*

Subsidiaries:

LBQ Foundry S.A. De C.V. (1)
Calle 2 No 18 Acceso 2, Zona industrial Benito Juarez, 76120, Santiago de Queretaro, Queretaro, Mexico
Tel.: (52) 4421927300
Web Site: http://www.lebelier.com.mx
Aluminum Foundry Mfr
N.A.I.C.S.: 331524

LE Belier Lushun (Dalian) Foundry Co., Ltd. (1)
Lushun Development Zone, Dalian, 116052, China
Tel.: (86) 41186281008
Automotive Cast Aluminium Part Mfr
N.A.I.C.S.: 331524

LE FOYER STEPHANAIS
42 bis Avenue Ambroise Croizat, BP 20, 76801, Saint Etienne-du-Rouvray, CEDEX, Rouvray, France

Tel.: (33) 232919320
Web Site: http://www.foyer-stephanais.fr
Year Founded: 1929
Apartment Building Operator
N.A.I.C.S.: 531110

LE GAGA HOLDINGS LIMITED
Unit 1105 The Metropolis Tower 10 Metropolis Drive Hung Hom, Kowloon, China (Hong Kong)
Tel.: (852) 31628585 Ky
Web Site: http://www.legaga.com.hk
Year Founded: 2004
Vegetable Whlsr
N.A.I.C.S.: 111219
Shing Yung Ma *(CEO)*

LE GROUPE MASTER S.E.C
1675 boul de Montarville, Boucherville, J4B 7W4, QC, Canada
Tel.: (514) 527-2301
Web Site: http://www.master.ca
Year Founded: 1952
Rev: $127,202,400
Emp.: 350
Air Conditioning, Refrigeration & Heating Products Distr
N.A.I.C.S.: 423730
Michel Ringuet *(CEO)*

LE JEAN BLEU INC.
1895 46th E Avenue, Lachine, H8T 2N9, QC, Canada
Tel.: (514) 631-3300 Ca
Web Site: http://www.jeanbleu.com
Sales Range: $25-49.9 Million
Emp.: 100
Blue Jeans Distr & Retailer
N.A.I.C.S.: 424350
Allan Berlach *(Owner & Pres)*

LE LAVOIR LTD.
Digvijay Plot Street No 51 Opp Makhicha Nivas Jamnagar, Jamnagar, 361005, Gujrat, India
Tel.: (91) 3365035881 In
Web Site: https://www.rholdings.org
Year Founded: 1981
539814—(BOM)
Rev: $260,374
Assets: $726,691
Liabilities: $134,508
Net Worth: $592,183
Earnings: $68,248
Fiscal Year-end: 03/31/23
Textile Products Distr
N.A.I.C.S.: 424310
Piyushbhai Jentilal Malde *(Exec Dir)*

LE NOBLE AGE SANTE SA
7 Boulevard Auguste Priou, 44120, Vertou, France
Tel.: (33) 240160161 FR
Web Site: https://www.lna-sante.com
Year Founded: 1990
LNA—(EUR)
Sales Range: $700-749.9 Million
Senior Care Center Operator
N.A.I.C.S.: 623312
Jean-Paul Siret *(Chm & CEO)*

LE PETIT BASQUE
Zac La Prade, 33650, Bordeaux, France
Tel.: (33) 557970260
Web Site: http://www.cailles-lait-brebis.com
Rev: $21,000,000
Emp.: 55
Fluid Milk
N.A.I.C.S.: 311511
Lionel Vasselle *(Mgr-DP)*

LE PUBLIC SYSTEME
40 rue Anatole France, 92594, Levallois-Perret, Cedex, France

LE PUBLIC SYSTEME

Le Public Systeme—(Continued)
Tel.: (33) 141342000
Web Site: http://www.le-public-systeme.com
Year Founded: 1993
Sales Range: $75-99.9 Million
Emp.: 400
Public Relations
N.A.I.C.S.: 541820
Lionel Chouchan *(Pres)*

LE SAUNDA HOLDINGS LIMITED

Suites 1104-6 11/F 1063 King's Road, Quarry Bay, China (Hong Kong)
Tel.: (852) 36783200
Web Site: http://www.lesaunda.com.hk
0738—(HKG)
Rev.: $53,298,018
Assets: $103,500,001
Liabilities: $17,903,843
Net Worth: $85,596,158
Earnings: ($6,612,418)
Emp.: 1,120
Fiscal Year-end: 02/28/23
Shoe Mfr
N.A.I.C.S.: 316210
Jacky Kwan Ho Chui *(Exec Dir)*

LE TANNEUR & CIE SA

7 rue Tronchet, 75008, Paris, France
Tel.: (33) 1 44724000
Web Site: http://www.letanneuretcie.com
ALTAN—(EUR)
Sales Range: $50-74.9 Million
Emp.: 570
Leather Goods Mfr & Distr
N.A.I.C.S.: 315250
Patricia Moulon *(Dir-Fin & Legal)*

Subsidiaries:

Le Tanneur & Cie Bruxelles S.A. (1)
Galerie Du Roi 22, Brussels, 1000, Belgium
Tel.: (32) 25131536
Web Site: http://www.letanneur.com
Sales Range: $25-49.9 Million
Emp.: 4
Leather Goods Mfr
N.A.I.C.S.: 315210
Christine Lericq *(Mgr)*

LE TEMPS SA

Pont Bessieres 3, PO Box 6714, 1002, Lausanne, Switzerland
Tel.: (41) 582692900 CH
Web Site: http://www.letemps.ch
Sales Range: $50-74.9 Million
Emp.: 120
Newspaper Publishers
N.A.I.C.S.: 513110

LE TREMAIL

Pavillon A4 7 Allee De Sete, 94150, Rungis, France
Tel.: (33) 146860832
Rev.: $23,600,000
Emp.: 48
Fish & Seafoods
N.A.I.C.S.: 424460
Colette Benisty *(Mgr)*

LEACH RHODES WALKER LTD.

Ground Floor West 50 Dearmans Place, Manchester, M3 5LH, United Kingdom
Tel.: (44) 1618330211
Web Site: http://www.lrw.co.uk
Sales Range: $25-49.9 Million
Emp.: 90
Architectural Design Services
N.A.I.C.S.: 541310

LEACY MG LTD.

Aston Lane, Perry Barr, Birmingham, B20 3BW, United Kingdom
Tel.: (44) 121 356 3003
Web Site: http://www.leacyclassics.com
Vintage Car Parts Mfr
N.A.I.C.S.: 441330
David Keene *(CEO)*

Subsidiaries:

The London Taxi Corporation Limited (1)
Holyhead Road, Coventry, CV5 8JJ, United Kingdom
Tel.: (44) 24 7657 2040
Web Site: http://www.london-taxis.co.uk
Emp.: 70
Taxi Mfr
N.A.I.C.S.: 336110
Peter Johansen *(VP-Ops-UK)*

LEAD DATA INC.

7F 5 No 3 Songjiang Rd, Zhongshan Dist, Taipei, 303, Taiwan
Tel.: (886) 225020788
Web Site: http://www.leaddata.com.tw
Year Founded: 1996
2443—(TAI)
Rev.: $737,586
Assets: $17,502,101
Liabilities: $1,867,786
Net Worth: $15,634,315
Earnings: $2,801,728
Emp.: 750
Fiscal Year-end: 12/31/22
Optical Disc Mfr & Distr
N.A.I.C.S.: 334112
Ming-Ho Huang *(Chm)*

Subsidiaries:

ChungHong Holdings Limited (1)
Suzhou New Technology Industrial Park New District, Suzhou, Jiangsu, China
Tel.: (86) 51268255365
Web Site: http://www.chunghong.com
Electric Equipment Mfr
N.A.I.C.S.: 334419
Lin Teng-Kuei *(Chm)*

Subsidiary (Non-US):

ChungHong Electronics Poland Sp. z o.o. (2)
ul Innowacyjna 4, Biskupice Podgorne, 55-040, Wroclaw, Poland
Tel.: (48) 717694720
Web Site: http://www.chunghong.com.pl
Emp.: 260
Electric Equipment Mfr
N.A.I.C.S.: 334419
Damian Kontek *(Deputy Dir-Plant)*

E-Top Union Inc. (1)
3F No 178 Sec 2 Xinyi Rd, Da`an Dist, Taipei, 106, Taiwan
Tel.: (886) 225282166
Web Site: http://www.u-wish.com.tw
Medical Instrument Mfr
N.A.I.C.S.: 339112
Jason Hwang *(VP)*

Subsidiary (Non-US):

Suzhou U-wish Joint Medical Devices Co., Ltd. (2)
Workshop 5 Area 1 No 98 Hengshan Road, New District, Suzhou, China
Tel.: (86) 51268076518
Medical Instrument Mfr
N.A.I.C.S.: 339112

LEAD EASTERN INVESTMENT CO., LTD.

A1A2 18F Tower A, Yifeng Business Mansion, Datong, 037008, Shanxi, China
Tel.: (86) 1059407655
000673—(SSE)
Rev.: $31,915,175
Assets: $234,155,439
Liabilities: $244,710,076
Net Worth: ($10,554,637)
Earnings: $3,782,755
Fiscal Year-end: 12/31/20
Television Program Distribution Services
N.A.I.C.S.: 516120
Gang Liu *(Vice Chm & Deputy Gen Mgr)*

LEAD FINANCIAL SERVICES LIMITED

101 Sita Ram Mansion 718-21Joshi Road Karol Bagh, New Delhi, 110 005, India
Tel.: (91) 1123549822
Web Site: https://www.leadfinancialservices.in
Year Founded: 1993
531288—(BOM)
Rev.: $8,272
Assets: $1,375,797
Liabilities: $636,691
Net Worth: $739,107
Earnings: ($14,605)
Emp.: 3
Fiscal Year-end: 03/31/21
Financial Services
N.A.I.C.S.: 523999
Vijay Kumar *(Mgr)*

LEAD INNOVATION CORP.

Building 4 Block 8 188 South 4th Ring West Road, Fengtai District, Beijing, 100070, China
Tel.: (86) 13702361616
Year Founded: 2010
LEIC—(OTCIQ)
Rev.: $6,966,000
Assets: $132,189,000
Liabilities: $12,083,000
Net Worth: $120,106,000
Earnings: ($499,000)
Fiscal Year-end: 11/30/22
Electric Power Distribution Services
N.A.I.C.S.: 221122
Jared Manhein *(VP-Operations)*

LEAD REAL ESTATE CO., LTD.

6F MFPR Shibuya Nanpeidai Building 16-11 Nampeidai-cho, Shibuya-ku, Tokyo, 150-0036, Japan
Tel.: (81) 357845127 JP
Web Site: https://lead-real.co.jp
Year Founded: 2001
LRE—(NASDAQ)
Rev.: $125,060,918
Assets: $113,395,307
Liabilities: $93,728,477
Net Worth: $19,666,830
Earnings: $3,850,326
Emp.: 62
Fiscal Year-end: 06/30/23
Real Estate Development Services
N.A.I.C.S.: 531190
Eiji Nagahara *(Pres)*

LEADCORP INC.

14-15 Yeouido-Dong, Yeongdeungpo-gu, Seoul, 150871, Korea (South)
Tel.: (82) 221265000
Web Site: http://www.leadcorp.co.kr
Year Founded: 1977
012700—(KRS)
Rev.: $496,842,188
Assets: $927,372,868
Liabilities: $600,284,322
Net Worth: $327,088,546
Earnings: $24,529,563
Emp.: 381
Fiscal Year-end: 12/31/22
Petroleum Product Whslr
N.A.I.C.S.: 424720
Jae-Jung Lee *(CEO)*

LEADDESK OYJ

INTERNATIONAL PUBLIC

Hameentie 15, 00500, Helsinki, Finland
Tel.: (358) 931544800
Web Site: https://www.leaddesk.com
Year Founded: 2010
LEADD—(HEL)
Emp.: 180
Software Development Services
N.A.I.C.S.: 541511
Henri Perttila *(Country Mgr)*

LEADER AUTO RESOURCES, LAR INC.

2525 Trans Canada Hwy, Pointe-Claire, H9R 4V6, QC, Canada
Tel.: (514) 694-6880
Web Site: http://www.larnet.com
Year Founded: 1979
Sales Range: $10-24.9 Million
Emp.: 90
New & Used Car Dealers
N.A.I.C.S.: 441110
Robert B. Issenman *(Pres & CEO)*

LEADER CAPITAL HOLDINGS CORP.

Suite 2311 23 F BEA Tower Millennium City 5418 Kwun Tong Road, Kwun Tong, China (Hong Kong)
Tel.: (852) 54117661 NV
Web Site: http://www.leader-capital.com
Year Founded: 2017
LCHD—(OTCIQ)
Rev.: $95,166
Assets: $3,924,771
Liabilities: $3,610,516
Net Worth: $314,255
Earnings: ($11,693,492)
Emp.: 63
Fiscal Year-end: 08/31/21
Holding Company
N.A.I.C.S.: 551112
Yi-Hsiu Lin *(Pres, CEO, Treas & Sec)*

LEADER ELECTRONICS CORPORATION

2-6-33 Tsunashima-Higashi, Yokohama, 223-8505, Japan
Tel.: (81) 45542121
Web Site: http://www.leader.co.jp
Year Founded: 1954
Sales Range: $25-49.9 Million
Emp.: 175
Sales of Electrical Measuring Equipment Mfr
N.A.I.C.S.: 334515
Kozo Nagao *(Pres)*

Subsidiaries:

JiaLong LEADER (Beijing) Trading Co., Ltd. (1)
Unit 2008 Jialong International Tower 20F, Chaoyang Park Road No 19, Chaoyang District, Beijing, 100125, China
Tel.: (86) 10 85118606
Electronic Test & Measuring Equipment Distr & Marketer
N.A.I.C.S.: 423610

Leader Instruments Corporation (1)
1501 E Orangethorpe Ave Ste 140, Fullerton, CA 92831-5252
Tel.: (714) 527-9300
Web Site: http://www.leaderamerica.com
Sales Range: $25-49.9 Million
Emp.: 25
Electronic Test & Measuring Equipment Distr & Marketer
N.A.I.C.S.: 423610
Masahiro Sawa *(Pres)*

LEADER ELECTRONICS INC.

8F No 138 Ln 235 Baoqiao Rd, Xindian Dist, New Taipei City, 23145, Taiwan
Tel.: (886) 281953058
Web Site: https://www.lei.com.tw

AND PRIVATE COMPANIES

Year Founded: 1970
3058—(TAI)
Rev.: $123,336,468
Assets: $143,294,936
Liabilities: $91,399,486
Net Worth: $51,895,449
Earnings: $1,368,161
Emp.: 1,778
Fiscal Year-end: 12/31/23
Power Supply Product Distr
N.A.I.C.S.: 423610
Chung-Yue Pao *(Chm & Gen Mgr)*

Subsidiaries:

Dongguan Leader Electronics Inc. (1)
No 1 Industrial Area, Tang Xia Town, Dongguan, 523710, Guangdong, China
Tel.: (86) 76987937136
Audio Transformer Mfr
N.A.I.C.S.: 334416

Jiangsu Leader Electronics Co., Ltd. (1)
No 99 Weijia Lane, Dantu New City Dantu District, Zhenjiang, 212028, Jiangsu, China
Tel.: (86) 51184565918
Power Converter Mfr & Distr
N.A.I.C.S.: 335311

Jiangsu Leader Electronics Inc. (1)
No 99 Weijia Lane Dantu New City, Dantu District, Zhenjiang, 212028, Jiangsu, China
Tel.: (86) 51184565918
Audio Transformer Mfr
N.A.I.C.S.: 334416

LEI Industries (H.K.) Limited (1)
Tel.: (852) 27576683
Audio Transformer Mfr
N.A.I.C.S.: 334416

LEI Japan Co., Ltd. (1)
2F Espoir Bld 3-41-8 Minami-Otsuka, Toshima-ku, Tokyo, 170-005, Japan
Tel.: (81) 367091381
Audio Transformer Mfr
N.A.I.C.S.: 334416

LEI Malaysia Sdn. Bhd. (1)
Unit 326 73-3-1 Ideal The one Jalan Mahsuri, 11950, Penang, Malaysia
Tel.: (60) 46485500
Audio Transformer Mfr
N.A.I.C.S.: 334416

Leader & Crescendo Electronics International Pte Ltd. (1)
2 Kallang Pudding Road 08-06 Mactech Building, Singapore, 349307, Singapore
Tel.: (65) 67431093
Audio Transformer Mfr
N.A.I.C.S.: 334416

Leader Electronics N.A. Inc. (1)
2901 South Harbor Blvd, Santa Ana, CA 92704
Audio Transformer Mfr
N.A.I.C.S.: 334416

Leader Electronics Philippine Branch Incorporated (1)
Cavite Economic Zone-CEZ Phase 2 Block 7, Rosario, Cavite, Philippines
Tel.: (63) 464373058
Audio Transformer Mfr
N.A.I.C.S.: 334416

LEADER ENVIRONMENTAL TECHNOLOGIES LIMITED
No 6 Block E Unit 608 Guang Yuan Dong Road Bo Hui Street, Tian He District, Guangzhou, 130033, China
Tel.: (86) 43186787555   SG
LS9—(SES)
Rev.: $2,104,493
Assets: $15,552,153
Liabilities: $11,344,281
Net Worth: $4,217,871
Earnings: ($9,936,894)
Fiscal Year-end: 12/31/20
Environmental Protection Services
N.A.I.C.S.: 541620

LEADER HARMONIOUS DRIVE SYSTEMS CO., LTD.
No 19 Muxu West Road, Wuzhong, Suzhou, 215101, China
Tel.: (86) 51266362298
Web Site: https://www.leaderdrive.com
Year Founded: 2011
688017—(SHG)
Rev.: $62,582,654
Assets: $339,093,827
Liabilities: $67,476,928
Net Worth: $271,616,899
Earnings: $21,804,471
Fiscal Year-end: 12/31/22
Transmission Device Mfr & Distr
N.A.I.C.S.: 333613
Yuyu Zuo *(Chm)*

LEADER HILL CORPORATION
Flat 1204 Block B Mei Li Yuan Hong Ling Middle Road, Luohu, Shenzhen, 518000, China
Tel.: (86) 18665342668   NV
Web Site: http://www.leaderhill.com
Year Founded: 2017
LHIL—(OTCIQ)
Liabilities: $33,395
Net Worth: ($33,395)
Earnings: ($33,900)
Emp.: 12
Fiscal Year-end: 11/30/21
Business Consulting Services
N.A.I.C.S.: 541611
Chia Yee Seah *(Founder)*

LEADER STEEL HOLDINGS BERHAD
Plot 85 Lorong Perusahaan Utama Kawasan Perusahaan, Bukit Tengah, 14000, Penang, Seberang Perai Tenga, Malaysia
Tel.: (60) 45071515
Web Site: https://www.leadersteel.my
Year Founded: 1987
LSTEEL—(KLS)
Rev.: $46,939,571
Assets: $60,547,210
Liabilities: $20,246,717
Net Worth: $40,300,493
Earnings: $1,373,473
Emp.: 169
Fiscal Year-end: 12/31/22
Steel Products Mfr
N.A.I.C.S.: 331110
Pak Say Tan *(Mng Dir)*

Subsidiaries:

Leader Steel Sdn. Bhd. (1)
Lot 841 Block 7 MTLD Demak Laut Industrial Park Phase 3, 93050, Kuching, Sarawak, Malaysia
Tel.: (60) 82439393
Steel Products Mfr
N.A.I.C.S.: 331110

Leader Steel Service Centre Sdn. Bhd. (1)
Lot 6483 Jalan Sungai Puloh KU 5 Kawasan Perindustrian Sungai Puloh, 42100, Klang, Selangor, Malaysia
Tel.: (60) 332905525
Steel Products Mfr
N.A.I.C.S.: 331110

LEADERLEASE S.A.
14 rue Hector Berlioz, 90000, Belfort, France
Tel.: (33) 3 84 46 13 45
Sales Range: $1-9.9 Million
Industrial Machinery Leasing Services
N.A.I.C.S.: 532490

LEADERS COSMETICS CO., LTD.
The Classic C404 90 Neungdong-ro, Gwangjin-gu, Seoul, 05065, Korea (South)
Tel.: (82) 234538768
Web Site: https://www.leaderscosmetics.com
Year Founded: 1986
016100—(KRS)
Rev.: $66,466,495
Assets: $60,995,772
Liabilities: $27,756,967
Net Worth: $33,238,805
Earnings: ($581,810)
Emp.: 162
Fiscal Year-end: 12/31/22
Cosmetics Products Mfr
N.A.I.C.S.: 325620
Jin-gu Kim *(CEO)*

LEADERS TECHNOLOGY INVESTMENT CO., LTD.
619 Bongeunsa-ro 6th floor JBK Tower Building, Gangnam-gu, Seoul, Korea (South)
Tel.: (82) 220519640
Web Site: https://plutusinvestment.co.kr
Year Founded: 1986
019570—(KRS)
Assets: $83,816,094
Liabilities: $36,366,089
Net Worth: $47,450,005
Earnings: ($8,828,313)
Emp.: 16
Fiscal Year-end: 03/31/22
Investment Management Service
N.A.I.C.S.: 523999
Jong-hun Song *(Exec Dir)*

LEADERSHIP DEVELOPMENT SOLUTIONS SRL
Alexandrov Constanstenescu 47 Sector 1, Bucharest, 11472, Romania
Tel.: (40) 212247124
Web Site: http://www.kfi.ro
Sales Range: $10-24.9 Million
Emp.: 20
Executive Search Service
N.A.I.C.S.: 541612
Radu Furnica *(Pres & Mng Dir)*

LEADING EDGE MATERIALS CORP.
14th Floor 1040 West Georgia Street, Vancouver, V6E 4H1, BC, Canada
Tel.: (778) 373-6727   BC
Web Site: https://www.leadingmaterials.com
Year Founded: 2010
LEMIF—(OTCQB)
Rev.: $19,946
Assets: $18,643,624
Liabilities: $4,299,445
Net Worth: $14,344,179
Earnings: ($2,824,447)
Emp.: 5
Fiscal Year-end: 10/31/22
Investment Services
N.A.I.C.S.: 523999
Nick DeMare *(Sec)*

LEADING HOLDINGS GROUP LIMITED
46/F Tower A Leading International Finance Center No 151, 2nd Tianfu Street Gaoxin District, Chengdu, Sichuan, China   Ky
Year Founded: 2019
6999—(HKG)
Rev.: $2,560,578,755
Assets: $4,714,052,254
Liabilities: $4,349,231,280
Net Worth: $364,820,974
Earnings: ($136,455,749)
Emp.: 928
Fiscal Year-end: 12/31/23
Holding Company
N.A.I.C.S.: 551112
Changlin Luo *(CFO)*

LEADING INVESTMENT & SECURITIES CO., LTD.
8th Road 27-8 NH Nonghyup Capital Building, Seoul, Korea (South)
Tel.: (82) 2009 7000   JP
Web Site: http://www.leading.co.kr
Year Founded: 2000
Sales Range: $75-99.9 Million
Emp.: 117
Investment Services
N.A.I.C.S.: 523999
Ho Kim Chun *(CEO)*

LEADING LEASING FINANCE & INVESTMENT COMPANY LTD.
C 233 G/F Back Side West Patel Nagar, New Delhi, 110008, India
Tel.: (91) 1165632288
Web Site: https://llflltd.in
Year Founded: 1983
540360—(BOM)
Rev.: $1,605,622
Assets: $9,367,695
Liabilities: $8,136,451
Net Worth: $1,231,244
Earnings: $107,999
Fiscal Year-end: 03/31/21
Finance Services
N.A.I.C.S.: 523150
Jinen Manoj Shah *(CFO)*

LEADING TECHNOLOGY GROUP PTY LTD.
Level 1 5 Lakeside Drive, Burwood, 3151, Australia
Tel.: (61) 3 9803 0045
Web Site: http://www.leadingtechnology.com
Technology Investment Services
N.A.I.C.S.: 523999

Subsidiaries:

Life Research Pty Ltd. (1)
1 Dalmore Drive Caribbean Park, Scoresby, 3179, Australia
Tel.: (61) 3 97 64 25 66
Web Site: http://www.liferesearch.com
Research & Development Services
N.A.I.C.S.: 541715
Scott Needham *(Mng Dir)*

Subsidiary (Domestic):

Mimotopes Pty. Ltd. (2)
11 Duerdin Street, Clayton, 3168, VIC, Australia (100%)
Tel.: (61) 395651111
Web Site: http://www.mimotopes.com
Emp.: 27
Research-Grade Peptides for Biological & Pharmaceutical Applications Developer
N.A.I.C.S.: 325412
Sonja Plompen *(Mng Dir)*

LEADTEK RESEARCH INC.
18F No166 Jian 1st Rd, Zhonghe Dist, Taipei, 23511, Taiwan
Tel.: (886) 282265800
Web Site: https://www.leadtek.com
Year Founded: 1986
2465—(TAI)
Rev.: $139,838,348
Assets: $85,287,645
Liabilities: $52,264,755
Net Worth: $33,022,890
Earnings: ($5,231,891)
Emp.: 352
Fiscal Year-end: 12/31/23
Graphic & Multimedia Design Services
N.A.I.C.S.: 541430
Kun-Shan Lu *(Founder, Chm & CEO)*

LEADTREND TECHNOLOGY CORP.
Floor 4 1 No 1 Taiyuan 2nd Street, Hsinchu County, Zhubei, 302, Taiwan

LEADTREND TECHNOLOGY CORP.

Tel.: (886) 35543588
Web Site:
 http://www.leadtrend.com.tw
Year Founded: 2002
3588—(TAI)
Rev.: $38,221,131
Assets: $61,417,605
Liabilities: $7,689,198
Net Worth: $53,728,406
Earnings: $943,916
Emp.: 180
Fiscal Year-end: 12/31/23
Power Regulator Mfr
N.A.I.C.S.: 333613
Yu-Kun Kao *(Pres-Interim & VP)*

LEADWAY ASSURANCE COMPANY LIMITED

121/123 Funso Williams Avenue, Iponri Surulere, Lagos, Nigeria
Tel.: (234) 1 270 0700
Web Site: http://www.leadway.com
Year Founded: 1970
Sales Range: $25-49.9 Million
Emp.: 300
Commercial, Personal & Life Insurance Services; Financial Services
N.A.I.C.S.: 524113
Oye Hassan-Odukale *(CEO & Mng Dir)*

LEADWAY TECHNOLOGY INVESTMENT GROUP LIMITED

Units 4108 - 4110 41st Floor Manhattan Place 23 Wang Tai Road, Kowloon, China (Hong Kong)
Tel.: (852) 82008188   Ky
Web Site: http://www.hnatechinv.com
Year Founded: 1995
2086—(HKG)
Rev.: $12,014,835
Assets: $12,978,225
Liabilities: $3,042,023
Net Worth: $9,936,203
Earnings: $143,565
Emp.: 122
Fiscal Year-end: 12/31/22
Holding Company; Card & Reader Technologies
N.A.I.C.S.: 551112
Chi Wong *(Exec Dir)*

LEAF CLEAN ENERGY COMPANY

Ugland House, PO Box 309, Georgetown, KY1-1104, Grand Cayman, Cayman Islands
Tel.: (345) 949 8066
Web Site:
 http://www.leafcleanenergy.com
Year Founded: 2007
LEAF—(AIM)
Sales Range: Less than $1 Million
Alternative Fuels, Renewable Power Generation & Other Environmentally Safe Technologies
N.A.I.C.S.: 221118
Jim Potochny *(CFO)*

Subsidiaries:

Johnstown Regional Energy LLC   (1)
368 Sandplant Rd, Cairnbrook, PA 15924
Tel.: (814) 754-5801
Natural Gas Distribution Services
N.A.I.C.S.: 221210

Telogia Power LLC   (1)
20082 Telogia Power Rd Hwy 65, Bristol, FL 32360
Tel.: (850) 379-8341
Eletric Power Generation Services
N.A.I.C.S.: 221118

LEAF MOBILE, INC.

2080-1055 West Georgia Street, Vancouver, V6E 3R5, BC, Canada

Tel.: (604) 288-4417
Web Site: http://www.leafmobile.io
LEAF—(TSXV)
Rev.: $6,183,996
Assets: $11,597,985
Liabilities: $4,118,269
Net Worth: $7,479,716
Earnings: ($141,508)
Fiscal Year-end: 06/30/20
Software Development Services
N.A.I.C.S.: 541511
Darcy Taylor *(Co-Founder & CEO)*

LEAF RESOURCES LIMITED

Suite 7/1 Westlink Court, Darra, Brisbane, 4076, QLD, Australia
Tel.: (61) 731889040   AU
Web Site:
 http://www.leafresources.com.au
LER—(ASX)
Rev.: $138,773
Assets: $9,762,843
Liabilities: $4,638,017
Net Worth: $5,124,826
Earnings: ($4,621,860)
Fiscal Year-end: 06/30/22
Plant Biomass Products Mfr
N.A.I.C.S.: 325414
Alex Baker *(Mng Dir)*

LEAGAS DELANEY LIMITED

1 Alfred Place, London, WC1E 7EB, United Kingdom
Tel.: (44) 207 758 1758   UK
Web Site:
 http://www.leagasdelaney.co.uk
Year Founded: 1980
Sales Range: $300-349.9 Million
Emp.: 60
Holding Company; Advertising Services
N.A.I.C.S.: 551112

Subsidiaries:

Leagas Delaney Hamburg
GmbH   (1)
Einseuetteler Strass 64, 22769, Hamburg, Germany
Tel.: (49) 40 54 80 40
Web Site: http://www.leagasdelaney.de
Emp.: 55
Advertising Services
N.A.I.C.S.: 541810
Hermann Waterkamp *(Owner)*

Leagas Delaney Italia S.r.l.   (1)
Via Pontaccio 12, 20121, Milan, Italy
Tel.: (39) 02 85 46 471
Web Site: http://www.leagasdelaney.it
Emp.: 21
Advertising Services
N.A.I.C.S.: 541810

Leagas Delaney London Limited   (1)
1 Alfred Place, London, WC1E 7EB, United Kingdom
Tel.: (44) 20 7758 1758
Web Site: http://www.leagasdelaney.co.uk
Advetising Agency
N.A.I.C.S.: 541810
Tim Delaney *(Founder, Chm & Exec Creative Dir)*

Leagas Delaney Shanghai Co., Ltd.   (1)
Anfu No 288 16F, Shanghai, 200031, China
Tel.: (86) 21 64371878
Web Site: http://www.leagasdelaney.cn
Advertising Agency Services
N.A.I.C.S.: 541810
Kien Lim *(Mng Partner)*

Leagas Delaney Tokyo   (1)
8F Pacific Century Place 1-11-1 Marunouchi, Chiyoda-Ku, Tokyo, 100-6208, Japan
Tel.: (81) 3 6860 8324
Web Site: http://www.leagasdelaney.jp
Advetising Agency
N.A.I.C.S.: 541810
Brian Shaw *(Chm)*

Leagas Delaney USA Inc.   (1)

11400 West Olympic Blvd Ste 330, Los Angeles, CA 90064
Tel.: (310) 266-3048
Web Site: http://www.leagasdelaney.us
Advertising Services
N.A.I.C.S.: 541810
Maria Escandon *(CEO & Mng Partner)*

LEAGUE PIPELINE SERVICES LTD.

PO Box 2198, Brooks, T1R 1C8, AB, Canada
Tel.: (403) 793-2648
Web Site:
 http://www.leaguepipeline.ca
Rev.: $25,822,650
Emp.: 130
Pipeline & Facility Services
N.A.I.C.S.: 213112
Bob Kubinchak *(Co-Owner & CEO)*

LEAGUER SHENZHEN MICRO-ELECTRONICS CORP.

1101 11F Research Building Tsinghua Information Port, High-tech Industrial Park Xili Subdistrict Nanshan District, Shenzhen, 518057, Guangdong, China
Tel.: (86) 75526719968
Web Site:
 https://www.leaguerme.com
Year Founded: 2002
688589—(SHG)
Rev.: $70,736,735
Assets: $145,235,488
Liabilities: $30,616,242
Net Worth: $114,619,247
Earnings: $10,540,263
Fiscal Year-end: 12/31/22
Electronic Product Mfr & Distr
N.A.I.C.S.: 334419
Zhen He *(Chm)*

LEAHY ORCHARDS INC.

1772, Route 209, Grande-Riviere, J0S 1E0, QC, Canada
Tel.: (450) 827-2544
Web Site: http://www.appleshax.com
Year Founded: 1979
Rev.: $26,060,239
Emp.: 210
Fruit & Vegetable Canning
N.A.I.C.S.: 311421
Doug Anderson *(VP-Sls & Mktg)*

LEALEA ENTERPRISE CO., LTD.

11F No 162 Songjiang Rd, Zhongshan Dist, Taipei, 104, Taiwan
Tel.: (886) 221001188
Web Site:
 https://www.lealeagroup.com.tw
Year Founded: 1979
1444—(TAI)
Rev.: $266,493,760
Assets: $624,960,538
Liabilities: $234,261,183
Net Worth: $390,699,354
Earnings: ($10,303,280)
Emp.: 1,041
Fiscal Year-end: 12/31/23
Polyester Filament Mfr & Distr
N.A.I.C.S.: 325220

LEALEA HOTELS & RESORTS CO., LTD.

3F No 162 Songjiang Road, Taipei, 104, Taiwan
Tel.: (886) 225152128
Web Site:
 https://www.lealeahotel.com
5364—(TPE)
Rev.: $12,499,922
Assets: $31,348,560
Liabilities: $20,678,892
Net Worth: $10,669,668
Earnings: ($1,283,682)

Fiscal Year-end: 12/31/22
Hotel Operator
N.A.I.C.S.: 721110
Tsai Chung *(Chm & CEO)*

LEANLIFE HEALTH INC.

580 Hornby Street Suite 380, Vancouver, V6C 3B6, BC, Canada
Tel.: (604) 674-2949   BC
Web Site:
 https://www.leanlifehealth.com
Year Founded: 2014
LLP—(CNSX)
Assets: $1,025,443
Liabilities: $842,279
Net Worth: $183,164
Earnings: ($2,925,308)
Fiscal Year-end: 03/31/21
Thermoplastic Sulphur Polymer Mfr
N.A.I.C.S.: 325199
Stan Lis *(CEO)*

LEAP HOLDINGS GROUP LTD.

Units 1-2 27/F Win Plaza 9 Sheung Hei Street, San Po Kong, Kowloon, China (Hong Kong)
Tel.: (852) 27147411   Ky
Web Site: http://www.leapholdings.hk
Holding Company
N.A.I.C.S.: 551112
Ying Chau Ip *(Co-Founder, Chm & CEO)*

LEAPING GROUP CO., LTD.

2010 Huaruntiexi Center Tiexi District, Shenyang, Liaoning, China
Tel.: (86) 2422598763   Ky
Web Site: http://www.yzcmmedia.cn
Year Founded: 2018
Rev.: $11,679,690
Assets: $11,099,020
Liabilities: $5,106,048
Net Worth: $5,992,972
Earnings: $5,188,919
Emp.: 50
Fiscal Year-end: 06/30/19
Holding Company
N.A.I.C.S.: 551112
Bo Jiang *(Chm)*

LEARN AFRICA PLC

52 Oba Akran Avenue, Ikeja, Lagos, Nigeria
Tel.: (234) 14393111
Web Site:
 https://www.learnafricaplc.com
LEARNAFRCA—(NIGE)
Rev.: $3,023,333
Assets: $3,599,429
Liabilities: $928,626
Net Worth: $2,670,803
Earnings: $8,286
Emp.: 176
Fiscal Year-end: 03/31/24
Educational Book Publisher
N.A.I.C.S.: 611710

LEARNING EDGE ACADEMY OF PROFESSIONALS LTD.

82 LGF Sukhdev Vihar Near Sukhdev Vihar Bus Depot, New Delhi, 110 025, India
Tel.: (91) 9818324060
Web Site: http://www.learnedge.in
Year Founded: 2009
Educational Support Services
N.A.I.C.S.: 611710
Bhagwan Kewal Ramani *(Mng Dir)*

LEARNING TECHNOLOGIES GROUP PLC

3 New Street Square, London, EC4A 3BF, United Kingdom
Tel.: (44) 2078323440
Web Site: https://www.ltgplc.com

AND PRIVATE COMPANIES

LTG—(AIM)
Rev.: $753,473,870
Assets: $1,107,326,433
Liabilities: $569,204,746
Net Worth: $538,121,686
Earnings: $38,381,722
Emp.: 5,000
Fiscal Year-end: 12/31/22
E-Learning Services & Technologies
N.A.I.C.S.: 541519
Jonathan Satchell *(CEO)*

Subsidiaries:

Epic Group (1)
52 Old Steine, Brighton, BN1 1NH, E Sussex, United Kingdom
Tel.: (44) 1273728686
Web Site: http://www.epic.co.uk
Sales Range: $25-49.9 Million
Emp.: 143
E-learning & Knowledge Solutions
N.A.I.C.S.: 611710

Subsidiary (US):

Epic Learning Inc. (2)
11 Broadway Ste 466, New York, NY 10004
Tel.: (212) 574-8233
Web Site: http://www.epiclearninggroup.com
Online Learning Software Development Services
N.A.I.C.S.: 541511

Subsidiary (Non-US):

LEO Learning Brasil (2)
Av Journalist Ricardo Marinho 360 room 301, Barra da Tijuca, Rio de Janeiro, 22631-350, Brazil
Tel.: (55) 95 686 7514
Web Site: https://leolearning.com.br
Online Learning Services
N.A.I.C.S.: 513199

Eukleia Training Limited (1)
15 Fetter Lane, London, EC4A 1BW, United Kingdom
Tel.: (44) 207 832 3440
Web Site: http://www.eukleia.com
Professional Training & Coaching Services
N.A.I.C.S.: 611430

GP Strategies Corporation (1)
70 Corporate Ctr 11000 Broken Land Pkwy Ste 200, Columbia, MD 21044
Tel.: (443) 367-9600
Web Site: http://www.gpstrategies.com
Rev.: $473,107,000
Assets: $381,776,000
Liabilities: $158,430,000
Net Worth: $223,346,000
Earnings: $7,068,000
Emp.: 4,343
Fiscal Year-end: 12/31/2020
Training, E-Learning Solutions, Management Consulting & Engineering Service
N.A.I.C.S.: 541611
Don Duquette *(Exec VP)*

Subsidiary (Non-US):

Effective People A/S (2)
Lerso Parkalle 107, 2100, Copenhagen, Denmark
Tel.: (45) 70702601
Web Site: http://www.effective-learning.com
Educational Support Services
N.A.I.C.S.: 611710

Subsidiary (Domestic):

Emantras, Inc. (2)
41350 Christy St, Fremont, CA 94538
Tel.: (813) 997-5254
Web Site: http://www.emantras.com
Educational Support Services
N.A.I.C.S.: 611710

Subsidiary (Non-US):

GP Strategies (Hong Kong) Limited (2)
Level 19 Cheung Kong Center 2 Queen's Road, Central, China (Hong Kong)
Tel.: (852) 34695010
Management Consulting Services
N.A.I.C.S.: 541611

GP Strategies (India) Pvt. Limited (2)
No 4/363 Kandanchavadi Old Mahabalipuram Road, Block B 1st & 2nd Floor Behind Max Showroom, Chennai, 600096, Tamil Nadu, India
Tel.: (91) 4466525516
Emp.: 100
Management Consulting Services
N.A.I.C.S.: 541612

GP Strategies (Shanghai) Co., Ltd. (2)
20 Ally 1228 Jiangchang Road Unit 501 Jing an District, Jinjiang Xiangyang Building, Shanghai, 200072, China
Tel.: (86) 2156297100
Sales Range: $25-49.9 Million
Emp.: 6
Management Consulting Services
N.A.I.C.S.: 541612
Roxanne Filaseta *(Gen Mgr-Asia Pacific)*

Branch (Domestic):

GP Strategies Corp. - Alexandria (2)
810 King St 2, Alexandria, VA 22314
Tel.: (703) 548-0320
Web Site: http://www.gpstrategies.com
Management Consulting Services
N.A.I.C.S.: 541612

Subsidiary (Non-US):

GP Strategies Danyimanlyk Limited Sirketi (2)
Hakki Yeten Cad Selenium Plaza No 10/C K 5 Fulya, Besiktas, 34349, Istanbul, Turkiye
Tel.: (90) 2123818746
Administrative Management Consulting Services
N.A.I.C.S.: 541611

GP Strategies Ltd. (2)
First Floor 266 Kings Court Solihull Parkway, The Crescent Birmingham Business Park, Solihull, B37 7YE, West Midlands, United Kingdom
Tel.: (44) 1212812700
Web Site: http://www.gpstrategies.com
Information Technology Training Services
N.A.I.C.S.: 611710

GP Strategies Malaysia Sdn Bhd (2)
Tel.: (60) 341418228
Management Consulting Services
N.A.I.C.S.: 541612

GP Strategies Nordic A/S (2)
Oster Alle 56 1 Th, 2100, Copenhagen, Denmark
Tel.: (45) 70702601
Educational Support Services
N.A.I.C.S.: 611710

GP Strategies Poland sp. z.o.o (2)
Ocean Office Park Building A 4th floor Pana Tadeusza 2, 30-727, Krakow, Poland
Tel.: (48) 122251421
Construction Engineering Services
N.A.I.C.S.: 541330

GP Strategies Singapore (Asia) Pte. Ltd. (2)
18 Robinson Road Level 02-03, Singapore, 048547, Singapore
Tel.: (65) 69557827
Management Consulting Services
N.A.I.C.S.: 541612

GP Strategies Switzerland GmbH (2)
Innere Margarethenstrasse 5 5th Floor, Basel, 4051, Switzerland
Tel.: (41) 612044555
Management Consulting Services
N.A.I.C.S.: 541611

GP Strategies Training Ltd (2)
Floor 4A Kingsgate Wellington Road North, Stockport, SK4 1LW, Cheshire, United Kingdom
Tel.: (44) 3301000610
Web Site: http://www.gpstl-apprenticeships.co.uk
Emp.: 250
Information Technology Training Services
N.A.I.C.S.: 611710

General Physics (UK) Ltd. (2)
Unit 2 Bredbury Business Park Bredbury Parkway, Bredbury, Stockport, SK6 2SN, United Kingdom
Tel.: (44) 1614064880
Educational Support Services
N.A.I.C.S.: 611710

TTI Peru S.A.C. (2)
German Schreiber 291 Oficina 301, Santiago de Surco, Lima, Peru
Tel.: (51) 12753478
Web Site: http://www.ttiperu.com
Web Hosting Services
N.A.I.C.S.: 518210

Subsidiary (Domestic):

TTi Global (2)
6001 N Adams Ste 185, Bloomfield Hills, MI 48304
Tel.: (248) 853-5550
Web Site: http://www.tti-global.com
Recruitment Services; Training, Staffing & Consulting
N.A.I.C.S.: 561311

Learning Technologies Group (Hong Kong) Limited (1)
18/F Siu On Centre 188 Lockhart Road, Wanchai, China (Hong Kong) **(100%)**
Tel.: (852) 3615 0366
Educational & Training Software Publisher
N.A.I.C.S.: 513210

Learning Technologies Group GmbH (1)
Dieningholt 9, 59387, Ascheberg, Germany **(100%)**
Tel.: (49) 25939299297
Educational & Training Software Publisher
N.A.I.C.S.: 513210

Learning Technologies Group Pty Limited (1)
19 Northcote Street, Haberfield, Sydney, 2045, NSW, Australia **(100%)**
Tel.: (61) 2 9798 0894
Educational & Training Software Publisher
N.A.I.C.S.: 513210

Leo Learning Limited (1)
52 Old Steine, Brighton, BN1 1NH, East Sussex, United Kingdom
Tel.: (44) 1273728686
Web Site: http://leolearning.com
Professional Training & Coaching Services
N.A.I.C.S.: 611430
James Greenwood *(Mng Dir)*

PeopleFluent Inc. (1)
300 5th Ave, Waltham, MA 02451
Tel.: (781) 530-2000
Web Site: http://www.peoplefluent.com
Talent Acquisition & Workforce Compliance Software & Consulting Services
N.A.I.C.S.: 513210
Stephen Bruce *(Mng Dir)*

Subsidiary (Non-US):

NetDimensions (Holdings) Limited (2)
18/F Siu On Centre 188 Lockhart Road, Wanchai, China (Hong Kong)
Tel.: (852) 3615 0366
Holding Company; Educational & Training Software Publisher
N.A.I.C.S.: 551112

Subsidiary (Non-US):

NetDimensions (UK) Limited (3)
15 Fetter Lane, London, EC4A 1BW, United Kingdom
Tel.: (44) 20 7832 3440
Educational & Training Software Publisher
N.A.I.C.S.: 513210

Subsidiary (US):

NetDimensions, Inc. (3)
434 Fayetteville St 9th Fl, Raleigh, NC 27601
Tel.: (919) 645-2800
Educational & Training Software Publisher
N.A.I.C.S.: 513210

Subsidiary (Domestic):

PeopleFluent, Inc. - Raleigh (2)
434 Fayetteville St, Raleigh, NC 27601
Tel.: (919) 645-2800
Talent Acquisition & Workforce Compliance Software & Consulting Services
N.A.I.C.S.: 513210

Preloaded Limited (1)
The Arts Building Morris Place Finsbury Park, London, N4 3JG, United Kingdom
Tel.: (44) 2076843505
Web Site: https://www.preloaded.com
Sales Range: $1-9.9 Million
Computer Games Developer
N.A.I.C.S.: 513210

Rustici Software LLC. (1)
210 Gothic Ct Ste 100, Franklin, TN 37067
Tel.: (615) 376-9867
Web Site: https://rusticisoftware.com
Sales Range: $1-9.9 Million
Emp.: 19
Software Product Development Services
N.A.I.C.S.: 541511

Watershed Systems, Inc. (1)
210 Gothic Ct Ste 100, Franklin, TN 37067
Web Site: https://www.watershedlrs.com
Software Development Services
N.A.I.C.S.: 541511
Mike Rustici *(Founder)*

getBridge LLC (1)
10961 S River Front Pkwy, South Jordan, UT 84095
Tel.: (214) 687-5725
Web Site: https://www.getbridge.com
Professional Development Training Services
N.A.I.C.S.: 611430

LEASE OPERATORS LIMITED

Otaheite Industrial Park, South Oropouche, Trinidad & Tobago
Tel.: (868) 6777531
Year Founded: 1988
Oil & Gas Exploration Services
N.A.I.C.S.: 211130
Christopher Brash *(CTO)*

Subsidiaries:

Trinity Exploration & Production plc (1)
3rd Floor Southern Supplies Limited Building 40-44 Sutton Street, PO Box 3519, La Romain, San Fernando, Trinidad & Tobago
Tel.: (868) 6120067
Web Site: https://www.trinityexploration.com
Rev.: $69,826,000
Assets: $114,123,000
Liabilities: $65,078,000
Net Worth: $49,045,000
Earnings: ($6,804,000)
Emp.: 281
Fiscal Year-end: 12/31/2023
Oil & Gas Exploration Services
N.A.I.C.S.: 211120
Bruce Alan Ian Dingwall *(Chm)*

LEASING GROUP JSC

pr Al-Farabi house 17/1 PFC Block 5B n/p, Bostandyk district, 050059, Almaty, Kazakhstan
Tel.: (7) 273111548
Web Site: https://www.lease.kz
Year Founded: 2005
LZGR—(KAZ)
Assets: $44,503,584
Liabilities: $27,586,434
Net Worth: $16,917,150
Earnings: $2,206,613
Fiscal Year-end: 12/31/23
Equipment Leasing Services
N.A.I.C.S.: 532412
Ravil Kabdolrahimov *(Chm)*

LEASING KHODRO GHADIR CO.

No 11 Ostad Motahari Ave, Tehran, Iran
Tel.: (98) 21 88835629
Financial Lending Services
N.A.I.C.S.: 522390
Siamak Chaman Zibaiee *(Chm)*

LEASING TOTAL S.A.

Leasing khodro Ghadir Co.—(Continued)

LEASING TOTAL S.A.
Av Jose Pardo N 231 Piso 13, Miraflores, Lima, Peru
Tel.: (51) 710 2300
Web Site:
http://www.leasingtotal.com.pe
Year Founded: 1997
Financial Lending Services
N.A.I.C.S.: 522320

LEATEC FINE CERAMICS CO., LTD.
No 160 Sec 1 Pingdong Rd, Pingzhen Dist, Taoyuan, 32473, Taiwan
Tel.: (886) 34507531
Web Site: https://www.leatec.com
Year Founded: 1991
6127—(TPE)
Rev.: $24,497,764
Assets: $107,624,050
Liabilities: $72,076,572
Net Worth: $35,547,478
Earnings: ($1,046,681)
Emp.: 395
Fiscal Year-end: 12/31/22
Ceramic Materials Mfr
N.A.I.C.S.: 327110
Chen Qing-Jin (Pres)

Subsidiaries:

LEATEC Fine Ceramics (Kunshan) Co., Ltd. (1)
No 1 Yinxing Road Zhengyi, Kunshan, Jiang Su, China
Tel.: (86) 51257898888
Alumina Chip Resistor Mfr
N.A.I.C.S.: 334416

LEATHER UP LIMITED
23-C 15th Commercial Street Phase-II Extension DHA, Karachi, Pakistan
Tel.: (92) 21358986417
Web Site:
https://www.leatherupltd.com
LEUL—(PSX)
Rev.: $97,696
Assets: $158,923
Liabilities: $87,737
Net Worth: $71,186
Earnings: ($11,830)
Emp.: 4
Fiscal Year-end: 06/30/23
Leather Goods Distr
N.A.I.C.S.: 458320
Khalid H. Shah (CEO)

LEATT CORPORATION
12 Kiepersol Drive Atlas Gardens Contermanskloof Road, Durbanville, 7550, Western Cape, South Africa
Tel.: (27) 215577257
Web Site: https://www.leatt-corp.com
Year Founded: 2005
LEAT—(OTCQB)
Rev.: $47,241,187
Assets: $47,607,372
Liabilities: $7,326,848
Net Worth: $40,280,524
Earnings: $803,159
Emp.: 89
Fiscal Year-end: 12/31/23
Protective Equipment Mfr & Whslr
N.A.I.C.S.: 339920
Christopher James Leatt (Chm & Head-R&D)

LEAVENS VOLKSWAGEN INC.
2360 Auto Mall Avenue, London, N5V 0B4, ON, Canada
Tel.: (519) 455-2580
Web Site:
https://www.leavensvw.com
Year Founded: 1958

New & Used Car Dealers
N.A.I.C.S.: 441110
Ed Leavens (Founder)

LEAVITT MACHINERY LTD.
102 19433 96th Ave, Surrey, V4N 4C4, BC, Canada
Tel.: (604) 607-8000
Web Site:
http://www.leavittmachinery.com
Year Founded: 2001
Rents, Sells & Services New & Used Materials Handling Equipment & Parts
N.A.I.C.S.: 423830
Tom Leavitt (Pre & CEO)

LEAX GROUP AB
Nya Hamnvagen 4, Koping, 731 36, Sweden
Tel.: (46) 22134600
Web Site: http://www.leax.com
Year Founded: 1982
Sales Range: $50-74.9 Million
Emp.: 1,300
Mechanical & Electromechanical Products for Vehicle, Power Generation & Construction & Mining Industries Mfr
N.A.I.C.S.: 333613
Frank Johansen (VP-New Bus & Innovation)

Subsidiaries:

LEAX Arkivator Sweden AB (1)
Goteborgsvagen 5, PO Box 743, 521 22, Falkoping, Sweden
Tel.: (46) 515 72 36 00
Industrial Supplies Whslr
N.A.I.C.S.: 423840
Thomas Wikman (Mng Dir)

LEAX Arkivator Telecom AB (1)
Stridsvagnsvagen 14, 291 39, Kristianstad, Sweden
Tel.: (46) 8 752 02 20
Telecommunication Servicesb
N.A.I.C.S.: 517810
Fredrik Ulin (VP-Sls)

LEAX Hungary Zrt. (1)
Szihalmi ut 7, 3400, Mezokovesd, Hungary
Tel.: (36) 49 505 400
Industrial Supplies Whslr
N.A.I.C.S.: 423840
Andras Farkas (Mng Dir)

LEAX Industry (Kunshan) Co., Ltd. (1)
78 Changyang Road, Yushan, 215300, Kunshan, China
Tel.: (86) 512 50178500
Industrial Supplies Whslr
N.A.I.C.S.: 423840
Shpetim Arifi (Mng Dir)

LEAX Rezekne SIA (1)
Tevini Ozolaines Pagasts, 4601, Rezekne, Latvia
Tel.: (371) 646 38 078
Web Site: http://www.leax.com
Industrial Supplies Whslr
N.A.I.C.S.: 423840
Gints Jacuks (Plant Mgr)

LEAX do Brasil Ltda. (1)
Rua Francisco Galarda 333, Capela Velha, 83706-493, Araucaria, Parana, Brazil
Tel.: (55) 41 3079 7583
Industrial Supplies Whslr
N.A.I.C.S.: 423840
Bernardino Sena (Mng Dir)

Leax Baltix SIA (1)
Vecpagrabs p/n Pinki, Babites Pagasts, LV-2107, Riga, Latvia (100%)
Tel.: (371) 67490950
Web Site: http://www.leax.lv
Sales Range: $25-49.9 Million
Emp.: 70
Mechanical Power Transmission Equipment Mfr
N.A.I.C.S.: 333613
Peter Luberts (Mng Dir)

Leax Brinkmann GmbH (1)
Remmighauser Strasse 85, 32760, Detmold, Germany
Tel.: (49) 5231 562 0
Web Site: http://www.leax-brinkmann.de
Industrial Supplies Whslr
N.A.I.C.S.: 423840
Ingmar Sandahl (Mgr)

Leax Components AB (1)
Svetsarevagen 2, 771 42, Ludvika, Sweden (100%)
Tel.: (46) 24059100
Web Site: http://www.leax.se
Mechanical Power Transmission Equipment Mfr
N.A.I.C.S.: 333613

Leax Falun AB (1)
Frambyvagen 30, 79152, Falun, Sweden (100%)
Tel.: (46) 23775601
Web Site: http://www.leax.se
Mechanical Power Transmission Equipment Mfr
N.A.I.C.S.: 333613
Hans Jansson (Pres)

Leax Mekaniska AB (1)
Nya Hamnvagen 4, Koping, 73136, Sweden (100%)
Tel.: (46) 22134600
Web Site: http://www.leax.se
Sales Range: $50-74.9 Million
Emp.: 500
Mechanical Power Transmission Equipment Mfr
N.A.I.C.S.: 333613
Roger Berggren (Mng Dir)

Leax Quality AB (1)
Nya Hamnvagen 4, Koping, 73139, Sweden (100%)
Tel.: (46) 22134600
Web Site: http://www.leax.com
Sales Range: $50-74.9 Million
Emp.: 200
Mechanical Power Transmission Equipment Mfr
N.A.I.C.S.: 333613
Roger Berggrem (Mng Dir)

LEBTECH BERHAD
Wisma Lebar Daun No 2 Jalan Tengku Ampuan Zabedah J9/J, Seksyen 9, 40000, Shah Alam, Selangor, Malaysia
Tel.: (60) 355111333
Web Site:
https://www.lebtech.com.my
Year Founded: 2002
9628—(KLS)
Rev.: $4,269,250
Assets: $36,239,864
Liabilities: $11,598,149
Net Worth: $24,641,715
Earnings: $8,061
Emp.: 33
Fiscal Year-end: 12/31/22
Investment Holding Company
N.A.I.C.S.: 523999
Norazmi Mohamed Nurdin (Mng Dir)

LEC, INC.
Kyobashi Trust Tower 8F 2-1-3 Kyobashi, Chuo-Ku, Tokyo, 104-0031, Japan
Tel.: (81) 335272650
Web Site: https://www.lecinc.co.jp
Year Founded: 1979
7874—(TKS)
Rev.: $401,775,630
Assets: $589,902,840
Liabilities: $341,413,110
Net Worth: $248,489,730
Earnings: $5,261,560
Emp.: 928
Fiscal Year-end: 03/31/24
Household Utensil Mfr & Whslr
N.A.I.C.S.: 332215
Takaki Nagamori (Pres)

LECHE GLORIA S.A.

Av Republica de Panama 2461 Urb, Santa Catalina La Victoria, Lima, Peru
Tel.: (51) 4707170
Web Site: http://www.gloria.com.pe
Year Founded: 1941
GLORIAI1—(LIM)
Rev.: $1,447,054,489
Assets: $1,194,497,341
Liabilities: $718,268,156
Net Worth: $476,229,185
Earnings: $52,535,017
Fiscal Year-end: 12/31/23
Dairy Product Mfr & Distr
N.A.I.C.S.: 311514
Jorge Columbo Rodriguez (Chm)

LECHLER GMBH
Ulmer Strasse 128, 72555, Metzingen, Germany
Tel.: (49) 71239620
Web Site: https://www.lechler.com
Year Founded: 1928
Sales Range: $75-99.9 Million
Emp.: 470
Precision Spray Nozzles & Demister Mfr
N.A.I.C.S.: 332919
Guido Kunzmann (Mng Dir)

Subsidiaries:

Lechler (Tianjin) International Trading Company Ltd. (1)
Room 418 Landmark Tower 2 8 Dong San Huan Bei Lu, Beijing, 100004, China
Tel.: (86) 10 84537968
Web Site: http://www.lechler.com.cn
Emp.: 35
Spray Nozzle Mfr
N.A.I.C.S.: 332919
Ryan Xu (Engr-Sls)

Lechler AB (1)
Sparrgatan 8, 653 41, Karlstad, Sweden
Tel.: (46) 54 137030
Web Site: http://www.lechler.se
Spray Nozzle Distr
N.A.I.C.S.: 423840

Lechler France S.A (1)
Immeuble CAP2 B51 66-72 rue Marceau, 93558, Montreuil, France
Tel.: (33) 1 49 88 26 00
Web Site: http://www.lechler.fr
Spray Nozzle Distr
N.A.I.C.S.: 423840

Lechler India Pvt. Ltd. (1)
Plot B-2 Main Road Wagle Industrial Estate, Thane, 400604, Maharashtra, India
Tel.: (91) 22 40634444
Web Site: http://www.lechler.in
Emp.: 160
Spray Nozzle Mfr
N.A.I.C.S.: 332919
Suresh Vasani (Mng Dir)

Lechler Ltd. (1)
1 Fell Street, Newhall, Sheffield, S9 2TP, United Kingdom
Tel.: (44) 114 249 2020
Web Site: http://www.lechler.co.uk
Emp.: 34
Spray Nozzle Mfr
N.A.I.C.S.: 332919
Craig Burgess (Mng Dir)

Lechler Oy (1)
Jaspilankatu 18, 04250, Kerava, Finland
Tel.: (358) 207 856 882
Spray Nozzle Distr
N.A.I.C.S.: 423840

Lechler S.A./N.V. (1)
Avenue Mercator 6, 1300, Wavre, Belgium
Tel.: (32) 10 225022
Spray Nozzle Distr
N.A.I.C.S.: 423840

Lechler, Inc. (1)
445 Kautz Rd, Saint Charles, IL 60174-5301
Tel.: (630) 377-6611
Web Site: http://www.lechler.com

AND PRIVATE COMPANIES

Sales Range: $1-9.9 Million
Emp.: 70
Industrial Spray Nozzles & Systems Mfr
N.A.I.C.S.: 332919
Adolf Pfeiffer (Pres & CEO)

Lechler, S.A. (1)
Avda Pirineos 7 - Oficina B7 Edificio IN-BISA I, San Sebastian de los Reyes, 28700, Madrid, Spain
Tel.: (34) 91 658 6346
Web Site: http://www.lechler.com
Spray Nozzle Distr
N.A.I.C.S.: 423840

LECICO EGYPT S.A.E.
PO Box 358, Alexandria, Egypt
Tel.: (20) 35180011 EG
Web Site:
https://www.lecicoegypt.com
Year Founded: 1959
LCSW—(EGX)
Rev.: $156,690,618
Assets: $176,507,274
Liabilities: $103,328,719
Net Worth: $73,178,555
Earnings: $15,301,076
Emp.: 6,000
Fiscal Year-end: 12/31/23
Tile & Sanitary Ware Mfr
N.A.I.C.S.: 332999
Gilbert Gargour (Chm)

Subsidiaries:

International Ceramics S.A.E. (1)
3rd Industrial Zone Block 25 Plot 2, New Borg El Arab, Alexandria, Egypt
Tel.: (20) 34598911
Ceramic Tile Mfr
N.A.I.C.S.: 327120

Lecico (UK) Ltd. (1)
37 Thurloe Street, London, SW7 2LQ, United Kingdom
Tel.: (44) 2075815711
Sales Range: $50-74.9 Million
Emp.: 4
Investment Management Service
N.A.I.C.S.: 523940
Taher Gargour (CEO)

Subsidiary (Non-US):

Lecico France SARL (2)
12 Avenue De La Republique, 51300, Vitry-le-Francois, France
Tel.: (33) 326741563
Sanitaryware Distr
N.A.I.C.S.: 423720

Lecico Poland (2)
ul Warszawska 187 lok 5, Minsk Mazowiecki, 05-300, Warsaw, Poland
Tel.: (48) 257595400
Sanitaryware Distr
N.A.I.C.S.: 423720

The Lebanese Ceramics Industries (S.A.L.) (1)
Lecico Building Warwar Area, Kfarshima, Lebanon
Tel.: (961) 5434222
Sales Range: $100-124.9 Million
Emp.: 40
Sanitary Ware Mfr
N.A.I.C.S.: 332999
Koji Hayashi (Gen Mgr)

LECIP HOLDINGS CORPORATION
1260-2 Kaminoho Motosu, Gifu, 501-0401, Japan
Tel.: (81) 583243121
Web Site: https://www.lecip.co.jp
Year Founded: 1953
7210—(NGO)
Rev.: $149,881,947
Assets: $131,804,879
Liabilities: $86,337,716
Net Worth: $45,467,163
Earnings: $15,967,164
Emp.: 600
Fiscal Year-end: 03/31/24

Neon Transformers & Interior Fluorescent Lighting Mfr for Buses
N.A.I.C.S.: 334416
Makoto Sugimoto (Pres & CEO)

Subsidiaries:

Gifu DS Operation Ltd. (1)
1260-2 Kaminoho, Motosu, 501-0401, Gifu, Japan
Tel.: (81) 583236283
Electric Equipment Mfr
N.A.I.C.S.: 335999

Lecip (Singapore) Pte Ltd (1)
1 Yishun Industrial Street 1 05-09 A Posh Bizhub, Singapore, 768160, Singapore
Tel.: (65) 65079680
Web Site: https://www.lecip.sg
Electrical Equipment Distr
N.A.I.C.S.: 423610

Lecip Arcontia AB (1)
Krokslatts Fabriker 30, 431 37, Molndal, Sweden
Tel.: (46) 3 149 9930
Web Site: https://leciparcontia.se
Peripheral Equipment Mfr
N.A.I.C.S.: 334118

Lecip Corporation (1)
1260-2 Kaminoho, Motosu, 501-0401, Gifu, Japan
Tel.: (81) 583243121
Electric Equipment Mfr
N.A.I.C.S.: 335999

Lecip Digital Signage Corporation (1)
1260-2 Kamiyasu, Motosu, 501-0401, Gifu, Japan
Tel.: (81) 583236283
Web Site: https://www.lecip.co.jp
Digital Sign Mfr
N.A.I.C.S.: 334515

Lecip Electronics Corporation (1)
1260-2 Kaminoho, Motosu, 501-0401, Gifu, Japan
Tel.: (81) 583233911
Electric Equipment Mfr
N.A.I.C.S.: 335999

Lecip Engineering Corporation (1)
1260-2 Kaminoho, Motosu, 501-0401, Gifu, Japan
Tel.: (81) 583236053
Electric Equipment Mfr
N.A.I.C.S.: 335999

Lecip Inc. (1)
881 IL Route 83, Bensenville, IL 60106
Tel.: (312) 626-2525
Electrical Equipment Distr
N.A.I.C.S.: 423610

Lecip SLP Corporation (1)
1260-2 Kaminoho, Motosu, 501-0401, Gifu, Japan
Tel.: (81) 583235766
Electric Equipment Mfr
N.A.I.C.S.: 335999

Lecip Sangyo Ltd. (1)
1260-2 Kaminoho, Motosu, 501-0401, Gifu, Japan
Tel.: (81) 583235155
Electric Equipment Mfr
N.A.I.C.S.: 335999

Lecip Thai Co., Ltd. (1)
18/8 Fico Place Building 5th Floor Sukhumvit 21 Asoke Road, KhlongtoeiNuea Watthana, Bangkok, 10110, Thailand
Tel.: (66) 26657317
Web Site: https://www.lecip.co.th
Electrical Equipment Distr
N.A.I.C.S.: 423610

LECRON INDUSTRIAL DEVELOPMENT GROUP CO., LTD.
Room 909 Block B Kechuang Building No 366 Huaguang Road, Zhangdian District, Zibo, 255000, Shandong, China
Tel.: (86) 5332752999
Web Site: https://www.lecron.cn
Year Founded: 2003

300343—(SSE)
Rev.: $266,338,732
Assets: $333,038,705
Liabilities: $208,577,030
Net Worth: $124,461,676
Earnings: ($13,387,490)
Fiscal Year-end: 12/31/20
Foam Polyether Products Mfr
N.A.I.C.S.: 326140
Li Hongpeng (Chm)

LECTRA SA
16-18 rue Chalgrin, 75016, Paris, France
Tel.: (33) 153644200
Web Site: https://www.lectra.com
LET—(DEU)
Rev.: $527,187,328
Assets: $893,275,196
Liabilities: $432,010,156
Net Worth: $461,265,040
Earnings: $36,002,870
Emp.: 2,578
Fiscal Year-end: 12/31/23
Mfr of Computer Aided Design & Computer Aided Manufacturing Systems
N.A.I.C.S.: 541511
Daniel Harari (Chm & CEO)

Subsidiaries:

A. Morante y Cia SA (1)
Las Agatas 189, 13, Lima, Peru (100%)
Tel.: (51) 4722872
Sales Range: $25-49.9 Million
Emp.: 30
Mfr of Computer Aided Design & Computer Aided Manufacturing Systems
N.A.I.C.S.: 541512

Gemini CAD Systems S.A. (1)
Tudor Vianu 2A street, 700490, Iasi, Romania
Tel.: (40) 232237546
Web Site: https://www.geminicad.com
Automotive Furniture Distr
N.A.I.C.S.: 441330

Lec Hellas SA (1)
31 Salaminos St, Nea Chalkidona, 14343, Athens, Greece
Tel.: (30) 210 258 9040
Web Site: https://www.lec.gr
Sales Range: $25-49.9 Million
Emp.: 10
Computer Aided Design & Computer Aided Manufacturing Systems Mfr
N.A.I.C.S.: 541512

Lectra (1)
Dendermondesteenweg 636, 9070, Destelbergen, Gent, Belgium (100%)
Tel.: (32) 92222026
Sales Range: $25-49.9 Million
Emp.: 25
Computer Aided Design & Computer Aided Manufacturing Systems Mfr
N.A.I.C.S.: 541512
Jean Patrice Gros (Gen Mgr)

Lectra Australia Pty Ltd (1)
Unit 18 104 Ferntree Gully Road, Victoria, 3166, VIC, Australia (100%)
Tel.: (61) 39 912 5499
Web Site: http://www.lectra.com
Sales Range: $25-49.9 Million
Emp.: 7
Computer Aided Design & Computer Aided Manufacturing Systems Mfr
N.A.I.C.S.: 541512

Lectra Baltic OU (1)
Tartu Mnt 173/2 Moigu, Peetri, Harju, Estonia
Tel.: (372) 6093390
Emp.: 10
Software Development Services
N.A.I.C.S.: 541511

Lectra Brasil Ltda (1)
Al Jau 1754 - 3 andar, Jardim Paulista, Sao Paulo, 01420-002, Brazil (100%)
Tel.: (55) 1138949144
Sales Range: $25-49.9 Million
Mfr of Computer Aided Design & Computer Aided Manufacturing Systems

N.A.I.C.S.: 541512

Division (Domestic):

Lectra (2)
Condominio Alameda Office Rua Coronel Vidal Ramos 01-sala 106, Vila Nova, Blumenau, 89010-330, SC, Brazil (100%)
Tel.: (55) 4733221222
Web Site: http://www.lectra.com
Mfr of Computer Aided Design & Computer Aided Manufacturing Systems
N.A.I.C.S.: 541512

Lectra Canada Inc (1)
3700-1 Place Ville-Marie, Montreal, H3B 3P4, QC, Canada (100%)
Tel.: (514) 383-4613
Sales Range: $25-49.9 Million
Mfr of Computer Aided Design & Computer Aided Manufacturing Systems
N.A.I.C.S.: 541512

Lectra Chile SA (1)
Av Santos Dumont 267 Correo Centra, PO Box 56, Recoleta, Santiago, Chile (99%)
Tel.: (56) 27356137
Sales Range: $25-49.9 Million
Emp.: 8
Mfr of Computer Aided Design & Computer Aided Manufacturing Systems
N.A.I.C.S.: 541512
Patricia Gutierrez (Mgr-Ops)

Lectra Danmark A/S (1)
Vestergade 41, 7400, Herning, Denmark (100%)
Tel.: (45) 97154966
Web Site: https://www.lectra.com
Sales Range: $25-49.9 Million
Emp.: 6
Computer Aided Design & Computer Aided Manufacturing Systems Mfr
N.A.I.C.S.: 541512

Lectra Deutschland GmbH (1)
Adalpero Strasse 80, 85737, Ismaning, Germany (100%)
Tel.: (49) 89996260
Sales Range: $200-249.9 Million
Emp.: 50
Computer Aided Design & Computer Aided Manufacturing Systems Mfr
N.A.I.C.S.: 541512
Chris Nicolaes (Mng Dir)

Lectra Hong Kong Ltd. (1)
Units 805B-806 8/F Tower B Manulife Financial Centre, Wai Yip Street KKT, Hong Kong, 223-231, China (Hong Kong) (100%)
Tel.: (852) 27225687
Web Site: https://www.lectra.com
Computer Aided Design & Computer Aided Manufacturing Systems Mfr
N.A.I.C.S.: 541512

Lectra Israel Ltd (1)
5 Arye Regev St, PO Box 8309, New Industrial Area, 42504, Netanya, Israel (100%)
Tel.: (972) 98355227
Sales Range: $25-49.9 Million
Computer Aided Design & Computer Aided Manufacturing Systems Mfr
N.A.I.C.S.: 541512
Ruthi Baron (Mgr-Admin)

Lectra Italia SpA (1)
Via Gaetano Crespi 12, 20134, Milan, Italy (100%)
Tel.: (39) 02210471
Web Site: https://www.lectra.com
Computer Aided Design & Computer Aided Manufacturing Systems mfr.
N.A.I.C.S.: 541512

Lectra Japan Ltd (1)
4F Nomura Fudousan Osaka Building 1-8-15 Azuchimachi, Chuo-ku, Osaka, 541-0052, Japan
Tel.: (81) 649641251
Computer Aided Design & Computer Aided Manufacturing Systems Mfr
N.A.I.C.S.: 541512
Akihiko Tanaka (Mng Dir)

Lectra Korea Ltd. (1)
Tel.: (82) 220262392
Information Technology Services
N.A.I.C.S.: 541511

LECTRA SA

Lectra SA—(Continued)

Lectra Maroc Sarl (1)
(19%)
Tel.: (212) 522774420
Web Site: https://www.lectra.com
Sales Range: $25-49.9 Million
Emp.: 100
Computer Aided Design & Computer Aided Manufacturing Systems Mfr
N.A.I.C.S.: 541512

Lectra Philippines Inc (1)
Unit 501 Prime Land Bldg Market St, Madrigal Business Park 2 Alabang, Muntinlupa, 1780, Manila, Philippines (99%)
Tel.: (63) 2 725 8693
Web Site: http://www.lectraglovines.com
Sales Range: Less than $1 Million
Emp.: 4
Computer Aided Design & Computer Aided Manufacturing Systems Mfr
N.A.I.C.S.: 541512

Lectra Portugal Lda (1)
Av Dr Antunes Guimaraes 521, 4450-621, Leca da Palmeira, Portugal (100%)
Tel.: (351) 22 999 1000
Web Site: http://www.lectra.com
Sales Range: $25-49.9 Million
Emp.: 26
Computer Aided Design & Computer Aided Manufacturing Systems Mfr
N.A.I.C.S.: 541512

Lectra Russia OOO (1)
26 Appt IV Room 24, Leninskaya Sloboda, 115280, Moscow, Russia
Tel.: (7) 84994180391
Information Technology Services
N.A.I.C.S.: 541511

Lectra Singapore Pte Ltd (1)
101 Thomson Road 08-05 United Square, United Sq, Singapore, 307591, Singapore (100%)
Tel.: (65) 6 353 9788
Sales Range: $25-49.9 Million
Emp.: 10
Computer Aided Design & Computer Aided Manufacturing Systems Mfr
N.A.I.C.S.: 541512

Lectra Sistemas Espanola SA (1)
Via de los Poblados 1-1a Plta Edif C P E Alvento, 28033, Madrid, Spain
Tel.: (34) 917888800
Sales Range: $25-49.9 Million
Emp.: 50
Computer Aided Design & Computer Aided Manufacturing Systems Mfr
N.A.I.C.S.: 541512

Lectra Suomi Oy (1)
Mannerheimintie 12B 5th floor, 00100, Helsinki, Finland
Tel.: (358) 97594430
Web Site: https://www.lectra.com
Sales Range: $25-49.9 Million
Emp.: 9
Fashion Design Software Mfr
N.A.I.C.S.: 334610

Lectra Sverige AB (1)
Skaraborgsvagen 3A, PO Box 974, 506 30, Boras, Sweden (100%)
Tel.: (46) 33237870
Sales Range: $25-49.9 Million
Emp.: 5
Computer Aided Design & Computer Aided Manufacturing Systems Mfr
N.A.I.C.S.: 541512

Lectra Systemes CAD CAM AS (1)
Koza Plaza A Blok Kt 13 No 49 Esenler, Istanbul, 34235, Turkiye
Tel.: (90) 2126569009
Web Site: http://www.lectra.com
Sales Range: $25-49.9 Million
Emp.: 28
Computer Aided Design & Computer Aided Manufacturing Systems Mfr
N.A.I.C.S.: 541512

Lectra Systemes SA de CV (1)
Insurgentes Sur 1602 - 701, Col Credito Constructor Benito Juarez, 03930, Mexico, DF, Mexico (100%)
Tel.: (52) 5555639191
Web Site: https://www.lectra.com

Sales Range: $25-49.9 Million
Mfr of Computer Aided Design & Computer Aided Manufacturing Systems
N.A.I.C.S.: 541512

Lectra Systemes Tunisie SA (1)
Royal Garden building 3rd fl offices n B7B8, Avenue el Riel cite les pins, 1053, Tunis, Tunisia (100%)
Tel.: (216) 70248181
Web Site: http://www.lectra.com
Sales Range: $25-49.9 Million
Emp.: 50
Computer Aided Design & Computer Aided Manufacturing Systems Mfr
N.A.I.C.S.: 541512

Lectra Systems (Canada) Inc. (1)
1120 Finch Avenue West Suite 506, Toronto, M3J 3H7, ON, Canada
Tel.: (416) 661-5544
Mfr of Computer Aided Design & Computer Aided Manufacturing Systems
N.A.I.C.S.: 541512

Lectra Systems (Shanghai) Co. Ltd (1)
5 & 6 Floors Bldg 91 Phase 13 Caohejing Hi-Tech Park No 1122, North Qinzhou Road, Shanghai, 200233, China (100%)
Tel.: (86) 2153891688
Computer Aided Design & Computer Aided Systems Mfr
N.A.I.C.S.: 541512

Lectra Systems Inc. (1)
Ste 303 1601 Galbraith Ave SE, Grand Rapids, MI 49546-6479 (100%)
Tel.: (616) 361-1139
Web Site: http://www.lectra.com
Sales Range: $50-74.9 Million
Emp.: 25
Apparel Design Software
N.A.I.C.S.: 711410

Lectra Systems Inc. (1)
Empire State Building 350 5th Ave Ste 4630, New York, NY 10018-2531
Tel.: (212) 730-4444
Web Site: http://www.lectra.com
Sales Range: $25-49.9 Million
Mfr of Computer Aided Design & Computer Aided Manufacturing Systems
N.A.I.C.S.: 541512

Lectra Systems SA (Pty) Ltd. (1)
46 Henwood Rd, Morningside, Durban, 4001, Kwazulu Natal, South Africa (100%)
Tel.: (27) 313031203
Sales Range: $25-49.9 Million
Emp.: 12
Computer Aided Design & Computer Aided Manufacturing Systems
N.A.I.C.S.: 541512

Lectra Taiwan Co. Ltd (1)
2F 38 1 Sec 1 Mingshen N Rd, Guishan Shiang Gayuan, Taipei, 33391, Taiwan (100%)
Tel.: (886) 33267210
Sales Range: $25-49.9 Million
Emp.: 4
Computer Aided Design & Computer Aided Manufacturing Systems Mfr
N.A.I.C.S.: 541512

Lectra Technologies India Private Ltd (1)
Unit 402 4th Floor Embassy Square no148 Infantry Road, Basavanagudi, Bengaluru, 560 001, Karnataka, India
Tel.: (91) 8040018000
Software Development Services
N.A.I.C.S.: 541511

Lectra UK Ltd (1)
Jade Building Albion Mills Albion Road, Greengates, Bradford, BD10 9TQ, West Yorkshire, United Kingdom (100%)
Tel.: (44) 1274623080
Sales Range: $25-49.9 Million
Emp.: 20
Computer Aided Design & Computer Aided Manufacturing Systems Mfr
N.A.I.C.S.: 541512

Lectra USA Inc. (1)
5000 Highlands Pkwy Ste 250, Smyrna, GA 30082
Tel.: (770) 422-8050

Web Site: http://www.lectra.com
Sales Range: $25-49.9 Million
Mfr of Computer Aided Design & Computer Aided Manufacturing Systems
N.A.I.C.S.: 541512

Luiv Amaro (1)
Rua Anita Garibaldi 1786, Rm 711, Porto Alegre, 9048 0200, Brazil (100%)
Tel.: (55) 515946592
Mfr of Computer Aided Design & Computer Aided Manufacturing Systems
N.A.I.C.S.: 541512

Neteven S.A. (1)
40-44 Rue Letort, 75018, Paris, France
Tel.: (33) 485374649
Web Site: https://www.neteven.com
Software Development Services
N.A.I.C.S.: 541511

Record Confecciones Importaciones Ltda. (1)
Av Tte Walter Vega 71/79, 127, Santa Cruz, Bolivia
Tel.: (591) 3 33 62 636
Web Site: http://www.record.com.bo
Apparels Mfr
N.A.I.C.S.: 315990

Retviews SA (1)
Avenue Louise 231, 1000, Brussels, Belgium
Tel.: (32) 477787082
Web Site: http://www.retviews.com
Fashion Designing Services
N.A.I.C.S.: 541490
Loic Winckelmans *(Co-Founder & CEO)*

LED INTERNATIONAL HOLDINGS LIMITED

Unit A1 6/F One Capital Place 18 Luard Road, Wanchai, China (Hong Kong)
Tel.: (852) 2243 3100   HK
Web Site: http://www.led-intl.com
Sales Range: $1-9.9 Million
Emp.: 164
Light Emitting Diode Display Screen Mfr & Distr
N.A.I.C.S.: 334419
Gordon Chin *(Sec)*

Subsidiaries:

Kepu Electronic Technology (Shenzhen) Company Limited (1)
3 building 4/5 floor zhongxinbao Sci&Tech Park, huangtian Town baoan District, Shenzhen, GuangDong, China
Tel.: (86) 755 29303001
Web Site: http://www.szkepu.com
Electronic Products Mfr
N.A.I.C.S.: 334419

LED International Holdings Limited - Shenzhen Factory (1)
5/F No 3 Building 1st Phase of Zhongxingbao Hi-Tech Park, Xixiang Town Baoan District, Shenzhen, Guangdong, China
Tel.: (86) 755 2868 4326
Electric Equipment Mfr
N.A.I.C.S.: 334419

LEDA FURNITURE LTD

350 Clayson Rd, Toronto, M9M 2H2, ON, Canada
Tel.: (416) 745-9588
Web Site:
http://www.ledafurniture.com
Year Founded: 1967
Rev.: $11,051,669
Emp.: 25
Furniture Mfr
N.A.I.C.S.: 337122
Marco L. Confalone *(Pres & COO)*

LEDAX CO., LTD.

2F Shin Kioicho Building 4-1 Kioi-cho, Chiyoda-ku, Tokyo, 102-8578, Japan
Tel.: (81) 332393100
Web Site: https://www.ledax.co.jp
Year Founded: 1987

INTERNATIONAL PUBLIC

7602—(TKS)
Rev.: $126,065,920
Assets: $47,968,770
Liabilities: $14,694,030
Net Worth: $33,274,740
Earnings: $482,530
Fiscal Year-end: 03/31/24
Holding Company
N.A.I.C.S.: 551112
Masayuki Kabata *(Chm & Co-CEO)*

Subsidiaries:

Carchs Co., Ltd. (1)
2F Shin Kioicho Building 4-1 Kioi-cho, Chiyoda-ku, Tokyo, 102-8578, Japan
Tel.: (81) 33 239 3180
Automobile Product Distr
N.A.I.C.S.: 423120

Carchs Kyushu Sales Co., Ltd. (1)
768-2 Yoshikai Mitsuhashi Yanagawa, Fukuoka, 832-0802, Japan
Tel.: (81) 944751500
Automotive Distr
N.A.I.C.S.: 423110

Takatoku Co., Ltd. (1)
2-12-3 Ichinoe, Edogawa-ku, Tokyo, 132-0024, Japan
Tel.: (81) 356788060
Web Site: http://www.takatoku.co.jp
Automobile Parts Distr
N.A.I.C.S.: 423120

LEDCOR GROUP OF COMPANIES

1067 W Cordova St Ste 1200, Vancouver, V6C 1C7, BC, Canada
Tel.: (604) 681-7500
Web Site: http://www.ledcor.com
Year Founded: 1947
Sales Range: $900-999.9 Million
Emp.: 7,200
Construction, Property Development, Pipeline & Telecommunication Services
N.A.I.C.S.: 236220
Dave Lede *(Chm & CEO)*

Subsidiaries:

Ledcor Construction (1)
1100 1st Street SE Ste 400, Calgary, T2G 1B1, AB, Canada
Tel.: (403) 264-9155
Sales Range: $25-49.9 Million
Emp.: 45
Construction Services
N.A.I.C.S.: 236220

Ledcor Industrial (1)
7008 Roper Rd, PO Box 4098, Edmonton, T6E 4S8, AB, Canada
Tel.: (780) 462-4211
Web Site: http://www.ledcor.com
Sales Range: $25-49.9 Million
Emp.: 4
Construction Services
N.A.I.C.S.: 236210
Ron Stevenson *(Pres & COO)*

Summit Helicopters, Inc. (1)
27 Yellowknife Airport 100 Dickins Street, Yellowknife, X1A 3T2, NT, Canada
Tel.: (867) 765-5969
Web Site: http://summithelicopters.ca
Helicopter Passenger Carrier Services
N.A.I.C.S.: 481111
Lane Zimhelt *(COO)*

LEDDARTECH HOLDINGS INC.

4535 boulevard Wilfrid-Hamel Suite 240, Quebec, G1P 2J7, QC, Canada
Tel.: (418) 653-9000   Ca
Web Site: https://leddartech.com
Year Founded: 2007
LDTC—(NASDAQ)
Holding Company
N.A.I.C.S.: 551112
Derek Aberle *(Chm)*

Subsidiaries:

LeddarTech Inc. (1)

AND PRIVATE COMPANIES

2740 Einstein Street, Quebec, G1P 4S4,
QC, Canada
Tel.: (418) 653-9000
Web Site: http://www.leddartech.com
Detection & Ranging Systems Mfr
N.A.I.C.S.: 334513
Frantz Saintelemy *(Pres & COO)*

Prospector Capital Corp. (1)
1250 Prospect St Ste 200, La Jolla, CA
92037
Tel.: (650) 396-7700
Rev.: $4,764,441
Assets: $329,802,135
Liabilities: $330,728,842
Net Worth: ($926,707)
Earnings: $3,763,805
Emp.: 2
Fiscal Year-end: 12/31/2022
Investment Services
N.A.I.C.S.: 523999
Steven R. Altman *(Chm)*

LEDER REINHARDT GMBH
An der Urfall 3, 72793, Pfullingen,
Germany
Tel.: (49) 712197520 De
Web Site: http://www.leder-
reinhardt.de
Year Founded: 1986
Sales Range: $10-24.9 Million
Leather Products Whslr
N.A.I.C.S.: 316110
Jochen Reinhardt *(Co-Mng Dir)*

LEDERMANN IMMOBILIEN AG
Seefeldstrasse 60, CH-8008, Zurich,
Switzerland
Tel.: (41) 44 396 15 85
Web Site: http://www.ledermann.com
Rev.: $675,654,320
Emp.: 15
Real Estate Investment & Management
N.A.I.C.S.: 531390
Urs Ledermann *(Chm)*

LEDESMA S.A.A.I.
Av Corrientes 415, C1043AAE, Buenos Aires, Argentina
Tel.: (54) 1143781555
Web Site:
https://www.ledesma.com.ar
Year Founded: 1908
Emp.: 5,000
Sugar, Syrups, Alcohol, Meat, Fruits,
Juices & Paper Mfr & Distr
N.A.I.C.S.: 311314
Carlos Herminio Blaquier *(Chm)*

Subsidiaries:

Alpamsa S.A. (1)
San Ignacio 040 Quilicura, Santiago,
Chile (100%)
Tel.: (56) 27386989
Web Site: http://www.alpamsa.cl
Wine & Distilled Alcoholic Beverage Whslr
N.A.I.C.S.: 424810

La Biznaga S.A. (1)
Avenida Corrientes 415 Ciudad De, Buenos
Aires, Argentina (100%)
Tel.: (54) 1143265131
Beef Cattle Ranching & Farming
N.A.I.C.S.: 112111

Ledesma S.A. (1)
Avenida Corrientes 415, Buenos Aires, Argentina
Tel.: (54) 1143781555
Cane Sugar Refining
N.A.I.C.S.: 311314

Productores de Alcohol de Melaza
S.A. (1)
Maipu 267 12th Fl, C1084ABE, Buenos Aires, Argentina (100%)
Tel.: (54) 1143265953
Web Site: http://www.pamsa.com.ar
Sales Range: $25-49.9 Million
Emp.: 15
Chemical & Allied Products Merchant Whslr
N.A.I.C.S.: 424690

LEDLINK OPTICS, INC.
15F No 655 Bannan Rd, Chung-Ho,
New Taipei City, Taiwan
Tel.: (886) 282276126
Web Site: https://www.ledlink-
optics.com
Year Founded: 2008
5230—(TPE)
Rev.: $37,578,276
Assets: $69,533,971
Liabilities: $33,401,119
Net Worth: $36,132,852
Emp.: 540
Fiscal Year-end: 12/31/22
Lighting Equipment Mfr
N.A.I.C.S.: 335139
Telung Tang *(CEO)*

LEDMAN OPTOELECTRONIC CO., LTD.
Building 8 Block 2 Baimang Baiwangxin Industrial Park Xili Area, Nanshan District, Shenzhen, China
Tel.: (86) 75586139688
Web Site: https://www.ledman.com
300162—(CHIN)
Rev.: $152,091,108
Assets: $198,550,872
Liabilities: $100,804,392
Net Worth: $97,746,480
Earnings: $4,366,440
Emp.: 520
Fiscal Year-end: 12/31/22
LED Components, Displays & Lighting Products Mfr
N.A.I.C.S.: 334419
Martin Lee *(Founder & CEO)*

Subsidiaries:

Shenzhen Apexls Optoelectronic Co.,
Ltd. (1)
Building 1st Lougang Block Songgang
Street, Baoan District, Shenzhen, 518105,
China
Tel.: (86) 18025376105
Emp.: 300
Light Emitting Diode Product Mfr & Distr
N.A.I.C.S.: 334413

Shenzhen Torshare Technology Co.,
Ltd. (1)
Torshare Industrial Park No 5 Minying
Road, NO 3 Industrial Area Shilongzai Shiyan Street Bao'an District, Shenzhen,
Guangdong, China
Tel.: (86) 75536861686
Web Site: https://www.torshare.com
Lighting Equipment Mfr & Distr
N.A.I.C.S.: 335139
Mandy Xing *(Mgr-Sls-Intl)*

LEDO TEA COMPANY LIMITED
Sir R N M House 3rd Floor 3B Lal
Bazar Street, Kolkata, 700001, West
Bengal, India
Tel.: (91) 3322306686 In
Web Site: http://www.ledotea.com
Year Founded: 1983
508306—(BOM)
Rev.: $1,708,666
Assets: $1,893,992
Liabilities: $2,762,869
Net Worth: ($868,877)
Earnings: $28,174
Emp.: 712
Fiscal Year-end: 03/31/21
Tea Mfr
N.A.I.C.S.: 311920
N. K. Lohia *(Chm & Mng Dir)*

LEDS-C4, S.A.
c Afores sn, 25750, Tora, Spain
Tel.: (34) 973468100
Web Site: http://www.leds-c4.com
Emp.: 330
Lighting Solutions Designer & Mfr
N.A.I.C.S.: 335132
Laura Monso *(Mgr-HR)*

Subsidiaries:

C&G Carandini S.A. (1)
Carrerada esq Verneda Martorelles, Barcelona, 08107, Spain
Tel.: (34) 933174008
Web Site: http://www.carandini.com
Electrical Equipment Distr
N.A.I.C.S.: 423440

Subsidiary (Domestic):

C&G Caradini (2)
Carrerada esq Verneda Martorelles,
E-08107, Barcelona, Spain (100%)
Tel.: (34) 933174008
Web Site: http://www.carandini.com
Sales Range: $100-124.9 Million
Outdoor & Industrial Lights Mfr
N.A.I.C.S.: 335132

LEDSTIERNAN AB
Malmskillnadsgatan 39, 111 38,
Stockholm, Sweden
Tel.: (46) 854503500
Web Site: http://www.ledstiernan.se
Sales Range: $50-74.9 Million
Emp.: 300
Investment Services
N.A.I.C.S.: 523999
Adam Gillberg *(Mng Dir)*

Subsidiaries:

Ledstiernan Venture AB (1)
Malmskillnadsgatan 39, 111 38, Stockholm,
Sweden
Tel.: (46) 854503500
Web Site: http://www.ledstiernan.se
Sales Range: $25-49.9 Million
Emp.: 3
Investment Management Service
N.A.I.C.S.: 541618

Polstiernan Industri AB (1)
C O Pallco AB Ekenasjjon, PO Box 2023,
574 02, Vetlanda, Sweden
Tel.: (46) 38334800
Web Site: http://www.pallco.se
Sales Range: $75-99.9 Million
Emp.: 150
Steel Aluminium Copper Supplies
N.A.I.C.S.: 423510
Gorgen Ekdahl *(Pres)*

LEDTECH ELECTRONICS CORPORATION
5F No 542-5 Zhongzheng Rd, Xindian Dist, New Taipei City, 231, Taiwan
Tel.: (886) 222186891 TW
Web Site: https://www.ledtech.com.tw
Year Founded: 1977
6164—(TAI)
Rev.: $23,449,785
Assets: $52,925,797
Liabilities: $17,034,860
Net Worth: $35,890,937
Earnings: ($844,436)
Emp.: 1,380
Fiscal Year-end: 12/31/23
Light Emitting Diode (LED) Display
Lamps & LED Displays Mfr
N.A.I.C.S.: 335132

Subsidiaries:

Energyled Electronics
Corporation (1)
Zone 22 North Guiyuan Rd West Jiqi Rd,
Duanzhou, Zhaoqing, Guangdong, China
Tel.: (86) 7582833488
Display Product Mfr
N.A.I.C.S.: 334419

Gelwin Technology Ltd (1)
Unit 17 7f Hong Leong Ind Complex 4
Wang Kwong Rd, Kowloon Bay, China
(Hong Kong)
Tel.: (852) 27950770
Web Site: http://www.gelwin.com
LED Mfr
N.A.I.C.S.: 334413

LEDUC CHRYSLER JEEP

LEE & MAN PAPER MANUFACTURING LIMITED

6102 46A Street, Leduc, T9E 7A7,
AB, Canada
Tel.: (780) 986-2051
Web Site: http://leducchrysler.com
Year Founded: 1952
New & Used Car Dealers
N.A.I.C.S.: 441110
Richard Rivard *(Dealer Principal)*

LEE & MAN CHEMICAL COMPANY LIMITED
8/Floor Liven House 61-63 King Yip
Street Kwun Tong, Kowloon, China
(Hong Kong)
Tel.: (852) 23199888
Web Site:
http://www.leemanhandbags.com
0746—(HKG)
Rev.: $748,047,218
Assets: $902,235,135
Liabilities: $184,022,408
Net Worth: $718,212,728
Earnings: $147,488,813
Emp.: 2,250
Fiscal Year-end: 12/31/22
Trading & Manufacturing of Chemical
Products
N.A.I.C.S.: 325998
Siu Kee Wai *(Chm)*

Subsidiaries:

Dongguan Jia Xin Handbag Company
Limited (1)
Liu Wu Shek Kit, Dongguan, Guangdong,
China
Tel.: (86) 76986631383
Handbag Mfr
N.A.I.C.S.: 316990

Dongguan Wei Hua Handbag Company Limited (1)
16 Zhen Xing Nan Road, Gao Bu, Dongguan, Guangdong, China
Tel.: (86) 76988871735
Handbag Mfr
N.A.I.C.S.: 316990

Jiangsu Lee & Man Chemical
Limited (1)
Xinggang Road Yanjiang Industrial Park,
Changshu Economic Development Zone,
Suzhou, 215536, Jiangsu, China
Tel.: (86) 51252259898
Chemical Product Mfr & Distr
N.A.I.C.S.: 325998
Wu Zeng Long *(Dir-Sls)*

Jiangxi Lee & Man Chemical
Limited (1)
Liwen Road Matou Industrial Park,
Ruichang, 332207, Jiangxi, China
Tel.: (86) 7928996998
Chemical Product Mfr & Distr
N.A.I.C.S.: 325998
Yang Zuo Ning *(Gen Mgr)*

Lee & Man Development Limited (1)
8/F Liven House 61-63 King Yip Street,
Kwun Tong, Kowloon, China (Hong Kong)
Tel.: (852) 23199888
Handbag Mfr
N.A.I.C.S.: 316990
Wai Siu Kee *(Exec Dir)*

Lee Wai Handbag Manufacturing Co.,
Ltd. (1)
8/F Liven House 61-63 King Yip Street,
Kwun Tong, Kowloon, China (Hong Kong)
Tel.: (852) 23199888
Handbag Mfr
N.A.I.C.S.: 316990

LEE & MAN PAPER MANUFACTURING LIMITED
5th Floor Liven House 61-63 King Yip
Street, Kwun Tong, Kowloon, China
(Hong Kong)
Tel.: (852) 23199889
Web Site:
http://www.leemanpaper.com
Year Founded: 1994

LEE & MAN PAPER MANUFACTURING LIMITED

Lee & Man Paper Manufacturing Limited—(Continued)
2314—(HKG)
Rev.: $3,719,226,255
Assets: $6,416,524,838
Liabilities: $2,769,145,853
Net Worth: $3,647,378,985
Earnings: $167,941,725
Emp.: 10,000
Fiscal Year-end: 12/31/22
Paper Mfr
N.A.I.C.S.: 322299
Raymond Man Chun Lee (Founder & Chm)

Subsidiaries:

Chongqing Lee & Man Paper Manufacturing Limited (1)
Zhoutou Town Yongchuan, 402191, Chongqing, China (100%)
Tel.: (86) 2349603333
Converted Paper Product Mfr
N.A.I.C.S.: 322299

Guangdong Lee & Man Paper Manufacturing Limited (1)
He Xi Industrial Park Hongmei, Dongguan, 523160, Guangdong, China (100%)
Tel.: (86) 7698 843 2168
Web Site: https://www.leemanpaper.com
Converted Paper Product Mfr
N.A.I.C.S.: 322299

Jiangsu Lee & Man Paper Manufacturing Company Limited (1)
Lee and Man Road Yanjiang Industrial Park, Changshu Economic Development Zone, Jiangsu, China (100%)
Tel.: (86) 5125 265 3333
Web Site: https://www.leemanpaper.com
Sales Range: $25-49.9 Million
Emp.: 100
Paperboard Mills
N.A.I.C.S.: 322130

LEE & NEE SOFTWARE EXPORTS LTD.

14B Camac Street, Kolkata, 700017, India
Tel.: (91) 3340695100
Web Site: https://www.lnsel.com
517415—(BOM)
Rev.: $1,127,845
Assets: $7,810,762
Liabilities: $212,066
Net Worth: $7,598,696
Earnings: $28,406
Emp.: 100
Fiscal Year-end: 03/31/23
Information Technology Software
N.A.I.C.S.: 541511
Ajay Kumar Agarwal (Co-Chm)

LEE & NIGHTINGALE ADVERTISING LTD.

2 White Friars, Chester, CH1 1NQ, Wales, United Kingdom
Tel.: (44) 151 346 2000
Year Founded: 1854
Rev.: $16,520,000
Emp.: 30
Advertising Agencies, Consumer Marketing, Recruitment
N.A.I.C.S.: 541810

LEE FEED MILL PUBLIC COMPANY LIMITED

28th Floor Wall Street Tower 33/137 Surawong Road, Bangrak, Bangkok, 10500, Thailand
Tel.: (66) 26327300
Web Site: http://www.leepattana.com
Year Founded: 1983
LEE—(THA)
Rev.: $87,111,514
Assets: $90,274,177
Liabilities: $9,985,834
Net Worth: $80,288,343
Earnings: $2,524,328
Emp.: 660
Fiscal Year-end: 12/31/23
Feed Mfr
N.A.I.C.S.: 311611
Visith Leelasithorn (Chm)

Subsidiaries:

Lee Pattana Agro Silo Co., Ltd. (1)
33 1 Mu 7 Phaholyothin Rd, Daorueng Muang District, Saraburi, 18000, Thailand
Tel.: (66) 3622 3372
Crop Drying Services
N.A.I.C.S.: 111998

Lee Pattana Feed Mill Co., Ltd. (1)
33 137 Surawong Rd, Bangkok, 10500, Thailand
Tel.: (66) 26327300
Web Site: http://www.leepattana.com
Livestock & Domestic Animals Food Production Services
N.A.I.C.S.: 311119

LEE HEDGES PLC

No 353 Galle road, PO Box 84, 3, Colombo, Sri Lanka
Tel.: (94) 112301732
Web Site: https://leehedgesplc.com
Year Founded: 1852
SHAW—(COL)
Rev.: $567,411
Assets: $21,456,809
Liabilities: $3,018,694
Net Worth: $18,438,115
Earnings: $1,437,183
Emp.: 8
Fiscal Year-end: 03/31/23
Investment Management Service
N.A.I.C.S.: 523940

LEE HING DEVELOPMENT LIMITED

Suite 1506-07 15th Floor 9 Queens Road, Central, China (Hong Kong)
Tel.: (852) 25263271
Web Site: http://www.lhd.com.hk
Rev.: $2,588,746
Assets: $127,746,120
Liabilities: $28,706,056
Net Worth: $99,040,065
Earnings: ($61,849,447)
Emp.: 9
Fiscal Year-end: 12/31/19
Investment Holding Services
N.A.I.C.S.: 523940
Boon Seng Tan (Chm & Mng Dir)

LEE KEE HOLDINGS LIMITED

16 Dai Fat Street Tai Po Industrial Estate, Hong Kong, New Territories, China (Hong Kong)
Tel.: (852) 27890282
Web Site: https://www.leekeegroup.com
0637—(HKG)
Rev.: $328,869,206
Assets: $144,090,136
Liabilities: $25,012,060
Net Worth: $119,078,076
Earnings: $2,391,160
Emp.: 180
Fiscal Year-end: 03/31/22
Metal Distr
N.A.I.C.S.: 213114
Clara Yuen Shan Chan (Vice Chm & CEO)

Subsidiaries:

Essence Metal (Asia) Company Limited (1)
16 Dai Fat Street Tai Po Industrial Estate, Hong Kong, New Territories, China (Hong Kong)
Tel.: (852) 27890282
Metal Mining Services
N.A.I.C.S.: 213114

Genesis Alloys (Ningbo) Limited (1)
8 Wangfang Road, Wangjia Village Xiepu Development Zone Zhenhai District, Ningbo, 315203, Zhejiang, China
Tel.: (86) 57486507398
Metal Mining Services
N.A.I.C.S.: 213114

Horizon Commodities & Futures Company Limited (1)
16 Dai Fat Street Tai Po Industrial Estate, Hong Kong, New Territories, China (Hong Kong)
Tel.: (852) 22352767
Web Site: http://www.hcfl.com.hk
Financial Services
N.A.I.C.S.: 523940

LKG (Singapore) Private Limited (1)
2 Venture Drive Vision Exchange 13-25, Singapore, 608526, Singapore
Tel.: (65) 69777595
Web Site: https://www.leesingmaterials.com
Metal Mining Services
N.A.I.C.S.: 213114

LKG Elite (Guangzhou) Company Limited (1)
Room 6017 Bai Ling Business Building 143 Liu Rong Road, Yuexiu District, Guangzhou, 510180, Guangdong, China
Tel.: (86) 2081064094
Metal Mining Services
N.A.I.C.S.: 213114

LKG Elite (Shenzhen) Company Limited (1)
Units E-G 28/F Block B HongLong Century Plaza 4002 Shennan Road East, Luohu District, Shenzhen, 518001, Guangdong, China
Tel.: (86) 75525181429
Metal Mining Services
N.A.I.C.S.: 213114

LKG Elite (Wuxi) Company Limited (1)
Unit AB 16/F Block B Oriental Plaza No 359 Zhongshan Road, Wuxi, 214002, Jiangsu, China
Tel.: (86) 51082444137
Metal Mining Services
N.A.I.C.S.: 213114

Lee Kee Group Limited (1)
16 Dai Fat Street Tai Po Industrial Estate, Tai Po Industrial Estate, Hong Kong, New Territories, China (Hong Kong)
Tel.: (852) 27890282
Web Site: https://www.leekeegroup.com
Metal Mining Services
N.A.I.C.S.: 213114

Mega International Resources Company Limited (1)
18F-7 No 201 Sec 2 Wenxin Road, Xitun District, Taichung, 40758, Taiwan
Tel.: (886) 422598747
Web Site: https://www.mircmq.com
Metal Mining Services
N.A.I.C.S.: 213114

Promet Metals Testing Laboratory Limited (1)
16 Dai Fat Street Tai Po Industrial Estate, Tai Po Industrial Estate, Hong Kong, New Territories, China (Hong Kong)
Tel.: (852) 39650806
Web Site: https://www.prometlab.com
Testing Laboratory Services
N.A.I.C.S.: 541380

LEE KIM TAH HOLDINGS LTD.

20 Jalan Afifi 07 01 Cisco Centre 2, Singapore, 409179, Singapore
Tel.: (65) 67453318 SG
Web Site: http://www.leekimtah.com
Sales Range: $75-99.9 Million
Emp.: 188
Holding Company; Real Estate Investment, Development, Construction Project Management & Property Management Services
N.A.I.C.S.: 551112
Lee Kim Tah (Founder & Chm)

Subsidiaries:

LKT Holdings Pty Ltd (1)
176 Campbell St, Surry Hills, 2010, NSW, Australia
Tel.: (61) 293929888
Sales Range: $50-74.9 Million
Emp.: 15
Asset Development & Management Services
N.A.I.C.S.: 533110

Subsidiary (Domestic):

Cienna (Project Marketing) Pty Ltd (2)
176 Campbell St, Surry Hills, 2010, NSW, Australia
Tel.: (61) 293929888
Sales Range: $50-74.9 Million
Emp.: 8
Real Estate Agencies
N.A.I.C.S.: 531210
Miranda Budiman (Mgr-Project Mktg)

Grosvenor Pacific Pty Ltd (2)
176 Campbell St, Surry Hills, 2010, NSW, Australia
Tel.: (61) 293929888
Web Site: http://www.leekimtah.com
Emp.: 3
Real Estate Agencies
N.A.I.C.S.: 531210

Lee Kim Tah (Pte) Ltd (1)
Certis Cisco Ctr I 20 Jalan Afifi No 07-01, Singapore, 409179, Singapore
Tel.: (65) 67453318
Web Site: http://www.info.com.sg
Sales Range: $25-49.9 Million
Emp.: 60
Building Construction Services
N.A.I.C.S.: 236220
Lee Teck (Chm)

LEE KU INDUSTRIAL CO., LTD.

42 Poseunggongdan-ro, Poseungeup, Pyeongtaek, Gyeonggi-do, Korea (South)
Tel.: (82) 314942929
Web Site: http://www.leeku.net
Year Founded: 1968
025820—(KRS)
Rev.: $329,517,583
Assets: $258,641,935
Liabilities: $161,069,691
Net Worth: $97,572,244
Earnings: $4,387,833
Emp.: 204
Fiscal Year-end: 12/31/22
Nonferrous Metal Products Mfr
N.A.I.C.S.: 331420
Kwon Deukho (COO)

LEE LONGLAND & CO. LTD.

224 Broad Street, Birmingham, B15 1AZ, United Kingdom
Tel.: (44) 1216439101
Web Site: http://www.leelonglands.com
Year Founded: 1902
Sales Range: $25-49.9 Million
Emp.: 130
Furniture Retailer
N.A.I.C.S.: 449110
Robert Lee (Mng Dir)

LEE SWEE KIAT GROUP BERHAD

Wisma LSK Lot 6122 Jalan Haji Abdul Manan Off Jalan Meru, 41050, Kelang, Selangor, Malaysia
Tel.: (60) 333924488
Web Site: https://www.lsk.com.my
Year Founded: 1975
LEESK—(KLS)
Rev.: $27,798,651
Assets: $25,649,325
Liabilities: $8,987,375
Net Worth: $16,661,950
Earnings: $2,967,349
Emp.: 384
Fiscal Year-end: 12/31/23
Laminated Foam Mfr

AND PRIVATE COMPANIES — LEEPORT (HOLDINGS) LIMITED

N.A.I.C.S.: 326140
Peir Chyun Wong *(Co-Sec)*

LEE'S PHARMACEUTICAL HOLDINGS LIMITED
1/F Building 20E Phase 3, Hong Kong Science Park, Sha Tin, China (Hong Kong)
Tel.: (852) 2314 1282   Ky
Web Site: http://www.leespharm.com
Rev.: $156,520,618
Assets: $467,443,347
Liabilities: $149,315,533
Net Worth: $318,127,814
Earnings: $8,134,131
Emp.: 1,308
Fiscal Year-end: 12/31/19
Holding Company; Pharmaceutical Mfr
N.A.I.C.S.: 551112
Xiaoyi Li *(CEO & Chief Technical Officer)*

Subsidiaries:

Guangzhou Zhaoke Lian Fa Pharmaceutical Limited (1)
1 Meide 3rd Road Pearl River Industrial Park, Nansha District, Guangzhou, 511462, China
Tel.: (86) 2034351732
Pharmaceutical Preparation Mfr
N.A.I.C.S.: 325412

Lee's Pharmaceutical (HK) Limited (1)
1/F Building 20E Phase 3 Hong Kong Science Park, Sha Tin, China (Hong Kong)
Tel.: (852) 23141282
Pharmaceutical Preparation Mfr
N.A.I.C.S.: 325412

Powder Pharmaceuticals Incorporated (1)
Ground Floor Wireless Center No 3 Science Park East Avenue, Hong Kong Science Park, Sha Tin, New Territories, China (Hong Kong)
Tel.: (852) 23146600
Web Site: http://www.powderpharma.com
Emp.: 100
Pharmaceuticals Product Mfr
N.A.I.C.S.: 325412

Zhaoke Pharmaceutical (Hefei) Co. Limited (1)
No 30 Tian Zhi Road New and High-Tech Industrial Development Zone, Hefei, 230088, Anhui, China
Tel.: (86) 55165310808
Pharmaceutical Preparation Mfr
N.A.I.C.S.: 325412

LEEBO B.V.
Touwslager 18, 5253 RK, Nieuwkuijk, Netherlands
Tel.: (31) 73 513 29 50
Web Site: http://www.leebo.nl
Emp.: 30
Building Facade Mfr
N.A.I.C.S.: 332323

LEECHI ENTERPRISES CO., LTD.
No 112 Sec 1 Shipai Rd, Chang-Hua, Taiwan
Tel.: (886) 47382121
Web Site: http://www.leechi.com.tw
Year Founded: 1973
1517—(TAI)
Rev.: $61,886,096
Assets: $147,564,303
Liabilities: $22,773,340
Net Worth: $124,790,963
Earnings: ($5,178,096)
Fiscal Year-end: 12/31/23
Bicycle Components Mfr
N.A.I.C.S.: 336991
Yuxin Lin *(Chm & Gen Mgr)*

LEEDS BUILDING SOCIETY
105 Albion Street, Leeds, LS1 5AS, United Kingdom
Tel.: (44) 113 225 7555   UK
Web Site: http://www.leedsbuildingsociety.com
Year Founded: 1886
Rev.: $610,287,480
Assets: $27,291,510,480
Liabilities: $25,866,981,720
Net Worth: $1,424,528,760
Earnings: $86,827,920
Emp.: 1,434
Fiscal Year-end: 12/31/19
Housing Services Organization
N.A.I.C.S.: 925110
Richard Fearon *(CEO)*

Subsidiaries:

Leeds Financial Services Ltd. (1)
105 Albion Street, Holbeck House, Leeds, LS1 5AS, United Kingdom   (100%)
Tel.: (44) 1132257777
Web Site: http://www.leedsbuildingsociety.co.uk
Sales Range: $150-199.9 Million
Emp.: 300
Financial Planning, Home Insurance & Other Financial Services
N.A.I.C.S.: 523991

Leeds Mortgage Funding Ltd. (1)
105 Albion St Holbeck House, Leeds, LS15 AS, United Kingdom   (100%)
Tel.: (44) 1132252000
Sales Range: $150-199.9 Million
Emp.: 400
Real Estate Credit Services
N.A.I.C.S.: 522292

LEEF BRANDS INC
789 West Pender Street Suite 810, Vancouver, V6C 1H2, BC, Canada
Tel.: (604) 687-2038
Web Site: http://www.icaninc.com
LEEEF—(OTCQB)
Rev.: $30,520,783
Assets: $43,768,409
Liabilities: $45,010,241
Net Worth: ($1,241,832)
Earnings: ($34,206,432)
Fiscal Year-end: 12/31/23
Pharmaceutical Cannabis Product Mfr
N.A.I.C.S.: 325411

LEEJAM SPORTS CO
Thumamah Road, PO Box 295254, Riyadh, 11351, Saudi Arabia
Tel.: (966) 112101015
Web Site: https://www.leejam.com.sa
1830—(SAU)
Rev.: $284,172,454
Assets: $719,410,741
Liabilities: $469,167,011
Net Worth: $250,243,730
Earnings: $68,593,289
Emp.: 2,490
Fiscal Year-end: 12/31/22
Fitness Center Operator
N.A.I.C.S.: 713940
Justin Musgrove *(CEO)*

LEEK UNITED BUILDING SOCIETY
50 St Edward Street, Leek, ST13 5DL, Staffordshire, United Kingdom
Tel.: (44) 1538 384151
Web Site: http://www.leekunited.co.uk
Year Founded: 1863
Rev.: $28,177,103
Assets: $1,431,522,211
Liabilities: $1,344,222,115
Net Worth: $87,300,096
Earnings: $2,556,308
Emp.: 194
Fiscal Year-end: 12/31/19
Housing Services Organization
N.A.I.C.S.: 925110
John Kelly *(Dir-Ops)*

LEEL ELECTRICALS LTD.
159 Okhla Industrial Estate Phase-III, New Delhi, 110020, India
Tel.: (91) 1140627200   In
Web Site: https://www.leelelectric.com
Year Founded: 1987
Rev.: $370,762,124
Assets: $387,135,912
Liabilities: $182,408,324
Net Worth: $204,727,588
Earnings: $79,360,668
Emp.: 552
Fiscal Year-end: 03/31/18
Heat Exchanger Coil Mfr
N.A.I.C.S.: 332410

Subsidiaries:

Lloyd Coils Europe s.r.o. (1)
Vrazska 143, 15300, Prague, Czech Republic
Tel.: (420) 257 881 129
Web Site: http://www.lloydcoils.eu
Electrical Products Mfr
N.A.I.C.S.: 334416

Lloyd Coils, L.P. (1)
2640 Fountain View Dr Ste 126, Houston, TX 77057
Tel.: (713) 992-3029
Web Site: http://www.lloydcoils.com
Engineeering Services
N.A.I.C.S.: 541330

LEEN ALKHAIR TRADING COMPANY
King Fahd Road, Olaya, Riyadh, Saudi Arabia
Tel.: (966) 920019522
Web Site: https://www.leenalkhair.com
Year Founded: 2006
9555—(SAU)
Rev.: $67,021,147
Assets: $79,429,616
Liabilities: $40,449,055
Net Worth: $38,980,561
Earnings: $3,197,248
Emp.: 282
Fiscal Year-end: 12/31/23
Vegetable & Fruit Distr
N.A.I.C.S.: 424480
Abdullah Muhammad Al Shuraim *(CEO)*

LEENGATE VALVES LIMITED
Grange Close Clover Nook Industrial Estate, Somercotes, Alfreton, DE55 4QT, Derbyshire, United Kingdom
Tel.: (44) 1773 521 555   UK
Web Site: http://www.leengatevalves.co.uk
Sales Range: $10-24.9 Million
Emp.: 21
Valve Whslr
N.A.I.C.S.: 423720
Steve Pickering *(Mng Dir)*

LEENO INDUSTRIAL, INC.
Tel.: (82) 518313232
Web Site: https://www.leeno.com
Year Founded: 1978
058470—(KRS)
Rev.: $247,298,290
Assets: $407,651,395
Liabilities: $29,379,587
Net Worth: $378,271,808
Earnings: $87,717,028
Emp.: 645
Fiscal Year-end: 12/31/22
Semiconductor Product Mfr
N.A.I.C.S.: 334413
Chae Yoon Lee *(Founder & CEO)*

LEEPORT (HOLDINGS) LIMITED
1st Floor Block 1 Golden Dragon Industrial Centre, 152-160 Tai Lin Pai Road, Kwai Chung, New Territories, China (Hong Kong)
Tel.: (852) 24277991
Web Site: https://www.leeport.com.hk
0387—(HKG)
Rev.: $111,436,403
Assets: $127,184,693
Liabilities: $67,273,718
Net Worth: $59,910,975
Earnings: $1,043,970
Emp.: 237
Fiscal Year-end: 12/31/22
Production Equipment & Tools Distr
N.A.I.C.S.: 444140
Joseph Sou Leung Lee *(Founder, Chm & CEO)*

Subsidiaries:

Grassinger Technologies GmbH (1)
Seemuhle 5a, 78183, Hufingen, Germany
Tel.: (49) 77116284000
Web Site: http://www.grassinger-technologies.com
Industrial Automation Products Mfr
N.A.I.C.S.: 334512

Leeport (Singapore) Pte Ltd (1)
No 66 Tannery Lane Unit 01-06 Sindo Building, Singapore, 347805, Singapore
Tel.: (65) 6 745 2666
Web Site: http://www.leeport.com.sg
Sales Range: $25-49.9 Million
Emp.: 11
Measuring Instruments & Machine Tools Distr
N.A.I.C.S.: 423830

Leeport Machine Tool (Shenzhen) Company Limited (1)
1/F Block A Intelig Technology Digital Park 8 Hongmian Road, Futian Free Trade Zone, Shenzhen, 518038, Guangdong, China
Tel.: (86) 7558 832 1888
Web Site: http://www.leeport.hk
Emp.: 50
Precision Cutting Tools Mfr
N.A.I.C.S.: 333515

Leeport Machine Tool Trading (China) Limited (1)
Room 102 Building 3 No 138 XinJunHuan Road, Minhang District, Shanghai, 201114, China
Tel.: (86) 215 046 1011
Web Site: http://www.leeport.com.hk
Machine Tool Distr
N.A.I.C.S.: 333517

Leeport Machinery (Shanghai) Company Limited (1)
Room 530 5th Floor No 456 Futebei Road Pilot Free Trade Zone, Shanghai, 200131, China
Tel.: (86) 215 046 1011
Web Site: http://www.leeport.com.hk
Sales Range: $75-99.9 Million
Emp.: 150
Machine Tool Distr
N.A.I.C.S.: 423830

Leeport Machinery (Taiwan) Co., Limited (1)
No 155-12 Duhuei S St, LongJing Dist, Taichung, 434018, Taiwan
Tel.: (886) 426313728
Metal Cutting Machinery Whslr
N.A.I.C.S.: 423830

Leeport Metalforming Machinery Limited (1)
1/F Block 1 Golden Dragon Industrial Centre 152-160 Tai Lin Pai Road, Kwai Chung, N T, China (Hong Kong)
Tel.: (852) 24277991
Web Site: http://www.leeport.com.hk
Emp.: 50
Metal Cutting Machinery Distr
N.A.I.C.S.: 423830

Leeport Metrology (Dongguan) Limited (1)
No 26 Guan Chang Rd Chong Tou Zone Chang An Town, Chan An Town, Dongguan, 523855, Guangdong, China
Tel.: (86) 76985417
Measuring Equipment Mfr

Leeport (Holdings) Limited—(Continued)
N.A.I.C.S.: 334515

Leeport Metrology Macao Commercial Offshore Limited (1)
8A Nam Yue Comml Ctr No 19 Calcada De Santo Agostinho, Macau, China (Macau)
Tel.: (853) 28355669
Machine Tool Distr
N.A.I.C.S.: 423830

Leeport Precision Machine Tool Company Limited (1)
1 F Block 1 Golden Dragon Indus Ctr 152-160 Tai Lin Pai Rd, Kwai Chung, New Territories, China (Hong Kong)
Tel.: (852) 24277991
Web Site: http://www.leeport.com.hk
Sales Range: $50-74.9 Million
Emp.: 100
Metal Cutting Machinery Supplier
N.A.I.C.S.: 423830

Leeport Tools Limited (1)
1 F Block 1 Golden Dragon Indus Ctr 152-160 Tai Lin Pai Rd, Kwai Chung, New Territories, China (Hong Kong)
Tel.: (852) 24277991
Web Site: http://www.leeport.com.hk
Sales Range: $75-99.9 Million
Emp.: 150
Machine Tool Distr
N.A.I.C.S.: 423830

Leeport Tools Macao Commercial Offshore Limited (1)
8A Nam Yue Comml Ctr No 19 Calcada De Santo Agostinho, Macau, China (Macau)
Tel.: (853) 28355601
Machine Tool Distr
N.A.I.C.S.: 423830

PT. Leeport Indonesia (1)
Soho Capital Unit SC 4101 Podomoro City Jl Letjend S Parman kav 28, Kelurahan Tanjung Duren Selatan Kecamatan Grogol Petamburan, Jakarta Barat, 11470, Indonesia
Tel.: (62) 212 789 3345
Investment Services
N.A.I.C.S.: 523999

PT. Leeport Machine Tool Indonesia (1)
Soho Capital Unit SC 4101 Podomoro City Jl Letjend S Parman Kav 28, Kelurahan Tanjung Duren Selatan Kecamatan Grogol Petamburan, Jakarta, 11470, Indonesia
Tel.: (62) 2127893345
Metal Cutting Machinery Whslr
N.A.I.C.S.: 423830

Rapman (Dongguan) Limited (1)
No 168-169 Tang Keng Baotun Village, Houjie Town, Dongguan, Guangdong, China
Tel.: (86) 76985038778
Web Site: http://www.rapman.hk
Rapid Prototypes Mfr
N.A.I.C.S.: 333248

Rapman Limited (1)
1/F Block 1 Golden Dragon Industrial Centre 152-160 Tai Lin Pai Road, Kwai Chung, New Teritories, China (Hong Kong)
Tel.: (852) 2 494 1728
Web Site: https://www.rapman.hk
Emp.: 7
Product Design & Rapid Prototypes Mfr
N.A.I.C.S.: 339910

LEEUWIN METALS LTD.
2 68 Hay St, Subiaco, 6008, WA, Australia
Tel.: (61) 865566427 AU
Web Site: https://www.leeuwinmetals.com
Year Founded: 2021
LM1—(ASX)
Rev.: $77,690
Assets: $2,374,932
Liabilities: $175,534
Net Worth: $2,199,398
Earnings: ($4,084,806)
Fiscal Year-end: 06/30/24
Metal Exploration Services
N.A.I.C.S.: 213114

Christopher Piggott *(Mng Dir)*

LEFORM BERHAD
PT 16077 & PT16078 Jalan Kesidang 4 Kawasan Perindustrian Sungai Choh, 48200, Serendah, Selangor, Malaysia
Tel.: (60) 360990666
Web Site: https://www.leformgroup.com.my
Year Founded: 1995
LEFORM—(KLS)
Rev.: $80,543,318
Assets: $99,378,973
Liabilities: $52,369,831
Net Worth: $47,009,143
Earnings: ($1,119,068)
Emp.: 273
Fiscal Year-end: 12/31/23
Steel Fabrication Product Mfr
N.A.I.C.S.: 331110

LEFROY EXPLORATION LIMITED
Level 3 7 Rheola St, West Perth, 6005, WA, Australia
Tel.: (61) 893210984 VG
Web Site: https://www.lefroyex.com
Year Founded: 1990
LEX—(ASX)
Rev.: $74,786
Assets: $16,688,034
Liabilities: $649,706
Net Worth: $16,038,328
Earnings: ($2,128,072)
Fiscal Year-end: 06/30/24
Investment Services
N.A.I.C.S.: 523999
Susan Hunter *(Sec)*

LEG IMMOBILIEN SE
Flughafenstrasse 99, 40474, Dusseldorf, Germany
Tel.: (49) 21145680 De
Web Site: https://www.leg-wohnen.de
Year Founded: 1970
LEG—(MUN)
Rev.: $1,512,081,126
Assets: $21,308,664,932
Liabilities: $13,070,262,348
Net Worth: $8,238,402,584
Earnings: ($1,731,640,869)
Emp.: 1,908
Fiscal Year-end: 12/31/23
Real Estate Manangement Services
N.A.I.C.S.: 531190
Michael Zimmer *(Chm-Supervisory Bd)*

Subsidiaries:

LEG Management GmbH (1)
Hans Bockler Strasse 38, 40476, Dusseldorf, Germany (100%)
Tel.: (49) 21145680
Web Site: http://www.leg-nrw.de
Residential & Commercial Real Estate Acquisition, Development & Property Management Services
N.A.I.C.S.: 531311

LEGACY FOOTWEAR LIMITED
House No 133 Ground Floor Lane No 01 West Side DOHS Baridhara, Dhaka, 1206, Bangladesh
Tel.: (880) 28415983
Web Site: https://www.legacyfootwearltd.com
Year Founded: 1996
LEGACYFOOT—(CHT)
Rev.: $16,034
Assets: $5,978,181
Liabilities: $1,581,240
Net Worth: $4,396,941
Earnings: $30,466
Emp.: 125
Fiscal Year-end: 06/30/23
Footwear Mfr

N.A.I.C.S.: 316210
Shahnaz Sultana *(Chm)*

LEGACY IRON ORE LIMITED
Tel.: (61) 894212000 AU
Web Site: https://www.legacyiron.com.au
LCY—(ASX)
Rev.: $3,056,132
Assets: $30,785,336
Liabilities: $8,028,130
Net Worth: $22,757,206
Earnings: ($6,254,006)
Fiscal Year-end: 03/31/24
Gold Ore Mining
N.A.I.C.S.: 212220
Benjamin Donovan *(Sec)*

LEGACY MERCANTILE LTD.
A - 4 First Floor Acharya Niketan Mayur Vihar Phase - I, Opp Fine Home Society, New Delhi, 110 091, India
Tel.: (91) 1132409091
Web Site: http://www.legacymercantile.com
Textile Product Mfr & Distr
N.A.I.C.S.: 314999
Ankit Brijpuriya *(Officer-Compliance & Co-Sec)*

LEGACY MINERALS HOLDINGS LIMITED
401/54 Miller Street, North Sydney, 2060, NSW, Australia
Tel.: (61) 299593520 AU
Web Site: https://www.legacyminerals.com.au
Year Founded: 2021
LGM—(ASX)
Rev.: $40,647
Assets: $3,742,836
Liabilities: $464,633
Net Worth: $3,278,203
Earnings: ($617,273)
Fiscal Year-end: 06/30/23
Holding Company
N.A.I.C.S.: 551112
Ian Morgan *(CFO & Sec)*

LEGACY PHARMACEUTICALS SWITZERLAND GMBH
Ruhrbergstrasse 21, 4127, Birsfelden, Switzerland
Tel.: (41) 613161600
Web Site: http://www.legacypharma.com
Year Founded: 2007
Sales Range: $25-49.9 Million
Emp.: 180
Pharmaceuticals Product Mfr
N.A.I.C.S.: 325412
Doris Arab *(Dir-Supply Chain)*

LEGACY VENTURES INTERNATIONAL, INC.
Unit 01 82/F International Commerce Centre 1 Austin Road West, Kowloon, China (Hong Kong)
Tel.: (852) 39606394 NV
Year Founded: 2014
LGYV—(OTCEM)
Assets: $21,000
Liabilities: $31,000
Net Worth: ($10,000)
Earnings: $307,000
Emp.: 5
Fiscal Year-end: 06/30/22
Real Estate Management Consulting Services
N.A.I.C.S.: 541611
Pak Hong Wan *(Chm, Pres, CEO, CFO, Treas & Sec)*

LEGAL & GENERAL GROUP PLC
One Coleman Street, London, EC2R 5AA, United Kingdom
Tel.: (44) 1737370370 UK
Web Site: https://group.legalandgeneral.com
Year Founded: 1836
LGEN—(LSE)
Assets: $618,240,942,000
Liabilities: $603,619,516,500
Net Worth: $14,621,425,500
Earnings: $2,758,305,000
Fiscal Year-end: 12/31/22
Financial Investment Services
N.A.I.C.S.: 523999
Geoffrey Timms *(Gen Counsel & Sec)*

Subsidiaries:

Banner Construction Limited (1)
84 High Street, London, NW10 4SJ, United Kingdom
Tel.: (44) 2080599670
Web Site: http://www.bannercontractors.co.uk
Civil Engineering Services
N.A.I.C.S.: 541330

CALA Group Limited (1)
Adam House 5 Mid New Cultins, Edinburgh, EH11 4DU, United Kingdom (100%)
Tel.: (44) 1315355200
Web Site: https://www.cala.co.uk
Sales Range: $900-999.9 Million
Holding Company; Residential Real Estate Development, Construction & Sales
N.A.I.C.S.: 551112

Subsidiary (Domestic):

CALA Homes (East) Limited (2)
Anderson House 25 Abercrombie Court Prospect Road, Westhill, Aberdeen, AB32 6FE, United Kingdom
Tel.: (44) 1224 737 800
Web Site: http://www.cala.co.uk
Residential Real Estate Development, Construction & Sales
N.A.I.C.S.: 236117

CALA Homes (Midlands) Limited (2)
CALA House Arleston Way, Solihull, B90 4LH, Midlands, United Kingdom
Tel.: (44) 121 711 5310
Web Site: http://www.cala.co.uk
Residential Real Estate Development, Construction & Sales
N.A.I.C.S.: 236117

CALA Homes (South) Limited (2)
CALA House 54 The Causeway, Staines-upon-Thames, TW18 3AX, United Kingdom
Tel.: (44) 1784 225 300
Web Site: http://www.cala.co.uk
Residential Real Estate Development, Construction & Sales
N.A.I.C.S.: 236117

CALA Homes (West) Limited (2)
Cairnlee House Callendar Road, Callendar Business Park, Falkirk, FK1 1XE, United Kingdom
Tel.: (44) 132 460 0000
Web Site: https://www.cala.co.uk
Residential Real Estate Development, Construction & Sales
N.A.I.C.S.: 236117

CALA Homes (Chiltern) Limited (1)
Gemini House Mercury Park, Wooburn Green, HP10 0HH, Buckinghamshire, United Kingdom
Tel.: (44) 1628552300
Home Rental Services
N.A.I.C.S.: 531110
Andrew Aldridge *(Dir-Land)*

CALA Homes (North Home Counties) Limited (1)
1 Falcon Gate Shire Park, Welwyn Garden City, AL7 1TW, United Kingdom
Tel.: (44) 17073971100
Home Rental Services
N.A.I.C.S.: 531110
Duncan Jackson *(Mng Dir)*

CALA Homes (Scotland) Limited (1)
Adam House 5 Mid New Cultins, Edinburgh,

EH11 4DU, United Kingdom
Tel.: (44) 1315355200
Home Rental Services
N.A.I.C.S.: 531110

CALA Homes (South Home Counties) Limited (1)
Tilford House Farnham Business Park Weydon Lane, Farnham, GU9 8QT, Surrey, United Kingdom
Tel.: (44) 1252736750
Home Rental Services
N.A.I.C.S.: 531110

CALA Homes (Thames) Limited (1)
Cala House 54 The Causeway, Staines-upon-Thames, TW18 3AX, United Kingdom
Tel.: (44) 1784225300
Home Rental Services
N.A.I.C.S.: 531110

Legal & General (Unit Trust Managers) Limited (1)
1 Coleman Street, London, EC2R 5AA, United Kingdom
Tel.: (44) 20 3124 3000
Web Site: http://www.legalandgeneral.com
Financial Management Services
N.A.I.C.S.: 523999

Legal & General America Inc. (1)
3275 Bennett Creek Ave, Frederick, MD 21704
Tel.: (301) 279-4800
Web Site: http://www.lgamerica.com
Sales Range: $75-99.9 Million
Holding Company
N.A.I.C.S.: 551112
Andrew D. Love *(CFO & Sr VP)*

Subsidiary (Domestic):

Banner Life Insurance Company (2)
3275 Bennett Creek Ave, Frederick, MD 21704 **(100%)**
Tel.: (301) 279-4800
Sales Range: $300-349.9 Million
Emp.: 203
Life, Health & Accident Insurance
N.A.I.C.S.: 524113
David J. Orr *(Chief Actuary & Sr VP)*

Subsidiary (Domestic):

William Penn Life Insurance Company of New York (3)
100 Quentin Roosevelt Blvd, Garden City, NY 11530 **(100%)**
Tel.: (516) 794-3700
Web Site: http://www.lgamerica.com
Emp.: 300
Life Insurance Underwriting
N.A.I.C.S.: 524113

Legal & General Assurance (Pensions Management) Limited (1)
1 Coleman Street, London, EC2R 5AA, United Kingdom
Tel.: (44) 2031243000
Insurance & Pension Management Services
N.A.I.C.S.: 524210

Legal & General Assurance Society Limited (1)
1 Comann Street, London, AC2R 5AA, United Kingdom **(100%)**
Tel.: (44) 2075286200
Web Site: http://www.legalandgeneral.com
Life & General Insurance
N.A.I.C.S.: 524113

Legal & General Bank (France) SA (1)
58 Rue De La Victoire, Paris, 75009, France
Tel.: (33) 155312400
Web Site: http://www.lgfrance-partners.com
Commercial Banking Services
N.A.I.C.S.: 522110

Legal & General Homes Modular Limited (1)
Sherburn Enterprise Park Hurricane Way South, Sherburn-in-Elmut, LS25 6PT, United Kingdom
Tel.: (44) 3302020850
General Life Insurance Services
N.A.I.C.S.: 524113
Tracey Jackson *(Head-HR)*

Legal & General Investment Management Limited (1)
1 Common Street, London, EC2R 5AA, United Kingdom **(100%)**
Tel.: (44) 2031242000
Web Site: http://www.legalgeneral.com
Sales Range: $50-74.9 Million
Emp.: 100
Investment Management
N.A.I.C.S.: 525910
Mark Zinkula *(Co-CEO)*

Subsidiary (Domestic):

LGV Capital Ltd. (2)
One Coleman Street, London, EC2R 5AA, United Kingdom
Tel.: (44) 2031242900
Web Site: http://www.lgvcapital.com
Privater Equity Firm
N.A.I.C.S.: 523999
Michael Mowlem *(Mng Dir)*

Subsidiary (US):

Legal & General Investment Management America Inc. (2)
8755 W Higgins Rd Ste 600, Chicago, IL 60631
Tel.: (773) 867-1650
Web Site: http://www.lgima.com
Sales Range: $50-74.9 Million
Emp.: 28
Investment Advisory Services
N.A.I.C.S.: 523940
John Bender *(CIO-Fixed Income)*

Legal & General Pensions Limited (1)
1 Coleman Street, London, EC2R 5AA, United Kingdom
Tel.: (44) 20 3124 3000
Pension Fund Management Services
N.A.I.C.S.: 525110

Legal & General Property Limited (1)
1 Coleman St, London, EC2R 5AA, United Kingdom
Tel.: (44) 2031242000
Fund Management Services
N.A.I.C.S.: 523940
James O'Neill *(Head-Intl Distr)*

Holding (Domestic):

Northampton Shopping Centre Limited Partnership (2)
Grosvenor Centre Management Office 2 Union Street, Northampton, NN1 2EW, United Kingdom
Tel.: (44) 1604 637268
Web Site: http://www.grosvenorshoppingcentre.co.uk
Sales Range: $50-74.9 Million
Shopping Mall Management Services
N.A.I.C.S.: 531120

Legal & General Resources Limited (1)
1 Coleman St, London, EC2R 5AA, United Kingdom
Tel.: (44) 20 3124 3000
Web Site: http://www.legalandgeneralgroup.com
Financial Management Services
N.A.I.C.S.: 523999

Legal & General Surveying Services Limited (1)
Unit 1-5 Churchfield Court, Barnsley, S70 2JT, South Yorkshire, United Kingdom
Tel.: (44) 1226230500
General Life Insurance Services
N.A.I.C.S.: 524113
Kevin Webb *(Mng Dir)*

LEGEND HOLDINGS CORPORATION
B-17 Raycom Info Tech Park No 2 Ke Xue Yuan South Road, Haidian District, Beijing, 100190, China
Tel.: (86) 1062509999 CN
Web Site: https://www.legendholdings.com.cn
Year Founded: 1984

3396—(HKG)
Rev.: $67,906,242,659
Assets: $95,622,813,187
Liabilities: $81,280,163,297
Net Worth: $14,342,649,890
Earnings: $1,459,313,809
Emp.: 102,187
Fiscal Year-end: 12/31/22
Investment Holding Company
N.A.I.C.S.: 551112
Chuanzhi Liu *(Founder)*

Subsidiaries:

Banque Internationale a Luxembourg S.A. (1)
69 Rte D'Esch, Luxembourg, 2953, Luxembourg **(89.9%)**
Tel.: (352) 45905000
Web Site: http://www.bil.com
Domestic & International Banking Services
N.A.I.C.S.: 522299
Luc Frieden *(Gen Mgr)*

Subsidiary (Domestic):

BIL Lease S.A. (2)
42 rue de la Vallee, Luxembourg, 2661, Luxembourg **(100%)**
Tel.: (352) 2277331
Web Site: http://www.bil.com
Equipment Rental & Leasing Services
N.A.I.C.S.: 532490
Charlotte Lies *(Gen Mgr)*

Subsidiary (Non-US):

Banque Internationale a Luxembourg (Suisse) SA (2)
Boulevard Georges-Favon 7, 1204, Geneva, Switzerland
Tel.: (41) 588108858
Web Site: http://ch.bil.com
Pension, Health & Welfare Funds
N.A.I.C.S.: 524292

Subsidiary (Domestic):

Belair House SA (2)
10 Rue Henri M Schnadt, Luxembourg, 2530, Luxembourg
Tel.: (352) 2732841
Web Site: http://www.belairhouse.lu
Finance & Banking Services
N.A.I.C.S.: 522110
Jeanne Ranaivoson *(COO)*

Hony Capital (Beijing) Co., Ltd. (1)
6th Floor South Tower C Raycom InfoTech Park No 2 Ke Xue Yuan Nan Lu, Haidian, Beijing, 100190, China
Tel.: (86) 1082655888
Web Site: http://www.honycapital.com
Sales Range: $25-49.9 Million
Emp.: 100
Private Equity Investments
N.A.I.C.S.: 523999
John Ling Huan Zhao *(Chm & CEO)*

Subsidiary (Non-US):

Hony Capital Ltd. (2)
Suite 06-11 70F Two International Finance Centre No 8 Finance Street, Central, China (Hong Kong) **(100%)**
Tel.: (852) 39619700
Web Site: https://www.honycapital.com
Middle-Market Private Equity Investments
N.A.I.C.S.: 523999

Holding (Non-US):

PizzaExpress Ltd. (2)
Hunton House Highbridge Estate, Oxford Road, Uxbridge, UB8 1LX, Mddx, United Kingdom **(100%)**
Tel.: (44) 8453899489
Web Site: http://www.pizzaexpress.com
Sales Range: $10-24.9 Million
Emp.: 60
Pizza Restaurants Operator
N.A.I.C.S.: 722511
Charlotte Maxwell *(Dir-Comml)*

Legend Capital Co., Ltd (1)
10F Tower A Raycom Infotech Park No 2 Kexueyuan South Road, Zhongguancun Haidian District, Beijing, China
Tel.: (86) 10 6250 8000

Web Site: http://www.legendcapital.com.cn
Private Equity & Venture Capital Investment Services
N.A.I.C.S.: 523999
Linan Zhu *(Co-Founder, Mng Dir & CEO)*

Levima Advanced Materials Corporation (1)
Rooms 1606-1609 South Building Tower C No 2 Kexueyuan South Road, Raycom Infotech Park Haidian District, Beijing, 100190, China
Tel.: (86) 1062508855
Web Site: https://www.levima.cn
Rev.: $1,145,241,396
Assets: $1,973,219,508
Liabilities: $938,002,572
Net Worth: $1,035,216,936
Earnings: $121,621,500
Fiscal Year-end: 12/31/2022
Chemical Product Mfr & Distr
N.A.I.C.S.: 325520
Haili Zhao *(Sr VP-Production & Ops)*

LEGEND MEDIA, INC.
Room 609 Gehua Tower A Qinglong Hutong Building No 1, Beijing, 100007, China
Tel.: (86) 10 8418 6112 NV
Web Site: http://www.legend-media.com
Year Founded: 1998
Sales Range: $1-9.9 Million
Radio Advertising Services
N.A.I.C.S.: 541890
BaoChun Ju *(CEO)*

LEGEND MINING LIMITED
Level 1 8 Kings Park Road, West Perth, 6005, WA, Australia
Tel.: (61) 892120600
Web Site: https://www.legendmining.com.au
LEG—(ASX)
Rev.: $437,940
Assets: $37,615,941
Liabilities: $873,198
Net Worth: $36,742,743
Earnings: ($3,418,922)
Emp.: 8
Fiscal Year-end: 12/31/23
Base Metal & Precious Metal Mining & Exploration
N.A.I.C.S.: 212220
Michael William Atkins *(Chm)*

LEGEND POWER SYSTEMS INC.
1480 Frances Street, Vancouver, V5L 1Y9, BC, Canada
Web Site: https://legendpower.com
Year Founded: 2001
LPS—(TSXV)
Rev.: $835,228
Assets: $3,948,663
Liabilities: $932,299
Net Worth: $3,016,364
Earnings: ($3,157,821)
Fiscal Year-end: 09/30/23
Electric Equipment Mfr
N.A.I.C.S.: 335999
Randy Buchamer *(CEO)*

LEGEND SPICES, INC.
14 Kajaznuni Street Apt 70, Yerevan, 0070, Armenia
Tel.: (374) 99432000 NV
Web Site: https://sacredspices.com
Year Founded: 2021
LGSP—(OTCIQ)
Rev.: $5,794
Assets: $4,946
Liabilities: $41,995
Net Worth: ($37,049)
Earnings: ($62,820)
Fiscal Year-end: 12/31/23
Packaged Food Product Mfr
N.A.I.C.S.: 311412

LEGEND STRATEGY INTERNATIONAL HOLDINGS GROUP

Legend Spices, Inc.—(Continued)

LEGEND STRATEGY INTERNATIONAL HOLDINGS GROUP
Suite 1705 17/F World-Wide House 19 Des Voeux Road Central, Central, China (Hong Kong)
Tel.: (852) 37003000 **Ky**
Web Site: http://www.legend-strategy.com
1355—(HKG)
Rev.: $8,032,755
Assets: $25,011,420
Liabilities: $27,672,855
Net Worth: ($2,661,435)
Earnings: ($2,249,993)
Emp.: 120
Fiscal Year-end: 12/31/22
Hotel Operator
N.A.I.C.S.: 721110
Tin Yan Chung *(CFO & Sec)*

Subsidiaries:

Grand China Industrial Limited (1)
E1 22/F Shui Sum Industrial Bldg 8-10 Kwai Sau Road, Kwai Chung, China (Hong Kong)
Tel.: (852) 24013618
Web Site: https://www.grand-china.com.hk
Toy & Sporting Good Mfr
N.A.I.C.S.: 339930
Jovida Chan *(Mgr-Sls & Mktg)*

LEGEND UPSTAR HOLDINGS LIMITED
Rooms 2505-8 25th Floor World-Wide House 19 Des Voeux Road, Central, China (Hong Kong)
Tel.: (852) 29956459 **Ky**
Web Site: http://www.midlandici.com.hk
0459—(HKG)
Rev.: $57,385,583
Assets: $232,116,810
Liabilities: $86,623,245
Net Worth: $145,493,565
Earnings: ($465,630)
Emp.: 577
Fiscal Year-end: 12/31/22
Industrial, Commercial & Shops Investor & Acquirer
N.A.I.C.S.: 531390
Daniel Hon Shing Wong *(CEO & Exec Dir)*

Subsidiaries:

EVI Education Asia Limited (1)
Rm 02-03 13 Fl Park Commercial Ctr Tung Lo Wan Rd, Causeway Bay Plz, Causeway Bay, China (Hong Kong)
Tel.: (852) 21873090
Web Site: http://www.evi.com.hk
Sales Range: $10-24.9 Million
Emp.: 20
Internet Education Provider
N.A.I.C.S.: 611710
Kenneth Wong *(Mgr)*

EVI Services Limited (1)
No 9 G/F Upper Floor Long Shing Wan Plaza 8 Hoi Fai Road, Tai Kok Tsui, Kowloon, China (Hong Kong)
Tel.: (852) 21873090
Web Site: https://www.evigarten.com
Internet Education Provider
N.A.I.C.S.: 611420

Hong Kong Property Services IC&I Limited (1)
Hankow rd 3941 Maxwell centre 3 F, 580A Nathan Rd Mongkok, Kowloon, China (Hong Kong)
Tel.: (852) 29286333
Web Site: http://www.hkpici.com.hk
Emp.: 60
Property Managing Services
N.A.I.C.S.: 531312

Midland IC&I Surveyors Limited (1)
Room 2505-08 25th Floor Global Building 19 Des Voeux Road Central, Central, China (Hong Kong)
Tel.: (852) 28014930

Real Estate Services
N.A.I.C.S.: 531390

Midland Realty (Comm. & Ind.)Limited (1)
Hoi Yuen Rd, Kwun Tong, China (Hong Kong)
Tel.: (852) 23318222
Web Site: http://www.iando7midlandici.com
Property Managing Services
N.A.I.C.S.: 531312
Stane Chow *(Gen Mgr)*

Midland Realty (Comm.) Limited (1)
18th Fl One Grand Tower, 639 Nathan Rd, Kowloon, China (Hong Kong)
Tel.: (852) 25231198
Property Management
N.A.I.C.S.: 531312

Midland Realty (Shops) Limited (1)
18th Fl One Grand Tower, 639 Nathan Rd, Kowloon, China (Hong Kong)
Tel.: (852) 23112733
Property Managing Services
N.A.I.C.S.: 531312

Princeton Residence (HK) Limited (1)
33 Java Road, North Point, China (Hong Kong)
Tel.: (852) 37558888
Residence Services
N.A.I.C.S.: 721199

Silicon Workshop Limited (1)
Skyway House 11 Kok Cheung St, Tai Kok Tsui, China (Hong Kong)
Tel.: (852) 27870909
Web Site: http://www.silicon.com.hk
Sales Range: $25-49.9 Million
Emp.: 15
Display Electronics Mfr
N.A.I.C.S.: 334513

LEGENDARY MOTORCAR COMPANY LTD.
8220 5th Line, Halton Hills, L7G 4S6, ON, Canada
Tel.: (905) 875-4700
Web Site: http://www.legendarymotorcar.com
Year Founded: 1985
Sales Range: $1-9.9 Million
Emp.: 15
Classic Car Restoration & Sales
N.A.I.C.S.: 811198

LEGENDARY VENTURES, INC.
5615 Doctor Peddle Crescent, Mississauga, L5M 0K4, ON, Canada
Tel.: (647) 478-6365 **NV**
Year Founded: 2012
Sales Range: Less than $1 Million
Pest Control Services
N.A.I.C.S.: 561710
Zahoor Ahmad *(Pres, CEO, CFO, Treas & Sec)*

LEGION (H.K.) LIMITED
Rm 902 Yue Shing Commercial Bldg, No 15 Queen Victoria St, Central, China (Hong Kong)
Tel.: (852) 25303099 **HK**
Web Site: http://www.legionhk.com
Kitchen Furniture
N.A.I.C.S.: 337110
Sam Chong *(Gen Mgr)*

LEGION CONSORTIUM LIMITED
Unit 912 9/F Two Harbourfront 22 Tak Fung Street, Hunghom, Kowloon, China (Hong Kong)
Tel.: (852) 35858646 **Ky**
Web Site: http://www.legionconsortium.com
Year Founded: 1995
2129—(HKG)
Logistic Services
N.A.I.C.S.: 541614
Choon Eng Ng *(Chm & CEO)*

Subsidiaries:

Radiant Overseas Pte. Ltd. (1)
7 Keppel Rd, Singapore, 089053, Singapore
Tel.: (65) 62241600
Freight Forwarding Services
N.A.I.C.S.: 488510

Real Time Forwarding Pte. Ltd. (1)
7 Keppel Road 03-43/44 Tanjong Pagar Complex, Singapore, 089053, Singapore
Tel.: (65) 62243346
Web Site: http://www.rtf.com.sg
Freight Forwarding Services
N.A.I.C.S.: 488510

Rejoice Container Services (Pte) Ltd. (1)
7 Keppel Road 03-20/21/22/23/24 Tanjong Pagar Complex, Singapore, 089053, Singapore
Tel.: (65) 62275836
Web Site: http://www.rejoicecontainer.com
Logistic Services
N.A.I.C.S.: 488510

Richwell Global Forwarding Pte. Ltd. (1)
19 Loyang Way 04-28/29 Changi Logistics Centre, Singapore, 508724, Singapore
Tel.: (65) 65439060
Web Site: http://www.richwellglobal.com
Logistic Services
N.A.I.C.S.: 488510
Stephen Yeo *(Mng Dir)*

LEGMAS S.A.
Str Aviator C H Agarici nr 2, Navodari, Constanta, Romania
Tel.: (40) 241 768939
Web Site: http://www.legmas.ro
Year Founded: 1962
Sales Range: $1-9.9 Million
Emp.: 53
Agricultural Machinery Mfr
N.A.I.C.S.: 333111

LEGOCHEM BIOSCIENCES INC.
10 Gukjegwahak 10-ro, Yuseong-gu, Daejeon, 34302, Korea (South)
Tel.: (82) 428610688
Web Site: https://www.legochembio.com
Year Founded: 2006
141080—(KRS)
Rev.: $25,627,037
Assets: $193,690,855
Liabilities: $25,258,479
Net Worth: $168,432,376
Earnings: ($34,585,406)
Emp.: 146
Fiscal Year-end: 12/31/22
Biopharmaceutical Researcher, Developer & Mfr
N.A.I.C.S.: 325412
Young Lag Cho *(Chief Dev Officer)*

Subsidiaries:

LegoChem Biosciences Inc. - Anseong Plant (1)
354 Wondang-ro Wongok-myeon, Anseong, 17557, Gyeonggi-do, Korea (South)
Tel.: (82) 7043337906
Biopharmaceutical Product Distr
N.A.I.C.S.: 424210

LEGRAND S.A.
128 Av du Marechal de Lattre de Tassigny, 87045, Limoges, France
Tel.: (33) 555068787 **FR**
Web Site: https://www.legrandgroup.com
Year Founded: 1860
LR—(EUR)
Rev.: $9,000,000,000
Assets: $15,557,090,438
Liabilities: $8,388,085,474
Net Worth: $7,169,004,964
Earnings: $1,078,674,725

Emp.: 33,895
Fiscal Year-end: 12/31/22
Electrical Telecommunications Products & Power Wiring Systems & Services
N.A.I.C.S.: 335929
John Selldorff *(Pres & CEO-North & Central America)*

Subsidiaries:

Australian Plastic Profiles Pty. Ltd. (1)
12 Cawarra Rd, Caringbah, 2229, NSW, Australia
Tel.: (61) 0295278800
Web Site: http://www.app.net.au
Sales Range: $25-49.9 Million
Emp.: 120
Plastics, Metal & Electronics Mfr
N.A.I.C.S.: 326220
John Hills *(Pres & CEO)*

Kenall Manufacturing Co, (1)
10200 55th St, Kenosha, WI 53144
Tel.: (262) 891-9700
Web Site: http://www.kenall.com
Electrical & Electronic Product Mfr
N.A.I.C.S.: 335999
Vic Fernandez *(VP-Ops & Dir-Mfg)*

Legrand France SA (1)
128 Avenue du Marechal de Lattre de Tassigny, 87045, Limoges, Cedex, France
Tel.: (33) 555068787
Low Voltage Electrical Fitting Accessories Mfr & Distr
N.A.I.C.S.: 335999

Subsidiary (Non-US):

Electro Andina Ltda (2)
Vicuna Mackenna, 1292, Santiago, Chile
Tel.: (56) 225505200
Web Site: http://www.legrand.cl
Electrical Products & Equipment Marketing
N.A.I.C.S.: 423610

Subsidiary (Domestic):

Groupe Arnould SAS (2)
5 Rue Jean Nicot, BP, 155, 93691, Pantin, France
Tel.: (33) 1 48 10 69 67
Web Site: http://www.legrandgroup.com
Sales Range: $50-74.9 Million
Electric Adapter Retailer
N.A.I.C.S.: 444180

ICM Group S.A. (2)
1 Route De Semur, 21500, Montbard, France
Tel.: (33) 3 80 89 58 15
Web Site: http://www.legrandgroup.com
Sales Range: $25-49.9 Million
Fiber Protection Cable Mfr
N.A.I.C.S.: 332618

Subsidiary (Non-US):

Inform Elektronik San. ve Tic. A.S. (2)
Esensehir Mah Hale Sk No 6/1, Umraniye, Istanbul, Turkiye
Tel.: (90) 2166225800
Web Site: https://www.informups.com
Industrial Electronic System Mfr
N.A.I.C.S.: 334419

LEGRAND SCANDINAVIA APS (2)
Avedoreholmen 48, 2650, Hvidovre, Denmark
Tel.: (45) 36 34 05 90
Cable Tray & Ladder Mfr
N.A.I.C.S.: 332618

LEGRAND SLV D.O.O (2)
Planjava 2, 1236, Trzin, Slovenia
Tel.: (386) 1 562 01 70
Sales Range: $50-74.9 Million
Emp.: 5
Electrical Cable Distr
N.A.I.C.S.: 423610
Gregor Svigelj *(Country Mgr)*

LEGRAND Ukraine Ltd (2)
Turivska 31, 04080, Kiev, Ukraine
Tel.: (380) 443511200
Web Site: http://www.legrand.ua

AND PRIVATE COMPANIES — LEGRAND S.A.

Sales Range: $25-49.9 Million
Electrical Component Mfr
N.A.I.C.S.: 335999

Legrand (Suisse) S.A. (2)
Industriestrasse 3, 5242, Birr, Switzerland
Tel.: (41) 56 464 67 67
Web Site: http://www.legrandgroup.com
Sales Range: $25-49.9 Million
Electrical Equipment Installation Services
N.A.I.C.S.: 238210

Legrand China (2)
30th Floor Shanghai Oriental Center No 699 Nanjing West Road, 200041, Shanghai, China (100%)
Tel.: (86) 2152110111
Web Site: http://www.legrand.com.cn
Electrical Wiring Mfr
N.A.I.C.S.: 423610

Legrand Colombia SA (2)
Calle 65 A No 93-91, Bogota, Colombia
Tel.: (57) 14376700
Web Site: https://www.legrand.com.co
Electrical Equipment Installation Services
N.A.I.C.S.: 238210

Legrand Electric Ltd (2)
Great King Street North, Birmingham, B19 2LF, United Kingdom
Tel.: (44) 3456054333
Web Site: https://www.legrand.co.uk
Emp.: 100
Wiring Device Mfr & Distr
N.A.I.C.S.: 335931
Ian Larner *(Mgr-Sls-Gulf Countries)*

Subsidiary (Domestic):

CP Electronics Limited (3)
Brent Crescent, London, NW10 7XR, United Kingdom
Tel.: (44) 333 900 0671
Web Site: http://www.cpelectronics.co.uk
Energy Saving Electronic Control Mfr
N.A.I.C.S.: 334512

Subsidiary (Non-US):

Legrand Electrica S.A. (2)
Estrada da Alagoa 96, Carcavelos, 2775-716, Cascais, Portugal
Tel.: (351) 214548800
Sales Range: $100-124.9 Million
Emp.: 20
Electrical Equipment Installation Services
N.A.I.C.S.: 238210

Legrand Electrical (2)
5f 2nd Bldg No 508 Chundong Rd, Minhang Dist, Shanghai, 201108, China
Tel.: (86) 2164780178
Electrical Equipment Distr
N.A.I.C.S.: 423610

Legrand Electrique SA (2)
Kouterveldstraat 9, 1831, Diegem, Belgium
Tel.: (32) 2 719 17 11
Web Site: http://www.legrand.be
Sales Range: $50-74.9 Million
Turbine Driven Power Station Installation Services & Distr
N.A.I.C.S.: 423610

Legrand Elektrik San. A.S. (2)
Sishane Refik Saydam Cad No 179, 34430, Istanbul, Turkiye
Tel.: (90) 212 368 28 00
Web Site: http://www.legrand.com
Electrical Component Mfr
N.A.I.C.S.: 335999

Legrand Espana SL (2)
Hierro 56, 28850, Torrejon de Ardoz, Madrid, Spain
Tel.: (34) 91 656 18 12
Web Site: http://www.legrand.com
Electric Equipment Mfr
N.A.I.C.S.: 335999

Legrand GmbH (2)
Am Silberg 14, 59494, Soest, Germany
Tel.: (49) 2921104317
Web Site: http://www.legrandgroup.com
Sales Range: $50-74.9 Million
Electronic Components Mfr
N.A.I.C.S.: 334419

Legrand Group Pty Ltd (2)
Bldg 4 43-47 Lyn Parade, Prestons, Sydney, 2170, NSW, Australia
Tel.: (61) 287194333
Web Site: http://www.hpmlegrand.com.au
Sales Range: $100-124.9 Million
Emp.: 30
Electrical Equipment Installation Services
N.A.I.C.S.: 238210

Legrand India Pvt Ltd (2)
61/62 Kalpataru Square 6th Floor Off Andheri-Kurla Road, Andheri East, Mumbai, 400 059, India
Tel.: (91) 2230416201
Web Site: http://www.legrand.co.in
Sales Range: $200-249.9 Million
Electrical Wiring Supplies Mfr
N.A.I.C.S.: 335931

Unit (Domestic):

Legrand India Pvt Ltd - Jalgaon Manufacturing Unit (3)
D-4 MIDC Industrial Estate, Jalgaon, 425 003, Maharashtra, India
Tel.: (91) 257 2272401
Web Site: http://www.legrand.co.in
Sales Range: $75-99.9 Million
Electrical Wiring Supplies Mfr
N.A.I.C.S.: 335931
Pramod Parulekar *(Gen Mgr)*

Legrand India Pvt Ltd - Nashik Manufacturing Unit (3)
A-2 MIDC Industrial Area Malegaon Village, Sinnar, Nasik, 422 113, India
Tel.: (91) 2551 230959
Web Site: http://www.legrand.co.in
Emp.: 500
Electrical Wiring Supplies Mfr
N.A.I.C.S.: 335931
Shripad Kulkarni *(Gen Mgr)*

Subsidiary (Non-US):

Legrand Nederland B.V. (2)
Van Salmstraat 76, 5281 RS, Boxtel, Netherlands (100%)
Tel.: (31) 411653111
Web Site: https://www.legrand.nl
Electrical Telecommunications Products & Power Wiring Systems & Services
N.A.I.C.S.: 334290

Subsidiary (Non-US):

Bticino SpA (3)
Via Messina 38, 20154, Milan, Italy (100%)
Tel.: (39) 0234801
Web Site: http://www.bticino.it
Design, Manufacture & Marketing of Electrical Products & Systems
N.A.I.C.S.: 423620

Subsidiary (Non-US):

Bticino Chile Ltda (4)
Roger de Flor 2901, Las Condes, Santiago, Chile
Tel.: (56) 2 585 3600
Web Site: http://www.Bticino.com
Emp.: 8
Electrical Component Mfr & Distr
N.A.I.C.S.: 335999

Bticino Chile S.A. (4)
Vicuna Mackenna, 1292, Santiago, Chile (100%)
Tel.: (56) 225505200
Web Site: http://www.bticino.cl
Mfr & Distr of Low Voltage Electrical Products
N.A.I.C.S.: 335999

Bticino China (4)
30F Oriental Center No 699 Nanjing West Road, 200041, Shanghai, China (100%)
Tel.: (86) 2152110111
Sales Range: $25-49.9 Million
Emp.: 20
Electronic Products for Home, Office & Industry
N.A.I.C.S.: 423620

Bticino de Mexico SA de CV (4)
Carretera Queretaro-San Luis Potosi No 22512 Int 6, Santa Rosa Jaurequi, CP 76220, Queretaro, Mexico
Tel.: (52) 4422380400
Web Site: https://www.bticino.com.mx

Designs, Manufactures & Markets Electrical Products & Systems
N.A.I.C.S.: 335999

Subsidiary (US):

Legrand Holding Inc. (4)
60 Woodlawn St, West Hartford, CT 06110
Tel.: (860) 233-6251
Web Site: http://www.legrand.us
Holding Company
N.A.I.C.S.: 551112
Steve Schneider *(CFO)*

Subsidiary (Domestic):

Legrand North America, LLC (5)
60 Woodlawn St, West Hartford, CT 06110
Tel.: (877) 295-3472
Web Site: http://www.legrand.us
Electronic Mfr & Installation
N.A.I.C.S.: 238210
John Selldorff *(Pres & CEO)*

Subsidiary (Domestic):

Cables to Go (6)
3555 Kettering Blvd, Moraine, OH 45439
Tel.: (937) 224-8646
Web Site: http://www.cablestogo.com
Sales Range: $25-49.9 Million
Sales of Computer Connectivity Products
N.A.I.C.S.: 238210

Branch (Domestic):

Cables to Go (7)
2351 South 2300 West, Salt Lake City, UT 84119-2048
Tel.: (801) 973-6090
Web Site: http://www.cablestogo-oem.com
Sales Range: $10-24.9 Million
Emp.: 40
Provides Connectivity Solutions to OEM
N.A.I.C.S.: 332322

Subsidiary (Domestic):

Cablofil Inc. (6)
8319 State Route 4, Mascoutah, IL 62258
Tel.: (618) 566-3244
Web Site: http://www.legrand.us
Emp.: 100
Electronic Cable Mfr
N.A.I.C.S.: 335921
Paul Courson *(Mng Dir)*

Focal Point, LLC (6)
4141 S Pulaski Rd, Chicago, IL 60632-3415
Tel.: (773) 247-9494
Web Site: https://www.focalpointlights.com
Architectural Lighting Fixture Mfr
N.A.I.C.S.: 335131
Peter Thornton Sr. *(Founder & Chm)*

Kenall Manufacturing Co. (6)
10200 55th St, Kenosha, WI 53144
Tel.: (262) 891-9700
Web Site: https://www.kenall.com
Commercial, Industrial & Institutional Electric Lighting Fixture Mfr
N.A.I.C.S.: 335132
Jim Hawkins *(CEO)*

Legrand AV, Inc. (6)
6436 City West Pkwy, Eden Prairie, MN 55344
Audio Visual, Mounting Equipment & Display Solutions Designer, Marketer & Distr
N.A.I.C.S.: 334310
Katia Desmichels *(Sls Mgr-France & Spain)*

Unit (Domestic):

Da-Lite (7)
3100 N Detroit St, Warsaw, IN 46582
Tel.: (574) 267-8101
Web Site: http://www.legrandav.com
Projection Screens & Accessories Mfr
N.A.I.C.S.: 334220
Tim Henson *(Dir-Screen Tech)*

Subsidiary (Non-US):

Legrand AV Netherlands B.V. (7)
Franklinstraat 14, 6003 DK, Weert, Netherlands
Tel.: (31) 495 580 840
Web Site: http://www.legrandav.com
Projection Screen Mfr
N.A.I.C.S.: 334310

Unit (Domestic):

Vaddio (7)
131 Cheshire Ln Ste 500, Minnetonka, MN 55305
Tel.: (763) 971-4400
Web Site: http://www.vaddio.com
Photographic & Photocopying Equipment Mfr
N.A.I.C.S.: 333310

Subsidiary (Non-US):

Legrand Canada, Inc. (6)
9024 Keele St, Vaughan, L4K 2N2, ON, Canada
Tel.: (905) 738-9195
Web Site: http://www.legrand.ca
Sales Range: $25-49.9 Million
Electrical Controls Mfr
N.A.I.C.S.: 334519

Subsidiary (Domestic):

Middle Atlantic Products Inc. (6)
300 Fairfield Rd, Fairfield, NJ 07004
Tel.: (973) 839-1011
Web Site: http://www.middleatlantic.com
Sales Range: $100-124.9 Million
Emp.: 345
Mfr of Support & Protection Products to Mount Audio & Video Equipment
N.A.I.C.S.: 332322

NuVo Technologies, LLC (6)
3015 Kustom Dr, Hebron, KY 41048
Tel.: (859) 817-7200
Web Site: http://www.nuvotechnologies.com
Sales Range: $10-24.9 Million
Whole-Home Audio Products Designer, Mfr & Distr
N.A.I.C.S.: 334310
David Rodarte *(Pres & CEO)*

On-Q/LeGrand (6)
301 Fulling Mill Rd Ste G, Middletown, PA 17057
Tel.: (717) 702-2532
Web Site: http://www.onqlegrand.com
Sales Range: $50-74.9 Million
Emp.: 125
Structured Wiring Systems
N.A.I.C.S.: 423610
Doug Fikse *(Pres)*

Pass & Seymour/Legrand (6)
50 Boyd Ave, Syracuse, NY 13209 (100%)
Tel.: (315) 468-6211
Rev.: $160,000,000
Emp.: 1,200
Mfr of Electrical Wiring Devices
N.A.I.C.S.: 335931
Pat Davin *(VP & Gen Mgr)*

Subsidiary (Domestic):

Ortronics/Legrand (7)
125 Eugene O'Neill Dr, New London, CT 06320-6417
Tel.: (860) 445-3800
Web Site: http://www.ortronics.com
Sales Range: $125-149.9 Million
Emp.: 80
Cabling Systems & Networking Equipment
N.A.I.C.S.: 334118
Mark Panico *(Pres-Data comm Div)*

Subsidiary (Domestic):

Pinnacle Architectural Lighting, Inc. (6)
3801 Havana St, Denver, CO 80239
Tel.: (303) 322-5570
Web Site: https://www.pinnacle-ltg.com
Commercial Lighting Fixtures Mfr
N.A.I.C.S.: 335132

Quiktron, Inc. (6)
21 B Ave W, Albia, IA 52531
Tel.: (641) 932-3503
Web Site: http://www.quiktron.com
Emp.: 50
Audio & Video Cable Mfr
N.A.I.C.S.: 334220
Pammi Griffin *(Dir-Sls)*

Plant (Domestic):

Quiktron, Inc. - East Production Facility (7)
925 Old Lenoir Rd, Hickory, NC 28601

LEGRAND S.A.

Legrand S.A.—(Continued)
Tel.: (828) 327-6009
Fiber Optic Cable Mfr
N.A.I.C.S.: 335921

Subsidiary (Domestic):

Raritan, Inc. (6)
270 Davidson Aven Ste 601, Somerset, NJ 08873-1238
Tel.: (732) 764-8886
Web Site: https://www.raritan.com
Power Distribution Units Meters & Switches Mfr
N.A.I.C.S.: 335311
Doug Fikse (Pres)

Subsidiary (Non-US):

Raritan Australia Pty Ltd (7)
4 Forbes Close, Knoxfield, 3180, VIC, Australia
Tel.: (61) 3 9866 6887
Web Site: http://www.raritan.com
Power Distribution Units Meters & Switches Mfr
N.A.I.C.S.: 335311

Branch (Domestic):

Raritan Australia Pty Ltd - Sydney (8)
Building 4 Nexus Industry Park 43-47 Lyn Parade, Prestons, Sydney, 2170, NSW, Australia
Tel.: (61) 290292558
Web Site: http://www.raritan.com
Power Distribution Units Meters & Switches Mfr
N.A.I.C.S.: 335311

Subsidiary (Non-US):

Raritan Computer France (7)
19 Boulevard Georges Bidault, 77183, Croissy-Beaubourg, France
Tel.: (33) 164616191
Web Site: http://www.raritan.com
Power Distribution Units Meters & Switches Mfr
N.A.I.C.S.: 335311

Raritan Europe BV (7)
Jan van Galenstraat 59, 3115 JG, Schiedam, Netherlands
Tel.: (31) 102844040
Web Site: http://www.raritan.com
Power Distribution Units Meters & Switches Mfr
N.A.I.C.S.: 335311

Raritan Germany GmbH (7)
Kaistrasse 18, 40221, Dusseldorf, Germany
Tel.: (49) 3752713494799
Web Site: http://www.raritan.com
Power Distribution Units Meters & Switches Mfr
N.A.I.C.S.: 335311

Raritan Inc. - India (7)
210 Block B Vipul Square Sushant Lok 1, Gurgaon, 122 002, Haryana, India
Tel.: (91) 1244107881
Web Site: http://www.raritan.com
Power Distribution Units Meters & Switches Mfr
N.A.I.C.S.: 335311

Raritan, Inc. - Singapore (7)
17 Neythal Road, Singapore, 628582, Singapore
Tel.: (65) 68179017
Web Site: http://www.raritan.com
Power Distribution Units Meters & Switches Mfr
N.A.I.C.S.: 335311

Raritan Inc. - Taiwan (7)
5F 121 Lane 235 Pao-Chiao Road, Xindian District, Taipei, 231, Taiwan
Tel.: (886) 289191333
Web Site: http://www.raritan.com
Power Distribution Units Meters & Switches Mfr
N.A.I.C.S.: 335311

Raritan Inc. - UK (7)
4th Floor 25-26 Lime Street, London, EC3M 7HR, United Kingdom
Tel.: (44) 2070901390

Web Site: http://www.raritan.com
Power Distribution Units Meters & Switches Mfr
N.A.I.C.S.: 335311

Raritan Japan, Inc. (7)
14th Floor Shinagawa Center Building 23-17 Takanawa 3-chome, Minato ku, Tokyo, 108-0074, Japan
Tel.: (81) 357953170
Web Site: http://www.raritan.com
Power Distribution Units Meters & Switches Mfr
N.A.I.C.S.: 335311

Subsidiary (Domestic):

Server Technology, Inc. (6)
1040 Sandhill Rd, Reno, NV 89521
Tel.: (775) 284-2000
Web Site: https://www.servertech.com
Intelligent Power Distribution Products
N.A.I.C.S.: 327910
Brandon Ewing (Pres)

The Original Cast Lighting, Inc. (6)
11902 Lackland Rd, Saint Louis, MO 63146
Tel.: (314) 863-1895
Web Site: https://www.ocl.com
Sales Range: $10-24.9 Million
Emp.: 60
Lighting Fixture Mfr
N.A.I.C.S.: 335132
Josh Shapiro (Pres)

The Wiremold Company (6)
60 Woodlawn St, West Hartford, CT 06110-2326
Tel.: (860) 233-6251
Web Site: http://www.legrand.us
Sales Range: $200-249.9 Million
Emp.: 900
Supplier of Wire Management Solutions for Lighting, Electrical, Electronic & Communication Markets
N.A.I.C.S.: 335932

Subsidiary (Domestic):

Brooks Electronics Inc. (7)
13200 Townsend Rd, Philadelphia, PA 19154-1014
Tel.: (215) 969-3803
Web Site: http://www.brookselectronics.com
Sales Range: $50-74.9 Million
Emp.: 130
Noncurrent-Carrying Wiring Devices
N.A.I.C.S.: 335932

Shape LLC (7)
2105 Corporate Dr, Addison, IL 60101-1484
Tel.: (630) 620-8394
Web Site: https://www.shapellc.com
Sales Range: $25-49.9 Million
Emp.: 55
Power, Distribution & Specialty Transformers
N.A.I.C.S.: 335311
Greg Babecki (Pres)

Wiremold International Sales Corporation (7)
60 Woodlawn St, West Hartford, CT 06110-2326
Tel.: (860) 233-6251
Web Site: http://www.wiremold.com
Sales Range: $125-149.9 Million
Emp.: 400
Mfg. of Electrical Equipment
N.A.I.C.S.: 335932

Subsidiary (Domestic):

Vantage Controls, Inc. (6)
1061 S 800 E, Orem, UT 84097
Tel.: (801) 229-2800
Web Site: http://www.vantagecontrols.com
Sales Range: $25-49.9 Million
Emp.: 100
Wired or Wireless Electrical or Electronic Controls Mfr
N.A.I.C.S.: 335311
Randy Thomas (Dir-Bus Dev)

Watt Stopper/Legrand (6)
2800 De La Cruz Blvd, Santa Clara, CA 95050-2619 (100%)
Tel.: (408) 988-5331
Web Site: http://www.wattstopper.com
Sales Range: $25-49.9 Million
Emp.: 25

Remote Lighting Controls, Occupancy Sensors & Energy Efficient Power Strips
N.A.I.C.S.: 335931
Kelly Brambila (Mgr-Project Svcs)

Subsidiary (Non-US):

Legrand Romania SRL (2)
Ghetarilor No 15 Sect 1, 14354, Bucharest, Romania
Tel.: (40) 21 232 07 77
Web Site: http://www.legrand.ro
Sales Range: $25-49.9 Million
Emp.: 27
Electrical Control System Distr
N.A.I.C.S.: 423610
Calin Pascalau (Gen Mgr)

Legrand s.r.o. (2)
Meteor Centre Office Park Sokolovska 100/94, 186 00, Prague, Czech Republic
Tel.: (420) 246 007 668
Web Site: http://www.legrand.cz
Electric Wiring Supplies Distr
N.A.I.C.S.: 423610

Subsidiary (Domestic):

Planet-Wattohm SNC (2)
5 Rue Jean Nicot, BP 155, 93691, Pantin, Cedex, France
Tel.: (33) 1 48 10 69 67
Web Site: http://www.planet-wattohm.fr
Electrical Cable Installation Services
N.A.I.C.S.: 238210

Subsidiary (Non-US):

Rocom Electric Company Limited (2)
5-10 22/F - Ever Gain Plaza Tower II - 88-100 Container Port Road, Kwai Chung, New Territories, China (Hong Kong)
Tel.: (852) 2481 1820
Electrical Equipment Mfr & Distr
N.A.I.C.S.: 423610

Starline Holdings LLC (1)
168 Georgetown Rd, Canonsburg, PA 15317
Tel.: (724) 597-7800
Web Site: https://www.starlinepower.com
Electrical & Electronic Product Mfr
N.A.I.C.S.: 335999
Ravi Ramanathan (VP & Gen Mgr)

LEHAR FOOTWEARS LIMITED

A 243 A Road No 6 V K I Area, Jaipur, 302013, Rajasthan, India
Tel.: (91) 1414157777
Web Site: https://www.leharfootwear.com
Year Founded: 1994
532829—(BOM)
Rev.: $20,184,009
Assets: $19,114,737
Liabilities: $10,959,312
Net Worth: $8,155,425
Earnings: $133,279
Emp.: 478
Fiscal Year-end: 03/31/21
Footwear Mfr
N.A.I.C.S.: 316210
Raj Kumar Agarwal (Mng Dir)

Subsidiaries:

Lawreshwar Footcare Private Limited (1)
F-263 Road No 13 VKI Area, Jaipur, 302 013, India
Tel.: (91) 1414041880
Footwear Mfr & Distr
N.A.I.C.S.: 316210

LEHNER INVESTMENTS AG

Friedenstrasse 7, 60311, Frankfurt am Main, Germany
Tel.: (49) 69242418240
Web Site: https://www.lehnerinvestments.de
Year Founded: 1990
LEH—(DEU)
Assets: $10,056,298
Liabilities: $287,007
Net Worth: $9,769,290

INTERNATIONAL PUBLIC

Earnings: ($35,423,336)
Fiscal Year-end: 12/31/23
Asset Management Services
N.A.I.C.S.: 523999
Siddharath Lugani (Mng Dir)

LEHTO GROUP OYJ

Voimatie 6, 90440, Kempele, Finland
Tel.: (358) 207600900
Web Site: https://www.lehto.fi
Year Founded: 1976
LEHTO—(HEL)
Rev.: $372,103,389
Assets: $288,407,080
Liabilities: $216,562,702
Net Worth: $71,844,377
Earnings: ($28,762,141)
Emp.: 664
Fiscal Year-end: 12/31/22
Engineering Construction Services
N.A.I.C.S.: 237990
Seppo Laine (Chm)

LEIBER GMBH

Hafenstrasse 24, Bramsche, 49565, Germany
Tel.: (49) 546193030
Web Site: http://www.leibergmbh.de
Year Founded: 1954
Rev.: $21,008,262
Emp.: 83
Yeast Products Mfr
N.A.I.C.S.: 311514

Subsidiaries:

Inter Yeast Sp. z oo (1)
Ul Leczycka 38, 99-340, Krosniewice, Poland
Tel.: (48) 242510360
Web Site: http://www.leiberspzoo.pl
Yeast Products Mfr
N.A.I.C.S.: 311514
Dariusz Piorkowski (Mgr-Ops)

LEIFHEIT AG

Leifheitstrasse 1, 56377, Nassau, Germany
Tel.: (49) 26049770
Web Site: http://www.leifheit.de
LEI—(MUN)
Rev.: $285,118,582
Assets: $224,781,048
Liabilities: $110,166,226
Net Worth: $114,614,822
Earnings: $3,532,384
Emp.: 1,032
Fiscal Year-end: 12/31/23
Household Appliances
N.A.I.C.S.: 335220
Karsten Schmidt (Deputy Chm-Supervisory Bd)

Subsidiaries:

Alimport do Brasil Ltda. (1)
Rua Cruzeiro 443, Barra Funda, Sao Paulo, 01137-010, SP, Brazil
Tel.: (55) 1133992202
Household Product Distr
N.A.I.C.S.: 423620

D. & J. Damkalidis S.A. (1)
44 Zefyrou, 17564, Palaion Faliron, Greece
Tel.: (30) 2109410888
Web Site: http://www.damkalidis.gr
Emp.: 30
Electronic Product Distr
N.A.I.C.S.: 423690
Tom Damkalidis (Owner & Gen Mgr)

Fackelmann Housewares Pty. Ltd. (1)
105 Vanessa Street, Kingsgrove, 2208, NSW, Australia
Tel.: (61) 1800709714
Web Site: http://www.fackelmannhousewares.com.au
Houseware Product Distr
N.A.I.C.S.: 423620

HERBY Industrie S.A. (1)
Zone Industrielle, PO Box 30050, 28240, La

AND PRIVATE COMPANIES

Loupe, France (100%)
Tel.: (33) 237811891
Web Site: http://www.herby.fr
Sales Range: $25-49.9 Million
Emp.: 75
Laundry Dryer Mfr
N.A.I.C.S.: 335220

LEIFHEIT International U.S.A. Inc (1)
510 Broadhollow Rd Ste 201, Melville, NY 11747-3606
Tel.: (631) 501-1054
Web Site: http://www.leifheitusa.com
Household Appliances Mfr & Whslr
N.A.I.C.S.: 335220

Leifheit AG (1)
Via Creta 31, 25124, Brescia, Italy
Tel.: (39) 030222420
Household Product Distr
N.A.I.C.S.: 423620

Leifheit CZ a.s. (1)
Logistic areal-Logport Prague West Mezi stromy-hall O3, 252 25, Hostivice, Czech Republic
Tel.: (420) 313104500
Web Site: https://www.leifheit.cz
Household Product Distr
N.A.I.C.S.: 423990
Martina Jirovcova (Mktg Mgr-Eastern Europe)

Leifheit Distribution S.R.L. (1)
Str SOS Pipera 48 Corp B2 Supanta 3 Sector 2, 014254, Bucharest, Romania
Tel.: (40) 726503103
Web Site: https://leifheit.ro
Cleaning Product Retailer
N.A.I.C.S.: 459999

Leifheit Espana S.A. (1)
Calle Princesa 25 1 Pl Oficina 6 Edificio Hexagono, 28008, Madrid, Spain
Tel.: (34) 915425929
Household Product Distr
N.A.I.C.S.: 423620

Leifheit Osterreich GmbH (1)
IZ-NO Sud Strasse 16 Obj 69/5/II, 2355, Wiener Neudorf, Austria
Tel.: (43) 2236649 23
Web Site: https://www.leifheit.at
Household Product Distr
N.A.I.C.S.: 423620

Leifheit Polska Sp. z o.o. (1)
Ul Sienna 73, 00-833, Warsaw, Poland
Tel.: (48) 222440099
Web Site: https://www.leifheitsklep.pl
Household Product Distr
N.A.I.C.S.: 423620
Katarzyna Bronowska (Mgr-E-commerce & Mktg)

Leifheit-Birambeau S.A.S. (1)
3 Rue Rondelet, 75012, Paris, France
Tel.: (33) 155785555
Web Site: http://www.birambeau.com
Rev.: $37,600,000
Emp.: 41
Household Appliances Mfr
N.A.I.C.S.: 335220
Georges Raynaud (Mgr-DP)

Robke B.V. (1)
Nieuwe's-Gravelandseweg 40, 1405 HM, Bussum, Netherlands
Tel.: (31) 356997244
Web Site: https://www.roebke.nl
Household Product Distr
N.A.I.C.S.: 423620
Gertrude Ziermans (Mgr-Social Media & Content)

Sonee Hardware Pvt. Ltd. (1)
181 Boduthakurufaanu Magu, 20181, Male, Maldives
Tel.: (960) 3336699
Web Site: https://www.sonee.com.mv
Household Hardware Product Retailer
N.A.I.C.S.: 444140
Hassan Hameez (Asst Gen Mgr)

Vesteh Ltd. (1)
204-V Borshchagovskaya str, 03058, Kiev, Ukraine
Tel.: (380) 443511324
Household Product Distr
N.A.I.C.S.: 423620

LEINER PAK GELATINE LIMITED

17/G Gulberg-2, GPO Box 3529, Lahore, Pakistan
Tel.: (92) 4235756953 PK
Web Site: https://www.leinerpakgelatine.com
Year Founded: 1983
LPGL—(PSX)
Rev.: $8,400,248
Assets: $6,617,069
Liabilities: $3,739,659
Net Worth: $2,877,410
Earnings: $239,856
Emp.: 163
Fiscal Year-end: 06/30/23
Gelatin Mfr
N.A.I.C.S.: 325412
Khwaja Imtiaz Ahmed (CEO & Mng Dir)

LEISURE & RESORTS WORLD CORPORATION

26th Floor West Tower Philippine Stock Exchange Center Exchange Road, Cor Pearl Drive Ortigas Center, Pasig, 1605, Philippines
Tel.: (63) 286375291
Web Site: http://www.lrwc.com.ph
PLUS—(PHI)
Rev.: $492,029,444
Assets: $536,515,532
Liabilities: $194,804,783
Net Worth: $341,710,749
Earnings: $73,934,332
Emp.: 192
Fiscal Year-end: 12/31/23
Home Management Services
N.A.I.C.S.: 721110
Alejandro P. Alonte (VP)

Subsidiaries:

AB Leisure Exponent, Inc. (1)
26th Fl W Tower Philippine Stock Exchange Ctr Exchange Rd, Ortigas Ctr, Pasig, 1605, Philippines
Tel.: (63) 26375291
Web Site: http://www.bingob.com
Entertainment Services
N.A.I.C.S.: 713120

Subsidiary (Domestic):

Alabang Numbers & Gaming Corporation (2)
Festival Supermall, Alabang, Muntinlupa, Philippines
Tel.: (63) 28503853
Gaming & Entertainment Services
N.A.I.C.S.: 713120

Cebu Entertainment Gallery, Inc. (2)
Elizabeth Mall Leon Kilat St, Cebu, 6000, Philippines
Tel.: (63) 322558045
Sales Range: $25-49.9 Million
Entertainment Services
N.A.I.C.S.: 713120
Jose Rafael Mercurio (Mgr)

Topmost Gaming Corp. (2)
5th Floor Nova Plaza Mall Quirino Highway Novaliches, Quezon City, Philippines
Tel.: (63) 29830797
Entertainment Services
N.A.I.C.S.: 713120

First Cagayan Converge Data Center, Inc. (1)
Cyberpark, Santa Ana, Manila, Cagayan, Philippines
Tel.: (63) 27298808
Web Site: https://www.fccdci.com
Information Technology Management Services
N.A.I.C.S.: 541513

First Cagayan Leisure & Resorts Corporation (1)
26th Fl W Tower Philippine Stock Exchange Ctr Exchange Rd, Ortigas Ctr, Pasig, 1605, Philippines
Tel.: (63) 26385556
Web Site: http://www.firstcagayan.com
Entertainment Services
N.A.I.C.S.: 713120

LEJAY LAGOUTE

47 Boulevard Des Acieries, 13010, Marseille, Bouches Du Rhone, France
Tel.: (33) 380784359
Web Site: http://www.lejay-lagoute.com
Sales Range: $25-49.9 Million
Emp.: 94
Spirit Mfr
N.A.I.C.S.: 312140
Christian Albouy (Gen Mgr)

LEJU HOLDINGS LIMITED

Level G Building G No 8 Dongfeng South Road, Chaoyang District, Beijing, 100016, China
Tel.: (86) 1058951000 Ky
Web Site: https://www.leju.com
Year Founded: 2013
LEJUY—(OTCIQ)
Rev.: $316,854,430
Assets: $102,191,231
Liabilities: $103,487,126
Net Worth: ($1,295,895)
Earnings: ($55,772,572)
Emp.: 871
Fiscal Year-end: 12/31/23
Online Real Estate Services
N.A.I.C.S.: 531390
Xin Zhou (Chm)

LEKOIL LIMITED

Churchgate Tower 1 9th Floor PC 30 Churchgate Street, Victoria Island, Lagos, Nigeria
Tel.: (234) 1 277 0560
Web Site: http://www.lekoil.com
Year Founded: 2010
LEK—(AIM)
Rev.: $3,061,000
Assets: $135,224,000
Liabilities: $1,525,000
Net Worth: $133,699,000
Earnings: ($237,164,000)
Emp.: 6
Fiscal Year-end: 12/31/21
Oil Exploration
N.A.I.C.S.: 211120
Olalekan Akinyanmi (Founder & CEO)

LELON ELECTRONICS CORP.

147 Sec 1 Guoguang Rd, Dali Dist, Taichung, 41262, Taiwan
Tel.: (886) 424181856
Web Site: http://www.lelon.com
Year Founded: 1976
2472—(TAI)
Rev.: $294,262,882
Assets: $483,236,320
Liabilities: $139,452,855
Net Worth: $343,783,466
Earnings: $40,824,878
Emp.: 2,632
Fiscal Year-end: 12/31/23
Aluminum Electrolytic Capacitors Mfr
N.A.I.C.S.: 334416
T. C. Wu (Founder & Chm)

Subsidiaries:

Lelon Electronics (Huizhou) Co., Ltd. (1)
Taiyang Industrial Zone, Baihua Town Huidong County, Huizhou, 516369, Guangdong, China
Tel.: (86) 7528768222
Electrolytic Capacitor Mfr
N.A.I.C.S.: 334416

Lelon Electronics (Suzhou) Co., Ltd. (1)
1220 Zhongshan North Road, Songling Town, Wujiang, 215200, Jiangsu, China
Tel.: (86) 51263457588
Capacitor Mfr
N.A.I.C.S.: 334416

Lifu Machinery Industrial Co., Ltd. (1)
10 Wugong 3rd Rd, Wufeng Dist, Taichung, Taiwan
Tel.: (886) 423334274
Electrolytic Capacitor Mfr
N.A.I.C.S.: 334416

Liton Technology Corp. (1)
No 8 Duxing Rd, East Dist, Hsinchu, Taiwan
Tel.: (886) 35787722
Electrolytic Capacitor Mfr
N.A.I.C.S.: 334416

Surge/Lelon LLC (1)
95E Jefryn Blvd, Deer Park, NY 11729
Tel.: (631) 595-1818
Electrolytic Capacitor Mfr
N.A.I.C.S.: 334416

LEM HOLDING SA

Avenue Beauregard 1, 1700, Fribourg, Switzerland
Tel.: (41) 264601030
Web Site: https://www.lem.com
LEHN—(SWX)
Rev.: $449,863,636
Assets: $381,735,033
Liabilities: $185,862,528
Net Worth: $195,872,506
Earnings: $72,424,612
Emp.: 1,574
Fiscal Year-end: 03/31/24
Electric Measurement Product Mfr
N.A.I.C.S.: 334515
François Gabella (CEO-Grp)

Subsidiaries:

Filial af LEM Europe GmbH (1)
Haraldsvej 60, 8960, Randers, Denmark
Tel.: (45) 6 043 1953
Electrical Equipment Distr
N.A.I.C.S.: 423610

LEM Belgium sprl-bvba (1)
Route de Petit-Roeulx 95, 7090, Braine-le-Comte, Hainaut, Belgium
Tel.: (32) 67550114
Sales Range: $50-74.9 Million
Emp.: 2
Electrical Meters Mfr
N.A.I.C.S.: 423610

LEM Electronics Co. Ltd (1)
No 28 Linhe Street Linhe Industrial Zone, Shunyi District, Beijing, 101300, China
Tel.: (86) 1089455288
Web Site: http://www.lem.com
Emp.: 700
Electrical Meters Distr
N.A.I.C.S.: 423610
Zong Hui Jhang (Chm)

LEM Europe GmbH (1)
Frankfurter Strasse 74, 64521, Gross-Gerau, Germany
Tel.: (49) 615293010
Electrical Equipment Distr
N.A.I.C.S.: 423610

LEM France S.a.r.l. (1)
15 Avenue Galois, 92340, Bourg-la-Reine, Hauts-de-Seine, France
Tel.: (33) 145364620
Electrical Meters Mfr & Distr
N.A.I.C.S.: 335999
Paul Leens (Mng Partner)

LEM International S.A. (1)
8 Chemin des Aulx, 1228, Plan-les-Ouates, Geneva, Switzerland
Tel.: (41) 227061111
Web Site: http://www.lem.com
Sales Range: $150-199.9 Million
Emp.: 300
Electrical Meters Distr
N.A.I.C.S.: 423610

LEM Italia S.r.l. (1)
Via Vincenzo Bellini 7, 35030, Selvazzano Dentro, Padua, Italy
Tel.: (39) 0498056060
Electrical Meters Distr

LEM HOLDING SA

LEM Holding SA—(Continued)
N.A.I.C.S.: 423610
Paul Leens (Pres)

LEM Japan K.K. (1)
2-1-2 Nakamachi, Machida, 194-0021, Tokyo, Japan
Tel.: (81) 427258151
Web Site: http://www.lem.co.jp
Sales Range: $50-74.9 Million
Emp.: 100
Electrical Meters Distr
N.A.I.C.S.: 423610
Hiroaki Mizoguchi (Pres)

LEM Russia Ltd. (1)
Str Starickoe Shosse 15, 170040, Tver, Russia
Tel.: (7) 4822655672
Electrical Equipment Distr
N.A.I.C.S.: 423610

LEM UK Ltd. (1)
West Lancashire Investment Centre, Skelmersdale, WN8 9TG, Lancashire, United Kingdom
Tel.: (44) 1695712560
Web Site: http://www.lem.com
Sales Range: $50-74.9 Million
Emp.: 3
Electronic Component Sales
N.A.I.C.S.: 423690

LEM USA Inc. (1)
11665 W Bradley Rd, Milwaukee, WI 53224
Tel.: (414) 353-0711
Web Site: http://www.lem.com
Sales Range: $25-49.9 Million
Emp.: 12
Current & Voltage Transducers Mfr & Distr
N.A.I.C.S.: 334419

TVELEM Ltd. (1)
TVELEM Str Staritskoye shosse 15, 170023, Tver, Russia
Tel.: (7) 4822743951
Web Site: http://www.lem.com
Electrical Meters Distr
N.A.I.C.S.: 423610

LEMARNE CORPORATION LIMITED
5th Floor 437 St Kilda Road, Melbourne, 3004, VIC, Australia
Tel.: (61) 398202400
Web Site: http://www.lemarne.com.au
Sales Range: Less than $1 Million
Specialized Technology, Products & Services
N.A.I.C.S.: 541990
Peter Anthony Murphy (CEO & Mng Dir)

LEMAUVIEL AUTOMOBILES VIRE
Route De Caen, 14500, Vire, Calvados, France
Tel.: (33) 231680078
Web Site: http://www.lemauviel.com
New & Used Car Dealers
N.A.I.C.S.: 441110
Christophe Lemauviel (Co-Pres)

LEMAY ONLINE
3500 St Jacques St, Montreal, H4C 1H2, QC, Canada
Tel.: (514) 932-5101
Web Site: http://www.lemayonline.com
Architectural & Design Services
N.A.I.C.S.: 541310
Louis T. Lemay (Pres)

Subsidiaries:

AE Design, Inc. (1)
277 Broadway Ste 1300, New York, NY 10007
Tel.: (212) 219-9810
Sales Range: $1-9.9 Million
Emp.: 35
Interior Design Services
N.A.I.C.S.: 541410
Andres Escobar (Pres)

LEMBAGA KEMAJUAN TANAH PERSEKUTUAN
Platinum Park No 11, Persiaran KLCC, 50088, Kuala Lumpur, Malaysia
Tel.: (60) 3 2191 2191
Web Site: http://www.felda.net.my
Year Founded: 1956
Land Development Organization
N.A.I.C.S.: 813990
Mohd Bakke Salleh (Chm)

Subsidiaries:

Encorp Berhad (1)
46G Jalan PJU 522 Encorp Strand Pusat Perdagangan Kota Damansara, Kota Damansara PJU 5, 47810, Petaling Jaya, Malaysia
Tel.: (60) 362867777
Web Site: https://www.encorp.com.my
Rev.: $29,099,259
Assets: $254,155,767
Liabilities: $164,622,857
Net Worth: $89,532,910
Earnings: ($3,852,698)
Emp.: 109
Fiscal Year-end: 12/31/2022
Property Development & Construction Management Services
N.A.I.C.S.: 236220
William Seow (Head-Fin)

Subsidiary (Domestic):

Must Ehsan Development Sdn Bhd (2)
No 46G Jalan PJU 5 22 The Strand Encorp, Kota Damansara PJU 5, 47180, Petaling Jaya, Selangor, Malaysia
Tel.: (60) 3 6286 7671
Property Development Services
N.A.I.C.S.: 531390

LEMBAGA TABUNG ANGKATAN TENTERA
12th Floor, Bangunan LTAT, Jalan Bukit Bintang, Kuala Lumpur, 55100, Malaysia
Tel.: (60) 0348158888
Web Site: https://www.ltat.gov.my
Year Founded: 1973
Financial Services
N.A.I.C.S.: 523999

Subsidiaries:

Boustead Holdings Berhad (1)
28th Floor Menara Boustead 69 Jalan Raja Chulan, 50200, Kuala Lumpur, Malaysia (59.42%)
Tel.: (60) 321419044
Web Site: http://www.boustead.com.my
Rev.: $3,197,714,286
Assets: $3,363,280,423
Liabilities: $2,247,365,079
Net Worth: $1,115,915,344
Earnings: $21,904,762
Emp.: 12,975
Fiscal Year-end: 12/31/2022
Holding Company; Oil Palm Cultivation, Property, Finance, Investment & Pharmaceutical Services
N.A.I.C.S.: 551112
Affendi Mohd Yob (Head-Secretarial-Grp)

Subsidiary (Domestic):

Boustead Cruise Centre Sdn Bhd (2)
Persiaran Pelabuhan Barat Bandar Armada Putra Pulau Indah, PO Box 278, 42009, Port Klang, Selangor, Malaysia
Tel.: (60) 331011333
Web Site: http://www.bousteadcruise.com
Marine Transportation Services
N.A.I.C.S.: 488390

Boustead Langkawi Shipyard Sdn Bhd (2)
Bukit Malut Mukim Kedawang Langkawi, 07000, Kedah, Malaysia
Tel.: (60) 4 966 5555
Web Site: https://www.blsy.com.my
Construction Engineering Services
N.A.I.C.S.: 541330

Raja Mohamed B. Mustafa (Gen Mgr)

Boustead Plantations Berhad (2)
28th Floor Menara Boustead, 69 Jalan Raja Chulan, 50200, Kuala Lumpur, Malaysia
Tel.: (60) 321452121
Web Site: http://www.bousteadplantations.com.my
Rev.: $249,089,524
Assets: $896,451,217
Liabilities: $291,522,751
Net Worth: $604,928,466
Earnings: $124,612,910
Emp.: 5,154
Fiscal Year-end: 12/31/2022
Upstream Oil Palm Plantations
N.A.I.C.S.: 311224
Ismail La Sim (Chm)

Boustead Shipping Agencies Sdn Bhd (2)
Blok B-4-7 Jalan Intan 1/KS1 Intania, Teluk Gadong Besar, 41200, Klang, Selangor, Malaysia
Tel.: (60) 333854256
Web Site: https://www.bousteadshipping.com.my
Transportation Services
N.A.I.C.S.: 488510

Boustead Travel Services Sdn Bhd (2)
14th Floor Menara Boustead 69 Jalan Raja Chulan, 50200, Kuala Lumpur, Malaysia
Tel.: (60) 358703268
Web Site: https://bousteadtravel.com
Food Transportation Services
N.A.I.C.S.: 488490

MHs Aviation Berhad (2)
No 18 Block H Jalan PJU. 1A/3 Taipan Damansara 2 Ara Damansara, 47301, Petaling Jaya, Malaysia
Tel.: (60) 378428500
Web Site: http://www.mhsaviation.com
Oil & Gas Production Services
N.A.I.C.S.: 213112
Mohsein Ma som (CEO)

Mutiara Rini Sdn Bhd (2)
18th Floor Menara Boustead 69 Jalan Raja Chulan, 50200, Kuala Lumpur, Malaysia
Tel.: (60) 321419044
Web Site: http://www.mutiararini.com.my
Real Estate Services
N.A.I.C.S.: 531390

Pharmaniaga Berhad (2)
No 7 Lorong Keluli 1B Kawasan Perindustrian Bukit Raja Selatan, Seksyen 7, 40000, Shah Alam, Selangor Darul Ehsan, Malaysia (86.8%)
Tel.: (60) 333429999
Web Site: https://www.pharmaniaga.com
Rev.: $743,000,423
Assets: $384,922,963
Liabilities: $433,040,635
Net Worth: ($48,117,672)
Earnings: ($128,052,910)
Emp.: 3,778
Fiscal Year-end: 12/31/2022
Pharmaceuticals Mfr
N.A.I.C.S.: 325412
Norai'ni Mohamed Ali (CFO)

Subsidiary (Domestic):

Pharmaniaga Biovention Sdn Bhd (3)
No 7 Lorong Keluli 1B Kawasan Perindustrian Bukit Raja Selatan, Seksyen 7, 40000, Shah Alam, Selangor Darul Ehsan, Malaysia
Tel.: (60) 3 3342 9999
Web Site: http://www.pharmaniaga.com
Pharmaceuticals Mfr
N.A.I.C.S.: 325412

Pharmaniaga International Corporation Sdn Bhd (3)
No 7 Lorong Keluli 1B, Kawasan Perindustrian Bukit Raja Selatan, Seksyen 7, 40000, Shah Alam, Malaysia
Tel.: (60) 3 3342 9999
Web Site: http://www.pharmaniaga.com
Emp.: 600
Pharmaceuticals Mfr
N.A.I.C.S.: 325412

Subsidiary (Non-US):

PT Millennium Pharmacon International Tbk (4)

INTERNATIONAL PUBLIC

Crown Bungur Arteri 2-4th floors Jl Sultan Iskandar Muda No 18, Senayan, Jakarta, 12240, Indonesia
Tel.: (62) 212 708 5961
Web Site: https://mpi-indonesia.ddns.net
Healthcare Product Distr
N.A.I.C.S.: 423450

Division (Domestic):

Pharmaniaga Logistics Sdn Bhd (3)
No 7 Lorong Keluli 1B Kawasan Perindustrian Bukit Raja Selatan, Seksyen 7, 40000, Shah Alam, Selangor Darul Ehsan, Malaysia
Tel.: (60) 3 3342 9999
Web Site: http://www.pharmaniaga.com
Emp.: 400
Pharmaceuticals Mfr
N.A.I.C.S.: 325412

Subsidiary (Domestic):

Pharmaniaga Biomedical Sdn Bhd (4)
No 7 Lorong Keluli 1B, Kawasan Perindustrian Bukit Raja Selatan Seksyen 7, 40000, Shah Alam, Malaysia
Tel.: (60) 333429999
Pharmaceuticals Mfr
N.A.I.C.S.: 325412

Branch (Domestic):

Pharmaniaga Logistics Sdn Bhd-Juru (4)
1/3/5 Lorong IKS Juru 8, Taman Perindustrian Ringan Juru, Penang, 14100, Malaysia
Tel.: (60) 4 508 3330
Web Site: http://www.pharmaniaga.com
Emp.: 46
Pharmaceutical Logistics Services & Distr
N.A.I.C.S.: 541614

Division (Domestic):

Pharmaniaga Manufacturing Berhad (3)
11A Jalan P1 Kawasan Perusahaan Bangi, 43650, Bandar Baru Bangi, Malaysia
Tel.: (60) 3 8925 7880
Web Site: http://www.pharmaniaga.com
Emp.: 470
Pharmaceuticals Mfr
N.A.I.C.S.: 325412

Subsidiary (Domestic):

Pharmaniaga LifeScience Sdn Bhd (4)
Lot 7 Jalan PPU 3, Taman Perindustrian Puchong Utama, 47100, Puchong, Selangor Darul Ehsan, Malaysia
Tel.: (60) 3 8061 2006
Web Site: http://www.pharmaniagalifescience.com
Emp.: 17
Pharmaceuticals Mfr
N.A.I.C.S.: 325412

Pharmaniaga Research Centre Sdn Bhd (4)
11A Jalan P1 Kawasan Perusahaan Bangi, Bandar Baru Bangi, 43650, Selangor Darul Ehsan, Malaysia
Tel.: (60) 3 8925 7880
Pharmaceutical Research
N.A.I.C.S.: 541715

Division (Domestic):

Pharmaniaga Marketing Sdn Bhd (3)
No 7 Lorong Keluli 1B Kawasan Perindustrian Bukit Raja Selatan, Seksyen 7, 40000, Shah Alam, Selangor Darul Ehsan, Malaysia
Tel.: (60) 3 3342 9999
Pharmaceutical Products Marketing
N.A.I.C.S.: 541613

Subsidiary (Domestic):

The University of Nottingham in Malaysia Sdn Bhd (2)
Jalan Broga, 43500, Semenyih, Selangor, Malaysia
Tel.: (60) 389248000
Web Site: https://www.nottingham.edu.my
Educational Support Services
N.A.I.C.S.: 611710

AND PRIVATE COMPANIES

UAC Berhad (2)
Level 10 Menara Uac 12 Jalan Pju 7/5, Mutiara Damansara, 47800, Petaling Jaya, Selangor Darul Ehsan, Malaysia
Tel.: (60) 37 721 9393
Web Site: https://www.uac.com.my
Sales Range: $50-74.9 Million
Emp.: 653
Cement Mfr & Distr
N.A.I.C.S.: 327310
B. T. Gan *(CEO & Mng Dir)*

LEMBAGA TABUNG HAJI
201 Jalan Tun Razak, Kuala Lumpur, 50732, Malaysia
Tel.: (60) 3 2054 2000
Web Site:
http://www.tabunghaji.gov.my
Financial Services
N.A.I.C.S.: 523999
Johan Abdullah *(CEO & Mng Dir)*

Subsidiaries:

BIMB Holdings Berhad (1)
31st Floor Menara Bank Islam 22 Jalan Perak, 50450, Kuala Lumpur, Malaysia **(51.47%)**
Tel.: (60) 327812999
Web Site: http://www.bimbholdings.com
Rev.: $1,178,089,853
Assets: $21,262,700,498
Liabilities: $19,492,313,693
Net Worth: $1,770,386,805
Earnings: $214,805,498
Emp.: 6,600
Fiscal Year-end: 12/31/2020
Investment Holding Company
N.A.I.C.S.: 551112
Ambrin Buang *(Chm)*

Holding (Domestic):

Bank Islam Malaysia Berhad (2)
Level 32 Menara Bank Islam No 22 Jalan Perak, 50450, Kuala Lumpur, Malaysia **(100%)**
Tel.: (60) 3 2088 8000
Web Site: http://www.bankislam.com.my
Rev.: $620,531,585
Assets: $12,557,322,241
Liabilities: $11,568,224,240
Net Worth: $989,098,002
Earnings: $119,753,169
Emp.: 4,559
Fiscal Year-end: 12/31/2016
Retail & Commercial Banking
N.A.I.C.S.: 522110
Hizamuddin Jamalluddin *(Head-Strategic Mgmt)*

Syarikat Takaful Malaysia Keluarga Berhad (2)
14th Floor Annexe Block Menara Takaful Malaysia, No 4 Jalan Sultan Sulaiman, 50000, Kuala Lumpur, Malaysia **(65.22%)**
Web Site:
http://www.takaful-malaysia.com.my
Rev.: $640,428,607
Assets: $3,194,577,731
Liabilities: $2,821,439,723
Net Worth: $373,138,009
Earnings: $75,550,501
Emp.: 996
Fiscal Year-end: 12/31/2023
Insurance Services
N.A.I.C.S.: 524298
Why Chong Leem *(Deputy CEO)*

TH Plantations Berhad (1)
Level 23 Menara TH Selborn 153 Jalan Tun Razak, 50400, Kuala Lumpur, Malaysia **(63.34%)**
Tel.: (60) 26034800
Web Site: https://www.thplantations.com.my
Rev.: $186,509,841
Assets: $567,290,370
Liabilities: $290,653,757
Net Worth: $276,636,614
Earnings: $18,610,794
Emp.: 5,303
Fiscal Year-end: 12/31/2022
Oil Mfr
N.A.I.C.S.: 324110
Maizura Mohamed *(Head-Strategic & Corp Svcs)*

Subsidiary (Domestic):

TH Bakti Sdn. Bhd. (2)
Peti Surat 3 Bandar Al Muktafi Billah Shah, Dungun, 23400, Terengganu, Malaysia
Tel.: (60) 9 8221884
Emp.: 7
Oil Palm Cultivation Services
N.A.I.C.S.: 115112
Mustaming Binabu *(Mng Dir)*

TH Pelita Gedong Sdn. Bhd. (2)
KM 8 Jalang Gedong Serian, Serian, 94700, Sarawak, Malaysia
Tel.: (60) 82895513
Emp.: 284
Oil Palm Cultivation Services
N.A.I.C.S.: 115112

TH Pelita Sadong Sdn. Bhd. (2)
KM 8 Jalang Gedong, 94700, Serian, Sarawak, Malaysia
Tel.: (60) 82895512
Oil Palm Cultivation Services
N.A.I.C.S.: 115112

THP Kota Bahagia Sdn. Bhd. (2)
Peti Surat 19, 26700, Bandar Muadzam Shah, Pahang, Malaysia
Tel.: (60) 94524826
Web Site: http://www.talntations.com
Sales Range: $10-24.9 Million
Emp.: 15
Oil Palm Cultivation Services
N.A.I.C.S.: 115112

THP Saribas Sdn. Bhd. (2)
Ladang Kenyalang No 12 Ground Floor Jalan Feeder Pusa Bazaar, New Shophouse Pusa, 94950, Betong, Sarawak, Malaysia
Tel.: (60) 83465822
Oil Palm Cultivation Services
N.A.I.C.S.: 115112

Theta Edge Berhad (1)
Lot 11B Jalan 223 Seksyen 51A, 46100, Petaling Jaya, Selangor, Malaysia
Tel.: (60) 60430000
Web Site: https://www.theta-edge.com
Rev.: $19,951,746
Assets: $29,195,556
Liabilities: $13,746,878
Net Worth: $15,448,677
Earnings: $1,610,370
Emp.: 189
Fiscal Year-end: 12/31/2022
Information Technology Services
N.A.I.C.S.: 541511
Cynthia Gloria Louis *(Co-Sec)*

LEMKEN GMBH & CO. KG
Weseler Strasse 5, 46519, Alpen, Germany
Tel.: (49) 2802810
Web Site: http://www.lemken.com
Year Founded: 1844
Sales Range: $100-124.9 Million
Emp.: 1,470
Agricultural Machinery Mfr & Distr
N.A.I.C.S.: 333111

Subsidiaries:

LEMKEN Agricultural Machinery (Qingdao) Co. Ltd. (1)
No 766 Huadong Road National High-Tech Zone, Qingdao, 266109, China
Tel.: (86) 532 5567 9566
Agricultural Equipment Distr
N.A.I.C.S.: 423820
Jens Stelter *(Plant Mgr)*

LEMKEN Austria GmbH (1)
Wiener Strasse 132, A-2020, Hollabrunn, Austria
Tel.: (43) 2952 202210
Web Site: http://lemken.com
Agricultural Machinery Mfr & Whslr
N.A.I.C.S.: 333111
Reinhold Kogler *(Reg Sls Mgr-East Austria)*

LEMKEN Belgium BVBA (1)
Varendonk 10, Sleidinge, 9940, Evergem, Belgium
Tel.: (32) 474 97 46 22
Agricultural Equipment Distr
N.A.I.C.S.: 423820

LEMKEN CANADA INC. (1)
1500 Ste Catherine Ouest, PO Box 55119, Montreal, H3G 2W5, QC, Canada
Tel.: (514) 443-6828
Web Site: http://www.lemken.ca
Emp.: 5
Agricultural Equipment Distr
N.A.I.C.S.: 423820
Laurent Letzter *(Mgr-Sls)*

LEMKEN CZECH, s.r.o. (1)
Veselska 34/290, Popuvky, 664 41, Troubsko, Czech Republic
Tel.: (420) 724151797
Web Site: http://www.lemken.cz
Agricultural Equipment Distr
N.A.I.C.S.: 423820

LEMKEN France sarl (1)
94 avenue Denis Papin, 45801, Saint Jean de Braye, Cedex, France
Tel.: (33) 2 38611112
Agricultural Equipment Distr
N.A.I.C.S.: 423820

LEMKEN Hungaria Kft. (1)
Hrsz 058/066, PF 53, 2351, Alsonemedi, Hungary
Tel.: (36) 29 537200
Agricultural Equipment Distr
N.A.I.C.S.: 423820

LEMKEN IBERIA S.L (1)
Apartado correos 62031, 28042, Madrid, Spain
Tel.: (34) 673 566 259
Agricultural Equipment Distr
N.A.I.C.S.: 423820
Alberto Pinero Panadero *(Area Mgr-Sls-East)*

LEMKEN ITALIA s.r.l. (1)
Corso Porto Nuova 11, 37122, Verona, Italy
Tel.: (39) 0335 8121111
Agricultural Equipment Distr
N.A.I.C.S.: 423820

LEMKEN India Agro Equipment Pvt Ltd. (1)
D-59 MIDC Butibori, Nagpur, 441 108, Maharashtra, India
Tel.: (91) 7104 305400
Web Site: http://www.lemken.in
Agricultural Equipment Mfr
N.A.I.C.S.: 333111
Vijay Rawal *(CFO)*

LEMKEN Nederland B.V. (1)
Zeilmaker 11, 3894 CL, Zeewolde, Netherlands
Tel.: (31) 6 53527135
Agricultural Equipment Distr
N.A.I.C.S.: 423820

LEMKEN POLSKA Sp.z.o.o. (1)
Zalecino 21, 73-115, Dolice, Poland
Tel.: (48) 91 563 76 46
Web Site: http://www.lemken.com.pl
Agricultural Equipment Distr
N.A.I.C.S.: 423820

LEMKEN ROMANIA SRL (1)
Comlosu-Mic nr 425, 307121, Comlosu Mic, Romania
Tel.: (40) 256 365532
Agricultural Equipment Distr
N.A.I.C.S.: 423820

LEMKEN SLOVAKIA s.r.o. (1)
Nitrianska cesta 5, 91701, Trnava, Slovakia
Tel.: (421) 3 35 35 37 98
Agricultural Equipment Distr
N.A.I.C.S.: 423820

LEMKEN Skandinavien ApS (1)
Varnaesvej 568, Felstedskov, 6200, Aabenraa, Denmark
Tel.: (45) 30 52 52 57
Agricultural Equipment Distr
N.A.I.C.S.: 423820
Nis Peter Albrechtsen *(Area Mgr-Sls)*

LEMKEN South Africa pty. Ltd. (1)
Unit 6 Garsfontein Office Park 645 Jacqueline Drive, Garsfontein, Pretoria, 0042, South Africa
Tel.: (27) 82 412 2577
Web Site: http://www.lemken.com
Emp.: 5
Agricultural Equipment Distr
N.A.I.C.S.: 423820
Blackie Swart *(Area Mgr-Sls-West)*

LEMKEN USA INC (1)
485 N Whitewater Park Blvd Apt B307, Boise, ID 83702
Tel.: (208) 680-7015
Web Site: http://www.lenken.com
Agricultural Equipment Distr
N.A.I.C.S.: 423820
Cord Diekmann *(Area Mgr-Sls)*

LEMKEN-Niederlassung Schweiz (1)
Oberifang 7, 8444, Henggart, Switzerland
Tel.: (41) 523 163480
Agricultural Equipment Distr
N.A.I.C.S.: 423820

Lemken UK (1)
46 Fuller Rd Harleston Industrial Pk, Harleston, Norfolk, IP20 9EA, United Kingdom **(100%)**
Tel.: (44) 1379855449
Web Site: http://www.lemken.co.uk
Sales Range: $25-49.9 Million
Emp.: 10
Mfr & Sales of Agricultural Machinery
N.A.I.C.S.: 333111
Richard Dixon *(Mgr-Area Svc-Northern England & Ireland)*

Lemken Werk Hetzerath AG (1)
Bahnhofstrasse 65, Hetzerath, 54523, Cologne, Germany **(100%)**
Tel.: (49) 650891490
Sales Range: $10-24.9 Million
Emp.: 50
Soil Preparation Planting & Cultivating
N.A.I.C.S.: 115112

Lemken Werk Meppen AG (1)
An Der Rutodrhm 31, 59733, Haren, Germany **(100%)**
Tel.: (49) 593570560
Web Site: http://www.lemken.com
Sales Range: $10-24.9 Million
Emp.: 30
Soil Preparation Planting & Cultivating
N.A.I.C.S.: 115112

OOO LEMKEN-RUS (1)
s Detschino ul Industrialnaja 2 Malojaroslavezkij rajon, 249080, Kaluga, Russia
Tel.: (7) 48431 57 000
Agricultural Equipment Distr
N.A.I.C.S.: 423820

TOO LEMKEN KAZ (1)
Imanova 19 office 403, Nur-Sultan, 010000, Kazakhstan
Tel.: (7) 7172 787043
Agricultural Equipment Distr
N.A.I.C.S.: 423820

LEMO S.A.
Chemin de Champs-Courbes 28, PO Box 194, Ecublens, 1024, Switzerland
Tel.: (41) 216951600
Web Site: http://www.lemo.com
Year Founded: 1946
Sales Range: $250-299.9 Million
Emp.: 1,400
Electrical, Optic & Fluidic Connectors
N.A.I.C.S.: 335931
Albert Meylan *(Dir-Fin)*

Subsidiaries:

LEMO Asia Pte Ltd (1)
4 Leng Kee Road Suite 06-09 SiS Building, Singapore, 159088, Singapore
Tel.: (65) 6476 0672
Electrical Connector Distr
N.A.I.C.S.: 423610

LEMO Canada, Inc (1)
44 East Beaver Creek Road Unit 20, Richmond Hill, L4B 1G8, ON, Canada
Tel.: (905) 889-5678
Web Site: http://www.lemo.com
Emp.: 7
Electrical Connector Distr
N.A.I.C.S.: 423610
Mario Colacino *(Gen Mgr)*

LEMO Connectors Nederland BV (1)
De Trompet 1060, Heemskerk, 1967 DA, Netherlands
Tel.: (31) 251 25 78 20
Electrical Connector Distr
N.A.I.C.S.: 423610

LEMO S.A.

Lemo S.A.—(Continued)

LEMO Denmark A/S (1)
Gammel Mosevej 46, 2820, Gentofte, Denmark
Tel.: (45) 45 20 44 0
Electrical Connector Distr
N.A.I.C.S.: 423610

LEMO Electronics (Shanghai) Co., Ltd. (1)
5th Floor Block 6 City of ELITE 1000 Jinhai Road, Shanghai, 201206, China
Tel.: (86) 21 58997721
Electrical Connector Distr
N.A.I.C.S.: 423610

LEMO Elektronik GesmbH (1)
Lembockgasse 49/E6-3, 1230, Vienna, Austria
Tel.: (43) 1 914 23 20 0
Web Site: http://www.lemo.com
Emp.: 3
Electrical Connector Distr
N.A.I.C.S.: 423610
Mathemaier Wilfried *(Gen Mgr)*

LEMO France Sarl (1)
24/28 Avenue Graham Bell Espace Vinci, Bussy Saint Georges, Marne-la-Vallee, Cedex, France
Tel.: (33) 8 635 60 60
Electrical Connector Distr
N.A.I.C.S.: 423610

LEMO Hong Kong Ltd (1)
Unit 1207 12/F Corporation Square 8 Lam Lok Street, Kowloon Bay, Kowloon, China (Hong Kong)
Tel.: (852) 21 74 04 68
Electrical Connector Distr
N.A.I.C.S.: 423610

LEMO Italia Srl (1)
Viale Lunigiana 25, 20125, Milan, Italy
Tel.: (39) 02 66 71 10 46
Electrical Connector Distr
N.A.I.C.S.: 423610

LEMO Nordic AB (1)
Box 8201, 163 08, Spanga, Sweden
Tel.: (46) 8 635 60 60
Electrical Connector Distr
N.A.I.C.S.: 423610

LEMO Norway A/S (1)
Soerumsandvegen 69, 1920, Lillestrom, Norway
Tel.: (47) 22 91 70 40
Electrical Connector Distr
N.A.I.C.S.: 423610

Lemo GmbH (1)
Hanns Schwinntq Strasse 6, Munich, 81829, Germany **(100%)**
Tel.: (49) 89427703
Web Site: http://www.lemo.de
Sales Range: $50-74.9 Million
Emp.: 150
N.A.I.C.S.: 335931

Lemo Japan (1)
Kada-Yushima Bluiding Yushima 3-14-8, 113, Tokyo, Bunko-Ku, Japan
Tel.: (81) 356888931
Web Site: http://www.lemo.co.jp
N.A.I.C.S.: 335931

Lemo U.K. (1)
12-20 N St, Worthing, BN11 1DU, W Sussex, United Kingdom **(100%)**
Tel.: (44) 1903234543
Web Site: http://www.lemo.co.uk
Sales Range: $25-49.9 Million
Emp.: 43
N.A.I.C.S.: 335931

Lemo U.S.A., Inc. (1)
635 Park Ct, Rohnert Park, CA 94928-7940 **(100%)**
Tel.: (707) 578-8811
Web Site: http://www.lemo.com
Sales Range: $75-99.9 Million
Emp.: 110
Mfr of Electronic Connectors
N.A.I.C.S.: 423690
Dean Pohwala *(Gen Mgr)*

Subsidiary (Domestic):

Northwire, Inc. (2)
110 Prospect Way, Osceola, WI 54020
Tel.: (715) 294-2121
Web Site: http://www.northwire.com
Emp.: 250
Wire & Cable, Retractile Cords, Cable Assemblies, Connectors & Harnesses Mfr & Distr
N.A.I.C.S.: 332618
Fabian Weber *(VP-Innovation & Bus Dev)*

Lemo Verkauf AG (1)
Grundstrasse 22, 6343, Rotkreuz, Switzerland
Tel.: (41) 41 790 49 40
Electrical Connector Distr
N.A.I.C.S.: 423610

LEMON CO., LTD.

1105-65 Sanho-daero Sandong-eup, Gumi, Gyeongsangbuk-do, Korea (South)
Tel.: (82) 544708800
Web Site: https://www.lemonano.co.kr
Year Founded: 2012
294140—(KRS)
Rev.: $30,503,005
Assets: $21,286,224
Liabilities: $12,237,479
Net Worth: $9,048,745
Earnings: ($12,546,826)
Emp.: 170
Fiscal Year-end: 12/31/22
Synthetic Fiber Mfr & Distr
N.A.I.C.S.: 325220
Kim Hyo-Gyu *(CEO)*

LEMON SISTEMI S.P.A.

Via IV Novembre 23, 90041, Balestrate, Italy
Tel.: (39) 0918884361
Web Site: https://www.lemonsistemi.it
Year Founded: 2009
LS—(ITA)
Solar Equipment Product Distr
N.A.I.C.S.: 423690

LEMON TREE HOTELS LTD.

Asset No 6 IGI Airport, Aerocity Hospitality, New Delhi, 110037, India
Tel.: (91) 1146050101
Web Site: https://www.lemontreehotels.com
Year Founded: 1992
LEMONTREE—(NSE)
Rev.: $36,169,661
Assets: $520,723,599
Liabilities: $311,200,426
Net Worth: $209,523,173
Earnings: ($25,462,942)
Emp.: 711
Fiscal Year-end: 03/31/21
Hotel & Resort Operator
N.A.I.C.S.: 721110
Patanjali Govind Keswani *(Chm & Mng Dir)*

LEMONSOFT OYJ

Vaasanpuistikko 20 A, 65100, Vaasa, Finland
Tel.: (358) 103281010
Web Site: https://www.lemonsoft.fi
Year Founded: 2006
LEMON—(HEL)
Rev.: $28,426,506
Assets: $52,762,789
Liabilities: $20,235,269
Net Worth: $32,527,520
Earnings: $5,719,836
Emp.: 220
Fiscal Year-end: 12/31/23
Software Development Services
N.A.I.C.S.: 541511
Christoffer Haggblom *(Chm)*

LEMPRIERE PTY. LTD.

Level 7 460 Collins Street, Melbourne, 3000, VIC, Australia
Tel.: (61) 3 8625 6508 AU
Web Site: http://www.lempriere.com
Investment Holding Company
N.A.I.C.S.: 551112
William Lempriere *(Chm)*

Subsidiaries:

Ceres Capital Management Pty. Ltd. (1)
Level 7 460 Collins Street, Melbourne, 3000, VIC, Australia
Tel.: (61) 3 8625 6508
Web Site: http://www.lemprierecapital.com
Investment Management Service
N.A.I.C.S.: 523940
William Lempriere *(Chm)*

Lempriere (Australia) Pty. Ltd. (1)
Level 7 460 Collins Street, Melbourne, 3000, VIC, Australia
Tel.: (61) 3 8625 6513
Web Site: http://www.lglogistics.com.au
Logistics Consulting Servies
N.A.I.C.S.: 541614
Jack Ohanian *(Gen Mgr)*

Lempriere Grain Pty. Ltd. (1)
Level 7 460 Collins Street, Melbourne, 3000, VIC, Australia
Tel.: (61) 3 8625 6551
Web Site: http://www.lemprieregrain.com.au
Grain Wholesale Trade Distr
N.A.I.C.S.: 425120

Worldwide Wool Pty. Ltd. (1)
Level 7 460 Collins Street, Melbourne, 3000, VIC, Australia
Tel.: (61) 3 8625 6500
Web Site: http://www.lempriererwool.com
Holding Company; Wool Processing & Whslr
N.A.I.C.S.: 551112
William Lempriere *(Chm & Mng Dir)*

Subsidiary (Non-US):

New Zealand Wool Services International Limited (2)
First Floor 30 Sir William Pickering Drive, PO Box 29383, Russley, Christchurch, 8053, New Zealand
Tel.: (64) 33578700
Web Site: http://www.woolserv.co.nz
Sales Range: $150-199.9 Million
Emp.: 14
Holding Company; Wool Processor & Whslr
N.A.I.C.S.: 551112
John Dawson *(Gen Mgr)*

Subsidiary (Domestic):

Kaputone Wool Scour Limited (3)
20 Station Road Belfast, Canterbury, Christchurch, 8051, New Zealand
Tel.: (64) 3323 8788
Wool Processing Services
N.A.I.C.S.: 314999
Don Caradus *(Gen Mgr)*

Subsidiary (Non-US):

New Zealand Wool Services International Ltd. (China) Limited (3)
No 14 Zhuqao Zhujianj Road, Nanjing, China
Tel.: (86) 25 8445 0511
Wool Wholesale Trade Agency
N.A.I.C.S.: 425120
Mark Chen *(Mgr-China)*

Subsidiary (Domestic):

Whakatu Wool Scour Limited (3)
Railway Road, PO Box 65, Whakatu, Napier, 4250, Hawkes Bay, New Zealand
Tel.: (64) 68700521
Sales Range: $25-49.9 Million
Emp.: 40
Wool Processing Services
N.A.I.C.S.: 314999
Adrian Donnelly *(Gen Mgr)*

LEMTECH HOLDINGS CO., LTD.

12F 3 No 3 Yuanqu St, Nangang Dist, Taipei, Taiwan
Tel.: (886) 286841618

INTERNATIONAL PUBLIC

Web Site: https://www.ky-lemtech.com
Year Founded: 2003
4912—(TAI)
Rev.: $195,940,475
Assets: $227,353,447
Liabilities: $135,134,592
Net Worth: $92,218,855
Earnings: $16,181,611
Emp.: 800
Fiscal Year-end: 12/31/20
Metal Stamping
N.A.I.C.S.: 332119
Chifeng Hsu *(Chm)*

Subsidiaries:

Kunshan Lemtech Electronics Technology Co., Ltd. (1)
Plant 5 No 128 Weita Road, Zhangpu Town, Kunshan, Jiangsu, China
Tel.: (86) 51236861556
Electronic Components & Mechanical Equipment Whslr
N.A.I.C.S.: 423690

Kunshan Lemtech Slide Technology Co., Ltd. (1)
Factory No 6 No 211 Zijing Road, Zhangpu Town, Kunshan, Jiangsu, China
Tel.: (86) 51250136519
Slide Rail Mfr & Distr
N.A.I.C.S.: 334519

LDC Precision Engineering Co., Ltd. (1)
2F No 1 Dingan Rd, Zhongli Dist, Taoyuan, 320030, Taiwan
Tel.: (886) 32866260
Electrical Appliance Mfr & Distr
N.A.I.C.S.: 335210

LemTech Global Industries Ltd. (1)
No 109 Dazhu Rd, Luzhu Dist, Taoyuan, Taiwan
Tel.: (886) 32866260
Electronic Equipment Mfr & Distr
N.A.I.C.S.: 336320

Lemtech Electronics Technology (Changsu) Co., Ltd. (1)
Building A2 No 8 Baixuexin Road, Shajiabang Town, Changshu, Jiangsu, China
Tel.: (86) 51257123772
Electronic Components Mfr & Distr
N.A.I.C.S.: 334419

Lemtech Energy Solutions Corporation (1)
No 39 Ruiyuan St, Bade Dist, Taoyuan, Taiwan
Tel.: (886) 286841618
Electrical Appliance Mfr & Distr
N.A.I.C.S.: 335210

Lemtech Global Solution Co. Ltd. (1)
3rd Floor Standard Chartered Tower, Cybercity, 72201, Ebene, Mauritius
Tel.: (230) 886286841618
Metal Stamping Components Mfr & Distr
N.A.I.C.S.: 333517

Lemtech Industrial Services Ltd. (1)
Offshore Chambers, PO Box 217, Apia, Samoa (Western)
Tel.: (685) 886286841618
Electronic & Computer Peripheral Parts Distr
N.A.I.C.S.: 423430

Lemtech International Limited (1)
Room 2702-03 CC Wu Building 302-8 Hennessy Road, Wanchai, Hong Kong, China (Hong Kong)
Tel.: (852) 886286841618
Investment Services
N.A.I.C.S.: 531110

Lemtech Precision Engineering (Tianjin) Co., Ltd. (1)
Building No 4 No 28 Saida Wuzhi Road, XiQing Economic & Technological Development Zone, Tianjin, China
Tel.: (86) 2258105173
Automotive Parts Mfr & Distr
N.A.I.C.S.: 336310

Lemtech Precision Material (CZECH) s.r. o. (1)

AND PRIVATE COMPANIES

Logisticke centrum Jihlava LCJ/Jipocar Hala B cp 3, 588 11, Stritez u Jihlavy, Czech Republic
Tel.: (420) 567575600
Machine Tools Mfr
N.A.I.C.S.: 333517

Lemtech Precision Material (China) Co., Ltd. (1)
128 Weita Rd, Zhangpu Town, Kunshan, Jiangsu, China
Tel.: (86) 51257175855
Electronic Components Mfr & Distr
N.A.I.C.S.: 334419

Lemtech Technology Limited (1)
Room 2702-03 CC Wu Building 302-8 Hennessy Road, Wanchai, Hong Kong, China (Hong Kong)
Tel.: (852) 886286841618
Electronic & Computer Peripheral Parts Distr
N.A.I.C.S.: 423430

Lemtech USA Inc. (1)
185 Estancia Dr Ste 117, San Jose, CA 95134
Tel.: (408) 886-0306
Business Information Collection & Development Services
N.A.I.C.S.: 561439

Lemtech-Eahwa Precision Technonlogy Co., Ltd. (1)
No 191-47 Shigu Rd, Changhua County, Shengang, Taiwan
Tel.: (886) 47988090
Electronic Equipment Mfr & Distr
N.A.I.C.S.: 336320

Zhenjiang Emtron Surface Treatment Limited Company (1)
No 199 Yuehe Street Zhenjiang New Area, Dagang Town, Jiangsu, China
Tel.: (86) 51183377959
Automotive Components & Electronic Services
N.A.I.C.S.: 811111

LEN CHEONG HOLDING BERHAD
PO BoxR 2 Lot 4 9556 Kawasan Perindustrian Bukit Rambai, 75250, Melaka, Malaysia
Tel.: (60) 3514911
Web Site: http://www.lcfurniture.com
Year Founded: 1995
Saw Mills & Furniture Mfr
N.A.I.C.S.: 321912

LENA LIGHTING S.A.
Kornicka street 52, 63-000, Sroda Wielkopolska, Poland
Tel.: (48) 612860300
Web Site: https://lenalighting.com
Year Founded: 1989
LEN—(WAR)
Rev.: $42,334,349
Assets: $35,537,856
Liabilities: $6,895,071
Net Worth: $28,642,784
Earnings: $2,509,654
Emp.: 420
Fiscal Year-end: 12/31/23
Lighting Equipment Mfr
N.A.I.C.S.: 335139
Andrzej Tomaszewski *(Chm/Chm-Supervisory Bd)*

LENAJA SA DISTRIBUTION
9 Rue Saint Antoine, 94150, Rungis, Val De Marne, France
Tel.: (33) 156300202
Web Site: http://lenaja.fr
Rev.: $16,000,000
Emp.: 26
N.A.I.C.S.: 424470
Philippe Leprince *(Dir)*

LENDINVEST PLC
Two Fitzroy Place 8 Mortimer Street, London, W1T 3JJ, United Kingdom
Tel.: (44) 2038361837   UK
Web Site: https://www.lendinvest.com
Year Founded: 2012
LINV—(AIM)
Rev.: $84,566,580
Assets: $1,568,145,040
Liabilities: $1,473,147,340
Net Worth: $94,997,700
Earnings: $14,156,520
Emp.: 275
Fiscal Year-end: 03/31/23
Investment Management Service
N.A.I.C.S.: 523999

LENDLEASE CORPORATION LIMITED
Level 14 Tower Three Intl Towers Sydney, Exchange Place 300 Barangaroo Avenue, Barangaroo, 2000, NSW, Australia
Tel.: (61) 292366111   AU
Web Site: https://www.lendlease.com
Year Founded: 1958
LLC—(ASX)
Rev.: $6,256,009,590
Assets: $11,199,252,091
Liabilities: $7,942,708,301
Net Worth: $3,256,543,790
Earnings: ($1,002,938,030)
Emp.: 3,191
Fiscal Year-end: 06/30/24
Shopping Centers & Residential Housing Projects; Real Estate Investment Management Services
N.A.I.C.S.: 531312
Anthony Peter Lombardo *(CEO-Global)*

Subsidiaries:

Actus Lend Lease (1)
2300 York Mont Rd Ste 700, Charlotte, NC 28217
Tel.: (704) 357-1919
Web Site: http://www.lendleaseactus.com
Rev.: $15,500,000
Emp.: 10
Military Housing Development Services
N.A.I.C.S.: 236115

Bovis Lend Lease (1)
Desguinlei 22, 1050, Antwerp, Belgium
Tel.: (32) 32572994
Web Site: http://www.bovislendlease.com
Pharmaceutical Services
N.A.I.C.S.: 325412

Bovis Lend Lease (1)
105 Embassy Sq, 148 Infantry Rd, Bengaluru, 560 001, India
Tel.: (91) 8022099777
Sales Range: $25-49.9 Million
Emp.: 100
Construction Services
N.A.I.C.S.: 236220

Bovis Lend Lease (HK) Ltd. (1)
Level 2 K Wah Centre 1010 Huai Hai Road, Shanghai, 200031, China
Tel.: (86) 2161962988
Web Site: http://www.bovislendlease.com
Sales Range: $50-74.9 Million
Emp.: 10
Real Estate Investment
N.A.I.C.S.: 525990

Bovis Lend Lease BV (1)
Westblaak 163, 3012 KJ, Rotterdam, Netherlands
Tel.: (31) 102759697
Sales Range: $75-99.9 Million
Emp.: 70
Real Estate Services
N.A.I.C.S.: 531390

Bovis Lend Lease Bau GmbH (1)
Industriezentrum Neiderosterreich Sud Strasse 6, Objeckt 17, Wiener Neudorf, 2355, Austria   (100%)
Tel.: (43) 22369010
Web Site: http://www.bovislendlease.com
Real Estate Services
N.A.I.C.S.: 531390
Christian Schaetz *(Mgr)*

Bovis Lend Lease Construction & Project Management Ltd (1)
Sari Kanarya Sokak No 14 k2 Plaza Kat 3, Kozyatagi, Istanbul, Turkiye
Tel.: (90) 2163840808
Web Site: http://www.bovislendlease.com
Real Estate Services
N.A.I.C.S.: 531390

Bovis Lend Lease Corp (1)
Level 2 825 Bourke Street, Victoria Harbour, Melbourne, Australia
Tel.: (61) 386006200
Web Site: http://www.lendlease.com
Sales Range: $25-49.9 Million
Emp.: 50
Real Estate Leasing & Development
N.A.I.C.S.: 531390

Bovis Lend Lease General Construction L.L.C. (1)
52 Egialieas St Fl 4, Marousi, 15125, Athens, Greece
Tel.: (30) 2106848499
Web Site: http://www.lendlease.com
Sales Range: $25-49.9 Million
Emp.: 16
N.A.I.C.S.: 236220

Bovis Lend Lease GmbH (1)
Kaisserstrasse 45, Staircase 2 - 5th Floor, A-1070, Vienna, Austria
Tel.: (43) 15248114
Real Estate Investment
N.A.I.C.S.: 525990

Bovis Lend Lease Inc. (1)
1 N Wacker Dr Ste 850, Chicago, IL 60606-2807   (100%)
Tel.: (312) 245-1000
Web Site: http://www.lendlease.com
Sales Range: $25-49.9 Million
Emp.: 200
Construction Management
N.A.I.C.S.: 541618

Bovis Lend Lease Ireland (1)
Kiscaobeoy, Dublin, 22, AB, Ireland   (1%)
Tel.: (353) 18561266
Web Site: http://www.bovislendlease.com
Real Estate Services
N.A.I.C.S.: 531390

Bovis Lend Lease Japan Inc. (1)
Akasaka Enokizaka Mori Building 3F, 1-7-1 Akasaka Minato-ku, Tokyo, 107-0052, Japan   (75%)
Tel.: (81) 3 6866 5600
Web Site: http://www.lendlease.com
Sales Range: $25-49.9 Million
Emp.: 50
Project Management & Construction Services
N.A.I.C.S.: 531390

Bovis Lend Lease Kft (1)
c/o Klapka u 11, H-1134, Budapest, Hungary
Tel.: (36) 14523733
Web Site: http://www.bovislendlease.com
Real Estate Services, Develop, Construct & Manage Real Estate Assets
N.A.I.C.S.: 531390

Bovis Lend Lease LMB (1)
200 Princeton South Corporate Ctr Ste 200, Ewing, NJ 08628-3434
Tel.: (617) 598-4300
Web Site: http://www.Bovislendlease.com
Sales Range: $75-99.9 Million
Emp.: 150
Real Estate Development & Leasing
N.A.I.C.S.: 531390

Bovis Lend Lease Pharmaceutical Division (1)
510 Thomson Rd #07-02 SLF Bldg, 298135, Singapore, Singapore
Tel.: (65) 62588777
Web Site: http://www.lendlease.com
Sales Range: $25-49.9 Million
Emp.: 50
Pharmaceutical Operations
N.A.I.C.S.: 325412

Bovis Lend Lease Portugal Lda. (1)
Edificio Atrium Saldanha Praca Duque De Saldanha, N 1 Piso 8 Escritorio 7 N, 1050 094, Lisbon, Portugal
Tel.: (351) 213583540
Web Site: http://www.bovislendlease.com

LENDLEASE CORPORATION LIMITED

Sales Range: $25-49.9 Million
Emp.: 2
Project Management & Construction Services, Including Consultation, Design/Build Services & Construction Management
N.A.I.C.S.: 541611

Bovis Lend Lease Pte Ltd (1)
510 Thomson Road #07-02 SLF Building, 298135, Singapore, Singapore
Tel.: (65) 62588777
Sales Range: $50-74.9 Million
Emp.: 70
Real Estate Investment
N.A.I.C.S.: 525990

Bovis Lend Lease S.A. (1)
10th ave de l'Enterprise Galilee 2, 95863, Cergy, France
Tel.: (33) 134226137
Web Site: http://www.bovislendlease.com
Sales Range: $25-49.9 Million
Emp.: 30
Real Estate Services
N.A.I.C.S.: 531390
Mahjoub Anes *(Country Mgr)*

Bovis Lend Lease SA (1)
Paseo de la Castallena 259C 20th Fl South, 28046, Madrid, Spain   (100%)
Tel.: (34) 915902490
Web Site: http://www.bovislendlease.com
Sales Range: $25-49.9 Million
Emp.: 50
Real Estate Services
N.A.I.C.S.: 531390

Bovis Lend Lease Sp. z o.o (1)
City Gate 58 Ogrodowa, 00-876, Warsaw, Poland   (100%)
Tel.: (48) 225202270
Web Site: http://www.bovis.com.pl
Sales Range: $50-74.9 Million
Emp.: 15
Real Estate Investment
N.A.I.C.S.: 525990

Bovis Lend Lease a.s. (1)
Sokolovska 192 79, 186 00, Prague, 8, Czech Republic   (100%)
Tel.: (420) 221775213
Web Site: http://www.bovislendlease.com
Sales Range: $75-99.9 Million
Emp.: 100
Project & Construction Management Projects
N.A.I.C.S.: 531390

Bovis Lend Lease, S.A. de C.V. (1)
Jaime Balmes No 11 Torre A, Piso 7 Col Polanco, Mexico, 11510, DF, Mexico
Tel.: (52) 5553879980
Web Site: http://www.bovislendlease.com
Sales Range: $50-74.9 Million
Emp.: 65
Real Estate Services
N.A.I.C.S.: 531390

Cadelta Group (1)
Minafree Port Area Minazayad, PO Box 47029, Abu Dhabi, United Arab Emirates
Tel.: (971) 6732111
Real Estate Services, Develop, Construct & Manage Real Estate Assets
N.A.I.C.S.: 531390

Capella Capital Lend Lease Pty Limited (1)
Level 31 AMP Centre 50 Bridge St, Sydney, 2000, NSW, Australia
Tel.: (61) 2 8224 3888
Web Site: http://www.capellacapital.com.au
Sales Range: $50-74.9 Million
Emp.: 15
Real Estate Managment Services
N.A.I.C.S.: 531390
John Bowyer *(Mng Dir)*

Lehrer McGovern International Ltd (1)
123 Lochside Crescent, Edinburgh, EH12 9DL, United Kingdom
Tel.: (44) 1315494000
Real Estate Development Services
N.A.I.C.S.: 531390

Lend Lease (Australia) Communities Limited (1)
Level 4 The Bond 30 Hickson Rd, Millers Point, 2000, NSW, Australia

LENDLEASE CORPORATION LIMITED

Lendlease Corporation Limited—(Continued)
Tel.: (61) 292366111
Emp.: 1,000
Real Estate Management Services
N.A.I.C.S.: 531390
Steve McCann *(Grp CEO & Mng Dir)*

Lend Lease (Scotland) Ltd (1)
33 Bothwell Street 1st Floor, Glasgow,
G26NL, United Kingdom (100%)
Tel.: (44) 1412268500
Web Site: http://www.lendlease.com
Sales Range: $25-49.9 Million
Emp.: 30
Real Estate Services
N.A.I.C.S.: 531390
Gillian Folgen *(Office Mgr)*

Lend Lease (Taiwan) Pty. Ltd. (1)
16th Fl No 99 Fu Hsing N Rd, 105, Taipei,
Taiwan
Tel.: (886) 227183997
Web Site: http://www.lendlease.com
Sales Range: $50-74.9 Million
Emp.: 4
Real Estate Investment
N.A.I.C.S.: 525990

Lend Lease (US) Capital, Inc. (1)
200 Park Ave, New York, NY 10166
Tel.: (212) 592-6700
Real Estate Development Services
N.A.I.C.S.: 531390
Kurt Lorenz *(Gen Mgr-Multi Site Grp-Americas)*

Lend Lease (US) Construction Holdings, Inc. (1)
200 Park Ave Fl 9, New York, NY 10166
Tel.: (212) 592-6800
Web Site: http://www.lendlease.com
Investment Management Service
N.A.I.C.S.: 523999
Ivelisse Laguna *(Gen Mgr)*

Lend Lease (US) Construction Inc (1)
71 Stevenson St Ste 800, San Francisco,
CA 94105-2919
Tel.: (415) 512-0586
Web Site: http://www.lendlease.com
Sales Range: $25-49.9 Million
Emp.: 13
Construction & Management Consultants
N.A.I.C.S.: 236220

Lend Lease (US) Construction, LMB, Inc. (1)
200 Park Ave 9th Fl, New York, NY 10166
Tel.: (212) 592-6700
Web Site: http://www.lendlease.com
Building Construction Services
N.A.I.C.S.: 236220
Claire Johnston *(CEO)*

Lend Lease (US) Healthcare Development LLC (1)
11360 Jog Rd Ste 200, Palm Beach Gardens, FL 33418
Tel.: (561) 691-9900
Sales Range: $25-49.9 Million
Emp.: 45
Medical Real Estate Investment Services
N.A.I.C.S.: 531390

Lend Lease (US) Holdings, Inc. (1)
200 Park Ave Fl 9, New York, NY 10166
Tel.: (212) 592-6700
Investment Management Service
N.A.I.C.S.: 523999

Lend Lease (US) Public Partnerships LLC (1)
1201 Demonbreun St Ste 800, Nashville,
TN 37203
Tel.: (615) 324-8800
Web Site: http://www.lendlease.com
Sales Range: $75-99.9 Million
Emp.: 120
Property Management Services
N.A.I.C.S.: 531312
Philip Carpenter *(COO)*

Lend Lease Building Japan Inc. (1)
Akasaka Enokizaka Mori Bldg 3F 1-7-1
Akasaka, Minato-ku, Tokyo, 107-0052, Japan
Tel.: (81) 3 6866 5600
Web Site: http://www.lendlease.com

Property Management & Construction Services
N.A.I.C.S.: 531390
Andrew Gauci *(Mng Dir)*

Lend Lease Building Pty. Ltd. (1)
Level 4 30 The Bond, Millers Point, 2000,
NSW, Australia
Tel.: (61) 292366111
Emp.: 2,000
Real Estate Investment
N.A.I.C.S.: 525990

Branch (Domestic):

Lend Lease Building Pty. Ltd. (2)
Level 13 SAP House Corner of Bunda St,
And Akuna Street, Canberra, 2601, Australia
Tel.: (61) 262760600
Sales Range: $50-74.9 Million
Emp.: 80
Real Estate Investment
N.A.I.C.S.: 525990

Lend Lease Building Pty. Ltd. (2)
Delfin House 155 Brebner Drive, Milton,
5021, NSW, Australia
Tel.: (61) 882317311
Real Estate Leasing & Developments
N.A.I.C.S.: 531390

Branch (Non-US):

Lend Lease Building Pty. Ltd. - New Zealand (2)
Level 3 16 High Street, Auckland, 1140,
New Zealand
Tel.: (64) 9 236 6111
Real Estate Services
N.A.I.C.S.: 531390

Lend Lease Communities (Australia) Limited (1)
Level 14 Tower Three International Towers
Sydney Exchange Place, 300 Barangaroo
Avenue, Barangaroo, 2000, NSW, Australia
Tel.: (61) 292366111
Emp.: 1,000
Real Estate Development Services
N.A.I.C.S.: 531390

Lend Lease Communities Inc. (1)
1675 Larimer St Ste 675, Denver, CO
80202
Tel.: (303) 623-8100
Web Site: http://www.lendlease.com.au
Real Estate Investments & Leasing
N.A.I.C.S.: 525990

Lend Lease Construction (EMEA) Limited (1)
1 Old Park Lane, Manchester, M41 7HG,
United Kingdom
Tel.: (44) 1612541700
Sales Range: $25-49.9 Million
Emp.: 55
Building Construction Services
N.A.I.C.S.: 236220

Lend Lease Construction Holdings (EMEA) Limited (1)
Bovis House 142 Northolt Road, Harrow,
HA2 0EE, Middlesex, United Kingdom
Tel.: (44) 2082718000
Building Construction Services
N.A.I.C.S.: 236220

Lend Lease Consulting (EMEA) Limited (1)
20 Triton Street Regent's Place, London,
NW1 3BF, United Kingdom
Tel.: (44) 2034309000
Web Site: http://www.lendlease.com
Construction Engineering Services
N.A.I.C.S.: 236220

Lend Lease Delfin Development (1)
Edgewater on the Maribyrnong Gordon
Street, Off Monash Street, Maribyrnong,
3032, Australia
Tel.: (61) 393184699
Web Site: http://www.lendlease.com
Sales Range: $25-49.9 Million
Emp.: 15
Real Estate Development & Leasing
N.A.I.C.S.: 531390

Lend Lease Development Inc. (1)
Level 4 30 The Bond 30 Hickson Road,

Millers Point, 2000, NSW, Australia
Tel.: (61) 292366111
Sales Range: $150-199.9 Million
Emp.: 500
Real Estate Development
N.A.I.C.S.: 531390

Lend Lease Development Inc. (1)
Level 2 19 Lang Pde, Milton, 4064, QLD,
Australia
Tel.: (61) 732922200
Web Site: http://www.lendlease.com
Sales Range: $25-49.9 Million
Emp.: 35
Real Estate Leasing & Developments
N.A.I.C.S.: 531390
Kirstien South *(Office Mgr)*

Lend Lease Development Inc. (1)
Level 2 10 Ord St, 6005, Perth, WA, Australia
Tel.: (61) 892232888
Web Site: http://www.lendlease.com
Sales Range: $50-74.9 Million
Emp.: 45
Real Estate Investments & Development
N.A.I.C.S.: 525990
Michael Glendinning *(Gen Mgr)*

Lend Lease Development Limited (1)
Langthorne Building, London, E15 2EG,
United Kingdom
Tel.: (44) 2032886100
Real Estate Management Services
N.A.I.C.S.: 531390

Lend Lease Espana S.A. (1)
Torre De Crital Ievel 20 S Castellana 259C,
28046, Madrid, Spain
Tel.: (34) 915902490
Web Site:
http://www.dhehave.lendlease.com
Real Estate Investment
N.A.I.C.S.: 525990
Alberto De Frutos *(Gen Mgr)*

Lend Lease Europe GP Limited (1)
20 Triton Street, Regent's Place, London,
NW1 3BF, United Kingdom
Tel.: (44) 2071829000
Real Estate Development Services
N.A.I.C.S.: 531390

Lend Lease Europe Limited (1)
Level 9 5 Merchant Square, London, W2
1BQ, United Kingdom
Tel.: (44) 2034309000
Real Estate Management Services
N.A.I.C.S.: 531390

Lend Lease Facilities Management (EMEA) Limited (1)
20 Triton Street, London, NW1 3BF, United
Kingdom
Tel.: (44) 2082762500
Facility Management Services
N.A.I.C.S.: 561210

Lend Lease Finance Limited (1)
L4 30 The Bond 30 Hickson Rd, Sydney,
2000, NSW, Australia
Tel.: (61) 292772169
Financial Lending Services
N.A.I.C.S.: 522220

Lend Lease Global Investment Plc (1)
Bovis House 142 Northolt Road, Harrow,
HA2 0EE, Middlesex, United Kingdom
Tel.: (44) 2082718000
Sales Range: $25-49.9 Million
Emp.: 50
Building Construction Services
N.A.I.C.S.: 236220

Lend Lease Infrastructure Pty Limited (1)
Locked Bag 1, Millers Point, 2000, NSW,
Australia (100%)
Tel.: (61) 2 8667 6000
Web Site: http://www.lendlease.com
Emp.: 200
Engineering, Construction & Asset Management Contractor
N.A.I.C.S.: 541330
Douglas Moss *(Exec Dir-Infrastructure Svcs)*

Subsidiary (Domestic):

Baulderstone Pty Limited (2)

INTERNATIONAL PUBLIC

Triniti Business Campus Level 5, 39 Delhi
Road, North Ryde, 2113, NSW,
Australia (100%)
Tel.: (61) 299357000
Web Site: http://www.baulderstone.com.au
Sales Range: $650-699.9 Million
Commercial Building Construction & Civil
Engineering Services
N.A.I.C.S.: 236220
Ian Luck *(Mng Dir)*

Lend Lease Engineering Pty Limited (2)
Level 20 Zenith Tower B, 821 Pacific Hwy,
Chatswood, 2067, NSW, Australia (100%)
Tel.: (61) 294990999
Web Site: http://www.lendlease.com
Sales Range: $1-4.9 Billion
Civil & Commercial Construction & Engineering Services
N.A.I.C.S.: 237990
Kate Perumal *(Gen Counsel)*

Lend Lease Infrastructure Pty Limited (2)
Level 5 7 Eden Park Drive, Macquarie Park,
2113, NSW, Australia (100%)
Tel.: (61) 281987100
Sales Range: $1-4.9 Billion
Emp.: 6,800
Holding Company
N.A.I.C.S.: 551112

Lend Lease International Pty Limited (1)
L 4 30 The Bond 30 Hickson Rd, Millers
Point, 2000, NSW, Australia
Tel.: (61) 292366111
Real Estate Development Services
N.A.I.C.S.: 531390

Lend Lease Investment Management Pte. Ltd. (1)
60 Anson Road 17-01 Mapletree Anson,
Singapore, 79914, Singapore
Tel.: (65) 62587116
Investment Management Service
N.A.I.C.S.: 523999

Lend Lease Japan Pty Ltd (1)
7 Chome-7-7 Roppongi, Main Tower
2-17-22 Akasaka, Minato-ku, Tokyo, 106-0032, Japan
Tel.: (81) 354141870
Real Estate Investment
N.A.I.C.S.: 525990

Lend Lease Primelife Limited (1)
Level 9 30 Convention Centre Place, South
Wharf, South Melbourne, 3006, VIC, Australia
Tel.: (61) 386993300
Web Site:
http://www.retirementbylendlease.com.au
Sales Range: $75-99.9 Million
Emp.: 944
Assisted Living Communities Developer &
Manager
N.A.I.C.S.: 623312
Rob Fehring *(CEO)*

Lend Lease Project Management & Construction (Australia) Pty Limited (1)
L 4 30 Hickson Rd, Millers Point, 2000,
NSW, Australia
Tel.: (61) 292366111
Construction Engineering Services
N.A.I.C.S.: 236220
Murray Woolcock *(Exec Gen Mgr-Strategic Bus-Americas)*

Lend Lease Project Management & Construction (Shanghai) Co. (1)
20/F Evergo Tower No 1325 Huaihai M Rd,
Xuhui District, Shanghai, 20031, China
Tel.: (86) 2161962988
Sales Range: $75-99.9 Million
Emp.: 200
Real Estate Management Services
N.A.I.C.S.: 531390
Mason Watebury *(Project Mgr)*

Lend Lease Property Management Pty Limited (1)
L 4 30 Hickson Rd, Millers Point, 2000,
NSW, Australia
Tel.: (61) 292366111
Real Estate Development Services

AND PRIVATE COMPANIES

N.A.I.C.S.: 531390

Lend Lease Real Estate Investment Services Ltd (1)
York House 23 Kingsway Strand, London, WC2B 6UJ, United Kingdom
Tel.: (44) 2071829000
Real Estate Manangement Services
N.A.I.C.S.: 531390

Lend Lease Real Estate Investments Ltd (1)
Level 14 Tower Three International Towers Sydney Exchange Place, 300 Barangaroo Avenue, Barangaroo, 2000, NSW, Australia
Tel.: (61) 292366111
Emp.: 1,000
Real Estate Development Services
N.A.I.C.S.: 531390

Lend Lease Residential Group (EMEA) Limited (1)
20 Triton Street Regent Place, London, NW1 3BF, United Kingdom
Tel.: (44) 2034309000
Real Estate Development Services
N.A.I.C.S.: 531390

Lend Lease Responsible Entity Limited (1)
30 The Bond L 4 30 Hickson Rd, Millers Point, 2000, NSW, Australia
Tel.: (61) 292366111
Investment Management Service
N.A.I.C.S.: 523999

Lend Lease Singapore Pte Limited (1)
60 Anson Road, Singapore, 79914, Singapore
Tel.: (65) 66716600
Real Estate Manangement Services
N.A.I.C.S.: 531390

Lend Lease Ventures Pty Ltd (1)
Level 14 Tower Three International Towers Sydney Exchange Place 300, Sydney, 2000, NSW, Australia
Tel.: (61) 292366111
Sales Range: $300-349.9 Million
Emp.: 1,000
Real Estate Manangement Services
N.A.I.C.S.: 531390

ML Bovis Holdings Limited (1)
200 Park Ave Fl 9, New York, NY 10166-0999
Tel.: (212) 592-6700
Investment Management Service
N.A.I.C.S.: 523999

LENDLEASE GLOBAL COMMERCIAL REIT
2 Tanjong Katong Road 05-01 Paya Lebar Quarter - PLQ 3, Singapore, 437161, Singapore
Tel.: (65) 66717374   SG
Web Site: https://www.lendleaseglobalreit.com
Year Founded: 1958
JYEU—(SES)
Rev.: $151,915,554
Assets: $2,837,239,267
Liabilities: $1,183,127,019
Net Worth: $1,654,112,248
Earnings: $87,846,988
Emp.: 69
Fiscal Year-end: 06/30/23
Real Estate Investment Trust Services
N.A.I.C.S.: 531190
Kelvin Chow (CEO)

LENDLOCK GROUP LIMITED
Guilden Sutton Lane No 86, Chester, CH3 7EX, United Kingdom
Tel.: (44) 1282412500   UK
Web Site: https://www.lendlockgroup.co.uk
Holding Company
N.A.I.C.S.: 551112

Subsidiaries:

Specialist Anodising Company Limited (1)
New Hall Works Elm Street, Burnley, BB10 1NY, United Kingdom
Tel.: (44) 1282412500
Web Site: https://sacoltd.com
Personal Care Product Mfr
N.A.I.C.S.: 456120

Subsidiary (Domestic):

Integrated Aluminium Components Limited (2)
Edward Street, Nelson, BB9 8TJ, Lancashire, United Kingdom
Tel.: (44) 1282699921
Web Site: http://www.iacltd.uk.com
Sales Range: $50-74.9 Million
Emp.: 130
Aluminum Component Mfr
N.A.I.C.S.: 331318
Danielle Oliver (Acct Mgr)

LENNARDS NIGERIA PLC
Kilometre 16 Ikorodu Road, Ojota, Lagos, Nigeria
Tel.: (234) 1 8132666
Footwear Whslr
N.A.I.C.S.: 424340
C. I. Ezeh (Chm)

LENNEPER GMBH & CO.KG
Gelpestrasse 75, 51647, Gummersbach, Germany
Tel.: (49) 2263903600
Web Site: http://www.lenneper.de
Sales Range: $10-24.9 Million
Emp.: 240
Light Mfr
N.A.I.C.S.: 335132
Elli Radmacher (Mng Dir)

LENNTECH BV
Rotterdamseweg 402 M, 2629 HH, Delft, Netherlands
Tel.: (31) 15 261 0900
Web Site: http://www.lenntech.com
Year Founded: 1993
Water Purification Systems Developer & Mfr
N.A.I.C.S.: 221310

LENOVO GROUP LIMITED
23/F Lincoln House Taikoo Place, 979 King s Road, Quarry Bay, China (Hong Kong)
Tel.: (852) 25163838   HK
Web Site: http://www.lenovo.com
Year Founded: 1988
LNVGF—(OTCIQ)
Rev.: $61,946,854,000
Assets: $38,920,057,000
Liabilities: $32,873,036,000
Net Worth: $6,047,021,000
Earnings: $1,680,831,000
Emp.: 77,000
Fiscal Year-end: 03/31/23
Holding Company; Personal Computer & Other Information Technology Products Developer, Mfr & Distr
N.A.I.C.S.: 551112
Wai Ming Wong (CFO & Exec VP)

Subsidiaries:

LLC Lenovo (East Europe / Asia) (1)
Boulevard Builders 4 Building 1 Section A 7th Floor, Krasnogorsk, Russia
Tel.: (7) 4986750600
Web Site: http://www.lenovo.com
Computer Peripheral Equipment Whslr
N.A.I.C.S.: 423430

Lenovo (Beijing) Limited (1)
Building 1 No 10 Yard Xibeiwang East Road, Haidian District, Beijing, 100085, China   (100%)
Tel.: (86) 1058868888
Web Site: http://www.lenovo.com
Sales Range: $1-4.9 Billion
Emp.: 9,000
Research & Manufacturing Centers & Sales of Computers & Computer Related Products
N.A.I.C.S.: 334118

Unit (Domestic):

Lenovo (Shenzhen) Advanced System Design Centre (2)
Lenovo R&D Building High Technology Park, Shen Nan Road, Shenzhen, 518057, China
Tel.: (86) 75526955888
Web Site: http://www.lenovo.com
Sales Range: $400-449.9 Million
Emp.: 1,200
Advanced System Computer Design Center
N.A.I.C.S.: 334118

Lenovo (Danmark) ApS (1)
Vandtarnsvej 83A, 2860, Soborg, Denmark
Tel.: (45) 8 988 1536
Computer Peripheral Equipment Whslr
N.A.I.C.S.: 423430

Lenovo (Deutschland) GmbH (1)
Meitnerstr 9, 70563, Stuttgart, Germany
Tel.: (49) 7116 569 0807
Computer Peripheral Equipment Whslr
N.A.I.C.S.: 423430

Lenovo (France) SAS (1)
20 Rue Des 2 Gares, PO Box 70072, 92842, Rueil-Malmaison, Cedex, France
Tel.: (33) 155704056
Web Site: http://www.lenovo.com
Personal Computer & Other Computer Products Whslr
N.A.I.C.S.: 423620

Lenovo (Italy) S.r.l. (1)
Segreen Business Park Via San Bovio 3 Building, San Felice, 20068, Segrate, MI, Italy
Tel.: (39) 028 707 4720
Computer Peripheral Equipment Whslr
N.A.I.C.S.: 423430

Lenovo (Japan) Ltd. (1)
1623-14 Shimotsumura, Yamato, 242-8502, Japan   (100%)
Tel.: (81) 462761111
Web Site: http://www.lenovo.com
Develops, Manufactures & Markets Personal Computers, Mobile Handsets & Related Products
N.A.I.C.S.: 334111

Lenovo (Schweiz) GmbH (1)
Baslerstrasse 60, 8048, Zurich, Switzerland
Tel.: (41) 43 508 4583
Computer Peripheral Equipment Whslr
N.A.I.C.S.: 423430

Lenovo (Singapore) Pte. Ltd. (1)
151 Lorong Chuan 02-01 New Tech Park, Singapore, 556741, Singapore   (100%)
Tel.: (65) 68271000
Emp.: 200
Mfr, Sales & Research of Computer Products
N.A.I.C.S.: 334118
Sumir Bhatia (VP-Data Center Grp-Asia Pacific)

Lenovo (South Africa) (Pty) Limited (1)
Wedgefield Office Park 17 Muswell Road South, PO BOX 69118, Bryanston, Johannesburg, South Africa
Tel.: (27) 11 514 7500
Computer Peripheral Equipment Whslr
N.A.I.C.S.: 423430

Lenovo (Sweden) A.B. (1)
Knarrarnasgatan 7, Box 1242, 164 28, Kista, Sweden
Tel.: (46) 84 030 0181
Computer Peripheral Equipment Whslr
N.A.I.C.S.: 423430

Lenovo (United States) Inc. (1)
1009 Think Pl, Morrisville, NC 27560
Tel.: (919) 294-2500
Web Site: http://www.lenovo.com
Computer Hardware
N.A.I.C.S.: 334118
Torod Neptune (VP-Global Comm)

Branch (Domestic):

Lenovo (United States) Inc. - US Sales Headquarters (2)
1009 Think Pl, Morrisville, NC 27560
Tel.: (919) 254-1924
Web Site: http://www.lenovo.com

LENOVO GROUP LIMITED

Sales & Distribution of Computer Systems
N.A.I.C.S.: 541512

Subsidiary (Domestic):

Motorola Mobility Holdings, Inc. (2)
222 W Merchandise Mart Plz Ste 1800, Chicago, IL 60654
Tel.: (800) 668-6765
Web Site: http://www.motorola.com
Holding Company; Wireless Communication, Information & Entertainment Technologies Developer, Mfr, Distr & Support Services
N.A.I.C.S.: 551112
Iqbal Arshad (Sr VP-Product Dev Engrg-Global)

Subsidiary (Non-US):

Motorola Comercial, S.A. de C.V. (3)
Paseo de los Tamarindos No 100 Piso 1 Oficina 101 Col Bosques de, las Lomas Del Cuajimalpa, Mexico, 05120, D F, Mexico
Tel.: (52) 5541662843
Web Site: http://www.motorola.com.mx
Wireless Communications Equipment Distr & Technical Support Services
N.A.I.C.S.: 423620

Motorola Industrial Ltda. (3)
Av Chedid Jafel n 222 Vila Olmpia 2nd Floor, Sao Paulo, 04551-065, SP, Brazil
Tel.: (55) 1138476686
Web Site: http://www.motorola.com.br
Wireless Communications Equipment Mfr & Distr
N.A.I.C.S.: 334220

Motorola Mobility Canada Ltd. (3)
55 Idema Road, Markham, L3R 1A9, ON, Canada
Web Site: http://www.motorola.ca
Wireless Communications Equipment Distr & Technical Support Services
N.A.I.C.S.: 423620

Motorola Mobility Espana, S.L. (3)
Martínez Villergas 52 Bloque 3, 28027, Madrid, Spain
Tel.: (34) 914002000
Web Site: http://www.motorola.es
Wireless Communications Equipment Distr & Technical Support Services
N.A.I.C.S.: 423620

Motorola Mobility Germany GmbH (3)
Telco Kreisel 1, 65510, Idstein, Germany
Tel.: (49) 6126 2246 0
Web Site: http://www.motorola.de
Wireless Communications Equipment Distr & Technical Support Services
N.A.I.C.S.: 423620

Motorola Mobility Italia S.r.l. (3)
Via Privata Maria Teresa 7, 20123, Milan, Italy
Tel.: (39) 0269430777
Web Site: http://www.motorola.it
Wireless Communications Equipment Distr & Technical Support Services
N.A.I.C.S.: 423620

Subsidiary (Domestic):

Motorola Mobility LLC (3)
222 W Merchandise Mart Plz Ste 1800, Chicago, IL 60654
Web Site: http://www.motorola.com
Wireless Communication, Information & Entertainment Technologies Developer, Mfr, Distr & Support Services
N.A.I.C.S.: 334220
Sanjay Vanjani (CFO)

Subsidiary (Non-US):

Motorola Mobility UK Ltd. (3)
Chineham Park Redwood, Basingstoke, RG24 8WQ, United Kingdom
Tel.: (44) 1256790790
Web Site: http://www.motorola.co.uk
Wireless Communications Equipment Distr & Technical Support Services
N.A.I.C.S.: 423620

Lenovo Enterprise Solutions (Singapore) Pte. Ltd. (1)
151 Lorong Chuan 02-01 New Tech Park, Singapore, 556741, Singapore

LENOVO GROUP LIMITED   INTERNATIONAL PUBLIC

Lenovo Group Limited—(Continued)
Tel.: (65) 6 827 1000
Computer Peripheral Equipment Whslr
N.A.I.C.S.: 423430

Lenovo Mexico, S. de R.L. de C.V. (1)
Ave Batallon de San Patricio 109 Sur Piso 6 - Int 617 Col Valle, Oriente San Pedro Garza Garcia, 66260, Monterrey, Nuevo Leon, Mexico **(100%)**
Tel.: (52) 8110015333
Web Site: http://www.lenovo.com
Sales Range: $50-74.9 Million
Emp.: 150
Mfr & Fulfillment Center
N.A.I.C.S.: 334118

Lenovo Technology (United Kingdom) Limited (1)
Redwood 3 Crockford Lane, Chineham Business Park, Basingstoke, RG24 8WQ, United Kingdom
Tel.: (44) 125 677 4500
Computer Peripheral Equipment Whslr
N.A.I.C.S.: 423430

Lenovo Technology B.V. Sp. z o.o. (1)
Oddzial W Polsce, Al Krakowska 271, 02-133, Warsaw, Poland **(100%)**
Tel.: (48) 223956476
Web Site: http://www.lenovopolska.pl
Computer Manufacturing Center
N.A.I.C.S.: 334111

Lenovo Tecnologia (Brasil) Ltda. (1)
Est Municipal Jose Costa de Mesquita 200-Mod 11, Neighborhood Chacara Alvorada, Indaiatuba, 13337-200, Sao Paulo, Brazil
Tel.: (55) 112 895 0432
Computer Peripheral Equipment Whslr
N.A.I.C.S.: 423430

MEDION AG (1)
Am Zehnthof 77, D-45307, Essen, Germany **(79.82%)**
Tel.: (49) 20183830
Web Site: https://www.medion.com
Rev.: $807,616,011
Assets: $692,270,047
Liabilities: $248,131,963
Net Worth: $444,138,083
Earnings: $18,422,115
Emp.: 897
Fiscal Year-end: 03/31/2024
Consumer Electronics Mfr & Distr
N.A.I.C.S.: 334111
Gerd Brachmann *(Chm-Mgmt Bd & CEO)*

Subsidiary (Domestic):

Allgemeine Multimedia Service GmbH (2)
Am Zehnthof 51, 45307, Essen, Nordrhein-Westfalen, Germany
Tel.: (49) 20183830
Personal Computers Retailer
N.A.I.C.S.: 449210

Subsidiary (Non-US):

MEDION Electronics Limited (2)
120 Faraday Park Faraday Road, Dorcan, Swindon, SN3 5JF, Wiltshire, United Kingdom
Tel.: (44) 3333213106
Web Site: http://www.medion.com
Home Electrical Appliances & Personal Computers Retailer
N.A.I.C.S.: 423620

MEDION Iberia, S.L. (2)
C/ Serrano Galvache N 56 Parque Empresarial Parque Norte, Edificio Abedul Planta 3, 28003, Madrid, Spain
Tel.: (34) 917896882
Web Site: http://www.medion.com
Sales Range: $25-49.9 Million
Emp.: 8
Consumer Electronics Retailer
N.A.I.C.S.: 423620

MEDION Nordic A/S (2)
Naverland 29 Floor 1, 2600, Glostrup, Denmark
Tel.: (45) 70200111
Web Site: http://www.medion.dk

Sales Range: $25-49.9 Million
Emp.: 5
Consumer Electronics Retailer
N.A.I.C.S.: 423620
Carsten Yde Ibsen *(Mng Dir)*

MEDION Schweiz Electronics AG (2)
Baslerstrasse 60, Altstetten, 8048, Zurich, Switzerland
Tel.: (41) 848333332
Web Site: http://www.medion.com
Sales Range: $25-49.9 Million
Emp.: 7
Consumer Electronics Retailer
N.A.I.C.S.: 423620

Subsidiary (US):

MEDION USA, Inc. (2)
493 Laurel Ave, Highland Park, IL 60035
Tel.: (866) 633-4660
Electronics Distr
N.A.I.C.S.: 423430

LENS TECHNOLOGY CO., LTD.
Lens Technology Park National Biomedical Industrial Estate, Changsha, 410311, Hunan, China
Tel.: (86) 73183859999
Web Site: https://www.hnlens.com
Year Founded: 2011
300433—(CHIN)
Rev.: $6,556,476,420
Assets: $10,999,727,856
Liabilities: $4,768,527,348
Net Worth: $6,231,200,508
Earnings: $43,710,432
Emp.: 120,000
Fiscal Year-end: 12/31/22
Electronic Components Mfr
N.A.I.C.S.: 334419
Qunfei Zhou *(Chm & Gen Mgr)*

LENSWISTA AG
Magnusstrasse 11, D 12489, Berlin, Germany
Tel.: (49) 3063926372
Web Site: http://www.lenswista.com
Contact Lens Mfr & Distr
N.A.I.C.S.: 333310
Thomas Kordick *(CEO)*

LENT TORMOZ IRAN COMPANY
11th Km Karaj Special Road Opposite The Pars Electric, Tehran, 13998 11498, Iran
Tel.: (98) 21 44905501
Year Founded: 1963
Brake Shoe Mfr
N.A.I.C.S.: 336340
Sayed Hussien Lagordi *(Chm)*

LENTEX S.A.
ul Powstancow Slaskich 54, 42-700, Lubliniec, Poland
Tel.: (48) 343515600
Web Site: https://www.lentex.pl
Year Founded: 1911
LTX—(WAR)
Rev.: $86,293,191
Assets: $113,002,794
Liabilities: $19,875,254
Net Worth: $93,127,540
Earnings: $6,452,236
Fiscal Year-end: 12/31/23
Floor Covering Mfr
N.A.I.C.S.: 321918
Barbara Trenda *(Member-Mgmt Bd & Dir-Fin & Economics)*

Subsidiaries:

Gamrat S.A. (1)
ul Mickiewicza 108, 38-200, Jaslo, Poland
Tel.: (48) 134916000
Web Site: http://gamrat.pl
Drainage Channel & Piping System Construction Services

N.A.I.C.S.: 237110
Anna Pawlak *(Chm)*

LENTUO INTERNATIONAL INC.
West of Beihuayuan Village Gaobeidian Township, Chaoyang District, Beijing, 100024, China
Tel.: (86) 10 8735 8388   Ky
Web Site: http://www.lentuo.net
Year Founded: 1994
Sales Range: $550-599.9 Million
Car Dealership Owner & Operator
N.A.I.C.S.: 441110
Hetong Guo *(Founder & Chm)*

LENZE SE
Hans-Lenze-Strasse 1, 31855, Aerzen, Germany
Tel.: (49) 5154820
Web Site: http://www.lenze.com
Year Founded: 1947
Sales Range: $800-899.9 Million
Emp.: 3,300
Holding Company
N.A.I.C.S.: 551112
Christian Wendler *(CEO)*

Subsidiaries:

Encoway GmbH (1)
Buschhohe 2, 28357, Bremen, Germany **(85.5%)**
Tel.: (49) 421246770
Software Publisher
N.A.I.C.S.: 513210

IOOO Lenze (1)
Masjukovschina Str 2-a Administrative & Amenity Building Office 5, 220124, Minsk, Belarus
Tel.: (375) 17 509 59 55
Electrical Equipment Distr
N.A.I.C.S.: 423610

Lenze A/S (1)
Roskiltevej 22, 2620, Albertslund, Denmark
Tel.: (45) 46966666
Web Site: http://www.lenze.com
Sales Range: $25-49.9 Million
Emp.: 20
Scientific & Technical Consulting Services
N.A.I.C.S.: 541690
Peter Nielsen *(Mgr-Mktg)*

Lenze AB (1)
Teknikringen 8, 583 30, Linkoping, Sweden
Tel.: (46) 13355800
Industrial Automation Products Mfr
N.A.I.C.S.: 335314

Lenze AC Technology Corp. (1)
630 Douglas St, Uxbridge, MA 01569
Tel.: (508) 278-9100
Web Site: http://www.lenzeamerica.com
Holding Company
N.A.I.C.S.: 551112
David Cybulski *(VP-Fin)*

Lenze AS (1)
Stallbakken 5, 2005, Raelingen, Norway
Tel.: (47) 64802510
Web Site: http://www.lenze.no
Sales Range: $50-74.9 Million
Emp.: 5
Holding Company
N.A.I.C.S.: 551112
Peter Nelson *(Gen Mgr)*

Lenze Americas Corporation (1)
630 Douglas St, Uxbridge, MA 01569
Tel.: (508) 278-9100
Industrial Automation Products Mfr
N.A.I.C.S.: 335314
Murphy Lenze *(Supvr-Production)*

Lenze Antriebstechnik GmbH (1)
Ipf-Landesstrasse 1, Asten, 4481, Austria
Tel.: (43) 72242100
Web Site: http://www.lenze.com
Sales Range: $25-49.9 Million
Emp.: 50
Holding Company
N.A.I.C.S.: 551112
Reinhard Pachl *(Mgr)*

Lenze Antriebstechnik Handelsgesellschaft mbH (1)

Gyarutca 2, PO Box 322, 2040, Budaors, Hungary
Tel.: (36) 23501320
Web Site: http://www.lenze.hu
Sales Range: $50-74.9 Million
Emp.: 6
Holding Company
N.A.I.C.S.: 551112
Fuchs Mario *(Gen Mgr)*

Lenze Argentina Automatizacion S.A. (1)
2667 Campillo St, C1427DCE, Buenos Aires, Argentina
Tel.: (54) 11 4523 0047
Web Site: http://www.lenze.com
Emp.: 100
Electrical Equipment Distr
N.A.I.C.S.: 423610
Paulo Taborda *(Mgr)*

Lenze Austria Holding GmbH (1)
Ipf-Landesstrasse 1, 4481, Asten, Austria
Tel.: (43) 7224210124
Industrial Automation Products Mfr
N.A.I.C.S.: 335314
Lukas Sittig *(CFO)*

Lenze Automation GmbH (1)
Grunstrasse 36, Meerbusch, 40667, Germany
Tel.: (49) 213299040
Web Site: http://www.lenze.de
Sales Range: $25-49.9 Million
Emp.: 40
Engineering & Technical Services
N.A.I.C.S.: 541330

Lenze B.V. (1)
Postbus 31 01, 's-Hertogenbosch, 5232BR, Netherlands
Tel.: (31) 736456500
Web Site: http://www.lenze.nl
Sales Range: $50-74.9 Million
Emp.: 5
Holding Company
N.A.I.C.S.: 551112
Vanden Broak *(Gen Mgr)*

Lenze B.V.B.A. (1)
Rijksweg 10c, Bornem, 2880, Belgium
Tel.: (32) 35426200
Web Site: http://www.lenze.com
Sales Range: $25-49.9 Million
Emp.: 8
Speed Changer Industrial High-Speed Drive & Gear Mfr
N.A.I.C.S.: 333612

Lenze Bachofen AG (1)
Ackerstrasse 45, 8610, Uster, Switzerland
Tel.: (41) 433991414
Web Site: http://www.lenze-bachofen.ch
Sales Range: $25-49.9 Million
Emp.: 40
Measuring Displaying & Controlling Industrial Process Variables Instruments & Related Products Mfr
N.A.I.C.S.: 334513
Conrad Mayer *(Mng Dir)*

Lenze Brasil Automacao Ltda. (1)
Rua Alfredo Acchar 970, Vinhedo, Sao Paulo, 13280-000, Brazil
Tel.: (55) 19 3846 3500
Electrical Equipment Distr
N.A.I.C.S.: 423610
Fabricio Lopes *(Key Acct Mgr-Automotive Indus)*

Lenze Delegacion Bilbao Srl (1)
Cullera 73-4 D, 46035, Valencia, Benimamet, Spain
Tel.: (34) 902 02 7904
Web Site: http://www.lenze.com
Holding Company: Technology & Automated Systems Mfr
N.A.I.C.S.: 551112

Lenze Drive Systems (Shanghai) Co. Ltd. (1)
No 2989 Jiangshan Road, Lingang, 201306, Shanghai, China
Tel.: (86) 2138280200
Web Site: http://www.lenze.com.cn
Sales Range: $75-99.9 Million
Emp.: 150
Holding Company
N.A.I.C.S.: 551112
Gary Chan *(Gen Mgr)*

AND PRIVATE COMPANIES

Lenze Drive Systems France Sarl (1)
ZI de Ruitz Secteur les Hallots, 25 Rue des Dames Ruitz, 62620, Lille, France
Tel.: (33) 391801530
Web Site: http://www.lenze.com
Sales Range: $25-49.9 Million
Emp.: 55
Electronic Computer Mfr
N.A.I.C.S.: 334111

Lenze Drive Systems GmbH (1)
Hans-Lenze-Strasse 1, Aerzen, 31855, Germany
Tel.: (49) 5154820
Web Site: http://www.lenze.com
Measuring Displaying & Controlling Industrial Process Variables Instruments & Related Products Mfr
N.A.I.C.S.: 334513
Verena Liane Ottermann (Mgr)

Lenze Drives Oy (1)
Piispanristingie 2C, 20520, Turku, Finland
Tel.: (358) 22748180
Sales Range: $50-74.9 Million
Emp.: 6
Holding Company
N.A.I.C.S.: 551112

Lenze Gerit S.r.l. (1)
Viale Monza 338, Milan, 20128, Italy
Tel.: (39) 02270981
Web Site: http://www.lenzeitalia.it
Holding Company
N.A.I.C.S.: 551112

Lenze GmbH & Co KG (1)
Buchenweg 1, Hans Lenze, Aerzen, 32699, Germany
Tel.: (49) 5154820
Web Site: http://www.lenze.com
Sales Range: $50-74.9 Million
Emp.: 200
Holding Company
N.A.I.C.S.: 551112
Carsten Helbk (CFO)

Lenze Hajtastechnika Kft. (1)
Gyar utca 2, PO Box 322, 2040, Budaors, Hungary
Tel.: (36) 23 501 320
Electrical Equipment Distr
N.A.I.C.S.: 423610

Lenze Italia S.r.l. (1)
Viale Tibaldi 7, 20136, Milan, Italy
Tel.: (39) 02270981
Industrial Automation Products Mfr
N.A.I.C.S.: 335314
Carlo De Regis (Mng Dir)

Lenze Ltd. (1)
Fraser Road Priory Business Park, Bedford, MK44 3WH, United Kingdom (100%)
Tel.: (44) 1234321321
Web Site: http://www.lenze.co.uk
Sales Range: $50-74.9 Million
Emp.: 107
N.A.I.C.S.: 333612

Lenze Mechatronics Pvt. Ltd. (1)
Lenze Plot No 46A Sector 10, Pcntda Industrial Area Bhosari, 411026, Pune, India
Tel.: (91) 2066318100
Web Site: http://www.lenze.com
Sales Range: $25-49.9 Million
Emp.: 20
Holding Company
N.A.I.C.S.: 551112

Lenze Muhendislik San. ve. Tic. A.S. (1)
Ataturk Mahallesi Cumhuriyet Caddesi Yurt Sokak No 7, Umraniye, 34764, Istanbul, Turkiye
Tel.: (90) 216 316 5138
Electrical Equipment Distr
N.A.I.C.S.: 423610

Lenze Pogonska Teknika, d.o.o. (1)
Kidriceva 2A, 3000, Celje, Slovenia
Tel.: (386) 34264640
Web Site: http://www.lenze.com
Sales Range: $50-74.9 Million
Emp.: 4
Holding Company; Power Regeneration
N.A.I.C.S.: 551112
Leon Strmcnik (Mgr-HR)

Lenze Polska Sp. z o.o. (1)
Ul Rydygiera 47, Torun, 879100, Poland
Tel.: (48) 566582800
Web Site: http://www.lenze.pl
Sales Range: $25-49.9 Million
Emp.: 10
Holding Company
N.A.I.C.S.: 551112
Radoslaw Kotkiewicz (Mgr-Sls)

Lenze S.E.A. Sdn. Bhd. (1)
No 28 Jalan PJU 3 47 Sunway Damansara Technology Park, 47810, Petaling Jaya, Selangor, Malaysia
Tel.: (60) 378031428
Web Site: http://www.lenze.com
Sales Range: $25-49.9 Million
Emp.: 5
Automotive Mechanical & Electrical Repair & Maintenance
N.A.I.C.S.: 811114

Lenze SAS (1)
44 rue Blaise Pascal ZI des Mardelles, 93600, Aulnay-sous-Bois, France
Tel.: (33) 1 48 79 62 00
Electrical Equipment Distr
N.A.I.C.S.: 423610

Lenze Service GmbH (1)
Breslauer Str 3, Extertal, 32699, Bielefeld, Germany
Tel.: (49) 1805202426
Holding Company
N.A.I.C.S.: 551112

Lenze Slovakia, s.r.o. (1)
Trencianska cesta 17, 915 01, Nove Mesto nad Vahom, Slovakia
Tel.: (421) 32 7430 778
Web Site: http://www.lenze.com
Electrical Equipment Distr
N.A.I.C.S.: 423610
Marek Engr-Application (Engr-Application)

Lenze South East Asia Pte. Ltd (1)
18 Sin Ming Lane 03-16, Midview City, Singapore, 573960, Singapore
Tel.: (65) 6694 1596
Electrical Equipment Distr
N.A.I.C.S.: 423610
Randy de Guzman (Mng Dir)

Lenze Transmisiones S.A. (1)
Edificio TCA C/ Henri Dunant 9, 08173, Sant Cugat del Valles, Barcelona, Spain
Tel.: (34) 937 207 680
Web Site: http://www.lenze.com
Electrical Equipment Distr
N.A.I.C.S.: 423610
Oscar Chaves Cayuela (Mng Dir)

Lenze UAB (1)
Breslaujos g 3, 44403, Kaunas, Lithuania
Tel.: (370) 37407174
Web Site: http://www.lenze.lt
Sales Range: $50-74.9 Million
Emp.: 9
Holding Company
N.A.I.C.S.: 551112
Liztroskrs Lenrs (Gen Mgr)

Lenze Verbindungstechnik GmbH (1)
Ipf-Landesstrasse 1, 4481, Asten, Austria
Tel.: (43) 72242100
Web Site: http://www.lenze.com
Sales Range: $150-199.9 Million
Emp.: 260
Holding Company
N.A.I.C.S.: 551112
Petra Kinast (Mgr-Mktg)

Lenze Zadvizhvasta Tehnika EOOD (1)
Bul Maritza 21 Office 204, 4003, Plovdiv, Bulgaria
Tel.: (359) 32940373
Web Site: http://www.Lenze.bg
Sales Range: $50-74.9 Million
Emp.: 5
Holding Company
N.A.I.C.S.: 551112

Lenze mehatronika-pogonska tehnika d.o.o. (1)
Ulica grada Gospica 3, 10000, Zagreb, Croatia
Tel.: (385) 1 249 8056
Electrical Equipment Distr
N.A.I.C.S.: 423610

Lenze, S.r.o. (1)
Central Trade Pk D1, Humpolec, 39601, Prague, Czech Republic
Tel.: (420) 565507111
Web Site: http://www.lenze.cz
Sales Range: $50-74.9 Million
Emp.: 10
Holding Company
N.A.I.C.S.: 551112

Logicline GmbH (1)
Planiestrasse 10, 71063, Sindelfingen, Germany
Tel.: (49) 7031611770
Web Site: http://www.logicline.de
Software Development Services
N.A.I.C.S.: 334610
Edgar Schuber (Mng Dir)

OOO Lenze (1)
Schelkovskoye shosse 5, 105122, Moscow, Russia
Tel.: (7) 4958492350
Electrical Equipment Distr
N.A.I.C.S.: 423610

Schmidhauser AG (1)
Obere Neustrasse 1, Romanshorn, 8590, Switzerland
Tel.: (41) 714661111
Web Site: http://www.lenze-schmidhauser.ch
Sales Range: $50-74.9 Million
Emp.: 80
Holding Company
N.A.I.C.S.: 551112
David Cesaretti (CFO)

LENZING AKTIENGESELLSCHAFT

Werkstrasse 2, 4860, Lenzing, Austria
Tel.: (43) 76727010 AT
Web Site: https://www.lenzing.com
LNZ—(VIE)
Rev.: $2,357,563,988
Assets: $3,495,159,210
Liabilities: $1,772,970,191
Net Worth: $1,722,189,019
Earnings: $137,525,527
Emp.: 7,036
Fiscal Year-end: 12/31/19
Cellulose Fiber Mfr
N.A.I.C.S.: 325220
Veit Sorger (Deputy Chm-Supervisory Bd)

Subsidiaries:

BZL-Bildungszentrum Lenzing GmbH (1)
Im Gruntal 2, A-4860, Lenzing, Austria (75%)
Tel.: (43) 76727013531
Web Site: https://www.bzl.at
Emp.: 90
Educational Support Services
N.A.I.C.S.: 611710

Gemeinnutzige Siedlungsgesellschaft m.b.H. (1)
Oberer Markt 12, 66538, Neunkirchen, Germany
Tel.: (49) 682192380
Web Site: http://www.gsg-nk.de
Real Estate Services
N.A.I.C.S.: 531390

LD Celulose S.A. (1)
Tel.: (55) 1146320625
Synthetic Fiber & Filament Mfr
N.A.I.C.S.: 325220

Lenzing (Nanjing) Fibers Co., Ltd. (1)
No 2 Kangqiang Road Xiongzhou Street, Luhe District, Nanjing, 211511, Jiangsu, China (100%)
Tel.: (86) 2557639888
Web Site: https://www.nanjing.com
Sales Range: $10-24.9 Million
Emp.: 100
Cellulosic Organic Fiber Mfr
N.A.I.C.S.: 325220

Lenzing (Thailand) Co., Ltd. (1)
599 Moo 2, ThaToom Sub-District SriMaha-Phot District, Bangkok, 25140, PrachinBuri, Thailand
Tel.: (66) 37624123
Synthetic Fiber & Filament Mfr
N.A.I.C.S.: 325220

Lenzing Beteiligungs GmbH (1)
Werkstr 2, Lenzing, 4860, Austria (100%)
Tel.: (43) 76727010
Web Site: http://www.lenzing.com
Sales Range: $300-349.9 Million
Emp.: 3,000
Holding Company
N.A.I.C.S.: 551112

Lenzing Biocel Paskov a.s (1)
Mistecka 762, 739 21, Paskov, Czech Republic
Tel.: (420) 558461111
Synthetic Fiber & Filament Mfr
N.A.I.C.S.: 325220

Lenzing Fibers (Hong Kong) Ltd (1)
Units 804 2806 8Th Fl Lu Plaza, 2 Wing Yip Street, Kwun Tong, China (Hong Kong) (100%)
Tel.: (852) 37185600
Web Site: http://www.lenzing.com
Emp.: 20
Textile Product Mills
N.A.I.C.S.: 314999

Lenzing Fibers (Shanghai) Co., Ltd. (1)
968 Beijing West Road Garden Square, Unit 06-08 Floor 15th, Shanghai, 200041, China (100%)
Tel.: (86) 21331524380
Sales Range: $10-24.9 Million
Cellulosic Organic Fiber Mfr
N.A.I.C.S.: 325220

Lenzing Fibers GmbH (1)
Industriegelande 1, Heiligenkreuz, 7561, Vienna, Austria (100%)
Tel.: (43) 33254100
Sales Range: $10-24.9 Million
Emp.: 180
Cellulosic Organic Fiber Mfr
N.A.I.C.S.: 325220

Lenzing Fibers Grimsby Limited (1)
Energy Park Way, Grimsby, DN31 2TT, United Kingdom
Tel.: (44) 1472244700
Fiber Mfr
N.A.I.C.S.: 325220

Lenzing Fibers Holding GmbH (1)
Industriegelande 1, Heiligenkreuz, 7561, Lenzing, Austria
Tel.: (43) 33254100
Web Site: https://www.lenzing.com
Sales Range: $300-349.9 Million
Holding Company
N.A.I.C.S.: 551112

Lenzing Fibers Inc. (1)
530 7th Ave Ste 808, New York, NY 10018-3508 (100%)
Tel.: (212) 944-7400
Nonwoven Fabric Mills
N.A.I.C.S.: 313230

Lenzing Fibers India Private Limited (1)
Srivari Shrimat 5th floor rear side 1045 Avinashi Road, Coimbatore, 641018, India
Tel.: (91) 4224292800
Fiber Mfr
N.A.I.C.S.: 325220

Lenzing Holding GmbH (1)
Werkstr 2, 4860, Lenzing, Austria (100%)
Tel.: (43) 76727010
Web Site: https://www.lenzing.com
Sales Range: $300-349.9 Million
Emp.: 3,500
Holding Company
N.A.I.C.S.: 551112

Lenzing Korea Yuhan Hoesa (1)
Rm 501 16-8 Teheran-ro 64-gil, Gangnam-gu, Seoul, 06192, Korea (South)
Tel.: (82) 27826131
Synthetic Fiber & Filament Mfr
N.A.I.C.S.: 325220

Lenzing Singapore Pte. Ltd. (1)
10 Anson Road Floor Level 5 Suite 5192

LENZING AKTIENGESELLSCHAFT

Lenzing Aktiengesellschaft—(Continued)

International Plaza, Singapore, 079903, Singapore
Tel.: (65) 65506733
Synthetic Fiber & Filament Mfr
N.A.I.C.S.: 325220

Lenzing Taiwan Fibers Ltd. (1)
7F No 53 Dongxing Road, Xinyi District, Taipei, 110, Taiwan
Tel.: (886) 287681023
Fiber Mfr
N.A.I.C.S.: 335991

Lenzing Technik GmbH (1)
Werkstrasse 2, 4860, Lenzing, Austria **(100%)**
Tel.: (43) 76727010
Web Site: http://www.lenzing-technik.com
Sales Range: $25-49.9 Million
Emp.: 500
Heavy & Civil Engineering Construction
N.A.I.C.S.: 237990

PT South Pacific Viscose (1)
Sampoerna Strategic Square South Tower 22nd Floor, Jl Jend Sudirman KAV 45-46, Jakarta, 12930, Indonesia **(90.56%)**
Tel.: (62) 215771630
Web Site: http://www.pt-spv.com
Sales Range: $10-24.9 Million
Emp.: 25
Production of Viscose Fibers
N.A.I.C.S.: 325220

Pulp Trading GmbH (1)
P A Lenzing Ag, 4860, Lenzing, Austria **(100%)**
Tel.: (43) 76727012892
Web Site: https://www.lenzing.com
Sales Range: $300-349.9 Million
Emp.: 3,500
Durable Goods Whslr
N.A.I.C.S.: 423990

RVL Reststoffverwertung Lenzing GmbH (1)
P A Lenzing Ag, 4860, Lenzing, Austria **(50%)**
Tel.: (43) 76727013361
Web Site: http://www.lenzing.com
Sales Range: $200-249.9 Million
Emp.: 3,000
Industrial Pattern Mfr
N.A.I.C.S.: 332999

LENZLINGER SOHNE AG
Grossrietstrasse 7, 8606, Nanikon, Switzerland
Tel.: (41) 58 944 5858 CH
Web Site: http://www.lenzlinger.ch
Year Founded: 1862
Sales Range: $25-49.9 Million
Emp.: 230
Construction & Engineering Services
N.A.I.C.S.: 541330
Karin Lenzlinger Diedenhofen (Deputy Chm)

Subsidiaries:

Lenzlinger Sohne AG - Uster (1)
Seestrasse 64, 8610, Uster, Switzerland
Tel.: (41) 58 944 5353
Web Site: http://www.lenzlinger.ch
Flooring Construction Components
N.A.I.C.S.: 324122
Markus Buhler (Mgr-Bus Unit)

LEO ACQUISITIONS CORP.
2300 Yonge Street Suite 1500, Toronto, M4P 1E4, ON, Canada
Tel.: (416) 780-2244 ON
Year Founded: 2009
Assets: $252,403
Liabilities: $95,639
Net Worth: $156,764
Earnings: ($56,230)
Emp.: 2
Fiscal Year-end: 06/30/17
Investment Services
N.A.I.C.S.: 523999
Gerald Goldberg (Pres & CEO)

LEO GLOBAL LOGISTICS PUBLIC COMPANY LIMITED
251-251/1 Soi Pakdee Rama III Road, Bangkorleam, Bangkok, 10120, Thailand
Tel.: (66) 26891122 TH
Web Site:
https://www.leogloballogistics.com
Year Founded: 1991
LEO—(THA)
Rev.: $40,078,093
Assets: $45,510,310
Liabilities: $18,481,173
Net Worth: $27,029,137
Earnings: $2,229,945
Emp.: 322
Fiscal Year-end: 12/31/23
Logistic Services
N.A.I.C.S.: 541614
Sanee Dangwang (Chm)

Subsidiaries:

Leo Myanmar Logistics Company Limited
422/426 International Commercial Center Tower 10-08, Corner of Strand Road and Botahtaung Pagoda Road Botahtaung Township, Yangon, Myanmar
Tel.: (95) 1202092
Logistic Services
N.A.I.C.S.: 488510

LEO GROUP CO., LTD.
Building A Oriental International Yuanzhong Building, Putuo District 2900 Zhongshan North Road, Shanghai, 200063, China
Tel.: (86) 2160158601
Web Site: http://www.leogroup.cn
Year Founded: 1995
002131—(SSE)
Rev.: $2,845,674,936
Assets: $2,729,001,132
Liabilities: $1,092,178,620
Net Worth: $1,636,822,512
Earnings: ($62,215,452)
Fiscal Year-end: 12/31/22
Pumps Mfr
N.A.I.C.S.: 333914
Wang Xiangrong (Chm & Gen Mgr)

LEO MOTORS, INC.
ES Tower 7F Teheranro 52 Gil 17, Gangnamgu, Seoul, 06212, Korea (South)
Tel.: (82) 7046993583 NV
Web Site: http://www.leomotors.com
Year Founded: 1986
LEOM—(OTCIQ)
Sales Range: $1-9.9 Million
Emp.: 73
Electric Vehicle Mfr
N.A.I.C.S.: 336211
Jeongyoul Choi (CFO)

LEO PHARMA A/S
Industriparken 55, DK-2750, Ballerup, Denmark
Tel.: (45) 44945888 DK
Web Site: http://www.leo-pharma.com
Year Founded: 1908
Rev.: $1,619,777,550
Assets: $3,711,771,600
Liabilities: $2,499,299,520
Net Worth: $1,212,472,080
Earnings: ($192,934,170)
Emp.: 5,820
Fiscal Year-end: 12/31/19
Pharmaceuticals Mfr
N.A.I.C.S.: 325412
Kim Kjoeller (Exec VP-R&D)

Subsidiaries:

LEO Farmaceuticos Lda. (1)
Rua Soeiro Pereira Gomes Lote 1-5 A, 1600-196, Lisbon, Portugal

Tel.: (351) 21 711 07 60
Web Site: http://www.leo-pharma.pt
Sales Range: $1-4.9 Billion
Pharmaceutical Products Distr
N.A.I.C.S.: 424210

LEO Laboratories Ltd. (1)
Horizon Honey Lane, Hurley, SL6 6RJ, Berkshire, United Kingdom
Tel.: (44) 1844 347 333
Web Site: http://www.leo-pharma.co.uk
Pharmaceutical Products Distr
N.A.I.C.S.: 424210
Geraldine Murphy (VP)

LEO Pharma AB (1)
Hyllie Stationsvag 42, Box 404, 201 24, Malmo, Sweden
Tel.: (46) 40 35 22 00
Web Site: http://www.leo-pharma.se
Pharmaceutical Products Distr
N.A.I.C.S.: 424210

LEO Pharma AS (1)
Fornebuveien 37, 1366, Lysaker, Norway
Tel.: (47) 22 51 49 00
Web Site: http://www.leo-pharma.no
Pharmaceutical Products Distr
N.A.I.C.S.: 424210

LEO Pharma Asia PTE Ltd. (1)
3791 Jalan Bukit Merah 07-21 E-Centre Redhill, 159471, Singapore, Singapore
Tel.: (65) 6285 3683
Pharmaceutical Products Distr
N.A.I.C.S.: 424210

LEO Pharma BV (1)
John M Keynesplein 5, 1066 EP, Amsterdam, Netherlands
Tel.: (31) 20 510 41 41
Web Site: http://www.leo-pharma.nl
Emp.: 40
Pharmaceutical Products Distr
N.A.I.C.S.: 424210
Marcel Bakker (Mgr-Access & Contract)

LEO Pharma GmbH (1)
Modecenterstrasse 17-19 Unit 4, 1110, Vienna, Austria
Tel.: (43) 1 503 69 79
Web Site: http://www.leo-pharma.com
Emp.: 15
Pharmaceutical Products Distr
N.A.I.C.S.: 424210

LEO Pharma GmbH (1)
Frankfurter Strasse 233 A3, 63263, Neu-Isenburg, Germany
Tel.: (49) 6102 201,0
Web Site: http://www.leo-pharma.de
Pharmaceutical Products Distr
N.A.I.C.S.: 424210

LEO Pharma Inc. (1)
7 Giralda Farms - 2nd Fl, Madison, NJ 07940
Tel.: (973) 637-1690
Web Site: http://www.leo-pharma.us
Pharmaceutical Products Distr
N.A.I.C.S.: 424210
Keith Bernius (CFO & VP-Bus Ops)

LEO Pharma Inc. (1)
3389 Steeles Avenue East Suite 110, Toronto, M2H 3S8, ON, Canada
Tel.: (905) 886-9822
Web Site: http://www.leo-pharma.ca
Emp.: 130
Pharmaceutical Products Distr
N.A.I.C.S.: 424210

LEO Pharma K.K. (1)
Jinbocho Mitsui Building 9F 1-105 Kanda-Jinbocho, Chiyoda-ku, Tokyo, 101-0051, Japan
Tel.: (81) 3 5809 2468
Web Site: http://www.leo-pharma.jp
Pharmaceutical Products Distr
N.A.I.C.S.: 424210

LEO Pharma Ltd. (1)
17/F Seoul City Tower 581 Namdaemunno 5-ga, Jung-gu, Seoul, 100 741, Korea (South)
Tel.: (82) 2 771 1110
Pharmaceutical Products Distr
N.A.I.C.S.: 424210

LEO Pharma NV (1)
Duwijckstraat 17, 2500, Lier, Belgium

INTERNATIONAL PUBLIC

Tel.: (32) 3 740 78 68
Web Site: http://www.leo-pharma.be
Emp.: 30
Pharmaceutical Products Distr
N.A.I.C.S.: 424210
Hilde Defawes (Country Mgr)

LEO Pharma OY (1)
Karhumaentie 3, 01530, Vantaa, Finland
Tel.: (358) 20 721 8440
Web Site: http://www.leo-pharma.fi
Pharmaceutical Products Distr
N.A.I.C.S.: 424210

LEO Pharma Pty Ltd (1)
Level 3 Tower One 25 Montpelier Road, Bowen Hills, 4006, QLD, Australia
Tel.: (61) 7 3250 1200
Web Site: http://www.leo-pharma.com.au
Pharmaceutical Products Distr
N.A.I.C.S.: 424210

LEO Pharma S.p.A. (1)
Via Elio Vittorini 129, 00144, Rome, Italy
Tel.: (39) 06 52625 500
Web Site: http://www.leo-pharma.it
Pharmaceutical Products Distr
N.A.I.C.S.: 424210

LEO Pharma SARL (1)
Rue du Lac Michigan - Residence Arcadia Appt 21 - 2eme etage, Les Berges du Lac, 1053, Tunis, Tunisia
Tel.: (216) 71 964 882
Pharmaceutical Products Distr
N.A.I.C.S.: 424210

LEO Pharma Sp. z o.o. (1)
Marynarska 15, 02-674, Warsaw, Poland
Tel.: (48) 22 244 18 40
Pharmaceutical Products Distr
N.A.I.C.S.: 424210

LEO Pharma s.r.o. (1)
Lomnickeho 1705/7, 140 00, Prague, Czech Republic
Tel.: (420) 721546611
Web Site: http://www.leopharma.cz
Pharmaceutical Products Distr
N.A.I.C.S.: 424210

LEO Pharmaceutical Products LLC (1)
72 Leningradsky Prospekt building 2, 125315, Moscow, Russia
Tel.: (7) 4957891160
Web Site: http://www.leo-pharma.ru
Pharmaceutical Products Distr
N.A.I.C.S.: 424210

LEO Pharmaceutical Products Sarath Ltd. (1)
Eichwatt 5, Postfach 1154, 8105, Regensdorf, Switzerland
Tel.: (41) 43 343 75 75
Web Site: http://www.leo-pharma.ch
Pharmaceutical Products Distr
N.A.I.C.S.: 424210

LEO Pharmaceuticals, S. de R.L. de C.V. (1)
Torre Pedregal Periferico Sur/Blvd Adolfo Ruiz Cortines 3642 Piso 12, Col Jardines Del Pedregal, 01900, Mexico, Mexico
Tel.: (52) 55 3684 7400
Web Site: http://www.latinoamerica.leo-pharma.com
Pharmaceutical Products Distr
N.A.I.C.S.: 424210

LEO US Holding, Inc. (1)
7 Giralda Farms 2nd FL, Madison, NJ 07940
Tel.: (877) 494-4536
Web Site: https://www.leo-pharma.us
Holding Company
N.A.I.C.S.: 551112

Subsidiary (Domestic):

Peplin, Inc. (2)
1 Sylvan Way Ste 1, Parsippany, NJ 07054-3880
Tel.: (510) 653-9700
Sales Range: $1-9.9 Million
Emp.: 40
Dermatological Disease Pharmaceutical Products Developer & Mfr
N.A.I.C.S.: 325412

Subsidiary (Non-US):

Peplin Limited (3)

AND PRIVATE COMPANIES

Level 3 Tower 1 25 Montpelier Rd, Bowen Hills, 4006, QLD, Australia
Tel.: (61) 732501200
Web Site: http://www.leo-pharma.com
Emp.: 100
Dermatological Disease Pharmaceutical Products Developer & Mfr
N.A.I.C.S.: 325412

Laboratoires LEO S.A (1)
39 Route de Chartres, BP 60009, 28501, Vernouillet, Cedex, France
Tel.: (33) 2 37 38 88 00
Web Site: http://www.leo-pharma.com
Pharmaceutical Products Distr
N.A.I.C.S.: 424210

Leo Laboratories, Ltd. (1)
285 Cashel Road, D12 E923, Dublin, Ireland
Tel.: (353) 1 490 8924
Web Site: http://www.leo-pharma.com
Emp.: 500
Pharmaceuticals Product Mfr
N.A.I.C.S.: 325412
Diarmaid Marrinan *(Dir-Mfg)*

Peplin Operations Pty Ltd (1)
Ashmore Plaza, PO Box 4446, Ashmore, 4214, QLD, Australia
Tel.: (61) 7 3250 1200
Pharmaceutical Products Distr
N.A.I.C.S.: 424210

Wexport Ltd. (1)
Wallingstown, Little Island, Cork, Ireland
Tel.: (353) 21 35 41 02
Pharmaceutical Products Distr
N.A.I.C.S.: 424210

LEOCH INTERNATIONAL TECHNOLOGY LIMITED
5th Floor Xinbaohui Building Nanhai Blvd, Nanshan, Shenzhen, 518054, China
Tel.: (86) 75586036060
Web Site: http://www.leoch.com
Year Founded: 1999
0842—(HKG)
Rev.: $1,803,558,604
Assets: $1,473,413,058
Liabilities: $906,725,664
Net Worth: $566,687,394
Earnings: $65,207,516
Emp.: 12,787
Fiscal Year-end: 12/31/22
Power Battery Mfr
N.A.I.C.S.: 335910
Li Dong *(Founder)*

Subsidiaries:

Anhui Leoch Power Supply Corp. (1)
Economic Development Zone, Huaibei, 235100, Suixi Anhui, China
Tel.: (86) 5617082222
Battery Mfr & Distr
N.A.I.C.S.: 335910

DBS Leoch Limited (1)
Unit B5 Welland Business Park, Market Harborough, LE16 7PS, Leicestershire, United Kingdom
Tel.: (44) 1858433330
Web Site: https://www.leochbattery.co.uk
Car Battery Distr
N.A.I.C.S.: 423610
Chris North *(Dir-Sls)*

LEOCH EMEA S.A. (1)
1 Deligiorgi 5 Filikon Str, 12131, Athens, Greece
Tel.: (30) 2105760318
Web Site: https://leoch.eu
Emp.: 20
Battery Distr
N.A.I.C.S.: 423120
Elia Mitropoulou *(Mgr-Mktg)*

Leoch Accupower (M) Sdn Bhd (1)
Lot 13338 & 2493 Jalan Sukepi Kawasan Perindustrian, Jenjarom, 42600, Kuala Langat, Selangor, Malaysia
Tel.: (60) 357406022
Web Site: http://www.leoch-accupower.com
Battery Mfr & Distr

N.A.I.C.S.: 335910
Amelia Adams *(CEO)*

Leoch Batteries India Private Limited (1)
BBMP No 117/26 NILE TOWERS 4th Main, Ganganagar, Bengaluru, 560032, India
Tel.: (91) 8028367720
Web Site: https://www.leoch.in
Battery Distr
N.A.I.C.S.: 423120

Leoch Battery (Jiangsu) Corp. (1)
Industry Park, Jiangsu, Jinhu County, China
Tel.: (86) 51786986335
Battery Mfr & Distr
N.A.I.C.S.: 335910

Leoch Battery Company Limited (1)
Workshop C 33/F TML Tower No 3 Hoi Shing Road, Tsuen Wan, New Territories, China (Hong Kong)
Tel.: (852) 35786666
Battery Distr
N.A.I.C.S.: 423120

Leoch Battery Corporation (1)
19751 Descartes Unit A, Foothill Ranch, CA 92610
Tel.: (949) 588-5853
Web Site: http://www.leoch.us
Battery Distr
N.A.I.C.S.: 423120
Philip Armstrong Noznesky *(Pres)*

Leoch Battery Pte. Ltd. (1)
1 Tech Park Crescent, Singapore, 638131, Singapore
Tel.: (65) 68636078
Web Site: https://leoch.sg
Emp.: 32
Battery Distr
N.A.I.C.S.: 423120
Henry Tow *(Gen Mgr)*

Leoch Battery UK Ltd. (1)
Unit B5 Welland Business Park, Market Harborough, LE16 7PS, Leicestershire, United Kingdom
Tel.: (44) 1858433330
Web Site: https://www.leochbattery.co.uk
Lead Acid Battery Mfr & Distr
N.A.I.C.S.: 335999

Leoch Italia S.R.L. (1)
Via Fornace 2, 40023, Castel Guelfo di Bologna, Italy
Tel.: (39) 0542013440
Lead Acid Battery Distr
N.A.I.C.S.: 423610

Leoch Lanka (Private) Ltd. (1)
No 71 Deanston Place, Colombo, Sri Lanka
Tel.: (94) 117394220
Battery Mfr & Distr
N.A.I.C.S.: 335910

Shenzhen Leoch Battery Technology Co., Ltd. (1)
Unit C D&E 22nd Floor Xinbaohui Bldg Nanyou Blvd, Nanshan, Shenzhen, China
Tel.: (86) 75526067212
Battery Mfr & Distr
N.A.I.C.S.: 335910

Zhaoqing Leoch Battery Technology Co., Ltd. (1)
Linjiang Industrial Park Hi-Tech Industry Development Zone Daw, Zhaoqing, 526238, China
Tel.: (86) 7583602988
Battery Mfr & Distr
N.A.I.C.S.: 335910

LEOCLAN CO., LTD.
2-4-26 Senrioka, Settsu, 566-0001, Osaka, Japan
Tel.: (81) 663871554
Web Site: https://www.leoclan.co.jp
Year Founded: 2001
7681—(TKS)
Rev.: $188,820,880
Assets: $104,173,370
Liabilities: $63,590,210
Net Worth: $40,583,160
Earnings: $1,921,390
Emp.: 114
Fiscal Year-end: 09/30/23

Medical Equipment Distr
N.A.I.C.S.: 423450
Shogo Sugita *(Board of Directors, Founder, Chm & Pres)*

LEOCOR GOLD, INC.
Suite 303 750 West Pender Street, Vancouver, V6C 2T7, BC, Canada
Tel.: (604) 681-0084
Web Site:
https://www.leocorgold.com
Year Founded: 2018
LECRF—(OTCQB)
Rev.: $56,491
Assets: $12,077,091
Liabilities: $411,233
Net Worth: $11,665,858
Earnings: ($396,230)
Fiscal Year-end: 10/31/22
Mineral Exploration Services
N.A.I.C.S.: 213115
Zula Kropivnitski *(CFO)*

LEOFOO DEVELOPMENT CO., LTD.
No 60 Gungtzgou Renan Li Guansi Jen, Hsinchu, 306, Taiwan
Tel.: (886) 35475665
Web Site: http://www.leofoo.com.tw
Year Founded: 1968
2705—(TAI)
Rev.: $72,307,627
Assets: $511,439,760
Liabilities: $353,629,340
Net Worth: $157,810,419
Earnings: ($3,196,442)
Emp.: 704
Fiscal Year-end: 12/31/23
Theme Park Operator
N.A.I.C.S.: 713110

LEON FUAT BERHAD
No 11 Lorong Keluli 1B Kawasan Perindustrian Bukit Raja Selatan, Seksyen 7, 40000, Shah Alam, Selangor Darul Ehsan, Malaysia
Tel.: (60) 333753333 MY
Web Site:
https://www.leonfuat.com.my
Year Founded: 1972
LEONFB—(KLS)
Rev.: $216,956,141
Assets: $220,119,111
Liabilities: $101,982,967
Net Worth: $118,136,144
Earnings: $6,251,390
Emp.: 399
Fiscal Year-end: 12/31/22
Steel Products Processor & Distr
N.A.I.C.S.: 332111
Ooi Seng Khong *(Mng Dir)*

Subsidiaries:

ASA Steel (M) Sdn. Bhd. (1)
No 8 Jalan 3 Off Jalan Sg Besi, 55200, Kuala Lumpur, Malaysia
Tel.: (60) 3 9222 4121
Web Site: http://www.asasteel.com
Steel Product Mfr & Distr
N.A.I.C.S.: 332111

Leon Fuat Hardware Sdn. Bhd. (1)
No 15 Lot 424 Jalan 3/89C Off Jalan Chan Sow Lin, 55200, Kuala Lumpur, Malaysia
Tel.: (60) 92237777
Web Site: https://www.leonfuat.com.my
Steel Product Distr
N.A.I.C.S.: 423510

LEON GROSSE
1 rue de l'Avenir, 73100, Aix-les-Bains, France
Tel.: (33) 4 79 88 74 88
Web Site: http://www.leongrosse.fr
Year Founded: 1881
Sales Range: $600-649.9 Million
Emp.: 3,000
Construction Engineering Services

LEONARDO S.P.A.

N.A.I.C.S.: 237990

Subsidiaries:

LEON GROSSE AQUITAINE (1)
15 rue Laplace, Espace Merignac Phare, 33700, Merignac, France
Tel.: (33) 5 56 13 23 70
Civil Engineering Services
N.A.I.C.S.: 237990

LEON GROSSE ELECTRICITE (LGE) (1)
165 avenue Roland-Garros, 78530, Buc, France
Tel.: (33) 1 30 97 09 90
Construction Engineering Services
N.A.I.C.S.: 237990

LEON TECHNOLOGY CO LTD
No 518 Yanshan Street, Urumqi Economic and Technological Development Zone Toutunhe District, Xinjiang, 830000, China
Tel.: (86) 9915300603
Web Site: http://www.leon.top
Year Founded: 1996
300603—(CHIN)
Rev.: $101,794,549
Assets: $328,178,922
Liabilities: $121,719,626
Net Worth: $206,459,296
Earnings: $1,049,544
Fiscal Year-end: 12/31/23
Security Systems Integration Services
N.A.I.C.S.: 541512
Gang Wang *(Chm)*

LEON'S FURNITURE LIMITED
45 Gordon MacKay Road, Toronto, M9N 3X3, ON, Canada
Tel.: (416) 243-7880 ON
Web Site: https://www.leons.ca
Year Founded: 1909
LNF—(OTCIQ)
Rev.: $1,747,357,434
Assets: $1,629,910,694
Liabilities: $929,131,451
Net Worth: $700,779,243
Earnings: $81,826,348
Emp.: 8,599
Fiscal Year-end: 12/31/19
Home Furnishings Mfr & Retailer
N.A.I.C.S.: 449110
Mark Joseph Leon *(Chm)*

Subsidiaries:

The Brick Ltd. (1)
2067 Sumas Way, Abbotsford, V2S 8H6, BC, Canada
Tel.: (604) 504-1771
Web Site: http://www.thebrick.com
Furniture Distr
N.A.I.C.S.: 449110

LEONARDO S.P.A.
Piazza Monte Grappa n 4, 00195, Rome, Italy
Tel.: (39) 06324731 IT
Web Site: https://www.leonardo.com
Year Founded: 1948
LDO—(ITA)
Rev.: $15,878,480,466
Assets: $30,846,104,036
Liabilities: $22,537,232,894
Net Worth: $8,308,871,142
Earnings: $1,005,827,757
Emp.: 50,286
Fiscal Year-end: 12/31/22
Aerospace Products Mfr
N.A.I.C.S.: 551112
Luciano Carta *(Chm)*

Subsidiaries:

AgustaWestland S.p.A. (1)
Viale Giovanni Agusta 520, 21017, Cascina della Costa, Varese, Italy (100%)
Tel.: (39) 0331229111
Web Site: http://www.agustawestland.com

LEONARDO S.P.A.
INTERNATIONAL PUBLIC

Leonardo S.p.A.—(Continued)
Sales Range: $1-4.9 Billion
Emp.: 5,200
Helicopter & Rotorcraft Components Designer, Mfr & Marketer
N.A.I.C.S.: 336411

Subsidiary (Non-US):

Agusta Aerospace Services - A.A.S. (2)
Liege Airport 60, Grace-Hollogne, 4460, Belgium
Tel.: (32) 4 2342323
Web Site: http://www.agustawestland.com
Sales Range: $25-49.9 Million
Emp.: 50
Airport Management Services
N.A.I.C.S.: 488119

AgustaWestland Australia Pty. Ltd. (2)
Level 1 39 Torrens Street, Braddon, Canberra, 2612, ACT, Australia
Tel.: (61) 2 62 62 66 60
Aircraft Part Mfr
N.A.I.C.S.: 336413

Subsidiary (US):

AgustaWestland Inc. (2)
2345 crytal Dr Ste 906, Arlington, VA 22202
Tel.: (703) 373-8000
Web Site: http://www.agustawestland.com
Emp.: 20
Oil Transportation Services
N.A.I.C.S.: 488999
Clyde M. Woltman (CEO)

Subsidiary (Domestic):

AgustaWestland Philadelphia Corporation (3)
3050 Red Lion Rd, Philadelphia, PA 19114
Tel.: (215) 281-1400
Web Site: http://www.agustausa.com
Helicopter Mfr
N.A.I.C.S.: 336411
William Hunt (CEO)

Subsidiary (Non-US):

AgustaWestland International Limited (2)
Lysander Road, Yeovil, BA20 2YB, Somerset, United Kingdom
Tel.: (44) 1935475222
Web Site: http://www.agustawestland.com
Sales Range: $700-749.9 Million
Emp.: 3,000
Aircraft Part Mfr
N.A.I.C.S.: 336413

AgustaWestland Limited (2)
25 Templer Ave, Farnborough, HAM GU14, United Kingdom
Tel.: (44) 1252 386451
Web Site: http://www.agustawestland.com
Emp.: 400
Aircraft Mfr
N.A.I.C.S.: 336411

Subsidiary (Domestic):

AgustaWestland Holdings Limited (3)
Lysander Road, Yeovil, BA20 2YB, United Kingdom
Tel.: (44) 19 3547 5222
Investment Management Service
N.A.I.C.S.: 523999
Raymond Edgar Edwards (Mng Dir)

Subsidiary (US):

AgustaWestland North America Inc (4)
11700 Plaza America Dr, Reston, VA 20190-4751
Tel.: (703) 373-8005
Helicopter Mfr
N.A.I.C.S.: 336411

Subsidiary (Domestic):

Westland Transmissions Limited (4)
AgustaWestland, Yeovil, BA20 2YB, Somerset, United Kingdom
Tel.: (44) 19 35 47 52 22
Emp.: 3,500
Industrial Furnace Mfr
N.A.I.C.S.: 333994
Geoss Munday (Mng Dir)

Plant (Domestic):

AgustaWestland Ltd. - Yeovil Plant (3)
Lysander Road, Yeovil, BA20 2YB, Somerset, United Kingdom
Tel.: (44) 1935475222
Web Site: http://www.agustawestland.com
Sales Range: $800-899.9 Million
Helicopter Mfr
N.A.I.C.S.: 336411

Subsidiary (Domestic):

AgustaWestland UK Pension Scheme (Trustee) Limited (3)
Westland Works Lysander Road, Box 205, Yeovil, BA20 2YB, Somerset, United Kingdom
Tel.: (44) 1935475222
Web Site: http://www.awpension.co.uk
Sales Range: $1-4.9 Billion
Pension Fund Management Services
N.A.I.C.S.: 525110
Mike Nixon (Head-Pension)

Subsidiary (Non-US):

AgustaWestland Malaysia Sdn, Bhd. (2)
Hangar B Old Cargo Complex Sultan Abdul Aziz Shah Airport, 47200, Subang Jaya, 47200, Malaysia
Tel.: (60) 3 7842 3026
Aircraft Maintenance Services
N.A.I.C.S.: 488190

AgustaWestland Portugal SA (2)
Rua Castilho 165, Lisbon, 1070-050, Portugal
Tel.: (351) 211924980
Engineeering Services
N.A.I.C.S.: 541330

AgustaWestland do Brasil Ltda. (2)
Av Alberto Jackson Bayton 2784, 62276-000, Osasco, Sao Paulo, Brazil
Tel.: (55) 11 3601 2269
Web Site: http://www.agustawestland.com
Aircraft Transportation Services
N.A.I.C.S.: 488190

Joint Venture (Domestic):

Rotorsim S.r.l. (2)
2 Via Indipendenza, 21100, Sesto Calende, Italy (50%)
Tel.: (39) 0331915573
Web Site: https://www.cae.com
Helicopter Flight Training Services
N.A.I.C.S.: 611512

Alenia Aermacchi S.p.A. (1)
Via Ing Paolo Foresio 1, Venegono Superiore, Varese, 21040, Italy
Tel.: (39) 0331813111
Web Site: http://www.alenia.it
Sales Range: $400-449.9 Million
Emp.: 1,800
Military Trainer Aircraft Mfr
N.A.I.C.S.: 336411
Giancarlo Grasso (Chm)

Alenia Aeronautica S.p.A. (1)
Piazza Monte Grappa 4, 187, Rome, Italy
Tel.: (39) 06420881
Web Site: http://www.alenia-aeronautica.it
Sales Range: $1-4.9 Billion
Emp.: 13,900
Commercial & Military Aircraft Mfr
N.A.I.C.S.: 336411

Subsidiary (US):

Alenia North America, Inc. (2)
1625 Eye St NW Ste 1200, Washington, DC 20006
Tel.: (202) 292-2664
Web Site: http://www.aleniana.com
Aircraft Manufacturing
N.A.I.C.S.: 336411
Fabrizio Lombardi (CFO)

Subsidiary (Domestic):

Alenia SIA SpA (2)
Strada del Lionetto 6, 10146, Turin, Italy
Tel.: (39) 011 4090111
Defense Aircraft Mfr
N.A.I.C.S.: 336411

Alenia Spazio S.p.A. (2)
Via Saccomuro 24, 00131, Rome, Italy (100%)
Tel.: (39) 0641511
Web Site: http://www.alespazio.it
Sales Range: $500-549.9 Million
Emp.: 2,400
Satellite & Space Structure Developer & Mfr
N.A.I.C.S.: 336414

Joint Venture (Non-US):

Avions de Transport Regional (2)
1 Allee Pierre Nadot, 31712, Blagnac, France (50%)
Tel.: (33) 562216221
Web Site: http://www.atr-aircraft.com
Sales Range: $1-4.9 Billion
Emp.: 1,000
Turboprop Commuter Aircraft Mfr
N.A.I.C.S.: 336411
Jean-Pierre Cousserans (Sr VP-Customer Svcs)

Subsidiary (Domestic):

Officine Aeronavali Venezia S.p.A. (2)
Via Triestina 214, 30030, Tesero, Venice, Italy (100%)
Tel.: (39) 0412693978
Web Site: http://www.aeronavali.com
Sales Range: $400-449.9 Million
Emp.: 1,600
Maintenance Services for Commercial & Military Aircraft
N.A.I.C.S.: 488119

Subsidiary (Non-US):

WING NED BV (2)
Weena 210 - 212, Rotterdam, 3012 NJ, Netherlands
Tel.: (31) 10 2013600
Web Site: http://www.freelandgroup.com
Emp.: 12
Aircraft Mfr
N.A.I.C.S.: 336411
Tim Koster (Dir Gen)

WORLD'S WING SA (2)
Rue Du Rhone 65, 1204, Geneva, Switzerland
Tel.: (41) 227189010
Emp.: 1
Investment Management Service
N.A.I.C.S.: 523999
Caruso Donatella (CEO)

Consorzio S3log S.p.A. (1)
Via Tiburtina 1020, 00156, Rome, Italy (60%)
Tel.: (39) 0645470201
Web Site: http://www.s3log.it
Sales Range: $25-49.9 Million
Emp.: 16
IT Services
N.A.I.C.S.: 541512

E - Geos SpA (1)
Via Tiburtina 965, 00156, Rome, Italy
Tel.: (39) 0640791
Web Site: https://www.e-geos.it
Geographical Information Providing Services
N.A.I.C.S.: 541370
Paolo Minciacchi (CEO)

ED Contact srl (1)
Via Laurentina 760, 00143, Rome, Italy
Tel.: (39) 06 50264 1
Customer Relationship Management
N.A.I.C.S.: 561421

ELSACOM NV (1)
Strawinskylaan 3111, 1077 ZX, Amsterdam, Noord-Holland, Netherlands
Tel.: (31) 20 4420460
Investment Management Service
N.A.I.C.S.: 523999

Earthlab Luxembourg S.A. (1)
49 Rue du Baerendall, 8212, Mamer, Luxembourg
Tel.: (352) 62 138 1427
Web Site: https://www.earthlab.lu
Information Technology Solutions Services

N.A.I.C.S.: 541519
Thomas Friederich (Gen Mgr)

FATA LOGISTIC SYSTEMS SpA (1)
Via dei Prati 7, 10044, Pianezza, Turin, Italy
Tel.: (39) 011 96681
Web Site: http://www.fatalogistic.it
Sales Range: $75-99.9 Million
Emp.: 500
Logistics Consulting Servies
N.A.I.C.S.: 541614

FINMECCANICA GROUP REAL ESTATE SPA (1)
Via Vittoria 14, 00187, Rome, Italy
Tel.: (39) 0632110820
Real Estate Manangement Services
N.A.I.C.S.: 531390

Finmeccanica Group Services S.p.A. (1)
Piazza Monte Grappa 4, 00195, Rome, Italy
Tel.: (39) 0632473419
Business Management Consulting Services
N.A.I.C.S.: 541611

Finmeccanica North America Inc. (1)
1625 I St NW 12th Fl, Washington, DC 20006
Tel.: (202) 292-2626
Web Site: http://www.finmeccanicausa.com
Holding Company; Regional Managing Office
N.A.I.C.S.: 551112

Subsidiary (Domestic):

AnsaldoBreda Inc. (2)
101 Embarcadero Ste 210, San Francisco, CA 94105
Tel.: (415) 397-7010
Web Site: http://www.ansaldobredainc.com
Railroad Transit System Mfr
N.A.I.C.S.: 336510
Russell Rowe (Mgr)

Leonardo DRS, Inc. (2)
2345 Crystal Dr Ste 1000, Arlington, VA 22202
Tel.: (703) 416-8000
Web Site: https://www.leonardodrs.com
Rev.: $2,826,000,000
Assets: $3,921,000,000
Liabilities: $1,596,000,000
Net Worth: $2,325,000,000
Earnings: $168,000,000
Emp.: 6,600
Fiscal Year-end: 12/31/2023
Military Communications, Surveillance, Reconnaissance & Sustainment Systems & Equipment Developer & Mfr
N.A.I.C.S.: 334511
William J. Lynn III (CEO)

Subsidiary (Domestic):

Advanced Acoustic Concepts, LLC (3)
425 Oser Ave Unit 1, Hauppauge, NY 11788
Tel.: (631) 273-5700
Web Site: http://www.aactech.com
Sales Range: $100-124.9 Million
Sonar System Development Services
N.A.I.C.S.: 334511

Unit (Domestic):

Advanced Acoustic Concepts, Inc. - Columbia (4)
7100 Columbia Gateway Dr # 190, Columbia, MD 21046
Tel.: (410) 872-0024
Sales Range: $25-49.9 Million
Emp.: 20
Sonar System Development Services
N.A.I.C.S.: 334511

Advanced Acoustic Concepts, Inc. - Lemont Furnace (4)
1080 Eberly Way, Lemont Furnace, PA 15456
Tel.: (724) 434-5100
Web Site: http://www.advancedacousticconcepts.com
Sonar System Development Services
N.A.I.C.S.: 334511

Subsidiary (Domestic):

DRS C3 & Aviation Company (3)

AND PRIVATE COMPANIES

1060 Consolidated Rd, Elizabeth City, NC
27909-7835
Tel.: (252) 338-0288
Web Site: http://www.drs.com
Aircraft & Military Equipment Maintenance Services
N.A.I.C.S.: 811198
Bill Lynn *(Pres)*

DRS C3 Systems, LLC (3)
645 Anchors St, Fort Walton Beach, FL 32548 **(100%)**
Tel.: (850) 302-3000
Sales Range: $200-249.9 Million
Naval Display & Sensor Control Systems Mfr
N.A.I.C.S.: 334513

Subsidiary (Domestic):

DRS C3 Systems, Inc. (4)
485 Cayuga Rd, Buffalo, NY 14225-1309
Tel.: (716) 631-6200
Web Site: http://www.drs-ds.com
Sales Range: $25-49.9 Million
Emp.: 250
Naval Display & Sensor Control Systems Mfr
N.A.I.C.S.: 334513

DRS C3 Systems, Inc. (4)
400 Professional Dr, Gaithersburg, MD 20879 **(100%)**
Tel.: (301) 921-8100
Web Site: http://www.drs.com
Sales Range: $25-49.9 Million
Emp.: 140
Naval Display & Sensor Control Systems Mfr
N.A.I.C.S.: 334513

DRS C3 Systems, Inc. (4)
767 Electronic Dr Ste A, Horsham, PA 19044-2228 **(100%)**
Tel.: (215) 233-4100
Web Site: http://www.drs.com
Sales Range: $25-49.9 Million
Emp.: 40
Naval Display & Sensor Control Systems Mfr
N.A.I.C.S.: 334513

Subsidiary (Domestic):

DRS Data & Imaging Systems Inc (3)
133 Bauer Dr, Oakland, NJ 07436 **(100%)**
Tel.: (201) 337-3800
Web Site: http://www.drs.com
Sales Range: $1-9.9 Million
Ruggedized Mission Recording Products & High Capacity Data Storage Systems for Government & Commercial Applications
N.A.I.C.S.: 334511

DRS Defense Solutions, LLC (3)
530 Gaither Rd Ste 900, Rockville, MD 20850
Tel.: (240) 238-3900
Search & Navigation Equipment Mfr
N.A.I.C.S.: 334511

Subsidiary (Domestic):

DRS CenGen, LLC (4)
9250 Bendix Rd N, Columbia, MD 21045
Tel.: (410) 715-1300
Web Site: http://www.cengen.com
Communication Software Development Services
N.A.I.C.S.: 541511

DRS Consolidated Controls, Inc. (4)
21 S St, Danbury, CT 06810
Tel.: (203) 798-3030
Web Site: http://www.drs-cci.com
Nuclear Power Plant Construction Services
N.A.I.C.S.: 237130
Peter Kirk *(VP-Bus Dev)*

DRS ICAS LLC (4)
2601 Mission Point Blvd Ste 250, Beavercreek, OH 45431
Tel.: (937) 429-7408
Communication Equipment Mfr
N.A.I.C.S.: 334290

DRS SIGNAL SOLUTIONS, INC. (4)
700 Quince Orchard Rd, Gaithersburg, MD 20878
Tel.: (301) 944-8616

Electronic Equipment Whslr
N.A.I.C.S.: 423690
Gary Glotfelty *(Controller)*

Subsidiary (Domestic):

DRS SONETICOM INC (5)
100 N Babcock St, Melbourne, FL 32935
Tel.: (321) 733-0400
Business Consulting Services
N.A.I.C.S.: 561499
Rowland Huss *(VP-Bus Line)*

Subsidiary (Domestic):

DRS TECHNICAL SERVICES, INC. (4)
12930 Worldgate Dr Ste 700, Herndon, VA 20170
Tel.: (703) 896-7100
Communication & Security System Mfr & Whslr
N.A.I.C.S.: 334290
Tom Adams *(Dir-Proposal Ops)*

Subsidiary (Domestic):

DRS Integrated Defense Systems and Servies Group (3)
400 Professional Dr Ste 400, Gaithersburg, MD 20879
Tel.: (240) 238-3900
Web Site: http://www.drs.com
Electronic Product Mfr & Whslr
N.A.I.C.S.: 334419

Subsidiary (Non-US):

DRS Pivotal Power (3)
150 Bluewater Rd, Bedford, B4B 1G9, NS, Canada
Tel.: (902) 835-7268
Web Site: http://www.drspowersolutions.com
Sales Range: $25-49.9 Million
Power Conversion Equipment Mfr
N.A.I.C.S.: 335999
Geroge Mullally *(Gen Mgr)*

Subsidiary (Domestic):

DRS Power & Control Technologies, Inc. (3)
4265 N 30th St, Milwaukee, WI 53216-1821
Tel.: (414) 875-2900
Web Site: http://www.drs.com
Emp.: 150
Power Conversion Equipment Whslr
N.A.I.C.S.: 444230

Subsidiary (Domestic):

DRS POWER TECHNOLOGY, INC. (4)
625 Main St, Fitchburg, MA 01420-3168
Tel.: (978) 353-5416
Steam Turbine & Pump Mfr
N.A.I.C.S.: 333611

Subsidiary (Domestic):

DRS Power Solutions (3)
141 N Ave, Bridgeport, CT 06606
Tel.: (703) 378-6100
Web Site: http://www.drspowersolutions.com
Sales Range: $50-74.9 Million
Power Generation & Conversion Equipment Mfr & Distr
N.A.I.C.S.: 335999

DRS RSTA, Inc. (3)
100 N Babcock St, Melbourne, FL 32935-6715 **(100%)**
Tel.: (321) 984-9030
Web Site: http://www.drs.com
Sales Range: $125-149.9 Million
Targeting & Sighting Systems Mfr
N.A.I.C.S.: 333310

DRS Surveillance Support Systems, Inc. (3)
6200 118th Ave, Largo, FL 33773-3726 **(100%)**
Tel.: (727) 541-6681
Web Site: http://www.drs.com
Sales Range: $50-74.9 Million
Radar & Other Military Surveillance Systems Support Pedestals & Antenna Systems Mfr
N.A.I.C.S.: 333310

DRS Sustainment Systems, Inc. (3)

201 Evans Ln, Saint Louis, MO 63121 **(100%)**
Tel.: (314) 553-4000
Web Site: http://www.drs-ssi.com
Sales Range: $1-4.9 Billion
Environmental Control Systems Mfr & Military Logistics Services
N.A.I.C.S.: 541614

Subsidiary (Domestic):

DRS Defense Technical Services, Inc. (4)
201 Evans Ln, Saint Louis, MO 63121-1126
Tel.: (314) 553-4272
Web Site: http://www.drs.com
Sales Range: $125-149.9 Million
Mfr of Environmental Control Systems & Developer of Military Logistics Services
N.A.I.C.S.: 334511

Plant (Domestic):

DRS Fermont (4)
141 N Ave, Bridgeport, CT 06606-5120
Tel.: (203) 366-5211
Web Site: http://www.drspowersolutions.com
Sales Range: $25-49.9 Million
Emp.: 150
Mfr of Engine Generator Sets, Air Cargo Loaders, Standby Power Sources & Solid State Controls
N.A.I.C.S.: 335312
Carl Geary *(Dir-Bus Dev)*

Subsidiary (Domestic):

DRS Test & Energy Management, LLC (3)
110 Wynn Dr NW, Huntsville, AL 35805
Tel.: (256) 895-2000
Web Site: http://www.drs-tem.com
Sales Range: $50-74.9 Million
Ground Vehicle Diagnostic & Test Equipment Mfr
N.A.I.C.S.: 332994

Daylight Solutions, Inc. (3)
15378 Ave of Science Ste 200, San Diego, CA 92128
Tel.: (858) 432-7500
Web Site: http://www.daylightsolutions.com
Emp.: 50
Molecular Detection & Imaging Instruments Mfr
N.A.I.C.S.: 334413
Timothy Day *(Co-Founder, Chm, CEO & CTO)*

Laurel Technologies Partnership (3)
246 Airport Rd, Johnstown, PA 15904-7224 **(80%)**
Tel.: (814) 534-8900
Web Site: http://www.drs.com
Sales Range: $200-249.9 Million
Circuit Card & Cable Assembly DRS Mfr
N.A.I.C.S.: 334412

Subsidiary (Domestic):

MECCANICA HOLDINGS USA, INC. (2)
1625 I St NW Fl 12, Washington, DC 20006
Tel.: (202) 292-2620
Investment Management Service
N.A.I.C.S.: 523999

MSSC COMPANY (2)
767 Electronic Dr Ste A, Horsham, PA 19044-2228
Tel.: (215) 242-7226
Radar & Navigation Equipment Mfr
N.A.I.C.S.: 334511

OTO MELARA NORTH AMERICA INC (2)
11700 Plaza America Dr Ste 1010, Reston, VA 20190
Tel.: (202) 459-6900
Web Site: http://www.otomelara.it
Military Weapon Mfr & Whslr
N.A.I.C.S.: 336992

Finmeccanica UK Limited (1)
8-10 Great George Street, London, SW1P 3AE, United Kingdom
Tel.: (44) 20 7340 6100
Web Site: http://www.finmeccanica.co.uk
Sales Range: $25-49.9 Million
Emp.: 30

LEONARDO S.P.A.

Aerospace Security & Transportation Services
N.A.I.C.S.: 488190

Kopter Group AG (1)
Binzstrasse 31, 8620, Wetzikon, Switzerland
Tel.: (41) 44 552 3333
Web Site: https://koptergroup.com
Aircraft Mfr
N.A.I.C.S.: 336411
Gian Piero Cutillo *(Chm)*

Leonardo (China) Co., Ltd. (1)
Unit 16A1 Hanwei Plaza n 7 Guanghua Road, Chaoyang Dist, Beijing, 100022, China
Tel.: (86) 108 567 9168
Aircraft Defense Services
N.A.I.C.S.: 928110

Leonardo Australia Pty. Ltd. (1)
130-188 Todd Road, Port Melbourne, 3207, VIC, Australia
Tel.: (61) 39 698 0400
Aircraft Defense Services
N.A.I.C.S.: 928110

Leonardo Canada Co. (1)
55 Metcalfe Street Suite 540, Ottawa, K1P 6L5, ON, Canada
Tel.: (613) 235-0353
Aircraft Defense Services
N.A.I.C.S.: 928110

Leonardo Do Brasil Ltda. (1)
Saus Quadra 01 Bloco M Edificio Libertas salas 1205-1211 Asa Sul, Brasilia, 70070-935, Federal District, Brazil
Tel.: (55) 613 221 5450
Aircraft Mfr
N.A.I.C.S.: 336411

Leonardo For Trading Of Machinery Equipment & Devices WLL (1)
Mazaya Towers 2 26th Floor Office B1 Khalid Ibn Al Waleed St, PO Box 2997, Mirqab Al-Safat, Kuwait, 13030, Kuwait
Tel.: (965) 2 209 0977
Aircraft Defense Services
N.A.I.C.S.: 928110

Leonardo Germany GmbH (1)
Raiffeisenstrasse 10, 41470, Neuss, Germany
Tel.: (49) 2 137 7820
Web Site: https://www.leonardogermany.com
Homeland Security Services
N.A.I.C.S.: 928110
Maurizio De Mitri *(Mng Dir)*

Leonardo Global Solutions SpA (1)
Via Pastrengo 20, 00185, Rome, Italy
Tel.: (39) 0645 5381
Web Site: https://www.leonardoglobalsolutions.com
Real Estate Services
N.A.I.C.S.: 531390

Leonardo Helicopters USA, Inc. (1)
3050 Red Lion Rd, Philadelphia, PA 19114
Tel.: (215) 281-1400
Helicopter Mfr
N.A.I.C.S.: 336411

Leonardo Hispania SAU (1)
Pol gono Industrial Mas a del Conde Calle 4 n 47, Parcela M 1-3 Sector 10 Loriguilla, 46393, Valencia, Spain
Tel.: (34) 96 152 0602
Web Site: https://www.leonardohispania.es
Aircraft Defense Services
N.A.I.C.S.: 928110

Leonardo International SpA (1)
Via Flaminia 135, 00196, Rome, Italy
Tel.: (39) 0632 6731
Aircraft Defense Services
N.A.I.C.S.: 928110

Leonardo Malaysia Sdn Bhd (1)
Office Suite A-13-1 Menara Amplewest No 6 Jalan P Ramlee, 50250, Kuala Lumpur, Malaysia
Tel.: (60) 32 058 2412
Emp.: 150
Aircraft Defense Services
N.A.I.C.S.: 928110

Leonardo Poland Sp. z o.o. (1)

LEONARDO S.P.A.

INTERNATIONAL PUBLIC

Leonardo S.p.A.—(Continued)

Plac Trzech Krzyzy 10/14, 00-499, Warsaw, Poland
Tel.: (48) 81 722 5700
Aircraft Defense Services
N.A.I.C.S.: 928110
Marco Lupo (Pres)

Leonardo Portugal S.A. (1)
Rua Joshua Benoliel 6 9A, 1250-133, Lisbon, Portugal
Tel.: (351) 21 192 4971
Aircraft Defense Services
N.A.I.C.S.: 928110
Garry Perks (Gen Mgr)

Leonardo Romania Aerospace, Defence & Security S.A. (1)
Km 8 Ploiesti-Targoviste Road, Prahova County, Ploiesti, Romania
Emp.: 160
Telecommunications Equipment Mfr
N.A.I.C.S.: 334290

Leonardo Singapore Pte. Ltd. (1)
8 Ubi Road 2 07-02/03 Zervex Building, Singapore, 408538, Singapore
Tel.: (65) 6 411 6520
Aircraft Defense Services
N.A.I.C.S.: 928110

Leonardo Technologies & Services Ltd. (1)
Watermark Business Park Ndege Road, PO Box 2015, Karen, 00502, Nairobi, Kenya
Air Traffic Management Services
N.A.I.C.S.: 488111

Leonardo Turkei Havacilik Savunma Ve Guvenlik Sistemleri A.S. (1)
Karaoglan Mah Ankara Cad No 225, Golbasi, 06830, Ankara, Turkiye
Tel.: (90) 312 484 5181
Web Site: https://leonardocompany.com.tr
Aircraft Mfr
N.A.I.C.S.: 336411
Sinan Senol (Chm & Gen Mgr)

Leonardo Us Aircraft Inc. (1)
1235 S Clark St Ste 700, Arlington, VA 22202
Tel.: (703) 413-2100
Logistics & Engineering Services
N.A.I.C.S.: 541330

MBDA Holdings S.A.S. (1)
37 Boulevard de Montmorency, 75016, Paris, France (25%)
Tel.: (33) 142242424
Web Site: http://www.mbda-systems.com
Holding Company; Guided Missiles & Missle Systems Mfr
N.A.I.C.S.: 551112
Antoine Bouvier (CEO)

Subsidiary (Non-US):

MBDA Deutschland GmbH (2)
Hagenauer Forst 27, Schrobenhausen, 86529, Germany
Tel.: (49) 8252 99 0
Aircraft Machinery Mfr
N.A.I.C.S.: 336413
Thomas Homberg (Mng Dir)

Subsidiary (Domestic):

Bayern-Chemie Gesellschaft fur Flugchemische Antriebe mbH (3)
Liebigstrasse 17, PO Box 11, 84544; Aschau, Germany
Tel.: (49) 86386010
Web Site: http://bayern-chemie.com
Sales Range: $50-74.9 Million
Emp.: 160
Rocket Propulsion Systems Mfr
N.A.I.C.S.: 336415

TDW-Gesellschaft fur verteidigungstechnische Wirksysteme GmbH (3)
Hagenauer Forst 27, 86529, Schrobenhausen, Germany
Tel.: (49) 8252 99 0
Web Site: http://www.eads.com
Sales Range: $200-249.9 Million
Emp.: 1,000
Aircraft Part Mfr
N.A.I.C.S.: 336413
Thomas Homberg (Gen Mgr)

Subsidiary (Domestic):

MBDA France SAS (2)
1 ave Reaumur, 92350, Le Plessis-Robinson, France
Tel.: (33) 171541000
Web Site: http://www.mbda-systems.com
Sales Range: $25-49.9 Million
Emp.: 100
Missiles & Missile Systems
N.A.I.C.S.: 336412

Joint Venture (Domestic):

EUROSAM (3)
Centre d'affaires de la Boursidiere Batiment Kerguelen, Le Plessis-Robinson, 92357, France
Tel.: (33) 1 4187 1416
Web Site: http://www.eurosam.com
Emp.: 70
Missile Defense Systems Mfr
N.A.I.C.S.: 336414
Michelle Vigneras (Mng Dir)

ROXEL S.A.S. (3)
La Boursidi Immeuble Jura, 92357, Le Plessis-Robinson, France (50%)
Tel.: (33) 141 07 82 95
Web Site: http://www.roxelgroup.com
Propulsion System Mfr
N.A.I.C.S.: 336415

Subsidiary (Domestic):

ROXEL France (4)
Route D Ardon, 45240, La Ferte-Saint-Aubin, France
Tel.: (33) 238516666
Sales Range: $100-124.9 Million
Emp.: 300
Rocket Propulsion Systems Mfr
N.A.I.C.S.: 335312

Subsidiary (Non-US):

MBDA Italia SpA (2)
Via Monte Flavio 45, 00131, Rome, Italy
Tel.: (39) 06 87711
Web Site: http://www.mbda-systems.com
Missile Systems Mfr
N.A.I.C.S.: 336414

MBDA UK Ltd. (2)
Six Hills Way, Stevenage, SG1 2DA, United Kingdom
Tel.: (44) 1438312422
Web Site: http://www.mbda.co.uk
Sales Range: $350-399.9 Million
Emp.: 2,000
Missile Mfr
N.A.I.C.S.: 336414

Branch (Domestic):

MBDA UK (3)
Six Hills Way, Stevenage, SG1 2DA, Hertfordshire, United Kingdom
Tel.: (44) 1438752000
Web Site: http://www.mbda.co.uk
Emp.: 4,000
Missile Mfr
N.A.I.C.S.: 336414
Chris Allam (Mng Dir)

OTO MELARA IBERICA SA (1)
Poligono Industrial Masia del Conde Calle en Proyecto 4 Parcela, Loriguilla, Valencia, 46393, Spain
Tel.: (34) 961 520 602
Web Site: http://www.otomelaraiberica.es
Sales Range: $25-49.9 Million
Emp.: 15
Logistics Consulting Servies
N.A.I.C.S.: 541614
Marco Busolli (Mng Dir)

OTO MELARA SpA (1)
Via Valdilocchi 15, 19136, La Spezia, Italy
Tel.: (39) 0187 581111
Web Site: http://www.otomelara.it
Rev.: $560,006,720
Emp.: 1,217
Military Weapon Services & Mfr
N.A.I.C.S.: 336992

Subsidiary (Domestic):

CISDEG SPA (2)
1231 Via Tiburtina, 00131, Rome, Italy
Tel.: (39) 064 417 041

Welding Equipment Mfr
N.A.I.C.S.: 333992

Orizzonte Sistemi Navali S.p.A. (1)
Viale Brigata Bisagno 45 R, 16129, Genoa, Italy (49%)
Tel.: (39) 0109817111
Web Site: https://www.orizzontesn.it
Contract Naval Vessel Design & Engineering Services
N.A.I.C.S.: 541490

PIVOTAL POWER, INC. (1)
150 Bluewater Road, Bedford, B4B 1G9, NS, Canada
Tel.: (902) 835-7268
Web Site: http://www.prs.com
Emp.: 38
Power Conversion Equipment Mfr
N.A.I.C.S.: 335999

Precision Aviation Services Pty. Ltd. (1)
Hangar 109 Lindvelt Avenue Wonderboom National Airport, Wonderboom, Pretoria, 0182, Gauteng, South Africa
Tel.: (27) 12 543 0371
Web Site: https://www.pasaviation.co.za
Aircraft Maintenance & Repair Services
N.A.I.C.S.: 488190

Precision Aviation Training Academy Pty. Ltd. (1)
Hangar 109 Lindvelt Avenue Wonderboom National Airport, Wonderboom, Pretoria, 0182, Gauteng, South Africa
Tel.: (27) 12 543 0371
Web Site: https://patahelicopters.co.za
Aviation Training Services
N.A.I.C.S.: 611512

Rartel S.A. (1)
70 Dr Iacob Felix Street, 011041, Bucharest, Romania
Tel.: (40) 21 319 6804
Web Site: https://www.rartel.ro
Satellite Services
N.A.I.C.S.: 517410

Regionalny Park Przemyslowy Swidnik Sp. z o.o. (1)
Al Lotnikow Polskich 1, 21-045, Swidnik, Poland
Tel.: (48) 81 722 60 22
Web Site: http://www.pafck.svidnik.pl
Sales Range: $50-74.9 Million
Emp.: 4
Investment Management Service
N.A.I.C.S.: 523999
Pawel Chojnacki (Gen Mgr)

SELEX ELSAG S.p.A. (1)
Via Puccini 2, 16154, Genoa, Italy
Tel.: (39) 01065821
Web Site: http://www.selex-es.com
Sales Range: $1-4.9 Billion
Emp.: 7,400
Defence Electronic Equipment Mfr
N.A.I.C.S.: 334419

Subsidiary (US):

ELSAG North America LLC (2)
7 Sutton Pl, Brewster, NY 10509
Tel.: (336) 379-7135
Automatic Number Plate Recognition System Mfr & Whslr
N.A.I.C.S.: 334419

Subsidiary (Domestic):

Electron Italia S.r.l. (2)
Via Tiburtina 1262, 00131, Rome, Italy
Tel.: (39) 06417 981
Electric Power Distribution Services
N.A.I.C.S.: 221122

Branch (Domestic):

Elsag Datamat S.p.A. (2)
Via Laurentina 760, 00143, Rome, Italy
Tel.: (39) 0650271
Web Site: http://www.elsagdatamat.com
Sales Range: $300-349.9 Million
Emp.: 1,500
Information, Communication & Technology Solution Services
N.A.I.C.S.: 541512

Subsidiary (Domestic):

LARIMART SpA (2)

Via Torrevecchia 12, 00168, Rome, Italy
Tel.: (39) 06 30 34 31
Electric Equipment Mfr
N.A.I.C.S.: 334419

Net Service SRL (2)
via Nuovalucello 47G, 95100, Catania, Italy
Tel.: (39) 095 221653
Web Site: http://www.net-serv.it
Internet Service Provider
N.A.I.C.S.: 517111

ORANGEE SRL (2)
Lungotevere dei Mellini 44, Rome, 00193, Italy
Tel.: (39) 06 36 00 44 39
Information & Communication Services
N.A.I.C.S.: 519290

Subsidiary (Non-US):

SELEX Communications Romania SRL (2)
Str DR Louis Pasteur No 8 Floor, Bucharest, 50535, Romania
Tel.: (40) 21 4109530
Telecommunication Servicesb
N.A.I.C.S.: 517810
Massimo Basile (Mng Dir)

Subsidiary (Domestic):

S.C. Elettra Communications SA (3)
Ploiesti-Mumbai Highway Km 8, 100302, Ploiesti, Romania
Tel.: (40) 244434022
Web Site: http://www.elettra.ro
Sales Range: $25-49.9 Million
Emp.: 100
Communication Equipment Mfr
N.A.I.C.S.: 334290
Sandor Lovasz (Dir Gen)

Subsidiary (Domestic):

SIRIO PANEL SPA (2)
Localita Levanella Becorpi, 52025, Montevarchi, Arezzo, Italy
Tel.: (39) 055 913671
Web Site: http://www.siriopanel.it
Rev.: $59,462,550
Emp.: 230
Aircraft Lighting Equipment Mfr
N.A.I.C.S.: 335139

Subsidiary (US):

Sirio Panel Inc. (3)
Ste 2A 1385 Stonycreek Rd, Troy, OH 43026
Tel.: (937) 524-5069
Web Site: http://www.siriopanel.it
Emp.: 10
Aircraft Lighting System Mfr
N.A.I.C.S.: 336413

Subsidiary (Non-US):

VEGA Deutschland GmbH (2)
Industriestrasse 161, D-50999, Cologne, Germany
Tel.: (49) 22367480
Web Site: http://www.vega.de
Sales Range: $100-124.9 Million
Emp.: 400
Civil & Military Technology Consulting & Support Services
N.A.I.C.S.: 541990

SELEX Galileo S.p.A. (1)
Via Albert Einstein 35, Campi Bisenzio Fl, 50013, Campi Bisenzio, Italy
Tel.: (39) 05589501
Web Site: http://www.selexgalileo.it
Sales Range: $1-4.9 Billion
Emp.: 7,000
Defense Electronics Mfr
N.A.I.C.S.: 334511

Subsidiary (Non-US):

Leonardo MW Limited (2)
Sigma House Christopher Martin Road, Basildon, SS14 3EL, Essex, United Kingdom (100%)
Tel.: (44) 1268823400
Web Site: http://www.uk.leonardocompany.com
Emp.: 7,400
Electronic Flight System Mfr
N.A.I.C.S.: 334511

AND PRIVATE COMPANIES

Norman Bone *(Chm & Mng Dir)*

Subsidiary (Domestic):

SELEX Galileo (Projects) Ltd. (3)
Sigma House Christopher Martin Road, Basildon, SS14 3EL, Essex, United Kingdom
Tel.: (44) 1268887075
Electrical Products Mfr & Whslr
N.A.I.C.S.: 335999
Jan Boyes *(Project Mgr)*

SELEX Galileo Infrared Ltd. (3)
Robinson House First Avenue, Southampton, SO15 0LG, Hants, United Kingdom
Tel.: (44) 23 8070 2300
Sales Range: $50-74.9 Million
Emp.: 200
Military & Industrial Detector Mfr
N.A.I.C.S.: 334511
Ian Bancroft *(Gen Mgr)*

SELEX PENSION SCHEME (TRUSTEE) LIMITED (3)
Sigma House Christopher Martin Road, Basildon, SS14 3EL, Essex, United Kingdom
Tel.: (44) 1268522822
Pension Management Services
N.A.I.C.S.: 525110

Subsidiary (US):

SELEX Galileo Inc. (2)
201 12th St S Ste 704, Arlington, VA 22202
Tel.: (703) 418-7280
Web Site: http://www.selexgalileo.com
Sales Range: $25-49.9 Million
Emp.: 200
Defense Electronics Mfr
N.A.I.C.S.: 334511

SELEX Sistemi Integrati S.p.A. (1)
Via Tiburtina Km 12 400 AS, IT-00131, Rome, Italy
Tel.: (39) 0641501
Web Site: http://www.selex-si.com
Sales Range: $900-999.9 Million
Emp.: 3,500
Scientific, Technical & Management Consulting & Support Services
N.A.I.C.S.: 541990
Alberto de Benedictis *(Chm)*

Subsidiary (Non-US):

SELEX SISTEMI INTEGRATI DO BRASIL LTDA (2)
Rua da Assembleia 10 - Sala 3101, 20011-901, Rio de Janeiro, Brazil
Tel.: (55) 21 2292 7743
Military Component Mfr
N.A.I.C.S.: 336992

Subsidiary (US):

SELEX SYSTEMS INTEGRATION INC. (2)
11300 W 89th St, Overland Park, KS 66214
Tel.: (913) 495-2600
Web Site: http://www.selex-si-us.com
Sales Range: $25-49.9 Million
Emp.: 100
Navigation Equipment Distr
N.A.I.C.S.: 423690
Mike Warner *(CEO)*

Subsidiary (Non-US):

SELEX Sistemi Integrati GmbH (2)
Raiffeisenstrasse 10, 41470, Neuss, Germany
Tel.: (49) 21377820
Web Site: http://www.gematronik.com
Sales Range: $50-74.9 Million
Emp.: 150
Scientific, Technical & Management Consulting & Support Services
N.A.I.C.S.: 541990

SELEX Systems Integration Ltd. (2)
430 Bristol Business Park Coldharbour Lane, Bristol, BS16 1EJ, United Kingdom (100%)
Tel.: (44) 117 900 8975
Web Site: http://www.selex-si.co.uk
Scientific, Technical & Management Consulting & Support Services
N.A.I.C.S.: 541990

Selex ES Saudi Arabia Ltd. (1)
Granada Business Park Building A4 Floor 8, PO Box 9743, Riyadh, 11423, Saudi Arabia
Tel.: (966) 11 511 7400
Aircraft Defense Services
N.A.I.C.S.: 928110

So.Ge.Pa. - Societa Generale Di Partecipazioni SpA (1)
Via Sardegna n 38 piano 5 interni 9 e 10, 00187, Rome, RM, Italy
Tel.: (39) 064 553 8311
Web Site: https://www.sogepaspa.com
Aircraft Defense Services
N.A.I.C.S.: 928110

TeleSPAzio Argentina S.A. (1)
Avenida Juan B Justo no 837 Piso 3, C1425FSC, Buenos Aires, Argentina
Tel.: (54) 114 852 8700
Satellite Services
N.A.I.C.S.: 517410

TeleSPAzio Iberica S.L. (1)
Julian Camarillo 4 Edificio B 4 D, 28037, Madrid, Spain
Tel.: (34) 91 553 3865
Web Site: https://www.telespazio.es
Satellite Services
N.A.I.C.S.: 517410
Miguel Bermudo *(CEO)*

TeleSPAzio Vega Deutschland GmbH (1)
Europaplatz 5, 64293, Darmstadt, Germany
Tel.: (49) 61 518 2570
Web Site: https://www.telespazio.de
Information Technology Solutions Services
N.A.I.C.S.: 541519
Sigmar Keller *(CEO)*

Telespazio SpA (1)
Via Tiburtina 965, 156, Rome, Italy (67%)
Tel.: (39) 0640791
Web Site: http://www.telespazio.com
Emp.: 2,500
Satellite Services
N.A.I.C.S.: 517410

Subsidiary (Non-US):

Telespazio Deutschland GmbH (2)
Talhofstrasse 28A, 82205, Gilching, Pavaria, Germany
Tel.: (49) 810538430
Web Site: http://www.telespazio.com
Operational Services for Space Systems
N.A.I.C.S.: 334511

Telespazio VEGA UK Ltd. (2)
350 Capability Green, Luton, LU1 3LU, Bedforshire, United Kingdom
Tel.: (44) 1582 399 000
Web Site: http://www.vegaspace.com
Sales Range: $100-124.9 Million
Emp.: 400
Space Sector Technology Consulting & Support Services
N.A.I.C.S.: 541990
Patrick Lacey *(CFO & Sec)*

Subsidiary (Non-US):

VEGA Space GmbH (3)
Europaplatz 5, Darmstadt, 64293, Germany
Tel.: (49) 61518257100
Web Site: http://www.vegaspace.de
Sales Range: $50-74.9 Million
Emp.: 200
Space Sector Technology Consulting & Support Services
N.A.I.C.S.: 541990

VEGA Technologies SAS (3)
Parc Technologique du Canal 12 avenue de l'Europe, Villa San Diego, F-31520, Ramonville-Saint-Agne, France
Tel.: (33) 567771999
Web Site: http://www.vegatechnologies.fr
Sales Range: $25-49.9 Million
Emp.: 60
Space Sector Technology Consulting & Support Services
N.A.I.C.S.: 541990

Tti Tactical Technologies Inc. (1)
2685 Queensview Dr, Ottawa, K2B 8K2, ON, Canada
Tel.: (613) 828-0775
Web Site: https://leonardocompany.ca

Aircraft Protection Software Development Services
N.A.I.C.S.: 541511

Vitrociset Belgium Sprl (1)
Rue Devant les Hetres 2, Transinne, 6890, Libin, Belgium
Tel.: (32) 6 123 0004
Web Site: https://www.vitrocisetbelgium.com
Aircraft Support Services
N.A.I.C.S.: 488190
Federico Rossi *(Pres & CEO)*

Vitrociset France SARL (1)
Innopolis -Bat A 1149 La Pyreneenne, 31670, Labege, France
Tel.: (33) 58 191 9043
Aircraft Support Services
N.A.I.C.S.: 488190

Vitrociset SpA (1)
Via Tiburtina 1020, 00156, Rome, Italy
Tel.: (39) 0688201
Web Site: https://www.vitrociset.it
Defense & Security Services
N.A.I.C.S.: 928110
Paolo Solferino *(CEO & Gen Mgr)*

WHITEHEAD ALENIA SISTEMI SUBACQUEI SPA (1)
Via di Levante 48, 57124, Livorno, Italy
Tel.: (39) 0586 840 111
Web Site: http://www.wass.it
Sales Range: $100-124.9 Million
Emp.: 400
Underwater Surveillance System Mfr
N.A.I.C.S.: 334511

Wytwornia Sprzetu Komunikacyjnego S.A. (1)
ul Czestochowska 140, 62-800, Kalisz, Poland
Tel.: (48) 62 504 6100
Web Site: https://www.wsk.kalisz.pl
Aircraft Mfr
N.A.I.C.S.: 336411
Jacek Jankowski *(Pres)*

ZAKLAD OBROBKI PLASTYCZNEJ SP. Z O.O. (1)
ul Kuznicza 13, Swidnik, 21-045, Lublin, Poland
Tel.: (48) 81 751 26 00
Web Site: http://www.kuznia-zop.pl
Sales Range: $25-49.9 Million
Emp.: 50
Metal Product Distr
N.A.I.C.S.: 423510
Kida Franciszek *(Pres)*

ZAKLAD REMONTOWY SP. Z O.O. (1)
Il Armii Wojska Polskiego 35, 59-220, Legnica, Poland
Tel.: (48) 76 854 21 04
Electrical Equipment Installation Services
N.A.I.C.S.: 238210

ZAKLAD UTRZYMANIA RUCHU SP. Z O.O. (1)
Metalowa 13, 21-045, Swidnik, Poland
Tel.: (48) 81 751 27 05
Electrical Equipment Installation Services
N.A.I.C.S.: 238210

LEONE FILM GROUP S.P.A

Via Birmania 74/76, 00144, Rome, Italy
Tel.: (39) 065924548
Web Site: https://www.iubenda.com
Year Founded: 1989
LFG—(ITA)
Sales Range: Less than $1 Million
Film Production & Distribution
N.A.I.C.S.: 512110
Andrea Leone *(Pres & Co-CEO)*

LEONG HUP INTERNATIONAL BERHAD

3rd Floor Wisma Westcourt 126 Jalan Klang Lama, Wilayah Persekutuan, 58000, Kuala Lumpur, Malaysia
Tel.: (60) 379808086   MY
Web Site:
   https://www.leonghupnational.com
Year Founded: 1978

LHI—(KLS)
Rev.: $1,913,799,365
Assets: $1,395,174,815
Liabilities: $847,116,614
Net Worth: $548,058,201
Earnings: $51,613,545
Emp.: 12,522
Fiscal Year-end: 12/31/22
Animal Feed Mfr
N.A.I.C.S.: 311999
Lau Tuang Nguang *(CEO)*

Subsidiaries:

Emivest Feedmill Vietnam Co., Limited (1)
01-03-05 Road D2 Saigonpearl Shophouse 3rd Floor No 92, Nguyen Huu Canh Street Ward 22 Binh Thanh District, 717066, Ho Chi Minh City, Vietnam
Tel.: (84) 2835120123
Animal & Poultry Feed Mfr
N.A.I.C.S.: 311119

F. E. Venture Sdn. Bhd. (1)
Lot 3 and 5 Jalan PJS 11/8 Bandar Sunway, 46150, Petaling Jaya, Selangor, Malaysia
Tel.: (60) 356333493
Web Site: https://www.feventure.com
Animal Health Product Distr
N.A.I.C.S.: 424910

Hup Heng Poultry Industries Pte. Ltd. (1)
No 30 Senoko Crescent Woodlands East Ind Estate, Singapore, 758279, Singapore
Tel.: (65) 62570366
Web Site: http://huphengp.com.sg
Meat Product Distr
N.A.I.C.S.: 424470

Leong Hup (Philippines), Inc. (1)
Penthouse 6 Landsdale Tower 86 Mother Ignacia St Timog Ave, Quezon City, Philippines
Tel.: (63) 83721671
Poultry Farming Services
N.A.I.C.S.: 112390

Leong Hup Food Pte. Ltd. (1)
4 Senoko Way, Singapore, 758029, Singapore
Tel.: (65) 67572121
Web Site:
   https://www.leonghupsingapore.com.sg
Meat Product Distr
N.A.I.C.S.: 424470

PT Malindo Food Delight (1)
JI RS Fatmawati No 15 Komplek Golden Plaza Blok G No 17-22, Jakarta, 12420, Indonesia
Tel.: (62) 217661727
Web Site: https://www.malindofeedmill.com
Meat Processed Mfr
N.A.I.C.S.: 311612

Prestige Fortune Sdn. Bhd. (1)
No 37 Jalan Besi Taman Sri Putri, 81300, Skudai, Johor, Malaysia
Tel.: (60) 75548799
Web Site: https://prestigefortune.com
Poultry Farming Services
N.A.I.C.S.: 112390

Ritma Premier Pte. Ltd. (1)
7030 Ang Mo Kio Ave 5 03-22 Northstar AMK, Singapore, 569880, Singapore
Tel.: (65) 64931930
Web Site: https://ritmapres.com
Animal Food Distr
N.A.I.C.S.: 424910

The Baker's Cottage Sdn. Bhd. (1)
3rd Floor Wisma Westcourt 126 Jalan Klang Lama, 58000, Kuala Lumpur, Malaysia
Tel.: (60) 379808086
Web Site: https://thebakerscottage.com
Food Mfr & Distr
N.A.I.C.S.: 311999

LEONHARD KURZ GMBH & CO. KG

Schwabacher Str 482, 90763, Furth, Germany
Tel.: (49) 91171410

LEONHARD KURZ GMBH & CO. KG

Leonhard Kurz GmbH & Co. KG—(Continued)

Web Site: http://www.kurz.de
Year Founded: 1892
Sales Range: $1-4.9 Billion
Emp.: 2,600
Security Broker Services
N.A.I.C.S.: 523150

Subsidiaries:

INTERCOM - KURZ LTD (1)
Beysan San Sit Dereboyu Cad No 41 Beylikduz B Cekmece, 34524, Istanbul, Turkiye
Tel.: (90) 212 422 04 04
Web Site: http://www.Intercom-Kurz.com
Stamping Foil Mfr
N.A.I.C.S.: 332119

KURZ - FORWARD COMPANY LTD. (1)
Flat 2-7 14/F Westlands Centre 20 Westlands Road, Quarry Bay, China (Hong Kong)
Tel.: (852) 2 880 90 83
Stamping Foil Mfr
N.A.I.C.S.: 332119

KURZ DO BRASIL (1)
Rua Achilles Orlando Curtolo 195, 01144-010, Sao Paulo, Brazil
Tel.: (55) 11 38 71 73 40
Web Site: http://www.kurz.com.br
Stamping Foil Mfr
N.A.I.C.S.: 332119
Claudio Sthamer (Gen Mgr)

KURZ MEXICO S.de R.L.de C.V. (1)
Emilio Cardenas no 45 Col Fraccionamiento Industrial, 54000, Tlalnepantla, Mexico
Tel.: (52) 55 55657589
Web Site: http://www.kurz.com.mx
Stamping Foil Mfr
N.A.I.C.S.: 332119

KURZ NORTH AFRICA SARL (1)
56 Bis Rue de l'Industrie La Charguia I, 2035, Tunis, Tunisia
Tel.: (216) 71 804 991
Web Site: http://www.kurz-na.com
Stamping Foil Mfr
N.A.I.C.S.: 332119

KURZ TYPOFOL GmbH (1)
Sormitzer Strasse 6/7, 04720, Dobeln, Germany
Tel.: (49) 3431 5 76 80
Web Site: http://www.kurz-typofol.de
Emp.: 18
Stamping Foil Mfr
N.A.I.C.S.: 332119

Kurz (India) Pvt. Ltd. (1)
56 Rama Road, New Delhi, 110 015, India
Tel.: (91) 1125170903
Web Site: http://www.kurzin.com
Sales Range: $25-49.9 Million
Emp.: 20
Metal Stamping
N.A.I.C.S.: 332119

Kurz (Thailand) Ltd. (1)
2869-2869/1 Rimtangrodfaisaipaknam Rd, Phrakanong Sub-District Klongtoey District, Bangkok, 10110, Thailand
Tel.: (66) 26717505
Web Site: http://www.kurz.co.th
Automobile Parts Mfr
N.A.I.C.S.: 336390
Supreecha Muangsaen (Mng Dir)

Kurz CS spol.sr.o. (1)
Za Humny 749/16, Strelice, Brno, 66447, Czech Republic
Tel.: (420) 547 23 98 20
Web Site: http://www.kurzcs.cz
Sales Range: $25-49.9 Million
Emp.: 5
Metal Stamping Foils
N.A.I.C.S.: 332119

Kurz Cheers Inc. (1)
No 14-16 Lane 123 Sec 6, Min Chuan East Road, Taipei, 114, Taiwan
Tel.: (886) 227926686
Web Site: http://www.kurz.com.tw
Sales Range: $25-49.9 Million
Emp.: 11
Metal Stamping Foils Whslr

Chih Jung Hsien (Mng Dir)

Kurz Digital Solutions GmbH & Co. KG
Schwabacher Str 106, 90763, Furth, Germany
Tel.: (49) 91171418787
Web Site: http://www.kurzdigital.com
Information Technology Services
N.A.I.C.S.: 541519
Andreas Kurz (Co-Chm)

Kurz France S.A.R.L. (1)
15 bis Rue de la Pierre Levee, 75011, Paris, France
Tel.: (33) 143571670
Web Site: http://www.kurz.fr
Sales Range: $25-49.9 Million
Emp.: 50
Metal Stamping
N.A.I.C.S.: 332119
Christoff Hervette (Dir-Admin)

Kurz Japan Ltd. (1)
16-24 Toyotsu-cho, Suita, Osaka, 564 0051, Japan
Tel.: (81) 663305050
Web Site: http://www.kurzjapan.com
Sales Range: $25-49.9 Million
Emp.: 40
Metal Stamping Foils Whslr
N.A.I.C.S.: 423510
Bunji Ando (Mgr-Sls)

Kurz New Zealand Ltd. (1)
665 B Great S Rd, Penrose, Auckland, 1642, New Zealand
Tel.: (64) 92743932
Web Site: http://www.kurz.com.au
Sales Range: $50-74.9 Million
Emp.: 5
Metal Stamping Foils Whslr
N.A.I.C.S.: 332119
Hainince Coohlein (Mgr-Australia & New Zealand)

Kurz Pragefolien AG (1)
Hertestrasse 27, 8304, Wallisellen, Switzerland
Tel.: (41) 432116800
Web Site: http://www.kurzag.ch
Sales Range: $25-49.9 Million
Emp.: 20
Metal Stamping Foils & Equipment Whslr
N.A.I.C.S.: 332119

Kurz Stamping Technology (Hefei) Co., Ltd. (1)
Hefei Economic & Technological Development Zone, 168 Jinxiu Road, Hefei, 230601, Anhui, China
Tel.: (86) 5513859000
Web Site: http://www.kurz.com.cn
Sales Range: $50-74.9 Million
Emp.: 200
Metal Stamping
N.A.I.C.S.: 332119

Kurz Transfer Products L.P. (1)
1575 Sismet Road Unit 9, Mississauga, L4W 1P9, ON, Canada
Tel.: (905) 625-6944
Packaging Product Distr
N.A.I.C.S.: 424130

Kurz Transfer Products, Inc. (1)
4939 Hwy 150 N, Lexington, NC 27295
Tel.: (336) 397-1700
Web Site: http://www.kurzusa.com
Sales Range: $50-74.9 Million
Emp.: 85
Metal Foil Products Mfr
N.A.I.C.S.: 423830
LaRue Cribb (Office Mgr)

Kurz Transfer Products, L.P. (1)
3200 Woodpark Blvd, Charlotte, NC 28206 (100%)
Tel.: (704) 927-3700
Web Site: http://www.kurzusa.com
Rev: $28,000,000
Emp.: 100
Metal Foil & Leaf Manufacturing
N.A.I.C.S.: 332999
Drew Barringer (COO)

Leonhard Kurz (Aust.) Pty. Ltd. (1)
Unit 4 81 Frenchs Forest Road, Frenchs Forest, Sydney, 2086, NSW, Australia

Tel.: (61) 2 8977 7277
Web Site: http://www.kurz.com.au
Sales Range: $25-49.9 Million
Emp.: 11
Metal Stamping Foils Whslr
N.A.I.C.S.: 332119

Leonhard Kurz (Far East) Ltd. (1)
Unit 202 2/F Westland Ctr 20 Westlands Rd, Quarry Bay, China (Hong Kong)
Tel.: (852) 28336167
Web Site: http://www.kurzfe.com.hk
Sales Range: $25-49.9 Million
Emp.: 28
Metal Stamping Foils Whslr
N.A.I.C.S.: 332119
Kin Sun Chan (Mng Dir)

Leonhard Kurz (U.K.) Ltd. (1)
Garnet Close, Greycaine Industrial Estate, Watford, WD24 7JW, Hertfordshire, United Kingdom
Tel.: (44) 1923249988
Web Site: http://www.kurz.co.uk
Sales Range: $25-49.9 Million
Emp.: 42
Metal Stamping Foils
N.A.I.C.S.: 332119
Andrew Ferrar (Gen Mgr)

Leonhard Kurz Benelux B.V. (1)
Roggeweg 24, Nijmegen, AJ-6534, Netherlands
Tel.: (31) 243781840
Web Site: http://www.kurz.nl
Sales Range: $25-49.9 Million
Emp.: 15
Metal Stamping Foils
N.A.I.C.S.: 332119
Rena Goossens (Mng Dir)

Leonhard Kurz Hungaria Kft (1)
Tarkaret u 8-10, 1106, Budapest, Hungary
Tel.: (36) 12605053
Web Site: http://www.kurz.hu
Emp.: 5
Metal Stamping Foils
N.A.I.C.S.: 332119
Laszlo Dosa (Mng Dir)

Leonhard Kurz Ireland Ltd. (1)
Unit 15 Churchtown Business Park Beaumont Ave, Churchtown, Dublin, 14, Ireland
Tel.: (353) 12963696
Web Site: http://www.kurz.ie
Sales Range: $25-49.9 Million
Emp.: 3
Metal Stamping Foils
N.A.I.C.S.: 332119
Ray O'Brien (Mng Dir)

Leonhard Kurz South-East Europe Kft. (1)
Tarkaret u 8-10, 1106, Budapest, Hungary
Tel.: (36) 14334321
Web Site: http://www.kurz.hu
Chemical Products Mfr
N.A.I.C.S.: 325998
Tamas Kristof (Sls Mgr)

Luxoro S.R.L. (1)
Via delle Rose 3, 27020, Parona, Pavia, Italy
Tel.: (39) 0384254011
Web Site: http://www.luxoro.it
Construction Materials Distr
N.A.I.C.S.: 423390
Valentina Pozzati (Bus Mgr)

Mayerhofer Argentina S.A. (1)
Av Elcano 3931, C1427CHD, Buenos Aires, Argentina
Tel.: (54) 1145554003
Web Site: http://www.mayerhofer.com.ar
Construction Materials Distr
N.A.I.C.S.: 423390

OVD Kinegram AG (1)
Zahlerweg 11, 6300, Zug, Switzerland
Tel.: (41) 415552000
Web Site: http://www.kinegram.com
Electric Equipment Mfr
N.A.I.C.S.: 335999

LEONHARD MOLL BETONWERKE GMBH & CO KG

Anderter Strasse 95, D-30629, Hannover, Germany
Tel.: (49) 511 51 98 97 0

Web Site: http://www.moll-betonwerke.de
Year Founded: 1929
Building Contractors
N.A.I.C.S.: 238190

Subsidiaries:

ZPSV s.r.o. (1)
Trebizskeho 207, Uhersky Ostroh, 687 24, Czech Republic
Tel.: (420) 572419311
Web Site: http://www.zpsv.cz
Sales Range: $150-199.9 Million
Civil Engineering Services
N.A.I.C.S.: 237990
Michal Sucha (Mgr-Quality)

Subsidiary (Domestic):

ZPSV Servis, s.r.o. (2)
Trebizskeho 207, 687 24, Uhersky Ostroh, Czech Republic
Tel.: (420) 572419311
Web Site: http://www.zpsv.com
Sales Range: $200-249.9 Million
Civil Engineering Services
N.A.I.C.S.: 237990

Subsidiary (Non-US):

ZPSV a.s. Cana (2)
Osloboditel'ov 127, 044 14, Cana, Slovakia
Tel.: (421) 55 6999528
Web Site: http://www.zpsvcana.sk
Railway Gravel & Concrete Prefabrication & Concrete Railway Sleepers
N.A.I.C.S.: 488210

LEONI AG

Marienstrabe 7, 90402, Nuremberg, Germany
Tel.: (49) 91120230 De
Web Site: https://www.leoni.com
LEO—(DEU)
Rev: $5,076,976,713
Assets: $4,295,171,247
Liabilities: $3,968,502,396
Net Worth: $326,668,852
Earnings: ($405,200,061)
Emp.: 101,007
Fiscal Year-end: 12/31/20
Wires, Cables & Wiring Systems Mfr
N.A.I.C.S.: 335929

Subsidiaries:

Adaptricity AG (1)
Hohlstrasse 190, 8004, Zurich, Switzerland
Tel.: (41) 44 500 9245
Web Site: https://www.adaptricity.com
Electronic Cable Mfr
N.A.I.C.S.: 335929
Mario Baumgartner (CEO)

Bizlink Tailor-Made Cable UK Limited (1)
Units 12-14 Boythorpe Business Units Dock Walk, Boythorpe, Chesterfield, S40 2QR, United Kingdom
Tel.: (44) 1246558618
Web Site: http://www.leoni.com
Sales Range: $50-74.9 Million
Emp.: 5
Fiber Optic Cable Distr
N.A.I.C.S.: 423610

Haarlander Gmbh (1)
Regensburger Ring 14, 91154, Roth, Germany
Tel.: (49) 917196180
Web Site: https://www.haarlaender-gmbh.com
Emp.: 25
Copper Wires Mfr
N.A.I.C.S.: 335929
Georg Brenner (Mng Dir)

KB Kabel Beteiligungs-GmbH (1)
Marienstr 7, Nuremberg, 90402, Germany
Tel.: (49) 9112023217
Fabricated Wire Products Distr
N.A.I.C.S.: 423610
Dieter Bella (Mng Dir)

LEONI Bordnetz-Systeme GmbH & Co., KG (1)

AND PRIVATE COMPANIES

LEONI AG

Flugplatzstrasse 74, 97318, Kitzingen, Germany
Tel.: (49) 9 321 3040
Web Site: https://www.leoni-wiring-systems.com
Sales Range: $200-249.9 Million
Emp.: 650
Wiring System Solutions
N.A.I.C.S.: 335932

LEONI Cable de Chihuahua S.A. de C.V. (1)
Av Rio Conchos No 9700 Parque Industrial Cuauhtemoc, Cuauhtemoc, 31543, Chihuahua, Mexico
Tel.: (52) 6255902000
Electronic Cable Mfr
N.A.I.C.S.: 335929

LEONI Draht GmbH (1)
Windorfer Strasse 1, Bad Kotzting, 93444, Cham, Germany
Tel.: (49) 91419180
Sales Range: $50-74.9 Million
Emp.: 130
Textile & Creative Wire Product
N.A.I.C.S.: 331222

LEONI Electrical Systems (Jining) Co., Ltd. (1)
7th Park of Jining High New Tech Industries Development Zone, Jining, 272104, China
Tel.: (86) 5375040200
Electronic Cable Mfr
N.A.I.C.S.: 335929

LEONI Electrical Systems (Penglai) Co., Ltd. (1)
Liujiagou Gongyeyuan, Penglai, Yantai, 265608, Shandong, China
Tel.: (86) 5355967978
Electronic Cable Mfr
N.A.I.C.S.: 335929

LEONI Engineering Products & Services Inc. (1)
100 Kay Industrial Dr, Lake Orion, MI 48359-1831
Tel.: (248) 484-5500
Web Site: https://www.leoni.com
Sales Range: $1-9.9 Million
Emp.: 32
Robotic Equipment & Services
N.A.I.C.S.: 333248

LEONI Fiber Optics GmbH (1)
An Der Lande 3, 91154, Roth, Germany
Tel.: (49) 9171 804 2133
Web Site: https://www.leoni-fiber-optics.com
Sales Range: $100-124.9 Million
Emp.: 300
Fiber Optics
N.A.I.C.S.: 335921
Bruno Uebbing (Mng Dir)

LEONI Fiber Optics GmbH (1)
Muhldamm 6, Foritztal, 96524, Neuhaus-Schierschnitz, Germany
Tel.: (49) 367 648 1100
Web Site: https://www.leoni-fiber-optics.com
Sales Range: $25-49.9 Million
Emp.: 100
Fiber Optics
N.A.I.C.S.: 335921
Nils Klippel (Member-Mgmt Bd)

LEONI Fiber Optics Inc. (1)
209 Bulifants Blvd, Williamsburg, VA 23188
Tel.: (757) 258-4805
Web Site: http://www.leoni-northamerica.com
Sales Range: $50-74.9 Million
Emp.: 55
Fiber Optic Cable Distr
N.A.I.C.S.: 423610

LEONI Italy S.r.l. (1)
Strada Padana 10 Ovest 17/19, 15023, Fe-lizzano, AL, Italy
Tel.: (39) 0131792411
Electronic Product Mfr & Distr
N.A.I.C.S.: 335313

LEONI Kabel GmbH (1)
An der Lande 3, 91154, Roth, Germany
Tel.: (49) 91718040
Sales Range: $200-249.9 Million
Emp.: 800
Automotive & Standard Cables
N.A.I.C.S.: 335932

LEONI Middle East FZE (1)
JAZFA View Buildings No 19 Office 603 Jebel Ali Free Zone, PO Box 16913, 15023, Dubai, United Arab Emirates
Tel.: (971) 48850660
Electronic Cable Mfr
N.A.I.C.S.: 335929

LEONI Slovakia spol. s.r.o. (1)
Mestska Cast Dobra 1356, Trencianska Tepla, 914 01, Trencin, Slovakia
Tel.: (421) 326550570
Electronic Cable Mfr
N.A.I.C.S.: 335929

LEONI Special Cables GmbH (1)
Eschstrasse 1, 26169, Friesoythe, Germany
Tel.: (49) 4 491 2910
Web Site: https://www.leoni.com
Sales Range: $100-124.9 Million
Emp.: 500
Specialty Cables
N.A.I.C.S.: 335932

LEONI Wiring Systems (Tieling) Co., Ltd. (1)
No 1288 Yuanyi Road Taiwan Industrial Parking, Tieling, Liaoning, China
Tel.: (86) 2472267501
Electronic Cable Mfr
N.A.I.C.S.: 335929

LEONI Wiring Systems Ain Sebaa SA (1)
44 Avenue Khalid Bnou Loualid, BP 2580, Ain Sebaa, Casablanca, 20250, Morocco
Tel.: (212) 22667700
Automotive Wiring Harness Mfr
N.A.I.C.S.: 336320

LEONI Wiring Systems Bouskoura SA (1)
Zone Industriel, BP. 75, 20180, Bouskoura, Morocco
Tel.: (212) 22334170
Automotive Wiring Harness Mfr
N.A.I.C.S.: 336320

LEONI Wiring Systems Czech, s.r.o. (1)
Mirova p/K-Bela 116, 511 01, Turnov, Czech Republic
Tel.: (420) 4848404415
Electronic Product Mfr & Distr
N.A.I.C.S.: 335313

LEONI Wiring Systems Egypt S.A.E. (1)
Public Free Zone, Nasr City, Cairo, Egypt
Tel.: (20) 22 274 7715
Web Site: https://www.leoni-egypt.com
Sales Range: $1-4.9 Billion
Emp.: 6,700
Automotive Electric Wire Distr
N.A.I.C.S.: 423120

LEONI Wiring Systems Italy s.r.l. (1)
Strada Padana 10 Ovest 17/19, 15023, Fe-lizzano, Italy
Tel.: (39) 013 179 2411
Web Site: https://www.leoni.com
Fabricated Wire Product Mfr
N.A.I.C.S.: 332618

LEONI Wiring Systems RO S.R.L. (1)
Street Tarpiului Road no 24, 420062, Bis-trita, Romania
Tel.: (40) 751257671
Electronic Cable Mfr
N.A.I.C.S.: 335929

LEONI Wiring Systems Southeast d.o.o. (1)
Pane Dukica 1, 18400, Prokuplje, Serbia
Tel.: (381) 27319111
Electronic Cable Mfr
N.A.I.C.S.: 335929

LEONI Wiring Systems Spain S.L. (1)
Pol Ind Armenteres Carrer Riera Pahissa n 14-16, 8980, Santa Perpetua de Mogoda, Spain
Tel.: (34) 936354400
Web Site: http://www.leoni
Sales Range: $25-49.9 Million
Emp.: 25
Fiber Optic Cables Whslr
N.A.I.C.S.: 423610

LEONI Wiring Systems Tunisia SARL (1)
Zone Industrielle-Messadine, 4013, Sousse, Tunisia
Tel.: (216) 73102000
Electronic Cable Mfr
N.A.I.C.S.: 335929

LEONI Wiring Systems de Durango S.A. de CV (1)
Calle Antiguo Camino a Contreras 201 Col 20 de Noviembre, 34237, Durango, Mexico
Tel.: (52) 6181501500
Emp.: 2,500
Fabricated Wire Products Distr
N.A.I.C.S.: 423610

LEONI Wiring Systems de Torreon S.A. de CV (1)
Antiguo Camino A Contreras 20 Col 20 De Noviembre, Durango, 34236, Mexico
Tel.: (52) 6181501500
Web Site: http://www.leoni-wiring-systems.com
Fiber Optic Cable Mfr
N.A.I.C.S.: 335921

LKH LEONI Kabelgyar Hungaria Kft. (1)
Kolcsey u 53, 3000, Hatvan, Hungary
Tel.: (36) 37544400
Sales Range: $50-74.9 Million
Emp.: 170
Automotive Wiring Harness Mfr
N.A.I.C.S.: 336320

Leoni (S.E.A) Pte Ltd (1)
237 Alexandra Road 04-14 The Alexcier, Singapore, 159929, Singapore
Tel.: (65) 6 958 1150
Web Site: http://www.leoni.com.sg
Sales Range: $25-49.9 Million
Emp.: 16
Logistics Management Consulting Services
N.A.I.C.S.: 541614

Leoni Autokabel Polska sp.z.o.o (1)
ul Przemyslowa Nr 24, 63-500, Ostrzeszow, Poland
Tel.: (48) 627309100
Web Site: http://www.leoni.com
Fiber Optic Cable Mfr
N.A.I.C.S.: 335921

Leoni Autokabel Slowakia Spol s.r.o (1)
Soblahovska 2050, 91101, Trencin, Slovakia
Tel.: (421) 32 3234 321
Web Site: http://www.leoni.com
Sales Range: $450-499.9 Million
Electrical Cable Wire Mfr & Distr
N.A.I.C.S.: 335921

Leoni Automotive Leads Gmbh (1)
Heinrich-addicks-strasse 1-3, 26919, Brake, Germany
Tel.: (49) 44019305
Fiber Optic Cable Mfr
N.A.I.C.S.: 335921

Leoni Automotive do Brasil Ltda (1)
Rua Lazaro Adriano 500, Bairro Itaim Guacu, Itu, 13312-650, Sao Paulo, Brazil
Tel.: (55) 1140229200
Web Site: http://www.leoni.com
Fiber Optic Cable Mfr
N.A.I.C.S.: 335921

Leoni Cable (Changzhou) Co Ltd (1)
Gaotian Industry Park 109 West Hanjiang Rd, New District, Changzhou, 213022, Jiangsu, China
Tel.: (86) 51989887268
Fiber Optic Cable Mfr
N.A.I.C.S.: 335921

Leoni Cable (Xiamen) Co Ltd (1)
No 666 Yangguang Road Xinyang Industrial Area, Xiamen, 361026, China
Tel.: (86) 592 6377 750
Sales Range: $100-124.9 Million
Emp.: 500
Fiber Optic Cable Mfr
N.A.I.C.S.: 335921

Leoni Cable Assemblies Gmbh (1)
Stieberstrasse 5, Roth, 91154, Germany
Tel.: (49) 9171 804 2640
Sales Range: $25-49.9 Million
Emp.: 9
Electric Cable Mfr & Distr
N.A.I.C.S.: 335921
Christoph Wolf (Mng Dir)

Leoni Cable Belgium N.V (1)
Kempische Steenweg 293 Bus 10, 3500, Hasselt, Belgium
Tel.: (32) 11260260
Web Site: http://www.leoni.com
Emp.: 13
Optical Fibers & Cable Distr
N.A.I.C.S.: 423610

Leoni Cable Maroc SARL (1)
Parc Logistique Ain Harrouda ZI Bd Chefchaouni Casablanca, Ex Route N 110, Casablanca, Morocco
Tel.: (212) 522 346 126
Fiber Optic Cable Distr
N.A.I.C.S.: 335921

Leoni Cable S.A de C.V. (1)
Av Rio Conchos No 9700 Parque Industrial Cuauhtemoc, 31543, Cuauhtemoc, Chih, Mexico
Tel.: (52) 6255902000
Electrical Cable Mfr & Distr
N.A.I.C.S.: 335921
Everardo Avila (Mng Dir)

Leoni Cable Slovakia Spol S.r.o (1)
Nam Dr Schweitzera 194, 91601, Stara Tura, Slovakia
Tel.: (421) 323213188
Web Site: http://www.leoni.com
Cable Assembling Services
N.A.I.C.S.: 561990

Leoni Cable Solutions (India) Private Limited (1)
Indospace Rohan Industrial Park Gat No 428 Off Chakan Talegaon Road, Mahalunge Khed, Pune, 410 501, India
Tel.: (91) 2135634600
Sales Range: $25-49.9 Million
Emp.: 65
Electrical Cable Mfr & Distr
N.A.I.C.S.: 335921
Pushpendra Singh (Mng Dir)

Leoni Electrical Systems (Shanghai) Co. Ltd. (1)
No 1288 Jiasong Bei Road, Jiading, Shanghai, 201806, China
Tel.: (86) 21 39939000
Sales Range: $800-899.9 Million
Emp.: 300
Fiber Optic Cable Mfr
N.A.I.C.S.: 335921

Leoni Elocab Ltd (1)
258 McBrine Drive, Kitchener, N2R 1H8, ON, Canada
Tel.: (519) 893-1155
Web Site: https://www.leoni.com
Sales Range: $25-49.9 Million
Emp.: 50
Fiber Optic Cable Mfr
N.A.I.C.S.: 335921

Leoni Furas S.L (1)
C/Doctor Maluquer 2, 25750, Tora, Spain
Tel.: (34) 973473004
Web Site: http://www.leoni-electrical-appliances.com
Sales Range: $25-49.9 Million
Emp.: 20
Electrical Cable Distr
N.A.I.C.S.: 423610

Leoni HighTemp Solutions Gmbh (1)
Alfred-jung-strasse 1, 58553, Halver, Germany
Tel.: (49) 235366870
Emp.: 11
Fiber Optic Cable Mfr
N.A.I.C.S.: 335921
Klaus Rudolf Bitterwolf (Gen Mgr)

Leoni Kabel Holding Gmbh (1)
Future An der Lande 3, 91154, Roth, Germany
Tel.: (49) 91718040
Fiber Optic Cable Mfr
N.A.I.C.S.: 335921

Leoni Kabel Polska sp.z.o.o (1)
ul Olawska 10, Wierzbice, 55040, Kobierzyce, Poland

LEONI AG

INTERNATIONAL PUBLIC

LEONI AG—(Continued)
Tel.: (48) 713605502
Web Site: https://www.leoni-polska.com
Sales Range: $25-49.9 Million
Emp.: 100
Fiber Optic Cable Mfr
N.A.I.C.S.: 335921

Leoni Kabelgyar Hungaria Kft (1)
Kolcsey u 53, 3000, Hatvan, Hungary
Tel.: (36) 37544400
Emp.: 180
Automotive & Twisted Pair Cables Mfr
N.A.I.C.S.: 335921
Achim Weinstock *(Mng Dir)*

Leoni Kabelsysteme GmbH (1)
Thalfinger Strasse 140, 89233, Neu-Ulm, Germany
Tel.: (49) 73 193 5930
Web Site: https://www.leoni-special-vehicles.com
Emp.: 100
Motor Vehicle Cables Mfr
N.A.I.C.S.: 336390
Matthias Heiligenthal *(Member-Mgmt Bd)*

Leoni Kablo ve Teknolojileri Sanayi Ve Ticaret Limited Sirketi (1)
Ata District Free Zone Muge Street No 13, Muge Caddesi No 13, 16600, Gemlik, Turkiye
Tel.: (90) 2242754000
Web Site: https://www.leoni.com.tr
Sales Range: $50-74.9 Million
Emp.: 140
Fiber Optic Cable Mfr
N.A.I.C.S.: 335921

Leoni Kerpen Gmbh (1)
Zweifaller Strasse 275-287, 52224, Stolberg, Germany
Tel.: (49) 2402 17 1
Web Site: http://www.leoni.com
Fiber Optic Cable Mfr
N.A.I.C.S.: 335921

Leoni Protec Cable Systems Gmbh (1)
Brusseler Strasse 12, 30539, Hannover, Germany
Tel.: (49) 5111 235 7630
Web Site: https://www.leoni.com
Emp.: 15
Fiber Optic Cable Mfr
N.A.I.C.S.: 335921

Leoni Schweiz AG (1)
Herrenmattstrasse 20, Postfach 63, 4658, Daniken, Switzerland
Tel.: (41) 622888282
Web Site: http://www.leoni-schweiz.ch
Sales Range: $25-49.9 Million
Emp.: 5
Electrical Cables Mfr & Distr
N.A.I.C.S.: 335921

Leoni Silitherms s.r.l (1)
SS 10 Via Breda, 29010, Monticelli d'Ongina, Italy
Tel.: (39) 0523815711
Web Site: http://www.silitherm.com
Sales Range: $25-49.9 Million
Emp.: 55
Fiber Optic Cable Mfr
N.A.I.C.S.: 335921

Leoni Slowakia Spol s.r.o (1)
Mestska Cast Dobra 1356, 914 01, Trencianske Teplice, Slovakia
Tel.: (421) 32 655 0570
Web Site: http://www.leoni.com
Sales Range: $200-249.9 Million
Emp.: 600
Electrical Cables Mfr
N.A.I.C.S.: 335921

Leoni Special Cables (Changzhou) Co Ltd (1)
No 21 Taihu West Road New Area, Changzhou, 213022, China
Tel.: (86) 5198 988 7105
Web Site: http://www.leoni.com
Fiber Optic Cable Mfr
N.A.I.C.S.: 335921

Leoni Special Cables Iberica S.A (1)
Pol Ind Can Calderon C/ Riera Fonollar 41-B, 08830, Sant Boi de Llobregat, Barcelona, Spain
Tel.: (34) 936354400
Sales Range: $25-49.9 Million
Emp.: 15
Fiber Optic Cables Whslr
N.A.I.C.S.: 423610
Robert Manich *(Gen Mgr)*

Leoni Studer Gmbh (1)
Stahlbaustrasse 56, Riedstadt, 64560, Germany
Tel.: (49) 615892080
Web Site: http://www.leoni-infrastructure-datacom.com
Emp.: 2
Fiber Optic Cable Mfr
N.A.I.C.S.: 335921

Leoni Temco Ltd (1)
Whimsey Industrial Estate, Cinderford, GL14 3HZ, Glos, United Kingdom
Tel.: (44) 159 482 0100
Web Site: http://www.leoni.com
Sales Range: $25-49.9 Million
Emp.: 80
Copper Wires Mfr
N.A.I.C.S.: 331420

Leoni Tunisie Sarl (1)
Zone Industrielle, Sousse, 4013, Tunisia
Tel.: (216) 73102000
Fiber Optic Cable Mfr
N.A.I.C.S.: 335921

Leoni Wire & Cable Solutions Japan K.K (1)
113 Todagai, Nagakute, 480-1124, Aichi, Japan
Tel.: (81) 561628365
Sales Range: $25-49.9 Million
Emp.: 5
Electrical Cables Mfr & Distr
N.A.I.C.S.: 335921

Leoni Wire (Changzhou) Co Ltd (1)
No 209 Chaohu Road, New district, Changzhou, 213022, China
Tel.: (86) 51989887016
Web Site: http://www.leoni.com
Sales Range: $50-74.9 Million
Emp.: 150
Electrical Cables Mfr
N.A.I.C.S.: 335921

Leoni Wire Inc (1)
301 Griffith Rd, Chicopee, MA 01022
Tel.: (413) 593-6618
Sales Range: $25-49.9 Million
Emp.: 10
Copper Wires Mfr
N.A.I.C.S.: 335929

Leoni Wiring System U.K Ltd (1)
Lower Milehouse Lane, Newcastle-under-Lyme, ST5 9BT, Staffordshire, United Kingdom
Tel.: (44) 1782604200
Web Site: https://www.leoni.co.uk
Emp.: 400
Electrical Cables Mfr & Distr
N.A.I.C.S.: 335921

Leoni Wiring System UA GmbH (1)
LEONI Str 1, village Nezhukhiv Stryi district, Lviv, 82431, Ukraine
Tel.: (380) 32 459 2700
Web Site: http://www.leoni.com
Fiber Optic Cable Mfr
N.A.I.C.S.: 335921

Leoni Wiring Systems (Changchun) Co. Ltd. (1)
No 10110 Donghuan Road, Changchun, 130036, Jilin, China
Tel.: (86) 4318 582 8121
Web Site: http://www.leoni.com
Sales Range: $25-49.9 Million
Emp.: 5
Fiber Optic Cable Mfr
N.A.I.C.S.: 335921

Leoni Wiring Systems (Pune) Pvt Ltd (1)
201B P T Gera Centre Bund Garden Road, Pune, 411001, Maharashtra, India
Tel.: (91) 206 792 9600
Web Site: http://www.leoni.com
Steel Wire Drawing Mfr
N.A.I.C.S.: 331110

Leoni Wiring Systems Arad SRL (1)
Arad West Industrial Zone no 11, 319589, Arad, Romania
Tel.: (40) 372225369
Fiber Optic Cable Mfr
N.A.I.C.S.: 335921

Leoni Wiring Systems France S.A (1)
5 avenue Newton, 78180, Montigny-le-Bretonneux, France
Tel.: (33) 130853085
Sales Range: $100-124.9 Million
Emp.: 400
Automobile Parts Mfr
N.A.I.C.S.: 336390

Leoni Wiring Systems Hermosillo S.A de C.V (1)
Calle Antonio de Quiroga S/N Col El Llanito Parque Ind El Progresso, 83320, Hermosillo, Sonora, Mexico
Tel.: (52) 6622897100
Web Site: https://www.leoni.com
Electrical Cable Mfr & Distr
N.A.I.C.S.: 335921

Leoni Wiring Systems Korea Inc (1)
607 RIT Building 705 Haean-ro, Sangrok-Gu, Ansan, Gyeonggi-do, Korea (South)
Tel.: (82) 3180849000
Fiber Optic Cable Mfr & Distr
N.A.I.C.S.: 335921

Leoni Wiring Systems Mateur Nord SA (1)
Zone Industrielle de Mateur North Route de Bizerte, 7030, Matir, Tunisia
Tel.: (216) 72468 600
Web Site: http://www.leoni.com
Fiber Optic Cable Mfr
N.A.I.C.S.: 335921

Leoni Wiring Systems Mexicana S.A de C.V (1)
Calle Antonio de Quiroga S/N Col El Llanito Parque Ind El Progresso, 83320, Hermosillo, Sonora, Mexico
Tel.: (52) 6622897100
Electrical Cable Mfr & Distr
N.A.I.C.S.: 335921

Leoni Wiring Systems Pitesti SRL (1)
Street Serelor No 19, 117045, Bascov, Romania
Tel.: (40) 248208413
Fiber Optic Cable Mfr
N.A.I.C.S.: 335921
Limiur Vincat *(Gen Mgr)*

Leoni Wiring Systems, Inc. (1)
3100 N Campbell Ave Ste 101, Tucson, AZ 85719
Tel.: (520) 741-0895
Electronic Cable Mfr
N.A.I.C.S.: 335929

Leoni elocab Gmbh (1)
Obere Lerch 34, 91166, Georgensgmund, Germany
Tel.: (49) 91 726 9800
Web Site: http://www.leoni.com
Fiber Optic Cable Mfr
N.A.I.C.S.: 335921

Leonische Holding Inc. (1)
3100 N Campbell Ave Ste 101, Tucson, AZ 85719
Tel.: (520) 741-0895
Investment Management Service
N.A.I.C.S.: 523999

Leonische Portugal Lda (1)
Rua San Martinho Sao Claudio de Barco, 4809-004, Guimaraes, Portugal
Tel.: (351) 253479840
Sales Range: $100-124.9 Million
Emp.: 500
Fiber Optic Cable Mfr
N.A.I.C.S.: 335921

Neumatic CZ s.r.o (1)
D5 Logistics Park 1, 3490 01, Ostrov u Stribra, Czech Republic
Tel.: (420) 37 334 0911
Web Site: https://www.leoni.com
Emp.: 150
Electrical Cables Mfr
N.A.I.C.S.: 335921

OOO LEONI Wiring Systems (1)
PO Box 00047, 423800, Naberezhnye Chelny, Tatarstan, Russia
Tel.: (7) 8552 330624
Web Site: http://www.leoni.com
Fabricated Wire Products Distr
N.A.I.C.S.: 423610

OOO LEONI Wiring Systems (1)
1 Leoni Street, Zavolzhie, 606520, Nizhniy Novgorod, Russia
Tel.: (7) 8316193096
Automobile Parts Distr
N.A.I.C.S.: 423120

j-fiber GmbH (1)
Im Semmicht 1, 07751, Jena, Germany (51%)
Tel.: (49) 3641352100
Web Site: https://www.j-fiber.com
Sales Range: $10-24.9 Million
Emp.: 135
Fiber Optic Technology Designer & Mfr
N.A.I.C.S.: 335921

Subsidiary (Domestic):

FiberCore Machinery Jena GmbH (2)
Im Semmicht 1, 7751, Jena, Germany
Tel.: (49) 3641352500
Fiber Processing Machinery Mfr
N.A.I.C.S.: 333248
Lothar Brehm *(Mng Dir)*

LEONOVUS INC.
2611 Queensview Drive Suite 125, Ottawa, K2B 8K2, ON, Canada
Tel.: (613) 319-5117 ON
Web Site: https://www.leonovus.com
Year Founded: 2008
LE4A—(DEU)
Assets: $80,043
Liabilities: $1,252,744
Net Worth: ($1,172,701)
Earnings: ($40,021)
Fiscal Year-end: 12/31/23
Internet Platform Developer
N.A.I.C.S.: 517810
Michael Gaffney *(Chm & CEO)*

LEONTEQ AG
Europaallee 39, Zurich, Switzerland
Tel.: (41) 588001000 CH
Web Site: https://www.leonteq.com
Year Founded: 2007
LEON—(SWX)
Rev.: $505,965,632
Assets: $13,694,839,246
Liabilities: $12,730,277,162
Net Worth: $964,562,084
Earnings: $173,443,459
Emp.: 556
Fiscal Year-end: 12/31/22
Financial Holding Company
N.A.I.C.S.: 551112
Lukas T. Ruflin *(CEO)*

Subsidiaries:

Leonteq Securities (Europe) GmbH (1)
Neue Mainzer Strasse 28, D-60311, Frankfurt am Main, Germany
Tel.: (49) 69970979900
Financial Holding Company
N.A.I.C.S.: 551112

Leonteq Securities (Hong Kong) Ltd. (1)
Room 2802 28th floor Prosperity Tower 39 Queen s Road, Central, China (Hong Kong)
Tel.: (852) 39725500
Financial Holding Company
N.A.I.C.S.: 551112

Leonteq Securities (Japan) Ltd. (1)
Ark Hills South Tower 9F 1-4-5 Roppongi, Minato-ku, Tokyo, 106-0032, Japan
Tel.: (81) 345631000
Financial Holding Company
N.A.I.C.S.: 551112

Leonteq Securities (Monaco) SAM (1)

AND PRIVATE COMPANIES

Villa Alexandra 35 Boulevard Princesse
Charlotte, MC 98000, Monaco, Monaco
Tel.: (377) 93151166
Financial Holding Company
N.A.I.C.S.: 551112

Leonteq Securities (Singapore) Pte.
Ltd. (1)
8 Marina View Asia Square Tower 1 Unit
31-02, Singapore, 018960, Singapore
Tel.: (65) 66905200
Financial Holding Company
N.A.I.C.S.: 551112

Leonteq Securities AG (1)
Europaallee 39, 8004, Zurich, Switzerland
Tel.: (41) 588001000
Financial Holding Company
N.A.I.C.S.: 551112

LEOPALACE21 CORPORATION

2-54-11 Honcho, Nakano-ku, Tokyo,
164-8622, Japan
Tel.: (81) 5020162895 JP
Web Site: https://leopalace21.co.jp
Year Founded: 1973
8848—(TKS)
Rev.: $2,793,855,310
Assets: $1,355,050,000
Liabilities: $881,251,810
Net Worth: $473,798,190
Earnings: $278,029,820
Emp.: 3,869
Fiscal Year-end: 03/31/24
Apartment Construction & Leasing
Services
N.A.I.C.S.: 236116
Hiroshi Takeda (Exec Officer-Wealth
Mgmt Dept & First Wealth Mgmt
Dept-East Japan)

Subsidiaries:

Azu Life Care Co., Ltd. (1)
1-12-8 Honcho, Nakano-ku, Tokyo, 164-
0012, Japan
Tel.: (81) 36 316 1813
Web Site: https://www.az-lifecare.co.jp
Nursing Care Services
N.A.I.C.S.: 623110

Leopalace Guam Corporation (1)
221 Lk View Dr, Yona, GU
96915-6002 (100%)
Tel.: (671) 471-0001
Resort Management Services
N.A.I.C.S.: 721110

Leopalace Insurance Co., Ltd. (1)
2-29-12 Honcho Nf Building 5f, Nakano-Ku,
Tokyo, 164-0012, Japan
Tel.: (81) 353335921
Resort Operating Services
N.A.I.C.S.: 721110

Leopalace Leasing Corporation (1)
Daiwa Nakano Sakaue Building 3F 3-31-11
Honcho, Nakano-ku, Tokyo, 164-0012, Japan
Tel.: (81) 36 362 5555
Web Site: https://www.leosumu.co.jp
Housing Management Agency Services
N.A.I.C.S.: 531311

Leopalace Power Corporation (1)
2-54-11 Honcho, Nakano-ku, Tokyo, 164-
8622, Japan
Tel.: (81) 502 016 2909
Web Site: https://www.leopower.co.jp
Solar Electric Power Generation Services
N.A.I.C.S.: 221114

Leopalace Smile Co., Ltd. (1)
1F 2-54-11 Honcho, Nakano-ku, Tokyo,
164-8622, Japan
Tel.: (81) 35 350 1498
Web Site: https://www.leo-smile.co.jp
Logistic Services
N.A.I.C.S.: 484110

Leopalace21 (Thailand) Co., Ltd. (1)
9/15 Jermjompol Road, Si Racha, Chon
Buri, 20110, Thailand
Tel.: (66) 82 341 3396
Web Site: https://www.leopalace21-th.com
Property Brokerage Services

N.A.I.C.S.: 531210

Leopalace21 Business Consulting
(Shanghai) Co., Ltd. (1)
Room 2006 Ascendas Plaza 333 Tian Yao
Qiao Road, Xuhui District, Shanghai, China
Tel.: (86) 216 387 0077
Real Estate Manangement Services
N.A.I.C.S.: 531311

Leopalace21 Philippines Inc. (1)
23F Tower 6789 Ayala Avenue 6789,
Makati, 1209, Manila, Philippines
Tel.: (63) 28 801 3417
Real Estate Manangement Services
N.A.I.C.S.: 531311

Leopalace21 Singapore Pte. Ltd. (1)
30/F Singapore Land Tower 50 Raffles
Place, Singapore, 048623, Singapore
Tel.: (65) 6 632 3519
Real Estate Manangement Services
N.A.I.C.S.: 531311

Plaza Guarantee Co., Ltd. (1)
1-8-8 Arai Leopalace Nakano Building 6th
Floor, Nakano-ku, Tokyo, 165-0026, Japan
Tel.: (81) 35 345 5607
Web Site: https://www.plazaguarantee.co.jp
Building Leasing Services
N.A.I.C.S.: 531110

Woori & Leo PMC Ltd. Co., Ltd. (1)
4F Sehwan Building 90, Banpo-daero
Seocho-gu, Seoul, 06649, Korea (South)
Tel.: (82) 1 566 3733
Web Site: https://www.woorileopmc.com
Housing Rental Management Services
N.A.I.C.S.: 531110

LEOPOLD KOSTAL GMBH & CO. KG

An der Bellmerei 10, 58513, Luden-
scheid, Germany
Tel.: (49) 2351160
Web Site: http://www.kostal.com
Year Founded: 1912
Sales Range: $10-24.9 Million
Emp.: 13,000
Electronics Mfr
N.A.I.C.S.: 334419
Andreas Kostal (Chm & CEO-
Automotive Electrical Sys)

Subsidiaries:

Compleo Charging Solutions AG (1)
Ezzestrasse 8, 44309, Dortmund, Germany
Tel.: (49) 23153492370
Web Site: https://www.compleo-
charging.com
Emp.: 411
Electric Vehicle Mfr
N.A.I.C.S.: 336320
Jens Stolze (COO)

Subsidiary (Domestic):

Compleo Connect GmbH (2)
Paderborner Str 76, 33189, Schlangen,
Germany
Tel.: (49) 23153492370
Web Site: https://www.wallbe.de
Power Charging Station Equipment Mfr &
Distr
N.A.I.C.S.: 335999

KOSTAL (Changchun) Automotive
Electric Co., Ltd. (1)
No 2877 Dalian Road, Technological Devel-
opment Area, Changchun, 130033, China
Tel.: (86) 43187062177
Electronic & Electromechanical Product Mfr
N.A.I.C.S.: 335999

KOSTAL (Shanghai) Kontakt Systeme
Manufacturing Co., Ltd. (1)
No 3033 Xiangfang Road, Anting Jiading,
Shanghai, 201814, China
Tel.: (86) 2159570077
Electronic & Electromechanical Product Mfr
N.A.I.C.S.: 335999

KOSTAL Bulgaria Automotive
EOOD (1)
Sinitevska Street 4, 4400, Pazardzhik, Bul-
garia
Tel.: (359) 879411727

Web Site: http://www.kostal.bg
Electronic & Mechatronic Component Mfr
N.A.I.C.S.: 334419
Aleksandar Valkov (Controller-Fin)

KOSTAL Bulgaria Ltd. (1)
1 Trakyia St, Smolyan, 4700, Bulgaria
Tel.: (359) 30186711
Electronic Components Distr
N.A.I.C.S.: 423690
Zahari Shopov (Mgr-Maintenance)

KOSTAL CR, spol. s r.o. (1)
Cernin 89, 26751, Beroun, Czech Republic
Tel.: (420) 311 653 911
Electronics Mfr
N.A.I.C.S.: 334419

KOSTAL Electrica S. A. (1)
Notari Jesus Led 10, Pol Ind Can Clapers,
Barcelona, 8181, Spain
Tel.: (34) 93 739 88 00
Electronics Mfr
N.A.I.C.S.: 334419

KOSTAL Eletromecanica Ltda. (1)
Rua General Bertoldo Klinger 277, Vila
Pauliceia, Sao Paulo, Brazil
Tel.: (55) 112139 6100
Electronics Mfr
N.A.I.C.S.: 334419

KOSTAL France (1)
Parc d'Affaires de Guyancourt Quebec 11
rue Jacques Cartier, 78280, Guyancourt,
France
Tel.: (33) 161383939
Electronic Components Distr
N.A.I.C.S.: 423690

KOSTAL India Private Limited (1)
Plot No 11A, SIPCOT Industrial Complex
Ranipet, 632403, Vellore, India
Tel.: (91) 4172304600
Electronic & Electromechanical Product Mfr
N.A.I.C.S.: 335999
Rajesh K. (Mgr-IT)

KOSTAL Industrie Elektrik GmbH (1)
Lange Eck 11, Hagen, 58099, Germany
Tel.: (49) 2331 8040 4811
Electronics Mfr
N.A.I.C.S.: 334419

KOSTAL Ireland GmbH (1)
Baltydaniel, Limerick Road Mal, Cork, Ire-
land
Tel.: (353) 22 440 00
Web Site: http://www.kostal.com
Emp.: 700
Electronics Mfr
N.A.I.C.S.: 334419
Michael Genster (Mng Dir)

KOSTAL Italia s. r. l. (1)
Via Genova 57, 10098, Rivoli, Italy
Tel.: (39) 011 978 2411
Electronics Mfr
N.A.I.C.S.: 334419

KOSTAL Japan Co., Ltd. (1)
6-1-1 Sakae, Tachikawa, Tokyo, 190 0003,
Japan
Tel.: (81) 42 538 0161
Electronics Mfr
N.A.I.C.S.: 334419

KOSTAL Kontakt Systeme
GmbH (1)
Cenkov 8, Pribram, 262 23, Czech Republic
Tel.: (420) 318 493 313
Web Site: http://www.kostal.com
Electronics Mfr
N.A.I.C.S.: 334419
Peter Kasik (Gen Mgr)

KOSTAL Kontakt Systeme
GmbH (1)
Lange Eck 11, Hagen, 58099, Germany
Tel.: (49) 2331 8040
Electronics Mfr
N.A.I.C.S.: 334419

KOSTAL Kontakt Systeme, Inc. (1)
1350 West Hamlin Rd, Rochester Hills, MI
48309
Tel.: (248) 284-7600
Web Site: http://www.kostal.com
Electronics Mfr
N.A.I.C.S.: 334419

Thomas Paul Stack (Dir-Pur & Supply
Chain)

KOSTAL Korea Ltd. (1)
Hanarom-Bldg 5F, 109-2 Yangjae-Dong,
Seoul, Seocho-Gu, Korea (South)
Tel.: (82) 2 2057 5676
Electronics Mfr
N.A.I.C.S.: 334419

KOSTAL Maroc, SARL (1)
AU Zone Franche d Exportation TFZ Ilot no
79 Deuxieme Tranche, 90000, Tangiers,
Morocco
Tel.: (212) 34937050315
Electronic & Electromechanical Product Mfr
N.A.I.C.S.: 335999
Marius Valles Segura (Mgr-Site)

KOSTAL Mexicana, S.A. de C.V. (1)
Acceso II No 36, Fracc Industrial Benito
Juare, 76120, Queretaro, Mexico
Tel.: (52) 442 211 9500
Electronics Mfr
N.A.I.C.S.: 334419

KOSTAL NTTF Automotive India Pvt.
Ltd. (1)
Shed No T12 T13, First East Cross Road,
Vellore, 632006, India
Tel.: (91) 416 30566 00
Electronics Mfr
N.A.I.C.S.: 334419

KOSTAL S.A. (1)
Parc d Affaires de Guyancourt Quebec 11,
rue Jacques Cartier, 78280, Guyancourt,
France
Tel.: (33) 161383939
Electronic & Electromechanical Product Mfr
N.A.I.C.S.: 335999

KOSTAL SofiaSoft Bulgaria OOD (1)
26-30 Bacho Kiro St, Sofia, 1000, Bulgaria
Tel.: (359) 2 9833143
Electronics Mfr
N.A.I.C.S.: 334419
Krassimir Paskalev (Mng Dir)

KOSTAL Solar Electric France
SARL (1)
11 rue Jacques Cartier, 78280, Guyancourt,
France
Tel.: (33) 161384117
Electronic & Electromechanical Product Mfr
N.A.I.C.S.: 335999

KOSTAL Solar Electric GmbH (1)
Hanferstr 6, 79108, Freiburg im Breisgau,
Germany
Tel.: (49) 761 47744 100
Web Site: http://www.kostal-solar-
electric.com
Solar Electric Module Mfr
N.A.I.C.S.: 335131

Subsidiary (Non-US):

KOSTAL SOLAR ELECTRIC HELLAS
E.P.E. (2)
47 Steliou Kazantzidi st 1st building - 2nd
entrance Pilea, PO Box 60080, 55535,
Thessaloniki, Greece
Tel.: (30) 2310477550
Solar Electric Module Distr
N.A.I.C.S.: 423690
Athanasios Katevainis (Acct Mgr)

KOSTAL Solar Electric Iberica
S.L. (2)
Edificio abm Ronda Narciso Monturiol y Es-
tarriol 3 Torre B despachos 2, Parque
Tecnologico de Valencia, 46980, Valencia,
Spain
Tel.: (34) 961824934
Solar Electric Module Distr
N.A.I.C.S.: 423690

KOSTAL Solar Electric Italia Srl (2)
Via Genova 57, 10098, Rivoli, Italy
Tel.: (39) 0119782420
Solar Electric Module Distr
N.A.I.C.S.: 423690
Alberto Bussi (Dir-Sls)

KOSTAL Sweden AB (1)
Lindholmspiren 3B, 417 56, Gothenburg,
Sweden
Tel.: (46) 733882272
Electronic & Electromechanical Product Mfr
N.A.I.C.S.: 335999

LEOPOLD KOSTAL GMBH & CO. KG

Leopold Kostal GmbH & Co, KG—(Continued)
Joakim Gulliksen (Acct Mgr)

KOSTAL UK Ltd. (1)
Goldthorpe Industrial Estate, Commercial Road, Rotherham, S63 9BL, United Kingdom
Tel.: (44) 1709 88 22 00
Electronics Mfr
N.A.I.C.S.: 334419

KOSTAL Ukraina TOV (1)
Chervonoarviytsiv 2, 08400, Kiev, Ukraine
Tel.: (380) 44 6758672
Electronics Mfr
N.A.I.C.S.: 334419

KOSTAL da Amazonia Industria e Comercio de Auto Pecas Ltda. (1)
Avenida Abiurana 449-Bloco 2, Distrito Industrial, 69075-010, Manaus, Amazonas, Brazil
Tel.: (55) 9221294000
Electronic & Electromechanical Product Mfr
N.A.I.C.S.: 335999

KOSTAL da Amazonia Industria e Comurcio de Auto Pecas Ltda (1)
Avenida Abiurana 449 Bloco 2, Distrito Industrial, Manaus, Brazil
Tel.: (55) 92 2129 4000
Electronics Mfr
N.A.I.C.S.: 334419

KOSTAL of America, Inc. (1)
350 Stephenson Hwy, Troy, MI 48083
Tel.: (248) 284-6500
Web Site: http://www.kostal.us
Emp.: 2,530
Electronic Components Mfr
N.A.I.C.S.: 334419
Jon Jackson (Project Mgr)

SOMA GmbH (1)
Gewerbering 9, 58579, Schalksmuhle, Germany
Tel.: (49) 2355 508280
Electronics Mfr
N.A.I.C.S.: 334419

Shanghai KOSTAL - Huayang Automotive Electric Co. Ltd. (1)
No 77 Yuan Gao Road, Shanghai, 201814, China
Tel.: (86) 21 59570077
Emp.: 3,000
Electronics Mfr
N.A.I.C.S.: 334419

LEOVEGAS AB
Luntmakargatan 18, SE-111 37, Stockholm, Sweden
Tel.: (46) 841036766
Web Site:
  http://www.leovegasgroup.com
Year Founded: 2011
LEO—(OMX)
Rev.: $475,898,783
Assets: $306,184,265
Liabilities: $185,594,433
Net Worth: $120,589,831
Earnings: $22,737,179
Emp.: 794
Fiscal Year-end: 12/31/20
Mobile Application Development Services
N.A.I.C.S.: 541511
Gustaf Hagman (CEO-Grp)

Subsidiaries:

Dynamic Web Marketing B.V. (1)
Koopmanslaan 12, 7005 BK, Doetinchem, Netherlands
Tel.: (31) 6700220
Web Site: http://www.dwmarketing.com
Web Development Services
N.A.I.C.S.: 541511

Pixel Digital Ltd. (1)
7 The Plaza Business Centre Bisazza Street, Sliema, SLM 1640, Malta
Tel.: (356) 99394268
Web Site: http://www.pixel.bet
Gambling Services
N.A.I.C.S.: 713290

LEPANTO CONSOLIDATED MINING COMPANY
21st Floor Lepanto Building 8747 Paseo de Roxas, 1226, Makati, 1226, Philippines
Tel.: (63) 28159447
Web Site:
  https://www.lepantomining.com
Year Founded: 1936
LECBF—(OTCEM)
Rev.: $44,934,567
Assets: $283,149,135
Liabilities: $192,904,034
Net Worth: $90,245,102
Earnings: ($1,940,995)
Fiscal Year-end: 12/31/23
Gold Mining
N.A.I.C.S.: 212220
Felipe U. Yap (Chm & CEO)

Subsidiaries:

Diamond Drilling Corporation of the Philippines (1)
1300 Domestic Road, PO Box 7507, Domestic Airport Post Office, Pasay, Philippines
Tel.: (63) 28120451
Diamond Drilling
N.A.I.C.S.: 213114

Far Southeast Gold Resources, Inc. (1)
Domestic Airport Post Office, PO Box 7507, 1300 Domestic Road, Pasay, Philippines (60%)
Tel.: (63) 28120451
Coal Mining
N.A.I.C.S.: 213113

Lepanto Investment & Development Corporation (1)
21st Floor Lepanto Building, 8747 Paseo des Roxas, Makati, 1226, Philippines
Tel.: (63) 28159447
Web Site: http://www.lepantomining.com
Emp.: 20
Insurance & Investment Activities
N.A.I.C.S.: 524298

Subsidiary (Domestic):

Diamant Boart Philippines, Inc. (2)
345 Km 14 West Service Road, South Superhighway Brgy Sun, 1700, Paranaque, Philippines (80%)
Tel.: (63) 8238173
Diamond Tool Mfr
N.A.I.C.S.: 333517

Shipside, Inc. (1)
1300 Domestic Road, PO Box 7507, Domestic Airport Post Office, Pasay, Philippines
Tel.: (63) 28120451
Web Site: http://www.shipsideinc.com
Marine Terminal Facilities
N.A.I.C.S.: 488320

LEPENSKI VIR A.D.
Radnicka bb, 19220, Donji Milanovac, Serbia
Tel.: (381) 30 590 221
Web Site:
  http://www.hotellepenskivir.co.rs
Year Founded: 1978
LPNS—(BEL)
Sales Range: Less than $1 Million
Emp.: 77
Home Management Services
N.A.I.C.S.: 721110
Dragan Ivanic (Exec Dir)

LEPERMISLIBRE SA
29 Avenue Joannes Masset, 69009, Lyon, France
Tel.: (33) 426229177
Web Site: https://www.lepermislibre.fr
Year Founded: 2014
ALLPL—(EUR)
Driving School Services
N.A.I.C.S.: 611692
Lucas Tournel (CEO)

LEPIDICO LTD.
Tel.: (61) 893637800 AU
Web Site: http://www.lepidico.com
Year Founded: 1979
LPD—(ASX)
Rev.: $9,088
Assets: $73,017,402
Liabilities: $14,448,645
Net Worth: $58,568,757
Earnings: ($6,084,575)
Fiscal Year-end: 06/30/22
Mineral Exploration Services
N.A.I.C.S.: 212230
Tom Dukovcic (Gen Mgr-Geology)

LEPU BIOPHARMA CO., LTD.
No 651 Lianheng Road, Minhang District, Shanghai, 201112, China CN
Web Site:
  https://en.lepubiopharma.com
Year Founded: 2018
2157—(HKG)
Rev.: $31,201,817
Assets: $330,126,551
Liabilities: $207,078,810
Net Worth: $123,047,740
Earnings: ($4,195,420)
Emp.: 428
Fiscal Year-end: 12/31/23
Biotechnology Research & Development Services
N.A.I.C.S.: 541714
Yunyi Li (CFO)

Subsidiaries:

Shanghai Miracogen Inc. (1)
No 1238 Zhangjiang Rd Building 3 Suite 4E, Pudong District, Shanghai, 201203, China
Tel.: (86) 2161637960
Web Site: https://www.miracogen.com.cn
Clinical Research Services
N.A.I.C.S.: 541714

LEPU MEDICAL TECHNOLOGY (BEIJING) CO., LTD.
Building 3 37 Chaoqian Road, Changping District, Beijing, 102200, China
Tel.: (86) 1080120666
Web Site:
  http://www.lepumedical.com
Year Founded: 1999
Sales Range: $50-74.9 Million
Emp.: 500
Medical Device Mfr & Sales
N.A.I.C.S.: 339112
Jianke Sun (Chm)

Subsidiaries:

Shaanxi Qinming Medical Co., Ltd (1)
18 Yingda Road, Weibin District, Baoji, 721006, Shaanxi, China
Tel.: (86) 9173314561
Medical Device Mfr & Distr
N.A.I.C.S.: 339112

Shanghai Shape Memory Alloy Co., Ltd (1)
Building 41 No 258 Shenzhuan Highway, Songjiang Hi-Tech Park Caoh, Shanghai, 201612, China
Tel.: (86) 2137013390
Medical Device Mfr & Distr
N.A.I.C.S.: 339112

LEPU SCIENTECH MEDICAL TECHNOLOGY (SHANGHAI) CO., LTD.
Building 41 258 Xinzhuan Road, Songjiang District, Shanghai, 201612, China
Tel.: (86) 2137015633 CN
Web Site:
  https://en.scientechmed.com
Year Founded: 1994

2291—(HKG)
Rev.: $37,945,521
Assets: $277,252,033
Liabilities: $9,973,052
Net Worth: $267,278,982
Earnings: ($3,035,550)
Emp.: 236
Fiscal Year-end: 12/31/22
Information Technology Services
N.A.I.C.S.: 541512
Juan Chen (Chm)

LERADO FINANCIAL GROUP COMPANY LIMITED
FT F G 4/F Golden Sun Centre 59 - 67 Bonham Strand West, 198 Wellington Street, Sheung Wan, China (Hong Kong)
Tel.: (852) 37009600 BM
Web Site: http://www.lerado.com
Year Founded: 1988
Rev.: $27,767,717
Assets: $261,967,409
Liabilities: $125,806,189
Net Worth: $136,161,219
Earnings: ($8,503,909)
Emp.: 210
Fiscal Year-end: 12/31/21
Investment Services
N.A.I.C.S.: 523999
Chun Chieh Chen (Exec Dir)

Subsidiaries:

Lerado China Limited (1)
Rm 1-3 30/F Universal Trade Ctr 3 - 5A Arbuthnot Rd, Central District, Hong Kong, China (Hong Kong)
Tel.: (852) 28689918
Toy Product Distr
N.A.I.C.S.: 423920

Lerado Global (Macao Commercial Offshore) Limited (1)
Ctro Cml Chong Fok, Macau, China (Macau)
Tel.: (853) 2872 6501
Toy Product Distr
N.A.I.C.S.: 423920

Lerado Group (Holding) Company Limited - Zhongshan Factory (1)
No 202 Kui Xing Road, Dong Sheng Town, Zhongshan, 528414, Guang Dong, China
Tel.: (86) 760 23372206
Toy Product Mfr
N.A.I.C.S.: 339930

Shanghai Lerado Daily Article Co., Ltd. (1)
No 665 Fulian Road, Baoshan District, Shanghai, 201906, China
Tel.: (86) 21 36042512
Toy Product Mfr & Distr
N.A.I.C.S.: 339930

LERTHAI GROUP LIMITED
Room 3303 Tower Two Lippo Centre 89 Queensway Admiralty, Hong Kong, China (Hong Kong)
Tel.: (852) 2530 3313 HK
Web Site: http://www.lth.com.hk
Year Founded: 1952
Rev.: $142,058,442
Assets: $3,094,007,618
Liabilities: $2,381,305,280
Net Worth: $712,702,338
Earnings: $17,554,417
Emp.: 169
Fiscal Year-end: 12/31/19
Investment Services
N.A.I.C.S.: 523999
Longfei Yang (Chm & Co-CEO)

Subsidiaries:

LT Design Studio (1)
350 S Grand Ave Ste 3950, Los Angeles, CA 90071
Tel.: (213) 225-6350
Web Site: http://www.ltdesignstudiola.com
Graphic Design Services
N.A.I.C.S.: 541430

AND PRIVATE COMPANIES

Alex Lin *(Co-Founder & Exec Dir)*

LES ACIERS SOFATEC INC.
867 5e Avenue, Sainte-Anne-des-Plaines, J0N 1H0, QC, Canada
Tel.: (450) 478-3365
Web Site: http://www.sofatec.com
Year Founded: 1997
Rev.: $11,910,019
Emp.: 80
Mechanical Welding of Steel & Machinery Mfr
N.A.I.C.S.: 331210
Michel Doucet *(Pres & CEO)*

LES AGENCES DE PAPA S.A
25 Avenue Jean Medecin, 06000, Nice, France
Tel.: (33) 980083232
Web Site:
https://www.lesagencesdepapa.fr
Year Founded: 2019
MLPAP—(EUR)
Real Estate Development Services
N.A.I.C.S.: 531190
Frederic Ibanez *(Chm)*

LES ALIMENTS DA VINCI LTD.
5655 Beaulieu, Montreal, H4E 3E4, QC, Canada
Tel.: (514) 769-1234
Web Site:
http://www.davincifoods.com
Year Founded: 1970
Rev.: $16,258,706
Emp.: 120
Pizzas & Other Food Products Mfr
N.A.I.C.S.: 311999
Frank Mazzaferro *(Chm)*

LES BOISERIES ROUSSEAU INC.
207 route 132, Metis-sur-Mer, G0J 1S0, QC, Canada
Tel.: (418) 936-3918
Web Site:
http://www.boiseriesrousseau.com
Year Founded: 1975
Rev.: $10,744,500
Emp.: 90
Wood Cabinet Mfr
N.A.I.C.S.: 337110
Roger Rousseau *(Pres & Gen Mgr)*

LES BOISES LA FLEUR INC.
219 Rue Francois-Bourgeois, Victoriaville, G6T 2G9, QC, Canada
Tel.: (819) 758-9441
Web Site: http://www.blf-inc.com
Year Founded: 1984
Rev.: $12,740,333
Emp.: 44
Hardwood, Veener & Plywood Mfr
N.A.I.C.S.: 321211

LES BRASSERIES DU CAMEROUN SA
77 rue Prince Bell, BP 4036, Douala, Littoral, Cameroon
Tel.: (237) 33429133
Web Site:
http://www.lesbrasseries.com
Sales Range: $600-649.9 Million
Alcoholic Beverage Mfr & Distr
N.A.I.C.S.: 312120

LES CABLES BEN-MOR INC.
1105 Lemire, Saint-Hyacinthe, J2T 1L8, QC, Canada
Tel.: (450) 778-0022
Web Site: http://www.ben-mor.com
Year Founded: 1992
Rev.: $25,080,000
Emp.: 75
Fittings & Cables Mfr
N.A.I.C.S.: 332913
Benoit Frappier *(Owner)*

LES CASTORS ANGEVINS
16 Rue De Bretagne, 49100, Angers, Maine Et Loire, France
Tel.: (33) 241241380
Web Site: http://www.castors-anjou.fr
Rev.: $15,100,000
Emp.: 20
Foundation Construction Services
N.A.I.C.S.: 531210
Gerard Gautier *(VP)*

LES CHANTIERS DE CHIBOUGAMAU LTEE
521 Chemin Merrill, PO Box 216, Chibougamau, G8P 2K7, QC, Canada
Tel.: (418) 748-6481
Web Site: http://www.chibou.com
Sales Range: $50-74.9 Million
Emp.: 600
Wood Products Mfr
N.A.I.C.S.: 321215

Subsidiaries:

Nordic Engineered Wood (1)
185 Dorval ave suite 304, Montreal, H9S 5J9, QC, Canada
Tel.: (514) 633-9661
Web Site: http://www.nordicwp.com
Wood Products Mfr
N.A.I.C.S.: 321211

LES CHAUSSURES STC INC.
10100 Colbert, Anjou, H1J 2J8, QC, Canada
Tel.: (514) 355-0026
Web Site:
http://www.stcfootwear.com
Year Founded: 1991
Rev.: $13,038,400
Emp.: 126
Footwear Mfr
N.A.I.C.S.: 316210
Alain Croteau *(VP-Sls)*

LES CIMENTS DE BIZERTE
Baie de Sebra, 7018, Bizerte, Tunisia
Tel.: (216) 72510444
Web Site:
http://www.lescimentsdebizerte.ind
Sales Range: $150-199.9 Million
Emp.: 750
Cement Mfr
N.A.I.C.S.: 327310
Abderrahman Touhami *(Pres)*

LES COLLECTIONS SHAN INC.
4390 Autoroute Laval Ouest, Laval, H7T 2P7, QC, Canada
Tel.: (450) 687-7101
Web Site: http://www.shan.ca
Year Founded: 1985
Rev.: $24,300,000
Emp.: 100
Apparels Mfr
N.A.I.C.S.: 315990
Chantal Levesque *(Founder)*

LES CONSTRUCTEURS DU BOIS SA
9 Allee des Chenes, 88000, Epinal, France
Tel.: (33) 329685212
Web Site:
https://www.lesconstructeurs.fr
Year Founded: 2010
MLLCB—(EUR)
Construction Engineering Services
N.A.I.C.S.: 541330
Francois Duchaine *(Chm)*

LES DISTRIBUTIONS MARC BOIVIN INC.
149 rue D'Amsterdam, Saint-Augustin-de-Desmaures, G3A 2V5, QC, Canada

Tel.: (418) 878-3373 QC
Web Site: http://www.dmb-distribution.com
Year Founded: 1981
Emp.: 200
Food Trucking & Warehousing Services
N.A.I.C.S.: 484230
Francois Mascouche *(Dir-Ops-Quebec City)*

LES DOCKS DES PETROLES D'AMBES SA
Avenue des Guerlandes Bassens, 33565, Carbon-Blanc, Cedex, France
Tel.: (33) 556338356 FR
Web Site: https://www.dpasa.fr
Year Founded: 1934
DPAM—(EUR)
Sales Range: $10-24.9 Million
Petroleum Product Transportation Services
N.A.I.C.S.: 486910
Patrick Sylvain Brzokewicz *(Chm & CEO)*

LES EAUX MINERALES D'OULMES SA
ZI Bouskoura, 20180, Casablanca, Morocco
Tel.: (212) 22102210
Web Site: https://www.oulmes.ma
Year Founded: 1934
OUL—(CAS)
Sales Range: Less than $1 Million
Bottled Water Mfr
N.A.I.C.S.: 312112
Miriem Bensalah Chaqroun *(CEO & VP)*

LES ENPHANTS GROUP
3F 17 Po Ai Rd, Taipei, Taiwan
Tel.: (886) 87976699
Web Site: https://www.enphants.com
Year Founded: 1971
2911—(TAI)
Rev.: $100,495,729
Assets: $127,350,137
Liabilities: $97,680,856
Net Worth: $29,669,282
Earnings: ($17,113,280)
Fiscal Year-end: 12/31/23
Children Apparels Mfr
N.A.I.C.S.: 313220
Eric Lin *(Founder)*

Subsidiaries:

PT Les Enphants Indonesia Co., Ltd. (1)
JL Paralon No 10, Cigondewah, Bandung, 40214, West Java, Indonesia
Tel.: (62) 226003049
Infant Clothing Distr
N.A.I.C.S.: 424350

Shanghai Les Enphants Children Articles Co., Ltd. (1)
1855 QiXing Road, Shanghai, 201101, China
Tel.: (86) 2164783678
Baby Clothing Retailer
N.A.I.C.S.: 424350

LES GARAGES SARCELLOIS SA
21 Avenue Paul Valery, 95200, Sarcelles, France
Tel.: (33) 134452777
Sales Range: $10-24.9 Million
Emp.: 46
New & Used Car Dealers
N.A.I.C.S.: 441110
Cyrille Paumier *(Pres)*

LES GRANDS GARAGES DE LANNION

LES LABORATOIRES SERVIER SAS

Lieu Dit Cruguil, 22300, Lannion, Cotes D Armor, France
Tel.: (33) 296482666
Web Site:
http://concessions.peugeot.fr
Rev.: $22,200,000
Emp.: 41
New & Used Car Dealers
N.A.I.C.S.: 441110
Bruno Courtois *(Pres)*

LES HUILES DIESEL A. ROY INC.
3939 boul St Jean Baptiste, Montreal, H1B 5V4, QC, Canada
Tel.: (514) 645-2212
Web Site: http://www.groupearoy.ca
Year Founded: 1935
Sales Range: $10-24.9 Million
Emp.: 25
Petroleum Product Distr
N.A.I.C.S.: 424720
Nathalie Roy *(Co-Owner)*

LES INDUSTRIES MAIBEC INC
660 rue Lenoir, Sainte-Foy, G1X 3W3, QC, Canada
Tel.: (418) 653-5280
Web Site: http://www.maibec.com
Sales Range: $150-199.9 Million
Emp.: 650
Wood Processing Services
N.A.I.C.S.: 321992
Francois Tardif *(Pres & CEO)*

LES INDUSTRIES TOUCH INC.
4025 Lesage, Sherbrooke, J1L 2Z9, QC, Canada
Tel.: (819) 822-4140
Web Site:
http://www.industriestouch.com
Year Founded: 1921
Rev.: $19,000,000
Emp.: 100
Wood & Plastic Products Mfr
N.A.I.C.S.: 321211
Gervais Morier *(Pres)*

LES LABORATOIRES SERVIER SAS
50 Rue Carnot, 92284, Suresnes, Cedex, France
Tel.: (33) 1 55 72 60 00
Web Site: http://www.servier.com
Year Founded: 1954
Sales Range: $5-14.9 Billion
Emp.: 20,000
Pharmaceuticals Mfr
N.A.I.C.S.: 325412
Jacques Servier *(Founder)*

Subsidiaries:

Egis Gyogyszergyar Nyrt (1)
Keresztruti ut 30-38, 1106, Budapest, Hungary
Tel.: (36) 18035555
Web Site: http://www.egis.hu
Pharmaceutical Ingredient Mfr
N.A.I.C.S.: 325412
Peter Mazsar *(Dir-Comml)*

Subsidiary (Non-US):

EGIS Bulgaria EOOD (2)
Industrialna Str 11 Floor 9, 1202, Sofia, Bulgaria
Tel.: (359) 29876040
Web Site: http://www.egis.bg
Pharmaceutical Preparation Mfr
N.A.I.C.S.: 325412

EGIS Ilaclari (Turkey) Ltd. (2)
Ekinciler Cad Kat 2 No 1, Kavacik-Beykoz, 34810, Istanbul, Turkiye
Tel.: (90) 2166802929
Web Site: http://www.egisturkey.com

LES LABORATOIRES SERVIER SAS

Les Laboratoires Servier SAS—(Continued)

Sales Range: $25-49.9 Million
Emp.: 5
Pharmaceutical Products Distr
N.A.I.C.S.: 424210
Sackin Aguday *(Gen Mgr)*

EGIS Polska Dystrybucja Ltd. (2)
Ul Annopol 4a, 03-236, Warsaw, Poland
Tel.: (48) 224179186
Web Site: http://www.egis.pl
Pharmaceutical Products Distr
N.A.I.C.S.: 424210

EGIS Praha spol.s.r.o. (2)
Ovocny trh 1096/8, 110 00, Prague, Czech Republic
Tel.: (420) 227129111
Web Site: http://www.egispraha.cz
Emp.: 70
Pharmaceuticals Product Mfr
N.A.I.C.S.: 325412

EGIS RUS LLC (2)
St Yartsevskaya 19 block B floor 13, 121552, Moscow, Russia
Tel.: (7) 4953633966
Web Site: http://www.egis.ru
Emp.: 100
Pharmaceuticals Mfr
N.A.I.C.S.: 325412
Tamas Endrenyi *(Gen Mgr)*

Plant (Domestic):

Egis Gyogyszergyar Nyrt - EGIS PLC Lacta Plant (2)
Matyas kir u 65, Kormend, 100, Vas, Hungary
Tel.: (36) 94593100
Pharmaceutical Preparation Mfr
N.A.I.C.S.: 325412

Subsidiary (Non-US):

Egis Pharmaceuticals PLC (2)
Str Poland no 68 - 72 3rd Floor Sector 1, Bucharest, 010505, Romania
Tel.: (40) 214120017
Web Site: http://www.egis.ro
Sales Range: $250-299.9 Million
Emp.: 650
Pharmaceutical Products Mfr & Distr
N.A.I.C.S.: 325412

Subsidiary (Domestic):

Hungaropharma Trading Co (2)
Kiraly U 12, 1061, Budapest, Hungary
Tel.: (36) 1 327 6700
Web Site: http://www.hungaropharma.hu
Pharmaceuticals Distr
N.A.I.C.S.: 424210

Medimpex Office Block Ltd. (2)
Vorosmarty ter 4, 1051, Budapest, Hungary
Tel.: (36) 12668252
Web Site: http://www.ihaz.hu
Pharmaceutical Preparations Mfr & Sales
N.A.I.C.S.: 325412

Medimpex Trading Close Co. Ltd (2)
Lehel u 11, 1134, Budapest, Hungary
Tel.: (36) 12881400
Web Site: http://www.medimpex.hu
Sales Range: $50-74.9 Million
Emp.: 60
Pharmaceuticals Import & Distr
N.A.I.C.S.: 424210

Subsidiary (Non-US):

Serdix (Russia) Ltd. (2)
Sofjino Bldg 1-1, Moscow, 142150, Russia
Tel.: (7) 495225 8010
Web Site: http://www.egis.hu
Pharmaceutical Mfr & Distr
N.A.I.C.S.: 325412
Federick Casecail *(Gen Mgr)*

Servier Laboratories Ltd. (1)
Rowley Wexham Springs Framewood Road, Wexham, Slough, SL3 6PJ, United Kingdom
Tel.: (44) 1753 662744
Web Site: http://www.servier.co.uk
Pharmaceuticals Mfr
N.A.I.C.S.: 325412

Symphogen A/S (1)
Pederstrupvej 93, DK-2750, Ballerup, Denmark
Tel.: (45) 4526 5050
Web Site: http://www.symphogen.com
Rev.: $26,152,353
Assets: $95,539,718
Liabilities: $196,237,068
Net Worth: ($100,697,350)
Earnings: ($68,568,471)
Emp.: 129
Fiscal Year-end: 12/31/2018
Medical Laboratories & Research Services
N.A.I.C.S.: 621511
Karin Garre *(Gen Mgr)*

Subsidiary (US):

Receptor Biologix, Inc. (2)
3350 W Byshore Rd, Palo Alto, CA 94303
Tel.: (650) 266-4600
Research & Development in Biotechnology
N.A.I.C.S.: 541714

Symphogen Inc. (2)
50 Division St Ste 503, Somerville, NJ 08876
Tel.: (908) 378-9630
Pharmaceuticals Product Mfr
N.A.I.C.S.: 325412

LES MOTOCYCLES ARDOIN SAINT AMND &CIE SA
8 rue des Petites Ecuries, 75010, Paris, France
Tel.: (33) 145233835
Year Founded: 1972
MLARD—(EUR)
Sales Range: Less than $1 Million
Motor Vehicle Distr
N.A.I.C.S.: 423110
Jean-Pierre Ardoin Saint Amand *(Chm & CEO)*

LES MOULINS DE LA CONCORDE LTTE
Cargo Peninsula Quay D, Port Louis, Mauritius
Tel.: (230) 2179100
Web Site: https://www.lmlc.mu
Year Founded: 1989
LMLC—(MAU)
Rev.: $74,087,317
Assets: $73,786,668
Liabilities: $23,247,615
Net Worth: $50,539,053
Earnings: $4,094,646
Fiscal Year-end: 06/30/23
Flour Product Distr
N.A.I.C.S.: 424490

LES PETROLES R.L. INC.
460 rue Racine Est, Chicoutimi, G7H 5C8, QC, Canada
Tel.: (418) 543-0775
Web Site: http://www.petrolesrl.com
Year Founded: 1970
Rev.: $20,200,000
Emp.: 40
Petroleum Product Distr
N.A.I.C.S.: 424720
Eric Larouche *(CEO)*

LES PLASTIQUES TPI INC.
271 rue Saint Jacques South, Coaticook, J1A 2P3, QC, Canada
Tel.: (819) 849-2786
Rev.: $10,070,767
Emp.: 150
Plastics Product Mfr
N.A.I.C.S.: 326199
Angy Potvin *(CEO)*

LES PRODUITS PLASTIQUE QUALIPAK INC.
2590 rue Debray, Laval, H7S 2J8, QC, Canada
Tel.: (450) 978-9258
Rev.: $12,607,018
Emp.: 140
Containers & Packaging Products Mfr
N.A.I.C.S.: 423840

Michel St-Onge *(Pres)*

LES SERVICES MENAGERS ROY LTEE
9000 rue de l Innovation, Anjou, H1J 2X9, QC, Canada
Tel.: (514) 354-6666
Rev.: $13,444,526
Emp.: 1,000
Carpet Cleaning Services
N.A.I.C.S.: 561740

LES THERMES DE SAUJON SA
Thermes de Saujon, BP 30, 17600, Saujon, France
Tel.: (33) 546235015
Web Site: http://www.thermes.net
Health Care Srvices
N.A.I.C.S.: 621610
Olivier Dubois *(Chm & CEO)*

LES TOQUES BLANCHES DU MONDE SARL
5 place Edgar Quinet, 69006, Lyon, France
Tel.: (33) 481919660
Web Site: http://www.lestoquesblanches.com
Food Products Distr
N.A.I.C.S.: 445110
Patrick Marche *(Chm & CEO)*

LES TROIS CHENES SA
Parc dActivite La Terre Ronde, 69770, Villecheneve, France
Tel.: (33) 474702020
Web Site: http://www.3chenes.fr
Cosmetic Product Mfr & Distr
N.A.I.C.S.: 325620
Hubert Jaricot *(Chm & CEO)*

LES VERANDAS 4 SAISONS
Rue du Parc Industriel 15, 6900, Marche-en-Famenne, Belgium
Tel.: (32) 84314077
Web Site: http://www.lesveras4saisons.com
MLV4S—(EUR)
Sales Range: $1-9.9 Million
Emp.: 20
Wood & Aluminum Porches Mfr
N.A.I.C.S.: 337122
Patrick Maniquet *(Chm, Dir-Legal & Mng Dir)*

LES VIGNERONS D UNI-MEDOC
14 Route De Soulac, 33340, Gaillon, Gironde, France
Tel.: (33) 556410312
Web Site: http://www.unimedoc.com
Sales Range: $100-124.9 Million
Emp.: 18
Winery
N.A.I.C.S.: 312130
Pedro Rojo *(Pres)*

LES VIGNERONS DE CALVISSONS
Rte De La Cave Cooperative, 30420, Calvisson, Gard, France
Tel.: (33) 466012021
Rev.: $11,800,000
Emp.: 16
Winery
N.A.I.C.S.: 312130
Joel Bruguiere *(Mng Partner)*

LESAKA TECHNOLOGIES, INC.
4th Floor President Place Cnr Jan Smuts Avenue Bolton Road, Rosebank, Johannesburg, 2196, South Africa
Tel.: (27) 113432000   ZA

INTERNATIONAL PUBLIC

Web Site: https://lesakatech.com
Year Founded: 1997
LSAK—(NASDAQ)
Rev.: $564,222,000
Assets: $558,450,000
Liabilities: $382,593,000
Net Worth: $175,857,000
Earnings: ($17,440,000)
Emp.: 2,531
Fiscal Year-end: 06/30/24
Electronic Payment Systems
N.A.I.C.S.: 522320
Kuben Pillay *(Chm)*

Subsidiaries:

Cash Paymaster Services (North West) (Pty) Limited (1)
C P S Bldg 71 Osborn Tce, Eshowe, Natal, 3815, South Africa
Tel.: (27) 354744886
Sales Range: $50-74.9 Million
Emp.: 21
Electronic Payment & Transaction Processing Services
N.A.I.C.S.: 522320

Cash Paymaster Services (Proprietary) Limited (1)
4th Floor President Place Hood Avenue, Johannesburg, 2196, Gauteng, South Africa
Tel.: (27) 113432000
Web Site: http://www.net1.co.za
Sales Range: $75-99.9 Million
Emp.: 300
Payroll Processing Services
N.A.I.C.S.: 541214

Subsidiary (Domestic):

Cash Paymaster Services (Kwa-Zulu Natal) (Pty) Ltd (2)
4 Simpson Place, Pinetown, 3610, South Africa
Tel.: (27) 113432125
Mobile Payment Services
N.A.I.C.S.: 522320

Cash Paymaster Services (Northern Cape) (Pty) Limited (2)
8 South Circular, Kimberley, Northern Cape, South Africa
Tel.: (27) 53 832 1540
Sales Range: $25-49.9 Million
Emp.: 50
Mobile Payment Services
N.A.I.C.S.: 522320

Cash Paymaster Services (Northern) (Pty) Limited (2)
1 D Industrial Street, Polokwane, 0700, South Africa
Tel.: (27) 15 297 0119
Mobile Payment Services
N.A.I.C.S.: 522320

DNI Retail (Pty) Ltd. (1)
25 Commerce Crescent Kramerville Sandton, Johannesburg, South Africa
Mobile Accessory Distr
N.A.I.C.S.: 449210

EasyPay (Proprietary) Limited (1)
Ground Floor EasyPay House Belmont Office Park 14 Belmont Road, Rondebosch, Cape Town, 7700, South Africa
Tel.: (27) 21 680 0100
Web Site: http://www.easypay.co.za
Electronic Fund Transfer Services
N.A.I.C.S.: 522320

Friedland 035 Investments (Pty) Ltd (1)
President Place Cnr Jan Smuts & Bolton Avenue, Rosebank, South Africa
Tel.: (27) 113432000
Financial Transaction System Development Services
N.A.I.C.S.: 541511

KSNET, Inc. (1)
Tel.: (82) 234205800
Web Site: http://www.ksnet.co.kr
Credit Card Processing Services
N.A.I.C.S.: 522320

M4JAM (Pty) Ltd. (1)
Workshop 17 146 Campground Rd 3rd floor, Snakepit Building Newlands, Cape

AND PRIVATE COMPANIES

Town, 7780, South Africa
Tel.: (27) 1003800
Mobile Application Development Services
N.A.I.C.S.: 513210

Masterpayment A.G. (1)
Petersbrunner Str 1B, 82319, Starnberg, Germany
Tel.: (49) 8151187590
Web Site: http://www.masterpayment.com
Financial Transaction Services
N.A.I.C.S.: 522320
Philippus Stefanus Meyer *(Mng Dir)*

MediKredit Integrated Healthcare Solutions (Proprietary) Limited (1)
132 Jan Smuts Ave, Parkwood, Johannesburg, 2193, South Africa
Tel.: (27) 11 770 6000
Web Site: http://www.medikredit.co.za
Sales Range: $25-49.9 Million
Emp.: 164
Healthcare Software Development Services
N.A.I.C.S.: 541511
Krish Pather *(Dir-Performance Health)*

Subsidiary (Domestic):

Performance Health (Pty) Ltd (2)
132 Jan Smuts Avenue Parkwood, Randburg, 2193, South Africa
Tel.: (27) 117706000
Medical Instrument Distr
N.A.I.C.S.: 423450

Subsidiary (US):

Xeohealth Corporation (2)
241 E 4th St Ste 202, Frederick, MD 21701
Tel.: (301) 685-6517
Web Site: http://www.xeohealth.com
Emp.: 3
Information Technology Healthcare Services
N.A.I.C.S.: 541512
Lisa S. Miller *(CEO)*

Moneyline Financial Services (Pty) Ltd (1)
Shop No 4 - 32 Tanner Road, Empangeni, 3880, South Africa
Tel.: (27) 357870152
Electronic Products Mfr
N.A.I.C.S.: 335999

Net 1 Universal Technologies (Austria) GmbH (1)
Gersthoferstrasse 131, 1180, Vienna, Austria
Tel.: (43) 1 47601 0
Web Site: http://www.at.net1.com
Mobile Phone Payment Services
N.A.I.C.S.: 522320
Serge Christian Pierre Belamant *(Chm & CEO)*

Subsidiary (Non-US):

Net1 Universal Technologies India Pvt. Ltd (2)
105 Shanti Kunj Main Ram Mandir Lane Vasant Kunj, New Delhi, 110 070, India
Tel.: (91) 11 64530936
Financial Transaction System Development Services
N.A.I.C.S.: 541511
Dhruv Chopra *(Mng Dir & Head-India)*

Net1 Applied Technologies Austria GmbH (1)
Gersthoferstrasse 131, 1180, Vienna, Austria
Tel.: (43) 1 476 01 0
Financial Transaction System Development Services
N.A.I.C.S.: 541511

Net1 Applied Technologies South Africa (Pty) Ltd (1)
4th Floor President's Place Cnr Jan Smuts Ave & Bolton Road Rosebank, Johannesburg, 2196, South Africa
Tel.: (27) 11 343 2000
Web Site: http://www.net1.co.za
Emp.: 500
Electronic Payment Services
N.A.I.C.S.: 522320

Subsidiary (Domestic):

PBel (Pty) Limited (2)
Bryanston Ridge Office Park Building 3 1st Floor, Corner Bruton And Main Road, Bryanston, 2196, South Africa
Tel.: (27) 11 463 7 233
Web Site: http://www.pbel.co.za
Sales Range: $25-49.9 Million
Emp.: 80
Mobile Software Development Services
N.A.I.C.S.: 541511
Philip Belamant *(Mng Dir)*

Prism Payment Technologies (Pty) Limited (2)
3th Floor President Place Jan Smuts & Bolton, 2196, Johannesburg, Gauteng, South Africa
Tel.: (27) 113432000
Electronic Payment Services
N.A.I.C.S.: 522320

Net1 Applied Technologies South Africa (Pty) Ltd (1)
3rd Floor President Place Cnr Jan Smuts Ave & Bolton Rd, Rosebank, 2121, South Africa
Tel.: (27) 113432000
Electronic Products Mfr
N.A.I.C.S.: 335999

Net1 FIHRST Holdings (Pty) Ltd (1)
5th Floor North Wing President Place Cnr Bolton and Jan Smuts Avenue, Rosebank, Johannesburg, 2196, South Africa
Tel.: (27) 115056801
Web Site: http://www.fihrst.com
Information Management Services
N.A.I.C.S.: 541512

Net1 Mobile Solutions (Pty) Ltd. (1)
Druton Rd, 2021, Johannesburg, Gauteng, South Africa
Tel.: (27) 114637233
Information Technology Services
N.A.I.C.S.: 541511
Eyasu Habtemariam *(Engr-Software)*

The Starterpack Company (Pty) Ltd. (1)
4 Monza Close Kyalami Park Kyalami, Johannesburg, South Africa
Tel.: (27) 114661813
Web Site: http://tspc.co.za
Multi Network Sim Distr
N.A.I.C.S.: 424990

Transact24 Limited (1)
Unit 2801 Wu Chung House 213 Queens Road East Wan Chai, Hong Kong, China (Hong Kong)
Tel.: (852) 28510145
Web Site: http://www.transact24.com
Financial Services
N.A.I.C.S.: 522320

Zazoo Limited (1)
111 Buckingham Palace Road, London, SW1W 0SR, United Kingdom
Tel.: (44) 2073406300
Web Site: http://www.zazooltd.com
Software Developing Services
N.A.I.C.S.: 541511

LESHA INDUSTRIES LTD
7th floor Ashoka Chambers Mithakali Six Roads, Ahmedabad, 380006, India
Tel.: (91) 7926463227
Web Site: https://www.lesha.in
533602—(BOM)
Rev.: $989,251
Assets: $3,079,903
Liabilities: $614,239
Net Worth: $2,465,664
Earnings: $54,697
Emp.: 2
Fiscal Year-end: 03/31/22
Steel Products Mfr & Distr
N.A.I.C.S.: 331210
Ashok Chinubhai Shah *(Chm & Mng Dir)*

LESHAN ELECTRIC POWER CO., LTD.
No 46 Jiading North Road, Shizhong District, Leshan, 614000, Sichuan, China
Tel.: (86) 8332445800
Web Site: http://www.lsep.com.cn
Year Founded: 1988
600644—(SHG)
Rev.: $403,297,863
Assets: $570,933,385
Liabilities: $286,561,539
Net Worth: $284,371,846
Earnings: $9,909,615
Fiscal Year-end: 12/31/22
Electric Power Generation & Distribution Services
N.A.I.C.S.: 221111
Liu Jiang *(Chm)*

LESHAN GIANTSTAR FARMING & HUSBANDRY CORPORATION
Xinhua Village, Zhugen Town Wutongqiao District, Leshan, 614800, Sichuan, China
Tel.: (86) 2862050265
Web Site: http://www.zhenjinggufen.com
Year Founded: 2013
603477—(SHG)
Rev.: $557,098,537
Assets: $1,018,452,488
Liabilities: $497,521,496
Net Worth: $520,930,992
Earnings: $22,195,780
Fiscal Year-end: 12/31/22
Leather Product Mfr & Distr
N.A.I.C.S.: 316990
Duan Lifeng *(Chm)*

LESICO LTD
Sderot Yerushalayim 152, Holon, Israel
Tel.: (972) 747500600
Web Site: https://www.lesico.com
Year Founded: 1969
LSCO—(TAE)
Rev.: $223,915,178
Assets: $169,498,547
Liabilities: $110,991,019
Net Worth: $58,507,528
Earnings: $2,664,180
Fiscal Year-end: 12/31/23
Commercial & Institutional Building Construction
N.A.I.C.S.: 236220
Shlomo Leshman *(Founder)*

Subsidiaries:

Poldmir Ltd. (1)
The Magic Carpet 8, Gedera, Israel
Tel.: (972) 88597553
Web Site: https://www.poldmir.co.il
Building Construction Services
N.A.I.C.S.: 236115

LESK AO
Pobedy Ave 87a, Lipetsk, 398024, Russia
Tel.: (7) 8002200009
Web Site: https://www.lesk.ru
Year Founded: 2005
LPSB—(MOEX)
Sales Range: Less than $1 Million
Electric Power Distribution Services
N.A.I.C.S.: 221122
Vorobtsov Sergey Viktorovich *(Gen Dir)*

LESKOVACKI SAJAM AD
Mlinska BB, Leskovac, Serbia
Tel.: (381) 16 243 001
Web Site: http://www.lesajam.co.rs
Year Founded: 1955
Sales Range: Less than $1 Million
Meeting & Trade Show Organizing Services
N.A.I.C.S.: 561920

LESNINA D.D.

LETECH CORPORATION

Cesta na Bokalce 40, 1000, Ljubljana, Slovenia
Tel.: (386) 12412100
Web Site: http://www.lesnina.si
Year Founded: 1949
Sales Range: $250-299.9 Million
Emp.: 1,150
Furniture Retailer
N.A.I.C.S.: 449110
Bojan Papic *(Chm-Mgmt Bd)*

LESOTHO TELECOMMUNICATIONS CORPORATION
PO Box 1037, Maseru, Lesotho
Tel.: (266) 22211000
Web Site: http://www.telecom.co.ls
Sales Range: $100-124.9 Million
Emp.: 350
Telecommunication Servicesb
N.A.I.C.S.: 517111
Wonder Nyakudya *(CFO)*

LESSON NINE GMBH
Max-Beer-Str 2, 10119, Berlin, Germany
Tel.: (49) 30779079400
Web Site: http://www.babbel.com
Online Language Learning Services
N.A.I.C.S.: 923110
Hermione McKee *(CFO)*

Subsidiaries:

Babbel (1)
Bergmannstr 5, 10961, Berlin, Germany
Tel.: (49) 30 43655 9387
Web Site: http://www.babbel.com
Online Language Learning Services
N.A.I.C.S.: 923110
Markus Witte *(CEO)*

LET GROUP HOLDINGS LIMITED
Unit 1705 17th Floor West Tower Shun Tak Centre 168-200 Connaught Road, Connaught Road Central, Central, China (Hong Kong)
Tel.: (852) 25981180
Web Site: https://www.letgroupholdings.com
Year Founded: 2002
1383—(HKG)
Rev.: $87,552,444
Assets: $589,427,755
Liabilities: $833,467,061
Net Worth: ($244,039,306)
Earnings: ($215,976,823)
Emp.: 152
Fiscal Year-end: 12/31/19
Property Development & Leasing Services
N.A.I.C.S.: 531390
Cheok Wa Chau *(Chm)*

LETCHWORTH INVESTMENTS LTD.
Dorchester House Station Road, Letchworth, SG6 3AW, United Kingdom
Tel.: (44) 8703515802
Holding Company
N.A.I.C.S.: 551112
David Kleeman *(Founder)*

Subsidiaries:

Fayrewood Ltd. (1)
Dorchester House, Station Way, Letchworth, SG6 3AW, United Kingdom
Tel.: (44) 8703515802
Sales Range: $250-299.9 Million
Emp.: 258
Software Programming & Data Processing Services
N.A.I.C.S.: 541511

LETECH CORPORATION
Nihon Seimei Umeda Bldg 10F 3-3

LETECH CORPORATION

LeTech Corporation—(Continued)

Doyamacho, Kita-ku, Osaka, 530-0027, Japan
Tel.: (81) 668092551
Web Site: http://www.legaterrace.com
Year Founded: 2000
3497—(TKS)
Real Estate Development Services
N.A.I.C.S.: 531311
Tetsuji Hirano *(Chm, Pres & CEO)*

LETHO RESOURCES CORP.

300-1455 Bellevue Avenue, Vancouver, V7T 1C3, BC, Canada
Tel.: (604) 341-1531   BC
Web Site:
   https://www.lethoresources.com
Year Founded: 2005
LET.H—(TSXV)
Rev.: $507
Assets: $611,954
Liabilities: $1,855,545
Net Worth: ($1,243,591)
Earnings: ($898,893)
Fiscal Year-end: 12/31/21
Mineral Exploration Services
N.A.I.C.S.: 213114
Brian Patrick Morrison *(CFO)*

LETHUILLIER SA

6 Rue De La Republique, Gonneville La Mallet, 76280, Le Havre, Seine Maritime, France
Tel.: (33) 232792670
Web Site: http://www.lethuillier.com
Sales Range: $25-49.9 Million
Emp.: 37
Farm Supplies Mfr & Distr
N.A.I.C.S.: 424910
Patrick Crevon *(Mgr-DP)*

LETONG CHEMICAL CO., LTD.

Letong Industrial Park Guantang Village, Jinding Town, Zhuhai, 519085, Guangdong, China
Tel.: (86) 7563383338
Web Site: https://www.letongink.com
Year Founded: 1996
002319—(SSE)
Rev.: $56,645,784
Assets: $89,026,236
Liabilities: $78,689,988
Net Worth: $10,336,248
Earnings: ($4,412,772)
Fiscal Year-end: 12/31/22
Ink Product Mfr
N.A.I.C.S.: 325910
Zhou Yubin *(Chm & Pres)*

Subsidiaries:

Shanghai Letong Packaging Materials Co., Ltd.   (1)
No 271 Jiugan Road Sijin Town Songjiang District, Shanghai, 201601, China
Tel.: (86) 2157626335
Printing Ink Distr
N.A.I.C.S.: 423840

Zhuhai Letong New Materials & Technology Co., Ltd.   (1)
Letong Industrial Yard Fushan Industrial Zone Qianwu Town, Doumen District, Zhuhai, 519175, China
Tel.: (86) 7565653388
Emp.: 57
Printing Ink Mfr & Distr
N.A.I.C.S.: 325910

LETS HOLDINGS GROUP CO., LTD.

No 62 Hubin South Road, Siming District, Xiamen, 361004, Fujian, China
Tel.: (86) 5922273752
Web Site: https://www.lets.com
Year Founded: 2004
002398—(SSE)
Rev.: $593,036,075
Assets: $834,505,760
Liabilities: $331,630,706
Net Worth: $502,875,055
Earnings: $57,063,065
Fiscal Year-end: 12/31/20
Construction Engineering Services
N.A.I.C.S.: 541330
Yong Tai Cai *(Chm & Gen Mgr)*

LETSHEGO FINANCIAL SERVICES (PTY) LTD.

1st Floor Letshego Place, 22 Khama Crescent, Gaborone, Botswana
Tel.: (267) 364 3000
Web Site: http://www.letshego.co.bw
Year Founded: 1998
Sales Range: $100-124.9 Million
Emp.: 127
Bank Holding Company
N.A.I.C.S.: 551111
Enos Banda *(Chm)*

LETTERONE HOLDINGS S.A.

1 - 3 Boulevard de la Foire, 1528, Luxembourg, Luxembourg
Tel.: (352) 26 3877 1   LU
Web Site: http://www.letterone.com
Year Founded: 2013
Rev.: $29,000,000,000
Investment Holding Company
N.A.I.C.S.: 551112
Mikhail Fridman *(Chm)*

Subsidiaries:

DEA Norge AS   (1)
Karenslyst alle 53, PO Box 243, Skoyen, 0213, Oslo, Norway
Tel.: (47) 23132000
Web Site: http://www.dea-norge.com
Emp.: 100
Oil Exploration Services
N.A.I.C.S.: 213112
Geir Diesen *(Head-Production)*

Distribuidora Internacional de Alimentacion S.A.   (1)
C/ Jacinto Benavente 2 A, Las Rozas, 28232, Madrid, Spain   (70.84%)
Tel.: (34) 913985400
Web Site: https://www.diacorporate.com
Rev.: $6,344,942,047
Assets: $2,900,248,372
Liabilities: $2,975,452,037
Net Worth: ($75,203,665)
Earnings: ($73,426,427)
Emp.: 22,825
Fiscal Year-end: 12/31/2023
Grocery Distr
N.A.I.C.S.: 445110
Stephan DuCharme *(Chm)*

L1 Energy Limited   (1)
35 Park Lane, London, W1K 1RB, United Kingdom
Tel.: (44) 20 3053 4030
Web Site: http://www.letterone.lu
Energy Industry Investment Holding Company
N.A.I.C.S.: 551112
Dmitry Avdeev *(Mng Dir)*

LetterOne Investment Holdings S.A.   (1)
1-3 Boulevard de la Foire, L31528, Luxembourg, Luxembourg
Tel.: (352) 26 38 77 1
Web Site: http://www.letterone.lu
Investment Holding Company
N.A.I.C.S.: 551112

Subsidiary (Domestic):

LetterOne Treasury Services S.A.   (2)
3 boulevard de la Foire, 1528, Luxembourg, Luxembourg
Tel.: (352) 26 3877 1
Web Site: http://www.letterone.lu
Rev.: $14,000,000,000
Investment Management Service
N.A.I.C.S.: 523940
Jonathan Muir *(Chm)*

Subsidiary (Non-US):

LetterOne Treasury Services LLP   (3)
35 Park Lane, London, W1K 1RB, United Kingdom
Tel.: (44) 20 3053 4030
Web Site: http://www.letterone.com
Emp.: 40
Investment Management Service
N.A.I.C.S.: 523940
Yves Leysen *(Chief Investment Officer)*

LetterOne Telecom Limited   (1)
6 Chesterfield Gardens, London, W1J 5BQ, United Kingdom
Tel.: (44) 20 7046 6150
Web Site: http://www.letterone.lu
Rev.: $13,500,000,000
Telecommunications Industry Investment Holding Company
N.A.I.C.S.: 551112
Alexey Reznikovich *(CEO & Mng Partner)*

LETUS CAPITAL S.A.

Al Jerozolimskie 85/21, 02-001, Warsaw, Poland
Tel.: (48) 780612815
Web Site: https://www.letuscap.com
Year Founded: 1990
LET—(WAR)
Investment Management Service
N.A.I.C.S.: 523999
Tomasz Andrzejczak *(Pres)*

LEU & GYGAX AG

Fellstrasse 1, 5413, Birmensdorf, Switzerland
Tel.: (41) 562014545   CH
Web Site: http://www.leugygax.ch
Sales Range: $10-24.9 Million
Emp.: 25
Chemical Products Sales
N.A.I.C.S.: 424690
Werner Ambauen *(Chm)*

LEV INS AD

Blvd Cherni Vrah 51 D, 1407, Sofia, Bulgaria
Tel.: (359) 29521225
Web Site: http://www.lev-ins.com
Year Founded: 1996
Sales Range: $100-124.9 Million
Insurance Services
N.A.I.C.S.: 524298
Stefan Sofianski *(CEO)*

LEV INVEST SPV

Tsarigradsko shose blvd 111-117 Evrotur business center flr 2 office 6, Mladost, 1784, Sofia, Bulgaria
Tel.: (359) 29628266
Web Site: https://levinvest.com
Year Founded: 2007
LEVI—(BUL)
Sales Range: Less than $1 Million
Financial Services
N.A.I.C.S.: 561499
Lozana Ljubenova Slavchova *(Exec Dir)*

LEVEL BIOTECHNOLOGY, INC.

No 80 Ln 169 Kangning St, Xizhi Dist, New Taipei City, 221, Taiwan
Tel.: (886) 226959935
Web Site: https://www.level.com.tw
Year Founded: 1989
3118—(TPE)
Rev.: $18,541,506
Assets: $25,405,059
Liabilities: $8,446,018
Net Worth: $16,959,041
Earnings: $1,828,034
Fiscal Year-end: 12/31/22
Healtcare Services
N.A.I.C.S.: 423450

Subsidiaries:

Ablaze Export Pvt. Ltd.   (1)
Block A 10 Rameshwari Ajwa Road Near Sardar Estate, Vadodara, 390019, Gujarat, India
Tel.: (91) 9377552542
Web Site: https://www.ablazeexport.com
Glass Reactor Mfr
N.A.I.C.S.: 334519
Ashita Mittal *(Head-Mktg)*

Aspect Imaging Ltd.   (1)
27 Shaked Street, PO Box 926, Industrial Area Hevel Modiin, Shoham, 60850, Israel
Tel.: (972) 37165606
Web Site: http://www.aspectimaging.com
Medicinal Product Mfr
N.A.I.C.S.: 339112

Aviva System Biology Corporation   (1)
7700 Ronson Rd Ste 100, San Diego, CA 92111
Tel.: (858) 552-6979
Web Site: http://www.avivasysbio.com
Biological Product Mfr
N.A.I.C.S.: 325414
Peter Jiang *(CEO)*

Biosensing Instrument Inc.   (1)
1007 E Warner Rd Ste 102, Tempe, AZ 85284
Tel.: (480) 491-2777
Web Site: https://www.biosensingusa.com
Biosensing Instrument Mfr
N.A.I.C.S.: 334513
Tianwei Jing *(Pres)*

Ibl-America, Inc.   (1)
8201 Central Ave NE Ste P, Minneapolis, MN 55432
Tel.: (763) 780-2955
Web Site: https://www.ibl-america.com
Biological Product Mfr
N.A.I.C.S.: 325414

Mill Creek Life Sciences, LLC   (1)
221 1st Ave SW Ste 209, Rochester, MN 55902
Tel.: (507) 287-6257
Web Site: https://www.millcreekls.com
Medical Devices
N.A.I.C.S.: 622110
Bill Mirsch *(CEO)*

Omega Bio-Tek, Inc.   (1)
400 Pinnacle Way Ste 450, Norcross, GA 30071
Tel.: (770) 931-8400
Web Site: https://www.omegabiotek.com
Rev.: $1,800,000
Emp.: 20
Biological Product Mfr
N.A.I.C.S.: 325414
Qi Guo *(Pres)*

Progenika Biopharma, S.A.   (1)
Ibaizabal Bidea Edificio 504 Parque Tecnologico de Bizkaia, 48160, Derio, Bizkaia, Spain
Tel.: (34) 944064525
Web Site: http://www.progenika.com
Medical Devices
N.A.I.C.S.: 622110
Antonio Martinez *(CEO)*

Wilson Wolf Corporation   (1)
2100 Old Hwy 8, Saint Paul, MN 55112
Tel.: (651) 628-9259
Web Site: https://www.wilsonwolf.com
Biological Product Mfr
N.A.I.C.S.: 325414
John Wilson *(CEO)*

LEVELJUMP HEALTHCARE CORP.

207-52 Scarsdale Rd, Toronto, M3B 2R7, ON, Canada
Tel.: (416) 900-0957
Web Site:
   https://eveljumphealthcare.com
JMPHF—(OTCQB)
Rev.: $4,267,995
Assets: $1,539,057
Liabilities: $1,283,173
Net Worth: $255,884
Earnings: ($9,045,536)
Fiscal Year-end: 12/31/20
Business Consulting Services
N.A.I.C.S.: 522299
Mitch Geisler *(Chm & CEO)*

AND PRIVATE COMPANIES

LEXIA SOLUTIONS GROUP LTD

LEVER STYLE CORPORATION
Room 76 Flat A 7/F Wing Tai Centre 12 Hing Yip Street, Kwun Tong, Kowloon, China (Hong Kong)
Tel.: (852) 27938000 Ky
Web Site: http://www.leverstyle.com
Year Founded: 1956
1346—(HKG)
Rev.: $217,209,081
Assets: $91,030,768
Liabilities: $43,271,833
Net Worth: $47,758,935
Earnings: $14,513,339
Emp.: 338
Fiscal Year-end: 12/31/22
Apparel Product Mfr & Distr
N.A.I.C.S.: 315990
Stanley Chi Yan Szeto *(Chm & CEO)*

LEVERE HOLDINGS CORP.
Boundary Hall Cricket Square, PO Box 1093, Grand Cayman, Georgetown, KY1-1102, Cayman Islands
Tel.: (345) 9498066 Ky
Web Site:
  http://www.levereholdings.com
Year Founded: 2021
LVRAU—(NASDAQ)
Rev.: $13,681,777
Assets: $275,771,052
Liabilities: $286,436,077
Net Worth: ($10,665,025)
Earnings: $12,515,341
Emp.: 3
Fiscal Year-end: 12/31/22
Investment Services
N.A.I.C.S.: 523999
Martin Varsavsky *(Chm & CEO)*

LEVIATHAN GOLD LTD.
Suite 488 1090 West Georgia Street, Vancouver, V6E 3V7, BC, Canada
Tel.: (604) 229-9445 BC
Web Site:
  https://www.leviathangold.com
Year Founded: 2020
LVXFF—(OTCQB)
Rev.: $15,354
Assets: $4,444,501
Liabilities: $92,947
Net Worth: $4,351,554
Earnings: ($2,725,481)
Fiscal Year-end: 06/30/22
Gold Exploration Services
N.A.I.C.S.: 212220
Luke Norman *(CEO)*

LEVIKOM EESTI OU
Parnu mnt 139C, Tallinn, 11317, Estonia
Tel.: (372) 6 840678
Web Site: http://www.levikom.ee
Telecommunication Servicesb
N.A.I.C.S.: 517112

Subsidiaries:

Uptime Systems OU (1)
Parnu mnt 158, Tallinn, 11317, Estonia
Tel.: (372) 603 1700
IT Infrastructure Services
N.A.I.C.S.: 541511
Eero Tohver *(CEO)*

LEVINSTEIN PROPERTIES LTD.
23 Menachem Begin Road, Tel Aviv, 66184, Israel
Tel.: (972) 37100200
Web Site: https://www.levinstein.co.il
LVPR—(TAE)
Rev.: $22,519,132
Assets: $609,072,238
Liabilities: $247,455,998
Net Worth: $361,616,240
Earnings: $12,779,942
Fiscal Year-end: 12/31/23

Offices of Real Estate Agents & Brokers
N.A.I.C.S.: 531210
Eran Amram *(Deputy CEO)*

LEWAG HOLDING AG
Industriestrasse 21 D, 37688, Beverungen, Germany
Tel.: (49) 5273905200
Web Site: https://www.lewag.de
Year Founded: 1873
KGR—(DEU)
Rev.: $146,417,927
Assets: $132,431,836
Liabilities: $87,945,689
Net Worth: $44,486,146
Earnings: $7,307,650
Emp.: 775
Fiscal Year-end: 12/31/23
Holding Company
N.A.I.C.S.: 551112

LEWEKO RESOURCES BERHAD
No 21B Laluan Tasek Timur 5 Pusat Perdagangan Tasek Indra, Ipoh Perak Darul Ridzuan, 31400, Ipoh, Perak, Malaysia
Tel.: (60) 55486663 MY
Web Site:
  https://www.snfcapital.com.my
Year Founded: 2002
Sales Range: $1-9.9 Million
Timber Product Mfr
N.A.I.C.S.: 321215
Chee Kheong Chan *(Sec)*

LEWINSKY-OFER LTD.
Azrieli Building 31 Round Tower, Tel Aviv, Israel
Tel.: (972) 35001500
Web Site: http://www.levinski-ofer.co.il
Year Founded: 1977
LEOF—(TAE)
Rev.: $3,213,980
Assets: $58,556,706
Liabilities: $50,087,304
Net Worth: $8,469,402
Earnings: ($3,590,827)
Fiscal Year-end: 12/31/23
New Multifamily Housing Construction (except For-Sale Builders)
N.A.I.C.S.: 236116
Yossi Lewinsky *(Co-Owner)*

LEWIS COMMUNICATIONS LIMITED
Millbank Tower, Millbank, London, SW1P 4RS, United Kingdom
Tel.: (44) 2078022626
Web Site: http://www.lewispr.co.uk
Sales Range: $25-49.9 Million
Emp.: 320
Public Relations
N.A.I.C.S.: 541820
Sarah Aitchison *(Dir-Global Ops)*

Subsidiaries:

Lewis PR - Dusseldorf (1)
Prinzenallee 5, 40549, Dusseldorf, Germany
Tel.: (49) 211 53 883 212
Web Site: http://www.lewispr.com
Emp.: 5
Public Relations
N.A.I.C.S.: 541820

Lewis PR - Eindhoven (1)
Meerenakkerplein 16, Eindhoven, 5652DJ, Netherlands
Tel.: (31) 40 235 46 00
Web Site: http://www.lewispr.com
Emp.: 32
Public Relations
N.A.I.C.S.: 541820
Yvonne van Bokhoven *(VP)*

Lewis PR - Madrid (1)

Cronos 63 3rd floor, Madrid, 28020, Spain
Tel.: (34) 91 770 15 16
Web Site: http://www.lewispr.com
Emp.: 20
Gen Mgr
Jorge Lopez *(VP-Southern Europe)*

Lewis PR - Manchester (1)
Imperial Court Exchange Quay, Manchester, M5 3EB, United Kingdom
Tel.: (44) 161 601 7740
Web Site: http://www.lewispr.com
Public Relations
N.A.I.C.S.: 541820

Lewis PR - Milan (1)
Via Lecco 12, Milan, 20124, Italy
Tel.: (39) 02 36531375
Emp.: 7
Public Relations
N.A.I.C.S.: 541820
Maria-Teresa Trifiletti *(Gen Mgr)*

Lewis PR - Mumbai (1)
Omprakash Arcade Unit No 401 Opposite Dr Ambedkar, Garden Chembur, Mumbai, 400 071, India
Tel.: (91) 22 2521 1020
Web Site: http://www.lewispr.com
Emp.: 6
Public Relations
N.A.I.C.S.: 541820

Lewis PR - Munich (1)
Baierbrunner Str 15, Munich, 81379, Germany
Tel.: (49) 89 17 30 19 0
Web Site: http://www.lewispr.com
Emp.: 30
Public Relations
N.A.I.C.S.: 541820
Rafael Rahn *(VP-Central-Eastern Europe)*

Lewis PR - Paris (1)
1 Place d'Estienne d'Orves, Paris, 75009, France
Tel.: (33) 1 55 31 98 00
Web Site: http://www.lewispr.fr
Emp.: 20
Public Relations
N.A.I.C.S.: 541820
Marie-Laure Laville *(Gen Mgr)*

Lewis PR - Singapore (1)
3 Pickering St #01-58/59 Nankin Row, 048660, Singapore, Singapore
Tel.: (65) 6534 7250
Web Site: http://www.lewispr.com
Public Relations
N.A.I.C.S.: 541820

Lewis PR - Stockholm (1)
Nybrogatan 34, 114 39, Stockholm, Sweden
Tel.: (46) 8 517 00 841
Web Site: http://www.lewispr.com
Emp.: 6
Public Relations
N.A.I.C.S.: 541820

Lewis PR - Sydney (1)
Suite 102 Level 1, 15 Blue St N, Sydney, 2060, Australia
Tel.: (61) 2 9409 3100
Web Site: http://www.lewispr.com
Emp.: 7
Public Relations
N.A.I.C.S.: 541820
Scott Pettet *(Gen Mgr)*

Lewis PR - Wanchai (1)
Rm 1611 16/F Harcourt House, 39 Gloucester Rd, Wanchai, China (Hong Kong)
Tel.: (852) 2151 4711
Web Site: http://www.lewispr.com
Public Relations
N.A.I.C.S.: 541820

Lewis PR Inc. (1)
575 Market St Ste 2550, San Francisco, CA 94105
Tel.: (415) 992-4400
Web Site: http://www.lewispr.com
Emp.: 25
Public Relations
N.A.I.C.S.: 541820
Cassie Katz *(Mgr-Bus Dev-Washington)*

Branch (Domestic):

Lewis PR - Boston (2)

535 Boylston St Ste 603, Boston, MA 02116
Tel.: (617) 226-8840
Web Site: http://www.lewispr.com
Rev.: $8,000,000
Emp.: 25
Public Relations
N.A.I.C.S.: 541820
Claire Rowberry *(Sr VP)*

Lewis PR - San Diego (2)
3131 Camino del Rio N Ste 200, San Diego, CA 92108
Tel.: (619) 516-2559
Web Site: http://www.lewispr.com
Public Relations
N.A.I.C.S.: 541810

Subsidiary (Domestic):

Piston Agency (2)
530 B St 19th Fl, San Diego, CA 92101
Tel.: (619) 308-5266
Web Site: http://www.pistonagency.com
Advetising Agency
N.A.I.C.S.: 541810
John Hartman *(Pres)*

LEWIS GROUP LIMITED
Universal House 53A Victoria Road, Woodstock, 7925, Cape Town, 7925, South Africa
Tel.: (27) 214604400 ZA
Web Site:
  https://www.lewisgroup.co.za
Year Founded: 1934
LEW—(JSE)
Rev.: $432,186,642
Assets: $397,839,005
Liabilities: $149,484,043
Net Worth: $248,354,962
Earnings: $23,046,293
Emp.: 10,000
Fiscal Year-end: 03/31/24
Furniture & Appliances Retailer
N.A.I.C.S.: 449110
Johan Enslin *(CEO)*

LEX NIMBLE SOLUTIONS LTD.
10th Floor Module A1 Quadrant 3 Cyber Towers Hitech City, Hyderabad, 500 081, India
Tel.: (91) 4023122330
Web Site: https://www.lexnimble.in
541196—(BOM)
Rev.: $604,280
Assets: $1,821,234
Liabilities: $83,928
Net Worth: $1,737,306
Earnings: $97,116
Emp.: 20
Fiscal Year-end: 03/31/23
Software Development Services
N.A.I.C.S.: 541511

LEXARIA BIOSCIENCE CORP.
100-740 McCurdy Road, Kelowna, V1X 2P7, BC, Canada
Tel.: (250) 765-6424 NV
Web Site:
  https://www.lexariabioscience.com
LEXX—(NASDAQ)
Rev.: $464,278
Assets: $8,867,789
Liabilities: $1,208,738
Net Worth: $7,659,051
Earnings: ($5,808,654)
Emp.: 5
Fiscal Year-end: 08/31/24
Food Sciences Services
N.A.I.C.S.: 325412
Christopher A. Bunka *(CEO)*

LEXIA SOLUTIONS GROUP LTD
Unit C Astra Park Parkside Lane, Leeds, W Yorks, United Kingdom
Tel.: (44) 113 270 0775
Web Site:
  http://www.lexiasolutionsgroup.co.uk
Year Founded: 2004

LEXIA SOLUTIONS GROUP LTD

Lexia Solutions Group Ltd—(Continued)
Holding Company
N.A.I.C.S.: 551112
Alexander De Graft-Hayford (Sec)

Subsidiaries:

Rhodar Ltd. (1)
Unit C Astra Park Parkside Lane, Leeds,
LS11 5SZ, W Yorks, United Kingdom
Tel.: (44) 0800834669
Construction Services
N.A.I.C.S.: 333120
Jason Davy (Dir)

LEXIBOOK S.A

6 Avenue des Andes Batiment 11,
91940, Les Ulis, France
Tel.: (33) 323036921
Web Site: https://www.lexibook.com
ALLEX—(EUR)
Rev.: $63,885,960
Assets: $37,469,756
Liabilities: $19,127,196
Net Worth: $18,342,560
Earnings: $5,387,387
Emp.: 69
Fiscal Year-end: 03/31/24
Leisure Electronic Products Mfr &
Distr
N.A.I.C.S.: 334419
Aymeric Le Cottier (Co-CEO)

LEXIN RESOURCES LTD.

1207 11th Avenue SW Suite 300,
Calgary, T3C 0M5, AB, Canada
Tel.: (403) 237-9400
Web Site: http://www.lexin.ca
Petroleum & Natural Gas Production
N.A.I.C.S.: 211120
Rob Jennings (COO)

LEXINFINTECH HOLDINGS LTD.

27/F CES Tower No 3099 Keyuan
South Road, Nanshan District, Shenzhen, 518057, China
Tel.: (86) 75536378888
Web Site: https://www.lexin.com
Year Founded: 2013
LX—(NASDAQ)
Rev.: $1,511,540,903
Assets: $3,488,699,407
Liabilities: $2,163,624,266
Net Worth: $1,325,075,141
Earnings: $125,594,204
Emp.: 3,872
Fiscal Year-end: 12/31/22
Online Financial Information Services
N.A.I.C.S.: 523940
Jay Wenjie Xiao (Founder, Chm & CEO)

LEXINGTON BIOSCIENCES, INC.

1055 West Hastings Street Suite
1900, Vancouver, V6E 2E9, BC, Canada
Tel.: (604) 343-4547
Medical Instrument Mfr
N.A.I.C.S.: 339112
Donald A. McInnes (CEO)

LEXINGTON COMPANY AB

St Eriksgatan 46, 11249, Stockholm, Sweden
Tel.: (46) 8 54 55 58 00
Web Site:
http://www.lexingtoncompany.com
LEX—(OMX)
Rev.: $32,635,646
Assets: $16,613,867
Liabilities: $7,689,819
Net Worth: $8,924,048
Earnings: $594,530
Emp.: 128
Fiscal Year-end: 12/31/20

Apparel & Home Textiles Mfr
N.A.I.C.S.: 315990
Kristina Lindhe (Founder)

LEXINGTON GOLD LTD.

Clarendon House, 2 Church Street,
Hamilton, HM 11, Bermuda
Tel.: (441) 7769325254   BM
Web Site:
https://www.lexingtongold.co.uk
Year Founded: 2003
LEX—(AIM)
Assets: $5,054,000
Liabilities: $95,000
Net Worth: $4,959,000
Earnings: ($924,000)
Fiscal Year-end: 12/31/22
Gemstone Mining
N.A.I.C.S.: 212390
Mike Allardice (Sec)

Subsidiaries:

TanzaniteOne Limited (1)
Clarendon House, 2 Church Street, Hamilton, HM 11, Bermuda (100%)
Tel.: (441) 295 1422
Web Site: http://www.tanzaniteone.com
Tanzanite Mining
N.A.I.C.S.: 212390
Mervyn Dettmer (Gen Mgr-Sls-Tanzania)

Subsidiary (Non-US):

Tanzanite One Mining Limited (2)
Plot 1087 Masaki, Dar es Salaam, Tanzania
Tel.: (255) 767 600 916
Web Site: http://www.tanzaniteone.com
Gemstone Mining
N.A.I.C.S.: 212390

LEXIS PUBLIC RELATIONS

8 Bolsover St, London, W1W 6AB, United Kingdom
Tel.: (44) 20 7908 6488
Emp.: 100
Public Relations
N.A.I.C.S.: 541820
Stephen Woodford (Chm)

LEXSTON LIFE SCIENCES CORP.

780789 West Pender St, Vancouver,
V6C 1H2, BC, Canada
Tel.: (604) 928-8913   BC
Web Site: https://www.lexston.ca
Year Founded: 2020
LEXTF—(OTCIQ)
Rev.: $269,314
Assets: $710,788
Liabilities: $59,000
Net Worth: $651,788
Earnings: ($1,730,880)
Fiscal Year-end: 05/31/22
Biotechnology Research & Development Services
N.A.I.C.S.: 541714
Jatinder Manhas (CFO)

LEXUS GRANITO (INDIA) LTD.

8 A National Highway Lakhadhipur
Road Morbi, 363 642, Rajkot, 363
642, India
Tel.: (91) 7567500158
Web Site:
https://www.lexusgranito.com
Year Founded: 2007
LEXUS—(NSE)
Rev.: $13,884,624
Assets: $19,666,950
Liabilities: $16,899,570
Net Worth: $2,767,380
Earnings: ($6,642,388)
Emp.: 107
Fiscal Year-end: 03/31/21
Ceramic & Tile Mfr
N.A.I.C.S.: 327120
Nilesh Babubhai Detroja (Mng Dir)

LEY CHOON GROUP HOLDINGS LIMITED

No 3 Sungei Kadut Drive, Singapore,
729556, Singapore
Tel.: (65) 67570900
Web Site: https://www.leychoon.com
Year Founded: 1987
Q0X—(CAT)
Rev.: $91,827,343
Assets: $74,002,223
Liabilities: $37,530,196
Net Worth: $36,472,027
Earnings: $6,921,082
Emp.: 941
Fiscal Year-end: 03/31/23
Underground Utilities Infrastructure
Services
N.A.I.C.S.: 237990
Choo Huat Toh (Co-Founder, Chm & CEO)

Subsidiaries:

Ultro Resources Pte Ltd (1)
1 Changi Business Park Avenue 1 05-01
Ultro Building, Singapore, 486058, Singapore
Tel.: (65) 6545 7811
Sales Range: $50-74.9 Million
Emp.: 8
Coal Distr
N.A.I.C.S.: 423520

LEYARD OPTOELECTRONIC CO., LTD.

9 West Zhenghongqi Street North of
Summer Palace, Haidian District, Beijing, 100091, China
Tel.: (86) 1062888888
Web Site: https://en.leyard.com
Year Founded: 1995
300296—(CHIN)
Rev.: $1,144,769,652
Assets: $2,090,932,272
Liabilities: $944,091,720
Net Worth: $1,146,840,552
Earnings: $39,508,560
Emp.: 5,000
Fiscal Year-end: 12/31/22
LED Products Mfr
N.A.I.C.S.: 334413
Li Jun (Chm & Pres)

Subsidiaries:

Leyard (Europe) Co., Ltd. (1)
Hundsschleestrasse 23, 72766, Reutlingen, Germany
Tel.: (49) 712 143 3030
Web Site: https://www.leyardeurope.eu
Light Emitting Diode Display Product Whslr
N.A.I.C.S.: 423690
Laurin Schmid (Sls Mgr)

Leyard (Japan) Co., Ltd. (1)
6F Nishiikebukuro Founded Shinkansen
Building, Toshima-ku, Tokyo, 171-0021, Japan
Tel.: (81) 36 915 2768
Web Site: https://leyard.jp
Light Emitting Diode Display Product Whslr
N.A.I.C.S.: 423690

Planar Systems, Inc. (1)
1195 NW Compton Dr, Beaverton, OR 97006
Tel.: (503) 748-1100
Web Site: http://www.planar.com
Sales Range: $150-199.9 Million
Emp.: 100
Flat-Panel Display Technologies Mfr & Distr
N.A.I.C.S.: 334419
Adam Schmidt (Exec VP-Sls, Mktg & Pro Svcs)

Subsidiary (Domestic):

NaturalPoint, Inc. (2)
3658 SW Descgutes St, Corvallis, OR 97333
Tel.: (541) 753-6645
Web Site: http://www.naturalpoint.com
Audio & Video Equipment Mfr
N.A.I.C.S.: 334310

Runco International, LLC (2)
1195 NW Compton Dr, Beaverton, OR 97006
Tel.: (503) 748-5790
Web Site: http://www.runco.com
Home Theater Products Mfr
N.A.I.C.S.: 334310
Zach Zhang (CEO)

Shenzhen Leyard Opto-Electronic Co., Ltd. (1)
Building 4 Jia'an Da Industrial Zone Dalang, Longhua Town, Shenzhen, 518109, China
Tel.: (86) 755 29671180
Web Site: http://www.leyard.com
Emp.: 650
Digital Display Mfr
N.A.I.C.S.: 339950

LEYSEN JEWELRY INC.

No 19 Huashen Avenue, Ningnan
New District Yuhuatai District, Nanjing, 210012, Jiangsu, China
Tel.: (86) 2552486808
Web Site:
https://www.leysen1855.com
Year Founded: 1999
603900—(SHG)
Rev.: $128,109,286
Assets: $357,123,757
Liabilities: $48,201,903
Net Worth: $308,921,853
Earnings: ($5,578,415)
Fiscal Year-end: 12/31/22
Jewelry Mfr & Distr
N.A.I.C.S.: 339910
Ma Jun (Chm)

LEZIER TRANSPORTS

ZA la Croisette, rue Champollion,
62300, Lens, France
Tel.: (33) 321134000
Web Site: http://www.lezier.fr
Sales Range: $10-24.9 Million
Emp.: 195
Trucking Service
N.A.I.C.S.: 484121

LF CORP.

870 Sinsa-dong Eonju-ro, Gangnam-gu, Seoul, Korea (South)
Tel.: (82) 215445114
Web Site: https://www.lfcorp.com
Year Founded: 1974
093050—(KRS)
Rev.: $1,509,870,460
Assets: $1,981,958,969
Liabilities: $711,156,471
Net Worth: $1,270,802,498
Earnings: $135,991,020
Emp.: 1,225
Fiscal Year-end: 12/31/22
Apparel Product Mfr
N.A.I.C.S.: 315250
Bon Keul Koo (Pres & CEO)

LFB S.A.

3 avenue des Tropiques, PO Box
40305, 91958, Courtaboeuf, Cedex, France
Tel.: (33) 169827010
Web Site: http://www.groupe-lfb.com
Year Founded: 1994
Sales Range: $550-599.9 Million
Emp.: 2,327
Biopharmaceutical Research & Development Services
N.A.I.C.S.: 325412
Sandrine Charrieres (Dir-Grp Comm)

Subsidiaries:

Europlasma GmbH (1)
Alserbachstrasse 18, 1090, Vienna, Austria
Tel.: (43) 1 319 53 63
Web Site: http://www.europlasma.at
Healtcare Services
N.A.I.C.S.: 621991

Europlasma sro (1)

AND PRIVATE COMPANIES

Roztylska 2321/19, 14800, Prague, Czech Republic
Tel.: (420) 272075555
Healtcare Services
N.A.I.C.S.: 621991

LFB Biomanufacturing SASU (1)
Impasse des Chenes Rouges, 30319, Ales, Cedex, France
Tel.: (33) 4 66 56 40 80
Web Site:
http://www.lfbbiomanufacturing.com
Pharmaceuticals Product Mfr
N.A.I.C.S.: 325412
Roland Beliard *(Pres)*

LFB Hemoderivados e Biotecnologia Ltda. (1)
Av das americas 500 Loja 101 bloco 11, Shopping downtown - Barra da tijuca, 22640-100, Rio de Janeiro, Brazil
Tel.: (55) 21 2492 4055
Pharmaceutical Products Distr
N.A.I.C.S.: 424210

LFB Lille (1)
59 rue de Trevise, BP 2006, 59011, Lille, Cedex, France
Tel.: (33) 3 20 49 44 44
Pharmaceutical Products Distr
N.A.I.C.S.: 424210

LFB USA Inc. (1)
175 Crossing Blvd, Framingham, MA 01702
Tel.: (508) 370-5100
Web Site: http://www.lfb-usa.com
Pharmaceutical Product Mfr & Distr
N.A.I.C.S.: 325412
William Gavin *(COO)*

rEVO Biologics, Inc. (1)
175 Crossing Blvd 4th Fl, Framingham, MA 01702-8868
Tel.: (508) 620-9700
Web Site: http://www.revobiologics.com
Sales Range: $25-49.9 Million
Biopharmaceutical Developer, Mfr & Marketer
N.A.I.C.S.: 325412
Robert Greif *(VP-Comml Ops)*

LFE CORPORATION BERHAD
D11G Block D1 Dana 1 Commercial Centre Jalan PJU 1A46, Ara Damansara, 50100, Kuala Lumpur, Malaysia
Tel.: (60) 326948899 MY
Web Site: https://www.lfe.com.my
Year Founded: 1967
LFECORP—(KLS)
Rev.: $15,497,850
Assets: $13,231,573
Liabilities: $62,201
Net Worth: $13,169,371
Earnings: $408,673
Fiscal Year-end: 12/31/22
Construction Engineering Services
N.A.I.C.S.: 541330
Kiam Woon Liew *(Mng Dir)*

Subsidiaries:

LFE Engineering Sdn. Bhd. (1)
Lot 43117 Off Jalan Balakong, 43300, Seri Kembangan, Selangor, Malaysia
Tel.: (60) 389958888
Engineeering Services
N.A.I.C.S.: 541330

Subsidiary (Domestic):

LFE Engineering (JB) Sdn. Bhd. (2)
No 43 Jalan Molek 2/30, 81100, Johor Bahru, Malaysia
Tel.: (60) 73539817
Engineeering Services
N.A.I.C.S.: 541330

LFG INVESTMENT HOLDINGS LIMITED
Room 1601 16/F China Building 29 Queens Road, Central, China (Hong Kong)
Tel.: (852) 2 128 9400 Ky
Web Site: http://www.legogroup.hk
Year Founded: 2015

3938—(HKG)
Rev.: $13,949,445
Assets: $44,351,837
Liabilities: $21,954,331
Net Worth: $22,397,506
Earnings: $2,060,327
Emp.: 53
Fiscal Year-end: 03/31/21
Holding Company
N.A.I.C.S.: 551112
Gary Ho Cheung Mui *(Chm & CEO)*

Subsidiaries:

Lego Asset Management Limited (1)
Room 301 3/F China Building 29 Queen's Road, Central, China (Hong Kong)
Tel.: (852) 21289400
Asset Management Services
N.A.I.C.S.: 523940
Chris Choy *(CIO)*

Lego Corporate Finance Limited (1)
Room 1601 16/F China Building 29 Queen's Road, Central, China (Hong Kong)
Tel.: (852) 21289400
Financial Advisory Services
N.A.I.C.S.: 523940
Constance Kong *(Asst Mgr)*

Lego Securities Limited (1)
Room 301 3/F China Building 29 Queen's Road, Central, China (Hong Kong)
Tel.: (852) 21289435
Web Site: https://www.legosecurities.hk
Underwriting & Security Margin Financing Services
N.A.I.C.S.: 523150
Lilian Lau *(VP)*

LFM PROPERTIES CORPORATION
3rd Floor Liberty Building 835 A Arnaiz Avenue, Makati, Philippines
Tel.: (63) 288937790
Web Site:
https://lfmproperty.wordpress.com
Year Founded: 1995
LPC—(PHI)
Rev.: $3,517,858
Assets: $38,114,738
Liabilities: $29,939,657
Net Worth: $8,175,081
Earnings: $932,150
Fiscal Year-end: 12/31/23
Real Estate Manangement Services
N.A.I.C.S.: 523999
John Carlos Uy *(Chm)*

LFNT RESOURCES CORP.
750 West Pender Street Suite 401, Vancouver, V6C 2T7, BC, Canada
Tel.: (604) 428-7050
Web Site: https://www.lfnt.ca
Year Founded: 2022
LFNT—(CNSX)
Mineral Exploration Services
N.A.I.C.S.: 212390
Shayne Taker *(CEO)*

LFOUNDR S.R.L.
Via Antonio Pacinotti 7, 67051, Avezzano, AQ, Italy
Tel.: (39) 08634231 IT
Web Site: http://www.lfoundry.com
Emp.: 1,400
Analog, Mixed-Signal & Specialized Technologies Mfr
N.A.I.C.S.: 334413
Gunther Ernst *(CEO)*

LFOUNDRY S.R.L. ZWEIGNIEDERLASSUNG LANDSHUT
Ludwig-Erhard-Strasse 6a, 84034, Landshut, Germany
Tel.: (49) 871 660665 0 De
Web Site: http://www.lfoundry.com
Emp.: 1,500
Analog, Mixed-Signal & Specialized Technology Mfr

N.A.I.C.S.: 334419
Gunther Ernst *(CEO)*

LG & DE LIMITED
Liongate Enterprise Park 80 Morden Road, Mitcham, CR4 4PH, Surrey, United Kingdom
Tel.: (44) 2086876000 UK
Web Site:
http://www.linguaphonegroup.com
Year Founded: 1901
Sales Range: $75-99.9 Million
Emp.: 30
Language Training Product & Services
N.A.I.C.S.: 611630
Clive A. Sawkins *(CEO)*

Subsidiaries:

Linguaphone Distributors Sdn. Bhd (1)
Ste 3 12 3rd Fl, Pudu Plz Jalan Landak, 55100, Kuala Lumpur, Malaysia (100%)
Tel.: (60) 321440612
Web Site: http://www.linguaphone.com.my
Sales Range: $25-49.9 Million
Language Training Products Distr
N.A.I.C.S.: 611710

Linguaphone Education Pte Ltd (1)
176 Orchard Rd, No 06 06 07 Ctr Pt, Singapore, 238843, Singapore (100%)
Tel.: (65) 62353098
Sales Range: $10-24.9 Million
Provider of Language Courses
N.A.I.C.S.: 611630

Linguaphone France S.A.R.L. (1)
La Grande Arche Paroi Nord, 92044, Paris, France
Tel.: (33) 1 47 78 45 80
Web Site: http://www.linguaphone.fr
Language Training Services
N.A.I.C.S.: 611630

Linguaphone Ireland Ltd. (1)
Suite 18 Information Age Park Gort Road, Co Clare, Ennis, Ireland
Tel.: (353) 65 6833066
Web Site: http://www.linguaphone.co.uk
Language Training Services
N.A.I.C.S.: 611630

Linguaphone Japan Limited (1)
Zenken Corporation 1-4-11 Zenken Plaza, Nishi-Shinjuku, Shinjuku, Japan
Tel.: (81) 3 3342 8202
Language Training Services
N.A.I.C.S.: 611630

LG CHEM LTD.
LG Twin Towers 128 Yeoui-daero, Yeongdeungpo-gu, Seoul, Korea (South)
Tel.: (82) 237731114 KS
Web Site: https://www.lgchem.com
Year Founded: 1947
051910—(KRS)
Rev.: $39,242
Assets: $47,044
Liabilities: $25,691
Net Worth: $21,353
Earnings: $3,376
Emp.: 13,682
Fiscal Year-end: 12/31/21
Chemical Products Mfr
N.A.I.C.S.: 325998
Young Soo Kwon *(Chm)*

Subsidiaries:

AVEO Pharmaceuticals, Inc. (1)
30 Winter St, Boston, MA 02108
Tel.: (857) 400-0101
Web Site: http://www.aveooncology.com
Rev.: $42,295,000
Assets: $105,341,000
Liabilities: $59,471,000
Net Worth: $45,870,000
Earnings: ($53,342,000)
Emp.: 115
Fiscal Year-end: 12/31/2021
Biopharmaceutical Developer & Mfr
N.A.I.C.S.: 325412

Michael P. Bailey *(Pres & CEO)*

FarmHannong Co., Ltd. (1)
5-6F FKI Tower 24 Yeoui-daero, Yeongdeungpo-gu, Seoul, 07320, Korea (South)
Tel.: (82) 23 159 5500
Web Site: https://www.farmhannong.com
Emp.: 2,000
Crop Protection Products, Fertilizers, Agrochemicals & Petrochemicals Mfr
N.A.I.C.S.: 325320
Jinsoo Park *(Co-CEO)*

Subsidiary (Domestic):

FarmBiotec Co., Ltd. (2)
Dongbu Finance Center, 891-10 Daechi-Dong Gangnam-gu, Seoul, Korea (South)
Tel.: (82) 234841500
Fertilizers, Seeds, Veterinary Pharmaceutials, Environment-Friendly Agricultural Materials Mfr & Distr
N.A.I.C.S.: 325311

FarmCeres Co., Ltd. (2)
39-23 Dongan-ro 1113 beon-gil yenomueup, Nonsan, Chungcheongnam-do, Korea (South)
Tel.: (82) 41 740 8020
Biological Research & Development Services
N.A.I.C.S.: 541380

Subsidiary (Non-US):

FarmHannong (Thailand) Ltd. (2)
44 Moo 5 San Klang, Sub-district San Pa Tong District, Chiang Mai, 50120, Thailand
Tel.: (66) 53111744
Agriculture Pesticide Distr
N.A.I.C.S.: 424910

Subsidiary (US):

Farmhannong America, Inc. (2)
111 Sylvan Ave S Bldg L3, Englewood Cliffs, NJ 07632
Tel.: (201) 408-9176
Agriculture Pesticide Distr
N.A.I.C.S.: 424910

Hyundai Petrochemical Co., Ltd. (1)
679 Daejuk-ri Daesan-eub, Seosan-si, Ch'onan, 756 712, Choongnam, Korea (South) (50%)
Tel.: (82) 23986600
Web Site: http://www.seetec.kr
Sales Range: $1-4.9 Billion
Emp.: 1,400
N.A.I.C.S.: 325998

LG Chem (Chongqing) Engineering Plastics Co., Ltd. (1)
No 24 Huanan Rd Eco and Tech Development Zone Yanjia, Changshou, Chongqing, China
Plastics Product Mfr
N.A.I.C.S.: 326199

LG Chem (Guangzhou) Information & Electronics Materials Co., Ltd. (1)
No 50 dongxiang road, Huangpu district, Guangzhou, Guangdong, China
Tel.: (86) 2028219500
Electronic Products Mfr
N.A.I.C.S.: 334419

LG Chem (Huizhou) Petrochemical Co., Ltd. (1)
No 57, Daya Bay District, Huizhou, 516082, Guangdong, China
Tel.: (86) 7523689000
Petrochemical Products Mfr
N.A.I.C.S.: 325110

LG Chem (Nanjing) Information & Electronics Materials Co., Ltd. (1)
No 17 Hengyi Road, Nanjing Economical and Technological Development Zone, Nanjing, 210038, China
Tel.: (86) 2585603000
Automotive Battery Mfr & Distr
N.A.I.C.S.: 335910

LG Chem (Taiwan), Ltd. (1)
5F No 58 Ruihu St, NeiHu Dist, Taipei, 11494, Taiwan
Tel.: (886) 287519977

LG CHEM LTD.

LG Chem Ltd.—(Continued)
Sales Range: $25-49.9 Million
Emp.: 20
Battery Mfr
N.A.I.C.S.: 335910

LG Chem (Tianjin) Engineering Plastics Co., Ltd. (1)
Tel.: (86) 2282113388
Chemical Product Mfr & Distr
N.A.I.C.S.: 325998

LG Chem Australia Pty. Ltd. (1)
Unit 12 35 Dunlop Rd, Mulgrave, 3170, VIC, Australia
Tel.: (61) 1300178064
Electronic Products Mfr
N.A.I.C.S.: 334419

LG Chem Brasil, Ltd. (1)
Tel.: (55) 1121597111
Emp.: 10
Chemical Products Mfr
N.A.I.C.S.: 325998

LG Chem China Investment Co., Ltd. (1)
22nd floor West Tower LG Twin Towers B-12 Jianguomenwai Avenue, Chaoyang District, Beijing, 100022, China
Tel.: (86) 1051208209
Investment Management Service
N.A.I.C.S.: 523999

LG Chem Display Materials (Beijing) Co., Ltd. (1)
No 21 Tongji South Road, Beijing Economic and Technological Development Area, Beijing, 100176, China
Tel.: (86) 1067856865
Polarizer Mfr
N.A.I.C.S.: 334516

LG Chem Europe GmbH (1)
Adolph-Prior-Strasse 16, 65936, Frankfurt am Main, Germany
Tel.: (49) 1736859324
Chemical Petroleum & Allied Product Whslr
N.A.I.C.S.: 424690

LG Chem Hai Phong Vietnam Co., Ltd. (1)
Lot E Trang Due Industry Park Dinh Vu-Cat Hai Economic Zone, Hong Phong Ward An Duong District, Haiphong, Vietnam
Tel.: (84) 2253240890
Electronic Products Mfr
N.A.I.C.S.: 334419

LG Chem Japan Co., Ltd. (1)
2-1-3 Kyobashi Trust Tower 12F Kyobashi, Chuo-ku, Tokyo, 104-0031, Japan
Tel.: (81) 352994530
Rubber Mfr
N.A.I.C.S.: 326291

LG Chem Malaysia Sdn. Bhd. (1)
Tel.: (60) 320221687
Petrochemical Products Mfr
N.A.I.C.S.: 325110
Audrey Yee *(Asst Mgr-Admin)*

LG Chem Mexico S.A. de C.V. (1)
Paseo de las palmas 830 piso 5 Col Lomas de Chapultepec Del, Acuamanala de Miguel Hidalgo, 11000, Mexico
Tel.: (52) 5559257321
Petrochemical Products Mfr
N.A.I.C.S.: 325110

LG Chem Nanjing Energy Solution Co., Ltd. (1)
No 739 Shengan Ave Binjiang Development Zone, Nanjing, China
Tel.: (86) 2585603000
Automotive Battery Mfr
N.A.I.C.S.: 335910

LG Chem Poland Sp. z o.o. (1)
ul LG 3 Biskupice Podgorne, Kobierzyce, 55-040, Wroclaw, Poland
Electronic Products Mfr
N.A.I.C.S.: 334419

LG Chem Tk Kimya Sanayi Ve Tic. Ltd. Sti. (1)
Maslak Mah AOS 55 Sok 42 Maslak Sitesi No A blok D 14 Ofis 3 ZK-06, Sariyer, Istanbul, Turkiye
Tel.: (90) 2122850171

Emp.: 10
Chemical Products Mfr
N.A.I.C.S.: 325998

LG Chem Wroclaw Energy sp. z o.o. (1)
Biskupice Podgorne LG 1A Street, Kobierzyce, 55-040, Wroclaw, Poland
Tel.: (48) 717338103
Web Site: https://lgensol.pl
Automotive Battery Mfr
N.A.I.C.S.: 335910

LG Chemical (Guangzhou) Engineering Plastics Co., Ltd. (1)
No 1 Yecheng 1st Rd East Area Of Economic And Technological, Guangzhou, 510530, China
Tel.: (86) 2082001570
Plastics Product Mfr
N.A.I.C.S.: 326199

LG Chemical America Inc. (1)
3475 Piedmont Rd NE Ste 1200, Atlanta, GA 30305 (100%)
Tel.: (404) 400-6101
Web Site: https://www.lgchem.com
Sales Range: $200-249.9 Million
Chemical & Finished Products Sales
N.A.I.C.S.: 423990

LG Chemical Co., Ltd. (1)
159 Sermmit Tower 19th Floor Asok Sukhumvit 21 Road Klongton-Nua, Wattana, Bangkok, 10110, Thailand
Tel.: (66) 26657419
Web Site: http://www.lgchem.com
Sales Range: $25-49.9 Million
Chemical Products Mfr
N.A.I.C.S.: 325998

LG Chemical India Private Ltd. (1)
3rd Fl Tower-b Dlf Bldg No 10 Phase-2 Dlf, Cyber City, 122002, Gurgaon, Haryana, India
Tel.: (91) 1244692603
Web Site: http://www.lgchem.com
Chemical Products Mfr
N.A.I.C.S.: 325998
Eric Lee *(Gen Mgr)*

Subsidiary (Domestic):

LG Polymers India Pvt. Ltd. (2)
601 and 602 A-Wing 6th Floor Delphi Orchard Avenue Hiranandani Gardens, Powai, Mumbai, 400 076, Maharashtra, India
Tel.: (91) 2261085352
Web Site: http://www.lgpi.co.in
Chemical Products Mfr
N.A.I.C.S.: 325998

LG Dow Polycarbonate Limited (1)
Hana Securities Building 23-3 Yoido-dong, Youngeungpo-ku, Seoul, Korea (South)
Tel.: (82) 237712625
Sales Range: $75-99.9 Million
Emp.: 100
Chemicals Mfr & Sales; 25% Owned by The Dow Chemical Company & 75 % Owned LG Chem, Ltd.
N.A.I.C.S.: 325998

LG Energy Solution Co., Ltd. (1)
108 Yeoui-daero, Yeongdeungpo-gu, Seoul, 07335, Korea (South)
Tel.: (82) 237771114
Web Site: https://www.lgensol.com
Battery Mfr & Sls
N.A.I.C.S.: 335910
Hak Cheol Shin *(Chm)*

Subsidiary (US):

NEC Energy Solutions, Inc. (2)
155 Flanders Rd, Westborough, MA 01581
Tel.: (508) 497-7319
Information Technology Consulting Services
N.A.I.C.S.: 541512

LG Life Sciences (Beijing) Co., Ltd. (1)
1103RM West Tower Twin Towers B-12 Jianguomenwai Avenue, Chaoyang District, Beijing, 100022, China
Tel.: (86) 1065632301
Pharmaceuticals Product Mfr
N.A.I.C.S.: 325412
In-Chull Kim *(Pres & CEO)*

LG Life Sciences (Thailand) Ltd. (1)

19th Floor CRC Tower All Seasons Place 87/2 Wireless Road, Phatumwan, Bangkok, 10330, Thailand
Tel.: (66) 26542323
Pharmaceutical Products Distr
N.A.I.C.S.: 424210

LG Life Sciences India Pvt. Ltd. (1)
Unit No 201 2nd Floor BPTP Park Centra Sector-30, Gurgaon, 122001, Haryana, India
Tel.: (91) 7926401031
Pharmaceuticals Product Mfr
N.A.I.C.S.: 325412
Anuj Kainth *(Sr Product Mgr)*

LG NanoH2O, Inc. (1)
21250 Hawthorne Blvd Ste 330, Torrance, CA 90503
Tel.: (424) 218-4000
Water Treatment Membrane Research Services
N.A.I.C.S.: 221310

LGC Petrochemical India Private Ltd. (1)
5 Floor building no-8C DLF Cyber City Phase-2, Gurgaon, 122002, Haryana, India
Synthetic Resin Mfr & Distr
N.A.I.C.S.: 325998

Leyou New Energy Materials (Wuxi) Co., Ltd. (1)
No 167 Ximei Road, Xinwu District, Wuxi, Jiangsu, China
Tel.: (86) 18261526162
Automotive Battery Mfr
N.A.I.C.S.: 335910

Tianjin LG BOTIAN Chemical Co., Ltd. (1)
Lingang Industrial Area No 1085 Haihe Road, Tanggu, Tianjin, 300452, China
Chemical Products Mfr
N.A.I.C.S.: 325998

Tianjin LG Bohai Chemical Co., Ltd. (1)
No 667 Haihe Rd, Harbor Economic Area Binhai New Area, Tianjin, 300452, China
Tel.: (86) 2259881120
Emp.: 400
Chemical Product Mfr & Distr
N.A.I.C.S.: 325998

UniSeal, Inc. (1)
1014 E Uhlhorn St, Evansville, IN 47710
Tel.: (812) 463-5230
Web Site: http://www.uniseal.com
Sealants & Adhesives Mfr
N.A.I.C.S.: 325520

LG CORP.
LG Twin Towers 128 Yeouidaero, Yeouideungpo-gu, Seoul, Korea (South)
Tel.: (82) 237771114
Web Site: https://www.lgcorp.com
Year Founded: 1947
003550—(KRS)
Rev.: $5,526,280,005
Assets: $22,455,268,471
Liabilities: $2,402,354,408
Net Worth: $20,052,914,063
Earnings: $936,136,306
Emp.: 195
Fiscal Year-end: 12/31/23
Chemical Products Mfr
N.A.I.C.S.: 551112
Kwang Mo Koo *(Chm & CEO)*

Subsidiaries:

HILOGIsTICS EUROPE B.V. (1)
Energieweg 10, Oosterhout, 4906 CG, Netherlands
Tel.: (31) 162447162
Web Site: http://www.hilogistics.co.in
Logistics Consulting Servies
N.A.I.C.S.: 541614
Henk Van Derek *(Mng Dir)*

Kunshan LGMSK Computer Co., Ltd. (1)
No 88 Qianjin E, Kunshan, Jiangsu, China
Tel.: (86) 51257718888
Web Site: http://www.lge.co.kr

Electronic Home Appliances Mfr
N.A.I.C.S.: 335220

LG Alina Electronics (1)
Beregovoy Pr-d 4/6 Bld 2, 121087, Moscow, Russia
Tel.: (7) 4959336090
Web Site: http://www.lg.com
Household Appliances Mfr
N.A.I.C.S.: 335220

LG CNS (1)
Prime Tower #10-1 Hoehyeon-dong, 2-ga Jung-gu, Seoul, Korea (South)
Tel.: (82) 2 6363 5000
Web Site: http://www.lgcns.com
Sales Range: $1-4.9 Billion
Emp.: 10,000
Information Technology Consulting, Solutions, Systems & Networks
N.A.I.C.S.: 541690
Dae Hoon Kim *(CEO)*

Subsidiary (Non-US):

Entrue Brasil Servicos de T.I. Ltda. (2)
Avenida Dr Chucri Zaidan 940 3F Vila Cordeira, Sao Paulo, 04583-110, Brazil
Tel.: (55) 11 2162 5461
Web Site: http://www.lgcns.com
Sales Range: $10-24.9 Million
Emp.: 40
Information Technology Consulting Services
N.A.I.C.S.: 541512
Taeyeon Lee *(Pres)*

LG CNS China Co., Ltd. (2)
4th Fl B401 Guomen Building No 1 Zuo Jia Zhang, Chaoyang District, Beijing, 100028, China
Tel.: (86) 1058287700
Web Site: http://www.lgcns.com.cn
Electrical Home Appliance Mfr
N.A.I.C.S.: 335220

LG CNS Europe B.V. (2)
Veluwezoom 15, 1327 AE, Almere, Netherlands
Tel.: (31) 365478915
Web Site: http://transportation.lgcns.com
Electronic Home Appliances Distr
N.A.I.C.S.: 423620

LG CNS India Pvt., Ltd. (2)
Embassy Tech Square Marathahalli Sarjapur Outer Ring Road, Bengaluru, 560 103, India
Tel.: (91) 8066674000
Web Site: http://www.lgcnsindia.com
Sales Range: $25-49.9 Million
Emp.: 50
Information Technology Consulting Services
N.A.I.C.S.: 541512
Jae Jang Yung *(Pres & Mng Dir)*

LG CNS India U.K. (2)
Building 3 Chiswick Park 566 Chiswick High Road, London, W4 5YA, United Kingdom
Tel.: (44) 2088495634
Web Site: http://transportation.lgcns.com
Electronic Home Appliances Mfr
N.A.I.C.S.: 335220

LG CNS Japan Co., Ltd. (2)
Hon-Kan 14F Akasaka Twin-Tower 2-17-22, Minato-ku, Tokyo, 107-0052, Japan
Tel.: (81) 335053999
Electrical Home Appliance Mfr
N.A.I.C.S.: 335220

LG CNS MIDDLE EAST (2)
Al Nasr Plaza Office Building 10th Street Oud Metha Road, PO Box 61445, Dubai, United Arab Emirates
Tel.: (971) 43573511
Web Site: http://transportation.lgcns.com
Sales Range: $75-99.9 Million
Emp.: 300
Logistics Consulting Services
N.A.I.C.S.: 541614
James Park *(Gen Mgr)*

Subsidiary (Domestic):

LG N-Sys Inc. (2)
Mapo Bldg No 275 Gongduk-dong Mapogu, Mapo-gu, Seoul, 121-721, Korea (South)
Tel.: (82) 237731114
Web Site: http://www.lgnsys.com

AND PRIVATE COMPANIES — LG CORP.

Sales Range: $400-449.9 Million
Emp.: 70
IT Solutions & Financial System Automation Equipment & Software
N.A.I.C.S.: 541511
Dohyun Kim *(CEO)*

Subsidiary (Non-US):

Pt. LG CNS Indonesia (2)
Wisma Prima Lt 2 Jl Kapten P Tendean No 34, Jakarta, 12790, Indonesia
Tel.: (62) 2179182121
Emp.: 10
Electronic Home Appliances Mfr
N.A.I.C.S.: 335220

Subsidiary (Domestic):

Ucess Partners Co., Ltd. (2)
22/F Daewoo Mirae Sarang City 337 Sindorim-Dong, Guro-Gu, Seoul, 152-070, Korea (South)
Tel.: (82) 234397600
Business Process Outsourcing Services
N.A.I.C.S.: 561499

V-ENS Co. Ltd (2)
236-1 Hhyosung dong, Kyeyang gu, Incheon, 407 040, Korea (South)
Tel.: (82) 325405500
Sales Range: $550-599.9 Million
Emp.: 550
Automobile Engineering & Consulting Services
N.A.I.C.S.: 541330
Woong-Pill Yang *(CTO)*

LG Chem Michigan Inc. (1)
1 Lg Way, Holland, MI 49423-8574
Tel.: (616) 494-7190
Web Site: http://www.lg.com
Sales Range: $50-74.9 Million
Emp.: 450
Chemical Products Mfr
N.A.I.C.S.: 325998
Nick Kaffoanof *(Gen Mgr)*

LG Economic Research Institute (1)
Sales Range: $25-49.9 Million
Emp.: 107
Economic Research & Consulting
N.A.I.C.S.: 541690

LG Electronics, Inc. (1)
LG Twin Tower 128 Yeoui-daero, Youngdeungpo-gu, Seoul, 07336, Korea (South) **(33.7%)**
Tel.: (82) 237771114
Web Site: https://www.lg.com
Rev.: $68,743,898,680
Assets: $49,202,959,760
Liabilities: $30,712,769,400
Net Worth: $18,490,190,360
Earnings: $1,301,774,240
Emp.: 37,612
Fiscal Year-end: 12/31/2021
Household Product Mfr & Distr
N.A.I.C.S.: 335220
Young-Soo Kwon *(Chm)*

Subsidiary (Domestic):

Hi Logistics Co., Ltd. (2)
LG Gangseo Bldg 36 Mullae-dong 6Ga, Youngdungpo-gu, Seoul, 150 096, Korea (South) **(100%)**
Tel.: (82) 221635518
Web Site: http://www.hilogistics.co.kr
Sales Range: $300-349.9 Million
Emp.: 435
Logistics Consulting Servies
N.A.I.C.S.: 541614
Changuk Choi *(CEO)*

Affiliate (Domestic):

LG Display Co., Ltd. (2)
128 Yeoui-daero, Yeongdeungpo-gu, Seoul, Korea (South) **(37.9%)**
Tel.: (82) 237731114
Web Site: https://www.lgdisplay.com
Rev.: $27,487,799,560
Assets: $35,102,153,800
Liabilities: $21,520,652,880
Net Worth: $13,581,500,920
Earnings: $1,226,860,480
Emp.: 70,707
Fiscal Year-end: 12/31/2021
Electronic Component Mfr & Distr
N.A.I.C.S.: 334419

James Hoyoung Jeong *(Pres & CEO)*

Joint Venture (US):

Global OLED Technology LLC (3)
107 Carpenter Dr Ste 225, Sterling, VA 20164
Tel.: (703) 870-3282
Web Site: https://www.globaloledtech.com
Professional, Scientific & Technical Services
N.A.I.C.S.: 541990

Subsidiary (Non-US):

LG Display Germany GmbH (3)
Berliner Str 93, 40880, Ratingen, Germany
Tel.: (49) 21025656235
Web Site: http://www.lgdisplay.com
Liquid Crystal Display Component Distr
N.A.I.C.S.: 423690

LG Display Japan Co., Ltd (3)
Kyobashi Trust Tower 12F 2-1-3 Kyobashi, Chuo-ku, Tokyo, 104-0031, Japan
Tel.: (81) 332240123
Electronic Components Mfr
N.A.I.C.S.: 334419

LG Display Shanghai Co., Ltd. (3)
18 Floor Longzhimeng Building 1018 Changning Road, Changning District, Shanghai, 200042, China
Tel.: (86) 2152416633
Electronic Display Component Distr
N.A.I.C.S.: 423440

LG Display Shenzhen Co., Ltd (3)
27th Floor Tower One UpperHills No 5001 Huanggang Road, the Third Phase of the Southern District Futian District, Shenzhen, Guangdong, China
Tel.: (86) 75533364087
Electronic Display Component Distr
N.A.I.C.S.: 423440

LG Display Singapore Pte. Ltd (3)
8 Temasek Boulevard 25-01 Suntec Tower 3, Singapore, 038988, Singapore
Tel.: (65) 63335914
Sales Range: $25-49.9 Million
Emp.: 28
Electronic Components Distr
N.A.I.C.S.: 423690

LG Display Taiwan Co., Ltd. (3)
9F No 89 Sec 2 Tiding Blvd, Neihu Dist, Taipei, 11493, Taiwan
Tel.: (886) 281785104
Electronic Components Distr
N.A.I.C.S.: 423690

LG Display Yantai Co., Ltd. (3)
No 2 Beijing Middle Road, Yantai, 264006, China
Tel.: (86) 5352167024
Home Appliance Mfr
N.A.I.C.S.: 335220

Subsidiary (Non-US):

LG Electronics (Hangzhou) Recording Media Co., Ltd (2)
9 No 23 Street Hangzhou Economic & Technological Development Area, Hangzhou, China
Tel.: (86) 57186729118
Household Appliances Mfr
N.A.I.C.S.: 335220

LG Electronics (Kunshan) Computer Co., Ltd (2)
No 88 Qianjin E, 215300, Kunshan, Jiangsu, China
Tel.: (86) 51286186000
Household Appliances Mfr
N.A.I.C.S.: 335220

LG Electronics (Thailand) Co., Ltd. (2)
75/81 Richmond Building 22nd Floor Sukhumvit 26 Sukhumvit Road, Khlong Tan Subdistrict Khlong Toei District, Bangkok, 10110, Thailand
Tel.: (66) 22048888
Web Site: https://www.lg.com
Home Appliance Distr
N.A.I.C.S.: 423620

LG Electronics Argentina S.A. (2)
Juana Manso 999 Piso 5 Torre Norte, C1107CBS, Buenos Aires, Puerto Madero, Argentina
Tel.: (54) 1153525454
Web Site: https://www.lg.com
Marketing Consulting Services
N.A.I.C.S.: 541613

LG Electronics Australia Pty Ltd (2)
2 Wonderland Dr, 2766 Easten, Eastern Creek, 2766, NSW, Australia
Tel.: (61) 296848000
Web Site: http://www.lge.com.au
Sales Range: $10-24.9 Million
Emp.: 50
Provider of Electronic Services
N.A.I.C.S.: 811310
Angus Jones *(Gen Mgr-Mktg)*

LG Electronics Benelux Sales BV (2)
Krijgsman 1, 1186 DM, Amstelveen, Netherlands
Tel.: (31) 204563112
Electronic Home Appliances Distr
N.A.I.C.S.: 423620
Vangerhulst Rik *(Gen Mgr-HR)*

LG Electronics CZ, s.r.o. (2)
Zlaty Andel Nadrazni 23/344, 151 34, Prague, Czech Republic
Tel.: (420) 234094600
Sales Range: $25-49.9 Million
Emp.: 100
Household Appliance Distr
N.A.I.C.S.: 423620

LG Electronics Canada, Inc. (2)
550 Matheson Blvd E, Mississauga, L4Z 4G3, ON, Canada
Tel.: (905) 568-6800
Web Site: http://www.lg.com
Sales Range: $25-49.9 Million
Emp.: 180
Electronic Appliances Whslr
N.A.I.C.S.: 532210
Andy Reed *(Dir-Air Conditioning-Energy Solutions-Surrey)*

LG Electronics Colombia Ltda. (2)
CRA 11 No 94 -34, Bogota, Colombia
Tel.: (57) 7559000
Household Appliance Distr
N.A.I.C.S.: 423620

LG Electronics Deutschland GmbH (2)
Jakob Kaiser Strasse 12, 47877, Willich, Germany
Tel.: (49) 21544920
Web Site: http://www.lge.de
Sales Range: $75-99.9 Million
Emp.: 262
Audio & Video Equipment Mfr
N.A.I.C.S.: 334310
Young W. Lee *(CEO)*

LG Electronics Egypt S.A.E. (2)
3/1 Crossroad El Laselky St With Palestine St Sabra Tower, Maadi, Cairo, Egypt
Tel.: (20) 2 2520 0336
Web Site: http://www.lg.com
Household Appliances Mfr
N.A.I.C.S.: 335220
Don Kwack *(Mng Dir)*

LG Electronics Espana S.A. (2)
Calle Chile 1, 28290, Las Rozas, Madrid, Spain
Tel.: (34) 912112200
Web Site: https://www.lg.com
Household Appliances Mfr
N.A.I.C.S.: 335220

LG Electronics European Logistics & Services B.V. (2)
Veluwezoom 15, 1327 AE, Almere, Netherlands
Tel.: (31) 365478888
Web Site: http://www.lg.com
Logistics Consulting Servies
N.A.I.C.S.: 541614

LG Electronics European Shared Service Center B.V. (2)
Veluwezoom 15, 1327 AE, Almere, Netherlands
Tel.: (31) 365478888
Web Site: http://www.lg.com
Household Appliances Mfr
N.A.I.C.S.: 335220

LG Electronics France S.A.R.L (2)
Paris Nord Il-117 Av des Nations, BP 59372, Roissy CDG, 95942, Villepinte, France
Tel.: (33) 149898949
Household Appliance Distr
N.A.I.C.S.: 423620

LG Electronics Gulf FZE (2)
Al-Nasr Plaza Office Building 4 Oud Metha, PO Box 61445, Dubai, United Arab Emirates
Tel.: (971) 43573466
Web Site: http://www.lg.com
Sales Range: $25-49.9 Million
Emp.: 10
Household Appliances Mfr
N.A.I.C.S.: 335220
Shik Paik Hyun *(Pres)*

LG Electronics HK Ltd. (2)
5F 633 King's Road, North Point, China (Hong Kong) **(49%)**
Tel.: (852) 35437777
Web Site: https://www.lg.com
Sales Range: $25-49.9 Million
Emp.: 3
Home Appliance Distr
N.A.I.C.S.: 423620

LG Electronics Hellas S.A. (2)
Ethnarcho Makariou 1 Delta of Palaio Faliro, PO Box 77331, 17501, Athens, Greece
Tel.: (30) 2104800500
Web Site: https://www.lg.com
Emp.: 100
Household Appliances Mfr
N.A.I.C.S.: 335220
Jordia Stvropulou *(Mgr-Mktg)*

LG Electronics India Pvt. Ltd (2)
Plot No 51 Surajpur Kasna Road, Noida, 201306, Uttar Pradesh, India
Tel.: (91) 1202560900
Web Site: http://www.lg.com
Sales Range: $700-749.9 Million
Emp.: 3,000
Electronic Home Appliances Mfr
N.A.I.C.S.: 335220
Soon Kwon *(Global Head-Info Display Bus)*

LG Electronics Italia S.p.A (2)
Via Dell Unione Europea 6, 20097, San Donato Milanese, Milan, Italy
Tel.: (39) 02518011
Web Site: http://www.lg.com
Household Appliance Distr
N.A.I.C.S.: 423620

LG Electronics Japan (2)
9th Floor Akasaka Twin Tower Honkan 2-17-22, Minato Ku, Tokyo, 107 8512, Japan
Tel.: (81) 335881911
Web Site: http://www.lg.com
Sales Range: $25-49.9 Million
Emp.: 67
Household Audio & Video Equipment Mfr
N.A.I.C.S.: 334310
Kyuhong Lee *(Pres)*

LG Electronics Latvia, LLC (2)
4a Gredu Str, Riga, 1019, Latvia
Tel.: (371) 67311337
Web Site: https://www.lg.com
Sales Range: $25-49.9 Million
Emp.: 70
Household Appliances Mfr
N.A.I.C.S.: 335220
Sergey Samoilenko *(Dir-Comml)*

LG Electronics Magyar KFT (2)
Konyves Kalman krt 3 / a, 1097, Budapest, Hungary
Tel.: (36) 615454054
Sales Range: $25-49.9 Million
Emp.: 100
Household Audio & Video Equipment Mfr
N.A.I.C.S.: 334310

LG Electronics Mexico S.A. DE C.V (2)
Sor Juan Ines De La Cruz 555, San Lorenzo Industrial, 54033, Tlalnepantla, Mexico
Tel.: (52) 53211900
Web Site: https://www.lg.com
Electronic Goods & Appliances Distr
N.A.I.C.S.: 423620

LG Electronics Mlawa Sp. z o.o. (2)

LG CORP.

LG Corp.—(Continued)

ul LG Electronics 7, 06-500, Mlawa, Poland
Tel.: (48) 236547404
Web Site: http://www.lg.com
Sales Range: $350-399.9 Million
Emp.: 2,500
Household Appliances Mfr
N.A.I.C.S.: 335220

LG Electronics Monterrey Mexico S.A. de C.V. (2)
Av Industrias 180 Parque Industrial Pimsa, 66603, Apodaca, Nuevo Leon, Mexico
Tel.: (52) 81965500
Web Site: http://www.lg.com
Household Appliances Mfr
N.A.I.C.S.: 335220

LG Electronics Morocco S.A.R.L. (2)
Lotiss Attaoufik Zenith Millennium Imm No 3 Et 4 5 Et, Sidi Maarouf, Casablanca, Morocco
Tel.: (212) 522588260
Web Site: https://www.lg.com
Sales Range: $50-74.9 Million
Emp.: 120
Electronic Home Appliances Distr
N.A.I.C.S.: 423620

LG Electronics Nordic AB (2)
Esbogatan 18 Akalla, Box 83, 164 94, Kista, Sweden
Tel.: (46) 856641500
Web Site: https://www.lg.com
Household Appliance Distr
N.A.I.C.S.: 423620
Bjorn Drablos (CEO)

LG Electronics Peru S.A. (2)
Tel.: (51) 14150000
Household Appliances Mfr
N.A.I.C.S.: 335220

LG Electronics Philippines, Inc. (2)
Sales Range: $50-74.9 Million
Emp.: 300
Electronic Services
N.A.I.C.S.: 811310

LG Electronics Portugal S.A. (2)
Qunita da Fonte Edificio D 2nd FL Rua Vitor Camara St No 2, Paço d'Arcos, 2770-229, Portugal
Tel.: (351) 211202200
Web Site: http://www.lg.com
Emp.: 50
Home Appliance Distr
N.A.I.C.S.: 423620
Oungnam Roh (Pres)

LG Electronics Qinhuangdao Inc (2)
Economic & Technical Development Zone, Qinhuangdao, China
Tel.: (86) 3358018550
Web Site: http://www.lg.com
Household Appliances Mfr
N.A.I.C.S.: 335220

LG Electronics RUS, LLC (2)
Building 9 86 Km of Minskoe Highway Rural Village Dorokhovskoe, Ruza District, Moscow, 143160, Russia
Tel.: (7) 4957851313
Household Appliances Mfr
N.A.I.C.S.: 335220
Song Dahon (Gen Dir)

LG Electronics S.A. (Pty) Ltd. (2)
Raceway Industrial Park Monte Carlo Drive Gosforth Park, Germiston, 1419, South Africa
Tel.: (27) 113238000
Web Site: https://www.lg.com
Home Appliance Distr
N.A.I.C.S.: 423620

LG Electronics Singapore Pte Ltd (2)
Suntec tower3 Temasek Blvd, Singapore, 038988, Singapore
Tel.: (65) 63336092
Web Site: https://www.lg.com
Home Appliance Distr
N.A.I.C.S.: 423620

LG Electronics Taiwan Taipei Co., Ltd (2)
6th Floor No 47 Lane 3 Jihu Road, Neihu District, Taipei, 11492, Taiwan
Tel.: (886) 226272788

Web Site: https://www.lg.com
Household Appliance Distr
N.A.I.C.S.: 423620

LG Electronics Ticaret A.S. (2)
Kaptanpasa Mahallesi Piyalepasa Bulvari No 73 Ortadogu Plaza K 7, Okmeydani SISLI, 34384, Istanbul, Turkiye
Tel.: (90) 2123145252
Web Site: https://www.lg.com
Household Appliances Mfr
N.A.I.C.S.: 335220

Subsidiary (US):

LG Electronics U.S.A., Inc. (2)
1000 Sylvan Ave, Englewood Cliffs, NJ 07632
Tel.: (201) 816-2000
Web Site: http://www.us.lge.com
Sales Range: $250-299.9 Million
Emp.: 200
Home Appliances, Personal Computers & Consumer Electronics
N.A.I.C.S.: 423430
John Herrington (VP-Natl Accts-Home Appliances)

Subsidiary (Domestic):

LG Electronics Alabama, Inc. (3)
201 James Record Rd SW, Huntsville, AL 35824
Tel.: (256) 772-0623
Web Site: http://www.lge.com
Sales Range: $125-149.9 Million
Television Sets & Microwave Ovens Mfr
N.A.I.C.S.: 334310
Wayne Kerr (CEO)

LG InfoComm U.S.A., Inc. (3)
10225 Willow Creek Rd, San Diego, CA 92131
Tel.: (858) 635-5300
Web Site: http://www.us.lge.com
Sales Range: $50-74.9 Million
Wireless Communication Products & Services
N.A.I.C.S.: 423690

Zenith Electronics Corp. (3)
2000 Millbrook Dr, Lincolnshire, IL 60069-3630
Tel.: (847) 941-8000
Web Site: https://www.zenith.com
Sales Range: $50-74.9 Million
Emp.: 160
TV, Video Cassette Recorders, Power Supplies, Video Display, CATV & STV Equipment & Accessories Mfr & Whlsr
N.A.I.C.S.: 334310
John I. Taylor (VP-PR)

Subsidiary (Non-US):

LG Electronics Ukraine Inc (2)
Bassdjmaya Street Building 6 6th Floor, Kiev, 1004, Ukraine
Tel.: (380) 44 201 4350
Web Site: http://www.lg.com
Home Appliance Mfr
N.A.I.C.S.: 335220
Sung Soo Kim (CEO)

LG Electronics United Kingdom Ltd. (2)
LG House 250 Bath Road, Slough, SL1 4DX, Berkshire, United Kingdom
Tel.: (44) 1753491500
Web Site: http://www.lg.com
Emp.: 2,000
Electronic Appliance Distr
N.A.I.C.S.: 423620

LG Electronics Venezuela S.A. (2)
Ed Parque Avila Torre HP Torre B Piso 10 Ave Francisco Miranda, Palos Grandes Chacão, Caracas, Venezuela
Sales Range: $25-49.9 Million
Emp.: 6
Household Appliances Mfr
N.A.I.C.S.: 335220

LG Electronics Vietnam Co., Ltd (2)
Km 17 5 Highway 5A, Van Lam District, Nhu Quynh, Hung Yen, Vietnam
Tel.: (84) 8001590
Web Site: http://www.lg.com
Electronic Components Distr
N.A.I.C.S.: 423690

LG Electronics Wroclaw Sp. z o.o. (2)
ul LG Electronics 1-2 Biskupice Podgorne, 55-040, Kobierzyce, Poland
Tel.: (48) 717929400
Household Appliances Mfr
N.A.I.C.S.: 335220

LG Electronics, Inc. Poland (2)
Sales Range: $25-49.9 Million
Emp.: 70
Electronic Services
N.A.I.C.S.: 811310

LG Electronics, Panama S.A. (2)
LG BUSINESS CENTER Calle Aquilino de la Guardia con Calle 48 Este, Marbella, Panama, Panama
Tel.: (507) 2106000
Web Site: https://www.lg.com
Sales Range: $25-49.9 Million
Emp.: 158
Electronic Services
N.A.I.C.S.: 811310

Subsidiary (Domestic):

LG Innotek Co., Ltd. (2)
Building E1/E3 30 Magokjungang 10-ro, Gangseo-gu, Seoul, 07796, Korea (South)
Tel.: (82) 237731114
Web Site: http://www.lginnotek.com
Sales Range: $500-549.9 Million
Emp.: 5,000
Communication Equipment Mfr
N.A.I.C.S.: 334290
Hyuksoo Moon (CEO)

Subsidiary (Non-US):

LG Micron (Fujian) Electronics Co., Ltd (2)
#5 Shangde Road Science Park of Economic & Technical Development Zone, Fuzhou, China
Tel.: (86) 59183977201
Electronic Components Mfr
N.A.I.C.S.: 334419

LG Mitr Electronics Co., Ltd. (2)
71/12 Moo 5 Bangna-Trad Rd Km 52 Thakarm Bangpakong, Bangkok, 24130, Chachangsao, Thailand
Tel.: (66) 28785757
Web Site: http://th.lge.com
Sales Range: $75-99.9 Million
Emp.: 300
Audio & Video Equipment
N.A.I.C.S.: 334310

P.T. LG Electronics Indonesia (2)
One Pacific Place 11th Floor Jl Jend Sudirman Kav 52-53 Sudirman, Central Business District, Jakarta, 12190, Indonesia
Tel.: (62) 21 5797 3113
Web Site: http://www.lg.com
Electronic Home Appliances Distr
N.A.I.C.S.: 423620

LG Household & Health Care Ltd. (1)
LG GwangHwaMoon Building 58 Saemunan-ro, Jongno-gu, Seoul, 110-602, Korea (South) (34%)
Tel.: (82) 800237007
Web Site: https://www.lghnh.com
Rev.: $5,050,872,883
Assets: $5,359,237,267
Liabilities: $1,240,562,326
Net Worth: $4,118,674,940
Earnings: $121,375,236
Emp.: 4,423
Fiscal Year-end: 12/31/2023
Cosmetic Product Distr
N.A.I.C.S.: 325998
Hong Ki Kim (CFO & Exec VP)

Subsidiary (Non-US):

Ginza Stefany Cosmetics Co., Ltd. (2)
1-5-1 Shinbashi Stephanie Ginza Chuudori Building, Minato-ku, Tokyo, Japan
Tel.: (81) 3 3289 1212
Web Site: http://www.ginza-stefany.com
Cosmetics Products Mfr & Distr
N.A.I.C.S.: 456120
Yi Ke Lee (CEO)

LG Household & Health Care (Taiwan), Ltd. (2)

9f 159 Keelung Road Sec 1, Taipei, 11070, Taiwan
Tel.: (886) 287878739
Cosmetics Products Mfr
N.A.I.C.S.: 325620

Subsidiary (US):

LG Household & Health Care America Inc. (2)
13102 Imperial Hwy, Santa Fe Springs, CA 90670
Tel.: (562) 653-8050
Web Site: http://www.lgcare.com
Sales Range: $25-49.9 Million
Emp.: 15
Cosmetic Product Distr
N.A.I.C.S.: 424210
Joseph Lee (Gen Mgr)

Subsidiary (Non-US):

LG Household & Health Care Trading (Shanghai) Co., Ltd (2)
5 7F Yong Feng Plaza No 98 South Wan Ping Road, Shanghai, 200030, China
Tel.: (86) 2154250011
Household Appliance Distr
N.A.I.C.S.: 423620

LG Innotek Huizhou Inc. (1)
Zhongkai Hi-Tech Industry Development Zone, District 18, Huizhou, 516-0016, Guangdong, China
Tel.: (86) 7522093602
Electronic Components Mfr
N.A.I.C.S.: 334419
Kinyong Tae (Gen Mgr)

LG Innotek Yantai Co., Ltd. (1)
36 TAIBEI North Road Development zone, Yantai, 264006, Shan dong, China
Tel.: (86) 18816388085
Electronic Components Mfr
N.A.I.C.S.: 334419

LG SILTRON - France (1)
6 Rue Du Docteur Finlay, Paris, 75015, France
Tel.: (33) 147668030
Web Site: http://www.lgsiltron.co.kr
Semiconductor Devices Mfr
N.A.I.C.S.: 334413
Shin Kyungchang (Mgr)

LG Soft India Private Limited (1)
Embassy Tech Square Marathahalli Sarjapur Outer Ring Road, Bengaluru, 560 103, India
Tel.: (91) 8066155000
Web Site: http://www.lgsoftindia.com
Sales Range: $75-99.9 Million
Emp.: 500
Software Development Services
N.A.I.C.S.: 541511
Joon Lee Hyun (Pres)

LG Sports (1)
Jamsil Station 10 Jamsil 1-dong, Songpa-gu, Seoul, 138-221, Korea (South)
Tel.: (82) 237971114
Web Site: http://www.lgtwins.com
Sales Range: $25-49.9 Million
Emp.: 50
Professional Baseball Management
N.A.I.C.S.: 711410
Sang Geon Nan (CEO)

LX Hausys, Ltd (1)
20 Yeouido-dong, Yeongdeungpo-gu, Seoul, 150721, Korea (South)
Tel.: (82) 800054000
Web Site: http://www.lghausys.co.kr
Rev.: $2,769,752,817
Assets: $1,905,020,143
Liabilities: $1,306,803,862
Net Worth: $598,216,281
Earnings: ($89,811,865)
Emp.: 3,092
Fiscal Year-end: 12/31/2022
Interior Construction Material Mfr
N.A.I.C.S.: 332321
Honggi Kim (CFO)

LX International Corp (1)
58 Seodaemunro, Jongno-gu, Seoul, 03184, Korea (South) (24.69%)
Tel.: (82) 237771114
Web Site: http://www.lgicorp.com
Rev.: $14,388,574,393
Assets: $5,920,478,625

AND PRIVATE COMPANIES

Liabilities: $3,591,502,091
Net Worth: $2,328,976,534
Earnings: $395,176,705
Emp.: 384
Fiscal Year-end: 12/31/2022
International Trade
N.A.I.C.S.: 522299
Chun Sung Yoon *(CEO)*

Subsidiary (US):

LG International (America), Inc. **(2)**
Ste 600 17777 Center Court Dr N, Cerritos, CA 90703-8575
Tel.: (562) 483-8000
Sales Range: $25-49.9 Million
Emp.: 40
Electronics Whslr
N.A.I.C.S.: 423690

Branch (Non-US):

LG International Corp. **(3)**
Level 14 Ste 201 Miller St, Sydney, 2060, NSW, Australia **(100%)**
Tel.: (61) 299574941
Web Site: http://www.lgicorp.com
Sales Range: $25-49.9 Million
Emp.: 4
Computer & Computer Peripherals Whlsr
N.A.I.C.S.: 541330

LG International Corp. **(3)**
Nueva Tajamar 481 Oficina 2004 Torre Sun, Las Condes, Santiago, Chile
Tel.: (56) 22036895
Web Site: http://www.lgicorp.com
Construction & Electronic Services
N.A.I.C.S.: 811310

LG International Corp. **(3)**
No 63 6th Fl Zafar St, Shareati Ave, Tehran, Iran **(100%)**
Tel.: (98) 2122770635
Engineering & Construction Services
N.A.I.C.S.: 541330

LG International Corp. Ho Chi Minh City Office **(3)**
8th Fl Yoco Office Bldg, 41 Nguyen Thi Minh Khai St 1, Ho Chi Minh City, Vietnam
Tel.: (84) 88220408
Web Site: http://www.lgicorp.com
Sales Range: $25-49.9 Million
Emp.: 6
Audio & Video Equipment Mfr
N.A.I.C.S.: 334310

Subsidiary (Non-US):

LG International (China) Corp. **(2)**
Rm 1513 Wandu Mansion No 8 Xingyi Rd, Changning Dist, 200336, Shanghai, China
Tel.: (86) 2152081118
Household Appliances Mfr
N.A.I.C.S.: 335210

LG International (Singapore) Pte., Ltd. **(2)**
8 Temasek Blvd 26-02 Suntec City Tower 3, Singapore, 038988, Singapore
Tel.: (65) 68321500
Emp.: 30
Electronic Home Appliances Mfr
N.A.I.C.S.: 335220

LG International Corp. Deutschland GMBH **(2)**
Lyoner Str 15, Frankfurt am Main, 60528, Germany
Tel.: (49) 6966300760
Electrical Home Appliance Mfr
N.A.I.C.S.: 335220

LG International DO Brazil Ltda **(2)**
Av Chucri Zaidan Dr 940 An 18 Cj 181 B - VI Cordeiro, Sao Paulo, 0458-3110, Brazil
Tel.: (55) 1121040075
Electronic Home Appliances Mfr
N.A.I.C.S.: 335220
Duseob Kim *(Pres)*

LG International Japan Ltd. **(2)**
Sakaisuji-Hom-Machi Center Bldg 2-1-6, Chuo-Ku, Osaka, 541-0053, Japan
Tel.: (81) 335829121
Electronic Home Appliances Mfr
N.A.I.C.S.: 335220

Pixdix Co., Ltd. **(1)**
9/F Gomwas Bldg 123 Hannam-Dong, Yongsan-Gu, Seoul, 140-889, Korea (South)
Tel.: (82) 27910834
Electronic Home Appliances Mfr
N.A.I.C.S.: 335220

Tianjin LG New Building Materials Co., Ltd. **(1)**
12 Quanta Road Wuqing DEV Area Tianjin Hitech Industry Zone, Tianjin, China
Tel.: (86) 2282125558
Web Site: http://www.lghausys.com
Building Materials Mfr
N.A.I.C.S.: 324122

LG UPLUS CORP.

Hangangno 3-ga 32 Hangang-daero, Yongsan-gu, Seoul, Korea (South)
Tel.: (82) 237731114
Web Site: https://www.lguplus.com
Year Founded: 1996
032640—(KRS)
Rev.: $12,344,216,840
Assets: $16,882,174,800
Liabilities: $9,843,057,920
Net Worth: $7,039,116,880
Earnings: $429,422,880
Emp.: 10,319
Fiscal Year-end: 12/31/20
Telecommunication Servicesb
N.A.I.C.S.: 517112
Hyeon Hoe Ha *(Vice Chm & CEO)*

Subsidiaries:

LG HelloVision Corp. **(1)**
Sinjeong dong Shintreetechnotown 807 276 Sinjeong-ro, Yangcheon-gu, Seoul, Korea (South) **(50%)**
Tel.: (82) 218551000
Web Site: http://www.lghellovision.net
Rev.: $895,754,754
Assets: $1,095,286,306
Liabilities: $615,511,077
Net Worth: $479,775,229
Earnings: ($19,960,863)
Emp.: 1,064
Fiscal Year-end: 12/31/2022
Cable TV Operator
N.A.I.C.S.: 516210
Gu Yeong Song *(CEO)*

LG2

3575 Saint-Laurent Boulevard Suite 900, Montreal, H2X 2T7, QC, Canada
Tel.: (514) 281-8901 Ca
Web Site: http://www.lg2.com
Emp.: 100
N.A.I.C.S.: 541810
Gilles Chouinard *(Assoc & VP-Creation)*

LGI LIMITED

57 Harvey Street North, Eagle Farm, 4009, QLD, Australia
Tel.: (61) 737112225 AU
Web Site: https://www.lgi.com.au
Year Founded: 2009
LGI—(ASX)
Rev.: $21,101,910
Assets: $41,313,816
Liabilities: $9,120,428
Net Worth: $32,193,389
Earnings: $4,198,996
Fiscal Year-end: 06/30/23
Renewable Energy Services
N.A.I.C.S.: 221210
Adam Bloomer *(Founder)*

LGM

La Boursidiere, BP 22, Le Plessis Robinson, 92357, Paris, Cedex, France
Tel.: (33) 1 45 37 34 00 FR
Web Site: http://www.lgm.fr
Rev.: $21,900,000
Emp.: 104
Engineering & Management Services
N.A.I.C.S.: 541330
Michel Monteillard *(Pres)*

Subsidiaries:

AXONE BV **(1)**
Keizersgracht 62 64, Amsterdam, 1015 CS, Netherlands **(100%)**
Tel.: (31) 205207518
Web Site: http://www.axone.nl
Sales Range: $25-49.9 Million
Emp.: 4
Engineering & Management Services
N.A.I.C.S.: 541330
Samuel Bate *(Gen Mgr)*

AXONE GmbH **(1)**
Technologiezentrum am Europaplatz, Dennwartstrasse 25 27, 52068, Aachen, Germany **(100%)**
Tel.: (49) 2419631763
Web Site: http://www.axone.eu
Engineeering Services
N.A.I.C.S.: 541330

LGM BELGIUM SPRL **(1)**
Rue de Rotterdam 23, 4000, Liege, Belgium
Tel.: (32) 4 274 32 45
Business Consulting Services
N.A.I.C.S.: 541611

LGMS BERHAD

A-11-01 Empire Office Tower Jalan SS 16/1, 47500, Subang Jaya, Selangor, Malaysia
Tel.: (60) 386050155
Web Site: https://www.lgms.global
Year Founded: 2005
LGMS—(KLS)
Rev.: $7,453,635
Assets: $20,825,860
Liabilities: $1,978,668
Net Worth: $18,847,192
Earnings: $2,442,751
Emp.: 118
Fiscal Year-end: 12/31/23
Information Technology Services
N.A.I.C.S.: 541512
Chu Gilbert *(Co-Founder & Co-CEO)*

LH FINANCIAL GROUP PUBLIC COMPANY LIMITED

1 Q House Lumpini Building 5th Floor South Sathorn Rd Thungmahamek, Sathorn, Bangkok, 10120, Thailand
Tel.: (66) 23590000
Web Site: https://www.lhfg.co.th
LHFG—(THA)
Rev.: $340,617,073
Assets: $9,438,421,917
Liabilities: $8,388,653,571
Net Worth: $1,049,768,346
Earnings: $61,195,711
Emp.: 1,789
Fiscal Year-end: 12/31/23
Financial Holding Company
N.A.I.C.S.: 551111
Rutt Phanijphand *(Chm)*

Subsidiaries:

CIMB Securities International (Thailand) Public Co Ltd **(1)**
130-132 1st and 2nd Floor Sindhorn Tower 2, 12th Floor Sindhorn Tower 3 Wireless Road Lumpini Patumwan, Bangkok, 10330, Thailand **(99.8%)**
Tel.: (66) 28419000
Sales Range: $75-99.9 Million
Investment Banking & Securities Dealing
N.A.I.C.S.: 523150

Land & Houses Securities Public Company Limited **(1)**
11 Q House Sathorn Building M Floor 10 South Sathorn Road, Thungmahamek Sathorn, Bangkok, 10120, Thailand
Tel.: (66) 20555100
Web Site: https://www.lhsec.co.th
Commercial Building Services
N.A.I.C.S.: 236220

LH HOTEL LEASEHOLD REAL ESTATE INVESTMENT TRUST

No 11 Q House Sathorn Building 14th Floor Sathorn Tai Road, Thung Maha Mek Subdistrict Sathorn District, Bangkok, 10120, Thailand
Tel.: (66) 22863484
LHHOTEL—(THA)
Rev.: $38,692,700
Assets: $658,785,710
Liabilities: $301,316,060
Net Worth: $357,469,650
Earnings: $27,711,001
Emp.: 94
Fiscal Year-end: 12/31/23
Investment Trust Management Services
N.A.I.C.S.: 523940

LH SHOPPING CENTERS LEASEHOLD REAL ESTATE INVESTMENT TRUST

No 11 Q House Sathorn Building 14th Floor Sathorn Tai Road, Thung Maha Mek Subdistrict Sathorn District, Bangkok, 10120, Thailand
Tel.: (66) 22863484
LHSC—(THA)
Rev.: $36,830,734
Assets: $208,682,323
Liabilities: $33,411,231
Net Worth: $175,271,092
Earnings: $15,224,076
Emp.: 92
Fiscal Year-end: 12/31/23
Real Estate Investment Trust Services
N.A.I.C.S.: 531190

LHN LIMITED

75 Beach Road 04 01, Singapore, 189689, Singapore
Tel.: (65) 63688328
Web Site:
https://www.lhngroup.com.sg
Year Founded: 1991
1730—(HKG)
Rev.: $69,391,627
Assets: $410,576,510
Liabilities: $248,998,888
Net Worth: $161,577,621
Earnings: $14,018,525
Emp.: 459
Fiscal Year-end: 09/30/23
Real Estate Manangement Services
N.A.I.C.S.: 531312
Kelvin Lim *(Chm & Mng Dir)*

Subsidiaries:

HLA Container Services Pte. Ltd. **(1)**
No 27 Benoi Sector, Singapore, 629859, Singapore
Tel.: (65) 62680151
Web Site: http://www.hlacs.com.sg
Container Depot Management Services
N.A.I.C.S.: 493110
Zaber Neo *(Reg Mgr-Depot)*

LHN Logistics Limited **(1)**
10 Raeburn Park 02-15B, Singapore, 088702, Singapore **(84.05%)**
Tel.: (65) 62697466
Web Site: https://www.lhnlogistics.com
Rev.: $19,083,020
Assets: $24,662,638
Liabilities: $14,342,999
Net Worth: $10,319,639
Earnings: ($2,224,722)
Fiscal Year-end: 09/30/2022
Transportation Services
N.A.I.C.S.: 541614
Kelvin Lim *(Chm)*

LHN Parking HK Limited **(1)**
31/F 148 Electric Road, North Point, China (Hong Kong)
Tel.: (852) 96530394
Web Site: https://www.lhnparking.com.hk
Container Depot Management Services
N.A.I.C.S.: 493110

LHN Parking Pte. Ltd. **(1)**
75 Beach Road 04-01, Singapore, 189689, Singapore
Tel.: (65) 68566600

LHN LIMITED

LHN Limited—(Continued)
Web Site: https://www.lhnparking.com.sg
Car Parking Management Services
N.A.I.C.S.: 812930

LHOIST S.A.
Rue Charles Dubois 28, 1342,
Limelette, Belgium
Tel.: (32) 10230711
Web Site: http://www.lhoist.com
Year Founded: 1889
Sales Range: $1-4.9 Billion
Emp.: 6,000
Lime & Dolomite Mfr
N.A.I.C.S.: 327410
Jean Pierre Berghmans (Chm)

Subsidiaries:

Chemical Lime Company (1)
3700 Hulen St, Fort Worth, TX 76107-6816
Tel.: (817) 429-3077
Web Site: http://www.lhoist.us
Sales Range: $25-49.9 Million
Emp.: 100
Chemical Processing Facilities
N.A.I.C.S.: 327410

Subsidiary (Domestic):

Chemical Lime Co. (2)
2093 Big Stony Creek Rd, Ripplemead, VA 24150-3036
Tel.: (540) 626-7163
Web Site: http://www.chemicallime.com
Sales Range: $50-74.9 Million
Lime Products
N.A.I.C.S.: 327410

Chemical Lime, Ltd (2)
350 Apg Ln, New Braunfels, TX 78132-5035 (100%)
Tel.: (830) 625-2327
Web Site: http://www.chemicallime.com
Sales Range: $25-49.9 Million
Emp.: 70
Mfr of Lime Products
N.A.I.C.S.: 327410

Plant (Domestic):

Lhoist North America, Inc - ARMAGOSA VALLEY PLANT (2)
498 E Imvite Rd, Amargosa Valley, NV 89020
Tel.: (775) 372-5341
Lime Product Mfr
N.A.I.C.S.: 327410

Lhoist North America, Inc - Alabaster (Minerals) Plant (2)
1152 Old Hwy 31, Alabaster, AL 35007
Tel.: (205) 621-3331
Lime Product Mfr
N.A.I.C.S.: 327410
Greg Littleton (Plant Mgr)

Lhoist North America, Inc - Anderson Plant (2)
2024 Crownover Rd, Sherwood, TN 37376
Tel.: (931) 598-5675
Lime Product Mfr
N.A.I.C.S.: 327410
Randy Downing (Plant Mgr)

Lhoist North America, Inc - Charleston Plant (2)
1385 Greenleaf St, Charleston, SC 29405
Tel.: (843) 965-5284
Lime Product Mfr
N.A.I.C.S.: 327410

Lhoist North America, Inc - Clifton Plant (2)
2861 FM 2602, Clifton, TX 76634
Tel.: (254) 315-2569
Lime Product Mfr
N.A.I.C.S.: 327410

Lhoist North America, Inc - Crab Orchard Plant (2)
10583 Hwy 70 E, Crab Orchard, TN 37723
Tel.: (931) 484-7578
Lime Product Mfr
N.A.I.C.S.: 327410
Geoff Fehr (Plant Mgr)

Lhoist North America, Inc - Crawford Plant (2)
8759 E 5th St, Crawford, TX 76638
Tel.: (254) 486-2105
Lime Product Mfr
N.A.I.C.S.: 327410
Keith Muron (Plant Mgr)

Lhoist North America, Inc - Dalton Plant (2)
821 Tilton Bridge Rd, Dalton, GA 30721
Tel.: (706) 277-3740
Lime Product Mfr
N.A.I.C.S.: 327410
Joe Gonzales (Plant Mgr)

Lhoist North America, Inc - Douglas Plant (2)
4753 W Paul Spur Rd, Douglas, AZ 85607
Tel.: (480) 368-4200
Lime Product Mfr
N.A.I.C.S.: 327410

Lhoist North America, Inc - Henderson Plant (2)
BMI Complex 8000 W Lake Mead Dr, Henderson, NV 89009
Tel.: (530) 878-7368
Lime Product Mfr
N.A.I.C.S.: 327410

Lhoist North America, Inc - Lowell Plant (2)
11661 NW Gainesville Rd, Ocala, FL 34482
Tel.: (352) 629-7990
Emp.: 30
Lime Product Mfr
N.A.I.C.S.: 327410
Phillip Curtin (Plant Mgr)

Lhoist North America, Inc - Natividad Plant (2)
11771 Old Stage Rd, Salinas, CA 93908
Tel.: (831) 449-9117
Lime Product Mfr
N.A.I.C.S.: 327410

Lhoist North America, Inc - Nolanville Plant (2)
Hwy FM 439, Nolanville, TX 76559
Tel.: (254) 698-6610
Lime Product Mfr
N.A.I.C.S.: 327410
Aaron Jones (Plant Mgr)

Lhoist North America, Inc - O'Neal Plant (2)
2885 Hwy 31 N, Calera, AL 35040
Tel.: (205) 665-1251
Lime Product Mfr
N.A.I.C.S.: 327410

Lhoist North America, Inc - Spinks Clay Plant (2)
275 Carothers Loop, Paris, TN 38242
Tel.: (731) 642-5414
Web Site: http://www.lhoist.com
Emp.: 68
Lime Product Mfr
N.A.I.C.S.: 327410
Dan Collins (Plant Mgr)

Lhoist North America, Inc - Ste. Genevieve Plant (2)
20947 White Sands Rd, Saint Genevieve, MO 63670
Tel.: (573) 883-3001
Web Site: http://www.lhoist.com
Emp.: 60
Lime Product Mfr
N.A.I.C.S.: 327410

Lhoist North America, Inc - Tenmile Plant (2)
1880 Tenmile Pass Rd, Bancroft, ID 83217
Tel.: (702) 373-3436
Lime Product Mfr
N.A.I.C.S.: 327410

Faxe Kalk A/S (1)
Hovedgaden 13, 4654, Faxe Ladeplads, Denmark
Tel.: (45) 56763500
Web Site: http://www.faxekalk.dk
Lime Product Distr
N.A.I.C.S.: 424910

Franklin Industrial Minerals (1)
9020 Overlook Blvd Ste 200, Brentwood, TN 37027
Tel.: (615) 259-4222
Web Site: http://www.frankmin.com
Rev.: $110,000,000
Emp.: 620
Crushed & Broken Limestone
N.A.I.C.S.: 212312
Rick Dunbar (Gen Mgr)

Grupo Calidra (1)
Av Vasco De Quiroga No 1800 Ph A 4 Piso, A 51, Mexico, Mexico
Tel.: (52) 152591033
Web Site: http://www.calidra.com
Lime & Dolomite Producer
N.A.I.C.S.: 327410

LE&LA Lhoist Engineering & Lime Application (1)
La Mallieue 95, 4470, Saint-Georges-sur-Meuse, Belgium
Tel.: (32) 4 275 84 11
Lime Product Mfr
N.A.I.C.S.: 327410

LHOIST INDUSTRIE S.A. (1)
Usine de On, Marche-en-Famenne, 6900, Belgium
Tel.: (32) 8 422 01 11
Web Site: http://www.carriere-boverie.be
Emp.: 90
Lime Product Mfr
N.A.I.C.S.: 327410
Geoffroy Fievet (Gen Mgr)

Lhoist (Malaysia) Sdn. Bhd. (1)
B-3 A-4 Northpoint Office Mid Valley City N 1 Medan Syed Putra Utara, 59200, Kuala Lumpur, Malaysia
Tel.: (60) 3 2284 1184
Web Site: http://www.lhoist.my
Lime Product Mfr
N.A.I.C.S.: 327410
Mandy Au (Mgr-Bus Dev)

Lhoist Benelux (1)
Parc Des Collines 50, 1300, Wavre, Belgium (100%)
Tel.: (32) 10 233811
Web Site: http://www.lhoist.be
Sales Range: $25-49.9 Million
Emp.: 75
Producer of Lime & Dolomite
N.A.I.C.S.: 327410
Jean-Marc Dewandre (Acct Dir-Europe)

Lhoist Bukowa Sp. z.o.o. (1)
ul Osiedlowa 10, Bukowa, 29-105, Krascoin, Poland
Tel.: (48) 413889105
Lime Product Mfr & Distr
N.A.I.C.S.: 327410

Lhoist Chile LTDA (1)
Avenida Apoquindo N 4499 Piso 4 Comuna de Las Condes, Las Condes, Santiago, Chile
Tel.: (56) 2 2353 9900
Lime Product Mfr & Distr
N.A.I.C.S.: 327410

Lhoist France SA (1)
Tour W 102 Terrasse Boieldieu, La Defense, 92085, Paris, Cedex, France (100%)
Tel.: (33) 153455345
Web Site: http://www.lhoist.com
Sales Range: $25-49.9 Million
Emp.: 50
Producer of Lime & Dolomite
N.A.I.C.S.: 327410

Lhoist India Pvt Ltd (1)
803 8th Floor Windfall Sahar Plaza Complex J B Nagar Andheri Kurla Roa, Andheri East, Mumbai, 400 059, India
Tel.: (91) 22 4502 1000
Web Site: http://www.lhoist.in
Lime Product Distr
N.A.I.C.S.: 424910
Satish Kulkarni (CEO & Mng Dir)

Lhoist Kalk GmbH (1)
Elisabethstrasse 38/1, 8010, Graz, Austria (100%)
Tel.: (43) 316339000
Web Site: http://www.lhoist.com
Sales Range: $25-49.9 Million
Emp.: 2
Producer of Lime & Dolomite
N.A.I.C.S.: 327410

INTERNATIONAL PUBLIC

Lhoist Nederland NV (1)
Galvanistraat 1, 6716 AE, Ede, Netherlands (100%)
Tel.: (31) 318754166
Web Site: http://www.lhoist.com
Sales Range: $100-124.9 Million
Emp.: 10
Producer of Lime & Dolime
N.A.I.C.S.: 327410
Marco Kluivers (Mng Dir)

Lhoist Polska (1)
Ul Morawskiego 5, PL 30102, Krakow, Poland (100%)
Tel.: (48) 00126291600
Web Site: http://www.lhoist.pl
Sales Range: $25-49.9 Million
Emp.: 30
Producer of Lime & Dolomite
N.A.I.C.S.: 327410

Lhoist S.A. - TEXADA LANGLEY PLANT (1)
20303-102B Avenue, Langley, V1M 3H1, BC, Canada
Tel.: (604) 888-2575
Lime Product Mfr
N.A.I.C.S.: 327410

Lhoist Singapore Pte Ltd (1)
3 Anson Road 27-01 Springleaf Tower, Singapore, 079909, Singapore
Tel.: (65) 9238 0652
Web Site: http://www.lhoist.sg
Chemical Products Distr
N.A.I.C.S.: 424690

Lhoist Trading (Shanghai) Co. Ltd. (1)
Suite 1402 Shanghai Mart 2299 West Yan'an Road, Shanghai, 200336, China
Tel.: (86) 21 6236 6330
Web Site: http://www.lhoist.cn
Lime Product Distr
N.A.I.C.S.: 424910

Lhoist UK (1)
Hindlow, Buxton, SK17 0EL, Derbys, United Kingdom (100%)
Tel.: (44) 01298768600
Web Site: http://www.lhoist.co.uk
Sales Range: $25-49.9 Million
Emp.: 75
Lime & Dolomite Producer
N.A.I.C.S.: 327310
Gwyn Watkins (Mgr-Sls)

Lhoist do Brasil Ltda (1)
Avenida Borges de Medeiros 633 sala 308, Leblon, Rio de Janeiro, 22430-041, Brazil
Tel.: (55) 21 3138 9451
Web Site: http://www.lhoist.com.br
Lime Product Mfr & Distr
N.A.I.C.S.: 327410

Lhoist sro (1)
Tman 200, 267 21, Prague, Czech Republic (100%)
Tel.: (420) 311657850
Web Site: http://www.lhoist.cz
Sales Range: $25-49.9 Million
Emp.: 150
Lime & Dolime Producer
N.A.I.C.S.: 327410
Milan Schuller (Mgr-Comml)

Rheinkalk GmbH & Co. KG (1)
Am Kalkstein 1, Wulfrath, 42489, Germany
Tel.: (49) 2058170
Web Site: http://www.rheinkalk.de
Lime & Dolime Mfr
N.A.I.C.S.: 327410

Zaklady Wapiennicze Lhoist S.A. (1)
ul Swierczewskiego 5, Opolski, 46-050, Tarnow, Poland
Tel.: (48) 774516200
Web Site: http://www.lhoist.com
Lime Product Mfr & Distr
N.A.I.C.S.: 327410
Pyotr Biskup (Gen Mgr)

LHT HOLDINGS LIMITED
27 Sungei Kadut Street 1, Singapore, 729335, Singapore
Tel.: (65) 62697890
Web Site: https://www.lht.com.sg
BEI—(SES)
Rev.: $23,274,256

AND PRIVATE COMPANIES

Assets: $58,176,172
Liabilities: $12,191,169
Net Worth: $45,985,003
Earnings: $3,290,919
Emp.: 262
Fiscal Year-end: 12/31/23
Timber Product Mfr
N.A.I.C.S.: 321215
Derek Kah Seng Neo *(Plant Mgr-Recycling)*

Subsidiaries:

Kim Hiap Lee Company Pte. Limited (1)
27 Sungei Kadut Street 1, Singapore, 729335, Singapore
Tel.: (65) 62697890
Wood Container & Pallet Mfr
N.A.I.C.S.: 321920

LHT Marketing Pte Ltd (1)
27 Sungei Kadut Street 1, Singapore, 729335, Singapore
Tel.: (65) 62697890
Sales Range: $25-49.9 Million
Emp.: 170
Timber & Wooden Pallets Distr
N.A.I.C.S.: 113110
May Yap *(Mng Dir)*

Lian Hup Packaging Industries Sdn. Bhd. (1)
15-2 Jalan USJ 9/5Q Subang Business Centre UEP, 47620, Subang Jaya, Selangor, Malaysia
Tel.: (60) 38 024 2681
Web Site: https://www.lianhuppackaging.com
Wood Container & Pallet Mfr
N.A.I.C.S.: 321920

Siri Belukar Packaging Sdn. Bhd. (1)
No PTB 1237 Jalan Tun Matahir 1 Industries Aarea Fase 2, Bandar Tenggara, Kulai, 81440, Johor, Malaysia
Tel.: (60) 78961387
Sales Range: $25-49.9 Million
Emp.: 100
Wooden Pallets Mfr & Distr
N.A.I.C.S.: 321920
Bey Ah Kuee *(Gen Mgr)*

LHV GROUP

Tartu mnt 2, 10145, Tallinn, Estonia
Tel.: (372) 6800400
Web Site: https://www.lhv.ee
Year Founded: 1999
LHV1T—(TAL)
Rev.: $371,586,268
Assets: $7,865,757,811
Liabilities: $7,251,599,515
Net Worth: $614,158,296
Earnings: $342,706,701
Emp.: 1,094
Fiscal Year-end: 12/31/23
All Other Business Support Services
N.A.I.C.S.: 561499
Rain Lohmus *(Chm-Supervisory Bd)*

Subsidiaries:

EveryPay AS (1)
Tartu maantee 2, 10145, Tallinn, Estonia
Tel.: (372) 6442201
Web Site: https://every-pay.com
Digital Payment Services
N.A.I.C.S.: 522320

LI & FUNG LIMITED

11/F LiFung Tower 888 Cheung Sha Wan Rd, Kowloon, China (Hong Kong)
Tel.: (852) 23002300   BM
Web Site: http://www.lifung.com
Rev.: $12,700,744,000
Assets: $5,341,091,000
Liabilities: $3,471,662,000
Net Worth: $1,869,429,000
Earnings: $30,965,000
Emp.: 16,840
Fiscal Year-end: 12/31/18
Holding Company
N.A.I.C.S.: 551112
William Kwok Lun Fung *(Chm)*

Subsidiaries:

Black Cat Fireworks Limited (1)
Standard Drive Crosland Hill, Huddersfield, HD4 7AD, United Kingdom
Tel.: (44) 1484640640
Web Site: http://www.blackcatfireworks.ltd.uk
Sales Range: $25-49.9 Million
Emp.: 30
Fireworks Mfr & Distr
N.A.I.C.S.: 423920

Bossini Fashion GmbH (1)
Harckesheyde 91-93, Norderstedt, 22844, Schleswig-Holstein, Germany
Tel.: (49) 40943640
Fashion Apparels Retailer
N.A.I.C.S.: 424350

Camberley Enterprises Limited (1)
2nd Floor Hong Kong Spinners Building 800 Cheung Sha Wan Road, Kowloon, 526060, China (Hong Kong)
Tel.: (852) 23107900
Women's Clothing Mfr
N.A.I.C.S.: 315250

Comet Feuerwerk GmbH (1)
Uberseering 22, 27580, Bremerhaven, Germany
Tel.: (49) 47190210
Web Site: http://www.comet-feuerwerk.de
Sales Range: $25-49.9 Million
Emp.: 60
Fireworks Mfr & Distr
N.A.I.C.S.: 325998
Richard Eickel *(Exec Dir)*

Direct Sourcing Group Pte. Ltd. (1)
10 Raeburn Park 03-08, Singapore, 088702, Singapore
Tel.: (65) 63338893
Web Site: http://www.lifung.com
Consumer Products Distr
N.A.I.C.S.: 424990

Hang Ten Group Holdings Limited (1)
Rm 912 9th Fl Stanhope House, 734 Kings Rd, Quarry Bay, China (Hong Kong)
Tel.: (852) 31738381
Web Site: http://www.hangten.com.hk
Sales Range: $300-349.9 Million
Emp.: 2,040
Apparel Design, Sales & Marketing Services
N.A.I.C.S.: 315210

Subsidiary (Non-US):

Hang Ten Enterprises (M) Sdn Bhd (2)
9 Jalan PJS 7 21 Bandar Sunway, Petaling Jaya, 46150, Selangor, Malaysia
Tel.: (60) 356355101
Web Site: http://www.hangten.com.my
Sales Range: $25-49.9 Million
Emp.: 5
Clothing Stores Operation Services
N.A.I.C.S.: 458110

Hang Ten Enterprises (Pte) Ltd. (2)
53 Serangoon North Avenue 4 03-02/03, Singapore, 555852, Singapore
Tel.: (65) 6483 0030
Web Site: http://www.hangten.com.sg
Casual Apparels Retailer
N.A.I.C.S.: 458110

Hang Ten Phils., Corp. (2)
76 F Mariano Avenue Anaconda Compound Brgy Dela Paz, Pasig, 10007, Philippines
Tel.: (63) 26475074
Web Site: http://www.hangten.com.ph
Casual Apparels Retailer
N.A.I.C.S.: 458110

Hanson Im-und Export GmbH (1)
Harckesheyde 91-93, Postfach 2240, Norderstedt, 22812, Schleswig-Holstein, Germany
Tel.: (49) 40943640
Web Site: http://www.hanson-import.de
Sales Range: $50-74.9 Million
Emp.: 200
Consumer Products Import & Distr
N.A.I.C.S.: 424990
Christopher Conzen *(Mgr)*

Heusel Textilhandelsgesellschaft mbH (1)
Harckesheyde 91-93, Norderstedt, 22844, Schleswig-Holstein, Germany
Tel.: (49) 4094364521
Fast Moving Consumer Goods Distr
N.A.I.C.S.: 424410

Homeworks Asia Limited (1)
1 F Hong Kong Spinners Industrial Building Ph I & li 800, Cheung Sha Wan Road, Kowloon, China (Hong Kong)
Tel.: (852) 23002300
Consumer Products Whslr
N.A.I.C.S.: 424490

IDS Manufacturing Sdn. Bhd. (1)
Lot 6 Persiaran Perusahaan Section 23, 40300, Shah Alam, Selangor, Malaysia
Tel.: (60) 3 5541 6600
Food & Beverage Products Mfr
N.A.I.C.S.: 311411

Imagine POS Limited (1)
2 F Hk Spinners Industrial Building Phase I Li 800 Cheung Sha Wan Road, Kowloon, China (Hong Kong)
Tel.: (852) 28107838
Web Site: http://www.lifung.com
Fast Moving Consumer Goods Distr
N.A.I.C.S.: 532289

Jac Tissot Solutions GmbH (1)
Harckesheyde 91-93, Norderstedt, 22844, Schleswig-Holstein, Germany
Tel.: (49) 40943640
Web Site: http://www.miles-fashion.de
Sales Range: $50-74.9 Million
Emp.: 2
Consumer Products Distr
N.A.I.C.S.: 424410

Jackel France SAS (1)
83 rue de Paris, 92200, Boulogne-Billancourt, Hauts-de-Seine, France
Tel.: (33) 146050784
Emp.: 60
Cosmetics Distr
N.A.I.C.S.: 456120

Jackel International Limited (1)
2 F Hk Spinners Building Phase I & li 800 Cheung Sha Wan Road, Kowloon Bay, Kowloon, China (Hong Kong)
Tel.: (852) 28107838
Web Site: http://www.jackelhk.com
Fast Moving Consumer Goods Distr
N.A.I.C.S.: 424990

Just Jamie and Paulrich Limited (1)
Woolworth House 242-246 Marylebone Road, London, NW1 6JQ, United Kingdom
Tel.: (44) 2076169395
Web Site: http://www.justjamie.com
Sales Range: $25-49.9 Million
Emp.: 50
Women Fashion Apparels Mfr & Distr
N.A.I.C.S.: 315250

LF Asia (Malaysia) Sdn. Bhd. (1)
Lot 6 Persiaran Perusahaan Seksyen 23, Shah Alam, 40300, Selangor, Malaysia
Tel.: (60) 355417748
Sales Range: $125-149.9 Million
Emp.: 400
Pharmaceutical Products Distr
N.A.I.C.S.: 424210

LF Beauty (UK) Limited (1)
Aintree Avenue White Horse Business Park, Trowbridge, BA14 0XB, Wiltshire, United Kingdom
Tel.: (44) 1225768491
Web Site: http://www.lfbeauty-uk.com
Emp.: 100
Cosmetic Products Mfr & Sales
N.A.I.C.S.: 456199
Gary Armstrong *(Mng Dir)*

LF Beauty Limited (1)
11 F Lifung Tower 888 Cheung Sha Wan Road, Kowloon, China (Hong Kong)
Tel.: (852) 23002300
Web Site: http://www.lifung.com
Sales Range: $1-4.9 Billion
Emp.: 3,000
Cosmetics Distr
N.A.I.C.S.: 424210

LI & FUNG LIMITED

LF Centennial Pte. Ltd. (1)
10 Raeburn Park 03-08, Singapore, 088702, Singapore
Tel.: (65) 63338893
Web Site: http://www.lifung.com
Consumer Products Retailer
N.A.I.C.S.: 424990

LF Centennial Services (Hong Kong) Limited (1)
1 F Hong Kong Spinners Industrial Building Ph I & li 800, Cheung Sha Wan Road, Kowloon, China (Hong Kong)
Tel.: (852) 23005000
Consumer Products Whslr
N.A.I.C.S.: 424490

LF Logistics Limited (1)
14/F LiFung Centre 2 On Ping Street, Siu Lek Yuen, Sha Tin, NT, China (Hong Kong)
Tel.: (852) 2635 5555
Web Site: http://www.lflogistics.com
Emp.: 8,500
Holding Company; Freight Forwarding & Warehousing Services
N.A.I.C.S.: 551112
Mike Lo *(Gen Mgr-Ops)*

Subsidiary (Non-US):

LF (Philippines), Inc. (2)
18th Floor One Corporate Centre Dona Julia Vargas Ave cnr Meralco Ave, Ortigas Center, Pasig, 1605, Philippines
Tel.: (63) 2 798 3864
Logistics Services & Consumer Goods Distr
N.A.I.C.S.: 541614

LF Logistics (Bangladesh) Limited (2)
ABC Heritage - GF Plot No 2 & 4 Jashim Uddin Ave Sec 03, Dhaka, 1230, Bangladesh
Tel.: (880) 289606332317
Freight Services
N.A.I.C.S.: 488510
Azad Mizan *(Asst Mgr-Bus Dev)*

LF Logistics (Cambodia) Limited (2)
No 8A/298 1/F Regency Complex A Mao Tse Toung Blvd Sangkat Tomnoubteuk, Khan Chamkarmorn, Phnom Penh, Cambodia
Tel.: (855) 23424177
Freight Services
N.A.I.C.S.: 488510
Vannear Pin *(Mgr-Fin)*

LF Logistics (China) Co., Ltd. (2)
7/F Tower Block Li & Fung Plaza 2000 Yishan Road, Shanghai, 201103, China
Tel.: (86) 2124164888
Freight Services
N.A.I.C.S.: 488510
Vincent Guo *(Gen Mgr)*

LF Logistics (India) Private Limited (2)
2/F S P Info City Tower B 243 Udyog Vihar Phase I, Gurgaon, 122 016, Haryana, India
Tel.: (91) 1244818082
Freight Services
N.A.I.C.S.: 488510
Anu Rana *(Asst Mgr)*

LF Logistics (Taiwan) Limited (2)
No 269 Daguan Road, Dayuan Township, Taoyuan, Taiwan
Tel.: (886) 339816885169
Logistics Management Consulting Services
N.A.I.C.S.: 541614
Tony Wang *(Mgr-Bus Dev)*

LF Logistics (UK) Limited (2)
2nd Floor Centenary House 1 Centenary Way, Manchester, M50 1RF, United Kingdom
Tel.: (44) 161 786 7569
Web Site: http://www.lflogistics.com
Freight Forwarding Services
N.A.I.C.S.: 484110
Martin Chrimes *(Mgr-Bus Dev)*

LF Logistics (Vietnam) Company Limited (2)
14/F Central Point Building 106 Nguyen Van Troi Str, Phu Nhuan District, Ho Chi Minh City, Vietnam
Tel.: (84) 2839991200
Freight Services

LI & FUNG LIMITED

Li & Fung Limited—(Continued)
N.A.I.C.S.: 488510
Hamza Harti (Dir-Country)

LF Logistics Japan Limited (2)
5-9-11 Osaki MT Building Kita-Shinagawa,
Shinagawa-ku, Tokyo, 141-0001, Japan
Tel.: (81) 477128711
Freight Services
N.A.I.C.S.: 488510

LF Logistics Korea Limited (2)
10/F 280 Gwangpyeong-ro, Gangnam-gu,
Seoul, 06367, Korea (South)
Tel.: (82) 34416220
Freight Services
N.A.I.C.S.: 488510
Yong Min Kim (VP)

LF Logistics Pakistan (Private) Limited (2)
8 Babar Block 1st Floor Asia Center, New Garden Town, Lahore, Pakistan
Tel.: (92) 4235940853
Freight Services
N.A.I.C.S.: 488510
Akhtar Pervez (Mgr-Fin)

LF Logistics Services Pte. Ltd. (2)
10 Bulim Avenue, Singapore, 648165, Singapore
Tel.: (65) 6430 7288
Web Site: http://www.fflogistics.com
Logistics Management Consulting Services
N.A.I.C.S.: 541614

Subsidiary (US):

LF Logistics USA Inc. (2)
230-59 International Airport Ctr Blvd Ste 270, Jamaica, NY 11413
Tel.: (212) 827-3308
Web Site: http://www.lflogistics.com
International Freight Handling & Logistics Services
N.A.I.C.S.: 488119

LF USA Inc. (1)
1359 Broadway Fl 16, New York, NY 10018
Tel.: (646) 562-5000
Rev.: $12,000,000
Emp.: 130
Womens Childrens & Infants Clothing & Accessories Merchant Whslr
N.A.I.C.S.: 424350
Valerie Lavion (Head-Childrenswear Platform & Dept Stores-North America)

Subsidiary (Domestic):

Briefly Stated Holdings, Inc. (2)
350 5th Ave 7th Fl, New York, NY 10118-7819
Tel.: (646) 839-7000
Nightwears Mfr
N.A.I.C.S.: 315250

Subsidiary (Domestic):

Briefly Stated, Inc. (3)
1359 Broadway Fl 18, New York, NY 10018-7839
Tel.: (212) 268-5400
Sleepwear Mfr
N.A.I.C.S.: 315250
David Lavington (Pres)

Subsidiary (Domestic):

Homestead International Group Ltd. (2)
1333 Broadway Fl 10, New York, NY 10018-7117
Tel.: (646) 839-7000
Web Site: http://www.lfusa.com
Consumer Goods Distr
N.A.I.C.S.: 424990

IDS USA Inc. (2)
2 Panasonic Way, Secaucus, NJ 07096
Tel.: (201) 520-2500
Oil Transportation Services
N.A.I.C.S.: 488190

Subsidiary (Domestic):

IDS USA West Inc. (3)
5151 Eucalyptus Ave, Chino, CA 91710-9206
Tel.: (909) 393-5840
Logistic Services

N.A.I.C.S.: 541614

Subsidiary (Domestic):

LF Accessories Group LLC (2)
1359 Broadway Fl 21, New York, NY 10018-7824
Tel.: (646) 839-7000
Consumer Goods Distr
N.A.I.C.S.: 424990

Group (Domestic):

Max Leather Group (2)
366 Fifth Ave, New York, NY 10001
Tel.: (212) 967-4120
Sales Range: $10-24.9 Million
Emp.: 125
Apparel Accessories Mfr & Sales
N.A.I.C.S.: 315990

Affiliate (Domestic):

Cipriani Accessories (3)
366 Fifth Ave, New York, NY 10001
Tel.: (212) 967-4120
Designer, Distr & Importer of Men's & Women's Accessories
N.A.I.C.S.: 315990
Evan Mittman (Pres)

Group (Domestic):

Oxford Apparel (2)
3 Park Ave 24th Fl, New York, NY 10016-5902 (100%)
Tel.: (212) 481-4901
Sales Range: $25-49.9 Million
Emp.: 60
Dress Sport Shirts & Mens Boys Sportswear Mfr
N.A.I.C.S.: 315250

Subsidiary (Domestic):

Pacific Alliance USA, Inc. (2)
1359 Broadway, New York, NY 10018-7102
Tel.: (646) 839-7000
Apparels Mfr
N.A.I.C.S.: 315990
Iric Browndorf (Sr VP)

Ralsey Group Limited (2)
1359 Broadway 16th Fl, New York, NY 10018
Tel.: (212) 730-0900
Sportswear Whslr
N.A.I.C.S.: 424350

Regatta Pacific Alliance USA Inc. (2)
1372 Broadway 21st 5th Fl, New York, NY 10018
Tel.: (212) 840-5600
Web Site: http://www.regattausa.com
Sales Range: $50-74.9 Million
Emp.: 100
Apparel Designer & Marketer
N.A.I.C.S.: 424350
Haim Dabah (Pres & Chief Mdsg Officer)

Rosetti Handbags and Accessories, Ltd. (2)
10 W 33rd St Ste 312, New York, NY 10001
Tel.: (212) 279-3470
Handbags Mfr & Sales
N.A.I.C.S.: 316990

VZI Investment Corp. (2)
1359 Broadway Fl 21, New York, NY 10018-7824
Tel.: (646) 839-7000
Investment Management Service
N.A.I.C.S.: 523999

Wear Me Apparel LLC (2)
350 5th Ave 4th Fl, New York, NY 10118
Tel.: (212) 736-9266
Sales Range: $150-199.9 Million
Womens, Childrens & Infant Clothing
N.A.I.C.S.: 424350

Lenci Calzature SpA (1)
Viale Puccini 1770/1772, 55016, Porcari, Lucca, Italy
Tel.: (39) 05832621
Web Site: http://www.lenci.it
Ladies Leather Shoes Mfr
N.A.I.C.S.: 316210

Li & Fung (Bangladesh) Limited (1)
ABC Heritage Plot 2 & 4 Uttara C A Jashim Uddin Avenue Setcor 3, Uttara Model Town, Dhaka, 1230, Bangladesh
Tel.: (880) 28960633
Consumer Products Whslr
N.A.I.C.S.: 424310

Li & Fung (Cambodia) Limited (1)
8A Street 245 Building Regency Complex A 1st Floor, Phnom Penh, 12306, Cambodia
Tel.: (855) 23424099
Wholesale Trade Agency
N.A.I.C.S.: 425120
Bunna Long (Sr Mgr)

Li & Fung (Guatemala) S.A. (1)
5a Avenue 5-55 Zona 14 12o Piso, Guatemala, 01014, Guatemala
Tel.: (502) 22855700
Consumer Goods Distr
N.A.I.C.S.: 424990

Li & Fung (India) Private Limited (1)
Tower B S P Infocity243 Udyog Vihar Phase I, Gurgaon, 122016, Haryana, India
Tel.: (91) 1246116666
Web Site: http://www.lifung.co.in
Ladies Apparels Retailer
N.A.I.C.S.: 458110

Li & Fung (Korea) Limited (1)
7 F Song Am Building 709 eonju-ro jangnan- gu, Kangnam-ku, Seoul, 135-734, Korea (South)
Tel.: (82) 234416500
Consumer Products Whslr
N.A.I.C.S.: 424990
Sonya Yoon (Exec VP)

Li & Fung (Mauritius) Limited (1)
Royal Road, Moka, Mauritius
Tel.: (230) 4335420
Consumer Products Whslr
N.A.I.C.S.: 424990

Li & Fung (Philippines) Inc. (1)
2-4 F Valderrama Building 107 Esteban Street, Legaspi Village, Makati, 1229, Philippines
Tel.: (63) 2 8439804
Web Site: http://www.lifung.com
Consumer Products Retailer
N.A.I.C.S.: 424990

Li & Fung (Portugal) Limited (1)
Rua da Lionesa nr 446 Building C-24 Centro Empresarial Da Lionesa, Leca do Balio, Matosinhos, Portugal
Tel.: (351) 22 0915000
Sales Range: $25-49.9 Million
Emp.: 60
Consumer Products Distr
N.A.I.C.S.: 424990
Francisco Barbosa (Gen Mgr)

Li & Fung (Singapore) Pte. Limited (1)
10 Raeburn Park unit 03-08 Block A, Singapore, 088702, Singapore
Tel.: (65) 63338893
Sales Range: $50-74.9 Million
Emp.: 150
Fashion Apparel Distr
N.A.I.C.S.: 424990
Cindy Chew (Mgr-Fin)

Li & Fung (Taiwan) Limited (1)
70 Rueiguang Road, Nanking E Road, Taipei, Taiwan
Tel.: (886) 226508000
Consumer Products Retailer
N.A.I.C.S.: 424990

Li & Fung (Trading) Limited (1)
11/F LiFung Tower 888 Cheung Sha Wan Road, Kowloon, China (Hong Kong)
Tel.: (852) 23002300
Web Site: http://www.lifung.com
Consumer Goods Distr
N.A.I.C.S.: 424990

Li & Fung Mumessillik Pazarlama Limited Sirketi (1)
Yenibosna Merkez Mahallesi Yalcin Kores Cad No 20, Bahcelievler, 34197, Istanbul, Turkiye
Tel.: (90) 2124967300
Web Site: http://www.lifung.com
Consumer Goods Distr
N.A.I.C.S.: 424310

Li & Fung Trading (Shanghai) Limited (1)

2000 Yishan Road, Shanghai, 201103, China
Tel.: (86) 2124055888
Web Site: http://www.lifung.com
Consumer Products Distr
N.A.I.C.S.: 424990

Lloyd Textile Trading Limited (1)
8 F Hk Spinners Industrial Building Ph 6 481-483 Castle Peak Road, Kowloon, China (Hong Kong)
Tel.: (852) 23002600
Consumer Products Whslr
N.A.I.C.S.: 424990

Miles Fashion GmbH (1)
Harckesheyde 91-93, Norderstedt, 22844, Schleswig-Holstein, Germany
Tel.: (49) 40943640
Web Site: http://www.miles-fashion.de
Sales Range: $100-124.9 Million
Emp.: 440
Fashion Apparels Mfr & Distr
N.A.I.C.S.: 315250
Christopher Conzen (Co-Mng Dir)

Miles Fashion Group France EURL (1)
Le Cruix, Druillat, 01160, Ain, France
Tel.: (33) 474390263
Family Clothing Whslr
N.A.I.C.S.: 424350

Miles GmbH (1)
Harckesheyde 91-93, 22844, Norderstedt, Germany
Tel.: (49) 40943640
Web Site: http://www.milesgroup.eu
Fashion Product & Household Appliance Whslr
N.A.I.C.S.: 423620
Boris Vogt (Mng Dir)

Modium Konfeksiyon Sanayi ve Ticaret Anonim Sirketi (1)
Yenibosna Merkez Mah Yalcin Kores Cad No 20 C Block 1 Kisim, Yenibosna Bahcelievler, 34197, Istanbul, Turkiye
Tel.: (90) 2124967800
Web Site: http://www.modium.com.tr
Textile Products Mfr
N.A.I.C.S.: 314999
Pinar Turktuzun (Gen Mgr)

P.T. Lifung Indonesia (1)
Wisma 76 2nd Floor JL Let Jen S Parman Kav 76 Slipi, Jakarta, 78, Indonesia
Tel.: (62) 2125678888
Household Furniture & Electronic Appliances Distr
N.A.I.C.S.: 423620

Peter Black Footwear & Accessories Limited (1)
Lawkholme Lane, Keighley, BD21 3JQ, West Yorkshire, United Kingdom
Tel.: (44) 2077244188
Web Site: http://www.pbfa.co.uk
Footwear Mfr & Distr
N.A.I.C.S.: 424340

PromOcean Spain SL (1)
Frederic Mompou 4 a 3-1, Sant Just Desvern, 8960, Barcelona, Spain
Tel.: (34) 934705464
Web Site: http://www.lifung.com
Sales Range: $25-49.9 Million
Emp.: 10
Consumer Products Distr
N.A.I.C.S.: 424350

STS Shenzhen Testing Service Limited (1)
1st Floor Building B Zhuo Ke Science Technology Park 190, Chongqing Road Baoan, Shenzhen, 518103, Guangdong, China
Tel.: (86) 75536886288
Web Site: http://www.stsapp.com
Wireless Communication Product Mfr
N.A.I.C.S.: 334220

Silvereed (Hong Kong) Limited (1)
926 Centennial Building Cheung Sha Wan Road, Cheung Sha Wan, Kowloon, China (Hong Kong)
Tel.: (852) 27553288
Web Site: http://www.hktdc.com
Emp.: 80
Consumer Goods Distr
N.A.I.C.S.: 532289

Texnorte Industrial Limited (1)
1 F Hong Kong Spinners Indl Building Ph I
& Ii 800 Cheung Sha Wan Road, Kowloon,
China (Hong Kong)
Tel.: (852) 23005000
Consumer Products Whslr
N.A.I.C.S.: 424490
Nikki Lee *(Asst Mgr-HR)*

Toy Island Manufacturing Company Limited (1)
1 F Hk Spinners Industrial Building Phase I
& II, 800 Cheung Sha Wan Road Cheung,
Kowloon, China (Hong Kong)
Tel.: (852) 23002300
Web Site: http://www.lifung.com
Toys Mfr & Sales
N.A.I.C.S.: 339930

Universal Pharmaceutical Laboratories Limited (1)
Units 1 - 5 1/F Eastern Center 1065 Kings
Road, Quarry Bay, China (Hong Kong)
Tel.: (852) 25628131
Web Site: http://www.upll.com.hk
Pharmaceuticals Products Mfr & Distr
N.A.I.C.S.: 325412

Ventana Bekleidungsfabrikation GmbH (1)
Harckesheyde 91-93, Norderstedt, 22844,
Schleswig-Holstein, Germany
Tel.: (49) 40943640
Fashion Apparels Retailer
N.A.I.C.S.: 315210

Verity Enterprises Limited (1)
7 F Centennial Building 924-926 Cheung
Sha Wan Road, Cheung Sha Wan, Kowloon, China (Hong Kong)
Tel.: (852) 23002600
Fast Moving Consumer Goods Distr
N.A.I.C.S.: 424990

Visage Group Limited (1)
Visage House Shaftesbury Avenue, South
Shields, NE34 9PH, Tyne And Wear, United
Kingdom
Tel.: (44) 1914271133
Sales Range: $25-49.9 Million
Emp.: 100
Womens Apparel Mfr & Distr
N.A.I.C.S.: 315250
Sanjeev Mehan *(Mng Dir)*

Visage Limited (1)
242 Marylebone Road, London, NW1 6JQ,
United Kingdom
Tel.: (44) 2075637227
Web Site: http://www.visage-group.com
Textile Product Mfr & Distr
N.A.I.C.S.: 314999

Wilson Textile Limited (1)
10 F Centennial Building 924-926 Cheung
Sha Wan Road, Kowloon, China (Hong Kong)
Tel.: (852) 23107800
Consumer Products Whslr
N.A.I.C.S.: 424990

LI AUTO INC.
11 Wenliang Street, Shunyi District,
Beijing, 101399, China
Tel.: (86) 1087427209   Ky
Web Site: http://www.lixiang.com
Year Founded: 2015
LI—(NASDAQ)
Rev.: $4,138,168,241
Assets: $9,475,871,961
Liabilities: $3,184,410,252
Net Worth: $6,291,461,710
Earnings: ($49,250,121)
Emp.: 11,901
Fiscal Year-end: 12/31/21
Holding Company
N.A.I.C.S.: 551112
Xiang Li *(Co-Founder, Chm & CEO)*

LI BANG INTERNATIONAL CORPORATION INC.
No 190 Xizhang Road, Gushan Town,
Jiangyin, Jiangsu, China
Tel.: (86) 51081630030   Ky
Web Site: https://ir.libangco.cn
Year Founded: 2021

LBGJ—(NASDAQ)
Rev.: $10,794,015
Assets: $25,079,568
Liabilities: $20,824,571
Net Worth: $4,254,997
Earnings: ($1,373,887)
Emp.: 141
Fiscal Year-end: 06/30/24
Holding Company
N.A.I.C.S.: 551112
Feng Huang *(CEO, Founder & Chm)*

LI BAO GE GROUP LIMITED
Room 2702 Tower 2 Kowloon Commerce Centre No 51 Kwai Cheong
Road, Kwai Chung, New Territories,
China (Hong Kong)
Tel.: (852) 25743326   Ky
Web Site:
 http://www.starofcanton.com.hk
1869—(HKG)
Rev.: $17,282,880
Assets: $18,095,310
Liabilities: $26,594,715
Net Worth: ($8,499,405)
Earnings: ($5,494,485)
Emp.: 408
Fiscal Year-end: 12/31/22
Restaurant Management Services
N.A.I.C.S.: 722511
Chun Kit Chan *(Chm & CEO)*

LI CHENG ENTERPRISE CO., LTD.
No 5 Dou-Kung 12 Road, Dou-Liu
City Yun-Lin, Hsien, 640, Taiwan
Tel.: (886) 55571010
Web Site: https://www.li-cheng.com.tw
Year Founded: 1992
4426—(TAI)
Rev.: $42,254,748
Assets: $155,998,686
Liabilities: $69,054,741
Net Worth: $86,943,945
Earnings: ($1,371,791)
Emp.: 650
Fiscal Year-end: 12/31/23
Fabrics Mfr
N.A.I.C.S.: 313230

LI HENG CHEMICAL FIBRE TECHNOLOGIES LIMITED
Binhai Industrial Zone, Changle,
350218, Fujian, China
Tel.: (86) 591 28513333
Web Site:
 http://www.lihengchem.com
Sales Range: $400-449.9 Million
Nylon Yarn Product Mfr & Sales
N.A.I.C.S.: 313110

LI KANG BIOMEDICAL CO., LTD.
No 29 Huangong Rd, Yongkang Dist,
T'ainan, 710, Taiwan
Tel.: (886) 62337068
Web Site: https://www.likangbio.com
6242—(TPE)
Rev.: $21,394,272
Assets: $21,537,661
Liabilities: $3,711,409
Net Worth: $17,826,251
Earnings: $3,504,799
Fiscal Year-end: 12/31/22
Pharmaceuticals Product Mfr
N.A.I.C.S.: 325412
Yu-Hsiu Cheng *(Chm & Pres)*

LI MING DEVELOPMENT CONSTRUCTION CO., LTD.
7F No 419 Sec 2 Kung Dao Wu Rd,
Hsinchu, Taiwan
Tel.: (886) 36886188
6212—(TPE)
Rev.: $38,468,186

Assets: $465,368,039
Liabilities: $378,565,238
Net Worth: $86,802,801
Earnings: $5,592,784
Fiscal Year-end: 12/31/22
Electronic Product Mfr & Distr
N.A.I.C.S.: 334413
Sen-Hsien Tseng *(Chm & CEO)*

LI NING CO., LTD.
No 8 Xing Guang 5th Street Opto-
Mechatronics Industrial Park, Zhongguancun Science & Technology Area
Tongzhou District, Beijing, 101111,
China
Tel.: (86) 1080800808   Ky
Web Site: http://www.lining.com
LNNGF—(OTCIQ)
Rev.: $3,821,235,462
Assets: $4,736,348,444
Liabilities: $1,357,050,565
Net Worth: $3,379,297,879
Earnings: $441,260,800
Emp.: 3,105
Fiscal Year-end: 12/31/23
Sportswear Mfr
N.A.I.C.S.: 339920
Ning Li *(Founder, Chm & Co-CEO)*

Subsidiaries:

Guangdong Yue Ao Sports Development Co., Ltd. (1)
Nanfeng Ave Xinan St, Sanshui Guangdong, 528100, Foshan, China
Tel.: (86) 757 87736877
Sports Goods Mfr
N.A.I.C.S.: 339920

Li Ning (China) Sports Goods Co., Ltd. (1)
No 8 Xing Guang 5th Street Opto-
Mechatronics Industrial Park, Zhongguancan Science and Technology Area
Tongzhou District, Beijing, 101111, China
Tel.: (86) 1080800818
Web Site: http://en.lining.com
Athletic Good Retailer
N.A.I.C.S.: 459110
Li Ning *(Founder)*

Li Ning Sports (China) Co., Ltd. (1)
No 8 Xing Guang 5th St Zhongguancun
Science & Technology Park, Tong Zhou District, 101111, Beijing, China
Tel.: (86) 1080800808
Sports Goods Sales Services
N.A.I.C.S.: 459110

LI PENG ENTERPRISE CO., LTD.
11F No 162 Songjiang Rd, Zhongshan Dist, Taipei, 104, Taiwan
Tel.: (886) 221002888
Web Site:
 https://www.lealeagroup.com.tw
1447—(TAI)
Rev.: $891,141,950
Assets: $616,052,184
Liabilities: $294,111,372
Net Worth: $321,940,812
Earnings: ($560,173)
Fiscal Year-end: 12/31/22
Textile Product Mfr & Distr
N.A.I.C.S.: 314999

LI-CYCLE HOLDINGS CORP.
207 Queens Quay West Suite 590,
Toronto, M5J 1A7, ON, Canada   Ca
Web Site: https://www.li-cycle.com
LICY—(NYSE)
Rev.: $18,300,000
Assets: $886,000,000
Liabilities: $509,600,000
Net Worth: $376,400,000
Earnings: ($13,800,000)
Emp.: 384
Fiscal Year-end: 12/31/23
Holding Company
N.A.I.C.S.: 551112

Ajay Kochhar *(Co-Founder, Pres & CEO)*

Subsidiaries:

Li-Cycle Corp. (1)
207 Queens Quay West Suite 590, Toronto,
M5J 1A7, ON, Canada
Tel.: (877) 542-9253
Lithium-ion Battery Recycling Technology
N.A.I.C.S.: 335910

LI-FT POWER LTD.
1218-1030 West Georgia Street, Vancouver, V6E 2Y3, BC, Canada
Tel.: (604) 609-6185   BC
Web Site: https://www.li-ft.com
Year Founded: 2021
LIFFF—(OTCQX)
Rev.: $782,300
Assets: $193,331,610
Liabilities: $12,204,329
Net Worth: $181,127,281
Earnings: $2,621,703
Fiscal Year-end: 11/30/23
Mineral Exploration Services
N.A.I.C.S.: 212390
Francis MacDonald *(CEO)*

LI3 LITHIUM CORP.
217 Queen Street West Suite 401,
Toronto, M5V 0R2, ON, Canada
Tel.: (416) 361-2827   Ca
Web Site: https://lithium3.com
Year Founded: 1989
WD9—(DEU)
Assets: $1,269,747
Liabilities: $33,640
Net Worth: $1,236,107
Earnings: ($675,572)
Fiscal Year-end: 11/30/22
Mineral Exploration Services
N.A.I.C.S.: 213114
Rex E. Loesby *(Chm)*

LIAN BENG GROUP LTD.
29 Harrison Road Lian Beng Building,
Singapore, 369648, Singapore
Tel.: (65) 62831468
Web Site:
 http://www.lianbeng.com.sg
L03—(SES)
Rev.: $388,424,515
Assets: $1,475,326,890
Liabilities: $828,437,641
Net Worth: $646,889,250
Earnings: $26,540,970
Emp.: 1,700
Fiscal Year-end: 05/31/21
Construction Services
N.A.I.C.S.: 236220
Lay Huan Ong *(Exec Dir)*

Subsidiaries:

Lian Beng Engineering & Machinery Pte Ltd (1)
63 Senoko Dr Woodland E Industrial Estate, Singapore, 758250, Singapore
Tel.: (65) 63626730
Web Site: http://www.lianbenggroup.com.sg
Scaffolding Contractors
N.A.I.C.S.: 238990
Ong Lee Yap *(Dir-Pur)*

Sinmix Pte Ltd (1)
63 Senoko Drive Woodlands East Industrial
Estate, Singapore, 758250, Singapore
Tel.: (65) 67591151
Web Site: http://www.sinmix.com.sg
Sales Range: $25-49.9 Million
Emp.: 8
Ready Mix Concrete Mfr & Distr
N.A.I.C.S.: 327320
David Goh *(Mng Dir)*

LIAN EE HYDRAULICS PTE LTD.
Blk 16D, Tuas Ave 1 #02-60, Singapore, 639536, Singapore
Tel.: (65) 62611611

Lian Ee Hydraulics Pte Ltd.—(Continued)
Web Site:
https://www.lianeehyd.com.sg
Year Founded: 1987
Industrial Services
N.A.I.C.S.: 236210
Subsidiaries:

GRP Pte Ltd (1)
33 Gul Circle, Singapore, 629570, Singapore
Tel.: (65) 62661622
Web Site: http://www.grppteltd.com
Marine Product Mfr
N.A.I.C.S.: 336612

LIAN HWA FOODS CORPORATION
148 Ti Hwa Street Sec 1, Taipei, Taiwan
Tel.: (886) 225534546
Web Site: http://www.lianhwa.com.tw
1231—(TAI)
Rev.: $354,925,131
Assets: $425,396,890
Liabilities: $236,414,131
Net Worth: $188,982,759
Earnings: $31,709,832
Fiscal Year-end: 12/31/23
Snack Food Mfr
N.A.I.C.S.: 311911

LIAN SHENG TECHNOLOGY CO., LTD.
Floor 1 No 8 Guanri Road Software Park Phase II, Torch High-tech Industrial Development Zone, Xiamen, 361008, Fujian, China
Tel.: (86) 5925397222
Web Site: http://www.35.com
Year Founded: 2004
300051—(CHIN)
Rev.: $24,916,788
Assets: $82,105,920
Liabilities: $56,811,456
Net Worth: $25,294,464
Earnings: ($4,522,284)
Emp.: 1,350
Fiscal Year-end: 12/31/22
Software & IT Products & Services
N.A.I.C.S.: 513210
Huang Mingliang *(Chm)*

LIANCHUANG ELECTRONIC TECHNOLOGY CO., LTD.
Lianchuang Electronic Audio-visual Technology Park, No 1699 Jingdong Ave High-tech Development Zone, Nanchang, 330096, Jiangxi, China
Tel.: (86) 79188320717
Web Site: https://www.lcetron.com
Year Founded: 2006
002036—(SSE)
Rev.: $589,653,324
Assets: $2,226,327,012
Liabilities: $1,619,881,848
Net Worth: $606,445,164
Earnings: ($39,237,588)
Fiscal Year-end: 12/31/22
Textile Products Mfr
N.A.I.C.S.: 314999
Zeng Jiyong *(Chm & Gen Mgr)*

LIANDI (NANJING) INFORMATION SYSTEMS CO., LTD
15F Bldg 2 Xincheng Sci-tech Park 68 Aoti Ave, Nanjing, 210019, China
Tel.: (86) 25 8324 9500
Web Site:
http://www.liandisys.com.cn
Year Founded: 1990
Software Development & IT Services
N.A.I.C.S.: 513210
Rong Ming Shen *(Gen Mgr)*

LIANDI CLEAN TECHNOLOGY INC.
4th Floor Tower B Wanliuxingui Building, Haidian District, Beijing, 100089, China
Tel.: (86) 1058720171 NV
LNDT—(OTCIQ)
Sales Range: Less than $1 Million
Downstream Flow Equipment & Engineering Services
N.A.I.C.S.: 333132
Jianzhong Zuo *(Chm, Pres & CEO)*

LIANE AUTOMOBILES
Z I De La Liane 20 Boulevard De La Liane, 62360, Saint Leonard, Pas De Calais, France
Tel.: (33) 321992112
Sales Range: $10-24.9 Million
Emp.: 41
New & Used Car Dealers
N.A.I.C.S.: 441110

LIANHE CHEMICAL TECHNOLOGY CO., LTD.
8 Yongjiao Road, Huangyan Economic Development Zone, Taizhou, 318020, Zhejiang, China
Tel.: (86) 57684275170
Web Site:
https://www.lianhetech.com
Year Founded: 1985
002250—(SSE)
Rev.: $1,104,311,988
Assets: $2,107,215,864
Liabilities: $1,093,818,492
Net Worth: $1,013,397,372
Earnings: $97,836,336
Fiscal Year-end: 12/31/22
Chemicals Mfr
N.A.I.C.S.: 325998
Maggie Wang *(Chm, Chm, Pres & Pres)*
Subsidiaries:

Fine Industries Limited (1)
Seal Sands, Middlesbrough, TS2 1UB, United Kingdom
Tel.: (44) 1642546666
Web Site: http://www.fineindustries.co.uk
Holding Company; Fine Chemicals Contract Mfr
N.A.I.C.S.: 551112

Subsidiary (Domestic):

Fine Environmental Services Limited (2)
Seal Sands, Middlesbrough, TS2 1UB, United Kingdom
Tel.: (44) 1642546666
Hazardous Liquid Waste Treatment Services
N.A.I.C.S.: 562211

Fine Organics Limited (2)
Seal Sands, Middlesbrough, TS2 1UB, United Kingdom
Tel.: (44) 1642 546 666
Web Site: http://www.fineindustries.co.uk
Chemicals Mfr
N.A.I.C.S.: 325199
James Rankin *(Dir-Comml-Pharmaceuticals)*

Division (Domestic):

Fine Contract Research Limited (3)
Seal Sands, Middlesbrough, TS2 1UB, United Kingdom
Tel.: (44) 1642 546 666
Web Site: http://www.fineindustries.co.uk
Synthetic Chemical Research Services
N.A.I.C.S.: 541715

LIANNEX CORPORATION (S) PTE. LTD.
18 Sungei Kadut Way, Singapore, 728789, Singapore
Tel.: (65) 63635133 SG
Web Site: http://www.liannex.com.sg
Year Founded: 1993
Emp.: 150
Holding Company; Coal, Cement & Construction Materials Trading; Bus Mfr; Warehousing, Shipping & Land Freight Transportation Services
N.A.I.C.S.: 551112
Han Weng Lim *(Founder)*
Subsidiaries:

Icon Offshore Berhad (1)
Icon Offshore Berhad Level 16 Menara Tan & Tan 207 Jalan Tun Razak, 50450, Kuala Lumpur, Malaysia (56.67%)
Tel.: (60) 327700500
Web Site: https://www.iconoffshore.com.my
Rev.: $59,996,297
Assets: $159,453,538
Liabilities: $74,263,639
Net Worth: $85,189,899
Earnings: $36,508,149
Emp.: 537
Fiscal Year-end: 12/31/2022
Offshore Support Vessel Services
N.A.I.C.S.: 488510
Arshad Tun Uda *(Chm)*

Yinson Corporation Sdn. Bhd. (1)
No 23 M Jalan 5/116B Kuchai Entrepreneurs Park, Off Jalan Kuchai Lama, 58200, Kuala Lumpur, Federal Territory, Malaysia
Tel.: (60) 379811000
Warehousing & Freight Forwarding Services
N.A.I.C.S.: 488510
Lim Han Joeh *(Mgr)*

LIAONING CHENGDA CO., LTD.
No 71 Renmin Road, Zhongshan District, Dalian, 116001, China
Tel.: (86) 41182511111
Web Site:
https://www.chengda.com.cn
Year Founded: 1993
600739—(SHG)
Rev.: $2,814,858,386
Assets: $7,356,813,266
Liabilities: $2,534,197,583
Net Worth: $4,822,615,684
Earnings: $330,829,417
Emp.: 200
Fiscal Year-end: 12/31/21
Textile Product Whslr
N.A.I.C.S.: 424990
Shuzhi Shang *(Chm)*
Subsidiaries:

Chengda International Co., Ltd. (1)
RM 303 Block A No 2679 Hechuan RD, Shanghai, 81234, China
Tel.: (86) 21 34792686
Clothing Accessory Distr
N.A.I.C.S.: 458110

Subsidiary (US):

Chengda International (New York) Co., Ltd. (2)
264 W 40th St Ste 501, New York, NY 10018
Tel.: (212) 730-7284
Web Site: http://www.chengdany.com
Clothing Accessory Distr
N.A.I.C.S.: 458110

LIAONING DARE INDUSTRIAL COMPANY LTD.
Fuxin Development Zone, Fuxin, 123004, China
Tel.: (86) 418 339 9123
Construction Materials Supplier
N.A.I.C.S.: 423390
Li Yi *(Chm)*
Subsidiaries:

Carcoustics International GmbH (1)
Neuenkamp 8, 51381, Leverkusen, Germany
Tel.: (49) 21719000
Web Site: http://www.carcoustics.com
Developer & Producer of Acoustic System For Cars

N.A.I.C.S.: 334310
Georg Brasch *(CFO & Member-Mgmt Bd)*

Subsidiary (Non-US):

Carcoustics Austria Ges.m.b.H. (2)
Treietstrasse 10, 6833, Klaus, Vorarlberg, Austria
Tel.: (43) 55 23 504 0
Web Site: http://www.carcoustics.com
Automobile Parts Distr
N.A.I.C.S.: 423120

Carcoustics Belgium N.V. (2)
Henry Fordlaan Z/N, Genk, 3600, Belgium
Tel.: (32) 89 62 05 00
Web Site: http://www.carcoustics.com
Audio & Video Equipment Mfr
N.A.I.C.S.: 334310

Subsidiary (Domestic):

Carcoustics Deutschland GmbH (2)
Neuenkamp 8, Sagerbaume 9, 51381, Leverkusen, Germany
Tel.: (49) 21719000
Web Site: http://www.carcoustics.com
Audio & Video Equipment Mfr
N.A.I.C.S.: 334310
Peter Scwebeenger *(CEO)*

Subsidiary (Non-US):

Carcoustics Espana SA (2)
Carrer dels Argenters46, Alcasser, 46290, Valencia, Spain
Tel.: (34) 961221280
Web Site: http://www.carcoustics.com
Motor Vehicle Parts Mfr
N.A.I.C.S.: 336390

Carcoustics France S.A.R.L. (2)
13 rue de Camilles-Desmoulins, 90150, Issy-les-Moulineaux, France
Tel.: (33) 1 5804 24 24
Web Site: http://www.carcoustics.com
Audio & Video Equipment Mfr
N.A.I.C.S.: 334310

Subsidiary (Domestic):

Carcoustics Haldensleben GmbH (2)
Jakob-Uffrecht-Strasse 26, Haldensleben, 39340, Hannover, Germany
Tel.: (49) 39046682600
Web Site: http://www.carcoustics.de
Audio & Video Equipment Mfr
N.A.I.C.S.: 334310

Subsidiary (Non-US):

Carcoustics Industrial De Mexico S de rl de C.V. (2)
Circuito Balvanera 24 Lote 40 Bodega 3, 76920, Queretaro, Mexico
Tel.: (52) 4423093800
Web Site: http://www.carcoustics.com
Motor Vehicle Parts Mfr
N.A.I.C.S.: 336390

Subsidiary (US):

Carcoustics Tech Center North America Inc. (2)
5455 Corporate Ste 300, Troy, MI 48098
Tel.: (248) 251-1737
Web Site: http://www.carcoustics.com
Audio & Video Equipment Mfr
N.A.I.C.S.: 334310

Carcoustics USA, Inc. (2)
1400 Durant Dr, Howell, MI 48843-8572
Tel.: (517) 548-6700
Web Site: http://www.carcoustics.com
Accoustics Products For Cars Developer & Producer
N.A.I.C.S.: 334310

LIAONING ENERGY INDUSTRY CO., LTD.
4F Qiyun Building No 96-6 Huanghe South Avenue, Huanggu District, Shenyang, 110000, Liaoning, China
Tel.: (86) 2486131586
600758—(SHG)
Rev.: $929,325,389
Assets: $2,096,461,589
Liabilities: $1,353,074,014
Net Worth: $743,387,575

Earnings: $27,342,507
Fiscal Year-end: 12/31/22
Electric Power Generation & Steam Supply Services
N.A.I.C.S.: 221112
Guang Zhao *(Chm)*

LIAONING FU-AN HEAVY INDUSTRY CO., LTD.
No 8 Anzheng Road, Qianshan District, Anshan, 114016, Liaoning, China
Tel.: (86) 4128432322
Web Site: https://www.lnfa.com.cn
Year Founded: 2004
603315—(SHG)
Rev.: $145,741,013
Assets: $389,390,876
Liabilities: $176,068,932
Net Worth: $213,321,944
Earnings: $11,490,750
Fiscal Year-end: 12/31/21
Heavy Steel Casting Provider
N.A.I.C.S.: 331513
Jianhua Mu *(Chm)*

LIAONING HE EYE HOSPITAL GROUP CO., LTD.
No 128 N Huanghe Street, Huangnan South Avenue Huanggu District, Shenyang, 110163, Liaoning, China
Tel.: (86) 4009090400
Web Site:
  https://www.hevisiongroup.com
Year Founded: 2009
301103—(SSE)
Rev.: $132,562,872
Assets: $365,799,564
Liabilities: $60,268,104
Net Worth: $305,531,460
Earnings: $13,957,164
Fiscal Year-end: 12/31/22
Health Care Srvices
N.A.I.C.S.: 621610
Wei He *(Chm & Gen Mgr)*

LIAONING HEZHAN ENERGY GROUP CO., LTD
Building No 38-1 No 42 Kunlunshan Road, Fanhe New District, Tieling, 112000, Liaoning, China
Tel.: (86) 2474997822
Web Site:
  http://www.tielingnewcity.com.cn
Year Founded: 1996
000809—(SSE)
Rev.: $31,145,451
Assets: $604,424,597
Liabilities: $200,289,852
Net Worth: $404,134,745
Earnings: ($5,071,922)
Fiscal Year-end: 12/31/22
Holding Company
N.A.I.C.S.: 551112
Sui Jingbao *(Chm & Deputy Gen Mgr)*

LIAONING KELONG FINE CHEMICAL CO., LTD.
No 36 Wanhe 7th Road, Hongwei District, Liaoyang, 111003, Liaoning, China
Tel.: (86) 4001555678
Web Site:
  https://www.kelongchem.com
Year Founded: 1988
300405—(CHIN)
Rev.: $109,684,692
Assets: $207,400,284
Liabilities: $115,921,260
Net Worth: $91,479,024
Earnings: ($16,672,500)
Emp.: 540
Fiscal Year-end: 12/31/22
Chemicals Mfr
N.A.I.C.S.: 325998

Yan Jiang *(Chm & Gen Mgr)*

LIAONING OXIRANCHEM GROUP CO., LTD.
No 38 Wanhe Road 7, Hongwei District, Liaoyang, 111003, Liangning, China
Tel.: (86) 4195167408
Web Site:
  http://www.oxiranchem.com
300082—(CHIN)
Rev.: $1,029,177,450
Assets: $1,036,209,789
Liabilities: $468,798,086
Net Worth: $567,411,703
Earnings: $53,966,690
Emp.: 340
Fiscal Year-end: 12/31/21
Chemicals Mfr
N.A.I.C.S.: 325998

LIAONING PORT CO., LTD.
Xingang Commercial Building Dayao Bay Dalian Free Trade Zone, Dalian, 116600, China
Tel.: (86) 41182798108 CN
Web Site: http://www.dlport.cn
Year Founded: 2005
DLPTF—(OTCIQ)
Rev.: $1,019,989,032
Assets: $4,528,815,620
Liabilities: $1,543,053,705
Net Worth: $2,985,761,915
Earnings: $145,674,707
Emp.: 6,152
Fiscal Year-end: 12/31/20
Oil & Chemical Port & Terminal Operations
N.A.I.C.S.: 488310
Wei Minghui *(Chm, Gen Mgr & Exec Dir)*

Subsidiaries:

Harbour Full Group Limited (1)
7701 Forsyth Blvd Ste 600, Saint Louis, MI 63105
Tel.: (314) 727-5550
Logistics Management Consulting Services
N.A.I.C.S.: 541614

LIAONING SG AUTOMOTIVE GROUP CO., LTD.
No 50 Shuguang Road, Zhenan District, Dandong, 118001, Liaoning, China
Tel.: (86) 4152263493
Web Site: https://www.huanghai-auto.com
Year Founded: 1993
600303—(SHG)
Rev.: $379,942,415
Assets: $654,490,139
Liabilities: $260,625,531
Net Worth: $393,864,608
Earnings: ($70,280,491)
Emp.: 1,031
Fiscal Year-end: 12/31/21
Automobile Parts Mfr & Distr
N.A.I.C.S.: 336390
Jia Muyun *(Chm)*

Subsidiaries:

Dandong Huanghai Motors LLC (1)
544 Huanghai Avenue, Dandong, 118008, Liaoning, China
Tel.: (86) 415 6272437
Automobile Parts Mfr & Distr
N.A.I.C.S.: 336390

Dandong SG Automobile Trading LLC (1)
No 51-18 Huayuan Road, Zhengxing District, Dandong, 118000, China
Tel.: (86) 41 5225 1718
New & Used Car Dealer
N.A.I.C.S.: 441110

Fengcheng SG Axle Shaft LLC (1)
No 242 Fengshan Road, Fengcheng,

118100, China
Tel.: (86) 41 5815 3000
Automobile Parts Mfr & Distr
N.A.I.C.S.: 336390

SG Technologies Inc. (1)
27404 Drake Rd, Farmington Hills, MI 48331
Tel.: (248) 489-8711
Automobile Parts Mfr & Distr
N.A.I.C.S.: 336390

LIAONING SHENGSHENG BIOTECHNOLOGY CO., LTD.
Tengao District, Haicheng, 114000, Liaoning, China
Tel.: (86) 412 2988160 DE
Web Site: http://www.biosheng.com
Year Founded: 2008
Sales Range: $10-24.9 Million
Emp.: 56
Holding Company: Plant Seedlings Researcher & Developer
N.A.I.C.S.: 551112
Baoquan Wang *(Chm & Pres)*

LIAONING SHENHUA HOLDINGS CO., LTD.
23rd Floor Shenhua Financial Building No 1 Ningbo Road, Shanghai, 200002, China
Tel.: (86) 2163372888
Web Site: https://www.shkg.com.cn
Year Founded: 1986
600653—(SHG)
Rev.: $835,214,567
Assets: $531,993,838
Liabilities: $357,641,566
Net Worth: $174,352,272
Earnings: ($24,247,838)
Fiscal Year-end: 12/31/22
Holding Company
N.A.I.C.S.: 551112
Yumin Qi *(Chm)*

LIAONING SHIDAI WANHENG CO., LTD.
No 7 Gangwan Street, Zhongshan District, Dalian, 116001, Liaoning, China
Tel.: (86) 41182357777
Web Site:
  https://www.shidaiwanheng.com
Year Founded: 1999
600241—(SHG)
Rev.: $131,427,303
Assets: $204,793,070
Liabilities: $65,750,303
Net Worth: $139,042,767
Earnings: $7,193,562
Fiscal Year-end: 12/31/22
Garment & Apparel Product Distr
N.A.I.C.S.: 315210
Jun Li *(Chm)*

LIAONING SHUIYUN QINGHE RICE INDUSTRY CO., LTD.
6F Fazhan Building No 658 Chaoyang Street, No 39 Hulan West Road Baoshan District, Hebei, China
Tel.: (86) 2166050886
SYQH—(OTCIQ)
Liabilities: $138,513
Net Worth: ($138,513)
Earnings: $71,309
Emp.: 1
Fiscal Year-end: 04/30/22
Investment Services
N.A.I.C.S.: 523999
Jiangou Wei *(Pres, CEO & Treas)*

LIAONING XINDE NEW MATERIAL TECHNOLOGY CO., LTD.
4th Floor No 295 Wensheng Road, Hongwei District, Liaoyang, 111003, Liaoning, China
Tel.: (86) 41185235213

Web Site: https://www.lnxdhg.com
Year Founded: 2000
301349—(CHIN)
Rev.: $126,882,288
Assets: $425,653,488
Liabilities: $32,241,456
Net Worth: $393,412,032
Earnings: $20,918,196
Fiscal Year-end: 12/31/22
Battery Product Mfr
N.A.I.C.S.: 335910
Hongtao Yin *(Chm & Gen Mgr)*

LIAT (1974) LTD.
VC Bird International Airport, PO Box 819, Saint John's, Coolidge, Antigua & Barbuda
Tel.: (268) 480 5601
Web Site: http://www.liatairline.com
Sales Range: $150-199.9 Million
Emp.: 890
Oil Transportation Services
N.A.I.C.S.: 481111
Jean Stewart Holder *(Chm)*

LIB WORK CO., LTD.
178-1 Nabeta, Yamaga, 861-0541, Kumamoto, Japan
Tel.: (81) 968443559
Web Site: https://www.libwork.co.jp
Year Founded: 1997
1431—(FKA)
Sales Range: $25-49.9 Million
Emp.: 99
Single Family Home Construction Services
N.A.I.C.S.: 236115
Chikara Seguchi *(Pres & CEO)*

LIBAS CONSUMER PRODUCTS LTD.
401 4th Floor Crescent Royale Off New Link Road Lokhandwala Complex, Andheri West, Mumbai, 400053, Maharashtra, India
Tel.: (91) 9928099603
Web Site:
  http://www.libasdesignsltd.com
LIBAS—(NSE)
Rev.: $9,839,302
Assets: $11,287,177
Liabilities: $2,547,737
Net Worth: $8,739,440
Earnings: $910,221
Emp.: 13
Fiscal Year-end: 03/31/23
Clothing Accessory Distr
N.A.I.C.S.: 458110
Nishant Mitrasen Mahimtura *(Chm & CFO)*

LIBERIS PUBLICATIONS SA
Ioannou Metaxa 80 Thesi Karela, 19400, Koropi, Greece
Tel.: (30) 2106688000
Web Site: http://www.liberis.gr
Sales Range: $100-124.9 Million
Emp.: 700
Book Publisher & Printer
N.A.I.C.S.: 513130
Antonios Liberis *(CEO)*

Subsidiaries:

IT Publications Hellas Ltd (1)
80 Ioannou Metaxa Street, Karelas Koropi Attica, 19400, Athens, Greece (95.58%)
Tel.: (30) 2106688040
Web Site: http://www.pcw.gr
Sales Range: $25-49.9 Million
Emp.: 50
Newspaper Publishers
N.A.I.C.S.: 513110

Libecom S.A. (1)
80 Ioan Metaxa, Nissiza Koropi, 19400, Athens, Greece (100%)
Tel.: (30) 2106688000
Web Site: http://www.pcmag.gr

LIBERIS PUBLICATIONS SA

Liberis Publications SA—(Continued)
Sales Range: $25-49.9 Million
Emp.: 5
Newspaper Publishers
N.A.I.C.S.: 513110

LIBERO COPPER & GOLD CORPORATION
Suite 905 1111 West Hastings, Vancouver, V6E 2J3, BC, Canada
Tel.: (604) 638-2545 BC
Web Site:
https://www.liberocopper.com
Year Founded: 2008
LBCMF—(OTCQB)
Assets: $2,186,887
Liabilities: $505,820
Net Worth: $1,681,067
Earnings: ($4,294,421)
Emp.: 19
Fiscal Year-end: 12/31/20
Mineral Exploration Services
N.A.I.C.S.: 213114
Ian Slater (CEO)

LIBERTA CO., LTD.
5F Cerulean Tower 261 Sakuragaokacho, Shibuya-ku, Tokyo, 150-8512, Japan
Tel.: (81) 354897670
Web Site: https://www.liberta-j.co.jp
Year Founded: 1997
4935—(TKS)
Rev.: $50,246,830
Assets: $39,136,800
Liabilities: $27,530,470
Net Worth: $11,606,330
Earnings: $786,990
Fiscal Year-end: 12/31/23
Toiletry Product Mfr & Distr
N.A.I.C.S.: 325620

LIBERTA PARTNERS HOLDING GMBH
Koniginstrasse 121, 80802, Munich, Germany
Tel.: (49) 89 901 44 110 De
Web Site: http://www.liberta-partners.com
Year Founded: 2016
Emp.: 10
Private Investment Firm
N.A.I.C.S.: 523999
Dominik Lanz (Partner)

Subsidiaries:

Skytron Energy GmbH (1)
Ernst-Augustin-Strasse 15, 12489, Berlin, Germany
Tel.: (49) 30 338 430 0
Web Site: http://www.skytron-energy.com
Photovoltaic System Installation Services
N.A.I.C.S.: 237130
Francisco Baraona (Mng Dir)

LIBERTAS 7, S.A.
Calle Caballeros 36, 46001, Valencia, 46001, Spain
Tel.: (34) 963913058
Web Site: https://www.libertas7.es
LIB—(MAD)
Sales Range: Less than $1 Million
Real Estate Development Services
N.A.I.C.S.: 531390
Agnes Noguera Borel (CEO)

LIBERTINE
Medius House 2 Sheraton St, London, W1F 8BH, United Kingdom
Tel.: (44) 207 434 4343
Web Site:
http://www.libertinelondon.com
Year Founded: 1993
Rev.: $116,515,000
Emp.: 35
N.A.I.C.S.: 541810
Mark Brandis (Mng Partner)

LIBERTINE HOLDINGS PLC
Unit 1 Coborn Avenue, Tinsley, Sheffield, S9 1DA, United Kingdom
Tel.: (44) 1142421161 UK
Web Site: https://www.libertine.co.uk
Year Founded: 2009
LIB—(AIM)
Rev.: $1,118,761
Assets: $11,129,231
Liabilities: $1,422,891
Net Worth: $9,706,340
Earnings: ($4,374,574)
Emp.: 13
Fiscal Year-end: 03/31/22
Offices of Other Holding Companies
N.A.I.C.S.: 551112

LIBERTY BANK JSC
74 Chavchavadze Ave, 0162, Tbilisi, Georgia
Tel.: (995) 322555500
Web Site: http://www.libertybank.ge
BANK—(GEOR)
Rev.: $93,759,599
Assets: $740,877,983
Liabilities: $634,063,492
Net Worth: $106,814,491
Earnings: $12,809,549
Fiscal Year-end: 12/31/19
Commercial Banking Services
N.A.I.C.S.: 522110
Vasil Khodeli (CEO)

LIBERTY DEFENSE HOLDINGS, LTD.
200 Granville Street Suite 1030, Vancouver, V6C 2R3, BC, Canada
Tel.: (604) 336-9820 ON
Web Site: http://libertydefense.com
Year Founded: 2012
SCAN—(OTCIQ)
Rev.: $28,221
Assets: $1,249,553
Liabilities: $1,101,887
Net Worth: $147,666
Earnings: ($11,587,120)
Fiscal Year-end: 12/31/19
Investment Services
N.A.I.C.S.: 523999
Jeremy Morton (Chm)

LIBERTY FINANCIAL GROUP LIMITED
Level 16 535 Bourke Street, Melbourne, 3000, VIC, Australia
Tel.: (61) 386358888
Web Site: https://www.lfgroup.com.au
Year Founded: 1997
LFG—(ASX)
Rev.: $665,935,571
Assets: $10,975,827,287
Liabilities: $10,120,654,279
Net Worth: $855,173,008
Earnings: $168,032,363
Emp.: 524
Fiscal Year-end: 06/30/22
Financial Investment Services
N.A.I.C.S.: 523999
Anne Bastian (Chief People Officer)

Subsidiaries:

LFI Group Pty. Ltd. (1)
Level 16 535 Bourke Street, Melbourne, 3000, VIC, Australia
Tel.: (61) 133677
Web Site: https://www.lfi.com.au
Insurance Services
N.A.I.C.S.: 524210

Minerva Funds Management Limited (1)
Townfield House 27-29 Townfield Street, Chelmsford, CM1 1QL, United Kingdom
Tel.: (44) 1245967190
Web Site: https://minerva-funds.com
Financial Institute Operator
N.A.I.C.S.: 522320

Money Place Assets Pty. Ltd. (1)
Level 16 535 Bourke Street, Melbourne, 3000, VIC, Australia
Tel.: (61) 386358888
Web Site: https://moneyplace.com.au
Financial Services
N.A.I.C.S.: 523999

LIBERTY FLOUR MILLS, INC.
Liberty Building 835 Antonio Arnaiz Avenue, Makati, 1200, Metro Manila, Philippines
Tel.: (63) 8925011 PH
Web Site:
http://www.libertygroup.com.ph
Year Founded: 1958
LFM—(PHI)
Rev.: $31,389,393
Assets: $76,570,314
Liabilities: $30,815,303
Net Worth: $45,755,011
Earnings: $247,843
Emp.: 60
Fiscal Year-end: 12/31/23
Flour & Flour Products Mfr
N.A.I.C.S.: 311212
Vicente S. Vargas (Corp Sec)

LIBERTY GLOBAL PLC
Griffin House 161 Hammersmith Road, London, W6 8BS, United Kingdom
Tel.: (44) 2084836300 UK
Web Site:
https://www.libertyglobal.com
Year Founded: 2013
LBTYA—(NASDAQ)
Rev.: $7,491,400,000
Assets: $42,087,900,000
Liabilities: $23,080,500,000
Net Worth: $19,007,400,000
Earnings: ($3,873,800,000)
Emp.: 9,860
Fiscal Year-end: 12/31/23
Media & Telecommunications Holding Company
N.A.I.C.S.: 551112
Charles H. R. Bracken (CFO & Exec VP)

Subsidiaries:

All3Media Holdings Ltd (1)
Berkshire House 168-173 High Holborn, London, WC1V 7AA, United Kingdom (50%)
Tel.: (44) 2078454377
Web Site: https://www.all3media.com
Holding Company
N.A.I.C.S.: 551114
Sara Geater (COO)

Subsidiary (Domestic):

Betty TV Limited (2)
Objective Media Group 89 Southwark Street, London, SE1 0HX, United Kingdom
Tel.: (44) 2072022300
Web Site: https://www.betty.co.uk
Emp.: 30
Motion Picture Production & Distribution Services
N.A.I.C.S.: 512110
David Harrison (Creative Dir)

Raw TV Ltd. (2)
Third Floor 13-21 Curtain Road, London, EC2A 3LT, United Kingdom
Tel.: (44) 2074560800
Web Site: https://www.raw.co.uk
Broadcasting & Media Production Company
N.A.I.C.S.: 516120
Joely Fether (CEO)

Azart-Sat Sp Zoo (1)
ul A Asnyka 12/13, 59-700, Boleslawiec, Poland
Tel.: (48) 757326079
Television Broadcasting Services
N.A.I.C.S.: 516120
Agnieszka Matczak (Head-Mktg & Promo)

Caviar Antwerp B.V. (1)
Liersesteenweg 38, 2800, Mechelen, Belgium

INTERNATIONAL PUBLIC

Tel.: (32) 15677675
Film Production Services
N.A.I.C.S.: 512110

Caviar Paris S.A.S. (1)
41 Rue de l Echiquier, 75010, Paris, France
Tel.: (33) 171181810
Film Production Services
N.A.I.C.S.: 512110

Companhia de Telecomunicacoes de Macau, S.A.R.L. (1)
Rua de Lagos Telecentro, PO Box 868, Taipa, China (Macau)
Tel.: (853) 8913880
Web Site: https://www.ctm.net
Telecommunication Servicesб
N.A.I.C.S.: 517111
Vandy Poon (CEO)

Esprit Telecom BV (1)
Tyro House Monitorweg 1, PO Box 60043, Almere, 1322 BJ, Netherlands
Tel.: (31) 880068000
Web Site: http://www.esprittelecom.nl
Telecommunication Servicesб
N.A.I.C.S.: 517810
Patrick de Moel (Sr Acct Mgr)

Liberty Global B.V. (1)
Boeing Avenue 53, 1119 PE, Schiphol-Rijk, Netherlands
Tel.: (31) 207789840
Internet Service Provider
N.A.I.C.S.: 517810
Claire Knapik (Mgr-HR Sys & Reporting)

Liberty Global Insurance Company Limited (1)
Development House St Anne Street, Floriana, FRN 9010, Malta
Tel.: (356) 21322076
Insurance Provider
N.A.I.C.S.: 524113
Gary O'Reilly (Dir-Grp Insurance Captive)

Liberty Global, Inc. (1)
12300 Liberty Blvd, Englewood, CO 80112
Tel.: (303) 220-6600
Web Site: http://www.lgi.com
Fiscal Year-end: 12/31/2019
Holding Company; Cable Network Communications Services
N.A.I.C.S.: 551112

Subsidiary (Non-US):

At Media Sp. z o.o (2)
North Gate Ul Bonifraterska 17, Warsaw, 00203, Poland
Tel.: (48) 222416950
Web Site: http://www.atmedia.pl
Emp.: 50
Advertising Services
N.A.I.C.S.: 541810

C-Cure NV (2)
Liersteenweg 4, Mechelen, 2800, Belgium
Tel.: (32) 15299250
Web Site: http://www.telenet.be
Emp.: 3,000
Business Security Services
N.A.I.C.S.: 561499

Cablecom GmbH (2)
Richtiplatz 5, Wallisellen, 8304, Switzerland
Tel.: (41) 800464646
Web Site: http://www.cablecom.ch
Sales Range: $100-124.9 Million
Emp.: 500
Cable & Other Subscription Programming
N.A.I.C.S.: 516210

Cablecom Kabelkommunikation GmbH (2)
Hauptstrasse 40, 6973, Hochst, Vorarlberg, Austria
Tel.: (43) 557874440
Web Site: http://www.cablecom.at
Cable & Other Subscription Services
N.A.I.C.S.: 516210

Liberty Global Europe Ltd. (2)
Michelin House 81 Fulham Road, London, SW3 6RD, United Kingdom
Tel.: (44) 2078382000
Sales Range: $25-49.9 Million
Emp.: 100
Television & Internet Communication Services
N.A.I.C.S.: 516120

AND PRIVATE COMPANIES

Enrique Rodriguez *(CTO & Exec VP)*

Subsidiary (Domestic):

Liberty Media International, Inc. (2)
12300 Liberty Blvd, Englewood, CO 80112
Tel.: (720) 875-5800
Web Site: https://www.libertymedia.com
Sales Range: $25-49.9 Million
Emp.: 120
Cable TV & Communications Services
N.A.I.C.S.: 517111

Subsidiary (Non-US):

NTL Irish Networks Ltd. (2)
Building P2 East Point Business Park, Clontarf, Dublin, Ireland
Tel.: (353) 12458686
Web Site: http://www.upc.ie
Emp.: 50
Cable & Subscription Services
N.A.I.C.S.: 516210

Netfront Information Technology Ltd. (2)
Room 802 Loon Kee Bldg 267-275 Des Voeux Rd Central, Sheung Wan, China (Hong Kong)
Tel.: (852) 2517 1209
Web Site: http://www.netfront.net
Emp.: 10
Internet Service Provider
N.A.I.C.S.: 517810
Lindo Yip *(Mng Dir)*

Telenet Group Holding NV (2)
Liersesteenweg 4, B-2800, Mechelen, Belgium (100%)
Tel.: (32) 15333000
Web Site: http://www2.telenet.be
Rev.: $3,151,120,433
Assets: $8,929,131,252
Liabilities: $9,530,742,909
Net Worth: ($601,611,657)
Earnings: $326,526,107
Emp.: 3,332
Fiscal Year-end: 12/31/2023
Holding Company; Cable Television, Internet & Telecommunications Services
N.A.I.C.S.: 551112
Patrick Vincent *(Exec VP-Customer Interaction Domain)*

Unit (Domestic):

Hostbasket (3)
Antwerpse Steenweg 19, Lochristi, 9080, Belgium
Tel.: (32) 9 326 90 92
Web Site: http://www.hostbasket.com
Emp.: 100
Web Hosting Services
N.A.I.C.S.: 518210

Affiliate (Domestic):

SBS Belgium NV (3)
Harensesteenweg 224, 1800, Vilvoorde, Belgium (50%)
Tel.: (32) 27151150
Web Site: https://www.playmedia.be
Sales Range: $25-49.9 Million
Emp.: 100
Television Broadcasting
N.A.I.C.S.: 516120

Subsidiary (Domestic):

Telenet Group pllc (3)
Neerveldstraat 105, 1200, Brussels, Belgium
Tel.: (32) 484 006 200
Web Site: http://www2.telenet.be
Emp.: 3,300
Telecommunications Products & Services
N.A.I.C.S.: 517810
John Porter *(CEO & Mng Dir)*

Telenet Mobile NV (3)
Zandvoortstraat 5, 2800, Mechelen, Belgium (100%)
Tel.: (32) 32873434
Mobile Communications Retailer & Supplier
N.A.I.C.S.: 517112

Telenet NV (3)
Liersesteenweg 4, 2800, Mechelen, Belgium
Tel.: (32) 15333000

Telecommunication & Business Consulting Services
N.A.I.C.S.: 541618

Subsidiary (Non-US):

UPC Broadband N.V. (2)
53 Boeing Avenue, 1119 PE, Schiphol-Rijk, Netherlands
Tel.: (31) 207789840
Cable Programming Services
N.A.I.C.S.: 516210

Subsidiary (Domestic):

UnitedGlobalCom, Inc. (2)
4643 S Ulster St Ste 1300, Denver, CO 80237
Tel.: (303) 770-4001
Web Site: http://www.lgi.com
Sales Range: $1-4.9 Billion
Emp.: 191
Cable Television Services
N.A.I.C.S.: 517111
Charles H. R. Bracken *(Co-CFO)*

Subsidiary (Non-US):

iCable ServiceGmbH (2)
In 9 Pichl bei, Wels, 4632, Austria
Tel.: (43) 724942820
Sales Range: $100-124.9 Million
Emp.: 40
Television & Internet Communication Services
N.A.I.C.S.: 517121
Peter Stefan *(Mng Dir)*

Liberty Latin America Ltd. (1)
2 Church Street, Hamilton, HM 11, Bermuda
Tel.: (441) 2955950
Web Site: http://www.lla.com
Rev.: $4,511,100,000
Assets: $13,594,600,000
Liabilities: $11,284,900,000
Net Worth: $2,309,700,000
Earnings: ($73,600,000)
Emp.: 10,600
Fiscal Year-end: 12/31/2023
Telecommunications Company
N.A.I.C.S.: 517121
Balan Nair *(Pres & CEO)*

Subsidiary (Non-US):

Cable & Wireless (Barbados) Ltd. (2)
Windsor Lodge Government Hill, Saint Michael, Barbados
Tel.: (246) 2925050
Telecommunication Servicesb
N.A.I.C.S.: 517111
Donald Austin *(Pres)*

Cable & Wireless Communications Limited (2)
161 Hammersmith Road, London, W6 8BS, United Kingdom
Tel.: (44) 2084836300
Web Site: https://www.cwc.com
Holding Company
N.A.I.C.S.: 551112
Inge Smidts *(CEO)*

Cable & Wireless Panama S.A. (2)
Plaza Internacional Torre B Piso 1 Via Espana, PO Box 0834-00659, Apartado, 00834-00659, Panama, Panama
Tel.: (507) 8002102
Web Site: https://www.masmovilpanama.com
Telecommunication Servicesb
N.A.I.C.S.: 517111

Claro Panama, S.A. (2)
Punta Pacifica Edificio Metrobank Piso 1 Y 7, Panama, Panama
Tel.: (507) 2169701
Web Site: http://www.claro.com.pa
Wireless Telecommunication Services
N.A.I.C.S.: 517112

Unit (Non-US):

LIME (2)
Windsor Lodge Government Hill, Saint Michael, Barbados
Tel.: (246) 2925050
Web Site: http://www.cwc.com
Telecommunication Servicesb

N.A.I.C.S.: 517111

Subsidiary (US):

Liberty Cablevision of Puerto Rico LLC (2)
279 Ave Ponce De Leon Hato Rey Norte SJ, San Juan, PR 00918-9675 (100%)
Tel.: (787) 355-3535
Web Site: http://www.libertypr.com
Cable Television Services
N.A.I.C.S.: 516210
Naji Khoury *(CEO)*

Subsidiary (Non-US):

Sonitel S.A. (2)
Calle Aquilino de la Guardia Torre Banco, General Marbella piso 12-14, Panama, Panama
Tel.: (507) 2947500
Web Site: http://www.ssasis.com
Hardware & Software System Integration Services
N.A.I.C.S.: 541512

The Bahamas Telecommunications Company Ltd. (2)
PO Box N-3048, Nassau, Bahamas
Tel.: (242) 2255282
Web Site: http://www.btcbahamas.com
Telecommunication Servicesb
N.A.I.C.S.: 517111
Helene Ferguson *(Dir-People)*

Lynx Europe 2 Limited (2)
38 Hans Crescent, London, SW1X 0LZ, United Kingdom
Tel.: (44) 13973108551
Telecommunication Servicesb
N.A.I.C.S.: 517810

MaRo N.V. (1)
Leegtestraat 6/8, Rudderverde, 8020, Oostkamp, Belgium
Tel.: (32) 50278431
Web Site: https://www.maro.be
Cooking Pot Distr
N.A.I.C.S.: 423220

Native Nation B.V. (1)
Harensesteenweg 224, 1800, Vilvoorde, Belgium
Tel.: (32) 498145429
Web Site: https://nativenation.eu
Advertising Services
N.A.I.C.S.: 541810

Net-Sat Media Sp Zoo (1)
Ul Chalubinskiego 25c, 80-807, Gdansk, Poland
Tel.: (48) 583005005
Cable TV Operator
N.A.I.C.S.: 516210

RAE Regionalantenne Ermatingen AG (1)
Hauptstrasse 50, PO Box 2131, 8280, Kreuzlingen, Switzerland
Tel.: (41) 716772080
Telecommunication Servicesb
N.A.I.C.S.: 517810

Sable International Finance Limited (1)
PO Box 709, Georgetown, KY1-1107, Cayman Islands
Tel.: (345) 9494544
Telecommunication Servicesb
N.A.I.C.S.: 517810
C. Bracken *(Sec)*

Sunrise UPC GmbH (1)
Thurgauerstrasse 101B, 8152, Opfikon, Switzerland
Tel.: (41) 800707505
Web Site: https://www.sunrise.ch
Telecommunications Company
N.A.I.C.S.: 517121
Andre Krause *(CEO)*

Subsidiary (Domestic):

Sunrise Communications Group AG (2)
Thurgauerstrasse 101B, 8152, Opfikon, Switzerland
Tel.: (41) 587779686
Web Site: http://www.sunrise.ch
Mobile Telecommunications & Internet Services

LIBERTY GLOBAL PLC

N.A.I.C.S.: 517112
Andre Krause *(CEO)*

UPC Schweiz GmbH (2)
Richtiplatz 5, 8304, Wallisellen, Switzerland
Tel.: (41) 800464646
Telecommunications Company
N.A.I.C.S.: 517121

Telco Lublin Sp Zoo (1)
Ul Naleczowska 51a, Lublin, 20-701, Poland
Tel.: (48) 815618000
Telecommunication Servicesb
N.A.I.C.S.: 517810

Teledistal SA (1)
Chemin sur la Croix 9, 1377, Oulens-sous-Echallens, Canton of Vaud, Switzerland
Tel.: (41) 218861086
Web Site: https://www.teledistal.ch
Cable TV Operator
N.A.I.C.S.: 516210

Telenet BVBA (1)
Liersesteenweg 4, 2800, Mechelen, Belgium
Tel.: (32) 15333000
Web Site: https://www2.telenet.be
Telecommunication Servicesb
N.A.I.C.S.: 517112

UPC Business Austria GmbH (1)
Wolfganggasse 58-60, A-1120, Vienna, Austria
Tel.: (43) 599992000
Web Site: http://business.upc.at
Internet Service Provider
N.A.I.C.S.: 517810

UPC Cablecom Austria GmbH (1)
Wolfganggasse 58-60, 1120, Vienna, Austria
Tel.: (43) 5572890900
Internet Service Provider
N.A.I.C.S.: 517810
Franz Jaeger *(Sr Engr-Network)*

UPC Cablecom GmbH (1)
Richtiplatz 5, 8304, Wallisellen, Switzerland
Tel.: (41) 442779111
Web Site: http://www.upc-cablecom.ch
Emp.: 1,300
Telecommunication Servicesb
N.A.I.C.S.: 517810

UPC DSL Telecom GmbH (1)
Wolfganggasse 58-60, Vienna, 1120, Austria
Tel.: (43) 599993000
Internet Service Provider
N.A.I.C.S.: 517810
Rene Schimek *(Head-Callcenter)*

UPC Nederland Netwerk 2 BV (1)
Kabelweg 51, 1014BA, Amsterdam, Noord-Holland, Netherlands
Tel.: (31) 207755000
Telecommunication Servicesb
N.A.I.C.S.: 517810

Unitymedia International GmbH (1)
Web Site: http://www.unitymedia.de
Internet Service Provider
N.A.I.C.S.: 517810
Winfried Rapp *(CEO)*

VMED O2 UK Limited (1)
Griffin House 161 Hammersmith Road, London, W6 8BS, United Kingdom (50%)
Tel.: (44) 1753565656
Web Site: https://news.virginmedia2.co.uk
Holding Company
N.A.I.C.S.: 551112
Lutz Schuler *(CEO)*

Subsidiary (Domestic):

Telefonica UK Limited (2)
260 Bath Road, Slough, SL1 4DX, United Kingdom
Tel.: (44) 1132722000
Web Site: http://www.o2.co.uk
Sales Range: $1-4.9 Billion
Emp.: 6,116
Mobile Communications Services
N.A.I.C.S.: 517112
Mark Evans *(CEO)*

Virgin Media Ltd. (2)
Bartley Wood Business Park Bartley Way,

4485

LIBERTY GLOBAL PLC

Liberty Global plc—(Continued)
Hook, RG27 9UP, Hampshire, United Kingdom
Tel.: (44) 8453026999
Web Site: http://www.virginmedia.com
Internet, Cable Television & Telecommunications Services
N.A.I.C.S.: 517810
Vani Bassi *(Head-Investor Relations)*

Subsidiary (Domestic):

Central Cable Limited (3)
Small Heath Business Park Talbot Way, Birmingham, B10 0HJ, United Kingdom
Tel.: (44) 1216281234
Cable Subscription Programming Services
N.A.I.C.S.: 516210

Subsidiary (Non-US):

TV3 Television Network Limited (3)
Westgate Business Park, Ballymount, Dublin, 24, Ireland
Tel.: (353) 14193333
Web Site: https://www.virginmediatelevision.ie
Television Station
N.A.I.C.S.: 516120

Subsidiary (Domestic):

Virgin Media Business Ltd. (3)
10-14 Bartley Way, Hook, RG27 9UP, United Kingdom
Tel.: (44) 8453026999
Web Site: http://www.virginmediabusiness.co.uk
Sales Range: $25-49.9 Million
Telecommunication & Internet Business Services
N.A.I.C.S.: 517111

Branch (Domestic):

Virgin Media Business Ltd. (4)
Communications House 5 Factory Ln, Croydon, CR9 3RA, United Kingdom
Tel.: (44) 2082515151
Web Site: http://www.virginmediabusiness.co.uk
Internet Services
N.A.I.C.S.: 517810

Virgin Media Inc. (1)
65 Bleecker St 6th Fl, New York, NY 10012
Tel.: (212) 906-8440
Web Site: http://www.virginmedia.co.uk
Sales Range: $1-4.9 Billion
Emp.: 13,000
Telecommunications & Broadband Internet Services
N.A.I.C.S.: 517810
Jeff Dodds *(COO)*

Subsidiary (Domestic):

Virgin Media Investment Holdings Limited (2)
65 Bleecker St 6th Fl, New York, NY 10012
Tel.: (212) 906-8440
Rev.: $3,980,700,000
Assets: $11,756,900,000
Liabilities: $7,382,700,000
Net Worth: $4,374,200,000
Earnings: $2,869,000,000
Fiscal Year-end: 12/31/2012
Cable Subscription Programming Services
N.A.I.C.S.: 516210

Virgin Media Ireland Ltd (1)
Macken House 39/40 Mayor Street Upper, Dublin, D01 C9W8, Ireland
Tel.: (353) 12458000
Web Site: https://www.virginmedia.ie
Media Content Management Services
N.A.I.C.S.: 541840
Tony Hanway *(CEO)*

Virgin Media Television Limited (1)
Westgate Business Park, Ballymount, Dublin, Ireland
Tel.: (353) 14193333
Web Site: https://www.virginmediatelevision.ie
Television Broadcasting Services
N.A.I.C.S.: 541890

Virgin WiFi Limited (1)
One Park Lane, Hemel Hempstead, HP2 4YJ, Hertfordshire, United Kingdom
Tel.: (44) 3333435036
Web Site: http://www.virginwifi.com
Broadband Internet Service Provider
N.A.I.C.S.: 516210

Ziggo B.V. (1)
Atoomweg 100, Utrecht, 3542 AB, Netherlands
Tel.: (31) 887170000
Web Site: http://www.ziggo.com
Cable Operator
N.A.I.C.S.: 516210
Ritchy Drost *(CFO)*

Subsidiary (Domestic):

Vodafone Libertel N.V. (2)
Avenue Ceramique 300, 6221 KX, Maastricht, Netherlands
Tel.: (31) 654500100
Web Site: https://www.vodafone.nl
Cellular Communications Network Operator
N.A.I.C.S.: 517112

Ziggo Group Holding BV (1)
Atoomweg 100, Utrecht, 3542 AB, Netherlands
Tel.: (31) 887170000
Emp.: 4,600
Holding Company
N.A.I.C.S.: 551112

Ziggo Services Employment B.V. (1)
Atoomweg 100, 3542 AB, Utrecht, Netherlands
Tel.: (31) 207755000
Television Broadcasting Services
N.A.I.C.S.: 516210

Zoranet Connectivity Services BV (1)
Assendorperdijk 2, Zwolle, 8012 EH, Netherlands
Tel.: (31) 384559560
Web Site: http://www.zoranet.nl
Internet Service Provider
N.A.I.C.S.: 517810

LIBERTY GOLD CORP.
Suite 610 815 West Hastings Street, Vancouver, V6C 3N9, BC, Canada
Tel.: (604) 632-4677   Ca
Web Site: https://libertygold.ca
Year Founded: 2010
LGDTF—(OTCQX)
Sales Range: Less than $1 Million
Gold Ore Exploration Services
N.A.I.C.S.: 213114
Robert Bruce R. Pease *(Chm)*

Subsidiaries:

Agola Madencilik Limited Sirketi (1)
Nilgun Sokak 14/15, Cankaya, Ankara, Turkiye
Tel.: (90) 3124682343
Web Site: http://www.agolamadencilik.com
Mineral Exploration Services
N.A.I.C.S.: 213114

LIBERTY LINEHAUL INC.
214 Boida Ave, Ayr, N0B 1E0, ON, Canada
Tel.: (519) 740-7072
Web Site: http://www.libertylinehaul.com
Year Founded: 1987
Sales Range: $10-24.9 Million
Emp.: 85
Freight Services
N.A.I.C.S.: 488510
Chris Gerber *(VP)*

LIBERTY MILLS LIMITED
A 51-A S I T E, Karachi, 75700, Pakistan
Tel.: (92) 2132578100
Web Site: http://www.libertymillslimited.com
Year Founded: 1964
Textile Fabric Mfr
N.A.I.C.S.: 313210

LIBERTY MINING INTERNATIONAL PTY. LTD.
No 193BEo St 63 Sangkat Boeung Keng Kang 1, Khan Chamcar Morn, Phnom Penh, Cambodia
Tel.: (855) 23 357 714
Web Site: http://www.libertymining.com.kh
Sales Range: $10-24.9 Million
Emp.: 15
Mineral Exploration Services
N.A.I.C.S.: 213115
Richard Stanger *(Mng Dir)*

LIBERTY SHOES LIMITED
19th Floor Magnum Global Park Tower -2 Golf Course Extension Road, Sector-58, Gurgaon, 122011, India
Tel.: (91) 1842255620
Web Site: https://www.libertyshoes.com
LIBERTSHOE—(NSE)
Rev.: $62,584,638
Assets: $70,625,173
Liabilities: $45,184,840
Net Worth: $25,440,333
Earnings: $34,296
Emp.: 1,849
Fiscal Year-end: 03/31/21
Footwear Mfr
N.A.I.C.S.: 316210
Shammi Bansal *(Exec Dir)*

LIBET SA
ul Powstancow Slaskich 5, 53-332, Wroclaw, Poland
Tel.: (48) 713351101
Web Site: http://www.libet.pl
Sales Range: $75-99.9 Million
Emp.: 460
Paving & Other Concrete Paving Materials Mfr
N.A.I.C.S.: 324121
Thomas Lehmann *(Pres & Mng Dir)*

LIBORD FINANCE LTD.
104 M K Bhavan 300 Shahid Bhagat Singh Road Fort, Mumbai, 400001, Maharashtra, India
Tel.: (91) 2222658108
Web Site: https://www.libord.com
Year Founded: 1994
511593—(BOM)
Rev.: $112,479
Assets: $1,893,084
Liabilities: $27,237
Net Worth: $1,865,847
Earnings: $9,504
Emp.: 3
Fiscal Year-end: 03/31/23
Financial & Management Consultancy Services
N.A.I.C.S.: 541618
Vandna Dangi *(Mng Dir)*

Subsidiaries:

Libord Advisors Pvt. Ltd. (1)
104 M K Bhavan 300 Shahid Bhagat Singh Road, Fort, Mumbai, 400001, Maharashtra, India
Tel.: (91) 2222658108
Web Site: https://www.libord.com
Banking Services
N.A.I.C.S.: 522110
Vandna Dangi *(Exec Dir)*

LIBORD SECURITIES LTD.
104 M K Bhavan 300 Shahid Bhagat Singh Road Fort, Mumbai, 400001, Maharashtra, India
Tel.: (91) 2222658108
Web Site: https://www.libord.com
Year Founded: 1994
531027—(BOM)
Rev.: $41,948
Assets: $491,697
Liabilities: $16,188
Net Worth: $475,509
Earnings: $8,806
Emp.: 2
Fiscal Year-end: 03/31/23
Financial Advisory Services
N.A.I.C.S.: 523940
Vandna Dangi *(Mng Dir)*

LIBRA GROUP LIMITED
13-14 Hobart Place, London, SW1W 0HH, United Kingdom
Tel.: (44) 20 7245 8700   UK
Web Site: https://www.libra.com
Emp.: 100
Diversified Holding Company
N.A.I.C.S.: 551112
George M. Logothetis *(Chm & CEO)*

Subsidiaries:

Libra Capital Limited (1)
13-14 Hobart Place, London, SW1W 0HH, United Kingdom
Tel.: (44) 20 7245 8700
Web Site: https://www.libra.com
Sales Range: $1-9.9 Million
Investment Management Service
N.A.I.C.S.: 523999

Subsidiary (US):

Americraft Marine Group LLC (2)
560 Stokes Landing Rd, Palatka, FL 32177
Tel.: (386) 328-6054
Web Site: https://americraftmarinegroup.com
Maritime & Shipbuilding Services
N.A.I.C.S.: 336611
Omear Khalid *(Pres & CEO)*

Subsidiary (Domestic):

St. Johns Ship Building, Inc. (3)
560 Stokes Landing Rd, Palatka, FL 32177-8485
Tel.: (386) 328-6054
Web Site: http://www.stjohnsshipbuilding.com
Shipbuilding & Repairing
N.A.I.C.S.: 336611
Bobby Barfield *(Gen Mgr)*

LIBRA HOLIDAYS GROUP PUBLIC LTD.
114 Antoni Loucaidi Str Oasis Complex Centre, Block E 4th Floor, 3031, Lemesos, Cyprus
Tel.: (357) 25884000
Web Site: http://www.libraholidaysgroup.com
Year Founded: 1996
Sales Range: $200-249.9 Million
Emp.: 850
Travel & Hotel Services
N.A.I.C.S.: 561599
Andreas Drakou *(CEO)*

Subsidiaries:

Astarti Development Plc (1)
284 Makarios III Ave Fortuna Court, 3105, Limassol, Cyprus
Tel.: (357) 25884000
Home Management Services
N.A.I.C.S.: 721110
Andreas Drakou *(Pres & Gen Dir)*

D.H. Cyprotels Plc (1)
114 Antoni Loukaidi Street Oasis Complex Centre Block C, 3727, Limassol, Cyprus
Tel.: (357) 25884000
Web Site: http://www.cyprotelshotels.com
Hotel Operator
N.A.I.C.S.: 721110

Helios Airways Limited (1)
22 Nietzsche Street, Next To Larnaca Airport, Larnaca, Cyprus
Tel.: (357) 25884000
Support Activities for Air Transportation
N.A.I.C.S.: 488190

LIBRA INFUSIONS LIMITED
I/7 Mirpur Industrial Estate Rupnagar Section-2, Dhaka, 1216, Bangladesh

Tel.: (880) 248040254
Web Site:
    https://www.libragroupbd.com
LIBRAINFU—(CHT)
Rev.: $2,266,634
Assets: $35,916,063
Liabilities: $13,607,082
Net Worth: $22,308,981
Earnings: $2,653
Fiscal Year-end: 06/30/21
Intravenous Fluids Mfr
N.A.I.C.S.: 325412
Roushon Alam *(Mng Dir)*

LIBRA SYSTEMS LTD.
Unit E Halesfield 10, Telford, TF7 4QP, Shropshire, United Kingdom
Tel.: (44) 1952 581150   UK
Web Site:
    http://www.librasystemsuk.com
Year Founded: 1967
Sales Range: $1-9.9 Million
Emp.: 40
Cold Rollforming High Quality Steel Section for Ceiling & Drywall Market Mfr
N.A.I.C.S.: 331221
Simon Scowcroft *(Mng Dir)*

LIBSTAR HOLDINGS LTD.
43 Bloulelie Crescent, Plattekloof, Cape Town, 7500, South Africa
Tel.: (27) 219111157
Web Site: https://www.libstar.co.za
Year Founded: 2005
LBR—(JSE)
Rev.: $674,337,716
Assets: $536,022,768
Liabilities: $247,685,823
Net Worth: $288,336,945
Earnings: $12,327,838
Emp.: 7,145
Fiscal Year-end: 12/31/23
Asset Management Services
N.A.I.C.S.: 523940
Robin Smith *(CFO)*
Subsidiaries:

Ambassador Foods Pty Ltd   (1)
11 Theo Kleynhans Street, White River, Nelspruit, 1240, South Africa
Tel.: (27) 137501192
Web Site:
    https://www.ambassadorfoods.co.za
Private Label Mfr
N.A.I.C.S.: 325998
Jaco Moolman *(Fin Mgr)*

Cape Foods (Pty.) Ltd.   (1)
1 Ruby Boulevard Montague Park Montague Gardens, Cape Town, 7441, South Africa
Tel.: (27) 215520800
Web Site: https://www.capefoods.com
Food Product Mfr & Distr
N.A.I.C.S.: 311999

Cape Herb & Spice (Pty) Ltd.   (1)
50 Bell Crescent Westlake Business Park, Tokai, Cape Town, 7945, South Africa
Tel.: (27) 217015140
Web Site: https://www.capeherb.co.za
Food Mfr
N.A.I.C.S.: 311999
Therona Pillay *(Mgr-HR)*

Cecil Vinegar Works (Pty) Ltd.   (1)
36 Chilwan Crescent, Helderberg Industrial Park Strand, Cape Town, 7140, Western Cape, South Africa
Tel.: (27) 218454001
Web Site: http://www.vinegar.co.za
Cider vinegar Mfr
N.A.I.C.S.: 311941
Nigel Pepperell *(Mng Dir)*

Chet Chemicals Pty. Ltd.   (1)
40 Steel Road, Spartan, Kempton Park, 1620, South Africa
Tel.: (27) 119715300
Household Products Mfr
N.A.I.C.S.: 335220

Contactim (Pty) Ltd.   (1)
17 Driftside Road, Pentrich, Pietermaritzburg, 3201, South Africa
Tel.: (27) 333461466
Web Site: http://www.contactim.co.za
Plastics Product Mfr
N.A.I.C.S.: 326199

Dickon Hall Foods (Pty) Ltd.   (1)
10 Landsborough Road, Robertsham, Johannesburg, 2135, South Africa
Tel.: (27) 116802537
Food Service
N.A.I.C.S.: 624210
Niel Heerden *(CEO)*

Finlar Fine Foods (Pty) Ltd.   (1)
82A Merino Avenue, City Deep, Johannesburg, 2001, South Africa
Tel.: (27) 116232665
Food Service
N.A.I.C.S.: 624210

Khoisan Tea (Pty) Ltd.   (1)
6 Gold Street Northgate Estate, Ysterplaat, Cape Town, 7405, South Africa
Tel.: (27) 215114991
Web Site: http://www.khoisantea.com
Tea Mfr
N.A.I.C.S.: 311920
Heinrich Toerien *(Ops Mgr)*

Lancewood Holdings Pty., Ltd.   (1)
1st Floor Rosenpark 1 High Street, Cape Town, 7530, South Africa
Tel.: (27) 219143912
Web Site: http://www.lancewood.co.za
Cheese Mfr
N.A.I.C.S.: 311513

Millennium Foods (Pty) Ltd.   (1)
19 Scheckter Road Killarney Gardens, Cape Town, South Africa
Tel.: (27) 215561603
Web Site:
    https://www.millenniumfoods.co.za
Food Mfr
N.A.I.C.S.: 311999
Ingrid Wolff *(Mgr-Technical)*

Natural Herbs & Spices Pty Ltd.   (1)
5 Rusper Street, Maitland, Cape Town, 7405, South Africa
Tel.: (27) 215108339
Web Site:
    http://www.naturalherbsandspices.com
Food Mfr
N.A.I.C.S.: 311999

LIBURNIA RIVIERA HOTELI D.D.
Marsala Tita 198, HR 51410, Opatija, Croatia
Tel.: (385) 51710300
Web Site: https://www.liburnia.hr
Year Founded: 1947
LRH—(ZAG)
Rev.: $35,120,925
Assets: $154,525,797
Liabilities: $70,477,075
Net Worth: $84,048,722
Earnings: ($14,905,614)
Emp.: 645
Fiscal Year-end: 12/31/21
Home Management Services
N.A.I.C.S.: 721110
Heimo Waldemar Hirn *(Chm-Mgmt Bd)*

LIBYAN INVESTMENT AUTHORITY
Office No 99 9th Floor El-Fata Tower, Tripoli, Libya
Web Site: http://www.lia.ly
Year Founded: 2006
Government Oil Investment Agency
N.A.I.C.S.: 926130
Abdurahman Benyezza *(Chm & Acting CEO)*

LIC HOUSING FINANCE LTD
131 Maker Tower-F Premises 13th Floor Cuffe Parade, Mumbai, 400 005, Maharashtra, India
Tel.: (91) 2222178600
Web Site: http://www.lichousing.com
500253—(BOM)
Rev.: $3,278,235,093
Assets: $35,012,362,725
Liabilities: $31,229,101,707
Net Worth: $3,783,261,019
Earnings: $572,002,017
Emp.: 2,462
Fiscal Year-end: 03/31/24
Financial Investment Services
N.A.I.C.S.: 523999
Nitin K. Jage *(Officer-Compliance, Sec & Gen Mgr-Taxation)*
Subsidiaries:

LICHFL Asset Management Company Limited   (1)
The Capital 211-212 A Wing, Bandra Kurla Complex Bandra East, Mumbai, 400 051, India
Tel.: (91) 2242065011
Web Site: https://www.lichflamc.com
Asset Management Services
N.A.I.C.S.: 523210
Surinder Mohan *(CFO)*

LICHFL Care Homes Limited   (1)
113-A B Wing 11th Floor Maker Tower F Premises, Cuffe Parade, Mumbai, 400 005, India
Tel.: (91) 2222152066
Web Site: https://www.lichflcarehomes.com
Construction Services
N.A.I.C.S.: 236220

LICHARZ GMBH
Industriepark Nord 13, 53567, Buchholz, Germany
Tel.: (49) 26839770   De
Web Site: http://www.licharz.de
Year Founded: 1962
Sales Range: $25-49.9 Million
Engineering Plastics Mfr
N.A.I.C.S.: 326199
Subsidiaries:

Licharz Ltd   (1)
34 Lanchester Way Royal Oak Ind Est, Daventry, NN11 8PH, Northants, United Kingdom
Tel.: (44) 1327877500
Plastic Product Distr
N.A.I.C.S.: 423830
Paul Charles *(Gen Mgr)*

Licharz plastique technique eurl.   (1)
Z I de Leveau Entree G, 38200, Vienne, France
Tel.: (33) 474318708
Web Site: http://www.licharz.fr
Plastic Product Distr
N.A.I.C.S.: 423830

LICHEN CHINA LIMITED
B2306 Block B Tower 3, Jinjiang Wanda Plaza Commercial Complex, Jinjiang, 362000, Fujian, China
Tel.: (86) 4008350088   Ky
Web Site: https://ir.lichenzx.com
Year Founded: 2016
LICN—(NASDAQ)
Rev.: $33,805,000
Assets: $46,525,000
Liabilities: $5,416,000
Net Worth: $41,109,000
Earnings: $7,818,000
Emp.: 399
Fiscal Year-end: 12/31/22
Holding Company
N.A.I.C.S.: 551112
Ya Li *(CEO & Chm)*

LICHTENERGIEWERKE AG
Friedrichstrasse 121, 10117, Berlin, Germany
Tel.: (49) 3027908656
Year Founded: 2002
Emp.: 124
Solar Power Generato
N.A.I.C.S.: 221118

Ole-Hagen Zachriat *(Chm-Supervisory Bd)*

LICHTREKLAME-ERZEUGUNG GMBH
Linzerstrasse 139-141, 3003, Gablitz, Austria
Tel.: (43) 2231 63430
Web Site: http://www.austroflex.at
Year Founded: 1967
Sales Range: $1-9.9 Million
Emp.: 93
Sign Mfr
N.A.I.C.S.: 339950
Michael Schmutzer *(Mng Dir)*

LICOGI 14 JOINT STOCK COMPANY
2068 Hung Vuong Avenue, Viet Tri, Phu Tho, Vietnam
Tel.: (84) 2103953543
Web Site: https://licogi14.vn
Year Founded: 1982
L14—(HNX)
Rev.: $22,569,319
Assets: $46,509,651
Liabilities: $16,383,582
Net Worth: $30,126,069
Earnings: $14,877,915
Emp.: 120
Fiscal Year-end: 12/31/21
Transportation & Industrial Building Construction Services
N.A.I.C.S.: 236210
Pham Gia Ly *(Chm-Mgmt Bd)*

LICOGI 16 JOINT STOCK COMPANY
24A Phan Dang Luu Street Ward 6, Binh Thanh District, Ho Chi Minh City, Vietnam
Tel.: (84) 838411375
Web Site: https://www.licogi16.vn
Year Founded: 2001
LCG—(HOSE)
Rev.: $82,727,499
Assets: $246,340,362
Liabilities: $141,766,357
Net Worth: $104,574,005
Earnings: $4,184,684
Fiscal Year-end: 12/31/23
Residential Building Construction Services
N.A.I.C.S.: 236116
Bui Duong Hung *(Chm)*

LIDA HOLDINGS LIMITED
Rm 1803 17F No 270 Sec 4 Zhongxiao E Rd, Da an Dist, Taipei, 11052, Taiwan
Tel.: (886) 227328616
Web Site:
    https://www.lidaholdings.com
Year Founded: 2016
4552—(TAI)
Rev.: $165,000,059
Assets: $241,203,791
Liabilities: $46,472,283
Net Worth: $194,731,508
Earnings: $13,135,648
Emp.: 1,082
Fiscal Year-end: 12/31/23
Air Compressor Mfr & Distr
N.A.I.C.S.: 333912
Chien-Neng Wu *(Chm)*
Subsidiaries:

Lida (China) Machine Equipment Company Limited   (1)
Taiwanest Investment Zone, Dongyuan Town, Quanzhou, 362122, Fujian, China
Tel.: (86) 59587597777
Web Site: http://www.lida-compressors.com
Electro Mechanical Product Mfr
N.A.I.C.S.: 334514

Lida Holdings Limited—(Continued)

LIDA RESOURCES, INC.
2 14 Street West, Vancouver, V7M
1P9, BC, Canada
Tel.: (604) 961-0296 Ca
Web Site:
http://www.lidaresources.com
LDDAF—(OTCIQ)
Assets: $36,435
Liabilities: $766,466
Net Worth: ($730,032)
Earnings: ($1,169,789)
Fiscal Year-end: 08/31/22
Metal Mining & Exploration Services
N.A.I.C.S.: 213114
Geoffrey Balderson (CFO)

LIDDS AB
Virdings alle 32b, 754 50, Uppsala,
Sweden
Tel.: (46) 706200400
Web Site:
https://www.liddspharma.com
Year Founded: 2003
LIDDS—(OMX)
Rev.: $46,658
Assets: $1,753,132
Liabilities: $373,260
Net Worth: $1,379,872
Earnings: ($3,991,701)
Emp.: 1
Fiscal Year-end: 12/31/23
Pharmaceuticals Mfr
N.A.I.C.S.: 325412
Niklas Axen (Dir-Biomaterials & Devices)

LIDER FAKTORING AS
Buyukdere Cad Maya Akar Center
100-102, K 25 No 96-97, Esentepe-
Sisli, 34394, Istanbul, Turkiye
Tel.: (90) 2122130040 TR
Web Site:
https://www.liderfaktoring.com.tr
Year Founded: 1992
LIDFA—(IST)
Rev.: $15,727,016
Assets: $70,529,938
Liabilities: $54,885,886
Net Worth: $15,644,052
Earnings: $6,389,894
Fiscal Year-end: 12/31/22
Financial Consulting Services
N.A.I.C.S.: 541611

LIDIS
Zae Avenue De L Europe, 24390,
Hautefort, Dordogne, France
Tel.: (33) 553517300
Web Site: http://www.lidis.fr
Rev.: $12,600,000
Emp.: 44
Biscuits, Confectionery, Chocolate &
Beverages
N.A.I.C.S.: 424490
Olivier Berbinau (Pres)

LIDYE CO., LTD.
12F 22 Nanking W Rd, Taipei, Taiwan
Tel.: (886) 225559231
Web Site: http://www.lidye.com.tw
Investment Company
N.A.I.C.S.: 523999

Subsidiaries:

Croslene Chemical Industries,
Ltd. (1)
11F No 22 Nanjing W Rd, Datong Dist, Taipei, 103, Taiwan
Tel.: (886) 225556661
Web Site: http://www.croslene.com
Synthetic Resins Mfr & Sales; Owned 50%
by Mitsui Takeda Chemicals, Inc. & 48% by
Lidye Co., Ltd.
N.A.I.C.S.: 325211

Lidye Chemical Co., Ltd. (1)
10th Fl The Lidye Commercial Bldg 22 Nanking West Road, Taipei, 103614, Taiwan
Tel.: (886) 225553271
Web Site: http://www.lidyechemical.com.tw
Synthetic Resins Mfr & Distr
N.A.I.C.S.: 325211

LIEBHERR-INTERNATIONAL AG
45 Rue De L'Industrie, 1630, Bulle,
Switzerland
Tel.: (41) 269133111
Web Site: http://www.liebherr.com
Year Founded: 1949
Sales Range: $5-14.9 Billion
Emp.: 37,800
Construction Machinery Mfr
N.A.I.C.S.: 333120
Willi Liebherr (Chm)

Subsidiaries:

EURL Liebherr Algerie (1)
Zone Industrielle Lot N 4 Oued Kerma, PO
Box 540, Saoula, 16305, Algiers, Algeria
Tel.: (213) 23 53 81 41
Construction Equipment Whslr
N.A.I.C.S.: 423830

Liebherr (Ireland) Holding Ltd. (1)
Fossa, Killarney, Co Kerry, Ireland (100%)
Tel.: (353) 646670200
Web Site: http://www.liebherr.com
Sales Range: $150-199.9 Million
Emp.: 700
Holding Company
N.A.I.C.S.: 551112
Gerry Bunyan (Mgr-Mktg & PR)

Subsidiary (Domestic):

Killarney Hotels Ltd. (2)
Fossa Killarney County Kerry, Killarney, Co
Kerry, Ireland (100%)
Tel.: (353) 6431900
Web Site: http://www.killarneyhotels.ie
Sales Range: $25-49.9 Million
Emp.: 150
Hotels, Farm
N.A.I.C.S.: 721110
Michael Brennan (Gen Mgr)

Liebherr Container Cranes Ltd. (2)
Fossa, Killarney, Co Kerry, Ireland (100%)
Tel.: (353) 646670200
Web Site: http://www.liebherr.com
Sales Range: $125-149.9 Million
Emp.: 400
Container & Cargo Holding Cranes Whslr
N.A.I.C.S.: 423830

Liebherr Appliances Kluang SDN.
BHD. (1)
No 7 Jalan Firma 2 Kawasan Perindustrian
Kluang II KM7 Jalan Mersing, 86007, Keluang, Johor, Malaysia
Tel.: (60) 7 778 6888
Web Site: http://www.liebherr.com
Emp.: 480
Refrigerator Mfr
N.A.I.C.S.: 335220
Sim Eng Beng (Gen Mgr)

Liebherr Brasil Guindastes e Maquinas Operatrizes Ltda. (1)
1 Bairro Vila Bela, 12522-640, Guaratingueta, SP, Brazil (100%)
Tel.: (55) 1231284200
Sales Range: $350-399.9 Million
Emp.: 600
Trade & Service Company
N.A.I.C.S.: 523160

Liebherr CMCtec India Pvt. Ltd. (1)
Gat No 196-199, Dhaygudewadi District,
Pune, 412 203, Maharashtra, India
Tel.: (91) 2117 305 300
Web Site: http://www.liebherr.com
Emp.: 90
Earthmoving Machine & Crane Distr
N.A.I.C.S.: 423830

Liebherr Chile SpA (1)
Av Nueva Tajamar 481 Of 2103 Y 2104 Edificio World Trade Center, Torre Sur Las
Condes, Santiago, Chile
Tel.: (56) 2 58 01499
Winding Machinery Distr

N.A.I.C.S.: 423810

Liebherr Components (Dalian) Co.
Ltd. (1)
201 West Huanghai Fourth Road Room 220
International Business Plaza Da, 116620,
Dalian, China
Tel.: (86) 411 8733 59 77
Web Site: http://www.liebherr.com
Construction Equipment Mfr
N.A.I.C.S.: 333310

Liebherr Components North America
Co. (1)
1465 Woodland Dr, Saline, MI 48176
Tel.: (734) 429-7225
Industrial Machinery & Equipment Distr
N.A.I.C.S.: 423830

Liebherr Concrete Technology
Co. (1)
4100 Chestnut Ave, Newport News, VA
23607
Tel.: (757) 928-8547
Web Site: http://www.liebherr.com
Emp.: 8
Construction Machinery Distr
N.A.I.C.S.: 423810
Herbert Botzenhart (Gen Mgr)

Liebherr Iberica, S.A. (1)
Catr Natl 2 km 41 del Aluminio 6 & 8 Poligono Indusl Miralcampo, Azuqueca De
Henares, Guadalajara, 19200,
Spain (100%)
Tel.: (34) 949348730
Web Site: http://www.liebherr.com
Sales Range: $50-74.9 Million
Emp.: 150
Importer, Exporter & Retailer of Construction Machinery
N.A.I.C.S.: 333120
Rudolf Lessmeister (Mng Dir)

Liebherr Iberica, S.L. (1)
Carretera Nacional II Km 41 Poligono Industrial Miralcampo C/Aluminio, 19200,
Azuqueca de Henares, Spain
Tel.: (34) 949 34 87 30
Web Site: http://www.liebherr.com
Earthmoving Machine & Crane Distr
N.A.I.C.S.: 423830

Liebherr India Private Limited (1)
Kesar Solitaire 25th and 26th Floor Plot no
5 Sector 19 Sanpada, Navi Mumbai, 400
705, India
Tel.: (91) 22 412675 00
Web Site: http://www.liebherr.com
Emp.: 80
Earthmoving Machine & Crane Distr
N.A.I.C.S.: 423830
Rahul Dandavate (Mng Dir)

Liebherr Industrias Metalicas,
S.A. (1)
Pol Agustinos St E, 31014, Pamplona, Navarre, Spain (100%)
Tel.: (34) 948297000
Web Site: http://www.liebherr.com
Sales Range: $100-124.9 Million
Emp.: 220
Construction Machinery & Construction
Cranes
N.A.I.C.S.: 333120
Helmut Dollerer (Gen Mgr)

Liebherr International Austria
GmbH (1)
Dr Hans Liebherr Strasse 4, A 5500, Bischofshofen, Austria (100%)
Tel.: (43) 64628880
Web Site: http://www.lah.liebherr.com
Sales Range: $25-49.9 Million
Emp.: 20
Holding Company
N.A.I.C.S.: 551112

Subsidiary (Domestic):

Hotel Lowen Schruns GmbH (2)
Silvrettastrasse 8, 6780, Schruns,
Austria (100%)
Tel.: (43) 55567141
Web Site: http://www.loewen-hotel.com
Sales Range: $10-24.9 Million
Hotel
N.A.I.C.S.: 721110

Interalpen-Hotel Tyrol GmbH (2)

Dr-Hans-Liebherr-Alpenstrasse 1, PO Box
96, 6410, Telfs, Austria (100%)
Tel.: (43) 5080930
Web Site: http://www.interalpen.com
Sales Range: $25-49.9 Million
Emp.: 240
Hotel
N.A.I.C.S.: 721110
Karl Brueggemann (Mng Dir)

Liebherr-Verkehrstechnik GmbH (2)
Liebherrstrasse 1, 2100, Korneuburg,
Austria (100%)
Tel.: (43) 22626020
Web Site: http://www.liebherr.com
Sales Range: $125-149.9 Million
Emp.: 400
Equipment for Rail Vehicles, Air Conditioning Systems, Ventilation & Air-Supported
Heating
N.A.I.C.S.: 423860
Adrian Gunis (Mng Dir & Head-Production
& Supply Chain)

Liebherr-Werk Bischofshofen
GmbH (2)
Dr Hans Liebherr Strasse 4, PO Box 49,
5500, Bischofshofen, Austria (100%)
Tel.: (43) 64628880
Web Site: http://www.lbh.liebherr.com
Construction Machinery & Wheel Loaders
N.A.I.C.S.: 333120
Manfred Santner (Mng Dir)

Liebherr-Werk Lienz GmbH (2)
Dr Hans Liebherr Strasse 1, A 9900, Lienz,
Austria (100%)
Tel.: (43) 48526010
Refrigerators & Freezers
N.A.I.C.S.: 335220

Liebherr-Werk Nenzing GmbH (2)
Dr Hans Liebherr St 1, PO Box 10, 6710,
Nenzing, Austria (100%)
Tel.: (43) 5525606
Emp.: 1,500
Ships' & Offshore Cranes; Harbor Cranes;
Hydraulic Rope Excavators
N.A.I.C.S.: 333120
Karl Weisskops (Mng Dir)

Subsidiary (Non-US):

Liebherr (HKG) Limited (3)
86 Ping Chen Rd, Fanling, China (Hong
Kong) (100%)
Tel.: (852) 31423150
Web Site: http://www.liebherr.com
Sales Range: $50-74.9 Million
Emp.: 85
Trading Company; Construction Machinery
N.A.I.C.S.: 523160
Fransico Kwok (Mng Dir)

Liebherr-Maritim Benelux (3)
Deeldschermweg 2, 3821 AH, Amersfoort,
Netherlands (100%)
Tel.: (31) 334500800
Web Site: http://www.liebherr.com
Sales Range: $25-49.9 Million
Emp.: 25
N.A.I.C.S.: 333120

Liebherr-Nenzing Service GmbH (3)
Am Neulander Baggerteich 1, D 21079,
Hamburg, Germany (100%)
Tel.: (49) 4076702200
Web Site: http://www.liebherr.com
Sales Range: $25-49.9 Million
Emp.: 40
Trade & Service for Mobile Harbour &
Ship's Cranes
N.A.I.C.S.: 333923
Greg Schmidt (Mng Dir)

Subsidiary (Domestic):

Liebherr-Werk Telfs GmbH (2)
Hans-Liebherr-Strasse 35, 6410, Telfs,
Austria (100%)
Tel.: (43) 508096100
Web Site: http://www.liebherr.com
Sales Range: $75-99.9 Million
Construction Machinery Loaders, Dozers
N.A.I.C.S.: 333120
Martin Liengle (Gen Mgr)

Liebherr Japan Co. Ltd. (1)
5 39 Daikoku Cho, Tsurumi Ku, Yokohama,
230, Japan (100%)

AND PRIVATE COMPANIES

LIEBHERR-INTERNATIONAL AG

Tel.: (81) 455058686
Web Site: http://www.liebherr.com
Sales Range: $50-74.9 Million
Emp.: 25
Trading Services
N.A.I.C.S.: 523160

Liebherr Machine Tools India Pvt. Ltd.
353/354 4th Main 9th Cross 4th Phase Peenya Industrial Area, Bengaluru, 560 058, India
Tel.: (91) 80 411785 91
Web Site: http://www.liebherr.com
Emp.: 30
Geat Cutting Machinery Mfr
N.A.I.C.S.: 333515
G. Sreedhar *(Gen Mgr)*

Liebherr Machinery (Dalian) Co., Ltd. (1)
30 Wanli Street Dalian Economic & Technological Development Zone, Dalian, 116600, Liaoning, China
Tel.: (86) 411 8733 5999
Crane Mfr
N.A.I.C.S.: 333310

Liebherr Machinery Service (Shanghai) Co. Ltd. (1)
Building No 1 88 Maji Road Waigaoqiao Free Trade Zone, Shanghai, 200131, China
Tel.: (86) 2150461988
Construction Machinery Sales
N.A.I.C.S.: 423810

Liebherr Makine Ticaret Servis Limited Sirketi (1)
Cumhuriyet Mah E-5 Yanyol No 39 Yakacik/Kartal, 34876, Istanbul, Turkiye
Tel.: (90) 216 4531000
Web Site: http://www.liebherr.com
Emp.: 70
Industrial Machinery Distr
N.A.I.C.S.: 423830
Danyel Temizkan *(CEO)*

Liebherr Maritime BeNeLux B.V. (1)
Beeldschermweg 2, 3821 AH, Amersfoort, Netherlands
Tel.: (31) 33 450 08 00
Crane Distr
N.A.I.C.S.: 423830

Liebherr Mexico S. de R.L. de C.V. (1)
Centro Aleman Av Santa Fe No 170/2-2-02 Col Lomas de Santa Fe, 01210, Mexico, Mexico
Tel.: (52) 55 5001 59 60
Mobile Crane Distr
N.A.I.C.S.: 423830

Liebherr Middle East, FZE. (1)
Jebel Ali Free Zone South Plot No S 10508, PO Box 2540, Dubai, United Arab Emirates
Tel.: (971) 4 88 60 199
Construction Machinery Whslr
N.A.I.C.S.: 423830

Liebherr Mobile Cranes Korea Ltd. (1)
Fine Bldg 4th Floor 673-5, Deungchon-Dong Gangseo-Gu, Seoul, 157-033, Korea (South)
Tel.: (82) 226 5922 90 2
Mobile Crane Distr
N.A.I.C.S.: 423830

Liebherr Monterrey, S. de R. L. de C. V. (1)
Carretera Monterrey-Garcia Km 11 Col El Durazno, Villa de Garcia, 66000, Mexico
Tel.: (52) 81 8988 8700
Web Site: http://www.liebherr.com
Emp.: 120
Bearing & Gear Ring Mfr
N.A.I.C.S.: 336390

Liebherr Nenzing Crane Co. (1)
15101 NW 112th Ave, Hialeah Gardens, FL 33018
Tel.: (305) 817-7500
Web Site: http://www.liebherr.com
Crane Distr
N.A.I.C.S.: 423830
Ines Relley *(Head-Fin & Admin)*

Liebherr Sales Kluang SDN. BHD. (1)
No 23 Jalan PJS 7/21 Bandar Sunway, 46150, Petaling Jaya, Selangor, Malaysia
Tel.: (60) 3 5638 1471
Refrigerator & Freezer Whslr
N.A.I.C.S.: 423620

Liebherr Sunderland Works Ltd. (1)
Ayres Quay Deptford Terrace, Tyne and Wear, Sunderland, SR4 6DD, United Kingdom
Tel.: (44) 191 514 3001
Emp.: 200
Crane Mfr
N.A.I.C.S.: 333310
Ralph Saelzer *(Mng Dir)*

Liebherr epitoipari-Gepek Magyarorszag Kft.
Szentivani Ut 19, 9027, Gyor, Hungary
Tel.: (36) 96 514 950
Earthmoving Machine & Crane Distr
N.A.I.C.S.: 423830

Liebherr-Aerospace & Transportation SAS
408 Avenue Des Etats-Unis, 31016, Toulouse, France
Tel.: (33) 5 613528 28
Construction Machinery Distr
N.A.I.C.S.: 423810

Liebherr-Aerospace Brasil Ltda. (1)
Rua Dr Hans Liebherr 1 Vila Bela, Guaratingueta, 12522-635, SP, Brazil
Tel.: (55) 1221314774
Sales Range: $25-49.9 Million
Emp.: 24
Joint Venture of Embraer-Empresa Brasileira de Aeronautica S/A (60%) & Liebherr-International AG (40%)
N.A.I.C.S.: 332911

Liebherr-Aerospace Nizhny Novgorod OOO (1)
Ul Liebherra 1/5, Nizhegorodskaya Oblast, 606023, Dzerzhinsk, Russia
Tel.: (7) 8313276101
Emp.: 270
Construction Machinery Mfr
N.A.I.C.S.: 333120

Liebherr-Aerospace Toulouse S.A. (1)
Av Des Etats Unis 408; PO Box 52010, F 31016, Toulouse, Cedex, France (100%)
Tel.: (33) 561352828
Web Site: http://www.liebherr.com
Sales Range: $200-249.9 Million
Emp.: 700
Aircraft Equipment
N.A.I.C.S.: 336413
Andre BenHanou *(Gen Mgr)*

Liebherr-Africa (Pty.) Ltd. (1)
Vlakfontein Rd Fulcrum Ind Township, PO Box 841, Springs, 1560, Transvaal, South Africa (100%)
Tel.: (27) 113652000
Web Site: http://www.liebherr.com
Sales Range: $50-74.9 Million
Emp.: 200
Construction Machinery & Equipment
N.A.I.C.S.: 333120
Dieter Schmid *(Dir-Fin)*

Liebherr-America Inc. (1)
4100 Chestnut Ave, Newport News, VA 23607-2420 (100%)
Tel.: (757) 245-5251
Web Site: http://www.liebherr.com
Sales Range: $150-199.9 Million
Emp.: 500
Holding Company
N.A.I.C.S.: 423810
Ana Cabiedes-Uranga *(Gen Mgr-Mktg)*

Subsidiary (Domestic):

HL Farm Corp. (2)
4100 Chestnut Ave, Newport News, VA 23607 (100%)
Tel.: (757) 245-5251
Web Site: http://www.liebherr.com
Sales Range: $75-99.9 Million
Emp.: 400
Sales of Farming Equipment
N.A.I.C.S.: 111998
Lena Hogue *(Pres)*

Liebherr Construction Equipment Co. (2)
4100 Chestnut Ave, Newport News, VA 23607 (100%)
Tel.: (757) 245-5251
Web Site: http://www.liebherr.com
Sales Range: $100-124.9 Million
Emp.: 400
Mfr & Sales of Construction Equipment
N.A.I.C.S.: 333923
Timothy Doucette *(Gen Mgr-Brand Strategy)*

Liebherr Mining Equipment Co. (2)
4100 Chestnut Ave, Newport News, VA 23607 (100%)
Tel.: (757) 245-5251
Web Site: http://www.liebherr-mining.com
Sales Range: $100-124.9 Million
Emp.: 400
Mfr & Sales of Mining Equipment
N.A.I.C.S.: 333923
Chen Qi *(Engr-Electrical Drive)*

Liebherr Nenzing Crane (2)
7075 Bennington St, Houston, TX 77028 (100%)
Tel.: (713) 636-4050
Web Site: http://www.liebherr.com
Sales Range: $50-74.9 Million
Offshore Crawler Cranes Mfr
N.A.I.C.S.: 333120
Matt Listro *(VP-Sls-Northeastern States)*

Liebherr-Aerospace Saline, Inc. (2)
1465 Woodland Dr, Saline, MI 48176-1259
Tel.: (734) 429-7225
Web Site: http://www.liebherr.com
Aircraft Equipment Mfr, Sales & Services
N.A.I.C.S.: 423830

Liebherr-Automation Systems Co. (2)
1465 Woodland Dr, Saline, MI 48176-1627 (100%)
Tel.: (734) 429-7225
Web Site: http://www.liebherr-us.com
Sales Range: $25-49.9 Million
Emp.: 15
Materials Flow Technology
N.A.I.C.S.: 423830
Peter Wiedemann *(Pres)*

Liebherr-Argentina S.A. (1)
Gral Mosconi 4587 Sur Lateral Ruta 40, C P 5425, Rawson, San Juan, Argentina
Tel.: (54) 264 42844 49
Mobile Crane Distr
N.A.I.C.S.: 423830

Liebherr-Australia Pty. Ltd. (1)
1 Dr Willi Liebherr Dr, Para Hills, 5096, SA, Australia (100%)
Tel.: (61) 883496888
Web Site: http://www.liebherr.com.au
Sales Range: $50-74.9 Million
Emp.: 120
Construction Machinery & Mining Equipment
N.A.I.C.S.: 333120

Liebherr-Azeri LLC (1)
20 A Jalilov Str Apt 19 1069, Baku, Azerbaijan
Tel.: (994) 12 489 026 5
Mobile Crane Distr
N.A.I.C.S.: 423830

Liebherr-Betonpumpen GmbH (1)
Lessingstrasse 4, 89231, Neu-Ulm, Germany
Tel.: (49) 731 72905 0
Emp.: 60
Construction Machinery Mfr
N.A.I.C.S.: 333120

Liebherr-Canada Ltd. (1)
1015 Sutton Drive, Burlington, L7L 5Z8, ON, Canada (100%)
Tel.: (905) 319-9222
Web Site: http://www.liebherr.com
Sales Range: $50-74.9 Million
Emp.: 108
Construction Machinery & Equipment Mfr
N.A.I.C.S.: 333120

Liebherr-Colombia SAS (1)
Via 40 No 69-58 Bodegas A09 & A10 Pq Ind Y Comercial Cia 40, Barranquilla, Colombia
Tel.: (57) 5 349 39 49
Construction Equipment Whslr
N.A.I.C.S.: 423830

Liebherr-Component Technologies AG (1)
45 Rue De Industrie, CH 1630, Bulle, Switzerland (100%)
Tel.: (41) 269133111
Web Site: http://www.liebherr.com
Sales Range: $25-49.9 Million
Emp.: 20
Mechanical Component Mfr
N.A.I.C.S.: 335999

Liebherr-Components AG (1)
Kirchweg 46, 5415, Nussbaumen, Switzerland
Tel.: (41) 56 296 4300
Web Site: http://www.liebherr.com
Industrial Machinery & Equipment Distr
N.A.I.C.S.: 423830

Liebherr-Components Biberach GmbH (1)
Betrieb Deggendorf Grosswalding 5, 94469, Deggendorf, Germany
Tel.: (49) 991 9959 831 0
Controlling Device Mfr
N.A.I.C.S.: 334519

Liebherr-Construction Equipment Ireland Limited (1)
Unit 23N Greenogue Industrial Estate, Rathcoole, Dublin, BS23 3TR, Ireland
Tel.: (353) 458 76 50
Construction Equipment Whslr
N.A.I.C.S.: 423830

Liebherr-Danmark ApS (1)
Vesterbrogade 18, 8722, Hedensted, Denmark
Tel.: (45) 75 79 03 21
Mobile Crane Distr
N.A.I.C.S.: 423830

Liebherr-EMtec Italia S.p.A. (1)
Via dell'Industria 8-12, 240240, Lallio, Italy
Tel.: (39) 035 69691 00
Construction Equipment Whslr
N.A.I.C.S.: 423830

Liebherr-Elektronik GmbH (1)
Peter-Dornier-Strasse 11, 88131, Lindau, Germany
Tel.: (49) 8382 2730 0
Emp.: 590
Electronic Components Mfr
N.A.I.C.S.: 334419

Liebherr-Ettlingen GmbH (1)
Hertzstrasse 9-15, 76275, Ettlingen, Germany
Tel.: (49) 7243 708 101
Emp.: 110
Motor Vehicle Component Mfr
N.A.I.C.S.: 336390

Liebherr-Finland OY Ab (1)
Pakkasraitti 8, 04360, Tuusula, Finland
Tel.: (358) 9 83 66 03 0
Earthmoving Machinery Distr
N.A.I.C.S.: 423830

Liebherr-France S.A. (1)
2 Ave Joseph Rey, F 68005, Colmars, France (100%)
Tel.: (33) 389213030
Web Site: http://www.liebherr.com
Sales Range: $400-449.9 Million
Emp.: 1,600
Construction Machinery & Hydraulic Excavators
N.A.I.C.S.: 333120
Wolfjanj Borjet *(Mng Dir)*

Subsidiary (Domestic):

Liebherr Grues Mobiles SAS (2)
2 Ave Gaef, PO Box 287, 68005, Colmars, Cedex, France (100%)
Tel.: (33) 389213030
Web Site: http://www.liebherr.com
Sales Range: $25-49.9 Million
Emp.: 29
Mobile Cranes
N.A.I.C.S.: 333120
Ala Boheh *(Gen Mgr)*

Liebherr Grues a Tour SAS (2)
Zone D Activete BP 44, FR 68127, Niederhergheim, Alsace, France (100%)
Tel.: (33) 389863300
Web Site: http://www.liebherr.com

LIEBHERR-INTERNATIONAL AG

INTERNATIONAL PUBLIC

Liebherr-International AG—(Continued)
Sales Range: $25-49.9 Million
Emp.: 25
Construction Cranes
N.A.I.C.S.: 333120
Helmut Limberg (Mng Dir)

Liebherr Malaxage & Techniques SAS
Zone D Actevite, FR 68127, Guebwiller, Cedex, France (100%)
Tel.: (33) 389863208
Web Site: http://www.liebherr.com
Sales Range: $25-49.9 Million
Emp.: 35
Concrete Equipment
N.A.I.C.S.: 333120

Liebherr-France Sas (1)
2 Avenue Joseph Rey, PO Box 90287, 68005, Colmar, France
Tel.: (33) 38 921 3030
Web Site: http://www.liebherr.com
Emp.: 1,250
Construction Equipment Whslr
N.A.I.C.S.: 423830

Liebherr-Great Britain Ltd. (1)
Travellers Ln, Welham Green, Hatfield, AL9 7HW, Hertfordshire, United Kingdom (100%)
Tel.: (44) 767602100
Web Site: http://www.liebherr.com
Sales Range: $700-749.9 Million
Emp.: 2,000
Trading & Service Company
N.A.I.C.S.: 523160

Liebherr-Hausgerate Lienz GmbH (1)
Dr-Hans-Liebherr-Strasse 1, 9900, Lienz, Austria
Tel.: (43) 5080 92 0
Emp.: 1,270
Refrigerator & Freezer Mfr
N.A.I.C.S.: 335220

Liebherr-Hausgerate Marica EOOD (1)
Plovdivska Obl, 4202, Radinovo, Bulgaria
Tel.: (359) 32 505 310
Emp.: 1,590
Air Conditioning System Mfr
N.A.I.C.S.: 333415

Liebherr-Hausgerate Ochsenhausen GmbH (1)
Memminger Strasse 77-79, 88416, Ochsenhausen, Germany
Tel.: (49) 7352 928 0
Emp.: 1,900
Refrigerator & Freezer Mfr
N.A.I.C.S.: 335220

Liebherr-Holding GmbH (1)
Hans Liebherr Strasse 45, Biberach an der Riss, 88396, Germany (100%)
Tel.: (49) 7351410
Web Site: http://www.liebherr.com
Sales Range: $550-599.9 Million
Emp.: 2,000
Holding Company
N.A.I.C.S.: 551112

Subsidiary (Domestic):

Liebherr Hydraulic Excavators GmbH (2)
Liebherr Hydraulik Bagger, DE 88457, Kirchdorf, Germany (100%)
Tel.: (49) 7354800
Sales Range: $550-599.9 Million
Emp.: 1,800
Real Estate & Hotel
N.A.I.C.S.: 531210
Joeehim Strobel (Mng Dir)

Liebherr Logistik GmbH (2)
Leibherstrasse 45, Biberach, 88400, Germany (100%)
Tel.: (49) 7351410
Web Site: http://www.lbc.liebherr.com
Sales Range: $450-499.9 Million
Emp.: 1,750
N.A.I.C.S.: 333120

Liebherr Verzahntechnik GmbH (2)
Hertzstrasse 9-15, 76275, Ettlingen, Germany (100%)
Tel.: (49) 72437080
Web Site: http://www.liebherr.com
Sales Range: $10-24.9 Million
Emp.: 100
Machine Tools Mfr
N.A.I.C.S.: 332216

Liebherr-Aerospace Lindenberg GmbH (2)
Pfanderstrasse 50 52, Lindenberg im Allgau, 88161, Germany (100%)
Tel.: (49) 8381460
Web Site: http://www.lli.liebherr.com
Sales Range: $350-399.9 Million
Emp.: 2,000
Aircraft Equipment
N.A.I.C.S.: 336413
Josef Gropper (Co-Pres)

Liebherr-Gutsverwaltung GmbH (2)
Hans Liebherr Strasse 45, 88400, Biberach an der Riss, Germany (100%)
Tel.: (49) 7351410
Web Site: http://www.liebherr.com
Sales Range: $550-599.9 Million
Emp.: 1,700
Real Estate Broker
N.A.I.C.S.: 531210

Liebherr-Hausgerate GmbH (2)
Memminger Str 77-79, Ochsenhausen, 88416, Germany (100%)
Tel.: (49) 73529280
Web Site: http://www.liebherr.com
Sales Range: $350-399.9 Million
Emp.: 2,000
Refrigerators & Freezers
N.A.I.C.S.: 335220
Walther Detlef (Mng Dir)

Liebherr-Hydraulikbagger GmbH (2)
Liebherrstrasse 12, D 88457, Kirchdorf, Iller, Germany (100%)
Tel.: (49) 7354800
Web Site: http://www.lhb.liebherr.com
Sales Range: $350-399.9 Million
Emp.: 1,700
Construction Machinery, Equipment & Excavations
N.A.I.C.S.: 333120
Klaus Springer (Dir-Mktg)

Subsidiary (Domestic):

Liebherr-Wupper GmbH (3)
Hacheneyer Kirchweg 150, 44265, Dortmund, Germany (100%)
Tel.: (49) 2314650100
Web Site: http://www.liebherr.com
Sales Range: $25-49.9 Million
Emp.: 83
N.A.I.C.S.: 333120

Subsidiary (Domestic):

Liebherr-Mietpartner GmbH (2)
Am Herrschaftsweiher 51, Ludwigshafen, 67071, Germany (100%)
Tel.: (49) 6237400660
Web Site: http://www.lmp.liebherr.com
Sales Range: $25-49.9 Million
Emp.: 40
Renting of Construction Equipment
N.A.I.C.S.: 532412
Gido Kahlert (Mgr-Sls)

Liebherr-Mischtechnik GmbH (2)
Im Elchgrund 12, Bad Schussenried, 88427, Germany (100%)
Tel.: (49) 75839490
Web Site: http://www.liebherr.com
Sales Range: $75-99.9 Million
Emp.: 700
Construction Machinery & Concrete Equipment
N.A.I.C.S.: 333120
Frank C. Furt (Gen Mgr)

Subsidiary (Non-US):

Liebherr-Russland o.o.o. (2)
1-st Borodinskaya street 5, 121059, Moscow, Russia (100%)
Tel.: (7) 4957108365
Web Site: http://www.liebherr.com
Sales Range: $25-49.9 Million
Emp.: 100
Construction Machinery Manufacturer
N.A.I.C.S.: 333120

Subsidiary (Domestic):

Liebherr-Verzahntechnik GmbH (2)
Kaufbeurer Strasse 141, 87437, Kempten, Allgau, Germany (100%)
Tel.: (49) 8317860
Web Site: http://www.liebherr.com
Rev.: $464,359,500
Emp.: 900
Machine Tool & Material Flow Technology
N.A.I.C.S.: 333517
Friedrich Hesemann (Mng Dir)

Liebherr-Werk Biberach GmbH (2)
Hans Liebherr St 45, 88400, Biberach an der Riss, Germany (100%)
Tel.: (49) 7351410
Web Site: http://www.lbc.liebherr.com
Sales Range: $350-399.9 Million
Construction Machinery & Construction Cranes
N.A.I.C.S.: 333120

Liebherr-Werk Ehingen GmbH (2)
Dr Hans Liebherr Str 1, Ehingen, 89584, Germany (100%)
Tel.: (49) 73915020
Web Site: http://www.liebherr.com
Sales Range: $350-399.9 Million
Emp.: 2,000
Construction Machinery & Mobile Cranes
N.A.I.C.S.: 333120
Mario Trunzer (Gen Mgr & Mgr-Fin)

Liebherr-Italia S.p.A. (1)
Via Chico Mendes N 17, 34074, Monfalcone, Italy
Tel.: (39) 0481496949
Web Site: http://www.liebherr.com
Tower Cranes, Mobile Cranes & Maritime Distr
N.A.I.C.S.: 423830

Liebherr-Mining Equipment Colmar SAS
49 Rue Frederic Hartmann CS 50038, 68025, Colmar, France
Tel.: (33) 3 6949 2000
Emp.: 600
Mining Equipment & Machinery Mfr
N.A.I.C.S.: 333131

Liebherr-Mining Ghana Limited (1)
1A Milne Close Airport Residential Area PMBKIA, Accra, Ghana
Tel.: (233) 30 27 43 777
Industrial Machinery Rental & Leasing Services
N.A.I.C.S.: 532490

Liebherr-Mozambique Lda. (1)
Pestana Rocuma Hotel Rua da Se Numero 114 4o Andar Porta 31, Maputo, Mozambique
Tel.: (258) 82 3220250
Winding Machinery Distr
N.A.I.C.S.: 423810

Liebherr-Nederland B.V. (1)
Beeldschermweg 2, NL 3821 AH, Amersfoort, Netherlands (100%)
Tel.: (31) 334500200
Web Site: http://www.liebherr.com
Sales Range: $25-49.9 Million
Emp.: 45
Trading & Service Company
N.A.I.C.S.: 523160

Liebherr-Nenzing Equipements SAS (1)
Zone d'Activite Rue Liebherr, 68127, Niederhergheim, France
Tel.: (33) 389 8633 33
Web Site: http://www.liebherr.com
Emp.: 28
Industrial Machinery Distr
N.A.I.C.S.: 423830
Olevier Terraer (Gen Dir)

Liebherr-Nigeria Ltd. (1)
182 Kofo Abayomi Street Plot 734B Industrial Area 1, Victoria Island Lagos, Abuja, Nigeria
Tel.: (234) 9871 672 2 103
Crane Distr
N.A.I.C.S.: 423830

Liebherr-Nouvelle-Caledonie SAS (1)
11 rue Auer - Z I Ducos, PO Box 27857, 98863, Noumea, Cedex, New Caledonia
Tel.: (687) 24 13 90
Web Site: http://www.liebherr.com
Emp.: 35
Earthmoving Machinery Distr
N.A.I.C.S.: 423830
Bedo Bertrand (Office Mgr)

Liebherr-Polska Sp. z o.o. (1)
ul Hansa Liebherra 8, 41-710, Ruda Slaska, Poland
Tel.: (48) 323426950
Construction Machinery Distr
N.A.I.C.S.: 423830

Liebherr-Romania S.R.L. (1)
Str Horia Closca Si Crisan No 61-63 Office Building II Etaj 3, Ilfov, 075100, Otopeni, Romania
Tel.: (40) 372 163 721
Mobile Crane Distr
N.A.I.C.S.: 423830

Liebherr-Singapore Pte. Ltd. (1)
No 8 Pandan Ave, Singapore, 609384, Singapore (100%)
Tel.: (65) 62652305
Web Site: http://www.liebherr.com
Sales Range: $50-74.9 Million
Emp.: 100
Trading Services
N.A.I.C.S.: 523160

Liebherr-Stavebni stroje CZ s.r.o. (1)
Vintrovna 17, Popuvky, 664 41, Brno, Czech Republic
Tel.: (420) 547 425 330
Web Site: http://www.liebherr.cz
Emp.: 40
Construction Equipment Distr
N.A.I.C.S.: 423830
Jarsolav Moravec (Mng Dir)

Liebherr-Sverige AB (1)
Fallskarmsvagen 5, 721 31, Vasteras, Sweden
Tel.: (46) 21 80 62 40
Earthmoving Machinery & Crane Distr
N.A.I.C.S.: 423830

Liebherr-Swissholding AG (1)
45 Rue De lIndustrie, CH 1630, Bulle, Switzerland (100%)
Tel.: (41) 269133111
Web Site: http://www.liebherr.com
Sales Range: $25-49.9 Million
Emp.: 30
Holding Company
N.A.I.C.S.: 551112
Anbrosini Claude (Mng Dir)

Subsidiary (Domestic):

Liebherr Machines Bulle S.A. (2)
45 Rue De lIndustrie, Bulle, 1630, Switzerland (100%)
Tel.: (41) 269133111
Web Site: http://www.liebherr.com
Emp.: 1,000
Diesel Engines & Hydraulic Components
N.A.I.C.S.: 333618
Claug Ambrosene (Dir-Fin)

Liebherr-Baumaschinen AG (2)
Industrieweg 18, 6260, Reiden, Switzerland (100%)
Tel.: (41) 627858111
Web Site: http://www.liebherr.com
Sales Range: $75-99.9 Million
Emp.: 120
Trading & Service Company
N.A.I.C.S.: 523160

Liebherr-Export AG (2)
General Guisanstrasse 14, Postfach 54, Nussbaumen, 5415, Switzerland (100%)
Tel.: (41) 562961111
Web Site: http://www.liebherr.com
Sales Range: $75-99.9 Million
Emp.: 140
Export Company Service
N.A.I.C.S.: 522299
Martin Stein (Dir-Fin)

Liebherr-Industrieanlagen AG (2)
45 Rue De Lindustrie, CH 1630, Bulle, Switzerland (100%)
Tel.: (41) 269133111
Web Site: http://www.liebherr.com
Sales Range: $25-49.9 Million
Emp.: 8
Industrial Plant & Engineering Services

AND PRIVATE COMPANIES

Liebherr-International AG (2)
Rue Hans-Liebherr 7, 1630, Bulle,
Switzerland (100%)
Tel.: (41) 269133111
Web Site: http://www.liebherr.com
Sales Range: $25-49.9 Million
Emp.: 22
Real Estate
N.A.I.C.S.: 531210

Liebherr-Intertrading AG (2)
Rue Hans-Liebherr 7, 1630, Bulle,
Switzerland (100%)
Tel.: (41) 269133111
Web Site: http://www.liebherr.com
Sales Range: $50-74.9 Million
Emp.: 5
Trading Services
N.A.I.C.S.: 523160

Liebherr-Service AG (2)
General Guisanstrasse 14, CH 5415, Nussbaumen, Switzerland (100%)
Tel.: (41) 562961111
Web Site: http://www.liebherr.com
Sales Range: $25-49.9 Million
Emp.: 145
Mfr & Sales of Earth Moving Equipment & Household Appliances
N.A.I.C.S.: 335220
Kai Friedrich *(Mng Dir)*

Liebherr-Thailand Co., Ltd. (1)
7 Moo Soi 11 Hwy 36 Km 26 3 Tambon,
Makam Ku Nikom Pattana, Rayong, 21180,
Thailand (100%)
Tel.: (66) 38689444
Sales Range: $50-74.9 Million
Emp.: 200
Construction Machinery, Concrete Equipment
N.A.I.C.S.: 333120

Liebherr-Transportation Systems GmbH (1)
Liebherrstrasse 1, 2100, Korneuburg, Austria
Tel.: (43) 2262 602 0
Emp.: 250
Air Conditioning & Hydraulic Equipment Mfr
N.A.I.C.S.: 333998

Liebherr-Transportation Systems Mannheim GmbH (1)
Weinheimer Strasse 64, 68309, Mannheim,
Germany
Tel.: (49) 621 73 405 0
Web Site: http://www.liebherr.com
Emp.: 20
Engineering Consulting Services
N.A.I.C.S.: 541330

Liebherr-Transportation Systems Marica EOOD (1)
Bezirk Plovidiv, 4202, Radinovo, Bulgaria
Tel.: (359) 32 505 780
Emp.: 270
Air Conditioning System Mfr
N.A.I.C.S.: 333415

Liebherr-Utensili S.r.l. (1)
Via Nazioni Unite 18, 10093, Collegno, Italy
Tel.: (39) 011 4 24 87 11
Emp.: 90
Gear Cutting Tool Mfr
N.A.I.C.S.: 333515

PT Liebherr-Indonesia Perkasa (1)
JL Mulawarman 17 RT 19, RW 04 Kel
Manggar, Balikpapan, 76116, East Kalimantan, Indonesia (95%)
Tel.: (62) 542764215
Web Site: http://www.liebherr.com
Sales Range: $50-74.9 Million
Emp.: 250
Trading & Service Company
N.A.I.C.S.: 333131
Charlie Clark *(Gen Mgr)*

Saudi Liebherr Company Ltd. (1)
KM 14 Madina Rd, PO Box 6403, Jeddah,
21442, Saudi Arabia (100%)
Tel.: (966) 26825333
Sales Range: $50-74.9 Million
Emp.: 52
Trading Company
N.A.I.C.S.: 523160

Xuzhou Liebherr Concrete Machinery Co. Ltd. (1)
Jinshanqiao Economic & Technological Development Zone, District 6A, Xuzhou,
221004, Jiangsu, China (50%)
Tel.: (86) 516 8798 2808
Web Site: http://www.liebherr.com
Emp.: 330
Concrete Equipment
N.A.I.C.S.: 333120
Eric Zhao *(Asst Gen Mgr)*

Zhejiang Liebherr Zhongche Transportation Systems Co. Ltd. (1)
37 Wangyun West Road, 311800, Zhuji,
Zhejiang, China
Tel.: (86) 575 8710 2861
Emp.: 110
Air Conditioning Equipment Mfr
N.A.I.C.S.: 333415

LIECHTENSTEIN GLOBAL TRUST AG

Herrengasse 12, PO Box 85, FL
9490, Vaduz, Liechtenstein
Tel.: (423) 2351122
Web Site: http://www.lgt.com
Year Founded: 1920
Sales Range: $200-249.9 Million
Emp.: 2,000
Bank Holding Company
N.A.I.C.S.: 551111
Urs Gahwilers *(Head-Legal & Tax)*

Subsidiaries:

LGT (Middle East) Ltd. (1)
DIFC The Gate Building West Level 2, PO
Box 506793, Dubai, United Arab Emirates
Tel.: (971) 4 436 7000
Commercial Banking Services
N.A.I.C.S.: 522110

LGT (Uruguay) Ltd. (1)
WTC Torre 3 - piso 8 oficina 875 Luis A de
Herrera 1248 CP, 11300, Montevideo, Uruguay
Tel.: (598) 2623 33 88
Commercial Banking Services
N.A.I.C.S.: 522110

LGT Bank (Singapore) Ltd. (1)
3 Temasek Avenue Suite 30-01 Centennial
Tower, Singapore, 039190, Singapore
Tel.: (65) 64 15 38 00
Commercial Banking Services
N.A.I.C.S.: 522110

LGT Bank Ltd. (1)
Herrengasse 12, 9490, Vaduz, Liechtenstein
Tel.: (423) 235 11 22
Web Site: http://www.lgt.com
Commercial Banking Services
N.A.I.C.S.: 522110

LGT Bank in Liechtenstein AG (1)
Herrengasse 12, 9490, Vaduz,
Liechtenstein (100%)
Tel.: (423) 2351122
Web Site: http://www.lgt.com
Sales Range: $200-249.9 Million
Emp.: 700
Private Banking Services
N.A.I.C.S.: 523150
Philipp von und zu Liechtenstein *(Chm)*

Subsidiary (Non-US):

LGT Bank (Ireland) Limited (2)
3rd Floor 30 Herbert Street, Dublin, 2,
Ireland (100%)
Tel.: (353) 14337400
Web Site: http://www.lgt.com
Sales Range: $50-74.9 Million
Emp.: 25
Banking Services
N.A.I.C.S.: 522320
Mariam Hynes *(Accountant)*

LGT Bank Switzerland (2)
Via Bossi 9, PO Box 2842, 6901, Lugano,
Switzerland (100%)
Tel.: (41) 919126969
Web Site: http://www.lgt.com
Sales Range: $25-49.9 Million
Emp.: 20
Branch Office
N.A.I.C.S.: 513110

LGT Bank in Switzerland Ltd. (2)
Lange Gasse 15, CH 4002, Basel, Switzerland
Tel.: (41) 612775600
Sales Range: $75-99.9 Million
Emp.: 122
Branch Office
N.A.I.C.S.: 522299
Heinrich Henckel *(CEO & Member-Exec Bd)*

LGT Capital Management Limited (1)
Herrengasse 12, PO Box 1133, 9490, Vaduz, Liechtenstein (100%)
Tel.: (423) 2351122
Web Site: http://www.lgt.com
Investment Services
N.A.I.C.S.: 523940

Subsidiary (Domestic):

LGT Financial Services Ltd (2)
Herrengasse 12, Vaduz, 9490, Liechtenstein
Tel.: (423) 2351122
Web Site: http://www.lgt.com
Investment Advisor
N.A.I.C.S.: 523940

Subsidiary (Non-US):

LGT Investment Management (Asia) Ltd. (1)
4203 Two Exchange Square, 8 Connaught
Pl, Central, China (Hong Kong) (100%)
Tel.: (852) 25229260
Web Site: http://www.lgtcp.com
Investment Advice
N.A.I.C.S.: 523940

LGT Capital Partners (Asia-Pacific) Ltd. (1)
Suite 4203 Two Exchange Square 8 Connaught Place, PO Box 13398, Hong Kong,
China (Hong Kong)
Tel.: (852) 2522 2900
Web Site: http://www.lgt-capital-partners.com
Commercial Banking Services
N.A.I.C.S.: 522110
Douglas Coulter *(Partner & Head-Private Equities)*

LGT Capital Partners (Australia) Pty Ltd. (1)
Level 36 Governor Phillip Tower 1 Farrer
Place, Sydney, 2000, NSW, Australia
Tel.: (61) 414 375 513
Commercial Banking Services
N.A.I.C.S.: 522110

LGT Capital Partners (Ireland) Limited (1)
3rd Floor 30 Herbert Street, Dublin, 2, Ireland
Tel.: (353) 1 433 74 40
Commercial Banking Services
N.A.I.C.S.: 522110

LGT Capital Partners (Japan) Co. Ltd. (1)
17th Floor Stage Building 2-7-2 Fujimi,
Chiyoda-ku, Tokyo, 102-0071, Japan
Tel.: (81) 3 6272 6442
Web Site: http://www.lgtcp.com
Commercial Banking Services
N.A.I.C.S.: 522110

LGT Capital Partners (U.K.) Limited (1)
35 Dover Street, London, W1S 4NQ, United Kingdom
Tel.: (44) 20 7529 0960
Web Site: http://www.lgt.com
Emp.: 10
Commercial Banking Services
N.A.I.C.S.: 522110
Baseera Green *(Office Mgr)*

LGT Capital Partners (USA) Inc. (1)
1133 Avenue of the Americas, New York,
NY 10036
Tel.: (212) 336-0650
Commercial Banking Services
N.A.I.C.S.: 522110

LGT Investment Consulting (Beijing) Limited (1)
Suite 15-16 15th Floor China World Tower 1
No1 Jianguomenwai Avenue, Chaoyang
District, Beijing, 100004, China
Tel.: (86) 10 6505 1523
Commercial Banking Services
N.A.I.C.S.: 522110

LGT Investment Management (Japan) Co. Ltd. (1)
8th Floor Pacific Century Place 1-11-1
Marunouchi, Chiyoda-ku, Tokyo, 100-6208,
Japan
Tel.: (81) 3 6860 8353
Commercial Banking Services
N.A.I.C.S.: 522110

LGT Investment Partners Ltd. (1)
Schuetzenstrasse 6, 8808, Pfaffikon, Switzerland
Tel.: (41) 55 415 7100
Commercial Banking Services
N.A.I.C.S.: 522110

LIECHTENSTEINISCHE LANDESBANK AG

Stadtle 44, PO Box 384, 9490, Vaduz, Liechtenstein
Tel.: (423) 2368811
Web Site: https://www.llb.li
Year Founded: 1926
LLBN—(SWX)
Rev.: $268,038,803
Assets: $27,955,504,435
Liabilities: $25,711,903,548
Net Worth: $2,243,600,887
Earnings: $165,687,361
Emp.: 915
Fiscal Year-end: 12/31/22
Banking Services
N.A.I.C.S.: 522110
Cyrill Sele *(Sec & Head-Grp Corp Comm & Sustainability)*

Subsidiaries:

Arch Capital Partners AG (1)
Am Schanzengraben 23, 8002, Zurich,
Switzerland
Tel.: (41) 582000400
Investment Management Service
N.A.I.C.S.: 523940

LLB Asset Management AG (1)
Stadtle 7, PO Box 201, 9490, Vaduz, Liechtenstein
Tel.: (423) 2369500
Sales Range: $25-49.9 Million
Emp.: 30
Asset Management Services
N.A.I.C.S.: 541611

LLB Fondsleitung AG (1)
Aeulestrasse 80, PO Box 1256, 9490, Vaduz, Liechtenstein
Tel.: (423) 2368140
Web Site: http://www.llb-funds.li
Sales Range: $50-74.9 Million
Emp.: 8
Investment Funds Management
N.A.I.C.S.: 523999
Loland Bartetze *(Mng Dir)*

LLB Fund Services AG (1)
Aulestrasse 80, PO Box 1238, 9490, Vaduz,
Liechtenstein
Tel.: (423) 2369400
Web Site: https://www.llb.li
Sales Range: $25-49.9 Million
Emp.: 20
Fund Management Services
N.A.I.C.S.: 541618

LLB Holding (Schweiz) AG (1)
Stampfenbachstrasse 114, 8006, Zurich,
Switzerland
Tel.: (41) 444214611
Web Site: http://www.liechtensteinischelandesbank.ch
Sales Range: $50-74.9 Million
Emp.: 25
Investment Management Service
N.A.I.C.S.: 523940

LLB Invest AGmvk (1)
Aulestrasse 80, Postfach 1256, 9490, Vaduz, Liechtenstein
Tel.: (423) 2368140

LIECHTENSTEINISCHE LANDESBANK AG

Liechtensteinische Landesbank AG—(Continued)
Web Site: http://www.llb.li
Investment Management Service
N.A.I.C.S.: 523999

LLB Investment Partners AG (1)
PO Box 362, Vaduz, 9490, Liechtenstein
Tel.: (423) 2369500
Web Site: http://www.llb.li
Sales Range: $350-399.9 Million
Emp.: 600
Research & Management of Funds for Liechtensteinische Landesbank
N.A.I.C.S.: 523920
Matt Rolland (CEO)

LLB Linth Holding AG (1)
Zurcherstrasse 3, 8730, Uznach, Switzerland (100%)
Tel.: (41) 844114411
Web Site: http://www.banklinth.ch
Holding Company
N.A.I.C.S.: 551111

LLB Swiss Investment AG (1)
Claridenstrasse 20, 8002, Zurich, Switzerland (100%)
Tel.: (41) 585239670
Web Site: https://www.lbswiss.ch
Investment Banking Services
N.A.I.C.S.: 523150
Dominik Rutishauser (Mng Dir)

LLB Treuhand AG (1)
Aeulestrasse 80, PO Box 568, 9490, Vaduz, Liechtenstein
Tel.: (423) 2368600
Web Site: http://www.llb-treuhand.li
Sales Range: $50-74.9 Million
Emp.: 50
Trust Management & Legal & Financial Advice
N.A.I.C.S.: 523991

Liechtensteinische Landesbank (Osterreich) AG (1)
Hebgasse 1, 1010, Vienna, Austria
Tel.: (43) 1536160
Web Site: https://www.llb.at
Sales Range: $50-74.9 Million
Emp.: 30
Commercial Banking Services
N.A.I.C.S.: 522110
Robert Low (Chm-Mgmt Bd)

Liechtensteinische Landesbank (Osterreich) AG (1)
Hessgasse 1, 1010, Vienna, Austria
Tel.: (43) 1536160
Web Site: https://www.llb.at
Banking & Investment Services
N.A.I.C.S.: 523150
Bernhard Ramsauer (CEO)

Liechtensteinische Landesbank (Schweiz) AG (1)
Stampfenbachstrasse 114, 8006, Zurich, Switzerland
Tel.: (41) 14214611
Web Site: http://www.llb.ch
Sales Range: $50-74.9 Million
Emp.: 65
Banking Services
N.A.I.C.S.: 522110

Liechtensteinische Landesbank Ltd. (1)
Gold & Diamond Park Building No 4 Office No 205-206, PO Box 30774, Dubai, 30774, United Arab Emirates
Tel.: (971) 43237970
Web Site: http://www.llb.li
Sales Range: $50-74.9 Million
Emp.: 10
Private Banking Services
N.A.I.C.S.: 522110

Swisspartners Advisors Ltd. (1)
Am Schanzengraben 23, 8022, Zurich, Switzerland
Tel.: (41) 582000800
Web Site: https://www.swisspartners-advisors.com
Sales Range: $50-74.9 Million
Emp.: 60
Financial Investment Advisory Services
N.A.I.C.S.: 523940
Gerhard Gottet (Partner & Chief Compliance Officer)

Swisspartners Insurance Company SPC Ltd. (1)
94 Solaris Avenue Fl 2, Camana Bay, KY1-1102, Cayman Islands
Tel.: (345) 914 8914
Web Site: http://www.swisspartners-insurance.com.ky
Emp.: 3
Fire Insurance Services
N.A.I.C.S.: 524113

Swisspartners Versicherung AG (1)
Stadtle 28, 9490, Vaduz, Liechtenstein
Tel.: (423) 2397979
Web Site: http://www.swisspartners.com
Emp.: 20
Asset Management Services
N.A.I.C.S.: 561110

LIEN CHANG ELECTRONIC ENTERPRISE CO., LTD.
11F No 501 Sec 6 Nanjing E Rd, Neihu Dist, Taipei, 114, Taiwan
Tel.: (886) 287921666
Web Site: https://www.lienchang.com.tw
Year Founded: 1968
2431—(TAI)
Rev.: $19,279,145
Assets: $50,665,422
Liabilities: $6,944,079
Net Worth: $43,721,343
Earnings: ($3,077,046)
Fiscal Year-end: 12/31/23
Power Supply Equipment Mfr
N.A.I.C.S.: 335999
Lian Zhaozhi (Chm)

Subsidiaries:

GENMAO ELECTRONICS (SUZHOU) CO., LTD. (1)
Tel.: (86) 51263401828
Web Site: http://www.lienchang.com.tw
Electronic Components Mfr
N.A.I.C.S.: 334416

LIEN HOE CORPORATION BERHAD
3rd Floor Plaza Armada Lot 6 Lorong Utara C Section 52, 46200, Petaling Jaya, Selangor, Malaysia
Tel.: (60) 379558808
Web Site: https://cms.lienhoecorporation.com
LIENHOE—(KLS)
Rev.: $5,734,219
Assets: $74,625,599
Liabilities: $20,445,364
Net Worth: $54,180,235
Earnings: ($3,303,004)
Emp.: 112
Fiscal Year-end: 12/31/23
Property Management Services
N.A.I.C.S.: 531312
Chong Keat Yeoh (Chm)

LIEN HWA INDUSTRIAL HOLDINGS CORP
10F No 209 Sec 1 Nangang Rd, Nangang Dist, Taipei, 115, Taiwan
Tel.: (886) 227861188
Web Site: https://www.lhiholdings.com
1229—(TAI)
Rev.: $385,403,652
Assets: $2,185,834,600
Liabilities: $515,193,228
Net Worth: $1,670,641,372
Earnings: $151,305,756
Emp.: 1,754
Fiscal Year-end: 12/31/22
Wheat Flour Processing Services
N.A.I.C.S.: 311211
John Miao (Vice Chm)

LIENHARD OFFICE GROUP AG
Grabenstrasse 1, 8606, Nanikon, Switzerland
Tel.: (41) 44 905 55 85
Web Site: http://www.lienhard-office.ch
Emp.: 300
Holding Company; Office Furniture Mfr
N.A.I.C.S.: 551112
Fredy A. Lienhard (Owner & Chm)

Subsidiaries:

Denz Office AG (1)
Werdmuhlestrasse 10, CH 8606, Zurich, Switzerland
Tel.: (41) 449055555
Web Site: http://www.denz.ch
Office Furniture Mfr & Retailer
N.A.I.C.S.: 337214

Lista Office AG (1)
Alfred Lienhard Strasse 2, Degersheim, 9113, Switzerland
Tel.: (41) 713725252
Web Site: http://www.lista-office.com
Sales Range: $100-124.9 Million
Emp.: 150
Office Furniture Mfr
N.A.I.C.S.: 337127
Markus Meili (CEO)

Branch (Domestic):

Lista Arnegg (2)
Muelimoos Strasse 8, CH 9212, Arnegg, Switzerland (100%)
Tel.: (41) 713889292
Web Site: http://www.lista-office.com
Sales Range: $50-74.9 Million
Emp.: 40
Office Furniture
N.A.I.C.S.: 337127
Markus Miele (CEO)

LIER CHEMICAL CO., LTD.
Block 5 No 11 Galileo Road Zhangjiang Hi-tech Park, Pudong New Area, Shanghai, 610052, Sichuan, China
Tel.: (86) 2158431502
Web Site: https://www.lierchem.com
Year Founded: 1993
002258—(SSE)
Rev.: $1,423,114,056
Assets: $1,806,435,540
Liabilities: $629,460,936
Net Worth: $1,176,974,604
Earnings: $254,472,192
Emp.: 2,000
Fiscal Year-end: 12/31/22
Pesticide Mfr
N.A.I.C.S.: 325320
Yin Yingsui (Chm)

Subsidiaries:

Jiangsu Kuaida Agrochemical Co., Ltd. (1)
Rudong Coastal Economic Development Zone, Yangkou Chemical Industry Park, Yangkou, 226407, Jiangsu, China
Tel.: (86) 51384415648
Web Site: https://www.kuaida-agrochem.com
Pesticide Mfr
N.A.I.C.S.: 325320
Shi Yongping (Gen Mgr)

LIETUVOS ENERGIJOS GAMYBA, AB
Elektrines G 21, Elektrenai, 26108, Lithuania
Tel.: (370) 5 278 2907
Web Site: http://www.gamyba.le.lt
Year Founded: 2011
Eletric Power Generation Services
N.A.I.C.S.: 221111
Rimgaudas kalvaitis (Chm-Mgmt Bd & CEO)

LIFAN TECHNOLOGY (GROUP) CO., LTD.
No 16 Fengxi Road, Caijiagang Town

INTERNATIONAL PUBLIC

Beibei District, Chongqing, 400707, China (Hong Kong)
Tel.: (852) 2361663307
Web Site: https://www.lifanmotos.net
Year Founded: 1922
601777—(SHG)
Rev.: $557,241,623
Assets: $2,748,664,005
Liabilities: $1,030,881,146
Net Worth: $1,717,782,860
Earnings: $8,901,501
Emp.: 5,170
Fiscal Year-end: 12/31/20
Motorcycle Part Mfr & Distr
N.A.I.C.S.: 336991
Gang Mou (Chm)

Subsidiaries:

American Lifan Inc. (1)
9272 Hyssop Dr, Rancho Cucamonga, CA 91730
Web Site: https://www.americanlifan.com
Motorcycle Mfr
N.A.I.C.S.: 336991

LIFE BANC & SPLIT CORP.
Bay Wellington Tower Brookfield Place Suite 2930 181 Bay Street, Box 793, Toronto, M5J 2T3, ON, Canada
Tel.: (416) 642-9061
Year Founded: 2000
74F—(DEU)
Rev.: $69,528,373
Assets: $551,448,096
Liabilities: $317,585,070
Net Worth: $233,863,026
Earnings: $43,823,308
Fiscal Year-end: 12/31/23
Investment Management Service
N.A.I.C.S.: 523940
Mark A. Caranci (Pres & CEO)

LIFE BOND HOLDING GMBH & CO. KG
Munchner Strasse 54, 82069, Hohenschaftlarn, Germany
Tel.: (49) 8178 9088 0
Web Site: http://www.lifebond.de
Life Insurance Funds Management Services
N.A.I.C.S.: 525190
Michael G. Hoesch (Mng Dir)

LIFE CONCEPTS HOLDINGS LIMITED
Room 806 8/F Stelux House 698 Prince Edward Road East San Po Kong, Kowloon, China (Hong Kong)
Tel.: (852) 39123800 Ky
Web Site: http://www.diningconcepts.com
Year Founded: 2002
8056—(HKG)
Rev.: $27,643,639
Assets: $32,391,263
Liabilities: $40,124,130
Net Worth: ($7,732,867)
Earnings: ($8,685,642)
Emp.: 357
Fiscal Year-end: 03/31/21
Restaurant Operators
N.A.I.C.S.: 722511
Xu Qiang (Chm)

Subsidiaries:

BLT Burger (HK) Limited (1)
Shop OT301-301A 3/F Ocean Terminal Harbour City 17 Canton Road, Tsim Tsa Tsui, China (Hong Kong)
Tel.: (852) 27302338
Restaurant Operators
N.A.I.C.S.: 722511
Sandip Gupta (Dir-Ops)

Wide Scope Holdings Limited (1)
32 Elgin St, Central, China (Hong Kong)
Tel.: (852) 25211608

AND PRIVATE COMPANIES

LIFEASSAYS AB

Restaurant Operators
N.A.I.C.S.: 722511
Mohit Sharma *(Gen Mgr)*

LIFE CORPORATION
2-2-22 Nishimiyahara, Yodogawa-Ku, Osaka, 532-0004, Japan
Tel.: (81) 661506111   JP
Web Site: http://www.lifecorp.co.jp
Year Founded: 1956
8194—(TKS)
Rev.: $5,740,836,810
Assets: $2,035,865,140
Liabilities: $1,065,563,190
Net Worth: $970,301,950
Earnings: $120,090,420
Fiscal Year-end: 02/29/24
Retail Grocery Stores Operator
N.A.I.C.S.: 445110
Nobutsugu Shimizu *(Chm & CEO)*

LIFE HEALTHCARE GROUP HOLDINGS LIMITED
Oxford Manor 21 Chaplin Road, 2196, Illovo, 2196, South Africa
Tel.: (27) 112199885
Web Site:
https://www.lifehealthcare.co.za
LTGHY—(OTCIQ)
Rev.: $1,195,671,691
Assets: $2,408,929,118
Liabilities: $1,284,656,576
Net Worth: $1,124,272,542
Earnings: $75,412,710
Emp.: 16,960
Fiscal Year-end: 09/30/23
Hospitals, Rehabiliation & Occupational Health Centers Owner & Operator
N.A.I.C.S.: 622110
Pieter Phillippus van der Westhuizen *(CEO-Acting & CFO)*
Subsidiaries:

Alliance Medical Group Limited (1)
38 Jermyn Street Princes House, London, SW1Y 6DN, United Kingdom
Tel.: (44) 1926482000
Web Site: http://www.alliancemedical.com
Diagnostic Imaging Services
N.A.I.C.S.: 621512
Charles Niehaus *(COO)*

Subsidiary (Non-US):

Alliance Diagnosticos, S.L. (2)
Calle la Granja 8 1 Izquierda, 28108, Alcobendas, Madrid, Spain
Tel.: (34) 916250126
Web Site:
http://www.alliancediagnosticos.es
Diagnostic Imaging Services
N.A.I.C.S.: 621512

Alliance Medical BV (2)
Piet Mondriaanplein 13, 3812 GZ, Amersfoort, Netherlands
Tel.: (31) 334543020
Web Site: http://www.alliancemedical.nl
Diagnostic Imaging Services
N.A.I.C.S.: 621512

Alliance Medical Diagnostic Imaging Ltd (2)
Portal House Raheen Business Park Raheen, Limerick, Ireland
Tel.: (353) 61585002
Web Site: http://www.alliancemedical.ie
Diagnostic Imaging Services
N.A.I.C.S.: 621512
Malcolm Banks *(Mng Dir)*

Alliance Medical GmbH (2)
Westring 168, 44575, Castrop-Rauxel, Germany
Tel.: (49) 2305921710
Web Site: http://www.alliancemedical.de
Diagnostic Imaging Services
N.A.I.C.S.: 621512
Axel Schmidt *(Mng Dir)*

Alliance Medical Italia S.R.L. (2)
Via Goffredo Mameli 42/a, 20851, Lissone, Italy
Tel.: (39) 039 2433 130
Web Site: http://www.alliancemedical.it
Diagnostic Imaging Services
N.A.I.C.S.: 621512
Francesco Martinelli *(Chief Medical Officer)*

LIFE HEALTHCARE GROUP LIMITED
Office A 18/F Aubin House 171-172 Gloucester Road, Wanchai, China (Hong Kong)
Tel.: (852) 1085968511   Ky
Web Site:
http://www.lifehealthcare.com
Year Founded: 2001
0928—(HKG)
Rev.: $13,161,248
Assets: $41,919,532
Liabilities: $3,910,932
Net Worth: $38,008,600
Earnings: ($302,587)
Emp.: 19
Fiscal Year-end: 03/31/21
Gene Detection Company
N.A.I.C.S.: 621511
Wai Lun Man *(Exec Dir)*

LIFE INSURANCE COMPANY FREEDOM FINANCE LIFE JSC
77/7 7a Al-Farabi Ave, Bostandyk District, Almaty, 050040, Kazakhstan
Tel.: (7) 272280607
Web Site: http://www.ffin.life
ASLF—(KAZ)
Assets: $288,424,387
Liabilities: $216,710,366
Net Worth: $71,714,022
Earnings: $35,103,940
Emp.: 300
Fiscal Year-end: 12/31/23
Fire Insurance Services
N.A.I.C.S.: 524113
Erdesov Azamat *(Co-Chm & Chm-Mgmt Bd)*

LIFE INSURANCE COMPANY STANDARD LIFE JSC
186 Kabanbai batyr St, Almaly District, 50012, Almaty, Kazakhstan
Tel.: (7) 272661198
Web Site: https://standardlife.kz
SKSL—(KAZ)
Assets: $104,558,567
Liabilities: $82,972,043
Net Worth: $21,586,524
Earnings: $4,513,761
Fiscal Year-end: 12/31/23
Fire Insurance Services
N.A.I.C.S.: 524113
Erzhan Konurbayev *(Chm-Mgmt Bd)*

LIFE INSURANCE CORPORATION OF INDIA
Yogakshema Jeevan Bima Marg, PO Box No - 19953, Nariman Point, Mumbai, 400 021, India
Tel.: (91) 2268276827
Web Site: https://www.licindia.in
LICI—(NSE)
Rev.: $57,146,788,754
Assets: $541,798,076,806
Liabilities: $536,240,859,829
Net Worth: $5,557,216,977
Earnings: $4,315,885,858
Emp.: 98,463
Fiscal Year-end: 03/31/23
Fire Insurance Services
N.A.I.C.S.: 524113
Hemant Bhargava *(Interim Chm)*
Subsidiaries:

LIC Fiji (1)
LICI House Butt Street, GPO Box 266, Suva, Fiji
Tel.: (679) 3314011
Web Site: http://www.licifiji.com
Fire Insurance Services
N.A.I.C.S.: 524113
S. K. Jain *(Gen Mgr)*

LIC Mauritius Offshore Ltd (1)
LIC Centre President John Kennedy Street, PO Box 310, Port Louis, Mauritius
Tel.: (230) 52081485
Web Site: http://www.lic.mu
Fire Insurance Services
N.A.I.C.S.: 524113
Biswajeet Ganguly *(Mgr)*

LIC Pension Fund Ltd. (1)
Industrial Assurance Building Churchgate Wing B 5th Fl, Veed Nariman Rd, Mumbai, 400020, India
Tel.: (91) 22 22882871
Web Site: http://www.licpensionfund.in
Emp.: 7
Fire Insurance Services
N.A.I.C.S.: 524113
Avinash C. Abhyankar *(Sec)*

Life Insurance Corporation (Lanka) Ltd. (1)
1st and 3rd Floor Sharnell Building 29/2 Visaka Road, Colombo, Sri Lanka
Tel.: (94) 2552277
Web Site: https://www.liclanka.com
Fire Insurance Services
N.A.I.C.S.: 524113
R. Rajnikanth *(CEO & Mng Dir)*

Life Insurance Corporation (Nepal) Ltd. (1)
Star Mall Putalisadak, Po Box No 21905, Kathmandu, 44621, Nepal
Tel.: (977) 14012613
Web Site: https://www.licnepal.com.np
Fire Insurance Services
N.A.I.C.S.: 524113
Laxmi Prasad Das *(CEO)*

Life Insurance Corporation (Singapore) Pte. Ltd. (1)
3 Raffles Place 07- 01 Bharat Building, Singapore, 048617, Singapore
Tel.: (65) 62234797
Web Site: https://www.licsingapore.com
Fire Insurance Services
N.A.I.C.S.: 524113
M. R. Kumar *(Chm)*

LIFE INTELLIGENT ENTERPRISE HOLDINGS CO., LTD.
8F Ginza Itchome East Bldg 1-19-7 Ginza, Chuo-ku, Tokyo, 104-0061, Japan
Tel.: (81) 355247851
Web Site: http://www.toriholdings.co.jp
Year Founded: 2004
5856—(TKS)
Rev.: $125,821,350
Assets: $39,765,760
Liabilities: $29,011,290
Net Worth: $10,754,470
Earnings: ($8,897,060)
Fiscal Year-end: 03/31/24
Holding Company
N.A.I.C.S.: 551112
Moritoshi Shinada *(Chm)*

LIFE IS HARD S.A.
Str A Iancu Nr 500, Floresti, Cluj-Napoca, Romania
Tel.: (40) 761326331
Web Site: https://www.lifeishard.ro
LIH—(BUC)
Rev.: $7,172,259
Assets: $14,290,219
Liabilities: $5,086,673
Net Worth: $9,203,546
Earnings: $999,141
Emp.: 128
Fiscal Year-end: 12/31/22
Software Development Services
N.A.I.C.S.: 541511
Ioan-Catalin Chis *(Pres)*

LIFE SCIENCE REIT PLC
29 Wellington Street Central Square, Leeds, LS1 4DL, United Kingdom
Tel.: (44) 3333001950   UK
Web Site:
https://www.lifesciencereit.co.uk
Year Founded: 2021
LABS—(LSE)
Real Estate Development Services
N.A.I.C.S.: 531190

LIFE SCIENCE TECHNOLOGY INC.
Suite B 1207 Gangseo Hangang Xi Tower 401 Yangcheon-ro, Gangseo-gu, Seoul, 07528, Korea (South)
Tel.: (82) 7086208020
Web Site: https://www.lstgrp.com
Year Founded: 2007
285770—(KRS)
Software Development Services
N.A.I.C.S.: 541511

LIFE SEMANTICS CORP.
533 Eonju-Ro, Gangnam-gu, Seoul, Korea (South)
Tel.: (82) 16612858
Web Site: http://www.lifesemantics.kr
Year Founded: 2012
347700—(KRS)
Rev.: $2,162,112
Assets: $20,044,766
Liabilities: $12,703,533
Net Worth: $7,341,233
Earnings: ($2,568,482)
Emp.: 58
Fiscal Year-end: 12/31/22
Software Development Services
N.A.I.C.S.: 541511
Rhee Gyu Jung *(CFO)*

LIFE SETTLEMENT ASSETS PLC
Den House Den Promenade, Teignmouth, Devon, TQ14 8SY, United Kingdom
Tel.: (44) 2072585990   UK
Web Site: https://www.lsaplc.com
Year Founded: 2017
LSAA—(LSE)
Rev.: $8,850,000
Assets: $113,370,000
Liabilities: $2,160,000
Net Worth: $111,210,000
Earnings: $600,000
Fiscal Year-end: 12/31/22
Investment Management Service
N.A.I.C.S.: 523940
Michael Baines *(Chm)*

LIFE SETTLEMENT HOLDING AG
Tuchlauben 11/18, 1010, Vienna, Austria
Tel.: (43) 153707210
Web Site:
https://www.lifesettlementholding.com
Insurance Services
N.A.I.C.S.: 524298

LIFE TRAVEL & TOURIST SERVICE CO., LTD.
2 3F No 28 Bo'ai 1st Rd, Sanmin Dist, Kaohsiung, 80757, Taiwan
Tel.: (886) 73231166
2745—(TPE)
Rev.: $9,099,459
Assets: $23,570,741
Liabilities: $15,505,143
Net Worth: $8,065,597
Earnings: ($2,377,325)
Fiscal Year-end: 12/31/22
Travel Tour Operator
N.A.I.C.S.: 713990
Shuen-Fu Hsu *(Chm)*

LIFEASSAYS AB

LIFEASSAYS AB

LifeAssays AB—(Continued)
Building Syret 9 Ideongatan 3A, SE-223 70, Lund, Sweden
Tel.: (46) 462865400
Web Site: http://www.lifeassays.com
Year Founded: 2000
Medical Equipment Device Mfr
N.A.I.C.S.: 339112
Anders Ingvarsson *(CEO)*

Subsidiaries:

AegirBio AB (1)
c/o LifeAssays AB Solvegatan 43A, 22371, Lund, Sweden
Tel.: (46) 462865400
Web Site: http://www.aegirbio.com
Therapeutic Drug Mfr
N.A.I.C.S.: 541714
Martin Linde *(CEO)*

LIFEBRANDZ LTD.

30 Cecil Street 19-08 Prudential Tower, Singapore, 49712, Singapore
Tel.: (65) 62219344
Web Site: https://www.lifebrandz.com
Year Founded: 2001
1D3—(CAT)
Rev.: $1,087,069
Assets: $1,333,827
Liabilities: $846,980
Net Worth: $486,847
Earnings: ($1,374,583)
Emp.: 25
Fiscal Year-end: 07/31/23
Entertainment Services
N.A.I.C.S.: 516210
Saito Hiroyuki *(Chm & CEO)*

Subsidiaries:

Luminox Pte. Ltd. (1)
3c River Valley Road 01-03 Clarke Quay Block C, Singapore, Singapore
Tel.: (65) 63056777
Watch Retailer
N.A.I.C.S.: 423940

Mulligan's Pte Ltd (1)
Block C The Cannery River Valley Road 01-02H, Singapore, 179022, Singapore
Tel.: (65) 63056726
Web Site: http://www.mulligans.lt
Sales Range: $10-24.9 Million
Emp.: 30
Pub & Restaurant Operators
N.A.I.C.S.: 722410

LIFECARE AS

Ytrebygdsvegen 215, Blomsterdalen, 5258, Bergen, Norway
Tel.: (47) 990251657
Web Site: https://www.lifecare.no
Year Founded: 2006
LIFE—(OSL)
Rev.: $1,286,439
Assets: $8,492,572
Liabilities: $1,959,747
Net Worth: $6,532,825
Earnings: ($3,460,946)
Emp.: 6
Fiscal Year-end: 12/31/23
Health Care Srvices
N.A.I.C.S.: 621610
Morten Foros Krohnstad *(Chm)*

LIFECLEAN INTERNATIONAL AB

Karrastrandvagen 124B, 451 76, Uddevalla, Sweden
Tel.: (46) 52210404
Web Site: https://www.lifeclean.se
Year Founded: 2012
LCLEAN—(OMX)
Rev.: $5,211,746
Assets: $6,811,007
Liabilities: $6,679,969
Net Worth: $131,038
Earnings: ($4,391,765)
Emp.: 33

Fiscal Year-end: 12/31/23
Cleaning Equipment Mfr
N.A.I.C.S.: 335999
Anders Lundstrm *(CEO)*

Subsidiaries:

Kempartner AB (1)
Smedjegatan 6, 131 54, Nacka, Sweden
Tel.: (46) 86838800
Web Site: https://eng.kempartner.se
Chemical Product Mfr & Distr
N.A.I.C.S.: 325998

LIFECOME BIOCHEMISTRY CO., LTD.

No 19 Industrial Park Pucheng, Nanping, Fujian, China
Tel.: (86) 5992846588
Web Site: https://www.lifecomepc.com
Year Founded: 2003
002868—(SSE)
Rev.: $46,310,940
Assets: $174,076,344
Liabilities: $89,934,624
Net Worth: $84,141,720
Earnings: ($17,120,376)
Fiscal Year-end: 12/31/22
Biopharmaceutical Product Mfr
N.A.I.C.S.: 325412

LIFEDRINK COMPANY INC.

10th Floor Umeda Dai Building 3310 Umeda, Kita-ku, Osaka, 530-0001, Japan
Tel.: (81) 664533201
Web Site: https://www.ld-company.com
2585—(TKS)
Rev.: $252,739,960
Assets: $202,570,060
Liabilities: $127,599,440
Net Worth: $74,970,620
Earnings: $20,854,550
Emp.: 607
Fiscal Year-end: 03/31/24
Non-alcoholic Beverage Products Mfr
N.A.I.C.S.: 312111
Kuniaki Okano *(Pres)*

LIFEIST WELLNESS INC.

666 Burrard St 2500, Vancouver, V6C 2X8, BC, Canada
Tel.: (786) 389-9771
Web Site: https://lifeist.com
Year Founded: 2005
LFSWF—(OTCQB)
Rev.: $22,308,648
Assets: $16,169,258
Liabilities: $5,714,467
Net Worth: $10,454,791
Earnings: ($12,074,882)
Emp.: 61
Fiscal Year-end: 11/30/22
Vaporizer Product Distr
N.A.I.C.S.: 424940
Meni Morim *(CEO)*

Subsidiaries:

NamasteMD Inc. (1)
1600-100 King Street West, Toronto, M5X 1G5, ON, Canada
Tel.: (800) 867-0267
Web Site: http://www.namastemd.com
Medical Consultation Services
N.A.I.C.S.: 541611

LIFENET INSURANCE COMPANY

2-14-2 Kojimachi Kojimachi NK Building 5F, Chiyoda-ku, Tokyo, 102-0083, Japan
Tel.: (81) 352167900
Web Site: https://ir.lifenet-seimei.co.jp
Year Founded: 2006
7157—(TKS)
Sales Range: $50-74.9 Million

Fire Insurance Services
N.A.I.C.S.: 524113
Haruaki Deguchi *(CEO)*

LIFESAFE HOLDINGS PLC

1 Sopwith Crescent, Essex, Wickford, SS11 8YU, Essex, United Kingdom
Web Site:
https://www.lifesafeholdingsplc.com
Year Founded: 2015
LIFS—(AIM)
Holding Company
N.A.I.C.S.: 551112

Subsidiaries:

LifeSafe Technologies Limited (1)
LifeSafe Technologies 1 Sopwith Crescent, Essex, Wickford, SS11 8YU, United Kingdom
Tel.: (44) 2078704890
Web Site:
https://www.lifesafetechnologies.co.uk
Fire Safety Equipment Mfr
N.A.I.C.S.: 333415

LIFESPEAK, INC.

2 Bloor St West Suite 1902, Toronto, M4W-3E2, ON, Canada
Tel.: (416) 687-6695
Web Site: https://lifespeak.com
Year Founded: 2004
LSPK—(TSX)
Rev.: $18,201,047
Assets: $71,768,848
Liabilities: $29,304,390
Net Worth: $42,464,458
Earnings: $20,593,176
Fiscal Year-end: 12/31/21
Mental Health & Wellness Services
N.A.I.C.S.: 621112
Jason Campana *(COO)*

Subsidiaries:

Wellbeats (1)
11600 96th Ave N, Maple Grove, MN 55369
Tel.: (855) 497-3908
Web Site: http://www.wellbeats.com
Sales Range: $1-9.9 Million
Emp.: 40
Fitness & Health Programs, Fitness Software Developer & Packaged Pre-recorded Fitness Programming
N.A.I.C.S.: 713940

LIFESPOT CAPITAL AG

Sendlinger-Tor-Platz 8, Munich, Germany
Tel.: (49) 89244192200
Web Site:
http://www.lifespotcapital.com
CDZ0—(MUN)
Rev.: $150,424,992
Assets: $123,667,071
Liabilities: $70,703,168
Net Worth: $52,963,903
Earnings: ($7,142,069)
Fiscal Year-end: 12/31/23
Software Development Services
N.A.I.C.S.: 541511
Andreas Empl *(Chm-Mgmt Bd & CEO)*

LIFESTAR HOLDING PLC

Testaferrata Street, Ta' Xbiex, 1403, XBX, Malta
Tel.: (356) 21342342
Web Site: https://lifestarholding.com
Year Founded: 1965
LSR—(MAL)
Rev.: $6,224,684
Assets: $156,571,188
Liabilities: $137,241,347
Net Worth: $19,329,841
Earnings: $721,857
Emp.: 64
Fiscal Year-end: 12/31/23
Financial Services

INTERNATIONAL PUBLIC

N.A.I.C.S.: 523999
Clinton V. Calleja *(Sec)*

LIFESTYLE CHINA GROUP LIMITED

20th Floor East Point Centre 555 Hennessy Road, Causeway Bay, China (Hong Kong)
Tel.: (852) 28338338
Web Site:
https://www.lifestylechina.com.hk
2136—(HKG)
Rev.: $158,313,355
Assets: $2,028,591,864
Liabilities: $512,431,358
Net Worth: $1,516,160,506
Earnings: $14,962,849
Emp.: 1,168
Fiscal Year-end: 12/31/22
Departmental Store Operator
N.A.I.C.S.: 455110
Thomas Luen Hung Lau *(Chm, CEO & Exec Dir)*

LIFESTYLE COMMUNITIES LIMITED

Level 5 101 Moray Street, South Melbourne, 3205, VIC, Australia
Tel.: (61) 394155000
Web Site:
https://www.lifestylecommunities.com
Year Founded: 1989
LIC—(ASX)
Rev.: $122,146,768
Assets: $1,009,368,319
Liabilities: $453,976,360
Net Worth: $555,391,958
Earnings: $33,372,730
Emp.: 186
Fiscal Year-end: 06/30/24
Holding Company; Retirement Community Property Development & Management Services
N.A.I.C.S.: 551112
James Kelly *(Founder & Mng Dir)*

Subsidiaries:

Brookfield Village Management Pty Ltd (1)
111-139 Coburns Road, Brookfield, Melbourne, 3338, VIC, Australia
Tel.: (61) 3 0050 5560
Property Management Services
N.A.I.C.S.: 531311
James Kelly *(CEO)*

Lifestyle Communities Development Pty. Ltd. (1)
Level 2 25 Ross Street, South Melbourne, 3205, VIC, Australia (100%)
Tel.: (61) 396822249
Sales Range: $25-49.9 Million
Emp.: 10
Retirement Community Property Development
N.A.I.C.S.: 237210

Lifestyle Communities Investments Cranbourne Pty Ltd (1)
2 Cameron Street Cranbourne East, Melbourne, 3977, VIC, Australia
Tel.: (61) 300505560
Sales Range: $50-74.9 Million
Emp.: 2
Property Management Services
N.A.I.C.S.: 531311

Lifestyle Communities Management Pty. Ltd. (1)
Level 2 25 Ross Street, South Melbourne, 3205, VIC, Australia (100%)
Tel.: (61) 396822249
Sales Range: $50-74.9 Million
Emp.: 10
Retirement Community Property Management Services
N.A.I.C.S.: 531311

Subsidiary (Domestic):

Lifestyle Seasons Pty. Ltd. (2)
13 Sundial Blvd, Tarneit, Melbourne, 3029, VIC, Australia (100%)

LIFESTYLE GLOBAL ENTERPRISE, INC.
3F No 86 Xinhu 1st Rd, Neihu Dist, Taipei, 114, Taiwan
Tel.: (886) 287925189
Web Site: https://www.lifestyle-global.com
8066—(TAI)
Rev.- $160,665,385
Assets: $52,002,222
Liabilities: $30,029,235
Net Worth: $21,972,987
Earnings: $1,475,817
Fiscal Year-end: 12/31/23
Furniture Distr
N.A.I.C.S.: 423210

Subsidiaries:

LF-International Holdings Limited (1)
Room 1303 13th Floor Ziwei Building No 267 Haining Avenue, Haining, Jiaxing, Zhejiang, China
Tel.: (86) 57387099098
Furniture Mfr & Distr
N.A.I.C.S.: 337121

LF-Shanghai Trading Limited (1)
Hall C5 No 5369 Jiasong Middle Road, Zhaoxing Town Qingpu District, Shanghai, China
Tel.: (86) 2169755311
Furniture Mfr & Distr
N.A.I.C.S.: 337121

LFN Limited (1)
529 Townsend Ave, High Point, NC 27263
Tel.: (336) 882-7900
Web Site: https://www.lfnlimited.com
Furniture Distr
N.A.I.C.S.: 449110

Lifestyle DCG Inc. (1)
529 Townsend Ave, High Point, NC 27263
Tel.: (336) 882-7900
Furniture Mfr & Distr
N.A.I.C.S.: 337121

Lifestyle Enterprise, Inc. (1)
529 Townsend Ave, High Point, NC 27263 (51%)
Tel.: (336) 882-7900
Web Site: http://www.lifestyle-us.com
Sales Range: $10-24.9 Million
Emp.: 25
Furniture Merchant Whslr
N.A.I.C.S.: 423210
William Hsieh *(Founder)*

LIFESTYLE INTERNATIONAL HOLDINGS LTD
20th Floor East Point Centre 555 Hennessy Road, Causeway Bay, China (Hong Kong)
Tel.: (852) 28338338
Web Site: http://www.lifestylehk.com.hk
1212—(HKG)
Rev.: $291,920,558
Assets: $2,930,356,088
Liabilities: $2,591,931,690
Net Worth: $338,424,398
Earnings: ($166,387,500)
Emp.: 675
Fiscal Year-end: 12/31/21
Department Store Retailer
N.A.I.C.S.: 455110
Kam Sen Lau *(Exec Dir)*

LIFETECH SCIENTIFIC CORPORATION
Cybio Electronic Building Langshan 2nd Street North Area of High-tech, Nanshan District, Shenzhen, 518057, China
Tel.: (86) 75586026250
Web Site: http://www.lifetechmed.com
Year Founded: 1999
1302—(HKG)
Rev.: $154,062,324
Assets: $518,090,461
Liabilities: $107,974,058
Net Worth: $410,116,403
Earnings: $44,750,956
Emp.: 1,299
Fiscal Year-end: 12/31/22
Medicinal Product Mfr
N.A.I.C.S.: 339112
Yuehui Xie *(Chm & CEO)*

Subsidiaries:

Lifetech Scientific (Shenzhen) Co., Ltd. (1)
14F LifeTech Scientific Building No 22 Keji 12th Road South, High-tech Industrial Park Nanshan District, Shenzhen, Guangdong, China
Tel.: (86) 75586026250
Medical Device Mfr & Whslr
N.A.I.C.S.: 339112

Lifetech Scientific India Private Limited (1)
No 521 9th Main Road 4th Cross Hal 2nd Stage Indiranagar, Bengaluru, 560038, India
Tel.: (91) 8041245252
Web Site: http://www.lifetechmed.com
Sales Range: $25-49.9 Million
Emp.: 31
Surgical Implant Distr
N.A.I.C.S.: 423450
Nandakumar Menon *(Acct Mgr & Mgr-Fin)*

Vast Medical Limited (1)
3 Klisouras, 16121, Athens, Greece
Tel.: (30) 2107254200
Web Site: https://www.vastmedical.gr
Medical Device Distr
N.A.I.C.S.: 423450

LIFETIME DISTRIBUTORS THE BOOK PEOPLE PTY. LIMITED
Suite 2 Level 10 8 West Street, North Sydney, 2060, NSW, Australia
Tel.: (61) 2 9899 9655
Web Site: http://www.booksgiftsdirect.com
Year Founded: 1990
Books & Periodicals Distr
N.A.I.C.S.: 424920
Joseph Craven *(Mng Dir)*

LIFEWAYS COMMUNITY CARE LIMITED
Fisher Building 118 Garratt Lane Wandsworth, London, SW18 4DJ, United Kingdom
Tel.: (44) 20 8877 1338
Web Site: http://www.lifeways.co.uk
Year Founded: 1995
Sales Range: $10-24.9 Million
Emp.: 5,194
Outpatient Health Care Services
N.A.I.C.S.: 621498
Peter Carroll *(Mgr)*

LIFEWORKS
25 York St 24th Floor, Toronto, M5J 2V5, ON, Canada
Tel.: (416) 445-2700
Year Founded: 1962
MSI—(TSX)
Rev.: $680,213,418
Assets: $1,170,984,022
Liabilities: $697,768,789
Net Worth: $473,215,533
Earnings: $14,515,072
Emp.: 6,000
Fiscal Year-end: 12/31/19
Holding Company; Corporate Consulting & Human Resource Outsourcing Services
N.A.I.C.S.: 551112
Jill Denham *(Chm)*

Subsidiaries:

Morneau Shepell Ltd. (1)
16 York St Suite 3300, Toronto, M5J 0E6, ON, Canada
Tel.: (416) 445-2700
Corporate Consulting & Human Resource Outsourcing Services
N.A.I.C.S.: 541611
William Morneau *(Chm)*

LIFEZONE METALS LIMITED
Commerce House 1 Bowring Road, Ramsey, IM8 2LQ, Isle of Man
Tel.: (44) 1624811611
Web Site: https://www.lifezonemetals.com
Year Founded: 2022
LZM—(NYSE)
Metal Mining Services
N.A.I.C.S.: 213114
Chris Showalter *(CEO)*

LIFFEY MILLS LTD.
Bunnow, Roscrea, Tipperary, E53 YR15, Ireland
Tel.: (353) 505 21477
Web Site: http://www.liffeymills.ie
Emp.: 100
Grain Mill Services & Retailer
N.A.I.C.S.: 111199
Pat Ryan *(Mng Dir)*

Subsidiaries:

Drummonds Limited (1)
Paddingstown Clonee, Meath, Ireland (100%)
Tel.: (353) 18255011
Web Site: http://www.drummonds.ie
Sales Range: $25-49.9 Million
Emp.: 30
Grain & Field Bean Merchant Whslr
N.A.I.C.S.: 424510

LIFOCOLOR FARBEN GMBH & CO. KG
Reundorfer Strasse 18, 96215, Lichtenfels, Germany
Tel.: (49) 95717890
Web Site: http://www.lifocolor.de
Year Founded: 1988
Emp.: 270
Color Concentrate Mfr
N.A.I.C.S.: 325130
Markus Blomenhofer *(Mgr-Quality)*

Subsidiaries:

Lifocolor Farbplast Sp.z o.o. (1)
ul B Raczkowskiego 2, 85-862, Bydgoszcz, Poland
Tel.: (48) 52 32381 60
Web Site: http://www.lifocolor.pl
Color Concentrate Mfr
N.A.I.C.S.: 325130

Lifocolor s.a.r.l. (1)
ZI Sud 951 rue de l'Ange, 01100, Bellignat, France
Tel.: (33) 4 7477 2697
Web Site: http://www.lifocolor.fr
Color Concentrate Mfr
N.A.I.C.S.: 325130

Lifocolor s.r.o. (1)
Olomoucka 89, 627 00, Brno, Czech Republic
Tel.: (420) 548 211 388
Web Site: http://www.lifocolor.cz
Color Concentrate Mfr
N.A.I.C.S.: 325130

LIFT GLOBAL VENTURES PLC
6 Heddon Street, London, W1B 4BT, United Kingdom
Tel.: (44) 2037451865
Web Site: https://www.liftgv.com
Year Founded: 2021
LFT—(AQSE)
Rev.: $611,011
Assets: $1,948,098
Liabilities: $117,666
Net Worth: $1,830,432
Earnings: ($554,785)
Emp.: 3
Fiscal Year-end: 06/30/23
Investment Management Service
N.A.I.C.S.: 523999

LIFULL CO., LTD.
1-4-4 Kojimachi, Chiyoda-ku, Tokyo, 102-0083, Japan
Tel.: (81) 367741600
Web Site: https://lifull.com
Year Founded: 1997
2120—(TKS)
Rev.: $258,111,450
Assets: $362,766,940
Liabilities: $131,959,080
Net Worth: $230,807,860
Earnings: $7,309,790
Emp.: 1,845
Fiscal Year-end: 09/30/23
Real Estate & Community Information Services
N.A.I.C.S.: 519290
Takashi Inoue *(Pres & CEO)*

Subsidiaries:

Lifull Bizas Co., Ltd. (1)
973-2 Kamobe, Kochi, 780-8050, Japan
Tel.: (81) 5055783777
Web Site: https://www.lifull-bizas.co.jp
Call Center Operation Services
N.A.I.C.S.: 561422

Lifull Fam Co., Ltd. (1)
1-4-4 Kojimachi, Chiyoda-ku, Tokyo, 102-0083, Japan
Tel.: (81) 364211886
Real Estate Development Services
N.A.I.C.S.: 531390

Lifull Investment Co., Ltd. (1)
1-4-4 Kojimachi, Chiyoda-ku, Tokyo, 102-0083, Japan
Tel.: (81) 362723659
Web Site: http://www.lifull-investment.co.jp
Financial Investment Services
N.A.I.C.S.: 523999

Lifull Marketing Partners Co., Ltd. (1)
1-15-1 Ebisu Minami A-PLACE Ebisu Minami 5F, Shibuya-ku, Tokyo, 150-0022, Japan
Tel.: (81) 368258575
Web Site: https://di-mp.co.jp
Real Estate Development Services
N.A.I.C.S.: 531390

Lifull Move Co., Ltd. (1)
1-4-4 Kojimachi, Chiyoda-ku, Tokyo, 102-0083, Japan
Tel.: (81) 367741658
Real Estate Development Services
N.A.I.C.S.: 531390

Lifull Space Co., Ltd. (1)
1-4-4 Kojimachi, Chiyoda-ku, Tokyo, 102-0083, Japan (94.3%)
Tel.: (81) 367741697
Web Site: https://lifull-space.co.jp
Real Estate Development Services
N.A.I.C.S.: 531390

Lifull Tech Vietnam Co., Ltd. (1)
TS Building 6 Floor 17 Street No 2, Cu Xa Do Thanh Ward 4 District 3, Ho Chi Minh City, Vietnam
Tel.: (84) 2838326737
Web Site: https://www.lifull-tech.vn
Real Estate Development Services
N.A.I.C.S.: 531390

LIG CO.,LTD
2nd Floor 524 Bongeunsa-ro, Gangnam-gu, Seoul, Korea (South)
Tel.: (82) 69001900
Web Site: http://www.ligcorp.co.kr
Holding Company
N.A.I.C.S.: 551112
Yoong-Jun Choi *(CEO)*

LIG NEX1 CO., LTD.

LIG NEX1 CO., LTD.

LIG Nex1 Co., Ltd.—(Continued)
207 Mabuk-ro, Giheung-gu, Yongin, Gyeonggi, Korea (South)
Tel.: (82) 16442005
Web Site: https://www.lignex1.com
Year Founded: 1976
079550—(KRS)
Rev.: $1,703,316,683
Assets: $2,310,761,780
Liabilities: $1,593,479,435
Net Worth: $717,282,345
Earnings: $94,294,664
Emp.: 3,780
Fiscal Year-end: 12/31/22
Space Vehicle Mfr
N.A.I.C.S.: 336414
Ickhyun Shin (CEO)

Subsidiaries:

LIG Pungshan ProTech Co., Ltd. (1)
2606-10 Hoguk-ro, Angang-eup, Gyeongju, Gyeongsangbuk-do, Korea (South)
Tel.: (82) 547625566
Web Site: https://m.ligpoongsan.co.kr
Rocket Propulsion Engine Mfr
N.A.I.C.S.: 336415

LIGA INDEPENDIENTE DE FUTBOL S.A.
Av Quilin 5942 Penalolen, Santiago, Chile
Tel.: (56) 22841010
Web Site: https://www.lif.cl
LINDEFUT—(SGO)
Sales Range: Less than $1 Million
Entertainment Facility Operator
N.A.I.C.S.: 713940
Rodrigo Malermo Navarro (CEO)

LIGAO FOODS CO., LTD.
5F Building 2 Hongding Yunjinghui No 559-571 Yuncheng East Road, Baiyun District, Guangzhou, 510420, Guangdong, China
Tel.: (86) 4007878788
Web Site: https://www.ligaofoods.com
Year Founded: 2000
300973—(SSE)
Rev.: $408,646,836
Assets: $400,806,900
Liabilities: $102,062,376
Net Worth: $298,744,524
Earnings: $20,185,308
Fiscal Year-end: 12/31/22
Packaged Food Product Mfr & Distr
N.A.I.C.S.: 311991
Yuhui Peng (Chm & Gen Mgr)

LIGEANCE AEROSPACE TECHNOLOGY CO., LTD.
No 2999 Xihanggang Avenue, Shuangliu District, Chengdu, 610200, Sichuan, China
Tel.: (86) 2885853290
Web Site: http://www.lsmin.com
Year Founded: 1993
000697—(SSE)
Rev.: $173,492,280
Assets: $391,331,304
Liabilities: $447,635,916
Net Worth: ($56,304,612)
Earnings: ($112,616,244)
Fiscal Year-end: 12/31/22
Metal Ore Smelting Services
N.A.I.C.S.: 331410
Xiong Huiran (Chm)

Subsidiaries:

Gardner Aerospace Holdings Ltd. (1)
Unit 9 Victory Park Victory Road, Derby, DE24 8ZF, United Kingdom
Tel.: (44) 1332274700
Web Site: https://gardner-aerospace.com
Aerospace Detailed Parts Mfr
N.A.I.C.S.: 336412

Nick Sanders (Chm)

LIGENTIA GROUP LTD.
Ligentia House 6 Butler Way, Leeds, LS28 6EA, United Kingdom
Tel.: (44) 113 344 4000
Web Site: http://www.ligentia.com
Year Founded: 1996
Sales Range: $75-99.9 Million
Emp.: 288
Supply Chain Distribution Services
N.A.I.C.S.: 423840
Nick Jones (Grp CEO)

Subsidiaries:

Ligentia (Thailand) Limited (1)
1103/2 Soi Sukhumvit 25 Sukhumvit Road, 1 Glas Haus Building 11th Floor North Klongtoey Wattana, Bangkok, 10110, Thailand
Tel.: (66) 22581265
Logistics Consulting Servies
N.A.I.C.S.: 541614

Ligentia Air Limited (1)
Unit C Parkway West Cranford Lane, Heston, TW5 9QA, United Kingdom
Tel.: (44) 2071277597
Logistics Consulting Servies
N.A.I.C.S.: 541614

Ligentia Asia Ltd (1)
8/F The Grande Building 398-402 Kwun Tong Road, Kwun Tong, China (Hong Kong)
Tel.: (852) 23171710
Web Site: http://www.ligentia-asia.com
Logistics Consulting Servies
N.A.I.C.S.: 541614
Gwen Choi (Asst Mgr-Freight Procurement)

Ligentia China (Guangzhou) Ltd (1)
No 33 Zhong Shan San Road, 5006-5007 Block B China International Center, Guangzhou, China
Tel.: (86) 2083888001
Logistics Consulting Servies
N.A.I.C.S.: 541614
Wallace Ho (Mgr-Station)

Ligentia China (Ningbo) Ltd (1)
404 A Crown World Trade Plaza No 11 Caihong South Road, Ningbo, China
Tel.: (86) 57487092035
Logistics Consulting Servies
N.A.I.C.S.: 541614

Ligentia China (Qingdao) Ltd (1)
8/F Top Yihe Building No 10 Hong Kong Middle Road, Qingdao, Shandong, China
Tel.: (86) 53280793858
Logistics Consulting Servies
N.A.I.C.S.: 541614

Ligentia China (Shanghai) Ltd (1)
1802-1804 Building A 2816 Yixian Road, Watts Gallop International Plaza Baoshan, Shanghai, China
Tel.: (86) 2161175656
Logistics Consulting Servies
N.A.I.C.S.: 541614

Ligentia China (Shenzhen) Ltd (1)
3018 Huishang Center Glittery City No 3027 Shennan Mid Road, Futian District, Shenzhen, China
Tel.: (86) 75583643058
Logistics Consulting Servies
N.A.I.C.S.: 541614

Ligentia China (Tianjin) Ltd (1)
1406 Haizhu Mansion No 166 Xinhua Road, Heping District, Tianjin, China
Tel.: (86) 2258292836
Logistics Consulting Servies
N.A.I.C.S.: 541614

Ligentia China (Xiamen) Ltd (1)
501-503 ChangJiang Building No 270 of ChangHao Road, Huli District, Xiamen, China
Tel.: (86) 5925688036
Logistics Consulting Servies
N.A.I.C.S.: 541614

Ligentia Logistics Limited (1)
Garnham Close Cotes Park Industrial Estate, Alfreton, DE55 4QH, Derbyshire, United Kingdom

Tel.: (44) 1773289000
Logistics Consulting Servies
N.A.I.C.S.: 541614

LIGHT S.A.
Rua Marechal Floriano n 168 Bloco 1 - 2 andar Centro, Rio de Janeiro, 20080-002, RJ, Brazil
Tel.: (55) 2122112828
Web Site: http://www.light.com.br
Year Founded: 1899
LIGT3—(BRAZ)
Rev.: $2,523,430,869
Assets: $4,239,633,787
Liabilities: $3,686,249,343
Net Worth: $553,384,444
Earnings: $45,612,698
Fiscal Year-end: 12/31/23
Electric Power Generation & Distribution Services
N.A.I.C.S.: 221111
Roberto Caixeta Barroso (Officer-Fin, IR & Bus Dev Areas)

Subsidiaries:

Axxiom Solucoes Tecnologicas S.A. (1)
Av Cristovao Colombo 485 - 6 Andar Savassi, Belo Horizonte, 30140-140, MG, Brazil
Tel.: (55) 3132804900
Web Site: http://www.axxiom.com.br
Electric Power Distribution Services
N.A.I.C.S.: 221122

Guanhaes Energia S.A. (1)
Rua Topazio 210 Iguacu, Ipatinga, 35162-132, MG, Brazil
Tel.: (55) 3138013900
Web Site: http://www.guanhaesenergia.com.br
Hydroelectric Power Generation Services
N.A.I.C.S.: 221111

LIGHT SCIENCE TECHNOLOGIES HOLDINGS PLC
1 Lowman Way Hilton Business Park, Hilton, Derby, DE65 5LJ, Derbyshire, United Kingdom
Tel.: (44) 1332410601
Web Site: https://www.lightscienceholding.com
Year Founded: 1997
LST—(AIM)
Rev.: $11,088,186
Assets: $9,594,206
Liabilities: $6,966,357
Net Worth: $2,627,849
Earnings: ($3,377,083)
Emp.: 86
Fiscal Year-end: 11/30/22
Holding Company
N.A.I.C.S.: 551112

Subsidiaries:

Light Science Technologies Limited (1)
Ednaston Park Business Centre Painters Lane Ednaston, Ashbourne, DE6 3FA, United Kingdom
Tel.: (44) 1332410601
Web Site: https://lightsciencetech.com
Agriculture Research & Development Services
N.A.I.C.S.: 541715

UK Circuits & Electronics Solutions Limited (1)
Greengate Industrial Estate Greenside Way, Manchester, Middleton, M24 1SW, United Kingdom
Tel.: (44) 1616545969
Web Site: https://www.ukcircuits.co.uk
Emp.: 60
Electronic Products Mfr
N.A.I.C.S.: 334511

LIGHTICO LTD.
121 Hahoshmanim Street, Tel Aviv, 6713328, Israel

INTERNATIONAL PUBLIC

Tel.: (972) 544273473
Web Site: https://www.lightico.com
Year Founded: 2015
Emp.: 103
Software Devolepment
N.A.I.C.S.: 513210

Subsidiaries:

Vizolution Ltd. (1)
Baglan Bay Innovation Centre, Baglan Energy Park, Port Talbot, SA12 7AX, West Glamorgan, United Kingdom
Tel.: (44) 8455391972
Web Site: http://www.vizolution.co.uk
Technology Support Services for Financial & Call Center Markets
N.A.I.C.S.: 541519
Bill Safran (CEO)

LIGHTING AND EQUIPMENT PUBLIC COMPANY LIMITED
16-17 Floor Gypsum Metropolitan Tower, 539/2 Sri-Ayudhya Rd Rajthevee, Bangkok, 10400, Thailand
Tel.: (66) 22488133
Web Site: http://www.lighting.co.th
Year Founded: 1993
L&E—(THA)
Rev.: $80,619,383
Assets: $96,779,158
Liabilities: $64,346,141
Net Worth: $32,433,016
Earnings: ($703,356)
Emp.: 1,263
Fiscal Year-end: 12/31/23
Lighting Equipment Mfr
N.A.I.C.S.: 335139
Yong Suptuaychone (Chm)

LIGHTINTHEBOX HOLDING CO., LTD.
Floor 5 Building 2 Yaxin Science Tech Park No 399 Shengxia Road, Pudong New Area, Shanghai, 201203, China
Tel.: (86) 2168772231
Web Site: http://www.lightinthebox.com
Year Founded: 2007
LITB—(NYSE)
Rev.: $503,568,000
Assets: $164,813,000
Liabilities: $160,937,000
Net Worth: $3,876,000
Earnings: ($56,582,000)
Emp.: 816
Fiscal Year-end: 12/31/22
Lifestyle Products Online Retailer & Mail Order
N.A.I.C.S.: 449210
Quji Guo (Co-Founder)

LIGHTNING MINERALS LTD.
Level 6 505 Little Collins Street, Melbourne, 3000, VIC, Australia
Tel.: (61) 894298806
Web Site: https://www.lightningminerals.com.au
Year Founded: 2021
L1M—(ASX)
Rev.: $42,217
Assets: $5,074,131
Liabilities: $148,339
Net Worth: $4,925,792
Earnings: ($2,214,779)
Fiscal Year-end: 06/30/24
Other Nonmetallic Mineral Mining & Quarrying
N.A.I.C.S.: 212390
Alex Biggs (CEO)

LIGHTPOWER GMBH
An der Talle 24-28, Paderborn, 33102, Germany
Tel.: (49) 525114320
Web Site: http://www.lightpower.de
Year Founded: 1978
Rev.: $35,257,464

AND PRIVATE COMPANIES

LIKE CO., LTD.

Emp.: 75
Stage Lighting & Show Technology Equipment Distr
N.A.I.C.S.: 423490
Ralph-Jorg Wezorke *(Mng Dir)*

LIGHTRON, INC.
68 Munpyeongdong-ro, Daedeok-gu, Daejeon, 34301, Korea (South)
Tel.: (82) 429307700
Web Site: https://www.lightron.co.kr
Year Founded: 1998
069540—(KRS)
Rev.: $40,311,966
Assets: $68,852,818
Liabilities: $26,457,982
Net Worth: $42,394,836
Earnings: ($550,663)
Emp.: 150
Fiscal Year-end: 12/31/22
Communication Devices Mfr
N.A.I.C.S.: 334220
Chanhee Park *(CEO)*

Subsidiaries:

Tomei Shoji Co., Ltd. (1)
5-23- 2-1F- A Daitakubo, Minamiku, Saitama, 336-0015, Japan
Tel.: (81) 487115919
Web Site: https://www.tomeishoji.co.jp
Automotive Distr
N.A.I.C.S.: 441110

LIGHTSCAPE TECHNOLOGIES, INC.
18/F 318 Hennessy Road W Square, Wanchai, China (Hong Kong)
Tel.: (852) 2546 1808   NV
Web Site: http://www.lightscape-tech.com
Year Founded: 1995
LTSC—(OTCIQ)
Sales Range: $1-9.9 Million
Emp.: 34
LED Lighting Products & Digital Billboards Mfr
N.A.I.C.S.: 334413

Subsidiaries:

Beijing Aihua New Enterprise Lighting Appliance Co., Ltd. (1)
No 7 Shuang Qiao Xili, Chaoyang District, Beijing, 100024, China
Tel.: (86) 1085362292
Lamp Mfr
N.A.I.C.S.: 335139

Lightscape Technologies (Greater China) Limited (1)
18/F 318 Hennessy Road West Square, Wanchai, China (Hong Kong)
Tel.: (852) 25461808
Lighting Systems Mfr & Distr
N.A.I.C.S.: 335132

LIGHTSPEED COMMERCE INC.
700 St Antoine Est, Montreal, H2Y 1A6, QC, Canada
Tel.: (514) 907-1801
Web Site: https://www.lightspeedhq.com
Year Founded: 2015
LSPD—(NYSE)
Rev.: $909,270,000
Assets: $2,575,154,000
Liabilities: $162,753,000
Net Worth: $2,412,401,000
Earnings: ($163,964,000)
Emp.: 3,000
Fiscal Year-end: 03/31/24
Hotel & Resort Operator
N.A.I.C.S.: 721110
JP Chauvet *(CEO)*

LIGHTSPEED DISCOVERIES INC.
10th Floor 595 Howe Street, Vancouver, V6C 2T5, BC, Canada
Tel.: (604) 719-8129
Web Site: http://www.monster-uranium.com
MURCF—(OTCEM)
Assets: $9,784
Liabilities: $527,056
Net Worth: ($517,272)
Earnings: ($139,058)
Fiscal Year-end: 12/31/23
Uranium Mining Services
N.A.I.C.S.: 212290
Kenneth Ralfs *(CFO)*

LIGHTWAVERF PLC
Assay Office 1 Moreton Street, Birmingham, B1 3AX, United Kingdom
Tel.: (44) 121 250 3625   UK
Web Site: http://www.lightwaverf.com
Year Founded: 2008
Sales Range: $1-9.9 Million
Home Automation System Mfr
N.A.I.C.S.: 238210
John Shermer *(CTO)*

Subsidiaries:

JSJS Designs (Europe) Limited (1)
Science Park Aston Faraday Wharf Holt Street, Birmingham, B7 4BB, United Kingdom
Tel.: (44) 1943830472
Web Site: http://www.jsdesigns.com
Sales Range: $25-49.9 Million
Emp.: 10
Home Automation Solutions
N.A.I.C.S.: 238210

LIGITEK ELECTRONICS CO., LTD.
NO 238 Bo-Ai St, Shulin District, New Taipei City, 238, Taiwan
Tel.: (886) 277036000
Web Site: https://www.ligitek.com
8111—(TPE)
Rev.: $26,337,898
Assets: $68,396,273
Liabilities: $23,063,753
Net Worth: $45,332,520
Earnings: $3,483,882
Fiscal Year-end: 12/31/22
Electric Equipment Mfr
N.A.I.C.S.: 333998
I-Hsing Tung *(Chm)*

Subsidiaries:

Lapling Electronics Co., Ltd. (1)
Central Avenue 29 in the 1421-1424 room, Nansha District, Guangzhou, China
Tel.: (86) 2084982000
Optoelectronic Component Mfr
N.A.I.C.S.: 334413

Ligitek Photovoltaic Co., Ltd. (1)
No 238 Bo-Ai St, Shulin District, New Taipei City, 238, Taiwan
Tel.: (886) 277036300
Optoelectronic Component Mfr
N.A.I.C.S.: 334413

US Ligitek Inc. (1)
4471 E Santa Ana St Ste C, Ontario, CA 91761
Tel.: (909) 605-6598
Optoelectronic Component Mfr
N.A.I.C.S.: 334413

LIGUA, INC.
Awajicho Park Building No 2 2-6-6 Awajicho, Chuo-Ku, Osaka, 541-0047, Osaka, Japan
Tel.: (81) 662321800
Web Site: https://www.ligua.jp
Year Founded: 2004
7090—(TKS)
Rev.: $22,672,300
Assets: $25,574,090
Liabilities: $21,581,650
Net Worth: $3,992,440
Earnings: $687,440

Fiscal Year-end: 03/31/24
Financial Management Consulting Services
N.A.I.C.S.: 541611
Norihiko Kawase *(Founder & Pres)*

LIHE TECHNOLOGY (HUNAN) CO., LTD.
No 668 Qingshan Road, High-tech Zone, Changsha, 410205, Hunan, China
Tel.: (86) 73188911456
Web Site: https://www.lihero.com
Year Founded: 1997
300800—(SSE)
Rev.: $72,798,804
Assets: $332,645,508
Liabilities: $45,433,440
Net Worth: $287,212,068
Earnings: $8,185,320
Fiscal Year-end: 12/31/22
Measuring Instruments Mfr
N.A.I.C.S.: 334513
Guangsheng Zhang *(Chm)*

LIHIT LAB., INC.
1-1-22 Noninbashi, Chuo Ku, Osaka, 540-8526, Japan
Tel.: (81) 669463931
Web Site: https://www.lihit-lab.com
Year Founded: 1938
7975—(TKS)
Rev.: $62,413,270
Assets: $92,999,530
Liabilities: $20,383,750
Net Worth: $72,615,780
Earnings: ($659,370)
Emp.: 177
Fiscal Year-end: 02/29/24
Stationery Product Mfr & Whslr
N.A.I.C.S.: 322230
Hirokazu Tanaka *(Pres)*

Subsidiaries:

Lihit Lab., Inc. - Shizuoka Factory (1)
1300-10 Kamo, Kikugawa, 439-0031, Shizuoka, Japan
Tel.: (81) 537351234
Stationery Product Mfr
N.A.I.C.S.: 339940

LIHNIDA OHRID
7-mi Noemvri No 183, Ohrid, North Macedonia
Tel.: (389) 46254141
Web Site: https://www.lihnida.com.mk
Year Founded: 1960
Plastic Pipe Fitting Products Mfr
N.A.I.C.S.: 326122
Petar Golaboski *(Owner & Gen Mgr)*

LIHTAI CONSTRUCTION & DEVELOPMENT CO., LTD.
No 7 Sec 7 Yen-Ping North Road, Taipei, Taiwan
Tel.: (886) 228103001
5520—(TPE)
Rev.: $105,439,296
Assets: $101,952,318
Liabilities: $30,600,882
Net Worth: $71,351,437
Earnings: $12,142,795
Fiscal Year-end: 12/31/22
Cement Product Mfr & Distr
N.A.I.C.S.: 327310
Liang-Tsai Wu *(Chm & CEO)*

LII HEN INDUSTRIES BHD.
Plo 43 Bukit Pasir Industrial Estate Jalan Raja Mukim Sungai Raya, 84300, Muar, Johor, Malaysia
Tel.: (60) 69857202
Web Site: https://www.liihenfurniture.com
LIIHEN—(KLS)
Rev.: $154,684,001

Assets: $132,474,261
Liabilities: $27,890,129
Net Worth: $104,584,131
Earnings: $16,130,171
Emp.: 2,497
Fiscal Year-end: 12/31/22
Furniture Mfr
N.A.I.C.S.: 321999
Bee Eng Tan *(Exec Dir)*

Subsidiaries:

CT Haup Heng Sdn Bhd (1)
Plo 9, Bukit Pasir Industrial Estate, 84300, Muar, Johor, Malaysia
Tel.: (60) 69857202
Furniture Mfr
N.A.I.C.S.: 337127

EF Furniture Sdn Bhd (1)
Plo 8, Bukit Pasir Industrial Estate, 84300, Muar, Johor, Malaysia
Tel.: (60) 69857202
Furniture Mfr
N.A.I.C.S.: 337127

Favourite Design Sdn Bhd (1)
Lot 1915 Jalan Tanjung Selabu GM 347, Mukim Sungai Raya Bukit Pasir, 84300, Muar, Johor, Malaysia
Tel.: (60) 69855222
Web Site:
   https://www.favouritedesign.com.my
Furniture Mfr
N.A.I.C.S.: 337127

Lii Hen Furniture Sdn Bhd (1)
Plo 43, Bukit Pasir Industrial Estate, 84300, Muar, Johor, Malaysia
Tel.: (60) 69857202
Furniture Mfr
N.A.I.C.S.: 337127

LIJIANG YULONG TOURISM CO., LTD.
760 Lijiang Shangri Avenue Old Town Yulong Tourism Building, Lijiang, 674100, Yunnan, China
Tel.: (86) 8885377777
Web Site:
   https://www.yulongtour.com
002033—(SSE)
Rev.: $44,445,024
Assets: $407,831,112
Liabilities: $39,693,888
Net Worth: $368,137,224
Earnings: $516,672
Fiscal Year-end: 12/31/22
Cable Car Operator
N.A.I.C.S.: 487990
Xianzhong He *(Chm)*

LIKE CO., LTD.
Umeda Hankyu Building Office Tower 19F 8-1 Kakuda-cho, Kita-ku, Osaka, 530-0017, Japan
Tel.: (81) 663640006
Web Site: http://www.like-gr.co.jp
Year Founded: 1995
2462—(TKS)
Rev.: $399,700,090
Assets: $254,504,830
Liabilities: $143,357,680
Net Worth: $111,147,150
Earnings: $16,174,670
Emp.: 5,223
Fiscal Year-end: 05/31/24
Employment Placement Services; Mobile Phone Sales
N.A.I.C.S.: 561311
Yasuhiko Okamoto *(Pres, Founder & CEO)*

Subsidiaries:

LIKE Care, Inc. (1)
17th floor Shibuya Mark City West 1-12-1 Dogenzaka, Shibuya-ku, Tokyo, 150-0043, Japan
Tel.: (81) 357845521
Emp.: 980
Nursing Home Services
N.A.I.C.S.: 621610

4497

LIKE CO., LTD.

LIKE Co., Ltd.—(Continued)

LIKE Kids, Inc. (1)
17th Floor Shibuya Mark City West 1-12-1 Dogenzaka, Shibuya-ku, Tokyo, 150-0043, Japan **(50.1%)**
Tel.: (81) 364319966
Web Site: https://www.like-kd.co.jp
Rev.: $157,850,880
Assets: $137,320,320
Liabilities: $98,834,400
Net Worth: $38,485,920
Earnings: $14,714,160
Fiscal Year-end: 04/30/2018
Child Care Services
N.A.I.C.S.: 624410

LIKE Staffing, Inc. (1)
17th Floor Shibuya Mark City West 1-12-1 Dogenzaka, Shibuya-ku, Tokyo, 150-0043, Japan
Tel.: (81) 357845522
Recruiting Services
N.A.I.C.S.: 561311
Kazunori Fukuhara *(Pres)*

LIKE Works, Inc. (1)
Shibuya Mark City West 17F 1-12-1 Dogenzaka, Shibuya-ku, Tokyo, 150-0043, Japan
Tel.: (81) 354565500
Recruiting Services
N.A.I.C.S.: 561311

Success Holdings Co., Ltd. (1)
1-1-8 Otemachi building Gotanda Building 7th floor, Shinagawa-ku, Tokyo, 141-0031, Japan **(50.1%)**
Tel.: (81) 3 6431 9899
Web Site: http://www.success-holdings.co.jp
Sales Range: $75-99.9 Million
Emp.: 3,979
Holding Company; Child Day Care Services
N.A.I.C.S.: 551112
Chi Jui Hong *(CEO)*

LIKEWISE GROUP PLC
Unit 4 Radial Park Solihull Parkway, Birmingham Business Park, Solihull, B37 7WN, United Kingdom
Tel.: (44) 1218172900 **UK**
Web Site: https://www.likewiseplc.com
Year Founded: 2012
LIKE—(AIM)
Rev.: $156,075,073
Assets: $122,454,398
Liabilities: $73,083,950
Net Worth: $49,370,448
Earnings: ($1,055,673)
Emp.: 455
Fiscal Year-end: 12/31/22
Floor Covering Retailer
N.A.I.C.S.: 449121

Subsidiaries:

H&V Carpets B.V.B.A. (1)
Nijverheidsstraat 26, 8760, Meulebeke, Belgium
Tel.: (32) 51320543
Carpet Whslr
N.A.I.C.S.: 423220

LIKHAMI CONSULTING LIMITED
62A Dr Meghnad Shah Sarani Room No 1 2nd Floor Southern Avenue, Kolkata, 700 029, West Bengal, India
Tel.: (91) 8232099092 **In**
Web Site: https://www.likhamiconsulting.com
Year Founded: 1982
029378—(KOL)
Rev.: $75,071
Assets: $4,197,338
Liabilities: $12,459
Net Worth: $4,184,878
Earnings: $20,846
Fiscal Year-end: 03/31/23
Business Management Services
N.A.I.C.S.: 541910
Pradip Kumar Ghosh *(Exec Dir)*

LIKHITHA INFRASTRUCTURE LIMITED
8-3-323 9th Floor Vasavi's Mpm Grand, Yellareddy Guda Ameerpet X Raods, Hyderabad, 500073, Telangana, India
Tel.: (91) 4023752657
Web Site: https://www.likhitha.co.in
Year Founded: 1998
LIKHITHA—(BOM)
Rev.: $26,335,915
Assets: $23,037,082
Liabilities: $2,097,487
Net Worth: $20,939,595
Earnings: $3,957,089
Emp.: 402
Fiscal Year-end: 03/31/21
Gas & Oil Exploration Services
N.A.I.C.S.: 211130
Sivasankara Parameshwara Kurup Pillai *(Chm)*

LILLO SPA
Zona Asi Capannone 18, 81030, Gricignano d'Aversa, CE, Italy
Tel.: (39) 081 8156 111 **IT**
Web Site: http://www.md-discount.it
Grocery & Department Store Operations
N.A.I.C.S.: 445110
Giuseppe Daloiso *(Ops Mgr)*

Subsidiaries:

Aclairo Pharmaceutical Development Group, Inc. (1)
1950 Old Gallows Rd Ste 300, Vienna, VA 22182
Tel.: (703) 506-6760
Web Site: http://www.aclairo.com
Scientific & Technical Consulting Services
N.A.I.C.S.: 541690
Hilary Sheevers *(Pres & CEO)*

Dedagroup SpA (1)
Loc Palazzine 120/f, 38121, Trento, Italy
Tel.: (39) 0461 997111
Web Site: http://www.dedagroup.it
Sales Range: $200-249.9 Million
Emp.: 1,600
Information & Communications Technology Solutions
N.A.I.C.S.: 541519
Gianni Camisa *(CEO)*

Subsidiary (US):

EPL, Inc. (2)
22 Inverness Center Pkwy, Birmingham, AL 35242-4814 **(70%)**
Tel.: (205) 408-5300
Web Site: http://www.eplinc.com
Sales Range: $1-9.9 Million
Emp.: 74
Data Processing Services
N.A.I.C.S.: 518210
Robin Kolvek *(Interim CEO)*

LILLY ASIA VENTURES
Room 2909 3 Corporate Avenue No 168 Hubin Road, Huangpu, Shanghai, 200021, China
Tel.: (86) 21 2316 9588
Web Site: http://www.lillyasiaventures.com
Holding Company
N.A.I.C.S.: 551112

LILONTEX CORPORATION
4F 6 No 369 Fushing N Road, Taipei, Taiwan
Tel.: (886) 2 2514 0077
Web Site: http://www.lilontex.com.tw
Rev.: $9,515,143
Assets: $88,299,686
Liabilities: $30,160,932
Net Worth: $58,138,754
Earnings: ($2,738,033)
Fiscal Year-end: 12/31/17
Yarn Mfr & Distr
N.A.I.C.S.: 313110

Chao-An Liu *(Pres)*

LILY GROUP CO.,LTD
Linjiang High-Tech Industrial Park, Hangzhou, Zhejiang, China
Tel.: (86) 57182963567
Web Site: https://www.lilygroup.cn
Year Founded: 2012
603823—(SHG)
Rev.: $346,513,504
Assets: $493,719,282
Liabilities: $157,483,296
Net Worth: $336,235,985
Earnings: $30,115,842
Fiscal Year-end: 12/31/22
Organic Pigments Mfr & Distr
N.A.I.C.S.: 325130

LILY TEXTILE CO., LTD.
6th Floor 70 Hsi Ning North Road, Taipei, Taiwan
Tel.: (886) 225557680
Web Site: http://www.lily.com.tw
1443—(TAI)
Rev.: $25,532,391
Assets: $229,787,394
Liabilities: $177,297,060
Net Worth: $52,490,335
Earnings: $4,667,517
Fiscal Year-end: 12/31/23
Textile Products Mfr
N.A.I.C.S.: 314999
Dongrong Su *(Chm)*

LILYCOLOR CO., LTD.
7-5-20 Nishi-Shinjuku, Shinjuku-ku, Tokyo, 160-8315, Japan
Tel.: (81) 333667845
Web Site: https://www.lilycolor.co.jp
Year Founded: 1949
9827—(TKS)
Sales Range: Less than $1 Million
Emp.: 475
Interior Product Mfr
N.A.I.C.S.: 314120
Toshiyuki Yamada *(Pres)*

LIM OVIN
185 rue de Nexon, 87015, Limoges, CEDEX 1, France
Tel.: (33) 555308687
Web Site: http://www.limovin.fr
Sales Range: $10-24.9 Million
Emp.: 25
Meat Packing Services
N.A.I.C.S.: 311611
Catherine Coeffeteau *(Mgr-Personnel)*

LIM WEN HENG CONSTRUCTION PTE LTD
41 Kim Chuan Drive #06-00 Lim Wen Heng Building, Singapore, 537091, Singapore
Tel.: (65) 67429133
Web Site: http://lwhconst.com.sg
Year Founded: 1994
Construction & Engineering Services
N.A.I.C.S.: 236220
Harry Lin Bing Cheng *(Mng Dir)*

Subsidiaries:

Presscrete Engineering Pte Ltd (1)
41 Kim Chuan Drive LWH Building 04-00, Singapore, 537091, Singapore
Tel.: (65) 65429315
Web Site: http://www.presscrete.com.sg
Civil Engineering Services
N.A.I.C.S.: 541330

LIMA GAS S.A.
Calle Bernini 149 4th floor, San Borja, Lima, Peru
Tel.: (51) 01 640 8888
Web Site: http://www.limagas.com
Year Founded: 1961
LPG Gas Mfr

INTERNATIONAL PUBLIC

N.A.I.C.S.: 213112

LIMA SP. Z O.O.
ul Ostrowite 37, 87-400, Golub-Dobrzyn, Poland
Tel.: (48) 564623143
Web Site: http://www.lima.pl
Year Founded: 1999
Helicopter Operator
N.A.I.C.S.: 481111
Piotr Majewski *(CEO & Mgr-Accountable)*

LIMAK HOLDING A.S.
Hafta Sokak No 9 GOP, 06700, Ankara, Turkiye
Tel.: (90) 3124468800
Web Site: http://www.limak.com.tr
Sales Range: $1-4.9 Billion
Holding Company
N.A.I.C.S.: 551112
Nihat Ozdemir *(Chm)*

LIME CHEMICALS LIMITED
404/405 NECO Chambers Plot No 48 Sector 11 CBD Belapur, Navi Mumbai, 400614, India
Tel.: (91) 2227561977
Web Site: https://www.limechem.com
Year Founded: 1970
507759—(BOM)
Rev.: $1,947,623
Assets: $2,397,336
Liabilities: $2,471,810
Net Worth: ($74,474)
Earnings: $1,337,140
Fiscal Year-end: 03/31/22
Lime Mfr
N.A.I.C.S.: 327410
A. H. Dawoodani *(Mng Dir)*

LIME TECHNOLOGIES AB
Tel.: (46) 462704800 **SE**
Web Site: https://www.lime-technologies.com
Year Founded: 1990
LIME—(OMX)
Rev.: $54,054,155
Assets: $65,275,787
Liabilities: $40,485,356
Net Worth: $24,790,432
Earnings: $7,809,529
Emp.: 412
Fiscal Year-end: 12/31/23
Software Development Services
N.A.I.C.S.: 541511
Nils Olsson *(CEO)*

Subsidiaries:

Userlike UG (1)
Probsteigasse 44-46, 50670, Koln, Germany
Tel.: (49) 22163060024
Web Site: https://www.userlike.com
Information Technology Services
N.A.I.C.S.: 541511

LIMERSTON CAPITAL LLP
12 -18 Grosvenor Gardens, London, SW1W 0DH, United Kingdom
Tel.: (44) 2038971860
Web Site: http://www.limerstoncap.com
Year Founded: 2015
Privater Equity Firm
N.A.I.C.S.: 523999
James Paget *(Partner-Founding)*

Subsidiaries:

Prism UK Medical Ltd. (1)
Unit 4 Jubilee Business Park Jubilee Way Grange Moor, Wakefield, WF4 4TD, W Yorks, United Kingdom
Tel.: (44) 1924 840 100
Web Site: http://www.prismmedical.co.uk
Emp.: 450
Medical Equipments Mfr & Distr
N.A.I.C.S.: 423450

AND PRIVATE COMPANIES — LIN YUAN INVESTMENT CO., LTD.

Stuart Meldrum (CEO)
Division (Domestic):

Prism Medical Manufacturing Centre (2)
Unit 1 Tir Llwyd Industrial Estate St Asaph Avenue, Kinmel Bay, Rhyl, LL18 5JZ, Conwy, United Kingdom
Tel.: (44) 1745 342 212
Web Site: http://www.prismmedical.co.uk
Medical Equipment Mfr
N.A.I.C.S.: 339112

Prism Medical UK - APLS Division (2)
Unit 4 Jubilee Business Park Jubilee Way Grange Moor, Wakefield, WF4 4TD, W Yorks, United Kingdom
Tel.: (44) 844 980 2275
Web Site: http://www.prismmedical.co.uk
Medical Equipments Moving Services
N.A.I.C.S.: 484210
Carole Shaw (Acct Mgr)

Prism Medical UK - Carefree Division (2)
13-15 Pennington Street, Hindley, Wigan, WN2 3AH, Lancs, United Kingdom
Tel.: (44) 844 980 2266
Web Site: http://prismmedical.co.uk
Patient Lifts & Handling Equipment Mfr
N.A.I.C.S.: 339112

Prism Medical UK - Healthcare Division (2)
Unit 4 Jubilee Business Park Jubilee Way Grange Moor, Wakefield, WF4 4TD, W Yorks, United Kingdom
Tel.: (44) 8449802278
Web Site: http://www.prismmedical.co.uk
Medical Equipments Moving Services
N.A.I.C.S.: 484210

Prism Medical UK - Liftech & Test Valley Division (2)
Unit 42 South Hampshire Industrial Park, Totton, Southampton, SO40 3SA, Hants, United Kingdom
Tel.: (44) 844 980 2272
Web Site: http://www.prismmedical.co.uk
Health Equipment Mfr
N.A.I.C.S.: 339112

Prism Medical UK - Saluss Division (2)
Unit 1 Tir Llwyd Industrial Estate St Asaph Avenue, Kinmel Bay, Rhyl, LL18 5JZ, Conwy, United Kingdom
Tel.: (44) 844 980 2290
Web Site: http://www.prismmedical.co.uk
Medical Equipment Repair & Maintenance Services
N.A.I.C.S.: 811210

Prism Medical UK - Westholme Division (2)
Unit 4 Jubilee Business Park Jubilee Way Grange Moor, Wakefield, WF4 4TD, W Yorks, United Kingdom
Tel.: (44) 1924 840 100
Web Site: http://www.prismmedical.co.uk
Patient Handling & Moving Equipment Mfr
N.A.I.C.S.: 339112

LIMES SCHLOSSKLINIKEN AG
Tel.: (49) 2203290140
Web Site: https://www.limes-schlosskliniken.de
LIK—(DEU)
Rev.: $41,898,712
Assets: $36,701,956
Liabilities: $18,330,447
Net Worth: $18,371,509
Earnings: $4,314,900
Emp.: 146
Fiscal Year-end: 12/31/23
Healthcare Services
N.A.I.C.S.: 621999
Gert Michael Frank (Chm-Mgmt Bd & CEO)

LIMIN GROUP CO., LTD.
Economic Development Zone, Xinyi, 221400, Jiangsu, China
Tel.: (86) 51688923527
Web Site: https://www.chinalimin.com
Year Founded: 1996
002734—(SSE)
Rev.: $323,755,380
Assets: $990,679,248
Liabilities: $591,924,996
Net Worth: $398,754,252
Earnings: $8,077,212
Emp.: 1,080
Fiscal Year-end: 12/31/22
Pesticide & Other Agricultural Chemical Mfr
N.A.I.C.S.: 325320
Li Xinsheng (Chm)

Subsidiaries:

Limin Chemical Co., Ltd. - International Business Unit (1)
B19 Kejichuangxin Building 5 Xinmofan Road, Nanjing, Jiangsu, China
Tel.: (86) 2566980134
Emp.: 30
Pesticide Mfr
N.A.I.C.S.: 325320

LIMING A.D.
Olge Jovanovic 14, Belgrade, Serbia
Tel.: (381) 11 2831 094
Year Founded: 1966
LMNG—(BEL)
Sales Range: Less than $1 Million
Roofing Services
N.A.I.C.S.: 238160
Milivoje Durkovic (Exec Dir)

LIMITED LIABILITY COMPANY "GROUP" SODRUZHESTVO
st Petrenko 18, Kherson, 73 025, Ukraine
Tel.: (380) 552 41 70 70
Web Site: http://www.sodruzhestvo.ua
Year Founded: 1988
Emp.: 5,000
Natural Gas Transportation Services
N.A.I.C.S.: 486210
Viktor Popov (Gen Dir)

Subsidiaries:

Gadyachgaz, PJSC (1)
26a Budka str c, Hadyach, Poltava, 37300, Ukraine
Tel.: (380) 5354 2 24 14
Natural Gas Distr
N.A.I.C.S.: 221210

LIMITLESS EARTH PLC
Suite 2 Northside House, Mount Pleasant, Barnet, EN4 9EB, Hertfordshire, United Kingdom
Tel.: (44) 2071170210
Web Site: https://www.limitlessearthplc.com
LME—(AIM)
Rev.: $37,450
Assets: $2,814,746
Liabilities: $127,217
Net Worth: $2,687,529
Earnings: ($68,555)
Fiscal Year-end: 01/31/21
Investment Services
N.A.I.C.S.: 523999
Nilesh Jagatia (CFO & CFO)

LIMOUSIN ADHESIFS
Parc Ocealim-16 Avenue Antoine de Saint Exupery, BP 39, 87270, Couzeix, France
Tel.: (33) 555300530
Web Site: http://www.lima.fr
Transformation Tape Mfr
N.A.I.C.S.: 424110
Bruno Daigueperse (Gen Mgr)

LIMURU TEA PLC
Kericho Highway, PO Box 1, 217, Limuru, Kenya
Tel.: (254) 722307394
Web Site: https://www.limuruteaplc.com
Year Founded: 1925
LIMT—(NAI)
Rev.: $879,697
Assets: $2,090,234
Liabilities: $354,127
Net Worth: $1,736,107
Earnings: ($33,352)
Emp.: 125
Fiscal Year-end: 12/31/20
Tea Mfr
N.A.I.C.S.: 311920
Gerridina Johanna Maria Ten Den (CEO)

LIN HORN TECHNOLOGY CO., LTD.
No 6 Zhongshan Road, Minxiong Industrial Zone, Chiayi, Taiwan
Tel.: (886) 522166968
Web Site: https://www.lhtech.com.tw
Year Founded: 1995
5464—(TPE)
Rev.: $43,141,669
Assets: $173,396,898
Liabilities: $128,629,835
Net Worth: $44,767,064
Earnings: $8,992,277
Fiscal Year-end: 12/31/22
Electronic Components Mfr
N.A.I.C.S.: 334419

LIN YUAN INVESTMENT CO., LTD.
No 296 Jen-Ai Road Sec 4, Taipei, 106, Taiwan
Tel.: (886) 227551399
Investment Holding Company
N.A.I.C.S.: 551112
Hong-Tu Tsai (Chm)

Subsidiaries:

Cathay Financial Holding Co., Ltd. (1)
No 296 Ren Ai Road Sec 4, Taipei, 106, Taiwan (15.52%)
Tel.: (886) 227087698
Web Site: http://www.cathayholdings.com.tw
Rev.: $9,616,891,349
Assets: $400,560,307,851
Liabilities: $375,501,818,904
Net Worth: $25,058,488,947
Earnings: $1,610,662,446
Emp.: 56,091
Fiscal Year-end: 12/31/2023
Financial Investment Services
N.A.I.C.S.: 523999
Hong-Tu Tsai (Chm)

Subsidiary (Domestic):

Cathay Century Insurance Co., Ltd. (2)
5th Fl 296 Jen Ai Rd Sec 4, 10639, Taipei, Taiwan (50%)
Tel.: (886) 227551299
Web Site: http://www.cathay-ins.com.tw
Sales Range: $200-249.9 Million
Emp.: 900
Motor, Fire, Marine, Engineering & Supplementary Insurance
N.A.I.C.S.: 524128
Wan-Hsing Chen (Sr Exec VP)

Cathay Life Insurance Co., Ltd. (2)
296 Jen-Ai Road Sec 4, Taipei, 106, Taiwan
Tel.: (886) 227551399
Web Site: http://www.cathaylife.com.tw
Sales Range: $15-24.9 Billion
Emp.: 31,379
Life & Other Insurance Services
N.A.I.C.S.: 524113

Subsidiary (US):

Conning & Company (3)
1 Financial Plz, Hartford, CT 06103-2627
Tel.: (860) 299-2000
Web Site: http://www.conning.com
Rev.: $80,600,000,000
Investment & Insurance Asset Management Services
N.A.I.C.S.: 524292
Richard L. Sega (Chief Investment Officer-North America)

Subsidiary (Non-US):

Conning Asset Management Limited (4)
24 Monument Street, London, EC3R 8AJ, United Kingdom
Tel.: (44) 2073371930
Web Site: http://www.conning.com
Asset Management Services
N.A.I.C.S.: 523150
Russell Busst (CEO & Chief Investment Officer)

Subsidiary (Domestic):

Conning, Inc. (4)
1 Financial Plz, Hartford, CT 06103-3408
Tel.: (860) 299-2000
Web Site: http://www.conning.com
Asset Management Services
N.A.I.C.S.: 523940
Michael Edward Haylon (Executives)

Octagon Credit Investors, LLC (4)
250 Park Ave 15th Fl, New York, NY 10177
Tel.: (212) 400-8400
Web Site: http://www.octagoncredit.com
Rev.: $14,500,000,000
Investment Management Service
N.A.I.C.S.: 523940
Andrew D. Gordon (CEO & Co-Chief Investment Officer)

Subsidiary (Domestic):

Cathay Securities Corporation Ltd. (2)
19F No 333 Sec 2 Dunhua S Rd Da'an Dist, Taipei, Taiwan
Tel.: (886) 2 2326 9888
Emp.: 359
Financial Support Services
N.A.I.C.S.: 523150
Chen-Hung Lin (Sr VP)

Cathay Securities Investment Trust Co., Ltd. (2)
18F No 296 Jen-Ai Rd Sec 4, Taipei, Taiwan
Tel.: (886) 2 27008399
Investment Management Service
N.A.I.C.S.: 523150
Mike Lee (Mgr-Fund)

Cathay United Bank (2)
218 Tun Hua South Rd Sec 2, Taipei, 106, Taiwan (100%)
Tel.: (886) 223776999
Web Site: http://www.cathay-bank.com.tw
Sales Range: $300-349.9 Million
Emp.: 1,000
Commericial Banking
N.A.I.C.S.: 522110
Sam Lin (CEO-Greater China)

Cathay United Bank Co., Ltd. (2)
No 7 Songren Road, Taipei, Taiwan
Tel.: (886) 2 8722 6666
Web Site: http://www.cathaybk.com.tw
Commercial Banking Services
N.A.I.C.S.: 522110

Subsidiary (Non-US):

Cathay United Bank (Cambodia) Corporation Limited (3)
No 68 Samdach Pan St St 214, Phnom Penh, Cambodia
Tel.: (855) 23 21 12 11
Web Site: http://www.sbc-bank.com
Commercial Banking Services
N.A.I.C.S.: 522110
Sreypoch Heng (Mgr-Compliance & Risk)

Cathay General Hospital (1)
280 Jen Ai Rd Section 4, Taipei, Taiwan
Tel.: (886) 227082121
Web Site: http://www.cgh.org.tw
Sales Range: $700-749.9 Million
Emp.: 2,000
Hospital Operator
N.A.I.C.S.: 622110
Kai-Mo Chen (Vice Chm)

LIN YUAN INVESTMENT CO., LTD.

Lin Yuan Investment Co., Ltd.—(Continued)

Cathay Real Estate Development Company Ltd. (1)
2F 218 Sec 2 Dun Hua South Road, Taipei, Taiwan
Tel.: (886) 223779968
Web Site: http://www.cathay-red.com.tw
Rev.: $506,227,850
Assets: $2,682,111,421
Liabilities: $1,749,106,846
Net Worth: $933,004,575
Earnings: $72,593,510
Emp.: 155
Fiscal Year-end: 12/31/2023
Real Estate Development & Construction Services
N.A.I.C.S.: 236220
Chin-Kuei Chang *(Chm)*

Subsidiary (Domestic):

San Ching Engineering Company Ltd. (2)
17th Fl 218 Tun Hua S Rd, Section 2, Taipei, Taiwan
Tel.: (886) 223779968
Sales Range: $25-49.9 Million
Emp.: 200
Contract Engineering
N.A.I.C.S.: 541330

LINAK A/S

Smedevanget 8 Guderup, 6430, Nordborg, Denmark
Tel.: (45) 73151515
Web Site: http://www.linak.com
Year Founded: 1907
Sales Range: $250-299.9 Million
Emp.: 2,200
Developer of Actuator Technology
N.A.I.C.S.: 333995
Bent Jensen *(Owner & CEO)*

Subsidiaries:

LINAK Actuators Sdn. Bhd. (1)
18-23-E Gurney Tower, Persiaran Gurney, Penang, 10250, Malaysia
Tel.: (60) 4 210 6500
Web Site: http://www.linak.my
Emp.: 4
Actuator Distr
N.A.I.C.S.: 423830
Jens Karing *(Mng Dir)*

LINAK Benelux (1)
Guldensporenpark 31, 9820, Merelbeke, Belgium
Tel.: (32) 92300109
Web Site: https://www.linak.be
Electric Linear Actuator Mfr & Distr
N.A.I.C.S.: 333995
Bram Van Meel *(Mgr Dir)*

LINAK Ith. Ihr. San. ve Tic. A.S. (1)
Birlik mah 455 Sk 20/1, Cankaya, Ankara, Turkiye
Tel.: (90) 312 4726338
Web Site: http://www.linak.com.tr
Actuator Distr
N.A.I.C.S.: 423830

LINAK Korea Ltd. (1)
1009 10F Daerung Post Tower 3-cha 27 Digital-ro 34-gil, Guro-gu, Seoul, 152-746, Korea (South)
Tel.: (82) 2 6231 1515
Web Site: http://www.linak.kr
Actuator Distr
N.A.I.C.S.: 423830

LINAK Polska (1)
Al Reunification 36, 01-830, Warsaw, Poland
Tel.: (48) 222950970
Web Site: https://www.linak.pl
Electric Linear Actuator Mfr & Distr
N.A.I.C.S.: 333995
Pawel Wolkiewicz *(Mgr)*

LINAK SLOVAKIA S.R.O. (1)
Logisticke centrum Maly Saris 486, 080 01, Presov, Slovakia
Tel.: (421) 517563 444
Actuator Mfr
N.A.I.C.S.: 333995

Linak (Shenzhen) Actuator Systems Ltd. (1)
Block B Shanghe Industrial Park Nanchang Road Xixiang Street, Baoan District, Shenzhen, 518126, China
Tel.: (86) 75586106656
Web Site: http://www.linak.com
Sales Range: $50-74.9 Million
Emp.: 80
Medical Dental & Hospital Equipment & Supply Merchant Distr
N.A.I.C.S.: 423450
Simon Jenkinson *(Mng Dir)*

Linak AG (1)
Bohnirainstrasse 9, 8800, Thalwil, Switzerland
Tel.: (41) 433883188
Web Site: http://www.linak.ch
Sales Range: $25-49.9 Million
Emp.: 5
Electrical Equipment & Component Mfr
N.A.I.C.S.: 335999
Bent Jenson *(Pres)*

Linak Actuadores S.L. (1)
Poligono Industrial Can Jardi, C-Compositor Strauss No 17 Nav, 08191, Rubi, Spain
Tel.: (34) 935882777
Web Site: http://www.linak.es
Sales Range: $25-49.9 Million
Emp.: 10
Business Support Services
N.A.I.C.S.: 561499
Soren Petersen *(Mng Dir)*

Linak Actuator-Systems B.V. (1)
Nikkelstraat 39, 4823AE, Breda, Netherlands
Tel.: (31) 765424440
Web Site: http://www.linak.nl
Sales Range: $25-49.9 Million
Emp.: 15
Durable Goods Whslr
N.A.I.C.S.: 423990
Saura Sylvia *(Office Mgr)*

Linak Actuator-Systems NV/SA (1)
Nijverheidsweg 1A, Merelbeke, 9820, Belgium
Tel.: (32) 92300109
Web Site: http://www.linak.be
Sales Range: $50-74.9 Million
Emp.: 7
Professional Equipment & Supplies Whslr
N.A.I.C.S.: 423490
Peter Godefroy *(Bus Mgr)*

Linak Australia Pty. Ltd. (1)
82-84 Abbott Road, Hallam, 3803, VIC, Australia
Tel.: (61) 387969777
Web Site: http://www.linak.com.au
Sales Range: $25-49.9 Million
Emp.: 25
Relay & Industrial Control Mfr
N.A.I.C.S.: 335314
Patrick Ramsden *(Mng Dir)*

Linak C&S S.r.o. (1)
Naves 37, 751 03, Majetin, Czech Republic
Tel.: (420) 581741814
Web Site: http://www.linak.cz
Sales Range: $50-74.9 Million
Emp.: 7
Medical Dental & Hospital Equipment & Supplies Whslr
N.A.I.C.S.: 423450
Richard Ponizil *(Mng Dir)*

Linak Canada Inc. (1)
81 The East Mall Ste 102, Suite 215, Toronto, M8Z 5W3, ON, Canada
Tel.: (502) 253-5595
Web Site: http://www.linak.ca
Sales Range: $25-49.9 Million
Emp.: 3
Relay & Industrial Control Mfr
N.A.I.C.S.: 335314

Linak Danmark A/S (1)
Monstedsvej 9, Silkeborg, 8600, Denmark
Tel.: (45) 86803611
Web Site: http://www.linak.dk
Sales Range: $25-49.9 Million
Emp.: 45
Electronic Parts & Equipment Whslr
N.A.I.C.S.: 423690
Peter Duch-Svenson *(Gen Mgr)*

Linak Do Brasil Comercio De Atuadores Ltda (1)
Rua Anhembi 90, 04728-010, Sao Paulo, SP, Brazil
Tel.: (55) 1128327070
Web Site: http://www.linak.com.br
Sales Range: $25-49.9 Million
Emp.: 6
Fluid Power Cylinder & Actuator Mfr
N.A.I.C.S.: 333995

Linak France Sarl (1)
13 Rue de la Claie, 49072, Beaucouze, Cedex, France
Tel.: (33) 241363434
Web Site: http://www.linak.fr
Sales Range: $25-49.9 Million
Emp.: 2,000
Industrial Machinery & Equipment Whslr
N.A.I.C.S.: 423830
Zerner Hansen *(Mng Dir)*

Linak GmbH (1)
An der Berufsschule 7, PO Box 1247, Nidda, Hessen, 63667, Germany
Tel.: (49) 604396550
Web Site: http://www.linak.de
Sales Range: $50-74.9 Million
Emp.: 60
Electrical Apparatus & Equipment Wiring Supplies & Construction Material Whslr
N.A.I.C.S.: 423610
Soren Rasmussen *(Gen Mgr)*

Linak Italia S.r.l. (1)
Via del Commercio 27, Buccinasco, 20090, Milan, Italy
Tel.: (39) 0248463366
Web Site: http://www.linak.it
Sales Range: $25-49.9 Million
Emp.: 15
Electrical Apparatus & Equipment Wiring Supplies & Construction Material Whslr
N.A.I.C.S.: 423610
Giorgio Bighiani *(Mng Dir)*

Linak K.K. (1)
2-5-1 Kita-Shinyokohama, Kohoku-ku, Yokohama, 223-0059, Kanagawa, Japan
Tel.: (81) 455330802
Web Site: http://www.linak.jp
Sales Range: $50-74.9 Million
Emp.: 14
Durable Goods Whslr
N.A.I.C.S.: 423990
Yoshitsugu Sato *(Mng Dir)*

Linak New Zealand Ltd. (1)
Unit G 61 Hugo Johnston Drive, Penrose, 1061, Auckland, New Zealand
Tel.: (64) 95802071
Web Site: http://www.linak.co.nz
Business Support Services
N.A.I.C.S.: 561499

Linak Norge AS (1)
Stoperigata 7 c, 3040, Drammen, Norway
Tel.: (47) 32829090
Web Site: http://www.linak.no
Sales Range: $25-49.9 Million
Emp.: 5
Store Retailers
N.A.I.C.S.: 459999
Tom B. Larsen *(CEO)*

Linak Oy (1)
Perintotie 2D, 01501, Vantaa, Finland
Tel.: (358) 108418700
Web Site: http://www.linak.fi
Sales Range: $50-74.9 Million
Emp.: 2
Electronic Part & Equipment Distr
N.A.I.C.S.: 423690
Jarno Viitanen *(Mng Dir)*

Linak Scandinavia AB (1)
Kanalvagen 10A, PO Box 7302, 19461, Taby, Sweden
Tel.: (46) 87322000
Web Site: http://www.linak.se
Sales Range: $25-49.9 Million
Emp.: 20
Commercial Equipment Whslr
N.A.I.C.S.: 423440
Anders Morin *(Pres)*

Linak UK Limited (1)
Actuation House Crystal Drive, Sandwell Business Park, Smethwick, B66 1RJ, West Midlands, United Kingdom

INTERNATIONAL PUBLIC

Tel.: (44) 1215442211
Web Site: http://www.linak.co.uk
Emp.: 2,000
Medical Dental & Hospital Equipment & Supplies Whslr
N.A.I.C.S.: 423450
Bent Jensen *(Owner & CEO)*

Linak US Inc. (1)
2200 Stanley Gault Pkwy, Louisville, KY 40223
Tel.: (502) 253-5595
Web Site: http://www.linak-us.com
Rev.: $11,700,000
Emp.: 100
Developer of Actuator Technology
N.A.I.C.S.: 423690
Soren Stig-Nielsen *(Pres)*

OOO LINAK (1)
FKV Centre Bolshaya Maryinskaya 9 Stroenie 1 Office 306, Moscow, 129085, Russia
Tel.: (7) 495 280 14 26
Web Site: http://www.linak.ru
Emp.: 3
Actuator Distr
N.A.I.C.S.: 423830
Ivan Lyapin *(Gen Mgr)*

LINAKS MICROELECTRONICS LTD.

12 6 Km Barabanki Road, Chinhat, Lucknow, 227105, Uttar Pradesh, India
Tel.: (91) 915226549493
Web Site: http://www.linaks.com
Year Founded: 1986
517463—(BOM)
Rev.: $36,350
Assets: $480,248
Liabilities: $3,280,545
Net Worth: ($2,800,298)
Earnings: ($112,408)
Fiscal Year-end: 03/31/22
Electronic Components Mfr
N.A.I.C.S.: 334419
Anil Kumar Singh *(Mng Dir)*

LINAMAR CORPORATION

287 Speedvale Avenue West, Guelph, N1H 1C5, ON, Canada
Tel.: (519) 836-7550 Ca
Web Site: https://www.linamar.com
Year Founded: 1966
LNR—(OTCIQ)
Rev.: $5,675,497,350
Assets: $5,799,606,269
Liabilities: $2,715,876,552
Net Worth: $3,083,729,716
Earnings: $329,390,671
Emp.: 27,000
Fiscal Year-end: 12/31/19
Automobile Parts Mfr
N.A.I.C.S.: 336390
Frank Hasenfratz *(Chm)*

Subsidiaries:

Eagle Manufacturing LLC (1)
7100 Industrial Rd, Florence, KY 41042-2908
Tel.: (859) 282-5900
Emp.: 250
Industrial Machinery Mfr
N.A.I.C.S.: 333248
William Balkovec *(Acct Mgr)*

Invar Manufacturing, Ltd. (1)
1 Parry Drive, Batawa, K0K1E0, Trenton, ON, Canada
Tel.: (613) 398-6106
Web Site: http://www.invar.com
Sales Range: $50-74.9 Million
Emp.: 120
Motor Vehicle Parts Mfr
N.A.I.C.S.: 336390

LPP Manufacturing Inc. (1)
347 Silvercreek Parkway North, Guelph, N1H 1E6, ON, Canada
Tel.: (519) 837-3055
Sales Range: $50-74.9 Million
Emp.: 150
Automotive Parts & Accessories Stores
N.A.I.C.S.: 441330

LINAMAR CORPORATION

Linamar Antriebstechnik GmbH (1)
Gewerbering 12, 8451, Crimmitschau, Germany
Tel.: (49) 3762 7045 0
Web Site: http://www.linamar.de
Sales Range: $100-124.9 Million
Emp.: 413
Engine Camshaft Machinery Mfr
N.A.I.C.S.: 336310

Linamar Automotive Systems (WUXI) Co., Ltd
No 106 Meiyu Rd Wuxi National Hi-Tech Industrial Development Zone, Wuxi, 214028, Jiangsu, China
Tel.: (86) 51088154686
Web Site: http://www.linamar.com
Sales Range: $200-249.9 Million
Emp.: 700
Motor Vehicle Parts Mfr
N.A.I.C.S.: 336390

Linamar Consumer Products Ltd. (1)
201 Woodlawn Road, Guelph, N1H 1B8, ON, Canada
Tel.: (519) 515-1000
Web Site: http://www.linamarconsumerproducts.com
Sales Range: $25-49.9 Million
Emp.: 7
Precision Metallic Component Mfr
N.A.I.C.S.: 332999

Linamar Corporation - Linamar Customs Facility (1)
700 woodlawn, Guelph, N1K 1G4, ON, Canada
Tel.: (519) 837-2580
Web Site: http://www.linamar.com
Emp.: 5
Precision Metallic Component Mfr
N.A.I.C.S.: 332999

Linamar Corporation - Linamar Gear Facility (1)
32 Independence Place, Guelph, N1K 1H8, ON, Canada
Tel.: (519) 827-9423
Web Site: http://www.linamar.com
Sales Range: $200-249.9 Million
Emp.: 612
Industrial Gear Machinery Mfr
N.A.I.C.S.: 333612

Linamar Driveline Systems Group (1)
32233 west 8th mile road, Livonia, MI 48152
Tel.: (248) 355-3533
Precision Metallic Component Mfr
N.A.I.C.S.: 332999

Plant (Non-US):

Linamar Driveline Systems Group - Corvex Mfg Facility (2)
12 Independence Place, Guelph, N1K 1H8, ON, Canada
Tel.: (519) 763-7786
Web Site: http://www.linamar.com
Sales Range: $25-49.9 Million
Emp.: 15
Automotive Transmission Equipment Mfr
N.A.I.C.S.: 336350

Linamar Driveline Systems Group - Linamar Gear Facility (2)
32 Independence Pl, Guelph, N1K 1H8, ON, Canada
Tel.: (519) 827-9423
Web Site: http://www.linamar.com
Sales Range: $75-99.9 Million
Emp.: 40
Automotive Gear System Mfr
N.A.I.C.S.: 336350

Linamar GmbH (1)
An der Hauptwache 7 60313, Frankfurt am Main, 8451, Germany
Tel.: (49) 69 65 606 97 102
Sales Range: $100-124.9 Million
Emp.: 6
Industrial Machinery Mfr
N.A.I.C.S.: 333248
Piet Strauss (Grp VP)

Linamar Hungary ZRT (1)
Csorvasi ut 27, 5900, Oroshaza, Hungary
Tel.: (36) 68514623
Web Site: http://www.linamar.hu
Agricultural Machinery Mfr
N.A.I.C.S.: 333111

Linamar Industrial, Commercial & Energy Manufacturing Group (1)
Travelers Twr 1 26555 Evergreen Rd Ste 900, Southfield, MI 48076
Tel.: (248) 355-3533
Industrial Machinery Mfr
N.A.I.C.S.: 333248

Plant (Non-US):

Linamar Industrial, Commercial & Energy Manufacturing Group - Camtac Mfg Facility (2)
148 Arrow Road, Guelph, N1K 1T4, ON, Canada
Tel.: (519) 780-2270
Web Site: http://www.linamar.com
Emp.: 40
Industrial Machinery Mfr
N.A.I.C.S.: 333248

Linamar Industrial, Commercial & Energy Manufacturing Group - Famer Rivoire Facility (2)
5 Rue Barrouin, BP50104, 42003, Saint Etienne, France
Tel.: (33) 477494501
Web Site: http://www.linamar.com
Sales Range: $25-49.9 Million
Emp.: 120
Industrial Machinery Mfr
N.A.I.C.S.: 333248

Linamar Industrial, Commercial & Energy Manufacturing Group - Famer Transmission Facility (2)
Avenue des Cevennes Suite 4290, 43290, Montfaucon-en-Velay, France
Tel.: (33) 4 71 65 65 65
Sales Range: $25-49.9 Million
Emp.: 10
Industrial Machinery Mfr
N.A.I.C.S.: 333248
Bernhard Lanzendorfer (Plant Mgr)

Linamar Industrial, Commercial & Energy Manufacturing Group - Linamar Fluid Products Facility (2)
87 Campbell Rd, Guelph, N1H 1B9, ON, Canada
Tel.: (519) 341-5996
Web Site: http://www.linamar.com
Fluid Machinery Mfr
N.A.I.C.S.: 334514

Linamar Industrial, Commercial & Energy Manufacturing Group - Linergy Manufacturing Facility (2)
87 Campbell Road, Guelph, N1H 1B9, ON, Canada
Tel.: (519) 341-5996
Web Site: http://www.linamar.com
Precision Metallic Component Mfr
N.A.I.C.S.: 332999

Linamar Industrial, Commercial & Energy Manufacturing Group - Linex Manufacturing Facility (2)
355 Massey Road, Guelph, N1K 1B2, ON, Canada
Tel.: (519) 837-0880
Precision Metallic Component Mfr
N.A.I.C.S.: 332999
Tim Feil (Gen Mgr)

Linamar Industrial, Commercial & Energy Manufacturing Group - Traxle Mfg Facility (2)
280 Speedvale Ave W, Guelph, N1H 1C4, ON, Canada
Tel.: (519) 824-8899
Web Site: http://www.linamar.com
Industrial Machinery Mfr
N.A.I.C.S.: 333248

Linamar Japan, Inc. (1)
Ranzan Ay Bldg 302 4-3-30, Shinjuku-ku, Tokyo, 160-0022, Japan
Tel.: (81) 3 3355 8825
Web Site: http://www.linamar.com
Emp.: 4
Automobile Parts Distr
N.A.I.C.S.: 423110

Linamar Manufacturing Group (1)
41 Minto Road 545 Elmira Road North, Guelph, N1K 1C2, ON, Canada
Tel.: (226) 326-0115
Industrial Equipment Whsr
N.A.I.C.S.: 423830

Subsidiary (Non-US):

Industrias de Linamar S.A. de C.V. (2)
Boulevard Mexico Km 4 Parque Industrial, Gomez Palacio, 35078, Durango, Mexico
Tel.: (52) 871 749 2700
Plastic Blow Molding Mfr
N.A.I.C.S.: 326199

Plant (Domestic):

Linamar Manufacturing Group - Ariss Manufacturing Group (2)
R R 1 Silvercreek Parkway Ext, Guelph, N0B 1B0, ON, Canada
Tel.: (519) 822-4080
Web Site: http://www.linamar.com
Precision Metallic Component Mfr
N.A.I.C.S.: 332999

Linamar Manufacturing Group - Autocom Manufacturing Facility (2)
375 Massey Road, Guelph, N1K 1B2, ON, Canada
Tel.: (519) 822-9008
Web Site: http://www.linamar.com
Automobile Parts Mfr
N.A.I.C.S.: 336390

Linamar Manufacturing Group - Camcor Mfg Facility (2)
150 Arrow Road, Guelph, N1K 1T4, ON, Canada
Tel.: (519) 837-0100
Web Site: http://www.linamar.com
Precision Metallic Component Mfr
N.A.I.C.S.: 332999

Linamar Manufacturing Group - Cemtol Mfg Facility (2)
41 Minto Road, Guelph, N1K 1H5, ON, Canada
Tel.: (519) 822-6627
Web Site: http://www.linamar.com
Precision Metallic Component Mfr
N.A.I.C.S.: 332999

Linamar Manufacturing Group - Comtech Mfg Facility (2)
355 Silvercreek Parkway North, Guelph, N1B 1E6, ON, Canada
Tel.: (519) 821-7576
Web Site: http://www.linamar.com
Sales Range: $75-99.9 Million
Emp.: 400
Industrial Machinery Mfr
N.A.I.C.S.: 333248

Plant (Non-US):

Linamar Manufacturing Group - Engicom Facility (2)
Industria Metalurgica 1004 Parque Industrial Ramos Arizpe, 25900, Ramos Arizpe, Coahuila, Mexico
Tel.: (52) 8442882000
Web Site: http://www.linamar.com
Emp.: 800
Industrial Machinery Mfr
N.A.I.C.S.: 333248

Plant (Domestic):

Linamar Manufacturing Group - Eston Manufacturing Facility (2)
277 Silvercreek Parkway North, Guelph, N1H 1E6, ON, Canada
Tel.: (519) 763-0063
Web Site: http://www.linamar.com
Emp.: 20
Industrial Machinery Mfr
N.A.I.C.S.: 333248

Linamar Manufacturing Group - Exkor Manufacturing Facility (2)
3590 Valtec Court, Windsor, N8N 5E6, ON, Canada
Tel.: (519) 739-3465
Web Site: http://www.linamar.com
Emp.: 75
Precision Metallic Component Mfr
N.A.I.C.S.: 332999

Linamar Manufacturing Group - Hastech Mfg Facility (2)
301 Massey Road, Guelph, N1K 1B2, ON, Canada
Tel.: (519) 836-7554
Sales Range: $75-99.9 Million
Emp.: 500
Precision Metallic Component Mfr
N.A.I.C.S.: 332999

Division (Non-US):

Linamar Manufacturing Group - Linamar Products Division (2)
Csorvasi Ut 27, 5900, Oroshaza, Hungary
Tel.: (36) 68 514 601
Industrial Machinery Mfr
N.A.I.C.S.: 333248

Linamar Manufacturing Group - OROS Division (2)
Csorvasi ut 27, Oroshaza, 5900, Hungary
Tel.: (36) 68 514 603
Precision Metallic Component Mfr
N.A.I.C.S.: 332999

Plant (Domestic):

Linamar Manufacturing Group - PowerCor Facility (2)
545 Elmira Road North, Guelph, N1K 1C2, ON, Canada
Tel.: (226) 326-0125
Web Site: http://www.linamar.com
Emp.: 200
Automotive Components Mfr
N.A.I.C.S.: 336390

Linamar Manufacturing Group - Quadrad Manufacturing Facility (2)
30 Malcom Road, Guelph, N1K 1A9, ON, Canada
Tel.: (519) 767-0219
Web Site: http://www.linamar.com
Cutting Tool Mfr
N.A.I.C.S.: 333515

Linamar Manufacturing Group - Roctel Manufacturing Facility (2)
415 Elmira Road, Guelph, N1K 1H3, ON, Canada
Tel.: (519) 763-5369
Web Site: http://www.linamar.com
Precision Metallic Component Mfr
N.A.I.C.S.: 332999

Linamar Manufacturing Group - Spinic Manufacturing Facility (2)
285 Massey Road, Guelph, N1K 1B2, ON, Canada
Tel.: (519) 763-0704
Web Site: http://www.linamar.com
Sales Range: $75-99.9 Million
Emp.: 30
Precision Metallic Component Mfr
N.A.I.C.S.: 332999

Linamar Manufacturing Group - Transgear Manufacturing Facility (2)
400 Massey Road, Guelph, N1K 1C4, ON, Canada
Tel.: (519) 763-5370
Web Site: http://www.linamar.com
Industrial Machinery Mfr
N.A.I.C.S.: 333248

Linamar Manufacturing Group - Vehcom Manufacturing Facility (2)
74 Campbell Road, Guelph, N1H 1C1, ON, Canada
Tel.: (519) 821-1650
Sales Range: $75-99.9 Million
Emp.: 500
Precision Metallic Component Mfr
N.A.I.C.S.: 332999
Thomas Horvat (Gen Mgr)

Subsidiary (Non-US):

Linamar de Mexico S.A. de C.V. (2)
3070 Prol Parque Industrial Saltillo, 25900, Ramos Arizpe, Coahuila, Mexico
Tel.: (52) 844 411 0600
Web Site: http://www.linamar.com
Emp.: 500
Motor Vehicle Parts & Accessories Mfr
N.A.I.C.S.: 336390

Linamar North Carolina, Inc. (1)
2169 Hendersonville Rd, Arden, NC 28704

LINAMAR CORPORATION

Linamar Corporation—(Continued)
Tel.: (828) 348-5343
Precision Metallic Component Mfr
N.A.I.C.S.: 332999

Linamar Transportation Inc. (1)
381 Massey Rd-700 Woodlawn Morre W,
Guelph, N1K 1g4, ON, Canada
Tel.: (519) 837-2056
Web Site: http://www.linamartransport.com
Emp.: 40
Logistics Consulting Servies
N.A.I.C.S.: 541614

Linamar U.S.A., Inc. (1)
9401 Harrison Rd, Romulus, MI 48174
Tel.: (734) 946-0610
Vending Machine Operators
N.A.I.C.S.: 445132

Linex Manufacturing, Inc. (1)
355 Massey Road, Guelph, N1K 1B2, ON,
Canada (100%)
Tel.: (519) 837-0880
Web Site: http://www.linamar.com
Sales Range: $100-124.9 Million
Emp.: 500
Automotive Parts & Accessories Stores
N.A.I.C.S.: 441330
Tim Feil *(Gen Mgr)*

MacDon Industries Ltd (1)
680 Moray Street, Winnipeg, R3J 3S3, MB,
Canada
Tel.: (204) 885-5590
Web Site: https://www.macdon.com
Agricultural Equipment Mfr
N.A.I.C.S.: 333111

MacDon, Inc. (1)
10708 N Pomona Ave, Kansas City, MO
64153-1924
Tel.: (816) 891-7313
Harvesting Equipment Mfr & Distr
N.A.I.C.S.: 333111

**McLaren Performance Technologies
Inc.** (1)
32233 W 8 Mile Rd, Livonia, MI 48152
Tel.: (248) 477-6240
Web Site:
http://www.mclarenperformance.com
Sales Range: $25-49.9 Million
Emp.: 100
Engineeering Services
N.A.I.C.S.: 541330

Montupet S.A. (1)
202 quai de Clichy, BP 77, 92110, Clichy,
Cedex, France
Tel.: (33) 1 4756 4756
Web Site: http://www.montupet.fr
Rev.: $530,098,656
Assets: $500,138,542
Liabilities: $228,306,536
Net Worth: $271,832,006
Earnings: $54,935,757
Emp.: 3,289
Fiscal Year-end: 12/31/2014
Automobile Parts Mfr
N.A.I.C.S.: 336390
M. Stephane Magnan *(Chm)*

Subsidiary (Non-US):

Alumalsa S.A. (2)
Ctra Castellon Km 6 4, 50720, Zaragoza,
Spain
Tel.: (34) 976 50 09 60
Web Site: http://www.alumalsa.com
Aluminum Parts Mfr
N.A.I.C.S.: 331318

OROS Division (1)
Csorvasi ut 27, H-5900, Oroshaza,
Hungary (100%)
Tel.: (36) 68514602
Web Site: http://www.linamar.hu
Sales Range: $400-449.9 Million
Emp.: 1,701
Mfr & Distr of Agricultural Harvesting Equipment, Components for Automotive Industry
& Machine Parts
N.A.I.C.S.: 333111

Quadrad Manufacturing Ltd. (1)
30 Malcolm Road, Guelph, N1K 1A9, ON,
Canada
Tel.: (519) 767-0219
Web Site: http://www.linamar.com

Sales Range: $50-74.9 Million
Emp.: 400
Electronic Components Mfr
N.A.I.C.S.: 334419

Roctel Manufacturing, Ltd. (1)
415 Elmira Road, Guelph, N1K 1H3, ON,
Canada
Tel.: (519) 763-5369
Web Site: http://www.linamar.com
Sales Range: $50-74.9 Million
Emp.: 200
Automotive Parts & Accessories Stores
N.A.I.C.S.: 441330

Seissenschmidt AG (1)
Daimlerstrasse 11, D-58840, Plettenberg,
Germany
Tel.: (49) 2391 915 0
Web Site: http://www.seissenschmidt.com
Sales Range: $300-349.9 Million
Emp.: 900
Motor Vehicle Parts Mfr
N.A.I.C.S.: 336390
Rudiger Groos *(Mng Dir)*

Subsidiary (Domestic):

**SEISSENSCHMIDT Heat Treatment
GmbH + Co. KG** (2)
Elberfelder Strasse 22, 58553, Halver, Germany
Tel.: (49) 235391590
Mechanical Component Mfr
N.A.I.C.S.: 334419
Hans-Otto Weber *(Mng Dir)*

Subsidiary (Non-US):

SEISSENSCHMIDT Precision Components Kft. (2)
Karacsondi ut 57, 3200, Gyongyos, Hungary
Tel.: (36) 37568402
Mechanical Component Mfr
N.A.I.C.S.: 334419
Marta Kuruc *(Plant Mgr)*

Subsidiary (US):

Seissenschmidt Corp. (2)
6121 Perimeter Rd, Oscoda, MI 48750-8750
Tel.: (989) 739-7300
Web Site: http://www.seissenschmidt.com
Motor Vehicle Parts Mfr
N.A.I.C.S.: 336390
Arnold Wespe *(Mng Partner)*

Skyjack, Inc. (1)
55 Campbell Road, Guelph, N1H 1B9, ON,
Canada (100%)
Tel.: (519) 837-0888
Web Site: https://www.skyjack.com
Sales Range: $200-249.9 Million
Emp.: 1,000
Mfr of Scissor Lift Machinery
N.A.I.C.S.: 333248

Subsidiary (Non-US):

Skyjack AB (2)
Marieholmsgatan 2, 415 02, Gothenburg,
Sweden
Tel.: (46) 31212245
Web Site: http://www.skyjack.com
Sales Range: $25-49.9 Million
Emp.: 5
Industrial Machinery Mfr
N.A.I.C.S.: 333248

Subsidiary (US):

Skyjack Equipment Services Inc. (2)
3451 Swenson Ave, Saint Charles, IL
60174
Tel.: (800) 965-4626
Construction Machinery Mfr
N.A.I.C.S.: 333120

Subsidiary (Non-US):

Skyjack Hebebuhnen GmbH (2)
Wullener Feld 27, Witten, 58454, Germany
Tel.: (49) 2302 202 6909
Web Site: http://www.linamar.com
Sales Range: $25-49.9 Million
Emp.: 5
Industrial Machinery Distr
N.A.I.C.S.: 423830

Skyjack Hungary Inc (2)
Csorvasi ut 27, 5900, Oroshaza, Hungary
Tel.: (36) 684 112 03
Web Site: http://www.linamar.com
Sales Range: $200-249.9 Million
Emp.: 1,000
Industrial Machinery Distr
N.A.I.C.S.: 423830

Skyjack SAS (2)
Lieudit Les Pretes 22 Bis Rue De I Avenir,
Chanas, France
Tel.: (33) 6 73 38 15 69
Web Site: http://www.skyjackparts.co.uk
Scissor Lift Mfr
N.A.I.C.S.: 333924

Skyjack UK Limited (2)
Unit 1 Maes-Y-Clawdd Maesbury Road Industrial Estate, Oswestry, SY10 8NN,
Shropshire, United Kingdom
Tel.: (44) 1691 676 235
Web Site: http://www.skyjack.com
Emp.: 30
Industrial Lift Mfr
N.A.I.C.S.: 333924

**Spinic Manufacturing Company,
Ltd.** (1)
285 Massey Road, Guelph, N1K 1B2, ON,
Canada (100%)
Tel.: (519) 763-0704
Web Site: http://www.linamar.com
Sales Range: $100-124.9 Million
Emp.: 300
Motor Vehicle Metal Stamping
N.A.I.C.S.: 336370

Traxle Mfg. Ltd. (1)
280 Speedvale Avenue West, Guelph, N1H
1C4, ON, Canada (100%)
Tel.: (519) 824-8899
Sales Range: $1-4.9 Billion
Emp.: 200
Industrial Machinery Mfr
N.A.I.C.S.: 333248
John Graham *(Gen Mgr)*

Vehcom Manufacturing Ltd. (1)
74 Campbell Road, Guelph, N1H 1C1, ON,
Canada (100%)
Tel.: (519) 821-1650
Web Site: http://www.linamar.com
Sales Range: $100-124.9 Million
Emp.: 400
Automotive Parts & Accessories Stores
N.A.I.C.S.: 441330

LINAS AB

S Kerbedzio Str 23, 35113, Panevezys, Lithuania
Tel.: (370) 45506100
Web Site: https://linas.lt
LNS1L—(RSE)
Rev.: $17,203,633
Assets: $14,330,868
Liabilities: $5,993,914
Net Worth: $8,336,954
Earnings: $632,023
Emp.: 113
Fiscal Year-end: 12/31/20
Textile Product Mf & Distr
N.A.I.C.S.: 313310
Egidijus Mikeliunas *(Chm-Mgmt Bd,
CFO & Head-Fin)*

LINAS AGRO GROUP AB

Smelynes St 2C, LT-35143, Panevezys, Lithuania
Tel.: (370) 45507303
Web Site: https://www.linasagro.lt
Year Founded: 1991
LNA1L—(VSE)
Rev.: $2,158,015,325
Assets: $965,166,199
Liabilities: $642,879,344
Net Worth: $322,286,855
Earnings: $22,466,005
Emp.: 4,739
Fiscal Year-end: 06/30/23
Holding Company; Agricultural Services
N.A.I.C.S.: 551112

INTERNATIONAL PUBLIC

LINC AB

Vasagatan 28, 111 20, Stockholm,
Sweden
Tel.: (46) 709358574
Web Site: https://www.linc.se
Year Founded: 1991
LINC—(OMX)
Rev.: $362,340
Assets: $350,623,430
Liabilities: $288,880
Net Worth: $350,334,550
Earnings: $61,494,630
Emp.: 2
Fiscal Year-end: 12/31/23
Investment Management Service
N.A.I.C.S.: 523999
Bengt Julander *(Chm)*

LINC LIMITED

Aurora Waterfront 18th Floor GN 34/1
GN Block Sector V Bidhannagar, Kolkata, 700091, India
Tel.: (91) 3368262100
Web Site: https://linclimited.com
531241—(BOM)
Rev.: $48,844,518
Assets: $27,520,693
Liabilities: $8,021,081
Net Worth: $19,499,612
Earnings: $1,110,168
Emp.: 881
Fiscal Year-end: 03/31/22
Pen & Mechanical Pencil Mfrs
N.A.I.C.S.: 322230
Aloke Jalan *(Exec Dir)*

LINCLUDEN MANAGEMENT LIMITED

201 City Centre Drive Suite 201, Mississauga, L5B 2T4, ON, Canada
Tel.: (905) 273-4240
Web Site: http://www.lincluden.com
Year Founded: 1982
Rev.: $2,793,728,000
Emp.: 20
Investment Management Service
N.A.I.C.S.: 523940
Philip Evans *(Pres & CEO)*

LINCOLN GOLD MINING INC.

Suite 400 - 789 West Pender Street,
Vancouver, V6C 1H2, BC, Canada
Tel.: (604) 688-7377
Web Site:
https://www.lincolnmining.com
LMG—(OTCIQ)
Rev.: $63
Assets: $529,032
Liabilities: $1,758,622
Net Worth: ($1,229,589)
Earnings: ($580,536)
Fiscal Year-end: 12/31/20
Mineral Exploration Services
N.A.I.C.S.: 213114
Paul Frederick Saxton *(Pres & CEO)*

Subsidiaries:

**Lincoln Resource Group
Corporation** (1)
912 N Division St, Carson City, NV 89703
Tel.: (775) 721-5435
Gold Ore Mining Services
N.A.I.C.S.: 212220

LINCOLN HEIGHTS FORD SALES

1377 Richmond Road, Ottawa, K2B
6R7, ON, Canada
Tel.: (613) 829-2120
Web Site:
http://www.lincolnheights.com
Year Founded: 1981
New & Used Car Dealers
N.A.I.C.S.: 441110
Brian Hoyt *(Sls Mgr)*

LINCOLN MINERALS LIMITED

AND PRIVATE COMPANIES

Suite 1 Level 1 852-858 Glenferrie Road, Hawthorn, 3122, VIC, Australia
Tel.: (61) 3 9191 3122
Web Site:
http://www.lincolnminerals.com.au
Rev.: $34,816
Assets: $6,327,118
Liabilities: $80,493
Net Worth: $6,246,624
Earnings: ($628,716)
Emp.: 12
Fiscal Year-end: 06/30/19
Iron Ore, Nickel-Cobalt, Uranium, Lead-Zinc-Copper-Silver Producer
N.A.I.C.S.: 212230
Jaroslaw K. Kopias *(Sec)*

LINCOLN PHARMACEUTICALS LTD.

Lincoln House B/h Satyam Complex Science City Road Sola, Ahmedabad, 380 062, Gujarat, India
Tel.: (91) 7941078000
Web Site:
https://www.lincolnpharma.com
531633—(BOM)
Rev.: $72,726,149
Assets: $80,160,335
Liabilities: $11,572,552
Net Worth: $68,587,783
Earnings: $9,950,754
Emp.: 1,700
Fiscal Year-end: 03/31/23
Pharmaceuticals Product Mfr
N.A.I.C.S.: 325412
Kishorbhai Meghji Shah *(Chm)*

LINCOLN VENTURES LTD.

650-669 Howe St, Vancouver, V6C 0B4, BC, Canada
Tel.: (778) 725-1487 BC
Year Founded: 2002
LX.H—(TSXV)
Assets: $104,722
Liabilities: $188,783
Net Worth: ($84,061)
Earnings: ($118,504)
Fiscal Year-end: 12/31/23
Investment Services
N.A.I.C.S.: 523999
John Graham Proust *(Pres)*

LINCOTRADE & ASSOCIATES HOLDINGS LIMITED

2 Bukit Merah Central 12-03, Singapore, 159835, Singapore
Tel.: (65) 62655918
Web Site:
https://www.lincotrade.com.sg
Sales Range: $25-49.9 Million
Boosters Mfr
N.A.I.C.S.: 332993
Rui Chen *(Sr Mgr-Safety, Tech & Integration)*

Subsidiaries:

Shandong Yinguang Technology Co., Ltd. (1)
No 1 Huagong Road, Feixian County, Linyi, Shandong, China
Tel.: (86) 5395039767
Web Site: http://www.sdyg.cc
Explosives Mfr
N.A.I.C.S.: 325920

LINDA NEKTAR AS

Kobela Antsla vald 66407, Voru, Estonia
Tel.: (372) 7855768
Web Site: http://www.lindanektar.ee
LINDA—(TAL)
Rev.: $2,748,415
Assets: $4,152,939
Liabilities: $311,826
Net Worth: $3,841,113
Earnings: ($144,232)
Emp.: 15
Fiscal Year-end: 12/31/23
Beer, Wine & Liquor Retailers
N.A.I.C.S.: 445320
Kadri Rauba *(CEO)*

LINDAB INTERNATIONAL AB

Stalhogavagen 115, SE-269 92, Bastad, Sweden
Tel.: (46) 43185000
Web Site:
https://www.lindabgroup.com
LIAB—(OMX)
Rev.: $1,158,223,046
Assets: $1,213,577,229
Liabilities: $581,265,747
Net Worth: $632,311,482
Earnings: $91,226,690
Emp.: 4,853
Fiscal Year-end: 12/31/22
Steel Products Mfr & Distr
N.A.I.C.S.: 423510
Olof Christensson *(Dir-Div Ventilation Sys)*

Subsidiaries:

Aer Faber AS (1)
Naeringsveien 13, 1820, Spydeberg, Norway
Tel.: (47) 69899080
Web Site: https://www.aerfaber.no
Sheet Metal Contracting Services
N.A.I.C.S.: 238160

Alig Ventilation AB (1)
Hammarsmedsgatan 15, 542 35, Mariestad, Sweden
Tel.: (46) 501278760
Web Site: https://alig.se
Ventilation System Distr
N.A.I.C.S.: 423730

Astron Buildings LLC (1)
Pozharskogo Str 73, 150066, Yaroslavl, Russia
Tel.: (7) 4852581600
Fabricated Metal & Hardware Mfr
N.A.I.C.S.: 332510

Astron Buildings S.A. (1)
Parc d Activite - 218 avenue des Pre Seigneurs, 01120, Montluel, France
Tel.: (33) 676891863
Web Site: http://www.astron.biz
Sales Range: $25-49.9 Million
Prefabricated Steel Building Mfr
N.A.I.C.S.: 332311

Subsidiary (Non-US):

Lindab-Astron GmbH (2)
Wilh-Theodor-Romheld-Str 32, 55130, Mainz, Germany
Tel.: (49) 61 31 83 09 00
Sheet Metal Roofing Installation Services
N.A.I.C.S.: 238160

Subsidiary (Domestic):

Lindab-Astron S.A.S. (2)
Parc d Activite - 218 avenue des Pre Seigneurs, 01120, Montluel, France
Tel.: (33) 676891863
Web Site: http://www.lindab.com
Sales Range: $25-49.9 Million
Sheet Metal Roofing Installation Services
N.A.I.C.S.: 238160

Subsidiary (Non-US):

Lindab-Astron Sp. z o.o. (2)
Ul Kolejowa 311 Sadowa, Lomianki, 05-092, Poland
Tel.: (48) 22 4898891
Construction Steel Materials Mfr
N.A.I.C.S.: 331210

Lindab-Astron s.r.o. (2)
Kojetinska 3228, 750 02, Prerov, Czech Republic
Tel.: (420) 581250222
Web Site: http://www.astron.biz
Sales Range: $50-74.9 Million
Structured Steel Building Construction Services
N.A.I.C.S.: 236210

Astron Buildings Sp. z o.o. (1)

Fiscal Year-end: 12/31/23
Beer, Wine & Liquor Retailers
N.A.I.C.S.: 445320
Kadri Rauba *(CEO)*

LINDAB INTERNATIONAL AB

Zeromskiego 77, 01-882, Warsaw, Poland
Tel.: (48) 224898891
Fabricated Metal & Hardware Mfr
N.A.I.C.S.: 332510

Astron Buildings s.r.o. (1)
Kojetinska 3228, 750 02, Prerov, Czech Republic
Tel.: (420) 581250222
Fabricated Metal & Hardware Mfr
N.A.I.C.S.: 332510

Benone AG (1)
Wildensteinerstrasse 21, Muttenz, 4132, Switzerland
Tel.: (41) 614679222
Air Conditioning Equipment Mfr
N.A.I.C.S.: 333415

Crenna Plat AB (1)
Kvartsgatan 19, 749 40, Enkoping, Sweden
Tel.: (46) 171478050
Web Site: https://www.crenna.se
Ventilation Product Mfr & Distr
N.A.I.C.S.: 333415

Disys Technologies Ltd. (1)
Units 24-25 Cross Hands Business Centre Heol Parc Mawr Cross Hands, Llanelli, SA14 6RE, United Kingdom
Tel.: (44) 1269842496
Web Site:
https://www.disystechnologies.com
Fire & Smoke Control System Mfr
N.A.I.C.S.: 334512

Ductmann Ltd. (1)
Broad Lanes, Bilston, WV14 0RX, West Midlands, United Kingdom
Tel.: (44) 1902408291
Web Site: https://www.ductmann.co.uk
Ductwork Product Mfr & Distr
N.A.I.C.S.: 333415

Ekovent AB (1)
Mejselgatan 7, 235 32, Vellinge, Sweden
Tel.: (46) 40421600
Web Site: https://www.ekovent.com
Ventilation Product Mfr & Distr
N.A.I.C.S.: 333415

Giroventilation AB (1)
Ekhagsvagen 6, 141 71, Segeltorp, Sweden
Tel.: (46) 86438380
Web Site: https://girovent.se
Duct System Mfr & Distr
N.A.I.C.S.: 332313

IVK-Tuote Oy (1)
Helmintie 8-10, Jyvaskyla, Finland
Tel.: (358) 207 229 670
Web Site: http://www.ivk-tuote.fi
Sales Range: $25-49.9 Million
Emp.: 80
Sound Attenuators Mfr
N.A.I.C.S.: 335999

KAMI, Kalix Mekaniska Industrier AB (1)
Vintervagen 16, 952 61, Kalix, Sweden
Tel.: (46) 92379850
Web Site: https://kami.se
Roof Product Mfr
N.A.I.C.S.: 327390

Klimatek Ventilationsmateriel A/S (1)
Fabriksvej 16 V Lyby, 7800, Skive, Denmark
Tel.: (45) 97536322
Web Site: https://www.klimatek.dk
Ventilating Product Mfr
N.A.I.C.S.: 333415

Lindab (IRL) Ltd (1)
Unit 2B Nangor Road Business Park, Dublin, Ireland
Tel.: (353) 14568200
Web Site: https://www.lindab.ie
Construction Materials Distr
N.A.I.C.S.: 423330

Subsidiary (Domestic):

A.C. Manufacturing Ltd. (2)
Unit 5 10B Stadium Business Park Ballycoolin Road, Dublin, D11 CKN7, Ireland
Tel.: (353) 18975000
Web Site: https://www.acmanufacturing.ie
Emp.: 30
Fabricated Metal & Hardware Mfr
N.A.I.C.S.: 332510

Lindab A/S (1)
Langkaer 20, 6100, Haderslev, Denmark
Web Site: https://www.lindab.dk
Ventilation Equipment Mfr
N.A.I.C.S.: 335210

Subsidiary (Non-US):

Lindab Door B.V. (2)
Tel.: (31) 88 022 2461
Web Site: https://www.lindab.com
Sales Range: $25-49.9 Million
Emp.: 26
Door & Door Frame Mfr
N.A.I.C.S.: 332321

Lindab GmbH (2)
Carl-Benz-Weg 18, 22941, Bargteheide, Germany
Tel.: (49) 453228590
Web Site: https://www.lindab.de
Emp.: 4,600
Security System Software Development Services
N.A.I.C.S.: 541511

Lindab N.V. (2)
Zeeschipstraat 149, 9000, Gent, Belgium
Tel.: (32) 93855011
Web Site: https://www.lindab.be
Sales Range: $25-49.9 Million
Emp.: 20
Steel Products Mfr
N.A.I.C.S.: 331110

Lindab Sp. z o.o. (2)
Wieruchow ul Sochaczewska 144, 05-850, Ozarow Mazowiecki, Poland
Tel.: (48) 222505050
Web Site: https://www.lindab-polska.pl
Sales Range: $25-49.9 Million
Metal Sheets Whslr
N.A.I.C.S.: 423510

Lindab AG (1)
Industriestrasse 24, 8112, Otelfingen, Switzerland
Tel.: (41) 588003100
Web Site: https://www.lindab.ch
Air Conditioning Equipment Mfr
N.A.I.C.S.: 333415

Lindab AS (1)
Saha-Loo tee 4, Iru village Joelahtme parish Harju County, 74206, Harjumaa, Estonia
Tel.: (372) 634 8200
Web Site: https://www.lindab.com
Sales Range: $25-49.9 Million
Emp.: 40
Roofing Metal Sheet Installation Services
N.A.I.C.S.: 238160

Lindab AS (1)
PO Box 171, Kalbakken, 0903, Oslo, Norway
Tel.: (47) 22803900
Fabricated Metal & Hardware Mfr
N.A.I.C.S.: 332510

Lindab Building Systems Kft. (1)
Derkovits 119, Nyiregyhaza, 4400, Hungary
Tel.: (36) 42501310
Web Site: http://www.lindabastron.biz
Sales Range: $25-49.9 Million
Emp.: 35
Metal Building System Mfr
N.A.I.C.S.: 332311

Lindab EOOD (1)
38 Captain Dimitar Spisarevski, 1592, Sofia, Bulgaria
Tel.: (359) 2 979 97 00
Web Site: http://www.lindab.bg
Sales Range: $25-49.9 Million
Emp.: 6
Metal Sheet Mfr & Distr
N.A.I.C.S.: 332322

Lindab France S.A.S. (1)
Tel.: (33) 478063641
Fabricated Metal & Hardware Mfr
N.A.I.C.S.: 332510

Lindab Havalandirma Ltd STI (1)
Mermerciler San Sit 8 Cad No 11/B Buyukcekmece Yakuplu, Istanbul, Turkiye
Tel.: (90) 2128766956
Industrial Machinery Mfr
N.A.I.C.S.: 333248
Leven Ozcan *(Mng Dir)*

LINDAB INTERNATIONAL AB — INTERNATIONAL PUBLIC

Lindab International AB—(Continued)

Lindab Holding A/S (1)
Langkaer 20, Haderslev, 6100, Denmark
Tel.: (45) 73232323
Emp.: 250
Holding Company
N.A.I.C.S.: 551112
Mette Proentum *(Gen Mgr)*

Lindab Kft. (1)
Allomas ut 1/a, 2051, Biatorbagy, Hungary
Tel.: (36) 23531300
Web Site: https://www.lindab.com
Sales Range: $50-74.9 Million
Emp.: 13
Metal Building Component Mfr
N.A.I.C.S.: 332311
Nabeel Alyyan *(Mng Dir)*

Lindab LLC (1)
Pr-d Serebryakova 6 Office 22, 129343, Moscow, Russia
Tel.: (7) 4992804037
Fabricated Metal & Hardware Mfr
N.A.I.C.S.: 332510

Lindab Ltd (1)
Building Products Division Unit 1 Block 1 Shenstone Trading Estate, Halesowen, B63 3XB, West Midlands, United Kingdom
Tel.: (44) 121 585 2780
Web Site: http://www.lindab.co.uk
Sales Range: $25-49.9 Million
Emp.: 15
Sheet Metal Products Mfr & Distr
N.A.I.C.S.: 332322

Subsidiary (Domestic):

CCL Lindab Ltd (2)
Unit 5 Eltruria Trad Estate Eturis Way, Basford, Stoke-on-Trent, ST4 6JQ, United Kingdom
Tel.: (44) 1782383460
Web Site: http://www.lindab.com
Ventilation Equipment Whslr
N.A.I.C.S.: 423730

Lindab Profil AB (1)
Vistorpsvagen 56, 269 71, Forslov, Sweden
Tel.: (46) 43185000
Roofing Metal Sheet Installation Services
N.A.I.C.S.: 238160

Lindab S.a.r.l (1)
Via Pisa 5-7, 10088, Volpiano, TO, Italy
Tel.: (39) 011 995 2099
Web Site: http://www.lindab.it
Ventilation Equipment Mfr
N.A.I.C.S.: 333415

Lindab SIA (1)
Ritausmas 11b, Ritausmas iela 11b, Riga, 1058, Latvia
Tel.: (371) 67804370
Web Site: https://www.lindab.com
Emp.: 10
Ventilation Equipment Mfr
N.A.I.C.S.: 333415
Maris Paulis *(Dir-Comml)*

Lindab SRL (1)
Soseaua deCentura nr 8, Ilfov, 077175, Stefanestii de Jos, Romania
Tel.: (40) 212094100
Fabricated Metal & Hardware Mfr
N.A.I.C.S.: 332510
Andrei Sulyok *(Country Mgr)*

Lindab Sp. z o.o. (1)
Wieruchow ul Sochaczewska 144, 05-850, Ozarow Mazowiecki, Poland
Tel.: (48) 222505050
Web Site: http://www.centrumklima.pl
Sales Range: $25-49.9 Million
Heating, Ventilation & Air Conditioning Materials Whslr & Mfr
N.A.I.C.S.: 423730
Piotr Wolak *(Pres, Member-Mgmt Bd & Country Mgr)*

Lindab Steel AB (1)
Tel.: (46) 43185000
Web Site: http://www.lindab.com
Emp.: 800
Steel Products Mfr
N.A.I.C.S.: 331110

Lindab Sverige AB (1)
Dolkvagen 16, Grevie, 262 74, Angelholm, Sweden
Tel.: (46) 43185000
Web Site: https://www.lindab.se
Emp.: 4,500
Roofing Metal Sheet Mfr
N.A.I.C.S.: 332322

Lindab Treasury AB (1)
Skjutbanevagen 6, Orebro, 703 69, Sweden
Tel.: (46) 43185000
Web Site: http://www.lindab.com
Emp.: 800
Roofing System Installation Services
N.A.I.C.S.: 238160
Johan Sofandberd *(Gen Mgr)*

Lindab Ventilation AB (1)
Stalhogavagen 115, 269 82, Bastad, Sweden
Tel.: (46) 4 318 5000
Web Site: http://www.lindabventilation.com
Emp.: 800
Ventilation System Installation Services
N.A.I.C.S.: 238220

Lindab a.s. (1)
Jamnik 278, Jamnik, 053 01, Spisska Nova Ves, Slovakia
Tel.: (421) 53 4176 226
Web Site: http://www.lindab.com
Sales Range: $25-49.9 Million
Steel Products Mfr
N.A.I.C.S.: 331110
Slavomir Janik *(Exec Dir)*

Lindab d.o.o. (1)
Franje Lucica 34, 10 090, Zagreb, Jankomir, Croatia
Tel.: (385) 1 6588 636
Web Site: http://www.lindab.com
Sheet Metal Roofing Installation Services
N.A.I.C.S.: 238160
Sasa Kolaric *(Dir)*

Lindab d.o.o. (1)
Godovic 150, Godovic, 5275, Idrija, Slovenia
Tel.: (386) 53756370
Fabricated Metal & Hardware Mfr
N.A.I.C.S.: 332510

Lindab s.r.o. (1)
Na Hurce 1081/6, Ruzyne, 161 00, Prague, Czech Republic
Tel.: (420) 233107100
Web Site: http://www.lindab.cz
Steel Sheet Mfr
N.A.I.C.S.: 332322

MP3 S.r.l. (1)
Via Muzza Spadetta 36, Bazzano, 40053, Valsamoggia, BO, Italy
Tel.: (39) 0516715811
Web Site: https://www.ilpa-mp3.com
Plastic Materials Mfr
N.A.I.C.S.: 325211

Muncholm A/S (1)
Tolsagervej 4, 8370, Hadsten, Denmark
Tel.: (45) 86215055
Web Site: https://muncholm.dk
Roofing Sheets Distr
N.A.I.C.S.: 423330

Oy Lindab Ab (1)
Juvan Teollisuuskatu 3, 02920, Espoo, Finland
Tel.: (358) 207851010
Web Site: https://www.lindab.fi
Industrial Machinery Mfr
N.A.I.C.S.: 333248

R-Vent Netherlands B.V. (1)
Boterdorpseweg 10, 2661, Bergschenhoek, Netherlands
Tel.: (31) 105242600
Web Site: https://www.r-vent.com
Ventilation System Mfr & Distr
N.A.I.C.S.: 333415

Spiral Helix Inc. (1)
500 Industrial Dr, Bensenville, IL 60106
Tel.: (224) 659-7870
Industrial Machinery Mfr
N.A.I.C.S.: 333248

Spiro International S.A. (1)
Industriestrasse 173, Bosingen, 3178, Fribourg, Switzerland
Tel.: (41) 317403100
Web Site: https://spiro.ch
Industrial Machinery Mfr
N.A.I.C.S.: 333248

Spiro Sweden AB (1)
Vallgatan 25, 411 16, Gothenburg, Sweden
Tel.: (46) 317129980
Web Site: https://spiro.se
Web Application Development Services
N.A.I.C.S.: 541511

Tecnovent SA (1)
Via Industria 31/33, 6934, Bioggio, Switzerland
Tel.: (41) 919309041
Web Site: https://www.tecnovent.ch
Ventilating Product Mfr
N.A.I.C.S.: 333415

U-nite Fasteners Technology AB (1)
Stora Bergavagen 5, 451 95, Uddevalla, Sweden
Tel.: (46) 522653390
Web Site: https://www.unitefasteners.com
Sales Range: $25-49.9 Million
Steel Fastener Mfr
N.A.I.C.S.: 339993
Madeleine Andersson *(Mng Dir-Fin & HR)*

UAB Lindab (1)
Mokslininku G 20, Vilnius, 8412, Lithuania
Tel.: (370) 52729729
Emp.: 6
Ventilation Equipment Mfr
N.A.I.C.S.: 333415

LINDBERGH S.P.A.

Via Guarneri Zanetti 22, Pescarolo Ed Uniti, 26033, Cremona, CR, Italy
Tel.: (39) 0372836220
Web Site: https://www.lindberghspa.it
Year Founded: 2006
LDB—(EUR)
Waste Disposal Services
N.A.I.C.S.: 562211
Michele Corradi *(CEO)*

LINDE PLC

Forge 43 ChurchStreet West, Surrey Research Park, Woking, GU21 6HT, Surrey, United Kingdom
Tel.: (44) 2038372000   IE
Web Site: https://www.linde.com
Year Founded: 2017
LIN—(NASDAQ)
Rev.: $32,854,000,000
Assets: $80,811,000,000
Liabilities: $39,729,000,000
Net Worth: $41,082,000,000
Earnings: $6,199,000,000
Emp.: 66,323
Fiscal Year-end: 12/31/23
Chemical Products Mfr
N.A.I.C.S.: 551112
Sanjiv Lamba *(CEO)*

Subsidiaries:

Linde AG (1)
Dr -Carl-von-Linde-Strasse 6-14, 82049, Pullach, Germany
Tel.: (49) 89357570
Industrial & Medical Gas Producer; Process Plant Construction
N.A.I.C.S.: 325120
Christian Bruch *(Member-Exec Bd)*

Subsidiary (Non-US):

Aries 94 s.r.o. (2)
Tuhovska 3, Bratislava, 831 06, Slovakia
Tel.: (421) 244462916
Web Site: http://www.aries94.sk
Medical Equipment Distr
N.A.I.C.S.: 423450

BOC Gas & Gear (2)
Bawtry Road Brinsworth, Rotherham, G72 7HN, United Kingdom
Tel.: (44) 1413033072
Industrial Gas & Welding Equipment Supplier
N.A.I.C.S.: 213112

BOGGY CREEK PTY LIMITED (2)
Riverside Corporate Park 10 Julius Avenue, North Ryde, Sydney, 2113, NSW, Australia
Tel.: (61) 288744400
Industrial Gas Mfr
N.A.I.C.S.: 325120

BOTSWANA OXYGEN COMPANY (PTY) LIMITED (2)
Plot 20595 Mabutswe Road Broadhurst Industrial, Gaborone, Botswana
Tel.: (267) 3905030
Natural Gas Distribution Services
N.A.I.C.S.: 221210

BRITISH INDUSTRIAL GASES LIMITED (2)
The Priestley Centre 10 Priestley Road, Guildford, GU2 7XY, Surrey, United Kingdom
Tel.: (44) 800111333
Industrial Gas Mfr
N.A.I.C.S.: 325120

CRYO Aktiebolag (2)
Oljevagen 105, Gothenburg, 418 78, Sweden
Tel.: (46) 31 646800
Cryogenic Equipment Mfr
N.A.I.C.S.: 333248

Compania de Operaciones de Nitrogeno, S.A. de C.V. (2)
Km 120 No 400 Carret Villahermosa-Cd Del Carme San Antonio Cardenas, Ciudad del Carmen, 24390, Campeche, Mexico
Tel.: (52) 9383811100
Industrial Gas Mfr
N.A.I.C.S.: 325120

Confederate Technology Co., Ltd. (2)
No 3 Lixing 4th Rd, East District, Hsinchu, 30078, Taiwan
Tel.: (886) 227866000
Industrial Gas Mfr
N.A.I.C.S.: 325120

Cryostar Cryogenic Equipments (Hangzhou) Co. Ltd. (2)
No 6 Kangyuan Road, Gongshu Dist, Hangzhou, 310015, China
Tel.: (86) 57185368331
Web Site: http://www.cryostar.com
Cryogenic Tank Mfr
N.A.I.C.S.: 332420

Cryostar Singapore Pte Ltd (2)
203 Henderson Road BLK B 10-09 Henderson Industrial Park, Singapore, 159546, Singapore
Tel.: (65) 62767441
Web Site: http://www.cryostar.com
Industrial Pump Distr
N.A.I.C.S.: 423830

EXPRESS INDUSTRIAL & WELDING SUPPLIES LIMITED (2)
10 Priestley Road Surrey Research Park, Guildford, GU2 7XY, Surrey, United Kingdom
Tel.: (44) 1159867880
Industrial & Welding Supplies Distr
N.A.I.C.S.: 423840

Eurogaz-Gdynia Sp. z o.o. (2)
Tel.: (48) 586605300
Web Site: http://www.eurogaz-gdynia.com.pl
Natural Gas Distribution Services
N.A.I.C.S.: 221210

FLEXIHIRE PTY LIMITED (2)
174 East Street, Rockhampton, 4700, QLD, Australia
Tel.: (61) 7 4927 6300
Web Site: http://www.flexihire.com.au
Heavy Construction Equipment Rental & Leasing Services
N.A.I.C.S.: 532412

Future Industrial & Welding Supplies Ltd. (2)
10 Priestley Road Surrey Research Park, Guildford, GU2 7XY, Surrey, United Kingdom
Tel.: (44) 1224212288
Welding Supplies Distr
N.A.I.C.S.: 423840

GI/LINDE ALGERIE (2)
23 Avenue De L Armee De Liberation Nationale Hussein Dey, Algiers, Algeria

AND PRIVATE COMPANIES

LINDE PLC

Tel.: (213) 497581
Chemical Products Distr
N.A.I.C.S.: 424690

GISTRANS Czech Republic s.r.o. (2)
Slavoninska 61, 779 00, Olomouc, Czech Republic
Tel.: (420) 585433251
Web Site: http://www.gistrans.cz
Industrial Gas Mfr
N.A.I.C.S.: 325120

GRANDPLAINS PROPERTIES, INC (2)
30th Floor Wynsum Corporate Plaza Emerald Avenue Ortigas Center, Pasig, 1605, Philippines
Tel.: (63) 26339112
Real Estate Management Services
N.A.I.C.S.: 531390

Grupo Linde Gas Argentina S.A. (2)
Calle 54 No 2075, 1650, San Martin, Buenos Aires, Argentina
Tel.: (54) 1147248888
Industrial Gas Mfr
N.A.I.C.S.: 325120

Subsidiary (Domestic):

Heins & Co. GmbH (2)
Etzestrasse 53, 22335, Hamburg, Germany
Tel.: (49) 406538119
Web Site: https://www.heins-trockenbau.de
Interior Design Services
N.A.I.C.S.: 541410

Subsidiary (Non-US):

IGL (PTY) LIMITED (2)
131 Mandume Ndemuayo Road Southern Industrial Area, Windhoek, Namibia
Tel.: (264) 61387000
Industrial Gas Mfr
N.A.I.C.S.: 325120
Eckhardt Vorster *(Mng Dir)*

INDUSTRIAL AND WELDING MANAGEMENT LIMITED (2)
10 Priestley Road Surrey Research Park, Guildford, GU2 7XY, Surrey, United Kingdom
Tel.: (44) 1159862357
Industrial Welding Supplies Distr
N.A.I.C.S.: 423840

INDUSTRIAL SUPPLIES & SERVICES LIMITED (2)
10 Priestley Road Surrey Research Park, Guildford, GU2 7XY, Surrey, United Kingdom
Tel.: (44) 1159867880
Welding Supplies Distr
N.A.I.C.S.: 423840

LIEN FUNG PRECISION TECHNOLOGY DEVELOPMENT CO., LTD (2)
66 Lane 245 Sha Tien Rd Sec 3, Taichung, 43241, Taiwan
Tel.: (886) 426992821
Precision Welding Equipment Mfr
N.A.I.C.S.: 333992

LINDE ELECTRONICS SAS (2)
Parc Technologique 4 Place Berthe Morisot, 69800, Saint Priest, France
Tel.: (33) 472476610
Web Site: http://www.linde-worldwide.com
Semiconductor Device & Solar Cell Mfr
N.A.I.C.S.: 334413

LINDE FINANCE (2)
The Priestly Centre 10 Priestley Road Surrey Research Park, Guildford, GU2 7XY, Surrey, United Kingdom
Tel.: (44) 1483 579 857
Web Site: http://www.linde-finance.com
Investment Management Service
N.A.I.C.S.: 523940

LINDE HADJIKYRIAKOS GAS LIMITED (2)
Limassol Avenue 260, Strovolos, 2029, Nicosia, Cyprus
Tel.: (357) 22482330
Industrial Gas Mfr
N.A.I.C.S.: 325120

LINDE MALAYSIA SDN. BHD. (2)
No 13 Jalan 222, 46100, Petaling Jaya, Selangor Darul Ehsan, Malaysia
Tel.: (60) 3 7955 4233
Web Site: http://www.linde.com.my
Industrial Gas Distr
N.A.I.C.S.: 424690
Ahmad Tajuddin Ali *(Chm)*

Subsidiary (US):

Lincare Holdings Inc. (2)
19387 US 19 N, Clearwater, FL 33764
Web Site: https://www.lincare.com
Holding Company; Home Health Respiratory Therapy Services & Supplies
N.A.I.C.S.: 551112
Jeff Barnhard *(CEO)*

Subsidiary (Domestic):

Alpha Respiratory Inc. (3)
1620 E Cypress Ave Ste #12, Redding, CA 96002-1356
Tel.: (530) 223-2080
Hospital Equipment & Supplies whslr
N.A.I.C.S.: 423450

American HomePatient, Inc. (3)
5200 Maryland Way Ste 400, Brentwood, TN 37027
Tel.: (615) 221-8884
Web Site: http://www.ahom.com
Home Health Care Services & Products Consisting Primarily of Respiratory & Infusion Therapies & Rentals & Sales of Home Medical Equipment & Home Health Care Supplies
N.A.I.C.S.: 621610
Pete Meekma *(Mgr-Data Center Ops)*

ConvaCare Services Inc. (3)
2599 W Fountain Dr, Bloomington, IN 47404-2782
Web Site: https://www.convacareservices.com
Supplier of Home Medical Equipment & Respiratory Services
N.A.I.C.S.: 423450
Chris Link *(Area Mgr)*

Health Care Solutions at Home Inc. (3)
7336 Whipple Ave NW, North Canton, OH 44720
Tel.: (330) 494-5906
Health Care Srvices
N.A.I.C.S.: 621610

Subsidiary (Domestic):

HCS Lancaster LLC (4)
2981 Hempland Rd Unit 3, Lancaster, PA 17601-1324
Tel.: (717) 291-5534
Hospital Equipment & Supplies whslr
N.A.I.C.S.: 423450

Subsidiary (Domestic):

Lincare Inc. (3)
12600 S Belcher Rd Ste 104 105, Largo, FL 33773
Tel.: (727) 545-3717
Health Care Srvices
N.A.I.C.S.: 621610
Micky Mckenzie *(Dir-Mktg & Bus Dev)*

Subsidiary (Non-US):

Lincare of Canada Inc. (4)
27 West Beaver Creek Rd #10, Richmond Hill, L4B 1M8, ON, Canada
Tel.: (905) 771-7397
Women Healthcare Services
N.A.I.C.S.: 621610

Subsidiary (Domestic):

Lincare of New York Inc. (4)
1160 Pittsford-victor Rd, Pittsford, NY 14534-3825
Tel.: (585) 385-7726
Health Care Srvices
N.A.I.C.S.: 621610

Subsidiary (Domestic):

MRB Acquisition Corp. (3)
1898 S Clyde Morris Blvd Ste 410, Daytona Beach, FL 32119
Web Site: https://www.uscootusa.com
Health Care Srvices

N.A.I.C.S.: 621610

Sleepcair, Inc. (3)
14333 W 95th St, Lenexa, KS 66215
Tel.: (913) 438-8200
Hospital Equipment & Supplies whslr
N.A.I.C.S.: 423450

mdINR, LLC (3)
45 Turner Dr, Middletown, NY 10941
Web Site: https://www.mdinr.com
Medical Laboratories
N.A.I.C.S.: 621511

Subsidiary (Non-US):

Linde (Australia) Pty. Ltd. (2)
Fl 2 54 Neridah Street, Chatswood, 2067, NSW, Australia
Tel.: (61) 294114111
Process Engineering Services
N.A.I.C.S.: 541330

Division (Domestic):

Linde AG - Engineering Division (2)
Dr Carl Von Linde Str 6 14 Pullach, 82049, Hollriegelskreuth, Germany
Tel.: (49) 8974450
Plant Engineering
N.A.I.C.S.: 541330

Subsidiary (Non-US):

Linde Engineering (Malaysia) Sdn. Bhd. (3)
Level 13 The Pinnacle Persiaran Lagoon, 46150, Bandar Sunway, Petaling Jaya, Malaysia
Tel.: (60) 79472635
Process Engineering Services
N.A.I.C.S.: 541330

Subsidiary (Domestic):

Linde Engineering Dresden GmbH (3)
Bodenbacher Strasse 80, 12775, Dresden, Germany
Tel.: (49) 35125030
Web Site: http://www.linde-engineering.de
Engineeering Services
N.A.I.C.S.: 541330

Subsidiary (Non-US):

Linde Engineering Korea, Ltd. (3)
25 Gukjegeumyung-ro 2-gil, Seoul, 150 763, Youngdeungpo, Korea (South)
Tel.: (82) 27800952
Web Site: http://www.linde-engineering.kr
Process Engineering Services
N.A.I.C.S.: 541330

Linde Engineering Middle East LLC (3)
Cl Tower Office 503 5th Floor Al Bateen Stree, Abu Dhabi, United Arab Emirates
Tel.: (971) 26981400
Process Engineering Services
N.A.I.C.S.: 541330

Linde Kryotechnik AG (3)
Dattlikonerstrasse St 5, 8422, Pfungen, Switzerland
Tel.: (41) 523040555
Web Site: http://www.linde-kryotechnik.ch
Process Engineering Services
N.A.I.C.S.: 541330

Subsidiary (US):

Selas Fluid Processing Corp. (3)
5 Sentry Pkwy E Ste 300, Blue Bell, PA 19422-2312
Tel.: (610) 834-0300
Web Site: http://leamericas.com
Engineering Design
N.A.I.C.S.: 541330

Subsidiary (Domestic):

Selas-Linde GmbH (3)
Wolfratshauser Str 138, 82049, Pullach, Germany
Tel.: (49) 8974450
Process Engineering Services
N.A.I.C.S.: 541330

Subsidiary (Non-US):

T-Thermal Company (3)

1 Blackwater Park, Holder Rd, Aldershot, GU12 4PQ, Hampshire, United Kingdom
Tel.: (44) 1252331351
Web Site: http://www.linde.co.uk
Compact Cryogenic Air Separation Plants
N.A.I.C.S.: 541330

Division (Domestic):

Linde AG - Gases Division (2)
Seitnerstrasse 70, 82049, Pullach, Germany
Tel.: (49) 803850000
Industrial, Medical & Special Gases Producer
N.A.I.C.S.: 325120

Subsidiary (Non-US):

AO "Linde Uraltechgaz" (3)
Montazhnikov Str 3, 620050, Ekaterinburg, Russia
Tel.: (7) 343 373 6747
Web Site: http://www.linde-gas.ru
Industrial Gas Mfr
N.A.I.C.S.: 325120

Ceylon Oxygen Limited (3)
No 50 Sri Pannananda Mawatha, 15, Colombo, Sri Lanka
Tel.: (94) 114760400
Web Site: https://www.linde-gas.lk
Industrial Gas Mfr & Distr
N.A.I.C.S.: 325120

ELGAS AUTOGAS PTY LIMITED (3)
10 Julius Ave, North Ryde, 2113, NSW, Australia
Tel.: (61) 280943200
Web Site: http://www.elgas.com.au
Petroleum Product Distr
N.A.I.C.S.: 424720

Grupo Linde Gas Argentina S.A. (3)
Calle 54 Ex Mitre No 2075, 1650, San Martin, Buenos Aires, Argentina
Tel.: (54) 1147248888
Web Site: http://www.linde-gas.com
Industrial Gas Mfr
N.A.I.C.S.: 325120

LINDE GAS SRBIJA Industrija gasova a.d. (3)
143 Petrovoselski Put, Becej, 21220, Serbia
Tel.: (381) 216811010
Web Site: https://www.linde-gas.rs
Industrial Gas Mfr
N.A.I.C.S.: 325120

LINDE GASES (SHANGHAI) CO., LTD. (3)
1525 Chuanqiao Road Jinqiao, Pudong, Shanghai, 201206, China
Tel.: (86) 21 6105 9889
Web Site: http://www.linde-gas.com.cn
Industrial Gas Mfr
N.A.I.C.S.: 325120

Branch (Domestic):

Linde AG - Gases Division, Hamburg (3)
Fangdiek Strasse 75, 22547, Hamburg, Germany
Tel.: (49) 1803850000
Web Site: http://www.linde-gas.de
Industrial Gas Mfr
N.A.I.C.S.: 325120

Subsidiary (Non-US):

Linde Gas (H.K.) Limited (3)
12 Chun Yat Street Tseung Kwan O Industrial Estate, Tseung Kwan O, Kowloon, China (Hong Kong)
Tel.: (852) 2572 2372
Industrial Gas Mfr
N.A.I.C.S.: 325120

Linde Gas A/S (3)
Lautruphoj 2-6, 2750, Ballerup, Denmark
Tel.: (45) 32836600
Web Site: https://www.linde-gas.dk
Industrial Gas Mfr
N.A.I.C.S.: 325120
Ole Kronborg *(VP)*

Linde Gas AB (3)
Rattarvagen 3, 169 68, Solna, Sweden
Tel.: (46) 87069500

4505

LINDE PLC

Linde plc—(Continued)
Web Site: https://www.linde-gas.se
Industrial Gas Mfr
N.A.I.C.S.: 325120

Linde Gas AS (3)
Gjerdrumsvie 8, 0484, Oslo, Norway
Tel.: (47) 23177200
Web Site: http://www.linde-gas.no
Industrial Gas Mfr
N.A.I.C.S.: 325120

Linde Gas Algerie S.p.A. (3)
23 Ave de l'ALN Hussein Dey, 16040, Algiers, Algeria
Tel.: (213) 21497391
Web Site: https://www.linde.dz
Industrial Gas Mfr
N.A.I.C.S.: 325120

Linde Gas Asia Pte Ltd (3)
80 Pasir Panjang Road 17 - 81 Mapletree Business City, Singapore, 117372, Singapore
Tel.: (65) 64850500
Industrial Gas Mfr
N.A.I.C.S.: 325120

Linde Gas Benelux B.V. (3)
(63.2%)
Industrial Gas Mfr
N.A.I.C.S.: 325120

Subsidiary (Non-US):

Linde Gas Belgium N.V. (4)
Westvaartdijk 85, B 1850, Grimbergen, Belgium
Web Site: http://www.linde-healthcare.nl
Mfr of Industrial Gases
N.A.I.C.S.: 325120

Subsidiary (Domestic):

Linde Gas Therapeutics Benelux B.V. (4)
De Keten 7, 5651 GJ, Eindhoven, Netherlands **(100%)**
Tel.: (31) 883276276
Mfr of Gases Used for Medical Purposes
N.A.I.C.S.: 325120

Subsidiary (Non-US):

Linde Gas Bulgaria EOOD (3)
9 Hristofor Kolumb Blvd, 1592, Sofia, Bulgaria
Tel.: (359) 29737302
Industrial Gas Mfr
N.A.I.C.S.: 325120

Linde Gas Chile S.A. (3)
Paseo Presidente Errazuriz Echaurren 2631 Piso 4 Providencia, Santiago, Chile
Tel.: (56) 800800242
Web Site: https://www.linde.cl
Industrial Gas Mfr
N.A.I.C.S.: 325120

Linde Gas Cryoservices B.V. (3)
De Keten 7, Eindhoven, 5651 GJ, North Brabant, Netherlands
Tel.: (31) 402825858
Web Site: http://www.linde-gascryoservices.com
Biomedical Cryogenic Equipment Distr
N.A.I.C.S.: 423830

Linde Gas Curacao N.V. (3)
Dokweg Koningsplein z/n, PO Box 3013, Willemstad, Curacao
Tel.: (599) 9 737 6777
Industrial Gas Mfr
N.A.I.C.S.: 325120

Linde Gas Espana SAU - Alcala de Henares Plant (3)
Poligono Industrial Banuelos Carretera Alcala Daganzo Km 3 8, 28036, Alcala de Henares, Spain
Tel.: (34) 902426464
Web Site: http://www.linde-gas.es
Industrial Gas Mfr
N.A.I.C.S.: 325120

Linde Gas GmbH (3)
Carl-von-Linde-Platz 1, 4651, Stadl Paura, Austria **(100%)**
Mfr of Industrial Gases
N.A.I.C.S.: 325120

Linde Gas Italia S.r.l. (3)
Via Guido Rossa 3, 200 10, Arluno, MI, Italy **(100%)**
Tel.: (39) 0290373501
Web Site: https://www.linde-gas.it
Industrial Gas Mfr
N.A.I.C.S.: 325120

Subsidiary (Domestic):

Linde Gas Produktionsgesellschaft mbH & Co. KG (3)
Sietnerstr 70, 82049, Pullach, Bavaria, Germany
Tel.: (49) 89 7446 0
Industrial Gas Mfr
N.A.I.C.S.: 325120

Subsidiary (Non-US):

Linde Gas SIA (3)
Tel.: (371) 67023900
Web Site: http://www.linde-gas.lv
Industrial Gas Mfr
N.A.I.C.S.: 325120

Linde Gas Shenzhen Ltd (3)
1F Siemens MRI Center Gaoxin C Ave 2nd Hi-Tech Industrial Park Middle, Shenzhen, 518057, China
Tel.: (86) 400 820 1798
Industrial Gas Mfr
N.A.I.C.S.: 325120

Linde Gas Singapore Pte. Ltd. (3)
Jurong Island facility 50 Jurong Island Highway, Jurong Industrial Estate, Singapore, 627877, Singapore **(100%)**
Tel.: (65) 68678998
Web Site: https://www.linde.com.sg
Mfr of Industrial Gases
N.A.I.C.S.: 325120

Subsidiary (Domestic):

Linde Gas Therapeutics GmbH & Co. KG (3)
Mittenheimer Strasse 62, 85764, Oberschleissheim, Germany
Tel.: (49) 89370000
Web Site: http://www.linde-healthcare.de
Industrial Gas Mfr
N.A.I.C.S.: 325120

Subsidiary (Non-US):

Linde Gas Tunisie S.A. (3)
Tel.: (216) 71409209
Industrial Gas Mfr
N.A.I.C.S.: 325120

Linde Gas UAB (3)
Didlaukio g 69, LV-08300, Vilnius, Lithuania
Web Site: http://www.linde-gas.lt
Industrial Gas Mfr
N.A.I.C.S.: 325120

Linde Gas Zhenhai Ltd. (3)
266 Xiepubeihai Road Chemical Industrial Park, Ningbo, 315807, China
Tel.: (86) 574 86809332
Industrial Gas Mfr
N.A.I.C.S.: 325120

Linde Gas a.s. (3)
U Technoplynu 1324, 198 00, Prague, 9, Czech Republic **(100%)**
Tel.: (420) 272100500
Mfr of Industrial Gases
N.A.I.C.S.: 325120

Linde Gas del Peru S.A. (3)
Av Nestor Gambetta 280, 1, Callao, Peru
Tel.: (51) 14132000
Web Site: http://www.linde-worldwide.com
Industrial Gas Mfr
N.A.I.C.S.: 325120

Linde Gas ehf (3)
Breidhofda 11, 110, Reykjavik, Iceland
Tel.: (354) 5773000
Industrial Gas Mfr
N.A.I.C.S.: 325120

Linde Gas k. s. (3)
Tuhovska 3, 831 06, Bratislava, Slovakia
Tel.: (421) 249102511
Web Site: https://www.linde-gas.sk
Industrial Gas Mfr
N.A.I.C.S.: 325120

Linde Gases (Changzhou) Company Limited (3)
6 Jianghua Road Binjiang Industrial Park, Changzhou, 213033, JiangSu, China
Tel.: (86) 519 8959 0159
Web Site: http://www.linde-gas.com.cn
Industrial Gas Mfr
N.A.I.C.S.: 325120

Linde Gases (Chengdu) Co., Ltd. (3)
11 West Park Of High-Tech Industrial Zone, Chengdu, 610016, China
Tel.: (86) 1590 2870 977
Web Site: http://www.linde-gas.com.cn
Industrial Gas Mfr
N.A.I.C.S.: 325120

Linde Gases (Fushun) Co., Ltd. (3)
2-1 Chengxiang Road, Dongzhou District, Fushun, 113109, Liaoning, China
Tel.: (86) 413 441 0288
Industrial Gas Mfr
N.A.I.C.S.: 325120

Linde Gases (Nanjing) Company Limited (3)
No. 3 Xin Gang Road, Nanjing, Jiangsu, China
Tel.: (86) 138 5142 7708
Industrial Gas Mfr
N.A.I.C.S.: 325120

Linde Gases (Suzhou) Company Limited (3)
99 Shishan Road, Gao Xin District, Suzhou, 215021, China
Tel.: (86) 512 6761 6226
Web Site: http://www.linde-gas.com.cn
Industrial Gas Mfr
N.A.I.C.S.: 325120

Linde Gaz A.S. (3)
Tel.: (90) 2626787400
Web Site: http://www.lindegaz.com.tr
Industrial Gas Mfr
N.A.I.C.S.: 325120

Linde Gaz Magyarorszag Zrt. (3)
Tel.: (36) 95588100
Industrial Gas Mfr
N.A.I.C.S.: 325120

Linde Gaz Polska Spolka z.o.o. (3)
Ul Rof. Michala Zyczkowskiego 17, 31-864, Krakow, Poland **(70%)**
Tel.: (48) 126439200
Mfr of Industrial Gases
N.A.I.C.S.: 325120

Linde Gaz Romania S.R.L. (3)
Highway A1 km 11 4, Bucharest, 077090, Romania **(100%)**
Tel.: (40) 213 181 920
Web Site: http://www.linde-gas.ro
Mfr of Industrial Gases
N.A.I.C.S.: 325120

Linde Healthcare Benelux (3)
De Keten 7, 5651 GJ, Eindhoven, Netherlands
Tel.: (31) 882626262
Web Site: https://www.linde-healthcare.nl
Medical & Hospital Equipment & Supplies Merchant Whlsr
N.A.I.C.S.: 423450

Linde Malaysia Sdn. Bhd. (3)
Tel.: (60) 800883888
Web Site: http://www.linde-gas.com.my
Industrial, Medical & Specialty Gases Mfr & Welding Products Distr
N.A.I.C.S.: 325120

Linde Uruguay Limitada (3)
Industrial Gas Mfr
N.A.I.C.S.: 325120

Subsidiary (Domestic):

Lindner GmbH & Co. KG (3)
Eschenbacher Str 7, 92690, Pressath, Germany
Tel.: (49) 96446896730
Web Site: http://www.linde-worldwide.com
Industrial Gas Mfr
N.A.I.C.S.: 325120

Subsidiary (Non-US):

Oy Linde Gas Ab (3)
Itsehallintokuja 6, 02600, Espoo, Finland

INTERNATIONAL PUBLIC

Tel.: (358) 102421
Industrial Gas Mfr
N.A.I.C.S.: 325120

PJSC "Linde Gas Ukraine" (3)
Kislorodnaya st 1, 4900, Dnepropetrovsk, Ukraine
Tel.: (380) 562351225
Web Site: http://www.linde.ua
Industrial Gas Distr
N.A.I.C.S.: 424690

PanGas AG (3)
Industriepark 10, CH 6252, Dagmersellen, Switzerland
Web Site: http://www.pangas.ch
Industrial Gas Mfr
N.A.I.C.S.: 325120
Denise Magli *(Mgr-Digital Mktg & E-Commerce)*

Group (Non-US):

The BOC Group Limited (3)
The Priestley Centre 10 Priestley Rd Surrey Research Pk, Guildford, GU2 7XY, Surrey, United Kingdom
Tel.: (44) 1483579857
Web Site: http://www.boc.com
Industrial Gas Products Mfr
N.A.I.C.S.: 424690

Subsidiary (Non-US):

African Oxygen Limited (4)
Afrox 23 Webber Street, Selby, Johannesburg, 2001, South Africa **(50.47%)**
Tel.: (27) 114900400
Web Site: http://www.afrox.co.za
Rev: $432,836,320
Assets: $514,197,600
Liabilities: $207,457,040
Net Worth: $306,740,560
Earnings: $450,900,800
Fiscal Year-end: 12/31/2019
Gases & Welding Products Supplier
N.A.I.C.S.: 325120
Johann Cilliers *(Head-Comm)*

Subsidiary (Non-US):

AFROX LESOTHO (PTY) LIMITED (5)
20 Mashoe Road, 100, Maseru, Lesotho
Tel.: (266) 223 13401
Web Site: http://www.afrox.co.za
Industrial Gas Mfr
N.A.I.C.S.: 325120

Subsidiary (Non-US):

Afrox Malawi Limited (4)
Johnstone Road Ginnery Corner, Blantyre, 3, Malawi
Tel.: (265) 671611
Industrial Gases & Welding Equipment Mfr
N.A.I.C.S.: 325120

BOC (China) Holdings Co., Ltd. (4)
Building No 9 27 Xin Jin Qiao Road, Pudong, Shanghai, 201206, China
Tel.: (86) 2161059888
Web Site: https://www.linde-gas.com.cn
Investment Management Service
N.A.I.C.S.: 523940

BOC (TRADING) LIMITED (4)
BOC Gases, PO Box 201, Dublin, 12, Ireland
Tel.: (353) 14091800
Web Site: http://www.boconline.ie
Industrial Gas Distr
N.A.I.C.S.: 424690

BOC Australia (4)
10 Julius Avenue Riverside Corporate Park, North Ryde, 2113, NSW, Australia
Tel.: (61) 288744400
Industrial Gases & Welding Products Mfr
N.A.I.C.S.: 325120

BOC GASES FINANCE LIMITED (4)
Riverside Corporate Park 10 Julius Avenue, North Ryde, Sydney, 2113, NSW, Australia
Tel.: (61) 288744400
Web Site: http://www.boc.com.au
Investment Management Service
N.A.I.C.S.: 523940

AND PRIVATE COMPANIES

LINDE PLC

BOC GASES MOZAMBIQUE LIMITED (4)
Ave Das Industrias 600, PO Box 2362, Machava, Maputo, Mozambique
Tel.: (258) 21750336
Industrial Gas Mfr
N.A.I.C.S.: 325120

BOC GASES SOLOMON ISLANDS LIMITED (4)
Ranadi Industrial Area Ranadi, PO Box R60, Honiara, Solomon Islands
Tel.: (677) 30528
Web Site: http://www.boc-gas-png.com
Industrial Gas Mfr
N.A.I.C.S.: 325120

BOC Gases (Nanjing) Company Limited (4)
8 Huanshan Road, Big Plant District, Nanjing, 210035, Jiangsu, China
Tel.: (86) 25 57025670
Web Site: http://www.linde-gas.com.cn
Industrial Gas Mfr
N.A.I.C.S.: 325120

BOC Gases (Suzhou) Co., Ltd. (4)
6 Hongfeng Road Suzhou Industrial Township, Suzhou, 215021, Jiangsu, China
Tel.: (86) 512 67616226
Web Site: http://www.linde-gas.com.cn
Industrial Gas Mfr
N.A.I.C.S.: 325120

BOC Gases (Tianjin) Company Limited (4)
No 6 4th Avenue Teda, Tianjin, 300457, China
Tel.: (86) 22 25325390
Web Site: http://www.linde-gas.com.cn
Industrial Gas Mfr
N.A.I.C.S.: 325120

BOC Gases (Wuhan) Co., Ltd. (4)
Room 11F Liangyou Building 318 Xinhua Road, Wuhan, 430015, Hubei, China
Tel.: (86) 27 85496230
Web Site: http://www.linde-gas.com.cn
Industrial Gas Mfr
N.A.I.C.S.: 325120

BOC Gases Aruba NV (4)
Balashi Z N, PO Box 387, Oranjestad, Aruba
Tel.: (297) 5852624
Web Site: http://www.boc-gases.com
Industrial Gases & Welding Products Mfr
N.A.I.C.S.: 325120

BOC Gases Fiji Ltd. (4)
Corner of Vetaia Nukuwatu St Suva, PO Box 687, Lami, Fiji
Tel.: (679) 3361011
Web Site: http://www.boc-gases.com
Industrial Gas Mfr
N.A.I.C.S.: 325120

BOC Gases Ireland Ltd. (4)
Tel.: (353) 14091800
Web Site: https://www.boconline.ie
Industrial Gases & Welding Products Mfr
N.A.I.C.S.: 325120

BOC Gases Nigeria plc (4)
Apapa-Oshodi Expressway Block H Plot 1-3, PO Box 1053, Oshodi, Lagos, Nigeria (60%)
Tel.: (234) 18750791
Web Site: http://www.boc-gas.com.ng
Industrial Gases & Welding Equipment Mfr
N.A.I.C.S.: 325120

BOC Gases Papua New Guinea Pty. Ltd. (4)
Mangola St, PO Box 93, Lae, Papua New Guinea
Tel.: (675) 4722377
Web Site: http://www.boc-gas-png.com
Industrial Gas Mfr
N.A.I.C.S.: 325120

Subsidiary (Domestic):

BOC INVESTMENT HOLDINGS LIMITED (4)
The Priestley Centre 10 Priestley Road Surrey Research Park, Guildford, GU2 7XY, Surrey, United Kingdom
Tel.: (44) 1483505211
Investment Management Service
N.A.I.C.S.: 523940

BOC INVESTMENTS NO.1 LIMITED (4)
The Priestley Centre 10 Priestley Road The Surrey Research Park, Guildford, GU2 7XY, Surrey, United Kingdom
Tel.: (44) 1483579857
Web Site: http://www.boc.com
Investment Management Service
N.A.I.C.S.: 523999

BOC INVESTMENTS NO.5 LIMITED (4)
The Priestley Centre 10 Priestley Road The Surrey Research Park, Guildford, GU2 7XY, Surrey, United Kingdom
Tel.: (44) 1483579857
Investment Management Service
N.A.I.C.S.: 523940

Subsidiary (Non-US):

BOC Intressenter AB (4)
Tel.: (46) 42178800
Web Site: http://www.linde-worldwide.com
Investment Management Service
N.A.I.C.S.: 523940

BOC Kenya Plc (4)
Kitui Road, PO Box 18010, Industrial Area, 00500, Nairobi, Kenya
Tel.: (254) 719069000
Web Site: https://www.boc.co.ke
Industrial, Medical & Scientific Gases, Refrigerants, Welding & Safety Equipment Mfr
N.A.I.C.S.: 325120

BOC Lienhwa Industrial Gases Co. Ltd. (4)
6th Fl 40 Cheng-The-Road Sec 1, Taipei, Taiwan
Tel.: (886) 225552260
Web Site: http://boclh.com.tw
Industrial Gas Mfr
N.A.I.C.S.: 325120

BOC Limited (4)
10 Julius Avenue, North Ryde, Sydney, 2113, NSW, Australia
Tel.: (61) 131262
Web Site: http://www.boc.com.au
Industrial Gas & Welding Equipment Mfr
N.A.I.C.S.: 325120
John Evans *(Mng Dir & Member-Exec Bd)*

Subsidiary (Domestic):

SOUTH PACIFIC WELDING GROUP PTY LIMITED (5)
7 Westgate St, Wacol, 4076, QLD, Australia
Tel.: (61) 300935337
Web Site: http://www.spwgroup.com.au
Industrial Welding Supplies Distr
N.A.I.C.S.: 423840

Subsidiary (Non-US):

BOC New Zealand Ltd. (4)
988 Great South Road, Penrose, 93300, Auckland, New Zealand
Tel.: (64) 800111333
Industrial Gases & Welding Equipment Mfr
N.A.I.C.S.: 325120

BOC Tanzania Limited (4)
Nyerere Road Plot 46/2, Box 40101, Dar es Salaam, Tanzania
Tel.: (255) 754315243
Web Site: http://www.afrox.co.za
Industrial Gas Mfr
N.A.I.C.S.: 325120

BOC Zimbabwe (Pvt) Limited (4)
BOC House Cnr Hull Road and Glasgow Road, PO Box 1282, Southerton, Harare, Zimbabwe
Tel.: (263) 4755750
Industrial Gases & Welding Products Mfr
N.A.I.C.S.: 325120

BOCLH Industrial Gases (Shanghai) Co., Ltd. (4)
No 766 Lishizhen Rd Zhangjiang High-Tech Park, Pudong New District, Shanghai, 201203, China
Tel.: (86) 2150805661
Industrial Gas Mfr
N.A.I.C.S.: 325120

BOCLH Industrial Gases (Songjiang) Co., Ltd. (4)
No 9 Bldg No 27 Xinjinqiao Rd, Pudong New Area, Shanghai, 201206, China
Tel.: (86) 2161059888
Industrial Gas Mfr
N.A.I.C.S.: 325120

BOCLH Industrial Gases (Xiamen) Co., Ltd. (4)
No 75 Sunban S Rd N Industrial Zone, Jimei Dist, Xiamen, 361021, China
Tel.: (86) 5926102990
Industrial Gas Mfr
N.A.I.C.S.: 325120

Cryostar SAS (4)
2 Rue de l'Industrie, 68220, Hesingue, France
Tel.: (33) 389702727
Web Site: https://www.cryostar.com
Emp.: 800
Cryogenic Equipment Mfr & Distr
N.A.I.C.S.: 333914

Subsidiary (Domestic):

Leengate Industrial & Welding Supplies Limited (4)
10 Priestley Road Surrey Research Park, Lenton, Guildford, GU2 7XY, Surrey, United Kingdom
Tel.: (44) 1159863121
Welding Equipment Mfr
N.A.I.C.S.: 333992

Subsidiary (Domestic):

Leengate Industrial & Welding Supplies (North East) Limited (5)
Unit 35D Pallion Industrial Estate European Way, Pallion, Sunderland, SR4 6SN, Tyne & Wear, United Kingdom
Tel.: (44) 1159862245
Welding Machinery & Equipment Mfr
N.A.I.C.S.: 333992

Leengate Industrial & Welding Supplies (Nottingham) Limited (5)
Redfield Road, Lenton, Nottingham, NG7 2UJ, Notts, United Kingdom
Tel.: (44) 1159862277
Welding Supplies Distr
N.A.I.C.S.: 423840

Leengate Industrial & Welding Supplies (Scotland) Limited (5)
Unit F/Pitreavie Business Park/Queensferry Rd, Dunfermline, KY11 8PU, United Kingdom
Tel.: (44) 1383729629
Welding Supplies Distr
N.A.I.C.S.: 423840

Subsidiary (Non-US):

Linde (Thailand) Public Company Limited (4)
15th FLoor Bangna Tower A 2/3 Moo 14, 10540, Samut Prakan, Thailand
Tel.: (66) 23386100
Web Site: http://www.linde.co.th
Industrial Gases Mfr & Distr
N.A.I.C.S.: 325120

Linde Bangladesh Limited (4)
285 Tejgaon Industrial Area, PO Box 56, Dhaka, 1208, Bangladesh
Tel.: (880) 28870322
Web Site: http://www.linde.com.bd
Industrial Gases & Welding Products Mfr
N.A.I.C.S.: 325120
Ayub Quadri *(Chm)*

Subsidiary (Non-US):

Linde Arabian Contracting Co., Ltd. (2)
Dammam-Khobar Highway, Riyadh, 31952, Saudi Arabia
Tel.: (966) 138218610
Web Site: http://www.linde-engineering.sa
Commercial Building Construction Services
N.A.I.C.S.: 236220

Linde Bangladesh Limited (2)
285 Tejgaon Industrial Area, Dhaka, 1208, Bangladesh
Tel.: (880) 2 8870 3227
Web Site: http://www.linde-gas.com.bd
Industrial Gas Mfr
N.A.I.C.S.: 325120
Ayub Quadri *(Chm)*

Linde CryoPlants Ltd. (2)
Blackwater Park Holder Road, Aldershot, GU12 4PQ, Surrey, United Kingdom
Tel.: (44) 1252331351
Web Site: http://www.linde-cryoplants.org
Compact Nitrogen & Oxygen Supplier
N.A.I.C.S.: 424690

Linde Electronics & Specialty Gases (Suzhou) Co Ltd. (2)
No 18 Chunhui Road Suzhou Industrial Park, Suzhou, 215021, Jiangsu, China
Tel.: (86) 51262752301
Web Site: http://www.linde.com.cn
Industrial Gas Mfr
N.A.I.C.S.: 325120

Linde Electronics B.V. (2)
Havenstraat 1, Schiedam, 3115 HC, South Holland, Netherlands
Tel.: (31) 102461616
Web Site: http://www.linde-worldwide.com
Electronic Components Distr
N.A.I.C.S.: 423690

Linde Electronics GmbH (2)
Waschenberger Strasse 13, Stadl Paura, 4651, Austria
Tel.: (43) 504273
Web Site: http://www.linde-worldwide.com
Electronic Product Distr
N.A.I.C.S.: 423690

Linde Engineering (Dalian) Co. Ltd. (2)
70 Ding Yuan Road Dalianwan Wan, Ganjingzi District, Dalian, 116113, China
Tel.: (86) 41139538810
Web Site: http://www.linde-engineering.com.cn
Industrial Machinery Mfr
N.A.I.C.S.: 333998

Linde Engineering (Hangzhou) Co. Ltd. (2)
North Building Lotus Business Center 333 Lianhua Street, 310012, Hangzhou, China
Tel.: (86) 57187858222
Web Site: http://www.linde-engineering.com.cn
Plant Construction Engineering Services
N.A.I.C.S.: 237990

Linde Engineering India Private Limited (2)
Tel.: (91) 2653056789
Plant Construction Engineering Services
N.A.I.C.S.: 237990

Linde Finance B.V. (2)
Strawinskylaan 3111, 1077 ZX, Amsterdam, Netherlands
Tel.: (31) 203013800
Web Site: http://www.linde-finance.com
Financial Investment Services
N.A.I.C.S.: 523999
Gerald Hobbs *(Chm-Supervisory Bd)*

Linde France S.A. (2)
523 Cours Du 3eme Millenaire, 69800, Saint Priest, Rhone, France
Tel.:
Web Site: http://www.linde-gas.fr
Industrial & Medical Gases Mfr
N.A.I.C.S.: 325120

Subsidiary (US):

Linde Gas North America LLC (2)
7390 Graham Road, Fairburn, GA 30213
Tel.: (770) 964-5072
Industrial Gas Mfr
N.A.I.C.S.: 325120

Subsidiary (Non-US):

Linde HKO Limited (2)
12 Chun Yat Street Tseung Kwan O Industrial Estate, Kowloon, China (Hong Kong)
Tel.:
Web Site: http://www.linde-healthcare.com.hk
Industrial Gas Mfr
N.A.I.C.S.: 325998

Linde Hellas E.P.E. (2)
Thesi Trypio Lithari, 19600, Mandra-Attikis, Greece (100%)
Tel.: (30) 211 1045 500

LINDE PLC

INTERNATIONAL PUBLIC

Linde plc—(Continued)
Web Site: http://www.linde.gr
Mfr of Industrial Gases
N.A.I.C.S.: 325120

Linde Holdings Netherlands B.V. (2)
Havenstraat 1, Schiedam, 3115 HC, Netherlands
Tel.: (31) 102461616
Web Site: http://www.linde.be
Investment Management Service
N.A.I.C.S.: 523999

Linde Homecare Benelux B.V. (2)
De Keten 7, 5391 BR, Eindhoven, Netherlands
Tel.: (31) 402825825
Home Care Services
N.A.I.C.S.: 621610

Linde Huachang (Zhangjiagang) Gas Co. Ltd. (2)
Yangtse River International Chemical Park, Zhangjiagang, 215633, Jiangsu, China
Tel.: (86) 512 5872 7111
Web Site: http://www.linde-gas.com.cn
Industrial Gas Mfr
N.A.I.C.S.: 325120

Linde India Limited (2)
Oxygen House P-43 Tartala Road, Kolkata, 700 088, India **(73.99%)**
Tel.: (91) 3366021600
Web Site: https://www.linde.in
Rev: $388,405,251
Assets: $527,520,532
Liabilities: $151,032,312
Net Worth: $376,488,220
Earnings: $64,511,600
Emp.: 207
Fiscal Year-end: 03/31/2023
Industrial, Medical & Specialty Gases Mfr
N.A.I.C.S.: 325120
Subhabrata Ghosh (CFO)

Linde Industrial Gases - Malaysian Sdn Bhd (2)
Web Site: http://www.linde.com.my
Mfr of Industrial Gases
N.A.I.C.S.: 325120

Linde Korea Co., Ltd. (2)
10th Fl Kiwoom Finance Square Bldg 18 Yoinaru-ro 4 Gil, Youngdeungpo-gu, Seoul, 150-886, Korea (South)
Tel.: (82) 27809331
Web Site: http://www.lindekorea.com
Industrial Gas Mfr
N.A.I.C.S.: 325120

Linde Medicale S.r.l. (2)
Via Guido Rossa 3, Arluno, 20010, Milan, Italy
Tel.: (39) 02 90373 1
Web Site: http://www.lindemedicale.it
Pharmaceuticals Product Mfr
N.A.I.C.S.: 325412

Linde Philippines, Inc. (2)
Tel.: (63) 27027500
Industrial Gas Mfr
N.A.I.C.S.: 325120

Subsidiary (US):

Linde RSS LLC (2)
208 W Main St, Livingston, TN 38570
Tel.: (931) 823-1440
Respiratory Care Services
N.A.I.C.S.: 622310

Subsidiary (Domestic):

Linde Schweisstechnik GmbH (2)
Glanzstoffstrasse 1, 63906, Erlenbach, Germany
Tel.: (49) 60222641030
Electrical Welding Equipment Mfr
N.A.I.C.S.: 333992
Walter Volpert (Mng Dir)

Subsidiary (Non-US):

Linde Sokolovska s.r.o. (2)
U Technoplynu 1324, Prague, 198 00, Czech Republic
Tel.: (420) 272 100 111
Web Site: http://www.linde-gas.cz
Industrial Gas Mfr
N.A.I.C.S.: 325120

MIG Production Company Limited (2)
20/1 Hemaraj Eastern Industrial Estate G-2 Prakornsongkrorad Road, PO Box 10540, T Huaypong A Muang, Rayong, 21150, Thailand
Tel.: (66) 23386100
Industrial Gas Mfr
N.A.I.C.S.: 325120

Subsidiary (Domestic):

MTA GmbH Medizin-Technischer Anlagenbau (2)
Bensbruchstrasse 11, 63533, Mainhausen, Germany
Tel.: (49) 6182992670
Web Site: http://www.linde-mta.de
Engineeering Services
N.A.I.C.S.: 541330

Subsidiary (Non-US):

NEW SINO GASES COMPANY LIMITED (2)
Tai Po Industrial Estate 18 Dai Shing Street, Tai Po, New Territories, China (Hong Kong)
Tel.: (852) 23050909
Industrial Gas Mfr
N.A.I.C.S.: 325120

Naamloze Vennootschap Linde Gas Benelux (2)
Havenstraat 1, Schiedam, 3115 HC, South Holland, Netherlands
Tel.: (31) 102461616
Web Site: http://www.linde-gas.nl
Industrial Gas Mfr
N.A.I.C.S.: 325120

P.T. Gresik Power Indonesia (2)
Jl Raya Romo Desa Romo Kec Manyar, Gresik, 61151, Indonesia
Tel.: (62) 313974225
Industrial Gas Mfr
N.A.I.C.S.: 325120

P.T. Townsville Welding Supplies (2)
71 Jl Mulawarman, Balikpapan, 76115, Indonesia
Tel.: (62) 542765385
Industrial Welding Supplies Distr
N.A.I.C.S.: 423840

PROVISIS Gase & Service GmbH (2)
Gewerbestrasse 1 (Au), Bad Wimsbach-Neydharting, 4654, Austria
Tel.: (43) 5042731777
Web Site: http://www.provisis.at
Industrial Gas Mfr
N.A.I.C.S.: 325120

PT. Linde Indonesia (2)
Jl Raya Bekasi Km 21, Pulogadung, Jakarta, 14250, Indonesia
Tel.: (62) 214601793
Web Site: https://www.linde.co.id
Industrial Gas Mfr
N.A.I.C.S.: 325120

Subsidiary (Domestic):

REMEO Deutschland GmbH (2)
Herbert-Tschape-Strasse 12-14, 15831, Blankenfelde-Mahlow, Germany
Tel.: (49) 337970070
Medical Instrument Distr
N.A.I.C.S.: 423450

Subsidiary (Non-US):

SERVICIOS DE OPERACIONES DE NITROGENO, S.A. DE C.V. (2)
Carr Villahermosa Km 120 400, Ciudad del Carmen, 24390, Campeche, Mexico
Tel.: (52) 9383811100
Industrial Gas Mfr
N.A.I.C.S.: 325120

Saudi Industrial Gas Company Ltd (2)
2nd Industrial city Dammam Makkah St Road 67, PO Box 291, Al Khobar, 31952, Saudi Arabia
Tel.: (966) 38121220
Web Site: https://www.linde-gas.sa
Industrial Gas Mfr
N.A.I.C.S.: 325120

Shanghai Huayi Microelectronic Material Co. Ltd. (2)
No 3 Tieli Road, Baoshan District, Shanghai, 200940, China
Tel.: (86) 2156846715
Industrial Organic Chemicals Mfr
N.A.I.C.S.: 325199

Tiamont Pty Ltd (2)
10 Julius Ave, North Ryde, Sydney, 2113, NSW, Australia
Tel.: (61) 280943200
Industrial Gas Mfr
N.A.I.C.S.: 325120

UNIGAS TRANSPORT FUELS PTY LTD (2)
10 Julius Ave, North Ryde, Sydney, 2113, NSW, Australia
Tel.: (61) 280943200
General Freight Trucking Services
N.A.I.C.S.: 484122

YUAN RONG INDUSTRIAL GASES COMPANY LIMITED (2)
3rd Floor No. 150 Chang'an West Road, Datong District, Taipei, 10355, Taiwan
Tel.: (886) 227866002
Industrial Gas Mfr
N.A.I.C.S.: 325120

Praxair, Inc. (1)
10 Riverview Dr, Danbury, CT, 06810-6268
Tel.: (203) 837-2000
Web Site: http://www.lindeus.com
Industrial Gases & Coatings Services
N.A.I.C.S.: 325120
Vanessa Abrahams-John (Dir-Diversity-Global)

Subsidiary (Non-US):

Almacenes Geneva S.A. (2)
Calle 64b Oeste Urbanizacion Industrial Los Angeles Bethania, Panama, Panama
Tel.: (507) 2322955
Industrial Gas Distr
N.A.I.C.S.: 424690
Marco Salazar (Gen Mgr)

Beijing Praxair Huashi Carbon Dioxide Co., Ltd. (2)
No 6 Huagong Road Dajiaoting Chaoyang District, Beijing, 100022, China
Tel.: (86) 1067888182
Industrial Gas Mfr
N.A.I.C.S.: 325120
Yonggang Fu (Supvr-Distr)

Beijing Praxair, Inc. (2)
6 Hua Gong Lu Dajiating, Chaoyang District, Beijing, 100022, China **(100%)**
Tel.: (86) 1067716715
Producer & Retailer of Industrial Gases
N.A.I.C.S.: 221210

Subsidiary (Domestic):

Carolina Home Care, Inc. (2)
1913 E Firetower Rd Ste G, Greenville, SC 27858
Tel.: (252) 758-9887
Web Site: http://www.carolinahomemedical.com
Medical Equipment Mfr
N.A.I.C.S.: 423450

Subsidiary (Non-US):

Famex Comercio Atacadista de Gas Carbonico Ltda. (2)
Rua Treze De Maio 345, Canhema, Diadema, 09941-400, SP, Brazil
Tel.: (55) 1121070280
Web Site: http://www.famexgas.com.br
Natural Gas Distribution Services
N.A.I.C.S.: 221210

Gama Gases Especials Ltda. (2)
Tel.: (55) 1143434000
Web Site: http://www.gamagases.com.br
Industrial Gas Mfr
N.A.I.C.S.: 325120

GemGas S.r.l. (2)
Via Cavalier Virginio Tedeschi 1, Settimo Torinese, 10036, Turin, Italy
Tel.: (39) 0112253916
Web Site: http://www.gemgas.it
Industrial Gas Distr

N.A.I.C.S.: 424690

Subsidiary (Domestic):

Home Care Medical, Inc. (2)
5665 S Westridge Dr Ste 100, New Berlin, WI 53151
Tel.: (262) 786-9870
Web Site: http://www.homecaremedical.com
Healthcare Equipment Mfr & Whslr
N.A.I.C.S.: 423450

Subsidiary (Non-US):

Industria Venezolana de Gas Inve-Gas, S.C.A. (2)
Zona Industrial Santa Rosalia Av Principal Parcela N 13, Cagua Edo, Caracas, Aragua, Venezuela
Tel.: (58) 244 400 4400
Web Site: http://www.praxair.com
Atmospheric, Process, Medical & Specialty Gas Distr
N.A.I.C.S.: 221210

Linde Canada Inc. (2)
1 City Center Drive Suite 1200, Mississauga, L5B 1M2, ON, Canada
Tel.: (905) 803-1600
Web Site: http://www.lindecanada.ca
Producer & Distributor Of Industrial, Medical & Specialty Gases, Intermediate Chemicals & Performance Processing Equipment
N.A.I.C.S.: 325998

Subsidiary (Domestic):

Linde Gas & Equipment Inc. (2)
10 Riverview Dr, Danbury, CT 06810 **(100%)**
Tel.: (716) 879-4077
Web Site: http://www.praxair.com
Industrial & Medical Gas Distr
N.A.I.C.S.: 325120

Subsidiary (Domestic):

Lake Welding Supply Company, Inc. (3)
363 Ottawa St, Muskegon, MI 49442
Tel.: (231) 722-3773
Welding Equipment, Supplies & Industrial Gas Distr
N.A.I.C.S.: 423830

Praxair Distribution Mid-Atlantic, LLC (3)
5275 Tilghman St, Allentown, PA 18104 **(100%)**
Tel.: (610) 398-2211
Web Site: http://www.praxair.com
Industrial Gases & Welding Supplies Distr
N.A.I.C.S.: 423840

Branch (Domestic):

Praxair Distribution, Inc. (3)
1725 Edsall Ave, Fort Wayne, IN 46803
Tel.: (260) 423-4468
Web Site: http://www.praxairwelding.com
Wholesale Gas Distr
N.A.I.C.S.: 221210

Praxair Distribution, Inc. - Georgia (3)
900 Westpark Dr Ste 100, Peachtree City, GA 30269
Tel.: (678) 364-8080
Web Site: http://www.praxair.com
Welding Gases & Equipment, Industrial Gases & Specialty Gases & Equipment Distribution
N.A.I.C.S.: 325120

Subsidiary (Domestic):

nexAir, LLC (3)
1385 Corp Ave, Memphis, TN 38132-1702 **(100%)**
Tel.: (901) 396-5050
Web Site: http://www.nexair.com
Sales Range: $75-99.9 Million
Emp.: 360
Gas Distribution Center.
N.A.I.C.S.: 424690
Betty Harris (VP-HR & Community Rels)

Division (Domestic):

Welders Supply & Equipment Co., Inc. (4)

AND PRIVATE COMPANIES — LINDE PLC

1600 River Falls St, Andalusia, AL 36420
Tel.: (334) 222-7894
Web Site: http://www.welders-supply.com
Sales Range: $1-9.9 Million
Emp.: 11
Welding & Medical Equipment, Gases & Safety Supplies Distr
N.A.I.C.S.: 423840

nexAir (4)
1350 Concourse Ave Ste 103, Memphis, TN 38104
Tel.: (901) 396-5050
Web Site: https://www.nexair.com
Sales Range: $25-49.9 Million
Emp.: 100
Wholesale Distribution of Welding Machinery & Equipment; Industrial Gases; Oxygen; Hospital Equipment & Supplies
N.A.I.C.S.: 423440
Betty Harris (Dir-HR)

Subsidiary (Non-US):

Liquido Carbonico Colombiana S.A. (2)
Cra. 19a 1525, Bogota, Colombia
Tel.: (57) 13607000
Chemical Products Distr
N.A.I.C.S.: 424690

NOxBOX Ltd. (2)
Tel.: (44) 1795859430
Web Site: http://www.noxboxltd.com
Medical Device Mfr
N.A.I.C.S.: 339113

Joint Venture (Domestic):

Niject Services Company (2)
222 Pennbright Dr Ste 300, Houston, TX 77090
Tel.: (512) 217-4833
Sales Range: $25-49.9 Million
Emp.: 2
Enhanced Oil Recovery Services
N.A.I.C.S.: 541990

Subsidiary (Domestic):

NuCO2 Inc. (2)
2800 SE Market Pl, Stuart, FL 34997-4965
Tel.: (772) 221-1754
Web Site: https://www.nuco2.com
Carbon Dioxide & Nitrogen Gas Solutions for Restaurant & Hospitality Industries
N.A.I.C.S.: 325120

Subsidiary (Domestic):

NuCO2 LLC (3)
2800 SE Market Pl, Stuart, FL 34997
Tel.: (772) 221-1754
Web Site: http://www.nuco2.com
Industrial Gas Distr
N.A.I.C.S.: 221210

Subsidiary (Non-US):

Oxigenos de Colombia Ltda. (2)
Ak 50 1 a, Bogota, DC, Colombia
Tel.: (57) 13607000
Web Site: http://www.linde.co
Atmospheric, Process, Medical & Specialty Gases Distr
N.A.I.C.S.: 221210

Oxigenos de Colombia Ltda. (2)
Cr36 12-172 Acopi, Valle del Cauca, Yumbo, Colombia
Tel.: (57) 26900777
Web Site: http://www.linde.co
Pharmaceuticals Product Mfr
N.A.I.C.S.: 325412

Oxygene Industriel Girardin, Inc. (2)
520 Chemin Larocque, Salaberry-de-Valleyfield, J6T 4C5, QC, Canada
Tel.: (450) 371-1444
Web Site: http://www.oxygeneindustrielgirardin.ca
Industrial Gas Mfr
N.A.I.C.S.: 325120
Mario Girardin (Pres)

Subsidiary (Domestic):

PG Technologies, LLC (2)
1500 Polco St Bldg 1405, Indianapolis, IN 46222
Tel.: (317) 240-2500

Industrial Gases & Coating Services
N.A.I.C.S.: 325120

Subsidiary (Non-US):

Praxair (China) Investment Co., Ltd. (2)
25th Floor Kerry Parkside No 1155 Fangdian Road, Pudong, Shanghai, China
Tel.: (86) 21 2894 7000
Web Site: http://www.linde-gas.com.cn
Industrial Gas Mfr
N.A.I.C.S.: 325120

Praxair (Shanghai) Co., Ltd. (2)
26/f Jialicheng, No1155, Fangdian, Shanghai, 201204, China
Tel.: (86) 21289470
Industrial Gas Mfr
N.A.I.C.S.: 325120

Praxair (Shanghai) Semiconductor Gases Co., Ltd. (2)
No 1509 Zuchongzhi Rd Zhangjiang Hi-Tech Park Pudong New Are, Shanghai, 201203, China
Tel.: (86) 21589540
Industrial Gas Distr
N.A.I.C.S.: 221210

Praxair (Thailand) Company Ltd. (2)
Premier Place building No 2 4th floor Soi Premier 2 Srinakarin Road, Nongbon Prawet, Bangkok, 10250, Thailand
Tel.: (66) 27151700
Carbon Dioxide Distr
N.A.I.C.S.: 221210

Praxair (Wuhan), Inc. (2)
No 8-3 Guandong Phase 2 Donghu De, Wuhan, 430074, China
Tel.: (86) 2787561360
Industrial Gas Distr
N.A.I.C.S.: 221210

Praxair Argentina S.A. (2)
Saavedra 2953, 1618 El Talar, Buenos Aires, Argentina
Tel.: (54) 1147366100
Web Site: http://www.praxair.com.ar
Producer & Retailer of Industrial Gases
N.A.I.C.S.: 221210

Praxair Asia Inc. (2)
26F Kerry Parkside No 1155 Fangdian Rd, Pudong, Shanghai, 201204, China (100%)
Tel.: (86) 2128947000
Web Site: http://www.lindeus.com
Industrial Gas Distr
N.A.I.C.S.: 221210

Joint Venture (Non-US):

Praxair Chemax Semiconductor Materials Co., Ltd. (2)
6th Floor No 145 Zhengjiu Road, Zhubei, Hsin-chu, 30251, Taiwan (50%)
Tel.: (886) 35543538
Gas, Chemical & Delivery System Solutions for Semiconductor Production
N.A.I.C.S.: 334413

Subsidiary (Non-US):

Praxair Chile Ltda (2)
Juana Weber 4725 Estacion Central, 9180183, Santiago, Metropolitana, Chile
Tel.: (56) 26802700
Industrial Gas Mfr & Services
N.A.I.C.S.: 325120
Sergio Novelli (Gen Mgr)

Praxair Consultoria y Administracion S de RL de CV (2)
Avenida Biologo Maximino Martinez 3804 S/ N, San Salvador Xochimanca, 2870, Mexico, Mexico
Tel.: (52) 55535495
Industrial Gas Distr
N.A.I.C.S.: 221210

Praxair Costa Rica, S.A. (2)
ProPark Industrial Park, Alajuela, Costa Rica
Tel.: (506) 24828500
Web Site: https://www.linde.cr
Atmospheric, Process, Specialty & Medical Gases & Welding & Medical Equipment
N.A.I.C.S.: 221210

Praxair Gases Industriales Ltda (2)
Av Cra 50 5C - 29, Bogota, Colombia
Tel.: (57) 7052000
Web Site: http://www.linde.co
Industrial Gas Mfr
N.A.I.C.S.: 325120

Praxair Gulf Industrial Gases LLC (2)
Al Quoz Industrial Area 1, PO Box 3763, Abu Dhabi, United Arab Emirates
Industrial Gas Distr
N.A.I.C.S.: 221210

Praxair India Pvt. Ltd. (2)
Web Site: http://www.praxair.co.in
Natural Gas Distr
N.A.I.C.S.: 221210
Anuj Sharma (Mng Dir)

Praxair Korea Co., Ltd. (2)
16th Fl Shinan Bldg 943-19 Daechi Kangnam, 943 19 Daechi Dong Kangnam Ku, Seoul, 135-280, Korea (South) (100%)
Tel.: (82) 221882213
Web Site: http://www.praxair.com
Producer & Retailer of Industrial Gases
N.A.I.C.S.: 221210

Praxair Mexico S. de R.L. de C.V. (2)
Biologo Maximino Martinez No 3804, 02870, Mexico, Mexico
Web Site: http://www.linde.com.mx
Natural Gas Distr
N.A.I.C.S.: 221210

Praxair Peru S.R.L. (2)
Av Alfredo Benavides 801 of 1102 Miraflores, Lima, Peru
Tel.: (51) 80011242
Web Site: http://www.praxair.com.pe
Atmospheric, Process, Medical & Specialty Gases Distr
N.A.I.C.S.: 221210

Subsidiary (Domestic):

Praxair Plainfield, Inc. (2)
2 Medori Blvd, Wilmington, DE 19801
Tel.: (302) 654-8755
Web Site: http://www.praxairusa.com
Industrial Gas Distr
N.A.I.C.S.: 221210

Subsidiary (Non-US):

Praxair Puerto Rico B. V. (2)
Van Heuven Goedhartlaan 935-A, 1181 LD, Amstelveen, Netherlands
Tel.: (31) 205646160
Chemical Products Distr
N.A.I.C.S.: 424690

Subsidiary (Domestic):

Praxair Puerto Rico, Inc. (2)
PO Box 307, Gurabo, PR 00778-0307
Tel.: (787) 258-7200
Producer & Retailer of Industrial Gases
N.A.I.C.S.: 325120

Subsidiary (Non-US):

Praxair Qingdao Co., Ltd. (2)
2 Shandong Rd Eastern Shangquan, Shinan, Qingdao, Shandong, China
Tel.: (86) 53283893686
Industrial Gas Mfr
N.A.I.C.S.: 325120

Praxair Republica Dominicana, SRL (2)
Ave Monumental 92, Santo Domingo, Dominican Republic
Tel.: (809) 560 2827
Web Site: http://www.praxair.com
Natural Gas Distribution Services
N.A.I.C.S.: 221210

Praxair S.r.l. (2)
Via Fleming 3, 28100, Novara, Italy
Tel.: (39) 0321674811
Industrial Gas Distr
N.A.I.C.S.: 221210

Praxair Services (UK) Limited (2)
27 Ivatt Way, Peterborough, PE37PH, Cambridgeshire, United Kingdom
Tel.: (44) 1733 267812
Web Site: http://www.praxair.com
Consulting Services

N.A.I.C.S.: 541690

Subsidiary (Domestic):

Praxair Services, Inc. (2)
1585 Sawdust Rd Ste 300, The Woodlands, TX 77380
Tel.: (281) 203-3600
Web Site: http://www.praxair.com
Industrial Gas Company; Nitrogen Pumping Services
N.A.I.C.S.: 221210

Praxair Surface Technologies, Inc. (2)
1500 Polco St, Indianapolis, IN 46222-3274 (100%)
Tel.: (317) 240-2500
Web Site: http://www.praxair.com
Surface Coatings Mfr
N.A.I.C.S.: 332812

Subsidiary (Non-US):

Praxair Surface Technologies Co., Ltd. (3)
204 Changwondae-ro, Seongsan-gu, Changwon, 51542, Gyeongsangnam-do, Korea (South)
Tel.: (82) 552601240
Web Site: http://www.praxairsurfacetechnologies.com
Industrial Gas Distr
N.A.I.C.S.: 221210

Praxair Surface Technologies GmbH (3)
Robert-Zapp-Strasse 7, 40880, Ratingen, Germany
Tel.: (49) 21024950
Surface Enhancing Material Distr
N.A.I.C.S.: 423710
Jann Steen (Gen Mgr)

Praxair Surface Technologies K.K. (3)
314 6 Chome Shimoishido, Kitamoto-shi, Saitama, 364-0028, Japan
Tel.: (81) 488257894
Web Site: http://www.praxairsurfacetechnologies.com
Industrial Gas Distr
N.A.I.C.S.: 221210

Praxair Surface Technologies Limited (3)
Whisby Road N Hykeham, Lincoln, LN6 3DL, United Kingdom
Tel.: (44) 1522878200
Web Site: http://www.praxairsurfacetechnologies.com
Industrial Gas Distr
N.A.I.C.S.: 221210

Praxair Surface Technologies S.A.S. (3)
42 Allee Jules Bigot ZI Molina la Chazotte, BP 80688, 42043, Saint Etienne, Cedex 1, France
Tel.: (33) 477426262
Web Site: http://www.praxairsurfacetechnologies.com
Industrial Gas Distr
N.A.I.C.S.: 221210

Praxair Surface Technologies do Brasil Ltda. (3)
Av Maringa 400, Pinhais, 83324-010, Brazil
Tel.: (55) 41366162
Web Site: http://www.praxairsurfacetechnologies.com
Industrial Gas Distr
N.A.I.C.S.: 423840

Subsidiary (Domestic):

Praxair Surface Techonologies, Inc. (3)
146 Pembroke Rd, Concord, NH 03301-5706
Tel.: (603) 224-9585
Web Site: http://www.praxairsurfacetechnologies.com
Mfr of Arc Spray Systems for Thermal Coatings
N.A.I.C.S.: 333912

Subsidiary (Non-US):

Praxair Uruguay Ltda. (2)

LINDE PLC

INTERNATIONAL PUBLIC

Linde plc—(Continued)

CNO Tomas Tomkinson 1468, Paso de la Arena, Montevideo, 12600, Uruguay
Tel.: (598) 2312 3359
Web Site: http://www.praxair.com.uy
Industrial Gas Mfr
N.A.I.C.S.: 325120

Affiliate (Non-US):

SIAD S.p.A. (2)
Via S Bernardino 92, 24126, Bergamo, Italy
Tel.: (39) 035328111
Web Site: https://www.siad.com
Gas Production; Industrial, Specialty & Medical Gases
N.A.I.C.S.: 325120

Subsidiary (Non-US):

Istrabenz plini, d.o.o. (3)
Sermin 8A, Bertoki, 6000, Koper, Slovenia
Tel.: (386) 56634600
Web Site: https://www.istrabenzplini.si
Industrial Gases
N.A.I.C.S.: 325120
Aldo Sraboti (Pres-Mgmt Bd)

SIAD Austria GmbH (3)
Tel.: (43) 627774470
Web Site: http://www.siad.com
Atmospheric, Process & Specialty Gases Distr
N.A.I.C.S.: 221210

SIAD Bulgaria EOOD (3)
4 Amsterdam Str, PO Box 28, 1528, Sofia, Bulgaria
Tel.: (359) 29785636
Atmospheric, Process & Specialty Gas Distr
N.A.I.C.S.: 221210

SIAD Czech spol. s r.o. (3)
K Hajum 2606 2b, Stodulky, 15500, Prague, Stodulky, Czech Republic
Tel.: (420) 235097520
Atmospheric, Process & Specialty Gas Distr
N.A.I.C.S.: 221210

Subsidiary (Domestic):

SIAD Healthcare S.p.A. (3)
Via Edison 6, Assago, 20090, Milan, Italy
Tel.: (39) 02457921
Web Site: http://www.siadhealthcare.com
Medical Product & Gas Distr
N.A.I.C.S.: 423450

Subsidiary (Non-US):

SIAD Hungary Kft (3)
Zsigmondy U 38, 3527, Miskolc, Hungary
Tel.: (36) 46501130
Atmospheric, Process & Specialty Gas Distr
N.A.I.C.S.: 221210

Subsidiary (Domestic):

SIAD Macchine Impianti S.p.A. (3)
Via Canovine 2/4, 24126, Bergamo, Italy
Tel.: (39) 035327611
Web Site: https://www.siadmi.com
Designs, Produces & Installs Compressors & Air Separation Units
N.A.I.C.S.: 333912

Subsidiary (Non-US):

SIAD Romania s.r.l. (3)
Tel.: (40) 213103658
Industrial Gases Mfr & Distr
N.A.I.C.S.: 325120

SIAD Rus o.o.o. (3)
Bolshaya Dmitrovka Street 12/1 Bldg 1 Floor 3, 107031, Moscow, Russia
Tel.: (7) 4957213026
Web Site: http://www.siad.com
Industrial Gases Mfr & Distr
N.A.I.C.S.: 325120

SIAD Slovakia spol. s r.o. (3)
Roznavska c 17, 831 04, Bratislava, Slovakia
Tel.: (421) 244460347
Atmospheric, Process & Specialty Gas Distr
N.A.I.C.S.: 221210

Subsidiary (Non-US):

Sermatech International Canada Corp. (2)

747 av Riddle, Dorval, H9P 1H4, QC, Canada
Tel.: (514) 631-2240
Web Site: http://www.praxairsurfacetechnology.com
Industrial Gas Mfr
N.A.I.C.S.: 325120

Sure/Arc Welding Supply (1977) Ltd. (2)
402 Neptune Crescent, London, N6M 1A1, ON, Canada
Tel.: (519) 455-4420
Web Site: http://www.surearcwelding.com
Emp.: 9
Welding Equipment Distr
N.A.I.C.S.: 423840
Morry Huber (Pres)

Technogas sp. Z o.o. (2)
ul Postepu 15c, 02-676, Warsaw, Poland
Tel.: (48) 327711650
Web Site: http://www.technogaz.pl
Industrial Gas Distr
N.A.I.C.S.: 424690

Tecnogas S/A (2)
Av Argentina 4040, Callao, 7001, Peru
Tel.: (51) 12098888
Industrial Gases & Coating Services
N.A.I.C.S.: 325120

Tecnoservizi Ambientali S.r.l. (2)
Via San Bernardino 92, 24126, Bergamo, Italy
Tel.: (39) 035328111
Web Site: https://www.tecnoserviziambientali.eu
Waste Management Services
N.A.I.C.S.: 562211

Subsidiary (Domestic):

Tradewinds Insurance, Inc. (2)
31975 SR 20 Ste 1, Oak Harbor, WA 98277
Tel.: (360) 679-4949
Web Site: https://www.tradewindsins.com
Insurance Services
N.A.I.C.S.: 524126
Robert Young (Principal)

Welco Acetylene Corp. (2)
321 Roanoke Ave, Newark, NJ 07105
Tel.: (973) 465-1043
Compressed Gas
N.A.I.C.S.: 424690

Westair Cryogenics Company (2)
117 S Texas Ave, El Paso, TX 79761
Tel.: (432) 580-7465
Welding Equipment Distr
N.A.I.C.S.: 423840

Subsidiary (Non-US):

White Martins Gases Industriais Ltda (2)
Rua Matura 1 gate A, Rio de Janeiro, 21530-340, Acari, Brazil **(100%)**
Web Site: http://www.whitemartins.com.br
Producer & Retailer of Industrial Gases
N.A.I.C.S.: 221210

White Martins Steel Gases Industriais Ltda. (2)
Web Site: http://www.praxair.com.br
Industrial Gas Distr
N.A.I.C.S.: 221210

Yateem Oxygen W.L.L. (2)
Building 9 Avenue 13 Block 0413 Al Musulla, PO Box 60, Manama, Bahrain
Tel.: (973) 17400675
Web Site: http://www.yateemoxygen.com
Industrial Gas Mfr & Distr
N.A.I.C.S.: 325120

LINDEMAN ASIA INVESTMENT CORP.

4-5/F 234 Teheran-ro, Gangnam-gu, Seoul, 06221, Korea (South)
Tel.: (82) 7070194071
Web Site: https://www.laic.kr
Year Founded: 2006
277070—(KRS)
Rev.: $7,499,955
Assets: $50,735,296
Liabilities: $8,845,198
Net Worth: $41,890,099
Earnings: $2,680,531
Emp.: 15
Fiscal Year-end: 12/31/22
Asset Management Services
N.A.I.C.S.: 523940
Jin Ha Kim (CEO)

LINDENGRUPPEN AB

Ruuthsesplanaden 2, Hoganas, 263 83, Sweden
Tel.: (46) 42338500
Web Site: http://www.lindengruppen.com
Sales Range: $900-999.9 Million
Holding Company
N.A.I.C.S.: 551112
Paul Schrotti (CEO)

Subsidiaries:

AB Wilh. Becker (1)
c/o Lindengruppen AB Bruksgarden, Hoganas, 263 83, Sweden **(100%)**
Tel.: (46) 42338500
Web Site: http://www.wilhbecker.se
Industrial Coating & Paint Mfr
N.A.I.C.S.: 325510

Division (Non-US):

Becker Industrial Coatings (2)
Cite Internationale 62 quai Charles de Gaulle, 69463, Lyon, France
Tel.: (33) 472690615
Web Site: http://www.beckers-bic.com
Sales Range: $25-49.9 Million
Emp.: 6
Mfr of Industrial Coatings
N.A.I.C.S.: 325510

Division (Domestic):

Becker Industrie S.A.S. (3)
40 Rue Du Champ De Mars, 42601, Montbrison, France
Tel.: (33) 477967050
Liquid & Powder Industrial Paint Mfr
N.A.I.C.S.: 325510

Subsidiary (Non-US):

ColArt International Holdings Ltd. (2)
21 Evesham Street, London, W11 4AJ, United Kingdom
Tel.: (44) 2084243200
Web Site: http://www.colart.com
Sales Range: $200-249.9 Million
Emp.: 1,480
Art Supply Mfr
N.A.I.C.S.: 325510
Thomas Brautigam (CEO)

Subsidiary (Non-US):

Bonny ColArt Co Ltd (3)
3-6-3 Rinkaicho, Edogawa-ku, Tokyo, 134-8576, Japan
Tel.: (81) 3 3877 5113
Web Site: http://www.bonnycolart.co.jp
Emp.: 20
Stationery Product Distr
N.A.I.C.S.: 424120
Eiichi Lshii (Pres)

Subsidiary (US):

ColArt Americas Inc. (3)
11 Constitution Ave, Piscataway, NJ 08855-1396
Tel.: (732) 562-0770
Stationery Product Distr
N.A.I.C.S.: 424120
Doug Johnson (Pres)

Subsidiary (Non-US):

ColArt Benelux b.v. (3)
Minervum 7491, 4817 ZP, Breda, Netherlands
Tel.: (31) 85 485 54 60
Stationery Product Distr
N.A.I.C.S.: 424120
Arie Baars (Mgr-Voormalig Pur)

ColArt Deutschland GmbH (3)
Gutenbergstrasse 4, 63477, Maintal, Germany
Tel.: (49) 6109 76 46 60
Stationery Product Distr
N.A.I.C.S.: 424120
Jasper van der Wurff (Mgr-Experienced Mktg & Sls)

Subsidiary (Domestic):

ColArt Fine Art & Graphics Ltd (3)
Goldthorn Road, Kidderminster, DY11 7JN, Worcestershire, United Kingdom
Tel.: (44) 1562 744522
Stationery Product Distr
N.A.I.C.S.: 424120

Subsidiary (Domestic):

Crown Artist Brush Ltd (4)
Crown Street West, Lowestoft, NR32 1SG, Suffolkshire, United Kingdom
Tel.: (44) 1502 573142
Web Site: http://www.crownartistbrush.co.uk
Stationery Product Distr
N.A.I.C.S.: 424120
Samantha Atkins (Mgr-Brush Dev)

Snazaroo Holdings Ltd (4)
Unit 1D Brunel Way Mart Road, Minehead, TA24 5BJ, Somerset, United Kingdom
Tel.: (44) 1643 707659
Web Site: http://www.snazaroo.com
Emp.: 60
Holding Company
N.A.I.C.S.: 551112

Subsidiary (Non-US):

ColArt Iberica SA (3)
c/ Capitan Haya n1 planta 15, 28020, Madrid, Spain
Tel.: (34) 912 844 601
Stationery Product Distr
N.A.I.C.S.: 424120
Pilar Bringas (Gen Mgr)

ColArt International SA (3)
5 rue Rene Panhard, ZI Nord, 72021, Le Mans, France
Tel.: (33) 2 43 83 83 00
Stationery Product Distr
N.A.I.C.S.: 424120

ColArt Italiana SpA (3)
via Monte Rosa 11, 20149, Milan, Italy
Tel.: (39) 0294755084
Web Site: http://www.colart.it
Stationery Product Distr
N.A.I.C.S.: 424120
Philippe Bonenfant (Gen Mgr)

ColArt Scandinavia AB (3)
Tuna Industrivag 35, 153 30, Jarna, Sweden
Tel.: (46) 8 709 34 20
Web Site: http://www.colart.se
Stationery Product Distr
N.A.I.C.S.: 424120
Per Johansson (CFO)

ColArt Tianjin Art Materials Co Ltd (3)
80 Xian Yang Road, Nankai District, Tianjin, 300113, China
Tel.: (86) 2227367907
Paint Distr
N.A.I.C.S.: 424950
Liu Canna (Mgr-Intl Bus)

Becker Industrial Coatings (M) Sdn Bhd (1)
No 3 & 5 Jalan Anggerik Mokara 31/54 Section 31, Kota Kemuning, 40460, Shah Alam, Selangor, Malaysia
Tel.: (60) 3 51227 540
Industrial Coating Material Mfr
N.A.I.C.S.: 324122

Moorbrook Textiles Limited (1)
March Street Mills March Street, Peebles, EH45 8ER, Scotland, United Kingdom
Tel.: (44) 1721 720146
Web Site: http://www.beggandcompany.com
Clothing Apparel Distr
N.A.I.C.S.: 424350

Subsidiary (Domestic):

Alex Begg & Co (2)
17 Viewfield Road, Ayr, KA8 8HJ, United Kingdom
Tel.: (44) 1292267615
Web Site: http://www.alex-begg.co.uk
Apparel Distr

AND PRIVATE COMPANIES

N.A.I.C.S.: 458110
Emily White *(Dir-Sls & Design)*

Secure Glass Holding AB (1)
Bruksgarden, 263 39, Hoganas, Sweden
Tel.: (46) 42 338514
Holding Company
N.A.I.C.S.: 551112

Subsidiary (Domestic):

Planglasteknik Stockholm AB (2)
Prastkragens vag 48, 132 45, Saltsjo-Boo, Sweden
Tel.: (46) 8 718 32 05
Glass Products Mfr
N.A.I.C.S.: 327215

Wilh. Becker Holding GmbH (1)
Kurfurstendamm 56, 10707, Berlin, Germany
Tel.: (49) 30 770 19 07 10
Holding Company
N.A.I.C.S.: 551112

Subsidiary (Non-US):

Becker Coating Boya Sanayi ve Ticaret Ltd. Sti. (2)
Guzeller Organize Sanayi Bolgesi Inonu mah Nursultan Nazarbayev sk, 41400, Gebze, Kocaeli, Turkiye
Tel.: (90) 5330964033
Paint Distr
N.A.I.C.S.: 424950

Becker Farby Przemyslowe Sp. z.o.o (2)
Beckera Wilhelma 7, 33-110, Tarnow, Poland
Tel.: (48) 146320200
Web Site: http://www.beckers-group.com
Emp.: 58
Metal Plating Services
N.A.I.C.S.: 331523
Danuta Zyder *(Mng Dir)*

Becker Industrial Coatings (Guangzhou) Ltd (2)
No 1 Xinzhuang 5th Road Yonghe Economic Zone, Guangzhou Economic & Tech Dev, Guangzhou, 511356, China
Tel.: (86) 20 3222 1888
Industrial Coating Material Mfr
N.A.I.C.S.: 324122

Becker Industrial Coatings (Korea) Ltd (2)
258-18 Songsan-ri, Yanggam-myun, Hwaseong, Kyonggi-do, Korea (South)
Tel.: (82) 31 354 4688
Industrial Coating Material Mfr
N.A.I.C.S.: 324122

Becker Industrial Coatings (Pty) Ltd (2)
105 Houtkop Road, Duncanville, Vereeniging, South Africa
Tel.: (27) 16428 4011
Industrial Coating Material Mfr
N.A.I.C.S.: 324122

Becker Industrial Coatings (Shanghai) Ltd (2)
100 Jiangtian East Road Songjiang Industrial Zone, Shanghai, 201600, China
Tel.: (86) 21 577 43 788
Web Site: http://www.beckers-group.com
Industrial Coating Material Mfr
N.A.I.C.S.: 324122
Mendi Yu *(Mgr-HR)*

Becker Industrial Coatings (Vietnam) Co. Ltd (2)
No 1B Dong An Industrial Park, Thuan An, VN-Binh Duong, Vietnam
Tel.: (84) 65 0376 8830
Industrial Coating Material Mfr
N.A.I.C.S.: 324122

Becker Industrial Coatings AB (2)
Brobyvagen 2, Box 2041, 195 02, Marsta, Sweden
Tel.: (46) 8 590 790 00
Industrial Coating Material Mfr
N.A.I.C.S.: 324122
Linda Snis *(Acct Mgr-Technical)*

Becker Industrial Coatings L.L.C. (2)
Ware House 2 - 9 Al-Khour Port Nakheel Area, PO Box 12795, 12795, Ras al Khaimah, United Arab Emirates
Tel.: (971) 3222 188 53
Painting & Coating Material Mfr
N.A.I.C.S.: 324122
Santhosh Jose *(Mng Dir)*

Becker Industrial Coatings Ltd (2)
Goodlass Road, Speke, Liverpool, L24 9HJ, United Kingdom
Tel.: (44) 1514481010
Paint Distr
N.A.I.C.S.: 424950
Richard Steele *(Dir-Bus)*

Subsidiary (Domestic):

Becker Industrielack GmbH (2)
Norfer Str 3, 41539, Dormagen, Germany
Tel.: (49) 21335010
Paint Distr
N.A.I.C.S.: 424950

Subsidiary (US):

Becker Specialty Corporation (2)
2550 Derby Ln, Elk Grove Village, IL 60007
Tel.: (847) 766-3555
Metal Coating & Allied Services
N.A.I.C.S.: 332812

Subsidiary (Non-US):

Beckers High Performance Coatings (Tianjin) Ltd (2)
32 Luyuan Road Wuqing Economic & Technology Development District, Tianjin, 301700, China
Tel.: (86) 22 5962 2818
Painting & Coating Material Mfr
N.A.I.C.S.: 325510

Beckers Industrial Coatings Italia SpA (2)
Via Grandi 1/A, Caleppio, 20090, Milan, Italy
Tel.: (39) 02 9509601
Painting & Coating Material Mfr
N.A.I.C.S.: 325510

Beckers Industrial Coatings Ltd (2)
Km 33 Lagos-Badagry Expressway Agbara, Lagos, Nigeria
Tel.: (234) 7033735655
Paint Distr
N.A.I.C.S.: 424950
Yetunde Odunuga *(Supvr-Quality Assurance & Quality Control)*

Berger Becker Bangladesh Limited (2)
8 Road 2 Sector 3, Uttara Model Town, Dhaka, 1230, Bangladesh
Tel.: (880) 2 8953665
Stationery Product Distr
N.A.I.C.S.: 424120
Md Shamim Iqbal *(Head-Bus)*

Berger Becker Coatings Pvt. Ltd. (2)
Plot No 114 Pilerne Industrial Estate IN-Post, Saligao, Goa, 403511, India
Tel.: (91) 8322407103
Paint Distr
N.A.I.C.S.: 424950
Sanjay Saxena *(Sr Gen Mgr-Sls & Mtkg)*

PT Beckers Indonesia (2)
Jalan Cendana Raya Blok F9 no 1B Kawa Silicon III Cikarang, 17550, Bekasi, Jawa barat, Indonesia
Tel.: (62) 21 29577693
Stationery Product Distr
N.A.I.C.S.: 424120
Aris Nuryadin *(Mgr-Sls)*

LINDIAN RESOURCES LIMITED
108 St Georges Terrace, Perth, 6000, WA, Australia
Tel.: (61) 865578838
Web Site:
https://www.lindianresources.com
LINIF—(OTCQB)
Rev.: $281,151
Assets: $52,840,732
Liabilities: $10,631,647
Net Worth: $42,209,085
Earnings: ($3,263,259)
Fiscal Year-end: 06/30/24
Mineral Exploration Services
N.A.I.C.S.: 212390
Shannon Green *(Mng Dir)*

LINDOPHARM GMBH
Neustrasse 82, 40721, Hilden, Germany
Tel.: (49) 21032065
Web Site: http://www.lindopharm.de
Year Founded: 1947
Emp.: 109
Pharmaceuticals Mfr
N.A.I.C.S.: 325412
Stephan Walz *(Mng Dir)*

Subsidiaries:

Esparma GmbH (1)
Seepark 7, D-39116, Magdeburg, Germany (100%)
Tel.: (49) 39163609870
Web Site: http://www.esparma.de
Sales Range: $10-24.9 Million
Pharmaceuticals Mfr
N.A.I.C.S.: 325412
Stephan Walz *(Mng Dir)*

LINDOR INC.
9600 Meilleur Street Suite 740, Montreal, H2N 2E3, QC, Canada
Tel.: (514) 384-5243
Web Site: http://www.lindor.ca
Year Founded: 1920
Rev.: $40,931,028
Emp.: 500
Women Apparel Mfr
N.A.I.C.S.: 458110
Herbert Liverant *(Chm & Pres)*

LINDSAY AUSTRALIA LIMITED
152 Postle Street, Acacia Ridge, 4110, QLD, Australia
Tel.: (61) 732404901
Web Site:
https://www.lindsayaustralia.com.au
LAU—(ASX)
Rev.: $537,104,031
Assets: $367,288,326
Liabilities: $267,551,415
Net Worth: $99,736,912
Earnings: $18,208,467
Emp.: 1,852
Fiscal Year-end: 06/30/24
Transportation & Logistics Services
N.A.I.C.S.: 488510
Michael Kim Lindsay *(CEO & Mng Dir)*

Subsidiaries:

Lindsay Brothers Holdings Pty Ltd (1)
44b Cambridge Street, Rocklea, 4106, Queensland, Australia
Tel.: (61) 732404900
Trucking & Courier Services
N.A.I.C.S.: 492110

LINDSELL TRAIN INVESTMENT TRUST PLC
Frostrow Capital LLP 25 Southampton Buildings, London, WC2A 1AL, United Kingdom
Tel.: (44) 2030084910
Web Site: https://www.ltit.co.uk
LTI—(LSE)
Other Financial Vehicles
N.A.I.C.S.: 525990
Julian Cazalet *(Chm)*

LINE GAMES CORP.
218 Teheran-ro Gangnam-gu, Seoul, 06221, Korea (South)
Tel.: (82) 16614467
Children Game Sets Mfr
N.A.I.C.S.: 339930

LINEAR INDUSTRIES LIMITED
116 11th Floor Maker Chamber 3, Nariman Point, Mumbai, 400 021, India
Tel.: (91) 22 22024342
Web Site:
http://www.linearindustries.in
Rev.: $16,402
Assets: $209,601
Liabilities: $1,672
Net Worth: $207,929
Earnings: ($629)
Emp.: 1
Fiscal Year-end: 03/31/16
Investment Management Service
N.A.I.C.S.: 523940

LINECROSS COMPOSITES LTD
Green Lane Bridgtown, Cannock, WS11 0JW, Staffordshire, United Kingdom
Tel.: (44) 1543 466 021
Web Site: http://www.linecross.co.uk
Sales Range: $25-49.9 Million
Emp.: 75
Automotive Components Mfr
N.A.I.C.S.: 336390
Stuart Fry *(Mng Dir)*

LINEDATA SERVICES SA
27 rue d Orleans, FR-92200, Neuilly-sur-Seine, France
Tel.: (33) 173437010
Web Site: https://www.linedata.com
Year Founded: 1998
LIN—(EUR)
Rev.: $186,352,256
Assets: $332,890,136
Liabilities: $226,030,650
Net Worth: $106,859,486
Earnings: $28,553,853
Emp.: 1,140
Fiscal Year-end: 12/31/22
Financial Information Technology Software & Solutions
N.A.I.C.S.: 513210
Anvaraly Jiva *(Founder, Chm & CEO)*

Subsidiaries:

Linedata CapitalStream (1)
1111 3rd Ave Ste 950, Seattle, WA 98101
Tel.: (206) 545-9522
Web Site: http://www.capitalstream.com
Sales Range: $25-49.9 Million
Emp.: 100
Technology Consulting Services
N.A.I.C.S.: 541690
Paul Kuralt *(Dir-QA)*

LINEKONG INTERACTIVE GROUP CO., LTD.
5/F Qiming International Mansion Wangjing Science Park, Wangjing North Road, Chaoyang District, Beijing, 100102, China
Tel.: (86) 1084148006
Web Site: http://www.linekong.com
8267—(HKG)
Rev.: $9,976,403
Assets: $51,221,009
Liabilities: $14,379,206
Net Worth: $36,841,802
Earnings: ($8,584,618)
Emp.: 103
Fiscal Year-end: 12/31/22
Game Developer
N.A.I.C.S.: 513210
Feng Wang *(Chm)*

LINETECH HOLDING SA
17 Stycznia 45D, 02 146, Warsaw, Poland
Tel.: (48) 722 008 008
Web Site: http://www.linetech.pl
Holding Company; Aircraft Maintenance & Repair Services
N.A.I.C.S.: 551112
Piotr Kaczor *(Chm-Mgmt Bd)*

LINEWELL SOFTWARE CO., LTD.

Linetech Holding SA—(Continued)

LINEWELL SOFTWARE CO., LTD.
Building 2 Linewell Building Fenghai Road, Fengze District, Quanzhou, 362000, Fujian, China
Tel.: (86) 59568288889
Web Site: http://www.linewell.com
Year Founded: 2002
603636—(SHG)
Rev.: $244,248,671
Assets: $758,655,949
Liabilities: $367,615,568
Net Worth: $391,040,381
Earnings: $19,359,812
Fiscal Year-end: 12/31/22
Software Development Services
N.A.I.C.S.: 541511
Zhixiong Wu (Chm, Pres & Sec-Party Committee)

LING YUE SERVICES GROUP LIMITED
44/F Tower A Leading International Finance Center No 151, 2nd Tianfu Street Gaoxin District, Chengdu, Sichuan, China   Ky
Web Site: https://www.lingyue-service.com
Year Founded: 2002
2165—(HKG)
Rev.: $84,334,432
Assets: $115,974,745
Liabilities: $39,866,111
Net Worth: $76,108,634
Earnings: $14,485,628
Emp.: 5,644
Fiscal Year-end: 12/31/23
Property Management Services
N.A.I.C.S.: 531311
Hongping Luo (CFO)

LING YUI HOLDINGS LIMITED
Unit 1702-03 17/F Stelux House 698 Prince Edward Rd East, San Po Kong Kln, Hong Kong, China (Hong Kong)
Tel.: (852) 28816878   Ky
Web Site: http://www.lingyui.com.hk
Year Founded: 2000
0784—(HKG)
Rev.: $31,082,761
Assets: $26,803,721
Liabilities: $13,313,445
Net Worth: $13,490,276
Earnings: ($70,939)
Emp.: 119
Fiscal Year-end: 03/31/21
Construction Management Services
N.A.I.C.S.: 238910
Kim Ming Lee (Exec Dir)

LINGARO SP Z O.O.
Ul Domaniewska 28, Warsaw, 02-672, Poland
Tel.: (48) 228253025
Web Site: http://www.lingarogroup.com
Investment Services
N.A.I.C.S.: 523999
Sam Mantle (CEO)

Subsidiaries:

Ostrow Reisin Berk & Abrams, Ltd.   (1)
455 N Cityfront Plz Dr Ste 1500, Chicago, IL 60611
Tel.: (312) 670-7444
Web Site: http://www.orba.com
Sales Range: $10-24.9 Million
Emp.: 115
Certified Public Accountants
N.A.I.C.S.: 541211
Jeffrey Newman (Chm-Real Estate Grp)

LINGBAO GOLD GROUP COMPANY LTD.
The intersection of Hangu Road and Jingshan Road, Lingbao, Henan, China
Tel.: (86) 3988862788   CN
Web Site: https://www.lbgold.com
3330—(HKG)
Rev.: $1,421,754,703
Assets: $969,307,981
Liabilities: $702,747,068
Net Worth: $266,560,913
Earnings: $32,329,908
Emp.: 4,176
Fiscal Year-end: 12/31/22
Gold Ore Mining Services
N.A.I.C.S.: 212220
Wang Pinran (Chm)

LINGDA GROUP CO., LTD.
Room 902 903 9th Floor No 32B Huoju Road, Dalian High-tech Industrial Park, Liaoning, 237300, China
Tel.: (86) 41184732565
Web Site: https://www.lingdagroup.com.cn
Year Founded: 2005
300125—(CHIN)
Rev.: $224,296,020
Assets: $299,815,776
Liabilities: $207,216,360
Net Worth: $92,599,416
Earnings: ($2,376,972)
Fiscal Year-end: 12/31/22
Heavy Engineering & Construction Services
N.A.I.C.S.: 237990
Zhendong Liu (Chm)

LINGKARAN TRANS KOTA HOLDINGS BERHAD
2nd Floor Kompleks Operasi Litrak KM 19, Lebuhraya Damansara-Puchong Bandar Sunway PJS 9 Subang Jaya, 47500, Petaling Jaya, Selangor Darul Ehsan, Malaysia
Tel.: (60) 374947000
Web Site: http://www.litrak.com.my
LITRAK—(KLS)
Rev.: $99,230,670
Assets: $457,685,168
Liabilities: $157,406,783
Net Worth: $300,278,385
Earnings: $40,304,880
Emp.: 486
Fiscal Year-end: 03/31/22
Highway Road Construction Management Services
N.A.I.C.S.: 237310
Chuah Lean Pin (Head-IT)

LINGNAN ECO&CULTURE-TOURISM CO. LTD.
No 33 Dongyuan Road, Dongcheng District, Dongguan, 523125, Guangdong, China
Tel.: (86) 76922000888
Web Site: https://www.lingnan.cn
Year Founded: 1998
002717—(SSE)
Sales Range: $350-399.9 Million
Ecological Environment & Garden Construction, Culture Tourism & Investment
N.A.I.C.S.: 561730
Hongwei Yin (Chm & Pres)

LINGON GARAGE
Le Moulin a Vent, Saint Geosmes, 52200, Langres, France
Tel.: (33) 325871183
Web Site: http://www.lingongarage.fr
Sales Range: Less than $1 Million
Emp.: 28
Automobile Dealers
N.A.I.C.S.: 441110
Martial Miquee (Mng Dir)

LINGOTES ESPECIALES, S.A.
Calle Colmenares N 5 Piso 1, 47004, Valladolid, Spain
Tel.: (34) 983305249
Web Site: https://www.lingotes.com
Year Founded: 1968
LGT—(MAD)
Sales Range: Less than $1 Million
Metal Parts Mfr
N.A.I.C.S.: 331511

Subsidiaries:

Frenos y Conjuntos S.A.   (1)
Avenida de Burgos No 53, Valladolid, 47000, Spain
Tel.: (34) 983 341 225
Metal Parts Mfr
N.A.I.C.S.: 331511

LINGSEN PRECISION INDUSTRIES, LTD.
No 5 1 South 2nd Road Taiwan Export Processing Zone, Tanzi Dist, Taichung, 42701, Taiwan
Tel.: (886) 425335120
Web Site: https://www.lingsen.com.tw
Year Founded: 1973
2369—(TAI)
Rev.: $185,099,931
Assets: $259,800,540
Liabilities: $74,026,649
Net Worth: $185,773,890
Earnings: ($5,236,633)
Emp.: 2,905
Fiscal Year-end: 12/31/23
Integrated Circuits Mfr
N.A.I.C.S.: 334413
Chun-Liang Lin (VP)

LINGYI ITECH (GUANGDONG) COMPANY
359 Jinou Road, Jianghai District, Jiangmen, 529000, Guangdong, China
Tel.: (86) 7503503601
Web Site: https://www.jpmf.com.cn
Year Founded: 1975
002600—(SSE)
Rev.: $4,655,207,713
Assets: $5,446,102,247
Liabilities: $3,018,906,528
Net Worth: $2,427,195,719
Earnings: $180,801,589
Emp.: 50,000
Fiscal Year-end: 12/31/21
Magnetic Material Mfr
N.A.I.C.S.: 334610
Zeng Fangqin (Chm & Gen Mgr)

Subsidiaries:

A-Core Jiangmen Electronics Co., Ltd.   (1)
No 88 Xinxing Road, High-tech Zone, Jiangmen, 529080, Guangdong, China
Tel.: (86) 7507360082
Web Site: https://www.acore-ferrite.com
Electronics Mfr
N.A.I.C.S.: 334419

Heshan Jiangci Wire & Cable Co., Ltd.   (1)
No 1 Dongping Road, East Industrial Zone Gonghe Town, Heshan, Guangdong, China
Tel.: (86) 7508308676
Web Site: http://www.hsjcxl.com.cn
Silo Mfr
N.A.I.C.S.: 332618

JPMF Jiangyi Co., Ltd.   (1)
359 Jinou Road, Jianghai District, Jiangmen, 529000, Guangdong, China
Tel.: (86) 7503503601
Magnetic Material Mfr
N.A.I.C.S.: 334610

Salcomp Plc   (1)
Joensuunkatu 13, PO Box 95, 24101, Salo, Finland
Tel.: (358) 201 875 511
Web Site: http://www.salcomp.com

INTERNATIONAL PUBLIC

Power Supplies Mfr
N.A.I.C.S.: 335999

Subsidiary (Non-US):

Salcomp (Shenzhen) Co., Ltd   (2)
Salcomp Road Furong Industrial Area Xinqiao Shajing, Baoan District, Shenzhen, 518125, China
Tel.: (86) 755 2725 5111
Power Supplies Mfr
N.A.I.C.S.: 335999

Salcomp Hong Kong Ltd   (2)
Cheung Kong Center 19th floor 2 Queens Road, Central, China (Hong Kong)
Tel.: (852) 255 077 117
Power Supplies Mfr
N.A.I.C.S.: 335999

Salcomp Industrial Eletronica da Amazonia LTDA   (2)
Avenida dos Oitis 5 055, Distrito Industrial II, Manaus, 69007-002, Amazonas, Brazil
Tel.: (55) 9221272600
Power Supplies Mfr
N.A.I.C.S.: 335999

Salcomp Japan   (2)
Azabu Green Terrace 5F 3-20-1 Minami-azabu, Minato-Ku, Tokyo, 1060047, Japan
Tel.: (81) 80 4155 2765
Power Supplies Mfr
N.A.I.C.S.: 335999

Salcomp LTDA   (2)
Rio Negro St 1084 1st Floor Room 12, Alphaville, 06454-000, Barueri, Sao Paulo, Brazil
Tel.: (55) 11 3167 0250
Power Supplies Mfr & Whslr
N.A.I.C.S.: 335999
Araujo Jane (Supvr-Quality)

Salcomp Manufacturing India Pvt Ltd   (2)
Nokia Telecom SEZ SIPCOT Industrial Area Phase III, Chennai Bangalore National Highway, Sriperumbudur, 602 105, India
Tel.: (91) 4437177777
Power Supplies Mfr
N.A.I.C.S.: 335999
Sasikumar Gendham (Mng Dir)

Salcomp Taiwan Co., Ltd   (2)
7F No 201 Sec 2 Tiding Blvd, Neihu Dist, Taipei, 11493, Taiwan
Tel.: (886) 226562358
Power Supplies Mfr
N.A.I.C.S.: 335999
Lin Phyllis (Mgr-HR)

Subsidiary (US):

Salcomp USA, L.L.C.   (2)
21162 Mill Branch Dr, Leesburg, VA 20175
Tel.: (817) 307-1185
Power Supplies Mfr
N.A.I.C.S.: 335999
Camilla Lento (Coord-Customer Svc)

Steelmag International S.A.S.   (1)
105 rue de Vaugraine, 38830, Saint-Pierre-d'Allevard, France
Tel.: (33) 476453845
Web Site: http://www.steelmaginternational.com
Magnetic Material Mfr
N.A.I.C.S.: 334610

LINGYUAN IRON & STEEL CO., LTD.
No 3 Gangtie Road, Lingyuan, 122500, Liaoning, China
Tel.: (86) 4216838003
Web Site: https://www.lggf.com.cn
Year Founded: 1994
600231—(SHG)
Rev.: $3,026,800,918
Assets: $2,334,722,902
Liabilities: $1,191,046,671
Net Worth: $1,143,676,231
Earnings: ($117,046,299)
Emp.: 5,840
Fiscal Year-end: 12/31/22
Iron & Steel Mfr
N.A.I.C.S.: 331110
Zhang Peng (Chm)

AND PRIVATE COMPANIES

LINGYUN INDUSTRIAL CORPORATION LIMITED
Songlindian Town, Zhuozhou, 072761, Hebei, China
Tel.: (86) 3123951002
Web Site: http://www.lingyun.com.cn
Year Founded: 1995
600480—(SHG)
Rev.: $2,343,108,405
Assets: $2,509,587,157
Liabilities: $1,321,832,192
Net Worth: $1,187,754,965
Earnings: $47,568,643
Emp.: 1,000
Fiscal Year-end: 12/31/22
Automotive Components Mfr
N.A.I.C.S.: 336320
Hufeng Xin *(Chm)*

LINHAI CO., LTD.
No 199 Yingchun West Road, Taizhou, 225300, Jiangsu, China
Tel.: (86) 52386551888
Web Site: https://www.linhai.cn
Year Founded: 1956
600099—(SHG)
Rev.: $128,918,555
Assets: $105,365,581
Liabilities: $29,928,041
Net Worth: $75,437,540
Earnings: $1,457,027
Emp.: 1,600
Fiscal Year-end: 12/31/21
Motor Vehicle Mfr & Distr
N.A.I.C.S.: 336211
Kangzhong Chang *(Chm & Pres)*

LINICAL CO., LTD.
10 Flr Shin-Osaka Brick Building 6-1 Miyahara 1-chome, Yodogawa-ku, Osaka, 532-0003, Japan
Tel.: (81) 661502478
Web Site: http://www.linical.co.jp
Year Founded: 2005
2183—(TKS)
Rev.: $81,349,270
Assets: $122,542,790
Liabilities: $68,109,440
Net Worth: $54,433,350
Earnings: $2,234,180
Emp.: 1,000
Fiscal Year-end: 03/31/24
Medical Contract Research Services
N.A.I.C.S.: 541715
Kazuhiro Hatano *(Pres & CEO)*

Subsidiaries:

Linical Accelovance America, Inc. (1)
2275 Research Blvd Ste 700, Rockville, MD 20850
Tel.: (240) 238-4900
Web Site: http://www.linical.com
Clinical Research & Development Services
N.A.I.C.S.: 541715
Vita Lanoce *(CEO)*

Subsidiary (Non-US):

Linical U.K. Limited (2)
Web Site: http://www.linical.com
Clinical Research & Development Services
N.A.I.C.S.: 541715

Subsidiary (Non-US):

THERAMetrics GmbH (3)
Zeche Katharina 6, 45307, Essen, Germany
Tel.: (49) 20189900
Clinical Research Services
N.A.I.C.S.: 541715

Linical France SARL (1)
15-17 rue Vulpian, 75013, Paris, France
Tel.: (33) 14 077 0570
Pharmaceuticals Product Mfr
N.A.I.C.S.: 325412

Linical Hungary Kft. (1)
Bojtar utca 39, 1037, Budapest, Hungary
Tel.: (36) 1 700 0040

Pharmaceuticals Product Mfr
N.A.I.C.S.: 325412

Linical Korea Co., Ltd. (1)
23F Seoul Finance Center Sejong-daero 136, Jung-gu, Seoul, 04520, Korea (South)
Tel.: (82) 22 038 8700
Pharmaceuticals Product Mfr
N.A.I.C.S.: 325412

Linical Netherlands B.V. (1)
Victorialaan 15, 5213 JG, 's-Hertogenbosch, Netherlands
Tel.: (31) 73 750 6636
Pharmaceuticals Product Mfr
N.A.I.C.S.: 325412

Linical Poland Sp. z o.o. (1)
Plac Ireneusza Gugulskiego 1, 02-661, Warsaw, Poland
Tel.: (48) 22 165 4600
Pharmaceuticals Product Mfr
N.A.I.C.S.: 325412

Linical Romania S.R.L. (1)
52 Take Ionescu Boulevard, 300073, Timisoara, Romania
Tel.: (40) 25 620 7271
Pharmaceuticals Product Mfr
N.A.I.C.S.: 325412

Linical Spain, S.L. (1)
Las Norias 92 Planta 2 Edificio Nuestra Senora del Pilar, Majadahonda, 28221, Madrid, Spain
Tel.: (34) 91 372 6000
Pharmaceuticals Product Mfr
N.A.I.C.S.: 325412

Linical Taiwan Co., Ltd. (1)
Room E 5F No 2 Sec 3 Minsheng E Rd, Zhongshan Dist, Taipei, 104, Taiwan
Tel.: (886) 22 503 8090
Pharmaceuticals Product Mfr
N.A.I.C.S.: 325412

Linical USA, Inc. (1)
68 3rd St, Brooklyn, NY 11231
Tel.: (561) 421-1446
Pharmaceuticals Product Mfr
N.A.I.C.S.: 325412

LINIU TECHNOLOGY GROUP
Alameda Dr Carlos D'Assumpcao No 181-187, Centro Com Grupo Brilhantismo Andar 12 Andar T, Macau, China (Macau)
Tel.: (853) 21119220 Ky
Year Founded: 2007
LINUF—(OTCIQ)
Sales Range: $25-49.9 Million
Emp.: 13
Gambling Establishments & Casino Hotels Operator
N.A.I.C.S.: 713290
Man Pou Lam *(Chm & CMO)*

LINIUS TECHNOLOGIES LIMITED
Suite 1 2A River Street, South Yarra, 3141, VIC, Australia
Tel.: (61) 386727186 AU
Web Site: https://www.linius.com
LNU—(ASX)
Rev.: $716,197
Assets: $873,657
Liabilities: $1,009,675
Net Worth: ($136,018)
Earnings: ($3,197,869)
Fiscal Year-end: 06/30/24
Investment Services
N.A.I.C.S.: 523999
Gerard Bongiorno *(Chm)*

LINK & MOTIVATION INC.
Kabukiza Tower 15F 4-12-15 Ginza, Chuo-ku, Tokyo, 104-0061, Japan
Tel.: (81) 367799494
Web Site: https://www.lmi.ne.jp
Year Founded: 2000
2170—(TKS)
Rev.: $240,840,210
Assets: $218,676,870
Liabilities: $126,932,270

Net Worth: $91,744,600
Earnings: $20,149,780
Emp.: 1,505
Fiscal Year-end: 12/31/23
Business Management Consulting Services
N.A.I.C.S.: 541618
Yoshihisa Ozasa *(Chm)*

Subsidiaries:

Dean Morgan K.K. (1)
12th Floor GINZA SIX 6-10-1 Ginza, Chuo-ku, Tokyo, 104-0061, Japan
Tel.: (81) 120335526
Web Site: http://www.rosettastone-lc.jp
Academy Services
N.A.I.C.S.: 611110
Dean R. Rogers *(Pres & CEO)*

Inbound Tech, Inc. (1)
Ohashi Building 9F 2313 Shinjuku, Shinjuku-ku, Tokyo, 160-0022, Japan
Tel.: (81) 362748400
Web Site: https://www.inboundtech.co.jp
Rev.: $21,931,980
Assets: $24,965,970
Liabilities: $7,237,950
Net Worth: $17,728,020
Earnings: $1,374,880
Fiscal Year-end: 03/31/2024
Application Development Services
N.A.I.C.S.: 541511
Yutaka Shimozono *(Chm)*

Link Academy Inc. (1)
Kabukiza Tower 15F 4-12-15 Ginza, Chuo-ku, Tokyo, 104-0061, Japan
Tel.: (81) 368538066
Web Site: https://www.link-academy.co.jp
Academy Services
N.A.I.C.S.: 611110

Link Corporate Communications Inc. (1)
4-12-15 Ginza Kabukiza Tower 15th floor, Chuo-ku, Tokyo, 104-0061, Japan
Tel.: (81) 368538060
Organizational Development Services
N.A.I.C.S.: 541715

Link Event Produce Inc. (1)
15th floor Kabukiza Tower 4-12-15 Ginza, Chuo-ku, Tokyo, 104-0061, Japan
Tel.: (81) 368538058
Web Site: https://www.event.link-ep.co.jp
Academy Services
N.A.I.C.S.: 611110

Link Global Solution Inc. (1)
Ginza Six 12F 6-10-1 Ginza, Chuo-ku, Tokyo, 104-0061, Japan
Tel.: (81) 367799420
Web Site: http://www.link-gs.co.jp
Organizational Consulting Services
N.A.I.C.S.: 541618
Yoshihisa Ozasa *(Chm & Dir-Rep)*

Link Interac Inc. (1)
15F 4-12-15 Ginza, Kabukiza Tower Chou-ku, Tokyo, 104-0061, Japan
Tel.: (81) 368538327
Web Site: http://www.interac.co.jp
Emp.: 3,600
Foreign Teachers for Schools & Commercial & Government Organizations
N.A.I.C.S.: 923110

Link Japan Careers Inc. (1)
Ginza Six 12F 6-10-1 Ginza, Kabukiza Tower Chou-ku, Tokyo, 104-0061, Japan
Tel.: (81) 367799460
Web Site: https://linkjapancareers.net
Consulting & Support Business Related Services
N.A.I.C.S.: 541614

Link-i Inc. (1)
4-12-15 Ginza Kabukiza Tower 15th Floor, Chuo-ku, Tokyo, 104-0061, Japan
Tel.: (81) 368538121
Training Education Services
N.A.I.C.S.: 611310

a2media corporation (1)
Ginza Six 12 Floor 6-10-1 Ginza, Chou-ku, Tokyo, 104-0061, Japan
Tel.: (81) 367799490
Web Site: http://www.a2media.co.jp
Business Software Development Services

LINK MOBILITY GROUP HOLDING ASA

N.A.I.C.S.: 541511
Kiyotaka Sakakibara *(Pres & CEO)*

LINK BILGISAYAR SISTEMLERI YAZILIMI VE DONANIMI SANAYI VE TICARET A.S.
Kisikli Caddesi No 2A/2 Ak is Merkezi Altunizade, Uskudar, 34662, Istanbul, Turkiye
Tel.: (90) 2165220000
Web Site: https://www.link.com.tr
Year Founded: 1984
LINK—(IST)
Sales Range: Less than $1 Million
Software Development Services
N.A.I.C.S.: 541511
Murat Kasaroglu *(Chm & Gen Mgr)*

LINK GLOBAL TECHNOLOGIES, INC.
1430-800 West Pender St, Vancouver, V6C 2V6, BC, Canada
Tel.: (403) 991-8587
Web Site: https://www.linkglobal.io
LNK—(CNSX)
Rev.: $991,052
Assets: $4,048,000
Liabilities: $5,643,442
Net Worth: ($1,595,442)
Earnings: ($3,651,865)
Fiscal Year-end: 11/30/20
Software Development Services
N.A.I.C.S.: 541511

LINK HOLDINGS LIMITED
Unit No 3503 35/F West Tower Shun Tak Centre, Nos 168-200 Connaught Road Central, Sheung Wan, China (Hong Kong)
Tel.: (852) 25810168 Ky
Web Site: http://www.linkholdingslimited.com
Year Founded: 2012
8237—(HKG)
Rev.: $6,339,144
Assets: $87,031,968
Liabilities: $58,892,523
Net Worth: $28,139,444
Earnings: ($14,760,591)
Emp.: 56
Fiscal Year-end: 12/31/21
Home Management Services
N.A.I.C.S.: 721110
Pak Tho Siew *(Compliance Officer)*

LINK MOBILITY GROUP HOLDING ASA
Gullhaug Torg 5, 484, Oslo, Norway
Tel.: (47) 22994400
Web Site: https://www.linkmobility.com
Year Founded: 2001
LINK—(OSL)
Rev.: $617,565,778
Assets: $1,148,290,102
Liabilities: $606,225,976
Net Worth: $542,064,125
Earnings: $3,770,595
Emp.: 686
Fiscal Year-end: 12/31/23
Mobilie Applications
N.A.I.C.S.: 513210
Jens Rugseth *(Founder & Chm)*

Subsidiaries:

Amm SpA (1)
Via Roma 26, 52100, Arezzo, Italy **(81.4%)**
Tel.: (39) 0575900732
Web Site: http://www.ammadv.it
Sales Range: Less than $1 Million
Advertising Agency Services
N.A.I.C.S.: 541810

LINK Mobility Hungary Kft. (1)
Andrassy ut 68 C 1 1, 1062, Budapest, Hungary
Tel.: (36) 702435625
Web Site: https://www.linkmobility.com

LINK MOBILITY GROUP HOLDING ASA

Link Mobility Group Holding ASA—(Continued)
Information Technology Services
N.A.I.C.S.: 541519

Link Mobility AS (1)
Gullhaug Torg 5, 0484, Oslo, Norway
Tel.: (47) 22994400
Web Site: https://www.linkmobility.com
Software Development Services
N.A.I.C.S.: 541511

Link Mobility EAD (1)
Bulgaria Square 1 NDK Administrative Building 7th Floor, 1463, Sofia, Bulgaria
Tel.: (359) 2 935 6969
Web Site: https://linkmobility.bg
Telecommunication Servicesb
N.A.I.C.S.: 517111

Link Mobility Oy (1)
Tynnyrintekijankatu 1 C, 00580, Helsinki, Finland
Tel.: (358) 104401010
Web Site: https://www.linkmobility.com
Telecommunication Servicesb
N.A.I.C.S.: 517111

Link Mobility SAS (1)
62 Ave Emile Zola, 92100, Boulogne-Billancourt, France
Tel.: (33) 183775900
Web Site: https://linkmobility.fr
Telecommunication Servicesb
N.A.I.C.S.: 517111

Link Mobility Sp. z o.o. (1)
Toszecka 101 5th Floor, 44-117, Gliwice, Poland
Tel.: (48) 327201206
Software Development Services
N.A.I.C.S.: 541511

MarketingPlatform ApS (1)
Birkmose Alle 37, 6000, Kolding, Denmark
Tel.: (45) 70261272
Web Site:
https://www.marketingplatform.com
Software Services
N.A.I.C.S.: 541511

MessageBroadcast, LLC (1)
4685 MacArthur Ct, Newport Beach, CA 92660-6476
Tel.: (949) 428-3111
Web Site:
https://www.messagebroadcast.com
Voice Messaging Services
N.A.I.C.S.: 517810
William H. Potter (Founder & CEO)

Teracomm RO SRL (1)
28 A Delea Veche Street Fl 2, 024102, Bucharest, 024102, Romania
Tel.: (40) 314255073
Web Site: https://www.teracomm.ro
Telecommunication Servicesb
N.A.I.C.S.: 517810

LINK MOTION INC.
No 4 Building 11 Heping Li East Street, Dongcheng District, Beijing, 100013, China
Tel.: (86) 1085655555 Ky
Web Site: http://www.lkmotion.com
Year Founded: 2005
Sales Range: $300-349.9 Million
Mobile Internet Security Software
N.A.I.C.S.: 513210
Vincent Wenyong Shi (Founder, Co-Chm & COO)

LINK PHARMA CHEM LTD.
Plot no 1611 162 G I D C, Nandesari, Baroda, 391 340, India
Tel.: (91) 2652840448
Web Site:
https://www.linkpharmachem.co.in
Year Founded: 1986
524748—(BOM)
Rev.: $4,754,849
Assets: $3,576,105
Liabilities: $1,861,585
Net Worth: $1,714,519
Earnings: $148,076
Emp.: 88

Fiscal Year-end: 03/31/21
Chemical Products Mfr
N.A.I.C.S.: 325199
Satish G. Thakur (Mng Dir)

LINK PROP INVESTMENT AB
c/o Wilfast Forvaltning AB Stora Badhusgatan 18, 411 21, Gothenburg, Sweden
Tel.: (46) 31171300
Web Site:
https://www.linkpropinvestment.se
Year Founded: 2015
LINKAB—(OMX)
Rev.: $3,604,110
Assets: $31,506,926
Liabilities: $19,861,942
Net Worth: $11,644,984
Earnings: $949,732
Fiscal Year-end: 12/31/22
Real Estate Investment
N.A.I.C.S.: 525990
Pontus Kagerman (Chm)

LINK RESERVATIONS, INC.
61 Bridge Street, Herefordshire, Kington, HR5 3DJ, United Kingdom
Tel.: (44) 3308080897
Web Site:
http://www.linkreservationsinc.com
LRSV—(OTCIQ)
Assets: $17,000
Liabilities: $271,000
Net Worth: ($254,000)
Earnings: ($96,000)
Fiscal Year-end: 12/31/20
Travel Agency Services
N.A.I.C.S.: 561510
Rene Lauritsen (Pres, CEO, Treas & Sec)

LINK SUSPENSIONS OF CANADA, LP
601 18th Ave, Nisku, T9E 7T7, AB, Canada
Tel.: (780) 955-2859
Web Site: http://www.linkmfg.com
Year Founded: 1992
Sales Range: $10-24.9 Million
Emp.: 40
Suspension Mfr
N.A.I.C.S.: 336330
Jim Huls (Pres)

LINK-ASIA INTERNATIONAL MEDTECH GROUP LIMITED
16/F Three Exchange Square 8 Connaught Place, Central, China (Hong Kong)
Tel.: (852) 21570118 Ky
Web Site: http://www.link-asia.com.hk
1143—(HKG)
Rev.: $67,479,503
Assets: $84,052,208
Liabilities: $37,895,168
Net Worth: $46,157,040
Earnings: ($6,631,148)
Emp.: 1,025
Fiscal Year-end: 12/31/22
Investment Services
N.A.I.C.S.: 523999
Darren Lin (Chm)

Subsidiaries:

Aiko Products Limited (1)
2-12 Au Pui Wan Street Sha Tin Unit D 2F Valiant Industrial Center, New Territories, Hong Kong, China (Hong Kong)
Tel.: (852) 29470160
Web Site: http://www.aikobeauty.com
Sales Range: $200-249.9 Million
Emp.: 600
Electronic Appliance Distr
N.A.I.C.S.: 423620

Subsidiary (Non-US):

Aiko Beauty (Shenzhen) Limited (2)

Room 1701 North Hubei Mansion No 9003 Binhe Road, Futian Dist, Shenzhen, 518033, Guangdong, China
Tel.: (86) 75583566313
Electronic Appliance Distr
N.A.I.C.S.: 423620

Fargo Telecom Holdings Limited (1)
Unit 3603-09 36/F 118 Connaught Road West, Hong Kong, China (Hong Kong) (53%)
Tel.: (852) 2869 0688
Web Site: http://www.fargotelecom.com
Holding Company; Telecommunications Equipment Designer, Mfr & Distr
N.A.I.C.S.: 551112

Subsidiary (Domestic):

Fargo Telecom Asia Limited (2)
36/F Yat Chau International Plaza No 118 Connaught Road, Cheung Sha Wan, Hong Kong, China (Hong Kong)
Tel.: (852) 2 869 0688
Web Site: http://www.fargotelecomasia.com
Telecommunication Equipment Distr
N.A.I.C.S.: 423690

Subsidiary (Non-US):

Fargo Telecom Technologies Pvt. Ltd. (3)
142/C Shubhangan 107 JP Road Opp Navrang Cinema, Andheri, Mumbai, 400058, India
Tel.: (91) 222 677 8586
Web Site: http://www.fargotelecomasia.com
Telecommunication Equipment Distr
N.A.I.C.S.: 423690

Subsidiary (Domestic):

Maestro Wireless Solutions Limited (2)
9th Floor Wing Cheong Factory Building, 121 King Lam Street Cheung Sha Wan, Kowloon, China (Hong Kong)
Tel.: (852) 39550222
Web Site: http://www.maestro-wireless.com
Wireless Communication Equipment Mfr
N.A.I.C.S.: 334220

Smart Gears Limited (2)
Unit 3603-09 36/F 118 Connaught Road West, Hong Kong, China (Hong Kong)
Tel.: (852) 2964 3240
Web Site: http://www.smart-gears.com
Wireless Communication Equipment Designer & Mfr
N.A.I.C.S.: 334220
Frank Tang (Dir-Technical)

Metro Creator Limited (1)
1Unit 609-610 6/F Bio-Informatics Centre No 2 Science Park West Avenue, Hong Kong Science Park, Sha Tin, NT, China (Hong Kong)
Tel.: (852) 3125 7388
Investment Holding Company
N.A.I.C.S.: 551112

Sino Achieve Limited (1)
Unit 609-610 6/F Bio-Informatics Centre No 2 Science Park West Avenue, Hong Kong Science Park, Sha Tin, NT, China (Hong Kong)
Tel.: (852) 3125 7388
Investment Holding Company
N.A.I.C.S.: 551112

Sota Acoustics Limited (1)
Unit 609-610 6/F Bio-Informatics Centre No 2 Science Park West Avenue, Hong Kong Science Park, Hong Kong, NT, China (Hong Kong)
Tel.: (852) 7876654436
Web Site: http://www.markaudiosota.co.uk
Loudspeaker Mfr & Distr
N.A.I.C.S.: 334310

Talent-Asia Holdings Co. Limited (1)
16F Three Exchange Square 8 Connaught Place, Central, China (Hong Kong)
Tel.: (852) 21570118
Web Site: https://www.talent-asia.com
Real Estate Services
N.A.I.C.S.: 531390

Telefield Limited (1)
Unit 613 6/F Building 12W Phase III No 12 Science Park West Avenue, Hong Kong

INTERNATIONAL PUBLIC

Science Park, Sha Tin, New Territories, China (Hong Kong)
Tel.: (852) 3 125 7368
Web Site: https://www.telefield.com.hk
Electronic Products Mfr
N.A.I.C.S.: 334419

Telefield NA, Inc. (1)
4915 SW Griffith Dr Ste 302, Beaverton, OR 97005
Tel.: (503) 511-3180
Web Site: https://www.rca4business.com
Cordless Phone Retailer
N.A.I.C.S.: 449210

TrekStor GmbH (1)
Kastanienallee 8-10, 64653, Lorsch, Hesse, Germany
Tel.: (49) 6251550400
Web Site: http://www.trekstor.de
Sales Range: $25-49.9 Million
Emp.: 60
Audio & Storage Device Mfr & Sales
N.A.I.C.S.: 334112
Shimon Szmigiel (CEO)

LINK-U GROUP INC
7th floor Sumitomo Fudousann Ochanomizu Building 2-2-3 Sotokanda, Chiyoda-Ku, Tokyo, 101-0021, Japan
Tel.: (81) 362609279
Web Site: https://link-u.group
Year Founded: 2013
4446—(TKS)
Rev.: $22,777,640
Assets: $28,848,360
Liabilities: $11,587,860
Net Worth: $17,260,500
Earnings: $1,424,380
Emp.: 157
Fiscal Year-end: 07/31/24
Application Development Services
N.A.I.C.S.: 541511
Yuki Matsubara (Founder, Pres & CEO)

LINKAGE ASSURANCE PLC
Plot 20 Block 94 Providence Street, Off Adewunmi Adebimpe Street Lekki Phase 1, Lagos, Nigeria
Tel.: (234) 70054652273
Web Site:
https://www.linkageassurance.com
Year Founded: 1991
LINKASSURE—(NIGE)
Rev.: $9,607,613
Assets: $29,605,599
Liabilities: $11,248,464
Net Worth: $18,357,135
Earnings: $1,900,007
Emp.: 160
Fiscal Year-end: 12/31/22
Non-Life Insurance Services
N.A.I.C.S.: 524298
Anthony Saiki (Head-Acting-Mktg)

LINKAGE GLOBAL INC.
2-23-3 Minami-Ikebukuro, Toshima-ku, Tokyo, 171-0022, Japan
Tel.: (81) 359279261 Ky
Web Site: https://www.linkagecc.com
Year Founded: 2022
LGCB—(NASDAQ)
Rev.: $22,028,303
Assets: $9,079,231
Liabilities: $6,344,678
Net Worth: $2,734,553
Earnings: $1,066,375
Emp.: 107
Fiscal Year-end: 09/30/22
Digital Marketing Services
N.A.I.C.S.: 541810
Zhihua Wu (CEO)

LINKAGE SOFTWARE CO., LTD.
No 96 Qitai Road Lingzhi Building, Industrial Park, Suzhou, 215028, Jiangsu, China
Tel.: (86) 2161659566

Web Site: https://www.linkstec.com
Year Founded: 2003
688588—(SHG)
Rev.: $91,893,485
Assets: $203,860,196
Liabilities: $15,358,342
Net Worth: $188,501,854
Earnings: $19,823,062
Fiscal Year-end: 12/31/22
Software Development Services
N.A.I.C.S.: 541511
Baoquan Zhang *(Chm & Gen Mgr)*

LINKBAL INC.
Tsukiji Riverfront 6F 7-14, Akashicho, Tokyo, 104-0044, Japan
Tel.: (81) 5017412300
Web Site: https://linkbal.co.jp
6046—(TKS)
Sales Range: $10-24.9 Million
Emp.: 114
Online Dating Services
N.A.I.C.S.: 812990

LINKDOC TECHNOLOGY LTD.
11/F Building A Zhonggang International Square, Haidian District, Beijing, 100080, China
Tel.: (86) 10 6268 0809 Ky
Year Founded: 2014
Rev.: $144,263,063
Assets: $130,805,936
Liabilities: $403,415,564
Net Worth: ($272,609,629)
Earnings: ($72,918,589)
Emp.: 1,250
Fiscal Year-end: 12/31/20
Information Technology Services
N.A.I.C.S.: 541512
Tianze Zhang *(Co-Founder & CEO)*

LINKERS INDUSTRIES LIMITED
Lot A99 Jalan 2A-3 A101 & A102 Jalan 2A Kawasan Perusahaan MIEL, Sungai Lalang Darul Aman, 08000, Sungai Petani, Kedah, Malaysia
Tel.: (60) 44417802 VG
Web Site: https://www.linkers-hk.com
Year Founded: 2022
LNKS—(NASDAQ)
Rev.: $4,756,203
Assets: $7,148,982
Liabilities: $3,504,925
Net Worth: $3,644,057
Earnings: ($424,001)
Emp.: 209
Fiscal Year-end: 06/30/24
Wire Product Mfr & Distr
N.A.I.C.S.: 335929

LINKGENESIS CO., LTD.
319 Daeryung Techno Town 15 Cha 401 Simin-daero, Dongan-gu, Anyang, 14057, Gyeonggi-do, Korea (South)
Tel.: (82) 314223581
Web Site: https://www.linkgenesis.co.kr
Year Founded: 2003
219420—(KRS)
Rev.: $13,244,490
Assets: $36,397,630
Liabilities: $2,877,346
Net Worth: $33,520,283
Earnings: $1,479,167
Emp.: 106
Fiscal Year-end: 12/31/22
Automation Software Development Services
N.A.I.C.S.: 541511
Sung-woo Jung *(CEO)*

LINKHOUSE INDUSTRIES LTD.
1st Floor B Poonam Chambers Chhindwara Road, Byramji Town, Nagpur, 440 013, India
Tel.: (91) 7126611216
Building Construction Services
N.A.I.C.S.: 236210
Nandkumar K. Harchandani *(Chm & Mng Dir)*

LINKLOGIS INC.
35/F 36/F & 39/F 36 CES Building No 3099 Keyuan South Road, Nanshan District, Shenzhen, 518063, Guangdong, China
Tel.: (86) 75523915717 Ky
Web Site: https://www.linklogis.com
Year Founded: 2016
9959—(HKG)
Rev.: $141,596,682
Assets: $1,826,930,583
Liabilities: $301,490,928
Net Worth: $1,525,439,655
Earnings: ($3,348,405)
Emp.: 981
Fiscal Year-end: 12/31/22
Information Technology Services
N.A.I.C.S.: 541512
Ka King Chau *(Vice Chm)*

Subsidiaries:

Linklogis International Company Limited (1)
Rm 05-06 49/F Central Plaza 18 Harbour Road, Wanchai, China (Hong Kong)
Tel.: (852) 37933339
Web Site: https://www.linklogis.com.hk
Bank Financing Services
N.A.I.C.S.: 522310

LINKSON INTERNATIONAL LTD.
B-103 Pushp Heritage Dhanukarwadi, Mahavir Nagar Kandivli West, Mumbai, 400067, Maharashtra, India
Tel.: (91) 7122553701
Year Founded: 1984
508982—(BOM)
Coal Product Distr
N.A.I.C.S.: 423520
Yashwant Sangla *(Mng Dir)*

LINKTEL TECHNOLOGIES CO., LTD.
No 19 Jiulonghu Street East Lake Hi-tech Development Zone, East-Lake Hi-tech Development Zone, Wuhan, 430205, Hubei, China
Tel.: (86) 2787929298
Web Site: https://linktel.com
Year Founded: 2011
301205—(CHIN)
Rev.: $115,789,284
Assets: $234,080,496
Liabilities: $36,151,596
Net Worth: $197,928,900
Earnings: $15,901,704
Fiscal Year-end: 12/31/22
Communication Transceiver Mfr
N.A.I.C.S.: 334220
Gavin Wu *(VP)*

LINMON MEDIA LIMITED
28/F Building A SOHO Renaissance Plaza, Huangpu, Shanghai, China
Tel.: (86) 2155698508 Ky
Web Site: https://www.linmon.cn
Year Founded: 2014
9857—(HKG)
Rev.: $169,161,498
Assets: $493,950,210
Liabilities: $137,483,800
Net Worth: $356,466,410
Earnings: $29,578,533
Emp.: 180
Fiscal Year-end: 12/31/23
Television Broadcasting Services
N.A.I.C.S.: 516120
Fei Chen *(CEO)*

LINNEA YACHT GROUP
Varvsvagen 1, 47331, Henan, Sweden
Tel.: (46) 304692300
Web Site: http://www.linneayachtgroup.se
Year Founded: 2008
Sales Range: $50-74.9 Million
Emp.: 100
Boat Building
N.A.I.C.S.: 336612
Perling Quist *(Mng Dir)*

Subsidiaries:

Najardvarvet AB (1)
Varvsvagen 1, 47331, Henan, Sweden
Tel.: (46) 304692300
Web Site: http://www.najad.se
Sales Range: $50-74.9 Million
Boat Building
N.A.I.C.S.: 336612
Magnus Ridderstad *(Mgr-Sls & Mktg)*

LINOCRAFT HOLDINGS LIMITED
Lot 1769 Jalan Belati Off Jalan Kempas Lama, Taman Perindustrian Maju Jaya, Johor Bahru, Johor Darul Takzim, Malaysia
Tel.: (60) 75540090 Ky
Web Site: http://www.linocraftprinters.com
Year Founded: 1972
8383—(HKG)
Rev.: $57,437,672
Assets: $69,290,794
Liabilities: $47,792,169
Net Worth: $21,498,624
Earnings: $1,238,730
Emp.: 974
Fiscal Year-end: 08/31/22
Packaging Services
N.A.I.C.S.: 561910
Yoong Nyock Ong *(Chm)*

Subsidiaries:

Linocraft Printers Philippines Inc. (1)
Bldg 2B Lot 3 Block 10 Light Industry & Science Park 3 LISP III, Sto Tomas, Batangas, 4243, Philippines
Tel.: (63) 433219207
Printing & Packaging Services
N.A.I.C.S.: 561910

Linocraft Printers Sdn. Bhd. (1)
Lot 1769 Jalan Belati Off Jalan Kempas Lama Taman Perindustrian, Maju Jaya Johor Darul Takzim, 81300, Johor Bahru, Malaysia
Tel.: (60) 75540090
Printing & Packaging Services
N.A.I.C.S.: 561910

Linocraft Singapore Pte. Ltd. (1)
Block 18 Boon Lay Way 03-111 Tradehub 21, Singapore, 609966, Singapore
Tel.: (65) 66591390
Printing & Packaging Services
N.A.I.C.S.: 561910

LINQ CAPITAL LIMITED
Level 1 17 Ord Street, West Perth, 6005, WA, Australia
Tel.: (61) 8 9488 8888 AU
Web Site: http://www.thelinqgroup.com
Emp.: 5
Investment Fund Management & Corporate Advisory Services
N.A.I.C.S.: 523940
Clive Donner *(Founder, Mng Dir & Partner)*

LINS TRADING LTD.
Lins House 38 Rosebery Avenue, London, EC1R 4RN, United Kingdom
Tel.: (44) 2078330707
Web Site: http://www.linstrading.net
Year Founded: 1990
Holding Company
N.A.I.C.S.: 551112

Subsidiaries:

Speciality Coatings (Darwen) Ltd. (1)
Dewhurst St, Southend Mill, Darwen, BB3 2EN, United Kingdom
Tel.: (44) 1254706026
Web Site: http://www.sclgroup.com
Sales Range: $25-49.9 Million
Emp.: 47
Wallcoverings, PVC Coatings & Plastisols
N.A.I.C.S.: 326199
Paul Phillips *(Mng Dir)*

LINTEC CORPORATION
23-23 Honcho, Itabashi-ku, Tokyo, 173-0001, Japan
Tel.: (81) 352487711
Web Site: https://www.lintec-global.com
Year Founded: 1934
7966—(TKS)
Rev.: $1,826,481,810
Assets: $2,205,373,620
Liabilities: $665,349,380
Net Worth: $1,540,024,240
Earnings: $34,656,230
Emp.: 5,476
Fiscal Year-end: 03/31/24
Adhesive Material Mfr & Whslr
N.A.I.C.S.: 325520
Gohei Kawamura *(Sr Mng Exec Officer & Exec Gen Mgr-Production & Quality Assurance)*

Subsidiaries:

LINTEC (SUZHOU) TECH CORPORATION (1)
No 30 Taishan Road, Suzhou New District, Suzhou, Jiangsu, China
Tel.: (86) 51266653110
Web Site: https://lintec-china.com
Adhesive Material Mfr & Distr
N.A.I.C.S.: 325520

LINTEC (THAILAND) CO., LTD. (1)
128/2 Moo 5 Bangna-Trad Rd, Bangsamak Bangpakong, Chachoengsao, 24130, Thailand
Tel.: (66) 33051195
Web Site: https://www.lintec.co.th
Adhesive Product Mfr & Distr
N.A.I.C.S.: 325520
Chawinda Phu *(Mgr)*

LINTEC (TIANJIN) INDUSTRY CO., LTD. (1)
No 85 Xi Hu Rd Nan Kai District, Tianjin, 300190, China
Tel.: (86) 22 2703 0923
Printing Machinery Mfr & Distr
N.A.I.C.S.: 333248

LINTEC ADVANCED TECHNOLOGIES (EUROPE) GMBH (1)
Konrad-Zuse-Platz 1, 81829, Munich, Germany
Tel.: (49) 89 998850 0
Web Site: http://www.linteceurope.com
Emp.: 25
Semiconductor Material Distr
N.A.I.C.S.: 423690
Michio Iwamoto *(Mng Dir)*

LINTEC ADVANCED TECHNOLOGIES (KOREA), INC. (1)
13F The Pinnacle Gangnam 343 Hakdong-Ro, Gangnam-Gu, Seoul, 06060, Korea (South)
Tel.: (82) 25481537
Emp.: 24
Semiconductor Product Distr
N.A.I.C.S.: 423690
Ukagaae Makoto *(Mgr)*

LINTEC ADVANCED TECHNOLOGIES (MALAYSIA) SDN. (1)
No 18-1 Jalan KPMB 1 Kompleks Perniagaan Musai Bistari, 75400, Melaka, Malaysia
Tel.: (60) 62883730
Semiconductor Material Distr
N.A.I.C.S.: 423690

LINTEC CORPORATION

LINTEC Corporation—(Continued)

LINTEC ADVANCED TECHNOLOGIES (PHILIPPINES), INC. (1)
Unit 1006 and 1007 CTP Asean Tower 2409 Asean Drive, Spectrum District Filinvest City Alabang, Muntinlupa, 1781, Philippines
Tel.: (63) 27723308
Web Site: http://www.lintech.com.sg
Emp.: 10
Semiconductor Material Distr
N.A.I.C.S.: 423690

LINTEC ADVANCED TECHNOLOGIES (SHANGHAI), INC. (1)
Room2802-05 Shanghai Maxdo Center No 8 Xing Yi Rd, Changning District, Shanghai, 200336, China
Tel.: (86) 2152082058
Semiconductor Material Distr
N.A.I.C.S.: 423690
Emil Xu *(Mng Dir)*

LINTEC ADVANCED TECHNOLOGIES (TAIWAN), INC. (1)
No 6 Zhongliu Road, Qianzhen District, Kaohsiung, 00806, Taiwan
Tel.: (886) 78117000
Web Site: https://www.lintec.com.tw
Semiconductor Material Distr
N.A.I.C.S.: 423690

LINTEC BKK PTE LIMITED (1)
11 Q-House Sathorn Bldg 8th Fl South Sathorn Rd Tungmahamek, Sathorn, Bangkok, 10120, Thailand
Tel.: (66) 2 287 0660
Adhesive Product Distr
N.A.I.C.S.: 424690

LINTEC EUROPE B.V. (1)
Schweitzerlaan 88, 1187 JD, Amstelveen, Netherlands
Tel.: (31) 206733566
Web Site: http://www.lintec-europe.com
Adhesive Material Distr
N.A.I.C.S.: 424690

LINTEC HI-TECH (TAIWAN), INC. (1)
10F-5 No 318 Songjiang Road, Zhongshan District, Taipei, 10468, Taiwan
Tel.: (886) 225717696
Web Site: https://www.lintec-ht.com.tw
Adhesive Product Distr
N.A.I.C.S.: 424690

LINTEC INDUSTRIES (MALAYSIA) SDN. BHD. (1)
783 Jalan Perindustrian Bukit Minyak Bukit Minyak Industrial Park, 14000, Bukit Mertajam, Penang, Malaysia
Tel.: (60) 45086236
Capacitor Mfr & Distr
N.A.I.C.S.: 334416
Norzila Mansor *(Mgr-Admin)*

LINTEC INDUSTRIES (SARAWAK) SDN. BHD. (1)
Lot 993 Block 12 Jalan Muara Tabuan Kawasan MIEL Sama Jaya, Free Industrial Zone, 93450, Kuching, Sarawak, Malaysia
Tel.: (60) 82364977
Capacitor Mfr & Distr
N.A.I.C.S.: 334416

LINTEC KOREA, INC. (1)
118 Gwahaksaneop 4-ro Ochang-eup, Cheongwon-gu, Cheongju, 28122, Chungcheongbuk, Korea (South)
Tel.: (82) 432155588
Web Site: http://www.lintec.co.kr
Semiconductor Product Mfr & Distr
N.A.I.C.S.: 334413

LINTEC OF AMERICA, INC. (1)
15930 S 48th St Ste 110, Phoenix, AZ 85048
Tel.: (480) 966-0784
Web Site: https://www.lintec-usa.com
Semiconductor Product Mfr & Distr
N.A.I.C.S.: 334413

Subsidiary (Domestic):

Morgan Adhesives Company, LLC (2)
4560 Darrow Rd, Stow, OH 44224
Web Site: https://www.mactac.com
Pressure Sensitive Packaging Materials Mfr & Distr
N.A.I.C.S.: 325520
Ed LaForge *(Pres & CEO)*

Subsidiary (Non-US):

Mactac Mexico, S.A. de C.V. (3)
Calle 13 Ext 270 int D Colonia Industrial Valle del Alamo, Guadalajara, Jalisco, Mexico
Tel.: (52) 336062548
Web Site: https://www.mactac.com
Pressure Sensitive Adhesive Products Mfr & Distr
N.A.I.C.S.: 325520

Mactac Scandinavia AB (3)
Hemsoegatan 10A, Box 50235, Malmo, 202 12, Sweden
Tel.: (46) 406803130
Web Site: http://www.mactacgraphics.eu
Pressure Sensitive Adhesive Products Mfr & Distr
N.A.I.C.S.: 325520

Mactac U.K. Limited (3)
37 Tenter Rd, Moulton Park Industrial Estate, Northampton, NN3 6AX, United Kingdom
Tel.: (44) 1604644697
Web Site: http://www.mactacgraphics.eu
Pressure Sensitive Adhesive Products Mfr & Distr
N.A.I.C.S.: 325520

Subsidiary (Domestic):

Spinnaker Coating, LLC (3)
518 E Water St, Troy, OH 45373-3445
Tel.: (937) 332-6500
Web Site: http://www.spinps.com
Mfr of Dry Gummed Papers, Pressure Sensitive Sheet & Roll Products, Label Papers, Conventional Gummed Papers, Gummed Tapes & Acid Free Adhesive Coated Products
N.A.I.C.S.: 322220
Braden L. Glett *(VP-Strategic Improvement)*

Plant (Domestic):

Spinnaker Coating, LLC - Plant 2 (4)
180 Marybill Dr, Troy, OH 45373
Coated Paper Mfr
N.A.I.C.S.: 322220

LINTEC PHILIPPINES (PEZA), INC. (1)
No 4 Lot 2 Blk 2 EZP Technohub Laguna Technopark Annex, Binan, 4024, Laguna, Philippines
Tel.: (63) 495300997
Web Site: http://www.lintec.com.sg
Emp.: 16
Adhesive Product Distr
N.A.I.C.S.: 424690

LINTEC SINGAPORE PRIVATE LIMITED (1)
20 Bendemeer Rd 04-11/14 BS Bendemeer Centre, Singapore, 339914, Singapore
Tel.: (65) 62215854
Web Site: https://www.lintec.com.sg
Semiconductor Product Mfr & Distr
N.A.I.C.S.: 334413

LINTEC SPECIALITY FILMS (KOREA), INC. (1)
35 Poseunggongdan-ro 117beon-gil, Poseung-eup, Pyeongtaek, 17956, Gyeonggi-do, Korea (South)
Tel.: (82) 316812266
Optical Products Mfr & Distr
N.A.I.C.S.: 333310

LINTEC SPECIALITY FILMS (TAIWAN), INC. (1)
2F-B No 32 Sec 2 Tainan Science Park Huandong Rd, Shanhua District, Tainan City, 741, Taiwan
Tel.: (886) 65053868
Optical Product Mfr & Distr
N.A.I.C.S.: 333310

LINTEC VIETNAM CO., LTD. (1)
No 40 VSIP II Street No 1 Vietnam-Singapore Industrial Park II, Hoa Phu Ward, Thu Dau Mot, Binh Duong, Vietnam
Tel.: (84) 2743628268
Web Site: http://www.lintec-global.com
Adhesive Product Distr
N.A.I.C.S.: 424690

Lintec Advanced Technologies (Europe) GmbH (1)
10 Openhaimer St The Science Park, Rehovot, 76701, Israel
Tel.: (972) 86521250
Semiconductor Related Parts Whslr
N.A.I.C.S.: 423690

Lintec Advanced Technologies (Malaysia) Sdn. Bhd. (1)
No 18-1 Jalan KPMB 1 Kompleks Perniagaan Musai Bistari, 75400, Melaka, Malaysia
Tel.: (60) 62883730
Adhesive Related Product Whslr
N.A.I.C.S.: 424690
Chee Siang Ooi *(Engr-Sls & Technical Svc)*

Lintec Asia Pacific Regional Headquarters Pte. Ltd. (1)
BS Bendemeer Centre 03-06 20 Bendemeer Rd, Singapore, 339914, Singapore
Tel.: (65) 68124188
Adhesive Related Product Mfr & Whslr
N.A.I.C.S.: 325520

Lintec Corporation (1)
Room CP2 19 03A 19F Tower 2 Capital Place Building 29 Lieu Giai St, Ngoc Khanh Ward Ba Dinh District, Hanoi, Vietnam
Tel.: (84) 436770088
Semiconductor Related Parts Whslr
N.A.I.C.S.: 423690

Lintec Europe (UK) Limited (1)
Unit 4 Century Point Halifax Road Cressex Business Park, High Wycombe, HP12 3SL, United Kingdom
Tel.: (44) 1628777766
Web Site: http://www.lintec-europe.com
Stationery Product Mfr & Whslr
N.A.I.C.S.: 323111

Lintec Europe B.V. (1)
Madach Imre ut 13-14 B, 1075, Budapest, Hungary
Tel.: (36) 12660322
Stationery Product Mfr & Whslr
N.A.I.C.S.: 323111

Lintec Hanoi Vietnam Co., Ltd. (1)
No 6 St 9 VSIP, Tu Son Town, Bac Ninh, Vietnam
Tel.: (84) 2413765861
Adhesive Related Product Whslr
N.A.I.C.S.: 424690

Lintec India Private Limited (1)
5F Unit No 507 508 Ashoka Estate Building 24 Barakhamba, New Delhi, 110001, India
Tel.: (91) 1144731800
Adhesive Related Product Whslr
N.A.I.C.S.: 424690

Lintec Kuala Lumpur Sdn. Bhd. (1)
No 9 Jalan Sejahtera 25/124 Seksyen 25, Axis Premier Industrial Park, 40400, Shah Alam, Selangor Darul Ehsan, Malaysia
Tel.: (60) 351201851
Adhesive Related Product Whslr
N.A.I.C.S.: 424690

Madico, Inc. (1)
9251 Belcher Rd N, Pinellas Park, FL 33782
Tel.: (727) 327-2544
Web Site: https://www.madico.com
Emp.: 350
Plastics Films Mfr
N.A.I.C.S.: 326113

Subsidiary (Domestic):

Madico Window Films Inc (2)
2630 Fairfield Ave S, Saint Petersburg, FL 33712
Tel.: (727) 327-2544
Plastic Film Mfr & Distr
N.A.I.C.S.: 326113

PT. LINTEC JAKARTA (1)
Talavera Office Park 11th Fl Jl Letjend TB Simatupang Kav 22-26, Jakarta, 12430, Indonesia
Tel.: (62) 2175925150
Web Site: https://www.lintecjakarta.co.id
Emp.: 20

INTERNATIONAL PUBLIC

Adhesive Material Distr
N.A.I.C.S.: 424690
Fajar Solihin *(Gen Mgr)*

PT. Lintec Indonesia (1)
Kawasan Industri Menara Permai Desa Dayeuh Jl Raya Narogong Km 23 85, Cileungsi, Bogor, 16820, Indonesia
Tel.: (62) 218231470
Adhesive Related Product Mfr & Whslr
N.A.I.C.S.: 325520

VDI, LLC (1)
1294 Old Fern Valley Rd, Louisville, KY 40219
Tel.: (502) 969-4227
Web Site: https://www.vdi-llc.com
Printing Plates, Holographic Materials & Industrial Products Mfr
N.A.I.C.S.: 332812

LINUS DIGITAL FINANCE AG

Karl-Liebknecht-Strasse 5, 10178, Berlin, Germany
Tel.: (49) 30629396810
Web Site: https://www.linus-finance.com
Year Founded: 2016
LDF—(BER)
Rev.: $5,916,768
Assets: $124,020,311
Liabilities: $110,762,777
Net Worth: $13,257,534
Earnings: ($5,894,690)
Emp.: 22
Fiscal Year-end: 12/31/23
Real Estate Development Services
N.A.I.C.S.: 531190
Julia Ariens *(Chief Risk Officer)*

Subsidiaries:

Linus Relationship Management GmbH (1)
Karl-Liebknecht-Strasse 5, 10178, Berlin, Germany
Tel.: (49) 30629396810
Investment Management Service
N.A.I.C.S.: 523999

LINUX GOLD CORP.

Suite 240 11780 Hammersmith Way, Richmond, V7A 5E9, BC, Canada
Tel.: (604) 278-5996
Year Founded: 1979
Gold Mining Services
N.A.I.C.S.: 212220
John George Robertson *(Pres & CEO)*

LINYI KAIYUAN BEARING CO., LTD.

Yinan Economic Development Zone, Yinan, Linyi, 276000, Shandong, China
Tel.: (86) 5393641049
Web Site: http://www.ym-bearing.cn
Bearing Mfr
N.A.I.C.S.: 332991
Zhang Anxi *(Pres)*

LINZ TEXTIL HOLDING AG

Wiener Strasse 435, 4030, Linz, Austria
Tel.: (43) 7323996
Web Site: https://www.linz-textil.at
LTH—(VIE)
Sales Range: $100-124.9 Million
Emp.: 597
Holding Company; Yarn & Fabric Mfr
N.A.I.C.S.: 551112
Anton Schneider *(Chm-Supervisory Bd)*

Subsidiaries:

Linz Textil Gesellschaft m.b.H. (1)
Wiener Strasse 435, 4030, Linz, Austria
Tel.: (43) 732 3996 0
Textile Products Mfr
N.A.I.C.S.: 314999

AND PRIVATE COMPANIES / LION CORPORATION

Subsidiary (Non-US):

Predionica Klanjec d.o.o. (2)
Novodvorska 7, 49290, Klanjec, Krapinsko-Zagorska, Croatia
Tel.: (385) 49 588300
Textile Products Mfr
N.A.I.C.S.: 314999

Subsidiary (Domestic):

Vossen GmbH & Co. KG (2)
Vossenlande 1, Jennersdorf, 8380, Austria
Tel.: (43) 3329 400 0
Web Site: http://www.vossen.com
Emp.: 150
Towel & Bathrobe Whslr
N.A.I.C.S.: 423220

Subsidiary (Non-US):

VOSSEN UK Ltd. (3)
Gothic House Barker Gate, Nottingham, NG1 1JU, United Kingdom
Tel.: (44) 115 95880 22
Web Site: http://www.vossen.com
Emp.: 1
Towel & Bathrobe Whslr
N.A.I.C.S.: 423220
Michael Ponberth *(Gen Mgr)*

LINZHOU HEAVY MACHINERY GROUP CO., LTD.

Intersection of Fengbao Avenue and Lingyang Avenue, Industrial Cluster District, Linzhou, 456561, Henan, China
Tel.: (86) 3723263686
Web Site: http://www.lzzj.com
Year Founded: 1987
002535—(SSE)
Rev.: $157,217,112
Assets: $589,396,392
Liabilities: $530,484,552
Net Worth: $58,911,840
Earnings: $2,417,688
Emp.: 1,900
Fiscal Year-end: 12/31/22
Mining Machinery Mfr & Whslr
N.A.I.C.S.: 333131
Luyun Han *(Chm)*

LION ASIAPAC LIMITED

10 Arumugam Road 10-00 Lion Building A, Singapore, 409957, Singapore
Tel.: (65) 66320500
Web Site:
 https://www.lionasiapac.com
Year Founded: 1968
BAZ—(SES)
Rev.: $22,494,998
Assets: $48,087,440
Liabilities: $4,916,636
Net Worth: $43,170,804
Earnings: ($2,226,010)
Emp.: 68
Fiscal Year-end: 06/30/23
Electronic Contract Mfr
N.A.I.C.S.: 334416
Chong Keen Sam *(Chm)*

Subsidiaries:

Compact Energy Sdn. Bhd. (1)
Lot 2319 Kawasan Perindustrian Olak Lempit, Tanjung Dua Belas, 42700, Banting, Selangor, Malaysia
Tel.: (60) 193772885
Web Site:
 https://www.compactenergy.com.my
Sales Range: $50-74.9 Million
Emp.: 40
Limestone Processing Services
N.A.I.C.S.: 212312

LION CAPITAL LLP

21 Grosvenor Place, London, SW1X 7HF, United Kingdom
Tel.: (44) 2072012200
Web Site: http://www.lioncapital.com
Year Founded: 2004
Rev.: $5,311,089,000
Emp.: 50

Privater Equity Firm
N.A.I.C.S.: 523999
Javier Ferran *(Partner)*

Subsidiaries:

Alain Afflelou Franchiseur SAS (1)
Batiment 264 45 Avenue Victor Hugo, 93300, Aubervilliers, France
Tel.: (33) 1 4937 7377
Web Site: http://www.alainafflelou.fr
Sales Range: $1-4.9 Billion
Eyeglasses Designer & Franchise Retailer
N.A.I.C.S.: 533110
Laurent Afflelou *(Mgr-Bus Dev)*

All Saints Retail Limited (1)
Units C15-17 Jacks Place 6 Corbet Place, London, E1 6NN, United Kingdom
Tel.: (44) 1332851600
Web Site: http://www.allsaints.com
Apparel Retailer
N.A.I.C.S.: 458110
Maria Giambrone *(Controller-Fin)*

Findus Group Limited (1)
77 Kingsway First Floor, London, WC2B 6SR, United Kingdom
Tel.: (44) 207 430 8181
Web Site: http://www.findusgroup.com
Sales Range: $1-4.9 Billion
Holding Company; Frozen Seafood & Foods Mfr & Whslr
N.A.I.C.S.: 551112
James Hill *(CEO)*

John Varvatos Enterprises, Inc. (1)
26 W 17th St, New York, NY 10011
Tel.: (212) 812-8000
Web Site: http://www.johnvarvatos.com
Footwear & Clothes Products Whslr
N.A.I.C.S.: 424340
John Varvatos *(Chm & Chief Creative Officer)*

Subsidiary (Domestic):

John Varvatos Apparel Corp. (2)
3411 Silverside Rd, Wilmington, DE 19810-4803
Footwear Products Whslr
N.A.I.C.S.: 424340

Picard Surgeles S.A. (1)
BP 93, 77792, Nemours, France
Tel.: (33) 810 13 12 11
Web Site: http://www.picard.fr
Frozen Food Retailer
N.A.I.C.S.: 424420

LION CHEMTECH CO., LTD.

36 Daedeokdae-ro 1277 beon-gil, Daedeok-gu, Daejeon, Korea (South)
Tel.: (82) 429303300
Web Site: https://www.lctkorea.com
Year Founded: 1973
171120—(KRS)
Rev.: $116,584,522
Assets: $116,459,767
Liabilities: $22,463,348
Net Worth: $93,996,419
Earnings: $6,786,432
Emp.: 268
Fiscal Year-end: 12/31/22
Plastic & Paint Additives, Synthetic & Natural Waxes Mfr
N.A.I.C.S.: 325998
Hee Won Park *(Pres)*

LION COPPER AND GOLD CORP.

Suite 1200-750 West Pender St, Vancouver, V6C 2T8, BC, Canada
Tel.: (604) 684-9384 BC
Web Site: https://www.lioncg.com
Year Founded: 1993
LCGMF—(OTCQB)
Rev.: $2,327,000
Assets: $10,839,000
Liabilities: $3,858,000
Net Worth: $6,981,000
Earnings: ($1,928,000)
Emp.: 8
Fiscal Year-end: 12/31/22

Precious Metal & Uranium Mining Services
N.A.I.C.S.: 212290
Steven A. Dischler *(CEO)*

LION CORPORATION

1-3-28 Kuramae, Taito-ku, Tokyo, 111-8644, Japan
Tel.: (81) 367393711
Web Site: https://www.lion.co.jp
Year Founded: 1891
4912—(TKS)
Rev.: $2,855,618,030
Assets: $3,448,313,670
Liabilities: $1,334,543,610
Net Worth: $2,113,770,060
Earnings: $103,684,160
Emp.: 7,550
Fiscal Year-end: 12/31/23
Mfr & Retailer Household & Beauty Products, Pharmaceuticals, Food & Chemicals
N.A.I.C.S.: 325620
Annette Ling *(Exec Officer)*

Subsidiaries:

Bushu Distribution Co., Ltd. (1)
14-14 Kamishinozaki 3-chome, Edogawa-ku, Tokyo, 133-0054, Japan (100%)
Tel.: (81) 336704141
Sales Range: $10-24.9 Million
Emp.: 100
N.A.I.C.S.: 325620

CJ Lion Corporation (1)
23 Seohae-daero 140beon-gil, Jung-gu, Incheon, Korea (South) (81%)
Tel.: (82) 32 881 2690
Web Site: http://www.lionkorea.co.kr
Household Detergent Mfr
N.A.I.C.S.: 325611

Global Eco Chemicals Singapore Pte. Ltd. (1)
56 Neil Road, Singapore, 088830, Singapore (50%)
Tel.: (65) 62160244
Toilet Preparation Mfr
N.A.I.C.S.: 325620

Subsidiary (Non-US):

Global Eco Chemicals Malaysia Sdn. Bhd. (2)
Industrial Complex Plo 116 Jalan Rumbia 1 Kampung Tanjung Langsat, 81700, Pasir Gudang, Johor, Malaysia
Tel.: (60) 72551224
Toilet Preparation Mfr
N.A.I.C.S.: 325620

Ipposha Oil Industries Co., Ltd. (1)
1516-1 Oda-cho, Ono, 675 1301, Hyogo, Japan (78.3%)
Tel.: (81) 794671456
Web Site: http://www.ipposha.co.jp
Sales Range: $50-74.9 Million
Emp.: 160
Mfr & Marketer of Surfactants & Other Chemicals
N.A.I.C.S.: 325199
Kiyotaka Aape *(Pres)*

Ketjen Black International Company (1)
Munekawa Bldg 12 8 Ryogoku 1 Chome, Sumida Ku, Tokyo, 130 0026, Japan (100%)
Tel.: (81) 336357011
Web Site: http://www.lion.co.jp
Sales Range: $25-49.9 Million
Emp.: 15
Mfr & Marketer of Carbon Black
N.A.I.C.S.: 325180

Kyuzituhack Co., Ltd. (1)
1-3-7 Honjo, Sumida-ku, Tokyo, 130-0004, Japan
Tel.: (81) 368223389
Web Site:
 https://www.about.kyuzituhack.com
Business Consulting Services
N.A.I.C.S.: 541611

Lion Akzo Co., Ltd. (1)
3 17 3-chome Obata, Yokkaichi, 510-0875,
Mie, Japan
Tel.: (81) 593468218
Web Site: http://www.lion.co.jp
Nitriles, Amines, Quarternary Ammonium Salts, Amine Oxides, Monoamides & Alkoxylated Amines Mfr; Joint Venture of Lion Corporation (50%) & Akzo Nobel N.V. (50%)
N.A.I.C.S.: 325998

Lion Business Service Co., Ltd. (1)
1-3-7 Honjo, Sumida-ku, Tokyo, 130-8644, Japan (100%)
Tel.: (81) 336216236
Toothpaste & Other Detergent Mfr & Whslr
N.A.I.C.S.: 325611

Lion Chemical Co., Ltd. (1)
22 1 Ban Nosu Cho, Sakaide, Kagawa, 762 0064, Japan (100%)
Tel.: (81) 877441811
Web Site: http://www.lion.co.jp
Sales Range: $25-49.9 Million
Emp.: 90
Mfr & Marketer of Ingredients for Detergents & Industrial Products
N.A.I.C.S.: 325611

Lion Chemical Co., Ltd. (1)
1-3-7 Honjo, Sumida-ku, Tokyo, 130-8644, Japan (100%)
Tel.: (81) 3 3621 6764
Web Site: http://www.lion.co.jp
Sales Range: $100-124.9 Million
Emp.: 83
Surfactant & Other Chemical Mfr & Distr
N.A.I.C.S.: 325199

Lion Chemical Industry (Taiwan) Co., Ltd. (1)
50 Sec 3 Chongsin Rd, Wugu District, New Taipei City, 24843, Taiwan
Tel.: (886) 222911140
Web Site: http://www.lion.co.jp
Toothpaste, Toothbrush & Laundry Detergents Mfr
N.A.I.C.S.: 339114
Peter Shu *(Mgr)*

Lion Cordial Support Co., Ltd. (1)
1-2-26 Yokoami, Sumida-Ku, Tokyo, 130-0015, Japan
Tel.: (81) 336216640
Temporary Staffing Services
N.A.I.C.S.: 561320

Lion Corporation (1)
Chungjeong Tower 12F 21 Seosomun-ro, Seodaemun-gu, Seoul, Korea (South)
Tel.: (82) 26 363 1114
Web Site: https://www.lionkorea.co.kr
Toilet Preparation Mfr
N.A.I.C.S.: 325620
Han Sang Hun *(CEO)*

Lion Corporation (Hong Kong) Ltd. (1)
Room 3701 37th Floor 148 Electric Road, North Point, China (Hong Kong)
Tel.: (852) 25715022
Web Site: https://lioncorphk.com
Sales Range: $25-49.9 Million
Emp.: 100
Personal Care Product Distr
N.A.I.C.S.: 424210
Christine Lo *(Deputy Gen Mgr-Mktg)*

Lion Corporation (Singapore) Pte Ltd (1)
221 Kallang Bahru Lion Building, Singapore, 339349, Singapore (100%)
Tel.: (65) 62966122
Web Site: http://www.lioncorp.com.sg
Sales Range: $25-49.9 Million
Emp.: 40
Oral Product Distr
N.A.I.C.S.: 325998

Lion Corporation (Thailand) Ltd. (1)
666 Rama 3 Rd, Yannawa Bangpongpang, Bangkok, 10120, Thailand (51%)
Tel.: (66) 22940191
Web Site: https://www.lion.co.th
Sales Range: $50-74.9 Million
Emp.: 200
Marketer of Consumer & Other Chemical Products
N.A.I.C.S.: 325998

Lion Corporation - Akashi Plant (1)

LION CORPORATION

Lion Corporation—(Continued)
800 Uozumichonishioka, Akashi, 674-0084, Hyogo, Japan
Tel.: (81) 789421111
Toilet Preparation Mfr
N.A.I.C.S.: 325620

Lion Corporation - Chiba Plant (1)
74-13 Yawatakaigandori, Ichihara, 290-0067, Chiba, Japan
Tel.: (81) 436438151
Toilet Preparation Mfr
N.A.I.C.S.: 325620

Lion Corporation - Odawara Plant (1)
100 Tajima, Odawara, 256-0811, Kanagawa, Japan
Tel.: (81) 465474151
Toilet Preparation Mfr
N.A.I.C.S.: 325620

Lion Corporation - Osaka Plant (1)
2-13 Chikkoshinmachi, Nishi-ku, Sakai, 592-8331, Osaka, Japan
Tel.: (81) 722418831
Toilet Preparation Mfr
N.A.I.C.S.: 325620

Lion Daily Necessities Chemicals (Qingdao) Co., Ltd. (1)
No 919 Weihe Road, Qingdao Economic and Technical Development Zone, Qingdao, 266510, Shandong, China **(100%)**
Tel.: (86) 53286897122
Web Site: http://www.lionchina.cn
Sales Range: $50-74.9 Million
Chemical Products Distr
N.A.I.C.S.: 325998

Lion Dental Products Co., Ltd. (1)
1-3-7 Honjo, Sumida-ku, Tokyo, 130-8644, Japan **(100%)**
Tel.: (81) 336216183
Web Site: http://www.lion.co.jp
Sales Range: $25-49.9 Million
Emp.: 30
Chemical Products Distr
N.A.I.C.S.: 325412

Lion Engineering Co., Ltd. (1)
(100%)
Web Site: http://www.lion-eng.co.jp
Sales Range: $25-49.9 Million
Emp.: 200
Chemical Products Distr
N.A.I.C.S.: 541330

Lion Expert Business Co., Ltd. (1)
1-3-28 Kuramae, Taito-ku, Tokyo, 111-8644, Japan
Tel.: (81) 367399015
Management Consulting Services
N.A.I.C.S.: 541618

Lion Field Marketing Co., Ltd. (1)
Fujii Nitto Bldg 17 10 Ryogoku 1 Chome, Sumida Ku, Tokyo, 130 0026, Japan **(100%)**
Tel.: (81) 336346825
Web Site: http://www.lion.co.jp
Sales Range: $25-49.9 Million
Emp.: 85
Sales Promotion Services
N.A.I.C.S.: 561990

Lion Home Products (International) Ltd. (1)
21 Fl Sing Pao Bldg, 101 Kings Rd, North Point, China (Hong Kong) **(100%)**
Tel.: (852) 25715022
Sales Range: $25-49.9 Million
Emp.: 30
Marketer of Consumer Products
N.A.I.C.S.: 922190
C. Y. Wong (Mng Dir)

Lion Home Products (Taiwan) Co., Ltd. (1)
18F-1 No 97 SEC 4 Chongsin Rd, Sanchong Dist, New Taipei City, 24161, Taiwan
Tel.: (886) 289726500
Web Site: https://www.lion-corp.com.tw
Toilet Preparation Mfr
N.A.I.C.S.: 325620

Lion Hygiene Co., Ltd. (1)
1-3-28 Kuramae, Taito-ku, Tokyo, 111-8644, Japan **(100%)**
Tel.: (81) 367399050

Web Site: https://www.lionhygiene.co.jp
Sales Range: $25-49.9 Million
Emp.: 90
Institutional-Use Cleaner Mfr & Distr
N.A.I.C.S.: 325620

Lion Idemitsu Composites Co., Ltd (1)
5F TIXTOWER UENO 4-8-1 Higashiueno, Taito-ku, Tokyo, 110-0015, Japan **(50%)**
Tel.: (81) 358300530
Web Site: https://www.idemitsu.com
Production & Sales of Special Composite Plastics
N.A.I.C.S.: 325211
Yasuyuki Kanehara (Pres)

Subsidiary (Non-US):

Lion Idemitsu Composites (Hong Kong) Limited (2)
Unit No 1509 15/F The Metropolis Tower 10 Metropolis Drive, Hung Hom, Kowloon, China (Hong Kong)
Tel.: (852) 25301000
Toilet Preparation Mfr
N.A.I.C.S.: 325620

Lion Idemitsu Composites (India) Private Limited (2)
No 503 5th Floor Suncity Business Tower Golf Course Road Sector 54, Gurgaon, Haryana, India
Tel.: (91) 1244233965
Toilet Preparation Mfr
N.A.I.C.S.: 325620

Lion Idemitsu Composites (Shanghai) Co., Ltd. (2)
Room 3806B Huaihai Plaza NO 1045 Huaihai Zhong Road, Xuhui District, Shanghai, 200031, China
Tel.: (86) 2154655055
Toilet Preparation Mfr
N.A.I.C.S.: 325620

Lion Idemitsu Composites (Thailand) Co., Ltd. (2)
571 RSU Tower 8 Floor Room 803 Sukhumvit Road Klongton Nua, Wattana, Bangkok, 10110, Thailand
Tel.: (66) 22596095
Toilet Preparation Mfr
N.A.I.C.S.: 325620

Lion Kallol Limited (1)
199 Tejgaon Industrial Area, Dhaka, Bangladesh
Tel.: (880) 258816004
Skin-care Product Mfr & Distr
N.A.I.C.S.: 325620

Lion Logistics Service Co., Ltd. (1)
1-3-7 Honjo, Sumida Ku, Tokyo, 130-8644, Japan **(100%)**
Tel.: (81) 336216961
Web Site: http://www.lion.co.jp
Sales Range: $10-24.9 Million
Emp.: 35
Shipping & Warehousing Services
N.A.I.C.S.: 493120

Lion Specialty Chemicals Co., Ltd. (1)
3-7 Honjo 1-chome, Sumida-Ku, Tokyo, 130-8644, Japan
Tel.: (81) 336216554
Web Site: http://www.lion-specialty-chem.co.jp
Emp.: 317
Chemical Products Mfr
N.A.I.C.S.: 325199
Osamu Yoshitake (Pres)

Lion Tomoni Co., Ltd. (1)
1-3-28 Kuramae, Taito-ku, Tokyo, 111-8644, Japan
Tel.: (81) 336216493
Emp.: 31
Toilet Preparation Mfr
N.A.I.C.S.: 325620

Lion Trading Co., Ltd. (1)
11Fl Arca Central 1-2-1 Kinshi, Sumida Ku, Tokyo, 130-0013, Japan **(100%)**
Tel.: (81) 336216911
Web Site: http://www.lion-pet.jp
Sales Range: $25-49.9 Million
Emp.: 78
Chemical Products Distr

N.A.I.C.S.: 424690

Lion pet Co., Ltd. (1)
1-3-28 Kuramae, Taito-ku, Tokyo, 111-8644, Japan
Tel.: (81) 367399011
Web Site: https://www.lion-pet.co.jp
Emp.: 83
Pet Care Services
N.A.I.C.S.: 812910

McCormick-Lion Ltd. (1)
3-38 Kanda Sakum-Cho, Chiyoda-ku, Tokyo, 101-0025, Japan
Tel.: (81) 358201311
Web Site: http://www.mccormickflavor.com
Sales Range: $25-49.9 Million
Emp.: 50
Mfr of Food Preparations & Flavorings;
Joint Venture of Lion Corporation (51%) & McCormick & Company (49%)
N.A.I.C.S.: 311930

PT Lion Wings (1)
Jl Inspeksi Cakung Drain Timur No 1, Jakarta, 13910, Indonesia **(100%)**
Tel.: (62) 2146826566
Web Site: http://www.lionwings.com
Sales Range: $200-249.9 Million
Emp.: 1,000
Health Care Product Mfr & Distr
N.A.I.C.S.: 339112

Planet Logistics Co., Ltd. (1)
4-5-9 Tsukiji Tsukijiyasudadai 2 Bldg 7f, Chuo-Ku, Tokyo, 104-0045, Japan
Tel.: (81) 363676635
Logistics Consulting Servies
N.A.I.C.S.: 541614

Planet, Inc. (1)
1-31 Hamamatsucho Cultural Broadcasting Media Plus Building 3rd Floor, Minato-ku, Tokyo, 105-0013, Japan
Tel.: (81) 35 962 0811
Web Site: https://www.planet-van.co.jp
Electronic Data Interchange Services
N.A.I.C.S.: 518210
Hiromasa Tamanyu (Chm)

Southern Lion Sdn. Bhd. (1)
3 Jalan Firma 2 Tebrau Industrial Estate, 81100, Johor Bahru, Johor, Malaysia **(100%)**
Tel.: (60) 73546042
Web Site: http://www.southernlion.com.my
Sales Range: $50-74.9 Million
Emp.: 200
Marketer of Consumer & Other Chemical Products
N.A.I.C.S.: 325998
Annette Ling (Mng Dir)

The Lion Foundation for Dental Health (1)
3 7 Honjo 1 Chome, Sumida Ku, Tokyo, 130 8644, Japan **(100%)**
Tel.: (81) 336266490
Web Site: http://www.lion.co.jp
Sales Range: $25-49.9 Million
Emp.: 50
Promoter of Dental Care
N.A.I.C.S.: 339114

LION E-MOBILITY AG

Poststrasse 6, 6300, Zug, Switzerland
Tel.: (41) 41 729 63 63
Web Site: http://www.lionemobility.de
Holding Company; Electrical Energy Storage & Battery
N.A.I.C.S.: 551112
Hany Magour (CFO & COO)

LION ENERGY LIMITED

Suite 7 295 Rokeby Road, Subiaco, 6008, WA, Australia
Tel.: (61) 892111500
Web Site: https://www.lionenergy.com.au
LIO—(ASX)
Rev.: $670,232
Assets: $8,152,104
Liabilities: $1,101,099
Net Worth: $7,051,005
Earnings: ($1,406,691)

Fiscal Year-end: 12/31/23
Oil & Gas Exploration Services
N.A.I.C.S.: 211120
Thomas Leo Soulsby (Chm)

Subsidiaries:

KRX Energy Pte Ltd (1)
4 Shenton Way 28-03 SGX Centre 2, Singapore, 068807, Singapore
Tel.: (65) 66328488
Holding Company
N.A.I.C.S.: 551112

LION GROUP HOLDING LTD.

Room 901-903 9/F Harbour Centre 25 Harbour Road, Wanchai, China (Hong Kong)
Tel.: (852) 28209000
Web Site:
https://www.liongrouphl.com
Year Founded: 2020
LGHL—(NASDAQ)
Rev.: $3,229,716
Assets: $86,634,384
Liabilities: $59,221,719
Net Worth: $27,412,665
Earnings: ($31,563,283)
Emp.: 38
Fiscal Year-end: 12/31/22
Holding Company
N.A.I.C.S.: 551112
Jian Wang (Chm)

LION GROUP MANAGEMENT SERVICES SDN BHD

Level 11 - 15, Lion Office Tower No. 1 Jalan Nagasari, 50200, Kuala Lumpur, Malaysia
Tel.: (60) 3 2142 0155
Web Site:
http://www.liongroup.com.my
Holding Company
N.A.I.C.S.: 551112
Seri Utama William Cheng (Exec Chm)

Subsidiaries:

Amsteel Mills Sdn Bhd (1)
Tel.: (60) 333412322
Web Site: http://www.lion.com.my
Sales Range: $50-74.9 Million
Emp.: 23,483
Steel Mfrs
N.A.I.C.S.: 331110
William H. J. Cheng (Chm & Mng Dir)

Changshu Lion Enterprise Co Ltd (1)
Room 505 Level 5 Dong Nang International Building, No 1 Dong Nan Road, Changshu, 215500, Jiangsu, China
Tel.: (86) 51252358668
Web Site: http://www.lion.com.my
Property Development Services
N.A.I.C.S.: 531210

Likom CMS Sdn Bhd (1)
Kawasan Perindustrian Cheng Fasa III, Mukim Cheng, 75250, Melaka, Malaysia
Tel.: (60) 6 334 5026
Sales Range: $50-74.9 Million
Emp.: 250
Computer Peripherals & Metal Case Mfr
N.A.I.C.S.: 334118

Likom Caseworks USA Inc. (1)
17890 Castleton St Ste 309, City of Industry, CA 91748-1756
Tel.: (626) 854-2029
Metal Stamping Mfr
N.A.I.C.S.: 332119

Subsidiary (Non-US):

Likom de Mexico S.A. de C.V. (2)
Calle Bufalo No 351 Parque Industrial Salvarcar, Ciudad Juarez, 32575, Chihuahua, Mexico
Tel.: (52) 6566830282
Web Site: http://www.likommexico.com
Sales Range: $125-149.9 Million
Emp.: 350

Metal Stampings & Injection Molded Plastic Products Mfr
N.A.I.C.S.: 326130
Azmi Sulaiman *(VP)*

Lion DRI Sdn. Bhd. (1)
2319 Kawasan Perindustrian Olak Lempit Mukim Tanjung Dua Belas, Banting, Kuala Langat, 42700, Malaysia
Tel.: (60) 331822200
Web Site: http://www.liongroup.com.my
Sales Range: $100-124.9 Million
Emp.: 500
Iron Product Mfr
N.A.I.C.S.: 331110
William Cheng *(CEO)*

LION INDUSTRIES CORPORATION BERHAD
Level 14 Lion Office Tower, No 1 Jalan Nagasari, 50200, Kuala Lumpur, Wilayah Persekutuan, Malaysia
Tel.: (60) 321420155
Web Site: https://www.lionind.com.my
Year Founded: 1924
LIONIND—(KLS)
Rev.: $1,037,749,433
Assets: $869,412,555
Liabilities: $364,833,068
Net Worth: $504,579,488
Earnings: $133,462,148
Fiscal Year-end: 12/31/21
Steel Bar Mfr
N.A.I.C.S.: 331110
Utama Nong Chik Zainal Abidin *(Chm)*

Subsidiaries:

Amsteel Mills Marketing Sdn Bhd (1)
Wisma Lion Lot 2319 Kawasan Perindustrian Olak Lempit Mukim Tanjung 12, 42700, Banting, Selangor, Malaysia **(99%)**
Tel.: (60) 331822000
Web Site: https://lionind.com.my
Steel Product Distr
N.A.I.C.S.: 423510
Pak Yii Wong *(Gen Mgr-Mktg)*

Subsidiary (Domestic):

Antara Steel Mills Sdn Bhd (2)
PLO 277 and 417 Jalan Gangsa 1, Pasir Gudang Industrial Estate Pasir Gudang, 81707, Johor Bahru, Johor, Malaysia
Tel.: (60) 7 259 8888
Web Site: http://www.antarasteel.com.my
Sales Range: $200-249.9 Million
Emp.: 800
Steel Bar Products Mfr & Sales
N.A.I.C.S.: 331110

Lion Courts Sdn Bhd (1)
Level 11-15 Office Tower No 1 Jalan Nagasari, Off Jalan Raja Chulan, Kuala Lumpur, 50200, Malaysia
Tel.: (60) 321420155
Steel Bar Mfr
N.A.I.C.S.: 331110

Lion Posim Berhad (1)
Level 14 Lion Office Tower No 1 Jalan Nagasari, 50200, Kuala Lumpur, Wilayah, Malaysia
Tel.: (60) 321420155
Web Site: http://www.lion.com.my
Rev.: $177,518,095
Assets: $186,973,122
Liabilities: $30,210,159
Net Worth: $156,762,963
Earnings: $127,196
Fiscal Year-end: 12/31/2022
Building Materials Distr
N.A.I.C.S.: 444180
Phooi Lin Wong *(Co-Sec)*

Subsidiary (Domestic):

Lion Petroleum Products Sdn Bhd (2)
Lot 72 Persiaran Jubli Perak, 40000, Shah Alam, Selangor, Malaysia
Tel.: (60) 51022999
Petroleum Product Mfr
N.A.I.C.S.: 324110

Posim Marketing Sdn Bhd (2)
Wisma Posim Lot 72 Persiaran Jubli Perak, 40000, Shah Alam, Selangor Darul Ehsan, Malaysia
Tel.: (60) 351022999
Web Site: https://www.posimmarketing.com.my
Sales Range: $50-74.9 Million
Emp.: 61
Industrial Equipment Mfr & Distr
N.A.I.C.S.: 423830
Evonne Chin *(Mgr-HR)*

Posim Petroleum Marketing Sdn Bhd (2)
No 3 Jalan Keluli 15/16 Seksyen 15, 40200, Shah Alam, Selangor Darul Ehsan, Malaysia
Tel.: (60) 351022999
Web Site: https://www.posim.com.my
Emp.: 300
Petroleum Product Distr
N.A.I.C.S.: 424720

Lion Rubber Industries Pte Ltd (1)
10 Arumugam Road 10-00, Singapore, 409957, Singapore
Tel.: (65) 67459677
Emp.: 50
Investment Management Service
N.A.I.C.S.: 523999

Lion Steel Sdn Bhd (1)
Wisma Lion Lot 2319, Kawasan Perindustrian Olak Lempit Mukim Tanjung 12, 42700, Banting, Selangor Darul Ehsan, Malaysia
Tel.: (60) 331825888
Web Site: https://www.lion.com.my
Flat Steel Product Mfr & Distr
N.A.I.C.S.: 331110

Malim Jaya (Melaka) Sdn Bhd (1)
G-30 Jln Pm 3 Plz Mahkota, Bandar Hilir, 75000, Melaka, Malaysia
Tel.: (60) 62833909
Sales Range: $50-74.9 Million
Emp.: 16
Property Management Services
N.A.I.C.S.: 531312
Allen Chen *(Mgr)*

Projek Jaya Sdn Bhd (1)
No 48-1 Jalan Temenggung 1/9 Section 9, Bandar Mahkota, 43200, Cheras, Selangor, Malaysia
Tel.: (60) 3806061712
Web Site: https://ppj.construction
Construction Contracting Services
N.A.I.C.S.: 236220

LION METAL WORKS TBK
Jl Raya Bekasi Km 24 5 Cakung, Jakarta, 13910, Indonesia
Tel.: (62) 214600779
Web Site: https://www.lionmetal.co.id
Year Founded: 1972
LION—(INDO)
Rev.: $29,361,610
Assets: $48,243,073
Liabilities: $16,332,618
Net Worth: $31,910,455
Earnings: $430,314
Emp.: 737
Fiscal Year-end: 12/31/23
Construction Equipment Mfr
N.A.I.C.S.: 333120
Sukmawati Syarif *(Sec)*

LION ONE METALS LIMITED
306-267 West Esplanade, North Vancouver, V7M 1A5, BC, Canada
Tel.: (604) 998-1250 BC
Web Site: https://www.liononemetals.com
Year Founded: 1996
LIO—(TSXV)
Rev.: $362,060
Assets: $105,053,083
Liabilities: $780,441
Net Worth: $104,272,642
Earnings: ($3,310,110)
Emp.: 115
Fiscal Year-end: 06/30/21

Gold Ore Exploration & Mining
N.A.I.C.S.: 212220
Walter H. Berukoff *(Founder, Chm & CEO)*

Subsidiaries:

Lion One Australia Pty Ltd. (1)
Level 1 - 31 Cliff Street, Fremantle, 6160, WA, Australia
Tel.: (61) 894353200
Mineral Exploration Services
N.A.I.C.S.: 213114

Lion One Limited (1)
Lot 1 and 6 Waimalika, Legalega Industrial Subdivision, Nadi, Fiji
Tel.: (679) 6049733032
Mineral Exploration Services
N.A.I.C.S.: 213114

LION PRINT CORPORATION
G Washington St 17/67, L'viv, Ukraine
Tel.: (380) 685511850 NV
Year Founded: 2013
Printing Services
N.A.I.C.S.: 323111
Liliia Yasinska *(Pres, CEO, CFO, Principal Acctg Officer, Treas & Sec)*

LION ROCK GROUP LTD
26/F 625 Kings Road, North Point, China (Hong Kong)
Tel.: (852) 82261010 BM
Web Site: http://www.lionrockgrouphk.com
1127—(HKG)
Rev.: $318,251,348
Assets: $356,721,540
Liabilities: $145,714,013
Net Worth: $211,007,528
Earnings: $36,440,648
Emp.: 1,683
Fiscal Year-end: 12/31/22
Printing Services
N.A.I.C.S.: 323111
Chuk Kin Lau *(Exec Dir)*

Subsidiaries:

1010 Printing (UK) Limited (1)
Office 10 Apsley House 176 Upper Richmond Road, London, SW15 2SH, United Kingdom
Tel.: (44) 208 780 7000
Commercial Printer Services
N.A.I.C.S.: 323111
Andrew Law *(Sls Dir)*

C.O.S. Printers Pte Limited (1)
9 Kian Teck Crescent, Singapore, 628875, Singapore
Tel.: (65) 6 265 9022
Web Site: https://www.cosprinters.com
Digital Printing Services
N.A.I.C.S.: 323111
Michael Chang *(Acct Mgr)*

Griffin Press Printing Pty. Ltd. (1)
168 Cross Keys Rd, Salisbury, 5106, SA, Australia
Tel.: (61) 882532000
Web Site: https://www.griffinpress.com.au
Book & Magazine Distr
N.A.I.C.S.: 424920

Left Field Printing Group Ltd. (1)
Level 11 East Wing NEO 123 Hoi Bun Road, Kwun Tong, Kowloon, China (Hong Kong)
Tel.: (852) 29762398
Web Site: https://www.leftfieldprinting.com
Rev.: $64,433,528
Assets: $47,701,065
Liabilities: $15,215,723
Net Worth: $32,485,343
Earnings: $1,431,060
Emp.: 325
Fiscal Year-end: 12/31/2022
Commercial Printing & Packaging Product Mfr
N.A.I.C.S.: 333993
Richard Francis Celarc *(Chm)*

Ligare Pty Ltd (1)
138 Bonds Road, Riverwood, 2210, NSW, Australia
Tel.: (61) 29 533 2555
Web Site: https://www.ligare.com.au
Book Printing Services
N.A.I.C.S.: 323117

Papercraft Sdn. Bhd. (1)
20 Jalan Perindustrian 3 20 Jalan Perindustrian 3, Kawasan Perindustrian Pontian, 82000, Johor, Malaysia
Tel.: (60) 7 686 1885
Web Site: https://www.papercraft.com.my
Emp.: 100
Converted Paper Product Mfr
N.A.I.C.S.: 322299

Regent Publishing Services Limited (1)
Units B C 7/F Genesis, No 33 - 35 Wong Chuk Hang Road, Hong Kong, China (Hong Kong) **(75%)**
Tel.: (852) 28977803
Web Site: https://www.regent-hk.com.hk
Publishing Company
N.A.I.C.S.: 513130

LION ROCK RESOURCES INC.
Suite 1450 789 West Pender Street, Vancouver, V6C 1H2, BC, Canada
Tel.: (604) 681-1568
Web Site: http://www.kingsbayres.com
Year Founded: 1998
KGB—(DEU)
Assets: $818,372
Liabilities: $1,366,620
Net Worth: ($548,248)
Earnings: ($2,292,488)
Fiscal Year-end: 12/31/23
Mineral Exploration Services
N.A.I.C.S.: 213114
Jody Bellefleur *(CFO)*

LION SELECTION GROUP LIMITED
Level 2/175 Flinders Lane, Melbourne, 3000, VIC, Australia
Tel.: (61) 396148008
Web Site: http://www.lionselection.com.au
Year Founded: 1997
LSX—(ASX)
Rev.: $2,261,619
Assets: $59,471,821
Liabilities: $713,809
Net Worth: $58,758,013
Earnings: $739,183
Emp.: 5
Fiscal Year-end: 07/31/24
Investment Services
N.A.I.C.S.: 523999
Craig K. Smyth *(CEO)*

LION TRAVEL SERVICE CO., LTD.
No 151 Shitan Rd, Neihu Dist, Taipei, 114, Taiwan
Tel.: (886) 287939000
Web Site: https://www.liontravel.com
2731—(TAI)
Rev.: $703,494,627
Assets: $309,742,491
Liabilities: $184,747,957
Net Worth: $124,994,534
Earnings: $46,937,014
Fiscal Year-end: 12/31/23
Travel Services
N.A.I.C.S.: 561599

LIONAX INTERNATIONAL INVESTMENT HOLDINGS LIMITED
Unit 601 6 F Beautiful Group Tower 77, Connaught Road, Central, China (Hong Kong)
Tel.: (852) 21379738
Sales Range: $1-9.9 Million

LIONAX INTERNATIONAL INVESTMENT HOLDINGS LIMITED   **INTERNATIONAL PUBLIC**

Lionax International Investment Holdings Limited—(Continued)
Holding Company; Tire Pressure Monitoring Systems & Digital Pressure Sensors Mfr
N.A.I.C.S.: 551112
Hongbing Liu (CTO)

LIONCO PHARMACEUTICAL GROUP CO.,LTD.
1F Building 2 Commercial-residential Building No 68 Naidong Road, Naidong County Zedang Town, Shannan, 856000, Xizang, China
Tel.: (86) 8937830999
Web Site:
http://www.lingkang.com.cn
Year Founded: 2003
603669—(SHG)
Rev.: $113,425,959
Assets: $385,225,096
Liabilities: $161,717,751
Net Worth: $223,507,344
Earnings: $10,096,539
Fiscal Year-end: 12/31/21
Pharmaceutical Product Mfr & Distr
N.A.I.C.S.: 325412
Lingping Tao (Chm & Gen Mgr)

LIONHEAD TECHNOLOGY DEVELOPMENT CO., LTD.
Room 0201 1st-2nd Floor Building 3, No 51 Binhe West Road Xinghua Street Wanbolin District, Taiyuan, 030027, Shanxi, China
Tel.: (86) 3516838977
Web Site:
http://www.lionhead.com.cn
Year Founded: 1999
600539—(SHG)
Rev.: $82,639,075
Assets: $98,476,167
Liabilities: $15,825,481
Net Worth: $82,650,686
Earnings: $2,459,682
Fiscal Year-end: 12/31/22
Cement Mfr & Distr
N.A.I.C.S.: 327310
Wu Jiahui (Chm)

LIONHUB GROUP LIMITED
Level 3A 148 Elizabeth Street, Sydney, 2000, NSW, Australia
Tel.: (61) 282813008
Web Site: http://www.lionhub.com.au
Rev.: $703
Assets: $5,139,835
Liabilities: $3,990,773
Net Worth: $1,149,061
Earnings: ($2,638,481)
Emp.: 30
Fiscal Year-end: 12/31/18
Real Estate Support Services
N.A.I.C.S.: 531190
Siew Goh (Head-Ops)

LIONMESH PRIMA TBK
Jalan Raya Bekasi Km 24 5, Cakung, Jakarta, 13910, Timur, Indonesia
Tel.: (62) 214600779
Web Site: https://www.lionmesh.com
LMSH—(INDO)
Rev.: $17,286,976
Assets: $13,239,887
Liabilities: $2,083,176
Net Worth: $11,156,711
Earnings: ($474,455)
Emp.: 61
Fiscal Year-end: 12/31/22
Steel Fabrication Product Mfr
N.A.I.C.S.: 332312
Tjoe Tjoe Peng (Chm)

LIONROCK CAPITAL LIMITED
Unit 1903-4 303 Hennessy Road, Wanchai, China (Hong Kong)
Tel.: (852) 28348000
Web Site:
http://www.lionrockcapitalhk.com
Year Founded: 2011
Private Equity
N.A.I.C.S.: 523940
Ning Li (Chm)
Subsidiaries:

HAGLOFS AB   (1)
Henry Bergstens vag 3 Hus B, 176 69, Jarfalla, Sweden
Tel.: (46) 22667000
Sports Product Mfr & Distr
N.A.I.C.S.: 339920

LIONS BAY CAPITAL INC.
585 Burwood Road, Hawthorn, VIC 3122, Australia
Tel.: (61) 392362800   BC
Web Site:
http://www.lionsbaycapital.com
Year Founded: 2010
LBI.P—(TSXV)
Sales Range: Less than $1 Million
Investment Services
N.A.I.C.S.: 523999
John Byrne (Chm)

LIONS GATE ENTERTAINMENT CORP.
250 Howe Street 20th Floor, Vancouver, V6C 3R8, BC, Canada
Tel.: (604) 687-4460   BC
Web Site: http://www.lionsgate.com
Year Founded: 1997
LGF.A—(NYSE)
Rev.: $3,604,300,000
Assets: $8,991,200,000
Liabilities: $6,307,800,000
Net Worth: $2,683,400,000
Earnings: ($188,200,000)
Emp.: 1,448
Fiscal Year-end: 03/31/22
Holding Company; Motion Picture, Television Programming, Video & Home Entertainment Products Marketer & Distr
N.A.I.C.S.: 551112
Jon Feltheimer (CEO)
Subsidiaries:

Entertainment One Ltd.   (1)
134 Peter Street Suite 700, Toronto, M5V 2H2, ON, Canada
Tel.: (416) 646-2400
Web Site: http://www.entertainmentone.com
Rev.: $689,871,364
Assets: $1,393,962,346
Liabilities: $870,108,687
Net Worth: $523,853,659
Earnings: $11,214,441
Emp.: 1,190
Fiscal Year-end: 03/31/2019
Retail Entertainment Distr
N.A.I.C.S.: 512250
Stuart Baxter (Pres-Intl- Television)

Subsidiary (Non-US):

Audio Network Limited   (2)
3rd Floor The Johnson Building 77 Hatton Garden, London, EC1N 8JS, United Kingdom
Tel.: (44) 207 566 1441
Web Site: http://www.audionetwork.com
Music Publishing Services
N.A.I.C.S.: 512230
Ali Johnson (Chief Creative Officer)

Subsidiary (Domestic):

E1 Television International Ltd.   (2)
175 Bloor Street East Ste 1400 North Tower, Toronto, M4W 3R8, ON, Canada
Tel.: (416) 646-2400
Sales Range: $75-99.9 Million
Emp.: 150
Entertainment Services
N.A.I.C.S.: 711510
Stuart Baxter (Pres)

E1 Television Productions Inc   (2)
134 Peter Street Suite 700, Toronto, M5V 2H2, ON, Canada
Tel.: (416) 646-2400
Web Site: http://www.Eonetv.com
Sales Range: $50-74.9 Million
Emp.: 400
Film Production Services
N.A.I.C.S.: 512110

Subsidiary (Non-US):

Entertainment One Benelux B.V.   (2)
Bergweg 46, 1217 SC, Hilversum, Netherlands
Tel.: (31) 356 25 12 00
Web Site: http://www.entertainmentone.com
Emp.: 35
Entertainment Services
N.A.I.C.S.: 512120

Subsidiary (Domestic):

Entertainment One Limited Partnership   (2)
5014 49th St, Yellowknife, X1A 3R7, NT, Canada
Tel.: (867) 873-4112
Sales Range: $50-74.9 Million
Emp.: 4
Music Entertainment Services
N.A.I.C.S.: 711130

Seville Pictures Inc.   (2)
455 St-Antoine Street West Suite 300, Montreal, H2Z 1J1, QC, Canada
Tel.: (514) 878-2282
Web Site:
http://www.sevilleinternational.com
Film Entertainment Services
N.A.I.C.S.: 512110

Holding (US):

The Mark Gordon Company   (2)
12200 W Olympic Blvd, Los Angeles, CA 90064   (100%)
Tel.: (310) 943-6401
Sales Range: $1-9.9 Million
Emp.: 25
Film & Television Broadcasting
N.A.I.C.S.: 516120
Mark Gordon (CEO)

Lions Gate Entertainment Inc.   (1)
2700 Colorado Ave, Santa Monica, CA 90404
Tel.: (310) 449-9200
Web Site: https://www.lionsgate.com
Motion Picture, Television Programming, Video & Home Entertainment Products Marketer & Distr
N.A.I.C.S.: 512110

Subsidiary (Domestic):

Arima, Inc.   (2)
2421 Riker Rdg Trl, Austin, TX 78748
Tel.: (512) 280-3200
Web Site: http://www.arimasoft.com
Custom Computer Programming Services
N.A.I.C.S.: 541511

Atom Productions, Inc.   (2)
1965 Adams Ave, San Leandro, CA 94577
Tel.: (510) 632-4629
Web Site:
http://www.atomicproductions.com
Emp.: 8
Motion Picture Production Services
N.A.I.C.S.: 512110
Lucy Nazareno (Mgr-Production)

CB Development, LLC   (2)
3251 Mount Pleasant St NW Fl 3, Washington, DC 20010
Tel.: (202) 750-3921
Web Site: https://cbdevllc.com
Motion Picture Production & Distribution Services
N.A.I.C.S.: 512110
Luke Bartelme (Dir-Ops)

CB Direct, LLC   (2)
1717 Turning Basin Dr, Houston, TX 77029-4050
Tel.: (346) 352-4046
Motion Picture Production & Distribution Services
N.A.I.C.S.: 512110

Chevalier Productions, Inc.   (2)
1706 Hillyer Robinson Industrial Pkwy S, Oxford, AL 36203
Tel.: (256) 835-0360
Web Site: https://chevalierproductions.com
Motion Picture Production & Distribution Services
N.A.I.C.S.: 512110

Subsidiary (Non-US):

Cine Groupe Corporation Inc.   (2)
1151 rue Alexandre De Seve, Montreal, H2L 2T7, QC, Canada   (100%)
Tel.: (514) 524-7567
Web Site: http://www.cinegroupe.com
Sales Range: $25-49.9 Million
Emp.: 125
Produces Animated Programming
N.A.I.C.S.: 512110
Jacques Pettigrew (Founder, Pres & CEO)

Subsidiary (Domestic):

Debmar-Mercury, LLC   (2)
2700 Colorado Ave, Santa Monica, CA 90404
Tel.: (310) 393-6000
Web Site: https://www.debmarmercury.com
Sales Range: $10-24.9 Million
Emp.: 12
Film & Television Syndication Services
N.A.I.C.S.: 512120
Mort Marcus (Co-Pres)

Grindstone Entertainment Group, LLC   (2)
2700 Colorado Ave, Santa Monica, CA 90404
Tel.: (310) 255-5762
Motion Picture & Video Distribution Services
N.A.I.C.S.: 512120

Journal Productions, Inc.   (2)
330 West St Fl 24, New York, NY 10014-3632
Tel.: (929) 425-8632
Entertainment Services
N.A.I.C.S.: 516210

Lady Prison Productions, Inc.   (2)
3412 36th St, Astoria, NY 11106
Tel.: (718) 706-4242
Emp.: 50
Motion Picture & Video Distribution Services
N.A.I.C.S.: 512120

Lamb Productions, Inc.   (2)
417 Market St, Sioux City, IA 51103
Tel.: (712) 255-9536
Emp.: 38
Motion Picture Theater Services
N.A.I.C.S.: 512131
Diana Woole (CEO)

Subsidiary (Non-US):

Lions Gate Studios   (2)
555 Brookes Bank Ave, North Vancouver, V7J 3S5, BC, Canada   (100%)
Tel.: (604) 983-5500
Web Site: http://www.lionsgatestudios.com
Sales Range: $1-9.9 Million
Emp.: 13
Television Studio Facilities
N.A.I.C.S.: 512110

Subsidiary (Domestic):

Lions Gate Television Corp.   (2)
2700 Colorado Ave Ste 200, Santa Monica, CA 90404
Tel.: (310) 449-9200
Web Site: http://www.lionsgate.com
Sales Range: $25-49.9 Million
Emp.: 100
Developer & Producer & Television Programs
N.A.I.C.S.: 512120
Kevin Beggs (Chm)

Subsidiary (Domestic):

Lions Gate Television Development LLC   (3)
2700 Colorado Ave Ste 200, Santa Monica, CA 90404
Tel.: (310) 255-3700
Emp.: 600
Motion Picture & Video Distribution Services
N.A.I.C.S.: 512120

AND PRIVATE COMPANIES ... LIPPO LIMITED

Subsidiary (Non-US):

Lions Gate UK Ltd. (2)
45 Mortimer Street 5th Floor, London, W1W 8HJ, United Kingdom
Tel.: (44) 2072998800
Web Site: https://www.lionsgatefilms.co.uk
Sales Range: $25-49.9 Million
Emp.: 45
Producer & Distr of Motion Pictures & Television Programs
N.A.I.C.S.: 512110
Zygi Kamasa (CEO-Europe)

Subsidiary (Domestic):

Kindle Entertainment Limited (3)
3rd Floor 106 Cleveland Street, London, W1T 6NX, United Kingdom
Tel.: (44) 2077485277
Web Site:
 https://www.kindleentertainment.co.uk
Television Broadcasting Services
N.A.I.C.S.: 516120
Anne Brogan (Mng Dir)

Subsidiary (Domestic):

Mandate Films, LLC (2)
2700 Colorado Ave Ste 500, Santa Monica, CA 90404
Tel.: (310) 360-1441
Motion Picture & Video Production Services
N.A.I.C.S.: 512110

Subsidiary (Non-US):

Maple Pictures Corp. (2)
2 Bloor W, Toronto, M4W 3E2, ON, Canada (100%)
Tel.: (416) 944-0104
Web Site: http://www.alliencefilms.com
Sales Range: $25-49.9 Million
Emp.: 100
Distr of Feature Films
N.A.I.C.S.: 512120

Subsidiary (Domestic):

Mucho Movies, Inc. (2)
2700 Colorado Ave Ste 300, Santa Monica, CA 90404
Tel.: (310) 255-3816
Emp.: 6
Motion Picture Production & Distribution Services
N.A.I.C.S.: 512110

Niche Productions, LLC (2)
PO Box 90383, Dayton, OH 45490
Tel.: (937) 528-2323
Web Site: http://www.nicheproductions.com
Entertainment Business Services
N.A.I.C.S.: 512110

Pilgrim Media Group, LLC (2)
12020 Chandler Blvd Ste 200, North Hollywood, CA 91607
Tel.: (818) 478-4500
Web Site:
 https://www.pilgrimmediagroup.com
Networking Software Development Services
N.A.I.C.S.: 541511

Rockhouse Images, LLC (2)
12020 Chandler Blvd, North Hollywood, CA 91607
Tel.: (818) 661-4917
Web Site:
 https://www.rockhouseimages.com
Digital Media Provider
N.A.I.C.S.: 512110
Rebecka Biejo (Officer-Data Protection)

Royals Productions, Inc. (2)
4210 Fidus Dr, Las Vegas, NV 89103
Tel.: (702) 362-4200
Web Site: https://www.royalpro.com
Motion Picture & Video Production Services
N.A.I.C.S.: 512110
Brenda Klingonsmith (Coord-Media)

South Shore Productions, Inc. (2)
17561 Otto Zeck Rd, Detroit Lakes, MN 56501
Tel.: (218) 849-1643
Web Site:
 http://www.southshoreproductions.net
Entertainment Services
N.A.I.C.S.: 516210

Starz Acquisition LLC (2)
8900 Liberty Cir, Englewood, CO 80112
Tel.: (720) 852-4100
Web Site: http://www.starz.com
Holding Company; Cable Television Network Operator
N.A.I.C.S.: 551112

Subsidiary (Domestic):

Starz, LLC (3)
8900 Liberty Cir, Englewood, CO 80112
Tel.: (720) 852-7700
Web Site: http://www.starz.com
Emp.: 771
Media Holding Company
N.A.I.C.S.: 551112
Scott MacDonald (CFO)

Joint Venture (Domestic):

Courtroom Television Network LLC (4)
1050 Techwood Dr NW, Atlanta, GA 30318-5604
Web Site: http://www.trutv.com
Cable Television Network
N.A.I.C.S.: 516210

Subsidiary (Domestic):

Film Roman, LLC (4)
6320 Canoga Ave Ste 490, Woodland Hills, CA 91367
Tel.: (818) 748-4056
Web Site: http://www.filmroman.com
Animation Studio
N.A.I.C.S.: 512110

Starz Entertainment, LLC (4)
8900 Liberty Cir, Englewood, CO 80112
Tel.: (720) 852-4100
Cable Television Programming
N.A.I.C.S.: 516210

Subsidiary (Domestic):

Leisure Arts, Inc. (5)
104 Champs Blvd Ste 100, Maumelle, AR 72113
Tel.: (501) 868-8800
Web Site: http://www.leisurearts.com
Emp.: 100
Lifestyle & Instructional Periodicals, Books & Software Publisher & Marketer
N.A.I.C.S.: 513120

Subsidiary (Domestic):

Starz Media, LLC (4)
8900 Liberty Cir, Englewood, CO 80112
Tel.: (720) 852-7700
Cable Television Programming
N.A.I.C.S.: 516120
Carmi Zlotnik (Pres)

Subsidiary (Domestic):

Anchor Bay Entertainment, LLC (5)
2401 W Big Beaver Rd Ste 200, Troy, MI 48084
Tel.: (248) 205-1688
Web Site: http://www.anchorbayent.com
Home Entertainment Video Distr
N.A.I.C.S.: 512120
Bill Clark (Pres)

Subsidiary (Domestic):

Starz Power Productions, LLC (4)
1438 N Gower St, Los Angeles, CA 90028
Tel.: (323) 468-7960
Entertainment Services
N.A.I.C.S.: 516210

Subsidiary (Domestic):

Step-Up Productions, Inc. (2)
8351 Roswell Rd Ste 251, Atlanta, GA 30350-2810
Tel.: (407) 963-6978
Web Site:
 http://www.stepupproductions.com
Entertainment Services
N.A.I.C.S.: 516210

Summit Entertainment, LLC (2)
1630 Stewart St Ste 120, Santa Monica, CA 90404
Tel.: (310) 309-8400
Web Site: http://www.summit-ent.com

Motion Picture & Video Production Services
N.A.I.C.S.: 512110

U.R.O.K. Productions, Inc. (2)
1201 W 5th St Ste M230, Los Angeles, CA 90017
Tel.: (310) 255-3983
Emp.: 9
Motion Picture & Video Distribution Services
N.A.I.C.S.: 512120

Lionsgate Studios Corp. (1)
250 Howe Street, 20th Floor, Vancouver, V6C 3R8, BC, Canada (87.2%)
Tel.: (877) 848-3866
Web Site:
 https://investors.lionsgatestudios.com
Film & Television Production & Dist.
N.A.I.C.S.: 512120

LIONTOWN RESOURCES LIMITED

Tel.: (61) 861864600
Web Site:
 http://www.ltresources.com.au
LTR—(ASX)
Rev.: $150,242
Assets: $924,769,152
Liabilities: $410,561,274
Net Worth: $514,207,877
Earnings: ($43,348,345)
Emp.: 5
Fiscal Year-end: 06/30/24
Minerals Exploration
N.A.I.C.S.: 213113
Antonino Ottaviano (CEO & Mng Dir)

LIONTRUST ASSET MANAGEMENT PLC

2 Savoy Court, London, WC2R 0EZ, United Kingdom
Tel.: (44) 2074121700 UK
Web Site: https://www.liontrust.co.uk
Year Founded: 1994
LIO—(LSE)
Rev.: $249,796,769
Assets: $538,199,950
Liabilities: $322,049,988
Net Worth: $216,149,962
Earnings: ($4,405,453)
Emp.: 213
Fiscal Year-end: 03/31/24
Investment Management Service
N.A.I.C.S.: 523940
John Ions (CEO)

Subsidiaries:

Liontrust Investment Management Limited (1)
2 Savoy Court, London, WC2R 0EZ, United Kingdom
Tel.: (44) 20 7412 1700
Investment Services
N.A.I.C.S.: 523999

LIORET SA

3 Rue Saint Charles, 71360, Epinac, France
Tel.: (33) 385824056
Web Site:
 http://www.lioretgroupe.com
Rev.: $21,200,000
Emp.: 104
Fabricated Pipe & Fittings
N.A.I.C.S.: 332996
Jean-Michel Cler (Dir-Admin)

LIPA A.D., NOVI PAZAR

Ul 37 Sandzacke Divizije 2, 36300, Novi Pazar, Serbia
Tel.: (381) 20 322 637 RS
Web Site: http://www.lipa.rs
Year Founded: 1998
Sales Range: $1-9.9 Million
Emp.: 55
Home Management Services
N.A.I.C.S.: 721110

LIPA A.D., SOMBOR

Vojvodanska br 26, 25000, Sombor, Serbia
Tel.: (381) 25 412 154 RS
Web Site: http://www.lipa-sombor.rs
Year Founded: 1962
Sales Range: Less than $1 Million
Bar Management Services
N.A.I.C.S.: 722410
Nevenka Pavlica (Dir)

LIPIGON PHARMACEUTICALS AB

Tvistevagen 48 C, 907 36, Umea, Sweden
Tel.: (46) 705781768
Web Site: https://www.lipigon.se
Year Founded: 2010
LPGO—(OMX)
Rev.: $1,629,043
Assets: $3,335,517
Liabilities: $512,240
Net Worth: $2,823,277
Earnings: ($1,204,161)
Emp.: 7
Fiscal Year-end: 12/31/23
Pharmaceutical Product Mfr & Distr
N.A.I.C.S.: 325412
Lars Ohman (Chm)

LIPP GMBH

Industriestrasse 27, 73497, Tannhausen, Germany
Tel.: (49) 796490030
Web Site: http://www.lipp-system.de
Rev.: $50,421,679
Emp.: 43
Tanks & Containers Mfr
N.A.I.C.S.: 332420
Xaver Lipp (Founder)

LIPPI SYSTEMS LIMITED

3rd Floor Satya Complex Opp IOC Petrol Pump Nr Ashwamegh-IV, 132 ft Ring Road Satellite, Ahmedabad, 380 015, Gujarat, India
Tel.: (91) 796750060
Web Site:
 https://www.lippisystems.com
526604—(BOM)
Rev.: $1,987,013
Assets: $3,735,088
Liabilities: $412,455
Net Worth: $3,322,633
Earnings: $114,354
Emp.: 73
Fiscal Year-end: 03/31/22
Printing Machinery System Mfr
N.A.I.C.S.: 333248
Nandlal J. Agrawal (Mng Dir)

LIPPO LIMITED

40th Floor Tower Two Lippo Centre 89 Queensway, Hong Kong, China (Hong Kong)
Tel.: (852) 28676888
Web Site: https://www.lippoltd.com.hk
0226—(HKG)
Rev.: $93,919,883
Assets: $2,140,630,500
Liabilities: $317,183,876
Net Worth: $1,823,446,624
Earnings: $87,173,971
Emp.: 830
Fiscal Year-end: 12/31/21
Property Investment & Financial Services
N.A.I.C.S.: 541611
Davy Kwok Fai Lee (Sec)

Subsidiaries:

Auric Pacific Group Limited (1)
06-03 OUE Bayfront 50 Collyer Quay, Singapore, 049321, Singapore
Tel.: (65) 63362262
Web Site: http://www.auricgroup.com

LIPPO LIMITED

Lippo Limited—(Continued)
Sales Range: $250-299.9 Million
Investment Holding Company
N.A.I.C.S.: 551112
Stephen T. Riady (Exec Dir)

Subsidiary (Domestic):

Auric Asset Management Pte Ltd (2)
50 Collyer Quay Unit 06-03 Oue, Singapore, 79120, Singapore **(100%)**
Tel.: (65) 63362262
Web Site: http://www.auricgroup.com
Sales Range: $50-74.9 Million
Emp.: 22
Miscellaneous Financial Investment Activities
N.A.I.C.S.: 523999
Saw Phaik Hwa (CEO)

Subsidiary (Non-US):

Auric Chun Yip Sdn Bhd (2)
Lot 35 Jalan Delima 1-3 Subang Hitech Insustrial Park Batu 3, Subang Hi-Tech Industrial Park, 40000, Shah Alam, Selangor, Malaysia **(58.33%)**
Tel.: (60) 351636363
Web Site: http://www.auricgruop.com
Emp.: 80
Other Grocery & Related Products Whslr
N.A.I.C.S.: 424490
Liew Kok Hong (Gen Mgr)

Subsidiary (Domestic):

Auric Pacific Food Industries Pte Ltd (2)
50 Collyer Quay 06-03 Oue Bay Front, 49321, Singapore, Singapore **(100%)**
Tel.: (65) 63362262
Web Site: http://www.auricgroup.com
Sales Range: $25-49.9 Million
Emp.: 20
Frozen Cakes Pies & Other Pastries Mfr
N.A.I.C.S.: 311813
Saw Thaik Hwa (CEO)

Subsidiary (Non-US):

Auric Pacific Food Processing Sdn Bhd (2)
Lot 35 Jalan Delima 1/3 Subang Hi-Tech, Industrial Park Batu Tiga, 40000, Shah Alam, Selangor Darul Ehsan, Malaysia **(58.33%)**
Tel.: (60) 351636363
Web Site: http://www.auric.com.sg
Sales Range: $25-49.9 Million
Emp.: 130
Food Service Contractors
N.A.I.C.S.: 722310

Delifrance (HK) Limited (2)
Flat A 2/F Tin Fung Industrial Building 63 Wong Chuk Hang Road, Hong Kong, China (Hong Kong)
Tel.: (852) 2873 3893
Web Site: http://www.delifrance.com.hk
Emp.: 200
Cafeteria Operator
N.A.I.C.S.: 722514
Frances Chan (Gen Mgr)

Subsidiary (Domestic):

Delifrance Asia Ltd (2)
230 Pandan Loop, Singapore, 128415, Singapore
Tel.: (65) 68749647
Web Site: http://www.delifranceasia.com
Bakeries Operating Services
N.A.I.C.S.: 311812

Delifrance Singapore Pte Ltd (2)
10 Pandan Crescent 05-01 Lobby 1, Singapore, 128466, Singapore
Tel.: (65) 68749652
Web Site: http://www.delifrance.com.sg
Commercial Bakeries
N.A.I.C.S.: 311812

Food Junction Holdings Limited (2)
91 Tanglin Rd 02-02 Tanglin Pl, Singapore, 247918, Singapore **(93.1%)**
Tel.: (65) 63388213
Web Site: http://www.foodjunction.com
Sales Range: $25-49.9 Million
Beverages Mfr
N.A.I.C.S.: 311421

Phaik Hwa Saw (Exec Dir)

Subsidiary (Non-US):

Malone's Limited (2)
6 Miami Avenue Waiheke Island, Auckland, 1701, New Zealand
Tel.: (64) 93728011
Food & Beverages Mfr
N.A.I.C.S.: 311999

Subsidiary (Domestic):

Sunshine Manufacturing Pte Ltd (2)
2 Senoko Avenue, 758298, Singapore, Singapore
Tel.: (65) 62578455
Web Site: http://www.sunshine.com.sg
Sales Range: $100-124.9 Million
Commercial Bakeries
N.A.I.C.S.: 311812
Albert Chan (Gen Mgr)

HongKong Chinese Limited (1)
40th Floor Tower Two Lippo Centre 89 Queensway, Hong Kong, China (Hong Kong) **(65.84%)**
Tel.: (852) 2 867 6888
Web Site: http://www.hkchinese.com.hk
Sales Range: $10-24.9 Million
Emp.: 68
Investment Holding Company; Property Investment & Development Services
N.A.I.C.S.: 551112
John Luen Wai Lee (CEO)

Lippo China Resources Limited (1)
40th Floor Tower Two Lippo Centre 89 Queensway, Hong Kong, China (Hong Kong)
Tel.: (852) 28676888
Web Site: https://www.lcr.com.hk
Rev.: $77,442,480
Assets: $559,984,718
Liabilities: $174,547,755
Net Worth: $385,436,963
Earnings: ($40,356,555)
Emp.: 740
Fiscal Year-end: 12/31/2022
Property Investment & Development Services
N.A.I.C.S.: 523940
Millie Yuen Fun Luk (Sec)

Subsidiary (Non-US):

China Gold Pte. Ltd. (2)
19 Keppel Road #03-05 Jit Poh Building, Singapore, 089058, Singapore
Tel.: (65) 6227 3613
Minerals Exploration
N.A.I.C.S.: 212220
Kwok Fai Lee (Mgr)

Lippo Investments Management Limited (1)
40/F Tower Two Lippo Centre 89 Queensway, Hong Kong, China (Hong Kong)
Tel.: (852) 2 867 6888
Web Site: https://www.lippo-im.com
Investment Management Service
N.A.I.C.S.: 523940

LIPPO MALLS INDONESIA RETAIL TRUST

6 Shenton Way 40-05 OUE Downtown 1, Singapore, 68809, Singapore
Tel.: (65) 64109138
Web Site: https://www.lmir-trust.com
D5IU—(SES)
Rev.: $149,411,497
Assets: $1,305,235,931
Liabilities: $782,436,567
Net Worth: $522,799,364
Earnings: ($95,422,252)
Emp.: 16
Fiscal Year-end: 12/31/23
Real Estate Investment Services
N.A.I.C.S.: 523999
Murray Dangar Bell (Chm)

Subsidiaries:

PT Cibubur Utama (1)
Jl Jambore 1 Cibubur Junction Lt 2, Jakarta, Indonesia
Tel.: (62) 218 7755678
Real Estate Investment Services

PT Graha Baru Raya (1)
Jl Gajah Mada 19-26 Gajah Mada Plaza Lt 3/1, Jakarta, Indonesia
Tel.: (62) 216 3872287
Real Estate Investment Services
N.A.I.C.S.: 523940

PT Indah Pesona Bogor (1)
Jl Siliwangi 123 Ekalokasari Plaza Office Lt, Mezzanine, Bogor, 16142, Jawa Barat, Indonesia
Tel.: (62) 251 8318788
Real Estate Investment Services
N.A.I.C.S.: 531390

PT Manunggal Wiratama (1)
Jl KH Zainul Arifin 7 Sun Plaza Level 4 Bl C/10, Medan, 20153, Indonesia
Tel.: (62) 614 501000
Real Estate Investment Services
N.A.I.C.S.: 523940

PT Megah Semesta Abadi (1)
Jl Merdeka 56 Bandung Indah Plaza Lt 1/52-53, Bandung, 40115, Jawa Barat, Indonesia
Tel.: (62) 224 230850
Real Estate Investment Services
N.A.I.C.S.: 531390

PT Primatama Nusa Indah (1)
Jl Jend Sudirman Kav 50 The Plaza Semanggi Lt LG, 10270, Jakarta, Indonesia
Tel.: (62) 212 5536465
Real Estate Investment Services
N.A.I.C.S.: 531390

PT Suryana Istana Pasundan (1)
Jl Pasirkaliki 121-123 Istana Plaza LG B-2, Bandung, Jawa Barat, Indonesia
Tel.: (62) 226 018625
Real Estate Investment Services
N.A.I.C.S.: 531390

LIPSPLUS B.V.

Fokkerstraat 574, 3125 BE, Schiedam, Netherlands
Tel.: (31) 10 232 26 66 NI
Web Site: http://www.lipsplus.nl
Year Founded: 2017
Emp.: 950
Healthcare Linen Supply & Laundry Services
N.A.I.C.S.: 812331
Eduard Molkenboer (CEO)

Subsidiaries:

LipsPlus Emmen B.V. (1)
Cornelis Houtmanstraat 15, 7825 VH, Emmen, Netherlands
Tel.: (31) 591632022
Web Site: http://www.lipsplus.nl
Healthcare Linen Supply & Laundry Services
N.A.I.C.S.: 812331

LipsPlus Gemert B.V. (1)
Lodderdijk 9, 5421 XB, Gemert, Netherlands
Tel.: (31) 492361309
Web Site: http://www.lipsplus.nl
Healthcare Linen Supply & Laundry Services
N.A.I.C.S.: 812331

LipsPlus Goes B.V. (1)
Verrijn Stuartweg 30, 4462 GE, Goes, Netherlands
Tel.: (31) 113233150
Web Site: http://www.lipsplus.nl
Healthcare Linen Supply & Laundry Services
N.A.I.C.S.: 812331

LipsPlus Raalte B.V. (1)
Aakstraat 3, 8102 HH, Raalte, Netherlands
Tel.: (31) 572 328 000
Web Site: http://www.lipsplus.nl
Healthcare Linen Supply & Laundry Services
N.A.I.C.S.: 812331

LipsPlus Tiel B.V. (1)
Latensteinse Rondweg 6, 4005 EH, Tiel, Netherlands
Tel.: (31) 344 67 91 00

INTERNATIONAL PUBLIC

Web Site: http://www.lipsplus.nl
Healthcare Linen Supply & Laundry Services
N.A.I.C.S.: 812331

LipsPlus Voorburg B.V. (1)
Populierendreef 972, 2272 HW, Voorburg, Netherlands
Tel.: (31) 70 386 24 23
Web Site: http://www.lipsplus.nl
Healthcare Linen Supply & Laundry Services
N.A.I.C.S.: 812331

LipsPlus Wasverzorging B.V. (1)
Latensteinse Rondweg 6, 4005 EH, Tiel, Netherlands
Tel.: (31) 344 67 9113
Web Site: http://www.lipsplus.nl
Healthcare Linen Laundry Services
N.A.I.C.S.: 812331

LIQTECH INTERNATIONAL, INC.

Industriparken 22C, DK 2750, Ballerup, Denmark
Tel.: (45) 44986000 NV
Web Site: https://www.liqtech.com
LIQT—(NASDAQ)
Rev.: $15,982,438
Assets: $40,125,655
Liabilities: $16,816,283
Net Worth: $23,309,372
Earnings: ($14,169,107)
Emp.: 105
Fiscal Year-end: 12/31/22
Ceramic Silicon Carbide Filters Mfr
N.A.I.C.S.: 336390
Mark E. Vernon (Chm)

Subsidiaries:

LiqTech International A/S (1)
Industriparken 22C, 2750, Ballerup, Denmark
Tel.: (45) 44986000
Web Site: https://www.liqtech.com
Emp.: 100
Remediation Services
N.A.I.C.S.: 562910

Provital Solutions A/S (1)
Benshoj Industrivej 24, DK 9500, Hobro, Denmark
Tel.: (45) 70207258
Web Site: http://www.provital.dk
Remediation Services
N.A.I.C.S.: 562910

LIQUEFIED NATURAL GAS LIMITED

Level 25 20 Bond Street, Sydney, 2000, NSW, Australia
Tel.: (61) 2 7201 8312
Web Site: http://www.lnglimited.com.au
Rev.: $1,172,877
Assets: $24,311,496
Liabilities: $2,538,086
Net Worth: $21,773,409
Earnings: ($23,455,442)
Emp.: 22
Fiscal Year-end: 06/30/19
Natural Gas Supplier
N.A.I.C.S.: 211130
John G. Baguley (COO)

Subsidiaries:

Gas Link Global Limited (1)
5 Ord Street, West Perth, 6005, WA, Australia
Tel.: (61) 893663788
Web Site: http://www.gaslinkglobal.com.au
Gas Plant Development Services
N.A.I.C.S.: 237120

LNG International Pty Ltd (1)
5 Ord Street, West Perth, 6005, WA, Australia
Tel.: (61) 893663700
Web Site: http://www.lnglimited.com.au
Sales Range: $75-99.9 Million
Natural Gas Supplier
N.A.I.C.S.: 221210

AND PRIVATE COMPANIES — LISI S.A.

Maurice Brand *(Mng Dir)*

LIQUICHEM HANDELS GMBH
Beselerstrasse 2a, D-22607, Hamburg, Germany
Tel.: (49) 408997890   De
Web Site: http://www.liquichem.de
Year Founded: 1994
Sales Range: $50-74.9 Million
Chemicals Whslr
N.A.I.C.S.: 424690
Bun-Jon Winkelmann *(Product Mgr)*

LIQUID AVATAR TECHNOLOGIES INC.
7934 Government Road, Burnaby, V5A 2E2, BC, Canada
Tel.: (604) 808-2225
LQAVF—(OTCEM)
Rev.: $11,765
Assets: $2,183,482
Liabilities: $1,869,977
Net Worth: $313,505
Earnings: ($8,394,720)
Fiscal Year-end: 12/31/21
Electric Power Distribution Services
N.A.I.C.S.: 221121
Bryan E. Loree *(CFO & Sec)*

LIQUID MEDIA GROUP LTD.
202 5626 Larch Street, Vancouver, V6M 4E1, BC, Canada
Tel.: (604) 602-0001   BC
Web Site: http://liquidmediagroup.co
Year Founded: 1986
YVRLF—(OTCEM)
Rev.: $767,000
Assets: $11,566,000
Liabilities: $4,525,000
Net Worth: $7,041,000
Earnings: ($12,779,000)
Fiscal Year-end: 11/30/21
Beverage Mfr, Distr, Retailer & Marketer
N.A.I.C.S.: 312111
Charles Brezer *(Pres)*

Subsidiaries:

IndieFlix Group, Inc.   (1)
911 E Pike St Ste 310, Seattle, WA 98122-3853
Tel.: (206) 829-9112
Web Site: http://www.indieflix.com
Educational & Entertainment Streaming Services
N.A.I.C.S.: 512110
Scilla Andreen *(Founder & CEO)*

Leading Brands of America, Inc.   (1)
1500 West Georgia Street, Suite 1800, Vancouver, V6G 2Z6, BC, Canada
Tel.: (604) 685-5200
Web Site: http://www.lbis.com
Sales Range: $25-49.9 Million
Emp.: 20
Beverage Mfr, Distr, Retailer & Marketer
N.A.I.C.S.: 312111

Leading Brands of Canada, Inc.   (1)
1500 West Georgia Street Suite 1800, Vancouver, V6G 2Z6, BC, Canada
Tel.: (604) 685-5200
Web Site: http://www.leadingbrands.com
Beverage Mfr, Distr, Retailer & Marketer
N.A.I.C.S.: 312111

LIQUN COMMERCIAL GROUP CO., LTD.
No 78 Xiangjiang Road, Economic & Technological Development Zone, Qingdao, 266100, Shandong, China
Tel.: (86) 53258668898
Web Site: https://www.liquncommercial.com
Year Founded: 1998
601366—(SHG)
Rev.: $1,103,568,598
Assets: $2,452,603,304
Liabilities: $1,855,779,668
Net Worth: $596,823,636
Earnings: ($24,265,444)
Fiscal Year-end: 12/31/22
Departmental Store Operator
N.A.I.C.S.: 455110
Xu Gongzao *(Chm)*

LIR S.R.L.
Via Feltrina Sud 6, Montebelluna, 31044, Italy
Tel.: (39) 0423617911
Investment Management Firm
N.A.I.C.S.: 525910

Subsidiaries:

Geox S.p.A.   (1)
Via Feltrina Centro 16 Biadene di Montebelluna, 31044, Treviso, Italy
Tel.: (39) 04232822
Web Site: https://www.geox.biz
Rev.: $656,981,891
Assets: $1,052,765,036
Liabilities: $847,393,482
Net Worth: $205,371,554
Earnings: ($157,466,509)
Emp.: 4,458
Fiscal Year-end: 12/31/2020
Shoes & Apparel Mfr
N.A.I.C.S.: 316210
Mario Moretti Polegato *(Chm)*

LIS CO., LTD.
38-13 Ojeon-Dong, Uiwang, 437817, Korea (South)
Tel.: (82) 314278492   KR
138690—(KRS)
Rev.: $1,853,199
Assets: $63,753,898
Liabilities: $9,281,247
Net Worth: $54,472,651
Earnings: ($5,186,731)
Emp.: 278
Fiscal Year-end: 12/31/23
Semiconductor Laser Equipment Mfr
N.A.I.C.S.: 334413

LISAM SYSTEMS INC.
Rue Jean Jaures 5, Ecaussinnes, 7190, Belgium
Tel.: (32) 67 49 00 03
Web Site: http://www.lisam.com
Year Founded: 1999
Environmental, Health & Safety (EH&S) Compliance Management Software Services
N.A.I.C.S.: 513210
Michel Hemberg *(CEO)*

Subsidiaries:

Perillon Software, Inc   (1)
33 Nagog Park, Acton, MA 01720
Tel.: (978) 263-0412
Web Site: http://www.perillon.com
EHS Compliance & Risk Management Software Developer
N.A.I.C.S.: 513210
John E. Niemoller *(CEO)*

LISANYDIS
Ctr Commercial La Valet Route Nationale 973, Puyvert, 84160, Apt, France
Tel.: (33) 490084073
Rev.: $21,800,000
Emp.: 100
Grocery Stores
N.A.I.C.S.: 445110
Renaud Martin *(Dir)*

LISCA, D.D.
Presernova 4, 8290, Sevnica, Slovenia
Tel.: (386) 78164100
Web Site: http://www.lisca.com
Sales Range: $50-74.9 Million
Emp.: 400
Women Underwear, Swimwear & Blouse Mfr
N.A.I.C.S.: 315120
Goran Kodelja *(Gen Mgr)*

Subsidiaries:

LISCA d.o.o - modna odeca   (1)
Pere Velimirovica 2a, Belgrade, 11000, Serbia
Tel.: (381) 11 266 3938
Sales Range: $50-74.9 Million
Emp.: 60
Lingerie Distr
N.A.I.C.S.: 424350

LISCA moda d.o.o.   (1)
Vrbanjusa 45-A, 71000, Sarajevo, Bosnia & Herzegovina
Tel.: (387) 33 272 680
Lingerie Distr
N.A.I.C.S.: 424350

Lisca Group Deutschland GmbH   (1)
MTC-Haus 1 Raum 38 Taunusstrasse 45, 80807, Munich, Germany
Tel.: (49) 89 381682460
Lingerie Distr
N.A.I.C.S.: 424350

Lisca Moda s.r.o.   (1)
Holeckova 31, Smichov, 15000, Prague, Czech Republic
Tel.: (420) 267 713 542
Sales Range: $50-74.9 Million
Emp.: 5
Lingerie Distr
N.A.I.C.S.: 424350
Sandra Aljancic *(Mgr-Client Rels)*

LISGRAFICA IMPRESSAO E ARTES GRAFICAS SA
St Marks Road 27, 2735-521, Cacem, Portugal
Tel.: (351) 214345400
Web Site: http://www.lisgrafica.pt
LIG—(EUR)
Sales Range: $10-24.9 Million
Printing Services
N.A.I.C.S.: 323111
Luciano Manuel Ribeiro da Silva Patrao *(Chm & CEO)*

LISHENG SPORTS (SHANGHAI) CO., LTD.
2F Building 8 518 Fuquan North Road, Changning District, Shanghai, 200335, China
Tel.: (86) 2162418755
Web Site: http://www.lsracing.cn
Year Founded: 2002
002858—(SSE)
Rev.: $36,265,643
Assets: $144,615,819
Liabilities: $36,902,329
Net Worth: $107,713,490
Earnings: ($10,725,942)
Fiscal Year-end: 12/31/22
Motor Sport Racing Operator
N.A.I.C.S.: 711219
Xia Qing *(Chm)*

LISI S.A.
6 Juvenal Street Viellard, CS 70431, Grandvillars, 90008, Belfort, Cedex, France
Tel.: (33) 384570077
Web Site: https://www.lisi-group.com
Year Founded: 1777
FII—(EUR)
Rev.: $1,874,097,583
Assets: $2,272,398,720
Liabilities: $1,236,151,893
Net Worth: $1,036,246,827
Earnings: $40,475,770
Emp.: 10,014
Fiscal Year-end: 12/31/23
Holding Company; Aerospace, Cosmetics & Automotive Businesses
N.A.I.C.S.: 551112
Emmanuel Viellard *(Dir Gen)*

Subsidiaries:

ANKIT Fasteners Pvt Ltd.   (1)
297 Haragadde Village Road No 4, Jigni Industrial Estate, Bengaluru, 562 106, India
Tel.: (91) 8039817900
Web Site: http://www.ankitfasteners.com
Aircraft Product Mfr
N.A.I.C.S.: 336411
Prashant Raju *(Mgr)*

Blanc Aero Industries UK Ltd.   (1)
Butlers Leap, Rugby, CV21 3RQ, Warwickshire, United Kingdom
Tel.: (44) 1788559000
Aircraft Product Mfr
N.A.I.C.S.: 336411

Ft Bestas A.S.   (1)
Ege Serbest Böl Ayfer Sok No 21, Izmir, Turkiye   (100%)
Tel.: (90) 2322517272
Web Site: http://www.lisi-aerospace.com
Sales Range: $100-124.9 Million
Emp.: 450
Aeronautical & Nautical System & Instrument Mfr
N.A.I.C.S.: 334511

Knipping Verbindungstechnik GmbH   (1)
In Der Helle 7, 58566, Kierspe, Germany   (100%)
Tel.: (49) 23596630
Web Site: http://www.knipping.com
Sales Range: $150-199.9 Million
Emp.: 300
Hardware Whslr
N.A.I.C.S.: 423710

Subsidiary (Domestic):

BETEO GmbH   (2)
Kirchhoffstrasse 3, 51647, Gummersbach, Germany
Tel.: (49) 2261 29045 0
Web Site: http://www.beteo.de
Sales Range: $25-49.9 Million
Emp.: 43
Automobile Assembly Parts Mfr
N.A.I.C.S.: 336390
Haenig Jens-Paul *(Gen Mgr)*

LISI AUTOMOTIVE NOMEL   (1)
Lieu-dit de la Foret du Chateau, 61550, La Ferte-Frenel, France
Tel.: (33) 233346629
Sales Range: $100-124.9 Million
Emp.: 30
Automobile Parts Mfr
N.A.I.C.S.: 336390
Ludovic Clebar *(Mgr)*

LISI AUTOMOTIVE SHANGHAI Co., Ltd   (1)
No 888 Huadan Road, Qingpu District, Shanghai, 201708, China
Tel.: (86) 21 6979 1388
Web Site: http://www.lisi-automotive.com
Automobile Assembly Parts Mfr
N.A.I.C.S.: 336390

LISI Automotive Hi-Vol Inc.   (1)
12955 Inkster Rd, Livonia, MI 48150
Tel.: (734) 266-6900
Screw & Bolt Mfr
N.A.I.C.S.: 332722
Randy Hinz *(Gen Mgr)*

LISI Automotive Knipping Espana S.A.   (1)
Calle Enebro 2, Fuenlabrada, 28 942, Madrid, Spain
Tel.: (34) 916490034
Screw & Bolt Mfr
N.A.I.C.S.: 332722
Lorenzo Jimenez Cano *(Gen Mgr)*

LISI Automotive SAS   (1)
2 Rue Juvenal Viellard, Grandvillars, 90600, Bourgogne, France
Tel.: (33) 384586300
Web Site: http://www.lisi-automotive.com
Screw & Bolt Mfr
N.A.I.C.S.: 332722
Sean Farrell *(Dir-Strategy & Mktg)*

LISI MEDICAL JEROPA INC.   (1)
950 Borra Pl, Escondido, CA 92029-2011
Tel.: (760) 432-9785
Web Site: http://www.lisi-medical.com
Surgical & Medical Instrument Mfr
N.A.I.C.S.: 339112

LISI Medical Orthopaedics   (1)
203 Blvd de la Grande Delle, BP 8, 14201,

LISI S.A.

LISI S.A.—(Continued)
Herouville-Saint-Clair, France **(100%)**
Tel.: (33) 2 3146 3300
Web Site: http://www.lisi-medical.com
Sales Range: $50-74.9 Million
Emp.: 250
Medical & Surgical Implants Mfr
N.A.I.C.S.: 339112

LISI Medical SAS (1)
19 Chemin de la Traille, 01700, Neyron, France
Tel.: (33) 478558000
Web Site: http://www.lisi-medical.com
Medical Equipment Mfr
N.A.I.C.S.: 339112
Jean-Marc Durano *(Mng Dir)*

Lisi Aerospace Additive Manufacturing SAS (1)
4 route Robert Algayon, Ayguemorte-les-Graves, 33640, Gironde, France
Tel.: (33) 626633834
Aircraft Product Mfr
N.A.I.C.S.: 336411

Lisi Aerospace North America, Inc. (1)
2600 Skypark Dr, Torrance, CA 90509-2976
Tel.: (310) 326-8110
Aircraft Product Mfr
N.A.I.C.S.: 336411
Paul Felski *(VP & Gen Mgr)*

Lisi Aerospace S.A.S. (1)
Tour Gamma A, 193, rue de Bercy, 75582, Paris, France **(100%)**
Tel.: (33) 144678585
Web Site: http://www.lisi-aerospace.com
Sales Range: $550-599.9 Million
Emp.: 3,309
Bolt Nut Screw Rivet & Washer Mfr
N.A.I.C.S.: 332722

Subsidiary (Domestic):

Blanc Aero Industries S.A. (2)
Tour Gamma A, Paris, France **(100%)**
Tel.: (33) 143473180
Sales Range: $25-49.9 Million
Emp.: 30
Bolt Nut Screw Rivet & Washer Mfr
N.A.I.C.S.: 332722

Blanc Aero Technologies S.A. (2)
Tour Gamma A, Paris, France **(100%)**
Tel.: (33) 143473180
Sales Range: $25-49.9 Million
Emp.: 30
Bolt Nut Screw Rivet & Washer Mfr
N.A.I.C.S.: 332722

Subsidiary (US):

HI-SHEAR CORPORATION (2)
2600 Skypark Dr, Torrance, CA 90509
Tel.: (310) 326-8110
Web Site: http://www.lisiaerospace.com
Sales Range: $150-199.9 Million
Emp.: 1,000
Aircraft Part Mfr
N.A.I.C.S.: 336413
Josee Martin *(Mgr-Inside Sls-Fasteners)*

Subsidiary (Non-US):

Lisi Aerospace Canada Corporation (2)
2000 Place Transcanadienne, Dorval, H9P 2X5, QC, Canada **(100%)**
Tel.: (514) 421-4567
Web Site: http://www.lisiaerospace.com
Sales Range: $25-49.9 Million
Emp.: 150
Industrial Machinery Mfr
N.A.I.C.S.: 333248
Farrell Campbell *(Mng Dir)*

Subsidiary (US):

Lisi Aerospace, Hi-Shear Corp. (2)
2600 Skypark Dr, Torrance, CA 90505-5373 **(100%)**
Tel.: (310) 784-4042
Web Site: http://www.lisi-aerospace.com
Sales Range: $200-249.9 Million
Emp.: 825
Holding Company
N.A.I.C.S.: 551112
Christian Darville *(CEO)*

Lisi Automotive Former S.A.S. (1)
28 Faubourg De Belfort, Delle, France **(100%)**
Tel.: (33) 384586335
Web Site: http://www.lisi-automotive.com
Bolt Nut Screw Rivet & Washer Mfr
N.A.I.C.S.: 332722

Lisi Automotive Kkp Gmbh & Co Kg (1)
Am Sandhugel 1, Mellrichstadt, 97638, Mellrichstadt, Germany **(100%)**
Tel.: (49) 9776630
Web Site: http://www.lisi-automotive.com
Sales Range: $50-74.9 Million
Emp.: 220
Automotive Parts & Accessories Stores
N.A.I.C.S.: 441330

Lisi Automotive Rapid S.A. (1)
1 Rue De Pontoise, Puiseux Pontoise, Paris, France **(100%)**
Tel.: (33) 134466000
Web Site: http://www.lisi-automotive.com
Sales Range: $50-74.9 Million
Emp.: 200
Prefabricated Metal Building & Component Mfr
N.A.I.C.S.: 332311

Lisi Automotive Sarl (1)
28 Faubourg De Belfort, 90101, Delle, France **(100%)**
Tel.: (33) 384586300
Web Site: http://www.lisi-automotive.com
Sales Range: $400-449.9 Million
Emp.: 2,000
Bolt Nut Screw Rivet & Washer Mfr
N.A.I.C.S.: 332722

Subsidiary (Non-US):

Beteo Gmbh & Co Kg (2)
Kirchhoffstrasse 3, 51647, Bochum, Germany
Tel.: (49) 2261290450
Web Site: http://www.beteo.de
Sales Range: $25-49.9 Million
Emp.: 40
Bolt Nut Screw Rivet & Washer Mfr
N.A.I.C.S.: 332722

Lisi Automotive Form A.S (2)
Cejc 276 Nadrazni, Hodonin, 696 14, Czech Republic **(100%)**
Tel.: (420) 518606600
Web Site: http://www.lisi-automotive.com
Sales Range: $25-49.9 Million
Emp.: 150
Machine Tools Mfr
N.A.I.C.S.: 333517

Lisi Automotive Mecano GmbH (2)
Dischinger Str 9, 69123, Heidelberg, Germany **(100%)**
Tel.: (49) 62217746
Web Site: http://www.lisi-automotive.com
Sales Range: $25-49.9 Million
Emp.: 20
Automotive Parts & Accessories Stores
N.A.I.C.S.: 441330

Subsidiary (Domestic):

LISI AUTOMOTIVE KKP GmbH (3)
Am Sandhugel 1, 97635, Mellrichstadt, Germany
Tel.: (49) 97 76 63 0
Sales Range: $50-74.9 Million
Automobile Assembly Parts Mfr
N.A.I.C.S.: 336390
Roger Schweigert *(Mgr)*

Subsidiary (Non-US):

Lisi Automotive Mohr und Friedrich GmbH (2)
Langenbacher Str 18, Vohrenbach, 78147, Germany
Tel.: (49) 7727926020
Web Site: http://www.lisi-automotive.com
Sales Range: $25-49.9 Million
Emp.: 91
Bolt Nut Screw Rivet & Washer Mfr
N.A.I.C.S.: 332722

Subsidiary (US):

Termax Corporation (2)
200 Telser Rd, Lake Zurich, IL 60047-0047

Tel.: (847) 519-1500
Web Site: http://www.termax.com
Dynamic Mfr & Engineering Company; Fastener, Button, Needle & Pin Mfr
N.A.I.C.S.: 339993
Bill Smith *(CEO)*

MONADNOCK (1)
16728 E Gale Ave, City of Industry, CA 91745
Tel.: (626) 964-6581
Web Site: http://www.monadnock.com
Fastening Systems Mfr
N.A.I.C.S.: 339993
Michael Reyes *(VP)*

SEIGNOL HUGUENY (1)
Zone D Acti De La Traille Chemin De La Traille, 1700, Neyron, France
Tel.: (33) 4 78 55 8000
Web Site: http://www.seignol.info
Medical & Surgical Equipment Mfr
N.A.I.C.S.: 339112

Subsidiary (Non-US):

LIXUS Industrie (2)
Lot 72 Lot No 01 Free Zone, Tangiers, Morocco
Tel.: (212) 539394470
Sales Range: $25-49.9 Million
Emp.: 27
Surgical & Medical Instrument Distr
N.A.I.C.S.: 423450
Jerome Caze *(Gen Mgr)*

TMX Canada Corp. (1)
5230 Burke Street, Windsor, N9A 6J3, ON, Canada
Tel.: (847) 519-1500
Engineeering Services
N.A.I.C.S.: 541330
Jackie Goodman *(Acct Mgr)*

TMX, S.A. de C.V. (1)
Av Del Marques No 45, Parque Industrial Bernardo Quintana, 76246, El Marques, Mexico
Tel.: (52) 4422216614
Metal & Rubber Product Mfr
N.A.I.C.S.: 326299

LISTER WILDER LTD

The Park Port Way Crowmarsh, Wallingford, OX10 8FG, Oxon, United Kingdom
Tel.: (44) 1491838388
Web Site:
http://www.listerwilder.co.uk
Year Founded: 1947
Sales Range: $50-74.9 Million
Emp.: 150
Agriculture & Construction Machinery Distr
N.A.I.C.S.: 423820
Ian Nutt *(Mng Dir)*

LISTER-PETTER LIMITED

Long St, Dursley, GL11 4HS, Gloucester, United Kingdom
Tel.: (44) 453544141 UK
Web Site: http://www.lister-petter.co.uk
Year Founded: 1867
Sales Range: $25-49.9 Million
Emp.: 250
Air & Water Cooled Medium & High Speed Diesel Engines for Industrial Applications
N.A.I.C.S.: 333618
Brian Fuller *(Mng Dir)*

Subsidiaries:

Lister Petter Africa (PTY) LTD (1)
4 Falcon Crescent Airport City, Cape Town, 7525, South Africa
Tel.: (27) 21 380 7700
Web Site: http://www.lister-petter.co.za
Emp.: 5
Industrial Engine & Power Generator Mfr
N.A.I.C.S.: 333618
Douglas Jones *(Gen Mgr)*

Lister Petter Americas Inc (1)
14350 NW 56 Ct Unit 105, Miami, FL 33054

Tel.: (305) 913-3300
Industrial Engine & Power Generator Mfr
N.A.I.C.S.: 333618
Dooky Schute *(Mng Dir)*

Lister Petter FZE (1)
DSO HQ Silicon Oasis, PO Box 341077, Dubai, United Arab Emirates
Tel.: (971) 43724315
Industrial Engine & Power Generator Mfr
N.A.I.C.S.: 333618

Lister Petter Global HUB (1)
Dorset Road 1 Hangar 21 F Site Aston Down, Quadrant Way Hardwicke, Gloucester, GL6 8GA, United Kingdom
Tel.: (44) 1452 229 990
Industrial Engine & Power Generator Mfr
N.A.I.C.S.: 333618

Lister Petter Oceania Ltd (1)
358 Neilson Street, Penrose, 1061, Auckland, New Zealand
Tel.: (64) 94 853 135
Industrial Engine & Power Generator Mfr
N.A.I.C.S.: 333618

Lister-Petter Inc. (1)
815 E 56 Hwy, Olathe, KS 66061 **(100%)**
Tel.: (913) 764-3512
Web Site: http://www.lister-petter.com
Sales Range: $25-49.9 Million
Emp.: 30
Sales & Service of Diesel Engines
N.A.I.C.S.: 423830
Brian Draper *(Pres & CEO)*

LITALICO, LNC.

Nakameguro GT Tower 15F / 16F / 20F 2-1-1 Kamimeguro, Meguro-ku, Tokyo, 153-0051, Japan
Tel.: (81) 357047355
Web Site: https://www.litalico.co.jp
Year Founded: 2005
7366—(TKS)
Rev.: $196,925,120
Assets: $167,305,710
Liabilities: $98,383,240
Net Worth: $68,922,470
Earnings: $23,432,450
Emp.: 4,714
Fiscal Year-end: 03/31/24
Infant School Management Services
N.A.I.C.S.: 611110
Atsumi Hasegawa *(Pres & Co-CEO)*

LITE ACCESS TECHNOLOGIES INC.

110 6039 196 Street, Surrey, V3S 7X4, BC, Canada
Tel.: (604) 247-4704 BC
Web Site: https://www.liteaccess.com
Year Founded: 2014
LTCCF—(OTCIQ)
Rev.: $5,622,792
Assets: $5,122,136
Liabilities: $3,188,698
Net Worth: $1,933,437
Earnings: $1,679,770
Fiscal Year-end: 09/30/21
Fiber Optic Mfr
N.A.I.C.S.: 335921
Robert David Toyoda *(Sec)*

LITE-ON SEMICONDUCTOR CORP.

4F 392 Ruey Kuang Road, Neihu, Taipei, 11492, Taiwan
Tel.: (886) 87982988
Web Site: http://www.liteon-semi.com
Year Founded: 1990
5305—(TAI)
Rev.: $5,589,242,970
Assets: $6,262,711,620
Liabilities: $3,625,497,967
Net Worth: $2,637,213,653
Earnings: $349,624,786
Emp.: 3,679
Fiscal Year-end: 12/31/20
Semiconductor Components Mfr
N.A.I.C.S.: 333242

AND PRIVATE COMPANIES

Subsidiaries:

Lite-On Semiconductor Corp - Hsin-chu Plant (1)
No 7 Industry East Road VII Science Based Industrial Park, Hsin-chu, Taiwan
Tel.: (886) 35771036
Semiconductor Devices Mfr
N.A.I.C.S.: 334413

Lite-On Semiconductor Corp. - Keelung Plant (1)
No 28 1 Wu Shin Street Ta Wu Lung Ind Zone, Keelung, 204, Taiwan
Tel.: (886) 224324123
Semiconductor Devices Mfr
N.A.I.C.S.: 334413

Lite-On Semiconductor Corp. - Philippines Plant (1)
Lot 1 & 2 Block 24 Phase 4, Peza Ecozone, Rosario, 4106, Cavite, Philippines
Tel.: (63) 464371002
Sales Range: $25-49.9 Million
Emp.: 80
Semiconductor Devices Mfr
N.A.I.C.S.: 334413

Lite-On Semiconductor Corp. - ShangHai Plant (1)
No 6 Zhen ye Road Dong Jung Ind Area, Song Jiang, Shanghai, 201601, China
Tel.: (86) 2157671670
Web Site: http://www.lite-onsemi.com
Semiconductor Devices Mfr
N.A.I.C.S.: 334413

LITE-ON TECHNOLOGY CORPORATION

No 392 Ruiguang Rd, Neihu, Taipei, 114, Taiwan
Tel.: (886) 287982888
Web Site: https://www.liteon.com
Year Founded: 1975
2301—(TAI)
Rev: $4,959,130,948
Assets: $6,179,804,862
Liabilities: $3,397,915,042
Net Worth: $2,781,889,819
Earnings: $477,412,160
Emp.: 27,765
Fiscal Year-end: 12/31/23
Computer Components Mfr & Marketer
N.A.I.C.S.: 334419
Raymond Soong *(Bd of Dirs & Chm/Chm-Grp)*

Subsidiaries:

DongGuan G-pro Computer Co., Ltd. (1)
1st Row Yinshan Rd Yinhu Industrial Zone Qingxi Town, Dongguan, 523730, Guangdong, China
Tel.: (86) 76987318190
Electronic Computer Mfr
N.A.I.C.S.: 334111

DragonJet Corporation (1)
No 24 Zhongyi St, Shulin, Taipei, Taiwan
Tel.: (886) 2 26896926
Web Site: http://www.dragonjet.com.tw
Injection Molded Plastic Products Mfr
N.A.I.C.S.: 326199

Plant (Domestic):

DragonJet Corporation - Dragonjet Kaohsiung Plant (2)
No 27 Jing 4th Rd, Nanzi Dist, Kaohsiung, Taiwan
Tel.: (886) 7 361 7163
Web Site: https://www.dragonjet.com.tw
Cash Register Cases Mfr
N.A.I.C.S.: 339940

Plant (Non-US):

DragonJet Corporation - Dragonjet Vietnam Plant (2)
D3 Que Vo Industrial Park, Bac Ninh, Vietnam
Tel.: (84) 241 3 634 188
Printer Mfr
N.A.I.C.S.: 334118

Huizhou Li Shin Electronic Co., Ltd. (1)
Yi Ho Houng Bo Industrial City, Lo Yang Town Bo Luo Hsien, Huizhou, Guangdong, China
Tel.: (86) 7526863222
Electronic Components Mfr
N.A.I.C.S.: 334419

Leotek Electronics Corp. (1)
50 Lung Yuan 7th Rd Lungtan Hsiang, Taoyuan, 32542, Taiwan
Tel.: (886) 34995939
Electronic Components Mfr
N.A.I.C.S.: 334419

Leotek Electronics USA LLC (1)
1955 Lundy Ave, San Jose, CA 95131
Tel.: (408) 380-1788
Web Site: http://www.leotek.com
Lighting Product Mfr
N.A.I.C.S.: 335139
Kenan Chen *(Mgr-Product)*

Lite-On Automotive Corp. (1)
37 Jhong Yang Rd N E P Z, Kaohsiung, 81170, Taiwan
Tel.: (886) 73611111
Car Alarm System Mfr
N.A.I.C.S.: 336320

Subsidiary (US):

Lite-On Automotive North America Inc. (2)
1050 S Milford Rd Ste 204, Highland, MI 48357-4878
Tel.: (248) 887-2800
Automotive Electronic Component Mfr
N.A.I.C.S.: 336320

Lite-On Automotive Electronics (Guang Zhou) Co., Ltd. (1)
No 25 Guangpu W Rd Guangbao Tech Park, Guangzhou, 510663, Guangdong, China
Tel.: (86) 2082373058
Automobile Parts Mfr
N.A.I.C.S.: 336390

Lite-On Automotive Electronics Europe B.V. (1)
Tweelingenlaan 57, Apeldoorn, 7324, Netherlands
Tel.: (31) 55 5261950
Web Site: http://www.liteon.com
Emp.: 2
Cruise Control System Mfr & Whslr
N.A.I.C.S.: 336320

Lite-On Clean Energy Technology Corp. (1)
19f 392 Jui Kuang Rd, Taipei, 11492, Taiwan
Tel.: (886) 287982888
Sales Range: $25-49.9 Million
Emp.: 6
Electronic Components Mfr
N.A.I.C.S.: 334419
C. Y. Ting *(VP)*

Lite-On Electronics (Dongguan) Co., Ltd. (1)
No 1 Zheng An Road, Shang Jiao Section Chang An Town, Dongguan, 523878, Guangdong, China
Tel.: (86) 76986070888
Automotive Electronic Product Mfr
N.A.I.C.S.: 336320

Lite-On Electronics (Europe) Ltd. (1)
23 Apex Business Village, Cramlington, NE23 7BF, Northumberland, United Kingdom
Tel.: (44) 191 250 4931
Web Site: http://www.liteon.com
Electronic Components Mfr
N.A.I.C.S.: 334419

Lite-On Electronics (Thailand) Co., Ltd. (1)
8/4 Moo 1 Rangsit Ongkarak Road, Bunyeetoh Tanyaburi, Bangkok, 12130, Patthumthani, Thailand
Tel.: (66) 2533120816
Electronic Components Mfr
N.A.I.C.S.: 334419

Lite-On Electronics Co., Ltd. (1)
Rm 904-905 9/F Intl Plz 20 Sheung Yuet Rd, Kowloon Bay, Kowloon, China (Hong Kong)
Tel.: (852) 27963012
Web Site: http://www.liteon.com
Sales Range: $25-49.9 Million
Emp.: 18
Electronic Components Mfr
N.A.I.C.S.: 334419

Subsidiary (Non-US):

Lite-On Technology (Guangzhou) Co., Ltd. (2)
No 2 Caipin Rd Science City High-Tech Industrial Development Zone, Guangzhou, 510663, Guangdong, China
Tel.: (86) 2028201000
Electronic Components Mfr
N.A.I.C.S.: 334419

Silitek Elec. (GuangZhou) Co., Ltd. (2)
Lingnan Industrial Area, Haotou Town, Guangzhou, 510935, China
Tel.: (86) 20 8237 3688
Computer Peripheral Equipment Mfr
N.A.I.C.S.: 334419

Lite-On Electronics H.K. Ltd. (1)
Rm 904-905 9/Fl International Plaza 20 Sheung Yuet Road, Kowloon Bay, Kowloon, 523878, China (Hong Kong)
Tel.: (852) 27963012
Web Site: http://www.optoelectronics.liteon.com
Sales Range: $25-49.9 Million
Optoelectronic Device Mfr
N.A.I.C.S.: 334413

Lite-On Electronics Tianjin Co., Ltd. (1)
No 11 Fu-Yuan Road, Wuqing Development Area, Tianjin, 301700, China
Tel.: (86) 2282193000
Web Site: http://www.optoelectronics.liteon.com
Optoelectronic Device Mfr
N.A.I.C.S.: 334413

Lite-On Green Technologies Inc. (1)
22F 392 Ruey Kuang Road, Neihu, Taipei, 114, Taiwan
Tel.: (886) 287982888
Web Site: http://www.liteongt.com
Solar Power Plant Construction Services
N.A.I.C.S.: 237130

Lite-On IT Corporation (1)
12F 392 Ruey Kuang Road, Neihu, Taipei, 114, Taiwan
Tel.: (886) 28 798 2886
Web Site: http://www.liteonit.com
Sales Range: $1-4.9 Billion
Emp.: 13,604
Optical Disk Drives Mfr & Distr
N.A.I.C.S.: 334112
Raymond Soong *(Chm)*

Subsidiary (Non-US):

Lite-On IT BV (2)
Meerenakkerplein 16, 5652 BJ, Eindhoven, Netherlands
Tel.: (31) 402508000
Web Site: http://www.liteonit.com
Playback Drives Distr
N.A.I.C.S.: 423430

Lite-On Opto Technology (Guangzhou) Ltd. (2)
Lite-on Science Park GuangPu West Road Guangzhou Science Park, Guangzhou, Guangdong, China
Tel.: (86) 20 8234 0168
Digital Camera & Optical Disk Drives Mfr
N.A.I.C.S.: 334118

Lite-On Japan Ltd. (1)
2-16-2 Sotokanda, Chiyoda-Ku, Tokyo, 101-0021, Japan **(100%)**
Tel.: (81) 332586501
Web Site: https://www.lite-on.co.jp
Rev: $122,322,000
Assets: $61,174,320
Liabilities: $36,807,600
Net Worth: $24,366,720
Earnings: $967,920
Fiscal Year-end: 12/31/2017
Electronic Components Distr
N.A.I.C.S.: 423690

Tetsuo Matakawa *(Pres & Gen Mgr-Bus Div)*

Subsidiary (Non-US):

Lite-On Japan (H.K.) Limited (2)
Unit No 01 15th Floor No 909 Cheung Sha Wan Road Cheung Sha Wan, Kowloon, China (Hong Kong)
Tel.: (852) 27717523
Electronic Parts Distr
N.A.I.C.S.: 423690

Lite-On Japan (Thailand) Co., Ltd. (2)
55 Wave Place 18FL Wireless Road Lumpini, Pathumwan, Bangkok, 10330, Thailand
Tel.: (66) 26553451
Electronic Parts Distr
N.A.I.C.S.: 423690

NL (Shanghai) Co., Ltd. (2)
Room 2706-1 Building 299 SOHO Dong Hai Plaza Tong-ren Road, Jing'an District, Shanghai, China
Tel.: (86) 2162368780
Electronic Parts Distr
N.A.I.C.S.: 423690

NL(Shanghai)Co., Ltd. (2)
Room 33A Block B Honglong Century Plaza 3001 Heping Road, Luohu District, Shenzhen, Guangdong, China
Tel.: (86) 75522919723
Electronic Parts Distr
N.A.I.C.S.: 423690

Lite-On Li Shin Technology (Ganzhou) Inc. (1)
South 3rd Road, Economic and Technological Development Zone Industria, Ganzhou, Jiangxi, China
Tel.: (86) 7978324999
Electronic Components Mfr
N.A.I.C.S.: 334419

Lite-On Mobile Oyj (1)
Ayritie 8 A, 01510, Vantaa, Finland
Tel.: (358) 9250071
Web Site: http://www.liteonmobile.com
Sales Range: $900-999.9 Million
Emp.: 10,200
Telecommunication Electronic Components Mfr
N.A.I.C.S.: 334419
Raymond Soong *(Chm)*

Subsidiary (Non-US):

CIM Precision Moulds (HK) Ltd. (2)
Hopeful Factory Centre Unit 1201, 10 Wo Shing Street, Fo Tan, Hong Kong, China (Hong Kong)
Tel.: (852) 23655221
Designer & Mfr of Telecommunication Electronic Components
N.A.I.C.S.: 334419

Subsidiary (Non-US):

Perlos Precision Molds (Shenzhen) Co. Ltd. (3)
Brightman Industrial Zone 1 3 F Block 9, Shawan, Shenzhen, China
Tel.: (86) 75589964088
Sales Range: $100-124.9 Million
Emp.: 350
Designer & Mfr of Telecommunication Electronic Components
N.A.I.C.S.: 334419

Subsidiary (Non-US):

Lite-On Mobile Industria e Comercio de Plasticos Ltda (2)
Avenida Torquato Tapajos 7891, 690 48660, Manaus, Taruma, Brazil
Tel.: (55) 9221237777
Web Site: http://www.liteonmobile.com
Sales Range: $75-99.9 Million
Emp.: 300
Designer & Mfr of Telecommunication Electronic Components
N.A.I.C.S.: 334419

Perlos (Beijing) Electronic & Telecommunication Components Co., Ltd. (2)
16 Zhonghe Road, Beijing Economic Devel Area, Perlos (Beijing), Beijing, China

LITE-ON TECHNOLOGY CORPORATION

Lite-On Technology Corporation—(Continued)
Tel.: (86) 10 6787 9009
Designer & Mfr of Telecommunication Electronic Components
N.A.I.C.S.: 334419

Perlos (Guangzhou) Engineering Plastics Co., Ltd. (2)
46 Dong Peng Avenue, Eastern Section GETDD, Guangzhou, 510530, China
Tel.: (86) 2032100000
Web Site: http://www.liteonmobile.com
Designer & Mfr of Telecommunication Electronic Components
N.A.I.C.S.: 334419

Perlos Asia Pte. Ltd. (2)
3 International Business Park, 05 28 Nordic European Centre, Singapore, 609927, Singapore
Tel.: (65) 6890 6200
Designer & Mfr of Telecommunication Electronic Components
N.A.I.C.S.: 334419

Perlos Japan (2)
Kotobuki Building 5th Floor, 1 11 1 Kita Shinagawa, Shinagawa-ku, 140 0001, Tokyo, Japan
Tel.: (81) 354633411
Designer & Mfr of Telecommunication Electronic Components
N.A.I.C.S.: 334419

Perlos Precision Plastics Moulding LLC (2)
Nokia Utca 3, PO Box 102, 2900, Komarom, Hungary
Tel.: (36) 34542700
Designer & Mfr of Telecommunication Electronic Components
N.A.I.C.S.: 334419

Perlos Telecommunication & Electronic Components India Pvt. Ltd. (2)
Nokia Telecom Special Economic Zone Plot 1A SIPCOT Bangalore Hwy, Kancheepuram Dist, Sriperumbudur, 602 105, Chennai, India
Tel.: (91) 4447112233
Sales Range: $700-749.9 Million
Emp.: 3,000
Designer & Mfr of Telecommunication Electronic Components
N.A.I.C.S.: 334419

Lite-On Overseas Trading Co., Ltd. (1)
Portcullis Trustnet Bvi Limited 4th Floor Ellen L Skelton Building, Road Town, Virgin Islands (British)
Tel.: (284) 4945296
Sales Range: $50-74.9 Million
Emp.: 20
Investment Management Service
N.A.I.C.S.: 523999

Lite-On Singapore Pte. Ltd. (1)
151 Lorong Chuan 03-03 New Tech Park, Singapore, 556741, Singapore
Tel.: (65) 63490918
Automotive Electronic Product Mfr
N.A.I.C.S.: 336320

Lite-On Technology (Changzhou) Co., Ltd. (1)
No 88 Yanghu Road, Wujin Hi-Tech Industrial Development Zone, Changzhou, 213166, Jiangsu, China
Tel.: (86) 51983068888
Automotive Electronic Product Mfr
N.A.I.C.S.: 336320

Lite-On Trading USA, Inc. (1)
720 S Hillview Dr, Milpitas, CA 95035
Tel.: (408) 946-4873
Web Site: https://www.us.liteon.com
Sales Range: $25-49.9 Million
Emp.: 35
Electric Component Whslr
N.A.I.C.S.: 423690

Lite-On, Inc. (1)
720 S Hillview Dr, Milpitas, CA 95035
Tel.: (408) 946-4873
Electronic Components Mfr
N.A.I.C.S.: 334419

Philips & Lite-On Digital Solutions Corporation (1)
16F 392 Ruey Kuang Road, Neihu Dist, Taipei, 114, Taiwan
Tel.: (886) 287982798
Web Site: http://www.pldsnet.com
Optical Disc Drive Mfr
N.A.I.C.S.: 334112

Power Innovations International, Inc. (1)
1305 S 630 E, American Fork, UT 84003
Tel.: (801) 785-4123
Web Site: https://powerinnovations.com
Electrical Equipment & Component Manufacturing
N.A.I.C.S.: 335999
Karen Gudmundson *(VP-Bus Dev)*

Silitech Technology Corporation Sdn. Bhd. (1)
1528 MK 15 Jalan Besar, Sg Jawi Seberang Perai Selatan, 14200, Penang, Pinang, Malaysia
Tel.: (60) 45872128
Web Site: https://www.silitech.com
Sales Range: $200-249.9 Million
Emp.: 700
Automobile Parts Mfr
N.A.I.C.S.: 336390
Lee Keong Tye *(Mng Dir)*

Skyla Corporation (1)
No 8 Dusing Road, Hsinchu Science Park, Hsinchu, 300, Taiwan
Tel.: (886) 36121288
Web Site: https://www.skyla.com
Biomedical Product Mfr
N.A.I.C.S.: 339112

LITEL PARTICIPACOES S.A.

Av Ayrton Senna 3000 - sala 4098, Barra da Tijuca, Rio de Janeiro, 22775-003, RJ, Brazil
Tel.: (55) 2135960400
Web Site: http://www.litelbrasil.com.br
Year Founded: 1995
LTEL3B—(BRAZ)
Sales Range: Less than $1 Million
Investment Management Service
N.A.I.C.S.: 523940
Carlos Eduardo Reich De Sampaio *(Dir-Investor Relations)*

LITEMAX ELECTRONICS, INC.

8F No 137 Ln 235 Baoqiao Rd, Xindian Dist, New Taipei City, 23145, Taiwan
Tel.: (886) 289191858
Web Site: https://www.litemax.com
Year Founded: 2000
4995—(TPE)
Rev.: $42,755,339
Assets: $54,335,960
Liabilities: $24,321,890
Net Worth: $30,014,070
Earnings: $6,573,117
Emp.: 181
Fiscal Year-end: 12/31/22
Electronic Product Mfr & Distr
N.A.I.C.S.: 334419
I. J. Lee *(Chm)*

LITERACY CAPITAL PLC

3rd Floor Charles House 5-11 Regent Street St Jamess, London, SW1Y 4LR, United Kingdom   UK
Web Site:
   https://www.literacycapital.com
Year Founded: 2017
BOOK—(LSE)
Rev.: $71,107,031
Assets: $398,682,575
Liabilities: $18,618,601
Net Worth: $380,063,974
Earnings: $60,849,044
Emp.: 6
Fiscal Year-end: 12/31/23
Asset Management Services
N.A.I.C.S.: 523999

Paul Pindar *(Chm)*
Subsidiaries:

Alufold Direct Ltd. (1)
6b Frontier Park Frontier Avenue, Blackburn, BB1 3AL, United Kingdom
Tel.: (44) 1706260700
Web Site: https://www.alufolddirect.co.uk
Aluminium Door Mfr
N.A.I.C.S.: 332321

Antler Homes Plc (1)
Knightway House Park Street, Bagshot, GU19 5AQ, Surrey, United Kingdom
Tel.: (44) 1276538941
Web Site: https://www.antlerhomes.co.uk
Construction Services
N.A.I.C.S.: 236220

EPM Bus Solutions Limited (1)
20 Harris Business Park Hanbury Road, Bromsgrove, B60 4DJ, United Kingdom
Tel.: (44) 1527556940
Web Site: https://www.epm-bus.com
Software Development Services
N.A.I.C.S.: 541511

Oxygen Freejumping Ltd. (1)
15 Vision Industrial Park, Kendal, W3 0AF, United Kingdom
Tel.: (44) 2080501315
Web Site: https://oxygenfreejumping.co.uk
Trampoline Park Operator
N.A.I.C.S.: 812930

Techpoint Group Ltd. (1)
Unit One Mundford Road Trading Estate, Thetford, Norfolk, United Kingdom
Tel.: (44) 1842767947
Web Site: https://techpoint.co.uk
Electronic Components Mfr
N.A.I.C.S.: 334419

Tyrefix UK Ltd. (1)
Spring Road, Brookside Ind Est, Ibstock, LE67 6LR, Leicestershire, United Kingdom
Tel.: (44) 1530244444
Web Site: https://www.tyrefixuk.com
Car Repair & Maintenance Services
N.A.I.C.S.: 811111

LITGRID AB

Karl Gustav Emil Manerheim st 8, LT-05131, Vilnius, Lithuania
Tel.: (370) 70702171
Web Site: https://www.litgrid.eu
Year Founded: 2010
LGD1L—(RSE)
Rev.: $217,559,682
Assets: $417,996,704
Liabilities: $198,089,796
Net Worth: $219,906,908
Earnings: $4,745,967
Emp.: 260
Fiscal Year-end: 12/31/19
Electric Power Distribution Services
N.A.I.C.S.: 221122
Daivis Virbickas *(CEO)*

LITHIUM & BORON TECHNOLOGY, INC.

60 East Ren-Min Road Dachaidan, XaiXi, Hangzhou, 817000, Qinghai, China
Tel.: (86) 977828122   NV
LBTI—(OTCBB)
Rev.: $6,166,318
Assets: $4,643,023
Liabilities: $6,007,611
Net Worth: ($1,364,588)
Earnings: ($4,193,202)
Emp.: 153
Fiscal Year-end: 12/31/21
Plate Heat Exchanger Products Mfr & Sales
N.A.I.C.S.: 332410
Jimin Zhang *(Chm & CEO)*

Subsidiaries:

SmartHeat (Shanghai) Trading Co., Ltd. (1)
Room 2E Jieyun Buliding No 2 Lane 600 Tianshan Road, Shanghai, 200051, China

Tel.: (86) 21 31338352
Web Site: http://www.smartheatgroup.com
Heat Exchanger Whslr
N.A.I.C.S.: 221330

LITHIUM AMERICAS CORP.

3260666 Burrard St, Vancouver, V6C 2X8, BC, Canada
Tel.: (778) 656-5820   BC
Web Site:
   https://www.lithiumamericas.com
Year Founded: 2007
LAAC—(NYSE)
Rev.: $64,586,000
Assets: $1,055,026,000
Liabilities: $226,095,000
Net Worth: $828,931,000
Earnings: $1,288,369,000
Emp.: 850
Fiscal Year-end: 12/31/23
Lithium Mining Services
N.A.I.C.S.: 212290
John Kanellitsas *(Vice Chm)*

Subsidiaries:

Arena Minerals Inc. (1)
1410-120 Adelaide Street West, Toronto, M5H 1T1, ON, Canada   (100%)
Tel.: (416) 818-8711
Web Site: http://www.arenaminerals.com
Assets: $763,332
Liabilities: $440,658
Net Worth: $322,675
Earnings: ($42,012)
Fiscal Year-end: 12/31/2020
Metal Mining Services
N.A.I.C.S.: 212290

Millennial Lithium Corp. (1)
1455 Bellevue Avenue Suite 300, West Vancouver, V7T 1C3, BC, Canada
Tel.: (604) 662-8184
Web Site: http://www.millenniallithium.com
Rev.: $73,069
Assets: $91,597,474
Liabilities: $743,528
Net Worth: $90,853,946
Earnings: ($7,749,325)
Emp.: 6
Fiscal Year-end: 02/28/2021
Mineral Exploration & Production
N.A.I.C.S.: 212390
Brian Patrick Morrison *(Sec)*

Minera Exar S. A. (1)
Carrilo Palm 54 PB San Salvador, La Puntilla, Salta, Jujuy, Argentina   (44.8%)
Tel.: (54) 3884831000
Web Site: http://www.mineraexar.com.ar
Lithium & Potassium Mining Services
N.A.I.C.S.: 212390
Waldo A. Perez *(Pres & CEO)*

RheoMinerals Inc. (1)
260 Logan Ln, Fernley, NV 89408
Tel.: (775) 302-4400
Web Site: https://www.rheominerals.com
Clay Mineral Product Mfr
N.A.I.C.S.: 327999
Jerry McNamara *(Pres & CEO)*

LITHIUM AUSTRALIA NL

Level 1 677 Murray Street, Perth, 6005, WA, Australia
Tel.: (61) 370172656   AU
Web Site: https://www.lithium-au.com
LIT—(ASX)
Rev.: $4,482,225
Assets: $12,337,658
Liabilities: $10,092,627
Net Worth: $2,245,030
Earnings: ($7,184,496)
Fiscal Year-end: 06/30/24
Gold & Copper Exploration Services
N.A.I.C.S.: 212220
Barry Woodhouse *(CFO & Sec)*

Subsidiaries:

Envirostream Australia Pty Ltd (1)
606 High Street, Kew, 3101, VIC, Australia
Tel.: (61) 1800727274
Web Site: http://www.envirostream.com.au
Recycle Battery Mfr

AND PRIVATE COMPANIES

Soluna Australia Pty. Ltd. (1)
1/677 Murray Street, West Perth, WA, Australia
Tel.: (61) 1300126888
Web Site: https://soluna.com.au
Power Bank Mfr
N.A.I.C.S.: 335910

VSPC Ltd. (1)
31 Westgate St, Wacol, Brisbane, 4076, QLD, Australia
Tel.: (61) 861450221
Web Site: https://www.vspc.com
Battery Material & Lithium Battery Mfr
N.A.I.C.S.: 335910
John Worsley (Plant Mgr)

LITHIUM CHILE INC.
700 903-8th Ave SW Calgary, Calgary, T2P 0P7, AB, Canada
Tel.: (587) 393-1990 AB
Web Site: https://www.lithiumchile.ca
Year Founded: 2010
KC3—(DEU)
Rev.: $895,152
Assets: $42,175,325
Liabilities: $2,104,585
Net Worth: $40,070,740
Earnings: $353,081
Fiscal Year-end: 12/31/23
Investment Services
N.A.I.C.S.: 523999
Al Kroontje (Chm)

LITHIUM ENERGI EXPLORATION INC.
161 Bay St 27th Floor, Toronto, M5J 2S1, ON, Canada
Tel.: (416) 276-6689 BC
Web Site: https://lithiumenergi.com
Year Founded: 1998
L09—(DEU)
Assets: $3,771,506
Liabilities: $8,748,531
Net Worth: ($4,977,024)
Earnings: ($3,475,611)
Emp.: 4
Fiscal Year-end: 02/28/23
Exploration Company; Lithium Brine Assets Acquisition, Exploration & Development
N.A.I.C.S.: 212290

LITHIUM ENERGY LIMITED
Suite 1 Level 1 680 Murray Street, West Perth, 6005, WA, Australia
Tel.: (61) 892149737 AU
Web Site: https://www.lithiumenergy.com.au
Year Founded: 2021
LEL—(ASX)
Rev.: $335,614
Assets: $21,725,362
Liabilities: $780,136
Net Worth: $20,945,226
Earnings: ($7,867,804)
Fiscal Year-end: 06/30/23
Mineral Exploration Services
N.A.I.C.S.: 212390
William Matthew Johnson (Chm & Exec Chm)

LITHIUM IONIC CORP.
36 Lombard Street Floor 4, Toronto, M5C 2X3, ON, Canada
Tel.: (647) 316-2500 ON
Web Site: https://www.lithiumionic.com
Year Founded: 2020
LTH—(TSX)
Rev.: $342,809
Assets: $24,496,807
Liabilities: $1,683,186
Net Worth: $22,813,621
Earnings: ($19,489,536)
Fiscal Year-end: 12/31/22
Mineral Mining Services
N.A.I.C.S.: 213115
Carlos Costa (VP)

LITHIUM PLUS MINERALS LTD.
Suite 403 Level 4 66 Hunter Street, Sydney, 2000, NSW, Australia
Tel.: (61) 280290666 AU
Web Site: https://www.lithiumplus.com.au
Year Founded: 2021
LPM—(ASX)
Rev.: $114,631
Assets: $15,159,640
Liabilities: $457,927
Net Worth: $14,701,713
Earnings: ($1,393,707)
Fiscal Year-end: 06/30/24
Mineral Exploration Services
N.A.I.C.S.: 212390
Bin Guo (Chm & Exec Chm)

LITHIUM ROYALTY CORP.
1133 Yonge Street 5th Floor, Toronto, M4W 2K9, ON, Canada
Tel.: (647) 792-1100
Web Site: https://www.lithiumroyaltycorp.com
Year Founded: 2017
LIRC—(TSX)
Emp.: 4
Lithium Battery Mfr
N.A.I.C.S.: 335910
Blair Levinsky (Chm)

LITHIUM SOUTH DEVELOPMENT CORPORATION
1681 Chestnut Street Suite 400, Vancouver, V6J 4M6, BC, Canada
Tel.: (604) 682-2928 Ca
Web Site: https://www.lithiumsouth.com
Year Founded: 1995
LIS—(OTCIQ)
Assets: $4,084,248
Liabilities: $1,121,423
Net Worth: $2,962,824
Earnings: ($2,336,107)
Fiscal Year-end: 12/31/20
Gold Exploration Services
N.A.I.C.S.: 212220
Adrian F. C. Hobkirk (Pres & CEO)

LITHIUM X ENERGY CORP.
3123-595 Burrard Street, PO Box 49139, Bentall III, Vancouver, V7X 1A0, BC, Canada
Tel.: (604) 609-6138 Ca
Web Site: http://www.lithium-x.com
Year Founded: 1997
Sales Range: Less than $1 Million
Lithium Mining Services
N.A.I.C.S.: 212390
William Randall (VP-Project Dev)

LITHIUM-FOR-EARTH INC.
11th floor 48 Achasan-ro 17-gil, Seongdong-gu, Seoul, Chungcheongnam-do, Korea (South)
Tel.: (82) 220387969
Web Site: https://www.lithium-for-earth.com
Year Founded: 1998
073570—(KRS)
Rev.: $15,893,178
Assets: $189,829,385
Liabilities: $47,220,220
Net Worth: $142,609,164
Earnings: ($68,716,690)
Emp.: 28
Fiscal Year-end: 12/31/22
Semiconductor Testing Equipment Mfr
N.A.I.C.S.: 334515
Jeon Woong (CEO)

LITHIUMBANK RESOURCES CORP.
2820-200 Granville Street, Vancouver, V6C 1S4, BC, Canada
Tel.: (647) 689-6041 BC
Web Site: https://www.lithiumbank.ca
Year Founded: 2019
LBNKF—(OTCQX)
Rev.: $33,395
Assets: $6,142,231
Liabilities: $218,973
Net Worth: $5,923,257
Earnings: ($2,583,932)
Emp.: 25
Fiscal Year-end: 09/30/22
Mineral Mining Services
N.A.I.C.S.: 213115
Kevin Piepgrass (COO)

LITHO FORMAS, SA
Avenida Barbosa du Bocage 113, 1050-031, Lisbon, Portugal
Tel.: (351) 219947620
Web Site: https://www.lithoformas.pt
Year Founded: 1966
LIT—(EUR)
Printed Form Product Mfr & Distr
N.A.I.C.S.: 334412
Benjamim Mendes (CEO)

LITHO SUPPLIES LTD
Manners Industrial Estate Units 1 & 2 Ashbourne Court, Ilkeston, DE7 8EF, United Kingdom
Tel.: (44) 8449840415
Web Site: http://www.litho.co.uk
Sales Range: $50-74.9 Million
Emp.: 274
Printing Supply & Equipment Distr
N.A.I.C.S.: 424120
B. C. Clark (Chm)

Subsidiaries:

Graphica Plus Limited (1)
Unit 8 Genesis Park, Sheffield Rd Templeborough, Rotherham, S60 1DX, South Yorkshire, United Kingdom
Tel.: (44) 8700 668 661
Web Site: http://www.andersons-uk.net
Sales Range: $25-49.9 Million
Emp.: 12
Printing Equipment Distr
N.A.I.C.S.: 424110
Lewis Stable (Office Mgr)

Litho Supplies (UK) Ltd (1)
Units 1 & 2 Ashbourne Ct Manners Industrial Estate, Breaston, Ilkeston, DE7 8EF, United Kingdom
Tel.: (44) 1159071660
Web Site: https://www.litho.co.uk
Sales Range: $25-49.9 Million
Emp.: 30
Printing Equipment Distr
N.A.I.C.S.: 333248

LITHORADE PACKAGING SOLUTIONS B.V.
Energielaan 2, 5405 AD, Uden, Netherlands
Tel.: (31) 413333666
Web Site: http://www.lithorade.nl
Sales Range: $25-49.9 Million
Emp.: 85
Commercial Printing
N.A.I.C.S.: 323111
Wim Hieltjes (Mng Dir)

LITHOS ENERGY LTD.
142 - 757 West Hastings Street, Vancouver, V6C 1A1, BC, Canada
Tel.: (604) 601-2049 BC
Web Site: https://lithosenergy.com
Year Founded: 2010
V1R—(DEU)
Assets: $12,726,306
Liabilities: $351,870
Net Worth: $12,374,436
Earnings: ($1,494,770)
Emp.: 15
Fiscal Year-end: 04/30/23
Metal Mining Services
N.A.I.C.S.: 212290
Nashirudeen Meghji (CFO)

LITIAN PICTURES HOLDINGS LIMITED
No 5A Tongniu Dianying Industrial Park, Chaoyang, Beijing, China
Tel.: (86) 1085164862 Ky
Web Site: https://www.litian.tv
Year Founded: 2013
9958—(HKG)
Rev.: $3,542,368
Assets: $125,736,842
Liabilities: $97,104,958
Net Worth: $28,631,885
Earnings: ($44,564,346)
Emp.: 47
Fiscal Year-end: 12/31/22
Holding Company
N.A.I.C.S.: 551112

LITIGATION CAPITAL MANAGEMENT LIMITED
Level 12 The Chifley Tower 2 Chifley Square, Sydney, 2000, NSW, Australia
Tel.: (61) 2 8098 1390 AU
Web Site: http://www.lcmfinance.com
Year Founded: 1998
Sales Range: $1-9.9 Million
Financial Management Services
N.A.I.C.S.: 551112
Patrick Moloney (CEO)

LITIUM AB
Convendum Birger Jarlsgatan 57, 111 37, Stockholm, Sweden
Tel.: (46) 858643400
Web Site: https://www.litium.com
Year Founded: 1998
LITI—(NASDAQ)
Emp.: 30
Online Shopping Services
N.A.I.C.S.: 425120
Daniel Hultgren (COO)

LITORINA CAPITAL MANAGEMENT AB
Sveavagen 9, 111 57, Stockholm, Sweden
Tel.: (46) 854518180 SE
Web Site: http://www.litorina.se
Year Founded: 1998
Rev.: $711,024,000
Emp.: 13
Investment Management Service
N.A.I.C.S.: 523940
Paul Steene (Partner)

Subsidiaries:

Atelje Margaretha AB (1)
Bryggaregatan 8, 503 38, Boras, Sweden (70%)
Tel.: (46) 33 16 99 50
Web Site: http://www.margaretha.se
Sales Range: $25-49.9 Million
Emp.: 7
Crafts Embroidery & Knitting Product Distr
N.A.I.C.S.: 424350
Mikael Rosendahl (CEO)

EuroFlorist Sverige AB (1)
Bellevuevagen 46, 217 72, Malmo, Sweden (59%)
Tel.: (46) 40 636 30 00
Web Site: http://www.euroflorist.se
Sales Range: $125-149.9 Million
Emp.: 100
Flower Delivery Service
N.A.I.C.S.: 459310

Gullbergs Sverige AB (1)
PO Box 1047, 262 21, Angelholm, Sweden (72%)
Tel.: (46) 431 44 52 00
Web Site: http://www.gullbergs.se

LITORINA CAPITAL MANAGEMENT AB

Litorina Capital Management AB—(Continued)
Sales Range: $75-99.9 Million
Office Supplies Distr
N.A.I.C.S.: 459410

LGT Logistics A/S (1)
Orionvej 18, 8700, Horsens, Denmark
Tel.: (45) 7015 5555
Web Site: http://www.lgtlogistics.com
Sales Range: $75-99.9 Million
Emp.: 325
Furniture Shipping Services
N.A.I.C.S.: 488510
John Riis (Mng Dir)

Subsidiary (Non-US):

LGT Logistics AB (2)
Fagelviksleden 4, PO Box 269, 543 23, Tibro, Sweden
Tel.: (46) 504 401 00
Web Site: http://www.lgtlogistics.se
Furniture Shipping Services
N.A.I.C.S.: 488510
Ulf Naversten (CEO)

Nordic Heat & Vent AB (1)
Sergels Torg 12, SE 11157, Stockholm, Sweden
Tel.: (46) 737906072
Ventilation & Heating Products
N.A.I.C.S.: 333413

Subsidiary (Domestic):

Dryson AB (2)
Kattkarrsvagen 4, Halleforsnas, 64831, Sweden
Tel.: (46) 157 76 90 00
Web Site: http://www.dryson.se
Develops, Manufactures & Markets Ventilation & Heating Products
N.A.I.C.S.: 333415
Jonas Jern (Mgr-Sls)

PAX Electro Products AB (2)
Kattkarrsvagen 4, SE 648 31, Halleforsnas, Sweden
Tel.: (46) 157 756 00
Web Site: http://www.pax.se
Develops, Manufactures & Markets Ventilation & Heating Products
N.A.I.C.S.: 333415
Urban Jangedahl (Mgr-Pur)

Pahlen AB (1)
Vallentunavagen 401, Box 728, 194 27, Upplands Vasby, Sweden (73%)
Tel.: (46) 8 594 110 50
Web Site: http://www.pahlen.com
Sales Range: $10-24.9 Million
Emp.: 55
Swimming Pool Products Developer, Mfr & Retailer
N.A.I.C.S.: 334519

Pelly Industri Holding AB (1)
Industrigatan 14-22, 330 33, Hillerstorp, Sweden (68%)
Tel.: (46) 370 37 35 00
Web Site: http://www.pellyindustri.se
Sales Range: $25-49.9 Million
Emp.: 170
Supplier of Flexible Storage Solutions
N.A.I.C.S.: 337215

Skandinavisk Kommunalteknik AB (1)
Reprovagen 5, PO Box 1444, 183 14, Taby, Sweden (82%)
Tel.: (46) 8 544 407 90
Web Site: http://www.kommunalteknik.se
Sales Range: $10-24.9 Million
Pressure Sewage Systems Mfr & Distr
N.A.I.C.S.: 333914
Torbjorn Jansson (CEO)

Subsidiary (Non-US):

SKT Suomi Oy (2)
Vesterbackantie 10, 01120, Vasterskog, Finland
Tel.: (358) 9 27 86 148
Pressure Sewage Systems Distr
N.A.I.C.S.: 423830

Skandinavisk Kommunalteknikk AS (2)
Osloveien 187, N 1441, Drobak, Norway
Tel.: (47) 94 00 88 01
Web Site: http://www.kommunalteknik.no
Emp.: 7
Pressure Sewage Systems Distr
N.A.I.C.S.: 423830
Peter Pritchard (Gen Mgr)

WA Wallvision AB (1)
Ryssnasgatan 8, 504 64, Boras, Sweden
Tel.: (46) 33 236400
Web Site: http://www.wallvision.se
Sales Range: $75-99.9 Million
Emp.: 120
Wallpaper Designer Mfr
N.A.I.C.S.: 444120
Ake Straberg (Pres & CEO)

Subsidiary (Non-US):

Cole & Son (Wallpapers) Ltd (2)
Lifford House 199 Eade Road, London, N4 1DN, United Kingdom
Tel.: (44) 208 442 8844
Web Site: http://www.cole-and-son.com
Wallpaper Designer, Mfr & Whslr
N.A.I.C.S.: 322299
Jess Burnett (Head-PR & Mktg)

Subsidiary (Domestic):

Eco-Borastapeter AB (2)
Ryssnassgatan 8, Boras, 504 64, Sweden
Tel.: (46) 33236400
Web Site: http://www.borastapeter.com
Sales Range: $50-74.9 Million
Wall Coverings Mfr & Distr
N.A.I.C.S.: 444120
Linda Andersson (Mgr-Acctg)

LITORIUM GROUP CORP.

5 Fuxin Complex North 402, Manzhouli, 021400, Inner Mongolia, China
Tel.: (86) 315 359 5955 NV
Year Founded: 2016
Emp.: 1
Online Food Delivery Services
N.A.I.C.S.: 455110
Maria Manzey (Pres, Treas & Sec)

LITTLE COMPANY OF MARY HEALTH CARE LIMITED

Level 12 135 King Street, Sydney, 2000, NSW, Australia
Tel.: (61) 2 9258 1700
Web Site:
http://www.calvarycare.org.au
Healthcare & Aged Care Services
N.A.I.C.S.: 813212
Martin Bowles (CEO)

Subsidiaries:

Japara Healthcare Limited (1)
Q1 Building Level 4 1 Southbank Boulevard, Southbank, 3006, VIC, Australia
Tel.: (61) 3 9649 2100
Web Site: http://www.japara.com.au
Rev.: $279,593,742
Assets: $964,203,533
Liabilities: $592,069,304
Net Worth: $372,134,229
Earnings: $11,493,076
Fiscal Year-end: 06/30/2019
Elderly Care & Retirement Facilities
N.A.I.C.S.: 623311
Bruce Paterson (Sec)

Subsidiary (Domestic):

Japara Retirement Living 4 (Cosgrove Cottages) Pty. Ltd. (2)
25 Waveney St South, Launceston, 7249, TAS, Australia
Tel.: (61) 363445566
Retirement Living Services
N.A.I.C.S.: 623311

Japara Retirement Living 6 (Barongarook) Pty. Ltd. (2)
8-32 Murray Street East, Colac, 3250, VIC, Australia
Tel.: (61) 352319999
Retirement Home Providing Services
N.A.I.C.S.: 623312

Japara Retirement Living 7 (The Homestead) Pty. Ltd. (2)
29 Homestead Avenue, Walkley Heights, Adelaide, 5098, SA, Australia
Tel.: (61) 882221222
Retirement Living Services
N.A.I.C.S.: 623311

LITTLE GREEN PHARMA LTD.

Kings Park Road, PO Box 690, West Perth, 6872, WA, Australia
Tel.: (61) 62800050
Web Site:
https://www.littlegreenpharma.com
Year Founded: 2016
LGP—(ASX)
Pharmaceutical Preparation Manufacturing
N.A.I.C.S.: 325412
Alistair Warren (Sec)

Subsidiaries:

Reset Mind Sciences Ltd. (1)
PO Box 690, West Perth, 6872, WA, Australia
Tel.: (61) 862800050
Web Site: https://www.resetmind.com.au
Pharmaceuticals Product Mfr
N.A.I.C.S.: 325412

LITTLE REAL ESTATE PTY. LTD.

41 Burwood Rd, Hawthorn, 3122, VIC, Australia
Tel.: (61) 300548853 AU
Web Site:
http://www.littlerealestate.com.au
Year Founded: 2009
Emp.: 380
Residential & Commercial Real Estate Development, Sales, Construction & Property Management Services
N.A.I.C.S.: 531390
Paul Little (Chm)

Subsidiaries:

Agentplus Pty Ltd (1)
107 High Street, Prahran, 3181, VIC, Australia
Tel.: (61) 1300267944
Web Site: http://www.agentplus.com.au
Software Development Services
N.A.I.C.S.: 541511

Little Projects Pty. Limited (1)
Llev 3 15 Callamont Street Sofia, Hawthorn, 3141, VIC, Australia
Tel.: (61) 3 8809 5999
Web Site: http://www.littleprojects.com.au
Residential & Commercial Real Estate Development & Construction Management Services
N.A.I.C.S.: 237210
Paris Lechte (Dir-Construction)

Little Real Estate Pty. Ltd. - Commercial Division (1)
41 Burwood Road, Hawthorn, 3122, VIC, Australia
Tel.: (61) 3 8809 5777
Web Site: http://www.littlerealestate.com.au
Commercial Real Estate Brokerage & Property Management Services
N.A.I.C.S.: 531210
Jeffrey Wilson (Dir-Sls Ops)

Little Real Estate Pty. Ltd. - Residential Division (1)
41 Burwood Road, Hawthorn, 3122, VIC, Australia
Tel.: (61) 3 8809 5888
Web Site: http://www.littleresidential.com.au
Emp.: 300
Residential Real Estate Brokerage & Property Management Services
N.A.I.C.S.: 531210
Jeffrey Wilson (Dir-Sls Ops)

LITU HOLDINGS LIMITED

Room 1201 AXA Centre Gloucester Road, Wanchai, Hong Kong, China (Hong Kong)
Tel.: (852) 39157888 Ky
Web Site: http://www.bcghk.cn
1008—(HKG)
Rev.: $125,523,113
Assets: $407,319,278
Liabilities: $91,739,310
Net Worth: $315,579,968
Earnings: $1,200,413
Emp.: 663
Fiscal Year-end: 12/31/22
Printing Services
N.A.I.C.S.: 323111
Song Qin (Vice Chm & CEO)

Subsidiaries:

Bengbu Jinhuangshan Rotogravure Printing Company Limited (1)
Chang Zheng Road New High Tech Industrial Development Zone 3F, Association Building, Bengbu, Anhui, China
Tel.: (86) 5524078719
Cigarette Mfr
N.A.I.C.S.: 312230

CT Printing Limited (1)
Ste 23012 23 F Tower 2 Nina Tower, 8 Yeung UK Rd, Tsuen Wan, China (Hong Kong)
Tel.: (852) 28519288
Sales Range: $25-49.9 Million
Emp.: 10
Books & Paper Mfr
N.A.I.C.S.: 424920
Yttox Kiong (Office Mgr)

HY-Link Science & Technology Co., Ltd. (1)
No 189 Zhongzhou West Road Chengnan Road Jingjiang, Taizhou, Jiangsu, China
Tel.: (86) 52384129190
Cigarette Mfr
N.A.I.C.S.: 312230

Shenzhen Kecai Printing Co., Ltd. (1)
Lan Zu East Road Great Industrial Park, Shenzhen, 518118, Guangdong, China
Tel.: (86) 75589938000
Cigarette Mfr
N.A.I.C.S.: 312230
Chen Huapei (Dir-Fin)

Zhaotong Antong Package Material Co., Ltd. (1)
Inside Zhaotong Cigarette Factory, Southern Suburb, Zhaotong, 657000, Yunnan, China
Tel.: (86) 8702130802
Cigarette Mfr
N.A.I.C.S.: 312230

LIU CHONG HING INVESTMENT LIMITED

23/F Chong Hing Bank Centre 24 Des Voeux Road, Central, China (Hong Kong)
Tel.: (852) 29837777 HK
Web Site: https://www.lchi.com.hk
Year Founded: 1970
0194—(HKG)
Rev.: $91,193,100
Assets: $2,018,662,365
Liabilities: $404,513,768
Net Worth: $1,614,148,598
Earnings: $11,321,873
Emp.: 629
Fiscal Year-end: 12/31/22
Residential & Commercial Building Investment Services
N.A.I.C.S.: 531311
Wai Hung Lee (Sec)

Subsidiaries:

Liu Chong Hing Godown Company, Limited (1)
25 Fl Chong Hing Bank Ctr 24 Des Voeux Rd, Central, China (Hong Kong)
Tel.: (852) 37689038
Web Site: http://www.chbank.com

AND PRIVATE COMPANIES

Sales Range: $25-49.9 Million
Emp.: 40
Property Investment Services
N.A.I.C.S.: 531312

Liu Chong Hing Property Management and Agency Limited (1)
23/F Chong Hing Bank Centre 24 Des Voeux Road, Central, China (Hong Kong)
Tel.: (852) 29837777
Web Site: http://www.lchi.com.hk
Emp.: 80
Real Estate Property Management Services
N.A.I.C.S.: 531311

One-Eight-One Hospitality Management Limited (1)
181 Connaught Road West, Hong Kong, China (Hong Kong)
Tel.: (852) 3 181 1688
Web Site: https://www.one-eight-one.com
Home Management Services
N.A.I.C.S.: 721110

LIUNA PENSION FUND OF CENTRAL AND EASTERN CANADA
6th Floor - 1315 North Service Road East, Oakville, L6H 1A7, ON, Canada
Tel.: (289) 291-3663
Web Site: https://www.lpfcec.org
Year Founded: 1967
Pension & Retirement Benefits
N.A.I.C.S.: 525110
Joseph Mancinelli (VP)

Subsidiaries:

Mack Fire Protection, LLC (1)
15 Industrial Park Pl, Middletown, CT 06457
Tel.: (860) 632-8053
Web Site: http://www.mackfire.com
Specialty Trade Contractors
N.A.I.C.S.: 238990
William J. Wells (Mgr)

LIUYANG FIREWORKS LIMITED
Far Ocean Building Beizheng North Road, Liuyang, Changsha, 410300, Hunan, China
Tel.: (86) 73183655555 BM
Web Site: http://www.liuyangfwk.com
Year Founded: 1993
Sales Range: $10-24.9 Million
Fireworks Mfr
N.A.I.C.S.: 325998
Mingyue Hu (Chm)

LIUZHOU CHEMICAL INDUSTRY CO., LTD.
26th Floor Huijin International No 106-8 Yuejin Road, Liuzhou, 545001, Guangxi, China
Tel.: (86) 7722519434
Web Site: https://www.lzhg.cn
Year Founded: 1967
600423—(SHG)
Rev.: $19,721,005
Assets: $72,045,123
Liabilities: $10,714,107
Net Worth: $61,331,016
Earnings: $2,226,225
Fiscal Year-end: 12/31/22
Chemical Fertilizer Mfr & Distr
N.A.I.C.S.: 325311
Lu Shengyun (Chm, Pres & Gen Mgr)

LIUZHOU IRON & STEEL CO. LTD.
No 117 Bei Que Road, Liuzhou, 545002, Guangxi, China
Tel.: (86) 7722595998
Web Site: https://www.liusteel.com
Year Founded: 2000
601003—(SHG)
Rev.: $11,333,827,529
Assets: $10,026,280,644
Liabilities: $6,858,511,555
Net Worth: $3,167,769,089
Earnings: ($328,813,641)
Emp.: 9,300
Fiscal Year-end: 12/31/22
Steel Products Mfr
N.A.I.C.S.: 331110
Pei Kan (Sec)

LIUZHOU LMZ CO., LTD.
No 282 Donghuan Road, Liuzhou, 545006, Guangxi, China
Tel.: (86) 7722068000
Web Site: https://www.lmz.com.cn
Year Founded: 1941
600249—(SHG)
Rev.: $93,954,557
Assets: $347,654,872
Liabilities: $53,997,980
Net Worth: $293,656,891
Earnings: ($5,417,531)
Fiscal Year-end: 12/31/22
Personal Care Product Mfr & Distr
N.A.I.C.S.: 325611
Zuanhuang Lin (Chm)

Subsidiaries:

JK Sucralose Inc. (1)
118 Renmin East Road, Sheyang County, Jiangsu, 224300, China
Tel.: (86) 5158 217 8858
Web Site: https://www.jksucralose.com
Food Ingredient Mfr & Distr
N.A.I.C.S.: 325199

Subsidiary (Non-US):

JK Sucralose Europe B.V. (2)
Minervum 7483, 4817 ZP, Breda, Netherlands
Tel.: (31) 765139169
Food Ingredient Distr
N.A.I.C.S.: 424690

JK Sucralose Inc. (2)
10F ASSORTI Bld 13-5 Nihombashi Kodenmacho, Chuo-Ku, Tokyo, Japan
Tel.: (81) 356950888
Web Site: http://www.jksucralose.com
Food Ingredient Mfr & Distr
N.A.I.C.S.: 325199

LMZ (Jiangsu) Industries Co., Ltd.
No 8 Xiyuan Road, Hangji Industrial Park Hangji town, Yangzhou, 225111, Jiangsu, China
Tel.: (86) 1891 212 8655
Web Site: https://www.lmzhotelamenities.com
Cosmetic Product Distr
N.A.I.C.S.: 424210

LIV CAPITAL ACQUISITION CORP.
Pedregal No 24 Piso 6-601 Col Molino del Rey, Mexico, 11040, Mexico
Tel.: (52) 5511002470 Ky
Web Site: http://www.livcapitalspac.mx
Year Founded: 2019
LIVK—(NASDAQ)
Rev.: $519,105
Assets: $81,257,598
Liabilities: $398,748
Net Worth: $80,858,850
Earnings: ($154,520)
Emp.: 1
Fiscal Year-end: 12/31/20
Investment Services
N.A.I.C.S.: 523999
Alexander R. Rossi (Chm, CEO & Mng Partner)

LIVA INSURANCE COMPANY
Al Aqiq King Fahad Rd, PO Box 6393, Sulaymaniyah, Riyadh, 11442, Saudi Arabia
Tel.: (966) 8002444481
Web Site: https://www.livainsurance.sa
Year Founded: 2009
Insurance Services
N.A.I.C.S.: 524210
Fadi Aboul Hosn (CFO)

LIVAL OY
Lukkarinmaentie 1, 04130, Sipoo, Finland
Tel.: (358) 9 235 511 FI
Web Site: http://www.lival.com
Ceramic & Shop Lighting Mfr
N.A.I.C.S.: 335132
Stig Lival-Lindstrom (CEO)

Subsidiaries:

Nordic Aluminium Plc (1)
Kaapelitie 68, FI-02490, Pikkala, Finland (73.94%)
Tel.: (358) 207660200
Web Site: http://www.nordicaluminium.fi
Sales Range: $75-99.9 Million
Emp.: 105
Aluminum Products Designer, Producer, Marketer & Supplier
N.A.I.C.S.: 331318
Peter Hogel (Dir-Export)

Subsidiary (US):

Nordic Aluminium, Inc. (2)
2310 Peachford Rd, Atlanta, GA 30338
Tel.: (770) 455-5986
Sales Range: $1-9.9 Million
Emp.: 17
Aluminum Products Designer, Producer, Marketer & Supplier
N.A.I.C.S.: 331318

LIVANIS PUBLICATIONS SA
Solonos Str 98, 10680, Athens, Greece
Tel.: (30) 2103661200
Web Site: https://www.livanis.gr
Year Founded: 1972
LIVAN—(ATH)
Sales Range: Less than $1 Million
Emp.: 32
Books Publishing Services
N.A.I.C.S.: 513130
Panagiota A. Livani (Chm & Pres)

LIVANOVA PLC
20 Eastbourne Terrace, London, W2 6LG, United Kingdom
Tel.: (44) 2033250660 UK
Web Site: https://www.livanova.com
LIVN—(NASDAQ)
Rev.: $1,021,805,000
Assets: $2,294,773,000
Liabilities: $1,087,149,000
Net Worth: $1,207,624,000
Earnings: ($86,246,000)
Emp.: 2,900
Fiscal Year-end: 12/31/22
Holding Company; Medical Technologies Developer & Mfr
N.A.I.C.S.: 551112
Paul R. Buckman (Pres-Advanced Circulatory Support)

Subsidiaries:

Alung Technologies, Inc. (1)
333 E Carson St, Pittsburgh, PA 15219
Tel.: (412) 697-3370
Web Site: http://www.alung.com
Rev.: $1,600,000
Emp.: 12
Electromedical & Electrotherapeutic Apparatus Mfr
N.A.I.C.S.: 334510
Peter DeComo (Chm & CEO)

Caisson Interventional, LLC (1)
6500 Wedgwood Rd N, Maple Grove, MN 55311
Tel.: (763) 220-4110
Medical Device Mfr
N.A.I.C.S.: 339112

CardiacAssist, Inc. (1)
620 Alpha Dr, Pittsburgh, PA 15238
Tel.: (412) 963-7770
Web Site: http://www.tandemlife.com

Medical Device Mfr
N.A.I.C.S.: 339112

Corcym S.r.l. (1)
Via Crescentino sn, 13040, Saluggia, VC, Italy
Tel.: (39) 0161487800
Web Site: http://www.corcym.com
Medical Device Mfr
N.A.I.C.S.: 339112
Christian Mazzi (CEO)

LivaNova (China) Medical Technology Co., Ltd. (1)
Room 3-9 Building D Guang Hua Soho No 9 Guang Hua Road, Chao Yang District, Beijing, 100020, China
Tel.: (86) 2123569550
Medical Device Mfr
N.A.I.C.S.: 339112

LivaNova Australia Pty. Limited (1)
1/63 Wells Road, Chelsea Heights, 3196, VIC, Australia
Tel.: (61) 397997444
Medical Equipment Mfr & Distr
N.A.I.C.S.: 334510
Elise Hogan (Mng Dir)

LivaNova Austria GmbH (1)
Regus Office MilleniumTower - Handelskai 94-96, 1200, Vienna, Austria
Tel.: (43) 720380016
Medical Equipment Mfr & Distr
N.A.I.C.S.: 334510
Bernhard Pfeifer (Project Mgr & Mgr-Education)

LivaNova Belgium N.V. (1)
Ikaroslaan 83, 1930, Zaventem, Belgium
Tel.: (32) 22453790
Emp.: 30
Medical Equipment Mfr & Distr
N.A.I.C.S.: 334510
Philip Blancquaert (Mgr)

LivaNova Canada Corp. (1)
5005 North Fraser Way, Burnaby, V5J 5M1, BC, Canada
Tel.: (604) 412-5650
Emp.: 300
Medical Equipment Mfr & Distr
N.A.I.C.S.: 334510

LivaNova Chile S.p.A. (1)
Miraflores n 222 Piso 28, Santiago, Chile
Tel.: (56) 233282638
Medical Device Mfr
N.A.I.C.S.: 339112

LivaNova Deutschland GmbH (1)
Lindberghstr 25, 80939, Munich, Germany
Tel.: (49) 89323010
Web Site: http://www.sorin.com
Medical Equipment Mfr & Distr
N.A.I.C.S.: 334510

LivaNova Espana, S.L. (1)
Avgda Diagonal 123 Planta 10, 08005, Barcelona, Spain
Tel.: (34) 935442244
Medical Equipment Mfr & Distr
N.A.I.C.S.: 334510

LivaNova France SAS (1)
4 Avenue Parc D Affaires Noveos, 92140, Clamart, France
Tel.: (33) 146013333
Medical Technologies Device Whslr
N.A.I.C.S.: 423450

LivaNova Japan K.K. (1)
Sanno Park Tower 10F 2-11-1 Nagatacho, Chiyoda-ku, Tokyo, 100-6110, Japan
Tel.: (81) 335957630
Web Site: http://www.livanova.com
Medical Device Distr
N.A.I.C.S.: 423450
Konomi Kawaeni (Pres)

LivaNova Polska Sp. z o.o. (1)
Ul Postepu 21, 02-676, Warsaw, Poland
Tel.: (48) 225020412
Medical Equipment Mfr & Distr
N.A.I.C.S.: 334510
Filipina Pilichowska (Gen Mgr)

LivaNova Portugal Lda. (1)
Edificio Zenith Rua Dr Antonio Loureiro Borges n 9/9A 6 A, 1495-131, Alges, Portugal

LIVANOVA PLC

LivaNova PLC—(Continued)
Tel.: (351) 21 413 9900
Medical Equipment Distr
N.A.I.C.S.: 423450

LivaNova S.A.S. (1)
200 Avenue de Paris, 92320, Chatillon, France
Tel.: (33) 146018909
Medical Device Mfr
N.A.I.C.S.: 339112

LivaNova Scandinavia AB (1)
Djupdalsvagen 16, 192 51, Sollentuna, Sweden
Tel.: (46) 850122400
Medical Equipment Mfr & Distr
N.A.I.C.S.: 334510

LivaNova Singapore Pte. Ltd. (1)
11 North Buona Vista Drive 13-09 The Metropolis Tower 2, Singapore, 138589, Singapore
Tel.: (65) 62931033
Web Site: http://www.livanova.com
Medical Equipment Mfr & Distr
N.A.I.C.S.: 334510

LivaNova Switzerland S.A. (1)
Rue du Grand-Pont 12 CH, 1003, Lausanne, Switzerland
Tel.: (41) 225675010
Medical Equipment Mfr & Distr
N.A.I.C.S.: 334510

LivaNova UK Ltd. (1)
1370 Montpellier Court-Gloucester Business Park, Gloucester, GL3 4AH, United Kingdom
Tel.: (44) 1452638500
Medical Equipment Mfr & Distr
N.A.I.C.S.: 334510
Linda Hoyle *(Mgr-Customer Svc & IMS)*

LivaNova USA, Inc
100 Cyberonics Blvd, Houston, TX 77058-2072
Tel.: (281) 228-7330
Web Site: http://www.cyberonics.com
Rev: $291,557,998
Assets: $315,944,195
Liabilities: $39,370,464
Net Worth: $276,573,731
Earnings: $57,847,534
Emp.: 660
Fiscal Year-end: 04/24/2015
Implantable Medical Devices Mfr for Epilepsy & Depression Treatment
N.A.I.C.S.: 334510

Subsidiary (Non-US):

Cyberonics Europe, S.A. (2)
Belgicastraat 9, Zaventem, 1831, Vlaams Brabant, Belgium (100%)
Tel.: (32) 27209593
Sales Range: $10-24.9 Million
Emp.: 30
Provider of Epilepsy Treatment Products
N.A.I.C.S.: 325412
Veronique Antoine *(Coord-HR)*

LivaNova USA, Inc. (1)
100 Cyberonics Blvd, Houston, TX 77058
Tel.: (281) 228-7200
Medical Technologies Device Whslr
N.A.I.C.S.: 423450
Jerry Goodwin *(Sr Mgr-Pur)*

Sorin Group Italia S.r.l. (1)
Via Enrico Cialdini 16, 20161, Milan, Italy
Tel.: (39) 0237014960
Web Site: http://www.sorin.com
Sales Range: $50-74.9 Million
Emp.: 90
Holding Company
N.A.I.C.S.: 551112

Subsidiary (Non-US):

Alcard Industria Mecanica Ltda (2)
Rua Liege 54-Vila Vermelha, 04298-070, Sao Paulo, Brazil
Tel.: (55) 11 2946 6406
Web Site: http://www.internology.com.br
Medical Equipment Mfr & Distr
N.A.I.C.S.: 334510

Subsidiary (US):

Sorin Group USA, Inc. (2)
14401 W 65th Way, Arvada, CO 80004-3503 (100%)
Tel.: (303) 425-5508
Web Site: http://www.sorin.com
Holding Company; Cardio-Medical & Renal Disease Device Mfr
N.A.I.C.S.: 551112

Subsidiary (Domestic):

California Medical Laboratories, Inc. (3)
1570 Sunland Ln, Costa Mesa, CA 92626
Tel.: (714) 556-7365
Web Site: http://www.calmedlab.com
Sales Range: $25-49.9 Million
Emp.: 20
Cardio-Medical & Renal Disease Device Mfr
N.A.I.C.S.: 339112

Sorin Group Japan K.K. (1)
Sanno Park Tower 10F 2-11-1 Nagatacho, Chiyoda-ku, Tokyo, 100-6110, Japan
Tel.: (81) 335 957 630
Medical Equipment Mfr & Distr
N.A.I.C.S.: 334510

LIVARNA TITAN, D.O.O.

28 Kovinarska Cesta, Kamnik, 1241, Slovenia
Tel.: (386) 8309354
Web Site: http://www.livarna-titan.eu
Year Founded: 1920
Steel Foundry
N.A.I.C.S.: 331513
Drago Brence *(Owner & Exec Dir)*

LIVE COMPANY GROUP PLC

3 Park Court Pyrford Road, West Byfleet, KT14 6SD, Surrey, United Kingdom
Tel.: (44) 2072252000
Web Site: https://www.livecompanygroup.com
Year Founded: 1987
LVCG—(AIM)
Rev.: $6,026,256
Assets: $10,552,891
Liabilities: $10,195,658
Net Worth: $357,233
Earnings: ($12,196,415)
Emp.: 25
Fiscal Year-end: 12/31/22
Sports Management & Marketing Services
N.A.I.C.S.: 711310
David Ciclitira *(Chm)*

Subsidiaries:

Bright Bricks Limited (1)
Unit 32 Woolmer Way, Bordon, GU35 9QF, Hampshire, United Kingdom
Tel.: (44) 1420488993
Web Site: https://bright-bricks.com
Emp.: 60
Brick Building Services
N.A.I.C.S.: 423320

Parallel Television (2001) Ltd (1)
Unit 312 Harbour Yard, Chelsea Harbour, London, SW10 0XD, United Kingdom
Tel.: (44) 2073494820
Sales Range: $50-74.9 Million
Emp.: 8
Sports Marketing & Event Management Services
N.A.I.C.S.: 711310

LIVE MOTION GAMES SA

ul Indiry Gandhi 23, 02-776, Warsaw, Poland
Tel.: (48) 530280462
Web Site: https://www.livemotiongames.com
Year Founded: 2017
LMG—(WAR)
Software Development Services
N.A.I.C.S.: 541511
Dorota Osowska *(CEO)*

LIVE VERDURE LTD.

Level 21 459 Collins Street, Melbourne, 3000, VIC, Australia
Tel.: (61) 386303321
Web Site: https://www.liveverdure.com.au
Year Founded: 2016
LV1—(ASX)
Rev.: $1,444,821
Assets: $1,625,588
Liabilities: $1,023,790
Net Worth: $601,798
Earnings: ($1,847,965)
Fiscal Year-end: 06/30/23
Biotechnology Research & Development Services
N.A.I.C.S.: 541714
Justin Mouchacca *(Sec)*

LIVEHIRE

Level 5 90 Queen Street Safe Deposit Building, Melbourne, 3000, VIC, Australia
Tel.: (61) 390210657
Web Site: https://www.livehire.com
Year Founded: 2012
LVH—(ASX)
Rev.: $5,015,780
Assets: $7,878,381
Liabilities: $5,708,863
Net Worth: $2,169,518
Earnings: ($5,810,694)
Emp.: 28
Fiscal Year-end: 06/30/24
Software Development Services
N.A.I.C.S.: 513210
Christy Forest *(CEO & Exec Dir)*

LIVENUP GROUP INC.

1-4-28 Mita 24th floor Mita International Building, Minato-Ku, Tokyo, 108-0073, Japan
Tel.: (81) 354185100
Web Site: https://livenup.co.jp
Year Founded: 2003
2977—(TKS)
Rev.: $43,553,870
Assets: $32,181,510
Liabilities: $22,943,240
Net Worth: $9,238,270
Earnings: $3,509,550
Emp.: 29
Fiscal Year-end: 09/30/23
Real Estate Development Services
N.A.I.C.S.: 531311
Masayuki Naito *(Founder & Pres)*

LIVERMORE INVESTMENTS GROUP LTD.

Trident Chambers, PO Box 146, Road Town, Tortola, Virgin Islands (British)
Tel.: (284) 48701436756
Web Site: https://www.livermore-inv.com
Year Founded: 1998
LIV—(AIM)
Rev.: $24,054,000
Assets: $139,692,000
Liabilities: $3,792,000
Net Worth: $135,837,000
Earnings: $13,888,000
Emp.: 4
Fiscal Year-end: 12/31/23
Real Estate Investment Services
N.A.I.C.S.: 531390
Noam Lanir *(Founder & CEO)*

LIVERPOOL PARTNERS PTY LTD

Suite 3 Level 36 60 Margaret Street, Sydney, 2000, NSW, Australia
Tel.: (61) 2 9269 9130
Web Site: http://www.liverpoolpartners.com
Privater Equity Firm
N.A.I.C.S.: 523999

INTERNATIONAL PUBLIC

William Best *(Chm)*

Subsidiaries:

Zenitas Healthcare Limited (1)
Level 9 417 St Kilda Road, Melbourne, 3004, VIC, Australia
Tel.: (61) 398213701
Web Site: http://www.zenitas.com.au
Healtcare Services
N.A.I.C.S.: 621491
Justin Walter *(CEO & Mng Dir)*

Subsidiary (Domestic):

Modern Medical Group Pty Ltd (2)
Office 1 379-381 Whitehorse Road, Balwyn, 3103, VIC, Australia
Tel.: (61) 388091200
Web Site: http://www.modernmedical.com.au
Health Care Services
N.A.I.C.S.: 621498
Todd Cameron *(Founder)*

NexttCare Pty Ltd (2)
Unit 2 Railway Parade Camberwell, Melbourne, 3124, VIC, Australia
Tel.: (61) 398299120
Web Site: http://www.nextt.com.au
Women Healthcare Services
N.A.I.C.S.: 621610

Zenitas Caring Choice Pty Ltd (2)
2/315 Unley Road, Malvern, 5061, SA, Australia
Tel.: (61) 881221433
Web Site: http://www.zenitascare.com.au
Women Healthcare Services
N.A.I.C.S.: 621610

Zenitas Ontrac Pty Ltd (2)
Whiteman s Arcade Ste 4 100 Argyle Street, Camden Park, 2570, NSW, Australia
Tel.: (61) 246552266
Web Site: http://ontrachealth.com.au
Exercise Physiology Services
N.A.I.C.S.: 621340

LIVESENSE INC.

10th floor Tokyo Port City Takeshiba 1-7-1 Kaigan, Minato-ku, Tokyo, 105-7510, Japan
Tel.: (81) 366830082
Web Site: https://www.livesense.co.jp
Year Founded: 2006
6054—(TKS)
Rev.: $40,086,860
Assets: $34,088,720
Liabilities: $5,863,430
Net Worth: $28,225,290
Earnings: $5,076,440
Emp.: 227
Fiscal Year-end: 12/31/23
Internet Information Services
N.A.I.C.S.: 541810
Taichi Murakami *(Pres)*

Subsidiaries:

Livesense Connect Inc. (1)
25170-0005 2-25-15 Minami-Otsuka South Shin-Otsuka Building 1F, Toshima, Tokyo, Japan
Tel.: (81) 356563415
Web Site: http://www.livesenseconnect.co.jp
Employment & Recruiting Services
N.A.I.C.S.: 561311

Phil Life Inc. (1)
7th floor Starts Nihonbashi Building 3-1-8 Nihonbashi, Chuo-ku, Tokyo, 103-0027, Japan
Tel.: (81) 335489800
Web Site: https://www.phillife.co.jp
Real Estate Investment Services
N.A.I.C.S.: 531390
Masato Yokoi *(Pres & CEO)*

LIVESTOCK FEED LIMITED

Claude Delaitre Road Les Guibies, Les Pailles, Mauritius
Tel.: (230) 2863900
Web Site: https://www.grouplfl.com
Year Founded: 1977

AND PRIVATE COMPANIES

LFL—(MAU)
Rev.: $116,314,289
Assets: $94,635,164
Liabilities: $35,802,824
Net Worth: $58,832,340
Earnings: $4,510,650
Emp.: 498
Fiscal Year-end: 06/30/23
Animal Feed Mfr
N.A.I.C.S.: 311119
Rocky Forget *(Mng Dir)*

Subsidiaries:

Agro Bulk Ltd. (1)
Industrial Zone, Riche Terre, Mauritius
Tel.: (230) 2482870
General Warehousing & Storage Services
N.A.I.C.S.: 493110
Alexandre Mazery *(Head-Procurement)*

LFL Madagascar SA (1)
Lot K7-97 bis II A Mamory Ivato 105, Antananarivo, Madagascar
Tel.: (261) 202426474
General Warehousing & Storage Services
N.A.I.C.S.: 493110

LIVESTOCK FEEDS PLC
1 Henry Carr Street, Ikeja, Lagos, 102212, Nigeria
Tel.: (234) 8077281600
Web Site: https://www.livestockfeedsplc.com
Year Founded: 1963
LIVESTOCK—(NIGE)
Rev.: $12,146,812
Assets: $5,520,178
Liabilities: $4,276,455
Net Worth: $1,243,723
Earnings: ($608,604)
Emp.: 87
Fiscal Year-end: 12/31/22
Animal Feed Mfr
N.A.I.C.S.: 311119
Adegboyega W. Adedeji *(Mng Dir-Acting)*

LIVESTOCK IMPROVEMENT CORPORATION LIMITED
Tel.: (64) 78560700
Web Site: http://www.lic.co.nz
LIC—(NZX)
Rev.: $179,040,347
Assets: $274,661,595
Liabilities: $63,187,158
Net Worth: $211,474,437
Earnings: $17,297,702
Emp.: 700
Fiscal Year-end: 05/31/21
Livestock Products & Services
N.A.I.C.S.: 112990
David Chin *(Gen Mgr-Ops & Svc)*

Subsidiaries:

Beacon Automation Pty Ltd (1)
30 Glen Munro Road, PO Box 855, Muswellbrook, 2333, NSW, Australia
Tel.: (61) 265412345
Web Site: https://www.beaconhd.com.au
Bovine Heat Detection Product Mfr
N.A.I.C.S.: 334519

Deer Improvement (1)
PO Box 1593, Queenstown, New Zealand
Tel.: (64) 78560700
Web Site: http://www.deerimprovement.co.nz
Sales Range: $25-49.9 Million
Emp.: 8
Deer Farming Services
N.A.I.C.S.: 112990
Bruce McGregor *(Gen Mgr)*

Eurogene AI Services IRL Ltd (1)
Carrigeen Commercial Park, Cahir, E21 X006, Tipperary, Ireland
Tel.: (353) 527442940
Web Site: https://www.eurogeneaiservices.com

Sales Range: $10-24.9 Million
Emp.: 50
Livestock Services
N.A.I.C.S.: 115210
Tom Baker *(Mgr-Bus & Breeding Dev)*

Gensur Ltda (1)
Nueva York, 1690, Montevideo, Uruguay
Tel.: (598) 2 924 6655
Web Site: https://www.gensur.com.uy
Sales Range: $25-49.9 Million
Emp.: 12
Livestock Breeding Services
N.A.I.C.S.: 115210
Martin Artucio *(Gen Mgr)*

LIC Deer Ltd (1)
Cnr Ruakura and Morrinsville Roads RD 4, Hamilton, 3240, New Zealand
Tel.: (64) 78560700
Web Site: http://www.lic.co.in
Sales Range: $75-99.9 Million
Emp.: 300
Animal Farming Services
N.A.I.C.S.: 112990

LIC Ireland Limited (1)
Unit 1A Carrigeen Industrial Estate, Cahir, Tipperary, E21 X006, Ireland
Tel.: (353) 527442517
Web Site: https://www.lic.ie
Farm Consultancy Services
N.A.I.C.S.: 112990
Mark Ryder *(Gen Mgr)*

LIC Latin America SA (1)
Independencia, 2415, Lujan, Buenos Aires, Argentina
Tel.: (54) 2323428799
Livestock Breeding Services
N.A.I.C.S.: 115210

LIC UK Ltd (1)
Unit 7 Town Farm Workshops, Sixpenny Handley, Salisbury, SP5 5PA, Wilts, United Kingdom
Tel.: (44) 1725553008
Livestock Breeding Services
N.A.I.C.S.: 115210

LIC USA Ltd (1)
10220 N Ambassador Dr, Kansas City, MO 64153-1367
Tel.: (816) 922-9988
Livestock Support Services
N.A.I.C.S.: 115210
Wayne Meyers *(Country Mgr)*

Livestock Improvement Australia Pty Ltd (1)
1/129 Ogilvie Avenue, PO Box 1129, Echuca, 3564, VIC, Australia
Tel.: (61) 49 990 0612
Web Site: https://licnz.com.au
Sales Range: $25-49.9 Million
Emp.: 12
Livestock Breeding Services
N.A.I.C.S.: 115210

Livestock Improvement Corporation (UK) Ltd (1)
Unit 7 Town Farm Workshops, Salisbury, SP5 5PA, United Kingdom
Tel.: (44) 1725553008
Emp.: 3
Livestock Farming Services
N.A.I.C.S.: 115210

Taurus Service Inc (1)
Grist Flat Rd, Mehoopany, PA 18629
Tel.: (570) 833-5123
Web Site: http://www.taurus-service.com
Sales Range: $50-74.9 Million
Emp.: 10
Dairy Product Whslr
N.A.I.C.S.: 424430
John Witter *(VP & Mgr-Ops & Distr)*

LIVESTOCK TRANSPORT & TRADING CO. K.S.C.
Sulaibiya agricultural area Block 12 Livestock Transport Trading Co, PO Box 23727, Safat, 13098, Kuwait, 13098, Kuwait
Tel.: (965) 1888822
Web Site: https://www.almawashi.com.kw

CATTL—(KUW)
Rev.: $136,902,447
Assets: $191,306,325
Liabilities: $92,616,611
Net Worth: $98,689,714
Earnings: ($14,263,772)
Emp.: 555
Fiscal Year-end: 12/31/22
Meat & Livestock Trading, Transportation & Production Services
N.A.I.C.S.: 424520
Bader Nasser AlSubaiee *(Co-Chm)*

LIVFORSAKRINGSAKTIEBOLAGET SKANDIA
Lindhagensgatan 86, 112 18, Stockholm, Sweden
Tel.: (46) 87881000
Web Site: http://www.skandia.se
Sales Range: $600-649.9 Million
Emp.: 2,000
Provider of Life Insurance Products
N.A.I.C.S.: 524113
Bengt-Ake Fagerman *(CEO)*

Subsidiaries:

Professional Life Assurance Ltd. (1)
Skandia House, PO Box 37, Portland Terrace, Southampton, SO14 7AY, United Kingdom
Tel.: (44) 2380334411
Web Site: http://www.skandia.co.uk
Sales Range: $500-549.9 Million
Emp.: 1,600
Life Insurance Products
N.A.I.C.S.: 524113

Royal Skandia Life Assurance Ltd. (1)
Skandia House, King Edward Rd, Onchan, IM99 1NU, United Kingdom
Tel.: (44) 624655555
Web Site: http://www.royalskandia.com
Sales Range: $150-199.9 Million
Emp.: 350
Offshore Manager of Investment Funds & Other Financial Products
N.A.I.C.S.: 524292

Skandia Holding de Colombia S.A. (1)
Centro Skandia Avenida 19 No 113 30, Apartado Aereo 103 970, Bogota, DC, Colombia
Tel.: (57) 16205566
Web Site: http://www.skandia.com.co
Sales Range: $75-99.9 Million
Emp.: 231
Holding Company for Managers of Pensions & Personal Investment Trusts & Providers of Insurance Products
N.A.I.C.S.: 524292

Subsidiary (Domestic):

Skandia Seguros de Vida S.A. (2)
Centro Skandia Avenida 19 No 113 30, Apartado Aereo 103 970, Bogota, DC, Colombia
Tel.: (57) 16205566
Web Site: http://www.skandia.com.co
Sales Range: $50-74.9 Million
Emp.: 231
Life Insurance Products
N.A.I.C.S.: 524113

Skandia Sociedad Fiduciaria S.A. (2)
Centro Skandia Avenida 19 109A 30, Bogota, DC, Colombia
Tel.: (57) 16584000
Web Site: http://www.skandia.com.co
Sales Range: $50-74.9 Million
Emp.: 231
Financial Advisement
N.A.I.C.S.: 523940

Skandia Life Assurance (Holdings) Ltd. (1)
Skandia House, PO Box 37, Portland Ter, Southampton, SO14 7AY, United Kingdom
Tel.: (44) 2380334411
Web Site: http://www.skandia.co.uk
Sales Range: $25-49.9 Million
Emp.: 100

Holding Company for Providers of Life Assurance Products
N.A.I.C.S.: 524113

Subsidiary (Domestic):

Skandia Life Assurance Ltd. (2)
Skandia House Portland Terrace, Southampton, SO14 7AY, United Kingdom
Tel.: (44) 2380334411
Web Site: http://www.skandia.co.uk
Emp.: 1,590
Life Insurance Products
N.A.I.C.S.: 524113
Paul Seeney *(CEO)*

Skandia Life Insurance Co. (Japan) Ltd. (1)
Hiroo Plz, 5 6 6 Hiroo, Minato Ku, Tokyo, 150 0012, Japan
Tel.: (81) 354881500
Web Site: http://www.skandia.co.jp
Emp.: 150
Life Insurance
N.A.I.C.S.: 524113

Skandia Lifeline (1)
Lindhagensgatan 86, Stockholm, 10655, Sweden
Tel.: (46) 87881000
Web Site: http://www.skandia.se
Sales Range: $75-99.9 Million
Emp.: 200
Provider of Group Health & Life Insurance Products
N.A.I.C.S.: 524114
Frans Lindelow *(CEO)*

Skandia Liv A/S (1)
Stamholmen 151, DK 2650, Hvidovre, Denmark
Tel.: (45) 70121213
Web Site: http://www.skandia.dk
Sales Range: $75-99.9 Million
Emp.: 180
Provider of Life Insurance Products
N.A.I.C.S.: 524113
Charsten Christensen *(CEO)*

Skandia Multifunds Ltd. (1)
Old Mutual House, PO Box 37, Portland Ter, Southampton, SO14 7AY, United Kingdom
Tel.: (44) 2380334411
Web Site: http://www.skandia.co.uk
Sales Range: $500-549.9 Million
Emp.: 1,500
Manager of Investment Funds
N.A.I.C.S.: 525910
Paul Penney *(Mng Dir)*

Skandia Property Asset Management (UK) Ltd. (1)
PO Box 37 Skandia House Portland Terrace, PO Box 37, Southampton, SO14 7AY, United Kingdom
Tel.: (44) 2380334411
Web Site: http://www.skandia.co.uk
Sales Range: $450-499.9 Million
Emp.: 500
Manager of Property Assets
N.A.I.C.S.: 531210
Tracey Hahn *(Mgr-HR)*

Skandia UK (1)
Skandia House Portland Terrace, Southampton, SO14 7AY, United Kingdom
Tel.: (44) 2380334411
Web Site: http://www.skandia.co.uk
Marine Insurance
N.A.I.C.S.: 524128
Peter Mann *(CEO)*

Skandia Vida S.A. de Seguros y Reaseguros (1)
Ruiz De Alarcon 11, E 28014, Madrid, Spain
Tel.: (34) 915243400
Web Site: http://www.skandia.es
Sales Range: $50-74.9 Million
Emp.: 100
Provider of Life Insurance Products
N.A.I.C.S.: 524113

Skandia Vita S.p.A. (1)
Via Fatebenefratelli 3, I-20121, Milan, Italy
Tel.: (39) 0236101010
Web Site: http://www.skandia.it
Sales Range: $75-99.9 Million
Emp.: 130
Life Insurance Products

LIVFORSAKRINGSAKTIEBOLAGET SKANDIA

Livforsakringsaktiebolaget Skandia—(Continued)
N.A.I.C.S.: 524113

SkandiaBanken Aktiebolag (1)
Lindhagensgatan 86, Stockholm, 10655, Sweden
Tel.: (46) 84636000
Web Site: http://www.skandia.se
Sales Range: $150-199.9 Million
Emp.: 300
Banking Services
N.A.I.C.S.: 522110
Frans Lindelow (Pres)

Subsidiary (Domestic):

Skandia Fonder AB (2)
Lindhagensgatan 86, 10655, Stockholm, Sweden
Tel.: (46) 87881940
Web Site: http://www.skandia.se
Manager of Funds
N.A.I.C.S.: 525190

SkandiaLink Livforsakerings (1)
86 Lindhagensgatan, 106 55, Stockholm, Sweden
Tel.: (46) 87881000
Web Site: http://www.skandia.se
Sales Range: $600-649.9 Million
Emp.: 1,300
Manager of Investment Funds
N.A.I.C.S.: 523940

Subsidiary (Non-US):

Skandia Link, S.A. de Seguros y Reaseguros (2)
Avda de las Castillos 33 Atica 7 2a Pl, Pozuelo de Alarcon, 28224, Madrid, Spain
Tel.: (34) 918298800
Web Site: http://www.skandia.es
Sales Range: $50-74.9 Million
Emp.: 10
Investment Fund
N.A.I.C.S.: 525910

SkandiaLink Multifond AB (1)
Lindhagensgatan 86, 112 18, Stockholm, Sweden
Tel.: (46) 87881000
Web Site: http://www.skandia.se
Sales Range: $300-349.9 Million
Emp.: 1,000
Manager of Investment Funds
N.A.I.C.S.: 525910

LIVIA CORPORATE DEVELOPMENT SE
Alter Hof 5, 80331, Munich, Germany
Tel.: (49) 89 5527 58 0
Web Site: http://www.livia-group.com
Private Investment Firm
N.A.I.C.S.: 523940
Peter Low (Chm)

LIVING 3D HOLDINGS, INC.
Rm 1801-02 Office Tower Two Grand Plaza 625 Nathan Road, Kowloon, China (Hong Kong)
Tel.: (852) 35639280   NV
Web Site: http://www.living3d.com
Year Founded: 1987
LTDH—(OTCEM)
Sales Range: Less than $1 Million
3D Image Display Devices
N.A.I.C.S.: 334413
Stephen Man Wah Yip (Chm, CEO & CTO)

LIVING CELL TECHNOLOGIES LIMITED
Level 7 330 Collins Street, Melbourne, 3000, VIC, Australia
Tel.: (61) 386899997
Web Site: http://www.lctglobal.com
1AI—(ASX)
Rev.: $83,601
Assets: $2,131,892
Liabilities: $119,157
Net Worth: $2,012,735
Earnings: ($1,399,291)
Fiscal Year-end: 06/30/24

Biological Pharmaceuticals & Products Mfr
N.A.I.C.S.: 325414
Bernie Tuch (Interim CEO & Interim Chm)

Subsidiaries:

Living Cell Technologies New Zealand Ltd. (1)
Unit 107 23 Edwin St, Mount Eden, Auckland, 1024, New Zealand
Tel.: (64) 92762690
Healtcare Services
N.A.I.C.S.: 621999

LIVING TECHNOLOGIES, INC.
8F Hourai Horidome Building 1-8-12 Nihonbashi Horidome-cho, Chuo-ku, Tokyo, 103-0012, Japan
Tel.: (81) 358478558
Web Site: https://www.lvn.co.jp
Year Founded: 2004
4445—(TKS)
Emp.: 100
Information Technology Services
N.A.I.C.S.: 541512
Daimu Kawai (Pres)

LIVINGBRIDGE EP LLP
2nd Floor 100 Wood Street, London, EC2V 7AN, United Kingdom
Tel.: (44) 20 7506 5600   UK
Web Site: http://www.livingbridge.com
Year Founded: 1995
Rev.: $2,159,872,000
Emp.: 50
Private Equity & Investment Management Services
N.A.I.C.S.: 523999
Wol Kolade (Mng Partner)

Subsidiaries:

Livingbridge VC LLP (1)
100 Wood Street, London, EC2V 7AN, United Kingdom
Tel.: (44) 20 7506 5600
Web Site: http://www.livingbridge.com
Investment Fund Management Services
N.A.I.C.S.: 523940
Adam Holloway (Partner)

Metronet (UK) Ltd. (1)
Turing House Archway 5, Hulme, Manchester, M15 5RL, United Kingdom
Tel.: (44) 161 822 2581
Web Site: http://www.metronet-uk.com
Sales Range: $25-49.9 Million
Emp.: 160
Data & Voice Connectivity Services
N.A.I.C.S.: 517810
Andy Lockwood (Chm)

Subsidiary (Domestic):

M247 Limited (2)
Ball Green Cobra Court, Manchester, M32 0QT, United Kingdom
Tel.: (44) 161 615 1270
Web Site: http://www.m247.com
Emp.: 260
Web Hosting Services
N.A.I.C.S.: 518210
Mike Darcey (Chm)

Subsidiary (Non-US):

M247 Europe SRL (3)
Sos Fabrica de Glucoza No 11B Etaj 1 District 2, Bucharest, Romania
Tel.: (40) 310800700
Web Site: http://www.m247.ro
Web Hosting Services
N.A.I.C.S.: 518210
Mike Darcey (Chm)

World of Books Limited (1)
Mulberry House Woods Way, Goring, BN12 4QY, W Sussex, United Kingdom
Tel.: (44) 1903 507 544
Web Site: http://www.worldofbooks.com
Used Book Whslr
N.A.I.C.S.: 424920
Ken Blair (Chm & Dir)

LIVINGSTON GROUP LTD.
Unit 1 Waverley Industrial Park Hailsham Drive, Harrow, HA1 4TR, Middlesex, United Kingdom
Tel.: (44) 2089430770   UK
Web Site: http://www.livingston-global.com
Year Founded: 2003
Sales Range: $25-49.9 Million
Emp.: 150
Holding Company; Information Technology, Testing & Measuring Equipment Rental Services
N.A.I.C.S.: 551112
Mel Porter (CEO & Mng Dir)

Subsidiaries:

Livingston Electronic Services GmbH (1)
Borsigstrasse 11, Darmstadt, 64291, Germany   (100%)
Tel.: (49) 615193440
Web Site: http://www.xtr-global.de
Sales Range: $75-99.9 Million
Emp.: 55
Information Technology Rental Services
N.A.I.C.S.: 532420

Livingston India Pvt. Ltd (1)
GF 04/4A Times Square B Block Sushant Lok 1, Gurgaon, 122 002, Haryana, India
Tel.: (91) 124 4 00 05 06
Web Site: http://www.livingston.co.in
Test & Measurement Equipment Rental Services
N.A.I.C.S.: 532490

Livingston Services SAS (1)
Parc Tertiaire Icade 43 avenue Robert Schumann, PO Box 10181, 94563, Rungis, France   (100%)
Tel.: (33) 145126565
Web Site: http://www.livingston.fr
Sales Range: $50-74.9 Million
Emp.: 30
Information Technology Testing & Measuring Equipment Rental Services
N.A.I.C.S.: 532490

Livingston T&M B.V. (1)
Nyjverheivslaan 41, 3903 AN, Veenendaal, Netherlands   (100%)
Tel.: (31) 318588688
Web Site: http://www.livingston.nl
Sales Range: $50-74.9 Million
Emp.: 7
Testing & Measuring Equipment Rental Services
N.A.I.C.S.: 532490
Reinier Treur (Gen Mgr)

Livingston T&M GmbH (1)
Borsigstrasse 11, Darmstadt, 64291, Germany
Tel.: (49) 6151360410
Web Site: http://www.livingstonrental.de
Test & Measurement Equipment Rental Services
N.A.I.C.S.: 532490

Livingston UK Ltd. (1)
Livingston House 2 Queens Road, Teddington, TW11 0LB, Mddx, United Kingdom   (100%)
Tel.: (44) 2086144006
Web Site: http://tm.livingston.co.uk
Sales Range: $25-49.9 Million
Emp.: 40
Testing & Measuring Equipment Rental Services
N.A.I.C.S.: 532490

LIVINGSTON S.P.A.
Via Giovanni XXIII 206, 21010, Cardano al Campo, VA, Italy
Tel.: (39) 0331 267 321   IT
Web Site: http://www.lauda.it
Year Founded: 2003
Sales Range: $300-349.9 Million
Commercial Airline Operator
N.A.I.C.S.: 481111
Pellegrino D'Aquino (CEO & Dir-Strategic Fin)

LIVINGSTONE HEALTH HOLDINGS LIMITED

INTERNATIONAL PUBLIC

217 Henderson Road 01-09 Henderson Industrial Park, Singapore, 159555, Singapore
Tel.: (65) 69327720   SG
Web Site: https://www.livingstonehealth.com.sg
PRH—(CAT)
Rev.: $24,392,655
Assets: $16,892,667
Liabilities: $12,202,966
Net Worth: $4,689,701
Earnings: $952,600
Emp.: 99
Fiscal Year-end: 03/31/23
Holding Company; Recycling & Waste Management Services
N.A.I.C.S.: 551112
Wing Kwan Teh (Chm & CEO)

Subsidiaries:

Apicare Pain Specialist Pte. Ltd. (1)
Farrer Park Medical Centre 1 Farrer Park Station Road 14-09/10, Connexion, Singapore, 217562, Singapore
Tel.: (65) 65133383
Web Site: http://www.apicarepainspecialist.com
Pain Management Anaesthesiology Services
N.A.I.C.S.: 621111

Ardennes Healthcare Pte. Ltd. (1)
60 Paya Lebar Rd 02-01/04, Singapore, 409051, Singapore
Tel.: (65) 69803045
Web Site: https://ardenneshealth.com.sg
Health Screening & Radiology Services
N.A.I.C.S.: 621512

Asiapac Recycling Pte Ltd (1)
65 Tech Park Crescent, 637787, Singapore, Singapore
Tel.: (65) 6264 4338
Web Site: http://www.advancesct.com
Sales Range: $25-49.9 Million
Metal Scrap Recycling Services
N.A.I.C.S.: 561990

Atlas Podiatry Pte. Ltd. (1)
333A Orchard Road 04-13 Mandarin Gallery, Singapore, 238897, Singapore
Tel.: (65) 62358616
Web Site: https://atlaspodiatry.com.sg
Podiatry Clinic Operator
N.A.I.C.S.: 621391

Cove Sports & Reconstruction Pte. Ltd. (1)
3 Mount Elizabeth 14-13, Singapore, 228510, Singapore
Tel.: (65) 96317637
Web Site: https://www.coveorthopedics.com.sg
Orthopaedic Clinic Operator
N.A.I.C.S.: 621111

Phoenix Medical Group Pte. Ltd. (1)
1 Seletar Road 02-11 Greenwich V, Singapore, 807011, Singapore
Tel.: (65) 65553512
Web Site: https://www.phoenixmedical.sg
Emp.: 25
Healtcare Services
N.A.I.C.S.: 622110

Precision Medical Services Pte. Ltd. (1)
14 Robinson Road 08-01A Far East Finance Building, Singapore, 48545, Singapore
Tel.: (65) 96741633
Web Site: https://www.precisionhealthcare.com.sg
Healtcare Services
N.A.I.C.S.: 622110

Quantum Orthopaedics Pte. Ltd. (1)
1 Orchard Boulevard 09-06, Singapore, 248649, Singapore
Tel.: (65) 62358781
Web Site: https://www.quantumortho.com.sg
Orthopaedic Surgeon Services
N.A.I.C.S.: 621111

SCT Copper Industry (Shenyang) Co., Ltd. (1)
106 Dong Da Ying Road North Xinmin City

Economic Development Zone, Shenyang, 110000, Liaoning, China
Tel.: (86) 2487526039
Copper Smelting Services
N.A.I.C.S.: 331410

SCT Technologies (Thailand) Co., Ltd. (1)
14/48-49 M 10 Phaholyothin Road, T Klongnueng, Khlong Luang, 12120, Pathum Thani, Thailand
Tel.: (66) 2 529 4646
Web Site: http://www.sctthailand.com
Sales Range: $25-49.9 Million
Emp.: 22
Printed Circuit Board Drilling Services
N.A.I.C.S.: 561990
Thirapan Piangkantha (Mgr)

The Bone and Joint Centre Pte. Ltd. (1)
Mount Elizabeth Medical Centre 3 Mount Elizabeth 14-15, Singapore, 228510, Singapore
Tel.: (65) 69705905
Web Site: https://www.bjc.sg
Orthopaedics Medical Services
N.A.I.C.S.: 621111

Virtuemed Pte. Ltd. (1)
Blk 105 Clementi Street 12 01-24, Singapore, 120105, Singapore
Tel.: (65) 63203830
Web Site: https://virtuemedical.com.sg
Healtcare Services
N.A.I.C.S.: 624410

LIVNICA AD LJUBIJA
27 Juni br 17, 79 000, Prijedor, Bosnia & Herzegovina
Tel.: (387) 52233117
Web Site: http://www.fortisgroup.ba
Year Founded: 1917
LIVN—(BANJ)
Sales Range: Less than $1 Million
Iron, Bronze & Silumin Mfr
N.A.I.C.S.: 212290

LIVNICA D.D.
Arnautovici bb, 71300, Visoko, Bosnia & Herzegovina
Tel.: (387) 3 273 5651
LVNCR—(SARE)
Rev.: $379,952
Assets: $1,720,938
Liabilities: $292,460
Net Worth: $1,428,478
Earnings: $648
Emp.: 8
Fiscal Year-end: 12/31/20
Iron Casting & Forging Services
N.A.I.C.S.: 332111

LIVNICA LJIG A.D.
Kralja Milana 4/IV-V, Belgrade, Serbia
Tel.: (381) 11 361 24 46
Web Site: http://www.livnicaljig.weebly.com
Year Founded: 1986
Sales Range: $1-9.9 Million
Emp.: 67
Iron Casting Services
N.A.I.C.S.: 331511

LIVZON PHARMACEUTICAL GROUP INC.
No 38 Chuangye North Road, Jinwan District, Zhuhai, 519090, Guangdong, China
Tel.: (86) 7568135992
Web Site: https://www.livzon.com.cn
Year Founded: 1985
000513—(SSE)
Rev.: $1,773,193,032
Assets: $3,491,022,132
Liabilities: $1,393,972,632
Net Worth: $2,097,049,500
Earnings: $268,078,356
Emp.: 8,000
Fiscal Year-end: 12/31/22
Pharmaceuticals Mfr

N.A.I.C.S.: 325412
Baoguo Zhu (Chm)

Subsidiaries:

Livzon New North River Pharmaceutical Co., Ltd. (1)
Renmin One Road, Qingcheng District, Qingyuan, 511515, Guangdong, China
Tel.: (86) 7633865316
Web Site: http://www.livzon-nnr.com
Chemical Products Mfr
N.A.I.C.S.: 325199

Livzon Syntpharm Co., Ltd. (1)
22 lianfeng road wanchai free trade zone, Xiangzhou District, Zhuhai, Guangdong, China
Tel.: (86) 7568686175
Web Site: https://syntpharm.livzon.cn
Emp.: 500
Antibiotic Mfr
N.A.I.C.S.: 325411

LIWANLI INNOVATION CO., LTD.
235 4th Floor No 258 Liancheng Road, Zhonghe District, New Taipei City, 235, Taiwan
Tel.: (886) 282213985
Web Site: https://www.liwanli.com.tw
3054—(TAI)
Rev.: $1,271,690
Assets: $27,279,276
Liabilities: $1,656,692
Net Worth: $25,622,583
Earnings: $166,879
Fiscal Year-end: 12/31/23
Portable Multimedia & Storage Products Mfr
N.A.I.C.S.: 334112

LIWE ESPANOLA S.A.
No 140 Calle Mayor, Puente Tocinos, 30006, Murcia, 30006, Spain
Tel.: (34) 968301944
Web Site: https://www.liwe.net
LIW—(MAD)
Sales Range: Less than $1 Million
Apparel Product Mfr & Whslr
N.A.I.C.S.: 315990
Juan Carlos Pardo Cano (Chm)

LIX DETERGENT JOINT STOCK COMPANY
No 3 Street No 2 Ward 4 Linh Trung Ward, Thu Duc City, Ho Chi Minh City, Vietnam
Tel.: (84) 2838963658
Web Site: https://www.lixco.com
LIX—(HOSE)
Rev.: $115,383,031
Assets: $53,808,724
Liabilities: $17,456,522
Net Worth: $36,352,202
Earnings: $7,829,689
Emp.: 1,166
Fiscal Year-end: 12/31/23
Detergents Mfr
N.A.I.C.S.: 325611
Thi Tam Doan (Member-Mgmt Bd)

LIXIANG EDUCATION HOLDING CO., LTD.
No 467 Chengbei Street No 818 Huayuan Road, Liandu District, Lishui, 323000, Zhejiang, China
Tel.: (86) 5782267142   Ky
Year Founded: 2018
LXEH—(NASDAQ)
Rev.: $7,035,807
Assets: $60,086,823
Liabilities: $38,335,201
Net Worth: $21,751,621
Earnings: ($17,582,779)
Emp.: 197
Fiscal Year-end: 12/31/23
Holding Company
N.A.I.C.S.: 551112

LIXIL GROUP CORPORATION
Osaki Garden Tower 1-1 Nishi-Shinagawa 1-chome, Shinagawa-ku, Tokyo, 141-0033, Japan
Tel.: (81) 336389300   JP
Web Site: https://www.lixil.com
Year Founded: 1949
5938—(NGO)
Rev.: $16,603,428,480
Assets: $18,659,468,640
Liabilities: $13,520,935,620
Net Worth: $5,138,533,020
Earnings: ($472,868,580)
Emp.: 62,940
Fiscal Year-end: 03/31/19
Holding Company; Building Materials & Housing Equipment Mfr
N.A.I.C.S.: 551112
Ryo Nihei (Sr Mng Dir, CTO & Exec Officer)

Subsidiaries:

Aiex, Inc. (1)
1-1-1 Sakurashimmachi, Setagaya-Ku, Tokyo, 154-0015, Japan
Tel.: (81) 337021122
Construction Materials Distr
N.A.I.C.S.: 423390

American Standard Philippines Limited, Co. (1)
18/F The Pearlbank Center 146 Valero Street, Salcedo Village, Makati, 1227, Philippines
Tel.: (63) 2 893 1315
Web Site: http://www.americanstandard.com.ph
Sales Range: $25-49.9 Million
Emp.: 36
Plumbing Fittings & Fixtures Mfr
N.A.I.C.S.: 332913

American standard Jiangmen Fittings Co., Ltd. (1)
No 3 Songyuan Avenue Duruan Town, Pengjiang Dist, Jiangmen, 529163, China
Tel.: (86) 7503672102
Plumbing Fitting & Fixtures Mfr
N.A.I.C.S.: 326191
Michael Liu (Pres)

Asahi Tostem Exterior Building Materials Co., Ltd. (1)
1-19-10 Mori 6F Emachukin Kinshicho Building, Koto-ku, Tokyo, 135-0001, Japan (80%)
Tel.: (81) 3 5638 5111
Web Site: http://www.asahitostem.co.jp
Building Materials Distr
N.A.I.C.S.: 423390

G Life Group, Inc. (1)
1-1-1 Sakurashimmachi, Setagaya-Ku, Tokyo, 154-0015, Japan
Tel.: (81) 357606011
Business Management Consulting Services
N.A.I.C.S.: 541611

GHS Corporation (1)
2-1-1 Ojima, Koto-Ku, Tokyo, 136-8535, Japan
Tel.: (81) 33 6388370
Sales Range: $50-74.9 Million
Emp.: 58
Housing Franchise Business
N.A.I.C.S.: 531210

Grohe AG (1)
Feldmuhleplatz 15, Dusseldorf, 40545, Germany
Tel.: (49) 21191303000
Web Site: http://www.grohe.com
Sales Range: $1-4.9 Billion
Faucets, Shower Heads & Fittings Mfr & Exporter
N.A.I.C.S.: 332913
Thomas Fuhr (Exec Dir-Ops)

Subsidiary (Domestic):

AQERO Vertriebs GmbH (2)
Parkstr 1 5 1335, 14974, Ludwigsfelde, Germany
Tel.: (49) 33788180
Web Site: http://www.grohe.de
Mfr of Faucets, Shower Heads & Fittings

N.A.I.C.S.: 332913

Dal-Georg Rost & Sohne Sanitararmaturen Gmbh (2)
Zur Porta 8 12, Porta Westfalica, 32457, Germany
Web Site: http://www.grohe.de
Sales Range: $25-49.9 Million
Emp.: 100
Shower Heads & Fittings Mfr
N.A.I.C.S.: 332913
Jorguwe Ramaker (Gen Mgr)

GROHEDAL Sanitarsysteme GmbH & Co. KG (2)
Zur Porta 8 12, 32457, Porta Westfalica, Germany
Tel.: (49) 57179510
Web Site: http://www.grohe.com
Sales Range: $25-49.9 Million
Emp.: 300
Faucets, Shower Heads & Fittings Mfr
N.A.I.C.S.: 332913

Subsidiary (Non-US):

Grohe A/S (2)
Sluseholmen 8c 2th, 2450, Copenhagen, Denmark
Tel.: (45) 44656800
Web Site: http://www.grohe.dk
Sales Range: $10-24.9 Million
Emp.: 50
Faucets, Shower Heads & Fittings Mfr
N.A.I.C.S.: 332913

Grohe AS (2)
Engebrets Vei 3, 0275, Oslo, Norway
Tel.: (47) 22072070
Web Site: http://www.grohe.no
Sales Range: Less than $1 Million
Emp.: 8
Faucets, Shower Heads & Fittings Mfr
N.A.I.C.S.: 332913

Subsidiary (US):

Grohe America, Inc. (2)
200 N Gary Ave Ste G, Roselle, IL 60172
Tel.: (630) 582-7711
Web Site: http://www.grohe.la
Sales Range: $25-49.9 Million
Emp.: 100
Distr of Faucets & Shower Heads
N.A.I.C.S.: 332913

Subsidiary (Domestic):

Grohe Deutschland Vertriebs GmbH (2)
Zur Porta 9, 32457, Porta Westfalica, Germany
Tel.: (49) 5713989333
Web Site: http://www.grohe.de
Sales Range: $25-49.9 Million
Emp.: 125
Faucets, Shower Heads & Fittings Mfr
N.A.I.C.S.: 332913

Subsidiary (Non-US):

Grohe Espana, S.A. (2)
Avenida de Sarria 106 8 Planta Edificio, Sarria Forum, 08017, Barcelona, Spain
Tel.: (34) 933368850
Web Site: http://www.grohe.es
Sales Range: $10-24.9 Million
Emp.: 40
Mfr Faucets, Shower Heads & Fittings
N.A.I.C.S.: 332913
Miguel Rubio (Mng Dir)

Grohe GmbH (2)
Wienerbergstrasse 11/A7, 1100, Vienna, Austria
Tel.: (43) 1 680 60
Web Site: http://www.grohe.at
Sales Range: $10-24.9 Million
Emp.: 45
Plumbing Fixture Mfr
N.A.I.C.S.: 332913
Robert H. Friedl (Mng Dir)

Grohe Japan Ltd. (2)
A-PLACE Aoyama 6F 2-11-3 Kita-Aoyama, Minato-ku, Tokyo, 107-0061, Japan
Tel.: (81) 357757500
Web Site: http://www.grohe.co.jp
Sales Range: Less than $1 Million
Emp.: 40
Faucets, Shower Heads & Fittings Mfr

LIXIL GROUP CORPORATION

LIXIL Group Corporation—(Continued)
N.A.I.C.S.: 332913

Grohe Limited (2)
World Business Centre 2 Newall Road London Heathrow Airport, Hounslow, TW6 2SF, Middlesex, United Kingdom
Tel.: (44) 2082832840
Web Site: http://www.grohe.co.uk
Faucets, Shower Heads & Fittings Mfr
N.A.I.C.S.: 332913
Paul Bailey *(Sr Mgr-Product)*

Grohe N.V. S.A. (2)
Leuvensesteenweg 369, 1932, Zaventem, Belgium
Tel.: (32) 28993077
Web Site: http://www.grohe.be
Sales Range: $10-24.9 Million
Emp.: 34
Faucets, Shower Heads & Fittings Mfr
N.A.I.C.S.: 332913
Jean Pierre Boogaerts *(Dir-Fin)*

Grohe Nederland B.V. (2)
Metaalstraat 2, 2718 SW, Zoetermeer, Netherlands
Tel.: (31) 793680133
Web Site: http://www.grohe.nl
Sales Range: $75-99.9 Million
Emp.: 75
Mfr of Faucets, Shower Heads & Fittings
N.A.I.C.S.: 332913
Loprop Maageun *(Mng Dir)*

Grohe Pacific Pte. Ltd. (2)
180 Clemenceau Avenue 06-02 Haw Par Centre, 239922, Singapore
Tel.: (65) 63113611
Web Site: http://www.grohe.sg
Sales Range: $10-24.9 Million
Emp.: 25
Faucets, Shower Heads & Fittings Mfr
N.A.I.C.S.: 332913

Grohe Polska Sp. zo.o. (2)
ul Pulawska 182, 02-670, Warsaw, Poland
Tel.: (48) 225432640
Web Site: http://www.grohe.pl
Sales Range: $10-24.9 Million
Emp.: 10
Plumbing Fixture Mfr
N.A.I.C.S.: 332913

Grohe S.a.r.l. (2)
60 Bld de la Mission Marchand, La Defense, 92418, Courbevoie, France
Tel.: (33) 149972900
Web Site: http://www.grohe.fr
Sales Range: $25-49.9 Million
Emp.: 150
Faucets, Shower Heads & Fittings Mfr
N.A.I.C.S.: 332913

Grohe S.p.A. (2)
Via Crocefisso 19, 20122, Milan, Italy
Tel.: (39) 02959401
Web Site: http://www.grohe.it
Sales Range: $10-24.9 Million
Emp.: 50
Faucets, Shower Heads & Fittings Mfr
N.A.I.C.S.: 332913

Subsidiary (Domestic):

Grohe Water Technology AG & Co. Kg (2)
Industriepark Edelburg, 58675, Hemer, Germany
Tel.: (49) 2372930
Faucets, Shower Heads & Fittings Mfr
N.A.I.C.S.: 332913

H.D. Eichelberg & Co. GmbH (2)
Werler Str 3, 58706, Menden, Germany
Tel.: (49) 2372930
Web Site: http://www.eichelberg-armaturen.de
Faucets, Shower Heads & Fittings Mfr
N.A.I.C.S.: 332913

JIO Corporation (1)
Landic Kanda Building 4F 2-6 Kanda-sudamachi, Chiyoda-ku, Tokyo, 101-0041, Japan
Tel.: (81) 3 6859 4800
Web Site: http://www.jio-kensa.co.jp
Sales Range: $75-99.9 Million
Emp.: 485
Home Inspection & Evaluation Services

N.A.I.C.S.: 541350

KYUSHU INAX Corporation (1)
1112-1 Nagacho Hamamachi, Kashima, 849-1322, Saga, Japan
Tel.: (81) 954622201
Office Machinery Mfr
N.A.I.C.S.: 333310

Kyodo Die-Works (Thailand) Co., Ltd. (1)
60/3 Soi Navanankorn11 Moo 19 Phaholyothin Rd, Klongnueng Klongluang, Pathumthani, 12120, Thailand
Tel.: (66) 252909426
Web Site: https://www.kdt.co.th
Sales Range: $50-74.9 Million
Emp.: 234
Extrusion Dies & Metal Mold Tools Mfr
N.A.I.C.S.: 333514
Itabashi Shigeo *(Pres)*

LIXIL (China) Investment Co., Ltd. (1)
Building 24 Gems Garden No 487 Tianlin Road, Shanghai, China
Tel.: (86) 2133952588
Web Site: http://www.lixil.cn
Building Material Equipment Mfr
N.A.I.C.S.: 333120

LIXIL Corporation (1)
36F Kasumigaseki Building 3-2-5 Kasumigaseki, Chiyoda-ku, Tokyo, 100 6036, Japan
Tel.: (81) 3 4335 6550
Web Site: http://www.lixil.co.jp
Building Materials & Housing Equipment Mfr & Distr
N.A.I.C.S.: 444180

Subsidiary (Non-US):

American Standard B&K (Thailand) Public Company Ltd. (2)
1 6 Phaholyothin Rd Km 32, Klongluang, Pathumthani, 12120, Thailand
Tel.: (66) 29014455
Web Site: http://www.americanstandard.co.th
Sales Range: $450-499.9 Million
Emp.: 1,200
Shower Enclosure & Bathroom Fixture Mfr & Distr
N.A.I.C.S.: 327110

American Standard Korea Inc. (2)
66 Yeongdong-daero 112-gil, Gangnam-gu, Seoul, Korea (South)
Tel.: (82) 15885903
Web Site: http://www.americanstandard.co.kr
Kitchen & Bath Accessories Mfr
N.A.I.C.S.: 327110

Subsidiary (Domestic):

Dinaone Corporation (2)
3-10-5 Hatchobori, Chuo-Ku, Tokyo, 104-0032, Japan
Tel.: (81) 367418003
Web Site: http://www.dinaone.co.jp
Emp.: 12
Construction Materials Whslr
N.A.I.C.S.: 423390

Subsidiary (Non-US):

INAX (China) Investment Co., Ltd. (2)
Room 704 Yongyin Bldg, 218 Xizan South Street, Shanghai, Luwan, China
Tel.: (86) 216334 3366
Web Site: http://www.inax.com.cn
Construction Materials Whslr
N.A.I.C.S.: 423390

Subsidiary (Domestic):

INAX ENGINEERING Corporation (2)
5-1 Koiehonmachi, Tokoname, 479-0838, Japan
Tel.: (81) 569360260
Environmental Engineering Services
N.A.I.C.S.: 541330

Subsidiary (Non-US):

INAX Italia S.r.l. (2)
Via Aurelio Saffi No.12, 20123, Milan, Italy

Tel.: (39) 02 4801 3109
Housing Materials Mfr
N.A.I.C.S.: 327110

Subsidiary (Domestic):

INAX MAINTENANCE Corporation (2)
25-7 Kitahamamachi, Chita, 478-0046, Aichi, Japan
Tel.: (81) 562310620
Home Furnishing Installation & Maintenance Services
N.A.I.C.S.: 238990

Subsidiary (Non-US):

INAX Malaysia Sdn. Bhd. (2)
Level1, Wisma Kemajuan, No.2, Jalan 19 B, 46300, Petaling Jaya, Selangor Darul Ehsan, Malaysia
Tel.: (60) 379601794
Housing Materials Mfr
N.A.I.C.S.: 327110

INAX Vietnam Co., Ltd. (2)
My Xuan Al Z, Tan Thanh District, Ba Ria-Vung Tau, Hanoi, Vietnam
Tel.: (84) 64 393 1873
Housing Materials Mfr
N.A.I.C.S.: 327110

INAX Vietnam Plumbing Fixtures Co., Ltd. (2)
2F Management Office Dien Nam-Dien Ngoc Industrial, Quang Nam, Quang Ninh, Vietnam
Tel.: (84) 5103947168
Web Site: http://www.inax.com.vn
Sales Range: $100-124.9 Million
Emp.: 300
Housing Materials Mfr
N.A.I.C.S.: 327110
Tetsuya Ito *(Gen Dir)*

INAX Vietnam Sanitary Ware Co., Ltd. (2)
18th Fl Charmvit Tower 117 Tran Duy Hung St, Hanoi, Vietnam
Tel.: (84) 435566153
Web Site: http://www.email.com.vn
Sales Range: $25-49.9 Million
Emp.: 50
Pottery Product Mfr
N.A.I.C.S.: 327110

Subsidiary (Domestic):

Japan Home Shield Corporation (2)
2-10-14 Ryogoku Citycore 17th Floor, Sumida-Ku, Tokyo, 130 0026, Japan
Tel.: (81) 356241545
Web Site: http://www.j-shield.co.jp
Sales Range: $50-74.9 Million
Emp.: 280
Ground Investigation for Houses & Improvement Work for Foundation of Houses
N.A.I.C.S.: 238190
Takeshi Saito *(Pres)*

LIXIL ENERGY Co., Ltd. (2)
3-3-2 Nihonbashihamacho Tornare Nihonbashihamacho Office To 8f, Chuo-Ku, Tokyo, 103-0007, Japan
Tel.: (81) 356497116
Sales Range: $25-49.9 Million
Emp.: 5
Solar Energy Generation System Distr
N.A.I.C.S.: 423690
Yusuke Ohta *(Gen Mgr)*

LIXIL INFORMATION SYSTEMS CORPORATION (2)
2-1-1 Ojima, Koto-Ku, Tokyo, 136-0072, Japan
Tel.: (81) 336388121
Information Technology Consulting Services
N.A.I.C.S.: 541512

Subsidiary (Non-US):

LIXIL Sanitary Fitting Manufacturing (Suzhou) Corp. (2)
No 86 Ta Yuan South Road, Suzhou New District, Suzhou, Jiangsu Province, China
Tel.: (86) 512 6825 9097
Web Site: http://www.lixil.co.th
Sales Range: $75-99.9 Million
Emp.: 500
Sanitary Ware Mfr

INTERNATIONAL PUBLIC

N.A.I.C.S.: 332913

Suzhou INAX Building Materials Co., Ltd. (2)
No 668 Chang Jiang Rd, Suzhou New Dist, Suzhou, Jiangsu Prov, China
Tel.: (86) 51265364555
Sales Range: $100-124.9 Million
Emp.: 300
Brick & Structural Clay Tile Mfr
N.A.I.C.S.: 327120

Subsidiary (Domestic):

TM.S Corporation (2)
4-1-3 Kudankita Hieikudankita Bldg 8f, Tokyo, Tokyo, 102-0073, Japan
Tel.: (81) 335569500
Web Site: http://www.tms.jp
Construction Materials Distr
N.A.I.C.S.: 423390
Masuda Haruhiko *(Gen Mgr)*

Subsidiary (Non-US):

TOSTEM HOUSING PRODUCTS (DALIAN) CO., LTD. (2)
No 25 Dongbei Da Street Dalian Economic & Technical Development Zone, Dalian, 116600, China
Tel.: (86) 411 8764 3871
Sales Range: $1-4.9 Billion
Emp.: 300
Interior Furnishing Materials Mfr & Distr
N.A.I.C.S.: 321999

Taiwan INAX Corporation (2)
No 132 Tian Mou W Road, Taipei, Peitou, Taiwan
Tel.: (886) 228265888
Web Site: http://www.inax.com.tw
Housing Materials Mfr
N.A.I.C.S.: 327110

Subsidiary (Domestic):

Tostem Management Systems Co., Ltd. (2)
Sumitomofudousan Kameido Bldg 12F 1-42-20, Koto-ku, Tokyo, Japan
Sales Range: $25-49.9 Million
Emp.: 158
Computer, Business, Accounting Support & Temporary Personnel Services
N.A.I.C.S.: 561320

Subsidiary (Non-US):

Tostem Thai Co., Ltd. (2)
60/2 Soi Navanakorn 11 Moo 19 Phaholyothin Road Klongnueng, Klongluang, Pathumthani, 12120, Thailand
Tel.: (66) 25290475
Web Site: http://www.tostemthailand.com
Metal Doors, Sash & Trim Mfr
N.A.I.C.S.: 332321

Tostem Thai Marketing Co., Ltd. (2)
Navanakorn Industrial Zone 60/2 Phaholyothin Rd, Khlong Nueng, Khlong Luang, 12120, Pathumthani, Thailand
Tel.: (66) 2959 0180
Web Site: http://www.lixil.tostem.co.th
Aluminium Door & Window Whslr
N.A.I.C.S.: 423510

LIXIL Global Manufacturing Vietnam Company Limited (1)
D1 St Long Duc IP, Long Duc Ward Long Thanh District, Long Thanh, Dong Nai, Vietnam
Tel.: (84) 2513681111
Web Site: http://www.lixilvina.com.vn
Emp.: 1,573
Building Material Equipment Mfr
N.A.I.C.S.: 333120

LIXIL Housing Research Institute, Ltd. (1)
1-5-7 Kameido Nittetsu ND Tower 4F, Koto-ku, Tokyo, 136 0071, Japan (100%)
Tel.: (81) 3 5626 8245
Sales Range: $25-49.9 Million
Emp.: 140
Planning & Operation of Homebuilding Franchise Chains
N.A.I.C.S.: 541618

LIXIL REALTY, Corp. (1)

AND PRIVATE COMPANIES

2-9-14 Meieki, Nishi-Ku, Nagoya, 451-0045, Japan
Tel.: (81) 525698228
Sales Range: $50-74.9 Million
Emp.: 60
Real Estate Development Services
N.A.I.C.S.: 531390
Yorihisa Yagami *(Mng Dir)*

LIXIL VIVA CORPORATION (1)
1-13-1 Kamikizaki, Urawa-ku, Saitama, 330-8671, Japan **(53.2%)**
Tel.: (81) 486100624
Web Site: http://www.vivahome.co.jp
Household Goods Distr
N.A.I.C.S.: 424990

Naniwa Exterior, Inc. (1)
3-20-7 Ebie, Fukushima-Ku, Osaka, 553-0001, Japan
Tel.: (81) 664587401
Construction Materials Distr
N.A.I.C.S.: 423390

Oita Tostem Co., Ltd. (1)
3-1994-245 Toyomi, Oita, 870-0018, Japan **(100%)**
Tel.: (81) 975362078
Construction Materials Distr
N.A.I.C.S.: 423390

PT American Standard Indonesia (1)
Alamanda Tower Building 31st Floor Jl T B Simatupang Kav 22-26, Cilandak, Jakarta Selatan, 12560, Indonesia
Tel.: (62) 2129660296
Web Site: http://www.americanstandard.co.id
Sanitary Equipment Mfr & Distr
N.A.I.C.S.: 332999

Tostem Hong Kong Ltd. (1)
Unit 16 C F Manulife Tower Electric Road, 169 Electric Road, North Point, China (Hong Kong) **(100%)**
Tel.: (852) 25776368
Sales Range: $10-24.9 Million
Emp.: 40
Residential Building Materials Mfr
N.A.I.C.S.: 561790
Koyanagi Tetsuya *(Gen Mgr)*

Tostem Viva Corporation (1)
298-1 Kami, 362-8555, Ageo, Saitama Pref, Japan
Tel.: (81) 36388112
Web Site: http://www.ithd.co.jp
Sales of DYI Products by Operation of Home Improvement Retailers
N.A.I.C.S.: 459910

LIZEE SAS
Z I Secteur C 1952 Route Des Pugets, 06700, Nice, Alpes Maritimes, France
Tel.: (33) 493311806
Web Site: http://www.lizee.com
Sales Range: $10-24.9 Million
Emp.: 49
Masonry & Other Stonework
N.A.I.C.S.: 238140

LIZHAN ENVIRONMENTAL CORPORATION
716 Qifu Road Wutong Street, Tongxiang, Wutong, 314500, Zhejiang, China
Tel.: (86) 57388986299 Ky
Web Site: http://www.lzencorp.com
Sales Range: $25-49.9 Million
Emp.: 515
Recycled Synthetic Leather & Other Fabrics Mfr & Distr
N.A.I.C.S.: 316990
Jianfeng Liu *(Chm, Pres & CEO)*

LIZHONG SITONG LIGHT ALLOYS GROUP CO., LTD.
No 359 Fazhan West Street, Qingyuan County, Baoding, 071000, Hebei, China
Tel.: (86) 3125806816
Web Site: https://www.stnm.com.cn

300428—(CHIN)
Rev.: $3,000,545,964
Assets: $2,379,038,688
Liabilities: $1,544,624,640
Net Worth: $834,414,048
Earnings: $69,134,364
Emp.: 350
Fiscal Year-end: 12/31/22
Master Alloy Materials Mfr
N.A.I.C.S.: 331420

LIZHONG WHEEL GROUP LTD
No 948 East Qiyi Rd, Baoding, 071000, Hebei, China
Tel.: (86) 3125997688
Web Site: http://www.lzwheel.com
Year Founded: 1995
Sales Range: $450-499.9 Million
Aluminum Alloy Wheels Mfr
N.A.I.C.S.: 331313
Ligen Zang *(Co-Founder & Chm)*

LJ INTERNATIONAL, INC.
1212 Block A Focal Indl Center 21 Man Lok St, Hunghom, Kowloon, China (Hong Kong)
Tel.: (852) 27643622 HK
Web Site: http://www.ljintl.com
Year Founded: 1987
Sales Range: $50-74.9 Million
Emp.: 3,200
Jewelry Designer, Marketing, Distr & Retailer
N.A.I.C.S.: 423940
Yu Chuan Yih *(Chm, Pres & CEO)*

Subsidiaries:

Lorenzo (Shenzhen) Co., Ltd. (1)
Unit C&D 7 Floor Gold Jewelry Building Shenyan Road, Yantian, Shenzhen, 518081, China
Tel.: (86) 755 25266385
Jewelry Mfr
N.A.I.C.S.: 339910

Lorenzo Crystal Ltd. (1)
Rm 11-12 12/F Focal Indl Ctr Blk-A 21 Man Lok St, Hung Hom, China (Hong Kong)
Tel.: (852) 27643622
Web Site: http://www.ljintl.com
Emp.: 7
Costume Jewelry Mfr
N.A.I.C.S.: 339910
Gabor Halasz *(Office Mgr)*

Lorenzo Jewelry Limited (1)
Unit 12 12/F Block A Focal Industrial Centre, 21 Man Lok Street Hung Hom, Kowloon, China (Hong Kong) **(100%)**
Tel.: (852) 27643622
Web Site: http://www.ljintl.com
Sales Range: $25-49.9 Million
Emp.: 72
Jewelry Mfr
N.A.I.C.S.: 339910
Yu Chuan Yih *(Pres & Mng Dir)*

LJECILISTE SLANA BANJA D.D.
ul Prvomajska br 351, Kiseljak, Tuzla, Bosnia & Herzegovina
Tel.: (387) 35271666
LSLBRK3—(SARE)
Rev.: $84,896
Assets: $3,273,934
Liabilities: $112,377
Net Worth: $3,161,557
Earnings: $7,297
Emp.: 2
Fiscal Year-end: 12/31/20
Hotel Operator
N.A.I.C.S.: 721110

LKB INTERNATIONAL
34 Avenue Jean Mermoz, 93120, La Courneuve, France
Tel.: (33) 148360411
Rev.: $24,100,000
Emp.: 119
Meats & Meat Products

N.A.I.C.S.: 424470
Louis Rouaud *(Mgr-Mktg)*

LKL INTERNATIONAL BERHAD
Wisma LKL No 3 Jalan BS7/18 Kawasan Perindustrian Bukit Serdang, Seksyen, 43300, Seri Kembangan, Selangor Darul Ehsan, Malaysia
Tel.: (60) 389482990 MY
Web Site: https://www.lklbeds.com
Year Founded: 2015
LKL—(KLS)
Rev.: $9,703,569
Assets: $46,792,843
Liabilities: $9,565,252
Net Worth: $37,227,591
Earnings: ($1,519,989)
Emp.: 225
Fiscal Year-end: 12/31/23
Investment Holding Services
N.A.I.C.S.: 551112
Ming Chang Lim *(Gen Mgr-Ops)*

Subsidiaries:

LKL Advance Metaltech Sdn. Bhd. (1)
No 33 & 35 Jalan Indah 2/16 Taman Universiti Indah, 43300, Seri Kembangan, Selangor, Malaysia
Tel.: (60) 389425230
Medical Equipment Mfr & Distr
N.A.I.C.S.: 339113
Calvin Lee *(CMO)*

LKP FINANCE LIMITED
203 Embassy Centre Nariman Point, Mumbai, 400 021, India
Tel.: (91) 40024785
Web Site: https://www.lkpsec.com
Year Founded: 1948
507912—(BOM)
Rev.: $133
Assets: $432
Liabilities: $86
Net Worth: $346
Earnings: $83
Emp.: 11
Fiscal Year-end: 03/31/21
Financial Support Services
N.A.I.C.S.: 523999
Mahendra V. Doshi *(Chm)*

LKP SECURITIES LTD.
203 Embassy Centre Nariman Point, Mumbai, 400021, India
Tel.: (91) 2240024785
Web Site: https://www.lkpsec.com
Year Founded: 1948
540192—(BOM)
Rev.: $10,806,555
Assets: $22,745,896
Liabilities: $13,665,998
Net Worth: $9,079,898
Earnings: $509,664
Emp.: 385
Fiscal Year-end: 03/31/23
Trading Services
N.A.I.C.S.: 523160
Pratik M. Doshi *(Mng Dir)*

Subsidiaries:

LKP Wealth Advisory Limited (1)
2nd Floor Gala Impecca Andheri Kurla Road, Near Hotel Courtyard Marriott Chakala Andheri East, Mumbai, 400059, India
Tel.: (91) 226902434
Web Site: https://www.lkpwealth.com
Investment Advisory Services
N.A.I.C.S.: 523940

LL LUCKY GAMES AB
Ostermalmstorg 1, 114 142, Stockholm, Sweden
Web Site: https://www.ladyluckgames.io
Year Founded: 2019

7HH—(DEU)
Software Development Services
N.A.I.C.S.: 541511
Martin Jensen *(CTO)*

LLEIDANETWORKS SERVEIS TELEMATICS SA
Calle Tellez 56 Local C, 28007, Madrid, Spain
Tel.: (34) 973282300 ES
Web Site: https://www.lleida.net
Year Founded: 1995
LLEIF—(OTCQX)
Rev.: $14,483,254
Assets: $12,057,387
Liabilities: $6,884,366
Net Worth: $5,173,021
Earnings: $646,555
Fiscal Year-end: 12/31/19
Telecommunications Consulting Services
N.A.I.C.S.: 541618
Francisco Jose Sapena Soler *(Founder, Chm & CEO)*

Subsidiaries:

Indenova, S.L. (1)
Dels Traginers 14 - 2 B, 46014, Valencia, Spain
Tel.: (34) 963819947
Web Site: https://www.indenova.com
Information Technology Services
N.A.I.C.S.: 541519

Lleida Chile SPA (1)
Avenida Apoquindo Nr 4700 Piso 11 Oficina 9, Santiago, Chile
Tel.: (56) 225708515
Digital Communication Services
N.A.I.C.S.: 517810

LLORENTE & CUENCA MADRID, S.L.
Lagasca 88-Planta 3, 28001, Madrid, Spain
Tel.: (34) 915637722 ES
Web Site: http://www.llorenteycuenca.com
Year Founded: 1995
Reputation, Communication & Public Affairs Management Consulting Services
N.A.I.C.S.: 541613
Jose Antonio Llorente *(Founder, Chm & Partner)*

Subsidiaries:

EDF Consulting, Inc. (1)
801 Brickell Ave 9th Fl, Miami, FL 33131-2945 **(70%)**
Tel.: (305) 606-8641
Web Site: http://www.edfpr.com
Reputation, Communication & Public Affairs Management Consulting Services
N.A.I.C.S.: 541613
Erich de la Fuente *(Founder & CEO)*

LLOYD AEREO BOLIVIANO S.A.
Ave Killmann Aeropuerto 1691 B Sud C, 132, Cochabamba, Bolivia
Tel.: (591) 44251270
Web Site: http://www.labairlinespunto.com.bo
Year Founded: 1925
Sales Range: $75-99.9 Million
Emp.: 360
Airline Services
N.A.I.C.S.: 481111
Milton Patino *(Mng Dir)*

LLOYD CAPITAL AG
An der Alster 42, 20099, Hamburg, Germany
Tel.: (49) 403256780
Web Site: http://www.lloydfonds.de
Year Founded: 1995

LLOYD CAPITAL AG

Lloyd Capital AG—(Continued)
L1OA—(MUN)
Rev.: $33,944,002
Assets: $159,652,718
Liabilities: $98,332,740
Net Worth: $61,319,978
Earnings: ($13,599,678)
Emp.: 158
Fiscal Year-end: 12/31/23
Securities
N.A.I.C.S.: 523910
Stefan Rindfleisch *(Chm-Supervisory Bd)*

Subsidiaries:

Lloyd Fonds Gesellschaft fur Immobilienbeteiligungen mbH & Co. KG (1)
Zippelhaus 2, 20457, Hamburg, Germany
Tel.: (49) 403256780
Sales Range: $50-74.9 Million
Emp.: 6
Real Estate Investment Services
N.A.I.C.S.: 531390

Lloyd Fonds Special Assets GmbH (1)
An Der Alster 42, 20099, Hamburg, Germany
Tel.: (49) 403256780
Web Site: http://www.lloydfonds.de
Sales Range: $50-74.9 Million
Investment Management Service
N.A.I.C.S.: 523999

Lloyd Shipping GmbH (1)
Amelungstrasse 8-10, 20354, Hamburg, Germany
Tel.: (49) 403256780
Sales Range: $25-49.9 Million
Ship Broking Services
N.A.I.C.S.: 488510
Torsten Teichert *(Mng Dir)*

Subsidiary (Non-US):

Lloyd Fonds Singapore Pte. Ltd. (2)
Level 57 Repub Plz 9 Raffles Pl, Singapore, Singapore
Tel.: (65) 68231544
Sales Range: $50-74.9 Million
Emp.: 2
Ship Management Services
N.A.I.C.S.: 532411

Lloyd Treuhand GmbH (1)
Amelungstrasse 8-10, 20354, Hamburg, Germany
Tel.: (49) 40325678400
Web Site: http://www.lloyd-treuhand.de
Sales Range: $50-74.9 Million
Emp.: 30
Trust Management Services
N.A.I.C.S.: 523991
Frank Ahrens *(Mng Dir)*

Lloyd Zweitmarkt GmbH (1)
Amelungstrasse 8-10, Hamburg, 20354, Germany
Tel.: (49) 403256780
Sales Range: $50-74.9 Million
Emp.: 3
Secondary Share Market Services
N.A.I.C.S.: 522299
Frank Ahrens *(Mng Dir)*

TradeOn AG (1)
Amelungstrasse 8-10, 20354, Hamburg, Germany
Tel.: (49) 40325678250
Web Site: http://www.tradeon-gmbh.de
Sales Range: $50-74.9 Million
Emp.: 3
Secondary Share Market Services
N.A.I.C.S.: 522299
Stefan Gieseke *(Mng Dir)*

LLOYD'S OF LONDON

1 Lime St, London, EC3M 7HA, United Kingdom
Tel.: (44) 2073271000
Web Site: http://www.lloyds.com
Sales Range: $300-349.9 Million
Emp.: 620
Insurance Services
N.A.I.C.S.: 561499

Richard Magrath *(Dir-Western US)*

Subsidiaries:

Additional Securities Limited (1)
One Lime Street, London, EC3M 7HA, United Kingdom
Tel.: (44) 2073271000
General Insurance Services
N.A.I.C.S.: 524298

LLOYD'S REGISTER FOUNDATION

71 Fenchurch Street, London, EC3M 4BS, United Kingdom
Tel.: (44) 20 7709 9166 UK
Web Site:
  http://www.lrfoundation.org.uk
Charity Foundation
N.A.I.C.S.: 813211
Richard Clegg *(CEO)*

Subsidiaries:

Lloyd's Register Group Limited (1)
71 Fenchurch Street, London, EC3M 4BS, United Kingdom
Tel.: (44) 20 7709 9166
Web Site: http://www.lr.org
Holding Company; Engineering, Technical Support & Assessment Services
N.A.I.C.S.: 551112
Thomas Thune Andersen *(Chm)*

Subsidiary (Domestic):

LR Senergy Limited (2)
2/3 Queens Terrace, Aberdeen, AB10 1XL, United Kingdom
Tel.: (44) 1224 213 440
Web Site: http://www.lr-senergy.com
Exploration, Production & Energy Consulting Services
N.A.I.C.S.: 541690
Steve Gilbert *(VP-Ops)*

Subsidiary (US):

Lloyd's Register Americas, Inc. (2)
1330 Enclave Pkwy Ste 200, Houston, TX 77077
Tel.: (281) 675-3100
Holding Company; Regional Managing Office
N.A.I.C.S.: 551112
Timothy Protheroe *(Pres)*

Subsidiary (Domestic):

Lloyd's Register North America, Inc. (3)
1330 Enclave Pkwy Ste 200, Houston, TX 77077
Tel.: (281) 675-3100
Holding Company; Engineering, Technical Support & Assessment Services
N.A.I.C.S.: 551112
Donna Grill *(Gen Counsel & Sec)*

Subsidiary (Domestic):

Lloyd's Register Technical Services, Inc. (4)
1330 Enclave Pkwy Ste 200, Houston, TX 77077
Tel.: (281) 675-3100
Technical Support Services
N.A.I.C.S.: 541990

Subsidiary (Domestic):

Lloyd's Register Group Services Limited (2)
71 Fenchurch Street, London, EC3M 4BS, United Kingdom
Tel.: (44) 20 7709 9166
Web Site: http://www.lr.org
Engineering & Technical Support Services
N.A.I.C.S.: 541330

Lloyd's Register Quality Assurance Limited (2)
1 Trinity Place Bickenhill Lane, Birmingham, B37 7ES, United Kingdom
Tel.: (44) 330 414 1271
Web Site: http://www.lrqa.com
Corporate Assessment Services
N.A.I.C.S.: 541990
Vincent Doumeizel *(VP-Food & Beverage)*

Subsidiary (US):

Lloyd's Register Quality Assurance, Inc. (3)
1330 Enclave Pkwy Ste 200, Houston, TX 77077
Tel.: (281) 398-7370
Web Site: http://www.lrqausa.com
Exploration, Production & Energy Consulting Services
N.A.I.C.S.: 541690
Chris Koci *(Pres)*

LLOYDS BANKING GROUP PLC

25 Gresham Street, London, EC2V 7HN, United Kingdom
Tel.: (44) 2073561808 UK
Web Site:
  https://www.lloydsbankinggroup.com
Year Founded: 1985
LYG—(NYSE)
Rev.: $50,838,467,680
Assets: $1,203,652,723,000
Liabilities: $1,131,487,189,560
Net Worth: $72,165,533,440
Earnings: $7,990,182,200
Emp.: 57,955
Fiscal Year-end: 12/31/21
Bank Holding Company
N.A.I.C.S.: 551111
Alan Dickinson *(Deputy Chm)*

Subsidiaries:

Birmingham Midshires Financial Services Ltd. (1)
Pendeford Business Park Wobaston Road, PO Box 81, Wolverhampton, WV9 5HZ, United Kingdom
Tel.: (44) 3456022828
Web Site:
  http://www.birminghammidshires.co.uk
Financial Saving Services
N.A.I.C.S.: 522180

Black Horse Offshore Ltd. (1)
9 Broad Street, Saint Helier, JE2 3RR, Jersey
Tel.: (44) 1534514700
Personal Finance Services
N.A.I.C.S.: 523999
Ronnie Herbert *(Branch Mgr-Interim)*

Blue Bay Travel Group Ltd. (1)
Unit A4 Bellringer Road Business Quarter, Trentham, Stoke-on-Trent, ST4 8GB, Staffordshire, United Kingdom
Tel.: (44) 1782647248
Web Site: https://www.bluebaytravel.co.uk
Travel Agency Services
N.A.I.C.S.: 561510
Nicola Holman *(Head-Sls)*

Cardnet Merchant Services Ltd. (1)
Phoenix House Christopher Martin Road, Basildon, SS14 3EZ, Essex, United Kingdom
Tel.: (44) 3456044635
Web Site: http://www.lloydsbankcardnet.com
Online Payment Services
N.A.I.C.S.: 522320

Connect Health Group Ltd. (1)
The Light Box Quorum Park Benton Lane, Newcastle upon Tyne, NE12 8EU, Tyne and Wear, United Kingdom
Tel.: (44) 1912504580
Web Site: https://www.connecthealth.co.uk
Community Health Care Services
N.A.I.C.S.: 621498
Andrew Walton *(Founder & Exec Dir)*

Lex Autolease Ltd. (1)
Heathside Park Heathside Park Road, Stockport, SK3 0RB, Cheshire, United Kingdom
Tel.: (44) 3456038725
Web Site: https://www.lexautolease.co.uk
Vehicle Leasing Services
N.A.I.C.S.: 532112

Lloyds Bank Commercial Finance Ltd.
12 High Street, Banbury, OX16 5EF, United Kingdom
Tel.: (44) 3456021997

Banking Services
N.A.I.C.S.: 522110

Lloyds Bank GmbH (1)
Karl-Liebknecht-Strasse 5, 10178, Berlin, Germany
Tel.: (49) 302804280
Banking Services
N.A.I.C.S.: 522110
Bertil Bos *(Co-Mng Dir)*

Lloyds Bank Pensions Property (Guernsey) Ltd. (1)
1 Smith St, Saint Peter Port, GY1 4BD, Guernsey
Tel.: (44) 1539736626
Banking Services
N.A.I.C.S.: 522110

Lloyds Bank plc (1)
25 Gresham Street, London, EC2V 7HN, United Kingdom (100%)
Tel.: (44) 2076261500
Web Site: http://www.lloydsbank.com
Rev.: $32,208,784,344
Assets: $770,725,655,564
Liabilities: $719,253,981,264
Net Worth: $51,471,674,301
Earnings: $6,628,898,817
Emp.: 60,686
Fiscal Year-end: 12/31/2023
Commercial, Private & International Banking
N.A.I.C.S.: 522110
William Chalmers *(CFO)*

Subsidiary (Domestic):

Black Horse Limited (2)
25 Gresham Street, London, EC2V 7HN, United Kingdom
Tel.: (44) 3448248888
Web Site: https://www.blackhorse.co.uk
Consumer Credit, Leasing & Related Services
N.A.I.C.S.: 522291

Joint Venture (Domestic):

Caley Ltd. (2)
3rd Floor Sunley House 4 Bedford Park, Croydon, CR0 2AP, United Kingdom
Tel.: (44) 2082404517
Sales Range: $50-74.9 Million
Emp.: 85
Holding Company; Property & Casualty Insurance Products & Services
N.A.I.C.S.: 551112

Subsidiary (Domestic):

Cheltenham & Gloucester plc (2)
Barnett Way, Gloucester, GL4 3RL, United Kingdom
Tel.: (44) 452372372
Web Site: http://www.cheltglos.co.uk
Sales Range: $1-4.9 Billion
Emp.: 3,500
Bank Mortgages & Investments, Savings & Property Related Insurance
N.A.I.C.S.: 522292

D&D London Ltd. (2)
16 Kirby Street, London, EC1N 8TS, United Kingdom
Tel.: (44) 2077160716
Web Site: https://www.danddlondon.com
Full-Service Restaurants
N.A.I.C.S.: 722511
Des Gunewardena *(Co-Founder, Chm & CEO)*

HBOS plc (2)
The Mound, PO Box 5, Edinburgh, EH1 1YZ, United Kingdom
Tel.: (44) 8706005000
Bank Holding Company; Business, Corporate & Retail Banking; Insurance & Investment Services
N.A.I.C.S.: 551111

Subsidiary (Domestic):

Bank of Scotland plc (3)
The Mound, PO Box 5, Edinburgh, EH1 1YZ, United Kingdom
Tel.: (44) 8706005000
Web Site: http://www.bankofscotland.co.uk
Commercial & Investment Banking Services
N.A.I.C.S.: 522110

AND PRIVATE COMPANIES — LLOYDS BANKING GROUP PLC

Division (Domestic):

Bank of Scotland Corporate Banking (4)
The Mound, PO Box 5, Edinburgh, EH1 1YZ, United Kingdom
Tel.: (44) 8706005000
Web Site: http://www.bankofscotland.co.uk
Corporate Financial Services
N.A.I.C.S.: 523999

Holding (Domestic):

Keepmoat Ltd. (5)
The Waterfront Lakeside Boulevard, Doncaster, DN4 5PL, United Kingdom
Tel.: (44) 1302896800
Web Site: https://www.keepmoat.com
Rev.: $815,400,000
Emp.: 2,550
New Home Construction Services
N.A.I.C.S.: 236115
Ian Hoad *(Chm-Yorkshire & North East)*

Unit (Domestic):

Birmingham Midshires (4)
Pendeford Business Park, PO Box 81, Wobaston Road, Wolverhampton, WV9 5HZ, W Midlands, United Kingdom
Sales Range: $700-749.9 Million
Emp.: 1,500
Banking Services
N.A.I.C.S.: 522110

Intelligent Finance (3)
1 Baird Rd, Kirkton Campus, Livingston, EH54 7AZ, United Kingdom
Tel.: (44) 8456094343
Web Site: http://www.if.com
Banking Services
N.A.I.C.S.: 522320
Heather Scott *(Head-Commun)*

Subsidiary (Non-US):

McCarthy & Stone (Developments) Ltd. (4)
Tel.: (44) 1202292480
Web Site: http://www.mccarthyandstone.co.uk
Sales Range: $550-599.9 Million
Emp.: 200
Retirement Community Housing Builder
N.A.I.C.S.: 623311
Paul Lester *(Chm)*

Subsidiary (Non-US):

HBOS Insurance & Investment Group Limited (3)
Tel.: (44) 1133 809 574
Web Site: http://www.halifax.co.uk
Investment Services
N.A.I.C.S.: 523940

Subsidiary (Non-US):

Clerical Medical Investment Group Ltd. (4)
Tel.: (44) 2079305474
Web Site: http://www.clericalmedical.co.uk
Sales Range: $5-14.9 Billion
Emp.: 9,000
Pension & Investment Financial Services
N.A.I.C.S.: 525110

HBOS Investment Fund Managers Limited (4)
Tel.: (44) 2073562305
Equity Investment Services
N.A.I.C.S.: 523999

Subsidiary (Domestic):

Halifax Plc (3)
Trinity Road, Halifax, HX1 2RG, W Yorkshire, United Kingdom
Tel.: (44) 1133809574
Web Site: http://www.halifax.co.uk
Sales Range: $600-649.9 Million
Emp.: 2,000
Commercial Bank Services
N.A.I.C.S.: 522320

Subsidiary (Domestic):

Lloyds Bank General Insurance Holdings Limited (2)
Charlton Place, Andover, SP10 1RE, Hampshire, United Kingdom (100%)
Tel.: (44) 1633810666
Web Site: http://www.lloydstsb.co.uk
Rev.: $9,504
Assets: $354,014,628
Net Worth: $354,014,628
Earnings: $1,358
Emp.: 2,500
Fiscal Year-end: 12/31/2020
Holding Company
N.A.I.C.S.: 551112
N. E. T. Prettejohn *(Chm)*

Subsidiary (Domestic):

Lloyds TSB General Insurance Limited (3)
Tredegar Park, Newport, NP10 8SB, South Wales, United Kingdom
Tel.: (44) 2392853853
Web Site: http://www.lloydstsb.co.uk
Sales Range: $350-399.9 Million
Emp.: 969
Insurance Services
N.A.I.C.S.: 524210

Lloyds TSB Insurance Services Limited (3)
25 Gresham Street, London, EC2V 7HN, United Kingdom
Tel.: (44) 1444475000
Insurance Services
N.A.I.C.S.: 524210

Subsidiary (Non-US):

Lloyds Bank International Limited (2)
9 Broad Street, PO Box 160, Saint Helier, JE2 3RR, Jersey (100%)
Tel.: (44) 1539736626
Investment, Trust & Financial Services
N.A.I.C.S.: 523940

Subsidiary (Domestic):

Lloyds Bank Leasing Limited (2)
25 Gresham Street, London, EC2V 7AE, United Kingdom (100%)
Tel.: (44) 2071582605
Consumer Sales Financing Services
N.A.I.C.S.: 522220

Lloyds Bank Private Banking Limited (2)
125 Colmore Row, Birmingham, B33SD, United Kingdom
Tel.: (44) 1216256520
Web Site: http://www.lloydsbank.com
Commerical Banking
N.A.I.C.S.: 522110

Lloyds Bank Unit Trust Managers Ltd. (2)
25 Gresham St, London, EC2V 7HN, United Kingdom (100%)
Tel.: (44) 2076261500
Web Site: http://www.lloydstsb.co.uk
Unit Trust Management
N.A.I.C.S.: 523991

Representative Office (US):

Lloyds Bank plc - New York Representative Office (2)
1095 Ave of Americas 34th Fl, New York, NY 10036
Tel.: (212) 930-5000
Web Site: http://www.lloydstsb-usa.com
Sales Range: $150-199.9 Million
Emp.: 300
Banking Services
N.A.I.C.S.: 921130

Subsidiary (Domestic):

Lloyds Development Capital (Holdings) Limited (2)
One Vine Street, London, W1J 0AH, United Kingdom (100%)
Tel.: (44) 2077583680
Rev.: $3,144,480,000
Emp.: 100
Equity Investment Firm
N.A.I.C.S.: 523999
Dale Alderson *(Head-North West)*

Subsidiary (Domestic):

Aspire Technology Solutions Ltd. (3)
Pipewell Quay Pipewellgate, Gateshead, NE8 2BJ, United Kingdom
Tel.: (44) 3301242700
Web Site: https://www.aspirets.com
Emp.: 100
Information Technology & Services
N.A.I.C.S.: 513210

Holding (Domestic):

Eley Limited (3)
Selco Way off First Avenue, Minworth Industrial Estate Minworth, Sutton Coldfield, B76 1BA, West Midlands, United Kingdom
Tel.: (44) 1213134567
Web Site: https://www.eley.co.uk
Ammunitions Mfr & Distr
N.A.I.C.S.: 332993
David Barton *(Dir-Sls & Mktg)*

Subsidiary (Domestic):

Fishawack Ltd. (3)
3 Booths Park Booths Hall, Knutsford, WA16 8GS, Cheshire England, United Kingdom
Tel.: (44) 1565756600
Web Site: https://fishawack.com
Emp.: 150
Medical Marketing & Communications Agency
N.A.I.C.S.: 541613
Fred Bassett *(Head-Consulting)*

Subsidiary (US):

Avalere Health, LLC (4)
1201 New York Ave NW Ste 1000, Washington, DC 20005
Tel.: (202) 207-1300
Web Site: http://www.avalere.com
Sales Range: $10-24.9 Million
Health Care Srvices
N.A.I.C.S.: 622110
Daniel N. Mendelson *(Founder)*

Carling Communications (4)
2305 Historic Decatur Rd, San Diego, CA 92106
Tel.: (619) 269-3000
Web Site: http://www.carling-communications.com
Management Consulting Services
N.A.I.C.S.: 541618
Didi Discar *(Founder)*

Skysis, LLC (4)
11445 E Via Linda Ste 2621, Scottsdale, AZ 85259
Tel.: (480) 748-3473
Web Site: http://www.skysisllc.com
Brand Management & Business Development Services
N.A.I.C.S.: 541618
Dan Twibell *(Co-Mng Dir)*

closerlook, LLC (4)
212 West Superior St Ste 300, Chicago, IL 60610
Tel.: (312) 640-3700
Web Site: http://www.closerlook.com
Rev.: $4,904,531
Emp.: 21
Healthcare Marketing Services
N.A.I.C.S.: 541810
Roy Schoenberg *(CEO)*

Subsidiary (Domestic):

Instinctif Partners Holdings Ltd (3)
65 Gresham Street, London, EC2V 7NQ, United Kingdom
Tel.: (44) 20 7457 2020
Web Site: http://www.instinctif.com
Advertising, Financial
N.A.I.C.S.: 541810
Warwick Smith *(Mng Partner-Pub Policy-Global)*

Branch (Domestic):

College Hill Life Sciences (4)
The Registry Royal Mint Court, London, EC3N 4QN, United Kingdom
Tel.: (44) 20 7457 2020
Rev.: $6,000,000
Emp.: 175
N.A.I.C.S.: 541820

College Hill Life Sciences (4)
Meadowside Mountbatten Way, Congleton, CW12 1DN, United Kingdom
Tel.: (44) 1260 296 500

Sales Range: $10-24.9 Million
Emp.: 12
N.A.I.C.S.: 541810

Subsidiary (Domestic):

LDC (Managers) Limited (3)
One Vine Street, London, W1J 0AH, United Kingdom
Tel.: (44) 20 7758 3680
Web Site: http://www.ldc.co.uk
Emp.: 40
Private Equity Investment Management Services
N.A.I.C.S.: 523940
Martin Draper *(CEO)*

Holding (Domestic):

MAMA Group Plc (3)
59-65 Worship St, London, EC2A 2DU, United Kingdom
Tel.: (44) 2076889000
Web Site: http://www.mamagroup.co.uk
Sales Range: $10-24.9 Million
Emp.: 100
Live Music Production, Artist Management & Magazine Publishing
N.A.I.C.S.: 711310

Network Group Holdings plc (3)
Network Court Meriden Hall Main Road, Meriden, Solihull, CV7 7PT, West Midlands, United Kingdom
Tel.: (44) 1676525000
Web Site: http://www.networkgroupholdings.co.uk
Sales Range: $75-99.9 Million
Staffing & Outsourcing Services
N.A.I.C.S.: 561499

Joint Venture (Domestic):

Pelsis Limited (3)
Sterling House Grimbald Crag Close, Knaresborough, HG5 8PJ, United Kingdom
Tel.: (44) 8009885359
Web Site: https://www.pelsis.com
Sales Range: $25-49.9 Million
Emp.: 100
Washroom Hygiene Product Mfr & Supplier
N.A.I.C.S.: 325612
Peter Mangion *(Mng Dir)*

Subsidiary (US):

Bird B Gone, Inc. (4)
1921 E Edinger Ave, Santa Ana, CA 92705
Tel.: (949) 472-3122
Web Site: http://www.birdbgone.com
Soap & Detergent Mfr
N.A.I.C.S.: 325611
Bruce Donoho *(Founder & CEO)*

Holding (Domestic):

SX Environmental Supplies Limited (4)
Unit 2 Scimitar Park Courtauld Road, Basildon, SS13 1ND, Essex, United Kingdom
Tel.: (44) 1702 524040
Web Site: http://www.pestcontrolonline.com
Sales Range: $50-74.9 Million
Emp.: 17
Pest Control Product Distr
N.A.I.C.S.: 424690
Mark Sutton *(Gen Mgr)*

Holding (Domestic):

SSP Limited (3)
Third Floor Bowling Mill Dean Clough, Halifax, HX3 5AX, West Yorkshire, United Kingdom
Tel.: (44) 1422330022
Insurance Technology & Financial Management Software Services
N.A.I.C.S.: 561499
Stephen Lathrope *(CEO)*

Subsidiary (US):

SSP (USA), Inc. (4)
6465 Greenwood Plz Blvd Ste 170, Centennial, CO 80111
Tel.: (303) 209-5900
Web Site: http://www.ssp-worldwide.com
Financial & Insurance Management Software Services
N.A.I.C.S.: 513210

LLOYDS BANKING GROUP PLC

Lloyds Banking Group plc—(Continued)

Branch (Domestic):

SSP Limited - Solihull (4)
2500 The Crescent Birmingham Business Park, Solihull, B37 7YE, W Midlands, United Kingdom
Tel.: (44) 1217798400
Web Site: http://www.ssp-worldwide.com
Insurance Technology & Financial Management Software Services
N.A.I.C.S.: 513210

Holding (Domestic):

Synexus Clinical Research Limited (3)
Sandringham House Ackhurst Park, Chorley, PR7 1NY, Lancs, United Kingdom
Tel.: (44) 1257 230723
Web Site: http://www.synexus.com
Medical Research & Development Services
N.A.I.C.S.: 541715

Subsidiary (Domestic):

Texecom Limited (3)
Bradwood Court St Crispin Way, Haslingden, BB4 4PW, Lancs, United Kingdom
Tel.: (44) 1706234800
Web Site: http://www.texe.com
Security Alarm System Mfr
N.A.I.C.S.: 334290
Jim Ludwig (Mng Dir)

Subsidiary (Domestic):

Lloyds TSB Commercial Finance Ltd. (2)
No 1 Brookhill Way, Banbury, OX16 3EL, United Kingdom (100%)
Tel.: (44) 1295272272
Web Site: http://www.lloydstsb.co.uk
Sales Range: $75-99.9 Million
Emp.: 200
Credit Factoring Services
N.A.I.C.S.: 522299

Scottish Widows plc (2)
69 Morrison Street, Edinburgh, EH3 8BW, United Kingdom
Tel.: (44) 8457678910
Web Site: https://www.scottishwidows.co.uk
Rev.: $714,363,210
Emp.: 4,000
Life Insurance, Pension & Investment Management Services
N.A.I.C.S.: 524113
Jeff Sayers (Mng Dir-Pensions & Investments)

Subsidiary (Domestic):

Scottish Widows Fund & Life Assurance Society (3)
69 Morrison Street, Edinburgh, EH3 8YF, United Kingdom
Tel.: (44) 8457678910
Sales Range: $1-4.9 Billion
Emp.: 4,000
Life Insurance & Pension Management
N.A.I.C.S.: 524292

Subsidiary (Domestic):

St. Andrew's Insurance plc (2)
St Andrews House Portsmouth Road, Esher, KT10 9SA, United Kingdom
Tel.: (44) 8453002456
General Insurance Services
N.A.I.C.S.: 524210

Subsidiary (Domestic):

St Andrew's Life Assurance plc (3)
St Andrews House, Esher, KT10 9SA, United Kingdom
Tel.: (44) 8709010137
Fire Insurance Services
N.A.I.C.S.: 524113

Subsidiary (Domestic):

The Agricultural Mortgage Corporation Plc (2)
Keens House Anton Mill Road, Andover, SP10 2NQ, Hampshire, United Kingdom
Tel.: (44) 2077143660
Web Site: https://www.amconline.co.uk

Sales Range: $50-74.9 Million
Emp.: 60
Business Credit Services; Mortgages
N.A.I.C.S.: 522310

Lloyds Hypotheken B.V. (1)
De Entree 254, 1101 EE, Amsterdam, Netherlands
Tel.: (31) 204622366
Web Site: http://www.lloydsbank.nl
Mortgage Services
N.A.I.C.S.: 522310

Lloyds Securities Inc. (1)
1095 Ave of the Americas 34th Fl, New York, NY 10036
Tel.: (212) 450-0800
Web Site: http://www.lbusa.com
Commercial Banking Services
N.A.I.C.S.: 522110
Andy Schaefer (CEO-Comml Banking-North America)

SARL Hiram (1)
16 Rue des Couturieres, 67240, Bischwiller, France
Tel.: (33) 388050626
Web Site: http://www.fr.hiram.de
Timber & Douglas Wood Product Mfr & Distr
N.A.I.C.S.: 321999

Scottish Widows Schroder Personal Wealth Ltd. (1)
25 Gresham Street, London, EC2V 7HN, United Kingdom
Tel.: (44) 2070316057
Web Site: https://www.spw.com
Financial Advice Services
N.A.I.C.S.: 523940

Specialist People Services Group Ltd. (1)
7 Bradford Business Park Kings Gate, Bradford, BD1 4SJ, West Yorkshire, United Kingdom
Tel.: (44) 1274361000
Web Site: https://www.spsgroup.uk.com
Recruitment Services
N.A.I.C.S.: 561311
Tony Rieger (Chm)

Stroma Group Ltd. (1)
4 Pioneer Way, Castleford, WF10 5QU, West Yorkshire, United Kingdom
Tel.: (44) 3301249660
Web Site: http://www.stroma.com
Construction Services
N.A.I.C.S.: 236220
Martin Holt (CEO)

The Mortgage Business plc (1)
Trinity Road, Halifax, HX1 2RG, United Kingdom
Tel.: (44) 3457253253
Web Site: http://www.t-m-b.co.uk
Mortgage Services
N.A.I.C.S.: 522310

Tuskerdirect Ltd. (1)
Building 4 Hatters Lane, Croxley Green Business Park, Watford, WD18 8YF, Hertfordshire, United Kingdom
Tel.: (44) 3334001010
Web Site: https://tuskercars.com
Software Development Services
N.A.I.C.S.: 541511
David Hosking (Deputy Chm)

LLOYDS METALS AND ENERGY LIMITED
A2 2nd Floor Madhu Estate Pandurang Budhkar Marg, Lower Parel, Mumbai, 400 013, India
Tel.: (91) 2262918111
Web Site: https://lloyds.in
Year Founded: 1977
512455—(BOM)
Rev.: $99,270,035
Assets: $112,449,696
Liabilities: $46,704,362
Net Worth: $65,745,334
Earnings: $13,291,947
Emp.: 415
Fiscal Year-end: 03/31/22
Steel & Related Products Mfr
N.A.I.C.S.: 331221

Babulal Kesar Deo Agarwal (Mng Dir)

LMG CORP.
Unit 1915 PSE Tower 5th Ave cor 28th Street BGC Taguig, Ortigas Center, Manila, 1635, Philippines
Tel.: (63) 86366686 PH
Web Site: https://www.lmg.ph
Year Founded: 1970
LMG—(PHI)
Rev.: $247,800
Assets: $4,731,932
Liabilities: $3,765
Net Worth: $4,728,167
Earnings: ($107,939)
Fiscal Year-end: 12/31/22
Holding Company; Chemical Mfr & Distr
N.A.I.C.S.: 551112
Robinson W. Siao (Vice Chm, Pres & CEO)

LMS CAPITAL PLC
3 Bromley Place, London, W1T6DB, United Kingdom
Tel.: (44) 2079353555 UK
Web Site: https://www.lmscapital.com
Year Founded: 2006
LMS—(LSE)
Rev.: $84,315
Assets: $106,056,225
Liabilities: $49,998,795
Net Worth: $56,057,430
Earnings: ($2,252,415)
Fiscal Year-end: 12/31/22
Investment Management Service
N.A.I.C.S.: 523999
Nick Friedlos (Mng Dir & Mng Dir)

Subsidiaries:

LMS Capital Group Limited (1)
100 George St, London, W1U 8NU, United Kingdom
Tel.: (44) 2079353555
Web Site: http://www.lmscapital.com
Emp.: 12
Investment Management Service
N.A.I.C.S.: 523999
Glenn Payne (CEO)

LMS Capital Holdings Limited (1)
100 George Street, London, W1U 8NU, United Kingdom
Tel.: (44) 20 7935 3555
Emp.: 20
Investment Management Service
N.A.I.C.S.: 523999
Nicholas Friedlos (CEO)

Nationwide Energy Partners, Ltd. (1)
Tel.: (614) 918-2031
Web Site: https://www.nationwideenergypartner.com
Energy Infrastructure Design, Installation, Operation & Maintenance for Private Communities
N.A.I.C.S.: 926130
Victoria Roach (Mgr-Customer Relationship)

Westpool Investment Trust plc (1)
100 George Street, London, W1U 8NU, United Kingdom
Tel.: (44) 2079353555
Web Site: http://www.lmscapital.com
Emp.: 12
Investment Management Service
N.A.I.C.S.: 523999
Nicholas Friedlos (Gen Mgr)

LMS CO. LTD.
53-73 Jinwisandan-ro Jinwi-myeon, Jinwi-myeon, Pyeongtaek, 17709, Gyeonggi, Korea (South)
Tel.: (82) 314212345
Web Site: https://www.lmsglobal.com
Year Founded: 1999
073110—(KRS)
Rev.: $75,856,446
Assets: $175,604,404
Liabilities: $101,491,731
Net Worth: $74,112,673

INTERNATIONAL PUBLIC

Earnings: $204,970
Emp.: 280
Fiscal Year-end: 12/31/22
Display Equipment Mfr
N.A.I.C.S.: 334419

LMS INVESTMENT COMPANY
river Moika house 11 lit A room 21 N, 191186, Saint Petersburg, Russia
Tel.: (7) 8123291999
Web Site: http://www.lmsic.com
Year Founded: 1994
Sales Range: Less than $1 Million
Securities Brokerage Services
N.A.I.C.S.: 523150

LMS PROLINK LTD.
480 University Ave Ste 800, Toronto, M5G 1V2, ON, Canada
Tel.: (416) 595-7484
Web Site: http://www.lmsprolink.ca
Sales Range: $10-24.9 Million
Emp.: 37
Financial Support & Insurance Planning Services
N.A.I.C.S.: 524298
Joseph V. McCabe (CEO)

LMS REINFORCING STEEL GROUP
6320 148th Street, Surrey, V3S 3C4, BC, Canada
Tel.: (604) 598-9930 Ca
Web Site: http://www.lmsgroup.ca
Year Founded: 1987
Rebar & Post Tensioning Fabrication & Installation
N.A.I.C.S.: 332312
Ron McNeil (Co-Founder & CEO)

Subsidiaries:

D. Kay Leonard, Inc. (1)
18059 Rosedale Hwy, Bakersfield, CA 93314
Tel.: (661) 589-0972
Web Site: http://www.johaseerebar.com
Sales Range: $1-9.9 Million
Emp.: 30
Reinforcing Steel (Rebar) Subcontractor
N.A.I.C.S.: 238190
Tamara Chapman (Mgr-Bus Ops)

LMT GMBH & CO. KG
Heidenheimer Str 84, 73447, Oberkochen, Germany
Tel.: (49) 7364 9579 0
Web Site: http://www.lmt-tools.com
Sales Range: $250-299.9 Million
Emp.: 2,000
Tool Mfr
N.A.I.C.S.: 333517
Michael Heinrich (CEO)

Subsidiaries:

LLC LMT Tools (1)
Serebryanicheskaya nab 27, 109028, Moscow, Russia
Tel.: (7) 4952807352
Tool Mfr
N.A.I.C.S.: 333517

LMT (India) Private Limited (1)
Old No 14 New No 29 IInd Main Road Gandhinagar, Adyar, 600 020, Chennai, India
Tel.: (91) 44 24405136
Tool Mfr
N.A.I.C.S.: 333517
Srikrishnan Narayanan (Dir-Sls)

LMT Asia PTE LTD. (1)
1 Clementi Loop 04-01 Clementi West District Park, 12 9808, Singapore, Singapore
Tel.: (65) 64 624214
Tool Mfr
N.A.I.C.S.: 333517
Robin Yin (Mng Dir)

LMT BELIN S.A.S. (1)
Lieu dit Les Cizes, 01590, Lavancia-Epercy, France
Tel.: (33) 474 758 989

AND PRIVATE COMPANIES

Web Site: http://www.belin-y.com
Sales Range: $10-24.9 Million
Emp.: 120
Machine Tools Mfr
N.A.I.C.S.: 333515
Dieter Brucklacher *(Mng Dir)*

LMT China Co. Ltd. (1)
No 8 Phoenix Road Jiangning Development Zone, 211100, Nanjing, China
Tel.: (86) 25 52128866
Tool Mfr
N.A.I.C.S.: 333517
Feng Si Yuan *(Dir-Fin)*

LMT Czech Republic s.r.o. (1)
Dusikova 3, Lesna, 63800, Brno, Czech Republic
Tel.: (420) 548218722
Web Site: http://www.lmt-fette.cz
Tool Mfr
N.A.I.C.S.: 333517

LMT Fette Werkzeugtechnik GmbH & Co. KG (1)
Grabauer Strasse 24, 21493, Schwarzenbek, Germany
Tel.: (49) 4151 12 0
Tool Mfr
N.A.I.C.S.: 333517
Uwe Kretzschmann *(Dir-R&D & Engrg)*

LMT KIENINGER GmbH (1)
Vogesenstrasse 23, 77933, Lahr, Germany
Tel.: (49) 7821 943 0
Web Site: http://www.kieninger.de
Tool Mfr
N.A.I.C.S.: 333517

LMT Korea Co. Ltd. (1)
Room 1212 Anyang Trade Center 161 Simin-daero, Dongan-Gu, Anyang, 431-817, Gyeonggi-Do, Korea (South)
Tel.: (82) 31 3848600
Tool Mfr
N.A.I.C.S.: 333517
Chang Soo Chung *(Pres)*

LMT Onsrud ONSRUD LP (1)
1081 S Northpoint Blvd, Waukegan, IL 60085
Tel.: (847) 362-1560
Web Site: http://www.onsrud.com
Tool Mfr
N.A.I.C.S.: 333517
Scott Feimster *(VP-Sls & Mktg)*

LMT Tool Systems GmbH (1)
Heidenheimer Strasse 84, 73447, Oberkochen, Germany
Tel.: (49) 7364 9579
Tool Mfr
N.A.I.C.S.: 333517
Dietmar Schoepf *(VP-Sls)*

LMT Tool Systems GmbH & Co. KG (1)
C/Agricultura local no 12 planta 1 no 16-18, El Masnou, 08320, Barcelona, Spain
Tel.: (34) 937127435
Cut Gear Cutting Tool Mfr
N.A.I.C.S.: 333515

LMT Tool Systems GmbH & Co. KG (1)
Mosetiggasse 1, 1230, Vienna, Austria
Tel.: (43) 6803106101
Cut Gear Cutting Tool Mfr
N.A.I.C.S.: 333515

LMT Tool Systems RO SRL (1)
Str Mihai Viteazu nr 245A, Selimbar, 557260, Sibiu, Romania
Tel.: (40) 269 246 092
Tool Mfr
N.A.I.C.S.: 333517

LMT Tools GmbH & Co. KG (1)
Grabauer Strasse 24, 21493, Schwarzenbek, Germany
Tel.: (49) 4151120
Cut Gear Cutting Tool Mfr
N.A.I.C.S.: 333515
David Szillat *(Dir-Rolling Sys)*

LMT Tools India Pvt. Ltd. (1)
Plot No A-40/1 Phase I MIDC Tal Khed, Chakan Village Nighoje, 410 501, Pune, India
Tel.: (91) 2135614900
Cut Gear Cutting Tool Mfr
N.A.I.C.S.: 333515
Ramakant Reddy *(Mng Dir)*

LMT Tools Mexico, SA de CV (1)
Adolfo Prieto No 1638 Colonia Del Valle Sur, 3100, Mexico, Mexico
Tel.: (52) 55 40000653
Tool Mfr
N.A.I.C.S.: 333517
Daniel Martinez *(Dir-Sls)*

LMT UK Ltd. (1)
5 Elm Court Copse Drive, Meriden, CV5 9RG, United Kingdom
Tel.: (44) 1676 523440
Web Site: http://www.lmt-tools.com
Emp.: 4
Tool Mfr
N.A.I.C.S.: 333517
David Flatman *(Mng Dir)*

LMT USA, Inc. (1)
1081 S Northpoint Blvd, Waukegan, IL 60085
Tel.: (630) 969-5412
Web Site: http://www.lmtusa.com
Sales Range: $25-49.9 Million
Emp.: 30
Tool Mfr
N.A.I.C.S.: 333517
Brian Nowicki *(Pres)*

Lmt Tools Brasil Ferramentas LTDA (1)
Av Cambaciica 1200 Modulo 11, 13097-160, Campinas, Sao Paolo, Brazil
Tel.: (55) 19 98243 9910
Tool Mfr
N.A.I.C.S.: 333517

LNOX WIND ENERGY LIMITED
3rd Floor ABS Towers, Old Padra Rd, Vadodara, 390007, Gujarat, India
Tel.: (91) 2656198111
Web Site: https://www.iwel.co.in
Year Founded: 2020
IWEL—(NSE)
Rev.: $90,557,113
Assets: $741,308,183
Liabilities: $455,899,442
Net Worth: $285,408,740
Earnings: ($79,621,857)
Emp.: 5
Fiscal Year-end: 03/31/23
Wind Energy Equipment Mfr
N.A.I.C.S.: 333611
Deepak Banga *(Sec & Compliance Officer)*
Subsidiaries:
Inox Wind Infrastructure Services Limited (1)
Survey No 1837 and 1834 Moje Jetalpur ABS Towers Second Floor, Old Padra Road, Vadodara, 390007, Gujarat, India
Tel.: (91) 265 619 8111
Web Site: https://www.igesl.co.in
Wind Energy Services
N.A.I.C.S.: 221115

LOABIRAN COMPANY
No 25 Sanei St North Gandi Ave Vanak sq, PO Box 15855/316, 1969945311, Tehran, Iran
Tel.: (98) 2188795138
Web Site: https://www.loabiran.com
Year Founded: 1981
LEAB—(THE)
Emp.: 241
Chemical Products Mfr
N.A.I.C.S.: 325199

LOADSTAR CAPITAL, K.K.
Prime Ginza Yanagidori Building 1-9-13 Ginza, Chuo-ku, Tokyo, 104-0061, Japan
Tel.: (81) 362644270   JP
Web Site: https://www.loadstarcapital.com
Year Founded: 2012
3482—(TKS)
Rev.: $203,667,340
Assets: $535,103,570
Liabilities: $398,316,200
Net Worth: $136,787,370
Earnings: $34,620,470
Emp.: 70
Fiscal Year-end: 12/31/23
Real Estate Management Services
N.A.I.C.S.: 531210
Takuya Kawabata *(Exec Dir)*
Subsidiaries:
Loadstar Funding K.K. (1)
Web Site: http://loadstarfunding.com
Emp.: 3
Investment Management Service
N.A.I.C.S.: 523940

LOANCOS GMBH
Plockstrasse 6-10, 35390, Giessen, Germany
Tel.: (49) 69 80 80 65 0
Web Site: http://loancos.de
Emp.: 80
Real Estate Advisory Services
N.A.I.C.S.: 531390
Sylvia Baumgarten *(CEO)*
Subsidiaries:
Hypotheken Management GmbH (1)
Gruneburgweg 16-18, D-60322, Frankfurt, Germany
Tel.: (49) 698080654100
Web Site: http://www.hypotheken-management.com
Money Transmission Services
N.A.I.C.S.: 522390
Eckhard Blauhut *(Mng Dir)*
Proceed Portfolio Services GmbH (1)
Friedrich-Ebert-Strasse 55, 45127, Essen, Germany
Tel.: (49) 201 177856 0
Web Site: http://www.portfolio-services.de
Commercial Real Estate Loans & Investment Services
N.A.I.C.S.: 522292
Tilo Knebusch *(Mng Dir)*

LOBA GMBH & CO. KG
Leonbergerstr 56 - 62, Ditzingen, 71254, Germany
Tel.: (49) 7156357220
Web Site: http://www.loba.de
Year Founded: 1922
Rev.: $17,932,200
Emp.: 80
Parquet & Hardwood Floors Treating Products Mfr
N.A.I.C.S.: 325612
Michael Fischer *(Gen Mgr)*

LOBE SCIENCES LTD.
Suite 1400-1199 West Hastings Street, Vancouver, V6E 3T2, BC, Canada
Tel.: (949) 505-5623   BC
Web Site: https://www.lobesciences.com
Year Founded: 2010
LOBEF—(OTCQB)
Rev.: $627,038
Assets: $1,715,420
Liabilities: $1,834,875
Net Worth: ($119,455)
Earnings: ($3,511,682)
Fiscal Year-end: 08/31/23
Psychedelic Medicines Research & Development
N.A.I.C.S.: 541715
Philip J. Young *(CEO)*

LOBSTER POINT PROPERTIES LTD.
757 Bedford Highway, Bedford, B4A 3Z7, NS, Canada
Tel.: (902) 457-2350
Investment Holding Company
N.A.I.C.S.: 551112

LOCALITY PLANNING ENERGY HOLDINGS LIMITED

John Carter Risley *(Owner)*
Subsidiaries:
Cognition Financial Corporation (1)
200 Clarendon St 3rd Fl, Boston, MA 02116
Tel.: (866) 296-3637
Web Site: http://www.cognitionfinancial.com
Sales Range: $25-49.9 Million
Consumer Lending & Student Loan Services
N.A.I.C.S.: 522291
Seth Gelber *(Pres)*
Subsidiary (Domestic):
FM Systems LLC (2)
171 Service Ave Ste 200, Warwick, RI 02886
Tel.: (401) 921-3700
Web Site: http://www.tuitionmanagementsystems.com
Payment Solutions Services
N.A.I.C.S.: 541214
Craig Lockwood *(Pres-Tuition Mgmt Sys)*

LOBTEX CO., LTD.
12-8 Shijo-cho, Higashi-osaka, 579-8053, Osaka, Japan
Tel.: (81) 729801111
Web Site: https://www.lobtex.co.jp
Year Founded: 1888
5969—(TKS)
Rev.: $39,164,250
Assets: $61,367,240
Liabilities: $27,682,680
Net Worth: $33,684,560
Earnings: $1,844,190
Emp.: 190
Fiscal Year-end: 03/31/24
Hand Tool Mfr & Distr
N.A.I.C.S.: 332216
Toshitame Jibiki *(Pres)*

LOCAFY LIMITED
246A Churchill Avenue, Subiaco, 6008, WA, Australia
Tel.: (61) 409999339   AU
Web Site: https://locafy.com
Year Founded: 2009
LCFY—(NASDAQ)
Rev.: $2,772,000
Assets: $4,112,000
Liabilities: $1,900,000
Net Worth: $2,212,000
Earnings: ($1,996,000)
Emp.: 40
Fiscal Year-end: 06/30/24
Software Development Services
N.A.I.C.S.: 541511
Gavin Burnett *(Founder, CEO & Mng Dir)*

LOCAL VIEW MARKETING INC.
1011 Upper Middle Rd East Suite 1429, Oakville, L6H 5Z9, ON, Canada
Tel.: (647) 977-9153
Web Site: http://www.localviewmarketing.com
Marketing & Advertising Services
N.A.I.C.S.: 541613
Puneet Mehta *(Co-Founder & CEO)*

LOCALITY PLANNING ENERGY HOLDINGS LIMITED
Level 8 8 Market Lane, PO Box 5737, Maroochydore, 4558, QLD, Australia
Tel.: (61) 1300433735
Web Site: https://www.localityenergy.com.au
LPE—(ASX)
Rev.: $27,073,863
Assets: $15,040,066
Liabilities: $7,762,697
Net Worth: $7,277,369
Earnings: $1,339,760
Emp.: 30

LOCALITY PLANNING ENERGY HOLDINGS LIMITED

Locality Planning Energy Holdings Limited—(Continued)

Fiscal Year-end: 06/30/24
Energy Production Services
N.A.I.C.S.: 221118
Damien Glanville *(Co-CEO, Co-Founder & Co-Mng Dir)*

LOCALIZA RENT A CAR S.A.
Av Bernardo Vasconcelos 377, Cachoeirinha, Belo Horizonte, 31150-000, MG, Brazil
Tel.: (55) 3132477024
Web Site: https://www.localiza.com
Year Founded: 1973
LZRFY—(OTCQX)
Rev.: $3,368,259,000
Assets: $12,435,557,000
Liabilities: $8,541,586,000
Net Worth: $3,893,971,000
Earnings: $348,730,000
Emp.: 18,581
Fiscal Year-end: 12/31/22
Passenger Car Rental & Leasing Services
N.A.I.C.S.: 532111
Mauricio Fernandes Teireixa *(CFO & Officer-IR)*

Subsidiaries:

Companhia de Locacao das Americas (1)
Avenida Raja Gabaglia n 1 781 Belo Horizonte 12 andar, Luxemburgo, Belo Horizonte, 30350-540, Brazil
Tel.: (55) 3133161981
Vehicle Leasing Services
N.A.I.C.S.: 532120

LOCALTAPIOLA GROUP
Revontulenkuja 1, 02100, Espoo, Finland
Tel.: (358) 94531
Web Site: http://www.lahitapiola.fi
Sales Range: $1-4.9 Billion
Emp.: 2,400
Holding Company Insurance Investment & Banking Product & Services
N.A.I.C.S.: 551112
Jari Sundstrom *(Co-CEO)*

Subsidiaries:

LocalTapiola General Mutual Insurance Company (1)
Revontulenkuja 1, 02010, Espoo, Finland
Tel.: (358) 9 4531
Web Site: http://www.lahitapiola.fi
Rev.: $33,492,839,142
Assets: $298,355,015,799
Liabilities: $136,377,364,987
Net Worth: $161,977,650,812
Earnings: $5,169,308,872
Emp.: 3,428
Fiscal Year-end: 12/31/2018
Non-Life Insurance Products & Services
N.A.I.C.S.: 524298
Erkki Moisander *(Chm & Pres)*

Subsidiary (Domestic):

LocalTapiola Bank Plc (2)
Revontulentie 7, 02100, Espoo, Finland (73.17%)
Tel.: (358) 9 4531
Web Site: http://www.lahitapiola.fi
Sales Range: $100-124.9 Million
Emp.: 113
Commercial & Investment Banking, Credit Cards & Securities Brokerage Services
N.A.I.C.S.: 522110
Erkki Moisander *(Pres)*

Subsidiary (Domestic):

LocalTapiola Asset Management Ltd. (3)
Revontulentie 7, Espoo, 2100, Finland
Tel.: (358) 9 4531
Web Site: http://www.lahitapiola.fi

Sales Range: $25-49.9 Million
Investment & Asset Management Services
N.A.I.C.S.: 523940

LocalTapiola Real Estate Asset Management Ltd. (3)
Revontulentie 7, 02100, Espoo, Finland
Tel.: (358) 9 4531
Web Site: http://www.lahitapiola.fi
Real Estate Investment & Asset Management Services
N.A.I.C.S.: 531390

LocalTapiola Mutual Life Insurance Company (1)
Revontulentie 7, 02100, Espoo, Finland
Tel.: (358) 9 4531
Web Site: http://www.lahitapiola.fi
Sales Range: $750-799.9 Million
Life Insurance Products & Services
N.A.I.C.S.: 524113
Minna Kohmo *(Mng Dir)*

LocalTapiola Mutual Pension Insurance Company (1)
Revontulentie 7, PO Box 9, 2010, Espoo, Finland
Tel.: (358) 9 4531
Web Site: http://www.tapiola.fi
Rev.: $1,775,314,027
Assets: $12,109,491,112
Liabilities: $12,028,553,517
Net Worth: $80,937,595
Earnings: $2,831,311
Emp.: 214
Fiscal Year-end: 12/31/2012
Pension Insurance Products & Services
N.A.I.C.S.: 524128
Satu Huber *(Mng Dir)*

LOCASOLOG SA
10 rue de la Grange Bateliere, 75009, Paris, France
Tel.: (33) 140220713
Real Estate Support Services
N.A.I.C.S.: 531390
Pierre Faure *(Chm & CEO)*

LOCH DUART LTD.
Badcall Salmon House Scourie, Lairg, Sutherland, IV27 4TH, United Kingdom
Tel.: (44) 1674 660161
Web Site: http://www.lochduart.com
Year Founded: 1999
Fish Farming
N.A.I.C.S.: 112511
Andy Bing *(Sls Dir)*

Subsidiaries:

The Edinburgh Salmon Company Ltd. (1)
1 Strathview, Dingwall Business Park, Dingwall, IV15 9XD, United Kingdom
Tel.: (44) 1349860600
Chilled Salmon Mfr & Distr
N.A.I.C.S.: 311710

LOCK&LOCK CO., LTD.
20F Grand Central A Sejong-daero 14, Jung-gu, Seoul, 04527, Korea (South)
Tel.: (82) 25209567
Web Site: https://www.locknlock.com
Year Founded: 1978
115390—(KRS)
Rev.: $399,772,762
Assets: $543,427,322
Liabilities: $81,630,355
Net Worth: $461,796,967
Earnings: ($11,806,141)
Emp.: 488
Fiscal Year-end: 12/31/22
Kitchenware Product Mfr
N.A.I.C.S.: 339999
Park Namki *(Mng Dir)*

Subsidiaries:

Beijing Lock&Lock Trading Co., Ltd. (1)
Kitchenware Sales
N.A.I.C.S.: 332215

Lock & Lock HCM Co., Ltd. (1)
Floor 9 Beautiful Saigon 2 77 Hoang Van Thai, Tan Phu Q 7, Ho Chi Minh City, Vietnam
Tel.: (84) 2854135750
Kitchen Appliance Retailer
N.A.I.C.S.: 423620
Chun Hae Woo *(CEO)*

Lock&Lock (Hong Kong) Company Limited (1)
2602-03 26/F Hopewell Centre 183 Queen's Road East, Wanchai, China (Hong Kong)
Tel.: (852) 2116 3559
Kitchenware Sales
N.A.I.C.S.: 332215

Lock&Lock (Thailand) Co., Ltd. (1)
388 Exchange Tower 20th Fl Unit 2002 and 21th Fl, Unit 2103 Sukhumvit Road Khlong Toei, Bangkok, 10110, Thailand
Tel.: (66) 22585210
Web Site: https://www.locknlock.co.th
Kitchenware Sales
N.A.I.C.S.: 332215

Lock&Lock Ghidini Srl (1)
Via Ponte Gandovere n 51, Gussago, 25064, Brescia, Italy
Tel.: (39) 030 314 718
Kitchenware Sales
N.A.I.C.S.: 332215

Lock&Lock GmbH (1)
Europa - Allee 88, 60486, Frankfurt am Main, Germany
Tel.: (49) 6977061010
Web Site: http://www.locknlock.de
Kitchenware Sales
N.A.I.C.S.: 332215

Lock&Lock HN Company Limited (1)
Kitchenware Sales
N.A.I.C.S.: 332215

Lock&Lock India Trading Private, Ltd. (1)
A-206 Universal Business Park Saki Vihar Road Chandivali, Powai Andheri E, Mumbai, 400 072, Maharashtra, India
Tel.: (91) 2240151960
Kitchenware Sales
N.A.I.C.S.: 332215

Lock&Lock Japan Co., Ltd. (1)
8F Shinbashi-Hara Building 2-10-5 Shinbashi, Minato-ku, Tokyo, 105-0004, Japan
Tel.: (81) 3 5501 0661
Kitchenware Sales
N.A.I.C.S.: 332215

Lock&Lock Phnom Penh Co., Ltd. (1)
443B Morivong Boulevard, Phnom Penh, Cambodia
Tel.: (855) 23 222 077
Kitchenware Sales
N.A.I.C.S.: 332215

Lock&Lock Retail Co., Ltd. (1)
191 Silom Complex Building 25th Floor 3-5 Unit C Silom Road, Silom Bangrak, Bangkok, 10500, Thailand
Tel.: (66) 2632 1794
Kitchenware Sales
N.A.I.C.S.: 332215

Lock&Lock Trade (Shenzhen) Co., Ltd. (1)
Tel.: (86) 75523993960
Kitchenware Sales
N.A.I.C.S.: 332215

PT Lock&Lock Indonesia (1)
Palma Tower Lt 17 Jl RA Kartini II-S Kav 6 Pondok Pinang, Kebayoran Lama, Jakarta, 12310, Selatan, Indonesia
Tel.: (62) 2157948200
Kitchenware Sales
N.A.I.C.S.: 332215

Shanghai Lock & Lock Trade Co., Ltd. (1)
Block D/H 3/F Hechuan Building No 2016 Yishan Road, Minhang District, Shanghai, China
Tel.: (86) 2154222228
Healthcare Food Distr
N.A.I.C.S.: 445298

INTERNATIONAL PUBLIC

Shanghai Lock&Lock Trading Co., Ltd. (1)
Block D/H 3/F Hechuan Building No 2016 Yishan Road, Minhang District, Shanghai, China
Tel.: (86) 2154222228
Kitchenware Sales
N.A.I.C.S.: 332215

LOCKSLEY RESOURCES LIMITED
216 Saint Georges Terrace, Perth, 6000, WA, Australia
Tel.: (61) 894810389 AU
Web Site: https://www.locksleyresources.com
Year Founded: 2018
LKY—(ASX)
Rev.: $43,385
Assets: $4,684,018
Liabilities: $218,406
Net Worth: $4,465,611
Earnings: ($978,212)
Fiscal Year-end: 06/30/23
Exploration & Mining Services
N.A.I.C.S.: 213115
Alan Armstrong *(Sec)*

LOCO HONG KONG HOLDINGS LIMITED
Unit 401 4/F Fairmont House 8 Cotton Tree Drive Admiralty, Hong Kong, China (Hong Kong)
Tel.: (852) 22030999 HK
Web Site: https://www.locohkholdings.com
Year Founded: 2014
8162—(HKG)
Rev.: $6,163,478
Assets: $6,202,620
Liabilities: $3,234,930
Net Worth: $2,967,690
Earnings: ($2,953,410)
Emp.: 24
Fiscal Year-end: 12/31/22
Metal Distr
N.A.I.C.S.: 423510
Wendong Wang *(Chm, CEO & Exec Dir)*

LOCONDO, INC.
7F 30-13 Motoyoyogi-cho, Shibuya-ku, Tokyo, 151-0062, Japan
Tel.: (81) 354658022
Web Site: https://jade-group.jp
Year Founded: 2010
3558—(TKS)
Rev.: $94,694,040
Assets: $83,534,380
Liabilities: $38,108,750
Net Worth: $45,425,630
Earnings: $7,097,090
Fiscal Year-end: 02/29/24
Online Fashion Product Distr
N.A.I.C.S.: 459999
Yusuke Tanaka *(CEO)*

LOCOSOCO GROUP PLC
8 Madeira Avenue, Leigh-on-Sea, SS9 3EB, Essex, United Kingdom
Tel.: (44) 2035380716
Web Site: http://www.locoso.co
LOCO—(VIE)
Rev.: $287,110
Assets: $425,758
Liabilities: $252,478
Net Worth: $173,280
Earnings: ($749,319)
Emp.: 2
Fiscal Year-end: 05/31/20
Aviation Consulting Services
N.A.I.C.S.: 813319
Simon Rendell *(Chm)*

LOCTEK ERGONOMIC TECHNOLOGY CORP.

15-19F Jindong Building No 536 Xueshi Road, Shounan Subdistrict Yinzhou District, Ningbo, 315100, Zhejiang, China
Tel.: (86) 57455007473
Web Site: http://www.loctek.com
Year Founded: 2002
300729—(CHIN)
Rev.: $549,555,515
Assets: $957,485,328
Liabilities: $529,713,511
Net Worth: $427,771,817
Earnings: $89,255,575
Fiscal Year-end: 12/31/23
Office Furniture Mfr & Distr
N.A.I.C.S.: 337126
Lehong Xiang *(Chm, Pres & Gen Mgr)*

LODE METALS INC.
918-1030 West Georgia St, Vancouver, V6E 2Y3, BC, Canada
Tel.: (775) 240-7731   BC
Web Site:
   https://www.lodemetals.com
Year Founded: 2018
3G7—(DEU)
Assets: $2,328,161
Liabilities: $66,476
Net Worth: $2,261,685
Earnings: ($434,679)
Fiscal Year-end: 01/31/23
Gold Exploration Services
N.A.I.C.S.: 212220
Ken Tullar *(Pres & CEO)*

LODE RESOURCES LTD.
Level 5 1 Margaret Street, Sydney, 2000, NSW, Australia
Tel.: (61) 290081381
Web Site:
   https://www.loderesources.com
Year Founded: 2019
LDR—(ASX)
Exploration & Mining Services
N.A.I.C.S.: 213115

LODESTAR INVESTMENT HOLDINGS CORPORATION
7th Floor Peaksun Bldg 1505 Princeton St corner Shaw Blvd Brgy, Wack Wack Greenhills East, Mandaluyong, Philippines
Tel.: (63) 2 920 9306
Web Site:
   http://www.lodestarholdings.com
Year Founded: 1974
LIHC—(PHI)
Rev.: $46,746
Assets: $5,020,708
Liabilities: $49,031
Net Worth: $4,971,677
Earnings: ($39,251)
Fiscal Year-end: 12/31/21
Mining & Natural Resource Exploration Services
N.A.I.C.S.: 212220
Delfin S. Castro Jr. *(Pres, CFO & Treas)*

LODESTAR LOGISTICS CORP.
1155 Appleby Line Unit E4, Burlington, L7L 5H9, ON, Canada
Tel.: (905) 332-2200
Web Site:
   https://www.lodestarlog.com
Rev.: $12,000,000
Emp.: 9
Liquid Petroleum Transport, Non-Local
N.A.I.C.S.: 484230

LODESTAR MINERALS LIMITED
1st Floor 31 Cliff Street, Fremantle, 6160, WA, Australia
Tel.: (61) 894353200
Web Site:
   https://www.lodestarminerals.com
LSR—(ASX)
Rev.: $427,774
Assets: $556,262
Liabilities: $667,911
Net Worth: ($111,649)
Earnings: ($3,081,390)
Fiscal Year-end: 06/30/24
Gold & Nickel Producer
N.A.I.C.S.: 212230
William Frank Clayton *(Mng Dir)*

LODGING MEDIA, INC.
Rua Leopoldo Miguez 159, 22060-020, Rio de Janeiro, Brazil
Tel.: (55) 21 6937 3056   NV
Year Founded: 2012
Rental Property Online Marketplace
N.A.I.C.S.: 531390
Joao Neto *(Pres, CEO, CFO, Treas & Sec)*

LODHA GROUP
Lodha Pavillion Apollo Mills Compound, NM Joshi Marg Mahalaxmi, Mumbai, 400011, India
Tel.: (91) 2223024400
Web Site: http://www.lodhagroup.com
Year Founded: 1980
Sales Range: $300-349.9 Million
Emp.: 1,300
Real Estate Developers
N.A.I.C.S.: 236116
Mangal Prabhat Lodha *(Founder)*

LODZIA-ROTEX INVESTMENT LTD.
2 Kaufman Yehezkel, Jaffa, Tel Aviv, 6801294, Israel
Tel.: (972) 563942
Web Site:
   https://www.lodziarotexinvest.com
Year Founded: 1924
LODZ—(TAE)
Rev.: $6,765,023
Assets: $134,430,168
Liabilities: $63,965,464
Net Worth: $70,464,704
Earnings: $2,790,717
Emp.: 4
Fiscal Year-end: 12/31/23
Real Estate Manangement Services
N.A.I.C.S.: 531390

LOEWEN
77 Hwy 52 W, Steinbach, RG5 1B2, MB, Canada
Tel.: (204) 326-6446
Web Site: http://www.loewen.com
Year Founded: 1905
Sales Range: $150-199.9 Million
Emp.: 700
Doors & Windows Mfr
N.A.I.C.S.: 321911

LOG COMMERCIAL PROPERTIES E PARTICIPACOES S.A.
Av Professor Mario Werneck 621, Buritis, Belo Horizonte, 30455-610, MG, Brazil
Tel.: (55) 3136158400
Web Site: http://www.logcp.com.br
LOGG3—(BRAZ)
Rev.: $39,355,034
Assets: $1,118,043,087
Liabilities: $450,872,157
Net Worth: $667,170,930
Earnings: $34,851,003
Fiscal Year-end: 12/31/23
Commercial Property Rental Services
N.A.I.C.S.: 531120
Rubens Menin Teixeira De Souza *(Chm)*

LOG-IN LOGISTICA INTERMODAL S.A.
Rua do Passeio n 78 12 andar Ed BVEP Nigri Plaza, Rio de Janeiro, 20021-280, Brazil
Tel.: (55) 21116762
Web Site:
   http://www.loginlogistica.com.br
LOGN3—(BRAZ)
Rev.: $412,214,578
Assets: $687,817,928
Liabilities: $513,201,516
Net Worth: $174,616,412
Earnings: $81,116,761
Fiscal Year-end: 12/31/22
Logistic Services
N.A.I.C.S.: 483113
Pascoal Cunha Gomes *(CFO & Dir-IR)*

Subsidiaries:

Oliva Pinto Logistica Ltda.   (1)
Rua Javari 1165 - Distrito Industrial, Manaus, Brazil
Tel.: (55) 9236157922
Web Site: https://www.olivapinto.com.br
Road Transport & Logistics Services
N.A.I.C.S.: 541614

Tecmar Transportes Ltda.   (1)
Rua da Congregacao No 206 Gramado Neighborhood, Embu, 06816-005, SP, Brazil
Tel.: (55) 1136135922
Web Site: https://www.tecmartransportes.com.br
Logistics & Transportation Services
N.A.I.C.S.: 541614

LOGAER MASCHINENBAU GMBH
Muhlenweg 2d, Leer, 26789, Germany
Tel.: (49) 491979280
Web Site: http://www.logaer.de
Year Founded: 1974
Sales Range: $25-49.9 Million
Emp.: 246
Metal Machining Services
N.A.I.C.S.: 332322
Alwin Kaffka *(Head-Fin)*

LOGAH TECHNOLOGY CORPORATION
No 15 Lane 62 Caigong 1st Road, Kaohsiung, 813, Tsoying, Taiwan
Tel.: (886) 3433776
Web Site: https://www.logah.com
3593—(TAI)
Rev.: $28,769,154
Assets: $46,617,350
Liabilities: $31,396,513
Net Worth: $15,220,837
Earnings: ($2,281,925)
Emp.: 594
Fiscal Year-end: 12/31/23
Inverters, High-Level Power Supply & Display Power Supply Mfr
N.A.I.C.S.: 334413
Alpha Hui-Fa Yu *(Chm & Pres-Interim)*

LOGAHOLIC B.V.
Ellermanstraat 15C, 1099 BW, Amsterdam, Netherlands
Tel.: (31) 20 3373075
Web Site: http://www.logaholic.com
Sales Range: $1-9.9 Million
Web Analytics Software
N.A.I.C.S.: 513210
Joe Bowab *(Pres)*

LOGAN COPPER INC.
1174 Gregory Road, Kelowna, V1Z 3A6, BC, Canada
Tel.: (604) 940-9157
Year Founded: 1999
Sales Range: Less than $1 Million
Copper Exploration Services
N.A.I.C.S.: 212230
Thalbinder S. Poonian *(Pres & CEO)*

LOGAN GROUP COMPANY LIMITED
15/F Tower B Logan Centrury Center, Xinghua Road South, Shenzhen, China
Tel.: (86) 75585288221
Web Site: https://www.logangroup.com
3380—(HKG)
Rev.: $6,530,625,138
Assets: $34,390,515,757
Liabilities: $29,858,308,872
Net Worth: $4,532,206,884
Earnings: ($1,226,477,625)
Emp.: 2,361
Fiscal Year-end: 12/31/23
Real Estate Manangement Services
N.A.I.C.S.: 531390
Hoi Pang Kei *(Founder & Chm)*

LOGHMAN PHARMACEUTICAL & HYGIENIC CO.
10th Km Karaj Road Lashgari Highway, Po Box 14155-1443, Tehran, 1389737611, Iran
Tel.: (98) 2144504121
Web Site: http://www.loghman-med.com
Year Founded: 1968
DLGM—(THE)
Sales Range: Less than $1 Million
Pharmaceuticals Product Mfr
N.A.I.C.S.: 325412

LOGIC INSTRUMENT S.A.
12 rue Ampere ZI Igny, 91430, Igny, France
Tel.: (33) 169331080
Web Site: https://www.logic-instrument.com
Year Founded: 1987
ALLOG—(EUR)
Sales Range: $10-24.9 Million
Personal Computer Mfr
N.A.I.C.S.: 334111

Subsidiaries:

Logic Instrument Deutschland GmbH   (1)
Taunusstr 51, 80807, Munich, Germany
Tel.: (49) 89 666 2 876
Personal Computer Distr
N.A.I.C.S.: 423430

Logic Instrument USA Inc.   (1)
3495 Piedmont Rd NE Bldg 11 Ste 710, Atlanta, GA 30305
Tel.: (678) 263-3103
Computer Peripheral Distr
N.A.I.C.S.: 423430

LOGICA VENTURES CORP.
365 Bay Street Suite 800, Toronto, M5H 2V1, ON, Canada
Tel.: (416) 831-3598
Web Site:
   http://www.logicaventures.com
LOG.P—(TSXV)
Sales Range: Less than $1 Million
Asset Management Services
N.A.I.C.S.: 523940
Thomas Tewoldemedhin *(Sec)*

LOGICAN TECHNOLOGIES INC.
150 Karl Clark Road, Edmonton, T6N 1E2, AB, Canada
Tel.: (780) 450-4400
Web Site: https://www.logican.com
Year Founded: 1994
Electronic Parts Mfr
N.A.I.C.S.: 334419
Sheldon Bekolay *(Mgr-Plng & Customer Svc)*

LOGICOM PUBLIC LTD

LogiCan Technologies Inc.—(Continued)

LOGICOM PUBLIC LTD
26 Stasinou Street, Ayia Paraskevi, 2003, Strovolos, Nicosia, Cyprus
Tel.: (357) 22551000 **CY**
Web Site: https://www.logicom.net
LOG—(CYP)
Rev.: $1,256,115,423
Assets: $665,709,035
Liabilities: $415,443,472
Net Worth: $250,265,563
Earnings: $28,893,455
Emp.: 873
Fiscal Year-end: 12/31/22
Computer Components & Peripherals Whslr
N.A.I.C.S.: 423430
Varnavas Irinarchos (Mng Dir)

Subsidiaries:

ENET Solutions - Logicom S.A. (1)
Thesi Roupaki, Aspropirgos, 19300, Athens, Greece
Tel.: (30) 2102883600
Marketing Consulting Services
N.A.I.C.S.: 541613

Elogicomnet Morocco Distribution SARL
California Garden Building A, Sidi Maarouf La colline, Casablanca, Morocco
Tel.: (212) 529079737
Information Technology Distribution Services
N.A.I.C.S.: 541511

ICT Logicom Solutions S.A. (1)
44 Kifissias Ave Monumental Plaza Building B 4th Floor, 151 25, Maroussi, Greece
Tel.: (30) 2111822800
Information Technology & Consulting Services
N.A.I.C.S.: 541690

Logicom (Middle East) SAL (1)
Maurice Jabra Bldg-GF, Dekwaneh Industrial Zone, Beirut, Lebanon
Tel.: (961) 1698220
Marketing Consulting Services
N.A.I.C.S.: 541613

Logicom Dubai LLC (1)
Al Kifaf Commercial Building Number 306 Trade Center Road, PO Box 54328, Bur Dubai, Dubai, United Arab Emirates
Tel.: (971) 48055399
Information Technology Services
N.A.I.C.S.: 541519

Logicom FZE (1)
Plot S 60608 Jebel Ali Free Zone, PO Box 54328, Dubai, United Arab Emirates
Tel.: (971) 48055399
Marketing Consulting Services
N.A.I.C.S.: 541613

Logicom Italia s.r.l. (1)
Via Vesuvio 1, 20834, Novate Milanese, MB, Italy
Tel.: (39) 03621822700
Computer Peripheral Equipment Whslr
N.A.I.C.S.: 423430

Logicom Jordan LLC (1)
Tel.: (962) 65166300
Computer Peripheral Equipment Whslr
N.A.I.C.S.: 423430

Logicom Kuwait for Computer Company W.L.L. (1)
Office No 16 16th Floor Al Shorouq Tower 2 Jaber Al Mubarak Street, Al-Sharq, Kuwait
Tel.: (965) 22411384
Information Technology Services
N.A.I.C.S.: 541519

Logicom LLC (1)
Knowledge Oasis Muscat 4 Ground Floor Office 6, Muscat, Oman
Tel.: (968) 24170555
Information Technology & Consulting Services
N.A.I.C.S.: 541690

Logicom Saudi Arabia LLC (1)
Office 417 419 Gate 2A King Fahad Branch Road, PO Box 87009, Offices Zone Riyadh Gallery Mall, Riyadh, 12262, Saudi Arabia
Tel.: (966) 112078450
Emp.: 100
Information Technology & Consulting Services
N.A.I.C.S.: 541690

Logicom Solutions Limited (1)
50 John Kennedy Avenue, 1076, Nicosia, Cyprus
Tel.: (357) 22551010
Web Site: https://solutions.logicom.net
Emp.: 100
Information Technology & Consulting Services
N.A.I.C.S.: 541690

Netcom Limited (1)
20 Charalampou Mouskou Str Office 209, 8010, Paphos, Cyprus
Tel.: (357) 26020600
Web Site: https://netcomcyprus.com.cy
Mobile Telecommunications Services
N.A.I.C.S.: 517810

Newcytech Business Solutions Ltd. (1)
45 Vyzantiou Street, CY-2064, Strovolos, Cyprus
Tel.: (357) 22558600
Web Site: https://newcytech.logicom.net
Information Technology & Consulting Services
N.A.I.C.S.: 541690

Newcytech Distribution Ltd. (1)
45 Vyzantiou Street, CY-2064, Strovolos, Cyprus
Tel.: (357) 22558600
Web Site: https://newcytechdistribution.logicom.net
Information Technology Services
N.A.I.C.S.: 541519

LOGIN PEOPLE S.A.
Buropolis 2 1240 route des Dolines, Valbonne, 06560, Sophia-Antipolis, France
Tel.: (33) 4 9333 0666
Web Site: http://www.loginpeople.com
Year Founded: 2004
Computer Security Solutions
N.A.I.C.S.: 541512
Francois-Pierre Le Page (Chm & CEO)

LOGINET JAPAN CO., LTD.
LNJ Sapporo Odori Park Building 2-6 Odori Nishi 8-chome, Chuo-ku, Sapporo, 060-0042, Japan
Tel.: (81) 112517755
Web Site: https://www.loginet-japan.com
Year Founded: 2005
9027—(SAP)
Rev.: $601,607,020
Assets: $294,320,320
Liabilities: $168,425,390
Net Worth: $125,894,930
Earnings: $19,513,760
Fiscal Year-end: 03/31/20
Transport Services
N.A.I.C.S.: 485999
Terumi Kimura (CEO)

LOGINTRADE SA
ul Legnicka 57D lok B/J, 54-203, Wroclaw, Poland
Tel.: (48) 717873534
Web Site: https://www.logintrade.pl
Online Marketing Services
N.A.I.C.S.: 541613
Mikolaj Maciejewski (Project Mgr-IT)

LOGIS CONFORT SOCIMI, S.A.
Avda Castilla 53-55 planta 2a local 20a, San Fernando de Henares, 28830, Madrid, Spain
Tel.: (34) 961753012 **ES**
Web Site: http://www.logisconfort.es
Year Founded: 2016

MLLOG—(EUR)
Sales Range: $1-9.9 Million
Emp.: 4
Real Estate Investment Services
N.A.I.C.S.: 525990
Salvador Vila Arcos (CFO)

LOGISCO
Rue De La Sablonniere, 14980, Caen, Rots, France
Tel.: (33) 233896410
Web Site: http://www.malherbe.fr
Rev.: $24,300,000
Emp.: 32
Local Trucking without Storage
N.A.I.C.S.: 484110
Denis Bertin (Dir)

LOGISMOS INFORMATION SYSTEMS S.A.
Thessaloniki ICT Business Park 9th. Km Thessaloniki-Thermi Str, PO Box 21094, Pylaia, 555 10, Thessaloniki, Greece
Tel.: (30) 2310502060
Web Site: https://www.logismos.gr
Year Founded: 1993
LOGISMOS—(ATH)
Sales Range: Less than $1 Million
Emp.: 53
Business Software Development Services
N.A.I.C.S.: 541511
Markos Doufos (Founder)

LOGISTEA AB
Kornhamnstorg 6, S-111 27, Stockholm, Sweden
Tel.: (46) 852228500
Web Site: https://www.oddmolly.com
Year Founded: 2002
LOGI—(OMX)
Rev.: $28,876,849
Assets: $34,981,574
Liabilities: $20,988,066
Net Worth: $13,993,508
Earnings: ($8,133,560)
Emp.: 71
Fiscal Year-end: 12/31/19
Women's Clothing Designer & Mfr
N.A.I.C.S.: 315250
Stig Waernes (Interim Chief Operating Officer)

Subsidiaries:

KMC Properties ASA (1)
Brattorkaia 13 B, 7010, Trondheim, Norway
Tel.: (47) 48003175
Web Site: https://kmcp.no
Rev.: $40,246,157
Assets: $652,854,791
Liabilities: $377,747,638
Net Worth: $275,107,158
Earnings: ($7,657,977)
Emp.: 14
Fiscal Year-end: 12/31/2023
Real Estate Services
N.A.I.C.S.: 531390
Stig Waernes (CEO)

Odd Molly Inc. (1)
860 S Los Angeles St, Los Angeles, CA 90014
Tel.: (310) 246-0226
Fashion Apparels Retailer
N.A.I.C.S.: 424350
Josephine Svedmark (Mgr-Fin)

LOGISTICS HOLDINGS LTD
72 Senoko Drive, Singapore, 739465, Singapore
Tel.: (65) 68910831
Web Site: https://www.logistics99.com.sg
Building Construction
N.A.I.C.S.: 236220

LOGISTICS VICEM JOINT STOCK COMPANY

INTERNATIONAL PUBLIC

405 Song Hanh Xa Lo Ha Noi Truong Tho Ward, Thu Duc City, Ho Chi Minh City, Vietnam
Tel.: (84) 02837404061
Web Site: https://www.vantaihatien.com.vn
Year Founded: 2000
HTV—(HOSE)
Rev.: $12,349,494
Assets: $16,789,330
Liabilities: $3,391,708
Net Worth: $13,397,622
Earnings: $339,323
Fiscal Year-end: 12/31/23
Transportation Services
N.A.I.C.S.: 488490
Khoi Xuan Le (Chm)

LOGISTIQUES TRANS-WEST INC
1900 52E Ave, Lachine, Montreal, H8T2X9, QC, Canada
Tel.: (514) 345-1090
Web Site: http://groupetranswest.com
Sales Range: $50-74.9 Million
Emp.: 650
Food Products Transportation
N.A.I.C.S.: 484220
Real Gagnon (CEO)

LOGISTRI FASTIGHETS AB
Box 7415, 103 91, Stockholm, Sweden
Tel.: (46) 700890466
Web Site: https://www.logistri.se
Year Founded: 2017
6DV—(DEU)
Real Estate Development Services
N.A.I.C.S.: 531190
Henrik Viktorsson (Pres)

LOGISYS INC.
Mapo dokmakro 281, Seoul, 121-727, Korea (South)
Tel.: (82) 221256300
Web Site: http://www.logisys.co.kr
Year Founded: 1996
067730—(KRS)
Rev.: $25,173,634
Assets: $18,475,063
Liabilities: $5,384,117
Net Worth: $13,090,946
Earnings: $156,759
Emp.: 353
Fiscal Year-end: 12/31/22
ATM & Office Equipment Maintenance & Repair Services
N.A.I.C.S.: 811210
Lee Tae Hwan (CFO)

LOGITRANS A/S
Hillerupvej 35, 6760, Ribe, Denmark
Tel.: (45) 76881600
Web Site: http://www.logitrans.com
Year Founded: 1940
Sales Range: $50-74.9 Million
Emp.: 100
Material Handling Equipment Mfr
N.A.I.C.S.: 333998
Erling Pedersen (Pres)

Subsidiaries:

Interthor Inc. (1)
1817 Beach St, Broadview, IL 60155
Tel.: (708) 345-1270
Web Site: http://www.interthor.com
Sales Range: $25-49.9 Million
Emp.: 20
Material Handling Equipment Mfr
N.A.I.C.S.: 333924

LOGIZARD CO., LTD.
3-3-6 Nihonbashi Ningyo-cho, Chuo-Ku, Tokyo, 103-0013, Japan
Tel.: (81) 356436228
Web Site: https://www.logizard-zero.com

AND PRIVATE COMPANIES — LOHMANN & RAUSCHER INTERNATIONAL GMBH & CO. KG

Year Founded: 2001
4391—(TKS)
Rev.: $17,298,160
Assets: $17,714,400
Liabilities: $2,836,240
Net Worth: $14,878,160
Earnings: $2,294,160
Emp.: 105
Fiscal Year-end: 06/30/22
Freight Forwarding & Logistics Consulting Services
N.A.I.C.S.: 488510
Shigenori Kanazawa (Pres & CEO)

LOGLY, INC.
Unosawa-Tokyu Building 7F 1-19-15 Ebisu, Shibuya-ku, Tokyo, 150-0013, Japan
Tel.: (81) 337703287
Web Site: https://corp.logly.co.jp
Year Founded: 2006
6579—(TKS)
Rev.: $13,576,940
Assets: $9,796,020
Liabilities: $5,327,660
Net Worth: $4,468,360
Earnings: ($304,060)
Emp.: 48
Fiscal Year-end: 03/31/24
Advertising & Marketing Services
N.A.I.C.S.: 541810
Hirokazu Yoshinaga (Founder, Pres & CEO)

LOGNET SYSTEMS
Ha Kidma 7, Yokneam, 203900, Israel
Tel.: (972) 49598700
Web Site: http://www.lognet-systems.com
Year Founded: 2001
Customer Management & Billing Solutions
N.A.I.C.S.: 541519
Yigal Goodman (CFO)

LOGO YAZILIM SANAYI VE TICARET A.S.
Gebze Organize Sanayi Bolgesi Sahabettin Bilgisu Caddesi No 609, 41400, Gebze, 41400, Kocaeli, Turkiye
Tel.: (90) 2626798000
Web Site: https://www.logo.com.tr
LOGO—(IST)
Rev.: $47,612,423
Assets: $82,372,720
Liabilities: $45,343,948
Net Worth: $37,028,772
Earnings: $13,107,442
Emp.: 1,507
Fiscal Year-end: 12/31/22
Software Development Services
N.A.I.C.S.: 541511
Tugrul Tekbulut (Chm)

Subsidiaries:

Elba Hr Insan Kaynaklari Egitim Ve Danismanlik A.S.
ITU Teknokent ARI 4, Building No 2 / 50 / 6 34467 Sariyer, Istanbul, Turkiye
Tel.: (90) 4445646
Medical Consulting Services
N.A.I.C.S.: 541611

Logo Infosoft Business Technology Private Limited (1)
Second Floor Raghu Leela Mall Arcade Vishwaroop Infotech Pvt Ltd, Plot No 34 35 38 Next to Mc Donalds Navi Mumbai, Vashi, 400703, Maharashtra, India
Tel.: (91) 8433733535
Web Site: https://jplatform.in
Software Development Services
N.A.I.C.S.: 541511

Logo Kobi Dijital Hizmetler A.S. (1)
Degirmenyolu Street Gulseren Murat Third Business Center No 35 Floor 7, Atasehir Icerenkoy District, 34752, Istanbul, Turkiye
Tel.: (90) 8502818800
Web Site: http://www.isbasi.com
Software Publishing Services
N.A.I.C.S.: 513210
Cahit Guvensoy (Mng Partner)

Total Soft S.A. (1)
Global City Business Park 10 Bucuresti-Nord Road Building O2 8th Floor, Ilfov, 077190, Voluntari, Romania
Tel.: (40) 213351709
Software Publisher Services
N.A.I.C.S.: 513210

Subsidiary (Domestic):

Architected Business Solutions SRL (2)
19 Eroii Sanitari Blvd, District 5, 050471, Bucharest, Romania
Tel.: (40) 212431296
Web Site: https://www.abs-europe.com
Business Management Consulting Services
N.A.I.C.S.: 541618

LOGORY LOGISTICS TECHNOLOGY CO., LTD.
No 2700 Chuangxin Avenue, Hightech District, Hefei, Anhui, China
Tel.: (86) 55162757168 CN
Web Site: https://www.logory.com
Year Founded: 2010
2482—(HKG)
Rev.: $950,587,308
Assets: $332,923,032
Liabilities: $247,969,159
Net Worth: $84,953,873
Earnings: $213,422
Emp.: 1,020
Fiscal Year-end: 12/31/22
Information Technology Services
N.A.I.C.S.: 541512
Bing Du (CEO)

LOGYCOM JSC
8 Aralskaya Street, 050056, Almaty, Kazakhstan
Tel.: (7) 7272275822
Web Site: https://www.logycom.kz
LOGC—(KAZ)
Rev.: $84,343,958
Assets: $123,920,525
Liabilities: $105,445,374
Net Worth: $18,475,151
Earnings: $2,084,348
Fiscal Year-end: 12/31/22
IT Products & Services
N.A.I.C.S.: 541519

LOH & LOH CORPORATION BERHAD
19 21 23 & 25 Jalan Sri Hartamas 7, Tamam Sri Hartamas, 50480, Kuala Lumpur, Malaysia
Tel.: (60) 3 6201 3888
Web Site: http://www.llc-bhd.com
Sales Range: $75-99.9 Million
Emp.: 80
Civil & Structural Engineering Services
N.A.I.C.S.: 541330
Loh Choon Quan (Mng Dir)

Subsidiaries:

Loh & Loh Construction Sdn Bhd (1)
19 & 21 Jalan Sri Hartamas 7, Taman Sri Hartamas, 50480, Kuala Lumpur, Malaysia
Tel.: (60) 6201 3888
Construction Services
N.A.I.C.S.: 237990

Water Engineering Technology Sdn Bhd (1)
No 20 Jalan Astaka U8/83 Seksyen U8, Bukit Jelutong, Shah Alam, 40150, Selangor Darul Ehsan, Malaysia
Tel.: (60) 3 7846 9888
Web Site: http://www.wetsb.com
Emp.: 850
Water Supply Engineering
N.A.I.C.S.: 221310
Tan Swee Heng (COO)

LOHA CO., LTD.
Room 818 Yisibo Software Building Haitian 2nd Road, Nanshan District, Shenzhen, 518000, Guangdong, China
Tel.: (86) 75533093707 Ky
Web Site: http://www.lohas.sh
Year Founded: 2019
Rev.: $85,186,000
Assets: $34,849,000
Liabilities: $6,647,000
Net Worth: $28,202,000
Earnings: $8,781,000
Emp.: 70
Fiscal Year-end: 09/30/18
Holding Company
N.A.I.C.S.: 551112
Yanyue Zhang (Founder, Chm & CEO)

LOHAKIT METAL PUBLIC COMPANY LIMITED
43 Thai CC Tower Rm 167-169 16th Floor South Sathorn Rd, Sathorn, Bangkok, 10120, Thailand
Tel.: (66) 26739559
Web Site: https://www.lohakit.co.th
Year Founded: 1989
LHK—(THA)
Rev.: $73,076,164
Assets: $54,891,802
Liabilities: $13,413,087
Net Worth: $41,478,715
Earnings: $3,304,128
Emp.: 187
Fiscal Year-end: 03/31/24
Steel Products Mfr
N.A.I.C.S.: 331110
Prasarn Akarapongpisak (CEO)

Subsidiaries:

Alternative Stainless Company Limited (1)
66/1 Moo 6 Soi Suksawas 76 Suksawas Road Bangjak, Prapradang, Samut Prakan, 10130, Thailand
Tel.: (66) 2463 0158
Web Site: http://www.d-stainless.co.th
Steel Product Distr
N.A.I.C.S.: 423510

Ngeck Seng Chiang Metal Co., Ltd (1)
108/8 Sripraya River View Condominium 1st Fl Yotha Road TaladNoi, Samphanthawong, Bangkok, 10100, Thailand
Tel.: (66) 2693 4151
Web Site: http://www.nscmetal.com
Steel Product Distr
N.A.I.C.S.: 423510

LOHIA CORP. LIMITED
D-3/A Panki Industrial Estate, Kanpur, 208022, India
Tel.: (91) 5122691221
Web Site: http://www.lohiagroup.com
Year Founded: 1981
Engineering Products & Services
N.A.I.C.S.: 326199
Anurag Lohia (Dir)

Subsidiaries:

Light & Strong, Ltd. (1)
38 Ha'adom Street Kanot Industrial Zone, PO Box 7042, 7070000, Gedera, Israel
Tel.: (972) 8 9333110
Web Site: http://www.light-and-strong.com
Sales Range: $1-9.9 Million
Composite Materials Mfr
N.A.I.C.S.: 325998
Gal Erez (Chm)

LOHIA SECURITIES LTD
4 Brabourne Road 5th Floor Passport Building, Kolkata, 700 001, India
Tel.: (91) 3340026600
Web Site: http://www.lohiasecurities.com
590082—(BOM)
Rev.: $29,579,018
Assets: $16,281,766
Liabilities: $5,822,909
Net Worth: $10,458,857
Earnings: $2,960,455
Emp.: 282
Fiscal Year-end: 03/31/23
Financial Services
N.A.I.C.S.: 541611
Narendra Kumar Rai (Compliance Officer)

Subsidiaries:

Trade City Barter Private Limited (1)

Trade City Real Estate Private Limited (1)
4 Biplabi Trailokya Maharaj Sarani 5th Floor, Kolkata, 700 001, India
Tel.: (91) 3340026600
Web Site: http://www.lohiasecurities.com
Rev.: $15,190
Assets: $906,471
Liabilities: $230,385
Net Worth: $676,087
Earnings: ($28,268)
Fiscal Year-end: 03/31/2018
Investment Banking & Security Dealing Services
N.A.I.C.S.: 523150

Trade City Securities Private Limited (1)
1602B Lady Ratan Tower 72 Dainik Shivner Marg Gandhi Nagar Worli, Mumbai, 400 018, India
Tel.: (91) 2222610552
Web Site: http://www.tradecity.biz
Rev.: $12,292
Assets: $359,060
Liabilities: $43,892
Net Worth: $315,168
Earnings: ($11,110)
Fiscal Year-end: 03/31/2018
Investment Banking & Security Dealing Services
N.A.I.C.S.: 523150
Natwar Lal Agarwal (Sec)

LOHILO FOODS AB
Hejaregatan 30, 352 46, Vaxjo, Sweden
Tel.: (46) 470729178
Web Site: https://www.lohilofoods.com
Year Founded: 1979
LOHILO—(OMX)
Rev.: $18,080,291
Assets: $8,243,493
Liabilities: $6,666,071
Net Worth: $1,577,422
Earnings: ($2,890,782)
Emp.: 23
Fiscal Year-end: 12/31/23
Food Products Mfr
N.A.I.C.S.: 311412
Daniel Broman (CFO)

LOHMANN & RAUSCHER INTERNATIONAL GMBH & CO. KG
Irlicher Strasse 55, 56567, Neuwied, Germany
Tel.: (49) 2634 99 0 De
Web Site: http://www.lohmann-rauscher.com
Year Founded: 1998
Emp.: 4,000
Holding Company Medical Devices & Hygiene Products Mfr & Whslr
N.A.I.C.S.: 551112

Subsidiaries:

L&R Medical UK Ltd. (1)
1 Wellington Court Lancaster Park, Needwood, Burton-on-Trent, DE13 9PS, Staffordshire, United Kingdom
Tel.: (44) 1283576800

LOHMANN & RAUSCHER INTERNATIONAL GMBH & CO. KG

Lohmann & Rauscher International GmbH & Co. KG—(Continued)
Web Site: http://www.lohmann-rauscher.co.uk
Medical Device Mfr & Distr
N.A.I.C.S.: 339112

L&R USA INC. (1)
3880 W Wheelhouse Rd, Milwaukee, WI 53208
Tel.: (414) 892-4140
Medical Device Mfr & Distr
N.A.I.C.S.: 339112
Jodi Loeffler (Dir-Customer Svc)

Laboratoires Lohmann & Rauscher s.a. (1)
Rue Vise-Voie 81 - Boite 2, 4000, Liege, Belgium
Tel.: (32) 43679711
Surgical & Medical Product Distr
N.A.I.C.S.: 423450

Lohmann & Rauscher A/S (1)
Hjnaesgaard Gongehusvej 252, 2950, Vedbaek, Denmark
Tel.: (45) 45890225
Surgical & Medical Product Distr
N.A.I.C.S.: 423450

Lohmann & Rauscher AB (1)
Gronegatan 1C 1tr, 22224, Lund, Sweden
Tel.: (46) 46328900
Surgical & Medical Product Mfr
N.A.I.C.S.: 339113

Lohmann & Rauscher AG (1)
Oberstrasse 222, 9014, Saint Gallen, Switzerland
Tel.: (41) 712742570
Surgical & Medical Product Mfr
N.A.I.C.S.: 339113
Urs Eisenring (Mng Dir)

Lohmann & Rauscher B.V. (1)
Antennestraat 86-B, 1322 AS, Almere, Netherlands
Tel.: (31) 365463020
Surgical & Medical Product Distr
N.A.I.C.S.: 423450

Lohmann & Rauscher China Medical Products Co., Ltd. (1)
Room 2207-2208 Changfeng Center No 1088 Yanan West Road, Changning District, Shanghai, 200052, China
Tel.: (86) 2162123679
Medical Device Retailer
N.A.I.C.S.: 423450

Lohmann & Rauscher GmbH (1)
Kirchengasse 17, 2525, Schonau an der Triesting, Austria
Tel.: (43) 1576700
Surgical & Medical Product Distr
N.A.I.C.S.: 423450

Lohmann & Rauscher GmbH & Co. KG (1)
Irlicher Strasse 55, 56567, Neuwied, Germany
Tel.: (49) 2634 99 0
Web Site: http://www.lohmann-rauscher.com
Medical Devices & Hygiene Products Mfr & Whslr
N.A.I.C.S.: 339113
Wolfgang Sussle (Pres, CEO, Chief Comml Officer & Member-Exec Bd)

Subsidiary (US):

Lohmann & Rauscher, Inc. (2)
6001 SW 6th Ave Ste 101, Topeka, KS 66615-1004
Tel.: (785) 862-1100
Web Site: http://www.lohmann-rauscher.us
Medical Devices & Supplies Mfr & Whslr
N.A.I.C.S.: 423450
Gary Keytel (Pres)

Subsidiary (Domestic):

Solaris, Inc. (3)
6737 W Washington St Ste 3260, West Allis, WI 53214
Tel.: (414) 918-9180
Web Site: http://www.solarismed.com
Medical Compression Bandage & Garment Mfr
N.A.I.C.S.: 315250

Jianne Wade (Dir-Design)

Lohmann & Rauscher Middle East DMCC (1)
Cluster N JBC 4 Office 2604/2605 Jumeirah Lakes Towers, PO Box 336 351, Dubai, United Arab Emirates
Tel.: (971) 44424621
Medical Device Mfr & Distr
N.A.I.C.S.: 339112
Salim Bouzidi (Mng Dir)

Lohmann & Rauscher Polska Sp. z o.o. (1)
ul Moniuszki 14, 95-200, Pabianice, Poland
Tel.: (48) 422155837
Surgical & Medical Product Distr
N.A.I.C.S.: 423450

Lohmann & Rauscher Pty. Ltd. (1)
321 Ferntree Gully Road, Mount Waverley, 3149, VIC, Australia
Tel.: (61) 1300572869
Medical Device Mfr & Distr
N.A.I.C.S.: 339112
Leon Hoare (Mng Dir)

Lohmann & Rauscher S.A.S. (1)
Chemin du Canal Z A de Choisy, 88200, Remiremont, France
Tel.: (33) 329623606
Surgical & Medical Product Distr
N.A.I.C.S.: 423450

Lohmann & Rauscher S.a.r.l. (1)
15 rue Saria Ben Zounaim Residence EN-NAS Quartier Palmier, Casablanca, Morocco
Tel.: (212) 2299127080
Medical Device Whslr
N.A.I.C.S.: 423450

Lohmann & Rauscher Tunisie s.a.r.l. (1)
Centre Urbain Nord Residence etoile du Nord Bloc B Apt No 5, Tunis, Tunisia
Tel.: (216) 71947135
Medical Device Whslr
N.A.I.C.S.: 423450
Atef Boutej (Country Mgr)

Lohmann & Rauscher d.o.o. (1)
Oreskoviceva 10a, 10010, Zagreb, Croatia
Tel.: (385) 16609543
Surgical & Medical Product Distr
N.A.I.C.S.: 423450

Lohmann & Rauscher s.r.l. (1)
Via E Fermi 4 Sarmeola di, 35030, Rubano, Italy
Tel.: (39) 0498976244
Surgical & Medical Product Distr
N.A.I.C.S.: 423450

Lohmann & Rauscher s.r.o. (1)
Jarosova 1, 831 03, Bratislava, Slovakia
Tel.: (421) 254777419
Medical Device Mfr & Distr
N.A.I.C.S.: 339112

Lohmann & Rauscher, s.l.o. (1)
C v Skoke 11, 2204, Maribor, Slovenia
Tel.: (386) 26296474
Surgical & Medical Product Distr
N.A.I.C.S.: 423450

Lohmann & Rauscher, s.r.o. (1)
Bucovicka 256, 68401, Slavkov u Brna, Czech Republic
Tel.: (420) 544425601
Surgical & Medical Product Distr
N.A.I.C.S.: 423450

LOHMANN GMBH & CO. KG
Irlicher Strasse 55, 56567, Neuwied, Germany
Tel.: (49) 2631340 De
Web Site: http://www.lohmann-tapes.com
Year Founded: 1851
Sales Range: $400-449.9 Million
Emp.: 1,600
Adhesives & Bonding Products Mfr
N.A.I.C.S.: 325520
Christina Barg-Becker (Head-Mktg, Comm & PR)

Subsidiaries:

Lohmann Adhesive Tape Technologies (Tianjin) Co., Ltd (1)

No 231 Mu Ning Road, Tianjin, 300457, China
Tel.: (86) 22 25328808
Web Site: http://www.lohmann-lttt.com.cn
Adhesive Mfr
N.A.I.C.S.: 325520
Hansson Yin (Mgr-Product Mgmt)

Lohmann Adhesive Tapes India Pvt. Ltd. (1)
Plot No OZ - 15 Hi Tech SEZ SIPCOT Industrial Growth Centre, Oragadam Mathur Village Sriperumbudur, Kanchipuram, 602 105, Tamil Nadu, India
Tel.: (91) 44 6714 1117
Adhesive Distr
N.A.I.C.S.: 424690
H. Vinodh (Mng Dir)

Lohmann Asia Pacific Pte. Ltd. (1)
20 Sing Ming Lane 07-54, Midview City, Singapore, 573968, Singapore
Tel.: (65) 6440 8551
Web Site: http://www.lohmann-tapes.com
Adhesive Distr
N.A.I.C.S.: 424690
Michael Boerner (Bus Mgr-South East Asia, Australia & New Zealand)

Lohmann Danmark ApS (1)
Kurreholmvej 33E, 3330, Gorlose, Denmark
Tel.: (45) 48106080
Web Site: http://www.lohmann-tapes.dk
Emp.: 6
Adhesive Mfr
N.A.I.C.S.: 325520
Norman Goldberg (CEO)

Lohmann France S.A.S. (1)
Allee des Marronniers Ecoparc, PO Box 706, 27407, Louviers, Cedex, France
Tel.: (33) 232 092323
Web Site: http://www.lohmann-tapes.fr
Adhesive Mfr
N.A.I.C.S.: 325520

Lohmann Italia s.r.l. (1)
Via Thomas A Edison 3/G, 31020, Villorba, Treviso, Italy
Tel.: (39) 0 422 911663
Web Site: http://www.lohmann-tapes.it
Adhesive Mfr
N.A.I.C.S.: 325520

Lohmann Klebebandsysteme Ges.m.b.H. (1)
Wiener Strasse 28, 2000, Stockerau, Austria
Tel.: (43) 2266 62050 0
Web Site: http://www.lohmann-tapes.at
Emp.: 40
Adhesive Mfr
N.A.I.C.S.: 325520
Markus Koch (Mng Dir)

Lohmann Korea Co. Ltd. (1)
C-1105 Poonglim I-want Plus 255-1 Seohyun-dong, Bundang-gu, Seongnam, 463-862, Gyeonggi-do, Korea (South)
Tel.: (82) 31 783 7441
Web Site: http://www.lohmann-papes.com
Adhesive Distr
N.A.I.C.S.: 424690
Sang Do Hah (Mng Dir)

Lohmann Netherlands BV (1)
De Trompet 1930, 1967 DB, Heemskerk, Netherlands
Tel.: (31) 251 257000
Web Site: http://www.lohmann-tapes.nl
Adhesive Mfr
N.A.I.C.S.: 325520

Lohmann Nordic AB (1)
Backvagen 34, 463 24, Vastra Gotaland, Sweden
Tel.: (46) 10 206 48 00
Web Site: http://www.lohmann-nordic.se
Emp.: 15
Adhesive Mfr
N.A.I.C.S.: 325520
Andreas Eklund (Mng Dir)

Lohmann Polska Sp. z o.o. (1)
ul Budowlanych 64, 80-298, Gdansk, Poland
Tel.: (48) 58 555 81 50
Web Site: http://www.lohmann-tapes.pl
Adhesive Mfr
N.A.I.C.S.: 325520

INTERNATIONAL PUBLIC

Leszek Pykosz (Mng Dir)

Lohmann Precision Die Cutting, LLC (1)
1766 Junction Ave, San Jose, CA 95112
Tel.: (408) 453-9400
Adhesive Distr
N.A.I.C.S.: 424690

Lohmann Spain S.A. (1)
Calle Miquel Torello i Pages 38 Poligono Industrial El Pla, 08750, Barcelona, Spain
Tel.: (34) 93 666 71 01
Web Site: http://www.lohmann-tapes.es
Adhesive Mfr
N.A.I.C.S.: 325520
Juan Plaza (Dir-Comml)

Lohmann Specialty Coatings LLC (1)
14218 Litchfield Dr, Orange, VA 22960
Tel.: (540) 661-0308
Adhesive Distr
N.A.I.C.S.: 424690
Steven Dejong (Pres)

Lohmann Technologies Corp. (1)
3000 Earhart Ct Ste 155, Hebron, KY 41048
Tel.: (859) 334-4900
Web Site: http://www.lohmanncorp.com
Sales Range: $25-49.9 Million
Emp.: 110
Coated & Laminated Paper Mfr
N.A.I.C.S.: 322220
Bill Payne (Dir-Sls & Mktg)

Lohmann Technologies UK Ltd. (1)
25 Kelvin Drive, Milton Keynes, MK5 8NH, United Kingdom
Tel.: (44) 1296 337888
Web Site: http://www.lohmann-tapes.co.uk
Adhesive Mfr
N.A.I.C.S.: 325520
Jeremy Parfitt (Mgr-Sls & Transportation)

Lohmann Turkey Yapistirici Bantlar Sanayi ve Ticaret Limited Sirketi (1)
Barbaros Mahallesi Halk Caddesi No 8/A Palladium Alisveris Merkezi No, Residance Kat 2 Atasehir, 34746, Istanbul, Turkiye
Tel.: (90) 216 663 6014
Adhesive Distr
N.A.I.C.S.: 424690

Lohmann Ukraina TOV (1)
34 Chervonopraporna street Office 1, 03680, Kiev, Ukraine
Tel.: (380) 44 537 03 20
Web Site: http://www.lohmann-tapes.ua
Adhesive Mfr
N.A.I.C.S.: 325520

Lohmann-koester GmbH & Co. KG (1)
Industriestrasse 2, 96146, Berlin, Germany
Tel.: (49) 9545 48 0
Adhesive Mfr
N.A.I.C.S.: 325520

Subsidiary (Non-US):

Lohmann-koester Asia Pacific Co. Ltd. (2)
Room 608 Building B Far East International Plaza No 317 Xianxia Road, Shanghai, 200051, China
Tel.: (86) 21 62351499
Adhesive Distr
N.A.I.C.S.: 424690

Lohmann-koester S. de R.L. de C.V. (2)
Av Juan Gil Preciado 2450 Nave 11-12 Parque Ind, Ecopark Col El Tigre, 45134, Zapopan, Jalisco, Mexico
Tel.: (52) 33 316 56 600
Adhesive Distr
N.A.I.C.S.: 424690

OOO Lohmann Rus (1)
Sofiyskaya ulitsa 72, 192289, Saint Petersburg, Russia
Tel.: (7) 8124483404
Web Site: http://www.lohmann-tapes.ru
Adhesive Mfr
N.A.I.C.S.: 325520

LOJAS HERING S/A
R Xv de Novembro 759 - 3 Floor,

89010902, Blumenau, SC, Brazil
Tel.: (55) 47 3035 3000
Web Site:
http://www.lojasheringsa.com.br
Sales Range: $1-9.9 Million
Emp.: 8
Apparel Whslr
N.A.I.C.S.: 424310
Ademar Klemz *(VP & Dir-IR)*

LOJAS RENNER S.A.
Av Joaquim Porto Villanova 401,
Porto Alegre, 91410-000, RS, Brazil
Tel.: (55) 5121217045   BR
Web Site:
https://www.lojasrennersa.com.br
Year Founded: 1965
LREN3—(BRAZ)
Rev.: $2,439,686,212
Assets: $3,662,901,531
Liabilities: $1,866,862,716
Net Worth: $1,796,038,815
Earnings: $174,515,825
Fiscal Year-end: 12/31/23
Holding Company; Retail Family Clothing Department Stores Owner & Operator
N.A.I.C.S.: 551112
Clarice Martins Costa *(Chief HR Officer)*

LOKESH MACHINES LTD
B-29 EEIE Stage-II Balanagar, Hyderabad, 500 037, Telangana, India
Tel.: (91) 4023079310
Web Site:
https://www.lokeshmachines.com
532740—(BOM)
Rev.: $27,663,035
Assets: $40,153,645
Liabilities: $19,781,566
Net Worth: $20,372,079
Earnings: $866,229
Emp.: 388
Fiscal Year-end: 03/31/22
Machine Tools Design, Development & Production
N.A.I.C.S.: 333517
K. Krishna Swamy *(Exec Dir-Technical)*

LOKMAN HEKIM ENGURUSAG SAGLIK TURIZM EGITIM HIZMETLERI VE INSAAT TAAHHUT A.S.
Zubeyde Hanim Mah Aslanbey Cad No 17 Iskitler Altindag, Ankara, Turkiye
Tel.: (90) 3125897000
Web Site:
http://www.lokmanhekim.com.tr
Year Founded: 1996
LKMNH—(IST)
Rev.: $64,194,851
Assets: $77,447,119
Liabilities: $32,485,241
Net Worth: $44,961,878
Earnings: $11,249,969
Emp.: 2,240
Fiscal Year-end: 12/31/23
Health Care Srvices
N.A.I.C.S.: 621999
Mustafa Sarioglu *(Chm)*

LOKUM DEWELOPER SA
ul Krawiecka 1 lok 101, 50-148, Wroclaw, Poland
Tel.: (48) 717966666
Web Site: https://lokumdeweloper.pl
Year Founded: 2004
LKD—(WAR)
Rev.: $114,661,585
Assets: $213,320,884
Liabilities: $75,728,658
Net Worth: $137,592,225

Earnings: $36,168,953
Fiscal Year-end: 12/31/23
Real Estate Manangement Services
N.A.I.C.S.: 531390
Bartosz Kuzniar *(Chm & Pres)*

LOLC HOLDINGS PLC
No 100 1 Sri Jayawardenapura Mawatha, Rajagirya, Sri Lanka
Tel.: (94) 0115880880
Web Site: https://www.lolc.com
Year Founded: 1980
Sales Range: $150-199.9 Million
Emp.: 500
Equipment Leasing Services
N.A.I.C.S.: 532490

Subsidiaries:

Eden Hotel Lanka PLC   (1)
100/1 Sri Jayawardenepura Mawatha, Rajagiriya, Colombo, Sri Lanka   **(88.92%)**
Tel.: (94) 115880880
Web Site: http://www.confifihotels.com
Rev.: $7,749,288
Assets: $228,740,417
Liabilities: $149,814,690
Net Worth: $78,925,727
Earnings: ($18,334,009)
Fiscal Year-end: 03/31/2023
Home Management Services
N.A.I.C.S.: 721110

Subsidiary (Domestic):

Serendib Hotels PLC   (2)
Hemas House 75 Braybrooke Place, Colombo, 02, Sri Lanka   **(56%)**
Tel.: (94) 114790500
Web Site: http://www.serendibleisure.com
Rev.: $4,799,855
Assets: $29,628,652
Liabilities: $11,996,197
Net Worth: $17,632,455
Earnings: ($1,503,201)
Emp.: 713
Fiscal Year-end: 03/31/2023
Hotel & Restaurant Operator
N.A.I.C.S.: 721110

LOLLANDS BANK A/S
Nybrogade 3, 4900, Nakskov, 4900, Denmark
Tel.: (45) 54921133
Web Site:
https://www.lollandsbank.dk
LOLB—(CSE)
Rev.: $27,920,302
Assets: $700,248,875
Liabilities: $595,103,529
Net Worth: $105,145,346
Earnings: $8,198,405
Emp.: 110
Fiscal Year-end: 12/31/22
Banking Services
N.A.I.C.S.: 522110
Allan Aaskov *(CEO)*

LOM FINANCIAL LIMITED
The LOM Building 27 Reid Street, Hamilton, HM 11, Bermuda
Tel.: (441) 2925000   BM
Web Site: https://www.lom.com
Year Founded: 1996
LOM.BH—(BERM)
Rev.: $18,281,932
Assets: $36,306,845
Liabilities: $1,655,265
Net Worth: $34,651,580
Earnings: $1,883,951
Emp.: 50
Fiscal Year-end: 12/31/22
Holding Company; Financial & Investment Services
N.A.I.C.S.: 551112
Scott Hill *(Mng Dir & Exec VP)*

Subsidiaries:

LOM (UK) Limited   (1)
6th Floor City Point Temple Gate, Bristol, BS1 6PL, United Kingdom
Tel.: (44) 1179254777

Administrative Management Services
N.A.I.C.S.: 541611
Justin Cornell *(CIO)*

LOM Asset Management Limited   (1)
The LOM Building 27 Reid Street, Hamilton, HM 11, Bermuda
Tel.: (441) 2925000
Web Site: https://www.lom.com
Asset Management Services
N.A.I.C.S.: 541611

LOM Capital Limited   (1)
The LOM Building 27 Reid Street, Hamilton, HM 11, Bermuda
Tel.: (441) 292 5000
Web Site: http://www.lom.com
Sales Range: $50-74.9 Million
Emp.: 20
Corporate Financial Services
N.A.I.C.S.: 523999

LOM Financial (Bahamas) Limited   (1)
LOM House 3 Pineapple Grove Old Fort Bay Rd, Nassau, Bahamas
Tel.: (242) 3275100
Financial Banking Services
N.A.I.C.S.: 522110
Craig D. Lines *(Pres)*

LOM Securities (Bahamas) Ltd.   (1)
Centre of Commerce 1 Bay Street Suite 309, PO Box AP59223 SL# 0436, Nassau, Bahamas
Tel.: (242) 323 0032
Investment Services
N.A.I.C.S.: 523940

LOM Securities (Bermuda) Ltd.   (1)
The LOM Building 27 Reid Street, Hamilton, HM 11, Bermuda
Tel.: (441) 292 5000
Investment Services
N.A.I.C.S.: 523940

LOMA NEGRA COMPANIA INDUSTRIAL ARGENTINA SOCIEDAD ANONIMA
25 Harbour Road, C1107CPG, Buenos Aires, Argentina
Tel.: (54) 1143193048   Ar
Web Site:
https://www.lomanegra.com
Year Founded: 1926
LOMA—(NYSE)
Rev.: $1,725,626,780
Assets: $2,412,402,728
Liabilities: $1,033,790,080
Net Worth: $1,378,612,648
Earnings: $21,483,791
Emp.: 2,886
Fiscal Year-end: 12/31/22
Cement Mfr
N.A.I.C.S.: 327310
Sergio Damian Faifman *(Pres & CEO)*

Subsidiaries:

Recycomb S.A.U.   (1)
Ruta 205 km82 Acceso Uribelarrea, Buenos Aires, Argentina
Tel.: (54) 2226493049
Web Site: https://www.recycomb.com.ar
Waste Energy Recovery Services
N.A.I.C.S.: 562998

LOMAK INDUSTRIAL CO. LTD.
188 202 Texaco Rd 14F Phase 1 Leader Industrial Ctr, Tsuen Wan, NT, China (Hong Kong)
Tel.: (852) 27568680
Web Site: http://www.lomak.com
Year Founded: 1976
Sales Range: $250-299.9 Million
Emp.: 1,350
Consumer Electronic Products, Lighting, Lighted Mirrors, Wine Coolers & Bath Accessories Mfr
N.A.I.C.S.: 335131
Eddie Lo Ying Hoi *(Founder & Mng Dir)*

LOMBARD BANK MALTA P.L.C.
67 Republic street, Valletta, VLT 1117, Malta
Tel.: (356) 25581117
Web Site:
https://www.lombard.com.mt
Year Founded: 1969
LOM—(MAL)
Rev.: $28,595,942
Assets: $1,298,742,715
Liabilities: $1,143,012,087
Net Worth: $155,730,628
Earnings: $19,022,232
Emp.: 942
Fiscal Year-end: 12/31/22
Banking Services
N.A.I.C.S.: 522110
Michael C. Bonello *(Chm)*

Subsidiaries:

MaltaPost Group P.L.C.   (1)
305 Triq Hal-Qormi, Marsa, 1001, Malta
Tel.: (356) 2 122 4421
Web Site: https://www.maltapost.com
Local Delivery Services
N.A.I.C.S.: 492210

Maltapost plc   (1)
Customer Care Department 305 Triq Hal-Qormi, Marsa, MTP 1001, Malta   **(67%)**
Tel.: (356) 21224421
Web Site: http://www.maltapost.com
Sales Range: $25-49.9 Million
Emp.: 637
Postal Service
N.A.I.C.S.: 491110
Joseph Gafa *(CEO)*

LOMBARD ET MEDOT SA
1 rue des Cotelles, BP 118, 51204, Epernay, France
Tel.: (33) 326595740
Web Site: https://www.champagne-lombard.com
MLCAC—(EUR)
Sales Range: $10-24.9 Million
Champagne Mfr
N.A.I.C.S.: 312130
Thierry Lombard *(Chm)*

LOMBARD MEDICAL, INC.
Lombard Medical House 4 Trident Park Basil Hill Road, Didcot, OX11 7HJ, Oxon, United Kingdom
Tel.: (44) 1 345 949 1040   Ky
Sales Range: $10-24.9 Million
Holding Company; Medical Products Mfr
N.A.I.C.S.: 551112

Subsidiaries:

Lombard Medical Technologies GmbH   (1)
Werner-Haas-Strasse 8, 86153, Augsburg, Germany
Tel.: (49) 171 522 4418
Medical Equipment Mfr
N.A.I.C.S.: 339112

Lombard Medical Technologies plc   (1)
Lombard Medical House 4 Trident Park, Didcot, OX11 7HJ, Oxfordshire, United Kingdom
Tel.: (44) 1235750800
Web Site: http://www.lombardmedical.com
Holding Company; Cardiovascular Medical Device Mfr
N.A.I.C.S.: 551112
Peter Phillips *(CTO)*

Subsidiary (Domestic):

Lombard Medical (Scotland) Limited (2)
6 Skye Road Shawfarm Industrial Park, Prestwick, KA9 2TA, S Ayrshire, United Kingdom
Tel.: (44) 1292 671763
Web Site: http://www.lombardmedical.com

LOMBARD MEDICAL, INC.

Lombard Medical, Inc.—(Continued)
Sales Range: $25-49.9 Million
Medical Fabric Products Mfr
N.A.I.C.S.: 339999

Subsidiary (US):

Lombard Medical Technologies, Inc. (2)
2050 E ASU Cir Ste 103, Tempe, AZ 85284
Tel.: (480) 289-7888
Web Site: http://www.lombardmedical.com
Sales Range: $25-49.9 Million
Cardiovascular Device Mfr
N.A.I.C.S.: 339112
Simon Hubbert (CEO)

LOMIKO METALS INC.
439 - 7184 120th Street, Surrey,
V3W 0M6, BC, Canada
Tel.: (778) 228-1170
Web Site: https://www.lomiko.com
Year Founded: 1987
LMRMF—(OTCQB)
Assets: $9,017,799
Liabilities: $391,731
Net Worth: $8,626,069
Earnings: ($1,357,808)
Fiscal Year-end: 07/31/21
Mineral Exploration Services
N.A.I.C.S.: 213114
A. Paul Gill (Chm)

Subsidiaries:

Lomiko Technologies Inc. (1)

LOMSKO PIVO AD
No 43 Al Stamboliiski str, 3600, Lom,
Bulgaria
Tel.: (359) 887498484
Web Site: https://www.lomskopivo.com
Year Founded: 1894
LOMP—(BUL)
Sales Range: Less than $1 Million
Beer Mfr
N.A.I.C.S.: 312120
Darin Iliev Dimitrov (Chm)

LONCIN MOTOR CO., LTD.
No 116 Juye road C area of Jiulong industrial park, Jiulongpo district,
Chongqing, 400052, China
Tel.: (86) 2389028829
Web Site: https://www.loncinindustries.com
Year Founded: 2007
603766—(SHG)
Rev.: $1,742,388,233
Assets: $1,766,992,083
Liabilities: $625,929,974
Net Worth: $1,141,062,109
Earnings: $74,036,247
Emp.: 10,000
Fiscal Year-end: 12/31/22
Motorcycle Mfr & Distr
N.A.I.C.S.: 336991
Ye Kejia (Sec)

LONCOR GOLD INC.
4120 Yonge Street Suite 304, Toronto, M2P 2B8, ON, Canada
Tel.: (416) 361-2510
Web Site: https://www.loncor.com
LO5—(DEU)
Rev.: $180,192
Assets: $42,888,714
Liabilities: $1,697,012
Net Worth: $41,191,702
Earnings: ($2,928,742)
Emp.: 26
Fiscal Year-end: 12/31/22
Gold Mining Services
N.A.I.C.S.: 212220
Arnold T. Kondrat (Founder & CEO)

LONDON & ASSOCIATED PROPERTIES PLC
12 Little Portland Street 2nd Floor,
London, W1W 8BJ, United Kingdom
Tel.: (44) 2074155000
Web Site: https://www.lap.co.uk
LAS—(LSE)
Rev.: $120,739,080
Assets: $143,239,140
Liabilities: $78,533,400
Net Worth: $64,705,740
Earnings: $25,499,265
Fiscal Year-end: 12/31/22
Property Investment & Development Services
N.A.I.C.S.: 531390
Michael A. Heller (Chm)

Subsidiaries:

Orchard Square Limited (1)
1 Orchard Square, Sheffield, S1 2FB, South Yorkshire, United Kingdom
Tel.: (44) 1142759992
Web Site: https://orchardsquare.co.uk
Personal Care Services
N.A.I.C.S.: 812990

LONDON & REGIONAL PROPERTIES LIMITED
55 Baker Street, London, W1U 8EW,
United Kingdom
Tel.: (44) 207 563 9000
Web Site: http://www.lrp.co.uk
Property Development Services
N.A.I.C.S.: 531190
Richard Luck (Dir-Fin)

LONDON AND ST. LAWRENCE INVESTMENT COMPANY PLC
Fair Lorna House Buckingham Road,
Singleborough, Milton Keynes, MK17 0RB, United Kingdom
Tel.: (44) 1296 711598
Web Site: http://www.londonstlawrence.com
Sales Range: $1-9.9 Million
Emp.: 1
Investment Services
N.A.I.C.S.: 523999

Subsidiaries:

Consistent Unit Trust Management Co. Ltd. (1)
Customer Service Centre, PO Box 10117, Chelmsford, CM1 9JB, Essex, United Kingdom
Tel.: (44) 845 026 4281
Web Site: http://www.consistentunittrust.co.uk
Investment Management Service
N.A.I.C.S.: 523999

LONDON BISCUITS BERHAD
1 Jalan Istimewa 2 Taman Perindustrian Desa Cemerlang, 81800, Ulu Tiram, Johor, Malaysia
Tel.: (60) 78615288
Web Site: http://www.londonbiscuits.com.my
LONBISC—(KLS)
Biscuit Mfr
N.A.I.C.S.: 311821
Leong Ching Sen (Co-Sec)

LONDON CAPITAL GROUP HOLDINGS PLC
77 Grosvenor Street Mayfair, London, W1K 3JR, United Kingdom
Tel.: (44) 2074567020
Web Site: http://www.lcg.com
Year Founded: 1990
Rev.: $29,140,588
Assets: $27,009,145
Liabilities: $10,902,958
Net Worth: $16,106,187
Earnings: ($9,750,725)
Emp.: 86
Fiscal Year-end: 12/31/16
Financial Management Services
N.A.I.C.S.: 523999

LONDON CAPITAL GROUP LIMITED
80 Cheapside, London, EC2V 6EE,
United Kingdom
Tel.: (44) 2074567000
Web Site: http://www.londoncapitalgroup.com
Online Financial Trading Services
N.A.I.C.S.: 522299
Mukid Chowdhury (CEO)

LONDON CITY EQUITIES LIMITED
Suite 212 Level 2 111 Harrington Street, Sydney, 2000, NSW, Australia
Tel.: (61) 292479315
Web Site: http://www.londoncity.com.au
LCE—(ASX)
Rev.: $832,773
Assets: $17,770,150
Liabilities: $3,455,716
Net Worth: $14,314,434
Earnings: ($4,328)
Fiscal Year-end: 06/30/24
Investment Services
N.A.I.C.S.: 523940
Peter E. J. Murray (Chm & COO)

LONDON CITY PLYMOUTH CHRYSLER (1995) LTD
1345 Driver Lane, London, N5V 0B4,
ON, Canada
Tel.: (519) 659-2489
Web Site: http://www.londoncitychrysler.com
Year Founded: 1995
Emp.: 16
New & Used Car Dealers
N.A.I.C.S.: 441110
Lisa Putman (Office Mgr)

LONDON DRUGS LIMITED
12831 Horseshoe Place, Richmond, V7A 4X5, BC, Canada
Tel.: (604) 272-7400
Web Site: https://www.londondrugs.com
Year Founded: 1945
Sales Range: $900-999.9 Million
Emp.: 6,000
Pharmacy Operator
N.A.I.C.S.: 456110
Brandt C. Louie (Chm & CEO)

LONDON FINANCE & INVESTMENT GROUP P.L.C.
25 Southampton Buildings Central Court, London, WC2A 1AL, United Kingdom
Tel.: (44) 2037098741
Web Site: https://www.city-group.com
Sales Range: $1-9.9 Million
Investment Finance & Management Services
N.A.I.C.S.: 921130
Edward Beale (CEO-City Group)

Subsidiaries:

City Group PLC (1)
1 Ely Place, London, EC1N 6RY, United Kingdom
Tel.: (44) 2077969060
Web Site: http://www.city-group.com
Secretarial Services
N.A.I.C.S.: 561499
Rod Venables (Head-Company Secretarial Dept)

LONDON MINING PLC
Nations House 103 Wigmore Street,
London, W1U 1QS, United Kingdom
Tel.: (44) 2074087500
Web Site: http://www.londonmining.com
Sales Range: $250-299.9 Million
Emp.: 1,450
Iron Ore & Other Metal Mining Services
N.A.I.C.S.: 212210
Thomas Credland (Head-IR)

LONDON PHILHARMONIC ORCHESTRA
89 Albert Embankment, London, SE1 7TP, United Kingdom
Tel.: (44) 2078404200
Web Site: http://www.lpo.org.uk
Year Founded: 1932
Sales Range: $50-74.9 Million
Emp.: 120
Symphony Orchestra
N.A.I.C.S.: 711130
Timothy Walker (CEO & Dir-Artistic)

LONDON SECURITY PLC
Premier House 2 Jubilee Way, Elland, HX5 9DY, West Yorkshire,
United Kingdom
Tel.: (44) 1422372852
Web Site: https://www.londonsecurity.org
Year Founded: 1897
LSC—(AIM)
Rev.: $238,447,362
Assets: $247,263,317
Liabilities: $63,148,195
Net Worth: $184,115,122
Earnings: $25,502,398
Emp.: 1,406
Fiscal Year-end: 12/31/22
Holding Company; Fire Protection Products & Services
N.A.I.C.S.: 551112
Jacques Gaston Murray (Chm)

Subsidiaries:

A.L.P.I. sarl (1)
10 rue Robert Krieps, L-4702, Petange, Luxembourg
Tel.: (352) 26313013
Web Site: https://www.alpi.lu
Emp.: 14
Fire Protection Installation Services
N.A.I.C.S.: 922160

All-Protec N.V. (1)
Kirchstrasse 42, 4710, Lontzen, Orientale, Belgium
Tel.: (32) 93752044
Web Site: https://www.all-protec.be
Sales Range: $50-74.9 Million
Emp.: 5
Fire Safety Services
N.A.I.C.S.: 922160
Robert Closset (Gen Mgr)

Amberfire Limited (1)
Back Lane Bleasby Moor Market, Market Rasen, LN8 3QL, Lincolnshire, United Kingdom
Tel.: (44) 167 388 5229
Web Site: https://www.amber-fire.co.uk
Fire Protection Installation Services
N.A.I.C.S.: 922160

Ansul BV (1)
Platinastraat 15, 8211 AR, Lelystad, Netherlands
Tel.: (31) 320240864
Web Site: https://www.ansul.nl
Sales Range: $50-74.9 Million
Fire Extinguishing Services
N.A.I.C.S.: 922160
Erik van Ekeris (Mng Dir)

Ansul S.A. (1)
Industrialaan 35, 1702, Groot-Bijgaarden, Belgium
Tel.: (32) 24677211
Web Site: https://www.ansul.be
Sales Range: $75-99.9 Million
Fire Fighting & Protection Services
N.A.I.C.S.: 922160

Ansul Solutions B.V. (1)

AND PRIVATE COMPANIES

Platinastraat 15, 8211 AR, Lelystad, Netherlands
Tel.: (31) 320240864
Web Site: https://www.ansulsolutions.nl
Fire Protection Services
N.A.I.C.S.: 922160

Asco Extinguishers Company Limited (1)
Unit 1 Pt 1 Festival Court Brand Place, Glasgow, G51 1DR, United Kingdom
Tel.: (44) 1414734821
Web Site: https://www.asco.uk.com
Sales Range: $50-74.9 Million
Extinguisher Suppliers
N.A.I.C.S.: 922160

Beta Fire Protection Limited (1)
Unit 18 Western Road Ind Estate, Stratford-upon-Avon, CV37 0AH, United Kingdom
Tel.: (44) 178 929 2050
Web Site: https://betafireprotection.com
Fire Protection Services
N.A.I.C.S.: 922160

Blesberger G.m.b.H (1)
Hasnerstrasse 12, 4020, Linz, Austria
Tel.: (43) 73 273 3234
Fire Protection Services
N.A.I.C.S.: 922160

Blusdesign B.V. (1)
Rechte Tocht 7d, 1507 BZ, Zaandam, Netherlands
Tel.: (31) 318508369
Web Site: https://www.blusdesign.nl
Fire Protection Services
N.A.I.C.S.: 922160

Braho Brandpreventie B.V. (1)
Maasdijkseweg 107, 2291 PJ, Wateringen, Netherlands
Tel.: (31) 793410708
Web Site: https://www.braho.nl
Fire Protection Services
N.A.I.C.S.: 922160

Brandpreventie Groep B.V. (1)
Rechte Tocht 7d, 1507 BZ, Zaandam, Netherlands
Tel.: (31) 756315558
Web Site: https://www.brandpreventiegroep.nl
Fire Protection Services
N.A.I.C.S.: 922160

City Fire Protection & Maintenance Services LLP (1)
Trenton House 59a Imperial Way, Croydon, CR0 4RR, Surrey, United Kingdom
Tel.: (44) 2039942352
Web Site: https://www.cityfire.co.uk
Fire Protection Installation Services
N.A.I.C.S.: 922160

Dimex Technics S.A. (1)
42 Rue De L'eglise, Lontzen, 4710, Herbesthal, Belgium
Tel.: (32) 87890401
Web Site: http://www.dimex-technics.be
Sales Range: $25-49.9 Million
Fire Safety Services
N.A.I.C.S.: 922160

Feuerschutz Hollmann G.m.b.H. (1)
Ihmerter Strasse 211, Ihmert, 58675, Hemer, Germany
Tel.: (49) 237281066
Web Site: https://www.feuerschutz-hollmann.de
Fire Protection Installation Services
N.A.I.C.S.: 922160

Firebreak Fire Securities Limited (1)
55 Rachel Drive, Duns, TD11 3LP, Berwickshire, United Kingdom
Tel.: (44) 136 188 4373
Web Site: https://www.firebreak.co
Fire Extinguisher Whslr
N.A.I.C.S.: 423990

GC Fire Protection Limited (1)
Premier House 2 Jubilee Way, Elland, HX5 9DY, West Yorkshire, United Kingdom
Tel.: (44) 2083917310
Fire Protection Installation Services
N.A.I.C.S.: 922160

GFA Premier Limited (1)
Premier House Jubilee Way, Elland, HX5 9DY, West Yorkshire, United Kingdom
Tel.: (44) 1422377521
Web Site: http://www.gfapremier.co.uk
Sales Range: $25-49.9 Million
Fire Extinguishing Products Mfr
N.A.I.C.S.: 922160

HP Fire Prevention Sprl (1)
Chaussee de Louvain 406, 1300, Wavre, Belgium
Tel.: (32) 1 060 4402
Web Site: https://www.hpfire.be
Fire Protection Installation Services
N.A.I.C.S.: 922160

Hoyles Fire & Safety Limited (1)
Premier House 2 Jubilee Way, Elland, HX5 9DY, West Yorkshire, United Kingdom
Tel.: (44) 8081964527
Web Site: https://www.hoyles.co.uk
Fire Extinguishing Services
N.A.I.C.S.: 922160

Importex SA (1)
Rue De L eglise 42 Lontzen, 4710, Herbesthal, Wallonie, Belgium
Tel.: (32) 87880242
Web Site: https://importex.be
Rubber Products Mfr
N.A.I.C.S.: 326299

KDN Fire Protection Limited (1)
6 Dollywaggon Way, South Rings Business Park Bamber Bridge, Preston, PR5 6EW, Lancashire, United Kingdom
Tel.: (44) 177 295 4650
Web Site: https://www.kdnfireprotection.co.uk
Fire Protection Installation Services
N.A.I.C.S.: 922160

KW Fire Protection Limited (1)
Albion House Under Lane, Chadderton, Oldham, OL9 7PS, United Kingdom
Tel.: (44) 161 519 5803
Web Site: https://www.kwfire.co.uk
Fire Protection Installation Services
N.A.I.C.S.: 922160

Kuhn Feuerschutz G.m.b.H. (1)
Schmuckebergsweg 12, 34576, Homberg (Ohm), Germany
Tel.: (49) 568199440
Web Site: https://www.kuhn-feuerschutz.de
Fire Protection Installation Services
N.A.I.C.S.: 922160

L.W. Safety Limited (1)
Premier House 2 Jubilee Way, Elland, HX5 9DY, United Kingdom
Tel.: (44) 208 106 1958
Web Site: https://www.lwsafety.co.uk
Fire Safety Services
N.A.I.C.S.: 922160

Linde Brandmateriel Aps (1)
Industrivej 51A, 4000, Roskilde, Denmark
Tel.: (45) 33313100
Web Site: https://www.lindebrand.dk
Fire Extinguisher Whslr
N.A.I.C.S.: 423990

MK Fire Limited (1)
56/69 Queens Road, High Wycombe, HP13 6AH, Buckinghamshire, United Kingdom
Tel.: (44) 149 476 9744
Web Site: http://www.mkfire.co.uk
Emp.: 50
Fire Extinguishing Services
N.A.I.C.S.: 922160

NL Brandbeveiliging B.V. (1)
Postbus 2097, 6802 CB, Arnhem, Netherlands
Tel.: (31) 26 376 0199
Web Site: https://www.nlbrandbeveiliging.nl
Fire Protection Services
N.A.I.C.S.: 922160

Nu-Swift International Limited (1)
Premier House 2 Jubilee Way, Elland, HX5 9DY, West Yorkshire, United Kingdom
Tel.: (44) 1422372852
Web Site: https://www.nu-swift.co.uk
Sales Range: $25-49.9 Million
Emp.: 50
Fire Extinguishing Product Suppliers
N.A.I.C.S.: 922160

Prevent Brandbeveiliging B.V. (1)
Maasdijkseweg 107, 2291 PH, Wateringen, Netherlands
Tel.: (31) 174526700
Web Site: https://www.preventbrandbeveiliging.nl
Fire Protection Services
N.A.I.C.S.: 922160

Pyrotec Fire Protection Limited (1)
8 Caburn Enterprise Park The Broyle, Ringmer, BN8 5NP, East Sussex, United Kingdom
Tel.: (44) 8085015936
Web Site: https://www.pyrotec.co.uk
Fire Protection Installation Services
N.A.I.C.S.: 922160

Record Brandbeveiliging B.V. (1)
Oostergracht 24, 3763 LZ, Soest, Netherlands
Tel.: (31) 356027966
Web Site: https://www.recordbrandbeveiliging.nl
Fire Protection Services
N.A.I.C.S.: 922160

S2 Fire Solutions Limited (1)
Unit 14 Littleton Drive, Huntington, Cannock, WS12 4TS, Staffordshire, United Kingdom
Tel.: (44) 8455198186
Web Site: https://s2fire.co.uk
Fire Protection Installation Services
N.A.I.C.S.: 922160
Simon Millward *(Founder)*

Somati FIE N.V. (1)
Industrielaan 19a, 9320, Erembodegem, Belgium
Tel.: (32) 53852222
Web Site: https://www.somatifie.be
Sales Range: $75-99.9 Million
Emp.: 110
Fire Extinguisher Suppliers
N.A.I.C.S.: 922160

TVF (UK) Limited (1)
Unit 1 59/69 Queens Road, High Wycombe, HP13 6AH, United Kingdom
Tel.: (44) 8085015856
Web Site: https://www.tvfltd.co.uk
Fire Protection Installation Services
N.A.I.C.S.: 922160

Total Firestop GmbH (1)
Tillmanngasse 5, 1220, Vienna, Austria
Tel.: (43) 125936310
Web Site: https://www.total.at
Sales Range: $25-49.9 Million
Emp.: 45
Fire Safety Services
N.A.I.C.S.: 922160

Trium N.V. (1)
Herseltsesteenweg 72, B3200, Aarschot, Belgium
Tel.: (32) 78158085
Web Site: https://www.trium.be
Emp.: 35
Fire Protection Installation Services
N.A.I.C.S.: 922160

Tunbridge Wells Fire Protection Limited (1)
Buckham Hill, Uckfield, TN22 5XY, United Kingdom
Tel.: (44) 189 235 4225
Fire Protection Installation Services
N.A.I.C.S.: 922160

United Fire Alarms Limited (1)
Premier House 2 Jubilee Way, Elland, HX5 9DY, West Yorkshire, United Kingdom
Tel.: (44) 1422372852
Web Site: http://www.nuswift.co.uk
Sales Range: $50-74.9 Million
Emp.: 60
Security Access Control Systems
N.A.I.C.S.: 423610

LONDON STOCK EXCHANGE GROUP PLC

10 Paternoster Square, London, EC4M 7LS, United Kingdom
Tel.: (44) 2077971000 UK
Web Site: https://www.lseg.com
Year Founded: 2007
LSEG—(LSE)
Rev.: $9,151,032,800
Assets: $1,068,673,631,480
Liabilities: $1,034,025,974,800
Net Worth: $34,647,656,680
Earnings: $4,430,240,360
Emp.: 23,261
Fiscal Year-end: 12/31/21
Financial Investment Services
N.A.I.C.S.: 551112
Catherine Johnson *(Group)*

Subsidiaries:

Beyond Ratings, S.A.S. (1)
51 rue Saint Anne, 75002, Paris, France
Tel.: (33) 986275757
Web Site: http://www.beyond-ratings.com
Financial Services
N.A.I.C.S.: 523999
Sylvain Chateau *(Founder & COO)*

Borsa Italiana S.p.A. (1)
Piazza degli Affari 6, 20123, Milan, Italy
Tel.: (39) 0272 4261
Web Site: https://www.borsaitaliana.it
Sales Range: $350-399.9 Million
Emp.: 300
Stock Exchange
N.A.I.C.S.: 523210
Antonella Amadei *(Dir-Intl Rels & Global Dev)*

Subsidiary (Domestic):

MTS S.p.A. (2)
Via Tomacelli 146, 00186, Rome, Italy
Tel.: (39) 0642120208
Web Site: https://www.mtsmarkets.com
Electronic Bond Trading Platform Operator
N.A.I.C.S.: 523150

Corporate Headquarters (Non-US):

MTS S.p.A. - UK Corporate Office (3)
110 Cannon Street, London, EC4N 6EU, United Kingdom
Tel.: (44) 207 076 0001
Web Site: https://www.mtsmarkets.com
Emp.: 25
Corporate Office; Electronic Bond Trading Platform Operator
N.A.I.C.S.: 551114

Subsidiary (Domestic):

Monte Titoli S.p.A. (2)
Piazza degli Affari 6, 20123, Milan, Italy
Tel.: (39) 02336351
Web Site: https://www.euronext.com
Sales Range: $75-99.9 Million
Emp.: 50
Central Depository & Settlement Services
N.A.I.C.S.: 541191
Alessandro Zignani *(Head-Post Trade Sls)*

Cassa di Compensazione e Garanzia S.p.A. (1)
Via Tomacelli 146, 00186, Roma, Italy (100%)
Tel.: (39) 0632395202
Web Site: http://www.ccg.it
Sales Range: $25-49.9 Million
Contract Monitoring Services
N.A.I.C.S.: 561499
Renato Tarantola *(CEO)*

Exactpro Systems LLC (1)
4040 Civic Ctr Dr Ste 200, San Rafael, CA 94903-4187
Tel.: (646) 340-3000
Web Site: http://www.exactpro.com
Emp.: 300
Software Developer
N.A.I.C.S.: 513210
Alexey Zverev *(Co-Founder & Co-CEO)*

FTSE International Limited (1)
10 Paternoster Square, Canary Wharf, London, EC4M 7LS, United Kingdom (100%)
Tel.: (44) 207 866 1810
Web Site: https://www.ftserussell.com
Sales Range: $75-99.9 Million
Emp.: 250
Equity, Bond & Alternative Asset Class Indices Creation & Management Services
N.A.I.C.S.: 519290
Catherine Johnson *(Chm)*

FTSE Italy S.p.A (1)
Piazza Affari 6, 20123, Milan, Italy
Tel.: (39) 0272426641

LONDON STOCK EXCHANGE GROUP PLC

London Stock Exchange Group plc—(Continued)
Financial Services
N.A.I.C.S.: 523999

Gatelab S.r.l. (1)
Viale dei Pentri 161, 86170, Isernia, Italy
Tel.: (39) 0865820201
Financial Services
N.A.I.C.S.: 523999

LCH Group Holdings Limited (1)
Aldgate House 33 Aldgate High Street, London, EC3N 1EA, United Kingdom (64.9%)
Tel.: (44) 2074267000
Web Site: http://www.lch.com
Rev.: $1,130,205,720
Net Worth: $1,698,259,680
Earnings: $371,445,120
Emp.: 797
Fiscal Year-end: 12/31/2019
Holding Company; Financial Transaction Processing & Clearinghouse Services
N.A.I.C.S.: 551112
Daniel Maguire (CEO)

LCH Limited (1)
Aldgate House Aldgate High Street, London, EC3N 1EA, United Kingdom
Tel.: (44) 2074267000
Web Site: http://www.lch.com
Financial Derivative Clearing Services
N.A.I.C.S.: 522320
Laurie Adams (Chm)

London Stock Exchange plc (1)
10 Paternoster Square, London, EC4M 7LS, United Kingdom
Tel.: (44) 207 797 1000
Web Site:
  https://www.londonstockexchange.com
Sales Range: $200-249.9 Million
Emp.: 400
Securities & Commodities Exchange
N.A.I.C.S.: 523210
Denzil Jenkins (Interim CEO)

Mergent Japan K.K. (1)
1-5-1 Otemachi Otemachi First Square East Tower 11th Floor, Chiyoda-ku, Tokyo, 100-0004, Japan
Tel.: (81) 345636315
Web Site: http://www.mergentjapan.com
Business & Financial Information Provider
N.A.I.C.S.: 519290

Mergent, Inc. (1)
580 Kingsley Park Dr, Fort Mill, SC 29715
Tel.: (704) 559-7601
Web Site: http://www.mergent.com
Corporate & Financial Data Processor & Publisher
N.A.I.C.S.: 513140

Millennium IT Software (Private) Limited (1)
1 Millennium Drive, Malabe, 10115, Sri Lanka
Tel.: (94) 112416000
Emp.: 70
Information Technology Consulting Services
N.A.I.C.S.: 541512
Knox Ngema (CEO)

Millennium Information Technologies (Private) Limited (1)
1 Millennium Drive, Malabe, Sri Lanka
Tel.: (94) 112416000
Web Site: http://www.milleniumit.com
Sales Range: $150-199.9 Million
Emp.: 600
Information Technology Consulting Services
N.A.I.C.S.: 541512
Tony Weeresinghe (Mng Dir)

Quantile Technologies Limited (1)
Cannon Green 27 Bush Lane, London, United Kingdom
Tel.: (44) 2039177544
Web Site: https://www.quantile.com
Counterparty Risk Optimisation Services
N.A.I.C.S.: 522320

Refinitiv Ireland Limited (1)
12/13 Exchange Place IFSC, Dublin, Ireland
Tel.: (353) 15825800
Management Consulting Services
N.A.I.C.S.: 541612

Refinitiv Norge AS (1)
Dronning Eufemias gate 16, 191, Oslo, Norway
Tel.: (47) 21631082
Financial Software Services
N.A.I.C.S.: 522320

Refinitiv US Holdings Inc. (1)
3 Times Square, New York, NY 10036 (55%)
Tel.: (646) 223-4000
Web Site: http://www.refinitiv.com
Emp.: 10,000
Data Analytic Services
N.A.I.C.S.: 518210
David Craig (CEO)

Subsidiary (Domestic):

Giact Systems, LLC (2)
700 Central Expy S Ste 300, Allen, TX 75013
Tel.: (214) 644-0450
Web Site: https://giact.com
Depository Credit Intermediation
N.A.I.C.S.: 522180
Merlin Bise (Co-Founder & CTO)

Scivantage, Inc. (2)
10 Exchange Pl 13th Fl, Jersey City, NJ 07302
Tel.: (646) 452-0050
Web Site: http://www.scivantage.com
Sales Range: $25-49.9 Million
Emp.: 110
Business IT & Customer Service Consulting Services
N.A.I.C.S.: 541618
Adnane Charchour (Pres & CEO)

The Stock Exchange (Properties) Ltd (1)
10 Paternoster Square, London, EC4M 7LS, United Kingdom
Tel.: (44) 2077971000
Web Site:
  http://www.londonstockexchange.com
Securities & Commodity Exchanges
N.A.I.C.S.: 523210

The Yield Book Inc. (1)
28 Liberty St 58th Fl, New York, NY 10005
Tel.: (646) 989-2200
Web Site: http://www.yieldbook.com
Software Development Services
N.A.I.C.S.: 541511
Sibasish Acharya (Dir)

Turquoise Services Ltd (1)
10 Paternoster Sq, London, EC4M 7LS, United Kingdom
Tel.: (44) 2073827600
Sales Range: $200-249.9 Million
Emp.: 500
Securities Brokerage Services
N.A.I.C.S.: 523150
Robert Barnes (CEO)

LONDON SYMPHONY ORCHESTRA LTD

Barbican Centre Silk Street, London, EC2Y 8DS, United Kingdom
Tel.: (44) 2075881116 UK
Web Site: http://www.lso.co.uk
Emp.: 100
Symphony Orchestra
N.A.I.C.S.: 711130
Colin Davis (Pres)

Subsidiaries:

London Symphony Orchestra American Foundation (1)
954 Lexington Ave Ste 337, New York, NY 10021
Tel.: (917) 405-0274
Web Site: http://lso.co.uk
Sales Range: $75-99.9 Million
Foundation
N.A.I.C.S.: 813990

London Symphony Orchestra St. Luke's (1)
161 Old Street, London, EC1V 9NG, United Kingdom
Tel.: (44) 2074903939
Web Site: http://www.lso.co.uk
Sales Range: $50-74.9 Million
Emp.: 20
Symphony Orchestra Services

N.A.I.C.S.: 711130
Anne Basley (Mgr-Facilities)

LONDONMETRIC PROPERTY PLC

One Curzon Street, London, W1J 5HB, United Kingdom
Tel.: (44) 2074849000 UK
Web Site:
  https://www.londonmetric.com
Year Founded: 2013
LMP—(LSE)
Rev.: $225,101,112
Assets: $8,188,321,522
Liabilities: $3,171,258,842
Net Worth: $5,017,062,681
Earnings: $151,541,961
Emp.: 47
Fiscal Year-end: 03/31/24
Real Estate Investment Trust
N.A.I.C.S.: 523999
Martin McGann (Dir-Fin)

Subsidiaries:

A&J Mucklow Group Plc (1)
60 Whitehall Road, Halesowen, B63 3JS, West Midlands, United Kingdom
Tel.: (44) 1215501841
Web Site: http://www.mucklow.com
Real Estate Development Services
N.A.I.C.S.: 531390
Rupert J. Mucklow (Chm)

CT Property Trust Limited (1)
7A Nightingale Way Quartermile 4 6th Floor, Edinburgh, EH3 9EG, United Kingdom
Tel.: (44) 2076288000
Web Site: http://www.bmogam.com
Rev.: $25,085,235
Assets: $579,189,775
Liabilities: $145,282,829
Net Worth: $433,906,946
Earnings: $113,237,921
Fiscal Year-end: 06/30/2022
Real Estate Investment Services
N.A.I.C.S.: 531210

LXI REIT plc (1)
1st Floor Senator House 85 Queen Victoria Street, London, EC4V 4AB, United Kingdom
Tel.: (44) 2076806550
Web Site: http://www.lxireit.com
Sales Range: $25-49.9 Million
Real Estate Investment Trust Services
N.A.I.C.S.: 523940
Alex Mattey (Head-IR)

Subsidiary (Domestic):

Secure Income REIT Plc (2)
Cavendish House 18 Cavendish Square, London, W1G 0PJ, United Kingdom
Tel.: (44) 207 647 7647
Web Site:
  http://www.secureincomereit.co.uk
Sales Range: $125-149.9 Million
Real Estate Investment Trust
N.A.I.C.S.: 525990

LONE STAR MERCEDES-BENZ

10 Heritage Meadows Road SE, Calgary, T2H 3C1, AB, Canada
Tel.: (403) 253-1333
Web Site:
  http://www.lonestarcalgary.com
Year Founded: 1971
Emp.: 100
New & Used Car Dealers
N.A.I.C.S.: 441110
Simon Clarke (Gen Mgr-Sls)

LONE WOLF REAL ESTATE TECHNOLOGIES INC.

231 Shearson Crescent Suite 310, Cambridge, N1T 1J5, ON, Canada
Tel.: (519) 624-1236
Web Site: https://www.lwolf.com
Tobacco Mfr
N.A.I.C.S.: 312230
Lorne Wallace (Founder & Chm)

INTERNATIONAL PUBLIC

Subsidiaries:

RE FormsNet, LLC (1)
18070 15 Mile Rd, Fraser, MI 48026
Tel.: (586) 840-0140
Web Site: http://www.ziplogix.com
Emp.: 200
Real Estate Forms & Transaction Management Software Publisher
N.A.I.C.S.: 513210
John McGonagle (Coord-Mktg)

Terradatum, Inc. (1)
14221 Metcalf Ave Ste 210, Overland Park, KS 66223
Tel.: (806) 398-2016
Web Site: http://www.terradatum.com
Activities Related to Real Estate
N.A.I.C.S.: 531390
Dan Biggs (VP-Tech)

LONG AN BOOK & EDUCATIONAL EQUIPMENT JSC

No 39 Hai Ba Trung Ward 1, Tan An, Long An, Vietnam
Tel.: (84) 723822374
Web Site:
  https://www.sachthietbila.com.vn
LBE—(HNX)
Rev.: $9,069,400
Assets: $2,638,200
Liabilities: $256,200
Net Worth: $2,382,000
Earnings: $156,500
Emp.: 35
Fiscal Year-end: 12/31/23
Books Publishing Services
N.A.I.C.S.: 513130
Truc Trung Dang (Chm-Mgmt Bd & Deputy Dir)

LONG AN FOOD PROCESSING EXPORT JOINT STOCK COMPANY

81B National Road 62 Ward 2, Tan An, Long An, Vietnam
Tel.: (84) 723823900
Web Site: https://www.lafooco.vn
Year Founded: 1985
LAF—(HOSE)
Rev.: $17,777,635
Assets: $13,684,003
Liabilities: $4,547,944
Net Worth: $9,136,059
Earnings: $1,179,062
Emp.: 180
Fiscal Year-end: 12/31/23
Agricultural Product Mfr
N.A.I.C.S.: 339999
Tien Hung Nguyen (Dir-Binh Phuoc Branch)

Subsidiaries:

Long An Food Processing Export Joint Stock Company - Long An Cashew Factory (1)
81B National Road 62 Ward 2, Tan An, Long An, Vietnam
Tel.: (84) 723823900
Cashew Nut Packaging & Sales
N.A.I.C.S.: 115114

LONG BON INTERNATIONAL CO., LTD

9F No 50 Sec 1 Zhongxiao W Rd, Zhongzheng District, Taipei, 100, Taiwan
Tel.: (886) 223756595
Web Site:
  https://www.longbon.com.tw
2514—(TAI)
Rev.: $286,677,110
Assets: $808,303,536
Liabilities: $474,158,959
Net Worth: $334,144,577
Earnings: $10,369,540
Fiscal Year-end: 12/31/22

AND PRIVATE COMPANIES

Insurance Management Services
N.A.I.C.S.: 524298
Mingbin Shao *(Chm)*

LONG FIOUL
72 Avenue Louis Blanc, 94214,
Champigny-sur-Marne, La Varenne,
France
Tel.: (33) 148864444
Rev.: $21,800,000
Emp.: 20
Miscellaneous Retail Stores
N.A.I.C.S.: 459999
Daniel Long *(Chm)*

LONG GIANG INVESTMENT & URBAN DEVELOPMENT JOINT-STOCK COMPANY
173 Xuan Thuy Str, Cau Giay District,
Hanoi, Vietnam
Tel.: (84) 437950595
Web Site:
  https://www.longgiangland.com.vn
Year Founded: 2001
LGL—(HOSE)
Rev.: $3,762,466
Assets: $55,496,276
Liabilities: $27,730,278
Net Worth: $27,765,998
Earnings: $685,032
Emp.: 204
Fiscal Year-end: 12/31/23
Civil Engineering Services
N.A.I.C.S.: 237990
Le Ha Giang *(Chm-Mgmt Bd & Gen Dir)*

LONG HARBOUR EXPLORATION CORP.
885 West Georgia Street Suite 1500,
Vancouver, V6C 3E8, BC, Canada
Tel.: (778) 871-8008
Web Site:
  http://www.longharbour.com
Year Founded: 2004
Mineral Exploration Services
N.A.I.C.S.: 213114

LONG HAU CORPORATION
Hamlet 3 Long Hau Ward, Can Giuoc
District, Can Giuoc, Long An, Vietnam
Tel.: (84) 906938599
Web Site:
  https://www.longhau.com.vn
LHG—(HOSE)
Rev.: $16,268,191
Assets: $125,871,232
Liabilities: $60,172,435
Net Worth: $65,698,797
Earnings: $6,846,904
Emp.: 136
Fiscal Year-end: 12/31/23
Real Estate Development Services
N.A.I.C.S.: 531390
Tran Hong Son *(Gen Dir)*

LONG MARCH CAPITAL LTD.
Suite 2111 Orient Plaza Block E1, 1
Chang An Avenue, Beijing, 100738,
China
Tel.: (86) 10 85151966
Web Site:
  http://www.longmarchproject.com
Emp.: 20
Private Equity Firm
N.A.I.C.S.: 523999
Alex Chun Yao *(Mng Partner)*
Subsidiaries:

Gold One Africa Limited (1)
Constantia Office Park Bridgeview House
Ground Fl, Weltevreden Park, Johannesburg, 1709, South Africa
Tel.: (27) 117261047
Web Site: http://www.gold1.co.za
Gold Resource Exploration, Development & Mining
N.A.I.C.S.: 212220
Jost Barenberg *(VP-Mining)*
Subsidiary (Domestic):

New Kleinfontein Mining Company Limited (2)
Clover Field Ave Outenikua Rd East Vail,
Private Bag X17, Weltevreden Park,
Springs, 1560, South Africa **(100%)**
Tel.: (27) 11730760
Holding Company; Gold Ore Exploration & Mining Services
N.A.I.C.S.: 551112
Izak Marais *(Gen Mgr)*
Subsidiary (Domestic):

New Kleinfontein Goldmine (Proprietary) Limited (3)
Postnet Suite 115, Private Bag X17, Weltevreden Park, Johannesburg, 1715, South Africa **(100%)**
Tel.: (27) 10 591 5200
Gold Ore Mining Services
N.A.I.C.S.: 212220

LONG MING GREEN ENERGY TECHNOLOGY ENGINEERING CO., LTD.
3rd Floor No 602 Mingshui Road,
Zhongshan District, Taipei, Taiwan
Tel.: (886) 285015778
Web Site: https://www.tkte.com.tw
Year Founded: 1996
3018—(TAI)
Rev.: $19,617,449
Assets: $39,653,061
Liabilities: $34,517,707
Net Worth: $5,135,354
Earnings: ($3,724,353)
Emp.: 72
Fiscal Year-end: 12/31/23
Civil Construction Services
N.A.I.C.S.: 541330

LONG RUN EXPLORATION LTD.
Livingston Place West Tower Suite
400, 250 - 2nd Street Southwest,
Calgary, T2P 0C1, AB, Canada
Tel.: (403) 261-6012 AB
Web Site:
  http://www.longrunexploration.com
Sales Range: $200-249.9 Million
Emp.: 227
Oil & Gas Exploration Services
N.A.I.C.S.: 213112
William E. Andrew *(Chm & CEO)*

LONG WELL INTERNATIONAL HOLDINGS LIMITED
21st Floor 80 Gloucester Road, Wan
Chai, Hong Kong, China (Hong Kong)
Tel.: (852) 26986093 Ky
Web Site: http://www.trcf.com.hk
Year Founded: 1987
Investment Holding Company;
Chemical Products, Insurance Brokerage & Crude Oil Sale
N.A.I.C.S.: 551112
Gan Xiaohua *(Exec Dir)*
Subsidiaries:

Wing Shing Chemical Company Limited (1)
Units 9-10 4 F Kinglet Indus Bldg 21-23
Shing Wan Rd, Tai Wai, Sha Tin, New Territories, China (Hong Kong)
Tel.: (852) 26986173
Web Site: http://www.petroasian.com
Solvents & Paints Mfr
N.A.I.C.S.: 325130

LONG YOUNG ELECTRONIC (KUNSHAN) CO., LTD.
No 99 Shunchang Road, Zhoushi
Town, Kunshan, 215313, Jiangsu,
China
Tel.: (86) 51257668990
Web Site:
  https://www.longyoung.com
Year Founded: 2000
301389—(CHIN)
Rev.: $52,853,580
Assets: $337,442,976
Liabilities: $10,531,404
Net Worth: $326,911,572
Earnings: $23,707,944
Fiscal Year-end: 12/31/22
Electronic Component Mfr & Distr
N.A.I.C.S.: 334419
Subsidiaries:

GHZ Composite Material Corp. (1)
No 20-B6 Guotai Rd, Zhunan Township Miaoli County, Hsinchu, 350, Taiwan
Tel.: (886) 37552738
Electronic Components Mfr
N.A.I.C.S.: 334419

Huaian Fuyang Electronic Material Co., Limited (1)
No 103 Shenzhen East Road, Huai'an Economic and Technological Development Zone, Jiangsu, China
Tel.: (86) 51783506888
Electronic Components Mfr
N.A.I.C.S.: 334419

Long Young Electric (Kunsan) Co., Ltd. (1)
No 99 ShunChang Road, Zhoushi Town, Kunshan, 215337, Jiangsu, China
Tel.: (86) 51257668990
Electromagnetic Shielding Material Mfr
N.A.I.C.S.: 334510

LONG YUAN CONSTRUCTION GROUP CO., LTD
Longyuan Group Building 99 Shouyang Road, Jingan District, Shanghai,
200072, China
Tel.: (86) 2165176909 CN
Web Site: https://www.lycg.com.cn
Year Founded: 1980
600491—(SHG)
Rev.: $2,000,123,700
Assets: $9,357,881,748
Liabilities: $7,471,956,389
Net Worth: $1,885,925,359
Earnings: $53,401,814
Fiscal Year-end: 12/31/22
Industrial & Public Utility Construction Services
N.A.I.C.S.: 236210
Zhenyuan Yuan Lai *(Chm & Sec)*
Subsidiaries:

Beijing Longyuan Hengxing Urban & Rural Planning & Design Co., Ltd. (1)
Room 3403 China Jin Greenland Center, Fourth District Wangjing East Park Chaoyang District, Beijing, China
Construction Services
N.A.I.C.S.: 236220

Beijing Mingshu Data Technology Co., Ltd. (1)
Room 502 5th Floor Block F Wangjing Science and Technology Park, Chaoyang District, Beijing, China
Tel.: (86) 108 620 3077
Web Site: https://www.bridata.com
Financial Services
N.A.I.C.S.: 523999

Hangzhou City Investment Construction Co., Ltd. (1)
8th Floor Building 5 Baima Lake, International Convention & Exhibition Center Binjiang District, Hangzhou, China
Construction Services
N.A.I.C.S.: 236220

Hangzhou Qingshan Lake Forest Silicon Valley Development Co., Ltd. (1)

LONGBOAT ENERGY PLC

Building 8 No 199 Yunan Road Jinbei Street, Linan District, Hangzhou, China
Tel.: (86) 5716 108 1290
Construction Services
N.A.I.C.S.: 236220

Longyuan Mingcheng Investment Management (Shanghai) Co., Ltd. (1)
Longyuan Group Lane 99 Shouyang Road, Shanghai, China
Tel.: (86) 216 510 3999
Web Site: https://www.lymcppp.com
Construction Services
N.A.I.C.S.: 236220

Longyuan Mingzhu Technology Co., Ltd. (1)
Room 1511 1512 Shimao Building 2299 Yanan West Road, Changning District, Shanghai, China
Tel.: (86) 216 522 0666
Construction Services
N.A.I.C.S.: 236220

Longyuan Municipal Maintenance (Shanghai) Co., Ltd. (1)
9th Floor Building 5 No 336 Changjiang Road, Binjiang District, Hangzhou, China
Construction Services
N.A.I.C.S.: 236220

Ningbo Longyuan Shenghong Ecological Construction Engineering Co., Ltd. (1)
No 408 Huanyuan South Road, Andong Town Industrial Park Hangzhou Bay New District, Ningbo, China
Tel.: (86) 5746 347 7805
Construction Services
N.A.I.C.S.: 236220

Shanghai Housing Architectural Design Institute Co., Ltd. (1)
Building 8 No 658 Daduhe Road, Putuo District, Shanghai, 200062, China
Web Site: https://www.sfsjy.com
Architectural Services
N.A.I.C.S.: 541310

Shanghai Longyuan Tiance Enterprise Management Co., Ltd. (1)
Room 3302 Building T1 SOHO Tianshan 1715 Tianshan Road, Changning District, Shanghai, China
Tel.: (86) 216 233 1325
Construction Services
N.A.I.C.S.: 236220

Shanghai Xinan Curtain Wall Building & Decoration Co., Ltd. (1)
Jiashan Road No 526 Middle Business Building Room 309, Xuhui District, Shanghai, 200031, China
Tel.: (86) 215 404 3857
Web Site: https://www.xinancn.com.cn
General Contracting Services
N.A.I.C.S.: 236220

Zhejiang Dadi Steel Structure Co., Ltd. (1)
Xiaoshan Economic and Technological Development Zone, Gianjiang Farm Qian Nong 6 All The Way, Hangzhou, Zhejiang, China
Tel.: (86) 57182831560
Web Site: http://www.en.cnzjdd.com
Steel Mfrs
N.A.I.C.S.: 331513

LONGBOAT ENERGY PLC
5th Floor One New Change, London,
EC4M 9AF, United Kingdom UK
Web Site: https://longboatenergy.com
Year Founded: 2019
LBE—(AIM)
Rev.: $190,443
Assets: $112,530,138
Liabilities: $86,106,179
Net Worth: $26,423,959
Earnings: ($19,531,188)
Emp.: 11
Fiscal Year-end: 12/31/22
Natural Gas Distribution Services
N.A.I.C.S.: 221210
James Menzies *(Chm)*

LONGCHAMP S.A.S.

Longboat Energy Plc—(Continued)

LONGCHAMP S.A.S.
12 rue Saint Florentin, Paris, 75001, France
Tel.: (33) 143160000
Web Site: http://www.longchamp.com
Sales Range: $200-249.9 Million
Emp.: 950
Handbags, Luggage & Leather Goods Mfr
N.A.I.C.S.: 316990
Jean Cassegrain *(Founder)*

Subsidiaries:

LONGCHAMP USA INC **(1)**
4 Applegate Dr Ste B, Robbinsville, NJ 08691
Tel.: (609) 581-5555
Web Site: http://www.longchampusa.com
Emp.: 40
Leather Goods Mfr
N.A.I.C.S.: 316990
Nina M. Richter *(Mgr-Mktg & Comm)*

LONGCHEER HOLDINGS LTD.
Building 1 No 401 Caobao Rd, Xuhui District, Shanghai, 200233, China
Tel.: (86) 21 6408 8898 BM
Web Site:
  http://www.longcheertel.com
Year Founded: 2002
Sales Range: Less than $1 Million
Holding Company
N.A.I.C.S.: 551112

LONGCHEN PAPER & PACKAGING CO., LTD.
No 1-1 Guangxing Ln Guangxing Vil, Erlin Township, Chang-Hua, 526002, Taiwan
Tel.: (886) 255811777
Web Site:
  http://www.longchenpaper.com
1909—(TAI)
Rev.: $1,527,585,181
Assets: $2,293,273,336
Liabilities: $1,569,777,827
Net Worth: $723,495,509
Earnings: ($33,727,884)
Emp.: 3,510
Fiscal Year-end: 12/31/23
Corrugated Board Mfr
N.A.I.C.S.: 322211
Ying-Pin Cheng *(Chm & Pres)*

Subsidiaries:

Long Chen Paper Co., Ltd. - Luzhu Plant **(1)**
No 100-1 Zhongshan S Rd, Luzhu Dist, Kaohsiung, 82151, Taiwan
Tel.: (886) 76968111
Paper Packaging Materials Mfr
N.A.I.C.S.: 322211

Long Chen Paper Co., Ltd. - Shengang Plant **(1)**
No 78 Xitou Road, Shengang Township, Taichung, 42953, Taiwan
Tel.: (886) 42561 5901
Corrugated Board Mfr
N.A.I.C.S.: 322211

Long Chen Paper Co., Ltd. - Yunlin Plant **(1)**
No 25 North Road, Douliu, 64059, Yunlin, Taiwan
Tel.: (886) 55510336
Paper Packaging Materials Mfr
N.A.I.C.S.: 322110

LONGDA CONSTRUCTION & DEVELOPMENT CORPORATION
18th Floor No 380 Minquan 2nd Road, Kaohsiung, Taiwan
Tel.: (886) 73367041
Web Site: https://www.longda.com.tw
5519—(TAI)
Rev.: $142,763,689

Assets: $434,046,780
Liabilities: $257,098,293
Net Worth: $176,948,487
Earnings: $26,435,363
Emp.: 200
Fiscal Year-end: 12/31/23
Residential & Commercial Buildings Construction
N.A.I.C.S.: 236116
Hann-Long Guo *(Gen Mgr)*

LONGFIELD CHEMICALS LIMITED
Weaver House Ashville Point, Sutton, WA7 3FW, Cheshire, United Kingdom
Tel.: (44) 1928 712900
Web Site: http://www.longchem.co.uk
Year Founded: 1968
Sales Range: $100-124.9 Million
Emp.: 18
Plastic Product Distr
N.A.I.C.S.: 424610
Mark Pepper *(Mng Dir & Dir-Fin)*

LONGFOR GROUP HOLDINGS LIMITED
Building 6 No 8 Beiyuan Street, Longfor Blue Ocean Engine Industrial Park Chaoyang District, Beijing, 100012, China
Tel.: (86) 87984288
Web Site: https://www.longfor.com
LGFRY—(OTCIQ)
Rev.: $34,692,776,224
Assets: $74,800,350,714
Liabilities: $42,514,809,897
Net Worth: $32,285,540,817
Earnings: $4,544,572,026
Emp.: 31,565
Fiscal Year-end: 12/31/22
Investment Holding Company; Real Estate Services
N.A.I.C.S.: 551112
Xuping Chen *(CEO)*

Subsidiaries:

Juntion Development Hong Kong (Holding) Limited **(1)**
15/F 1 Duddell Street, Central, China (Hong Kong)
Tel.: (852) 22349071
Investment Holding Services
N.A.I.C.S.: 551112

LONGHAI STEEL, INC.
1 Jingguang Road, Neiqiu County, Xingtai, 054000, Hebei, China
Tel.: (86) 3196861111 NV
Web Site:
  http://www.longhaisteelinc.com
Sales Range: $600-649.9 Million
Emp.: 816
Steel Pole Mfr
N.A.I.C.S.: 331222
Chaojun Wang *(Chm, Pres & CEO)*

LONGHUA TECHNOLOGY GROUP LUOYANG CO., LTD.
No 288 of Kaiyuan Avenue, Luoyang, 471000, Henan, China
Tel.: (86) 37967891167
Web Site:
  https://www.longhuatech.com
Year Founded: 1995
300263—(CHIN)
Rev.: $323,074,440
Assets: $854,853,480
Liabilities: $405,565,056
Net Worth: $449,288,424
Earnings: $9,027,720
Emp.: 1,000
Fiscal Year-end: 12/31/22
Heat Exchange Equipment Mfr
N.A.I.C.S.: 333415
Li Zhanqiang *(Chm & Deputy Secy-Party Committee)*

Subsidiaries:

Beijing CM Environment Engineering Corporation Limited **(1)**
10/F Tower B Techart Plaza No 30 Xueyuan Road, Haidian District, Beijing, 100083, China
Tel.: (86) 1062526909
Web Site: http://www.cmwater.com
Sewage Treatment System Services
N.A.I.C.S.: 221320

LONGHUI INTERNATIONAL HOLDINGS LIMITED
Room 1502 15/F Lucky Building, 39 Wellington Street, Central, China (Hong Kong)
Tel.: (852) 864598979533 Ky
Web Site: http://www.cre8ir.com
Year Founded: 2009
1007—(HKG)
Rev: $10,147,972
Assets: $6,163,841
Liabilities: $32,488,700
Net Worth: ($26,324,860)
Earnings: ($8,801,676)
Emp.: 350
Fiscal Year-end: 12/31/22
Holding Company
N.A.I.C.S.: 551112
Shui Chak Hung *(Chm)*

LONGI GREEN ENERGY TECHNOLOGY CO., LTD.
No 8369 Shangyuan Road Xian Economic and Technological Development Zone, Shaanxi, 710018, China
Tel.: (86) 2981566863
Web Site: https://www.longi.com
Year Founded: 2000
601012—(SHG)
Rev.: $17,860,837,339
Assets: $19,322,606,474
Liabilities: $10,702,992,260
Net Worth: $8,619,614,214
Earnings: $2,050,783,230
Emp.: 60,601
Fiscal Year-end: 12/31/22
Solar Component Mfr
N.A.I.C.S.: 334413
Baoshen Zhong *(Chm)*

Subsidiaries:

LERRI Solar Technology Co., Ltd. **(1)**
Block B Innovation Incubation Xi'an Service Outsourcing Industrial, Park No 8989 Shangji Road Xi'an Economic & Technological Development, Xi'an, 710018, China
Tel.: (86) 4009696199
Web Site: http://www.lerri.com
Crystal Mfr
N.A.I.C.S.: 334419
Kang Bowei *(Gen Mgr)*

LONGI Solar Technologie GmbH **(1)**
Bockenheimer Landstrasse 51-53, 60325, Frankfurt am Main, Germany
Tel.: (49) 69580070080
Monocrystalline Silicon Module Mfr
N.A.I.C.S.: 334413

LONGI Solar Technology K.K. **(1)**
Asahi Seimei Otemachi Building 24th Floor 2-6-1, Otemachi Chiyoda-ku, Tokyo, 100-1004, Japan
Tel.: (81) 335166300
Web Site: http://www.longisolar.co.jp
Silicone Products Mfr
N.A.I.C.S.: 334413

LONGi Solar Australia Pty. Ltd. **(1)**
Level 8 124 Walker Street, North Sydney, 2060, NSW, Australia
Tel.: (61) 284845806
Monocrystalline Silicon Module Mfr
N.A.I.C.S.: 334413

LONGi Solar Technology Co., Ltd. **(1)**
19th Floor Tower 3 Lujiazui Financial Plaza Century Avenue 826, Pudong, Shanghai, China
Tel.: (86) 2160578585
Web Site: http://www.en.longi-solar.com
Monocrystalline Silicon Module Mfr
N.A.I.C.S.: 334413
Hong Chen *(VP)*

LONGINO & CARDENAL SPA
Via Ambrogio Moroni 8, 20010, Pogliano Milanese, MI, Italy
Tel.: (39) 029396851
Web Site: https://www.longino.it
Year Founded: 1988
LON—(ITA)
Sales Range: Less than $1 Million
Catering Services
N.A.I.C.S.: 721110
Riccardo Uleri *(CEO)*

Subsidiaries:

Longino & Cardenal Limited **(1)**
5/FL No12 Wong Chuk Hang Road, Heung Wah industrial Building, Aberdeen, China (Hong Kong)
Tel.: (852) 27861238
Catering Services
N.A.I.C.S.: 722320
Beatrice Lombard *(Country Mgr)*

Longino & Cardenal NY LLC **(1)**
508 Franklin Ave, Mount Vernon, NY 10550
Tel.: (914) 292-5444
Catering Services
N.A.I.C.S.: 722320
Andrea Bertali *(Country Mgr)*

Longino & Cardenal Trading LLC **(1)**
3 Street 9b - Unit 12, Al Quoz Industrial, Dubai, United Arab Emirates
Tel.: (971) 43380108
Catering Services
N.A.I.C.S.: 722320
Marco Rosa *(Country Mgr)*

LONGJIAN ROAD & BRIDGE CO., LTD.
No 109 Songshan Road, Nangang District, Harbin, 150001, Heilongjiang, China
Tel.: (86) 45182281861
Web Site: https://www.longjianlq.com
Year Founded: 1993
600853—(SHG)
Rev.: $2,381,061,950
Assets: $4,560,867,127
Liabilities: $3,927,619,758
Net Worth: $633,247,370
Earnings: $49,047,954
Fiscal Year-end: 12/31/22
Road & Bridge Construction Services
N.A.I.C.S.: 237310
Tian Yulong *(Chm)*

LONGKOU UNION CHEMICAL CO., LTD.
Zhuyouguan Town Yantai, Longkou, 265705, Shandong, China
Tel.: (86) 5358575203
Web Site: https://www.lkunion.com.cn
Year Founded: 2007
301209—(CHIN)
Rev.: $76,093,992
Assets: $110,076,408
Liabilities: $16,265,340
Net Worth: $93,811,068
Earnings: $9,006,660
Fiscal Year-end: 12/31/22
Chemical Product Mfr & Distr
N.A.I.C.S.: 327120
Xiumei Li *(Chm)*

LONGLIDE INTELLIGENT TECHNOLOGY CO., LTD.
No 150 TIYU Road, Industrial park, Mingguang, 239400, Anhui, China
Tel.: (86) 4008366588
Web Site: https://www.llddl.com
Year Founded: 2010

AND PRIVATE COMPANIES

LONRHO LIMITED

300883—(SSE)
Rev.: $89,994,996
Assets: $287,885,988
Liabilities: $86,353,020
Net Worth: $201,532,968
Earnings: $4,400,136
Fiscal Year-end: 12/31/22
Information Technology Services
N.A.I.C.S.: 541512
Longping Xu *(Chm & Gen Mgr)*

Subsidiaries:

Fengqifeng Printing Technology (Shanghai) Co., Ltd. (1)
2199 Chuhua North Road, Zhelin Town Fengxian District, Shanghai, 201417, China
Tel.: (86) 2137586500
Packaging Services
N.A.I.C.S.: 561910

Longlide Packaging Technology (Shanghai) Co., Ltd. (1)
No 899 Zhangong Road, Fengxian District, Shanghai, 201417, China
Tel.: (86) 2157459111
Packaging Services
N.A.I.C.S.: 561910

LONGLIFE HOLDING CO., LTD.
Umeda Center Bldg 25F 2-4-12 Nakazakinishi, Kita-ku, Osaka, 530-0015, Japan
Tel.: (81) 663739191
Web Site: http://www.longlife-holding.co.jp
Year Founded: 1986
4355—(TKS)
Rev.: $121,958,765
Assets: $154,176,583
Liabilities: $153,236,646
Net Worth: $939,938
Earnings: ($1,277,944)
Fiscal Year-end: 10/31/22
Holding Company
N.A.I.C.S.: 551112
Kitamura Masami *(Chm)*

Subsidiaries:

L-Care Co., Ltd. (1)
Umeda Center Building 25F 2-4-12 Nakazakinish, Kita-ku, Osaka, 530-0015, Japan
Tel.: (81) 64 301 3785
Web Site: https://www.l-care.jp
Home Care Support Services
N.A.I.C.S.: 621610

LONGLIFE Dining Co., Ltd. (1)
25th floor of Umeda Center Building 2-4-12 Nakazakinishi, Kita-ku, Osaka, 530-0015, Japan
Tel.: (81) 64 709 0012
Web Site: https://www.lld.co.jp
Food Mfr & Distr
N.A.I.C.S.: 311999

LONGLIFE Global Consultant Co., Ltd. (1)
2-4-12 Umeda Center Building 25F Nakazakinishi, Kita-ku, Osaka, 530-0015, Japan
Tel.: (81) 663739191
Investment & Consulting Services
N.A.I.C.S.: 523940

LONGLIFE Medical Co., Ltd. (1)
2-4-12 Nakazakinishi Umeda Center Building 25th floor, Kita-ku, Osaka, 530-0015, Japan
Tel.: (81) 66 633 7507
Web Site: https://www.ll-p.co.jp
Health Care Srvices
N.A.I.C.S.: 621999

LONGO BROTHERS FRUIT MARKETS INC.
8800 Huntington Road, Vaughan, L4H 3M6, ON, Canada
Tel.: (905) 673-3099
Web Site: http://www.longos.com
Year Founded: 1956
Sales Range: $300-349.9 Million
Emp.: 2,200
Grocery Stores
N.A.I.C.S.: 445110
Anthony Longo *(Pres & CEO)*

LONGREACH OIL LIMITED
Level 27 25 Bligh Street, Sydney, 2000, NSW, Australia
Tel.: (61) 2 8277 6683   AU
Web Site: http://www.longreachoil.com
Year Founded: 1954
Sales Range: Less than $1 Million
Oil & Natural Gas Exploration Services
N.A.I.C.S.: 211120
Justin Rosenberg *(Mng Dir & Sec)*

LONGSHINE TECHNOLOGY GROUP CO LTD
Langxin Science and Technology Industrial Park, No 118 Jinghui East Road Xinwu district, Wuxi, Jiangsu, China
Tel.: (86) 51066676999
Web Site: https://www.longshine.com
Year Founded: 2003
300682—(CHIN)
Rev.: $665,838,684
Assets: $1,405,422,202
Liabilities: $329,784,331
Net Worth: $1,075,637,871
Earnings: $85,065,724
Fiscal Year-end: 12/31/23
Software Development Services
N.A.I.C.S.: 541511

LONGSHORE REOSURCES LTD.
555 605 5th Avenue SW, Calgary, T2P 3H5, AB, Canada
Tel.: (409) 984-1090
Web Site: https://www.longshore.ca
Year Founded: 2018
Exploration Services
N.A.I.C.S.: 213111
Byron Nodwell *(Pres & CEO)*

LONGUEUIL NISSAN INC.
760 boul Saint Charles Est, Longueuil, J4H 1C3, QC, Canada
Tel.: (450) 442-2000
Web Site: http://www.longueuilnissan.com
Rev.: $17,215,100
Emp.: 37
New & Used Car Dealers
N.A.I.C.S.: 441110
Andre Nolin *(VP)*

LONGVIEW TEA COMPANY LIMITED
16 Hare Street 1st Floor, Kolkata, 700 001, India
Tel.: (91) 3322482391
Web Site: https://www.longviewtea.org
Year Founded: 1879
526568—(BOM)
Rev.: $257,793
Assets: $1,961,699
Liabilities: $9,742
Net Worth: $1,951,958
Earnings: ($19,599)
Emp.: 2
Fiscal Year-end: 03/31/23
Tea Mfr & Distr
N.A.I.C.S.: 311920

LONGWEI PETROLEUM INVESTMENT HOLDING LIMITED
No 30 Dajingyu Street Xiaojingyu Xiang, Wan Bailin District, Taiyuan, 030024, Shanxi, China
Tel.: (86) 3516527388   CO
Web Site: http://www.longweipetro.com
Sales Range: $500-549.9 Million
Emp.: 77
Holding Company; Oil & Gas Services
N.A.I.C.S.: 551112
Yongjun Cai *(Chm & CEO)*

LONGWELL COMPANY
10th Fl No 36 Sec 1 Chang An E Road, Taipei, Taiwan
Tel.: (886) 225433567
Web Site: https://www.longwell.com
Year Founded: 1972
6290—(TPE)
Rev.: $243,497,108
Assets: $260,941,062
Liabilities: $99,318,200
Net Worth: $161,622,862
Earnings: $25,983,648
Emp.: 2,326
Fiscal Year-end: 12/31/22
Electronic Components Mfr
N.A.I.C.S.: 334419
Tsung-Cheng Lee *(Chm & CEO)*

LONGXING CHEMICAL INDUSTRY CO., LTD.
No 1 Longxing Street East Ring Road, Shahe, 054100, Hebei, China
Tel.: (86) 3198869002
Web Site: http://www.hb-lx.com.cn
Year Founded: 1994
002442—(SSE)
Rev.: $640,240,118
Assets: $474,550,091
Liabilities: $251,470,749
Net Worth: $223,079,342
Earnings: $14,558,216
Emp.: 1,300
Fiscal Year-end: 12/31/22
Carbon Black Mfr & Distr
N.A.I.C.S.: 325180

LONGXING CHEMICAL STOCK CO., LTD.
No 1 Longxing Street, Shahe, 54100, Hebei, China
Tel.: (86) 3198869002
Web Site: https://www.hb-lx.com
Year Founded: 1994
2442—(SSE)
Rev.: $631,384,969
Assets: $467,986,597
Liabilities: $247,992,662
Net Worth: $219,993,936
Earnings: $14,356,862
Emp.: 1,300
Fiscal Year-end: 12/31/22
Plastic Woven Product Mfr
N.A.I.C.S.: 314910
Pengda Liu *(Chm)*

LONGYAN KAOLIN CLAY CO., LTD.
10-12F Guozi Building No 260 Longyan Avenue, Xipi Subdistrict Xinluo District, Longyan, 364000, Fujian, China
Tel.: (86) 5973218228
Web Site: http://www.longgaogf.com
Year Founded: 2003
605086—(SHG)
Rev.: $39,038,669
Assets: $167,538,674
Liabilities: $11,867,731
Net Worth: $155,670,943
Earnings: $14,441,446
Fiscal Year-end: 12/31/22
Clay Mining Services
N.A.I.C.S.: 212323
Nengquan Wen *(Chm)*

LONGYAN ZHUOYUE NEW ENERGY CO., LTD.
Dongbao Industrial Concentration Zone Longzhou Industrial Park, Pinglin Tieshan Town Xinluo District, Longyan, 364000, Fujian, China
Tel.: (86) 5972342338
Web Site: https://www.zyxny.com
Year Founded: 2001
688196—(SHG)
Rev.: $610,034,209
Assets: $419,163,681
Liabilities: $28,317,360
Net Worth: $390,846,320
Earnings: $63,422,738
Fiscal Year-end: 12/31/22
Energy Distribution Services
N.A.I.C.S.: 221122
Huodong Ye *(Chm & Gen Mgr)*

Subsidiaries:

Xiamen Zhuoyue Biomass Energy Co., Ltd. (1)
Building A No 1153 Jicheng Road Torch High-tech Zone, Tongjiyuan; Xiamen, 361100, China
Tel.: (86) 5927890366
Biodiesel Product Mfr
N.A.I.C.S.: 325199

LONGZHOU GROUP CO., LTD.
No 112 Nanhuan West Road, Xinluo District, Longyan, 364000, Fujian, China
Tel.: (86) 5973100699
Web Site: http://www.lzgf.cn
Year Founded: 2003
002682—(SSE)
Rev.: $701,085,996
Assets: $1,037,512,476
Liabilities: $733,406,076
Net Worth: $304,106,400
Earnings: ($11,132,316)
Emp.: 5,260
Fiscal Year-end: 12/31/22
Passenger & Cargo Transportation
N.A.I.C.S.: 485999
Chen Mingsheng *(Chm)*

LONKEY INDUSTRIAL CO., LTD.
Room 201 No 87-93 Jinming Street, Tianhe District, Guangzhou, 510660, Guangdong, China
Tel.: (86) 2082162933
Web Site: https://www.lonkey.com.cn
000523—(SSE)
Rev.: $349,343,280
Assets: $328,422,276
Liabilities: $192,137,400
Net Worth: $136,284,876
Earnings: ($10,054,044)
Fiscal Year-end: 12/31/22
Chemical Products Mfr
N.A.I.C.S.: 325998
Guo Fu Yong *(Vice Chm & Gen Mgr)*

LONKING HOLDINGS LIMITED
26 Minyi Road Xinqiao, Shanghai, 201612, China
Tel.: (86) 2137602242
Web Site: http://www.lonkinggroup.com
3339—(OTCIQ)
Rev.: $1,543,840,552
Assets: $2,130,999,391
Liabilities: $780,872,702
Net Worth: $1,350,126,689
Earnings: $55,430,328
Emp.: 7,762
Fiscal Year-end: 12/31/22
Construction Machinery Mfr & Distr
N.A.I.C.S.: 333120
San Li *(Founder, Chm & CEO)*

LONRHO LIMITED
2nd Floor 25 Berkeley Square, London, W1J 6HB, United Kingdom
Tel.: (44) 2070165105
Web Site: http://www.lonrho.com
Year Founded: 1909

LONRHO LIMITED

Lonrho Limited—(Continued)
Sales Range: $300-349.9 Million
Emp.: 4,286
Investment Services
N.A.I.C.S.: 523999
Rainer-Marc Frey *(Vice Chm)*

Subsidiaries:

FastJet Plc (1)
6th Floor 60 Gracechurch Street, London,
EC3V 0HR, United Kingdom (54.79%)
Tel.: (44) 20 3651 6307
Web Site: http://www.fastjet.com
Rev.: $38,514,000
Assets: $35,155,000
Liabilities: $24,750,000
Net Worth: $10,405,000
Earnings: ($65,040,000)
Emp.: 263
Fiscal Year-end: 12/31/2018
Holding Company; Air Transportation
N.A.I.C.S.: 551112
Mark Hurst *(CEO)*

Fresh Direct Limited (1)
29 Clemow Drive, Mount Wellington, Auckland, 1546, New Zealand
Tel.: (64) 9 573 4100
Web Site: http://www.freshdirect.co.nz
Emp.: 29
Fruits & Vegetables Distr
N.A.I.C.S.: 424480
Jeffery Turner *(Chm)*

Hotel Cardoso SARL (1)
Avenida Martires de Mueda 707, PO Box 35, Maputo, Mozambique
Tel.: (258) 21491071
Web Site: http://www.hotelcardoso.co.mz
Home Management Services
N.A.I.C.S.: 721110
Pascal Demarchi *(Gen Mgr)*

KwikBuild Corporation (1)
8A Brentford Close, Beaconvale, Cape Town, 7530, South Africa
Tel.: (27) 21 931 8130
Web Site: http://www.e-kwikbuild.co.za
Sales Range: $25-49.9 Million
Emp.: 41
Prefabricated Buildings Mfr
N.A.I.C.S.: 321992

Oceanfresh Seafoods (Pty) Limited (1)
226 Albert Amon Rd, Meadowdale, Germiston, 1600, Gauteng, South Africa
Tel.: (27) 114532024
Web Site: http://www.oceanfresh.co.za
Sales Range: $25-49.9 Million
Emp.: 42
Seafood Processing Services
N.A.I.C.S.: 311710
Tom Pienaar *(Dir-Sls)*

Rollex (Pty) Limited (1)
Cnr Webb & Jones Road, PO Box 25219, Jet Park East Rand, Boksburg, 1462, South Africa
Tel.: (27) 115719800
Web Site: http://www.rollex.co.za
Sales Range: $75-99.9 Million
Emp.: 300
Logistics Consulting Servies
N.A.I.C.S.: 541614
Hammes Bornman *(Dir-Fin)*

LONSDALE CAPITAL PARTNERS LLP

21 Upper Brook Street, London, W1K 7PY, United Kingdom
Tel.: (44) 20 7514 1800 UK
Web Site: http://www.lonsdalepartners.com
Year Founded: 2010
Privater Equity Firm
N.A.I.C.S.: 523999
Alan Dargan *(Co-Founder)*

Subsidiaries:

Avalon Trustee Company Limited (1)
Brooke Court Lower Meadow Road, Handforth Dean, Wilmslow, SK9 3ND, Cheshire, United Kingdom
Tel.: (44) 161 486 2020
Web Site: http://www.avalonfuneralplans.co.uk
Pre-paid Funeral Trust Sales & Management Services
N.A.I.C.S.: 523991
Jason Gardner *(Head-Europe)*

Subsidiary (Non-US):

Avalon Europe S.L. (2)
Calle Albatera 1 - 68, La Finca Algorfa, 03169, Alicante, Spain
Tel.: (34) 966 799 070
Web Site: http://www.avalonfuneralplans.com
Pre-paid Funeral Trust Sales & Management Services
N.A.I.C.S.: 523991
Jason Gardner *(Mng Dir)*

Certeco Limited (1)
10 Eastcheap, London, EC3M 1AJ, United Kingdom
Tel.: (44) 207 099 0803
IT Services
N.A.I.C.S.: 541512

Cross Rental Limited (1)
Unit 9 Harewood Farm Andover Down London Road, Andover, SP11 6LJ, Hants, United Kingdom
Tel.: (44) 808 1691919
Web Site: http://www.crossrental.co.uk
Heating, Ventilation & Air Conditioning Services
N.A.I.C.S.: 333415
John Fogwill *(Sls Dir-UK)*

EMC Advisory Services Limited (1)
EMC House 38-40 Palace Avenue, Paignton, TQ3 3HE, Devon, United Kingdom
Tel.: (44) 800 0272484
Web Site: http://www.emcasclaims.co.uk
Financial Claims Management Services
N.A.I.C.S.: 524291
Craig Bernhardt *(CEO)*

OTEAC Limited (1)
Unit 4C The Core Berryhill Crescent, Bridge of Don, Aberdeen, AB23 8AN, United Kingdom
Tel.: (44) 1224 739 040
Web Site: http://www.oteac.co.uk
Sales Range: $1-9.9 Million
Integrated Safety Engineering Services
N.A.I.C.S.: 541330
John Singer *(Mgr-Fire & Security)*

Ocean Media Group Limited (1)
Suite 6 04 Exchange Tower 6th Floor 1 Harbour Exchange Square, Canary Wharf, London, E14 9GE, United Kingdom
Tel.: (44) 2077728300
Web Site: https://www.oceanmedia.co.uk
Magazine Publisher & Exhibition Organizer
N.A.I.C.S.: 513120
Declan Cassidy *(CFO)*

LONSDALE GROUP

8 rue Lavoisier, 75008, Paris, France
Tel.: (33) 1 43 12 67 00 FR
Web Site: http://www.lonsdale.fr
Emp.: 200
Holding Company; Advertising Agency
N.A.I.C.S.: 551112
Francois Serena *(Creative Dir)*

Subsidiaries:

Lonsdale Operations SAS (1)
8 rue Lavoisier, 75008, Paris, France
Tel.: (33) 1 4312 6700
Web Site: http://www.lonsdale.fr
Advetising Agency
N.A.I.C.S.: 541810
Frederic Messian *(Pres)*

Shiva Communication SASU (1)
8 rue Lavoisier, 75008, Paris, France
Tel.: (33) 1 4312 6700
Web Site: http://www.shivacom.fr
Advetising Agency
N.A.I.C.S.: 541810
Nicolas Sirot *(Founder & Grp Chief Digital Officer)*

Unedite SAS (1)
15 rue d'Argenteuil, 75001, Paris, France
Tel.: (33) 1 42 44 48 48
Advetising Agency
N.A.I.C.S.: 541810
Agnes Matheon *(Founder & Pres)*

LONSEAL CORPORATION

4-15-3 Midori, Sumida-Ku, Tokyo, 130-8570, Japan
Tel.: (81) 356001828
Web Site: https://www.lonseal.co.jp
Year Founded: 1928
4224—(TKS)
Rev.: $138,948,810
Assets: $174,675,860
Liabilities: $48,114,190
Net Worth: $126,561,670
Earnings: $5,519,350
Emp.: 372
Fiscal Year-end: 03/31/24
Plastic Product Mfr & Whslr
N.A.I.C.S.: 325211
Tamotsu Sato *(Mng Exec Officer & Dir-Transportation Flooring & Film Div)*

LONTRUE CO., LTD.

No 299 Langyuan Road Hi-Tech Industrial Park, Longkou, 265718, Shandong, China
Tel.: (86) 5358662568
Web Site: https://www.lontrue.com
Year Founded: 2002
300175—(CHIN)
Rev.: $30,274,452
Assets: $99,980,244
Liabilities: $24,838,164
Net Worth: $75,142,080
Earnings: ($3,897,504)
Fiscal Year-end: 12/31/22
Fresh & Dry Fruit Producer & Distr
N.A.I.C.S.: 424480
Zhao Zheng *(Chm)*

LONZA GROUP AG

Muenchensteinerstrasse 38, CH-4002, Basel, Switzerland
Tel.: (41) 613168111 CH
Web Site: https://www.lonza.com
Year Founded: 1897
LONN—(SWX)
Rev.: $2,919,514,139
Assets: $12,876,750,218
Liabilities: $3,665,270,686
Net Worth: $9,211,479,531
Earnings: $2,656,020,544
Emp.: 16,218
Fiscal Year-end: 12/31/21
Life Science Ingredients, Exclusive Synthesis & Biopharmaceuticals Mfr & Whslr
N.A.I.C.S.: 325199
Rodolfo J. Savitzky *(CFO)*

Subsidiaries:

Arch Chemicals, Inc. (1)
501 Merritt 7, Norwalk, CT 06851
Tel.: (203) 229-2900
Web Site: http://www.archchemicals.com
Sales Range: $1-4.9 Billion
Emp.: 2,504
Specialty Chemicals Mfr
N.A.I.C.S.: 325998
Mark E. Faford *(VP-IR & Corp Comm)*

Subsidiary (Non-US):

Arch Chemicals (China) Co., Ltd. (2)
No 9 Quingquiu Street Suzhou Industrial Park, Suzhou, 215024, Jiangsu, China
Tel.: (86) 512 62953072
Web Site: http://www.lonza.com
Sales Range: $75-99.9 Million
Emp.: 168
Personal Care Products Mfr & Distr
N.A.I.C.S.: 424210

Subsidiary (Domestic):

Arch International Trading (Shanghai) Co., Ltd. (3)

INTERNATIONAL PUBLIC

Room 2027 #1 Jilong Road, Waigaoqi Free Trade Zone, Shanghai, 200131, China
Tel.: (86) 2158690305
Web Site: http://www.archchemicals.com
Chemical Products Mfr
N.A.I.C.S.: 325998

Subsidiary (Non-US):

Arch Chemicals (Pty) Ltd. (2)
NCP Factory Site 9 Hytor Rd, Chloorkop, Kempton Park, 1620, South Africa
Tel.: (27) 113939000
Sales Range: $150-199.9 Million
Chemical Products Mfr
N.A.I.C.S.: 325998

Subsidiary (Domestic):

Arch Water Products South Africa Pty. Limited (3)
9 Hycor Rd, Chloorkop, Kempton Park, 1620, South Africa (100%)
Tel.: (27) 113939000
Web Site: http://www.lonza.com
Sales Range: $25-49.9 Million
Emp.: 240
Calcium Hypochlorite Mfr
N.A.I.C.S.: 325180
David Platt *(Mng Dir)*

Arch Wood Protection (SA) (Properietary) Limited (3)
16 Indus Road, Marburg, Port Shepstone, 4240, South Africa
Tel.: (27) 39 682 6019
Sales Range: $25-49.9 Million
Emp.: 19
Wood Protection Chemicals Distr
N.A.I.C.S.: 424690

Subsidiary (Non-US):

Arch Chemicals B.V. (2)
Watery Ln, Swords, Dublin, Ireland (100%)
Tel.: (353) 1 8908000
Web Site: http://www.archchemicals.com
Sales Range: $10-24.9 Million
Emp.: 50
Biocides for Personal Care & Industrial Use
N.A.I.C.S.: 325110

Subsidiary (Domestic):

Arch Chemicals Ireland B.V. (3)
Watery Lane, Swords, Co Dublin, Ireland
Tel.: (353) 1 8908000
Web Site: http://www.lonza.com
Personal Care & Industrial Biocides Mfr
N.A.I.C.S.: 325998

Subsidiary (Non-US):

Arch Chemicals Far East Ltd. (2)
80-6 Soo Song-Dong, Suktan Building 6F, Chongro-Ku, Seoul, Korea (South)
Tel.: (82) 2 737 2840
Web Site: http://www.archchemicals.com
Sales Range: $150-199.9 Million
Chemical Products Mfr
N.A.I.C.S.: 325998

Arch Chemicals GmbH (2)
An Der Poent 62 A, 40885, Ratingen, Germany (100%)
Tel.: (49) 151 14 10 28 65
Web Site: http://www.archchemicals.de
Sales Range: $50-74.9 Million
Emp.: 10
Chemical Products Sales & Distr
N.A.I.C.S.: 424690

Arch Chemicals Japan, Inc. (2)
Hamamatsucho DS Bldg 1 27 16 Hamamatsu-cho, Minato-ku, Tokyo, 105 0013, Japan (100%)
Tel.: (81) 354081770
Web Site: http://www.archchemicals.com
Sales Range: $10-24.9 Million
Emp.: 10
Chemical Products Mfr
N.A.I.C.S.: 325998

Arch Chemicals Ltd. (2)
Wheldon Rd, Castleford, WF10 2JT, West Yorkshire, United Kingdom (50%)
Tel.: (44) 1977 714000
Web Site: http://www.archchemicals.com
Sales Range: $10-24.9 Million
Emp.: 50
Timber Protection

AND PRIVATE COMPANIES — LONZA GROUP AG

N.A.I.C.S.: 325998

Subsidiary (Domestic):

Arch UK Biocides Ltd. (3)
Wheldon Road, Castleford, WF10 2JT,
West Yorkshire, United Kingdom
Tel.: (44) 1977 714200
Specialty Chemicals Mfr
N.A.I.C.S.: 325998
Caren Scott (CEO)

Division (Domestic):

Arch Water Products (3)
Wheldon Road, Castleford, WF10 2JT,
West Yorkshire, United Kingdom
Tel.: (44) 1977 714100
Emp.: 20
Water Treatment Chemical Distr
N.A.I.C.S.: 424690

Subsidiary (Domestic):

Lonza Wood Protection (3)
Wheldon Road, Castleford, WF10 2JT, W
Yorkshire, United Kingdom
Tel.: (44) 1977714000
Web Site: http://www.lonzawood.com
Timber Preservers
N.A.I.C.S.: 321114
David Lewis (Mng Dir)

Subsidiary (Non-US):

Arch Chemicals SAS (2)
28 rue Jean Jaures, Les Mureaux, 78130,
France
Tel.: (33) 130 999 888
Web Site: http://www.lonza.com
Sales Range: $25-49.9 Million
Emp.: 20
Specialty Chemicals Distr
N.A.I.C.S.: 424690

Subsidiary (Domestic):

Arch Water Products France S.A.S (3)
Zi La Boistardiere Chemin du Roi, 37400,
Amboise, France
Tel.: (33) 2 47 23 71 15
Web Site: http://www.archwater.fr
Sales Range: $75-99.9 Million
Emp.: 10
Waste Treatment Services
N.A.I.C.S.: 221310
Xavier Papillard (Dir-Sls-Export)

Subsidiary (Non-US):

Arch Chemicals Singapore Pte, Ltd. (2)
10 Science Park Road 02-12 The Alpha,
Science Park II, Singapore, 117684, Singapore
Tel.: (65) 67781181
Web Site: http://www.archchemicals.com
Sales Range: $150-199.9 Million
Chemical Products Mfr
N.A.I.C.S.: 325998

Plant (Non-US):

Arch Chemicals, Inc. - Kuala Lumpur (2)
No 1-1 Jalan 109E Desa Business Park
Taman Desa, Off Jalan Klang Lama, Kuala
Lumpur, 58100, Malaysia
Tel.: (60) 3 7981 4002
Web Site: http://www.lonza.com
Sales Range: $25-49.9 Million
Emp.: 20
Wood Protection Chemicals Distr
N.A.I.C.S.: 424690
Kenny Kong (Gen Mgr)

Subsidiary (Non-US):

Arch Chemicals, Inc. - Mississauga (2)
2000 Argentia Road Suite 320 Plaza IV,
Mississauga, L5N 1V9, ON, Canada
Tel.: (905) 826-9648
Web Site: http://www.lonza.com
Chemical Products Distr
N.A.I.C.S.: 424690

Plant (Non-US):

Arch Chemicals, Inc. - New Zealand (2)
102 Tosswill Rd, Tahunanui, Nelson, 7011,
New Zealand
Tel.: (64) 274 322 080
Web Site: http://www.lonza.com
Chemical Products Distr
N.A.I.C.S.: 424690

Arch Chemicals, Inc. - Sydney (2)
PO Box 519, North Sydney, 2059, Australia
Tel.: (61) 408 635940
Web Site: http://www.lonza.com
Sales Range: $75-99.9 Million
Emp.: 3
Waste Treatment Services
N.A.I.C.S.: 221310

Subsidiary (Non-US):

Arch Protection Chemicals Pvt. Ltd. (2)
162 6th Floor Solitaire 1 Solitaire Corporate
Park Andheri Kurla Park, Andheri East,
Mumbai, 400 093, India
Tel.: (91) 22 6713 6666
Web Site: http://www.lonza.com
Sales Range: $25-49.9 Million
Emp.: 28
Specialty Chemicals Distr
N.A.I.C.S.: 424690

Arch Quimica Argentina S.R.L. (2)
Calle Septiembre 151 Alt Km 47 5 Colectora Oeste de Panamerica, Ramal Escobar,
Buenos Aires, 1625, Argentina
Tel.: (54) 3488678600
Web Site: http://www.archchemicals.com
Sales Range: $150-199.9 Million
Chemical Products Mfr
N.A.I.C.S.: 325998

Arch Quimica Brasil Ltda. (2)
Av Brasilia 1500, Bairro Buru Salto, Sao
Paulo, 13327-901, Brazil
Tel.: (55) 1140288036
Web Site: http://www.archchemicals.com
Sales Range: $75-99.9 Million
Emp.: 250
Chemical Products Mfr
N.A.I.C.S.: 325998

Arch Quimica Colombia S.A. (2)
Of 301 Ak 15 86a71, Bogota, 110211, Colombia
Tel.: (57) 17451680
Web Site: http://www.lonza.com
Water Treatment Chemical Distr
N.A.I.C.S.: 424690

Arch Quimica Uruguay S.A. (2)
25 de Mayo 313 Of 328, Montevideo,
11100, Uruguay
Tel.: (598) 29153940
Web Site: http://www.archchemicals.com
Sales Range: $150-199.9 Million
Emp.: 2
Chemical Products Mfr
N.A.I.C.S.: 325998
Caldado Vlanco (Mgr)

Arch Quimica, S.A. de C.V. (2)
Av Lomas Verdes No 791-202 Jardines de
Satelite, Naucalpan, 53129, Mexico
Tel.: (52) 5553446486
Sales Range: $10-24.9 Million
Emp.: 4
Chemical Products Mfr
N.A.I.C.S.: 325998

Arch Timber Protection AB (2)
Grev Turegatan 70, 114 38, Stockholm,
Sweden
Tel.: (46) 708 52 24 64
Sales Range: $25-49.9 Million
Emp.: 1
Timber Protection Products Distr
N.A.I.C.S.: 423990

Arch Timber Protection BV (2)
Saltshof 1004, 6604 EA, Wijchen, Netherlands
Tel.: (31) 24 377 24 30
Web Site: http://www.lonza.com
Sales Range: $25-49.9 Million
Wood Protection Chemicals Distr
N.A.I.C.S.: 424690

Arch Wood Protection (Fiji) Ltd (2)
Nava Street Namoli Industrial Subdivision,
PO Box 4735, Lautoka, Fiji
Tel.: (679) 666 2237
Web Site: http://www.lonza.com
Sales Range: $25-49.9 Million
Emp.: 5
Wood Protection Products Mfr & Distr
N.A.I.C.S.: 321211
Firilo Mule (Mgr)

Arch Wood Protection (M) Sdn. Bhd. (2)
941 Jalan Kubang Semang, 14400, Bukit
Mertajam, Pulau Pinang, Malaysia
Tel.: (60) 4 5383500
Sales Range: $25-49.9 Million
Emp.: 7
Wood Protection Chemicals Mfr
N.A.I.C.S.: 325194

Arch Wood Protection (NZ) Limited (2)
265 James Fletcher Drive, PO Box 22148,
Otahuhu, Auckland, 1640, New Zealand
Tel.: (64) 9 276 3646
Web Site: http://www.lonza.com
Sales Range: $25-49.9 Million
Emp.: 15
Wood Protection Chemicals Mfr
N.A.I.C.S.: 325194

Subsidiary (Domestic):

Arch Wood Protection, Inc. (2)
360 Interstate N Pkwy Ste 450, Atlanta, GA
30339 (100%)
Tel.: (678) 627-2000
Web Site: http://www.wolmanizedwood.com
Wood Protection Chemicals Mfr
N.A.I.C.S.: 325194
Frank Kicklighter (VP & Grp Head-Wood
Protection Bus-Global)

Plant (Domestic):

Arch Wood Protection, Inc. - Conley Plant (3)
3941 Bonsal Rd, Conley, GA 30288-1207
Tel.: (404) 362-3970
Emp.: 110
Wood Protection Chemicals Mfr
N.A.I.C.S.: 325194

Arch Personal Care Products, L.P. (1)
412 Mt Kemble Ave Ste 200 S, Morristown,
NJ 07960
Tel.: (201) 316-9200
Rev.: $5,779,800
Emp.: 45
Healtcare Services
N.A.I.C.S.: 621491

Bend Research, Inc. (1)
1201 NW Wall St, Bend, OR 97703
Tel.: (541) 382-4100
Healtcare Services
N.A.I.C.S.: 621491
James Nightingale (Pres)

Capsugel Australia Pty. Ltd. (1)
Suite 610 12 Century Circuit, Norwest,
Baulkham Hills, 2153, NSW, Australia
Tel.: (61) 294212700
Pharmaceuticals Product Mfr
N.A.I.C.S.: 325412

Capsugel, Inc. (1)
412 Mt Kemble Ave Ste 200C, Morristown,
NJ 07960 (100%)
Tel.: (862) 242-1700
Web Site: http://www.capsugel.com
Capsule Products Mfr
N.A.I.C.S.: 325412

Subsidiary (Non-US):

Capsugel (Thailand) Co., Ltd. (2)
159 Serm-Mit Tower 18th Floor Sukumvit 21
Asoke Road, Wattana, Bangkok, 10110,
Thailand
Tel.: (66) 2 2603810 8
Web Site: http://www.capsugel.com
Capsule Products Mfr
N.A.I.C.S.: 325412

Capsugel Belgium NV (2)
Rijksweg 11, B-2880, Bornem, Belgium
Tel.: (32) 38900511
Capsule Products Mfr
N.A.I.C.S.: 325412

Capsugel France SAS (2)
10 Rue Timken, F-68027, Colmar, France
Tel.: (33) 389205709
Web Site: https://www.capsugel.com
Capsule Products Mfr
N.A.I.C.S.: 325412

Capsugel Japan Inc. (2)
4-3-36 Minamihashimoto, Chuo-ku, Sagamihara, 252-0253, Kanagawa, Japan
Tel.: (81) 427006700
Web Site: http://www.capsugel.com
Capsule Products Mfr
N.A.I.C.S.: 325412

Capsugel Ploermel (2)
ZI Camagnon, BP 320, 56 803, Ploermel,
Cedex, France
Tel.: (33) 297721000
Web Site: http://www.capsugel.com
Capsule Products Mfr
N.A.I.C.S.: 325412

Plant (Domestic):

Capsugel, Inc. - Greenwood (2)
535 N Emerald Rd, Greenwood, SC 29646-9669
Tel.: (800) 845-6973
Web Site: http://www.capsugel.com
Gelatin Capsules Mfr
N.A.I.C.S.: 325998

Subsidiary (Domestic):

Xcelience, LLC (2)
4910 Savarese Cir, Tampa, FL 33634
Tel.: (813) 286-0404
Web Site: http://www.capsugel.com
Pharmaceuticals Mfr
N.A.I.C.S.: 325412

Diacon Technologies Limited (1)
135-11960 Hammersmith Way, Richmond,
V7A 5C9, BC, Canada
Tel.: (604) 271-8855
Pharmaceuticals Product Mfr
N.A.I.C.S.: 325412

Hickson Ltd. (1)
9 Quarry Road, Winchester, SO23 0JF,
Hampshire, United Kingdom
Tel.: (44) 7799628540
Web Site: http://www.hicksonltd.com
Business Management Consulting Services
N.A.I.C.S.: 541618

InterHealth Nutraceuticals, Inc. (1)
5451 Industrial Way, Benicia, CA 94510
Tel.: (800) 783-4636
Web Site: http://www.interhealthusa.com
Nutritional Ingredients Mfr
N.A.I.C.S.: 325411
Fredrick Zilz (Head-Product Mgmt & Ops)

Komec Helsen N.V. (1)
Kernenergiestraat 79, 2610, Wilrijk, Belgium
Tel.: (32) 38283138
Web Site: http://www.komec.be
Metal Product Distr
N.A.I.C.S.: 423510
Werner Helsen (CEO & Mng Dir)

LLC Capsugel (1)
Office 3 Entrance No 3 Building 1/6 Logisticheskaya Str, Microdistrict Severniy Domodedovo, Moscow, Russia
Tel.: (7) 4959846042
Pharmaceuticals Product Mfr
N.A.I.C.S.: 325412

Lonza (China) Investments Co Ltd (1)
Room 1710-1716 Longemont Yes Tower No
369 Kai Xuan Road, Shanghai, 200051,
China
Tel.: (86) 2163403488
Sales Range: $50-74.9 Million
Emp.: 4
Investment Management Service
N.A.I.C.S.: 523999

Lonza (Thailand) Co., Ltd. (1)
Sukhumvit 21 Asoke Road 159 Serm-Mit
Tower, Bangkok, 10110, Thailand
Tel.: (66) 226038117
Biological Product Mfr
N.A.I.C.S.: 325414

Lonza Australia Pty Ltd (1)
541 Blackburn Road 2nd Floor, Mount Waverley, 3149, VIC, Australia
Tel.: (61) 3 9550 0883
Web Site: http://www.lonza.com

LONZA GROUP AG

Lonza Group AG—(Continued)

Sales Range: $50-74.9 Million
Specialty Chemicals Distr
N.A.I.C.S.: 424690
John Woods *(Mng Dir)*

Lonza Benelux BV (1)
Hoge Mosten 16, Breda, 4823 AL,
Netherlands **(100%)**
Tel.: (31) 765425100
Web Site: http://www.lonza.com
Sales Range: $50-74.9 Million
Life Science Ingredients & Biopharmaceuticals Whslr
N.A.I.C.S.: 424990

Lonza Biologics Ltd. (1)
No 1 Kangji Road, Huangpu District,
Guangzhou, 510555, Guangdong, China
Tel.: (86) 2089054201
Emp.: 400
Biological Product Mfr
N.A.I.C.S.: 325414

Lonza Biologics PLC (1)
Imperial House Lypiatt Rd, Cheltenham,
GL50 2QJ, Glos, United Kingdom **(100%)**
Tel.: (44) 1242513211
Web Site: http://www.lonzagroup.com
Sales Range: $50-74.9 Million
Emp.: 8
Sales of Chemicals
N.A.I.C.S.: 424690

Lonza Biologics Porrino, S.L. (1)
C/ La Relba s/n, 36410, Porrino, Pontevedra, Spain
Tel.: (34) 986344060
Sales Range: $100-124.9 Million
Emp.: 29
Therapeutic Protein Mfr
N.A.I.C.S.: 334510

Lonza Biologics Tuas Pte Ltd (1)
35 Tuas South Ave 6, Tuas, Singapore,
637377, Singapore
Tel.: (65) 65214000
Web Site: https://www.lonza.com.cn
Emp.: 500
Electrotherapeutic Apparatus Mfr
N.A.I.C.S.: 334510

Lonza Biologics plc (1)
228 Bath Rd, Slough, SL1 4DX, Berks,
United Kingdom **(100%)**
Tel.: (44) 1753777000
Web Site: http://www.lonzabiologics.com
Sales Range: $200-249.9 Million
Emp.: 800
Pharmaceuticals Product Mfr
N.A.I.C.S.: 325412
Gorden Bates *(Mng Dir)*

Lonza Biopharma Ltd (1)
Lonzastrasse, 3930, Visp, Switzerland
Tel.: (41) 27 948 51 11
Web Site: http://www.lonza.com
Pharmaceutical Products Mfr & Distr
N.A.I.C.S.: 325412
Stefan Troger *(Gen Mgr)*

Lonza Bioscience S.A.R.L. (1)
Rue Michel Renaud, 63360, Saint-Beauzire,
France
Tel.: (33) 140899900
Pharmaceuticals Product Mfr
N.A.I.C.S.: 325412

Lonza Bioscience Singapore Pte. Ltd. (1)
35 Tuas South Ave 6 Tuas, Singapore,
637377, Singapore
Tel.: (65) 65214379
Pharmaceuticals Product Mfr
N.A.I.C.S.: 325412

Lonza Biotec s.r.o. (1)
Okruzni 134, 281 61, Kourim, Czech
Republic **(100%)**
Tel.: (420) 321738666
Web Site: http://www.lonzabiotec.cz
Sales Range: $125-149.9 Million
Emp.: 260
Production of Chemicals & Chemical Products
N.A.I.C.S.: 325998
Ladiflav Kolek *(Mgr-Site)*

Lonza Canada Inc. (1)
4852 rue Burrill, Shawinigan, G9N 6T6, QC,
Canada
Tel.: (819) 539-9509
Sales Range: $25-49.9 Million
Emp.: 20
Bio Medical Component Mfr
N.A.I.C.S.: 325414

Lonza Cologne Gmbh (1)
Nattermannallee 1, Cologne, 50829, Germany
Tel.: (49) 221991990
Web Site: http://www.lonza.com
Sales Range: $50-74.9 Million
Emp.: 90
Biological Product Mfr
N.A.I.C.S.: 325412

Lonza Copenhagen ApS (1)
Strandhaven 12, 2665, Vallensbaek, Strand,
Denmark
Tel.: (45) 43567400
Web Site: http://www.lonza.com
Sales Range: $25-49.9 Million
Pharmaceuticals Mfr
N.A.I.C.S.: 325412

Lonza Costa Rica, S.A. (1)
Trejos Montealegre 7th Floor, Escazu Village San Refael de Escazu, San Jose,
Costa Rica
Tel.: (506) 12012498666
Pharmaceuticals Product Mfr
N.A.I.C.S.: 325412

Lonza France S.A.R.L. (1)
55 Rue Aristide Briand, Levallois-Perret,
92300, France **(100%)**
Tel.: (33) 140899900
Sales Range: $50-74.9 Million
Emp.: 10
Sales
N.A.I.C.S.: 424690
Sophie Lanjjlois *(Mgr)*

Lonza GmbH (1)
Morianstrasse 32, DE 42103, Wuppertal,
Germany **(100%)**
Tel.: (49) 2022453813
Web Site: http://www.lonza.com
Sales Range: $125-149.9 Million
Emp.: 9
N.A.I.C.S.: 221122

Lonza Guangzhou Engineering and Consulting Co Ltd (1)
Room 401 South Tower No 898 of
Guangzhou Avenue South, Haizhu District,
510305, Guangzhou, Guangdong, China
Tel.: (86) 20 3497 1118
Pharmaceutical Products Research & Development Services
N.A.I.C.S.: 541715

Lonza Guangzhou Ltd. (1)
39 Jinhui Rd, Haizhu District, Guangzhou,
510288, Guangdong, China **(100%)**
Tel.: (86) 2084338998
Web Site: http://www.lonza.com.cn
Sales Range: $700-749.9 Million
Emp.: 700
N.A.I.C.S.: 221122

Lonza Guangzhou Nansha Ltd (1)
68 Huangge Dadaobe, Nansha District,
Guangzhou, 511455, Guangdong, China
Tel.: (86) 20 3497 3888
Specialty Chemicals Distr
N.A.I.C.S.: 424690

Lonza Guangzhou Research and Development Center Ltd. (1)
68 Huangge Dadaobe, Nansha District,
Guangzhou, 511455, China
Tel.: (86) 20 3497 3888
Pharmaceutical Products Research & Development Services
N.A.I.C.S.: 541715

Lonza Hong Kong Ltd. (1)
Rm 601 6th Fl Central Hang Seng Bldg, 77
Des Voeux Rd, Hong Kong, China (Hong Kong) **(100%)**
Tel.: (852) 25456868
Web Site: http://www.lonza.com
Sales of Chemicals
N.A.I.C.S.: 424690

Lonza Iberica S.A. (1)
Via Augusta N 18 2 Fl Left Side, ES 08006,
Barcelona, Spain **(100%)**
Tel.: (34) 932385460
Web Site: http://www.lonzagroup.com
Sales Range: $50-74.9 Million
Emp.: 4
Sales of Chemicals
N.A.I.C.S.: 424690
Alsrado Jurge *(Mng Dir)*

Lonza Inc. (1)
90 Boroline Rd, Allendale, NJ
07401-1613 **(100%)**
Tel.: (201) 316-9200
Web Site: http://www.lonza.com
Sales Range: $75-99.9 Million
Emp.: 160
Mfr, Marketer & Retailer of Organic & Fine
Chemicals, Performance Chemicals, Plastics & Inorganics
N.A.I.C.S.: 325998

Subsidiary (Domestic):

Lonza Biologics, Inc. (2)
101 International Dr, Portsmouth, NH 03801
Tel.: (603) 334-6100
Sales Range: $125-149.9 Million
Bio Medical Component Mfr
N.A.I.C.S.: 325414

Lonza Rockland, Inc. (2)
191 Thomaston St, Rockland, ME 04841-2130
Tel.: (207) 594-3400
Sales Range: $25-49.9 Million
Bio Medical Supplies Mfr
N.A.I.C.S.: 325414

Lonza Walkersville, Inc. (2)
8830 Biggs Ford Rd, Walkersville, MD
21793-8415
Tel.: (301) 898-7025
Sales Range: $100-124.9 Million
Production of Biomedical Products; Cell
Cultures, Chemically Defined Media, Endotoxin Detection Products
N.A.I.C.S.: 325414

Lonza Waynec Inc. (2)
1255 Drummers Ln, Wayne, PA 19087
Tel.: (484) 253-1000
Web Site: http://www.lonza.com
Sales Range: $25-49.9 Million
Emp.: 20
Biological Research & Development Services
N.A.I.C.S.: 541715

Lonza India Private Limited (1)
Corpora 2nd Floor LBS Marg Bhandup
West, Mumbai, 400 078, India
Tel.: (91) 22 4342 4000
Web Site: http://www.lonza.com
Sales Range: $25-49.9 Million
Emp.: 28
Pharmaceutical Intermediates, Bioscience &
Microbial Control Actives & Formulations for
Hospitals & Pharma Clean Rooms
N.A.I.C.S.: 325412

Lonza Japan Ltd. (1)
Kyowa Shinkawa Building 8 Floor 2 20 8
Shinkawa, Chuo Ku, Tokyo, 104 0033,
Japan **(100%)**
Tel.: (81) 355660612
Web Site: http://www.lonza.co.jp
Sales Range: $25-49.9 Million
Emp.: 20
Chemical Distr
N.A.I.C.S.: 424690

Lonza K.K. (1)
39F St Luke's Tower 8-1 Akashi-cho, Chuo-ku, Tokyo, 104-6591, Japan
Tel.: (81) 362640600
Pharmaceuticals Product Mfr
N.A.I.C.S.: 325412

Lonza Microbial Control Asia Pacific Pte. Ltd. (1)
10 Science Park Road 02-12 The Alpha
Singapore Science Park II Tuas, Singapore,
637377, Singapore
Tel.: (65) 67781181
Pharmaceuticals Product Mfr
N.A.I.C.S.: 325412

Lonza Milano S.r.l. (1)
Via Rossini 1/3, I-24047, Treviglio, DG, Italy
Tel.: (39) 036545710
Web Site: http://www.milanolonza.com

INTERNATIONAL PUBLIC

Sales Range: $1-9.9 Million
Emp.: 10
Pharmaceuticals Mfr
N.A.I.C.S.: 325412

Lonza NZ Limited (1)
15 Hudson Rd, 4373, New Plymouth, New
Zealand
Tel.: (64) 67559234
Pharmaceuticals Product Mfr
N.A.I.C.S.: 325412

Lonza Nanjing Ltd (1)
No 201 East Dawai Road Nanjing Chemical
Industry Park, Nanjing, 210047, China
Tel.: (86) 25 5836 83 88
Web Site: http://www.lonza.com
Sales Range: $25-49.9 Million
Emp.: 93
Water Treatment Chemical Mfr
N.A.I.C.S.: 325998

Lonza Netherlands B.V. (1)
Oxfordlaan 70, 6229 EV, Maastricht, Netherlands
Tel.: (31) 433509910
Pharmaceuticals Product Mfr
N.A.I.C.S.: 325412

Lonza Sales Ltd (1)
Muenchensteinerstrasse 38, 4002, Basel,
Switzerland
Tel.: (41) 613168111
Sales Range: $150-199.9 Million
Emp.: 30
Chemical Products Distr
N.A.I.C.S.: 424690

Lonza Verviers Sprl (1)
Parc Industriel de Petit-Rechain, 4800, Verviers, Belgium **(100%)**
Tel.: (32) 87321611
Sales Range: $75-99.9 Million
Emp.: 130
Biotechnology Products Mfr & Distr
N.A.I.C.S.: 424210
Gechambre Bernard *(Mng Dir)*

Micro-Macinazione SA (1)
Via Cantonale 4, 6998, Monteggio, Switzerland
Tel.: (41) 916113636
Biological Product Mfr
N.A.I.C.S.: 325414

OOO Lonza Rus (1)
Building 1/6 Logisticheskaya Str, Microdistrict Severniy Domodedovo, 115419, Moscow, Russia
Tel.: (7) 4957212339
Web Site: http://www.lonza.com.cn
Specialty Chemicals Distr
N.A.I.C.S.: 424690

Octane Biotech Inc. (1)
369 Dalton Avenue, Kingston, K7K 6Z1,
ON, Canada
Tel.: (613) 634-6345
Web Site: http://www.octaneco.com
Medical Device Mfr
N.A.I.C.S.: 339112

LOOK INCORPORATED

8-5-30 Akasaka, Minato-ku, Tokyo,
107-0052, Japan
Tel.: (81) 364391650
Web Site: https://www.look-inc.jp
Year Founded: 1962
LOO—(DEU)
Emp.: 1,672
Clothing Apparel Mfr & Distr
N.A.I.C.S.: 314999
Kazuhiro Tada *(Pres)*

Subsidiaries:

I.D. LOOK LTD. (1)
580 Gangnam-daero, Gangnam-gu, Seoul,
06043, Korea (South)
Tel.: (82) 2 3438 9100
Web Site: http://www.idlook.co.kr
Emp.: 100
Apparels Mfr
N.A.I.C.S.: 315990

L.LOGISTICS INC. (1)
2-3-1 Akanehama, Narashino, Chiba, Japan
Tel.: (81) 47 455 2111
Apparels Mfr

AND PRIVATE COMPANIES — LOOMIS AB

N.A.I.C.S.: 315990

LAISSE PASSE CO., LTD. (1)
Claire Tours 4-5 Motoyoyogichou, Shibuya-ku, Tokyo, 151-0062, Japan (80%)
Tel.: (81) 3 5790 7201
Apparels Mfr
N.A.I.C.S.: 315990

LOOK CHINA CO., LTD. (1)
Fl3 Bld4 No 1151 Lianxi Rd, Pudong, Shanghai, 200127, China
Tel.: (86) 21 5039 1533
Apparels Mfr
N.A.I.C.S.: 315990

LOOK (H.K) LTD. (1)
7B Hing Wing Factory Bldg 110 How Ming Street, Kwun Tong, Kowloon, China (Hong Kong)
Tel.: (852) 2751 8773
Apparels Mfr
N.A.I.C.S.: 315990

LOOKERS PLC
Lookers House 3 Etchells Road West Timperley, Altrincham, WA14 5XS, United Kingdom
Tel.: (44) 1612910043 UK
Web Site: http://www.lookersplc.com
Year Founded: 1908
LOOK—(LSE)
Rev.: $5,499,716,404
Assets: $1,988,516,712
Liabilities: $1,486,703,400
Net Worth: $501,813,312
Earnings: $83,092,464
Emp.: 6,030
Fiscal Year-end: 12/31/21
Holding Company; Car Dealerships Owner & Operator
N.A.I.C.S.: 551112
Mark Douglas Raban (CEO)

Subsidiaries:

Charles Hurst Dublin Limited (1)
Unit 96 Bracken Rd Sandyford Business Park Sandyford, Dublin, Ireland
Tel.: (353) 19026814
Web Site: http://www.usedirectireland.ie
Used Car Distr
N.A.I.C.S.: 441120

Charles Hurst Limited (1)
62 Boucher Road, Belfast, BT12 6LR, Antrim, United Kingdom
Tel.: (44) 3301089261
Web Site: http://www.charleshurstgroup.co.uk
Emp.: 1,000
Motor Vehicle Retailers
N.A.I.C.S.: 423110

Subsidiary (Domestic):

Balmoral Motors Ltd (2)
62 Boucher Road, Belfast, BT12 6LR, United Kingdom
Tel.: (44) 2890381721
Web Site: http://www.charleshurstgroup.co.uk
Sales Range: $75-99.9 Million
Emp.: 200
Automobile Sales & Support Services
N.A.I.C.S.: 423120

Dutton-Forshaw Motor Co., Ltd. (1)
142 Rayne Road, Braintree, CM7 2QS, Essex, United Kingdom
Tel.: (44) 1376554218
Sales Range: $25-49.9 Million
Emp.: 12
Automobile Repair & Maintenance Services
N.A.I.C.S.: 811111
Marie Carr (Mgr)

Fleet Financial Limited (1)
62 Boucher Road Balmoral, County Antrim, Belfast, BT12 6LR, United Kingdom
Tel.: (44) 2890849777
Web Site: http://www.fleetfinancial.co.uk
Vehicle Leasing Services
N.A.I.C.S.: 532112
Damian Hughes (Mng Dir)

Howdens of Harrogate Limited (1)
Units B-C Claro Way, Harrogate, HG1 4DE, United Kingdom
Tel.: (44) 1423523202
Kitchen & Joinery Product Distr
N.A.I.C.S.: 423310

Lookers Birmingham Limited (1)
Star Park South Heartlands Parkway, Birmingham, B75 AH, West Midlands, United Kingdom
Tel.: (44) 1213257548
Sales Range: $25-49.9 Million
Emp.: 80
New & Used Car Dealers
N.A.I.C.S.: 441120

Lookers Leasing Limited (1)
Lookers House Cardale Park, Harrogate, HG3 1RY, North Yorkshire, United Kingdom
Tel.: (44) 1423853000
Web Site: http://www.lookersleasing.co.uk
Sales Range: $50-74.9 Million
Emp.: 10
Fleet Management Services
N.A.I.C.S.: 532112

Lookers Motor Group Limited (1)
Bircholt Road, Maidstone, ME15 9YN, Kent, United Kingdom
Tel.: (44) 1612910043
Web Site: http://www.lookers.co.uk
Motor Vehicle Dealerships Operator
N.A.I.C.S.: 441110

Platts Harris Limited (1)
34 Eldon Street, Tuxford, Newark, NG22 0LH, Nottinghamshire, United Kingdom
Tel.: (44) 1777870111
Web Site: http://www.plattsharris.co.uk
Sales Range: $10-24.9 Million
Emp.: 49
Construction & Groundcare Machinery Sales
N.A.I.C.S.: 423390
Kevin Petley (Mng Dir)

Rosedale Finance & Leasing Limited (1)
Suite A The Exchange Maingate Kingsway North, Gateshead, NE11 0BE, Tyne and Wear, United Kingdom
Tel.: (44) 1912981648
Web Site: http://www.rosedaleleasing.com
Car Lending Services
N.A.I.C.S.: 532112
Jason Smith (Head-Fleet Ops)

Taggarts Motor Group Ltd. (1)
262 Maryhill Road, Glasgow, G20 7YD, Lanarkshire, United Kingdom
Tel.: (44) 3442119163
Web Site: http://www.taggarts.co.uk
Automobile Sales
N.A.I.C.S.: 441110

LOOKING GLASS LABS LTD.
Suite 810-789 West Pender Street, Vancouver, V6C 1H2, BC, Canada
Tel.: (604) 687-2038 BC
Web Site: https://www.lgl.io
Year Founded: 2015
LGSLF—(OTCIQ)
Rev.: $5,225,908
Assets: $5,670,319
Liabilities: $2,965,273
Net Worth: $2,705,046
Earnings: ($8,882,531)
Emp.: 10
Fiscal Year-end: 07/31/22
Information Technology Services
N.A.I.C.S.: 541512
Arthur Francis Rowe (CFO)

LOOKS FINLAND OY
Sornaisten Rantatie 22E 2 krs, 00540, Helsinki, Finland
Tel.: (358) 400249424 FI
Web Site: http://www.looks.fi
Year Founded: 1998
Sales Range: $1-9.9 Million
Emp.: 100
Financial & Insurance Services
N.A.I.C.S.: 523999
Jussi Heino (Mng Dir)

LOOKS HEALTH SERVICES LIMITED
5 & 9 Plot - 27/33 Floor 1 & 2 Beaumon Chambers Nagindas Master Lane, Hutatma Chowk Fort, Mumbai, 400001, Maharashtra, India
Tel.: (91) 2262361730
Web Site: http://www.looksclinic.in
534422—(BOM)
Rev.: $54,866
Assets: $1,779,963
Liabilities: $5,276
Net Worth: $1,774,688
Earnings: ($2,122)
Emp.: 6
Fiscal Year-end: 03/31/24
Health Clinic
N.A.I.C.S.: 621399
Pritesh Champalal Doshi (Chm, CFO & Sec)

LOOMIS AB
Drottninggatan 82 4th Floor, PO Box 702, SE-101 33, Stockholm, Sweden
Tel.: (46) 852292000
Web Site: http://www.loomis.com
LOOM—(OMX)
Rev.: $2,296,691,040
Assets: $3,039,303,680
Liabilities: $1,968,417,920
Net Worth: $1,070,885,760
Earnings: $87,409,280
Emp.: 22,800
Fiscal Year-end: 12/31/20
Cash Handling Services
N.A.I.C.S.: 561613
Alf Goransson (Chm)

Subsidiaries:

Loomis Belgium NV (1)
Ottergemsesteenweg 419, 9000, Gent, Belgium
Tel.: (32) 9 243 7080
Web Site: https://www.loomis.be
Security Services
N.A.I.C.S.: 561612

Loomis Czech Republic a.s. (1)
Sezemicka 2853/4, Horni Pocernice ICO 261, 107 09, Prague, Czech Republic
Tel.: (420) 277003850
Web Site: https://loomis.cz
Security Cash Handling Services
N.A.I.C.S.: 522320

Loomis Danmark A/S (1)
Lithuania Alle 1, 2630, Taastrup, Denmark
Tel.: (45) 70264242
Web Site: https://dk.loomis.com
Sales Range: $25-49.9 Million
Emp.: 100
Cash Handling Services
N.A.I.C.S.: 561613

Loomis Digital Solution AB (1)
Drottninggatan 82, 111 36, Stockholm, Sweden
Tel.: (46) 101636300
Web Site: http://help.loomispay.com
Digital Payment Solution Services
N.A.I.C.S.: 522320

Loomis FX Gold and Services SAS (1)
42 rue Benoit Maon, 94250, Gentilly, France
Tel.: (33) 149705500
Web Site: https://www.loomis-fxgs.fr
Currencies & Gold Exchange Services
N.A.I.C.S.: 523210

Loomis Foreign Exchange AS (1)
Persveien 26, 0581, Oslo, Norway
Tel.: (47) 21525200
Web Site: http://www.loomis.no
Foreign Exchange Services
N.A.I.C.S.: 523160
Harald Welde (Acct Mgr)

Loomis France S.A.S. (1)
ZAC du Marcreux - 20 Rue Marcel Carne, 93300, Aubervilliers, France
Tel.: (33) 800155124
Web Site: https://www.loomis.fr

Sales Range: $650-699.9 Million
Emp.: 4,100
Cash Handling Services
N.A.I.C.S.: 561613
Michael Tresch (CEO)

Loomis Guvenlik Hizmetleri A.S. (1)
Tekfen Kagithane Ofispark B Blok Kat 1 Merkez Mahallesi, Baglar Cd No 14 Kagithane, 34406, Istanbul, Turkiye
Tel.: (90) 212 603 0370
Web Site: https://www.loomis.com.tr
Retail Banking Services
N.A.I.C.S.: 522110

Loomis Holder Spain SL (1)
Calle Retama 3, Madrid, 28045, Spain
Tel.: (34) 915062040
Cash Handling Services
N.A.I.C.S.: 522390

Loomis International Services GmbH (1)
Nordbahnstrasse 36/3, 1020, Vienna, Austria
Tel.: (43) 1 211 11 0
Web Site: http://www.loomis.at
Secured Cash Transportation Services
N.A.I.C.S.: 522320

Loomis Norge AS (1)
Persveien 26, 0581, Oslo, Norway
Tel.: (47) 2 152 5200
Web Site: https://www.loomis.no
Sales Range: $75-99.9 Million
Emp.: 420
Cash Handling Services
N.A.I.C.S.: 561613

Loomis Osterreich GmbH (1)
Fugbachgasse 22-24, 1020, Vienna, Austria
Tel.: (43) 1211111000
Web Site: https://at.loomis.com
Sales Range: $75-99.9 Million
Emp.: 370
Cash Handling Services
N.A.I.C.S.: 525990

Loomis Portugal, S.A (1)
Rua Rodrigues Lobo 2, 2799-553, Linda-a-Velha, Portugal
Tel.: (351) 210122500
Web Site: https://www.loomis.pt
Sales Range: $75-99.9 Million
Emp.: 320
Cash Handling Services
N.A.I.C.S.: 561613

Loomis Schweiz AG (1)
Steinackerstrasse 49, 8302, Kloten, Switzerland
Tel.: (41) 848803804
Web Site: https://www.loomis.ch
Sales Range: $25-49.9 Million
Emp.: 110
Cash Handling Services
N.A.I.C.S.: 561613

Loomis Slovensko, s.r.o. (1)
Vajnorska 140, 831 04, Bratislava, Slovakia
Tel.: (421) 232336101
Web Site: http://www.loomis.sk
Sales Range: $10-24.9 Million
Emp.: 35
Cash Handling Services
N.A.I.C.S.: 561613

Loomis Spain, S.A. (1)
C/ Ahumaos Number 35-37 Pl La Dehesa de Vicalvaro, Vicalvaro, 28052, Madrid, Spain
Tel.: (34) 917438900
Web Site: https://es.loomis.com
Sales Range: $300-349.9 Million
Emp.: 2,388
Cash Handling Services
N.A.I.C.S.: 561613

Loomis Suomi Oy (1)
Turvalaaksontie 1, 01740, Vantaa, Finland
Tel.: (358) 204303000
Web Site: https://fi.loomis.com
Emp.: 350
Cash Handling Services
N.A.I.C.S.: 561613

Loomis Sverige AB (1)
Staffans vag 2B, 192 78, Sollentuna, Sweden
Tel.: (46) 85 222 4600
Web Site: https://www.loomis.se

LOOMIS AB

Loomis AB—(Continued)
Cash Handling Services
N.A.I.C.S.: 523150

Subsidiary (Domestic):

Nokas Vardehantering AB (2)
Vastberga Alle 11, Stockholm, 126 17, Sweden
Tel.: (46) 102226000
Web Site: http://www.g4scash.se
Cash Handling Security System Services
N.A.I.C.S.: 561621
Kieran Doherty *(Gen Mgr)*

Loomis UK Ltd. (1)
6th Floor Regus East West Building 2, Tollhouse Hill, Nottingham, NG1 5FS, United Kingdom
Tel.: (44) 8453096419
Web Site: https://uk.loomis.com
Sales Range: $650-699.9 Million
Cost Management Services
N.A.I.C.S.: 561613

Loomis US Inc. (1)
2500 Citywest Blvd Ste 2300, Houston, TX 77042
Tel.: (713) 435-6700
Web Site: https://www.loomis.us
Sales Range: $500-549.9 Million
Emp.: 8,000
Cash Handling Services
N.A.I.C.S.: 561613
Pat Otero *(Sr VP-Admin)*

Loomis Value Solutions Oy (1)
Loomis Suomi Oy 1773520-6, PO Box 6000, 01511, Vantaa, Finland
Tel.: (358) 204303000
Web Site: https://www.loomis.fi
Cash & Financial Services
N.A.I.C.S.: 541611

Loomis d.o.o. (1)
Letaliska Cesta 10, 2312, Orehovica, Slovenia
Tel.: (386) 1 21196 326
Sales Range: $25-49.9 Million
Emp.: 20
Cash Handling Services
N.A.I.C.S.: 561613

Loomis eStore AB (1)
Tuna Industrivag 23, 153 30, Jarna, Sweden
Tel.: (46) 85 222 4770
Web Site: https://estore.loomis.se
Packaging Services
N.A.I.C.S.: 561910

LOOP INDUSTRIES, INC.

480 Fernand Poitras Street Terrebonne, Quebec, J6Y 1Y4, QC, Canada
Tel.: (450) 951-8555 NV
Web Site: https://www.loopindustries.com
Year Founded: 2010
LOOP—(NASDAQ)
Assets: $59,220,199
Liabilities: $13,225,218
Net Worth: $45,994,981
Earnings: ($44,920,956)
Emp.: 89
Fiscal Year-end: 02/28/22
Upcycling Technology Company;
Chemical Recycling
N.A.I.C.S.: 423930
Daniel Solomita *(Chm, Pres & CEO)*

LOOP TELECOMMUNICATION INTERNATIONAL, INC.

7F No 8 Hsin Ann Road Science-Based Industrial Park, Hsinchu, 300092, Taiwan
Tel.: (886) 35787696
Web Site: https://www.looptelecom.com
Year Founded: 1991
3025—(TAI)
Rev.: $21,226,887
Assets: $42,036,200
Liabilities: $14,461,918
Net Worth: $27,574,282
Earnings: $6,529,285
Emp.: 17
Fiscal Year-end: 12/31/23
Communication Equipment Mfr
N.A.I.C.S.: 238210
Marty Wu *(VP-Mktg & Sls-China & Asia)*

Subsidiaries:

Loop Telecom NA, Inc. (1)
2000 G Ave Ste 804, Plano, TX 75074
Tel.: (972) 366-0033
Web Site: https://www.looptelecomna.com
Telecommunication & Information Services
N.A.I.C.S.: 517810

LOOPSHARE LTD.

Suite 106 131 Water Street, Vancouver, V6B 4M3, BC, Canada
Tel.: (604) 568-1598 SK
Web Site: https://loopscooters.com
Year Founded: 2009
GFCOF—(OTCIQ)
Rev.: $376,595
Assets: $2,156,361
Liabilities: $1,430,448
Net Worth: $725,913
Earnings: ($4,337,887)
Fiscal Year-end: 06/30/22
Investment Services
N.A.I.C.S.: 523999
Matthew Clayton *(Chm & Co-CEO)*

LOOPUP GROUP PLC

52 Tabernacle Street, The Tea Building, London, EC2A 4NJ, United Kingdom
Tel.: (44) 2031070206
Web Site: https://www.loopup.com
Year Founded: 2003
LOOP—(LSE)
Rev.: $68,198,276
Assets: $130,114,381
Liabilities: $41,610,045
Net Worth: $88,504,336
Earnings: $8,855,050
Emp.: 241
Fiscal Year-end: 12/31/20
All Other Telecommunications
N.A.I.C.S.: 517810
Steve Flavell *(Co-Founder & Co-CEO)*

Subsidiaries:

Comfy MeetingZone AB (1)
Sodra Forstadsgatan 40A, 21143, Malmo, Sweden
Tel.: (46) 77 410 1049
Telecommunication Servicesb
N.A.I.C.S.: 517810

Confy MeetingZone AB (1)
Sodra Forstadsgatan 40A, 21143, Malmo, Sweden
Tel.: (46) 774101049
Software Development Services
N.A.I.C.S.: 541511

LoopUp (HK) Limited (1)
46/F Lee Garden One 33 Hysan Avenue, Causeway Bay, China (Hong Kong)
Tel.: (852) 3 905 3403
Software Development Services
N.A.I.C.S.: 541511

LoopUp Australia Pty Ltd (1)
Level 10 580 George Street, Sydney, 2000, NSW, Australia
Tel.: (61) 27 908 2612
Software Development Services
N.A.I.C.S.: 541511

MeetingZone GmbH (1)
Hardenbergstr 32, 10623, Berlin, Germany
Tel.: (49) 692 222 3969
Telecommunication Servicesb
N.A.I.C.S.: 517810

MeetingZone Ltd. (1)
The Tea Building 56 Shoreditch High St, Cardiff, E1 6JJ, United Kingdom
Tel.: (44) 203 107 0206
Web Site: https://www.meetingzone.com
Audio & Web Conferencing Services
N.A.I.C.S.: 517810
Steve O'Reilly *(Mgr-Data Strategy)*

LOOTOM TELCO-VIDEO NETWORK(WUXI).CO.,LTD

No 182 Luou East Road Binhu, Wuxi, 214161, Jiangsu, China
Tel.: (86) 15261520683
Web Site: https://www.lootom.com
Year Founded: 2007
300555—(CHIN)
Rev.: $25,650,715
Assets: $97,260,517
Liabilities: $16,071,365
Net Worth: $81,189,151
Earnings: ($4,853,268)
Fiscal Year-end: 12/31/23
Integrated Component Mfr & Distr
N.A.I.C.S.: 334413

LOPAM

Rue Bernard Gombert, 27300, Bernay, Eure, France
Tel.: (33) 232458405
Sales Range: $25-49.9 Million
Emp.: 44
Grocery Stores
N.A.I.C.S.: 445110
Laurent Boutbien *(CEO)*

LOPEZ, INC.

5th Floor Benpres Bldg Exchange Road cor Meralco Ave, Pasig, Philippines
Tel.: (63) 26313111
Web Site: http://www.lopezgroup.org
Holding Company Services
N.A.I.C.S.: 551112

Subsidiaries:

ABS-CBN Holdings Corporation (1)
16/F North Tower Rockwell Business Center, Sheridan St Corner United St Barangay Highway Hills, Mandaluyong, 1554, Philippines
Tel.: (63) 88780000
Web Site: https://www.edge.pse.com
Rev.: $102,736
Assets: $404,855
Liabilities: $404,854
Net Worth: $1
Fiscal Year-end: 12/31/2020
Holding Company
N.A.I.C.S.: 551112
Oscar M. Lopez *(Chm, Pres, CEO & COO)*

Lopez Holdings Corporation (1)
16/F North Tower Rockwell Business Center Sheridan Sheridan St, corner United St 1550 Bgy Highway Hills, Mandaluyong, Philippines (54.44%)
Tel.: (63) 28780000
Web Site: http://www.lopez-holdings.ph
Rev.: $2,378,629,330
Assets: $7,410,251,100
Liabilities: $3,840,855,900
Net Worth: $3,569,395,200
Earnings: $402,220,910
Emp.: 15
Fiscal Year-end: 12/31/2018
Holding Company; Broadcasting, Cable & Satellite; Telecommunications; Electric Power Distribution & Generation
N.A.I.C.S.: 551112
Enrique I. Quiason *(Sec)*

Subsidiary (Non-US):

ABS-CBN Australia Pty Ltd (2)
B6 12-14 Solent Circuit, 2153, Baulkham Hills, Australia
Tel.: (61) 288846188
Television Broadcasting
N.A.I.C.S.: 516120

Subsidiary (Domestic):

ABS-CBN Corporation (2)
Sgt E A Esguerra Ave, corner Mother Ignacia Street, Quezon City, Philippines (60.3%)
Tel.: (63) 234152272
Web Site: https://ent.abs-cbn.com
Rev.: $445,530,946
Assets: $1,225,664,482
Liabilities: $867,928,381
Net Worth: $357,736,101
Earnings: ($281,440,973)
Emp.: 4,939
Fiscal Year-end: 12/31/2020
Television Broadcasting & Related Services
N.A.I.C.S.: 516120
Augusto Almeda-Lopez *(Vice Chm)*

Subsidiary (Domestic):

ABS-CBN Film Productions Inc. (3)
2nd Floor ELJCC Building Eugenio Lopez Drive, Quezon City, 1103, Philippines
Tel.: (63) 24147825
Web Site: http://starcinema.abs-cbn.com
Sales Range: $100-124.9 Million
Emp.: 300
Film & Television Production
N.A.I.C.S.: 512110
Angie Pineda *(Asst VP-Distr)*

ABS-CBN Foundation, Inc. (3)
Mother Ignacia Ave Corner E Lopez Dr, Brgy S Diliman District, Quezon City, 1103, Philippines
Tel.: (63) 29224842
Web Site: http://www.abs-cbnfoundation.com
Sales Range: $1-9.9 Million
Emp.: 300
Outreach Programs for Children & Families
N.A.I.C.S.: 516120
Regina Paz Lopez *(Mng Dir)*

Subsidiary (US):

ABS-CBN International (3)
150 Shoreline Dr, Redwood City, CA 94065
Tel.: (650) 508-6000
Web Site: http://www.abs-cbnglobal.com
Sales Range: $25-49.9 Million
Emp.: 50
Television Broadcasting
N.A.I.C.S.: 516120
Elisha Lawrence *(Asst VP-Global Anti-Piracy)*

Subsidiary (Domestic):

Star Recording, Inc. (3)
2 F Roadrunner Bldg 282 Tomas Morato Ave, Diliman, Quezon City, 1100, Philippines
Tel.: (63) 24139159
Web Site: http://www.pari.com.ph
N.A.I.C.S.: 516120

Subsidiary (Domestic):

First Philippine Holdings Corporation (2)
6th Floor Rockwell Business Center Tower 3, Ortigas Avenue, Pasig, 1604, Philippines (51.04%)
Tel.: (63) 25558000
Web Site: https://www.fphc.com
Rev.: $2,978,279,289
Assets: $8,525,322,660
Liabilities: $4,103,656,186
Net Worth: $4,421,666,474
Earnings: $524,618,574
Emp.: 9,538
Fiscal Year-end: 12/31/2023
Power Generation Services
N.A.I.C.S.: 562213
Oscar M. Lopez *(Chief Strategic Officer)*

Subsidiary (Domestic):

Asian Eye Institute Inc. (3)
8th 9th and 10th Floors Phinma Plaza Rockwell Center, Makati, Philippines
Tel.: (63) 288982020
Web Site: http://www.asianeyeinstitute.com
Eye Care Service
N.A.I.C.S.: 621320

First Balfour, Inc. (3)
KM 19 West Service Road Barangay Marcelo Green Sucat, Paranaque, 1700, Philippines
Tel.: (63) 277914001
Web Site: http://www.firstbalfour.com
Construction & Engineering Services
N.A.I.C.S.: 541330
Federico R. Lopez *(Chm & CEO)*

AND PRIVATE COMPANIES

First Industrial Science & Technology School Inc. (3)
3/F Oasis Building Special Economic Zone R S Diaz Ave, Brgy Sta Anastacia First Philippine Industrial Park Santo Tomas, Batangas, 4234, Philippines
Tel.: (63) 9177134778
Web Site: http://www.firstschool.edu.ph
Industrial School Services
N.A.I.C.S.: 611110

First Philippine Electric Corporation (3)
5th floor Rockwell Business Center Tower 3 Ortigas Avenue, Pasig, Philippines
Tel.: (63) 9175394074
Web Site: http://www.firstphilec.com
Transformer Mfr
N.A.I.C.S.: 335311
Derrick Roy B. Degay *(Head-Ops)*

First Philippine Industrial Park, Inc. (3)
Barangay Sta Anastacia, Santo Tomas, 4234, Batangas, Philippines
Tel.: (63) 43 405 6020
Web Site: http://www.fpip.com
Industrial Park Development Services
N.A.I.C.S.: 531312
Alexander M. Roque *(Head-Park Mgmt & Dev)*

Rockwell Primaries Development Corporation (3)
8 Rockwell Building Hidalgo Drive Rockwell Center, Makati, 1200, Philippines
Tel.: (63) 9173278010
Web Site:
    http://www.rockwellprimaries.com.ph
Residential Building Services
N.A.I.C.S.: 236220
Leslie Constantino *(Sls Mgr)*

Terraprime, Inc. (3)
2F Prima Residences 243 Quezon Ave, Quezon City, 1113, Philippines
Tel.: (63) 23549373
Web Site: http://www.terraprime.ph
Real Estate Development Services
N.A.I.C.S.: 531390
Brenda Calaud *(Mgr-Building)*

Therma Prime Drilling Corporation (3)
6th Floor Rockwell Business Center Tower 3 Ortigas Avenue, Pasig, 1604, Philippines
Tel.: (63) 234887974
Web Site: http://www.thermaprime.com
Geothermal Drilling Services
N.A.I.C.S.: 237110
Federico R. Lopez *(Chm)*

LOPHOS HOLDINGS INC.
620 1111 Melville Street, Vancouver, V6E 3V6, BC, Canada BC
Year Founded: 2020
MESC—(CNSX)
Assets: $2,881,129
Liabilities: $1,788,548
Net Worth: $1,092,581
Earnings: ($943,106)
Fiscal Year-end: 03/31/24
Holding Company
N.A.I.C.S.: 551112

Subsidiaries:

Lophos Pharmaceuticals Corp. (1)

LOQUS
SUB008A Industrial Estate, San Gwann, SGN 3000, Malta
Tel.: (356) 23318000
Web Site:
    https://www.loqusgroup.com
LQS—(MAL)
Rev.: $11,514,811
Assets: $14,642,651
Liabilities: $7,477,814
Net Worth: $7,164,837
Earnings: $955,196
Emp.: 150
Fiscal Year-end: 06/30/23
Information Technology Services
N.A.I.C.S.: 541512

Walter Bonnici *(Chm)*
Subsidiaries:

Premiere Post Limited (1)
SUB008A Industrial Estate, San Gwann, Malta
Tel.: (356) 21420234
Web Site: http://www.premierepost.eu
Letter Distribution Services
N.A.I.C.S.: 541614
Francesca Bianchi *(Gen Mgr)*

LORAS HOLDING A.S.
Musalla Baglari Mahallesi Kule Caddesi Kule Plaza Kat 35 No 2 Selcuklu, 42060, Konya, Turkiye
Tel.: (90) 3322213999
Web Site:
    https://www.lorasholding.com
Year Founded: 1988
ITTFH—(IST)
Sales Range: $400-449.9 Million
Emp.: 3,822
Holding Company
N.A.I.C.S.: 551112
Mehmet Ali Korkmaz *(Chm)*

Subsidiaries:

ADESE PETROL URUNLERI TAS. SAN. TIC. A.S. (1)
Fatih Mah Eski Sanayi Futbol Sahasi Yani No 10/ D, Selcuklu, Konya, Turkiye
Tel.: (90) 332 237 41 00
Web Site: http://www.adesepetrol.com.tr
Gasoline Station Operator
N.A.I.C.S.: 457120

AES SIGORTA ARAC. HIZM. A.S. (1)
Feritpasa Mah Kule Cad Kule Plaza Zemin Kat No 4/2-A, Selcuklu, Konya, Turkiye
Tel.: (90) 332 233 23 01
Web Site: http://www.aessigorta.com.tr
Property & Casualty Insurance Services
N.A.I.C.S.: 524126

Adese Alisveris Merkezleri Ticaret A.S. (1)
Haci Yusuf Mescid Mh Gulcicek Sk No 4 Karatay, Konya, Turkiye
Tel.: (90) 332 2214242
Web Site: http://www.adese.com.tr
Sales Range: $800-899.9 Million
Emp.: 3,500
Supermarket Owner & Operator
N.A.I.C.S.: 445110
Musafa Ozeskiciler *(Gen Mgr)*

BELYA TURIZM INS. ENERJI BLS. SAN. ve TIC. A.S. (1)
Ardicli Mah Gurbulut Sok No 67/1, Konya, Turkiye
Tel.: (90) 332 262 00 12
Information Technology Consulting Services
N.A.I.C.S.: 541512

ELITE DANS. ARASTIRMA GELISTIRME REK. ve HLK. ILS. TIC. A.S (1)
Haciyusuf Mescit Mah Gulcicek Sok No 4/D, Konya, Turkiye
Tel.: (90) 332 345 44 06
Web Site: http://www.elitedanismanlik.com
Advetising Agency
N.A.I.C.S.: 541810

IMAS MAKINE SANAYI A.S. (1)
2 Osb Lalehan Cad No 61, Selcuklu, Konya, Turkiye
Tel.: (90) 332 239 01 41
Web Site: http://www.imas.com.tr
Industrial Machinery Mfr
N.A.I.C.S.: 333998

IRENT OTO KIRALAMA TIC. A.S. (1)
Ankara Cad No 138/A Jandarma Bolge Komutanligi Karsisi, Karatay, Konya, Turkiye
Tel.: (90) 332 237 67 00
New & Used Car Dealer
N.A.I.C.S.: 441110

KULE YON. ve ORG. ve DANISMANLIK A.S. (1)
Feritpasa Mah Kule Cd No 8, Selcuklu, Konya, Turkiye
Tel.: (90) 332 234 32 72
Web Site: http://www.kuleyonetim.com
Real Estate Manangement Services
N.A.I.C.S.: 531390

SEHA INSAAT MUH. MAD. TUR. SAN. ve TIC. A.S. (1)
Feritpasa Mahallesi Kule Oaddesi Kule Plaza Kat 33 No 56, Selcuklu, Konya, Turkiye
Tel.: (90) 332 221 39 00
Web Site: http://www.sehayapi.com
Construction Engineering Services
N.A.I.C.S.: 541330

SELET ENTEGRE ET VE SUT URUNLERI SAN. TIC. A.S. (1)
Haci Yusuf Mescid Mahallesi Gul cicek Sokak No 4/B, Karatay, 42300, Konya, Turkiye
Tel.: (90) 332 342 64 01
Web Site: http://www.selet.com.tr
Chicken Egg Production Services
N.A.I.C.S.: 112310

SELVA GIDA SANAYI A.S. (1)
Konya Organize Sanayi Bolgesi Buyuk Kayack Mah Guzelkonak Sok No 6, Selcuklu, 42050, Konya, Turkiye
Tel.: (90) 332 239 01 24
Web Site: http://www.selva.com.tr
Dry Pasta Mfr
N.A.I.C.S.: 311824

LORDCO PARTS LTD.
22866 Dewddney Trunk Road, Maple Ridge, V2X 3K6, BC, Canada
Tel.: (604) 467-1581
Web Site: http://www.lordco.com
Year Founded: 1974
Rev.: $203,722,834
Emp.: 1,300
Automobile Parts Distr
N.A.I.C.S.: 423120
Ed Coates *(Co-Founder)*

LORDOS HOTEL (HOLDINGS) PUBLIC LTD
10 Kantaras Str Pyla Larnaca, 7081, Larnaca, Cyprus
Tel.: (357) 24646880
Web Site: http://www.lordos.com.cy
Sales Range: $10-24.9 Million
Home Management Services
N.A.I.C.S.: 721110
Takis Kyriakides *(Chm)*

LORDOS HOTELS (HOLDINGS) PUBLIC LTD.
1 Neapoleos Street Lordos Forest Beach Block 1 Office 1 23, Voroklini, 7041, Larnaca, Cyprus
Tel.: (357) 24646880
Web Site: https://www.lordos.com.cy
LHH—(CYP)
Sales Range: Less than $1 Million
Holding Company
N.A.I.C.S.: 551112

LORDOS UNITED PLASTICS PUBLIC LTD
Epimitheos Street Industrial Area, 3056, Limassol, Cyprus
Tel.: (357) 25885555
Web Site:
    https://www.lordosunited.com
Year Founded: 1959
LPL—(CYP)
Sales Range: Less than $1 Million
Plastics Bottle & Pipe Fitting Mfr
N.A.I.C.S.: 326160
Petros Mitsides *(Exec Dir)*

LORDS CHLORO ALKALI LIMITED
Lords Chloro Alkali Limited A281 1st Floor and 2nd Floor, Defence Colony, New Delhi, 110024, India
Tel.: (91) 1140239034

LORENZO INTERNATIONAL LIMITED

Web Site:
    https://www.lordschloro.com
Year Founded: 1979
500284—(BOM)
Rev.: $40,471,458
Assets: $32,441,218
Liabilities: $9,332,901
Net Worth: $23,108,317
Earnings: $7,264,926
Emp.: 400
Fiscal Year-end: 03/31/23
Specialty Chemical Mfr & Distr
N.A.I.C.S.: 325998
Ajay Virmani *(Mng Dir)*

LORDS GROUP TRADING PLC
Second Floor 12-15 Hanger Green, London, W5 3EL, United Kingdom UK
Web Site:
    https://www.lordsgrouptrading.com
Year Founded: 1985
LORD—(AIM)
Rev.: $493,244,741
Assets: $233,947,375
Liabilities: $165,045,801
Net Worth: $68,901,575
Earnings: $7,662,972
Emp.: 638
Fiscal Year-end: 12/31/21
Ecommerce Retailer
N.A.I.C.S.: 459999

LORDS ISHWAR HOTELS LIMITED
Hotel Revival Near Sayaji Gardens Kala Ghoda Chowk University Road, Baroda, 390 002, Gujarat, India
Tel.: (91) 2652793535
Web Site:
    https://www.lordsishwar.com
Year Founded: 1985
530065—(BOM)
Rev.: $890,246
Assets: $1,103,387
Liabilities: $497,260
Net Worth: $606,127
Earnings: $13,608
Emp.: 60
Fiscal Year-end: 03/31/23
Home Management Services
N.A.I.C.S.: 721110
Ranjit Kumar Singh *(Compliance Officer & Sec)*

LORENZINI APPARELS LIMITED
C-64 Okhla Industrial Area Phase-I, New Delhi, 110020, India
Tel.: (91) 1140504731
Web Site:
    https://www.mymonteil.com
LAL—(NSE)
Rev.: $5,326,461
Assets: $5,033,109
Liabilities: $3,165,902
Net Worth: $1,867,207
Earnings: $305,327
Emp.: 75
Fiscal Year-end: 03/31/23
Textile Product Mfr & Distr
N.A.I.C.S.: 315210
Sandeep Jain *(Mng Dir)*

LORENZO INTERNATIONAL LIMITED
106 International Road 03-00, Singapore, 629175, Singapore
Tel.: (65) 68611949 SG
Web Site: https://www.lorenzo-international.com
Year Founded: 1983
Rev.: $23,290,697
Assets: $22,647,557
Liabilities: $23,780,333
Net Worth: ($1,132,776)
Earnings: ($7,906,975)

4557

LORENZO INTERNATIONAL LIMITED

Lorenzo International Limited—(Continued)
Emp.: 1,136
Fiscal Year-end: 03/31/18
Sofa Sets Mfr
N.A.I.C.S.: 337121
Pang Hern Lim *(Exec Dir)*

Subsidiaries:

Brezza Living Sdn. Bhd. (1)
Lot 621 Jln 2/87G Tmn Seputeh, 58000, Kuala Lumpur, Malaysia
Tel.: (60) 322735223
Web Site: http://www.brezzaliving.com
Mattress Mfr & Retailer
N.A.I.C.S.: 337121

Builders Shop Pte. Ltd. (1)
106 International Road 02-00, Singapore, 629175, Singapore
Tel.: (65) 68416636
Mattress Mfr & Retailer
N.A.I.C.S.: 337121
Paul Nicole Fonte *(Sls Mgr)*

Lorenzo International (Kunshan) Co., Ltd.
9 Dongyuan Rd, Dianshan Hu Town, Kunshan, 215345, Jiangsu, China
Tel.: (86) 51257639597
Web Site: http://www.lorenzo.com.sg
Furniture Mfr
N.A.I.C.S.: 337121

LORENZO SHIPPING CORPORATION
20th Floor Times Plaza Building United Nations Avenue, Corner Taft Avenue Ermita, Manila, 1000, Philippines
Tel.: (63) 285672180
Web Site: https://www.lorenzoshipping.com
Year Founded: 1972
LSC—(PHI)
Rev.: $59,238,001
Assets: $55,852,661
Liabilities: $47,429,167
Net Worth: $8,423,494
Earnings: $1,729,464
Emp.: 243
Fiscal Year-end: 12/31/23
Cargo Shipping Services
N.A.I.C.S.: 488320
Antony Louis Marden *(Vice Chm)*

LORMEDO SAS
Rue De La Gare, 88550, Pouxeux, Vosges, France
Tel.: (33) 329369717
Web Site: http://www.lormedo.com
Year Founded: 1986
Rev.: $12,600,000
Emp.: 44
Sheet Metal Work Mfg
N.A.I.C.S.: 332322
Stephane Chwartz *(Dir)*

Subsidiaries:

Lorraine Precision Mecanique sarl (1)
11 Avenue De La Republique, 54150, Briey, France
Tel.: (33) 382465252
Emp.: 19
Metal Stamping Services
N.A.I.C.S.: 332119

LORNE PARK CAPITAL PARTNERS INC.
1295 Cornwall Rd Unit A3, Oakville, L6J 7T5, ON, Canada
Tel.: (905) 337-2227   AB
Web Site: https://www.lpcp.ca
Year Founded: 2011
LPC—(TSXV)
Rev.: $22,203,888
Assets: $38,689,630
Liabilities: $15,634,860
Net Worth: $23,054,770

Earnings: $292,315
Fiscal Year-end: 12/31/23
Investment Management & Brokerage Services
N.A.I.C.S.: 523160
Robert Sewell *(Pres & CEO)*

LORNE STEWART PLC
Stewart House 420 Kenton Road, Harrow, HA3 9TU, Middlesex, United Kingdom
Tel.: (44) 2087322000
Web Site: http://www.lornestewart.com
Rev.: $297,014,154
Emp.: 1,406
Building Engineering Services
N.A.I.C.S.: 237990
Gary Worrall *(CEO-Engrg Div)*

LOS ANDES COPPER LTD.
1100-1199 West Hastings Street, Vancouver, V6E 3T5, BC, Canada
Tel.: (604) 639-3892
Web Site: https://www.losandescopper.com
LSANF—(OTCQX)
Rev.: $239,271
Assets: $83,730,226
Liabilities: $21,995,019
Net Worth: $61,735,207
Earnings: $(75,403)
Emp.: 11
Fiscal Year-end: 09/30/23
Mineral Exploration Services
N.A.I.C.S.: 213114
Pedro Loch *(Controller)*

Subsidiaries:

Compania Minera Vizcachitas Holding (1)
Suite 812 Augusto Leguia Norte 100, Las Condes, Santiago, Chile
Tel.: (56) 229540450
Copper Exploration Services
N.A.I.C.S.: 212230

Sociedad Legal Minera San Jose Uno de Lo Vicuna El Tartaro y Piguchen de Putaendo (1)

LOS CASTILLOS REAL ESTATE, INC.
Do It Center Administrative Offices, Section 0819-04859, Eldorado, Panama, Panama
Tel.: (507) 236 5066
LCAS—(PAN)
Sales Range: Less than $1 Million
Real Estate Investment Services
N.A.I.C.S.: 531390
Alex A. Cohen Solis *(Pres)*

LOSFELD DISTRIBUTION
15 Rue Du Luxembourg, Roubaix, 59100, Nord, France
Tel.: (33) 320289960
Rev.: $21,000,000
Emp.: 49
Dairy Products, Except Dried Or Canned
N.A.I.C.S.: 424430
Philippe Leleu *(Dir)*

LOSINJSKA PLOVIDBA - HOLDING D.D
Privlaka bb Splitska 2/4, Rijeka, Croatia
Tel.: (385) 51750204
Web Site: https://www.lp-holding.hr
Year Founded: 1958
LPLH—(ZAG)
Sales Range: Less than $1 Million
Ship Building Services
N.A.I.C.S.: 336611
Miroslav Ivic *(Chm-Supervisory Bd)*

LOSS MANAGEMENT GROUP LTD.
Bath & West Buildings, Lower Bristol Road, Bath, BA2 3EG, United Kingdom
Tel.: (44) 8452500990
Sales Range: $25-49.9 Million
Emp.: 100
Jewelry, Collectible, Art & Antiques Insurance Claim Management Services
N.A.I.C.S.: 524128
Julian Radcliffe *(Chm)*

Subsidiaries:

Guild Claims Service (1)
Bath & West Buildings, Lower Bristol Road, Bath, BA2 3EG, United Kingdom
Tel.: (44) 8450501749
Jewelry Stores
N.A.I.C.S.: 458310

The Guild of Valuers & Jewellers (1)
Bath & West Buildings Lower Bristol Road, Bath, BA2 3EG, United Kingdom
Tel.: (44) 1225788716
Web Site: http://www.gvj.org.uk
Jewelry Stores
N.A.I.C.S.: 458310

LOT POLISH AIRLINES S.A.
17 Stycznia 39, PL 00-906, Warsaw, Poland
Tel.: (48) 225776111   PL
Web Site: http://www.lot.com
Year Founded: 1929
Sales Range: $1-4.9 Billion
Emp.: 3,672
Oil Transportation Services
N.A.I.C.S.: 481111
Rafal Milczarski *(Chm)*

Subsidiaries:

EuroLOT SA (1)
17 Stycznia 39, 00-906, Warsaw, Poland
Tel.: (48) 226066467
Web Site: http://www.eurolot.com.pl
Sales Range: $125-149.9 Million
Emp.: 350
Urban Transit Systems
N.A.I.C.S.: 485119

GTL-LOT Uslugi Lotniskowe Sp. z o.o. (1)
Wolnosci 90, Ozarowice, 42-625, Bytom, Poland
Tel.: (48) 323927287
Web Site: http://www.lotnisko.com.pl
Sales Range: $125-149.9 Million
Emp.: 380
Urban Transit Systems
N.A.I.C.S.: 485119

LOT Auto Services Sp. z o.o. (1)
17 Stycznia 39, 02-148, Warsaw, Poland
Tel.: (48) 226069014
Web Site: http://www.lotauto.pl
Automotive Parts & Accessories Stores
N.A.I.C.S.: 441330

LOT Catering Sp. z o.o. (1)
Sekundowa 2, 02-178, Warsaw, Poland
Tel.: (48) 226066814
Web Site: http://www.lotcatering.com.pl
Restaurant
N.A.I.C.S.: 722511

LOT Polish Airlines SA (1)
500 5th Ave Ste 408, New York, NY 10110
Tel.: (212) 852-0244
Web Site: http://www.lot.com
Airline Services
N.A.I.C.S.: 481111

LOT TRAVEL LTD. (1)
43 I Chavchavadze av /1 Cholokashvili str, 0162, Tbilisi, Georgia
Tel.: (995) 32 255 44 55
Web Site: http://www.polishairlines.com
Emp.: 23
Oil Transportation Services
N.A.I.C.S.: 488190
George Litaltane *(Mgr)*

Nowy Przewoznik Sp. z o.o. (1)

Pl Zwyciestwa 2, 90-312, Lodz, Poland
Tel.: (48) 225580045
Travel Agencies
N.A.I.C.S.: 561510

WRO-LOT Uslugi Lotniskowe Sp. z o.o. (1)
ul Skarzynskiego 36, Wroclaw, 54530, Poland
Tel.: (48) 713581382
Web Site: http://www.wrolot.com.pl
Sales Range: $50-74.9 Million
Emp.: 200
Scheduled Passenger Air Transportation
N.A.I.C.S.: 481111
Daniel Frejek *(VP)*

LOT VACUUM CO., LTD.
1-20 Jigotjungang-ro, Osan, 18102, Gyeonggi-do, Korea (South)
Tel.: (82) 316774431
Web Site: https://www.lotvacuum.com
Year Founded: 2002
083310—(KRS)
Rev.: $287,009,454
Assets: $248,257,817
Liabilities: $86,020,288
Net Worth: $162,237,529
Earnings: $18,890,539
Emp.: 516
Fiscal Year-end: 12/31/22
Semiconductor Machinery Mfr
N.A.I.C.S.: 333242
Heung Sik Oh *(Pres & CEO)*

LOT78, INC.
65 Alfred Road Great Western Studios Studio 209, London, W2 5EU, United Kingdom
Tel.: (44) 7753331198   NV
Web Site: http://www.lot78.com
Year Founded: 2008
LOTE—(OTCIQ)
Sales Range: Less than $1 Million
Emp.: 6
Apparel Mfr & Distr
N.A.I.C.S.: 315990
Oliver Amhurst *(Pres & CEO)*

LOTARIJA NA MAKEDONIJA AD
11-a Marshall Tito Street, Skopje, North Macedonia
Tel.: (389) 23235124
Web Site: https://www.lotarija.com.mk
LOTO—(MAC)
Rev.: $496,542
Assets: $5,753,537
Liabilities: $341,876
Net Worth: $5,411,661
Earnings: $196,204
Fiscal Year-end: 12/31/19
Gambling Services
N.A.I.C.S.: 713210

LOTCE LIMITED
33 Queen Street, London, EC4R 1BR, United Kingdom
Tel.: (44) 20 3582 0250   UK
Web Site: http://www.lotce.com
Derivatives Exchange Operator
N.A.I.C.S.: 523210
Clive Richard Shiret *(CEO)*

LOTES CO., LTD.
No 15 Wusyun Street, Anle District, Keelung, 20446, Taiwan
Tel.: (886) 224331110
Web Site: http://www.lotes.cc
3533—(TAI)
Rev.: $800,662,614
Assets: $1,241,126,184
Liabilities: $280,303,368
Net Worth: $960,822,816
Earnings: $187,286,889
Emp.: 11,732

AND PRIVATE COMPANIES
LOTTE CO., LTD.

Fiscal Year-end: 12/31/23
Connector Mfr
N.A.I.C.S.: 334417
Te-Hsiang Chu *(Chm)*

Subsidiaries:

LOTES Guangzhou Co.,Ltd. (1)
No 526 North Jinglin Road, Guangzhou, 511458, Guangdong, China
Tel.: (86) 2084682476
Electronic Components Mfr
N.A.I.C.S.: 334419

LOTES Suzhou Co., Ltd. (1)
No 26 Caohu Road, Xiangcheng Economic Development Zone, Suzhou, 215143, Jiangsu, China
Tel.: (86) 51268838128
Connector Mfr
N.A.I.C.S.: 334417

LOTO-QUEBEC

500 Rue Sherbrooke Ouest, Montreal, H3A 3G6, QC, Canada
Tel.: (514) 282-8000
Web Site: http://www.loto-quebec.com
Year Founded: 1969
Rev.: $3,002,526,146
Assets: $982,720,423
Liabilities: $885,876,587
Net Worth: $96,843,836
Earnings: $1,063,819,658
Emp.: 992
Fiscal Year-end: 03/31/18
Numbers Games, Television Lotteries, Sport Betting, Video Lottery, Casinos, Network Bingo & Multimedia Games
N.A.I.C.S.: 713290
Lynne Roiter *(Pres & CEO)*

Subsidiaries:

Casiloc Inc. (1)
500 Rue Sherbrooke O Bureau 300, Montreal, H3A 3G6, QC, Canada
Tel.: (514) 282-8080
Project Construction Services
N.A.I.C.S.: 236220

Ingenio-Filiale de Loto-Quebec, Inc. (1)
500 Sherbrooke St W Ste 2100, Montreal, H3A 3G6, QC, Canada (100%)
Tel.: (514) 282-0210
Sales Range: $25-49.9 Million
Emp.: 51
Develops Games of Chance Based on Multimedia & New Technologies
N.A.I.C.S.: 334610

La Societe Des Bingos Du Quebec, Inc. (1)
500 Rue Sherbrooke Ouest, Ste 600, Montreal, H3A 3G6, QC, Canada
Tel.: (514) 282-7777
Web Site: http://www.bingo-quebec.com
Sales Range: $10-24.9 Million
Emp.: 35
Management of Daily Network Bingo Events
N.A.I.C.S.: 611620

La Societe Des Casinos Du Quebec, Inc. (1)
500 Sherbrooke St W, Montreal, H3A 3G6, QC, Canada
Tel.: (514) 282-8080
Web Site: http://www.casinos.qu.ca
Sales Range: $75-99.9 Million
Emp.: 120
Management & Operation of Casinos
N.A.I.C.S.: 713210
Claude Poisson *(Pres)*

La Societe Des Loteries Video Du Quebec, Inc. (1)
500 Sherbrooke St W 16 FL, Montreal, H3A 3G6, QC, Canada (100%)
Tel.: (514) 282-8090
Web Site: http://www.slvq.com
Sales Range: $50-74.9 Million
Emp.: 60
Management of State-Run Video Lottery Network

N.A.I.C.S.: 713290

Technologies Nter Inc (1)
1801 Av Mcgill College Bureau 930, Montreal, H3A 2N4, QC, Canada
Tel.: (514) 987-6837
Web Site: http://www.lotoquebec.com
Software Development Services
N.A.I.C.S.: 541511
Pierre Lazurre *(Sr Project Mgr-BI)*

LOTTE CO., LTD.

20-1 Nishi-shinjuku 3-chome, Shinjuku-ku, Tokyo, 160-0023, Japan
Tel.: (81) 333751211 JP
Web Site: https://www.lotte.co.jp
Year Founded: 1948
Sales Range: $50-74.9 Billion
Confectionery Mfr
N.A.I.C.S.: 311340
Takeo Shigemitsu *(Chm & CEO)*

Subsidiaries:

Chiba Lotte Marines Co., Ltd. (1)
6 Nakase 2 Chome, Mihama-Ku, Chiba, 261 7190, Japan (100%)
Tel.: (81) 432972101
Web Site: http://www.marines.co.jp
Sales Range: $25-49.9 Million
Emp.: 50
Professional Basketball Team
N.A.I.C.S.: 711211

Daehong Communications Inc. (1)
10 Tongil-ro, Jung-gu, Seoul, 04527, Korea (South)
Tel.: (82) 2 3671 6114
Web Site: http://www.daehong.com
Sales Range: $300-349.9 Million
Advertising Agency Services
N.A.I.C.S.: 541810

LOTTE Corp. (1)
300 Olympic-ro Songpa-gu, Seoul, 05551, Korea (South)
Tel.: (82) 226706114
Web Site: http://www.lotte.co.kr
Holding Company; Food Production & Distribution Services
N.A.I.C.S.: 551112
Dong-bin Shin *(Chm & CEO)*

Affiliate (Domestic):

Hotel Lotte Co., Ltd. (2)
30 Eulji-Ro, Jung-gu, Seoul, Korea (South)
Tel.: (82) 27711000
Web Site: https://www.lottehotel.com
Rev.: $3,682,192,735
Assets: $14,172,768,206
Liabilities: $8,859,476,750
Net Worth: $5,313,291,456
Earnings: ($3,424,315)
Emp.: 5,071
Fiscal Year-end: 12/31/2023
Hotel Operator
N.A.I.C.S.: 721110

Lotte Asset Development Co., Ltd. (2)
10F West Mirae Asset Center 1 Bldg 26 Eulji-ro 5-gil, Jung-gu, Seoul, Korea (South)
Tel.: (82) 2 2086 3333
Emp.: 360
Real Estate Manangement Services
N.A.I.C.S.: 531390
Kim Chang-kwon *(CEO)*

Lotte Capital Co., Ltd. (2)
4F Capital Tower 142 Teheran-ro, Gangnam-gu, Seoul, Korea (South)
Tel.: (82) 1577 7700
Financial Management Services
N.A.I.C.S.: 523999

Lotte Chemical Corporation (2)
Lotte World Tower 14F-16F 300 Olympic-ro, Songpa-gu, Seoul, 05551, Korea (South)
Tel.: (82) 28294114
Web Site: https://www.lottechem.com
Chemical Products Mfr
N.A.I.C.S.: 325998
Lee Hun-ki *(Pres & Co-CEO)*

Subsidiary (Domestic):

ILJIN Materials Co., Ltd. (3)

45 Mapo-daero, Mapo-Gu, Seoul, Korea (South) (53.3%)
Tel.: (82) 27079114
Web Site: https://www.iljin.co.kr
Emp.: 380
Fiscal Year-end: 12/31/2022
Copper Foils Mfr
N.A.I.C.S.: 332999
Jae-Myeong Heo *(Co-CEO)*

Subsidiary (Non-US):

Lotte Chemical Pakistan Ltd. (3)
EZ/1/P-4 Eastern Industrial Zone Port Qasim, PO Box 723, Karachi, 74200, Pakistan (75%)
Tel.: (92) 2134726005
Web Site: https://www.lottechem.pk
Rev.: $389,876,016
Assets: $177,268,683
Liabilities: $75,567,874
Net Worth: $101,700,808
Earnings: $35,692,605
Emp.: 235
Fiscal Year-end: 12/31/2019
Terephthalic Acid Mfr & Distr
N.A.I.C.S.: 325998
Humair Ijaz *(CEO)*

Holding (Non-US):

Lotte Chemical Titan Holding Berhad (3)
Lot 29 01 Level 29 1 Powerhouse No 1 Persiaran Bandar Utama, 47800, Petaling Jaya, Selangor Darul Ehsan, Malaysia (75.86%)
Tel.: (60) 320934222
Web Site: https://lottechem.my
Rev.: $2,120,440,847
Assets: $3,549,590,899
Liabilities: $475,803,598
Net Worth: $3,073,787,302
Earnings: ($157,683,810)
Emp.: 1,497
Fiscal Year-end: 12/31/2022
Investment Holding Company; Chemical Product Mfr
N.A.I.C.S.: 551112
Abdul Rahman Mamat *(Chm)*

Affiliate (Domestic):

Lotte Fine Chemical Co., Ltd. (3)
19 Yeocheon-ro 217 Beon-gil, Nam-gu, Ulsan, 680-090, Korea (South) (31.13%)
Tel.: (82) 522706701
Web Site: http://www.samsung-cellulose.com
Sales Range: $1-4.9 Billion
Chemical Products Mfr
N.A.I.C.S.: 325998
Hee-In Lee *(CFO & Head-Mgmt Support Div)*

Joint Venture (Domestic):

Lotte INEOS Chemical Co., Ltd. (3)
8F West Center 26 Eulji ro 5 gil, Jung gu, Seoul, 1320-10, Korea (South) (49%)
Tel.: (82) 522781100
Web Site: http://www.lotteineos.com
Sales Range: Less than $1 Million
Acetic Acid, Vinyl Acetate Monomer & Other Specialty Fine Chemicals Mfr
N.A.I.C.S.: 325998
Young Joon Kim *(CEO)*

Affiliate (Domestic):

Lotte Chilsung Beverage Co., Ltd. (3)
3th/4th/5th/9th Fl Lotte Castle Gold 269 Olympic-ro, Songpa-gu, Seoul, Korea (South)
Tel.: (82) 234799114
Web Site: http://www.lottechilsung.co.kr
Rev.: $2,179,619,987
Assets: $2,834,782,636
Liabilities: $1,751,651,176
Net Worth: $1,083,131,460
Earnings: $100,549,314
Fiscal Year-end: 12/31/2022
Soft Drink Bottler & Whslr; Liquor Distilleries & Products Whslr
N.A.I.C.S.: 312111
Yeong-Gu Lee *(Exec Dir)*

Plant (Domestic):

Lotte Chilsung Beverage Co., Ltd. - Anseong Plant (3)

17 Je2gongdan 1-gil, Miyang-myeon, Anseong, Gyeonggi-do, Korea (South)
Tel.: (82) 316774761
Web Site: http://www.lottechilsung.co.kr
Sales Range: $25-49.9 Million
Emp.: 180
Soft Drink Bottler & Syrup Mfr
N.A.I.C.S.: 312111

Lotte Chilsung Beverage Co., Ltd. - Bupyeong Plant (3)
27 Bupyeong-daero 313beon-gil, Bupyeong-gu, Incheon, Korea (South)
Tel.: (82) 32 502 0511
Sales Range: $100-124.9 Million
Emp.: 500
Soft Drink Bottler
N.A.I.C.S.: 312111

Lotte Chilsung Beverage Co., Ltd. - Opo Plant (3)
257 Yangbeol-ro, Opo-eup, Gwangju, Gyeonggi-do, Korea (South)
Tel.: (82) 31 764 7810
Web Site: http://www.lottechilsung.co.kr
Sales Range: $25-49.9 Million
Emp.: 240
Soft Drink Bottler
N.A.I.C.S.: 312111

Lotte Chilsung Beverage Co., Ltd. - Yangsan Plant (3)
28 Bukjeonggongdan 1-gil, Yangsan, Gyeongsangnam-do, Korea (South)
Tel.: (82) 55 388 5580
Web Site: http://www.lottechilsung.co.kr
Soft Drink Bottler & Syrup Mfr
N.A.I.C.S.: 312111

Affiliate (Domestic):

Lotte Data Communications Company (2)
179 Gasan digital 2-ro, Geumcheon-gu, Seoul, Korea (South)
Tel.: (82) 2 2626 4000
Software Development Services
N.A.I.C.S.: 541511
Ma Yong Deuk *(CEO)*

Subsidiary (Domestic):

Hyundai Information Technology Co., Ltd. (3)
Lotte Center 179 Gasan Digital 2-ro, Geumcheon-gu, Seoul, 08500, Korea (South) (100%)
Tel.: (82) 2 2626 6000
Web Site: http://www.hit.co.kr
Rev.: $147,986,278
Assets: $167,772,755
Liabilities: $120,584,790
Net Worth: $47,187,965
Earnings: $935,313
Emp.: 579
Fiscal Year-end: 12/31/2017
Computer System Integration & Management Services
N.A.I.C.S.: 541512

Affiliate (Domestic):

Lotte Engineering & Construction Co., Ltd. (2)
50-2 Jamwonn-Dong, Seocho-gu, Seoul, Korea (South)
Tel.: (82) 2 3480 9114
Web Site: http://www.lotte.co.kr
Civil Engineering Services
N.A.I.C.S.: 237990
Suk Joo Ha *(Pres & CEO)*

Lotte Engineering & Machinery Mfg. Co., Ltd. (2)
8 Yeomjeon-ro 333beon-gil, Nam-gu, Incheon, Korea (South)
Tel.: (82) 32 870 7100
Heating Equipment Installation Services
N.A.I.C.S.: 238220
YoungSoon Kim *(CEO)*

Lotte Global Logistics Co., Ltd. (2)
10 Tongil-ro, Jung-gu, Seoul, 04527, Korea (South) (44.59%)
Tel.: (82) 2 2170 3355
Web Site: http://www.lottelogis.com
Domestic Logistic Services
N.A.I.C.S.: 488510

Lotte LHP Corporation (2)

LOTTE CO., LTD.

Lotte Co., Ltd.—(Continued)
21-1 Seonyu-ro 47-gil, Yeongdeungpo-gu, Seoul, Korea (South)
Tel.: (82) 2 2169 3400
Confectionery Distr
N.A.I.C.S.: 424450

Lotte Logistics Co., Ltd. (2)
Yonsei Bongnae Bldg 36 Chilpae-ro, Jung-gu, Seoul, Korea (South)
Tel.: (82) 2 2095 3114
Logistics Consulting Servies
N.A.I.C.S.: 541614

Lotte Shopping Co., Ltd. (2)
81 Namdaemun, Jung-gu, Seoul, Korea (South)
Tel.: (82) 27712500
Web Site: https://www.lotteshoppingir.com
Rev.: $10,804,049,612
Assets: $22,745,942,651
Liabilities: $14,702,617,889
Net Worth: $8,043,324,762
Earnings: $125,573,710
Emp.: 19,227
Fiscal Year-end: 12/31/2023
Departmental Store Operator
N.A.I.C.S.: 455110
Heetae Kang (Chm & CEO)

Subsidiary (Domestic):

Korea Seven Co., Ltd (3)
3 Sowol-Ro, Jung-Gu, Seoul, 100778, Korea (South)
Tel.: (82) 15770711
Confectionery Distr
N.A.I.C.S.: 424450

Subsidiary (Domestic):

Lotte PS Net Co., Ltd. (4)
6F Lotte Center 179 Gasan digital 2-ro, Geumcheon-gu, Seoul, Korea (South)
Tel.: (82) 2 2028 8900
Financial Management Services
N.A.I.C.S.: 523999

Subsidiary (Domestic):

Lotte Boulangerie Co., Ltd. (3)
10F Daedong Bldg 340 Olympic-ro, Songpa-gu, Seoul, Korea (South)
Tel.: (82) 2 2675 8131
Confectionery Distr
N.A.I.C.S.: 424450

Lotte Himart Co., Ltd. (3)
Lv 3-8 HIMART Building 156 Samsung-ro, Gangnam-gu, Seoul, Korea (South)
Tel.: (82) 215880070
Web Site: https://www.e-himart.co.kr
Rev.: $2,559,341,593
Assets: $1,890,056,030
Liabilities: $896,563,567
Net Worth: $993,492,463
Earnings: ($404,892,462)
Emp.: 3,383
Fiscal Year-end: 12/31/2022
Electronics Retailer
N.A.I.C.S.: 449210
Seo Eun Lee (Exec Dir)

Affiliate (Domestic):

Lotte Wellfood Co.,Ltd (2)
Lotte Yangpyung Building 5 Yangpyung-Dong, Yeongdeungpo-Gu, Seoul, Korea (South)
Tel.: (82) 226706302
Web Site: http://www.lotteconf.co.kr
Rev.: $2,456,903,842
Assets: $3,148,733,790
Liabilities: $1,529,112,295
Net Worth: $1,619,621,495
Earnings: $33,655,975
Emp.: 7,060
Fiscal Year-end: 12/31/2022
Confectionery Products Mfr & Whslr
N.A.I.C.S.: 311352

Subsidiary (Non-US):

Chocolaterie Guylian NV (3)
Europark Oost 1, 9100, Saint-Niklaas, Belgium
Tel.: (32) 37609700
Web Site: http://www.guylian.be
Sales Range: $25-49.9 Million
Emp.: 200
Chocolate Mfr

N.A.I.C.S.: 311352
Mieke Callebaut (Gen Mgr)

JSC Rakhat (3)
2a Zenkov Street, 50002, Almaty, Kazakhstan (92.44%)
Tel.: (7) 7272584711
Web Site: https://www.rakhat.kz
Rev.: $210,868,425
Assets: $163,349,551
Liabilities: $18,926,088
Net Worth: $144,423,463
Earnings: $19,464,476
Emp.: 4,500
Fiscal Year-end: 12/31/2023
Confectionery Mfr & Distr
N.A.I.C.S.: 311351
Fedorets Konstantin Viktorovich (Chm)

Subsidiary (Domestic):

Argo Ltd (4)
Morozov Str 49, Shchuchinsk, Kazakhstan
Tel.: (7) 7163632085
Confectioneries Mfr
N.A.I.C.S.: 311351

Rakhat-Taldykorgan Ltd. (4)
Tynyshbaeva St 88, Taldyqorghan, Almaty, Kazakhstan
Tel.: (7) 7282272080
Confectioneries Mfr
N.A.I.C.S.: 311351

TD RAKHAT-Shymkent Ltd (4)
Zhybek Zholy St 60, Shymkent, Kazakhstan
Tel.: (7) 7252572193
Web Site: http://www.rakhat.kz
Confectionery Mfr
N.A.I.C.S.: 311351

Zhanel Ltd (4)
Kantsev St 2, Atyrau, Kazakhstan
Tel.: (7) 7122 354900
Web Site: http://www.rakhat.kz
Confectionery Mfr
N.A.I.C.S.: 311351

Subsidiary (Domestic):

Lotte Foods Co., Ltd. (3)
19 Yangpyeong-ro 19-gil, Yeongdeungpo-gu, Seoul, Korea (South)
Tel.: (82) 234693114
Web Site: http://www.lottefoods.co.kr
Rev.: $1,350,556,629
Assets: $1,068,058,913
Liabilities: $407,791,649
Net Worth: $660,267,264
Earnings: ($879,356)
Emp.: 1,940
Fiscal Year-end: 12/31/2021
Ice Cream, Dairy Products, Meat Products, Fats & Cooking Oil Mfr & Whslr
N.A.I.C.S.: 311999

Affiliate (Domestic):

Lotte.com Inc. (2)
158 Eulji-ro, Jung-gu, Seoul, Korea (South)
Tel.: (82) 2 1599 9731
Web Site: http://www.lotte.com
Confectionery Distr
N.A.I.C.S.: 424450
Hyun-Goo Kang (CEO)

Subsidiary (Domestic):

Lotte JTB Co., Ltd (3)
Yurim Bldg 626 Tongil-ro, Eunpyeong-ro, Seoul, Korea (South)
Tel.: (82) 2 3782 3000
Web Site: http://www.lottejtb.com
Emp.: 229
Travel Agency
N.A.I.C.S.: 561510
Gyu Dong Ahn (CEO)

Affiliate (Domestic):

Lotteria Co., Ltd. (2)
47 Hangang-daero 71-gil, Yongsan-gu, Seoul, Korea (South)
Tel.: (82) 2 709 1114
Web Site: http://www.lotteria.co.kr
Restaurants & Snack Shops Franchisee & Operator
N.A.I.C.S.: 722513
Il-sik Rho (CEO)

MYbi Co., Ltd. (2)
11F Centum IS Tower 60 Centum buk-daero, Haeundae, Busan, Korea (South) (66.12%)
Tel.: (82) 1588 8990
Web Site: http://www.mybi.co.kr
Financial Management Services
N.A.I.C.S.: 523999

Lotte China Foods Co., Ltd. (1)
No 8 Yong Chang North Road, ETD area, Beijing, 100176, China
Tel.: (86) 10 6787 3810
Confectionery Distr
N.A.I.C.S.: 424450
Park Kihong (Gen Mgr)

Lotte International Co., Ltd. (1)
302 Yeongdong-daero, Gangnam-gu, Seoul, Korea (South)
Tel.: (82) 2 3459 9600
Web Site: http://www.lotteintl.co.kr
Emp.: 112
Wholesale Trade Distr
N.A.I.C.S.: 425120
Kyuk-Ho Shin (CEO)

Subsidiary (US):

Lotte International America Corp. (2)
100 Challenger Rd Ste 710, Ridgefield Park, NJ 07660
Tel.: (201) 440-8050
Web Site: http://www.lotteintl.com
Wholesale Trade Distr
N.A.I.C.S.: 425120

Subsidiary (Non-US):

Lotte Vina International Co., Ltd. (2)
3rd Floor Beautiful Saigon Building No 02 Nguyen Khac Vien Street, Tan Phu Ward District 7, Ho Chi Minh City, Vietnam
Tel.: (84) 8 3775 2507
Wholesale Trade Distr
N.A.I.C.S.: 425120

Lotte Singapore Pte. Ltd. (1)
10 Anson Road, Singapore, Singapore
Tel.: (65) 62233708
Confectionery Distr
N.A.I.C.S.: 424450

Lotte U.S.A., Inc. (1)
5243 Wayne Rd, Battle Creek, MI 49037
Tel.: (269) 963-6664
Sales Range: $25-49.9 Million
Emp.: 13
Mfr of Confectionery Products
N.A.I.C.S.: 311340
John Hammons (Mgr-Pur)

Lotte Vietnam Co., Ltd. (1)
4th Floor Tuoi Tre Building, Ho Chi Minh City, Vietnam
Tel.: (84) 838479623
Confectionery Distr
N.A.I.C.S.: 424450

Mary Chocolate Co., Ltd. (1)
7-1-14 Omori-Nishi, Ota-ku, Tokyo, 143-8508, Japan
Tel.: (81) 3 3763 5111
Confectionery Distr
N.A.I.C.S.: 424450

Midori Shoji CO., LTD. (1)
1-1-10 Higashiikebukuro, Toshima-Ku, Tokyo, Japan
Tel.: (81) 339855155
Confectionery Distr
N.A.I.C.S.: 424450

PT Makro Indonesia (1)
Jl Lingkar Luar Selatan Kav 6, Ciracas, Jakarta, 13750, Indonesia
Tel.: (62) 218404080
Web Site: http://www.makro.co.id
Cash & Carry Warehouse Club & Superstore
N.A.I.C.S.: 455211

Thai Lotte Co., Ltd. (1)
Tower Building 3rd Floor 14/1 Sukhumvit Soi 1 North Sathorn Road, Bangkok, 10500, Thailand
Tel.: (66) 2267 3399
Web Site: http://www.lotte.co.th
Confectionery Distr
N.A.I.C.S.: 424450

Plant (Domestic):

Thai Lotte Co., Ltd. - Amatanakorn Factory (2)

INTERNATIONAL PUBLIC

700/830 Amata Nakorn Phase 8 Moo 6 Nong-tam-lung, Pan-thong, Phan Thong, 20160, Chonburi, Thailand
Tel.: (66) 3818 5255 8
Confectionery Mfr
N.A.I.C.S.: 311351

Thai Lotte Co., Ltd. - Sriracha Factory (2)
600/8 Moo 11 Sukaphiban Rd Soi 8 Nongkam, Si Racha, Chon Buri, Thailand
Tel.: (66) 3848 0564 5
Confectionery Mfr
N.A.I.C.S.: 311351

LOTTE REIT CO., LTD.
30F Lotteworld Tower 300 Olympic-Ro, Songpa-gu, Seoul, 05551, Korea (South)
Tel.: (82) 232138154
Web Site: https://www.lottereit.co.kr
Year Founded: 2019
330590—(KRS)
Rev.: $44,995,807
Assets: $1,796,868,583
Liabilities: $969,420,114
Net Worth: $827,448,469
Earnings: $4,498,854
Fiscal Year-end: 06/30/23
Real Estate Services
N.A.I.C.S.: 531210
Young Ju Yoon (Head-REIT Bus)

LOTTE RENTAL CO., LTD.
3F 6 10F 15F kt tower 422 Teheran-ro, Gangnam-gu, Seoul, Korea (South)
Tel.: (82) 15775100
Web Site: https://www.lotterental.com
Year Founded: 2005
089860—(KRS)
Motor Vehicle Rental Services
N.A.I.C.S.: 532111
Hyun-Soo Kim (Pres & CEO)

Subsidiaries:

Lotte Auto Lease Co., Ltd. (1)
11F Kt Tower 422 Teheran-ro, Gangnam-gu, Seoul, Korea (South)
Tel.: (82) 1 899 8700
Car Rental Services
N.A.I.C.S.: 532111

Lotte Rent-A-Car (Thailand) Co., Ltd. (1)
828 Oasis Work Place E Bldg 3rd Floor Rimklongsamsen Rd, Bangkapi Sub-district Huaykwang District, Bangkok, 10310, Thailand
Tel.: (66) 90 947 9583
Web Site: https://www.lotterentacar.co.th
Car Rental Services
N.A.I.C.S.: 532111

LOTTE TOUR DEVELOPMENT CO., LTD.
5th floor Gwanghwamun Building 149 Sejong-daero, Jongno-gu, Seoul, 03186, Korea (South)
Tel.: (82) 15773000
Web Site: https://www.lottetour.com
Year Founded: 1971
032350—(KRS)
Rev.: $140,875,585
Assets: $1,382,729,648
Liabilities: $1,205,024,868
Net Worth: $177,704,780
Earnings: ($172,351,158)
Emp.: 1,107
Fiscal Year-end: 12/31/22
Tour Arrangement Services
N.A.I.C.S.: 561520
Kim Hong Gyun (Dir-Investor Relations)

LOTTO SPORT ITALIA S.P.A.
Via Montebelluna 5/7, Trevignano, 31040, Treviso, Italy
Tel.: (39) 04236181   IT
Web Site: http://www.lotto.it

Year Founded: 1973
Sales Range: $300-349.9 Million
Emp.: 200
Athletic Footwear & Sportswear Mfr
N.A.I.C.S.: 316210

LOTTOTECH LTD.
Bank Street 18 Cybercity, Ebene, Mauritius
Tel.: (230) 4037117
Web Site: https://www.lottotech.mu
Year Founded: 2008
LOTO—(MAU)
Rev.: $67,593,643
Assets: $13,096,054
Liabilities: $9,164,342
Net Worth: $3,931,712
Earnings: $3,534,643
Emp.: 118
Fiscal Year-end: 12/31/23
Entertainment Services
N.A.I.C.S.: 711130
Michelle J. Carinci *(Mng Dir)*

LOTUS BAKERIES N.V.
Gentstraat 1 Lembeke, 9971, Brussels, Belgium
Tel.: (32) 93762600
Web Site:
https://www.lotusbakeries.com
LOTB—(EUR)
Rev.: $1,173,376,753
Assets: $1,372,671,377
Liabilities: $648,301,137
Net Worth: $724,370,240
Earnings: $142,767,414
Emp.: 2,746
Fiscal Year-end: 12/31/23
Mfr of Biscuit & Cake Products
N.A.I.C.S.: 311821
Jan Boone *(CEO & Mng Dir)*

Subsidiaries:

Koninklijke Peijnenburg B.V. (1)
Nieuwendijk 45, 5664 HB, Geldrop, Netherlands
Tel.: (31) 402807777
Web Site: https://peijnenburg.nl
Gingerbread Mfr & Distr
N.A.I.C.S.: 311999

Lotus Bakeries CZ s.r.o. (1)
Americka 415/36, 120 00, Prague, Czech Republic
Tel.: (420) 222511320
Cookies & Biscuit Mfr
N.A.I.C.S.: 311821

Lotus Bakeries GmbH (1)
Schumanstrasse 33, 52146, Wurselen, Nordrhein-Westfalen, Germany
Tel.: (49) 240541200
Web Site: http://www.der-lotus-moment.com
Bakery Goods Retailer
N.A.I.C.S.: 445291

Lotus Bakeries North America Inc. (1)
1000 Sansome St Ste 350, San Francisco, CA 94111
Tel.: (415) 956-8956
Web Site: http://www.biscoff.com
Sales Range: $10-24.9 Million
Emp.: 27
Specialty Food Items
N.A.I.C.S.: 424390

LOTUS BIO-TECHNOLOGY DEVELOPMENT CORP.
Unit 04 16/F Tower 2, Silvercord 30 Canton Road, Kowloon, China (Hong Kong)
Tel.: (852) 63980202 NV
Year Founded: 2011
LBTD—(OTCIQ)
Assets: $2,000
Liabilities: $44,000
Net Worth: ($42,000)
Earnings: ($9,000)
Fiscal Year-end: 03/31/22

Investment Services
N.A.I.C.S.: 523999
Zoltan Nagy *(Pres, CEO & Principal Fin Officer)*

LOTUS CAPITAL FINANCIAL SERVICES LTD.
7th Floor Vaman Techno Center, Marol Makwana Road Marol Naka, Mumbai, 400059, Andheri, India
Tel.: (91) 2242300800
Web Site:
http://www.lotuscapitalservices.com
Year Founded: 1995
Investment Services
N.A.I.C.S.: 523999

LOTUS EYE HOSPITAL AND INSTITUTE LTD.
770/12 Avinashi Road Civil Aerodrome Post, Coimbatore, 641014, India
Tel.: (91) 7397697774
Web Site: https://www.lotuseye.org
532998—(BOM)
Rev.: $5,432,113
Assets: $8,407,963
Liabilities: $953,889
Net Worth: $7,454,074
Earnings: $407,371
Emp.: 310
Fiscal Year-end: 03/31/22
Eye Care Hospital Owner & Operator
N.A.I.C.S.: 622310
S. K. Sundaramoorthy *(Founder)*

LOTUS HOLDINGS CO LTD
No 18 Lianhua Avenue, Xiangcheng, 466200, Henan, China
Tel.: (86) 3944298666
Web Site:
https://en.chinalotus.com.cn
Year Founded: 1983
600186—(SHG)
Rev.: $237,424,150
Assets: $340,801,063
Liabilities: $175,473,773
Net Worth: $165,327,290
Earnings: $6,481,875
Fiscal Year-end: 12/31/22
Flavouring Product Mfr
N.A.I.C.S.: 325199
Li Houwen *(Chm)*

LOTUS HORIZON HOLDINGS LIMITED
21/F Delta House 3 On Yiu Street, Shatin, Hong Kong, New Territories, China (Hong Kong)
Tel.: (852) 2 399 0911 Ky
Web Site:
http://www.lotushorizonholding.com
Year Founded: 2018
6063—(HKG)
Rev.: $28,477,236
Assets: $27,117,271
Liabilities: $4,775,485
Net Worth: $22,341,787
Earnings: $2,803,509
Emp.: 61
Fiscal Year-end: 03/31/21
Holding Company
N.A.I.C.S.: 551112
Kwok Fun Chu *(Chm & CEO)*

LOTUS HYDRO POWER PLC
2nd Floor No 168 Negombo Road, Peliyagoda, Colombo, Sri Lanka
Tel.: (94) 115117780
Web Site:
https://www.lotusreenergy.com
Year Founded: 2000
HPFL—(COL)
Rev.: $666,537
Assets: $3,224,822
Liabilities: $580,796

Net Worth: $2,644,026
Earnings: $145,500
Emp.: 51
Fiscal Year-end: 03/31/23
Electricity Power Generation Services
N.A.I.C.S.: 221118
Gary Donald Seaton *(Chm)*

LOTUS KFM BERHAD
Kawasan Lembaga Pelabuhan Kuantan KM 25 Jalan Kuantan / Kemaman, PO Box 387 Tanjung Gelang, 25740, Kuantan, Pahang Darul Makmur, Malaysia
Tel.: (60) 95833611
Web Site: http://www.kfmb.com.my
Rev.: $14,251,288
Assets: $8,826,331
Liabilities: $16,104,886
Net Worth: ($7,278,554)
Earnings: ($962,643)
Fiscal Year-end: 09/30/19
Flour Milling Services
N.A.I.C.S.: 311211
Mohd Rasli Muda *(Chm)*

LOTUS PHARMACEUTICAL CO., LTD.
17F No. 277 Song Ren Road Xin Yi District, Taipei, 110, Taiwan
Tel.: (886) 227005908 KR
Web Site: http://www.lotuspharm.com
Year Founded: 1966
Rev.: $305,060,105
Assets: $595,771,073
Liabilities: $338,288,759
Net Worth: $257,482,314
Earnings: $22,552,910
Emp.: 1,080
Fiscal Year-end: 12/31/19
Pharmaceuticals Product Mfr
N.A.I.C.S.: 325412
Petar Vazharov *(Gen Mgr)*

Subsidiaries:

Alvogen Korea Holdings Ltd. (1)
13F Two IFC Bldg 10 Gukjegeumyung-ro, Yeongdeungpo-gu, Seoul, Korea (South)
Tel.: (82) 220477700
Pharmaceutical Products Preparation & Mfr
N.A.I.C.S.: 325412

Subsidiary (Domestic):

Alvogen Korea Co., Ltd. (2)
13f Two Ifc Bldg 10 Gukjegeumyung-ro, Yeongdeungpo-Gu, Seoul, Korea (South) (100%)
Tel.: (82) 2 2047 7700
Web Site: http://en.alvogenkorea.com
Emp.: 500
Pharmaceutical Product Mfr & Distr
N.A.I.C.S.: 325412
Hee-Kyun Im *(CEO)*

Plant (Domestic):

Kunwha Pharmaceutical Co., Ltd. - Korea Plant (3)
55-8 Jeongannonggongdanjigil Jeonganmyeon, Gongju, Chungcheongnam-do, Korea (South)
Tel.: (82) 41 840 5300
Pharmaceuticals Product Mfr
N.A.I.C.S.: 325412

LOTUS PHARMACEUTICALS, INC.
16 Cheng Zhuang Road, Feng Tai District, Beijing, 100071, China
Tel.: (86) 1063899868
Web Site:
http://www.lotuspharma.com
LTUS—(OTCIQ)
Sales Range: Less than $1 Million
Emp.: 233
Pharmaceuticals Mfr
N.A.I.C.S.: 325412
Zhong Yi Liu *(Chm)*

LOTUS RESOURCES LIMITED
Tel.: (61) 892003427 AU
Web Site:
https://lotusresources.com.au
Year Founded: 2006
LOT—(ASX)
Rev.: $1,114,976
Assets: $112,728,488
Liabilities: $27,661,832
Net Worth: $85,066,656
Earnings: ($16,856,245)
Emp.: 19
Fiscal Year-end: 06/30/24
Phosphate Mining Services
N.A.I.C.S.: 212390
Keith Bowes *(Mng Dir)*

Subsidiaries:

Lotus Marula Pty. Ltd. (1)
Level 38 123 Eagle St, Brisbane, 4000, QLD, Australia
Tel.: (61) 863837836
Rev.: $3,697
Assets: $35,225,018
Liabilities: $373,018
Net Worth: $34,851,999
Earnings: ($3,995,393)
Fiscal Year-end: 06/30/2022
Mineral Exploration Services
N.A.I.C.S.: 212220
Angang Shen *(Chm)*

Subsidiary (Non-US):

A-Cap Resources Botswana (Pty.) Ltd. (2)
Delloite House Plot 64518 Fairgrounds, PO Box 50448, Gaborone, Botswana
Tel.: (267) 76647871
Uranium Mining Services
N.A.I.C.S.: 213115

LOUGHBOROUGH BUILDING SOCIETY
6 High Street, Loughborough, LE11 2QB, United Kingdom
Tel.: (44) 1509 610707
Web Site:
http://www.theloughborough.co.uk
Year Founded: 1867
Rev.: $10,170,146
Assets: $416,894,683
Liabilities: $386,272,758
Net Worth: $30,621,925
Earnings: $474,799
Emp.: 50
Fiscal Year-end: 10/31/19
Mortgage Lending & Other Financial Services
N.A.I.C.S.: 522310
Gary Brebner *(CEO)*

LOUIS DREYFUS ARMATEURS
Immeuble Les Ecluses 28 quai Gallieni, 92158, Suresnes, Cedex, France
Tel.: (33) 1 7038 6000 FR
Web Site: http://www.lda.fr
Year Founded: 1893
Emp.: 2,000
Holding Company; Freight Shipping, Maritime Engineering & Offshore Services
N.A.I.C.S.: 551112
Philippe Louis-Dreyfus *(Chm-Supervisory Bd)*

Subsidiaries:

LD Bulk Asia Pte Ltd. (1)
45B Club Street, Singapore, 69422, Singapore
Tel.: (65) 65766890
Logistics Consulting Servies
N.A.I.C.S.: 541614

LD Ports & Logistics (1)
45A Club Street, Singapore, 69422, Singapore
Tel.: (65) 65769877
Web Site: http://www.ldpl.com
Logistics Consulting Servies

LOUIS DREYFUS ARMATEURS

Louis Dreyfus Armateurs—(Continued)
N.A.I.C.S.: 541614
Lucian Pop (Mgr-Ops & Technical)

Louis Dreyfus Travocean (1)
Le Mistral C - ZA Athelia IV 375 av du Mistral, 60136, La Ciotat, France
Tel.: (33) 4 42 18 34 00
Web Site: http://www.ldtravocean.com
Emp.: 30
Cable Installation Services
N.A.I.C.S.: 516210
Sylvain Gouillon (Dir-Sls & Project)

LOUIS DREYFUS COMPANY B.V.

Westblaak 92, 3012 KM, Rotterdam, Netherlands
Tel.: (31) 10 20 624 40   NI
Web Site: http://www.ldc.com
Year Founded: 1851
Rev.: $33,643,000,000
Assets: $19,538,000,000
Liabilities: $14,740,000,000
Net Worth: $4,798,000,000
Earnings: $228,000,000
Emp.: 18,158
Fiscal Year-end: 12/31/19
Agricultural Goods Distr
N.A.I.C.S.: 424490
Margarita Louis-Dreyfus (Chm-Supervisory Bd)

Subsidiaries:

Ilomar Holding N.V. (1)
Noorderlaan 121B, 2030, Antwerp, Belgium
Tel.: (32) 35427300
Agricultural Food Product Distr
N.A.I.C.S.: 424490

LDC (China) Trading Company Ltd. (1)
Tower A 24F Pacific Century Place Workers Stadium North Road No 2, Chaoyang District, Beijing, 100027, China
Tel.: (86) 1058693666
Agricultural Food Product Distr
N.A.I.C.S.: 424490

LDC (Tianjin) Food Technology Limited Liability Company (1)
2068 40 Bohai Road Lingang economic zone, Binhai new area, Tianjin, 300452, China
Tel.: (86) 2259855888
Agricultural Food Product Distr
N.A.I.C.S.: 424490

LDC Argentina S.A. (1)
Olga Cossettini 240 Piso 2, C1107CCF, Buenos Aires, Argentina
Tel.: (54) 1143246900
Agricultural Food Product Distr
N.A.I.C.S.: 424490

LDC Enterprises Australia Pty. Ltd. (1)
Level 3 1 Breakfast Creek Rd, Newstead, Brisbane, 4006, QLD, Australia
Tel.: (61) 732535999
Agricultural Food Product Distr
N.A.I.C.S.: 424490

Louis Dreyfus (Shanghai) Co. Ltd. (1)
Tower 1 12th Floor Crystal Plaza No 1359 Yaolong Road, Pudong District, Shanghai, 200126, China
Tel.: (86) 2168593986
Agricultural Food Product Distr
N.A.I.C.S.: 424490

Louis Dreyfus (Zhangjiagang) Feed Protein Company Ltd. (1)
No 1 Baodao Road Free Trade Zone, Zhangjiagang, 215634, Jiangsu, China
Tel.: (86) 51258388187
Agricultural Food Product Distr
N.A.I.C.S.: 424490

Louis Dreyfus Company Africa Pty. Ltd. (1)
4th Floor 155 West Street, PO Box 784658, Johannesburg, Sandton, 2196, South Africa
Tel.: (27) 112175300

Agricultural Food Product Distr
N.A.I.C.S.: 424490

Louis Dreyfus Company Agricultural Industries LLC (1)
7344 State Route 15, Claypool, IN 46510
Tel.: (574) 566-2100
Agricultural Food Product Distr
N.A.I.C.S.: 424490

Louis Dreyfus Company Colombia S.A.S. (1)
Avenue 7 71-52 Torre A Office 1301, 11001, Bogota, Colombia
Tel.: (57) 17455300
Emp.: 100
Soybean Oil Distr
N.A.I.C.S.: 424590

Louis Dreyfus Company Cotton LLC (1)
1520 Texas Ave, Lubbock, TX 79401
Tel.: (806) 747-7836
Agricultural Food Product Distr
N.A.I.C.S.: 424490

Louis Dreyfus Company Distribution, France S.A.S. (1)
15 Avenue de la Grande Armee, 75116, Paris, France
Tel.: (33) 4374288
Agricultural Food Product Distr
N.A.I.C.S.: 424490

Louis Dreyfus Company Espana S.A. (1)
Calle Zurbano 45 4th Floor, 28010, Madrid, Spain
Tel.: (34) 915141200
Agricultural Food Product Distr
N.A.I.C.S.: 424490

Louis Dreyfus Company Grand Junction LLC (1)
1149 U Ave, Grand Junction, IA 50107
Tel.: (515) 738-2800
Agricultural Food Product Distr
N.A.I.C.S.: 424490

Louis Dreyfus Company Kenya Ltd. (1)
Shimanzi KPA Gate 12, PO Box 34256-80118, Mombasa, Kenya
Tel.: (254) 412223958
Agricultural Food Product Distr
N.A.I.C.S.: 424490

Louis Dreyfus Company Mexico S.A. de C.V. (1)
Insurgentes Sur 859 Piso 3 of 302, Col Napoles Deleg Benito Juarez, 3810, Mexico, Mexico
Tel.: (52) 2223728400
Agricultural Food Product Distr
N.A.I.C.S.: 424490

Louis Dreyfus Company Polska SP. z.o.o. (1)
Ul Bobrowiecka, 100-728, Warsaw, Poland
Tel.: (48) 225590800
Agricultural Food Product Distr
N.A.I.C.S.: 424490

Louis Dreyfus Company Ukraine Ltd. (1)
1-A Sportyvna sq 15th floor, Kiev, 01001, Ukraine
Tel.: (380) 442386888
Emp.: 400
Agricultural Food Product Distr
N.A.I.C.S.: 424490

Louis Dreyfus Company Wittenberg GmbH (1)
Dessauer Strasse 126, 6886, Lutherstadt Wittenberg, Germany
Tel.: (49) 34914200980
Vegetable Oil Mfr
N.A.I.C.S.: 311225

Namoi Cotton Limited (1)
259 Ruthven Street, PO Box 1333, Toowoomba, 4350, QLD, Australia
Tel.: (61) 46316100
Web Site: https://www.namoicotton.com.au
Rev.: $166,205,981
Assets: $130,501,328
Liabilities: $32,866,290
Net Worth: $97,635,038
Earnings: $4,699,952

Emp.: 150
Fiscal Year-end: 02/29/2024
Cotton Ginning
N.A.I.C.S.: 115111
Eimear McDonagh (Mgr-Export Mktg & Logistics-Namoi Cotton Alliance)

Affiliate (Domestic):

Ashley Ginning Services Pty Ltd (2)
Mungindi Road Ashley, Sydney, 2400, NSW, Australia   (51%)
Tel.: (61) 267542150
Web Site: http://www.namoicotton.com.au
Sales Range: $25-49.9 Million
Emp.: 5
Cotton Ginning; Owned 51% by Naomi Cotton Co-operative Ltd.& 49% by Australian Food & Fibre Ltd
N.A.I.C.S.: 115111

Subsidiary (Domestic):

Australian Classing Services Pty Ltd. (2)
27 Trucking Yards Lane, PO Box 143, Wee Waa, 2388, NSW, Australia
Tel.: (61) 437414939
Web Site: https://www.ausclass.com.au
Reinsurance Services
N.A.I.C.S.: 524130

Australian Cotton Ginning Company Pty Ltd. (2)
Roto Road Hillston, Sydney, 2675, NSW, Australia   (100%)
Tel.: (61) 269672951
Sales Range: $10-24.9 Million
Emp.: 35
Cotton Ginning
N.A.I.C.S.: 115111
Jamie McGowan (Gen Mgr)

Affiliate (Domestic):

Wathagar Ginning Company Pty Ltd (2)
Collarenebri Rd Moree, Sydney, 2400, NSW, Australia   (50%)
Tel.: (61) 267525200
Sales Range: $25-49.9 Million
Cotton Ginning
N.A.I.C.S.: 115111
Michael Murray (Gen Mgr)

Terminal Exportador De Santos S.A. (1)
Avenida Governador Mario Covas Junior S/N Armz XL XLII e 38, Estuario, Santos, 11020-300, SP, Brazil
Tel.: (55) 1332781700
Web Site: http://www.tessantos.com.br
Port Operation Services
N.A.I.C.S.: 488310

LOUIS DREYFUS S.A.S.

1 Rue Kepler, 75116, Paris, Cedex, France
Tel.: (33) 1 80 50 19 00   FR
Web Site:
http://www.louisdreyfus.com
Sales Range: $1-4.9 Billion
Holding Company
N.A.I.C.S.: 551112
Margarita Louis-Dreyfus (Chm-Supervisory Bd)

Subsidiaries:

Louis Dreyfus Commodities (1)
40 Danbury Rd, Wilton, CT 06897-4522
Tel.: (203) 761-2000
Web Site: http://www.ldcom.com
Sales Range: $200-249.9 Million
Emp.: 300
Agricultural Services; Trucking & Warehousing; Commodity Exporters
N.A.I.C.S.: 523160

Joint Venture (Domestic):

CLD Pacific Grain LLC (2)
800 N River St, Portland, OR 97227-1715
Tel.: (503) 281-9177
Sales Range: $1-9.9 Million
Emp.: 30
Grain Whslr & Storage Services
N.A.I.C.S.: 424510

INTERNATIONAL PUBLIC

Holding (Domestic):

Imperial Sugar Company (2)
3 Sugar creek Ctr Blvd Ste 500, Sugar Land, TX 77478
Tel.: (281) 491-9181
Web Site:
http://www.imperialsugarcompany.com
Sales Range: $150-199.9 Million
Emp.: 530
Pure Cane Sugar Refiner Packager Mfr
N.A.I.C.S.: 311314
Patrick D. Henneberry (Sr VP-Commodities & Sls)

Subsidiary (Domestic):

Colonial Sugar, Inc. (3)
1230 5th Ave, Gramercy, LA 70052-3360   (100%)
Tel.: (225) 869-5521
Sales Range: $100-124.9 Million
Emp.: 200
Sugar Refinery
N.A.I.C.S.: 311314

Imperial Sugar Company (3)
GA Hwy 25 N Oxnard Dr, Port Wentworth, GA 31407
Tel.: (912) 964-1361
Web Site: http://www.imperialsugar.com
Sales Range: $200-249.9 Million
Emp.: 450
Mfr of Sugar & Sugar Products; Liquid Animal Feeds, Warehousing & Transportation
N.A.I.C.S.: 311313
Gail Lange (Gen Mgr-Bus Dev)

Savannah Foods Industrial, Inc. (3)
201 Oxnard Ave, Port Wentworth, GA 31407
Tel.: (912) 964-1361
Web Site: http://www.impimperialsugar.com
Sales Range: $200-249.9 Million
Emp.: 350
Food Products Mfr
N.A.I.C.S.: 311313

Savannah Investment Company (3)
2751 Centerville Rd, Wilmington, DE 19808-1627
Tel.: (302) 427-5786
Sales Range: $250-299.9 Million
Mfr of Food Products, Primarily Refined Cane & Beet Sugar
N.A.I.C.S.: 311314

Savannah Sugar Refining Corp. (3)
201 Oxnard Dr, Port Wentworth, GA 31407
Tel.: (912) 964-1361
Web Site:
http://www.imperialsugarcompany.com
Sugar Refinery
N.A.I.C.S.: 311313

Subsidiary (Domestic):

Louis Dreyfus Citrus, Inc. (2)
355 9th St, Winter Garden, FL 34787
Tel.: (407) 656-1000
Web Site: http://www.ldcitrusfl.com
Sales Range: $100-124.9 Million
Citrus Growers & Producers
N.A.I.C.S.: 111320
Scott Hogan (Pres)

LOUIS PLC

11 Lemesou Aven, 2112, Nicosia, Cyprus
Tel.: (357) 22588168
Web Site:
https://www.louisgroup.com
Year Founded: 1998
LUI—(CYP)
Rev.: $20,239,661
Assets: $482,747,961
Liabilities: $431,872,085
Net Worth: $50,875,877
Earnings: $15,625,174
Fiscal Year-end: 12/31/20
Home Management Services
N.A.I.C.S.: 721110
Costakis Loizou (Chm)

Subsidiaries:

Celestyal Cruises Ltd. (1)
11 Lemesos Avenue, 2112, Nicosia, Cyprus

Tel.: (357) 22413500
Web Site: http://www.celestyal.com
Cruise Operator
N.A.I.C.S.: 483112
Bentlie Logan *(Mgr-Bus Dev-Northeast USA & Canada)*

Louis Hotels Public Company Ltd. (1)
Tel.: (357) 22588204
Web Site: https://www.louishotels.com
Hotel Operator
N.A.I.C.S.: 721110

LOUIS POULSEN AS
Kuglegardsvej 19-23, DK-1434, Copenhagen, K, Denmark
Tel.: (45) 70 33 14 14
Web Site:
  http://www.louispoulsen.com
Lighting Product Mfr
N.A.I.C.S.: 335132

Subsidiaries:

Louis Poulsen UK Limited (1)
St James House 13 Kensington Square, London, W8 5HD, United Kingdom
Tel.: (44) 2083974400
Commercial Industrial & Institutional Electric Lighting Fixture Mfr
N.A.I.C.S.: 335132

LOUISBOURG SEAFOODS LTD.
PO Box 5609, Louisbourg, B1C 1B5, NS, Canada
Tel.: (902) 733-2079
Web Site:
  https://www.louisbourgseafoods.ca
Year Founded: 1984
Rev.: $11,042,009
Emp.: 70
Seafood Canning
N.A.I.C.S.: 311710

Subsidiaries:

J.K. Marine Services Ltd. (1)
3 Commercial Street, Louisbourg, B1C 1B5, NS, Canada
Tel.: (902) 733-2739
Seafood Distr
N.A.I.C.S.: 424460
Bernard Kenendy *(Mgr)*

Ka' Le Bay Seafoods Ltd. (1)
-, PO Box 298, Glace Bay, B1A 5V4, NS, Canada
Tel.: (902) 842-9454
Seafood Mfr
N.A.I.C.S.: 311710
Jan Voutier *(Mgr)*

Northsyde Processing Limited (1)
139 Queen Street, North Sydney, B2A 1A9, NS, Canada
Tel.: (902) 794-8501
Seafood Mfr
N.A.I.C.S.: 311710
Hordur Bjarnason *(Gen Mgr & Plant Mgr)*

LOULIS FOOD INGREDIENTS S.A.
Loulis Port Almiros Magnesia, 370 08, Volos, Greece
Tel.: (30) 2421094550
Web Site: https://www.loulis.com
Year Founded: 1927
KYLO—(ATH)
Rev.: $213,585,366
Assets: $240,522,839
Liabilities: $135,248,692
Net Worth: $105,274,147
Earnings: $1,988,194
Emp.: 365
Fiscal Year-end: 12/31/22
Flour Production & Trading
N.A.I.C.S.: 311211
Konstantinos N. Dimopoulos *(Exec Dir)*

Subsidiaries:

Greek Baking School S.A. (1)
1 Spetson Str Fish Market, 91154, Keratsini, Greece
Tel.: (30) 2104090168
Web Site: http://www.greekbakingschool.gr
Emp.: 285
Bakery & Pastry Food Distr
N.A.I.C.S.: 424490

Kenfood S.A. (1)
Spetson 1, 187 55, Keratsini, Greece
Tel.: (30) 2105615410
Web Site: http://www.kenfood.com
Bakery & Pastry Food Distr
N.A.I.C.S.: 424490

LOUNGERS PLC
Loungers HQ 26 Baldwin St, Bristol, BS1 1SE, United Kingdom
Tel.: (44) 1179309971 JE
Web Site: https://www.loungers.co.uk
Year Founded: 2002
LGRS—(AIM)
Rev.: $106,371,931
Assets: $395,719,713
Liabilities: $242,410,044
Net Worth: $153,309,669
Earnings: ($15,127,716)
Emp.: 4,521
Fiscal Year-end: 04/18/21
Other Grocery & Related Products Merchant Wholesalers
N.A.I.C.S.: 424490
Alex Reilley *(Founder & Chm)*

LOUNOR EXPLORATION INC.
15 Gamble East Suite 204, Rouyn-Noranda, J9X 3B6, QC, Canada
Tel.: (819) 797-8668
Web Site: http://www.lounor.com
Year Founded: 1953
Sales Range: Less than $1 Million
Gold Exploration Services
N.A.I.C.S.: 212220
Gilles Fiset *(Pres & CEO)*

LOV GROUP INVEST SAS
5 rue Francois 1er, 75008, Paris, France
Tel.: (33) 144952300
Web Site: http://www.lovgroup.com
Holding Company; Entertainment, Online Casino & Luxury Hotel Operator
N.A.I.C.S.: 551112
Stephane Courbit *(Founder & CEO)*

Subsidiaries:

Banijay Holding SAS (1)
5 rue Francois 1er, 75008, Paris, France (67.1%)
Tel.: (33) 1 4318 9191
Web Site: http://www.banijay.com
Holding Company; Television & Digital Entertainment Content Production Services
N.A.I.C.S.: 551112
Stephane Courbit *(Chm)*

Subsidiary (Domestic):

Banijay Entertainment SAS (2)
5 rue Francois 1er, Paris, 75008, France
Tel.: (33) 1 4318 9191
Web Site: http://www.banijay.com
Television & Digital Entertainment Content Production Services
N.A.I.C.S.: 516210

Subsidiary (Domestic):

Air Productions (3)
Batiment 113 50 avenue du President Wilson, La Plaine Saint Denis, 93210, Saint Denis, France
Tel.: (33) 149178400
Web Site: http://www.airprod.com
Media Production Services
N.A.I.C.S.: 512191

Subsidiary (Non-US):

BRAINPOOL TV GmbH (3)
Schanzenstrasse 22, 51063, Cologne, Germany
Tel.: (49) 221 6509 0
Web Site: http://www.brainpool.de
Television Production
N.A.I.C.S.: 512110
Ralf Gunther *(Mng Dir)*

Banijay Finland Oy (3)
Tyopajankatu 10 A, 00580, Helsinki, Finland
Tel.: (358) 449875910
Web Site: https://www.banijay.fi
Media Production Services
N.A.I.C.S.: 512191
Rami Jahkonen *(CFO)*

Subsidiary (US):

Bunim/Murray Productions, Inc. (3)
6007 Sepulveda Blvd, Van Nuys, CA 91411
Tel.: (818) 756-5100
Web Site: http://www.bunim-murray.com
Sales Range: $25-49.9 Million
Emp.: 150
Cable Television Reality Programming Production & Distribution Services; Motion Picture & Music Production Services
N.A.I.C.S.: 512110
Jonathan Murray *(Founder)*

Subsidiary (Non-US):

Cuarzo Producciones S.L. (3)
Ile del Conde de Penalver 38, 28006, Madrid, Spain
Tel.: (34) 916592290
Web Site: https://www.cuarzotv.com
Media Production Services
N.A.I.C.S.: 512191
Ana Rosa Quintana *(CEO)*

Endemol India (3)
16th Floor Grandeur Veera Desai Road Extn Andheri West, Mumbai, 400053, Maharashtra, India
Tel.: (91) 2248905500
Web Site: https://endemolshine.co.in
Television & Other Audiovisual Entertainment Programming Services
N.A.I.C.S.: 516210

Subsidiary (Domestic):

H2O Productions SAS (3)
5 rue Francois 1er, 75008, Paris, France
Tel.: (33) 143189191
Video Production Services
N.A.I.C.S.: 512110

Subsidiary (Non-US):

Nonpanic Srl (3)
Via Pasubio 4, 00195, Rome, Italy
Tel.: (39) 06 888 05 187
Web Site: http://www.nonpanic.com
Media Production Services
N.A.I.C.S.: 512191
Filippo Cipriano *(CEO)*

Nordisk Film TV A/S (3)
Mosedalvej 14, 2500, Valby, Denmark
Tel.: (45) 36 18 82 00
Web Site: http://www.nordiskfilmtv.com
Television Production & Distribution
N.A.I.C.S.: 512110
Jacob Houlind *(CEO)*

Subsidiary (Non-US):

Nordisk Film TV AB (4)
Tel.: (46) 858782200
Web Site: http://www.nordiskfilmtv.se
Motion Picture & Video Production
N.A.I.C.S.: 512110
Kristoffer Graci *(CEO)*

Nordisk Film TV AS (4)
Drammensveien 130 A oppgang 4, 0277, Oslo, Norway
Tel.: (47) 21 04 28 10
Television Production
N.A.I.C.S.: 512110
Vibeke Gillebo *(Head-Production)*

Subsidiary (Non-US):

Screentime Limited (3)
Victoria Street West, PO Box 90530, Auckland, 1010, New Zealand
Tel.: (64) 9 303 3339
Web Site: http://www.screentime.co.nz
Media Production Services
N.A.I.C.S.: 512191
Philly de Lacey *(CEO)*

Screentime Pty Ltd (3)
Level 2 70-76 Alexander Street, Crows Nest, 2065, NSW, Australia
Tel.: (61) 294394911
Web Site: http://www.screentime.com.au
Media Production Services
N.A.I.C.S.: 512191
Bob Campbell *(Chm)*

Subsidiary (Domestic):

Beyond International Limited (4)
109 Reserve Road, Artarmon, 2064, NSW, Australia
Tel.: (61) 294372000
Web Site: http://www.beyond.com.au
Rev.: $87,726,456
Assets: $58,520,826
Liabilities: $42,364,944
Net Worth: $16,155,882
Earnings: $425,235
Emp.: 119
Fiscal Year-end: 06/30/2021
DVD Distribution
N.A.I.C.S.: 423990
Mikael Borglund *(CEO & Mng Dir)*

Subsidiary (Domestic):

Beyond Distribution Pty Ltd (5)
109 Reserve Road, Artarmon, 2064, NSW, Australia
Tel.: (61) 294372000
Web Site: http://www.beyond.com.au
Sales Range: $25-49.9 Million
Emp.: 16
Television Programme Distr
N.A.I.C.S.: 516120
Sarah McCormack *(Sr VP-Acquisitions & Co-Productions)*

Beyond Entertainment Pty Ltd (5)
109 Reserve Rd, Artarmon, 2064, NSW, Australia
Tel.: (61) 294372000
Sales Range: $50-74.9 Million
Movie Production & Distribution Services
N.A.I.C.S.: 512110
Mikael Borglund *(Gen Mgr)*

Beyond Films Limited (5)
109 Reserve Road, Artarmon, 2064, NSW, Australia
Tel.: (61) 294372000
Web Site: http://www.beyond.com.au
Sales Range: $50-74.9 Million
Emp.: 150
Motion Picture & Video Production Services
N.A.I.C.S.: 512110

Beyond Home Entertainment Pty Ltd (5)
701 Macarthur Ave, Eagle Farm, 4009, VIC, Australia
Tel.: (61) 393211200
Web Site:
  http://www.beyondhomeentertainment.com
Sales Range: $25-49.9 Million
Emp.: 15
Movies Distr
N.A.I.C.S.: 512120

Subsidiary (Domestic):

Arthur & Pat Laing Entertainment Pty Ltd (6)
61 Clinton Street, Goulburn, 2580, NSW, Australia
Tel.: (61) 248220007
Web Site: http://www.laing-entertainment.com.au
Events & Concerts Organizing Services
N.A.I.C.S.: 711310
Cathy Bell *(Office Mgr)*

Subsidiary (Domestic):

Beyond Productions Pty Ltd (5)
109 Reserve Road, Artarmon, 2064, NSW, Australia
Tel.: (61) 294372000
Web Site: http://www.beyond.com.au

LOV GROUP INVEST SAS

LOV Group Invest SAS—(Continued)
Sales Range: $25-49.9 Million
Emp.: 100
Motion Picture Production Services
N.A.I.C.S.: 512110
John Luscombe *(Exec VP & Gen Mgr)*

Beyond Properties Pty Ltd (5)
109 Reserve Rd, Artarmon, Sydney, 2064, NSW, Australia
Tel.: (61) 294372000
Sales Range: $75-99.9 Million
Emp.: 150
Property Management Services
N.A.I.C.S.: 531311
Tim McGee *(Gen Mgr-Bus & Product Dev)*

Subsidiary (Domestic):

Beyond Pty Ltd (6)
109 Reserve Rd, Artarmon, 2064, NSW, Australia
Tel.: (61) 294372000
Web Site: http://www.beyond.com.au
Sales Range: $25-49.9 Million
Emp.: 100
Motion Picture & Video Production Services
N.A.I.C.S.: 512110
Michael Borglund *(Mgr)*

Subsidiary (Domestic):

Eurocam Australia Pty Ltd (5)
Studio 47 90 Mona Vale Rd, Mona Vale, 2103, NSW, Australia
Tel.: (61) 2 9997 8899
Web Site: http://www.eurocam.com.au
Sales Range: $25-49.9 Million
Emp.: 7
Sports Program Production & Distribution Services
N.A.I.C.S.: 517111

dSp Beyond Pty Ltd (5)
Level 2 18-26 Dickson Ave, Artarmon, 2064, NSW, Australia
Tel.: (61) 284252430
Sales Range: $25-49.9 Million
Emp.: 20
Television Program Production Services
N.A.I.C.S.: 512110

Subsidiary (US):

Stephen David Entertainment (3)
247 W 37th St 10th Fl, New York, NY 10018
Tel.: (212) 575-8200
Web Site:
   https://www.stephenentertainment.com
Media Production Services
N.A.I.C.S.: 512191
Stephen David *(Pres)*

Subsidiary (Non-US):

Endemol Shine Group SPV B.V. (2)
MediArena 1, 1114 BC, Amsterdam, Netherlands (100%)
Tel.: (31) 208939000
Web Site:
   https://uat.endemolshinegroup.com
Holding Company; Entertainment Media Operator
N.A.I.C.S.: 551112
Peter Salmon *(Chief Creative Officer)*

Subsidiary (Non-US):

B&B Endemol AG (3)
Binzuhlestrasse 170d, 8050, Zurich, Switzerland
Tel.: (41) 44 557 24 24
Web Site: http://www.bbendemolshine.ch
Television & Other Audiovisual Entertainment Programming Services
N.A.I.C.S.: 516210

Brighter Pictures Ltd (3)
234-244 Stockwell Road 10th Floor Blue Star House, Charecroft Way Shepherds Bush, London, SW9 9SP, United Kingdom
Tel.: (44) 2077337333
Television & Other Audiovisual Entertainment Programming Services
N.A.I.C.S.: 516210

Cheetah Television Ltd (3)
Shepherds Building, Central, Charecroft Way Shepherds Bush, London, W14 0EE, United Kingdom
Tel.: (44) 870 333 1700
Television & Other Audiovisual Entertainment Programming Services
N.A.I.C.S.: 516210

Diagonal Television, S.L. (3)
C/ Larrard 20, 08024, Barcelona, Spain
Tel.: (34) 932688530
Web Site: https://www.diagonaltv.es
Television & Other Audiovisual Entertainment Programming Services
N.A.I.C.S.: 516210

Affiliate (Non-US):

Endemol Argentina S.A. (3)
Jose A Cabrera 5870, C1414CPJ, Buenos Aires, Argentina
Tel.: (54) 11 5218 9000
Television & Other Audiovisual Entertainment Programming Services
N.A.I.C.S.: 516210

Subsidiary (Non-US):

Endemol Belgie N.V. (3)
Schalienhoevedreef 20E, 2800, Mechelen, Belgium
Tel.: (32) 1565 2000
Web Site: http://www.endemolshine.com
Emp.: 40
Television & Other Audiovisual Entertainment Programming Services
N.A.I.C.S.: 516210
Nicole Plas *(Mng Dir)*

Endemol Brazil (3)
R General Furtado Nascimento 740 - cj 125 Alto de Pinheiros, Vila Madalena, Sao Paulo, 05434-080, Brazil
Tel.: (55) 1130223668
Television & Other Audiovisual Entertainment Programming Services
N.A.I.C.S.: 516210

Endemol Chile Lda. (3)
Miguel Claro 645 Providencia, Santiago, Chile
Tel.: (56) 2 719 4850
Television & Other Audiovisual Entertainment Programming Services
N.A.I.C.S.: 516210

Endemol Colombia SA (3)
Cl 63 F 28 B 15, Bogota, Colombia
Tel.: (57) 16409000
Television & Other Audiovisual Entertainment Programming Services
N.A.I.C.S.: 516210

Endemol Deutschland GmbH (3)
Am Coloneum 3-7 D, PO Box 320452, 50829, Cologne, Germany
Tel.: (49) 221 650 300
Television & Other Audiovisual Entertainment Programming Services
N.A.I.C.S.: 516210

Endemol Espana Holding, S.L. (3)
Avenida de Manoteras 18 6th Floor, 28050, Madrid, Spain
Tel.: (34) 902 12 02 04
Holding Company; Television & Other Audiovisual Entertainment Programming Services
N.A.I.C.S.: 551112

Endemol Fiction (3)
10 Rue Waldeck Rochet 521 Batiment, 93300, Aubervilliers, France
Tel.: (33) 1 53 56 40 00
Emp.: 200
Television & Other Audiovisual Entertainment Programming Services
N.A.I.C.S.: 516210
Nicolas Coppermann *(CEO)*

Endemol France (3)
Batiment 52, Ba10 Rue Waldeck Rochet, 93600, Aubervilliers, France
Tel.: (33) 1 53 56 40 00
Web Site: http://www.endemolsrance.com
Emp.: 100
Television & Other Audiovisual Entertainment Programming Services
N.A.I.C.S.: 516210

Endemol Globo S.A. (3)
Av Das Americas 700, PO Box 301, Barra da Tijuca, Rio de Janeiro, 22640-100, Brazil
Tel.: (55) 2125401569
Television & Other Audiovisual Entertainment Programming Services
N.A.I.C.S.: 516210

Endemol Italia Holding S.p.A (3)
Via Monte Zebio 32, 00195, Rome, Italy
Tel.: (39) 06 32 8191
Web Site: http://www.endemol.it
Television & Other Audiovisual Entertainment Programming Services
N.A.I.C.S.: 516210

Endemol Malaysia Entertainment Group Sdn (3)
Bhd B-20-1 Northpoint Office, Mid Valley City, Kuala Lumpur, 59200, Malaysia
Tel.: (60) 3 2282 1809
Television & Other Audiovisual Entertainment Programming Services
N.A.I.C.S.: 516210

Endemol MedyaProduction Ticaret Limited (3)
Cevdet Pasa Caddesi, Manolya Sok No:20, Istanbul, Turkiye
Tel.: (90) 212 287 00 50
Television & Other Audiovisual Entertainment Programming Services
N.A.I.C.S.: 516210

Endemol Middle East (3)
Dubai Studio City Boutique Studio 09 Office No 201 202, PO Box 299634, Dubai, United Arab Emirates
Tel.: (971) 44 331 590
Web Site: http://www.endemolme.com
Television & Other Audiovisual Entertainment Programming Services
N.A.I.C.S.: 516210

Endemol Middle East Productions S.A.L (3)
Damascus Road Chevrolet Roundabout, PO Box 11-2109, Palm Center 9th Floor, Beirut, Lebanon
Tel.: (961) 1283603
Television & Other Audiovisual Entertainment Programming Services
N.A.I.C.S.: 516210

Endemol Moscow (3)
Tverskaja Str 22a Build 3 3rd floor, 125009, Moscow, Russia
Tel.: (7) 495 626 5746
Web Site: http://www.endemolshine.de
Television & Other Audiovisual Entertainment Programming Services
N.A.I.C.S.: 516210

Subsidiary (Domestic):

Endemol Nederland, B.V. (3)
MediArena 2, 1114 BC, Amsterdam, Netherlands
Tel.: (31) 208931000
Web Site: http://www.endemolshine.nl
Sales Range: $50-74.9 Million
Emp.: 300
Television & Other Audiovisual Entertainment Programming Services
N.A.I.C.S.: 516210

Subsidiary (Non-US):

Endemol Nordic AB (3)
Palermog 17, 115 56, Stockholm, Sweden
Tel.: (46) 8 660 15 36
Television & Other Audiovisual Entertainment Programming Services
N.A.I.C.S.: 516210

Endemol Poland (3)
Ul Dominikanska 25A, 02-738, Warsaw, Poland
Tel.: (48) 22 847 4505
Web Site: http://www.endemolshine.pl
Television & Other Audiovisual Entertainment Programming Services
N.A.I.C.S.: 516210

Endemol Portugal Lda. (3)
Av Duque de Avila 141-5 Esq, 1050-081, Lisbon, Portugal
Tel.: (351) 213890800
Web Site: http://www.endemol.pt
Television & Other Audiovisual Entertainment Programming Services
N.A.I.C.S.: 516210

INTERNATIONAL PUBLIC

Endemol South Africa (Pty) Ltd. (3)
Studio Park 5 Concourse Crescent Lonehill, PO Box 71917, 2062, Johannesburg, South Africa
Tel.: (27) 11 799 2200
Web Site: http://www.endemol.co.za
Emp.: 50
Television & Other Audiovisual Entertainment Programming Services
N.A.I.C.S.: 516210

Endemol Sweden AB (3)
Linnegatan 87 A, Stockholm, 115 23, Sweden
Tel.: (46) 84597340
Television & Other Audiovisual Entertainment Programming Services
N.A.I.C.S.: 516210

Endemol UK Plc (3)
Shepherds Building Central, Charecroft Way Shepherds Bush, London, W14 0EE, United Kingdom
Tel.: (44) 2082224969
Web Site:
   http://www.endemolshinegroup.com
Emp.: 700
Entertainment Services
N.A.I.C.S.: 711410
Richard Johnson *(Mng Dir)*

Subsidiary (US):

Endemol USA Inc. (3)
9255 W Sunset Blvd Ste 1100, West Hollywood, CA 90069
Tel.: (310) 860-9914
Web Site: http://www.endemolusa.tv
Rev.: $47,000,000
Emp.: 30
Holding Company; Television & Other Audiovisual Entertainment Programming & Production Services
N.A.I.C.S.: 551112
Laurens Drillich *(Pres-Latino)*

Subsidiary (Domestic):

Authentic Entertainment, Inc. (4)
2860 N Naomi St, Burbank, CA 91504
Tel.: (323) 644-6144
Web Site: http://www.authentictv.com
Sales Range: $1-9.9 Million
Emp.: 20
Television Production
N.A.I.C.S.: 512110
Sara Reddy *(Exec VP-Current Programming)*

Subsidiary (Non-US):

Gestmusic Endemol S.A. (3)
C Santa Elionor 3, 08024, Barcelona, Spain
Tel.: (34) 932536700
Web Site: https://www.gestmusic.es
Emp.: 150
Television & Other Audiovisual Entertainment Programming Services
N.A.I.C.S.: 516210

Initial Film & Television Ltd (3)
Shepherds Building, Central, Charecroft Way Shepherds Bush, London, W14 0EE, United Kingdom
Tel.: (44) 8703331700
Television & Other Audiovisual Entertainment Programming Services
N.A.I.C.S.: 516210

META Productions GmbH (3)
Stralauer Allee 8, 10245, Berlin, Germany
Tel.: (49) 3061681100
Web Site: http://www.metaproductions.de
Television & Other Audiovisual Entertainment Programming Services
N.A.I.C.S.: 516210

Subsidiary (Domestic):

NL Film (3)
Johannes Vermeerstraat 20, 1071 DR, Amsterdam, Netherlands
Tel.: (31) 20 5747626
Web Site: http://www.nlfilm.tv
Emp.: 25
Television & Other Audiovisual Entertainment Programming Services
N.A.I.C.S.: 516210

SNP Holding B.V. (3)
MediArena 3, 1099CZ Duivendrecht, 1099

CZ, Amsterdam, Netherlands
Tel.: (31) 208936000
Web Site:
  http://www.endemolshinegroup.com
Television & Other Audiovisual Entertainment Programming Services
N.A.I.C.S.: 516210

Subsidiary (Non-US):

Shine Ltd. (3)
Primrose Studios, 109 Regents Park Rd, London, NW1 8UR, United Kingdom
Tel.: (44) 2079857000
Web Site: http://www.shinegroup.tv
Sales Range: $125-149.9 Million
Television Content Production & Distribution
N.A.I.C.S.: 512110

Subsidiary (US):

Brillante Entretenimiento, Inc. (4)
2121 Ave of The Stars, Los Angeles, CA 90067-5010
Tel.: (310) 402-2746
Television Broadcasting Services
N.A.I.C.S.: 516120

Subsidiary (Domestic):

Brown Eyed Boy (Vicious) Limited (4)
12-14 Amwell Street, London, EC1R 1UQ, United Kingdom
Tel.: (44) 2071176667
Web Site: http://browneyedboy.com
Motion Video Production Services
N.A.I.C.S.: 512110

ChannelFlip Media Limited (4)
The Shepherds Building Charecroft Way, London, W14 0EE, United Kingdom
Tel.: (44) 2078515711
Web Site: http://www.channelflip.com
Television Broadcasting Services
N.A.I.C.S.: 516120

Dragonfly Film & TV Limited (4)
Zetland House Unit H, 109 Clifton Street, London, EC2A 4LD, United Kingdom
Tel.: (44) 2070332300
Web Site: http://www.dragonfly.tv
Emp.: 60
Motion Video Production Services
N.A.I.C.S.: 512110
Leeanne Vinson (Head-Talent)

Subsidiary (Non-US):

Endemol Shine Australia Pty Ltd (4)
42-44 Victoria Street, McMahons Point, 2060, NSW, Australia
Tel.: (61) 285871110
Web Site:
  https://www.endemolshine.com.au
Television Production
N.A.I.C.S.: 512110
Carl Fennessy (Co-CEO)

Endemol Shine Nordics AB (4)
Palermogatan 17 Magasin 5, Stockholms Frihamn, 115 56, Stockholm, Sweden
Tel.: (46) 84597340
Web Site: https://www.endemolshine.se
Films, Television Programs & Commercials Production Services
N.A.I.C.S.: 512110

Subsidiary (Domestic):

Filmlance International AB (5)
Palermogatan 17 Magasin 5 Frihamnen, PO Box 27156, 102 52, Stockholm, Sweden
Tel.: (46) 84597380
Web Site: https://www.filmlance.se
Sales Range: $10-24.9 Million
Emp.: 18
Film & Television Program Production
N.A.I.C.S.: 512110
Anders Landstrom (Mng Dir)

Subsidiary (Non-US):

Metronome Productions A/S (5)
Raffinaderivej 8 2 sal, 2300, Copenhagen, Denmark
Tel.: (45) 32646565
Web Site: https://www.metronome.dk
Sales Range: $10-24.9 Million
Emp.: 100
Film & Television Program Production
N.A.I.C.S.: 512110
Anne K. Edelsgaard Andersen (Mgr-Legal)

Subsidiary (Non-US):

Friday TV AB (4)
PO Box 278 37, 115 93, Stockholm, Sweden
Tel.: (46) 703812810
Web Site: http://www.fridaytv.se
Sales Range: $10-24.9 Million
Emp.: 6
Television Broadcasting Services
N.A.I.C.S.: 516120

Subsidiary (US):

Hold It (4)
2411 N Atherton St, State College, PA 16803
Tel.: (814) 238-7050
Web Site: http://www.holditstatecollege.com
Personal Property Storage Services
N.A.I.C.S.: 531130

Ivy Productions, Inc. (4)
268 Devoe St Apt 4f, Brooklyn, NY 11211
Tel.: (917) 757-4967
Motion Video Distribution Services
N.A.I.C.S.: 512120

Subsidiary (Domestic):

Kudos (Law) Limited (4)
12-14 Amwell Street, London, EC1R 1UQ, United Kingdom
Tel.: (44) 2078123270
Web Site: http://www.kudos.co.uk
Emp.: 40
Television Broadcasting Services
N.A.I.C.S.: 516120

Kudos Film & Television Limited (4)
12-14 Amwell Street, London, EC1R 1UQ, United Kingdom
Tel.: (44) 3700420052
Web Site: https://www.kudos.co.uk
Emp.: 45
Television Broadcasting Services
N.A.I.C.S.: 512110
Anna Mynott (Head-Resources)

Lovely Day (Grantchester) Limited (4)
12-14 Amwell Street, London, EC1R 1UQ, United Kingdom
Tel.: (44) 2078123270
Web Site: http://www.lovely-day.co.uk
Motion Picture & Video Production Services
N.A.I.C.S.: 512110

Subsidiary (Non-US):

Magfive Content AB (4)
Fjarde Bassangvagen 11, PO Box 27837, Frihamnen, 115 93, Stockholm, Sweden
Tel.: (46) 86662084
Web Site: http://www.mag5.se
Emp.: 150
Motion Picture & Video Production Services
N.A.I.C.S.: 512110

Meter Television AB (4)
Stockholms Frihamnen Magasin 5, Box 287 37, 115 93, Stockholm, Sweden
Tel.: (46) 84597800
Web Site: https://www.meter.tv
Sales Range: $50-74.9 Million
Emp.: 300
Television Broadcasting Services
N.A.I.C.S.: 516120
Magnus Backlund (CFO)

Metronome Post AB (4)
Palermogatan 17 Frihamnen Magasin 5, PO Box 27837, 115 93, Stockholm, Sweden
Tel.: (46) 84597350
Television Broadcasting Services
N.A.I.C.S.: 516120

Subsidiary (US):

Metronome, LLC (4)
11216 Waples Mill Rd Ste 105, Fairfax, VA 22030
Tel.: (703) 957-4082
Web Site: http://wearemetronome.com
Emp.: 35
Information Technology Consulting Services
N.A.I.C.S.: 541512
Jennifer Virga (Co-Founder & CEO)

Subsidiary (Non-US):

Mutter Media AB (4)
Palermogatan 17 Magasin 5, PO Box 27837, 115 56, Stockholm, Sweden
Tel.: (46) 84597300
Television Broadcasting Services
N.A.I.C.S.: 516120

Rubicon TV AS (4)
Sandakerveien 24 C inng C3, PO Box 4414, Nydalen, 0473, Oslo, Norway
Tel.: (47) 23234500
Web Site: http://www.rubicontv.no
Emp.: 50
Motion Picture & Video Production Services
N.A.I.C.S.: 512110
Laila Ammoura (Dir-Fin)

Shine (Aust) PTY Limited (4)
Suite 1 The Upper Deck Jones Bay Wharf 26-32 Pirrama Road, Pyrmont, 2009, NSW, Australia
Tel.: (61) 285871111
Web Site: http://www.shineaustralia.com.au
Television & Digital Production Services
N.A.I.C.S.: 512199

Shine Australia Holdings PTY Limited (4)
26-32 Pirrama Rd, Pyrmont, 2009, NSW, Australia
Tel.: (61) 285871111
Web Site: http://www.shineaustralia.com.au
Holding Company
N.A.I.C.S.: 551112

Shine Finland Oy (4)
Saastopankinranta 2 A 6th floor, 00530, Helsinki, Finland
Tel.: (358) 207410500
Web Site: http://www.shinefinland.tv
Television & Digital Production Services
N.A.I.C.S.: 512199
Mika Toivainen (Mgr-Fin)

Shine Germany Film Und Fernsehproduktion GmbH (4)
Infanteriestr 19, 80797, Munich, Germany
Tel.: (49) 8918947630
Motion Picture & Video Production Services
N.A.I.C.S.: 512110

Shine Germany Film- und Fernsehproduktion GmbH (4)
Infanteriestrasse 19 Haus 4b, Munich, 80797, Germany
Tel.: (49) 89 1894763 0
Web Site: http://www.shinegermany.de
Film & Television Production
N.A.I.C.S.: 512110

Shine Iberia SLU (4)
Calle Mira Ceti 1 Aravaca, 28023, Madrid, Spain
Tel.: (34) 913576280
Web Site: http://www.shineiberia.tv
Emp.: 10
Motion Video Production Services
N.A.I.C.S.: 512110

Shine Nordic Formats AB (4)
Frihamnen Magasin 5, Box 27837, 115 93, Stockholm, Sweden
Tel.: (46) 702753915
Motion Picture & Video Production Services
N.A.I.C.S.: 512110

Shine Nordics AB (4)
Palermogatan 17 Magasin 5, Frihamn, 115 56, Stockholm, Sweden
Tel.: (46) 84597340
Motion Picture & Video Production Services
N.A.I.C.S.: 512110
Nicke Johansson (Head-Info)

Subsidiary (Non-US):

Societe Miss France (3)
10 r Waldeck Rochet, 93300, Aubervilliers, France
Tel.: (33) 153564001
Television & Other Audiovisual Entertainment Programming Services
N.A.I.C.S.: 516210

Telegenia, S.L (3)
Avda Manoteras 18, 28050, Madrid, Spain
Tel.: (34) 913025913
Television & Other Audiovisual Entertainment Programming Services
N.A.I.C.S.: 516210

WeiT Media (3)
1st Zachatievsky lane building 5, 119034, Moscow, Russia
Tel.: (7) 4959811914
Web Site: http://www.weitmedia.com
Television & Other Audiovisual Entertainment Programming Services
N.A.I.C.S.: 516210

Zeppelin Television, S.A. (3)
Avda Manoteras 18 Plt 6, 28050, Madrid, Spain
Tel.: (34) 91 768 4000
Television & Other Audiovisual Entertainment Programming Services
N.A.I.C.S.: 516210

Zeppotron Ltd (3)
Shepherds Building Central Charecroft Way Shepherd s Bush, London, W14 0EE, United Kingdom
Tel.: (44) 3700420042
Television & Other Audiovisual Entertainment Programming Services
N.A.I.C.S.: 516210

LOVABLE LINGERIE LIMITED

A 46 Road No 2 MIDC, Andheri E, Mumbai, 400093, India
Tel.: (91) 2228383581
Web Site: https://www.lovableindia.in
Year Founded: 1987
533343—(BOM)
Rev.: $11,636,080
Assets: $25,971,060
Liabilities: $3,068,313
Net Worth: $22,902,747
Earnings: $91,415
Emp.: 939
Fiscal Year-end: 03/31/21
Lingerie Mfr
N.A.I.C.S.: 315250
Raghunathan Govindarajan (CFO)

LOVE GROUP GLOBAL LTD

Level 8 99 St Georges Terrace, Perth, 6000, WA, Australia
Tel.: (61) 419768130   AU
Web Site: https://www.lovegroup.co
LVE—(ASX)
Rev.: $3,191,384
Assets: $1,764,955
Liabilities: $858,488
Net Worth: $906,466
Earnings: $408,021
Fiscal Year-end: 06/30/24
Internet Publishing & Broadcasting Services
N.A.I.C.S.: 516210
Michael Ye (Founder, CEO & Mng Dir)

LOVE INTERNATIONAL GROUP, INC.

Room 161 2nd Floor No 12 Building 115, Pu Dong New District, Shanghai, China
Tel.: (86) 02123563330   NV
Year Founded: 2013
LOVV—(OTCBB)
Sales Range: Less than $1 Million
Emp.: 32
Ecommerce Services
N.A.I.C.S.: 425120
Yong Qiang Yang (Chm & CEO)

LOVISA HOLDINGS LIMITED

Level 1 818-820 Glenferrie Road, Victoria, Hawthorn, 3122, VIC, Australia
Tel.: (61) 370426440   AU
Web Site: https://www.lovisa.com.au
Year Founded: 2010
LOV—(ASX)
Rev.: $466,522,434
Assets: $355,768,562
Liabilities: $302,158,786
Net Worth: $53,609,775

LOVISA HOLDINGS LIMITED

Lovisa Holdings Limited—(Continued)
Earnings: $55,028,712
Fiscal Year-end: 06/30/24
Jewellery Distr
N.A.I.C.S.: 423940
Brett Blundy (Chm)

Subsidiaries:

DCK Jewellery South Africa (Pty) Ltd (1)
264 Absa Bedford Centre 1 Bradford Rd, Bedfordview, Gauteng, South Africa
Tel.: (27) 118830918
Costume Jewellery Store Operator
N.A.I.C.S.: 458110

LOVISAGRUVAN AB
Hakansboda 1, PO Box 250, Stora, 711 04, Fors, Sweden
Tel.: (46) 58140941
Web Site: https://www.lovisagruvan.se
Year Founded: 2004
Metal Exploration Services
N.A.I.C.S.: 213114
Jan-Erik Bjorklund (CEO)

LOVITT RESOURCES INC.
1942 167 St, Surrey, V3S 9R4, BC, Canada
Tel.: (604) 725-9952
Web Site: https://lovittresources.com
Year Founded: 1979
LRCFF—(OTCEM)
Rev.: $1,402
Assets: $1,025,372
Liabilities: $1,967,003
Net Worth: ($941,631)
Earnings: ($256,575)
Fiscal Year-end: 06/30/22
Gold Mining Services
N.A.I.C.S.: 212220
C. Lorne Brown (Pres)

LOW CURRENT - TELECOM JOINT STOCK COMPANY
142 Le Duan, Kham Thien Ward Dong Da, Hanoi, Vietnam
Tel.: (84) 2463251712
Web Site: http://www.ltc.com.vn
Year Founded: 1989
Sales Range: $1-9.9 Million
Telecommunications Installation Services
N.A.I.C.S.: 238210
Ngo Trong Vinh (Chm)

LOW KENG HUAT (SINGAPORE) LIMITED
80 Marine Parade Road 18-05/09 Parkway Parade, Singapore, 449269, Singapore
Tel.: (65) 63442333   SG
Web Site: https://www.lkhs.com.sg
Year Founded: 1969
F1E—(SES)
Rev.: $72,076,325
Assets: $969,782,883
Liabilities: $500,456,465
Net Worth: $469,326,417
Earnings: ($23,635,421)
Emp.: 245
Fiscal Year-end: 01/31/23
Building Construction Services
N.A.I.C.S.: 236115
Keng Boon Low (Chm)

Subsidiaries:

Duxton Hotels International Pty Ltd (1)
1 St George s Terrace, Perth, 6000, WA, Australia
Tel.: (61) 892618000
Web Site: https://www.perth.duxtonhotels.com
Hotel Operator
N.A.I.C.S.: 721120

LOW VOLATILITY U.S. EQUITY INCOME FUND
121 King Street West Suite 2600, PO Box 113, Toronto, M5H 3T9, ON, Canada
Tel.: (416) 681-3992   ON
Web Site: http://www.strathbridge.com
Year Founded: 2012
Rev.: $95,872
Assets: $2,811,657
Liabilities: $79,323
Net Worth: $2,732,333
Earnings: ($108,929)
Fiscal Year-end: 12/31/18
Investment Services
N.A.I.C.S.: 523999
John P. Mulvihill (Chm, CEO & VP)

LOWES MANHATTAN PTY. LTD.
240 Princes Highway, Arncliffe, 2205, NSW, Australia
Tel.: (61) 295621111
Web Site: http://www.lowes.com.au
Year Founded: 1898
Men's Apparel Distr
N.A.I.C.S.: 424350
James Kondonis (CFO)

LOWLAND INVESTMENT COMPANY PLC
201 Bishopsgate, London, EC2M 3AE, United Kingdom
Tel.: (44) 2078181818
LWI—(LSE)
Rev.: $183,780,979
Assets: $622,419,580
Liabilities: $87,097,738
Net Worth: $535,321,842
Earnings: $178,961,073
Fiscal Year-end: 09/30/21
Investment Management Service
N.A.I.C.S.: 525990

LOWS OF DUNDEE LTD.
Marrbank House 6 Paradise Road, PO Box 300, Dundee, DD1 1JB, United Kingdom
Tel.: (44) 1382229251
Web Site: http://www.lowsofdundee.co.uk
Year Founded: 1913
Rev.: $15,655,981
Emp.: 29
Coated Fabrics & Textiles Distr
N.A.I.C.S.: 424310
Scott Kopel (Mgr-Sls)

LOXAM SAS
89 Avenue de la Grande Armee, 75219, Paris, Cedex 16, France
Tel.: (33) 158440400
Web Site: http://www.loxam.fr
Construction Equipment Rental Services
N.A.I.C.S.: 532412
Gerard Deprez (Pres)

Subsidiaries:

Lavendon Group Limited (1)
15 Midland Court Central Park, Lutterworth, LE17 4PN, Leics, United Kingdom
Tel.: (44) 1455558874
Web Site: http://www.lavendongroup.com
Sales Range: $350-399.9 Million
Emp.: 1,675
Holding Company; Powered Aerial Work Platform Equipment Rental Services
N.A.I.C.S.: 551112
Alan Merrell (Dir-Fin Grp)

Subsidiary (Non-US):

Lavendon Access Services (France) SA (2)
5 Avenue Gustave Eiffel, Zi Du Phare, 33692, Merignac, Cedex, France (100%)
Tel.: (33) 556184800
Web Site: http://www.lavendon.fr
Sales Range: $50-74.9 Million
Emp.: 80
Machinery & Equipment Rental & Leasing Office
N.A.I.C.S.: 532420

Subsidiary (Domestic):

Lavendon Access Services (UK) Limited (2)
15 Midland Court Central Park, Lutterworth, LE17 4PN, Leics, United Kingdom (100%)
Tel.: (44) 1455558874
Web Site: http://www.lavendongroup.co.uk
Sales Range: $50-74.9 Million
Emp.: 100
Machinery & Equipment Rental & Leasing Office
N.A.I.C.S.: 532420
Carin Moulds (Mgr-Mktg)

Subsidiary (Non-US):

Nationwide Platforms (2)
Unit 1 Latchmore Park Latchmore Road, Low Fields Road, LS10 2AA, Leeds, United Kingdom - England (100%)
Tel.: (44) 8457450000
Web Site: http://www.nationwideplatforms.co.uk
Sales Range: $150-199.9 Million
Emp.: 500
Machinery & Equipment Rental & Leasing Office
N.A.I.C.S.: 532490
Kate Liggins (Exec Dir-HR)

Subsidiary (Domestic):

Nationwide Platforms (2)
Unit 12 Dencora Way, Sundan Park Industrial Estate, Luton, LU3 3HP, Beds, United Kingdom (100%)
Tel.: (44) 1582578070
Web Site: http://www.nationwideplatforms.co.uk
Sales Range: $25-49.9 Million
Emp.: 50
Construction, Mining Forestry Machinery & Equipment Rental & Leasing
N.A.I.C.S.: 532412
Joe Brown (Gen Mgr)

Subsidiary (Non-US):

Rapid Access LLC (2)
Dubai Invesment Park 1, PO Box 38170, Dubai, United Arab Emirates
Tel.: (971) 43470131
Web Site: http://www.rapidaccess-gulf.com
Sales Range: $50-74.9 Million
Emp.: 70
Machinery & Equipment Rental & Leasing Office
N.A.I.C.S.: 532420
Paul Rankin (Mng Dir)

dk Rental N.V. (2)
Sprietestraat 164, Waregem, 8792, Belgium
Tel.: (32) 56622622
Web Site: http://www.dkrental.be
Sales Range: $50-74.9 Million
Emp.: 65
Forklift Rental Services
N.A.I.C.S.: 532412
Kurt Dobbels (Gen Mgr)

Ramirent Plc (1)
Tapulikaupungintie 37, 00750, Helsinki, Finland (98.22%)
Tel.: (358) 20750200
Web Site: http://www.ramirent.com
Rev.: $813,999,886
Assets: $986,618,385
Liabilities: $651,721,248
Net Worth: $334,897,137
Earnings: $54,710,907
Emp.: 2,905
Fiscal Year-end: 12/31/2018
Construction Machinery & Equipment Rental Services
N.A.I.C.S.: 532490
Jonas Soderkvist (CFO-Interim & Exec VP-Grp Bus Dev)

Subsidiary (Non-US):

OOO Ramirent (2)
607 Projezd Dom 32, 123458, Moscow, Russia
Tel.: (7) 4997401197
Web Site: http://www.ramirent.com
Machinery & Equipment Rental Services
N.A.I.C.S.: 532412

OTS Bratislava, Spol. S.R.O. (2)
Opletalova 65, 841 07, Bratislava, Slovakia
Tel.: (421) 269203811
Web Site: http://www.ramirent.sk
Sales Range: $75-99.9 Million
Emp.: 140
Equipment Rental Services
N.A.I.C.S.: 532412

Ramirent AB (2)
Frekvensvagen 2, 196 92, Kungsangen, Sweden
Tel.: (46) 31578400
Web Site: http://www.ramirent.se
Sales Range: $50-74.9 Million
Emp.: 20
Equipment Rental Services
N.A.I.C.S.: 532412

Ramirent AS (2)
Hvamsvingen 20, 2013, Skjetten, Norway
Tel.: (47) 9 8 9 0
Web Site: http://www.ramirent.no
Construction Equipment Rental
N.A.I.C.S.: 532412
Oyvind Emblem (Exec VP)

Ramirent Baltic AS (2)
Laki 11D, Tallinn, 12915, Estonia
Tel.: (372) 6501060
Web Site: http://www.ramirent.ee
Equipment Rental Services
N.A.I.C.S.: 532412

Subsidiary (Domestic):

Ramirent Finland Oy (2)
Tapulikaupungintie 37, 00750, Helsinki, Finland
Tel.: (358) 20750200
Web Site: http://www.ramirent.com
Construction Machinery & Equipment Rental Services
N.A.I.C.S.: 532490
Mikael Kampe (Exec VP)

Subsidiary (Domestic):

SRV Kalusto Oy (3)
Kalkkimaentie, 03100, Nummela, Finland
Tel.: (358) 201 45 5880
Construction Engineering Services
N.A.I.C.S.: 237990

Subsidiary (Non-US):

Ramirent Machinery LLC (2)
Umanski St 70A, 195248, Saint Petersburg, Russia
Tel.: (7) 8125292619
Web Site: http://www.ramirent.com
Machinery & Equipment Rental Services
N.A.I.C.S.: 532412

Ramirent S.R.O. (2)
V Jircharich 4, 110 00, Prague, Nove Mesto, Czech Republic
Tel.: (420) 244 062 327
Web Site: http://www.ramirent.cz
Equipment Rental Services
N.A.I.C.S.: 532412

Ramirent Ukraine LLC (2)
Saint Peter and Paul 14-A, 08130, Kiev, Ukraine
Tel.: (380) 444958315
Web Site: http://www.ramirent.com.ua
Sales Range: $50-74.9 Million
Emp.: 20
Machinery & Equipment Rental Services
N.A.I.C.S.: 532412

UAB Ramirent (2)
Titnago g 19, Vilnius, LT 02300, Lithuania
Tel.: (370) 52395303
Web Site: http://www.ramirent.lt
Sales Range: $25-49.9 Million
Emp.: 40
Construction Machinery Rental Services
N.A.I.C.S.: 532412

ZAO Ramirent (2)
Salova Str 56 lit Sh, 192102, Saint Petersburg, Russia

Tel.: (7) 8124495790
Sales Range: $75-99.9 Million
Emp.: 200
Construction Equipment Rental Services
N.A.I.C.S.: 532412

LOXLEY PUBLIC COMPANY LIMITED
102 Na Ranong Rd, Klong Toey, Bangkok, 10110, Thailand
Tel.: (66) 23488000
Web Site: https://www.loxley.co.th
Year Founded: 1939
LOXLEY—(THA)
Sales Range: $250-299.9 Million
Emp.: 900
Chemicals Mfr
N.A.I.C.S.: 325998
Dhongchai Lamsam *(Pres)*

Subsidiaries:

Green Natural Product Co., Ltd. (1)
No 102 Na Ranong Road, Klongtoey, Bangkok, Thailand
Tel.: (66) 2 521 2359
Health Care Product Mfr & Distr
N.A.I.C.S.: 424490

L Hardware & Services Co. Ltd (1)
44/385-389 Moo 10 Navamin Rd, Klongkhum Bungkhum, Bangkok, 10230, Thailand **(79%)**
Tel.: (66) 25085555
Web Site: http://www.lhs.co.th
Computer Peripheral Equipment Mfr
N.A.I.C.S.: 334118

Loxbit Public Co.Ltd (1)
8th Floor Siripinyo Building, 475 Sri Ayudthaya Road Rajthew, 10400, Bangkok, Thailand **(79%)**
Tel.: (66) 22013110
Web Site: http://www.loxbit.co.th
Sales Range: $25-49.9 Million
Emp.: 80
Telecommunications Resellers
N.A.I.C.S.: 517121

Subsidiary (Domestic):

Loxbit PA Plc (2)
2 Soi Phaholyothin 19 Phaholyothin Road, Chatuchak, Bangkok, 10900, Thailand
Tel.: (66) 2 515 8343
Web Site: http://www.loxbitpa.com
Information Technology Consulting Services
N.A.I.C.S.: 541512
Vasant Chatikavanij *(Chm)*

Loxdata Company Limited (1)
Siripinyo Building 11th Floor, 475 Sri Ayudthaya Rd Ratchathewi, 10400, Bangkok, Thailand **(79%)**
Tel.: (66) 220390003
Web Site: http://www.loxdata.co.th
Data Processing Services
N.A.I.C.S.: 518210

Loxley Intertrade (Guangzhou) Co., Ltd. (1)
Room 2011 20th Floor 33 Yian Plaza Jianshe Liu Road Yaexiu, Guangzhou, Guangdong, China
Tel.: (86) 20 8363 4055
Telecommunication Equipment Distr
N.A.I.C.S.: 423690

Loxley Trading Co. Ltd. (1)
1st and AA Floor Loxley Building, 102 Na Ranong Road Klongtoey, 10110, Bangkok, Thailand **(50%)**
Tel.: (66) 23502000
Web Site: http://www.loxtrade.com
Sales Range: $50-74.9 Million
Emp.: 100
Dairy Product Merchant Whslr
N.A.I.C.S.: 424430

Loxley Wireless Co. Ltd. (1)
555 RASA Tower Phaholyothin Rd, Chatuchak, Bangkok, 10900, Thailand **(99%)**
Tel.: (66) 29370099
Web Site: http://www.loxleywireless.co.th
Telecommunications Products, Datacom Products, Wireless Broadband Solutions & Products & Internet Broadband; Business Development & Engineering Services

N.A.I.C.S.: 423690

Mobile Innovation Co. Ltd (1)
128-224 227 228 21st Floor Payatai Plaza Building Phayathai Road, Kwaeng Thung-Phayathai Khet Ra, 10400, Bangkok, Thailand **(60%)**
Tel.: (66) 21293800
Web Site: http://www.mobileinnovation.co.th
Motor Vehicle Parts Mfr
N.A.I.C.S.: 336390
Centuro Makis *(Mng Dir)*

NetOne Network Solution Co. Ltd (1)
408-81 19 th Floor Phaholyotin Place Building, Phaholyotin Road Samsennai Pha, 10400, Bangkok, Thailand **(79%)**
Tel.: (66) 26190444
Web Site: http://www.net1.co.th
Sales Range: $25-49.9 Million
Emp.: 100
Satellite Telecommunications
N.A.I.C.S.: 517410
Pornrapee Abhakorn *(Pres)*

Poonsap Co Ltd (1)
562 Din-daeng Road, Din-daeng District, Bangkok, Thailand **(60%)**
Tel.: (66) 22468848
Web Site: http://www.loxley.co.th
Telecommunications Resellers
N.A.I.C.S.: 517121

Thai Fiber Optics Co., Ltd. (1)
9th Floor Siam Tower Building 989 Rama 1 Road, Pathumwan, Bangkok, 10330, Thailand **(100%)**
Tel.: (66) 26580670
Web Site: http://www.btc-tfoc.com
Sales Range: $25-49.9 Million
Emp.: 52
Fiber Optic Cable Mfr
N.A.I.C.S.: 335921
Y. Anzai *(Pres)*

Thai Gateway Co. Ltd. (1)
102 Na Ranong Road, Klongtoey, 10110, Bangkok, Thailand **(79%)**
Tel.: (66) 23488701
Web Site: http://www.thaigateway.co.th
Sales Range: $25-49.9 Million
Emp.: 10
Communication Equipment Mfr
N.A.I.C.S.: 334290
Suroj Lamsum *(Gen Mgr)*

LOYAL EQUIPMENTS LIMITED
Block No 33 34 35/1-2-3-4, Village Zak Taluka Dahegam, Ahmedabad, 382330, Gujarat, India
Tel.: (91) 2718247236
Web Site: https://www.loyalequipments.com
Year Founded: 1993
539227—(BOM)
Rev.: $3,868,263
Assets: $6,994,043
Liabilities: $4,039,765
Net Worth: $2,954,278
Earnings: $122,187
Fiscal Year-end: 03/31/21
N.A.I.C.S.: 333415
Rameshchandra Nathalal Patel *(Chm)*

Subsidiaries:

Loyal Sports Pvt. Ltd. (1)

LOYAL SOURCE MARKET SERVICES INC
13025 Klimovske, 01001, Zilina, Slovakia
Tel.: (421) 7029240620 NV
Year Founded: 2016
Emp.: 1
Home Air Purifier Distr
N.A.I.C.S.: 423690
Kamil Hornik *(Pres, Treas & Sec)*

LOYAL TEXTILE MILLS LIMITED
No 83 Old No 41 First Main Road R A Puram, Chennai, 600 028, Tamil Nadu, India
Tel.: (91) 4442277374
Web Site: https://www.loyaltextiles.com
Year Founded: 1956
514036—(BOM)
Rev.: $153,542,025
Assets: $136,463,145
Liabilities: $99,890,700
Net Worth: $36,572,445
Earnings: $4,482,660
Emp.: 1,590
Fiscal Year-end: 03/31/21
Textile Products Mfr
N.A.I.C.S.: 314999
P. Manivannan *(Exec Dir)*

LOYALIST EXPLORATION LIMITED
140 Cooks Lake Road, Timmins, P4R 0B7, ON, Canada
Tel.: (705) 288-0249
Web Site: http://www.goldenbirchresources.ca
GBRX—(CNSX)
Rev.: $19,051
Assets: $1,251,024
Liabilities: $531,558
Net Worth: $719,466
Earnings: ($2,240,535)
Fiscal Year-end: 12/31/20
Mineral Exploration Services
N.A.I.C.S.: 213115
Iain Martin *(Pres, CEO-Interim & Sec)*

LOYALTOUCH SA
22 rue Louis Blanc, 93400, Saint-Ouen, France
Tel.: (33) 158792020
Sales Range: $300-349.9 Million
Emp.: 264
Royalty, Club Discount & Marketing Consulting Services
N.A.I.C.S.: 541613
Christian Querou *(Chm-Supervisory Bd)*

LOYALTY ALLIANCE ENTERPRISE CORPORATION
Suite 6005 60/F Central Plaza 18 Harbour Road, Wanchai, China (Hong Kong)
Tel.: (852) 25110386
Web Site: http://www.loyalty-alliance.com
Sales Range: $10-24.9 Million
Emp.: 701
Data-Driven Multi-Channel Direct Marketing & Customer Loyalty Solutions
N.A.I.C.S.: 541613
Frederick Sum *(CEO)*

LOYALTY COMPANY SAS
100 allee des Frenes, 69760, Limonest, France
Tel.: (33) 4 26 23 06 54
Web Site: http://www.loyaltycompany.com
Brand & Customer Marketing Solutions
N.A.I.C.S.: 541810
Guillaume Chollet *(Founder, Chm & Mng Dir)*

LOYALTY FOUNDER CO., LTD.
No 225 Lane 54 Sec 2 An Ho Rond, Anhe Annan District, Tainan City, Taiwan
Tel.: (886) 63560606
5465—(TPE)
Rev.: $133,965,294
Assets: $128,517,525
Liabilities: $43,539,912
Net Worth: $84,977,613
Earnings: $10,719,195
Fiscal Year-end: 12/31/22
Electronic Products Mfr
N.A.I.C.S.: 334413
Chi-Yuan Ko *(Chm)*

LOYENS & LOEFF N.V.
Tel.: (31) 102246224
Web Site: http://www.loyensloeff.com
Year Founded: 2000
Emp.: 134
Law firm
N.A.I.C.S.: 541110
Marieke Bakker *(Partner)*

LOZNICAELEKTRO A.D.
Prvog maja bb, 15300, Loznica, Serbia
Tel.: (381) 15 871 834
Web Site: http://www.loelektro.co.rs
Year Founded: 1988
Sales Range: $1-9.9 Million
Electricity Distribution & Control Equipment Mfr
N.A.I.C.S.: 335999
Jevto Jevtic *(Exec Dir)*

LPA GROUP PLC
Light & Power House Shire Hill, Saffron Walden, CB11 3AQ, Essex, United Kingdom
Tel.: (44) 1799512800 UK
Web Site: https://www.lpa-group.com
LPA—(LSE)
Rev.: $24,798,756
Assets: $29,879,344
Liabilities: $10,717,842
Net Worth: $19,161,502
Earnings: ($46,162)
Emp.: 164
Fiscal Year-end: 09/30/21
Mfr of Electrical Connections & Other Electrical Components
N.A.I.C.S.: 335999
Peter Pollock *(Chm)*

Subsidiaries:

Channel Electric Equipment Holdings Ltd (1)
Light & Power House Shire Hill, Saffron Walden, CB11 3AQ, Essex, United Kingdom
Tel.: (44) 1635864866
Web Site: http://www.lpa-group.com
Sales Range: $25-49.9 Million
Emp.: 50
Electromechanical Products Mfr
N.A.I.C.S.: 334419

Channel Electric Equipment Ltd (1)
Bath Road, Thatcham, RB18 3ST, Berkshire, United Kingdom **(100%)**
Tel.: (44) 163 586 4866
Web Site: https://www.lpa-group.com
Sales Range: $25-49.9 Million
Emp.: 12
Mfr of Electrical Components
N.A.I.C.S.: 335999

LPA Excil Electronics Ltd (1)
Ripley Dr, Normanton, WF6 1QT, West Yorkshire, United Kingdom **(100%)**
Tel.: (44) 1924224100
Web Site: http://www.lpa-excil.com
Sales Range: $25-49.9 Million
Emp.: 63
Mfr of Electrical Components
N.A.I.C.S.: 335999

LPA Haswell Engineers Ltd (1)
Oakwood Business Park, Stephenson Rd W, Clacton-on-Sea, CO15 4TL, Essex, United Kingdom **(100%)**
Tel.: (44) 1255428424
Sales Range: $25-49.9 Million
Emp.: 50
Mfr of Electrical Components
N.A.I.C.S.: 335999

LPA Industries Ltd (1)
Light Power House Shire Hill, Debden Road, Saffron Walden, CB11 3AQ, Essex, United Kingdom

LPA GROUP PLC

LPA Group plc—(Continued)
Tel.: (44) 1799512800
Web Site: http://www.lpa-group.com
Sales Range: $25-49.9 Million
Emp.: 60
Electrical Component Mfr
N.A.I.C.S.: 334413

LPA Niphan Ltd (1)
Tudor Works Debden Rd, Saffron Walden, CB11 4AN, Essex, United Kingdom (100%)
Tel.: (44) 1799512800
Web Site: http://www.lpa-niphan.com
Sales Range: $25-49.9 Million
Emp.: 40
Mfr of Electrical Components
N.A.I.C.S.: 335999

LPI CAPITAL BHD
6th Floor Bangunan Public Bank, 6 Jalan Sultan Sulaiman, 50000, Kuala Lumpur, Malaysia
Tel.: (60) 322628688
Web Site: http://www.lpicapital.com
LPI—(KLS)
Rev.: $350,812,698
Assets: $1,086,515,132
Liabilities: $624,533,968
Net Worth: $461,981,164
Earnings: $58,541,164
Emp.: 827
Fiscal Year-end: 12/31/22
General Insurance Services
N.A.I.C.S.: 524128
Tammy Thian Mee Kong *(Co-Sec & Gen Mgr-Grp HR)*

LPK CO., LTD.
38 Sosam-ro, Sosa-gu, Bucheon, Korea (South)
Tel.: (82) 32 341 1645
Web Site: http://www.lpkrobo.com
Industrial Robots Mfr
N.A.I.C.S.: 334511

LPKF LASER & ELECTRONICS AG
Osteriede 7, 30827, Garbsen, Germany
Tel.: (49) 513170950
Web Site: https://www.lpkf.com
LPK—(MUN)
Rev.: $137,255,196
Assets: $163,891,579
Liabilities: $58,891,464
Net Worth: $105,000,114
Earnings: $1,931,772
Emp.: 755
Fiscal Year-end: 12/31/23
Industrial Machinery
N.A.I.C.S.: 333242
Markus Peters *(Chm-Supervisory Bd)*

Subsidiaries:

H&R Malaysia Sdn. Bhd. (1)
Lot 6579 Jalan Parang N Port, Locked Bag No 203, Port Klang, 42000, Selangor, Malaysia
Tel.: (60) 331768314
Sales Range: $50-74.9 Million
Emp.: 10
Petroleum Lubricants Sales
N.A.I.C.S.: 424720

LPKF France S.A.R.L (1)
Creteil Parc 16 rue Paul Sejourne, 94000, Creteil, France
Tel.: (33) 141941967
Web Site: http://www.lpkf.fr
Sales Range: $25-49.9 Million
Emp.: 12
Industrial Machiney Mfr & Sales
N.A.I.C.S.: 333998

LPKF Laser & Electronics (Asia) Ltd. (1)
Rm 1102-3 11 F Shun Kwong Com Bldg No 8 Des Voeux Rd W, Sheung Wan, China (Hong Kong)
Tel.: (852) 25454005
Web Site: http://www.lpkf.com
Sales Range: $25-49.9 Million
Emp.: 10
Laser & Mechanical Structuring Solar Cells Mfr & Sales
N.A.I.C.S.: 334413

LPKF Laser & Electronics Inc. (1)
12555 SW Leveton Dr, Tualatin, OR 97062-6073
Tel.: (503) 454-4200
Web Site: https://www.lpkfusa.com
Printed Circuit Board & Laser Equipments Sales
N.A.I.C.S.: 423690

LPKF Laser & Electronics K.K. (1)
LaLaport Mitsui Building 8F 2-1-1 Hamacho, Funabashi, 273-0012, Chiba, Japan
Tel.: (81) 474325100
Web Site: http://jp.lpkf.com
Electrical & Electronic Mfr
N.A.I.C.S.: 336320

LPKF Laser & Electronics Korea Ltd. (1)
Tel.: (82) 316893660
Electrical & Electronic Mfr
N.A.I.C.S.: 336320

LPKF Laser & Electronics d.o.o. (1)
Polica 33, SI-4202, Naklo, Slovenia
Tel.: (386) 59208800
Electrical & Electronic Mfr
N.A.I.C.S.: 336320

LPKF Motion & Control GmbH (1)
Mittelbergstr 17, 98527, Suhl, Thuringia, Germany
Tel.: (49) 368189240
Web Site: http://www.lpkf.com
Sales Range: $25-49.9 Million
Emp.: 80
Measuring & Control Devices Mfr
N.A.I.C.S.: 334513

LPKF SolarQuipment GmbH (1)
Mittelbergstr 17, D-98527, Suhl, Germany
Tel.: (49) 368189240
Web Site: http://www.lpkf.com
Sales Range: $25-49.9 Million
Emp.: 100
Laser & Mechanical Structuring Solar Cells Mfr & Sales
N.A.I.C.S.: 334419

LPKF Tianjin Co., Ltd. (1)
K1-6-202 No 6 Hi-Tech Develop 6th Rd Green Indus base, HuaYuan, Tianjin, 300384, China
Tel.: (86) 2223785318
Sales Range: $25-49.9 Million
Emp.: 60
Printed Circuit Boards Mfr & Distr
N.A.I.C.S.: 334412

LPKF WeldingQuipment GmbH (1)
Alfred-Nobel-Str 55 - 57, D-90765, Furth, Germany
Tel.: (49) 9116698590
Electrical & Electronic Mfr
N.A.I.C.S.: 336320

LaserMicronics GmbH (1)
Osteriede 7, 30827, Garbsen, Germany
Tel.: (49) 5131908110
Web Site: http://www.lasermicronics.com
Sales Range: $25-49.9 Million
Emp.: 10
Laser Micromachining Maintenance & Repair Services
N.A.I.C.S.: 811310

LPP S.A.
Lakowa 39/44, 80-769, Gdansk, Poland
Tel.: (48) 587696900
Web Site: https://www.lpp.com
Year Founded: 1991
LPP—(WAR)
Rev.: $4,372,757,876
Assets: $3,467,341,607
Liabilities: $2,282,344,370
Net Worth: $1,184,997,237
Earnings: $404,964,076
Emp.: 21,489
Fiscal Year-end: 01/31/24
Clothing Mfr & Distr
N.A.I.C.S.: 458110

Marek Piechocki *(Chm-Mgmt Bd)*

Subsidiaries:

LPP Hungary Kft (1)
Teve utca 1/AC 6th floor, 1139, Budapest, Hungary
Tel.: (36) 14900371
Web Site: https://www.reserved.com
Emp.: 100
Apparel & Accessories Mfr
N.A.I.C.S.: 315990

LPP Retail Latvia Ltd (1)
Braslas 27 k 1-2, Riga, 1084, Latvia
Tel.: (371) 67818214
Apparel & Accessories Retailer
N.A.I.C.S.: 458110

TORA Sp. z o.o. (1)
Tyska 12, Legnica, 59-220, Poland
Tel.: (48) 226223312
Apparel & Accessories Distr
N.A.I.C.S.: 424350

LPR LOGISTIC PACKAGING RETURN S.A.S.
5 Avenue Marcel Dassault, PO Box 45848, 31506, Toulouse, Cedex, France
Tel.: (33) 562716161 FR
Web Site: http://www.lpr.eu
Year Founded: 1992
Sales Range: $125-149.9 Million
Emp.: 200
Pallet Pooling Operator
N.A.I.C.S.: 561499
Debbie Pereira *(CFO)*

Subsidiaries:

LPR France (1)
8 rue de Vidailhan, BP 30083, 31132, Balma, Cedex, France
Tel.: (33) 562716161
Logistics Consulting Servies
N.A.I.C.S.: 541614

LPR Netherlands (1)
Rietveldenweg 49 F, 5222 AP, 's-Hertogenbosch, Netherlands
Tel.: (31) 736241464
Emp.: 80
Logistics Consulting Servies
N.A.I.C.S.: 541614
Sebastiaan Corver *(Country Mgr)*

LPR Portugal (1)
Complexo de Salemas Tocadelos Cabeco de Montachique, 2670-770, Loures, Portugal
Tel.: (351) 219758950
Logistics Consulting Servies
N.A.I.C.S.: 541614
Amadeo Remane *(Country Mgr)*

LPR S.r.l. (1)
Via Mecenate 90, 20138, Milan, Italy
Tel.: (39) 0236644310
Logistics Consulting Servies
N.A.I.C.S.: 541614
Fabio Benazzo *(Country Mgr)*

LPR UK Limited (1)
Studley Point Birmingham Road, Warwick, B80 7AS, United Kingdom
Tel.: (44) 1527523311
Logistics Consulting Servies
N.A.I.C.S.: 541614

La Palette Rouge Deutschland GmbH (1)
Rosental 8, 53332, Bornheim, Germany
Tel.: (49) 2222911380
Logistics Consulting Servies
N.A.I.C.S.: 541614
Sascha Olschewski *(Country Mgr)*

La Palette Rouge Iberica SA (1)
Calle Castrobarto 10 4 Planta Edificio Artemisa II, 28042, Madrid, Spain
Tel.: (34) 917472350
Logistics Consulting Servies
N.A.I.C.S.: 541614

La Palette Rouge Poland Sp. z o.o. (1)
Prologis Park Bonie I DC 7, Kopytow 44G, 05-870, Blonie, Poland

Tel.: (48) 222104555
Logistics Consulting Servies
N.A.I.C.S.: 541614
Tiago Costa *(Country Mgr)*

LPS BRASIL - CONSULTORIA DE IMOVEIS SA
Rua Estados Unidos n 1971, Sao Paulo, 01427-002, SP, Brazil
Tel.: (55) 1130670324 BR
Web Site: https://ri.lopes.com.br
Year Founded: 2007
LPSB3—(BRAZ)
Rev.: $32,561,627
Assets: $71,307,805
Liabilities: $34,535,134
Net Worth: $36,772,670
Earnings: $6,306,108
Emp.: 633
Fiscal Year-end: 12/31/23
Real Estate Brokerage & Consulting Services
N.A.I.C.S.: 531210
Marcello Rodrigues Leone *(CFO, Officer-IR & Member-Exec Bd)*

Subsidiaries:

LPS Raul Fulgencio Consultoria de Imoveis S.A. (1)
Avenida Ayrton Senna da Silva 702 Gleba Fazenda Palhano, Londrina, Brazil
Tel.: (55) 4333729000
Web Site: https://www.raulfulgencio.com.br
Real Estate Services
N.A.I.C.S.: 531390

LS 2 HOLDINGS LIMITED
1 Bukit Batok Crescent WCEGA Plaza 04-11, Singapore, 658064, Singapore
Tel.: (65) 62811843 SG
Web Site: https://www.ls2.sg
Year Founded: 1993
ENV—(CAT)
Rev.: $46,721,776
Assets: $24,555,392
Liabilities: $10,902,458
Net Worth: $13,652,934
Earnings: $1,154,923
Emp.: 1,654
Fiscal Year-end: 12/31/23
Holding Company
N.A.I.C.S.: 551112
Roger Tan *(Chm)*

Subsidiaries:

Urban Cobots Pte. Ltd. (1)
1 Bukit Batok Crescent WCEGA Plaza No 04-18, Singapore, 658064, Singapore
Tel.: (65) 81005500
Web Site: https://www.urbancobots.com
Cleaning Industry Machine Mfr
N.A.I.C.S.: 333241

LS CABLE & SYSTEM ASIA LTD.
4th Fl LS Yongsan Tower Hangangdaero 92, Yongsan-gu, Seoul, 04386, Gyeonggi-do, Korea (South)
Tel.: (82) 314280288
Web Site: https://lsecoenergy.com
Year Founded: 2015
229640—(KRS)
Rev.: $627,785,457
Assets: $388,664,041
Liabilities: $267,430,128
Net Worth: $121,233,913
Earnings: ($7,004,695)
Emp.: 19
Fiscal Year-end: 12/31/22
Cable Product Mfr & Distr
N.A.I.C.S.: 332618
Lee Sang-Ho *(CEO)*

Subsidiaries:

LS-Gaon Cable Myanmar Co., Ltd. (1)
Lot No BA3 Zone B Thilawa Special Eco-

nomic Zone, Industrial Area, Yangon, Myanmar
Tel.: (95) 12309268
Web Site: https://www.lsgmcable.com
Communication Cable Distr
N.A.I.C.S.: 423690

LS-VINA Cable & System Joint Stock Co. (1)
South Binh Bridge, So Dau Ward Hong Bang District, Haiphong, Vietnam
Tel.: (84) 2253540330
Web Site: http://www.lsvinacable.com.vn
Communication Cable Mfr
N.A.I.C.S.: 335929
Jong Pil Kim (Gen Dir)

LS CORP.
17F 18F LS Yongsan Tower 92 Hangang-daero, Yongsan-gu, Seoul, 04386, Korea (South)
Tel.: (82) 221899723
Web Site: https://www.lsholdings.com
Year Founded: 1936
006260—(KRS)
Rev.: $12,042
Assets: $11,616
Liabilities: $7,282
Net Worth: $4,333
Earnings: $324
Emp.: 70
Fiscal Year-end: 12/31/21
Holding Company
N.A.I.C.S.: 551112
Roe-Hyun Myung (Vice Chm, Pres & CEO)

Subsidiaries:

ALUTEK (1)
Level 4 & 6 GS Bldg 588 Guro-dong, Guro-gu, Seoul, Korea (South)
Tel.: (82) 2 6675 1361
Web Site: http://www.alutek.co.kr
Construction Engineering Services
N.A.I.C.S.: 541330
Chung Eun Taeg (CEO)

LS Cable & System Ltd. (1)
13th-17th Fl LS Tower 127 LS-ro, Dongan-gu, Anyang, 14119, Gyeonggi-do, Korea (South)
Tel.: (82) 221899114
Web Site: https://www.lscns.co.kr
Emp.: 4,700
Industrial Cable & Material Mfr & Distr
N.A.I.C.S.: 335929
Cha-Yub Koo (Chm)

Subsidiary (Domestic):

LS Alsco Co., Ltd. (2)
Daerong Post Tower 5 68 Digital-ro 9-gil, Geumcheon-gu, Seoul, Korea (South)
Tel.: (82) 266751361
Web Site: http://www.alsco.co.kr
Aluminum Mfr
N.A.I.C.S.: 331524

LS Ev Korea Ltd. (2)
181 Dangjeong-dong, Gunpo, Gyeonggi-do, Korea (South) (100%)
Tel.: (82) 266751376
Web Site: https://www.lsevkorea.com
High Voltage Connector Mfr
N.A.I.C.S.: 334417

LS Cable Ltd. (1)
Room Number 12 & 17 LS Tower, Hogye-dong Dongan-gu, 1026-6, Anyang, Korea (South)
Tel.: (82) 221899114
Web Site: http://www.lscable.com
Sales Range: $1-4.9 Billion
Emp.: 2,338
Wire & Cable Mfr
N.A.I.C.S.: 335929
Myung Roe Hyun (Pres)

Subsidiary (Non-US):

LS Cable India Pvt. Ltd. (2)
632-634 6th Floor Park Centra Sector 30, Gurgaon, 122 002, Haryana, India
Tel.: (91) 1244285800
Emp.: 400
Cable Mfr
N.A.I.C.S.: 335929

Plant (Domestic):

LS Cable Ltd. - Anyang Plant (2)
136 LS-ro Dongan-gu, Anyang, Gyeonggi-do, Korea (South)
Tel.: (82) 31 428 4114
Cable Mfr
N.A.I.C.S.: 335929

LS Cable Ltd. - Donghae Plant (2)
215 Daedong-ro, Donghae, Gangwon-do, Korea (South)
Tel.: (82) 33 820 3114
Cable Mfr
N.A.I.C.S.: 335929

LS Cable Ltd. - Gumi Plant (2)
228 Suchul-daero, Gumi, Gyeongsangbuk, Korea (South)
Tel.: (82) 54 469 7114
Wire & Cable Mfr
N.A.I.C.S.: 335929

LS Cable Ltd. - Indong Plant (2)
238 3gongdan 2-ro, Gumi, Gyeongsangbuk-do, Korea (South)
Tel.: (82) 54 469 1053
Fiber Optic Cable Mfr
N.A.I.C.S.: 335921

Subsidiary (US):

LSCA (2)
920 Sylvan Ave, Englewood Cliffs, NJ 07632
Tel.: (201) 266-2465
Cable Distr
N.A.I.C.S.: 423610

Subsidiary (Non-US):

LSCD (2)
12th Fl IFCI Tower 61 Nehru Place, New Delhi, 110019, India
Tel.: (91) 1244285800
Cable Distr
N.A.I.C.S.: 423610

LSCJ (2)
Tokyo Club Bldg 13F 3-2-6 Kasumigaseki, Chiyoda-ku, Tokyo, 100-0013, Japan
Tel.: (81) 362057188
Cable Mfr & Distr
N.A.I.C.S.: 335929

LSCM (2)
Lot 1192 Mukim 14 Permatang Tinggi 1400 Bukit Mertajam, Penang, 14000, Malaysia
Tel.: (60) 4 588 9609
Magnet Wire Mfr
N.A.I.C.S.: 331318

LSCT (2)
East of Jing-jin Express Yixingbu Entrance, Beichen, Tianjin, China
Tel.: (86) 22 2699 7618
Magnet Wire Mfr
N.A.I.C.S.: 331318

LSCU (2)
109 Building 3 Chiswick Business Park 566 Chiswick High Rd, London, W4 5YA, United Kingdom
Tel.: (44) 20 8899 6671
Cable Mfr & Distr
N.A.I.C.S.: 335929

LSCV (2)
Nhon Trach 2 - Loc Khang Industrial Zone, Nhon Trach District, Ho Chi Minh City, Dong Nai, Vietnam
Tel.: (84) 613569140
Cable Mfr
N.A.I.C.S.: 335929

LSCW (2)
LS Industrial Park Xin Mei Road, National High-tech Industrial Development Zone, Wuxi, 214028, Jiangsu, China
Tel.: (86) 51088119000
Wire & Cable Mfr
N.A.I.C.S.: 335929

LSHQ (2)
NO1 Tanjiahe Road, Dianjun District, Yichang, 443004, Hubei, China
Tel.: (86) 13911714020
Cable Mfr & Distr
N.A.I.C.S.: 335929

LSIC (2)
B-2301 Landgent Center No 20 Dongsanhuanzhong, Chaoyang, Beijing, 100022, China
Tel.: (86) 10 5761 3166
Cable Distr
N.A.I.C.S.: 423610

Subsidiary (US):

Superior Essex, Inc. (2)
5770 Powers Ferry Rd NW Ste 400, Atlanta, GA 30327
Tel.: (770) 657-6000
Web Site: http://www.superioressex.com
Sales Range: $1-4.9 Billion
Magnet Wire & Communications Cable Mfr
N.A.I.C.S.: 335921
Brian Kim (CEO)

Subsidiary (Domestic):

Essex Group, Inc. (3)
1601 Wall St, Fort Wayne, IN 46802-4352
Tel.: (260) 461-4000
Web Site: http://www.superioressex.com
Sales Range: $50-74.9 Million
Emp.: 200
Magnet Wire Mfr
N.A.I.C.S.: 331420

Division (Domestic):

Essex Brownell (4)
1601 Wall St, Fort Wayne, IN 46802-4352
Tel.: (260) 461-4000
Web Site: http://www.superioressex.com
Sales Range: $100-124.9 Million
Distr of Magnet Wire & Insulation Products
N.A.I.C.S.: 423610

Subsidiary (Non-US):

Lacroix + Kress GmbH (3)
Engterstrasse 34, 49565, Bramsche, Germany
Tel.: (49) 546195600
Web Site: https://lacroixundkress.de
Electric Power Cable Mfr
N.A.I.C.S.: 335921

Subsidiary (Domestic):

Lacroix + Kress GmbH (4)
Aussere Neukirchner Strasse 1, Neunburg vorm Wald, 92431, Neuenburg, Germany
Tel.: (49) 96725090
Electrical Wiring Mfr
N.A.I.C.S.: 335931

Subsidiary (Domestic):

Superior Essex International LP (3)
5770 Powers Ferry Rd NW Ste 300, Atlanta, GA 30327
Tel.: (770) 657-6000
Web Site: http://www.superioressex.com
Copper Communications Cables Mfr
N.A.I.C.S.: 335921

LS Global Inc. (1)
163 LS-ro, Gunpo, 15808, Gyeonggido, Korea (South)
Tel.: (82) 70 4355 1005
Web Site: http://www.lsglobalinc.com
Nonferrous Metal Distr
N.A.I.C.S.: 423510
Ik-Hee Lee (CEO)

LS Metal Co. Ltd. (1)
Trade Tower 7th Fl 511 Yeongdong-Daero, Gangnum-gu, Seoul, 135-798, Korea (South)
Tel.: (82) 2 6942 6114
Web Site: http://www.lsmetal.biz
Metal Product Mfr & Distr
N.A.I.C.S.: 331529
Myung-joo Moon (CEO)

LS Mtron (1)
11F LS Tower 1026-6 Hogye 1-dong, Dongan-gu, Anyang, Gyeonggi-do, Korea (South)
Tel.: (82) 316898288
Web Site: https://www.lsmtron.com
Emp.: 2,000
Industrial Equipment Distr
N.A.I.C.S.: 423830
Chai-ho Shin (CEO)

Subsidiary (Non-US):

LSEQ (2)
Yu-Huanging Industrial Area Xiazhuang, Chengyang Dt, Qingdao, 266109, China
Tel.: (86) 53280962200
Connector Mfr
N.A.I.C.S.: 334417

Subsidiary (US):

LSTA (2)
6900 Corporation Pkwy, Battleboro, NC 27809
Tel.: (252) 984-0700
Industrial Equipment Distr
N.A.I.C.S.: 423830

Subsidiary (Non-US):

YTLS (2)
No 79 Changjiang Road Development Zone, Yantai, Shandong, China
Tel.: (86) 535 8096 5618
Industrial Equipment Distr
N.A.I.C.S.: 423830

LS Mtron Ltd. - Engine Plant (1)
42 Udong-ro Bongdong-eup, Wonju, Jeolabuk, Korea (South)
Tel.: (82) 637163500
Electronic & Automotive Parts Mfr
N.A.I.C.S.: 336320

LS Mtron Ltd. - Jeonju Plant (1)
886 Gwahak-ro Bongdong-eup, Wonju, Jeollabuk, Korea (South)
Tel.: (82) 632795114
Electronic & Automotive Parts Mfr
N.A.I.C.S.: 336320

LS-Nikko Copper Inc. (1)
148 Sanam-ro Onsan-eup, Ulju-gun, Ulsan, 689-982, Korea (South) (100%)
Tel.: (82) 221899832
Web Site: http://www.lsnikko.com
Copper & Other Non-Ferrous Metal Smelting & Refining
N.A.I.C.S.: 331410
Suk-Goo Doh (CEO)

LS ELECTRIC CO., LTD.
LS Tower 127 LS-ro, Dongan-gu, Anyang, 14119, Gyeonggi-do, Korea (South)
Tel.: (82) 220344224
Web Site: https://www.ls-electric.com
Year Founded: 1974
010120—(KRS)
Rev.: $2,590,212,856
Assets: $2,548,591,418
Liabilities: $1,360,285,217
Net Worth: $1,188,306,201
Earnings: $69,958,070
Emp.: 3,112
Fiscal Year-end: 12/31/22
Electric Motor Mfr
N.A.I.C.S.: 335311
Ja-Kyun Koo (Chm, Chm & Co-CEO)

Subsidiaries:

Ls Energy Solutions LLC. (1)
9201 Forsyth Park Dr, Charlotte, NC 28273
Tel.: (980) 221-0654
Web Site: https://www.ls-es.com
Energy Storage Component Mfr
N.A.I.C.S.: 335910
Steven M. Fludder (Pres & CEO)

Ls Mecapion Co., Ltd. (1)
12-9 Hosandongro, in Daegu Hi-tech Industrial Complex Dalseogu, Daegu, Korea (South)
Tel.: (82) 535930066
Web Site: https://www.lsmecapion.com
Servo Motor Mfr
N.A.I.C.S.: 335312
Heung Koo Yun (CEO)

LS INTERNATIONAL CARGO GMBH
Teerhof 59, 28199, Bremen, Germany
Tel.: (49) 421360830
Web Site: http://www.ls-cargo.com
Rev.: $48,003,120
Emp.: 45

LS INTERNATIONAL CARGO GMBH

LS International Cargo GmbH—(Continued)
Freight & Logistics Services
N.A.I.C.S.: 484110
Bernd Oltmann *(Member-Mgmt Bd)*
Subsidiaries:

LS Cargo Logistics Middle East FZCO (1)
POB 54628, Dubai, United Arab Emirates
Tel.: (971) 42045728
Logistics Consulting Servies
N.A.I.C.S.: 541614
Dirk Rothig *(Mgr)*

LS Cargo Logistics Oy (1)
Nisulankatu 78, Jyvaskyla, Finland
Tel.: (358) 105053883
Logistics Consulting Servies
N.A.I.C.S.: 541614
Sakari Leppiaho *(Mgr)*

LS NETWORKS CORPORATION LIMITED

LS Yongsan Tower 92 Hanggangdaero, Yongsan-gu, Seoul, Korea (South)
Tel.: (82) 27997114
Web Site:
https://www.lsnetworks.co.kr
Year Founded: 1949
000680—(KRS)
Rev.: $278,352,761
Assets: $997,439,363
Liabilities: $574,150,101
Net Worth: $423,289,262
Earnings: ($1,838,670)
Emp.: 204
Fiscal Year-end: 12/31/22
Machinery Whslr
N.A.I.C.S.: 423830
Sung Joon Moon *(Pres & CEO)*
Subsidiaries:

LS Networks Trading (Beijing) Co., Ltd. (1)
Unit 07 25th Floor East Tower LG Twin Towers B-12 Jianguomenwai Avenue, Chaoyang, Beijing, 100022, China
Tel.: (86) 10 5120 8600
Telecommunication & Networking Services
N.A.I.C.S.: 517121
Wu Si *(Mgr-Mktg)*

LS SECURITIES CO., LTD.

24 Post Tower 60 Yeouinaru-ro, Yeongdeungpo-gu, Seoul, 07328, Korea (South)
Tel.: (82) 237790100
Web Site: https://ir.ebestsec.co.kr
Year Founded: 1999
078020—(KRS)
Rev.: $1,065,394,588
Assets: $4,874,236,539
Liabilities: $4,147,802,105
Net Worth: $726,434,433
Earnings: $23,470,137
Fiscal Year-end: 12/31/22
Financial Management Services
N.A.I.C.S.: 541611
Kim Won Kyu *(CEO)*

LS TELCOM AG

Im Gewerbegebiet 31-33, Lichtenau, 77839, Rastatt, Germany
Tel.: (49) 72279535600
Web Site: https://www.lstelcom.com
Year Founded: 1992
LSX—(DEU)
Rev.: $45,014,030
Assets: $44,463,630
Liabilities: $25,145,694
Net Worth: $19,317,937
Earnings: ($226,635)
Emp.: 286
Fiscal Year-end: 09/29/23
Wireless Telecommunication Services
N.A.I.C.S.: 517212

Georg Schone *(Co-Founder, CEO & Member-Exec Bd)*
Subsidiaries:

Colibrex GmbH (1)
Winnipeg Avenue B 112 / A5, 77836, Rheinmunster, Germany
Tel.: (49) 72279535600
Web Site: http://www.colibrex.com
Software & Hardware Development Services
N.A.I.C.S.: 541512

LS Telcom AG MKK (1)
Koztarsasag ut 11-13, 2600, Vac, Hungary
Tel.: (36) 302010581
Radio Communication Product Distr
N.A.I.C.S.: 423690

LS Telcom Inc. (1)
5021 Howerton Way Ste E, Bowie, MD 20715
Tel.: (301) 377-6966
Web Site: http://www.lstelcom.com
Software & Hardware Development Services
N.A.I.C.S.: 541512

LS of South Africa Radio Communication Services (Pty) Ltd. (1)
131 Gelding Avenue, Ruimsig, Johannesburg, 1724, South Africa
Tel.: (27) 119585153
Web Site: https://www.lsofsa.co.za
Emp.: 60
Radio Communication Services
N.A.I.C.S.: 517112

LS telcom Ltd. (1)
1145 Hunt Club Road Suite 100, Ottawa, K1V 0Y3, ON, Canada
Tel.: (613) 248-8686
Web Site: https://www.lstelcom.ca
Radio Communication Services
N.A.I.C.S.: 517112

LS telcom SAS (1)
47 Boulevard de Sebastopol, 75001, Paris, France
Tel.: (33) 184794195
Web Site: https://www.lstelcom.fr
Radio Communication Services
N.A.I.C.S.: 517112

LS telcom UK Limited (1)
Dowgate Hill House 14-16 Dowgate Hill, London, EC4R 2SU, United Kingdom
Tel.: (44) 2035762920
Web Site: https://www.lstelcom.co.uk
Radio Communication Services
N.A.I.C.S.: 517112
Daniel Nowok *(Reg Dir-Sls)*

LST Middle East FZ-LLC (1)
Office 2118 21st Floor Shatha Tower Dubai Media City, Dubai, United Arab Emirates
Tel.: (971) 43623437
Web Site: https://www.lst-middleeast.com
Radio Communication Product Distr
N.A.I.C.S.: 423690

Mountain Tower, Ltd. (1)
194 Professional Park Dr, Clarkesville, GA 30523
Web Site: http://www.radiosoft.com
Software Development Services
N.A.I.C.S.: 541512

SlivaCom d.o.o. (1)
Ulica Krajiskih Brigada Broj 113, 78000, Banja Luka, Bosnia & Herzegovina
Tel.: (387) 65004160
Telecommunication Servicesb
N.A.I.C.S.: 517810

Vision2Comm GmbH (1)
Im Gewerbegebiet 33, Lichtenau, 77839, Dusseldorf, Germany
Tel.: (49) 72279535960
Web Site: https://www.vision2comm.com
Telecommunication Servicesb
N.A.I.C.S.: 517112

LSE ELEKTRIK LTD.

Ataturk Mahallesi Demokrasi Caddesi Yurt Sokak No 7, Umraniye, Istanbul, 34764, Turkiye
Tel.: (90) 2163165138

Web Site: http://www.lse.com.tr
Sales Range: $25-49.9 Million
Emp.: 25
Measuring Displaying & Controlling Industrial Process Variables Instruments & Related Products Mfr
N.A.I.C.S.: 334513
Junaid Cuneyt *(Gen Mgr)*

LSI SOFTWARE S.A

Ul Przybyszewskiego 176/178, 93-120, Lodz, Poland
Tel.: (48) 426808000
Web Site: https://www.lsisoftware.pl
Year Founded: 1991
LSI—(WAR)
Rev.: $14,463,415
Assets: $17,079,268
Liabilities: $4,073,933
Net Worth: $13,005,335
Earnings: $810,213
Fiscal Year-end: 12/31/23
Custom Computer Programming Services
N.A.I.C.S.: 541511
Bartlomiej Grduszak *(Vice Chm-Mgmt Bd)*
Subsidiaries:

GiP Sp. z o.o. (1)
al Jerozolimskie 184 B, 02-486, Warsaw, Poland
Tel.: (48) 221003800
Web Site: http://www.gip.com.pl
Software Development Services
N.A.I.C.S.: 541511

LSI Software s.r.o. (1)
Roztylska 1860/1, Chodov, 148 00, Prague, Czech Republic
Tel.: (420) 736227799
Software Development Services
N.A.I.C.S.: 541511

Positive Software USA LLC (1)
1355 Remington Rd Ste B, Schaumburg, IL 60173
Tel.: (469) 250-5748
Software Development Services
N.A.I.C.S.: 541511

LSL PHARMA GROUP INC.

540 Rue d'avaugour, Boucherville, J4B 0G6, QC, Canada
Tel.: (514) 664-7700
Web Site:
https://www.groupelslpharma.com
LSL—(AIM)
Pharmaceuticals Mfr
N.A.I.C.S.: 325412
Subsidiaries:

Steri-Med Pharma Inc. (1)
540 Rue dAvaugour Suite 1800, Boucherville, J4B 0G6, QC, Canada
Tel.: (514) 664-7700
Web Site: https://sterimedpharma.com
Pharmaceutical Product Mfr & Distr
N.A.I.C.S.: 325412

LSL PROPERTY SERVICES PLC

3 St Mary's Court Blossom Street Howard House, York, YO24 1AH, United Kingdom
Tel.: (44) 1912334600
Web Site: https://www.lslps.co.uk
LSLPF—(OTCIQ)
Rev.: $387,535,830
Assets: $262,099,200
Liabilities: $104,249,475
Net Worth: $157,849,725
Earnings: ($76,509,840)
Fiscal Year-end: 12/31/22
Residential Property Service Providers
N.A.I.C.S.: 531311
Sapna Bedi FitzGerald *(Gen Counsel & Sec)*

INTERNATIONAL PUBLIC

Subsidiaries:

Direct Life & Pension Services Limited (1)
Friars House 52a East Street, Chichester, PO19 1JG, West Sussex, United Kingdom
Tel.: (44) 124 381 7900
Web Site: https://www.directlife.co.uk
Life Insurance Brokerage Services
N.A.I.C.S.: 524210
Rob Quayle *(CEO)*

Embrace Financial Services Ltd. (1)
Howard House 3 St Marys Court Blossom Street, York, YO24 1AH, United Kingdom
Tel.: (44) 139 245 3568
Web Site: https://www.embracefs.co.uk
Financial Services
N.A.I.C.S.: 522320
Oliver Blake *(Mng Dir)*

First2Protect Limited (1)
Howard House 3 St Marys Court Blossom Street, York, YO24 1AH, United Kingdom
Tel.: (44) 139 284 9750
Web Site: https://www.first2protect.co.uk
Insurance Services
N.A.I.C.S.: 524210

Insurance First Brokers Ltd. (1)
Strover House Crouch Street, Colchester, CO3 3ES, Essex, United Kingdom
Tel.: (44) 120 673 1806
Web Site: https://www.insurance-first.co.uk
Insurance Services
N.A.I.C.S.: 524210

LSL Corporate Client Services Limited (1)
1-2 Northenhay Place, Exeter, EX4 3YF, United Kingdom
Tel.: (44) 1392355542
Web Site: http://www.lsl-ccd.co.uk
Real Estate Services
N.A.I.C.S.: 531911
Martyn Alderton *(Mng Dir)*

LSL Land & New Homes Limited (1)
56 Hallgate, Doncaster, DN1 3NE, South Yorkshire, United Kingdom
Tel.: (44) 8453402940
Web Site:
http://www.lsllandandnewhomes.co.uk
Real Estate Services
N.A.I.C.S.: 531390
Shaun Peart *(Mng Dir)*

LSLi Limited (1)
4th Floor 13 Sun Street, London, EC2A 2EP, United Kingdom
Tel.: (44) 7974441102
Web Site: http://www.lsli.co.uk
Real Estate Services
N.A.I.C.S.: 531390
Greig Barker *(Dir-Fin)*

Lets Move Property Limited (1)
369 Hoe Street, Walthamstow, London, E17 9AP, United Kingdom
Tel.: (44) 2085218838
Web Site:
http://www.letsmoveproperties.co.uk
Real Estate Services
N.A.I.C.S.: 531390

Marsh & Parsons Limited (1)
80 Hammersmith Road, London, W14 8UD, United Kingdom
Tel.: (44) 2088462320
Web Site:
http://www.marshandparsons.co.uk
Emp.: 300
Real Estate Services
N.A.I.C.S.: 531390

Mortgages First Ltd. (1)
Strover House Crouch Street, Colchester, CO3 3ES, Essex, United Kingdom
Tel.: (44) 120 673 1800
Web Site: https://www.mortgages-first.co.uk
Financial Services
N.A.I.C.S.: 522320

Pygott & Crone Lincoln Lettings Limited (1)
19 Southgate, Sleaford, NG34 7SU, United Kingdom
Tel.: (44) 1529404254
Web Site: https://www.pygott-crone.com
Real Estate Mortgage Services

AND PRIVATE COMPANIES

RSC New Homes Limited (1)
1st Floor Landmark House Station Road, Cheadle Hulme, SK8 7BS, Cheshire, United Kingdom
Tel.: (44) 1614866278
Web Site: http://www.rscnewhomes.com
Home & Construction Services
N.A.I.C.S.: 236118

Reeds Rains Cleckheaton Limited (1)
20 Central Parade, Cleckheaton, BD19 3RU, United Kingdom
Tel.: (44) 1274870440
Real Estate Services
N.A.I.C.S.: 531390

St Trinity Limited (1)
1-2 Northernhay Place, Exeter, Ex4 3QH, Devon, United Kingdom
Tel.: (44) 1392355580
Web Site: http://www.sttrinityassetmanagement.co.uk
Real Estate Services
N.A.I.C.S.: 531390
Charlotte Buttle *(Mgr-Client Svcs)*

Templeton LPA Limited (1)
Castlebridge 2 Cowbridge Road East, Cardiff, CF11 9AB, United Kingdom
Tel.: (44) 2920231778
Web Site: http://www.templetonlpa.com
Financial Services
N.A.I.C.S.: 522320

Zenith Properties Limited (1)
Suite 14 Plot 3124 Landmark Plaza IBB Way, Maitama, Abuja, Nigeria
Tel.: (234) 803 705 4322
Web Site: https://www.zenithpropertiesmarket.com
Real Estate Services
N.A.I.C.S.: 531390

LT FOODS LTD
Unit-134 1st Floor Rectangle-1 Saket District Centre, Saket, New Delhi, 110017, India
Tel.: (91) 1243055100
Web Site: https://www.ltgroup.in
532783—(BOM)
Rev.: $744,004,279
Assets: $595,080,295
Liabilities: $301,754,994
Net Worth: $293,325,300
Earnings: $42,206,223
Emp.: 2,000
Fiscal Year-end: 03/31/22
Basmati Rice Packaging & Mfr
N.A.I.C.S.: 311212
Surinder Kumar Arora *(Mng Dir)*

Subsidiaries:

Nature Bio Foods Limited (1)
45 KM Stone G T Road, Kamaspur, Sonipat, 131021, Haryana, India **(82.5%)**
Tel.: (91) 1303541500
Web Site: http://naturebiofoods.organic
Sales Range: $25-49.9 Million
Emp.: 100
Food Products Mfr
N.A.I.C.S.: 311230

LT GROUP, INC.
Bonifacio Global City, Taguig, Manila, Phillipines
Tel.: (63) 288081266 PH
Web Site: https://www.ltg.com.ph
Year Founded: 1937
LTG—(PHI)
Rev.: $2,051,545,987
Assets: $23,618,730,556
Liabilities: $18,276,551,236
Net Worth: $5,342,179,321
Earnings: $452,330,991
Emp.: 12,951
Fiscal Year-end: 12/31/23
Tobacco Mfr
N.A.I.C.S.: 551112
Michael G. Tan *(Pres & COO)*

Subsidiaries:

Eton Properties Philippines, Inc. (1)
8F Philippine National Bank Center 6754 Ayala Avenue, Makati, Philippines **(99.3%)**
Tel.: (63) 8 548 4000
Web Site: https://www.eton.com.ph
Sales Range: $50-74.9 Million
Emp.: 241
Real Estate Services
N.A.I.C.S.: 531390
Lucio C. Tan *(Chm)*

Tanduay Distillers, Inc. (1)
348 J Nepomuceno Street, San Miguel District, Manila, 632, Philippines **(100%)**
Tel.: (63) 8 790 0500
Web Site: https://ph.tanduay.com
Distillery
N.A.I.C.S.: 312140
Janet Tan-Lee *(Sec)*

Subsidiary (Non-US):

Asia Pacific Beverage Pte. Ltd. (2)
9 Fourth Lok Yang Road, Singapore, 629706, Singapore
Tel.: (65) 6 858 2338
Web Site: https://www.pacbev.sg
Alcoholic Beverages Mfr
N.A.I.C.S.: 312140

LT KM BERHAD
102 Batu 1 1/2 Jalan Meru, 41050, Klang, Selangor Darul Ehsan, Malaysia
Tel.: (60) 33 342 2830
Web Site: http://www.ltkm.com.my
LTKM—(KLS)
Rev.: $49,913,155
Assets: $78,816,566
Liabilities: $25,245,667
Net Worth: $53,570,899
Earnings: $(3,984,081)
Emp.: 500
Fiscal Year-end: 03/31/22
Egg Mfr
N.A.I.C.S.: 112310
Yim Kong Ng *(Sec)*

LTC CO., LTD.
114 Cheongwonsandan 8-gil, Madomyeon, Hwaseong, 18543, Gyeonggi-do, Korea (South)
Tel.: (82) 313836525
Web Site: https://www.l-tech.co.kr
Year Founded: 2007
170920—(KRS)
Rev.: $168,300,772
Assets: $208,228,484
Liabilities: $136,677,188
Net Worth: $71,551,296
Earnings: $1,625,569
Emp.: 132
Fiscal Year-end: 12/31/22
Chemicals Mfr
N.A.I.C.S.: 325998
Ho-Sung Choi *(Chm, Pres & CEO)*

LTC CORPORATION LIMITED
10 Arumugam Road 10-00 Lion Building A, Singapore, 409957, Singapore
Tel.: (65) 6745 9677
Web Site: http://www.ltcgroup.com.sg
Sales Range: $125-149.9 Million
Emp.: 248
Iron Mfr; Property Development
N.A.I.C.S.: 331110
Theng Kee Cheng *(Chm)*

Subsidiaries:

Angkasa Amsteel Pte Ltd (1)
20 Woodlands Loop, Singapore, 738321, Singapore
Tel.: (65) 6759 5973
Web Site: http://www.angkasa.com.sg
Sales Range: $25-49.9 Million
Emp.: 100
Steel Reinforcement Bars Mfr & Distr
N.A.I.C.S.: 314994

LTC Building Materials Pte Ltd (1)
Lion Building A Unit 10-00 10 Arumugam Road, Singapore, 409957, Singapore
Tel.: (65) 67459677
Building Materials Distr
N.A.I.C.S.: 444180

Teck Chiang Realty Private Limited (1)
10 Arumugam Road Unit 10-00 Lion Industrial Building A, Singapore, 409957, Singapore
Tel.: (65) 67459677
Property Development Services
N.A.I.C.S.: 236210

LTKM BHD
102 Batu 1 1/2 Jalan Meru, 41050, Klang, Selangor, Malaysia
Tel.: (60) 333422830
Web Site: https://www.ltkm.com.my
Year Founded: 2000
7085—(KLS)
Rev.: $54,449,028
Assets: $71,955,796
Liabilities: $22,065,099
Net Worth: $49,890,697
Earnings: $4,365,484
Fiscal Year-end: 03/31/23
Chicken Egg Production Services
N.A.I.C.S.: 112310
Tan Kok *(Chm)*

Subsidiaries:

LTK (Melaka) Sdn. Bhd. (1)
Batu 11 1/2 Durian Tunggal, 76100, Melaka, Malaysia
Tel.: (60) 65531130
Chicken Egg Production Services
N.A.I.C.S.: 112310

LTK Development Sdn. Bhd. (1)
Wisma LTKM 102 Batu 1 1/2 Jalan Meru, 41050, Klang, Selangor, Malaysia
Tel.: (60) 33342830
Web Site: http://www.ltkdevelopment.my
Property Development Services
N.A.I.C.S.: 531390

LTS, INC.
14F 1-3-13 Motoakasaka, Minato-ku, Tokyo, 107-0051, Japan
Tel.: (81) 353127010
Web Site: https://www.lt-s.jp
Year Founded: 2002
6560—(TKS)
Rev.: $86,795,780
Assets: $84,909,840
Liabilities: $59,258,220
Net Worth: $25,651,620
Earnings: $3,233,040
Fiscal Year-end: 12/31/23
Business Management Consulting Services
N.A.I.C.S.: 541611
Hiroaki Kabashima *(Pres & CEO)*

Subsidiaries:

Assign Navi, Inc. (1)
2-8-6 Shinjuku KDX Shinjuku 286 Building 2F / 3F, Shinjuku-ku, Tokyo, 160-0022, Japan
Tel.: (81) 353127009
Web Site: www.assign-navi.com
Business Consulting Services
N.A.I.C.S.: 541611

HCS Holdings Co., Ltd. (1)
2-4-38 Toyo, Koto-ku, Tokyo, 135-0016, Japan
Tel.: (81) 356902201
Web Site: https://www.hcs-hd.co.jp
Emp.: 412
Computer Programming Services
N.A.I.C.S.: 541511

Hibiya Computer System Co., Ltd. (1)
Toyocho HCS Building 2-4-38 Toyo, Koto-ku, Tokyo, 135-0016, Japan
Tel.: (81) 356904701
Web Site: https://www.hibiya-cs.co.jp
Emp.: 161
Computer Programming Services

LU THAI TEXTILE CO., LTD.

N.A.I.C.S.: 541511

Hibiya Resource Planning Co., Ltd. (1)
2-4-38 Toyo, Koto-ku, Tokyo, 135-0016, Japan
Tel.: (81) 366667051
Web Site: https://www.hibiya-rp.co.jp
Emp.: 103
Computer Programming Services
N.A.I.C.S.: 541511

Isis Co., Ltd. (1)
7F Toyocho Square Building 2-1-12 Minamisuna, Koto-ku, Tokyo, 136-0076, Japan
Tel.: (81) 358575333
Web Site: https://www.i-si-s.co.jp
Emp.: 118
Computer Programming Services
N.A.I.C.S.: 541511

Lts Asia Co., Limited (1)
2nd Floor Eton Tower 8 Hysan Avenue, Causeway Bay, China (Hong Kong)
Tel.: (852) 353127010
Business Consulting Services
N.A.I.C.S.: 541611

LU GIA MECHANICAL ELECTRIC JOINT STOCK COMPANY
70 Lu Gia Street, Ward 15 District 11, Ho Chi Minh City, Vietnam
Tel.: (84) 2838686738
Web Site: http://www.lugiaco.com.vn
Year Founded: 1978
Electrical Steel Product Mfr
N.A.I.C.S.: 335132

LU HAI HOLDING CORP.
No 64 Shing-kong 5th Rd Tien-Chung, Industrial District, Chang-Hua, Taiwan
Tel.: (886) 48748122
Web Site: https://www.luhai.com.tw
Year Founded: 1980
2115—(TAI)
Rev.: $84,778,374
Assets: $154,711,267
Liabilities: $55,709,831
Net Worth: $99,001,435
Earnings: $5,723,797
Emp.: 821
Fiscal Year-end: 12/31/23
Tire Valves & Other Related Products & Accessories Mfr
N.A.I.C.S.: 332912
Hsin-Hsin Tsai *(Mgr-Admin Dept)*

Subsidiaries:

Luhai Intelligent Technology (kunshan) Co., Ltd. (1)
No 868 Jimingtang South Road, HuaQiao Town, Kunshan, Jiangsu, China
Tel.: (86) 51257601216
Valve Mfr
N.A.I.C.S.: 332919

Mega Power Co., Ltd. (1)
505-1 Hanam-dong, Gwangsan-Gu, Gwangju, Korea (South)
Tel.: (82) 629559700
Automobile Valve Mfr
N.A.I.C.S.: 334519

PT. Luhai Industrial (1)
D/A Jl Raya Cikande Rangkasbitung Km 4 5 Desa, Serang, Junti Jawilan, Indonesia
Tel.: (62) 2548488333
Automobile Valve Mfr
N.A.I.C.S.: 334519

Xiamen Xiahui Rubber Metal Industrial Co., Ltd. (1)
No 118 Guankou South Road, Guankou Town Jimei District, Xiamen, 361023, China
Tel.: (86) 5926210902
Tire Valve Mfr & Distr
N.A.I.C.S.: 326211

LU THAI TEXTILE CO., LTD.
No 81 Songling East Road, Zichuan District, Zibo, 255100, Shandong, China

LU THAI TEXTILE CO., LTD.

Lu Thai Textile Co., Ltd.—(Continued)
Tel.: (86) 5336027828
Web Site: https://www.lttc.com.cn
Year Founded: 1993
000726—(SSE)
Rev.: $974,142,936
Assets: $1,905,785,388
Liabilities: $552,499,272
Net Worth: $1,353,286,116
Earnings: $135,325,944
Fiscal Year-end: 12/31/22
Fabric Product Mfr
N.A.I.C.S.: 313310
Liu Zibin *(Chm & Pres)*

LU ZHOU LAO JIAO CO., LTD.
Luzhou Laojiao Command Center
Nanguang Road, Longmatan District,
Luzhou, 646000, China
Tel.: (86) 8302398999
Web Site: https://www.lzlj.com
Year Founded: 2000
000568—(SSE)
Rev.: $3,478,561,600
Assets: $7,114,737,677
Liabilities: $2,361,636,921
Net Worth: $4,753,100,756
Earnings: $1,435,171,591
Emp.: 2,040
Fiscal Year-end: 12/31/22
Beverage Product Distr
N.A.I.C.S.: 424820

LU-VE SPA
Via Caduti della Liberazione 53,
21040, Uboldo, Varese, Italy
Tel.: (39) 02 96716 1
Web Site: http://www.luve.it
Sales Range: Less than $1 Million
Refrigeration & Air Conditioning Products Mfr
N.A.I.C.S.: 333415
Matteo Liberali *(CEO)*

Subsidiaries:

Heat Transfer Systems s.r.o. (1)
Novosedly na Morave 238, 69182, Novosedly, Czech Republic
Tel.: (420) 519 501401
Web Site: http://www.htsystems.cz
Production of Heat Exchangers for Air Conditioning & Refrigeration Sector
N.A.I.C.S.: 333415

Industrial Stars of Italy S.p.A. (1)
Via Senato 20, 20121, Milan, Italy
Tel.: (39) 02 76 31 14 45
Web Site: http://www.indstars.it
Investment Services
N.A.I.C.S.: 523999
Giovanni Cavallini *(Chm & CEO)*

LU-VE Asia Pacific Ltd. (1)
Unit C 12/F Times Media Centre 133 Wan Chai Road, Wan Chai, Hong Kong, China (Hong Kong)
Tel.: (852) 2 289 12858
Web Site: http://www.luve.it
Sales of Air Conditioning & Refrigeration Products
N.A.I.C.S.: 423730

LU-VE Contardo Caribe S.A. (1)
Ofi-centro P de Belen local 2 1a planta,
San Antonio de Belen, Costa Rica
Tel.: (506) 2 239 10 76
Web Site: http://www.luve.it
Sales of Air Conditioning & Refrigeration Products
N.A.I.C.S.: 423730

LU-VE Contardo Deutschland GmbH (1)
Bruno Jacoby Weg 10, 70597, Stuttgart, Germany
Tel.: (49) 711 727211 0
Sales of Air Conditioning & Refrigeration Products
N.A.I.C.S.: 423730

LU-VE Contardo France S.a.r.l. (1)
17 rue Crepet, 69007, Lyon, France
Tel.: (33) 4 72779868

Sales of Air Conditioning & Refrigeration Products
N.A.I.C.S.: 423730

LU-VE Contardo Iberica S.L. (1)
Poligono Industrial Ventorro del Cano C/Villaconejos 8F Nave 43, Alcorcon, 28925, Madrid, Spain
Tel.: (34) 917 21 63 10
Sales of Air Conditioning & Refrigeration Products
N.A.I.C.S.: 423730

LU-VE Contardo Pacific Pty. Ltd. (1)
84 Northgate Drive, Thomastown, 3074, VIC, Australia
Tel.: (61) 3 946 41433
Web Site: http://www.luve.it
Emp.: 5
Sales of Air Conditioning & Refrigeration Products
N.A.I.C.S.: 423730
John Mignano *(Mng Dir)*

LU-VE Heat Exchangers (Changshu) Ltd (1)
Building A1 Southeast Ave, Changshu Southeast Economic Development Zone, Changshu, 215500, Jiangsu, China
Tel.: (86) 13913627371
Web Site: http://www.luve.it
Emp.: 40
Production of Heat Exchangers for Air Conditioning & Refrigeration Sectors
N.A.I.C.S.: 333415
Stefano Deleidi *(Gen Mgr)*

LU-VE India Corporation Private Limited (1)
423 Regus Business Centre Level 4 Rectangle 1 Commercial Complex D-4, Saket, New Delhi, India
Tel.: (91) 11 6654 4175
Refrigeration Equipment Distr
N.A.I.C.S.: 423740

LU-VE Sweden AB (1)
Sodra Industrivagen 2-4, 374 50, Asarum, Sweden
Tel.: (46) 45433400
Web Site: http://www.luve.it
Sales Range: $75-99.9 Million
Emp.: 20
Mfr of Heat Exchangers for Refrigeration, Air Conditioning & Industrial Applications
N.A.I.C.S.: 333415
Ann-Margreth Olsson *(Mgr-Purchase)*

LU-VE UK (1)
PO Box 3, Fareham, PO15 7YU, Hampshire, United Kingdom
Tel.: (44) 1 489 881503
Refrigeration Equipment Distr
N.A.I.C.S.: 423740

SEST S.p.A. (1)
Via Baorche 39, 32020, Limana, BL, Italy
Tel.: (39) 0437 966311
Air Conditioning Parts Mfr
N.A.I.C.S.: 333415

Subsidiary (Non-US):

OOO SEST-LUVE (2)
S E Z of I P T Lipetsk, Kazinka Gryazinsky District, 399071, Lipetsk, Russia
Tel.: (7) 4742709511
Web Site: http://www.luve.it
Mfr of Static Evaporator Coils for Refrigerated Counters & Display Cabinets
N.A.I.C.S.: 333415

SEST-LUVE-POLSKA Sp. Z.o.o. (2)
Ul Wyczolkowskiego 30, 44109, Gliwice, Poland
Tel.: (48) 32 3304050
Emp.: 200
Mfr of Static Evaporator Coils for Refrigerated Counters & Display Cabinets
N.A.I.C.S.: 333415
Tomasz Kolanda *(Pres)*

Tecnair LV S.p.A. (1)
Via Caduti della Liberazione 53, 21040, Uboldo, VA, Italy
Tel.: (39) 02 9699111
Web Site: http://www.luve.it
Emp.: 35
Air Conditioner Mfr
N.A.I.C.S.: 333415

Alberto Monti *(Gen Mgr)*

Thermo Glass Door S.p.A (1)
Via del Tovo 5, Travaco Siccomario, 27020, Pavia, Italy
Tel.: (39) 0382 482773
Web Site: http://www.tgd.it
Refrigeration Equipment Distr
N.A.I.C.S.: 423740

Zyklus Heat Transfer (1)
1488 N Bolton St, Jacksonville, TX 75766-4034
Tel.: (903) 589-3355
Plumbing, Heating & Air-Conditioning Contractors
N.A.I.C.S.: 238220

LUBAIR AVIATION TECHNOLOGY CO., LTD.
Room 3901 Block A Tanglang City Plaza, Next to Tanglang Depot Fuguang Community Taoyuan Street Nanshan Dist, Shenzhen, 518018, Guangdong, China
Tel.: (86) 75581782356
Web Site: https://www.lubair.com
Year Founded: 2005
001316—(SSE)
Rev.: $52,975,728
Assets: $158,452,632
Liabilities: $11,271,312
Net Worth: $147,181,320
Earnings: $7,111,260
Fiscal Year-end: 12/31/22
Aviation Fuel Distr
N.A.I.C.S.: 457210

LUBAWA S.A.
ul Staroprzygodzka 117, 63-400, Ostrow Wielkopolski, Poland
Tel.: (48) 627375777
Web Site: https://www.lubawa.com.pl
Year Founded: 1951
LBW—(WAR)
Rev.: $95,938,262
Assets: $142,352,896
Liabilities: $50,143,038
Net Worth: $92,209,857
Earnings: $11,522,358
Fiscal Year-end: 12/31/23
Safety Equipment Mfr
N.A.I.C.S.: 332994
Marcin Kubica *(Chm-Mgmt Bd)*

Subsidiaries:

CTF Group Closed Joint Stock Company (1)
Charentsavan Yesayan 1/1, Yerevan, Armenia
Tel.: (374) 77969728
Masking & Optical Net Mfr
N.A.I.C.S.: 339999

Effect-System S.A. (1)
ul Stanislawa Staszica 30, 58-400, Kamienna Gora, woj dolnoslaskie, Poland
Tel.: (48) 756454256
Web Site: https://www.effect-system.com
Screen Printing & Digital Printing Services
N.A.I.C.S.: 323113

Litex Promo Sp. z o.o (1)
ul Staroprzygodzka 117, 63-400, Ostrow Wielkopolski, Poland
Tel.: (48) 627375700
Web Site: https://litex.pl
Parasol & Tent Mfr
N.A.I.C.S.: 339999
Iwona Ratuszna *(Mgr-Export)*

Lubawa USA, Inc. (1)
140 Fairway Dr Ste 100, Lake Lure, NC 28746
Tel.: (540) 940-9744
Web Site: http://www.lubawausa.com
Bulletproof Vest Mfr
N.A.I.C.S.: 339113

Miranda Spolka z o.o. (1)
ul Jedwabnicza 1, 62-700, Turek, Wielkopolska, Poland
Tel.: (48) 632800100
Web Site: https://www.miranda.pl

Woven & Knitted Fabric Mfr
N.A.I.C.S.: 313240

LUBELSKI WEGIEL BOGDANKA SPOLKA AKCYJNA
Bogdanka, Puchaczow, 21-013, Lublin, Poland
Tel.: (48) 814625100
Web Site: http://www.lw.com.pl
LWB—(WAR)
Rev.: $615,915,942
Assets: $1,210,548,410
Liabilities: $279,114,958
Net Worth: $931,433,452
Earnings: $44,122,997
Fiscal Year-end: 12/31/22
Hard Coal Mfr
N.A.I.C.S.: 324199
Adam Partyka *(Vice Chm-Mgmt Bd-Labor & Social Affairs)*

Subsidiaries:

EkoTRANS Bogdanka Sp. z o.o. (1)
Bogdanka, Puchaczow, 21-013, Lublin, Poland
Tel.: (48) 814625215
Web Site: http://www.ekotrans-bogdanka.pl
Waste Management Rinsing & Cleaning Services
N.A.I.C.S.: 562998

Enea Wytwarzanie Sp. z o.o. (1)
ul Aleja Jozefa Zielinskiego 1, Swierze Gorne, 26-900, Kozienice, Poland
Tel.: (48) 6142414
Web Site: http://www.enea.pl
Energy Power Distr
N.A.I.C.S.: 221122

Leczynska Energetyka Sp. z o.o. (1)
Bogdanka, Puchaczow, 21-013, Lublin, Poland
Tel.: (48) 814625553
Web Site: http://lebog.com.pl
Energy Power Distr
N.A.I.C.S.: 221122
Artur Wasilewski *(Dir-Fin & Controlling)*

MR Bogdanka sp. z o.o. (1)
Bogdanka, Puchaczow, 21-013, Lublin, Poland
Tel.: (48) 814625334
Web Site: http://mrbogdanka.pl
Steel Structure & Maintenance Services
N.A.I.C.S.: 238120

RG Bogdanka Sp. z o.o. (1)
Bogdanka, Puchaczow, 21-013, Lublin, Poland
Tel.: (48) 814625086
Web Site: http://rgbogdanka.pl
Mining & Construction Product Distr
N.A.I.C.S.: 423810

LUBRICANT CONSULT GMBH
Gutenbergstr 11-13, 63477, Maintal, Germany
Tel.: (49) 610976500
Web Site: http://www.lubcon.com
Year Founded: 1980
Rev.: $35,450,580
Emp.: 86
Lubricant Mfr
N.A.I.C.S.: 324191
Heiko Engelke *(Gen Mgr)*

Subsidiaries:

LUBCON Bulgarien LTD (1)
1 A Drava Str, 4003, Plovdiv, Bulgaria
Tel.: (359) 877805093
Lubricant Distr
N.A.I.C.S.: 424720

LUBCON FRANCE S.A.R.L. (1)
70 Voie Christophe Colomb, Francin, 73800, Montmelian, France
Tel.: (33) 479843860
Web Site: http://www.lubcon.com
Lubricant Distr
N.A.I.C.S.: 424720

LUBCON LUBRICANTS ASIA PACIFIC INC. (1)

AND PRIVATE COMPANIES

Unit 1 Orient Goldcrest Laguna Technopark
Building 5 East Main Avenue, Loop Lot
3281-K Phase 6-A Laguna Technopark
SEZ, Binan, Laguna, Philippines
Tel.: (63) 495020502
Lubricant Distr
N.A.I.C.S.: 424720
Roland Metelmann *(Pres)*

LUBCON LUBRIFICANTI S.R.L. (1)
Via Cernaia 14, 10122, Turin, Italy
Tel.: (39) 01119703964
Lubricant Distr
N.A.I.C.S.: 424720
Francesco Cerra *(Country Mgr)*

LUBCON Lubricant Consult AG (1)
Pfadackerstr 9, 8957, Spreitenbach, Switzerland
Tel.: (41) 448823037
Lubricant Distr
N.A.I.C.S.: 424720

LUBCON Lubricants UK Ltd. (1)
Wilmot Hall Golden Butts Road, Ilkley, LS
29 8HS, West Yorkshire, United Kingdom
Tel.: (44) 1943601431
Lubricant Distr
N.A.I.C.S.: 424720

LUBCON Malaysia Sdn Bhd (1)
B-1-15 Block B 8th Avenue Jalan Sungai
Jernih 8/1, 46050, Petaling Jaya, Selangor, Malaysia
Tel.: (60) 196561648
Lubricant Distr
N.A.I.C.S.: 424720

LUBCON POLSKA Sp. z o.o. (1)
Ul Piasecka 162, 21-040, Swidnik, Poland
Tel.: (48) 817216830
Web Site: http://www.lubcon.com
Lubricant Distr
N.A.I.C.S.: 424720

LUBCON Turmo Lubrication, Inc. (1)
5460 33rd St SE, Grand Rapids, MI 49512
Tel.: (616) 575-6034
Lubricant Distr
N.A.I.C.S.: 424720

LUBCON d.o.o. (1)
Adamiceva ulica 26, 8000, Novo Mesto, Slovenia
Tel.: (386) 73380760
Web Site: http://www.lubcon.si
Lubricant Distr
N.A.I.C.S.: 424720

LUBCON s.r.o. (1)
Dlouha 783, 76321, Slavicin, Czech Republic
Tel.: (420) 577343618
Lubricant Distr
N.A.I.C.S.: 424720

Lubricant Service Kft (1)
Padragi ut 309, 8451, Ajka, Hungary
Tel.: (36) 209245567
Lubricant Distr
N.A.I.C.S.: 424720

Taiwan LUBCON Lubricants Co., Ltd. (1)
7F-1 No 61 Sec 2 Gongyi Road, Natun District, Taichung, 608, Taiwan
Tel.: (886) 423285825
Lubricant Distr
N.A.I.C.S.: 424720

LUCA WAY S.R.L.

Bd Barbu Vacarescu nr 313-321 et 3
4 si 5 Dist 2, Sector 2, Bucharest,
020276, Romania
Tel.: (40) 372 220715
Web Site: http://www.lucaway.ro
Emp.: 30
Engineeering Services
N.A.I.C.S.: 541330
Radu Luca *(Mng Dir)*

LUCAPA DIAMOND COMPANY LIMITED

34 Bagot Road, Subiaco, 6008, WA, Australia
Tel.: (61) 893815995
Web Site: http://www.lucapa.com.au
LOM—(ASX)
Rev.: $23,350,000
Assets: $101,969,000
Liabilities: $16,662,000
Net Worth: $85,307,000
Earnings: ($15,074,000)
Emp.: 1,200
Fiscal Year-end: 12/31/22
Diamond Mining Services
N.A.I.C.S.: 212311
Neil Kaner *(Chief Technical Officer)*

LUCARA DIAMOND CORP.

Suite 2800 Four Bentall Centre 1055
Dunsmuir Street, Vancouver, V7X
1L2, BC, Canada
Tel.: (604) 674-0272   BC
Web Site:
   https://www.lucaradiamond.com
LKT—(DEU)
Rev.: $177,371,000
Assets: $575,803,000
Liabilities: $333,672,000
Net Worth: $242,131,000
Earnings: ($20,191,000)
Emp.: 573
Fiscal Year-end: 12/31/23
Diamond Exploration & Mining
N.A.I.C.S.: 212390
Eira M. Thomas *(Pres & CEO)*

Subsidiaries:

Clara Diamond Solutions Limited
Partnership (1)
Suite 502 1250 Homer Street, Vancouver, V6B 2Y5, BC, Canada
Tel.: (604) 674-0272
Web Site: https://claradiamonds.ca
Polished Diamond Distr
N.A.I.C.S.: 423940

LUCAS BOLS B.V.

Paulus Potterstraat 14, 1071 CZ, Amsterdam, Netherlands
Tel.: (31) 205708575   NI
Web Site: https://www.lucasbols.com
Year Founded: 1575
BOLS—(EUR)
Rev.: $108,584,071
Assets: $381,755,882
Liabilities: $158,809,627
Net Worth: $222,946,255
Earnings: ($17,524,282)
Emp.: 70
Fiscal Year-end: 03/31/23
Distilled & Blended Liquors Mfr & Distr
N.A.I.C.S.: 312140
Huub L. M. P. van Doorne *(CEO & Member-Mgmt Bd)*

Subsidiaries:

Distilleerderijen Erven Lucas Bols
BV (1)
Watt St 61, 2723 RB, Zoetermeer,
Netherlands (100%)
Tel.: (31) 793305305
Web Site: http://www.lucasbols.com
Sales Range: $10-24.9 Million
Distillery
N.A.I.C.S.: 312140

LUCECO PLC

Caparo House 103 Baker Street,
London, W1U 6LN, United Kingdom
Tel.: (44) 1952238128
Web Site: https://www.luceco.com
LUCE—(LSE)
Rev.: $264,155,712
Assets: $223,458,038
Liabilities: $104,903,943
Net Worth: $118,554,095
Earnings: $21,107,179
Emp.: 1,590
Fiscal Year-end: 12/31/23
All Other Miscellaneous Electrical
Equipment & Component Manufacturing
N.A.I.C.S.: 335999
John Hornby *(CEO)*

Subsidiaries:

D.W. Windsor Limited (1)
Pindar Road, Hoddesdon, EN11 0DX,
United Kingdom
Tel.: (44) 1992474600
Web Site: https://www.dwwindsor.com
Street Lighting Equipment Mfr & Distr
N.A.I.C.S.: 334511

DW Windsor Group Limited (1)
Pindar Road, Hoddesdon, EN11 0DX,
United Kingdom
Tel.: (44) 1992474600
Web Site: https://www.dwwindsor.com
Street Lighting Equipment Mfr & Distr
N.A.I.C.S.: 334511

Fusion Lighting Limited (1)
18A High West Street, Dorset, Dorchester, DT1 1UW, United Kingdom
Tel.: (44) 1305251543
Web Site: https://www.fusion-lighting.co.uk
Table Lamp Mfr
N.A.I.C.S.: 334413

Luceco Electrical (Jiaxing)
Limited (1)
No 1438 Jiachuang Road Xiuzhou Industrial Park, Zhejiang, Jiaxing, 314031, China
Tel.: (86) 57383570200
Lighting Equipment Mfr & Distr
N.A.I.C.S.: 334511

Luceco Southern Europe SL (1)
Bobinadora 1-5, Mataro, 8302, Barcelona, Spain
Tel.: (34) 938295577
Electrical & Electronics Appliances Mfr & Distr
N.A.I.C.S.: 335999

Urban Control Limited (1)
Pindar Road, Hoddesdon, EN11 0DX, Hertfordshire, United Kingdom
Tel.: (44) 2034370777
Web Site: https://www.urban-control.co.uk
Environmental Engineering Services
N.A.I.C.S.: 541330

LUCENT INDUSTRIES LIMITED

Second Floor 448-D Scheme No 51
Sangam Nagar, Indore, 452 006,
Madhya Pradesh, India
Tel.: (91) 7312571451
Web Site: https://lucentindustries.life
Year Founded: 2010
539682—(BOM)
Assets: $2,204,172
Liabilities: $468,006
Net Worth: $1,736,167
Earnings: ($10,431)
Fiscal Year-end: 03/31/23
Professional Skill Development Services
N.A.I.C.S.: 611430
Dinesh Kumar Jangid *(Mgr)*

LUCIA S.A.

30 Ave George V, 75008, Paris, France
Tel.: (33) 156623100
Web Site: http://www.lucia-sa.com
Sales Range: Less than $1 Million
Emp.: 4
Real Estate Services
N.A.I.C.S.: 531390
Alain Aubert *(CFO & Sec)*

LUCIBEL SA

101 allee des Vergers Parc d Activites du Hoquet, 76360, Barentin, France
Tel.: (33) 180041231   FR
Web Site: http://www.lucibel.io
Year Founded: 2008
ALUCI—(EUR)
Rev.: $15,175,223
Earnings: ($13,452,878)
Fiscal Year-end: 12/31/19
LED Lighting Products Mfr

LUCKIN COFFEE INC.

N.A.I.C.S.: 334419
Yves-Henry Brepson *(CEO)*

Subsidiaries:

Lorenz Light Technic SARL (1)
7 A Rue Ampere, 67120, Duttlenheim, France
Tel.: (33) 388958680
Lighting Equipment Mfr
N.A.I.C.S.: 335139

Lucibel Middle East FZCO (1)
Dubai Silicon Oasis Suntech Tower Office
306, PO Box 341407, Dubai, United Arab Emirates
Tel.: (971) 43886691
Lighting Equipment Mfr
N.A.I.C.S.: 335139

Procedes Hallier SAS (1)
69 rue Victor Hugo, 93100, Montreuil, France
Tel.: (33) 148517988
Web Site: http://www.procedeshallier.fr
Lighting Equipment Mfr
N.A.I.C.S.: 335139

LUCIC PRIGREVICA A.D.

Ilije Vucetica 7, Novi Sad, Serbia
Tel.: (381) 255420033
Year Founded: 1989
SJPR—(BEL)
Rev.: $11,259,094
Assets: $39,274,026
Liabilities: $15,897,734
Net Worth: $23,376,292
Earnings: $525,632
Emp.: 18
Fiscal Year-end: 12/31/22
Cereal & Crop Farming Services
N.A.I.C.S.: 111140

LUCIDEON

Queens Road Penkhull, Stoke-on-Trent, ST4 7LQ, Staffordshire, United Kingdom
Tel.: (44) 1782411008
Web Site: http://www.lucideon.com
Material Testing Services
N.A.I.C.S.: 541380
Tony Kinsella *(CEO)*

Subsidiaries:

The M&P Lab, Inc. (1)
2210 Technology Dr, Schenectady, NY 12308
Tel.: (518) 382-0082
Web Site: http://www.mandplabs.com
Sales Range: $25-49.9 Million
Emp.: 30
Testing Laboratories
N.A.I.C.S.: 541380
Frank E. Anderson *(Pres)*

LUCIEN GEORGELIN SAS

La prairie de Londres, 47200, Bordeaux, France
Tel.: (33) 553201520
Web Site: http://www.lucien-georgelin.com
Food Mfr
N.A.I.C.S.: 445298
Lucien Georgelin *(CEO)*

LUCISANO MEDIA GROUP S.P.A.

Via Gian Domenico Romagnosi 20,
196, Rome, Italy
Tel.: (39) 063611377
Web Site:
   https://www.lucisanomediagroup.com
Year Founded: 1958
LMG—(ITA)
Sales Range: $25-49.9 Million
Film & Television Production & Distribution
N.A.I.C.S.: 512110
Fulvio Lucisano *(Chm)*

LUCKIN COFFEE INC.

LUCKIN COFFEE INC.

Luckin Coffee Inc.—(Continued)
28th Floor Building T3 Haixi Jingu Plaza 1-3 Taibei Road, Siming District, Xiamen, 361008, Fujian, China
Tel.: (86) 5923386666 Ky
Web Site: http://www.luckincoffee.com
Year Founded: 2017
LKNCY—(OTCIQ)
Rev.: $3,448,045,802
Assets: $2,532,673,073
Liabilities: $1,187,629,181
Net Worth: $1,345,043,891
Earnings: $394,319,478
Emp.: 29,217
Fiscal Year-end: 12/31/23
Holding Company
N.A.I.C.S.: 551112
Jinyi Guo (Co-Founder, Chm & CEO)

LUCKLAND CO., LTD.
3-18-20 Nishi-Shinjuku, Shinjuku-ku, Tokyo, 160-0023, Japan
Tel.: (81) 333779331
Web Site: https://www.luckland.co.jp
Year Founded: 1970
9612—(TKS)
Rev.: $319,872,440
Assets: $194,117,110
Liabilities: $122,869,700
Net Worth: $71,247,410
Earnings: $1,786,680
Emp.: 998
Fiscal Year-end: 12/31/23
Industrial Building Construction Services
N.A.I.C.S.: 236210

Subsidiaries:

Viet Bokuto Co., Ltd. (1)
28A Street 7 VSIP II, Hoa Phu Ward, Thu Dau Mot, Binh Duong, Vietnam
Tel.: (84) 2743628163
Web Site: https://www.bokuto.vn
Steel Mfrs
N.A.I.C.S.: 331110

LUCKY CEMENT CORPORATION
15th Floor No 237 Songjiang Rd, Taipei, Taiwan
Tel.: (886) 225092188
Web Site: https://www.luckygrp.com.tw
Year Founded: 1974
1108—(TAI)
Rev.: $166,787,462
Assets: $326,036,581
Liabilities: $160,209,550
Net Worth: $165,827,032
Earnings: $17,238,496
Emp.: 360
Fiscal Year-end: 12/31/23
Cement Mfr
N.A.I.C.S.: 327310
Liang-Chuan Chen (Chm)

Subsidiaries:

Lucky Cement Corporation - Dongao Plant (1)
No 101 Sec 3 Suhua Rd Nanao Village, Yilan, Yilan, Taiwan
Tel.: (886) 39986110
Cement Mfr
N.A.I.C.S.: 333994

Lucky Cement Corporation - Horen Plant (1)
No 73 Horeng Rd Hoping Village Xiulin Country, Hua-lien, Taiwan
Tel.: (886) 38681217
Cement Mfr
N.A.I.C.S.: 333994

Lucky Cement Corporation - Puxin Plant (1)
No 193 Sec 1 Meisi Rd Chengping Li, Taoyuan, Taiwan
Tel.: (886) 34814788

Cement Mfr
N.A.I.C.S.: 333994

LUCKY CEMENT LIMITED
6-A Muhammad Ali Housing Society A Aziz HashimTabba Street, Karachi, 75350, Pakistan
Tel.: (92) 21111786555 PK
Web Site: https://www.lucky-cement.com
Year Founded: 1993
LUCK—(KAR)
Rev.: $1,662,572,927
Assets: $2,244,279,220
Liabilities: $1,269,145,947
Net Worth: $975,133,273
Earnings: $175,301,618
Emp.: 2,541
Fiscal Year-end: 06/30/21
Cement Mfr
N.A.I.C.S.: 327310
Muhammad Ali A. Razzak Tabba (CEO)

Subsidiaries:

Lucky Commodities (Private) Limited (1)
7-A Muhammad Ali Housing Society A Aziz Hashim Tabba Street, Karachi, 75350, Pakistan
Tel.: (92) 2134168212
Web Site: https://www.lucky-commodities.com
Coal Distr
N.A.I.C.S.: 423520
Tahir Ahmed (CEO)

Lucky Core Industries Limited (1)
5 West Wharf, Karachi, 74000, Pakistan (75.81%)
Tel.: (92) 2132313717
Web Site: https://luckycore.com
Rev.: $626,383,002
Assets: $466,555,120
Liabilities: $259,816,445
Net Worth: $206,738,675
Earnings: $55,020,737
Emp.: 2,198
Fiscal Year-end: 06/30/2022
Specialty Chemicals Mfr.
N.A.I.C.S.: 325998
Muhammad Ali A. Razzak Tabba (Vice Chm)

Subsidiary (Domestic):

ICI Pakistan Ltd.-Soda Ash Works (2)
ICI Pakistan Ltd Soda Ash-Business Area, Khewra, Jhelum, Pakistan
Tel.: (92) 544211495
Web Site: http://www.icipakistan.com
Sales Range: $100-124.9 Million
Emp.: 500
Soda Ash Mfr
N.A.I.C.S.: 325180
Ali Aga (VP)

Lucky Electric Power Company Limited (1)
11th Floor Al-Tijarah Center 32-1-A PECHS Shahra-e-Faisal, Karachi, 74000, Pakistan
Tel.: (92) 213416880609
Web Site: https://www.luckyelectricpower.com
Electric Power Distribution Services
N.A.I.C.S.: 221122

Lucky Energy (Private) Limited (1)
L-A-2/B Block 21 Federal B Area, Karachi, Pakistan
Tel.: (92) 216322048
Web Site: https://www.luckyenergy.net
Electric Power Distribution Services
N.A.I.C.S.: 221122
Sohail Tabba (CEO)

Lucky Foods (Private) Limited (1)
7-A Muhammad Ali Housing Society, Karachi, 75350, Pakistan
Tel.: (92) 23097867865
Web Site: https://www.luckyfoods.com.pk
Dairy Products Distr
N.A.I.C.S.: 424430
Salman Hussain (CEO)

Lucky Holdings Limited (1)
6-A Muhammad Ali Housing Society A Aziz Hashim Tabba Street, Karachi, Pakistan
Tel.: (92) 111786555
Web Site: https://www.luckyholdings.com.pk
Cement Mfr
N.A.I.C.S.: 327310
Mohammad Ali Tabba (CEO)

Lucky Knits (Private) Limited (1)
L-A-2/B Block 21 Federal B Area, Karachi, Pakistan
Tel.: (92) 2136312380
Web Site: https://www.luckyknits.com
Apparels Mfr
N.A.I.C.S.: 315990

Y.B. Pakistan Limited (1)
First Floor Sindh Market M A Jinnah Road, Karachi, Sindh, Pakistan
Tel.: (92) 2132434874
Web Site: https://www.ybpakistan.com
Wheat & Rice Product Distr
N.A.I.C.S.: 424510
Muhammad Yunus Tabba (Chm)

Yunus Textile Mills Limited (1)
H-23/1 Landhi Industrial Area, Karachi, 75120, Sindh, Pakistan
Tel.: (92) 2135081305
Web Site: https://www.yunustextile.com
Fabric Textile Product Distr
N.A.I.C.S.: 424310
Mohammad Nisar Palla (COO)

LUCKY FILM CO., LTD.
No 6 Lekai South Street, Baoding, 071054, Hebei, China
Tel.: (86) 3127922692
Web Site: http://gufen.luckyfilm.com.cn
Year Founded: 1998
600135—(SHG)
Rev.: $290,316,466
Assets: $491,301,860
Liabilities: $113,063,727
Net Worth: $378,238,134
Earnings: $5,425,168
Emp.: 8,000
Fiscal Year-end: 12/31/22
Photographic Flim & Paper Mfr & Distr
N.A.I.C.S.: 325992
Wang Hongze (Chm)

LUCKY HARVEST CO., LTD.
No 893 Changan Jianan Road, Changan Town, Dongguan, 523870, Guangdong, China
Tel.: (86) 76989953999
Web Site: http://www.luckyharvest.cn
Year Founded: 2004
002965—(SSE)
Rev.: $363,225,672
Assets: $593,258,230
Liabilities: $303,034,059
Net Worth: $290,224,171
Earnings: $9,817,697
Fiscal Year-end: 12/31/21
Automotive Stamping Mfr & Distr
N.A.I.C.S.: 336370
Rong Chen (Chm)

LUCKY MINERALS INC.
1010- 789 W Pender St, Vancouver, V6C 1H2, BC, Canada
Web Site: https://www.luckyminerals.com
Year Founded: 2007
LKMNF—(OTCIQ)
Assets: $6,203,419
Liabilities: $1,175,101
Net Worth: $5,028,318
Earnings: ($3,160,156)
Fiscal Year-end: 10/31/22
Mineral Mining Services
N.A.I.C.S.: 212390
Francois Perron (Pres, CEO & Chm)

LUCKY-CAR FRANCHISE & BETEILIGUNGS GMBH

INTERNATIONAL PUBLIC

Seilergasse 8, 1010, Vienna, Austria
Tel.: (43) 5958259227
Web Site: http://www.luckycar-franchise.com
Year Founded: 2007
Car Paintwork & Bodywork Maintenance & Services
N.A.I.C.S.: 811121
Ostoja Matic (Mng Dir)

Subsidiaries:

Midas Autoservice GmbH (1)
Schoenbrunner Schlosstrasse 9, 1230, Vienna, Austria
Tel.: (43) 16677225
Web Site: http://www.midas.at
Sales Range: $25-49.9 Million
Emp.: 10
Auto Parts Stores
N.A.I.C.S.: 441330
Peter Bakucz (Mng Dir)

LUCTA, S.A.
Carrer de Can Parellada 28, Montornes del Valles, 08170, Barcelona, Spain
Tel.: (34) 93 845 88 88
Web Site: http://www.lucta.com
Year Founded: 1949
Emp.: 500
Fragrance Flavor & Animal Feed Additive Mfr
N.A.I.C.S.: 311930
Carlos Ventos (CEO)

Subsidiaries:

Lucta (Guangzhou) Flavours Co. Ltd. (1)
No 20 Suida Street, Guangzhou Economic & Technological Development District, Guangzhou, 510530, China
Tel.: (86) 20 82 21 05 46
Fragrance, Flavor & Animal Feed Additive Mfr
N.A.I.C.S.: 311999

Lucta Grancolombiana, S.A.S. (1)
Carretera Autodromo Termoelectrica Km 2, Tocancipa, Cundinamarca, Colombia
Tel.: (57) 1 593 4700
Fragrance, Flavor & Animal Feed Additive Mfr
N.A.I.C.S.: 311999

Lucta Mexicana S.A. de C.V. (1)
Poniente 122 n 673 Col Las Salinas Deleg Azcapotzalco, 02360, Mexico, Mexico
Tel.: (52) 55 53 33 60 03
Fragrance, Flavor & Animal Feed Additive Mfr
N.A.I.C.S.: 311999

Lucta Polska sp. z o.o. (1)
ul Kolejowa 57, 40 602, Katowice, Poland
Tel.: (48) 32 78 69 251
Fragrance, Flavor & Animal Feed Additive Mfr
N.A.I.C.S.: 311999

Lucta USA Inc. (1)
Pine Meadow Corporate Center 950 Technology Way Ste 110, Libertyville, IL 60048
Tel.: (847) 996-3400
Fragrance, Flavor & Animal Feed Additive Mfr
N.A.I.C.S.: 311999

Lucta do Brasil Comercial Ltda. (1)
Avenida Juvenal Arantes 2 500 Galpao 10 Bairro Medeiros, Jundiai, 13212-370, Brazil
Tel.: (55) 11 4525 1696
Web Site: http://www.lucta.com
Emp.: 5
Fragrance, Flavor & Animal Feed Additive Mfr
N.A.I.C.S.: 311999

LUCY SCIENTIFIC DISCOVERY INC.
301-1321 Blanshard Street, Victoria, V8W 0B6, BC, Canada
Tel.: (778) 410-5195 Ca
Year Founded: 2017

AND PRIVATE COMPANIES

LSDI—(NASDAQ)
Rev.: $7,048
Assets: $8,778,646
Liabilities: $4,099,757
Net Worth: $4,678,889
Earnings: ($8,988,456)
Emp.: 2
Fiscal Year-end: 06/30/23
Pharmaceuticals Product Mfr
N.A.I.C.S.: 325412
Steven E. Meyer (COO)

LUDAN ENGINEERING CO., LTD.
6 Granit St, PO B 3584, Petach Tikva, 49130, Israel
Tel.: (972) 39182000
Web Site: https://www.ludan-group.com
Engineeering Services
N.A.I.C.S.: 541330
Arnon Aharon (CEO)

LUDDEN & MENNEKES ENTSORGUNGS-SYSTEME GMBH
Essener Strasse 13, Meppen, 49716, Germany
Tel.: (49) 593272150
Web Site: http://www.ludden.de
Year Founded: 1991
Rev.: $35,864,400
Emp.: 165
Waste Disposal Equipment Mfr
N.A.I.C.S.: 562211
Dietmar Bentlage (Mgr-Sls)

LUDGATE INVESTMENTS LTD.
20 Old Bailey, London, EC4M 7AN, United Kingdom
Tel.: (44) 20364781000
Web Site: http://www.ludgate.com
Privater Equity Firm
N.A.I.C.S.: 523940

LUDLOW JUTE & SPECIALITIES LIMITED
KCI Plaza 4th Floor 23C Ashutosh Chowdhury Avenue, Kolkata, 700 019, India
Tel.: (91) 3340506300
Web Site: https://www.ludlowjute.com
LYPSAGEMS—(NSE)
Rev.: $74,735,115
Assets: $50,130,990
Liabilities: $25,956,840
Net Worth: $24,174,150
Earnings: $182,910
Emp.: 9,000
Fiscal Year-end: 03/31/23
Jute Product Mfr
N.A.I.C.S.: 313110
Rajesh Kumar Gupta (CFO)
Subsidiaries:

Sijberia Industries Ltd. (1)
KCI Plaza 23C Ashutosh Chowdhary Avenue, Kolkata, 700019, India
Tel.: (91) 3324543063
Jute Product Mfr
N.A.I.C.S.: 313110

LUDORUM PLC
10 The Old Power Station, 121 Mortlake High Street, London, SW14 8SN, United Kingdom
Tel.: (44) 20 8939 6280
Web Site: http://www.ludorumplc.com
Sales Range: $1-9.9 Million
Emp.: 9
Media Investment & Entertainment Services
N.A.I.C.S.: 516210
Rob Lawes (CEO)

LUDUSON G INC.
35/F Central Plaza 38 Harbour Road, Wanchai, China (Hong Kong)
Tel.: (852) 28187199 DE
Web Site: http://www.luduson.com
Year Founded: 2014
LDSN—(OTCQB)
Rev.: $52,361
Assets: $1,600,813
Liabilities: $966,523
Net Worth: $634,290
Earnings: ($336,418)
Emp.: 3
Fiscal Year-end: 12/31/22
Furniture Product Distr
N.A.I.C.S.: 423210
Eng Wah Kung (CFO & Sec)

LUDWIG BECK AG
Marienplatz 11, 80331, Munich, Germany
Tel.: (49) 89236910
Web Site: https://www.ludwigbeck.de
ECK—(DEU)
Rev.: $80,251,349
Assets: $187,437,126
Liabilities: $115,188,834
Net Worth: $72,248,292
Earnings: $474,664
Emp.: 408
Fiscal Year-end: 12/31/23
Departmental Store Operator
N.A.I.C.S.: 455110
Steffen Stremme (Chm-Supervisory Bd)
Subsidiaries:

LUDWIG BECK Verwaltungs GmbH (1)
Marienplatz 11, Munich, 80331, Germany
Tel.: (49) 89236910
Real Estate Manangement Services
N.A.I.C.S.: 531390

LUDWIG GORTZ GMBH
Spitalerstrasse 10, 20095, Hamburg, Germany
Tel.: (49) 40333000
Web Site: http://www.goertz.de
Sales Range: $500-549.9 Million
Emp.: 3,200
Shoe,Luggage,Accessory, Mail Order & Internet Retailer
N.A.I.C.S.: 423990
Frank Revermann (Mng Dir)

LUEN HENG F&B SDN. BHD.
Wisma LHA No 8 Jalan Kilang Midah, Taman Midah, 56000, Kuala Lumpur, Malaysia
Tel.: (60) 379839000 MY
Web Site: http://www.luenheng.com
Year Founded: 1956
Beer & Wine Distr
N.A.I.C.S.: 424820
Kenneth Soh (Mng Dir)

LUENMEI QUANTUM CO., LTD.
No 1 Yuanhang Middle Road, Hunnan New District, Shenyang, 110168, Liaoning, China
Tel.: (86) 2486318888
Web Site: https://en.luenmeilz.com
Year Founded: 2005
600167—(SHG)
Rev.: $484,428,747
Assets: $2,349,595,938
Liabilities: $726,132,682
Net Worth: $1,623,463,255
Earnings: $132,534,287
Fiscal Year-end: 12/31/22
Holding Company; Real Estate & Engineering Services
N.A.I.C.S.: 551112

LUFAPAK MONTAGE VERPACKEN LOGISTIK
Carl Borgward Strasse 20, Neuwied, 56566, Germany
Tel.: (49) 26313840
Web Site: http://www.lufapak.de
Rev.: $20,691,000
Emp.: 251
Logistics Consulting Servies
N.A.I.C.S.: 541614
Harald Fuchsel (Chm)

LUFAX HOLDING LTD.
No 1333 Lujiazui Ring Road, Pudong New District, Shanghai, China
Tel.: (86) 2138632121 Ky
Web Site: https://ir.lufaxholding.com
Year Founded: 2014
LU—(NYSE)
Rev.: $4,742,933,928
Assets: $32,817,762,655
Liabilities: $19,846,481,364
Net Worth: $12,971,281,292
Earnings: $143,232,997
Emp.: 36,215
Fiscal Year-end: 12/31/23
Holding Company
N.A.I.C.S.: 551112
Guangheng Ji (Chm)

LUGER GESELLSCHAFT M.B.H.
Tullnerbachstrasse 55, A-3011, Purkersdorf, Austria
Tel.: (43) 2231 635390
Web Site: http://www.luger.eu
Industrial Machinery & Equiment Mfr
N.A.I.C.S.: 333248
Thomas Luger (CEO)
Subsidiaries:

KraussMaffei Austria Ges.mbH (1)
Alfred-Feierfeil-Strasse 3, A-2380, Perchtoldsdorf, Austria
Tel.: (43) 18 65 58 63
Web Site: http://www.kraussmaffeigroup.com
Plastic Processing Machinery Mfr & Whslr
N.A.I.C.S.: 423830

LUHARUKA MEDIA & INFRA LIMITED
A-301 Hetal Arch SV Road Opposite Natraj Market, Malad West, Mumbai, 400064, India
Tel.: (91) 2268948500
Web Site: https://luharukamediainfra.com
Year Founded: 1994
512048—(BOM)
Rev.: $234,461
Assets: $1,822,775
Liabilities: $25,161
Net Worth: $1,797,614
Earnings: $80,974
Emp.: 7
Fiscal Year-end: 03/31/23
Property Development Services
N.A.I.C.S.: 531390
Ankur Anil Agrawal (Mng Dir)

LUIGI LAVAZZA S.P.A.
Corso Novara 59, Turin, 10154, Italy
Tel.: (39) 01123981 IT
Web Site: http://www.lavazza.com.it
Year Founded: 1894
Sales Range: $800-899.9 Million
Emp.: 1,000
Coffee & Related Products Mfr & Marketer
N.A.I.C.S.: 311920
Alberto Lavazza (Chm)
Subsidiaries:

Ercom S.p.A. (1)
Via Galileo Galilei 14, 20090, Segrate, MI, Italy
Tel.: (39) 022693181
Web Site: http://www.eraclea.it

Sales Range: $25-49.9 Million
Emp.: 60
Hot Chocolate & Tea Mfr
N.A.I.C.S.: 311999
Stefano Sacco (Pres)

Lavazza Coffee (UK) Ltd. (1)
36 Windsor St, Uxbridge, UB8 1AB, Middlesex, United Kingdom
Tel.: (44) 1895 209 750
Web Site: http://www.lavazza.com
Emp.: 45
Coffee Distribution
N.A.I.C.S.: 311920
David Rogers (Mng Dir)

Lavazza Deutschland GmbH (1)
Ziegelhuttenweg 43, 60598, Frankfurt, Germany
Tel.: (49) 6963155163
Web Site: http://www.lavazza.de
Grocery Product Whslr
N.A.I.C.S.: 424490
Oliva Knot (Mng Dir)

Lavazza Kaffee GmbH (1)
Johnstrasse 4-6, 1150, Vienna, Austria
Tel.: (43) 17899760
Web Site: http://www.lavazza.at
Sales Range: $25-49.9 Million
Emp.: 25
Grocery Product Whslr
N.A.I.C.S.: 424490

Lavazza Premium Coffees Corp. (1)
3 Park Ave 28th Fl 121 Wall St, New York, NY 10005
Tel.: (212) 725-8800
Web Site: http://www.lavazza.com
Sales Range: $75-99.9 Million
Emp.: 50
Coffee Mfr
N.A.I.C.S.: 424490
Ennio Khetarpaul (CEO-North America)

Lavazza do Brasil Ind. e com. Ltda (1)
Praia de Bortafogo 501, Salao 201, 22250-040, Rio de Janeiro, Brazil
Tel.: (55) 2125866163
Sales Range: $75-99.9 Million
Emp.: 160
Grocery Product Whslr
N.A.I.C.S.: 424490

Merrild Kaffe ApS (1)
Erritso Mollebanke 3, 7000, Fredericia, Denmark
Tel.: (45) 63 103 103
Web Site: http://www.merrild-kaffe.dk
Coffee Sales & Mfr
N.A.I.C.S.: 311920
Peter Falk (Mng Dir)

Siege Lavazza France S.A.S. (1)
9/11 Ave du Val de Fontenay, 94120, Paris, France
Tel.: (33) 148776600
Web Site: http://www.lavazza.fr
Grocery Product Whslr
N.A.I.C.S.: 424490

LUIRI GOLD LIMITED
1 King Place, South Perth, 6025, WA, Australia
Tel.: (61) 41202239
Web Site: http://www.luirigold.com
Sales Range: $1-9.9 Million
Gold Mining & Exploration Services
N.A.I.C.S.: 212220
Robert Brown (Chm)

LUK FOOK HOLDINGS (INTERNATIONAL) LIMITED
Floor 27 Metropole Square, No 2 On Yiu Street Shatin, Hong Kong, New Territories, China (Hong Kong)
Tel.: (852) 23081218 BM
Web Site: http://www.lukfook.com
Year Founded: 1991
0590—(HKG)
Rev.: $1,513,941,831
Assets: $2,092,090,296
Liabilities: $534,201,754
Net Worth: $1,557,888,541
Earnings: $179,583,626

LUK FOOK HOLDINGS (INTERNATIONAL) LIMITED

Luk Fook Holdings (International) Limited—(Continued)

Emp.: 6,000
Fiscal Year-end: 03/31/22
Jewelry Stores
N.A.I.C.S.: 458310
Wai Sheung Wong *(Co-Founder, Chm & CEO)*

Subsidiaries:

Hong Kong Resources Holdings
Company Limited **(1)**
Room 905 9th Floor Star House 3 Salisbury Road, Tsim Sha Tsui, Kowloon, China (Hong Kong) **(50.43%)**
Tel.: (852) 31012828
Web Site: http://www.hkrh.hk
Rev.: $116,336,607
Assets: $230,391,557
Liabilities: $253,484,136
Net Worth: ($23,092,579)
Earnings: ($15,065,380)
Emp.: 947
Fiscal Year-end: 06/30/2022
Electroplating Chemical Trading
N.A.I.C.S.: 332813
Wilfred Kwok Hing Lam *(Exec Dir)*

Luk Fook Jewellery & Goldsmith (HK)
Company Limited **(1)**
475 Hennessy Rd, Wanchai, China (Hong Kong)
Tel.: (852) 2838 8844
Jewelry Store Operator
N.A.I.C.S.: 458310

Luk Fook Jewellery & Goldsmith (Macao) Company Limited **(1)**
Rua de S Domingos no 4, Macau, China (Macau)
Tel.: (853) 2832 2755
Jewelry Store Operator
N.A.I.C.S.: 458310

LUK HING ENTERTAINMENT GROUP HOLDINGS LIMITED

Room 1505 15/F Shun Tak Centre West Tower 168-200 Connaught Road, Central, Sheung Wan, China (Hong Kong)
Tel.: (852) 37589000   Ky
Web Site: http://www.lukhing.com
8052—(HKG)
Rev.: $7,470,225
Assets: $5,304,255
Liabilities: $19,038,300
Net Worth: ($13,734,045)
Earnings: ($6,239,213)
Emp.: 79
Fiscal Year-end: 12/31/22
Pub Operator
N.A.I.C.S.: 722410
Yiu Ying Choi *(Chm & CEO)*

LUKA BEOGRAD A.D.

Zorza Klemansoa 37, Belgrade, Serbia
Tel.: (381) 11 2752 971
Web Site:
   http://www.lukabeograd.com
Year Founded: 1957
LBGD—(BEL)
Sales Range: $1-9.9 Million
Marine Cargo Handling Services
N.A.I.C.S.: 488320

LUKA DUNAV A.D.

Luka Dunav 1, Pancevo, Serbia
Tel.: (381) 13 302 303
Web Site: http://www.lukadunav.co.rs
Year Founded: 1947
Sales Range: $1-9.9 Million
Emp.: 95
Cargo Handling Services
N.A.I.C.S.: 488320

LUKA KOPER D.D.

Vojkovo nabrezje 38, 6000, Koper, Slovenia
Tel.: (386) 56656100   SI
Web Site: https://www.luka-kp.si
Year Founded: 1957
LKPG—(LJU)
Rev.: $251,650,279
Assets: $647,408,003
Liabilities: $214,145,413
Net Worth: $433,262,589
Earnings: $43,471,410
Emp.: 1,541
Fiscal Year-end: 12/31/19
Marine Cargo Handler
N.A.I.C.S.: 488320
Uros Ilic *(Chm-Supervisory Bd)*

Subsidiaries:

Adria Investicije, d.o.o. **(1)**
38 Vojkovo Nabrezje, 6000, Koper, Primorska, Slovenia
Tel.: (386) 56656100
Web Site: http://www.luka-kp.se
Investment Management Service
N.A.I.C.S.: 523940
Mojca Cerne Pucer *(Gen Mgr)*

Adria Terminali, d.o.o. **(1)**
Business unit Sezana Partizanska cesta 79, 6210, Sezana, Slovenia
Tel.: (386) 57312200
Web Site: https://www.adria-terminali.si
Sales Range: $25-49.9 Million
Emp.: 32
Logistics & Distribution Services
N.A.I.C.S.: 541614
Miha Kalcic *(Mng Dir)*

Adria Tow **(1)**
Vojkovo Nabrezje 38, 6000, Koper, Slovenia **(50%)**
Tel.: (386) 56656318
Web Site: http://www.adria-tow.si
Sales Range: $25-49.9 Million
Emp.: 30
Sea Transportation Services
N.A.I.C.S.: 483111
Robert Gerk *(Gen Mgr)*

Adriasole, d.o.o. **(1)**
Vojkovo Nabrezje 38, 6000, Koper, Primorska, Slovenia
Tel.: (386) 5 6300318
Solar Electric Power Generation Services
N.A.I.C.S.: 221118

Ecoporto Koper, d.o.o. **(1)**
38 Vojkovo Nabrezje, 6000, Koper, Slovenia
Tel.: (386) 56300318
Web Site: http://www.ecoporto.si
Waste Treatment Services
N.A.I.C.S.: 221320

Luka Koper INPO d.o.o. **(1)**
Vojkovo Nabrezje 38, 6000, Koper, Slovenia **(100%)**
Tel.: (386) 56656702
Web Site: https://www.luka-inpo.si
Sales Range: $25-49.9 Million
Emp.: 133
Maintenance Services
N.A.I.C.S.: 811412

Luka Koper Pristan, d.o.o. **(1)**
Vojkovo nabrezje 38, 6000, Koper, Slovenia
Tel.: (386) 56144000
Web Site: http://www.pristan-koper.si
Sales Range: $10-24.9 Million
Hotels & Motels
N.A.I.C.S.: 721110

LUKA PLOCE D.D.

Trg kralja Tomislava 21, 20340, Ploce, Croatia
Tel.: (385) 20679220
Web Site: https://www.luka-ploce.hr
Year Founded: 1998
LKPC—(ZAG)
Rev.: $103,337,682
Assets: $108,306,452
Liabilities: $38,666,331
Net Worth: $69,640,121
Earnings: $7,466,494
Emp.: 395
Fiscal Year-end: 12/31/22
Sea Transportation Services
N.A.I.C.S.: 488390

Hrvoje Livaja *(Chm-Mgmt Bd & CEO)*

Subsidiaries:

Luka Sped d.o.o. **(1)**
Trg Kralja Tomislava 21, 20340, Ploce, Croatia
Tel.: (385) 20676148
Freight Forwarding Services
N.A.I.C.S.: 488510

LUKA RIJEKA D.D.

Riva 1, 51000, Rijeka, Croatia
Tel.: (385) 51496000
Web Site: https://lukarijeka.hr
Year Founded: 1999
LKRI—(ZAG)
Rev.: $37,793,355
Assets: $159,677,669
Liabilities: $76,807,595
Net Worth: $82,870,074
Earnings: $9,029,694
Emp.: 655
Fiscal Year-end: 12/31/23
Port & Harbor Operations
N.A.I.C.S.: 488310
Alen Jugovic *(Chm-Supervisory Bd)*

Subsidiaries:

LUKA PRIVEZ - ODVEZ d.o.o. **(1)**
Riva 1, 51000, Rijeka, Croatia
Tel.: (385) 51 213 794
Emp.: 680
Ship Maintenance Services
N.A.I.C.S.: 488390
Zedran Devcic *(Mgr)*

Stanovi d.o.o. **(1)**
Dubrovacka Ulica 4, 51000, Rijeka, Croatia
Tel.: (385) 51672213
Web Site: https://stanovi-doo.com
Real Estate Services
N.A.I.C.S.: 531210

LUKA SENTA A.D.

Pristanisna br 1, 24400, Senta, Serbia
Tel.: (381) 24815233
Web Site: https://www.luka-senta.rs
Year Founded: 1991
PTSJ—(BEL)
Rev.: $2,582,992
Assets: $2,484,692
Liabilities: $485,644
Net Worth: $1,999,048
Earnings: $7,551
Emp.: 21
Fiscal Year-end: 12/31/23
Building Materials Whslr
N.A.I.C.S.: 423390
Mirko Kondic *(Mgr)*

LUKE REIT

Shandor Petyofi 13-15, Sofia, 1606, Bulgaria
Tel.: (359) 29804557
LUKE—(BUL)
Sales Range: Less than $1 Million
Real Estate Investment Services
N.A.I.C.S.: 531210
Gabriela Kirova *(Dir-IR)*

LUKOIL SRBIJA A.D.

Mihajla Pupina 165d, 11070, Novi Beograd, Serbia
Tel.: (381) 11 2220 200
Web Site: http://www.lukoil.rs
Year Founded: 1990
LOIL—(BEL)
Sales Range: $350-399.9 Million
Emp.: 191
Automotive Fuel Distribution Services
N.A.I.C.S.: 457210
Semenychev Igor *(Gen Dir)*

LUKOM A.D.

Cara Dusana 41, 76230, Samac, Bosnia & Herzegovina
Tel.: (387) 54611001

INTERNATIONAL PUBLIC

LKMS-R-A—(BANJ)
Emp.: 3
Apparel & Accessory Mfr
N.A.I.C.S.: 315990
Predrag Lukic *(Exec Dir)*

LUKOS SA

6 Rue Dicks, L 1417, Luxembourg, Luxembourg
Tel.: (352) 26 645 81   LU
Investment Holding Company
N.A.I.C.S.: 551112

Subsidiaries:

Banca Zarattini & Co. **(1)**
Via Balestra 17, 6901, Lugano, Switzerland
Tel.: (41) 919125555
Web Site: http://www.bancazarattini.ch
Sales Range: $50-74.9 Million
Emp.: 35
Commericial Banking
N.A.I.C.S.: 522110
Pablo Quaggio *(CEO)*

LUKS GROUP (VIETNAM HOLDINGS) COMPANY LIMITED

5th Floor Cheong Wah Factory Building 39-41 Sheung Heung Road, Tokwawan, Kowloon, China (Hong Kong)
Tel.: (852) 23620297
Web Site: http://www.luks.com.hk
0366—(HKG)
Rev.: $62,841,563
Assets: $374,643,960
Liabilities: $54,659,888
Net Worth: $319,984,073
Earnings: $6,183,495
Emp.: 990
Fiscal Year-end: 12/31/22
Cements & Chinese Medicine Product Mfr
N.A.I.C.S.: 325412
Martin Chiu Tat Fan *(Sec)*

Subsidiaries:

Luks Cement (Vietnam) Limited **(1)**
30 Thong Nhat Tu Ha, Huong Tra, Hue, Thua Thien Hue, Vietnam
Tel.: (84) 2343557012
Web Site: https://www.ximangluks.vn
Real Estate Services
N.A.I.C.S.: 531390

Luks Industrial Company Limited **(1)**
5F Cheong Wah Factory Bldg 39-41 Sheung Heung Rd, To Kwa Wan, Kowloon, China (Hong Kong)
Tel.: (852) 27644808
Web Site: http://www.luks.com
Sales Range: $50-74.9 Million
Emp.: 40
Property Management & Investment Holding Services
N.A.I.C.S.: 523940
Luk Yan *(Gen Mgr)*

Vigconic (International) Limited **(1)**
5F Cheong Wah Factory Bldg 39-41 Sheung Heung Rd, Tokwawan, Kowloon, China (Hong Kong)
Tel.: (852) 27656200
Web Site: http://www.vigconic.com
Sales Range: $25-49.9 Million
Emp.: 40
Chinese Medicine Products Mfr & Sales
N.A.I.C.S.: 325412

LUKS KADIFE TICARET VE SANAYII A.S.

Organize Sanayi Bolgesi 18 Cadde No 30, Melikgazi, 38125, Kayseri, Turkiye
Tel.: (90) 3523214061
Web Site:
   https://www.lukskadife.com.tr
LUKSK—(IST)
Rev.: $7,281,535
Assets: $18,973,614
Liabilities: $8,757,505
Net Worth: $10,216,109

AND PRIVATE COMPANIES

Earnings: $2,971,200
Fiscal Year-end: 12/31/22
Fabric Product Mfr
N.A.I.C.S.: 313210
Yilmaz Kucukcalik *(Chm)*

LULULEMON ATHLETICA INC.
1818 Cornwall Ave, Vancouver, V6J 1C7, BC, Canada
Tel.: (604) 732-6124   DE
Web Site: https://www.lululemon.com
Year Founded: 1998
LULU—(NASDAQ)
Rev.: $9,619,278,000
Assets: $7,091,941,000
Liabilities: $2,859,860,000
Net Worth: $4,232,081,000
Earnings: $1,550,190,000
Emp.: 38,000
Fiscal Year-end: 01/28/24
Sports Related Product Distr
N.A.I.C.S.: 459110
Calvin R. McDonald *(CEO)*

Subsidiaries:

Lululemon Hong Kong Limited   (1)
Rm 1402-1422 14/F Leighton Ctr 77 Leighton Rd, Causeway Bay, Hong Kong, China (Hong Kong)
Tel.: (852) 25768322
Fitness Equipment Whslr
N.A.I.C.S.: 423910

ivivva athletica canada inc.   (1)
2850-8882 170 St NW, Edmonton, T5T 4M2, AB, Canada
Tel.: (780) 486-3633
Athletic Apparel Mfr
N.A.I.C.S.: 339920

lululemon ahletica australia holdings Pty Ltd   (1)
30 Rupert Street, Collingwood, 3066, VIC, Australia
Tel.: (61) 394177848
Web Site: http://www.lululemon.com.au
Sportswear Retailer
N.A.I.C.S.: 459110

lululemon athletica CH GmbH   (1)
Zugerstrasse 76B, 6340, Baar, Switzerland
Tel.: (41) 434884343
Athletic Apparel Distr
N.A.I.C.S.: 423910

lululemon athletica NL BV   (1)
Hartenstraat 13, 1016 BZ, Amsterdam, Netherlands
Tel.: (31) 202993836
Athletic Apparel Distr
N.A.I.C.S.: 423910

lululemon athletica canada inc.   (1)
1818 Cornwall Ave, Vancouver, V6J 1C7, BC, Canada
Tel.: (604) 732-6124
Sportswear Mfr
N.A.I.C.S.: 339920

lululemon usa inc.   (1)
2625 NE University Vlg, Seattle, WA 98105
Tel.: (206) 524-6025
Athletic Apparel Retail Store Operating Services
N.A.I.C.S.: 458110

LULUMCO INC.
79 Saint Alphonse street, Saint-Luc, G0K 1P0, QC, Canada
Tel.: (418) 739-4881
Web Site: http://www.lulumco.com
Year Founded: 1892
Rev.: $14,509,129
Emp.: 90
Lumber & Fencing Products Mfr
N.A.I.C.S.: 423310

LUM CHANG HOLDINGS LIMITED
14 Kung Chong Road 08-01 Lum Chang Building, Singapore, 159150, Singapore
Tel.: (65) 62738888
Web Site: https://www.lumchang.com.sg
Year Founded: 1940
L19—(SES)
Rev.: $291,530,937
Assets: $327,353,835
Liabilities: $200,975,917
Net Worth: $126,377,918
Earnings: ($20,459,429)
Emp.: 879
Fiscal Year-end: 06/30/23
Construction Services
N.A.I.C.S.: 236220
Adrian Wen Hong Lum *(Dir-Property Dev)*

Subsidiaries:

Fabulous Range Sdn. Bhd.   (1)
Lot 10-03 Level 10 Menara Hla No 3 Jalan Kia Peng, 50450, Kuala Lumpur, Malaysia
Tel.: (60) 321712222
Web Site: https://www.lumchang.com.my
Real Estate Services
N.A.I.C.S.: 531390

Lum Chang Building Contractors Pte Ltd   (1)
14 Kung Chong Road 08-01 Lum Chang Building, Singapore, 159150, Singapore
Tel.: (65) 62738888
Web Site: https://www.lumchang.com.sg
Emp.: 100
Building Construction Services
N.A.I.C.S.: 236220

Nexus Sdn. Bhd.   (1)
Lot 10-03 Level 10 Menara HLA No 3 Jln Kia Peng, Kuala Lumpur, 50450, Malaysia
Tel.: (60) 321712222
Emp.: 40
Property Development Services
N.A.I.C.S.: 531210
Joan Bong *(Mgr-HR)*

Twin Palms Development Sdn. Bhd.   (1)
Twin Palms Sungai Long No 6 Jalan Palma 2/2A Taman Bukit Palma, 43000, Kajang, Selangor, Malaysia
Tel.: (60) 387406888
Web Site: https://www.twinpalms.com.my
Real Estate Services
N.A.I.C.S.: 531390

Venus Capital Corporation Sdn. Bhd.   (1)
Lum Chang Menara HLA Lot 10-03 Level 10 No 3 Jalan Kia Peng, 50450, Kuala Lumpur, Malaysia
Tel.: (60) 321712222
Sales Range: $50-74.9 Million
Emp.: 20
Property Development Services
N.A.I.C.S.: 531210

LUMA INVESTMENTS, LTD.
10 Ang Mo Kio Street 65 Techpoint #03-04, Singapore, 569059, Singapore
Tel.: (65) 6240 4655
Web Site: http://www.lumainvestments.com
Investment Holding Company
N.A.I.C.S.: 551112
James M. Gosart *(CEO)*

Subsidiaries:

LUXIM Corporation   (1)
1171 Borregas Ave, Sunnyvale, CA 94089
Tel.: (408) 734-1096
Web Site: http://www.luxim.com
Sales Range: $1-9.9 Million
Emp.: 55
Projection Display Lamps Mfr
N.A.I.C.S.: 335139
John Pena *(Sr VP-Sls & Mktg)*

Subsidiary (Non-US):

JK Yaming International Holdings Pte. Ltd.   (2)
160 Paya Lebar Rd 08-03/04 Orion Industria Bldg, 409022, Singapore, Singapore
Tel.: (65) 68469063

Sales Range: $150-199.9 Million
Holding Company; Industrial Light Mfr
N.A.I.C.S.: 551112

Subsidiary (Non-US):

Fujian Juan Kuang Yaming Electric Ltd.   (3)
Nanping Hi-Tech Zone, Nanping, 353001, Fujian, China
Tel.: (86) 599 860 9088
Web Site: http://www.fjjk.com
Electric Light Fixture Mfr
N.A.I.C.S.: 335132

LUMAX AUTO TECHNOLOGIES LTD
Plot No - 878 Udyog Vihar Phase - V, Gurgaon, 122016, Haryana, India
Tel.: (91) 1244760000
Web Site: https://www.lumaxworld.in
LUMAXAUTO—(NSE)
Rev.: $207,580,628
Assets: $155,460,915
Liabilities: $72,919,488
Net Worth: $82,541,427
Earnings: $11,175,774
Emp.: 1,072
Fiscal Year-end: 03/31/22
Sheet Metal Parts, Fabricated Assemblies & Tubular Parts Mfr
N.A.I.C.S.: 332322
Ashish Dubey *(CFO)*

LUMAX INDUSTRIES LTD
2nd Floor Harbans Bhawan II Commercial Complex Nangal Raya, New Delhi, 110064, India
Tel.: (91) 1149857832
Web Site: https://www.lumaxworld.in
517206—(BOM)
Rev.: $279,864,241
Assets: $223,687,657
Liabilities: $153,718,314
Net Worth: $69,969,342
Earnings: $12,358,995
Emp.: 2,514
Fiscal Year-end: 03/31/23
Automotive Lighting Solutions Provider
N.A.I.C.S.: 336320
Anmol Jain *(Co-Mng Dir)*

LUMAX INTERNATIONAL CORP., LTD.
12F No 3-1 Park Street, Nangang District, Taipei, 115603, Taiwan
Tel.: (886) 227883656   CN
Web Site: https://www.elumax.com
Year Founded: 1975
6192—(TAI)
Rev.: $220,025,303
Assets: $356,193,551
Liabilities: $144,777,849
Net Worth: $211,415,702
Earnings: $25,709,734
Emp.: 600
Fiscal Year-end: 12/31/23
Integrated Circuits Mfr
N.A.I.C.S.: 334413
C. K. Lin *(Chm)*

Subsidiaries:

Dalian FTZ Lumax International Trade Co., Ltd.   (1)
Emp.: 60
Passive Components Mfr
N.A.I.C.S.: 334416
Tony Yao *(Gen Mgr)*

Exodus Limited Company   (1)
10F-3 No 20 Dalong Rd, West Dist, Taichung, Taiwan
Tel.: (886) 423292339
Electronic Component & Process Control Equipment Mfr
N.A.I.C.S.: 334513

LUMAX Trading (Xiamen) Limited   (1)

LUMENS CO., LTD.

Unit 2F 2 XiangXing 3rd Road Xiangyu Free Trade Zone, Xiamen, 361006, Fujian, China
Tel.: (86) 592 6018026
Passive Components Mfr
N.A.I.C.S.: 334416

Lumax International (Shanghai) Co., Ltd.   (1)
Room 706 7F No 1733 Lianhua Road, Minhang District, Shanghai, 210002, China
Tel.: (86) 2164069680
Sales Range: $25-49.9 Million
Emp.: 20
Passive Components Mfr
N.A.I.C.S.: 334416
Simon Teng *(Mgr)*

WINMAX HI-TECH (SHENZHEN) CO., LTD.   (1)
No A2 Blag Tongfuyu Industry Park A-5 Buyong Village Shajing Town, Baoan District, Shenzhen, 518104, Guangdong, China
Tel.: (86) 75533655588
Web Site: http://www.elumax.com
Passive Components Mfr
N.A.I.C.S.: 334416

LUMENRADIO AB
Johan Willins gata 6, 416 64, Gothenburg, Sweden
Tel.: (46) 313010370
Web Site: https://lumenradio.com
LUMEN—(OMX)
Rev.: $25,070,979
Assets: $31,915,739
Liabilities: $11,076,697
Net Worth: $20,839,042
Earnings: $4,695,535
Emp.: 69
Fiscal Year-end: 12/31/23
Wireless Communication Products & Services
N.A.I.C.S.: 334220
Magnus Thousgaard Terrvik *(Chm)*

Subsidiaries:

Radiocrafts AS   (1)
Sandakerveien 64, NO-0484, Oslo, Norway
Tel.: (47) 40005195
Web Site: http://www.radiocrafts.com
Sales Range: $1-9.9 Million
Emp.: 10
RF Module Design, Marketing & Mfr
N.A.I.C.S.: 339999
Peder Martin Evjen *(Mng Dir)*

Wireless Solution Sweden AB   (1)
Sturexparksvagen 7, Uddevalla, 45155, Sweden
Tel.: (46) 522511511
Web Site: http://www.wirelessdmx.com
Sales Range: $10-24.9 Million
Wireless Lighting Systems
N.A.I.C.S.: 335139
Niclas Arwidsson *(Gen Mgr)*

LUMENS CO., LTD.
B-15F 58 Giheung-ro, Giheung-gu, Yongin, 16976, Gyeonggi-do, Korea (South)
Tel.: (82) 3180332000
Web Site: https://www.lumensleds.com
Year Founded: 2004
038060—(KRS)
Rev.: $127,555,849
Assets: $105,539,230
Liabilities: $33,689,150
Net Worth: $71,850,081
Earnings: $12,187,416
Emp.: 229
Fiscal Year-end: 12/31/22
LCD Products Mfr
N.A.I.C.S.: 334413
Damaged Hair *(Deputy Gen Mgr)*

Subsidiaries:

Soft-Epi, Inc.   (1)
240 Opo-ro Opo-eup, Gwangju, Gyeonggi-do, Korea (South)
Tel.: (82) 7049155500

LUMENS CO., LTD.

Lumens Co., Ltd.—(Continued)
Web Site: http://www.soft-epi.com
Semiconductor Devices Mfr
N.A.I.C.S.: 334413
Sung-min Hwang (Pres)

Topaz Co., Ltd. (1)
98 4SanDan3-Ro JikSan-Eup, Seobuk-gu, Cheonan, Chungcheongnam, Korea (South)
Tel.: (82) 419010000
Machine Tools Mfr
N.A.I.C.S.: 333517

LUMEX LTD.
Ul Obruchevykh 1 lit b, 195220, Saint Petersburg, Russia
Tel.: (7) 8123350336
Web Site:
http://www.lumexinstruments.com
Year Founded: 1991
Sales Range: $75-99.9 Million
Emp.: 400
Analytical Laboratory Instrument Mfr
N.A.I.C.S.: 334516
Alexander A. Stroganov (Pres)

Subsidiaries:

Ohio Lumex Co., Inc. (1)
9263 Ravenna Rd Ste A 3, Twinsburg, OH 44087
Tel.: (330) 405-0837
Web Site: http://www.ohiolumex.com
Sales Range: $25-49.9 Million
Emp.: 10
Analytical Laboratory Instrument Mfr
N.A.I.C.S.: 334516
Alexendra Sipershteyn (Dir-Mktg)

LUMI GRUPPEN AS
Sandakerveien 116, 0484, Oslo, Norway
Tel.: (47) 91504070   NO
Web Site:
https://www.lumigruppen.no
Year Founded: 1989
LUMI—(OSL)
Rev.: $39,053,390
Assets: $94,039,073
Liabilities: $52,433,216
Net Worth: $41,605,856
Earnings: ($25,516,996)
Emp.: 226
Fiscal Year-end: 12/31/23
Educational Support Services
N.A.I.C.S.: 611710
Erik Brandt (CEO)

Subsidiaries:

Norwegian School of Technology AS (1)
Pilestredet 56, 167, Oslo, Norway
Tel.: (47) 41260140
Web Site: https://ntech.no
Web Development & Design Education Services
N.A.I.C.S.: 611710

Oslo Nye Hoyskole AS (1)
Lovisenberggata 13, 456, Oslo, Norway
Tel.: (47) 23233820
Web Site: https://oslonyehoyskole.no
Research & Education Services
N.A.I.C.S.: 611710

Sonans Privatgymnas AS (1)
PO Box 943, 7409, Trondheim, Norway
Tel.: (47) 91504070
Web Site: https://sonans.no
Educational Program Services
N.A.I.C.S.: 611710

LUMI RENTAL COMPANY
Imam Saud bin Abdulaziz bin Muhammad Street, AlTaawun District, Riyadh, 12476, Saudi Arabia
Tel.: (966) 920028428
Web Site: https://www.lumirental.com
Year Founded: 2007
4262—(SAU)
Rev.: $208,649,425
Assets: $491,697,312
Liabilities: $266,809,014
Net Worth: $224,888,297
Earnings: $38,546,361
Emp.: 1,034
Fiscal Year-end: 12/31/22
Vehicle Rental Services
N.A.I.C.S.: 532120
Syed Mohammed Azfar Shakeel (CEO)

LUMIBIRD GROUP
2 rue Paul Sabatier, 22300, Lannion, France
Tel.: (33) 296050800
Web Site: https://www.lumibird.co
Year Founded: 1970
LBIRD—(EUR)
Rev.: $206,085,690
Assets: $401,515,217
Liabilities: $192,754,155
Net Worth: $208,761,062
Earnings: $12,252,320
Emp.: 1,001
Fiscal Year-end: 12/31/22
Solid-State Laser Developer & Mfr
N.A.I.C.S.: 335999
Marc Le Flohic (Chm & CEO)

Subsidiaries:

Big Sky Laser Technologies, Inc. (1)
601 Haggerty Ln Ste C, Bozeman, MT 59715
Tel.: (406) 586-0131
Web Site: http://www.quantelusa.com
Sales Range: $25-49.9 Million
Emp.: 55
Laser Product Mfr
N.A.I.C.S.: 334413
Bill Harn (CFO & Treas)

Ellex Australia Pty. Ltd. (1)
82 Gilbert St, Adelaide, 5000, SA, Australia   (100%)
Tel.: (61) 294821100
Sales Range: $75-99.9 Million
Emp.: 180
Diagnostic Ultrasound System Marketing Services
N.A.I.C.S.: 423450

EssMed AB (1)
Metallvagen 20, 435 33, Molnlycke, Sweden
Tel.: (46) 31 97 79 40
Web Site: http://www.essmed.se
Ophthalmology Products Distr
N.A.I.C.S.: 423450
Lars Gulijsson (Gen Mgr)

Halo Photonics Ltd. (1)
Unit 1 and 2 Bank Farm Brockamin, Leigh, WR6 5LA, Worcestershire, United Kingdom
Tel.: (44) 1886833489
Electrical Laser Mfr
N.A.I.C.S.: 335999

Keopsys Sa (1)
2 rue Paul Sabatier, 22300, Lannion, France
Tel.: (33) 296050800
Web Site: http://www.keopsys.com
Fiber Laser & Amplifier Mfr
N.A.I.C.S.: 335999
Marc Flohic (CEO)

Lumibird GmbH (1)
Worringer Str 30, 50668, Cologne, Germany
Tel.: (49) 221677856750
Electrical Laser Mfr
N.A.I.C.S.: 335999

Lumibird Japan Co., Ltd. (1)
Office Tower -0097 4-3-6-401 Nunobiki-cho, Chuo-ku, Tokyo, 104-6009, Japan
Tel.: (81) 363800390
Web Site: https://lumibird-japan.co.jp
Electrical Laser Mfr
N.A.I.C.S.: 335999
Takashi Kawauchi (Sls Mgr)

Lumibird Ltd. (1)
2680 Queensview Drive Suite 120, Ottawa, K2B 8J9, ON, Canada
Tel.: (613) 903-6350
Electrical Laser Mfr
N.A.I.C.S.: 335999
Nick Cristello (Mgr-R&D & Program)

Quantel Asia Pacific Ltd. (1)
Office No 3512 35F Central Plaza, 18 Harbour Road, Wanchai, China (Hong Kong)
Tel.: (852) 23661321
Web Site: http://www.quantel.com
Sales Range: $25-49.9 Million
Emp.: 5
Digital Technology Equipment Sales & Services
N.A.I.C.S.: 335999
Evita Won (Mgr-Engrg)

Quantel GmbH (1)
Worringer Str 30, 50668, Cologne, Germany
Tel.: (49) 221 677856750
Laser Mfr & Distr
N.A.I.C.S.: 335999
Norio Fukuda (Engr-Customer Support)

Quantel Laser Diodes (1)
Route de Nozay, BP 50005, Centre DATA 4, 91460, Marcoussis, Cedex, France
Tel.: (33) 1 6963 6896
Web Site: http://www.quantel-diodes.com
Sales Range: $1-9.9 Million
Emp.: 40
High-Power Laser Diodes Solutions
N.A.I.C.S.: 334413

Quantel Medical SA (1)
11 rue du Bois joli, CS 40015, 63808, Cournon-d'Auvergne, Cedex, France
Tel.: (33) 473745745
Web Site: http://www.quantel-medical.com
Sales Range: $25-49.9 Million
Emp.: 70
Medical Device Mfr
N.A.I.C.S.: 334519
Jean-Marc Gendre (CEO)

Quantel Medical, Inc. (1)
601 Haggerty Ln, Bozeman, MT 59715
Tel.: (406) 586-0424
Web Site: http://www.quantelmedical.com
Medical Device Mfr
N.A.I.C.S.: 334519

Sensup JSC (1)
4 Avenue des Peupliers - Batiment E, 35510, Cesson Sevigne, France
Tel.: (33) 299548978
Web Site: http://www.sensup-tech.com
Electrical Laser Mfr
N.A.I.C.S.: 335999
Pierre-Alain Tremblin (Project Mgr)

LUMIERA HEALTH INC.
26-4500 bl Kimber, Saint-Hubert, J3Y 8K5, QC, Canada
Web Site: http://www.mondias.ca
Year Founded: 2002
NHP—(TSXV)
Rev.: $493,341
Assets: $217,546
Liabilities: $1,797,898
Net Worth: ($1,580,352)
Earnings: ($2,167,163)
Fiscal Year-end: 11/30/22
Health Product Mfr
N.A.I.C.S.: 325411

LUMINA GOLD CORP.
410 - 625 Howe Street, Vancouver, V6C 2T6, BC, Canada
Tel.: (604) 646-1890   BC
Web Site:
https://www.luminagold.com
Year Founded: 1988
OMH2—(DEU)
Rev.: $198,497
Assets: $21,997,373
Liabilities: $29,964,895
Net Worth: $7,967,522
Earnings: ($17,252,512)
Fiscal Year-end: 12/31/23
Gold Exploration Services
N.A.I.C.S.: 213114
Marshall A. Koval (Pres & CEO)

Subsidiaries:

Condormining Corporation S.A. (1)
Catalina Aldaz No 34-131 Y Av Portugal, Quito, Ecuador
Tel.: (593) 2 333 2502
Metal Exploration Services
N.A.I.C.S.: 213114

LUMINA GROUP LIMITED
1/F and 6/F R&T Centre No 81-83 Larch Street Tai Kok Tsui, Kowloon, China (Hong Kong)
Tel.: (852) 2 305 5848   Ky
Web Site: http://www.lumina.com.hk
Year Founded: 2005
1162—(HKG)
Rev: $7,430,280
Assets: $18,799,738
Liabilities: $1,080,208
Net Worth: $17,719,530
Earnings: ($62,297)
Emp.: 40
Fiscal Year-end: 03/31/21
Security System Services
N.A.I.C.S.: 561621
Hau Fai Fok (Chm)

LUMINAR GROUP HOLDINGS PLC
Deltic Avenue Rooksley, Milton Keynes, MK13 8LW, United Kingdom
Tel.: (44) 1908544100   UK
Web Site: http://www.luminar.co.uk
Year Founded: 1988
Sales Range: $200-249.9 Million
Emp.: 2,699
Late-Night Leisure Venue Operator
N.A.I.C.S.: 722410
Tim Howard (Dir-Mktg)

Subsidiaries:

Liquid & Envy Portsmouth (1)
Connaught Drill Hall, Stanhope Road, Portsmouth, PO1 1DU, Hampshire, United Kingdom
Tel.: (44) 2392 862312
Web Site: http://www.liquidclubs.com
Sales Range: $25-49.9 Million
Emp.: 80
Night Clubs & Other Late Night Entertainment Services
N.A.I.C.S.: 722410
Bill Dearsley (Gen Mgr)

Luminar (1)
Luminar House Deltic Ave, Milton Keynes, MK13 8LW, Buckinghamshire, United Kingdom   (100%)
Tel.: (44) 1908544100
Web Site: http://www.luminar.co.uk
Sales Range: $25-49.9 Million
Emp.: 110
Operation of Dancing & Entertainment Businesses
N.A.I.C.S.: 611610
Peter Marks (CEO)

Luminar Dancing Scotland Ltd. (1)
1 Primrose Hill, Preston, United Kingdom   (100%)
Tel.: (44) 1772202626
Amusement & Recreation Industries
N.A.I.C.S.: 713990

Luminar Leisure Limited (1)
Luminar House Deltic Ave, Milton Keynes, MK13 8LW, United Kingdom   (100%)
Tel.: (44) 1908544253
Web Site: http://www.luminar.co.uk
Sales Range: $25-49.9 Million
Emp.: 150
Drinking Places
N.A.I.C.S.: 722410

LUMINAR MEDIA GROUP, INC.
260 Adelaide Street East Suite 177, Toronto, M5A 1N1, ON, Canada
Tel.: (347) 943-4835   DE
Web Site: http://www.luminarinc.com
Year Founded: 2010
LRGR—(OTCIQ)
Assets: $81,577
Liabilities: $202,759
Net Worth: ($121,182)

AND PRIVATE COMPANIES

Earnings: ($178,937)
Emp.: 2
Fiscal Year-end: 12/31/20
Investment Services
N.A.I.C.S.: 523999
Mirsad Jakubovic *(CFO)*

LUMINUS SYSTEMS LIMITED
349 Collins Street, Melbourne, 3000, VIC, Australia
Tel.: (61) 386148401
Web Site: http://www.luminussystems.com
Sales Range: Less than $1 Million
Emp.: 3
Digital Imaging & Data Management Technology Solutions
N.A.I.C.S.: 518210
Ian Pattison *(Deputy Chm, CFO & Sec)*

Subsidiaries:

Promim Pty Ltd. (1)
32 Miller St, Murarrie, 4172, QLD, Australia
Tel.: (61) 732922300
Web Site: http://www.promim.com.au
Emp.: 30
Hardware Installation & Maintenance Services
N.A.I.C.S.: 541513

LUMIRA CAPITAL CORP.
141 Adelaide Street Suite 770, Toronto, M5H 3L5, ON, Canada
Tel.: (416) 213-4223
Web Site: http://www.lumiraventures.com
Year Founded: 1988
Sales Range: $25-49.9 Million
Emp.: 15
Venture Capital Investment Services
N.A.I.C.S.: 523999
Jacki Jenuth *(Partner)*

LUMIRADX LIMITED
Windward 3 Regatta Office Park, PO Box 1350, Georgetown, KY1-1108, Cayman Islands
Tel.: (345) 6400540 Ky
Web Site: http://www.lumiradx.com
Year Founded: 2016
LMDX—(NASDAQ)
Rev.: $139,153,000
Assets: $515,095,000
Liabilities: $139,879,000
Net Worth: $375,216,000
Earnings: ($240,997,000)
Emp.: 1,022
Fiscal Year-end: 12/31/20
Biotechnology Research & Development Services
N.A.I.C.S.: 541714
Ron Zwanziger *(Co-Founder, Chm & CEO)*

LUMOS DIAGNOSTICS HOLDINGS LIMITED
Level 4 100 Albert Road, South Melbourne, 3205, VIC, Australia
Tel.: (61) 390871598 AU
Web Site: https://www.lumosdiagnostics.com
Year Founded: 2004
LDX—(ASX)
Rev.: $10,535,000
Assets: $25,419,000
Liabilities: $15,921,000
Net Worth: $9,498,000
Earnings: ($8,971,000)
Fiscal Year-end: 06/30/23
Holding Company
N.A.I.C.S.: 551112
Barrie Lambert *(CFO)*

Subsidiaries:

Lumos Diagnostics, Inc. (1)
2724 Loker Ave W, Carlsbad, CA 92010

Health Care Srvices
N.A.I.C.S.: 621498

LUMOSA THERAPEUTICS CO., LTD.
4th Floor No 3-2 Park Street, Nangang District, Taipei, 11503, Taiwan
Tel.: (886) 226557918
Web Site: https://www.lumosa.com.tw
Year Founded: 2000
6535—(TPE)
Rev.: $833,005
Assets: $58,959,072
Liabilities: $6,744,802
Net Worth: $52,214,270
Earnings: ($15,773,411)
Fiscal Year-end: 12/31/22
Biotechnology Research & Development Services
N.A.I.C.S.: 541714

LUMX GROUP LIMITED
Martello Court Admiral Park, Saint Peter Port, GY1 3HB, Guernsey
Tel.: (44) 1481 211 000 GY
Web Site: http://www.lumxgroup.com
Year Founded: 2007
Rev.: $8,256,000
Assets: $32,088,000
Liabilities: $16,923,000
Net Worth: $15,165,000
Earnings: ($8,652,000)
Emp.: 48
Fiscal Year-end: 12/31/18
Financial Investment Management Services
N.A.I.C.S.: 523940

LUNAR CAPITAL MANAGEMENT LTD.
HKRI Center One 41st Floor 288 Shimen Yi Road, No 227 North Huangpi Road, Shanghai, 200003, China
Tel.: (86) 21 6120 2080
Web Site: http://lunar.cn
Emp.: 30
Privater Equity Firm
N.A.I.C.S.: 523999
Y. R. Cheng *(Partner)*

Subsidiaries:

I Pinco Pallino S.p.A. (1)
Viale E Mattei 27/29, IT-24060, Entratico, BG, Italy
Tel.: (39) 035 4255 111
Web Site: http://www.ipincopallino.it
Sales Range: $10-24.9 Million
Luxury Children's Apparel Designer, Distr & Retailer
N.A.I.C.S.: 458110
Imelde Bronzieri Cavalleri *(Co-Founder)*

LUNDBECKFONDEN
Scherfigsvej 7, 2100, Copenhagen, Denmark
Tel.: (45) 3912 8000
Web Site: http://www.lundbeckfonden.com
Year Founded: 1954
Rev.: $5,253,351,300
Assets: $8,486,041,500
Liabilities: $3,215,843,700
Net Worth: $5,270,197,800
Earnings: $452,864,550
Emp.: 32,113
Fiscal Year-end: 12/31/18
Grantmaking Foundations
N.A.I.C.S.: 813211
Lene Skole *(CEO)*

Subsidiaries:

Lundbeckfond Invest A/S (1)
Scherfigsvej 7, 2100, Copenhagen, Denmark (100%)
Tel.: (45) 39128000
Investment Management Service
N.A.I.C.S.: 523940

Holding (Domestic):

A C Trafik A/S (2)
Kongebakken 1, Smorum, 2765, Denmark
Tel.: (45) 70235051
Food Transportation Services
N.A.I.C.S.: 488490

Holding (Non-US):

AB Previa (2)
S t Eriksgatan 113 V, Stockholm, Sweden
Tel.: (46) 77 123 00 00
Web Site: http://www.previa.se
Healtcare Services
N.A.I.C.S.: 621610

Holding (Domestic):

ALK-Abello A/S (2)
Boge Alle 6-8, DK-2970, Horsholm, Denmark (69%)
Tel.: (45) 45747576
Web Site: https://www.alk.net
Rev.: $576,259,370
Assets: $918,284,410
Liabilities: $397,818,700
Net Worth: $520,465,710
Earnings: $4,126,750
Emp.: 2,419
Fiscal Year-end: 12/31/2020
Allergy Vaccination Pharmaceutical Producer
N.A.I.C.S.: 325412
Lene Skole *(Vice Chm)*

Subsidiary (Non-US):

ALK - Abello Allergie-Service GmbH (3)
Backermuhlweg 59, 4030, Linz, Austria
Tel.: (43) 7323853720
Web Site: http://www.alk.net
Sales Range: $25-49.9 Million
Emp.: 25
Pharmaceuticals Product Mfr
N.A.I.C.S.: 325412

ALK - Abello Arzneimittel GmbH (3)
Griegstrasse 75 Haus 25, 22763, Hamburg, Germany
Tel.: (49) 407038450
Web Site: http://www.alk.de
Pharmaceutical Products Distr
N.A.I.C.S.: 424210

ALK - Abello Pharmaceuticals, Inc. (3)
35-151 Brunel Rd, Mississauga, L4Z 2H6, ON, Canada
Tel.: (905) 290-9952
Sales Range: $25-49.9 Million
Emp.: 15
Pharmaceuticals Product Mfr
N.A.I.C.S.: 325412

ALK Slovakia s.r.o. (3)
Tomasikova 64 Lake Side Park-10 floor, 831 04, Bratislava, Slovakia
Tel.: (421) 254650371
Web Site: http://www.alk.net
Pharmaceuticals Product Mfr
N.A.I.C.S.: 325412

ALK Sverige AB (3)
Smorhalevagen 3, Box 10073, Kungsbacka, SE-434 21, Sweden
Tel.: (46) 30018545
Web Site: http://www.alk.se
Sales Range: $25-49.9 Million
Emp.: 20
Allergy Treatment Products
N.A.I.C.S.: 325412
Hans Lindbergs *(Gen Mgr)*

ALK-Abello AG (3)
Industriestrasse 30, 8604, Volketswil, Switzerland
Tel.: (41) 449082100
Sales Range: $25-49.9 Million
Emp.: 14
Pharmaceutical Products Distr
N.A.I.C.S.: 424210

ALK-Abello B.V. (3)
Transistorstraat 23-2, 1322 CK, Almere, Netherlands
Tel.: (31) 36 539 78 40
Pharmaceuticals Product Mfr
N.A.I.C.S.: 325412

LUNDBECKFONDEN

ALK-Abello GmbH (3)
Backermuhlweg 59, Linz, 4030, Austria
Tel.: (43) 732385372
Web Site: http://www.alk-abello.com
Sales Range: $25-49.9 Million
Emp.: 20
Allergy Treatment Products
N.A.I.C.S.: 325412
Guenther Herpel *(Mng Dir)*

ALK-Abello Ltd. (3)
1 Tealgate, Hungerford, RG17 OYT, Berkshire, United Kingdom
Tel.: (44) 1488 68 60 16
Pharmaceuticals Product Mfr
N.A.I.C.S.: 325412

ALK-Abello Nordic A/S (3)
Linnoitustie 4, 02600, Espoo, Finland
Tel.: (358) 958422120
Web Site: http://www.alk.fi
Sales Range: $25-49.9 Million
Emp.: 2
Pharmaceuticals Product Mfr
N.A.I.C.S.: 325412

ALK-Abello Nordic A/S (3)
Skarersletta 18, 1473, Lorenskog, Norway
Tel.: (47) 99446040
Web Site: http://www.alk.no
Sales Range: $25-49.9 Million
Emp.: 6
Pharmaceuticals Product Mfr
N.A.I.C.S.: 325412

ALK-Abello S.A. (3)
Miguel Fleta 19, 28037, Madrid, Spain
Tel.: (34) 913276100
Web Site: http://www.alk.net
Sales Range: $50-74.9 Million
Emp.: 200
Allergy Treatment Products
N.A.I.C.S.: 325412

Subsidiary (Non-US):

ALK-Abello S.p.A. (4)
Via Nino Bixio 31, 20129, Milah, MI, Italy
Tel.: (39) 02937631
Web Site: http://www.alk.it
Sales Range: $25-49.9 Million
Emp.: 44
Allergy Treatment Products
N.A.I.C.S.: 325412

Subsidiary (Non-US):

ALK-Abello bv (3)
Transistorstraat 25, 1322 CK, Almere, Netherlands
Tel.: (31) 365397840
Web Site: http://www.alk.net
Sales Range: $25-49.9 Million
Emp.: 40
Allergy Treatment Products
N.A.I.C.S.: 325412

ALK-Abello sp. z.o.o. (3)
AL Pokoju 1, 31-548, Krakow, Poland
Tel.: (48) 123484000
Web Site: http://www.alk.net
Pharmaceuticals Product Mfr
N.A.I.C.S.: 325412

Subsidiary (US):

ALK-Abello, Inc. (3)
1700 Royston Ln, Round Rock, TX 78664
Tel.: (512) 251-0037
Web Site: http://www.alk-abello.us
Sales Range: $25-49.9 Million
Emp.: 75
Allergy Treatment Products
N.A.I.C.S.: 325412
Jorge Alderete *(Pres & Sr VP-Comml Ops)*

Subsidiary (Domestic):

Vespa Laboratories, Inc. (4)
Upper Georges Valley Rd, Spring Mills, PA 16875
Tel.: (814) 422-8165
Web Site: http://www.alkabello.com
Sales Range: $25-49.9 Million
Emp.: 20
Developer & Mfr of Hymenoptera Venoms for the Diagnosis & Treatment of Insect Sting Allergic Disease
N.A.I.C.S.: 325414
Miles Guralnick *(Pres)*

LUNDBECKFONDEN

Lundbeckfonden—(Continued)

Joint Venture (Non-US):

ALK-Scherax Arzneimittel GmbH (3)
PO Box 22876, Wedel, Germany
Tel.: (49) 408707070
Web Site: http://www.alkscherax.de
Sales Range: $25-49.9 Million
Emp.: 83
Allergy Treatment Sales
N.A.I.C.S.: 424210

Holding (Non-US):

ASG Ambulanz Leipzig GmbH (2)
Zschochersche Str 79C, 04229, Leipzig, Germany
Tel.: (49) 34149071
Healtcare Services
N.A.I.C.S.: 621610

AVD Consultancy N.V. (2)
Burgemeester Den Texlaan 50, 2111 CE, Aerdenhout, Netherlands
Tel.: (31) 620390322
Healtcare Services
N.A.I.C.S.: 621610

Holding (US):

Alford Safety Services, Inc. (2)
201 Clendenning Rd, Houma, LA 70363
Tel.: (985) 868-1860
Emp.: 20
Energy Equipment Mfr
N.A.I.C.S.: 334515
Bryan Lecompte (CEO)

Alford Services, Inc (2)
PO Box 516, Gunter, TX 75058
Tel.: (903) 433-1454
Web Site: http://www.alfordservicesinc.com
Residential Property Leasing Services
N.A.I.C.S.: 531311

Holding (Non-US):

CNS Pharma Pty Ltd. (2)
Level 5 Deutsche Bank Place 126 Phillip Street, Sydney, 2000, NSW, Australia
Tel.: (61) 286691068
Web Site: http://www.cnspharma.com.au
Pharmaceuticals Product Mfr
N.A.I.C.S.: 325412

EMI Panama S.A. (2)
El Dorado Cl 4 Edif Emi, Panama, Panama
Tel.: (507) 2366060
Healtcare Services
N.A.I.C.S.: 621610

Holding (Domestic):

Falck A/S (2)
Sydhavnsgade 18, DK-2450, Copenhagen, Denmark (59.15%)
Tel.: (45) 70333311
Web Site: http://www.falck.com
Rev.: $2,032,300,500
Assets: $1,889,411,550
Liabilities: $1,551,409,500
Net Worth: $338,002,050
Earnings: $(140,132,250)
Emp.: 14,000
Fiscal Year-end: 12/31/2018
Rescue & Safety Services
N.A.I.C.S.: 621910
Peter Schutze (Chm)

Subsidiary (Domestic):

ActivCare A/S (3)
Rojelskaer 11 2nd floor, 2840, Holte, Denmark
Tel.: (45) 70203000
Web Site: http://www.activcare.dk
Healtcare Services
N.A.I.C.S.: 621610
Gitte Hoelstad (Mgr-Fin)

Subsidiary (Non-US):

Falck AVD B.V. (3)
De Waal 28, Best, 5684 PH, Netherlands
Tel.: (31) 499 32 84 00
Fire & Ambulance Services
N.A.I.C.S.: 922160

Falck Aktiv Arbetsmedicin AB (3)
Box 3086, Stockholm, 103 61, Sweden
Tel.: (46) 84066700
Healtcare Services
N.A.I.C.S.: 621610
Stefan Pettersson (CEO)

Falck Chile S.A. (3)
La Concepcion 141 of 905, Providencia, Santiago, Chile
Tel.: (56) 2 2481 1780
Web Site: http://www.falck.cl
Fire & Ambulance Services
N.A.I.C.S.: 922160

Falck Emergency Services UK Ltd. (3)
Walker House George Street, Aylesbury, HP20 2HU, Bucks, United Kingdom
Tel.: (44) 1296 399311
Healtcare Services
N.A.I.C.S.: 621610

Falck Emergency a.s. (3)
Havlickova 2034, 580 01, Havlickuv Brod, Czech Republic
Tel.: (420) 569425113
Healtcare Services
N.A.I.C.S.: 621610

Falck Fire & Safety do Brasil S.A. (3)
Av Das Americas 3500 Edificio Hong Kong 2000, Condominio Empresarial Le Monde-Barra da Tijuca, Rio de Janeiro, 22640-102, Brazil
Tel.: (55) 2135130711
Fire & Ambulance Services
N.A.I.C.S.: 922160
Jens Gaardsvig (CFO)

Falck Fire Services NL B.V. (3)
Embankment 17, 3534 BD, Utrecht, Netherlands
Tel.: (31) 402304190
Fire & Ambulance Services
N.A.I.C.S.: 922160

Falck Global Assistance AB (3)
Mejerivagen 9, 117 43, Stockholm, Sweden
Tel.: (46) 858771717
Web Site: http://www.falck.com
Healtcare Services
N.A.I.C.S.: 621610

Falck Global Assistance Norway AS (3)
Maridalsveien 300, Serviceboks 4900 Nydalen, 0423, Oslo, Norway
Tel.: (47) 21492415
Healtcare Services
N.A.I.C.S.: 621610

Falck Healthcare AB (3)
Sveavagen 17 7th floor, 111 57, Stockholm, Sweden
Tel.: (46) 771505080
Web Site: http://www.falcksverige.se
Healtcare Services
N.A.I.C.S.: 621610

Subsidiary (Domestic):

Falck Hjaelpemidler A/S (3)
Gydevang 2D, 3450, Allerod, Denmark
Tel.: (45) 48171355
Web Site: http://www.falckhm.dk
Healtcare Services
N.A.I.C.S.: 621610

Subsidiary (Non-US):

Falck Holding B.V. (3)
Spoordijk 17, 3534 BD, Utrecht, Netherlands
Tel.: (31) 30 2427070
Healtcare Services
N.A.I.C.S.: 621610

Falck India Limited (3)
Upper Floor The Peach Tree Blok - C Sushant Lok - 1, Gurgaon, 122015, Haryana, India
Tel.: (91) 124 4498777
Healtcare Services
N.A.I.C.S.: 621610
Imrat Singh (Dir-Ops)

Falck Nutec (Thailand) Ltd (3)
919 Moo2 Tamboon Taibaan, Amphur Muang, 10280, Samut Prakan, Thailand
Tel.: (66) 27039773
Web Site: http://www.falck.com
Healtcare Services

N.A.I.C.S.: 621610

Falck Nutec AS (3)
Gravdalsveien 255, PO Box 6, Ytre Laksevag, 5848, Bergen, Norway
Tel.: (47) 55942000
Web Site: http://www.falcknutec.no
Healtcare Services
N.A.I.C.S.: 621610
Thomas Iversen (Mgr-Stavanger Center)

Falck Nutec B.V (3)
Beerweg 101 Harbour no 7033, Maasvlakte, Rotterdam, 3199 LM, Netherlands
Tel.: (31) 18 137 6666
Healtcare Services
N.A.I.C.S.: 621610

Falck Nutec Brasil Treinamentos em Seguranca Maritima Ltda (3)
Av Prefeito Aristeu Ferreira da Silva, 1277 Novo Cavaleiros, Macae, 27930-070, Brazil
Tel.: (55) 2221053361
Healtcare Services
N.A.I.C.S.: 621610
Furtado Lima (Mgr-Tech)

Falck Nutec Vietnam Limited (3)
Dong Xuyen IP No 11 Street, Rach Dua Ward, Vung Tau, Ba Ria-Vung Tau, Vietnam
Tel.: (84) 643616080
Healtcare Services
N.A.I.C.S.: 621610

Falck Oy (3)
Malmin kauppatie 8, Helsinki, 00700, Finland
Tel.: (358) 10 024 00
Web Site: http://www.falck.fi
Emp.: 50
Ambulance Service
N.A.I.C.S.: 621910
Maiju Pesonen (Mgr-Svc)

Subsidiary (Non-US):

Falck Autoabi OU (4)
Laki 11, 12915, Tallinn, Estonia
Tel.: (372) 6979179
Web Site: http://www.falck.ee
Healtcare Services
N.A.I.C.S.: 621610

Subsidiary (Non-US):

Falck Pharma s.r.o. (3)
J Jonasa 1, 843 02, Bratislava, Slovakia
Tel.: (421) 220868780
Healtcare Services
N.A.I.C.S.: 621610

Falck Pty Ltd. (3)
15 Catalano Road, Canning Vale, 6155, WA, Australia
Tel.: (61) 8 9452 6500
Web Site: http://www.falck.com.au
Healtcare Services
N.A.I.C.S.: 621610

Falck SCI, S.A. (3)
Av de las Cortes Valencianas 58, Sorolla Center local 10, 46015, Valencia, Spain
Tel.: (34) 963 540 300
Web Site: http://www.falck.es
Healtcare Services
N.A.I.C.S.: 621610

Falck SK a.s. (3)
Galvaniho ul 7/D, 82104, Bratislava, Slovakia
Tel.: (421) 232663501
Healtcare Services
N.A.I.C.S.: 621610
Maria Bokorova (Mgr-Mktg)

Falck Sverige Holding AB (3)
Forradsvagen 2, Lidingo, 181 41, Stockholm, Sweden
Tel.: (46) 8 7814070
Holding Company
N.A.I.C.S.: 551112

Falck UK Limited (3)
Foinavon Close Aberdeen Airport Dyce, Aberdeen, AB21 7EG, United Kingdom
Tel.: (44) 8444 142 142
Healtcare Services
N.A.I.C.S.: 621610

Subsidiary (US):

Falck USA, Inc. (3)

INTERNATIONAL PUBLIC

21540 30th Dr SE Ste 250, Bothell, WA 98021
Tel.: (855) 385-2591
Healtcare Services
N.A.I.C.S.: 621610

Subsidiary (Domestic):

Allergy Laboratories, Inc. (4)
1005 SW Second St, Oklahoma City, OK 73109
Tel.: (405) 235-1451
Web Site: http://www.allergylabs.com
Rev.: $6,666,666
Emp.: 30
Biological Product, except Diagnostic, Mfr
N.A.I.C.S.: 325414
Eric Bell (Mgr-Quality Control)

American Ambulance Service, Inc. (4)
6605 NW 74th Ave, Miami, FL 33166
Tel.: (305) 925-2000
Web Site: http://www.americanambulancesvc.com
Sales Range: $10-24.9 Million
Ambulance Service
N.A.I.C.S.: 621910
Charles Maymon (Pres & Co-CEO)

Cape Cod Medica Enterprises, Inc. (4)
62 Locust St Office, Falmouth, MA 02540
Tel.: (508) 775-0494
Ambulance Service
N.A.I.C.S.: 621910
Leo F. Gildea (Pres)

Care Ambulance Service, Inc. (4)
W Braden Ct, Orange, CA 92868-1125
Tel.: (714) 288-3800
Web Site: http://www.careambulance.net
Ambulance Service
N.A.I.C.S.: 621910
Bob Barry (Dir-Pub Affairs)

Falck Global Assistance LLC (4)
3210 Lake Emma Rd Ste 3090, Lake Mary, FL 32746
Web Site: http://www.falck.com
Medical, Security Risk Management & Crisis Management Services
N.A.I.C.S.: 812990
Claes Bloch Larsen (Dir-Global Ops)

Falck Northern California Corp. (4)
2190 S McDowell Blvd, Petaluma, CA 94954
Ambulance Service
N.A.I.C.S.: 621910
Chris Le Baudour (Gen Mgr)

Falck Northwest Corp. (4)
6405 218th St SW Ste 201, Mountlake Terrace, WA 98043
Tel.: (425) 248-4100
Ambulance Service
N.A.I.C.S.: 621910

Home Care Equipment, Inc. (4)
201 Center Park Dr, Knoxville, TN 37922
Tel.: (865) 966-2273
Health Care Services
N.A.I.C.S.: 621610

Robinson's Ambulance & Oxygen Service, Inc. (4)
920-14 Lincoln Ave, Holbrook, NY 11741
Tel.: (631) 289-1982
Web Site: http://www.robinsonsoxygen.com
Healtcare Services
N.A.I.C.S.: 621610

Subsidiary (Non-US):

Falck VL Servicios Sanitarios, S.L (3)
Pol Ind Coll de la Manya, 08403, Granollers, Spain
Tel.: (34) 902232022
Healtcare Services
N.A.I.C.S.: 621610

Falck Zachranna a.s. (3)
Baclkova 7, 040 01, Kosice, Slovakia
Tel.: (421) 55 28 13 300
Web Site: http://www.falck-zachranna.sk
Healtcare Services
N.A.I.C.S.: 621610

Falck fire Services DE GmbH (3)

AND PRIVATE COMPANIES

LUNDBECKFONDEN

Holstenhofweg 47b, 22043, Hamburg, Germany
Tel.: (49) 406695544620
Healtcare Services
N.A.I.C.S.: 621610

Subsidiary (Domestic):

Vikteam A/S (3)
Kongensgade 31 1 sal, 6700, Esbjerg, Denmark
Tel.: (45) 79141100
Web Site: http://www.vikteam.dk
Healtcare Services
N.A.I.C.S.: 621610
Kamilla Thuesen *(Country Mgr)*

Holding (Domestic):

H. Lundbeck A/S (2)
Ottiliavej 9, 2500, Valby, Denmark **(70%)**
Tel.: (45) 36301311
Web Site: https://www.lundbeck.com
Rev.: $2,917,117,040
Assets: $5,947,307,030
Liabilities: $3,145,573,920
Net Worth: $2,801,733,110
Earnings: $260,975,670
Emp.: 5,628
Fiscal Year-end: 12/31/2020
Holding Company; Brain Disease Pharmaceutical Research & Development, Mfr & Distr
N.A.I.C.S.: 551112
Anders Gotzsche *(CFO & Exec VP)*

Subsidiary (Non-US):

Falck Kazakhstan LLP (3)
Pushkina Street 64/30 ch A, Almaty, 050010, Kazakhstan
Tel.: (7) 727 291 77 88
Healtcare Services
N.A.I.C.S.: 621610
Eduard Li *(Dir-Fin & Bus Dev)*

H. Lundbeck A/S - Saudi Arabia (3)
Al Mousa Comml Housing Ctr Tower 3, Office No 221 A 2nd Fl, Riyadh, 11537, Saudi Arabia
Tel.: (966) 14610748
Web Site: http://www.lundbeck.com
Sales Range: $25-49.9 Million
Emp.: 17
Pharmaceutical Preparations
N.A.I.C.S.: 325412

Plant (Domestic):

H. Lundbeck A/S Lumsas (3)
Oddenvej 182 Lumsaas, Nykobing, 2500, Denmark
Tel.: (45) 3643 7000
Web Site: http://www.lundbeck.com
Sales Range: $100-124.9 Million
Emp.: 255
Pharmaceutical Preparations
N.A.I.C.S.: 325412
Paul Poyo Pahlperd *(Mng Dir)*

Subsidiary (Non-US):

H. Lundbeck AB (3)
Slagthuset Carlsgatan 12A, PO Box 23, 211 20, Malmo, Sweden
Tel.: (46) 406998200
Web Site: http://www.lundbeck.com
Sales Range: $25-49.9 Million
Emp.: 50
Pharmaceutical Preparations
N.A.I.C.S.: 325412

H. Lundbeck AS (3)
Strandveien 15, 1366, Lysaker, Norway
Tel.: (47) 91300800
Web Site: http://www.lundbeck.com
Sales Range: $25-49.9 Million
Emp.: 20
Pharmaceutical Preparations
N.A.I.C.S.: 325412

Lundbeck (Beijing) Pharmaceuticals Consulting Co., Ltd. (3)
Unit 03-06 12th Floor Tower A Beijing Chyau, Fwu Fang Cao Di No 9 Dong Da Qiao Road Chaoyang District, 100020, Beijing, China
Tel.: (86) 1058750088
Pharmaceutical Products Distr
N.A.I.C.S.: 424210

Lundbeck (Ireland) Limited (3)
4045 Kingswood RoadCitywest Business Park, Citywestco, D24 VO6K, Dublin, Ireland
Tel.: (353) 14689800
Web Site: http://www.lundbeck.com
Sales Range: $25-49.9 Million
Emp.: 11
Pharmaceutical Preparations
N.A.I.C.S.: 325412

Lundbeck (Schweiz) AG (3)
Balz-Zimmermann-Strasse 7 Zurich Airport, PO Box 5, Flughafen, 8058, Zurich, Switzerland **(100%)**
Tel.: (41) 582698181
Web Site: http://www.lundbeck.com
Sales Range: $25-49.9 Million
Emp.: 50
Pharmaceutical Preparations
N.A.I.C.S.: 325412

Lundbeck America Central S.A. (3)
Torre de las Americas Torre B Piso 6, Oficina 603, Panama, Panama
Tel.: (507) 2015556
Pharmaceutical Products Distr
N.A.I.C.S.: 424210
Itzel Herrera Batista *(Dir-Reg Sls)*

Lundbeck Argentina S.A. (3)
Dart Rocha 2858, Piso 2 Martinez, B1640FTR, Buenos Aires, Argentina
Tel.: (54) 1148360280
Web Site: http://www.lundbeck.com
Sales Range: $25-49.9 Million
Emp.: 50
Pharmaceutical Preparations
N.A.I.C.S.: 325412

Lundbeck Australia Pty Ltd. (3)
1 Innovation Road, North Ryde, 2113, NSW, Australia
Tel.: (61) 286691000
Web Site: http://www.lundbeck.com
Sales Range: $25-49.9 Million
Emp.: 25
Pharmaceutical Preparation Mfr
N.A.I.C.S.: 325412

Lundbeck Austria GmbH (3)
Mooslackengasse 17, 1190, Vienna, Austria
Tel.: (43) 12669108
Web Site: http://www.lundbeck.com
Sales Range: $25-49.9 Million
Emp.: 50
Pharmaceutical Preparations
N.A.I.C.S.: 325412

Lundbeck B.V. (3)
Herikerbergweg 292, PO Box 12021, 1101 CT, Amsterdam, Netherlands
Tel.: (31) 206971901
Web Site: http://www.lundbeck.com
Sales Range: $25-49.9 Million
Emp.: 50
Pharmaceutical Preparation Mfr
N.A.I.C.S.: 325412

Lundbeck Brasil Ltda. (3)
Joao Cabral de Mello Neto Avenue 400, Barra Da Tijuca, 1201, Rio de Janeiro, RJ, Brazil
Tel.: (55) 2138733000
Web Site: http://www.lundbeck.com
Sales Range: $25-49.9 Million
Emp.: 80
Pharmaceutical Preparations
N.A.I.C.S.: 325412

Lundbeck Business Service Centre Sp.z.o.o (3)
Al Bora-Komorowskiego 25c, 31-476, Krakow, Poland
Tel.: (48) 123486888
Pharmaceutical Products Distr
N.A.I.C.S.: 424210
Marcin Mlynarczyk *(Head-Fin)*

Lundbeck Canada, Inc. (3)
2600 Alfred-Nobel Boulevard Suite 400, Saint Laurent, H4S 0A9, QC, Canada **(100%)**
Tel.: (514) 844-8515
Web Site: https://www.lundbeck.com
Sales Range: $25-49.9 Million
Emp.: 60
Pharmaceutical Preparation Mfr
N.A.I.C.S.: 325412

Lundbeck Chile Farmaceutica Ltda. (3)
Ave Vitacura 5250 Officina 401 Vitacura, Santiago, Chile
Tel.: (56) 229538500
Web Site: http://www.lundbeck.com
Sales Range: $25-49.9 Million
Emp.: 15
Pharmaceutical Preparations
N.A.I.C.S.: 325412

Lundbeck Croatia Ltd. (3)
5th floor Grand Centar Hektoroviceva ulica 2, 10000, Zagreb, Croatia
Tel.: (385) 16448264
Web Site: http://www.lundbeck.com
Sales Range: $25-49.9 Million
Emp.: 7
Pharmaceutical Preparations
N.A.I.C.S.: 325412

Lundbeck Czech Republic s.r.o. (3)
Bozdechova 7, 150 00, Prague, Czech Republic
Tel.: (420) 225275600
Web Site: http://www.lundbeck.cz
Sales Range: $25-49.9 Million
Emp.: 15
Pharmaceutical Preparations
N.A.I.C.S.: 325412

Lundbeck Eesti A/S (3)
Weizenbergi 29, Tallinn, 10150, Estonia **(100%)**
Tel.: (372) 6059350
Web Site: http://www.lundbeck.com
Sales Range: $1-9.9 Million
Emp.: 5
Pharmaceutical Preparations
N.A.I.C.S.: 325412
Karin Toomela *(Country Mgr)*

Lundbeck Espana S.A. (3)
Av Diagonal 605 7-2 a, 08028, Barcelona, Spain
Tel.: (34) 934949620
Web Site: http://www.lundbeck.com
Sales Range: $50-74.9 Million
Emp.: 130
Pharmaceutical Preparations
N.A.I.C.S.: 325412

Subsidiary (Domestic):

Lundbeck Export A/S (3)
Ottiliavej 9, 2500, Valby, Denmark
Tel.: (45) 36301311
Web Site: http://www.lundbeck.com
Sales Range: $1-4.9 Billion
Pharmaceutical Preparations
N.A.I.C.S.: 325412

Subsidiary (Non-US):

Lundbeck Export A/S (3)
Armula 1, 108, Reykjavik, Iceland
Tel.: (354) 4147070
Web Site: http://www.lundbeck.com
Sales Range: $25-49.9 Million
Emp.: 3
Pharmaceutical Preparations
N.A.I.C.S.: 325412

Lundbeck Export A/S (3)
Horoshovskoe shosse Building 32A, Moscow, 103031, Russia
Tel.: (7) 4952472646
Web Site: http://www.lundbeck.com
Pharmaceutical Preparations
N.A.I.C.S.: 325412

Lundbeck Export A/S (3)
Sportivnaya 1a Square, 01601, Kiev, Ukraine **(100%)**
Tel.: (380) 444902910
Web Site: http://www.lundbeck.com
Sales Range: $1-9.9 Million
Emp.: 29
Pharmaceutical Preparations
N.A.I.C.S.: 325412

Lundbeck Export A/S (3)
MPC Building No 71-Ibn Ishaaq Office No 1F-16, PO Box 49886, Dubai, United Arab Emirates **(100%)**
Tel.: (971) 45502100
Web Site: http://www.lundbeck.com
Sales Range: $25-49.9 Million
Emp.: 16
Pharmaceutical Preparations
N.A.I.C.S.: 325412

Lundbeck Export A/S-Central European Regional Office (3)
Dresdner Strasse 82, 1200, Vienna, Austria
Tel.: (43) 1331070
Web Site: http://www.lundbeck.at
Sales Range: $25-49.9 Million
Emp.: 100
Pharmaceutical Preparations
N.A.I.C.S.: 325412

Lundbeck Export A/S-Southern Europe Regional Office (3)
Via Sequals 15, Labaro, 00188, Rome, Italy
Tel.: (39) 063361751
Web Site: http://www.lundbeck.com
Pharmaceutical Preparations
N.A.I.C.S.: 325412

Lundbeck GmbH (3)
Ericussspitze 2, 20457, Hamburg, Germany
Tel.: (49) 40236490
Web Site: http://www.lundbeck.com
Sales Range: $50-74.9 Million
Emp.: 115
Pharmaceutical Preparation Mfr
N.A.I.C.S.: 325412

Lundbeck Group Limited (Holding company) (3)
Lundbeck House Caldecotte Lk Bus Pk, Caldecotte, Milton Keynes, MK7 8LG, United Kingdom
Tel.: (44) 908649966
Pharmaceutical Preparations
N.A.I.C.S.: 325412

Lundbeck Hellas S.A. (3)
109 Kifisias Avenue, Athens, 15124, Greece
Tel.: (30) 2106105036
Web Site: http://www.lundbeck.com
Sales Range: $25-49.9 Million
Emp.: 65
Pharmaceutical Preparations
N.A.I.C.S.: 325412
Peter Anastasiou *(Exec VP-North America)*

Lundbeck Hong Kong (3)
Suite 4303 43/F Central Plaza 18 Harbour Road, Wanchai, China (Hong Kong) **(100%)**
Tel.: (852) 22448888
Web Site: http://www.lundbeck.com
Sales Range: $1-9.9 Million
Pharmaceutical Preparations
N.A.I.C.S.: 325412

Lundbeck Hungaria Kft. (3)
Szechenyi Istvan ter 7, 1051, Budapest, Hungary
Tel.: (36) 14369980
Web Site: http://www.lundbeck.com
Sales Range: $25-49.9 Million
Emp.: 17
Pharmaceutical Preparations
N.A.I.C.S.: 325412

Lundbeck Ilac Ticaret Limited Sirketi (3)
FSM Mah Poligon Caddesi Buyaka 2 Sitesi, No 8 1 Blok Kat 7 Umraniye, 34771, Istanbul, Kavacik Beykoz, Turkiye
Tel.: (90) 2165389600
Web Site: http://www.lundbeck.com
Sales Range: $25-49.9 Million
Emp.: 100
Pharmaceutical Preparations
N.A.I.C.S.: 325412

Lundbeck India Private Limited (3)
H M Towers I Floor Ste 58 Brigade Road Kodihalli BDA HAL II Stage, Bengaluru, 560 025, India
Tel.: (91) 8046544777
Web Site: http://www.lundbeck.com
Sales Range: $25-49.9 Million
Emp.: 20
Pharmaceutical Preparations
N.A.I.C.S.: 325412

Lundbeck Iran (3)
Unit No 1102 Anahita Buildiing, 184 Africa Expressway, Tehran, 1917643186, Iran
Tel.: (98) 21 879 4000
Web Site: http://www.lundbeck.com
Pharmaceutical Preparations
N.A.I.C.S.: 325412

Lundbeck Israel Ltd. (3)
4 Derech Hashalom, PO Box 7382, Tel Aviv, 61073, Israel
Tel.: (972) 39100100
Web Site: http://www.lundbeck.com

LUNDBECKFONDEN

Lundbeckfonden—(Continued)
Sales Range: $25-49.9 Million
Emp.: 15
Pharmaceutical Preparations
N.A.I.C.S.: 325412

Lundbeck Italia S.p.A. (3)
Via Joe Colombo 2, 20124, Milan,
Italy (100%)
Tel.: (39) 026774171
Web Site: http://www.lundbeck.com
Sales Range: $25-49.9 Million
Emp.: 34
Pharmaceutical Preparations
N.A.I.C.S.: 325412

Lundbeck Japan Kabushiki Kaisha (3)
7th floor Toto Building 1-4-4 Toranomon 5-chome, Minato-ku, Tokyo, 105-0001, Japan
Tel.: (81) 357338690
Web Site: http://www.lundbeck.com
Sales Range: $25-49.9 Million
Pharmaceutical Preparations
N.A.I.C.S.: 325412

Lundbeck Korea Co., Ltd. (3)
19F Korea AD Culture Center 137 Olympic-ro 35-gil, Songpa-gu, Seoul, 05510, Korea (South)
Tel.: (82) 24316600
Web Site: http://www.lundbeck.com
Sales Range: $25-49.9 Million
Emp.: 60
Pharmaceutical Preparations
N.A.I.C.S.: 325412
Pilsoo Oh (Mng Dir)

Lundbeck Limited (3)
2nd Floor Building 3 Abbey View Everard Close, Saint Albans, AL1 2PS, Hertfordshire, United Kingdom
Tel.: (44) 1908649966
Web Site: http://www.lundbeck.com
Sales Range: $25-49.9 Million
Emp.: 60
Pharmaceutical Preparation Mfr
N.A.I.C.S.: 325412

Lundbeck Malaysia (3)
A-05-01 Oasis Square Jalan PJU 1A/7A Ara Damansara, 47301, Petaling Jaya, Selangor Darul Ehsan, Malaysia
Tel.: (60) 78313060
Web Site: http://www.lundbeck.com
Sales Range: $25-49.9 Million
Emp.: 14
Pharmaceutical Preparations
N.A.I.C.S.: 325412

Lundbeck Mexico SA de CV (3)
Av Insurgentes Sur 1605 Piso 28 de Torre Mural, Col San Jose Insurgentes, 03900, Mexico, DF, Mexico
Tel.: (52) 5550626900
Web Site: http://www.lundbeck.com
Sales Range: $25-49.9 Million
Emp.: 100
Pharmaceutical Preparations
N.A.I.C.S.: 325412

Lundbeck Middle East A/S (3)
Regus 90 Kifisias Av, 15125, Maroussi, Greece
Tel.: (30) 2108099797
Web Site: http://www.lundbeck.com
Pharmaceutical Preparations
N.A.I.C.S.: 325412

Lundbeck Pakistan (Private) Limited (3)
40 T/4 Blessing Street Block-6 PECHS, 75400, Karachi, Pakistan (100%)
Tel.: (92) 2134392570
Web Site: http://www.lundbeck.com
Sales Range: $25-49.9 Million
Emp.: 27
Pharmaceutical Preparations
N.A.I.C.S.: 325412

Lundbeck Peru S.A.C. (3)
Av Camino Real 390, Torre Central Of 801, 1075, Lima, Peru
Tel.: (51) 12225252
Pharmaceutical Products Distr
N.A.I.C.S.: 424210

Subsidiary (Domestic):

Lundbeck Pharma A/S (3)
Ottiliavej 9, 2500, Valby, Denmark
Tel.: (45) 43714270
Web Site: http://www.lundbeck.com
Sales Range: $25-49.9 Million
Emp.: 1,800
Pharmaceutical Preparations
N.A.I.C.S.: 325412

Subsidiary (Non-US):

Lundbeck Pharma d.o.o. (3)
Titova c 8, 2000, Maribor, Slovenia (100%)
Tel.: (386) 22294500
Web Site: http://www.lundbeck.com
Sales Range: $400-449.9 Million
Emp.: 1,513
Pharmaceutical Preparations
N.A.I.C.S.: 325412
Valeria Bale Bable (Mng Dir)

Lundbeck Pharmaceuticals (Tianjin) Co., Ltd. (3)
Building D12-2 Saida International Industry Town, Xiqing Econmic Development District, Tianjin, 300385, China
Tel.: (86) 2287204906
Pharmaceutical Products Distr
N.A.I.C.S.: 424210

Lundbeck Pharmaceuticals Ireland Limited (3)
7 Riverwalk Citywest Business Campus, Dublin, Ireland
Tel.: (353) 14689800
Pharmaceutical Products Distr
N.A.I.C.S.: 424210

Lundbeck Pharmaceuticals Limited (3)
Lundbeck House, Caldecotte Lake Business Park, Milton Keynes, MK7 8LG, Bucks, United Kingdom
Tel.: (44) 1908 649 966
Web Site: http://www.lundbeck.com
Sales Range: $25-49.9 Million
Emp.: 65
Pharmaceutical Preparations
N.A.I.C.S.: 325412

Lundbeck Pharmaceuticals, Italy S.p.A. (3)
Via Joe Colombo 2, 20124, Milan, Italy
Tel.: (39) 026774171
Web Site: http://www.lundbeck.com
Pharmaceutical Preparations
N.A.I.C.S.: 325412

Lundbeck Pharmaceuticals, Italy S.p.A. (3)
Quarta Strada 2, 35129, Padua, Italy
Tel.: (39) 049 869 9311
Web Site: http://www.lundbeck.com
Pharmaceutical Products Distr
N.A.I.C.S.: 424210
Giulio Volpe (Mng Dir)

Lundbeck Poland Sp.z.o.o. (3)
Marszalkowska 142, 00-061, Warsaw, Poland
Tel.: (48) 226269300
Web Site: http://www.lundbeck.com
Rev.: $18,000,000
Emp.: 25
Pharmaceutical Preparations
N.A.I.C.S.: 325412
Koziejowski Wojciech (Country Mgr)

Lundbeck Portugal - Produtos Farmaceuticos Unipessoal Lda. (3)
Quinta Da Fonte Edificio, Dom Jose Piso 1, 2780 203, Paco d'Arcos, Portugal
Tel.: (351) 210045900
Web Site: http://www.lundbeck.com
Sales Range: $25-49.9 Million
Emp.: 15
Pharmaceutical Preparations
N.A.I.C.S.: 325412

Lundbeck RUS OOO (3)
2nd Krutitskiy pereulok 18 Building 1, 109044, Moscow, Russia
Tel.: (7) 4953803197
Emp.: 12
Pharmaceutical Products Distr
N.A.I.C.S.: 424210

Lundbeck SA (3)
Stephanie Square Center Avenue Louise 65, PO Box 11, 1050, Brussels, Belgium
Tel.: (32) 25357979

Web Site: http://www.lundbeck.com
Sales Range: $25-49.9 Million
Emp.: 80
Pharmaceutical Preparations
N.A.I.C.S.: 325412

Lundbeck SA (3)
Tour W 102 Terrasse Boieldieu, La Defense, 92085, Paris, France
Tel.: (33) 179412900
Web Site: http://www.lundbeck.com
Sales Range: $100-124.9 Million
Emp.: 500
Pharmaceutical Preparations
N.A.I.C.S.: 325412

Lundbeck SAS (3)
37-45 Quai du President Roosevelt, Issy-les-Moulineaux Cedex, 92445, Paris, France
Tel.: (33) 179412900
Pharmaceutical Products Distr
N.A.I.C.S.: 424210
Maria Greco (Office Mgr)

Lundbeck Singapore PTE. LTD. (3)
101 Thomson Road 13-05 United Square, Singapore, 307591, Singapore
Tel.: (65) 62556002
Pharmaceutical Products Distr
N.A.I.C.S.: 424210
Lot Yin Teng (Dir-Biometrics & Medical Writing)

Lundbeck Slovensko s.r.o. (3)
Eurovea Central 1 Pribinova 4, SK-811 09, Bratislava, Slovakia
Tel.: (421) 253414218
Web Site: http://www.lundbeck.com
Sales Range: $25-49.9 Million
Emp.: 14
Pharmaceutical Preparations
N.A.I.C.S.: 325412

Lundbeck South Africa (Pty) Limited (3)
252 Montrose Avenue, Northriding, 2194, South Africa
Tel.: (27) 116991600
Pharmaceutical Products Distr
N.A.I.C.S.: 424210

Lundbeck de Venezuela, C.A. (3)
Calle de los Laboratorios Torre Beta Piso 4, Oficina 404 Municipio Sucre Los Ruices, Caracas, Venezuela
Tel.: (58) 2122355311
Pharmaceutical Products Distr
N.A.I.C.S.: 424210
Ignacio Gardel (Mgr-Comml)

Subsidiary (US):

Lundbeck, LLC (3)
6 Pkwy N Ste 200, Deerfield, IL 60015
Tel.: (847) 282-1000
Web Site: http://www.lundbeck.com
Pharmaceutical Research, Development, Mfr & Distr
N.A.I.C.S.: 325412
Doug Williamson (Chief Medical Officer & VP-US Medical)

Subsidiary (Domestic):

Abide Therapeutics, Inc. (4)
10835 Rd to the Cure Ste 250, San Diego, CA 92121
Tel.: (858) 427-2590
Web Site: http://www.abidetx.com
Chemicals Mfr
N.A.I.C.S.: 325998
Cheryl Grice (VP-Chemistry)

Alder BioPharmaceuticals, Inc. (4)
11804 N Creek Pkwy S, Bothell, WA 98011
Tel.: (425) 205-2900
Web Site: http://www.alderbio.com
Rev.: $8,909,000
Assets: $426,239,000
Liabilities: $316,263,000
Net Worth: $109,976,000
Earnings: $(296,429,000)
Emp.: 202
Fiscal Year-end: 12/31/2018
Biopharmaceutical Mfr
N.A.I.C.S.: 325412
Jeffrey T. L. Smith (Mng Dir)

Lifestar Response Corp. (4)
657 Union Blvd, Totowa, NJ 07512-2445

INTERNATIONAL PUBLIC

Tel.: (973) 812-7271
Web Site: http://www.lifestarcompanies.com
Sales Range: $25-49.9 Million
Emp.: 700
Ambulance Service
N.A.I.C.S.: 621910

Subsidiary (Domestic):

Care Ambulance Inc. (5)
1150 S Panama St, Montgomery, AL 36107
Tel.: (334) 262-2550
Sales Range: $10-24.9 Million
Emp.: 50
Ambulance Service
N.A.I.C.S.: 621910

Lifestar Response Corp. - Holtsville (5)
664 Blue Point Rd, Holtsville, NY 11742
Tel.: (631) 447-2800
Sales Range: $25-49.9 Million
Emp.: 210
Ambulance Service
N.A.I.C.S.: 621910

Lifestar Response of Alabama, Inc. (5)
668 S Oates St, Dothan, AL 36301
Tel.: (334) 671-2273
Ambulance Service
N.A.I.C.S.: 621910
Jon Colin (Pres)

Lifestar Response of Maryland, Inc (5)
3710 Commerce Dr Ste 1006, Halethorpe, MD 21227
Tel.: (410) 247-1178
Healtcare Services
N.A.I.C.S.: 621610

Subsidiary (Domestic):

Lundbeck Research USA Inc. (4)
215 College Rd, Paramus, NJ 07652
Tel.: (201) 261-1331
Web Site: http://www.lundbeck.com
Sales Range: $25-49.9 Million
Emp.: 150
Biotechnology Research
N.A.I.C.S.: 325414
Christi Caramia (Assoc Dir-Ops)

Subsidiary (Non-US):

NUTEC AS (3)
Gravdalsveien 255, 5848, Bergen, Norway
Tel.: (47) 55942000
Web Site: http://www.nutec.no
Rev.: $75,745,000
Underwater Safety Training Programs
N.A.I.C.S.: 923110
Torben Harring (Gen Mgr)

Oy H. Lundbeck AB (3)
Logomo Byra Koydenpunojankatu 14, 20100, Turku, Finland
Tel.: (358) 22765000
Web Site: http://www.lundbeck.com
Sales Range: $25-49.9 Million
Emp.: 20
Pharmaceutical Preparations
N.A.I.C.S.: 325412

SIA Lundbeck Latvia (3)
Kleistuiela 24, Riga, 1067, Latvia
Tel.: (371) 67067884
Web Site: http://www.lundbeck.com
Sales Range: $25-49.9 Million
Emp.: 5
Pharmaceutical Preparations
N.A.I.C.S.: 325412
Radmila Korol (Product Mgr)

UAB Lundbeck Lithuania (3)
L Stuokos Guceviciaus 9 3, Vilnius, 1122, Lithuania
Tel.: (370) 52314188
Web Site: http://www.lundbeck.com
Sales Range: $25-49.9 Million
Emp.: 6
Pharmaceutical Preparations
N.A.I.C.S.: 325412
Leo Poldas (Mng Dir)

Holding (Non-US):

Haces Inversiones y Servicios S.A.S. (2)
Carrera 49 B 91-34, Bogota, Colombia

Tel.: (57) 6102877
Web Site: http://www.bhmsoluciones.com
Healtcare Services
N.A.I.C.S.: 621610

Kranken-Transport Herzig GmbH (2)
An den Kirchen 26-28, 59077, Hamm, Germany
Tel.: (49) 2381 996 990
Web Site: http://www.rettungsdienst-hamm.de
Healtcare Services
N.A.I.C.S.: 621610

Laboratoire Elaiapharm SA (2)
2881 Route des Cretes, BP 205, Sophia Antipolis Cedex, Valbonne, 06904, France
Tel.: (33) 493954949
Emp.: 200
Pharmaceuticals Product Mfr
N.A.I.C.S.: 325412

Lifehealth Limited (2)
Lundbeck House Caldecotte Lake, Business Park Caldecotte, Milton Keynes, MK7 8LG, United Kingdom
Tel.: (44) 1908649966
Pharmaceuticals Product Mfr
N.A.I.C.S.: 325412

MSTS Asia Sdn. Bhd. (2)
606 & 607 Jalan Melaka Raya 10, Taman Melaka Raya, 75000, Melaka, Malaysia
Tel.: (60) 6 2922069
Web Site: http://www.msts-my.org
Health Care Srvices
N.A.I.C.S.: 621610

Subsidiary (Non-US):

Falck Caspian Safe LLC (3)
Nobel Ave 36, Baku, Azerbaijan
Tel.: (994) 124965278
Web Site: http://www.caspiansafe.com
Healtcare Services
N.A.I.C.S.: 621610

Falck Prime Atlantic Limited (3)
9 Younis Bashorun Street, Off Ajose Adeogun Street Victoria Island, Lagos, Nigeria
Tel.: (234) 14606130
Web Site: http://www.falck.ng
Healtcare Services
N.A.I.C.S.: 621610
Michael Graham (Mgr-Ops)

Falck Safety Services Belgium BVBA (3)
Esplanadestraat 1 bus 8, 8400, Oostende, Belgium
Tel.: (32) 59295910
Web Site: http://www.falck.be
Healtcare Services
N.A.I.C.S.: 621610

Falck Safety Services Canada Ltd. (3)
20 Orion Court, Dartmouth, B2Y 4W6, NS, Canada
Tel.: (902) 700-6902
Web Site: http://www.falck.ca
Health Care Srvices
N.A.I.C.S.: 621610
Sean Fitzpatrick (Mgr-Ops)

MSTS Asia (Singapore) Pte Ltd (3)
No 67 Tuas South Avenue 1, Singapore, 637579, Singapore
Tel.: (65) 65158193
Web Site: http://www.msts.com
Survival Training Services
N.A.I.C.S.: 611699

Holding (Non-US):

S Reg AB (2)
Kungstorget 8, Knutpunkten level 2, Helsingborg, 252 24, Sweden
Tel.: (46) 4 24 90 79 00
Healtcare Services
N.A.I.C.S.: 327910

Skandinavisk Halsovard AB (2)
Barnhusgatan 22, 111 23, Stockholm, Sweden
Tel.: (46) 101783620
Web Site: http://www.shvab.se
Healtcare Services
N.A.I.C.S.: 621610

Subsidiary (Domestic):

Doc Care AB (3)
Barnhusgatan 22, Box 5156, 111 23, Stockholm, Sweden
Tel.: (46) 101783600
Web Site: http://www.shvab.se
Healtcare Services
N.A.I.C.S.: 621610

Ofelia Vard AB (3)
Vasagatan 45, 411 37, Gothenburg, Sweden
Tel.: (46) 101783620
Web Site: http://www.ofelia.se
Healtcare Services
N.A.I.C.S.: 621610

Holding (Non-US):

promedica Rettungsdienst Walbeck-Frankenberg GmbH & Co. KG (2)
Wilhelmstr 3, 34513, Waldeck, Hessen, Germany
Tel.: (49) 5634993078
Healtcare Services
N.A.I.C.S.: 621610

LUNDIN GOLD INC.
Suite 2800 Four Bentall Centre1055 Dunsmuir Street, Vancouver, V6C 3E8, BC, Canada
Tel.: (604) 689-7842   Ca
Web Site:
https://www.lundingold.com
Year Founded: 2002
LUG—(OMX)
Rev.: $815,666,000
Assets: $1,668,865,000
Liabilities: $816,784,000
Net Worth: $852,081,000
Earnings: $73,558,000
Emp.: 1,721
Fiscal Year-end: 12/31/22
Gold Exploration Services
N.A.I.C.S.: 212220
Lukas H. Lundin (Chm)

LUNDIN GROUP OF COMPANIES
Suite 2000 - 885 West Georgia Street, Vancouver, V6C 3E8, BC, Canada
Tel.: (604) 689-7842
Web Site:
https://www.thelundingroup.com
Emp.: 15
Holding Company; Metal Ore Mining & Oil & Gas Exploration Services
N.A.I.C.S.: 551112
Ian H. Lundin (Chm)

Subsidiaries:

International Petroleum Corporation (1)
Suite 2000 885 West Georgia Street, Vancouver, V6C 3E8, BC, Canada
Tel.: (604) 689-7842
Web Site:
https://www.international-petroleum.com
Rev.: $853,906,000
Assets: $2,062,985,000
Liabilities: $982,726,000
Net Worth: $1,080,259,000
Earnings: $172,979,000
Emp.: 271
Fiscal Year-end: 12/31/2023
Oil & Gas Exploration Services
N.A.I.C.S.: 213112
Mike Nicholson (CEO)

Subsidiary (Domestic):

BlackPearl Resources Inc. (2)
900 215 - 9th Ave SW, Calgary, T2P 1K3, AB, Canada   (100%)
Tel.: (403) 215-8313
Web Site:
http://www.blackpearlresources.ca
Sales Range: $10-24.9 Million
Oil & Natural Gas Exploration, Drilling & Extraction
N.A.I.C.S.: 211120
John Hunter Craig (Chm)

Subsidiary (Domestic):

Pearl E&P Canada Ltd. (3)
5208 62nd St, Lloydminster, T9V 2E4, AB, Canada
Tel.: (780) 808-8448
Web Site:
http://www.blackpearlresources.ca
Sales Range: $50-74.9 Million
Emp.: 20
Oil & Gas Field Exploration Services
N.A.I.C.S.: 211120

Subsidiary (Domestic):

Granite Oil Corp. (2)
432 222 3rd Ave SW, Calgary, T2P 0B4, AB, Canada
Tel.: (587) 349-9113
Web Site: http://www.graniteoil.ca
Sales Range: $50-74.9 Million
Emp.: 12
Oil & Gas Exploration Services
N.A.I.C.S.: 211120
Gail Hannon (CFO)

Lundin Energy AB (1)
Hovslagargatan 5, SE 111 48, Stockholm, Sweden
Tel.: (46) 84405450
Web Site: https://www.lundin-energy.com
Rev.: $2,564,400,000
Assets: $6,653,200,000
Liabilities: $8,422,300,000
Net Worth: ($1,769,100,000)
Earnings: $384,200,000
Emp.: 448
Fiscal Year-end: 12/31/2020
Oil Exploration & Production Services
N.A.I.C.S.: 211120
Teitur Poulsen (CFO)

Subsidiary (Non-US):

LLC PetroResurs (2)
19 Liter A Pom 4 North Ul Donskaya, Saint Petersburg, 199178, Russia
Tel.: (7) 8125523211
Crude Petroleum Extraction Services
N.A.I.C.S.: 211120

Lundin Banyumas BV (2)
Amaliastraat 3-5, Hague, 2514 JC, South Holland, Netherlands
Tel.: (31) 703717818
Natural Gas Extraction Services
N.A.I.C.S.: 211130

Lundin Netherlands Facilities BV (2)
Amaliastraat 3-5, Hague, 2514 JC, South-Holland, Netherlands
Tel.: (31) 703717818
Oil & Gas Exploration Services
N.A.I.C.S.: 213112

Lundin Oil & Gas BV (2)
Amaliastraat 3-5, Hague, 2514 JC, South-Holland, Netherlands
Tel.: (31) 703717818
Oil & Gas Exploration Services
N.A.I.C.S.: 213112

Lundin Petroleum (2)
5 chemin de la Pallanterie, CH-1222, Geneva, Vesenaz, Switzerland
Tel.: (41) 225951000
Web Site: http://www.lundin-petroleum.com
Sales Range: $50-74.9 Million
Emp.: 45
Oil & Petroleum Exploration Services
N.A.I.C.S.: 211120
Teitur Poulsen (CFO)

Lundin Petroleum BV (2)
Amaliastraat 3-5, 2514 JC, Hague, South Holland, Netherlands
Tel.: (31) 703717818
Crude Petroleum Extraction Services
N.A.I.C.S.: 211120

Subsidiary (Non-US):

Lundin International SA (3)
Maclaunay, Montmirail, 51210, Marne, France
Tel.: (33) 326817400
Sales Range: $50-74.9 Million
Emp.: 56
Oil & Gas Exploration Services
N.A.I.C.S.: 213112

Subsidiary (Domestic):

Lundin Malaysia BV (3)
Amaliastraat 5, Hague, 2514 JC, South-Holland, Netherlands
Tel.: (31) 703717818
Oil & Gas Exploration Services
N.A.I.C.S.: 213112

Lundin Marine BV (3)
Amaliastraat 3-5, Hague, 2514 JC, South-Holland, Netherlands
Tel.: (31) 703717818
Oil & Gas Exploration Services
N.A.I.C.S.: 213112

Subsidiary (Non-US):

Lundin Norway AS (3)
Strandveien 50d, 1366, Lysaker, Norway
Tel.: (47) 67107250
Sales Range: $75-99.9 Million
Emp.: 120
Crude Petroleum Extraction Services
N.A.I.C.S.: 211120

Subsidiary (Domestic):

Lundin Services BV (3)
Amaliastraat 3-5, Hague, 2514 JC, South-Holland, Netherlands
Tel.: (31) 703717818
Emp.: 7
Oil & Gas Exploration Services
N.A.I.C.S.: 213112

Subsidiary (Non-US):

Lundin Tunisia BV (3)
Rue Du Lac Tanganyika Imm Lundin Les Berges Du Lac, Tunis, 1053, Tunisia
Tel.: (216) 71964455
Sales Range: $50-74.9 Million
Emp.: 2
Oil & Gas Exploration Services
N.A.I.C.S.: 213112

Subsidiary (Non-US):

Lundin Russia Services BV (2)
Amaliastraat 3-5, Hague, 2514 JC, South Holland, Netherlands
Tel.: (31) 703717818
Oil & Gas Exploration Services
N.A.I.C.S.: 213112

Lundin Sareba BV (2)
Amaliastraat 3-5, Hague, 2514 JC, South-Holland, Netherlands
Tel.: (31) 703717818
Oil & Gas Exploration Services
N.A.I.C.S.: 213112

LUNDIN MINING CORPORATION
1055 Dunsmuir Street Suite 2800 Four Bentall Centre, PO Box 38, Vancouver, V7X 1L2, BC, Canada
Tel.: (604) 689-7842   Ca
Web Site:
https://www.lundinmining.com
LUN—(TSX)
Rev.: $1,892,713,000
Assets: $6,917,246,000
Liabilities: $2,619,846,000
Net Worth: $4,297,400,000
Earnings: $189,177,000
Emp.: 4,170
Fiscal Year-end: 12/31/19
Gold Ore & Metal Exploration, Mining & Processing Services
N.A.I.C.S.: 212220
Lukas H. Lundin (Chm)

Subsidiaries:

Barinas Enterprises Company Ltd (1)
7th Floor 16 Panteli Katelaris Street, Diagoras House, Nicosia, Cyprus   (100%)
Tel.: (357) 22660766
Sales Range: $50-74.9 Million
Emp.: 25
Open-End Investment Funds
N.A.I.C.S.: 525910

Josemaria Resources Inc. (1)
Suite 2000-885 West Georgia Street, Van-

LUNDIN MINING CORPORATION

Lundin Mining Corporation—(Continued)
couver, V6C 3E8, BC, Canada
Tel.: (604) 689-7842
Web Site: http://www.ngexresources.com
Rev.: $247,613
Assets: $14,334,352
Liabilities: $26,849,679
Net Worth: ($12,515,327)
Earnings: ($8,379,733)
Emp.: 27
Fiscal Year-end: 12/31/2019
Gold Mining, Exploration & Production Services
N.A.I.C.S.: 212220
Bob Carmichael (VP-Exploration)

Lundin Mining UK Ltd. (1)
Hayworthe House 2 Market Pl, Haywards Heath, RH16 1DB, West Sussex, United Kingdom
Tel.: (44) 1444411900
Web Site: http://www.lundinmining.com
Sales Range: $50-74.9 Million
Emp.: 18
Metallic Ore Mining Services
N.A.I.C.S.: 213114

North Atlantic Natural Resources AB (1)
Storlidensgruvan, Mala, Helsingborg, Sweden (100%)
Tel.: (46) 95350135
Sales Range: $25-49.9 Million
Emp.: 2
Engineeering Services
N.A.I.C.S.: 541330

Sociedade Mineira de Neves Corvo S.A (1)
Mina De Neves-corvo Santa Barbara De Padroes Apartado 12, 7780-409, Castro Verde, Portugal
Tel.: (351) 286689000
Web Site: http://somincor.com.pt
Copper & Zinc Ore Mining Services
N.A.I.C.S.: 212230

Somincor S.A. (1)
Minas De Neves de Neves Corvo Santa Barbara De Padroes, 7780-409, Castro Verde, Portugal
Tel.: (351) 286689000
Web Site: http://www.somincor.com
Sales Range: $350-399.9 Million
Emp.: 900
Precious Metal Mining Services
N.A.I.C.S.: 212290

Zinkgruvan Mining AB (1)
Centrumvagen 1, 696 81, Zinkgruvan, Sweden
Tel.: (46) 58382200
Web Site: http://www.zinkgruvanmining.com
Sales Range: $75-99.9 Million
Emp.: 350
Zinc, Lead & Copper Mining
N.A.I.C.S.: 212230

LUNG HWA ELECTRONICS CO., LTD.
15F No 32 Bade Road Section3, Songshan District, Taipei, 10559, Taiwan
Tel.: (886) 225787775
Web Site: https://www.lhsat.com
Year Founded: 1973
2424—(TAI)
Rev.: $3,488,374
Assets: $21,761,273
Liabilities: $12,217,371
Net Worth: $9,543,902
Earnings: ($6,505,837)
Fiscal Year-end: 12/31/23
Consumer Electronics Mfr
N.A.I.C.S.: 811210
Guangxiang Wang (Chm)

LUNG KEE BERMUDA HOLDINGS LTD.
Unit A 15th Floor Kings Wing Plaza 2 No 1 On Kwan Street, Sha Tin New Territories, Hong Kong, China (Hong Kong)
Tel.: (852) 23422248 BM

0255—(HKG)
Rev.: $204,182,708
Assets: $293,438,318
Liabilities: $40,149,240
Net Worth: $253,289,078
Earnings: $2,016,285
Emp.: 2,900
Fiscal Year-end: 12/31/22
Holding Company
N.A.I.C.S.: 551112

LUNG TEH SHIPBUILDING CO., LTD.
4F No 37 Ln 221 Gangqian Rd, Neihu Dist, Taipei, 00114, Taiwan
Tel.: (886) 226571830
Web Site: https://www.lungteh.com
Year Founded: 1979
6753—(TAI)
Rev.: $163,099,212
Assets: $296,518,286
Liabilities: $197,336,858
Net Worth: $99,181,428
Earnings: $18,803,688
Emp.: 798
Fiscal Year-end: 12/31/23
Ship Building Product Mfr
N.A.I.C.S.: 336611
Sheldon Huang (Chm)

LUNGYEN LIFE SERVICE CORPORATION, LTD.
No 111 Dongshi St, Xizhi Dist, New Taipei City, 221, Taiwan
Tel.: (886) 226602028
Web Site:
http://www.lungyengroup.com.tw
Year Founded: 1992
5530—(TPE)
Rev.: $134,000,485
Assets: $2,279,772,765
Liabilities: $1,510,415,915
Net Worth: $769,356,850
Earnings: $40,870,073
Emp.: 601
Fiscal Year-end: 12/31/23
Funeral Services
N.A.I.C.S.: 812210
Kelly Lee (Chm)

LUNIA BIO PTY. LTD.
2806 Ipswich Rd, Darra, 4076, QLD, Australia
Tel.: (61) 732739176 AU
Web Site: http://www.luinabio.com.au
Year Founded: 1990
Drug Development & Contract Mfr
N.A.I.C.S.: 325412
Les Tillack (CEO)

LUNIT, INC.
374 Gangnam-daero, Gangnam-gu, Seoul, Korea (South)
Tel.: (82) 221380827
Web Site: https://www.lunit.io
Year Founded: 2013
328130—(KRS)
Software Publisher
N.A.I.C.S.: 513210
Brandon B. Suh (CEO)

LUNNON METALS LIMITED
Level 3 33 Richardson Street, West Perth, 6005, WA, Australia
Tel.: (61) 864248848 AU
Web Site:
https://lunnonmetals.com.au
Year Founded: 2014
LM8—(ASX)
Rev.: $33,980
Assets: $35,436,347
Liabilities: $1,622,776
Net Worth: $33,813,571
Earnings: ($11,563,610)
Emp.: 25
Fiscal Year-end: 06/30/23

Metal Exploration Services
N.A.I.C.S.: 213114
Edmund Ainscough (Mng Dir)

LUO LIH-FEN HOLDING CO., LTD.
No 21 Longxiang Road Taiwanese Investment Area, Zhangzhou, China
Tel.: (86) 5966269800
Web Site: https://www.luolifen.com
Year Founded: 1986
6666—(TAI)
Rev.: $30,052,559
Assets: $73,951,809
Liabilities: $15,507,524
Net Worth: $58,444,284
Earnings: $3,696,292
Fiscal Year-end: 12/31/20
Beauty Product Mfr
N.A.I.C.S.: 325620

LUOKUNG TECHNOLOGY CORP.
No 9 Guanghua Road Miss Qinyu Zhao B9-8 Block B SOHO Phase II, Chaoyang District, Beijing, 100020, China
Tel.: (86) 1065065217
Web Site: https://www.luokung.com
Year Founded: 2009
LKCO—(NASDAQ)
Rev.: $10,236,235
Assets: $53,637,742
Liabilities: $106,661,696
Net Worth: ($53,023,954)
Earnings: ($181,722,229)
Emp.: 727
Fiscal Year-end: 12/31/23
Wireless Solutions & Software Developer
N.A.I.C.S.: 513210
Xuesong Song (Chm & CEO)

Subsidiaries:

Xi'an Kingtone Information Technology Co.Ltd (1)
3 F Borough A Block A No 181 South Tai Bai Road, Xi'an, 710065, Shaanxi, China
Tel.: (86) 2988231591
Web Site: http://www.kingtoneinfo.com
Sales Range: $25-49.9 Million
Wireless Software Application Development Services
N.A.I.C.S.: 541511
Li Tao (Chm)

LUOLAI LIFESTYLE TECHNOLOGY CO., LTD.
No 1699 Xinghu Avenue Economic & Technological Development Zone, Nantong, 226009, Jiangsu, China
Tel.: (86) 2123138999
Web Site: http://www.luolai.com.cn
Year Founded: 2002
002293—(SSE)
Rev.: $344,878,560
Assets: $980,254,548
Liabilities: $391,362,192
Net Worth: $588,892,356
Earnings: $39,949,416
Fiscal Year-end: 12/31/22
Home Textile Products Mfr & Distr
N.A.I.C.S.: 314120
Xue Xia (Sec)

Subsidiaries:

Lexington Furniture Industries, Inc. (1)
1300 National Hwy, Thomasville, NC 27360
Tel.: (336) 474-5300
Web Site: http://www.lexington.com
Home Furnishings Mfr & Whslr
N.A.I.C.S.: 551112
Craig Spooner (COO)

LUONG TAI INVESTMENT &

INTERNATIONAL PUBLIC CONSTRUCTION CORPORATION
173A Nguyen Van Troi Street Ward 11, Phu Nhuan District, Ho Chi Minh City, Vietnam
Tel.: (84) 838421026
Web Site:
http://www.luongtaigroup.com
Year Founded: 1987
LUT—(HNX)
Rev.: $5,370,000
Assets: $47,963,000
Liabilities: $37,088,700
Net Worth: $10,874,300
Earnings: ($7,482,100)
Emp.: 100
Fiscal Year-end: 12/31/22
Road & Industrial Building Construction Services
N.A.I.C.S.: 236220

LUONIUSHAN CO., LTD.
12th Floor Nongxin Building Hainan Mansion No 5 Guoxing Avenue, Meilan District, Haikou, 570203, Hainan, China
Tel.: (86) 89868581891
Web Site:
https://www.luoniushan.com
Year Founded: 1987
000735—(SSE)
Rev.: $404,944,488
Assets: $1,779,005,592
Liabilities: $1,101,902,724
Net Worth: $677,102,868
Earnings: $12,527,892
Fiscal Year-end: 12/31/22
Animal Breeding Services
N.A.I.C.S.: 112210
Xu Zili (Chm & Pres)

LUOSSAVAARA-KIIRUNAVAARA AB
Varvsgatan 45, Box 952, SE-971 28, Lulea, Sweden
Tel.: (46) 771760000 SE
Web Site: http://www.lkab.com
Year Founded: 1897
Rev.: $3,350,134,200
Assets: $8,003,562,770
Liabilities: $3,124,327,010
Net Worth: $4,879,235,760
Earnings: $1,090,240,410
Emp.: 4,300
Fiscal Year-end: 12/31/19
Minerals Products Mfr & Distr
N.A.I.C.S.: 327992
Leif Bostrom (Sr VP-Special Products Div)

Subsidiaries:

LKAB Berg & Betong AB (1)
Tippvagen 5, Box 817, 981 28, Kiruna, Sweden
Tel.: (46) 771 760 200
Web Site: http://www.lkabbergbetong.se
Mineral Ore Mining Services
N.A.I.C.S.: 212319

LKAB Far East Pte Ltd (1)
300 Beach Road 29-02 The Concourse, Singapore, 199555, Singapore
Tel.: (65) 6392 49 22
Mineral Ore Mining Services
N.A.I.C.S.: 212319

LKAB Fastigheter AB (1)
Kirunavaaravagen 1, 981 86, Kiruna, Sweden
Tel.: (46) 771 760 300
Web Site: http://www.lkabfastigheter.se
Real Estate Consulting Service
N.A.I.C.S.: 531210

LKAB Holdings Ltd. (1)
Raynesway, Derby, DE21 7BE, United Kingdom
Tel.: (44) 1332673131
Iron Ore Mfr
N.A.I.C.S.: 331110

AND PRIVATE COMPANIES — LUPIN LIMITED

Denise Roberts *(Comml Dir)*

LKAB Kimit AB (1)
Lkab Industriomrade, 981 86, Kiruna, Sweden
Tel.: (46) 771 760 220
Web Site: http://www.lkabkimit.se
Explosive Material Mfr & Distr
N.A.I.C.S.: 325920
Peter Soderman *(Pres)*

LKAB Malmtrafik AB (1)
Kiirunavaaravagen 1, 981 31, Kiruna, Sweden
Tel.: (46) 77 176 05 00
Freight Rail Transport Services
N.A.I.C.S.: 482111

LKAB Malmtrafikk AS (1)
Bolagsgata 40, 8514, Narvik, Norway
Tel.: (47) 7 692 3800
Web Site: http://www.lkab.com
Freight Rail Transport Services
N.A.I.C.S.: 482111

LKAB Mekaniska AB (1)
Lastv 14, PO Box 952, 971 28, Lulea, Sweden
Tel.: (46) 771760400
Web Site: http://www.lkabmekaniska.se
Industrial Machinery & Equipment Mfr
N.A.I.C.S.: 332999
Peter Soderman *(Pres)*

LKAB Minerals (Tianjin) Minerals Co. Ltd. (1)
Junyi Industrial Park Jungliangcheng, Dongli District, Tianjin, 300301, China
Tel.: (86) 22 2435 1706
Mineral Ore Mining Services
N.A.I.C.S.: 212319
James Qi *(Mng Dir)*

LKAB Minerals Asia Pacific Ltd. (1)
Rm 3407 China Resources Building 26 Harbour Road, Wanchai, China (Hong Kong)
Tel.: (852) 2827 3000
Web Site: http://www.lkabminerals.com
Emp.: 13
Mineral Ore Mining Services
N.A.I.C.S.: 212319

LKAB Minerals B.V. (1)
Vlasweg 19 Harbour M164, 4782 PW, Moerdijk, Netherlands
Tel.: (31) 168 388500
Web Site: http://www.lkabminerals.com
Emp.: 25
Mineral Ore Mining Services
N.A.I.C.S.: 212319

LKAB Minerals France (1)
85 Rue Jean Rache, 59310, Sameon, France
Tel.: (33) 320 055 167
Mineral Ore Mining Services
N.A.I.C.S.: 212319
Robert Egea *(Mgr-Bus Dev Refractories)*

LKAB Minerals GmbH (1)
Am Europa-Center 1a, 45145, Essen, Germany
Tel.: (49) 201 45060
Web Site: http://www.lkabminerals.com
Mineral Ore Mining Services
N.A.I.C.S.: 212319
Thomas Tepper *(Mgr-Sls-Civil Engrg & Construction-Europe)*

LKAB Minerals Greece (1)
13 N Kountouriotou str, 546 25, Thessaloniki, Greece
Tel.: (30) 2310 539073
Mineral Ore Mining Services
N.A.I.C.S.: 212319
Sakis Chatzinikolaou *(Mgr-Technical Sls-Central SE Europe)*

LKAB Minerals Ltd. (1)
Raynesway, Derby, DE21 7BE, United Kingdom
Tel.: (44) 1332673131
Web Site: http://www.lkabminerals.com
Emp.: 60
Mineral Ore Mining Services
N.A.I.C.S.: 212319
Darren Wilson *(CEO-Industrial Minerals Div)*

LKAB Minerals Oy (1)
Kaivoksentie 300, 71800, Siilinjarvi, Finland
Tel.: (358) 17 266 0160

Mineral Ore Mining Services
N.A.I.C.S.: 212319
Kari Laukkanen *(Mng Dir)*

LKAB Minerals Richmond Ltd. (1)
325 Coleford Road, Sheffield, S9 5NF, United Kingdom
Tel.: (44) 114 243 3141
Mineral Ore Mining Services
N.A.I.C.S.: 212319
Mark Connor *(Gen Mgr)*

LKAB Minerals Slovak Republic (1)
Panenska 13, 81103, Bratislava, Slovakia
Tel.: (421) 2 5930 5753
Mineral Ore Mining Services
N.A.I.C.S.: 212319
Marian Zilinsky *(Mgr-Sls)*

LKAB Minerals Spain (1)
C /Nord no 2 Ent 5, 08500, Vic, Spain
Tel.: (34) 93 886 1330
Mineral Ore Mining Services
N.A.I.C.S.: 212319
Albert Senyer *(Mgr-Technical Sls)*

LKAB Minerals, Inc. (1)
2150 Scripps Ctr 312 Walnut St, Cincinnati, OH 45202
Tel.: (513) 322-5530
Mineral Ore Mining Services
N.A.I.C.S.: 212319
Mats Drugge *(Pres)*

LKAB S.A. (1)
Chaussee de la Hulpe 150, 1170, Brussels, Belgium
Tel.: (32) 2 663 36 70
Mineral Ore Mining Services
N.A.I.C.S.: 212319
Goran Ottosson *(Pres)*

LKAB Schwedenerz GmbH (1)
Bredeneyer Strasse 182, 45133, Essen, Germany
Tel.: (49) 201 879 440
Logistics Consulting Servies
N.A.I.C.S.: 541614
Goran Ottosson *(VP-Mktg & Sls)*

LKAB Trading (Shanghai) Co. Ltd. (1)
Unit 2007 889 Yueda Plaza 1111 Changshou Road, Shanghai, 200042, China
Tel.: (86) 21 521 25103
Mineral Ore Mining Services
N.A.I.C.S.: 212319
Anders Lundgren *(Pres)*

LKAB Wassara AB (1)
Elektronvagen 4, Box 1067, 141 22, Huddinge, Sweden
Tel.: (46) 771 760 100
Web Site: http://www.wassara.com
Emp.: 41
Drilling System Mfr
N.A.I.C.S.: 333131

Minelco AB (1)
PO Box 952, Lulea, Sweden
Tel.: (46) 98071182
Web Site: http://www.minelco.com
Mineral Mfr
N.A.I.C.S.: 327992

Subsidiary (Non-US):

Minelco Ltd. (2)
Flixborough Industrial Estate, Scunthorpe, DN15 8SF, North Lincolnshire, United Kingdom (100%)
Web Site: http://www.minelco.com
Sales Range: $100-124.9 Million
Emp.: 400
Mineral Mfr
N.A.I.C.S.: 327992

LUOXIN PHARMACEUTICALS GROUP STOCK CO., LTD.
No 18 Huxi Rd National New & High-tech Industrial Development Zone, Linyi, 276017, Shandong, China
Tel.: (86) 5398241226   CN
Web Site: https://www.luoxin.cn
Year Founded: 1993
002793—(SSE)
Rev.: $503,692,020
Assets: $1,138,337,928
Liabilities: $674,108,136

Net Worth: $464,229,792
Earnings: ($172,065,816)
Fiscal Year-end: 12/31/22
Submersible Pump Mfr & Distr
N.A.I.C.S.: 333996
Liu Zhenteng *(Chm & Gen Mgr)*

LUOYANG GLASS COMPANY LIMITED
No 9 Tanggong Zhong Lu Xigong District, Luoyang, 471009, Henan, China
Tel.: (86) 37963908695   CN
Web Site: http://www.zhglb.com
Year Founded: 1994
Sales Range: $100-124.9 Million
Emp.: 1,102
Float Sheet Glass Mfr
N.A.I.C.S.: 327211
Zhisen Ni *(Gen Mgr)*

LUOYANG JIANLONG MICRO-NANO NEW MATERIALS CO., LTD.
Junmin Road, Industrial Cluster District Yanshi, Luoyang, 471900, Henan, China
Tel.: (86) 37967758531
Web Site: http://www.jalonmolecularsieve.com
Year Founded: 1998
688357—(SHG)
Rev.: $119,871,695
Assets: $306,922,782
Liabilities: $89,383,456
Net Worth: $217,539,326
Earnings: $27,779,221
Emp.: 480
Fiscal Year-end: 12/31/22
Chemical Product Mfr & Distr
N.A.I.C.S.: 325520
Jianbo Li *(Chm)*

LUOYANG NORTH GLASS TECHNOLOGY CO., LTD.
No 20 binhe road high-tech development zone, Luoyang, 471003, Henan, China
Tel.: (86) 37969920620
Web Site: https://www.northglass.global
Year Founded: 1995
002613—(SSE)
Rev.: $210,065,076
Assets: $339,975,792
Liabilities: $95,314,752
Net Worth: $244,661,040
Earnings: $4,988,412
Fiscal Year-end: 12/31/22
Glass Processing Equipment & Glass Products Mfr
N.A.I.C.S.: 333248
Gao Xueming *(Chm)*

Subsidiaries:

Shanghai North Glass Coating Technology Industrial Co., Ltd (1)
328 Guanghua Road, Xiaokunshan Town Songjiang District, Shanghai, 201614, China
Tel.: (86) 2157858680
Web Site: http://www.Northglass.com
Emp.: 900
Glass Processing Equipment Mfr
N.A.I.C.S.: 333248

Shanghai North Glass Technology Industrial Co., Ltd. (1)
No 328 Guanghua Road Songjiang Science & Technology Zone, Shanghai, 201614, China
Tel.: (86) 2157858601
Glass Products Mfr
N.A.I.C.S.: 327215
Li Gao *(Gen Mgr)*

LUOYANG XINQIANGLIAN SLEWING BEARING CO., LTD.

No 8 Jingjin Road, Luoxin Park Economic and Technological Development Zone Xin'an, Luoyang, 471800, Henan, China
Tel.: (86) 37962811096
Web Site: http://www.lyxqlbearing.com.cn
Year Founded: 2005
300850—(SSE)
Rev.: $379,481,253
Assets: $958,536,916
Liabilities: $421,048,658
Net Worth: $537,488,258
Earnings: $78,797,435
Fiscal Year-end: 12/31/21
Slewing Bearings Product Mfr & Distr
N.A.I.C.S.: 332991
Zhengqiang Xiao *(Chm)*

LUPAKA GOLD CORP.
1569 Dempsey Road, North Vancouver, V7K 1S8, BC, Canada
Tel.: (604) 669-7748
Web Site: https://www.lupakagold.com
Year Founded: 2000
LPK—(TSXV)
Assets: $107,654
Liabilities: $497,177
Net Worth: ($389,523)
Earnings: ($168,926)
Emp.: 22
Fiscal Year-end: 12/31/21
Gold Mining Services
N.A.I.C.S.: 212220
Gordon Ellis *(Chm)*

LUPATECH S.A.
Rua Alcides Lourenco da Rocha 167 8 andar, Sao Paulo, 04571-910, Brazil
Tel.: (55) 1121347000   BR
Web Site: https://www.lupatech.com.br
Year Founded: 1980
LUPA3—(BRAZ)
Rev.: $17,203,909
Assets: $96,274,604
Liabilities: $64,454,283
Net Worth: $31,820,321
Earnings: $10,499,352
Fiscal Year-end: 12/31/23
Oil Exploration Tools, Industrial Valves & Automotive Industry Parts Mfr
N.A.I.C.S.: 333914
Joao Marcos Cavichioli Feiteiro *(Pres)*

Subsidiaries:

Fiberware Equipamentos e Servicos para Industria Ltda (1)
Rio Das Ostras, Rio de Janeiro, Brazil
Tel.: (55) 21 2620 0145
Web Site: http://www.fiberware.com.br
Industrial Valve Mfr
N.A.I.C.S.: 332911

Mipel Ind. e Com. de Valvulas Ltda. (1)
Rua Casemiro Ecco 417, Vila Azul, 95330-000, Veranopolis, Rio Grande do Sul, Brazil
Tel.: (55) 54 3441 3636
Web Site: http://www.mipel.com.br
Industrial Valve Mfr
N.A.I.C.S.: 332911
Marco Miola *(Gen Mgr)*

Valmicro Ind. e Com. de Valvulas Limitada (1)
Rua Pequetita 145 4 Andar Bairro Vila Olimpia, 04552-060, Sao Paulo, Brazil
Tel.: (55) 11 2134 7000
Web Site: http://www.lupatech.com.br
Mfr of Both Manual & Automatic Ball Valves
N.A.I.C.S.: 332911

LUPIN LIMITED

LUPIN LIMITED

Lupin Limited—(Continued)

3rd Floor Kalpataru Inspire Off Western Expressway Highway, Santacruz East, Mumbai, 400 055, India
Tel.: (91) 2266402323
Web Site: https://www.lupin.com
LUPIN—(NSE)
Rev.: $2,088,347,625
Assets: $3,222,825,060
Liabilities: $1,331,193,045
Net Worth: $1,891,632,015
Earnings: $166,056,345
Emp.: 18,573
Fiscal Year-end: 03/31/21
Pharmaceutical Preparations & Medicines Mfr
N.A.I.C.S.: 325412
Vinita D. Gupta (CEO)

Subsidiaries:

GAVIS Pharmaceuticals, LLC (1)
400 Campus Dr, Somerset, NJ 08873
Tel.: (908) 603-6080
Web Site: http://www.gavispharma.com
Pharmaceutical Products Distr
N.A.I.C.S.: 424210
Veerappan Subramanian (Founder, Chm & CEO)

Generic Health Pty Ltd. (1)
Suite 2 Level 2 19-23 Prospect Street, Box Hill, 3128, VIC, Australia
Tel.: (61) 398097900
Web Site: https://www.generichealth.com.au
Pharmaceutical Products Distr
N.A.I.C.S.: 424210
Ashutosh Damle (CEO)

Hormosan Pharma GmbH (1)
Hanauer Landstrasse 139-143, 60314, Frankfurt am Main, Germany
Tel.: (49) 69478730
Web Site: https://www.hormosan.com
Pharmaceutical Product Mfr & Distr
N.A.I.C.S.: 325412
Anjan Selz (Mng Dir)

Lupin (Europe) Ltd. (1)
Suite 1 Victoria Court Bexton Road, Warrington, Knutsford, WA16 0PF, Cheshire, United Kingdom
Tel.: (44) 1565751378
Pharmaceuticals Product Mfr
N.A.I.C.S.: 325412

Lupin Atlantis Holdings SA (1)
Zweigniederlasssung Zug Landis Gyr Strasse 1, 6300, Zug, Switzerland
Tel.: (41) 526337000
Pharmaceutical Products Distr
N.A.I.C.S.: 424210

Subsidiary (Non-US):

Laboratorios Grin, S.A. de C.V. (2)
Rodriguez Saro No 630, 03100, Mexico, Mexico
Tel.: (52) 52002300
Web Site: https://www.laboratoriosgrin.com
Pharmaceutical Product Mfr & Distr
N.A.I.C.S.: 325412

Subsidiary (US):

Lupin Pharmaceuticals, Inc. (2)
Harborplace Tower 111 S Calvert St 21st Fl, Baltimore, MD 21202
Tel.: (410) 576-2000
Web Site: https://www.lupin.com
Pharmaceutical Products Distr
N.A.I.C.S.: 424210
Paul McGarty (Pres)

Subsidiary (Non-US):

Nanomi B.V. (2)
Zutphenstraat 51, 7575 EJ, Oldenzaal, Netherlands
Tel.: (31) 880040800
Web Site: https://www.nanomi.com
Pharmaceutical Product Mfr & Distr
N.A.I.C.S.: 325412
Rob Duwel (Principal)

Lupin Digital Health Limited (1)
Kalpataru Inspire 3rd Floor Off Western Express Highway, Santacruz East, Mumbai, 400 055, India
Tel.: (91) 7030200600
Web Site: https://lyfe.in
Digital Cardiology Therapeutics Services
N.A.I.C.S.: 621111

Lupin Investments Pvt. Limited (1)
159 CST Road Kalina Santacruz E, Mumbai, 400 098, India
Tel.: (91) 2266402323
Pharmaceuticals Product Mfr
N.A.I.C.S.: 325412

Lupin Pharma Canada Ltd. (1)
1001 De Maisonneuve East Suite 304, Montreal, H2L 4P9, QC, Canada
Tel.: http://www.lupinpharma.ca
Pharmaceutical Product Mfr & Distr
N.A.I.C.S.: 325412
Patrick Nadeau (Gen Mgr)

Medquimeca Industria Farmaceutica Ltda (1)
Rua Fernando Lamarca 255, Distrito Industrial, Juiz de Fora, 36092-030, MG, Brazil
Tel.: (55) 3221014000
Web Site: http://www.medquimica.ind.br
Pharmaceuticals Product Mfr
N.A.I.C.S.: 325412

Medquimica Industria Farmaceutica Ltda. (1)
Rua Fernando Lamarca N 255 Bairro Distrito Industrial, Juiz de Fora, CEP 36092-030, Minas Gerais, Brazil
Tel.: (55) 3221014000
Web Site: https://medquimica.ind.br
Pharmaceutical Mfr & Distr
N.A.I.C.S.: 325412

Multicare Pharmaceuticals Philippines, Inc. (1)
17th Floor Units A B 8 Rockwell Building, Hidalgo Drive Rockwell Center, Makati, 1226, Philippines
Tel.: (63) 28110636
Web Site: https://www.multicare.com.ph
Pharmaceutical Product Mfr & Distr
N.A.I.C.S.: 325412
Romeo Sy (Pres)

Novel Laboratories, Inc. (1)
400 Campus Dr, Somerset, NJ 08873
Tel.: (908) 603-6000
Web Site: https://www.novellabs.net
Emp.: 80
Specialty Generic Mfr & Distr
N.A.I.C.S.: 325412

LUR BERRI

Route de Sauveterre, 64120, Aicirits-Camou-Suhast, France
Tel.: (33) 5 5938 7200 FR
Web Site: http://www.lurberri.fr
Sales Range: $800-899.9 Million
Emp.: 4,000
Agricultural & Animal Farming Cooperative
N.A.I.C.S.: 813990
Gemin Olivier (CEO)

Subsidiaries:

Labeyrie Fine Foods SAS (1)
39 Route de Bayonne, 40230, Saint-Geours-de-Maremne, France (61%)
Tel.: (33) 558567300
Web Site: https://www.labeyrie-fine-foods.com
Holding Company; Fresh & Frozen Seafood, Poultry, Dessert & Specialty Foods Mfr & Whslr
N.A.I.C.S.: 551112
Steve Lawson (CFO)

Subsidiary (Domestic):

Labeyrie SA (2)
39 Route de Bayonne, 40230, Saint-Geours-de-Maremne, France
Tel.: (33) 558567300
Web Site: https://www.labeyrie.com
Sales Range: $150-199.9 Million
Emp.: 1,000
Smoked Salmon & Foie Gras Mfr & Whslr
N.A.I.C.S.: 311710
Xavier Govare (CEO)

LURA GRUPA DOO

Radnicka 47, 10 000, Zagreb, Croatia
Tel.: (385) 16285220
Web Site: http://www.lura-grupa.hr
Investment Services
N.A.I.C.S.: 523999

Subsidiaries:

PharmaS d.o.o. (1)
Radnicka cesta 47, Zagreb, 10000, Croatia
Tel.: (385) 15509375
Web Site: http://www.pharmas-group.com
Pharmaceutical Products Dist & Mfr
N.A.I.C.S.: 325412
Jerko Jaksic (CEO)

Subsidiary (Non-US):

Mabo Farma, s.a.u. (2)
Las Rejas 2 Pta 1 Of 6 and 7, 28821, Coslada, Madrid, Spain
Tel.: (34) 910376485
Web Site: https://www.mabofarma.com
Emp.: 70
Laboratory Instrument Mfr
N.A.I.C.S.: 334516

LUSAKA STOCK EXCHANGE

3rd Fl Exchange Bldg Central Park Cairo Rd, PO Box 34523, Lusaka, Zambia
Tel.: (260) 211228391
Web Site: http://www.lusa.co.zm
Year Founded: 1993
Sales Range: $25-49.9 Million
Emp.: 11
Stock Exchange Services
N.A.I.C.S.: 523210
Friday C. Ndhlovu (Chm)

LUSH COSMETICS LTD.

29 High Street, Poole, BH15 1AB, Dorsetshire, United Kingdom
Tel.: (44) 1202668545
Web Site: http://www.lush.com
Sales Range: $300-349.9 Million
Emp.: 4,280
Natural Cosmetics & Fragrances Mfr & Retailer
N.A.I.C.S.: 325620
Mark Constantine (Founder)

Subsidiaries:

LUSH Asia Limited (1)
Lai Chi Kok, Hong Kong, China (Hong Kong)
Tel.: (852) 2423 3833
Web Site: http://www.lush-hk.com
Cosmetic Product Distr
N.A.I.C.S.: 456120
Miranda Cheung (Mgr-Mktg & PR)

LUSH Bulgaria Ltd. (1)
The Mall Level 0 Tsarigradsko Shose 115, Sofia, 1784, Bulgaria
Tel.: (359) 882 648 644
Web Site: http://www.lushbg.com
Cosmetic Product Distr
N.A.I.C.S.: 456120
Aleksander Meghev (Gen Mgr)

LUSH Internet Inc. (1)
3625 S Las Vegas Blvd, Las Vegas, NV 89109
Tel.: (702) 778-9364
Web Site: http://www.lushusa.com
Cosmetic Product Distr
N.A.I.C.S.: 456120

LUSH LATVIJA (1)
Dzirnavu iela 70, Riga, Latvia
Tel.: (371) 67288048
Web Site: http://www.lush.lv
Cosmetic Product Distr
N.A.I.C.S.: 456120

LUSH Ukraine (1)
Volodymyra Sosyury St 6 202, Kiev, 01004, Ukraine
Tel.: (380) 44 235 1965
Web Site: http://www.lush.com.ua
Cosmetic Product Distr
N.A.I.C.S.: 456120

INTERNATIONAL PUBLIC

Lush (Switzerland) AG (1)
Gartenstrasse 2, 6300, Zug, Switzerland
Tel.: (41) 41 560 64 00
Web Site: http://www.lush.ch
Cosmetic Product Distr
N.A.I.C.S.: 456120

Lush Australia PTY Limited (1)
25 Carrington Road, Marrickville, 2204, NSW, Australia
Tel.: (61) 1300 587 428
Web Site: http://www.lush.com.au
Emp.: 50
Cosmetic Product Distr
N.A.I.C.S.: 456120
Mark Lincoln (Dir)

Lush BV (1)
Leidsestraat 14, 1017 PA, Amsterdam, Netherlands
Tel.: (31) 20 638 80 96
Web Site: http://www.lush.nl
Cosmetic Product Distr
N.A.I.C.S.: 456120

Lush Bosna i Hercegovina (1)
Trg Djece Sarajeva, Sarajevo, Bosnia & Herzegovina
Tel.: (387) 33 25 9375
Web Site: http://www.lush.ba
Cosmetic Product Distr
N.A.I.C.S.: 456120

Lush Ceska republika (1)
Republiky 1, Prague, 110 00, Czech Republic
Tel.: (420) 222 51 61 61
Web Site: http://www.lushcz.cz
Cosmetic Product Distr
N.A.I.C.S.: 456120

Lush Cosmetics SL (1)
C/ Alcala 104, 28009, Madrid, Spain
Tel.: (34) 91 522 88 09
Web Site: http://www.lush.es
Cosmetic Product Distr
N.A.I.C.S.: 456120
Mark Constantine (Mng Dir)

Lush Finland Oy (1)
Mannerheimintie 5, 00100, Helsinki, Finland
Tel.: (358) 50 464 3316
Web Site: http://www.lush.fi
Cosmetic Product Distr
N.A.I.C.S.: 456120
Hanna Songpraguy (Mgr-Store)

Lush France (1)
77 boulevard Voltaire, 75011, Paris, France
Tel.: (33) 1 49 70 98 34
Cosmetic Product Distr
N.A.I.C.S.: 456120
David Remy (Mgr-Digital)

Lush GmbH (1)
Barnabitengasse 6/16, 1060, Vienna, Austria
Tel.: (43) 1 533 25 50
Web Site: http://www.lush.at
Cosmetic Product Distr
N.A.I.C.S.: 456120

Lush GmbH (1)
Romerstrasse 13, 72469, Messstetten, Germany
Tel.: (49) 7579 92178 0
Web Site: http://www.lush-shop.de
Cosmetic Product Distr
N.A.I.C.S.: 456120

Lush Hrvatska (1)
Petrinjska 4, 10000, Zagreb, Croatia
Tel.: (385) 1 4100 361
Web Site: http://www.lush.hr
Emp.: 4
Cosmetic Product Distr
N.A.I.C.S.: 456120
Slavica Caleta (Dir)

Lush Hungary Kft. (1)
Szent Istvan korut 1, 1055, Budapest, Hungary
Tel.: (36) 70 428 3 428
Web Site: http://www.lush.hu
Cosmetic Product Distr
N.A.I.C.S.: 456120
Kati Lush (Country Mgr)

Lush Italia Srl (1)
Via Atto Vannucci 13, Milan, 20135, Italy
Tel.: (39) 02 55303036

AND PRIVATE COMPANIES

Web Site: http://www.lush.it
Cosmetic Product Distr
N.A.I.C.S.: 456120

Lush Lebanon (1)
Souk Ayass, Beirut, Lebanon
Tel.: (961) 1 991618
Web Site: http://www.lushlebanon.com
Cosmetic Product Distr
N.A.I.C.S.: 456120

Lush Ltd. (1)
29 High Street, Poole, BH15 1AB, Dorset, United Kingdom
Tel.: (44) 1202668545
Web Site: http://www.lush.co.uk
Holding Company; Natural Cosmetics & Fragrances
N.A.I.C.S.: 551112
Andrew Gerrie *(CEO)*

Subsidiary (Domestic):

Lush Ireland Limited (2)
12 Castle Ln, Belfast, BT1 5DA, United Kingdom
Tel.: (44) 2890438672
Web Site: http://www.lush.co.uk
Sales Range: $25-49.9 Million
Emp.: 12
Natural Cosmetics & Fragrances Retail
N.A.I.C.S.: 456120
Chloe Murray *(Mgr)*

Lush Manufacturing Ltd. (2)
Unit 17 Witney Road, Nuffield Industrial Estate, Poole, BH17 0GL, Dorset, United Kingdom
Tel.: (44) 1202 668 545
Web Site: http://www.lush.co.uk
Sales Range: $50-74.9 Million
Emp.: 318
Natural Cosmetics & Fragrances Mfr
N.A.I.C.S.: 325620
Margaret Constantine *(Founder)*

Lush Retail Ltd. (2)
29 High Street, Poole, BH15 1AB, Dorset, United Kingdom
Tel.: (44) 1202 672 217
Web Site: http://www.lush.co.uk
Sales Range: $200-249.9 Million
Emp.: 871
Natural Cosmetics, Bath Products & Fragrances Retail
N.A.I.C.S.: 456120

Subsidiary (Non-US):

Lush Fresh Handmade Cosmetics (3)
1b Charles Street, Canterbury, 2193, NSW, Australia
Tel.: (61) 297848500
Web Site: http://www.lush.com.au
Sales Range: $50-74.9 Million
Emp.: 200
Natural Cosmetics & Fragrances Retail
N.A.I.C.S.: 456120
Megan Taylor *(Mgr-PR)*

Lush Handmade Cosmetics Ltd (3)
4700 Kingsway Suite 1161, Burnaby, V5H 4M2, BC, Canada
Tel.: (604) 437-5874
Web Site: http://www.lush.ca
Natural Cosmetics & Fragrances Mfr & Retailer
N.A.I.C.S.: 456120
Brynn Diaz *(Mgr-Talent Resource)*

Lush Norge (1)
Lushnorge Dronningengsgate 14, 7011, Trondheim, Norway
Tel.: (47) 94131252
Web Site: http://www.lushnorge.no
Cosmetic Product Distr
N.A.I.C.S.: 456120

Lush Saudi Arabia (1)
Olaya Street, Riyadh, Saudi Arabia
Tel.: (966) 112113177
Web Site: http://www.lush.com.sa
Cosmetic Product Distr
N.A.I.C.S.: 456120

Lush Singapore (1)
277 Orchard Road 01-07 Orchard Gateway, Singapore, 238858, Singapore
Tel.: (65) 6702 6135
Web Site: http://www.lushsg.com

Cosmetic Product Distr
N.A.I.C.S.: 456120

Lush Slovenia (1)
Ciril Metodov Trg 21, Ljubljana, Slovenia
Tel.: (386) 1 43 47 477
Web Site: http://www.lush.si
Cosmetic Product Distr
N.A.I.C.S.: 456120

Lush South Africa (1)
Wharf Victoria & Alfred Waterfront, Cape Town, 7104, VIC, South Africa
Tel.: (27) 78 995 05 93
Web Site: http://www.lush.co.za
Cosmetic Product Distr
N.A.I.C.S.: 456120

Lush Sweden AB (1)
Hammarby fabriksvag 43, 120 30, Stockholm, Sweden
Tel.: (46) 8 68 40 50 30
Web Site: http://www.lush.se
Cosmetic Product Distr
N.A.I.C.S.: 456120

Lush TICINO SA (1)
Piazza Cioccaro 11, 6900, Lugano, Switzerland
Tel.: (41) 91 922 52 70
Cosmetic Product Distr
N.A.I.C.S.: 456120

Lush United Arab Emirates (1)
1st Floor Dubai Mall, Dubai, United Arab Emirates
Tel.: (971) 4 435 6114
Web Site: http://www.lush.ae
Cosmetic Product Distr
N.A.I.C.S.: 456120

LUSHANG HEALTH INDUSTRY DEVELOPMENT CO.,LTD.
8F Guodian Building No 9777 East Road Jingshi Road, Jinan, 250014, Shandong, China
Tel.: (86) 53166699999
Web Site: http://www.lshzy.com.cn
600223—(SHG)
Rev.: $1,818,382,625
Assets: $8,209,722,910
Liabilities: $7,428,131,470
Net Worth: $781,591,440
Earnings: $6,381,924
Fiscal Year-end: 12/31/22
Real Estate Support Services
N.A.I.C.S.: 531390
Honglin Dong *(Chm)*

LUSHANG LIFE SERVICE CO., LTD.
Room 202 Block 2 Lushang Guo'ao City No 9777 Jingshi Road, Lixia District, Jinan, Shandong, China
Tel.: (86) 6036688   CN
Web Site:
  https://www.lushangfuwu.com
Year Founded: 2006
2376—(HKG)
Rev.: $85,985,526
Assets: $124,723,600
Liabilities: $52,212,368
Net Worth: $72,511,231
Earnings: $5,574,359
Emp.: 1,437
Fiscal Year-end: 12/31/22
Property Management Services
N.A.I.C.S.: 531311
Zhongwu Wang *(Chm)*

LUSSIER CABINET D'ASSURANCES & SERVICES FINANCIERS INC
80 Rue Augusta, Sorel-Tracy, J3P 1A5, QC, Canada
Tel.: (450) 746-1000
Web Site:
  http://www.lussierassurance.com
Year Founded: 1915
Rev.: $133,634,388
Emp.: 325
Insurance Agencies

N.A.I.C.S.: 524210
Andre Lussier *(Pres)*

LUSTER INDUSTRIES BHD.
Plot 36 37 Jalan PKNK Utama Kawasan Perusahaan Sungai Petani, 08000, Sungai Petani, Kedah Darul Aman, Malaysia
Tel.: (60) 44417980
Web Site:
  https://www.lustergroup.com
Year Founded: 1986
LUSTER—(KLS)
Rev.: $33,027,230
Assets: $117,709,076
Liabilities: $57,609,262
Net Worth: $60,099,814
Earnings: ($3,937,922)
Fiscal Year-end: 12/31/22
Precision Plastic Parts Mfr
N.A.I.C.S.: 332216
Wooi Gee Liang *(Deputy Mng Dir)*

Subsidiaries:

Exzone Plastics Manufacturers Sdn. Bhd. (1)
Lot 38 Jalan 6, Bakar Arang Industrial Estate, 08000, Sungai Petani, Kedah, Malaysia
Tel.: (60) 44216232
Web Site: http://www.exzone.com.my
Plastic Mfr
N.A.I.C.S.: 325211

Glovconcept Sdn. Bhd. (1)
D1-1-1 Block D1 Dana 1 Commercial Centre Jalan PJU 1A/46, Ara Damansara, 47301, Petaling Jaya, Selangor Darul Ehsan, Malaysia
Tel.: (60) 124716861
Web Site: https://glovconcept.com
Stripped Glove Mfr & Distr
N.A.I.C.S.: 339113

Glovmaster Sdn. Bhd. (1)
D1-1-1 Block D1 Dana 1 Commercial Centre Jalan PJU 1A/46 Ara Damansara, 47301, Petaling Jaya, Selangor, Malaysia
Tel.: (60) 124716861
Web Site: https://glovmaster.com.my
Industrial Hand Gloves Mfr & Distr
N.A.I.C.S.: 339113

Winco Precision Engineering (Melaka) Sdn. Bhd. (1)
No 4 Jalan TP 4, Taman Perindustrian Bukit Rambai, 75000, Melaka, Malaysia
Tel.: (60) 63533717
Web Site: https://www.wincoprecision.com
Machine Whslr
N.A.I.C.S.: 423710
Zalbidi Mahmod *(Mng Dir)*

LUTRIJA RS A.D.
Vuka Karadzica 2, 78000, Banja Luka, Bosnia & Herzegovina
Tel.: (387) 51432700
Web Site: https://www.lutrijars.com
LTRS-R-A—(BANJ)
Sales Range: Less than $1 Million
Gambling Services
N.A.I.C.S.: 713290
Milos Acic *(Pres)*

LUX AMBER, CORP.
Shaoyaoju Beili 207, Beijing, 100029, China
Tel.: (86) 702 425 3256   NV
Web Site:
  http://www.luxdesignjewelry.com
Year Founded: 2018
LXAM—(OTCIQ)
Rev.: $998,947
Assets: $3,353,460
Liabilities: $2,468,547
Net Worth: $884,913
Earnings: ($1,984,197)
Emp.: 6
Fiscal Year-end: 04/30/21
Ornament Design Services
N.A.I.C.S.: 541490

E. Thomas Layton *(Chm & CEO)*

LUX GROUP HOLDINGS LIMITED
Hopton Workshop London Road, Devizes, SN10 2EU, Wilts, United Kingdom
Tel.: (44) 2033708000
Web Site: http://www.luxgh.com
Year Founded: 2009
Holding Company; Furniture Designer & Mfr
N.A.I.C.S.: 551112
Andrew P. *(Head-IT)*

Subsidiaries:

Poggenpohl Mobelwerke GmbH (1)
Poggenpohlstr 1, Herford, 32051, Germany
Tel.: (49) 52213810
Web Site: http://www.poggenpohl.com
Kitchen & Bathroom Furnishings for Construction Related Industries
N.A.I.C.S.: 238350
Thomas Kredatus *(Mng Dir)*

LUX INDUSTRIES LIMITED
P S Srijan Tech Park DN-52 Salt Lake City Sector V, Kolkata, 700091, West Bengal, India
Tel.: (91) 3340402121
Web Site:
  https://www.luxinnerwear.com
Year Founded: 1957
539542—(BOM)
Rev.: $287,468,377
Assets: $254,042,324
Liabilities: $81,286,494
Net Worth: $172,755,830
Earnings: $17,596,067
Emp.: 3,055
Fiscal Year-end: 03/31/23
Apparel Mfr & Distr
N.A.I.C.S.: 315250
Ashok Kumar Todi *(Chm)*

Subsidiaries:

Artimas Fashions Private Limited (1)
P S Srijan Tech Park DN -52 Sector-V, Salt Lake City, Kolkata, 700091, West Bengal, India
Tel.: (91) 3340402121
Web Site: https://www.artimas.in
Men Innerwear Mfr
N.A.I.C.S.: 315250

LUX ISLAND RESORTS LTD
Pierre Simonet Street, Floreal, Mauritius
Tel.: (230) 6989800
Web Site: https://www.luxresorts.com
Year Founded: 1987
NRL—(MAU)
Rev.: $178,139,826
Assets: $414,475,927
Liabilities: $240,679,668
Net Worth: $173,796,259
Earnings: $31,420,310
Emp.: 2,824
Fiscal Year-end: 06/30/23
Home Management Services
N.A.I.C.S.: 721110
Desire Elliah *(Co-CFO & Sec)*

Subsidiaries:

SAS Hotel Le Recif (1)
50 Avenue de Bourbon, Saint Gilles Les Bains, 97434, Saint-Paul, Reunion
Tel.: (262) 262700100
Web Site: http://www.hotellerecif.com
Restaurant Services
N.A.I.C.S.: 722511

LUXAT
Quartier Labiry, 64240, Hasparren, Pyrenees Atlantiques, France
Tel.: (33) 559296359
Web Site: http://www.luxat.fr
Rev.: $14,500,000

LUXAT

INTERNATIONAL PUBLIC

Luxat—(Continued)

Emp.: 75
Footwear Mfr
N.A.I.C.S.: 316210
Catherine Dubois (Dir)

LUXBRIGHT AB
Hulda Lindgrens gata 6b, 421 31, Vastra Frolunda, Sweden
Tel.: (46) 317960697
Web Site: https://www.luxbright.com
Year Founded: 2012
LXB—(OMX)
Rev.: $84,381
Assets: $4,039,351
Liabilities: $694,899
Net Worth: $3,344,452
Earnings: ($2,519,507)
Emp.: 10
Fiscal Year-end: 12/31/23
Health Care Srvices
N.A.I.C.S.: 621610
Mats Alm (CEO)

LUXCHEM CORPORATION BERHAD
Block N Jaya One 72A Jalan Prof Diraja Ungku Aziz Seksyen 13, 46200, Petaling Jaya, Selangor, Malaysia
Tel.: (60) 377282155 MY
Web Site: https://www.luxchem.com.my
Year Founded: 1991
LUXCHEM—(KLS)
Rev.: $169,898,572
Assets: $151,897,276
Liabilities: $27,243,593
Net Worth: $124,653,683
Earnings: $10,857,624
Emp.: 262
Fiscal Year-end: 12/31/22
Holding Company; Industrial Chemicals & Unsaturated Polyester Resin Mfr, Distr & Marketer
N.A.I.C.S.: 551112
Ying See Tang (CEO & Mng Dir)

Subsidiaries:

Lexis Chemical Sdn. Bhd. (1)
No 26 Jalan Bestari 2/KU7 Taman Perindustrian Kapar Bestari, Sungai Kapar Indah, 42200, Kapar, Selangor, Malaysia
Tel.: (60) 332911317
Web Site: https://www.lexischemical.com
Specialty Chemicals Mfr
N.A.I.C.S.: 325199

Luxchem Polymer Industries Sdn Bhd (1)
3 Jalan TTC 30 Taman Teknologai Cheng, Fesa 4A, 75250, Melaka, Malaysia
Tel.: (60) 63372728
Web Site: https://www.luxchem.com.my
Sales Range: $25-49.9 Million
Emp.: 45
Plastics Material & Resin Mfr
N.A.I.C.S.: 325211

Luxchem Trading Sdn Bhd (1)
Lot 3385 Jalan Banding Pandamaran, 42000, Port Klang, Selangor, Malaysia
Tel.: (60) 331674142
Chemical Products Distr
N.A.I.C.S.: 424690

Luxchem Vietnam Company Limited (1)
Room A06-06 Republic Plaza 18E Cong Hoa Street, Ward 4 Tan Binh District, Ho Chi Minh City, Vietnam
Tel.: (84) 839307232
Web Site: https://luxchem.com.my
Holding Company Services
N.A.I.C.S.: 551112

PT Luxchem Indonesia (1)
APL Tower LT 21 Suite 6 Jl Letjen Parman Kav 28 Tanjung, Duren Selatan Grogol Petamburan, Jakarta Barat, 11470, Jakarta, Indonesia
Tel.: (62) 2129670585
Web Site: https://www.luxchem.com.my
Holding Company Services
N.A.I.C.S.: 551112

Transform Master Sdn. Bhd. (1)
Lot P2 Lumut Port Industrial Park, Mukim Lumut Kampung Acheh, 32000, Sitiawan, Perak Darul Ridzuan, Malaysia
Tel.: (60) 56922299
Web Site: https://transformmaster.com.my
Holding Company Services
N.A.I.C.S.: 551112

LUXE GREEN ENERGY TECHNOLOGY CO., LTD.
4F-2 No 188 Section 5 Nanjing East Road, Datong Dist, Taipei, 103, Taiwan
Tel.: (886) 225591021
Web Site: https://www.luxe.com.tw
Year Founded: 1978
1529—(TAI)
Rev.: $24,604,139
Assets: $71,625,230
Liabilities: $11,838,582
Net Worth: $59,786,649
Earnings: $4,740,345
Emp.: 47
Fiscal Year-end: 12/31/23
Electronic Components Mfr
N.A.I.C.S.: 334419
Xinxian Liu (Gen Mgr)

LUXE HOLDINGS LIMITED
Tel.: (27) 116081999 ZA
Year Founded: 2000
LUX—(JSE)
Rev.: $24,695,917
Assets: $29,444,725
Liabilities: $20,558,381
Net Worth: $8,886,343
Earnings: ($2,492,101)
Emp.: 975
Fiscal Year-end: 02/28/21
Investment Management Service
N.A.I.C.S.: 523940
Claire Middlemiss (Sec)

Subsidiaries:

Scooters Pizza (Pty) Ltd. (1)
288 Main Avenue, Ferndale, Randburg, 2194, South Africa
Tel.: (27) 11 608 1999
Web Site: http://www.scooterspizza.co.za
Pizza Distribution Services
N.A.I.C.S.: 722513

LUXELL TECHNOLOGIES INC
2145 Meadowpine Blvd, Mississauga, L5N 6R8, ON, Canada
Tel.: (905) 363-0325
Web Site: http://www.luxell.com
Sales Range: $1-9.9 Million
Emp.: 71
Flat Panel Display Technologies Research, Development & Commercial Licensing
N.A.I.C.S.: 423690
Richard Pepperall (VP-Ops & Engrg)

LUXEMBOURG AIRPORT COMPANY
4 Rue de Treves, BP 635, 2016, Luxembourg, Luxembourg
Tel.: (352) 24640
Web Site: https://www.lux-airport.lu
Air Freight Forwarding Services
N.A.I.C.S.: 481212
Rene Steinhaus (CEO)

LUXEMPART SA
12 Rue Leon Laval, 3372, Leudelange, Luxembourg
Tel.: (352) 437435101
Web Site: https://www.luxempart.lu
LXMPR—(LUX)
Rev.: $40,178,828
Assets: $2,578,843,140
Liabilities: $13,939,728
Net Worth: $2,564,903,411
Earnings: $202,586,378
Emp.: 28
Fiscal Year-end: 12/31/23
Investment Holding Services
N.A.I.C.S.: 523940
Francois Tesch (Chm)

LUXEY INTERNATIONAL (HOLDINGS) LIMITED
Unit B 5/F Hang Cheong Factory Building, 1 Wing Ming Street Cheung Sha Wan, Kowloon, China (Hong Kong)
Tel.: (852) 2520 6020
Web Site: http://www.luxey.com.hk
8041—(HKG)
Rev.: $9,184,279
Assets: $10,413,071
Liabilities: $4,169,279
Net Worth: $6,243,793
Earnings: ($772,203)
Emp.: 88
Fiscal Year-end: 06/30/21
Holding Company; Shopping & Direct Mailing Services
N.A.I.C.S.: 551112
Hiu Kwan Chan (CEO, Officer-Compliance & Sec)

LUXFER HOLDINGS PLC
Lumns Lane, Manchester, M27 8LN, United Kingdom
Tel.: (44) 3308226000 UK
Web Site: https://www.luxfermeltech.com
LXFR—(NYSE)
Rev.: $405,000,000
Assets: $372,100,000
Liabilities: $159,500,000
Net Worth: $212,600,000
Earnings: ($1,900,000)
Emp.: 1,300
Fiscal Year-end: 12/31/23
Holding Company; Chemical Products Mfr
N.A.I.C.S.: 551112
Andrew William John Butcher (CEO)

Subsidiaries:

Luxfer Group Limited (1)
Anchorage Gateway 5 Anchorage Quay, Salford, M50 3XE, United Kingdom (100%)
Tel.: (44) 161 300 0600
Web Site: http://www.luxfer.com
Emp.: 20
Holding Company
N.A.I.C.S.: 551112

Subsidiary (US):

BA Holdings, Inc. (2)
3016 Kansas Ave, Riverside, CA 92507-3441 (100%)
Tel.: (951) 684-5110
Web Site: http://www.luxfercylinders.com
Sales Range: $200-249.9 Million
Holding Company
N.A.I.C.S.: 551112

Subsidiary (Domestic):

Luxfer, Inc. (3)
3016 Kansas Ave, Riverside, CA 92507-3441 (100%)
Tel.: (951) 684-5110
Web Site: http://www.luxfercylinders.com
Sales Range: $100-124.9 Million
Mfr of High Pressure Gas Cylinders
N.A.I.C.S.: 332999

Subsidiary (US):

Hart Metals, Inc. (2)
1415 E Broad St, Tamaqua, PA 18252
Tel.: (570) 668-0001
Rev.: $8,900,000
Emp.: 48
Mfr & Supplier of Magnesium Powders
N.A.I.C.S.: 325180

Subsidiary (Non-US):

Luxfer Australia Pty Limited (2)
Unit 4 171-175 Newton Road, Wetherill Park, 2164, NSW, Australia (100%)
Tel.: (61) 298300999
Web Site: http://www.luxfercylinders.com
Emp.: 4
Distr of High Pressure Gas Cylinders
N.A.I.C.S.: 423990

Luxfer Gas Cylinders (Shanghai) Co., Limited (2)
No 123 Lane 150 Pingbei Road, Minhang District, Shanghai, 201109, China (100%)
Tel.: (86) 2164904007
Mfr of High Pressure Aluminium & Carbon Composite Gas Cylinders
N.A.I.C.S.: 332999

Subsidiary (Domestic):

Luxfer Gas Cylinders Limited (2)
Colwick Industrial Estate, Nottingham, NG4 2BH, United Kingdom
Tel.: (44) 1159803800
Web Site: http://www.luxfercylinders.com
Designer & Mfr of High Pressure Aluminum & Composite Cylinders
N.A.I.C.S.: 331318

Subsidiary (Non-US):

Luxfer Gas Cylinders S.A.S. (2)
Rue de L'Industrie, BP 7, 63360, Gerzat, France (100%)
Tel.: (33) 473236400
Designer & Mfr of High Pressure Aluminium & Carbon Composite Gas Cylinders
N.A.I.C.S.: 332999

Subsidiary (US):

Luxfer Magtech Inc. (2)
2940 Highland Ave Unit 210, Cincinnati, OH 45212
Tel.: (513) 554-1200
Web Site: https://luxfermagtech.com
Heating Equipment Mfr
N.A.I.C.S.: 333414

MEL Chemicals, Inc. (2)
500 Barbertown Point Breeze Rd, Flemington, NJ 08822
Tel.: (908) 782-5800
Web Site: https://www.luxfermeltechnologies.com
Rev.: $2,333,333
Emp.: 70
Mfr & Supplier of Zirconium Chemicals & Oxides
N.A.I.C.S.: 325998

Subsidiary (Domestic):

Magnesium Elektron Limited (2)
PO Box 23, Swinton, Manchester, M27 8DD, United Kingdom (100%)
Tel.: (44) 161 911 1000
Web Site: http://www.magnesium-elektron.com
Development, Manufacture & Supply of Magnesium Products & Services
N.A.I.C.S.: 332999

Subsidiary (US):

Magnesium Elektron North America, Inc. (2)
1001 College St, Madison, IL 62060-1084
Tel.: (618) 452-5190
Web Site: https://luxferga.com
Sales Range: $75-99.9 Million
Emp.: 100
Magnesium & Magnesium Alloy Bars, Shapes, Sheets & Aluminum Plates Mfr
N.A.I.C.S.: 331491

Reade Manufacturing Company (2)
2590 Bridgeway Blvd, Manchester Township, NJ 08795 (100%)
Tel.: (732) 657-6451
Web Site: http://www.magnesium-elektron.com
Emp.: 35
Basic Inorganic Chemical Mfr
N.A.I.C.S.: 325180
James Gardella (Pres)

AND PRIVATE COMPANIES

Structural Composites Industries LLC (1)
336 Enterprise Pl, Pomona, CA 91768-3245
Tel.: (909) 594-7777
Sales Range: $25-49.9 Million
Emp.: 150
Composite Pressure Natural Gas Cylinder Mfr
N.A.I.C.S.: 332420

LUXI CHEMICAL GROUP CO., LTD.
Chemical Industrial Park, High Technology Industrial Development Zone, Liaocheng, 252000, Shandong, China
Tel.: (86) 4007000830
Web Site: https://en.luxichemical.com
Year Founded: 1998
000830—(SSE)
Rev.: $2,695,339,265
Assets: $4,981,269,235
Liabilities: $2,368,150,117
Net Worth: $2,613,119,118
Earnings: $126,372,204
Emp.: 12,000
Fiscal Year-end: 12/31/20
Chemical Products Mfr
N.A.I.C.S.: 325998
Wang Ligang *(Chm)*

LUXIN VENTURE CAPITAL GROUP CO., LTD
Tower A No 2788 Olympic Sports West Road, Jinan, 250101, Shandong, China
Tel.: (86) 53186566770
Web Site: http://www.600783.cn
Year Founded: 1993
600783—(SHG)
Rev.: $16,235,547
Assets: $1,194,730,009
Liabilities: $551,009,389
Net Worth: $643,720,620
Earnings: $67,512,196
Fiscal Year-end: 12/31/22
Abrasive Product Mfr & Distr
N.A.I.C.S.: 327910
Guo Xiangzhong *(Chm-Supervisory Bd)*

LUXKING GROUP HOLDINGS LIMITED
26 Lianfeng Road, Xiaolan Town, Zhongshan, 528415, Guangdong, China
Tel.: (86) 76022126315   BM
Web Site: https://www.newasiatapes.com
Year Founded: 1995
BKK—(SES)
Rev.: $88,153,204
Assets: $46,629,770
Liabilities: $27,775,441
Net Worth: $18,854,329
Earnings: $335,990
Emp.: 600
Fiscal Year-end: 06/30/22
Adhesive Mfr
N.A.I.C.S.: 325520
Chee Kwong Leung *(Founder, Chm & CEO)*

Subsidiaries:

Zhongshan New Asia Adhesive Products Co., Ltd (1)
Lianfeng Road Jiu Zhouji, Xiaolan Town, Zhongshan, 528415, Guangdong, China
Tel.: (86) 76022126315
Web Site: https://www.newasiatape.com
Adhesive Tape Products Distr
N.A.I.C.S.: 424690

LUXL CO., LTD.
3F 107 Bongeunsa-ro, Gangnam-gu, Seoul, 06120, Korea (South)
Tel.: (82) 7074629538
33600—(KRS)

Sales Range: $10-24.9 Million
Automobile Part Mfr & Distr
N.A.I.C.S.: 336390
Yeon-Soon Kim *(CEO)*

LUXOS SA
Z D'activite Hlm La Piche, 38430, Moirans, Isere, France
Tel.: (33) 476353167
Rev.: $11,400,000
Emp.: 80
Meat Pastry Catering
N.A.I.C.S.: 311612
Richard Luxos *(Pres)*

LUXPIA CO., LTD
10F 109 Gwanggyo-ro, Yeongtong-gu, Suwon, Gyeonggi-do, Korea (South)
Tel.: (82) 7086712400
Web Site: http://www.luxpialed.com
Year Founded: 2000
Light Emitting Diode Product Mfr
N.A.I.C.S.: 334413

Subsidiaries:

Luxpia Co., Ltd - Jeonju Plant (1)
948-1 Dunsan-li 46 Wanjusandan 7-ro Bongdong-eup, Jeonju, Wanju-Gun Jeollabuk, Korea (South)
Tel.: (82) 7086712500
Light Emitting Diode Mfr
N.A.I.C.S.: 334413

LUXSHARE PRECISION INDUSTRY CO., LTD.
2nd Floor Ho Street New Industrial Zone, West of Sanyo Bao'an District, Shenzhen, Guangdong, China
Tel.: (86) 76987892475
Year Founded: 2004
002475—(SSE)
Rev.: $30,049,585,956
Assets: $20,833,158,528
Liabilities: $12,579,903,180
Net Worth: $8,253,255,348
Earnings: $1,286,499,240
Emp.: 7,000
Fiscal Year-end: 12/31/22
Electronic Connector Mfr
N.A.I.C.S.: 334417
Grace Wang *(Chm)*

Subsidiaries:

Korea Luxshare-ICT Co., Ltd. (1)
30 Namdong daero 215beon gil, Namdong-gu, Incheon, 405-817, Seoul, Korea (South)
Tel.: (82) 328147730
Electronic Components Mfr
N.A.I.C.S.: 334419

Luxshare-ICT (Japan) Limited (1)
Room1405 14F Nisseki yokohama bldg 1-1-8 Sakuragi-cho, Naka-ku, Yokohama, 231-0062, Kanagawa, Japan
Tel.: (81) 456802680
Electronic Components Mfr
N.A.I.C.S.: 334419
Gina Ger *(Sls Mgr)*

Luxshare-ICT Europe Limited (1)
Lowton Business Park Newton Road Lowton St Mary's, Warrington, WA3 2AP, United Kingdom
Tel.: (44) 1942675874
Electronic Components Mfr
N.A.I.C.S.: 334419
Dawn Stephen *(Office Mgr-Sls)*

Luxshare-ICT, Inc. (1)
Tel.: (408) 957-0535
Electronic Components Mfr
N.A.I.C.S.: 334419
Charles Fan *(Sls Dir)*

SuK Kunststoffrechnik GmbH (1)
Am Funkenhof 10, 58566, Kierspe, Germany
Tel.: (49) 2359294980
Web Site: https://www.suk-gmbh.de
Electronic Components Mfr
N.A.I.C.S.: 334419

LUXURY CONCEPTS WATCHES & JEWELLERY SDN. BHD.
Level 5 Annexe Block Lot 10 Shopping Centre, 50 Jalan Sultan Ismail, Kuala Lumpur, 50250, Malaysia
Tel.: (60) 321426328   MY
Web Site: http://www.luxuryconcepts.com.my
Year Founded: 2005
Sales Range: $25-49.9 Million
Emp.: 40
Holding Company; Watch & Jewelry Brand Management & Retailer
N.A.I.C.S.: 551112
Charmaine Low *(Gen Mgr)*

Subsidiaries:

Bedat & Co. SA (1)
8 rue du Rhone, 1204, Geneva, Switzerland
Tel.: (41) 228108587
Web Site: http://www.bedat.com
Sales Range: $25-49.9 Million
Emp.: 10
Luxury Watch Mfr & Distr
N.A.I.C.S.: 334519
Gan Kollros *(CEO)*

LUXURY FOR LESS LIMITED
Unit H2 Grovelands Industrial Estate Longford Road Exhall, Coventry, CV7 9ND, United Kingdom
Tel.: (44) 2476 389052
Web Site: http://www.bathempire.com
Year Founded: 2009
Sales Range: $10-24.9 Million
Emp.: 55
Bathroom Product Whslr
N.A.I.C.S.: 423220
Dave Steptoe *(Mgr-Warehouse)*

LUXVISIONS INNOVATION LIMITED
3F No 136 Jian 1st Rd Zhonghe Dist, New Taipei City, Taiwan
Tel.: (886) 2 8024 3066
Web Site: http://www.luxvisions-inno.com
Camera Lenses Mfr
N.A.I.C.S.: 333310

Subsidiaries:

Guangzhou Luxvisions Innovation Technology Limited (1)
No 25 Guangpu West Road Science City, Guangzhou Hi-tech Industrial Developemt Zone, Guangzhou, China
Tel.: (86) 20 6661599
Camera Lenses Mfr
N.A.I.C.S.: 333310

LUXXFOLIO HOLDINGS, INC.
119-6th Ave SW, Calgary, T2P 0P8, AB, Canada
Web Site: https://www.luxxfolio.com
LUXX—(OTCIQ)
Holding Company
N.A.I.C.S.: 551112
Zeke Iribar *(CTO)*

LUXXO, INC.
Bukit Jalil City Signature Shop-Offices N-9-1 N-9-2 N-9-3, Pusat Perdagangan Bandar Bukit Jalil Persiaran Jalil 2, 57000, Kuala Lumpur, Malaysia
Tel.: (60) 3 8605 3699   DE
Year Founded: 2016
Assets: $200,705
Liabilities: $44,270
Net Worth: $156,435
Earnings: ($87,936)
Emp.: 4
Fiscal Year-end: 08/31/19
Medical & Healthcare Services
N.A.I.C.S.: 621610
Ch'ng Wee Ling *(Co-Founder & Pres)*

LUXXU GROUP LIMITED
Room 17 7/F Block 1 Enterprise Square 9 Sheung Yuet Road, Kowloon, China (Hong Kong)
Tel.: (852) 5962600781
Web Site: http://www.time2u.com
1327—(HKG)
Rev.: $9,043,024
Assets: $21,787,132
Liabilities: $5,167,282
Net Worth: $16,619,850
Earnings: ($6,773,879)
Emp.: 56
Fiscal Year-end: 12/31/22
Watch Mfr
N.A.I.C.S.: 339910
Ching Chuen See *(Exec Dir)*

LUYAN (FUJIAN) PHARMA CO., LTD.
Xiamen Huatai Road Building 3 A, Huli District, Xiamen, 361006, Fujian, China
Tel.: (86) 592 8128888
Web Site: http://www.luyan.com.cn
Holding Company
N.A.I.C.S.: 551112
Belinda Han *(Gen Mgr)*

Subsidiaries:

Goodman Medical Supplies Limited (1)
Unit C 6/F Block II Camelpaint Building 62 Hoi Yuen Road, Kwun Tong, Kowloon, China (Hong Kong) (100%)
Tel.: (852) 2332 4455
Web Site: http://www.goodman.hk
Emp.: 26
Medical Equipment & Accessories Whslr
N.A.I.C.S.: 423450

LUYE MEDICAL GROUP
137 Telok Ayer Street #05-05, Singapore, 068602, Minhang, Singapore
Tel.: (65) 622 00 119   SG
Web Site: http://www.luyemedical.com
Year Founded: 2015
Emp.: 10,000
Medical Devices
N.A.I.C.S.: 622110
Charles Chong Guang Wang *(CEO)*

Subsidiaries:

Healthe Care Australia Pty Ltd. (1)
Level 13 160 Sussex Street, Sydney, 2000, NSW, Australia
Tel.: (61) 2 9215 8200
Web Site: http://www.healthecare.com.au
Emp.: 7,000
Health Care Srvices
N.A.I.C.S.: 621498
Geoff Sam *(Exec Gen Mgr-Clinical Governance, Risk & Quality)*

Subsidiary (Domestic):

Pulse Health Limited (2)
Level 22 227 Elizabeth Street, Sydney, 2000, NSW, Australia
Tel.: (61) 0282787300
Web Site: http://www.pulsehealth.net.au
Healtcare Services
N.A.I.C.S.: 621999
Stuart Bruce James *(Chm)*

Subsidiary (Domestic):

Forster Private Hospital Pty. Ltd. (3)
29-41 S St, Forster, 2428, NSW, Australia
Tel.: (61) 265551333
Web Site: http://www.forsterprivate.com.au
Medical & Surgical Hospitals
N.A.I.C.S.: 622110
Jenny Bullivant *(Gen Mgr & Dir-Nursing)*

Gympie Private Hospital Pty. Ltd. (3)
78-82 Channon St, Gympie, 4570, QLD, Australia
Tel.: (61) 754830500
Web Site: http://www.gympieprivate.com.au
Medical & Surgical Hospitals

LUYE MEDICAL GROUP

Luye Medical Group—(Continued)
N.A.I.C.S.: 622110
Helen Chalmers (Gen Mgr)

Westmead Rehabilitation Hospital Pty. Ltd. (3)
7 Coleman St, South Wentworthville, Newcastle, 2145, NSW, Australia
Tel.: (61) 288333555
Web Site: http://www.westmeadrehab.net.au
Rehabilitation Hospital Services
N.A.I.C.S.: 622310
Amanda Jones (Gen Mgr)

Subsidiary (Domestic):

Shellharbour Private Hospital Pty. Ltd. (2)
27 Captain Cook Drive, Barrack Heights, Shellharbour, 2528, NSW, Australia
Tel.: (61) 2 4295 2999
Web Site: http://www.shellharbourprivate.com.au
Hospital Operator
N.A.I.C.S.: 622110
Chris Walsh (CEO)

South Coast Private Pty. Ltd. (2)
112 Burelli Street, Wollongong, 2500, NSW, Australia
Tel.: (61) 800 250 000
Web Site: http://www.southcoastprivate.com.au
Psychiatric Hospital Operator
N.A.I.C.S.: 622210
Kim Capp (CEO)

LUYIN INVESTMENT GROUP CO., LTD.
26th Floor Building 3 Guotai Wealth Plaza No 8777 Tourism Road, High-tech Zone, Jinan, 250101, Shandong, China
Tel.: (86) 53159596777
Web Site: https://www.luyin.cn
Year Founded: 1993
600784—(SHG)
Rev.: $531,972,904
Assets: $735,369,121
Liabilities: $334,353,797
Net Worth: $401,015,324
Earnings: $45,554,058
Fiscal Year-end: 12/31/22
Iron & Steel Product Mfr & Distr
N.A.I.C.S.: 331110
Yang Yaodong (Chm)

LUZERNER KANTONALBANK
Pilatusstrasse 12, 6003, Lucerne, Switzerland
Tel.: (41) 844822811
Web Site: https://www.lukb.ch
Year Founded: 1850
LUKN—(SWX)
Sales Range: $400-449.9 Million
Emp.: 1,000
Banking Services
N.A.I.C.S.: 522110
Daniel Salzmann (CEO & Member-Mgmt Bd)

Subsidiaries:

LKB Expert Fondsleitung AG (1)
Pilatusstrasse 12, PO Box 3567, 6002, Lucerne, Switzerland
Tel.: (41) 412101214
Sales Range: $150-199.9 Million
Emp.: 600
Fund Management Services
N.A.I.C.S.: 541618

LUZHOU BANK CO., LTD.
Building 1 No 18 Section 3 Jiucheng Avenue, Jiangyang District, Luzhou, 646000, Sichuan, China
Tel.: (86) 8302362606   CN
Web Site: http://www.lzccb.cn
1983—(HKG)
Rev.: $1,052,316,814
Assets: $20,867,627,711
Liabilities: $19,436,163,224

Net Worth: $1,431,464,486
Earnings: $113,377,072
Emp.: 1,408
Fiscal Year-end: 12/31/22
Commercial Banking Services
N.A.I.C.S.: 522110
Jiang You (Chm)

LUZHOU BIO-CHEM TECHNOLOGY LIMITED
No 18 Luzhou Road, Yishui, 276400, Shandong, China
Tel.: (86) 5392322711
Web Site: http://www.luzhou.com.sg
Rev.: $292,232,237
Assets: $148,290,953
Liabilities: $163,104,378
Net Worth: ($14,813,426)
Earnings: ($15,505,171)
Fiscal Year-end: 12/31/19
Bio Technology Services
N.A.I.C.S.: 541714
Ke Zhang (Deputy Gen Mgr-Grp)

Subsidiaries:

Luzhou Bio-Chem Technology (Liaoning) Co., Ltd. (1)
Gaowan Economic Zone Economic Development Area, Fushun, 113123, Liaoning, China
Tel.: (86) 4136102188
Corn Starch Product Mfr & Distr
N.A.I.C.S.: 311221

Luzhou Bio-Chem Technology (Shaanxi) Co., Ltd. (1)
NO 54 Xingyu Road, Xingping, 713100, Shaanxi, China
Tel.: (86) 9108736125
Corn Starch Product Mfr & Distr
N.A.I.C.S.: 311221

LUZHOU XINGLU WATER (GROUP) CO., LTD.
16 Baizi Road, Jiangyang District, Luzhou, Sichuan, China
Tel.: (86) 8303194768   CN
Web Site: https://www.lzss.com
Year Founded: 1958
2281—(HKG)
Rev.: $190,020,065
Assets: $1,002,535,722
Liabilities: $603,656,552
Net Worth: $398,879,170
Earnings: $31,343,008
Emp.: 933
Fiscal Year-end: 12/31/22
Water Supply Services
N.A.I.C.S.: 221310
Zhang Qi (Chm, Sec-Party Committee & Exec Dir)

LVGEM (CHINA) REAL ESTATE INVESTMENT COMPANY LIMITED
Room 2501 Greenview NEO Building 123 Hoi Bun Road Kwun Tong, Kowloon, China (Hong Kong)
Tel.: (852) 21239530   Ky
Web Site: https://www.lvgem-china.com
0095—(HKG)
Rev.: $328,665,308
Assets: $13,998,524,857
Liabilities: $9,649,422,572
Net Worth: $4,349,102,285
Earnings: ($41,632,110)
Emp.: 2,379
Fiscal Year-end: 12/31/22
Property Development & Property Investment Services
N.A.I.C.S.: 531312
Jingshu Huang (Chm)

Subsidiaries:

Shenzhen LVGEM Hotel Co., Ltd. (1)
No 3099 Xinzhou Road, Futian District,

Shenzhen, 518048, China
Tel.: (86) 2086009099
Web Site: http://www.lvgemhotelshenzhen.com
Home Management Services
N.A.I.C.S.: 721110

LVJI TECHNOLOGY HOLDINGS INC.
Room 501 238 Gaotang Road, Tianhe, Guangzhou, China   Ky
Web Site: https://www.lvji.cn
Year Founded: 2013
1745—(HKG)
Rev.: $81,052,697
Assets: $143,763,569
Liabilities: $17,044,611
Net Worth: $126,718,958
Earnings: $20,099,551
Emp.: 54
Fiscal Year-end: 12/31/23
Holding Company
N.A.I.C.S.: 551112
Lei Wang (Vice Chm)

LVJING HOLDING CO., LTD.
Floor 35 Hai Hang Building No 8 Linhe Middle Road, Tianhe District, Guangzhou, 510610, Guangdong, China
Tel.: (86) 202 208 2956
Web Site: http://www.000502.cn
000502—(SSE)
Rev.: $2,258,315
Assets: $35,480,372
Liabilities: $6,212,666
Net Worth: $29,267,706
Earnings: ($2,826,725)
Fiscal Year-end: 12/31/20
Holding Company
N.A.I.C.S.: 551112
Wang Bin (Pres)•

LVL ENERGY FUND PLC
Tel.: (94) 112439201
Web Site: https://www.lvlenergyfund.lk
Year Founded: 2006
LVEF.N0000—(COL)
Rev.: $917,388
Assets: $30,330,059
Liabilities: $11,255,901
Net Worth: $19,074,158
Earnings: ($975,219)
Fiscal Year-end: 03/31/23
Eletric Power Generation Services
N.A.I.C.S.: 221118
Sumith Arangala (CEO)

LVMC HOLDINGS
10th Floor Pearl Plaza Building 561A Dien Bien Phu, Ward 25 Binh Thanh District, Ho Chi Minh City, Vietnam
Tel.: (84) 7086154824
Web Site: http://www.lvmcholdings.net
Year Founded: 2009
900140—(KRS)
Rev.: $199,528,253
Assets: $505,537,142
Liabilities: $181,131,218
Net Worth: $324,405,924
Earnings: ($31,716,352)
Emp.: 49
Fiscal Year-end: 12/31/23
Holding Company; Automobiles & Related Parts Sales; Motorcycle Mfr & Sales
N.A.I.C.S.: 551112
Sei-Young Oh (Chm & Co-CEO)

LVMH MOET HENNESSY LOUIS VUITTON SE
22 avenue Montaigne, 75008, Paris, France
Tel.: (33) 144132222   FR
Web Site: https://www.lvmh.com

INTERNATIONAL PUBLIC

Year Founded: 1987
MC—(EUR)
Rev.: $92,977,552,342
Assets: $155,076,624,218
Liabilities: $87,408,806,389
Net Worth: $67,667,817,829
Earnings: $16,375,998,273
Emp.: 192,287
Fiscal Year-end: 12/31/23
Personal care Product Mfr
N.A.I.C.S.: 551112
Antonio Belloni (Gen Mgr)

Subsidiaries:

Acqua Di Parma LLC (1)
208 Fernwood Ave, Edison, NJ 08837-3839
Tel.: (732) 346-6990
Cosmetic Product Distr
N.A.I.C.S.: 456120

Avenue M International SCA (1)
23 Rue du Pont Neuf, 75001, Paris, France (100%)
Tel.: (33) 1 44 13 23 44
Sales Range: $50-74.9 Million
Emp.: 85
Holding Company
N.A.I.C.S.: 551112

Beauty in Motion Sdn. Bhd. (1)
Starhill Gallery Terrace 181 Jalan Bukit Bintang, 55100, Kuala Lumpur, Malaysia
Tel.: (60) 3 2141 6688
Cosmetic & Perfume Distr
N.A.I.C.S.: 456120

Belmond Ltd. (1)
Shackleton House 4 Battle Bridge Lane, London, SE1 2HP, United Kingdom
Web Site: http://www.belmond.com
Leisure Properties Owner & Manager
N.A.I.C.S.: 721110

Subsidiary (Non-US):

80 Westcliff (Pty) Ltd. (2)
The Westcliff, 67 Jan Smuts Ave, Johannesburg, South Africa (100%)
Tel.: (27) 114816000
Web Site: http://www.westcliff.co.za
Sales Range: $25-49.9 Million
Emp.: 200
Hotel Operator
N.A.I.C.S.: 721110

Belmond Cap Juluca Ltd (2)
Maundays Bay British West Indies, Anguilla, AI-2640, Anguilla
Tel.: (264) 4976666
Hotel Services
N.A.I.C.S.: 721110
Tiago Moraes Sarmento (Gen Mgr)

Belmond Castello di Casole S.r.l. (2)
Localita Querceto Casole D Elsa, 53013, Siena, Italy
Tel.: (39) 0577961501
Web Site: http://www.belmond.com
Hotel Operator
N.A.I.C.S.: 721110

Belmond Italia S.r.l. (2)
Corso Vercelli 2, 20145, Milan, Italy
Tel.: (39) 01852678460
Web Site: http://www.belmond.com
Holding Company; Hotel Management Services
N.A.I.C.S.: 551112
Marcello Scaccabarozzi (Dir-Sls-Italy)

Subsidiary (Domestic):

Hotel Caruso S.r.l. (3)
Piazza San Giovanni Del Toro 2, 84010, Ravello, Italy
Tel.: (39) 089 858 801
Web Site: http://www.hotelcaruso.com
Home Management Services
N.A.I.C.S.: 721110

Hotel Cipriani S.r.l. (3)
Giudecca 10, 30133, Venice, Italy (100%)
Tel.: (39) 041240801
Web Site: http://www.hotelcipriani.com
Sales Range: $25-49.9 Million
Emp.: 200
Hotel Operator
N.A.I.C.S.: 721110

AND PRIVATE COMPANIES

Hotel Splendido S.r.l. (3)
Salita Baratta 16, 16034, Portofino, Italy
Tel.: (39) 0185267801
Web Site: http://www.hotelsplendido.com
Sales Range: $25-49.9 Million
Emp.: 200
Hotel Operator
N.A.I.C.S.: 721110

Villa San Michele S.r.l. (3)
Via Doccia 4 Fiesole, 50014, Florence,
Italy (100%)
Tel.: (39) 0555678200
Web Site: http://www.villasanmichele.orient-express.com
Sales Range: $10-24.9 Million
Emp.: 80
Hotel & Resort Operator
N.A.I.C.S.: 721110

Subsidiary (Domestic):

Belmond Management Limited (2)
1st Floor Shackleton House 4 Battle Bridge Lane, London, SE1 2HP, United Kingdom
Tel.: (44) 2079214000
Web Site: http://www.belmond.com
Emp.: 137
Home Management Services
N.A.I.C.S.: 721110
Ralph Aruzza *(Chief Sls & Mktg Officer)*

Subsidiary (Domestic):

Belmond (UK) Limited (3)
1st Floor Shackleton House 4 Battle Bridge Lane, London, SE1 2HP, United Kingdom
Tel.: (44) 2031171300
Web Site: http://www.belmond.com
Sales Range: $25-49.9 Million
Emp.: 100
Hotel, Cruises & Tourist Train Operations
N.A.I.C.S.: 721110

Subsidiary (Non-US):

Belmond Mount Nelson Hotel Ltd. (3)
76 Orange Street, Gardens, Cape Town, 8001, South Africa (100%)
Tel.: (27) 214831000
Web Site: http://www.mountnelson.co.za
Sales Range: $10-24.9 Million
Emp.: 200
Hotel Operator
N.A.I.C.S.: 721110
Amy Brandt *(VP-Fin & IR)*

Subsidiary (US):

Belmond USA Inc. (2)
441 Lexington Ave Ste 504, New York, NY 10017
Tel.: (212) 302-5055
Web Site: http://www.belmond.com
Hotel & Tourist Train Operations
N.A.I.C.S.: 721110
Richard M. Levine *(Chief Legal Officer)*

Subsidiary (Domestic):

21 Club Inc. (3)
21 W 52nd St, New York, NY 10019
Tel.: (212) 582-7200
Web Site: http://www.21club.com
Home Management Services
N.A.I.C.S.: 721110
Phil Pratt *(Dir-Wine)*

Belmond Reservation Services Inc (3)
205 Meeting St, Charleston, SC 29401
Tel.: (843) 937-9068
Hotel Services
N.A.I.C.S.: 721110

Charleston Place Holdings Inc. (3)
205 Meeting St, Charleston, SC 29401-3107
Tel.: (843) 722-4900
Web Site: http://www.charlestonplace.com
Emp.: 620
Hotel Operations
N.A.I.C.S.: 721110
Paul Stracey *(Mng Dir)*

El Encanto Inc. (3)
1900 Lasuen Rd, Santa Barbara, CA 93103
Tel.: (805) 667-5000
Web Site: http://www.elencantohotel.com
Rev.: $12,700,000
Emp.: 3
Hotel Operator
N.A.I.C.S.: 721110

Inn at Perry Cabin Corporation (3)
308 Watkins Ln, Saint Michaels, MD 21663
Tel.: (410) 745-2200
Web Site: http://www.perrycabin.com
Home Management Services
N.A.I.C.S.: 721110
Claus Kabelitz *(Gen Mgr)*

Keswick Corporation (3)
850 Black Cat Rd, Keswick, VA 22947
Tel.: (434) 245-0900
Home Management Services
N.A.I.C.S.: 721110

Venice Simplon-Orient-Express Inc. (3)
1114 Ave of the Americas 3rd Fl, New York, NY 10036-7703
Tel.: (212) 302-5055
Travel Services
N.A.I.C.S.: 561510

Windsor Court Hotel Inc. (3)
300 Gravier St, New Orleans, LA 70130
Tel.: (504) 523-6000
Web Site: http://www.windsorcourthotel.com
Hotel Operator
N.A.I.C.S.: 721110
Megan Uram *(Dir-Sls & Mktg)*

Subsidiary (Domestic):

Blanc Restaurants Ltd. (2)
Promenade, Cheltenham, GL50 1NN, Gloucestershire, United Kingdom
Tel.: (44) 1242266800
Restaurant Operating Services
N.A.I.C.S.: 721110

Collection Venice Simplon-Orient-Express Ltd. (2)
Shackleton House 4 Battle Bridge Lane, London, SE1 2HP, United Kingdom
Tel.: (44) 6563950678
Web Site: http://www.orient-express.com
Emp.: 15
Home Management Services
N.A.I.C.S.: 721110

Subsidiary (Non-US):

Copacabana Palace Hotel (2)
Avenida Atlantica 1702, Rio de Janeiro, 22021-001, Brazil
Tel.: (55) 2135000292
Web Site: http://www.copacabanapalace.com.br
Sales Range: $50-74.9 Million
Emp.: 492
Hotel Operator
N.A.I.C.S.: 721110
Andrea Natal *(Mng Dir)*

E&O Services (Singapore) Ltd. (2)
100 Beach Rd 18, Singapore, 189702, Singapore (100%)
Tel.: (65) 63923500
Sales Range: $25-49.9 Million
Emp.: 6
Provider of Transportation Services
N.A.I.C.S.: 488210
Nicoles Pillet *(Gen Mgr)*

Subsidiary (Domestic):

Harry's Bar Ltd. (2)
26 South Audley Street, London, W1K 2PD, United Kingdom (100%)
Tel.: (44) 2074080844
Web Site: http://www.harrysbar.co.uk
Restaurant
N.A.I.C.S.: 722511

Subsidiary (Non-US):

Island Hotel (Madeira) Ltd. (2)
Estrada Monumental 139, 9004-549, Funchal, Portugal
Tel.: (351) 291717171
Web Site: http://www.belmond.com
Sales Range: $50-74.9 Million
Emp.: 214
Home Management Services
N.A.I.C.S.: 721110
Cereco Campus *(Gen Mgr)*

LLC Europe Hotel (2)
Baikalskaya Str 69, 664047, Irkutsk, Russia
Tel.: (7) 3952291515
Web Site: http://www.europehotel.ru
Hotel Operating Services
N.A.I.C.S.: 721110

La Samanna S.A.S. (2)
PO Box 4077, 97064, Saint Martin, Cedex, Guadeloupe
Tel.: (590) 590 87 64 00
Web Site: http://www.lasamanna.com
Sales Range: $25-49.9 Million
Emp.: 150
Home Management Services
N.A.I.C.S.: 721110
Michael Schoonewagen *(Mng Dir)*

Luxury Trains S.r.l. (2)
Via Parco Ferroviario 1, Marghera, 30170, Venice, Italy
Tel.: (39) 0415205300
Train Transportation Services
N.A.I.C.S.: 488999

OEH Peru Ltd. (2)
Av Malecon De La Reserva 1035, Miraflores, Lima, 18, Peru (50%)
Tel.: (51) 12423000
Web Site: http://www.mira-park.com
Sales Range: $25-49.9 Million
Emp.: 140
Hotel Operator
N.A.I.C.S.: 721110

Reid's Palace Hotel (2)
Estrada Monumental 139, 9000-098, Funchal, Portugal (100%)
Tel.: (351) 291717171
Web Site: http://www.belmond.com
Sales Range: $25-49.9 Million
Emp.: 200
Hotel Operator
N.A.I.C.S.: 721110
Sireacco Campus *(Gen Mgr)*

Subsidiary (Domestic):

The Great Scottish & Western Railway Company Ltd. (2)
78 Shore, Edinburgh, EH6 6RG, United Kingdom
Tel.: (44) 1315551344
Home Management Services
N.A.I.C.S.: 721110

Venice Simplon-Orient-Express Ltd. (2)
Sea Containers House 20 Upper Grd, London, SE1 9PF, United Kingdom (100%)
Tel.: (44) 2078055000
Web Site: http://www.belmond.com
Sales Range: $300-349.9 Million
Emp.: 100
Railway Operator; Hotel Marketing Services
N.A.I.C.S.: 721110

Subsidiary (Non-US):

Venice Simplon-Orient-Express Deutschland GmbH (3)
Beethovenstr 3, 50670, Cologne, Germany
Tel.: (49) 2213380300
Web Site: http://www.belmond.com
Emp.: 4
Home Management Services
N.A.I.C.S.: 721110

Venice Simplon-Orient-Express Voyages S.A. (3)
5 Rue du Provence, 75001, Paris, France
Tel.: (33) 1 44 50 10 70
Emp.: 5
Travel Arrangement Services
N.A.I.C.S.: 561520
Gary Franklin *(Mgr)*

BeneFit Cosmetics SAS (1)
55 rue St Placide, 75006, Paris, France
Tel.: (33) 8 99 69 65 05
Web Site: http://www.benefitcosmetics.fr
Cosmetic Product Distr
N.A.I.C.S.: 456120

BeneFit Cosmetics Services Canada Inc (1)
2 Bloor Street W Suite 2000, Toronto, M4W 3E2, ON, Canada
Tel.: (416) 963-6544
Cosmetic Product Distr
N.A.I.C.S.: 456120

LVMH MOET HENNESSY LOUIS VUITTON SE

Bulgari France SAS (1)
21 Boulevard Madeleine, Paris, 75001, France
Tel.: (33) 1 40 20 01 59
Cosmetic Product Distr
N.A.I.C.S.: 456120

Bulgari SA (1)
Rue Du Rhone 30, Geneva, 1204, Switzerland
Tel.: (41) 22 319 06 60
Jewel & Accessories Distr
N.A.I.C.S.: 423940

Celine Korea Ltd (1)
2 FL Louis Vuitton Building - 99-18 Chungdam-Dong, Kangnam-Ku, Seoul, 135-100, Korea (South)
Tel.: (82) 2 548 8626
Leather Product Mfr
N.A.I.C.S.: 316990

Chaumet UAE (1)
2nd Floor BurJuman Centre New Extension Sheikh Khalifa Bin Zayed Road, Dubai, 52356, United Arab Emirates
Tel.: (971) 4 3516228
Jewellery Distr
N.A.I.C.S.: 423940

Christian Dior Couture S.A. (1)
30 avenue Montaigne, 75008, Paris, France (100%)
Tel.: (33) 140737373
Web Site: http://www.dior.com
Fashion Designer & Mfr
N.A.I.C.S.: 315250
Pietro Beccari *(Chm & CEO)*

Colgin Cellars (1)
PO Box 254, Saint Helena, CA 94574
Tel.: (707) 963-0999
Web Site: http://www.colgincellars.com
Beverages Mfr
N.A.I.C.S.: 312130

Cpc International Ltd (1)
17/F North Point, Hong Kong, China (Hong Kong)
Tel.: (852) 29686880
Cosmetic Product Distr
N.A.I.C.S.: 456120

Creare Pte Ltd (1)
One Raffles Quay North Tower 1 Raffles Quay 27-01, Singapore, 048583, Singapore
Tel.: (65) 64119374
Insurance Management Services
N.A.I.C.S.: 524298

Creare SA (1)
Rue De Merl 74, 2146, Luxembourg, Luxembourg
Tel.: (352) 496951
Emp.: 2
Cosmetic Product Distr
N.A.I.C.S.: 424210

DFS Cotai Limitada (1)
1/F The Shoppes At Four Seasons Est Da Baia De N S/N Cotai Strip, Taipa, China (Macau)
Tel.: (853) 28282833
Jewels & Watches Distr
N.A.I.C.S.: 423940

Di Regie Sas (1)
16 Rue Du 4 Septembre, Paris, 75002, France
Tel.: (33) 144884260
Web Site: http://www.lesechos.fr
Emp.: 600
Wine & Spirit Whslr
N.A.I.C.S.: 424820
Morel Friendies *(Gen Mgr)*

Emilio Pucci Hong Kong Co Ltd (1)
633 Kings Road 17 floor, Quarry Bay, China (Hong Kong)
Tel.: (852) 2968 6818
Wine & Spirit Whslr
N.A.I.C.S.: 424820

Enilec Gestion SARL (1)
16 Rue Vivienne 2, 75002, Paris, France
Tel.: (33) 155801212
Home Management Services
N.A.I.C.S.: 721110

Eutrope SAS (1)
Hameau Les Gros, Gordes, 84220, France

LVMH MOET HENNESSY LOUIS VUITTON SE

INTERNATIONAL PUBLIC

LVMH Moet Hennessy Louis Vuitton
SE—(Continued)
Tel.: (33) 490722958
Cosmetic Product Distr
N.A.I.C.S.: 456120

Fendi (Singapore) Pte Ltd (1)
583 Orchard Road No 10-02 - Forum, Singapore, 238884, Singapore
Tel.: (65) 6738 6862
Cosmetic Product Distr
N.A.I.C.S.: 456120

Fendi Adele S.R.L (1)
Via Flaminia 968, 00189, Rome, Italy
Tel.: (39) 06334501
Cosmetic Product Distr
N.A.I.C.S.: 456120

Fendi Dis Ticaret Lsi (1)
Buyukdere Cad Onurls Hani K 5 D 118 Zincirlikuyu, Istanbul, Turkiye
Tel.: (90) 212 288 99 01
Cosmetic Product Distr
N.A.I.C.S.: 456120

Fendi Silk SA (1)
Centro Galleria 3, Manno, 6928, Ticino, Switzerland
Tel.: (41) 919237809
Cosmetic Product Distr
N.A.I.C.S.: 456120

Fendi Taiwan Ltd (1)
No 105 Tun Hwa South Road Section 2, 106, Taipei, Taiwan
Tel.: (886) 2 2705 1680
Cosmetic Product Distr
N.A.I.C.S.: 456120

Green Bell BV (1)
Julianalaan 3, 2159 LA, Kaag, Netherlands
Tel.: (31) 252 547 123
Business Management Consulting Services
N.A.I.C.S.: 541618

Groupe Les Echos SA (1)
46 Rue de la Boetie, Paris, 75381, France
Tel.: (33) 1 49 53 65 65
Web Site: http://www.lesechos.fr
Newspaper & Magazine Publisher
N.A.I.C.S.: 513110

Subsidiary (Domestic):

D.I. Group (2)
51 rue Vivienne, 75095, Paris, Cedex 02, France (100%)
Tel.: (33) 144884799
Print Media
N.A.I.C.S.: 513199

EUROSTAF - Europe Strategie Analyse Financiere SAS (2)
16 rue du Quatre Septembre, Paris, 75002, France
Tel.: (33) 1 49 53 65 65
Web Site: http://www.eurostaf.fr
Marketing Research Consulting Services
N.A.I.C.S.: 541910
Karine Gauthier *(Mgr-Comml)*

La Fugue (2)
32 rue Washington, Paris, F-75008, France
Tel.: (33) 1 43 59 10 14
Web Site: http://www.lafugue.com
Tour & Music Event Organizer
N.A.I.C.S.: 561520
Frederic Pfeffer *(Chm & CEO)*

Les Echos SA (2)
16 rue du Quatre Septembre, 75002, Cedex 02, France
Tel.: (33) 149536565
Web Site: http://www.lesechos.fr
Business Publications
N.A.I.C.S.: 513110

Joint Venture (Domestic):

Mezzo S.A. (3)
28 rue Francois 1er, 75008, Paris, France (50%)
Tel.: (33) 1 56 36 51 00
Web Site: http://www.mezzo.tv
Sales Range: $25-49.9 Million
Emp.: 11
Television Broadcasting Services
N.A.I.C.S.: 516120
Christophe Winckel *(Mng Dir)*

Subsidiary (Domestic):

ONLINE SAS (3)
BP 438, Paris, 75366, France
Tel.: (33) 173502000
Web Site: http://www.online.net
Data Processing Services
N.A.I.C.S.: 518210

Subsidiary (Domestic):

Les Echos Services SAS (2)
16 rue du Quatre Septembre, 75002, Paris, France
Tel.: (33) 1 44 88 41 00
Newspaper Publishing Services
N.A.I.C.S.: 513110

Radio Classique SAS (2)
12 bis place Henri Bergson, Paris, 75382, France
Tel.: (33) 1 40 08 50 00
Web Site: http://www.radioclassique.fr
Radio Station Operator
N.A.I.C.S.: 516110

SID Developpement SAS (2)
48 Rue Notre Dame des Victoires, Paris, 75002, France
Tel.: (33) 1 44 88 41 00
Web Site: http://www.siddeveloppement.fr
Business Support Services
N.A.I.C.S.: 561499

SID Presse SAS (2)
Au capital de 1 728 750, BP 1119, 86061, Poitiers, France
Tel.: (33) 5 49 60 20 60
Apparel & Fashion Accessory Retailer
N.A.I.C.S.: 458110

Hainan DFS Retail Company Limited (1)
1/F 2/F Meilan International Airport, Haikou, 570000, China
Tel.: (86) 898 65760222
Cosmetic Product Distr
N.A.I.C.S.: 456120

Kenzo Uk Ltd (1)
81 Aldwych, London, WC2B 4HN, United Kingdom
Tel.: (44) 207 493 8448
Cosmetic Product Distr
N.A.I.C.S.: 456120

L Capital Asia Advisors PLC (1)
608 St James Ct St Denis St, Port Louis, Mauritius
Tel.: (230) 210 9000
Sales Range: $50-74.9 Million
Emp.: 60
Investment Advisory Services
N.A.I.C.S.: 523940

L Capital Management SAS (1)
18 rue Francois 1er, Paris, 75008, France
Tel.: (33) 1 44 13 23 30
Web Site: http://www.lcapital.eu
Venture Capital Services
N.A.I.C.S.: 523940
Daniel Piette *(Chm & Mng Partner)*

LVJ Group KK (1)
One Omotesando 3-5-29 Kita-Aoyama, Minato-ku, Tokyo, 1070061, Japan
Tel.: (81) 3 3478 3694
Web Site: http://www.lvmh.com
Leather Goods Retailer
N.A.I.C.S.: 458320

LVMH Asia Pacific Ltd. (1)
16 F Dorset House Taikoo Pl, Quarry Bay, China (Hong Kong) (100%)
Tel.: (852) 29689288
Web Site: http://www.lvmh.com
Holding Company
N.A.I.C.S.: 551112

LVMH Fashion Group France Snc (1)
2 Rue du Pont-Neuf, Paris, 75001, France
Tel.: (33) 1 55 80 32 00
Clothing Wear Distr
N.A.I.C.S.: 424350

LVMH Fashion Group S.A. (1)
2 Rue Du Pont Neuf, 75034, Paris, Cedex, France (100%)
Tel.: (33) 155803200

Sales Range: $550-599.9 Million
Emp.: 1,200
Holding Company
N.A.I.C.S.: 551112
Sidney Toledano *(Chm & CEO)*

Subsidiary (Non-US):

Atlantic Luggage Company Ltd (2)
Butterfield Pl 67 Front St, Hamilton, HM12, Bermuda
Tel.: (441) 296 1940
Luggage Distr
N.A.I.C.S.: 423990

Subsidiary (Domestic):

Berluti S.A. (2)
120 rue du Faubourg Saint-Honore, 75008, Paris, France (100%)
Tel.: (33) 1 53 83 67 00
Web Site: http://www.berluti.com
Sales Range: $350-399.9 Million
Emp.: 1,200
Footwear Mfr & Retailer
N.A.I.C.S.: 458210
Antoine Arnault *(CEO)*

Subsidiary (Non-US):

Berluti Hong Kong Company Ltd (3)
Ocean Terminal, Tsim Sha Tsui, Kowloon, China (Hong Kong)
Tel.: (852) 2376 3533
Leather Goods Retailer
N.A.I.C.S.: 458320
Martina Chang *(Gen Mgr)*

Berluti Italia (3)
Via Tommasoo Grossi 2, 20121, Milan, Italy
Tel.: (39) 0272334220
Web Site: http://www.berluti.com
Sales Range: $25-49.9 Million
Emp.: 3
Mfr & Retailer of Men's Shoes
N.A.I.C.S.: 316210

Berluti Japan (3)
Aoyama Twin W 1st Fl, 1 1 1 Minami Aoyama Minato-Ku, Tokyo, 107-0062, Japan (100%)
Tel.: (81) 357753451
Web Site: http://www.berluti.co.jp
Sales Range: $25-49.9 Million
Emp.: 10
Mfr of Men's Shoes
N.A.I.C.S.: 316210

Subsidiary (US):

Berluti LLC (3)
677 Madison Ave, New York, NY 10019
Tel.: (212) 439-6400
Web Site: http://www.berluti.com
Emp.: 15
Leather Shoe Retailer
N.A.I.C.S.: 458210

Subsidiary (Non-US):

Berluti UK (3)
43 Conduit St, London, W1S 2YJ, United Kingdom (100%)
Tel.: (44) 2074371740
Web Site: http://www.berluti.com
Sales Range: $25-49.9 Million
Emp.: 12
Mfr of Men's Shoes
N.A.I.C.S.: 316210
John-Paul O'Dea *(Mgr-Shop)*

Holding (Non-US):

Bulgari S.p.A. (2)
Lungotevere Marzio 11, 00186, Rome, Italy (98.09%)
Tel.: (39) 06688101
Web Site: http://www.bulgari.com
Sales Range: $1-4.9 Billion
Fine Jewelry, Watches, Leather Goods & Perfume Mfr & Retailer
N.A.I.C.S.: 339910
Jean-Christophe Babin *(CEO)*

Subsidiary (Non-US):

Bulgari (Taiwan) Ltd. (3)
15F No 101 Fusing N Rd, Songshan, Taipei, Taiwan
Tel.: (886) 2 27188585
Perfume & Skincare Product Distr

N.A.I.C.S.: 424210

Bulgari (Thailand) Ltd. (3)
999 Gaysorn Tower 5th Floor Unit 5A-1 Ploenchit Road, Lumpini Patumwan, 10330, Bangkok, Thailand
Tel.: (66) 26109388
Sales Range: $50-74.9 Million
Emp.: 9
Cosmetic Product Distr
N.A.I.C.S.: 424210

Bulgari Asia Pacific Ltd. (3)
25th Fl No 979 King's Rd Taikoo Pl, Central, China (Hong Kong)
Tel.: (852) 2905 1212
Sales Range: $25-49.9 Million
Emp.: 40
Jewelry & Skincare Product Retailer
N.A.I.C.S.: 458310

Bulgari Australia Pty Ltd (3)
Ste 1 64 Castle High St, Sydney, 2000, NSW, Australia (100%)
Tel.: (61) 282571000
Sales Range: $25-49.9 Million
Emp.: 30
Jewelry Stores
N.A.I.C.S.: 458310
Julie Ann Morrison *(Mng Dir)*

Bulgari Belgium S.A. (3)
Boulevard de Waterloo 36-37, 1000, Brussels, Belgium
Tel.: (32) 2 5116701
Watch & Jewelry Distr
N.A.I.C.S.: 423940

Subsidiary (US):

Bulgari Corporation of America (3)
625 Madison Ave, New York, NY 10022
Tel.: (212) 315-9700
Web Site: http://www.bulgari.com
Sales Range: $25-49.9 Million.
Emp.: 75
Import of Fine Jewelry & Watches
N.A.I.C.S.: 458310
Annette Berthod *(Dir-Mktg)*

Subsidiary (Non-US):

Bulgari Deutschland GmbH (3)
Thierschplatz 6, 80539, Munich, Germany
Tel.: (49) 89 24 23 86 24
Web Site: http://www.bulgari.com
Jewelry Stores
N.A.I.C.S.: 458310

Bulgari Espana S.A. Unipersonal (3)
Calle Serrano 49, Madrid, 28006, Spain
Tel.: (34) 915 750 141
Jewelry & Luxury Product Retailer
N.A.I.C.S.: 458310

Subsidiary (Domestic):

Bulgari Gioielli SpA (3)
Lungotevere Marzio 11, Rome, 186, Italy
Tel.: (39) 06 68810501
Jewelry & Luxury Product Distr
N.A.I.C.S.: 423940

Subsidiary (Non-US):

Bulgari Global Operations SA (3)
Rue de Monruz 34, Neuchatel, 2000, Switzerland
Tel.: (41) 32 722 78 78
Web Site: http://www.bulgari.com
Sales Range: $125-149.9 Million
Emp.: 400
Watch & Jewelry Distr
N.A.I.C.S.: 423940
Pius Steiner *(Dir-Fin)*

Subsidiary (Domestic):

Bulgari Italia SpA (3)
Condotti, 00187, Rome, Italy
Tel.: (39) 066 793 876
Web Site: http://it.bulgari.com
Cosmetic & Jewelry Retailer
N.A.I.C.S.: 456120

Subsidiary (Non-US):

Bulgari Japan Ltd. (3)
7F 2-7-12 Ginza, Chuo-Ku, Tokyo, 104-0061, Japan
Tel.: (81) 3 6362 0144
Web Site: http://www.bulgari.com

AND PRIVATE COMPANIES — LVMH MOET HENNESSY LOUIS VUITTON SE

Sales Range: $100-124.9 Million
Emp.: 500
Watch & Jewelry Retailer
N.A.I.C.S.: 458310
Hiroshi Okagaki *(Sr Mgr-IT)*

Bulgari Korea Ltd. (3)
10th Fl Doowon Bldg 503-5 Sinsa-dong, Gangnam-gu, Seoul, 135-746, Korea (South)
Tel.: (82) 2 2056 0100
Watch & Jewelry Whslr
N.A.I.C.S.: 423940

Bulgari South Asian Operations Pte Ltd (3)
583 Orchard Rd #16-02 The Forum, Singapore, 238884, Singapore (100%)
Tel.: (65) 67335337
Web Site: http://www.bulgari.com
Sales Range: $50-74.9 Million
Emp.: 100
Jewelry Stores
N.A.I.C.S.: 423940

Bulgari UK Limited (3)
168-169 New Bond St, London, W1S 4RB, United Kingdom
Tel.: (44) 2078729969
Jewelry & Watches Retail
N.A.I.C.S.: 423940

Subsidiary (Domestic):

Celine S.A. (2)
23-25 Rue Du Pont Neuf, 75001, Paris, France (100%)
Tel.: (33) 155801212
Web Site: http://www.celine.com
Sales Range: $25-49.9 Million
Emp.: 200
Mfr of Ready-to-Wear, Leather Goods, Shoes & Accessories
N.A.I.C.S.: 316990

Subsidiary (Non-US):

Celine (Hong Kong) Ltd (3)
G3-5 The Landmark 15 Queen's Road, Central, China (Hong Kong) (100%)
Tel.: (852) 2525 1281
Web Site: http://www.celine.com
Mfr of Fashion & Leather Goods
N.A.I.C.S.: 458110

Celine Boutique Taiwan Co. Ltd. (3)
1 Fl Annex 246 Sec 1 Tun Hau South Rd, Tun Hwa South Rd, Taipei, 106, Taiwan (100%)
Tel.: (886) 227111218
Web Site: http://www.celine.com
Sales Range: $25-49.9 Million
Emp.: 25
Mfr of Ready to Wear Apparel
N.A.I.C.S.: 315990

Subsidiary (US):

Celine Hawaii Inc. (3)
2255 Kuhio Ave Ste 1400, Honolulu, HI 96815
Tel.: (808) 971-8444
Web Site: http://www.celine.com
Mfr of Fashion & Leather Goods
N.A.I.C.S.: 316990

Celine Inc. (3)
19 E 57th St, New York, NY 10022
Tel.: (212) 931-2080
Web Site: http://www.celine.com
Sales Range: $25-49.9 Million
Emp.: 20
Mfr of Fashion & Leather Goods, Perfumes & Cosmetics
N.A.I.C.S.: 458110

Subsidiary (Non-US):

Celine Italia S.r.l. (3)
via Monte Napoleone 25, 20121, Milan, Italy
Tel.: (39) 0276015579
Web Site: http://www.celine.com
Emp.: 10
Fashion Goods
N.A.I.C.S.: 458110

Celine Japan KK (3)
3-5-29 Kita-aoyama, Minato-ku, Tokyo, 107 0061, Japan (100%)
Tel.: (81) 354142150
Web Site: http://www.celine.com

Sales Range: $25-49.9 Million
Emp.: 170
Fashion & Leather Goods Mfr
N.A.I.C.S.: 316990
Naoko Kariya *(Sec)*

Celine Monaco SA (3)
Sporting D Hiver, Place Du Casino, 98000, Monaco, Monaco (100%)
Tel.: (377) 93309278
Web Site: http://www.celine.com
Sales Range: $25-49.9 Million
Emp.: 8
Mfr of Fashion Goods
N.A.I.C.S.: 458320
Evelin Boyer *(Gen Mgr)*

Celine Monte-Carlo SA (3)
Sporting d'Hiver Place du Casino, Monte Carlo, 98000, Monaco
Tel.: (377) 93 30 92 78
Sales Range: $25-49.9 Million
Emp.: 8
Leather Goods Retailer
N.A.I.C.S.: 458320

Celine Production S.R.L (3)
Via di Meleto (localita Palagione), Frazione Strada in Chianti, Florence, 50027, Greve in Chianti, Italy
Tel.: (39) 0558547321
Web Site: http://www.celine.com
Mfr of Fashion & Leather Goods
N.A.I.C.S.: 316990

Celine Suisse SA (3)
47 rue du Rhone, 1204, Geneva, Switzerland
Tel.: (41) 22 312 14 60
Web Site: http://www.celine.com
Sales Range: $25-49.9 Million
Emp.: 5
Leather Goods Retailer
N.A.I.C.S.: 458320
Augaey Ramey *(Gen Mgr)*

Celine UK Ltd. (3)
1112 Clifford St, London, W1S 2LL, United Kingdom (100%)
Tel.: (44) 2076600990
Web Site: http://www.celine.com
Sales Range: $25-49.9 Million
Emp.: 100
Ready to Wear Apparel
N.A.I.C.S.: 315990
White Ley *(Mng Dir)*

Louis Vuitton Korea (3)
133 Gil 20 Eonju-Ro Gangnam-gu, Seoul, 135 010, Korea (South) (100%)
Tel.: (82) 2 548 8626
Web Site: http://www.lvmh.com
Sales Range: $25-49.9 Million
Emp.: 32
Mfr of Fashion & Leather Goods
N.A.I.C.S.: 316990

Subsidiary (Domestic):

Fred S.A. (2)
21 Pl Vendome, 75009, Paris, France (100%)
Tel.: (33) 0153452870
Web Site: http://www.fred.fr
Sales Range: $25-49.9 Million
Emp.: 50
Mfr of Watches & Jewelry
N.A.I.C.S.: 334519

Subsidiary (Domestic):

Fred Paris SA (3)
8 Place de l Opera, Paris, 75009, France
Tel.: (33) 1 53 45 28 70
Web Site: http://www.fred.com
Sales Range: $25-49.9 Million
Emp.: 30
Watch & Jewelry Retailer
N.A.I.C.S.: 458310

Subsidiary (Non-US):

Fun Fashion Kuwait Co. W.L.L. (2)
Salhia Complex Grnd Fl Shop No 1 Fendi, Kuwait, Kuwait
Tel.: (965) 22493985
Apparel & Accessory Retailer
N.A.I.C.S.: 458110

Fun Fashion Napoli Srl (2)
24 Vico Filangieri, 80144, Naples, Italy

Tel.: (39) 081413 261
Apparel, Accessory & Jewelry Retailer
N.A.I.C.S.: 458110

Subsidiary (Domestic):

Givenchy S.A. (2)
3 Ave George 5, 75008, Paris, France (100%)
Tel.: (33) 0144315000
Web Site: http://www.givenchy.fr
Sales Range: $75-99.9 Million
Emp.: 150
Holding Company; Mfr of Ready-to-Wear, Haute Couture, Shoes, Leather Goods & Accessories
N.A.I.C.S.: 551112
Julia Erdman *(Dir-Comm & Mktg-Americas)*

Subsidiary (Non-US):

Givenchy China Company Limited (3)
Office B 18 Fl 633 King Rd, Quarry Bay, China (Hong Kong) (100%)
Tel.: (852) 25769083
Web Site: http://www.givenchy.com
Sales Range: $25-49.9 Million
Emp.: 100
Mfr of Ready-to-Wear, Haute Couture, Shoes, Leather Goods & Accessories
N.A.I.C.S.: 316990

Subsidiary (US):

Givenchy Corp. (3)
19 E 57th St, New York, NY 10022
Tel.: (212) 931-2500
Web Site: http://www.givenchy.com
Mfr of Ready-to-Wear, Haute Couture, Shoes, Leather Goods & Accessories
N.A.I.C.S.: 424210
Renaud de Lesquen *(Pres & CEO)*

Subsidiary (Non-US):

Givenchy Japan Co. Ltd (3)
Sumitomo Hanzomon Bldg 6th Fl Hayabusa Cho, Chiyoda-ku, 102 0092, Tokyo, Japan (100%)
Tel.: (81) 352751861
Web Site: http://www.givenchy.com
Sales Range: $25-49.9 Million
Emp.: 3
Mfr of Ready-to-Wear, Haute Couture, Shoes, Leather Goods & Accessories
N.A.I.C.S.: 316990

Subsidiary (Domestic):

Parfums Givenchy S.A. (3)
77 Rue Anatole France, 92532, Levallois-Perret, France (100%)
Tel.: (33) 173026000
Web Site: http://www.parfumsgivenchy.fr
Emp.: 300
Mfr of Perfume & Beauty Products
N.A.I.C.S.: 325620
Lorenzo Alain *(CIO)*

Subsidiary (Non-US):

Givenchy Shanghai Commercial and Trading Co Ltd (4)
Rm 1103 Pudong Holiday Inn No 899 Dongfang Rd, Pudong, Shanghai, 200122, China
Tel.: (86) 2168751363
Fashion & Leather Goods Retailer
N.A.I.C.S.: 458320

LVMH Perfumes & Cosmetics Taiwan Fa Hua Fragrance & Cosmetic Co., Ltd. (4)
10 Fl N 285 Chung Hsiao East Rd, Section 4, Taipei, 10692, Taiwan (100%)
Tel.: (886) 227771334
Web Site: http://www.tw-givenchy.com
Sales Range: $25-49.9 Million
Emp.: 100
Mfr of Perfumes & Cosmetics
N.A.I.C.S.: 325620

Parfumes Givenchy (4)
Langebrogade 6 E, 1411, Copenhagen, Denmark (100%)
Tel.: (45) 32837373
Mfr of Perfume & Cosmetics
N.A.I.C.S.: 325620

Parfums Givenchy (4)

Avenida Europa 140 Jardim Europa, PO Box 140, 01449-000, Sao Paulo, Brazil (100%)
Tel.: (55) 138967299
Web Site: http://www.parfums.givenchy.com
Sales Range: $25-49.9 Million
Emp.: 50
Mfr of Perfumes & Cosmetics
N.A.I.C.S.: 325620

Parfums Givenchy Argentine SA (4)
Edificio Columbus, Av. Paseo Colon 746 - Piso 2, 1063, Buenos Aires, Argentina
Web Site: http://www.parfums.givenchy.com
Mfr of Perfumes & other Cosmetics
N.A.I.C.S.: 325620

Parfums Givenchy Asia Pacific Pte. Ltd. (4)
1 Kim Seng Promenade #14-09/10, Great World City West Tower, 237994, Singapore, Singapore
Tel.: (65) 6733 6161
Web Site: http://www.lvmh.com
Mfr of Perfumes & Cosmetics
N.A.I.C.S.: 325620

Parfums Givenchy Benelux (4)
Ave Louise 523, 1050, Brussels, Belgium (100%)
Tel.: (32) 26422970
Web Site: http://www.parfums.givenchy.fr
Sales Range: $25-49.9 Million
Emp.: 50
Mfr of Perfumes & Cosmetics
N.A.I.C.S.: 325620
Philip Labrot *(Gen Mgr)*

Parfums Givenchy GmBH (4)
Haus Am Rhein, Rotterdamerstrasse 40, 40474, Dusseldorf, Germany (100%)
Tel.: (49) 211471540
Web Site: http://www.givenchy.com
Sales Range: $25-49.9 Million
Emp.: 90
Mfr of Perfume & Beauty Products
N.A.I.C.S.: 325620

Subsidiary (US):

Parfums Givenchy Inc. (4)
19 E 57th St 7th Fl, New York, NY 10022-8101
Tel.: (212) 759-7566
Web Site: http://www.parfumsgivenchy.com
Fragrances & Cosmetics Marketing
N.A.I.C.S.: 424210

Subsidiary (Non-US):

Parfums Givenchy Italia S.r.l. (4)
Via Ripamonti 99, Milan, 20141, Italy
Tel.: (39) 025522881
Web Site: http://www.parfumsgivenchy.fr
Mfr of Perfume & Beauty Products
N.A.I.C.S.: 325620

Parfums Givenchy KK (4)
Sumitomo Hanzomon Bldg 4th Fl, 3 16 Hayabusa Cho, Tokyo, 102 0092, Japan (100%)
Tel.: (81) 332643941
Web Site: http://www.parfumsgivenchy.co.jp
Sales Range: $1-9.9 Million
Emp.: 20
Perfume & Beauty Products Mfr
N.A.I.C.S.: 325620

Parfums Givenchy Mexico (4)
216 Piso 17 Col Anzures, 11590, Mexico, Mexico (100%)
Tel.: (52) 5525811200
Web Site: http://www.parfums.givenchy.com
Sales Range: $25-49.9 Million
Emp.: 120
Mfr of Perfumes & Cosmetics
N.A.I.C.S.: 325620

Parfums Givenchy Spain (4)
Isla De Java 33, 28034, Madrid, Spain (99%)
Tel.: (34) 917286900
Web Site: http://www.parfumsgivenchy.com
Sales Range: $25-49.9 Million
Emp.: 200
Mfr of Perfumes & Cosmetics
N.A.I.C.S.: 325620
Juan Pedro Abeneicar *(Pres)*

Parfums Givenchy UK Ltd. (4)
UK House - 6th Floor 180, Oxford Street,

LVMH MOET HENNESSY LOUIS VUITTON SE · INTERNATIONAL PUBLIC

LVMH Moet Hennessy Louis Vuitton SE—(Continued)
London, W1D 1AB, United Kingdom **(100%)**
Tel.: (44) 2075638800
Web Site: http://www.lvmh-pc.com
Sales Range: $25-49.9 Million
Emp.: 100
Mfr of Perfume & Beauty Products
N.A.I.C.S.: 325620

Subsidiary (Domestic):

Guerlain S.A. (2)
125 Rue De President, Wilson, Levallois-Perret, 92300, France **(59%)**
Tel.: (33) 141273100
Web Site: http://www.guerlain.com
Sales Range: $100-124.9 Million
Emp.: 300
Mfr of Perfumes & Cosmetics
N.A.I.C.S.: 325620

Subsidiary (Non-US):

Guerlain Argentina (FACSA) (3)
Torre Alem Plaza, Leandro N. Alem 855 Piso 2, 1001, Buenos Aires, Argentina
Tel.: (54) 11 45 90 81 50
Web Site: http://www.guerlain.com
Mfr & Wholesaler of Perfumes & Cosmetics
N.A.I.C.S.: 325620

Guerlain Asia Pacific Ltd (3)
16/F Dorset House Taikoo Place 979 King's Road, Quarry Bay, China (Hong Kong)
Tel.: (852) 2524 6129
Web Site: http://www.lvmh.com
Personal Care Product Retailer
N.A.I.C.S.: 456120

Guerlain Benelux S.A. (3)
Ave Louise 523, 1050, Brussels, Belgium **(100%)**
Tel.: (32) 26422970
Web Site: http://www.guerlain.fr
Sales Range: $25-49.9 Million
Emp.: 20
Mfr of Perfumes & Cosmetics
N.A.I.C.S.: 325620
Deroen Van Derdossen (Mng Dir)

Guerlain Benelux S.A. (3)
Crystal Bldg B Rivium Blvd 212, 2909 LK, Capelle aan den IJssel, Netherlands **(100%)**
Tel.: (31) 102041177
Web Site: http://www.guerlain.com
Sales Range: $25-49.9 Million
Emp.: 5
Mfr of Perfumes & Cosmetics
N.A.I.C.S.: 325620
Guy Beaugrenier (Gen Mgr)

Guerlain Canada Ltd. (3)
2515 Leger Street, Montreal, H8N 2V9, QC, Canada **(100%)**
Tel.: (514) 363-0432
Web Site: http://www.guerlain.com
Sales Range: $25-49.9 Million
Emp.: 20
Mfr of Perfumes & Cosmetics
N.A.I.C.S.: 325620

Guerlain Ges. m.b.H. (3)
Singerstrase 6, 1030, Vienna, Austria **(100%)**
Tel.: (43) 15336565
Web Site: http://www.guerlain.com
Sales Range: $25-49.9 Million
Emp.: 50
Mfr of Perfumes & Cosmetics
N.A.I.C.S.: 325620
Natalie Dellers (Gen Mgr)

Guerlain GmbH (3)
Singerstrasse 6, 1010, Vienna, Austria
Tel.: (43) 1 5336565 0
Sales Range: $25-49.9 Million
Emp.: 15
Perfume & Cosmetic Product Distr
N.A.I.C.S.: 424210
Maya Bolze (Gen Mgr)

Guerlain KK (3)
3 16 Hayabusa Cho, Sumitomo Hanzomon Building, Tokyo, 102 0092, Japan **(100%)**
Tel.: (81) 332343601
Web Site: http://www.guerlain.co.jp

Sales Range: $25-49.9 Million
Emp.: 30
Mfr of Perfumes & Cosmetics
N.A.I.C.S.: 325620

Guerlain Korea (3)
LVMH F & C Korea Ltd 11 F Sera Bldg, 50 1 & 2 Nonhyun Dong, Seoul, 185010, Korea (South) **(100%)**
Tel.: (82) 234389500
Web Site: http://www.guerlain.com
Sales Range: $25-49.9 Million
Emp.: 90
Mfr of Perfumes & Cosmetics
N.A.I.C.S.: 325620

Guerlain Ltd. (3)
180 Oxford St, London, W1D 1AB, United Kingdom **(100%)**
Tel.: (44) 2075637555
Web Site: http://www.guerlain.com
Sales Range: $50-74.9 Million
Emp.: 200
Mfr of Perfumes & Cosmetics
N.A.I.C.S.: 325620
Immanuel Noel (Mng Dir)

Guerlain Parfumeur GmbH (3)
Rotterdamerstr 40, 40474, Dusseldorf, Germany **(100%)**
Tel.: (49) 211650455
Web Site: http://www.cosmoty.de
Sales Range: $25-49.9 Million
Emp.: 90
Mfr of Perfumes & Cosmetics
N.A.I.C.S.: 325620

Guerlain S.A.E. (3)
Isla De Java 33, 28034, Madrid, Spain **(100%)**
Tel.: (34) 917286900
Web Site: http://www.lvmh-iberica.es
Mfr of Perfumes & Cosmetics
N.A.I.C.S.: 325620

Guerlain SpA (3)
Via Ripamonti 99, Milan, 20121, Italy **(100%)**
Tel.: (39) 025522881
Web Site: http://www.guerlain.com
Sales Range: $50-74.9 Million
Emp.: 118
Mfr of Perfumes & Cosmetics
N.A.I.C.S.: 325620

Guerlain Taiwan Co. Ltd. (3)
Section 4 10 F N 285 Chung Hsiao East Road, 106, Taipei, Taiwan **(100%)**
Tel.: (886) 227771334
Web Site: http://www.guerlain.com
Sales Range: $125-149.9 Million
Emp.: 300
Mfr of Perfumes & Cosmetics
N.A.I.C.S.: 325620

Guerlain de Portugal Lda. (3)
LVMH Perfumes e Cosmetica LDA Rua Castilho no 50 - 54 Andar, Salas 50-52, 1250-066, Lisbon, Portugal
Tel.: (351) 213583560
Web Site: http://www.guerlain.com
Sales Range: $25-49.9 Million
Emp.: 30
Mfr of Perfumes & Cosmetics
N.A.I.C.S.: 325620
Maria Andrade (Gen Mgr)

Subsidiary (US):

Guerlain, Inc. (3)
19 E 57th St 7th Fl, New York, NY 10022
Tel.: (212) 931-2400
Web Site: http://www.guerlain.com
Mfr of Perfumes & Cosmetics
N.A.I.C.S.: 424210

Subsidiary (Non-US):

LVMH Perfumes & Cosmetics China Ltd (3)
Ste 2901 2906 Plz 66 29 Fl, 1266 W Nanjing Rd, Shanghai, China **(100%)**
Tel.: (86) 2162881688
Web Site: http://www.lvmh.com
Sales Range: $50-74.9 Million
Emp.: 300
Mfr of Perfumes & Cosmetics
N.A.I.C.S.: 325620

LVMH Perfumes and Cosmetic of Brazil (3)

LVMH Parfums Et Cosmetiques Do Brasil Ltda, PO Box 140, Jardim Europa, Sao Paulo, 1449000, Brazil **(100%)**
Tel.: (55) 38967299
Web Site: http://www.pcblvmh.com.br
Sales Range: $25-49.9 Million
Emp.: 100
Mfr of Perfumes & Cosmetics
N.A.I.C.S.: 325620

Subsidiary (Non-US):

Heng Long International Ltd. (2)
50 Defu Ln 7, 539356, Singapore, Singapore
Tel.: (65) 62822622
Web Site: http://henglong.listedcompany.com
Sales Range: $50-74.9 Million
Crocodile Leather Products Mfr
N.A.I.C.S.: 316990
Choon Heong Koh (Exec Dir)

Subsidiary (Domestic):

Heng Long Leather Co (Pte) Ltd (3)
50 Defu Lane 7, Singapore, 539356, Singapore
Tel.: (65) 62822622
Sales Range: $25-49.9 Million
Emp.: 180
Leather Product Mfr
N.A.I.C.S.: 316990
Chon Tong Koh (Mng Dir)

Subsidiary (Non-US):

Interservices & Trading SA (2)
Via Moree 16, 6850, Mendrisio, Switzerland
Tel.: (41) 91 802 92 00
Leather Goods Retailer
N.A.I.C.S.: 458320

Subsidiary (Domestic):

Kenzo SA (2)
1 Rue Du Pont Neuf, 75001, Paris, France **(100%)**
Tel.: (33) 173042000
Web Site: http://www.kenzo.fr
Sales Range: $10-24.9 Million
Emp.: 27
Mfr of Fashion & Leather Goods
N.A.I.C.S.: 316990

Subsidiary (Non-US):

Kenzo Belgique SA (3)
Rue De Namur 44, Brussels, 1000, Belgium
Tel.: (32) 2 514 04 48
Web Site: http://www.kenzo.fr
Jewelry Retailer
N.A.I.C.S.: 458310
Olivia Lejrand (Mgr-Store)

Kenzo Deutschland GmbH (3)
Koenigsallee 62, 40212, Dusseldorf, Germany
Tel.: (49) 211864700
Mfr of Perfumes & Cosmetics
N.A.I.C.S.: 325620

Kenzo Fashion Iberica (3)
Jorge Juan 15, 28001, Madrid, Spain **(100%)**
Tel.: (34) 914356593
Web Site: http://www.kenzo.fr
Mfr of Perfumes & Cosmetics
N.A.I.C.S.: 325620
Lola Mateo (Gen Mgr)

Subsidiary (Domestic):

Kenzo Homme SA (3)
Trois Place des Vectoires, 75002, Paris, France
Tel.: (33) 140397261
Web Site: http://www.kenzo.com
Men's Fashion Retailer
N.A.I.C.S.: 458110

Kenzo Parfums (3)
3 Place des Victoires, 75001, Paris, France **(100%)**
Tel.: (33) 140397202
Web Site: http://www.kenzo.com
Mfr of Perfumes & Cosmetics
N.A.I.C.S.: 325620

Subsidiary (Non-US):

Kenzo Parfums (4)

Rua Sao Tome 86 6th Fl, Vila Olimpia, Sao Paulo, 04551-080, Brazil **(100%)**
Tel.: (55) 138967299
Sales Range: $25-49.9 Million
Emp.: 120
Mfr of Perfumes & Cosmetics
N.A.I.C.S.: 325620

Kenzo Parfums (4)
Edificio Columbus, Av. Paseo Colon 746 Piso 2, 1063, Buenos Aires, Argentina
Tel.: (54) 41218000
Web Site: http://www.kenzo.com
Mfr of Perfumes & Cosmetics
N.A.I.C.S.: 325620

Subsidiary (US):

Kenzo Parfums (4)
19 E 57th st, New York, NY 10022
Tel.: (212) 931-2652
Web Site: http://www.kenzousa.com
Perfumes & Cosmetics Mfr & Sales
N.A.I.C.S.: 325620

Subsidiary (Non-US):

Kenzo Parfums Italia S.R.L (4)
Via Ripamonti 99, 20141, Milan, Italy **(100%)**
Tel.: (39) 025522881
Web Site: http://www.kenzo.com
Mfr of Perfumes & Cosmetics
N.A.I.C.S.: 325620

Kenzo Parfums Mexico (4)
216 Piso 7 Col Anzures, 11570, Mexico, Mexico **(100%)**
Tel.: (52) 25811290
Mfr of Perfumes & Cosmetics
N.A.I.C.S.: 325620
Carlos De la Pena (HR Mgr)

Kenzo Parfums Spain (4)
Isla De Java 33, 28034, Madrid, Spain **(100%)**
Tel.: (34) 917286900
Web Site: http://www.kenzo.com
Sales Range: $25-49.9 Million
Emp.: 10
Mfr of Perfumes & Cosmetics
N.A.I.C.S.: 325620

Kenzo Parfums Switzerland (4)
4 Chemin de la Graviere, 1211, Geneva, Switzerland
Tel.: (41) 223423388
Web Site: http://www.kenzo.com
Mfr of Perfumes & Cosmetics
N.A.I.C.S.: 325620

Subsidiary (Non-US):

Kenzo Paris K.K (3)
TTS Building 7th Floor, 6 12 1 Minami Aoyama, Tokyo, 107 0062, Japan **(100%)**
Tel.: (81) 354856411
Web Site: http://www.kenzo.com
Mfr & Wholesaler of Designer Fashions
N.A.I.C.S.: 458110

Subsidiary (Non-US):

LVMH FG Brasil Ltda (2)
Rua Capote Valente 73, Pinheiros, 05409-000, Sao Paulo, Brazil
Tel.: (55) 11 3897 7700
Fashion & Leather Goods Distr
N.A.I.C.S.: 458320

LVMH FG Services UK Ltd (2)
15 Saint George Street, London, W1S 1FH, United Kingdom
Tel.: (44) 207 408 74 00
Web Site: http://www.lvmh.com
Clothing Accessory Retailer
N.A.I.C.S.: 458110

LVMH Fashion Group Brasil Ltda (2)
Rua Capote Valente 73, 05409-000, Sao Paulo, Brazil **(100%)**
Tel.: (55) 138977700
Web Site: http://www.louisvuitton.com
Sales Range: $25-49.9 Million
Emp.: 100
Luggage & Leather Goods
N.A.I.C.S.: 458320
Francois Rosset (Pres)

LVMH Fashion Group Korea (2)
2F Louis Vuitton Building, Kangnam-Ku,

AND PRIVATE COMPANIES — LVMH MOET HENNESSY LOUIS VUITTON SE

99-18 Chungdam-dong, 135-100, Seoul, Korea (South)
Tel.: (82) 25488626
Web Site: http://www.vuitton.com
Sales Range: $10-24.9 Million
Emp.: 40
Luxury Goods Mfr & Retailer
N.A.I.C.S.: 315990
Ok Cho *(Chm)*

LVMH Fashion Group Pacific Ltd. (2)
22 F Dorset House, 979 Kings Rd, Quarry Bay, China (Hong Kong) **(100%)**
Tel.: (852) 29681338
Web Site: http://www.lvmh.com
Mfr & Retailer of Perfumes, Cosmetics, Leather & Fashion Goods.
N.A.I.C.S.: 325620

LVMH Fashion Group Singapore (2)
583 Orchard Rd 10 02 Forum Singapore, 3918 Orchard Rd 13 01 Ngee Ann, Singapore, 238884, Singapore **(100%)**
Tel.: (65) 68351233
Web Site: http://www.louisvuitton.com
Sales Range: $10-24.9 Million
Emp.: 30
Fashion & Leather Goods Mfr
N.A.I.C.S.: 316990
Jean-Christophe Tebenin *(Mng Dir)*

LVMH Fashion Group Switzerland S.A. (2)
5 Quai Du Mont Blanc, Geneva, 1204, Switzerland **(100%)**
Tel.: (41) 223113070
Web Site: http://www.vuitton.ch
Sales Range: $25-49.9 Million
Emp.: 30
Luggage & Leather Goods
N.A.I.C.S.: 458320

LVMH Fashion Group Thailand (2)
Unit 1601 16th Fl UBC II Tower, PO Box 33, North Klongton, Bangkok, 10110, Thailand **(100%)**
Tel.: (66) 22620140
Web Site: http://www.louisvuitton.com
Sales Range: $25-49.9 Million
Emp.: 60
Fashion & Leather Goods
N.A.I.C.S.: 316990
Rachaya Veerapsont *(Gen Mgr)*

LVMH Fashion Group UK Ltd (2)
1 Pancras Square, London, M1C4AG, United Kingdom **(100%)**
Tel.: (44) 2073994000
Web Site: http://www.lvmh.com
Sales Range: $25-49.9 Million
Emp.: 200
Mfr of Luggage & Leather Goods
N.A.I.C.S.: 316990

LVMH Fashion Trading Co. Ltd (2)
Room 1106 1110 1111 1112 1114 1115 No 500 Bingke Road, Waigaoqiao Free Trade Zone, Shanghai, China **(100%)**
Tel.: (86) 2162893399
Fashion Goods
N.A.I.C.S.: 541490

Les Ateliers Horlogers Louis Vuitton SA (2)
6 Avenue Louis-Joseph Chevrolet, La Chaux-de-Fonds, 2301, Switzerland
Tel.: (41) 32 925 34 34
Sales Range: $25-49.9 Million
Emp.: 25
Luxury Watch & Jewelry Mfr
N.A.I.C.S.: 339910

Loro Piana S.p.A. (2)
Corso Rolandi 10, 13017, Quarona, Italy **(80%)**
Tel.: (39) 0163 20 11
Web Site: http://www.loropiana.com
Wool & Cashmere Mfr
N.A.I.C.S.: 313110

Subsidiary (US):

Loro Piana USA, LLC
711 5th Ave 11th Fl, New York, NY 10022
Tel.: (212) 319-5971
Web Site: http://www.loropiana.com
Sales Range: $1-9.9 Million
Emp.: 50
Clothing Stores
N.A.I.C.S.: 458110
Pier Guerci *(Pres & CEO)*

Subsidiary (Domestic):

Louis Vuitton Malletier S.A. (2)
2 Rue Du Pont Neuf, 75034, Paris, Cedex 01, France **(100%)**
Tel.: (33) 155803200
Web Site: http://www.louisvuittonfr.com
Sales Range: $300-349.9 Million
Emp.: 1,200
Leather Goods
N.A.I.C.S.: 316990
Youssef Marquis *(Dir-Fashion Comm)*

Subsidiary (US):

LVMH Fashion Group Micronesia (3)
Pacific Pl Level 3 Ste 302 1411 Pale San Vitores Rd, Tumon Bay, GU 96911
Tel.: (671) 642-5800
Web Site: http://www.lvmh.com
Sales Range: $50-74.9 Million
Emp.: 85
Luxury Goods Mfr & Retailer
N.A.I.C.S.: 315990

Subsidiary (Non-US):

LVMH Moet-Hennessy Louis Vuitton (Japan) KK (3)
211 Hirakawa, Chiyada-ku, Tokyo, 102 0093, Japan **(100%)**
Tel.: (81) 332631031
Web Site: http://www.lvmh.jp
Sales Range: $25-49.9 Million
Emp.: 21
Mfr & Wholesaler of Distilled & Blended Liquors; Fashion Goods; Perfumes & Cosmetics
N.A.I.C.S.: 312130
Emmanuel Cart *(Dir)*

Louis Vuitton (China) Co Ltd (3)
Rm 4001 40f Phase I Plz 66 No 1266 Nanjing W Rd, Shanghai, 200040, China
Tel.: (86) 2161332888
Web Site: http://www.louisvuitton.cn
Jewelry & Leather Product Retailer
N.A.I.C.S.: 458310

Louis Vuitton (Philippines) Inc (3)
Ground Floor Greenbelt 4 Ayala Center, Makati, 1226, Philippines
Tel.: (63) 27560637
Clothing Accessory Distr
N.A.I.C.S.: 424350
Rhea de Vera-Aguirre *(Country Mgr)*

Louis Vuitton (Thailand) Ltd. (3)
591 Unit 1601-1602 16th Floor Samatchawanich 2 Tower Soi Sukhumvit 33, Klongtonnua Wattana, 10110, Bangkok, Thailand
Tel.: (66) 2 262 0130
Web Site: http://www.lvmh.com
Leather Goods Retailer
N.A.I.C.S.: 458320

Louis Vuitton Argentina S.A. (3)
Olga Cossenttini 240 Piso 4, Dique 4 Puerto Madero, C1107 BVA, Buenos Aires, Argentina
Tel.: (54) 11 4321 5000
Web Site: http://www.lvmh.com
Luxury Goods Mfr & Retailer
N.A.I.C.S.: 316990

Louis Vuitton Australia Pty Ltd. (3)
Level 4 70 King Street, Sydney, 2000, NSW, Australia **(100%)**
Tel.: (61) 292234311
Web Site: http://www.louisvuitton.com
Sales Range: $25-49.9 Million
Emp.: 30
Luxury Goods Mfr & Retailer
N.A.I.C.S.: 315990

Louis Vuitton Autriche (3)
Kohlmarkt 6, Vienna, 1010, Austria
Tel.: (43) 15 33 79 33
Sales Range: $50-74.9 Million
Emp.: 170
Leather Product Distr
N.A.I.C.S.: 424990
Karim Fettous *(Mgr)*

Louis Vuitton Bahrain W.L.L (3)
Moda Mall Bahrain World Trade Center, Manama, Bahrain
Tel.: (973) 17537543

Leather Goods Retailer
N.A.I.C.S.: 458320

Louis Vuitton Belgium S.A. (3)
Gallerie de la Porte Louise 203, 1050, Brussels, Belgium **(100%)**
Tel.: (32) 25511010
Web Site: http://www.louisvuitton.com
Sales Range: $25-49.9 Million
Emp.: 12
Luggage, Fashion & Leather Goods
N.A.I.C.S.: 458320

Louis Vuitton Canada Inc. (3)
150 Bloor Street West, Toronto, M5S 2X9, ON, Canada **(100%)**
Tel.: (416) 968-3993
Web Site: https://ca.louisvuitton.com
Sales Range: $25-49.9 Million
Emp.: 16
Luggage & Leather Goods
N.A.I.C.S.: 458320

Louis Vuitton Ceska S.R.O (3)
Parizska 13, 11000, Prague, Czech Republic **(100%)**
Tel.: (420) 224812774
Web Site: http://www.vuitton.com
Sales Range: $25-49.9 Million
Emp.: 30
Mfr of Leather Fashions & Goods
N.A.I.C.S.: 316990

Louis Vuitton Chile Ltda (3)
Alonso De Cordova 2460, Vitacura, 6670196, Santiago, Chile **(100%)**
Tel.: (56) 22083477
Web Site: http://www.vuitton.com
Luxury Goods Mfr & Retailer
N.A.I.C.S.: 315990

Louis Vuitton Colombia S.A. (3)
Calle 81 No 11-68 Ofca 407, Bogota, Colombia
Tel.: (57) 1 618 0532
Web Site: http://www.lvmh.com
Sales Range: $25-49.9 Million
Emp.: 5
Luxury Leather & Fashion Goods Mfr & Retailer
N.A.I.C.S.: 316990

Louis Vuitton Cyprus Limited (3)
29 Stassikratous St, Nicosia, 1065, Cyprus
Tel.: (357) 22873787
Leather Product Distr
N.A.I.C.S.: 424990

Louis Vuitton Danmark A/S (3)
Amagertorv 2, 1100, Copenhagen, Denmark **(100%)**
Tel.: (45) 33151022
Web Site: http://www.louisvuitton.com
Sales Range: $25-49.9 Million
Emp.: 10
Luxury Goods Mfr & Retailer
N.A.I.C.S.: 315990

Louis Vuitton Deutschland GmbH (3)
Konigsallee 62, 40212, Dusseldorf, Germany **(100%)**
Tel.: (49) 211323230
Web Site: http://www.louisvuitton.com
Sales Range: $25-49.9 Million
Emp.: 20
Fashion Goods; Luggage & Leather Goods
N.A.I.C.S.: 458320
Beate Klingenberg *(Country Mgr)*

Louis Vuitton Espana S.A. (3)
Maria de Molina 40, 41 6 Planta, Madrid, 28006, Spain
Tel.: (84) 914364084
Web Site: http://www.vuitton.com
Sales Range: $25-49.9 Million
Emp.: 15
Luggage & Leather Goods
N.A.I.C.S.: 458320
Carlos Velso *(Gen Mgr)*

Subsidiary (US):

Louis Vuitton Guam Inc (3)
Pacific Pl Level 3 Ste 302 1411 Pale San Vitores Rd, Tumon Bay, GU 96913
Tel.: (671) 642-5800
Luxury Goods & Leather Product Retailer
N.A.I.C.S.: 458110

Louis Vuitton Hawaii, Inc (3)
2255 Kuhio Ave Ste 1400, Honolulu, HI 96815-2642
Tel.: (808) 971-8444
Web Site: http://www.vuitton.com
Sales Range: $50-74.9 Million
Emp.: 240
Luxury Goods Mfr & Retailer
N.A.I.C.S.: 458320

Subsidiary (Non-US):

Louis Vuitton Hellas SCA (3)
Voukourestiou St 19, 10671, Athens, Greece
Tel.: (30) 2103613938
Web Site: http://www.vuitton.com
Luxury Goods Mfr & Retailer
N.A.I.C.S.: 315990

Louis Vuitton Hong Kong Ltd (3)
2202 Dorset House - 979 Kings Rd, Quarry Bay, China (Hong Kong)
Tel.: (852) 2968 1338
Fashion And Leather Goods
N.A.I.C.S.: 316990

Louis Vuitton Hungaria Sarl (3)
VI ker Andrassy ut 24, 1061, Budapest, Hungary
Tel.: (36) 1 3730487
Leather Goods Retailer
N.A.I.C.S.: 458320

Louis Vuitton Italia SpA (3)
Via Montenapoleone 2, 20121, Milan, Italy **(100%)**
Tel.: (39) 02 77 71711
Web Site: http://www.louisvuitton.com
Sales Range: $25-49.9 Million
Emp.: 100
Luggage & Leather Goods
N.A.I.C.S.: 458320
Gitti Sodano *(Mng Dir)*

Louis Vuitton Japan KK (3)
3 5 29 One Omotesando, Minato-ku Kita Aoyama, Tokyo, 107 0061, Japan **(100%)**
Tel.: (81) 334783694
Web Site: http://www.lvmh.co.jp
Sales Range: $50-74.9 Million
Emp.: 150
Luggage & Leather Goods
N.A.I.C.S.: 458320

Louis Vuitton Kuwait (3)
Sahlia Commercial Complex, PO Box 21074, Safat, 13071, Kuwait, Kuwait **(100%)**
Tel.: (965) 22404982
Web Site: http://www.louisvuitton.com
Sales Range: $75-99.9 Million
Emp.: 450
Luxury Goods Mfr & Retailer
N.A.I.C.S.: 315990

Louis Vuitton Ltd (3)
Heh B'iyar Street 32, 62998, Tel Aviv, Israel
Tel.: (972) 3 695 80 65
Web Site: http://www.lvmh.com
Leather Goods Retailer
N.A.I.C.S.: 458320
Benjamin Cercio *(Dir-Press, Influencers & Entertainment Rels)*

Louis Vuitton Luxembourg SARL (3)
Ave de la Porte Neuve 2, Luxembourg, 2227, Luxembourg
Tel.: (352) 22632626
Leather Goods Distr
N.A.I.C.S.: 424990
Olivier Coustet *(Mgr)*

Louis Vuitton Malaysia Sdn Bhd (3)
Muse Floor Annexe Block Starhill Gallery, 181 Jalan Bukit Bintang, Kuala Lumpur, 55100, Malaysia **(100%)**
Tel.: (60) 327102525
Web Site: http://www.louisvuitton.com
Sales Range: $25-49.9 Million
Emp.: 50
Luggage & Leather Goods
N.A.I.C.S.: 458320
Kathy Lan *(Gen Mgr)*

Louis Vuitton Mexico SA de RL de CV (3)
Ave Ejercito Nacional 216 17th Fl, Col Anzures, Mexico, 11590, Mexico **(100%)**
Tel.: (52) 5525811200
Web Site: http://www.lvmh.com

LVMH MOET HENNESSY LOUIS VUITTON SE

LVMH Moet Hennessy Louis Vuitton SE—(Continued)
Sales Range: $25-49.9 Million
Emp.: 120
Luxury Goods Mfr & Retailer
N.A.I.C.S.: 315990
Benjamin Gelas *(Gen Mgr)*

Louis Vuitton New Zealand Ltd. (3)
56 Queen St Level 3, PO Box 105002, Auckland, New Zealand **(100%)**
Tel.: (64) 93580422
Web Site: http://www.louisvuitton.com
Sales Range: $25-49.9 Million
Emp.: 14
Luxury Goods Mfr & Retailer
N.A.I.C.S.: 315990

Louis Vuitton Norge AS (3)
Akersgata 20, Oslo, 0158, Norway
Tel.: (47) 22 82 88 00
Web Site: http://www.louisvuitton.eu
Leather Bag Retailer
N.A.I.C.S.: 458320
Nina Horgen *(Office Mgr)*

Subsidiary (US):

Louis Vuitton North America Inc. (3)
19 E 57th St, New York, NY 10022
Tel.: (212) 931-2000
Web Site: http://www.vuitton.com
Luxury Goods Mfr & Retailer
N.A.I.C.S.: 458320

Subsidiary (Non-US):

Louis Vuitton Österreich GesmbH (3)
Borsegasse 12, 1010, Vienna, Austria **(100%)**
Tel.: (43) 015337933
Web Site: http://www.vuitton.com
Sales Range: $25-49.9 Million
Emp.: 20
Luxury Goods Mfr & Retailer
N.A.I.C.S.: 315990

Louis Vuitton Panama Inc (3)
Mall Multiplaza Pacific Corregimiento de San Francisco Camino del, Sol Primer Nivel Local NA-261, Panama, Panama
Tel.: (507) 302 6802
Web Site: http://www.louisvuitton.com.au
Sales Range: $25-49.9 Million
Emp.: 11
Handbag Retailer
N.A.I.C.S.: 458110

Louis Vuitton Portugal Maleiro Limitada (3)
Rua Augusta 196, 1100-055, Lisbon, Portugal
Tel.: (351) 213468600
Web Site: http://www.vuitton.com
Luxury Goods Mfr & Retailer
N.A.I.C.S.: 315990

Subsidiary (US):

Louis Vuitton Saipan Inc. (3)
DFS Galleria PMB A54, Saipan, MP 96950
Tel.: (670) 233-0637
Web Site: http://www.vuitton.com
Sales Range: $25-49.9 Million
Emp.: 14
Luxury Goods Retailer
N.A.I.C.S.: 315990

Subsidiary (Non-US):

Louis Vuitton South Africa Ltd (3)
Shop 26 Upper Level Sandton City Shopping Centre, Sandton, Johannesburg, 2196, South Africa
Tel.: (27) 11 881 57 25
Web Site: http://www.louisvuitton.com
Emp.: 17
Clothing Accessory Retailer
N.A.I.C.S.: 458110
Rebecca Fletcher *(Mgr-Retail)*

Louis Vuitton South Europe Srl (3)
Via Tommaso Grossi 2, Milan, 20121, Italy
Tel.: (39) 02006608100
Clothing Accessory & Leather Goods Retailer
N.A.I.C.S.: 458110

Louis Vuitton Suisse SA (3)
5 Quai du Mont-Blanc, Geneva, 1201, Switzerland
Tel.: (41) 22 311 30 70
Web Site: http://www.louisvuittonsuisse.com
Sales Range: $50-74.9 Million
Emp.: 150
Jewelry & Leather Goods Retailer
N.A.I.C.S.: 458310

Louis Vuitton Suomy Oy (3)
Pohjoisesplanadi 35, Helsinki, 00100, Finland
Tel.: (358) 9 6811 6615
Web Site: http://eu.vuitton.com
Leather Goods Retailer
N.A.I.C.S.: 458320
Pekka Ylanko *(Country Mgr)*

Louis Vuitton Taiwan Ltd. (3)
Ste A 18th Fl No 105 Tun Hwa S Rd, Section 2, Taipei, 106, Taiwan **(100%)**
Tel.: (886) 227051680
Web Site: http://www.vuitton.com
Luxury Goods Mfr & Retailer
N.A.I.C.S.: 315990

Louis Vuitton Venezuela SA (3)
Centro Sambil Locales Fr 37 & 38, Avenida Libertador, 1060, Caracas, Venezuela **(100%)**
Tel.: (58) 2122678709
Web Site: http://www.vuitton.com
Sales Range: $25-49.9 Million
Emp.: 8
Luxury Goods Mfr & Retailer
N.A.I.C.S.: 316990

Louis Vuitton Vietnam Company Ltd (3)
161 Dong Khoi St Opera View Bldg Gb Area ben Nghe W, Dist 1, 70000, Ho Chi Minh City, Vietnam
Tel.: (84) 8 38276318
Web Site: http://www.louisvuittonvietnam.net
Sales Range: $25-49.9 Million
Emp.: 20
Luxury Goods Retailer
N.A.I.C.S.: 459999
Vi Truong *(Reg Mgr)*

Louis Vuitton Vostock LLC (3)
Stoleshnikov pereulok 10/18, 107031, Moscow, Russia
Tel.: (7) 8007005058
Web Site: http://www.lvmh.com
Fashion Apparel & Leather Goods Retailer
N.A.I.C.S.: 458110

PT Louis Vuitton Indonesia LLC (3)
Jalan Jendral Sudirman Kav 54-55 Plaza Bapindo Mandiri Tower Lantai 21, Jakarta, Indonesia
Tel.: (62) 21 5275428
Leather Goods Retailer
N.A.I.C.S.: 458320

Subsidiary (Domestic):

Societe des Ateliers Louis Vuitton (3)
2 Rue Du Pont Neuf, 75034, Paris, Cedex, France **(100%)**
Tel.: (33) 155803200
Web Site: http://www.louisvuitton.com
Sales Range: $150-199.9 Million
Emp.: 789
Mfr of Leather Goods
N.A.I.C.S.: 316990
Yves Carcelles *(Pres)*

Societe des Magasins Louis Vuitton-France (3)
2 rue du Pont Neuf, 75001, Paris, Cedex, France **(100%)**
Tel.: (33) 155803200
Web Site: http://www.louisvuitton.fr
Sales Range: $550-599.9 Million
Emp.: 1,200
Holding Company; Retail Stores
N.A.I.C.S.: 551112

Subsidiary (Domestic):

Make Up For Ever Paris (2)
5 Rue De La Boetie, 75008, Paris, France **(100%)**
Tel.: (33) 141479900
Web Site: http://www.makeupforever.fr
Sales Range: $50-74.9 Million
Emp.: 200
Mfr of Cosmetics

INTERNATIONAL PUBLIC

N.A.I.C.S.: 325620

Subsidiary (Non-US):

Make Up For Ever Canada Ltd (3)
1260 Crescent street suite 100, Montreal, H3G 2A9, QC, Canada
Tel.: (514) 288-4445
Web Site: https://www.makeupforever.com
Cosmetic & Beauty Product Distr
N.A.I.C.S.: 424210
Francine Blauer *(Gen Mgr)*

Subsidiary (US):

Make Up For Ever LLC (3)
853 Broadway 10 th Fl, New York, NY 10003
Tel.: (212) 377-3960
Web Site: http://www.makeupforeverusa.com
Sales Range: $25-49.9 Million
Emp.: 50
Cosmetic Product Retailer
N.A.I.C.S.: 456120
Floriane David *(Dir-Education)*

Subsidiary (Non-US):

Manufacture de Souliers Louis Vuitton Srl (2)
35 Via Cavour, 30032, Fiesso d'Artico, Italy
Tel.: (39) 0499804311
Sales Range: $75-99.9 Million
Emp.: 400
Luxury Goods & Jewelry Mfr
N.A.I.C.S.: 339910
Patrice Guillemin *(Dir-Investor)*

Maxelle SA (2)
Avenue Des Champs-Montants 12, 2074, Marin, Switzerland
Tel.: (41) 327 56 66 70
Sales Range: $25-49.9 Million
Emp.: 30
Watch & Jewelry Distr
N.A.I.C.S.: 423940
Patrick Lassigne *(Gen Mgr)*

Montaigne KK (2)
1-1-1 Minamiaoyama, Minato-Ku, Tokyo, 107-0062, Japan
Tel.: (81) 334783910
Clothing Accessory Distr
N.A.I.C.S.: 424350

Rossimoda Spa (2)
Via Venezia 22, 35010, Vigonza, Padua, Italy
Tel.: (39) 049 828 42 11
Web Site: http://www.rossimoda.com
Sales Range: $75-99.9 Million
Emp.: 300
Footwear Mfr
N.A.I.C.S.: 316210
Frederic Munoz *(Pres)*

Subsidiary (Domestic):

Sephora (2)
65 Ave Edouard Vaillant, 92100, Boulogne-Billancourt, France **(100%)**
Tel.: (33) 144132222
Web Site: http://www.sephora.com
Sales Range: $50-74.9 Million
Emp.: 120
Holding Company
N.A.I.C.S.: 551112
Calandra MacGregor *(Mgr-Loss Prevention-Natl)*

Subsidiary (Non-US):

Sephora Danmark ApS (3)
Rathsacksvej 1 4th, 1862, Frederiksberg, Denmark
Tel.: (45) 38 41 38 80
Web Site: http://www.sephora.dk
Cosmetic & Personal Care Product Distr
N.A.I.C.S.: 424210

Sephora Deutschland GmbH (3)
Limbeckerstrasse 66-68, 45127, Essen, Germany
Tel.: (49) 2012436190
Perfumes & Cosmetics Retailer
N.A.I.C.S.: 325620

Subsidiary (Domestic):

Sephora France SA (3)
Parc Technologique Orleans-Charbonniere, 1, Route de Boigny, 45760, Boigny-sur-Bionne, France
Tel.: (33) 232787474
Web Site: http://www.sephora.fr
Perfume & Cosmetics Retailer
N.A.I.C.S.: 325620

Subsidiary (Non-US):

Sephora Italia SpA (3)
Via del Vecchio, Polotechnico 7, Milan, 20121, Italy
Web Site: http://www.sephora.it
Retailer of Perfumes & Cosmetics
N.A.I.C.S.: 325620

Sephora Luxembourg SARL (3)
C C Auchan Kirchberg 5 rue A Weiker, 2721, Luxembourg, Luxembourg
Tel.: (352) 42 81 611
Leather Goods Mfr
N.A.I.C.S.: 424990

Sephora Marinopoulos S.A. (3)
P. Marinopoulou 7, Athens, 17456, Alimos, Greece
Tel.: (30) 2109898011
Web Site: http://www.sephora.com
Perfumes & Cosmetics Retailer
N.A.I.C.S.: 325620

Sephora Monaco SAM (3)
17 avenue des Spelugues - Galerie commerciale du Metropole, Premises no 101-103 & 147, Monaco, 98000, Monaco
Tel.: (377) 97 77 28 00
Leather Goods Retailer
N.A.I.C.S.: 458320

Sephora Nederland BV (3)
Derkinderenstraat 24, 1062 DB, Amsterdam, Netherlands
Tel.: (31) 20 5127500
Web Site: http://www.sephora.nl
Sales Range: $50-74.9 Million
Emp.: 10
Cosmetic Product Distr
N.A.I.C.S.: 424210

Sephora Pologne sp.zo.o. (3)
Al. Jerozolimskie 92, 00-807, Warsaw, Poland
Tel.: (48) 225295200
Web Site: http://www.sephora.pl
Mfr of Perfumes & Cosmetics
N.A.I.C.S.: 325620

Sephora Portugal Perfumeria Lda (3)
Avenida da Liberdade 49, 5. E, Lisbon, Portugal
Tel.: (351) 213241780
Web Site: http://www.sephora.pt
Perfume & Cosmetics Retailer
N.A.I.C.S.: 325620

Sephora Spain SA (3)
Avenida Partenon 4 Planta Tercera, 28042, Madrid, Spain **(100%)**
Tel.: (34) 917212230
Web Site: http://www.sephora.es
Perfumes & Cosmetics Retailer
N.A.I.C.S.: 456120

Subsidiary (Non-US):

Somarest SARL (2)
Str Transilvaniei Nr 1 Cisnadie, 555300, Sibiu, Romania
Tel.: (40) 269 563 294
Sales Range: $75-99.9 Million
Emp.: 500
Footwear Mfr
N.A.I.C.S.: 316210

Taramax SA (2)
Fendi Tiemepiece Av des Champs-Montants 12 A, 2074, Marin, Switzerland
Tel.: (41) 32 756 66 70
Luxury Watches Mfr
N.A.I.C.S.: 334519

Subsidiary (US):

Taramax USA Inc (3)
600 Warren Ave, Spring Lake, NJ 07762-2039
Tel.: (732) 282-0300
Jewelry Retailer
N.A.I.C.S.: 458310

AND PRIVATE COMPANIES

LVMH MOET HENNESSY LOUIS VUITTON SE

Subsidiary (Non-US):

Thomas Pink Holdings Ltd. (2)
1 Palmerston Ct, Palmerston Way, London,
SW1Y 6JD, United Kingdom **(100%)**
Tel.: (44) 2074982202
Web Site: http://www.thomaspink.com
Sales Range: $25-49.9 Million
Emp.: 70
Holding Company
N.A.I.C.S.: 551112
Jonathan Hilbron *(Mng Dir)*

Subsidiary (Non-US):

Thomas Pink Belgium SA (3)
23 24 Blvd De Waterloo, 1000, Brussels,
Belgium **(100%)**
Tel.: (32) 25020508
Web Site: http://www.thomaspink.co.uk
Mfr of Leather & Leather Fashions
N.A.I.C.S.: 316990

Thomas Pink France (3)
19 Rue Francois 1st Er, 75008, Paris,
France **(100%)**
Tel.: (33) 147237200
Web Site: http://www.thomaspink.co.uk
Sales Range: $25-49.9 Million
Emp.: 6
Mfr & Retailer of Mens' & Ladies' Fashions
N.A.I.C.S.: 315210

Subsidiary (US):

Thomas Pink Inc. (3)
520 Madison Ave, New York, NY
10022 **(100%)**
Tel.: (212) 838-1928
Sales Range: $25-49.9 Million
Emp.: 20
Mfr & Retailer of Mens' & Ladies' Fashions
N.A.I.C.S.: 458110
Michael Bragg *(Dir-Comm)*

Subsidiary (Non-US):

Thomas Pink Ireland Ltd. (3)
29 Dawson St, Hatch Street, Dublin, 2,
Ireland **(100%)**
Tel.: (353) 16703720
Web Site: http://www.thomaspink.com
Sales Range: $25-49.9 Million
Emp.: 7
Mfr of Mens' & Ladies' Fashions
N.A.I.C.S.: 315210
David Galvin *(Mgr-Stores)*

Subsidiary (Domestic):

Thomas Pink Ltd. (3)
1 Palmerston Ct, London, SW8 4AJ, United
Kingdom **(100%)**
Tel.: (44) 2074982202
Web Site: http://www.thomaspink.co.uk
Sales Range: $25-49.9 Million
Emp.: 101
Mfr & Retailer of Mens' & Ladies' Fashions
N.A.I.C.S.: 315210
Jonathan Heilbron *(CEO)*

LVMH Finance SA (1)
22 Ave Montaine, 92100, Boulogne-
Billancourt, Paris, France
Tel.: (33) 144132222
Financial Advisory Services
N.A.I.C.S.: 523940

**LVMH Fragrance Brands Canada
Ltd** (1)
2 Vloor Street West Suite 1602, Toronto,
M4W3E2, ON, Canada
Tel.: (416) 929-3499
Cosmetic Product Distr
N.A.I.C.S.: 456120

LVMH Fragrance Brands GmbH (1)
Haus am Rhein Rotterdamerstr 40, 40474,
Dusseldorf, Germany
Tel.: (49) 21 16 50 455
Cosmetic Product Distr
N.A.I.C.S.: 456120

LVMH Fragrance Brands LLC (1)
19 E 57th St, New York, NY 10022
Tel.: (212) 931-2700
Cosmetic Product Distr
N.A.I.C.S.: 456120

LVMH Fragrance Brands Ltd (1)
2 Vloor Street West Suite 1602, Toronto,
M4W3E2, ON, Canada
Tel.: (416) 929-3499
Cosmetic Product Distr
N.A.I.C.S.: 456120

LVMH Fragrance Brands SA (1)
77 rue Anatole France, 92300, Levallois-
Perret, France
Tel.: (33) 1 73 02 60 00
Web Site: http://www.lvmh.com
Perfume & Cosmetic Product Retailer
N.A.I.C.S.: 456120

Subsidiary (Non-US):

LVMH Fragrance Brands Austria (2)
Fingerstrasse 6, Vienna, 1010, Austria
Tel.: (43) 1 533 65 65
Web Site: http://www.lvmh.com
Perfume & Cosmetic Product Distr
N.A.I.C.S.: 424210
Maya Bolcli *(Gen Mgr)*

LVMH Fragrance Brands KK (2)
Sumitomo Hanzomon Building 3-16
Hayabusa-cho, Chiyoda-Ku, 102-8606, To-
kyo, Japan
Tel.: (81) 3 3264 5500
Web Site: http://www.lvmh.com
Watch & Jewelry Retailer
N.A.I.C.S.: 458310

LVMH Fragrance Brands Ltd (2)
UK House - 6th Floor 180 Oxford Street,
W1D 1AB, London, United Kingdom - Eng-
land
Tel.: (44) 2075638800
Web Site: http://www.lvmh.com
Sales Range: $50-74.9 Million
Emp.: 140
Perfume & Cosmetic Product Distr
N.A.I.C.S.: 424210

LVMH Italia S.p.A. (1)
Via Tommaso Grossi 2, 20121, Milan, Italy
Tel.: (39) 02723341
Web Site: http://www.lvmh.com
Retailer of Textiles & Leather Fashion
Goods, Accessories & Luggage
N.A.I.C.S.: 458110
Gabriella Scarpa *(Chm)*

**LVMH MoEt Hennessy Louis Vuitton
KK** (1)
Sumitomo Hanzomon Bldg 3 rd Floor- 3-16
Hayabusa-cho, Chiyoda-Ku, Tokyo, 102-
0092, Japan
Tel.: (81) 3 32 63 10 31
Sales Range: $25-49.9 Million
Emp.: 25
Luxury Goods Retailer
N.A.I.C.S.: 458310
Yukari Ogawa *(Mgr)*

LVMH P&K GmbH (1)
Rotterdamer Str 40, 40474, Dusseldorf,
Germany
Tel.: (49) 211650455
Cosmetic Product Distr
N.A.I.C.S.: 456120

**LVMH Parfums et Cosmetiques do
Brasil Ltda** (1)
R Sao Tome 86, Sao Paulo, 04551-080,
Brazil
Tel.: (55) 11 38 96 72 99
Cosmetic Product & Perfume Distr
N.A.I.C.S.: 456120

LVMH Participations BV (1)
Oude Utrechtseweg 22, Baarn, 3743KN,
Netherlands
Tel.: (31) 356946907
Sales Range: $50-74.9 Million
Emp.: 5
Financial Management Services
N.A.I.C.S.: 523999
Marco de Ruite *(Mng Dir)*

LVMH Perfumes & Cosmetics (1)
22 avenue Montaigne, Paris, 75008, France
Tel.: (33) 1 44 13 22 22
Perfumes & Cosmetics Distr
N.A.I.C.S.: 424990
Claude Martinez *(Mng Dir)*

Subsidiary (Non-US):

Fresh Cosmetics Ltd (2)
92 Marylebone High Street, London, W1U
4RD, United Kingdom
Tel.: (44) 20 7486 4100
Emp.: 6
Cosmetic Product Retailer
N.A.I.C.S.: 456120

LVMH Cosmetics KK (2)
Sumitomo Hanzomon Bldg 3-16 Hayabusa-
cho, Chiyoda-Ku, Tokyo, 102-0092, Japan
Tel.: (81) 3 3234 1101
Web Site: http://www.lvmh.com
Sales Range: $25-49.9 Million
Emp.: 50
Perfume & Cosmetic Retailer
N.A.I.C.S.: 456120
Sayaka Nakajima *(Mgr-Back Office Applica-
tion)*

**LVMH Fragrances & Cosmetics (Sin-
gapore) Pte. Ltd.** (2)
1 King Seng Promenade 14 09 10, Great
World City West Tower, Singapore, 237994,
Singapore **(100%)**
Tel.: (65) 67372188
Web Site: http://www.christiandior.com
Sales Range: $25-49.9 Million
Emp.: 25
Mfr of Perfumes & Cosmetics
N.A.I.C.S.: 325620

LVMH P&C de Mexico SA de CV (2)
Av Ejercito National - No 216 Piso 17, Col
Anzures, 11590, Mexico, Mexico
Tel.: (52) 55 25 81 12 00
Perfume & Cosmetic Retailer
N.A.I.C.S.: 456120

**LVMH Parfums & Cosmetiques do
Brasil Ltda** (2)
Rua Sao Tome 86 Vila Olimpia, Sao Paulo,
04551-080, Brazil
Tel.: (55) 11 3896 7299
Web Site: http://www.lvmh.com
Perfume & Cosmetic Product Distr
N.A.I.C.S.: 424210

**LVMH Parfums & Kosmetik
Deutschland GmbH** (2)
Rotterdamerstrasse 40, Dusseldorf, 40474,
Germany
Tel.: (49) 211882320
Perfume & Personal Care Product Distr
N.A.I.C.S.: 424210
Bart de Boever *(Gen Mgr)*

**LVMH Perfumes & Cosmeticos
Iberica SA** (2)
Isla De Java 33, Madrid, 28034,
Spain **(100%)**
Tel.: (34) 917286900
Web Site: http://www.lvmh.com
Sales Range: $100-124.9 Million
Emp.: 400
Mfr of Perfumes & Cosmetics
N.A.I.C.S.: 325620
Matia DeAlzua *(Gen Mgr)*

**LVMH Perfumes & Cosmetics (Korea)
Ltd.** (2)
12 F Sera Bldg 50 1 & 2 Nonhyun Dong,
Kangnam Ku, Seoul, 135 010, Korea
(South) **(100%)**
Tel.: (82) 234389500
Web Site: http://www.lvmh.com
Sales Range: $1-9.9 Million
Emp.: 500
Perfumes & Cosmetics
N.A.I.C.S.: 325620

**LVMH Perfumes & Cosmetics (Malay-
sia) Sdn. Bhd.** (2)
Ste 7 2 & 7th Fl, Jalan Semangat Section
14, Petaling Jaya, 46100, Selangor,
Malaysia **(100%)**
Tel.: (60) 379552919
Sales Range: $25-49.9 Million
Emp.: 40
Mfr & Distr of Perfumes & Cosmetics
N.A.I.C.S.: 325620

**LVMH Perfumes & Cosmetics (Thai-
land) Ltd** (2)
16th Fl Italthai Tower 2034 New Petchburi
Rd, Bangkapi Huay Kwang, 10320, Bang-
kok, Thailand **(100%)**
Tel.: (66) 271618229
Web Site: http://www.lvmh.com
Sales Range: $200-249.9 Million
Emp.: 530
Mfr of Perfumes & Cosmetics
N.A.I.C.S.: 325620

**LVMH Perfumes & Cosmetics Asia
Pacific Ltd** (2)
34 F Dorset House, 979 Kings Rd, Quarry
Bay, China (Hong Kong) **(100%)**
Tel.: (852) 29689168
Perfumes & Cosmetics Mfr & Retailer
N.A.I.C.S.: 325620

**LVMH Perfumes & Cosmetics
GmbH** (2)
Rotterdamerstrasse 40, 40474, Dusseldorf,
Germany **(100%)**
Tel.: (49) 21143840
Sales Range: $25-49.9 Million
Emp.: 100
Mfr of Perfumes & Cosmetics
N.A.I.C.S.: 325620

**LVMH Perfumes & Cosmetics Group
Pty Ltd** (2)
Locked Bag 3, Ste 1 13 Lord St, Botany,
2019, New South Wales, Australia **(100%)**
Tel.: (61) 296954800
Web Site: http://www.lvmh.com
Sales Range: $25-49.9 Million
Emp.: 90
Sale of Perfumes & Cosmetics
N.A.I.C.S.: 325620

**LVMH Perfumes & Cosmetics Italia
S.p.A** (2)
Via Ripamonti 99, Milan, 20141,
Italy **(100%)**
Tel.: (39) 025522881
Web Site: http://www.lvmh.com
Sales Range: $50-74.9 Million
Emp.: 200
Mfr & Retailer of Perfumes & Cosmetics
N.A.I.C.S.: 325620

**LVMH Perfumes & Cosmetics Shang-
hai Co. Ltd.** (2)
1266 Nanjing Xi Lu, Ste 2901 2906 Plz 66,
Shanghai, 200040, China **(100%)**
Tel.: (86) 2162881688
Web Site: http://www.dior.com
Sales Range: $25-49.9 Million
Emp.: 70
Mfr of Perfumes, Cosmetics & other Toilet
Preparations
N.A.I.C.S.: 325620

**LVMH Perfumes & Cosmetics
Thailand** (2)
16th Fl Italthai Tower 2034 New Petchburi
Rd, Bankapi, Bangkok, 10320,
Thailand **(100%)**
Tel.: (66) 271618229
Web Site: http://www.dior.com
Sales Range: $25-49.9 Million
Emp.: 30
Mfr of Perfumes & Cosmetics
N.A.I.C.S.: 325620
Pasica Silapajan *(Country Gen Mgr)*

**LVMH Perfumes & Cosmetics
UK** (2)
UK House - 6th Floor 180 Oxford Street,
W1D 1AB, London, United Kingdom - Eng-
land
Tel.: (44) 207 563 6300
Sales Range: $50-74.9 Million
Emp.: 140
Perfume & Cosmetic Product Distr
N.A.I.C.S.: 424210

**LVMH Perfumes & Cosmetics de
Mexico S.A. de C.V.** (2)
Av Ejercito National No 216 Pisos 16 17 Y
18 8th fl, Col Anzures, Mexico, 11590,
Mexico **(100%)**
Tel.: (52) 5525811203
Web Site: http://www.lvmh.com
Sales Range: $25-49.9 Million
Emp.: 40
Mfr of Perfumes & Cosmetics
N.A.I.C.S.: 325620

**LVMH Perfumes & Cosmetics do Bra-
sil Ltda.** (2)
Avda Europa 140, Sao Paulo, 1449000,
Brazil **(100%)**
Tel.: (55) 138967299
Sales Range: $50-74.9 Million
Emp.: 200
Perfumes & Cosmetics
N.A.I.C.S.: 325620

LVMH MOET HENNESSY LOUIS VUITTON SE

LVMH Moet Hennessy Louis Vuitton
SE—(Continued)

LVMH Perfumes e Cosmetica Lda (2)
Rua Castilho n 5 - 5 Andar Salas 50-52,
1250-066, Lisbon, Portugal
Tel.: (351) 213 583 560
Emp.: 60
Perfume & Cosmetic Product Distr
N.A.I.C.S.: 424210
Sergi Figuerola *(Mng Dir)*

Pardior, S.A. de C.V. (2)
Av Ejercito Nacional No 216 Piso 17 Anzures, Seccion Miguel Hidalgo, Mexico,
11590, Mexico
Tel.: (52) 5525811200
Perfume Stores
N.A.I.C.S.: 456120
Silvia Silo *(Gen Mgr)*

Subsidiary (Domestic):

Parfums Christian Dior SA (2)
33 Ave Hoche, 75008, Paris,
France (100%)
Tel.: (33) 0149538500
Web Site: http://www.dior.com
Sales Range: $100-124.9 Million
Emp.: 300
Mfr of Perfume & Beauty Products
N.A.I.C.S.: 325620
Laurent Kleitman *(Pres & CEO)*

Subsidiary (Non-US):

Christian Dior (Thailand) (3)
591 Unit 1601-1602 16th Fl Samatjawanich
2 Tower Soi Sukhumvit 33, Klongtonnua
Wattana, 10110, Bangkok,
Thailand (100%)
Tel.: (66) 22620130
Web Site: http://www.lvmh.com
Mfr of Perfumes & Cosmetics
N.A.I.C.S.: 325620

Christian Dior Korea (3)
8 F Youlim Bldg 49 Chungdam Dong, Kangnam Ku, Seoul, 135-954, Korea
(South) (100%)
Tel.: (82) 25185233
Web Site: http://www.dior.com
Sales Range: $25-49.9 Million
Emp.: 23
Mfr of Perfume & Cosmetics
N.A.I.C.S.: 325620

Parfums Christian Dior (3)
Isla De Java 33, Madrid, 28034,
Spain (100%)
Tel.: (34) 917286900
Sales Range: $25-49.9 Million
Emp.: 100
Mfr of Perfumes & Cosmetics
N.A.I.C.S.: 325620
Juan Pedro Abeniacar *(Gen Mgr)*

Parfums Christian Dior (3)
Avenida Europe 140, Sao Paulo, 01449
000, Brazil (100%)
Tel.: (55) 138967299
Sales Range: $25-49.9 Million
Emp.: 100
Mfr of Perfumes & Cosmetics
N.A.I.C.S.: 325620

Parfums Christian Dior (Australia) Pty Ltd (3)
Unit 1 13 Lord St, Locked Bag 3, Botany,
2019, Australia (100%)
Tel.: (61) 296954800
Web Site: http://www.parfums.givenchy.fr
Sales Range: $25-49.9 Million
Emp.: 75
Mfr of Perfumes & Cosmetics
N.A.I.C.S.: 325620

Parfums Christian Dior A/S (3)
Langebrogade 6 a, Copenhagen, 1411,
Denmark (100%)
Tel.: (45) 32837373
Web Site: http://www.dior.com
Sales Range: $25-49.9 Million
Emp.: 25
Mfr of Perfumes & Cosmetics
N.A.I.C.S.: 325620
Stephane Previdi *(Gen Mgr)*

Parfums Christian Dior AB (3)
Kungsholms Strand 127, PO Box 49143,
Stockholm, 10029, Sweden (100%)
Tel.: (46) 84425240
Web Site: http://www.dior.com
Sales Range: Less than $1 Million
Emp.: 12
Sales of Perfumes & Cosmetics
N.A.I.C.S.: 316990
Aenetha Stahl *(Country Mgr)*

Parfums Christian Dior AG (3)
Buckhauserstrasse 32, CH 8048, Zurich,
Switzerland (100%)
Tel.: (41) 14068686
Sales Range: $25-49.9 Million
Emp.: 100
Mfr of Perfume & Beauty Products
N.A.I.C.S.: 325620

Parfums Christian Dior BV (3)
Max Euwelaan 55, Postbus 8806, 3062 MA,
Rotterdam, Netherlands (100%)
Tel.: (31) 104524677
Web Site: http://www.dior.com
Sales Range: $25-49.9 Million
Emp.: 30
Mfr of Perfume & Beauty Products
N.A.I.C.S.: 325620

Parfums Christian Dior Canada Inc. (3)
2 Bloor St W, Toronto, M4W 3E2, ON,
Canada (100%)
Tel.: (416) 929-6299
Sales Range: $25-49.9 Million
Emp.: 20
Mfr of Perfume & Beauty Products
N.A.I.C.S.: 325620

Parfums Christian Dior GmbH (3)
Haus Am Rhein, Rotterdamerstrasse 40,
40474, Dusseldorf, Germany (100%)
Tel.: (49) 21143840
Web Site: http://www.diormail.com
Sales Range: $25-49.9 Million
Emp.: 100
Mfr of Perfume & Beauty Products
N.A.I.C.S.: 325620

Parfums Christian Dior GmbH (3)
Esslinggasse 16/18, Vienna, 1010, Austria
Tel.: (43) 1 533 91 81
Web Site: http://www.dior.com
Perfume & Cosmetic Product Distr
N.A.I.C.S.: 456120

Parfums Christian Dior Hellas S.A. (3)
32 Ave Kifissias, Athens, 15125, Greece
Tel.: (30) 210 81 11 500
Web Site: http://www.dior.com
Sales Range: $25-49.9 Million
Emp.: 40
Cosmetic & Perfume Distr
N.A.I.C.S.: 424210
Aimilia Papathanasopoulou *(Mgr-Adv & PR)*

Parfums Christian Dior Japan KK (3)
Sumitomo Hanzomon Bldg 5th Fl, 3 16
Hayabusha Cho, Tokyo, 102 0092,
Japan (100%)
Tel.: (81) 332635777
Web Site: http://www.i-love-dior.jp
Sales Range: $25-49.9 Million
Emp.: 60
Mfr of Perfume & Beauty Products
N.A.I.C.S.: 325620

Parfums Christian Dior Ltd. (3)
34 Fl Dorset House Taikoo Pl, 979 Kings
Rd, Quarry Bay, China (Hong
Kong) (100%)
Tel.: (852) 29689168
Web Site: http://www.dior.com
Sales Range: $25-49.9 Million
Emp.: 50
Mfr of Perfume & Beauty Products
N.A.I.C.S.: 325620

Parfums Christian Dior New Zealand Ltd. (3)
74 Richard Pearse Drive Airport Oaks,
Auckland, New Zealand
Tel.: (64) 9 255 1588
Web Site: http://www.lvmh.com
Perfumes & Cosmetics
N.A.I.C.S.: 325620

Parfums Christian Dior Osterreich GmbH (3)
Esslinggasse 16-18, Vienna, 1010,
Austria (100%)
Tel.: (43) 15339181
Web Site: http://www.dior.com
Sales Range: $25-49.9 Million
Emp.: 9
Mfr of Perfume & Cosmetics
N.A.I.C.S.: 325620

Parfums Christian Dior SAB (3)
Ave Lousie 523, B1050, Brussels,
Belgium (100%)
Tel.: (32) 26422611
Web Site: http://www.dior.com
Sales Range: $25-49.9 Million
Emp.: 60
Mfr of Perfume & Beauty Products
N.A.I.C.S.: 325620
Bruno Ruelhat *(Gen Mgr)*

Parfums Christian Dior Singapore Pte. Ltd. (3)
1 Kim Seng Promenade 14 09 10, Singapore, 237994, Singapore (100%)
Tel.: (65) 67372188
Web Site: http://www.christiandior.com
Sales Range: $25-49.9 Million
Emp.: 50
Mfr of Perfume & Beauty Products
N.A.I.C.S.: 325620

Parfums Christian Dior SpA (3)
Via Ripamonti 99, 20141, Milan,
Italy (100%)
Tel.: (39) 025522881
Mfr of Perfume & Beauty Products
N.A.I.C.S.: 325620

Subsidiary (US):

Parfums Christian Dior, Inc (3)
19 E 57th St, New York, NY 10022-2508
Tel.: (212) 931-2200
Web Site: http://www.dior.com
Sales Range: $25-49.9 Million
Emp.: 40
Perfumes, Eau de Cologne, Eau de Toilette,
Dusting Powder, Bath Items, Lipstick, Nail
Enamel, Men's Toiletries, Nail Conditioners,
Makeup, Skin Care
N.A.I.C.S.: 456120

Subsidiary (Non-US):

Parfums Christina Dior Argentina SA (3)
Avenida Corrientes 222 4 piso, Buenos Aires, 1043, Argentina
Tel.: (54) 11 4338 8100
Web Site: http://www.lvmh.com
Emp.: 100
Mfr of Perfumes & Cosmetics
N.A.I.C.S.: 325620

LVMH Publica SA (1)
Avenue Louise 326, 1050, Brussels, Belgium
Tel.: (32) 26444354
Cosmetic Product Distr
N.A.I.C.S.: 456120

LVMH Services BV (1)
Oude Utrechtseweg 22-24, Baarn, 3743,
Netherlands
Tel.: (31) 356946907
Emp.: 3
Watch & Jewelry Retailer
N.A.I.C.S.: 458310
Marco Rueter *(Gen Mgr)*

LVMH Swiss Manufactures SA (1)
Rue Des Billodes 34, Neuchatel, Le Locle,
2400, Switzerland
Tel.: (41) 32 930 62 62
Cosmetic Product Distr
N.A.I.C.S.: 456120

La Minute & ses Complications SA (1)
Chemin des Cytises 8, 1347, Le Sentier,
Switzerland
Tel.: (41) 218456666
Cosmetic Product Distr
N.A.I.C.S.: 456120

Le Bon Marche SA (1)
24 Rue De Sevres, Paris, 75007,
France (100%)
Tel.: (33) 00144398000
Web Site: http://www.lebonmarche.fr

INTERNATIONAL PUBLIC

Clothing Stores
N.A.I.C.S.: 458110

Subsidiary (Domestic):

Franck & Fils SA (2)
80 Rue de Passy, 75016, Paris, France
Tel.: (33) 1 44 14 38 00
Web Site: http://www.francketfils.fr
Clothing Apparel Distr
N.A.I.C.S.: 424350

La Grande Epicerie (2)
38 rue de Sevres, 75007, Paris, France
Tel.: (33) 144398100
Web Site: http://www.lagrandeepicerie.fr
Sales Range: $25-49.9 Million
Gourmet Food Retailer
N.A.I.C.S.: 445298
Alexandre Boutoille *(Mgr)*

Le Jardin D'Acclimatation (1)
Bois De Boulogne, Paris, 75116,
France (100%)
Tel.: (33) 140679085
Web Site: http://www.jardindacclimatation.fr
Theme Park
N.A.I.C.S.: 713110
Asonso Morais Bruno *(Mgr-HR)*

Les Ateliers Joaillers Louis Vuitton SAS (1)
2 Rue Du Pont Neuf, 75001, Paris, France
Tel.: (33) 8 99 96 39 84
Jewellery Distr
N.A.I.C.S.: 423940

Les Echos Formation SAS (1)
16 rue du Quatre Septembre, 75112, Paris,
France
Tel.: (33) 1 49 53 65 65
Web Site: http://www.lesechos-formation.fr
Training & Educational Support Services
N.A.I.C.S.: 611430

Les Echos Medias SNC (1)
16 Rue Du 4 Septembre, 75002, Paris,
France
Tel.: (33) 149536565
Cosmetic Product Distr
N.A.I.C.S.: 456120

Loewe Fashion (M) Sdn Bhd (1)
Annexe Block Level 11 Starhill Shopping
Center 181, Jalan Bukit Bintang, Kuala
Lumpur, Malaysia
Tel.: (60) 3 2710 2525
Cosmetic Product Distr
N.A.I.C.S.: 456120

Louis Vuitton (Aruba) N.V (1)
LG Smith Boulevard 82, Oranjestad, Aruba
Tel.: (297) 582 6271
Cosmetic Product Distr
N.A.I.C.S.: 456120

Louis Vuitton Eau Llc (1)
PO Box 60912, Dubai, United Arab Emirates
Tel.: (971) 4 3592535
Cosmetic Product Distr
N.A.I.C.S.: 456120

Lvmh Fashion Group Services Sas (1)
65 Avenue Edouard Vaillant, 92100,
Boulogne-Billancourt, France
Tel.: (33) 1 55 80 32 00
Fashion Leather Goods Distr
N.A.I.C.S.: 458320

Lvmh Fashion Group Trading Korea Ltd (1)
Louis Vuitton Building 2 nd Floor 99-18
Chungdam-dong, Kangnam-ku, Seoul, 135-100, Korea (South)
Tel.: (82) 2 548 86 26
Fashion Leather Goods Distr
N.A.I.C.S.: 458320

Lvmh Iberia Sl (1)
Isla de Java 33, Madrid, 2834, Spain
Tel.: (34) 91 728 69 00
Emp.: 300
Cosmetic Product Distr
N.A.I.C.S.: 456120
Juan Pedro Abeniacar *(Gen Mgr)*

Lvmh Moet Hennessy Louis Vuitton Inc. (1)
19 E 57th St, New York, NY 10022

AND PRIVATE COMPANIES / LVMH MOET HENNESSY LOUIS VUITTON SE

Tel.: (212) 931-2000
Leather Accessories Mfr & Distr
N.A.I.C.S.: 316990

Lvmh Watch And Jewelry Taiwan Ltd Cortech Sa (1)
14/F 270 Chung Hsiao East Road Section 4, Taipei, Taiwan
Tel.: (886) 2 2778 7266
Cosmetic Product Distr
N.A.I.C.S.: 456120

Moet Hennessy Czech Republic Sro (1)
608/2 Radlicka, 15023, Prague, Czech Republic
Tel.: (420) 251 552 644
Wine & Spirit Whslr
N.A.I.C.S.: 424820

Moet Hennessy Do Brasil Vinhos E Destilados Ltda (1)
Av Brasil 1 814, Sao Paulo, 01430-001, Brazil
Tel.: (55) 1130628388
Emp.: 150
Wine & Spirit Mfr
N.A.I.C.S.: 312120
Davide Marcovitch (Pres)

Moet Hennessy Investissements (1)
65 Avenue Edouard Vaillant, 92100, Boulogne-Billancourt, France
Tel.: (33) 8 99 96 31 90
Investment Management Service
N.A.I.C.S.: 523999

Moet Hennessy Latin America & Caribbean (1)
Av Brasil 1814 Jd America, 01430-001, Sao Paulo, Brazil
Tel.: (55) 11 30 62 83 88
Wine & Spirit Whslr
N.A.I.C.S.: 424820

Moet Hennessy Norge As (1)
Radmann Halmrastsvei 14, Veritasveien 2, Sandvika, 1337, Norway
Tel.: (47) 6711 87 40
Wine & Spirit Whslr
N.A.I.C.S.: 424820

Moet-Hennessy SNC (1)
65 Avenue de la Grande Armee, Paris, 75016, France (66%)
Tel.: (33) 144132222
Web Site: http://www.lvmh.fr
Mfr of Wines & Spirits
N.A.I.C.S.: 312130

Subsidiary (Domestic):

Champagne Mercier (2)
68-70 Ave De Champagne, Epernay, 51333, France (100%)
Tel.: (33) 326512000
Web Site: http://www.champagnemercier.fr
Sales Range: $10-24.9 Million
Emp.: 50
Champagne Mfr
N.A.I.C.S.: 312130

Champagne Moet & Chandon S.A. (2)
20 Ave De Champagne, PO Box 140, Epernay, 51200, France (100%)
Tel.: (33) 326512000
Web Site: http://www.moet.com
Sales Range: $150-199.9 Million
Emp.: 1,000
Production of Champagne, Wines & other Spirits
N.A.I.C.S.: 312130

Subsidiary (Domestic):

Champagne Ruinart (3)
4 Rue Des Crayeres, PO Box 85, Reims, 51100, France (100%)
Tel.: (33) 326775151
Web Site: http://www.ruinart.com
Sales Range: $25-49.9 Million
Emp.: 75
Mfr of Wines & Champagnes
N.A.I.C.S.: 312130
Frederick Dufour (Pres)

Subsidiary (Non-US):

Ruinart UK Ltd. (4)
13 Grosvenor Crescent, London, SW1X 7EE, United Kingdom (100%)
Tel.: (44) 74160592
Web Site: http://www.ruinart.com
Sales Range: $10-24.9 Million
Mfr of Wines & Champagnes
N.A.I.C.S.: 312130

Subsidiary (US):

Clicquot Inc (2)
85 10th Ave, New York, NY 10011
Tel.: (212) 888-7575
Web Site: http://www.veuve-clicquot.com
Beverages Mfr
N.A.I.C.S.: 312120

Subsidiary (Domestic):

Distillerie de la Groie SARL (2)
Rue La Groie, 16100, Cognac, France
Tel.: (33) 5 45 82 15 15
Alcoholic Beverages Mfr
N.A.I.C.S.: 312120

Subsidiary (US):

Domaine Chandon, Inc. (2)
1 California Dr, Yountville, CA 94599
Tel.: (707) 944-8844
Web Site: http://www.chandon.com
Sales Range: $10-24.9 Million
Emp.: 100
Mfr of Wines & Champagnes
N.A.I.C.S.: 722511
Matt Wood (Dir-Estate)

Subsidiary (Non-US):

Bodega Chandon Argentina S.A. (3)
Avda Paseo Colon 746 Piso 2 Edificio Colombus, C1063ACH, Buenos Aires, Argentina
Tel.: (54) 41218000
Web Site: http://www.chandon.com.ar
Wine & Champagne Producer
N.A.I.C.S.: 312130

Bodegas Terrazas de los Andes (3)
Thames Y Cochabamba, Perdriel-Lujan de Cuyo, Mendoza, 5509, Argentina
Tel.: (54) 2614880058
Web Site: http://www.terrazasdelosandes.com
Mfr of Wines
N.A.I.C.S.: 312130
Ezequiel Acosta (Mgr-Mktg)

Chandon do Brasil (3)
Rod Sao Vendelino Rio Grande do Sul, Sao Paulo, 95720, Garibaldi, Brazil (100%)
Tel.: (55) 1130628388
Web Site: http://www.chandon.com.br
Mfr of Wines & Spirits
N.A.I.C.S.: 312130
Philippe Mevel (Mng Dir)

Domaine Chandon Australia Pty Ltd (3)
727 Maroondah Highway, Coldstream, 3770, Australia (100%)
Tel.: (61) 3 9738 9219
Web Site: http://www.chandon.com.au
Mfr of Wines & Champagnes
N.A.I.C.S.: 312130

Subsidiary (Domestic):

Newton Vineyards (3)
1 California Dr, Yountville, CA 94599-1426
Tel.: (707) 963-9000
Web Site: http://www.newtonvineyard.com
Mfr of Wines
N.A.I.C.S.: 312130
Su Hua Newton (Owner)

Subsidiary (Domestic):

Jas Hennessy & Co SCS (2)
1 rue de la Richonne, Cognac, 16101, France
Tel.: (33) 5 45 35 72 72
Sales Range: $150-199.9 Million
Emp.: 600
Alcoholic Beverages Mfr
N.A.I.C.S.: 312120
Bernard Peillon (Mgr)

Subsidiary (US):

Joseph Phelps Vineyards Inc. (2)
200 Taplin Rd, Saint Helena, CA 94574-9601
Tel.: (707) 963-2745
Web Site: http://www.jpvwines.com
Sales Range: $10-24.9 Million
Emp.: 25
Mfr of Wines
N.A.I.C.S.: 312130
Stephen Pavy (Dir-Hospitality)

Subsidiary (Domestic):

Krug, Vins fins de Champagne S.A. (2)
5 rue Coquebert, Reims, 51100, France
Tel.: (33) 326844420
Web Site: http://www.krug.com
Sales Range: $10-24.9 Million
Emp.: 50
Mfr of Champagne
N.A.I.C.S.: 312130
Margart Henriquez (Gen Mgr)

Subsidiary (Non-US):

LVMH WINES & SPIRITS SUISSE SA (2)
Chemin des Coquelicots 16, Case Postale 552, 1215, Geneva, Switzerland
Tel.: (41) 22 939 35 00
Sales Range: $10-24.9 Million
Emp.: 40
Wine & Spirit Mfr
N.A.I.C.S.: 312130

MH Champagnes and Wines Korea Ltd (2)
9/F Ann Jay Tower 718-2 Yeoksam-dong, Gangnam-gu, Seoul, 135-080, Korea (South)
Tel.: (82) 2 2188 5100
Web Site: http://www.lvmh.com
Sales Range: $25-49.9 Million
Emp.: 22
Beverages Mfr
N.A.I.C.S.: 312120
Gunhee Kim (Sr Mgr-Mktg)

Subsidiary (US):

Millennium Import LLC (2)
25 Main St SE, Minneapolis, MN 55414
Tel.: (612) 331-6230
Web Site: http://www.belvederevodka.com
Sales Range: $25-49.9 Million
Emp.: 20
Vodka Importer
N.A.I.C.S.: 424820
Charles Gibb (Pres)

Moet Hennessy USA (2)
85 10th Ave 2nd Fl, New York, NY 10011
Tel.: (212) 251-8200
Web Site: http://www.mhusa.com
Sales Range: $25-49.9 Million
Emp.: 220
Sales & Marketing Services
N.A.I.C.S.: 541613
Rodney Williams (Exec VP-Brands)

Subsidiary (Domestic):

Moet-Hennessy Diageo SAS (2)
105 Boulevard de la Mission Marchand, 92400, Courbevoie, France
Tel.: (33) 141883200
Sales Range: $25-49.9 Million
Emp.: 250
Retail Operations
N.A.I.C.S.: 445320

Subsidiary (Non-US):

Bodegas Chandon Argentina SA (3)
Ortis Be Ccanco Ave 2839, Buenos Aires, 8125, Argentina
Tel.: (54) 11 4121 8000
Web Site: http://www.chandon.com.ar
Sales Range: $25-49.9 Million
Emp.: 18
Beverage Mfr & Distr
N.A.I.C.S.: 312130
Milagros Maciel (Mgr-Brand Mktg)

Diageo Moet Hennessy (Thailand) Limited (3)
17/F Empire Tower 195 South Sathorn Road Yannawa, Sathorn, Bangkok, 10120, Thailand
Tel.: (66) 26856999
Sales Range: $100-124.9 Million
Wines, Cognac & Spirits Marketer & Distr
N.A.I.C.S.: 424820

France Korea Wines & Spirits Ltd. (3)
1 Floor Sangwon Building 995-25 Daechi-Dong, Kangnam-Ku, Seoul, Korea (South)
Tel.: (82) 25015950
Distilled Wines & Spirits
N.A.I.C.S.: 312130

MHD Moet Hennessy Diageo K.K. (3)
13F, Jimbocho Mitsui Building 1-105 Kanda Jimbocho, Chiyoda-ku, Tokyo, 101-0051, Japan
Tel.: (81) 334340761
Web Site: http://www.mhdkk.com
Emp.: 235
Wines & Spirits Whslr
N.A.I.C.S.: 445320
James Paton (Pres)

Moet Hennessy Argentina (3)
Avenida Ortiz de Ocampo 2839, Buenos Aires, C1425 DSD, Argentina
Tel.: (54) 11 4121 8000
Web Site: http://www.bodegaschandon.com.ar
Wine & Spirit Mfr
N.A.I.C.S.: 312130

Moet Hennessy Australia Ltd (3)
Level 7/201 Coward St, Roseberry, Mascot, 2020, NSW, Australia
Tel.: (61) 2 8344 9900
Web Site: http://www.lvmh.com
Wine & Spirit Distr
N.A.I.C.S.: 424820

Moet Hennessy Danmark A/S (3)
Langebrogade 6A, 1411, Copenhagen, Denmark
Tel.: (45) 32 83 73 60
Web Site: http://www.moet-hennessy.dk
Sales Range: $25-49.9 Million
Emp.: 16
Beverage Product Mfr
N.A.I.C.S.: 312120
Jeanette Andersen (Brand Mgr)

Moet Hennessy Deutschland GmbH (3)
Nymphenburger Strasse 21, 80335, Munich, Germany (100%)
Tel.: (49) 89994210
Web Site: http://www.veuve-clicquot-service.de
Sales Range: $25-49.9 Million
Emp.: 50
Wine & Champagne
N.A.I.C.S.: 445320
Gardt Hausen (Mng Dir)

Subsidiary (Domestic):

Veuve Clicquot Import GmbH (4)
Seidl St 23, Munich, 80335, Bavaria, Germany (100%)
Tel.: (49) 89994210
Sales Range: $25-49.9 Million
Importer of Wine & Champagne
N.A.I.C.S.: 445320

Subsidiary (Non-US):

Moet Hennessy Diageo Hong Kong Ltd. (3)
15F Dorset House 979 King's Road, Quarry Bay, China (Hong Kong) (100%)
Tel.: (852) 29761888
Web Site: http://www.mhdhk.com
Sales Range: Less than $1 Million
Emp.: 25
Wines & Spirits Marketer & Sales
N.A.I.C.S.: 424820
Rosemary Yu (Dir-Channel Sls)

Moet Hennessy Diageo Shanghai Ltd. (3)
Plaza 66 30/F 1266 Nan Jing Road W, Shanghai, 200040, China
Tel.: (86) 2162881888
Web Site: http://www.lvmh.com
Sales Range: $25-49.9 Million
Marketing & Distr of Wines & Spirits
N.A.I.C.S.: 445320
Manfred Chen (Mgr-Mktg)

LVMH MOET HENNESSY LOUIS VUITTON SE

LVMH Moet Hennessy Louis Vuitton SE—(Continued)

Moet Hennessy Espana SA (3)
Consell De Cent 334 336 Pta 3, Barcelona, 8009, Spain **(100%)**
Tel.: (34) 934960730
Web Site: http://www.moethennessy.com
Sales Range: $25-49.9 Million
Emp.: 40
Mfr of Wines & Spirits
N.A.I.C.S.: 312130
Rodolph Veleusse *(Mng Dir)*

Moet Hennessy Osterreich GmbH (3)
Anton Frank Gasse 7, 1180, Vienna, Austria
Tel.: (43) 1 53 50 010
Web Site: http://www.moet-hennessy.at
Sales Range: $25-49.9 Million
Emp.: 19
Alcoholic Beverages Mfr
N.A.I.C.S.: 312120

Moet Hennessy Polska SP Z.O.O. (3)
Plac Trzech Krzyzy 18, Warsaw, 00499, Poland
Tel.: (48) 22 550 59 00
Web Site: http://www.lvmh.com
Sales Range: $25-49.9 Million
Emp.: 23
Wine & Spirit Mfr
N.A.I.C.S.: 312130
Anna Mowel *(Office Mgr)*

Moet Hennessy Suomi OY (3)
Korkeavuorenkatu 22, 130, Helsinki, Finland
Tel.: (358) 20 741 8220
Web Site: http://www.moet-hennessy.fi
Sales Range: $25-49.9 Million
Emp.: 6
Beverages Mfr
N.A.I.C.S.: 312120
Pekka Ylanko *(Gen Mgr)*

Moet Hennessy Sverige AB (3)
Kungsholms Strand 127, 112 33, Stockholm, Sweden
Tel.: (46) 8 545 724 20
Web Site: http://www.moet-hennessy.se
Sales Range: $25-49.9 Million
Emp.: 8
Beverage Product Mfr
N.A.I.C.S.: 312120

Moet Hennessy Taiwan (3)
5F No 95 Sec 2 Dunhua South Road, Taipei, 10682, Taiwan
Tel.: (886) 27008665
Web Site: http://www.hennessy.com
Wines & Spirits
N.A.I.C.S.: 312130

Moet Hennessy UK Ltd (3)
18 Grosvenor Gardens, London, SW1W0DH, United Kingdom
Tel.: (44) 20 7808 4400
Web Site: http://www.lvmh.com
Emp.: 150
Wine & Spirit Mfr
N.A.I.C.S.: 312130

Moet Hennessy de Mexico, SA de C.V. (3)
Avenida Ejercito Nacional N 216 - Piso 17, Colonia Anzures, 11590, Mexico, Mexico
Tel.: (52) 55 25 81 12 90
Sales Range: $25-49.9 Million
Emp.: 40
Beverages Mfr
N.A.I.C.S.: 312130
Jarome Seignon *(Gen Mgr)*

Moet-Hennessy (Suisse) S.A. (3)
Chemin Des Coquelicots 16, PO Box 496, Geneva, 1215, Switzerland **(100%)**
Tel.: (41) 229393400
Web Site: http://www.moet.com
Sales Range: $25-49.9 Million
Emp.: 50
Wine & Champagne
N.A.I.C.S.: 445320

Subsidiary (Domestic):

Veuve Clicquot (Suisse) S.A. (4)
Chemin des Coquelicots 16, 1215, Geneva, Switzerland **(100%)**
Tel.: (41) 229393400
Web Site: http://www.veuve-clicquot.com
Rev.: $29,758,050
Emp.: 42
Mfr of Wines & Brandy
N.A.I.C.S.: 312130

Subsidiary (Non-US):

Moet-Hennessy Italia SpA (3)
Via Tonale 26, 20125, Milan, Italy
Tel.: (39) 026714111
Web Site: http://www.moethennessy.it
Sales Range: $25-49.9 Million
Emp.: 30
Mfr of Wines & other Alcoholic Beverages
N.A.I.C.S.: 312130
Cristiano Talassi *(Dir-Mktg)*

Moet-Hennessy Nederland B.V. (3)
Oudeutrechtseweg 22 24, 3743 KN, Baarn, 3743 KN, Netherlands **(100%)**
Tel.: (31) 356946014
Web Site: http://www.moethennessy.nl
Sales Range: $25-49.9 Million
Emp.: 20
Mfr & Wholesaler of Wines & Spirits
N.A.I.C.S.: 445320
Bob Bron *(Gen Mgr)*

Subsidiary (Domestic):

S.A. Du Chateau D'Yquem (2)
Chateau D Yquem, 33210, Gironde, France **(100%)**
Tel.: (33) 557980707
Web Site: http://www.chateau-yquem.fr
Sales Range: $25-49.9 Million
Emp.: 62
Mfr of Wines & Spirits
N.A.I.C.S.: 312130

Societe JAS Hennessy & Co. S.A. (2)
1 Rue De La Richonne, PO Box 20, Cognac, 16101, France **(100%)**
Tel.: (33) 545357272
Web Site: http://www.hennessy-cognac.com
Sales Range: $200-249.9 Million
Emp.: 650
Wines, Champagne, Cognac, Hypo-Allergenic Beauty Products, Horticulture Holding Company
N.A.I.C.S.: 551112
Belnalg Peillom *(Mng Dir)*

Subsidiary (Non-US):

Jas Hennessy & Co. Ltd. (3)
Estuary House Lock P7, East point Buisness park Fabio, Dublin, 3, Ireland **(100%)**
Tel.: (353) 18558548
Web Site: http://www.hennessy.com
Sales Range: $25-49.9 Million
Emp.: 1
Mfr of Cognac & Spirits
N.A.I.C.S.: 312130

Subsidiary (Domestic):

Societe Viticole de Reims SA (2)
20 Av de Champagne, 51200, Epernay, France
Tel.: (33) 3 26 61 62 55
Beverage Distr
N.A.I.C.S.: 424820

Sodepa SARL (2)
1 rue de la Rishon, Cognac, 16100, France
Tel.: (33) 5 45 35 72 16
Cosmetic Product Distr
N.A.I.C.S.: 424210

Subsidiary (Non-US):

The Glenmorangie Company (2)
18 Westerton Road, Broxburn, EH52 5AQ, West Lothian, United Kingdom
Tel.: (44) 01506852929
Sales Range: $75-99.9 Million
Emp.: 400
Single-Malt Whiskey Distiller
N.A.I.C.S.: 312130
Paul Skipworth *(Sr VP-Strategy)*

The Scotch Malt Whisky Society Ltd (2)
The Vaults 87 Giles Street, Edinburgh, EH6 6BZ, United Kingdom
Tel.: (44) 1315552929
Web Site: http://www.smws.co.uk
Alcoholic Beverage Distr

N.A.I.C.S.: 424820
Jan Damen *(Gen Mgr)*

Subsidiary (Domestic):

Thomas Hine & Cie (2)
16 Quai Del Orangerie, PO Box 8, 16200, Jarnac, France **(100%)**
Tel.: (33) 545355959
Web Site: http://www.hine.com
Sales Range: $25-49.9 Million
Emp.: 17
Production of Cognac & Spirits
N.A.I.C.S.: 312130

Parfums Christian Dior A/S Ltd (1)
Radmann Halmrasts Vei 14, Sandvika, 1337, Norway
Tel.: (47) 67 11 08 50
Emp.: 30
Cosmetic Product Distr
N.A.I.C.S.: 456120
Annebrit Carr *(Gen Mgr)*

Parfums Christian Dior Hong Kong Ltd (1)
34/F Dorest House Taikoo Place 979 Kings Road, Quarry Bay, China (Hong Kong)
Tel.: (852) 29689168
Cosmetic Product Distr
N.A.I.C.S.: 456120

Percier Publications SNC (1)
16 Rue Du 4 Septembre, 75002, Paris, France
Tel.: (33) 1 49536800
Periodical Publishing Services
N.A.I.C.S.: 513120

Probinvest SAS (1)
48 Bis Avenue De La Cour De france, 91260, Juvlsy-sur-Orge, France
Tel.: (33) 1 69 21 76 78
Investment Management Service
N.A.I.C.S.: 523999

Profusion SARL (1)
Route des Avouillons 14, 1196, Gland, Switzerland
Tel.: (41) 22 995 15 50
Cosmetic Product Distr
N.A.I.C.S.: 456120

RVL Holding BV (1)
Galvanistraat 15, 3817KP, Amersfoort, Netherlands
Tel.: (31) 334616399
Investment Management Service
N.A.I.C.S.: 523999

Royal Hawaiian Insurance Company Ltd (1)
655 Montgomery St Fl 18, San Francisco, CA 94111-2635
Tel.: (415) 397-4400
Insurance Management Services
N.A.I.C.S.: 524298

S+ (1)
65 av Edouard Vaillant, 92100, Boulogne-Billancourt, France
Tel.: (33) 899963486
Cosmetic Product Distr
N.A.I.C.S.: 456120

SCI Edison (1)
1 rue Edison, 80210, Feuquieres-en-Vimeu, France
Tel.: (33) 3 22 60 33 33
Cosmetic Product Distr
N.A.I.C.S.: 456120

SICA de Bagnolet (1)
Rue Saulnier, 16100, Cognac, France
Tel.: (33) 5 45 82 15 15
Cosmetic Product Distr
N.A.I.C.S.: 456120

Sephora Middle East FZE (1)
Jebel Ali Free Zone, PO Box 18536, Dubai, United Arab Emirates
Tel.: (971) 4 804 5852
Web Site: http://www.sephora-me.com
Cosmetic Product Distr
N.A.I.C.S.: 456120

Sephora Unitim Kozmetik AS (1)
Levent Buyukdere Cad Ecza Sok No 6 K 6, Istanbul, Turkiye
Tel.: (90) 2123199000
Cosmetic Product Distr

INTERNATIONAL PUBLIC

N.A.I.C.S.: 456120

Societe Louis Vuitton Services SNC (1)
2 R Du Pont Neuf, 75001, Paris, France
Tel.: (33) 8 10 81 00 10
Leather Goods Distr
N.A.I.C.S.: 424990

Sofidiv S.A (1)
30 Ave Hoche, 75008, Paris, France **(99.99%)**
Tel.: (33) 0144132222
Web Site: http://www.lvmh.fr
Holding Company
N.A.I.C.S.: 551112

Subsidiary (Non-US):

Acqua Di Parma S.R.L (2)
Via G Ripamonti 99, I-20141, Milan, Italy
Tel.: (39) 025522881
Web Site: http://www.acquadiparma.com
Sales Range: $10-24.9 Million
Emp.: 20
Perfumes & Cosmetics Mfr
N.A.I.C.S.: 325620
Laura Burdese *(Pres & CEO)*

DFS Group Ltd. (2)
Chinachem Golden Plaza 77 Mody Road Tsimshatsui East, Central, China (Hong Kong)
Tel.: (852) 2899 2200
Web Site: http://www.dfs.com
Luxury Goods Retailer
N.A.I.C.S.: 459999
John Woodhouse *(VP-Airport Strategy)*

Subsidiary (Non-US):

DFS India Private Ltd (3)
Chhatrapati Shivaji International Airport Terminal 2 c Airside, Arrival Level Sahar, Mumbai, 400 099, India
Tel.: (91) 98 2098 2249
Web Site: http://www.dfsgalleria.com
Emp.: 500
Tobacco Product Distr
N.A.I.C.S.: 424940
T. Sujesh *(Head-HR)*

DFS Seoul Ltd (3)
822 Changkang Building 22 Dohwa-dong, Mapo-gu, 121-763, Seoul, Korea (South)
Tel.: (82) 2 713 6566
Web Site: http://www.lvmh.com
Apparel & Accessory Retailer
N.A.I.C.S.: 315130

DFS Venture Singapore (Pte) Ltd (3)
Singapore Changi Airport, PO Box 51, Singapore, 918142, Singapore
Tel.: (65) 6891 9168
Web Site: http://www.dfsgalleria.com
Perfume Retailer
N.A.I.C.S.: 456120

DFS Vietnam LLC (3)
17-19-21 Ly Tu Trong St, District 1, Ho Chi Minh City, Vietnam
Tel.: (84) 8 3823 7180
Retail Management Services
N.A.I.C.S.: 541618

Subsidiary (Non-US):

Emilio Pucci S.r.l. (2)
Palazzo Pucci, Via De Pucci 6, Florence, 50122, Italy **(100%)**
Tel.: (39) 055261841
Web Site: http://www.emiliopucci.com
Sales Range: $10-24.9 Million
Emp.: 50
Mfr & Retailer of Apparel
N.A.I.C.S.: 315990
Laudomia Pucci *(Founder)*

Subsidiary (US):

Emilio Pucci Ltd (3)
855 Madison Ave, New York, NY 10021
Tel.: (212) 752-4777
Web Site: http://www.emiliopucci.com
Mfr & Retailer of apparel
N.A.I.C.S.: 458110

Subsidiary (Non-US):

Fendi SRL (2)
Longo Goldoni, Rome, Italy **(100%)**

AND PRIVATE COMPANIES

Tel.: (39) 06334501
Web Site: http://www.fendi.it
Apparel & Accessories Mfr & Retailer
N.A.I.C.S.: 315990
Serge Brunschwig *(Chm & CEO)*

Subsidiary (Non-US):

Fendi France SAS (3)
2 Rue du Pont-Neuf, Paris, 75001, France
Tel.: (33) 1 55 80 32 00
Jewelry & Luxury Goods Retailer
N.A.I.C.S.: 458310

Fendi Germany GmbH (3)
Neuhauser Str 18, Munich, 80331, Germany
Tel.: (49) 89 24216080
Web Site: http://www.fendi.com
Fashion Apparel & Accessory Retailer
N.A.I.C.S.: 458110

Subsidiary (US):

Fendi North America Inc (3)
677 5th Ave 4th Fl, New York, NY 10022
Tel.: (212) 920-8115
Web Site: http://www.lvmh.com
Fashion Apparels Retailer
N.A.I.C.S.: 458110

Subsidiary (Non-US):

Hublot SA (2)
Ch de la Vuarpilliere 33, 1260, Nyon, Switzerland
Tel.: (41) 22 990 90 00
Web Site: http://www.hublot.com
Sales Range: $75-99.9 Million
Emp.: 300
Luxury Watches Mfr
N.A.I.C.S.: 339910
Ricardo Guadalupe *(CEO)*

Subsidiary (Non-US):

Hublot Japan KK Ltd (3)
Kamiyacho Annex 6F 5-3-2 Toranomon, Minato-ku, Tokyo, 105-0001, Japan
Tel.: (81) 3 3434 3002
Web Site: http://www.hublot.com
Sales Range: $25-49.9 Million
Emp.: 12
Watch & Jewelry Retailer
N.A.I.C.S.: 458310
Seji Kamijia *(Dir-Sls)*

Subsidiary (Domestic):

Hublot SA Geneve (3)
Rue de la Fontaine 7, 1204, Geneva, Switzerland
Tel.: (41) 223101919
Wrist Watch Mfr
N.A.I.C.S.: 334519

Subsidiary (US):

Hublot of America, Inc (3)
The Galleria Corp Ctr 2455 E Sunrise Blvd Ste 402, Fort Lauderdale, FL 33304
Tel.: (954) 568-9400
Web Site: http://www.lvmh.com
Emp.: 20
Watch & Jewelry Retailer
N.A.I.C.S.: 458310
Jason Morrison *(VP-Sls & Mktg)*

Subsidiary (US):

LVMH Inc. (2)
19 E 57th St 5th Fl, New York, NY 10022-2508
Tel.: (212) 931-2700
Web Site: http://www.lvmh.com
Sales Range: $200-249.9 Million
Emp.: 750
Holding Company
N.A.I.C.S.: 458320
Anish Melwani *(Chm & CEO)*

Subsidiary (Domestic):

BeneFit Cosmetics LLC (3)
225 Bush St Fl 20, San Francisco, CA 94104-4279
Tel.: (415) 781-8153
Web Site: http://www.benefitcosmetics.com
Sales Range: $25-49.9 Million
Emp.: 270
Perfumes & Cosmetics Mfr & Whslr

N.A.I.C.S.: 456120
Julie Bell *(VP-Mktg)*

Subsidiary (Non-US):

BeneFit Cosmetics Hong Kong Limited (4)
Faces Harbour City, Tsim Sha Tsui, Kowloon, China (Hong Kong)
Tel.: (852) 2110 3950
Web Site: http://www.benefitcosmetics.hk
Sales Range: $25-49.9 Million
Emp.: 14
Cosmetic & Perfume Distr
N.A.I.C.S.: 424210

BeneFit Cosmetics UK Ltd (4)
Greenwood House New London Road, Chelmsford, CM2 0PP, Essex, United Kingdom
Tel.: (44) 12 4534 7138
Web Site: http://www.benefitcosmetics.co.uk
Emp.: 68
Personal Care Product Retailer
N.A.I.C.S.: 456120
Amanda Erlking *(Mgr-Mktg)*

Subsidiary (Domestic):

Cosmetic of France Inc (3)
100 Biscayne Blvd 2400, Miami, FL 33132-2306
Tel.: (305) 371-7181
Web Site: http://www.lvmh.com
Sales Range: $25-49.9 Million
Emp.: 40
Cosmetic & Perfume Retailer
N.A.I.C.S.: 456120
Leonardo Ferracina *(Dir-Travel Retail)*

Cruise Line Holdings Co. (3)
8400 NW 36th St Ste 600, Doral, FL 33166
Tel.: (786) 845-7300
Holding Company; Cruise Ship Retailer
N.A.I.C.S.: 551112
J. P. Miquel *(Chm)*

Subsidiary (Domestic):

Starboard Cruise Services, Inc. (4)
8400 NW 36th St Ste 600, Doral, FL 33166-6620
Tel.: (786) 845-7300
Web Site: http://www.starboardcruise.com
Emp.: 1,800
Cruise Ship Retail Services
N.A.I.C.S.: 455219
Lisa Bauer *(Pres & CEO)*

Starboard Holdings Ltd (4)
8400 NW 36th St Ste 600, Doral, FL 33166
Tel.: (786) 845-7300
Investment Management Service
N.A.I.C.S.: 523999
Shawn Paul *(Office Mgr)*

Subsidiary (Domestic):

DFS Group Ltd. - USA (3)
First Market Tower 525 Market St 31st Fl, San Francisco, CA 94105-2708 (61%)
Tel.: (415) 977-2700
Web Site: http://www.dfsgalleria.com
Retailer for International Travellers
N.A.I.C.S.: 458310
Robert Miller *(Founder)*

Subsidiary (Non-US):

DFS Australia Pty. Ltd. (4)
155 George St on the Rocks, PO Box 3680, Sydney, 2000, NSW, Australia
Tel.: (61) 282438666
Web Site: http://www.dfsgalleria.com
Retailer for International Travellers
N.A.I.C.S.: 459420

Subsidiary (Domestic):

DFS Group L.P. (4)
1296 Pale San Vitores Rd, Tumon Bay, GU 96913
Tel.: (671) 646-9640
Web Site: http://www.dfsgalleria.com
Luxury Items Retailer
N.A.I.C.S.: 458110

Subsidiary (Non-US):

DFS Hong Kong Ltd. (4)
6 F Chinachem Golden Plz 77 Mody Rd,

Tsimshatsui E, Kowloon, Hong Kong, China (Hong Kong) (100%)
Tel.: (852) 27325211
Web Site: http://www.dfsgalleria.com
Sales Range: $150-199.9 Million
Emp.: 700
Retailer of Luxury Goods
N.A.I.C.S.: 459999
Tim Deessio *(Mng Dir)*

DFS Japan KK (4)
Shin Ohsaki Kangyo Bldg 6F, 1-6-4 Oshaki, Tokyo, 1410032, Shingawa-ku, Japan (60%)
Tel.: (81) 354340181
Web Site: http://www.dfsgalleria.com
Sales Range: $25-49.9 Million
Emp.: 16
Retailer for International Travellers
N.A.I.C.S.: 459420

DFS Korea Ltd. (4)
822 Chang Kang Bldg, 22 Dohwa-dong, Seoul, 121-763, Mapo-gu, Korea (South)
Tel.: (82) 27136566
Web Site: http://www.dfsgalleria.com
Retailer for International Travellers
N.A.I.C.S.: 561599

DFS New Zealand Ltd. (4)
119 Tom Pearce Dr, PO Box 73 018, Auckland International Airport, Auckland, 1730, New Zealand (51%)
Tel.: (64) 9275029
Web Site: http://www.dfsgalleria.com
Sales Range: $10-24.9 Million
Emp.: 50
Retailer for International Travellers
N.A.I.C.S.: 561599

Subsidiary (Domestic):

DFS Saipan Limited (4)
PO Box 500528, Saipan, MP 96950-0528
Tel.: (670) 234-6615
Web Site: http://www.dfsgalleria.com
Sales Range: $25-49.9 Million
Emp.: 200
Retailer for International Travellers
N.A.I.C.S.: 459420

Subsidiary (Non-US):

DFS Taiwan Ltd (4)
3 F No 21 1 Ln 45, Chung Shan Rd Section 2, Taipei, Taiwan (100%)
Tel.: (886) 225619122
Web Site: http://www.dfsgalleria.com
Retailer for International Travellers
N.A.I.C.S.: 561599

Subsidiary (Domestic):

Gabrielle Studio Inc (3)
300 Old Niskayuna Rd, Latham, NY 12110-3514
Tel.: (518) 782-1410
Beauty Saloon & Bridal Shop Operator
N.A.I.C.S.: 812112

LV US Manufacturing, Inc (3)
321 W Covina Blvd, San Dimas, CA 91773
Tel.: (909) 599-2411
Leather Goods Mfr
N.A.I.C.S.: 316990
Joanne Maillard *(CFO)*

LVMH Fragrance Brands WHD Inc (3)
100 N Biscayne Blvd Ste 2400/2300, Miami, FL 33132
Tel.: (305) 416-2555
Web Site: http://www.lvmh.com
Perfume & Cosmetic Product Distr
N.A.I.C.S.: 424210
Alberto Luis Goulart Goncalves *(Gen Mgr)*

Marc Jacobs International LLC (3)
72 Spring St 8th Fl, New York, NY 10012
Tel.: (212) 343-0222
Web Site: http://www.marcjacobs.com
Sales Range: $1-9.9 Million
Emp.: 45
Fashion & Leather Goods Designer & Retailer
N.A.I.C.S.: 315990
Robert Duffy *(Pres)*

Nowness LLC (3)
598 Madison Ave 8th Fl, New York, NY 10022

LVMH MOET HENNESSY LOUIS VUITTON SE

Tel.: (917) 281-2886
Web Site: http://www.nowness.com
Cosmetic & Leather Goods Retailer
N.A.I.C.S.: 456120
Anna Higgs *(Dir-Creative)*

On Board Media Inc (3)
1691 Michigan Ave Ste 600, Miami Beach, FL 33166
Tel.: (305) 673-0400
Web Site: http://www.onboardmedia.com
Online Media Publishing & Broadcasting Services
N.A.I.C.S.: 516210
Alexandra Iturriza *(Coord-Creative Svcs)*

Parazul LLC (3)
1691 Michigan Ave Ste 600, Miami Beach, FL 33139
Tel.: (866) 249-9487
Web Site: http://www.parazul.com
Leather Handbag Mfr & Distr
N.A.I.C.S.: 316990
Robin Rosenbaum-Andras *(Founder)*

San Dimas Luggage Company (3)
2095 S Archibald Ave, Ontario, CA 91761-8579
Tel.: (909) 510-8820
Leather Goods Retailer
N.A.I.C.S.: 458320

Sephora USA Inc (3)
525 Market St 11th Fl, San Francisco, CA 94105-2708
Tel.: (415) 284-3300
Web Site: http://www.sephora.com
Sales Range: $50-74.9 Million
Emp.: 220
Perfumes & Cosmetics Retailer
N.A.I.C.S.: 456120
Deborah Yeh *(Sr VP-Mktg & Brand)*

Subsidiary (Domestic):

Ole Henriksen of Denmark, Inc. (4)
16665 Arminta St, Van Nuys, CA 91406-1611
Tel.: (818) 787-9301
Web Site: http://www.olehenriksen.com
Sales Range: $25-49.9 Million
Emp.: 30
Cosmetics Mfr
N.A.I.C.S.: 325620
Ole Henriksen *(Founder & Dir-Creative)*

Subsidiary (Non-US):

LVMH Moet Hennessy Louis Vuitton BV (2)
8a Cattenhagestraat, Naarden, Netherlands
Tel.: (31) 356946014
Web Site: http://www.moet.com
Holding Company
N.A.I.C.S.: 551112

Subsidiary (Non-US):

Loewe S.A. (3)
Palacio De Miraflores 15 3 A Planta, Jeronimo, 28014, Madrid, Spain (100%)
Tel.: (34) 913606100
Web Site: http://www.loewe.es
Sales Range: $150-199.9 Million
Emp.: 1,000
Mfr of Leather Goods, Ready to Wear, Shoes, Fragrances & Accessories
N.A.I.C.S.: 316990
Charlie Smith *(Chief Mktg Officer)*

Subsidiary (Non-US):

Loewe Australia Pty Ltd. (4)
135 King St Level 14, Sydney, 2000, Australia (100%)
Tel.: (61) 292234311
Web Site: http://www.louisvuition.com
Sales Range: $10-24.9 Million
Emp.: 30
Mfr of Fashion & Leather Goods
N.A.I.C.S.: 316990

Loewe Fashion Sdn. Bhd (4)
Mufe Fl Starhill Gallery, 181 Jalan Bukit Bintang, 55100, Kuala Lumpur, Malaysia (100%)
Tel.: (60) 327102525
Web Site: http://www.loewe.com
Sales Range: $10-24.9 Million
Emp.: 40
Mfr of Luggage & Leather Goods

LVMH MOET HENNESSY LOUIS VUITTON SE

INTERNATIONAL PUBLIC

LVMH Moet Hennessy Louis Vuitton
SE—(Continued)
N.A.I.C.S.: 316990

Subsidiary (US):

Loewe Hawaii Inc. (4)
2255 Kuhio Ave Ste 1400, Honolulu, HI
96815
Tel.: (808) 971-8400
Web Site: http://www.loewe.es
Retailers of Textile & Leather Fashion
Goods, Accessories & Luggage
N.A.I.C.S.: 458110

Subsidiary (Non-US):

Loewe Hermanos (U.K.) Ltd (4)
12 Clifford St, London, W1X 1RB, United
Kingdom **(100%)**
Tel.: (44) 2073994010
Web Site: http://www.loewe.es
Mfr of Fashion & Leather Goods
N.A.I.C.S.: 316990

Branch (Domestic):

Loewe Hermanos (U.K.) Ltd (5)
130 New Bond Street, London, W1S 2TH,
United Kingdom
Tel.: (44) 2074933914
Fashion & Leather Goods Retailer
N.A.I.C.S.: 424990

Subsidiary (Domestic):

Loewe Hermanos S.A (4)
Isle Gave 23, Jeronimo, 28034, Madrid,
Spain **(100%)**
Tel.: (34) 913606100
Web Site: http://www.loewe.es
Mfr of Fashion & Leather Goods
N.A.I.C.S.: 316990

Subsidiary (Non-US):

Loewe Hong Kong Ltd. (4)
16 Fl Dorset House Taikoo Pl, 979 Kings
Rd, Quarry Bay, China (Hong
Kong) **(100%)**
Tel.: (852) 29685313
Web Site: http://www.loewe.com
Luggage & Leather Goods Stores
N.A.I.C.S.: 458320

Loewe Japan KK (4)
One Omotesando 3-5-29 Kita-Aoyama
Minato-ku, Tokyo, 107 0061,
Japan **(100%)**
Tel.: (81) 334040631
Web Site: http://www.loewe.es
Sales Range: $10-24.9 Million
Emp.: 50
Mfr of Luggage & Leather Goods
N.A.I.C.S.: 316990
Masayoshi Saijo *(Gen Mgr)*

Loewe Macao Ltd (4)
Shop G5 One Central Macau Avenida de
Sagres, Nape, Macau, China (Macau)
Tel.: (853) 2875 0744
Web Site: http://www.loewe.com
Luxury Jewelry & Watch Distr
N.A.I.C.S.: 423940

Subsidiary (US):

Loewe Saipan Inc. (4)
Beach Rd & 1st Ave Garapan, Saipan, MP
96950
Tel.: (670) 233-0576
Web Site: http://www.loewe.es
Sales Range: $25-49.9 Million
Emp.: 4
Luggage & Leather Goods
N.A.I.C.S.: 458320

Subsidiary (Non-US):

Loewe Taiwan Ltd. (4)
Suite A 18F, Sec 2, 105 Tun Hwa South Rd,
Taipei, 106, Taiwan
Tel.: (886) 227051680
Web Site: http://www.loewe.es
Luggage & Leather Goods Mfr
N.A.I.C.S.: 316990

Subsidiary (Domestic):

Manufacturas Loewe S.L (4)
Eratostenes 2 C Pol Ind El Lomo, 28906,
Madrid, Spain **(100%)**
Tel.: (34) 916653119
Web Site: http://www.loewe.es
Sales Range: $25-49.9 Million
Emp.: 200
Textile Mfr
N.A.I.C.S.: 313210

Perfumes Loewe S.A (4)
Isla de Java 33, 28034, Madrid,
Spain **(100%)**
Tel.: (34) 917286900
Web Site: http://www.loewe.es
Sales Range: $350-399.9 Million
Mfr of Perfumes & Cosmetics
N.A.I.C.S.: 325620

Subsidiary (Domestic):

Royal Van Lent Shipyard BV (3)
Julianalaan 3, 2159 LA, Kaag,
Netherlands **(91%)**
Tel.: (31) 252547123
Web Site: http://www.royalvanlent.nl
Yacht Building Services
N.A.I.C.S.: 336611

Subsidiary (Domestic):

LVMH Montres et Joaillerie (2)
22 Ave Mongaigne, 75008, Paris,
France **(100%)**
Tel.: (33) 0144132222
Web Site: http://www.lvmh.fr
Sales Range: $25-49.9 Million
Emp.: 50
Holding Company
N.A.I.C.S.: 551112

Subsidiary (Non-US):

Bulgari Horlogerie SA (3)
Chemin des Labours 5, 2350, Saignelegier,
Switzerland
Tel.: (41) 32 951 11 33
Luxury Jewelry & Watch Mfr & Distr
N.A.I.C.S.: 339910

Subsidiary (Domestic):

Chaumet International SA (3)
12 Pl Vendome, 75001, Paris,
France **(100%)**
Tel.: (33) 44772400
Web Site: http://www.chaumet.com
Sales Range: $50-74.9 Million
Emp.: 140
Mfr of Watches & Jewelry
N.A.I.C.S.: 423940

Subsidiary (Non-US):

Chaumet (London) Ltd. (4)
49 Sloane St, London, SW1X 9SN, United
Kingdom **(100%)**
Tel.: (44) 2072450045
Web Site: http://www.chaumet.com
Sales Range: $25-49.9 Million
Emp.: 6
Mfr & Retailer of Watches & Jewelry
N.A.I.C.S.: 423940

Chaumet Horlogerie S.A. (4)
Route de Champ Colin 2C, Nyon, 1260,
Switzerland **(100%)**
Tel.: (41) 22 994 21 00
Web Site: http://www.chaumet.com
Emp.: 13
Mfr of Jewelry & Watches
N.A.I.C.S.: 423940
Sergio Schiazza *(Gen Mgr)*

Subsidiary (Non-US):

**LVMH Relojeria & Joyeria Espana
SA** (3)
Francisco Silvela 42, Madrid, 28028, Spain
Tel.: (34) 917810782
Sales Range: $25-49.9 Million
Watch Distr
N.A.I.C.S.: 423940

LVMH Relojeria S.A. (3)
Farancisco Silvela 42 3 FL, 28028, Madrid,
Spain **(100%)**
Tel.: (34) 917810782
Web Site: http://www.tagheuer.com
Sales Range: $25-49.9 Million
Emp.: 30
Watches & Jewelry Whslr
N.A.I.C.S.: 334519

Eanpansano Blanca *(CEO)*

**LVMH W&J Services (Suisse)
SA** (3)
Passage de la Bonne-Fontaine 41, 2300,
La Chaux-de-Fonds, Switzerland
Tel.: (41) 32 925 37 37
Web Site: http://www.dior.com
Sales Range: $25-49.9 Million
Emp.: 45
Watch & Jewelry Retailer
N.A.I.C.S.: 458310

Subsidiary (US):

LVMH W&J USA Inc. (3)
966 S Springfield Ave, Springfield, NJ
07081
Tel.: (973) 467-1890
Web Site: http://www.lvmh.com
Watches & Clocks Whslr & Repair
N.A.I.C.S.: 423940

Subsidiary (Non-US):

**LVMH Watch & Jewellery Australia
Pty. Limited** (3)
Level 5 Rialto North Tower, 525 Collins
Street, Melbourne, 3000, VIC, Australia
Tel.: (61) 386144300
Web Site: http://www.tagheuer.com
Watch & Jewelry Store
N.A.I.C.S.: 423940

LVMH Watch & Jewellery UK Ltd (3)
2nd Floor 13 Crescent Place, London, SW3
2EA, United Kingdom
Tel.: (44) 207 371 6166
Watch & Jewelry Distr
N.A.I.C.S.: 423940

**LVMH Watch & Jewelry (Shanghai)
Commercial Co., Ltd.** (3)
Room 1701-1707 17/F Plaza 66 1266 Nan-
jing Road West, 200040, Shanghai, China
Tel.: (86) 21 6133 2688
Web Site: http://www.lvmh.com
Sales Range: $25-49.9 Million
Emp.: 100
Watch & Jewelry Disttr
N.A.I.C.S.: 423940
Benoit Toulin *(Pres)*

**LVMH Watch & Jewelry Australia Pty.
Ltd.** (3)
Level 2 Rialto N Twr, 525 Collins St, Mel-
bourne, 3000, VIC, Australia **(100%)**
Tel.: (61) 386144300
Web Site: http://www.lvmh.com
Sales Range: $25-49.9 Million
Emp.: 20
Mfr of Watches
N.A.I.C.S.: 334519
Philip Richards *(Mng Dir)*

**LVMH Watch & Jewelry Central
Europe** (3)
Zimmersmuhlenweg 71, 61440, Oberursel,
Germany **(100%)**
Tel.: (49) 617169660
Mfr of Watches
N.A.I.C.S.: 334519

**LVMH Watch & Jewelry Holding Italy
S.p.A** (3)
Via G Lorenzini 4, Milan, 20139, Italy
Tel.: (39) 02202371
Web Site: http://www.lvmh.com
Holding Company
N.A.I.C.S.: 551112

Subsidiary (Domestic):

**LVMH Watch & Jewelry Italy
S.p.A** (4)
Via G Lorenzini 4, 20139, Milan, Italy
Tel.: (39) 02202371
Web Site: http://www.lvmh.com
Mfr of Watches & Jewelry
N.A.I.C.S.: 334519

Subsidiary (Non-US):

**LVMH Watch & Jewelry Hong Kong
Ltd** (3)
24th Floor Oxford House 979 King's Road
Taikoo Place Island East, Hong Kong,
China (Hong Kong)
Tel.: (852) 2881 1631
Watch & Jewelry Distr

N.A.I.C.S.: 423940

**LVMH Watch & Jewelry India Pvt
Ltd** (3)
International Trade Tower No 301-312 3rd
Floor Block F Nehru Place, 110 019, New
Delhi, India
Tel.: (91) 11 4747 4141
Watch & Jewelry Retailer
N.A.I.C.S.: 458310

**LVMH Watch & Jewelry Japan
KK** (3)
Sumitomo Hanzomon Building 3-16
Hayabusa-cho, Chiyoda-ku, 102-0092, To-
kyo, Japan
Tel.: (81) 3 3263 9420
Web Site: http://www.tagheuer.co.jp
Watch & Jewelry Distr
N.A.I.C.S.: 423940

LVMH Watch & Jewelry K.K. (3)
2-1-1 Hirakawa-cho, 3 16 Hayabusa Cho,
Tokyo, 102-0093, Japan **(100%)**
Tel.: (81) 332639420
Web Site: http://www.lvmh.com
Sales Range: $100-124.9 Million
Mfr of Watches & Clocks
N.A.I.C.S.: 334519

**LVMH Watch & Jewelry Malaysia Sdn
Bhd** (3)
Ste 2305 06 23rd Fl Central Plz, 34 Jalan
Sultan Ismail, Kuala Lumpur, 50250,
Malaysia **(100%)**
Tel.: (60) 321416328
Web Site: http://www.lvmh.com
Sales Range: $25-49.9 Million
Emp.: 20
Mfr of Watches & Clocks
N.A.I.C.S.: 334519
Lee Chingpei *(Dir-Fin & Ops)*

**LVMH Watch & Jewelry Singapore
Pte Ltd** (3)
250 N Bridge Rd 32-04 Raffles City Tower,
179101, Singapore, Singapore
Tel.: (65) 6338 6848
Web Site: http://www.lvmh.com
Watch & Jewelry Distr
N.A.I.C.S.: 423940

LVMH Watch & Jewelry UK Ltd (3)
58 Pembroke Road, London, W8 6NX,
United Kingdom
Tel.: (44) 207 371 61 66
Watch & Jewelry Retailer
N.A.I.C.S.: 458310

Subsidiary (US):

LVMH Watch & Jewelry USA Inc (3)
966 S Springfield Ave, Springfield, NJ
07081
Tel.: (973) 467-1890
Web Site: http://www.lvmh.com
Watch & Jewelry Retailer
N.A.I.C.S.: 423415
Francois-Xavier Lamy *(CFO)*

Subsidiary (Non-US):

**LVMH Watches & Jewelry
(Switzerland)** (3)
Lue 6a Lan Chaox De Fonds, 2300, Marin,
Switzerland **(100%)**
Tel.: (41) 327556000
Web Site: http://www.tagheuer.com
Sales Range: $25-49.9 Million
Emp.: 100
Mfr of Watches & Clocks
N.A.I.C.S.: 334519

**LVMH Watches & Jewelry Hong Kong
Ltd.** (3)
24th Floor Oxford House 979 King's Road
Taikoo Place Island East, Hong Kong,
China (Hong Kong) **(100%)**
Tel.: (852) 28811631
Sales Range: $25-49.9 Million
Emp.: 70
Mfr of Watches & Clocks
N.A.I.C.S.: 334519
Benoit Toulin *(Pres)*

LVMH Watches & Jewelry Ltd. (3)
Duval House 16 18 Harcourt St, Worsley,
Manchester, M28 5GN, United
Kingdom **(100%)**
Tel.: (44) 204861168

AND PRIVATE COMPANIES

Sales Range: $100-124.9 Million
Emp.: 300
Watches & Jewelry Whlsr
N.A.I.C.S.: 334519

LVMH Watches & Jewelry Singapore Pte. Ltd. (3)
250 N Bridge Rd, 32 04 Raffles City Tower, Singapore, 179101, Singapore (100%)
Tel.: (65) 63386848
Web Site: http://www.tagheuer.com
Sales Range: $25-49.9 Million
Emp.: 32
Mfr of Watches & Clocks
N.A.I.C.S.: 334519

LVMH Watches & Jewelry Taiwan Ltd (3)
14th Fl 270 Chung Hsiao E Rd, Section 4, 10694, Taipei, Taiwan (100%)
Tel.: (886) 227787266
Sales Range: $25-49.9 Million
Mfr of Watches & Clocks
N.A.I.C.S.: 334519
Lily Chang *(Gen Mgr)*

Les Ateliers Horlogers LVMH SA (3)
Alphonse-Large 11, Meyrin, 1217, Switzerland (100%)
Tel.: (41) 32 925 34 34
Web Site: http://www.louisvuitton.com
Mfr of Luxury Watches & Clocks
N.A.I.C.S.: 423940
Jose Fernandez *(Gen Mgr)*

TAG Heuer S.A. (3)
6A Rue Louis-Joseph Chevrolet, 2300, La Chaux-de-Fonds, Switzerland
Tel.: (41) 329198000
Web Site: http://www.tagheuer.com
Luxury Watches Mfr
N.A.I.C.S.: 334519
Benjamin Beaufils *(Pres-North America)*

Subsidiary (Non-US):

TAG Heuer Canada Ltd. (4)
30E Beaver Creek Rd Ste 212, Richmond Hill, L4B 1J2, ON, Canada (100%)
Tel.: (905) 882-9500
Web Site: http://www.tagheuer.com
Sales Range: $25-49.9 Million
Emp.: 10
Mfr of Clocks & Watches
N.A.I.C.S.: 334519

Subsidiary (Domestic):

Zenith Time France S.A. (3)
1 Rue du Stade, 25130, Villers-le-Lac, France
Tel.: (33) 3 81 68 12 22
Web Site: http://www.lvmh.com
Mfr of Watches & Clocks
N.A.I.C.S.: 423940

Subsidiary (Non-US):

LVMH Watch & Jewelry GmbH (4)
Zimmersmuehlenweg 71, 61440, Oberursel, Germany (100%)
Tel.: (49) 617169660
Web Site: http://www.lvmh.com
Sales Range: $25-49.9 Million
Emp.: 10
Mfr of Watches & Clocks
N.A.I.C.S.: 334519

Zenith International S.A. (4)
Billodes 34 36, Le Locle, 2400, Switzerland (100%)
Tel.: (41) 329306262
Web Site: http://www.zenith-watches.com
Sales Range: $50-74.9 Million
Emp.: 200
Mfr of Watches & Jewelry
N.A.I.C.S.: 423940
Julien Tornare *(CEO-Swiss Luxury Watch Brand)*

StefanoBi S.r.l. (1)
Via Cimarosa 7, 44100, Ferrara, Italy
Tel.: (39) 0532903020
Web Site: http://www.lvmh.com
Mfr of Footwear
N.A.I.C.S.: 316210

Thelios S.p.A.
Zona Industriale Villanova 16, 32013, Villanova, Italy
Tel.: (39) 0437571111
Web Site: https://www.thelios.com
Sunglasses, Jewelries & Accesories Whslr
N.A.I.C.S.: 423460

Thomas Pink Bv (1)
Oude Utrechtseweg 22 24, 3743KN, Baarn, Netherlands
Tel.: (31) 356946907
Cosmetic Product Distr
N.A.I.C.S.: 456120

Tiffany & Co. (1)
200 5th Ave, New York, NY 10010
Tel.: (212) 755-8000
Web Site: http://www.tiffany.com
Rev.: $4,424,000,000
Assets: $6,660,100,000
Liabilities: $3,324,700,000
Net Worth: $3,335,400,000
Earnings: $541,100,000
Emp.: 14,100
Fiscal Year-end: 01/31/2020
Fine Jewelry, China, Crystal, Sterling Silver, Timepieces, Clocks, Stationery, Leather, Scarves & Fragrance Retailer
N.A.I.C.S.: 458310
Andrew W. Hart *(Sr VP-Diamond & Jewelry Supply)*

Subsidiary (Domestic):

Judel Products Corp. (2)
1 Judel Plz, Salem, WV 26426-0287 (100%)
Tel.: (304) 782-3991
Sales Range: $50-74.9 Million
Emp.: 110
Crystal Glassware Mfr
N.A.I.C.S.: 327212

Subsidiary (Non-US):

Laurelton Diamonds (Botswana) (Proprietary) Limited (2)
PO Box 26517, Gaborone, Botswana
Tel.: (267) 3187470
Jewelry Polishing Services
N.A.I.C.S.: 339910
Binu Phillip *(Gen Mgr)*

Laurelton Diamonds, Inc. (2)
Schupstraat 9, Po Box 11, 2018, Antwerp, Belgium
Tel.: (32) 32292700
Web Site: http://www.laureltondiamonds.com
Jewelry Retailer
N.A.I.C.S.: 458310

Subsidiary (Domestic):

Laurelton Diamonds Belgium Bvba (3)
Schupstraat 9-11 3rd Floor Block B, Antwerp, Belgium
Tel.: (32) 32292700
Fine Jewelry & Crystal Retailer
N.A.I.C.S.: 458310

Subsidiary (Non-US):

Tiffany & Co. (2)
6 Rue de la Paix, Paris, 75002, France
Tel.: (33) 140202020
Web Site: http://www.tiffany.fr
Jewelry & Specialty Retailer
N.A.I.C.S.: 458310

Tiffany & Co. (Canada) LP (2)
150 Bloor Street West, Toronto, M5S 2X9, ON, Canada
Tel.: (416) 921-3900
Web Site: https://www.tiffany.ca
Emp.: 115
Jewelry Store Operator
N.A.I.C.S.: 458310

Tiffany & Co. (Shanghai) Commercial Company Limited (2)
Shop A105 No 1266 Nanjing West Road, Jingan District, Shanghai, 200040, China
Tel.: (86) 2162887208
Web Site: http://www.tiffany.cn
Jewelry Store Operator
N.A.I.C.S.: 458310

Tiffany & Co. (UK) Holdings Limited (2)
25 Old Bond Street, London, W1S 4QB, United Kingdom
Tel.: (44) 8001601330

Holding Company
N.A.I.C.S.: 551112

Subsidiary (Non-US):

Tiffany & Co. (Australia) Pty. Ltd. (3)
90 King Street, Sydney, 2000, NSW, Australia (100%)
Tel.: (61) 1800829152
Web Site: http://www.tiffany.com
Fine Jewelry, China, Crystal, Sterling Silver, Timepieces, Clocks, Stationery, Leather, Scarves & Fragrance Retailer
N.A.I.C.S.: 458310

Tiffany & Co. (Switzerland) Jewelers S.A.R.L. (3)
Bahnhofstrasse 14, 8001, Zurich, Switzerland (100%)
Tel.: (41) 442111010
Web Site: http://www.international.tiffany.com
Sales Range: $50-74.9 Million
Emp.: 20
Jewelry, China, Crystal, Sterling Silver, Timepieces, Clocks, Stationery, Leather, Scarves & Fragrance Retailer
N.A.I.C.S.: 458310

Tiffany & Co. Belgium Sprl (3)
66 Boulevard de Waterloo, 1000, Brussels, Belgium
Tel.: (32) 25016633
Jewelry Store Operator
N.A.I.C.S.: 458310

Tiffany & Co. Italia S.p.A. (3)
via della Spiga 19 / A, 20121, Milan, Italy (100%)
Tel.: (39) 0276022321
Web Site: http://www.tiffany.it
Sales Range: $50-74.9 Million
Emp.: 45
Jewelry Stores
N.A.I.C.S.: 458310

Subsidiary (Domestic):

Tiffany & Co. Limited (3)
25 Old Bond St, Mayfair, London, W1S 4QB, United Kingdom
Tel.: (44) 8001601837
Fine Jewelry, Watches & Other Accessories Mfr & Distr
N.A.I.C.S.: 458310

Subsidiary (Non-US):

Tiffany & Co. Netherlands B.V. (3)
PC Hooftstraat 86-88, 1071 CB, Amsterdam, Netherlands
Tel.: (31) 203050920
Web Site: http://nl.tiffany.com
Jewelry Store Operator
N.A.I.C.S.: 458310

Tiffany of New York (Spain) S.L. (3)
Calle Jose Ortega y Gasset 10, Salamanca, 28006, Madrid, Spain
Tel.: (34) 917818555
Web Site: http://www.tiffany.es
Jewelry Store Operator
N.A.I.C.S.: 458310

Subsidiary (Domestic):

Tiffany & Co. International (2)
6 E 57th St, New York, NY 10022 (100%)
Tel.: (212) 755-8000
Web Site: http://www.international.tiffany.com
Holding Company
N.A.I.C.S.: 551112

Subsidiary (Non-US):

Tiffany & Co. Japan Inc. (3)
Meiji Yasuda Life Building 15th Floor 2-1-1 Marunouchi, Chiyoda-ku, Tokyo, 100-0005, Japan (100%)
Tel.: (81) 120488712
Web Site: http://www.tiffany.com
Jewelry Stores
N.A.I.C.S.: 458310

Tiffany & Co. Pte. Ltd. (3)
Ngee Ann City 391 Orchard Road 01- 05/06 & 02-05/06, Singapore, 238872, Singapore (100%)
Tel.: (65) 67358823
Web Site: http://www.tiffany.com

LVMH MOET HENNESSY LOUIS VUITTON SE

Sales Range: $25-49.9 Million
Emp.: 80
Jewelry Stores
N.A.I.C.S.: 458310

Tiffany & Co. Taiwan Limited (3)
1F No 246 Sec 1 Dunhua S Rd, Sec 2 Taipei, Taipei, 104, Taiwan (100%)
Tel.: (886) 227789661
Web Site: http://www.tiffany.com
Sales Range: $50-74.9 Million
Emp.: 50
Jewelry Stores
N.A.I.C.S.: 458310

Tiffany & Co. of New York Limited (3)
88 Queensway Shop 323 Level 3, Admiralty, Hong Kong, China (Hong Kong) (100%)
Tel.: (852) 29189992
Web Site: http://www.tiffany.com
Sales Range: $25-49.9 Million
Emp.: 10
Jewelry Stores
N.A.I.C.S.: 458310

Tiffany Switzerland Watch Company SAGL (3)
Bahnhofstrasse 14, 8001, Zurich, Switzerland (100%)
Tel.: (41) 442111010
Web Site: http://www.tiffany.com
Sales Range: $10-24.9 Million
Emp.: 12
Watch Retailer
N.A.I.C.S.: 334519

Subsidiary (Non-US):

Tiffany & Co. Mexico, S.A. de C.V. (2)
Masaryk 450 Col Polanco, 11560, Mexico, Mexico (100%)
Tel.: (52) 5552815222
Web Site: http://www.tiffany.com.mx
Sales Range: $50-74.9 Million
Emp.: 35
Jewelry Stores
N.A.I.C.S.: 458310

Subsidiary (Domestic):

Tiffany (NJ) LLC (2)
15 Sylvan Way, Parsippany, NJ 07054 (100%)
Tel.: (973) 254-7000
Sales Range: $700-749.9 Million
Emp.: 1,200
Jewelry, China, Crystal, Sterling Silver, Timepieces, Clocks, Stationery, Leather, Scarves & Fragrance Retailer
N.A.I.C.S.: 458310

Subsidiary (Non-US):

Tiffany Korea Ltd. (2)
515 Apgujeong-dong The Galleria East 1st Floor, Gangnam-gu, Seoul, 135-110, Korea (South) (100%)
Tel.: (82) 262508620
Sales Range: $150-199.9 Million
Emp.: 200
Jewelry Stores
N.A.I.C.S.: 458310
Michelle Kim *(Mng Dir)*

Tower Holding BV (1)
Kwadijk 39, Kwadijk, 1471 CB, Netherlands
Tel.: (31) 299 62 33 00
Investment Management Service
N.A.I.C.S.: 523999

Tumon Aquarium Llc (1)
1245 Pale San Vitores Rd Ste 400, Tumon, GU 96913
Tel.: (671) 649-9191
Web Site: http://www.uwwguam.com
Emp.: 400
Aquarium
N.A.I.C.S.: 712130
Jeff Schindler *(Gen Mgr)*

Van der Loo Yachtinteriors BV (1)
Coenecoop 208, 2741 PK, Waddinxveen, Netherlands
Tel.: (31) 182 612810
Web Site: http://www.vanderlooyachtinteriors.nl

LVMH MOET HENNESSY LOUIS VUITTON SE

LVMH Moet Hennessy Louis Vuitton SE—(Continued)
Sales Range: $25-49.9 Million
Emp.: 70
Yacht & Marine Furniture Mfr
N.A.I.C.S.: 337212
Pieter Zuidam *(Gen Mgr)*

Veuve Clicquot Ponsardin S.A. (1)
12 Rue Du Temple, 51100, Reims, France
Tel.: (33) 326895440
Web Site: http://www.veuveclicquot.com
Wines & Spirits Mfr
N.A.I.C.S.: 312130

Subsidiary (Non-US):

Cape Mentelle Vineyards Ltd. (2)
331 Wallcliffe Rd, PO Box 110, Margaret River, 6285, WA, Australia (100%)
Tel.: (61) 897570888
Web Site: http://www.capementelle.com.au
Wine Mfr
N.A.I.C.S.: 312130

Cloudy Bay Vineyards Ltd (2)
Jacksons Rd, PO Box 376, Blenheim, 7240, Marlborough, New Zealand
Tel.: (64) 35209140
Web Site: http://www.cloudybay.co.nz
Wine & Champagne Mfr
N.A.I.C.S.: 445320

Subsidiary (US):

Moet Hennessy (2)
85 10th Ave Fl 2, New York, NY 10011
Tel.: (212) 251-8200
Web Site: http://www1.mhusa.com
Wine Importer
N.A.I.C.S.: 424820
Geraud Leclercq *(VP)*

Subsidiary (Domestic):

Roederer Estate Inc. (3)
4501 Hwy 128, Philo, CA 95466-0365
Tel.: (707) 895-2288
Wine & Alcoholic Beverages Mfr
N.A.I.C.S.: 312130

Subsidiary (Non-US):

Mountadam Vineyards Pty Limited (2)
High Eden Rd, Eden Valley, 5235, Australia
Tel.: (61) 427089836
Web Site: http://www.mountadam.com
Wine Mfr
N.A.I.C.S.: 312130

LVYUAN GREEN BUILDING MATERIAL TECHNOLOGY CORP.
Room 1216 Building 3 Incubator Mansion Development Zone, Daqing, 150000, Heilong, China
Tel.: (86) 75522184466 NV
Year Founded: 2013
LVYN—(OTCIQ)
Liabilities: $27,000
Net Worth: ($27,000)
Earnings: ($77,000)
Fiscal Year-end: 04/30/22
Investment Services
N.A.I.C.S.: 523999
James A. Tilton *(Pres, Treas & Sec)*

LW BOGDANKA SA
Bogdanka, Puchaczow, 21-013, Lublin, Poland
Tel.: (48) 814625100
Web Site: https://www.lw.com.pl
LWB—(WAR)
Rev.: $989,621,665
Assets: $1,447,562,679
Liabilities: $366,308,345
Net Worth: $1,081,254,334
Earnings: $172,623,223
Emp.: 6,132
Fiscal Year-end: 12/31/23
Coal Distr
N.A.I.C.S.: 423520
Artur Wasil *(Pres)*

LWP TECHNOLOGIES LIMITED
Suite 29 Level 54 111 Eagle Street, Brisbane, 4000, QLD, Australia
Tel.: (61) 7 3122 2233
Web Site: http://lwptech.com
LWP—(ASX)
Sales Range: Less than $1 Million
Investment Services
N.A.I.C.S.: 523999
David Henson *(CEO-Americas)*

LWS KNITWEAR LIMITED
B-XXXII 933 Village Bhura G T Road West, Ludhiana, 141 008, Punjab, India
Tel.: (91) 9877815974
Web Site: https://www.lwsknitwear.com
531402—(BOM)
Rev.: $7,507,507
Assets: $6,035,690
Liabilities: $4,742,568
Net Worth: $1,293,123
Earnings: $35,100
Emp.: 8
Fiscal Year-end: 03/31/23
Woolen & Acrylic Garment Whslr
N.A.I.C.S.: 315210
Girish Kapoor *(Mng Dir)*

LX HOLDINGS CORP.
58 Saemunhan-Ro, Jongno-Gu, Seoul, Korea (South)
Tel.: (82) 269243114
Web Site: https://www.lxholdings.co.kr
Year Founded: 2021
383800—(KRS)
Holding Company
N.A.I.C.S.: 551112
Song Chi Ho *(Pres & Co-CEO)*

Subsidiaries:

Hi Logistics Egypt S.A.E. (1)
7St Mostafa Refaat Sheratoon, Cairo, Egypt
Tel.: (20) 128 678 7334
Logistic Services
N.A.I.C.S.: 541614

LX Pantos (Cambodia) Co., Ltd. (1)
4F No 66 Norodom Blvd, Sangkat Chey Chomneas Khan Doun Penh, Phnom Penh, Cambodia
Tel.: (855) 2 321 3425
Logistic Services
N.A.I.C.S.: 541614

LX Pantos (Thailand) Co., Ltd. (1)
193/77 Lake Rajada Office Complex 19th Floor Rachadapisek Rd, Klongtoey, Bangkok, 10110, Thailand
Tel.: (66) 2 260 6320
Logistic Services
N.A.I.C.S.: 541614

LX Pantos Australia Pty Ltd (1)
7/4 Ave of the Americas, Newington, 2127, NSW, Australia
Tel.: (61) 28 305 3777
Logistic Services
N.A.I.C.S.: 541614

LX Pantos Germany GmbH (1)
Waldecker Str 6-12, 64546, Moerfelden-Walldorf, Germany
Tel.: (49) 61 054 0530
Logistic Services
N.A.I.C.S.: 541614

LX Pantos Hungary Kft. (1)
Regus 306 EMKE Rakoczi ut 42, Budapest, Hungary
Tel.: (36) 30 515 7440
Logistic Services
N.A.I.C.S.: 541614

LX Pantos India Private Limited (1)
Pioneer Urban Square 7th Floor Tower-D Sector-62, Gurgaon, 122005, Haryana, India
Tel.: (91) 981 027 3425
Logistic Services
N.A.I.C.S.: 541614

LX Pantos Japan Inc. (1)
14F Kyobashi Trust Tower 1-3 Kyobashi 2-chome, Chuo-ku, Tokyo, 104-0031, Japan
Tel.: (81) 35 299 4450
Logistic Services
N.A.I.C.S.: 541614

LX Pantos Logistics (Hong Kong) Co., Ltd. (1)
Unit 01-03 and 11-12 13F Tower 1 Ever Gain Plaza, 88 Container Port Rd, Kwai Chung, China (Hong Kong)
Tel.: (852) 2 403 4400
Logistic Services
N.A.I.C.S.: 541614

LX Pantos Logistics (Shanghai) Co., Ltd. (1)
23 / F The New Bund Times Square No 399, Haiyang West Roa Pudong New Area, Shanghai, China
Tel.: (86) 213 856 8200
Logistic Services
N.A.I.C.S.: 541614

LX Pantos Malaysia Sdn. Bhd. (1)
Unit 10-01 Level 10 Blok I Sumurwang Tower No 3, Prsn Multimedia I-City Seksyen 7, 40000, Shah Alam, Selangor, Malaysia
Tel.: (60) 35 870 1399
Logistic Services
N.A.I.C.S.: 541614

LX Pantos Mexico, S.A.de C.V. (1)
Torre VAO2 Piso11 David Alfaro Siqueiros 104, Col Valle Oriente San Pedro Garza Garcia, 66269, Monterrey, Mexico
Tel.: (52) 815 515 3104
Logistic Services
N.A.I.C.S.: 541614

LX Pantos Netherlands B.V. (1)
Tupolevlilaan 48, 1119 NZ, Schiphol-Rijk, Netherlands
Tel.: (31) 20 659 0101
Logistic Services
N.A.I.C.S.: 541614

LX Pantos Panama S.A. (1)
Calle Aquilino de la Guardia con Calle 48 Este, Panama, Panama
Tel.: (507) 265 1712
Logistic Services
N.A.I.C.S.: 541614

LX Pantos Phillippines, Inc. (1)
Unit 2503 25th Floor The Trade and Financial Tower, 7th Avenue corner 32nd Street Bonifacio Global City, Taguig, Philippines
Tel.: (63) 2 717 4426
Logistic Services
N.A.I.C.S.: 541614

LX Pantos Poland Sp. z o.o. (1)
Ul Dzialkowa 121C, 02-234, Warsaw, Poland
Tel.: (48) 22 358 2760
Logistic Services
N.A.I.C.S.: 541614

LX Pantos Singapore Pte. Ltd. (1)
7 Changi South Street 2 Xilin Districentre Building C 01-02, Singapore, 486415, Singapore
Tel.: (65) 6 546 0733
Logistic Services
N.A.I.C.S.: 541614

LX Pantos Spain S.L. (1)
C/De la Balsa 1 Parcela A-4 1 Nave 1 Pol Ind La Reva Sector 12, Riba-roja de Turia, 46394, Valencia, Spain
Tel.: (34) 96 339 2633
Logistic Services
N.A.I.C.S.: 541614

LX Pantos UK Ltd. (1)
776 Buckingham Avenue, Slough, SL1 4NL, Berkshire, United Kingdom
Tel.: (44) 175 361 0400
Logistic Services
N.A.I.C.S.: 541614

LX Pantos Vietnam Company Limited (1)
12A Floor Handico Building Pham Hung, Tu Liem, Hanoi, Vietnam
Tel.: (84) 243 936 2814
Logistic Services
N.A.I.C.S.: 541614

INTERNATIONAL PUBLIC

Lx Pantos Logistics Taiwan Co., Ltd. (1)
6F No 216 Sec 2 Dunhua South Rd, Taipei, Taiwan
Tel.: (886) 22 737 1100
Logistic Services
N.A.I.C.S.: 541614

PT. LX Pantos Indonesia (1)
Kawasan Industri MM 2100 Blok G Jalan Bali No 1, Jatiwangi Cikarang Barat-Gandamekar Kec Cikarang Bar, Bekasi, 17530, West Java, Indonesia
Tel.: (62) 218 998 2855
Logistic Services
N.A.I.C.S.: 541614

Pantos Logistics (China) Co., Ltd. (1)
RooM 322 3F Fortune Center No 18-2 Qinling Road, Laoshan District, Qingdao, China
Tel.: (86) 5328 666 0588
Logistic Services
N.A.I.C.S.: 541614

Pantos Logistics France SARL (1)
5 Rue du Noyer aux Perdrix, 77170, Servon, France
Tel.: (33) 16 062 3712
Logistic Services
N.A.I.C.S.: 541614

Pantos Logistics LLC (1)
2nd Floo Office No 8 Emitac Building Al Garhoud, Dubai, United Arab Emirates
Tel.: (971) 4 805 1447
Logistic Services
N.A.I.C.S.: 541614

Pantos Logistics Swedan AB (1)
Skrittvagen 3, 567 92, Vaggeryd, Sweden
Tel.: (46) 39 339 0151
Logistic Services
N.A.I.C.S.: 541614

Pantos North America Inc. (1)
111 Sylvan Ave S Bldg L2, Englewood Cliffs, NJ 07632
Tel.: (201) 627-1600
Logistic Services
N.A.I.C.S.: 541614

LX SEMICON CO., LTD.
222 Techno 2-ro, Yuseong-gu, Daejeon, Korea (South)
Tel.: (82) 269243114
Web Site: https://www.lxsemicon.com
Year Founded: 1999
108320—(KRS)
Rev.: $1,625,537,894
Assets: $989,137,422
Liabilities: $260,210,804
Net Worth: $728,926,618
Earnings: $179,242,178
Emp.: 1,604
Fiscal Year-end: 12/31/22
Semiconductor Mfr
N.A.I.C.S.: 334413
Yuntae Lee *(Pres & CEO)*

LXB COMMUNICATIONS MARKETING
55 Mont Royal Ave W Ste 801, Montreal, H2T 2S6, QC, Canada
Tel.: (514) 284-3010
Year Founded: 1989
Rev.: $10,000,000
Emp.: 30
Advetising Agency
N.A.I.C.S.: 541810
Paul Bergeron *(Mng Dir & Exec VP)*

Subsidiaries:

LXB Communications Marketing (1)
2590,Blvd Laurier Tour Belle Cour Bureau, Quebec, G1V 4M6, QC, Canada
Tel.: (418) 529-9761
Emp.: 14
N.A.I.C.S.: 541810
Marc Lacroix *(Pres)*

LXB RETAIL PROPERTIES PLC

AND PRIVATE COMPANIES

44 Esplanade, Saint Helier, JE4 9WG, Jersey
Tel.: (44) 1534504000 JE
Web Site: http://www.lxbretailproperties.com
Year Founded: 2009
Rev.: $53,514,712
Assets: $40,077,579
Liabilities: $14,817,421
Net Worth: $25,260,158
Earnings: ($15,635,189)
Fiscal Year-end: 09/30/18
Real Estate Investment Services
N.A.I.C.S.: 531390
Timothy Paul Walton (CEO)

LXRANDCO
7399 St-Laurent Boulevard, Montreal, H2R 1W7, QC, Canada
Web Site: http://www.lxrco.com
Luggage Product Retailer
N.A.I.C.S.: 458320
Valerie Sorbie (Pres)

LY CORPORATION LIMITED
No 15 Jalan Wawasan Utama Kawasan Perindustrian, Sri Gading Batu Pahat, Johor, 83300, Malaysia
Tel.: (60) 74558828
Web Site: http://www.lyfurniture.com
1H8—(CAT)
Rev.: $43,287,332
Assets: $64,825,425
Liabilities: $18,332,826
Net Worth: $46,492,599
Earnings: ($1,787,549)
Emp.: 1,145
Fiscal Year-end: 12/31/23
Investment Holding Company
N.A.I.C.S.: 551114
Kwee Chai Tan (Co-Founder & Chm)

Subsidiaries:

LY Furniture Sdn. Bhd. (1)
No 15 Jalan Wawasan Utama Kawasan Perindustrian, Sri Gading, 83300, Batu Pahat, 83300, Johor, Malaysia
Tel.: (60) 74558828
Emp.: 1,000
Household Furniture Mfr
N.A.I.C.S.: 337122

LYC HEALTHCARE BERHAD
Level 2 Podium BlockPlaza VADS 1 Jalan TunMohd Fuad, Taman Tun Dr Ismail, 60000, Kuala Lumpur, Malaysia
Tel.: (60) 377339222 MY
Web Site: https://www.lychealth.com
Year Founded: 1992
LYC—(KLS)
Rev.: $27,553,439
Assets: $51,396,613
Liabilities: $34,987,725
Net Worth: $16,408,889
Earnings: ($3,154,286)
Fiscal Year-end: 03/31/24
Investment Holding Services
N.A.I.C.S.: 551112
Diong Hoe Sui (CEO & Mng Dir)

Subsidiaries:

HC Orthopaedic Surgery Pte. Ltd. (1)
3 Mount Elizabeth 15-14, Singapore, 228510, Singapore
Tel.: (65) 67328848
Clinic & General Medical Services
N.A.I.C.S.: 621491

LYC Child Care Centre Sdn. Bhd. (1)
Plaza Vads T-G-1 and T-M-2 No 1 Jalan Tun Mohd Fuad, Taman Tun Dr Ismail, 60000, Kuala Lumpur, Malaysia
Tel.: (60) 377339622
Web Site: https://www.lychealth.com
Child Care Services
N.A.I.C.S.: 624410

Mohana Thanabal (Head-Operations)

LYC Medicare (Singapore) Pte. Ltd. (1)
435 Orchard Road 21-05 Wisma Atria, Singapore, 238877, Singapore
Tel.: (65) 69622517
Web Site: https://www.lycmedicare.com
Medical Equipment Distr
N.A.I.C.S.: 423450

LYC Medicare Sdn Bhd (1)
Ground Floor Plaza VADS No 1 Jalan Tun Mohd Fuad, Taman Tun Dr Ismail, 60000, Kuala Lumpur, Malaysia
Tel.: (60) 377327622
Web Site: https://www.lychealth.com
Primary Healthcare Services
N.A.I.C.S.: 621999

LYC Senior Living Care Centre Sdn. Bhd. (1)
No 12 Jalan Gallagher, Taman Duta, 50480, Kuala Lumpur, Malaysia
Tel.: (60) 326021994
Nursing Care Services
N.A.I.C.S.: 623110

LYC Senior Living Sdn Bhd (1)
No 12 Jalan Gallagher Taman Duta, 50480, Kuala Lumpur, Malaysia
Tel.: (60) 326021994
Nursing Care Services
N.A.I.C.S.: 623110

Locktech International Sdn. Bhd. (1)
No 79B Gf 3rd Miles Old Klang Road, 58000, Kuala Lumpur, Malaysia
Tel.: (60) 379820098
Web Site: http://www.locktechinternational.com
Hardware Distr
N.A.I.C.S.: 423710

Tonerex Technologies Sdn. Bhd. (1)
1-12B-15 Suntech Penang Cybercity Lintang Mayang Pasir 3 Bayan Baru, 11950, Penang, Malaysia
Tel.: (60) 46445898
Web Site: http://www.tonerex.com
Testing Equipment Distr
N.A.I.C.S.: 423610

LYCAON RESOURCES LIMITED
Level 2 22 Mount St, Perth, 6000, WA, Australia
Tel.: (61) 861888181 AU
Web Site: https://www.lycaonresources.com
Year Founded: 2021
HYR—(ASX)
Exploration & Mining Services
N.A.I.C.S.: 213115

LYCATEL GROUP
Wallbrook Building 195 Marsh Wall, London, E14 9SG, United Kingdom
Tel.: (44) 20 7536 6450
Web Site: http://www.lycatel.com
Year Founded: 2004
Sales Range: $700-749.9 Million
Emp.: 953
Mobile Telecommunications Services
N.A.I.C.S.: 517112
Subaskaran Allirajah (Chm)

Subsidiaries:

Lycamobile UK Ltd (1)
3rd Floor Walbrook Building 195 Marsh Wall, London, E14 9SG, United Kingdom
Tel.: (44) 207 132 0322
Web Site: http://www.lycamoney.co.uk
Telecommunication Servicesb
N.A.I.C.S.: 517112
Subaskaran Allirajah (Founder & Grp Chm)

Lycatel Canada Inc (1)
304-305 Milner Avenue, Scarborough, M1B 3V4, ON, Canada
Web Site: https://www.lycatalk.ca
Telecommunication Servicesb
N.A.I.C.S.: 517112

Lycatel GmbH (1)

Hermetschloostrasse 73, 8048, Zurich, Switzerland
Tel.: (41) 442403838
Telecommunication Servicesb
N.A.I.C.S.: 517112

Lycatel Ireland Limited (1)
Dominick Court 41 Lower Dominick Street, Dublin, Ireland
Tel.: (353) 18728052
Telecommunication Servicesb
N.A.I.C.S.: 517112

LYCKEGARD GROUP AB
Trollebergsvagen 102-28, 245 61, Staffanstorp, Sweden
Tel.: (46) 702566705
Web Site: https://lyckegardgroup.se
Year Founded: 2008
F55—(DEU)
Farm Machinery & Equipment Mfr
N.A.I.C.S.: 333111
Christian Bjarntoft (CEO)

Subsidiaries:

Lyckegard Finland Oy AB (1)
Kuninkaankartanontie 37A, 653 80, Vaasa, Finland
Tel.: (358) 500567611
Farm Equipment Distr
N.A.I.C.S.: 423820

LYCOPODIUM LIMITED
Level 5 1 Adelaide Terrace, Perth, 6004, WA, Australia
Tel.: (61) 862105222
Web Site: https://www.lycopodium.com
LYL—(ASX)
Rev.: $232,958,959
Assets: $144,928,245
Liabilities: $59,831,968
Net Worth: $85,096,278
Earnings: $34,009,446
Emp.: 1,300
Fiscal Year-end: 06/30/24
Engineering Consulting Services
N.A.I.C.S.: 541330
Peter De Leo (Mng Dir)

Subsidiaries:

Lycopodium (Ghana) Limited (1)
One Airport Square Commercial 3rd Floor 1 Plot 21, Ashongman, Accra, Ghana
Tel.: (233) 302790563
Web Site: http://www.lycopodium.com.au
Mineral Mfr
N.A.I.C.S.: 327999

Lycopodium (Ghana) Pty Ltd (1)
83 Osu Badu St Airport W, Accra, Ghana
Tel.: (233) 21762247
Mineral Mfr
N.A.I.C.S.: 327999

Lycopodium (Philippines) Pty Ltd (1)
25th floor High Street South Corporate Plaza Tower 1, 26th Street Corner 9th Avenue Fort Bonifacio Global City Metro Manila, Taguig, Philippines
Tel.: (63) 288582400
Web Site: http://www.lycopodium.com
Sales Range: $25-49.9 Million
Emp.: 60
Mineral Mfr
N.A.I.C.S.: 327999

Orway Mineral Consultants (WA) Pty Ltd (1)
Level 5 1 Adelaide Terrace East, Perth, 6004, WA, Australia
Tel.: (61) 862105601
Web Site: http://www.orway.com.au
Sales Range: $25-49.9 Million
Emp.: 15
Metallurgical Consultancy Services
N.A.I.C.S.: 541618

LYCOS ENERGY INC.
215 - 2nd Street SW Suite 1900, Calgary, T2P 1M4, AB, Canada
Tel.: (403) 453-1950
Web Site: https://lycosenergy.com

LYKOS METALS LIMITED

Year Founded: 2006
SCD—(TSXV)
Rev.: $20,754
Assets: $105,076
Liabilities: $188,741
Net Worth: ($83,666)
Earnings: ($36,988)
Fiscal Year-end: 10/31/21
Natural Gas Exploration Service
N.A.I.C.S.: 211130
Dave Burton (Pres)

LYGEND RESOURCES & TECHNOLOGY CO., LTD.
0-11/F Building C10 R&D Park Lane 299 Guanghua Road, Yinzhou, Ningbo, 315000, Zhejiang, China
Tel.: (86) 57427702203 CN
Web Site: https://www.lygend.com
Year Founded: 2009
2245—(HKG)
Rev.: $2,915,833,518
Assets: $4,247,855,007
Liabilities: $2,380,698,660
Net Worth: $1,867,156,347
Earnings: $238,354,287
Emp.: 9,176
Fiscal Year-end: 12/31/23
Information Technology Services
N.A.I.C.S.: 541512
Jianyong Cai (Chm)

Subsidiaries:

Xi'an Pengyuan Metallurgical Equipment Co., Ltd. (1)
20th Floor Commercial Building No F1, Guorun City Fengdong New City Xixian New District, Shaanxi, China
Tel.: (86) 2933291785
Web Site: https://www.xapyyj.com
Industrial Machinery Mfr
N.A.I.C.S.: 333924

LYKA LABS LIMITED
Spencer Building Ground Floor 30 Forjett Street, Near Bhatia Hospital Grant Road, Mumbai, 400007, India
Tel.: (91) 2266112200
Web Site: https://www.lykalabs.com
500259—(BOM)
Rev.: $11,692,625
Assets: $18,364,563
Liabilities: $12,829,275
Net Worth: $5,535,289
Earnings: ($1,594,071)
Emp.: 296
Fiscal Year-end: 03/31/23
Drug Mfr
N.A.I.C.S.: 325412
Nehal Narendra Gandhi (Chm)

LYKIS LIMITED
Lotus Grandeur Building 4th Floor Opp Gundecha Symphony, Veera Desai Road Andheri W, Mumbai, 400 053, India
Tel.: (91) 2240694069
Web Site: https://www.lykis.com
Year Founded: 1984
530689—(BOM)
Rev.: $55,342,162
Assets: $22,379,762
Liabilities: $19,037,223
Net Worth: $3,342,538
Earnings: $1,906,815
Emp.: 77
Fiscal Year-end: 03/31/23
Tea Mfr & Distr
N.A.I.C.S.: 311920
Prince Tulsian (Mng Dir)

LYKOS METALS LIMITED
Level 48 152-158 St Georges Terrace, Perth, 6000, WA, Australia
Tel.: (61) 766767154 AU
Web Site: https://www.lykosmetals.com

LYKOS METALS LIMITED

Lykos Metals Limited—(Continued)
Year Founded: 2021
LYK—(ASX)
Rev.: $26,467
Assets: $4,552,424
Liabilities: $85,357
Net Worth: $4,467,067
Earnings: ($3,048,463)
Emp.: 22
Fiscal Year-end: 06/30/23
Metal Exploration Services
N.A.I.C.S.: 213114
Candice Van Der Plas *(Sec)*

Subsidiaries:

Lykos Balkan Metals d.o.o. (1)
Majevickih brigada Street Block 52 Number 8, Novi Dvorovi, 76 300, Bijeljina, Bosnia & Herzegovina
Tel.: (387) 66767154
Web Site: https://lykosbalkanmetals.com
Biological Research Services
N.A.I.C.S.: 541715

LYNAS RARE EARTHS LIMITED

Level 4 1 Howard Street, Perth, 6000, WA, Australia
Tel.: (61) 862413800   AU
Web Site: https://lynasrareearths.com
Year Founded: 1983
LYSCF—(OTCIQ)
Rev.: $374,685
Assets: $1,132,115
Liabilities: $302,009
Net Worth: $830,106
Earnings: $120,355
Emp.: 848
Fiscal Year-end: 06/30/21
Mineral Mining & Exploration Services
N.A.I.C.S.: 212390
Andrew Arnold *(Gen Counsel & Co-Sec)*

Subsidiaries:

Lynas Malaysia Sdn Bhd (1)
PT17212 Jalan Gebeng 3, Kawasan Perindustrian Gebeng, 26080, Kuantan, Pahang Darul Makmur, Malaysia
Tel.: (60) 95825200
Web Site: https://lynasrareearths.com
Rare Earth Material Mining Services
N.A.I.C.S.: 212290

LYNCH GROUP HOLDINGS LIMITED

8b Williamson Road, Ingleburn, 2170, NSW, Australia
Tel.: (61) 282340111   AU
Web Site: https://www.lynchgroup.com.au
LGL—(ASX)
Rev.: $600,644,694
Assets: $610,383,810
Liabilities: $247,919,701
Net Worth: $362,464,110
Earnings: $15,104,824
Emp.: 1,762
Fiscal Year-end: 07/02/23
Holding Company
N.A.I.C.S.: 551112
Steve Wood *(CFO & Sec)*

LYNX EQUITY LIMITED

692 Queen Street East Unit 205, Toronto, M4M 1G9, ON, Canada
Tel.: (416) 323-3512
Web Site: http://www.lynxequity.com
Year Founded: 2007
Private Equity Services
N.A.I.C.S.: 551112
Brad Nathan *(Pres)*

Subsidiaries:

Flooring Solutions Inc. (1)
330 Wright Brothers Ave, Livermore, CA 94551
Tel.: (925) 294-5200
Web Site: http://www.flooring-solutions.com
Floor Laying & Floor Work Services
N.A.I.C.S.: 238330
Jim Foley *(Acct Mgr)*

G&W Commercial Flooring, Inc. (1)
6407 S 211th St, Kent, WA 98032-2308
Tel.: (253) 479-1760
Web Site: http://www.gwcommercialflooring.com
Flooring Contractors
N.A.I.C.S.: 238330
James Gravalis *(Pres)*

Granite Electric Limited (1)
3655 48 Ave SE, Calgary, T2B 3N8, AB, Canada
Tel.: (403) 212-0363
Web Site: http://www.graniteelectric.net
Fiber Optic Specialists & Licensed Electricians
N.A.I.C.S.: 335921
Philip Sparrow *(Gen Mgr)*

Prime Flooring LLC (1)
7132 Basin St SW, Ephrata, WA 98823
Web Site: http://www.primeflooringllc.com
Full-Service Flooring Company
N.A.I.C.S.: 238330
Tanner Halley *(Co-Founder & Pres)*

LYNX GLOBAL DIGITAL FINANCE CORPORATION

375 Water Street Suite 413, Vancouver, V6B 1B8, BC, Canada
Tel.: (604) 876-8850
Web Site: http://www.cannaonetech.com
LYNX—(CNSX)
Assets: $249,550
Liabilities: $976,921
Net Worth: ($727,370)
Earnings: ($762,718)
Fiscal Year-end: 10/31/20
Software Development Services
N.A.I.C.S.: 541511
Solomon Riby-Williams *(Founder, Pres & CEO)*

LYNX MACHINERY & COMMERCIALS LIMITED

Warden House 340 J J Road Byculla, Mumbai, 400008, Maharashtra, India
Tel.: (91) 2223027900
Web Site: https://www.lynxmachinery.com
Year Founded: 1960
505320—(BOM)
Rev.: $1,192
Assets: $229,104
Liabilities: $211,437
Net Worth: $17,666
Earnings: ($58,690)
Fiscal Year-end: 03/31/21
Warehousing Services
N.A.I.C.S.: 493110

LYON POCHE PRESSE

3 Rue de la Claire, 69009, Lyon, France
Tel.: (33) 478648464   FR
Web Site: http://www.lyonpoche.com
Emp.: 12
Periodical Publishing
N.A.I.C.S.: 513120
Patrick Deschamps *(Chm & CEO)*

LYONDELLBASELL INDUSTRIES N.V.

Delftseplein 27E, 3013 AA, Rotterdam, Netherlands
Tel.: (31) 102755500   NI
Web Site: https://www.lyondellbasell.com
Year Founded: 2007
LYB—(NYSE)
Rev.: $41,107,000,000
Assets: $37,000,000,000
Liabilities: $24,056,000,000
Net Worth: $12,944,000,000
Earnings: $2,114,000,000
Emp.: 20,000
Fiscal Year-end: 12/31/23
Chemicals, Petrochemicals & Plastics Mfr
N.A.I.C.S.: 325998
Jacques Aigrain *(Chm)*

Subsidiaries:

A. Schulman, Inc. (1)
3637 Ridgewood Rd, Fairlawn, OH 44333
Tel.: (330) 666-3751
Web Site: http://www.aschulman.com
Rev.: $2,461,124,000
Assets: $1,753,780,000
Liabilities: $1,546,748,000
Net Worth: $207,032,000
Earnings: $33,026,000
Emp.: 4,900
Fiscal Year-end: 08/31/2017
Plastic Resins & Compounds Mfr
N.A.I.C.S.: 325220

Subsidiary (Non-US):

A. Schulman Belgium (2)
Nijverheidslaan 1520, 3660, Opglabbeek, Belgium
Tel.: (32) 89869490
Plastic Product & Additive Mfr
N.A.I.C.S.: 325211
Martin Manteleers *(Plant Mgr)*

A. Schulman Castellon, S.L. (2)
CR Valencia-Barcelona km 61 5, 12550, Almazora, Castellon, Spain
Tel.: (34) 964504450
Plastic Product & Additive Mfr
N.A.I.C.S.: 325211
Facundo Mendez *(Plant Mgr)*

Subsidiary (Domestic):

A. Schulman Custom Compounding NE, Inc. (2)
53 Millbrook St, Worcester, MA 01606
Tel.: (508) 756-0002
Web Site: http://www.ecmplastics.com
Plastic Product & Additive Mfr
N.A.I.C.S.: 325211

Subsidiary (Non-US):

A. Schulman Europe Verwaltungs GmbH (2)
Schumanstr 33, 52146, Wurselen, Nordrhein-Westfalen, Germany
Tel.: (49) 240545270
Investment Management Service
N.A.I.C.S.: 551112

A. Schulman GmbH (2)
Huttenstr 130-138, 50170, Kerpen, Germany
Tel.: (49) 22735610
Web Site: http://www.aschulman.com
Plastic Resins & Compounds Mfr
N.A.I.C.S.: 325211

Subsidiary (Non-US):

A. Schulman Hungary Kft. (3)
Vendel Park Budai Ut 8, Biatorbagy, 2051, Hungary
Tel.: (36) 23814300
Sales Range: $25-49.9 Million
Emp.: 20
Plastic Resin Mfr
N.A.I.C.S.: 325211

Subsidiary (Non-US):

A. Schulman Inc. Limited (2)
Maes-Yr-Haf Lane, Croespenmaen Industrial Estate, Newport, NP11 3AF, United Kingdom (100%)
Tel.: (44) 1495244090
Web Site: http://www.aschulman.com
Sales Range: $50-74.9 Million
Emp.: 100
Mfr of Plastic Compounds
N.A.I.C.S.: 325991

A. Schulman International Services BVBA (2)
Technologielaan 7, 1840, Londerzeel, Belgium

INTERNATIONAL PUBLIC

Tel.: (32) 52750500
Sales Range: $25-49.9 Million
Emp.: 100
Plastic Compound & Resins Mfr
N.A.I.C.S.: 325211
Petrus Johannes Maria Speek *(Pres)*

Subsidiary (Non-US):

A. Schulman Poznan Sp Zoo (3)
ul Roosevelta 18, 60-829, Poznan, Poland
Tel.: (48) 616681900
Management Consulting Services
N.A.I.C.S.: 541611
Lucyna Kruchlik *(Mgr-Process Improvement)*

Subsidiary (Non-US):

A. Schulman L'Arbresle SAS (2)
ZI la Ponchonniere Savigny, BP 58, 69592, L'Arbresle, Cedex, France
Tel.: (33) 474720646
Plastics Product Mfr
N.A.I.C.S.: 326199
Emmanuel Lely *(Plant Mgr)*

A. Schulman Nordic AB (2)
Bronsgatan 1, 265 39, Astorp, Sweden
Tel.: (46) 42377500
Web Site: http://www.aschulman.se
Emp.: 48
Plastic Compounds & Resins Mfr
N.A.I.C.S.: 325211
Alf Jensen *(Mng Dir)*

A. Schulman Plasticos do Brasil Ltda. (2)
Rod Anhanguera s/n Parque das Industrias Nova Veneza, Sumare, 13177-435, Sau Paulo, Brazil
Tel.: (55) 1938389600
Web Site: https://aschulmanbrasil.business.site
Plastic Resins & Compounds Mfr
N.A.I.C.S.: 325211

A. Schulman Plastics S.L. (2)
BCIN - Pol Ind Les Guixeres s/n, 08915, Barcelona, Spain
Tel.: (34) 934648043
Sales Range: $25-49.9 Million
Emp.: 10
Plastic Resins & Compounds Mfr
N.A.I.C.S.: 325211

A. Schulman Plastics SpA (2)
Via Baragiola 6, Gorla Maggiore, 21050, Varese, Italy
Tel.: (39) 033160741
Plastic Resins Distr
N.A.I.C.S.: 424610

A. Schulman Plastics s.r.o. (2)
Rigeleho 1, 811 02, Bratislava, Slovakia
Tel.: (421) 232660293
Plastic Product & Additive Mfr
N.A.I.C.S.: 325211

A. Schulman Plastics, BV (2)
Pedro Colomalaan 25, Industriepark, 2880, Bornem, Belgium (100%)
Tel.: (32) 38904211
Mfr & Supplier of Chemical Compounds, Masterbatches & Distribution Products
N.A.I.C.S.: 325180

A. Schulman Plastik Sanayi Ve Tic A.S. (2)
Fsm Mah Poligon Cad Buyaka 2 Sitesi Kule 3 No 61, Istanbul, 34771, Turkiye
Tel.: (90) 2164569050
Web Site: http://aschulman.com
Sales Range: $25-49.9 Million
Emp.: 8
Plastic Resins & Compounds Mfr
N.A.I.C.S.: 325211

A. Schulman Saint Germain Laval S.A.S. (2)
1 rue des argiles vertes ZA de Merlange Saint Germain, 77130, Laval, France
Tel.: (33) 160397000
Plastic Resin Mfr
N.A.I.C.S.: 325211
Nathalie Lasseron *(Head-Personnel & Payroll)*

AND PRIVATE COMPANIES

LYONDELLBASELL INDUSTRIES N.V.

A. Schulman Thermoplastic Compounds Limited (2)
1 Kingsland Grange, Woolston, Warrington, WA1 4RA, Cheshire, United Kingdom
Tel.: (44) 1925810608
Web Site: http://www.perrite.com
Sales Range: $125-149.9 Million
Emp.: 100
Plastic Compounds Mfr
N.A.I.C.S.: 325211

A. Schulman Thermoplastic Compounds Sdn. Bhd. (2)
PTD 43022 Jalan Murni 12 Taman Perindustrian Murni, 81400, Senai, Johor, Malaysia
Tel.: (60) 75999189
Web Site: http://www.aschulman.com
Emp.: 150
Plastic Product & Additive Mfr
N.A.I.C.S.: 325211

A. Schulman de Mexico, S.A. de C.V. (100%)
Avenida Cfe 730 Entre Eje 134 Y Eje 136, Zona Industrial Del Potosi, San Luis Potosi, 78395, Mexico
Tel.: (52) 4448700700
Web Site: http://www.aschulman.com.mx
Sales Range: $25-49.9 Million
Emp.: 200
Mfr & Sales of Plastic Compounds, Resins & High-Performance Color Additive Concentrates
N.A.I.C.S.: 325991

Subsidiary (Domestic):

A. Schulman, Inc. - East Chicago (2)
4404 Euclid Ave, East Chicago, IN 46312
Tel.: (219) 392-3375
Web Site: http://www.aschulman.com
Polymer Product Mfr
N.A.I.C.S.: 325211

Plant (Domestic):

A. Schulman, Inc. - Filled & Reinforced Plastics (2)
5001 O'Hara Dr, Evansville, IN 47711
Tel.: (812) 423-5218
Sales Range: $25-49.9 Million
Emp.: 75
Filled & Reinforced Plastics Mfr
N.A.I.C.S.: 325211
John Finnegan (Mgr-Sls)

A. Schulman, Inc. - Liquid Coatings & Dispersions (2)
1301 N Flora St, Plymouth, IN 46563-1344
Tel.: (574) 935-5131
Sales Range: $25-49.9 Million
Emp.: 50
Thermoset Gelcoats, Color Dispersions, Thermoplastic Liquid Color & Purging Compounds Mfr
N.A.I.C.S.: 325991
Karen Ray (Mgr-Ops)

A. Schulman, Inc. - Plastic Colorants (2)
103 Railroad Ave, Stryker, OH 43557-9492
Tel.: (419) 682-3311
Sales Range: $50-74.9 Million
Emp.: 150
Plastics Coloring Compound Mfr
N.A.I.C.S.: 325991

A. Schulman, Inc. - Specialty Plastics, Carpentersville Plant (2)
400-A Maple Ave, Carpentersville, IL 60110-0729
Tel.: (847) 426-3350
Emp.: 50
Specialty Plastic Resins, Dyes & Pigments Mfr
N.A.I.C.S.: 325211

Subsidiary (Non-US):

A. Schulman, S.A.S. (2)
Immeuble Dynasteur 10/12 Rue Andras Beck, Meudon-la-Foret, 92360, Paris, France
Tel.: (33) 141077500
Sales Range: $25-49.9 Million
Emp.: 40
Plastic Compounds & Resins Mfr

N.A.I.C.S.: 325211
Franck Pietrantoni (Pres)

Subsidiary (Domestic):

ASI Investments Holding Co. (2)
3550 W Market St, Fairlawn, OH 44333-2658
Tel.: (330) 666-3751
Sales Range: $25-49.9 Million
Emp.: 90
Plastic Compounds Mfr
N.A.I.C.S.: 325211

Citadel Plastics Holdings, Inc. (2)
1600 Powis Ct, West Chicago, IL 60185
Tel.: (630) 377-1065
Holding Company; Thermoplastic Compounds & Thermoset Resins Mfr
N.A.I.C.S.: 551112

Subsidiary (Domestic):

Bulk Molding Compounds Inc. (3)
12600 Eckel Rd, Perrysburg, OH 43551
Tel.: (888) 665-3262
Web Site: http://www.bulkmolding.com
Custom Compound Purchased Resins Whslr & Distr
N.A.I.C.S.: 325991

Subsidiary (Non-US):

Lyondellbasell Advanced Polyolefins Pty Ltd (2)
Factory 10 19-23 Japaddy Street, Mordialloc, 3195, VIC, Australia
Tel.: (61) 383746400
Web Site: http://www.aschulman.com
Plastic Product & Additive Mfr
N.A.I.C.S.: 325211

Subsidiary (Domestic):

Network Polymers Inc. (2)
1353 Exeter Rd, Akron, OH 44306
Tel.: (330) 773-2700
Plastics Resins
N.A.I.C.S.: 424610

Subsidiary (Non-US):

Wedco (2)
Mijlweg 7, 3295 KG, 's-Gravendeel, Netherlands
Tel.: (31) 786738111
Plastic Material & Resin Mfr
N.A.I.C.S.: 325211
Esmeralda de Vlaam (Mgr-HR)

BMC Dongguan Limited (1)
No 8 Qiaoxin Road, Qiaotou, Dongguan, 523525, Guangdong, China
Tel.: (86) 76983452480
Engineering Consulting Services
N.A.I.C.S.: 541330

BMC Far East Limited (1)
Unit 2 3/F Block A New Trade Plaza 6 On Ping Street, Shatin, Yuen Long, China (Hong Kong)
Tel.: (852) 26378822
Engineering Consulting Services
N.A.I.C.S.: 541330

Basell (Thailand) Holdings B.V. (1)
Delftseplein 27 E, 3013 AA, Rotterdam, Netherlands
Tel.: (31) 102755500
Holding Company
N.A.I.C.S.: 551112

Basell Advanced Polyolefins (Suzhou) Co. Ltd. (1)
36 Fang Da Street, Suzhou Industrial Park, Suzhou, 215024, China
Tel.: (86) 51268952355
Plastics Product Mfr
N.A.I.C.S.: 326199
Shi Kelin (Supvr-Maintenance)

Basell Advanced Polyolefins (Thailand) Company Ltd. (1)
Eastern Seaboard Industrial Estate 64/17 Moo 4, Tambol Plukdaeng Amphur Pluakdeang, Rayong, 21140, Thailand
Tel.: (66) 38951000
Plastics Product Mfr
N.A.I.C.S.: 326199
Anchalee Eiamsam-ang (Mgr-HR)

Basell Arabie Investissements SAS (1)
Chemin Demartemental 54 Raffinerie De Berre, 13130, Berre-l'Etang, France
Tel.: (33) 892977271
Holding Company
N.A.I.C.S.: 551112

Basell Asia Pacific Consulting (Shanghai) Co., Ltd. (1)
Unit 04-06 14/f Zone 2 Jinmao Tower 88 Century Boulevard, Pudong New District, Shanghai, 200121, China
Tel.: (86) 2160819888
Plastic & Chemical Product Mfr
N.A.I.C.S.: 326199

Basell Asia Pacific Ltd. (1)
32/F Dorset House Taikoo Place 979 King's Road, Quarry Bay, China (Hong Kong)
Tel.: (852) 25773855
Web Site: http://www.lyondellbasell.com
Sales Range: $25-49.9 Million
Emp.: 50
Mfr of Polypropylene & Polyethylene
N.A.I.C.S.: 325211

Basell Asia Pacific Ltd. (1)
Central Plaza Office Building 9th Floor Unit 902 17 Le Duan Boulevard, District 1, Ho Chi Minh City, Vietnam
Tel.: (84) 28382355023
Polymers Mfr
N.A.I.C.S.: 325211

Basell Bayreuth Chemie GmbH (1)
Weiherstrasse 40, 95448, Bayreuth, Germany
Tel.: (49) 9218070
Web Site: https://www.lyondellbasell.com
Emp.: 130
Chemical Products Mfr
N.A.I.C.S.: 325998

Basell Benelux B.V. (1)
Chemieweg 3 Industrial Area, 4782 SJ, Moerdijk, Netherlands
Tel.: (31) 168384400
Emp.: 120
Plastic & Chemical Product Mfr
N.A.I.C.S.: 326199

Basell Brasil Ltd. (1)
Av Pres Juscelino Kubitschek 1600 - Conj 41, Campo, Sao Paulo, 04543-000, Brazil
Tel.: (55) 1151848400
Web Site: http://www.basell.com
Mfr of Polypropylene & Polyethylene
N.A.I.C.S.: 325211

Basell Chemie Koln GmbH (1)
Bruhler Strasse 60, 50389, Wesseling, Germany
Tel.: (49) 2236720
Chemical, Petrochemical & Plastic Mfr
N.A.I.C.S.: 325110

Basell Holdings Middle East GmbH (1)
Bruhler Str 60, 50389, Wesseling, Germany
Tel.: (49) 2236722801
Chemical, Petrochemical & Plastic Mfr
N.A.I.C.S.: 325110

Basell International Trading FZE (1)
Building 2W Office No 206, PO Box 293611, Dubai Airport Free Zone, Dubai, United Arab Emirates
Tel.: (971) 42045970
Chemical, Petrochemical & Plastic Mfr
N.A.I.C.S.: 325110
Lakshman Krishnan Iyer (Bus Mgr & Mgr-JV Off-take)

Basell Italia S.r.l (1)
Piazza Indro Montanelli 20, 20099, Sesto San Giovanni, Italy
Tel.: (39) 02243421
Chemical, Petrochemical & Plastic Mfr
N.A.I.C.S.: 325110

Basell Poliolefinas Comercial Espagnola S.L. (1)
Av Diagonal 615 4th floor, 08028, Barcelona, Spain
Tel.: (34) 933652000
Web Site: http://www.lyondellbasell.com
Chemical, Petrochemical & Plastic Mfr
N.A.I.C.S.: 325110

Basell Poliolefinas Ltda. (1)
Av Julio de Paula Claro 687, Pindamonhangaba, 12441-400, Sao Paulo, Brazil
Tel.: (55) 1236046060
Web Site: https://www.lyondellbasell.com
Chemical, Petrochemical & Plastic Mfr
N.A.I.C.S.: 325211

Basell Poliolefine Italia S.r.l. (1)
Sito di Ferrara Piazzale G Donegani 12, 44122, Ferrara, Italy
Tel.: (39) 0532467111
Web Site: https://www.lyondellbasell.com
Emp.: 800
Chemical, Petrochemical & Plastic Mfr
N.A.I.C.S.: 325110

Basell Polyolefin Istanbul Ticaret Limited Sirketi (1)
Barbaros Mahallesi Kardelen Sokak Palladium Tower No 2 Kat 4 Daire 15, Atasehir, 34752, Istanbul, Turkiye
Tel.: (90) 2166556800
Chemical, Petrochemical & Plastic Mfr
N.A.I.C.S.: 325110
326199 Tamakan (Gen Mgr)

Basell Polyolefine GmbH (1)
Berghauser Weg 50, 85126, Munchsmunster, Germany
Tel.: (49) 840276329
Web Site: https://www.lyondellbasell.com
Emp.: 220
Chemical, Petrochemical & Plastic Mfr
N.A.I.C.S.: 325110

Basell Polyolefins Company BVBA (1)
Woluwe Garden, Woluwedal 24, Zaventem, 1932, Belgium
Tel.: (32) 27158000
Web Site: http://www.lyondellbasell.com
Polypropylene & Polyethylene Products Mfr
N.A.I.C.S.: 325211

Basell Polyolefins India Private Limited (1)
101-104 1st Floor Godrej Two Pirojshanagar Eastern Express Highway, Vikhroli-East, Mumbai, 400079, India
Tel.: (91) 2269161111
Chemical, Petrochemical & Plastic Mfr
N.A.I.C.S.: 325110

Basell Polyolefins Korea Ltd. (1)
Chong-Kun-Dang Bldg 906 Choongjeong-Ro 8, Seodaemun-gu, Seoul, 03742, Korea (South)
Tel.: (82) 221250300
Chemical, Petrochemical & Plastic Mfr
N.A.I.C.S.: 325110

Basell Polyolefins UK Limited (1)
Bramley Road Mount Farm, Bletchley, Milton Keynes, MK1 1LZ, Buckinghamshire, United Kingdom
Tel.: (44) 1908360000
Web Site: http://www.lyondellbasell.com
Chemical, Petrochemical & Plastic Mfr
N.A.I.C.S.: 325110

Basell Sales & Marketing Company B.V. (1)
Delftseplein 27E, 3013 AA, Rotterdam, Netherlands
Tel.: (31) 102755500
Chemical & Petrochemical Product Distr
N.A.I.C.S.: 424690

Bulk Molding Compounds do Brazil Ltda. (1)
Rua Meridian 55, Rio Claro, 13505-610, SP, Brazil
Tel.: (55) 1935261207
Polymers Mfr
N.A.I.C.S.: 325211

Channelview Complex Equistar Chemicals, LP (1)
8280 Sheldon Rd, Channelview, TX 77530
Tel.: (281) 862-4000
Emp.: 1,900
Petrochemical Mfr
N.A.I.C.S.: 325110

Compagnie de Distribution des Hydrocarbures SAS (1)
Chemin Departemental 54 BP 14, Berre-l'Etang, 13131, France
Tel.: (33) 442744274

LYONDELLBASELL INDUSTRIES N.V.

LyondellBasell Industries N.V.—(Continued)
Chemical, Petrochemical & Plastic Mfr
N.A.I.C.S.: 325110

Complejo Industrial Taqsa A.I.E. (1)
Carretera Valencia tarragona Kilometro 1155, Reus, 43206, Spain
Tel.: (34) 977389225
Architectural Engineering Services
N.A.I.C.S.: 541310

EPS Ethylen-Pipeline-Sud GmbH & Co. KG (1)
Lise-Meitner-Str 1, 85716, Unterschleissheim, Germany
Tel.: (49) 8923239170
Web Site: https://www.eps-pipeline.de
Natural Gas Distr
N.A.I.C.S.: 486210

Equistar Chemicals LP (1)
11530 Northlake Dr, Cincinnati, OH 45249
Tel.: (513) 530-4000
Polymers Mfr
N.A.I.C.S.: 325211

Equistar GP, LLC (1)
1221 McKinney St Ste 700, Houston, TX 77010
Tel.: (713) 309-4560
Chemical, Petrochemical & Plastic Mfr
N.A.I.C.S.: 325110

HMC Polymers Company Limited (1)
20/F Sathorn City Tower 175 South Sathorn Road, Thungmahamek Sathorn, Bangkok, 10120, Thailand
Tel.: (66) 26143700
Web Site: https://www.hmcpolymers.com
Polypropylene Product Mfr
N.A.I.C.S.: 325211

Houston Refining LP (1)
12000 Lawndale, Houston, TX 77017
Tel.: (713) 321-4111
Web Site: http://www.lyondellbasell.com
Oil Refining Services
N.A.I.C.S.: 324110

ICO Europe B.V. (1)
Mijlweg 7, 3295 ZH, 's-Gravendeel, Netherlands
Tel.: (31) 786738111
Web Site: http://www.icopolymers.com
Sales Range: $25-49.9 Million
Emp.: 80
Plastic Powders Mfr
N.A.I.C.S.: 326199

Subsidiary (Non-US):

A. Schulman Gainsborough Ltd (2)
Sandars Road Heapham Road Ind Est, Gainsborough, DN21 1RZ, Lincolnshire, United Kingdom
Tel.: (44) 1427676767
Sales Range: $25-49.9 Million
Emp.: 70
Plastic Resins & Compounds Mfr
N.A.I.C.S.: 325220
Dereck Blister *(Pres-Europe & Asia Pacific)*

Industriepark Munchsmunster GmbH & Co. KG (1)
Berghauser Weg 50, 85126, Munchsmunster, Germany
Tel.: (49) 8402760
Chemical, Petrochemical & Plastic Mfr
N.A.I.C.S.: 325110

Industriepark Munchsmunster Verwaltungsgesellschaft mbH (1)
Berghauser Weg 50, 85126, Munchsmunster, Germany
Tel.: (49) 211650410
Chemical, Petrochemical & Plastic Mfr
N.A.I.C.S.: 325110

Infraserv GmbH & Co. Hochst KG (1)
Industriepark Hochst, 65926, Frankfurt am Main, Germany
Tel.: (49) 693050
Web Site: https://www.infraserv.com
Environmental & Waste Management Services
N.A.I.C.S.: 562998
Joachim Kreysing *(Mng Dir)*

LYB International Finance II B.V. (1)
Delftseplein 27 E, 3013 AA, Rotterdam, Netherlands
Tel.: (31) 102755500
Petrochemical Mfr
N.A.I.C.S.: 325110

Lyondell Chemical Company (1)
4025 Midway Dr, Carrollton, TX 75007
Tel.: (214) 775-2995
Web Site: http://www.lyondell.com
Sales Range: $800-899.9 Million
Emp.: 7,340
Chemical & Polymer Mfr & Refiner
N.A.I.C.S.: 325180
Bhavesh V. Patel *(Chm-Mgmt Bd & CEO)*

Subsidiary (Domestic):

Equistar Chemicals, LP (2)
1221 McKinney St Ste 700, Houston, TX 77010
Tel.: (713) 652-7200
Sales Range: $10-24.9 Million
Polyethylene & Special Polymers & Chemicals Mfr
N.A.I.C.S.: 325998

Subsidiary (Non-US):

Lyondell Asia Pacific, Ltd. (2)
12/F Caroline Centre Lee Gardens, Two 28 Yun Ping Rd, Causeway Bay, China (Hong Kong)
Tel.: (852) 28822668
Web Site: http://www.lyondellbasell.com
Chemicals Mfr
N.A.I.C.S.: 325998

Lyondell Brussels (2)
Silversquare Business Center 35 Square de Meeus, B1200, Brussels, Belgium
Tel.: (32) 27742511
Chemicals Mfr
N.A.I.C.S.: 325998

Lyondell Chemical Europe, Inc. (2)
Delftseplein 27E, 3013 AA, Rotterdam, Netherlands
Tel.: (31) 0102755500
Web Site: http://www.lyondellbasell.com
Sales Range: $25-49.9 Million
Emp.: 250
Chemicals Mfr
N.A.I.C.S.: 325199

Lyondell Chemical Italia srl (2)
6 Largo Richini, Milan, 20122, Italy
Tel.: (39) 0272582151
Chemicals Mfr
N.A.I.C.S.: 325199

Lyondell Chemie Nederland B.V. (2)
Theemsweg 14 Portnumber 5103 Botlek, 3197 KM, Rotterdam, Netherlands
Tel.: (31) 181294000
Web Site: http://www.lyondellbafell.com
Sales Range: $50-74.9 Million
Emp.: 220
Chemicals Mfr
N.A.I.C.S.: 325199

Lyondell Chimie France SNC (2)
Les Marches De L oise, 100 Rue Louis Blanc, 60160, Montataire, France
Tel.: (33) 344249200
Technical Services
N.A.I.C.S.: 561499

Lyondell Chimie France, SAS (2)
Route du Quai Mineralier, ZIP de Fos-Caban, 13270, Fos-sur-Mer, France
Tel.: (33) 442475100
Web Site: http://www.lyondellbasell.com
Chemicals Mfr
N.A.I.C.S.: 325998

Subsidiary (Domestic):

LyondellBasell Advanced Polyolefins USA, Inc. (2)
100 S Mitchell Rd, Mansfield, TX 76063
Tel.: (817) 792-1400
Web Site: http://www.apo.lyondellbasell.com
Sales Range: $25-49.9 Million
Emp.: 300
Custom-Engineered Polyolefin Materials
N.A.I.C.S.: 325211

LyondellBasell Industries (2)
LyondellBasell Tower 1221 McKinney St Ste 300, Houston, TX 77010
Tel.: (713) 309-7200
Web Site: http://www.lyondellbasell.com
Emp.: 1,000
Holding Company: Chemicals & Fuels
N.A.I.C.S.: 551112

Subsidiary (Non-US):

Tronox Pigmentos do Brasil S.A. (2)
Highway BA -099 Coco road, Camacari, 42829- 710, Bahia, Brazil
Tel.: (55) 7136349304
Web Site: https://www.tronox-ri.com.br
Rev.: $102,861,941
Assets: $173,858,525
Liabilities: $51,873,222
Net Worth: $121,985,303
Earnings: $6,433,921
Emp.: 7,000
Fiscal Year-end: 12/31/2023
Chemical Products Mfr
N.A.I.C.S.: 325998
Paulo Roberto Dantas Oliveira *(Member-Exec Bd)*

Lyondell Greater China, Ltd. (1)
7F-6 No 101 Fu Hsing N Road, Taipei, 105, Taiwan
Tel.: (886) 277079010
Web Site: http://www.lyondell.com
Emp.: 12
Chemical, Petrochemical & Plastic Mfr
N.A.I.C.S.: 325110

Lyondell Japan, Inc. (1)
Yurakucho ITOCiA 12/F 2-7-1 Yurakucho, Chiyoda-ku, Tokyo, 100-0006, Japan
Tel.: (81) 368604790
Chemical, Petrochemical & Plastic Mfr
N.A.I.C.S.: 325110

Lyondell Quimica do Brasil Ltda. (1)
Av Roque Petroni Junior 999-12 andar, Sao Paulo, 04707-910, Brazil
Tel.: (55) 1151848400
Chemical & Plastic Product Distr
N.A.I.C.S.: 424690

Lyondell Refining Company LLC (1)
1221 McKinney St Ste 1600, Houston, TX 77010
Tel.: (713) 309-4980
Oil Refinery Mfr
N.A.I.C.S.: 324110

Lyondell South Asia Pte Ltd (1)
78 Shenton Way 25-01, Singapore, 079120, Singapore
Tel.: (65) 68802345
Chemical, Petrochemical & Plastic Mfr
N.A.I.C.S.: 325110

LyondellBasell Acetyls, LLC (1)
1515 Miller Cut-Off Rd, La Porte, TX 77571
Tel.: (713) 209-7000
Web Site: https://www.lyondellbasell.com
Chemical, Petrochemical & Plastic Mfr
N.A.I.C.S.: 325110

LyondellBasell Brasil Ltda. (1)
Av Pres Juscelino Kubitschek 1600 - Conj 41, 1600-Conj 41, Sao Paulo, 04543-000, Brazil
Tel.: (55) 1151848400
Petrochemical Mfr
N.A.I.C.S.: 325110
Sinclair Fittipaldi *(Dir-Sls)*

LyondellBasell Egypt LLC (1)
203 Airport Ave No 6 Nozha, Heliopolis, Cairo, Egypt
Tel.: (20) 222671047
Polyolefin Product Mfr
N.A.I.C.S.: 325211
Khaled Dyab *(Sls Mgr)*

Matagorda Complex Equistar Chemicals, LP (1)
17042 State Hwy 60 S, Bay City, TX 77414
Tel.: (979) 245-1225
Polymers Mfr
N.A.I.C.S.: 325211

Pipeline Operations Equistar Chemicals, LP (1)
16055 Space Ctr Blvd Ste 350, Houston, TX 77062
Gas Pipeline Operation Services
N.A.I.C.S.: 237120

INTERNATIONAL PUBLIC

PolyMirae Co., Ltd. (1)
17F Three IFC Gukjegeumyung-ro 10, Yeongdeungpo-gu, Seoul, 07326, Korea (South)
Tel.: (82) 221678914
Web Site: https://www.polymirae.com
Polypropylene Product Mfr
N.A.I.C.S.: 325211
Mitchell Ian Killeen *(Pres)*

PolyPacific Polymers Sdn. Bhd. (1)
Lot 8936 Jalan Telok Gong Darul Ehsan, Pandamaran, 42000, Port Klang, Selangor, Malaysia
Tel.: (60) 331342850
Polypropylene Product Mfr
N.A.I.C.S.: 325211
Malcolm Fisher *(Gen Mgr)*

QCP B.V. (1)
Polymeerstraat 1, 6161 RE, Geleen, Netherlands (50%)
Tel.: (31) 886000500
Web Site: http://www.qcpolymers.com
Polyethylene & Polypropylene Compound Mfr
N.A.I.C.S.: 325211
Raf Bemelmans *(Co-Founder)*

RIGK GmbH Gesellschaft zur Ruckfuhrung industrieller & gewerblicher Kunstoffverpackungen mbH (1)
Friedrichstrasse 6, 65185, Wiesbaden, Germany
Tel.: (49) 6113086000
Web Site: http://www.rigk.de
Waste Management Services
N.A.I.C.S.: 562998
Markus Dambeck *(Mng Dir & Gen Mgr)*

TRV Thermische Ruckstandsverwertung GmbH & Co. KG (1)
Rodenkirchener Strasse, 50389, Wesseling, Germany
Tel.: (49) 2236943240
Web Site: https://www.trv-wesseling.de
Industrial Waste Collection & Recycling Services
N.A.I.C.S.: 562111

TRV Thermische Ruckstandsverwertung Verwaltungs-GmbH (1)
Rodenkirchener Str, 50389, Wesseling, Germany
Tel.: (49) 2236943240
Industrial Waste Collection & Recycling Services
N.A.I.C.S.: 562111

YNCORIS GmbH & Co. KG (1)
Chemical Park Knapsack Industriestrasse 300, 50354, Hurth, Germany
Tel.: (49) 2233481212
Web Site: https://www.yncoris.com
Environmental Services
N.A.I.C.S.: 541620
Pierre Kramer *(Head-Site Dev)*

tetra-DUR Kunststoff-Produktion GmbH (1)
Brookdamm 3, 21217, Seevetal, Germany
Tel.: (49) 407698320
Web Site: http://www.tetra-dur.de
Polyester Resin Mfr
N.A.I.C.S.: 325211
Peter Kirchner *(Dir-Sls & Application)*

LYONS CORPORATE MARKET LIMITED

33A Jawahar Lal Nehru Road, Chatterjee International Centre 6th Floor Suit No A- 5, Kolkata, 700071, West Bengal, India
Tel.: (91) 3340123123
Web Site: https://lyonscorporate.co.in
Year Founded: 1994
22036—(CSE)
Emp.: 9
Non Banking Financial Services
N.A.I.C.S.: 523999
ram Karan Gupta *(Compliance Officer)*

LYPPARD AUSTRALIA LIMITED

14-16 Fiveways Blvd, Keysborough, 3173, VIC, Australia
Tel.: (61) 387690500
Web Site: http://www.lyppard.com.au
Year Founded: 1988
Sales Range: $250-299.9 Million
Emp.: 100
Veterinary Distr
N.A.I.C.S.: 541940
Brian Oakley *(Mng Dir)*

LYPSA GEMS & JEWELLERY LIMITED
Wing A 2nd Block 202-302 Orchid Complex Opp, HDFC Bank Chhapi Pirojpura Road Vadgam Banaskantha, Mumbai, 385210, India
Tel.: (91) 2223679792
Web Site: https://www.lypsa.in
Year Founded: 1995
534532—(BOM)
Rev.: $1,148,088
Assets: $13,806,688
Liabilities: $9,474,260
Net Worth: $4,332,428
Earnings: ($23,696)
Fiscal Year-end: 03/31/21
Jewelry Mfr
N.A.I.C.S.: 339910
Dipankumar Babulal Patwa *(Chm & Co-Mng Dir)*

LYRECO S.A.S.
Rue de 19 Mars 1962, 59770, Marly, France
Tel.: (33) 327236400
Web Site: http://www.group.lyreco.com
Sales Range: $1-4.9 Billion
Emp.: 10,000
Office Supplie & Furniture Distr
N.A.I.C.S.: 459410
Georges Gaspard *(Chm)*

Subsidiaries:

LYRECO Australia (1)
Building A1 2 Unwin Street, Rosehill, Sydney, 2142, NSW, Australia
Tel.: (61) 288465001
Web Site: http://www.lyreco.com
Sales Range: $125-149.9 Million
Emp.: 460
Office Supplies & Equipment
N.A.I.C.S.: 459410
Michael Milwirj *(Mng Dir)*

LYRECO Benelux SA (1)
Berchemstadionstraat 72, 2600, Berchem, Belgium
Tel.: (32) 4 361 99 23
Emp.: 729
Office Supplies Distr
N.A.I.C.S.: 424120

Lyreco (Canada) Limited (1)
7303 Warden Avenue Suite 200, Markham, L3R 5Y6, ON, Canada
Tel.: (877) 597-3261
Emp.: 268
Office Supplies Distr
N.A.I.C.S.: 424120

Lyreco (Hong Kong) Co. Ltd. (1)
6/F Yuen Fat Wharf & Godown, No 1 Fat Tseung Street, Kowloon, NT, China (Hong Kong)
Tel.: (852) 27542821
Web Site: http://www.lyreco.com.hk
Sales Range: $50-74.9 Million
Emp.: 100
Stationery & Office Supplies Whslr
N.A.I.C.S.: 424120

Lyreco (Japan) Co. Ltd. (1)
Oak Minami-Azabu Bldg-11th Fl, 3-19-23 Minami-Azabu Minato-KU, Tokyo, 106-0047, Japan
Tel.: (81) 354470455
Web Site: http://www.lyreco.jp
Sales Range: $75-99.9 Million
Emp.: 115
Stationery & Office Supplies Whslr
N.A.I.C.S.: 424120

Lyreco (Korea) Co., Ltd. (1)
3rd Floor Nobel Building 16 Teheran-ro 78-gil, Gangnam-gu, Seoul, 135840, Korea (South)
Tel.: (82) 15883734
Web Site: http://www.lyreco.co.kr
Sales Range: $50-74.9 Million
Emp.: 100
Stationery & Office Supplies Whslr
N.A.I.C.S.: 424120

Lyreco (Singapore) Pte Ltd. (1)
391B Orchard Road No 23-01 Ngee Ann City Tower B, Singapore, 238874, Singapore
Tel.: (65) 62357887
Web Site: http://www.lyreco.com.sg
Sales Range: $50-74.9 Million
Emp.: 70
Stationery & Office Supplies Whslr
N.A.I.C.S.: 424120
Gregory Lienare *(Mng Dir-Asian Pacific)*

Lyreco CE/SE (1)
Na Strzi 65/1702, 140 00, Prague, Czech Republic
Tel.: (420) 800 100 914
Emp.: 51
Office Supplies Distr
N.A.I.C.S.: 424120
Juraj Nemjo *(Mng Dir)*

Lyreco Danmark A/S (1)
Lykkegardsvej 10, Roskilde, 4000, Denmark
Tel.: (45) 70100500
Web Site: http://www.lyreco.dk
Sales Range: $150-199.9 Million
Emp.: 339
Office Equipment Whslr
N.A.I.C.S.: 423420
Henrik Brandt *(Mng Dir)*

Lyreco Deutschland GmbH (1)
Rohrer Weg 10, 71032, Boblingen, Germany
Tel.: (49) 70312840
Web Site: http://www.lyreco.de
Sales Range: $200-249.9 Million
Emp.: 765
Office Furniture Mfr
N.A.I.C.S.: 337214

Lyreco Espana, S.A. (1)
Carretera de Hospitalet 147-149 Edif Paris D, Cornella de Llobregat, 08940, Barcelona, Spain
Tel.: (34) 902100016
Web Site: http://www.lyreco.com
Stationery & Office Supply Distr
N.A.I.C.S.: 424120

Lyreco Finland Oy (1)
Vaino Tannerin tie 3, 01510, Vantaa, Finland
Tel.: (358) 10 500 1500
Web Site: http://www.lyreco.com
Emp.: 140
Office Supplies Distr
N.A.I.C.S.: 424120
Harry Jiliniu *(Gen Mgr)*

Lyreco Ireland Ltd (1)
Unit 41 Park West Industrial Park Nangor Road, Dublin, Ireland
Tel.: (353) 1850 882276
Web Site: http://www.ireland-corp.lyreco.com
Emp.: 73
Office Supplies Distr
N.A.I.C.S.: 424120

Lyreco Italia Spa (1)
Via Papa Giovanni Paolo, 20040, Cambiago, Italy
Tel.: (39) 02959441
Web Site: http://www.lyreco.it
Sales Range: $150-199.9 Million
Emp.: 455
Stationery & Office Supplies Whslr
N.A.I.C.S.: 424120

Lyreco Luxembourgh SA (1)
rue Jean Fischbach 2, rue Jean Fischb, Leudelange, Luxembourg
Tel.: (352) 34 63 65
Office Supplies Distr
N.A.I.C.S.: 424120

Lyreco Nederland B.V (1)
Europalaan 460 gebouw 400 7 et, 3526 KS, Utrecht, Netherlands
Tel.: (31) 88 6032001
Office Supplies Distr
N.A.I.C.S.: 424120

Lyreco Norge AS (1)
Heiaveien 6, 1900, Oslo, Fetsund, Norway
Tel.: (47) 21030300
Web Site: http://www.lyreco.com
Sales Range: $50-74.9 Million
Emp.: 110
Office Supplier of Paper, Office Products, IT, Catering, Safety & Cleaning Products
N.A.I.C.S.: 424120

Lyreco Office Supplies (M) Sdn. Bhd. (1)
No 68 Jalan i-Park SAC 8 Taman Perindustrian i-Park SAC, 81400, Senai, Malaysia
Tel.: (60) 75975555
Web Site: http://www.lyreco.com
Sales Range: $50-74.9 Million
Emp.: 40
Stationery & Office Supplies Whslr
N.A.I.C.S.: 424120
Xavier Etienne *(Mng Dir)*

Lyreco Polska SA (1)
ul Sokolowska 33, Sokolow, 05-806, Komorow, Poland
Tel.: (48) 801300002
Web Site: http://www.lyreco.com.pl
Sales Range: $250-299.9 Million
Emp.: 695
Stationery & Office Supplies Whslr
N.A.I.C.S.: 424120

Lyreco Portugal, S.A. (1)
Avenida da Liberdade 110 2 piso escritorio n 220, 1269-046, Lisbon, Portugal
Tel.: (351) 808 206 070
Web Site: http://www.portugal-corp.lyreco.com
Emp.: 15
Office Supplies Distr
N.A.I.C.S.: 424120

Lyreco Sverige AB (1)
Sjoakravagen 27, PO Box 501, Bankeryd, 56428, Jonkoping, Sweden (100%)
Tel.: (46) 36198900
Web Site: http://www.lyreco.se
Sales Range: $75-99.9 Million
Emp.: 212
Stationery & Office Supplies Whslr
N.A.I.C.S.: 424120

Lyreco Switzerland AG (1)
Riedstrasse 4, 8953, Dietikon, Switzerland
Tel.: (41) 447444111
Web Site: http://www.lyreco.com
Sales Range: $150-199.9 Million
Emp.: 300
Stationery & Office Supply Whslr
N.A.I.C.S.: 424120
Thomas Illi *(Mng Dir)*

Lyreco UK Ltd. (1)
Deer Park Court, Donnington Wood, Telford, TF2 7NB, United Kingdom
Tel.: (44) 8457676999
Web Site: http://www.lyreco.co.uk
Sales Range: $1-4.9 Billion
Emp.: 3,000
Office Supplies & Stationery Distr
N.A.I.C.S.: 459410
Dave Longsley *(Mng Dir)*

LYSAGHT GALVANIZED STEEL BERHAD
No 11 Jalan Majistret U1/26 Seksyen U1 Hicom-Glenmarie Industrial Park, 40150, Shah Alam, Selangor Darul Ehsan, Malaysia
Tel.: (60) 378803750
Web Site: https://www.lysaghtgalvanized.com
LYSAGHT—(KLS)
Rev.: $18,355,018
Assets: $40,776,949
Liabilities: $1,694,967
Net Worth: $39,081,982
Earnings: $2,448,506
Emp.: 335
Fiscal Year-end: 12/31/23
Steel Mfrs
N.A.I.C.S.: 331110
Tia Bon Chua *(CEO)*

Subsidiaries:

Lysaght Marketing (S) Pte. Ltd. (1)
50 Tuas Ave 11 02-28 Tuas Lot, Singapore, 639107, Singapore
Tel.: (65) 68617122
Steel Pipe Whslr
N.A.I.C.S.: 423510

Lysaght Marketing Sdn. Bhd. (1)
No 11 Jalan Majistret U1/26 Seksyen U1, PO Box 7818, Hicom-Glenmarie Ind Park, 40150, Shah Alam, Selangor, Malaysia
Tel.: (60) 37 880 3750
Web Site: https://lysaghtmarketing.com
Marketing Agent Services
N.A.I.C.S.: 541613

LYSOGENE
18-20 rue Jacques Dulud18-20 rue Jacques Dulud, 92 200, Neuilly-sur-Seine, France
Tel.: (33) 1 41 43 03 90 FR
Web Site: http://www.lysogene.com
Year Founded: 2009
Biopharmaceutical Research & Development Services
N.A.I.C.S.: 541714
Karen Aiach *(Founder, Chm & CEO)*

LYTUS TECHNOLOGIES HOLDINGS PTV. LTD.
Tel.: (91) 2844942810 VG
Web Site: https://www.lytuscorp.com
Year Founded: 2020
LYT—(NASDAQ)
Rev.: $23,003,342
Assets: $31,563,423
Liabilities: $15,584,298
Net Worth: $15,979,125
Earnings: $653,174
Emp.: 3
Fiscal Year-end: 03/31/24
Holding Company
N.A.I.C.S.: 551112
Dharmesh Pandya *(CEO)*

M & A EQUITY HOLDINGS BERHAD
No 47-11 The Boulevard Mid Valley City, Lingkaran Syed Putra, 57000, Kuala Lumpur, Selangor Darul Ehsan, Malaysia
Tel.: (60) 322842911
Web Site: https://www.syf.com.my
Year Founded: 1963
SYF—(KLS)
Rev.: $58,802,869
Assets: $96,081,634
Liabilities: $37,539,453
Net Worth: $58,542,180
Earnings: ($10,718,402)
Emp.: 96
Fiscal Year-end: 07/31/19
Rubber Wood Furniture Mfr
N.A.I.C.S.: 321911
Hong Leong Chee *(Exec Dir)*

Subsidiaries:

M & A Securities Sdn. Bhd. (1)
5th and 6th Floor and Unit 8A M and A Building 52A, Jalan Sultan Idris Shah, 30000, Ipoh, Perak Darul Ridzuan, Malaysia
Tel.: (60) 52419800
Web Site: https://www.mnaonline.com.my
Sales Range: $50-74.9 Million
Emp.: 60
Stock Broking Services
N.A.I.C.S.: 523150
Thong Kok Yoon *(Exec Dir)*

M & C SERVICES PRIVATE LIMITED
112 Robinson Road 05-01, Singapore, 068902, Singapore
Tel.: (65) 6227 6660

M & C SERVICES PRIVATE LIMITED

M & C Services Private Limited—(Continued)
Web Site:
http://www.mncsingapore.com
Sales Range: $10-24.9 Million
Emp.: 60
Share Registration & Corporate Secretarial Services
N.A.I.C.S.: 561499
Grace Chan *(Dir-Secretarial Svcs)*

M & N CONSTRUCTION LTD.
4511 Victoria Ave, PO Box 249, Coronation, T0C 1C0, AB, Canada
Tel.: (403) 578-2016
Web Site:
http://www.mnconstruction.com
Rev.: $22,269,603
Emp.: 50
Pipeline Construction Services
N.A.I.C.S.: 237120
Archie Merchant *(Pres)*

M AND J WOODCRAFTS LTD.
1 - 7338 Progress Way, Delta, V4G 1L4, BC, Canada
Tel.: (604) 946-4767
Web Site:
https://www.mjwoodcrafts.com
Year Founded: 1980
Cabinetry Mfr
N.A.I.C.S.: 337110

M C SPINNERS PVT LTD
Gowtham Centre Avinashi Rd, Coimbatore, 641018, Tamil Nadu, India
Tel.: (91) 4285223530
Year Founded: 2011
Sales Range: $25-49.9 Million
Emp.: 220
Yarn Mfr
N.A.I.C.S.: 313110

M DEVELOPMENT LTD.
4 Shenton Way No 17-01 SGX Centre 2, Singapore, 068807, Singapore
Tel.: (65) 65350550 **SG**
Year Founded: 2002
Rev.: $1,686,094
Assets: $2,408,705
Liabilities: $953,106
Net Worth: $1,455,599
Earnings: $1,103,557
Fiscal Year-end: 12/31/19
Accommodation & Lodging Services
N.A.I.C.S.: 721199
Claudia Kwee Yee Teo *(Sec)*

M K LAND HOLDINGS BERHAD
No 19 Jalan PJU 8/5H Perdana Business Center Bandar Damansara Perdana, 47820, Petaling Jaya, Selangor Darul Ehsan, Malaysia
Tel.: (60) 377268866
Web Site:
https://www.mkland.com.my
Year Founded: 1984
MKLAND—(KLS)
Rev.: $48,695,625
Assets: $409,266,000
Liabilities: $104,964,503
Net Worth: $304,301,498
Earnings: $3,991,928
Emp.: 478
Fiscal Year-end: 06/30/22
Property Development & Management Services
N.A.I.C.S.: 531312
Kamarulzaman Abu Bakar *(Deputy COO)*

Subsidiaries:

Bukit Merah Resort Sdn. Bhd. (1)
Jalan Bukit Merah, 34400, Kampong Gunong Semanggol, Perak Darul Ridzuan, Malaysia
Tel.: (60) 58908888
Web Site:
https://www.bukitmerahresort.com.my
Resort Operating Services
N.A.I.C.S.: 721110

Medan Prestasi Sdn. Bhd. (1)
No 19 Jalan Pju 8/5H Perdana Business Center, Bandar Damansara Perdana, 47820, Petaling Jaya, Selangor, Malaysia
Tel.: (60) 377254510
Housing Project Development Services
N.A.I.C.S.: 236115

Paramoden Sdn. Bhd. (1)
1 Cyberia SmartHomes Jalan Multimedia Cyberjaya, 63000, Sepang, Selangor, Malaysia
Tel.: (60) 383180290
Residential Property Development Services
N.A.I.C.S.: 236116

Pujaan Pasifik Sdn. Bhd. (1)
Lot 78 Jalan Kuala Muda, Langkawi, 07100, Kampung Padang Masirat, Kedah Darul Aman, Malaysia
Tel.: (60) 49558181
Web Site:
https://www.ombakvillalangkawi.com
Sales Range: $25-49.9 Million
Emp.: 184
Resort Management Services
N.A.I.C.S.: 721110

Saujana Triangle Sdn. Bhd. (1)
No 19 Jalan PJU 8/5H Persana Business Centre Bandar Damansara Perdana, Petaling Jaya, 47820, Selangor Darul Ehsan, Malaysia (100%)
Tel.: (60) 377278870
Web Site: http://www.mkland.com.my
Property Development Services
N.A.I.C.S.: 531390

M LAKHAMSI INDUSTRIES LIMITED
505 Churchgate Chambers 5 New Marine Lines, Mumbai, 400 020, India
Tel.: (91) 2222620722 **In**
Web Site: https://m.lakhamsi.com
512153—(BOM)
Rev.: $12,285
Assets: $81,185
Liabilities: $93,782
Net Worth: ($12,597)
Earnings: $550
Fiscal Year-end: 03/31/21
Financial Investment Services
N.A.I.C.S.: 523999
Shreyas Ramniklal Mehta *(Chm & Mng Dir)*

M N C WIRELESS BHD
100-3 011 Block J 129 Offices Jaya One No 72A, Jalan Profesor Diraja Ungku Aziz, 46200, Petaling Jaya, Selangor, Malaysia
Tel.: (60) 74911880
Web Site: https://www.mnc.com.my
Year Founded: 2002
0103—(KLS)
Rev.: $2,631,874
Assets: $18,583,679
Liabilities: $2,056,367
Net Worth: $16,527,312
Earnings: ($1,406,276)
Fiscal Year-end: 04/30/23
Mobile Game Development Services
N.A.I.C.S.: 713120
Wong Kok Seong *(Chm)*

M VEST WATER AS
Espehaugen 54, Blomsterdalen, 5258, Bergen, Norway
Tel.: (47) 55989999 **NO**
Web Site:
https://www.mvestwater.com
Year Founded: 2017
MVW—(EUR)
Rev.: $1,082,136
Assets: $4,195,155
Liabilities: $1,538,158
Net Worth: $2,656,997
Earnings: ($2,783,744)
Emp.: 13
Fiscal Year-end: 12/31/23
Waste Treatment Services
N.A.I.C.S.: 221310
Atle Mundheim *(CTO)*

M VISION PCL
11/1 Soi Ramkhamhaeng 121 Ramkhamhaeng Rd Huamak, Bangkapi, Bangkok, 10240, Thailand
Tel.: (66) 27351201
Web Site:
http://www.mvisioncorp.com
Year Founded: 2002
MVP—(THA)
Rev.: $9,468,672
Assets: $12,021,541
Liabilities: $6,437,133
Net Worth: $5,584,408
Earnings: ($8,452,085)
Fiscal Year-end: 12/31/23
Advertising Agency Services
N.A.I.C.S.: 541810
Opas Cherdpunt *(Founder & CEO)*

M WINKWORTH PLC
13 Charles II Street, London, SW1Y 4QU, United Kingdom
Tel.: (44) 2073550205 **UK**
Web Site:
https://www.winkworthplc.com
Year Founded: 1835
WINK—(LSE)
Rev.: $8,697,554
Assets: $10,814,240
Liabilities: $3,445,893
Net Worth: $7,368,346
Earnings: $1,679,500
Emp.: 33
Fiscal Year-end: 12/31/20
Real Estate Development Services
N.A.I.C.S.: 533110
Dominic C. M. Agace *(CEO)*

Subsidiaries:

Winkworth Client Services Limited (1)
4th Floor 1 Lumley Street, London, W1K 6TT, United Kingdom
Tel.: (44) 207 870 4878
Web Site: https://www.winkworth.co.uk
Real Estate Services
N.A.I.C.S.: 531390

M&A CAPITAL PARTNERS CO., LTD.
36F Yaesu Central Tower Tokyo Midtown Yaesu 2-2-1 Yaesu, Chuo-ku, Tokyo, 104-0028, Japan
Tel.: (81) 367704300
Web Site: https://www.ma-cp.com
Year Founded: 2005
6080—(TKS)
Rev.: $133,395,360
Assets: $328,087,440
Liabilities: $46,840,800
Net Worth: $281,246,640
Earnings: $31,069,440
Emp.: 313
Fiscal Year-end: 09/30/24
Mergers & Acquisitions Services
N.A.I.C.S.: 561499
Satoru Nakamura *(Founder & Pres)*

Subsidiaries:

RECOF Corporation (1)
Kojimachi Diamond Building 4-1-1 Kojimachi, Chiyoda-ku, Tokyo, 102-0083, Japan
Tel.: (81) 33 221 4943
Web Site: https://www.recof.co.jp
Emp.: 70
Business Support Services
N.A.I.C.S.: 561499
Yoichi Inada *(CEO)*

INTERNATIONAL PUBLIC

M&A RESEARCH INSTITUTE INC.
Marunouchi Trust Tower N Building 17F 1-8-1 Marunouchi, Chiyoda-ku, Tokyo, 100-0005, Japan
Web Site:
https://www.masouken.com
Year Founded: 2018
9552—(TKS)
Rev.: $115,181,040
Assets: $83,513,040
Liabilities: $20,740,800
Net Worth: $62,772,240
Earnings: $40,284,480
Fiscal Year-end: 09/30/24
Investment Management Service
N.A.I.C.S.: 523999
Shunsaku Sagami *(CEO)*

M&B ZEITSCHRIFTEN-PRODUKTIONS GMBH
Toepsen Tasse 8, Vienna, 111140, Austria
Tel.: (43) 191751180 **AT**
Web Site: http://www.austria-today.at
Sales Range: $10-24.9 Million
Emp.: 7
Business Information Publisher
N.A.I.C.S.: 513140
Thomas Brey *(Mng Dir)*

M&C S.P.A.
Via Ciovassino 1/A, 20121, Milan, Italy
Tel.: (39) 02 727371 **IT**
Web Site: http://www.mecinv.com
Year Founded: 2005
Rev.: $121,950
Assets: $74,791,942
Liabilities: $1,107,181
Net Worth: $73,684,761
Earnings: ($1,238,759)
Emp.: 2
Fiscal Year-end: 12/31/16
Investment Holding Company
N.A.I.C.S.: 551112
Luisa Graziani *(CEO)*

Subsidiaries:

Botto Fila S.p.A. (1)
Via roma 99, Valle Mosso, 13825, Biella, Italy
Tel.: (39) 0157091
Web Site: http://www.bottofila.it
Fabrics Mfr
N.A.I.C.S.: 313210

Treofan Holdings GmbH (1)
Am Prime Parc 17, 65479, Raunheim, Germany (98.75%)
Tel.: (49) 61422003000
Web Site: http://www.treofan.com
Emp.: 1,100
Holding Company; Polypropylene Films Mfr
N.A.I.C.S.: 551112
Walter Bickel *(CEO, CFO & Mng Dir)*

Subsidiary (Domestic):

Treofan Germany GmbH & Co. KG (2)
Bergstrasse, 66539, Neunkirchen, Germany
Tel.: (49) 61422003000
Web Site: http://www.treofan.com
Polypropylene Film Mfr
N.A.I.C.S.: 326113

Plant (Non-US):

Treofan Italy S.p.A. - Battipaglia Plant (2)
Zona Industriale, 84091, Battipaglia, Salerno, Italy
Tel.: (39) 0828615111
Web Site: http://www.treofan.com
Polypropylene Film Mfr
N.A.I.C.S.: 326113

Treofan Italy S.p.A. - Terni Plant (2)
Piazzale Donegani 4, 05100, Terni, Italy
Tel.: (39) 0744 8021
Web Site: http://www.treofan.com

AND PRIVATE COMPANIES

Polypropylene Film Mfr
N.A.I.C.S.: 326113

M&C SAATCHI PLC
36 Golden Square, London, W1F 9EE, United Kingdom
Tel.: (44) 2075434500 UK
Web Site: https://www.mcsaatchi.com
Year Founded: 1995
SAA—(AIM)
Rev.: $557,117,385
Assets: $350,593,815
Liabilities: $304,593,960
Net Worth: $45,999,855
Earnings: $313,170
Emp.: 2,597
Fiscal Year-end: 12/31/22
Advertising Services
N.A.I.C.S.: 541810
David A. Kershaw *(Co-Founder)*

Subsidiaries:

Brands In Space Pty Limited (1)
99 Macquarie St, Sydney, 2000, NSW, Australia
Tel.: (61) 2 9019 6703
Web Site: http://www.brandsinspace.com.au
Shops & Showroom Interior Design Services
N.A.I.C.S.: 541410

Clear Ideas Ltd. (1)
The Poppy Factory Petersham Rd, Richmond, TW10 6UW, London, United Kingdom
Tel.: (44) 2084398280
Web Site: http://www.clear-ideas.com
Sales Range: $25-49.9 Million
Emp.: 70
Brand Consulting Services
N.A.I.C.S.: 541611
Damian Symons *(CEO-Global)*

Branch (US):

Clear M&C Saatchi (2)
88 Pine St 30th Fl, New York, NY 10005
Tel.: (917) 287-9992
Web Site: https://www.clearstrategy.com
Emp.: 20
N.A.I.C.S.: 541810
Adam Garrett *(Mng Dir)*

LIDA (1)
36 Golden Square, London, W1F 9EE, United Kingdom
Tel.: (44) 20 7544 3700
Web Site: http://www.lida.com
Rev.: $19,835,170
Emp.: 75
Advertising Services
N.A.I.C.S.: 541810
Tori Winn *(Exec Dir-Creative)*

Unit (US):

Principle MCD, Inc. (2)
138 W 25th St Fl 5, New York, NY 10001
Tel.: (212) 500-4500
Web Site: http://www.mcdpartnes.com
Sales Range: $1-9.9 Million
Emp.: 40
Professional, Scientific & Technical Services
N.A.I.C.S.: 541990
Ian Magnani *(Sec)*

LIDA Australia Pty. Ltd. (1)
Transport House 99 Macquarie Street, Sydney, 2000, NSW, Australia
Tel.: (61) 290196000
Web Site: http://www.lidaaustralia.com.au
Digital Marketing Services
N.A.I.C.S.: 541613
Brendon Harrington *(Gen Mgr)*

Lean Mean Fighting Machine Ltd. (1)
2nd Floor 17 Ferdinand Street, London, NW1 8EU, United Kingdom
Tel.: (44) 2072676016
Web Site: http://www.leanmeanfightingmachine.com
Sales Range: $10-24.9 Million
Emp.: 40
Advertising Services
N.A.I.C.S.: 541810
Tom Bazeley *(Mng Dir)*

M&C Saatchi (1)
99 MacQuarie St, Sydney, 2000, NSW, Australia
Tel.: (61) 290196000
Web Site: http://www.mcsaatchi.com
Sales Range: $25-49.9 Million
Emp.: 400
Full Service
N.A.I.C.S.: 541810
Tom Dery *(Chm)*

M&C Saatchi (1)
Level 1 129 York Street, Melbourne, 3205, VIC, Australia
Tel.: (61) 396931400
Web Site: http://www.mcsaatchi.com
Sales Range: $25-49.9 Million
Emp.: 30
Full Service
N.A.I.C.S.: 541810
Cam Blackley *(Chief Creative Officer)*

M&C Saatchi (1)
2032 Broadway, Santa Monica, CA 90404
Tel.: (310) 401-6070
Web Site: http://www.mcsaatchi.com
Sales Range: $25-49.9 Million
Emp.: 45
N.A.I.C.S.: 541810
Kate Bristow *(Chief Strategy Officer)*

M&C Saatchi (1)
115 Amoy Street, Singapore, 069935, Singapore
Tel.: (65) 6372 4212
Web Site: http://www.mcsaatchi.com
Full Service
N.A.I.C.S.: 541810
Tanuj Philip *(CEO & Partner)*

M&C Saatchi (1)
Level 10 Grand Central Building 76-86 Manners Street, Wellington, New Zealand
Tel.: (64) 4 499 9868
Web Site: http://www.mcsaatchi.com
Sales Range: $25-49.9 Million
Emp.: 8
Full Service
N.A.I.C.S.: 541810

M&C Saatchi (1)
Level 2 18 Shortland St, Auckland, 1140, New Zealand
Tel.: (64) 9 307 1166
Web Site: http://www.mcsaatchi.com
Sales Range: $25-49.9 Million
Emp.: 15
Full Service
N.A.I.C.S.: 541810

M&C Saatchi (1)
4F 376 Wu Kang Lu, Xuhui Qu, Shanghai, 200020, China
Tel.: (86) 2164668930
Web Site: http://www.mcsaatchi.com
Full Service
N.A.I.C.S.: 541810

M&C Saatchi (1)
29 F Cambridge House Taikoo Place, 979 Kings Road, Quarry Bay, China (Hong Kong)
Tel.: (852) 2525 2843
Web Site: http://www.mcsaatchi.com
N.A.I.C.S.: 541810
Yvonne Lo *(CEO)*

M&C Saatchi (1)
Unit 10 2 10Th Floor Bangunan Malaysian RE-7 Lorong Dungun, Damansara Heights, 50490, Kuala Lumpur, Malaysia
Tel.: (60) 3 2094 6355
Web Site: http://www.mcsaatchi.com
Sales Range: $25-49.9 Million
Emp.: 80
Advertising Agencies
N.A.I.C.S.: 541810
Menyalara Hussein *(CEO & Partner)*

M&C Saatchi (1)
1-26-1 Ebisu West, Shibuya-Ku, Tokyo, 150-0021, Japan
Tel.: (81) 3 5456 6355
Web Site: http://www.mcsaatchi.co.jp
Sales Range: $25-49.9 Million
Emp.: 13
Advertising Agencies
N.A.I.C.S.: 541810
Tamio Koshino *(CEO)*

M&C Saatchi (1)

32 rue Notre-Dame des Victoires, Paris, 75002, France
Tel.: (33) 1 55 80 1000
Web Site: http://www.mcsaatchi.com
Sales Range: $25-49.9 Million
Emp.: 60
Advertising Agencies
N.A.I.C.S.: 541810
Gilles Masson *(Co-Founder, Pres & Dir-Publication)*

M&C Saatchi (1)
204 Solitaire Plz Sikandarpur MG Rd, Gurgaon, 122 002, Haryana, India
Tel.: (91) 124 4659000 29
Sales Range: $25-49.9 Million
Emp.: 33
N.A.I.C.S.: 541810
Richa Sinha *(Exec Dir-Creative)*

M&C Saatchi (1)
Munzstrasse 21-23, 10178, Berlin, Germany
Tel.: (49) 3060960000
Web Site: http://www.mcsaatchi.de
Sales Range: $25-49.9 Million
Emp.: 45
Advetising Agency
N.A.I.C.S.: 541810
Dominik Tiemann *(CEO & Mng Dir)*

M&C Saatchi (S) Pte. Ltd. (1)
59 Mohamed Sultan Road 02-08, Singapore, 238999, Singapore
Tel.: (65) 2075434500
Advertising Agency Services
N.A.I.C.S.: 541810

M&C Saatchi (Switzerland) SA (1)
Boulevard Bd des Promenades 8, 1227, Geneva, Switzerland
Tel.: (41) 225961890
Web Site: http://www.mcsaatchi.ch
Advertising Agency Services
N.A.I.C.S.: 541810
Olivier Girard *(Founder & Creative Dir)*

M&C Saatchi Connect (Pty.) Limited (1)
Media Quarter 5th Floor Corner Somerset & De Smit Street, De Waterkant, Cape Town, 8005, South Africa
Tel.: (27) 214211024
Web Site: https://mcsaatchiconnect.co.za
Advertising Services
N.A.I.C.S.: 541810

M&C Saatchi Fluency Limited (1)
36 Golden Square, London, W1F 9EE, United Kingdom
Tel.: (44) 2075434500
Web Site: https://fluency.mcsaatchi.com
Digital Advertising & Mobile Marketing Services
N.A.I.C.S.: 541613

M&C Saatchi LA Inc. (1)
2032-2034 Broadway, Santa Monica, CA 90404
Tel.: (310) 401-6070
Web Site: http://www.mcsaatchi-la.com
Advertising Agency Services
N.A.I.C.S.: 541810
Kate Bristow *(Partner & Chief Strategy Officer)*

M&C Saatchi Little Stories SAS (1)
32 rue Notre-Dame des Victoires, 75102, Paris, France
Tel.: (33) 155801000
Web Site: http://www.mcslittlestories.com
Public Relation Agency Services
N.A.I.C.S.: 541820

M&C Saatchi Madrid SL (1)
Gran Via 27 Planta 3, 28013, Madrid, Spain
Tel.: (34) 913600247
Web Site: http://www.mcsaatchimadrid.com
Communication & Creative Agency Services
N.A.I.C.S.: 541810
andres Martinez *(CEO, Partner & Exec Creative Dir)*

M&C Saatchi S.A. DE. C.V (1)
Darwin 74 Piso 1 Colonia Anzures, 11590, Mexico, Mexico
Tel.: (52) 15544944337
Advertising Agency Services
N.A.I.C.S.: 541810

M&C Saatchi Social Ltd. (1)

M&G GROUP LIMITED

36 Golden Square, London, W1F 9JG, United Kingdom
Tel.: (44) 2039678750
Web Site: https://www.mcsaatchisocial.com
Social Media Marketing Services
N.A.I.C.S.: 541613

M&C Saatchi SpA (1)
Viale Monte Nero 76, 20135, Milan, Italy
Tel.: (39) 0236748250
Web Site: http://www.mcsaatchi-milano.com
Advertising Agency Services
N.A.I.C.S.: 541810
Daniele Dionisi *(Creative Dir)*

M&C Saatchi Sport & Entertainment (1)
36 Golden Square, London, W1F 9EE, United Kingdom
Tel.: (44) 20 7543 4531
Web Site: http://www.mcsaatchi.com
Sales Range: $25-49.9 Million
Emp.: 25
N.A.I.C.S.: 541810
Steve Martin *(CEO-Global)*

M&C Saatchi Talk Limited (1)
36 Golden Square, London, W1F 9EE, United Kingdom
Tel.: (44) 2075443600
Web Site: https://www.mcsaatchitalk.com
Communications Advertising Services
N.A.I.C.S.: 541890

Mark. (1)
Level 3 99 Macquarie St, Sydney, 2000, NSW, Australia
Tel.: (61) 290161600
Web Site: http://www.marksydney.com
Sales Range: $25-49.9 Million
Emp.: 30
N.A.I.C.S.: 541810

Scarecrow M&C Saatchi Limited (1)
2nd Floor Kamini Chambers 32 Ramjibhai Kamani Marg, Opp Neville House Ballard Estate, Mumbai, 400 038, India
Tel.: (91) 2243321600
Web Site: https://www.scarecrowmcsaatchi.com
Communications Advertising Services
N.A.I.C.S.: 541890

Talk PR (1)
3-5 Rathbone Pl, London, W1T 1HJ, United Kingdom
Tel.: (44) 207 544 3777
Web Site: http://www.talkpr.com
Sales Range: Less than $1 Million
Emp.: 30
N.A.I.C.S.: 541820

This Film Studio Pty. Ltd. (1)
99 Macquarie Street, Sydney, 2000, NSW, Australia
Tel.: (61) 290196000
Web Site: https://www.thisfilmstudio.com
Film Production Services
N.A.I.C.S.: 512110

Thread Innovation Limited (1)
36 Golden Square, London, W1F 9EE, United Kingdom
Tel.: (44) 2075443603
Web Site: https://www.threadinnovation.io
Digital Advertising & Mobile Marketing Services
N.A.I.C.S.: 541613

Tricky Jigsaw Pty. Ltd. (1)
99 Macquarie Street, Sydney, 2000, NSW, Australia
Tel.: (61) 290196000
Web Site: https://www.trickyjigsaw.com
Marketing Services
N.A.I.C.S.: 541613
Ben Cooper *(Mng Dir)*

Walker Media (1)
Middlesex House 34-42 Cleveland St, London, W1T 4JE, United Kingdom
Tel.: (44) 20 7447 7500
Web Site: http://www.walkermedia.com
Emp.: 200
Advertising Services
N.A.I.C.S.: 541810
Phil Georgiadis *(CEO & Founding Partner)*

M&G GROUP LIMITED

M&G GROUP LIMITED

M&G Group Limited—(Continued)
Laurence Pountney Hill, London,
EC4R 0HH, United Kingdom
Tel.: (44) 2076264588 UK
Web Site: http://www.mandg.co.uk
Year Founded: 1931
Sales Range: $800-899.9 Million
Emp.: 1,468
Holding Company; Asset Management Services
N.A.I.C.S.: 551112
William Nott *(CEO-Securities)*

Subsidiaries:

Associated British Ports Holdings Ltd. (1)
25 Bedford Street, London, WC2E 9ES, United Kingdom (10%)
Tel.: (44) 2074301177
Web Site: https://www.abports.co.uk
Holding Company; Marine Ports Operator & Cargo Handling Activities
N.A.I.C.S.: 551112
Harm van Weezel *(CIO)*

Unit (Domestic):

ABP Ayr (2)
Port Office North Harbour Street, Ayr, KA8 8AH, United Kingdom
Tel.: (44) 1292281687
Sales Range: $100-124.9 Million
Emp.: 30
Marine Cargo Handling
N.A.I.C.S.: 488320

ABP Barrow (2)
Port Office Ramsey Way, Barrow-in-Furness, LA14 2GR, Cumbria, United Kingdom
Tel.: (44) 1229822911
Sales Range: $25-49.9 Million
Emp.: 30
Marine Cargo Handling Distr
N.A.I.C.S.: 488320
Paul Jervis *(Mgr-Port)*

ABP Cardiff (2)
QA House Cargo Road, Cardiff, CF10 4LY, United Kingdom
Tel.: (44) 8706096699
Sales Range: $25-49.9 Million
Emp.: 100
Marine Cargo Handling
N.A.I.C.S.: 488320
Matthew Kennerley *(Dir-Ports-South Wales)*

ABP Fleetwood (2)
Dock Office, Fleetwood, FY7 6PP, Lancs, United Kingdom
Tel.: (44) 1253872323
Sales Range: $100-124.9 Million
Emp.: 15
Marine Cargo Handling
N.A.I.C.S.: 488320
Nick Ridehalgh *(Dir-Short-Sea Ports)*

ABP Garston (2)
Port Office Garston, Liverpool, L19 2JW, United Kingdom
Tel.: (44) 1514275971
Sales Range: $25-49.9 Million
Emp.: 20
Marine Cargo Handling
N.A.I.C.S.: 488320
Paul Jervis *(Mgr-Port)*

ABP Goole (2)
Port Office East Parade, Goole, DN14 5RB, East Yorkshire, United Kingdom
Tel.: (44) 1482327171
Web Site: http://www.abport.co.uk
Sales Range: $50-74.9 Million
Emp.: 250
Marine Cargo Handling
N.A.I.C.S.: 488320
Phil Coombes *(Mgr-Comml)*

ABP Hull (2)
Port House Northern Gateway, PO Box 1, Hull, HU9 5PQ, Yorkshire, United Kingdom
Tel.: (44) 1482327171
Sales Range: $25-49.9 Million
Emp.: 125
Port & Harbor Operations
N.A.I.C.S.: 488310

ABP Ipswich (2)
Old Custom House Key Street, Ipswich, IP4 1BY, United Kingdom
Tel.: (44) 1473231010
Sales Range: $25-49.9 Million
Emp.: 23
Marine Cargo Handling
N.A.I.C.S.: 488320
Alastair MacFarlane *(Mgr-Port)*

ABP Plymouth (2)
Port Office Millbay Docks, Plymouth, PL1 3EF, Devon, United Kingdom
Tel.: (44) 1752662191
Sales Range: $25-49.9 Million
Emp.: 22
Passenger Ferry & Marine Cargo Handling Services
N.A.I.C.S.: 488320

M&G Alternatives Investment Management Limited (1)
Laurence Pountney Hill, London, EC4R 0HH, United Kingdom (100%)
Tel.: (44) 20 7626 4588
Web Site: http://www.mandg.com
Alternative Investment Management Services
N.A.I.C.S.: 523940
Gary Cotton *(COO)*

M&G Investment Management Limited (1)
Laurence Pountney Hill, London, EC4R 0HH, United Kingdom
Tel.: (44) 20 7626 4588
Web Site: http://www.mandg.com
Investment Management Service
N.A.I.C.S.: 523940
Gary Cotton *(COO)*

Division (Domestic):

Infracapital (2)
One Angel Lane, London, EC4R 3AB, United Kingdom
Tel.: (44) 20 7548 2214
Web Site: http://www.infracapital.co.uk
Infrastructure Asset Fund Management Services
N.A.I.C.S.: 523940
Martin Lennon *(Co-Founder & Head-Infracapital)*

Joint Venture (Non-US):

Adven Oy (3)
Karhumaenkuja 2, 01530, Vantaa, Finland
Tel.: (358) 10 344 5000
Web Site: https://adven.com
Sales Range: $125-149.9 Million
Emp.: 400
Heating & Cooling Services
N.A.I.C.S.: 221330
Esa Aarnio *(VP-Bus Dev)*

Subsidiary (Non-US):

Adven Eesti AS (4)
Kassi 13, 12618, Tallinn, Estonia
Tel.: (372) 667 8600
Web Site: https://adven.com
Heating & Cooling Services
N.A.I.C.S.: 221330
Urmo Heinam *(Chm-Mgmt Bd & CEO)*

Joint Venture (Non-US):

Kelda Group Limited (3)
Tel.: (44) 1274600111
Web Site: https://www.keldagroup.com
Emp.: 3,500
Holding Company; Water, Sewage, Environmental & Land Management Services
N.A.I.C.S.: 551112

Joint Venture (Domestic):

SSE Telecommunications Limited (3)
Inveralmond House 200 Dunkeld Road, Perth, PH1 3AQ, United Kingdom
Tel.: (44) 3450701997
Web Site: http://www.ssetelecoms.com
Telecommunication Servicesb
N.A.I.C.S.: 517810
Colin Douglas Sempill *(Mng Dir)*

M&G Securities Limited (1)
Laurence Pountney Hill, London, EC4R

0HH, United Kingdom
Tel.: (44) 20 7626 4588
Web Site: http://www.mandg.co.uk
Securities Trading Services
N.A.I.C.S.: 523150
William Nott *(CEO)*

M&G PLC
10 Fenchurch Avenue, London, EC3M 5AG, United Kingdom
Tel.: (44) 2076264588 UK
Web Site: https://www.mandg.com
Year Founded: 1901
MNG—(LSE)
Rev.: $4,906,589,245
Assets: $239,361,272,406
Liabilities: $234,206,008,584
Net Worth: $5,155,263,822
Earnings: $374,905,327
Emp.: 6,093
Fiscal Year-end: 12/31/23
Financial Investment Services
N.A.I.C.S.: 523999
Alan Porter *(Sec)*

Subsidiaries:

Investment Funds Direct Limited (1)
10 Fenchurch Avenue, London, EC3M 5AG, United Kingdom
Tel.: (44) 3450766140
Web Site: https://www.mandg.com
Investment Services
N.A.I.C.S.: 541690

M&G International Investments Switzerland AG (1)
Zollstrasse 17, 8005, Zurich, Switzerland
Tel.: (41) 434438200
Web Site: https://www.mandg.com
Investment Services
N.A.I.C.S.: 541690

M&G Investments (Hong Kong) Limited (1)
Unit 1002 LHT Tower 31 Queen's Road, Central, China (Hong Kong)
Tel.: (852) 37253188
Web Site: https://www.mandg.com
Investment Services
N.A.I.C.S.: 541690

M&G Investments (Singapore) Pte. Ltd. (1)
138 Market Street CapitaGreen 35-01, Singapore, 048946, Singapore
Tel.: (65) 69827770
Asset Management Services
N.A.I.C.S.: 531390

M&G Real Estate Korea Co., Ltd. (1)
17th Floor Kyobo Building 1 Jongno, Jongno-gu, Seoul, 110714, Korea (South)
Tel.: (82) 262201400
Investment Services
N.A.I.C.S.: 541690

MandG Investments (Namibia) (Pty.) Ltd. (1)
Maerua Mall Office Tower 2nd floor Corner of Robert Mugabe Avenue and, PO Box 25743, Jan Jonker Road, Windhoek, Namibia
Tel.: (264) 61256166
Web Site: https://www.mandg.com.na
Investment Services
N.A.I.C.S.: 541690

MandG Investments Life South Africa (RF) Ltd. (1)
5th Floor Protea Place 30 Dreyer Street, Claremont, Cape Town, 7700, South Africa
Tel.: (27) 216705100
Web Site: https://www.mandg.co.za
Investment Services
N.A.I.C.S.: 541690

Prudential Polska sp. Z o.o (1)
Ul Pulawska 182, 02-670, Warsaw, Poland
Tel.: (48) 226675820
Web Site: https://www.pru.pl
Financial Processing & Insurance Services
N.A.I.C.S.: 522320

Prudential Staff Pensions Limited (1)

INTERNATIONAL PUBLIC

10 Fenchurch Avenue, London, EC3M 5AG, United Kingdom
Tel.: (44) 1245673515
Web Site: https://prudentialstaffps.co.uk
Pension Services
N.A.I.C.S.: 524292

ResponsAbility Africa Ltd. (1)
Merchant Square Block D 5th Floor Riverside Drive, PO Box 293, Riverside, Nairobi, Kenya
Tel.: (254) 113927412
Investment Services
N.A.I.C.S.: 541690

ResponsAbility America Latina S.A.C. (1)
Av 28 de Julio 753 Interior 801 Urb Leuro, Miraflores, 15074, Lima, Peru
Tel.: (51) 12559292
Investment Services
N.A.I.C.S.: 541690

ResponsAbility France S.A.S. (1)
5 Rue du Helder, 75009, Paris, France
Tel.: (33) 153245320
Investment Services
N.A.I.C.S.: 541690

ResponsAbility India Business Advisors Pvt. Ltd. (1)
Green Acre 1st Floor 31 Union Park Road 5 Khar West, Mumbai, 400052, India
Tel.: (91) 2230770300
Investment Services
N.A.I.C.S.: 541690

ResponsAbility Investments AG (1)
Zollstrasse 17, 8605, Zurich, Switzerland
Tel.: (41) 444030500
Web Site: https://www.responsability.com
Investment Services
N.A.I.C.S.: 541690

ResponsAbility Thailand Ltd. (1)
Unit 1102 11th Floor Thaniya Tower B 62 Silom Road, Suriyawongse Bangrak, Bangkok, 10500, Thailand
Tel.: (66) 21171907
Investment Services
N.A.I.C.S.: 541690

M&L HOLDINGS GROUP LIMITED

21st Floor Empress Plaza 17-19 Chatham Road South, Tsimshatsui, Kowloon, China (Hong Kong)
Tel.: (852) 25118186 Ky
Web Site: https://www.mleng.com
8152—(HKG)
Rev.: $11,098,493
Assets: $24,840,825
Liabilities: $12,699,255
Net Worth: $12,141,570
Earnings: ($1,093,313)
Emp.: 44
Fiscal Year-end: 12/31/22
Industrial Equipment Mfr & Distr
N.A.I.C.S.: 333248
Lai Ming Ng *(Founder, Chm, CEO & Exec Dir)*

Subsidiaries:

M&L Engineering & Materials Pte Limited (1)
5 Yishun Industrial Street 1 02-04/05 North Spring Bizhub, Singapore, 768161, Singapore
Tel.: (65) 63699662
Construction Equipment Whslr
N.A.I.C.S.: 423810

M&L PROPERTY & ASSETS PLC

First Floor Jubilee Buildings Victoria Street, Douglas, IM1 2LR, Isle of Man
Tel.: (44) 1624 699000
Sales Range: Less than $1 Million
Investment Management Service
N.A.I.C.S.: 523940
Barry Curtis Smith *(Sec)*

M+S ELEKTRONIK AG

AND PRIVATE COMPANIES / M+W GROUP GMBH

Nordring 55, Niedernberg, Miltenberg, 63843, Germany
Tel.: (49) 60289440
Information Technology Consulting Services
N.A.I.C.S.: 541512
Georg Kunze *(Member-Mgmt Bd)*

M+S HYDRAULIC AD-KAZANLAK

68 Kozloduy Str, 6100, Kazanlak, 6100, Bulgaria
Tel.: (359) 43165167
Web Site: https://www.ms-hydraulic.com
Year Founded: 1963
MSH—(BUL)
Rev.: $119,170,245
Assets: $76,127,093
Liabilities: $16,332,117
Net Worth: $59,794,976
Earnings: $18,074,281
Fiscal Year-end: 12/31/22
Hydraulic Motor Mfr
N.A.I.C.S.: 336390
M. Marinov *(Fin Mgr)*

Subsidiaries:

M+S Hydraulic Power Transmission GmbH (1)
Robert-Bosch-Str 46, 63225, Langen, Germany
Tel.: (49) 6103706470
Fluid Power Pump & Motor Mfr
N.A.I.C.S.: 333996

M+W GROUP GMBH

Loewentorbogen 9b, 70376, Stuttgart, Germany
Tel.: (49) 71188040   De
Web Site: http://www.mwgroup.net
Year Founded: 1912
Sales Range: $1-4.9 Billion
Emp.: 5,900
Holding Company; Facility Engineering & Management Services
N.A.I.C.S.: 551112
Wolfgang Buchele *(CEO)*

Subsidiaries:

Exyte GmbH (1)
Loewentorbogen 9B, 70376, Stuttgart, Germany
Tel.: (49) 71188040
Web Site: http://www.exyte.net
Engineeering Services
N.A.I.C.S.: 541330
Wolfgang Buchele *(CEO)*

Subsidiary (US):

Airgard, Inc. (2)
1755 McCarthy Blvd, Milpitas, CA 95035
Tel.: (408) 573-0701
Web Site: http://www.airgard.net
Mfg Analytical Instruments
N.A.I.C.S.: 334516
Dyana Chargin *(CFO)*

Subsidiary (Domestic):

Kinetics Holding GmbH (2)
Am Dillhof 5, 63863, Eschau, Germany
Tel.: (49) 9374 9722 0
Web Site: http://www.kinetics.net
Holding Company; Heating, Ventilation, Air-Conditioning, Plumbing & Mechanical Contractor
N.A.I.C.S.: 551112
Peter M. Maris *(Pres & CEO)*

Subsidiary (US):

Kinetic Systems, Inc. (3)
48400 Fremont Blvd, Fremont, CA 94538   (100%)
Tel.: (510) 683-6000
Web Site: http://www.kinetics.com
Emp.: 1,500
Heating, Ventilation, Air-Conditioning, Plumbing & Mechanical Contractor
N.A.I.C.S.: 238220
Peter M. Maris *(Pres & CEO)*

Subsidiary (Non-US):

Kinetics Germany GmbH (4)
Am Dillhof 5, 63863, Eschau, Germany   (100%)
Tel.: (49) 9374 9722 0
Web Site: http://www.kinetics.net
Heating, Ventilation, Air-Conditioning, Plumbing & Mechanical Contractor
N.A.I.C.S.: 238220
Hans-Peter Casel *(Exec VP-Bus Dev-Global)*

Branch (Domestic):

Kinetics Germany GmbH - Dresden Office (5)
Grenzstrasse 20, 01109, Dresden, Germany
Tel.: (49) 351 476 990
Web Site: http://www.kinetics.net
Sales Range: $25-49.9 Million
Emp.: 500
Heating Ventilation Air-Conditioning Plumbing & Mechanical Contractor Services
N.A.I.C.S.: 238220
Rajeev Nair *(CIO)*

Subsidiary (Non-US):

Kinetics Process Systems (Shanghai) Ltd. (4)
Room 801 Building 3 No 400 Tangqiao Road, Pudong, Shanghai, 200127, China   (100%)
Tel.: (86) 2150395162
Web Site: http://www.kinetics.net
Heating, Ventilation, Air-Conditioning, Plumbing & Mechanical Contractor
N.A.I.C.S.: 238220
Christine Zhang *(Mgr-Ops)*

Kinetics Process Systems Pte. Ltd. (4)
1 Clenenti Loop 02-01, Singapore, 129808, Singapore   (100%)
Tel.: (65) 63491000
Web Site: http://www.kinetics.com
Emp.: 70
Heating, Ventilation, Air-Conditioning, Plumbing & Mechanical Contractor
N.A.I.C.S.: 238220
Meng Kwang Koh *(Dir-Ops)*

Kinetics Systems Malaysia Sdn. Bhd. (4)
12A Jalan Ringgit 23/11 Section 23, 40300, Shah Alam, Selangor Darul Ehsan, Malaysia   (100%)
Tel.: (60) 3 5542 2288
Web Site: http://www.kinetics.net
Heating, Ventilation, Air-Conditioning, Plumbing & Mechanical Contractor
N.A.I.C.S.: 238220
Chooi Choon Keet *(Gen Mgr-Southeast Asia)*

Branch (Domestic):

Kinetics Systems Malaysia Sdn. Bhd. - Kulim Office (5)
No 574 Kawasan Industri Waja II, Jalan Waja, 09000, Kulim, Kedah D.A., Malaysia
Tel.: (60) 4 489 1478
Web Site: http://www.kinetics.com
Heating, Ventilation, Air-Conditioning, Plumbing & Mechanical Contractor
N.A.I.C.S.: 238220
Ban Chuan Lok *(Dir-Ops)*

Subsidiary (Domestic):

Wafab International (4)
6161-A Industrial Way, Livermore, CA 94551
Tel.: (925) 455-5252
Web Site: http://www.wafabintl.com
Microelectronic Wafer Processing & Plastic Thermoforming Equipment Designer & Mfr
N.A.I.C.S.: 333248
Jorge Freitas *(Gen Mgr)*

Hargreaves Ductwork Limited (1)
Lord Street, Bury, BL9 0RG, Lancashire, United Kingdom   (100%)
Tel.: (44) 1617645082
Web Site: http://www.mw-hargreaves.net
Sales Range: $25-49.9 Million
Emp.: 400
Ductwork, Air Handling, Air Distribution Equipment, Rolled Metallic Sections & Presswork
N.A.I.C.S.: 221330

Lead Management Engineering & Construction Pte. Ltd. (1)
16 International Business Park 03-00, Singapore, 609929, Singapore
Tel.: (65) 63662532
Web Site: http://www.leadgrp.net
Semiconductor Device Distr
N.A.I.C.S.: 423690
Karthigeyan K S *(Project Mgr)*

Lead Management Engineering (Malaysia) Sdn. Bhd. (1)
No 45 Jalan Saujana 2 Taman Industri Saujana, Kulim, 09000, Kedah, Malaysia
Tel.: (60) 44102128
Engineeering Services
N.A.I.C.S.: 541330

Lead Management Engineering (Shanghai) Co., Ltd. (1)
Room 307 - 312 No 12 Building No 31 South Kaixuan Road, 200232, Shanghai, China
Tel.: (86) 2164569658
Engineeering Services
N.A.I.C.S.: 541330

M+W (Thailand) Ltd. (1)
219/39 Asoke Towers 11th Floor Soi Asoke Sukhumvit 21 Rd, Watthana, Bangkok, 10110, Thailand
Tel.: (66) 26408017
Engineeering Services
N.A.I.C.S.: 541330

M+W Asia Limited (1)
16 International Business Park, Singapore, 609929, Singapore
Tel.: (65) 67259500
Engineeering Services
N.A.I.C.S.: 541330

M+W Brasil Projetos Tecnicos Ltda. (1)
Rua Paes Leme 524 - 12 andar - Cjs 124/125, 05424-904, Sao Paulo, Brazil
Tel.: (55) 1156412816
Engineering Services
N.A.I.C.S.: 541330

M+W Central Europe Sp. z o.o. (1)
ul Trzy Lipy 3, 80-172, Gdansk, Poland
Tel.: (48) 587354300
Engineeering Services
N.A.I.C.S.: 541330

M+W Facility Engineering GmbH (1)
Standard Invest Building 3rd Floor Dbaye Highway, Beirut, Lebanon
Tel.: (961) 4549000
Engineeering Services
N.A.I.C.S.: 541330

M+W France S.a.r.l. (1)
Rousset Parc Club 118 avenue Francis Perrin, 13106, Rousset, France
Tel.: (33) 442612612
Engineeering Services
N.A.I.C.S.: 541330

M+W High Tech Projects (Malaysia) Sdn. Bhd. (1)
20th Floor Unit A Gurney Tower No 18, Gurney, 10250, Penang, Malaysia
Tel.: (60) 43704500
Engineeering Services
N.A.I.C.S.: 541330

M+W High Tech Projects Israel Ltd. (1)
3 Pekeris St Rorberg Science Center, PO Box 342, 76702, Rehovot, Israel
Tel.: (972) 89393600
Engineeering Services
N.A.I.C.S.: 541330
Raoul Ronen *(CEO)*

M+W High Tech Projects LLC (1)
1-st Derbenevsky Pereulok 5 Entrance 4 Office 605, 115114, Moscow, Russia
Tel.: (7) 4956623220
Engineeering Services
N.A.I.C.S.: 541330

M+W High Tech Projects Mexico, S. de. R.L. de C.V. (1)
Del Benito Juarez Col Del Valle Corporativo Coyoacan Av Coyoacan, 1622 Edificio 4 1er piso, 03100, Mexico, Mexico
Tel.: (52) 5515553800
Engineeering Services
N.A.I.C.S.: 541330
David Martinez Salazar *(Mng Dir & Dir Gen)*

M+W High Tech Projects Philippines Inc. (1)
10th Floor Unit 1002 DPC Place Bldg 2322 Don Chino Roces Ave, 1231, Makati, Philippines
Tel.: (63) 28899891
Engineeering Services
N.A.I.C.S.: 541330

M+W High Tech Projects Taiwan Co., Ltd (1)
8F No 118 Sec1 Tong Ta Road, Hsinchuang, Taiwan
Tel.: (886) 35421415
Engineeering Services
N.A.I.C.S.: 541330

M+W Italy S.r.l. (1)
Centro Colleoni - Palazzo Andromeda 2 Via Paracelso 18, Agrate Brianza, 20041, Milan, Italy
Tel.: (39) 039657331
Web Site: http://www.ita.mwgroup.net
Engineeering Services
N.A.I.C.S.: 541330

M+W Middle East Ltd. (1)
Masdar City, Abu Dhabi, United Arab Emirates
Tel.: (971) 26137000
Engineeering Services
N.A.I.C.S.: 541330

M+W Power Solutions GmbH (1)
Industriestrasse 70, 04435, Schkeuditz, Germany
Tel.: (49) 3420467290
Engineeering Services
N.A.I.C.S.: 541330

M+W Process Engineering d.o.o. (1)
Milutina Milankovica 136 B Unit 2B 2nd Floor, 11070, Belgrade, Serbia
Tel.: (381) 116557905
Engineeering Services
N.A.I.C.S.: 541330

M+W Products (Shanghai) Co. Ltd. (1)
No 139 Beimin Road Che dun, Songjiang, 201611, Shanghai, China
Tel.: (86) 2137838360
Engineeering Services
N.A.I.C.S.: 541330

M+W Saudi Arabia Ltd. (1)
Ncci Towers Abraj Aitawaniyah King Fahad Road North Tower 13th Floor, Olaya, Riyadh, Saudi Arabia
Tel.: (966) 112180444
Engineeering Services
N.A.I.C.S.: 541330

M+W Shanghai Co., Ltd. (1)
10th Floor No 436 Hengfeng Road, Zhabei, Shanghai, 200070, China
Tel.: (86) 2122201888
Web Site: http://www.chn.mwgroup.net
Construction Engineering Services
N.A.I.C.S.: 541330
Frank Lorenzetto *(CEO)*

M+W U.S., Inc. (1)
1001 Klein Rd St 400, Plano, TX 75074
Tel.: (972) 535-7300
Web Site: http://www.usa.mwgroup.net
Sales Range: $75-99.9 Million
Emp.: 252
Holding Company; Industrial Engineering, Architecture & Construction Services
N.A.I.C.S.: 551112
Ralf Graber *(Exec VP)*

Subsidiary (Domestic):

Gehrlicher Solar America Corp. (2)
21 Fadem Rd, Springfield, NJ 07091
Tel.: (908) 219-4379
Web Site: http://www.gehrlichersolar.us
Engineeering Services
N.A.I.C.S.: 541330
Jerry Shinn *(Pres)*

M+W GROUP GMBH

M+W Group GmbH—(Continued)

Spectrum Engineering Solutions, Inc. (2)
25560 Mound Rd, Warren, MI 48091
Tel.: (586) 754-8400
Web Site: http://www.sesdirect.com
Sales Range: $10-24.9 Million
Emp.: 150
Full-Service Controls Engineering Services
N.A.I.C.S.: 541330
Anthony F. Pingston (Dir-Ops)

Total Facility Solutions, Inc. (2)
1001 Klein Rd Ste 400, Plano, TX 75074 (100%)
Tel.: (972) 535-7361
Web Site: http://www.tfs-us.com
Sales Range: $125-149.9 Million
Emp.: 50
Mfr Industry Mechanical, Process Piping, Heating, Ventilation, Air-Conditioning & Electrical Contracting Services
N.A.I.C.S.: 238220
Rick Whitney (CEO)

Subsidiary (Domestic):

Ray L Hellwig Plumbing & Heating Co, Inc. (3)
1301 Laurelwood Rd, Santa Clara, CA 95054
Tel.: (408) 727-5612
Web Site: http://www.rlhellwig.com
Sales Range: $1-9.9 Million
Emp.: 80
Plumbing, Heating, Air-Conditioning, Nsk
N.A.I.C.S.: 238220
Glen Bollenbacher (Pres)

M+W Vietnam Co., Ltd. (1)
4th Floor Simco Building 28 Pham Hung, Hanoi, Vietnam
Tel.: (84) 437856339
Engineeering Services
N.A.I.C.S.: 541330

MW High Tech Projects India Pvt. Ltd. (1)
2nd & 3rd Floor Sai Shikha Plot No 1264 Road No 36 Jubilee Hills, 500 033, Hyderabad, India
Tel.: (91) 4044543650
Web Site: http://www.ind.mwgroup.net
Engineeering Services
N.A.I.C.S.: 541330
Kumar Mahesh (Sr Mgr-HR)

PAN ELECTRICS SDN BHD (1)
No 124/125 Jalan Persiaran 6 Kulim Avenue Kulim Hi-Tech Park, Kulim, 09000, Kedah, Malaysia
Tel.: (60) 44102128
Electrical Engineering Services
N.A.I.C.S.: 541330

True Value Solar Pty. Ltd. (1)
Level 2 850 Collins Street, Docklands, 3008, VIC, Australia
Tel.: (61) 386675900
Web Site: http://www.truevaluesolar.com.au
Solar Panel Distr
N.A.I.C.S.: 423720

M-BRAIN OY

Kuortaneenkatu 1, 00520, Helsinki, Finland
Tel.: (358) 20 7737 600 FI
Web Site: http://www.m-brain.com
Year Founded: 2011
Sales Range: $25-49.9 Million
Emp.: 400
Holding Company; Print, Radio, Television & Social Media Content Monitoring & Analysis Services
N.A.I.C.S.: 551112
Kimmo Valtonen (CTO)

Subsidiaries:

Global Intelligence Alliance Group Oy (1)
Itamerenkatu 1, 00180, Helsinki, Finland
Tel.: (358) 10 613 2000
Web Site: http://www.globalintelligence.com
Marketing Consulting Services
N.A.I.C.S.: 541613
Markko Vaarnas (CEO)

Subsidiary (Non-US):

Global Intelligence Alliance Benelux B.V. (2)
Amstel Business Park Joop Geesinkweg 901, 1096 AZ, Amsterdam, Netherlands
Tel.: (31) 2056 160 15
Marketing Consulting Services
N.A.I.C.S.: 541613

Global Intelligence Alliance Hong Kong (2)
31/F Tower One Times Square 1 Matheson Street, Causeway Bay, China (Hong Kong)
Tel.: (852) 28248511
Marketing Consulting Services
N.A.I.C.S.: 541613

Global Intelligence Alliance Asia-Pacific Pte. LTD. (2)
8 Eu Tong Sen Street, 23-81 The Central, Singapore, 059818, Singapore
Tel.: (65) 6423 1681
Marketing Consulting Services
N.A.I.C.S.: 541613
Nicolas Pechet (Sr VP)

Global Intelligence Alliance Estrategia e Consultoria em Marketing Ltda (2)
Rua Joaquim Floriano 466 cj 306, Itaim Bibi, 04534-002, Sao Paulo, Brazil
Tel.: (55) 11 2165 6810
Marketing Consulting Services
N.A.I.C.S.: 541613
Natan Rodeguero (VP-Intelligence Svcs)

Global Intelligence Alliance Germany GmbH (2)
Dorotheenstrasse 1, 45130, Essen, Germany
Tel.: (49) 201 266 900
Web Site: http://www.m-brain.com
Emp.: 25
Marketing Consulting Services
N.A.I.C.S.: 541613
Carlton Jaiel (Mng Dir)

Global Intelligence Alliance Greater China LTD (2)
Unit 2602 United Power International Plaza 1158 Jiangning Road, Shanghai, 200060, China
Tel.: (86) 21 6279 0197
Marketing Consulting Services
N.A.I.C.S.: 541613

Global Intelligence Alliance North America Inc. (2)
174 Spadina Avenue Suite 302, Toronto, M5T 2C2, ON, Canada
Tel.: (416) 231-0828
Marketing Consulting Services
N.A.I.C.S.: 541613

Global Intelligence Alliance UK Ltd. (2)
55 Old Broad Street, London, EC2M 1RX, United Kingdom
Tel.: (44) 207 997 6320
Marketing Consulting Services
N.A.I.C.S.: 541613

Subsidiary (US):

Global Intelligence Alliance USA Inc. (2)
1 Penn Plz 36th fl, New York, NY 10119
Tel.: (212) 786-7368
Marketing Consulting Services
N.A.I.C.S.: 541613
Jouko Virtanen (Sr VP)

M-Brain GmbH (1)
Schweinfurter Strasse 28, 97076, Wurzburg, Germany
Tel.: (49) 931299290
Sales Range: $25-49.9 Million
Emp.: 12
Information Monitoring & Analysis Services
N.A.I.C.S.: 519290
Gunter Habermann (Mgr-Production)

M-Brain Information AB (1)
Sankt Eriksgatan 46 B, 112 34, Stockholm, Sweden
Tel.: (46) 8 556 08 800
Web Site: http://www.m-brain.com
Sales Range: $25-49.9 Million
Emp.: 15
Information Monitoring & Analysis Services
N.A.I.C.S.: 519290
Goran Eriksson (Mgr-Production)

M-Brain Information Sdn. Bhd. (1)
Suite 13-10 13th Floor Wisma UOA II No 21 Jalan Pinang, 50450, Kuala Lumpur, Malaysia
Tel.: (60) 321645755
Sales Range: $10-24.9 Milllion
Emp.: 35
Information Monitoring & Analysis Services
N.A.I.C.S.: 519290
Quek Kian Chzen (Mgr)

M-Brain Insight Oy (1)
Kumpulantie 3, FI-00520, Helsinki, Finland
Tel.: (358) 20 7737 600
Web Site: http://www.m-brain.com
Emp.: 30
Editorial & Social Media Content Monitoring, Analysis & Consulting Services
N.A.I.C.S.: 519290
Kim Nyberg (Gen Mgr)

Subsidiary (Non-US):

M-Brain Ab (2)
Sankt Eriksgatan 46B, 112 34, Stockholm, Sweden
Tel.: (46) 8 55608800
Emp.: 13
Marketing Consulting Services
N.A.I.C.S.: 541613
Christina Wihlner Lentell (Mng Dir)

M-Brain Limited (1)
County House 3rd Floor 17 Friar Street, Reading, RG1 1DB, United Kingdom
Tel.: (44) 118 9565 820
Web Site: http://www.m-brain.com
Sales Range: $25-49.9 Million
Emp.: 50
Information Monitoring & Analysis Services
N.A.I.C.S.: 519290

M-Brain Media Oy (1)
Kuortaneenkatu 1, 00520, Helsinki, Finland
Tel.: (358) 20 7737 600
Web Site: http://www.m-brainmedia.com
Emp.: 200
Print, Radio & Television Content Monitoring & Analysis Services
N.A.I.C.S.: 519290
Joakim Nyberg (Mgr-Mktg)

OOO M-Brain (1)
Business-Center Zolotaya Shpalernaya Office B-24, 191015, Saint Petersburg, Russia
Tel.: (7) 812 333 0886
Sales Range: $25-49.9 Million
Emp.: 25
Information Monitoring & Analysis Services
N.A.I.C.S.: 519290
Yekaterina Levochskaya (Gen Dir)

M-GRASS ECOLOGY AND ENVIRONMENT (GROUP) CO., LTD.

Mengcao Seed Industry Center Shenggaiying Lane Huheta West Street, Xincheng District, Hohhot, 010070, China
Tel.: (86) 4716695191
Web Site: https://www.mengcao.com
Year Founded: 2001
300355—(CHIN)
Rev.: $266,790,901
Assets: $2,244,773,705
Liabilities: $1,411,585,516
Net Worth: $833,188,189
Earnings: $35,089,862
Fiscal Year-end: 12/31/23
Biological Landscape Construction, City Landscape Engineering Construction, Plants Distribution & Engineering Design
N.A.I.C.S.: 561730
Fan Junmei (Chm & Pres)

M-MART, INC.

6-5-1 Nishishinjuku, Shinjku-Ku, Tokyo, 163-1326, Japan
Tel.: (81) 3 6811 0124
Web Site: http://www.m-mart.co.jp
Year Founded: 2000

4380—(TKS)
E Commerce Site Operator
N.A.I.C.S.: 455211

M-RESOURCES GROUP LIMITED

26th Floor Times Tower 391-407 Jaffe Road, Wanchai, China (Hong Kong)
Tel.: (852) 25438223 BM
Web Site: http://www.irresources.com.hk
Rev.: $3,933,070
Assets: $9,572,195
Liabilities: $7,740,426
Net Worth: $1,831,769
Earnings: ($1,935,909)
Emp.: 43
Fiscal Year-end: 12/31/19
Wood Product Distr
N.A.I.C.S.: 423990
Ching Hang Chan (Compliance Officer)

Subsidiaries:

Nine Rivers Capital Partners Limited (1)
26/F Times Tower 391-407 Jaffe Road, Wanchai, China (Hong Kong)
Tel.: (852) 34697000
Web Site: http://www.nineriverscapitalpartners.com
Security Dealing Services
N.A.I.C.S.: 523150

M-UP HOLDINGS, INC.

Shibuya Minami Tokyu Building 5th 9th and 10th floors 3-12-18 Shibuya, Shibuya-ku, Tokyo, 150-0002, Japan
Tel.: (81) 354677125
Web Site: https://m-upholdings.co.jp
Year Founded: 2004
3661—(TKS)
Rev.: $122,774,140
Assets: $129,218,890
Liabilities: $82,016,880
Net Worth: $47,202,010
Earnings: $9,789,410
Emp.: 60
Fiscal Year-end: 03/31/24
Mobile Phones & PC Equipment Distr
N.A.I.C.S.: 423690

M-VENTURE INVESTMENT, INC.

36 Teheran-ro 87-gil, Gangnam-gu, Seoul, Korea (South)
Tel.: (82) 260005533
Web Site: http://www.m-vc.co.kr
Year Founded: 1999
Investment Services
N.A.I.C.S.: 523999
Sung-Hyeok Hong (Chm & CEO)

Subsidiaries:

M-Venture Investment Management (Shanghai) Co., Ltd. (1)
G/2F No 369 Jiangsu Road Zhaofeng Shimao Building, Shanghai, 200050, China
Tel.: (86) 21 5240 1133
Web Site: http://www.m-vc.com.ch
Sales Range: $50-74.9 Million
Emp.: 16
Investment Management Service
N.A.I.C.S.: 523999

M-WISE INC.

3 Sapir Street, Herzeliya Pituach, Tel Aviv, 46852, Israel
Tel.: (972) 73 2620000 DE
Web Site: http://www.m-wise.com
Year Founded: 2000
MWIS—(OTCIQ)
Sales Range: $1-9.9 Million
Emp.: 14
Content Management & Delivery Platform (CDP), Service Delivery Plat-

form (SDP) & Related Data Engines for Mobile Operators, Wireless ASPs & Large Content & Media Providers
N.A.I.C.S.: 517112
Zach Sivan (CEO)

M. A. STEWART & SONS LTD.
12900 - 87th Avenue, Surrey, V3W 3H9, BC, Canada
Tel.: (604) 594-8431
Web Site: http://www.mastewart.com
Year Founded: 1955
Sales Range: $10-24.9 Million
Pipe Valve & Fittings Distr
N.A.I.C.S.: 423720
John Makarchuk (Exec VP-Sls & Mktg)

Subsidiaries:

MAS (USA) ltd. (1)
803 Pressley Rd Ste 107, Charlotte, NC 28217
Tel.: (704) 527-0722
Web Site: http://www.mastewartusa.com
Pipe Fitting Product Distr
N.A.I.C.S.: 423720
Jerry Priest (VP-Ops)

M. ABUHAB PARTICIPACOES S.A.
Av Santiago Dumont 935, Joinville, 89218 105, Brazil
Tel.: (55) 47 2101 6500   BR
Holding Company
N.A.I.C.S.: 551112
Miguel Abuhab (Chm)

Subsidiaries:

NeoGrid Informatica Ltda. (1)
Av Santiago Dumont 935, Joinville, 89218 105, Brazil
Tel.: (55) 4721016500
Web Site: http://www.neogrid.com
Supply Chain Management Solutions
N.A.I.C.S.: 541614

Subsidiary (Non-US):

Trace One UK (2)
Verulam Point Station Way, Saint Albans, AL1 5HE, Herts, United Kingdom
Tel.: (44) 1727744700
Sales Range: $25-49.9 Million
Emp.: 50
Sourcing, Product Management, Data Processing, Business Intelligence & Supply Chain Solutions
N.A.I.C.S.: 518210
Jerome Malavoy (Founder & CEO)

M. DIAS BRANCO S.A. INDUSTRIA E COMERCIO DE ALIMENTOS
Rod BR 116 - Km 18, 61760-000, Eusebio, 61760-000, Ceara, Brazil
Tel.: (55) 8007025509   BR
Web Site: https://www.mdiasbranco.com.br
Year Founded: 1951
MDIA3—(BRAZ)
Rev.: $2,161,786,818
Assets: $2,461,061,322
Liabilities: $944,520,491
Net Worth: $1,516,540,832
Earnings: $177,216,871
Emp.: 16,588
Fiscal Year-end: 12/31/23
Food Product Mfr & Whslr
N.A.I.C.S.: 311999
Maria Consuelo Saraiva Leao Dias Branco (Chm-Acting)

Subsidiaries:

Industria de Produtos Alimenticios Piraque S.A (1)
Matriz Rua Leopoldino de Oliveira 335, Turiacu, Rio de Janeiro, 21360-060, Brazil
Tel.: (55) 8540052754
Web Site: http://www.piraque.com.br
Biscuit Product Mfr

N.A.I.C.S.: 311821

M. Dias Branco S.A. Industria e Comercio de Alimentos - Gorduras e Margarinas Especiais Plant (1)
Rua Jose Setubal Pessoa 255 - Mucuripe, Fortaleza, 60180-560, Ceara, Brazil
Tel.: (55) 8533918200
Biscuit & Pasta Mfr
N.A.I.C.S.: 311821

M. Dias Branco S.A. Industria e Comercio de Alimentos - Grande Moinho Aratu Plant (1)
Rod BA 528 Estrada da Base Naval s/n Sao Tome de Paripe, Salvador, 40820-260, Bahia, Brazil
Tel.: (55) 7134137500
Biscuit & Pasta Mfr
N.A.I.C.S.: 311824

M. Dias Branco S.A. Industria e Comercio de Alimentos - Grande Moinho Potiguar Plant (1)
Avenida Hildebrando Gois 1/117 - Ribeira, Natal, 59010-700, Rio Grande do Norte, Brazil
Tel.: (55) 8440082500
Pasta, Flour & Wheat Mfr
N.A.I.C.S.: 311824

M. Dias Branco S.A. Industria e Comercio de Alimentos - Grande Moinho Tambau Plant (1)
Rua Conde Augusto Chiericartte s/n - Centro, Cabedelo, Joao Pessoa, 58100-355, Paraiba, Brazil
Tel.: (55) 8340094800
Pasta, Flour & Wheat Mfr
N.A.I.C.S.: 311824

M. Dias Branco S.A. Industria e Comercio de Alimentos - Moinho Dias Branco Plant (1)
Esplanada do Mucuripe s/n Patio B1- Mucuripe, Fortaleza, 60191-070, Ceara, Brazil
Tel.: (55) 8540093599
Pasta, Flour & Wheat Mfr
N.A.I.C.S.: 311824

M. Dias Branco S.A. Industria e Comercio de Alimentos - Moinho Dias Branco Rolandia Plant (1)
Rodovia BR 369 KM 178-Gleba Tres Bocas, Rolandia, 86600-970, Parana, Brazil
Tel.: (55) 8540055105
Pasta, Flour & Wheat Mfr
N.A.I.C.S.: 311824

M.DIAS BRANCO S.A. IND COM DE ALIMENTOS - Fortaleza Plant (1)
BR 116 KM 18 - Jabuti, Eusebio, 61760-000, Brazil
Tel.: (55) 8540055500
Cookie & Cracker Mfr
N.A.I.C.S.: 311821

M. G. INTERNATIONAL TRANSPORTS GMBH
Koblenzer Strasse 40, 57072, Siegen, Germany
Tel.: (49) 27140930
Web Site: http://www.mgint.de
Year Founded: 1891
Sales Range: $100-124.9 Million
Emp.: 25
Freight Transportation Services
N.A.I.C.S.: 488510

M.C.S. STEEL PUBLIC COMPANY LIMITED
70 Moo 2 Changyai, Bangsai, Ayutthaya, 13290, Thailand
Tel.: (66) 35372961
Web Site: https://www.mcssteel.com
Year Founded: 1992
MCS—(THA)
Rev.: $169,870,498
Assets: $153,893,775
Liabilities: $44,054,271
Net Worth: $109,839,504
Earnings: $4,221,102
Emp.: 592

Fiscal Year-end: 12/31/23
Steel Designing & Fabrication Services
N.A.I.C.S.: 238120
Phairat Viwatborvornwong (Chief Plng & Construction Officer)

Subsidiaries:

M.C.S. Steel - Xiamen Co., Ltd. (1)
No 68 Shanbian Road Dongfu Town, Haicang District, Xiamen, 361027, Fujian, China
Tel.: (86) 5926511711
Fabricated Steel Mfr & Distr
N.A.I.C.S.: 332312

M.H. ALSHAYA CO. W.L.L.
PO Box 181, Safat, Kuwait, 13002, Kuwait
Tel.: (965) 2242000
Web Site: http://www.alshaya.com
Year Founded: 1890
Sales Range: $1-4.9 Billion
Emp.: 7,000
Retail Store Owner
N.A.I.C.S.: 455219
Mohammed H. Alshaya (Chm)

M.H. DADABHOY GROUP OF COMPANIES
Office 4 Second Floor Plot 30C Ittehad Lane 12, Phase VII Defence Officer Housing Authority, Karachi, 75950, Pakistan
Tel.: (92) 21 35312002 03   PK
Web Site: http://www.mhdadabhoy.com
Holding Company
N.A.I.C.S.: 551112
Muhammad Hussain Dadabhoy (Chm)

Subsidiaries:

DADABHOY CEMENT INDUSTRIES LIMITED (1)
Office 4 Second Floor Plot 30C Ittehad Lane 12, Phase VII Defence Officer Housing Authority, Karachi, 74000, Pakistan
Tel.: (92) 2135312002
Web Site: https://mhdadabhoy.com
Cement Mfr
N.A.I.C.S.: 327310
Muhammad Hussain Dadabhoy (Chm)

DADABHOY CONSTRUCTION TECHNOLOGY LIMITED (1)
Office 4 Second Floor Plot 30C Ittehad Lane 12, Phase VII, Karachi, Pakistan
Tel.: (92) 2135312002
Rev.: $526
Assets: $430,805
Liabilities: $480,293
Net Worth: ($49,488)
Earnings: ($60,926)
Fiscal Year-end: 06/30/2019
Prefabricated Construction Materials Mfr
N.A.I.C.S.: 236210
Muhammad Hussain Dadabhoy (Chm)

DADABHOY SACK LIMITED (1)
C-30/II 24th Commercial St Phase II-Ext PDOHA, Karachi, 74000, Pakistan
Tel.: (92) 2135312002
Web Site: http://www.mhdadabhoy.com
Kraft Paper Sack Mfr
N.A.I.C.S.: 314910
Muhammad Hussain Dadabhoy (Chm)

M.I. CEMENT FACTORY LIMITED
Delta Life Tower 3rd and 6th Floor Plot 37 Rd 45 S & 90 NGulshan 2, Dhaka, 1212, Bangladesh
Tel.: (880) 802222263631
Web Site: https://www.crowncement.com
Year Founded: 1998
CROWNCEMNT—(DHA)
Rev.: $220,591,805
Assets: $208,433,653
Liabilities: $137,698,367

Net Worth: $70,735,285
Earnings: $5,568,240
Emp.: 1,480
Fiscal Year-end: 06/30/23
Cement Mfr
N.A.I.C.S.: 327310
Mohammad Mahfuzul Hoque (Gen Mgr-Supply Chain Mgmt)

M.J. INTERNATIONAL CO., LTD.
No 126 Danuan Rd Tucheng Dist, New Taipei City, 236, Taiwan
Tel.: (886) 222684666   TW
Web Site: https://www.mjig.com
Year Founded: 1982
8466—(TAI)
Rev.: $88,375,483
Assets: $204,815,617
Liabilities: $124,776,836
Net Worth: $80,038,782
Earnings: $3,127,081)
Fiscal Year-end: 12/31/23
Wood Floor Mfr & Distr
N.A.I.C.S.: 327120
Brandon Liao (Mgr-IT)

M.J. MAILLIS S.A.
7 Kavalieratou Taki Str, 145 64, Kifissia, Athens, Greece
Tel.: (30) 2106285000   GR
Web Site: http://www.maillis.gr
Year Founded: 1968
MAIK—(ATH)
Sales Range: $350-399.9 Million
Emp.: 1,376
Mfr & Distributor of End Line Industrial Solutions, Including Strapping, Wrapping & Taping Packaging Material, Strapping Tools & Machines
N.A.I.C.S.: 425120
Michael J. Maillis (Chm)

Subsidiaries:

3L SRL (1)
Via Dei Falegnami 11, 41049, Sassuolo, Modena, Italy
Tel.: (39) 0536813143
Electronic Components Mfr
N.A.I.C.S.: 334419

M.J. Maillis Espana, S.L. (1)
CL Palau de Plegamans 21-23, 08213, Polinya, Barcelona, Spain
Tel.: (34) 937133222
Web Site: http://www.maillis.es
Packaging Machinery Import & Distr
N.A.I.C.S.: 423830

M.J. Maillis France SAS (1)
10 rue de la grande ourse, 95800, Cergy, Val-d'Oise, France
Tel.: (33) 134407080
Web Site: http://www.maillis.com
Sales Range: $50-74.9 Million
Emp.: 12
Packaging Machinery Import & Distr
N.A.I.C.S.: 423830
Konstantinos Marinakis (Mgr)

M.J. Maillis Hungary Packing Systems Ltd. (1)
Totharpad 1, Budapest, 1183, Hungary
Tel.: (36) 12906385
Web Site: http://www.maillis.com
Sales Range: $50-74.9 Million
Emp.: 7
Packaging Machinery Import & Distr
N.A.I.C.S.: 423830
Dimitrios Kelesidis (Country Mgr)

M.J. Maillis Romania S.A. (1)
DN Bucuresti Targoviste Nr 1 km 16 5, Buftea, Ilfov, Romania
Tel.: (40) 21 3050800
Sales Range: $10-24.9 Million
Emp.: 20
Packaging Material Mfr & Distr
N.A.I.C.S.: 322220
Michail Maillis (CEO)

M.J.Maillis Czech s.r.o. (1)

M.J. MAILLIS S.A.

M.J. Maillis S.A.—(Continued)

Sterboholska 1434/102a, 102 19, Prague, Czech Republic
Tel.: (420) 272011341
Web Site: http://www.maillis.cz
Sales Range: $50-74.9 Million
Emp.: 10
Packaging Machinery Import & Distr
N.A.I.C.S.: 423830

MARFLEX-M.J.Maillis Poland Sp. z o.o. (1)
ul Przemyslowa 4, 05-480, Karczew, Masovian, Poland
Tel.: (48) 227181800
Web Site: http://www.maillis.pl
Sales Range: $50-74.9 Million
Emp.: 200
Packaging Machinery Mfr
N.A.I.C.S.: 333993
Tomasz Sikorski *(Mgr-Logistics)*

Straptech AE (1)
Takhkabalearipou 7, Kifissia, Athens, 14564, Greece
Tel.: (30) 2106285300
Web Site: http://www.maillis.com
Emp.: 60
Packaging Machinery Import & Distr
N.A.I.C.S.: 423830
John Lentzos *(COO)*

M.K. PROTEINS LTD.
Naraingarh Road, Village Garnala, Ambala, 134003, Haryana, India
Tel.: (91) 1712679358
Web Site: https://www.mkproteins.in
MKPL—(NSE)
Rev.: $42,471,419
Assets: $9,193,718
Liabilities: $5,189,023
Net Worth: $4,004,695
Earnings: $1,418,080
Emp.: 38
Fiscal Year-end: 03/31/21
Vegetable Refined Oil Mfr
N.A.I.C.S.: 311225
Vinod Kumar *(Mng Dir)*

M.M. WARBURG & CO. KGAA
Ferdinandstrasse 75, 20095, Hamburg, Germany
Tel.: (49) 4032820   De
Web Site:
    http://www.mmwarburg.com
Year Founded: 1798
Rev.: $214,851,698
Assets: $6,149,459,482
Liabilities: $5,824,219,053
Net Worth: $325,240,429
Emp.: 684
Fiscal Year-end: 12/31/18
Banking Services
N.A.I.C.S.: 522320
Jens Kruse *(Exec Dir)*

Subsidiaries:

Allgemeine Verwaltungsgesellschaft mbH (1)
Kuferstr 9 -11, 67551, Worms, Germany
Tel.: (49) 6247908900
Financial Advisory Services
N.A.I.C.S.: 523940

Bankhaus Carl F. Plump & Co. (1)
Am Markt 19, 28195, Bremen, Germany (51%)
Tel.: (49) 42136850
Web Site: http://www.bankhaus-plump.de
Sales Range: $50-74.9 Million
Emp.: 35
Commercial Banking Services
N.A.I.C.S.: 522110
Peter Hiel *(Mgr-Personnel)*

Bankhaus Hallbaum AG & Co. Kommanditgesellschaft (1)
An der Borse 7, 30159, Hannover, Germany (100%)
Tel.: (49) 51130120
Web Site: http://www.hallbaum-bank.de
Sales Range: $50-74.9 Million
Emp.: 100
Commercial Bank
N.A.I.C.S.: 522110

Hamburgische Seehandlung Gesellschaft fur Schiffsbeteiligungen mbH & Co. KG (1)
Brodschrangen 3-5, 20457, Hamburg, Germany
Tel.: (49) 40348420
Web Site: http://www.seehandlung.de
Sales Range: $50-74.9 Million
Emp.: 8
Investment Services
N.A.I.C.S.: 525910

Hansa Hamburg Shipping International GmbH & Co. KG (1)
Ballindamm 6, Hamburg, 20095, Germany (100%)
Tel.: (49) 403500460
Web Site: http://www.hansahamburg.de
Sales Range: $25-49.9 Million
Emp.: 14
Provider of Shipping Services
N.A.I.C.S.: 488330
Harald Block *(Mng Dir)*

Lederwerke Wieman GmbH (1)
Ferdinandstr 75, 20095, Hamburg, Germany
Tel.: (49) 4032822
Financial Advisory Services
N.A.I.C.S.: 523940

M.M. Warburg & CO Hypothekenbank AG (1)
Colonnaden 5, Hamburg, 20354, Germany (79%)
Tel.: (49) 403553340
Web Site: http://www.warburghyp.de
Sales Range: $50-74.9 Million
Emp.: 27
Commercial Bank
N.A.I.C.S.: 522110
Klaus Ruepke *(Mgr-Capital Market)*

M.M. Warburg & CO Luxembourg S.A. (1)
2 Pl Dargent, Luxembourg, 1413, Luxembourg (100%)
Tel.: (352) 4245451
Web Site: http://www.mmwarburg.lu
Sales Range: $50-74.9 Million
Emp.: 100
Commercial Bank
N.A.I.C.S.: 522110
Riener Scheffels *(Gen Mgr)*

M.M. Warburg & Co. Assekuranzmakler GmbH (1)
Neuer Wall 77, D20354, Hamburg, Germany (100%)
Tel.: (49) 32825220
Web Site: http://www.mmwarburg.com
Sales Range: $50-74.9 Million
Emp.: 6
Provider of Investment Banking Services
N.A.I.C.S.: 525910

M.M. Warburg & Co. Fonds-Vertrieb (1)
Ferdinandstrasse 75, Hamburg, 20095, Germany (100%)
Tel.: (49) 4032820
Web Site: http://www.mmwarburg.com
Sales Range: $150-199.9 Million
Emp.: 500
Asset Management & Banking Services
N.A.I.C.S.: 531390
Philip Marx *(Gen Mgr)*

M.M. Warburg & Co. Schiffahrtstreuhand GmbH (1)
Ferdinandstrasse 75, 20095, Hamburg, Germany (100%)
Tel.: (49) 4032820
Web Site: http://www.mmwarburg.de
Sales Range: $50-74.9 Million
Emp.: 420
Provider of Investment Services
N.A.I.C.S.: 525910
Ingrid Kinsmueller *(Mng Dir)*

M.M. Warburg Bank (Schweiz) AG (1)
Parkring 12, CH 8027, Zurich, Switzerland (100%)
Tel.: (41) 12062323
Web Site: http://www.mmwarburg.ch
Sales Range: $50-74.9 Million
Emp.: 27
Commercial Bank
N.A.I.C.S.: 522110
Thomas Vorwerk *(CEO)*

Subsidiary (Domestic):

Mandatropa AG (2)
Angererstrasse 6, PO Box 370, 8027, Zurich, Switzerland
Tel.: (41) 1 208 99 88
Web Site: http://www.mandatropa.ch
Auditing & Business Consulting Services
N.A.I.C.S.: 541219
Wolfgang A. Kaemmler *(CEO & Gen Mgr)*

M.M. Warburg-LuxInvest S.A. (1)
2 Place Dargent, Luxembourg, 1413, Luxembourg
Tel.: (352) 424491
Web Site: http://www.luxinvest.lu
Sales Range: $50-74.9 Million
Emp.: 100
Provider of Investment Services
N.A.I.C.S.: 525910
Sabeena Bucher *(Mng Dir)*

Marcard Family Office Treuhand GmbH (1)
Ballindamm 36, 20095, Hamburg, Germany
Tel.: (49) 40320990
Web Site: http://www.marcard.de
Commercial Banking Services
N.A.I.C.S.: 522110

Marcard, Stein & Co. GmbH & Co. KG (1)
Ballindamm 36, D 20095, Hamburg, Germany (100%)
Tel.: (49) 40320990
Web Site: http://www.marcard.de
Rev.: $15,000,000
Emp.: 50
Commercial Bank
N.A.I.C.S.: 522110

NESTOR-Fonds-Vertriebs-GmbH (1)
Ottostr 5, 80333, Munich, Germany
Tel.: (49) 8954590380
Commercial Banking Services
N.A.I.C.S.: 522110

RHL Hamburger Lloyd Shipping Trust GmbH (1)
Raboisen 38, 20095, Hamburg, Germany
Tel.: (49) 40380881300
Commercial Banking Services
N.A.I.C.S.: 522110

Schwabische Bank AG (1)
Konigstrabe 28, 70173, Stuttgart, Germany
Tel.: (49) 711229220
Web Site: http://www.schwaebische-bank.de
Commercial Banking Services
N.A.I.C.S.: 522110

Verwaltung MS Pacific Beteiligungsgesellschaft mbH (1)
Neuer Wall 42, 20354, Hamburg, Germany
Tel.: (49) 403500460
Emp.: 6
Commercial Banking Services
N.A.I.C.S.: 522110
Harald Block *(Gen Mgr)*

Warburg - Henderson Kapitalanlagegesellschaft fur Immobilien mbH (1)
Gertrudenstrasse 9, 20095, Hamburg, Germany (50%)
Tel.: (49) 40 32 82 36 00
Web Site: http://www.warburg-hih.com
Sales Range: $50-74.9 Million
Emp.: 15
Investment Services
N.A.I.C.S.: 525910
Andreas Beckers *(Chief Scientific Officer)*

Warburg Alternative Investments AG (1)
Ager Street 6, 8002, Zurich, Switzerland
Tel.: (41) 442059444
Web Site: http://www.warburg-ai.com
Sales Range: $50-74.9 Million
Emp.: 10
Financial Services
N.A.I.C.S.: 523999

INTERNATIONAL PUBLIC

Siegmar Thakur-Weigold *(Mng Dir)*

Warburg Asset Management GmbH (1)
Liebig Str 6, D 60323, Frankfurt am Main, Hessen, Germany (100%)
Tel.: (49) 6917097410
Web Site: http://www.warburg-fonds.de
Sales Range: $50-74.9 Million
Emp.: 35
Provider of Asset Management Services
N.A.I.C.S.: 525910

Warburg Invest Kapitalanlagegesellschaft mbH (1)
20095 Hamburg Ferdinand Strassee, D 65627, Hamburg, Germany (100%)
Tel.: (49) 69170970
Web Site: http://www.warburg-funds.com
Sales Range: $50-74.9 Million
Emp.: 13
Asset Management & Banking Services
N.A.I.C.S.: 531390

Warburg Research GmbH (1)
Hermannstrasse 9, Hamburg, 20095, Germany (100%)
Tel.: (49) 403095370
Web Site: http://www.warburg-research.com
Sales Range: $25-49.9 Million
Emp.: 35
Financial Research Services
N.A.I.C.S.: 541720
Henner Ruschmeier *(Member-Mgmt Bd)*

M.P. AGRO INDUSTRIES LIMITED
924 9th Floor Fortune Tower Sayajigunj, Vadodara, 390020, India
Tel.: (91) 2653152583
Web Site:
    https://www.mpagroindustries.in
506543—(BOM)
Rev.: $30,106
Assets: $721,758
Liabilities: $13,999
Net Worth: $707,760
Earnings: $2,618
Emp.: 5
Fiscal Year-end: 03/31/23
Fertilizer Mfr & Whslr
N.A.I.C.S.: 325314
Yunus R. Memon *(Mng Dir)*

M.P. EVANS GROUP PLC
3 Clanricarde Gardens Tunbridge Wells, Tunbridge Wells, TN1 1HQ, Kent, United Kingdom
Tel.: (44) 1892516333
Web Site:
    https://www.mpevans.co.uk
MPE—(AIM)
Rev.: $326,917,000
Assets: $590,258,000
Liabilities: $101,414,000
Net Worth: $488,844,000
Earnings: $78,361,000
Emp.: 11,500
Fiscal Year-end: 12/31/22
Holding Company; Agricultural Products Developer
N.A.I.C.S.: 551112
Peter E. Hadsley-Chaplin *(Chm)*

Subsidiaries:

P.T. Dharma Agung (1)
Alamanda Tower 22nd Floor Jl TB Simatupang Kav 23-24 Cilandak Barat, Jakarta Selatan, Indonesia
Tel.: (62) 2129661956
Web Site: https://www.daw.co.id
Renewable Energy Generation Services
N.A.I.C.S.: 221114

Supara Company Limited (1)
363-375 Rama 4 Rd Rongmuang Pathumwan, Bangkok, Thailand
Tel.: (66) 22151541
Sales Range: $25-49.9 Million
Emp.: 50
Rubber Products Mfr & Export Services
N.A.I.C.S.: 325212

AND PRIVATE COMPANIES

M.R. ORGANISATION LIMITED
4th Floor D Block Sumel-11 Nr Relaince Mart Namaste Circle Shaibaug, Ahmedabad, 380052, India
Tel.: (91) 7929098077
Web Site:
  http://www.mrorganisation.com
Year Founded: 1984
MRO—(NSE)
Electronic Part Mfr & Distr
N.A.I.C.S.: 334419
Mayur Kamdar (Mng Dir)

M.S. JACOVIDES & CO. LTD.
8 Ayios Nicolaos St, 1055, Nicosia, Cyprus
Tel.: (357) 22757188
Web Site:
  http://www.msjacovides.com.cy
Sales Range: $50-74.9 Million
Emp.: 400
Pharmaceutical, Medical & Consumer Health Products Distr
N.A.I.C.S.: 325412
Sotos M. Jacovides (Mng Dir)

M.S.A. FORD SALES LTD.
30295 Automall Drive, Abbotsford, V2T5M1, BC, Canada
Tel.: (604) 857-2293
Web Site: http://www.msaford.com
Year Founded: 1951
Rev.: $23,574,955
Emp.: 65
New & Used Car Dealers
N.A.I.C.S.: 441110
Mike McDonald (Pres)

M.T.L. PRINT LTD.
David Navon 5 Str, Magshimim, 56910, Israel
Tel.: (972) 3 9082800
Printing Technology Developer
N.A.I.C.S.: 333248
Ran Emanuel (CEO)

M.Y GROUP LIMITED
Lot 26 Latui Road, Wailada Lami, Suva, Fiji
Tel.: (679) 3300192   FJ
Web Site: http://www.my-groupfiji.com
Holding Company
N.A.I.C.S.: 551112
Mohammed Aiyub (CEO)

M/S NILA SPACES LIMITED
1st Floor Sambhaav House Opp Chief Justices Bungalow Bodakdev, Ahmedabad, 380015, India
Tel.: (91) 7940036817
Web Site:
  https://www.nilaspaces.com
542231—(BOM)
Rev.: $415,377
Assets: $21,999,073
Liabilities: $8,160,190
Net Worth: $13,838,883
Earnings: ($492,351)
Emp.: 24
Fiscal Year-end: 03/31/23
Real Estate Manangement Services
N.A.I.C.S.: 531390
Anand Patel (Exec Dir)

M1 D.D. LJUBLJANA
Vojkova cesta 58, 1000, Ljubljana, Slovenia
Tel.: (386) 12340150
Web Site: http://www.m1-dd.si
MR1R—(LJU)
Sales Range: $10-24.9 Million
Emp.: 5
Investment Services
N.A.I.C.S.: 523999

M1 KLINIKEN AG
Grunauer Strasse 5, 12557, Berlin, Germany
Tel.: (49) 30347474414
Web Site: https://www.m1-kliniken.de
Year Founded: 2007
M12—(DEU)
Rev.: $304,919,220
Assets: $210,580,045
Liabilities: $57,687,538
Net Worth: $152,892,507
Earnings: $7,556,458
Emp.: 292
Fiscal Year-end: 12/31/22
Holding Company
N.A.I.C.S.: 551112
Attila Strauss (Co-CEO & Member-Mgmt Bd)

Subsidiaries:

BEAUTY Now GmbH (1)
Murrhardterweg 11, Baden-Wurttemberg, 71732, Tamm, Germany
Tel.: (49) 71415058318
Beauty Care Services
N.A.I.C.S.: 812112

HAEMATO Pharm GmbH (1)
Lilienthalstrasse 3a, D-12529, Schonefeld, Germany
Tel.: (49) 306779867600
Web Site: https://www.haemato.de
Drug & Cosmetic Product Distr
N.A.I.C.S.: 424210

Haemato AG (1)
Lilienthalstrasse 3a, 12529, Schonefeld, Germany
Tel.: (49) 30897308670
Web Site: https://haemato.de
Pharmaceuticals Mfr
N.A.I.C.S.: 325412

Haemato Med GmbH (1)
Lilienthalstrasse 3a, 12529, Schonefeld, Germany
Tel.: (49) 30516538535
Pharmaceuticals Mfr
N.A.I.C.S.: 325412

M1 Med Beauty Croatia d.o.o. (1)
Meduliceva ulica 21, 10 000, Zagreb, Croatia
Tel.: (385) 17776840
Aesthetic Treatment Services
N.A.I.C.S.: 812199

M1 Med Beauty Hungary Kft. (1)
Andrassy ut 1 1 em 2, 1061, Budapest, Hungary
Tel.: (36) 12197070
Aesthetic Treatment Services
N.A.I.C.S.: 812199

M1 Med Beauty Netherlands B.V. (1)
Minervalaan 15HS, 1077 NJ, Amsterdam, Netherlands
Tel.: (31) 203697169
Web Site: https://www.m1-beauty.nl
Cosmetics Whslr
N.A.I.C.S.: 424210

M1 Med Beauty UK Ltd. (1)
164 New Cavendish Street, London, W1W 6YT, United Kingdom
Tel.: (44) 2036701772
Web Site: https://www.m1-beauty.co.uk
Cosmetics Whslr
N.A.I.C.S.: 424210

M1 LIMITED
10 International Business Park, Singapore, 609928, Singapore
Tel.: (65) 66551111
Web Site: http://www.m1.com.sg
Year Founded: 1994
Rev.: $801,164,339
Assets: $949,232,170
Liabilities: $628,425,641
Net Worth: $320,806,529
Earnings: $99,126,285
Emp.: 1,541
Fiscal Year-end: 12/31/17
Telecommunication Servicesb
N.A.I.C.S.: 517112
Kok Chew Lee (CFO)

Subsidiaries:

M1 Net Ltd. (1)
9 International Business Park, Singapore, 609915, Singapore
Tel.: (65) 66555633
Web Site: http://www.m1net.com.sg
Mobile Telecommunications Services
N.A.I.C.S.: 517112

M2 COMMUNICATIONS LTD
Normans Media Ltd Stokewood House, Warminster Road, Limpley Stoke, BA2 7GB, Bath, United Kingdom
Tel.: (44) 2070470200
Web Site: http://www.m2.com
Sales Range: $25-49.9 Million
Emp.: 46
Business & News Publisher
N.A.I.C.S.: 513120
Thomas A. Naysmith (Mng Dir)

M2I CORPORATION
M2I Bldg 11-35 Simin-daero 327beon-gil, Dongan-gu, Anyang, 14055, Gyeonggi-do, Korea (South)
Tel.: (82) 314653366
Web Site: https://www.m2i.co.kr
Year Founded: 1999
347890—(KRS)
Rev.: $31,970,583
Assets: $60,796,786
Liabilities: $4,799,756
Net Worth: $55,997,030
Earnings: $8,042,613
Emp.: 100
Fiscal Year-end: 12/31/22
Software Development Services
N.A.I.C.S.: 541511

Subsidiaries:

Kien Tao Engineering Co., Ltd. (1)
118/9/3 Le Loi Street, Go Vap District, Ho Chi Minh City, Vietnam
Tel.: (84) 2862928567
Web Site: https://www.kientaosaigon.com
Electronic Equipment Distr
N.A.I.C.S.: 423690

Perfect Automation Private Limited (1)
Unit No 141 First Floor B Wings Nahar & Seth Industrial Premises, CHS Ltd Pannalal Silk Mills Compound LBS Marg Bhandup W, Mumbai, 400078, Maharashtra, India
Tel.: (91) 9930994983
Web Site: https://www.perfectautomation.net
Electronic Components Mfr
N.A.I.C.S.: 334419

RJ Connect S.A. (1)
1 Avocet Close, Bromhof, Johannesburg, 2154, South Africa
Tel.: (27) 117810777
Web Site: https://rjconnect.co.za
Industrial Automation Services
N.A.I.C.S.: 541420

Retronic Sdn. Bhd. (1)
37A Jalan SS18/1B, Subang Jaya, 47500, Petaling Jaya, Malaysia
Tel.: (60) 356354613
Web Site: https://www.retronic.com.my
Industrial Automation Services
N.A.I.C.S.: 541420

Roboreps, Inc. (1)
5782 James Dr, Stevensville, MI 49127
Web Site: https://www.roboreps.com
Industrial Equipment Mfr
N.A.I.C.S.: 333413

Sebong Vina Company Limited (1)
OTM3 Can So 7-8 khu nha Pho TM du an Cat Tuong Smart City, Yen Trung, Yen Phong, Bac Ninh, Vietnam
Tel.: (84) 393665382
Web Site: https://sebongvina.com
Automation Product Mfr
N.A.I.C.S.: 335314

Serad S.A.R.L. (1)
271 Route des Cretes, 44440, Teilhet, France
Tel.: (33) 240972454
Web Site: https://www.serad.com
Industrial Automation Services
N.A.I.C.S.: 541420

Suer LLC (1)
St Dmitry Shamshurina 10 floor 1, Novosibirsk, Russia
Tel.: (7) 83833750050
Web Site: https://www.suer.ru
Industrial Automation Services
N.A.I.C.S.: 541420

YT Automation Singapore Pte. Ltd. (1)
21 Bukit Batok Crescent 22-79 WCEGA Tower, Singapore, 658065, Singapore
Tel.: (65) 66840702
Web Site: https://www.ytautomation.com
Electronic Equipment Distr
N.A.I.C.S.: 423690

M2I SA
18-19 Place des Reflets, 92400, Courbevoie, France
Tel.: (33) 144533600
Web Site: https://www.m2iformation.fr
Year Founded: 1985
ALMII—(EUR)
Information Technology Services
N.A.I.C.S.: 541512
Georges Seban (Chm)

M2M GROUP SA
16 Rue Abdelhak Ben Mehyou, Quartier Palmiers, 20040, Casablanca, Morocco
Tel.: (212) 522435300
Web Site:
  https://www.m2mgroup.com
Year Founded: 1990
M2M—(CAS)
Sales Range: $10-24.9 Million
Emp.: 160
Computer Peripheral Equipment Whslr
N.A.I.C.S.: 423430
Brahim Eddahbi (Dir-Fin & Fin Mgr-Administration)

M2N CO., LTD.
13F Hanwha Bldg 109 Sogong-ro, Jung-gu, Seoul, Korea (South)
Tel.: (82) 226362431
Web Site: http://www.m2ncorp.com
Year Founded: 1965
033310—(KRS)
Rev.: $21,821,729
Assets: $141,960,441
Liabilities: $33,493,865
Net Worth: $108,466,576
Earnings: $3,950,608
Emp.: 57
Fiscal Year-end: 12/31/22
Steel Drum Mfr & Whslr
N.A.I.C.S.: 332439
Lee Seung Geon (Mng Dir)

M3 METALS CORP.
300-1455 Bellevue Ave West, Vancouver, V6E 2K3, BC, Canada
Tel.: (604) 669-2279   Ca
Web Site:
  https://www.m3metalscorp.com
Year Founded: 2007
MT—(OTCIQ)
Assets: $827,722
Liabilities: $189,083
Net Worth: $638,639
Earnings: ($1,684,800)
Fiscal Year-end: 08/31/21
Gold Exploration & Mining Services
N.A.I.C.S.: 212220
Brian Patrick Morrison (CFO)

M3 MINING LIMITED

M3 MINING LIMITED

M3 Mining Limited—(Continued)
225 St Georges Terrace, Perth, 6000, WA, Australia
Tel.: (61) 24366581 AU
Web Site: https://www.m3mining.com.au
Year Founded: 2020
M3M—(ASX)
Mining Services
N.A.I.C.S.: 212290
Ben Donovan *(Sec)*

M3 STEEL STRUCTURES LTD.
405 Mount Paul Way, Kamloops, V2H 1A8, BC, Canada
Tel.: (250) 374-1074
Web Site: https://www.m3steel.com
Sales Range: $10-24.9 Million
Emp.: 50
Fabricated Structural Steel & Metal Mfr
N.A.I.C.S.: 332312
Vance Smelland *(Gen Mgr)*

MA FINANCIAL GROUP LIMITED
Level 27 Brookfield Place 10 Carrington Street, Sydney, 2000, NSW, Australia
Tel.: (61) 282885555 AU
Web Site: https://mafinancial.com
Year Founded: 2009
MAF—(ASX)
Rev.: $521,337,783
Assets: $2,434,346,434
Liabilities: $2,120,226,142
Net Worth: $314,120,292
Earnings: $21,169,539
Emp.: 600
Fiscal Year-end: 12/31/23
Financial Advisory Services
N.A.I.C.S.: 523940
Andrew Pridham *(Vice Chm-Grp)*

Subsidiaries:

Redcape Hotel Group Pty Ltd (1)
Level 1 287 Military Rd, Cremorne, 2090, NSW, Australia
Tel.: (61) 297194000
Web Site: https://www.redcape.com.au
Emp.: 1,000
Hotel Operator
N.A.I.C.S.: 721120
Dan Brady *(CEO)*

MA KUANG HEALTHCARE HOLDINGS LTD.
106A Henderson Crescent, Singapore, 151106, Singapore
Tel.: (65) 68844772
Web Site: https://makuang.com.sg
Year Founded: 2011
4139—(TPE)
Rev.: $33,103,367
Assets: $48,505,831
Liabilities: $33,238,564
Net Worth: $15,267,267
Earnings: $(1,110,527)
Fiscal Year-end: 12/31/22
Health Care Srvices
N.A.I.C.S.: 621999

Subsidiaries:

MA KUANG HEALTHCARE GROUP Pte. Ltd. (1)
106A Henderson Crescent, Singapore, 151106, Singapore
Tel.: (65) 68844772
Web Site: https://www.makuang.com.sg
Healthcare Services
N.A.I.C.S.: 621498

MAA GROUP BERHAD
13th Floor No 566 Jalan Ipoh, 51200, Kuala Lumpur, Malaysia
Tel.: (60) 362568000 MY
Web Site: https://www.maa.my

Year Founded: 1968
MAA—(KLS)
Rev.: $59,967,831
Assets: $174,202,540
Liabilities: $98,377,143
Net Worth: $75,825,397
Earnings: $(2,407,417)
Fiscal Year-end: 06/30/23
Fire Insurance Services
N.A.I.C.S.: 524113
Lily Kam May Yin *(Sec)*

Subsidiaries:

10Star Cinemas Sdn. Bhd. (1)
Suite 11 05 11th Floor 566 Jalan Ipoh, 51200, Kuala Lumpur, Malaysia
Tel.: (60) 147034962
Web Site: https://www.10star.com.my
Digital Entertainment Services
N.A.I.C.S.: 541330

MAA General Assurance Philippines, Inc. (1)
10th Flr Pearlbank Centre 146 Valero Street, Salcedo Village, Makati, Philippines
Tel.: (63) 28672452
Web Site: http://www.maa.com.ph
General Insurance Services
N.A.I.C.S.: 524210
Santiago J. Ranada *(Chm)*

Maax Factor Sdn. Bhd. (1)
13th Floor No 566 Jalan Ipoh, 51200, Kuala Lumpur, Malaysia
Tel.: (60) 362568000
Web Site: https://www.maaxfactor.my
Trade Finance Services
N.A.I.C.S.: 522291

MAA JAGDAMBE TRADELINKS LTD.
Gala No 1 Ground Floor Ajinkyatara Compound, Near Basra Studio Road No 2 Singh Estate Samata Nagal Kandivali E, Mumbai, 400101, India
Tel.: (91) 2265121144
Web Site: http://www.jaajtl.com
Year Founded: 1985
Sales Range: $1-9.9 Million
Textile Mfr & Sales
N.A.I.C.S.: 314999
Kailash Bhageria *(CEO, CFO & Compliance Officer)*

MAABAROT PRODUCTS LTD.
Emek Hefer Kibbutz, Ma'abarot, 40230, Israel
Tel.: (972) 98984101
Baby Food & Ingredient Mfr
N.A.I.C.S.: 311422
Efrat Gilat *(CEO)*

MAAGH ADVERTISING & MARKETING SERVICES LIMITED
302 Kuber Complex 3rd Floor New Link Road, Opp Laxmi Industrial Estate Andheri West, Mumbai, 400053, Maharashtra, India
Tel.: (91) 2246033045
Web Site: https://www.maaghadvertising.in
Year Founded: 2013
543624—(BOM)
Advertising Agency Services
N.A.I.C.S.: 541810

MAAN ALUMINIUM LTD.
4/5 1st Floor Asaf Ali Road, New Delhi, 110002, India
Tel.: (91) 114 008 1800
Web Site: http://www.maanaluminium.in
532906—(NSE)
Rev.: $78,834,633
Assets: $23,401,888
Liabilities: $11,884,946
Net Worth: $11,516,942
Earnings: $3,000,147

Emp.: 204
Fiscal Year-end: 03/31/22
Aluminum Mfr
N.A.I.C.S.: 325180
Ravinder Nath Jain *(Chm & Mng Dir)*

MAAS GROUP HOLDINGS LIMITED
20L Sheraton Road, Dubbo, 2830, NSW, Australia
Tel.: (61) 258521800 AU
Web Site: https://www.maasgroup.com.au
Year Founded: 2002
MGH—(ASX)
Rev.: $525,085,740
Assets: $941,411,619
Liabilities: $531,101,910
Net Worth: $410,309,709
Earnings: $42,969,942
Emp.: 1,800
Fiscal Year-end: 06/30/23
Holding Company
N.A.I.C.S.: 551112
Craig Bellamy *(CFO)*

Subsidiaries:

A1 Earthworx Mining & Civil Pty. Limited (1)
176 Wilbetree Road, PO Box 706, Mudgee, 2850, NSW, Australia
Tel.: (61) 263729238
Web Site: https://www.a1earthworx.com.au
Earthmoving & Civil Construction Services
N.A.I.C.S.: 541330

Brett Harvey Constructions Pty. Limited (1)
76 Azure Avenue, PO Box 2768, Dubbo, 2830, NSW, Australia
Tel.: (61) 268825971
Web Site: https://www.brettharvey.com.au
Drafting Services
N.A.I.C.S.: 541340

Dandy Premix Quarries Pty. Limited (1)
21-23 Bennet Street, Dandenong, 3175, VIC, Australia
Tel.: (61) 97038222
Web Site: https://www.dandypremix.com
Emp.: 150
Quarry Material & Cement Distr
N.A.I.C.S.: 423320

Garde Services Pty. Limited (1)
14 Carter Street, Lidcombe, 2141, NSW, Australia
Tel.: (61) 297378484
Web Site: https://www.garde.com.au
Cable Installation Services
N.A.I.C.S.: 238210

Jacon Equipment Pty. Limited (1)
1388 Kingsford Smith Drive, Pinkenba, 4008, QLD, Australia
Tel.: (61) 732601331
Web Site: https://www.jacon.com.au
Construction Machinery Mfr
N.A.I.C.S.: 333120

Regional Group Australia Pty. Limited (1)
20L Sheraton Road, Dubbo, 2880, NSW, Australia
Tel.: (61) 1800472835
Web Site: https://regionalgroupaustralia.com.au
Construction Materials Whslr
N.A.I.C.S.: 423320

MAAT PHARMA SA
70 Avenue Tony Garnier, 69007, Lyon, France
Tel.: (33) 428291400
Web Site: https://www.maatpharma.com
Year Founded: 2014
MAAT—(EUR)
Biotechnology Research & Development Services
N.A.I.C.S.: 541714
Herve Affagard *(Founder)*

INTERNATIONAL PUBLIC

MAAYAN VENTURES LTD.
Omer Industrial Park, PO Box 3010, Omer, 84965, Israel
Tel.: (972) 86255888
Web Site: http://www.myv.co.il
Year Founded: 1996
Sales Range: Less than $1 Million
Financial Investment Services
N.A.I.C.S.: 523999

MAB MANNESMANN GMBH
Theodorstr 182, 40472, Dusseldorf, Germany
Tel.: (49) 2116590
Web Site: http://www.mmec-mannesmann.com
Holding Company; Oil & Gas Industry Engineering & Construction Services
N.A.I.C.S.: 551112

Subsidiaries:

MMEC Mannesmann GmbH (1)
Theodorstr 182, 40472, Dusseldorf, Germany
Tel.: (49) 211 659 0
Web Site: http://www.mmec-mannesmann.com
Emp.: 250
Oil & Gas Plant Construction Engineering Services
N.A.I.C.S.: 237120
Claudia Burk *(Head-Procurement)*

MABANEE COMPANY S.A.K.
Al Rai Area Sheikh Zayed bin Sultan Al Nahyan Road, The Avenues - 2nd Avenue Entrance 9, Kuwait, Kuwait
Tel.: (965) 22244444
Web Site: https://www.mabanee.com
Year Founded: 1964
MABANEE—(KUW)
Rev.: $367,975,261
Assets: $3,687,957,525
Liabilities: $1,562,994,865
Net Worth: $2,124,962,660
Earnings: $197,837,102
Emp.: 313
Fiscal Year-end: 12/31/22
Real Estate Investment & Construction Services
N.A.I.C.S.: 531390
Mohammed Abdullatif Latif Alshaya *(Vice Chm)*

Subsidiaries:

Shomoul Holding Company L.L.C. (1)
K S A King Saud Bin Abdulaziz Road, Sipchem Tower, Al Khobar, 31952, Saudi Arabia
Tel.: (966) 138644422
Web Site: http://www.shomoul.sa
Real Estate Services
N.A.I.C.S.: 531390

MABION SA
gen Mariana Langiewicza 60, 95-050, Konstantynow Lodzki, Poland
Tel.: (48) 422077890
Web Site: https://www.mabion.eu
Year Founded: 2007
MAB—(WAR)
Rev.: $38,536,077
Assets: $52,910,061
Liabilities: $22,987,297
Net Worth: $29,922,764
Earnings: $10,485,010
Fiscal Year-end: 12/31/23
Pharmaceutical Preparation Manufacturing
N.A.I.C.S.: 325412
Slawomir Jaros *(Member-Mgmt Bd)*

MABPHARM LIMITED
Block G79 Lujia Road East & Koutai Road West, China Medical City, Taizhou, 225300, Jiangsu, China Ky
Web Site: https://www.mabpharm.cn

AND PRIVATE COMPANIES

Year Founded: 2018
2181—(HKG)
Rev.: $8,567,197
Assets: $140,573,392
Liabilities: $79,144,762
Net Worth: $61,428,630
Earnings: ($32,299,579)
Emp.: 417
Fiscal Year-end: 12/31/22
Pharmaceutical Product Mfr & Distr
N.A.I.C.S.: 325412
Jing Tao *(VP)*

MABUCHI MOTOR CO., LTD.
430 Matsuhidai, Matsudo, 270-2280, Chiba, Japan
Tel.: (81) 477101111 JP
Web Site: https://www.mabuchi-motor.co.jp
Year Founded: 1954
MBUMY—(OTCIQ)
Rev.: $1,035,388,173
Assets: $2,033,604,229
Liabilities: $182,431,450
Net Worth: $1,851,172,778
Earnings: $94,449,950
Emp.: 20,248
Fiscal Year-end: 12/31/22
Motor & Generator Mfr
N.A.I.C.S.: 335312
Hiroo Okoshi *(Pres & CEO)*

Subsidiaries:

Mabuch Precision (Jiangmen) Co., Ltd. (1)
No 3 315-A-1F 4F New Fortune Environmental Electroplating Base, Yamen Xinhui District, Jiangmen, 529000, Guangdong, China
Tel.: (86) 7506238301
Electric Motor & Parts Mfr
N.A.I.C.S.: 335312

Mabuchi Industry Co., Ltd. (1)
Office E 19/F Maxgrand Plaza No 3 Tai Yau Street, San Po Kong, Kowloon, China (Hong Kong)
Tel.: (852) 2 328 5575
Web Site: http://www.mabuchi-motor.co.jp
Electric Motor Distr
N.A.I.C.S.: 423610

Mabuchi Motor (Dongguan) Co., Ltd. (1)
Guancheng Sci & Technol Park Shilong Rd, Guancheng Science Technology Park, Dongguan, 523119, Guangdong, China
Tel.: (86) 76922267409
Sales Range: $200-249.9 Million
Emp.: 700
Electric Motor Mfr
N.A.I.C.S.: 333618

Mabuchi Motor (Europe) GmbH (1)
Herriotstrasse 1, 60528, Frankfurt am Main, Germany
Tel.: (49) 69 669 0220
Web Site: http://www.mabuchi-motor.co.jp
Sales Range: $25-49.9 Million
Electric Motor Sales
N.A.I.C.S.: 423610

Mabuchi Motor (Jiangsu) Co., Ltd. (1)
No 100 Liuxu Road Wujiang Economic and Technological Development Zone, Jiangsu, 215200, China
Tel.: (86) 51263451111
Electric Motor Mfr & Whslr
N.A.I.C.S.: 335312

Mabuchi Motor (Jiangxi) Co., Ltd. (1)
No 62 Jinlong Road Ganzhou Economic Technology Development Zone, Jiangxiang, 341000, Jiangxi, China
Tel.: (86) 7975555368
Electric Motor Mfr
N.A.I.C.S.: 335312

Mabuchi Motor (Shanghai) Co., Ltd. (1)
Room 1506-1510 Metro Plaza No 555 Lou Shan Guan Road, Changning District, Shanghai, 200051, China
Tel.: (86) 2162085666
Web Site: http://www.mabuchi-motor.co.jp
Sales Range: $25-49.9 Million
Electric Motor Mfr
N.A.I.C.S.: 335312

Mabuchi Motor (Singapore) Pte Ltd. (1)
111 North Bridge Road 12-05 Peninsula Plaza, Singapore, 179098, Singapore
Tel.: (65) 6 339 9991
Web Site: http://www.mabuchi-motor.co.jp
Sales Range: $25-49.9 Million
Emp.: 15
Small Electric Motor Distr
N.A.I.C.S.: 423610

Mabuchi Motor (Thailand) Co., Ltd. (1)
No 4345 Bhiraj Tower at BITEC Unit 2411-2412 24th Floor Sukhumvit Road, South-Bangna Sub-District Bangna District, Bangkok, 10260, Thailand
Tel.: (66) 20910624
Electric Motor Whslr
N.A.I.C.S.: 423610

Mabuchi Motor America Corp. (1)
3001 W Big Beaver Rd Ste 328, Troy, MI 48084
Tel.: (248) 816-3100
Small Electric Motor Distr
N.A.I.C.S.: 423610

Mabuchi Motor Dalian Co.,Ltd. (1)
No 41 Harbin Road, Dalian Economic and Technical Development Zone, Dalian, 116600, Liaoning, China
Tel.: (86) 4118 761 1111
Web Site: http://www.mabuchi-motor.co.jp
Sales Range: $800-899.9 Million
Electric Motor Mfr
N.A.I.C.S.: 335312

Mabuchi Motor Danang Ltd. (1)
LotA2 No 3 street Hoa Khanh Industrial Zone, Hoa Khanh Bac Ward Lien Chieu District, Da Nang, Vietnam
Tel.: (84) 236 373 1931
Web Site: http://www.mabuchi-motor.co.jp
Sales Range: $800-899.9 Million
Emp.: 5,000
Electric Motor Mfr & Distr
N.A.I.C.S.: 335312

Mabuchi Motor Dongguan Daojiao Co., Ltd. (1)
No 220 Yue Hui Road, Daojiao Town, Dongguan, 523179, Guangdong, China
Tel.: (86) 76988831848
Electric Motor Mfr
N.A.I.C.S.: 335312

Mabuchi Motor Electromag SA (1)
Chemin du Devent 7 Z I Larges Pieces A, 1024, Ecublens, Switzerland
Tel.: (41) 216941600
Web Site: https://www.electromagmotor.com
Electric Motor Distr
N.A.I.C.S.: 423610

Mabuchi Motor Korea Co.,Ltd. (1)
Ace High-End Tower III 1403 145 Gasan Digital 1-Ro, Geumcheon-Gu; Seoul, 08506, Korea (South)
Tel.: (82) 2 534 8131
Web Site: http://www.mabuchi-motor.co.jp
Electric Motor Whslr
N.A.I.C.S.: 423610

Mabuchi Motor Mexico S.A. De C.V. (1)
Circuito Cerezos Oriente 105 Parque Industrial San Francisco IV, 20305, San Francisco de los Romo, Aguascalientes, Mexico
Tel.: (52) 4494783200
Electric Motor Mfr & Whslr
N.A.I.C.S.: 335312

Mabuchi Motor Oken Co., Ltd. (1)
706 Yanokuchi, Inagi, Tokyo, 206-0812, Japan
Tel.: (81) 423780078
Web Site: https://www.okenseiko.com
Emp.: 55
Pumps Mfr
N.A.I.C.S.: 333914

Mabuchi Motor Poland Sp. Z o.o. (1)
Adolfa Mitery 14, 32-700, Bochnia, Poland
Tel.: (48) 122257711
Electric Motor Mfr
N.A.I.C.S.: 335312

Mabuchi Motor Taiwan Ltd. (1)
No 18 Chunghwa Road, Hsinchu Industrial District, Hsinchu, 30352, Taiwan
Tel.: (886) 35981111
Web Site: http://www.mabuchi-motor.co.jp
Sales Range: $100-124.9 Million
Emp.: 400
Electric Motor Mfr & Distr
N.A.I.C.S.: 335312

Mabuchi Motor Trading (Shenzhen) Co., Ltd (1)
Unit 1601 Excellence Times Plaza No 4068 Yitian Road, Futian District, Shenzhen, 518017, Guangdong, China
Tel.: (86) 75523998568
Web Site: http://www.mabuchi-motor.co.jp
Sales Range: $25-49.9 Million
Small Electric Motors Whslr
N.A.I.C.S.: 423610

Mabuchi Motor Vietnam Ltd. (1)
No 2 5A St Bienhoa II Indus Zone, Bien Hoa, Dongnai, Vietnam
Tel.: (84) 2513836711
Sales Range: $1-4.9 Billion
Emp.: 7,000
Small Electric Motors Mfr
N.A.I.C.S.: 333618

Mabuchi Motor Wafangdian Co.,Ltd. (1)
Laohutun Town, Wafangdian, 116322, Liangning, China
Tel.: (86) 4118 537 0241
Web Site: http://www.mabuchi-motor.co.jp
Electric Motor Mfr
N.A.I.C.S.: 335312

Mabuchi Taiwan Co., Ltd. (1)
No 18 Chunghwa Road, Hsinchu Industrial District, Hsinchu, 30352, Taiwan
Tel.: (886) 35981111
Electric Motor Mfr & Whslr
N.A.I.C.S.: 335312

MABUHAY HOLDINGS CORPORATION
35th Floor Rufino Pacfic Tower 6784 Ayala Avenue, Makati, 1223, Philippines
Tel.: (63) 288502000 PH
Web Site: https://www.mabuhayholdings.com
Year Founded: 1988
MHC—(PHI)
Rev.: $427,906
Assets: $14,531,936
Liabilities: $6,721,194
Net Worth: $7,810,742
Earnings: ($1,169,713)
Emp.: 8
Fiscal Year-end: 12/31/23
Investment Services
N.A.I.C.S.: 523940
Araceli C. Molina *(Officer-Compliance, Treas, VP & Mgr-Fin)*

MAC ALPHA LIMITED
Commerce House Wickhams Cay 1 Road Town, Tortola, VG1110, Virgin Islands (British) UK
Web Site: https://www.mac-alpha.com
Year Founded: 2021
MACA—(LSE)
Rev.: $10,631
Assets: $708,239
Liabilities: $74,547
Net Worth: $633,692
Earnings: ($408,310)
Fiscal Year-end: 06/30/23
Investment Management Service
N.A.I.C.S.: 523999
James Corsellis *(Chm)*

MAC HOTELS LTD.
Beach Plaza Behind hotel Miramar Nomoim Miramar Panaji, Panaji, 403 002, Goa, India
Tel.: (91) 8322461824
Web Site: https://www.machotels.net
541973—(BOM)
Rev.: $652,541
Assets: $836,595
Liabilities: $846,255
Net Worth: ($9,660)
Earnings: ($9,163)
Emp.: 30
Fiscal Year-end: 03/31/23
Hotel & Restaurant Operator
N.A.I.C.S.: 721110
Edgar Maximiano Do Rosario Cotta *(Mng Dir)*

MAC'S OYSTERS LTD.
7162 South Island Highway, Fanny Bay, V0R 1W0, BC, Canada
Tel.: (250) 335-2129 Ca
Web Site:
http://www.macsoysters.com
Year Founded: 1947
Fish & Seafood Whslr
N.A.I.C.S.: 424460

MAC-HOUSE CO., LTD.
Shin-Koenji Twin Building 1-7-7 Umesato, Suginami-ku, Tokyo, 166-0011, Japan
Tel.: (81) 333161911
Web Site: https://www.mac-house.co.jp
Year Founded: 1990
7603—(TKS)
Emp.: 339
Clothing Accessories Stores
N.A.I.C.S.: 458110
Koshiro Sugiura *(Mng Dir)*

MACA LIMITED
45 Division Street, Welshpool, 6106, WA, Australia
Tel.: (61) 8 6242 2600
Web Site: http://www.maca.net.au
Year Founded: 2002
MLD—(ASX)
Rev.: $927,548,848
Assets: $772,963,886
Liabilities: $475,982,512
Net Worth: $296,981,374
Earnings: $15,883,119
Emp.: 3,000
Fiscal Year-end: 06/30/21
Contract Mining, Civil Earthworks, Crushing, Screening & Material Haulage Solutions
N.A.I.C.S.: 212390
Geoff Baker *(Exec Dir-Ops)*

MACARTHUR AUSTRALIA LIMITED
Level 20 10 Eagle Street, Brisbane, 4000, QLD, Australia
Tel.: (61) 732211796 AU
Web Site:
http://www.macarthuraustralia.com
Iron Exploration Services
N.A.I.C.S.: 212210

MACARTHUR MINERALS LIMITED
Suite G03 555 Coronation Drive, Toowong, 4066, QLD, Australia
Tel.: (61) 732211796 AU
Web Site:
http://www.macarthurminerals.com
Year Founded: 2002
MMLA—(DEU)
Rev.: $69,544
Assets: $50,655,680
Liabilities: $1,135,051
Net Worth: $49,520,629
Earnings: ($3,756,720)
Emp.: 8

MACARTHUR MINERALS LIMITED

Macarthur Minerals Limited—(Continued)
Fiscal Year-end: 03/31/24
Gold, Nickel & Iron Ore Mining Services
N.A.I.C.S.: 212220
Joe Phillips (CEO)

Subsidiaries:

Internickel Australia Pty Ltd (1)
Level 2 220 Saint Georges Terrace, Perth, 6000, WA, Australia
Tel.: (61) 8 9322 1342
Web Site:
http://www.macarthurminerals.com
Sales Range: $50-74.9 Million
Emp.: 10
Mineral Mining Services
N.A.I.C.S.: 212390

MACARTNEY A/S
Gl Guldagervej 48, 6710, Esbjerg, Denmark
Tel.: (45) 76132000 DK
Web Site: http://www.macartney.com
Year Founded: 1978
Emp.: 200
Underwater Technology Products & Systems Sales & Service
N.A.I.C.S.: 541330
Hans-Jorgen Hansen (VP-Sls)

Subsidiaries:

MacArtney Australia Pty Ltd. (1)
5/177 Bannister Rd, Canning Vale, 6155, WA, Australia
Tel.: (61) 862 58 5670
Web Site: http://www.macartney.com
Underwater Technology Product & System Distr
N.A.I.C.S.: 423610
Steen Frejo (Mng Dir-Ops-Asia Pacific)

MacArtney Benelux BV (1)
Mandenmakerstraat 188, Hoogvliet, 3194 DG, Rotterdam, Netherlands
Tel.: (31) 10 2041166
Web Site: http://www.macartney.com
Underwater Technology Products & Systems Sales & Service
N.A.I.C.S.: 423610
Ron Voerman (Mng Dir)

MacArtney France SAS (1)
Avenue Olivier Perroy Les Portes de Rousset Bat E, 13790, Rousset, France
Tel.: (33) 442 394 985
Web Site: http://www.macartney.com
Underwater Technology Products & Systems Mfr, Sales & Service
N.A.I.C.S.: 423610
David Mazzochi (Mng Dir)

MacArtney Inc. (1)
2901 W Sam Houston Pkwy N Ste D2-60, Houston, TX 77043-1625
Tel.: (713) 266-7575
Web Site: http://www.macartney.com
Underwater Technology Solutions & Services
N.A.I.C.S.: 541330
Francis Peronard (Gen Mgr)

Subsidiary (Non-US):

MacArtney Canada Ltd. (2)
25 Parker Street - Unit 301, Dartmouth, B2Y 4T5, NS, Canada
Tel.: (902) 434-1798
Web Site: http://www.macartney.com
Underwater Technology Products & Systems Sales & Service
N.A.I.C.S.: 423610
Thomas J. Knox (Gen Mgr)

MacArtney Norge AS (1)
Fabrikkveien 34, 4033, Stavanger, Norway
Tel.: (47) 5195 1800
Web Site: http://www.macartney.com
Underwater Technology Products & Systems Sales & Service
N.A.I.C.S.: 423610
Mats Ekstrom (Mng Dir)

MacArtney Singapore Pte. Ltd. (1)
18 Tampines Industrial Crescent #05-07A, Singapore, 528605, Singapore

Tel.: (65) 6542 4500
Web Site: http://www.macartney.com
Underwater Technology Products & Systems Sales & Service
N.A.I.C.S.: 423610
Steen Frejo (Mng Dir-Ops-Asia Pacific)

MacArtney UK Ltd. (1)
Howemoss Avenue Kirkhill Industrial Estate, Dyce, Aberdeen, AB21 0GP, United Kingdom
Tel.: (44) 1224 358 500
Emp.: 40
Underwater Technology Solutions
N.A.I.C.S.: 541330
David Buchan (Mng Dir)

MACAU E&M HOLDING LIMITED
No 56-68 Edificio Industrial Lee Cheung 13 Andar D, Estrada Marginal do Hipodromo, Macau, China (Macau)
Tel.: (853) 28720006 Ky
Web Site: https://www.macauem.com
Year Founded: 2011
1408—(HKG)
Rev.: $15,943,896
Assets: $32,274,076
Liabilities: $6,739,706
Net Worth: $25,534,371
Earnings: ($467,194)
Emp.: 64
Fiscal Year-end: 12/31/23
Holding Company
N.A.I.C.S.: 551112
Ka Wo Cheong (CEO)

MACAU LEGEND DEVELOPMENT LIMITED
Palace Building Macau Fisherman s Wharf Avenida da Amizade e Avenida, Dr Sun Yat Sen, Macau, China (Macau)
Tel.: (853) 28222211
Web Site:
http://www.macaulegend.com
1680—(OTCIQ)
Rev.: $90,943,423
Assets: $913,821,616
Liabilities: $439,910,540
Net Worth: $473,911,076
Earnings: ($77,601,569)
Emp.: 814
Fiscal Year-end: 12/31/22
Entertainment & Casino Gaming Facilities Owner & Operator
N.A.I.C.S.: 721120
David Kam Fai Chow (Chm)

Subsidiaries:

Grand Merit Retail Group Limited (1)
1st Floor Rome Building Macau Fishermans Wharf Avenida Dr Sun Yat-Sen, Macau, China (Macau)
Tel.: (853) 28222200
Web Site: https://www.grandmerit.com
Emp.: 2,000
Hotel Services
N.A.I.C.S.: 721110

Macau Fisherman's Wharf International Investment Limited (1)
360 Virtual Tour Avenida da Amizade e Avenida Dr Sun Yat-Sen, Macau, China (Macau)
Tel.: (853) 82993300
Web Site:
https://www.fishermanswharf.com.mo
Hotel Services
N.A.I.C.S.: 721110

MACAU PROPERTY OPPORTUNITIES FUND LTD.
Offshore Incorporations Centre, PO Box 957, Road Town, VG1110, Tortola, Virgin Islands (British)
Tel.: (284) 1481726511
Web Site: https://www.mpofund.com
Year Founded: 2006

MPO—(LSE)
Rev.: $1,122,000
Assets: $182,628,000
Liabilities: $116,944,000
Net Worth: $65,684,000
Earnings: ($12,007,000)
Fiscal Year-end: 06/30/23
Investment Management Service
N.A.I.C.S.: 525990
Mark Huntley (Chm)

MACAU RESOURCES GROUP LIMITED
Galaxy Resort Hotel, Galaxy Macau Cotai, Macau, China (Macau)
Tel.: (853) 2882 8668 VG
Year Founded: 2011
Holding Company
N.A.I.C.S.: 551112
Long Jin Chung (Chm)

MACAUTO INDUSTRIAL CO., LTD.
No 6 Yongke 5th Rd, Yongkang Dist, Tainan City, 710, Taiwan
Tel.: (886) 62331088
Web Site: https://www.macautogroup.com
Year Founded: 1979
9951—(TPE)
Rev.: $151,644,123
Assets: $177,012,069
Liabilities: $71,508,051
Net Worth: $105,504,018
Earnings: $12,880,968
Fiscal Year-end: 12/31/22
Cordless Garden Tool Mfr
N.A.I.C.S.: 333515
Yu-Shan Chou (Chm & Pres)

Subsidiaries:

Kunshan Macauto Automobile Parts Industry Co., Ltd. (1)
No 9 Jinyang Middle Rd, Lujia, Kunshan, Jiangsu, China
Tel.: (86) 51257876699
Automotive Parts Mfr & Distr
N.A.I.C.S.: 336390

MACAUTO MEXICO, S.A. de C.V. (1)
Av Industria en Telecomunicaciones 103 B Parque Industrial Stiva, San Jose de Cementos Guanajuato, 37555, Leon, Mexico
Tel.: (52) 14773902223
Automotive Interior Product Mfr & Distr
N.A.I.C.S.: 336360

Macauto Group GmbH (1)
Hauptstrasse 47, 42579, Heiligenhaus, Germany
Tel.: (49) 20569884600
Automotive Interior Product Mfr
N.A.I.C.S.: 336360

MACAY HOLDINGS, INC.
137 Yakal Street, San Antonio Village, Makati, 1203, Philippines
Tel.: (63) 8930733
Web Site:
https://www.macayholdings.com.ph
Year Founded: 1930
MACAY—(PHI)
Rev.: $79,341,641
Assets: $218,973,412
Liabilities: $99,807,200
Net Worth: $119,166,211
Earnings: ($16,226,610)
Fiscal Year-end: 12/31/23
Holding Company
N.A.I.C.S.: 551112
Alfredo M. Yao (Chm)

MACBEE PLANET, INC.
4F 5F IVY East Building 3-11-11 Shibuya, Shibuya-Ku, Tokyo, 150-0002, Japan
Tel.: (81) 334068858

Web Site: https://www.macbee-planet.com
Year Founded: 2015
7095—(TKS)
Rev.: $260,467,050
Assets: $133,707,080
Liabilities: $67,402,170
Net Worth: $66,304,910
Earnings: $15,084,020
Emp.: 159
Fiscal Year-end: 04/30/24
Media Advertising Services
N.A.I.C.S.: 541840
Yusuke Kojima (Founder & Pres)

Subsidiaries:

Net Marketing Co., Ltd. (1)
Floor 3 and 4 Lattice Aoyama Square 2-6 Minami Aoyama 1-chome, Tokyo, 107-0062, Japan
Tel.: (81) 368940139
Web Site: http://www.net-marketing.co.jp
Sales Range: $75-99.9 Million
Media Advertising Services
N.A.I.C.S.: 541840
Kunihiko Miyamoto (Pres & CEO)

MACCARTHY MOTORS (TERRACE) LTD.
5004 Highway 16 West, Terrace, V8G 5S5, BC, Canada
Tel.: (250) 635-4941
Web Site:
http://www.maccarthygm.com
Rev.: $16,152,440
Emp.: 36
New & Used Car Dealers
N.A.I.C.S.: 441110

MACCURA BIOTECHNOLOGY CO., LTD.
16 No Baichuan Road Hi-tech Zone, Chengdu, 611731, Sichuan, China
Tel.: (86) 2887826777
Web Site: https://en.maccura.com
Year Founded: 1994
300463—(CHIN)
Rev.: $506,620,764
Assets: $1,145,926,548
Liabilities: $229,160,880
Net Worth: $916,765,668
Earnings: $99,396,180
Emp.: 990
Fiscal Year-end: 12/31/22
In-Vitro Diagnostic Substance Mfr
N.A.I.C.S.: 325413
Tang Yong (Chm)

Subsidiaries:

Guizhou Maccura Science & Technology Co., Ltd (1)
Rm B The 18th Floor Yonglixingzuo Building No 188 Xintian street, Yunyan District, Guiyang, 550004, China
Tel.: (86) 8515213070
In-Vitro Diagnostic Reagent Distr
N.A.I.C.S.: 424210

Maccura Biotechnology (Xinjiang Hongkang) Co., Ltd. (1)
Room 903-907 Building 2 Luda International 1080 Liyushan South Road, Xinshi Zone, Urumqi, 830054, China
Tel.: (86) 991 662 4493
In-Vitro Diagnostic Product Mfr & Distr
N.A.I.C.S.: 325413

Sichuan Maccura Industry Co., Ltd. (1)
8 Anhe 2nd Road, Hi-tech Zone, Chengdu, 611731, China
Tel.: (86) 288 173 1888
In-Vitro Diagnostic Product Mfr & Distr
N.A.I.C.S.: 325413

Yunnan Maccura Science & Technology Co., Ltd (1)
No 53 Keyi Road, High-tech Zone, Kunming, 650051, Yunnan, China
Tel.: (86) 87168012999
Web Site: https://www.botanee.com

In-Vitro Diagnostic Reagent Distr
N.A.I.C.S.: 424210

MACDONALD HOTELS & RESORTS
Whiteside House, Bathgate, EH48 2RX, West Lothian, United Kingdom
Tel.: (44) 1506815200
Web Site:
http://www.macdonaldhotels.co.uk
Sales Range: $550-599.9 Million
Emp.: 5,570
Owner & Operator of Hotels & Motels
N.A.I.C.S.: 721110
Donald J. MacDonald *(Founder)*

MACDONALD MINES EXPLORATION LTD.
145 Wellington Street West Suite 1001, Toronto, M5J 1H8, ON, Canada
Tel.: (416) 364-4986
Web Site:
https://www.macdonaldmines.com
MCDMD—(OTCIQ)
Rev.: $39,231
Assets: $1,352,973
Liabilities: $481,202
Net Worth: $871,771
Earnings: ($2,421,662)
Emp.: 3
Fiscal Year-end: 12/31/21
Nickel, Zinc & Copper Mining Services
N.A.I.C.S.: 212230
Fiona Fitzmaurice *(CFO)*

MACDONALD PONTIAC BUICK GMC LTD
111 Baig Blvd, Moncton, E1C 8T6, NB, Canada
Tel.: (506) 853-6200
Web Site:
http://www.macdonaldpontiac.com
Sales Range: $50-74.9 Million
Emp.: 120
Automobile Dealers
N.A.I.C.S.: 441110
Douglas MacDonald *(Co-Pres)*

MACDONALD REAL ESTATE GROUP INC.
2105 W 38th Avenue, Vancouver, V6M 1R8, BC, Canada
Tel.: (604) 263-1911
Web Site: https://www.macrealty.com
Year Founded: 1944
Sales Range: $1-4.9 Billion
Emp.: 1,000
Real Estate Brokerage & Services
N.A.I.C.S.: 531210
Lynn Hsu *(Chm & CEO)*

MACDONALD STEEL LIMITED
200 Avenue Road, Cambridge, N1R 8H5, ON, Canada
Tel.: (519) 620-0400
Web Site:
http://www.macdonaldsteel.com
Year Founded: 1957
Rev.: $27,822,384
Emp.: 240
Fabricated Metal Products Mfr
N.A.I.C.S.: 332999
Ken MacDonald *(Pres)*

MACE LIMITED
155 Moorgate, London, EC2M 6XB, United Kingdom
Tel.: (44) 20 3522 3000   UK
Web Site: http://www.macegroup.com
Year Founded: 1990
Construction Consultancy Services
N.A.I.C.S.: 541330
Stephen Pycroft *(Chm)*

Subsidiaries:

Mace (China) Ltd. (1)
Room 323 Apollo Building No 1440 Middle Yan'an Road, Jingan, Shanghai, 200040, China
Tel.: (86) 2161331825
Project Management & Construction Services
N.A.I.C.S.: 541330

Mace (Russia) Limited (1)
7/5 Bolshaya Dmitrovka bld 2, Moscow, 125009, Russia
Tel.: (7) 4952879508
Project Management & Construction Services
N.A.I.C.S.: 541330

Mace Australia Pty Ltd (1)
Suite 1605 Level 16 44 Market Street, Sydney, 2000, NSW, Australia
Tel.: (61) 291268010
Project Management & Construction Services
N.A.I.C.S.: 541330
Jeremy Oakes *(Mng Dir)*

Mace Egypt LLC (1)
10 Obour Buildings Salah Salim St Apartment 10, Cairo, Egypt
Tel.: (20) 24054682
Project Management & Construction Services
N.A.I.C.S.: 541330
Rana Farouk Abdelhamid *(Mgr-Cost)*

Mace GmbH (1)
Hamburger Allee 45, 60486, Frankfurt am Main, Germany
Tel.: (49) 697137300
Web Site: http://www.macegmbh.de
Project Management & Construction Services
N.A.I.C.S.: 541330

Mace Holding Limited (1)
Al Mousa Centre Tower 4 Unit 435 Olaya Street, PO Box 9817, Riyadh, 12241, Saudi Arabia
Tel.: (966) 14620599
Project Management & Construction Services
N.A.I.C.S.: 541330
Jeremy Oakes *(Mng Dir)*

Mace Insaat Yonetim ve Danismanlk Hizmetleri Ltd (1)
Macka Cad Tuncer Building No 29 D 13 F 4, Macka Sisli, Istanbul, Turkiye
Tel.: (90) 2122361646
Project Management & Construction Services
N.A.I.C.S.: 541330
Jyldyza Sydykova *(Mgr-Bus Dev)*

Mace International (Vietnam) BIDV (1)
Tower 13/F 194 Tran Quang Khai Street, Hoan Kiem, Hanoi, Vietnam
Tel.: (84) 422205656
Project Management & Construction Services
N.A.I.C.S.: 541330

Mace International Limited (1)
PO Box 37501, Abu Dhabi, United Arab Emirates
Tel.: (971) 26349600
Emp.: 450
Project Management & Construction Services
N.A.I.C.S.: 541330
Ruchira Kulatilaka *(Mgr-Comml)*

Mace International Ltd (1)
PO Box 3427, 111, Muscat, Oman
Tel.: (968) 24391900
Project Management & Construction Services
N.A.I.C.S.: 541330

Mace Management Services (Pty) Ltd (1)
The Pavilion 12 Wessel Road, Rivonia, Johannesburg, 2128, South Africa
Tel.: (27) 105910222
Project Management & Construction Services
N.A.I.C.S.: 541330

Mace Management Services Limited (1)
1C Etim Inyang Crescent Victoria Island, Lagos, Nigeria
Tel.: (234) 12955114
Project Management & Construction Services
N.A.I.C.S.: 541330

Mace Management Services S.A. (1)
Edificio Cuzco III Paseo de la Castellana 135 Planta 3, 28046, Madrid, Spain
Tel.: (34) 913198531
Project Management & Construction Services
N.A.I.C.S.: 541330

Mace Polska Sp.o.o. (1)
Atrium Plaza al Jana Pawla II 29, 00-867, Warsaw, Poland
Tel.: (48) 226537100
Project Management & Construction Services
N.A.I.C.S.: 541330
Monika Szczepanczyk *(Project Mgr)*

Mace Portugal, Consulmace Lda (1)
Edificio Novo Chiado 16 - 3 C, Travessa da Trindade, 1200-466, Lisbon, Portugal
Tel.: (351) 213242560
Project Management & Construction Services
N.A.I.C.S.: 541330

Mace Project and Cost Management Pvt. Ltd. (1)
703 Vatika City Point M G Road, Gurgaon, 110075, Haryana, India
Tel.: (91) 1244368216
Project Management & Construction Services
N.A.I.C.S.: 541330

Mace Projets Sarl (1)
6 Place de la Madeleine, 75008, Paris, France
Tel.: (33) 142988888
Project Management & Construction Services
N.A.I.C.S.: 541330

Mace d.o.o. (1)
Osijek Koscela 18, 31000, Osijek, Croatia
Tel.: (385) 31280706
Project Management & Construction Services
N.A.I.C.S.: 541330

Mace d.o.o. (1)
Heroja Milana Tepica 3, 11000, Belgrade, Serbia
Tel.: (381) 114000222
Web Site: http://www.mace.co.rs
Project Management & Construction Services
N.A.I.C.S.: 541330
Ognjen Dulovic *(Sr Project Mgr)*

Mace d.o.o. (1)
Kralja Nikole 27a Zgrada Celebic, 81000, Podgorica, Montenegro
Tel.: (382) 20634905
Project Management & Construction Services
N.A.I.C.S.: 541330

Mace doel (1)
Bulevar Partizanski Odredi 80-1/5, 1000, Skopje, North Macedonia
Tel.: (389) 71344586
Project Management & Construction Services
N.A.I.C.S.: 541330

MACEDONIAN AIRLINES AD
Vasil Glavinov 3, 1000, Skopje, North Macedonia
Tel.: (389) 23292333   GR
Year Founded: 1994
Sales Range: $25-49.9 Million
Emp.: 156
Oil Transportation Services
N.A.I.C.S.: 481111
Zlatko Petrovksi *(Pres)*

MACEWEN AGRICENTRE INC.
40 Catherine Street West, Maxville, K0C 1T0, ON, Canada
Tel.: (613) 527-2175
Web Site:
http://www.macewenag.com
Year Founded: 1983
Sales Range: $10-24.9 Million
Feed, Seeds & Fertilizers Mfr
N.A.I.C.S.: 325314
Jim MacEwen *(Pres)*

MACEWEN PETROLEUM INC.
18 Adelaide Street, PO Box 100, Maxville, K0C 1T0, ON, Canada
Tel.: (613) 527-2100
Web Site: https://www.macewen.ca
Year Founded: 1976
Rev.: $31,015,600
Emp.: 80
Gasoline & Lubricating Oil Whslr
N.A.I.C.S.: 424720
Allan MacEwen *(Founder)*

MACFARLANE GROUP PLC
3 Park Gardens, Glasgow, G3 7YE, United Kingdom
Tel.: (44) 1413339666   UK
Web Site:
https://www.macfarlanegroup.com
Year Founded: 1949
MACF—(LSE)
Rev.: $312,314,974
Assets: $234,491,821
Liabilities: $126,175,635
Net Worth: $108,316,186
Earnings: $13,809,370
Emp.: 910
Fiscal Year-end: 12/31/20
Holding Company; Labels & Packaging Products Mfr & Packaging Distr
N.A.I.C.S.: 551112
Peter D. Atkinson *(CEO)*

Subsidiaries:

Ecopac (U.K.) Limited (1)
H2 Ashendon Rd, Westcott Venture Park, Westcott, Aylesbury, HP18 0XB, United Kingdom
Tel.: (44) 129 665 2700
Web Site: https://www.ecopac.co.uk
Packaging Material Distr
N.A.I.C.S.: 424610
Andy Haines *(Ops Mgr)*

Macfarlane Group Sweden AB (1)
Kullagatan 6, Helsingborg, 252 20, Scania, Sweden
Tel.: (46) 42137555
Web Site: http://www.reseal-it.se
Self Adhesive Mfr
N.A.I.C.S.: 325520

Macfarlane Group UK Ltd (1)
Siskin Parkway East, Middlemarch Industrial Estate, Coventry, CV3 4PE, United Kingdom
Tel.: (44) 800 288 8444
Web Site:
https://www.macfarlanepackaging.com
Sales Range: $250-299.9 Million
Emp.: 600
Industrial & Personal Service Paper Whslr
N.A.I.C.S.: 424130
Ivor Gray *(Mng Dir)*

Macfarlane Labels (Ireland) Ltd (1)
Newtownmountkennedy County, Wicklow, Ireland (100%)
Tel.: (353) 18320220
Sales Range: $25-49.9 Million
Emp.: 15
Paper Mills
N.A.I.C.S.: 322120
Gregor Williamson *(Mng Dir)*

Macfarlane Labels Ltd (1)
22 Bentinck Street, Kilmarnock, KA1 4AS, United Kingdom
Tel.: (44) 1563525151
Web Site: https://www.macfarlanelabels.com
Sales Range: $25-49.9 Million
Emp.: 96
Paper Mills

MACFARLANE GROUP PLC

Macfarlane Group PLC—(Continued)
N.A.I.C.S.: 322120

Macfarlane Packaging Limited (1)
Unit 5 Lanesfield Drive Spring Road Industrial Estate, Wolverhampton, WV4 6UA, Ettingshall, United Kingdom
Tel.: (44) 1902496666
Web Site:
    http://www.macfarlanepackaging.com
Sales Range: $25-49.9 Million
Packaging Materials & Equipment Distr
N.A.I.C.S.: 423840
Peter Atkinson (Grp CEO)

Nottingham Recycling Limited (1)
Abbeyfield Road, Nottingham, NG7 2SZ, United Kingdom
Tel.: (44) 115 986 7181
Web Site:
    https://www.nottinghamrecyclingltd.co.uk
Recycling Services
N.A.I.C.S.: 562111

Online Packaging Limited (1)
Waterwells Business Pk Waterwells Dr, Quedgeley, Gloucester, GL2 2AA, Gloucestershire, United Kingdom
Tel.: (44) 1452555550
Web Site:
    http://www.macfarlanepackaging.net
Sales Range: $25-49.9 Million
Emp.: 20
Packaging Product Distr
N.A.I.C.S.: 423840
Chris Martin (Bus Mgr)

MACFOS LTD.
S No 78/1 Sumant Building Bhosari Alandi Road, Dynamic Logistics Trade Park Dighi, Pune, 411015, Maharashtra, India
Tel.: (91) 2268197600
Year Founded: 2012
543787—(BOM)
Electronic Parts Distr
N.A.I.C.S.: 423690
Sagar Subhash Gulhane (Sec)

MACGREGORS MEAT & SEAFOOD LTD.
265 Garyray Drive, Toronto, M9L 1P2, ON, Canada
Tel.: (416) 746-3663
Web Site:
    http://www.macgregors.com
Year Founded: 1949
Rev.: $86,114,143
Emp.: 175
Sea Food & Poultry Products Distr
N.A.I.C.S.: 424440
Duncan Macgregor (Pres)

MACHHAPUCHCHHRE BANK LIMITED
MBL Tower Lazimpat, Kathmandu, Nepal
Tel.: (977) 15970555
Web Site:
    https://www.machbank.com
Year Founded: 1998
MBL—(NEP)
Rev.: $144,550,326
Assets: $1,397,119,298
Liabilities: $1,275,319,341
Net Worth: $121,799,956
Earnings: $12,257,868
Emp.: 1,558
Fiscal Year-end: 07/16/23
Banking Services
N.A.I.C.S.: 522110
Bijay Bahadur Shrestha (Deputy Gen Mgr)

Subsidiaries:

Machhapuchchhre Capital Limited (1)
Investment Banking Services
N.A.I.C.S.: 523999
Amita Dongol (Head-Merchant Banking)

MACHINAGE PICHE
414 3e rue, PO Box 147, Daveluyville, G0Z 1C0, QC, Canada
Tel.: (819) 367-3333
Web Site: http://www.picheinc.com
Year Founded: 1983
Rev.: $14,713,600
Emp.: 85
Wood & Processing Equipment Mfr
N.A.I.C.S.: 321999

MACHINEFABRIEK GOUDKUIL APELDOORN B.V.
Europaweg 200, 7336 AR, Apeldoorn, Netherlands
Tel.: (31) 55 5332023
Web Site: http://www.goudkuil.com
Year Founded: 1912
Laundry Machine Parts & Services
N.A.I.C.S.: 335220

Subsidiaries:

Washex, Inc. (1)
300 Great Hill Rd, Naugatuck, CT 06770-2000 (100%)
Tel.: (940) 855-3990
Web Site: http://www.washex.com
Industrial Laundry Equipment
N.A.I.C.S.: 423850
Ambrose Ethington (Pres)

MACHINES ROGER INTERNATIONAL INC.
1161 Des manufacturiers, Val d'Or, J9P 6Y7, QC, Canada
Tel.: (819) 825-4657
Web Site: http://www.machines-roger.ca
Year Founded: 1988
Rev.: $18,084,550
Emp.: 200
Drilling Machines Mfr
N.A.I.C.S.: 333519

MACHINO PLASTICS LTD.
3 Maruti JV Complex Udyog Vihar, Gurgaon, 122015, Haryana, India
Tel.: (91) 1242341218
Web Site: https://www.machino.com
523248—(BOM)
Rev.: $40,181,218
Assets: $21,557,129
Liabilities: $15,381,856
Net Worth: $6,175,273
Earnings: $193,375
Emp.: 392
Fiscal Year-end: 03/31/23
Plastics Product Mfr
N.A.I.C.S.: 326199
Sanjiivv Jindal (Exec Dir-Strategy)

MACHVISION, INC.
No 2-3 Industry East Road II Science Park, Hsinchu, 30075, Taiwan
Tel.: (886) 35638599
Web Site:
    https://www.machvision.com.tw
Year Founded: 1998
3563—(TAI)
Rev.: $57,575,131
Assets: $188,446,116
Liabilities: $19,122,371
Net Worth: $169,323,745
Earnings: $13,493,541
Emp.: 181
Fiscal Year-end: 12/31/23
Semiconductor Product Mfr
N.A.I.C.S.: 334413
Guang-Shiah Wang (Chm)

Subsidiaries:

Machvision (Dongguan) Inc. (1)
Room 2801 Block 4 Diwang Plaza Changing South Road 303, Changan Town, Dongguan, Guangdong, China
Tel.: (86) 76985845780
Measuring & Testing Equipment Distr
N.A.I.C.S.: 423830

MACIF GESTION
1 rue Vernier, 75017, Paris, France
Tel.: (33) 156888383
Web Site: http://www.macif-gestion.fr
Sales Range: $25-49.9 Million
Emp.: 20
Insurance Services
N.A.I.C.S.: 524126
Hugues Fournier (CEO & Dir Gen)

MACINTOSH RETAIL GROUP NV
Amerikalaan 100, 6199 AE, Maastricht, Netherlands
Tel.: (31) 433280780
Web Site: http://www.macintosh.nl
MACIN—(EUR)
Sales Range: $1-4.9 Billion
Emp.: 10,461
Consumer Products & Services Distr
N.A.I.C.S.: 459999
C. Henk van Dalen (Chm-Supervisory Bd)

Subsidiaries:

Dolcis BV (1)
Larenweg 70, 5234 KC, 's-Hertogenbosch, Netherlands
Tel.: (31) 73 6483 483
Web Site: http://www.dolcis.nl
Emp.: 5
Clothing Apparel & Accessories Retailer
N.A.I.C.S.: 458110

GP Decors BV (1)
Staalweg 7, Culemborg, Netherlands
Tel.: (31) 345 533733
Interior Decoration Services
N.A.I.C.S.: 541410

GP Decors SNC (1)
27 bis Rue du General Leclerc, 80110, Montreuil, France (100%)
Tel.: (33) 322353637
Web Site: http://www.gpdecors.fr
Home Furnishings & Accessories
N.A.I.C.S.: 449129

Halfords Belgium NV (1)
Boomsesteenweg 936, 2610, Antwerp, Belgium (100%)
Tel.: (32) 38773394
Web Site: http://www.halfords.be
Automobile & Bicycle Accessory Retailer
N.A.I.C.S.: 459999

Hoogenbosch Retail Group BV (1)
Larenweg 70, 5234 KC, 's-Hertogenbosch, Netherlands (100%)
Tel.: (31) 736483483
Web Site: http://www.dolcis.nl
Sales Range: $25-49.9 Million
Emp.: 180
Shoe Retailer
N.A.I.C.S.: 458210
G. Seger (Dir-Fin)

Invito BV (1)
Larenweg 70, 's-Hertogenbosch, 5234 KC, Netherlands
Tel.: (31) 73 6483 483
Web Site: http://www.invito.com
Sales Range: $25-49.9 Million
Emp.: 25
Clothing Apparel Retailer
N.A.I.C.S.: 458110
Eric Coorens (Gen Mgr)

Klerkx Groep BV (1)
Reigerbosweg 2, 5144, Waalwijk, Netherlands (100%)
Tel.: (31) 416673673
Web Site: http://www.pietklerkx.nl
Home Furnishings Retailer
N.A.I.C.S.: 449129

Kwantum Belgium BV (1)
Rijksweg 220, 3630, Maasmechelen, Belgium (100%)
Tel.: (32) 89770168
Web Site: http://www.kwantum.be
Sales Range: $25-49.9 Million
Emp.: 55
Discount Home Furnishing & Decoration Products & Services
N.A.I.C.S.: 449129

INTERNATIONAL PUBLIC

E.M.H. Coorens (Mng Dir)

Kwantum Nederland BV (1)
Belle Van Zuylenstraat 10, Postbus 90160, Tilburg, 5000 LK, Netherlands (100%)
Tel.: (31) 134626626
Web Site: http://www.kwantum.nl
Sales Range: $25-49.9 Million
Emp.: 100
Discount Home Furnishing & Decoration Products & Services
N.A.I.C.S.: 449129
Rob Berns (Gen Mgr)

Macintosh Hong Kong Ltd (1)
Unit 1018-1019 10Fl Peninsula Ctr, 57 Mody Rd, Kowloon, China (Hong Kong) (100%)
Tel.: (852) 27357939
Web Site: http://www.macintoshretail.com
Sales Range: $25-49.9 Million
Emp.: 6
E-Business Services & Software
N.A.I.C.S.: 541519
Jeff Kuperus (Mng Dir)

Macintosh International BV (1)
Amerikalaan 100, Maastricht Airport, Maastricht, 6199 AE, Netherlands
Tel.: (31) 433280780
Web Site: http://www.macintosh.nl
Sales Range: $25-49.9 Million
Emp.: 4
Clothing Apparel Retailer
N.A.I.C.S.: 458110
Kurc Staelens (Gen Mgr)

Macintosh Intragroup Services NV (1)
Rijksweg 376, Maasmechelen, 3630, Belgium (100%)
Tel.: (32) 89770150
Web Site: http://www.macintosh.nl
Sales Range: $25-49.9 Million
Emp.: 10
Business Services
N.A.I.C.S.: 541519
Geert Jacobs (Mng Dir)

Muys NV (1)
Kwadelapstraat 2, 9320, Erembodegem, Belgium
Tel.: (32) 9 210 45 20
Web Site: http://www.muys.be
Emp.: 35
Clothing Accessories & Shoe Retailer
N.A.I.C.S.: 458110
Franck Borgnon (Gen Mgr)

Pro sport BV (1)
Larenweg 70, 5234 KC, 's-Hertogenbosch, Netherlands
Tel.: (31) 73 6483 483
Sporting Goods Retailer
N.A.I.C.S.: 459110

MACINTYRE CHEVROLET CADILLAC LIMITED
101 Disco Street, Sydney, B1P 6H2, NS, Canada
Tel.: (902) 564-4491
Web Site:
    http://www.macintyrechevrolet.com
Year Founded: 1981
Rev.: $17,890,400
Emp.: 40
New & Used Car Dealers
N.A.I.C.S.: 441110
Susan Tanner (Bus Mgr)

MACK STE-FOY INC.
2550 Watt avenue, Sainte-Foy, G1P 3T4, QC, Canada
Tel.: (418) 651-9847
Web Site: http://www.mackstefoy.com
Year Founded: 1985
Rev.: $17,657,452
Emp.: 49
New & Used Truck Dealers
N.A.I.C.S.: 532120
Simon Poire (Founder & Pres)

MACK TRADING COMPANY LIMITED
5C Sindhu House Nanabhai Lane

Flora Fountain, Fort, Mumbai, 400 001, India
Tel.: (91) 22047644
Web Site:
http://www.macktradingco.com
Year Founded: 1980
Rev.: $2,015,194
Assets: $3,407,749
Liabilities: $476,056
Net Worth: $2,931,693
Earnings: $1,237,195
Emp.: 2
Fiscal Year-end: 03/31/18
Investment Management Service
N.A.I.C.S.: 523999
Pooja Garg *(Compliance Officer)*

MACKENZIE MASTER LIMITED PARTNERSHIP
180 Queen Street West, Toronto, M5V 3K1, ON, Canada
Tel.: (416) 922-5322
Web Site:
https://www.mackenzie.com
Year Founded: 1995
MKZ.UN—(TSX)
Rev.: $864,760
Assets: $825,125
Liabilities: $254,129
Net Worth: $570,995
Earnings: $570,995
Fiscal Year-end: 12/31/19
Financial Services
N.A.I.C.S.: 525990

MACKINNON TRANSPORT INC.
405 Laird Road, Guelph, N1G 4P7, ON, Canada
Tel.: (519) 763-1600
Web Site:
http://www.mackinnontransport.com
Year Founded: 1929
Rev.: $54,936,062
Emp.: 300
Transportation, Warehousing & Logistics Services
N.A.I.C.S.: 493110
William MacKinnon *(Chm)*

MACKMYRA SVENSK WHISKY AB
Kolonnvagen 2, 802 67, Gavle, Sweden
Tel.: (46) 26541880
Web Site: https://www.mackmyra.se
Year Founded: 1999
MACK.B—(OMX)
Rev.: $10,799,197
Assets: $37,188,010
Liabilities: $23,401,515
Net Worth: $13,786,494
Earnings: ($3,788,142)
Emp.: 59
Fiscal Year-end: 12/31/20
Whisky Producer
N.A.I.C.S.: 312140

Subsidiaries:

Mat och Upplevelser i Kungsback AB (1)
Nobelvagen 2, 802 67, Gavle, Sweden
Tel.: (46) 8 55602590
Liquor Mfr
N.A.I.C.S.: 312130

MACKWELL ELECTRONICS LIMITED
Vigo Place, Walsall, Aldridge, WS9 8UG, West Midlands, United Kingdom
Tel.: (44) 1922458255
Web Site: http://www.mackwell.com
Year Founded: 1979
Sales Range: $25-49.9 Million
Emp.: 150
Emergency Lighting Components Mfr
N.A.I.C.S.: 335132
Nick Brangwin *(Mng Dir)*

Subsidiaries:

Mackwell Hong Kong (1)
Unit 1102-1103 11F Wing Tuck Commercial Centre 177-183 Wing Lok Street, Sheung Wan, China (Hong Kong)
Tel.: (852) 9389 4747
Electrical Equipment Distr
N.A.I.C.S.: 423610
Nicolas Ragiot *(Gen Mgr)*

Mackwell Middle East (1)
PO Box 122195, Sharjah, United Arab Emirates
Tel.: (971) 6 552 8328
Electrical Equipment Distr
N.A.I.C.S.: 423610

MACKWOODS LIMITED
10 Gnanartha Pradeepa Mawatha, Colombo, 8, Sri Lanka
Tel.: (94) 11 269 7965 LK
Web Site:
http://www.mackwoods.com
Year Founded: 1841
Holding Company
N.A.I.C.S.: 551112
Chris Nonis *(Co-Chm)*

Subsidiaries:

Mackwoods I.T. (Pvt) Ltd. (1)
10 Gnanartha Pradeepa Mawatha, Colombo, Sri Lanka
Tel.: (94) 11 266 9482
Web Site: http://www.mackwoods.com
Software & Web Portal Development Services; Information Technology Consultancy Services
N.A.I.C.S.: 541511

Mackwoods International Tours & Travels (Pvt) Ltd. (1)
10 Gnanartha Pradeepa Mawatha, Colombo, 8, Sri Lanka
Tel.: (94) 11 269 7970
Web Site: http://www.mackwoods.com
Travel Arrangement & Tour Services
N.A.I.C.S.: 561599

Mackwoods Tea (Pvt) Ltd. (1)
10 Gnanartha Pradeepa Mawatha, Colombo, 8, Sri Lanka
Tel.: (94) 11 266 7711
Web Site: http://www.mackwoodstea.com
Tea Farming & Mfr
N.A.I.C.S.: 311920

MACLAB ENTERPRISES LTD
3400 10205 100 Avenue, Edmonton, T5J 4B5, AB, Canada
Tel.: (780) 420-4040
Web Site: https://www.maclab.com
Year Founded: 1954
Rev.: $34,000,000
Emp.: 250
General Building Contractors
N.A.I.C.S.: 236220
Sandy Mctaggart *(Chm)*

MACLAREN MINERALS LTD.
615 800 West Pender Street, Vancouver, V6C 2V6, BC, Canada
Tel.: (604) 787-7356 BC
Year Founded: 2022
MRN—(CNSX)
Assets: $169,352
Liabilities: $53,690
Net Worth: $115,661
Earnings: ($65,876)
Fiscal Year-end: 06/30/23
Mineral Exploration Services
N.A.I.C.S.: 213115

MACMAHON HOLDINGS LIMITED
15 Hudswell Road Perth Airport, Perth, 6105, WA, Australia
Tel.: (61) 892321000 AU
Web Site:
http://www.macmahon.com.au
MAH—(ASX)
Rev.: $1,356,344,145
Assets: $969,117,250
Liabilities: $546,097,086
Net Worth: $423,020,164
Earnings: $35,540,865
Emp.: 9,676
Fiscal Year-end: 06/30/24
Construction & Mining Business
N.A.I.C.S.: 213113
Michael Finnegan *(CEO & Mng Dir)*

Subsidiaries:

Decmil Group Limited (1)
20 Parkland Road, Osborne Park, 6017, WA, Australia
Tel.: (61) 893688877
Web Site: https://decmil.com
Rev.: $289,311,045
Assets: $171,913,115
Liabilities: $142,536,624
Net Worth: $29,376,491
Earnings: ($79,093,794)
Emp.: 343
Fiscal Year-end: 06/30/2022
Civil Works Industrial & Non Process Infrastructure
N.A.I.C.S.: 541330
Alison Thompson *(Sec)*

Subsidiary (Non-US):

Decmil Australia Pty. Ltd. (2)
Tel.: (61) 89 368 8877
Web Site: http://www.decmil.com.au
Sales Range: $75-99.9 Million
Emp.: 300
Construction Engineering Services
N.A.I.C.S.: 541330

Doorn-Djil Yoordaning Mining and Construction Pty Ltd (1)
27-31 Troode St, Perth, 6005, WA, Australia
Tel.: (61) 892321415
Sales Range: $25-49.9 Million
Emp.: 5
Mining & Construction Services
N.A.I.C.S.: 541330
Tony Noonan *(Gen Mgr)*

Macmahon Construction Pty. Ltd. (1)
Level 3 27-31 Troode St, 6005, West Perth, WA, Australia (100%)
Tel.: (61) 893651111
Web Site: http://www.macmahon.com.au
Civil Engineering & Construction Services
N.A.I.C.S.: 237990

Macmahon Contractors Pty Ltd (1)
Level 21, 127 Creek Street, Brisbane, 4000, QLD, Australia (100%)
Tel.: (61) 73 840 5300
Web Site: http://www.macmahon.com.au
Mining & Engineering Services
N.A.I.C.S.: 541330
Syerendt Baneyk *(CEO)*

Macmahon Mining Services Pty. Ltd. (1)
13 Heath Street, PO Box 277, Lonsdale, 5160, SA, Australia
Tel.: (61) 881869600
Mining Services
N.A.I.C.S.: 213114

Macmahon Sdn. Bhd. (1)
No 60 - 1 Jalan 1/76D, Desa Pandan, Kuala Lumpur, 55100, Malaysia
Tel.: (60) 39 282 6129
Web Site: https://www.macmahon.com.au
Sales Range: $25-49.9 Million
Emp.: 50
Commercial Building Construction Contract Services
N.A.I.C.S.: 236220

TMM Group Pty. Ltd. (1)
Level 13 300 Ann Street, Brisbane, 4000, QLD, Australia
Tel.: (61) 738405300
Web Site: http://www.tmmgroup.com.au
Engineeering Services
N.A.I.C.S.: 541330
Carl O'Hehir *(Gen Mgr)*

MACMASTER CHEVROLET CADILLAC BUICK GMC LTD.
1350 Driver Ln, London, N5V 0B4, ON, Canada
Tel.: (519) 455-6200
Web Site:
https://www.macmasterchev.ca
New & Used Car Dealers
N.A.I.C.S.: 441110
Jim Arnold *(Mgr-Sls)*

MACMOR INDUSTRIES LTD.
1175 Sherwin Road, Winnipeg, R3H 0V1, MB, Canada
Tel.: (204) 786-5891
Web Site: https://www.macmor.com
Rev.: $16,380,429
Emp.: 72
Industrial & Safety Products Distr
N.A.I.C.S.: 423840
Jean Marc Roy *(Pres)*

MACNICA GALAXY, INC.
14F 207-5 Sec 3 Peihsin Rd, Hsintien, Taipei, 23143, Taiwan
Tel.: (886) 289132200
Year Founded: 1979
6227—(TPE)
Rev.: $469,047,025
Assets: $294,863,427
Liabilities: $219,873,839
Net Worth: $74,989,588
Earnings: $18,087,234
Emp.: 200
Fiscal Year-end: 12/31/22
Integrated Circuit Mfr & Distr
N.A.I.C.S.: 334413

Subsidiaries:

Macnica Atd Europe Gmbh (1)
Nurnberger Str 34, 85055, Ingolstadt, Germany
Tel.: (49) 84188198102
Web Site: https://www.macnica.eu
Semiconductor Distr
N.A.I.C.S.: 423690

Macnica Dhw Ltda. (1)
Rua Patricio Farias 101 8 andar Infinity Office Bairro Itacorubi, Florianopolis, 88034-132, Brazil
Tel.: (55) 4832255052
Web Site: https://www.macnicadhw.com.br
Semiconductor Distr
N.A.I.C.S.: 423690

Macnica Korea, Limited (1)
No 1629 Gongdeok-Dong Hyundai Hyel 173 Mapodaero, Mapo-gu, Seoul, 04130, Korea (South)
Tel.: (82) 27020520
Semiconductor Product Mfr & Distr
N.A.I.C.S.: 333242

Macnica Networks USA, Inc. (1)
303 Almaden Blvd Ste 140, San Jose, CA 95110
Tel.: (408) 205-7141
Web Site: https://www.macnica-nw.com
Information Technology Services
N.A.I.C.S.: 518210

Macnica Uk Ltd. (1)
Suite 35 MK Business Centre, Milton Keynes, MK14 6GD, United Kingdom
Tel.: (44) 7770995766
Web Site: https://www.macnica.co.uk
Semiconductor Product Mfr & Distr
N.A.I.C.S.: 333242

MACNICA HOLDINGS, INC.
1-6-3 Shin-Yokohama, Kouhoku-ku, Yokohama, 222-8561, Kanagawa, Japan
Tel.: (81) 454708980
Web Site:
https://holdings.macnica.co.jp
Year Founded: 2015
3132—(TKS)
Rev.: $6,799,825,980
Assets: $3,650,332,840
Liabilities: $1,955,396,640
Net Worth: $1,694,936,200

MACNICA HOLDINGS, INC.

Macnica Holdings, Inc.—(Continued)
Earnings: $317,736,090
Fiscal Year-end: 03/31/24
Holding Company
N.A.I.C.S.: 551112
Shigeyuki Sano *(Mng Exec Officer)*

Subsidiaries:

Fuji Electronics Co., Ltd. (1)
Ochanomizu Center Building 2-12 3-chome, Hongo Bunkyo-ku, Tokyo, 113-8444, Japan
Tel.: (81) 338141411
Web Site: http://www.fujiele.co.jp
Rev.: $7,292,244,540
Assets: $8,402,460,140
Liabilities: $4,030,130,220
Net Worth: $4,372,329,920
Earnings: $498,083,330
Fiscal Year-end: 03/31/2024
Semiconductor Device Whslr
N.A.I.C.S.: 334413

Macnica Networks Corp. (1)
Macnica Building No 2 1-5-5, Shin-Yokohama Kouhoku-ku, Yokohama, 222-8562, Japan
Tel.: (81) 454762010
Web Site: http://www.macnica.net
Software Development Services
N.A.I.C.S.: 541511

Macnica, Inc. (1)
Macnica Bldg No 1 1-6-3, Shin-Yokohama Kohoku-ku, Yokohama, 222-8561, Japan
Tel.: (81) 454709870
Emp.: 3,499
Semiconductor Components & Electronic Devices Mfr
N.A.I.C.S.: 334419
Kiyoshi Nakashima *(Pres & CEO)*

Subsidiary (Non-US):

Cytech Technology Ltd. (2)
Suites 4001-4003 40/F AIA Kowloon Tower Landmark East 100 How Ming St, Kwun Tong, Kowloon, China (Hong Kong)
Tel.: (852) 2375 8866
Web Site: http://www.cytech.com
Emp.: 300
Electronic Components Distr
N.A.I.C.S.: 423690
Horace Lai *(CTO)*

Subsidiary (Domestic):

GLOSEL Co., Ltd. (2)
1 Kanda Tsukasa-machi 2-chome, Chiyoda-ku, Tokyo, 101-0048, Japan **(85.56%)**
Tel.: (81) 362750600
Web Site: http://www.rene-easton.com
Rev.: $661,095,600
Assets: $365,749,120
Liabilities: $126,875,760
Net Worth: $238,873,360
Earnings: $8,440,960
Emp.: 362
Fiscal Year-end: 03/31/2023
Electronic Parts Distr
N.A.I.C.S.: 423690
Hitoshi Ishii *(Pres)*

Subsidiary (Domestic):

EASTON WORKS CO., LTD. (3)
18-9 Buzo 1-chome, Minami-ku, Saitama, 336-0025, Japan
Tel.: (81) 488441051
Emp.: 30
Electrical Equipment Distr
N.A.I.C.S.: 423690

Subsidiary (Non-US):

Glosel Electronics Singapore Pte. Ltd. (3)
10 Anson Road 09-18/19 International Plaza, Singapore, 079903, Singapore
Tel.: (65) 6 224 4177
Semiconductor Product Mfr
N.A.I.C.S.: 334413

Glosel Hong Kong Limited (3)
522 Chinachem Golden Plaza 77 Mody Road, Tsimshatsui East, Kowloon, China (Hong Kong)
Tel.: (852) 2 376 3633
Semiconductor Product Mfr
N.A.I.C.S.: 334413

Daisuke Nibuya *(Mng Dir)*
Glosel Shanghai Trading Co., Ltd. (3)
Room 3401 Zhao Feng Plaza 1027 Changning Road, Shanghai, 200050, China
Tel.: (86) 215 240 0066
Semiconductor Product Mfr
N.A.I.C.S.: 334413
Kimikazu Taniguchi *(Mng Dir)*

Glosel Taiwan Co., Ltd. (3)
Room No A107 10FI No 51 Herngyang Rd, Taipei, 100-45, Taiwan
Tel.: (886) 22 313 1395
Electronic Parts Distr
N.A.I.C.S.: 423690
Takashi Maeda *(Mng Dir)*

RENESAS EASTON (HONG KONG) LTD. (3)
522 Chinachem Golden Plaza 77 Mody Road, Tsimshatsui, Kowloon, China (Hong Kong)
Tel.: (852) 2376 3633
Semiconductor Device Distr
N.A.I.C.S.: 423690

RENESAS EASTON (SHANGHAI) TRADING CO., LTD. (3)
Room 1305 Zhao Feng Plaza 1027 Changning road, Shanghai, 200050, China
Tel.: (86) 21 5240 0066
Emp.: 100
Electronic Components Distr
N.A.I.C.S.: 423690

RENESAS EASTON (SINGAPORE) PTE. LTD. (3)
100 Tras Street 09-03 100AM, Singapore, 079027, Singapore
Tel.: (65) 6224 4177
Semiconductor Device Distr
N.A.I.C.S.: 423690

RENESAS EASTON (TAIWAN) CO., LTD. (3)
Room No A107 10FI No 51 Herngyang Rd, Taipei, 100-45, Taiwan
Tel.: (886) 2 2313 1395
Electronic Components Distr
N.A.I.C.S.: 423690

RENESAS EASTON (THAILAND) CO., LTD. (3)
Unit 5 Floor 22 Silom Complex 191 Silom Road Kwaeng Silom, Khet Bangrak, Bangkok, 10500, Thailand
Tel.: (66) 2632 1081
Semiconductor Device Distr
N.A.I.C.S.: 423690

Subsidiary (US):

RENESAS EASTON AMERICA INC. (3)
27780 Novi Rd Ste 270, Novi, MI 48377
Tel.: (248) 513-4460
Emp.: 6
Semiconductor Device Distr
N.A.I.C.S.: 423690
Nakatsui Akimasa *(Pres)*

Subsidiary (US):

Macnica Americas, Inc. (2)
380 Stevens Ave Ste 206, Solana Beach, CA 92075
Tel.: (858) 771-0846
Semiconductor Distr
N.A.I.C.S.: 423690

Subsidiary (Non-US):

Macnica GmbH (2)
Nurnberger Str 34, 85055, Ingolstadt, Germany
Tel.: (49) 84188198102
Web Site: https://www.macnica.eu
Semiconductor & Electronic Components Distr
N.A.I.C.S.: 423690
Juergen Poeschel *(Mng Dir)*

MACPAC FILMS LIMITED
Plot 21 Maqboolabad Jinnah Cooperative Housing Society, Tipu Sultan Road, Karachi, 75400, Pakistan
Tel.: (92) 2134305811
Web Site:
https://www.macpacfilms.net
Year Founded: 1993
MACFL—(LAH)
Rev.: $17,342,136
Assets: $17,922,426
Liabilities: $13,236,479
Net Worth: $4,685,947
Earnings: ($1,679,529)
Emp.: 114
Fiscal Year-end: 06/30/19
Formulated Films Mfr
N.A.I.C.S.: 322220
Ehtesham Maqbool Elahi *(Mng Dir)*

MACPEK INC
2970 avenue Watt, Quebec, G1X 4P7, QC, Canada
Tel.: (418) 659-1144
Web Site: http://www.macpek.com
Year Founded: 1974
Rev.: $14,713,600
Emp.: 100
Truck Parts Distr
N.A.I.C.S.: 423120
Jean-Francois Pouliot *(Pres)*

MACPHEE FORD SALES
580 Portland St, Dartmouth, B2W 2M3, NS, Canada
Tel.: (902) 434-7700
Web Site:
https://www.macpheeford.com
Year Founded: 1971
Sales Range: $10-24.9 Million
Emp.: 60
Car Dealer
N.A.I.C.S.: 441110
Don McLeod *(Mgr-New Vehicle Sls)*

MACPHEE PONTIAC BUICK GMC LTD
636 Portland St, Dartmouth, B2W 2M3, NS, Canada
Tel.: (902) 434-4100
Web Site:
http://www.macpheepontiac.com
Sales Range: $125-149.9 Million
Emp.: 236
Automobile Dealers
N.A.I.C.S.: 441110
Debbie O'Connor *(Treas & Sec)*

MACPOWER CNC MACHINES LTD.
Plot No 2234 Near Kranti Gate GIDC Metoda, 360021, Rajkot, 360021, Gujarat, India
Tel.: (91) 7998799816
Web Site:
https://www.macpowercnc.com
Year Founded: 2003
MACPOWER—(NSE)
Rev.: $24,235,957
Assets: $17,166,837
Liabilities: $5,583,598
Net Worth: $11,583,238
Earnings: $1,545,471
Emp.: 554
Fiscal Year-end: 03/31/23
Farm Machinery & Equipment Mfr
N.A.I.C.S.: 333111
Rupesh Mehta *(Chm)*

MACQUARIE GROUP LIMITED
50 Martin Place, Sydney, 2000, NSW, Australia
Tel.: (61) 282323333
Web Site:
https://www.macquarie.com
Year Founded: 1969
MCQEF—(OTCIQ)
Rev.: $4,378,120,800
Assets: $258,943,347,200
Liabilities: $236,174,181,600
Net Worth: $22,769,165,600

INTERNATIONAL PUBLIC

Earnings: $3,459,503,200
Emp.: 20,509
Fiscal Year-end: 03/31/23
Bank Holding Company
N.A.I.C.S.: 551111
Alex H. Harvey *(CFO)*

Subsidiaries:

Bennett Lawrence Management, LLC (1)
757 3rd Ave Fl 19, New York, NY 10017
Tel.: (212) 508-6400
Web Site:
http://www.delawareinvestments.com
Sales Range: $1-9.9 Million
Emp.: 19
Investment Advice
N.A.I.C.S.: 523940
Jane Fisher *(Specialist-Investments)*

Broadview Energy Prime II, LLC (1)
4365 Executive Dr St 1470, San Diego, CA 92121-2131
Tel.: (858) 450-6800
Infrastructure Investment Services
N.A.I.C.S.: 523999

Central Park Group, LLC (1)
12 E 49th St Fl 14, New York, NY 10017
Tel.: (212) 317-9200
Web Site: http://www.centralparkgroup.com
Sales Range: $1-9.9 Million
Emp.: 12
Investment Advice
N.A.I.C.S.: 523940
Michael Mascis *(CFO)*

DTG Enterprises, Inc. (1)
8504 192nd Ave NE, Redmond, WA 98053
Tel.: (425) 549-4905
Web Site: http://www.dtgrecycle.com
Recycling Services
N.A.I.C.S.: 562998

East Jersey Railroad and Terminal Company (1)
PO Box 67, Bayonne, NJ 07002-0067
Tel.: (201) 437-2200
Emp.: 8
Infrastructure Investment Services
N.A.I.C.S.: 523999
Shawn Gannon *(Gen Mgr)*

ITT-USA, Inc. (1)
10720 W Sam Houston Pkwy Ste 250, Houston, TX 77064
Tel.: (713) 888-0501
Web Site: https://www.intermodaltank.com
Tanker Trucking Services
N.A.I.C.S.: 484230

ITT-Virginia, Inc. (1)
621 Lynnhaven Pkwy Ste 355, Virginia Beach, VA 23452
Tel.: (757) 431-0609
Tanker Trucking Services
N.A.I.C.S.: 484230

International Tank Terminals, LLC (1)
11842 River Rd, Saint Rose, LA 70087
Tel.: (504) 468-3997
Petroleum Bulk Storage Services
N.A.I.C.S.: 493190
Richard Courtney *(Pres)*

MCT Holdings LLC (1)
3351 Augusta Ln, Onalaska, WI 54650
Tel.: (608) 781-4048
Holding Company
N.A.I.C.S.: 551112

Macquarie Bank Europe Designated Activity Company (1)
1st Floor Connaught House 1 Burlington Road, Dublin, Ireland
Tel.: (353) 12383401
Asset Management Services
N.A.I.C.S.: 523940

Macquarie Bank Limited (1)
1 Shelley Street, Sydney, 2000, NSW, Australia **(100%)**
Tel.: (61) 282323333
Web Site: https://www.macquarie.com.au
Rev.: $5,371,976,267
Assets: $215,702,549,390
Liabilities: $202,432,679,142
Net Worth: $13,269,870,248

AND PRIVATE COMPANIES

MACQUARIE GROUP LIMITED

Earnings: $2,546,130,273
Emp.: 20,500
Fiscal Year-end: 03/31/2023
Banking Services
N.A.I.C.S.: 522110
Peter Hastings Warne *(Chm)*

Holding (Non-US):

Chartreuse & Mont Blanc (2)
98 rue Louis Barran, 38430, Saint-Jean-de-Moirans, France
Tel.: (33) 438038038
Web Site: http://www.rossignol.com
Holding Company
N.A.I.C.S.: 551112
Bruno Cercley *(Pres & CEO)*

Corona Energy (2)
Edward Hyde Building, 38 Clarendon Road, Watford, WD17 1JW, United Kingdom
Tel.: (44) 8442646464
Web Site: http://www.coronaenergy.co.uk
Sales Range: $100-124.9 Million
Emp.: 150
Distr of Natural Gas to Business Customers
N.A.I.C.S.: 221210
Neil Mitchell *(CEO)*

Subsidiary (Domestic):

MQ Portfolio Management Limited (2)
No 1 Martin Place, Sydney, 2000, NSW, Australia
Tel.: (61) 2 8232 3333
Asset Management Services
N.A.I.C.S.: 523940

Macquarie Agricultural Funds Management Limited (2)
1 Shelley Street, Sydney, 2000, NSW, Australia
Tel.: (61) 2 8232 3333
Financial Management Services
N.A.I.C.S.: 523999

Subsidiary (Domestic):

Vitalharvest Freehold Trust (3)
Level 18 123 Pitt Street, Sydney, 2000, WA, Australia **(24.72%)**
Tel.: (61) 1300 117 902
Web Site: http://www.vitalharvest.com.au
Rev.: $11,279,063
Assets: $199,767,465
Liabilities: $82,143,356
Net Worth: $117,624,110
Earnings: $7,494,663
Fiscal Year-end: 06/30/2020
Real Estate Investment Services
N.A.I.C.S.: 531190

Subsidiary (Domestic):

Macquarie Alternative Assets Management Limited (2)
1 Martin Pl, Sydney, 2000, NSW, Australia
Tel.: (61) 2 82323333
Portfolio Management Services
N.A.I.C.S.: 523940

Subsidiary (Non-US):

Macquarie Asset Finance Japan Limited (2)
4-1 Kioicho, Chiyoda-Ku, Tokyo, 102-0094, Japan
Tel.: (81) 3 3512 7272
Asset Management Services
N.A.I.C.S.: 523940

Macquarie Bank International Limited (2)
Ropemaker Place 28 Ropemaker Street, London, EC2Y 9HD, United Kingdom
Tel.: (44) 20 3037 4625
Financial Banking Services
N.A.I.C.S.: 523150

Subsidiary (Domestic):

Macquarie Capital (Australia) Limited (2)
Level 7 No 1 Martin Place, Sydney, 2000, NSW, Australia
Tel.: (61) 282323333
Financial Advisory Services
N.A.I.C.S.: 523940
John Katzenmeyer *(Mng Dir-San Francisco)*

Subsidiary (Non-US):

Macquarie Capital (Europe) Limited (2)
Level 35 CityPoint 1 Ropemaker Street, London, EC2Y 9HD, United Kingdom
Tel.: (44) 20 3037 2000
Web Site: http://www.macquarie.co.uk
Financial Management Services
N.A.I.C.S.: 523999
Oliver Bradley *(Mng Dir-Digital Infrastructure)*

Macquarie Capital (India) Private Limited (2)
92 Level 9 2 North Avenue Maker Maxity Bandra Kurla Complex, Bandra East, Mumbai, 400 051, India
Tel.: (91) 22 6720 4000
Emp.: 14
Investment Management Service
N.A.I.C.S.: 523999

Macquarie Capital Advisers Korea (2)
3rd Floor Hanwha Building Sogong-dong 109 Sogong-ro, Jung-gu, Seoul, 100-755, Korea (South)
Tel.: (82) 237058500
Web Site: http://www.macquarie.kr
Sales Range: $50-74.9 Million
Investment & Financial Services
N.A.I.C.S.: 523940
John Walker *(CEO)*

Subsidiary (Domestic):

Macquarie Capital Group Limited (2)
No 1 Martin Place, Sydney, 2000, NSW, Australia
Tel.: (61) 2 8232 3333
Web Site: http://www.macquarie.com.au
Investment Advisory & Financing Services
N.A.I.C.S.: 523940
Nick Butcher *(Vice Chm-Infrastructure & Energy & Sr Mng Dir)*

Joint Venture (US):

Macquarie Capital Venture Studio (3)
125 West 55th St, New York, NY 10019
Tel.: (212) 231-1000
Web Site: http://www.macquarie.com
Venture Capital Firm
N.A.I.C.S.: 523999

Subsidiary (Non-US):

Macquarie Capital Korea Limited (2)
3 Floor Hanwha Building Sogong-dong 109 Sogong-ro, Jung-gu, Seoul, 100-755, Korea (South)
Tel.: (82) 2 3705 8500
Financial Management Services
N.A.I.C.S.: 523999

Macquarie Capital Securities (India) Private Limited (2)
92 Level 9 2 North Avenue Maker Maxity Bandra Kurla Complex, Bandra East, Mumbai, 400 051, India
Tel.: (91) 22 6720 4000
Security Brokerage Services
N.A.I.C.S.: 523150

Macquarie Capital Securities (Japan) Limited (2)
20F The New Otani Garden Court 4-1 Kioicho, Chiyoda-ku, Tokyo, 102-0094, Japan
Tel.: (81) 3 3512 7900
Web Site: http://www.macquarie.jp
Financial Security Brokerage Services
N.A.I.C.S.: 523150

Subsidiary (Domestic):

Macquarie Corporate and Asset Finance Limited (2)
Level 4 & 8, 432 St Kilda Road, Melbourne, 3004, VIC, Australia
Tel.: (61) 3 9864 2800
Asset Management Services
N.A.I.C.S.: 523940
Ben Brazil *(Co-Head)*

Unit (Domestic):

Macquarie Equipment Finance (2)
Level 4 9 Hunter Street, Sydney, 2000, NSW, Australia
Tel.: (61) 282323333
Web Site: http://www.macquarie.com
Office Equipment Sales Financing, Leasing & Asset Management Services
N.A.I.C.S.: 522220

Subsidiary (Non-US):

Macquarie Finance Korea Co., Limited (3)
9th Floor Hanwha Building Sogong-dong 109, Sogong-ro Jung-gu, Seoul, 100-755, Korea (South)
Tel.: (82) 2 3705 8500
Financial Management Services
N.A.I.C.S.: 523999
Peter Hain *(CEO)*

Subsidiary (Domestic):

Macquarie Equities Limited (2)
No 1 Market Place, Sydney, 2000, NSW, Australia
Tel.: (61) 282323333
Web Site: http://www.macquarie.com
Sales Range: $25-49.9 Million
Emp.: 400
Financial Services
N.A.I.C.S.: 523150
Peter Maher *(Chm)*

Subsidiary (Non-US):

Macquarie Equities New Zealand Limited (2)
Level 12 Tower 2 205 Queen Street, 1010, Auckland, New Zealand
Tel.: (64) 9 357 6931
Web Site: http://www.macquarie.com
Sales Range: $50-74.9 Million
Emp.: 85
Financial Security Brokerage Services
N.A.I.C.S.: 523150

Macquarie Finance (India) Pvt. Ltd. (2)
92 Level 9 2 North Avenue Maker Maxity Bandra Kurla Complex, Bandra East, Mumbai, 400 051, India
Tel.: (91) 22 6720 4000
Financial Management Services
N.A.I.C.S.: 523999

Subsidiary (Domestic):

Macquarie Financial Holdings Limited (2)
No 1 Martin Place, Sydney, 2000, NSW, Australia
Tel.: (61) 2 8232 3333
Investment Management Service
N.A.I.C.S.: 523999

Macquarie Financial Products Management Limited (2)
No 1 Martin Place, Sydney, 2000, NSW, Australia
Tel.: (61) 282323333
Web Site: http://www.macquarie.com
Investment Management Service
N.A.I.C.S.: 523999

Subsidiary (Non-US):

Macquarie First South Advisers (Proprietary) Limited (2)
The Place South Building 1 Sandton Drive, Sandton, 2196, Johannesburg, South Africa
Tel.: (27) 11 583 2000
Emp.: 15
Investment Advisory Services
N.A.I.C.S.: 523940
Michel Lamarche *(CEO)*

Macquarie Global Services Private Limited (2)
Level 1 DLF Building 9B DLF Phase III Cyber City, Gurgaon, 122 002, Haryana, India
Tel.: (91) 12 4481 3000
Web Site: http://www.macquarieglobal.com
Financial Management Services
N.A.I.C.S.: 523999

Subsidiary (US):

Macquarie Holdings (USA) Inc. (2)
Level 8 15-23 Ground 125 W 55th St, New York, NY 10019
Tel.: (212) 231-1000
Web Site: http://www.macquarie.com
Security Brokerage Services
N.A.I.C.S.: 523150
Michael Gray *(Mng Dir & Head-Intl Sls Trading-Securities)*

Subsidiary (Domestic):

Macquarie Asset Management, Inc. (3)
17th Fl Ste 1700 225 Franklin St, Boston, MA 02110
Tel.: (617) 457-0645
Web Site: https://www.macquarie.com
Investment Fund Management Services
N.A.I.C.S.: 523940
Martin Stanley *(Head)*

Affiliate (Domestic):

Macquarie Equipment Leasing Fund, LLC (4)
225 Franklin St 17th Fl Ste 1740, Boston, MA 02110
Tel.: (617) 457-0645
Web Site: http://www.macquarie.com
Rev.: $7,968,177
Earnings: $4,592,481
Fiscal Year-end: 12/31/2017
Equipment Leasing Services Investment Fund
N.A.I.C.S.: 525990
Brett Beldner *(Chief Acctg Officer)*

Subsidiary (Domestic):

Waddell & Reed Financial, Inc. (4)
6300 Lamar Ave, Overland Park, KS 66202
Tel.: (913) 236-2000
Web Site: http://www.waddell.com
Rev.: $1,049,497,000
Assets: $1,153,831,000
Liabilities: $426,074,000
Net Worth: $727,757,000
Earnings: $70,457,000
Emp.: 1,116
Fiscal Year-end: 12/31/2020
Mutual Funds & Life Insurance
N.A.I.C.S.: 523910
Brent Kyle Bloss *(Pres)*

Subsidiary (Domestic):

Fiduciary Trust Co. of New Hampshire (5)
6300 Lamar Ave, Shawnee Mission, KS 66202 **(100%)**
Tel.: (913) 236-2000
Sales Range: $1-4.9 Billion
Trust Company
N.A.I.C.S.: 523940
Hank Herrmann *(Pres)*

Ivy Investment Management Company (5)
6300 Lamar Ave, Overland Park, KS 66202-4247
Tel.: (913) 236-2000
Web Site: http://www.ivyinvestments.com
Investment Management Service
N.A.I.C.S.: 523940
Amy Scupham *(Pres)*

Waddell & Reed Financial Services, Inc. (5)
680 Andersen Dr Ste 350, Pittsburgh, PA 15220
Tel.: (412) 922-9101
Investment Advisory Services
N.A.I.C.S.: 523940

Waddell & Reed Investment Management Co. (5)
6300 Lamar Ave, Shawnee Mission, KS 66202 **(100%)**
Tel.: (913) 236-2000
Web Site: http://www.waddell.com
Sales Range: $650-699.9 Million
Investment Advisor
N.A.I.C.S.: 523150

Waddell & Reed Services Co. (5)
6300 Lamar Ave, Shawnee Mission, KS 66202-4247 **(100%)**
Tel.: (913) 236-2000
Web Site: http://www.waddell.com
Rev.: $9,542,417
Emp.: 900
Shareholder Services to United Group of Mutual Funds

4625

MACQUARIE GROUP LIMITED   INTERNATIONAL PUBLIC

Macquarie Group Limited—(Continued)
N.A.I.C.S.: 523940

Waddell & Reed, Inc. (5)
6300 Lamar Ave, Shawnee Mission, KS 66202-4247
Tel.: (913) 236-2000
Web Site: http://www.waddell.com
Sales Range: $150-199.9 Million
Emp.: 100
Insurance General Agency
N.A.I.C.S.: 523940
Shawn M. Mihal *(Pres)*

Subsidiary (Domestic):

Macquarie Global Opportunities Partners, L.P.
125 W 55th St, New York, NY 10019-5369
Tel.: (212) 231-1000
Privater Equity Firm
N.A.I.C.S.: 523999
Michael Cook *(Sr Mng Dir)*

Holding (Domestic):

Sentient Flight Group, LLC (4)
100 Grossman Dr, Braintree, MA 02184
Tel.: (781) 763-0200
Web Site: http://www.sentient.com
Sales Range: $75-99.9 Million
Emp.: 200
Holding Company
N.A.I.C.S.: 551112
Charles Starkowsky *(Chief Safety Officer)*

Subsidiary (Domestic):

Sentient Jet, LLC (5)
26180 Curtiss Wright Pkwy, Cleveland, OH 44143
Tel.: (216) 261-3500
Web Site: http://www.sentient.com
Sales Range: $50-74.9 Million
Emp.: 200
Private Jet Management & Transportation Services
N.A.I.C.S.: 481111
Charles Starkowsky *(Chief Safety Officer)*

Subsidiary (Domestic):

Macquarie Infrastructure & Real Assets Limited (2)
50 Martin Place, Sydney, 2000, NSW, Australia
Tel.: (61) 282372330
Web Site: http://www.mirafunds.com
Sales Range: $100-149.9 Billion
Alternative Investment Fund Management Services
N.A.I.C.S.: 523940

Subsidiary (Domestic):

BINGO Industries Limited (3)
305 Parramatta Rd, Auburn, 2144, NSW, Australia
Tel.: (61) 1300424646
Web Site: https://www.bingoindustries.com.au
Waste Management Services
N.A.I.C.S.: 562111
Daniel Tartak *(CEO & Mng Dir)*

Subsidiary (Domestic):

Toro Waste Equipment (Aust) Pty. Ltd. (4)
299 Parramatta Rd, Auburn, 2144, NSW, Australia
Tel.: (61) 1300556570
Web Site: http://www.torowasteequipment.com.au
Water Equipment Mfr
N.A.I.C.S.: 333310

Subsidiary (Non-US):

Macquarie Infrastructure & Real Assets (Europe) Limited (3)
Ropemaker Place 28 Ropemaker Street, London, EC2Y 9HD, United Kingdom
Tel.: (44) 2030372000
Web Site: http://www.mirafunds.com
Alternative Investment Fund Management Services
N.A.I.C.S.: 523940

Holding (Non-US):

Ceske Radiokomunikace a.s. (4)
Skokanska 2117/1, 169 00, Prague, Czech Republic
Tel.: (420) 242411111
Web Site: https://www.cra.cz
Sales Range: $150-199.9 Million
Emp.: 800
Telecommunications & Broadcasting Services
N.A.I.C.S.: 516120
Milos Mastnik *(Chief Comml Officer)*

Joint Venture (Non-US):

Enel Green Power Hellas SA (4)
4 Gravias Str Maroussi, 15125, Athens, Greece (50%)
Tel.: (30) 2111808500
Eletric Power Generation Services
N.A.I.C.S.: 221118

Financiere Eiffarie (4)
163 quai du Docter Dervaux, Asnieres-sur-Seine, 92600, France
Tel.: (33) 141328000
Holding Company
N.A.I.C.S.: 551112

Subsidiary (Domestic):

Autoroutes Paris-Rhin-Rhone (5)
36 rue du Docteur-Schmitt, 21800, Saint Apollinaire, France
Tel.: (33) 380776700
Web Site: http://www.parisrhinrhone.com
Sales Range: $1-9.9 Million
Emp.: 3,800
Motorways, Telecoms, Secure Car Parks & Railroad Transportation Services
N.A.I.C.S.: 488999
Philippe Nourry *(CEO)*

Subsidiary (Domestic):

AREA Societe des Autoroutes Rhones-Alpes SA (6)
260 avenue Jean Monnet, BP 48, Bron, Cedex, Bron, France
Tel.: (33) 472353200
Web Site: http://www.appr.fr
Sales Range: $450-499.9 Million
Emp.: 150
Bus Terminal & Service Facilities
N.A.I.C.S.: 237310
Philippe Nourry *(Pres)*

Holding (Domestic):

KCOM Group Limited (4)
37 Carr Lane, Hull, HU1 3RE, United Kingdom
Tel.: (44) 1482602100
Web Site: http://www.kcomplc.com
Rev.: $407,296,630
Assets: $385,904,983
Liabilities: $249,383,483
Net Worth: $136,521,500
Earnings: $37,071,119
Fiscal Year-end: 03/31/2018
Telecommunication Servicesb
N.A.I.C.S.: 517112
Sean Royce *(Exec VP-Tech, Svc & Ops-Hull & East Yorkshire)*

Subsidiary (Domestic):

Affiniti Integrated Solutions Ltd. (5)
37 Carr Lane, Hull, HU1 3RE, United Kingdom (100%)
Tel.: (44) 1482 602 100
Emp.: 600
Telecommunication Servicesb
N.A.I.C.S.: 517810
Dale Raneberg *(CEO)*

KC Ltd. (5)
37 Carr Lane, Hull, HU1 3RE, United Kingdom
Tel.: (44) 14 82602100
Web Site: http://www.kcomgroupltd.com
Telecommunication Servicesb
N.A.I.C.S.: 517810

KCOM Contact Centres Ltd. (5)
Prospect House Prospect St, Hull, HU2 8PU, United Kingdom
Tel.: (44) 1482 602 100
Web Site: http://www.kccontactcentres.co.uk
Call Center Operation Services
N.A.I.C.S.: 561422
Tony Joplin *(Head-Contact Centres)*

Kingston Information Services Ltd. (5)
Warehouse 6 Princes Dock Street, Hull, HU1 2LP, United Kingdom
Tel.: (44) 1482 602602
Telephone Directory Publishing Services
N.A.I.C.S.: 513140

Smart421 Technology Group Ltd. (5)
N Felaw Maltings 48 Felaw St, Ipswich, IP2 8PN, Suffolk, United Kingdom
Tel.: (44) 1473421421
Web Site: http://www.kcom.com
Sales Range: $25-49.9 Million
Emp.: 100
Software Consulting Services
N.A.I.C.S.: 541512
Dale Raneberg *(CEO)*

Joint Venture (Non-US):

Open Grid Europe GmbH (4)
Kallenbergstr 5, 45141, Essen, Germany
Tel.: (49) 201 3642 0
Web Site: http://www.open-grid-europe.com
Holding Company; Natural Gas Pipeline Transportation Services
N.A.I.C.S.: 551112
Jorg Bergmann *(Chm-Mgmt Bd)*

Joint Venture (Domestic):

MEGAL Mittel-Europaische-Gasleitungsgesellschaft mbH & Co. KG (5)
Kallenbergstrasse 5, D-45141, Essen, Germany
Tel.: (49) 20136420
Web Site: http://www.open-grid-europe.com
Natural Gas Pipeline Transportation Services
N.A.I.C.S.: 486210
Hans Jurgen Plattner *(Mng Dir)*

Subsidiary (Domestic):

Mittelrheinische Erdgastransportleitungsgesellschaft mbH (5)
Neuer Markt 29, 42781, Haan, Germany (100%)
Tel.: (49) 212993530
Sales Range: $25-49.9 Million
Emp.: 3
Natural Gas Pipeline Transportation Services
N.A.I.C.S.: 486210

PLEdoc Gesellschaft fur Dokumentationserstellung und -pflege mbH (5)
Gladbecker Str 404, 45326, Essen, Germany (100%)
Tel.: (49) 201 3659 0
Web Site: http://www.pledoc.de
Sales Range: $25-49.9 Million
Emp.: 130
Technical Consulting Services
N.A.I.C.S.: 541690
Anne-Kathrin Wirtz *(Mng Dir & Member-Mgmt Bd)*

Joint Venture (Non-US):

TDC Holding A/S (4)
Teglholmsgade 1, 0900, Copenhagen, C, Denmark (50%)
Tel.: (45) 70110330
Web Site: http://www.tdcgroup.com
Rev.: $2,302,027,000
Assets: $9,226,189,000
Liabilities: $6,451,042,500
Net Worth: $2,775,146,500
Earnings: $246,246,000
Emp.: 6,433
Fiscal Year-end: 12/31/2022
Holding Company; Telecommunications Services
N.A.I.C.S.: 551112
Mike Parton *(Chm)*

Subsidiary (Domestic):

Nuuday A/S (5)
Teglholmsgade 1, 2450, Copenhagen, Denmark
Tel.: (45) 70110330
Web Site: https://nuuday.com
Emp.: 3,075

Digital Media Streaming & Telecommunications Services
N.A.I.C.S.: 517121

Punktum dk A/S (5)
Ørestads Boulevard 108 11, 2300, Copenhagen, Denmark
Tel.: (45) 33646000
Web Site: https://www.punktum.dk
Sales Range: $10-24.9 Million
Emp.: 43
Internet Domain Name Registration & Hosting Services
N.A.I.C.S.: 518210
Jakob Bring Truelsen *(CEO)*

TDC Solutions A/S (5)
Teglholmsgade 1 G 455, 0900, Copenhagen, C, Denmark
Tel.: (45) 70110330
Telecommunications, Internet & Business Management Services
N.A.I.C.S.: 517111

YouSee A/S (5)
Teglholmsgade 1, DK-0900, Copenhagen, Denmark
Tel.: (45) 70704040
Web Site: http://yousee.dk
Cable Television & Internet Services
N.A.I.C.S.: 516210

Subsidiary (Domestic):

DKTV A/S (6)
Teglholmsgade 1,, 2450, Copenhagen, Denmark
Tel.: (45) 43324700
Web Site: https://www.dktv.dk
Emp.: 422
Cable Television & Internet Services
N.A.I.C.S.: 516210

Branch (Domestic):

Dansk Kabel TV A/S - Esbjerg (7)
Skjoltsgate 49, 6700, Esbjerg, Denmark
Tel.: (45) 43324700
Web Site: https://www.dktv.dk
Cable Television & Internet Services
N.A.I.C.S.: 516210

Holding (Domestic):

Thames Water plc (4)
Clearwater Ct, Vastern Rd, Reading, RG1 8DB, Verkshire, United Kingdom
Tel.: (44) 1183738650
Web Site: http://www.thameswater.co.uk
Sales Range: $1-4.9 Billion
Emp.: 4,000
Water & Wastewater Services
N.A.I.C.S.: 221310
Kelly MacFarlane *(Mng Dir-Customer Svc & Retail)*

Holding (Non-US):

Viesgo, S.L. (4)
Ed Torre Picasso Pza Pablo Ruiz Picasso Floor 19, 28020, Madrid, Spain
Tel.: (34) 91 4184400
Web Site: http://www.viesgo.com
Electric Power Generation & Distribution Services
N.A.I.C.S.: 221118
Miguel Antonanzas *(Pres & CEO)*

Subsidiary (US):

Macquarie Infrastructure & Real Assets Inc. (3)
Level 15 125 W 55th St, New York, NY 10019
Tel.: (212) 231-1000
Web Site: http://www.mirafunds.com
Alternative Investment Fund Management Services
N.A.I.C.S.: 523940
Christopher J. Leslie *(Chm)*

Holding (Domestic):

Aquarion Water Company (4)
200 Monroe Tpke, Monroe, CT 06468
Tel.: (203) 445-7310
Web Site: http://www.aquarionwater.com
Public Water Supply & Utility Management Services
N.A.I.C.S.: 221310
Donald J. Morrissey *(Pres)*

AND PRIVATE COMPANIES MACQUARIE GROUP LIMITED

Subsidiary (Domestic):

Aquarion Water Company of Connecticut (5)
600 Lindley St, Bridgeport, CT 06606-5044
Tel.: (203) 337-5991
Web Site: http://www.aquarionwater.com
Sales Range: $125-149.9 Million
Emp.: 227
Water Service Company
N.A.I.C.S.: 221310
Lucy Teixeira (VP-Admin)

Aquarion Water Company of Massachusetts & New Hampshire (5)
200 Cordwainer Dr Ste 200, Norwell, MA 02061
Tel.: (508) 865-0555
Web Site: http://www.aquarion.com
Sales Range: $75-99.9 Million
Emp.: 60
Water Utility Company
N.A.I.C.S.: 221310
Chuck Firlo (Pres & CEO)

Holding (Domestic):

Duquesne Light Holdings, Inc. (4)
411 Seventh Ave, Pittsburgh, PA 15219
Tel.: (412) 393-6000
Sales Range: $900-999.9 Million
Emp.: 1,500
Holding Company; Electric Services
N.A.I.C.S.: 221122
Mike Doran (VP-Ops)

Subsidiary (Domestic):

DQE Energy Services (5)
411 7th Ave, Pittsburgh, PA 15219
Tel.: (412) 393-6000
Sales Range: $25-49.9 Million
Emp.: 20
Utility Holding Company
N.A.I.C.S.: 541611

Duquesne Light Company (5)
411 7th Ave 6-1, Pittsburgh, PA 15219-1919
Tel.: (412) 393-7100
Web Site: http://www.duquesnelight.com
Emp.: 1,700
Electric Utility Services
N.A.I.C.S.: 221122
David T. Fisfis (Gen Counsel, Sec & VP-Rates & Regulatory Affairs)

Joint Venture (Domestic):

Elizabeth River Crossings Opco, LLC (4)
99 Canal Ctr Plz Ste 125, Alexandria, VA 22314-1559 (50%)
Tel.: (757) 334-0404
Web Site: http://www.driveert.com
Highway, Street & Bridge Construction
N.A.I.C.S.: 237310
Leila Rice (Mgr-Pub Affairs)

Affiliate (Domestic):

Macquarie Infrastructure Corporation (4)
125 W 55th St, New York, NY 10019
Tel.: (212) 231-1000
Web Site: http://www.micinc.com
Rev.: $847,000,000
Assets: $4,179,000,000
Liabilities: $3,285,000,000
Net Worth: $894,000,000
Earnings: ($928,000,000)
Emp.: 2,224
Fiscal Year-end: 12/31/2020
Holding Company; Infrastructure Assets Investment
N.A.I.C.S.: 551112
Christopher Timothy Frost (CEO)

Subsidiary (Domestic):

AA Charter Brokerage LLC (5)
3700 Airport Rd, Boca Raton, FL 33431
Tel.: (561) 368-1110
Web Site: http://www.aurajets.com
Aircraft Leasing Services
N.A.I.C.S.: 532411

ACM Property Services, LLC (5)
111 Roberts St Ste G1, East Hartford, CT 06108-3666
Tel.: (860) 291-8777
Real Estate Manangement Services
N.A.I.C.S.: 531210

Ascend Dvpt HWD, LLC (5)
20193 Skywest Dr Hayward Executive Airport, Hayward, CA 94541
Tel.: (510) 264-5553
Web Site: http://www.parkavion.com
Aviation Real Estate & Consulting Services
N.A.I.C.S.: 237210
Gary W. Briggs (Founder)

Atlantic Aviation FBO, Inc. (5)
6504 International Pkwy, Plano, TX 75093
Tel.: (972) 447-4200
Fixed Base Operator
N.A.I.C.S.: 488119

Atlantic Aviation Flight Support, Inc. (5)
207 N Frank Luke Dr, San Antonio, TX 78226
Tel.: (210) 923-5305
Aviation Services
N.A.I.C.S.: 488190

Atlantic Aviation LLC-PHF (5)
1200 Bland Blvd, Newport News, VA 23602
Tel.: (757) 886-5755
Web Site: http://www.atlanticaviation.com
Emp.: 15
Owner, Operator & Developer of Airports, Fixed-Base Operations & Aviation-Related Facilities
N.A.I.C.S.: 488119
Richard Martinez (Gen Mgr)

Atlantic Aviation Oklahoma City Inc. (5)
6401 S Portland Pl, Oklahoma City, OK 73159
Tel.: (405) 787-4043
Web Site: http://www.atlanticaviation.com
Aviation Services
N.A.I.C.S.: 488190
Todd Batek (Gen Mgr)

Atlantic Aviation Oregon FBO, Inc. (5)
90454 Boeing Dr, Eugene, OR 97402
Tel.: (541) 688-9291
Web Site: http://www.atlanticaviation.com
Sales Range: $25-49.9 Million
Aviation Services
N.A.I.C.S.: 488190

Atlantic Aviation Philadelphia, Inc. (5)
8375 Enterprise Ave, Philadelphia, PA 19153
Tel.: (215) 492-7060
Web Site: http://www.atlanticaviation.com
Aviation Services
N.A.I.C.S.: 488190
John S. Butterworth (Gen Mgr)

Atlantic Aviation Stewart LLC (5)
1032 1st St Bldg 112, New Windsor, NY 12553
Tel.: (845) 567-9800
Web Site: http://www.atlanticaviation.com
Sales Range: $25-49.9 Million
Aviation Services
N.A.I.C.S.: 488190
Michael Carey (Gen Mgr)

Atlantic Aviation of Santa Monica, L.P. (5)
2828 Donald Douglas Loop N, Santa Monica, CA 90405
Tel.: (310) 396-6770
Web Site: http://www.atlanticaviation.com
Aviation Services
N.A.I.C.S.: 327910
Gregory S. Wain (Gen Mgr)

Atlantic Aviation-Kansas City LLC (5)
1001 NW Lou Holland Dr, Kansas City, MO 64116
Tel.: (816) 949-8900
Web Site: http://www.atlanticaviation.com
Aircraft Support Services
N.A.I.C.S.: 488190

Atlantic Aviation-Orlando Executive LLC (5)
400 Herndon Ave, Orlando, FL 32803
Tel.: (407) 894-7331
Aircraft Support Services
N.A.I.C.S.: 488190

Atlantic Aviation-Orlando LLC (5)
9245 Tradeport Dr, Orlando, FL 32827
Tel.: (407) 851-8304
Web Site: http://www.atlanticaviation.com
Aircraft Leasing Services
N.A.I.C.S.: 532411
Tony Sherbert (Gen Mgr-Area)

Atlantic Aviation-St. Augustine LLC (5)
4900 US 1 N, Saint Augustine, FL 32095
Tel.: (904) 824-1995
Web Site: http://www.atlanticaviation.com
Emp.: 50
Aircraft Leasing Services
N.A.I.C.S.: 532411

Atlantic Aviation-Steamboat-Hayden LLC (5)
PO Box 1030, Hayden, CO 81639
Tel.: (970) 276-3743
Aircraft Leasing Services
N.A.I.C.S.: 532411

Atlantic Aviation-Stuart LLC (5)
2240 SE Witham Field Dr, Stuart, FL 34996
Tel.: (772) 781-4720
Aircraft Leasing Services
N.A.I.C.S.: 532411
Don Pipes (Mgr-Customer Svc)

Atlantic Aviation-West Palm Beach LLC (5)
3800 Southern Blvd, West Palm Beach, FL 33406
Tel.: (561) 683-4121
Aircraft Leasing Services
N.A.I.C.S.: 532411

Atlantic SMO Holdings LLC (5)
6504 International Pkwy Ste 1100, Plano, TX 75093-8221
Tel.: (972) 447-4200
Investment Management Service
N.A.I.C.S.: 551112

Aviation Contract Services, Inc. (5)
2828 Donald Douglas Loop N, Santa Monica, CA 90405
Tel.: (310) 396-6770
Aviation Services
N.A.I.C.S.: 488190
David Price (Pres)

BASI Holdings, LLC (5)
5575 Trowbridge Dr, Atlanta, GA 30338-2923
Tel.: (770) 396-5033
Investment Management Service
N.A.I.C.S.: 551112

Brainard Airport Services, Inc. (5)
20 Lindbergh Dr Ste 6, Hartford, CT 06114
Tel.: (860) 548-9334
Aviation Services
N.A.I.C.S.: 488190

Charter Oak Aviation, Inc. (5)
20 Lindbergh Dr Million Al, Hartford, CT 06101
Tel.: (860) 548-9334
Aviation Services
N.A.I.C.S.: 488190

Corporate Wings-CGF, LLC (5)
355 Richmond Rd, Richmond Heights, OH 44143
Tel.: (216) 261-1111
Aviation Services
N.A.I.C.S.: 488190

Flightways of Long Island, Inc. (5)
Route 109, Farmingdale, NY 11735
Tel.: (631) 752-9022
Web Site: http://www.atlanticaviation.com
Aviation Services
N.A.I.C.S.: 488190
Arthur Volk (Pres)

Macquarie Americas Parking Corporation (5)
125 W 55th St, New York, NY 10019
Tel.: (212) 231-1000
Sales Range: $10-24.9 Million
Emp.: 50
Off-Site Airport Parking Operations
N.A.I.C.S.: 812930

Subsidiary (Domestic):

Parking Company of America, LLC (6)
523 W 6th St Ste 528, Los Angeles, CA 90014
Tel.: (562) 862-2118
Sales Range: $10-24.9 Million
Emp.: 20
Automobile Parking
N.A.I.C.S.: 812930
Nadine Chaves (Owner)

Branch (Domestic):

Parking Company of America Airports, LLC (7)
176-192 McClellan St, Newark, NJ 07114
Tel.: (973) 297-0430
Web Site: http://www.fasttrack.com
Airport Transportation Services
N.A.I.C.S.: 812930

Subsidiary (Domestic):

Macquarie Aviation North America 2 Inc. (5)
1131 Standiford Ave, Louisville, KY 40213-2015
Tel.: (502) 368-1515
Sales Range: $25-49.9 Million
Emp.: 40
Airport Management Services
N.A.I.C.S.: 488190
Louis Peppper (Pres)

Mercury Air Center-Tulsa, LLC (5)
7500 E Apache St, Tulsa, OK 74115
Tel.: (918) 836-6592
Aircraft Management Services
N.A.I.C.S.: 488190
Sherry Levine (Gen Mgr)

Mercury Air Centers, Inc. (5)
6411 W Imperial Hwy Los Angeles International Airport, Los Angeles, CA 90045
Tel.: (310) 215-5745
Aircraft Management Services
N.A.I.C.S.: 488190

Newport FBO Two LLC (5)
19711 Campus Dr, Santa Ana, CA 92707
Tel.: (949) 851-5061
Aviation Services
N.A.I.C.S.: 488190

Palm Springs FBO Two LLC (5)
145 N Gene Autry Trl, Palm Springs, CA 92262
Tel.: (760) 320-7704
Web Site: http://www.atlanticaviation.com
Aviation Services
N.A.I.C.S.: 488190

Rifle Air, LLC (5)
375 County Rd 352, Rifle, CO 81650-8411
Tel.: (970) 625-1662
Aviation Services
N.A.I.C.S.: 488190

Rifle Jet Center, LLC (5)
375 County Rd 352 Ste 2070, Rifle, CO 81650
Tel.: (970) 625-4833
Web Site: http://www.atlanticaviation.com
Emp.: 17
Fixed Base Operator
N.A.I.C.S.: 488119

SBN, Inc. (5)
1516 Grant Ave, Novato, CA 94945-3165
Tel.: (415) 892-7749
Aircraft Management Services
N.A.I.C.S.: 488190

SJJC Airline Services, LLC (5)
6504 International Pkwy Ste 2400, Plano, TX 75093
Tel.: (972) 447-1973
Aircraft Management Services
N.A.I.C.S.: 488190

SJJC Aviation Services, LLC (5)
1250 Aviation Ave, San Jose, CA 95110-1119
Tel.: (408) 297-7552
Web Site: http://www.atlanticaviation.com
Fixed Base Operator
N.A.I.C.S.: 488119
Tim Murray (Gen Mgr)

Sun Valley Aviation, Inc. (5)
2230 Aviation Dr Friedman Memorial Airport, Hailey, ID 83333
Tel.: (208) 788-9511

MACQUARIE GROUP LIMITED

Macquarie Group Limited—(Continued)

Aviation Services
N.A.I.C.S.: 488190
Michael Rasch *(Gen Mgr)*

The Gas Company LLC (5)
515 Kamakee St, Honolulu, HI 96814
Tel.: (808) 535-5933
Web Site: http://www.hawaiigas.com
Sales Range: $250-299.9 Million
Emp.: 300
Natural Gas Distr
N.A.I.C.S.: 221210
Alicia E. Moy *(Pres & CEO)*

Trajen Flight Support, LP (5)
3131 Briarcrest Dr Ste 100, Bryan, TX 77802
Tel.: (979) 260-4000
Aircraft Maintenance Services
N.A.I.C.S.: 488190

Trajen Limited, LLC (5)
1007 N Orange St, Wilmington, DE 19801
Tel.: (302) 472-9185
Aircraft Maintenance Services
N.A.I.C.S.: 488190

Subsidiary (Domestic):

Macquarie Infrastructure Partners Inc. (4)
125 W 55th St, New York, NY 10019
Tel.: (212) 231-1000
Web Site: http://www.macquarie.com
Asset Management Services
N.A.I.C.S.: 523999
Karl Kuchel *(CEO)*

Holding (Domestic):

Bluebird Network, LLC (5)
2005 W Broadway Bldg A Ste 215, Columbia, MO 65203
Tel.: (573) 777-4200
Web Site: http://www.bluebirdnetwork.com
Internet & Fiber Transport Services
N.A.I.C.S.: 517810
Michael C. Morey *(Pres & CEO)*

Cincinnati Bell Inc. (5)
221 E 4th St, Cincinnati, OH 45202
Tel.: (513) 397-9900
Web Site: https://www.altafiber.com
Rev.: $1,796,000,000
Assets: $4,435,600,000
Liabilities: $2,857,300,000
Net Worth: $1,578,300,000
Earnings: ($130,900,000)
Emp.: 5,800
Fiscal Year-end: 12/31/2022
Local Phone Service & Regional Wireless Voice & Data Communications
N.A.I.C.S.: 517111
Joshua T. Duckworth *(CFO)*

Subsidiary (Domestic):

Agile Network Builders, LLC (6)
213 Market Ave N Ste 310, Canton, OH 44702
Tel.:
Web Site: http://www.agilenetworks.com
Wireless Communication Tower Services
N.A.I.C.S.: 517112
Kyle Quillen *(Founder & CEO)*

Cincinnati Bell Technology Solutions Inc. (6)
221 E 4th St, Cincinnati, OH 45202
Tel.: (513) 841-5000
Web Site: http://www.cbts.com
Sales Range: $10-24.9 Million
Emp.: 62
Information Technology & Communications Solutions
N.A.I.C.S.: 541690
Shannon M. Mullen *(Sr VP-Admin Svcs)*

Subsidiary (Non-US):

OnX Enterprise Solutions Ltd. (7)
165 Commerce Valley Dr West Suite 300, Thornhill, L3T 7V8, ON, Canada
Tel.: (905) 482-2292
Web Site: http://www.onx.com
End-to-End Communications Services; Digital & Application Services
N.A.I.C.S.: 517810
Paul Khawaja *(Pres)*

Subsidiary (Domestic):

Cincinnati Bell Telephone Company LLC (6)
2120 Dana Ave, Cincinnati, OH 45207
Tel.: (513) 565-2400
Telecommunication Servicesb
N.A.I.C.S.: 517121

Cincinnati Bell Wireless LLC (6)
221 E Fourth St, Cincinnati, OH 45202
Tel.: (513) 397-9900
Web Site: http://www.cincinnatibell.com
Sales Range: $75-99.9 Million
Emp.: 250
Retail Cellular Telephones
N.A.I.C.S.: 517112

Hawaiian Telcom Holdco, Inc. (6)
1177 Bishop St, Honolulu, HI 96813
Tel.: (808) 546-4511
Web Site: https://www.hawaiiantel.com
Holding Company; Communication Services
N.A.I.C.S.: 551112
Kevin T. Paul *(Sr VP-Advanced Svcs)*

Subsidiary (Domestic):

Hawaiian Telcom Communications, Inc. (7)
1177 Bishop St Ste 5, Honolulu, HI 96813
Tel.: (808) 643-3377
Web Site: http://www.hawaiiantel.com
Telecommunication Servicesb
N.A.I.C.S.: 517810

Hawaiian Telcom, Inc. (7)
1177 Bishop St, Honolulu, HI 96813
Tel.: (808) 643-3456
Web Site: https://www.hawaiiantel.com
Telecommunication Services Provider
N.A.I.C.S.: 517810
Kevin T. Paul *(Sr VP-Advanced Svcs)*

SystemMetrics Corporation (7)
1177 Bishop St Ste 13, Honolulu, HI 96813
Tel.: (808) 791-7000
Web Site: http://systemmetrics.hawaiiantel.com
Business Critical Data Infrastructure & Protection Services
N.A.I.C.S.: 541512

Wavecom Solutions Corporation (7)
1132 Bishop St Ste 800, Honolulu, HI 96813
Tel.: (808) 791-3000
Web Site: http://www.wavecomsolutions.com
Telecommunication Services Provider
N.A.I.C.S.: 517810

Subsidiary (Non-US):

Momentum Digital Solutions Inc. (6)
20 Toronto Street Suite 1100, Toronto, M5C 2B8, ON, Canada
Tel.: (461) 971-6612
Web Site: http://www.momentum.com
Communication Services; Digital, Mobile & Social Marketing
N.A.I.C.S.: 541511

Holding (Domestic):

LRS Holdings, LLC (5)
5500 Pearl St, Rosemont, IL 60018
Tel.: (773) 685-8811
Web Site: https://www.lrsrecycles.com
Holding Company; Recycling Services
N.A.I.C.S.: 551112
Alan T. Handley *(CEO)*

Subsidiary (Domestic):

Lakeshore Recycling Systems, LLC (6)
5500 Pearl St, Rosemont, IL 60018
Tel.: (773) 685-8811
Web Site: http://www.lrsrecycles.com
Waste Management & Recycling Services
N.A.I.C.S.: 562211
Alan T. Handley *(CEO)*

Subsidiary (Domestic):

Junoll Services (7)
1020 Webster St, South Bend, IN 46619
Tel.: (574) 231-9844
Web Site: http://www.junoll.com
Waste Collection

N.A.I.C.S.: 562119
Lee Fairleigh *(Mgr-Sls)*

Lee's Trash Services, Inc. (7)
9505 US-64, 72823, Atkins, AR
Tel.: (479) 968-3465
Web Site: http://www.leestrashservice.com
Waste Collection Services
N.A.I.C.S.: 562119

Michiana Recycling & Disposal, LLC (7)
2275 Reum Rd, Niles, MI 49120
Tel.: (269) 684-0900
Web Site: http://www.michianarecyclingdisposal.com
Sales Range: $1-9.9 Million
Emp.: 30
Hazardous Waste Treatment & Disposal Services
N.A.I.C.S.: 562211
Henry Valekma *(Pres)*

Roy Strom Family of Companies (7)
1201 Greenwood Ave, Maywood, IL 60153-2319
Tel.: (708) 344-5000
Web Site: http://www.roystrom.com
Waste Management Services
N.A.I.C.S.: 562998
Roy Strom *(CEO)*

Sunshine Sanitation, LLC (7)
750 County Rd 106 SE, Stewartville, MN 55976
Tel.: (507) 285-5550
Web Site: http://www.sunshinesanitation.us
Waste Collection
N.A.I.C.S.: 562119

Holding (Domestic):

Wheelabrator Technologies Inc. (5)
100 Arboretum Dr Ste 310, Portsmouth, NH 03801
Tel.: (603) 929-3000
Web Site: https://www.wtienergy.com
Emp.: 1,200
Waste-To-Energy Facilities & Independent Power Production Facilities Owner & Operator
N.A.I.C.S.: 221118
Robert C. Boucher Jr. *(Pres & CEO)*

Subsidiary (Domestic):

Tunnel Hill Partners LP (6)
8 Viaduct Rd, Stamford, CT 06907
Tel.: (516) 806-6232
Web Site: http://www.tunnelhillpartners.com
Solid Waste Treatment Services
N.A.I.C.S.: 562219
Kevin McEnery *(CFO)*

Subsidiary (Domestic):

City Carting Holding Company, Inc. (7)
8 Viaduct Rd, Stamford, CT 06907
Tel.: (203) 324-4090
Web Site: http://www.citycarting.net
Rev.: $5,000,000
Emp.: 40
Garbage & Recycling Treatment & Disposal
N.A.I.C.S.: 562219
Anthony Farina *(CEO)*

Subsidiary (Domestic):

Wheelabrator Baltimore, L.P. (6)
1801 Annapolis Rd, Baltimore, MD 21230
Tel.: (410) 234-0808
Web Site: http://www.wtienergy.com
Power Generation & Solid Waste Management Services
N.A.I.C.S.: 562998
Dave Jones *(Plant Mgr-South Broward)*

Wheelabrator Concord Company, L.P. (6)
11 Whitney Rd, Penacook, NH 03303
Tel.: (603) 753-8411
Web Site: http://www.wtienergy.com
Solid Waste Landfill Services
N.A.I.C.S.: 562212
John LaRiviere *(Plant Mgr)*

Wheelabrator Connecticut Inc. (6)
6 Howard Ave, Bridgeport, CT 06605-1822
Tel.: (203) 579-2607
Web Site: http://www.wtienergy.com

INTERNATIONAL PUBLIC

Emp.: 70
Solid Waste Landfill Services
N.A.I.C.S.: 562212

Wheelabrator Falls Inc. (6)
1201 New Ford Mill Rd, Morrisville, PA 19067-3701
Tel.: (215) 736-1760
Web Site: http://www.wtienergy.com
Waste-to-Energy Conversion Services
N.A.I.C.S.: 562213
Fred Lodini *(Plant Mgr)*

Wheelabrator Frackville Energy Company Inc. (6)
475 Morea Rd, Frackville, PA 17931
Tel.: (570) 773-0405
Web Site: http://www.wtienergy.com
Renewable Electric Power Generation Services
N.A.I.C.S.: 221112

Wheelabrator Gloucester Company, L.P. (6)
600 US Route 130, Westville, NJ 08093
Tel.: (856) 742-1484
Web Site: http://www.wtienergy.com
Renewable Electric Power Generation Services
N.A.I.C.S.: 562213
Ludwig Saenz *(Plant Mgr)*

Wheelabrator Lisbon, Inc. (6)
425 S Burnham Hwy, Lisbon, CT 06351
Tel.: (860) 885-3512
Web Site: http://www.wtienergy.com
Refuse Systems Collection & Disposal Services
N.A.I.C.S.: 562219
John Horgan *(Plant Mgr)*

Wheelabrator McKay Bay Inc. (6)
107 N 34th St, Tampa, FL 33605
Tel.: (813) 248-1457
Web Site: http://www.wtienergy.com
Power Generation & Solid Waste Management Services
N.A.I.C.S.: 562998

Wheelabrator Millbury Inc. (6)
331 SW Cutoff Rd, Millbury, MA 01527
Tel.: (508) 791-8900
Web Site: http://www.wtienergy.com
Waste-to-Energy Conversion Systems
N.A.I.C.S.: 562998

Wheelabrator North Andover Inc. (6)
285 Holt Rd, North Andover, MA 01845
Tel.: (978) 688-9011
Web Site: http://www.wheelabrator-northandover.com
Waste Recycling Services
N.A.I.C.S.: 562920

Wheelabrator Norwalk Energy Company Inc. (6)
11400 Norwalk Blvd, Norwalk, CA 90650
Tel.: (562) 929-0887
Web Site: http://www.wtienergy.com
Eletric Power Generation Services
N.A.I.C.S.: 221118
Brian Hagerty *(Plant Mgr)*

Wheelabrator Portsmouth Inc. (6)
3809 Elm Ave, Portsmouth, VA 23704
Tel.: (757) 393-3100
Web Site: http://www.wtienergy.com
Renewable Electric Power Generation Services
N.A.I.C.S.: 562213

Wheelabrator Putnam Inc. (6)
200 Technology Park Dr, Putnam, CT 06260
Tel.: (508) 845-6987
Web Site: http://www.wtienergy.com
Ash Waste Disposal Services
N.A.I.C.S.: 562219
Donald W. Musial *(Gen Mgr)*

Wheelabrator Ridge Energy Inc. (6)
3131 K-Ville Ave, Auburndale, FL 33823
Tel.: (863) 665-2255
Web Site: http://www.wtienergy.com
Eletric Power Generation Services
N.A.I.C.S.: 221118
Rodney Williams *(Plant Mgr)*

Wheelabrator Saugus Inc. (6)
100 Salem Tpke, Saugus, MA 01906-1819
Tel.: (781) 233-7600

AND PRIVATE COMPANIES — MACQUARIE GROUP LIMITED

Web Site: http://www.wtienergy.com
Solid Waste Landfill Services
N.A.I.C.S.: 562212

Wheelabrator Shasta Energy Company Inc. (6)
20811 Industry Rd, Anderson, CA 96007
Tel.: (530) 365-9173
Web Site: http://www.wtienergy.com
Wood-Fired Electric Power Distribution Services
N.A.I.C.S.: 221122

Wheelabrator South Broward Inc. (6)
4400 S State Rd 7, Fort Lauderdale, FL 33314-4022
Tel.: (954) 581-6606
Web Site: http://www.wtienergy.com
Waste Management Systems
N.A.I.C.S.: 562219

Joint Venture (Domestic):

Puget Energy, Inc. (4)
355 110th Ave NE, Bellevue, WA 98004
Tel.: (425) 454-6363
Web Site: https://www.pugetenergy.com
Rev.: $4,221,162,000
Assets: $17,187,514,000
Liabilities: $5,560,052,000
Net Worth: $11,627,462,000
Earnings: $414,345,000
Emp.: 3,250
Fiscal Year-end: 12/31/2022
Holding Company; Electric Power & Gas Distr
N.A.I.C.S.: 551112
Steven W. Hooper (Chm)

Subsidiary (Domestic):

Puget Sound Energy, Inc. (5)
355 110th Ave NE, Bellevue, WA 98004
Tel.: (425) 454-6363
Web Site: https://www.pse.com
Rev.: $4,216,173,000
Assets: $15,200,242,000
Liabilities: $5,542,394,000
Net Worth: $9,657,848,000
Earnings: $490,952,000
Emp.: 3,250
Fiscal Year-end: 12/31/2022
Electric Power & Natural Gas Distribution & Generation Services
N.A.I.C.S.: 221122
Steven W. Hooper (Chm)

Subsidiary (Domestic):

Puget Western, Inc. (6)
19515 North Creek Pkwy Ste 310, Bothell, WA 98011-8200
Tel.: (425) 487-6550
Web Site: http://www.pugetwestern.com
Sales Range: $25-49.9 Million
Emp.: 5
Real Estate Holding & Developing
N.A.I.C.S.: 237210
Joel Molander (Pres)

Joint Venture (Domestic):

Vocus Group Ltd. (3)
Level 12 60 Miller Street, North Sydney, 2060, NSW, Australia
Tel.: (61) 289998999
Web Site: http://www.vocus.com.au
Sales Range: $550-599.9 Million
Telecommunication Servicesb
N.A.I.C.S.: 517810
Ashe-lee Jegathesann (Gen Counsel & Sec)

Subsidiary (Domestic):

Amnet Broadband Pty. Ltd. (4)
Level 6 202 Pier St, Perth, 6000, WA, Australia
Tel.: (61) 1300539986
Web Site: http://www.amnet.com.au
Emp.: 150
Broadband Internet Providers
N.A.I.C.S.: 517810
Ryan Punter (Bus Mgr)

Eftel Pty Limited (4)
Level 10 452 Flinders Street, Melbourne, 3000, VIC, Australia
Tel.: (61) 3 9090 2525
Web Site: http://www.eftel.com

Broadband Network Operator
N.A.I.C.S.: 517810

Subsidiary (Domestic):

Engin Limited (5)
Level 3 28 Rodborough Road, French's Forest, 2086, NSW, Australia
Tel.: (61) 290044444
Web Site: http://www.engin.com.au
Sales Range: $10-24.9 Million
VoIP Services
N.A.I.C.S.: 517810

OntheNet (5)
165 Varsity Parade Level 1, PO Box 102, Varsity Lakes, Gold Coast, 4227, QLD, Australia
Tel.: (61) 7 55539222
Web Site: http://www.onthenet.com.au
Internet Services, DSL & Broadband Services
N.A.I.C.S.: 517111

Subsidiary (Domestic):

LSP Communications Pty Limited (4)
U 3a 100 Station St, Nunawading, VIC, Australia
Tel.: (61) 398722935
Electronic Parts & Equipment Merchant Whslr
N.A.I.C.S.: 423690

M2 Commander Pty. Ltd. (4)
76 Berry Street, Sydney, 2060, NSW, Australia
Tel.: (61) 2 9030 1605
Web Site: http://www.commander.com.au
Business Telecommunications Products & Services
N.A.I.C.S.: 561499

Multelink Services Pty Limited (4)
Suite101 29-31 Solent Circuit, 2153, Baulkham Hills, NSW, Australia
Tel.: (61) 1300309360
Web Site: http://www.multelink.com.au
Telecommunications
N.A.I.C.S.: 517810
Vaughan Bowen (CEO & Mng Dir)

Perth International Exchange Pty Ltd (4)
1 William Street, Perth, 6000, WA, Australia
Tel.: (61) 892166600
Web Site: http://www.perthix.com
Information Technology Consulting Services
N.A.I.C.S.: 541512

Primus Telecom Pty. Ltd. (4)
Level 3 538 Collins Street West, Melbourne, 3000, VIC, Australia
Tel.: (61) 399230785
Web Site: http://www.iprimus.com.au
Holding Company; Telecommunications & Internet Services
N.A.I.C.S.: 551112

Subsidiary (Domestic):

0014 Pty. Ltd. (5)
GPO Box 4618, Melbourne, 3001, VIC, Australia
Tel.: (61) 1300140014
Web Site: http://www.0014.com.au
Discounted International Telecommunications Services
N.A.I.C.S.: 517810

Primus Telecommunications (Australia) Pty. Ltd. (5)
Level 3 538 Collins Street West, Melbourne, 3000, VIC, Australia
Tel.: (61) 300854485
Web Site: http://www.iprimus.com.au
Telecommunication Servicesb
N.A.I.C.S.: 517112

Subsidiary (Domestic):

Vocus Fibre Pty Limited (4)
L 1 189 Miller St, North Sydney, North Sydney, 2060, NSW, Australia
Tel.: (61) 1300889988
Web Site: http://www.vocus.com.au
Sales Range: $25-49.9 Million
Emp.: 80
Telecommunication & Data Centre Services
N.A.I.C.S.: 517810

Alex West (Mng Dir)

Vocus Group Limited (4)
L 1 Vocus House 189 Miller St, North Sydney, Sydney, 2060, NSW, Australia
Tel.: (61) 2 8999 8999
Web Site: http://www.vocus.com.au
Emp.: 55
Telecommunication Servicesb
N.A.I.C.S.: 517810
Robert Mansfield (Chm)

Vocus Pty Limited (4)
L 1 Vocus House 189 Miller St, North Sydney, Sydney, 2060, NSW, Australia
Tel.: (61) 289998999
Web Site: http://www.vocus.com.au
Emp.: 12
Telecommunication Servicesb
N.A.I.C.S.: 517810
Doug Sayce (CEO)

Subsidiary (Non-US):

Macquarie International Housing and Land Consulting (Shanghai) Co., Ltd (2)
Level 3 The Centre 989 Changle Road, Xuhui District, Shanghai, 200031, China
Tel.: (86) 21 2412 9000
Properties Management Consulting Services
N.A.I.C.S.: 541611

Macquarie Investment Advisory (Beijing) Co., Ltd (2)
No1 East Chang An Avenue Towers Oriental Plaza Suite 1702 Block E2, Dong Cheng District, Beijing, 100738, China
Tel.: (86) 10 6521 6000
Investment Advisory Services
N.A.I.C.S.: 523940

Macquarie Investment Management Austria Kapitalanlage AG (2)
Karntner Strasse 28, 1010, Vienna, Austria
Tel.: (43) 1904000
Web Site: https://www.macquarieinvestments.at
Sales Range: $50-74.9 Million
Investment Management Service
N.A.I.C.S.: 523999
Konrad Kontriner (Member-Mgmt Bd & Dir-Div)

Subsidiary (Domestic):

Macquarie Investment Management Limited (2)
1 Martin Place, Sydney, 2000, NSW, Australia
Tel.: (61) 282454900
Web Site: http://www.macquarie.com.au
Sales Range: $800-899.9 Million
Emp.: 1,800
Securities Funds Management
N.A.I.C.S.: 523940

Subsidiary (US):

Delaware Management Holdings Inc. (3)
100 Independence 610 Market St, Philadelphia, PA 19106-2354 (100%)
Tel.: (215) 225-2300
Web Site: http://www.delawareinvestments.com
Sales Range: $300-349.9 Million
Holding Company; Investment Advisor Marketing Services
N.A.I.C.S.: 525910
Bruce A Ulmer (VP & Dir-Internal Audit)

Subsidiary (Domestic):

Macquarie Investment Services Limited (2)
No 1 Martin Place, Sydney, 2000, NSW, Australia
Tel.: (61) 2 8232 3333
Investment Management Service
N.A.I.C.S.: 523999

Subsidiary (Non-US):

Macquarie Korea Asset Management Co., Limited (2)
17th and 18th Floor Unit A Centropolis 26 Ujeongguk-ro, Jongno-gu, Seoul, 03161, Korea (South)

Tel.: (82) 37058500
Web Site: http://www.macquarie.kr
Asset Management Services
N.A.I.C.S.: 523940

Macquarie North America Ltd. (2)
Level 32 Brookfield Place 181 Bay St Suite 3200, Toronto, M5J 2T3, ON, Canada
Tel.: (416) 848-3500
Web Site: http://www.macquarie.com
Sales Range: $75-99.9 Million
Emp.: 250
Financial Services
N.A.I.C.S.: 523999

Subsidiary (Domestic):

Macquarie Cook Energy Canada Ltd (3)
Suite 3100 421 7th Avenue SW, Calgary, T2P 1C9, AB, Canada
Tel.: (403) 294-9541
Electric Power & Natural Gas Distribution Services
N.A.I.C.S.: 221122

Macquarie Essential Assets Partnership (3)
Brookfield Pl 181 Bay st Ste 3100, Toronto, M5J 2T3, ON, Canada
Tel.: (416) 607-5166
Web Site: http://www.macquarie.com.au
Asset Management Services
N.A.I.C.S.: 523999
James Cowan (Mng Dir)

Macquarie Financial Limited (3)
Level 32 Brookfield Place 181 Bay St Suite 3200, Toronto, M5J 2T3, ON, Canada
Tel.: (416) 848-3500
Web Site: http://www.macquarie.com
Sales Range: $50-74.9 Million
Emp.: 64
Residential Mortgage Services
N.A.I.C.S.: 522310

Macquarie Global Investments (3)
Brookfield Place 181 Bay Street Suite 3100, Toronto, M5J 2T3, ON, Canada
Tel.: (416) 848-3500
Web Site: http://www.macquarieglobalinvestments.ca
Investment Management Service
N.A.I.C.S.: 523999

Macquarie Metals and Energy Capital (Canada) Ltd (3)
Level 31 TD Canada Trust Tower 421 7th Avenue S W, Calgary, T2P 4K9, AB, Canada
Tel.: (403) 294-9541
Investment Management Service
N.A.I.C.S.: 523999

Macquarie Resource Capital Canada Ltd (3)
Suite 2400 Bentall 5 550 Burrard Street, Vancouver, V6C 2B5, BC, Canada
Tel.: (604) 605-3944
N.A.I.C.S.: 523999

Subsidiary (Non-US):

Macquarie Securities (New Zealand) Limited (2)
Level 17 Lumley Centre 88 Shortland Street, Auckland, New Zealand
Tel.: (64) 9 357 6931
Web Site: http://www.macquarie.co.nz
Securities Brokerage Services
N.A.I.C.S.: 523150

Macquarie Securities (Thailand) Limited (2)
28th Floor CRC Tower All Seasons Place 87/2 Wireless Road, Lumpini Patumwan, Bangkok, 10330, Thailand
Tel.: (66) 2 694 7999
Web Site: http://www.macquarie.com
Financial Security Brokerage Services
N.A.I.C.S.: 523150

Macquarie Securities Korea Limited (2)
17th and 18th Floor Unit A Centropolis 26 Ujeongguk-ro, Jongno-gu, Seoul, 03161, Korea (South)
Tel.: (82) 37058500
Web Site: http://www.macquarie.kr
Securities Brokerage Services

MACQUARIE GROUP LIMITED

INTERNATIONAL PUBLIC

Macquarie Group Limited—(Continued)
N.A.I.C.S.: 523150

Macquarie Securities South Africa (Pty) Ltd (2)
2nd Fl N Wing Great westerford 240 Main Rd, Rondebosch, Cape Town, 7700, South Africa
Tel.: (27) 21 813 2600
Sales Range: $50-74.9 Million
Emp.: 5
Financial Management Services
N.A.I.C.S.: 523999
James Mason *(Mng Dir)*

Subsidiary (Domestic):

Macquarie Securitisation Limited (2)
L 6 1 Martin Pl, Sydney, 2000, NSW, Australia
Tel.: (61) 2 8232 3333
Mortgage Loan Brokerage Services
N.A.I.C.S.: 522310

Macquarie Specialised Asset Management Limited (2)
Level 12 680 George Street, Sydney, 2000, NSW, Australia
Tel.: (61) 2 8280 7111
Web Site: http://www.macquarie.com
Asset Management Services
N.A.I.C.S.: 523940

Joint Venture (Domestic):

Medallist Developments Pty. Limited (2)
Level 12 1 Martin Place, Sydney, 2000, NSW, Australia
Tel.: (61) 800 667 626
Sales Range: $1-9.9 Million
Emp.: 53
Golf Course Real Estate Developer & Residential Housing Construction; Owned by Great White Shark Enterprises, Inc. & by Macquarie Group Limited
N.A.I.C.S.: 237210

Subsidiary (US):

Medallist Developments Inc. (3)
200 Blue Moon Crossing Ste 100, Pooler, GA 31322
Tel.: (912) 450-2280
Web Site: http://www.medallist.com
Golf Course Real Estate Developer & Residential Housing Construction
N.A.I.C.S.: 237210

Subsidiary (Non-US):

PT. MPM Indonesia (2)
Indonesia Stock Exchange Building Tower I, Jakarta, 12190, Indonesia
Tel.: (62) 21 2598 8300
Financial Management Services
N.A.I.C.S.: 523999

PT. Macquarie Capital Securities Indonesia (2)
The Indonesia Stock Exchange Building Tower I 8th Floor Jalan, Jenderal Sudirman Kav 52-53, Jakarta, 12190, Indonesia
Tel.: (62) 21 2598 8300
Web Site: http://www.macquarie.com
Sales Range: $50-74.9 Million
Securities Brokerage Services
N.A.I.C.S.: 523150

Holding (Non-US):

The Isle of Man Steam Packet Company Ltd. (2)
Imperial Buildings, IM1 2BY, Douglas, Isle of Man **(100%)**
Tel.: (44) 1624645645
Web Site: https://www.steam-packet.com
Sales Range: $100-124.9 Million
Ferry Boat Operator
N.A.I.C.S.: 483114
Mark Woodward *(CEO)*

Macquarie Capital France Societe Anonyme (1)
59 Avenue Marceau Floor 4, 75016, Paris, France
Tel.: (33) 156525450
Asset Management Services
N.A.I.C.S.: 523940

Macquarie Capital Limited (1)
Level 22 One International Finance Centre 1 Harbour View Street, Central, China (Hong Kong)
Tel.: (852) 39221888
Asset Management Services
N.A.I.C.S.: 523940

Macquarie Capital Securities (Philippines) Inc. (1)
Levels 25 29 30 31 Tower 1 The Enterprise Center, 6766 Ayala Avenue corner Paseo de Roxas, Makati, 1226, Philippines
Tel.: (63) 279171999
Asset Management Services
N.A.I.C.S.: 523940

Macquarie Commodities Trading (Shanghai) Co., Ltd. (1)
Level 27 Tower 2 HKRI Taikoo Hui No 288 Shimen Yi Road, Jing'an, Shanghai, China
Tel.: (86) 2124129000
Asset Management Services
N.A.I.C.S.: 523940

Macquarie Commodities Trading SA (1)
81 route de Florissant, 1206, Geneva, Switzerland
Tel.: (41) 228187509
Asset Management Services
N.A.I.C.S.: 523940

Macquarie Emerging Markets Asian Trading Pte. Limited (1)
9 Straits View 21-07 Marina One West Tower, Singapore, 018937, Singapore
Tel.: (65) 66010888
Asset Management Services
N.A.I.C.S.: 523940

Macquarie Energy Canada Ltd. (1)
Level 31 TD Canada Trust Tower 421 7th Avenue S W, Calgary, T2P 4K9, AB, Canada
Tel.: (403) 294-9541
Asset Management Services
N.A.I.C.S.: 523940

Macquarie Energy LLC (1)
1 Allen Ctr 500 Dallas Ste 3100, Houston, TX 77002
Tel.: (713) 275-6100
Asset Management Services
N.A.I.C.S.: 523940
Jim Rexroad *(Mng Dir)*

Macquarie Group - Frankfurt (1)
Untermainanlage 1, 60329, Frankfurt, Germany
Tel.: (49) 69 50957 8000
Financial Management Services
N.A.I.C.S.: 523999

Macquarie Group - Geneva (1)
81 route de Florissant, 1206, Geneva, Switzerland
Tel.: (41) 228187509
Web Site: http://www.macquarie.com
Emp.: 5
Financial Management Services
N.A.I.C.S.: 523999

Macquarie Group - Munich (1)
Sternstrasse 5, 80538, Munich, Germany
Tel.: (49) 89 20300 76000
Web Site: http://www.macquarie.de
Financial Management Services
N.A.I.C.S.: 523999

Macquarie Group - Vienna (1)
Karntner Strasse 28, 1010, Vienna, Austria
Tel.: (43) 120530020
Web Site: http://www.macquarie.at
Financial Management Services
N.A.I.C.S.: 523999

Macquarie Group Brazil (1)
Av Antonio Diederichsen 400 - Conj 1609 Edificio Metropolitan, Jardim America, Riberao Preto, 14020-250, Sao Paulo, Brazil
Tel.: (55) 16 3515 2600
Web Site: http://www.macquarie.com.br
Commercial Banking & Financial Advisory Services
N.A.I.C.S.: 523940

Macquarie Group Hong Kong (1)
Level 18 one International Finance Centre 1 Harbour View Street, Central, China (Hong Kong)
Tel.: (852) 3922 1888
Web Site: http://www.macquarie.hk
Banking & Investment Advisory Services
N.A.I.C.S.: 523940

Macquarie Group Ireland (1)
1st Floor Connaught House 1 Burlington Road, Dublin, 4, Ireland
Tel.: (353) 12383401
Web Site: http://www.macquarie.com
Banking & Financial Advisory Services
N.A.I.C.S.: 523940

Macquarie Group Netherlands (1)
Strawinskylaan 1021, 107XX, Amsterdam, Netherlands
Tel.: (31) 202382145
Web Site: http://www.macquarie.com
Banking & Financial Services
N.A.I.C.S.: 523150

Macquarie Group Philippines (1)
Level 22 6750 Office Tower Ayala Avenue, Makati, 1226, Philippines
Tel.: (63) 2 857 0888
Web Site: http://www.macquarie.com
Financial Advisory Services
N.A.I.C.S.: 523940

Subsidiary (Domestic):

Macquarie Offshore Services Pty Ltd (2)
Level 29 Tower 1 The Enterprise Center 6766 Ayala Avenue, corner Paseo de Roxas, Makati, 1226, Philippines
Tel.: (63) 279171999
Web Site: http://www.macquarie.com
Financial Management Services
N.A.I.C.S.: 523999

Macquarie Group Services Australia Pty Limited (1)
1 Martin Place Level 11, Sydney, 2000, NSW, Australia
Tel.: (61) 2 8232 3333
Investment Advisory Services
N.A.I.C.S.: 523940
Larry Handen *(Mng Dir)*

Macquarie Group Singapore (1)
10 Marina Boulevard 17-01 Tower 2 Marina Bay Financial Centre, Singapore, 18983, Singapore
Tel.: (65) 6601 0888
Financial Banking & Advisory Services
N.A.I.C.S.: 522110

Macquarie Insurance Facility Luxembourg S.A R.L. (1)
20 Boulevard Royal, 2449, Luxembourg, Luxembourg
Tel.: (352) 24619343
Asset Management Services
N.A.I.C.S.: 523940

Macquarie Securities (NZ) Limited (1)
Level 13 PWC Tower Commercial Bay 15 Customs Street West, Auckland, 1010, New Zealand
Tel.: (64) 93576931
Asset Management Services
N.A.I.C.S.: 523940

Maher Terminals, LLC (1)
1210 Corbin St, Elizabeth, NJ 07201 **(80%)**
Tel.: (908) 527-8200
Web Site: https://www.maherterminals.com
Marine Container Terminal Services
N.A.I.C.S.: 488320
Gary Cross *(Pres & CEO)*

Mercury Air Center-Reno, LLC (1)
655 S Rock Blvd, Reno, NV 89502-4118
Tel.: (775) 858-7300
Aircraft Maintenance Services
N.A.I.C.S.: 488190

Newfoundland Transshipment Limited (1)
Suite 201 2nd Floor Baine Johnston Centre 10 Fort William Place, Saint John's, A1C 1K4, NL, Canada
Tel.: (709) 570-3200
Web Site: http://www.ntl.net
Petroleum Bulk Storage Services
N.A.I.C.S.: 493190

Oil Mop, L.L.C. (1)
131 Keating Dr, Belle Chasse, LA 70037
Tel.: (504) 394-6110
Web Site: http://www.omies.com
Waste Management Services
N.A.I.C.S.: 562119
Kyle Prest *(VP-Admin & Controller)*

Premier Technical Services Group plc (1)
11-14 Flemming Court Whistler Drive, Glasshoughton, Castleford, WF10 5HW, United Kingdom
Tel.: (44) 1977668771
Web Site: http://www.ptsg.co.uk
Rev.: $87,685,672
Assets: $123,314,668
Liabilities: $52,505,087
Net Worth: $70,809,581
Earnings: $3,870,832
Emp.: 850
Fiscal Year-end: 12/31/2018
Facade Access & Fall Arrest Equipment Services, Electrical Testing, High-Level Cleaning & Specialist Electrical & Mechanical Services
N.A.I.C.S.: 238210
John Foley *(Chm)*

ProAir Aviation Maintenance, LLC (1)
732 W Deer Vly Rd, Phoenix, AZ 85027
Tel.: (623) 869-5011
Web Site: http://www.proair-dvt.com
Emp.: 20
Aircraft Maintenance Services
N.A.I.C.S.: 488190
Daniel Faurie *(Gen Mgr)*

Reden Solar SAS (1)
ZAC Des Champs de Lescaze, 47310, Roquefort, France
Tel.: (33) 553772131
Web Site: http://www.reden.solar
Emp.: 100
Solar Energy Services
N.A.I.C.S.: 221118

Wavenet Limited (1)
1 Central Boulevard Blythe Valley Park Solihull, Birmingham, B90 8BG, United Kingdom
Tel.: (44) 3332340011
Web Site: https://www.wavenetuk.com
Telecommunications & Internet Services
N.A.I.C.S.: 517111

Subsidiary (Domestic):

AdEPT Technology Group plc (2)
77 Mount Ephraim, Tunbridge Wells, TN4 8BS, Kent, United Kingdom
Tel.: (44) 3445577200
Web Site: http://www.adept.co.uk
Rev.: $78,545,460
Assets: $114,060,699
Liabilities: $89,473,748
Net Worth: $24,586,951
Earnings: ($461,625)
Emp.: 375
Fiscal Year-end: 03/31/2021
Telecommunications & Internet Services
N.A.I.C.S.: 517111
Ian Fishwick *(Chm)*

Subsidiary (Domestic):

Atomwide Limited (3)
Unit 2-3 Ravensquay Business Centre Cray Avenue, Orpington, BR5 4BQ, Kent, United Kingdom
Tel.: (44) 1689814700
Web Site: http://www.atomwide.com
Online Cashless Payment Services
N.A.I.C.S.: 522320

Centrix Limited (3)
Flagship House Reading Road North, Fleet, GU51 4WP, Hampshire, United Kingdom
Tel.: (44) 8701434343
Web Site: http://www.centrix-uk.com
Information Technology Services
N.A.I.C.S.: 541511

Comms Group UK Limited (3)
Unit 2 IO Centre Barn Way Lodge Farm, Northampton, NN5 7UW, United Kingdom
Tel.: (44) 1604653362
Web Site: http://www.commsgroup.com
Emp.: 28
Fiber Data Services

AND PRIVATE COMPANIES   MACROGEN INC.

N.A.I.C.S.: 518210
Emma Archer *(Dir-Ops)*

Our IT Department Limited (3)
Bridge House 181 Queen Victoria Street, London, EC4V 4EG, United Kingdom
Tel.: (44) 2085017676
Web Site: http://www.ouritdept.co.uk
IT Support Services
N.A.I.C.S.: 541519
Ben Montague *(Acct Mgr-Technical)*

Shift F7 Limited (3)
Blackbrook House The Dorking Business Park Station Road, Dorking, RH4 1HJ, Surrey, United Kingdom
Tel.: (44) 1306873900
Web Site: http://www.shiftf7.com
IT Support Services
N.A.I.C.S.: 541519

MACQUARIE LEASING PTY LIMITED
Level 6 50 Martin Place, Sydney, 2000, NSW, Australia
Tel.: (61) 282323333   AU
Financial Investment Services
N.A.I.C.S.: 523940
Jon Moodie *(Mng Dir)*

MACQUARIE TELECOM GROUP LIMITED
Level 15 2 Market St, Sydney, 2000, NSW, Australia
Tel.: (61) 282217112
Web Site:
   https://www.macquarietelecom.com
MAQ—(ASX)
Rev.: $236,990,229
Assets: $362,081,473
Liabilities: $250,461,381
Net Worth: $111,620,092
Earnings: $6,478,903
Emp.: 446
Fiscal Year-end: 06/30/22
Offices of Other Holding Companies
N.A.I.C.S.: 551112
David Tudehope *(Co-Founder & CEO)*

Subsidiaries:

Macquarie Technology Group Pty. Ltd. (1)
Level 15 2 Market St, Sydney, NSW, Australia
Tel.: (61) 1800004943
Web Site:
   https://macquarietechnologygroup.com
Telecommunication & Data Centre Services
N.A.I.C.S.: 518210

Macquarie Telecom Pty Limited (1)
Level 14 2 Market St, Sydney, 2000, NSW, Australia
Tel.: (61) 800004943
Web Site:
   http://www.macquarietelecom.com
Sales Range: $100-124.9 Million
Telecommunications & Hosting Services
N.A.I.C.S.: 517121

MACRO ENTERPRISES INC.
6807-100th Avenue, Fort Saint John, V1J 4M6, BC, Canada
Tel.: (250) 785-0033
Web Site:
   http://www.macroenterprises.ca
Year Founded: 1994
MCR—(TSXV)
Rev.: $209,359,250
Assets: $143,287,881
Liabilities: $62,108,338
Net Worth: $81,179,542
Earnings: ($9,639,254)
Emp.: 46
Fiscal Year-end: 12/31/20
Oil & Gas Construction Services
N.A.I.C.S.: 237120
Frank Miles *(Founder, Pres & CEO)*

Subsidiaries:

Macro Industries Inc. (1)
PO Box 6781, Fort Saint John, V1J 4J2, BC, Canada
Tel.: (250) 785-0033
Web Site: https://www.macroindustries.ca
Sales Range: $150-199.9 Million
Oil & Gas Pipeline Transportation Services
N.A.I.C.S.: 486110
Frank Miles *(Co-Founder, Pres & CEO)*

MACRO INTERNATIONAL LIMITED
24/147 ground floor Plaza Kalpana, Birhana Road, Kanpur, 208 001, India
Tel.: (91) 5122332481
Web Site: https://www.miel.co.in
Year Founded: 1993
512600—(BOM)
Rev.: $27,721
Assets: $724,517
Liabilities: $17,967
Net Worth: $706,550
Earnings: $822
Fiscal Year-end: 03/31/21
Real Estate Development Services
N.A.I.C.S.: 531390
Sudhir Kumar Parasrampuria *(Chm & Mng Dir)*

MACRO KIOSK BERHAD
The Troika Tower B Level 3 19 Persiaran KLCC, 50450, Kuala Lumpur, Malaysia
Tel.: (60) 3 2164 8100   MY
Web Site:
   http://www.macrokiosk.com
Year Founded: 2000
Wireless & Telecommunications Services
N.A.I.C.S.: 517810
Kenny Goh *(Co-Founder & CEO)*

Subsidiaries:

Macro Kiosk (Australia) Pty Ltd (1)
Level 21 Tower 2 Darling Park, 201 Sussex Street, Sydney, 2000, NSW, Australia
Tel.: (61) 2 9006 3306
Mobile Telecommunications Services
N.A.I.C.S.: 517112

Macro Kiosk (Guangzhou) Technology Co. Ltd (1)
Suite 2902 29th Floor Block A Zhongtai International Plaza, No 161 Lin He Xi Road TianHe District, Guangzhou, 510620, Guangdong, China
Tel.: (86) 20 3892 1135
Web Site: http://www.macrokiosk.com
Mobile Telecommunications Services
N.A.I.C.S.: 517810

Macro Kiosk (HK) Limited (1)
Suite 2 25th Floor Grandion Plaza, 932 Cheung Sha Wan Road, Kowloon, China (Hong Kong)
Tel.: (852) 2989 9160
Web Site: http://www.macrokiosk.com
Mobile Telecommunications Services
N.A.I.C.S.: 517810

Macro Kiosk (India) Private Limited (1)
409-409A International Trade Tower Nehru Place, New Delhi, 110 019, India
Tel.: (91) 8587970827
Telecommunication Servicesb
N.A.I.C.S.: 517810

Macro Kiosk Co. Ltd. (1)
Suite 2 4th Floor No 925 Sec 4 Taiwan Boulevard, Xitun District, Taichung, 407, Taiwan
Tel.: (886) 4 2358 5100
Mobile Telecommunications Services
N.A.I.C.S.: 517810

Macro Kiosk FZ-LLC (1)
Suite 215 Building 12, PO Box 500493, Dubai Internet City, Dubai, United Arab Emirates
Tel.: (971) 4421 8434

Wireless Telecommunication Services
N.A.I.C.S.: 517810

Macro Kiosk Joint Stock Company (1)
Suite 1104 11th Floor TNR Tower Nguyen Cong Tru, 180-192 Nguyen Cong Tru Street Nguyen Thai Binh Ward District 1, Ho Chi Minh City, Vietnam
Tel.: (84) 8 3821 7047
Web Site: http://www.macrokiosk.com
Wireless Telecommunication Services
N.A.I.C.S.: 517810

Macro Kiosk Limited (1)
57 Park Ventures Ecoplex 15th Floor Suite 1508 Wireless Road, Lumpini Pathumwan, Bangkok, 10330, Thailand
Tel.: (66) 2 115 8800
Web Site: http://www.macrokiosk.com
Wireless & Telecommunications Services
N.A.I.C.S.: 517810

Macro Kiosk Philippines, Inc. (1)
Suite 11 11th Floor Tower One Ayala Triangle Ayala Avenue, Makati City, Manila, 1227, Philippines
Tel.: (63) 2 887 6335
Web Site: http://www.macrokiosk.com
Mobile Telecommunications Services
N.A.I.C.S.: 517112

Macro Kiosk Pte Ltd (1)
152 Beach Road 24-07 The Gateway East, Singapore, 189721, Singapore
Tel.: (65) 6339 0870
Web Site: http://www.macrokiosk.com
Wireless Telecommunication Services
N.A.I.C.S.: 517810

PT Permata Cipta Rejeki (1)
Menara DEA Tower 1 Suite 1205 12th Floor Kawasan Mega Kuningan, Jl Mega Kuningan Barat Kav E 4 3 No 1-2, Jakarta, 12950, Indonesia
Tel.: (62) 21 5785 3254
Web Site: http://www.macrokiosk.com
Mobile Telecommunications Services
N.A.I.C.S.: 517810

MACRO METALS LIMITED
Suite 23 513 Hay Street, Subiaco, 6904, WA, Australia
Tel.: (61) 861436707   AU
Web Site:
   https://macrometals.com.au
M4M—(ASX)
Rev.: $12,025
Assets: $6,282,452
Liabilities: $507,618
Net Worth: $5,774,834
Earnings: ($9,315,324)
Emp.: 2
Fiscal Year-end: 06/30/24
Iron Mining
N.A.I.C.S.: 212210
Simon Rushton *(Mng Dir)*

MACROASIA CORPORATION
12th Floor PNB Allied Bank Center 6754 Ayala Avenue, Makati, 1226, Philippines
Tel.: (63) 288402001
Web Site:
   https://www.macroasiacorp.com
MAC—(PHI)
Rev.: $40,536,385
Assets: $217,777,819
Liabilities: $115,067,670
Net Worth: $102,710,149
Earnings: ($3,139,240)
Emp.: 5,999
Fiscal Year-end: 12/31/21
Geological Exploration & Development Services
N.A.I.C.S.: 541360
Marivic T. Moya *(Chief Compliance Officer, Officer-Corp Information & Sr VP-HR)*

Subsidiaries:

MacroAsia Air Taxi Services, Inc (1)
Planters Hangar Domestic Airport, Manila Domestic Airport, Pasay, 1301, Philippines
Tel.: (63) 28539723
Sales Range: $25-49.9 Million
Emp.: 4
Helicopter Charter Services
N.A.I.C.S.: 481211
Joseph T. Chua *(Pres & CEO)*

MacroAsia Airport Services Corporation (1)
3rd Floor Bldg A Skyfreight Center Ninoy Aquino Avenue Brgy, Sto Nino, Paranaque, 1704, Philippines
Tel.: (63) 28785000
Web Site: http://mascorp.ph
Airport Ground Handling Services
N.A.I.C.S.: 488119
Emerson S. Bonoan *(Gen Mgr)*

MacroAsia Catering Services, Inc (1)
West Service Road Merville Exit, NAIA, Pasay, 1300, Philippines
Tel.: (63) 288282011
Web Site:
   http://www.macroasiacatering.com
Sales Range: $50-74.9 Million
Emp.: 400
Aircraft Catering Services
N.A.I.C.S.: 722320
Rhodel Esteban *(COO)*

MacroAsia Properties Development Corporation (1)
Macroasia Special Econimic Zone Villamor Airbase, Pasay, 1309, Philippines
Tel.: (63) 28535201
Web Site: http://www.macroasiacorp.com
Aircraft Support Services
N.A.I.C.S.: 481211
Joseph T. Chua *(Pres)*

MacroAsia SATS Food Industries Corporation (1)
Mapdc Bldg Esat Service Road Sucat, Muntinlupa, 1771, Philippines
Tel.: (63) 282979000
Catering Services
N.A.I.C.S.: 722320

MACROBLOCK, INC.
6F-4 No 18 Pu-Ting Rd, Hsinchu, 30072, Taiwan
Tel.: (886) 35790068
Web Site: https://www.mblock.com.tw
Year Founded: 1999
3527—(TPE)
Rev.: $79,243,598
Assets: $100,457,837
Liabilities: $16,456,805
Net Worth: $84,001,032
Earnings: $8,953,038
Emp.: 286
Fiscal Year-end: 12/31/22
Electronic Components Mfr
N.A.I.C.S.: 334419
Li-Chang Yang *(Chm)*

MACROGEN INC.
238 Teheran-ro, Geumcheon-gu, Seoul, Korea (South)
Tel.: (82) 221807000
Web Site: https://www.macrogen.com
Year Founded: 1997
038290—(KRS)
Rev.: $106,319,614
Assets: $214,856,384
Liabilities: $76,060,980
Net Worth: $138,795,404
Earnings: ($16,878,106)
Emp.: 555
Fiscal Year-end: 12/31/22
Bio Technology Services
N.A.I.C.S.: 541714
Changhoon Kim *(CEO)*

Subsidiaries:

Macrogen Asia Pacific Pte. Ltd. (1)
3 Biopolis Drive 05-18 Synapse, Singapore, 138623, Singapore
Tel.: (65) 63390927
Biotechnology Research Services
N.A.I.C.S.: 541714

4631

MACROGEN INC.

Macrogen Inc.—(Continued)

Macrogen Corp. (1)
Meibergdreef 57, 1105 BA, Amsterdam, Netherlands
Tel.: (31) 203337563
Web Site: https://www.macrogen-europe.com
Sales Range: $25-49.9 Million
Business Management Consulting Services
N.A.I.C.S.: 541611

Macrogen Corp. (1)
1330 Piccard Dr Ste 103, Rockville, MD 20850
Tel.: (301) 251-1007
Web Site: https://www.psomagen.com
Emp.: 100
Laboratory Testing Services
N.A.I.C.S.: 541380

Macrogen Corp. (1)
Tokyo University of Agriculture No 11 Building 3F 1-1-1 Sakuragaoka, Setagaya-Ku, Tokyo, 156-8502, Japan
Tel.: (81) 3 5799 4788
Laboratory Testing Services
N.A.I.C.S.: 541380

Macrogen Japan Corp. (1)
2-4-32 Aomi Time24 Building 16F, Koto-ku, Tokyo, 135-0064, Japan
Tel.: (81) 359621124
Biotechnology Research Services
N.A.I.C.S.: 541714

Psomagen, Inc. (1)
1330 Piccard Dr Ste 103, Rockville, MD 20850
Tel.: (301) 918-5784
Web Site: https://www.psomagen.com
Biotechnology Research Services
N.A.I.C.S.: 541714

MACROLINK CAPITAL HOLDINGS LIMITED

15/F COFCO Tower 262 Gloucester Road, Causeway Bay, China (Hong Kong)
Tel.: (852) 35292657
Web Site: http://macrolinkcapital.etnet.com.hk
0758—(HKG)
Rev.: $97,424,535
Assets: $34,869,338
Liabilities: $25,700,430
Net Worth: $9,168,908
Earnings: ($577,065)
Emp.: 26
Fiscal Year-end: 12/31/22
Property Management Consultancy Service Provider
N.A.I.C.S.: 531311
Jianren Zhou *(Exec Dir)*

Subsidiaries:

Lima Airlines S.A.C (1)
Av Republica De Panama 3545 Piso 14, San Isidro, Peru
Tel.: (51) 987214374
Web Site: http://www.limaairlines.com
Charter Air Freight Services
N.A.I.C.S.: 481212

MACROLINK CULTURALTAINMENT DEVELOPMENT CO., LTD.

8F Macrolink Group Headquarters Building Government Avenu, Taihu Town Tongzhou District, Beijing, 101116, China
Tel.: (86) 1080559199
Web Site: http://www.macrolink.com.cn
Year Founded: 1993
000620—(SSE)
Rev.: $38,063,492
Assets: $449,994,623
Liabilities: $71,993,379
Net Worth: $378,001,244
Earnings: $16,136,077
Fiscal Year-end: 12/31/20
Real Estate Services

N.A.I.C.S.: 531390
Ma Chenshan *(Chm)*

Subsidiaries:

New Silkroad Culturaltainment Limited (1)
15/F COFCO Tower 262 Gloucester Road, Causeway Bay, China (Hong Kong)
Tel.: (852) 25919919
Web Site: https://www.newsilkroad472.com
Rev.: $47,105,130
Assets: $273,455,753
Liabilities: $42,651,810
Net Worth: $230,803,943
Emp.: 353
Fiscal Year-end: 12/31/2022
Investment Holding Company
N.A.I.C.S.: 551112
Paul Kwong Chue Ng *(Sec)*

MACROMILL EMBRAIN CO., LTD.

7 9 Floor 9 Myeongdal-ro, Seocho-gu, Seoul, Korea (South)
Tel.: (82) 234444000
Web Site: https://www.embrain.com
Year Founded: 1998
169330—(KRS)
Rev.: $47,166,626
Assets: $41,987,652
Liabilities: $14,852,483
Net Worth: $27,135,169
Earnings: $5,569,455
Emp.: 232
Fiscal Year-end: 06/30/22
Digital Marketing Services
N.A.I.C.S.: 541870
In-Su Choi *(CEO)*

Subsidiaries:

Centan Inc. (1)
11F Shinagawa East One Tower 2 16 1 Konan, Tokyo, 1080075, Japan
Tel.: (81) 366706722
Marketing Consulting Services
N.A.I.C.S.: 541613

H.M. Marketing Research, Inc. (1)
Yamaman Building 8F 6-1 Nihonbashi Koamicho, Chuo-ku, Tokyo, 103-0016, Japan
Tel.: (81) 355432311
Web Site: https://www.hmmr.co.jp
Marketing Analysis Services
N.A.I.C.S.: 541910

Macromill Carenet, Inc. (1)
Shinagawa East One Tower 11F 2-16-1, Konan Minato-ku, Tokyo, 108-0075, Japan
Tel.: (81) 367167108
Web Site: https://www.macromillcarenet.jp
Medical Research Services
N.A.I.C.S.: 541715

MACRONIX INTERNATIONAL CO., LTD.

16 Li-Hsin Road Science Park, Hsin-chu, ROC, Taiwan
Tel.: (886) 35786688
Web Site: https://www.macronix.com
Year Founded: 1989
2337—(TAI)
Rev.: $903,352,201
Assets: $2,544,604,796
Liabilities: $964,240,717
Net Worth: $1,580,364,079
Earnings: ($55,565,811)
Emp.: 4,025
Fiscal Year-end: 12/31/23
Memory Products Mfr for Consumer Electronics
N.A.I.C.S.: 334413
Miin Chyou Wu *(Founder, Chm & CEO)*

Subsidiaries:

InfoMax Communication Co., Ltd. (1)
4F No 3 Creation Road III Science Park, Hsin-chu, Taiwan
Tel.: (886) 36668866

Web Site: http://www.infomax.com.tw
Emp.: 90
Electronic Components Mfr
N.A.I.C.S.: 334419
Michael Chien *(Mgr-Sls Dept)*

Macronix (BVI) Co Ltd (1)
C-o Offshore Incorporations Limited, PO Box 957, Road Town, Virgin Islands (British)
Tel.: (284) 4948184
Holding Company
N.A.I.C.S.: 551112

Subsidiary (Non-US):

Macronix (Asia) Limited (2)
Ichigo Kawasaki Bldg 5F 1-2 Higashida-cho, Kawasaki-Ku, Kawasaki, 210-0005, Kanagawa, Japan
Tel.: (81) 442469100
Web Site: http://www.mxic.co.jp
Semiconductor Equipment Mfr
N.A.I.C.S.: 334413
Harrison Tu *(Gen Mgr)*

Macronix (Hong Kong) Co., Limited (1)
702-703 7/F Building 9, Hong Kong Science Park 5 Science Park West Avenue, Sha Tin, NT, China (Hong Kong)
Tel.: (852) 34605188
Integrated Device Mfr
N.A.I.C.S.: 334413

Macronix America Inc. (1)
680 N McCarthy Blvd Ste 200, Milpitas, CA 95035
Tel.: (408) 262-8887
Integrated Device Mfr
N.A.I.C.S.: 334413
Arthur Yang *(Pres)*

Macronix Europe NV (1)
Koningin Astridlaan 49 B6, 1780, Wemmel, Belgium
Tel.: (32) 24568020
Sales Range: $50-74.9 Million
Emp.: 6
Electronic Parts & Equipment Whslr
N.A.I.C.S.: 423690

Macronix Microelectronics (Suzhou) Co., Ltd (1)
No 55 Suhong West Road, Suzhou Industrial Park, Suzhou, 215021, China
Tel.: (86) 51262580888
Web Site: https://www.mxic.cn
Semiconductor Equipment Mfr
N.A.I.C.S.: 334413

Macronix Pte Ltd (1)
1 Marine Parade Central 11-03 Parkway Centre, Singapore, 449408, Singapore
Tel.: (65) 63465505
Electronic Components Mfr
N.A.I.C.S.: 334419

Magic Pixel Inc (1)
5th Fl No 3 Creation Rd III, Science-Based Industrial Park, Hsin-chu, Taiwan
Tel.: (886) 36668822
Web Site: http://www.magicpixel.com.tw
Computer System Design Services
N.A.I.C.S.: 541512

MaxRise Inc. (1)
9F No 16 Li Hsin Road Science Park, Hsin-chu, Taiwan
Tel.: (886) 36687667
Web Site: http://www.maxrise.com.tw
Sales Range: $50-74.9 Million
Emp.: 60
Digital Television Distr
N.A.I.C.S.: 423620

MoDioTek Co., Ltd. (1)
4F No 3 Creation Road III Science Park, Hsin-chu, 300, Taiwan
Tel.: (886) 36668881
Web Site: http://www.modiotek.com.tw
Semiconductor Equipment Mfr
N.A.I.C.S.: 334413

Mxtran Inc. (1)
9F No 16 Li Hsin Road Science Park, Hsin-chu, 00300, Taiwan
Tel.: (886) 277022168
Web Site: http://www.mxtran.com
Information Technology Consulting Services
N.A.I.C.S.: 541512

INTERNATIONAL PUBLIC

New Trend Technology Inc. (1)
1342 Alessandro Dr, Thousand Oaks, CA 91320
Tel.: (650) 822-7101
Web Site: http://www.newtrendtechnology.com
Plastic Injection Mold Mfr
N.A.I.C.S.: 326199
Felix Alanis *(CEO)*

MACROWELL OMG DIGITAL ENTERTAINMENT CO., LTD.

7F-1 No 19-2 Sanchong Rd, Nangang District, Taipei, 115, Taiwan
Tel.: (886) 226550051
3687—(TPE)
Rev.: $52,211,081
Assets: $261,375,387
Liabilities: $146,255,479
Net Worth: $115,119,907
Earnings: $10,206,422
Fiscal Year-end: 12/31/22
Software Development Services
N.A.I.C.S.: 541511
Mark Lo *(Chm & CEO)*

MACSA ID, S.A.

Calle Girona 46-48, 08242, Manresa, Barcelona, Spain
Tel.: (34) 938 738 798
Web Site: http://www.macsalaser.com
Year Founded: 1908
Sales Range: $25-49.9 Million
Emp.: 51
Marking Laser Mfr & Distr
N.A.I.C.S.: 333248
Xavi Rodriguez Robles *(Mgr-Bus Dev)*

Subsidiaries:

Macsa Portugal Lda. (1)
Rua Frederico Ulrich n 2650, 4470-605, Moreira, Portugal
Tel.: (351) 229962204
Web Site: http://www.macsa.pt
Lasers Distr
N.A.I.C.S.: 423690

MACSTEEL HOLDINGS LUXEMBOURG S.A.R.L.

7 Brook Road Industrial Sites, Lilianton, Boksburg, Gauteng, South Africa
Tel.: (27) 118710000
Holding Company
N.A.I.C.S.: 551112

Subsidiaries:

Macsteel International Holdings B.V. (1)
World Trade Center Amsterdam Strawinskylaan 333 Tower B 3rd Floor, 1077 XX, Amsterdam, Netherlands
Tel.: (31) 20 642 4361
Web Site: http://www.macsteelinternational.com
Holding Company; Steel Production & Distr
N.A.I.C.S.: 551112
Adriaan Veltema *(Sec)*

Subsidiary (Non-US):

Macsteel International Australia Pty Limited (2)
Level 1 40 Burwood Road, Hawthorn, 3122, VIC, Australia
Tel.: (61) 3 9805 0400
Web Site: http://www.mitgr.com.au
Steel Product Distr
N.A.I.C.S.: 331513

Macsteel International FZCO (2)
25th Floor AG Tower Jumeirah Lake Towers, PO Box 61030, Dubai, United Arab Emirates
Tel.: (971) 44402100
Steel Product Distr
N.A.I.C.S.: 331513

Subsidiary (US):

Macsteel International USA Corp. (2)

333 Westchester Ave Ste S101, White Plains, NY 10604
Tel.: (914) 872-2700
Web Site:
 http://www.macsteelinternational.com
Steel Alloy, Carbon Rod & Wire Distr
N.A.I.C.S.: 423390
Steven Cohen *(Chief Strategy Officer)*

Subsidiary (Non-US):

Macsteel Service Centres SA (Pty) Ltd. (2)
7 Brook Rd Lillianton Industrial Sites, Lillianton, Boksburg, Gauteng, South Africa
Tel.: (27) 118710000
Web Site: http://www.macsteel.co.za
Steel Product Mfr & Distr
N.A.I.C.S.: 331513
Mike Benfield *(CEO)*

MACTER INTERNATIONAL LTD.

F 216 Site, Karachi, Pakistan
Tel.: (92) 2132591000
Web Site: https://www.macter.com
Year Founded: 1992
MACTER—(KAR)
Rev.: $27,015,362
Assets: $21,155,793
Liabilities: $13,685,219
Net Worth: $7,470,574
Earnings: $277,229
Fiscal Year-end: 06/30/19
Pharmaceuticals Product Mfr
N.A.I.C.S.: 325412
Asif Misbah *(CEO)*

MACWIN STEEL INC

380 Pelissier St 210, Windsor, N9A 6W8, ON, Canada
Tel.: (519) 256-3137
Web Site:
 http://www.macwinsteel.com
Rev.: $16,836,346
Emp.: 6
Steel Distr
N.A.I.C.S.: 423510
Norm Smith *(Pres)*

MAD PAWS HOLDING LIMITED

55 Pyrmont Bridge Road, Pyrmont, 2009, NSW, Australia
Tel.: (61) 280466536   AU
Web Site:
 https://www.madpaws.com.au
Year Founded: 2014
MPA—(ASX)
Rev.: $16,030,445
Assets: $20,785,408
Liabilities: $8,655,658
Net Worth: $12,129,750
Earnings: ($4,876,649)
Emp.: 125
Fiscal Year-end: 06/30/23
Holding Company
N.A.I.C.S.: 551112

MADARA COSMETICS AS

Zeltinu Iela 131, Marupe, 2167, Latvia
Tel.: (371) 66154811
Web Site:
 https://www.madaracosmetics.com
MDARA—(RSE)
Rev.: $22,336,039
Assets: $18,572,058
Liabilities: $3,005,370
Net Worth: $15,566,687
Earnings: $1,763,306
Emp.: 215
Fiscal Year-end: 12/31/23
Skin Care Product Mfr
N.A.I.C.S.: 325611
Anna Ramata-Stunda *(Chm-Supervisory Bd)*

Subsidiaries:

Cosmetics Nord SIA (1)
Zeltinu str 131, Marupe, LV-2167, Latvia
Tel.: (371) 66154811
Web Site: http://cosmeticsnord.com
Cosmetics Products Mfr
N.A.I.C.S.: 325620

MADARA EUROPE AD

82 Kniaz Boris I Blvd 2nd Floor Apt 3, 9002, Varna, Bulgaria
Tel.: (359) 52610368
Web Site:
 https://www.madaraeurope.eu
6MF—(BUL)
Real Estate Services
N.A.I.C.S.: 531390
Hristo Hristos *(Exec Dir)*

MADE IN JAPAN TERIYAKI EXPERIENCE

700 Kerr St Ste 100, Oakville, L6K 3W5, ON, Canada
Tel.: (905) 337-7777
Web Site:
 http://www.teriyakiexperience.com
Year Founded: 1981
Sales Range: $10-24.9 Million
Emp.: 25
Restaurant Operators
N.A.I.C.S.: 722511
Lou Donato *(Founder & CEO)*

MADE SA

167 Impasse de la Garrigue, 83210, La Farlede, France
Tel.: (33) 494088053   FR
Web Site: https://www.made-sa.com
Year Founded: 1991
MLMAD—(EUR)
Sales Range: $1-9.9 Million
Search & Measurement Equipment Mfr & Distr
N.A.I.C.S.: 334511
Didier Spada *(Pres)*

MADE TECH GROUP PLC

4 O Meara Street, London, SE1 1TE, United Kingdom
Tel.: (44) 2033977846   UK
Web Site: https://www.madetech.com
Year Founded: 2008
MTEC—(AIM)
Rev.: $50,738,450
Assets: $25,472,103
Liabilities: $6,271,144
Net Worth: $19,200,959
Earnings: ($2,018,430)
Emp.: 430
Fiscal Year-end: 05/31/23
Digital Marketing Services
N.A.I.C.S.: 541810

Subsidiaries:

Made Tech Limited (1)
4 O Meara Street, London, SE1 1TE, United Kingdom
Tel.: (44) 2033977846
Web Site: https://www.madetech.com
Digital Data & Technology Services
N.A.I.C.S.: 518210

MADEIRA MINERALS LTD.

Suite 1100 1111 Melville Street, Vancouver, V6E 3V6, BC, Canada
Tel.: (604) 924-8000   BC
Year Founded: 2006
Assets: $94,554
Liabilities: $9,642
Net Worth: $84,912
Earnings: ($22,244)
Fiscal Year-end: 09/30/19
Investment Services
N.A.I.C.S.: 523999
Thomas Kovacs *(CEO)*

MADEMOISELLE DESSERTS CORBY LTD.

10 Princewood Road Earlstrees Industrial Estate, Corby, NN17 4AP, United Kingdom
Tel.: (44) 1536 463250
Web Site:
 http://www.mdesserts.co.uk
Desserts Mfr
N.A.I.C.S.: 311811
Frans Visser *(Mng Dir)*

Subsidiaries:

Ministry of Cake Ltd (1)
Frobisher Way Bindon Road, Taunton, TA2 6AB, Somerset, United Kingdom
Tel.: (44) 1823 257 922
Web Site: http://www.ministryofcake.co.uk
Emp.: 400
Frozen Cake & Dessert Mfr
N.A.I.C.S.: 311813
Garry Hewings *(Mgr-New Product Dev)*

MADHAV COPPER LTD.

202/203 D and I Excelus Opp Home School Bhavnagar, Waghawadi Road, 364001, Gujarat, 364001, India
Tel.: (91) 2783001034
Web Site:
 https://www.madhavcopper.com
Year Founded: 2012
MCL—(NSE)
Rev.: $24,759
Assets: $12,394,077
Liabilities: $7,622,852
Net Worth: $4,771,225
Earnings: ($529,273)
Emp.: 23
Fiscal Year-end: 03/31/23
Copper Product Mfr
N.A.I.C.S.: 335921
Nilesh Patel *(Chm)*

MADHAV INFRA PROJECTS LIMITED

Madhav House Plot 4 Nr Panchratna Tower Beside Amul Apartment, Subhanpura, Vadodara, 390 023, Gujarat, India
Tel.: (91) 2652290722   In
Web Site:
 www.madhavcorp.com
Year Founded: 2010
539894—(BOM)
Rev.: $65,635,824
Assets: $69,545,324
Liabilities: $48,888,795
Net Worth: $20,656,528
Earnings: $4,111,189
Emp.: 549
Fiscal Year-end: 03/31/23
Eletric Power Generation Services
N.A.I.C.S.: 221114
Amit Ashok Khurana *(Mng Dir)*

MADHAV MARBLES AND GRANITES LIMITED

First Floor Mumal Tower 16 Saheli Marg, Udaipur, 313 001, Rajasthan, India
Tel.: (91) 2942981666
Web Site:
 https://www.madhavmarbles.com
Year Founded: 1989
MADHAV—(NSE)
Rev.: $8,929,254
Assets: $20,893,154
Liabilities: $3,071,877
Net Worth: $17,821,278
Earnings: ($59,266)
Emp.: 187
Fiscal Year-end: 03/31/21
Granite & Marble Mfr
N.A.I.C.S.: 339999
Ravi Kumar Krishnamurthi *(Chm)*

Subsidiaries:

Madhav Marbles and Granites Limited - Granite Factory (1)
Thoppur, Dharmapuri, 636 352, Tamilnadu, India
Tel.: (91) 7708961299
Web Site: http://www.madhavmarbles.com
Emp.: 200
Granite & Marble Mfr
N.A.I.C.S.: 327991

MADHUCON PROJECTS LIMITED

Madhucon House Road No 36 Plot No 1129/A Jubilee Hills, Hyderabad, 500033, Telangana, India
Tel.: (91) 4023556001
Web Site:
 https://www.madhucon.com
Year Founded: 1983
531497—(BOM)
Rev.: $250,137,372
Assets: $498,099,203
Liabilities: $783,791,177
Net Worth: ($285,691,973)
Earnings: ($21,471,186)
Emp.: 738
Fiscal Year-end: 03/31/23
Construction Services
N.A.I.C.S.: 236210
N. Seethaiah *(CEO & Mng Dir)*

Subsidiaries:

Madhucon Infra Limited (1)
Madhucon House Road No 36 Jubilee Hills, Hyderabad, 500033, India
Tel.: (91) 40 23556001
Web Site: http://www.madhucon.com
Emp.: 20
Power Line Construction Engineering Services
N.A.I.C.S.: 237130
M.V.S Nageshwara Roa *(Gen Mgr)*

Subsidiary (Domestic):

Simhapuri Energy Private Limited (2)
Plot No 6-3- 866 / 2 3rd Floor Madhucon Greenlands, Begumpet, Hyderabad, 500 016, India
Tel.: (91) 40 2341 2196
Web Site: http://www.simhapurienergy.com
Sales Range: $75-99.9 Million
Thermal Power Generation Services
N.A.I.C.S.: 221118
Nama Nageswara Rao *(Founder)*

TN(DK) Expressways Limited (2)
6-3-866/2 Green Lands, Begumpet, 500 016, Hyderabad, India
Tel.: (91) 40 23550914
Commercial Building Construction Services
N.A.I.C.S.: 236220

PT Madhucon Indonesia (1)
Menara Bidakara 3rd Floor Jl Gatot Subroto Kay 71-73, 12870, Jakarta, Indonesia
Tel.: (62) 21 8379 3105
Web Site: http://www.madhucon.com
Coal Mining Services
N.A.I.C.S.: 212115

MADHUR CAPITAL & FINANCE LTD.

Madhur Complex Stadium Cross Road Navarangpura, Ahmedabad, 380009, Gujarat, India
Tel.: (91) 79 6563422
Web Site:
 http://www.madhurcapital.co.in
Year Founded: 1993
Assets: $27,466
Liabilities: $96,853
Net Worth: ($69,387)
Earnings: ($7,043)
Fiscal Year-end: 03/31/18
Financial Management Services
N.A.I.C.S.: 523999
Shalin V. Parikh *(Compliance Officer)*

MADHUR INDUSTRIES LIMITED

Madhur Complex 3rd Floor Stadium

MADHUR INDUSTRIES LIMITED

Madhur Industries Limited—(Continued)
Cross Road, Navarangpura, Ahmedabad, 380 009, India
Tel.: (91) 7926445023
Web Site: https://www.madhur.co
Year Founded: 1973
519279—(BOM)
Assets: $799,000
Liabilities: $164,519
Net Worth: $634,481
Earnings: ($57,972)
Emp.: 1
Fiscal Year-end: 03/31/23
Food Products Mfr
N.A.I.C.S.: 311999
Shalin Vinitbhai Parikh *(Mng Dir & CFO)*

MADHUSUDAN INDUSTRIES LIMITED
Rakhial Station Taluka Dehgam, Gandhinagar, 382715, Gujarat, India
Tel.: (91) 2716267270
Web Site: https://www.madhusudan-india.com
515059—(BOM)
Rev.: $797,736
Assets: $3,160,194
Liabilities: $279,381
Net Worth: $2,880,813
Earnings: $489,118
Emp.: 5
Fiscal Year-end: 03/31/21
Horticulture Services
N.A.I.C.S.: 115112
Thomas Koshy *(CEO)*

MADHUSUDAN SECURITIES LIMITED
37 National Storage Building Plot No 424-B Nr, Johnson & Johnson Building S B Road Mahim West, Mumbai, 400 016, Maharashtra, India
Tel.: (91) 2266347377
Year Founded: 1983
511000—(BOM)
Rev.: $9,468
Assets: $2,535,035
Liabilities: $216,571
Net Worth: $2,318,464
Earnings: ($9,673)
Fiscal Year-end: 03/31/21
Financial Investment Services
N.A.I.C.S.: 523999

MADHYA BHARAT AGRO PRODUCTS LTD.
Wing A1 1st Floor Ostwal Heights Urban Forest, Bhilwara, 311001, Rajasthan, India
Tel.: (91) 1482237104
Web Site: https://www.mbapl.com
Year Founded: 1997
MBAPL—(NSE)
Rev.: $118,366,896
Assets: $89,069,324
Liabilities: $49,696,997
Net Worth: $39,372,328
Earnings: $14,891,637
Emp.: 308
Fiscal Year-end: 03/31/23
Phosphatic Fertilizer Mfr
N.A.I.C.S.: 325312
Pankaj Ostwal *(Chm & Mng Dir)*

MADHYA PRADESH TODAY MEDIA LIMITED
Plot No 5 Press Complex Zone-I M P Nagar, Bhopal, 462011, India
Tel.: (91) 7557185600
Web Site: https://www.pradeshtoday.com
Year Founded: 2010
MPTODAY—(NSE)
Rev.: $2,640,297
Assets: $5,715,724

Liabilities: $1,054,193
Net Worth: $4,661,531
Earnings: $292,405
Emp.: 211
Fiscal Year-end: 03/31/23
Newspaper Publisher Services
N.A.I.C.S.: 513110
Hradayesh Kumar Dixit *(Chm & Mng Dir)*

MADI MINERALS LTD.
615-800 West Pender Street, Vancouver, V6C 2V6, BC, Canada
Tel.: (604) 787-7356   BC
Year Founded: 2021
PGA—(CNSX)
Assets: $604,550
Liabilities: $209,231
Net Worth: $395,319
Earnings: ($1,369,364)
Fiscal Year-end: 08/31/23
Mineral Exploration Services
N.A.I.C.S.: 212220
Gary Musil *(Pres & CEO)*

MADICOB SA
10 Boulevard des Martyrs de Chateaubriand, 95100, Saint-Ouen-l'Aumone, Val D Oise, France
Tel.: (33) 139475156
Web Site: http://www.madicob.fr
Rev.: $17,800,000
Emp.: 20
Technical Equipment Related to Smoke & Ventilation Designer & Mfr
N.A.I.C.S.: 335999
France Polet *(Dir-Personnel)*

MADILL MOTORS PTY LTD
35 Mellor St, Gympie, 4570, QLD, Australia
Tel.: (61) 0754805500
Web Site: http://www.madill.com.au
Year Founded: 1935
Sales Range: $50-74.9 Million
Emp.: 200
Car Dealership Owner & Operator
N.A.I.C.S.: 441110
Garth Madill *(Founder & Mng Dir)*

MADINET NASR FOR HOUSING & DEVELOPMENT
4 Youssif Abbas Street, District 2 Nasr City, Cairo, Egypt
Tel.: (20) 222619570
Web Site: https://www.mnhd.com
Year Founded: 1959
MNHD.CA—(EGX)
Rev.: $171,102,493
Assets: $389,574,666
Liabilities: $232,119,644
Net Worth: $157,455,022
Earnings: $45,018,511
Fiscal Year-end: 12/31/23
Real Estate Development Services
N.A.I.C.S.: 531390
Ahmed El Hitamy *(CEO-Expert)*

MADISON COMMUNICATIONS
349 Business Point Western Express Highway, Andheri East, Mumbai, 400 069, India
Tel.: (91) 2266401500
Web Site: http://www.madisonindia.com
Year Founded: 1989
Rev.: $239,800,000
Emp.: 1,000
N.A.I.C.S.: 541810
Sam Balsara *(Chm & Mng Dir)*

Subsidiaries:

Anugrah Madison Advertising Pvt. Ltd.   (1)
Jammi Bldg 1 Floor, 125 Royapettah High Rd, Chennai, 600 004, India
Tel.: (91) 44 2498 5751

N.A.I.C.S.: 541810
R.V. Rajan *(Chm)*

Madison Creative   (1)
Koch House Ground Fl Jerbai Wadia Rd, Sewree West, Mumbai, 400 015, India
Tel.: (91) 22 24154467
N.A.I.C.S.: 541810
Prabha Prabhu *(Partner & Exec Dir)*

Madison Creative   (1)
Everest House Flat No 12G 12th Fl, 46-C Chowringhee Rd, Kolkata, 700 071, India
Tel.: (91) 033 22883064
N.A.I.C.S.: 541810
Rajotavo Dasgupta *(Branch Head)*

Madison Media   (1)
349 Business Point Western Express Hwy, Andheri E, Mumbai, 400069, India
Tel.: (91) 22 66401500
N.A.I.C.S.: 541830
Prema Singh *(Branch Head)*

Madison Media Plus   (1)
38 Okhla Indus Estate Phase III, New Delhi, 110 020, India
Tel.: (91) 11 41002561
Sales Range: $550-599.9 Million
Emp.: 100
N.A.I.C.S.: 541830
Amit Duggal *(Dir-Digital-Delhi & Kolkata)*

Madison PR   (1)
3rd Fl Zoroastrian Bldg Horniman Circle, Fort, Mumbai, 400023, India
Tel.: (91) 22 66548341
Emp.: 100
N.A.I.C.S.: 541820
Madhu Chhibber *(CEO)*

Madison Retail Paradigm Pvt. Ltd.   (1)
Koch House Ground Floor Jerbai Wadia Rd, Sewri West, Mumbai, 400015, India
Tel.: (91) 22 24115650
N.A.I.C.S.: 541810
Rachna Lanewala *(Dir-Design)*

Madison Teamworks fp&e   (1)
303 VIP Plaza Off Andheri Link Rd B7 Veera Industrial Estate, Andheri West, Mumbai, 400053, India
Tel.: (91) 22 65028490
Emp.: 20
N.A.I.C.S.: 541810
Priya Goradia *(Dir-HR)*

Moms Outdoor Media Solutions Pvt. Ltd.   (1)
Koch House Ground Fl Jerbai Wadia Rd, Sewri West, Mumbai, 400015, India
Tel.: (91) 22 24173742
Sales Range: Less than $1 Million
N.A.I.C.S.: 541810
Rajneesh Bahl *(COO-West & South)*

MADISON HOLDINGS GROUP LIMITED
10/F North Point Industrial Building 499 Kings Road, North Point, China (Hong Kong)
Tel.: (852) 2 973 2317   Ky
Web Site: http://www.madison-wine.com
Year Founded: 1997
8057—(HKG)
Rev.: $16,830,858
Assets: $79,776,968
Liabilities: $57,042,050
Net Worth: $22,734,918
Earnings: ($2,228,516)
Emp.: 124
Fiscal Year-end: 03/31/22
Holding Company; Wine Products
N.A.I.C.S.: 551112
Kwan Kuo *(Exec Dir)*

MADISON PACIFIC PROPERTIES INC.
389 W 6th Ave, Vancouver, V5Y 1L1, BC, Canada
Tel.: (604) 732-6540   Ca
Web Site: https://www.madisonpacific.ca

INTERNATIONAL PUBLIC

MPC—(TSX)
Sales Range: $10-24.9 Million
Emp.: 9
Real Estate Investment & Development
N.A.I.C.S.: 531190
Dino Di Marco *(CFO)*

MADISON SYSTEMS, INC.
1111 Davis Dr Unit 23, Newmarket, L3Y 9E5, ON, Canada
Tel.: (289) 716-9172   FL
Year Founded: 1997
MADI—(OTCEM)
Sales Range: Less than $1 Million
Business Support Services
N.A.I.C.S.: 561499

MADMAN ENTERTAINMENT PTY. LIMITED
21-31 Goodwood Street, Richmond, 3121, VIC, Australia
Tel.: (61) 3 9261 9200   AU
Web Site: http://www.madman.com.au
Year Founded: 1996
Sales Range: $25-49.9 Million
Emp.: 100
ideo Distribution & Entertainment Rights Management Services
N.A.I.C.S.: 512120
Tim Anderson *(Co-Founder & Mng Dir)*

Subsidiaries:

Madman Entertainment NZ   (1)
PO Box 47426, Ponsonby, Auckland, New Zealand
Tel.: (64) 93700188
Web Site: http://www.madman.co.nz
Sales Range: $50-74.9 Million
Emp.: 7
Digital Video Discs Whslr
N.A.I.C.S.: 532282
Michael Eldred *(Mgr-Theatrical Sls)*

Madman Production Company Pty. Limited   (1)
1-35 Wellington Street, Collingwood, 3066, VIC, Australia
Tel.: (61) 394170977
Web Site: http://www.madmanproduction.com.au
Sales Range: $25-49.9 Million
Motion Picture Production & Distribution Services
N.A.I.C.S.: 512110

MADORO METALS CORP.
Suite 1450 - 789 West Pender Street, Vancouver, V6C 1H2, BC, Canada
Tel.: (604) 681-1568   Ca
Web Site: https://madorometals.com
Year Founded: 1984
M5Q—(DEU)
Assets: $1,374,205
Liabilities: $63,933
Net Worth: $1,310,272
Earnings: ($466,704)
Fiscal Year-end: 02/28/23
Mineral Exploration Services
N.A.I.C.S.: 213114
Dusan Berka *(Pres & CEO)*

MADRAS FERTILIZERS LIMITED
Manali, Chennai, 600068, India
Tel.: (91) 4425941001
Web Site: https://www.madrasfert.co.in
Year Founded: 1966
MADRASFERT—(NSE)
Rev.: $210,218,190
Assets: $165,301,500
Liabilities: $260,200,395
Net Worth: ($94,898,895)
Earnings: $391,755
Emp.: 539

Fiscal Year-end: 03/31/21
Chemicals & Fertilizers Mfr
N.A.I.C.S.: 212390
Muralidharan V. *(Officer-Compliance, Sec & Gen Mgr-Fin & Acct)*

MADRIGALL SA
17 rue de l'Universite, 75007, Paris, France
Tel.: (33) 1 49 54 42 00
Sales Range: $25-49.9 Million
Emp.: 6
Holding Company
N.A.I.C.S.: 551112
Antoine Gallimard *(Chm & CEO)*

Subsidiaries:

Editions Gallimard SA (1)
5 rue Gaston-Gallimard, 75328, Paris, cedex 07, France
Tel.: (33) 1 49 54 42 00
Web Site: http://www.gallimard.fr
Emp.: 500
Book Publishers
N.A.I.C.S.: 513130
Antoine Gallimard *(CEO)*

Subsidiary (Domestic):

Flammarion S.A. (2)
87 quai Panhard et Levassor, 75647, Paris, cedex 13, France   **(100%)**
Tel.: (33) 1 40 51 31 00
Web Site: http://www.groupe-flammarion.com
Book Publishing
N.A.I.C.S.: 513130

Subsidiary (Non-US):

Editions Casterman S.A. (3)
47 Cantersteen, 1000, Brussels, Belgium
Tel.: (32) 2 209 83 00
Books Publishing Services
N.A.I.C.S.: 513130

Editions Flammarion Ltee (3)
3700A boul, Montreal, H2X 2V4, QC, Canada   **(100%)**
Tel.: (514) 277-8807
Web Site: http://www.flammarion.qc.ca
Emp.: 20
Book Publishers
N.A.I.C.S.: 513130
Guy Gougeon *(Gen Mgr)*

Subsidiary (Domestic):

Editions J'ai Lu S.A. (3)
87 quai Panhard et Levassor, F 75013, Paris, France
Tel.: (33) 144393470
Web Site: http://www.jailu.com
Book Publishers
N.A.I.C.S.: 513130

La Hune S.A.S. (3)
16 Rue De l, 75006, Paris, France
Tel.: (33) 1 45 48 35 85
Sales Range: $25-49.9 Million
Book Retailer
N.A.I.C.S.: 459210
Olivia Place *(Gen Mgr)*

UD-Union Distribution S.A.S. (3)
106 Rue Petit Leroy, 94550, Chevilly-Larue, France
Tel.: (33) 141802020
Newspaper Publishing Services
N.A.I.C.S.: 513110

MADSEN MOTORS LTD.
50 King St, Sioux Lookout, P8T 1A8, ON, Canada
Tel.: (807) 737-1450
Web Site: http://www.madsengm.com
Rev.: $10,197,056
Emp.: 30
New & Used Car Dealers
N.A.I.C.S.: 441110
John Madsen *(Mgr-Sls)*

MADURO & CURIEL'S BANK N.V.
Plasa Jojo Correa 2-4, PO Box 305, Willemstad, Curacao
Tel.: (599) 9 466 1111
Web Site: http://www.mcb-bank.com
Year Founded: 1916
Rev.: $278,713,798
Assets: $4,392,639,669
Liabilities: $3,886,677,508
Net Worth: $505,962,161
Earnings: $82,408,495
Emp.: 1,497
Fiscal Year-end: 12/31/19
Banking Services
N.A.I.C.S.: 522110
Michael de Sola *(Mng Dir)*

Subsidiaries:

Caribbean Mercantile Bank N.V. (1)
Caya G F Betico Croes 53, PO Box 28, Oranjestad, Aruba
Tel.: (297) 5223000
Web Site: http://www.cmbnv.com
Sales Range: $100-124.9 Million
Emp.: 247
Banking Services
N.A.I.C.S.: 522299

Maduro & Curiel's Bank (Bonaire) N.V. (1)
Bulevar Gobernador N Debrot 70, Kralendijk, Bonaire, Netherlands
Tel.: (31) 715 5520
Web Site: http://www.mcbbonaire.com
Investment Banking Services
N.A.I.C.S.: 523150
Leonard Domacasse *(Mng Dir)*

Maduro & Curiel's Insurance Services N.V. (1)
Lio Capriles Banking Center Rooi Catootje, PO Box 305, Willemstad, Curacao
Tel.: (599) 9 466 1855
Web Site: http://www.mcb-insurance.com
Insurance Management Services
N.A.I.C.S.: 524298
Roelf Bos *(Sr Acct Mgr-Comml)*

MADVERTISE S.A.
13 Rue Aristide Briand, 92300, Levallois-Perret, France
Tel.: (33) 146216616
Web Site: https://www.metadvertise.io
Year Founded: 2011
ALMNG—(EUR)
Sales Range: $1-9.9 Million
Advertising & Marketing Services
N.A.I.C.S.: 541613
Paul Amsellem *(Chm & CEO)*

MAEDA CORPORATION
2-10-2 Fujimi, Chiyoda-ku, Tokyo, 102-8151, Japan
Tel.: (81) 332655551   JP
Web Site: http://www.maeda.co.jp
Year Founded: 1919
1824—(TKS)
Rev.: $6,563,611,120
Assets: $8,991,645,520
Liabilities: $5,433,974,480
Net Worth: $3,557,671,040
Earnings: $225,302,000
Emp.: 6,929
Fiscal Year-end: 03/31/21
Building & Civil Engineering Contractor
N.A.I.C.S.: 236220
Soji Maeda *(Pres)*

Subsidiaries:

GKMC Construction & Consulting Inc. (1)
Tekstilkent Koza Plaza A Blok K 34, Esenler, 34235, Istanbul, Turkiye
Tel.: (90) 2124672901
Construction Services
N.A.I.C.S.: 236220

Hikarigaoka Corporation (1)
5-8-20 Takamatsu J City 17th Floor, Nerima-ku, Tokyo, 179-0075, Japan
Tel.: (81) 353724611
Web Site: http://www.jcity-hikari.co.jp
Construction Machinery Mfr & Distr
N.A.I.C.S.: 333120

JM Corporation (1)
Kojimachi Square 5th floor 3, Nibancho Chiyoda-ku, Tokyo, 102-0084, Japan
Tel.: (81) 352757048
Web Site: http://www.matabee.com
Sales Range: $75-99.9 Million
Emp.: 200
Building & Facilities Management Services
N.A.I.C.S.: 236118
Kazuhito Nishida *(Exec Officer)*

Koho Co., Ltd. (1)
MK Hall 3-11-18, Iidabashi Chiyoda-ku, Tokyo, 102-0072, Japan
Tel.: (81) 332650611
Web Site: http://www.kohocome.co.jp
Emp.: 158
Commercial Printing & Book Binding Services
N.A.I.C.S.: 323111
Ryuichiro Maeda *(Pres)*

Maeda (Beijing) Business Consulting Co., Ltd. (1)
Beijin Hotel Rm No D 6304 No 33 Dong Chang An St, Beijing, China
Tel.: (86) 1065259523
Business Consulting Services
N.A.I.C.S.: 561499

Maeda Corporation (1)
Rm D Maeda Pacific Corp Bldg 150 Harmon Sink Rd, Tamuning, GU 96913
Tel.: (671) 649-7617
Web Site: http://www.maeda.co.jp
Sales Range: $25-49.9 Million
Emp.: 2
Engineeering Services
N.A.I.C.S.: 236220

Maeda Corporation India Private Ltd. (1)
7th Floor Unit No 702 DLF South Court Saket, New Delhi, India
Tel.: (91) 1149738888
Construction Services
N.A.I.C.S.: 236220

Maeda Corporation, U.S.A. (1)
39209 6 Mile Rd Ste 204, Livonia, MI 48152   **(100%)**
Tel.: (734) 462-2230
Web Site: http://www.maedacorpusa.com
Sales Range: $50-74.9 Million
Emp.: 2
General Construction Contractor
N.A.I.C.S.: 236210
Susumu Morita *(Pres & CEO)*

Maeda Road Construction Co., Ltd. (1)
1-11-3 Osaki, Shinagawa-ku, Tokyo, Japan   **(100%)**
Tel.: (81) 3 54870011
Web Site: http://ssl.maedaroad.co.jp
Rev.: $2,271,044,160
Assets: $2,157,962,400
Liabilities: $574,701,600
Net Worth: $1,583,260,800
Earnings: $162,140,000
Fiscal Year-end: 03/31/2021
Pavement Construction Services
N.A.I.C.S.: 237310

Maeda Seisakusho Co., Ltd. (1)
No 1095 Onbegawa Shinonoi, Nagano, 388-8522, Japan   **(100%)**
Tel.: (81) 262922228
Web Site: http://www.maesei.co.jp
Rev.: $330,735,300
Assets: $284,230,320
Liabilities: $180,130,920
Net Worth: $104,099,400
Earnings: $8,534,520
Emp.: 536
Fiscal Year-end: 03/31/2019
Industrial Machinery Mfr
N.A.I.C.S.: 333248
Masaaki Shioiri *(Pres)*

Subsidiary (US):

Maeda USA LLC (2)
8505 S Loop E, Houston, TX 77017
Tel.: (713) 715-1500
Web Site: http://www.maedausa.com
Crane Distr
N.A.I.C.S.: 423830
Tony Inman *(Pres)*

Maeda Thien Duc Co., Ltd. (1)
Floor 9 Block 6 Vista Building 628C Hanoi Highway Residential Zone 4, Dist 2 An Phu, Ho Chi Minh City, Vietnam
Tel.: (84) 862586611
Construction Services
N.A.I.C.S.: 236220

Maeda Vietnam Co., Ltd. (1)
Room 9 Area B 19th Floor Vincom Center 72 Le Thanh Ton Street, Ben Nghe Ward District, Ho Chi Minh City, Vietnam
Tel.: (84) 2839369000
Web Site: http://www.maedavietnam.com.vn
Sales Range: $25-49.9 Million
Emp.: 12
Civil Engineering Services
N.A.I.C.S.: 327910

Miyama Kogyo Co., Ltd. (1)
3-11-18 Iidabashi Chiyoda-Ku, Chiyoda-ku, Tokyo, 102-0072, Japan
Tel.: (81) 332304305
Web Site: http://www.miyamak.co.jp
Sales Range: $25-49.9 Million
Emp.: 66
Civil Engineering Services
N.A.I.C.S.: 541330
Imai Tsutomu *(Pres)*

Seiyu Real Estate Co., Ltd. (1)
3-11-18 Iidabashi Koho Building 7Fl, Chiyoda-ku, Tokyo, 102-0072, Japan
Tel.: (81) 332304977
Web Site: http://www.seiyujisyo.co.jp
Sales Range: $50-74.9 Million
Emp.: 14
Property Management Services
N.A.I.C.S.: 531311

Thai Maeda Corporation (1)
18th Fl Thaniya Plaza Bldg 52 Silom Rd, Bangrak, Bangkok, 10500, Thailand
Web Site: http://www.thai-maeda.com
Construction Engineering Services
N.A.I.C.S.: 541330

MAEDA KOSEN CO., LTD.
38-3 Okinunome Harue-cho, Sakai, 919-0422, Fukui, Japan
Tel.: (81) 776513535
Web Site: https://www.maedakosen.jp
Year Founded: 1972
7821—(TKS)
Rev.: $347,281,260
Assets: $499,111,460
Liabilities: $110,224,620
Net Worth: $388,886,840
Earnings: $49,629,380
Emp.: 1,218
Fiscal Year-end: 06/30/24
Construction Materials, Plastic Products & Textile Goods Mfr & Sales
N.A.I.C.S.: 423320
Yukitoshi Maeda *(Chm & CEO)*

Subsidiaries:

BBS Japan Co., Ltd. (1)
12F Shiba Park Building A 2-4-1 Shibakoen, Minato-ku, Tokyo, 105-0011, Japan
Tel.: (81) 36 402 4090
Web Site: https://bbs-japan.co.jp
Automotive Distr
N.A.I.C.S.: 441110
Yukitoshi Maeda *(Chm)*

Mirai Kosen Co., Ltd. (1)
10-10-2 Yunoo Minamiechizen-cho, Nanjo-gun, Fukui, 919-0101, Japan
Tel.: (81) 778452325
Web Site: https://www.mirai-kosen.jp
Wiping Cloths & Gloves Mfr & Distr
N.A.I.C.S.: 313310
Tomiji Shirasaki *(Pres)*

Seven Chemical Inc. (1)
2-4-1 Shibakoen Shiba Park Building A Building 12F, Minato-ku, Tokyo, 105-0011, Japan
Tel.: (81) 36 809 2597
Web Site: https://www.seven-chemical.co.jp

MAEDA KOSEN CO., LTD.

Maeda Kosen Co., Ltd.—(Continued)
Synthetic Resin Mfr
N.A.I.C.S.: 325211

MAEIL HOLDINGS CO., LTD.
The Twin Towers K 50 Jong-ro 1-gil, Jongno-gu, Seoul, Korea (South)
Tel.: (82) 215881539
Web Site: https://www.maeil.com
Year Founded: 1969
005990—(KRS)
Rev.: $1,518,093,479
Assets: $975,261,350
Liabilities: $461,855,792
Net Worth: $513,405,558
Earnings: $4,997,550
Emp.: 38
Fiscal Year-end: 12/31/22
Dairy Products Mfr
N.A.I.C.S.: 311514
Seon-hee Kim (CEO)

Subsidiaries:

Les Vins de Maeil Co., Ltd. (1)
5F Yongjin Building 48 Yangjaecheon-ro 19-gil, Seocho-gu, Seoul, 427-070, Korea (South)
Tel.: (82) 234976888
Web Site: http://www.lesvinsdemaeil.com
Emp.: 70
Wine Distr
N.A.I.C.S.: 424820
Yoo Ji-chan (CEO)

M's Beverage Co., Ltd. (1)
8F 18 Baumoe-ro 37-gil Seocho-gu, Seoul, 137-888, Korea (South)
Tel.: (82) 221409323
Web Site: http://www.sapporobeer.kr
Beer Distr
N.A.I.C.S.: 424810
Hong Seung Won (Mgr-Sls Plng & Mgmt Team)

Maeil Dairies Co., Ltd. - Asan Plant (1)
61-23 Yeongin-ro202beon-gil Yeongin-myeon, Asan, Chungcheongnam-do, Korea (South)
Tel.: (82) 415381600
Milk Product Mfr
N.A.I.C.S.: 311514

Maeil Dairies Co., Ltd. - Cheongyang Plant (1)
1355-58 Chungjeol-ro Cheongyang-eup, Cheongyang, Chungcheongnam-do, Korea (South)
Tel.: (82) 419405210
Milk Product Mfr
N.A.I.C.S.: 311514

Maeil Dairies Co., Ltd. - Gwangju Plant (1)
511 Eodeung-daero Gwangsan-gu, Gwangju, Korea (South)
Tel.: (82) 629495000
Milk Product Mfr & Distr
N.A.I.C.S.: 311514

Maeil Dairies Co., Ltd. - Gyeongsan Plant (1)
1090 Daehak-ro Jillyang-eup, Gyeongsan, Gyeongsangbuk-do, Korea (South)
Tel.: (82) 538591700
Milk Product Mfr
N.A.I.C.S.: 311514

Maeil Dairies Co., Ltd. - Pyeongtaek Plant (1)
63 Jinwiseo-ro Jinwi-myeon, Pyeongtaek, Gyeonggi-do, Korea (South)
Tel.: (82) 316609100
Milk Product Mfr
N.A.I.C.S.: 311514

Maeil Dairies Co., Ltd. - Sangha Plant (1)
412 Jinamgusipo-ro Sangha-myeon, Kochang, Jeollabuk-do, Korea (South)
Tel.: (82) 635604500
Milk Product Mfr
N.A.I.C.S.: 311514

Maeil Dairies Co., Ltd. - Yeongdong Plant (1)
730-20 Gwaebangnyeong-ro Maegok-myeon, Yeongdong, Chungcheongbuk-do, Korea (South)
Tel.: (82) 437409400
Milk Product Mfr
N.A.I.C.S.: 311514

MAESTRO LOCADORA DE VEICULOS S.A.
Avenida Queiroz Filho 1560, Torre Beija Flor 2nd floor conj 219, Sao Paulo, Brazil
Tel.: (55) 1147850200
Web Site:
https://www.maestrolocadora.com.br
MSRO3—(BRAZ)
Rev.: $31,460,288
Assets: $48,004,861
Liabilities: $34,802,380
Net Worth: $13,202,481
Earnings: $1,820,847
Fiscal Year-end: 12/31/23
Management Consulting Services
N.A.I.C.S.: 541618
Fabio Lewkowicz (CEO & Chief Comml Officer)

MAEZAWA INDUSTRIES, INC.
5-11 Naka-cho, Kawaguchi, 332-8556, Saitama, Japan
Tel.: (81) 482515511
Web Site: https://www.maezawa.co.jp
Year Founded: 1937
6489—(TKS)
Rev.: $241,337,710
Assets: $271,975,060
Liabilities: $87,589,110
Net Worth: $184,385,950
Earnings: $23,339,910
Emp.: 650
Fiscal Year-end: 05/31/24
Water Supply & Sewage Equipment Mfr & Distr
N.A.I.C.S.: 333310
Tadashi Matsubara (Pres)

MAEZAWA KASEI INDUSTRIES CO., LTD.
Nihonbashi Koamicho Building 17-10, Chuo-ku, Tokyo, 103-0016, Japan
Tel.: (81) 359620711
Web Site: https://www.maezawa-k.co.jp
Year Founded: 1937
7925—(TKS)
Rev.: $158,144,250
Assets: $326,223,330
Liabilities: $59,047,130
Net Worth: $267,176,200
Earnings: $9,002,820
Emp.: 567
Fiscal Year-end: 03/31/24
Pipe Valve Mfr & Whslr
N.A.I.C.S.: 332919
Junichi Kubo (Pres)

Subsidiaries:

NIIGATA MOLDING CO., LTD. (1)
7-4 Bunsuikoyo, Tsubame, Niigata, Japan
Tel.: (81) 256985181
Web Site: http://www.niigata-seikei.co.jp
Plastic Product Mfr & Distr
N.A.I.C.S.: 326199

MAEZAWA KYUSO INDUSTRIES CO., LTD.
14-4 Takaban, Meguro-ku, Tokyo, 152-8510, Japan
Tel.: (81) 337161511
Web Site: http://www.qso.co.jp
Year Founded: 1957
6485—(TKS)
Rev.: $211,572,880
Assets: $303,828,650
Liabilities: $45,780,860
Net Worth: $258,047,790
Earnings: $11,111,410
Emp.: 482
Fiscal Year-end: 03/31/24
Water Supply Equipment Mfr
N.A.I.C.S.: 332911
Yuichi Tanigo (Pres & CEO)

MAFIA TRENDS LIMITED
Shop No-1 2 3 4 5 Prabhu Kuthir Complex Sandesh Press Road, Bodakdev, Ahmedabad, 380015, India
Tel.: (91) 7778043457
Web Site:
https://www.mafiastores.com
Year Founded: 2011
543613—(BOM)
Rev.: $923,997
Assets: $1,675,931
Liabilities: $807,338
Net Worth: $868,593
Earnings: $24,651
Emp.: 23
Fiscal Year-end: 03/31/23
Investment Management Service
N.A.I.C.S.: 523999

MAFRA HOSPITALAR S/A
Av Luiz Maggioni 2727, Distrito Empresarial Pref Luiz Roberto Jabali, 14072-055, Ribeirao Preto, Sao Paulo, Brazil
Tel.: (55) 16 3995 9400
Web Site:
http://www.mafrahospitalar.com.br
Year Founded: 1996
Holding Company, Medical Equipment Pharmaceutical & Supply Distr
N.A.I.C.S.: 551112
Cristhiane Lopes Coutinho (Mgr-Comml)

Subsidiaries:

CM Hospitalar SA (1)
Avenida Luiz Maggioni 2727, Distrito Empresarial Pref Luiz Roberto Jabali, CEP 14072-055, Ribeirao Preto, SP, Brazil
Tel.: (55) 16 3995 9400
Medical Equipment, Pharmaceuticals & Supplies Distr
N.A.I.C.S.: 423450

Subsidiary (Domestic):

Cremer S.A. (2)
R Iguacu 291/363, 89030-030, Blumenau, SC, Brazil (91.09%)
Tel.: (55) 4721238411
Web Site: http://www.cremer.com.br
Surgery Product Mfr & Whslr
N.A.I.C.S.: 339113
Hessica Magalhaes (Mgr-HR)

MAG FRUITS
5 Rue Pierre Et Marie Curie, 45140, Ingre, Loiret, France
Tel.: (33) 238227575
Web Site: http://www.mag-fruits.fr
Rev.: $15,200,000
Emp.: 46
Fruits Producer
N.A.I.C.S.: 424480
Adeline Costa (Gen Mgr & Mgr-Quality)

MAG HOLDINGS BERHAD
B-3-12 Gateway Corporate Suites Gateway Kiaramas, Jalan Desa Kiara, 50480, Kuala Lumpur, Malaysia
Tel.: (60) 364191385
Web Site:
https://magholdings.com.my
Year Founded: 2002
MAG—(KLS)
Rev.: $43,795,556
Assets: $233,746,948
Liabilities: $66,680,617
Net Worth: $167,066,330
Earnings: $7,417,597
Fiscal Year-end: 06/30/23

Vegetable Oil Mfr & Distr
N.A.I.C.S.: 311224

MAG INTERACTIVE AB
Drottninggatan 95A, 113 60, Stockholm, Sweden
Tel.: (46) 86443540
Web Site:
https://www.maginteractive.com
Year Founded: 2010
MAGI—(OMX)
Rev.: $37,188,457
Assets: $40,746,392
Liabilities: $8,974,215
Net Worth: $31,772,177
Earnings: $52,544
Emp.: 112
Fiscal Year-end: 08/31/23
Software Development Services
N.A.I.C.S.: 541511
Magnus Wiklander (CFO)

MAG SILVER CORP.
38 Harbour Road, Vancouver, V6C 2V6, BC, Canada
Tel.: (604) 630-1399
Web Site: https://www.magsilver.com
Year Founded: 1999
MAG—(NYSEAMEX)
Rev.: $40,767,000
Assets: $407,829,000
Liabilities: $6,133,000
Net Worth: $401,696,000
Earnings: $17,644,000
Emp.: 11
Fiscal Year-end: 12/31/22
Silver Mining Services
N.A.I.C.S.: 212220
Peter K. Megaw (Chief Exploration Officer)

Subsidiaries:

Gatling Exploration Inc. (1)
Suite 1680 - 200 Burrard St, Vancouver, V6C 3L6, BC, Canada
Tel.: (604) 678-5308
Web Site: http://www.gatlingexploration.com
Metal Exploration Services
N.A.I.C.S.: 213114
Jason Billan (Pres & CEO)

Minera Los Lagartos, S.A. de C.V (1)
Trece 100 Col Bugambilias, Zacatecas, Hermosillo, Mexico
Tel.: (52) 4929232086
Mineral Mining Services
N.A.I.C.S.: 212390

MAG-PRIM
541 avenue de L'Europe, 77246, Vert, Cedex, Cesson, France
Tel.: (33) 160565040
Web Site: http://www.mag-fruits.fr
Rev.: $12,600,000
Emp.: 33
Fruit, Vegetables & Flowers Producer
N.A.I.C.S.: 424480
Dominique Pele (Gen Mgr)

MAGADANENERGO OAO
Sovetskaya st 24, Magadan, 685000, Russia
Tel.: (7) 4132629275
Web Site:
https://www.magadanenergo.ru
Year Founded: 1966
MAGE—(MOEX)
Sales Range: Less than $1 Million
Power Generation Services
N.A.I.C.S.: 221116
Vladimir Evaldovich Milotvorskiy (Chm-Mgmt Bd, CEO & Gen Dir)

MAGAZINE LUIZA S.A.
Rua Amazonas da Silva 27, Sao Paulo, 02051-000, Brazil
Tel.: (55) 1135042727

AND PRIVATE COMPANIES

Web Site:
   https://ri.magazineluiza.com.br
Year Founded: 1957
MGLU3—(BRAZ)
Rev.: $7,332,365,939
Assets: $7,469,352,278
Liabilities: $5,552,803,470
Net Worth: $1,916,548,808
Earnings: ($195,254,562)
Fiscal Year-end: 12/31/23
Department Store Retailer
N.A.I.C.S.: 455110
Luiza Helena Trajano Inacio Rodrigues *(Chm)*

Subsidiaries:

Netshoes (Cayman) Limited (1)
Rua Vergueiro 961, Liberdade, 01504-001, Sao Paulo, Brazil **(100%)**
Tel.: (55) 1130283528
Web Site: http://www.netshoes.com
Sales Range: $400-449.9 Million
Online Sports & Lifestyle Product Distr
N.A.I.C.S.: 455110
Marcio Kumruian *(Founder, Chm & CEO)*

MAGEAN HOLDING PLC
Riga Fereou 2 Limasson Centre
Block B Office 401, Limassol, Cyprus
Tel.: (357) 22600700
Grocery Distr
N.A.I.C.S.: 445110

MAGEBA S.A.
Solistrasse 68, 8180, Bulach, Switzerland
Tel.: (41) 448724050   CH
Web Site: http://www.mageba.in
Year Founded: 1963
Sales Range: $10-24.9 Million
Emp.: 900
Bridge Bearings & Expansion Joints Mfr
N.A.I.C.S.: 332991

Subsidiaries:

mageba (Korea) Co. Ltd. (1)
Hanshin Intervalley 24 Bldg East Hall 1708-9 707-34 Yeoksam 2 Dong, Gangnam, Seoul, 135-918, Korea (South)
Tel.: (82) 2 2183 2020
Web Site: http://www.mageba.co.kr
Construction Materials Mfr
N.A.I.C.S.: 327120

mageba (Shanghai) Ltd. (1)
No 388 Bei Huan Road, Shanghai, 201402, China
Tel.: (86) 21 5740 7637
Web Site: http://www.mageba.cn
Construction Materials Mfr
N.A.I.C.S.: 327120
Gianni Moor *(Chm & CEO)*

mageba A.S. (1)
241/17 Parsel Sekerpinar Mah Aycicegi No 17, Cayirova, Kocaeli, Turkiye
Tel.: (90) 262 658 23 80
Web Site: http://www.mageba.com.tr
Construction Materials Mfr
N.A.I.C.S.: 327120

mageba USA LLC (1)
575 Lexington Ave 4th Fl, New York, NY 10022
Tel.: (212) 644-3335
Web Site: http://www.magebausa.com
Construction Materials Mfr
N.A.I.C.S.: 327120
Juan Carlos Lopez *(Project Mgr)*

mageba bridge products Ltd. (1)
45 Jhowtala Road 3rd Floor, Kolkata, 700 019, India
Tel.: (91) 33 229 00 250
Web Site: http://www.mageba.in
Construction Materials Mfr
N.A.I.C.S.: 327120
Chinmoy Ghosh *(COO)*

mageba gmbh (1)
Seglerweg 1, Fussach, 6972, Austria
Tel.: (43) 5578 75593
Web Site: http://www.mageba.at

Emp.: 14
Construction Materials Mfr
N.A.I.C.S.: 327120
Knut Mettner *(Gen Mgr)*

MAGELLAN AEROSPACE CORPORATION
3160 Derry Road East, Mississauga, L4T 1A9, ON, Canada
Tel.: (905) 677-1889   ON
Web Site: https://www.magellan.aero
Year Founded: 1996
4M7A—(DEU)
Rev.: $664,216,389
Assets: $774,053,124
Liabilities: $217,214,799
Net Worth: $556,838,325
Earnings: $6,982,595
Emp.: 3,848
Fiscal Year-end: 12/31/23
Aerospace, Defense & Space Systems & Components Mfr & Designer
N.A.I.C.S.: 336412
N. Murray Edwards *(Chm)*

Subsidiaries:

Magellan Aerospace (UK) Limited (1)
Rackery Lane, Llay, Wrexham, LL12 0PB, United Kingdom
Tel.: (44) 1978 852101
Airframe Component Mfr
N.A.I.C.S.: 336413
Donna Bennett *(Dir-HR-European Ops)*

Magellan Aerospace Limited (1)
3160 Derry Road East, Mississauga, L4T 1A9, ON, Canada
Tel.: (905) 677-1889
Web Site: http://www.magellan.aero
Sales Range: $100-124.9 Million
Airframe Component Mfr
N.A.I.C.S.: 336413

Subsidiary (Domestic):

Bristol Aerospace Limited (2)
660 Berry St, PO Box 874, Winnipeg, R3C 2S4, MB, Canada **(100%)**
Tel.: (204) 775-8331
Web Site: http://www.bristol.ca
Sales Range: $100-124.9 Million
Emp.: 700
N.A.I.C.S.: 336412

Chicopee Manufacturing Limited (2)
975 Wilson Ave, Kitchener, N2C 1J1, ON, Canada **(100%)**
Tel.: (519) 893-7575
Web Site: http://www.magellan.ca
Sales Range: $50-74.9 Million
Emp.: 150
Mfr of Precision Machined Components & Sub-Assemblies for Aerospace Industry
N.A.I.C.S.: 336413
Ken Nadalin *(Mgr-Mktg)*

Haley Industries Limited (2)
634 Magnesium Rd, Haley Station, K0J 1Y0, ON, Canada **(100%)**
Tel.: (613) 432-8841
Web Site: http://www.magellen.aero
Mfr of Light Alloy Castings for Aerospace Industry
N.A.I.C.S.: 331513
James C. Lemenchick *(Gen Mgr)*

Subsidiary (US):

Magellan Aerospace, Bethel, Inc. (2)
159 Grassy Plain St Rte 53, Bethel, CT 06801-2806
Tel.: (203) 798-9373
Web Site: http://www.magellan.aero
Sales Range: $25-49.9 Million
Emp.: 44
Aircraft Part Mfr
N.A.I.C.S.: 336412

Magellan Aerospace, Glendale, Inc. (2)
5401 W Luke Ave, Glendale, AZ 85301
Tel.: (623) 939-9441
Web Site: http://www.magellan.aero

Sales Range: $50-74.9 Million
Magnesium & Aluminum Castings Mfr
N.A.I.C.S.: 331524

Magellan Aerospace, Haverhilll, Inc. (2)
20 Computer Dr, Haverhill, MA 01832-2450 **(100%)**
Tel.: (978) 774-6000
Web Site: http://www.magellan.aero
Sales Range: $50-74.9 Million
Critical Rotating & Non-Rotating Parts for Major Commercial & Military Engine Builders; Production of Major Castings & Structural Engine Components & Turbine Engines
N.A.I.C.S.: 336412

Magellan Aerospace, Middletown, Inc. (2)
2320 Wedekind Dr, Middletown, OH 45042-1716 **(100%)**
Tel.: (513) 422-2751
Web Site: http://www.magellan.aero
Sales Range: $50-74.9 Million
Emp.: 170
Mfr of Aerospace Components, Aircraft Structures; Jet Engine Components; Brazed & Bonded Honeycomb Structures
N.A.I.C.S.: 336412

Magellan Aerospace, New York, Inc. (2)
97-11 50th Ave, New York, NY 11368-2740
Tel.: (718) 699-4000
Web Site: http://www.magellan.aero
Sales Range: $125-149.9 Million
Mfr of Complex Components & Sub-Assemblies for OEMs of Commercial & Military Aircraft
N.A.I.C.S.: 336413

MAGELLAN FINANCIAL GROUP LIMITED
Level 36 25 Martin Place, Sydney, 2000, NSW, Australia
Tel.: (61) 292354888   AU
Web Site:
   http://www.magellangroup.com.au
Year Founded: 2006
MFG—(ASX)
Rev.: $252,821,847
Assets: $727,326,386
Liabilities: $46,551,148
Net Worth: $680,775,238
Earnings: $159,427,750
Emp.: 109
Fiscal Year-end: 06/30/24
Holding Company; Investment Banking & Asset Management Services
N.A.I.C.S.: 551112
Leo Quintana *(Chief Legal Officer)*

Subsidiaries:

Frontier Partners Inc. (1)
400 Skokie Blvd Ste 500, Northbrook, IL 60062-2815
Tel.: (847) 509-9860
Web Site: https://www.frontierpartners.com
Administrative Management & General Management Consulting Service
N.A.I.C.S.: 541611
William D. Forsyth *(Founder & Pres)*

Magellan Asset Management Ltd. (1)
Level 36 25 Martin Place, Sydney, 2000, NSW, Australia
Tel.: (61) 292354888
Web Site: http://www.magellangroup.com.au
Sales Range: $50-74.9 Million
Emp.: 26
Asset Management Services
N.A.I.C.S.: 523940
Mark Jordan *(Key Acct Mgr)*

Magellan Global Trust (1)
Level 36 19 Martin Place, Sydney, 2000, NSW, Australia
Tel.: (61) 292354888
Web Site: http://www.magellangroup.com.au
Investment Management Service
N.A.I.C.S.: 525910

MAGELLANIC CLOUD LIMITED

MAGICMICRO CO., LTD.

Dallas Center 6th Floor 83/1 Plot No A1 Knowledge City Rai Durg, Borivali West, Mumbai, 400 103, India
Tel.: (91) 4043366058
Web Site: https://www.magellanic-cloud.com
Year Founded: 1981
538891—(BOM)
Rev.: $29,221,995
Assets: $21,150,961
Liabilities: $13,854,707
Net Worth: $7,296,254
Earnings: $243,415
Emp.: 95
Fiscal Year-end: 03/31/21
Financial Support Services
N.A.I.C.S.: 523999
Jagan Mohan Reddy Thumma *(Exec Dir)*

Subsidiaries:

JNIT Technologies, Inc. (1)
3145 Bordentown Ave Ste D1, Parlin, NJ 08859
Tel.: (732) 993-6835
Web Site: https://www.jnitinc.com
Software Development Services
N.A.I.C.S.: 513210
Joseph Thumma *(CEO)*

Subsidiary (Domestic):

Motivity Labs, Inc. (2)
222 W Las Colinas Blvd Ste 755E, Irving, TX 75039 **(68%)**
Tel.: (214) 519-1719
Web Site: http://www.MotivityLabs.com
Sales Range: $1-9.9 Million
Emp.: 160
Information Technology Consulting Services
N.A.I.C.S.: 541511
Venkat Yellapragada *(COO)*

MAGFORCE AG
Max-Planck-Strasse 3, 12489, Berlin, Germany
Tel.: (49) 303083800
Web Site: https://magforce.de
Year Founded: 1997
MF6—(DEU)
Rev.: $1,952,408
Assets: $41,053,959
Liabilities: $24,582,979
Net Worth: $16,470,980
Earnings: ($9,777,051)
Emp.: 26
Fiscal Year-end: 12/31/19
Nanotechnology Medical Services
N.A.I.C.S.: 541713
Ben J. Lipps *(Chm-Mgmt Bd & CEO)*

MAGIC EMPIRE GLOBAL LIMITED
3/F 8 Wyndham Street, Central, China (Hong Kong)
Tel.: (852) 35778770   VG
Web Site: https://meglmagic.com
Year Founded: 2016
MEGL—(NASDAQ)
Rev.: $1,444,351
Assets: $18,586,899
Liabilities: $1,002,595
Net Worth: $17,584,304
Earnings: ($495,577)
Emp.: 9
Fiscal Year-end: 12/31/22
Holding Company
N.A.I.C.S.: 551112
Johnson Sze Hon Chen *(CEO)*

MAGICMICRO CO., LTD.
15 shinwon-ro 133beon-gil, Danwon-gu, Ansan, Gyeonggi-do, Korea (South)
Tel.: (82) 7086803792
Web Site:
   http://www.magicmicro.co.kr
Year Founded: 2008

MAGICMICRO CO., LTD.

Magicmicro Co., Ltd.—(Continued)
127160—(KRS)
Rev: $45,059,711
Assets: $73,676,811
Liabilities: $55,578,901
Net Worth: $18,097,909
Earnings: ($43,620,442)
Emp.: 38
Fiscal Year-end: 12/31/20
Semiconductor & LED Display Products Mfr
N.A.I.C.S.: 334413
Jae Hun Choi (CEO)

MAGICSTEM GROUP CORP.
Room 803 8th Floor Lippo Sun Plaza
28 Canton Road, Tsim Sha Tsui,
Hong Kong, China (Hong Kong)
Tel.: (852) 2871 8000 NV
Year Founded: 2012
MGGI—(OTCIQ)
Sales Range: Less than $1 Million
Stem Cell Cryo-Preserved Banking
N.A.I.C.S.: 325413
Chi Man Ng (Pres & CEO)

MAGILLEM DESIGN SERVICES
251 rue du Faubourg Saint-Martin,
75010, Paris, France
Tel.: (33) 140213550
Web Site: http://www.magillem.com
Year Founded: 2006
Computer Related Services
N.A.I.C.S.: 541519
Vincent Thibaut (Chief Strategy Officer)

Subsidiaries:

MAGILLEM ISRAEL (1)
15 HaTzivoni St, PO Box 7043, Tel Mond, 40600, Israel
Tel.: (972) 77 2060 282
Information Technology Consulting Services
N.A.I.C.S.: 541512

MAGILLEM JAPAN (1)
KECK Technology Koji Nakamura 1-28-7, Matsugaoka, Funabashi, 274-0064, Chiba, Japan
Tel.: (81) 80 3085 8521
Information Technology Consulting Services
N.A.I.C.S.: 541512

MAGILLEM KOREA (1)
No 6 1st Rd Yeoksam-Dong, Gangnam-Gu, Seoul, Korea (South)
Tel.: (82) 70 4047 4060
Information Technology Consulting Services
N.A.I.C.S.: 541512

MAGILLEM USA (1)
161 W 54th St Ste 202A, New York, NY 10019
Tel.: (212) 378-4409
Information Technology Consulting Services
N.A.I.C.S.: 541512

MAGIS S.P.A.
Via Triestina Accesso E-Z I Ponte Tezze, Torre di Mosto, 30020, Venice, Italy
Tel.: (39) 0421319600
Web Site:
   https://www.magisdesign.com
Year Founded: 1976
MGS—(ITA)
Furniture Product Mfr
N.A.I.C.S.: 337121

MAGISTRALA A.D.
Tosin bunar 198, Novi Beograd, Belgrade, Serbia
Tel.: (381) 112696499
Web Site: https://www.magistrala.rs
Year Founded: 1945
MGST—(BEL)
Rev: $4,123,689
Assets: $8,777,743
Liabilities: $4,512,122
Net Worth: $4,265,291

Earnings: $163,596
Emp.: 120
Fiscal Year-end: 12/31/23
Road Maintenance & Construction Services
N.A.I.C.S.: 237310
Nebojsa Bascarevic (Dir Gen)

MAGIX AG
Quedlinburger Str 1, 10589, Berlin, Germany
Tel.: (49) 30 293920
Web Site: http://www.magix.com
Sales Range: $25-49.9 Million
Emp.: 342
Software Developer
N.A.I.C.S.: 513210
Klaus Schmidt (CEO)

Subsidiaries:

MAGIX Development GmbH. (1)
August-Bebel-Str 48, Dresden, 01219, Germany
Tel.: (49) 351479620
Web Site: http://www.magix.com
Sales Range: $25-49.9 Million
Emp.: 80
Multimedia Software Development Services
N.A.I.C.S.: 541511

MAGIX Entertainment S. A. R. L. (1)
38 rue du Mont Thabor, 75001, Paris, France
Tel.: (33) 144501134
Web Site: http://www.magix.com
Sales Range: $25-49.9 Million
Emp.: 3
Entertainment & Multimedia Software Development Services
N.A.I.C.S.: 541511

MAGIX Online Services GmbH. (1)
Friedrichstr 200, Berlin, 10117, Germany
Tel.: (49) 30293920
Web Site: http://www.magix.com
Sales Range: $75-99.9 Million
Emp.: 180
Online Website Hosting & Album Maker Services
N.A.I.C.S.: 518210
Jurgen Jaron (Mng Dir)

Xara Group Ltd. (1)
Gaddesden Pl, Hemel Hempstead, HP2 6EX, Hertfordshire, United Kingdom
Tel.: (44) 1442351000
Web Site: http://www.xara.com
Emp.: 23
Graphic Software Development Services
N.A.I.C.S.: 541511
Charles Moir (Mng Dir)

mufin GmbH. (1)
Quedlinburger Str 1, 10589, Berlin, Germany
Tel.: (49) 30270041800
Web Site: http://www.mufin.com
Online Music Search Engine Services
N.A.I.C.S.: 519210
Juergen Jaron (Pres)

MAGLE CHEMOSWED HOLDING AB
Agneslundsvagen 27, 212 15, Malmo, Sweden
Tel.: (46) 761643312
Web Site:
   https://www.maglechemoswed.com
Year Founded: 1944
MAGLE—(OMX)
Rev: $16,919,809
Assets: $27,098,100
Liabilities: $11,390,395
Net Worth: $15,707,706
Earnings: $1,208,132
Emp.: 78
Fiscal Year-end: 12/31/23
Holding Company
N.A.I.C.S.: 551112
Hans Henrik Lidgard (Founder)

Subsidiaries:

Magle Chemoswed AB (1)

Agneslundsvagen 27, 212 15, Malmo, Sweden
Tel.: (46) 40383300
Web Site: https://maglechemoswed.com
Pharmaceuticals Product Mfr
N.A.I.C.S.: 325412

MAGMA D.D.
Bastjanova 52a, 10000, Zagreb, Croatia
Tel.: (385) 13656888
Web Site: http://www.magma.hr
MGMA—(ZAG)
Sales Range: $150-199.9 Million
Clothes & Sporting Goods Retailer
N.A.I.C.S.: 423910
Goranko Fizulic (CEO)

Subsidiaries:

Magma International ltd. (1)
Suite 810 Ocean Centre 5 Canton Road, Tsim Sha Tsui, Kowloon, China (Hong Kong)
Tel.: (852) 23773288
Sales Range: $25-49.9 Million
Emp.: 12
Clothing Retail Stores Operation Services
N.A.I.C.S.: 458110

MAGMA GMBH
Kackertstrasse 11, 52072, Aachen, Germany
Tel.: (49) 241889010
Web Site: http://www.magmasoft.de
Year Founded: 1988
Rev: $11,611,260
Emp.: 81
Casting Services
N.A.I.C.S.: 331523
Erwin Flender (Mng Dir)

Subsidiaries:

MAGMA Bilisim ve Teknoloji Hizmetleri Ltd. Sti. (1)
Kuzguncuk Mah Pasalimani Cad Bogazici Apt No 112/B D 1, Uskudar, Istanbul, Turkiye
Tel.: (90) 2165576400
Web Site: http://www.magmasoft.com.tr
Software Development Services
N.A.I.C.S.: 541511

MAGMA Engenharia do Brasil Ltda. (1)
Alexandre Dumas 1708 1st floor, 04717-004, Sao Paulo, Brazil
Tel.: (55) 1155351381
Web Site: http://www.magmasoft.com.br
Software Development Services
N.A.I.C.S.: 541511
Vinicius Da Rocha Ubeda (Acct Mgr)

MAGMA Engineering (Suzhou) Co., Ltd. (1)
Room 615 CIQ Tower No 98 Suhui Road, Suzhou Industrial Park, Suzhou, 215021, Jiangsu, China
Tel.: (86) 51262725820
Web Site: http://www.magmasoft-china.com
Software Development Services
N.A.I.C.S.: 541511
Michael Er (Gen Mgr)

MAGMA Engineering Asia Pacific Pte Ltd. (1)
25 International Business Park 02-24/25 German Centre, Singapore, 609916, Singapore
Tel.: (65) 65643435
Web Site: http://www.magmasoft.com.sg
Emp.: 60
Software Development Services
N.A.I.C.S.: 541511
Jan Eilers (Mgr-Sls & Mktg)

MAGMA Engineering Korea Co., Ltd. (1)
Suite 902 Hyundai 41 Tower 917-9 Mokdong, Yangchungu, Seoul, 158-050, Korea (South)
Tel.: (82) 221683575
Web Site: http://www.magmasoft.co.kr
Software Development Services
N.A.I.C.S.: 541511

INTERNATIONAL PUBLIC

MAGMA Foundry Technologies Inc. (1)
10 N Martingale Rd Ste 425, Schaumburg, IL 60173
Tel.: (847) 969-1001
Web Site: http://www.magmasoft.com
Software Development Services
N.A.I.C.S.: 541511
Benji Johnson (Mgr-Technical Applications)

MAGMA Giessereitechnologie GmbH (1)
K Vinici 1256 studio 8, 53002, Pardubice, Czech Republic
Tel.: (420) 773154664
Software Development Services
N.A.I.C.S.: 541511

SIGMA Engineering GmbH (1)
Kackertstr 11, 52072, Aachen, Germany
Tel.: (49) 241894950
Web Site: http://www.sigmasoft.de
Software Development Services
N.A.I.C.S.: 541511
Thomas Klein (Member-Mgmt Bd)

MAGMAG, INC.
3-12-14 Nishigotanda, Shinagawa-Ku, Tokyo, 141-0031, Japan
Tel.: (81) 357195703
Web Site: https://mag2.co.jp
Year Founded: 1999
4059—(TKS)
Media Advertising Services
N.A.I.C.S.: 541840
Yasufumi Matsuda (Pres)

MAGMATIC RESOURCES LIMITED
14 Edward Street, Orange, 2800, NSW, Australia
Tel.: (61) 263620716 AU
Web Site:
   https://www.magmaticresources.com
MAG—(ASX)
Rev: $123,002
Assets: $6,952,398
Liabilities: $740,885
Net Worth: $6,211,512
Earnings: ($2,257,853)
Fiscal Year-end: 06/30/24
Gold Exploration Services
N.A.I.C.S.: 212220
David Richardson (Chm)

MAGNA ELECTRO CASTINGS LIMITED
43 Balasundaram Road, Coimbatore, 641 018, Tamilnadu, India
Tel.: (91) 4222240109
Web Site:
   https://www.magnacast.com
517449—(BOM)
Rev: $20,353,880
Assets: $14,450,967
Liabilities: $3,014,462
Net Worth: $11,436,505
Earnings: $2,075,223
Emp.: 235
Fiscal Year-end: 03/31/23
Ductile Iron Casting Services
N.A.I.C.S.: 331523
Narayanaswamy Krishna Samaraj (Mng Dir)

MAGNA GOLD CORP.
82 Richmond Street East, Toronto, M5C 1P1, ON, Canada
Tel.: (647) 259-1790
Web Site:
   https://www.magnagoldcorp.com
MGLQF—(OTCIQ)
Rev: $98,508,000
Assets: $83,141,000
Liabilities: $60,182,000
Net Worth: $22,959,000
Earnings: $5,244,000
Emp.: 270
Fiscal Year-end: 12/31/21

AND PRIVATE COMPANIES — MAGNA INTERNATIONAL INC.

Gold Exploration & Mining Services
N.A.I.C.S.: 212220
Leslie Kapusiynyk *(Sec)*

MAGNA INDUSTRIES & EXPORTS LIMITED
No-2 Pittalwala Bldg 17 Tilak Road,
Santacruz West, Mumbai, 400 054,
India
Tel.: (91) 22 26059978
Rev.: $3,042,753
Assets: $2,777,764
Liabilities: $585,114
Net Worth: $2,192,651
Earnings: $98,265
Fiscal Year-end: 03/31/16
Export Trading Services
N.A.I.C.S.: 522299
Ramnath K. Warkar *(Compliance Officer)*

MAGNA INTERNATIONAL INC.
337 Magna Drive, Aurora, Toronto,
L4G 7K1, ON, Canada
Tel.: (905) 726-2462   ON
Web Site: https://www.magna.com
Year Founded: 1957
MGA—(NYSE)
Rev.: $42,797,000,000
Assets: $32,255,000,000
Liabilities: $19,978,000,000
Net Worth: $12,277,000,000
Earnings: $1,213,000,000
Emp.: 179,000
Fiscal Year-end: 12/31/23
Automobile Parts Mfr
N.A.I.C.S.: 336390
Vincent J. Galifi *(CFO & Exec VP)*

Subsidiaries:

Cosma International Inc.   (1)
2550 Steeles Avenue East, Brampton, L6T 5R3, ON, Canada   (100%)
Tel.: (905) 799-7600
Web Site: http://www.cosma.com
Sales Range: $25-49.9 Million
Emp.: 20
Automotive Metalforming Supplier
N.A.I.C.S.: 336370

Subsidiary (US):

Cosma International of America, Inc.   (2)
1807 E Maple Rd, Troy, MI 48083-4212
Tel.: (248) 524-5300
Automotive Parts Mfr & Whslr
N.A.I.C.S.: 336390

Subsidiary (Non-US):

MAGNA BDW technologies GmbH   (2)
Tel.: (49) 81214200
Web Site: http://www.bdw-technologies.com
Sales Range: $75-99.9 Million
Emp.: 320
Aluminum Alloy Casting
N.A.I.C.S.: 331523

Subsidiary (Non-US):

MAGNA BDW technologies Hungary Kft.   (3)
Verseci utca 1-15, H 8050, Szekesfehervar, Hungary
Tel.: (36) 22520430
Sales Range: $10-24.9 Million
Emp.: 82
Aluminium Products Mfr
N.A.I.C.S.: 331318

Subsidiary (Domestic):

MAGNA BDW technologies Soest GmbH   (3)
Overweg 24, 59494, Soest, Germany
Tel.: (49) 29219700
Web Site: http://www.bdw-technologies.com
Sales Range: $25-49.9 Million
Emp.: 280
Automotive Castings & Extrusions
N.A.I.C.S.: 331523

Day Tech Industries   (1)
319 Pokagon Trl, Angola, IN 46703-9325
Tel.: (260) 665-1070
Flywheel Assembly
N.A.I.C.S.: 441330

HE System Electronic GmbH & Co. KG   (1)
Reitweg 1, 90587, Veitsbronn, Germany
Tel.: (49) 911975810
Web Site: http://www.he-system.com
Sales Range: $25-49.9 Million
Emp.: 100
Electronic Module & Microelectronic Subassemblies Mfr
N.A.I.C.S.: 334419
Axel Weber *(Mng Dir)*

Magna Donnelly Corporation   (1)
49 W 3rd St, Holland, MI 49423
Tel.: (616) 786-7000
Web Site: http://www.donnelly.com
International Supplier of Automotive Parts & Component Systems
N.A.I.C.S.: 327215

Subsidiary (Domestic):

Magna Donnelly Electronics   (2)
10410 N Holly Rd, Holly, MI 48442
Tel.: (810) 606-0444
Web Site: http://www.magna.com
Sales Range: $50-74.9 Million
Emp.: 250
Electronic Component & Sub Assemblies Mfr
N.A.I.C.S.: 334419

Subsidiary (Non-US):

Magna Donnelly Euroglas Systems   (2)
1 Rue Des Allies, Haute-Marne, 52201, France
Tel.: (33) 325843434
Web Site: http://www.magnadonnelly.com
Sales Range: $25-49.9 Million
Emp.: 54
Modular Windows Mfr
N.A.I.C.S.: 337211

Subsidiary (Domestic):

Optera, Inc.   (2)
215 Central Ave Ste 200, Holland, MI 49423   (100%)
Tel.: (616) 786-5300
Web Site: http://www.optera.com
Sales Range: $50-74.9 Million
Emp.: 165
Specialty Coated Glass for the Touch Screen Industry Mfr
N.A.I.C.S.: 327215

Magna International AG   (1)
Technologiestrasse 8, 1120, Vienna, Austria
Tel.: (43) 18125565
Holding Company; Regional Managing Office
N.A.I.C.S.: 551112
Gunther Apfalter *(Pres)*

Subsidiary (Domestic):

Magna Powertrain AG & Co. KG   (2)
Industries Strasse 35, 8502, Lannach, Austria
Tel.: (43) 50444
Automotive Components Mfr
N.A.I.C.S.: 336330

Magna Steyr AG & Co. KG   (2)
Liebenauer Hauptstrasse 317, 8041, Graz, Austria
Tel.: (43) 3164040
Web Site: http://www.magnasteyr.com
Emp.: 6,000
Holding Company; Motor Vehicle Components Mfr
N.A.I.C.S.: 551112
Karl Stracke *(Pres)*

Subsidiary (Domestic):

Magna Steyr Engineering AG & Co. KG   (3)
Liebenauer Hauptstrasse 317, 8041, Graz, Austria
Tel.: (43) 3164040
Web Site: http://www.magnasteyr.com

Automotive Components Developer
N.A.I.C.S.: 336330

Magna Steyr Fahrzeugtechnik AG & Co. KG   (3)
Liebenauer Hauptstrasse 317, 8041, Graz, Austria
Tel.: (43) 3164040
Emp.: 7,000
Automotive Components Mfr
N.A.I.C.S.: 336330

Unit (Domestic):

Magna Steyr Heavy Stamping   (3)
Frank Stronach Strasse 1, 8200, Albersdorf, Austria
Tel.: (43) 31128080
Web Site: http://www.cosma.com
Automotive Components Mfr
N.A.I.C.S.: 336330

Subsidiary (US):

Magna Steyr LLC   (3)
1965 Research Dr Ste 100, Troy, MI 48083
Tel.: (248) 307-8000
Web Site: http://www.magnasteyr.com
Motor Vehicle Engines & Parts
N.A.I.C.S.: 423120

Magna International China   (1)
8F Tower A Eton Place 69 Dongfang Road, Pudong, Shanghai, 201120, China
Tel.: (86) 2161651500
Producer of Framed Glass Products for the Asian Automotive Industry
N.A.I.C.S.: 327211

Magna PT B.V. & Co. KG   (1)
Hermann-Hagenmeyer Strasse 1, 74199, Untergruppenbach, Germany
Tel.: (49) 713164440
Web Site: http://www.getrag.com
Emp.: 16,300
Motor Vehicle Parts & Accessories Mfr
N.A.I.C.S.: 336390
Stephan Weng *(Exec VP)*

Group (Non-US):

GETRAG Asia Pacific   (2)
8F Tower A Eton Place 69 Dongfang Road, Pudong, Shanghai, 200120, China
Tel.: (86) 21 5033 3266
Web Site: http://www.getrag.com
Emp.: 93
Holding Company; Regional Managing Office
N.A.I.C.S.: 551112
Peter Seidl *(Dir)*

Subsidiary (Domestic):

GETRAG (Jiangxi) Transmission Co. Ltd   (3)
169 Meilin Street, Nanchang, 330013, Jiangxi, China
Tel.: (86) 791 88 555 5018
Web Site: http://www.getrag.com
Emp.: 3,943
Vehicle Parts Mfr
N.A.I.C.S.: 336390
Weixiang Cai *(Plant Dir-Nanchang)*

GETRAG Asia Pacific Transmission Technology (Shanghai) Co. Ltd.   (3)
8F Tower A Eton Place 69 Dongfang Road, Pudong, Shanghai, 200120, China
Tel.: (86) 21 5033 3266
Web Site: http://www.getrag.com
Emp.: 93
Motor Vehicle Parts Mfr & Distr
N.A.I.C.S.: 336390
Peter Seidl *(Dir)*

Plant (Domestic):

GETRAG B.V. & Co. KG - Bad Windsheim Plant   (3)
Burgbernheimer Strasse 5, 91438, Bad Windsheim, Germany
Tel.: (49) 98414070
Web Site: http://www.getrag.com
Emp.: 404
Vehicle Parts Mfr
N.A.I.C.S.: 336390
Jorg Schwarz *(Plant Dir)*

GETRAG B.V. & Co. KG - Neuenstein Plant   (2)

Hermann-Hagenmeyer-Strasse, 74632, Neuenstein, Germany
Tel.: (49) 7942 9930
Web Site: http://www.getrag.com
Emp.: 934
Vehicle Parts Mfr
N.A.I.C.S.: 336390
Aldo Cirili *(Plant Dir)*

GETRAG B.V. & Co. KG - Rosenberg Plant   (2)
Hermann-Hagenmeyer-Strasse 1, 74749, Rosenberg, Germany
Tel.: (49) 6295180
Web Site: http://www.getrag.com
Emp.: 523
Vehicle Parts Mfr
N.A.I.C.S.: 336390
Jorg Schwarz *(Plant Dir)*

Joint Venture (Domestic):

GETRAG Ford Transmissions GmbH   (2)
Scarletallee 2, 50735, Cologne, Germany
Tel.: (49) 22158970
Web Site: http://www.getrag.com
Emp.: 506
Transmissions Systems & Components Mfr
N.A.I.C.S.: 333613
Hans Terbrueggen *(VP-Sls & Customer Strategy)*

Plant (Non-US):

GETRAG Ford Transmissions GmbH - Bordeaux Plant   (3)
Zone Industrielle 65 Rue Jean Duvert, BP 123, 33294, Blanquefort, Cedex, France
Tel.: (33) 557 535 100
Web Site: http://www.getrag.com
Emp.: 1,090
Vehicle Parts Mfr
N.A.I.C.S.: 336390
Andor Paizer *(Plant Dir)*

Plant (Domestic):

GETRAG Ford Transmissions GmbH - Cologne-Merkenich   (3)
Spessartstrasse, 50725, Cologne, Germany
Tel.: (49) 221 903 8202
Web Site: http://www.getrag.com
Emp.: 106
Vehicle Parts Mfr
N.A.I.C.S.: 336390
Erik Muller *(Plant Dir)*

Plant (Non-US):

GETRAG Ford Transmissions GmbH - Halewood Plant   (3)
Speke Boulevard, Liverpool, L24 9LE, United Kingdom
Tel.: (44) 151 485 6959
Web Site: http://www.getrag.com
Emp.: 639
Vehicle Parts Mfr
N.A.I.C.S.: 336390
Andy Roche *(Plant Dir)*

Subsidiary (Non-US):

GETRAG Ford Transmissions Slovakia sro   (3)
Perinska cesta 282, Kechnec, 044 58, Kosice, Slovakia
Tel.: (421) 556148300
Web Site: http://www.getrag.com
Emp.: 1,009
Vehicle Parts Mfr
N.A.I.C.S.: 336390
Andy Roche *(Dir)*

Subsidiary (Non-US):

GETRAG SpA   (2)
Via dei Ciclamini 4, 70026, Modugno, Bari, Italy
Tel.: (39) 0805858111
Web Site: http://www.getrag.com
Emp.: 868
Vehicle Parts Mfr
N.A.I.C.S.: 336390
Bob Taylor *(Plant Dir)*

Subsidiary (Domestic):

GETRAG Systemtechnik GmbH   (2)

MAGNA INTERNATIONAL INC.

Magna International Inc.—(Continued)

Industriestrasse 5, 78112, Saint Georgen, Germany
Tel.: (49) 772494120
Web Site: http://www.getrag.com
Emp.: 93
Vehicle Parts Mfr
N.A.I.C.S.: 336390
Frank Nageleisen *(Dir)*

Subsidiary (Non-US):

GETRAG s.r.o. (2)
Perinska cesta 282, Kechnec, 044 58, Kosice, Slovakia
Tel.: (421) 556148300
Web Site: http://www.getrag.com
Vehicle Parts Mfr
N.A.I.C.S.: 336390

Magna Powertrain Inc. (1)
245 Edward St, Aurora, L4G 3M7, ON, Canada (100%)
Tel.: (905) 713-0746
Web Site: http://www.magna.com
Sales Range: $1-4.9 Billion
Emp.: 11,000
Unimotion-Gear Parts & Accessories
N.A.I.C.S.: 333612

Subsidiary (US):

Magna Powertrain USA, Inc. (2)
1235 E Big Beaver, Troy, MI 48083-4232
Tel.: (248) 528-6474
Web Site: http://www.magnapowertrain.com
Sales Range: $50-74.9 Million
Emp.: 300
Engineeering Services
N.A.I.C.S.: 336390
Brent Kearns *(VP-HR)*

Subsidiary (Domestic):

New Process Gear Inc. (3)
6600 New Venture Gear Dr, East Syracuse, NY 13057-1209
Tel.: (315) 432-4000
Web Site: http://www.magnadrivetrain.com
Motor Vehicle Gear Mfr
N.A.I.C.S.: 336390

Magna Seating Inc. (1)
400 Courtneypark Drive East Unit 1, Mississauga, L5T 2S5, ON, Canada
Tel.: (905) 696-1000
Web Site: http://www.magnaseating.com
Sales Range: $100-124.9 Million
Emp.: 350
Seating System Mfr
N.A.I.C.S.: 336360
Shea Hardman *(CEO)*

Subsidiary (US):

Magna Seating of America, Inc. (2)
30020 Cabot Dr, Novi, MI 48377
Tel.: (248) 567-4000
Web Site: http://www.magna.com
Emp.: 500
Motor Vehicle Interior Seating Mfr & Whslr
N.A.I.C.S.: 336360

Joint Venture (Domestic):

Bloomington-Normal Seating Company (3)
2031 Warehouse Rd, Normal, IL 61761-1038
Tel.: (309) 452-7878
Web Site: http://www.bnseating.com
Sales Range: $25-49.9 Million
Emp.: 55
Mfr of Automotive Seating; Joint Venture of Namba Press Works Co., Ltd. & Magna Interior Systems (50%)
N.A.I.C.S.: 336360
Hank Inoue *(Pres)*

Magna Structural Systems Inc. (1)
1 Cosma Court, Saint Thomas, N5P 4J5, ON, Canada
Tel.: (519) 637-3200
Web Site: http://www.magna.com
Sales Range: $25-49.9 Million
Emp.: 1,100
Automotive Components Mfr
N.A.I.C.S.: 336330

MAGNA MINING NL
Level 1 47 Ord Street, West Perth, 6005, WA, Australia
Tel.: (61) 8 9322 7822
Web Site:
http://www.magnamining.com.au
Sales Range: Less than $1 Million
Metals & Semi-Precious Stones Mining & Exploration Services
N.A.I.C.S.: 212290
Gary Stokes *(CEO)*

MAGNA POLONIA S.A.
Ul Grzybowska 4/Lok 96, 00-131, Warsaw, Poland
Tel.: (48) 226307700
Web Site:
http://www.magnapolonia.com.pl
Year Founded: 1997
06N—(WAR)
Rev.: $50,826,982
Assets: $25,474,339
Liabilities: $921,748
Net Worth: $24,552,591
Earnings: $17,389,482
Fiscal Year-end: 12/31/23
Telecommunication Servicesb
N.A.I.C.S.: 517810
Miroslaw Janisiewicz *(Chm-Mgmt Bd & CEO)*

MAGNA PRIMA BERHAD
Lot 4 01 Level 4 IDCC Corporate Tower, Jalan Pahat L 15/L Seksyen 15, 40200, Shah Alam, Selangor, Malaysia
Tel.: (60) 358804810 MY
Web Site:
https://www.magnaprima.com.my
Year Founded: 1995
MAGNA—(KLS)
Rev.: $18,063,492
Assets: $123,291,788
Liabilities: $33,904,668
Net Worth: $89,387,120
Earnings: $10,382,762
Fiscal Year-end: 12/31/22
Construction Engineering Services
N.A.I.C.S.: 541330
Adzmi Abdul Wahab *(Chm)*

MAGNA TERRA MINERALS INC.
20 Adelaide St East Suite 401, Toronto, M2C 2T6, ON, Canada
Tel.: (647) 478-5307
Web Site:
https://www.magnaterramineral.com
Year Founded: 2009
MTT—(TSXV)
Rev.: $15,559
Assets: $134,750
Liabilities: $663,814
Net Worth: ($529,064)
Earnings: ($722,570)
Fiscal Year-end: 08/31/23
Mineral Exploration Services
N.A.I.C.S.: 212290
Lewis Lawrick *(Pres & CEO)*

MAGNACHIP SEMICONDUCTOR CORPORATION
c/o MagnaChip Semiconductor SA 1 Allee Scheffer, L-2520, Luxembourg, Luxembourg
Tel.: (352) 456262 DE
Web Site: http://www.magnachip.com
MX—(NYSE)
Rev.: $337,658,000
Assets: $516,645,000
Liabilities: $88,492,000
Net Worth: $428,153,000
Earnings: ($8,036,000)
Emp.: 897
Fiscal Year-end: 12/31/22

Holding Company; Analog & Mixed-Signal Semiconductor Products Designer & Mfr
N.A.I.C.S.: 551112
Young-Joon Kim *(CEO)*

MAGNAGHI AERONAUTICA S.P.A.
Via Galileo Ferraris 76/80, 80142, Naples, Italy
Tel.: (39) 0815 977111 IT
Web Site: http://www.magroup.net
Year Founded: 1936
Aerospace Component Mfr
N.A.I.C.S.: 336413
Paolo Graziano *(CEO)*

Subsidiaries:

Blair Industries, Inc. (1)
3671 Horseblock Rd, Medford, NY 11763
Tel.: (631) 924-6600
Gears' assembling, Hydraulic Testing & Painting Mfr
N.A.I.C.S.: 333612
William R. Lehmann Jr. *(CEO)*

MAGNANIMOUS TRADE & FINANCE LIMITED
Ground Floor Shop No 188/2, Shyam Dham Heights Rampura Patrakar Colony, Jaipur, 302034, Rajasthan, India
Tel.: (91) 1412373676
Web Site: http://mtfl.co.in
Year Founded: 1985
512377—(BOM)
Rev.: $102,734
Assets: $1,067,053
Liabilities: $14,942
Net Worth: $1,052,112
Earnings: $50,984
Fiscal Year-end: 03/31/23
Real Estate Management Services
N.A.I.C.S.: 531390
Parwati Parasrampuri *(Mng Dir)*

MAGNET ADVERTISING
32 Kifissias Ave Atrina ctr, 151 25, Maroussi, Athens, Greece
Tel.: (30) 210 68 92 151
Web Site: http://www.magnetad.gr
Year Founded: 1988
Rev.: $25,000,000
Emp.: 25
N.A.I.C.S.: 541810
Effie Karakitsou *(Mng Dir)*

MAGNETEC GMBH
Industriestrasse 7, 63505, Langenselbold, Germany
Tel.: (49) 618492020
Web Site: http://www.magnetec.de
Year Founded: 1984
Rev.: $17,932,200
Emp.: 450
Ring Cores Mfr
N.A.I.C.S.: 339999
Martin Ferch *(Mng Dir)*

Subsidiaries:

MAGNETEC Magnetic Device Co. Ltd. (1)
6/F Building 2 Huangzhou Industrial Zone Chebei Road, Tianhe District, Guangzhou, 510660, China
Tel.: (86) 2038662129
Web Site: http://www.magnetec-china.com
Electronic Component Mfr & Distr
N.A.I.C.S.: 335999

MAGNETEC-Ungarn Kft. (1)
Pipishegy, 3200, Gyongyos, Hungary
Tel.: (36) 37509100
Electronic Product Distr
N.A.I.C.S.: 423690

MAGNETIC NORTH ACQUISITION CORPORATION

INTERNATIONAL PUBLIC

1000 250 2nd Street SW, Calgary, T2P 0C1, AB, Canada
Tel.: (403) 470-4355 AB
Web Site:
https://www.magneticnac.com
MNC—(TSXV)
Industrial Minerals Integrated Miner, Processor & Marketer
N.A.I.C.S.: 212319
Andrew Osis *(Co-CEO)*

MAGNETIC RESOURCES NL
1st Floor 44A Kings Park Road, West Perth, 6005, WA, Australia
Tel.: (61) 892261777 AU
Web Site:
https://www.magres.com.au
MAU—(ASX)
Rev.: $41
Assets: $6,502,521
Liabilities: $591,455
Net Worth: $5,911,066
Earnings: ($8,261,905)
Emp.: 10
Fiscal Year-end: 06/30/24
Mineral Mining & Exploration Services
N.A.I.C.S.: 212290
George Sakalidis *(Mng Dir)*

MAGNETITE MINES LIMITED
Suite 16 1st Floor 22 Greenhill Road, Wayville, 5034, SA, Australia
Tel.: (61) 884270516
Web Site:
https://www.magnetitemines.com
MGT—(ASX)
Rev.: $248,301
Assets: $25,524,935
Liabilities: $922,989
Net Worth: $24,601,946
Earnings: ($3,237,083)
Emp.: 15
Fiscal Year-end: 06/30/24
Uranium & Iron Ore Mining Services
N.A.I.C.S.: 212290
Tim Dobson *(CEO)*

MAGNI-TECH INDUSTRIES BERHAD
Level 18 Penas Tower Midlands Park Centre Jalan Burmah, 10350, Penang, Malaysia
Tel.: (60) 42288826
Web Site: https://www.magni-tech.com.my
MAGNI—(KLS)
Rev.: $256,589,399
Assets: $194,017,361
Liabilities: $22,127,089
Net Worth: $171,890,272
Earnings: $20,184,372
Emp.: 1,005
Fiscal Year-end: 04/30/23
Garments Mfr
N.A.I.C.S.: 315250
Peng Loon Lee *(Co-Sec)*

Subsidiaries:

Inter-Pacific Packaging Sdn. Bhd. (1)
Lot 897 984 985 13th Mile Jalan Kelang, 47100, Puchong, Selangor Darul Ehsan, Malaysia
Tel.: (60) 380611301
Web Site: https://www.ippsb.com.my
Electrical & Electronic Mfr
N.A.I.C.S.: 336320
Zabidi Ab Aziz *(Mgr-QA)*

South Island Plastics Sdn. Bhd. (1)
Plot 541 Lorong Perusahaan Baru Dua, Prai Industrial Park, 13600, Prai, Penang, Malaysia
Tel.: (60) 43992988
Web Site: https://www.siplas.com
Plastic Materials Mfr
N.A.I.C.S.: 325211

MAGNIFICENT HOTEL INVESTMENTS LIMITED
3rd Floor Shun Ho Tower 24-30 Ice House Street, Central, China (Hong Kong)
Tel.: (852) 25253788   HK
Web Site:
  https://www.magnificenthotelinv.com
0201—(HKG)
Rev.: $56,033,955
Assets: $671,352,270
Liabilities: $131,674,860
Net Worth: $539,677,410
Earnings: $75,500,783
Emp.: 334
Fiscal Year-end: 12/31/22
Hotel Operators; Property Investment & Development
N.A.I.C.S.: 561110
Albert Wing Ho Hui (Exec Dir)

Subsidiaries:

Grand View Hotel Limited   (1)
No 88 Chun Yeung Street, North Point, China (Hong Kong)
Tel.: (852) 21303388
Web Site:
  https://www.ramadahongkonggrand.com
Hotel Services
N.A.I.C.S.: 721110

Magnificent International Hotel Limited   (1)
381 Xizang South Road, Shanghai, 200021, China
Tel.: (86) 2153838588
Web Site: https://www.magnificenthotel-shanghai.com
Hotel Services
N.A.I.C.S.: 721110

MAGNIS ENERGY TECHNOLOGIES LTD
Tel.: (61) 283979888   AU
Web Site: http://www.magnis.com.au
Year Founded: 2005
MNS—(OTCIQ)
Rev.: $474,721
Assets: $104,725,614
Liabilities: $53,008,376
Net Worth: $51,717,238
Earnings: ($8,692,519)
Emp.: 12
Fiscal Year-end: 06/30/21
Metal Exploration Services
N.A.I.C.S.: 212290
Jurgen Behrens (CFO)

MAGNIT PJSC
15/5 Solnechnaya Street, Krasnodar, 350072, Russia
Tel.: (7) 8612109810   RU
Web Site: https://www.magnit.com
Year Founded: 1994
MGNT—(MOEX)
Rev.: $25,001,383,457
Assets: $16,291,205,710
Liabilities: $13,880,275,348
Net Worth: $2,410,930,361
Earnings: $647,985,961
Emp.: 359,000
Fiscal Year-end: 12/31/21
Convenience Store Owner & Operator
N.A.I.C.S.: 445131
Sergey Galitsky (Chm-Mgmt Bd)

MAGNOLIA BOSTAD AB
Turegatan 11A, Box 5853, 102 40, Stockholm, Sweden
Tel.: (46) 84705080
Web Site:
  http://www.magnoliabostad.se
MAG—(OMX)
Rev.: $53,293,621
Assets: $647,016,400
Liabilities: $436,745,436
Net Worth: $210,270,964
Earnings: ($80,830,219)
Emp.: 104
Fiscal Year-end: 12/31/22
Real Estate Property Management Services
N.A.I.C.S.: 531311

MAGNOLIA CAPITAL PARTNERS LTD.
Shenhav Offices Or Towers Building B 11th Floor Hanechoshet St 4, Ramat Hachaya, Tel Aviv, 69710, Israel
Year Founded: 2004
Investing Services
N.A.I.C.S.: 523999

MAGNORA ASA
Karenlyst Alle 2, 278, Oslo, Norway
Tel.: (47) 22122550
Web Site:
  https://www.magnoraasa.com
MGN—(OSL)
Rev.: $8,414,927
Assets: $52,115,278
Liabilities: $12,229,817
Net Worth: $39,885,461
Earnings: $1,154,628
Emp.: 32
Fiscal Year-end: 12/31/22
Floating Units for Offshore Oil & Gas Production, Storage & Offloading Designing, Engineering, Construction, Ownership & Operation
N.A.I.C.S.: 213112
Erling Overland (Co-Chm)

Subsidiaries:

Kanfa Aragon AS   (1)
Fantoftveien 14P, 5072, Bergen, Norway   (50%)
Tel.: (47) 55602350
Web Site: http://www.aragon.no
Sales Range: $25-49.9 Million
Emp.: 100
Natural Gas Transportation Services
N.A.I.C.S.: 486210

Mator AS   (1)
Heroya Industrial Park, 3936, Porsgrunn, Norway
Tel.: (47) 35574900
Web Site: http://www.mator.com
Sales Range: $50-74.9 Million
Emp.: 7
Oil & Gas Field Services
N.A.I.C.S.: 213112

Sevan 300 Pte Ltd   (1)
350 Orchard Rd Unit No 15-08, Shaw House, Singapore, 238868, Singapore
Tel.: (65) 62201314
Sales Range: $50-74.9 Million
Emp.: 20
Natural Gas Production Services
N.A.I.C.S.: 211130

Sevan Drilling AS   (1)
Kittelsbuktveien 5, 4836, Arendal, Norway
Tel.: (47) 37404000
Oil & Gas Field Drilling Services
N.A.I.C.S.: 213111

Sevan Drilling ASA   (1)
Drammensveien 288, 0283, Oslo, Norway
Tel.: (47) 22 33 00 00
Web Site: http://www.sevandrilling.com
Oil & Gas Field Drilling Services
N.A.I.C.S.: 213111
Scott McReaken (CEO)

Sevan Drilling Rig Pte Ltd   (1)
350 Orchard Rd Show House Nlt 015-08, Singapore, 238868, Singapore
Tel.: (65) 62201314
Oil & Gas Field Drilling Services
N.A.I.C.S.: 213111

Sevan Holding I AS   (1)
Kittelsbuktveien 5, 4836, Arendal, Norway
Tel.: (47) 37404000
Investment Management Service
N.A.I.C.S.: 541618

Sevan Holding I Pte Ltd   (1)
350 Orchard Rd #15-08 Shaw House, Singapore, 238868, Singapore
Tel.: (65) 62201314
Web Site: http://www.sevanmarine.com
Sales Range: $25-49.9 Million
Emp.: 8
Investment Management Service
N.A.I.C.S.: 541618

Sevan Invest AS   (1)
Kystveien 2D, Arendal, 4841, Norway
Tel.: (47) 37404000
Web Site: http://www.sevanmarine.com
Emp.: 75
Investment Management Service
N.A.I.C.S.: 541618

Sevan Marine do Brasil Ltda   (1)
Av Wilson Pres 231, 1004, Rio de Janeiro, Brazil
Tel.: (55) 21 3861 7950
Sales Range: $50-74.9 Million
Emp.: 20
Oil & Gas Field Services
N.A.I.C.S.: 213112

Sevan Production AS   (1)
Kittelsbuktveien 5, 4836, Arendal, Norway
Tel.: (47) 51 94 49 60
Sales Range: $150-199.9 Million
Liquified Natural Gas Production Services
N.A.I.C.S.: 211130

Sevan Production General Partnership
350 Orchard Road 15-08 Shaw House, 238868, Singapore, Singapore
Tel.: (65) 62201314
Natural Gas Production Services
N.A.I.C.S.: 211130

Sevan Pte Ltd   (1)
350 Orchard Rd Ste 15-08 Shaw House, 238868, Singapore, Singapore
Tel.: (65) 62201314
Web Site: http://www.sevanmarine.com
Sales Range: $50-74.9 Million
Emp.: 20
Natural Gas Production Services
N.A.I.C.S.: 211130

MAGNOTTA WINERY CORPORATION
271 Chrislea Road, Vaughan, L4L 8N6, ON, Canada
Tel.: (905) 738-9463   ON
Web Site: http://www.magnotta.com
Year Founded: 1985
Sales Range: $10-24.9 Million
Emp.: 100
Winery & Brewery Operator & Sales
N.A.I.C.S.: 312130
Rossana Di Zio Magnotta (Chm, Pres, CEO & Sec)

Subsidiaries:

Kittling Ridge Ltd.   (1)
271 Chrislea Road, Vaughan, L4L 8N6, ON, Canada
Tel.: (905) 738-9463
Web Site: http://www.kittlingridge.com
Sales Range: $10-24.9 Million
Whisky Brandy Liqueur Retail Stores
N.A.I.C.S.: 445320
Terry Martin (Mgr-Mktg)

Magnotta Brewery (Vaughan) Ltd   (1)
271 Chrislea Rd, Woodbridge, ON, Canada
Tel.: (905) 738-9463
Wine & Alcoholic Beverages Mfr
N.A.I.C.S.: 312130

Magnotta Cellars Corporation   (1)
4701 Ontario St, Beamsville, L0R 1B4, ON, Canada
Tel.: (905) 563-5313
Web Site: http://www.magnotta.com
Wine Mfr
N.A.I.C.S.: 312130
Melinda Konkle (Gen Mgr)

Magnotta Distillery Ltd   (1)
271 Chrislea Rd, Vaughan, L4L 8N6, ON, Canada
Tel.: (905) 738-9463
Web Site: http://www.magnotta.com
Alcoholic Beverages Mfr
N.A.I.C.S.: 312130

Magnotta Winery Estates Limited   (1)
271 Chrislea Rd, Woodbridge, L4L 8N6, ON, Canada
Tel.: (905) 738-9463
Wine Mfr
N.A.I.C.S.: 312130

Magnotta Wines Ltd   (1)
1760 Midland Ave, Scarborough, M1P 3C2, ON, Canada
Tel.: (416) 701-9463
Web Site: http://www.magnotta.com
Emp.: 8
Alcoholic Beverages Mfr
N.A.I.C.S.: 312130
David Whalley (Mgr)

MAGNUM BERHAD
35th Floor Menara Multi-Purpose Capital Square, No 8 Jalan Munshi Abdullah, 50100, Kuala Lumpur, Malaysia
Tel.: (60) 326988033   MY
Web Site:
  https://www.magnum.com.my
Year Founded: 1975
3859—(KLS)
Rev.: $429,862,434
Assets: $743,745,608
Liabilities: $233,358,942
Net Worth: $510,386,667
Earnings: $21,391,746
Emp.: 371
Fiscal Year-end: 12/31/22
Investment Holding Company
N.A.I.C.S.: 551114
Kuan Ying Leong (Co-Sec)

MAGNUM ENERGY INC.
1350 734 - 7th Avenue SW, Calgary, T2P 3P8, AB, Canada
Tel.: (403) 264-5980   Ca
Web Site:
  http://www.magnumenergyinc.com
Year Founded: 2003
Sales Range: $1-9.9 Million
Oil & Natural Gas Exploration Services
N.A.I.C.S.: 213112
Bob Stinn (Pres)

MAGNUM GOLDCORP INC.
2489 Bellevue Avenue, Vancouver, V7V 1E1, BC, Canada
Tel.: (604) 922-2030   AB
Web Site:
  https://www.magnumgoldcorp.com
Year Founded: 2011
MGIDD—(OTCIQ)
Rev.: $462
Assets: $2,669,330
Liabilities: $112,637
Net Worth: $2,556,693
Earnings: ($56,761)
Fiscal Year-end: 05/31/24
Investment Services
N.A.I.C.S.: 523999
Daniel B. Evans (CFO)

MAGNUM INDUSTRIAL PARTNERS, S.L.
Fortuny 14 2, 28010, Madrid, Spain
Tel.: (34) 913106342   ES
Web Site:
  http://www.magnumpartners.com
Year Founded: 2006
Privater Equity Firm
N.A.I.C.S.: 523999
Angel Corcostegui (Gen Partner)

Subsidiaries:

Grupo Vendap, SA   (1)
EN 118 Km 22 Vil Figueiras - Apartado 107, 2136-901, Samora Correia, Portugal
Tel.: (351) 212 349 900
Web Site: http://www.grupovendap.com
Industrial Equipment Rental Services
N.A.I.C.S.: 532490

MAGNUM INDUSTRIAL PARTNERS, S.L.

Magnum Industrial Partners, S.L.—(Continued)

Pretersa-Prenavisa Estructuras de Hormigon S.L. (1)
Pol Ind Venta del Barro S/N, La Puebla de Hijar, 44511, Teruel, Spain
Tel.: (34) 978 820 640
Web Site: http://www.pretersa.com
Precast Concrete Structures Mfr
N.A.I.C.S.: 327390

MAGNUM INTEGRATED TECHNOLOGIES, INC.
200 First Gulf Blvd, Brampton, L6W 4T5, ON, Canada
Tel.: (905) 595-1998
Web Site: http://www.magnum-integrated.com
Sales Range: $25-49.9 Million
Emp.: 60
Mfr of Machine Control, Automation & Equipment for Ferrous & Non-Ferrous Industries
N.A.I.C.S.: 334519

Subsidiaries:

Hill-Acme (1)
4 Thomas Dr Unit 5, Gorham, ME 04092
Tel.: (207) 854-9791
Sales Range: $25-49.9 Million
Emp.: 35
Mfr of Metal Punching, Shearing, Grinding, Continuous & Semi-Ccontinuous Casting Equipment
N.A.I.C.S.: 333519

Waterbury Farrel Technologies (1)
200 First Gulf Blvd, Brampton, L6W 4T5, ON, Canada **(100%)**
Tel.: (905) 455-0106
Web Site: http://www.waterburyfarrel.com
Sales Range: $25-49.9 Million
Emp.: 30
Mfr of Machine Tools
N.A.I.C.S.: 333517
Andre Nazarian *(Pres)*

MAGNUM LIMITED
502 Kiran Appartment Asha Kiran Flats, Vejalpur, Ahmedabad, 380015, Gujarat, India
Tel.: (91) 79 2676 8844 In
Year Founded: 1992
Assets: $423,248
Liabilities: $137,146
Net Worth: $286,102
Earnings: ($988,060)
Fiscal Year-end: 03/31/18
Investment Holding Company
N.A.I.C.S.: 551112
Santosh Kumar Awasthi *(Chm)*

MAGNUM MINING AND EXPLORATION LIMITED
311-313 Hay Street, Subiaco, 6008, WA, Australia
Tel.: (61) 864890600
Web Site: https://www.mmel.com.au
MGU—(ASX)
Rev.: $256,451
Assets: $8,549,142
Liabilities: $591,905
Net Worth: $7,957,237
Earnings: ($2,253,344)
Emp.: 1
Fiscal Year-end: 12/31/23
Tantalum Ore Mining & Exploration Services
N.A.I.C.S.: 212290
Grant Michael Button *(CEO & Sec)*

MAGNUM OPUS ACQUISITION LIMITED
Floor 15 Nexxus Building 77 Des Voeux Road, Central, China (Hong Kong)
Tel.: (852) 37579857 Ky
Web Site: http://www.opusacquisition.com

Year Founded: 2021
OPA—(NYSE)
Rev.: $2,830,785
Assets: $203,759,547
Liabilities: $215,648,688
Net Worth: ($11,889,141)
Earnings: $15,271,867
Emp.: 3
Fiscal Year-end: 12/31/22
Investment Services
N.A.I.C.S.: 523999
Jonathan Lin *(Co-Founder, Chm & CEO)*

MAGNUM VENTURES LIMITED
18-41 Site-IV Industrial Area Sahibabad, Ghaziabad, 201 010, UP, India
Tel.: (91) 1204199200
Web Site: https://www.magnumventures.in
Year Founded: 1980
532896—(NSE)
Rev.: $55,811,858
Assets: $125,019,112
Liabilities: $55,006,618
Net Worth: $70,012,493
Earnings: $8,496,013
Emp.: 1,421
Fiscal Year-end: 03/31/23
Paper & Paperboard Mfr
N.A.I.C.S.: 322120
Pradeep Kumar Jain *(Mng Dir)*

MAGNUS CONCORDIA GROUP LIMITED
Units 02-03 7/F Tung Wai Commercial Building 109-111 Gloucester Road, Wanchai, China (Hong Kong)
Tel.: (852) 21603088 Ky
Web Site: https://www.mcgrouphk.com
Year Founded: 1990
1172—(HKG)
Rev.: $204,736,274
Assets: $197,134,580
Liabilities: $112,969,713
Net Worth: $84,164,867
Earnings: ($34,823,697)
Emp.: 237
Fiscal Year-end: 03/31/22
Holding Company; Securities Investment & Trading Business; Printing Facilities
N.A.I.C.S.: 551112
Qing Li *(Exec Dir)*

MAGNUS ENERGY GROUP LTD.
32 Loyang Crescent, Singapore, 508992, Singapore
Tel.: (65) 63251850
Web Site: http://www.magnusenergy.com.sg
41S—(SES)
Rev.: $12,528,279
Assets: $6,661,905
Liabilities: $4,123,988
Net Worth: $2,537,917
Earnings: ($2,462,272)
Emp.: 26
Fiscal Year-end: 12/31/21
Crude Oil Mfr
N.A.I.C.S.: 211120
Thein Htike Maung *(Pres-Mid-Continent Equipment Inc)*

Subsidiaries:

Mid-Continent Environmental Project Pte. Ltd. (1)
32 Loyang Crescent, Singapore, 508992, Singapore
Tel.: (65) 65785088
Drilling Equipment Distr
N.A.I.C.S.: 423830

Mid-Continent Equipment Group Pte Ltd (1)

32 Loyang Crescent, Singapore, 508992, Singapore
Tel.: (65) 65059200
Web Site: http://www.mid-continents.com
Sales Range: $50-74.9 Million
Emp.: 60
Oil Drilling Equipment & Tools Distr
N.A.I.C.S.: 424690

Subsidiary (Non-US):

Mid-Continent Equipment (Australia) Pty Ltd (2)
130 Mills Street, Welshpool, Perth, 6101, WA, Australia
Tel.: (61) 894518800
Web Site: http://www.mid-continents.com
Sales Range: $50-74.9 Million
Emp.: 10
Oil & Gas Field Equipments Distr
N.A.I.C.S.: 532412

Subsidiary (Domestic):

Tubular Leasing Astralia Pty Ltd (3)
130 Mills Street, Welshpool, 6106, WA, Australia
Tel.: (61) 894518800
Web Site: http://www.tlaust.com.au
Sales Range: $50-74.9 Million
Emp.: 10
Drill Pipes & Drilling Accessories Leasing Services
N.A.I.C.S.: 532412
Kelly Duncan *(Gen Mgr)*

Subsidiary (US):

Mid-Continent Equipment, Inc. (2)
5234 Brittmoore Rd, Houston, TX 77041
Tel.: (713) 849-3422
Web Site: http://www.mid-continents.com
Sales Range: $25-49.9 Million
Emp.: 6
Oil Field Equipment Distr
N.A.I.C.S.: 423830
Tim Htlke *(Gen Mgr)*

MAGNUS POIRIER INC.
7388 Viau Blvd, Montreal, H1S 2N9, QC, Canada
Tel.: (514) 727-2847
Web Site: http://www.magnuspoirier.com
Year Founded: 1923
Sales Range: $10-24.9 Million
Funeral Services
N.A.I.C.S.: 812210
Claude Poirier *(Chm)*

MAGNUSSEN HOME FURNISHINGS LTD.
66 Hincks Street, New Hamburg, N3A 2A3, ON, Canada
Tel.: (519) 662-3040
Web Site: http://www.magnussen.com
Year Founded: 1931
Rev.: $19,127,889
Emp.: 100
Home Furniture Mfr
N.A.I.C.S.: 337126
Kent MacFarlane *(CFO)*

MAGONTEC LIMITED
Suite 201 139 Macquarie Street, Potts Point, Sydney, 2000, NSW, Australia
Tel.: (61) 280847813
Web Site: https://www.magontec.com
MGL—(ASX)
Rev.: $69,720,727
Assets: $58,012,397
Liabilities: $19,427,151
Net Worth: $38,585,246
Earnings: $317,417
Emp.: 311
Fiscal Year-end: 12/31/23
Magnesium Mining Services
N.A.I.C.S.: 212290
Nicholas William Andrews *(Chm)*

INTERNATIONAL PUBLIC

Subsidiaries:

AMT North America Inc (1)
4241 Augusta Ct, Howell, MI 48843
Tel.: (734) 853-8076
Alloy Product Mfr
N.A.I.C.S.: 331110

Advanced Magnesium Technologies Pty Ltd (1)
Office 10 Level 8 139 Macquarie Street, Sydney, 2000, NSW, Australia
Tel.: (61) 282317085
Web Site: http://www.magontec.com
Magnesium Alloys Mfr & Sales
N.A.I.C.S.: 331529

Australian Magnesium Corporation Limited (1)
Hondecoeterstraat 2A, 1071 LR, Amsterdam, Netherlands
Tel.: (31) 20 305 2010
Provider of Mining Services
N.A.I.C.S.: 212323

Magontec GmbH (1)
Industriestrasse 61, PO Box 101153, 46240, Bottrop, Germany
Tel.: (49) 204199070
Sales Range: $10-24.9 Million
Emp.: 100
Magnesium Smelting & Die Casting Services
N.A.I.C.S.: 331492

MAGOR CORPORATION
Suite 400 1 Antares Dr, Ottawa, K2E 8C4, ON, Canada
Tel.: (613) 686-1731 ON
Web Site: http://www.magorcorp.com
Year Founded: 2009
Rev.: $1,406,004
Assets: $530,411
Liabilities: $11,473,820
Net Worth: ($10,943,409)
Earnings: ($3,162,395)
Fiscal Year-end: 04/30/17
Video Communications Software Publisher
N.A.I.C.S.: 513210

MAGRIS RESOURCES INC.
Bay Adelaide Centre West Tower 333 Bay Street Suite 1101, PO Box 27, Toronto, M5H 2R2, ON, Canada
Tel.: (416) 901-9877
Web Site: http://www.magrisresources.com
Metal Exploration & Mining
N.A.I.C.S.: 212290
Aaron William Regent *(Pres & CEO)*

Subsidiaries:

Niobec Inc. (1)
3400 route du Columbium, Saint-Honore, G0V 1L0, QC, Canada
Tel.: (418) 673-4694
Web Site: http://www.niobec.com
Metal Mining Services
N.A.I.C.S.: 331410
Aaron William Regent *(Chm & CEO)*

MAGRIS SPA
Via Pastrengo, Seriate, 24068, Bergamo, Italy
Tel.: (39) 0354525911
Web Site: http://www.magrisplanet.it
Cleaning Products Whlsr
N.A.I.C.S.: 423990
Umberto Magris *(Pres)*

MAGROS VELETRGOVINA D.D.
Vrbanja br 1, 71000, Sarajevo, Bosnia & Herzegovina
Tel.: (387) 33407278
MGVSR—(SARE)
Rev.: $12,126,637
Assets: $115,169,910
Liabilities: $28,188,785
Net Worth: $86,981,125

Earnings: $300,116
Emp.: 114
Fiscal Year-end: 12/31/20
Management Consulting Services
N.A.I.C.S.: 541618

MAGROS-METAL D.D.
Halilovici broj 6, Sarajevo, 71000, Bosnia & Herzegovina
Tel.: (387) 3 345 4124
Web Site: http://www.magros-metal.ba
MMTSRK4—(SARE)
Rev.: $363,775
Assets: $4,850,676
Liabilities: $71,831
Net Worth: $4,778,845
Earnings: $40,936
Emp.: 6
Fiscal Year-end: 12/31/20
Metal Processing Services
N.A.I.C.S.: 332811

MAGTICOM LTD.
Polytkovskaya 5, Tbilisi, 0186, Georgia
Tel.: (995) 32322331 GE
Web Site: http://www.magticom.ge
Year Founded: 1997
Sales Range: $150-199.9 Million
Mobile Telecommunications Services
N.A.I.C.S.: 517112
David Lee (Gen Dir)

MAGYAR NEMZETI BANK
1054 Szabadsag ter 9, 1850, Budapest, Hungary
Tel.: (36) 14282600 HU
Web Site: http://www.mnb.hu
Year Founded: 1930
Rev.: $1,119,350,500
Assets: $39,509,519,100
Liabilities: $37,967,228,700
Net Worth: $1,542,290,400
Earnings: $169,572,850
Emp.: 1,434
Fiscal Year-end: 12/31/18
Central Bank
N.A.I.C.S.: 521110
Gyorgy Matolcsy (Governor)

Subsidiaries:

Budapesti Ertektozsde Zrt. (1)
Szabadsag Square 7, 5th district, H-1054, Budapest, Hungary
Tel.: (36) 14296700
Web Site: http://www.bse.hu
Rev.: $8,300,046
Assets: $26,597,480
Liabilities: $3,454,029
Net Worth: $23,143,451
Earnings: $1,053,292
Emp.: 57
Fiscal Year-end: 12/31/2018
Stock Exchange Operator
N.A.I.C.S.: 523210
Mihaly Patai (Chm)

MAH SING GROUP BERHAD
Wisma Mah Sing Penthouse Suite 1 No 163, Jalan Sungai Besi, 57100, Kuala Lumpur, Malaysia
Tel.: (60) 392218888
Web Site: https://www.mahsing.com.my
MAHSING—(KLS)
Rev.: $490,418,624
Assets: $1,352,315,132
Liabilities: $593,126,772
Net Worth: $759,188,360
Earnings: $39,533,968
Emp.: 2,063
Fiscal Year-end: 12/31/22
Property Development & Management Services
N.A.I.C.S.: 531312
Hui Fang Kuan (Co-Sec)

Subsidiaries:

Icon City Development Sdn. Bhd. (1)
No 1 Jalan SS 8/2 Sungai Way, 47300, Petaling Jaya, Malaysia
Tel.: (60) 374513697
Web Site: http://icon-city.com.my
Property Development & Management Services
N.A.I.C.S.: 531312

M Vertica Sdn. Bhd. (1)
Wisma Mah Sing Penthouse Suite 1 No 163, Jalan Sungai Besi, 57100, Kuala Lumpur, Malaysia
Tel.: (60) 392216888
Web Site: https://mvertica.com.my
Property Development & Management Services
N.A.I.C.S.: 531312

Mah Sing Plastics Industries Sendirian Berhad (1)
Lot 9 Lingkaran Sultan Mohamed 1, Kawasan Perindustrian Bandar Sultan Suleiman, 42000, Port Klang, Selangor Darul Ehsan, Malaysia
Tel.: (60) 331763718
Web Site: https://www.msplastics.com.my
Plastics Product Mfr
N.A.I.C.S.: 326199

Meridin East Sdn. Bhd. (1)
Meridin East Sales Gallery Jalan Kong Kong, 81700, Pasir Gudang, Johor, Malaysia
Tel.: (60) 72913218
Web Site: https://meridin-east.com.my
Property Development & Management Services
N.A.I.C.S.: 531312

PT. Mah Sing Indonesia (1)
Kawasan Industri Jababeka Jalan Jababeka XIIB, Block W17-20 Cikarang Industrial Estate, Bekasi, Indonesia
Tel.: (62) 218935123
Automotive Plastic Parts & Component Mfr
N.A.I.C.S.: 336390

Southville City Sdn. Bhd. (1)
E-G-01 Savanna Boulevard Retail Jalan Southville City 2, Dengkil, 43800, Bangi, Malaysia
Tel.: (60) 392120199
Web Site: https://www.southville-city.com
Property Development & Management Services
N.A.I.C.S.: 531312

MAHA ENERGY AB
Eriksbergsgatan 10 SE114 30, 114 51, Stockholm, Sweden
Tel.: (46) 86110511 SE
Web Site: https://maha-energy.com
Year Founded: 2016
MAHA.A—(OMX)
Rev.: $5,226,000
Assets: $201,900,000
Liabilities: $47,075,000
Net Worth: $154,825,000
Earnings: ($5,307,000)
Emp.: 41
Fiscal Year-end: 12/31/23
Holding Company; Oil & Gas Exploration & Extraction Services
N.A.I.C.S.: 551112
Jonas Lindvall (CEO & Mng Dir)

Subsidiaries:

Maha Energy Inc. (1)
240 23 Sunpark Drive SE, Calgary, T2X 3V1, AB, Canada
Tel.: (403) 454-7560
Web Site: http://www.mahaenergy.ca
Oil & Gas Exploration & Extraction Services
N.A.I.C.S.: 213112
Alan Johnson (COO)

MAHA RASHTRA APEX CORPORATION LIMITED
3rd Floor North Block The Manipal Centre 47 Dickenson Road, Bengaluru, 560042, India
Tel.: (91) 8025587132
Web Site: https://www.maharashtraapex.com
Year Founded: 1943
523384—(BOM)
Sales Range: $1-9.9 Million
Emp.: 20
Financial Lending Services
N.A.I.C.S.: 522220
S. R. Gowda (Exec Dir)

MAHAAN FOODS LIMITED
Office No 406 4th Floor Worldmark 2, Aerocity Hospitality District, New Delhi, 110037, India
Tel.: (91) 1143107200
Web Site: https://www.mahaanfoods.com
Year Founded: 1987
519612—(BOM)
Rev.: $137,155
Assets: $2,307,705
Liabilities: $51,314
Net Worth: $2,256,391
Earnings: $69,600
Emp.: 2
Fiscal Year-end: 03/31/23
Dairy Products Mfr
N.A.I.C.S.: 112120
Sanjeev Goyal (Chm & Mng Dir)

MAHACHAI HOSPITAL PCL
927/43 Sethakij-1 Road Tambol Mahachai, Amphoe Muang, Samut Sakhon, 74000, Thailand
Tel.: (66) 344249904
Web Site: https://www.mahachaihospital.com
Year Founded: 1989
M.CHAI—(THA)
Rev.: $195,852,138
Assets: $356,045,700
Liabilities: $290,931,260
Net Worth: $65,114,441
Earnings: $8,434,436
Fiscal Year-end: 12/31/23
Health Care Srvices
N.A.I.C.S.: 621999
Pongpat Patanavanich (Chm, Vice Chm, CEO & Mng Dir)

MAHAJAYA BERHAD
No 1-1-1 Wisma Mahajaya Block A, Megan Salak Park Jalan 2/125E Taman Desa Petaling, 57100, Kuala Lumpur, Malaysia
Tel.: (60) 390513333
Web Site: http://www.mahajaya.com
Sales Range: $100-124.9 Million
Emp.: 500
Civil Engineering Services
N.A.I.C.S.: 541330
Beng Hong Tan (Exec Dir)

MAHALAXMI BIKAS BANK LTD.
2nd Floor Annapurna Arcade II, Durbarmarg, Kathmandu, Nepal
Tel.: (977) 15368719
Web Site: https://www.mahalaxmibank.com
MLBL—(NEP)
Rev.: $50,779,342
Assets: $468,878,896
Liabilities: $420,025,046
Net Worth: $48,853,850
Earnings: $2,861,866
Emp.: 871
Fiscal Year-end: 07/16/23
Commercial Banking Services
N.A.I.C.S.: 522110
Rajesh Upadhyay (Chm)

MAHALAXMI RUBTECH LIMITED
YSL Avenue Opp Ketav Petrol Pump, Polytechnic Road, Ahmedabad, 380 015, Gujarat, India
Tel.: (91) 7940008000
Web Site: https://www.mrtglobal.com
MHLXMIRU—(NSE)
Rev.: $33,104,435
Assets: $25,497,523
Liabilities: $14,914,848
Net Worth: $10,582,675
Earnings: $1,023,328
Emp.: 344
Fiscal Year-end: 03/31/23
Industrial Machinery Mfr
N.A.I.C.S.: 333248
Jeetmal Bhoorchand Parekh (Chm)

MAHALAXMI SEAMLESS LTD
54-A Virwani Industrial Estate Western Express Highway, Goregoan E, Mumbai, 400 063, India
Tel.: (91) 2265013491
Web Site: http://www.mahalaxmitubes.com
513460—(BOM)
Rev.: $232,401
Assets: $496,811
Liabilities: $433,787
Net Worth: $63,024
Earnings: $46,953
Fiscal Year-end: 03/31/23
Iron & Steel Products Mfr
N.A.I.C.S.: 331210
M. P. Jalan (Chm & Mng Dir)

MAHAMAYA STEEL INDUSTRIES LIMITED
B 8-9 Sector-C Urla Industrial Complex, Sarora, Raipur, 493 221, Chhattisgarh, India
Tel.: (91) 7714910058
Web Site: https://www.mahamayagroup.in
513554—(NSE)
Rev.: $34,309,971
Assets: $30,608,774
Liabilities: $15,395,548
Net Worth: $15,213,225
Earnings: $119,874
Emp.: 212
Fiscal Year-end: 03/31/21
Metal Products Mfr
N.A.I.C.S.: 332312
Rajesh Agrawal (Mng Dir)

MAHAN AIR PJSC
Mahan Tower 21 Azadegan Street, PO Box 14515-411, MA Jenah Expressway, Tehran, Iran
Tel.: (98) 21 44 07 6081
Web Site: http://www.mahan.aero
Year Founded: 1992
Sales Range: $300-349.9 Million
Emp.: 1,400
Oil Transportation Services
N.A.I.C.S.: 481111

MAHAN INDUSTRIES LIMITED
3rd Floor D K House Under Bridge, Mithakhali, Ahmedabad, 380 006, Gujarat, India
Tel.: (91) 7926568789
Web Site: https://www.mahan.co.in
Year Founded: 1995
531515—(BOM)
Rev.: $45,311
Assets: $833,254
Liabilities: $385,034
Net Worth: $448,220
Earnings: ($438,991)
Emp.: 5
Fiscal Year-end: 03/31/21
Security Brokerage Services
N.A.I.C.S.: 523150
Yogendrakumar Prabhudayal Gupta (Chm, Mng Dir & Officer-Compliance)

MAHANAGAR GAS LIMITED

Mahanagar Gas Limited—(Continued)

MAHANAGAR GAS LIMITED
MGL House Block G-33 Bandra-Kurla Complex Bandra East, Mumbai, 400 051, India
Tel.: (91) 2266785000　In
Web Site:
　https://www.mahanagargas.com
Year Founded: 1995
MGL—(NSE)
Rev.: $330,098,469
Assets: $628,055,979
Liabilities: $186,837,310
Net Worth: $441,218,669
Earnings: $84,572,329
Emp.: 496
Fiscal Year-end: 03/31/21
Electric Power Transmission Services
N.A.I.C.S.: 221210
Sanjib Datta *(Mng Dir)*

Subsidiaries:

Unison Enviro Private Limited　(1)
S No 861 Ashoka House Ashoka Marg Ashoka Nagar, Wadala, Nashik, 422 011, India
Tel.: (91) 2536638696
Web Site: http://www.unisonenviro.com
Infrastructure Developing Services
N.A.I.C.S.: 237310

MAHANAGAR TELEPHONE NIGAM LIMITED
5th Floor 9 CGO Complex Lodhi Road, New Delhi, 110003, India
Tel.: (91) 1124319020
Web Site: http://www.mtnl.net.in
Year Founded: 1986
MTNL—(NSE)
Rev.: $255,646,755
Assets: $1,825,735,275
Liabilities: $4,015,809,525
Net Worth: ($2,190,074,250)
Earnings: ($335,961,990)
Emp.: 3,907
Fiscal Year-end: 03/31/21
Telecommunication Servicesb
N.A.I.C.S.: 517211
S. R. Sayal *(Officer-Compliance & Sec)*

Subsidiaries:

MTNL-STPI IT Services Limited　(1)
12th Floor Jeevan Bharthi Building Tower, 124 Conaught Circus, 110001, New Delhi, India　(50%)
Tel.: (91) 11 23327225
Web Site: http://www.mtnl-stpi.in
Telecommunications
N.A.I.C.S.: 517810

Mahanagar Telephone (Mauritius) Ltd.　(1)
MTML Square 63 Cyber City, Ebene, Mauritius
Tel.: (230) 52943333
Web Site: https://www.chili.mu
Telecommunication Servicesb
N.A.I.C.S.: 517810

MAHANIVESH (INDIA) LIMITED
13/34 WEA IVth Floor Main Arya Samaj Road, Karol Bagh, New Delhi, 110 005, India
Tel.: (91) 1125763401
Web Site:
　http://www.mahaniveshltd.com
Year Founded: 1994
Rev.: $13,226
Assets: $3,876,725
Liabilities: $6,930
Net Worth: $3,869,795
Earnings: $81
Fiscal Year-end: 03/31/18
Securities Brokerage Services
N.A.I.C.S.: 523150
A. K. Singh *(Chm & CEO)*

MAHARAJA SHREE UMAID MILLS LTD.
7 Munshi Premchand Sarani Hastings, Kolkata, 700 022, India
Tel.: (91) 3322230016　In
Web Site: http://www.msumindia.com
Year Founded: 1918
Rev.: $70,272,875
Assets: $129,529,355
Liabilities: $60,272,885
Net Worth: $69,256,469
Earnings: $4,470,675
Fiscal Year-end: 03/31/22
Textiles Composite Mills
N.A.I.C.S.: 315210
Lakshmi Niwas Bangur *(Chm & Mng Dir)*

Subsidiaries:

Kiran Vyapar Ltd.　(1)
Tel.: (91) 3322230016
Web Site: http://www.lnbgroup.com
Rev.: $8,137,929
Assets: $207,808,117
Liabilities: $26,155,063
Net Worth: $181,653,054
Earnings: $4,619,963
Emp.: 14
Fiscal Year-end: 03/31/2023
Financial Support Services
N.A.I.C.S.: 523999
Lakshmi Niwas Bangur *(Chm)*

MAHARASHTRA CORPORATION LIMITED
907/908 Dev Plaza SV Road, Andheri W, Mumbai, 400058, India
Tel.: (91) 2267424815
Web Site: https://mcl.visagar.com
Year Founded: 1982
505523—(BOM)
Rev.: $135,615
Assets: $3,424,843
Liabilities: $12,721
Net Worth: $3,412,122
Earnings: $86,374
Fiscal Year-end: 03/31/23
Textile Products Distr
N.A.I.C.S.: 424990
Kanwarlal Rathi *(Exec Dir)*

MAHARASHTRA POLYBUTENES LTD.
Plot No R-802 TTC Industrial Area Thane Belapur Road Mahape, Navi Mumbai, 400 701, India
Tel.: (91) 02227782210　In
Web Site:
　http://www.maharashtrapoly.com
Year Founded: 1988
Polybutenes Mfr
N.A.I.C.S.: 326140
Kumari Shikha *(Sr Mgr)*

MAHARASHTRA SEAMLESS LTD
Pipe Nagar Village Sukeli N H-17 B K G Road, Dist Raigad, Gurgaon, 402 126, Maharashtra, India
Tel.: (91) 2194238511
Web Site: https://www.jindal.com
MAHSEAMLES—(NSE)
Rev.: $327,019,302
Assets: $731,041,721
Liabilities: $280,756,012
Net Worth: $450,285,709
Earnings: $16,576,956
Emp.: 1,444
Fiscal Year-end: 03/31/21
Seamless Pipe & Tube Mfr
N.A.I.C.S.: 331210
D. P. Jindal *(Chm)*

MAHASAGAR TRAVELS LIMITED
Kalva Chowk Jayshree Cinema Road, Junagadh, 362001, Gujarat, India
Tel.: (91) 2852650427
Web Site:
　https://mahasagartravels.com
526795—(BOM)
Rev.: $6,642,758
Assets: $1,744,237
Liabilities: $1,811,794
Net Worth: ($67,558)
Earnings: $22,565
Emp.: 106
Fiscal Year-end: 03/31/23
Travel Arrangement Services
N.A.I.C.S.: 561510
Bhagchand G. Sukhwani *(CEO & Co-Mng Dir)*

MAHASHREE TRADING LIMITED
Unit-B/21 Grd Floor Raj Industrial Complex Raj Industrial Complex, Premises Co Op Soc Ltd Military Road Marol Andheri E, Mumbai, 400059, India
Tel.: (91) 2224124591
Web Site:
　https://www.mahashreetrading.co.in
512337—(BOM)
Rev.: $137,506
Assets: $188,848
Liabilities: $6,964
Net Worth: $181,884
Earnings: ($425,754)
Fiscal Year-end: 03/31/21
Financial Investment Services
N.A.I.C.S.: 523999
Rajesh Malpani *(Exec Dir)*

MAHAVEER INFOWAY LTD.
7-1-24 /2/C 301/A Dhansi Surabhi Complex Greenlands, Hyderabad, 500 016, Andhra Pradesh, India
Tel.: (91) 4066134054
Web Site: https://www.minfy.com
539383—(BOM)
Rev.: $508,967
Assets: $1,051,302
Liabilities: $525,215
Net Worth: $526,087
Earnings: ($38,071)
Fiscal Year-end: 03/31/23
Information Technology Services
N.A.I.C.S.: 519290
Prasanna Ramesh Dixit *(Dir-Bus Dev & Ops)*

MAHAVIR GREEN CROP LIMITED
Mahavir Estate 40 Nr C T M Mills Narol-Naroda High Way Amraiwadi, Ahmedabad, 380 026, Gujarat, India
Tel.: (91) 79 25856971
Web Site:
　http://www.narmadaagroindltd.com
Sales Range: Less than $1 Million
Seed Production Services
N.A.I.C.S.: 111422

MAHAVIR INDUSTRIES LIMITED
TO- D 44 / 253 AAMANTRAN CHS Ground Floor Sector 2, Charkop Kandivali west, Mumbai, 400067, India
Tel.: (91) 2265350073
Web Site: http://www.miltd.co.in
531648—(BOM)
Rev.: $18,482
Assets: $132,602
Liabilities: $132,227
Net Worth: $375
Earnings: ($505)
Fiscal Year-end: 03/31/20
Wire Product Mfr
N.A.I.C.S.: 332618
Nirmala Bansal *(Mng Dir)*

INTERNATIONAL PUBLIC

MAHAWELI REACH HOTEL
Tel.: (94) 812472727
Web Site: https://www.mahaweli.com
Year Founded: 1970
MRH.N0000—(COL)
Rev.: $1,677,535
Assets: $12,729,048
Liabilities: $5,110,142
Net Worth: $7,618,906
Earnings: ($40,075)
Emp.: 227
Fiscal Year-end: 03/31/23
Hotel & Restaurant Operator
N.A.I.C.S.: 721110
M. U. Maniku *(Chm)*

MAHDIA GOLD CORP.
c/o Ken Wise & Associates 1240 Bay Street Suite 202, Toronto, M5R 2A7, ON, Canada
Tel.: (416) 924-6231　AB
Web Site:
　http://www.mahdiagold.com
Year Founded: 1987
Gold Exploration Services
N.A.I.C.S.: 212220
Edward K. Chan *(Interim CEO)*

MAHE HUBERT SA
Z I De Lann Sevelin 516 Rue Jacques Ange Gabriel, 56850, Caudan, Morbihan, France
Tel.: (33) 297767075
Rev.: $12,700,000
Emp.: 102
Demolitions, Sawing & Removal of Rubble
N.A.I.C.S.: 238910
David Poulain *(Dir)*

MAHESH DEVELOPERS LIMITED
Uma Shikhar Ground Floor13th Road Behind Khar Telephone Exchange, Khar West, Mumbai, 400052, India
Tel.: (91) 2226000038
Web Site:
　https://www.maheshdevelopers.com
Year Founded: 1970
542677—(BOM)
Rev.: $983
Assets: $3,627,023
Liabilities: $2,911,968
Net Worth: $715,055
Earnings: ($18,482)
Fiscal Year-end: 03/31/21
Construction Services
N.A.I.C.S.: 236220
Mahesh Ratilal Sapariya *(Mng Dir)*

MAHESHWARI LOGISTICS LIMITED
Mll House A2-3/2 Opp Upl 1St Phase Gidc, Vapi, Valsad, 396195, India
Tel.: (91) 2602431024
Web Site: https://www.mlpl.biz
Year Founded: 2006
MAHESHWARI—(NSE)
Rev.: $92,544,229
Assets: $50,175,093
Liabilities: $31,231,678
Net Worth: $18,943,415
Earnings: $1,267,744
Emp.: 562
Fiscal Year-end: 03/31/21
Logistic Services
N.A.I.C.S.: 541614
Vinay Maheshwari *(Chm)*

MAHICKRA CHEMICALS LIMITED
Plot No-1201/1202 Phase-3, Vatva Gidc, Ahmedabad, 382445, India
Tel.: (91) 7948994608
Web Site: https://www.mahickra.com

AND PRIVATE COMPANIES

MAHICKRA—(NSE)
Rev.: $12,216,912
Assets: $7,875,907
Liabilities: $4,200,328
Net Worth: $3,675,579
Earnings: $424,158
Fiscal Year-end: 03/31/21
Dyestuff Mfr & Distr
N.A.I.C.S.: 325130
Mitesh Gandhi *(Chm & Mng Dir)*

MAHINDRA & MAHINDRA LIMITED

Gateway Building St Steven Street
Apollo Bunder, Mumbai, 400 001, India
Tel.: (91) 8001004175
Web Site: https://www.mahindra.com
Year Founded: 1945
MHID—(LSE)
Rev.: $12,435,843,420
Assets: $23,766,397,200
Liabilities: $16,009,749,210
Net Worth: $7,756,647,990
Earnings: $990,035,865
Emp.: 21,297
Fiscal Year-end: 03/31/22
Automobile Mfr
N.A.I.C.S.: 336110
Anand G. Mahindra *(Chm)*

Subsidiaries:

Aerostaff Australia Pty Limited (1)
32 Network Drive, Port Melbourne, 3207, Australia
Tel.: (61) 3 8671 2300
Web Site: http://www.aerostaff.com.au
Sales Range: $25-49.9 Million
Emp.: 13
Precision Sheet Metal Component Mfr
N.A.I.C.S.: 332312
Stephen Roebuck *(CEO)*

Bristlecone (Malaysia) Sdn Bhd (1)
Level 40 Tower 2 Petronas Twin Tower, 50088, Kuala Lumpur, Federal Territory, Malaysia
Tel.: (60) 321684428
Sales Range: $25-49.9 Million
Emp.: 4
Engineering Consulting Services
N.A.I.C.S.: 541330
Uday Tata *(Mgr-Bus Dev)*

Bristlecone (Singapore) Pte. Limited (1)
12 Marina Boulevard 17-01 Tower 3 Marina Bay Financial Centre, 3 Temasek Avenue, Singapore, 018982, Singapore
Tel.: (65) 6 809 7426
Web Site: http://www.bcone.com
Sales Range: $25-49.9 Million
Emp.: 10
Engineering Consulting Services
N.A.I.C.S.: 541330
Gaurav Bhardwaj *(Mgr-Bus Dev)*

Bristlecone (UK) Limited (1)
8 The Square, Stockley Park, Uxbridge, UB11 1FW, Middlesex, United Kingdom
Tel.: (44) 2071666319
Information Technology Services
N.A.I.C.S.: 541512

Bristlecone GmbH (1)
Kennedyallee 97 A, 60596, Frankfurt am Main, Hessen, Germany
Tel.: (49) 62278147418
Information Technology Services
N.A.I.C.S.: 541511

Bristlecone Inc (1)
10 Almaden Blvd Ste 990, San Jose, CA 95113
Tel.: (650) 386-4000
Web Site: https://www.bristlecone.com
Sales Range: $25-49.9 Million
Emp.: 35
Business Process & Technology Consulting Firm
N.A.I.C.S.: 541611
Tom Rauch *(Mng Partner-Client Engagement-North America & VP)*

Bristlecone India Limited (1)
2nd Floor Techniplex - I Techniplex Complex Off Veer Savarkar Flyover, Goregaon W, Mumbai, 400062, Maharashtra, India
Tel.: (91) 226 722 7000
Web Site: https://www.bristlecone.com
Analytics & Data Management Services
N.A.I.C.S.: 541618
Ashok Santhanam *(Pres & CEO)*

Bristlecone Limited (1)
10 Almaden Blvd Ste 990, San Jose, CA 95113
Tel.: (650) 386-4000
Web Site: https://www.bristlecone.com
Information Technology Consulting Services
N.A.I.C.S.: 541512
Nancy Faber *(Mgr-Global Supply Chain)*

Subsidiary (Non-US):

Bristlecone International AG (2)
Rheinweg 7, 8200, Schaffhausen, Switzerland
Tel.: (41) 526248717
Information Technology Services
N.A.I.C.S.: 541511

CIE Automotive India Limited (1)
Suite F9D Grand Hyatt Plaza Lobby Level, Off Western Express Highway Santacruz E, Mumbai, 400055, India
Tel.: (91) 2262411031
Web Site: https://www.cie-india.com
Rev.: $1,152,373,950
Assets: $1,358,925,750
Liabilities: $649,589,850
Net Worth: $709,335,900
Earnings: $53,630,850
Emp.: 4,113
Fiscal Year-end: 12/31/2021
Forged Products Mfr
N.A.I.C.S.: 332111
Ander Arenaza Alvarez *(Exec Dir)*

Erkunt Sanayi A.S. (1)
Bahcekapi Mahallesi Fen Isleri Caddesi No 2, Etimesgut, 06370, Ankara, Turkiye
Tel.: (90) 3123972500
Web Site: http://www.erkunt.com.tr
Ductile Iron Casting Mfr & Distr
N.A.I.C.S.: 331511
Tuna Armagan *(Chm & CEO)*

Erkunt Traktor Sanayii A.S. (1)
Organize Sanayi Bolgesi Bati Hun Cad No 2, Sincan, 06930, Ankara, Turkiye
Tel.: (90) 3122674488
Web Site: http://www.armatrac.com
Tractor Mfr & Distr
N.A.I.C.S.: 333111

Gipps Aero Pty Limited (1)
Latrobe Regional Airport, PO Box 881, Morwell, 3840, VIC, Australia
Tel.: (61) 3 5172 1200
Web Site: http://www.gippsaero.com
Sales Range: $50-74.9 Million
Emp.: 110
Aircraft Components Mfr
N.A.I.C.S.: 336413
Marguerite Morgan *(Mgr-Global Sls)*

Gromax Agri Equipment Limited (1)
Near Vishwamitri Railway Over bridge Vishwamitry Twp Wing A Viswamitri, Vadodara, 390011, Gujarat, India
Tel.: (91) 2652339547
Web Site: http://www.trakstartractor.com
Armored Vehicle Mfr & Distr
N.A.I.C.S.: 336992

Hisarlar Makina Sanayi ve Ticaret Anonim Sirketi (1)
Hisar Mh 1047 Cd No 2, Tepebasi, 26550, Eskisehir, Turkiye
Tel.: (90) 2224112430
Web Site: http://www.hisarlar.com.tr
Emp.: 800
Agricultural Machinery Mfr & Distr
N.A.I.C.S.: 333111

Holiday Club Resorts Oy (1)
Hitsaajankatu 22, 00810, Helsinki, Finland
Tel.: (358) 300870900
Web Site: http://www.holidayclubresorts.com
Holiday & Tourism Accommodation Services
N.A.I.C.S.: 721110
Maisa Romanainen *(Mng Dir)*

Mahindra & Mahindra Financial Services Limited (1)
Mahindra Towers A Wing 3rd Floor, PK Kurne Chowk Worli, Mumbai, 400 018, India
Tel.: (91) 2266526000
Web Site: https://www.mahindrafinance.com
Rev.: $1,661,273,250
Assets: $11,684,535,135
Liabilities: $9,517,526,655
Net Worth: $2,167,008,480
Earnings: $106,508,220
Emp.: 19,952
Fiscal Year-end: 03/31/2021
Rural & Semi-Urban Financial Lending Services
N.A.I.C.S.: 522291
Dhananjay Mungale *(Chm)*

Subsidiary (Domestic):

Mahindra Insurance Brokers Limited (2)
Ground Floor Sadhana House Behind Mahindra Towers, 570 P B Marg Worli, Mumbai, 400 018, Maharashtra, India **(100%)**
Tel.: (91) 2266423800
Web Site: https://www.mahindrainsurance.com
Sales Range: $50-74.9 Million
Emp.: 100
Insurance Brokerage Services
N.A.I.C.S.: 524210
Jaideep Devare *(Mng Dir)*

Mahindra Rural Housing Finance Limited (2)
Sadhana House Behind Mahindra Towers Ground Floor 570, P B Marg Worli, Mumbai, 400 018, India
Tel.: (91) 22 6642 3800
Housing Loan Mortgage Services
N.A.I.C.S.: 522299

Mahindra & Mahindra Limited - Defense Systems Division (1)
1st Floor 2A Bhikaji Cama Place, New Delhi, 110066, India
Tel.: (91) 114 122 0300
Web Site: https://www.mahindra.com
Aircraft Part Mfr
N.A.I.C.S.: 336413

Mahindra & Mahindra South Africa (Proprietary) Limited (1)
Southdowns Ridge Office Park Block A 1st Floor, CNR John Vorster and Nellmapius Dr Southdowns, Centurion, 169, Highveld Park, South Africa
Tel.: (27) 12 661 3161
Web Site: https://www.mahindra.co.za
Sales Range: $25-49.9 Million
Emp.: 40
Cars Import & Distr
N.A.I.C.S.: 441110
Aviansh Bapat *(CEO)*

Mahindra Aerospace Private Limited (1)
Touch Down Building 3rd Floor Hal Industrial Area, Vibhutipura Marathahalli, Bengaluru, 560037, India **(91.59%)**
Tel.: (91) 80 42131459
Sales Range: $25-49.9 Million
Emp.: 5
Aircraft Components Mfr
N.A.I.C.S.: 336413
Arvind Mehra *(CEO)*

Mahindra Agri Solutions Limited (1)
Farm Equipment Sector 5th Floor EPU Building Gate No 4 Akurli Road, Kandivali East, Mumbai, 400101, Maharashtra, India
Tel.: (91) 2228029086
Web Site: http://www.mahindraagri.com
Farming Management Services
N.A.I.C.S.: 115116
Pawan Kumar Goenka *(Chm)*

Mahindra Automotive Australia Pty. Ltd. (1)
1 Kiora Road, Miranda, 2228, NSW, Australia
Tel.: (61) 2 8545 8380
Web Site: http://www.mahindraautomotive.com.au
Commercial Vehicle Distr
N.A.I.C.S.: 441110

Mahindra Bangladesh Pvt. Ltd. (1)
Taj Casilina 4th Floor SW I 4 25 Gulshan Avenue, Dhaka, 1212, Bangladesh
Tel.: (880) 29853346
Web Site: http://www.mahindra.com.bd
Automobile Mfr
N.A.I.C.S.: 336110

Mahindra Castings Limited (1)
Bhosari Industrial Estate, Pune, 411026, Maharashtra, India
Tel.: (91) 2027120811
Web Site: http://www.hinoday.com
Sales Range: $200-249.9 Million
Emp.: 1,000
Ductile Iron Castings Mfr
N.A.I.C.S.: 331511
Vinayak Kadaskar *(Gen Mgr-HR)*

Mahindra Consulting Engineers Limited (1)
Mahindra Towers Ground Floor No 17/18 Pattullous Road, Chennai, 600 002, India
Tel.: (91) 442 854 2325
Web Site: https://www.mahindrace.com
Sales Range: $25-49.9 Million
Emp.: 110
Engineering Consulting Services
N.A.I.C.S.: 541330

Mahindra Conveyor Systems Private Limited (1)
Gat No 316-319 Ambadvet Pune-Paud Road, Pimpri, Pune, 412108, Maharastra, India
Tel.: (91) 206 792 8400
Web Site: https://www.mahindra-tsubaki.com
Material Handling Equipment & Systems Distr
N.A.I.C.S.: 423490

Mahindra Emirates Vehicle Armouring FZ-LLC (1)
Al Jazeera Al Hamra FreeZone WFZ-08, PO Box 39893, Rakia Industrial Park, Ras al Khaimah, United Arab Emirates
Tel.: (971) 72432824
Web Site: http://www.mahindraarmored.com
Armored Vehicle Mfr & Distr
N.A.I.C.S.: 336992
Rajiv Gupta *(CEO)*

Mahindra Engineering Services Limited (1)
Gateway Bldg Apollo Bunder, 28849588, 400 001, Mumbai, India
Tel.: (91) 2222021031
Web Site: http://www.mahindraengineering.com
Aerospace & Automotive Engineering Services
N.A.I.C.S.: 541330
Hemant Luthra *(Pres)*

Subsidiary (Non-US):

Mahindra Engineering Services (Europe) Limited (2)
Atrium Court Ring, Bracknell, RG12 1BW, Berkshire, United Kingdom
Tel.: (44) 1344 397590
Engineeering Services
N.A.I.C.S.: 541330

Mahindra Europe s.r.l. (1)
Via Cancelliera 35, Ariccia, 00040, Rome, Italy
Tel.: (39) 0693490043
Web Site: http://www.mahindraeurope.com
Cars Import & Distrimport
N.A.I.C.S.: 441110
Pawan Goenka *(Pres)*

Mahindra First Choice Wheels Limited (1)
Mahindra Towers Ground Floor Dr G M Bhosale Marg, P K Kurne Chowk Worli, Mumbai, 400 018, Maharashtra, India
Tel.: (91) 2224936505
Web Site: http://www.mahindrafirstchoice.com
Used Car Dealers
N.A.I.C.S.: 441120
Anand G. Mahindra *(Chm)*

Mahindra Forgings Europe AG (1)
Ulmer Strasse 112, 73431, Aalen, Baden-Wurttemberg, Germany
Tel.: (49) 73615970
Web Site: http://www.mahindraforgings.eu

MAHINDRA & MAHINDRA LIMITED

Mahindra & Mahindra Limited—(Continued)
Sales Range: $400-449.9 Million
Emp.: 2,000
Iron & Steel Forgings Mfr
N.A.I.C.S.: 331110
Burkard Rausch *(Dir-Fin & HR)*

Mahindra Gears & Transmissions Private Limited
Plot No 01 31 to 34 Galaxy Industrial Estate, Shapar Kotdasangani, Rajkot, 360 024, Gujarat, India
Tel.: (91) 2827252590
Sales Range: $200-249.9 Million
Emp.: 750
Gears & Transmission Components Mfr
N.A.I.C.S.: 333612
Romesh Kaul *(Mng Dir)*

Mahindra Graphic Research Design s.r.l. (1)
Via Padova 16, 10092, Beinasco, Torino, Italy
Tel.: (39) 0113499487
Web Site: http://www.mgrd.it
Sales Range: $25-49.9 Million
Emp.: 40
Industrial Design Services
N.A.I.C.S.: 541420
Elisabetta Fedon *(CFO)*

Mahindra Gujarat Tractor Limited (1)
Near Vishwamitri Railway Overbridge, Vishwamitri, Vadodara, 390011, Gujarat, India
Tel.: (91) 265 231 1617
Web Site: http://www.mahindragujarat.com
Emp.: 400
Tractor Mfr
N.A.I.C.S.: 333924
Anand Mahindra *(CEO)*

Mahindra Holidays & Resorts India, Ltd. (1)
Mahindra Towers 2nd Floor 17/18 Pathullos Road Mount Road, Chennai, 600 002, Tamilnadu, India
Tel.: (91) 4435041000
Web Site: https://www.clubmahindra.com
Rev.: $252,151,495
Assets: $1,163,182,293
Liabilities: $1,150,783,848
Net Worth: $12,398,445
Earnings: ($1,911,601)
Emp.: 4,702
Fiscal Year-end: 03/31/2021
Hotel & Resort Owner & Operator
N.A.I.C.S.: 721110
Arun Kumar Nanda *(Chm)*

Subsidiary (Non-US):

BAH Hotelanlagen AG (2)
Hilberstrasse 8, 6080, Innsbruck, Tirol, Austria
Tel.: (43) 512377600
Web Site: http://www.innsbruck-hotels.at
Sales Range: $10-24.9 Million
Emp.: 17
Home Management Services
N.A.I.C.S.: 721110
Klaus Stiebleichinger *(Owner)*

Mahindra Intertrade Limited (2)
Mahindra Towers P K Kurne Chowk Worli, Mumbai, 400 018, India
Tel.: (91) 222 493 5185
Web Site: https://www.mahindraaccelo.com
Material Handling Equipment & Systems Distr
N.A.I.C.S.: 423830
Sumit Issar *(Mng Dir)*

Subsidiary (Domestic):

Mahindra Auto Steel Private Limited (2)
Mahindra Towers P K Kurne Chowk, Worli, Mumbai, 400018, India
Tel.: (91) 2224935185
Flat Steel Mfr
N.A.I.C.S.: 331221
Zhooben Bhiwandiwala *(Chm)*

Subsidiary (Non-US):

Mahindra MiddleEast Electrical Steel Service Centre (FZC) (2)
P3 11-12 Sharjah Airport International Free Zone, PO Box 8114, Sharjah, United Arab Emirates
Tel.: (971) 6 557 3435
Web Site: http://www.mahindra.com
Sales Range: $25-49.9 Million
Emp.: 20
Steel Distr
N.A.I.C.S.: 423510

Subsidiary (Domestic):

Mahindra Steel Service Centre Limited (2)
Mahindra Towers P K Kurne Chowk, Worli, Mumbai, 400 018, Maharashtra, India
Tel.: (91) 2224948131
Emp.: 50
Steel Processing Services
N.A.I.C.S.: 238120
Sumit Issar *(Mng Dir)*

Mahindra Lifespace Developers Ltd. (1)
5thFloor Mahindra Towers, Mumbai, 400 018, India
Tel.: (91) 2267478600
Web Site: https://www.mahindralifespaces.com
Rev.: $25,637,280
Assets: $351,171,339
Liabilities: $122,795,932
Net Worth: $228,375,406
Earnings: ($9,752,516)
Emp.: 507
Fiscal Year-end: 03/31/2021
Real Estate Construction
N.A.I.C.S.: 236220
Suhas Kulkarni *(Gen Counsel & Sec)*

Subsidiary (Domestic):

Mahindra Residential Developers Limited (2)
Canopy Block-A 2nd Floor Unit - II 2nd Ave Mahindra World City, Natham Sub Chengalpet, Chennai, 603 002, India
Tel.: (91) 44 47410000
Web Site: http://www.mahindralifespaces.com
Sales Range: $25-49.9 Million
Emp.: 8
Property Development Services
N.A.I.C.S.: 531390
Vijay Nadarajan *(Gen Mgr-Sls & Mktg)*

Mahindra World City (Jaipur) Limited (2)
PO Mahindra World City, Tehsil Sanganer, Jaipur, 302037, Rajasthan, India
Tel.: (91) 141 668 3454
Web Site: https://www.mahindraworldcity.com
Sales Range: $25-49.9 Million
Emp.: 40
Industrial Building Construction Services
N.A.I.C.S.: 236210

Mahindra World City Developers Limited (2)
Administrative Block Central Avenue Mahindra World City, Chengelpet Taluk, Kanchipuram, 603 004, Tamilnadu, India
Tel.: (91) 4449400000
Web Site: http://www.mahindraworldcity.com
Real Estate Development Services
N.A.I.C.S.: 531390

Mahindra Logistics Limited (1)
Mahindra Tower P K Kurne chowk Worli, Goregaon East, Mumbai, 400018, Maharashtra, India
Tel.: (91) 222 871 6800
Web Site: https://www.mahindralogistics.com
Logistics Consulting Servies
N.A.I.C.S.: 541614
Ravi Begur *(Head-Bus Dev, Strategy & People)*

Mahindra Navistar Automotives Limited (1)
Marketing Department 3rd Floor Mahindra Towers, Worli, Mumbai, 400018, Maharashtra, India
Tel.: (91) 2027473600
Web Site: http://www.mahindranavistar.com
Sales Range: $150-199.9 Million
Emp.: 800
Trucks Mfr
N.A.I.C.S.: 333924

Mahindra Punjab Tractors Private Limited (1)
Phase IV Industrial Area SAS Nagar, Mohali, 160055, India
Tel.: (91) 17 2227 1620
Web Site: http://www.mahindratractor.com
Tractor Mfr & Whslr
N.A.I.C.S.: 333111
Viren Poply *(CEO)*

Mahindra Retail Private Limited (1)
No 1 Prim Park Primrose Road Off MG Road, Bengaluru, 560025, Karnataka, India
Tel.: (91) 8042665042
Web Site: http://www.momandme.in
Emp.: 80
Baby Care Products Retailer
N.A.I.C.S.: 458110
Prakash Wakankar *(CEO)*

Mahindra Tractor Assembly Inc. (1)
1055 W Square Lake Rd, Troy, MI 48098
Web Site: http://www.genze.com
Automobile Mfr & Distr
N.A.I.C.S.: 336110

Mahindra Two Wheelers Limited (1)
D-1 Block Plot No 18/2 MIDC, Chinchwad, Pune, 411 019, Maharashtra, India (80%)
Tel.: (91) 20 27602029
Web Site: http://www.mahindratwowheelers.com
Two Wheelers Mfr
N.A.I.C.S.: 336991
Anoop Mathur *(Pres)*

Subsidiary (Non-US):

Peugeot Motocycles S.A. (2)
Rue Du 17 Novembre, 25350, Mandeure, France (51%)
Tel.: (33) 38 136 8000
Web Site: https://peugeot-motocycles.com
Emp.: 300
Motor Vehicle Mfr & Distr
N.A.I.C.S.: 336110
Costantino Sambuy *(CEO)*

Mahindra USA Inc (1)
9020 Jackrabbit Rd, Houston, TX 77095
Tel.: (281) 449-7771
Web Site: http://www.mahindrausa.com
Sales Range: $25-49.9 Million
Emp.: 30
Farm Equipment Mfr
N.A.I.C.S.: 333111
Anjanikumar Choudhari *(Chm)*

Mahindra Vehicle Manufacturers Limited (1)
3rd Floor Mahindra Towers Dr G M Bhosle Marg P K Kurne, Chowk Road No 13 Worli, Mumbai, 400018, Maharashtra, India
Tel.: (91) 2228849588
Sales Range: $400-449.9 Million
Emp.: 180
Automobile Parts Mfr
N.A.I.C.S.: 336390

Metal Castello S.P.A (1)
Via Don Fornasini 12, Castel di casio, 40030, Bologna, Italy
Tel.: (39) 05 342 0511
Web Site: https://www.metalcastello.it
Sales Range: $50-74.9 Million
Emp.: 250
Gear Mfr
N.A.I.C.S.: 333612

NBS International Limited (1)
Standford Bldg S V Road & Juhu Lane Junction, Andheri W Nr Shoppers Stop, Mumbai, 400 058, Maharashtra, India
Tel.: (91) 865 751 7839
Web Site: https://www.nbsmahindra.com
Sales Range: $25-49.9 Million
Emp.: 50
Automotive Distr
N.A.I.C.S.: 423110

Origin Direct Asia (Shanghai) Trading Co., Ltd. (1)
Room E 22/F 238 East Nandang Road, Xu Hui District, Shanghai, 200030, China
Tel.: (86) 2152986007
Web Site: http://www.origindirectasia.com
Fruit Product Distr
N.A.I.C.S.: 424480

INTERNATIONAL PUBLIC

Origin Fruit Direct B.V. (1)
Albert Plesmanweg 250 - Port 2450, 3088 GD, Rotterdam, Netherlands
Tel.: (31) 882449300
Web Site: http://www.originfruitdirect.nl
Fruit Product Distr
N.A.I.C.S.: 424480

Origin Fruit Services South America SpA (1)
Limache 3405 -Office 126, Vina del Mar, Chile
Tel.: (56) 322158605
Fruit Product Distr
N.A.I.C.S.: 424480

Pininfarina S.p.A. (1)
Via Nazionale 30, Cambiano, 10020, Turin, Italy (76.14%)
Tel.: (39) 0119438111
Web Site: https://www.pininfarina.it
Rev.: $82,287,615
Assets: $126,746,750
Liabilities: $84,696,963
Net Worth: $42,049,788
Earnings: ($30,015,347)
Emp.: 639
Fiscal Year-end: 12/31/2020
Automotive Design, Engineering & Mfr
N.A.I.C.S.: 336110
Paolo Pininfarina *(Chm)*

Subsidiary (Non-US):

Pininfarina Deutschland GmbH (2)
Frankfurter Ring 81, 80807, Munich, Germany (100%)
Tel.: (49) 893 577 5060
Web Site: https://www.pininfarina.it
Automotive Design, Engineering & Mfr
N.A.I.C.S.: 336110
Rocco Venneri *(Mng Dir & CFO)*

Subsidiary (Domestic):

Pininfarina Extra s.r.l. (2)
Via Nazionale 30, Cambiano, 10020, Turin, Italy (100%)
Tel.: (39) 0119438111
Web Site: http://www.pininfarina.it
Automobile Design, Engineering & Mfr
N.A.I.C.S.: 336110

Schoeneweiss & Co. GmbH (1)
Delsterner Strasse 170, 58091, Hagen, Germany
Tel.: (49) 2 331 7860
Web Site: https://schoeneweiss-gmbh.de
Sales Range: $100-124.9 Million
Emp.: 450
Forgings Mfr
N.A.I.C.S.: 331110

Ssangyong European Parts Center B.V. (1)
IABC 5253-5254, Breda, 4814 RD, Netherlands
Tel.: (31) 765247799
Sales Range: $50-74.9 Million
Emp.: 5
Automobile Parts Distr
N.A.I.C.S.: 423120
S. T. Yang *(Gen Mgr)*

Stokes Group Limited (1)
Cochrane Road, Dudley, DY2 0SE, West Midlands, United Kingdom
Tel.: (44) 1384342550
Web Site: http://www.stokesforgings.com
Sales Range: $50-74.9 Million
Emp.: 150
Iron & Steel Forgings Mfr
N.A.I.C.S.: 331110
Paul Morgan *(Mng Dir)*

Subsidiary (Domestic):

Stokes Forgings Dudley Limited (2)
Cochrane Road, Dudley, DY2 0SF, West Midlands, United Kingdom
Tel.: (44) 1384342550
Web Site: http://www.stokesforgings.com
Sales Range: $25-49.9 Million
Emp.: 200
Forgings Mfr
N.A.I.C.S.: 331110
Paul Morgan *(Mng Dir)*

Swaraj Engines Ltd (1)
Phase-IV Industrial Area S A S Nagar, Mo-

hali, 160055, Punjab, India **(52.13%)**
Tel.: (91) 1722271620
Web Site: https://www.swarajenterprise.com
Rev.: $156,675,806
Assets: $62,981,755
Liabilities: $21,257,009
Net Worth: $41,724,747
Earnings: $14,943,242
Emp.: 335
Fiscal Year-end: 03/31/2022
Diesel Engine Mfr
N.A.I.C.S.: 333618
Rajesh Kumar Kapila *(Compliance Officer & Sec)*

Tech Mahindra Limited **(1)**
Gateway Building Apollo Bunder, Mumbai, 400001, Maharashtra, India
Tel.: (91) 2066018100
Web Site: https://www.techmahindra.com
Rev.: $6,389,329,177
Assets: $5,533,637,072
Liabilities: $2,129,200,887
Net Worth: $3,404,436,185
Earnings: $582,339,188
Emp.: 106,222
Fiscal Year-end: 03/31/2023
Software Development Services
N.A.I.C.S.: 541690
C. P. Gurnani *(CEO & Mng Dir)*

Subsidiary (US):

DigitalOnUs Inc. **(2)**
84 W Santa Clara St Ste 740, San Jose, CA 95113
Tel.: (408) 228-3490
Web Site: https://www.digitalonus.com
Sales Range: $10-24.9 Million
Emp.: 178
Information Technology Development Services
N.A.I.C.S.: 541512
Surinder Chawla *(CEO)*

Subsidiary (Non-US):

Leadcom de Colombia S.A **(2)**
Cra 49 No 102a-26 Barrio Pasadena, Bogota, Colombia
Tel.: (57) 1 2574900
Web Site: http://www.leadcom-is.com
Telecommunication Network Services
N.A.I.C.S.: 517111

Subsidiary (US):

Lightbridge Communications Corporation **(2)**
2201 Coperative Way Ste 600, Herndon, VA 20171
Tel.: (703) 788-6750
Web Site: https://www.lcc.com
Emp.: 5,000
Telecommunication Servicesb
N.A.I.C.S.: 517810

Subsidiary (Non-US):

LCC Belgium N.V. **(3)**
Leuvensesteenweg 555, 1930, Zaventem, Belgium
Tel.: (32) 27215985
Web Site: http://www.lcc.com
Computer Network & Business Consulting Services
N.A.I.C.S.: 541690
Amaury Desgress du Lou *(Mng Dir)*

LCC, United Kingdom, Limited **(3)**
450 Bath Road Longford, Heathrow, UB7 0EB, United Kingdom
Tel.: (44) 2087578920
Web Site: http://www.lcc.com
Computer Networking & Business Consulting Services
N.A.I.C.S.: 541690
Alejandro Medina *(Mng Dir-Engrg Div)*

Leadcom Integrated Solutions Limited **(3)**
Hahagana 10 st, Or Yehuda, Israel
Tel.: (972) 3 970 6000
Web Site: https://www.leadcom-is.com
Sales Range: $10-24.9 Million
Integrated Telecommunications Products Mfr
N.A.I.C.S.: 334290

Subsidiary (Non-US):

Leadcom Costa Rica S.A **(4)**
Sabana Sur Calle Morenos 150 Mt Sur del Supermecado AMPM, Edificio Color Papaya, San Jose, Costa Rica
Tel.: (506) 40302587
Web Site: http://www.leadcom-is.com
Telecommunication Network Services
N.A.I.C.S.: 517111

Leadcom Peru S.A.C **(4)**
Canaval y Moreyra # 340, San Isidro, Lima, Lima 27, Peru
Tel.: (51) 4402014
Web Site: http://www.leadcom-is.com
Telecommunication Network Services
N.A.I.C.S.: 517111

Leadcom Tanzania Ltd. **(4)**
2379/34 Winding Avenue Oyster Bay, Dar es Salaam, Tanzania
Tel.: (255) 787563365
Web Site: http://www.leadcom-is.com
Telecommunication Engineering Services
N.A.I.C.S.: 517810

Leadcom Telecomunicationes de Chile S.A **(4)**
San Antonio 378 Oficina 808, Santiago, Chile
Tel.: (56) 2 26567886
Web Site: http://www.leadcom-is.com
Telecommunication Network Services
N.A.I.C.S.: 517111

Leadcom del Ecuador S.A **(4)**
Kenedy Norte Manzana 1010 Solares 7 8 y 9, Guayaquil, Ecuador
Tel.: (593) 4 2684315
Web Site: http://www.leadcom-is.com
Telecommunication Network Services
N.A.I.C.S.: 517111

STA Burkina **(4)**
06 BP 9286, Ouagadougou, Burkina Faso
Tel.: (226) 77049081
Web Site: http://www.leadcom-is.com
Telecommunication Network Services
N.A.I.C.S.: 517111

STA Cote D'Ivoire **(4)**
01 Abidjan 01, PO Box 8240, Abidjan, Cote d'Ivoire
Tel.: (225) 21353446
Web Site: http://www.sta-ci.com
Telecommunication Network Services
N.A.I.C.S.: 517111

Subsidiary (US):

Mahindra Satyam **(2)**
2901 Tasman Dr Ste 106, Santa Clara, CA 95054
Tel.: (408) 988-3100
Sales Range: $25-49.9 Million
Emp.: 20
Custom Computer Programming Services
N.A.I.C.S.: 541511
Saurabh Misra *(Acct Mgr)*

Subsidiary (Non-US):

S&V Management Consultants NV **(2)**
Bellevue 5 box 801, 8th floor, Gent, 9050, East Flanders, Belgium
Tel.: (32) 92202336
Web Site: http://www.pwc.be
Sales Range: $25-49.9 Million
Emp.: 60
Management Consulting Services
N.A.I.C.S.: 541618

SOFGEN HOLDINGS LIMITED **(2)**
Arch Makariou III 229 Meliza Court 4th floor, 3105, Limassol, Cyprus
Tel.: (357) 25 585 069
Web Site: http://sofgen.com
Bank Systems & Information Technology Consulting Services
N.A.I.C.S.: 541690
Eva Agathangelou *(Dir)*

Subsidiary (Non-US):

SC Compania SOFGEN SRL **(3)**
Calea Floreasca nr 167 bis etaj 6 Sector 1, 14472, Bucharest, Romania
Tel.: (40) 31 424 06 80
Web Site: http://sofgen.com
Bank Systems & Information Technology Consulting Services
N.A.I.C.S.: 541618

Ramona Arpad *(Mgr)*

SOFGEN (UK) Limited **(3)**
3rd Floor Ormond House 63 Queen Victoria Street, London, EC4N 4UA, United Kingdom
Tel.: (44) 1908546100
Web Site: http://sofgen.com
Bank Systems & Information Technology Consulting Services
N.A.I.C.S.: 519290
Marcel McCann *(CEO)*

SOFGEN Africa Ltd **(3)**
6th Floor Mayfair Center Ralph Bunche Road, Nairobi, Kenya
Tel.: (254) 20 204 5085
Web Site: http://sofgen.com
Bank Systems & Information Technology Consulting Services
N.A.I.C.S.: 541618
Tunde Oladele *(Exec VP & Gen Mgr)*

Subsidiary (US):

SOFGEN Americas, Inc. **(3)**
880 Apollo St Ste 357, El Segundo, CA 90245
Tel.: (310) 752-5431
Web Site: http://sofgen.com
Bank Systems & Information Technology Consulting Services
N.A.I.C.S.: 541618
Ashok Sharma *(Pres)*

Subsidiary (Non-US):

SOFGEN Australia Pty Ltd **(3)**
29 The Mall South Hurstville, NSW 2221, Sydney, Australia
Tel.: (61) 2 9546 3594
Web Site: http://sofgen.com
Bank Systems & Information Technology Consulting Services
N.A.I.C.S.: 541618
Tony Ward *(Chm & CEO)*

SOFGEN Consulting AG **(3)**
Lintheschergasse 13, 8001, Zurich, Switzerland
Tel.: (41) 84 876 3436
Web Site: http://sofgen.com
Bank Systems & Information Technology Consulting Services
N.A.I.C.S.: 541618
Armin Heeb *(CEO)*

SOFGEN India Private Ltd **(3)**
3A KG 360 IT Park 232/1 Dr MGR Salai OMR Bypass Road, Perungudi, Chennai, 600 096, India
Tel.: (91) 4466955000
Web Site: http://sofgen.com
Bank Systems & Information Technology Consulting Services
N.A.I.C.S.: 541618
Rammohan Duraikannu *(CTO & Head-India Unit)*

SOFGEN S.A. **(3)**
Chemin du Chateau-Bloch 11, Le Lignon, 1219, Geneva, Switzerland
Tel.: (41) 22879 95 70
Web Site: http://sofgen.com
Bank Systems & Information Technology Services
N.A.I.C.S.: 541618
Rosita Nattier *(Office Mgr)*

SOFGEN Sdn Bhd **(3)**
Global Solution Center Lot 12122 Persiaran Apec, Cyberjaya, 63000, Kuala Selangor, Malaysia
Tel.: (60) 327247094
Web Site: http://sofgen.com
Bank Systems & Information Technology Consulting Services
N.A.I.C.S.: 541618

SOFGEN Services Pte Ltd **(3)**
Plaza 8 CBP 1 Changi Business Park Crescent 04-04/05/06, Singapore, 486025, Singapore
Tel.: (65) 64392088
Web Site: http://sofgen.com
Bank Systems & Information Technology Consulting Services
N.A.I.C.S.: 541618

Subsidiary (US):

Tech Mahindra (Americas), Inc. **(2)**

5700 Democracy Dr Ste 2000, Plano, TX 75024
Tel.: (214) 974-9907
Web Site: http://www.techmahindra.com
Sales Range: $1-9.9 Million
Emp.: 7,500
Information Technology Services & Solutions to the Telecom Industry
N.A.I.C.S.: 517810

Subsidiary (Domestic):

Tech Mahindra (R&D Services) Limited **(2)**
Plot No 45 - 47 KIADB Industrial Area Phase - II, Electronic City, Bengaluru, 560 100, Karnataka, India
Tel.: (91) 8067807777
Web Site: http://www.techmahindra.com
Sales Range: $75-99.9 Million
Emp.: 274
Telecommunications IT Services & Solutions
N.A.I.C.S.: 541519
C. P. Gurnani *(CEO & Mng Dir)*

Subsidiary (US):

Tech Mahindra (R&D Services) Inc. **(3)**
2140 Lake Park Blvd Ste 300, Richardson, TX 75080
Tel.: (972) 991-2900
Web Site: http://www.techmahindra.com
Sales Range: $25-49.9 Million
Emp.: 26
Telecommunication Servicesb
N.A.I.C.S.: 517810
Anand G. Mahindra *(Chm)*

Subsidiary (Non-US):

Tech Mahindra (Singapore) Pte. Limited **(2)**
150 Kampong Ampart #01-01 KA Centre, Singapore, 189721, Singapore
Tel.: (65) 6303 8752
Web Site: http://www.techmahindra.com
Telecommunications IT Services & Solutions
N.A.I.C.S.: 519290

Subsidiary (Domestic):

Tech Mahindra BPO Limited **(2)**
Infocity - Special Economic Zone Tower - I Plot No 22 to 34, Hi-Tech City Madhapur, Hyderabad, 500081, Telangana, India
Tel.: (91) 4066361300
Web Site: http://www.techmahindra.com
Sales Range: $300-349.9 Million
Emp.: 2,000
Outsourcing Services
N.A.I.C.S.: 561421
Vijay Ranigineni *(Head-Enterprise Global Ops)*

Tech Mahindra Foundation **(2)**
Mahindra Towers Bhikaji Cama Place, New Delhi, 110066, India
Tel.: (91) 11 4573 4722
Web Site: http://www.techmahindrafoundation.org
Telecommunications IT Services & Solutions
N.A.I.C.S.: 541519
Vikrant Gandhe *(Sec)*

Subsidiary (Non-US):

Tech Mahindra GmbH **(2)**
Fritz-Vomfelde-Str 8, 40547, Dusseldorf, Germany
Tel.: (49) 2115 239 1248
Web Site: https://www.techmahindra.com
Telecommunications IT Services & Solutions
N.A.I.C.S.: 541519

Tech Mahindra Ltd **(2)**
Room No 23102-23104 23202-23204 No 498 Guoshoujing Road, Zhangjiang Hitech Park, Shanghai, Jiangsu, China
Tel.: (86) 215 080 7600
Web Site: http://www.techmahindra.com
Sales Range: $25-49.9 Million
Emp.: 100
Information Technology Services
N.A.I.C.S.: 513199

MAHINDRA & MAHINDRA LIMITED

INTERNATIONAL PUBLIC

Mahindra & Mahindra Limited—(Continued)

The BIO Agency Ltd. (2)
90-92 Pentonville Rd, London, N1 9HS, United Kingdom
Tel.: (44) 207 079 2450
Web Site: https://www.thebioagency.com
Sales Range: $10-24.9 Million
Emp.: 95
Digital Advertising Services
N.A.I.C.S.: 541810
Peter Veash *(Founder & CEO)*

MAHINDRA EPC IRRIGATION LIMITED
12 Tupper Blvd, Amherst, B4H 4S7, NS, Canada
Tel.: (902) 667-7241
Web Site: http://www.polycello.com
Year Founded: 1956
Rev: $23,408,000
Emp.: 350
Flexographic Packaging Services
N.A.I.C.S.: 561910
Stephen Emmerson *(Pres & CEO)*

MAHIP INDUSTRIES LTD.
Survey No 127 Jalalpur-Godhneshwar Dholka Bagodara Highway, Ahmedabad, 387810, India
Tel.: (91) 9825033335
Web Site:
 https://www.mahipindustriesltd.in
Year Founded: 1995
Rev: $19,192,702
Assets: $12,879,577
Liabilities: $6,631,537
Net Worth: $6,248,039
Earnings: $704,481
Fiscal Year-end: 03/31/19
Corrugated Carton Box Mfr
N.A.I.C.S.: 322211
Rajiv Agrawal *(Mng Dir)*

MAHLE GMBH
Pragstrasse 26-46, 70376, Stuttgart, Germany
Tel.: (49) 7115010
Web Site: http://www.mahle.com
Year Founded: 1920
Rev: $13,493,375,677
Assets: $9,404,495,811
Liabilities: $6,333,335,754
Net Worth: $3,071,160,057
Earnings: ($236,903,023)
Emp.: 77,015
Fiscal Year-end: 12/31/19
Automotive Products Mfr
N.A.I.C.S.: 333618
Michael Frick *(Member-Mgmt Bd)*
Subsidiaries:

ABYO TM S.L. (1)
Rua Francisco Cruz 322, Jardim Vila Mariana, Sao Paulo, 04117-091, Brazil
Tel.: (55) 11976093682
Tunnelling Mining Services
N.A.I.C.S.: 213115

Ertunnel Mak. San. Tic. Ltd. Sti. (1)
Mustafa Kemal Mahallesi 2155 Street NEP Office No 4/47, Cankaya, Ankara, Türkiye
Tel.: (90) 3122194047
Web Site: https://ertunnel.com.tr
Tunnelling Product Mfr
N.A.I.C.S.: 334516

MAHLE Aftermarket GmbH (1)
Pragstrasse 26-46, 70376, Stuttgart, Germany
Tel.: (49) 7115010
Web Site: https://www.mahle-aftermarket.com
Automobile Aftermarket Parts Whslr
N.A.I.C.S.: 423120

MAHLE Behr GmbH & Co. KG (1)
Mauserstr 3, 70469, Stuttgart, Germany **(51%)**
Tel.: (49) 7115010
Sales Range: $5-14.9 Billion
Emp.: 17,285
Air Conditioning & Engine Cooling Products Mfr
N.A.I.C.S.: 333415

Subsidiary (US):

MAHLE Behr Charleston Inc. (2)
4500 Leeds Ave, Charleston, SC 29405
Tel.: (843) 745-1233
Air Conditioning & Engine Cooling Products Mfr
N.A.I.C.S.: 336390
James Wojdyla *(Mgr-Process Plng)*

MAHLE Behr Dayton L.L.C. (2)
1600 Webster St, Dayton, OH 45404-1144
Tel.: (937) 369-2900
Sales Range: $600-649.9 Million
Automotive Heaters & Air Conditioning Units, Air Conditioning Compressors, Radiators, Heat Exchangers, Oil Coolers & Condensers Mfr
N.A.I.C.S.: 333618

Subsidiary (Non-US):

MAHLE Behr France Hamback S.A.S. (2)
Rue Herbert Roth Zone Europole, 57910, Hambach, Cedex, France **(100%)**
Tel.: (33) 387283400
Emp.: 450
Mfr of Air Conditioning & Engine Cooling Products
N.A.I.C.S.: 333415
Gouph Ferannrg *(Gen Mgr)*

MAHLE Behr France Rouffach S.A.S. (2)
5 avenue de la Gare, 68250, Rouffach, France **(100%)**
Tel.: (33) 389735800
Sales Range: $400-449.9 Million
Emp.: 1,000
Air Conditioning & Engine Cooling Products Mfr
N.A.I.C.S.: 333415
Fernand Gouth *(Pres)*

MAHLE Behr Japan K.K. (2)
1-9-12 Kita-otsuka, Toshima-ku, Tokyo, 170-0004, Japan **(100%)**
Tel.: (81) 5033630001
Sales Range: $25-49.9 Million
Emp.: 40
Air Conditioning & Engine Cooling Products Mfr
N.A.I.C.S.: 333415

Subsidiary (Domestic):

MAHLE Behr Kirchberg GmbH (2)
Bahnhofstrasse 26, 08107, Kirchberg, Germany **(100%)**
Tel.: (49) 376026720
Sales Range: $100-124.9 Million
Emp.: 300
Mfr of Air Conditioning & Engine Cooling Products
N.A.I.C.S.: 333415

MAHLE Behr Kornwestheim GmbH (2)
Enzstrasse 25-33, 70806, Kornwestheim, Germany **(100%)**
Tel.: (49) 71541330
Emp.: 370
Air Conditioning & Engine Cooling Products Mfr
N.A.I.C.S.: 333415

Subsidiary (US):

MAHLE Behr Service America L.L.C. (2)
5020 Augusta Dr, Fort Worth, TX 76106
Tel.: (817) 624-7273
Automobile Climate Control Systems Mfr
N.A.I.C.S.: 336390

Subsidiary (Domestic):

MAHLE Behr Service GmbH (2)
Mauserstrasse 3, 70469, Stuttgart, Germany **(100%)**
Tel.: (49) 7115010
Sales Range: $200-249.9 Million
Emp.: 600
Air Conditioning & Engine Cooling Products Mfr
N.A.I.C.S.: 333415

MAHLE Behr Service GmbH (2)
Dr Manfred Behr Str 1, 74523, Schwablsch Hall, Germany **(100%)**
Tel.: (49) 79078750
Sales Range: $50-74.9 Million
Emp.: 140
Air Conditioning & Engine Cooling Products Mfr
Juergen Laucher *(Mng Dir)*

MAHLE Clevite Inc. (1)
1240 Eisenhower Pl, Ann Arbor, MI 48108-3282
Tel.: (734) 975-4777
Web Site: http://www.us.mahle-aftermarket.com
Sales Range: $50-74.9 Million
Emp.: 55
Transportation Components, Bushings, Bearings, Pistons & Sleeves Whslr
N.A.I.C.S.: 423120
Jim Markle *(Mgr-Bus Dev-Service Solutions)*

MAHLE Engine Components Japan Corporation (1)
2-17 Akabori, Okegawa, 363-0002, Saitama, Japan **(100%)**
Tel.: (81) 5033633888
Emp.: 880
Automotive Pistons & Cylinder Liners Mfr
N.A.I.C.S.: 336390
Ivan A. Lenehan *(Pres)*

Subsidiary (Domestic):

MAHLE Electric Drives Japan Corporation (2)
3744 Ooka, Numazu, 410-0022, Shizuoka, Japan
Tel.: (81) 5033635000
Sales Range: $125-149.9 Million
Engine Electric Appliance & Motor Mfr
N.A.I.C.S.: 336320
Rikio Yoshikawa *(Pres)*

MAHLE Engine Components USA, Inc. (1)
2020 Sanford St, Muskegon, MI 49444-1025
Tel.: (231) 722-1300
Sales Range: $50-74.9 Million
Emp.: 225
Engine Parts Mfr
N.A.I.C.S.: 336390

MAHLE Filter Systems Japan Corporation (1)
1-9-12 Kita-otsuka, Toshima-ku, Tokyo, 170-0004, Japan **(100%)**
Tel.: (81) 5033530799
Web Site: http://www.jp.mahle.com
Emp.: 681
Automotive Filter Systems Mfr
N.A.I.C.S.: 336390
Takahisa Yamashita *(Pres)*

MAHLE Industries, Incorporated (1)
23030 MAHLE Dr, Farmington Hills, MI 48335
Tel.: (248) 305-8200
Web Site: https://www.us.mahle.com
Engines & Transportation Equipment Mfr
N.A.I.C.S.: 333618

MAHLE Letrika d.o.o (1)
Polje 15, 5290, Sempeter pri Gorici, Slovenia
Tel.: (386) 53393000
Web Site: http://www.mahle.com
Starters, Alternators, Electric Motors, Controllers, Electronics & Components Mfr
N.A.I.C.S.: 336320

Subsidiary (Domestic):

Letrika Lab d.o.o. (2)
Polje 15, 5290, Sempeter pri Gorici, Slovenia
Tel.: (386) 5 33 93 000
Web Site: http://www.mahle.com
Electric Motor Controller Mfr
N.A.I.C.S.: 336320

Subsidiary (Non-US):

MAHLE Aftermarket France S.A.S. (2)
Parc d Activites des Pivolles6 rue de Catalogne, 69150, Decines-Charpieu, France
Tel.: (33) 472156868
Automotive Motor Spare Parts Distr
N.A.I.C.S.: 423120

MAHLE Letrika (Suzhou) Automotive Electrics Co., Ltd. (2)
No 11 Ou'jiang Road Shuangfeng Town, Taicang, 215 416, Suzhou, Jiangsu, China
Tel.: (86) 512 8160 7768
Web Site: http://www.mahle.com
Motor Vechicle Electrical & Electronic Equipment Mfr
N.A.I.C.S.: 336320

Subsidiary (Domestic):

MAHLE Letrika Bovec d.o.o. (2)
Industrijska Cona 3, Bovec, 5230, Ljubljana, Slovenia
Tel.: (386) 538 79 001
Web Site: http://www.mahle.com
Engine Equipment Mfr
N.A.I.C.S.: 333618

Subsidiary (Non-US):

MAHLE Letrika Deutschland GmbH (2)
Danziger Strasse 1, 71691, Freiberg am Neckar, Germany
Tel.: (49) 7141702690
Web Site: http://www.mahle.com
Motor Vehicle Supplies & New Parts Whslr
N.A.I.C.S.: 423120

MAHLE Letrika Italia S.r.l. (2)
Via Ragazzi del 99 n 39, 42124, Reggio Emilia, Italy
Tel.: (39) 0 522 506 285
Web Site: http://www.mahle.com
Motor Vehicle Parts Distr
N.A.I.C.S.: 423140

Subsidiary (Domestic):

MAHLE Letrika Komen d.o.o. (2)
Komen 139, Komen, 6223, Ljubljana, Slovenia
Tel.: (386) 57395700
Web Site: http://www.mahle.com
Aluminum Die-Casting Foundries
N.A.I.C.S.: 331523

Subsidiary (Non-US):

MAHLE Letrika Laktasi d.o.o. (2)
Nemanjina 63a, 78250, Laktasi, Bosnia & Herzegovina
Tel.: (387) 51535315
Web Site: http://www.mahle.com
Electronic Components Mfr
N.A.I.C.S.: 334419

MAHLE Letrika UK Ltd. (2)
Unit A6 Redlands Ullswater Crescent, Surrey, Coulsdon, CR5 2HT, United Kingdom
Tel.: (44) 2086687141
Web Site: http://www.mahle.com
Equipment Wiring Supplies & Construction Material Whslr
N.A.I.C.S.: 423610
Janez Iponitck *(Mng Dir)*

Subsidiary (US):

MAHLE Letrika USA Inc. (2)
4814 American Rd, Rockford, IL 61109
Tel.: (815) 874-4022
Web Site: http://www.mahle.com
Motor & Generator Mfr
N.A.I.C.S.: 335312
Bruce Olson *(Pres)*

MAHLE Powertrain Ltd. (1)
Costin House St James Mill Road, Northampton, NN5 5TZ, United Kingdom
Tel.: (44) 1604738000
Web Site: https://www.mahle-powertrain.com
Sales Range: $50-74.9 Million
High Performance Engines & Sub Assemblies for Road & Racing Cars Mfr
N.A.I.C.S.: 333618
Pernd Mahr *(CEO)*

TUNROCK S.R.L. (2)
Via Manzoni 3, 24069, Cenate Sotto, Italy
Tel.: (39) 03356390680
Web Site: https://www.tunrock.com

AND PRIVATE COMPANIES

Tunnelling Product Distr
N.A.I.C.S.: 423840

MAHLE METAL LEVE S.A.
Av Ernst Mahle 2000, 13846-146,
Mogi-Guacu, 13846-146, SP, Brazil
Tel.: (55) 1938619100   BR
Web Site: http://www.mahle.com
Year Founded: 1950
LEVE3—(BRAZ)
Rev.: $14,149,272,549
Assets: $9,055,003,865
Liabilities: $7,276,897,010
Net Worth: $1,778,106,855
Earnings: $28,667,623
Emp.: 72,373
Fiscal Year-end: 12/31/23
Automobile Parts Mfr
N.A.I.C.S.: 336310
Sergio Pancini (Dir-Investor Relations)

MAHLER BESSE SA
49 Rue Camille Godard, 33000, Bordeaux, Gironde, France
Tel.: (33) 556560430
Web Site: http://www.mahler-besse.com
Rev.: $12,900,000
Emp.: 35
Wines Producer
N.A.I.C.S.: 424820
Laurent Carrau (Dir-Admin)

MAHLO GMBH & CO. KG
Donaustrasse 12, PO Box 53, Saal, 93342, Germany
Tel.: (49) 94416010
Web Site: http://www.mahlo.ge
Year Founded: 1945
Sales Range: $25-49.9 Million
Emp.: 300
Electronic Equipment for the Textile Industry
N.A.I.C.S.: 333248
Thomas Hopfl (Mgr-Sls)

Subsidiaries:

Mahlo America Inc.   (1)
575 Simuel Rd, Spartanburg, SC 29304   **(100%)**
Tel.: (864) 576-6288
Web Site: http://www.mahloamerica.com
Sales Range: $50-74.9 Million
Emp.: 9
Machinery for Textile Industry
N.A.I.C.S.: 423830
Alan Lavore (Exec VP)

Mahlo Asia Ltd.   (1)
764 Thetsaban Nimit Nua Rd, PO Box 1, Ladyaw Chatuchak, Bangkok, 10900, Thailand   **(100%)**
Tel.: (66) 29544883
Web Site: http://www.mahlo.com
Sales Range: $25-49.9 Million
Emp.: 5
Technical Consulting With Respect to Electronic Monitoring & Control Systems; Installation, Repairs & Maintenance Used in Textile
N.A.I.C.S.: 333248

Mahlo Espana Sistemas de Regulacion y Control S.L.   (1)
C/Santa Margarida s/n Nave Bitchass n 13 Poligono Riera de Caldes, Boada Vell Palau Solita i Plegamans, 08184, Barcelona, Spain
Tel.: (34) 90 20062 30
Textile Equipment Distr
N.A.I.C.S.: 423830
Michel Bruni (Area Mgr-Sls)

Mahlo Italia S.R.L.   (1)
Via Fiume 62, 21020, Daverio, Italy   **(100%)**
Tel.: (39) 0332949558
Web Site: http://www.mahlo.com
Sales Range: $25-49.9 Million
Emp.: 6

Technical Consulting With Respect to Electronic Monitoring & Control Systems; Installation, Repairs & Maintenance Used in Textile
N.A.I.C.S.: 333248
Michel Bruni (CEO & Mgr-Sls)

Mahlo Ouest S.a.r.l.   (1)
18 Rue Ju Jura, BP 50005, 68391, Sausheim, Cedex, France
Tel.: (33) 389617661
Provider of Control & Automation Systems For The Textile Finisher.
N.A.I.C.S.: 333248

Mahlo do Brasil Controle de Processos Ltda.   (1)
Rua dos Lirios 849 e 851 Cidade Jardim II, Americana, 13466-580, Brazil
Tel.: (55) 19 3407 7954
Textile Equipment Distr
N.A.I.C.S.: 423830
Miguel Lessel (Area Mgr-Sls)

MAHMOOD GROUP OF COMPANIES LLC
Mehr Manzil O S Lohari Gate, PO Box 28, Multan, Pakistan
Tel.: (92) 61111181181
Web Site: http://www.mahmoodgroup.com
Year Founded: 1935
Sales Range: $200-249.9 Million
Emp.: 11,000
Owns & Manages Various Companies
N.A.I.C.S.: 551112
Khawaja Muhammad Masood (Chm)

Subsidiaries:

Khawaja Tanneries Pvt. Ltd.   (1)
Mahmood Group Mehr Manzil Lohari Gate, PO Box No 28, Multan, 60000, Pakistan
Tel.: (92) 61 111 181181
Web Site: http://www.mahmoodgroup.com
Cow, Buffalo & Goat Finished Leather Mfr
N.A.I.C.S.: 316110

MG Agri Foods (Pvt) Ltd.   (1)
Mehr Manzil O/S Lohari Gate, PO Box No 2, Multan, Pakistan
Tel.: (92) 3477749111
Web Site: https://mgagrifoods.com
Fresh Fruit & Vegetable Distr
N.A.I.C.S.: 424480

Mahmood Power Generation Limited   (1)
Mahmood Group Mehr Manzil Lohari Gate, PO Box 28, Multan, 60000, Pakistan
Tel.: (92) 61111181181
Web Site: http://www.mahmoodgroup.com
Electric Power
N.A.I.C.S.: 221122

Mahmood Textile Mills Limited   (1)
Mehr Manzil Lohari Gate, PO Box 28, Multan, Pakistan
Tel.: (92) 61111181181
Web Site: https://www.mahmoodgroup.com
Rev.: $196,522,587
Assets: $184,807,182
Liabilities: $135,324,707
Net Worth: $49,482,476
Earnings: $4,324,016
Emp.: 6,017
Fiscal Year-end: 06/30/2023
Cotton & Yarn Mfr
N.A.I.C.S.: 115111
Muhammad Iqbal (CEO)

Multan Fabrics (Pvt.) Limited   (1)
Toyota Multan Motors Building Bosan Road, Multan, Punjab, Pakistan
Tel.: (92) 61 6522481
Textile Products Distr
N.A.I.C.S.: 424990

Roomi Enterprises Pvt. Ltd.   (1)
Mahmood Group Mehr Manzil Lohari Gate, Multan, Pakistan
Tel.: (92) 61511158
Web Site: http://www.mahmoodgroup.com
Fabric Trading
N.A.I.C.S.: 332999

MAHMOOD SALEH ABBAR COMPANY
Medina Road, PO Box 461, Jeddah, 21411, Saudi Arabia
Tel.: (966) 26519449
Web Site: http://www.abbar-sa.com
Year Founded: 1954
Sales Range: $50-74.9 Million
Emp.: 400
Electrical Appliances Distr
N.A.I.C.S.: 449210

MAHOGANY OY
Kiviniemenkatu 4, Lohja, 08100, Finland
Tel.: (358) 207418230   FI
Web Site: http://www.mahogany.fi
Year Founded: 1908
Plywood & Veneer Mfr
N.A.I.C.S.: 321211
Markku Tamminen (Mng Dir)

MAHOU, S.A.
C/ Titan 15, 28045, Madrid, Spain
Tel.: (34) 915269100   ES
Web Site: http://www.mahou-sanmiguel.com
Year Founded: 1890
Sales Range: $1-4.9 Billion
Emp.: 2,500
Beer & Non-Alcoholic Beer Brewer Mfr
N.A.I.C.S.: 312120
Beatriz Martinez-Falero (Dir-Legal Affairs)

Subsidiaries:

Avery Brewing Company   (1)
4910 Nautilus Ct, Boulder, CO 80301   **(70%)**
Tel.: (303) 440-4324
Web Site: http://www.averybrewing.com
Sales Range: $1-9.9 Million
Emp.: 9
Breweries
N.A.I.C.S.: 312120
Adam Avery (Founder & CEO)

Mahou, S.A. - Barcelona   (1)
Calle Urgell 240, PO Box 8, 08036, Barcelona, Spain
Tel.: (34) 932272300
Web Site: http://www.mahou-sanmiguel.com
Executive Office; Beer Bewer & Whslr
N.A.I.C.S.: 921110

MAHRAM MFG. GROUP
No 343 and 345 Ostad Motahari Avenue, Tehran, 15957 13111, Iran
Tel.: (98) 21 88726194
Web Site: http://www.mahramco.ir
MRAM—(THE)
Sales Range: Less than $1 Million
Food Products Mfr
N.A.I.C.S.: 311941

MAHUBE INFRASTRUCTURE LTD
Tel.: (27) 116841230
Web Site: https://mahube.africa
Year Founded: 2015
MHB—(JSE)
Rev.: $51,296
Assets: $31,663,843
Liabilities: $78,527
Net Worth: $31,585,315
Earnings: $2,878,738
Fiscal Year-end: 02/29/24
Asset Management Services
N.A.I.C.S.: 523940
Gontse Moseneke (CEO)

MAHULI LAGHUBITTA BITTIYA SANSTHA LIMITED
Aganisair Krishanasawaran6 Mahuli, Saptari, Nepal
Tel.: (977) 31411005
Web Site: https://www.mslbsl.com.np

MAIDEN HOLDINGS, LTD.

MSLB—(NEP)
Rev.: $5,181,289
Assets: $33,610,695
Liabilities: $29,062,186
Net Worth: $4,548,509
Earnings: $332,035
Fiscal Year-end: 12/31/23
Asset Management Services
N.A.I.C.S.: 523940
Prabhu Narayan Chaudhary (Chm)

MAI LINH CENTRAL JOINT STOCK COMPANY
No 92 Road 2/9, Hai Chau District, Da Nang, Vietnam
Tel.: (84) 511 6257888
Web Site: http://www.mailinh.vn
Year Founded: 1993
MNC—(HNX)
Sales Range: $1-9.9 Million
Transportation, Construction & Telecommunication Services
N.A.I.C.S.: 517810
Ho Huy (Chm)

MAI LINH NORTH JOINT STOCK COMPANY
Dich Vong Cau Giay, Hanoi, Vietnam
Tel.: (84) 2439725888
Logistic Services
N.A.I.C.S.: 488510

MAIDEN FORGINGS LIMITED
E-201 Kavi Nagar Industrial Area, Ghaziabad, 201002, Uttar Pradesh, India
Web Site: https://www.maidenforgings.in
Year Founded: 2005
543874—(BOM)
Steel Products Mfr
N.A.I.C.S.: 331210
Nivedita Garg (Chm)

MAIDEN HOLDINGS, LTD.
94 Pitts Bay Road, Pembroke, HM 08, Bermuda
Tel.: (441) 2984900   BM
Web Site: https://www.maiden.bm
Year Founded: 2007
MHLD—(NASDAQ)
Rev.: $58,132,000
Assets: $1,846,866,000
Liabilities: $1,562,287,000
Net Worth: $284,579,000
Earnings: $(60,041,000)
Emp.: 49
Fiscal Year-end: 12/31/22
Holding Company; Reinsurance Services
N.A.I.C.S.: 551112
Lawrence Frederic Metz (Vice Chm & Grp Pres)

Subsidiaries:

Maiden Holdings North America, Ltd.   (1)
6000 Midlantic Dr Ste 200S, Mount Laurel, NJ 08054
Tel.: (856) 359-2400
Holding Company
N.A.I.C.S.: 551112
Thomas H. Highet (Pres)

Subsidiary (Domestic):

Maiden Re Insurance Services, LLC   (2)
6000 Midlantic Dr, Mount Laurel, NJ 08054
Tel.: (856) 359-2400
Web Site: http://www.maidenre.com
Sales Range: $300-349.9 Million
Emp.: 42
Reinsurance Underwriting Services
N.A.I.C.S.: 524298

OVS Opel VersicherungsService GmbH   (1)

MAIDEN HOLDINGS, LTD.   INTERNATIONAL PUBLIC

Maiden Holdings, Ltd.—(Continued)
Hietzinger Kai 101105, A-1130, Vienna, Austria
Tel.: (43) 18134613
Web Site: http://www.opel.at
Insurance Agency & Brokerage Services
N.A.I.C.S.: 524210

MAIDER MEDICAL INDUSTRY EQUIPMENT CO., LTD.
No 3 Tianyou Road, Binggang Industrial Zone Yuhuan County, Taizhou, 317607, Zhejiang, China
Tel.: (86) 57687498999
Web Site:
  https://www.maiderchina.com
Year Founded: 2003
688310—(SHG)
Rev.: $53,841,982
Assets: $145,771,802
Liabilities: $29,295,611
Net Worth: $116,476,191
Earnings: $9,410,535
Emp.: 500
Fiscal Year-end: 12/31/22
Medical Product Mfr & Distr
N.A.I.C.S.: 339112
Junhua Lin *(Chm & Gen Mgr)*

MAIER + PARTNER AG
Moorhof 11, Hamburg, 22399, Germany
Tel.: (49) 4060761830
MPRK—(DEU)
Sales Range: Less than $1 Million
Financial Support Services
N.A.I.C.S.: 523940

MAIKE TUBE INDUSTRY HOLDINGS LIMITED
Meigui Zone of Industrial Park, Pingyin, Jinan, 250400, China
Tel.: (86) 53187666798
Web Site:
  http://www.mechpipingtech.com
Year Founded: 2013
1553—(HKG)
Rev.: $295,863,516
Assets: $180,056,401
Liabilities: $48,096,828
Net Worth: $131,959,573
Earnings: $19,486,116
Emp.: 1,059
Fiscal Year-end: 12/31/22
Holding Company
N.A.I.C.S.: 551112
Linglei Kong *(Chm)*

Subsidiaries:

Jinan Mech Piping Technology Co., Ltd. (1)
Meigui Zone of Industrial Park, Pingyin, Jinan, 250400, China
Tel.: (86) 53187666798
Web Site: https://www.mechpipingtech.com
Steel Pole Mfr
N.A.I.C.S.: 331210

MAIL MARKETING (SCOTLAND) LIMITED
42 Methil Street, Glasgow, G14 0SZ, United Kingdom
Tel.: (44) 141 950 2222   UK
Web Site:
  http://www.mailmarkscot.co.uk
Year Founded: 1950
Emp.: 30
Advertising Services
N.A.I.C.S.: 541810
Mara McWhirter *(Acct Dir)*

MAIL.RU GROUP LIMITED
Leningradsky prospekt 39 bld 79, 125167, Moscow, Russia
Tel.: (7) 4957256357
Web Site: http://www.corp.mail.ru

MAIL—(LSE)
Rev.: $1,483,933,114
Assets: $4,478,958,773
Liabilities: $2,941,779,764
Net Worth: $1,537,179,008
Earnings: ($383,260,906)
Emp.: 14,422
Fiscal Year-end: 12/31/23
Internet Communications & Entertainment Services
N.A.I.C.S.: 519290
Dmitry Grishin *(Founder & Chm)*

MAILBOX MEDIA MBM AB
Enhagsvagen 7, 18 740, Taby, Sweden
Tel.: (46) 854496351
Web Site:
  http://www.mailboxmedia.se
Sales Range: $25-49.9 Million
Emp.: 6
Commercial Printing Mfr
N.A.I.C.S.: 323111
Odd B. Westman *(CEO-Sls)*

MAIN CAPITAL PARTNERS B.V.
Paleisstraat 6, 2514 JA, Hague, Netherlands
Tel.: (31) 703243433
Web Site: http://www.main.nl
Year Founded: 2003
Portfolio Management & Software Services
N.A.I.C.S.: 523940
Charly Zwemstra *(Mng Partner)*

Subsidiaries:

HYPE Softwaretechnik GmbH (1)
Trierer Str 70-72, 53115, Bonn, Germany
Tel.: (49) 22822760
Web Site: https://www.hypeinnovation.com
Software Publr
N.A.I.C.S.: 513210
Frank Henningsen *(CEO)*

Subsidiary (Non-US):

Planbox, Inc. (2)
3090 Le Carrefour Blvd #750, Laval, H7T 2J7, QC, Canada
Tel.: (855) 752-6269
Web Site: http://www.planbox.com
Cloud Based AI Powered Agile Work Innovations Solutions
N.A.I.C.S.: 513210
Ludwig Melik *(CEO)*

Lux Scientiae, Inc. (1)
46 Central St, Somerville, MA 02143
Tel.: (800) 441-6612
Web Site: http://www.luxsci.com
Software Publisher
N.A.I.C.S.: 513210
Erik Kangas *(Founder & CEO)*

PeakAvenue GmbH (1)
Maria-Goeppert-Str1 5, 23562, Lubeck, Germany
Tel.: (49) 4519309860
Web Site: https://www.peakavenue.com
Software Publr
N.A.I.C.S.: 513210
Ulrich Mangold *(CEO)*

Subsidiary (US):

Isograph Ltd. (2)
2020 Main St Ste 1180, Irvine, CA 92614-8263
Tel.: (949) 502-5919
Web Site: http://www.isograph.com
Computer & Computer Peripheral Equipment & Software Merchant Whslr
N.A.I.C.S.: 423430
Jeremy Hynek *(VP)*

MAIN FINE INTERNATIONAL LTD.
Workshop A06H 6/F Block A Hong Kong Industrial Centre, No 489-491 Castle Peak Road Cheung Sha Wan, Kowloon, China (Hong Kong)

Tel.: (852) 23323028
Web Site: http://www.mainfine.com
Year Founded: 1992
Sales Range: $25-49.9 Million
Emp.: 4
Window Covering Parts & Accessory Mfr
N.A.I.C.S.: 337920
T. Chen *(Gen Mgr)*

Subsidiaries:

Main Fine International, LLC (1)
1328 E Hackberry Ave Ste D, McAllen, TX 78501
Tel.: (956) 682-5570
Window Covering Products Distr
N.A.I.C.S.: 423220

Taiwan Main Fine International Co., Ltd (1)
5F-11 No 178 Fuxing N Rd, Zhongshan Dist, Taipei, 10487, Taiwan
Tel.: (886) 2 25456736
Blind & Shade Mfr
N.A.I.C.S.: 337920

MAIN STREET COMPLEX PLC
Antoine De Paule Square, Paola, Malta
Tel.: (356) 21227436
Web Site:
  http://www.mainstreetcomplex.com
Year Founded: 2004
Shopping Mall Services
N.A.I.C.S.: 722310
Bettina Azzopardi *(Mng Dir)*

MAIN STREET COMPLEX PLC
Antoine De Paule Square, Paola, PLA 1262, Malta
Tel.: (356) 21227436
Web Site:
  https://www.mainstreetcomplex.com
Year Founded: 2004
MSC—(MAL)
Rev.: $783,024
Assets: $16,019,621
Liabilities: $1,945,169
Net Worth: $14,074,453
Earnings: $296,764
Fiscal Year-end: 12/31/21
Real Estate Agency Services
N.A.I.C.S.: 531210
Joseph A. Gasan *(Chm)*

MAINFREIGHT LTD.
2 Railway Lane, Otahuhu, Auckland, 1062, New Zealand
Tel.: (64) 92595500   NZ
Web Site:
  http://www.mainfreight.co.nz
Year Founded: 1978
MFT—(NZX)
Rev.: $3,394,562,799
Assets: $2,059,238,636
Liabilities: $1,026,458,134
Net Worth: $1,032,780,502
Earnings: $255,069,378
Emp.: 11,311
Fiscal Year-end: 03/31/23
Freight Forwarding & Logistics Services
N.A.I.C.S.: 488510
Bruce Plested *(Founder & Chm)*

Subsidiaries:

CaroTrans International, Inc. (1)
100 Walnut Ave Ste 202, Clark, NJ 07066-5745
Tel.: (732) 540-8100
Web Site: http://www.carotrans.com
Sales Range: $25-49.9 Million
Emp.: 50
International Exports
N.A.I.C.S.: 484121
Mary White *(Mgr-Customer Svc-Export)*

Daily Freight (1994) Ltd (1)
42 O'Rorke Rd, Penrose, 09, Auckland, New Zealand

Tel.: (64) 95792089
Sales Range: $25-49.9 Million
Emp.: 100
Logistic Services
N.A.I.C.S.: 541614
Edward Creasy *(Mgr-Sls)*

Daily Freight Ltd. (1)
42 O'Rorke Road, PO Box 12441, Penrose, Auckland, 1061, New Zealand (100%)
Tel.: (64) 95792089
Web Site: http://www.dailyfreight.co.nz
Sales Range: $50-74.9 Million
Emp.: 120
General Freight Trucking, Local
N.A.I.C.S.: 484110

Mainfreight (1)
1400 Glenn Curtiss St, Carson, CA 90746-4030
Tel.: (310) 900-1974
Web Site: http://www.mainfreightusa.com
Sales Range: $200-249.9 Million
Emp.: 60
Provider of Logistics Services
N.A.I.C.S.: 488510
Denis Dillon *(VP-Ops)*

Mainfreight (Thailand) Co., Ltd. (1)
193/64 16th Floor Lake Rajada Office Complex Ratchadapisek Road, Klongtoey, Bangkok, 10110, Thailand
Tel.: (66) 22640390
Freight Transportation Services
N.A.I.C.S.: 488510
Chatchawan Channim *(Asst Mgr-Sls)*

Mainfreight Air & Ocean-Brisbane (1)
63a Lavarack Avenue, Eagle Farm, 4009, QLD, Australia (100%)
Tel.: (61) 736383900
Web Site: http://www.mainfreight.com
Emp.: 40
Freight Transportation Arrangement
N.A.I.C.S.: 488510
Drew Bowler *(Mgr-Sales)*

Mainfreight BV (1)
Dockworks IV Waalhaven O z 77 5th Floor, 3087 BM, Rotterdam, Netherlands
Tel.: (31) 102992828
Freight Transportation Services
N.A.I.C.S.: 488510

Mainfreight Chile SpA (1)
Av Las Condes 11283 Oficina 204, Las Condes, Santiago, Chile
Tel.: (56) 227634900
Freight Transportation Services
N.A.I.C.S.: 488510
Beatriz Osorio *(Branch Mgr)*

Mainfreight Distribution Pty Ltd (1)
1653 Centre Road, Clayton, 3168, VIC, Australia (100%)
Tel.: (61) 392655300
Web Site: http://www.mainfreight.com.au
Sales Range: $25-49.9 Million
Emp.: 100
General Freight Trucking, Local
N.A.I.C.S.: 484110
Don Braid *(Mng Dir)*

Mainfreight Express Ltd (1)
Floor 10 City Point Mansion 1600 Zhong Hua Road, Shanghai, 200021, China
Tel.: (86) 2163736699
Freight Transportation Services
N.A.I.C.S.: 481212

Mainfreight Forwarding Belgium NV (1)
Bertha De Vriesestraat 2, 9052, Zwijnaarde, Belgium
Tel.: (32) 93112400
Freight Transportation Services
N.A.I.C.S.: 488510

Mainfreight Global Taiwan Ltd. (1)
Rm 1002 10th Fl No 65 Nanking East Rd Sec 3, Taipei, 10487, Taiwan
Tel.: (886) 225016800
Freight Transportation Services
N.A.I.C.S.: 488510
Eric Peng *(Mgr-Bus Dev)*

Mainfreight GmbH (1)
Freight Transportation Services
N.A.I.C.S.: 488510

AND PRIVATE COMPANIES / MAINSTREET EQUITY CORP

Mainfreight Holdings Pty Ltd (1)
154 Melrose Dr, Tullamarine, 3043, VIC, Australia
Tel.: (61) 393306000
Web Site: http://www.mainfreight.com
Emp.: 130
Freight Transportation Services
N.A.I.C.S.: 488510

Mainfreight Hong Kong Ltd. (1)
8/F Tower 2 Magnet Place 38-42 Kwai Fung Crescent, Kwai Fong, China (Hong Kong)
Tel.: (852) 22648188
Freight Transportation Services
N.A.I.C.S.: 488510
Alma She (Head-Trade Lane)

Mainfreight International Ltd (1)
40 Ron Guthrey Road Christchurch Airport, Sockburn, Christchurch, 8042, New Zealand
Tel.: (64) 33415750
Web Site: http://www.mainfreight.co.nz
Sales Range: $25-49.9 Million
Emp.: 15
Freight Forwarding Services
N.A.I.C.S.: 488510

Mainfreight Italy SRL (1)
Via Cassanese 224 Palazzo Caravaggio, 20090, Segrate, Italy
Tel.: (39) 0235979100
Freight Transportation Services
N.A.I.C.S.: 488510

Mainfreight Japan Co., Ltd. (1)
Higashi Nihonbashi Green Bldg Annex 8F 2-8-5 Higashi Nihonbashi, Chuo-ku, Tokyo, Japan
Tel.: (81) 368685607
Freight Transportation Services
N.A.I.C.S.: 488510
Rui Kawasaki (Branch Mgr)

Mainfreight Korea Ltd. (1)
8 Floor Queens Park 13 798-11, Magok-Dong Gangseo-Gu, Seoul, Korea (South)
Tel.: (82) 226648998
Freight Transportation Services
N.A.I.C.S.: 488510
Chris Jeong (Mgr-Bus Dev)

Mainfreight Logistics (Malaysia) Sdn. Bhd. (1)
Tower B 5-2 The Landmark MTBBT2 Jalan Batu Nilam 16, Bandar Bukit Tinggi 2, 41200, Klang, Selangor, Malaysia
Tel.: (60) 331623088
Freight Transportation Services
N.A.I.C.S.: 488510
Buwana Baba (Country Mgr)

Mainfreight N.V. (1)
Vliegveld 753, 1820, Steenokkerzeel, Belgium
Tel.: (32) 22513500
Freight Transportation Services
N.A.I.C.S.: 488510

Mainfreight Poland Sp z o.o. (1)
ul Rajdowa 3A, Konotopa, 05-850, Ozarow Mazowiecki, Poland
Tel.: (48) 222709649
Freight Transportation Services
N.A.I.C.S.: 488510

Mainfreight Russ LLC (1)
Startovaya Street 8a Office 404, 196210, Saint Petersburg, Russia
Tel.: (7) 8126111010
Freight Transportation Services
N.A.I.C.S.: 488510

Mainfreight SAS (1)
182 rue de l'aeropostale, Colombier Saugnieu, 69124, Lyon, France
Tel.: (33) 472237461
Freight Transportation Services
N.A.I.C.S.: 488510

Mainfreight Sp z o.o. (1)
Al Krakowska 106 / 130, 02-256, Warsaw, Poland
Tel.: (48) 222094134
Freight Transportation Services
N.A.I.C.S.: 488510

Mainfreight Spain, S.L.U. (1)
Carrer de la Selva 4 - Edificio Muntadas II, 08820, El Prat de Llobregat, Spain
Tel.: (34) 672407892
Freight Transportation Services

N.A.I.C.S.: 488510
Claudi Calvera (Branch Mgr)

Mainfreight Ukraine LLC (1)
Str Marshla Timoshenka 21 Block 12-A Office 209, Kiev, 04212, Ukraine
Tel.: (380) 445005560
Freight Transportation Services
N.A.I.C.S.: 488510

Mainfreight Vietnam Company Ltd. (1)
9th Floor Vietjet Plaza 60A Truong Son Street, Ward 2 Tan Binh District, Ho Chi Minh City, 70000, Vietnam
Tel.: (84) 2838488300
Freight Transportation Services
N.A.I.C.S.: 488510
Richard Nguyen (Country Mgr)

Mainline Global Logistics Pte. Ltd. (1)
10 Raeburn Park 01-23, Singapore, 088702, Singapore
Tel.: (65) 62658836
Freight Transportation Services
N.A.I.C.S.: 488510
Adrian He (Mgr-Bus Dev)

Owens Group Ltd. (1)
6 Harrison Road, Mount Wellington, Auckland, New Zealand (100%)
Tel.: (64) 95251700
Web Site: http://www.owensglobal.com
Courier Service
N.A.I.C.S.: 492110

Owens Transport Ltd. (1)
2 Railway Lane, Otahuhu, Auckland, 1062, New Zealand (100%)
Tel.: (64) 92595500
Web Site: http://www.owens.co.nz
Sales Range: $25-49.9 Million
Emp.: 80
General Freight Trucking, Local
N.A.I.C.S.: 484110
Paul Tolson (Branch Mgr-Auckland Mainfreight Transport)

Owens Transport Pty Ltd. (1)
37-39 Riverside Rd, Chipping Norton, NSW, Australia (100%)
Tel.: (61) 297553555
General Freight Trucking, Local
N.A.I.C.S.: 484110
Cloete Cameron (Gen Mgr)

SystemPlus Logistics Services NV (1)
Geleenlaan 33, 3600, Genk, Belgium
Tel.: (32) 89623750
Freight Transportation Services
N.A.I.C.S.: 488510

MAINI CORPORATE PVT LTD.
Maini Sadan, No. 38, 7th Cross, Lavelle Road,, Bangalore, 560 001, India
Tel.: (91) 8040723800
Web Site: https://www.mainigroup.com
Year Founded: 1973
Emp.: 1,500
Motor Vehicles Mfr
N.A.I.C.S.: 336211

MAINICHICOMNET CO. LTD.
15F Otemachi Nomura Bldg 2-1-1 Ote-machi, Chiyoda-Ku, Tokyo, 100-0004, Japan
Tel.: (81) 335482111
Web Site: https://www.maicom.co.jp
Year Founded: 1972
8908—(TKS)
Rev.: $137,302,920
Assets: $190,506,810
Liabilities: $109,468,210
Net Worth: $81,038,600
Earnings: $9,809,240
Emp.: 261
Fiscal Year-end: 05/31/24
Real Estate Development Services
N.A.I.C.S.: 531390
Mamoru Ito (Pres & CEO)

MAINLAND HEADWEAR HOLDINGS LTD.
Unit 01-05 23/F FTLife Tower 18 Sheung Yuet Street, Kowloon Bay, Kowloon, China (Hong Kong)
Tel.: (852) 27980483
Web Site: http://www.mainland.com.hk
1100—(HKG)
Rev.: $206,400,890
Assets: $215,334,690
Liabilities: $98,979,123
Net Worth: $116,355,567
Earnings: $17,697,475
Emp.: 7,845
Fiscal Year-end: 12/31/21
Headwear Products Mfr & Retailer
N.A.I.C.S.: 315210
Hoi Ying Chan (Sec)

Subsidiaries:

Drew Pearson International (Europe) Ltd. (1)
3 Warner House Harrovian Business Village Bessborough Road, Middlesex, Harrow, HA1 3EX, United Kingdom
Tel.: (44) 2088635628
Headwear Product Mfr & Distr
N.A.I.C.S.: 315990

Exquisite Property Limited (1)
1110 Lincoln Road, Werrington, Peterborough, PE4 6BP, United Kingdom
Tel.: (44) 173 382 2988
Web Site: https://www.exquisiteproperty.com
Property Selling Services
N.A.I.C.S.: 531210

H3 Sportgear LLC (1)
2875 Whiptail Loop E, Carlsbad, CA 92010
Tel.: (760) 804-9765
Web Site: https://www.h3sportgear.com
Custom Headwear & Apparel Whslr
N.A.I.C.S.: 424350
Omar Cantu (CEO)

San Diego Hat Company (1)
PO Box 131390, Carlsbad, CA 92013
Tel.: (760) 804-9780
Web Site: http://www.sandiegohat.com
Sales Range: $10-24.9 Million
Emp.: 25
Hat Mfr & Distr
N.A.I.C.S.: 458110

Simplylife LLC (1)
PO Box 7224, Watchung, NJ 07069
Tel.: (908) 424-9197
Web Site: http://www.simplylifellc.com
Other Personal Services
N.A.I.C.S.: 812990
Tahira Hair (Founder)

Top Super Sportswear (Shenzhen) Co., Ltd. (1)
NO 1 Zhen Han Road Gan Keng, Jihua Longgang, Shenzhen, China
Tel.: (86) 75528558111
Headwear Product Mfr & Distr
N.A.I.C.S.: 315990

Unimas Sportswear Ltd. (1)
Anika Industrial Garden Bagh Bari, Kashimpur, Gazipur, Bangladesh
Tel.: (880) 1912452426
Headwear Product Mfr & Distr
N.A.I.C.S.: 315990

Wintax Caps (Shenzhen) Co., Ltd. (1)
NO 1 Zhen Han Road Gan Keng, Jihua Longgang, Shenzhen, China
Tel.: (86) 75528558111
Headwear Product Mfr & Distr
N.A.I.C.S.: 315990

MAINOSKENTTA OY
Rongankatu 4 D, 33100, Tampere, Finland
Tel.: (358) 3 313 661
Web Site: http://www.mainoskentta.fi
Year Founded: 1967
Sales Range: $10-24.9 Million
Emp.: 25
Advertising & Public Relations

N.A.I.C.S.: 541810
Juhani Salonen (Chm)

MAINOVA AG
Solmsstrasse 38, 60486, Frankfurt am Main, Germany
Tel.: (49) 800880000
Web Site: https://mainova.de
MNV6—(DEU)
Rev.: $2,780,735,360
Assets: $4,014,993,736
Liabilities: $2,441,249,824
Net Worth: $1,573,743,912
Earnings: $220,591,904
Emp.: 2,853
Fiscal Year-end: 12/30/20
Natural Gas Distribution Services
N.A.I.C.S.: 221210
Mayor Mike Josef (Chm-Supervisory Bd)

Subsidiaries:

mobiheat GmbH (1)
Winterbruckenweg 58, Derching, 86316, Friedberg, Germany
Tel.: (49) 821710110
Web Site: http://www.creationell.de
Mobile Heating Services
N.A.I.C.S.: 238220

MAINSPED BANSE GMBH & CO. KG
Stahlstrasse 30, 65428, Russelsheim, Germany
Tel.: (49) 61428740
Web Site: http://www.mainsped.de
Year Founded: 1962
Rev.: $12,827,730
Emp.: 85
Freight Trucking Services
N.A.I.C.S.: 484110
Thomas Banse (Gen Mgr)

MAINSTAR TECHNOLOGIES COMPANY
64/A Siddheswari 4th Floor, Ramna, Dhaka, 1217, Bangladesh
Tel.: (880) 29335662 BD
Web Site: http://www.mainstarbd.com
Year Founded: 2013
Power Distribution Services
N.A.I.C.S.: 221122

MAINSTAY MEDICAL LIMITED
77 Sir John Rogersons Quay Block C Grand Canal Docklands, Dublin, D02VK60, Ireland
Tel.: (353) 1 8970270
Web Site: http://www.mainstay-medical.com
Sales Range: Less than $1 Million
Emp.: 39
Medical Device Mfr
N.A.I.C.S.: 339112
Prashant Rawat (COO)

MAINSTREAM MINERALS CORPORATION
400-365 Bay Street, Toronto, M5H 2V1, ON, Canada
Tel.: (416) 361-2820 Ca
Web Site: http://www.mainstreamminerals.com
Year Founded: 2006
Precious Metal Mining Exploration & Development Services
N.A.I.C.S.: 212290
Jessica Whitton (CEO)

MAINSTREET EQUITY CORP
305-10 Avenue SE, Calgary, T2G 0W2, AB, Canada
Tel.: (403) 215-6060
Web Site: https://www.mainst.biz
MEQ—(TSX)
Rev.: $105,306,972
Assets: $1,573,352,571

MAINSTREET EQUITY CORP

Mainstreet Equity Corp—(Continued)
Liabilities: $960,927,173
Net Worth: $612,425,398
Earnings: $44,908,109
Emp.: 384
Fiscal Year-end: 09/30/19
Multi-Family Residential Rental Property Acquisition & Management Services
N.A.I.C.S.: 541618
Navjeet Dhillon *(Founder, Pres & CEO)*

MAINTEL HOLDINGS PLC
160 Blackfriars Road, Southwark, London, SE1 8EZ, United Kingdom
Tel.: (44) 3448711122   UK
Web Site: https://www.maintel.co.uk
Year Founded: 1991
MAI—(AIM)
Rev.: $114,915,425
Assets: $117,178,743
Liabilities: $92,705,125
Net Worth: $24,473,618
Earnings: ($5,504,923)
Emp.: 493
Fiscal Year-end: 12/31/22
Telecommunications Support & Maintenance Services
N.A.I.C.S.: 811210
Dan Davies *(CTO)*

Subsidiaries:

Maintel Europe Limited   (1)
160 Blackfriars Road, London, SE1 8EZ, United Kingdom
Tel.: (44) 3448711122
Sales Range: $50-74.9 Million
Emp.: 600
Telecommunication Support & Maintenance Services
N.A.I.C.S.: 517112

Maintel Voice and Data Limited   (1)
61 Webber St, London, SE1 0RF, United Kingdom
Tel.: (44) 8704015600
Telecommunication Support & Maintenance Services
N.A.I.C.S.: 517112
Helena Hope *(Mgr-Mktg)*

MAINZ BIOMED N.V.
Sirius Gutenberg Park Robert-Koch-Strasse 50, 55129, Mainz, Germany
Tel.: (49) 6131265140   NL
Web Site: https://www.mainzbiomed.com
Year Founded: 2021
MYNZ—(NASDAQ)
Rev.: $895,479
Assets: $15,409,028
Liabilities: $12,159,802
Net Worth: $3,249,226
Earnings: ($26,295,727)
Emp.: 65
Fiscal Year-end: 12/31/23
Biotechnology Research & Development Services
N.A.I.C.S.: 541714
William J. Caragol *(CFO)*

MAIQUER GROUP CO., LTD.
Maiquer Avenue, Changji, 831100, China
Tel.: (86) 9946568908
Web Site: http://www.maiquer.cn
Year Founded: 2002
002719—(SSE)
Rev.: $138,868,236
Assets: $198,410,472
Liabilities: $120,759,444
Net Worth: $77,651,028
Earnings: ($49,309,884)
Emp.: 670
Fiscal Year-end: 12/31/22
Dairy & Bakery Products Mfr; Bakery Store Operations

N.A.I.C.S.: 311511
Yong Li *(Chm)*

MAIRE TECNIMONT S.P.A.
Viale Castello Della Magliana 27, 00148, Rome, Italy
Tel.: (39) 06602161
Web Site: https://www.mairetecnimont.com
Year Founded: 2003
MT—(ITA)
Rev.: $134,232,474
Assets: $1,836,131,069
Liabilities: $1,249,860,532
Net Worth: $586,270,537
Earnings: $90,571,602
Emp.: 2,882
Fiscal Year-end: 12/31/21
Engineering & Construction Services
N.A.I.C.S.: 237990
Fabrizio Di Amato *(Chm)*

Subsidiaries:

MABE Chile Ltda.   (1)
Av Presidente Riesco 5711 of 1403, Las Condes, 7561114, Chile
Tel.: (56) 2 376 8635
Construction Engineering Services
N.A.I.C.S.: 541330

Met NewEn S.p.A.   (1)
Viale Monte Grappa 3, Milan, 20124, Italy
Tel.: (39) 0263131
Civil Engineering Services
N.A.I.C.S.: 541330

Met T&S Ltd.   (1)
75-77 Brook Street, London, W1K 4HX, United Kingdom
Tel.: (44) 7775536067
Web Site: https://www.met-ts.co.uk
Engineering & Construction Equipment Distr
N.A.I.C.S.: 423830

Nextchem S.p.A.   (1)
Via di Vannina 88/94, 00156, Rome, Italy
Tel.: (39) 069356771
Web Site: https://www.nextchem.it
Emp.: 7,000
Oil & Gas Pipeline Services
N.A.I.C.S.: 237120
Tommaso Verani *(Mgr-Grp-Media Rels)*

OOO MT Russia   (1)
Tel.: (7) 4957306314
Engineering, Procurement & Construction Services
N.A.I.C.S.: 541330

Protecma S.r.l.   (1)
29 Via Della Tecnica, 36075, Montecchio Maggiore, Vicenza, Italy
Tel.: (39) 0444695869
Web Site: http://www.protecma.com
Sales Range: $25-49.9 Million
Emp.: 40
Electric Power Supplies & Wiring Equipment Mfr
N.A.I.C.S.: 335999

SOFREGAZ   (1)
Tour Vista-52 Quai De Dion Button, 92806, Puteaux, France
Tel.: (33) 180603000
Web Site: http://www.sofregaz.fr
Sales Range: $25-49.9 Million
Engineeering Services
N.A.I.C.S.: 541330

Stamicarbon BV   (1)
Mercator 3, 6135 KW, Sittard, Netherlands
Tel.: (31) 464237000
Web Site: https://www.stamicarbon.com
Sales Range: $25-49.9 Million
Emp.: 130
Urea Licensing
N.A.I.C.S.: 926150
Stephen Zwart *(VP)*

TPI Tecnimont Planung und Industrieanlagenbau GmbH   (1)
Neue Strasse 20, Innenstadt, 38100, Braunschweig, Germany
Tel.: (49) 53123440201
Engineering, Procurement & Construction Services
N.A.I.C.S.: 541330

Tecnimont Civil Construction   (1)
Via Gaetano de Castillia 6A, 20124, Milan, Italy   **(70%)**
Tel.: (39) 02 6313 1
Web Site: http://www.mairetecnimont.com
Sales Range: $600-649.9 Million
Emp.: 400
Engineering, Building & Infrastructure Services
N.A.I.C.S.: 541330

Subsidiary (Non-US):

Tecnimont ICB Pvt. Ltd.   (2)
Tecnimont ICB House Chincholi Bunder 504 Link Road, Malad, Mumbai, 400064, India
Tel.: (91) 22 6694 5555
Web Site: http://www.ticb.com
Sales Range: $150-199.9 Million
Construction Engineering Services
N.A.I.C.S.: 541330
Gianni Bardazzi *(Chm)*

Tecnimont Russia   (2)
Ul Petra Romanova 14 k1, Moscow, 115193, Russia
Tel.: (7) 495 3801417
Oil & Gas Plant Construction Services
N.A.I.C.S.: 213112

Tecnimont ICB Qatar WLL.   (1)
Airport Road Behind Qatar Airways Building, PO Box 16852, Doha, Qatar
Tel.: (974) 44622443
Construction Engineering Services
N.A.I.C.S.: 541330
B. Venugopalan *(Mgr)*

Tecnimont Mexico SA de CV   (1)
Campos Eliseos 345 piso 7 oficina 702, Colonia Chapultepec Polanco, 11560, Mexico, Mexico
Tel.: (52) 5575870093
Engineering, Procurement & Construction Services
N.A.I.C.S.: 541330

Tecnimont Nigeria Ltd.   (1)
101 Jubril Martins Street Off Ajose Adebogun Street, Victoria Island, Lagos, Nigeria
Tel.: (234) 94612456
Web Site: http://www.mairetecnimont.it
Sales Range: $25-49.9 Million
Emp.: 5
Oil & Gas Plant Construction Services
N.A.I.C.S.: 237120

Tecnimont Philippines Inc.   (1)
12 Fl Net One Center 26th Street Corner 3rd Avenue Crescent Park West, Bonifacio Global City, Taguig, 1634, Metro Manila, Philippines
Tel.: (63) 28194700
Engineering, Procurement & Construction Services
N.A.I.C.S.: 541330

Tecnimont Private Limited   (1)
Tecnimont House Chincholi Bunder 504 Link Road, Malad W, Mumbai, 400 064, India
Tel.: (91) 2266945555
Web Site: https://careers.tecnimont.in
Emp.: 2,000
Engineering, Procurement & Construction Services
N.A.I.C.S.: 541330
Sathiamoorthy Gopalsamy *(VP-Svcs Projects & Engineering)*

MAISON ANTOINE BAUD SA
MAB 27 route du Cendre CS 40159, 63808, Cournon-d'Auvergne, Cedex, France
Tel.: (33) 473847736
Web Site: https://www.mab-immobilier.com
Year Founded: 1864
MLMAB—(EUR)
Sales Range: $10-24.9 Million
Real Estate Support Services
N.A.I.C.S.: 531390
Patrick Dupre *(CEO)*

MAISON BLEUE
Impasse de la Grotte, BP 19, 85250, La Rabateliere, Vendee, France

INTERNATIONAL PUBLIC

Tel.: (33) 251431600
Web Site: http://www.maisonbleue.fr
Sales Range: $10-24.9 Million
Emp.: 750
Diversified Constructions Services
N.A.I.C.S.: 236220
Emmanuelle Thiebaut George *(Mgr-Comm)*

MAISON CHARLOIS SAS
Le Bourg, 58700, Murlin, France
Tel.: (33) 386381755   FR
Web Site: http://www.groupecharlois.com
Emp.: 20
Oak Barrel Mfr & Whslr
N.A.I.C.S.: 321920
Sylvain Charlois *(Pres)*

MAISON CLIO BLUE SA
55 rue de Turbigo, 75003, Paris, France
Tel.: (33) 142743400   FR
Web Site: https://www.maisonclioblue.com
Year Founded: 1981
MLCLI—(EUR)
Sales Range: $1-9.9 Million
Jewelry Mfr & Distr
N.A.I.C.S.: 339910
Patrick Morineau *(Chm, CEO & Dir-IR)*

MAISON DAUPHINE SAVOIE
8 Avenue De Chambery, 74000, Annecy, Haute Savoie, France
Tel.: (33) 450101112
Web Site: http://www.maisons-ds.com
Sales Range: $10-24.9 Million
Emp.: 12
Architectural & Construction Services
N.A.I.C.S.: 236115

MAISON F E TRIMBACH SA
15 Route De Bergheim, 68150, Ribeauville, Haut Rhin, France
Tel.: (33) 389736030
Web Site: http://www.maison-trimbach.com
Sales Range: $10-24.9 Million
Emp.: 28
Wines Producer
N.A.I.C.S.: 424820
Bernard Heydt Trimbach *(Gen Mgr)*

MAISONS & DOMAINES HENRIOT FRANCE SASU
81 re Coquebert, Reims, 51100, Paris, France
Tel.: (33) 326 895300
Web Site: http://www.champagne-henriot.com
Wine Distr
N.A.I.C.S.: 424820

Subsidiaries:

Beaux Freres, LLC   (1)
15155 NE North Vly Rd, Newberg, OR 97132
Tel.: (503) 537-1137
Web Site: http://www.beauxfreres.com
Vineyard & Wine Mfr
N.A.I.C.S.: 111332
Michael G. Etzel *(Pres)*

MAISONS AQUITAINES SARL
116 Avenue Jean Mermoz, 64000, Pau, Pyrenees Atlantiques, France
Tel.: (33) 559142121
Web Site: http://www.maisons-aquitaine.fr
Rev.: $17,400,000
Emp.: 30
Residential Construction
N.A.I.C.S.: 236115
Pascal Mazouat *(Mgr)*

AND PRIVATE COMPANIES

MAISONS AXIAL
169 Avenue Jean Jaures, 69007, Lyon, Rhone, France
Tel.: (33) 478247451
Web Site: http://www.maisons-axial.com
Rev.: $10,900,000
Emp.: 33
Land Developer
N.A.I.C.S.: 531210
Pierre Bonnet *(Pres)*

MAISONS COUDRELLE
Route de Rouen, BP 326, 27300, Menneval, Menneval, France
Tel.: (33) 232430914
Web Site: http://www.maisons-coudrelle.fr
Rev.: $10,400,000
Emp.: 15
Residential Construction
N.A.I.C.S.: 236115
Max Masson *(Pres)*

MAISONS D'EN FRANCE
4 rue du General Foy, 75008, Paris, France
Tel.: (33) 251070701
Web Site: http://www.maisonsdenfrance.com
Year Founded: 1986
Sales Range: $10-24.9 Million
Emp.: 34
Real Estate Services
N.A.I.C.S.: 531210
Alain Coutelot *(Pres)*

MAISONS DE THE MARIAGE FRERES
35 Rue Du Bourg Tibourg, 75004, Paris, France
Tel.: (33) 143471854
Web Site: http://www.mariagefreres.com
Rev.: $19,200,000
Emp.: 102
Caterers
N.A.I.C.S.: 445298
Patricia Touitou *(Dir)*

MAISONS DELMAS
Rue de la Hayette, 77100, Meyreuil, France
Tel.: (33) 164331121
Web Site: http://www.maisonsdelmas.com
Year Founded: 1987
Home Construction Services
N.A.I.C.S.: 236115

MAISONS DOMINIQUE CHARLES
71 rue Lavoisier Parc d'activities de Ragon, 44119, Treillieres, Loire Atlantique, France
Tel.: (33) 240729090
Web Site: http://www.maisonsdominique.fr
Sales Range: $10-24.9 Million
Emp.: 19
Home Construction Services
N.A.I.C.S.: 236115
Navaud pascal *(Pres)*

MAISONS DU MARAIS
Sarl Les Maisons Du Marais 4 Rue Martin Luther King, 79000, Niort, Deux Sevres, France
Tel.: (33) 549332211
Web Site: http://www.maisonsdumarais.com
Rev.: $14,400,000
Emp.: 21
Individual Home Design & Construction
N.A.I.C.S.: 236115
Jean-Philippe Bodin *(Dir-Pur)*

MAISONS DU MONDE SA
Le Portereau route du Port Aux Meules, 44120, Vertou, France
Tel.: (33) 251711717
Web Site: https://www.maisonsdumonde.com
MDM—(EUR)
Sales Range: $1-4.9 Billion
Furniture Mfr & Distr
N.A.I.C.S.: 337121
Gilles Petit *(CEO)*

MAISONS ECUREUIL
Z Europarc 15 C Rue Le Corbusier, 94000, Creteil, Val De Marne, France
Tel.: (33) 142075428
Web Site: http://www.maisonsecureuil.com
Rev.: $12,200,000
Emp.: 28
Individual Home Construction
N.A.I.C.S.: 236115
Salomon Hazziza *(Mng Dir, Mng Dir & Chm)*

MAISONS FRANCE CONFORT SA
2 route d'Ancinnes, BP 17, 61001, Alencon, Cedex, France
Tel.: (33) 2 33 80 66 66   FR
Web Site: http://www.maisons-france-confort.fr
Year Founded: 1919
Rev.: $915,644,184
Earnings: $34,857,726
Fiscal Year-end: 12/31/17
Residential Construction Services
N.A.I.C.S.: 236115

Subsidiaries:

Maine Construction SAS   (1)
74 Avenue Du General Leclerc, 72000, Le Mans, Sarthe, France
Tel.: (33) 243247075
Web Site: http://www.maine-construction.fr
Sales Range: $10-24.9 Million
Emp.: 15
Masonry & Other Stonework
N.A.I.C.S.: 238140
Claude Tourteau *(Pres)*

MAISONS LELIEVRE
21 rue des Mardelles BP 5, 72390, Le Luart, France
Tel.: (33) 243934519
Sales Range: $10-24.9 Million
Emp.: 34
Housing Construction Services
N.A.I.C.S.: 236115
Georges Lelievre *(Gen Mgr)*

MAISONS LES NATURELLES
69 Rue Charles de gaulle, 80220, Gamaches, Somme, France
Tel.: (33) 322309396
Web Site: http://www.maisonslesnaturelles.fr
Year Founded: 1968
Rev.: $11,100,000
Emp.: 32
Housing Construction Services
N.A.I.C.S.: 236115
Beatrice Wynands *(Dir-Publication)*

MAISONS PARTOUT
15 bis Avenue des Volontaires, 15000, Aurillac, France
Tel.: (33) 471481717
Web Site: http://www.maisonspartout.fr
Year Founded: 1988
Housing Construction Services
N.A.I.C.S.: 236115
Yoann Canet *(Pres)*

MAISTRO PLC
3 Kew Court Pynes Hill, Exeter, EX2 5AZ, United Kingdom
Tel.: (44) 800 048 8664
Web Site: http://www.maistro.com
Business to Business Electronic Markets
N.A.I.C.S.: 425120

MAITONG SUNSHINE CULTURAL DEVELOPMENT CO., LIMITED
Room 202 Gate 6 Building 9 Yayuan Anhui Beili, Chaoyang District, Beijing, 100000, China
Tel.: (86) 1064927946   NV
Web Site: https://www.maitongsunshine.com
Year Founded: 2023
MGSD—(OTCQB)
Rev.: $804,887
Assets: $752,334
Liabilities: $760,083
Net Worth: ($7,749)
Earnings: ($30,810)
Emp.: 12
Fiscal Year-end: 09/30/24
Tour Operator
N.A.I.C.S.: 561520

MAITRI ENTERPRISES LTD.
Gayatri House Ashok Vihar Near Maitri Avenue, Society Opp Govt Eng College Motera Sabarmati, Ahmedabad, India
Tel.: (91) 7927506840
Web Site: https://www.maitrienterprises.com
Rev.: $862,128
Assets: $712,919
Liabilities: $459,671
Net Worth: $253,248
Earnings: $1,762
Fiscal Year-end: 03/31/19
Metals Mfr
N.A.I.C.S.: 332312
Alpeshkumar M. Patel *(CEO)*

MAJ INVEST HOLDING A/S
Gammeltorv 18, 1457, Copenhagen, Denmark
Tel.: (45) 3338 7300   DK
Web Site: http://www.majinvest.com
Year Founded: 2005
Emp.: 100
Holding Company; Equity Investment & Asset Management Services
N.A.I.C.S.: 551112
Jeppe Christiansen *(CEO)*

Subsidiaries:

Fondsmaeglerselskabet Maj Invest A/S   (1)
Gammeltorv 18, 1457, Copenhagen, K, Denmark
Tel.: (45) 3338 7300
Web Site: http://www.majinvest.com
Investment Advisory & Asset Management Services
N.A.I.C.S.: 523940
Jeppe Christiansen *(CEO)*

Maj Invest Equity A/S   (1)
Gammeltorv 18, 1457, Copenhagen, Denmark
Tel.: (45) 3338 7300
Web Site: http://www.majinvest.com
Equity Investment Firm
N.A.I.C.S.: 523999
Jeppe Christiansen *(CEO)*

Holding (Domestic):

Bang & Olufsen Medicom A/S   (2)
Gimsinglund Vej 20, Struer, 7600, Denmark   (91%)
Tel.: (45) 70301600
Web Site: http://www.medicomnordic.com
Sales Range: $50-74.9 Million
Emp.: 80
Medical Device Mfr

MAJAN COLLEGE (UNIVERSITY COLLEGE) SAOG

N.A.I.C.S.: 334510
Soren Vestergard Jacobsen *(VP-R&D & Ops)*

Interbuild A/S   (2)
Allegade 2 1 sal, DK 8700, Horsens, Denmark   (51%)
Tel.: (45) 75757516
Sales Range: $50-74.9 Million
Emp.: 2
Construction Product Mfr
N.A.I.C.S.: 321215

Subsidiary (Domestic):

Lilleheden A/S   (3)
Hovedvejen 114, Hirtshals, 9850, Denmark
Tel.: (45) 88969200
Web Site: http://www.lilleheden.dk
Sales Range: $25-49.9 Million
Glulam Mfr
N.A.I.C.S.: 321999
Christian Esbensen *(Mgr)*

Subsidiary (Non-US):

Lilleheden Ltd.   (4)
Redbrook Business Park Wilthtorpe Road, Barnsley, S75 1JN, United Kingdom
Tel.: (44) 1226205449
Web Site: http://www.lilleheden.dk
Sales Range: $25-49.9 Million
Emp.: 5
Glulam Mfr
N.A.I.C.S.: 321999

Lilleheden Sp. z o.o.   (4)
Ul Chylonska 191, 81 007, Gdynia, Poland
Tel.: (48) 586600088
Web Site: http://www.lilleheden.pl
Glulam Mfr
N.A.I.C.S.: 321999
Marek Ciesielski *(Mng Dir)*

Verkaufsburo Lilleheden GmbH   (4)
Grebenstrasse 21, D 27283, Verden, Germany
Tel.: (49) 423198910
Web Site: http://www.lilleheden.dk
Glulam Mfr
N.A.I.C.S.: 321999

Subsidiary (Domestic):

PLUS A/S   (3)
Sdr Ringvej 1-6, 6600, Vejen, Denmark
Tel.: (45) 79963333
Web Site: http://www.plus.dk
Mfr of Wooden Products for Outdoor Use
N.A.I.C.S.: 321999

Holding (Domestic):

PF Group A/S   (2)
Sverigesvej 2-4, 7480, Vildbjerg, Denmark   (76%)
Tel.: (45) 9713 1200
Web Site: http://www.pcp.dk
Sales Range: $50-74.9 Million
Emp.: 270
Holding Company; Metal Gratings Mfr
N.A.I.C.S.: 551112
John Nielsen *(CEO)*

Subsidiary (Domestic):

PcP. A/S   (3)
Sverigesvej 2-4, 7480, Vildbjerg, Denmark
Tel.: (45) 9713 1200
Web Site: http://en.pcp.dk
Emp.: 80
Metal Gratings Mfr
N.A.I.C.S.: 332323
John Nielsen *(CEO)*

MAJAN COLLEGE (UNIVERSITY COLLEGE) SAOG
Way No 2621, PO Box 710, Mutrah, Ruwi, Oman
Tel.: (968) 24704300
Web Site: https://www.majancollege.edu.om
Year Founded: 1965
BACS—(MUS)
Rev.: $11,447,210
Assets: $36,381,500

MAJAN COLLEGE (UNIVERSITY COLLEGE) SAOG

Majan College (University College) SAOG—(Continued)
Liabilities: $4,135,036
Net Worth: $32,246,465
Earnings: $1,300,307
Emp.: 150
Fiscal Year-end: 08/31/23
Educational Support Services
N.A.I.C.S.: 611710
Aly Darwish Hagi Aly Al Shamali, *(Chm)*

MAJAN GLASS COMPANY SAOG
Sohar Industrial Estate, PO Box 17, 327, Sohar, Oman
Tel.: (968) 26751655
Web Site:
https://www.majanglass.com
Year Founded: 1997
MGCI—(MUS)
Rev.: $28,280,545
Assets: $33,216,070
Liabilities: $22,219,040
Net Worth: $10,997,030
Earnings: ($1,576,434)
Emp.: 248
Fiscal Year-end: 12/31/19
Glass Container Mfr
N.A.I.C.S.: 327213
Vivek Varadan *(Deputy Chm)*

MAJEDIE INVESTMENTS PLC
Dashwood House Old Broad Street, London, EC2M 1QS, United Kingdom
Tel.: (44) 2034689910
Web Site:
https://www.majedieinvestment.com
MAJE—(LSE)
Rev.: $7,914,194
Assets: $201,427,658
Liabilities: $29,171,296
Net Worth: $172,256,363
Earnings: ($23,086,783)
Emp.: 3
Fiscal Year-end: 09/30/20
Investment Trust Services
N.A.I.C.S.: 523999
J. William M. Barlow *(CEO)*

MAJENCIA S.A.
17 Allees de l'Europe, F 92588, Clichy, France
Tel.: (33) 825886927
Web Site: http://www.majencia.com
Sales Range: $125-149.9 Million
Emp.: 742
Office Furnishings Supplier
N.A.I.C.S.: 423210
Vincent Gruau *(Chm & CEO)*

MAJESTIC GOLD CORP.
306 - 1688 152nd Street, Surrey, V4A 4N2, BC, Canada
Tel.: (604) 560-9060   BC
Web Site:
https://www.majesticgold.com
MJS—(OTCIQ)
Rev.: $52,363,436
Assets: $126,715,193
Liabilities: $36,623,513
Net Worth: $90,091,680
Earnings: $15,062,301
Fiscal Year-end: 12/31/20
Gold Mining Services
N.A.I.C.S.: 212220
Stephen Patrick Kenwood *(Pres & CEO)*

MAJESTIC HORIZON HOLDINGS LTD
564 St Kilda Road Level 7, Melbourne, 3004, VIC, Australia
Tel.: (61) 385303400
Real Estate Manangement Services
N.A.I.C.S.: 531210

Khen Peng Wee *(CEO & Mng Dir)*

MAJESTIC RESEARCH SERVICES & SOLUTIONS LTD
C-509 5th Floor Kanakia Zillion LBS Marg, Kurla West, Mumbai, 400070, India
Tel.: (91) 9326926803
Web Site: https://www.mrssindia.com
539229—(BOM)
Rev.: $2,828,662
Assets: $11,006,077
Liabilities: $5,016,293
Net Worth: $5,989,784
Earnings: $102,102
Emp.: 31
Fiscal Year-end: 03/31/20
Market Research Services
N.A.I.C.S.: 541910
Rajendra Kumar Sharma *(Chm & CFO)*

MAJEVICA A.D.
Cara Dusana 51, 75240, Lopare, Bosnia & Herzegovina
Tel.: (387) 55650021
MJVC-R-A—(BANJ)
Rev.: $6,035
Assets: $608,485
Liabilities: $103,813
Net Worth: $504,672
Earnings: ($8,634)
Emp.: 1
Fiscal Year-end: 12/31/12
Home Management Services
N.A.I.C.S.: 721110
Jovo Maksimovic *(Chm-Mgmt Bd)*

MAJEVICA HOLDING A.D.
Zarka Zrenjanina 123, 21400, Backa Palanka, Serbia
Tel.: (381) 21 751 388
Web Site: http://www.majevica.co.rs
Year Founded: 2000
Sales Range: $1-9.9 Million
Emp.: 274
Investment Management Service
N.A.I.C.S.: 523940

MAJOR CINEPLEX GROUP PLC
1839 1839/1-6 Phaholyothin Rd Ladyao, Chatuchak, Bangkok, 10900, Thailand
Tel.: (66) 25115427
Web Site:
https://investor.majorcineplex.com
Year Founded: 1995
MAJOR—(THA)
Rev.: $249,629,292
Assets: $421,122,019
Liabilities: $242,696,220
Net Worth: $178,425,799
Earnings: $31,050,021
Emp.: 1,925
Fiscal Year-end: 12/31/23
Recreational Services
N.A.I.C.S.: 713990
Somchainuk Engtrakul *(Chm)*

MAJOR DEVELOPMENT PUBLIC COMPANY LIMITED
141 Major Tower 16th Fl Soi Thonglor 10 Sukhumvit 55 Klongton Nua, Wattana, Bangkok, 10110, Thailand
Tel.: (66) 20301111
Web Site: https://www.mjd.co.th
MJD—(THA)
Rev.: $65,298,567
Assets: $507,013,374
Liabilities: $371,507,122
Net Worth: $135,506,252
Earnings: ($9,636,949)
Emp.: 629
Fiscal Year-end: 12/31/23
Residential Real Estate Developer

N.A.I.C.S.: 531390
Chumroen Poolvoralaks *(Chm)*

Subsidiaries:

MJ ONE Company Limited (1)
398 Marche Ram 53 3rd Fl Building A Soi Ramkhamhaeng 53, Chan Sri Chawala Phlab Phla Wangthonglang, Bangkok, 10310, Thailand
Tel.: (66) 21388077
Real Estate Services
N.A.I.C.S.: 531320

MJV2 Company Limited (1)
141 Soi Sukhumvit 63 Ekkamai Sukhumvit Rd, Klongton Nua Wattana, Bangkok, 10110, Thailand
Tel.: (66) 20301111
Real Estate Services
N.A.I.C.S.: 531320

MJV3 Company Limited (1)
141 Soi Sukhumvit 63 Ekkamai Sukhumvit Rd, Klongton Nua Wattana, Bangkok, 10110, Thailand
Tel.: (66) 20301111
Real Estate Services
N.A.I.C.S.: 531320

MJV4 Company Limited (1)
141 Soi Sukhumvit 63 Ekkamai Sukhumvit Rd Klongton Nua, Wattana, Bangkok, 10110, Thailand
Tel.: (66) 20301111
Property Management Services
N.A.I.C.S.: 921190

Major SPV One Company Limited (1)
141 Soi Sukhumvit 63 Ekkamai Sukhumvit Rd, Klongton Nua Wattana, Bangkok, 10110, Thailand
Tel.: (66) 23921111
Real Estate Services
N.A.I.C.S.: 531320

Peoplescape Company Limited (1)
141 Soi Sukhumvit 63 Ekkamai Sukhumvit Rd, Klongton Nua Wattana, Bangkok, 10110, Thailand
Tel.: (66) 23921111
Real Estate Services
N.A.I.C.S.: 531320

MAJOR DRILLING GROUP INTERNATIONAL INC.
111 St George St, Moncton, M5S 2E8, NB, Canada
Tel.: (506) 857-8636   Ca
Web Site:
https://www.majordrilling.com
Year Founded: 1994
MJDLF—(OTCIQ)
Rev.: $508,806,646
Assets: $435,792,542
Liabilities: $154,361,054
Net Worth: $281,431,488
Earnings: $41,819,907
Emp.: 3,800
Fiscal Year-end: 04/30/22
Provider of Mining & Mineral Exploration Services
N.A.I.C.S.: 213115
David B. Tennant *(Chm)*

Subsidiaries:

Forage Major Kennebec Drilling Ltd (1)
4169 boul Frontenac est, Thetford Mines, G6H 4G3, QC, Canada
Tel.: (418) 338-3141
Sales Range: $50-74.9 Million
Emp.: 20
Nonmetallic Mineral Mining
N.A.I.C.S.: 212390

Major Drilling America, Inc. (1)
2200 S 4000 W, Salt Lake City, UT 84120
Tel.: (801) 974-0645
Web Site: http://www.majordrilling.com
Sales Range: $50-74.9 Million
Emp.: 40
Support Activities for Metal Mining
N.A.I.C.S.: 213114
Larry Pisto *(VP)*

INTERNATIONAL PUBLIC

Major Drilling Chile S.A. (1)
Calle Cinco 1271, Barrio Industrial, Casilla Postal 314, Coquimbo, Chile
Tel.: (56) 51 241 815
Support Activities for Metal Mining
N.A.I.C.S.: 213114
Normand Doyon *(Mgr)*

Major Drilling De Mexico, S.A. De C.V. (1)
Calle de los Nogales No 29 -Esquina Calle de los Pimas, Parque Indus de Hermosillo, 83299, Hermosillo, Mexico
Tel.: (52) 6622510265
Sales Range: $50-74.9 Million
Emp.: 100
Drilling Oil & Gas Wells
N.A.I.C.S.: 213111
David Boucher *(Branch Mgr)*

Major Drilling Environmental, LLC (1)
2200 S 4000 W, Salt Lake City, UT 84120
Tel.: (801) 974-0645
Web Site: http://www.smdservices.net
Environmental Drilling & Geotechnical Sampling Services
N.A.I.C.S.: 238990
Denis Despres *(Gen Mgr)*

Major Drilling Group Australasia Pty Ltd (1)
42 Suscatand St, Rocklea, 4106, QLD, Australia
Tel.: (61) 738504750
Mineral Mining Services
N.A.I.C.S.: 212390

Major Drilling International Inc. (1)
2 Rendezvous Road, Christchurch, Barbados
Tel.: (246) 4342649
Web Site: http://www.majordrilling.com
Sales Range: $50-74.9 Million
Emp.: 1
Support Activities for Metal Mining
N.A.I.C.S.: 213114
Ryan Highland *(Dir)*

Subsidiary (Non-US):

Major Drilling Tanzania Limited (2)
PO Box 2409, Mwanza, Tanzania
Tel.: (255) 787 571857
Oil & Gas Drilling Services
N.A.I.C.S.: 213111

Major Drilling Namibia (Pty) Limited (1)
161 Mandume Ndemufayo Street, Southern Industrial, Windhoek, Namibia
Tel.: (264) 64417600
Web Site: http://www.majordrilling.com
Support Activities for Metal Mining
N.A.I.C.S.: 213114

Major Drilling Pty Ltd (1)
42 Suscatand St, 4106, Rocklea, QLD, Australia
Tel.: (61) 738504750
Sales Range: $50-74.9 Million
Emp.: 35
Support Activities for Metal Mining
N.A.I.C.S.: 213114

Major Drilling South Africa (Pty) Limited (1)
98 Sesmylspruit Street, PO Box 204, Centurion, 157, South Africa
Tel.: (27) 126668793
Web Site: http://www.majordrilling.com
Sales Range: $100-124.9 Million
Emp.: 8
Support Activities for Metal Mining
N.A.I.C.S.: 213114
Greig Rodgers *(Reg Mgr-African Drilling Ops)*

Major Perforaciones S.A. (1)
Carril Ponce 1740, Mendoza, 5525, Argentina
Tel.: (54) 2614919100
Support Activities for Metal Mining
N.A.I.C.S.: 213114
Normand Brear *(Country Mgr)*

North Star Drilling LLC. (1)
18505 State Hwy 371, Brainerd, MN 56401-6825
Tel.: (218) 829-0892

AND PRIVATE COMPANIES

Web Site: http://www.nsdrilling.com
Sales Range: $25-49.9 Million
Emp.: 10
Commercial Water Wells Installation Services
N.A.I.C.S.: 237110
Milo Backowski (Office Mgr)

PT Pontil Indonesia (1)
Wisma GKBI Suite 1703, 17th Floor Jin Jenderal Sudirman, 10210, Jakarta, Indonesia
Tel.: (62) 215741040
Web Site: http://www.majordrilling.com
Emp.: 7
Support Activities for Metal Mining
N.A.I.C.S.: 213114
Keryyn Hornby (Mng Dir)

MAJOR HOLDINGS LIMITED
Suites 509-510 South Tower World Finance Centre, Harbour City TST, Kowloon, China (Hong Kong)
Tel.: (852) 2 723 9399   Ky
Web Site: http://www.majorcellar.com
Year Founded: 2013
1389—(HKG)
Rev.: $13,902,625
Assets: $22,358,425
Liabilities: $6,054,450
Net Worth: $16,303,975
Earnings: ($1,123,932)
Emp.: 25
Fiscal Year-end: 03/31/22
Holding Company
N.A.I.C.S.: 551112
Chun To Cheung (Chm)

MAJOR TEAM HOLDINGS BERHAD
1st Floor Regal House No 1 Jalan U-Thant, Kuala Lumpur, 55000, Malaysia
Tel.: (60) 3 2148 9822
Web Site: http://www.mteam.com.my
Sales Range: $1-9.9 Million
Dimension Stone Mfr
N.A.I.C.S.: 327991
See Kuan Kong (Exec Dir)

Subsidiaries:

Stone World Sdn Bhd (1)
PLO 466 Jalan Gangsa Pasir Gudang Industrial Estate, Pasir Gudang, 81700, Johor, Malaysia
Tel.: (60) 7 251 7632
Web Site: http://www.stoneworld.com.my
Emp.: 200
Dimension Stone Mfr
N.A.I.C.S.: 327991

MAJOREL GROUP LUXEMBOURG S.A.
18 boulevard de Kockelscheuer, 1821, Luxembourg, Luxembourg
Web Site: https://www.majorel.com
Year Founded: 2018
MAJ—(EUR)
Rev.: $2,579,304,000
Assets: $1,757,611,440
Liabilities: $1,072,253,520
Net Worth: $685,357,920
Earnings: $208,800,800
Emp.: 21
Fiscal Year-end: 12/31/22
Management Consulting Services
N.A.I.C.S.: 541613
Otmane Serraj (Chief Shared Svcs Officer)

Subsidiaries:

Alembo B.V. (1)
Teleportboulevard 126, 1043 EJ, Amsterdam, Netherlands
Tel.: (31) 727370000
Web Site: https://alembo.nl
Outsourcing Business Services
N.A.I.C.S.: 561990

Findasense Espana, S.L. (1)
Calle de los Martires de Alcala 4, 28015, Madrid, Spain
Tel.: (34) 911875236
Web Site: https://es.findasense.com
Digital Transformation Services
N.A.I.C.S.: 518210

Isilis S.A.S. (1)
23 rue de Vienne, 75008, Paris, France
Tel.: (33) 140899680
Web Site: https://public.isilis.fr
Emp.: 30
Financial Services
N.A.I.C.S.: 523999

Junokai GmbH (1)
Schumannstrasse 17, 10117, Berlin, Germany
Tel.: (49) 30577048990
Web Site: https://www.junokai.de
Business Management Consulting Services
N.A.I.C.S.: 541611

Majorel Brandenburg GmbH (1)
Wilhelmsdorfer Landstrasse 43, 14776, Brandenburg, Germany
Tel.: (49) 33812143122
Web Site: https://brandenburg-majorel.career.softgarden.de
Customer Services
N.A.I.C.S.: 561990

Majorel Munster GmbH (1)
Holtenweg 33, 48155, Munster, Germany
Tel.: (49) 25191547018
Web Site: https://muenster-majorel.career.softgarden.de
Customer Services
N.A.I.C.S.: 561990

Majorel Nordhorn GmbH (1)
Bentheimer Strasse 118a, 48529, Nordhorn, Germany
Tel.: (49) 30886673900
Web Site: https://nordhorn-majorel.career.softgarden.de
Customer Services
N.A.I.C.S.: 561990

MAJORICA, S.A.
Paseo de Gracia 74 4th Fl, E 08008, Barcelona, Spain
Tel.: (34) 932703660
Web Site: http://www.majorica.com
Sales Range: $25-49.9 Million
Emp.: 300
Mfr of Jewelry
N.A.I.C.S.: 334519
Claude Ries (Chm)

Subsidiaries:

Majorica Jewelry, Ltd. (1)
366 5th Ave Rm 507, New York, NY 10001
Tel.: (212) 695-1756
Web Site: http://www.majorica.com
Sales Range: $25-49.9 Million
Emp.: 31
Organic Man-Made Pearl Grower; Jewelry & Watch Mfr
N.A.I.C.S.: 423940

MAJUBA HILL COPPER CORP.
Royal Centre Suite 1500 1055 West Georgia Street, Vancouver, V6E 4N7, BC, Canada
Tel.: (604) 318-0114
Web Site: https://www.majubahillcopper.com
YW5—(DEU)
Assets: $8,472,013
Liabilities: $145,823
Net Worth: $8,326,190
Earnings: ($2,187,209)
Fiscal Year-end: 06/30/24
Investment Services
N.A.I.C.S.: 523999
David Greenway (Pres & CEO)

MAJUPERAK HOLDINGS BERHAD
Aras 1 Bazar Ipoh Jalan Sultan Nazrin Shah, Bandar Meru Raya, 31350, Ipoh, Perak Darul Ridzuan, Malaysia
Tel.: (60) 2262888
Web Site: https://www.majuperak.com.my
Year Founded: 1976
MJPERAK—(KLS)
Rev.: $5,567,834
Assets: $64,395,622
Liabilities: $21,889,945
Net Worth: $42,505,677
Earnings: ($2,751,211)
Fiscal Year-end: 12/31/22
Property Development Services
N.A.I.C.S.: 531311
Abd Karim Nast Mohd Alias (Gen Mgr-Land & Assets Mgmt)

Subsidiaries:

Nexus Jade Sdn Bhd (1)
No 3 Jalan Meru Impian A3 Pusat Perniagaan Meru Impian, 30020, Ipoh, Perak, Malaysia
Tel.: (60) 55251457
Web Site: http://www.nexusjade.com.my
Graphic Design Services
N.A.I.C.S.: 541430

MAK AD
9 Treti Mart blvd, 5300, Gabrovo, 5300, Bulgaria
Tel.: (359) 66801264
Web Site: https://www.mak.bg
4MK—(BUL)
Sales Range: Less than $1 Million
Textile Product Mfr & Distr
N.A.I.C.S.: 314999
Dimitar Georgiev Bizhev (Chm)

MAKALOT INDUSTRIAL CO., LTD.
8F No 550 Sec 4 Zhongxiao E Rd, Xinyi Dist, Taipei, 110, Taiwan
Tel.: (886) 223455588
Web Site: https://www.makalot.com.tw
Year Founded: 1990
1477—(TAI)
Rev.: $1,061,471,100
Assets: $813,490,960
Liabilities: $292,648,604
Net Worth: $520,842,356
Earnings: $131,953,656
Emp.: 27,954
Fiscal Year-end: 12/31/23
Apparels Mfr
N.A.I.C.S.: 315120
Li-Ping Chou (Chm, Pres & CEO)

Subsidiaries:

Makalot Industrial Co., Ltd. - Eastern China Factory (1)
3F/4F No 1346 Gonghexin Road, Zhabei District, Shanghai, 200070, China
Tel.: (86) 21 6608 6060
Sales Range: $750-799.9 Million
Emp.: 3,100
Apparels Mfr
N.A.I.C.S.: 315210

MAKARONY POLSKIE S.A.
ul Podkarpacka 15a, 35-082, Rzeszow, Poland
Tel.: (48) 178753010   PL
Web Site: https://makarony.pl
Year Founded: 2002
MAK—(WAR)
Rev.: $90,153,455
Assets: $60,489,837
Liabilities: $22,564,024
Net Worth: $37,925,813
Earnings: $8,356,453
Emp.: 404
Fiscal Year-end: 12/31/23
Frozen Specialty Food Manufacturing
N.A.I.C.S.: 311412
Zenon Danilowski (Chm-Mgmt Bd)

Subsidiaries:

Stoczek Natura Sp. z o.o. (1)
ul Dwernickiego 5, Stoczek Lukowski, 21-450, Lublin, Poland
Tel.: (48) 257970197
Web Site: http://www.stoczek.com.pl
Food Products Mfr
N.A.I.C.S.: 311999

MAKATI FINANCE CORPORATION
3/F Mazda Makati Building Don Chino Roces Ave Extension, Makati, 2301, Philippines
Tel.: (63) 27518132
Web Site: https://www.makatifinance.ph
Year Founded: 1966
MFIN—(PHI)
Rev.: $3,765,013
Assets: $27,338,221
Liabilities: $16,287,876
Net Worth: $11,050,345
Earnings: $225,208
Emp.: 181
Fiscal Year-end: 12/31/20
Investment Management Service
N.A.I.C.S.: 523999
Max Francisco O. Borromeo (Vice Chm)

MAKE IT CHEAPER LIMITED
4th Floor 33 King William Street, London, EC4R 9AS, United Kingdom
Tel.: (44) 845 8339422
Web Site: http://www.makeitcheaper.com
Year Founded: 2007
Sales Range: $10-24.9 Million
Emp.: 67
Business Cost Saving Services
N.A.I.C.S.: 541611
Jonathan Elliott (Founder, CEO & Mng Dir)

MAKEDONIJATURIST A.D SKOPJE
ul Filip Vtori Makedonski br 5, 1000, Skopje, North Macedonia
Tel.: (389) 23292731
Web Site: https://makedonijaturist.com.mk
Year Founded: 1963
MTUR—(MAC)
Rev.: $5,636,237
Assets: $48,028,367
Liabilities: $1,109,480
Net Worth: $46,918,887
Earnings: $1,916,310
Emp.: 300
Fiscal Year-end: 12/31/19
Home Management Services
N.A.I.C.S.: 721110

MAKEDONSKI TELEKOM AD
Kej 13 Noemvri No 6, 1000, Skopje, North Macedonia
Tel.: (389) 2 310 0200
Web Site: http://www.telekom.mk
Year Founded: 2001
Rev.: $197,268,766
Assets: $359,399,346
Liabilities: $81,691,087
Net Worth: $277,708,259
Earnings: $27,187,434
Emp.: 1,060
Fiscal Year-end: 12/31/19
Telecommunication Servicesb
N.A.I.C.S.: 517810
Slavko Projkoski (CFO)

MAKERS LABORATORIES LIMITED
54-D Government Industrial Estate Charkop, Kandivali W, Mumbai, Maharashtra, India
Tel.: (91) 2228688544
Web Site: https://www.makerslabs.com

MAKERS LABORATORIES LIMITED | **INTERNATIONAL PUBLIC**

Makers Laboratories Limited—(Continued)
506919—(BOM)
Rev.: $12,550,721
Assets: $18,458,154
Liabilities: $5,165,580
Net Worth: $13,292,574
Earnings: ($265,610)
Emp.: 121
Fiscal Year-end: 03/31/23
Pharmaceuticals Product Mfr
N.A.I.C.S.: 325412
Saahil U. Parikh (CEO)

MAKETOWIN HOLDING PUBLIC CO LTD
9/70 Moo 3 Tumbon Om Yai Amphoe Sam Phran, Nakhon Pathom, 73160, Thailand
Tel.: (66) 34100368
Web Site:
 https://www.maketowin.com
Year Founded: 1996
MTW—(THA)
Rev.: $15,441,968
Assets: $27,757,185
Liabilities: $11,161,842
Net Worth: $16,595,343
Earnings: $1,583,372
Fiscal Year-end: 12/31/22
Holding Company
N.A.I.C.S.: 551112
Chun Chen (Founder, CEO & Mng Dir)

MAKHEIA GROUP SA
125 rue de Saussure, 75017, Paris, France
Tel.: (33) 1 53 23 35 35
Web Site: http://www.makheia.com
Sales Range: $25-49.9 Million
Emp.: 230
Marketing Consulting, Corporate & Financial Communication, Brand Strategy & Advertising Services
N.A.I.C.S.: 541613
Edouard Rencker (Chm & CEO)

MAKINA TAKIM ENDUSTRISI AS
Balcik Mahallesi 3257 Sokak No 15/A, 41480, Gebze, Kocaeli, Turkiye
Tel.: (90) 2627441880
Web Site:
 https://www.makinatakim.com
Year Founded: 1957
MAKTK—(IST)
Rev.: $7,115,766
Assets: $15,962,013
Liabilities: $6,042,933
Net Worth: $9,919,080
Earnings: $2,039,182
Emp.: 190
Fiscal Year-end: 12/31/22
Cutting Tool Mfr
N.A.I.C.S.: 333515
Ali Ulker (Chm)

MAKING SCIENCE GROUP, S.A.
Calle Lopez de Hoyos 135 4, 28002, Madrid, Spain
Tel.: (34) 913090209
Web Site:
 https://www.makingscience.com
Year Founded: 2001
MAKS—(MAD)
Rev.: $224,043,048
Assets: $142,300,862
Liabilities: $126,688,993
Net Worth: $15,611,869
Earnings: ($4,861,650)
Emp.: 901
Fiscal Year-end: 12/31/22
Management Consulting Services
N.A.I.C.S.: 541613

Jose Antonio Martnez Aguilar (Founder)

MAKINO MILLING MACHINE CO., LTD.
3-19 Nakane 2-chome, Meguro-ku, Tokyo, 152-8578, Japan
Tel.: (81) 337171151   JP
Web Site: https://www.makino.co.jp
Year Founded: 1937
95B—(DEU)
Rev.: $1,634,652,450
Assets: $2,498,465,370
Liabilities: $1,080,332,580
Net Worth: $1,418,132,790
Earnings: $115,243,410
Emp.: 4,692
Fiscal Year-end: 03/31/23
Industrial Machines Mfr & Sales
N.A.I.C.S.: 333248
Shinichi Inoue (Chm & Pres)

Subsidiaries:

KANTO BUSSAN Co., Ltd.   (1)
Nihonbashi Life Science Building 10 4F 1-5-9 Nihonbashi Honcho, Chiyoda-Ku, Tokyo, 103-0023, Japan
Tel.: (81) 352040201
Web Site: http://www.kanbutsu.co.jp
Sales Range: $50-74.9 Million
Emp.: 52
Metal Working Machinery Distr
N.A.I.C.S.: 423830
Hiroshi Yamamoto (Pres)

MAKINO TECHNICAL SERVICE Co., Ltd.   (1)
1-2-5 Katsuragi, Aomori, 030-0844, Japan
Tel.: (81) 177774069
Web Site: http://www.makino-mts.co.jp
Machine Tool Maintenance Services
N.A.I.C.S.: 811310

Makino Asia Pte Ltd   (1)
2 Gul Avenue, Singapore, 629649, Singapore
Tel.: (65) 68615722
Web Site: http://www.makino.com.sg
Sales Range: $100-124.9 Million
Emp.: 500
Metalworking Machines Mfr
N.A.I.C.S.: 333519

Makino China Co., Ltd.   (1)
2 Mu Ye Road, Yu Shan, Kunshan, 215-316, Jiangsu, China
Tel.: (86) 51257778000
Web Site: http://www.makino.com.cn
Computer Numerical Control Machine Mfr
N.A.I.C.S.: 333517

Makino Europe GmbH   (1)
Kruichling 18, 73230, Kirchheim unter Teck, Germany
Tel.: (49) 70215030
Web Site: http://www.makino.eu
Holding Company
N.A.I.C.S.: 551112

Makino Europe GmbH   (1)
1 Warshavskoye sh bld 1-2 Office A201, 117105, Moscow, Russia
Tel.: (7) 4959898220
Industrial Machinery Mfr & Distr
N.A.I.C.S.: 333248

Makino France S.A.S.   (1)
22 Avenue des Nations Parc Silic Batiment Ronsard Hall A, Roissy Charles De Gaulle, 95912, Villepinte, Cedex, France
Tel.: (33) 178784320
Web Site: http://www.makino.fr
Sales Range: $50-74.9 Million
Emp.: 10
Industrial Machinery & Equipment Whslr
N.A.I.C.S.: 423830

Makino Giken Co., Ltd.   (1)
3579 Katsuyama Fujikawaguchikomachi, Minamitsuru, Yamanashi, 401-0310, Japan
Tel.: (81) 555205700
Computer Numerical Control Machinery Mfr
N.A.I.C.S.: 333248

Makino GmbH   (1)
Kruichling 18, 73230, Kirchheim unter Teck, Germany
Tel.: (49) 70215030
Industrial Machinery Mfr & Distr
N.A.I.C.S.: 333248

Makino Iberia SL   (1)
C/ Agricultura 16-18 2 4a, El Masnou, 08320, Barcelona, Spain
Tel.: (34) 935559515
Industrial Machinery Mfr & Distr
N.A.I.C.S.: 333248
Ricardo Delvillar (Country Mgr)

Makino India Private Limited   (1)
No 11 EPIP Whitefield Road, Bengaluru, 560066, India
Tel.: (91) 8067419500
Web Site: http://makinoindia.co.in
Industrial Machinery Mfr
N.A.I.C.S.: 333248

Makino Italia S.r.l.   (1)
Via Codognino Laudense 40, Cornegliano, 26854, Padua, LO, Italy
Tel.: (39) 0371697211
Sales Range: $25-49.9 Million
Emp.: 30
Industrial Machinery & Equipment Whslr
N.A.I.C.S.: 423830

Makino J Co., Ltd.   (1)
4007 Nakatsu, Aiko-gun, Aikawa, 243-0303, Kanagawa, Japan   (100%)
Tel.: (81) 462868350
Web Site: http://www.makinoj.co.jp
Sales Range: $25-49.9 Million
Emp.: 200
Engineeering Services
N.A.I.C.S.: 541330
Yasuyuki Tamura (Exec VP)

Makino Korea Co., Ltd.   (1)
Nambudaero 390, Osan, 18151, Gyeonggi-do, Korea (South)
Tel.: (82) 313771580
Industrial Machinery Mfr & Distr
N.A.I.C.S.: 333248

Makino Logistics Co., Ltd.   (1)
6804 Nakatsu, Aikawa, 243-0303, Kanagawa, Japan
Tel.: (81) 462866009
Logistics Consulting Servies
N.A.I.C.S.: 541614
Matsuda Yasuhiro (Mgr-Overseas Logistics)

Makino Mexico S de R.L. de C.V.   (1)
Retomo El Marques No 3 Parque Industrial El Marques, El Marques, 76246, Queretaro, Coahuila, Mexico
Tel.: (52) 4421016000
Web Site: http://www.makino.com
Sales Range: $25-49.9 Million
Emp.: 25
Numerical Control Machinery Mfr
N.A.I.C.S.: 334513

Makino Philippines Inc.   (1)
Unit 1 Ground Floor Admin 1 Annex 2 Building North Main Avenue, Laguna Technopark, Binan, Laguna, Philippines
Tel.: (63) 9178049589
Industrial Machinery Mfr & Distr
N.A.I.C.S.: 333248

Makino Resource Development Pte Ltd.   (1)
2 Gul Avenue, 629649, Singapore, Singapore
Tel.: (65) 68615722
Web Site: http://www.makino.com
Sales Range: $25-49.9 Million
Emp.: 11
Rolling Mill Machinery & Equipment Mfr
N.A.I.C.S.: 333517
PharkWee Chua (Pres)

Makino S.r.o.   (1)
Tuhovska 31, Bratislava, 831 06, Slovakia
Tel.: (421) 24 961 2100
Web Site: http://www.makino.eu
Emp.: 45
Machine Tool (Metal Cutting Types) Mfr
N.A.I.C.S.: 333517
Reanhard Jeruber (Mng Dir)

Makino SAS   (1)
Batiment Ronsard Hall A Paris Nord 2 22 Avenue de Nations, CS 45045, Roissy Charles De Gaulle, 95912, Villepinte, Cedex, France
Tel.: (33) 178784320
Industrial Machinery Mfr & Distr
N.A.I.C.S.: 333248

Makino Sp. z.o.o.   (1)
Ul Nowa 10, 05-500, Stara Iwiczna, Poland
Tel.: (48) 223781950
Industrial Machinery Mfr & Distr
N.A.I.C.S.: 333248

Makino Thailand Co., Ltd.   (1)
1555 Pattanakarn Road, Suanluang District Suanluang Sub-District, Bangkok, 10250, Thailand
Tel.: (66) 20170123
Web Site: http://www.makino.co.th
Sales Range: $25-49.9 Million
Emp.: 60
Machine Tool (Metal Cutting Types) Mfr
N.A.I.C.S.: 333517

Makino USA Inc.   (1)
7680 Innovation Way, Mason, OH 45040-9695   (100%)
Tel.: (513) 573-7200
Web Site: http://www.makino.com
Sales Range: $125-149.9 Million
Emp.: 300
Holding Company
N.A.I.C.S.: 333517
Don Lane (Pres)

Subsidiary (Domestic):

Makino Inc.   (2)
7680 A Innovation Way, Mason, OH 45040
Tel.: (513) 573-7200
Web Site: http://www.makino.com
Sales Range: $50-74.9 Million
Emp.: 250
Mfr System Designer, Mfr & Retailer
N.A.I.C.S.: 333517
Mark Rentschler (Mgr-Mktg)

Single Source Technologies, Inc.   (2)
2600 Superior Ct, Auburn Hills, MI 48326
Tel.: (248) 232-6232
Web Site: https://www.singlesourcetech.com
Sales Range: $1-9.9 Million
Emp.: 45
Industrial Machinery & Equipment Merchant Whslr
N.A.I.C.S.: 423830
Ricardo Marin (Engr-Sls)

Makino Vietnam Co., Ltd.   (1)
Level 2 VMT Building Lot A1F Duy Tan Street, Dich Vong Hau Ward Cau Giay District, Hanoi, Vietnam
Tel.: (84) 2437957022
Industrial Machinery Mfr & Distr
N.A.I.C.S.: 333248
Nguyen Hoa (Country Mgr)

Makino do Brasil Ltda.   (1)
Ua Emilia Marengo 260 S/91, Sao Paulo, 03336-000, SP, Brazil
Tel.: (55) 1166712532
Industrial Machinery Mfr & Distr
N.A.I.C.S.: 333248

Makino-Cnc Ileri Teknoloji ve Pazarlama Limited Sirketi   (1)
Istanbul Trakya Serbest Bolgesi Ataturk Blv Begonya Sk, Blok 1 Catalca, Istanbul, 34540, Turkiye
Tel.: (90) 2127866200
Web Site: http://www.cnc.com.tr
Sales Range: $25-49.9 Million
Emp.: 75
Machine Tool (Metal Cutting Types) Mfr
N.A.I.C.S.: 333517

PT Makino Indonesia   (1)
Jl Sriwijaya Kavling 6-8, Lippo Cikarang, Bekasi, 17550, Indonesia
Tel.: (62) 2189903366
Industrial Machinery Mfr & Distr
N.A.I.C.S.: 333248

Single Source Technologies S. de R.L. de C.V.   (1)
Retorno el Marques 3, Parque Industrial El Marques, 76246, Queretaro, Mexico
Tel.: (52) 442 101 6000
Web Site: https://www.singlesourcetech.com
Engineeering Services
N.A.I.C.S.: 541330

AND PRIVATE COMPANIES

MAKITA CORPORATION

Eduardo Medrano *(Pres)*

MAKITA CORPORATION
3-11-8 Sumiyoshi-cho, Anjo, 446-8502, Aichi, Japan
Tel.: (81) 566981711   JP
Web Site: https://www.makita.biz
Year Founded: 1915
MK2A—(DEU)
Rev: $4,900,594,510
Assets: $6,978,890,880
Liabilities: $1,193,779,220
Net Worth: $5,785,111,660
Earnings: $288,797,510
Emp.: 17,669
Fiscal Year-end: 03/31/24
Electric Power Tools, Pneumatic Tools & Garden Tools Mfr
N.A.I.C.S.: 333991
Masahiko Goto *(Chm)*

Subsidiaries:

Dolmar GmbH (1)
Jenfelder Strasse 38, Hamburg, 22045, Germany (100%)
Tel.: (49) 40669860
Web Site: http://www.dolomar.de
Sales Range: $100-124.9 Million
Emp.: 350
Garden Tool Mfr
N.A.I.C.S.: 333991
Rainer Bergseld *(Gen Mgr)*

Makita (Australia) Pty. Ltd. (1)
2 Litton Close, Pemulwuy, Sydney, 2145, NSW, Australia (100%)
Tel.: (61) 1300361690
Web Site: http://www.makita.com.au
Sales Range: $25-49.9 Million
Emp.: 50
Sale of Electric Power Tools
N.A.I.C.S.: 444140
Terry Nozawa *(Mng Dir)*

Makita (China) Co., Ltd. (1)
288 Huangpujiang Road Kunshan Economic & Technical Development Zone, Kunshan, 215335, Jiangsu, China (100%)
Tel.: (86) 512 577 07710
Web Site: http://www.makita.com.cn
Sales Range: $800-899.9 Million
Emp.: 3,000
Mfr of Electric Power Tools
N.A.I.C.S.: 333991

Makita (Kunshan) Co., Ltd. (1)
Nanzi Road, Kunshan Comprehensive Free Trade Zone, Jiangsu, 215301, China
Tel.: (86) 51257367368
Tool Mfr
N.A.I.C.S.: 333519

Makita (New Zealand) Ltd. (1)
(100%)
Tel.: (64) 9 479 8251
Web Site: https://www.makita.co.nz
Emp.: 25
Sale of Electric Power Tools
N.A.I.C.S.: 444140

Makita (Taiwan) Ltd. (1)
No 798 Sec 2 Wenhua 3rd Rd, Linkou Dist, New Taipei City, 24459, Taiwan
Tel.: (886) 286019898
Automotive Products Whslr
N.A.I.C.S.: 423120

Makita (U.K.) Ltd. (1)
Michigan Drive, Tongwell, Milton Keynes, MK15 8JD, Bucks, United Kingdom (100%)
Tel.: (44) 190 821 1678
Web Site: https://www.makitauk.com
Sales Range: $50-74.9 Million
Emp.: 150
Electric Power Tools Sales
N.A.I.C.S.: 444140
Kevin Brannigan *(Mgr-Mktg)*

Makita Benelux B.V. (1)
Park Forum 1101 Bedrijfsnummer 6051, 5657 HK, Eindhoven, Netherlands (100%)
Tel.: (31) 402064040
Web Site: http://www.makita.nl
Sales Range: $25-49.9 Million
Emp.: 70
Sale of Electric Power Tools

N.A.I.C.S.: 444140

Makita Bulgaria EOOD (1)
Street Sofia circle road No 373, Sofia, 1186, Bulgaria
Tel.: (359) 29737153
Web Site: http://www.makita.bg
Hand Tool Mfr
N.A.I.C.S.: 333991

Makita Canada, Inc. (1)
1950 Forbes Street, Whitby, L1N 7B7, ON, Canada (100%)
Tel.: (905) 571-2200
Web Site: http://www.makita.ca
Sales Range: $100-124.9 Million
Emp.: 150
Portable Electric & Cordless Power Tools Mfr
N.A.I.C.S.: 333991
Todd Okochi *(Pres)*

Makita Chile Comercial Ltda. (1)
Avenida El Parque, Santiago, Chile
Tel.: (56) 22 540 0400
Web Site: https://www.makita.cl
Sales Range: $25-49.9 Million
Emp.: 50
Electric Power Tools Sales
N.A.I.C.S.: 444140

Makita Colombia, S.A. (1)
Bodega 4 y 7 Lote 5 Hacienda Potrero Chico, Medellin, Colombia
Tel.: (57) 18966199
Sales Range: $25-49.9 Million
Emp.: 12
Hand Tool Mfr
N.A.I.C.S.: 333991

Makita Corporation - Okazaki Plant (1)
22-1 Watarishima, Nemunoki, Okazaki, 444-0232, Japan
Tel.: (81) 564433111
Hand Tool Mfr
N.A.I.C.S.: 333991

Makita Corporation of Taiwan (1)
Sec 798 Cultural Road, Taipei, 24459, Linkou District, Taiwan (100%)
Tel.: (886) 2 8601 9898
Sale of Electric Power Tools
N.A.I.C.S.: 333991

Makita Elektromos Kisgepertekesito Kft. (1)
Takarodo U 2, 8000, Szekesfehervar, Hungary (100%)
Tel.: (36) 2 250 7472
Web Site: https://www.makita.hu
Sales Range: $25-49.9 Million
Emp.: 40
Electric Power Tools Sales
N.A.I.C.S.: 444140
Shingi Heredi *(COO)*

Makita Elvaerktoj Danmark (1)
Erhvervsbyvej 14, 8700, Horsens, Denmark
Tel.: (45) 76254400
Web Site: http://www.makita.dk
Sales Range: $25-49.9 Million
Emp.: 50
Hand Tool Mfr
N.A.I.C.S.: 333991

Makita Engineering Germany GmbH (1)
Jenfelder Strasse 38, 22045, Hamburg, Germany
Tel.: (49) 40669860
Web Site: http://makita-engineering.de
Mechanical Services
N.A.I.C.S.: 238220

Makita France S.A.S. (1)
37 avenue Graham Bell ZAC Leonard de Vinci, PO Box 119, Bussy-Saint-Georges, 77607, Marne-la-Vallee, Cedex, France (55%)
Tel.: (33) 16 094 6400
Web Site: https://www.makita.fr
Sales Range: $25-49.9 Million
Emp.: 65
Electric Power Tools Sales
N.A.I.C.S.: 444140

Makita Gulf FZE (1)
Jebel Ali, PO Box 17133, Jafza, Dubai, United Arab Emirates (100%)

Tel.: (971) 4 886 0804
Web Site: https://makita.ae
Sales Range: $25-49.9 Million
Emp.: 25
Sale of Electric Power Tools
N.A.I.C.S.: 444140

Makita Hellas S.A. (1)
Tatoiou Ave 34, Athens, 13677, Acharnes, Athens, Greece (100%)
Tel.: (30) 2108071241
Web Site: https://www.makita.gr
Sales Range: $25-49.9 Million
Emp.: 25
Sale of Electric Power Tools
N.A.I.C.S.: 444140

Makita Herramientas Electricas de Argentina S.A.
Calle 11 Lote 9C Fraccion 6 Parque Industrial de Pilar, Buenos Aires, CP 1629, Argentina (100%)
Tel.: (54) 11 2322 441 100
Sales Range: Less than $1 Million
Emp.: 10
Sale of Electric Power Tools
N.A.I.C.S.: 444140

Makita International Europe Ltd. (1)
Michigan Dr, Milton Keynes, MK15 8JD, Bucks, United Kingdom (100%)
Tel.: (44) 1908211678
Sales Range: $50-74.9 Million
Emp.: 100
Sale of Electric Power Tools
N.A.I.C.S.: 423610
Koji Kato *(Mng Dir)*

Makita Kazakhstan LLP (1)
Kommunalnaya 39, 50016, Almaty, Kazakhstan
Tel.: (7) 7272330827
Tool Mfr
N.A.I.C.S.: 333519

Makita Korea Co., Ltd. (1)
Ste 901 Seocho Plz 1573 1 Seocho Dong Seocho Ku, Seoul, 137 874, Korea (South) (100%)
Tel.: (82) 234713111
Web Site: http://www.makita.co.kr
Sales Range: $25-49.9 Million
Emp.: 2
Sale of Power Tools
N.A.I.C.S.: 444140

Makita LLC (1)
1 build 1 Permskaya str, 107143, Moscow, Russia
Tel.: (7) 4959158866
Web Site: http://www.makita.ru
Hand Tool Mfr
N.A.I.C.S.: 333991

Makita Latin America Inc. (1)
10801 NW 97th St Ste 13, Medley, FL 33178
Tel.: (305) 882-0522
Web Site: https://www.makitalatinamerica.com
Sales Range: $25-49.9 Million
Emp.: 20
Industrial Power Driven Hand Tool Mfr
N.A.I.C.S.: 333991

Makita Manufacturing (Thailand) Co., Ltd. (1)
219/1 Moo 6 Tambol Bowin, Amphur Sriracha, Chon Buri, Thailand
Tel.: (66) 33004750
Tool Mfr
N.A.I.C.S.: 333519

Makita Manufacturing Europe Ltd. (1)
Hortonwood Industrial Estate Road 7, Telford, TF1 7YX, Shropshire, United Kingdom (100%)
Tel.: (44) 1952677688
Web Site: http://www.makitauk.com
Sales Range: $100-124.9 Million
Emp.: 300
Mfr of Electric Power Tools
N.A.I.C.S.: 333991
Masanori Nabetani *(Mng Dir)*

Makita Mexico, S.A. de C.V. (1)
Norte 35 780 C Col Industrial Vallejo, Del Azcapotzalco, 02300, Mexico, Mexico (100%)

Tel.: (52) 1555 368 1105
Web Site: https://www.makita.com.mx
Sales Range: $25-49.9 Million
Emp.: 100
Sale of Electric Power Tools
N.A.I.C.S.: 423610

Makita Nederland B.V. (1)
Park Forum 1101, 5657 HK, Eindhoven, Netherlands
Tel.: (31) 402064040
Web Site: http://www.makita.nl
Emp.: 8
Hand Tool Mfr
N.A.I.C.S.: 333991

Makita Norway (1)
Loxaveien 15, 1351, Rud, Norway
Tel.: (47) 67176900
Web Site: http://www.makita.no
Power Tool Distr
N.A.I.C.S.: 423710

Makita Numazu Corporation (1)
35 Ohoka Numazu, Shizuoka, 410-8535, Japan (89.35%)
Tel.: (81) 559631111
Web Site: http://www.makita.biz
Sales Range: $75-99.9 Million
Emp.: 300
Engines, Agricultural & Forestry Machinery Mfr
N.A.I.C.S.: 333618

Makita Oy (1)
Teilimaki 4, 01530, Vantaa, Finland (100%)
Tel.: (358) 9 857 8830
Web Site: https://www.makita.fi
Power Tool Mfr
N.A.I.C.S.: 333991
Yoshinori Matsumoto *(Mng Dir)*

Makita Peru S.A. (1)
Av Argentina 3119 - Zona B, Lima, Peru
Tel.: (51) 15620220
Hand Tool Mfr
N.A.I.C.S.: 333991

Makita Power Tools (H.K.) Ltd. (1)
3/F Wellness Centre 8 On Ping Street, Sha Tin, NT, China (Hong Kong) (100%)
Tel.: (852) 2 648 8683
Web Site: https://www.makita.com.hk
Sales Range: $25-49.9 Million
Emp.: 25
Sale of Electric Power Tools
N.A.I.C.S.: 444140

Makita Power Tools (Malaysia) Sdn. Bhd. (1)
Lot 824 Jalan Subang 5 Taman Perindustrian Subang, 47500, Subang Jaya, Selangor, Malaysia
Tel.: (60) 380230824
Web Site: http://www.makita.my
Automotive Products Whslr
N.A.I.C.S.: 423120

Makita Power Tools India Private Ltd. (1)
Unit II Sy No 93/3 93/4, Koralur Village Kasaba Hobli Hoskote Taluk, Bengaluru, 560067, Karnataka, India
Tel.: (91) 8022058200
Web Site: http://www.makita.in
Emp.: 4
Power Driven Hand Tool Distr
N.A.I.C.S.: 423710

Makita Romania S.R.L. (1)
Urziceni nr 31, Expo Market Doraly Pavilion R, Bucharest, 77010, Romania (100%)
Tel.: (40) 213511382
Web Site: http://www.makita.ro
Sales Range: $25-49.9 Million
Emp.: 15
Power Tools Mfr & Whslr
N.A.I.C.S.: 333991

Makita S.p.A. (1)
Via Don Luigi Sturzo 56/58, 20004, San Vittore Olona, MI, Italy (100%)
Tel.: (39) 033 152 4111
Web Site: https://www.makita.it
Sales Range: $25-49.9 Million
Emp.: 18
Sale of Electric Power Tools
N.A.I.C.S.: 444140

Makita SA (1)

MAKITA CORPORATION

Makita Corporation—(Continued)

Chemin du Vuasset 7, 1028, Préverenges, Switzerland **(100%)**
Tel.: (41) 21 811 5656
Web Site: https://www.makita.ch
Sales Range: $25-49.9 Million
Emp.: 20
Mfr of Power Tools
N.A.I.C.S.: 333991

Makita Singapore Pte. Ltd. (1)
7 Changi South Street 3, Singapore, 486348, Singapore **(100%)**
Tel.: (65) 6 546 8700
Web Site: https://www.makita.com.sg
Sales Range: $25-49.9 Million
Emp.: 20
Sale of Power Tools
N.A.I.C.S.: 444140

Makita Sp. z.o.o. (1)
ul Bestwinska 103, 43 346, Bielsko-Biala, Poland **(100%)**
Tel.: (48) 33 484 0200
Web Site: https://www.makita.pl
Sales Range: $10-24.9 Million
Emp.: 35
Sale of Electric Power Tools
N.A.I.C.S.: 423990

Makita Sweden (1)
Bergkallavagen 36 A, Box 7049, 192 07, Sollentuna, Sweden
Tel.: (46) 850581900
Web Site: http://www.makita.se
Sales Range: $25-49.9 Million
Emp.: 2
Power Tool Mfr
N.A.I.C.S.: 333991

Makita U.S.A., Inc. (1)
14930 Northam St, La Mirada, CA 90638 **(100%)**
Tel.: (714) 522-8088
Web Site: https://www.makitatools.com
Sales Range: $75-99.9 Million
Emp.: 140
Portable Electric Power Tools Mfr & Sales
N.A.I.C.S.: 423710
Ken Hefley (Exec VP-Marketing)

Subsidiary (Domestic):

Makita Corporation of America (2)
2650 Buford Hwy, Buford, GA 30518-6045 **(100%)**
Tel.: (770) 932-2901
Web Site: https://www.makitatools.com
Sales Range: $50-74.9 Million
Emp.: 125
Electric Power Tools Mfr
N.A.I.C.S.: 333991
Bradley Gillespie (Engr-Quality)

Makita Ukraine LLC (1)
Street Oleg Onikienko bldg 61, Kyiv Region, Brovary, 07400, Ukraine
Tel.: (380) 444942370
Web Site: http://www.makita.ua
Hardware & Plumbing Equipment Distr
N.A.I.C.S.: 423720

Makita Vietnam Co., Ltd. (1)
Unit 4-5-6 Block 16 18 L1-2 Street 3 VSIPII, Hoa Phu Ward, Thu Dau Mot, 084, Binh Duong, Vietnam
Tel.: (84) 2743628338
Web Site: http://makita.com.vn
Emp.: 40
Hand Tool Mfr
N.A.I.C.S.: 333991

Makita Werkzeug GmbH (1)
Kolpingstrasse 13, 1232, Vienna, Austria **(100%)**
Tel.: (43) 16162730
Web Site: http://www.makita.at
Sales Range: $25-49.9 Million
Emp.: 50
Sale of Electric Power Tools
N.A.I.C.S.: 444140

Makita Werkzeug GmbH (1)
Makita-Platz 1, 40885, Ratingen, Germany **(100%)**
Tel.: (49) 21 021 0040
Web Site: https://www.makita.de
Sales Range: $50-74.9 Million
Emp.: 160
Sale of Electric Power Tools

N.A.I.C.S.: 444140

Makita d.o.o. (1)
Brnciceva 17, Crnuce, 1231, Ljubljana, Slovenia
Tel.: (386) 59083600
Web Site: http://www.makita.si
Hardware & Plumbing Equipment Distr
N.A.I.C.S.: 423720

Makita do Brasil Ferramentas Eletricas LTDA. (1)
Rua Makita Brasil No 200 Bairro Dos Alvarengas, Sao Bernardo do Campo, 09852-080, Brazil **(90%)**
Tel.: (55) 143922411
Web Site: http://www.makita.com.br
Sales Range: $50-74.9 Million
Emp.: 230
Mfr & Sale of Electric Power Tools
N.A.I.C.S.: 333991

Makita s.r.o. (1)
Jegorovova 35, 974 01, Banska Bystrica, Slovakia
Tel.: (421) 484161772
Web Site: http://www.makita.sk
Sales Range: $25-49.9 Million
Emp.: 36
Hand Tool Mfr
N.A.I.C.S.: 333991
Ladislav Taborsky (Mgr-Sls)

Makita, F.E.S.U. Lda. (1)
Centro Empresarial de Alverca Vale das Ervas Armazem C2, 2615-187, Alverca do Ribatejo, Portugal
Tel.: (351) 219936750
Web Site: http://www.makita.pt
Sales Range: $25-49.9 Million
Emp.: 7
Hand Tool Mfr
N.A.I.C.S.: 333991

Makita, S.A. (1)
C/ Juan de la Cierva 7-15, Coslada, 28820, Coslada, Spain **(100%)**
Tel.: (34) 91 671 1262
Web Site: https://www.makita.es
Sale of Electric Power Tools
N.A.I.C.S.: 444140
Kuniyuki Imai (Mng Dir)

Makita, spol. s r.o. (1)
Kastanova 555/125d, 620 00, Brno, Czech Republic **(100%)**
Tel.: (420) 54 521 9572
Web Site: https://www.makita.cz
Sales Range: $25-49.9 Million
Emp.: 25
Electric Power Tools Sales
N.A.I.C.S.: 423610

S.A. Makita N.V. (1)
Mechelsesteenweg 323, Industriezone Guldendelle, 1800, Vilvoorde, Belgium **(100%)**
Tel.: (32) 2 257 1840
Web Site: http://www.makita.be
Sales Range: $25-49.9 Million
Emp.: 65
Sale of Electric Power Tools
N.A.I.C.S.: 444140

SC Makita EU SRL (1)
Str IC Bratianu nr164, Comuna Branesti jud Ilfov, Bucharest, 077030, Romania
Tel.: (40) 213107675
Tool Mfr
N.A.I.C.S.: 333519

MAKIVIK CORPORATION

PO Box 179, Kuujjuaq, J0M 1C0, QC, Canada
Tel.: (819) 964-2925
Web Site: http://www.makivik.org
Year Founded: 1978
Holding Company
N.A.I.C.S.: 551112
Andy Moorhouse (Corp Sec)

MAKIYA CO., LTD.

2373 Obuchi, Fuji, 417-0801, Shizuoka, Japan
Tel.: (81) 545361000
Web Site: https://www.makiya-group.co.jp
Year Founded: 1972

9890—(TKS)
Rev: $507,059,710
Assets: $251,794,730
Liabilities: $123,765,640
Net Worth: $128,029,090
Earnings: $9,610,940
Emp.: 3,200
Fiscal Year-end: 03/31/24
Supermarket Operator
N.A.I.C.S.: 445110
Yasuo Kawarasaki (Pres)

MAKKAH CONSTRUCTION & DEVELOPMENT COMPANY

Al-Aziziyah Main Street Faqih Commercial Center - 7th Floor, PO Box 7134, Makkah, 21955, Saudi Arabia
Tel.: (966) 125570377
Web Site: https://www.mcdc.com.sa
Year Founded: 1989
4100—(SAU)
Rev.: $194,905,084
Assets: $1,232,545,391
Liabilities: $141,497,742
Net Worth: $1,091,047,649
Earnings: $89,126,895
Emp.: 1,152
Fiscal Year-end: 12/31/23
Construction & Real Estate Services
N.A.I.C.S.: 531390
Abdul Rahman Abdul Qader Fakieh (Chm)

MAKKAH MADINAH HOLDINGS LTD

7th Floor Rose Rayhaan Tower Sheikh Zayed Road, PO Box 125168, Dubai, United Arab Emirates
Tel.: (971) 43503596
Web Site: http://www.mm-holdings.com
Sales Range: $1-9.9 Million
Investment Services
N.A.I.C.S.: 523999
Muin El Saleh (CEO)

MAKLOC BUILDINGS INC.

706 17 Avenue, Nisku, T9E 7T1, AB, Canada
Tel.: (780) 955-2951
Web Site: http://www.makloc.com
Year Founded: 1971
Rev.: $10,626,605
Emp.: 50
Building Construction Services
N.A.I.C.S.: 236220

MAKO GOLD LIMITED

Level 6 144 Edward Street, Brisbane, 4000, QLD, Australia
Tel.: (61) 730760727 AU
Web Site: https://www.makogold.com.au
Year Founded: 2015
MKG—(ASX)
Rev.: $12,585
Assets: $24,132,786
Liabilities: $412,873
Net Worth: $23,719,914
Earnings: ($830,056)
Fiscal Year-end: 06/30/24
Mining & Exploration Services
N.A.I.C.S.: 213114
Peter Ledwidge (Mng Dir)

MAKO HYDROCARBONS LIMITED

14 Emerald Terrace, West Perth, 6005, WA, Australia
Tel.: (61) 8 9226 0443
Web Site: http://www.makohydrocarbons.com
Sales Range: Less than $1 Million
Oil & Gas Exploration
N.A.I.C.S.: 211120
Robert Paul Griese (Pres & Mng Dir)

INTERNATIONAL PUBLIC

MAKO MINING CORP.

595 Burrard Street Suite 2833, Vancouver, V7X 1K8, BC, Canada
Tel.: (203) 862-7059 BC
Web Site: http://www.makominingcorp.com
Year Founded: 2004
MAKOF—(OTCQX)
Rev.: $1,398,000
Assets: $49,429,000
Liabilities: $32,519,000
Net Worth: $16,910,000
Earnings: ($12,129,000)
Fiscal Year-end: 12/31/20
Mineral Exploration Services
N.A.I.C.S.: 213114
Akiba Leisman (CEO)

Subsidiaries:

Goldsource Mines Inc. (1)
570 Granville Street Suite 501, Vancouver, V6C 3P1, BC, Canada
Tel.: (604) 694-1760
Web Site: https://www.goldsourcemines.com
Assets: $9,334,307
Liabilities: $646,816
Net Worth: $8,687,491
Earnings: ($7,134,242)
Fiscal Year-end: 12/31/2020
Mineral Exploration Services
N.A.I.C.S.: 213114
N. Eric Fier (Chm & COO)

MAKOLAB SA

Ogrodowa 8, 91-062, Lodz, Poland
Tel.: (48) 422392850
Web Site: https://www.makolab.com
Year Founded: 1989
Business Consulting Services
N.A.I.C.S.: 541611
Michal Hertel (Head-Comm & Bus Dev)

MAKOTEX A.D.

Nikola Parapunov St 41, 1000, Skopje, North Macedonia
Tel.: (389) 23238927
Web Site: https://www.makotex.com.mk
Year Founded: 1949
MAKS—(MAC)
Rev.: $318,235
Assets: $3,903,398
Liabilities: $129,346
Net Worth: $3,774,052
Earnings: $248,686
Fiscal Year-end: 12/31/19
Textile Product Whslr
N.A.I.C.S.: 424990

MAKOTO CONSTRUCTION CO., LTD.

46 Fukuda, Naka-ku, Sakai, 599-8241, Osaka, Japan
Tel.: (81) 722348410
Web Site: https://www.makoto-gr.com
Year Founded: 1991
8995—(TKS)
Rev.: $21,079,290
Assets: $39,805,420
Liabilities: $13,616,600
Net Worth: $26,188,820
Earnings: $865,910
Emp.: 23
Fiscal Year-end: 03/31/24
Building Construction Services
N.A.I.C.S.: 236115

MAKPETROL A.D.

Sv Kiril I Metodij br 4, 1000, Skopje, North Macedonia
Tel.: (389) 23112144
Web Site: https://www.makpetrol.com.mk
Year Founded: 1947
MPT—(MAC)
Rev.: $543,480,456
Assets: $167,187,368

Liabilities: $26,268,525
Net Worth: $140,918,842
Earnings: $14,121,588
Fiscal Year-end: 12/31/23
Crude Oil & Oil Products Distr & Producer
N.A.I.C.S.: 211120

MAKPROMET AD
Dr Slobodan Jovanovski 3, 2000, Stip, 2000, North Macedonia
Tel.: (389) 32390552
Web Site: https://www.makpromet.com.mk
Year Founded: 1973
MAKP—(MAC)
Rev.: $6,002,837
Assets: $11,316,161
Liabilities: $5,914,614
Net Worth: $5,401,547
Earnings: $251,395
Fiscal Year-end: 12/31/19
Food Products Mfr
N.A.I.C.S.: 311423

MAKSTIL A.D.
16 Makedonska Brigada 18, 1000, Skopje, North Macedonia
Tel.: (389) 23287023
Web Site: https://www.makstil.com
Year Founded: 1997
STIL—(MAC)
Rev.: $148,810,755
Assets: $145,687,177
Liabilities: $81,536,874
Net Worth: $64,150,302
Earnings: $6,394,155
Emp.: 973
Fiscal Year-end: 12/31/23
Rolled Steel Products Mfr
N.A.I.C.S.: 331221

MAKUS, INC.
73 Bongeunsa-ro 44-gil, Gangnam-gu, Seoul, 06146, Korea (South)
Tel.: (82) 234909500
Web Site: https://www.makus.co.kr
Year Founded: 1997
093520—(KRS)
Rev.: $148,616,597
Assets: $219,790,619
Liabilities: $148,184,580
Net Worth: $71,606,039
Earnings: $16,976,002
Emp.: 49
Fiscal Year-end: 12/31/22
Semiconductor Product Distr
N.A.I.C.S.: 423690

MALABAR RESOURCES LIMITED
Level 26 259 George Street, Sydney, 2000, NSW, Australia
Tel.: (61) 2 8248 1272
Web Site: http://www.malabarcoal.com.au
Coal Mining
N.A.I.C.S.: 212115
Wayne Seabrook *(Chm)*

MALACCA STRAITS ACQUISITION COMPANY LIMITED
Unit 601-2 St George's Building 2 Ice House Street, Central, China (Hong Kong)
Tel.: (852) 21060888   Ky
Year Founded: 2019
MLAC—(NASDAQ)
Rev.: $266,386
Assets: $5,512,051
Liabilities: $14,571,649
Net Worth: ($9,059,598)
Earnings: $3,008,083
Emp.: 2
Fiscal Year-end: 12/31/22
Investment Services

N.A.I.C.S.: 523999
Gordon Lo *(Pres & CEO)*

MALACCA TRUST WUWUNGAN INSURANCE PT
Chase Plaza 7th Floor Jl Jend Sudirman Kav 21, Jakarta, 12920, Indonesia
Tel.: (62) 2125989835
Web Site: https://www.mtwi.co.id
MTWI—(INDO)
Rev.: $65,717,157
Assets: $105,682,895
Liabilities: $87,455,318
Net Worth: $18,227,577
Earnings: $795,479
Emp.: 112
Fiscal Year-end: 12/31/23
Investment Management Service
N.A.I.C.S.: 525990
Vientje Harijanto *(Chm)*

MALAM SYSTEMS LTD.
11 Gush Etzion St, Giv'at Shemu'el, 54030, Israel
Tel.: (972) 35312300
Web Site: http://www.malam.com
Year Founded: 1996
Sales Range: $100-124.9 Million
Emp.: 900
Provider of Computer Programming Services
N.A.I.C.S.: 541511
Shai Basson *(Sr Exec VP-Projects)*

Subsidiaries:

Modern Software Technologies Ltd.   (1)
6 Ravnizki St, Petah Tiqwa, 49277, Israel   (66%)
Tel.: (972) 39115511
Web Site: http://www.mostsoftware.com
Sales Range: $25-49.9 Million
Emp.: 80
Software Conversion Tools & Services
N.A.I.C.S.: 541512

MALAM-TEAM LTD.
7 Martin Gehl Street, Petah Tiqwa, Israel
Tel.: (972) 39278444
Web Site: https://www.malamteam.com
Year Founded: 1972
MLTM—(TAE)
Rev.: $836,841,263
Assets: $647,141,031
Liabilities: $477,655,470
Net Worth: $169,485,562
Earnings: $17,736,427
Emp.: 4,200
Fiscal Year-end: 12/31/23
Computer System Design Services
N.A.I.C.S.: 541512
Udi Weintraub *(Co-CEO)*

Subsidiaries:

4Cast Ltd.   (1)
53 Avshalom Gissin Street, Petah Tikva, 4922450, Israel
Tel.: (972) 39787659
Web Site: http://4cast-solutions.com
Economic Research Services
N.A.I.C.S.: 541720
Nissim Titan *(CEO)*

Subsidiary (US):

4Cast Inc.   (2)
259 W Front St Ste 6, Missoula, MT 59802
Tel.: (406) 926-2840
Defense & Security Services
N.A.I.C.S.: 928110

Comtec Ltd.   (1)
18 Hasivim st, PO Box 7431, Petach Tikva, 49517, Israel
Tel.: (972) 39201666
Web Site: https://www.comtecglobal.com
Information Technology & Services

N.A.I.C.S.: 541511
Subsidiary (Domestic):

Knowledge Control Systems Ltd.   (2)
18 Hasivim St, PO Box 7431, Petach Tikva, 49517, Israel
Tel.: (972) 37710555
Web Site: http://www.kc-sys.com
Information Technology & Services
N.A.I.C.S.: 541511

Eltel Technologistics, Ltd.   (1)
7 Martin Gehl Street, Petach Tikva, Israel
Tel.: (972) 39205253
Web Site: http://www.eltel.co.il
Computer Software Development Services
N.A.I.C.S.: 541511

Etype-Omnitech Ltd.   (1)
Haofan 5, Petach Tikva, Israel
Tel.: (972) 700702323
Web Site: http://www.etype.co.il
Information Technology & Services
N.A.I.C.S.: 541511

Malam Payroll Ltd.   (1)
Am Veolamo 8, PO Box 34060, Jerusalem, 91340, Israel
Tel.: (972) 26707066
Web Site: http://www.malam-payroll.com
Payroll Services
N.A.I.C.S.: 541214
Uri Salah *(CEO)*

Subsidiary (Domestic):

Malam Provident Fund Operation Ltd.   (2)
7 Martin Gehl Street, Petah Tikva, Israel
Tel.: (972) 26707066
Web Site: http://www.malam-gemel.com
Computer Software Development Services
N.A.I.C.S.: 541511

McKit Systems Ltd.   (1)
Gush Etzion St, Giv'at Shemu'el, 54030, Israel
Tel.: (972) 3734450013
Web Site: https://www.mckit.co.il
Emp.: 100
Information Technology & Services
N.A.I.C.S.: 541511

TEAM Ltd.   (1)
7 Martin Gehl Street, Petah Tiqwa, Israel
Tel.: (972) 39278220
Emp.: 1,200
Computer System Design Services
N.A.I.C.S.: 541512

The Information Experts Ltd.   (1)
18 Aharon Bart St, Petach Tikva, 49514, Israel
Tel.: (972) 36226201
Web Site: https://www.t-i-e.co.il
Information Technology & Services
N.A.I.C.S.: 541511
Avi Norman *(CEO)*

MALANI PADAYACHEE & ASSOCIATES (PTY) LTD.
147 Bram Fischer Drive Ferndale, Randburg, 2194, Johannesburg, South Africa
Tel.: (27) 11 781 9710
Web Site: http://www.mpamot.co.za
Engineering & Other Consulting Services
N.A.I.C.S.: 541330
Malani Padayachee-Saman *(CEO)*

MALATH COOPERATIVE INSURANCE COMPANY
Prince Mohammed Bin Abdulaziz Road, PO Box 99763, Riyadh, 11625, Saudi Arabia
Tel.: (966) 114168222
Web Site: http://www.malath.com.sa
Year Founded: 2007
8020—(SAU)
Rev.: $241,337,688
Assets: $365,848,554
Liabilities: $276,140,515
Net Worth: $89,708,039
Earnings: ($7,549,660)

Emp.: 331
Fiscal Year-end: 12/31/22
Insurance Management Services
N.A.I.C.S.: 524298

MALAWI STOCK EXCHANGE
Old Reserve Bank Building Victoria Avenue, Private Bag 270, Blantyre, Malawi
Tel.: (265) 184233
Web Site: http://www.mse.co.mw
Stock Exchange Services
N.A.I.C.S.: 523210
Augustine Chithenga *(Chm)*

MALAYAN BANKING BERHAD
Menara Maybank, 100 Jalan Tun Perak, 50050, Kuala Lumpur, Malaysia
Tel.: (60) 320708833
Web Site: https://www.maybank.com
Year Founded: 1960
1155—(KLS)
Rev.: $15,633,250,380
Assets: $219,822,667,268
Liabilities: $197,905,943,070
Net Worth: $21,916,724,198
Earnings: $2,059,574,963
Emp.: 42,000
Fiscal Year-end: 12/31/21
Commercial Banking Services
N.A.I.C.S.: 522110
Amirul Feisal Wan Zahir *(CFO-Grp)*

Subsidiaries:

Amanah Mutual Berhad   (1)
34th Floor Menara PNB 201-A Jalan Tun Razak, 50400, Kuala Lumpur, Malaysia
Tel.: (60) 320340800
Investment Management Service
N.A.I.C.S.: 523940

BinaFikir Sdn. Bhd   (1)
31 Menara Maybank 100 Jalan Tun Perak, 50050, Kuala Lumpur, Malaysia
Tel.: (60) 3 2059 1989
Web Site: http://www.binafikir.com
Emp.: 11
Financial Advisory Services
N.A.I.C.S.: 523999
Zain Bador *(Dir)*

Etiqa General Insurance (Cambodia) Plc.   (1)
Maybank Tower Level 3 No 43, Preah Norodom Boulevard Sangkat Phsar Thmey 3 Khan Daun Penh, Phnom Penh, Cambodia
Tel.: (855) 23212311
Web Site: http://www.etiqa.com.kh
Insurance Services
N.A.I.C.S.: 524210
Mohd Najib Abdullah *(Chm)*

Etiqa General Insurance Berhad   (1)
Ground Floor Akademi Etiqa 23 Jalan Melaka, 50100, Kuala Lumpur, Malaysia   (100%)
Tel.: (60) 1300138888
Rev.: $332,087,338
Assets: $1,267,433,976
Liabilities: $1,008,793,078
Net Worth: $258,640,898
Earnings: $18,669,172
Fiscal Year-end: 12/31/2019
Life Insurance Sales & Services
N.A.I.C.S.: 524298
Fukhairudin Mohd Yusof *(CEO)*

Etiqa Insurance & Takaful Berhad   (1)
Level 19 Mayban Life Tower Dataran Maybank 1 Jalan Maarof, 59000, Kuala Lumpur, Malaysia   (100%)
Tel.: (60) 3 2785 6565
Web Site: http://www.etiqa.com.my
Life Insurance Products & Financial Advice Services
N.A.I.C.S.: 524298

Etiqa Insurance Pte. Ltd.   (1)
One Raffles Quay 22-01 North Tower, Singapore, 048583, Singapore
Tel.: (65) 68878777
Web Site: https://www.etiqa.com.sg

MALAYAN BANKING BERHAD

Malayan Banking Berhad—(Continued)
Insurance Services
N.A.I.C.S.: 524210
Yap Chee Keong *(Chief Risk Officer)*

Etiqa Life & General Assurance Philippines Inc. (1)
2/F and 3/F Morning Star Center 347 Sen Gil J Puyat Avenue, Makati, 1209, Philippines
Tel.: (63) 288901758
Web Site: https://etiqa.com.ph
General Insurance Services
N.A.I.C.S.: 524210

Etiqa Life Insurance (Cambodia) Plc. (1)
Maybank Tower Level 3 No 43, Preah Norodom Boulevard Sangkat Phsar Thmey 3 Khan Daun Penh, Phnom Penh, Cambodia
Tel.: (855) 15212321
Insurance Services
N.A.I.C.S.: 524210
Johan Ariffin *(Chm)*

Etiqa Offshore Insurance (L) Ltd. (1)
Level 11B Block 4 Office Tower Financial Park Complex Jalan Merdeka, 87000, Labuan, Malaysia
Tel.: (60) 87417672
Web Site: https://www.etiqa.com.my
Sales Range: $50-74.9 Million
Emp.: 15
Insurance Management Services
N.A.I.C.S.: 524298

MIB Securities India Private Limited (1)
Unit No 1101 11th Floor A Wing Kanakia Wallstreet, Chakala Andheri E, Mumbai, 400 093, India
Tel.: (91) 2242232600
Investment Banking & Security Services
N.A.I.C.S.: 523150

Mayban (Nominees) Sdn Bhd (1)
14 Floor Menara Maybank, 100 Jalan Tun Perak, 50050, Kuala Lumpur, Malaysia (100%)
Tel.: (60) 32347812
Web Site: http://www.maybank2u.com.my
Stock, Shares, Unit Trusts, Income Collection, Corporate & Proxy Services
N.A.I.C.S.: 523150

Mayban (Nominees) Sendirian Berhad (1)
14 Floor Menara Maybank 100 Jalan Tun Perak, 50050, Kuala Lumpur, Malaysia
Tel.: (60) 3 234 7812
Commercial Banking Services
N.A.I.C.S.: 522110
Redwan Hashim *(Mgr)*

Mayban International Trust (Labuan) Bhd (1)
Level 16 (B) Main Office Tower Financial Park Complex, Jalan Merdeka, 87000, Labuan, FT, Malaysia (100%)
Tel.: (60) 87416621
Web Site: http://www.maybank2u.com.my
Trust & Administrative Services
N.A.I.C.S.: 523150

Mayban Investment Management Sdn. Bhd (1)
Level 13 Tower C No 1 Jalan Maarof, 59000, Kuala Lumpur, Malaysia
Tel.: (60) 3 2297 7888
Web Site: http://www.maybank.com
Investment Management Service
N.A.I.C.S.: 523999

Mayban Life International (Labuan) Ltd. (1)
Level 11 B Block 4 Office Tower Financial Park, Labuan Complex, Jalan Merdeka, 87000, Labuan, WP, Malaysia (100%)
Tel.: (60) 87582588
Web Site: http://www.maybank2u.com.my
Offshore Life Insurance & Investment Products
N.A.I.C.S.: 524210

Mayban Nominees (Asing) Sdn. Bhd. (1)
Level 14 14th Flr Menara Maybank 100 Jln Tun Perak, Kuala Lumpur, 50050, Malaysia
Tel.: (60) 320747812

Web Site: http://www.maybank.com.my
Commercial Banking Services
N.A.I.C.S.: 522110

Mayban Trustees Berhad (1)
Level 8 Menara Maybank 100 Jalan Tun Perak, 50050, Kuala Lumpur, Malaysia
Tel.: (60) 320788363
Web Site: http://www.maybank.com
Sales Range: $50-74.9 Million
Emp.: 50
Commercial Banking Services
N.A.I.C.S.: 522110

Mayban Ventures Sdn. Bhd. (1)
41st Floor Menara Maybank 100 Jalan Tun Perak, 50050, Kuala Lumpur, Malaysia
Tel.: (60) 3 2032 2188
Web Site: http://www.maybanventures.com.my
Sales Range: $50-74.9 Million
Emp.: 20
Financial Services
N.A.I.C.S.: 523999

Mayban-JAIC Capital Management Sdn. Bhd (1)
Tingkat 20 West Wing Menara Maybank No 100 Jalan Tun Perak, Kuala Lumpur, 50050, Malaysia
Tel.: (60) 3 20322188
Web Site: http://www.maybank.com
Commercial Banking Services
N.A.I.C.S.: 522110

Maybank Asset Management Group Berhad (1)
Level 5 Tower A Dataran Maybank 1 Jalan Maarof, 59000, Kuala Lumpur, Malaysia (100%)
Tel.: (60) 322977833
Web Site: https://www.maybank-am.com
Banking Services
N.A.I.C.S.: 523150
Idris Kechot *(Chm)*

Maybank Asset Management Singapore Pte Ltd. (1)
2 Battery Road 08-01 Maybank Tower, Singapore, 049907, Singapore
Tel.: (65) 62315080
Web Site: https://www.maybank-am.com.sg
Investment Banking & Security Services
N.A.I.C.S.: 523150

Maybank International (L) Limited (1)
Level 16B Main Office Tower Financial Park, Jalan Merdeka, 87000, Labuan, Malaysia (100%)
Tel.: (60) 87414406
Web Site: http://www.maybank2u.com.my
Sales Range: $50-74.9 Million
Offshore Banking Services Including Foreign Currency Deposits & Loans, Trade Financing, Treasury Services & Islamic Banking Solutions
N.A.I.C.S.: 522110

Maybank International Islamic Banking Operations (1)
Level 16 (B) Main Office Tower Financial Park, Jalan Merdeka, 87000, Labuan, Malaysia (100%)
Tel.: (60) 87414406
Web Site: http://www.maybank2u.com.my
Sales Range: $50-74.9 Million
Emp.: 31
Offshore Islamic Banking Solutions
N.A.I.C.S.: 522110

Maybank Islamic Asset Management Sdn Bhd (1)
Level 12 Tower C Dataran Maybank1 Jalan Maarof, 59000, Kuala Lumpur, Malaysia
Tel.: (60) 322977872
Web Site: https://www.maybank-am.com
Investment Banking & Security Services
N.A.I.C.S.: 523150

Maybank Kim Eng Holdings Limited (1)
50 North Canal Road, Singapore, 59304, Singapore (96.87%)
Tel.: (65) 6231 5000
Web Site: http://www.maybank-ke.com
Sales Range: $300-349.9 Million
Emp.: 500
Investment Services
N.A.I.C.S.: 523150

Subsidiary (Non-US):

Kim Eng Securities (Hong Kong) Limited (2)
Level 30 3 Pacific Place, 1 Queen's Road East, Central, China (Hong Kong) (100%)
Tel.: (852) 2268 0800
Sales Range: $50-74.9 Million
Emp.: 55
Investment Services
N.A.I.C.S.: 523150

Kim Eng Securities India Private Limited (2)
2nd Fl the International 16 Maharishi Karve Marg Churchgate, Mumbai, 400 020, India
Tel.: (91) 22 6623 2600
Investment Services
N.A.I.C.S.: 523999
Jigar Shah *(CEO)*

Maybank ATR Kim Eng Capital Partners, Inc. (2)
17/F Tower One and Exchange Plaza Ayala Triangle Ayala Avenue, Makati, 1226, Metro Manila, Philippines
Tel.: (63) 2 849 8988
Web Site: http://www.atrkimeng.com
Sales Range: $50-74.9 Million
Emp.: 100
Investment Banking Services
N.A.I.C.S.: 523150

Subsidiary (Domestic):

ATR Asset Management, Inc. (3)
8th Floor 8 Rockwell Bldg Hidalgo Drive, Rockwell Center, Makati, Philippines (82.7%)
Tel.: (63) 288147800
Web Site: http://www.atram.com.ph
Sales Range: $50-74.9 Million
Emp.: 30
Mutual Fund Management Services
N.A.I.C.S.: 523150

ATR KimEng Land, Inc. (3)
Unit 811 Tower One & Exchange Plaza, Ayala Triangle Ayala Avenue, Makati, 1226, Philippines
Tel.: (63) 28931150
Web Site: http://www.maybank-atrke.com
Emp.: 2
Real Estate Development Services
N.A.I.C.S.: 531390

AsianLife & General Assurance Corporation (3)
2/F and 3/F Morning Star Center 347 Sen Gil J Puyat Avenue, Makati, 1200, Philippines
Tel.: (63) 28901758
Web Site: http://www.asianlife.com.ph
Emp.: 200
Insurance Services
N.A.I.C.S.: 524113
Manuel N. Tordesillas *(Pres & CEO)*

Subsidiary (Domestic):

AsianLife Financial Assurance Corporation (4)
Ground Floor - 3rd Floor Morning Star Center 347 Sen Gil J Puyat Ave, Makati, 1200, Philippines (70%)
Tel.: (63) 28901758
Web Site: http://www.asianlife.com.ph
Fire Insurance Services
N.A.I.C.S.: 524113

Subsidiary (Domestic):

Maybank ATR Kim Eng Securities, Inc. (3)
17/F Tower One & Exchange Plaza, Ayala Triangle Ayala Avenue, Makati, 1226, Metro Manila, Philippines (100%)
Tel.: (63) 28 849 8888
Web Site: http://www.atrkimengsecurities.com
Sales Range: $50-74.9 Million
Emp.: 100
Investment Services
N.A.I.C.S.: 523150
Lorenzo Andres T. Roxas *(Chm & Pres)*

Subsidiary (Non-US):

Maybank Investment Bank Berhad (2)

INTERNATIONAL PUBLIC

32nd Floor Menara Maybank 100 Jalan Tun Perak, 50050, Kuala Lumpur, Malaysia
Tel.: (60) 320591888
Web Site: https://www.maybank2u.com.my
Emp.: 500
Investment Services
N.A.I.C.S.: 523999
John Chong *(CEO)*

Maybank Kim Eng Securities (London) Ltd. (2)
1st Fl Pnb House, 77 Queen Victoria St, London, EC4V 4AY, United Kingdom (100%)
Tel.: (44) 20 7332 0221
Web Site: http://www.maybank-ke.com
Sales Range: $50-74.9 Million
Emp.: 10
Securities Brokerage
N.A.I.C.S.: 523150

Maybank Kim Eng Securities (Thailand) Public Company Limited (2)
999/9 The Offices at Central World Floors 20 21 & 24, Rama 1 Road Pathumwan, Bangkok, 10330, Thailand (100%)
Tel.: (66) 2 658 6300
Web Site: http://www.kimeng.co.th
Securities Dealer
N.A.I.C.S.: 523150

Maybank Kim Eng Securities JSC (2)
1st Floor 255 Tran Hung Dao Street, District 1, Ho Chi Minh City, Vietnam
Tel.: (84) 8 3838 6636
Investment Services
N.A.I.C.S.: 523999

Subsidiary (Domestic):

Maybank Kim Eng Securities Pte. Ltd (2)
50 North Canal Road, Singapore, 59304, Singapore (100%)
Tel.: (65) 6231 5000
Web Site: http://www.maybank-ke.com.sg
Rev.: $57,900,000
Emp.: 250
Stock & Share Brokers
N.A.I.C.S.: 523150

Subsidiary (US):

Maybank Kim Eng Securities USA Inc. (2)
400 Park Ave 11th Fl, New York, NY 10022 (100%)
Tel.: (212) 688-8886
Web Site: http://www.kimeng.com
Sales Range: $50-74.9 Million
Emp.: 12
Investment Services
N.A.I.C.S.: 523150
Benedict Perez *(Mng Dir-Asian Equity Sls)*

Subsidiary (Non-US):

PT Kim Eng Securities (2)
Plaza Bapindo Citibank Tower 17th Floor Jl Jend Sudirman Kav 54-55, Jakarta, 12190, Indonesia
Tel.: (62) 21 255 71188
Investment Services
N.A.I.C.S.: 523999

Maybank Nominees (Singapore) Private Limited (1)
16 Raffles Quay 01-04 Hong Leong Bldg, Singapore, 048581, Singapore
Tel.: (65) 62200190
Securities Brokerage Services
N.A.I.C.S.: 523150

Maybank Philippines, Incorporated (1)
Legaspi Towers 300 Roxas Blvd, Corner P Ocampo Sr Street, Manila, 1100, Malate, Philippines (100%)
Tel.: (63) 25237777
Web Site: http://www.maybank.com.my
Financial Products & Services for Philippine Retail & Business Sectors
N.A.I.C.S.: 525990

Maybank Securities (London) Limited (1)
1st Floor PNB House 77 Queen Victoria St, London, EC4V 4AY, United Kingdom
Tel.: (44) 2073320221

Investment Banking & Security Services
N.A.I.C.S.: 523150

Maybank Securities (Thailand) Public Company Limited (1)
999/9 The Offices at Central World 20th - 21st Floor and 25th Floor, Rama 1 Road Pathumwan, Bangkok, 10330, Thailand
Tel.: (66) 26586300
Investment Banking & Security Services
N.A.I.C.S.: 523150

Maybank Securities Pte Ltd. (1)
50 North Canal Road, Singapore, 059304, Singapore
Tel.: (65) 64321888
Web Site: https://www.maybank.com
Investment Banking & Security Services
N.A.I.C.S.: 523150

Maybank Securities USA Inc. (1)
400 Park Ave 11th Fl, New York, NY 10022
Tel.: (212) 688-8886
Investment Banking & Security Services
N.A.I.C.S.: 523150

Maybank Securities, Inc. (1)
17/F Tower One and Exchange Plaza Ayala Triangle Ayala Avenue, Makati, 1226, Philippines
Tel.: (63) 288498888
Web Site: https://www.maybank-atrke.com
Investment Banking & Security Services
N.A.I.C.S.: 523150

PT Asuransi Etiqa Internasional Indonesia (1)
CHUBB Square Level Mezzanine unit A and B Jalan MH Thamrin Kav 10, Central Jakarta Administrative City, Jakarta, 10230, Indonesia
Tel.: (62) 2129261801
Web Site: https://www.etiqa.co.id
Insurance Services
N.A.I.C.S.: 524210

PT Bank Maybank Indocorp (1)
17th Floor Sona Topas Tower Jalan Jenderal Sudirman Kav 26, Jakarta, 12920, Indonesia
Tel.: (62) 21 250 6446
Commercial Banking Services
N.A.I.C.S.: 522110

PT Bank Maybank Indonesia Tbk. (1)
Gedung Sentral Senayan III Floor Jl Asia Afrika No 8, Senayan Gelora Bung Karno, Jakarta, 10270, Pusat, Indonesia (97.29%)
Tel.: (62) 2129228857
Web Site: http://www.maybank.co.id
Sales Range: $5-14.9 Billion
Financial Banking Services
N.A.I.C.S.: 521110

PT Maybank Asset Management (1)
Sentral Senayan 3 Building Mezzanine Floor Jl Asia Afrika No 8, Senayan-Gelora Bung Karno Jakarta, Jakarta, 10270, Indonesia
Tel.: (62) 2180657701
Web Site: https://www.maybank-am.co.id
Banking Services
N.A.I.C.S.: 523150
Badrul Hisyam Abu Bakar (Commissioner)

PT Maybank Indonesia Finance (1)
Central Senayan 3 22nd Floor Jl Asia Africa No 8, Gelora Bung Karno Senayan, Jakarta, 10270, Indonesia
Tel.: (62) 2180668500
Web Site: https://www.maybank-ke.co.id
Investment Banking & Security Services
N.A.I.C.S.: 523150

MALAYAN DACHING CO. PTE. LTD.
5 Tanjong Penjuru Crescent, Singapore, 608970, Singapore
Tel.: (65) 6763 4545   SG
Web Site:
  http://www.malayandaching.com
Year Founded: 1955
Mechanical Scale & Measurement Equipment Mfr; Industrial & Civil Engineering & Construction Services
N.A.I.C.S.: 333998

Chris Chong (Dir-Plant Engrg & Construction Svcs)
Subsidiaries:

Metall-Treat Industries Pte. Ltd. (1)
28/30 Gul Ave, Singapore, 629670, Singapore
Tel.: (65) 63040018
Web Site: http://www.metall-treat.com
Emp.: 33
Metal Surface Treatment & Coating Services
N.A.I.C.S.: 332812
Lim Tay Yan (Mng Dir)

MALAYAN FLOUR MILLS BERHAD
Suite 28 01 Level 28 Menara Citibank 165 Jalan Ampang, 50450, Kuala Lumpur, Malaysia
Tel.: (60) 321700999
Web Site: https://www.mfm.com.my
Year Founded: 1961
MFLOUR—(KLS)
Rev.: $617,051,852
Assets: $578,079,788
Liabilities: $267,795,556
Net Worth: $310,284,233
Earnings: $32,592,593
Emp.: 2,837
Fiscal Year-end: 12/31/22
Flour Mills
N.A.I.C.S.: 311211
Wai Mun Mah (Sec)
Subsidiaries:

Mekong Flour Mills Ltd. (1)
Road No 3 Phu My I Industrial Zone, Phu My Ward Phu My Town, Vung Tau, Vietnam
Tel.: (84) 2543895588
Web Site: https://www.mekongflour.com
Flour Product Mfr
N.A.I.C.S.: 311211

Vimaflour Ltd. (1)
Cai Lan Industrial Park, Ha Long, Quang Ninh, Vietnam
Tel.: (84) 2033845263
Web Site: https://vimaflour.vn
Flour Product Mfr
N.A.I.C.S.: 311211

MALAYAN UNITED INDUSTRIES BERHAD
189 Jalan Ampang, 50450, Kuala Lumpur, Malaysia
Tel.: (60) 321451366
Web Site: https://www.muiglobal.com
Year Founded: 1960
MUIIND—(KLS)
Rev.: $102,219,048
Assets: $559,554,497
Liabilities: $287,337,354
Net Worth: $272,217,143
Earnings: $3,338,624
Fiscal Year-end: 06/30/23
Holding Company
N.A.I.C.S.: 551112
Chik Siong Lee (Co-Sec)
Subsidiaries:

Corus Hotels Plc (1)
Traditional Barn Rossway Park, Berkhamsted, HP4 3TZ, Hertfordshire, United Kingdom
Tel.: (44) 1442285070
Web Site: https://www.corushotels.com
Sales Range: $150-199.9 Million
Emp.: 25
Hotel
N.A.I.C.S.: 721110

Subsidiary (Domestic):

County Hotels Group Plc (2)
Great Hey Dr, Telford, TF7 4DT, United Kingdom
Tel.: (44) 1952429977
Web Site: http://www.qhotels.co.uk
Hotel Operator
N.A.I.C.S.: 721110

Steven Essex (Mgr)

MUI Properties Berhad (1)
189 Jln Ampang Taman U Thant, 50450, Kuala Lumpur, Malaysia
Tel.: (60) 321451366
Web Site:
  https://www.muiproperties.com.my
Rev.: $17,577,566
Assets: $102,421,799
Liabilities: $8,882,963
Net Worth: $93,538,836
Earnings: $8,738,413
Fiscal Year-end: 06/30/2023
Property Development Services
N.A.I.C.S.: 531311
Chik Siong Lee (Co-Sec)

Subsidiary (Non-US):

Ming Court Hotel (Vancouver) Ltd (2)
8911 Beckwith Rd Suite 220, Vancouver, V6X 1V4, BC, Canada
Tel.: (604) 207-2251
Mortgage Banking Services
N.A.I.C.S.: 522310

Malayan United Security Services Sdn Bhd (1)
G-15-1 Jalan Kolam Air 2 Nongchik Riverside Commercial, 80100, Johor Bahru, Malaysia
Tel.: (60) 72073770
Web Site:
  https://unitedsecurityservices.com.my
Security Guard Services
N.A.I.C.S.: 561612

Natloyal (M) Sdn Bhd (1)
189B 21st Floor Jalan Ampang, Kuala Lumpur, 50450, Malaysia
Tel.: (60) 321451366
Property Investment Services
N.A.I.C.S.: 531311

Network Foods Industries Sdn Bhd (1)
Lot 3 Persiaran Raja Muda Seksyen 16, 40000, Shah Alam, Selangor, Malaysia
Tel.: (60) 355192606
Web Site: https://www.networkfoods.com
Chocolate Mfr & Distr
N.A.I.C.S.: 311351
Ng Lai Fah (Asst Gen Mgr)

Pan Malaysia Corporation Berhad (1)
189 Jln Ampang Taman U Thant, 55000, Kuala Lumpur, Malaysia
Tel.: (60) 321451366
Web Site:
  https://www.pmcorporation.com.my
Rev.: $26,292,668
Assets: $84,968,978
Liabilities: $26,112,488
Net Worth: $58,856,490
Earnings: $742,500
Fiscal Year-end: 06/30/2022
Confectionery Mfr
N.A.I.C.S.: 311351
Azmi Khalid (Chm)

Subsidiary (Domestic):

A&W (Malaysia) Sdn Bhd (2)
1 Jalan Nilam 2 Taman Perindustrian Teknologi Tinggi, Subang Jaya, 47500, Malaysia (51%)
Tel.: (60) 358887600
Web Site: https://anwmalaysia.com.my
Food Mfr
N.A.I.C.S.: 311999

West Synergy Sdn Bhd (1)
No 27-G Jalan Springhill 9/12 Persiaran Springhill, Bandar SpringhillPort Dickson, 71000, Negeri Sembilan, Malaysia
Tel.: (60) 66516512
Web Site: https://bandarspringhill.com
Real Estate Services
N.A.I.C.S.: 531210

MALAYSIA AIRPORTS HOLDINGS BERHAD
Malaysia Airports Corporate Office Persiaran Korporat KLIA, 64000, Sepang, Selangor, Malaysia
Tel.: (60) 387777000
Web Site:
  https://mahb.listedcompany.com
AIRPORT—(KLS)
Rev.: $1,069,699,615
Assets: $4,452,546,830
Liabilities: $2,711,101,455
Net Worth: $1,741,445,375
Earnings: $118,241,185
Emp.: 8,177
Fiscal Year-end: 12/31/23
Airport Management Services
N.A.I.C.S.: 488119
Azmi Murad (COO)
Subsidiaries:

Malaysia Airports (Niaga) Sdn. Bhd. (1)
3rd Fl Airport Management Ctr, Kuala Lumpur Intl Airport, Sepang, 64000, Selangor, Malaysia
Tel.: (60) 387768600
Airport Management Services
N.A.I.C.S.: 488119

Malaysia Airports (Properties) Sdn. Bhd. (1)
Block C Ground Floor Short Term Car Park, Sepang, 64000, Selangor, Malaysia
Tel.: (60) 387768401
Sales Range: $25-49.9 Million
Emp.: 7
Airport Management Services
N.A.I.C.S.: 488119

Malaysia Airports (Sepang) Sdn. Bhd. (1)
Persiaran Korporat KLIA, 64000, Sepang, Selangor, Malaysia
Tel.: (60) 387777000
Web Site:
  http://www.malaysiaairports.com.my
Airport Operation Services
N.A.I.C.S.: 488119

Malaysia Airports Consultancy Services Sdn. Bhd. (1)
Malaysia Airports Corporate Office Persiaran Korporat KLIA, 64000, Sepang, Selangor, Malaysia
Tel.: (60) 387777000
Sales Range: $25-49.9 Million
Emp.: 25
Airport Operation & Maintenance Services
N.A.I.C.S.: 488119

Malaysia Airports Technologies Sdn. Bhd. (1)
3rd Floor Airport Management Centre, Kuala Lumpur Intl Airport, Sepang, 64000, Selangor, Malaysia
Tel.: (60) 387768341
Emp.: 300
Airport Maintenance & Operation Services
N.A.I.C.S.: 488119
Meznida Mohamad (Gen Mgr)

Malaysia International Aerospace Centre Sdn. Bhd. (1)
Unit M8 & M9 Skypark Terminal Sultan Abdul Aziz Shah Airport, Subang Jaya, 47200, Selangor, Malaysia
Tel.: (60) 378463870
Aviation Support Services
N.A.I.C.S.: 488119

Sama-Sama Hotel KL International Airport (1)
Jalan CTA 4B KLIA, 64000, Sepang, Malaysia
Tel.: (60) 387873333
Web Site: http://samasamahotels.com
Home Management Services
N.A.I.C.S.: 721110

Sinmah Axis Healthcare Sdn. Bhd. (1)
Unit A-2-6 Level 2 Empire Tower Empire Subang Jalan SS16/1, Empire Subang, 47500, Subang Jaya, Selangor, Malaysia
Tel.: (60) 356135366
Web Site: https://sinmah-amegajaya-healthcare-sdn-bhd.business.site
Hospital & Health Care Services
N.A.I.C.S.: 622110

MALAYSIA BUILDING SOCIETY BERHAD

MALAYSIA BUILDING SOCIETY BERHAD

Malaysia Building Society Berhad—(Continued)
Level 11 Wisma MBSB 48 Jalan Dungun Damansara Heights, 50490, Kuala Lumpur, Malaysia
Tel.: (60) 320963000
Web Site: https://www.mbsb.com.my
MBSB—(KLS)
Rev.: $570,263,280
Assets: $11,629,270,899
Liabilities: $9,733,145,397
Net Worth: $1,896,125,503
Earnings: $97,394,286
Emp.: 2,361
Fiscal Year-end: 12/31/22
Retail Financing Services
N.A.I.C.S.: 523940
Nor Azam M. Taib (Chief Bus Officer)
Subsidiaries:

Malaysian Industrial Development Finance Berhad (1)
Level 19 Menara MIDF 82 Jalan Raja Chulan, 50200, Kuala Lumpur, Malaysia
Tel.: (60) 321738888
Web Site: http://www.midf.com.my
Investment Banking Services
N.A.I.C.S.: 523150
Encik Azlan Hussin (Head-Asset Mgmt Div)

MALAYSIA MARINE AND HEAVY ENGINEERING HOLDINGS BERHAD
Level 31 Menara Dayabumi Jalan Sultan Hishamuddin, 50050, Kuala Lumpur, Malaysia
Tel.: (60) 322730266
Web Site: https://mhb.com.my
Year Founded: 1989
MHB—(KLS)
Rev.: $349,554,074
Assets: $710,714,074
Liabilities: $336,214,603
Net Worth: $374,499,471
Earnings: $14,314,921
Emp.: 3,365
Fiscal Year-end: 12/31/22
Marine Construction & Heavy Engineering Services
N.A.I.C.S.: 237990
Nasarudin Md Idris (Chm)
Subsidiaries:

Malaysia Marine & Heavy Engineering Sdn Bhd (1)
PLO 3 Jalan Pekeliling, PO Box 77, 81700, Pasir Gudang, Johor, Malaysia
Tel.: (60) 72512111
Marine & Heavy Engineering Construction Services
N.A.I.C.S.: 237990

Subsidiary (Domestic):

MMHE-EPIC Marine & Services Sdn Bhd (2)
Warehouse 18 Kemaman Supply Base, 24007, Kemaman, Terengganu, Malaysia
Tel.: (60) 98549837
Marine & Heavy Engineering Construction Services
N.A.I.C.S.: 237990

Techno Indah Sdn Bhd (2)
PLO 3 Jalan Pekeliling, PO Box 77, 81700, Pasir Gudang, Johor, Malaysia
Tel.: (60) 72682891
Marine & Heavy Engineering Construction Services
N.A.I.C.S.: 237990

MALAYSIA STEEL WORKS (KL) BHD
29C Off Jalan Tandang Section 51, 46050, Petaling Jaya, Selangor, Malaysia
Tel.: (60) 377811611
Web Site:
https://www.masteel.com.my
Year Founded: 1971
MASTEEL—(KLS)
Rev.: $376,357,460
Assets: $381,683,810
Liabilities: $199,047,831
Net Worth: $182,635,979
Earnings: $4,036,190
Emp.: 821
Fiscal Year-end: 12/31/22
Steel Bar Mfr
N.A.I.C.S.: 331110
Yit Chan Tai (Co-Sec)

MALAYSIAN AE MODELS HOLDINGS BERHAD
No 9 Jalan Wawasan 12 Kawasan, Perindustrian Sri Gading, 83300, Batu Pahat, Johor Darul Takzim, Malaysia
Tel.: (60) 74556333
Web Site: http://www.ae.com.my
Sales Range: $150-199.9 Million
Coal & Mineral Conveyor Systems Mfr
N.A.I.C.S.: 333922

MALAYSIAN BULK CARRIERS BERHAD
Suite 8 01 Level 8 Menara Binjai No 2 Jalan Binjai, KL Eco City, 50450, Kuala Lumpur, Wilayah Persekutuan, Malaysia
Tel.: (60) 323867899
Web Site:
https://www.maybulk.com.my
Year Founded: 1988
MAYBULK—(KLS)
Rev.: $32,757,460
Assets: $135,294,392
Liabilities: $32,214,603
Net Worth: $103,079,788
Earnings: $19,720,847
Fiscal Year-end: 12/31/22
Cargo Handling Services
N.A.I.C.S.: 488320
Weng Yew Hor (CEO)
Subsidiaries:

PSM Perkapalan Sdn Bhd (1)
Level 17 & 18 PJ Tower No 18 Jalan Persiaran Barat Off Jalan Timur, 46050, Petaling Jaya, Selangor, Malaysia
Tel.: (60) 379661602
Cargo Handling Services
N.A.I.C.S.: 488320

Pacific Ship-Managers Sdn Bhd (1)
Level 17 & 18 PJ Tower No 18 Jalan Persiaran Barat Off Jalan Timur, 46050, Petaling Jaya, Selangor, Malaysia
Tel.: (60) 379661688
Cargo Handling Services
N.A.I.C.S.: 488320

MALAYSIAN GENOMICS RESOURCE CENTRE BERHAD
8F Jalan Teknologi 3/6 Taman Sains Selangor 1, Kota Damansara, 59200, Petaling Jaya, Malaysia
Tel.: (60) 378900015
Web Site: https://www.mgrc.com.my
MGRC—(KLS)
Rev.: $2,721,715
Assets: $5,439,895
Liabilities: $765,347
Net Worth: $4,674,548
Earnings: ($5,014,927)
Fiscal Year-end: 12/31/23
Genome Sequencing & Analysis Services
N.A.I.C.S.: 541715
Robert George Hercus (Co-Founder & Mng Dir)
Subsidiaries:

Clinipath (Malaysia) Sdn Bhd (1)
No 23 Galeri Empire Jalan Empayar Off Persiaran Sultan Ibrahim/ KU1, 41150, Klang, Selangor, Malaysia
Tel.: (60) 333422828
Web Site: https://www.clinipath.com.my
Pathology Laboratory Services
N.A.I.C.S.: 621511

MALAYSIAN RESOURCES CORPORATION BERHAD
Level 30 Menara Allianz Sentral, No 203 Jalan Tun Sambanthan Kuala Lumpur Sentral, 50470, Kuala Lumpur, Malaysia
Tel.: (60) 327868080
Web Site: https://www.mrcb.com.my
MRCB—(KLS)
Rev.: $552,348,719
Assets: $1,925,237,932
Liabilities: $924,000,224
Net Worth: $1,001,237,708
Earnings: $22,003,918
Emp.: 1,669
Fiscal Year-end: 12/31/23
Property Development & Management Services
N.A.I.C.S.: 531311
Mohammad Noor Rahim Yahaya (Sec)
Subsidiaries:

Country Annexe Sdn. Bhd. (1)
Level 30 Menara Allianz Sentral No 203 Jalan Tun Sambanthan, Kuala Lumpur Sentral, 50470, Kuala Lumpur, Malaysia
Tel.: (60) 32 727 7510
Web Site: https://www.sentralsuites.com.my
Real Estate Services
N.A.I.C.S.: 531210

MRCB Land Sdn. Bhd. (1)
Level 30 Menara Allianz Sentral No 203 Jalan Tun Sambanthan, Kuala Lumpur Sentral, 50470, Kuala Lumpur, Malaysia
Tel.: (60) 327868080
Web Site: http://www.mrcbland.com.my
Real Estate Services
N.A.I.C.S.: 531210

Subsidiary (Domestic):

Crystal Hallmark Sdn. Bhd. (2)
Level 30 Menara Allianz Sentral No 203 Jalan Tun Sambanthan, Kuala Lumpur Sentral, 50470, Kuala Lumpur, Malaysia
Tel.: (60) 32 718 1771
Web Site: https://www.kalista.com.my
Real Estate Services
N.A.I.C.S.: 531210

Penang Sentral DCS Sdn. Bhd. (1)
5130 Terminal Pengangkutan Penang Sentral Jalan Bagan Dalam, Butterworth, 12100, Pulau Penang, Malaysia
Tel.: (60) 43139888
Transportation Hub Services
N.A.I.C.S.: 488490

Penang Sentral Sdn. Bhd. (1)
5130 Terminal Pengangkutan Penang Sentral Jalan Bagan Dalam, 12100, Butterworth, Penang, Malaysia
Tel.: (60) 43139888
Transport Terminal Services
N.A.I.C.S.: 488310

Semasa Parking Sdn. Bhd. (1)
Unit No 11 & 12 Level 2 Stesen Sentral, 50470, Kuala Lumpur, Malaysia
Tel.: (60) 327868080
Web Site: https://semasaparking.com
Parking Operation & Management Services
N.A.I.C.S.: 561790

MALDIVES TRANSPORT & CONTRACTING COMPANY PLC
7th Floor MTCC Tower Boduthakurufaanu, Magu, Maldives
Tel.: (960) 3326822
Web Site: http://www.mtcc.com.mv
Year Founded: 1980
Emp.: 3,000
Marine Cargo Handling Services
N.A.I.C.S.: 488320
Ibrahim Ziyath (CEO)

INTERNATIONAL PUBLIC

Subsidiaries:

Housing Development Corporation Limited (1)
HDC Building 3rd Floor, Male, Maldives
Tel.: (960) 3353535
Web Site: http://www.hdc.com
Housing Development Services
N.A.I.C.S.: 236116

Maldives Airport Company Limited (1)
Ibrahim Nasir International Airport, Male, 22000, Maldives
Tel.: (960) 3315366
Web Site: http://www.macl.aero
Airport Services
N.A.I.C.S.: 485999

State Trading Organization Plc (1)
STO Head Office Building, Boduthakurufaanu Magu Maafannu, Male, 20345, Maldives
Tel.: (960) 3344511
Web Site: http://www.stomaldives.com
Home Appliance Distr
N.A.I.C.S.: 449210
Ahmed Niyaz (Chm)

MALDIVIAN
26 Ameer Ahmed, Magu, 20026, Maldives
Tel.: (960) 3335566
Web Site: http://www.maldivian.aero
Sales Range: $100-124.9 Million
Emp.: 360
Oil Transportation Services
N.A.I.C.S.: 481111
Ahmed Saleem (Dir-Property & Maintenance)

MALEE GROUP PUBLIC COMPANY LIMITED
401/1 Phaholyothin Road Lam Luk Ka, Pathumthani, 12130, Thailand
Tel.: (66) 20807899
Web Site: https://www.malee.co.th
MALEE—(THA)
Rev.: $231,898,090
Assets: $161,633,603
Liabilities: $102,077,897
Net Worth: $59,555,706
Earnings: $2,339,153
Emp.: 1,337
Fiscal Year-end: 12/31/23
Fruit & Beverage Products Mfr & Distr
N.A.I.C.S.: 424480
Chintana Boonyarat (Chm)
Subsidiaries:

Long Quan Safe Food JSC (1)
A100 Le Thi Rieng, Thoi An Ward District 12, Ho Chi Minh City, Vietnam
Tel.: (84) 837652979
Food & Beverage Services
N.A.I.C.S.: 722310

Malee Enterprise Company Limited. (1)
No 401/1 Moo 8 Phahonyothin Road, Lam Luk Ka, Pathumthani, 12130, Thailand (100%)
Tel.: (66) 20807899
Web Site: http://www.malee.co.th
Fruit & Vegetable Canning
N.A.I.C.S.: 311421

MALEK SPINNING MILLS LIMITED
Tower-117 117/A Tejgaon Industrial Area, Dhaka, 1208, Bangladesh
Tel.: (880) 28878065
Web Site:
https://www.malekspinning.com
MALEKSPIN—(DHA)
Rev.: $174,460,937
Assets: $258,410,332
Liabilities: $153,864,713
Net Worth: $104,545,620
Earnings: $7,567,972

Emp.: 1,214
Fiscal Year-end: 06/30/21
Spinning Mills
N.A.I.C.S.: 313110

MALEV LTD.
Konyes Kalman 12214, H 1097, Budapest, Hungary
Tel.: (36) 1 235 3646 HU
Web Site: http://www.malev.hu
Year Founded: 1954
Sales Range: $450-499.9 Million
Emp.: 2,610
Oil Transportation Services
N.A.I.C.S.: 481111
Geza Fehervary *(COO)*

MALIN CORPORATION PLC
2 Harbour Square Crofton Road, Dun Laoghaire, Ireland
Web Site: http://www.malinplc.com
Life Sciences Investment Services
N.A.I.C.S.: 523999
Darragh Fergal Lyons *(CFO)*

Subsidiaries:

Malin Life Sciences (US) Inc. (1)
195 Church St Fl 9, New Haven, CT 06510
Tel.: (203) 654-3282
Financial Management Services
N.A.I.C.S.: 551112
G. Kelly Martin *(CEO)*

MALION NEW MATERIALS CO., LTD
No 1 Meilian Road, Shantou, 515064, Guangdong, China
Tel.: (86) 75482489555
Web Site: https://en.malion.cn
Year Founded: 2000
300586—(SSE)
Rev.: $336,750,804
Assets: $422,334,432
Liabilities: $151,803,288
Net Worth: $270,531,144
Earnings: $44,520,840
Fiscal Year-end: 12/31/22
Masterbatch Mfr & Distr
N.A.I.C.S.: 325998
Huang Weishan *(Chm)*

MALITA INVESTMENTS P.L.C.
Clock Tower Level 1 Tigne' Point, Sliema, TP 01, Malta
Tel.: (356) 21323503 Mt
Web Site: https://www.malitainvestments.com
MLT—(MAL)
Rev.: $10,167,844
Assets: $323,433,349
Liabilities: $139,059,074
Net Worth: $184,374,275
Earnings: $27,214,167
Emp.: 5
Fiscal Year-end: 12/31/23
Financial Investment Services
N.A.I.C.S.: 523999
Kenneth Farrugia *(Chm)*

MALKOWSKI-MARTECH S.A.
Ul Kornicka 4, Konarskie Kornik, 62-035, Radzewo, Poland
Tel.: (48) 612227500
Web Site: http://www.malkowski.pl
Year Founded: 1990
Building Construction Services
N.A.I.C.S.: 236220
Marcin Malkowski *(Pres)*

MALLCOM INDIA LTD.
EN-12 Sector-V, Salt Lake, Kolkata, 700 091, India
Tel.: (91) 3340161000
Web Site: https://www.mallcom.in
Year Founded: 1983
539400—(BOM)
Rev.: $43,694,428

Assets: $34,471,696
Liabilities: $15,158,148
Net Worth: $19,313,549
Earnings: $3,858,609
Emp.: 347
Fiscal Year-end: 03/31/21
Personal Protective Equipment Mfr
N.A.I.C.S.: 315990
Ajay Kumar Mall *(Founder, Chm & Mng Dir)*

MALLEE RESOURCES LIMITED
Suite 4 38 Colin Street, West Perth, 6005, WA, Australia
Tel.: (61) 861478100
Web Site:
  http://www.myanmarmetals.com.au
Rev.: $138,637
Assets: $32,203,615
Liabilities: $1,784,393
Net Worth: $30,419,222
Earnings: ($11,506,609)
Fiscal Year-end: 06/30/19
Uranium Metals Exploration
N.A.I.C.S.: 213114
John Lamb *(Chm & CEO)*

MALLINCKRODT PUBLIC LIMITED COMPANY
College Business and Technology Park Cruiserath, Blanchardstown, Dublin, 15, Ireland
Tel.: (353) 16960000 IE
Web Site:
  https://www.mallinckrodt.com
Year Founded: 1867
MNKKQ—(OTCIQ)
Rev.: $2,213,400,000
Assets: $9,715,400,000
Liabilities: $8,696,200,000
Net Worth: $1,019,200,000
Earnings: ($944,600,000)
Emp.: 3,100
Fiscal Year-end: 12/25/20
Holding Company; Pharmaceutical Developer, Mfr & Distr
N.A.I.C.S.: 551112
Bryan M. Reasons *(CFO, Principal Acctg Officer & Exec VP)*

Subsidiaries:

Dritte CORSA Verwaltungsgesellschaft GmbH (1)
Gewerbepark 1, 93333, Neustadt, Germany
Tel.: (49) 94459590
Pharmaceuticals Product Mfr
N.A.I.C.S.: 325412

Ikaria Australia Pty Ltd (1)
Ground Floor 17 Cotham Road, Kew, 3101, VIC, Australia
Tel.: (61) 398519100
Web Site: https://www.mallinckrodt.com.au
Pharmaceuticals Product Mfr
N.A.I.C.S.: 325412

Ikaria Canada Inc. (1)
6345 Dixie Road Unit 1, Mississauga, L5T 2E6, ON, Canada
Tel.: (289) 548-5520
Web Site: http://www.ikaria.ca
Medical Care Management Services
N.A.I.C.S.: 621999

Mallinckrodt LLC (1)
675 McDonnell Blvd, Hazelwood, MO 63042-2301
Tel.: (314) 654-8622
Pharmaceuticals Product Mfr
N.A.I.C.S.: 339112

Subsidiary (Domestic):

CNS Therapeutics, Inc. (2)
332 Minnesota St W1750, Saint Paul, MN 55101
Tel.: (651) 207-6959
Pharmaceuticals Product Mfr
N.A.I.C.S.: 325412

Cadence Pharmaceuticals, Inc. (2)

12481 High Bluff Dr Ste 200, San Diego, CA 92130
Tel.: (858) 436-1400
Emp.: 210
Pharmaceutical Preparation Mfr
N.A.I.C.S.: 325412
Cam L. Garner *(Co-Founder & Chm)*

INO Therapeutics LLC (2)
6 Route 173 W, Clinton, NJ 08809
Tel.: (908) 238-6600
Pharmaceuticals Product Mfr
N.A.I.C.S.: 325412
David Trueblood *(Dir-Regulatory Affairs)*

InfaCare Pharmaceutical Corporation (2)
1405 U S 206 Bedminster, Bedminster, NJ 07921
Tel.: (267) 515-5850
Neonatal & Pediatrics Pharmaceutical Products Developer, Mfr & Marketer
N.A.I.C.S.: 325412

Lafayette Pharmaceuticals LLC (2)
526 N Earl Ave, Lafayette, IN 47904-2819
Tel.: (765) 449-8002
Pharmaceuticals Product Mfr
N.A.I.C.S.: 325412
James O. Rollans *(Chm)*

Mallinckrodt CB LLC (2)
675 James S Mcdonnell Blvd, Hazelwood, MO 63042
Tel.: (314) 654-2000
Pharmaceuticals Product Mfr
N.A.I.C.S.: 325412

Mallinckrodt Hospital Products Inc. (2)
12481 High Bluff Dr Ste 200, San Diego, CA 92130
Tel.: (858) 436-1400
Pharmaceuticals Product Mfr
N.A.I.C.S.: 325412

Mallinckrodt Inc. (2)
172 Railroad Ave, Hobart, NY 13788
Tel.: (607) 538-9124
Pharmaceutical Equipment Whslr
N.A.I.C.S.: 423450

Ocera Therapeutics, Inc. (2)
525 University Ave Ste 610, Palo Alto, CA 94301
Tel.: (650) 475-0158
Web Site: http://mallinckrodt.com
Pharmaceuticals Mfr
N.A.I.C.S.: 325412

Mallinckrodt Specialty Pharmaceuticals Ireland Limited (1)
Unit 7 Sandyford Business Centre, Dublin, 18, Ireland
Tel.: (353) 12902501
Medical Product Distr
N.A.I.C.S.: 325412
Stephanie Keenan *(Mgr-Admin Svcs)*

Mallinckrodt UK Ltd (1)
154 Fareham Road, Gosport, PO13 0AS, United Kingdom
Tel.: (44) 1329224000
Pharmaceutical Equipment Whslr
N.A.I.C.S.: 423450

Therakos (UK), Ltd (1)
3 Lotus Park The Causeway, Staines-Upon-Thames, TW18 3AG, Surrey, United Kingdom
Tel.: (44) 1784636700
Web Site: http://www.therakos.co.uk
Pharmaceuticals Product Mfr
N.A.I.C.S.: 325412
Christopher Hirt *(Dir)*

MALLIOUHANA HOTEL & SPA
PO Box 173, Meads Bay, AI-2640, Anguilla
Tel.: (264) 4976111
Web Site:
  http://www.aubergeresorts.com
Sales Range: $10-24.9 Million
Emp.: 170
Hotel & Spa Owner & Operator
N.A.I.C.S.: 721110
John Vasatka *(Gen Mgr)*

MALLOUPPAS & PAPACOSTAS PUBLIC CO LTD
Office Level 10 21 Akadimias St, Aglantzia, 2107, Nicosia, Cyprus
Tel.: (357) 22 550 400
Web Site: http://www.mppublic.com
Year Founded: 1978
MPT—(CYP)
Sales Range: Less than $1 Million
Home Appliance Distr
N.A.I.C.S.: 449210
Polys Mallouppas *(Chm)*

MALMBERG TRUCK TRAILER EQUIPMENT LTD.
1621 Michael St, Ottawa, K1B 3T3, ON, Canada
Tel.: (613) 741-3360
Web Site:
  http://www.malmbergtruck.com
Year Founded: 1950
Rev.: $20,285,222
Emp.: 70
Truck Equipment Mfr & Distr
N.A.I.C.S.: 336120
Steve Malmberg *(Pres)*

MALMBERGS ELEKTRISKA AB
Vastra Bangatan 54, Box 144, 692 23, Kumla, Sweden
Tel.: (46) 19587700
Web Site:
  https://www.malmbergs.com
Year Founded: 1981
MEAB.B—(OMX)
Rev.: $75,378,296
Assets: $65,622,883
Liabilities: $25,356,016
Net Worth: $40,266,867
Earnings: $3,320,576
Emp.: 170
Fiscal Year-end: 12/31/20
Electrical Component Distr
N.A.I.C.S.: 423610

Subsidiaries:

Malmberg-Elektro OY (1)
Juhanilantie 1, 01740, Vantaa, Finland
Tel.: (358) 98553430
Electronic Equipment Whslr
N.A.I.C.S.: 423690
Petteri Mattinen *(Mng Dir)*

Malmbergs Elektriske A/S (1)
Generatorvej 14, 2860, Soborg, Denmark
Tel.: (45) 44500377
Electronic Equipment Whslr
N.A.I.C.S.: 423690

Malmbergs Elektriske AS (1)
Kleverveien 6 Verpet, 1540, Vestby, Norway
Tel.: (47) 64986800
Electronic Equipment Whslr
N.A.I.C.S.: 423690

MALPAC HOLDINGS BERHAD
2nd Floor No 23, Jalan Kong Sang, 70000, Seremban, Negeri Sembilan, Malaysia
Tel.: (60) 67653816
Web Site: http://www.malpac.com.my
Year Founded: 1976
MALPAC—(KLS)
Rev.: $1,338,756
Assets: $38,706,377
Liabilities: $2,173,036
Net Worth: $36,533,341
Earnings: $557,556
Fiscal Year-end: 06/30/23
Investment Holding Company
N.A.I.C.S.: 551112
Bee Lian Ng *(Co-Sec)*

MALPREH A.D.
Vidovdanska 53, 78000, Banja Luka, Bosnia & Herzegovina
Tel.: (387) 51 218 158

MALPREH A.D.

Malpreh a.d.—(Continued)
Sales Range: Less than $1 Million
Emp.: 8
Real Estate Prorperty Leasing Services
N.A.I.C.S.: 531190
Darko Blagojevic *(Chm-Mgmt Bd)*

MALTA PROPERTIES COMPANY PLC
Tel.: (356) 21230032
Web Site:
https://www.maltaproperties.com.mt
Year Founded: 2011
MPC—(MAL)
Rev.: $5,448,291
Assets: $109,369,330
Liabilities: $47,123,282
Net Worth: $62,246,048
Earnings: $2,277,207
Emp.: 7
Fiscal Year-end: 12/31/23
Property Rental Services
N.A.I.C.S.: 531120
Deepak Srinivas Padmanabhan *(Chm & CEO)*

MALTON BERHAD
Level 19 Pavilion Tower No 75 Jalan Raja Chulan, 50200, Kuala Lumpur, Malaysia
Tel.: (60) 320882888
Web Site:
https://www.malton.com.my
MALTON—(KLS)
Rev.: $176,067,090
Assets: $542,758,730
Liabilities: $347,565,503
Net Worth: $195,193,228
Earnings: ($20,915,767)
Emp.: 338
Fiscal Year-end: 06/30/23
Property Development & Management Services
N.A.I.C.S.: 531311
Lay Chuan Hong *(Exec Dir)*

Subsidiaries:

Kumpulan Gapadu Sdn Bhd (1)
Level 19 Pavilion Tower No 75 Jalan Raja Chulan, 50200, Kuala Lumpur, Malaysia
Tel.: (60) 320882888
Construction Services
N.A.I.C.S.: 236220

MALU PAPER MILLS LIMITED
Heera Plaza 4th Floor Near Telephone Exchange Central Avenue, Nagpur, 400008, Maharashtra, India
Tel.: (91) 7122760308
Web Site:
https://www.malupaper.com
Year Founded: 1994
532728—(BOM)
Rev.: $28,121,492
Assets: $18,090,666
Liabilities: $17,327,954
Net Worth: $762,712
Earnings: ($1,253,366)
Emp.: 224
Fiscal Year-end: 03/31/23
Paper Products Mfr
N.A.I.C.S.: 322299
Punamchand Malu *(Co-Mng Dir)*

MALVAUX INDUSTRIES S.A.
21 rue de la Gare, 17330, Loulay, France
Tel.: (33) 5 4633 6800   FR
Web Site: http://www.malvaux.fr
Year Founded: 1928
Sales Range: $50-74.9 Million
Emp.: 100
Wood Panels & Plywood Mfr & Distr
N.A.I.C.S.: 321211
Philippe Heripret *(Gen Mgr)*

MALWA COTTON SPINNING MILLS LTD.
208-209 Pragati Tower 2nd Floor, Rajendra Place, New Delhi, 110008, India
Tel.: (91) 1140460000
Web Site:
http://www.malwagroup.com
Year Founded: 1976
Textile Mill Operator
N.A.I.C.S.: 314999
Jangi Lal Oswal *(Chm)*

MALWATTE VALLEY PLANTATIONS PLC
No 280 Dam Street 12, Colombo, Sri Lanka
Tel.: (94) 112800400
Web Site: https://malwattevalley.com
MAL.N0000—(COL)
Rev.: $31,060,562
Assets: $32,295,507
Liabilities: $13,521,546
Net Worth: $18,773,961
Earnings: $7,179,925
Emp.: 4,274
Fiscal Year-end: 12/31/22
Farm Management Services
N.A.I.C.S.: 115116
Lucas Bogtstra *(Mng Dir)*

MAMAIA SA
Mamaia Vila 26, Constanta, Romania
Tel.: (40) 241 831780
Sales Range: Less than $1 Million
Emp.: 16
Accommodation Services
N.A.I.C.S.: 721110

MAMBA EXPLORATION LIMITED
Level 2 25 Richardson St, West Perth, 6005, WA, Australia
Tel.: (61) 865576616   AU
Web Site:
https://www.mambaexploration.com
Year Founded: 2020
M24—(ASX)
Rev.: $24,273
Assets: $3,603,744
Liabilities: $209,456
Net Worth: $3,394,288
Earnings: ($1,998,463)
Fiscal Year-end: 06/30/23
Exploration & Mining Services
N.A.I.C.S.: 213115

MAMIYA-OP CO., LTD
6-18-1 Nishi-Shinjuku, Shinjuku-ku, Tokyo, 160-0023, Japan
Tel.: (81) 362737481
Web Site: https://www.mamiya-op.co.jp
Year Founded: 1948
7991—(TKS)
Rev.: $181,074,340
Assets: $254,286,700
Liabilities: $118,166,970
Net Worth: $136,119,730
Earnings: $25,461,720
Emp.: 1,519
Fiscal Year-end: 03/31/24
Electronic Equipment & Sporting Goods Mfr
N.A.I.C.S.: 336320
Satoshi Suzuki *(Pres)*

MAMMOTH RESOURCES CORP.
410 - 150 York Street, Toronto, M5H 3S5, ON, Canada
Tel.: (416) 509-4326   BC
Web Site:
https://www.mammothresources.ca
Year Founded: 2011
MTH—(TSXV)
Assets: $28,276
Liabilities: $280,786
Net Worth: ($252,510)
Earnings: ($321,929)
Fiscal Year-end: 01/31/24
Precious Metal & Mineral Exploration
N.A.I.C.S.: 212390
Richard P. Geo Simpson *(VP-Exploration)*

MAMMY MART CO., LTD.
2-44-1 Miyahara-cho, Kita-ku, Saitama, 331-0812, Japan
Tel.: (81) 486542511
Web Site: https://www.mamimart.com
Year Founded: 1950
9823—(TKS)
Rev.: $1,028,340,690
Assets: $470,974,520
Liabilities: $229,815,260
Net Worth: $241,159,260
Earnings: $30,579,170
Emp.: 940
Fiscal Year-end: 09/30/23
Supermarket Operator
N.A.I.C.S.: 445110
Hirofumi Iwasaki *(Pres)*

MAMUN AGRO PRODUCTS LTD.
House 22 4th Floor Road 01, Dhanmondi, Dhaka, 1205, Bangladesh
Tel.: (880) 29635143
Web Site:
https://www.mamunagroprod.com
Year Founded: 2003
Agricultural Services
N.A.I.C.S.: 541690
Nasrin Jahan Mamun *(Chm)*

MAN GROUP PLC
Riverbank House 2 Swan Lane, London, EC4R 3AD, United Kingdom
Tel.: (44) 2071441000
Web Site: https://www.man.com
Year Founded: 1783
EMG—(LSE)
Rev.: $939,000,000
Assets: $2,608,000,000
Liabilities: $1,111,000,000
Net Worth: $1,497,000,000
Earnings: $138,000,000
Emp.: 1,400
Fiscal Year-end: 12/31/20
Alternative Investment Products & Solutions Services
N.A.I.C.S.: 523940
Robyn Grew *(COO-Grp & Gen Counsel)*

Subsidiaries:

GLG Partners, Inc. (1)
390 Park Ave 20th Fl, New York, NY 10022
Tel.: (212) 224-7200
Web Site: http://www.glgpartners.com
Sales Range: $300-349.9 Million
Emp.: 393
Investment Services
N.A.I.C.S.: 523999
Pierre Philippe Alexandre Lagrange *(Sr Mng Dir)*

Subsidiary (Non-US):

GLG Partners LP (2)
Riverbank House 2 Swan Lane, London, EC4R 3AD, United Kingdom (100%)
Tel.: (44) 2070167000
Web Site: http://www.glgpartners.com
Sales Range: $100-124.9 Million
Asset Management Services
N.A.I.C.S.: 523940

Man (Europe) AG (1)
Austrasse 56, 9490, Vaduz, Liechtenstein
Tel.: (423) 3751045
Investment Management Service
N.A.I.C.S.: 523940

INTERNATIONAL PUBLIC

Man Global Private Markets (USA) Inc. (1)
Morrison Blvd 6836 Ste 430, Charlotte, NC 28211
Tel.: (980) 321-7560
Investment Management Service
N.A.I.C.S.: 523940
Ian Swallow *(COO)*

Man Group Japan Limited (1)
27th Floor Akasaka Biz Tower 5-3-1, Akasaka Minato-ku, Tokyo, 107-6327, Japan
Tel.: (81) 364412460
Investment Management Service
N.A.I.C.S.: 523940

Man Investment Management (Shanghai) Co., Ltd. (1)
Room 1817 222 Yan An Road East, Huangpu District, Shanghai, China
Tel.: (86) 2161933514
Investment Management Service
N.A.I.C.S.: 523940

Man Investments (Hong Kong) Ltd. (1)
Suite 2206 Man Yee Building 68 Des Voeux Road, Central, China (Hong Kong)
Tel.: (852) 2 230 7231
Web Site: https://www.man.com
Investment Management Service
N.A.I.C.S.: 523940

Man Investments (Luxembourg) S.A. (1)
21st Century 19 Rue de Bitbourg, Luxembourg, 1273, Luxembourg
Tel.: (352) 2600021491
Web Site: http://www.man.com
Sales Range: $50-74.9 Million
Emp.: 2
Investment Management Service
N.A.I.C.S.: 523150

Man Investments (Singapore) Pte. Ltd. (1)
50 Collyer quay 0605 oue Payfront, Singapore, 049321, Singapore
Tel.: (65) 67406602
Web Site:
http://www.search.mangroupplc.com
Sales Range: $50-74.9 Million
Emp.: 10
Investment Management Service
N.A.I.C.S.: 523940

Man Investments (USA) LLC (1)
123 N Wacker Dr 28th Fl, Chicago, IL 60606
Tel.: (312) 881-6800
Investment Management Service
N.A.I.C.S.: 523940

Man Investments AG (1)
La Cumparsita 1373 Oficce 801, Montevideo, 11200, Uruguay
Tel.: (598) 29022016
Web Site: http://www.maninvestments.com
Sales Range: $50-74.9 Million
Emp.: 12
Investment Management Service
N.A.I.C.S.: 523940

Man Investments AG (1)
Huobstrasse 3, 8808, Pfaffikon, Switzerland
Tel.: (41) 55 417 6000
Web Site: http://www.man.com
Sales Range: $100-124.9 Million
Asset Management Services
N.A.I.C.S.: 523999

Man Investments Australia Ltd. (1)
Level 28 Chifley Tower 2 Chifley Square, Sydney, 2000, NSW, Australia
Tel.: (61) 28 259 9999
Web Site:
http://www.maninvestment.com.au
Sales Range: $50-74.9 Million
Emp.: 50
Investment Management Service
N.A.I.C.S.: 523940

Man Investments Inc. (1)
123 N Wacker Dr, Chicago, IL 60606-1743
Tel.: (312) 881-6800
Sales Range: $50-74.9 Million
Emp.: 55
Hedge Fund Management Services
N.A.I.C.S.: 523999

AND PRIVATE COMPANIES

Man Investments Ltd. (1)
Riverbank House 2 Swan Lane, London, EC4R 3AD, United Kingdom
Tel.: (44) 2071441000
Web Site: http://www.maninvestments.com
Sales Range: $50-74.9 Million
Asset Management Services
N.A.I.C.S.: 523999

Man Investments Middle East Ltd. (1)
Level 5 West Wing The Gate Dubai International Financial Centre, PO Box 73221, Dubai, United Arab Emirates
Tel.: (971) 43604999
Web Site: http://www.man.com
Sales Range: $50-74.9 Million
Emp.: 16
Investment Management Service
N.A.I.C.S.: 523940

Man Investments Netherlands B.V. (1)
Beurs-World Trade Center 19th Floor Beursplein 37, Rotterdam, 3011 AA, Zuid-Holland, Netherlands
Tel.: (31) 102051260
Web Site: http://www.man.com
Sales Range: $50-74.9 Million
Emp.: 5
Investment Management Service
N.A.I.C.S.: 523150

Man Investments SGR S.p.A. (1)
Via Durini 23, Milan, 20122, Italy
Tel.: (39) 0236006900
Sales Range: $50-74.9 Million
Emp.: 5
Investment Management Service
N.A.I.C.S.: 523150

Man Investments Securities Japan Ltd. (1)
Imperial Hotel Tower 16th Fl 1-1-1 Uchisaiwaicho, Chiyoda-ku, Tokyo, 100 0011, Japan
Tel.: (81) 335193880
Investment Management Service
N.A.I.C.S.: 523940

Numeric Investors LLC (1)
200 Pier 4 Blvd 5th Fl, Boston, MA 02210
Tel.: (617) 897-7800
Web Site: http://www.numeric.com
Sales Range: $75-99.9 Million
Emp.: 72
Investment Services
N.A.I.C.S.: 523999
Douglas W. Hamilton *(COO)*

MAN INDUSTRIES INDIA LTD.
Man House 101 S V Road Vile Parle W, Mumbai, 400 056, India
Tel.: (91) 2266477500
Web Site: https://www.mangroup.com
513269—(NSE)
Rev.: $288,145,303
Assets: $243,776,251
Liabilities: $129,815,513
Net Worth: $113,960,738
Earnings: $13,765,629
Emp.: 832
Fiscal Year-end: 03/31/21
Carbon Steel Line Pipe Mfr
N.A.I.C.S.: 331210
Ramesh C. Manusukhani *(Chm)*

Subsidiaries:

Man Infraprojects Limited (1)
Man House 102 S V Road Vile Parle, Mumbai, 400 056, India
Tel.: (91) 22 6712 7000
Real Estate Manangement Services
N.A.I.C.S.: 531390

MAN INFRACONSTRUCTION LTD.
12th Floor Krushal Commercial Complex Above Shoppers Stop, G M Road Chembur West, Mumbai, 400 089, India
Tel.: (91) 2242463999
Web Site: http://www.maninfra.com
Sales Range: $125-149.9 Million

Emp.: 750
Infrastructure Construction Services
N.A.I.C.S.: 237310
Parag K. Shah *(Mng Dir)*

MAN KING HOLDINGS LIMITED
Unit D 10/ F Skyline Tower 18 Tong Mi Road Mongkok, Kowloon, China (Hong Kong)
Tel.: (852) 2 398 8001   Ky
Web Site: http://www.manking.com.hk
Year Founded: 2014
2193—(HKG)
Rev.: $52,649,636
Assets: $53,641,234
Liabilities: $17,639,950
Net Worth: $36,001,285
Earnings: $4,762,200
Emp.: 171
Fiscal Year-end: 03/31/22
Civil Engineering Services
N.A.I.C.S.: 541330
Yuen Cheong Lo *(Chm)*

MAN SHING AGRICULTURAL HOLDINGS, INC.
Unit 611-612 Sixth floor No 1 Huacheng Road, Tianhe District, Guangzhou, 510000, Shandong, China
Tel.: (86) 15112038735   NV
Web Site: https://msahinc.com
Year Founded: 2000
MSAH—(OTCIQ)
Sales Range: $25-49.9 Million
Vegetables Mfr & Processor
N.A.I.C.S.: 311411
Liu Yue *(CEO & Officer)*

MAN SHING GLOBAL HOLDINGS LIMITED
Unit 10 11/F Trans Asia Centre 18 Kin Hong Street, Kwai Chung, China (Hong Kong)
Tel.: (852) 2 406 2881   Ky
Web Site: http://www.manshing.com.hk
Year Founded: 1987
8309—(HKG)
Rev.: $74,879,339
Assets: $25,595,307
Liabilities: $12,502,934
Net Worth: $13,092,373
Earnings: $3,690,763
Emp.: 5,187
Fiscal Year-end: 03/31/21
Janitorial Services
N.A.I.C.S.: 561720
Shing Chong Wong *(Co-Founder & Chm)*

Subsidiaries:

Man Shing Cleaning Service Company Limited (1)
Unit 10 11/F Trans Asia Centre 18 Kin Hong Street, Kwai Chung, New Territories, China (Hong Kong)
Tel.: (852) 24062881
Cleaning Service
N.A.I.C.S.: 561720

MAN SHUN GROUP (HOLDINGS) LIMITED
Room 8 19/F Cheung Fung Industrial Building 23-39 Pak Tin Par Street, Tsuen Wan, China (Hong Kong)
Tel.: (852) 26336866   Ky
Web Site: http://www.manshungroup.com.hk
Year Founded: 1996
1746—(HKG)
Rev.: $15,948,593
Assets: $20,957,303
Liabilities: $1,685,933

Net Worth: $19,271,370
Earnings: $30,345
Emp.: 71
Fiscal Year-end: 12/31/22
Electrical Contracting Services
N.A.I.C.S.: 238210
Yuen Tung Cheung *(Chm)*

MAN WAH HOLDINGS LIMITED
1/F Wah Lai Industrial Center 10-14 Kwei Tei Street, Fotan, New Territories, China (Hong Kong)
Tel.: (852) 27120091
Web Site: http://www.manwahholdings.com
MAWHY—(OTCIQ)
Rev.: $2,212,266,015
Assets: $2,504,162,220
Liabilities: $906,871,545
Net Worth: $1,597,290,675
Earnings: $236,917,695
Emp.: 25,832
Fiscal Year-end: 03/31/23
Recliner Sofa Mfr & Sales
N.A.I.C.S.: 337121
Man Li Wong *(Founder, Chm & Mng Dir)*

Subsidiaries:

Man Wah Furniture Manufacturing (Huizhou) Co., Ltd. (1)
Western Section of Daya Bay, Economic and Technological Development Zone, Huizhou, Guangdong, China
Tel.: (86) 7525206588
Furniture Product Mfr
N.A.I.C.S.: 337121

MAN YUE TECHNOLOGY HOLDINGS LIMITED
Unit 03 6/F Harbour Centre Tower 2 8 Hok Cheung Street, Hung Hom, Kowloon, China (Hong Kong)
Tel.: (852) 28975277   BM
Web Site: http://www.manyue.com
Year Founded: 1979
0894—(HKG)
Rev.: $235,435,763
Assets: $411,996,743
Liabilities: $219,980,978
Net Worth: $192,015,765
Earnings: $5,059,710
Emp.: 2,501
Fiscal Year-end: 12/31/22
Aluminum Electrolytic Capacitors Mfr
N.A.I.C.S.: 334416
Chor Lin Kee *(Founder & Chm)*

Subsidiaries:

Luminous Town Electric Co., Ltd. (1)
7F-3 No 306 Zhongzheng 1st Rd, Lingya Dist, Kaohsiung, 802, Taiwan
Tel.: (886) 77276589
Web Site: https://www.ltec.com.tw
Emp.: 800
Electrolytic Capacitor Mfr & Distr
N.A.I.C.S.: 334416

Plant (Non-US):

Luminous Town Electric Co., Ltd. - Dong Guan Factory (2)
No 67 Nan Chang South Road, Chi Jiao Village Wang Niou Duen Town, Dongguan, Guangdong, China
Tel.: (86) 76988850216
Electronic Component Mfr & Whslr
N.A.I.C.S.: 334419

Luminous Town Electric Co., Ltd. - Kunshan Factory (2)
No 22-1 Zhuzhu Roan, Lu Jia Town, Kunshan, Jiang Su, China
Tel.: (86) 51288165958
Electronic Component Mfr & Whslr
N.A.I.C.S.: 334419

Man Yue Electronics Company Limited (1)
Unit 3402 34th Floor Grand Millennium

MANAC INCORPORATED

Plaza No 183 Queen's Road, Cosco Tower, Central, China (Hong Kong)
Tel.: (852) 28975277
Electronic Component Mfr & Whslr
N.A.I.C.S.: 334419

Rifeng Qingyuan Electronic Co., Ltd. (1)
No 2 Taiji Industrial Park, Hi-Tech Industrial Development Zone, Qingyuan, 511517, Guangdong, China
Tel.: (86) 7636883380
Emp.: 200
Aluminum Foil Mfr
N.A.I.C.S.: 331315

Rihong (Yaan) Electronics Co., Ltd. (1)
28 Xiangyang Road, Lushan Town, Ya'an, 625600, Sichuan, China
Tel.: (86) 8358706968
Emp.: 200
Aluminum Foil Mfr
N.A.I.C.S.: 331315

Samxon Electronic Components LLC (1)
1141 Ringwood Ct, San Jose, CA 95131   (100%)
Tel.: (408) 956-9738
Sales Range: $25-49.9 Million
Emp.: 5
Electronic Components Mfr
N.A.I.C.S.: 334419

Samxon Electronics (Dongguan) Co., Ltd. (1)
Xin Xing Industrial Area Wu Sha Village Xing Fa South Road, Chang An Town, Dongguan, 523857, Guangdong, China
Tel.: (86) 76982286000
Emp.: 2,900
Aluminum Foil Mfr
N.A.I.C.S.: 331315

Wuxi Man Yue Electronics Company Limited (1)
148 Chunhui East Road Xishan Economic Development Zone, Dongting Town, Wuxi, 214101, Jiangsu, China
Tel.: (86) 51088662688
Emp.: 600
Aluminum Foil Mfr
N.A.I.C.S.: 331315

MAN ZAI INDUSTRIAL CO., LTD.
No 260 Sec 2 Zhongshan Rd, Guanmiao Dist, Tainan City, 718, Taiwan
Tel.: (886) 65952614
Web Site: https://www.manzai.com.tw
Year Founded: 1984
4543—(TPE)
Rev.: $30,143,482
Assets: $76,035,112
Liabilities: $24,890,754
Net Worth: $51,144,358
Earnings: $4,368,258
Emp.: 325
Fiscal Year-end: 12/31/22
Aluminium Products Mfr
N.A.I.C.S.: 331315

MANABI HOLDING S.A.
275 Rua Humaita 10 andar Parte 1, CEP 22261-005, Rio de Janeiro, Brazil
Tel.: (55) 21 2538 4939   BR
Web Site: http://www.manabi.com
Sales Range: $25-49.9 Million
Industrial Metals & Mining Operations
N.A.I.C.S.: 212290
Patricia Coelho *(CEO)*

MANAC INCORPORATED
6F Nihonbashi Sakuradori Bldg 8-4 Nihonbashi 3-chome, Chuo-ku, Tokyo, 103-0027, Japan
Tel.: (81) 332422561
Web Site: http://www.manac-inc.co.jp
Year Founded: 1948
4364—(TKS)
Rev.: $92,172,960

MANAC INCORPORATED

Manac Incorporated—(Continued)
Assets: $126,382,080
Liabilities: $31,856,880
Net Worth: $94,525,200
Earnings: $5,314,320
Emp.: 198
Fiscal Year-end: 03/31/21
Chemical Products Mfr
N.A.I.C.S.: 325199
Shoji Suginohara (Chm)

Subsidiaries:

HAKKO TSUSHO CO., LTD. (1)
2-7-6 Nihombashi-Kayabacyo Chuo-ku, Tokyo, 103-0025, Japan
Tel.: (81) 3 3639 4477
Web Site: http://www.hakko-tsusho.co.jp
Chemical Mfr & Distr
N.A.I.C.S.: 325199

Plant (Domestic):

HAKKO TSUSHO CO., LTD. -
Kashima Plant (2)
2668-32 Sunayama, Kamisu, Ibaraki, Japan
Tel.: (81) 479464420
Chemicals Mfr
N.A.I.C.S.: 325199

Iodo-Finechem Corporation (1)
7F Toshin Shoji Bldg 2-12-6 Kyobashi Chuo-ku, Tokyo, 104-0031, Japan
Tel.: (81) 3 5250 2890
Web Site: http://www.iodo-finechem.com
Emp.: 9
Chemical Mfr & Distr
N.A.I.C.S.: 325199

Plant (Domestic):

Iodo-Finechem Corporation - Chiba
Plant (2)
1365 Nanaido Chosei-mura, Chosei, Chiba, Japan
Tel.: (81) 475327601
Chemicals Mfr
N.A.I.C.S.: 325199

MANAC (SHANGHAI) CO., LTD. (1)
Rm 502A Huawen International Bldg No 999 Zhongshan road west, Shanghai, 200051, China
Tel.: (86) 2132503616
Chemical Distr
N.A.I.C.S.: 424690

Manac Incorporated - Gobun
Factory (1)
950-1 Gobun-cho, Fukuyama, Hiroshima, Japan
Tel.: (81) 849512501
Chemicals Mfr
N.A.I.C.S.: 325199

MANAFAE HOLDING COMPANY K.S.C

Al Sharq Khalid Bin Waleed Street Al-Shaheed Tower Floor 11, PO Box 3132, Safat, Kuwait, 13032, Kuwait
Tel.: (965) 22925888
Web Site: http://www.manafae.com
Sales Range: $1-9.9 Million
Investment Holding Company
N.A.I.C.S.: 551112

MANAGEMENT CAPITAL HOLDING AG

Residenz Strasse 27, D 80333, Munich, Germany
Tel.: (49) 89552797900
Web Site: http://www.management-capital.com
Year Founded: 2007
Sales Range: $25-49.9 Million
Emp.: 5
Privater Equity Firm
N.A.I.C.S.: 523999
Michael Hengstmann (Co-Founder & Partner)

Subsidiaries:

EPP Professional Publishing Group
GmbH (1)

Residenzstr 27, Preysing Palais, Munich, D 80333, Germany
Tel.: (49) 89 452 444 88 0
Web Site: http://www.eppg.de
Information Publishing Services
N.A.I.C.S.: 519290

Subsidiary (Domestic):

ATEC Business Information
GmbH (2)
Hackerbruecke 6, Munich, 80335, Germany
Tel.: (49) 89898170
Web Site: http://www.atec-bi.de
Sales Range: $50-74.9 Million
Trade Magazine Publisher & Information Services
N.A.I.C.S.: 513120

LPV Lebensmittel Praxis Verlag
Neuwied GmbH (2)
Am Hammergraben 14, 56567, Neuwied, Germany (100%)
Tel.: (49) 26318790
Web Site: http://www.lebensmittelpraxis.de
Sales Range: $25-49.9 Million
Emp.: 55
Newspapers & Periodicals Publishing
N.A.I.C.S.: 513110
Eckhard Lenz (Mng Dir)

MANAGEMENT CENTRE TURKIYE

Sungurlar is Merkezi Yildiz Caddesi No 45/5, Besiktas, 34353, Istanbul, Turkiye
Tel.: (90) 212 310 17 00
Web Site: http://www.mct.com.tr
Year Founded: 1992
Management Consulting Services
N.A.I.C.S.: 541618
Alper Utku (Founder & Chm)

MANAGEMENT CONSULTING GROUP PLC

St Paul's House 10 Warwick Lane, London, EC4M 7BP, United Kingdom UK
Tel.: (44) 20 7710 5000
Web Site: http://www.mcgplc.com
Year Founded: 1946
Rev.: $35,894,231
Assets: $31,066,879
Liabilities: $30,069,429
Net Worth: $997,450
Earnings: ($17,423,645)
Emp.: 147
Fiscal Year-end: 12/31/18
Management Consulting Services
N.A.I.C.S.: 541611
Nicholas S. Stagg (Chm & CEO)

Subsidiaries:

Alexander Proudfoot Company (1)
1355 Peachtree St NE Ste 700, Atlanta, GA 30309
Tel.: (404) 260-0600
Web Site: http://www.proudfoot.com
Sales Range: $25-49.9 Million
Emp.: 150
Consulting Services
N.A.I.C.S.: 541618
John Little (CFO)

Subsidiary (Non-US):

Alexander Proudfoot (Europe)
Limited (2)
10 Fleet Place, London, EC4M 7RB, United Kingdom
Tel.: (44) 20 7710 5100
Web Site: http://www.alexanderproudfoot.com
Management Consulting Services
N.A.I.C.S.: 541611

Alexander Proudfoot Canada (2)
Canada Trust Tower Brookfield Pl, PO Box 508, 161 Bay Street 27th Floor, Toronto, M5J 2S1, ON, Canada
Tel.: (416) 572-2032
Web Site: http://www.proudfootconsulting.com
Consulting Services
N.A.I.C.S.: 541618

Alexander Proudfoot South
Africa (2)
3rd Floor 4 Sandown Valley Crescent, Sandton, 2196, South Africa (100%)
Tel.: (27) 115821200
Web Site: http://www.alexanderproudfoot.com
Sales Range: $10-24.9 Million
Emp.: 45
Management Consulting Services
N.A.I.C.S.: 541618
David Kitchen (Pres)

Alexander Proudfoot UK (2)
10 Fleet Place, London, EC4M 7RB, United Kingdom (100%)
Tel.: (44) 2077105100
Web Site: http://www.proudfootconsulting.com
Sales Range: $25-49.9 Million
Emp.: 25
Management Consulting Services
N.A.I.C.S.: 541618

Proudfoot Consulting GmbH (2)
An der Welle 4, 60322, Frankfurt am Main, Germany (100%)
Tel.: (49) 6975938185
Web Site: http://www.proudfootconsulting.com
Management Consulting Services
N.A.I.C.S.: 541611

Proudfoot Consulting SA (2)
159 avenue Charles-de-Gaulle, 92521, Neuilly-sur-Seine, France (100%)
Tel.: (33) 155243700
Web Site: http://www.alexanderproudfoot.com
Sales Range: $10-24.9 Million
Emp.: 27
Management Consulting Services
N.A.I.C.S.: 541611
Jean Baron-Mazloumian (Pres)

Proudfoot Consulting Spain (2)
Capitan Haya 60, 2nd Fl, 28020, Madrid, Spain (100%)
Tel.: (34) 915720086
Web Site: http://www.proudfootconsulting.com
Sales Range: $25-49.9 Million
Emp.: 1
Management Consulting Services
N.A.I.C.S.: 541611

Proudfoot Japan Ltd. (2)
6002 Gluck Heim Kioicho 3-29 Kioicho, Chiyoda-ku, Tokyo, 102-0094, Japan (100%)
Tel.: (81) 352123903
Web Site: http://www.proudfoot.co.jp
Sales Range: $25-49.9 Million
Emp.: 90
Management Consulting Services
N.A.I.C.S.: 541611
Kiichiro Hasegawa (Pres)

MCG Holdings Netherlands BV (1)
Weena 327, Rotterdam, 3013 AL, Netherlands
Tel.: (31) 102064600
Web Site: http://www.sgggroup.com
Emp.: 30
Investment Management Service
N.A.I.C.S.: 523999
Andre Nagelmaker (Gen Mgr)

MANAGEMENT RESOURCE SOLUTIONS PLC

8th Floor Reading Bridge House, Reading, RG1 8LS, United Kingdom
Tel.: (44) 7785 234447 UK
Web Site: http://www.mrsplc.net
Year Founded: 2007
Rev.: $70,643,971
Assets: $51,091,174
Liabilities: $46,069,750
Net Worth: $5,021,425
Earnings: ($14,550,259)
Fiscal Year-end: 06/30/17
Human Capital Resource Consulting Services
N.A.I.C.S.: 541612
Timothy Jones (Fin Dir)

MANAGEMENT SOLUTIONS CO., LTD.

INTERNATIONAL PUBLIC

Midtown tower 29F 9-7-1 Akasaka, Minato-ku, Tokyo, 107-6229, Japan
Tel.: (81) 354138808
Web Site: https://www.msols.com
Year Founded: 2005
7033—(TKS)
Rev.: $120,040,790
Assets: $49,856,880
Liabilities: $19,355,700
Net Worth: $30,501,180
Earnings: $11,485,800
Emp.: 867
Fiscal Year-end: 10/31/23
Management Consulting Services
N.A.I.C.S.: 541613
Junichi Fukushima (CFO)

Subsidiaries:

MSOL-TW Ltd. (1)
5 7th Floor No 58 Section 3 Minquan East Road, Zhongshan Dist, Taipei, 10477, Taiwan
Tel.: (886) 225000625
Web Site: http://www.msol.tw
Consulting Management Services
N.A.I.C.S.: 541611

MANAGEMENT TRUST HOLDING AG

Argentinierstrasse 42/6, 1040, Vienna, Austria
Tel.: (43) 1 535 61 03
Web Site: http://www.mth-gruppe.at
Holding Company
N.A.I.C.S.: 551112
Martin Waldhausl (Chm-Exec Bd)

Subsidiaries:

MTH Retail Group Holding
GmbH (1)
Industriestrasse 7a, A - 2353, Guntramsdorf, Austria
Tel.: (43) 223680990
Web Site: http://www.mth-retailgroup.com
Holding Company
N.A.I.C.S.: 551112

Subsidiary (Non-US):

Office World AG (2)
Gewerbestrasse 16, Bolligen, 3065, Zurich, Switzerland
Tel.: (41) 844822816
Web Site: http://www.officeworld.ch
Office Equipment Retailer
N.A.I.C.S.: 423420

MANAGEMENT, CONSULTING & LIST-BROKING SERVICES S.A.

Henri Dunantlaan 13, B-2900, Schoten, Belgium
Tel.: (32) 36583883
Year Founded: 1990
Sales Range: $10-24.9 Million
Emp.: 15
Direct Marketing Services
N.A.I.C.S.: 541613
Frans Hendrickx (Founder)

MANAGEPAY SYSTEMS BERHAD

Wisma MPSB Lot 109-113 Jalan USJ21/10, 47630, Subang Jaya, Selangor Darul Ehsan, Malaysia
Tel.: (60) 1700816729
Web Site: https://www.mpay.my
Year Founded: 2000
MPAY—(KLS)
Rev.: $3,818,206
Assets: $18,045,949
Liabilities: $1,832,241
Net Worth: $16,213,708
Earnings: ($2,265,350)
Emp.: 134
Fiscal Year-end: 12/31/22
Electronic Payment Solutions Including Software & Hardware
N.A.I.C.S.: 522320

AND PRIVATE COMPANIES

Chee Seng Chew *(Founder, CEO & Mng Dir)*
Subsidiaries:

Multimedia Prospect Sdn Bhd (1)
UEP USJ21/1 Lot 118 Jalan Wisma MPSB, 47630, Subang Jaya, Selangor, Malaysia
Tel.: (60) 380231880
Web Site: http://1226-my.all.biz
Computer Software Development Services
N.A.I.C.S.: 541511

QuicKash Malaysia Sdn. Bhd. (1)
Lot 107-113 Jalan USJ 21/10, 47630, Subang Jaya, Selangor, Malaysia
Tel.: (60) 380231880
Web Site: https://www.quickash.com
Financial Services
N.A.I.C.S.: 921130

MANAKSIA LTD
Turner Morrison Building 6 Lyons Range Mezzanine Floor, North-West Corner, Kolkata, 700 001, India
Tel.: (91) 3322310055
Web Site: https://www.manaksia.com
532932—(BOM)
Rev.: $121,987,702
Assets: $159,559,041
Liabilities: $26,057,168
Net Worth: $133,501,873
Earnings: $8,819,715
Emp.: 21
Fiscal Year-end: 03/31/21
Metal Packaging Products
N.A.I.C.S.: 332119
Suresh Kumar Agrawal *(Mng Dir)*
Subsidiaries:

BKM Industries Limited (1)
3rd Floor Bikaner Building 8/1 Lal Bazar Street, Kolkata, 700 001, India
Tel.: (91) 3322310050
Web Site: http://bkmindustries.com
Rev.: $11,875,500
Assets: $524,078,100
Liabilities: $313,704,300
Net Worth: $210,373,800
Earnings: ($39,885,300)
Emp.: 60
Fiscal Year-end: 03/31/2020
Plastic & Metal Packaging Mfr
N.A.I.C.S.: 326112
Basant Kumar Agrawal *(Chm & Mng Dir)*

Euroasian Ventures FZE (1)
JAFZA View 19 25th Fl Ofc No 07, PO Box 17707, Jebel Ali Free Zone, Dubai, United Arab Emirates
Tel.: (971) 48865838
Web Site: http://www.euroasian-ventures.com
Sales Range: $25-49.9 Million
Emp.: 10
Copper Wires Mfr
N.A.I.C.S.: 332618

Manaksia Aluminium Company Limited (1)
Bikaner Building 8/1 Lalbazar Street 3rd Floor, Kolkata, 700 001, India
Tel.: (91) 3322435053
Web Site: https://www.manaksiaaluminium.com
Rev.: $37,638,305
Assets: $44,006,167
Liabilities: $29,166,242
Net Worth: $14,839,925
Earnings: ($431,736)
Emp.: 297
Fiscal Year-end: 03/31/2021
Packaging Products Mfr
N.A.I.C.S.: 326112
Vivek Jain *(Officer-Compliance & Sec)*

Manaksia Coated Metals & Industries Limited (1)
Bikaner Building 8/1 Lalbazar Street 3rd Floor, Kolkata, 700 001, India
Tel.: (91) 3322310050
Web Site: https://www.manaksiacoatedmetals.com
Rev.: $78,813,105
Assets: $65,721,444
Liabilities: $51,423,740
Net Worth: $14,297,704
Earnings: $1,122,103
Emp.: 309
Fiscal Year-end: 03/31/2023
Packaging Products Mfr
N.A.I.C.S.: 326112
Ajay Kumar Chakraborty *(Chm)*

Manaksia Steels Limited (1)
Turner Morrison Building 6 Lyons Range 1st Floor, Kolkata, 700 001, India
Tel.: (91) 3322310055
Web Site: https://www.manaksiasteels.com
Rev.: $69,826,015
Assets: $47,623,608
Liabilities: $17,208,378
Net Worth: $30,415,230
Earnings: $3,623,160
Emp.: 175
Fiscal Year-end: 03/31/2021
Packaging Products Mfr
N.A.I.C.S.: 326112
Vineet Agrawal *(CEO)*

Mark Steels Ltd. (1)
Com House 1st Fl, 2 Ganesh Chandra Av, Kolkata, 700013, West Bengal, India
Tel.: (91) 3322132299
Stainless Steel Mfr
N.A.I.C.S.: 331110

MANALI PETROCHEMICALS LTD
SPIC House Floor 88 Mount Road, Guindy, Chennai, 600032, India
Tel.: (91) 4422351098
Web Site: https://www.manalipetro.com
Year Founded: 1986
MANALIPETC—(NSE)
Rev.: $146,064,180
Assets: $154,430,616
Liabilities: $27,852,972
Net Worth: $126,577,644
Earnings: $6,141,204
Emp.: 386
Fiscal Year-end: 03/31/23
Petrochemical Mfr
N.A.I.C.S.: 325110
Ashwin C. Muthiah *(Chm)*
Subsidiaries:

Notedom Limited (1)
4 Golden Acres Lane, Binley Industrial Estate, Coventry, CV3 2RT, United Kingdom
Tel.: (44) 2476635192
Web Site: http://www.notedome.com
Chemical Products Mfr
N.A.I.C.S.: 325998
Gordon Alderley *(CEO)*

MANALTO LIMITED
Level 11 London House 216 St Georges Terrace, Perth, 6000, WA, Australia
Tel.: (61) 8 9481 0389
Web Site: http://www.manalto.com
Rev.: $62,939
Assets: $1,267,650
Liabilities: $1,117,505
Net Worth: $150,145
Earnings: ($1,762,023)
Fiscal Year-end: 06/30/18
Internet Services
N.A.I.C.S.: 541519
Colin Joseph Marland *(CEO & Mng Dir)*

MANAPPURAM FINANCE LIMITED
IV/470 old W638A New Manappuram House, Valapad, Thrissur, 680 567, Kerala, India
Tel.: (91) 4873050000
Web Site: https://www.manappuram.com
Year Founded: 1992
MANAPPURAM—(BOM)
Rev.: $836,241,861
Assets: $4,615,140,348
Liabilities: $3,470,662,241
Net Worth: $1,144,478,108
Earnings: $181,368,233
Emp.: 27,564
Fiscal Year-end: 03/31/22
Finance Services
N.A.I.C.S.: 523999
V. P. Nandakumar *(CEO & Mng Dir)*
Subsidiaries:

Asirvad Micro Finance Limited (1)
9th and 10th Floor No 9 Club House Road Anna Salai, Chennai, 600002, Tamil Nadu, India
Tel.: (91) 4435298100
Web Site: https://www.asirvadmicrofinance.co.in
Home Finance Services
N.A.I.C.S.: 522299
Rajesh Krn Namboodiripad *(CFO)*

Manappuram Home Finance Limited (1)
Kanakia Wall Street A-Wing 3rd Floor Unit No 301 to 315 Andheri, Kurla Road Andheri East, Mumbai, 400093, Maharashtra, India
Tel.: (91) 8002101373
Web Site: https://www.manappuramhomefin.com
Home Finance Services
N.A.I.C.S.: 522299
V. P. Nandakumar *(Chm)*

MANAS PROPERTIES LIMITED
Dev Plaza 10th Floor Opp Andheri Fire Station S V Road Andheri West, Mumbai, 400 058, India
Tel.: (91) 2240383838
Web Site: https://www.manasproperties.co.in
Year Founded: 2004
540402—(BOM)
Rev.: $23,224
Assets: $8,312,660
Liabilities: $3,724,486
Net Worth: $4,588,174
Earnings: ($150,902)
Emp.: 3
Fiscal Year-end: 03/31/21
Property Management Services
N.A.I.C.S.: 531120
Vijay Thakordas Thakkar *(Exec Dir)*
Subsidiaries:

Dev Land and Housing Private Limited (1)
Dev Plaza 10th Floor S V Road Opp Fire Brigade Station, Andheri W, Mumbai, 400058, India
Tel.: (91) 2240383838
Web Site: https://www.dlh.co.in
Construction Services
N.A.I.C.S.: 236220

MANAV INFRA PROJECTS LTD.
209 Gundecha Industrial Complex, Akurli Road Near Growels Mall Kandivali, Mumbai, 400101, India
Tel.: (91) 2228540694
Web Site: https://www.manavinfra.com
Year Founded: 1995
MANAV—(NSE)
Rev.: $1,446,978
Assets: $1,149,857
Liabilities: $1,536,737
Net Worth: ($386,880)
Earnings: $71,740
Emp.: 10
Fiscal Year-end: 03/31/23
Building Construction Services
N.A.I.C.S.: 236220
Mahendra Narayan Raju *(Chm & Mng Dir)*

MANAZEL HOLDING CO.
Shuhada Street Kre Tower 17 Floor, PO Box 26131, Safat, Kuwait, 13121, Kuwait
Tel.: (965) 22324476
Web Site: https://www.manazelholding.com
Year Founded: 1983
MANAZEL—(KUW)
Rev.: $20,272,689
Assets: $166,574,469
Liabilities: $121,180,567
Net Worth: $45,393,902
Earnings: ($1,138,915)
Emp.: 12
Fiscal Year-end: 12/31/23
Holding Company
N.A.I.C.S.: 551112
Adnan Abdul Wahab Nisf Al-Nisf *(Chm)*

MANAZEL REAL ESTATE
Prestige Towers Mohammed bin Zayed City, PO Box 33322, Abu Dhabi, United Arab Emirates
Tel.: (971) 26444466
Web Site: https://www.manazelgroup.com
Year Founded: 2008
Real Estate Services
N.A.I.C.S.: 531390
Yaqoob Al Doseri *(CEO)*

MANCHES LLP
Aldwych House 81 Aldwych, London, WC2B 4RP, United Kingdom
Tel.: (44) 20 7404 4433   UK
Web Site: http://www.manches.com
Year Founded: 1937
Emp.: 140
Law firm
N.A.I.C.S.: 541110
Derek Brookes *(Partner)*

MANCHESTER & LONDON INVESTMENT TRUST PLC
12a Princes Gate Mews, London, SW7 2PS, United Kingdom
Tel.: (44) 2075845733
Web Site: https://www.mlcapman.com
MNL—(LSE)
Rev.: $39,625,838
Assets: $277,331,194
Liabilities: $2,421,510
Net Worth: $274,909,684
Earnings: $35,701,750
Fiscal Year-end: 07/31/23
Investment Management Service
N.A.I.C.S.: 523940
David Harris *(Mgr-Fund)*

MANCHESTER UNITED PLC
Sir Matt Busby Way, Old Trafford, Manchester, M16 0RA, United Kingdom
Tel.: (44) 1618688000   Ky
Web Site: https://www.manutd.com
Year Founded: 2012
MANU—(NYSE)
Rev.: $971,347,319
Assets: $1,699,680,230
Liabilities: $1,516,553,334
Net Worth: $183,126,896
Earnings: ($143,021,992)
Emp.: 1,140
Fiscal Year-end: 06/30/24
Holding Company; Professional Soccer Team & Sports Related Assets Owner & Operator
N.A.I.C.S.: 551112
Joel M. Glazer *(Co-Chm)*
Subsidiaries:

Red Football Limited (1)
Sir Matt Busby Way, Old Trafford, Manchester, M16 0RA, United Kingdom   (100%)
Tel.: (44) 1618688000
Web Site: http://www.manutd.com
Holding Company; Football Association

MANCHESTER UNITED PLC   INTERNATIONAL PUBLIC

Manchester United plc—(Continued)
N.A.I.C.S.: 551112
Holding (Domestic):

Manchester United Limited (2)
Sir Matt Busby Way, Old Trafford, Manchester, M16 0RA, United
Kingdom (72%)
Tel.: (44) 1618688000
Web Site: http://www.manutd.com
Professional Soccer Team
N.A.I.C.S.: 711211
Joel M. Glazer *(Co-Chm)*

MANCOR CANADA INC.
2485 Speers Rd, Oakville, L6L 2X9, ON, Canada
Tel.: (905) 827-3737   Ca
Web Site: http://www.mancor.com
Sales Range: $100-124.9 Million
Emp.: 644
Metal Component Mfr
N.A.I.C.S.: 333517
Dale Harber *(Pres)*

Subsidiaries:

Mancor Ohio Inc. (1)
1008 Leonhard St, Dayton, OH 45404-1666
Tel.: (937) 228-6141
Web Site: http://www.mancor.com
Sales Range: $125-149.9 Million
Emp.: 300
Aluminum & Steel Truck Component Machining & Fabrication
N.A.I.C.S.: 332999
Joe Rimkus *(Controller)*

MANDALA AIRLINES
Jl Tomang Raya 33-37, Jakarta, 11440, Barat, Indonesia
Tel.: (62) 215665434
Web Site: http://www.mandalaair.com
Year Founded: 1969
Sales Range: $300-349.9 Million
Emp.: 1,300
Oil Transportation Services
N.A.I.C.S.: 481111

MANDALAY RESOURCES CORPORATION
155 University Ave Suite 720, Toronto, M5H 3B7, ON, Canada
Tel.: (647) 258-9722   BC
Web Site: https://www.mandalayresource.com
Year Founded: 1997
MND—(TSX)
Rev.: $178,974,000
Assets: $301,284,000
Liabilities: $165,505,000
Net Worth: $135,779,000
Earnings: $9,309,000
Emp.: 467
Fiscal Year-end: 12/31/20
Precious Metal Ore Mining Exploration, Property Developer & Support Services
N.A.I.C.S.: 213114
Bradford A. Mills *(Exec Chm)*

MANDARAKE INC.
5-52-15 Nakano, Nakano-ku, Tokyo, 164-0001, Japan
Tel.: (81) 332280007
Web Site: https://www.mandarake.co.jp
Year Founded: 1987
2652—(TKS)
Sales Range: $75-99.9 Million
Used Book & Toy Whslr
N.A.I.C.S.: 459510
Masuzo Furukawa *(Chm, Pres & CEO)*

MANDARIN CAPITAL MANAGEMENT SA
10 Rue Jans Antoine, 1820, Luxembourg, Luxembourg
Tel.: (352) 267385   LU
Web Site: http://www.mandarincp.com
Investment Management Service
N.A.I.C.S.: 523940
Alberto Forchielli *(Mng Partner-China)*

Subsidiaries:

Mandarin Advisory S.r.l. (1)
Via Brera 3, 20121, Milan, Italy
Tel.: (39) 02 809 401
Web Site: http://www.mandarincp.com
Emp.: 8
Privater Equity Firm
N.A.I.C.S.: 523940

Mandarin Capital Advisory Ltd. (1)
Kerry Center 1515 Nanjing Xi Lu, Shanghai, 200040, China
Tel.: (86) 21 5298 6600
Web Site: http://www.mandarincp.com
Privater Equity Firm
N.A.I.C.S.: 523940
Alberto Forchielli *(Mng Partner)*

Mandarin Capital Management II SA (1)
9 Via Pioda, 6901, Lugano, Switzerland
Tel.: (41) 919663068
Financial Investment Management Services
N.A.I.C.S.: 523940

MANDARIN HOTEL PUBLIC COMPANY LIMITED
662 Rama IV Road, Bang Rak, Bangkok, 10500, Thailand
Tel.: (66) 2380230
Web Site: https://www.mandarin-bkk.com
Year Founded: 1965
MANRIN—(THA)
Rev.: $9,504,905
Assets: $22,156,705
Liabilities: $10,838,595
Net Worth: $11,318,311
Earnings: $1,012,378
Fiscal Year-end: 12/31/23
Hotel & Motel Services
N.A.I.C.S.: 721110
Piengchai Harnpanich *(Chm-Exec Bd & Mng Dir)*

MANDATUM AND CO LTD
Fabianinkatu 23, PO Box 95, FIN-000131, Helsinki, Finland
Tel.: (358) 102365450
Web Site: http://www.mandatum.fi
Emp.: 100
Investment Banking & Securities Dealing
N.A.I.C.S.:

MANDERS INDUSTRIES B.V.
Keizersveld 16, 5803 AN, Venray, Netherlands
Tel.: (31) 478510004   NI
Web Site: https://www.mandersautomate.com
Year Founded: 1984
Sales Range: $75-99.9 Million
Emp.: 475
Holding Company; Custom Automation & Process Technologies Designer & Mfr
N.A.I.C.S.: 551112
Gustaaf Merkx *(CFO)*

Subsidiaries:

Edgewater Automation, LLC (1)
481 Renaissance Dr, Saint Joseph, MI 49085
Tel.: (269) 983-1300
Web Site: http://www.edgewaterautomation.com
Sales Range: $1-9.9 Million
Emp.: 50
Industrial Automated Assembly & Test Equipment Mfr

N.A.I.C.S.: 333248
Richard Blake *(Founder & Pres)*

Eutomation & Scansys SA/NV (1)
Industriestrasse 28B, 4700, Eupen, Belgium
Tel.: (32) 8756 1008
Web Site: http://www.eutomation.be
Emp.: 40
Industrial Assembly & Test Machinery Designer & Mfr
N.A.I.C.S.: 333248
Jan Peelaerts *(Mng Dir-Peelaerts Mgmt)*

Manders Automation B.V. (1)
Keizersveld 16, 5803 AN, Venray, Netherlands
Tel.: (31) 478 510 004
Web Site: http://www.mandersautomation.nl
Emp.: 53
Industrial Automated Application Developer & Mfr
N.A.I.C.S.: 333248
John Thijssen *(Mng Dir)*

Montair Process Technology B.V. (1)
Heuvelsestraat 14, Kronenberg, 5976 NG, Netherlands
Tel.: (31) 774672473
Web Site: http://www.montair.nl
Sales Range: $1-9.9 Million
Emp.: 50
Industrial Process Technologies Designer, Mfr & Distr
N.A.I.C.S.: 333248
Rene Francken *(Mng Dir)*

MANDM DIRECT HOLDINGS PLC
Clinton Road, Leominster, HR6 0SP, Herefordshire, United Kingdom
Tel.: (44) 1568 618521
Web Site: http://www.mandmdirect.com
Online Retailer
N.A.I.C.S.: 425120
Alan White *(Chm)*

MANDOM CORPORATION
5-12 Juniken-cho, Chuo-ku, Osaka, 540-8530, Japan
Tel.: (81) 667675001   JP
Web Site: https://www.mandom.co.jp
Year Founded: 1927
4917—(TKS)
Rev.: $484,070,130
Assets: $616,481,650
Liabilities: $132,583,380
Net Worth: $483,898,270
Earnings: $17,192,610
Emp.: 2,672
Fiscal Year-end: 03/31/24
Cosmetics & Personal Care Products Mfr
N.A.I.C.S.: 325620
Motonobu Nishimura *(Chm, Co-Pres & Exec Officer)*

Subsidiaries:

Guinot Japan Corporation (1)
Tokyo Head Office 4F Yoyogi Uehara West Building 45-18 Oyama-cho, Shibuya-ku, Tokyo, 151-0065, Japan (100%)
Tel.: (81) 334006444
Web Site: https://www.guinot.co.jp
Sales Range: $1-9.9 Million
Emp.: 1,000
Mfr of Facial & Body Care Beauty Products
N.A.I.C.S.: 325620

MBS Corporation (1)
1-4-18 Asahicho Goto Building Haf, Kashiwa, 277-0852, Chiba, Japan
Tel.: (81) 471469640
Insurance Services
N.A.I.C.S.: 524113

Mandom (Malaysia) Sdn. Bhd. (1)
1001C Level 10 Tower C Uptown 5 5 Jalan SS21/39, Damansara Uptown, 47400, Petaling Jaya, Selangor Darul Ehsan, Malaysia
Tel.: (60) 377101100
Web Site: http://www.gatsby.com.my

Sales Range: $50-74.9 Million
Emp.: 71
Cosmetic Product Distr
N.A.I.C.S.: 424210

Mandom China Corporation (1)
Room 306 No 688 Nanjing W Road, Jing An District, Shanghai, 200041, China
Tel.: (86) 2152288882
Web Site: http://www.gatsby.cn
Emp.: 73
Beauty & Personal Care Products Distr
N.A.I.C.S.: 424210

Mandom Corporation (Singapore) Pte. Ltd. (1)
1 Kim Seng Promenade 10-08/09 Great World City West Tower, Singapore, 237994, Singapore
Tel.: (65) 62356700
Web Site: https://www.gatsby.sg
Sales Range: $25-49.9 Million
Emp.: 34
Cosmetic Product Distr
N.A.I.C.S.: 424210

Mandom Corporation (Thailand) Ltd. (1)
No 98 Sathorn Square Building 28th Floor North Sathorn Road, Silom Subdistrict Bang Rak District, Bangkok, 10500, Thailand
Tel.: (66) 2163282831
Web Site: https://www.gatsbythailand.com
Emp.: 44
Cosmetic & Other Product Retailer
N.A.I.C.S.: 456120

Mandom Korea Corporation (1)
10th Floor 110 Teheran-ro Yeoksam-dong Cambridge Gangnam Building, Gangnam-gu, Seoul, 06232, Korea (South)
Tel.: (82) 15228223
Web Site: https://www.mandom.co.kr
Sales Range: $25-49.9 Million
Emp.: 26
Cosmetic Product Distr
N.A.I.C.S.: 424210

Mandom Philippines Corporation (1)
18th/F 6788 Ayala Avenue Oledan Square, Makati, 1266, Philippines
Tel.: (63) 28866201
Web Site: https://www.mandom.com.ph
Cosmetic Product Distr
N.A.I.C.S.: 424210

Mandom Taiwan Corporation (1)
12F No 76 Sec 1 Min Quan E Rd, Zhong Shan Dist, Taipei, 10451, Taiwan
Tel.: (886) 225231255
Web Site: http://www.gatsby.com.tw
Emp.: 25
Cosmetic Product Distr
N.A.I.C.S.: 424210

PT. Mandom Indonesia Tbk. (1)
Wisma 46 Kota BNI Suite 7 01 7th floor, Jl Jend Sudirman Kav 1, Jakarta, 10220, Indonesia (60.8%)
Tel.: (62) 29809500
Web Site: https://www.mandom.co.id
Rev.: $133,156,876
Assets: $155,308,329
Liabilities: $32,845,300
Net Worth: $122,463,030
Earnings: $2,475,253
Emp.: 1,475
Fiscal Year-end: 12/31/2023
Cosmetics Mfr
N.A.I.C.S.: 325620
Muhammad Makmun Arsyad *(Vice Chm)*

Piacelabo Corporation (1)
5-12 Jugengencho, Chuo-ku, Osaka, 540-8530, Japan (100%)
Tel.: (81) 667675027
Web Site: https://www.piacelabo.co.jp
Sales Range: $25-49.9 Million
Emp.: 50
Hair Care Products Mfr
N.A.I.C.S.: 325620
Masao Yoshida *(Pres)*

Zhongshan City Rida Fine Chemical Co., Ltd. (1)
No 4 Haijing Road, Zhongshan, 528402, Guangdong, China
Tel.: (86) 76088711788
Web Site: http://www.mandom.co.id
Emp.: 113

AND PRIVATE COMPANIES

Cosmetics Whslr
N.A.I.C.S.: 424210

MANDRAKE RESOURCES LIMITED
Level 1 10 Outram Street, West Perth, 6005, WA, Australia
Tel.: (61) 892003743 AU
Web Site:
https://www.mandrakeresource.com
MAN—(ASX)
Assets: $14,750,091
Liabilities: $281,643
Net Worth: $14,468,448
Earnings: ($2,381,733)
Fiscal Year-end: 06/30/21
Cosmetic Mfr & Distr
N.A.I.C.S.: 325620
Lloyd Flint (Sec)

MANDRIVA S.A.
12 rue Vivienne, 75002, Paris, France
Tel.: (33) 17 664 1660
Web Site: http://www.mandriva.com
Year Founded: 1998
MLMAN—(EUR)
Sales Range: $1-9.9 Million
Software Development Services
N.A.I.C.S.: 541511
Arnaud Laprevote (CEO)

Subsidiaries:

Mandriva Brasil (1)
Rua Oyapock n 448 Cristo Rei, Curitiba, Brazil
Tel.: (55) 41 3360 2600
Software Development Services
N.A.I.C.S.: 541511

MANDVIWALLA MAUSER PLASTIC INDUSTRIES LIMITED
Mandviwalla Building Old Queens Road, Karachi, 74000, Pakistan
Tel.: (92) 212441116
Web Site:
https://www.mandviwalla.com
Year Founded: 1989
MWMP—(PSX)
Rev.: $2,229,774
Assets: $1,353,195
Liabilities: $1,545,037
Net Worth: ($191,842)
Earnings: $146,415
Emp.: 46
Fiscal Year-end: 06/30/23
Plastics Product Mfr
N.A.I.C.S.: 326199

MANFORCE GROUP BHD
No 1302 Jalan PJU 520E Pusat Perdagangan Kota Damansara, 47810, Petaling Jaya, 47810, Selangor, Malaysia
Tel.: (60) 361422222
Web Site: https://www.manforce.net
3015—(KLS)
Rev.: $17,504,427
Assets: $9,647,343
Liabilities: $5,026,531
Net Worth: $4,620,812
Earnings: ($852,413)
Fiscal Year-end: 09/30/20
Human Resource Consulting Services
N.A.I.C.S.: 561320
Paul Wong Boon Ming (Mng Dir)

MANFRED HUCK GMBH
Asslarer Weg 13-15, Berghausen, 35614, Asslar, Germany
Tel.: (49) 6443630
Web Site: http://www.huck.net
Year Founded: 1963
Sales Range: $10-24.9 Million
Sports Equipment Mfr
N.A.I.C.S.: 423910
Stefan Huck (Mng Dir)

MANGAL CREDIT & FINCORP LIMITED
A 1701 1702 Lotus Corporate Park Ram Mandir Road Off Western, Express Highway Goregaon East, Mumbai, 400 063, Maharashtra, India
Tel.: (91) 2242461300 In
Web Site:
https://www.mangalfincorp.com
Year Founded: 1961
505850—(BOM)
Rev.: $1,557,516
Assets: $15,862,777
Liabilities: $2,243,057
Net Worth: $13,619,720
Earnings: $779,561
Emp.: 31
Fiscal Year-end: 03/31/21
Holding Company
N.A.I.C.S.: 551112
Meghraj Sohanlal Jain (Chm & Mng Dir)

Subsidiaries:

Indtrans Container Lines Private Limited (1)
A-1701-1702 Lotus Corporate Park Ram Mandir Road Off Western Highway, Goregaon East, Mumbai, 400 063, Maharashtra, India
Tel.: (91) 2242461300
Web Site: https://www.indtrans.in
Freight Forwarding Services
N.A.I.C.S.: 488510

Mangal Compusolution Private Limited (1)
A-1701-1702 Lotus Corporate Park Ram Mandir Road Off Western Highway, Goregaon East, Mumbai, 400 063, Maharashtra, India
Tel.: (91) 2240360500
Web Site:
https://www.mangalcompusolution.com
IT Services
N.A.I.C.S.: 541513

Mangal Mines & Minerals Pvt. Ltd. (1)
No 11 1/F Bawa Road, Alwarpet, Chennai, 600 018, India
Tel.: (91) 4443534141
Web Site: http://www.glrminerals.com
Mineral & Chemical Exploration Services
N.A.I.C.S.: 212390

Satco Capital Markets Limited (1)
17 Noble Chambers Janmabhoomi Marg Fort, Mumbai, 400001, India
Tel.: (91) 2266556777
Web Site: http://www.satcodirect.com
Stock Brokerage Services
N.A.I.C.S.: 523150
S. T. Gerela (Chm)

Satco Wealth Manager Private Ltd. (1)
101- A Wing Devrup CHS Ltd 36 Turner Road TPS -3 Opp Tavaa Restaurant, Bandra W, Mumbai, 400 050, India
Tel.: (91) 9820300745
Web Site: http://www.satcowealth.com
Insurance Services
N.A.I.C.S.: 524210
Sanjib Parhi (Co-Founder)

MANGALAM ALLOYS LIMITED
3123/24/25/26 GIDC Chattral, Gandhinagar, 382729, Gujarat, India
Tel.: (91) 9727762813
Web Site:
https://www.mangalamalloys.com
Year Founded: 1988
MAL—(NSE)
Emp.: 780
Steel Products Mfr
N.A.I.C.S.: 331110
Uttam Chand Mehta (Chm)

MANGALAM CEMENT LTD
Birla Building 10th Floor 9/1 R N Mukherjee Road, Kolkata, 700 001, India
Tel.: (91) 3322438706
Web Site:
https://www.mangalamcement.com
MANGLMCEM—(NSE)
Rev.: $217,502,362
Assets: $263,239,062
Liabilities: $161,930,728
Net Worth: $101,308,334
Earnings: $10,606,801
Emp.: 1,114
Fiscal Year-end: 03/31/22
Cement Mfr
N.A.I.C.S.: 327310
Anshuman Vikram Jalan (Exec Dir)

MANGALAM DRUGS & ORGANICS LTD.
Rupam Building 3rd Floor 239 P D Mello Road near GPO, Mumbai, 400 001, Maharashtra, India
Tel.: (91) 2222616200
Web Site:
https://www.mangalamdrugs.com
532637—(BOM)
Rev.: $52,533,554
Assets: $35,878,711
Liabilities: $18,002,425
Net Worth: $17,876,286
Earnings: $3,818,042
Emp.: 462
Fiscal Year-end: 03/31/21
Specialty Chemicals Mfr
N.A.I.C.S.: 325199
Govardhan M. Dhoot (Chm & Mng Dir)

Subsidiaries:

Mangalam Drugs & Organics Ltd. - VAPI - UNIT II (1)
1203 Phase 3 GIDC, Wapi, 396 195, India
Tel.: (91) 260 2424970
Sales Range: $75-99.9 Million
Emp.: 200
Pharmaceutical Product Whslr
N.A.I.C.S.: 424210

MANGALAM GLOBAL ENTERPRISE LIMITED
101 Mangalam Corporate House 42 Shrimali Society, Netaji Marg Mithakhali Navrangpura, Ahmedabad, 380 009, Gujarat, India
Tel.: (91) 7961615000
Web Site:
https://www.groupmangalam.com
Year Founded: 1942
MGEL—(NSE)
Rev.: $171,505,341
Assets: $52,654,589
Liabilities: $38,936,383
Net Worth: $13,718,206
Earnings: $1,522,259
Emp.: 170
Fiscal Year-end: 03/31/23
Refined Castor Oil Mfr
N.A.I.C.S.: 311225
Chanakya Prakash Mangal (Mng Dir & COO)

MANGALAM ORGANICS LIMITED
812 Tulsiani Chamber 212 Nariman Point, Mumbai, 400021, Maharashtra, India
Tel.: (91) 2249204089
Web Site:
https://www.mangalamorganics.com
514418—(BOM)
Rev.: $46,312,493
Assets: $42,492,436
Liabilities: $8,138,899
Net Worth: $34,353,536
Earnings: $11,585,831
Emp.: 322
Fiscal Year-end: 03/31/23
Chemical Products Mfr & Distr
N.A.I.C.S.: 325199
Kamalkumar Dujodwala (Chm)

MANGALAM SEEDS LIMITED
202 Sampada Mithakhali Six Roads, Navrangpura, Ahmedabad, 380 009, Gujarat, India
Tel.: (91) 7926447302
Web Site:
https://www.mangalamseeds.com
539275—(BOM)
Rev.: $5,623,645
Assets: $7,357,456
Liabilities: $1,876,422
Net Worth: $5,481,034
Earnings: $837,926
Emp.: 54
Fiscal Year-end: 03/31/21
Agricultural Product Mfr & Distr
N.A.I.C.S.: 325320
Mafatlal Jethabhai Patel (Founder & Chm)

MANGALAM TIMBER PRODUCTS LTD.
Birla Building 9/1 R N Mukherjee Road 10th Floor, Kolkata, 700 001, India
Tel.: (91) 3322438707
Web Site:
http://www.mangalamtimber.com
516007—(BOM)
Rev.: $652,634
Assets: $15,427,244
Liabilities: $23,863,790
Net Worth: ($8,436,546)
Earnings: ($2,010,781)
Emp.: 248
Fiscal Year-end: 03/31/20
Fiber Board Mfr & Sales
N.A.I.C.S.: 321999
Yaswant Mishra (Pres)

MANGALAM VENTURES LIMITED
94 Arcadia Nariman Point, Mumbai, 400 021, Maharashtra, India
Tel.: (91) 22 22833216
Web Site:
http://www.mangalamventures.com
Sales Range: $1-9.9 Million
Garments Mfr & Distr
N.A.I.C.S.: 315250
Vinod Kumar Ahuja (Chm)

MANGALORE CHEMICALS & FERTILIZERS LTD
Level-11 UB Towers UB City No 24 Vittal Mallya Road, Bengaluru, 560 001, India
Tel.: (91) 8045855599
Web Site:
https://www.mangalorechemical.com
Year Founded: 1966
MANGCHEFER—(NSE)
Rev.: $440,281,782
Assets: $318,823,752
Liabilities: $222,523,985
Net Worth: $96,299,766
Earnings: $16,144,728
Emp.: 605
Fiscal Year-end: 03/31/23
Fertilizers Nitrogenous
N.A.I.C.S.: 325314
K. Prabhakar Rao (Dir-Works)

MANGALYA SOFT-TECH LIMITED
302 Samruddhi Nr CU Shah commerce college IncomeTax Circle Ashram Road, Ahmedabad, 380 014, India

Mangalya Soft-Tech Limited—(Continued)
Tel.: (91) 79 27543839
Year Founded: 1992
Rev.: $12,347
Assets: $1,813,023
Liabilities: $311
Net Worth: $1,812,712
Earnings: $201
Fiscal Year-end: 03/31/18
Software Product Mfr & Distr
N.A.I.C.S.: 334610

MANGANESE X ENERGY CORP.
145 Rue Graveline, Saint Laurent, H4T 1R3, QC, Canada
Tel.: (514) 802-1814 BC
Web Site: https://www.manganeseenergy.com
Year Founded: 2007
MNXXF—(OTCQB)
Assets: $2,944,083
Liabilities: $79,710
Net Worth: $2,864,373
Earnings: ($2,113,611)
Fiscal Year-end: 03/31/23
Mineral Exploration Services
N.A.I.C.S.: 213114
Jacques Arsenault (CFO)

MANGATA HOLDING S.A.
Cechowa 6/8, 43-300, Bielsko-Biala, Poland
Tel.: (48) 334752008
Web Site: https://www.mangata.com.pl
Year Founded: 1946
MGT—(WAR)
Rev.: $238,215,192
Assets: $229,264,481
Liabilities: $87,087,398
Net Worth: $142,177,083
Earnings: $14,710,112
Fiscal Year-end: 12/31/23
Industrial Valve Mfr
N.A.I.C.S.: 332911
Jerzy Kozuch (Chm-Mgmt Bd)
Subsidiaries:
Kuznia Polska S.A. (1)
ul Gorecka 32, 43-430, Skoczow, Poland
Tel.: (48) 338548283
Web Site: http://kuzniapolska.com
Die Forging Distr
N.A.I.C.S.: 423510
Michal Jankowiak (Pres & Gen Dir)

MCS Sp. z o. o. (1)
ul Strazacka 43, 44-240, Zory, Poland
Tel.: (48) 324724070
Web Site: http://mcs-zory.com.pl
Machine Casting & Forging Mfr
N.A.I.C.S.: 333517

Masterform Spolka z o.o. (1)
ul Mikulicza 6a, 58-160, Swiebodzice, Poland
Tel.: (48) 748583970
Web Site: http://masterform.pl
CNC Machine Product Mfr
N.A.I.C.S.: 333517

ZETKAMA R&D SP. Z O.O. (1)
Ul 3 Maja 12, 57-410, Scinawka Srednia, Poland
Tel.: (48) 748652111
Web Site: http://zetkama-rnd.pl
Construction Development Services
N.A.I.C.S.: 236220

MANGAZEYA MINING LTD.
Craigmuir Chambers, PO Box 71, Road Town, Tortola, VG1110, Virgin Islands (British)
Tel.: (284) 74956475555 VG
Web Site: http://mangazeyamining.ru
Year Founded: 2016
MGZ.H—(TSXV)
Rev.: $151,229,587
Assets: $308,234,748
Liabilities: $244,758,984
Net Worth: $63,475,764
Earnings: $40,553,395
Fiscal Year-end: 12/31/21
Gold Mining Services
N.A.I.C.S.: 212220
Liudmila Arutiuniian (Chm)
Subsidiaries:
Century Mining Corporation (1)
288 Martin St Ste 310, Blaine, WA 98230
Tel.: (360) 332-4653
Web Site: http://www.centurymining.com
Sales Range: $10-24.9 Million
Emp.: 240
Gold Mining & Exploration Services
N.A.I.C.S.: 212220

MANGELS INDUSTRIAL S.A.
Rua Jose Versolato 101 Torre A 9th floor, Baeta Neves Sao Bernardo do Campo, Sao Paulo, 09750-730, SP, Brazil
Tel.: (55) 1143411580
Web Site: https://www.mangels.com.br
Year Founded: 1928
MGEL4—(BRAZ)
Rev.: $165,865,997
Assets: $132,609,889
Liabilities: $125,284,672
Net Worth: $7,325,217
Earnings: $6,086,234
Fiscal Year-end: 12/31/23
Steel Products Mfr
N.A.I.C.S.: 331110
Robert Max Mangels (Chm)

MANGISTAU REGIONAL ELECTRICITY NETWORK CO JSC
29A building 97 district of poultry farm, PO Box 250, Micro District, 130000, Aktau, Kazakhstan
Tel.: (7) 292200201
Web Site: https://www.mrek.kz
Year Founded: 1966
MREK—(KAZ)
Rev.: $33,361,957
Assets: $136,751,590
Liabilities: $68,549,844
Net Worth: $68,201,746
Earnings: $4,090,691
Fiscal Year-end: 12/31/20
Electric Power Distribution Services
N.A.I.C.S.: 221122

MANGISTAUMUNAIGAZ JSC
1 6th Microdistrict, 130000, Aktau, 130000, Kazakhstan
Tel.: (7) 7292215517
Web Site: https://www.mmg.kz
Year Founded: 1963
MMGZ—(KAZ)
Rev.: $2,034,946,825
Assets: $1,222,069,447
Liabilities: $545,770,621
Net Worth: $676,298,826
Earnings: $221,351,020
Fiscal Year-end: 12/31/22
Oil Extraction Services
N.A.I.C.S.: 211120
Bakyt Imanbaev (Gen Dir)

MANGO EXCELLENT MEDIA CO., LTD.
Golden Eagle Film and Television Cultural City, Kaifu District, Changsha, 410003, Hunan, China
Tel.: (86) 73182967188 CN
Web Site: http://www.happigo.com
Year Founded: 2005
300413—(CHIN)
Rev.: $1,924,089,336
Assets: $4,078,573,668
Liabilities: $1,438,167,744
Net Worth: $2,640,405,924
Earnings: $256,220,172
Emp.: 1,130
Fiscal Year-end: 12/31/22
Television Shopping & E-Commerce Services
N.A.I.C.S.: 455219
Cai Huaijun (Chm & Pres)

MANGO GIDA SANAYI VE TICARET AS
Eyup Sultan Mah Mehmet Akif Ersoy Cad No 30, Sancaktepe, Istanbul, Turkiye
Tel.: (90) 216 5612000
Year Founded: 2000
Fruit & Vegatable Whslr
N.A.I.C.S.: 424480
Muhammet Ali Erkisi (Vice Chm)

MANGOLD FONDKOMMISSION AB
Engelbrektsplan 2, 114 34, Stockholm, Sweden
Tel.: (46) 850301550
Web Site: https://www.mangold.se
Year Founded: 2000
Rev.: $16,298,414
Assets: $60,679,654
Liabilities: $49,705,446
Net Worth: $10,974,208
Earnings: $1,192,802
Emp.: 66
Fiscal Year-end: 12/31/19
Investment Advisor
N.A.I.C.S.: 523940
Charles Wilken (Head-Investment Banking)

MANGROVE HOLDINGS PTE LTD.
Level 25 One Raffles Quay, 048583, Singapore, Singapore
Tel.: (65) 98776688
Web Site: http://mangroveholdings.com
Asset Management Services
N.A.I.C.S.: 523999
Neil Johnson (CEO)

MANHATTAN CORPORATION
Tel.: (61) 893226677
MHC—(OTCIQ)
Rev.: $827
Assets: $6,224,908
Liabilities: $61,659
Net Worth: $6,163,248
Earnings: ($458,963)
Emp.: 9
Fiscal Year-end: 06/30/21
Uranium Mining Services
N.A.I.C.S.: 212290
Kell Nielsen (CEO & Exec Dir)

MANHO ROPE & WIRE LTD.
6 7th 14 Jungang-daero 116 Beon-gil, Jung-gu, Busan, Korea (South)
Tel.: (82) 516010300
Web Site: https://www.manhorope.com
Year Founded: 1953
001080—(KRS)
Rev.: $180,434,009
Assets: $237,582,450
Liabilities: $23,164,778
Net Worth: $21,441,767
Earnings: $796,223
Emp.: 189
Fiscal Year-end: 06/30/21
Rope & Steel Wire Product Mfr
N.A.I.C.S.: 331110
Dong Su Kim (Chm)
Subsidiaries:
Manho Rope & Wire Ltd. - Busan Factory (1)
71 Noksanhwajeon-ro, Gangseo-gu, Busan, Korea (South)
Tel.: (82) 51 831 5611
Rope & Steel Wire Product Mfr
N.A.I.C.S.: 332618

Manho Rope & Wire Ltd. - Changwon Factory (1)
670 Ungnam-ro, Seongsan-gu, Changwon, 51557, Gyeongsangnam-do, Korea (South)
Tel.: (82) 55 283 3131
Emp.: 200
Rope & Steel Wire Product Mfr
N.A.I.C.S.: 332618
Jang Bong Kyu (Gen Mgr)

Manho Rope & Wire Ltd. - Yangsan Factory (1)
31 Yusangongdan 8-gil, Yangsan, Gyeongsangnam-do, Korea (South)
Tel.: (82) 55 387 5831
Rope & Steel Wire Product Mfr
N.A.I.C.S.: 331110

MANI INC.
8-3 Kiyohara Industrial Park Utsunomiya, Tochigi, 321-3231, Japan
Tel.: (81) 286671811
Web Site: https://www.mani.co.jp
Year Founded: 1959
7730—(TKS)
Rev.: $177,350,860
Assets: $355,640,940
Liabilities: $30,148,340
Net Worth: $325,492,600
Earnings: $39,098,920
Emp.: 4,154
Fiscal Year-end: 08/31/24
Medical Equipment Mfr
N.A.I.C.S.: 339112
Masaaki Matsutani (Co-Chm & Mng Dir)
Subsidiaries:
Mani Inc. - KIYOHARA Factory (1)
8-3 Kiyohara Industrial Park, Utsunomiya, 321-3231, Tochigi, Japan
Tel.: (81) 286671811
Web Site: http://www.mani.co.jp
Emp.: 350
Medical Instrument Mfr
N.A.I.C.S.: 339112

MANIKER CO., LTD.
278 Guseong-ro, Giheung-gu, Yongin, 16914, Gyeonggi-do, Korea (South)
Tel.: (82) 312815300
Web Site: https://www.maniker.net
Year Founded: 1985
027740—(KRS)
Rev.: $245,862,833
Assets: $133,938,247
Liabilities: $96,372,971
Net Worth: $37,565,276
Earnings: $502,751
Emp.: 525
Fiscal Year-end: 12/31/22
Chicken Slaughtering & Processing Services
N.A.I.C.S.: 311615
Ahn Jeong-Won (CEO)

MANIKER F&G CO., LTD.
36-2 144 St Baekokdaero Yidongmyeon, Cheoin-gu Hwasan-ri, Yongin, 63701, Gyeonggi-do, Korea (South)
Tel.: (82) 313386700
Web Site: https://www.manikerfng.com
Year Founded: 2004
195500—(KRS)
Rev.: $68,541,287
Assets: $79,319,332
Liabilities: $29,606,956
Net Worth: $49,712,376
Earnings: ($201,220)
Emp.: 155
Fiscal Year-end: 12/31/22
Processed Food Distr
N.A.I.C.S.: 424490

Sin-Jae Kang (Dir)

MANILA BROADCASTING COMPANY
MBC Media Group MBC Building Vicente Sotto Street, Pasay, 1308, Philippines
Tel.: (63) 88400000
Web Site:
https://mbcmediagroup.com
Year Founded: 1946
MBC—(PHI)
Rev.: $18,749,935
Assets: $50,554,544
Liabilities: $20,784,888
Net Worth: $29,769,656
Earnings: $1,007,548
Emp.: 278
Fiscal Year-end: 12/31/23
Radio Broadcasting Services
N.A.I.C.S.: 516210
Juan Manuel Elizalde (Sr VP-Ops)

MANILA BULLETIN PUBLISHING CORPORATION
Muralla Cor Recoletos Sts Intramuros, PO Box 769, Manila, 1002, Philippines
Tel.: (63) 85278121
Web Site: https://www.mb.com.ph
Year Founded: 1900
MB—(PHI)
Rev.: $13,476,403
Assets: $148,994,060
Liabilities: $44,356,051
Net Worth: $104,638,009
Earnings: $1,100,446
Fiscal Year-end: 12/31/23
Newspaper Publication Services
N.A.I.C.S.: 513110
Aurora Capellan- Tan (VP-Exec Office & Asst Sec)

MANILA ELECTRIC COMPANY
G/F Lopez Building Meralco Center Ortigas Avenue, Brgy Ugong, Pasig, 1605, Philippines
Tel.: (63) 286328884
Web Site:
https://company.meralco.com.ph
Year Founded: 1903
MAEOY—(OTCIQ)
Rev.: $7,905,165,840
Assets: $10,443,268,440
Liabilities: $7,461,643,860
Net Worth: $2,981,624,580
Earnings: $689,241,960
Emp.: 10,011
Fiscal Year-end: 12/31/23
Electric Power Distribution & Generation Services
N.A.I.C.S.: 221122
Roberto R. Almazora (Sr VP & Head-MPower)

Subsidiaries:

CIS Bayad Center Inc. (1)
G/F Business Solutions Center Meralco Complex Ortigas Avenue, Pasig, 0300, Philippines
Tel.: (63) 286725777
Web Site: https://www.bayad.com
Collection Agencies
N.A.I.C.S.: 561440
Manuel L. Tuason (Pres & CEO)

Subsidiary (Domestic):

Customer Frontline Solutions, Inc. (2)
Business Solutions Center Meralco Complex Ortigas Ave, Pasig, 300, Philippines
Tel.: (63) 26328061
Web Site:
http://www.customerfrontlinesolutions.com
Business Outsourcing Services
N.A.I.C.S.: 561499
Ramon B. Segismundo (Head-Human Resources)

Clark Electric Distribution Corporation (1)
Bldg N2830 Bayanihan St, Clark Freeport Zone, Pampanga, 2023, Philippines (65%)
Tel.: (63) 455993146
Web Site: https://www.clarkelectric.ph
Sales Range: $50-74.9 Million
Electric Bulk Power Transmission & Control
N.A.I.C.S.: 221121
Redel M. Domingo (Pres & CEO)

E-Meralco Ventures, Inc. (1)
2nd Fl Business Solutions Ctr Bldg, Meralco Ctr Ortigas Ave, 0300, Pasig, Philippines
Tel.: (63) 26315602
Web Site: http://www.e-mvi.com
Sales Range: $25-49.9 Million
Emp.: 75
Wired Telecommunications Carriers
N.A.I.C.S.: 517111

First Pacific Leadership Academy (1)
Km 27 Sumulong Hwy, Antipolo, Quezon City, 1870, Philippines
Tel.: (63) 26328111
Web Site: http://www.fpacademy.net
Emp.: 100
Social Advocacy Organization
N.A.I.C.S.: 813319
Norman Mark T. Sayno (Head-Sales)

Landbees Corporation (1)
2nd Floor B & G Building, Meralco Ctr Ortigas Avenue, Pasig, 1657, Philippines
Tel.: (63) 26321899
Web Site: http://www.miescor.net
Sales Range: $250-299.9 Million
Emp.: 1,000
Hydronics Plumbing & Heating Equipment & Supplies Whslr
N.A.I.C.S.: 423720

MRail, Inc. (1)
3/F Business Solutions Center Brgy Ugong Ortigas Ave, Pasig, 1604, Philippines
Tel.: (63) 216226601
Web Site: http://www.mrail.com.ph
Engineering & Construction Services
N.A.I.C.S.: 541330
Katherine Bayona-Baldueza (Head-Fin & Admin)

MSpectrum, Inc. (1)
3/F Business Solutions Center Meralco Center Ortigas Avenue, Metro Manila, Pasig, 1605, Philippines
Tel.: (63) 16223039
Web Site: https://www.mspectrum.com.ph
Solar Energy Services
N.A.I.C.S.: 221114

Meralco Energy, Inc. (1)
3rd Fl Business Solutions Ctr Bldg, Meralco Ctr Ortigas Ave, 0300, Pasig, Philippines
Tel.: (63) 216226900
Sales Range: $75-99.9 Million
Emp.: 10
Electric Bulk Power Transmission & Control
N.A.I.C.S.: 221121

Meralco Financial Services Corporation (1)
12F Lopez Building, Meralco Center Ortigas Avenue, 300, Pasig, Philippines
Tel.: (63) 216223070
Web Site: http://www.meralco.com.ph
Financial Investment
N.A.I.C.S.: 523999

Meralco Industrial Engineering Services Corp. (1)
5th Fl Renaissance 1000 Twr, Meralco Ave Ortigas Ctr, Pasig, 1600, Philippines
Tel.: (63) 286355901
Web Site: https://www.miescor.ph
Heavy & Civil Engineering Construction
N.A.I.C.S.: 237990

Meralco Millennium Foundation, Inc. (1)
Gr Fl Lopez Bldg Ortigas Ave, Pasig, Philippines
Tel.: (63) 26328301
Web Site: http://www.meralco.com.ph
Sales Range: $25-49.9 Million
Emp.: 5
Social Advocacy Organization

N.A.I.C.S.: 813319

Meralco Powergen Corporation (1)
8th Floor Rockwell Business Center Tower One Ortigas Avenue, Brgy Ugong, Pasig, Philippines
Tel.: (63) 284641600
Web Site:
https://www.meralcopowergen.com.ph
Electric Power Distribution Services
N.A.I.C.S.: 221122
Rogelio L. Singson (Pres & CEO)

Subsidiary (Domestic):

Atimonan One Energy, Inc. (2)
2/F Marie Parco Building Quezon Corner Rizal Street, Atimonan, Quezon City, Philippines
Tel.: (63) 427174975
Web Site: http://www.atimonan1energy.ph
Electric Power Distribution Services
N.A.I.C.S.: 221122

San Buenaventura Power Limited (2)
62 H Dela Costa Street Barangay Daungan, Mauban, Quezon City, 4330, Philippines
Tel.: (63) 427840295
Web Site: https://www.sbpl.com.ph
Power Plant & Coal Construction Services
N.A.I.C.S.: 221112
Mike Rondario (Mgr-Commercial)

Miescor Builders, Inc. (1)
283 Katipunan Rd Loyola Heights, Quezon, Quezon City, Philippines
Tel.: (63) 29209804
Web Site: http://www.miescor.com.ph
Sales Range: $200-249.9 Million
Emp.: 1,000
Heavy & Civil Engineering Construction
N.A.I.C.S.: 237990

Miescor Logistics Inc. (1)
2nd Floor B & G Building Meralco Center Ortigas Avenue, Pasig, 1600, Philippines
Tel.: (63) 286355901
Web Site: https://www.miescor.ph
Emp.: 2,600
Engineering & Construction Services
N.A.I.C.S.: 541330
Richard O. Ochava (Pres & CEO)

Rockwell Land Corporation (1)
8 Rockwell Hidalgo Drive Rockwell Center, Makati, 1200, Philippines
Tel.: (63) 77930088
Web Site: https://www.e-rockwell.com
Rev.: $334,224,263
Assets: $1,346,881,760
Liabilities: $763,786,885
Net Worth: $583,094,876
Earnings: $61,380,373
Emp.: 876
Fiscal Year-end: 12/31/2023
Real Estate Developers
N.A.I.C.S.: 237210
Nestor J. Padilla (Pres & CEO)

MANILA JOCKEY CLUB, INC.
14th Floor Strata 100 Building F Ortigas Jr Road, Ortigas Center, Pasig, 1605, Philippines
Tel.: (63) 89144846
Web Site:
https://www.manilajockey.com
MJC—(PHI)
Rev.: $8,587,157
Assets: $66,176,161
Liabilities: $26,194,719
Net Worth: $39,981,442
Earnings: ($3,999,038)
Fiscal Year-end: 12/31/21
Horse Race Track Construction & Maintenance Services
N.A.I.C.S.: 711212
Ferdinand A. Domingo (Gen Counsel & Sec)

Subsidiaries:

MJC Investments Corporation (1)
12 F Strata 100 Building Emerald Avenue, Ortigas Center, Pasig, 1605, Philippines
Tel.: (63) 26327373

Web Site:
http://www.mjcinvestmentscorp.com
Rev.: $14,625,426
Assets: $119,986,101
Liabilities: $112,146,022
Net Worth: $7,840,079
Earnings: ($12,636,389)
Fiscal Year-end: 12/31/2019
Investment Management Service
N.A.I.C.S.: 523999
Ferdinand A. Domingo (Gen Counsel & Sec)

MANILA MINING CORPORATION
20th Floor Lepanto Bldg, 8747 Paseo de Roxas, Makati, 2117, Philippines
Tel.: (63) 2 815 9447
Web Site:
http://www.manilamining.com
Year Founded: 1949
Mining Company
N.A.I.C.S.: 212220
Felipe U. Yap (Chm & CEO)

MANILA WATER COMPANY, INC.
489 Katipunan Road MWSS Administration Building, Balara, Quezon City, 1105, Philippines
Tel.: (63) 9175900
Web Site:
https://www.manilawater.com
MWTCF—(OTCIQ)
Rev.: $554,479,860
Assets: $3,785,996,204
Liabilities: $2,519,959,499
Net Worth: $1,266,036,705
Earnings: $106,008,627
Emp.: 2,663
Fiscal Year-end: 12/31/23
Water Production, Treatment & Distribution Services
N.A.I.C.S.: 221310
Abelardo P. Basilio (COO-Ops)

Subsidiaries:

Clark Water Corporation (1)
Depot 1901 Bicentennial Hill Clark Freeport Zone, Pampanga, 2023, Philippines
Tel.: (63) 455995757
Web Site: https://www.clarkwater.com
Water Sewage Treatment Services
N.A.I.C.S.: 221320

United Utilities Pacific Holdings BV (1)
Teleportboulevard 140, 1043, Amsterdam, Netherlands (100%)
Tel.: (31) 205405800
Web Site: http://www.orangefieldtrust.com
Sales Range: $200-249.9 Million
Emp.: 500
Trusts Estates & Agency Accounts
N.A.I.C.S.: 525920

MANIPAL FINANCE CORPORATION LIMITED
Manipal House, Udupi, Manipal, 576 104, Karnataka, India
Tel.: (91) 8202570741
Web Site: https://mfgroupco.com
Year Founded: 1984
507938—(BOM)
Sales Range: Less than $1 Million
Financial Lending Services
N.A.I.C.S.: 522220
T. Narayan M. Pai (Mng Dir)

MANIPAL UNIVERSAL LEARNING (P) LTD.
14 Manipal Towers HAL Airport Road, Bengaluru, 560008, India
Tel.: (91) 80 40789100
Web Site: http://www.manipalu.com
Sales Range: $150-199.9 Million
Emp.: 300
Distance Learning
N.A.I.C.S.: 923110

MANIPAL UNIVERSAL LEARNING (P) LTD.

Manipal Universal Learning (P) Ltd.—(Continued)
S. Vaitheeswaran *(CEO & Mng Dir)*

MANITEX CAPITAL INC.
16667 Hymus Boulevard, Kirkland, H9H 4R9, QC, Canada
Tel.: (514) 693-8830
Web Site:
http://www.manitexcapital.com
Year Founded: 1986
MNX—(TSXV)
Rev.: $124,747
Assets: $13,190,352
Liabilities: $1,103,061
Net Worth: $12,087,290
Earnings: ($5,914,719)
Fiscal Year-end: 10/31/19
Investment Management Service
N.A.I.C.S.: 523999

MANITOK ENERGY INC.
Suite 700 444 7th Avenue SW, Calgary, T2P 0X8, AB, Canada
Tel.: (403) 984-1750   AB
Web Site:
http://www.manitokenergy.com
Year Founded: 2009
Rev.: $36,000,883
Assets: $192,541,526
Liabilities: $136,014,504
Net Worth: $56,527,021
Earnings: ($18,802,999)
Emp.: 27
Fiscal Year-end: 12/31/16
Petroleum & Natural Gas Exploration, Development & Extraction
N.A.I.C.S.: 211120
Massimo Mario Geremia *(Founder, Pres & CEO)*

MANITOU BF S.A.
430 rue de l'Aubiniere, BP 10249, 44158, Ancenis, Cedex, France
Tel.: (33) 240091011   FR
Web Site: https://www.manitou-group.com
Year Founded: 1945
MTU—(EUR)
Rev.: $2,548,701,705
Assets: $1,902,814,591
Liabilities: $1,048,531,189
Net Worth: $854,283,402
Earnings: $59,060,004
Emp.: 5,009
Fiscal Year-end: 12/31/22
Small Industrial Vehicles Mfr & Distr
N.A.I.C.S.: 333924
Herve Rochet *(CFO & Sec)*

Subsidiaries:

Chariots Elevateurs Manitou Canada Inc (1)
1 Rue Provost Suite 113, Lachine, H8S 4H2, QC, Canada
Tel.: (514) 639-3805
Sales Range: $50-74.9 Million
Emp.: 5
Fork Lift Trucks Rental Services
N.A.I.C.S.: 532120

Cie Industrielle De Materiels De Manutention (1)
Sussis Souzis, 49440, Cande, France
Tel.: (33) 241929474
Industrial Machinery Mfr
N.A.I.C.S.: 333248
Elizabeth Viauv *(Mng Dir)*

Compagnie Francaise de Manutention (1)
510 Blvd Pierre And Marie Curie, PO Box 75, 44152, Ancenis, France **(85%)**
Tel.: (33) 240091313
Web Site:
http://www.toyotamanutention.com
Sales Range: $50-74.9 Million
Emp.: 60
Distr of Toyota Industrial Trucks

N.A.I.C.S.: 423830
Jean-Pierre Guerand *(Bus Mgr)*

De Ladderspecialist BV (1)
Scottweg 17, 4462 GS, Goes, Netherlands
Tel.: (31) 113251335
Web Site: http://www.ladderspecialist-goes.nl
Sales Range: $50-74.9 Million
Emp.: 6
Construction Equipment Rental Services
N.A.I.C.S.: 532412

Empilhadores de Portugal (Centro) Lda (1)
Rua Das Valeiras N 1 Pelariga, 3105-295, Pombal, Portugal
Tel.: (351) 236 209 200
Web Site: http://www.pt.manitou.com
Construction Machinery Handling Services
N.A.I.C.S.: 811310

Loc Manutention (1)
7 Ave Fief Du Sies, Saint-Ouen, 95310, France **(66.48%)**
Tel.: (33) 134326500
Web Site: http://www.loc.fr
Sales Range: $25-49.9 Million
Emp.: 12
Industrial Vehicle Mfr
N.A.I.C.S.: 333924

MLM SAS (1)
Voie Parc D Activite Aerodrome, 76430, Saint-Romain-de-Colbosc, France
Tel.: (33) 2 35 20 39 76
Industrial Machinery Mfr
N.A.I.C.S.: 333248

Manitou Americas, Inc. (1)
1 Gehl Way, West Bend, WI 53095-3415
Tel.: (262) 334-9461
Web Site: http://www.gehl.com
Sales Range: $450-499.9 Million
Emp.: 375
Designer, Mfr & Retailer of Equipment Used in the Light-Construction & Agricultural Equipment Industries
N.A.I.C.S.: 332216
James Green *(Gen Counsel & Corp Sec, VP)*

Subsidiary (Domestic):

C E Attachments, Inc. (2)
PO Box 179, West Bend, WI 53095
Tel.: (262) 387-1372
Web Site: http://www.ceattachment.com
Sales Range: $25-49.9 Million
Emp.: 5
Equipment Construction Products Mfr
N.A.I.C.S.: 484122
Daniel Miller *(Pres)*

Compact Equipment Attachments Inc (2)
N19w6721 Commerce Ct, Cedarburg, WI 53012
Tel.: (262) 387-1210
Web Site: http://www.compactequip.com
Sales Range: $25-49.9 Million
Emp.: 6
Construction Machinery Parts Distr
N.A.I.C.S.: 423120
Greg Hammann *(Gen Mgr)*

Gehl Power Products, Inc. (2)
900 Ferdig St, Yankton, SD 57078-3208
Tel.: (605) 665-6500
Web Site: http://www.gehl.com
Sales Range: $25-49.9 Million
Emp.: 50
Construction Machinery & Equipment Mfr
N.A.I.C.S.: 333924
Dave Ewald *(Gen Mgr)*

Division (Domestic):

Manitou Americas (2)
6401 Emperial Dr, Waco, TX 76712
Tel.: (254) 799-0232
Web Site: http://www.manitou-group.com
Sales Range: $25-49.9 Million
Emp.: 100
Rough Terrain Lift Trucks, Masts & Kurb Dressers Mfr
N.A.I.C.S.: 333924
Brian Riddle *(Mgr-Ops)*

Subsidiary (Domestic):

Mustang Manufacturing Company, Inc. (2)

1880 Austin Rd 1 Gehl Way, West Bend, WI 53095
Tel.: (262) 334-9461
Web Site: http://www.mustangmfg.com
Sales Range: $25-49.9 Million
Emp.: 150
Skid Steer Loaders, Mini Excavators & Telehandlers Mfr
N.A.I.C.S.: 333120

Manitou Asia Pte Ltd. (1)
57 Tuas South Avenue 1, Singapore, 637327, Singapore
Tel.: (65) 68620771
Sales Range: $50-74.9 Million
Emp.: 30
Machinery Spare Parts Sales & Rental Services
N.A.I.C.S.: 532490

Manitou Benelux SA (1)
2 Rue des Andains, 1360, Perwez, Belgium
Tel.: (32) 81654262
Sales Range: $25-49.9 Million
Emp.: 20
Automobile Parts Distr
N.A.I.C.S.: 423110
Stefaan Forret *(Gen Dir)*

Manitou Deutschland Gmbh (1)
Dieselstr 34, 61239, Obermorlen, Germany
Tel.: (49) 600291990
Web Site: https://www.manitou-center.de
Sales Range: $25-49.9 Million
Emp.: 21
Automotive Part Whslr
N.A.I.C.S.: 423110
Francois Piffard *(Mng Dir)*

Manitou Equipment India Private Ltd (1)
Plot No 66 Ecotech II Surajpur Great Value logistics Industrial Park, PO Surajpur, Gautam Buddha Nagar, Noida, 201306, Uttar Pradesh, India **(100%)**
Tel.: (91) 1204194100
Construction Equipment Mfr
N.A.I.C.S.: 333120

Manitou Polska Sp.z.o.o. (1)
Kowanowko Ul Obornicka 1 A, 64-600, Oborniki, Poland
Tel.: (48) 612977535
Web Site: http://www.pl.manitou.com
Construction Machinery Whslr
N.A.I.C.S.: 423810

Manitou Portugal SA (1)
Quinta Do Cabo Lote 10 Z Industrial Apartment 215, 2601-997, Vila Franca de Xira, Portugal
Tel.: (351) 263200900
Web Site: http://www.pt.manitou.com
Construction Machinery Handling Services
N.A.I.C.S.: 811310
Carlos Suarez *(Mng Dir)*

Manitou Southern Africa Pty. Ltd. (1)
122 Plane Road Spartan Ext, PO Box 1310, Isando, 1600, South Africa
Tel.: (27) 119757770
Web Site: http://www.manitou.co.com
Sales Range: $75-99.9 Million
Emp.: 80
Handling & Lifting Machinery Distr
N.A.I.C.S.: 423810
Lindsay Shankland *(Mng Dir)*

Manitou UK Ltd (1)
34 Blackmoor Road Ebblake Industrial Estate, Verwood, BH31 6BB, Dorset, United Kingdom
Tel.: (44) 1202810400
Web Site: http://www.uk.manitou.com
Sales Range: $75-99.9 Million
Emp.: 48
Forklift Truck Distr
N.A.I.C.S.: 423110
Mark Ormond *(Mng Dir)*

Societe Audoise de Vehicules Industriels et de Manutention (1)
ZAE La Baume RN 9, 34290, Servian, France **(75%)**
Tel.: (33) 467392929
Web Site: http://www.savim.com
Sales Range: $25-49.9 Million
Emp.: 36
Construction Equipment Distr
N.A.I.C.S.: 423810

INTERNATIONAL PUBLIC

Marc Sourice *(Mng Dir)*

MANITOU INVESTMENT MANAGEMENT LTD.
150 King Street West Suite 2003, PO Box 31, 66 Wellington Street West, Toronto, M5H 1J9, ON, Canada
Tel.: (416) 628-6519
Web Site:
http://www.manitouinvestment.com
Year Founded: 1998
Emp.: 14
Investment Management Service
N.A.I.C.S.: 523940
Stephen R. Scotchmer *(Founder)*

MANITOULIN GROUP OF COMPANIES
154 Hwy 540B, PO Box 390, Gore Bay, P0P 1H0, ON, Canada
Web Site:
http://www.manitoulingroup.com
Year Founded: 1953
Transportation & Logistic Services
N.A.I.C.S.: 488510

Subsidiaries:

Mid Arctic Transportation Co. Ltd (1)
18151 107 Avenue, Edmonton, T5S 1K4, AB, Canada
Tel.: (780) 484-8800
Web Site: http://www.matco.ca
Sales Range: $10-24.9 Million
Freight Transportation Services
N.A.I.C.S.: 484122
Jeff King *(Pres)*

MANIYAR PLAST LTD.
Maniyar Estate, Jalgaon, 425103, Maharashtra, India
Tel.: (91) 258855381
526321—(BOM)
Plastic Packaging Products Mfr
N.A.I.C.S.: 326112
Sreekant S. Maniyar *(Mng Dir)*

MANJEERA CONSTRUCTIONS LTD
711 Manjeera Trinity Corporate, JNTU-Hitech City Road KPHB, Hyderabad, 500072, India
Tel.: (91) 4066479600
Web Site: https://www.manjeera.com
533078—(BOM)
Rev.: $8,925,134
Assets: $70,255,690
Liabilities: $71,989,158
Net Worth: ($1,733,468)
Earnings: ($6,956,695)
Emp.: 37
Fiscal Year-end: 03/31/21
Building Construction
N.A.I.C.S.: 236210
G. Yoganand *(Chm & Mng Dir)*

MANJUSHREE FINANCE LIMITED
Omkar Building Second Floor Naya Baneshwor, PO Box 23170, Kathmandu, Nepal
Tel.: (977) 14792517
Web Site:
https://www.manjushreefinance.com
MFIL—(NEP)
Rev.: $16,001,806
Assets: $127,818,391
Liabilities: $112,173,525
Net Worth: $15,644,866
Earnings: $1,872,254
Fiscal Year-end: 07/16/23
Financial Services
N.A.I.C.S.: 523999
Santosh Niraula *(CEO)*

MANKICHI SOFTWARE (VIETNAM) CO., LTD.

AND PRIVATE COMPANIES

4th Floor S15 Saigon Pearl Building
No 92C Nguyen Huu Canh Street,
Ward 22 Binh Thanh District, Ho Chi
Minh City, Vietnam
Tel.: (84) 2836208460 VN
Software Development Services
N.A.I.C.S.: 541511

MANKIND PHARMA LTD.
208 Okhla Industrial Estate Phase-III,
Delhi, 110020, India
Tel.: (91) 1147476600 In
Web Site:
https://www.mankindpharma.com
Year Founded: 1991
543904—(BOM)
Rev.: $1,064,444,554
Assets: $1,164,852,119
Liabilities: $250,843,019
Net Worth: $914,009,100
Earnings: $157,026,054
Emp.: 18,468
Fiscal Year-end: 03/31/23
Pharmaceutical Product Mfr & Distr
N.A.I.C.S.: 325412
Sanjay Koul *(CMO)*

Subsidiaries:

Appify Infotech LLP (1)
S 61 Second Floor Panchsheel Park Near Shivalik Road Malviya Nagar, Delhi, New Delhi, 110017, India
Tel.: (91) 8955800800
Web Site: https://appifyinfotech.co.in
Software Development Services
N.A.I.C.S.: 541511

Bharat Serums & Vaccines
Limited (1)
3rd Floor Liberty tower Plot No K 10 Behind Reliable Plaza, Kalwa Industrial Estate Airoli Navi, Mumbai, 400708, India
Tel.: (91) 2245043456
Web Site: https://bsvgroup.com
Pharmaceutical Products Manufacturer
N.A.I.C.S.: 325412
Sanjiv Navangul *(CEO & Mng Dir)*

Lifestar Pharma LLC (1)
1200 MacArthur Blvd, Mahwah, NJ 07430
Tel.: (551) 236-5700
Web Site: https://www.lifestarpharma.com
Pharmaceutical Mfr & Distr
N.A.I.C.S.: 325412

Mankind Agritech Private Limited (1)
208 Okhla Industrial Estate Phase-III, New Delhi, 110020, India
Tel.: (91) 1146846700
Web Site: https://mankindag.com
Agricultural Product Mfr & Distr
N.A.I.C.S.: 333111

Mankind Specialities (1)
208 Okhla Industrial Estate Phase 3 Rd Okhla Phase III, Okhla Industrial Area Delhi, New Delhi, 110020, India
Tel.: (91) 1146541111
Web Site: https://mankindspecialities.com
Pharmaceutical Mfr & Distr
N.A.I.C.S.: 325412

Mediforce Healthcare Private
Limited (1)
Plot No 8-13 Industrial Area Gondpur, Paonta Sahib, 173025, Himachal Pradesh, India
Tel.: (91) 9805034195
Web Site: https://medifocehealthcare.com
Emp.: 1,000
Pharmaceutical Mfr & Distr
N.A.I.C.S.: 325412

Packtime Innovations Private
Limited (1)
B - 38/1 Chakan Industrial Area Phase II, Village - Vasuli Talkhed, Pune, 410501, Maharashtra, India
Tel.: (91) 2249689856
Web Site: https://pack-time.com
Packing Material Mfr & Distr
N.A.I.C.S.: 326112

Penta Latex LLP (1)
Plot No 49 & 50 Sector-2 Sidkul, Bhel Township, Haridwar, 249403, Uttarakhand, India
Tel.: (91) 9811040115
Web Site: https://www.pentalatex.com
Pharmaceutical Mfr & Distr
N.A.I.C.S.: 325412

Upakarma Ayurveda Private
Limited (1)
789-790 7th Floor Aggarwal Cyber Plaza-II Netaji Subhash Place, Pitampura North West DL, Delhi, 110034, India
Tel.: (91) 9319217217
Web Site: https://upakarma.in
Ayurveda Product Mfr & Distr
N.A.I.C.S.: 325412

MANKOTA STOCKMEN'S WEIGH CO. LTD
178 Railway Ave E, Mankota, S0H 2W0, SK, Canada
Tel.: (306) 478-2229
Web Site:
http://www.mankotastockmens.com
Year Founded: 1956
Sales Range: $25-49.9 Million
Emp.: 50
Livestock Whslr
N.A.I.C.S.: 424520
Evelyn Chanig *(Office Mgr)*

MANN+HUMMEL GMBH
Schwieberdinger Strasse 126, 71636, Ludwigsburg, Germany
Tel.: (49) 7141980 De
Web Site: http://www.mann-hummel.com
Year Founded: 1941
Sales Range: $1-4.9 Billion
Emp.: 14,338
Industrial Filters & Filtration Systems
N.A.I.C.S.: 333413
Manfred Wolf *(Pres/Gen Mgr-Automotive & Indus)*

Subsidiaries:

Changchun MANN+HUMMEL Fawer
Filter Co., Ltd. (1)
No 2177 Feng Yue Road, Automobile Economical and Technological Development Zone, Changchun, 130013, China
Tel.: (86) 43185808305
Industrial Filter Distr
N.A.I.C.S.: 423120

Fluid Brasil Sistemas e Tecnologia
Ltda. (1)
Rua Antonio Ovidio Rodrigues 845, Parque Industrial Jundiai III, 13213-180, Jundiai, SP, Brazil
Tel.: (55) 1133787500
Web Site: http://www.fluidbrasil.com.br
Industrial Filter Distr
N.A.I.C.S.: 423120
Alfred Weber *(Chm)*

Hydromation France S.A.R.L. (1)
3 Rue du colonel Mol, 75017, Paris, France
Tel.: (33) 243498000
Web Site: http://www.mann-hummel.com
Mfr of Industrial Filters & Filtration Systems For The Engineering Industry & Units & Systems For Materials Handling In The Plastics Processing Industry.
N.A.I.C.S.: 333998

I2M GmbH (1)
Hanauer Landstrasse 291 B, 60314, Frankfurt am Main, Germany
Tel.: (49) 15112258207
Filtration Equipment Mfr
N.A.I.C.S.: 333413
Sebastian Spielhoff *(Product Mgr)*

J. Riveros S.A.I.C. (1)
San Nicolas 912 / 960, San Miguel, 1200, Santiago, Chile
Tel.: (56) 23974444
Web Site: http://www.jriveros.cl
Emp.: 300
Service Paper-Wholesale
N.A.I.C.S.: 424130
Juan Riveros *(Gen Mgr)*

Jack Filter Hungaria Kft. (1)
Jack Filter Telep 1, Polgardi, Szekesfehervar, Hungary
Tel.: (36) 22576470
Filtration Equipment Mfr
N.A.I.C.S.: 333413
Eszter Varga *(Coord-Logistics)*

Jack Filter Lufttechnik GmbH (1)
Bundesstrasse 16, Steindorf am Ossiacher See, 9552, Feldkirchen bei Graz, Austria
Tel.: (43) 4243205420
Filtration Equipment Mfr
N.A.I.C.S.: 333413
Stefan Wiery *(Mgr-Ops & Plant)*

MANN VE HUMMEL Filtre Sanayi Ve
Ticaret Limited Sirketi (1)
Sahrayicedid Mh Halk Sk Pakpen Plaza No 44, Kozyatagi, 34734, Istanbul, Turkiye
Tel.: (90) 2164117900
Filtration Equipment Mfr
N.A.I.C.S.: 333413

MANN and HUMMEL Filter Private
Limited (1)
2nd Floor Prasad Enclave 118, 119 Industrial Suburb 2nd Stage 5th Main Yeshwantpura, Bengaluru, 560022, India
Tel.: (91) 8066207200
Industrial Filter Distr
N.A.I.C.S.: 423120
Christian Stummer *(VP-Fin & Controller)*

Plant (Domestic):

MANN and HUMMEL Filter Private
Limited - Plant 1 (2)
No 27 28 & 29 Block A Antharasanahalli Industrial Area Phase II, Tumkur, 572106, India
Tel.: (91) 8163051300
Industrial Filter Distr
N.A.I.C.S.: 423120

MANN and HUMMEL Filter Private
Limited - Plant 2 (2)
Plot No 19 Phase-II Sector-5 Bawal Industrial Growth Centre, Bawal, 123 501, Rewari, India
Tel.: (91) 1284263000
Industrial Filter Distr
N.A.I.C.S.: 423120

MANN and HUMMEL Thailand
Ltd. (1)
247 Lumpini 2 Tower Room 101 FL 1st Ratchadamri Road Lumpini, Pathumwan, Bangkok, 10330, Thailand
Tel.: (66) 265187901
Industrial Filter Distr
N.A.I.C.S.: 423120
Thanapong Longtong *(Mgr-Bus Dev)*

MANN+HUMMEL Atex Filter Verwaltungsgesellschaft mbH (1)
Eichenhofer Weg 14-16, 45549, Sprockhovel, Germany
Tel.: (49) 233912800
Industrial Filter Mfr
N.A.I.C.S.: 333248

MANN+HUMMEL BA J.S.C. (1)
Tesanj Bukva b b, 74260, Tesanj, Bosnia & Herzegovina
Tel.: (387) 32650585
Industrial Filter Mfr
N.A.I.C.S.: 333248
Arjana Krivdic *(Sec & Mgr-HR)*

MANN+HUMMEL BRASIL TECNOLOGIA EM AGUA PARTICIPACOES
LTDA. (1)
Alameda Filtros Mann 555, 13344-580, Indaiatuba, SP, Brazil
Tel.: (55) 1938949400
Industrial Filter Distr
N.A.I.C.S.: 423120

MANN+HUMMEL FT Poland Spolka
z Ograniczona Odpowiedzialnoscia
sp.k. (1)
Ul Wroclawska 145, 63-800, Gostyn, Poland
Tel.: (48) 655728900
Filtration Equipment Mfr
N.A.I.C.S.: 333413

MANN+HUMMEL KOREA CO.
LTD. (1)

MANN+HUMMEL GMBH

77-1 Donghwagongdan, Munmak, Anyang, 220-801, Gangwon, Korea (South)
Tel.: (82) 337604098
Industrial Filter Distr
N.A.I.C.S.: 423120

MANN+HUMMEL Middle East
FZE (1)
Office 1013 Bldg 7WA Dubai Airport Free Zone, PO Box 293882, Dubai, United Arab Emirates
Tel.: (971) 46091746
Industrial Filter Distr
N.A.I.C.S.: 423120

MANN+HUMMEL Togliatti OOO (1)
24 Menzelinskiy Trakt, 423800, Naberezhnye Chelny, Russia
Tel.: (7) 8552473037
Industrial Filter Distr
N.A.I.C.S.: 423120

MANN+HUMMEL Vokes Air AB (1)
Spinnaregatan 4, 51253, Svenljunga, Sweden
Tel.: (46) 325661600
Industrial Filter Distr
N.A.I.C.S.: 423120

MANN+HUMMEL Vokes Air AS (1)
Avedoreholmen 88, 2650, Hvidovre, Denmark
Tel.: (45) 36496600
Industrial Filter Distr
N.A.I.C.S.: 423120
Johnny Martens *(Mgr-Sls)*

MANN+HUMMEL Vokes Air
GmbH (1)
Ortsstrasse 18, 2331, Voesendorf, Austria
Tel.: (43) 169866770
Industrial Filter Distr
N.A.I.C.S.: 423120

MANN+HUMMEL Vokes Air SAS (1)
12 rue de Jamard, 77390, Ozouer-le-Voulgis, France
Tel.: (33) 164076125
Industrial Filter Distr
N.A.I.C.S.: 423120

MANN+HUMMEL Vokes Air SL (1)
Marina 7-Pol Ind Feliu Vila, Premia de Dalt, 08338, Barcelona, Spain
Tel.: (34) 937522718
Industrial Filter Distr
N.A.I.C.S.: 423120

MANN+HUMMEL Vokes Air SrL (1)
Via Zara 28, 20096, Pioltello, Italy
Tel.: (39) 0226926321
Industrial Filter Distr
N.A.I.C.S.: 423120
Carlo Coltri *(Mgr-Bus Dev)*

MANN+HUMMEL Vokes-Air
Limited (1)
Farrington Road, Burnley, BB11 5SY, United Kingdom
Tel.: (44) 1282413131
Industrial Filter Distr
N.A.I.C.S.: 423120

MICRODYN-NADIR GmbH (1)
Industrial Park Kalle Albert Building D512 Kasteler Strasse 45, 65203, Wiesbaden, Germany
Tel.: (49) 6119626001
Web Site: http://www.microdyn-nadir.com
Emp.: 220
Industrial Filter Distr
N.A.I.C.S.: 423120
Evelyn Vondikaki *(Reg Mgr-Sls)*

Subsidiary (Non-US):

MICRODYN-NADIR Singapore Pte
Ltd. (2)
2 Tuas Avenue 10, Singapore, 639126, Singapore
Tel.: (65) 64577533
Industrial Filter Distr
N.A.I.C.S.: 423120

Subsidiary (US):

TriSep Corp. (2)
93 S La Patera Lane, Goleta, CA 93117 (100%)
Tel.: (805) 964-8003
Web Site: http://www.trisep.com

MANN+HUMMEL GMBH

Mann+Hummel GmbH—(Continued)
Sales Range: $1-9.9 Million
Emp.: 52
Reverse Osmosis, Spiral Wound Membrane Separation & Chemical Support Products for Water Treatment
N.A.I.C.S.: 221310
Jon Goodman *(Sr VP-Comml)*

MICRODYN-NADIR Oltremare S.p.A. (1)
Via della Pineta 23, 61032, Fano, PU, Italy
Tel.: (39) 07211796201
Filtration Equipment Mfr
N.A.I.C.S.: 333413

Mann & Hummel Filters South Africa (Pty) Ltd. (1)
Clearwater Estates Block A First Floor West Atlas Road, 1459, Boksburg, South Africa
Tel.: (27) 115927000
Filtration Equipment Mfr
N.A.I.C.S.: 333413

Mann+Hummel (CZ) s.r.o. (1)
Nova Ves 66, 67521, Okrisky, Czech Republic **(100%)**
Tel.: (420) 568898111
Web Site: http://www.mannhummel.com
Emp.: 500
Industrial Filters & Filtration Systems
N.A.I.C.S.: 333998
Jiri Paroulek *(Mng Dir)*

Mann+Hummel (UK) Ltd. (1)
Hilton Cross Bus Park, Featherstone, Wolverhampton, WV10 7QZ, United Kingdom **(100%)**
Tel.: (44) 1902384000
Web Site: http://www.mann-hummel.com
Sales Range: $50-74.9 Million
Emp.: 250
Air Filtration Systems & Fuel Filtration Components
N.A.I.C.S.: 238290
Harald Spaeth *(Mng Dir)*

Mann+Hummel Argentina S.A. (1)
Sdor F Quindimil 4495, Valentin Alsina, 1822, Buenos Aires, Argentina **(100%)**
Tel.: (54) 40017200
Sales Range: $75-99.9 Million
Emp.: 220
Paper-Wholesale
N.A.I.C.S.: 424110

Mann+Hummel Brasil Ltda. (1)
Alameda Filtros Mann 555, Caixa Postal 210, CEP 1333-970, 13344-710, Indaiatuba, Brazil
Tel.: (55) 938949400
Web Site: http://www.mann-hummel.com.br
Emp.: 850
Industrial Filters & Filtration Systems
N.A.I.C.S.: 333998

Mann+Hummel Colombia S.A.S. (1)
Edificio Prime Tower Oficina 303 Avenida Calle 100 19-54, 110111, Bogota, Colombia
Tel.: (57) 4329066
Filtration Equipment Mfr
N.A.I.C.S.: 333413

Mann+Hummel Filter (Chongqing) Co., Ltd. (1)
Yuguan Avenue 225, Yuzui Town Jiangbei District, Chongqing, 401133, China
Tel.: (86) 2388798266
Filtration Equipment Mfr
N.A.I.C.S.: 333413

Mann+Hummel Filter Technology (S.E.A.) Pte. Ltd. (1)
1 International Business Park 03-15 The Synergy, 03 02 03 German Districentre, Singapore, 609917, Singapore
Tel.: (65) 65868181
Emp.: 20
Filters & Oil Cleaners
N.A.I.C.S.: 238220

Mann+Hummel Filtration Technology Canada ULC (1)
1035 Industrial Road, Ayr, N0B 1E0, ON, Canada
Tel.: (519) 622-4545
Filtration Equipment Mfr
N.A.I.C.S.: 333413
Bert Verriet *(Mgr-Mktg & Customer Rels)*

Mann+Hummel Filtration Technology Mexico S. de R.L.de C.V. (1)
Blvd Alpha 1655 Parque Industrial, Santa Maria, 25900, Ramos Arizpe, Mexico
Tel.: (52) 568448662201
Filtration Equipment Mfr
N.A.I.C.S.: 333413

Mann+Hummel Filtration Technology Venezuela C.A. (1)
Avenida Branger intersection, Iribarren Borges Industrial Zone Sur II, Valencia, Venezuela
Tel.: (58) 2413002000
Filtration Equipment Mfr
N.A.I.C.S.: 333413

Mann+Hummel GmbH - Marklkofen (1)
Kollbacher Strasse 31, 84163, Marklkofen, Germany
Tel.: (49) 8732200
Web Site: http://www.mann-hummel.com
Sales Range: $400-449.9 Million
Emp.: 2,500
Industrial Filters & Filtration Systems
N.A.I.C.S.: 333998

Mann+Hummel GmbH - Speyer (1)
Brunckstrasse 15, 67346, Speyer, Germany
Tel.: (49) 62325380
Web Site: http://www.mann-hummel.com
Sales Range: $200-249.9 Million
Emp.: 600
Industrial Filters & Filtration Systems
N.A.I.C.S.: 333998

Mann+Hummel Hydromation N.V. (1)
Luikersteenweg 220 1 Ste A F D, PO Box 99, 3700, Tongeren, Belgium **(100%)**
Tel.: (32) 12399310
Web Site: http://www.mannhummel.com
Sales Range: $25-49.9 Million
Emp.: 80
Industrial Filters & Filtration Systems
N.A.I.C.S.: 333998
Christian Stummer *(Mng Dir)*

Mann+Hummel Iberica S.A (1)
Pertusa 8, 501970, Zaragoza, Spain
Tel.: (34) 976720200
Web Site: http://www.mann-hummel.com
Emp.: 600
Industrial Filters & Filtration Systems
N.A.I.C.S.: 333998
Javier Sanz *(Gen Mgr)*

Mann+Hummel Japan K.K. (1)
Ys Shin Yokohama Bldg 2nd Fl 2-15-10, Shin Yokohama Kohoku-Ku, Yokohama, 222-0033, Japan **(100%)**
Tel.: (81) 454700808
Web Site: http://www.mannhummel.com
Sales Range: $25-49.9 Million
Emp.: 48
Paper-Wholesale
N.A.I.C.S.: 424130

Mann+Hummel Mexico, S.A. de C.V. (1)
Vialidad el Pueblito No 104 Parque Industrial Queretaro, Santa Rosa Jauregui, CP 76220, Queretaro, Mexico
Tel.: (52) 4421031100
Sales Range: $200-249.9 Million
Emp.: 800
Industrial Filters & Filtration Systems
N.A.I.C.S.: 333998

Mann+Hummel ProTec GmbH (1)
Groemer Strasse 50, 71636, Ludwigsburg, Germany **(100%)**
Tel.: (49) 7141980
Web Site: http://www.mann-hummel.com
Sales Range: $25-49.9 Million
Emp.: 100
Industrial Filters & Filtration Systems
N.A.I.C.S.: 333998
Alfert Weber *(CEO)*

Mann+Hummel Trading (Shanghai) Co., Ltd. (1)
29B Times Square 500 Zhang Yang Road, Shanghai, 200122, China
Tel.: (86) 2151759988
Filtration Equipment Mfr
N.A.I.C.S.: 333413

Mann+Hummel, Inc. (1)
6400 S Sprinkle Rd, Portage, MI 49002-9706 **(100%)**
Tel.: (269) 329-3900
Web Site: http://www.mann-hummel.com
Emp.: 25
Holding Company; Regional Managing Office; Filtration Products Mfr & Distr
N.A.I.C.S.: 551112

Subsidiary (Domestic):

Mann+Hummel USA, Inc. (2)
6400 S Sprinkle Rd, Portage, MI 49002-9706
Tel.: (269) 329-3900
Web Site: http://www.mann-hummel.com
Sales Range: $125-149.9 Million
Emp.: 257
Filtration Products Mfr & Distr
N.A.I.C.S.: 333998
Jack Endres *(Dir-Engrg & Tech)*

Subsidiary (Domestic):

MANN+HUMMEL Filtration Technology US LLC (3)
1 Wix Way, Gastonia, NC 28054
Tel.: (704) 864-3421
Web Site: http://www.wixfilters.com
Air, Oil, Fuel, Hydraulic, Cooling & Specialty Filters Mfr
N.A.I.C.S.: 333310
Jeff Blocher *(Dir-Sls)*

Mann+Hummel Advanced Filtration Concepts, Inc. (3)
2285 Franklin Rd Ste 200, Bloomfield Hills, MI 48302-0325
Tel.: (502) 935-9333
Web Site: http://www.mann-hummel.com
Sales Range: $25-49.9 Million
Emp.: 71
Mfr of Heavy Metal
N.A.I.C.S.: 333998

Mann+Hummel Purolator Filters LLC (3)
3200 Natal St, Fayetteville, NC 28306 **(100%)**
Tel.: (910) 425-4181
Web Site: http://www.purolatorautofilters.net
Automotive Filter Mfr & Distr
N.A.I.C.S.: 336390
Ken Robinson *(Mgr-IT)*

Universal Dynamics, Inc. (3)
13600 Dabney Rd, Woodbridge, VA 22191 **(100%)**
Tel.: (703) 490-7000
Web Site: http://www.unadyn.com
Rev.: $15,000,000
Emp.: 125
Mfr of Industrial Dryers & Auxiliary Equipment for The Plastics Industry
N.A.I.C.S.: 333415
Bill Godserv *(Pres)*

MANNAI CORPORATION QPSC

Building No 72 Zone No 57 East Industrial Street, PO Box 76, Doha, Qatar
Tel.: (974) 44558888
Web Site: https://www.mannai.com
MCCS (QE)
Rev.: $3,375,613,575
Assets: $4,608,441,433
Liabilities: $3,972,323,249
Net Worth: $636,118,184
Earnings: $3,936,791
Emp.: 2,000
Fiscal Year-end: 12/31/20
Engineering, Oil Rigging, Construction, Trading, Distribution & Automotive Services
N.A.I.C.S.: 541330
Alekh Grewal *(Mng Dir-Intl)*

Subsidiaries:

Damas International Limited (1)
36 Gate Village DIFC Bldg 4 Level 3, PO Box 113355, Dubai, United Arab Emirates **(100%)**
Tel.: (971) 44459000
Web Site: http://www.damasjewel.com

INTERNATIONAL PUBLIC

Sales Range: $800-899.9 Million
Jewelry & Watch Retailer
N.A.I.C.S.: 458310

Subsidiary (Domestic):

Damas LLC (2)
3rd Fl Gold Ctr Bldg, Deira, United Arab Emirates
Tel.: (971) 42266036
Jewelry & Watch Retailer
N.A.I.C.S.: 458310

Egyptian International Motors Egypt (1)
38 Abo Baker Elseddeik Mahkama Square, Cairo, Egypt
Tel.: (20) 26386395
Web Site: http://www.eim-eg.com
Automotive Services
N.A.I.C.S.: 811198

Gfi International SA (1)
Chemin des Aulx 10, 1228, Plan-les-Ouates, Switzerland
Tel.: (41) 227062711
Application Development Services
N.A.I.C.S.: 541511

Inetum SA (1)
5-7 rue Touzet Gaillard, 93400, Saint-Ouen, France **(100%)**
Tel.: (33) 144045000
Web Site: https://www.inetum.com
Rev.: $1,355,826,590
Assets: $1,136,612,220
Liabilities: $750,999,525
Net Worth: $385,612,695
Earnings: $44,690,959
Emp.: 14,375
Fiscal Year-end: 12/31/2017
Information Technology Services
N.A.I.C.S.: 541512
Jacques Pommeraud *(CEO)*

Subsidiary (Non-US):

GFI BeLux (2)
Technologielaan 11- 0102, 3001, Heverlee, Belgium
Tel.: (32) 16 38 11 11
Web Site: http://www.gfi.be
Emp.: 500
Business Management Software Development Services
N.A.I.C.S.: 541511

GFI Informatique Maroc (2)
1100 Bd El Qods Casablanca Nearshore Park 2B - 3eme etage, Quartier Sidi Maarouf, 20190, Casablanca, Morocco **(100%)**
Tel.: (212) 522949779
Web Site: http://www.gfimaroc.com
Emp.: 260
Financial Software Development Services
N.A.I.C.S.: 541511
Saloua Karkri Belkeziz *(Founder, CEO & Dir)*

GFI Portugal (2)
Atlantis Building Avenida D Joao Ii, 1990 095, Lisbon, Portugal
Tel.: (351) 21 049 99 50
Web Site: http://gfi.world
Public Administration, Healthcare, Media & Communications, Financial Services; Industry & Utilities, Transportation & Logistics Consulting & Outsourcing Services
N.A.I.C.S.: 541614
Nuno Santos *(CEO & Mng Dir)*

Grupo Corporativo GFI Informatica S.A. (2)
C Serrano Galvache 56 Planta Septima, Edificio Encina, 28033, Madrid, Spain
Tel.: (34) 91 383 63 20
Web Site: http://www.gfi.es
Emp.: 2,500
Business Management Software Development Services
N.A.I.C.S.: 541511
Carlos Munoz *(CEO)*

RealDolmen NV (2)
A Vaucampslaan 42, 1654, Huizingen, Belgium
Tel.: (32) 28015555
Web Site: https://www.realdolmen.com
Sales Range: $250-299.9 Million
Emp.: 1,950

Information & Communication Technology Developer
N.A.I.C.S.: 541512
Paul De Schrijver (CFO)

Subsidiary (Non-US):

Oriam SA (3)
8 Parvis de Saint Maur, 94106, Saint Maur-des-Fosses, France
Tel.: (33) 155970320
Sales Range: $25-49.9 Million
Emp.: 15
Software Consulting Services
N.A.I.C.S.: 541511

Real Solutions SA (3)
33 Rue d Eich, Luxembourg, 1461, Luxembourg
Tel.: (352) 4365221
Web Site: http://www.real.lu
Sales Range: $25-49.9 Million
Emp.: 80
Software Services
N.A.I.C.S.: 541511

Subsidiary (Domestic):

Supply Chain Software NV (3)
A Vaucampsl 28 N 42, Huizingen, 1654, Belgium
Tel.: (32) 32902536
Sales Range: $150-199.9 Million
Emp.: 1,000
Software Services
N.A.I.C.S.: 541511

Mannai Marine Co, Limited (1)
Ramada Signel, PO Box 776, Doha, Qatar (100%)
Tel.: (974) 4415025
Provider of Construction Services for Oil & Gas Industries
N.A.I.C.S.: 237120

Mannai Trading Company WLL (1)
Auto Service Center Mannai Complex, PO Box 76, Doha, Qatar (100%)
Tel.: (974) 4 455 8000
Web Site: https://www.mannaiautos.com
Provider of Trading & Distribution Services
N.A.I.C.S.: 561499

Mansal Offshore Limited (1)
Salwa Rd, PO Box 1310, Doha, Qatar (100%)
Tel.: (974) 4425755
Sales Range: $125-149.9 Million
Emp.: 500
Provider of Marine Services & Facilities to Offshore Oil & Gas Industry
N.A.I.C.S.: 488330

Manweir Limited (1)
CB-50 Phase-1 Ras Laffan Support Services Area, PO Box 4038, Ras Laffan Industrial City, Doha, Qatar (100%)
Tel.: (974) 44335381
Web Site: https://www.manweir.com
Sales Range: $200-249.9 Million
Emp.: 300
Repair & Maintenance Services for Oil, Gas, Petrochemical & Power Generation Industries
N.A.I.C.S.: 213112

Mideast Constructors Limited (MECON) (1)
Rayyan Rd, PO Box 3325, Doha, Qatar (100%)
Tel.: (974) 4415025
Sales Range: $350-399.9 Million
Emp.: 1,500
Provider of Electromechanical Services to Gas & Oil Industry
N.A.I.C.S.: 541330

Technical Services Co. Limited (TECHSERV) (1)
PO Box 76, Doha, Qatar
Tel.: (974) 4558888
Web Site: http://www.mannaicorp.com
Products & Services to Oil, Gas & Petroleum Industries
N.A.I.C.S.: 213112

MANNING GOTTLIEB OMD

Seymour Mews House 26-37 Seymour Mews, London, W1H 6BN, United Kingdom
Tel.: (44) 207 470 5300
Web Site: http://www.omd.com
Year Founded: 1990
Rev.: $462,295,673
Emp.: 400
N.A.I.C.S.: 541810
George Manas (CEO)

MANNING VENTURES, INC.

Suite 303 750 West Pender Street, Vancouver, V6C 2T7, BC, Canada
Tel.: (604) 681-0084
Web Site: https://www.manning-ventures.com
1H50—(DEU)
Rev.: $563
Assets: $6,756,050
Liabilities: $567,564
Net Worth: $6,188,486
Earnings: ($1,714,295)
Fiscal Year-end: 11/30/23
Mineral Exploration Services
N.A.I.C.S.: 213115
Alex Klenman (CEO)

MANOIR INDUSTRIES

37 Rue de Liege, 75008, Paris, France
Tel.: (33) 144698810
Web Site: http://www.manoir-industries.com
Year Founded: 1950
Sales Range: $250-299.9 Million
Emp.: 2,300
Forged Metal Component For Use in Petrochemical Industry Aeronautics Armaments Energy & Railroad Construction Mfr
N.A.I.C.S.: 332111
Pons Fernand (Chm, Pres & CEO)

Subsidiaries:

Hi-Tech Fabrication Ltd. (1)
Bretby Business Park Ashby Road, Burton-on-Trent, DE15 0YZ, Staffordshire, United Kingdom
Tel.: (44) 1283817900
Web Site: http://www.hitechfab.co.uk
Machinery Equipment Mfr
N.A.I.C.S.: 333248

Manoir Industries (1)
Ste 1300 11757 Katy Fwy, Houston, TX 77079-1725 (100%)
Tel.: (281) 548-1050
Web Site: http://www.manoirusa.com
Mfr f Forged Metal Components For Use In Petrochemical Industries
N.A.I.C.S.: 423510

Manoir Industries (1)
1 2 9 Nishi Shinbashi, Hibiya Central Bldg 14 Fl, 1050003, Tokyo, Minato Ku, Japan (100%)
Tel.: (81) 355327280
Web Site: http://www.manoir-industries.com
Sales Range: $300-349.9 Million
Emp.: 1
Mfr of Metal Products
N.A.I.C.S.: 332111

Manoir Industries (1)
Sede Italiana Via A Diaz 10, 21047, Saronno, VA, Italy (100%)
Tel.: (39) 0296703334
Sales Range: $25-49.9 Million
Emp.: 2
Mfr of Metal Products
N.A.I.C.S.: 332111

Manoir Industries - Manoir Bouzonville Plant (1)
Route de Guerstling, BP 11, 57320, Bouzonville, France
Tel.: (33) 3 87 39 78 78
Iron & Steel Forging Mfr
N.A.I.C.S.: 331110

Manoir Industries - Manoir Engrenages Plant (1)
Rue d'Oradour sur Glane, BP 28, 95270, Chaumontel, France
Tel.: (33) 1 3029 58 88
Iron & Steel Forging Mfr
N.A.I.C.S.: 331110

Manoir Petro India Limited (1)
Universal Business Park 602 B - Wing - Chandivali Farm Road E, Andheri, Mumbai, 400 072, India
Tel.: (91) 9920167307
Chemicals Mfr
N.A.I.C.S.: 325998
Jayarajan Nambiar (CEO)

MANOJ VAIBHAV GEMS N JEWELLERS LIMITED

47-15-8 V Square Zone-A Opp TSR Complex Station Road Dwarakanagar, Visakhapatnam, 530016, Andhra Pradesh, India
Tel.: (91) 8916667777
Web Site: https://www.vaibhavjewellers.com
Year Founded: 1989
543995—(BOM)
Jewelry Mfr
N.A.I.C.S.: 339910
Bharata Mallika Ratna Kumari Grandhiq (Chm)

MANOLETE PARTNERS PLC

21 Gloucester Place, London, W1U 8HR, United Kingdom
Tel.: (44) 2038593490 UK
Web Site: https://www.manolete-partners.com
Year Founded: 2009
MANO—(AIM)
Rev.: $26,196,668
Assets: $78,866,448
Liabilities: $29,433,224
Net Worth: $49,433,224
Earnings: ($3,943,449)
Emp.: 25
Fiscal Year-end: 03/31/23
Financial Brokerage Services
N.A.I.C.S.: 523160
Steven Cooklin (Founder & CEO)

MANOMAY TEX INDIA LIMITED

32 Heera Panna Market Pur Road, Bhilwara, 311 001, Rajsthan, India
Tel.: (91) 1482246983
Web Site: https://www.manomaytexindia.com
Year Founded: 1978
MANOMAY—(NSE)
Rev.: $83,835,406
Assets: $47,116,983
Liabilities: $33,216,462
Net Worth: $13,900,522
Earnings: $1,552,713
Emp.: 588
Fiscal Year-end: 03/31/23
Textile Material Mfr & Distr
N.A.I.C.S.: 313210
Kailashchandra Hiralal Laddha (Chm)

MANOR ESTATES & INDUSTRIES LIMITED

S No 321 Kallakal Village Toopran Mandal, Medak, 502336, Telangana, India
Tel.: (91) 8897642711
Web Site: https://www.meilmedak.in
Year Founded: 1992
526115—(BOM)
Rev.: $3,441
Assets: $18,092
Liabilities: $289,683
Net Worth: ($271,590)
Earnings: ($71,950)
Fiscal Year-end: 03/31/23
Sock Mfr & Sales
N.A.I.C.S.: 315120

MANOR FRESH LIMITED

Holbeach Hurn, Spalding, PE12 8LR, Lincolnshire, United Kingdom
Tel.: (44) 1406301001
Web Site: http://www.manorfresh.co.uk
Sales Range: $10-24.9 Million
Emp.: 250
Potato Production & Supply
N.A.I.C.S.: 111211

MANORAMA INDUSTRIES LIMITED

F 6 Anupam Nagar, Raipur, 492007, India
Tel.: (91) 7712283071
Web Site: https://www.manoramagroup.co.in
MANORAMA—(NSE)
Rev.: $42,794,149
Assets: $50,885,630
Liabilities: $15,119,993
Net Worth: $35,765,638
Earnings: $3,569,990
Emp.: 279
Fiscal Year-end: 03/31/23
Agricultural Services
N.A.I.C.S.: 115116
Divya Bhootra (Compliance Officer & Sec)

MANPOWERGROUP GREATER CHINA LIMITED

37/F Building A Xin Mei Union Square No 999 Pudong Road, Pudong New Area, Shanghai, China
Tel.: (86) 4008200711 Ky
Web Site: http://www.manpowergrc.com
Year Founded: 1997
2180—(HKG)
Rev.: $644,219,784
Assets: $270,988,848
Liabilities: $109,381,849
Net Worth: $161,606,999
Earnings: $19,020,971
Emp.: 1,384
Fiscal Year-end: 12/31/22
Human Resource Consulting Services
N.A.I.C.S.: 541612
Jianhua Yuan (Pres & CEO)

Subsidiaries:

Manpower Outsourcing Services (Macau) Limited (1)
Unit E 15/F Circle Square 61 Avenida De Almeida Ribeiro, Macau, China (Macau)
Tel.: (853) 28355521
Recruitment Process Outsourcing Services
N.A.I.C.S.: 561312

MANRAJ HOUSING FINANCE LIMITED

3 Pushpa Apartments General Vaidya Chowk, Jalgaon, 425 002, India
Tel.: (91) 2575612488
530537—(BOM)
Rev.: $39,290
Assets: $2,667,511
Liabilities: $2,693,016
Net Worth: ($25,505)
Earnings: $1,958
Fiscal Year-end: 03/31/21
Financial Services
N.A.I.C.S.: 522291
Ishwarlal S. Jain (Chm & Mng Dir)

MANROC DEVELOPMENTS INC.

7 Black Road, Manitouwadge, P0T 2C0, ON, Canada
Tel.: (807) 826-4564
Web Site: https://www.manroc.com
Year Founded: 1986
Rev.: $12,761,546
Emp.: 100
Mining Contractors

MANROC DEVELOPMENTS INC.

Manroc Developments Inc.—(Continued)
N.A.I.C.S.: 212390
Craig Robertson (Mgr-Health & Safety)

MANSEI CORPORATION
7-15-5 Fukushima, Fukushima-ku, Osaka, 553-0003, Japan
Tel.: (81) 664548211
Web Site: https://www.mansei.co.jp
Year Founded: 1947
7565—(TKS)
Rev.: $172,858,110
Assets: $158,362,380
Liabilities: $68,836,540
Net Worth: $89,525,840
Earnings: $7,079,310
Emp.: 183
Fiscal Year-end: 03/31/24
Electrical Equipment Whslr
N.A.I.C.S.: 423610
Masahiro Urabe (Pres & Chm)

Subsidiaries:

Mansei Denki HK Ltd. (1)
Unit A2 7/F Office Plus Mongkok No 998 Cazton Road, Kowloon, China (Hong Kong)
Tel.: (852) 26251770
Electrical Equipment Distr
N.A.I.C.S.: 423690
Hiroyuki Itou (Pres)

Mansei Denki Shanghai Ltd. (1)
Rm 2112 Block A Far East International Plaza No 319 Xianxia Road, Shanghai, 200051, China
Tel.: (86) 2162788190
Electrical Equipment Distr
N.A.I.C.S.: 423690

MANSFELDER METALS LTD.
Suite 803 Dina House Ruttonjee Centre, 11 Duddell Street, Central, 200070, China (Hong Kong)
Tel.: (852) 5373161   DE
Year Founded: 1977
MNSF—(OTCIQ)
Sales Range: $75-99.9 Million
Emp.: 126
Holding Company; Aluminum Products Mfr & Distr
N.A.I.C.S.: 551112
J. Randall Nelson (Pres & CEO)

Subsidiaries:

AFM Aluminiumfolie Merseburg GmbH (1)
August-Bebel Strasse 1, 06217, Merseburg, Germany **(100%)**
Tel.: (49) 34612840
Web Site: http://www.afm-aluminium.de
Sales Range: $25-49.9 Million
Emp.: 56
Aluminum Processor
N.A.I.C.S.: 331313
Bernd Gebhardt (Plant Mgr)

MAW Mansfelder Aluminiumwerke GmbH (1)
Lichtloecherberg 40, 06333, Hettstedt, Germany **(100%)**
Tel.: (49) 3476398301
Web Site: http://www.mansfelder-aluminiumwerk.de
Sales Range: $25-49.9 Million
Emp.: 70
Aluminium Products Mfr
N.A.I.C.S.: 331318
Harald Springer (Gen Mgr-Pur & Production)

MANSFIELD BUILDING SOCIETY
Regent House Regent Street, Mansfield, NG18 1SS, United Kingdom
Tel.: (44) 1623 676300
Web Site: http://www.mansfieldbs.co.uk
Year Founded: 1869
Rev.: $16,764,871

Assets: $568,854,036
Liabilities: $529,916,567
Net Worth: $38,937,469
Earnings: $2,482,859
Emp.: 65
Fiscal Year-end: 12/31/19
Residential Mortgage Lending & Financial Services Organization
N.A.I.C.S.: 925110
Paul Wheeler (CEO)

MANSI FINANCE (CHENNAI) LIMITED
No 22B Mullah Sahib Street Sowcarpet, Chennai, 600079, India
Tel.: (91) 4426445533
Web Site: https://www.mansi.in
511758—(BOM)
Rev.: $1,038,281
Assets: $8,878,622
Liabilities: $4,800,553
Net Worth: $4,078,069
Earnings: $238,726
Emp.: 19
Fiscal Year-end: 03/31/21
Financial Services
N.A.I.C.S.: 523999
Suresh Bafna (Chm & Mng Dir)

MANSION HOUSE CONSULTING LIMITED
Dowgate Hill House 14 - 16 Dowgate Hill, London, EC4R 2SU, United Kingdom
Tel.: (44) 2036977140
Web Site: http://www.mansion-house.co.uk
Year Founded: 2009
Sales Range: $10-24.9 Million
Emp.: 20
Information Technology Consultancy Services
N.A.I.C.S.: 541512
Eric Werner (Chm)

Subsidiaries:

Mansion House Consulting Inc. (1)
14 Wall St 20th Fl, New York, NY 10005
Tel.: (212) 618-1234
Business Management Consulting Services
N.A.I.C.S.: 541611
Jon Reece (Country Mgr)

MANSION INTERNATIONAL HOLDINGS LIMITED
East Wing 5/F 822 Lai Chi Kok Road, Kowloon, China (Hong Kong)
Tel.: (852) 2 481 7632   Ky
Web Site: http://www.mansionintl.com
Year Founded: 1993
8456—(HKG)
Rev.: $11,257,116
Assets: $6,542,897
Liabilities: $9,460,296
Net Worth: ($2,917,399)
Earnings: ($8,363,708)
Emp.: 63
Fiscal Year-end: 03/31/21
Clothing Product Mfr & Distr
N.A.I.C.S.: 315250
Desmond Lap Wai Cheung (Chm & CEO-Acting)

Subsidiaries:

Babies Trendyland Limited (1)
East Wing 5th Floor 822 Lai Chi Kok Road, Kowloon, China (Hong Kong)
Tel.: (852) 22661000
Web Site: http://www.mides.com.hk
Baby Clothing & Accessory Retailer
N.A.I.C.S.: 458110

Mantex Supplies Company Limited (1)
East Wing 5/F 822 Lai Chi Kok Road, Kowloon, China (Hong Kong)
Tel.: (852) 24817632

Web Site: http://www.mantex.com
Baby Clothing & Accessory Distr
N.A.I.C.S.: 424350

MANSOON TRADING CO., LTD.
203 2nd Floor M-Space, Next to Minatai Thackeray Blood Bank Sitaram Patkar Marg Goregaon West, Mumbai, 400001, India
Tel.: (91) 2138400000
Web Site: https://www.mansoontrading.co.in
Year Founded: 1985
512303—(BOM)
Rev.: $1,854,385
Assets: $32,013,728
Liabilities: $18,071,578
Net Worth: $13,942,150
Earnings: ($1,554,415)
Emp.: 1
Fiscal Year-end: 03/31/23
Financial Services
N.A.I.C.S.: 523150
Abhijeet Chandrakant Salvi (CFO)

MANSOUR GROUP
Smart Village 6 October Mantrac ECG Building B17, Mohandessin, Cairo, Egypt
Tel.: (20) 235314163
Web Site: http://www.mansourgroup.com
Sales Range: $1-4.9 Billion
Emp.: 60,000
Holding Services
N.A.I.C.S.: 551112
Youssef Mansour (Co-Chm)

Subsidiaries:

Al Mansour Holding Company (1)
Zahraa El Maadi Industrial Zone, PO Box 97, New Maadi, Cairo, Egypt
Tel.: (20) 2 2754 8360
Web Site: http://www.mmd.mansourgroup.com
Consumer Products Distr
N.A.I.C.S.: 424490
Youssef L. Mansour (CEO)

Al-Mansour Automotive Company (1)
54 Gameat El Dowal St, Mohandiseen, Cairo, Egypt
Tel.: (20) 2 3444177
Web Site: http://www.almansourauto.com
Motor Vehicle Distr
N.A.I.C.S.: 423110

Delta Rassis KSA (1)
Al-Safawah Center Gate 1 Ground Floor Office 1005 - Sulemania, Riyadh, Saudi Arabia
Tel.: (966) 114167775
Web Site: http://www.deltarassis.com
Computer Peripheral Equipment Distr
N.A.I.C.S.: 423430

Mantrac Egypt (1)
Amreya Km 28 Alex-Cairo Desert Road, Alexandria, Egypt
Tel.: (20) 3 4541000
Web Site: http://www.mantracgroup.com
Construction & Mining Equipment Distr
N.A.I.C.S.: 423810

Mantrac Ghana Ltd. (1)
Ring Road West, PO Box 5207, Accra, Ghana
Tel.: (233) 30 2213720
Web Site: http://www.mantracghana.com
Construction & Mining Equipment Distr
N.A.I.C.S.: 423810

Mantrac ITD Egypt (1)
13th St 294 New Maadi in front of Modern Academy, Cairo, Egypt
Tel.: (20) 2 3300 1414
Web Site: http://www.mantrac-itd.com
Computer Peripheral Equipment Distr
N.A.I.C.S.: 423430

Mantrac Iraq (1)

INTERNATIONAL PUBLIC

Dist 923 - St 29 - University St, Baghdad, Iraq
Tel.: (964) 1 7783 783
Web Site: http://www.iratrac.com
Construction & Mining Equipment Distr
N.A.I.C.S.: 423810

Mantrac Kenya Ltd. (1)
Mansour Complex Witu Road off Lusaka Road, PO Box 30067, Nairobi, Kenya
Tel.: (254) 20 4995300
Web Site: http://www.mantrackenya.com
Emp.: 30
Construction & Mining Equipment Distr
N.A.I.C.S.: 423810

Mantrac Nigeria Ltd. (1)
2 Billingsway Off Secretariat Road Oregun Industrial Estate, Oregun PMB 21480 Ikeja, Lagos, Nigeria
Tel.: (234) 1 2716300
Web Site: http://www.mantracnigeria.com
Construction & Mining Equipment Distr
N.A.I.C.S.: 423810

Mantrac Russia (1)
15 Steklozavodskoye shosse, Bor Nizhegorodskaya oblast, 606440, Nizhniy Novgorod, Russia
Tel.: (7) 8315920530
Web Site: http://www.mantracvostok.com
Construction & Mining Equipment Distr
N.A.I.C.S.: 423810

Mantrac Sierra Leone Ltd. (1)
6-8 Blackhall Road, PO Box 127, Freetown, Sierra Leone
Tel.: (232) 22 223317
Web Site: http://www.mantrac-sl.com
Emp.: 13
Construction & Mining Equipment Distr
N.A.I.C.S.: 423810

Mantrac Tanzania Ltd. (1)
Plot no 4A Nyerere Road, PO Box 9262, Dar es Salaam, Tanzania
Tel.: (255) 22 286 0161
Web Site: http://www.mantractanzania.com
Emp.: 200
Construction & Mining Equipment Distr
N.A.I.C.S.: 423810
Hatem Farouk (Mng Dir)

Mantrac Uganda Ltd. (1)
Plot 17/41 7th Street Industrial Area, PO Box 7126, Kampala, Uganda
Tel.: (256) 414 304000
Web Site: http://www.mantracuganda.com
Emp.: 22
Construction & Mining Equipment Distr
N.A.I.C.S.: 423810

MANSOURA POULTRY CO.
10th of Ramadan City AreaB3 Plot 49, Sharkia, Egypt
Tel.: (20) 554500511
Web Site: https://mpcopoultry.com
Year Founded: 1983
MPCO.CA—(EGX)
Sales Range: Less than $1 Million
Veal Product Mfr
N.A.I.C.S.: 311615
Islam Muhammad Naguib Hussein (Chm)

MANTARO PRECIOUS METALS CORP.
704-595 Howe Street, Vancouver, V6C-2T5, BC, Canada   BC
Web Site: https://www.mantaroprecious.com
Year Founded: 2008
MNTR—(TSXV)
Assets: $7,659,693
Liabilities: $243,157
Net Worth: $7,416,536
Earnings: ($3,572,880)
Fiscal Year-end: 02/28/22
Gold Exploration & Mining Services
N.A.I.C.S.: 212220

MANTEX AB
Torshamnsgatan 28A, 16440, Kista, Sweden

AND PRIVATE COMPANIES

MANULI RUBBER INDUSTRIES S.P.A.

Tel.: (46) 728573248
Web Site: https://www.mantex.se
Year Founded: 1895
MANTEX—(OMX)
Rev.: $639,711
Assets: $3,348,413
Liabilities: $721,197
Net Worth: $2,627,216
Earnings: ($1,563,217)
Emp.: 10
Fiscal Year-end: 12/31/23
Industrial Equipment Distr
N.A.I.C.S.: 423830
Per Grunewald *(Chm)*

MANTHAN SOFTWARE SERVICES PVT. LTD.
40/4 Lavelle Road, Bengaluru, 560001, Karnataka, India
Tel.: (91) 8022990585
Web Site: http://www.manthan.com
Cloud Analytics Company
N.A.I.C.S.: 518210
Atul Jalan *(CEO)*

MANTIS VISION LTD.
94 Shlomo Shmeltzer road Kiryat Arie, Petach Tikva, 4970602, Israel
Tel.: (972) 35611660
Web Site: http://www.mantis-vision.com
Year Founded: 2005
Sales Range: Less than $1 Million
3D Technologies Developer
N.A.I.C.S.: 513210
Gur Arie Bitan *(CEO)*

MANTLE MINERALS LIMITED
Ground Floor 168 Stirling Hwy, Nedlands, 6009, WA, Australia
Tel.: (61) 861022656   AU
Web Site:
  https://www.caeneus.com.au
Year Founded: 1998
MTL—(ASX)
Rev.: $56,033
Assets: $604,595
Liabilities: $581,900
Net Worth: $22,696
Earnings: ($1,728,913)
Fiscal Year-end: 06/30/24
Mineral Exploration Services
N.A.I.C.S.: 212390
Johnathon Busing *(Sec)*

MANUFACT LOGISTICS LTD
3655 Western Rd, North York, M9L 1V8, ON, Canada
Tel.: (416) 739-8411
Web Site:
  http://www.mvrwholesale.com
Sales Range: $125-149.9 Million
Emp.: 40
Supermarket Business Provider
N.A.I.C.S.: 445110
Robert Commisso *(VP)*

MANUFACTURE DE PANNEAUX BOIS DU SUD SA
Route de Gabes Km 1 5, 3003, Sfax, Tunisia
Tel.: (216) 74468044
Web Site: https://www.mpbs.com.tn
MPBS—(BVT)
Sales Range: Less than $1 Million
Wood Products Mfr
N.A.I.C.S.: 321999

MANUFACTURIER DE BAS IRIS INC.
6767 Leger Boulevard, Montreal, H1E 7J8, QC, Canada
Tel.: (514) 328-9334
Rev.: $120,000,000
Emp.: 1
Hosiery Mfr

N.A.I.C.S.: 315120
Andrew Badia *(Pres)*

MANUFACTURING INTEGRATION TECHNOLOGY LTD
Blk 5004 0501 Ang Mo Kio Ave 5 TECHplace II, Singapore, 569872, Singapore
Tel.: (65) 68678052
Web Site: https://www.mitech-ltd.com.sg
M11—(SES)
Rev.: $6,338,711
Assets: $11,202,757
Liabilities: $3,559,797
Net Worth: $7,642,960
Earnings: ($2,613,042)
Emp.: 70
Fiscal Year-end: 12/31/23
Automated Equipment Mfr
N.A.I.C.S.: 518210
Dennis Piau Yew Foo *(VP-Corporate Sls)*

Subsidiaries:

Casem (Asia) Pte. Ltd.   (1)
Blk 5004 05-01 Ang Mo Kio Ave 5 TECHplace II, Singapore, 569872, Singapore
Tel.: (65) 68678052
Industrial Automation Equipment Mfr & Distr
N.A.I.C.S.: 334413

MIT (Shanghai) Co. Ltd.   (1)
No 268 Hui Tong Road, Jia Ding District, Shanghai, 201815, China
Tel.: (86) 2139561933
Web Site: http://www.mitech-ltd.com.sg
Semiconductor Product Whslr
N.A.I.C.S.: 423690

MIT Technologies Pte. Ltd.   (1)
31 Woodlands Close Woodlands Horizon 04-17, Singapore, 737855, Singapore
Tel.: (65) 67423850
Web Site: https://www.mit-tec.com
Automated Equipment Mfr & Distr
N.A.I.C.S.: 334413

MANUGRAPH INDIA LTD
Sidhwa House N A Sawant Marg Colaba, Mumbai, 400 005, Maharashtra, India
Tel.: (91) 2235121178
Web Site:
  https://www.manugraph.com
MANUGRAPH—(NSE)
Rev.: $9,850,966
Assets: $20,844,109
Liabilities: $8,827,978
Net Worth: $12,016,132
Earnings: ($1,336,339)
Emp.: 368
Fiscal Year-end: 03/31/23
Web Offset Presses Mfr
N.A.I.C.S.: 333248
Sanat M. Shah *(Founder)*

Subsidiaries:

Manugraph DGM Inc   (1)
PO Box 573, Elizabethville, PA 17023
Tel.: (717) 362-3243
Web Site:
  http://www.manugraphdgmusa.com
Offset Printing Machines Mfr
N.A.I.C.S.: 333248
Ron Ehrhardt *(VP)*

Manugraph India Ltd - Manufacturing Unit No.1   (1)
Plot No D1 MIDC Industrial Estate Shiroli Pulachi, Kolhapur, 416 122, Maharastra, India
Tel.: (91) 2302468581
Web Site: http://www.manugraph.com
Offset Printing Press Mfr
N.A.I.C.S.: 333248

Manugraph India Ltd - Manufacturing Unit No.2   (1)
Warnanagar Kodoli Panhala, Kolhapur, 416 114, Maharastra, India
Tel.: (91) 2328288400

Web Site: http://www.manugraph.com
Sales Range: $200-249.9 Million
Emp.: 400
Offset Printing Press Mfr
N.A.I.C.S.: 333248

Manugraph Kenya Limited   (1)
Office Block NO 4 79 Sunview Complex Enterprise Road, PO Box 39787-00623, Nairobi, Kenya
Tel.: (254) 20537155
Web Site: http://www.manugraph.com
Sales Range: $25-49.9 Million
Emp.: 10
Offset Printing Machines Mfr
N.A.I.C.S.: 333248

Mercon Graphic FZC   (1)
A3/60 Sharjah Airport International Free Zone, PO Box 8219, Sharjah, United Arab Emirates
Tel.: (971) 65570708
Web Site: http://www.manugraph.com
Sales Range: $50-74.9 Million
Emp.: 10
Printing Equipment Material Sales Services
N.A.I.C.S.: 423830
Dinesh Raorane *(Gen Mgr-Middle East)*

MANUKA RESOURCES LIMITED
201-207 Kent Street, Sydney, 2000, NSW, Australia
Tel.: (61) 272532020   AU
Web Site:
  https://www.manukaresources.com
Year Founded: 2016
MKR—(ASX)
Rev.: $6,454,915
Assets: $40,102,794
Liabilities: $27,100,268
Net Worth: $13,002,526
Earnings: ($17,175,470)
Fiscal Year-end: 06/30/23
Exploration & Mining Services
N.A.I.C.S.: 213115
Dennis Karp *(Chm)*

MANULI RUBBER INDUSTRIES S.P.A.
Via Paleocapa 7, 20121, Milan, Italy
Tel.: (39) 0262713349   IT
Web Site:
  http://www.manulirubber.com
Year Founded: 1935
Sales Range: $400-449.9 Million
Emp.: 3,069
Fluid Conveying Reinforced Rubber & Metal Components & Systems for Automotive, Hydraulic, Oil & Marine Applications Designer, Mfr & Distr
N.A.I.C.S.: 326220
Mario Manuli *(Mng Dir)*

Subsidiaries:

Manuli Fluiconnecto (Pty) Ltd.   (1)
183 Kuschke St, 1614, Edenvale, Gauteng, South Africa
Tel.: (27) 114545155
Web Site: http://www.fluiconnecto.com
Sales Range: $25-49.9 Million
Emp.: 19
Rubber Products Mfr
N.A.I.C.S.: 326299
Neil Prenton *(Gen Mgr)*

Manuli Hydraulics (Americas) Inc.   (1)
410 Keystone Dr, Warrendale, PA 15086-7567   **(100%)**
Tel.: (724) 778-3340
Web Site: http://www.manuli-hydraulics.com
Sales Range: $25-49.9 Million
Emp.: 20
Steel Reinforced Hoses & Metal Fittings Mfr
N.A.I.C.S.: 326220
Fabien Artese *(Gen Mgr)*

Manuli Hydraulics (Shanghai) Co. S.p.A.   (1)
Room 605 UC Tower 500 Fushan Rd Pudong New District, Shanghai, 200122, China   **(100%)**

Tel.: (86) 2158665108
Web Site: http://www.manuli-hydraulics.com
Sales Range: $25-49.9 Million
Emp.: 30
Assembly & Distributor of Hoses & Belting Products
N.A.I.C.S.: 326220

Manuli Hydraulics Europe S.r.o   (1)
Prumyslova 1500, 691 23, Pohorelice, Czech Republic
Tel.: (420) 519 301 711
Web Site: http://www.manuli-hydraulics.com
Sales Range: $50-74.9 Million
Emp.: 250
Hydraulic System Mfr
N.A.I.C.S.: 333995

Manuli Hydraulics GmbH   (1)
Otto-Lilienthal-Str 4, 88046, Friedrichshafen, Germany   **(100%)**
Tel.: (49) 7541387960
Web Site: http://www.manuli-hydraulics.com
Sales Range: $50-74.9 Million
Emp.: 3
Hydraulic Products Distr
N.A.I.C.S.: 423830

Manuli Hydraulics Korea Co. Ltd.   (1)
51/17 Ung Namdong Gyenongman, Changwon, 642 290, Korea (South)   **(100%)**
Tel.: (82) 552376211
Web Site: http://www.manulihydraulics.com
Sales Range: $1-9.9 Million
Emp.: 54
Assembly & Distribution of Hoses & Belting Products
N.A.I.C.S.: 326220
Jeong Jaegyeong *(Mng Dir)*

Manuli Hydraulics Ltd.   (1)
Unit 26 Piccadilly Trading Estate, Adair St, Manchester, M1 2NP, United Kingdom   **(100%)**
Tel.: (44) 1612737383
Web Site: http://www.manuli-hydraulics.com
Sales Range: $1-9.9 Million
Emp.: 13
Hydraulic Products Distr
N.A.I.C.S.: 423830

Manuli Hydraulics Polska S.A.   (1)
Ul Brzezinska 50, 41-404, Myslowice, Poland   **(93%)**
Tel.: (48) 322220201
Web Site: http://www.manuli-hydraulics.com
Sales Range: $200-249.9 Million
Emp.: 670
Mfr & Distributor of Metal Fittings & Hose Assemblies for Hydraulics Applications
N.A.I.C.S.: 326220

Manuli Hydraulics Suzhou Co., Ltd   (1)
85 Xinglin St Suzhou Industrial Park, 215021, Suzhou, Jiangsu, China
Tel.: (86) 51262837099
Industrial Machinery Mfr
N.A.I.C.S.: 333248

Manuli Oil & Marine (USA) Inc.   (1)
2755 E Oakland Pk Blvd, Fort Lauderdale, FL 33306-1637   **(100%)**
Tel.: (954) 561-3777
Web Site: http://www.manulirubber.com
Sales Range: $100-124.9 Million
Emp.: 500
Designs, Produces & Markets Floating & Subsea Marine Hoses & Long Length Elastomeric Pipelines
N.A.I.C.S.: 237120

Manuli Otim S.A.   (1)
La Fouquetiere Rue Branly 44 Gusgaze Eissel, PO Box 40121, 44154, Ancenis, Cedex, France   **(100%)**
Tel.: (33) 240988302
Web Site: http://www.manuli-otim.fr
Sales Range: $1-9.9 Million
Emp.: 9
Mfr & Distributor of Assemblies for Hydraulics Applications
N.A.I.C.S.: 326220

Manuli Refrigeration Connectors S.p.A.   (1)
Via Bizzarri 21, Calderara Di Reno, 40012, Bologna, Italy   **(100%)**
Tel.: (39) 0516460911

MANULI RUBBER INDUSTRIES S.P.A.

Manuli Rubber Industries S.p.A.—(Continued)
Web Site: http://www.manulirubber.com
Sales Range: $25-49.9 Million
Emp.: 59
Mfr, Designer & Distributor of Metal Fittings & Hose Assemblies for Automotive Applications
N.A.I.C.S.: 332919

Manuli Rubber Industries - Flexmatic Division (1)
Via Bizzari 19, Calderara di Reno, 40012, Bologna, ER, Italy (100%)
Tel.: (39) 0516464911
Web Site: http://www.manuli-hydraulics.com
Hoses & Belting Products Mfr
N.A.I.C.S.: 326220

Manuli Rubber Industries - OEM Division (1)
Zona Industriale Campolongo, 63100, Ascoli Piceno, Marche, Italy (100%)
Tel.: (39) 07363091
Sales Range: $25-49.9 Million
Emp.: 100
Mfr of Hoses & Belting Products
N.A.I.C.S.: 326220

MANULIFE FINANCIAL CORPORATION
200 Bloor Street East, Toronto, M4W 1E5, ON, Canada
Tel.: (416) 926-3000 ON
Web Site: https://www.manulife.com
Year Founded: 1887
MFC—(NYSE)
Rev.: $48,361,331,880
Assets: $717,853,766,040
Liabilities: $671,801,724,720
Net Worth: $46,052,041,320
Earnings: $5,407,119,360
Emp.: 38,000
Fiscal Year-end: 12/31/21
Insurance & Financial Holding Company
N.A.I.C.S.: 551112
Steven A. Finch *(Chief Actuary)*

Subsidiaries:

Manulife Asset Management (Thailand) Company Limited (1)
18/F Singha Complex 1788 New Phetchaburi Road, Bang Kapi Huai Khwang, Bangkok, 10310, Thailand
Tel.: (66) 28440123
Web Site: http://www.manulife-asset.co.th
Asset Management Services
N.A.I.C.S.: 523940
Sumetha Lewchalermwong *(Deputy CEO & Chief Investment Officer)*

Manulife Insurance Berhad (1)
12 th Floor Menara Manulife 6 Jalan Gelenggang, Damansara Heights, 50490, Kuala Lumpur, Malaysia
Tel.: (60) 327199112
Web Site: http://www.manulife.com.my
Financial Investment Services
N.A.I.C.S.: 523940
Arthur Jay Belfer *(Chm)*

Manulife Investment Management (Malaysia) Bhd (1)
13th Floor Menara Manulife 6 Jalan Gelenggang, Damansara Heights, 50490, Kuala Lumpur, Malaysia
Tel.: (60) 327199228
Web Site: http://www.manulifeinvestment.com.my
Financial Investment Services
N.A.I.C.S.: 523940
Gianni Fiacco *(Chief Strategy Officer & Head-Emerging Markets)*

Manulife Investment Management (Singapore) Pte. Ltd. (1)
8 Cross Street 16-01 Manulife Tower, Singapore, 048424, Singapore
Tel.: (65) 65015438
Web Site: http://www.manulifeam.com.sg
Financial Investment Services
N.A.I.C.S.: 523940
Carl Wong *(Mng Dir & Head-Media Rels & Social)*

Manulife Investment Management (US) LLC (1)
197 Clarendon St, Boston, MA 02116
Tel.: (617) 375-1500
Web Site: https://www.manulifeim.com
Insurance Services
N.A.I.C.S.: 524298

Subsidiary (Domestic):

Serverfarm, LLC (2)
444 N Nash St, El Segundo, CA 90245
Tel.: (310) 563-1700
Web Site: https://www.serverfarmllc.com
Software Publisher
N.A.I.C.S.: 513210
Avner Papouchado *(Founder & CEO)*

The Manufacturers Life Insurance Company (1)
500 King Street North, PO Box 1669, Waterloo, N2J 4C6, ON, Canada (100%)
Tel.: (519) 747-7000
Web Site: http://www.manulife.ca
Sales Range: $700-749.9 Million
Emp.: 1,200
Life Insurance Products & Services
N.A.I.C.S.: 524113

Subsidiary (Domestic):

FNA Financial Inc. (2)
200 Bloor Street East, Toronto, M4W 1E5, ON, Canada (100%)
Tel.: (416) 926-0100
Web Site: https://www.manulifeim.com
Holding Company
N.A.I.C.S.: 551112

Subsidiary (Non-US):

Manulife Asset Management Limited (3)
Sales Range: $50-74.9 Million
Emp.: 16
Asset Management Services
N.A.I.C.S.: 523940
Warren Alfred Thomson *(Chm)*

Subsidiary (US):

John Hancock Financial Corporation (2)
197 Clarendon St, Boston, MA 02116
Tel.: (617) 572-6000
Web Site: https://www.johnhancock.com
Sales Range: $5-14.9 Billion
Individual Life, Group & Personal Health Insurance & Specialty Investment Products
N.A.I.C.S.: 524113
Brooks Tingle *(Pres & CEO)*

Subsidiary (Domestic):

John Hancock Insurance Agency, Inc. (3)
901 Dulaney Valley Rd Ste 700, Towson, MD 21204
Tel.: (410) 823-3399
Web Site: http://www.johnhancock.com
Insurance Agency Services
N.A.I.C.S.: 524298
Michael J. Doughty *(Exec VP)*

Subsidiary (Non-US):

John Hancock Life Insurance Company (3)
Tel.: (617) 572-6000
Web Site: http://www.johnhancock.com
Sales Range: $1-4.9 Billion
Fire Insurance Services
N.A.I.C.S.: 524113
Alex Silva *(CFO)*

Subsidiary (Domestic):

Hancock Natural Resource Group Inc. (4)
197 Clarendon St 8th Fl, Boston, MA 02116
Tel.: (617) 747-1600
Web Site: http://www.hnrg.com
Sales Range: $25-49.9 Million
Emp.: 100
Investment Services
N.A.I.C.S.: 523999
Oliver S. Williams *(Sr Mng Dir & Head-Agricultural Investments)*

Group (Domestic):

Hancock Timber Resource Group (5)
99 High St Fl 26, Boston, MA 02110-2320
Tel.: (617) 747-1600
Web Site: http://www.hancocktimber.com
Sales Range: $50-74.9 Million
Real Estate Invenstors
N.A.I.C.S.: 523999
Brent Keefer *(Pres & Mng Dir)*

Subsidiary (Domestic):

John Hancock Financial Network, Inc. (4)
197 Clarendon St, Boston, MA 02116
Tel.: (617) 572-6857
Web Site: http://www.johnhancockfinancial.com
Financial Service Distribution Organization
N.A.I.C.S.: 525990

Subsidiary (Domestic):

Symetra Investment Services, Inc. (5)
777 108th Ave NE Ste 1200, Bellevue, WA 98004-5135 (100%)
Tel.: (425) 256-8000
Web Site: http://www.symetra.com
Investment Services
N.A.I.C.S.: 523999

Subsidiary (Domestic):

John Hancock Life Insurance Company of New York (4)
100 Summit Lake Dr 2nd Fl, Valhalla, NY 10595
Web Site: http://www.johnhancocknewyork.com
Life Insurance Products & Services
N.A.I.C.S.: 524113

John Hancock Signature Services, Inc. (4)
380 Stuart St, Boston, MA 02116
Tel.: (617) 572-4403
Web Site: http://www.jhfunds.com
Sales Range: $75-99.9 Million
Emp.: 215
Life Insurance Mutual Funds & Annuity
N.A.I.C.S.: 523940

Subsidiary (Domestic):

John Hancock Funds, LLC (5)
200 Berkeley St, Boston, MA 02116 (100%)
Tel.: (617) 663-3021
Web Site: https://www.jhinvestments.com
Mutual Fund Management Services
N.A.I.C.S.: 525910
Andrew G. Arnott *(Pres & CEO)*

Subsidiary (Domestic):

John Hancock Variable Life Insurance Company (4)
601 Congress St, Boston, MA 02210
Tel.: (617) 572-6000
Web Site: http://www.johnhancock.com
Sales Range: $650-699.9 Million
Emp.: 8,000
Provider of Individual, Variable & Universal Life Insurance & Annuities
N.A.I.C.S.: 524210

Subsidiary (Domestic):

John Hancock Retirement Plan Services LLC (3)
601 Congress St, Boston, MA 02210
Tel.: (617) 663-4747
Web Site: http://www.johnhancockretirement.com
Emp.: 450
Retirement Plan Fund Administration Services
N.A.I.C.S.: 524292

Subsidiary (Domestic):

MFC Insurance Company Limited (2)
500 King St N, PO Box 1602, Waterloo, N2J 4C6, ON, Canada (100%)
Tel.: (519) 747-7000
Web Site: http://www.manulife.ca

INTERNATIONAL PUBLIC

Provider of Life & Health Insurance
N.A.I.C.S.: 524113

Unit (Domestic):

Manulife Affinity Markets (2)
2 Queen St E, Toronto, M5C 3G7, ON, Canada (100%)
Tel.: (519) 747-7000
Web Site: http://www.manulife.com
Sales Range: $50-74.9 Million
Emp.: 100
Marketer of Financial Services
N.A.I.C.S.: 523940

Subsidiary (Non-US):

Manulife Asset Management (Europe) Limited (2)
1 London Wall, London, EC2 Y5EA, United Kingdom (100%)
Tel.: (44) 2072563500
Web Site: http://www.manulifeam.com
Sales Range: $50-74.9 Million
Emp.: 15
Fund Portfolio Management Services
N.A.I.C.S.: 523940

Subsidiary (Domestic):

Manulife Asset Management Limited (2)
200 Bloor Street East, Toronto, M4W 1E5, ON, Canada
Tel.: (514) 499-6844
Web Site: https://www.manulifeim.com
Investment Management Service
N.A.I.C.S.: 523999
R. James Robertson *(Portfolio Mgr-10 Funds)*

Manulife Bank of Canada (2)
500 King Street North Suite 500-MA, PO Box 1602, STN Waterloo, Waterloo, N2J 4C6, ON, Canada (100%)
Tel.: (519) 747-7000
Web Site: https://www.manulifebank.ca
Sales Range: $700-749.9 Million
Emp.: 1,200
Provider of Banking Products & Services
N.A.I.C.S.: 522180

Manulife Canada Ltd. (2)
500 King St N, Waterloo, N2J 4C6, ON, Canada
Tel.: (519) 747-7000
Web Site: https://www.manulife.ca
Insurance Management Services
N.A.I.C.S.: 524298
Michael J. Doughty *(Pres & CEO)*

Unit (Domestic):

Manulife Canadian Group Pensions (2)
25 Water St S, PO Box 800, Kitchener, N2G 4Y5, ON, Canada (100%)
Tel.: (519) 747-7000
Web Site: http://www.manulife.ca
Sales Range: $700-749.9 Million
Manager of Pension Plans
N.A.I.C.S.: 525110

Manulife Financial Group Benefits (2)
380 Weber St N, PO Box 1650, Waterloo, N2J 3J3, ON, Canada (100%)
Tel.: (519) 747-7000
Web Site: http://www.manulife.ca
Provider of Group Benefits Products
N.A.I.C.S.: 524292

Manulife Global Investments (2)
200 Bloor St E, Toronto, M4W 1E5, ON, Canada (100%)
Tel.: (416) 926-5727
Sales Range: $350-399.9 Million
Emp.: 1,000
Provider of Investment Services
N.A.I.C.S.: 523940

Subsidiary (Non-US):

Manulife Holdings (Bermuda) Limited (2)
O'Hara House 3rd Floor 3 Bermudiana Road Tower 2, PO Box 2455, Hamilton, HM08, Bermuda (100%)
Tel.: (441) 2952131

AND PRIVATE COMPANIES

MANUTAN INTERNATIONAL SA

Web Site:
https://www.manulifebermuda.com
Sales Range: $50-74.9 Million
Emp.: 4
Holding Company
N.A.I.C.S.: 551112

Subsidiary (Non-US):

Manufacturers P&C Limited (3)
The Goddard Building Haggatt Hall, Saint Michael, BB11059, Barbados
Tel.: (246) 2284910
Emp.: 18
Property Insurance Management Services
N.A.I.C.S.: 524298

Manulife (International) Limited (3)
Twr A 21F Manulife Financial Ctr 2231 Way Yip St, Kwun Tong, China (Hong Kong) (100%)
Tel.: (852) 25105600
Web Site: http://www.manulife.com.hk
Provider of Life Insurance Products
N.A.I.C.S.: 524113
Isabella Lau *(Chief Customer Officer)*

Joint Venture (Non-US):

Manulife-Sinochem Life Insurance Company Ltd. (4)
21st Fl Jin Mao Bldg 88 Century Rd Pu Dong, Shanghai, 200121, China (51%)
Tel.: (86) 2150492288
Web Site: https://www.manulife-sinochem.com
Sales Range: $75-99.9 Million
Emp.: 200
Life Insurance Products & Services
N.A.I.C.S.: 524113

Subsidiary (Non-US):

Manulife (Singapore) Pte. Ltd. (3)
491 B River Valley Road, 07-00 Valley Pt, Singapore, 248373, Singapore (100%)
Tel.: (65) 7371221
Web Site: http://www.manulife.com.sg
Sales Range: $100-124.9 Million
Emp.: 200
Asset Management & Reinsurance Products & Services
N.A.I.C.S.: 523940
Steven Yeo *(Chm)*

Manulife (Vietnam) Limited (3)
2nd Floor Manulife Plaza Building 75 Hoang Van Thai, Tan Phu Ward District 7, Ho Chi Minh City, Vietnam (100%)
Tel.: (84) 2854166888
Web Site: https://www.manulife.com.vn
Sales Range: $10-24.9 Million
Emp.: 290
Life Insurance Products
N.A.I.C.S.: 524128

Manulife Asset Management International Holdings Limited (3)
Manulife Place, Bishop's Court Hill, Collymore Rock, Saint Michael, Barbados (100%)
Tel.: (246) 2284910
Sales Range: $25-49.9 Million
Holding Company
N.A.I.C.S.: 551112

Subsidiary (Non-US):

Manulife Asset Management (Hong Kong) Limited (4)
16/F Lee Garden One 33 Hysan Avenue, Causeway Bay, China (Hong Kong)
Tel.: (852) 25103388
Investment Management & Advisory of Mutual Funds
N.A.I.C.S.: 523150

Subsidiary (Non-US):

Manulife Holdings Berhad (3)
16th Floor Menara Manulife 6 Jalan Gelenggang, Damansara Heights, 50490, Kuala Lumpur, Malaysia
Tel.: (60) 327199228
Web Site: https://www.manulife.com.my
Rev.: $373,240,890
Assets: $1,645,643,093
Liabilities: $1,409,635,508
Net Worth: $236,007,585
Earnings: $21,522,600

Fiscal Year-end: 12/31/2021
Fire Insurance Services
N.A.I.C.S.: 524113
Siew Chuan Chua *(Co-Sec)*

Manulife Insurance (Thailand) Public Company Limited (3)
43 Thai CC Tower 33rd Floor South Sathorn Road, Yannawa Sathorn, Bangkok, 10120, Thailand
Tel.: (66) 20339000
Insurance Management Services
N.A.I.C.S.: 524298

Manulife Life Insurance Company
30th floor Tokyo Opera City Tower 3-20-2 Nishi -Shinjuku, Shinjuku-ku, Tokyo, 163-1430, Japan (100%)
Tel.: (81) 120063730
Web Site: https://www.manulife.co.jp
Emp.: 2,692
Provider of Life Insurance Products
N.A.I.C.S.: 524128
Suzumiko Asai *(CMO & Mng Exec Officer)*

Manulife Provident Funds Trust Company Limited (3)
22/F Tower A Manulife Financial Centre 223-231 Wai Yip Street, Kwun Tong, Kowloon, China (Hong Kong) (100%)
Tel.: (852) 23105600
Manager of Funds
N.A.I.C.S.: 525110

The Manufacturers Life Insurance Co. (Phils.), Inc. (3)
10th Floor NEX Tower 6786 Ayala Avenue, Makati, 1229, Philippines
Tel.: (63) 288847000
Web Site: https://www.manulife.com.ph
Life Insurance Management Services
N.A.I.C.S.: 524298

Unit (Domestic):

Manulife Mutual Funds (2)
500 King St North Del Stn 500 G-B, Waterloo, N2J 4C6, ON, Canada
Tel.: (416) 581-8300
Web Site:
http://www.manulifemutualfunds.ca
Mutual Fund Administration Services
N.A.I.C.S.: 523940

Manulife Real Estate (2)
250 Bloor St E 8th Fl, Toronto, M4W 1E5, ON, Canada (100%)
Tel.: (416) 926-5500
Sales Range: $50-74.9 Million
Emp.: 55
Provider of Real Estate Services
N.A.I.C.S.: 531390

Subsidiary (Domestic):

Manulife Reinsurance Limited (2)
200 Bloor St E NT 9, Toronto, N4W 1E5, ON, Canada (100%)
Tel.: (416) 926-3507
Web Site: http://manulife.com
Sales Range: $100-124.9 Million
Emp.: 140
Provider of Financial Reinsurance
N.A.I.C.S.: 524130

Manulife Securities Incorporated (2)
-1235 North Service Road West Ste 500, Oakville, L6M 2W2, ON, Canada
Tel.: (905) 469-2100
Web Site: http://www.manulifesecurities.ca
Investment Advisory & Portfolio Management Services
N.A.I.C.S.: 523940

Subsidiary (Domestic):

Manulife Securities Investment Services Inc. (3)
1235 N Service Road W, Oakville, L6M 2W2, ON, Canada
Tel.: (905) 469-2100
Sales Range: $100-124.9 Million
Emp.: 25
Investment Management Service
N.A.I.C.S.: 523999
Rick Annaert *(CEO)*

Subsidiary (Non-US):

P.T. Asuransi Jiwa Manulife Indonesia (2)

Sampoerna Strategic Square, North Tower GF Floor and South Tower Floors 3-14 JI Jenderal Sudirman, Jakarta, 12930, Indonesia (71%)
Tel.: (62) 2125557777
Web Site: https://www.manulife.co.id
Life Insurance Products & Services; Joint Venture of Manulife Financial Corporation (71%) & P.T. Tirta Dhana Nugraha (20%)
N.A.I.C.S.: 524113

MANULIFE US REAL ESTATE INVESTMENT TRUST
8 Cross Street 16-03 Manulife Tower, Singapore, 48424, Singapore
Tel.: (65) 62380222   SG
Web Site:
https://www.manulifeusreit.sg
Year Founded: 2015
BTOU—(SES)
Rev.: $208,025,000
Assets: $1,588,270,000
Liabilities: $979,635,000
Net Worth: $608,635,000
Earnings: ($379,963,000)
Emp.: 17
Fiscal Year-end: 12/31/23
Trust Management Services
N.A.I.C.S.: 523940
Robert Wong *(CFO)*

MANULOC GROUP
7 Rue Teilhard De Chardin ZI Two Fountains CS 90015, 57063, Metz, Cedex 2, France
Tel.: (33) 387305353
Web Site: http://www.manuloc.fr
Sales Range: $125-149.9 Million
Emp.: 660
Industrial Equipment
N.A.I.C.S.: 333310
Catherine Barthelemy *(Chm & Pres)*

Subsidiaries:

FMS SA (1)
9 Rue Robert Moinon, F 95192, Goussainville, France (100%)
Tel.: (33) 00139339696
Sales Range: $25-49.9 Million
Emp.: 31
Transportation - Freight
N.A.I.C.S.: 488510

MANUTAN INTERNATIONAL SA
ZAC du Parc des Tulipes Avenue du 21eme Siecle, 95506, Gonesse, Cedex, France
Tel.: (33) 134533587   FR
Web Site: http://www.manutan.com
Year Founded: 1966
MAN—(EUR)
Rev.: $957,664,869
Assets: $895,673,140
Liabilities: $304,085,203
Net Worth: $591,587,937
Earnings: $45,708,952
Emp.: 2,108
Fiscal Year-end: 09/30/20
Industrial & Office Equipment Distr & Mail Order
N.A.I.C.S.: 423420
Xavier Guichard *(CEO)*

Subsidiaries:

Camif Collectivites-Entreprises SA (1)
ZA le Geneteau Chauvray, 79074, Niort, Deux-Sevres, France
Tel.: (33) 549346200
Web Site: http://www.camif-collectivites.fr
Business Equipment Distr
N.A.I.C.S.: 423420

Essex Electrical Wholesalers Ltd. (1)
East Street, Braintree, CM7 3JW, Essex, United Kingdom
Tel.: (44) 1376551876

Web Site:
http://www.essexelectricalwholesalers.com
Electrical Product Whslr
N.A.I.C.S.: 423690

Fabritec-Overtoom GmbH (1)
Hirsrutiweg, 4303, Kaiseraugst, Aargau, Switzerland
Tel.: (41) 618159600
Web Site: http://www.fabritec.ch
Sales Range: $50-74.9 Million
Emp.: 8
Business Equipment Distr
N.A.I.C.S.: 423420
Pascal Weber *(Mgr)*

Ikaros Cleantech AB (1)
Argongatan 5, 431 53, Molndal, Sweden
Tel.: (46) 317975500
Web Site: https://www.ikaros.net
Industrial Machinery & Equipment Distr
N.A.I.C.S.: 423830
Frida Svedberg *(Mgr-Nordic Campaign)*

Subsidiary (Non-US):

Ikaros Finland Oy (2)
Metsanneidonkuja 8, 02130, Espoo, Finland
Tel.: (358) 207418751
Web Site: http://www.ikaros.fi
Environmental Consulting Services
N.A.I.C.S.: 541620
Etienne De Terrasson *(CEO)*

IronmongeryDirect Ltd. (1)
Scimitar Park Courtauld Road, Basildon, SS13 1ND, Essex, United Kingdom
Tel.: (44) 3301622541
Web Site:
http://www.ironmongerydirect.co.uk
Office Furniture & Equipment Distr
N.A.I.C.S.: 459410
Marco Verdonkschot *(Mng Dir)*

Kruizinga BV (1)
Ir RR van der Zeelaan 1, 8191 JH, Wapenveld, Netherlands
Tel.: (31) 885331555
Web Site: http://www.kruizinga.nl
Warehouse Transport Equipment Distr
N.A.I.C.S.: 423830
Boris Vildosola Bustos *(Mng Dir)*

Manutan B.V. (1)
Elandlaan 2, 3734 CP, Den Dolder, Netherlands
Tel.: (31) 302296211
Web Site: http://www.manutan.nl
Emp.: 1,600
Business Machines & Equipments Whslr
N.A.I.C.S.: 423420
Ramon Kok *(Mng Dir & Gen Mgr)*

Manutan Collectivites SAS (1)
143 Bd Ampere, CS 90000, Chauray, 79074, Niort, Cedex, France
Tel.: (33) 533060041
Web Site: http://www.manutan-collectivites.fr
Office Furniture & Equipment Retailer
N.A.I.C.S.: 459410

Manutan Hungaria Kft (1)
Budaors Office Park - Building C Szabadsag ut 117, 2040, Budaors, Pest, Hungary
Tel.: (36) 23445980
Web Site: http://www.manutan.hu
Sales Range: $50-74.9 Million
Emp.: 5
Business Machines & Equipments Whslr
N.A.I.C.S.: 423420

Manutan Italia Spa (1)
Via De Amicis 67, 20092, Cinisello Balsamo, MI, Italy
Tel.: (39) 0266010823
Web Site: http://www.manutan.it
Warehouse Transport Equipment Distr
N.A.I.C.S.: 423830
Niccolo Oggionni *(Sls Dir)*

Manutan NV (1)
Bergensesteenweg 1424, 1070, Brussels, Belgium
Tel.: (32) 25830101
Web Site: https://www.manutan.be
Sales Range: $25-49.9 Million
Emp.: 20
Business Machines & Equipments Whslr
N.A.I.C.S.: 423420
David Van Den Bogaert *(Mng Dir)*

MANUTAN INTERNATIONAL SA

Manutan International SA—(Continued)

Manutan Polska Sp z.o.o (1)
ul Woloska 5 budynek Taurus, 02-675, Warsaw, Poland
Tel.: (48) 228743265
Web Site: http://www.manutan.pl
Sales Range: $50-74.9 Million
Emp.: 9
Business Equipment Distr
N.A.I.C.S.: 423420

Manutan S.L. (1)
Avenida Diagonal 640 6a planta, 8017, Barcelona, Spain
Tel.: (34) 934776000
Web Site: http://www.manutan.es
Emp.: 3
Business Machines & Equipments Whslr
N.A.I.C.S.: 423420

Manutan SA (1)
ZAC du Parc des Tulipes Avenue du XXIeme siecle, 95500, Gonesse, France
Tel.: (33) 134533535
Web Site: http://www.manutan.fr
Business Equipment Whslr
N.A.I.C.S.: 423420

Manutan Slovakia s.r.o (1)
Obchodna 507/2, Bratislava, 811 06, Slovakia
Tel.: (421) 243634306
Web Site: http://www.manutan.sk
Emp.: 6
Business Machines & Equipments Whslr
N.A.I.C.S.: 423420

Manutan UK Ltd. (1)
Black Moor Road, Ebblake Industrial Estate, Verwood, BH31 6AT, Dorset, United Kingdom
Tel.: (44) 1202822214
Web Site: https://www.manutan.co.uk
Office Furniture & Equipment Distr
N.A.I.C.S.: 459410
Jonathan Metcalfe *(Mng Dir)*

Manutan Unipessoal Lda (1)
Avenida do Forte N 3 Edf Suecia III Piso-1, 2794-042, Carnaxide, Portugal
Tel.: (351) 214241060
Web Site: http://www.manutan.pt
Sales Range: $25-49.9 Million
Emp.: 13
Business Equipment Whslr
N.A.I.C.S.: 423420
Bertrand Soucadauch *(Mng Dir)*

Manutan o.o.o (1)
Wilis Latsis St House 27 Bldg 1, 125480, Moscow, Russia
Tel.: (7) 495 228 0 668
Web Site: http://www.manutan.ru
Business Equipment Distr
N.A.I.C.S.: 423420

Manutan s.r.o (1)
Provozni 5493/5, Trbovice, 722 00, Ostrava, Czech Republic
Tel.: (420) 800242424
Web Site: http://www.manutan.cz
Sales Range: $25-49.9 Million
Emp.: 50
Business Equipment Whslr
N.A.I.C.S.: 423420

Overtoom International Belgium NV (1)
Industrielaan 30, 1740, Ternat, Flemish Brabant, Belgium
Tel.: (32) 25830101
Web Site: http://www.overtoom.be
Sales Range: $50-74.9 Million
Emp.: 60
Business Equipment Distr
N.A.I.C.S.: 423420
Ramos Koko *(Gen Mgr)*

Papeteries Pichon SAS (1)
ZAC l'Orme les Sources - 750 rue Colonel Louis Lemaire, Veauche, 42340, Saint-Etienne, Cedex, France
Tel.: (33) 477434620
Web Site: https://www.pichon.fr
Stationery Item Distr
N.A.I.C.S.: 424120
Marc Gillot *(Project Dir)*

Rapid Racking Ltd (1)
Kemble Enterprise Park, Kemble, Cirences-ter, GL7 6BQ, Gloucestershire, United Kingdom
Tel.: (44) 1285686869
Web Site: http://www.rapidracking.com
Sales Range: $25-49.9 Million
Emp.: 80
Racking & Storage Solutions
N.A.I.C.S.: 493110
Jerome Braud *(Mng Dir)*

SCI Philippe Auguste (1)
32 bis Blvd de Picpus, 75012, Paris, France
Tel.: (33) 1 53 33 40 00
Sales Range: $25-49.9 Million
Emp.: 50
Business Equipment Whslr
N.A.I.C.S.: 423420

Trovatar a.s. (1)
Provozni 5493 5, Trebovice, 722 00, Ostrava, Czech Republic
Tel.: (420) 595 697 111
Web Site: http://www.trovatar.cz
Business Equipment Whslr
N.A.I.C.S.: 423420

WITRE AB (1)
Argongatan 5, PO Box 341, 431 53, Molndal, Vastergotland, Sweden
Tel.: (46) 313088891
Web Site: http://www.witre.se
Sales Range: $25-49.9 Million
Emp.: 50
Business Equipment Whslr
N.A.I.C.S.: 423420

Subsidiary (Non-US):

WITRE A/S (2)
Lamg Bryggo, PO Box 235, 1752, Halden, Ostfold, Norway
Tel.: (47) 69178700
Web Site: http://www.witre.no
Sales Range: $25-49.9 Million
Emp.: 10
Office Equipment Whslr
N.A.I.C.S.: 423420
Tove Buras *(Dir-Acct)*

WITRE Danmark A/S (2)
Hjulmagervej 8D, 7100, Vejle, Denmark
Tel.: (45) 89877003
Web Site: http://www.witre.dk
Sales Range: $25-49.9 Million
Emp.: 6
Business Equipment Whslr
N.A.I.C.S.: 423420

WITRE Oy (2)
PL 3980, 00002, Helsinki, Finland
Tel.: (358) 942452556
Web Site: http://www.witre.fi
Business Equipment Whslr
N.A.I.C.S.: 423420

MANUTENCOOP SOCIETA COOPERATIVA

Via Piemonte 12, Zola Predosa, 40069, Bologna, Italy
Tel.: (39) 0513515111
Web Site: http://www.manutencoop.coop
Real Estate & Facility Management Services
N.A.I.C.S.: 531390
Claudio Levorato *(Chm & CEO)*

Subsidiaries:

Firing S.r.l. (1)
Via Varese 38, 20020, Lainate, Milan, Italy
Tel.: (39) 02 93559352
Web Site: http://www.firing.it
Sprinkler System Mfr
N.A.I.C.S.: 333998

Protec S.r.l. (1)
Via Zamenhof 363, 36100, Vicenza, Italy
Tel.: (39) 0444 246080
Web Site: http://www.grupposicura.it
Emp.: 20
Industrial Machinery Mfr
N.A.I.C.S.: 333998
Michele Dalla Mora *(Gen Mgr)*

Servizi Ospedalieri S.p.A. (1)
Via Calvino 33, 44122, Ferrara, Italy
Tel.: (39) 0532 599711
Web Site: http://www.serviziospedalieri.it
Hospital Support Services
N.A.I.C.S.: 812331

Sies S.r.l. (1)
via Gentilin 2, Carbonera, 31030, Treviso, Italy
Tel.: (39) 0422 445098
Web Site: http://www.sies.it
Software Development Services
N.A.I.C.S.: 541511

MANX FINANCIAL GROUP PLC

Clarendon House Victoria Street, Douglas, IM1 2LN, Isle of Man
Tel.: (44) 1624694694
Web Site: https://www.mfg.im
MFX—(AIM)
Rev.: $57,741,566
Assets: $611,973,268
Liabilities: $566,162,956
Net Worth: $45,810,312
Earnings: $7,816,677
Emp.: 177
Fiscal Year-end: 12/31/23
Financial Service Provider
N.A.I.C.S.: 522291
Denham Eke *(CEO)*

Subsidiaries:

Blue Star Business Solutions Limited (1)
Fourth Floor East Matrix House Basing View, Basingstoke, RG21 4FF, Hampshire, United Kingdom
Tel.: (44) 1256581111
Web Site: https://www.bluestarleasing.com
Financial Lending Services
N.A.I.C.S.: 523999

Conister Bank Limited (1)
Clarendon House Victoria Street, IM1 2LN, Douglas, Isle of Man
Tel.: (44) 1624694694
Web Site: https://www.conisterbank.co.im
Financial Banking Services
N.A.I.C.S.: 522110
Douglas Grant *(Mng Dir)*

Conister Finance & Leasing Ltd. (1)
Fourth Floor East Matrix House Basing View, Medstead, Basingstoke, RG21 4FF, Hampshire, United Kingdom
Tel.: (44) 1256581000
Web Site: https://www.conister.co.uk
Commercial Banking Services
N.A.I.C.S.: 523999
Douglas Grant *(Exec Dir)*

Edgewater Associates Limited (1)
1st Floor Clarendon House Victoria Street, IM1 2LN, Douglas, Isle of Man
Tel.: (44) 7624220860
Web Site: https://www.edgewater.co.im
Financial Investment Services
N.A.I.C.S.: 523999
Sandra Cardwell *(Mng Dir)*

Manx FX Limited (1)
1st Floor Clarendon House Victoria Street, Douglas, IM1 2LN, Isle of Man
Tel.: (44) 1624694722
Web Site: https://www.mfx.im
Money Transaction Services
N.A.I.C.S.: 522320
David Shimmin *(Mgr-Bus Dev)*

MANY BRIGHT IDEAS TECHNOLOGIES INC.

598 East Kent Avenue South, Vancouver, V5X 4V6, BC, Canada
Tel.: (604) 732-7332   BC
Web Site: https://www.medbiogene.com
Year Founded: 2002
MBI.H—(TSXV)
Assets: $2,312
Liabilities: $129,297
Net Worth: ($126,985)
Earnings: ($58,112)
Fiscal Year-end: 12/31/23
Genomic-Based Clinical Laboratory Diagnostic Tests for Cancer Treatment

INTERNATIONAL PUBLIC

N.A.I.C.S.: 325414

MANY IDEA CLOUD HOLDINGS LIMITED

12/F ERKE Group Mansion 11 Guanyin Shan Hualien Road, Siming, Xiamen, Fujian, China   Ky
Web Site:
https://www.manyidea.cloud
Year Founded: 2012
6696—(HKG)
Rev.: $165,047,630
Assets: $107,309,066
Liabilities: $27,278,052
Net Worth: $80,031,015
Earnings: $4,576,733
Emp.: 136
Fiscal Year-end: 12/31/23
Holding Company
N.A.I.C.S.: 551112
Jianhui Liu *(Chm)*

MANYCORE TECH INC.

Floor 11 Building 1 Matrix International No 515 Yuhangtang Road, Gongshu District, Hangzhou, 310000, China
Tel.: (86) 571 8993 6057   Ky
Year Founded: 2013
KOOL—(NASDAQ)
Rev.: $54,147,172
Assets: $147,018,784
Liabilities: $328,440,720
Net Worth: ($181,421,936)
Earnings: ($65,883,058)
Emp.: 2,073
Fiscal Year-end: 12/31/20
Software Development Services
N.A.I.C.S.: 541511
Xiaohuang Huang *(Co-Founder & Chm)*

MANYO FACTORY CO., LTD.

518 Gonghang-daero, Gangseo-gu, Seoul, Korea (South)
Tel.: (82) 260130855
Web Site: https://www.manyo.co.kr
Year Founded: 2012
439090—(KRS)
Cosmetics Products Mfr
N.A.I.C.S.: 325620
Seongkuk Chu *(CFO)*

MANZ AG

Steigaeckerstrasse 5, 72768, Reutlingen, Germany
Tel.: (49) 712190000
Web Site: https://www.manz.com
M5Z—(MUN)
Rev.: $275,051,288
Assets: $307,560,259
Liabilities: $197,769,349
Net Worth: $109,790,910
Earnings: ($2,638,249)
Emp.: 1,435
Fiscal Year-end: 12/31/23
Robotic, Image Processing & Control Engineering Systems & Services
N.A.I.C.S.: 333248
Dieter Manz *(Deputy Chm-Supervisory Bd)*

Subsidiaries:

Intech Machines (Suzhou) Co. Ltd (1)
123 Nan Hu Rd, Wu Zhong, Suzhou, Jiang Su, China
Tel.: (86) 51265136050
Web Site: http://www.manz.com.tw
Sales Range: $100-124.9 Million
Emp.: 350
PCB Manufacturer
N.A.I.C.S.: 334412

Intech Technical (Shenzhen) Co. Ltd. (1)
3F Bldg T Dong Bao Industrial Area Sha Si Vlg, Sha Jing Baoan, Shenzhen, China

AND PRIVATE COMPANIES

Tel.: (86) 755 27567244
Electronic Components Mfr
N.A.I.C.S.: 334419

Manz AG - Tubingen (1)
Jopestrasse 14, 72072, Tubingen, Germany
Tel.: (49) 7121 9000 0
Web Site: http://www.manz.com
Sales Range: $25-49.9 Million
Emp.: 120
Industrial Engineering Services
N.A.I.C.S.: 541330

Manz Automation (Shanghai) Co. Ltd. (1)
No 717 German Centre, Zhangjiang Hi-Tech Park Pudong, 201203, Shanghai, China
Tel.: (86) 2128986072
Web Site: http://www.manz-automation.com
Sales Range: $25-49.9 Million
Emp.: 6
Industrial Engineering Services
N.A.I.C.S.: 541330

Manz Automation India Private Limited (1)
AKC House E-27, Ring Rd Defence Colony, New Delhi, 110 024, India
Tel.: (91) 1141553200
Web Site: http://www.manz-automation.com
Industrial Engineering Services
N.A.I.C.S.: 541330

Manz Automation Spain S.L. (1)
Parque Empresarial San Fernando Avda De Castilla 2, San Fernando de Henares, 28830, Madrid, Spain
Tel.: (34) 916771213
Web Site: http://www.manz-automation.com
Automation Parts Supplier
N.A.I.C.S.: 423690

Manz Automation Taiwan Ltd. (1)
1F No 290 Jhongjheng Rd, Shanhua Township, T'ainan, Taiwan
Tel.: (886) 65831116
Web Site: http://www.manz-automation.com
Industrial Machinery Mfr
N.A.I.C.S.: 541330

Manz China Suzhou Ltd. (1)
No 405 Jialingjiang Road, Suzhou New District, Suzhou, 215153, Jiangsu, China
Tel.: (86) 51262782588
Emp.: 200
Chemical Processing Equipment Mfr
N.A.I.C.S.: 333248

Manz Hungary Kft. (1)
Hatar ut 1 c, 4031, Debrecen, Hungary
Tel.: (36) 52530798
Web Site: http://www.manz-automation.com
Emp.: 100
Solar Cell Mfr
N.A.I.C.S.: 334413

Manz Intech Machines Co. Ltd (1)
2F No 3 Tzu Chiang 3rd Rd, Chungli Industrial Park, Taoyuan, 320, Taiwan
Tel.: (886) 34632746
Sales Range: $100-124.9 Million
Emp.: 350
Printed Circuit Board & LCD Equipments Mfr
N.A.I.C.S.: 334412

Manz Italy S.r.l. (1)
Via San Lorenzo 19, 40037, Sasso Marconi, BO, Italy
Tel.: (39) 0510287228
Emp.: 100
Electronic Products Mfr
N.A.I.C.S.: 334111

Manz Slovakia s.r.o. (1)
Rybarska 4, Trencin, 91501, Slovakia (100%)
Tel.: (421) 327740211
Web Site: http://www.manz.com
Sales Range: $75-99.9 Million
Emp.: 250
Electronic Parts & Equipment Whslr
N.A.I.C.S.: 423690

Manz Taiwan Ltd. (1)
4F No 168-1 Zhongyuan Rd, Zhongli Dist, Taoyuan, 320021, Taiwan
Tel.: (886) 34529811
Emp.: 200
Chemical Processing Equipment Mfr
N.A.I.C.S.: 333248

Manz USA Inc. (1)
376 Dry Bridge Rd Bldg B-2, North Kingstown, RI 02852
Tel.: (401) 295-2150
Sales Range: $25-49.9 Million
Emp.: 8
Industrial Equipment Mfr
N.A.I.C.S.: 333248

MAO BAO INC.
23 Floor No 97 Section 4 Chongsin Road, Sanchong District, New Taipei City, 24161, Taiwan
Tel.: (886) 289762277
Web Site: https://www.maobao.com.tw
1732—(TAI)
Rev.: $18,125,478
Assets: $21,319,467
Liabilities: $5,724,288
Net Worth: $15,595,179
Earnings: ($198,077)
Fiscal Year-end: 12/31/23
Washing Detergents Powder & Soap Mfr
N.A.I.C.S.: 325611

MAOMING PETRO-CHEMICAL SHIHUA CO., LTD.
No 162 Guandu Road, Maoming, 525000, Guangdong, China
Tel.: (86) 6682276176
Web Site: http://www.mhsh0637.com.cn
Year Founded: 1988
000637—(SSE)
Rev.: $850,731,336
Assets: $406,219,320
Liabilities: $261,375,660
Net Worth: $144,843,660
Earnings: ($18,371,340)
Fiscal Year-end: 12/31/22
Petrochemical Mfr
N.A.I.C.S.: 325110
Wang Zhihua (Chm)

MAOYAN ENTERTAINMENT
40th Floor Sunlight Tower No 248 Queens Road Eas, Wanchai, China (Hong Kong)
Tel.: (852) 30512780 Ky
Web Site: http://www.maoyan.com
Year Founded: 2017
1896—(HKG)
Rev.: $325,654,571
Assets: $1,440,225,727
Liabilities: $292,627,717
Net Worth: $1,147,598,010
Earnings: $14,715,605
Emp.: 724
Fiscal Year-end: 12/31/22
Internet Publishing Services
N.A.I.C.S.: 513199
Zhihao Zheng (CEO)

MAOYE COMMERCIAL CO., LTD.
29th Floor Building A Maoye Tiandi No 19 Dongyu Street, Jinjiang District, Chengdu, 610016, Sichuan, China
Tel.: (86) 2886672679
Web Site: https://www.maoyeshangye.cn
Year Founded: 1953
600828—(SHG)
Rev.: $478,672,923
Assets: $2,879,021,466
Liabilities: $1,796,504,163
Net Worth: $1,082,517,303
Earnings: $47,986,909
Fiscal Year-end: 12/31/22
Investment Services
N.A.I.C.S.: 523999
Gao Hongbiao (Chm)

MAOYE INTERNATIONAL HOLDING LIMITED
38/F Tower A World Finance Centre 4003 Shennan East Road, Luohu District, Shenzhen, China
Tel.: (86) 75525983885 Ky
Web Site: http://www.maoye.cn
Year Founded: 1996
0848—(HKG)
Rev.: $757,594,890
Assets: $7,053,260,620
Liabilities: $4,759,392,643
Net Worth: $2,293,867,976
Earnings: $28,807,834
Emp.: 4,001
Fiscal Year-end: 12/31/22
Department Store Owner & Operator
N.A.I.C.S.: 455110
Mao Ru Huang (Founder, Chm & CEO)

Subsidiaries:

Shenzhen Maoye Department Store Shennan Co., Ltd. (1)
No 2020 Mid Shennan Rd, Futian, Shenzhen, 518000, Guangdong, China
Tel.: (86) 75583696699
General Department Stores
N.A.I.C.S.: 455110

Zhuhai Maoye Department Store Co., Ltd. (1)
No 301 Zijing Rd, Xiangzhou, Zhuhai, 519000, Guangdong, China
Tel.: (86) 7562129888
Web Site: http://www.maoye.cn
General Department Stores
N.A.I.C.S.: 455110

MAOYE INTERNATIONAL HOLDINGS LTD.
38th Floor World Financial Center 4003 Shennan East Road, Shenzhen, 518001, China
Tel.: (86) 75525983904
Web Site: http://www.maoye.cn
Year Founded: 2007
Departmental Store Operator
N.A.I.C.S.: 455110
Haung Mao Ru (Founder, Chm & CEO)

MAPAL COMMUNICATIONS LTD.
Raoul Wallenberg Street, Tel Aviv, Israel
Tel.: (972) 37684000
Web Site: http://www.mapal.co.il
Year Founded: 1999
Investment Banking & Securities Dealing
N.A.I.C.S.: 523150
Nadav Palti (Co-Founder & Chm)

Subsidiaries:

BMI Ltd. (1)
2232 Highway 325, PO Box 366, Bridgewater, B4V 2W9, NS, Canada
Tel.: (902) 543-2446
Web Site: https://www.bmiltd.ca
Metal Products Mfr
N.A.I.C.S.: 331110

Subsidiary (Non-US):

RMS Ltd. (2)
Mowpen Brow High Legh, Knutsford, WA16 6NZ, Cheshire, United Kingdom
Tel.: (44) 1925752165
Web Site: http://www.rms-ltd.com
Environmental Management Services
N.A.I.C.S.: 541620

Upex Brands (1)
Unit 55, Talmei Elazar, Israel
Tel.: (972) 46275425
Toiletry Product Distr
N.A.I.C.S.: 424210

MAPAUTO
Les Barestes Route Nationale 7, 83480, Puget-sur-Argens, Var, France

Tel.: (33) 494197664
Web Site: http://www.mapauto.fr
Sales Range: $10-24.9 Million
Emp.: 9
Automobile Dealers
N.A.I.C.S.: 441110
Harold Bakalian (Gen Mgr)

MAPEI SPA
Via Cafiero 22, 20158, Milan, Italy
Tel.: (39) 02376731
Web Site: http://www.mapei.com
Sales Range: $1-4.9 Billion
Emp.: 3,000
Mfr of Adhesives, Sealants & Building Construction Supplies
N.A.I.C.S.: 325520
Giorgio Squinzi (CEO)

Subsidiaries:

AO Mapei (1)
Derbenevskaya Nab 7 Building 4, 115114, Moscow, Russia
Tel.: (7) 4952585520
Web Site: https://www.mapei.com
Construction Materials Mfr
N.A.I.C.S.: 327120

Adesital Spa (1)
Via XX Settembre 12/14, Ubersetto di Fiorano, 41042, Modena, Italy
Tel.: (39) 0536 927511
Web Site: http://www.adesital.it
Ceramic Tile & Stone Installation Services
N.A.I.C.S.: 238340
Riccardo Sighinolfi (Mng Dir)

Cercol S.p.A. (1)
Via Valle d Aosta 48, 41049, Sassuolo, Modena, Italy
Tel.: (39) 0536 801007
Web Site: http://www.cercol.it
Adhesive Mfr
N.A.I.C.S.: 325520
Andrea Ferroni (Mgr-Lab)

Subsidiary (Non-US):

Cercol Iberia S.L. (2)
C Cantabria N 11 - Poligono Industrial El Colador, 12200, Onda, Castellon, Spain
Tel.: (34) 9 64 532922
Adhesive Mfr
N.A.I.C.S.: 325520

Gorka Cement Sp. z o.o. (1)
ul 22 Lipca 58, 32-540, Trzebinia, Poland
Tel.: (48) 32 758 10 99
Web Site: http://www.gorka.com.pl
Cement Mfr & Distr
N.A.I.C.S.: 327310
Piotr Palichleb (Mgr-Sls)

Lusomapei S.A. (1)
Business Parque Tejo XXI Estrada Nacional 1 - Km 29, 2600-659, Castanheira do Ribatejo, Portugal
Tel.: (351) 263 860 360
Web Site: http://www.mapei.pt
Adhesive Distr
N.A.I.C.S.: 424690
Arnaldo Sousa (Area Mgr)

MAPEFIN Deutschland GmbH (1)
Otto-von-Guericke-Ring 11, 65205, Wiesbaden, Germany
Tel.: (49) 611 1707 160
Web Site: http://www.mapefin.com
Emp.: 9
Adhesive Distr
N.A.I.C.S.: 424690
Micheal Hecker (CEO)

MAPEI Argentina S.A. (1)
Rondeau 51 - 1 Piso, Wilde, B1875DZA, Buenos Aires, Argentina
Tel.: (54) 11 4207 0009
Web Site: http://www.mapei.com.ar
Adhesive Mfr
N.A.I.C.S.: 325520
Carlos Bonifacio (Mgr-Fin)

MAPEI Corporation (1)
1144 E Newport Center Dr, Deerfield Beach, FL 33442
Tel.: (954) 618-9555
Web Site: http://www.mapei.com

MAPEI SPA

Mapei SpA—(Continued)
Emp.: 170
Adhesives & Sealants Mfr & Distr
N.A.I.C.S.: 325520
Luigi Di Geso *(Pres & CEO)*

Subsidiary (Domestic):

General Resource Technology, Inc. (2)
2978 Center Ct, Eagan, MN 55121
Tel.: (651) 454-4151
Web Site: http://www.grtinc.com
Sales Range: $10-24.9 Million
Emp.: 29
Concrete Admixtures & Auxiliary Products Mfr & Whslr
N.A.I.C.S.: 325998
Travis Collins *(Gen Mgr)*

Subsidiary (Non-US):

Mapei De Venezuela C.A. (2)
Calle Orinoco Torre D&D PB Lc 11 y 12
Urb. Las Mercedes, 1080, Caracas, Miranda, Venezuela
Tel.: (58) 212 991 1797
Web Site: http://www.mapei.com.ve
Adhesive Mfr & Distr
N.A.I.C.S.: 325520

Subsidiary (Domestic):

Mapei East Corp (2)
Whitehead Ave, South River, NJ 08882
Tel.: (732) 254-4830
Adhesive Distr
N.A.I.C.S.: 424690

Subsidiary (Non-US):

Mapei de Mexico, S.A. DE C.V. (2)
Pirineos 515 Bodega 45 Microparque Santiago - Zona Ind Benito Juarez, Queretaro, Mexico
Tel.: (52) 442 209 5022
Web Site: http://www.mapei.mx
Adhesive Distr
N.A.I.C.S.: 424690

MAPEI Inc. (1)
2900 Francis-Hughes Avenue, Laval, H7L 3J5, QC, Canada
Tel.: (450) 662-1212
Web Site: https://www.mapei.com
Emp.: 100
Adhesive Mfr & Distr
N.A.I.C.S.: 325520
Yoanna Pergantis *(Mgr-Mktg)*

Subsidiary (US):

Mapei Caribe Inc. (2)
Rd 2 km 26 2 BO Espinosa, Dorado, PR 00646
Tel.: (787) 270-4162
Adhesive Mfr & Distr
N.A.I.C.S.: 325520

MAPEI Romania S.R.L. (1)
22th Tudor Vladimirescu Str Green Gate Building 6th floor Sector 5, Bucharest, Romania
Tel.: (40) 21 311 78 19
Web Site: http://www.mapei.ro
Emp.: 60
Adhesive Mfr
N.A.I.C.S.: 325520
Florin Ciobanu *(Gen Mgr)*

MAPEI SK s.r.o. (1)
Nadrazna 39, 900 28, Ivanka pri Dunaji, Slovakia
Tel.: (421) 2 4020 4511
Web Site: http://www.mapei.sk
Adhesive Distr
N.A.I.C.S.: 424690
Peter Drozda *(CFO)*

MAPEI, spol. s r.o. (1)
Smetanova 192, Olomouc, 779 00, Czech Republic
Tel.: (420) 585 201 151
Web Site: http://www.mapei.cz
Adhesive Distr
N.A.I.C.S.: 424690

MAPINTEC S.r.l. (1)
Via Romea 8, Malcontenta di Mira, 30034, Venice, Italy
Tel.: (39) 041 698079
Web Site: http://www.mapintec.it
Soil Remediation Services
N.A.I.C.S.: 562910

MBP (NZ) Ltd. (1)
88 Carbine Road, Mount Wellington, Auckland, 1060, New Zealand
Tel.: (64) 9 921 1994
Web Site: https://www.mapei.com
Construction Materials Mfr
N.A.I.C.S.: 327120

Mape Peru S.A.C. (1)
Av Los Eucaliptos Sublote 1-C2 Santa Genoveva Lurin Lima, Lima, Peru
Tel.: (51) 1 500 6180
Web Site: https://www.mapei.com
Construction Materials Mfr
N.A.I.C.S.: 327120

Mapei AB (1)
Smidesvagen 10, 171 41, Solna, Sweden
Tel.: (46) 8 525 090 80
Web Site: http://www.mapei.se
Adhesive Distr
N.A.I.C.S.: 424690

Mapei AS (1)
Vallsetvegen 6, 2120, Sagstua, Norway
Tel.: (47) 62 97 20 00
Web Site: http://www.mapei.no
Emp.: 160
Adhesive Distr
N.A.I.C.S.: 424690
Espen Bothner *(Mgr-Sls)*

Mapei Australia Pty. Ltd. (1)
180 Vikking Drive Wacol, Brisbane, 4076, QLD, Australia
Tel.: (61) 7 3276 5000
Web Site: http://www.mapei.com.au
Adhesive Distr
N.A.I.C.S.: 424690
Troy Bartlett *(Mgr-Sls-Resilient)*

Mapei Benelux S.A./N.V. (1)
Zoning Industriel - Rue de l Avenir 40, 4460, Grace-Hollogne, Belgium
Tel.: (32) 4 239 70 70
Web Site: http://www.mapei.be
Adhesive Distr
N.A.I.C.S.: 424690

Mapei Betontechnik G.m.b.H. (1)
Grazer Strasse 80, 8665, Langenwang, Austria
Tel.: (43) 3854 25 101 0
Web Site: http://www.mapei-betontechnik.com
Emp.: 60
Construction Materials Distr
N.A.I.C.S.: 423320
Andreas Wolf *(Gen Mgr)*

Mapei Brasil Construction Materials Ltda (1)
Avenida Paulista 1636 cj 508 Bela Vista, Sao Paulo, 01310-200, Brazil
Tel.: (55) 113 386 5151
Web Site: https://www.mapei.com
Construction Materials Mfr
N.A.I.C.S.: 327120

Mapei China Ltd (1)
9/F Linkchart Centre 2 Tai Yip Street, Kwun Tong, Kowloon, China (Hong Kong)
Tel.: (852) 21486816
Web Site: http://www.mapei.com.hk
Adhesive Mfr
N.A.I.C.S.: 325520

Subsidiary (Non-US):

Mapei Construction Materials Company Ltd (2)
Room 2003-4 Hong Fu Loi International Building No 313, Yan Jiang Zhong Road, Guangzhou, China
Tel.: (86) 20 8365 3489
Web Site: http://www.mapei.com.cn
Ceramic Tile Mfr
N.A.I.C.S.: 327120

Mapei Colombia S.A.S. (1)
Carrera 48 no 100 D Sur 250 La Estrella, 055460, Antioquia, Colombia
Tel.: (57) 4 444 6515
Web Site: https://www.mapei.com
Construction Materials Mfr
N.A.I.C.S.: 327120

INTERNATIONAL PUBLIC

Mapei Construction Chemicals LLC (1)
Plot no 597-191 - Dubai Investments Park 2, 73869, Dubai, United Arab Emirates
Tel.: (971) 4 815 6666
Web Site: https://www.mapei.ae
Construction Materials Mfr
N.A.I.C.S.: 327120

Mapei Construction Chemicals Panama Sa (1)
Via Transistmica Complejo Bodegas America, Panama, Panama
Tel.: (507) 261 9549 50
Adhesive Distr
N.A.I.C.S.: 424690

Mapei Construction Products India Ltd. (1)
No 402 Tudor Court 40 Lavelle Road, Bengaluru, 560001, India
Tel.: (91) 80 22221820
Web Site: http://www.mapei.in
Emp.: 100
Adhesive Distr
N.A.I.C.S.: 424690
Santhosh Prakash *(Product Mgr)*

Mapei Croatia d.o.o. (1)
Purgarija 14, Kerestinec, Sveta Nedelja, Croatia
Tel.: (385) 1 3647 790
Web Site: http://www.mapei.hr
Adhesive Distr
N.A.I.C.S.: 424690
Zoran Spoler *(Mgr-Sls)*

Mapei Denmark A/S (1)
Bostrupvej 4 Jebjerg, 7870, Roslev, Denmark
Tel.: (45) 69 60 74 80
Web Site: http://www.mapei.dk
Adhesive Distr
N.A.I.C.S.: 424690
Brian Norskov *(Product Mgr)*

Mapei East Africa Ltd. (1)
14th Riverside 6th Floor Grosvenor Building, Tatu City ALP 2 Kiambu, Nairobi, Kenya
Tel.: (254) 70 904 5000
Web Site: https://www.mapei.com
Construction Materials Mfr
N.A.I.C.S.: 327120

Mapei Egypt for Construction Chemicals S.A.E. (1)
15 N Teseen Street Fifth Settlement, New Cairo, Egypt
Tel.: (20) 22 537 0000
Construction Materials Mfr
N.A.I.C.S.: 327120

Mapei Far East Pte. Ltd. (1)
28 Tuas West Road, Singapore, 638383, Singapore
Tel.: (65) 68623488
Web Site: http://www.mapei.com
Emp.: 75
Adhesive Mfr
N.A.I.C.S.: 325520
Yt Lim *(Sr Mgr-Sls)*

Subsidiary (Non-US):

MAPEI Malaysia Sdn. Bhd. (2)
PT 521 Batu 23 - Jalan Rawang/Jalan, Batang Berjuntai, 48000, Rawang, Selangor, Malaysia
Tel.: (60) 3 6093 5799
Web Site: http://www.mapei.com.my
Adhesive Mfr & Distr
N.A.I.C.S.: 325520
S. A. Ang *(Asst Mgr-Sls)*

Mapei France S.A. (1)
CS 40021 - 29 av Leon Jouhaux, 31141, Paris, Cedex, France
Tel.: (33) 5 61 35 73 05
Web Site: http://www.mapei.fr
Adhesive Mfr
N.A.I.C.S.: 325520
Mario Pallmer *(Mng Dir)*

Mapei G.m.b.H. (1)
Frauleinmuhle 2, 3134, Nussdorf ob der Traisen, Austria
Tel.: (43) 2783 8891
Web Site: http://www.mapei.at
Adhesive Distr
N.A.I.C.S.: 424690

Mapei GmbH (1)
Bahnhofsplatz 10, 63906, Erlenbach, Germany
Tel.: (49) 9372 9895 0
Web Site: http://www.mapei.de
Ceramic Tile Installation Services
N.A.I.C.S.: 238340

Mapei Hellas SA (1)
PO Box 19243, Chalkida, 34100, Greece
Tel.: (30) 22620 71906
Web Site: http://www.mapei.gr
Emp.: 40
Adhesive Distr
N.A.I.C.S.: 424690
Nikolaos Markopoulos *(Product Mgr)*

Mapei Kft (1)
Sport Utca 2, 2040, Budaors, Hungary
Tel.: (36) 23 501667
Web Site: http://www.mapei.hu
Emp.: 156
Adhesive Mfr & Distr
N.A.I.C.S.: 325520
Csaba Szautner *(Head-Technical Dept)*

Mapei Korea Ltd. (1)
121-914 14th floor 361 Office-dong World Cup-ro, Seoul, Korea (South)
Tel.: (82) 2 6393 2300
Web Site: http://www.mapei.co.kr
Emp.: 30
Adhesive Mfr
N.A.I.C.S.: 325520
Jintak Han *(Country Mgr)*

Mapei Nederland B.V. (1)
Twentepoort Oost 27, 7609 RG, Almelo, Netherlands
Tel.: (31) 546 83 60 40
Web Site: http://www.mapei.nl
Emp.: 26
Adhesive Distr
N.A.I.C.S.: 424690
Frank Tijhuis *(Controller)*

Mapei New Zealand Ltd (1)
30 Fisher Crescent - Mt Wellington, Auckland, 1060, New Zealand
Tel.: (64) 9 9211994
Web Site: http://www.mapei.co.nz
Emp.: 15
Adhesive Distr
N.A.I.C.S.: 424690
Warren Millar *(Acct Mgr-Retail & Comml)*

Mapei Oy (1)
Tillinmaentie 1, 2330, Espoo, Finland
Tel.: (358) 9 867 8900
Web Site: http://www.mapei.fi
Emp.: 3
Adhesive Distr
N.A.I.C.S.: 424690
Laura Halonen *(Country Mgr)*

Mapei Philippines Inc. (1)
Building 7 Panorama Compound 6 LTI Extension, Laguna Technopark, Binan, 4024, Laguna, Philippines
Tel.: (63) 49 250 2427
Construction Materials Mfr
N.A.I.C.S.: 327120

Mapei Polska Sp.z o.o. (1)
ul Gustawa Eiffela 14, 44-109, Gliwice, Poland
Tel.: (48) 32 775 44 50
Web Site: http://www.mapei.pl
Adhesive Mfr
N.A.I.C.S.: 325520

Mapei SRB d.o.o. (1)
Save Kovacevica bb, Lestane, 11 309, Belgrade, Serbia
Tel.: (381) 11 8036 150
Web Site: http://www.mapei.rs
Adhesive Distr
N.A.I.C.S.: 424690

Mapei South Africa Pty (Ltd) (1)
Unit 2C Anchor Industrial Park Springbok & Taaljard Road Bartlett, Johannesburg, South Africa
Tel.: (27) 11 552 8476
Web Site: http://www.mapei.co.za
Adhesive Distr
N.A.I.C.S.: 424690
Christo van der Merwe *(Gen Mgr)*

Mapei Spain S.A. (1)
C / Valencia 11 - Pol Ind Can Oller, Santa

AND PRIVATE COMPANIES MAPFRE S.A.

Perpetua de Mogoda, 08130, Barcelona, Spain
Tel.: (34) 93 343 5050
Web Site: https://www.mapei.es
Construction Materials Mfr
N.A.I.C.S.: 327120

Mapei Suisse SA (1)
Route Principale 127, 1642, Sorens, Switzerland
Tel.: (41) 26 915 9000
Web Site: http://www.mapei.ch
Adhesive Mfr & Distr
N.A.I.C.S.: 325520

Mapei UK Ltd. (1)
Mapei House, Steel Park Road, Halesowen, B62 8HD, West Midlands, United Kingdom
Tel.: (44) 121 5086970
Web Site: http://www.mapei.co.uk
Emp.: 300
Adhesives & Sealants Mfr & Distr
N.A.I.C.S.: 325520

Mapei Vietnam Ltd (1)
Plot 8 Street No 4 Northern Part of Chu Lai I Z, Tam Hiep, Quang Nam, Vietnam
Tel.: (84) 510 3565801
Web Site: http://www.mapei.com
Adhesive Distr
N.A.I.C.S.: 424690
Thai Ha Nguyen *(Mgr-Mktg)*

Mapei Yapi Kimyasallari Ins.San. ve Tic.A.S. (1)
Umit Mah 2527 Sok No 10/1-2 Toyko Bolgesi, Umitkoy, Ankara, Turkiye
Tel.: (90) 312 227 84 84
Web Site: http://www.mapei.com.tr
Adhesive Distr
N.A.I.C.S.: 424690
Alper Ozer *(Gen Mgr)*

Mapei d.o.o. (1)
Distribucijsko skladisce v Grosupljem Brezje pri Grosupljem 1c, 1290, Grosuplje, Slovenia
Tel.: (386) 786 50 50
Web Site: http://www.mapei.si
Adhesive Distr
N.A.I.C.S.: 424690
Marko Hafner *(Mgr-Sls & Mktg)*

Mosaico+ Srl (1)
Via San Lorenzo 58/59, Casalgrande, Reggio Emilia, 42013, Italy
Tel.: (39) 0522990011
Construction Materials Distr
N.A.I.C.S.: 423320

PT Mapei Indonesia Construction Solution (1)
CIBIS Nine JI T B Simatupang No 2 6th Floor Unit A2, 12560, Jakarta Selatan, Indonesia
Tel.: (62) 21 782 6976
Web Site: https://www.mapei.co.id
Construction Materials Mfr
N.A.I.C.S.: 327120

Polyglass S.p.A. (1)
Via dell Artigianato 34, Ponte di Piave, 31047, Italy
Tel.: (39) 04227547
Web Site: http://www.polyglass.it
Roofing Product Mfr
N.A.I.C.S.: 327120
Debora Sinigaglia *(Product Mgr)*

Subsidiary (Non-US):

Polyglass Great Britain Ltd (2)
1 Electrium Point Ashmore Lake Way, Willenhall, WV12 4LF, West Midlands, United Kingdom
Tel.: (44) 1902 637422
Web Site: http://www.polyglass.com
Insulation Material Distr
N.A.I.C.S.: 423330

Polyglass Romania Srl (2)
B-dul Chimiei nr 6D, 700291, Iasi, Romania
Tel.: (40) 232 242042
Web Site: http://www.polyglass.com
Insulation Material Distr
N.A.I.C.S.: 423330
Cristian Opria *(Gen Mgr)*

Subsidiary (US):

Polyglass USA, Inc. (2)
1111 W Newport Center Dr, Deerfield Beach, FL 33442
Tel.: (866) 802-8017
Web Site: http://www.polyglass.com
Insulation Material Mfr
N.A.I.C.S.: 327215
Jeff Barksdale *(Plant Mgr)*

Sopro Bauchemie GmbH (1)
Biebricher Strasse 74, 65102, Wiesbaden, Germany
Tel.: (49) 611 1707239
Web Site: http://www.de-en.sopro.com
Building Chemical Product Mfr
N.A.I.C.S.: 327331
Andreas Wilbrand *(Mng Dir)*

Subsidiary (Non-US):

Sopro Bauchemie GmbH (2)
Lagerstrasse 7, 4481, Asten, Austria
Tel.: (43) 7224 67141 0
Web Site: http://at.sopro.com
Adhesive Distr
N.A.I.C.S.: 424690

Sopro Hungaria Kft. (2)
Szoloskert u 21, 2092, Budakeszi, Hungary
Tel.: (36) 23 458 040
Web Site: http://www.sopro.hu
Adhesive Distr
N.A.I.C.S.: 424690

Sopro Nederland BV (2)
Kruyderlaan 21 A, 3431 BM, Nieuwegein, Netherlands
Tel.: (31) 30 6050214
Web Site: http://www.sopro.com
Adhesive Distr
N.A.I.C.S.: 424690

Sopro Polska Sp. z o.o. (2)
ul Poleczki 23/F, 02-822, Warsaw, Poland
Tel.: (48) 22 335 23 00
Web Site: http://www.sopro.pl
Adhesive Distr
N.A.I.C.S.: 424690
Piotr Sokulski *(Mgr-Mktg)*

Sopro Netherland Bv (2)
Kruyderlaan 21a, 3431 BM, Nieuwegein, Netherlands
Tel.: (31) 30 605 0214
Web Site: https://www.sopro.com
Construction Materials Mfr
N.A.I.C.S.: 327120

Tecnopol de Sistemas SL (1)
Finlandia 33, Les Franqueses del Valles, 08520, Barcelona, Spain
Tel.: (34) 93 568 2111
Web Site: https://www.tecnopolgroup.com
Advanced Construction Material Whslr
N.A.I.C.S.: 423320

U.S. Sassuolo Calcio Srl (1)
Piazza Risorgimento 47, Sassuolo, 41049, Modena, Italy
Tel.: (39) 0536 882645
Web Site: http://www.sassuolocalcio.it
Sports Club Operator
N.A.I.C.S.: 711211

VINAVIL S.p.A. (1)
Via Valtellina 63, 20159, Milan, Italy
Tel.: (39) 02 695541
Web Site: http://www.vinavil.it
Polymer Product Mfr & Distr
N.A.I.C.S.: 325998
Cesare Casetta *(Mgr-Sls)*

Plant (Domestic):

VINAVIL S.p.A. - Ravenna Plant (2)
Via Baiona 107, 48123, Ravenna, Italy
Tel.: (39) 0544 685211
Polymer Product Mfr
N.A.I.C.S.: 325998

VINAVIL S.p.A. - Villadossola Plant (2)
Via Toce 7, 28844, Villadossola, Italy
Tel.: (39) 0324 5031
Polymer Product Mfr
N.A.I.C.S.: 325998

Vaga Srl (1)
Localita Sostegno - SP199, 27010, Costa de' Nobili, Italy
Tel.: (39) 0382 727111
Web Site: http://www.vagaedilizia.it

Building Materials Mfr
N.A.I.C.S.: 327120

Vinavil Americas Corp. - ILLINOIS Facility (1)
530 Industrial Dr, West Chicago, IL 60185-1828
Tel.: (630) 293-5800
Polymer Product Mfr
N.A.I.C.S.: 325998

Vinavil Americas Corporation (1)
1144 E Newport Center Dr, Deerfield Beach, FL 33442
Tel.: (954) 246-8770
Web Site: https://www.vinavil.com
Dispersion Polymer Mfr
N.A.I.C.S.: 325211

Vinavil Americas Inc. (1)
2900 avenue Francis-Hughes, Laval, H7L 3J5, QC, Canada
Tel.: (450) 662-6278
Dispersion Polymer Mfr
N.A.I.C.S.: 325211

Vinavil Egypt for Chemicals S.A.E. (1)
15 Road 90 Lafarge Building 5th Settlement, 11835, New Cairo, Egypt
Tel.: (20) 22 537 0000
Web Site: https://www.vinavil.com
Dispersion Polymer Mfr
N.A.I.C.S.: 325211

ZAO Mapei (1)
Derbenevskaya nab 7 building 4 3-d floor, 115114, Moscow, Russia
Tel.: (7) 4952585520
Web Site: http://www.mapei.com
Emp.: 30
Adhesive Mfr
N.A.I.C.S.: 325520
Valentina Rosi *(Deputy Gen Dir)*

MAPFRE S.A.
Carretera de Pozuelo-Majadahonda 52, 28222, Majadahonda, Spain
Tel.: (34) 915812318 ES
Web Site: https://www.mapfre.com
Year Founded: 1933
MAP—(MAD)
Rev.: $26,744,010,360
Assets: $59,299,697,820
Liabilities: $48,878,480,466
Net Worth: $10,421,217,354
Earnings: $1,366,932,873
Emp.: 28,908
Fiscal Year-end: 12/31/23
Real Estate Manangement Services
N.A.I.C.S.: 531390
Antonio Nunez Tovar *(Vice Chm)*

Subsidiaries:

Aseguradora Valenciana SA de Seguros y Reaseguros (1)
Plaza de la Legion Espanola 8, Entresuelo, 46010, Valencia, Spain
Tel.: (34) 963 87 5900
Insurance Brokerage Services
N.A.I.C.S.: 524298

Banco MAPFRE, S.A. (1)
Carretera de Pozuelo Alarcon 52, Majadahonda, 28222, Madrid, Spain (49%)
Tel.: (34) 915811100
Banking, Credit, Financial Services
N.A.I.C.S.: 522299

Bankia MAPFRE Vida, S.A. de Seguros y Reaseguros (1)
Avenida General Peron 49, ES 28020, Madrid, Spain (51%)
Tel.: (34) 902136524
Life Insurance
N.A.I.C.S.: 524113

MAPFRE America, S.A. (1)
Carretera De Pozuelo de Alarcon a Majadahonda 52, 28220, Madrid, Spain (99.26%)
Tel.: (34) 91 581 10 92
Web Site: http://www.mapfre.com
Holding Company
N.A.I.C.S.: 551112

Subsidiary (Non-US):

MAPFRE Argentina S.A. (2)

Avda Juana Manso 205 5 piso, Puerto Madero, Buenos Aires, C1107CBE, Argentina (100%)
Tel.: (54) 1143206700
Web Site: http://www.mapfre.com.ar
Sales Range: $500-549.9 Million
Emp.: 1,200
Holding Company
N.A.I.C.S.: 551112

Subsidiary (Domestic):

Surassur SA (3)
Lavalle 362 7 piso, C1047AAH, Buenos Aires, Argentina (100%)
Tel.: (54) 11 5777 2154
Web Site: http://www.surassur.com.ar
Sales Range: $150-199.9 Million
Emp.: 400
Insurance Brokers
N.A.I.C.S.: 524210

Subsidiary (Non-US):

MAPFRE Asistencia, S.A. (2)
Philpot Ln 2 3, London, EC3M 8AN, United Kingdom (100%)
Tel.: (44) 2076264800
Web Site: http://www.mapfreasistencia-uk.com
Sales Range: $25-49.9 Million
Emp.: 9
Provider of Travel Assistance
N.A.I.C.S.: 561510

MAPFRE Paraguay Compania de Seguros, S.A. (2)
Ave Mariscal Lopez 910 Esq Gral Aquino Corner, Asuncion, Paraguay (89.54%)
Tel.: (595) 212176000
Web Site: http://www.mapfre.com.py
Insurance Services
N.A.I.C.S.: 524128
Raquel Riveros *(Dir Gen-Fin, Ops & Media)*

Subsidiary (US):

MAPFRE Puerto Rico (2)
297 Ave Carlos Chardon, San Juan, PR 00918 (100%)
Tel.: (787) 250-6500
Web Site: http://www.mapfrepr.com
Earnings: $1,058,874
Emp.: 850
Holding & Insurance Company
N.A.I.C.S.: 524210

Subsidiary (Domestic):

MAPFRE Insurance Company of Florida (3)
5959 Blue Lagoon Dr Ste 400, Miami, FL 33126-2052 (100%)
Tel.: (305) 529-2000
Web Site: http://www.mapfreflorida.com
Earnings: $721,262
Emp.: 50
Holding Company
N.A.I.C.S.: 524210
Jo Ann S. Ellerbe *(Branch Mgr-Jacksonville)*

Affiliate (Domestic):

Head-Beckhan Amerinsurance, Inc. (4)
2500 NW 79th Ave Ste 101, Miami, FL 33122-1052 (23.79%)
Tel.: (305) 714-4400
Web Site: http://www.hbains.com
Insurance Brokering
N.A.I.C.S.: 524210
Bill Beckham *(Pres)*

Subsidiary (Domestic):

MAPFRE MGA, Inc. (4)
5959 Blue Lagoon Dr Ste 400, Miami, FL 33126 (100%)
Tel.: (305) 477-5552
Web Site: http://www.mapfre.com
Broker & Manager of Insurance Products
N.A.I.C.S.: 541611

Subsidiary (Domestic):

Pan American Insurance Company (3)
Urb Tres Monjitas Industrial 297 Ave Carlos Chardon, San Juan, PR 00918-1410 (100%)

MAPFRE S.A.

MAPFRE S.A.—(Continued)
Tel.: (787) 250-6500
Sales Range: $350-399.9 Million
Emp.: 530
Insurance Services
N.A.I.C.S.: 524210

Subsidiary (Domestic):

Pan American Finance
Corporation **(4)**
297 Ave Carlos Chardon, San Juan, PR
00918 **(62.78%)**
Tel.: (787) 250-6500
Web Site: http://www.praico.com
Sales Range: $250-299.9 Million
Emp.: 530
Financial Investment Services
N.A.I.C.S.: 522220

Subsidiary (Domestic):

Puerto Rican American Insurance
Company **(3)**
297 Ave Carlos Chardon, San Juan, PR
00918 **(100%)**
Tel.: (787) 250-6500
Web Site: http://www.praico.com
Sales Range: $350-399.9 Million
Emp.: 530
Insurance Services
N.A.I.C.S.: 524210

Puerto Rican Insurance Agency
Inc. **(3)**
297 Ave Carlos Chardon, San Juan, PR
00936-8333 **(100%)**
Tel.: (787) 250-6500
Sales Range: $350-399.9 Million
Emp.: 530
Insurance Brokers
N.A.I.C.S.: 524210
Jose Pagan *(Exec VP- Life)*

Subsidiary (Non-US):

MAPFRE Seguros Generales de Co-
lombia, S.A. **(2)**
Cra 14 No 96-34, Bogota, DC,
Colombia **(94.5%)**
Tel.: (57) 16503300
Web Site: http://www.mapfre.com.co
Financial Service Provider
N.A.I.C.S.: 522320

Affiliate (Non-US):

MAPFRE Tepeyac, S.A. **(2)**
Av Magnocentro 5 Col C San Fernando,
Hixquilucan, Mexico, Mexico **(49%)**
Tel.: (52) 5552307000
Web Site: http://www.mapfre.com.mx
Sales Range: $300-349.9 Million
Emp.: 800
Insurance Carrier
N.A.I.C.S.: 524126

Subsidiary (Domestic):

Ase Rent, S.A. de C.V.
Arquimedes 199 3 A, Polanco, Mexico, DF,
Mexico **(50.95%)**
Provider of Leasing Services
N.A.I.C.S.: 532490

Unidad Movil de Diagnostico,
S.A. **(3)**
Humboldt 56, Mexico, DF, Mexico **(100%)**
Provider of Medical Services
N.A.I.C.S.: 621410

Subsidiary (US):

MAPFRE U.S.A. Corp. **(2)**
211 Main St, Webster, MA 01570-2249
Tel.: (508) 943-9000
Web Site: http://www.mapfreinsurance.com
Emp.: 2,500
Fire, Marine & Casualty Insurance Services
N.A.I.C.S.: 524126
Jesse Zimmerman *(VP-Comml Lines)*

Subsidiary (Domestic):

American Commerce Insurance
Company **(3)**
3590 Twin Creeks Dr, Columbus, OH
43204-1628
Tel.: (614) 272-6951

Web Site: http://www.acilink.com
Rev.: $100,000,000
Emp.: 150
Property & Casualty Insurance
N.A.I.C.S.: 524128

Commerce Insurance Company **(3)**
11 Gore Rd, Webster, MA 01570
Tel.: (508) 943-9000
Web Site:
http://www.commerceinsurance.com
Rev.: $570,000
Emp.: 2,000
Insurance & Agent Services
N.A.I.C.S.: 524210

Commerce West Insurance
Company **(3)**
6130 Stoneridge Mall Rd Ste 400, Pleasan-
ton, CA 94588-3145
Tel.: (925) 734-1700
Web Site: http://www.commercewest.net
Sales Range: $50-74.9 Million
Emp.: 100
Fire, Marine & Casualty Insurance
N.A.I.C.S.: 524126
Regan P. Remillard *(Pres & Gen Mgr)*

State-Wide Insurance Company **(3)**
901 Franklin Ave, Garden City, NY 11530-
4020
Tel.: (516) 564-8000
Sales Range: $75-99.9 Million
Emp.: 150
Insurance Services
N.A.I.C.S.: 524126

Subsidiary (Non-US):

MAPFRE Vida e Previdencia,
S.A. **(2)**
Av Maria Coelho Aguiar 215, Bloco C 7 An-
dar, 05804-900, Sao Paulo, SP,
Brazil **(25%)**
Tel.: (55) 11 3741 1148
Web Site: http://www.mapfrevida.com.br
Provider of Insurance Products
N.A.I.C.S.: 524128

Vera Cruz Seguradora, S.A. **(2)**
Av Maria Coelho Aguiar 215, Bloco C 7 An-
dar, CEP 05804-906, Sao Paulo, SP,
Brazil **(64.86%)**
Web Site: http://www.veracruz.br
Provider of Insurance Products
N.A.I.C.S.: 524128

Affiliate (Domestic):

Seguradora Roma, S.A. **(3)**
Avda 9 de Julio 4017, Sao Paulo,
Brazil **(46.03%)**
Insurance
N.A.I.C.S.: 524298

MAPFRE Asistencia Cia. Internacio-
nal de Seguros y Reaseguros,
S.A. **(1)**
Sor Angela de la Cruz 6, Madrid, 28020,
Spain **(100%)**
Tel.: (34) 902140214
Earnings: $997,490
Emp.: 200
Provider of Insurance & Reinsurance Prod-
ucts
N.A.I.C.S.: 524128

Subsidiary (Non-US):

Andi Asistencia, S.A. **(2)**
Carrera 11 N 93 46 Fl 3, Bogota,
Colombia **(94.89%)**
Tel.: (57) 16354646
Web Site: http://www.andiasistencia.com.co
Sales Range: $25-49.9 Million
Emp.: 200
Travel Assistance Services
N.A.I.C.S.: 561510

Caribe Asistencia, S.A. **(2)**
Avda Tiradentes esq Presidente Gonzalez,
Edificio La Cumbre 6, Ens Piantini, Santo
Domingo, Dominican Republic **(52%)**
Tel.: (809) 5405403
Provider of Travel Assistance Services
N.A.I.C.S.: 561599

Eurosos Assistance, S.A. **(2)**
473 Mesogion Ave, Athens,
Greece **(61%)**
Tel.: (30) 2106504000

Web Site: http://www.eurosos.gr
Sales Range: $25-49.9 Million
Emp.: 60
Travel Services
N.A.I.C.S.: 561510
John Athanasiou *(Gen Mgr)*

Subsidiary (US):

Federal Assist **(2)**
7300 Corporate Center Dr Ste 601, Miami,
FL 33126 **(100%)**
Tel.: (305) 913-1842
Travel Assistance
N.A.I.C.S.: 561510

Subsidiary (Non-US):

Gulf Assist E.C. **(2)**
Manama Ctr Bldg 3 3rd Fl, PO Box 2790,
Manama, Bahrain **(69%)**
Tel.: (973) 017215214
Web Site: http://www.gulfassist.com
Sales Range: $10-24.9 Million
Emp.: 24
Travel Agency
N.A.I.C.S.: 561510

Ibero Asistencia, S.A. **(2)**
Av Paseo Colon 484 BS AS, C1063ACR,
Buenos Aires, Argentina **(50%)**
Tel.: (54) 11 5300 8040
Web Site: http://www.iberoasistencia.com.ar
Sales Range: $25-49.9 Million
Emp.: 80
Travel Assistance
N.A.I.C.S.: 561510

Subsidiary (Domestic):

Iberoasistencia, S.A. **(2)**
Sason Anvel Ade La Cruz 6, 28020, Madrid,
Spain **(100%)**
Tel.: (34) 915815290
Web Site: http://www.iberoasistencia.es
Travel Assistance
N.A.I.C.S.: 561510

Subsidiary (Non-US):

Mexico Asistencia, S.A. **(2)**
Paseo de la Reforma 243, 06500, Mexico,
Mexico **(99.99%)**
Tel.: (52) 55 5480 3840
Web Site: http://www.mapfre-asistencia.com
Sales Range: $75-99.9 Million
Emp.: 150
Marketer of Insurance & Reinsurance Pro-
grams, Travel Assistance for Insurance
Companies, Corporations & Private Indi-
viduals
N.A.I.C.S.: 524298
Juan Carlos Lanau *(Mng Dir)*

Sur Asistencia S.A. **(2)**
Av Apoquindo N 4499 Piso 7, Las Condes,
Santiago, CP 6761682, Chile **(50%)**
Tel.: (56) 23407090
Web Site: http://www.surasistencia.cl
Travel Assistance
N.A.I.C.S.: 561510

Veneasistencia, C.A. **(2)**
Edificio Torre Maracaibo Ph A Avenida Lib-
ertador, La Campina, Caracas, 1050,
Venezuela **(99%)**
Tel.: (58) 2127624905
Travel Assistance
N.A.I.C.S.: 561510

MAPFRE Caja Madrid Holding de
Entidades Aseguradoras, S.A. **(1)**
Carretera De Pozuelo A Majadahonda 52,
28220, Madrid, Spain **(51%)**
Tel.: (34) 915812100
Holding Company
N.A.I.C.S.: 551112

Subsidiary (Domestic):

MAPFRE Caja Salud de Seguros y
Reaseguros, S.A. **(2)**
Pase Retoletos 29, Madrid, 28004,
Spain **(74%)**
Tel.: (34) 915814800
Web Site: http://www.mapfre.com
Sales Range: $50-74.9 Million
Emp.: 100
Provider of Health Insurance
N.A.I.C.S.: 524113

Subsidiary (Domestic):

Centro Medico de Chequeos MAP-
FRE Vida **(3)**
8 Les Palmas, Madrid, 28034,
Spain **(99.95%)**
Tel.: (34) 917283680
Provider of Medical Services
N.A.I.C.S.: 524114

Subsidiary (Domestic):

MAPFRE Seguros Generales, Cia. de
Seguros y Reaseguros, S.A. **(2)**
Sor Angela de la Cruz 6, 28020, Madrid,
Spain **(100%)**
Tel.: (34) 902140214
Web Site: http://www.mapfre.com
Sales Range: $600-649.9 Million
Emp.: 2,319
Homeowners, Burial, Vehicle, Civil Liability
& Other Insurance & Reinsurance Products
N.A.I.C.S.: 524126

Subsidiary (Domestic):

Funespana, S.A. **(3)**
Sufli 4 Rotonda Cuesta Los Callejones,
Almeria, 04009, Spain **(100%)**
Tel.: (34) 950 624290
Web Site: http://www.funespana.es
Funeral Services
N.A.I.C.S.: 812210
Alberto Ortiz Jover *(CEO)*

Itsemap S.A. **(3)**
Carretera de pozuelo 52, Majadahonda,
28222, Madrid, Spain **(100%)**
Tel.: (34) 915813378
Web Site: http://www.itsemap.com
Sales Range: $50-74.9 Million
Emp.: 50
Provider of Research, Training & Consulting
Services
N.A.I.C.S.: 524298

MAPFRE Guanarteme Cia. de Se-
guros Generales y Reaseguros de
Canarias, S.A. **(3)**
Poeta Agustin Millares 3, Las Palmas,
35008, Spain **(70%)**
Tel.: (34) 928309200
Earnings: $1,419,505
Emp.: 250
Provider of Homeowners, Burial, Vehicle,
Civil Liability & Other Insurance & Reinsur-
ance Products
N.A.I.C.S.: 524126

MAPFRE Industrial, S.A. de
Seguros **(3)**
Paseo De Recoletos 23, Madrid, 28004,
Spain **(100%)**
Tel.: (34) 902136524
Web Site: http://www.mapfre.com
Provider of Industrial Insurance & Reinsur-
ance Products
N.A.I.C.S.: 524130

Subsidiary (Non-US):

MAPFRE Seguros Gerais
(PORTUGAL) **(3)**
Rua Castilho 52, 1250 071, Lisbon,
Portugal **(66%)**
Tel.: (351) 213819700
Web Site: http://www.mapfre.pt
Earnings: $23,019
Emp.: 300
Retailers of Insurance Products
N.A.I.C.S.: 524298
Antonio Mponiobelo *(Gen Mgr)*

Subsidiary (Domestic):

MAPFRE Vida, S.A. de Seguros y
Reaseguros sobre la Vida
Humana **(2)**
Carretera Pozuelo Majadahonda 50 Build-
ing 4, Majadahonda, 28222, Spain **(99%)**
Tel.: (34) 915811400
Web Site: http://www.mapfrevida.com
Sales Range: $50-74.9 Million
Emp.: 100
Provider of Life Insurance & Reinsurance
Products
N.A.I.C.S.: 524130
Antonio Huertas *(Pres)*

AND PRIVATE COMPANIES

MAPLE FINANCIAL GROUP INC.

Affiliate (Domestic):

Club Vida Agencia de Viajes, S.A. (3)
Avenida Gen Peron 14, 28080, Madrid, Spain (25%)
Tel.: (34) 915815631
Travel Agency
N.A.I.C.S.: 561510

Subsidiary (Domestic):

Gestion Moda Shopping S.A. (3)
Avda General Peron 40, Madrid, 28020, Spain (99.82%)
Tel.: (34) 915811525
Web Site: http://www.modashopping.com
Commercial Centers Administrator & Manager
N.A.I.C.S.: 236220

MAPFRE Inversion Dos, Sociedad Gestora de Instituciones de Inversion Colectiva, S.A. (3)
Carretera de Pozuelo 50, Madrid, 28222, Spain (90%)
Tel.: (34) 915813700
Web Site: http://www.mapfreinversion.com
Sales Range: $50-74.9 Million
Emp.: 11
Manager of Pension & Mutual Funds
N.A.I.C.S.: 525910

Affiliate (Domestic):

MAPFRE Inversion G.I.I.C (3)
Carretera de Pozuelo 50, Madrid, 2822, Spain (38%)
Tel.: (34) 915813700
Web Site: http://www.mapfre.com
Sales Range: $25-49.9 Million
Emp.: 100
Advertising Agency; Production, Sales & Distribution of Videos
N.A.I.C.S.: 541810
Sebastian Homet Dupra *(Mng Dir)*

Subsidiary (Domestic):

MAPFRE Inversion Sociedad de Valores, S.A. (3)
Carretera de Pozuelo Majadahonda 50, Madrid, 2832, Spain (100%)
Tel.: (34) 915813700
Web Site: http://www.mapfreinversion.com
Sales Range: $50-74.9 Million
Emp.: 100
Provider of Investment Services
N.A.I.C.S.: 523999

Subsidiary (Domestic):

MAPFRE Vida Pensiones Entidad Gestora de Fondos de Pensiones, S.A. (4)
Avda General Peron 40, Madrid, 28020, Spain (99%)
Tel.: (34) 915813700
Sales Range: $50-74.9 Million
Emp.: 10
Manager of Pension Funds
N.A.I.C.S.: 524292

MAPFRE Inmuebles, S.A. (1)
Tozelo 52 2 1st Fl, 28020, Madrid, Spain (91%)
Tel.: (34) 915811017
Web Site: http://www.mapfreinmuebles.com
Earnings: $1,204,661
Emp.: 70
Provider of Real Estate Services
N.A.I.C.S.: 531210

Subsidiary (Domestic):

Desarrollos Urbanos Ci., S.A. (2)
Calle Prietog Urena No 6, 28016, Madrid, Spain (100%)
Tel.: (34) 915816331
Sales Range: $50-74.9 Million
Emp.: 5
Provider of Real Estate Services
N.A.I.C.S.: 531210

MAPFRE Panama, S.A. (1)
Avenida Balboa y calle 4l E Bella Vista Apartado No 8911 Zona 5, Panama, Panama
Tel.: (507) 207 8700
Insurance Agency Services
N.A.I.C.S.: 524210

MAPFRE Paraguay S.A. (1)
Avda Mcal Lopez esq Gral Aquino 910, Asuncion, Paraguay
Tel.: (595) 21 217 6000
Insurance Agency Services
N.A.I.C.S.: 524210

MAPFRE Re Cia. Reaseguros, S.A. (1)
Paseo De Recoletos 25, Madrid, 28004, Spain (83%)
Tel.: (34) 915811600
Web Site: http://www.mapfre.com
Sales Range: $1-4.9 Billion
Emp.: 130
Provider of Reinsurance Products
N.A.I.C.S.: 524130

Affiliate (Non-US):

Benelux Assist S.A. (2)
Rue De Treves 45, 1040, Brussels, Belgium
Tel.: (32) 22381400
Sales Range: $25-49.9 Million
Emp.: 40
Insurance & Reinsurance
N.A.I.C.S.: 524298

Subsidiary (Non-US):

Itsemap Mexico, Servicos Tecnologicos MAPFRE, S.A. (2)
Porfirio Diaz 102, Colonia Nochebuena, 03720, Mexico, DF, Mexico (100%)
Tel.: (52) 54803880
Sales Range: $50-74.9 Million
Emp.: 15
Provider of Insurance Consulting Services
N.A.I.C.S.: 524298

Itsemap Venezuela, Servicos Tecnologicos MAPFRE, S.A. (2)
Torre Maracaibo Apto Penthouse B Avda Libertador, La Campina, Caracas, 1050, Venezuela (100%)
Tel.: (58) 2127621625
Provider of Insurance Consulting Services
N.A.I.C.S.: 524298

MAPFRE Chile Reaseguros, S.A. (2)
Isidora Goyenechea 3520 Las Condes, Santiago, CP 7550071, Chile
Tel.: (56) 2 694 7566
Web Site: http://www.mapfreseguros.cl
Sales Range: $300-349.5 Million
Reinsurance Carriers
N.A.I.C.S.: 524130
Miguel Barcia Gozalbo *(CEO)*

Subsidiary (Domestic):

Mapfre Asistencia Chile (3)
Av Apoquindo 4499 Piso 7 Las Condes, Santiago, 7580575, Chile (100%)
Tel.: (56) 2 2340 7090
Web Site: http://www.mapfregrupo.com
Sales Range: $50-74.9 Million
Emp.: 1
Insurance Services, Assistance, & Specialty Risks
N.A.I.C.S.: 524210

Sociedad Constructora y de Inversiones Martin Zamora Ltd. (3)
Avda. Apoquindo 4499, piso 8, Santiago, Chile (50%)
Real Estate Agency
N.A.I.C.S.: 531210

Subsidiary (Non-US):

MAPFRE R.E. (2)
Va Privata Mangili 2, 20121, Milan, Italy (100%)
Tel.: (39) 0026554412
Sales Range: $50-74.9 Million
Emp.: 7
Dormant Company
N.A.I.C.S.: 524128
Edoardo Radaelli *(Gen Mgr)*

MAPFRE Reinsurance Co. (2)
24 A Lime St, London, EC3M 7HJ, United Kingdom (88%)
Tel.: (44) 2072837877
Web Site: http://www.mapfrere.com

Sales Range: $50-74.9 Million
Emp.: 7
Reinsurance Carriers
N.A.I.C.S.: 524130
Javier San Basilio *(Gen Mgr)*

Maplux Reinsurance Company Ltd. (2)
5 Place de la Gare, L-1616, Luxembourg, Luxembourg (99.9%)
Tel.: (352) 402190
Web Site: http://www.mapfre.com
Reinsurance
N.A.I.C.S.: 524130

MAPFRE Reinsurance (1)
Paseo De Recoletos 25, Madrid, 28004, Spain (97%)
Tel.: (34) 915811600
Web Site: http://www.mapfrere.com
Earnings: ($1,074,220)
Emp.: 265
Insurance & Reinsurance
N.A.I.C.S.: 524130

Subsidiary (Domestic):

MAPFRE Servicios de Caucion, S.A. (2)
Avda General Peron 38, 28020, Madrid, Spain (100%)
Tel.: (34) 915815271
Other Direct Insurance (except Life, Health & Medical) Carriers
N.A.I.C.S.: 524128

MAPFRE Seguros Guatemala, S.A. (1)
Avenida La Reforma 9-55 Zone 10 Edificio Reforma 10, Guatemala, Guatemala
Tel.: (502) 2 375 5000
Support Services
N.A.I.C.S.: 561990

MAPFRE Seguros Honduras, S.A. (1)
Plaza Azul Building Berlin Avenue, Calle Viena Colonia Lomas de Guijarro Sur 7mo Floor, Tegucigalpa, Honduras (100%)
Tel.: (504) 216 2672
Insurance Agency Services
N.A.I.C.S.: 524210

MAPFRE Seguros Nicaragua S.A. (1)
Invercasa Building 1st Floor, Managua, Nicaragua
Tel.: (505) 2 276 8890
Insurance Agency Services
N.A.I.C.S.: 524210

MAPFRE Soft, S.A. (1)
Carretera Pozuelo-Majadahonda, Majadahonda Km 3800, Madrid, 28220, Spain (55%)
Tel.: (34) 915812318
Web Site: http://www.mapfre.com
Sales Range: $800-899.9 Million
Emp.: 3,000
Data Processing Services
N.A.I.C.S.: 518210

Mapfre Middlesea p.l.c. (1)
Middle Sea House, Floriana, FRN1442, Malta
Tel.: (356) 21246262
Web Site: https://www.mapfre.com.mt
Rev.: $271,356,572
Assets: $2,665,862,292
Liabilities: $2,422,788,690
Net Worth: $243,073,602
Earnings: $15,802,935
Emp.: 290
Fiscal Year-end: 12/31/2022
Insurance & Reinsurance Products
N.A.I.C.S.: 524126
Martin Galea *(Chm)*

Subsidiary (Domestic):

Euro Globe Holdings Ltd. (2)
Middle Sea House, PO Box 337, 1442, Floriana, Malta (100%)
Tel.: (356) 21246262
Web Site: http://www.middlesea.com
Sales Range: $100-124.9 Million
Emp.: 150
Direct Life Insurance Carriers
N.A.I.C.S.: 524113
Joseph F. X. Zahra *(Mng Dir)*

Growth Investments Ltd. (2)
Middle Sea House, PO Box 337, VLT16, Floriana, Malta (100%)
Tel.: (356) 21246262
Web Site: http://www.growthinvestmentsonline.com
Sales Range: $100-124.9 Million
Emp.: 150
Direct Life Insurance Carriers
N.A.I.C.S.: 524113

Middlesea Valletta Life Assurance Company Ltd. (2)
Middle Sea House, PO Box 337, Floriana, FRN1420, Malta (100%)
Tel.: (356) 21246262
Web Site: http://www.msvlife.com
Sales Range: $100-124.9 Million
Emp.: 70
Direct Life Insurance Carriers
N.A.I.C.S.: 524113
David Curmi *(CEO)*

Verti Versicherung AG (1)
Rheinstrasse 7A, 14513, Teltow, Germany
Tel.: (49) 3089 000 3003
Web Site: https://www.verti.de
Insurance Agency Services
N.A.I.C.S.: 524210

MAPI - PHARMA LTD.

Weizmann Science Park 16 Einstein Street, PO Box 4113, 74140, Nes Ziyyona, Israel
Tel.: (972) 73 712 1213
Web Site: http://www.mapi-pharma.com
Year Founded: 2008
Sales Range: $1-9.9 Million
Emp.: 31
Pharmaceuticals Mfr
N.A.I.C.S.: 325412
Ehud Marom *(Chm & CEO)*

MAPLE ENERGY PLC

Av Victor Andres Belaunde 147 Via Principal 140 Oficina 201, Edificio Real Seis, San Isidro, 27, Peru
Tel.: (51) 16114000
Web Site: http://www.maple-energy.com
Sales Range: $125-149.9 Million
Emp.: 898
Crude Oil & Natural Gas Exploration Services
N.A.I.C.S.: 211120
Rafael Guillermo Ferreyros *(CEO)*

MAPLE FINANCIAL GROUP INC.

79 Wellington St W Ste 3500, Toronto, M5K 1K7, ON, Canada
Tel.: (416) 350-8200
Web Site: http://www.maplefinancial.com
Sales Range: $400-449.9 Million
Emp.: 350
Financial Services
N.A.I.C.S.: 522320
Tom Higgins *(Pres & CEO)*

Subsidiaries:

Maple Securities (U.K.) Limited (1)
Ryder Court 14 Ryder Street, London, SW1Y 6QB, United Kingdom
Tel.: (44) 20 7570 2000
Securities Trading Services
N.A.I.C.S.: 523150
Jason Dunn *(COO)*

Maple Securities U.S.A. Inc. (1)
525 Washington Blvd 14th Fl, Jersey City, NJ 07310
Tel.: (201) 369-3000
Web Site: http://www.securities.com
Emp.: 30
Securities Trading Services
N.A.I.C.S.: 523150
John Malosky *(CEO)*

Maple Trade Finance Inc. (1)
5475 Spring Garden Rd 7th Floor, Halifax,

MAPLE FINANCIAL GROUP INC.

Maple Financial Group Inc.—(Continued)
B3J 3T2, NS, Canada
Tel.: (902) 444-5566
Web Site: http://www.mapletradefinance.ca
Financial Management Services
N.A.I.C.S.: 523999
Mike Miller *(COO)*

MAPLE GATE FREIGHT SYSTEMS INC.
6535 Millcreek Dr Unit 27, Mississauga, L5N 2M2, ON, Canada
Tel.: (905) 567-8810
Web Site:
 http://www.maplegatefreight.com
Rev.: $24,000,000
Emp.: 24
Logistics Solutions Services
N.A.I.C.S.: 541614
Julie Levert *(Controller)*

MAPLE GOLD MINES LTD.
1111 W Hastings St 6th Floor, Vancouver, V6E 2J3, BC, Canada
Tel.: (647) 265-8688   Ca
Web Site:
 https://www.maplegoldmines.com
Year Founded: 2010
MGMLF—(OTCQB)
Rev.: $491,596
Assets: $4,465,822
Liabilities: $1,925,391
Net Worth: $2,540,431
Earnings: ($2,807,376)
Emp.: 12
Fiscal Year-end: 12/31/19
Gold Mining Services
N.A.I.C.S.: 212220
Joness Lang *(Exec VP)*

MAPLE LEAF FOODS, INC.
6897 Financial Drive, Mississauga, L5N 0A8, ON, Canada
Tel.: (905) 285-5000   ON
Web Site:
 https://www.mapleleaffoods.com
Year Founded: 1927
MFI—(OTCIQ)
Rev.: $3,016,227,896
Assets: $2,689,080,143
Liabilities: $1,196,961,625
Net Worth: $1,492,118,519
Earnings: $48,989,900
Emp.: 13,000
Fiscal Year-end: 12/31/19
Food Processor
N.A.I.C.S.: 311999
Lynda J. Kuhn *(Sr VP & Chm-Maple Leaf Centre for Action on Food Security)*

Subsidiaries:

Cold Springs Farms Limited   (1)
149 Brock Street, Thamesford, N0M 2M0, ON, Canada
Tel.: (519) 285-3940
Sales Range: $125-149.9 Million
Emp.: 675
Poultry Slaughtering & Processing
N.A.I.C.S.: 311615

Lightlife Foods, Inc.   (1)
153 Industrial Blvd, Turners Falls, MA 01376
Tel.: (800) 769-3279
Web Site: http://www.lightlife.com
Vegetarian & Soy Food Products Mfr
N.A.I.C.S.: 311999
Roy Lubetkin *(CEO)*

Maple Leaf Consumer Foods   (1)
870 Lagimodiere Blvd, Winnipeg, R2J 0T9, MB, Canada   **(100%)**
Tel.: (204) 233-2421
Web Site: https://www.mapleleaffoods.com
Sales Range: $25-49.9 Million
Emp.: 50
Meat Packing
N.A.I.C.S.: 311611

Maple Leaf Consumer Foods   (1)
150 Bartor Rd, Weston, M9M 1H1, ON, Canada   **(100%)**
Tel.: (416) 741-7181
Web Site: http://www.mapleleaf.com
Sales Range: $100-124.9 Million
Emp.: 350
Prepared Meats & Salads
N.A.I.C.S.: 311991

Maple Leaf Consumer Foods   (1)
321 Courtland Avenue East, Kitchener, N2G 3X8, ON, Canada   **(100%)**
Tel.: (519) 741-5000
Web Site: http://www.mapleleaf.ca
Sales Range: $750-799.9 Million
Emp.: 1,100
Meat Products & Grocery Items for Retail & Food Service Markets Mfr
N.A.I.C.S.: 311615

The Field Roast Grain Meat Co.   (1)
3901 7th Ave S, Seattle, WA 98108
Web Site: http://www.fieldroast.com
Veal Product Mfr
N.A.I.C.S.: 311612

MAPLE LEAF GREEN WORLD INC.
Suite 203 1222 - 11th Ave SW, Calgary, T3C 0M4, AB, Canada
Tel.: (403) 907-3715   AB
Web Site:
 https://www.mlgreenworld.com
Year Founded: 2005
4HV0—(DEU)
Assets: $439,756
Liabilities: $6,964,161
Net Worth: ($6,524,405)
Earnings: ($890,836)
Emp.: 1
Fiscal Year-end: 12/31/22
Nursery Product Mfr
N.A.I.C.S.: 111421
Terence Lam *(CFO & Sec)*

MAPLE LODGE FARMS LTD.
8301 Winston Churchill Blvd, Brampton, L6Y 0A2, ON, Canada
Tel.: (905) 455-8340
Web Site:
 http://www.maplelodgefarms.com
Year Founded: 1955
Sales Range: $250-299.9 Million
Emp.: 2,200
Poultry & Deli Products Processor & Mfr
N.A.I.C.S.: 311615
Wendy Robson *(Sec)*

Subsidiaries:

Fleming Chicks Limited   (1)
4412 Ontario Street, Beamsville, L0R 1B0, ON, Canada
Tel.: (905) 563-4914
Sales Range: $25-49.9 Million
Emp.: 60
Poultry Producer
N.A.I.C.S.: 112390
Dianne Lumley *(Mgr-Hatchery)*

Golden Cut Poultry Ltd.   (1)
42 Taber Rd, Toronto, M9W 3A8, ON, Canada
Tel.: (416) 746-6367
Sales Range: $25-49.9 Million
Emp.: 120
Poultry Processing
N.A.I.C.S.: 311615

MAPLETREE COMMERCIAL TRUST
10 Pasir Panjang Road 13-01 Mapletree Business City, Singapore, 117438, Singapore
Tel.: (65) 63776111   SG
Web Site:
 http://www.mapletreetrust.com
Year Founded: 2005
N2IU—(SES)
Rev.: $2,136,609,264

Assets: $42,234,479,348
Liabilities: $19,032,221,385
Net Worth: $23,202,257,963
Earnings: $1,347,476,045
Emp.: 2,400
Fiscal Year-end: 03/31/23
Real Estate Investment Services
N.A.I.C.S.: 531390
Kwong Weng Wan *(Co-Sec)*

MAPLETREE INDUSTRIAL TRUST
10 Pasir Panjang Road No 13-01 Mapletree Business City, Singapore, 117438, Singapore
Tel.: (65) 63776111   SG
Web Site:
 https://www.mapletreetrust.com
Year Founded: 2008
MAPIF—(OTCIQ)
Rev.: $516,733,604
Assets: $6,420,426,818
Liabilities: $2,501,396,070
Net Worth: $3,919,030,748
Earnings: $89,387,180
Emp.: 186
Fiscal Year-end: 03/31/24
Real Estate Investment Services
N.A.I.C.S.: 525990
Peter Che Heng Tan *(Head-Investment)*

MAPLETREE LOGISTICS TRUST
10 Pasir Panjang Road 13-01, Mapletree Business City, Singapore, 117438, Singapore
Tel.: (65) 63776111
Web Site:
 https://www.mapletreetrust.com
M44U—(SES)
Rev.: $541,419,785
Assets: $9,946,791,404
Liabilities: $4,372,560,948
Net Worth: $5,574,230,456
Earnings: $421,652,464
Emp.: 345
Fiscal Year-end: 03/31/23
Real Estate Investment Trust
N.A.I.C.S.: 525990
Kwong Weng Wan *(Co-Sec)*

MAPLETREE NORTH ASIA COMMERCIAL TRUST MANAGEMENT LTD.
10 Pasir Panjang Road #13 01, Mapletree Business City, Singapore, 117438, Singapore
Tel.: (65) 6 377 6111
Web Site:
 http://www.mapletreenorthasia.com
RW0U—(SES)
Rev.: $297,054,271
Assets: $6,106,705,455
Liabilities: $2,796,069,144
Net Worth: $3,310,636,311
Earnings: ($199,736,373)
Fiscal Year-end: 03/31/21
Real Estate Investment Services
N.A.I.C.S.: 523999
Cindy Pei Pei Chow *(CEO)*

MAPNA GROUP
No 231 Mirdamad Blvd, PO Box 1918953651, 1918953651, Tehran, Iran
Tel.: (98) 21231510012
Web Site:
 https://www.mapnagroup.com
Year Founded: 1993
MAPN1—(THE)
Sales Range: Less than $1 Million
Power Plant Contractor Services
N.A.I.C.S.: 237130
Abbas Aliabadi *(Chm)*

INTERNATIONAL PUBLIC

Subsidiaries:

Alborz Turbine Company   (1)
Mapna Blvd Fardis, Karaj, Tehran, Iran
Tel.: (98) 2636185911
Gas Turbines Repair & Maintenance Services
N.A.I.C.S.: 811310

MAPNA Boiler & Equipment Engineering & Manufacturing Company   (1)
No 77 Golkhaneh Alley Africa Highway, Tehran, Iran
Tel.: (98) 2127582424
Boiler & Engineering Equipment Mfr
N.A.I.C.S.: 332410

MAPNA Combined Cycle Power Plants Construction & Development Company   (1)
Africa Highway-South of Haqqani Crossroads - No 15, 1518614411, Tehran, Iran
Tel.: (98) 2145357000
Web Site: http://www.mapnamd2.com
Construction Development Services
N.A.I.C.S.: 236220

MAPNA Drilling Company   (1)
No 20 23rd St Gandhi St Vanak Sq, 1517935111, Tehran, Iran
Tel.: (98) 2196880880
Web Site: http://www.mapnadrilling.com
Offshore Drilling Services
N.A.I.C.S.: 213111
Fazel Jamalzadeh *(Mng Dir)*

MAPNA Electric & Control Engineering & Manufacturing Company   (1)
Iran Mir Damad No 231, PO Box 193 956 448, Tehran, Iran
Tel.: (98) 2181981890
Web Site: http://www.mapnaec.com
Gas Turbine Mfr
N.A.I.C.S.: 335999

MAPNA Generator Engineering & Manufacturing Company   (1)
No 231 Mirdamad Blvd, PO Box 19395/5448, 1918953651, Tehran, Iran
Tel.: (98) 2123151850
Web Site: http://www.mapnagenerator.com
Generator Mfr
N.A.I.C.S.: 335312
Mohammad Reza Shakeri *(Mng Dir)*

MAPNA Healthcare Company   (1)
4th Floor No 46 East Arash Blvd Farid Afshar St, Vahid Dastgerdi Zafar St, Tehran, Iran
Tel.: (98) 2123153149
Healtcare Services
N.A.I.C.S.: 621610

MAPNA Locomotive Engineering & Manufacturing Company   (1)
New Razakan St Standard Sq, Karaj, 3173655111, Tehran, Iran
Tel.: (98) 2636186000
Web Site: http://www.mapnalocomotive.com
Rail Transport Equipment Mfr
N.A.I.C.S.: 336510
Babak Ahmadi *(Chm)*

MAPNA Management Consulting Company   (1)
Third floor No 231 Mirdamad Blvd, Tehran, Iran
Tel.: (98) 2123151180
Web Site: http://www.mapnamc.com
Management Consulting Services
N.A.I.C.S.: 541611
Mohammad-Hossein Mirhadi *(Mng Dir)*

MAPNA Operation & Maintenance Company   (1)
No 4 1st St Mosaddeq North Naft St Mirdamad Blvd, 1919613871, Tehran, Iran
Tel.: (98) 2123151800
Web Site: http://www.mapnaom.com
Oil & Gas Operation Services
N.A.I.C.S.: 213112
Mohammad Reza Sharifi *(CEO)*

MAPNA Power Plants Construction & Development Company   (1)
No 15 Africa Ave South of Haghani Crossroads, Post Box 15175/617, 1518614411, Tehran, Iran

AND PRIVATE COMPANIES

Tel.: (98) 2182980000
Web Site: http://www.mapnamd1.com
Renewable Energy Services
N.A.I.C.S.: 221114

MAPNA Railway Operation Development & Maintenance Company (1)
Mapna Reyli East Railroad between Shoosh and Behesht Street, Rajai street, Tehran, Iran
Tel.: (98) 2155650652
Web Site: http://www.mapnamrm.com
Railcar Repair Services
N.A.I.C.S.: 488210

MAPNA STS Company (1)
Andishmandan 20 Alavijeh Road in Front of Traffic Police, Bozorge Isfahan Industrial Zone Isfahan-Tehran Freeway, 8331134386, Isfahan, Iran
Tel.: (98) 3145233271
Web Site: http://www.mapnasts.ir
Industrial Equipment Mfr
N.A.I.C.S.: 333248

MAPNA Special Projects Construction & Development Company (1)
No 43 Kish Alley Jahan Koodak Crossroad Nelson Mandela Africa Ave, 1518813413, Tehran, Iran
Tel.: (98) 21846200001
Web Site: http://www.mapnamd3.com
Construction Development Services
N.A.I.C.S.: 236220

MAPNA Turbine Blade Engineering & Manufacturing Company (1)
3rd Floor No 231 No 3 Mapna Building Mirdamad Blvd, PO Box 19395-5316, 1918953651, Tehran, Iran
Tel.: (98) 2181981830
Web Site: http://www.mapnablade.com
Turbine Blade Mfr
N.A.I.C.S.: 333611

MAPNA Turbine Engineering & Manufacturing Company (1)
231 Mirdamad Ave, PO Box 15875-5643, Tehran, Iran
Tel.: (98) 2122908581
Web Site: http://www.mapnaturbine.com
Gas Turbine Mfr
N.A.I.C.S.: 335999
Majid Bahmani (CEO)

Mavadkaran Company (1)
Mapna Boulevard 7th Km Malard Road, Karaj, 3167643685, Tehran, Iran
Tel.: (98) 2636196243
Web Site: http://www.mavadkaran.com
Turbine Blade Mfr
N.A.I.C.S.: 333611

Monenco Consultancy Services Company (1)
No 12 Attar st Valiasr Ave, PO Box 15875-8717, 1994643315, Tehran, Iran
Tel.: (98) 2181961
Web Site: http://www.monencogroup.com
Engineeering Services
N.A.I.C.S.: 541330

Nasb Niroo Company (1)
No 45 West 27th St Kurdistan Highwa, PO Box 14155/6514, Tehran, Iran
Tel.: (98) 2196663100
Web Site: http://www.nasbniroo.com
Construction Development Services
N.A.I.C.S.: 236220

Neyrperse Company (1)
No 38 -West Armaghan St- Vali-e-Asr Ave, 1967843116, Tehran, Iran
Tel.: (98) 2123534000
Web Site: http://www.mapnanyp.com
Construction Development Services
N.A.I.C.S.: 236220

MAPROM GMBH
Rohrweg 33, 37671, Hoxter, Germany
Tel.: (49) 527197190
Web Site: http://www.maprom.de
Year Founded: 1987
Rev.: $15,725,160
Emp.: 70
Promotional Textiles Distr
N.A.I.C.S.: 424990

Henner Marquardt (Mng Dir)

MAPS SPA
Via Paradigna 38/A, 43122, Parma, Italy
Tel.: (39) 0521052300
Web Site: https://www.mapsgroup.it
Year Founded: 2002
MAPS—(ITA)
Sales Range: Less than $1 Million
Software Development Services
N.A.I.C.S.: 541511
Maurizio Pontremoli (CEO)

Subsidiaries:

IG Consulting S.r.l. (1)
Viale Virgilio 54/F, 41123, Modena, MO, Italy
Tel.: (39) 059460534
Web Site: http://igconsulting.mapsgroup.it
Information Technology Services
N.A.I.C.S.: 541511

MAPSPEOPLE A/S
Stigsborgvej 60, Norresundby, Denmark
Tel.: (45) 31234872
Web Site: https://www.mapspeople.com
Year Founded: 1997
Software Publisher
N.A.I.C.S.: 513210
Morten Brogger (CEO)

Subsidiaries:

Point Inside, Inc. (1)
12827 SE 40th Pl Ste 100, Bellevue, WA 98006
Tel.: (425) 590-9522
Web Site: http://www.pointinside.com
Sales Range: $25-49.9 Million
Computer Technology Development Services
N.A.I.C.S.: 541511
Jon Croy (Co-Founder)

MAQ ADMINISTRACION URBANAS SOCIMI, SA
Marques de Larios N 5 2-2, 29015, Malaga, Spain
Tel.: (34) 952223673
Web Site: https://www.maqau.es
Year Founded: 2014
MLMAQ—(EUR)
Rev.: $1,810,230
Assets: $9,827,831
Liabilities: $901,346
Net Worth: $8,926,485
Earnings: $1,352,804
Fiscal Year-end: 12/31/21
Real Estate Investment Trust Services
N.A.I.C.S.: 525990
Jose Torres Quesada (Pres)

MAQBOOL TEXTILE MILLS LTD.
2 Industrial Estate Multan, Multan, 60000, Punjab, Pakistan
Tel.: (92) 616537155
Web Site: https://www.maqboolgroup.com
Year Founded: 1958
MQTM—(PSX)
Rev.: $35,389,140
Assets: $30,584,784
Liabilities: $21,127,387
Net Worth: $9,457,397
Earnings: ($897,697)
Emp.: 1,703
Fiscal Year-end: 06/30/23
Textile & Fabric Material Mfr
N.A.I.C.S.: 313310
Mian Tanvir Ahmad Sheikh (Chm)

MAR CITY PLC
Ground Floor Touchstone Pinewood Business Park Coleshill Road, Solihull, B37 7HG, United Kingdom
Tel.: (44) 1212007260 UK
Web Site: http://www.marcityplc.co.uk
Sales Range: $25-49.9 Million
Emp.: 38
Real Estate Consulting Service
N.A.I.C.S.: 531390
Tony Ryan (CEO)

Subsidiaries:

Mar City Developments Limited (1)
Mar House 11 Hockley Ct 2401 Stratford Road Hockley Heath, Shirley, Solihull, B94 6NW, West Midlands, United Kingdom
Tel.: (44) 121 733 3011
Web Site: http://www.marcity.com
Sales Range: $50-74.9 Million
Emp.: 23
Real Estate Development Services
N.A.I.C.S.: 531390
Tony Ryan (Chm)

Mar City Homes Limited (1)
113-115 Great Hampton St, Shirley, Birmingham, B18 6ES, United Kingdom
Tel.: (44) 1212007260
Web Site: http://www.marcityplc.com
Emp.: 50
Real Estate Development Services
N.A.I.C.S.: 531390
Mark Grady (Mng Dir)

MARAC ELECTRONICS SA
455 Dimokratias Ave, Perama, 188 63, Piraeus, Greece
Tel.: (30) 2104314361
Web Site: http://www.marac.gr
Emp.: 81
Network Design & Installation Services
N.A.I.C.S.: 541512

Subsidiaries:

MARAC BULGARIA EOOD (1)
70A Eng Ivan Blvd, Vazrazdane, 1303, Sofia, Bulgaria
Tel.: (359) 29305050
Telecommunication Servicesb
N.A.I.C.S.: 517810

Marac Albania Sh.p.k (1)
Rr Sami Frasheri Nr 17/1 Kati 7, Tirana, Albania
Tel.: (355) 4 2271 281
Telecommunication Servicesb
N.A.I.C.S.: 517810

UNIAXIS SRL (1)
11 Stefan Mihaileanu Str Sector 2, 024021, Bucharest, Romania
Tel.: (40) 21 3232372
Web Site: http://www.uniaxis.ro
Communication Equipment Distr
N.A.I.C.S.: 423690

Ukravtomatika (1)
25 Klimenko St Office 217, 03110, Kiev, Ukraine
Tel.: (380) 44 275 02 33
Web Site: http://www.ukravtomatika.com.ua
Telecommunication Servicesb
N.A.I.C.S.: 517810

MARAL OVERSEAS LIMITED
Maral Sarovar V & PO Khalbujurg Tehsil Khasrawad, Khargone, 451660, Madhya Pradesh, India
Tel.: (91) 7285265401
Web Site: https://www.maraloverseas.com
MARALOVER—(NSE)
Rev.: $87,337,641
Assets: $60,274,755
Liabilities: $46,946,418
Net Worth: $13,328,338
Earnings: $1,710,468
Emp.: 2,642
Fiscal Year-end: 03/31/21
Textile Mfr
N.A.I.C.S.: 313220
Shekhar Agarwal (CEO & Mng Dir)

MARANGONI S.P.A.

MARAND D.O.O.
Koprska ulica 100, 1000, Ljubljana, Slovenia
Tel.: (386) 14703100
Web Site: http://www.marand.si
Sales Range: $25-49.9 Million
Emp.: 150
Software Services
N.A.I.C.S.: 541511
Tomaz Gornik (CEO)

MARANGONI S.P.A.
Via del Garda 6, 38068, Rovereto, Trentino, Italy
Tel.: (39) 0464301111
Web Site: http://www.marangoni.com
Year Founded: 1984
Sales Range: $350-399.9 Million
Emp.: 1,300
Mfr & Distribution of Tires & Retreaded Tires
N.A.I.C.S.: 441340
Dino Maggioni (CEO)

Subsidiaries:

Marangoni Argentina SA (1)
Parque Industrial Alvear-Ruta provincial 21 Km Alvera, Santa Fe, Argentina
Tel.: (54) 41 317 7575
Car Tire Mfr
N.A.I.C.S.: 326211

Marangoni Industrial Tyres Lanka Pvt Ltd (1)
Lot 10 Block B, Biyagama, Sri Lanka
Tel.: (94) 11 4815990
Car Tire Mfr
N.A.I.C.S.: 326211

Marangoni Industrie Manutention SAS (1)
4 Rue Jean-Pierre Timbaud, Goussainville, 95190, France
Tel.: (33) 1 30189898
Tire Distr
N.A.I.C.S.: 423130

Marangoni Kaucuk Ticaret A.S. (1)
Bornova Caddesi No 14/18, Bornova, Izmir, Isikkent, Turkiye
Tel.: (90) 2165945853
Web Site: http://marangoni.com.tr
Tires & Retreaded Tires Mfr
N.A.I.C.S.: 441340

Marangoni Meccanica S.p.A. (1) (100%)
Via E Ferni 29, 38068, Rovereto, Italy
Tel.: (39) 0464485200
Web Site: http://www.tyremachinery.marangoni.com
Sales Range: $25-49.9 Million
Emp.: 100
Mfr & Distribution of Tires & Retreaded Tires
N.A.I.C.S.: 441340
Riccardo Mastronardi (CEO)

Marangoni Pneumatici S.p.A (1) (100%)
Via Del Garda 6, 38068, Rovereto, Trento, Italy
Tel.: (39) 0464301111
Web Site: http://www.marangoni.com
Sales Range: $100-124.9 Million
Emp.: 340
Tire & Retreaded Tire Mfr & Distr
N.A.I.C.S.: 326211

Marangoni Retreading Systems Deutschland GmbH (1)
Immenhacken 5, 24558, Henstedt-Ulzburg, Germany
Tel.: (49) 419390060
Web Site: http://www.marangoni.com
Tires & Retreaded Tires Mfr & Distr
N.A.I.C.S.: 441340
Matthias Leppert (Mng Dir)

Marangoni Shanghai Trading Co., Ltd. (1)
Room 2506-2507 161 East Lujiazhui Road, Shanghai, 200120, Pudong, China
Tel.: (86) 21 588 25068
Tire Retreading Services
N.A.I.C.S.: 326212

MARANGONI S.P.A.

Marangoni S.p.A.—(Continued)

Marangoni Tread (UK) Ltd (1)
Lymedale Bus Pk Dalewood Rd, Newcastle,
ST5 9QH, Staffs, United Kingdom **(100%)**
Tel.: (44) 782566625
Sales Range: $25-49.9 Million
Emp.: 6
Mfr & Distribution of Tires & Retreaded Tires
N.A.I.C.S.: 441340

Marangoni Tread S.p.A (1)
Strada Comunale ASI 1/S 10-14, 3013, Ferentino, Italy **(100%)**
Tel.: (39) 077580061
Web Site: http://www.marangoni.com
Sales Range: $50-74.9 Million
Emp.: 180
Mfr & Distribution of Tires & Retreaded Tires
N.A.I.C.S.: 441340
Rabuffo Nicola (Mng Dir)

Marangoni Tyre GmbH (1)
Hoch Str 11, 32120, Hiddenhausen, Germany **(100%)**
Tel.: (49) 5223878766
Web Site: http://www.marangoni.com
Sales Range: $25-49.9 Million
Emp.: 5
Mfr & Distribution of Tires & Retreaded Tires
N.A.I.C.S.: 441340

Marangoni do Brasil, Ltda (1)
Rodovia LMG 800 Km 01 Distrito Industrial
Genesco Aparecido Oliveira, Lagoa Santa,
CEP 33400 000, Brazil **(100%)**
Tel.: (55) 3136899200
Web Site: http://www.marangoni.com.br
Sales Range: $50-74.9 Million
Emp.: 130
Mfr & Distribution of Tires & Retreaded Tires
N.A.I.C.S.: 441340

Pneusmarket S.p.A (1)
Via E Fermi 11B, 37135, Verona, Italy
Tel.: (39) 0459215500
Web Site: http://www.pneusmarket.it
Sales Range: $25-49.9 Million
Emp.: 25
Mfr & Distribution of Tires & Retreaded Tires
N.A.I.C.S.: 441340

TRM S.r.l. (1)
Via Alessandro Volta 54, Ala, 38061, Italy
Tel.: (39) 0464 670560
Car Tire Mfr
N.A.I.C.S.: 326211

MARATHON INVESTMENTS LTD.
HaNagar St, Holon, 58816, Israel
Tel.: (972) 36540822
Web Site: http://www.marathon.co.il
Year Founded: 1993
Sales Range: $10-24.9 Million
Privater Equity Firm
N.A.I.C.S.: 523999
Rafi Silman (Chm)

MARATHON NEXTGEN REALTY LTD.
702 Marathon Max Mulund-Goregaon
Link Road Mulund W, Western Railway Lower Parel, Mumbai, 400080,
Maharashtra, India
Tel.: (91) 7677501501
Web Site:
  https://www.marathonnextgen.com
503101—(BOM)
Rev.: $30,459,839
Assets: $231,986,145
Liabilities: $148,156,636
Net Worth: $83,829,509
Earnings: $2,174,199
Emp.: 55
Fiscal Year-end: 03/31/21
Real Estate Development Services
N.A.I.C.S.: 531390
Chetan Ramniklal Shah (Chm & Mng Dir)

MARATHON TYRES PTY. LIMITED
10 Friesian Close, Sandgate,
Newcastle, 2304, NSW, Australia
Tel.: (61) 2 4960 2144   AU
Web Site:
  http://www.marathontyres.com.au
Year Founded: 1970
Tire Distr
N.A.I.C.S.: 423130
Greg Nesbitt (Mng Dir)

MARBLE ARTS AD
103 James Bourchier Blvd 1st floor,
1407, Sofia, Bulgaria
Tel.: (359) 2 962 14 88
Web Site: http://www.marblearts.eu
Marble Product Distr
N.A.I.C.S.: 424990

MARBLE CITY INDIA LIMITED
A 30 IInd Floor Kailash Colony, New
Delhi, 110048, India
Tel.: (91) 1126654053
Web Site: https://www.pgil.com
531281—(BOM)
Rev.: $13,675,547
Assets: $13,338,877
Liabilities: $9,795,792
Net Worth: $3,543,085
Earnings: $92,405
Emp.: 38
Fiscal Year-end: 03/31/23
Marble Mfr
N.A.I.C.S.: 327991
Saket Dalmia (Mng Dir)

Subsidiaries:

P G Industry Limited - Alwar Factory (1)
E-237 I-2 Phase - II RIICO Industrial Area,
Behror, Alwar, 301701, Rajasthan, India
Tel.: (91) 1494 516116
Marble Mfr
N.A.I.C.S.: 327991
Neeraj Budhiraja (Mng Dir)

MARBLE DESIGN FACTORY COMPANY
8416 Sadus Industrial Area 5678
59268, Riyadh, 13968, Saudi Arabia
Tel.: (966) 920000988
Web Site:
  https://www.marbledesign.sa.com
9575—(SAU)
Rev.: $13,648,318
Assets: $29,264,796
Liabilities: $2,835,653
Net Worth: $26,429,143
Earnings: $5,843,236
Emp.: 103
Fiscal Year-end: 12/31/23
Stone Product Mfr
N.A.I.C.S.: 327991
Abdullah AlKharashi Ahmad (Founder & Chm)

MARBLE POINT LOAN FINANCING LIMITED
1st & 2nd Floors Elizabeth House
Les Ruettes Brayes, Saint Peter Port,
GY1 1EW, Guernsey
Tel.: (44) 2072591500   GY
Web Site:
  https://www.mplflimited.com
Year Founded: 2016
MPLF—(LSE)
Rev.: $9,339,894
Assets: $145,292,086
Liabilities: $41,357,137
Net Worth: $103,934,949
Earnings: $17,040,324
Fiscal Year-end: 12/31/23
Investment Management Service
N.A.I.C.S.: 523940

Thomas P. Majewski (Mgr-Marble Point)

MARBOUR SAS
2 Boulevard Faidherbe, 13012, Marseille, France
Tel.: (33) 4 91 34 89 12
Web Site: http://www.marbour.eu
Food, Beverage & Agricultural Product Mfr
N.A.I.C.S.: 311999

Subsidiaries:

Coroi International (1)
2 Boulevard Faidherbe, 13012, Marseille, France
Tel.: (33) 491348912
Web Site: http://www.coroi-international.com
Chemical Products Distr
N.A.I.C.S.: 424690

Coroi Maurice (1)
Grewals Lane, Port Louis, Mauritius
Tel.: (230) 4055700
Web Site: https://www.coroi.mu
Chemical Products Mfr
N.A.I.C.S.: 325199

FEI Foods Ltd (1)
Viking Way Winch Wen Industrial Estate,
Swansea, SA1 7DA, United Kingdom
Tel.: (44) 1792312910
Web Site: http://www.feifoods.co.uk
Food Products Mfr
N.A.I.C.S.: 311919

Rol-Ryz Sp. zo.o (1)
ul Celna 2, 81 337, Gdynia, Poland
Tel.: (48) 586205028
Web Site: http://www.rol-ryz.pl
Rice Distr
N.A.I.C.S.: 424490

Van Sillevoldt Rijst b.v. (1)
Ketelweg 34, 3356 LE, Papendrecht, Netherlands
Tel.: (31) 786420720
Web Site: http://www.vsr-rice.com
Rice Processing Services
N.A.I.C.S.: 311212

MARC CONLETH INDUSTRIES SDN. BHD.
Lot 24645 Jln KPB5 Kws Perindustrian Kampung Baru Balakong,
43300, Seri Kembahgan, Selangor, Malaysia
Tel.: (60) 389641330
Web Site: http://www.mci.com.my
Year Founded: 2010
Oil & Gas Equipment Mfr
N.A.I.C.S.: 333132

MARC O'POLO INTERNATIONAL GMBH
Hofgartenstrasse 1, Stephanskirchen,
83071, Germany
Tel.: (49) 8036900
Web Site: http://www.marc-o-polo.de
Year Founded: 1967
Sales Range: $200-249.9 Million
Emp.: 700
Apparel & Accessories Mfr, Designer, Marketer & Retailer
N.A.I.C.S.: 315990
Werner Bock (CEO & Corp Mktg & Licensing Officer)

MARCATEL S.A. DE C.V.
Ave San Jeronimo 210 Pte, Col San
Jeronimo, Monterrey, 64640, Mexico
Tel.: (52) 8147777000
Web Site: http://www.marcatel.com
Year Founded: 1996
Voice, Data & Telecommunication Infrastructure Services
N.A.I.C.S.: 517111
Gustavo M. de la Garza Ortega (Founder & Pres)

INTERNATIONAL PUBLIC

Subsidiaries:

STi Prepaid, LLC (1)
1250 Broadway 26th Fl, New York, NY 10001
Tel.: (212) 660-2700
Web Site: http://www.stiprepaid.com
Sales Range: $600-649.9 Million
Emp.: 270
Prepaid Phone Card Whslr
N.A.I.C.S.: 517121

MARCEGAGLIA S.P.A.
Via Bresciani 16, Gazoldo degli Ippoliti, 46040, Italy
Tel.: (39) 03766851
Web Site:
  http://www.marcegaglia.com
Year Founded: 1959
Sales Range: $5-14.9 Billion
Emp.: 6,000
Producer of Welded Carbon Steel & Stainless Steel Tubes, Sheets, Sections, Drawn Steel & Colded Rolled Strips
N.A.I.C.S.: 331513

Subsidiaries:

Albarella S.p.A. (1)
Isola di Albaralla Via Po di Levante 4,
45010, Rosolina, RO, Italy **(100%)**
Tel.: (39) 0426 332600
Web Site: http://www.albarella.it
Sales Range: $25-49.9 Million
Emp.: 20
Tourism Services
N.A.I.C.S.: 721110

Appia Energy S.r.l. (1)
Contrada Console, Massafra, 74016,
Taranto, Italy
Tel.: (39) 0998804187
Web Site: http://www.appiaenergy.com
Power Plant Construction Services
N.A.I.C.S.: 237130
Luca Tagliente (Plant Mgr)

Bre.M.A. Warmwalz (1)
Carl-Benz Strasse 30, D-28237, Bremen, Germany
Tel.: (49) 4216480
Web Site:
  http://www.gruppomarcegaglia.com
N.A.I.C.S.: 332919

CCT (1)
via A.Volta, 50, 21010, Varese, Italy
Tel.: (39) 0331232411
N.A.I.C.S.: 332919

Earcanal (1)
Langileria B, Lamiako, E 48940, Leioa,
Vizcaya, Spain
Tel.: (34) 944806188
Sales Range: $50-74.9 Million
Emp.: 100
N.A.I.C.S.: 332919

Elet.Ca (1)
Via Pistoiese 155/A, Signa, 50058, Florence, Firenze, Italy
Tel.: (39) 0558951944
Web Site: http://www.eletca.it
Sales Range: $50-74.9 Million
Emp.: 16
Steel & Metal Valve Sales
N.A.I.C.S.: 332919

Eta S.p.A. (1)
Via Canova 36, 20020, Lainate, Milano, Italy
Tel.: (39) 0029379251
Sales Range: $25-49.9 Million
Emp.: 40
N.A.I.C.S.: 332919

Euroenergy Group (1)
Via G Alessi 2, I-20020, Lainate, Milano,
Italy
Tel.: (39) 0293796872
Web Site: http://www.euroenergygroup.com
N.A.I.C.S.: 332919

IMAT (1)
via P Zorutti 13/14/16, Fontanafredda,
33074, Pordenone, Italy **(100%)**
Tel.: (39) 0434567111

AND PRIVATE COMPANIES

Web Site: http://www.imat.it
Sales Range: $25-49.9 Million
Emp.: 50
Metal Products Mfr
N.A.I.C.S.: 332999

LLC MARCEGAGLIA RU (1)
Str B Nizhegorodskaya - Nr 92 B, PO Box 8, 600020, Vladimir, Russia
Tel.: (7) 4922405662
Web Site: http://www.marcegaglia.ru
Steel Products Mfr
N.A.I.C.S.: 331210
Marco Redeghieri *(Gen Mgr)*

La Gaiana S.p.A. (1)
Via X X Settembre 28, 16121, Genoa, Italy
Tel.: (39) 010585760
Web Site: http://www.lagaiana.it
Sales Range: $50-74.9 Million
Emp.: 4
Real Estate Developers
N.A.I.C.S.: 531210

Made
via Bresciani 16, I 46040, Gazoldo degli Ippoliti, Mantova, Italy
Tel.: (39) 03766851
Emp.: 1,400
N.A.I.C.S.: 332919
Arnaldo Barini *(Gen Mgr)*

Marcegaglia Albignasego (1)
via Battaglia 85, 35020, Albignasego, Padova, Italy **(100%)**
Tel.: (39) 049680011
Web Site: http://www.marcegaglia.com
Sales Range: $25-49.9 Million
Emp.: 46
Valve Mfr
N.A.I.C.S.: 332919
Punto Fabio *(Mgr)*

Marcegaglia Buildtech (1)
via Giovanni della Casa 12, 20151, Milan, Italy
Tel.: (39) 02 30 7041
Web Site: http://www.marcegaglia.com
Welded Carbon Steel, Stainless Steel Tubes, Drawn Steel & Colded Rolled Strips Mfr
N.A.I.C.S.: 331513

Marcegaglia Casalmaggiore (1)
S Da Sabbionetana 420, I 26041, Casalmaggiore, Cremona, Italy **(100%)**
Tel.: (39) 03752821
Web Site: http://www.marcegaglia.com
Sales Range: $150-199.9 Million
Emp.: 350
Steel tube Mfr
N.A.I.C.S.: 332919

Marcegaglia China Co., Ltd. (1)
No 1 Marcegaglia Road Guangling Economic Development Zone, 225006, Yangzhou, China
Tel.: (86) 51489996000
Web Site: http://www.marcegaglia.cn
Tube Mfr
N.A.I.C.S.: 331210
Moon Meng *(Mgr-HR & Admin)*

Marcegaglia Contino (1)
via AIDO 3 Contino di Volta Mantovana, I 46049, Mantua, Italy
Tel.: (39) 0376 84601
Web Site: http://www.marcegaglia.com
Metal Products Mfr
N.A.I.C.S.: 332919

Marcegaglia Corsico (1)
via Canova 7/9, Corsico, I 20094, Milan, Italy **(100%)**
Tel.: (39) 02486981
Web Site: http://www.marcegaglia.com
Sales Range: $50-74.9 Million
Emp.: 15
Steel Processor & Machinery Mfr
N.A.I.C.S.: 331221

Marcegaglia Deutschland (1)
Opitzstrasse 12, 40470, Dusseldorf, Germany **(100%)**
Tel.: (49) 2116187810
Web Site: http://www.marcegaglia.com
Sales Range: $50-74.9 Million
Emp.: 11
Steel Products Mfr
N.A.I.C.S.: 332919
Davide Comparini *(Gen Mgr)*

Marcegaglia Engineering Division S.P.A. (1)
Via Ramazzotti 33, 21047, Saronno, Varese, Italy **(100%)**
Tel.: (39) 029601050
Web Site: http://www.marcegagliaimpianti.it
Sales Range: $50-74.9 Million
Emp.: 10
N.A.I.C.S.: 332919

Marcegaglia Finanziaria (1)
Via Bresciani 16, 46040, Gazoldo degli Ippoliti, Italy **(100%)**
Tel.: (39) 03766851
Web Site: http://www.marcegaglia.com
Sales Range: $600-649.9 Million
Emp.: 6,500
Steel & Metal Valve Sales
N.A.I.C.S.: 332919

Marcegaglia Forli (1)
Via Mattei 20, I 47034, Forlimpopoli, Forli, Italy **(100%)**
Tel.: (39) 0543470111
Web Site: http://www.marcegaglia.com
Sales Range: $150-199.9 Million
Emp.: 345
N.A.I.C.S.: 332919

Marcegaglia Iberica (1)
Calle Solsona 3 Santa Perpetua De Mogoda, 08130, Barcelona, Spain **(100%)**
Tel.: (34) 935448011
Web Site: http://www.marcegaglia.com
Welded Carbon Steel & Stainless Steel Tubes, Sheets, Sections, Drawn Steel & Colded Rolled Strips Mfr
N.A.I.C.S.: 331513

Marcegaglia Ireland (1)
AIB Internationl Ctr, PO Box 132 Greystones, Dublin, 1, Ireland **(100%)**
Tel.: (353) 12760854
Web Site: http://www.marcegaglia.com
Sales Range: $50-74.9 Million
Emp.: 1
N.A.I.C.S.: 332919

Marcegaglia Poland Sp Z O O (1)
ul Przemyslowa 1, Ligota Dolna, 46-200, Kluczbork, Poland
Tel.: (48) 77 45 98 200
Web Site: http://www.marcegaglia.pl
Steel Tube Mfr
N.A.I.C.S.: 331210
Filippo Nicoli *(Gen Mgr)*

Marcegaglia Poland Sp Z O O - Praszka Plant (1)
ul Kaliska 72, 46-320, Praszka, Poland
Tel.: (48) 343501500
Steel Tube Mfr
N.A.I.C.S.: 331210

Marcegaglia Ravenna (1)
Via Baiona 141, Ravenna, 48123, Italy **(100%)**
Tel.: (39) 0544516611
Web Site: http://www.marcegaglia.com
Sales Range: $1-4.9 Billion
Emp.: 5,500
Valve Mfr
N.A.I.C.S.: 332919
Aldo Siorini *(Plant Mgr)*

Marcegaglia Romania Srl (1)
Taietura Turcului Nr 47, 400221, Cluj-Napoca, Romania
Tel.: (40) 264560560
Web Site: http://www.marcegaglia.ro
Building Panel Mfr
N.A.I.C.S.: 327390
Ciprian Pop *(Mgr-Sls-Steel Div)*

Marcegaglia S.p.A. (1)
Via Fermi 33, I 33058, San Giorgio di Nogaro, Italy **(100%)**
Tel.: (39) 0431624111
Web Site: http://www.marcegaglia.com
N.A.I.C.S.: 332919

Marcegaglia S.p.A. - BENELUX Plant
Mc-Square offices Stockholm Building 7 019 Leonardo Da Vincilaan 19, 1831, Diegem, Belgium
Tel.: (32) 27190265
Steel Tube Mfr
N.A.I.C.S.: 331210

Marcegaglia S.p.A. - Boltiere Plant (1)
via Marcegaglia 2, Boltiere, 24040, Bergamo, Italy
Tel.: (39) 0354197811
Emp.: 230
Tube Mfr
N.A.I.C.S.: 331210

Marcegaglia S.p.A. - Castel Monastero Plant (1)
Monastero d Ombrone, Castelnuovo Berardenga, 53019, Siena, Italy
Tel.: (39) 0577570570
Web Site: http://www.castelmonastero.com
Steel Tube Mfr
N.A.I.C.S.: 331210

Marcegaglia S.p.A. - ETA Division (1)
via Canova 36, Lainate, 20020, Milan, Italy
Tel.: (39) 029379251
Steel Tube Distr
N.A.I.C.S.: 423510

Marcegaglia S.p.A. - Foggia Plant (1)
loc Pugnochiuso, Vieste, 71019, Foggia, Italy
Tel.: (39) 0884713111
Web Site: http://www.pugnochiuso.com
Steel Tube Mfr
N.A.I.C.S.: 331210

Marcegaglia S.p.A. - Guardrail Division (1)
strada Roveri 4, Pozzolo Formigaro, 15068, Alessandria, Italy
Tel.: (39) 01437761
Tube Mfr
N.A.I.C.S.: 331210

Marcegaglia S.p.A. - LIMA Plant (1)
Avenida Camino Real 1121Oficina 910, San Isidro, Lima, Peru
Tel.: (51) 12222215
Steel Tube Distr
N.A.I.C.S.: 423510

Marcegaglia S.p.A. - LYON Plant (1)
Le Bois des Cotes II RN 6 - n 300, 69760, Limonest, France
Tel.: (33) 478663700
Web Site: http://www.marcegaglia.fr
Steel Tube Mfr
N.A.I.C.S.: 331210

Marcegaglia S.p.A. - Lomagna Plant (1)
via Milano 41, Lomagna, 23871, Lecco, Italy
Tel.: (39) 03992211
Tube Mfr
N.A.I.C.S.: 331210

Marcegaglia S.p.A. - Montechiarugolo Plant (1)
via dell'Industria 7, Basilicanova di Montechiarugolo, 43022, Parma, Italy
Tel.: (39) 0521681231
Tube Mfr
N.A.I.C.S.: 331210

Marcegaglia S.p.A. - San Giorgio di Nogaro Plant (1)
via Enrico Fermi 33, San Giorgio di Nogaro, 33058, Udine, Italy
Tel.: (39) 0431624111
Metal Plate Mfr
N.A.I.C.S.: 332999

Marcegaglia S.p.A. - Sesto al Reghena Plant (1)
via Giotto di Bondone 79/a, Sesto al Reghena, 33079, Pordenone, Italy
Tel.: (39) 043469355264
Tube Mfr
N.A.I.C.S.: 331210

Marcegaglia S.p.A. - Stintino Plant (1)
loc Tonnara Saline, Stintino, 07040, Sassari, Italy
Tel.: (39) 07952231
Tube Mfr
N.A.I.C.S.: 331210

Marcegaglia S.p.A. - TRISIDER Division (1)

MARCHE CORPORATION

via Basse 15, Tezze sul Brenta, 36056, Vicenza, Italy
Tel.: (39) 0424535400
Stainless Steel Distr
N.A.I.C.S.: 423510

Marcegaglia S.p.A. - Teramo Plant (1)
zona Industriale S Atto, 64100, Teramo, Italy
Tel.: (39) 086158176
Tube Mfr
N.A.I.C.S.: 331210

Marcegaglia UK (1)
New Rd, Netherton, Dudley, DY2 8TA, W Midlands, United Kingdom **(100%)**
Tel.: (44) 1384242812
Sales Range: $75-99.9 Million
Emp.: 150
N.A.I.C.S.: 332919
Nigel Grinsell *(Controller)*

Marcegaglia USA, Inc. (1)
1001 E Waterfront Dr, Munhall, PA 15120-1098
Tel.: (412) 462-2185
Web Site: http://www.marcegaglia-usa.com
Sales Range: $75-99.9 Million
Emp.: 130
N.A.I.C.S.: 332919

Morteo Nord (1)
S Da Roveri 4, I 15068, Pozzolo Formigaro, Alessandria, Italy **(100%)**
Tel.: (39) 0001437761
Sales Range: $50-74.9 Million
Emp.: 100
N.A.I.C.S.: 332919

Oskar (1)
Via Lumaca 3, Mezzolara di Budrio, 40054, Bologna, Italy
Tel.: (39) 0518049111
Web Site: http://www.oskaritalia.it
Sales Range: $50-74.9 Million
Emp.: 100
Steel & Metal Valve Sales
N.A.I.C.S.: 332919

Oto Mills USA (1)
10 E Ontario St Ste 472, Chicago, IL 60611
Tel.: (630) 690-7805
Web Site: http://www.otomills.com
Sales Range: $25-49.9 Million
Emp.: 5
Sales Office for Industrial Machinery
N.A.I.C.S.: 333515

Ponteggi Dalmine (1)
Via Giovanni Della Casa 12, Milan, 20151, Italy **(100%)**
Tel.: (39) 02307041
Web Site: http://www.marcegaglia.com
Sales Range: $50-74.9 Million
Emp.: 85
Construction Equipment Sales
N.A.I.C.S.: 333120
Giancarlo Spotti *(CEO)*

Ponteggi Dalmine (1)
Via San Colombano 63, I-26813, Graffignano, Lodi, Italy
Tel.: (39) 037120681
N.A.I.C.S.: 332919

MARCEL JACQUART ET FILS SAS

131 Rue du Bois, 59200, Tourcoing, France
Tel.: (33) 320280170   FR
Web Site: http://www.jacquart.fr
Year Founded: 1949
Sales Range: $25-49.9 Million
Emp.: 120
Mattress & Bedding Mfr
N.A.I.C.S.: 337910
Patrick Dumesnil *(Chm & CEO)*

MARCHE CORPORATION

2-20-14 Hannan-cho, Abeno-ku, Osaka, 545-0021, Japan
Tel.: (81) 666248100
Web Site: https://www.marche.co.jp
Year Founded: 1972
7524—(TKS)
Sales Range: $75-99.9 Million

MARCHE CORPORATION

Marche Corporation—(Continued)
Restaurant Operators
N.A.I.C.S.: 722511
Hirotsugu Kato (Pres & CEO)

MARCHESI ANTINORI S.P.A
Via Cassia per Siena, 133, 50026, Firenze, Italy
Tel.: (39) 05523595
Web Site: https://www.antinori.it
Year Founded: 1385
Wine Mfr
N.A.I.C.S.: 312130

Subsidiaries:

Stag's Leap Wine Cellars, LLC (1)
5766 Silverado Trail, Napa, CA 94558
Tel.: (707) 944-2020
Web Site: http://www.cask23.com
Sales Range: $1-9.9 Million
Emp.: 110
Mfg Wines/Brandy/Spirits
N.A.I.C.S.: 312130
Warren P. Winiarski (Founder)

MARCO CABLES & CONDUCTORS LIMITED
Shop No 100 Opp Bhai Gangaram Market Main Road Ulhasnagar, Thane, 421005, Maharashtra, India
Tel.: (91) 2512530332   In
Web Site: https://marcocables.com
Year Founded: 1989
MARCO—(NSE)
Rev.: $6,906,260
Assets: $8,410,683
Liabilities: $6,226,005
Net Worth: $2,184,678
Earnings: $374,844
Emp.: 79
Fiscal Year-end: 03/31/23
Electrical Equipment Mfr & Distr
N.A.I.C.S.: 333414
Priyanka Vinod Patil (Sec)

MARCO HOLDINGS BERHAD
No 8 & 10 2nd Floor Jalan Segambut, 51200, Kuala Lumpur, Malaysia
Tel.: (60) 22954822
Web Site: https://marco-groups.com
MARCO—(KLS)
Rev.: $37,728,633
Assets: $53,070,995
Liabilities: $5,283,565
Net Worth: $47,787,430
Earnings: $4,168,141
Emp.: 100
Fiscal Year-end: 12/31/22
Timepiece & Jewelry Mfr
N.A.I.C.S.: 334519
Shien Yin Tan (Sec)

Subsidiaries:

Marco Corporation (M) Sdn. Bhd. (1)
25th Floor Menara JKG No 282 Jalan Raja Laut, 50350, Kuala Lumpur, Malaysia
Tel.: (60) 32 777 8222
Web Site: http://www.marco.com.my
Sales Range: $25-49.9 Million
Watch Mfr
N.A.I.C.S.: 334519

Marco Worldwide Sdn. Bhd. (1)
25th Floor Menara Jkg No 282 Jalan Raja Laut, 50350, Kuala Lumpur, Malaysia
Tel.: (60) 327778222
Caterpillar Timepiece Whslr
N.A.I.C.S.: 423940

MARCO POLO HOTELS MANAGEMENT LIMITED
5/F Marco Polo Hongkong Hotel Harbour City, Kowloon, China (Hong Kong)
Tel.: (852) 21187232
Web Site: http://www.marcopolohotels.com

Sales Range: $75-99.9 Million
Emp.: 60
Hotel Management & Operation Services
N.A.I.C.S.: 721110
Kitty Liu (Dir-Sls-Shanghai)

MARCO POLO MARINE LTD.
66 Kallang Pudding Road 05-01 Hor Kew Business Centre, Singapore, 349324, Singapore
Tel.: (65) 67412545
Web Site: https://marcopolomarine.com.sg
Year Founded: 1991
5LY—(SES)
Rev.: $94,202,297
Assets: $169,752,501
Liabilities: $33,488,700
Net Worth: $136,263,801
Earnings: $19,104,113
Fiscal Year-end: 09/30/23
Shipyard Services
N.A.I.C.S.: 336611
Liely Lee (Exec Dir)

Subsidiaries:

PT. Marcopolo Shipyard (1)
Batu Aji Kav Lama Dapur 12, Batam, Indonesia
Tel.: (62) 7787368800
Web Site: http://www.marcopoloshipyard.com
Ship Building Services
N.A.I.C.S.: 336611
K. S. Chan (Deputy Gen Mgr-Comml)

MARCONS SA
Bdul Bucuresti 27 Maramures, Baia Mare, Romania
Tel.: (40) 262 220040
Sales Range: $10-24.9 Million
Emp.: 27
Real Estate Prorperty Leasing Services
N.A.I.C.S.: 531190
Cornel Gherman (Pres & Gen Mgr)

MARCOPOLO S.A.
Av Rio Branco 4889 Bairro Ana Rech, Caxias do Sul, 95060-145, RS, Brazil
Tel.: (55) 5421014000   BR
Web Site: https://www.marcopolo.com.br
Year Founded: 1949
POMO3—(BRAZ)
Rev.: $1,068,192,328
Assets: $1,285,850,799
Liabilities: $701,955,156
Net Worth: $583,895,643
Earnings: $52,494,140
Emp.: 14,187
Fiscal Year-end: 12/31/19
Holding Company; Commercial Bus Body, Light Commercial Motor Vehicle Parts & Components & Other Plastic Products Mfr
N.A.I.C.S.: 551112

Subsidiaries:

Banco Moneo SA (1)
Av Marcopolo 280 Room 101, 95086 200, Caxias do Sul, Rio Grande do Sul, Brazil
Tel.: (55) 5429911000
Web Site: http://www.bancomoneo.com.br
Sales Range: $1-4.9 Billion
Emp.: 13,000
Financial Services
N.A.I.C.S.: 523999

Brasa Middle East FZE (1)
PO Box 17939, Jebel Ali, United Arab Emirates
Tel.: (971) 4 8833680
Web Site: http://www.marcopolo.br
Emp.: 10
Automobile Parts Distr
N.A.I.C.S.: 423140

Michael Mensch (Gen Mgr)

Ciferal Industria de Onibus Ltda. (1)
Rua Pastor Avelino de Souza 2064, Xerem, Duque de Caxias, Brazil
Tel.: (55) 21 2679 1011
Bus Mfr
N.A.I.C.S.: 336110

GB Polo Bus Manufacturing Company (1)
Economic & Industrial Zone, North West Suez Gulf, Suez, Egypt
Tel.: (20) 2 4215 0790
Bus Mfr; Joint Venture of Marcopolo S.A. & Ghabbour Auto S.A.E.
N.A.I.C.S.: 336110

Marcopolo Auto Components Co., Ltd (1)
167 Cheng Jiang Zhong Road, Jiangyin, 214400, Jiangsu, China
Tel.: (86) 51086406336
Web Site: http://www.marcopolochina.com
Sales Range: $50-74.9 Million
Emp.: 200
Bus Mfr
N.A.I.C.S.: 336110
Wang Chong (Mng Dir)

Marcopolo South Africa Pty. Ltd. (1)
2 Barlow Rd Industrial West, Germiston, 1400, South Africa
Tel.: (27) 114180800
Web Site: http://www.marcopolo.br
Sales Range: $200-249.9 Million
Emp.: 600
Bus Mfr
N.A.I.C.S.: 336110
Joeo Letur (Mng Dir)

Polomex S.A. de C.V. (1)
Carretera a Garcia Km 6.5 B Industrial Zone, El Obispo Garcia, 66000, Monterrey, Mexico
Tel.: (52) 8181302300
Web Site: http://www.marcopolo.br
Bus Mfr
N.A.I.C.S.: 336110

Superpolo S.A. (1)
Km 1.6 Via Siberia, Cota, Cundinamarca, Colombia   (50%)
Tel.: (57) 1 8776399
Web Site: http://www.superpolo.com.co
Bus Mfr
N.A.I.C.S.: 336110

MARCVENTURES HOLDINGS, INC.
4th Floor Citibank Center, Paseo de Roxas, Makati, 8741, Philippines
Tel.: (63) 28314479
Web Site: https://www.marcventures.com
Year Founded: 1957
MARC—(PHI)
Rev.: $36,483,629
Assets: $107,645,412
Liabilities: $22,284,400
Net Worth: $85,361,012
Earnings: $4,130,470
Emp.: 320
Fiscal Year-end: 12/31/23
Holding Company; Nickel Mining Services
N.A.I.C.S.: 551112
Rolando S. Santos (Treas & Sr VP-Fin & Admin)

MARDIA SAMYOUNG CAPILLARY TUBES COMPANY LIMITED
J-55 MIDC Industrial Area, Tarapur Boisar, Thane, 401 506, Maharashtra, India
Tel.: (91) 22 24969685
Year Founded: 1992
Sales Range: Less than $1 Million
Metal Product Mfr & Distr
N.A.I.C.S.: 327910
Ravindra Mardia (Chm & Mng Dir)

INTERNATIONAL PUBLIC

MARDIN CIMENTO SANAYI VE TICARET A.S.
Savur Yolu 6 Km, 47019, Mardin, Turkiye
Tel.: (90) 4822266430
Web Site: http://www.mardincimento.com.tr
Year Founded: 1969
Cement Mfr
N.A.I.C.S.: 327310
Recep Karakose (Mgr-Production & R&D)

MARECHALE CAPITAL PLC
46 New Broad Street, London, EC2M 1JH, United Kingdom
Tel.: (44) 2076285582
Web Site: https://www.marechalecapital.com
MAC—(AIM)
Rev.: $845,748
Assets: $4,329,723
Liabilities: $100,985
Net Worth: $4,228,738
Earnings: ($227,216)
Fiscal Year-end: 04/30/24
Investment Banking Services
N.A.I.C.S.: 523150
Mark Warde-Norbury (Chm)

MAREL HF
Austurhraun 9, 210, Gardabaer, Iceland
Tel.: (354) 5638000   IS
Web Site: https://www.marel.com
Year Founded: 1983
MAREL—(ICE)
Rev.: $1,900,209,736
Assets: $2,869,853,185
Liabilities: $1,720,057,402
Net Worth: $1,149,795,783
Earnings: $34,220,113
Emp.: 7,500
Fiscal Year-end: 12/31/23
Food Processing Machinery & Equipment
N.A.I.C.S.: 333241
Arnar Thor Masson (Vice Chm)

Subsidiaries:

Butina A/S (1)
Ydervang 5, 4300, Holbaek, Denmark
Tel.: (45) 59450450
Web Site: http://www.butina.eu
Food Processing Machinery & Equipment Mfr
N.A.I.C.S.: 333241
Steen Weihe (Mgr-R&D & Engrg)

MAJA-Maschinenfabrik Hermann Schill GmbH (1)
Hermann-Schill-Strasse 1, Goldscheuer, 77694, Kehl, Germany
Tel.: (49) 78541840
Web Site: https://marel.com
Emp.: 200
Meat Processing Equipment Mfr
N.A.I.C.S.: 333241
Farid Maqsudi (Mgr-Area Sls)

Marel A/S (1)
PO Pedersens Vej 18, Aarhus N, 8200, Aarhus, Denmark
Tel.: (45) 89304444
Food Processing Machinery & Equipment Mfr
N.A.I.C.S.: 333241
Morten Munk Rasmussen (Mgr-Fin)

Marel Australia Pty. Ltd. (1)
42 Borthwick Ave, Murarrie, 4172, QLD, Australia
Tel.: (61) 1800462735
Food Processing Machinery & Equipment Mfr
N.A.I.C.S.: 333241

Marel Brasil Commercial e Industrial Ltda (1)
Av Comendador Leopoldo Dedini 150, 13422-210, Piracicaba, Brazil
Tel.: (55) 1934149000

AND PRIVATE COMPANIES

Food Processing Machinery & Equipment Mfr
N.A.I.C.S.: 333241

Marel Carnitech (Thailand) Ltd. (1)
No 97 Soi Rama IX 59 Rama IX Rd, Pattanakarn sub-district Suanluang district, Bangkok, 10250, Thailand
Tel.: (66) 24020600
Web Site: http://www.marel.com
Sales Range: $25-49.9 Million
Emp.: 13
Food Product Machinery Mfr
N.A.I.C.S.: 333241

Marel Chile S.A. (1)
Camino Lo Boza 107 Modulo A13 Flex Center, Pudahuel, Santiago, Chile
Tel.: (56) 652754138
Web Site: http://www.marel.cl
Sales Range: $25-49.9 Million
Emp.: 12
Food Products Machinery
N.A.I.C.S.: 333241

Marel Food Systems (1)
R4-53 Hung Phuoc 3 Phu My Hung, Tan Phong Ward District, Ho Chi Minh City, Q1, Vietnam
Tel.: (84) 389868778
Fish & Seafood Whslr
N.A.I.C.S.: 424460

Marel Food Systems A/S (1)
PO Pedersens veg 8200, Stovring, 9530, Arhus, Denmark
Tel.: (45) 99864100
Web Site: http://www.marel.dk
Sales Range: $25-49.9 Million
Emp.: 13
Food Product Machinery Mfr
N.A.I.C.S.: 333241

Marel Food Systems GB Ltd. (1)
Wincolls Rd Federal Industrial Park, Colchester, CO49HW, Essex, United Kingdom
Tel.: (44) 1162843500
Web Site: http://www.scanvaegt.co.uk
Snack Food Mfr
N.A.I.C.S.: 311919

Marel Food Systems GmbH (1)
Hakenbusch 9, 49078, Osnabruck, Germany
Tel.: (49) 54 150 0970
Web Site: https://www.marel.com
Sales Range: $10-24.9 Million
Emp.: 45
Waste Management Services
N.A.I.C.S.: 562998

Marel Food Systems LLC (1)
Marshala Proshlyakova street Building 30 Office 602, 123458, Moscow, Russia
Tel.: (7) 4952280700
Web Site: http://www.marel.com
Food Service Contractors
N.A.I.C.S.: 722310

Marel Food Systems Sarl (1)
ZI Du Dresseve, 56150, Baud, France
Tel.: (33) 297391616
Web Site: http://marel.com
Industrial Machinery & Equipment Whslr
N.A.I.C.S.: 423830

Marel Food Systems Sp. z o.o. (1)
Ul Oplotek 29, 01-940, Warsaw, Poland
Tel.: (48) 225695280
Web Site: http://www.marelfoodsystems.pl
Sales Range: $25-49.9 Million
Emp.: 50
Fish & Seafood Whslr
N.A.I.C.S.: 424460

Marel France S.A.R.L. (1)
ZI Du Dresseve, 56150, Baud, 56150, France
Tel.: (33) 297391616
Food Processing Machinery & Equipment Mfr
N.A.I.C.S.: 333241

Marel Further Processing B.V. (1)
Handelstraat 3, 5831 AV, Boxmeer, 5831 AV, Netherlands
Tel.: (31) 485586111
Food Processing Machinery & Equipment Mfr
N.A.I.C.S.: 333241

Marel GmbH & Co. KG (1)
Hakenbusch 9, 49078, Osnabruck, Germany
Tel.: (49) 541500970
Web Site: http://marel.com
Sales Range: $25-49.9 Million
Farm Machinery & Equipment Mfr
N.A.I.C.S.: 333111

Marel GmbH & Co. KG (1)
Hook Bush 9, Osnabruck, 49078, Germany
Tel.: (49) 541500970
Food Processing Machinery & Equipment Mfr
N.A.I.C.S.: 333241

Marel Holding B.V. (1)
Handelstraat 3, 5831 AV, Boxmeer, 5831 AV, Netherlands
Tel.: (31) 485586111
Food Processing Machinery & Equipment Mfr
N.A.I.C.S.: 333241

Marel Iceland ehf. (1)
Austurhraun 9, 210, Gardabaer, Iceland
Tel.: (354) 5638000
Food Processing Machinery & Equipment Mfr
N.A.I.C.S.: 333241
Arnbjorn Eyporsson (Mgr-Technical)

Marel Italia S.r.l. (1)
Piazza Francesco Buffoni 5, 21013, Gallarate, VA, Italy
Tel.: (39) 0331 126 0750
Web Site: http://marel.com
Sales Range: $25-49.9 Million
Meat Processing Equipment Retailer
N.A.I.C.S.: 333241

Marel New Zealand Ltd (1)
Unit B 17 Hobill Avenue, Auckland, 2104, New Zealand
Tel.: (64) 92630366
Web Site: http://www.marel.com
Sales Range: $25-49.9 Million
Emp.: 20
Food Mfr
N.A.I.C.S.: 311999

Marel Norge AS (1)
Vestbygata 55 B, 2003, Lillestrom, 2003, Norway
Tel.: (47) 64838000
Food Processing Machinery & Equipment Mfr
N.A.I.C.S.: 333241

Marel Polska Sp. z.o.o. (1)
Amsterdam Office Building Lobby II Ul Poleczki 35, 02-822, Warsaw, Poland
Tel.: (48) 224902101
Food Processing Machinery & Equipment Mfr
N.A.I.C.S.: 333241
Adam Skrzypko (Mgr-Technical Svc)

Marel Poultry B.V. (1)
PO Box 118, 5830 AC, Boxmeer, Netherlands
Tel.: (31) 485586111
Poultry Meat & Fish Processing Services
N.A.I.C.S.: 114111

Marel Red Meat B.V. (1)
PO Box 160, 7130 AD, Lichtenvoorde, Netherlands
Tel.: (31) 544390500
Food Processing Equipment Mfr & Distr
N.A.I.C.S.: 333241

Marel Red Meat Slaughtering B.V. (1)
Albert Schweitzerstraat 33, 7131 PG, Lichtenvoorde, Netherlands
Tel.: (31) 544390500
Web Site: http://marel.com
Advanced Slaughtering Systems & Logistic Systems for the Meat Processing Industry
N.A.I.C.S.: 311611
Mark Pillen (Mgr-Fabrication)

Marel Red Meat Slaughtering B.V. (1)
Albert Schweitzerstraat 33, Lichtenvoorde, 7130 AD, Netherlands
Tel.: (31) 544390500
Meat Processing Equipment Mfr
N.A.I.C.S.: 333241

Mark Pillen (Mgr-Fabrication)

Marel Salmon AS (1)
Juelstrupparken 14 Newline, 9400, Stovring, Denmark
Tel.: (45) 98921511
Web Site: http://www.marelsalmon.com
Sales Range: $50-74.9 Million
Emp.: 200
Meat & Meat Product Whslr
N.A.I.C.S.: 424470
Lars Joeker (Chm)

Marel Singapore Pte. Ltd.-Freezing & Temperature Division (1)
21 Jurong Gateway Road 04-05 CPF Jurong Building, Singapore, 608546, Singapore
Tel.: (65) 62812878
Emp.: 8
Frozen & Temperature Processing & Equipment Mfr
N.A.I.C.S.: 311615
Ann Tan (Gen Mgr)

Marel Spain & Portugal S.L. (1)
C/de la Pagesia 22-24, Rubi, Barcelona, 08191, Spain
Tel.: (34) 931223437
Food Processing Machinery & Equipment Mfr
N.A.I.C.S.: 333241

Marel Stork Poultry Processing B.V. (1)
Handelstraat 3, 5831 AV, Boxmeer, Netherlands
Tel.: (31) 48 558 6111
Web Site: http://www.storkpoultry.com
Poultry Processing
N.A.I.C.S.: 311615

Marel Sytems AS (1)
Vestbygata 55B, Lillestrom, 2003, Skedsmokorset, Norway
Tel.: (47) 64838000
Web Site: http://www.marel.com
Sales Range: $25-49.9 Million
Oil & Gas Field Machinery & Equipment Mfr
N.A.I.C.S.: 333132

Marel Townsend Further Processing (1)
401 SW 7th St, Des Moines, IA 50309
Tel.: (515) 265-8181
Web Site: http://www.marel.com
Meat Processing Equipment Mfr
N.A.I.C.S.: 333241

Marel, Inc. (1)
8145 Flint St, Lenexa, KS 66214
Tel.: (913) 888-9110
Web Site: http://www.marel.com
Sales Range: $25-49.9 Million
Fish & Seafood Markets
N.A.I.C.S.: 445250
Debra Bernas (CFO)

Division (Domestic):

Marel Seattle Inc. (2)
2001 W Garfield Terminal 91 Bldg A1, Seattle, WA 98119
Tel.: (206) 781-1827
Web Site: http://www.marel.com
Sales Range: $50-74.9 Million
Emp.: 75
Processing Solutions for Salmon, Whitefish, Shellfish, Surimi, Freezing Solutions, Scales, Software Solutions & Customized Equipment & Service
N.A.I.C.S.: 311710

Scanvaegt AB (1)
Datavagen 12, Askim, 436 32, Gothenburg, Sweden
Tel.: (46) 317090707
Web Site: http://www.scanvaegt.com
General Purpose Machinery Mfr
N.A.I.C.S.: 333998

Scanvaegt International A/S (1)
Johan Gutenbergsvej 5-9, 8200, Arhus, Denmark
Tel.: (45) 86785500
Web Site: http://www.scanvaegt.dk
Sales Range: $50-74.9 Million
Food Processing Machinery Mfr
N.A.I.C.S.: 333998

Stork Titan B.V. (1)
Handelstraat 3, 5831 AV, Boxmeer, Netherlands
Tel.: (31) 485586122
Web Site: http://www.storkfoodsystems.com
Sales Range: $150-199.9 Million
Emp.: 1,000
Poultry Processing
N.A.I.C.S.: 311615

Valka ehf. (1)
Vesturvor 29, 200, Kopavogur, Iceland
Tel.: (354) 4300601
Food Processing Equipment Mfr & Distr
N.A.I.C.S.: 333241

Wenger Manufacturing Inc. (1)
15 Commerce Dr, Sabetha, KS 66534-1825
Tel.: (785) 284-2133
Web Site: https://www.wenger.com
Sales Range: $25-49.9 Million
Emp.: 250
Mfr of Commercial Extrusion Processing Systems
N.A.I.C.S.: 333241

MARESCO LIMITED

171 Basaltic Road Unit 2, Concord, L4K 1G4, ON, Canada
Tel.: (905) 669-5700
Web Site:
http://www.marescolimited.com
Year Founded: 1974
Rev.: $13,100,000
Emp.: 45
Building Construction Services
N.A.I.C.S.: 541330
Helmut Kruger (Pres)

MARETERRA GROUP HOLDING SRL

Via Alberto Caroncini 45, Rome, 00197, Italy
Tel.: (39) 0636306351
Energy Investment Group
N.A.I.C.S.: 523940

MARFIN INVESTMENT GROUP HOLDINGS S.A.

10 Eleftheriou Venizelou str, 106 71, Athens, Greece
Tel.: (30) 2103504000
Web Site:
https://www.marfininvestment.com
MIG—(ATH)
Rev.: $8,445,685
Assets: $236,361,099
Liabilities: $105,548,519
Net Worth: $130,812,581
Earnings: $4,290,468
Emp.: 56
Fiscal Year-end: 12/31/23
Holding Company
N.A.I.C.S.: 551112
Panagiotis Throuvalas (Chm)

Subsidiaries:

Alysis Ltd. (1)
Delta Velestino, 375 00, Volos, Magnesia, Greece
Tel.: (30) 2425024248
Web Site: http://www.analysis-ltd.com.gr
Electric Equipment Mfr
N.A.I.C.S.: 335999

Barba Stathis S.A. (1)
A5 St, Industrial Area Thessaloniki, 570 22, Sindos, Greece
Tel.: (30) 2310798483
Web Site: http://www.barbastathis.com
Nutritional Food Distr
N.A.I.C.S.: 456191
Zeta Papadopoulou (Mgr-Social Media)

Delta Greek Foods USA Inc. (1)
9204 Baltimore Ave, College Park, MD 20740
Tel.: (240) 764-9095
Web Site: http://www.greekfoodsusa.com
Food Products Distr
N.A.I.C.S.: 424490

Hellenic Catering S.A. (1)

MARFIN INVESTMENT GROUP HOLDINGS S.A.

Marfin Investment Group Holdings S.A.—(Continued)
1st - Industrial Zone, 570 22, Thessaloniki, Greece
Tel.: (30) 2310970700
Web Site: http://helleniccatering.gr
Emp.: 286
Catering Services
N.A.I.C.S.: 722320
Nikos Markopoulos (Gen Mgr)

Olympic Engineering S.A. (1)
Anthens international airport Elllis venizelos building 56, Koropi, 194 00, Spata, Greece
Tel.: (30) 2103550509
Sales Range: $25-49.9 Million
Emp.: 3
Aircraft Repair & Maintenance Services
N.A.I.C.S.: 488190

Olympic Handling S.A (1)
1st Km Koropiou Varis Ave Ifaistou Street, PO Box 19400, Spata, Attica, Greece
Tel.: (30) 2106607310
Web Site: http://www.olympichandling.com
Sales Range: $200-249.9 Million
Emp.: 1,000
Cargo Handling Services
N.A.I.C.S.: 488119
Iosif Mastorantonakis (CEO)

Professional Computer Services S.A. (1)
Lochagou Dedousi 1, Cholargos, 155 62, Athens, Greece
Tel.: (30) 2106266900
Web Site: http://www.pcs.gr
Emp.: 35
Banking & Financial Software Development Services
N.A.I.C.S.: 541511
George Xenofos (CEO)

Singular Logic S.A. (1)
Achaias 3 & Trizinias st, Kifissia, 145 64, Athens, Greece
Tel.: (30) 2106266500
Web Site: http://portal.singularlogic.eu
Emp.: 300
Software & Integrated Information Technology Solutions
N.A.I.C.S.: 541511

SingularLogic Business Services S.A. (1)
Achaias 3 & Trizinias Street, PO Box 14234, Nea Ionia, Nea Kifissia, 14564, Greece
Tel.: (30) 210 62 66 800
Web Site: http://www.singularlogic.eu
Business Management Software Development Services
N.A.I.C.S.: 541511
John Theodoropoulos (CEO)

SingularLogic Integrator S.A. (1)
Alexandrou Panagouli Str and Sinisioglou Str, Nea Ionia, 142 34, Athens, Greece
Tel.: (30) 2106266100
Web Site: http://www.singularlogic.eu
Computer Software Consulting Services
N.A.I.C.S.: 541512
Marica Labrou (CEO)

Singularlogic Cyprus Ltd. (1)
70 Kyrillou Loukareos, PO Box 70225, Kato Polemidia, 4156, Limassol, Cyprus
Tel.: (357) 25818044
System Integration Services
N.A.I.C.S.: 541512

System Soft S.A. (1)
61 Lagoumitzi Street, 117 44, Athens, Greece
Tel.: (30) 2109020002
Web Site: http://www.systemsoft.gr
Sales Range: $25-49.9 Million
Emp.: 15
Enterprise Resource Planning Software Development Services
N.A.I.C.S.: 541511

Vivartia Holdings S.A. (1)
Everest A E International Airport Eleftherios Venizelos Building 14B, 151 23, Spata, Greece **(92.08%)**
Tel.: (30) 2103494000
Web Site: http://www.vivartia.com
Sales Range: $1-4.9 Billion
Emp.: 7,000
Holding Company; Dairy, Beverages, Frozen Foods Mfr & Marketer
N.A.I.C.S.: 551112

Subsidiary (Non-US):

Everest Holdings & Investments S.A. (2)
Ul Stawki 2, 00-193, Warsaw, Poland
Tel.: (48) 221100025
Web Site:
http://www.everestinvestments.com
Investment Services
N.A.I.C.S.: 523999

Subsidiary (Non-US):

Varelas S.A. (3)
4 Eleftherias Street, 145 64, Kifissia, Greece
Tel.: (30) 2105281900
Web Site: http://www.varelas.gr
Pharmaceutical & Chemical Distr
N.A.I.C.S.: 424690

MARFOGLIA CONSTRUCTION INC.
9031 Parkway Blvd, Anjou, H1J 1N4, QC, Canada
Tel.: (514) 325-8700
Web Site: http://www.marfoglia.ca
Rev.: $13,282,870
Emp.: 55
Interior Decoration & Design Services
N.A.I.C.S.: 541410
Michael Marfoglia (Pres)

MARFRIG GLOBAL FOODS S.A.
Av Queiroz Filho 1 560 Sabia Tower-3 Floor, Vila Hamburguesa, Sao Paulo, 05319-000, SP, Brazil
Tel.: (55) 1137928600 BR
Web Site: https://ri.marfrig.com.br
Year Founded: 1986
MRFG3—(BRAZ)
Rev.: $12,973,324,527
Assets: $4,054,079,373
Liabilities: $3,378,500,761
Net Worth: $675,578,612
Earnings: $871,056,297
Emp.: 32,010
Fiscal Year-end: 12/31/20
Food Products Mfr
N.A.I.C.S.: 311813
Marcos Antonio M. dos Santos (Chm)

Subsidiaries:

Marfood USA, Inc. (1)
21655 Trolley Industrial Dr, Taylor, MI 48180
Tel.: (313) 292-4100
Web Site: http://www.marfoodusa.com
Emp.: 25
Fresh & Frozen Meat Products Mfr & Distr
N.A.I.C.S.: 311612
Fernando Momente (VP)

Marfrig Chile S.A. (1)
Camino La Vara 03645, San Bernardo, 750-0014, Santiago, Chile
Tel.: (56) 2 2 4132400
Web Site: http://www.marfrig.cl
Poultry Processing Services
N.A.I.C.S.: 311615

Subsidiary (Domestic):

Frigorifico Patagonia S.A. (2)
Lautaro Navarro 375, Punta Arenas, Chile
Tel.: (56) 61 2 24 10 92
Web Site:
http://www.frigorificopatagonia.com
Animal Slaughtering Services
N.A.I.C.S.: 311611
Juan Gysling (Pres)

National Beef Packing Company, LLC (1)
12200 N Ambassador Dr Ste 500, Kansas City, MO 64163-1244 **(81.73%)**
Tel.: (800) 449-2333
Web Site: http://www.nationalbeef.com
Meat Packing Plants
N.A.I.C.S.: 311611
Timothy M. Klein (CEO)

Subsidiary (Domestic):

Iowa Premium, LLC (2)
3337 L Ave, Tama, IA 52339
Tel.: (641) 484-2220
Web Site: http://www.iowapremium.com
Animal Feed Mfr
N.A.I.C.S.: 311119

Kansas City Steak Company, LLC (2)
100 Osage Ave, Kansas City, KS 66105
Tel.: (800) 524-1844
Web Site: http://www.kansascitysteaks.com
Meats & Meat Products Whslr
N.A.I.C.S.: 424470

Plant (Domestic):

National Beef - Dodge City (2)
2000 E Trail St, Dodge City, KS 67801-9018
Tel.: (620) 227-7135
Web Site: http://www.nationalbeef.com
Meat Packing
N.A.I.C.S.: 311611

National Beef - Liberal (2)
1501 E 8th St, Liberal, KS 67901
Tel.: (620) 624-1851
Web Site: http://www.nationalbeef.com
Meat Packing
N.A.I.C.S.: 311611

Subsidiary (Domestic):

National Beef Leathers, LLC (2)
205 Florence Rd, Saint Joseph, MO 64504-0459
Tel.: (816) 279-7468
Leather Tanning Services
N.A.I.C.S.: 316110
Robert Hein (Sr VP)

National Carriers, Inc. (2)
3925 Carbon Rd, Irving, TX 75038
Tel.: (800) 835-9180
Web Site: http://www.nationalcarriers.com
Trucking Service
N.A.I.C.S.: 484110

Weston Importers Ltd (1)
Kitchen Range Building Kingfisher Way, Huntingdon, PE29 6FJ, Cambridgeshire, United Kingdom
Tel.: (44) 1480 414 112
Meat Product Distr
N.A.I.C.S.: 424470

MARG LTD
Sri Sai Subhodhaya Apartments No 57/2B East Coast Road, Thiruvanmiyur, Chennai, 600 041, Tamil Nadu, India
Tel.: (91) 4424541111
Web Site:
https://www.marggroup.com
530543—(BOM)
Rev.: $5,045,040
Assets: $462,808,710
Liabilities: $522,212,145
Net Worth: ($59,403,435)
Earnings: ($1,781,325)
Emp.: 29
Fiscal Year-end: 03/31/21
Construction Housing
N.A.I.C.S.: 236117
G. R. K. Reddy (Chm & Mng Dir)

Subsidiaries:

Akarsh Constructions Private Limited (1)
575 8th Main MC Road Vijay Nagar, Bengaluru, 560040, India
Tel.: (91) 8023402350
Sales Range: $25-49.9 Million
Emp.: 8
Building Contractors
N.A.I.C.S.: 236220

New Chennai Township Private Limited (1)
392 & 393 Rajiv Gandhi Salai, Kotivakkam, Chennai, 600041, India
Tel.: (91) 4424542311
Web Site:
http://www.margswarnabhoomi.com
Sales Range: $75-99.9 Million
Emp.: 300
Engineeering Services
N.A.I.C.S.: 541330
G. R. K. Reddy (Mng Dir)

Trusted Properties (KPO) Private Limited (1)
4/318 Marg Axis Old Mahabalipuram Rd, Kottivakam, Chennai, 600041, India
Tel.: (91) 9003097462
Sales Range: $50-74.9 Million
Emp.: 6
Real Estate Outsourcing Agencies
N.A.I.C.S.: 531210

MARG TECHNO PROJECTS LIMITED
406 Royal Trade Centre Opp Star Bazar Adajan, Surat, 395 009, India
Tel.: (91) 2612782501 In
Web Site:
http://www.margtechno.com
Year Founded: 1993
540254—(BOM)
Rev.: $609,868
Assets: $3,143,277
Liabilities: $2,351,849
Net Worth: $791,427
Earnings: $59,013
Emp.: 8
Fiscal Year-end: 03/31/23
Finance Management Services
N.A.I.C.S.: 522291
Arun Madhavan Nair (Mng Dir)

MARGANEC ZHAIREMA JSC
Saransk Highway 8, Karaganda region Qazybek bi district, 100019, Karaganda, Kazakhstan
Tel.: (7) 212930500
MNZH—(KAZ)
Assets: $13,272,109
Liabilities: $3,303,685
Net Worth: $9,968,424
Earnings: ($563,074)
Fiscal Year-end: 12/31/20
Non-ferrous Metal Mining Services
N.A.I.C.S.: 212290
Nurlanov Abaj (CEO & Gen Dir)

MARGARET LAKE DIAMONDS INC.
Suite 303 - 1080 Howe Street, PO Box 11121, Vancouver, V6Z 2T1, BC, Canada
Tel.: (604) 684-2180 BC
Web Site:
http://www.margaretlakediamonds.ca
Year Founded: 2011
DIA—(TSXV)
Assets: $115,153
Liabilities: $372,846
Net Worth: ($257,693)
Earnings: ($896,909)
Fiscal Year-end: 05/31/24
Investment Services
N.A.I.C.S.: 523999
Jared Lazerson (CEO)

MARGO FINANCE LIMITED
Office No 3 Plot No 266 Village Alte Kumbhoj Road, Taluka Hatkanangale, Kolhapur, 416109, Maharashtra, India
Tel.: (91) 2302463100 In
Web Site:
https://www.margofinance.com
Year Founded: 1991
500206—(BOM)
Rev.: $78,419
Assets: $11,310,062
Liabilities: $2,689,569
Net Worth: $8,620,494
Earnings: $22,782
Emp.: 2

AND PRIVATE COMPANIES

Fiscal Year-end: 03/31/21
Financial Management Services
N.A.I.C.S.: 541611
Dass Maheshwari *(CFO & Dir-Fin)*

MARI PETROLEUM COMPANY LIMITED
21 Mauve Area 3rd Road G-10/4, PO Box 1614, Islamabad, 44000, Pakistan
Tel.: (92) 518020200
Web Site: https://www.mpcl.com.pk
Year Founded: 1957
MARI—(PSX)
Rev.: $513,521,443
Assets: $933,897,886
Liabilities: $216,434,447
Net Worth: $717,463,439
Earnings: $195,272,885
Emp.: 1,293
Fiscal Year-end: 06/30/21
Crude Oil Extraction Services
N.A.I.C.S.: 211120
Assad Rabbani *(Sec & Gen Mgr-Corp Affairs)*

MARIA MALLABAND CARE GROUP LTD.
Westcourt Gelderd Road, Leeds, LS12 6DB, United Kingdom
Tel.: (44) 113 238 2690
Web Site: http://www.mmcgcarehomes.co.uk
Year Founded: 1996
Sales Range: $50-74.9 Million
Emp.: 1,600
Nursing Home Operator
N.A.I.C.S.: 623110
Philip Burgan *(Founder, Chm & CEO)*

MARIBORSKA LIVARNA MARIBOR, D.D.
Oresko Nabrezje 9, 2000, Maribor, Slovenia
Tel.: (386) 22346100
Web Site: http://www.mlm-mb.si
Year Founded: 1924
Sales Range: $50-74.9 Million
Emp.: 1,011
Metal Products Mfr
N.A.I.C.S.: 331314
Davor Senija *(Chm-Mgmt Bd)*

Subsidiaries:

MLM Armal, d.o.o (1)
Ul Kapetant Misina 16, 11000, Belgrade, Serbia (100%)
Tel.: (381) 11 180967
Metal Forging & Stamping; Radiators & Central Heating Boilers Mfr; Taps & Valves Mfr; Machine Tool Mfr; Heating Products, Pipes, Valves, Radiators & Central Heating Boilers Whslr & Sales
N.A.I.C.S.: 332111

MLM Storitv d.o.o (1)
Oresko Nabrezje 9, 2001, Maribor, Slovenia (100%)
Tel.: (386) 22346100
Web Site: http://www.mlm-storitv.com
Sales Range: $100-124.9 Million
Emp.: 130
Metal Forging & Stamping; Radiators & Central Heating Boilers Mfr; Taps & Valves Mfr; Machine Tool Mfr; Electrical, Plumbing, Gas & Sanitary Installer; Design & Engineering Consulting Services
N.A.I.C.S.: 332111

MLM Vertriebs GmbH (1)
Mozartstrasse 12, 97753, Karlstadt, Germany (100%)
Tel.: (49) 935379060
Semi-Finished & Non-Ferrous Products Wholesale Distr & Sales
N.A.I.C.S.: 423510

MARICO KAYA ENTERPRISES LIMITED
9th Floor Grande Palladium 175 CST Road Kalina, Santacruz East, Mumbai, 400098, Maharashtra, India
Tel.: (91) 22 6648 0279
Web Site: http://www.maricokaya.com
Hair & Skin Care Products Distr
N.A.I.C.S.: 424210
Harsh Mariwala *(Chm & Mng Dir)*

MARICO LIMITED
7th Floor Grande Palladium 175 CST Road Kalina, Santacruz East, Mumbai, 400 098, India
Tel.: (91) 2266480480
Web Site: https://www.marico.com
531642—(BOM)
Rev.: $1,200,849,600
Assets: $841,855,200
Liabilities: $362,388,000
Net Worth: $479,467,200
Earnings: $160,226,400
Emp.: 1,806
Fiscal Year-end: 03/31/23
Hair & Skin Care Products & Services
N.A.I.C.S.: 325620
Hemangi Ghag *(Officer-Compliance & Sec)*

Subsidiaries:

MBL Industries Limited (1)
Media House B 86/1 Okhla Industrial Estate Phase II, Delhi, 110020, India
Tel.: (91) 1141613145
Sales Range: $25-49.9 Million
Emp.: 50
Skincare Products Mfr & Distr
N.A.I.C.S.: 325620

Marico Bangladesh Limited (1)
The Glass House Level-06 Plot 02 Block SE B Gulshan Avenue, Dhaka, 1212, Bangladesh
Tel.: (880) 29897180
Web Site: https://marico.com
Rev.: $128,940,446
Assets: $106,138,603
Liabilities: $73,425,700
Net Worth: $32,712,904
Earnings: $35,322,558
Emp.: 355
Fiscal Year-end: 03/31/2023
Hair & Skin Care Products & Services
N.A.I.C.S.: 325620
Saugata Gupta *(Chm, CEO & Mng Dir)*

Marico Malaysia Sdn. Bhd. (1)
806 Level 8 Block A Phileo Damansara 1, 9 Jalan 16/11 Off Jalan Damansara, 46350, Petaling Jaya, Selangor, Malaysia
Tel.: (60) 376623369
Consumer Goods Services
N.A.I.C.S.: 532289

Marico Middle East FZE (1)
Office No 122 3rd Floor Oasis Center Al Quoz - 1, Dubai, United Arab Emirates
Tel.: (971) 43576620
Consumer Goods Services
N.A.I.C.S.: 532289

Marico South Africa (Pty) Limited (1)
1474 South Coast Road, Durban, 4052, Kwazulu-Natal, South Africa
Tel.: (27) 314513900
Hair Care Products Mfr & Distr
N.A.I.C.S.: 325620

Marico for Consumer Care Products SAE (1)
Building number 3 section 1141 34 Ibad Elrahman Street, Masaken Sheraton Nouza District, Cairo, 11799, Egypt
Tel.: (20) 222698611
Consumer Goods Services
N.A.I.C.S.: 532289

MARID INDUSTRIES LIMITED
99 Windsor Junction Rd, Windsor, B2T 1G7, NS, Canada
Tel.: (902) 860-1138
Web Site: https://marid.ca
Year Founded: 1983
Sales Range: $10-24.9 Million
Emp.: 120
Structural Steel & Metals Fabricators Supplier
N.A.I.C.S.: 332999
Phillip Read *(CFO)*

MARIDIVE & OIL SERVICES CO.
37 Corrnish El Nile, El Maadi, Cairo, Egypt
Tel.: (20) 223585204
Web Site: https://maridive-group.com
Year Founded: 1978
MOIL.CA—(EGX)
Rev.: $102,442,834
Assets: $653,664,615
Liabilities: $726,962,156
Net Worth: ($73,297,541)
Earnings: ($106,341,967)
Fiscal Year-end: 12/31/22
Marine Support Services
N.A.I.C.S.: 488390
Shahira Mohamed Magdy Zeid *(Chm)*

MARIE BRIZARD WINE & SPIRITS S.A.
10 avenue Charles Jaffelin, Beaune, France
Tel.: (33) 380229383 FR
Web Site: http://www.belvedere.fr
Year Founded: 1755
Sales Range: $450-499.9 Million
Emp.: 2,493
Wines & Distilled Spirits Mfr & Distr
N.A.I.C.S.: 312130
Benoit Herault *(Chm)*

Subsidiaries:

Augustowianka Sp. z o.o. (1)
Turystyczna 18 Street, 16-300, Augustow, Podlaskie, Poland
Tel.: (48) 876443132
Web Site: http://www.augustowianka.com.pl
Bottled Mineral Water Whslr
N.A.I.C.S.: 424490

Belvedere Slovensko, s. r. o. (1)
Liptovska 2 Ruzinov, Bratislava, Slovakia
Tel.: (421) 253419996
Web Site: http://www.belvedere.sk
Sales Range: $50-74.9 Million
Emp.: 2
Alcoholic Beverages Whslr
N.A.I.C.S.: 424820

CENTRUM TMT Sp. z o.o. (1)
ul Kilnskiego 15, 58-200, Dzierzoniow, Lower Silesian, Poland
Tel.: (48) 748323901
Web Site: http://www.centrumtmt.com
Alcoholic Beverages Whslr
N.A.I.C.S.: 424810

Destylernia Polmos Krakowie SA (1)
ul Fabryczna 13, 31 553, Krakow, Poland
Tel.: (48) 12 411 4843
Web Site: http://www.polmos.krakow.pl
Emp.: 300
Alcoholic Beverages Mfr & Distr
N.A.I.C.S.: 312120
Leszek Wojtan *(Chm)*

Domain Menada Sp. z o.o. (1)
Al Krakowska 110/114, Warsaw, 1022, Masovian, Poland
Tel.: (48) 226097295
Web Site: http://www.domainmenada.pl
Sales Range: $25-49.9 Million
Emp.: 80
Alcoholic Beverages Mfr & Whslr
N.A.I.C.S.: 312130

Dubar Industria E Comercio De Bebidas Ltda (1)
Rua Bento Pires 24 Vila Arens, Jundiai, 13202-661, Sao Paulo, Brazil
Tel.: (55) 11 7864 4405
Web Site: http://www.dubar.com.br
Alcoholic Beverages Whslr
N.A.I.C.S.: 424820
Carlos Donizete *(VP-Sls)*

Galerie Alkoholi Sp. z o.o. (1)
ul Dabrowskiego 249, 93-231, Lodz, Poland
Tel.: (48) 426772929
Web Site: http://www.galerialkoholi.pl
Alcoholic Beverages Whslr
N.A.I.C.S.: 424820

Hasis Sp. z o.o. (1)
ul Techniczna 4, 05-500, Piaseczno, Masovian, Poland
Tel.: (48) 22 756 8083
Alcoholic Beverages Whslr
N.A.I.C.S.: 424820

Imperial Brands, Inc. (1)
11505 Fairchild Gardens Ave Ste 204, Palm Beach Gardens, FL 33410
Tel.: (561) 624-5662
Web Site: http://www.ibrandsinc.com
Sales Range: $25-49.9 Million
Emp.: 9
Wines & Spirits Importer & Marketer
N.A.I.C.S.: 424820
David Bitran *(Dir-Mktg)*

Jimbo Sp. z o.o. (1)
Wojska Polskiego 38, 06-100, Pultusk, Masovian, Poland
Tel.: (48) 23 692 0745
Alcoholic Beverages Whslr
N.A.I.C.S.: 424820

Marie Brizard & Roger International SAS (1)
130-142 rue Fondaudege, BP 557, 33002, Bordeaux, France (100%)
Tel.: (33) 556018585
Web Site: http://www.mariebrizard.com
Sales Range: $100-124.9 Million
Emp.: 750
Holding Company; Wines & Distilled Spirits Mfr & Distr
N.A.I.C.S.: 551112
Erick Antony Skora *(Gen Dir)*

Subsidiary (Domestic):

COGNAC GAUTIER SA (2)
28 rue des Ponts, Aigre, 16140, Charenta, Angouleme, France
Tel.: (33) 545211002
Web Site: http://www.cognac-gautier.com
Sales Range: $25-49.9 Million
Emp.: 35
Alcoholic Beverages Whslr
N.A.I.C.S.: 424820
Olivier Bernazeau *(Gen Mgr)*

Subsidiary (Non-US):

Marie Brizard Espana S.A. (2)
Capitan Haya 56 Bajo, ES-28020, Madrid, Spain (100%)
Tel.: (34) 915714289
Web Site: http://www.mariebrizard.com
Sales Range: $25-49.9 Million
Emp.: 15
Wine & Distilled Spirits Distr
N.A.I.C.S.: 424820

Subsidiary (Domestic):

Moncigale S.A.S. (2)
6 Quai de la Paix, Beaucaire, Gard, France
Tel.: (33) 466597400
Alcoholic Beverages Whslr
N.A.I.C.S.: 424820

Multihurt. Sp. z o.o. (1)
ul Chopina 5, Sztum, Pomeranian, Poland
Tel.: (48) 552772278
Spirits Whslr
N.A.I.C.S.: 424820

Polmos Lancut S.A. (1)
ul Kolejowa 1, 37-100, Lancut, Subcarpathian, Poland
Tel.: (48) 172254261
Web Site: http://www.polmoslancut.com.pl
Emp.: 300
Liquor Mfr
N.A.I.C.S.: 312130

Redo Sp.z.o.o. (1)
ul Tytoniowa 10, 16-300, Augustow, Podlaskie, Poland
Tel.: (48) 876432362
Web Site: http://www.redo.pl
Sales Range: $25-49.9 Million
Emp.: 50
Alcoholic Beverage Distr
N.A.I.C.S.: 424820
Wojciech Wojtulewicz *(Dir-Admin)*

MARIE BRIZARD WINE & SPIRITS S.A.

Marie Brizard Wine & Spirits S.A.—(Continued)

Rokicki sp z.o.o. (1)
ul Mszczonowska 155, Skierniewice, Lodz, Poland
Tel.: (48) 468336276
Alcoholic Beverages Whslr
N.A.I.C.S.: 424820

Sobieski International Sp. z o.o (1)
Bellottiego 1, 01-022, Warsaw, Masovian, Poland
Tel.: (48) 22 838 9518
Alcoholic Beverages Whslr
N.A.I.C.S.: 424820

Sobieski Sarl (1)
10 Avenue Charles Jaffelin, Beaune, Cote D Or, France
Tel.: (33) 380229383
Sales Range: $50-74.9 Million
Emp.: 8
Alcoholic Beverages Whslr
N.A.I.C.S.: 424820

TRITEX Sp. z o.o. (1)
ul Bytomska 60, 41-940, Piekary Slaskie, Silesian, Poland
Tel.: (48) 323919030
Web Site: http://www.tritex.com.pl
Alcoholic Beverages Whslr
N.A.I.C.S.: 424820

William Pitters International S.A.S (1)
1 Rue Banlin, BP 6, Lormont, 33305, Bordeaux, France
Tel.: (33) 557809999
Emp.: 50
Alcoholic Beverages Whslr
N.A.I.C.S.: 424820

MARIELLA BURANI FASHION GROUP S.P.A.
Via della Repubblica 86, Cavriago, 42025, Italy
Tel.: (39) 0522373131
Web Site:
http://www.marielloburani.com
Sales Range: $750-799.9 Million
Emp.: 226
Designer & Mfr of Luxury Clothing, Footwear, Jewelry & Accessories
N.A.I.C.S.: 315250
Carol Scarlatti Brumer *(Head-IR & Strategic Dev)*

MARIGOLD FORD LINCOLN SALES
1120 Dundas St East, Whitby, L1N 5V3, ON, Canada
Tel.: (905) 668-5893
Web Site:
http://www.marigoldfordsales.com
Rev.: $16,515,422
Emp.: 47
New & Used Car Dealers
N.A.I.C.S.: 441110
Janet Nobbs *(Mgr-Parts)*

MARIMACA COPPER CORP.
Suite 1504 Cerro El Plomo, 5420, Las Condes, Santiago, Chile
Tel.: (56) 224317608 BC
Web Site: http://www.marimaca.com
Year Founded: 2004
E2E1—(DEU)
Rev.: $597,000
Assets: $95,599,000
Liabilities: $1,204,000
Net Worth: $94,395,000
Earnings: ($7,113,000)
Emp.: 23
Fiscal Year-end: 12/31/23
Copper, Nickel, Lead & Zinc Mining
N.A.I.C.S.: 212230
Sergio L. Rivera *(VP-Exploration)*

MARIMEKKO CORPORATION
Puusepankatu 4, 00880, Helsinki, Finland
Tel.: (358) 975871
Web Site: http://www.marimekko.com
Year Founded: 1951
MMO1V—(HEL)
Rev.: $179,710,771
Assets: $123,667,170
Liabilities: $63,846,320
Net Worth: $59,820,850
Earnings: $24,508,957
Emp.: 451
Fiscal Year-end: 12/31/22
Fashion Apparel Mfr & Distr
N.A.I.C.S.: 315250
Elina Bjorklund *(Vice Chm)*

Subsidiaries:

Marimekko AB (1)
Skomakaregatan 6, Malmo, 21134, Sweden
Tel.: (46) 40 128 300
Clothing Accessories Distr
N.A.I.C.S.: 458110

Marimekko Australia Pty. Ltd. (1)
2A Kipling St, Richmond, 3121, VIC, Australia
Tel.: (61) 1300853671
Clothing & Bag Design Services
N.A.I.C.S.: 541490

Marimekko GmbH (1)
Querstrasse 2, Frankfurt am Main, 60322, Germany
Tel.: (49) 69 749084
Sales Range: $50-74.9 Million
Emp.: 10
Fabric Clothes & Accessories Distr
N.A.I.C.S.: 424350
Michael Hoppe *(Gen Mgr)*

Marimekko Kitee Oy (1)
Karhutie 1, Kitee, 82500, Pohjois-Karjala, Finland
Tel.: (358) 13414761
Outerwear Clothing Mfr
N.A.I.C.S.: 315250

Marimekko North America LLC (1)
401 Broadway, New York, NY 10013
Tel.: (212) 295-4311
Web Site: http://company.marimekko.com
Clothing & Accessories Distr
N.A.I.C.S.: 458110

Marimekko Tuotanto Oy (1)
Puusepankatu 4, 00880, Helsinki, Uusimaa, Finland
Tel.: (358) 975871
Web Site: http://www.marimekko.com
Sales Range: $25-49.9 Million
Clothing & Accessories Mfr
N.A.I.C.S.: 315250

Marimekko UK Ltd (1)
16-17 St Christophers Place 15-22 St Christophers Place, London, W1U 1NL, United Kingdom
Tel.: (44) 2074866454
Web Site: http://www.marimekko.com
Emp.: 6
Textile Products Mfr
N.A.I.C.S.: 314999

MARIMO REGIONAL REVITALIZATION REIT, INC.
1121 Toranomon, Minato-ku, Tokyo, 105-0001, Japan
Tel.: (81) 362054755
Web Site: https://www.marimo-reit.co.jp
3470—(TKS)
Sales Range: $10-24.9 Million
Real Estate Investment Services
N.A.I.C.S.: 531210
Takashi Kitagata *(Exec Dir)*

MARINE & GENERAL BERHAD
Level 23 Plaza VADS No 1 Jalan Tun Mohd Fuad Taman Tun Dr Ismail, 60000, Kuala Lumpur, Malaysia
Tel.: (60) 77356300
Web Site: https://www.marine-general.com.my
Year Founded: 1996
Sales Range: $125-149.9 Million
Holding Company

N.A.I.C.S.: 551112
Mohammed Azlan Hashim *(Chm)*

MARINE ATLANTIC INC.
355 Purves St, North Sydney, B2A 3V2, NS, Canada
Tel.: (709) 772-8957
Web Site: http://www.marine-atlantic.ca
Sales Range: $25-49.9 Million
Emp.: 1,200
Ferry Service
N.A.I.C.S.: 483114

MARINE CHRYSLER DODGE JEEP LTD.
450 SE Marine Dr, Vancouver, V5X 4V2, BC, Canada
Tel.: (604) 321-1236
Web Site:
http://www.marinechrysler.com
Year Founded: 1990
Rev.: $22,854,000
Emp.: 55
New & Used Car Dealers
N.A.I.C.S.: 441110
Ted Warkentin *(Pres)*

MARINE ELECTRICALS (INDIA) LIMITED
B-1 Udyog Sadan-3 Midc Marol Industrial Area, Andheri East, Mumbai, 400093, India
Tel.: (91) 2240334300
Web Site:
https://www.marineelectricals.com
Year Founded: 1978
MARINE—(NSE)
Electrical & Electronic Parts Mfr
N.A.I.C.S.: 336320
Vinay Uchil *(Chm)*

MARINE HARVEST ROLMER S.A.S.
Rue des Quatre Vents, 85300, Chalans, Vendee, France
Tel.: (33) 251495466
Sales Range: $10-24.9 Million
Emp.: 62
Seafood Processing Services
N.A.I.C.S.: 311710
Laurent Mauray *(Owner)*

MARINE PRODUCE AUSTRALIA LIMITED
34 Bagot Road, Subiaco, 6008, WA, Australia
Tel.: (61) 8 93814483
Web Site:
http://www.marineproduce.com
Sales Range: $1-9.9 Million
Emp.: 5
Aquaculture Projects
N.A.I.C.S.: 112519
Desiree Allen *(Mng Dir)*

MARINE SUPPLY & ENGINEERING SERVICE JOINT STOCK COMPANY
8A Van My Street, Van My Ward Ngo Quyen District, Haiphong, Vietnam
Tel.: (84) 2253766561
Web Site:
https://www.maserco.com.vn
MAC—(HNX)
Rev.: $4,628,496
Assets: $9,186,748
Liabilities: $1,956,576
Net Worth: $7,230,173
Earnings: $44,576
Fiscal Year-end: 12/31/20
Ship Building & Repairing Services
N.A.I.C.S.: 336611
Nguyen Van Cuong *(Chm-Mgmt Bd)*

INTERNATIONAL PUBLIC

MARINER CORPORATION LIMITED
Level 9 32 Walker Street, North Sydney, 2060, NSW, Australia
Tel.: (61) 294679980
Web Site:
http://www.marinercorporation.com
MCX—(ASX)
Rev.: $65,659
Assets: $178,993
Liabilities: $231,191
Net Worth: ($52,198)
Earnings: ($456,461)
Emp.: 10
Fiscal Year-end: 06/30/21
Investment Banking Services
N.A.I.C.S.: 523150
Adrian Olney *(Sec)*

MARINETEK GROUP OY
Vattuniemenkatu 3, 00210, Helsinki, Finland
Tel.: (358) 9 682 410 0
Web Site: http://www.marinetek.net
Year Founded: 1994
Sales Range: $10-24.9 Million
Emp.: 100
Marina Developer; Marine Equipment Mfr
N.A.I.C.S.: 237990
Ilkka Seppala *(Pres & CEO)*

Subsidiaries:

Marinetek Group Oy Hakkila Factory (1)
Mittalinja 2, 1260, Vantaa, Finland
Tel.: (358) 93436770
Marine Support Services
N.A.I.C.S.: 488510

Marinetek Latvia Sia (1)
Rigas iela 6, Olaine, Riga, Latvia
Tel.: (371) 29210966
Web Site: http://www.marinetek.lv
Marine Support Services
N.A.I.C.S.: 488510
Albert Sulackis *(Project Mgr)*

Marinetek Middle East and North Africa (1)
LOB 16 Office 16223 Jebel Ali Free Zone, PO Box 262893, Dubai, United Arab Emirates
Tel.: (971) 48817090
Marine Support Services
N.A.I.C.S.: 488510

Marinetek NCP d.o.o. (1)
Coast Jerko Sizgorica 1, 22000, Sibenik, Croatia
Tel.: (385) 22312960
Web Site: http://www.marinetek.hr
Marine Support Services
N.A.I.C.S.: 488510

Marinetek SPB ZAO (1)
Baltis Plaza office 336 Sredniy pr V O 88, Saint Petersburg, Russia
Tel.: (7) 8126001809
Marine Support Services
N.A.I.C.S.: 488510

Marinetek South East Asia Pte Ltd. (1)
10 Raeburn Park 04-02, 088702, Singapore, Singapore
Tel.: (65) 90920305
Marine Support Services
N.A.I.C.S.: 488510

Marinetek Sweden AB (1)
Kasenabbevagen 3H, 451 50, Uddevalla, Sweden
Tel.: (46) 52840270
Web Site: http://www.marineteksweden.net
Steel Products Whslr
N.A.I.C.S.: 423510

MARINETRANS INDIA LIMITED
Vindhya commercial Complex
801/802 8th Floor Plot No 1 Sector 11 br, CBD Belapur, Navi Mumbai, 400614, Maharashtra, India

AND PRIVATE COMPANIES

Tel.: (91) 7777045320
Web Site: https://www.marinetrans.in
Year Founded: 2004
MARINETRAN—(NSE)
Rev.: $24,636,603
Assets: $2,767,117
Liabilities: $1,038,442
Net Worth: $1,728,676
Earnings: $228,607
Emp.: 46
Fiscal Year-end: 03/31/22
Freight Transportation Services
N.A.I.C.S.: 488510

MARINOMED BIOTECH AG
Hovengasse 25, 2100, Korneuburg, Austria
Tel.: (43) 226290300
Web Site: https://www.marinomed.com
Year Founded: 2006
MARI—(VIE)
Rev.: $12,169,113
Assets: $24,052,018
Liabilities: $28,538,420
Net Worth: ($4,486,402)
Earnings: ($6,904,490)
Emp.: 44
Fiscal Year-end: 12/31/22
Pharmaceuticals Product Mfr
N.A.I.C.S.: 325412
Andreas Grassauer *(CEO)*

MARIS SPINNERS LIMITED
11 Cathedral Road, Chennai, 600086, India
Tel.: (91) 4428115910
Web Site: http://www.maris.co.in
Year Founded: 1981
531503—(BOM)
Rev.: $14,830,425
Assets: $12,002,909
Liabilities: $8,228,848
Net Worth: $3,774,061
Earnings: $896,737
Emp.: 317
Fiscal Year-end: 03/31/21
Cotton Yarn Mfr
N.A.I.C.S.: 313110
Anandkumar Rengaswamy *(Mng Dir)*

Subsidiaries:

Maris Spinners Limited - UNIT I   (1)
Kattemalalavadi Village, Hunsur Taluk
Mysore District, Mysore, 571 134, India
Tel.: (91) 8222252683
Fabric Product Mfr
N.A.I.C.S.: 313320

MARIS-TECH LTD.
2 Yitzhak Modai st, Rehovot, 7608804, Israel
Tel.: (972) 722424022
Web Site: https://maris-tech.com
Year Founded: 2008
MTEK—(NASDAQ)
Rev.: $4,031,103
Assets: $11,333,906
Liabilities: $4,439,416
Net Worth: $6,894,490
Earnings: ($2,709,596)
Emp.: 12
Fiscal Year-end: 12/31/23
Digital Video Equipment Mfr
N.A.I.C.S.: 334310
Hanan Samet *(CFO)*

MARISA LOJAS S.A.
Rua James Holland 422Barra Funda
Sao Paulo SP, Sao Paulo, 1138-050, Brazil
Tel.: (55) 1121096269   BR
Web Site: http://www.marisa.com.br
Year Founded: 1948
AMAR3—(BRAZ)
Rev.: $294,255,905
Assets: $438,657,324
Liabilities: $438,573,843
Net Worth: $83,481
Earnings: ($62,742,531)
Fiscal Year-end: 12/31/23
Apparel Store Operator
N.A.I.C.S.: 458110

MARITIME BANK JSC
Varshavskoye highway building 1A room 1/5, 117105, Moscow, Russia
Tel.: (7) 4957771177
Web Site: http://www.maritimebank.ru
Sales Range: Less than $1 Million
Insurance Brokerage Services
N.A.I.C.S.: 524210
Yuriy Vladimirovich Bardin *(Chm-Mgmt Bd)*

MARITIME BROADCASTING SYSTEM LTD.
90 Lovett Lake Court, Halifax, B3S 0H6, NS, Canada
Tel.: (902) 425-1225
Web Site: https://www.mbsradio.com
Sales Range: $75-99.9 Million
Emp.: 500
Radio Broadcasting Services
N.A.I.C.S.: 516110
Robert Pace *(Chm)*

Subsidiaries:

CFAN Radio   (1)
396 Pleasant St, Miramichi Bay, E1V 1X3, NB, Canada
Tel.: (506) 622-3311
Web Site: http://www.theriver993.com
Sales Range: $25-49.9 Million
Emp.: 8
Radio Stations
N.A.I.C.S.: 516110

CFCY Radio   (1)
5 Prince Street, Charlottetown, C1A 4P4, PE, Canada   (100%)
Tel.: (902) 892-1066
Web Site: https://www.cfcy.fm
Sales Range: $25-49.9 Million
Emp.: 36
Radio Broadcasting
N.A.I.C.S.: 516110

CFCY-AM/CHLQ-FM   (1)
5 Prince Street, Charlottetown, C1A 4P4, PE, Canada
Tel.: (902) 892-1066
Web Site: http://www.cfcy.fm
Sales Range: $25-49.9 Million
Emp.: 35
Radio Broadcasting Stations
N.A.I.C.S.: 516110
Rick McLeod *(Gen Mgr-Sls)*

CHNS/CHFX Radio   (1)
90 Lovett Lake Court Suite 201, Halifax, B3S 0H6, NS, Canada   (100%)
Tel.: (902) 422-1651
Web Site: http://www.fax101.ca
Sales Range: $25-49.9 Million
Emp.: 44
Radio Broadcasting
N.A.I.C.S.: 516110
Robert Pace *(Chm)*

CIOK/CJYC/CFBC Radio   (1)
226 Union, Saint John, E2L 1B1, NB, Canada
Tel.: (506) 658-5100
Web Site: http://www.k100.ca
Sales Range: $25-49.9 Million
Emp.: 15
Radio Stations
N.A.I.C.S.: 516110
Kelly O'Neill *(Gen Mgr-Sls)*

CJCW Radio   (1)
6 Marble St, PO Box 5900, Sussex, E0E 1P0, NB, Canada   (100%)
Tel.: (506) 432-2529
Web Site: http://www.favourites590.com
Sales Range: $25-49.9 Million
Emp.: 5
Radio Broadcasting
N.A.I.C.S.: 516110

CKCW-AM/CFQM-FM   (1)
1000 St George Blvd, Moncton, E1E 4M7, NB, Canada
Tel.: (506) 858-1220
Web Site: http://www.radiomoncton.com
Sales Range: $25-49.9 Million
Emp.: 30
Radio Broadcasting Stations
N.A.I.C.S.: 516110
Paddy Kearns *(Mgr-Acctg)*

CKCW/CFQM Radio   (1)
1000 Saint George Blvd, Moncton, E1E4M7, NB, Canada   (100%)
Tel.: (506) 858-1220
Web Site: http://www.radiomoncton.com
Sales Range: $25-49.9 Million
Emp.: 20
Radio Broadcasting
N.A.I.C.S.: 516110
Wayne Keeping *(Mgr-Sls)*

CKDH Radio-AM   (1)
38 Highway 6, PO Box 670, Amherst, B4H 4B8, NS, Canada
Tel.: (902) 667-3875
Web Site: http://www.ckdh.com
Sales Range: $25-49.9 Million
Emp.: 3
Radio Broadcasting Stations
N.A.I.C.S.: 516110
Robert Pace *(Pres)*

CKNB-AM   (1)
74 Water Street, Campbellton, E3N 1B1, NB, Canada
Tel.: (506) 753-4415
Web Site: https://hits100fm.ca
Sales Range: $25-49.9 Million
Emp.: 5
Radio Broadcasting Stations
N.A.I.C.S.: 516110

Magic 94.9   (1)
29 Oakdene Avenue, PO Boc 310, Kentville, B4N 1H5, NS, Canada
Tel.: (902) 678-2111
Web Site: http://www.magic949.ca
Radio Broadcasting
N.A.I.C.S.: 516110

Maritime Broadcasting - Sydney   (1)
318 Charlotte St 318, Sydney, B1P 1C8, NS, Canada   (100%)
Tel.: (902) 564-5596
Web Site: http://www.mbsradio.com
Sales Range: $25-49.9 Million
Emp.: 20
Radio Broadcasting
N.A.I.C.S.: 516110
Dwayne Keller *(Mgr-Ops)*

MARITIME ONTARIO FREIGHT LINES LIMITED
1 Maritime Ontario Blvd, Brampton, L6S 6G4, ON, Canada
Tel.: (905) 792-6100
Web Site: http://www.m-o.com
Sales Range: $75-99.9 Million
Emp.: 300
Freight Transportation
N.A.I.C.S.: 484122
Mike Morra *(VP-Corp Affairs)*

MARITIME PAPER PRODUCTS LIMITED
25 Borden Avenue, PO Box 668, Dartmouth, B3B 1C7, NS, Canada
Tel.: (902) 468-5353
Web Site: https://www.maritimepaper.com
Year Founded: 1931
Rev.: $46,925,901
Emp.: 300
Corrugated Cartons & Custom Packaging Mfr
N.A.I.C.S.: 322211
Thomas Jennegren *(Dir-Export Sls)*

MARITIME RESOURCES CORP.
1900 - 110 Yonge St, Toronto, M5C 1T4, ON, Canada
Tel.: (416) 365-5321
Web Site: https://www.maritimeresources.com
Year Founded: 2007
MRTMF—(OTCIQ)
Rev.: $722,998
Assets: $39,964,896
Liabilities: $10,535,960
Net Worth: $29,428,936
Earnings: ($1,920,843)
Fiscal Year-end: 12/31/23
Mineral Exploration Services
N.A.I.C.S.: 213114
Germaine M. Coombs *(CFO)*

MARITIME TRAVEL INC
202-2000 Barrington Street Cogswell Tower, Halifax, B3J 3K1, NS, Canada
Tel.: (902) 420-1554
Web Site: http://www.maritimetravel.ca
Sales Range: $100-124.9 Million
Emp.: 500
Travel Agency
N.A.I.C.S.: 561510
Rob Dexter *(Chm & CEO)*

MARITSATEX AD
Vasil Levski 144, Plovdiv, 4003, Bulgaria
Tel.: (359) 32969070
Web Site: http://www.maritzatex.com
MTEX—(BUL)
Sales Range: Less than $1 Million
Cotton Product Mfr & Distr
N.A.I.C.S.: 314999
Stoil Vylchev Kavanozov *(Dir-IR)*

MARIUS PEDERSEN A/S
Orbaekvej 49, 5863, Fjerritslev, Denmark
Tel.: (45) 70134040   DK
Web Site: http://www.mariuspedersen.dk
Emp.: 2,500
Waste Management Services
N.A.I.C.S.: 562998
Jeanett Vikkelsoe *(Dir-Sls & Mktg)*

Subsidiaries:

Marius Pedersen A/S - Aalborg Plant   (1)
Korinthvej 103, 9220, Aalborg, Denmark
Tel.: (45) 98 17 68 11
Sales Range: $10-24.9 Million
Emp.: 4
Waste Material Recycling Services
N.A.I.C.S.: 562998
Morgan Petersen *(Gen Mgr)*

Marius Pedersen A/S - Aarhus Plant   (1)
Olstedvej 20B, 8200, Arhus, Denmark
Tel.: (45) 87 30 40 70
Emp.: 6
Waste Material Recycling Services
N.A.I.C.S.: 562998

Marius Pedersen A/S - Broby Plant   (1)
Landevejen 5, 5672, Broby, Denmark
Tel.: (45) 63909909
Waste Material Recycling Services
N.A.I.C.S.: 562998

Marius Pedersen A/S - Esbjerg Plant   (1)
Made Industrivej 25, 6705, Esbjerg, Denmark
Tel.: (45) 76 12 23 00
Waste Material Recycling Services
N.A.I.C.S.: 562998

Marius Pedersen A/S - Herning Plant   (1)
Sandagervej 40, 7400, Herning, Denmark
Tel.: (45) 96 26 53 00
Sales Range: $10-24.9 Million
Emp.: 5
Waste Material Recycling Services
N.A.I.C.S.: 562998
Christian Moller *(Mng Dir)*

MARIUS PEDERSEN A/S

Marius Pedersen A/S—(Continued)

Marius Pedersen A/S - Kolding Plant (1)
Virkelyst 10, 6000, Kolding, Denmark
Tel.: (45) 75 52 21 44
Web Site: http://www.mariuspedersen.dk
Waste Material Recycling Services
N.A.I.C.S.: 562998

Marius Pedersen A/S - Odense Plant (1)
Havnegade 90, 5000, Odense, Denmark
Tel.: (45) 65 90 40 50
Web Site: http://www.mariuspedersen.dk
Waste Material Recycling Services
N.A.I.C.S.: 562920

Marius Pedersen A/S - Roedekro Plant (1)
Malmovej 3-5, 6230, Rodekro, Denmark
Tel.: (45) 7466 9382
Web Site: http://www.mariuspedersen.dk
Waste Material Recycling Services
N.A.I.C.S.: 562998

Marius Pedersen A/S - Roedovre Plant (1)
Islevdalvej 119, 2610, Rodovre, Denmark
Tel.: (45) 70 13 40 40
Waste Material Recycling Services
N.A.I.C.S.: 562998

Marius Pedersen A/S - Sakskobing Plant (1)
Nykobingvej 76 Bygn 54, 4990, Sakskobing, Denmark
Tel.: (45) 54 60 10 78
Web Site: http://www.mariuspedersen.dk
Waste Material Recycling Services
N.A.I.C.S.: 562998
Jan Kasttcup *(Mgr)*

Marius Pedersen A/S - Svinninge Plant (1)
Strandvejen 28, 4520, Svinninge, Denmark
Tel.: (45) 70134040
Waste Material Recycling Services
N.A.I.C.S.: 562998

Marius Pedersen a.s (1)
Opatovska 1735, PO Box 33, 911 01, Trencin, Slovakia **(100%)**
Tel.: (421) 327437543
Web Site: http://www.mariuspedersen.sk
Sales Range: $25-49.9 Million
Emp.: 100
Waste Management Services
N.A.I.C.S.: 562998
Oliver Sujan *(Gen Dir)*

Marius Pedersen a.s (1)
Prubezna 1940/3, 500 09, Hradec Kralove, Czech Republic
Tel.: (420) 495 500 550
Web Site: http://www.mariuspedersen.cz
Waste Management Services
N.A.I.C.S.: 562998

MARKA PJSC
Building 9 Level 3 Dubai Design District, PO Box 34771, Dubai, United Arab Emirates
Tel.: (971) 45593000
Web Site:
 http://www.markaholding.com
Year Founded: 2014
Rev.: $27,113,842
Assets: $52,682,602
Liabilities: $49,119,478
Net Worth: $3,563,125
Earnings: ($66,061,035)
Fiscal Year-end: 12/31/17
Fashion Retail Store Operator
N.A.I.C.S.: 458110
Khalid Jasem Kalban *(Chm)*

MARKA YATIRIM HOLDING AS
Ortabayir Mh Sair Celebi Sokak Gurtas Is Merkezi Apartmani No 1/13, Kagithane, Istanbul, Türkiye
Tel.: (90) 2122863330
Web Site: https://markaholding.com.tr
MARKA—(IST)
Rev.: $655,783

Assets: $2,292,860
Liabilities: $1,533,157
Net Worth: $759,704
Earnings: $313,108
Fiscal Year-end: 12/31/22
Investment Management Service
N.A.I.C.S.: 525990
Mine Tozlu *(Chm)*

MARKERSTUDY INSURANCE SERVICES LIMITED
Markerstudy House 45 Westerham Road, Bessels Green, Sevenoaks, TN13 2QB, Kent, United Kingdom
Tel.: (44) 1732745400
Web Site:
 http://www.markerstudy.com
Year Founded: 2001
Insurance Agencies & Brokerages
N.A.I.C.S.: 524210
Kevin Spencer *(Grp CEO)*

Subsidiaries:

CIS General Insurance Ltd (1)
Miller Street, Manchester, M60 0AL, United Kingdom
Tel.: (44) 1618328686
General Insurance Services
N.A.I.C.S.: 524298

MARKET CREATORS LTD.
Creative Castle 70 Sampatrao Colony, Opp Masonic Hall Productivity Road, Vadodara, 390 007, Gujarat, India
Tel.: (91) 2652354075
Web Site:
 https://www.sharemart.co.in
Year Founded: 1991
526891—(BOM)
Rev.: $870,879
Assets: $3,096,838
Liabilities: $1,795,560
Net Worth: $1,301,277
Earnings: ($150,168)
Fiscal Year-end: 03/31/21
Securities Brokerage Services
N.A.I.C.S.: 523150
Kalpesh J. Shah *(Compliance Officer)*

MARKET HARBOROUGH BUILDING SOCIETY
Welland House The Square, Market Harborough, LE16 7PD, Leics, United Kingdom
Tel.: (44) 1858 412250
Web Site: http://www.mhbs.co.uk
Year Founded: 1870
Rev.: $21,258,413
Assets: $696,787,500
Liabilities: $639,848,321
Net Worth: $56,939,179
Earnings: $3,583,291
Emp.: 101
Fiscal Year-end: 12/31/19
Mortgage Lending
N.A.I.C.S.: 522310
Mark T. Robinson *(CEO)*

MARKETBOOMER PTY. LTD.
Level 1 343 Pacific Highway, Sydney, 2060, NSW, Australia
Tel.: (61) 282157131
Web Site:
 http://www.marketboomer.com
Year Founded: 1997
Online Procurement Services
N.A.I.C.S.: 518210
Nathan Gyaneshwar *(Founder & CEO)*

Subsidiaries:

Marketboomer China Limited (1)
Room 1401 1322 Nan Kai Building Lujiabang Road, Hangpu District, Shanghai, 200011, China
Tel.: (86) 2152863155

Web Site: http://www.marketboomer.com.cn
Online Procurement Services
N.A.I.C.S.: 518210
Kelly Leong *(Gen Mgr)*

Marketboomer International Limited (1)
The Digital Hub 10-13 Thomas St, Dublin, 8, Ireland
Tel.: (353) 766024000
Web Site: http://www.marketboomer.com
Online Procurement Services
N.A.I.C.S.: 518210
Jonathan Santos *(Gen Mgr)*

MARKETECH INTERNATIONAL CORP.
6F No 3-2 Yuancyu St, Nangang Dist, Taipei, 115603, Taiwan
Tel.: (886) 226558899
Web Site: https://www.micb2b.com
Year Founded: 1988
6196—(TAI)
Rev.: $1,840,469,926
Assets: $1,527,084,020
Liabilities: $1,159,641,050
Net Worth: $367,442,970
Earnings: $68,714,769
Emp.: 1,242
Fiscal Year-end: 12/31/23
Integrated Circuits Mfr
N.A.I.C.S.: 334413
Hsin-Ming Kao *(Chm & CEO)*

Subsidiaries:

MIC-TECH(WUXI)CO., LTD. (1)
No 11 Xin Xi Rd Wuxi National High-Tech DEV Zone, Wuxi, Jiangsu, China
Tel.: (86) 51085200505
Web Site: http://www.micb2b.com
Precision Cleaning Services
N.A.I.C.S.: 561720

Marketech Co., Ltd. (1)
R1-08-09 The EverRich 968 3-2 St, 15 Ward Dist 11, Ho Chi Minh City, Vietnam
Tel.: (84) 2822250692
Engineeering Services
N.A.I.C.S.: 541330

Marketech Engineering Pte. Ltd. (1)
86 Kaki Bukit Industrial Terrace, Singapore, 416166, Singapore
Tel.: (65) 67476678
Web Site: https://marketech.com.sg
Engineeering Services
N.A.I.C.S.: 541330

Marketech Integrated Manufacturing Company Limited (1)
Lot No B-12 Thilawa Sez Zone A, Thanlyin Township, Yangon, Myanmar
Tel.: (95) 1535927
Automated Component Mfr
N.A.I.C.S.: 336390

Marketech International Corp. - Hukou Factory (1)
No 35 Guangfu South Road Hsinchu Industrial Park, Hukou, 303, Hsinchu, Taiwan
Tel.: (886) 3 597 4779
Web Site: http://www.micb2b.com
Electronic Components Mfr
N.A.I.C.S.: 334419

Marketech Netherlands B.V. (1)
European Business Center Luchthavenweg 81 207, 5657 EA, Eindhoven, Netherlands
Tel.: (31) 40 282 6087
Machinery Equipment Mfr & Distr
N.A.I.C.S.: 333248

Mic-Tech Electronics Engineering Corp. (1)
Room 701-706 No 36 Lane 2777 Jinxiu East Road, Pilot Free Trade Zone, Shanghai, China
Tel.: (86) 2150323399
Web Site: https://www.jiweicn.com
Engineering Services
N.A.I.C.S.: 541330

PT Marketech International Indonesia (1)
VIP Chamber 2 Wisma GKBI Lt 39 Jl Jend Sudirman No 28, Jakarta Pusat, Indonesia

INTERNATIONAL PUBLIC

Tel.: (62) 215 799 8000
Machinery Equipment Mfr & Distr
N.A.I.C.S.: 333248

Vertex System Corporation (1)
21F-7 No 77 Sec 1 Xintai 5th Rd, Xizhi Dist, New Taipei City, 221, Taiwan
Tel.: (886) 226981369
Web Site: https://vertexsystem.com.tw
Telecommunication Servicesb
N.A.I.C.S.: 532490

eZoom Information, Inc. (1)
10th Floor-2 No 3-2 Yuanyuan Street, Nangang District, Taipei, 11503, Taiwan
Tel.: (886) 226557299
Information Technology Services
N.A.I.C.S.: 541511

MARKETENTERPRISE CO., LTD.
Tokyo Tatemono Kyobashi Building 3F 3-6-18 Kyobashi, Chuo-ku, Tokyo, 1040031, Japan
Tel.: (81) 351594060
Web Site:
 https://www.marketenterprise.co.jp
Year Founded: 2006
3135—(TKS)
Rev.: $118,229,760
Assets: $33,245,900
Liabilities: $25,122,580
Net Worth: $8,123,320
Earnings: ($2,960,720)
Emp.: 677
Fiscal Year-end: 06/30/24
Second Hand Products Online Retailer
N.A.I.C.S.: 459999
Yasushi Kobayashi *(Pres & CEO)*

MARKETING & RESERVATIONS INTERNATIONAL LTD.
9 Galena Road, London, W6 0LT, United Kingdom
Tel.: (44) 20 8741 5333
Web Site: http://www.rexresorts.com
Hotel Booking Services
N.A.I.C.S.: 561599
Richard Bryson *(Mng Dir)*

Subsidiaries:

Discovery Bay Beach Hotel (1)
St. James Beach, Holetown, Saint James, Barbados **(100%)**
Tel.: (246) 4321301
Web Site: http://www.rexresorts.com
Travel Agency Services
N.A.I.C.S.: 561510

Hawksbill Beach Hotel (1)
Five Islands, PO Box 108, Saint John's, Antigua & Barbuda
Tel.: (268) 4620301
Web Site: http://www.rexresorts.com
Sales Range: $10-24.9 Million
Emp.: 36
Hotel & resort without casino Services
N.A.I.C.S.: 721110
John St.Luce *(Gen Mgr)*

Marketing & Reservations (USA) Inc. (1)
1150 NW 72nd Ave Ste 510, Miami, FL 33126
Tel.: (305) 471-6170
Resort Operator
N.A.I.C.S.: 721110

MARKETING RESOURCE GROUP
B702 Beijing Hanwei Office Building, Chaoyang District, Beijing, 100020, China
Tel.: (86) 105921 1188
Sales Range: $75-99.9 Million
Emp.: 96
N.A.I.C.S.: 541820
Lucas Lee *(Pres)*

Subsidiaries:

Marketing Resource Group (1)

AND PRIVATE COMPANIES
MARKUSSON NEW HOLLAND OF REGINA LTD.

24th Fl Huamin Empire Plaza, Shanghai, 200050, China
Tel.: (86) 21 5240 2999
N.A.I.C.S.: 541820
Edward Sun *(Gen Mgr)*

Marketing Resource Group (1)
1502 S Security Bldg 140-148 E Rd, Guangzhou, 510620, China
Tel.: (86) 20 3887 8488
N.A.I.C.S.: 541820
Carven Hu *(Gen Mgr)*

MARKETING V F LIMITED
Imperial Works Block C Perren Street, London, NW5 3ED, United Kingdom
Tel.: (44) 2035953800
Web Site: http://www.mvfglobal.com
Year Founded: 2009
Sales Range: $10-24.9 Million
Emp.: 130
Digital Marketing Services
N.A.I.C.S.: 541613
David Walton *(Co-Founder)*

Subsidiaries:

MVF US LLC (1)
14th Fl 600 Congress Ave, Austin, TX 78701
Tel.: (512) 643-1896
Marketing Consultancy Services
N.A.I.C.S.: 541613

MARKLINES CO., LTD.
Sanno Park Tower 14 Nagata-cho 2-11-1, Chiyoda-ku, Tokyo, 100-6114, Japan
Tel.: (81) 342413907
Web Site: https://www.marklines.com
Year Founded: 2001
3901—(TKS)
Rev.: $34,351,050
Assets: $53,061,560
Liabilities: $14,038,200
Net Worth: $39,023,360
Earnings: $9,805,470
Emp.: 250
Fiscal Year-end: 12/31/23
Internet Automotive Information Services
N.A.I.C.S.: 519290
Makoto Sakai *(Pres & CEO)*

Subsidiaries:

MarkLines Europe GmbH (1)
Hanauer Landstr 114, 60314, Frankfurt am Main, Germany
Tel.: (49) 6990438700
Automobile Parts Distr
N.A.I.C.S.: 423120

MarkLines Mexicana S.A. de C.V. (1)
Boulevard Mariano Escobedo No 3634 Colonia Oriental Anaya, interior 503 y 504 Guanajuato, 37510, Leon, Mexico
Tel.: (52) 4777960560
Automotive Parts Mfr & Distr
N.A.I.C.S.: 336390

MarkLines North America Incorporated (1)
400 Galleria Officentre Ste 415, Southfield, MI 48034-2172
Tel.: (248) 327-6987
Emp.: 7
Internet Automotive Information Services
N.A.I.C.S.: 519290

MARKOLINES TRAFFIC CONTROLS LIMITED
6th Floor Wing-A Shree Nand Dham Sector-11 Cbd Belapur, Navi Mumbai, 400614, Maharashtra, India
Tel.: (91) 2262661111
Web Site: https://www.markolines.com
Year Founded: 2002
543364—(BOM)
Road Construction Services

N.A.I.C.S.: 237310
Sanjay Patil *(Co-Founder, Chm & Mng Dir)*

MARKOR INTERNATIONAL HOME FURNISHINGS CO., LTD.
No 506 South Beijing Road, Xinjiang Uygur Autonomous Region, Urumqi, 830011, Xinjiang, China
Tel.: (86) 2259819058
Web Site: http://www.markorfurniture.com
Year Founded: 1995
600337—(SHG)
Rev.: $631,214,265
Assets: $1,359,942,677
Liabilities: $773,382,379
Net Worth: $586,560,298
Earnings: ($41,793,022)
Fiscal Year-end: 12/31/22
Furniture Mfr & Whslr
N.A.I.C.S.: 337126
Feng Lu *(Chm)*

MARKS & SPENCER GROUP PLC
Waterside House 35 North Wharf Road, London, W2 1NW, United Kingdom
Tel.: (44) 2079354422 UK
Web Site: https://corporate.marksspencer.com
Year Founded: 1894
MAKSY—(OTCQX)
Rev.: $14,778,917,972
Assets: $12,821,493,048
Liabilities: $8,859,801,860
Net Worth: $3,961,691,188
Earnings: $419,535,480
Emp.: 47,108
Fiscal Year-end: 04/02/22
Departmental Store Operator
N.A.I.C.S.: 455110
Archie Norman *(Chm)*

Subsidiaries:

Gist Limited (1)
Rosewood Crockford Ln, Chineham Business Park, Basingstoke, RG24 8UB, Hampshire, United Kingdom
Tel.: (44) 1256891111
Web Site: https://www.gistworld.com
Logistics & Supply Chain Services
N.A.I.C.S.: 488510
Martin Gwynn *(CEO)*

Subsidiary (Non-US):

Gist Nederland B.V. (2)
Klappolder 130 Naast Dock 63, Bleiswijk, 2665 LP, South Holland, Netherlands
Tel.: (31) 88 003 4000
Web Site: http://www.gistworld.eu
Logistics & Supply Chain
N.A.I.C.S.: 541614

Marks & Spencer (Ireland) Limited (1)
24 29 Mary St, Dublin, 1, Ireland (100%)
Tel.: (353) 18728833
Web Site: http://www.marksandspencer.co.uk
Sales Range: $125-149.9 Million
Emp.: 350
Department Stores
N.A.I.C.S.: 455110
Pettie Moore *(Gen Mgr)*

Marks & Spencer Property Developments Limited (1)
35 North Wharf Rd Waterside House, W2 1NW, London, W2 1NW, United Kingdom - England (100%)
Tel.: (44) 2079354422
Web Site: http://www.marksandspencer.com
Sales Range: $900-999.9 Million
Emp.: 3,500
Real Property Developers
N.A.I.C.S.: 237210
Stuart Rose *(Chm)*

Marks and Spencer (Bradford) Limited (1)
Duckworth Ln, Bradford, BD9 6RJ, United Kingdom
Tel.: (44) 1274480743
Men & Women Clothing & Footwear Retailer
N.A.I.C.S.: 424340

Marks and Spencer 2005 (Chester Store) Limited (1)
22 Foregate Street, Chester, CH1 1HP, United Kingdom
Tel.: (44) 1244348441
Men & Women Clothing & Footwear Retailer
N.A.I.C.S.: 424340

Marks and Spencer 2005 (Glasgow Sauchiehall Store) Limited (1)
172 Sauchiehall Street, Glasgow, G2 3EE, United Kingdom
Tel.: (44) 1413326097
Men & Women Clothing & Footwear Retailer
N.A.I.C.S.: 424340

Marks and Spencer 2005 (Hedge End Store) Limited (1)
Tollbar Way Hedge End, Southampton, SO30 2UH, United Kingdom
Tel.: (44) 1489798844
Men & Women Clothing & Footwear Retailer
N.A.I.C.S.: 424340

Marks and Spencer 2005 (Kensington Store) Limited (1)
113 Kensington High Street, London, W8 5SQ, United Kingdom
Tel.: (44) 2079383711
Men & Women Clothing & Footwear Retailer
N.A.I.C.S.: 424340

Marks and Spencer 2005 (Kingston-on-Thames Store) Limited (1)
26 Clarence Street, Kingston upon Thames, KT1 1NU, United Kingdom
Tel.: (44) 2085499933
Men & Women Clothing & Footwear Retailer
N.A.I.C.S.: 424340

Marks and Spencer 2005 (Warrington Gemini Store) Limited (1)
Europa Boulevard, Warrington, WA5 7WG, United Kingdom
Tel.: (44) 1925710077
Men & Women Clothing & Footwear Retailer
N.A.I.C.S.: 424340

Marks and Spencer Pension Trust Limited (1)
Hartshead House 2 Cutlers Gate, Sheffield, S4 7TL, United Kingdom
Tel.: (44) 3330037080
Web Site: https://www.mandspensionscheme.com
Pension Fund Management Services
N.A.I.C.S.: 523940

The Sports Edit Limited (1)
Waterside House 35 North Wharf Road, London, W2 1NW, United Kingdom
Tel.: (44) 2037930964
Web Site: https://www.thesportsedit.com
Yoga Training Services
N.A.I.C.S.: 611699

MARKS ELECTRICAL GROUP PLC
4 Boston Rd, Leicester, LE4 1AU, United Kingdom
Tel.: (44) 1162515515 UK
Web Site: https://group.markselectrical.co.uk
Year Founded: 1987
MRK—(AIM)
Rev.: $121,390,917
Assets: $40,789,405
Liabilities: $23,622,761
Net Worth: $17,166,643
Earnings: $6,403,963
Emp.: 250

Fiscal Year-end: 03/31/23
Electronic Components Distr
N.A.I.C.S.: 423620
Mark Smithson *(CEO)*

Subsidiaries:

Marks Electrical Limited (1)
4 Boston Rd, Leicester, LE4 1AU, United Kingdom
Tel.: (44) 1162515515
Web Site: https://www.markselectrical.co.uk
Electrical Equipment Distr
N.A.I.C.S.: 423440

MARKSANS PHARMA LTD
11th Floor Grandeur Off Veera Desai Road Opp Gundecha Symphony, Andheri W, Mumbai, 400 053, India
Tel.: (91) 2240012000
Web Site: https://www.marksanspharma.com
524404—(BOM)
Rev.: $229,177,148
Assets: $262,620,826
Liabilities: $50,994,185
Net Worth: $211,626,641
Earnings: $31,811,162
Emp.: 852
Fiscal Year-end: 03/31/23
Pharmaceuticals
N.A.I.C.S.: 424210
Mark Saldanha *(Chm & Mng Dir)*

Subsidiaries:

Bell Sons & Co (Druggists) Limited (1)
Cheshire House Gorsey Lane, Widnes, WA8 0RP, Cheshire, United Kingdom
Tel.: (44) 1514221200
Web Site: https://www.bells-healthcare.com
Sales Range: $25-49.9 Million
Emp.: 150
Pharmaceuticals Whslr
N.A.I.C.S.: 424210

Nova Pharmaceuticals Australasia Pty Ltd (1)
Suite 305 10 Norbrik Drive, Bella Vista, 2153, NSW, Australia
Tel.: (61) 280907855
Web Site: https://www.novapharm.com.au
Sales Range: $25-49.9 Million
Emp.: 9
Pharmaceutical Services
N.A.I.C.S.: 456110
Lydia Chi *(CFO)*

Relonchem Limited (1)
Cheshire House Gorsey Lane, Widnes, London, WA8 0RP, Cheshire, United Kingdom
Tel.: (44) 1515561860
Web Site: https://www.relonchem.com
Sales Range: $25-49.9 Million
Emp.: 25
Pharmaceuticals Whslr
N.A.I.C.S.: 424210
Sathish Kumar *(Mng Dir)*

MARKSMEN ENERGY INC.
Suite 500 400 3rd Ave SW, Calgary, T2P 4H2, AB, Canada
Tel.: (403) 265-7270 Ca
Web Site: https://www.marksmenenergy.com
Year Founded: 1997
MKSEF—(OTCQB)
Rev.: $540,619
Assets: $1,452,556
Liabilities: $1,726,445
Net Worth: ($273,889)
Earnings: ($3,579,017)
Emp.: 1
Fiscal Year-end: 12/31/23
Oil Exploration Services
N.A.I.C.S.: 213112
Archibald J. Nesbitt *(Pres & CEO)*

MARKUSSON NEW HOLLAND OF REGINA LTD.

Markusson New Holland of Regina Ltd.—(Continued)
26 Great Plains Road, Emerald Park, S4L 1B6, SK, Canada
Tel.: (306) 781-2828
Web Site: http://www.markusson.com
Year Founded: 1961
Sales Range: $10-24.9 Million
Farm Machinery & Equipment Dealer
N.A.I.C.S.: 423820
Garth Luedtke *(Asst Mgr-Parts)*

MARLBOROUGH WINE ESTATES GROUP LIMITED
Level 6 5-7 Kingdon St, Auckland Central, Auckland, New Zealand
Tel.: (64) 92156650
Web Site: https://www.nzmwe.com
Year Founded: 2015
MWE—(NZX)
Rev.: $5,637,832
Assets: $25,712,215
Liabilities: $7,123,447
Net Worth: $18,588,769
Earnings: $176,551
Emp.: 23
Fiscal Year-end: 06/30/23
Wine Product Mfr & Distr
N.A.I.C.S.: 312130
Min Jia *(Chm)*

Subsidiaries:

Otuwhero Trustee Limited (1)
Level 3 - Tower One 205 Queen Street, PO Box 105920, Auckland, 1143, New Zealand
Tel.: (64) 92156650
Web Site: http://www.otuwine.com
Winery Product Retailer
N.A.I.C.S.: 424820

MARLEY SPOON GROUP SE
9 Rue de Bitbourg, L-1273, Luxembourg, Luxembourg
Web Site: https://ir.marleyspoongroup.com
MS1—(DEU)
Food Delivery Services
N.A.I.C.S.: 722310

Subsidiaries:

BistroMD, Inc. (1)
1575 Pine Rdg Rd Ste 21, Naples, FL 34109
Tel.: (239) 514-0700
Web Site: http://www.bistromd.com
Professional, Scientific & Technical Services
N.A.I.C.S.: 541990
Edward Cederquist *(Mgr)*

MARLIN GLOBAL LIMITED
Level 1 67-73 Hurstmere Road, Private Bag 93502, Takapuna, Auckland, 0740, New Zealand
Tel.: (64) 94840365
Web Site: https://www.marlin.co.nz
MLN—(NZX)
Rev.: $16,529,306
Assets: $121,032,297
Liabilities: $5,750,000
Net Worth: $115,282,297
Earnings: $14,113,636
Fiscal Year-end: 06/30/23
Investment Management Service
N.A.I.C.S.: 523940
Alistair Ryan *(Chm)*

MARLOK AUTOMOTIVE GMBH
Wolf Hirth Strasse 9, 73730, Esslingen, Germany
Tel.: (49) 7113154250
Web Site: http://www.marlok-automotive.com
Sales Range: $10-24.9 Million
Emp.: 90
Automobile Sound System Mfr
N.A.I.C.S.: 336390
Siegfried Otto Marlok *(Mng Dir)*

MARLOWE PLC
20 Grosvenor Place, London, SW1X 7HN, United Kingdom
Tel.: (44) 2038138498 BZ
Web Site: https://www.marloweplc.com
MRL—(AIM)
Rev.: $577,980,270
Assets: $1,056,672,540
Liabilities: $506,492,910
Net Worth: $550,179,630
Earnings: ($4,716,180)
Fiscal Year-end: 03/31/23
Investment Management Service
N.A.I.C.S.: 523999
Alex Dacre *(Founder & CEO)*

Subsidiaries:

Aquatreat Chemical Products Limited
Aquatreat House Unit 7 24 Willow Lane, Abbey Industrial Estate, Mitcham, CR4 4NA, Surrey, United Kingdom
Tel.: (44) 2084018391
Web Site: http://www.aquatreat.uk.com
Water Treatment Chemical Distr
N.A.I.C.S.: 424690

Atana Limited (1)
Hydrus House Dromintee Road Bardon Hill, Hilltop Industrial Estate, Coalville, LE67 1TX, Leicestershire, United Kingdom
Tel.: (44) 1530830020
Web Site: http://www.atana.co.uk
Waste Water Treatment Services
N.A.I.C.S.: 221320
Alan Wakeling *(Dir-Technical)*

BBC Fire Protection Limited (1)
St Florian House Ayton Road, Wymondham, NR18 0QH, Norfolk, United Kingdom
Tel.: (44) 195 385 7700
Web Site: https://www.bbcfire.co.uk
Fire Protection Services
N.A.I.C.S.: 922160
Gemma Perry *(Engr-Sys Proposal)*

Clearwater Technology Ltd. (1)
1 Archipelago Lyon Way, Frimley, GU16 7ER, United Kingdom
Tel.: (44) 12 762 1155
Web Site: http://www.clearwater.eu.com
Waste Treatment Services
N.A.I.C.S.: 221310
Blake Hatt *(Acct Mgr)*

FSE Fire Safety Systems Limited (1)
Unit 8 Ruddington Lane, Wilford Industrial Estate Wilford, Nottingham, NG11 7EP, United Kingdom
Tel.: (44) 1159812624
Web Site: http://www.fsefiresafetysystems.co.uk
Fire Alarm Maintenance & Repair Services
N.A.I.C.S.: 561621
Stuart Rye *(Mng Dir)*

Fire Alarm Fabrication Services Limited (1)
Unit 3 Roebuck Place 110 Roebuck Road, Chessington, KT9 1EU, Surrey, United Kingdom
Tel.: (44) 2089741177
Web Site: https://fafsfireandsecurity.com
Security System Services
N.A.I.C.S.: 561621
Dave Quinney *(Head-Sls)*

Flamefast Fire Systems Limited (1)
9 Brunel Close, Park Farm Industrial Estate, Wellingborough, NN8 6QX, Northants, United Kingdom
Tel.: (44) 3300457000
Web Site: http://www.flamefast-fire-suppression.co.uk
Fire Protection Services
N.A.I.C.S.: 922160
Nigel Roddie *(Mng Dir)*

Kingfisher Environmental Services Limited (1)
Unit 17 Wheatstone Court Davy Way, Quedgeley, Gloucester, GL2 2AQ, United Kingdom
Tel.: (44) 192 087 1700
Web Site: https://www.kingfisher-es.co.uk

Commercial Swimming Pool Testing Services
N.A.I.C.S.: 561790
Max Coyle *(Engr-Water Treatment)*

Managed Occupational Health Limited (1)
St Michaels House Sawmills Road, Diss, IP22 4DA, United Kingdom
Tel.: (44) 1379646650
Web Site: https://www.mohuk.co.uk
Occupational Health Services
N.A.I.C.S.: 621112
Tom Grant *(Mng Dir)*

MARMAGOA STEEL LIMITED
280 Eclate Curtorim, Salcette, Goa, 403 709, India
Tel.: (91) 832 2784289
Web Site: http://www.marmagoasteel.com
Sales Range: $25-49.9 Million
Steel Products Mfr
N.A.I.C.S.: 331110
Ashok Mittal *(Chm)*

MARMARIS ALTINYUNUS TURISTIK TESISLERI A.S.
Fevzi Cakmak Caddesi No 30, 07100, Antalya, Turkiye
Tel.: (90) 2422486800 TR
Web Site: https://www.mares.com.tr
Year Founded: 1986
Hotel & Restaurant Operator
N.A.I.C.S.: 721110
Semahat Sevim Arsel *(Chm)*

MARMEN, INC.
845 Berlinguet Street, Trois Rivieres, G8T 8N9, QC, Canada
Tel.: (819) 379-0453
Web Site: http://www.marmeninc.com
Year Founded: 1972
Machinery Parts Distr
N.A.I.C.S.: 423830
Annie Pellerin *(VP-HR & Comm)*

MARNLEN MANAGEMENT LTD
400 Cochrane Dr, Markham, L3R8E3, ON, Canada
Tel.: (905) 475-0523
Web Site: http://www.marnlen.com
Sales Range: $50-74.9 Million
Emp.: 425
Label Design Mfr
N.A.I.C.S.: 541490
Owen Duckman *(CEO)*

MAROC LEASING SA
57 Angle Bd Abdelmounmen et Rue Pinel, Casablanca, Morocco
Tel.: (212) 522429595
Web Site: http://www.marocleasing.ma
Year Founded: 1965
MLE—(CAS)
Sales Range: $25-49.9 Million
Financial Services
N.A.I.C.S.: 523999
Aziz Boutaleb *(Gen Mgr)*

MAROLINE DISTRIBUTING INC.
3300 Orlando Drive, Mississauga, L4V 1C6, ON, Canada
Tel.: (905) 671-4747
Web Site: http://www.maroline.com
Rev.: $20,000,000
Emp.: 10
Kitchen Products & Appliances Supplier
N.A.I.C.S.: 449210
David Amiel *(VP)*

MARPIN 2K4 LTD.
5-7 Great Marlborough St, Roseau, Dominica
Tel.: (767) 5004107 DM

Web Site: http://www.marpin2k4.com
Year Founded: 1982
Sales Range: $50-74.9 Million
Emp.: 120
Cable Television Broadcasting, Telephony & Internet Services
N.A.I.C.S.: 516210
Brian Doctrove *(Mgr-Svcs & Install)*

MARPOSS S.P.A.
Via Saliceto 13, Bentivoglio, 40010, Bologna, Emilia-Romagna, Italy
Tel.: (39) 051899111
Web Site: http://www.marposs.com
Year Founded: 1952
Mfr of Environmental Controls
N.A.I.C.S.: 334512
Stefano Possati *(Pres)*

Subsidiaries:

BRANKAMP GmbH (1)
Max-Planck-Str 9, 40699, Erkrath, Germany
Tel.: (49) 211250760
Web Site: http://www.brankamp.com
Sales Range: $10-24.9 Million
Process Monitoring Systems Distr
N.A.I.C.S.: 423840
Hans-Georg Conrady *(Mng Dir)*

MARPOSS (NANJING) AUTOMATION Co., Ltd. (1)
No 7 Jing Ming Street Riverside Economic Development Zone, Jiangning, Nanjing, 211199, Jiangsu, China
Tel.: (86) 25 8495 0111
Machine Tools Mfr
N.A.I.C.S.: 333517

MARPOSS AB (1)
Elementvagen 2, 691 42, Karlskoga, Sweden
Tel.: (46) 586 721130
Web Site: http://www.marposs.com
Emp.: 10
Machine Tool & Gauge Distr
N.A.I.C.S.: 423830
Markus Edvardsson *(Gen Mgr)*

MARPOSS AG (1)
Aemmenmattstrasse 18, 3123, Belp, Switzerland
Tel.: (41) 31 9602020
Measurement Equipment Mfr
N.A.I.C.S.: 334519

MARPOSS APARELHOS ELETRONICOS DE MEDICAO Ltda. (1)
Rua Dom Vilares 166, Vila Brasilina, Sao Paulo, 04160-000, Brazil
Tel.: (55) 11 23535656
Machine Tools Mfr
N.A.I.C.S.: 333517

MARPOSS AUSTRALIA Pty. Ltd. (1)
4/76 Rushdale St, Knoxfield, 3180, VIC, Australia
Tel.: (61) 3 97636889
Machine Tool & Gauge Distr
N.A.I.C.S.: 423830

MARPOSS CANADA CORP. (1)
333 Denison Street Unit 21, Markham, L3R 1B7, ON, Canada
Tel.: (905) 475-6277
Machine Tool & Gauge Distr
N.A.I.C.S.: 423830

MARPOSS COMPANY LIMITED (1)
3/4F JS Tower 184 Pangyoyeok-ro, Bundang-gu, Seongnam, 463-400, Gyeonggi-do, Korea (South)
Tel.: (82) 31 8038 8300
Machine Tool Mfr & Distr
N.A.I.C.S.: 333517

MARPOSS GmbH (1)
Willicher Damm 145, 41066, Monchengladbach, Germany
Tel.: (49) 2161 69750
Machine Tool & Gauge Distr
N.A.I.C.S.: 423830

MARPOSS INDIA Pvt. Ltd. (1)
IMT Manesar 147 Sector 7, Gurgaon, 122 050, Haryana, India
Tel.: (91) 124 4735700
Web Site: http://www.marposs.net.in

AND PRIVATE COMPANIES

Emp.: 56
Machine Tool & Gauge Distr
N.A.I.C.S.: 423830
Narender Narwal *(Deputy Mgr-HR)*

MARPOSS KABUSHIKI KAISHA (1)
Marposs Bldg 5-34-1 Minamimagome, Ota, 143-0025, Tokyo, Japan
Tel.: (81) 3 37727011
Emp.: 145
Machine Tool Mfr & Distr
N.A.I.C.S.: 333517

MARPOSS Limited (1)
Leofric Business Park Progress Way, Coventry, CV3 2TJ, United Kingdom
Tel.: (44) 24 76636688
Emp.: 30
Machine Tool & Gauge Distr
N.A.I.C.S.: 423830

MARPOSS S.A. (1)
Paseo de la Zona Franca 83-95 4a planta, Barcelona, 08038, Spain
Tel.: (34) 93 2232133
Emp.: 27
Machine Tool & Gauge Mfr & Distr
N.A.I.C.S.: 333517

MARPOSS S.A. de C.V. (1)
Boulevard Adolfo Lopez Mateos 40 Club de Golf Bellavista, 52995, Ciudad Lopez Mateos, Mexico
Tel.: (52) 55 53705533
Emp.: 44
Automobile Component Distr
N.A.I.C.S.: 423120

MARPOSS S.A.S (1)
10 Rue Lionel Terray, 92500, Rueil-Malmaison, France
Tel.: (33) 1 41390270
Machine Tool & Gauge Distr
N.A.I.C.S.: 423830

MARPOSS T&E Co., Ltd. (1)
405 284 Gongdan-ro, Gunpo, 435-862, Gyeonggi-do, Korea (South)
Tel.: (82) 70 5001 1820
Web Site: http://www.marposs.com
Machine Tools Mfr
N.A.I.C.S.: 333517

MARPOSS s.r.o. (1)
Nachodska 149/199, 193 00, Prague, Czech Republic
Tel.: (420) 2 55702000
Emp.: 9
Machine Tool & Gauge Distr
N.A.I.C.S.: 423830

MG ASIA Limited (1)
1111 Kings Road Suites 1109-10 Cityplaza One, Taikoo Shing Island East, Hong Kong, China (Hong Kong)
Tel.: (852) 2807 1783
Web Site: http://www.marposs.com
Machine Tool & Gauge Distr
N.A.I.C.S.: 423830

MG S.p.A. (1)
Via dei Metalli 1, 25039, Brescia, Italy
Tel.: (39) 030 2149 1
Web Site: http://www.marposs.com
Leak Testing System & Gauge Distr
N.A.I.C.S.: 423830

Marposs Austria GmbH (1)
Triesterstrasse 14, Ikano Burohaus 2, 2351, Wiener Neudorf, Austria
Tel.: (43) 2236 86 66 62
Machine Tool & Gauge Distr
N.A.I.C.S.: 423830

Marposs Corporation (1)
3300 Cross Creek Pkwy, Auburn Hills, MI 48326
Tel.: (248) 370-0404
Web Site: http://www.marposs.com
Sales Range: $50-74.9 Million
Emp.: 100
Measuring & Testing Equipment; Electrical
N.A.I.C.S.: 423830
Mario Gelsi *(Chm)*

Movomatic SA (1)
Rue Du Tombet 29, Peseux, 2034, Switzerland
Tel.: (41) 327325200
Web Site: https://www.movomatic.com
Semiconductor Devices Mfr

N.A.I.C.S.: 334413

Solarius Development, Inc. (1)
550 E Weddell Dr, Sunnyvale, CA 94089
Tel.: (408) 541-0151
Web Site: http://www.solarius-inc.com
Rev: $1,000,000
Emp.: 10
Totalizing Fluid Meter & Counting Device Mfr
N.A.I.C.S.: 334514
Adam Donoghue *(VP-Mktg)*

MARQUARD & BAHLS AG

MARQUARD & BAHLS AG
Admiralitaetstr 55, 20459, Hamburg, Germany
Tel.: (49) 40370040   De
Web Site: http://www.marquard-bahls.de
Sales Range: $10-24.9 Million
Emp.: 4,920
Holding Company; Oil Trading, Tank-Terminal Storage & Aviation Fueling Services
N.A.I.C.S.: 551112
Inga Tolke *(Head-Excise Dept & Customs Dept)*

Subsidiaries:

B.W.O.C. Limited (1)
BW Estate Oldmixon Crescent, Weston-super-Mare, BS24 9BA, United Kingdom
Tel.: (44) 1934 886982
Web Site: http://www.bwoc.co.uk
Petroleum Product Distr
N.A.I.C.S.: 424720

Bomin Bunker Holding GmbH & Co. KG (1)
Koreastrasse 7, 20457, Hamburg, Germany
Tel.: (49) 40 37004 0
Web Site: http://www.bomin.com
Holding Company; Marine Fuels & Lubricants Trading & Supply Services
N.A.I.C.S.: 551112
Jan Christensen *(Mng Dir)*

Subsidiary (Non-US):

AS Bominflot Estonia (2)
Parnu mnt 21, 10141, Tallinn, Estonia
Tel.: (372) 681 1550
Petroleum Product Distr
N.A.I.C.S.: 424720

BOMIN Bunker Oil Ltd. (2)
Room 1402 400 Middle Zhejiang Road Chunshengjiang Building, Shanghai, 200001, China
Tel.: (86) 21 63 51 2072 3
Petrol Transportation Services
N.A.I.C.S.: 484220

BOMINFLOT Fujairah L.L.C (2)
PO Box 1415, Fujairah, United Arab Emirates
Tel.: (971) 92 23 21 24
Petrol Transportation Services
N.A.I.C.S.: 484220
Stephen Robinson *(Mng Dir)*

BOMINFLOT do Brasil Comercio Ltda. (2)
Av Almirante Barroso 63 - Conj 1809, 20031-003, Rio de Janeiro, Brazil
Tel.: (55) 21 22 20 47 73
Petrol Transportation Services
N.A.I.C.S.: 484220
Alvaro Marques *(Mng Dir)*

Subsidiary (Domestic):

Benol Energieservice GmbH & Co. KG (2)
Carl-Benz-Strasse 35, 60386, Frankfurt am Main, Germany
Tel.: (49) 69 42 40 44
Web Site: http://www.benol.de
Petroleum Product Distr
N.A.I.C.S.: 424720

Bomin Linde LNG GmbH & Co. KG (2)
Dornbusch 2, 20095, Hamburg, Germany
Tel.: (49) 40 468959 0
Web Site: http://www.bominlinde.com
Natural Gas Distr

N.A.I.C.S.: 221210

Subsidiary (Non-US):

Bomin Oil Pvt. Ltd. (2)
5th Floor Bharat Bhavan No 1 4&6 Currimbhoy Road Ballard Estate, Mumbai, 400 001, India
Tel.: (91) 22 22 71 36 33
Petrol Transportation Services
N.A.I.C.S.: 484220

Subsidiary (Domestic):

Bomin Tanklager Kiel GmbH & Co. KG (2)
Uferstr 48, 24106, Kiel, Germany
Tel.: (49) 431 30119 0
Emp.: 12
Petrol Transportation Services
N.A.I.C.S.: 484220

Subsidiary (Non-US):

Bominflot (Gibraltar) Limited (2)
Watergardens Block 5 Suite 12/13, Gibraltar, Gibraltar
Tel.: (350) 20 04 76 16
Petrol Transportation Services
N.A.I.C.S.: 484220
Alberto Grande *(Office Mgr)*

Bominflot Bunkergesellschaft fur Mineralowle mbH & Co. KG (2)
Reconquista 1048 Floor 6, A1003ABV, Buenos Aires, Argentina
Tel.: (54) 11 43 12 08 40
Emp.: 3
Petrol Transportation Services
N.A.I.C.S.: 484220
Ariel Gryner *(Gen Mgr)*

Bominflot Greece S. A. (2)
77 Posidonos Avenue, Alimos, Athens, Greece
Tel.: (30) 21 08 99 58 44
Petrol Transportation Services
N.A.I.C.S.: 484220
Maria Assimakis *(Coord-Lubricants)*

Bottcher Energie GmbH & Co. KG (1)
Maxhuttenstr 7, 93055, Regensburg, Germany
Tel.: (49) 9 41 560333 34
Web Site: http://www.boettcher-energie.de
Petroleum Product Distr
N.A.I.C.S.: 424720
Gerhart Grambow *(Mng Dir)*

Deglmann Energie GmbH & Co. KG (1)
Hinterm Rangierbahnhof 24, 92637, Weiden, Germany
Tel.: (49) 9 61 4 71 00 0
Web Site: http://www.deglmann.de
Petroleum Product Distr
N.A.I.C.S.: 424720

Emstank GmbH (1)
Stedinger Strasse 26, Emden, 26723, Germany
Tel.: (49) 4921 96 00 0
Petroleum Product Distr
N.A.I.C.S.: 424720

Gesellschaft fur Mineralol-Analytik und Qualitatsmanagement mbH + Co. KG (1)
Dieselstrasse 4-16, 60314, Frankfurt am Main, Germany
Tel.: (49) 69426811
Web Site: http://www.gma-analytik.de
Fuel Quality Control Solutions
N.A.I.C.S.: 541990

Greiner GmbH (1)
Riedbachstrasse 5, 74385, Pleidelsheim, Germany
Tel.: (49) 7144 8112 0
Web Site: http://www.greiner-gmbh.de
Chair Mfr
N.A.I.C.S.: 337211
Kristina Greiner *(Mng Dir & Gen Mgr)*

JB German Oil GmbH & Co. KG (1)
Wolzower Weg 13 - 19, 19243, Witten, Germany
Tel.: (49) 38852 90620
Web Site: http://www.jb-germanoil.de

Petroleum Product Distr
N.A.I.C.S.: 424720

Kaiser Sohne Mineralole GmbH & Co. KG (1)
Wagenbergstrasse 73, 59759, Arnsberg, Germany
Tel.: (49) 29 32 97 81 0
Web Site: http://www.kaiser-soehne.de
Petroleum Product Distr
N.A.I.C.S.: 424720

Klindworth-Kronol Energie GmbH & Co. KG (1)
Pelzerstrasse 4, 20095, Hamburg, Germany
Tel.: (49) 40 23 78 32 0
Web Site: http://www.klindworth-kronol.de
Petroleum Product Distr
N.A.I.C.S.: 424720

LSA Lubes Services GmbH & Co. KG (1)
Olhafen Lobau, Vienna, 1220, Austria
Tel.: (43) 12851400
Petroleum Product Distr
N.A.I.C.S.: 424720

Lipps MineralOle GmbH (1)
Gotenweg 18, 58119, Hagen, Germany
Tel.: (49) 23 34 95 80 0
Web Site: http://www.lippsenergy.de
Petroleum Product Distr
N.A.I.C.S.: 424720

Mabanaft Austria GmbH & Co. KG (1)
Wohllebengasse 19, 1040, Vienna, Austria
Tel.: (43) 1 3704506
Petroleum Product Distr
N.A.I.C.S.: 424720

Mabanaft Hungary Kft. (1)
Meszaros utca 58/b, 1016, Budapest, Hungary
Tel.: (36) 1 450 29 60
Web Site: http://www.mabanaft.hu
Petroleum Product Distr
N.A.I.C.S.: 424720

Mabanaft Limited (1)
20th Floor Portland House Bressenden Place, London, SW1E 5BH, United Kingdom
Tel.: (44) 207 802 3300
Web Site: http://www.mabanaft.co.uk
Petroleum Product Distr
N.A.I.C.S.: 424720

Mabanaft Moldova SRL (1)
90 Columna str, 2012, Chisinau, Moldova
Tel.: (373) 22 200 725
Petroleum Product Distr
N.A.I.C.S.: 424720

Mabanaft Pte. Ltd. (1)
83 Clemenceau Avenue 12-08 UE Square, Singapore, 239920, Singapore
Tel.: (65) 6305 8000
Petroleum Product Distr
N.A.I.C.S.: 424720

Manfred Mayer MMM Mineralol Vertriebsgesellschaft m.b.H. (1)
Schreinergasse 1, 7201, Neudorfl, Burgenland, Austria
Tel.: (43) 5 77 240 1
Web Site: http://www.mmm-energie.at
Petroleum Product Distr
N.A.I.C.S.: 424720

Matrix Marine Fuels L LC (1)
3 Allen Ctr 333 Clay St Ste 2400, Houston, TX 77002
Tel.: (281) 459-5100
Petroleum Product Distr
N.A.I.C.S.: 424720
Beverly Squyres *(Coord-Office Support)*

Mineralolvertrieb Brakel GmbH & Co. KG (1)
Driburger Str 7, 33034, Brakel, Germany
Tel.: (49) 52 72 39 49 6 0
Web Site: http://www.mvb-oil.de
Petroleum Product Distr
N.A.I.C.S.: 424720

Muhlenbruch Stinnes GmbH & Co. KG (1)
Osterholzer Mohle Damm 42-44, 28325, Bremen, Germany

MARQUARD & BAHLS AG

INTERNATIONAL PUBLIC

Marquard & Bahls AG—(Continued)
Tel.: (49) 421420071
Web Site: http://www.muehlenbruch-stinnes.de
Petroleum Product Distr
N.A.I.C.S.: 424720

OIL! Tankstellen AG (1)
Spitalstrasse 72, 8630, Ruti, Switzerland
Tel.: (41) 55 251 53 07
Web Site: http://www.oil-tankstellen.ch
Petroleum Product Distr
N.A.I.C.S.: 424720

Oiltanking GmbH (1)
Admiralitaetstrasse 55, 20459, Hamburg, Germany
Tel.: (49) 40 37099 0
Web Site: http://www.oiltanking.com
Holding Company; Petroleum & Chemical Storage Terminals Operator
N.A.I.C.S.: 551112
Rance Fromme (Gen Mgr-Asia, Middle East & Africa)

Joint Venture (Non-US):

Advario Singapore Chemical Pte. Ltd. (2)
1 Seraya Avenue, Jurong Island, Singapore, 628208, Singapore
Tel.: (65) 64731700
Web Site: https://advario.com
Petroleum & Chemical Storage Terminal Operator
N.A.I.C.S.: 493190

Subsidiary (Non-US):

Colon Oil and Services S. A. (2)
Cocosolo Norte Calle Culebra, Colon, Panama
Tel.: (507) 4307330
Petroleum Product Distr
N.A.I.C.S.: 424710

IOT Anwesha Engineering & Construction Limited (2)
Senate square A - Tower Vuda Road Gotri, Vadodara, 390021, India
Tel.: (91) 265 3936200
Web Site: http://www.iotaec.com
Emp.: 120
Engineeering Services
N.A.I.C.S.: 541330
Asim Chandra (Mng Dir)

Unit (Domestic):

IOT Anwesha Engineering & Construction Limited - Storage & Maintenance Unit (3)
Plot No 716 Road No C Plot No 301 & 305 Road N0 12 GIDC, Manjusar Savli, Vadodara, 391775, India
Tel.: (91) 9228023304
Engineeering Services
N.A.I.C.S.: 541330

Subsidiary (Non-US):

IOT Infrastructure & Energy Services Ltd. (2)
Plot No Y2 Near Nahur Railway Station Off CEAT Tyre Road, Nahur, Mumbai, 400078, India
Tel.: (91) 22 6152 4500
Web Site: http://www.iotinfraenergy.com
Logistics Consulting Servies
N.A.I.C.S.: 541614

JSZ Kazakhstancaspishelf (2)
7 Begailin str, 050010, Almaty, Kazakhstan
Tel.: (7) 727 396 94 45
Web Site: http://www.ksp.kazkom.info
Geological Services
N.A.I.C.S.: 541360

Logistica de Quimicos del Sur S.A.C. (2)
Terminal Portuario de Matarani s/n, Arequipa, Islay, Peru
Tel.: (51) 54 557 185
Petroleum Product Distr
N.A.I.C.S.: 424710

Subsidiary (US):

Newsco USA Inc. (2)
1630 Welton St, Denver, CO 80202
Tel.: (303) 623-2173
Petroleum Product Distr
N.A.I.C.S.: 424710

Subsidiary (Non-US):

Oiltanking (Nanjing) Co., Ltd (2)
Nanjing Chemical Industrial Park, Nanjing, 211512, Jiangsu, China
Tel.: (86) 25 57129018
Petroleum Product Distr
N.A.I.C.S.: 424710

Oiltanking Amsterdam B.V. (2)
Heining 100 Westpoort No 6450, 1047 AH, Amsterdam, Netherlands
Tel.: (31) 20 4070 100
Petroleum Product Distr
N.A.I.C.S.: 424710

Oiltanking Bulgaria A.D. (2)
Industrial Zone Port Varna West, Devnya, 9160, Varna, Bulgaria
Tel.: (359) 519 92646
Petroleum Product Distr
N.A.I.C.S.: 424720

Oiltanking Colombia S. A. (2)
Cra 7 80-49 Oficina 304 Edificio EL Nogal, Bogota, Colombia
Tel.: (57) 1 3217183
Petroleum Product Distr
N.A.I.C.S.: 424710

Oiltanking Copenhagen A/S (2)
Provestenen S-vej 4, 2300, Copenhagen, Denmark
Tel.: (45) 32 959 595
Web Site: http://www.oiltanking.com
Petroleum Product Distr
N.A.I.C.S.: 424710

Oiltanking Daya Bay Co. Ltd. (2)
301 Shi Hua Da Dao Dayawan Petrochemical Industrial Park, Huizhou, 516082, Guangdong, China
Tel.: (86) 752 309 8980
Petroleum Product Distr
N.A.I.C.S.: 424710

Subsidiary (Domestic):

Oiltanking Deutschland GmbH & Co. KG (2)
Admiralitatstrasse 55, 20459, Hamburg, Germany
Tel.: (49) 40 37099 0
Web Site: http://www.oiltanking.com
Petroleum & Chemical Storage Terminals Operator
N.A.I.C.S.: 493190

Subsidiary (Non-US):

Oiltanking Ghent N.V. (2)
Moervaartkaai 12, 9042, Gent, Belgium
Tel.: (32) 9 3422 727
Petroleum Product Distr
N.A.I.C.S.: 424710

Oiltanking Hungary Kft. (2)
Gaz utca 1, 1211, Budapest, Hungary
Tel.: (36) 1 4257 645
Petroleum Product Distr
N.A.I.C.S.: 424710

Oiltanking Malta Ltd (2)
Port of Marsaxlokk Kalafrana, BBG 3011, Birzebbuga, Malta
Tel.: (356) 21 650 230
Petroleum Product Distr
N.A.I.C.S.: 424710

Joint Venture (Non-US):

Oiltanking Odfjell Terminals & Co. LLC (2)
322 Falaj Al Qabail, PO Box 369, Plot 28 Sohar Industrial Port, Sohar, Oman (51.74%)
Tel.: (968) 2670 0300
Web Site: http://www.oiltanking.com
Petroleum & Chemical Storage Terminal Operator
N.A.I.C.S.: 493190

Subsidiary (Non-US):

Oiltanking Peru S. A. C. (2)
Av Alfredo Benavides 768 Oficina 1105, Miraflores, Lima, Peru
Tel.: (51) 1 241 59 19
Petroleum Product Distr
N.A.I.C.S.: 424710

Subsidiary (US):

Oiltanking Port Neches, LLC (2)
100 E Port Neches Ave, Port Neches, TX 77651
Tel.: (409) 835-5381
Petroleum Product Distr
N.A.I.C.S.: 424710

Subsidiary (Non-US):

Oiltanking Sonmarin Oy (2)
Mussalo Terminal Port of Mussalo, 48310, Kotka, Finland
Tel.: (358) 5 2109 781
Petroleum Product Distr
N.A.I.C.S.: 424710

Oiltanking Stolthaven Antwerp N. V. (2)
Haven 623 Scheldelaan 450, 2040, Antwerp, Belgium
Tel.: (32) 3 5611 500
Petroleum Product Distr
N.A.I.C.S.: 424710

Oiltanking Terminais Ltda. (2)
Av Paisagista Jose Silva de Azevedo Neto 200 Bloco O2 sala 104, Barra da Tijuca, 22775-056, Rio de Janeiro, Brazil
Tel.: (55) 21 2516 2966
Petroleum Product Distr
N.A.I.C.S.: 424710

Oiltanking Terneuzen B.V. (2)
Elementenweg 1 Haven 85, 4542 SM, Terneuzen, Netherlands
Tel.: (31) 115 670 800
Petroleum Product Distr
N.A.I.C.S.: 424710

Subsidiary (US):

Oiltanking Texas City, L.P. (2)
2800 Loop 197 S, Texas City, TX 77590
Tel.: (409) 797-1700
Web Site: http://www.oiltanking.com
Crude & Refined Petroleum Storage Terminal Operator
N.A.I.C.S.: 493190
Jan Vogel (Gen Mgr)

Subsidiary (Non-US):

PT Oiltanking Merak (2)
JI Yos Sudarso Desa Lebak Gede Kecamatan Pulo Merak, Cilegon, Banten, Indonesia
Tel.: (62) 254 572 740
Petroleum Product Distr
N.A.I.C.S.: 424710

Star Energy Resources Ltd. (2)
PO Box 16811, Jebel Ali Free Zone, Dubai, United Arab Emirates
Tel.: (971) 4 8816 733
Petroleum Product Distr
N.A.I.C.S.: 424710

Subsidiary (US):

United Bulk Terminals Davant LLC (2)
14537 Hwy 15, Washington, LA 70040
Tel.: (504) 333-7400
Petroleum Product Distr
N.A.I.C.S.: 424710

Oiltech Lubes Service GmbH & Co. KG (1)
Max-Planck-Strasse 1, 40699, Erkrath, Germany
Tel.: (49) 211 68 78 41 0
Web Site: http://www.oiltech.de
Petroleum Product Distr
N.A.I.C.S.: 424720
Klaus-Jurgen Huber (Mng Dir)

Oliehandel Klaas de Boer B. V. (1)
Postbus 3, 8320 AA, Urk, Netherlands
Tel.: (31) 527 681343
Web Site: http://www.klaasdeboer.nl
Petroleum Product Distr
N.A.I.C.S.: 424720

Ostsee MineralOl-Bunker GmbH (1)
Thomas-Mann-Strasse 20, 18055, Rostock, Germany
Tel.: (49) 381 252230
Petroleum Product Distr
N.A.I.C.S.: 424720

Petrocargo MineralOl-Logistik GmbH (1)
Bunder Strasse 184, 32120, Hiddenhausen, Germany
Tel.: (49) 52 21 68 86 0
Petroleum Product Distr
N.A.I.C.S.: 424720

SBI (Sea Bunkering International) B. V. (1)
Hereplein 5, 9711 GA, Groningen, Netherlands
Tel.: (31) 50 4099 160
Web Site: http://www.sbigroup.nl
Petroleum Product Distr
N.A.I.C.S.: 424720
Dave Gregory (Mng Dir)

Skytanking Holding GmbH (1)
Admiralitatstrasse 55, Hamburg, 20459, Germany
Tel.: (49) 4037099
Web Site: http://www.skytanking.com
Aviation Fuel Handling Services
N.A.I.C.S.: 488190
Paul Workman (Mng Dir)

Subsidiary (Non-US):

IndianOil Skytanking Delhi Ltd. (2)
New Delhi Indira Gandhi Intl Airport Fuel Farm Facility, Shahabad Mohamadpur, New Delhi, 110061, India
Tel.: (91) 986 850 28 69
Petroleum Product Distr
N.A.I.C.S.: 424720
A. P. Acharya (VP)

Luxfuel S.A. (2)
Aeroport de Luxembourg, 1110, Sandweiler, Luxembourg
Tel.: (352) 43 19 29 1
Petroleum Product Distr
N.A.I.C.S.: 424720

Skytanking Bordeaux SAS (2)
Aeroport de Bordeaux Merignac, 33700, Bordeaux, France
Tel.: (33) 5 56 34 51 63
Petroleum Product Distr
N.A.I.C.S.: 424720
Philippe Dutilh (Mgr)

Skytanking Calulo Ltd. (2)
King Shaka International Airport, PO Box 57917, Durban, 4407, South Africa
Tel.: (27) 32 436 6477
Petroleum Product Distr
N.A.I.C.S.: 424720
Keith MacQuillin (Gen Mgr)

Subsidiary (Domestic):

Skytanking GmbH & Co. KG (2)
Flughafen Frankfurt Gebaude 123c, 60549, Frankfurt am Main, Germany
Tel.: (49) 69 690 27743
Petroleum Product Distr
N.A.I.C.S.: 424720

Subsidiary (Non-US):

Skytanking N.V./S.A. (2)
Ikaroslaan 17, Brussels Airport, 1930, Zaventem, Belgium (63%)
Tel.: (32) 2 709 7070
Web Site: http://www.skytanking.com
Sales Range: $1-9.9 Million
Emp.: 50
Aviation Fuel Handling Services
N.A.I.C.S.: 488190
Luc Maes (Mgr-Ops)

Skytanking Nice SAS (2)
Aeroport de Nice Cote d'Azur, 06056, Nice, Cedex, France
Tel.: (33) 4 93 21 39 88
Petroleum Product Distr
N.A.I.C.S.: 424720
Andre Troncale (Deputy Mgr)

Skytanking Ostend N. V. (2)
Ostend Bruges Airport Nieuwpoortesteenweg 889, Postbus 16, 8400, Oostende, Belgium
Tel.: (32) 59 80 16 48
Fuel Storage Services
N.A.I.C.S.: 424710

AND PRIVATE COMPANIES

Tim Hallam (Gen Mgr)

Subsidiary (Domestic):

Skytanking Stuttgart GmbH & Co. KG (2)
Flughafen Stuttgart Flughafenstr 100, 70629, Stuttgart, Germany
Tel.: (49) 711 948 25 33
Fuel Storage Services
N.A.I.C.S.: 424710
Thomas Stitzl (Gen Mgr)

Staack Pooltankstellen GmbH & Co. KG (1)
Konig-Georg-Deich 8, 21107, Hamburg, Germany
Tel.: (49) 40 31 76 17 0
Web Site: http://www.staack-pooltankstellen.de
Gas Storage Services
N.A.I.C.S.: 424710

Thomas Silvey Ltd. (1)
Unit 5 Badminton Road Trading Estate Yate, Bristol, BS37 5NS, United Kingdom
Tel.: (44) 1454 333020
Web Site: http://www.silvey.co.uk
Petroleum Product Distr
N.A.I.C.S.: 424720

Uhlenbruck Energie GmbH (1)
Duisburger Strasse 351-353, 45478, Mulheim an der Ruhr, Germany
Tel.: (49) 208 58955 0
Web Site: http://www.uhlenbruck.de
Petroleum Product Distr
N.A.I.C.S.: 424720

MARQUEE RESOURCES LIMITED
22 Townshend Road, Subiaco, 6008, WA, Australia
Tel.: (61) 893880051 AU
Web Site:
  https://www.marqueeresources.com
MQR—(ASX)
Rev.: $29,612
Assets: $9,776,090
Liabilities: $281,404
Net Worth: $9,494,685
Earnings: ($4,705,066)
Fiscal Year-end: 06/30/24
Mineral Exploration Services
N.A.I.C.S.: 213113
Charles Thomas (Exec Chm, Chm & Mng Dir)

MARQUEST ASSET MANAGEMENT INC.
161 Bay Street Suite 4420, PO Box 204, Toronto, M5J 2S1, ON, Canada
Tel.: (416) 777-7350
Web Site: http://www.marquest.ca
Year Founded: 1985
Investment & Wealth Management Services
N.A.I.C.S.: 523940
Jean-claude Major (Exec VP)

MARS GROUP HOLDINGS CORPORATION
1-10-7 Shinjuku, Shinjuku-ku, Tokyo, 160-0022, Japan
Tel.: (81) 333528555
Web Site: https://www.mars-ghd.co.jp
Year Founded: 1974
6419—(TKS)
Rev.: $241,760,750
Assets: $554,949,160
Liabilities: $83,960,220
Net Worth: $470,988,940
Earnings: $56,746,850
Emp.: 436
Fiscal Year-end: 03/31/24
Holding Company; Electronic Devices Mfr; Software Developer
N.A.I.C.S.: 551112
Akihiro Matsunami (Chm & Pres)

MARSA MARSA ALAM FOR TOURISM DEVELOPMENT
6A Aswan Square Mohandessin, Cairo, Egypt
Tel.: (20) 2 33041115
Web Site:
  http://www.badawimarsaalam.com
Year Founded: 2003
MMAT.CA—(EGX)
Sales Range: Less than $1 Million
Home Management Services
N.A.I.C.S.: 721110
Ahmad Kamal Al Olaimi (Chm)

MARSALIS BYGG SVERIGE AB
Salve 3A, 11612, Tallinn, Estonia
Tel.: (372) 6 777 110 SE
Web Site: http://www.marsalis.ee
Year Founded: 2008
Sales Range: $50-74.9 Million
Emp.: 350
Structural Steel & Concrete Engineering Contractor
N.A.I.C.S.: 541330
Erich Reimets (Mgr)

MARSAN FOODS LIMITED
160 Thermos Road, Toronto, M1L4W2, ON, Canada
Tel.: (416) 755-9262
Web Site:
  http://www.marsanfoods.com
Year Founded: 1970
Rev.: $30,675,436
Emp.: 100
Frozen Products Distr
N.A.I.C.S.: 311710
James Jewett (VP)

MARSDEN BUILDING SOCIETY
6-20 Russell Street, Nelson, BB9 7NJ, Lancashire, United Kingdom
Tel.: (44) 1282 440500
Web Site:
  http://www.themarsden.co.uk
Year Founded: 1860
Rev.: $19,563,826
Assets: $754,451,994
Liabilities: $701,364,984
Net Worth: $53,087,010
Earnings: $2,417,279
Emp.: 72
Fiscal Year-end: 12/31/19
Mortgage Lending
N.A.I.C.S.: 522310
Rob M. Pheasey (CEO)

MARSDEN MARITIME HOLDINGS LIMITED
8 Marsden Bay Drive Marsden Point, Ruakaka, 0171, New Zealand
Tel.: (64) 94325033
Web Site:
  https://www.marsdenmaritime.co.nz
MMH—(NZX)
Rev.: $6,730,046
Assets: $117,119,709
Liabilities: $21,108,033
Net Worth: $96,011,675
Earnings: $4,741,607
Emp.: 15
Fiscal Year-end: 06/30/23
Port & Investment Management Services
N.A.I.C.S.: 488320
Gavin Carroll (Controller-Fin)

Subsidiaries:

Counties Energy Ltd. (1)
14 Glasgow Road, Pukekohe, 2120, Auckland, New Zealand
Tel.: (64) 9 237 0300
Web Site: https://www.countiesenergy.co.nz
Electric Power Distribution Services
N.A.I.C.S.: 221122
Vern Dark (Chm)

NPC Corporate Services Ltd. (1)
PO Box 848, Whangarei, 0140, Northland, New Zealand
Tel.: (64) 9 438 1279
Web Site:
  http://www.northlandportcorp.co.nz
Business Management Services
N.A.I.C.S.: 561110

MARSH GLOBAL HOLDINGS LTD
Suite 3206 32/F Tower 6 The Gateway Harbour City 9 Canton Rd, Tsim Sha Tsui, Kowloon, China (Hong Kong)
Tel.: (852) 26258288
Web Site: https://www.marsh-global.net
Emp.: 100
Industrial Machinery & Equipment Mfr & Distr
N.A.I.C.S.: 444180
William Marsh (Founder & Chm)

Subsidiaries:

Federal Heath Sign Company, LLC (1)
2300 N Highway 121, Euless, TX 76039
Tel.: (817) 685-9075
Web Site: http://www.federalheath.com
Custom Electric Signs Mfr
N.A.I.C.S.: 339950

Branch (Domestic):

Federal Heath Sign Co. (2)
2300 N Hwy 121, Euless, TX 76039
Tel.: (817) 685-9076
Web Site: http://www.federalheath.com
Sales Range: $10-24.9 Million
Emp.: 150
Custom Neon Signs Mfr
N.A.I.C.S.: 339950

MARSHALL AMPLIFICATION PLC
Denbigh Road, Bletchley, Milton Keynes, MK1 1DQ, Bucks, United Kingdom
Tel.: (44) 1908375411 UK
Web Site:
  http://www.marshallamps.com
Year Founded: 1962
Sales Range: $25-49.9 Million
Emp.: 250
Amplifiers Mfr
N.A.I.C.S.: 334310
John Ellery (Chm)

MARSHALL BOYA VE VERNIK SANAYII AS
1 Tuna Cd Dilovasi Organize Sanayi Bolgesi 1 Kisim Dilovasi Osb, Dilovasi, 41455, Kocaeli, Turkiye
Tel.: (90) 4448800
Web Site:
  https://www.marshallboya.com
MRSHL—(IST)
Sales Range: Less than $1 Million
Chemical Products Mfr
N.A.I.C.S.: 325998
Johannes Petrus Van Kesteren (Chm)

MARSHALL CONSTRUCTION LIMITED
The Whins, Alloa, FK10 3TA, Scotland, United Kingdom
Tel.: (44) 1259219500
Web Site:
  http://www.marshallconstruction.com
Year Founded: 1983
Rev.: $54,035,207
Emp.: 322
Construction Services
N.A.I.C.S.: 236220
John Marshall (Founder)

MARSHALL OF CAMBRIDGE (HOLDINGS) LIMITED

Subsidiaries:

Marshall Construction Limited - Scaffold Division (1)
Balquharn Farm, Alva, FK12 5NZ, United Kingdom
Tel.: (44) 1259763930
Architectural Design & Engineering Services
N.A.I.C.S.: 541310
Billy Carson (Mgr-Ops)

MARSHALL FENN COMMUNICATIONS LTD.
1300 Yonge Street Suite 701, Toronto, M4T 1X3, ON, Canada
Tel.: (416) 962-3366
Web Site: http://www.marshall-fenn.com
Year Founded: 1955
Rev.: $23,000,000
Emp.: 20
Public Relations & Advertising Services
N.A.I.C.S.: 541820
Jim Kabrajee (Partner)

Subsidiaries:

Marshall Fenn Communications Ltd. (1)
2320 Paseo del Prado Ste 208, Las Vegas, NV 89102
Tel.: (702) 367-6667
Sales Range: $25-49.9 Million
Emp.: 5
Public Relations & Advertising Agency
N.A.I.C.S.: 541820

MARSHALL MACHINES LTD.
C 86 Phase-V Focal Point, Ludhiana, 141010, India
Tel.: (91) 1615012406
Web Site:
  https://www.marshallcnc.com
MARSHALL—(NSE)
Rev.: $4,436,054
Assets: $16,940,175
Liabilities: $12,200,582
Net Worth: $4,739,593
Earnings: ($827,232)
Emp.: 195
Fiscal Year-end: 03/31/23
Farm Machinery & Equipment Mfr
N.A.I.C.S.: 333111
Phulljit Singh Grover (CEO)

MARSHALL MONTEAGLE PLC
11 Sunbury Park Douglas Saunders Drive, La Lucia, Durban, 4051, South Africa
Tel.: (27) 315667600
Web Site:
  https://monteaglegroup.com
MMP—(JSE)
Rev.: $89,491,000
Assets: $121,302,000
Liabilities: $30,737,000
Net Worth: $90,565,000
Earnings: $2,278,000
Fiscal Year-end: 03/31/24
Financial Investment Services
N.A.I.C.S.: 523999
Warwick H. Marshall (CEO)

MARSHALL OF CAMBRIDGE (HOLDINGS) LIMITED
The Airport, Cambridge, CB5 8RY, United Kingdom
Tel.: (44) 1223 373 737 UK
Web Site:
  http://www.marshallgroup.co.uk
Year Founded: 1909
Rev.: $3,152,172,077
Assets: $1,198,959,944
Liabilities: $871,499,485
Net Worth: $327,460,459
Earnings: $38,760,947
Emp.: 5,786
Fiscal Year-end: 12/31/18

MARSHALL OF CAMBRIDGE (HOLDINGS) LIMITED

Marshall of Cambridge (Holdings) Limited—(Continued)
Investment Holding Company
N.A.I.C.S.: 551112
Robert D. Marshall *(Vice Chm)*

Subsidiaries:

Marshall Group Properties Limited (1)
The Airport Newmarket Road, Cambridge, CB5 8RX, United Kingdom
Tel.: (44) 122 337 3247
Web Site: https://www.marshallgroupproperties.co.uk
Property Development Services
N.A.I.C.S.: 531390
Richard Howe *(Mng Dir)*

Marshall Land Systems Limited (1)
Airport House The Airport, Newmarket Road, Cambridge, CB5 8RX, United Kingdom
Tel.: (44) 1223 373737
Web Site: http://www.marshall-ls.com
Sales Range: $250-299.9 Million
Emp.: 600
Holding Company; Industrial & Military Vehicle Designer & Mfr
N.A.I.C.S.: 551112

Subsidiary (Domestic):

Marshall Fleet Solutions Limited (2)
Airport House The Airport Newmarket Road, Cambridge, CB5 8RX, United Kingdom
Tel.: (44) 8007311685
Web Site: http://www.marshallfleetsolutions.co.uk
Refrigeration Vehicle Fleet Management Services
N.A.I.C.S.: 811114
E. Gedney *(Comml Dir)*

Marshall Vehicle Engineering Limited (2)
Galaxy Site Hampstead Avenue, Mildenhall Industrial Estate, Mildenhall, IP28 7RE, Suffolk, United Kingdom
Tel.: (44) 1223 373221
Emp.: 56
Military Armored Vehicle & Protective Systems Designer & Mfr
N.A.I.C.S.: 336992

Marshall of Cambridge (Airport Properties) Limited (1)
Cambridge City Airport Newmarket Road, Cambridge, CB5 8RX, United Kingdom (100%)
Tel.: (44) 1223373535
Web Site: http://cambridgeairport.com
Sales Range: $550-599.9 Million
Emp.: 2,000
Airport Operator
N.A.I.C.S.: 488119
Jon Harper *(Mgr-Bus Dev)*

Marshall of Cambridge (Motor Holdings) Limited (1)
Airport House The Airport, Newmarket Road, Cambridge, CB5 8RX, United Kingdom (100%)
Tel.: (44) 1223377000
Sales Range: $750-799.9 Million
Emp.: 2,000
Holding Company; Motor Vehicle Dealerships & Leasing Services
N.A.I.C.S.: 551112
Daksh Gupta *(CEO)*

Subsidiary (Domestic):

Marshall Motor Group Limited (2)
Airport House The Airport, Newmarket Road, Cambridge, CB5 8RX, United Kingdom
Tel.: (44) 1223377000
Web Site: http://www.marshallweb.co.uk
Holding Company; New & User Car Dealerships Operator
N.A.I.C.S.: 551112
F. Laud *(Dir-Fin)*

Subsidiary (Domestic):

Marshall Cambridge Peugeot (3)
Teversham House, Cambridge, CB5 8AA, United Kingdom
Tel.: (44) 1223411442
Web Site: http://www.marshallweb.co.uk
Passenger Car Leasing Distr
N.A.I.C.S.: 532112

Marshall of Cambridge Aerospace Limited (1)
Airport House The Airport Newmarket Road, Cambridge, CB5 8RX, United Kingdom
Tel.: (44) 1223373737
Web Site: http://www.marshallaerospace.com
Sales Range: $150-199.9 Million
Emp.: 2,000
Aircraft Design & Engineering Services
N.A.I.C.S.: 541330
Steve J. Fitz-Gerald *(CEO)*

Subsidiary (Domestic):

Aeropeople Limited (2)
Concorde House Newmarket Road, Cambridge, CB5 8AA, United Kingdom
Tel.: (44) 1223 373333
Web Site: http://www.aeropeople.com
Contract Manpower Services
N.A.I.C.S.: 561320
Kevan Bishop *(Mng Dir)*

Subsidiary (Non-US):

Marshall Aerospace Australia PTY Limited (2)
PO Box 954, Richmond, 2753, NSW, Australia
Tel.: (61) 245873665
Emp.: 12
Aircraft Maintenance Services
N.A.I.C.S.: 488190
Greig Barton *(Gen Mgr)*

Marshall Aerospace Canada, Inc. (2)
141 Laurier Avenue West Suite 900, Ottawa, K1P 5J3, ON, Canada
Tel.: (613) 321-0161
Web Site: https://www.marshallaerospace.com
Aircraft Maintenance Services
N.A.I.C.S.: 488190

Marshall Aerospace Netherlands B.V. (2)
Haagse Schouwweg 8m, 2332 KG, Leiden, Netherlands
Tel.: (31) 71 579 59 21
Web Site: http://www.marshalladg.com
Emp.: 10
Aircraft Maintenance Services
N.A.I.C.S.: 488190

S.G. Smith (Motors) Beckenham Limited (1)
237 Croydon Road, Beckenham, London, BR3 3PT, United Kingdom
Tel.: (44) 203 811 0213
Car Dealing Services
N.A.I.C.S.: 441120

S.G. Smith (Motors) Croydon Limited (1)
414 Purley Way, Croydon, London, CR0 4NZ, United Kingdom
Tel.: (44) 203 131 8012
Car Dealing Services
N.A.I.C.S.: 441120

S.G. Smith (Motors) Sydenham Limited (1)
140-149 Mayow Road, Sydenham, London, SE26 4HZ, United Kingdom
Tel.: (44) 203 811 0276
Car Dealing Services
N.A.I.C.S.: 441120

The Cambridge Aero Club Limited (1)
The Airport Newmarket Rd, Cambridge, CB58RX, United Kingdom (100%)
Tel.: (44) 1223373717
Web Site: http://www.cambridgeaeroclub.co.uk
Emp.: 5
Aircraft Engine & Engine Parts Mfr
N.A.I.C.S.: 336412
Terry Holloway *(Mng Dir)*

Wood of Salisbury Limited (1)
Chaussee De Treycovagnes 10D, Tansley, Matlock, DE4 5FY, United Kingdom
Tel.: (44) 162 958 2272
Web Site: https://www.salisburyandwood.co.uk
Building Materials Distr
N.A.I.C.S.: 423390

MARSHALL WACE LLP

George House 131 Sloane Street, London, SW1X 9AT, United Kingdom
Tel.: (44) 20 7316 2280 UK
Web Site: http://www.mwam.com
Year Founded: 1997
Sales Range: $150-199.9 Million
Emp.: 300
Asset Management Services
N.A.I.C.S.: 523940
Paul Marshall *(Founder, Chm, CIO & Partner-London)*

Subsidiaries:

Marshall Wace Asia Limited (1)
23/F LHT Tower 31 Queen's Road, Central, China (Hong Kong)
Tel.: (852) 3761 5000
Web Site: http://www.mwam.com
Emp.: 30
Investment Fund Management Services
N.A.I.C.S.: 523940
Chris Pearce *(COO)*

Marshall Wace North America LP (1)
Harborside 3 River Rd, Greenwich, CT 06807-2717
Tel.: (203) 625-3200
Investment Fund Management Services
N.A.I.C.S.: 523940

MARSHALLS (EAST AFRICA) LIMITED

Kampala Road, PO Box 30366, Nairobi, 00100, Kenya
Tel.: (254) 202229547
Web Site: http://www.marshalls-ea.com
Sales Range: $1-9.9 Million
Motor Vehicle Whslr
N.A.I.C.S.: 423110
Joseph Kimeu *(Mgr-Bus Dev)*

MARSHALLS PLC

Landscape House Premier Way Lowfields Business Park, Elland, HX5 9HT, United Kingdom
Tel.: (44) 1422312000
Web Site: https://www.marshalls.co.uk
MSLH—(LSE)
Rev.: $866,481,165
Assets: $1,456,083,915
Liabilities: $659,825,100
Net Worth: $796,258,815
Earnings: $31,967,430
Fiscal Year-end: 12/31/22
Landscape Products Mfr
N.A.I.C.S.: 541320
Cathy Baxandall *(Sec)*

Subsidiaries:

Alton Glasshouses Limited (1)
Blythe Park Cresswell, Stoke-on-Trent, ST11 9RD, Staffordshire, United Kingdom
Tel.: (44) 1782385409
Web Site: http://www.altongreenhouses.co.uk
Cedar Wood Mfr
N.A.I.C.S.: 337122

Edenhall Limited (1)
Danygraig Road, Risca, NP11 6DP, United Kingdom
Tel.: (44) 1633600806
Web Site: http://www.edenhall.co.uk
Concrete Product Distr
N.A.I.C.S.: 423320

Marshalls Mono Limited (1)
Landscape House Premier Way Lowfields Business Park, Elland, HX5 9HT, United Kingdom
Tel.: (44) 845 309 313
Concrete Products Mfr
N.A.I.C.S.: 327390

INTERNATIONAL PUBLIC

Subsidiary (Domestic):

CPM Group Ltd. (2)
Mells Road Mells, Frome, BA11 3PD, Somerset, United Kingdom
Tel.: (44) 1179 814 500
Web Site: http://www.cpm-group.com
Precast Concrete Products Mfr
N.A.I.C.S.: 327332

Marshalls NV (1)
Nieuwstraat 4a, 2840, Rumst, Belgium
Tel.: (32) 3 880 86 06
Web Site: http://www.marshalls.be
Specialty Trade Contracting Services
N.A.I.C.S.: 238990

Stonemarket Limited (1)
Oxford Road, Ryton on Dunsmore, Rugby, CV8 3EJ, Warwickshire, United Kingdom
Tel.: (44) 3453020603
Web Site: http://www.stonemarket.co.uk
Landscaping Development Services
N.A.I.C.S.: 561730

Viridian Solar Limited (1)
68 Stirling Way, Papworth, Cambridge, United Kingdom
Tel.: (44) 1480839865
Web Site: https://www.viridiansolar.co.uk
Roof Integrated Solar Panel Mfr & Distr
N.A.I.C.S.: 335999

Woodhouse Group Limited (1)
207 Madison Ave S, Kitchener, N2G 3M7, ON, Canada
Tel.: (519) 749-3790
Web Site: https://www.woodhouse.ca
Construction Engineering Services
N.A.I.C.S.: 541330

MARSILLI & CO. S.P.A.

Via Per Ripalta Arpina 14, 26012, Castelleone, Italy
Tel.: (39) 03743551
Web Site: http://www.marsilli.com
Year Founded: 1938
Sales Range: $25-49.9 Million
Emp.: 190
Electronic Coils
N.A.I.C.S.: 334416
Gianbatti Parati *(Pres)*

Subsidiaries:

MARSILLI Automation Technology (Beijing) Co., Ltd (1)
Rm 701 Bldg B Sinolight Plaza No 4 Qiyang Rd, Wangjing Chaoyang District, Beijing, 100102, China
Tel.: (86) 10 6477 8841
Web Site: http://www.marsilli.cn
Winding Machinery Distr
N.A.I.C.S.: 423830

Marsilli Automation Technology (Suzhou) Co. Ltd.
No 101 Bldg 4 OETPark Science Park No 69 Weixin Road SIP, Suzhou, 215122, Jiangsu, China
Tel.: (86) 512 8099 1171
Winding Machinery Distr
N.A.I.C.S.: 423830

Marsilli Deutschland GmbH (1)
Freudenstadter Strasse 132, 75337, Enzklosterle, Germany
Tel.: (49) 7085 920634
Winding Machinery Distr
N.A.I.C.S.: 423830

Marsilli India Pvt. Ltd. (1)
5-B-5 Ranka Park Lalbagh Road, Bengaluru, 560027, Karnataka, India
Tel.: (91) 80 4211 4632
Winding Machinery Distr
N.A.I.C.S.: 423830
B. S. Raghavendra *(Engr-Sls)*

Marsilli North America Inc. (1)
11445A Cronridge Dr Ste S, Owings Mills, MD 21117
Tel.: (410) 654-2425
Rev.: $14,500,954
Emp.: 11
Coils, Electronic
N.A.I.C.S.: 423690
Katherine Hull *(Supvr-Sls-Spare Parts)*

AND PRIVATE COMPANIES

MARSONS LTD.
Marsons House Budge Budge Trunk Road, Maheshtala, Kolkata, 700142, India
Tel.: (91) 3322127189
Web Site:
  https://www.marsonsonline.com
Year Founded: 1976
517467—(BOM)
Rev.: $44,936
Assets: $3,359,456
Liabilities: $3,196,639
Net Worth: $162,817
Earnings: ($303,986)
Fiscal Year-end: 03/31/21
Power Transmission Equipment Mfr
N.A.I.C.S.: 333613
Binay Kumar Agarwal *(Exec Dir)*

MARSOVIN LTD.
The Winery Wills Street, Paola, PLA 2234, Malta
Tel.: (356) 21824920
Web Site:
  http://www.marsovin.com.mt
Year Founded: 1919
Sales Range: $25-49.9 Million
Emp.: 150
Wine Producer & Marketer
N.A.I.C.S.: 312130
George Agius *(CEO)*

MARSSENGER KITCHEN-WARE CO., LTD.
No 366 Xincheng Road, Jianshan New District, Haining, 314415, Zhejiang, China
Tel.: (86) 57387019995
Web Site:
  http://www.marssenger.com
Year Founded: 2010
300894—(SSE)
Rev.: $355,244,963
Assets: $367,526,276
Liabilities: $141,256,556
Net Worth: $226,269,721
Earnings: $57,565,593
Fiscal Year-end: 12/31/21
Household Appliance Mfr & Distr
N.A.I.C.S.: 335220
Weibin Huang *(Chm & Gen Mgr)*

MARSTON PROPERTIES LIMITED
1 Mills Yard Hugon Road, Fulham, London, SW6 3AQ, United Kingdom
Tel.: (44) 2077367133   UK
Web Site:
  http://www.marstonproperties.co.uk
Year Founded: 1938
Sales Range: $50-74.9 Million
Real Estate Investment, Development & Property Management Services
N.A.I.C.S.: 531390
Caroline Marston *(Mng Dir)*

MARSTON'S PLC
St Johns House, St John's Square, Wolverhampton, WV2 4BH, United Kingdom
Tel.: (44) 1902711811
Web Site:
  https://www.marstonspubs.co.uk
MARS—(LSE)
Rev.: $1,110,502,869
Assets: $3,124,634,004
Liabilities: $2,309,739,029
Net Worth: $814,894,975
Earnings: $11,839,593
Emp.: 11,000
Fiscal Year-end: 09/30/23
Holding Company; Pub & Brewery Operator
N.A.I.C.S.: 551112
Ralph Findlay *(CEO)*

Subsidiaries:

Marston's Pubs Limited   (1)
The Brewery Shobnall Road, Burton-on-Trent, DE14 2BG, Staffs, United Kingdom
Tel.: (44) 1283531131
Web Site: http://www.marstons.co.uk
Sales Range: $25-49.9 Million
Emp.: 150
Pub Developer & Operator
N.A.I.C.S.: 722410

Marston's Telecoms Limited   (1)
Marstons House Brewery Road, Wolverhampton, WV1 4JT, United Kingdom
Tel.: (44) 190 228 3300
Web Site: https://marstonstelecoms.com
Telecommunication Servicesb
N.A.I.C.S.: 517111
Tony Ford *(Mng Dir)*

MARTELA OYJ
Miestentie 1, PO Box 44, FI-00371, Helsinki, Finland
Tel.: (358) 1034550
Web Site: https://www.martela.com
MARAS—(HEL)
Rev.: $115,162,961
Assets: $67,264,192
Liabilities: $52,317,073
Net Worth: $14,947,118
Earnings: $2,756,313
Emp.: 400
Fiscal Year-end: 12/31/22
Furniture Mfr & Distr
N.A.I.C.S.: 423210
Eero Leskinen *(Vice Chm)*

Subsidiaries:

Irodabutor Martela kft   (1)
Robert Karoly Krt 59, 1134, Budapest, Hungary
Tel.: (36) 17840484
Web Site: http://www.martela.co.hu
Office Furniture Mfr
N.A.I.C.S.: 337214

Kidex Oy   (1)
Savikontie 25, 82500, Kitee, Finland
Tel.: (358) 50 470 7934
Web Site: https://www.kidex.fi
Emp.: 13
Household Furniture Mfr & Distr
N.A.I.C.S.: 337121
Ari Honkonen *(Dir-Sls)*

Martela A/S   (1)
Sundkaj 153 st th Pakhus 48, Nordhavn, 2150, Copenhagen, Denmark
Tel.: (45) 7 020 4830
Web Site: http://www.martela.dk
Sales Range: $25-49.9 Million
Emp.: 20
Office Furniture Distr
N.A.I.C.S.: 423210

Martela AB   (1)
Storgatan 49A, Box 21, 571 21, Nassjo, Podafors, Sweden
Tel.: (46) 380371900
Web Site: https://www.martela.com
Sales Range: $25-49.9 Million
Emp.: 5
Office Furniture Distr
N.A.I.C.S.: 423210

Martela AS   (1)
Drammensveien 130, 0277, Oslo, Norway
Tel.: (47) 23283850
Web Site: https://www.martela.com
Office Furniture Mfr
N.A.I.C.S.: 337211

P.O. Korhonen Oy   (1)
Tuotekatu 13, 21200, Raisio, Finland
Tel.: (358) 10 345 7100
Web Site: http://www.po-korhonen.fi
Rev.: $9,910,600
Emp.: 60
Wooden Furniture Mfr & Distr
N.A.I.C.S.: 321999

MARTELLO TECHNOLOGIES GROUP, INC.
390 March Road Suite 110, Kanata, K2K 0G7, ON, Canada
Tel.: (613) 271-5989
Web Site:
  https://www.martellotech.com
DRKOF—(OTCIQ)
Rev.: $12,010,052
Assets: $15,034,962
Liabilities: $15,980,523
Net Worth: ($945,560)
Earnings: ($18,791,441)
Emp.: 104
Fiscal Year-end: 03/31/23
Information Technology Services
N.A.I.C.S.: 541512
John Proctor *(Pres & CEO)*

MARTI GAYRIMENKUL YATIRIM ORTAKLIGI AS
Omer Avni Mah Inonu Cad Dersan Han No 46/3, Gumussuyu Beyoglu, Istanbul, Turkiye
Tel.: (90) 2123348850
Web Site: https://martigyo.com.tr
Year Founded: 1967
MRGYO—(IST)
Sales Range: Less than $1 Million
Real Estate Investment Services
N.A.I.C.S.: 531390
Mine Narin *(Chm)*

MARTI OTEL ISLETMELERI A.S.
Dumen Sok Dumen Apt No 3/8, Omer Avni Mah Beyoglu, Istanbul, Turkiye
Tel.: (90) 2123348850
Web Site: https://www.marti.com.tr
Year Founded: 1967
MARTI—(IST)
Rev.: $17,961,071
Assets: $436,041,438
Liabilities: $287,090,166
Net Worth: $148,951,272
Earnings: $1,754,967
Fiscal Year-end: 03/31/22
Home Management Services
N.A.I.C.S.: 721110

MARTIFER SGPS S.A.
Zona Industrial Apartado 17, 3684-001, Oliveira de Frades, Portugal
Tel.: (351) 232767700
Web Site: https://www.martifer.com
MAR—(EUR)
Rev.: $203,005,792
Assets: $261,977,107
Liabilities: $224,574,145
Net Worth: $37,402,961
Earnings: $15,095,003
Emp.: 1,331
Fiscal Year-end: 12/31/22
Metal Structure & Energy Infrastructure Construction Services
N.A.I.C.S.: 237990
Carlos Manuel Marques Martins *(Pres)*

Subsidiaries:

Martifer - Construcciones Metalicas Espana, S.A.   (1)
C/Bruselas n 6-B, Poligono Industrial Europolis Las Rozas, 28232, Madrid, Spain
Tel.: (34) 916378282
Metallic Construction Services
N.A.I.C.S.: 236210

Martifer - Construcoes Metalicas Angola, S.A.   (1)
KM 25 S/N Apartado 21, Polo Industrial de Viana, Luanda, Angola
Tel.: (244) 923551797
Metallic Construction Services
N.A.I.C.S.: 236210

Martifer Constructions, SAS   (1)
1 rue Le Corbusier, CP 90216, 94518, Rungis, Cedex, France
Tel.: (33) 146868046
Metallic Construction Services
N.A.I.C.S.: 236210

Navalria - Docas, Construcoes e Reparacoes Navais, S.A.   (1)
Apartado 39 Porto Comercial Terminal Sul, PO Box 39, 3811-901, Aveiro, Portugal
Tel.: (351) 234378970
Web Site: https://www.navalria.pt
Emp.: 50
Ship Building & Repair Services
N.A.I.C.S.: 336611

Saudi Martifer Constructions LLC   (1)
4055 Prince Mamduh Ibn Abdul Aziz Unit n 4060 - Office 105, Al Sulaimaniyah Dist, Riyadh, 12242-7637, Saudi Arabia
Tel.: (966) 112936696
Metallic Construction Services
N.A.I.C.S.: 236210

MARTIN & CO (UK) LTD.
2 St Stephens Court St Stephens Road, Bournemouth, BH2 6LA, Dorset, United Kingdom
Tel.: (44) 207 861 3232   UK
Web Site: http://www.martinco.com
Year Founded: 1986
Sales Range: $10-24.9 Million
Emp.: 39
Real Estate Development Services
N.A.I.C.S.: 531390
Richard Martin *(Chm)*

MARTIN BURN LIMITED
Martin Burn House 1/F 1 R N Mukherjee Road, Kolkata, 700 001, West Bengal, India
Tel.: (91) 3340828282
Web Site:
  https://www.martinburnltd.com
Year Founded: 1946
523566—(BOM)
Rev.: $1,000,638
Assets: $13,613,851
Liabilities: $7,010,110
Net Worth: $6,603,741
Earnings: $222,348
Emp.: 20
Fiscal Year-end: 03/31/22
Civil Engineering Services
N.A.I.C.S.: 237990
Kedar Nath Fatehpuria *(Chm, CEO & Mng Dir)*

MARTIN CURRIE GLOBAL PORTFOLIO TRUST PLC
5 Morrison Street 2nd floor, Edinburgh, EH3 8BH, United Kingdom
Tel.: (44) 1312295252   UK
Web Site:
  https://www.martincurrie.com
Year Founded: 1999
MNP—(LSE)
Assets: $338,018,835
Liabilities: $37,170,870
Net Worth: $300,847,965
Earnings: ($35,833,875)
Fiscal Year-end: 01/31/23
Investment Management Service
N.A.I.C.S.: 525990
Zehrid Osmani *(Mgr-Portfolio)*

MARTIN DAWES SYSTEMS
Network House Cinnamon Park, Fearnhead, Warrington, Cheshire, United Kingdom
Tel.: (44) 1925555300
Web Site:
  http://www.martindawessystems.com
Sales Range: $50-74.9 Million
Emp.: 200
Software & Services; Billing & CRM Solutions for the Telecommunications Industry
N.A.I.C.S.: 423430
Martin Dawes *(Founder & Chm)*

Subsidiaries:

Martin Dawes Analytics   (1)
321 Summer St 5th Fl, Boston, MA 02210

MARTIN DAWES SYSTEMS

Martin Dawes Systems—(Continued)
Tel.: (617) 345-5422
Web Site: http://www.mda-data.com
Sales Range: $25-49.9 Million
Emp.: 25
Revenue Assurance & Cost Management Software
N.A.I.C.S.: 541511

MARTIN OLSSON HANDELS AB
Grosshandlarvagen 7, Arsta, 12044, Sweden
Tel.: (46) 87222500
Web Site: http://www.martinolsson.se
Food Whslr
N.A.I.C.S.: 424410
Martin Oldmark *(Chm & CEO)*

Subsidiaries:

Martin & Servera AB (1)
Strandbergsgatan 61, SE 112 89, Stockholm, Sweden
Tel.: (46) 8 672 84 00
Web Site: http://www.martinservera.se
Sales Range: $1-4.9 Billion
Emp.: 2,500
Food Industry Services
N.A.I.C.S.: 722310
Christer Lind *(CEO)*

Subsidiary (Domestic):

Fallmans Kott AB
Elektravagen 15, 126 30, Hagersten, Sweden
Tel.: (46) 8 556 139 00
Web Site: http://www.fallmanskott.se
Meat Product Distr
N.A.I.C.S.: 424470

Galatea AB (2)
Gustavslundsvagen 133, 167 51, Bromma, Sweden
Tel.: (46) 20 21 24 10
Web Site: http://www.galatea.se
Beer & Wine Distr
N.A.I.C.S.: 445320
Dan Samson *(Brand Mgr-Beer)*

Martin Olsson Cashar AB (2)
Ranhammarsvagen 10, 168 67, Bromma, Sweden
Tel.: (46) 8 501622 50
Web Site: http://www.martinolssoncashar.se
Restaurant Operators
N.A.I.C.S.: 722511
Douglas Thulin *(Mgr-Strategic Procurement)*

RP Frukt AB (2)
PL 5246 Roinge, 28192, Hasslehom, Sweden
Tel.: (46) 451 351 63
Web Site: http://www.rpfrukt.se
Fruit & Vegetable Distr
N.A.I.C.S.: 424480

MARTIN-BAKER AIRCRAFT COMPANY LIMITED
Higher Denham, Uxbridge, UB9 5AJ, Middx, United Kingdom
Tel.: (44) 1895832214   UK
Web Site: http://www.martin-baker.co.uk
Sales Range: $125-149.9 Million
Emp.: 700
Aircraft Ejection Seats Mfr
N.A.I.C.S.: 336413
John S. Martin *(Co-Mng Dir)*

Subsidiaries:

Martin-Baker America Inc. (1)
423 Walters Ave, Johnstown, PA 15904
Tel.: (814) 262-9325
Web Site: http://www.martin-baker.com
Sales Range: $50-74.9 Million
Emp.: 101
Aircraft Ejection Seats Mfr
N.A.I.C.S.: 336413
Mike Santoro *(Gen Mgr)*

MARTINA MINERALS CORPORATION
1800-130 King Street West, Toronto, M5X 1E3, ON, Canada
Tel.: (416) 945-6628
Web Site: http://www.martinaminerals.com
Year Founded: 2005
MTN.H—(TSXV)
Assets: $12,235
Liabilities: $1,809,771
Net Worth: ($1,797,536)
Earnings: ($8,520)
Fiscal Year-end: 06/30/24
Mineral Exploration Services
N.A.I.C.S.: 212290

MARTINREA INTERNATIONAL, INC.
3210 Langstaff Road, Vaughan, L4K 5B2, ON, Canada
Tel.: (416) 749-0314   ON
Web Site: https://www.martinrea.com
Year Founded: 1987
03M—(DEU)
Rev.: $4,032,343,065
Assets: $3,012,724,918
Liabilities: $1,906,337,441
Net Worth: $1,106,387,477
Earnings: $116,035,515
Emp.: 19,000
Fiscal Year-end: 12/31/23
Fabricator & Engineering of Industrial Products
N.A.I.C.S.: 334513
Robert P. Wildeboer *(Founder & Exec Chm)*

Subsidiaries:

Industrias Martinrea, S.A de C.V (1)
Antigua Carretera A Arteaga No 2653, Saltillo, 25298, Mexico
Tel.: (52) 844 438 9250
Sales Range: $100-124.9 Million
Emp.: 500
Automobile Parts Mfr
N.A.I.C.S.: 336390
David Rashid *(Gen Mgr)*

Martinrea Automative Systems (USA) LLC (1)
2003 Oakland Pky, Columbia, TN 38401-6530
Tel.: (931) 490-4231
Automobile Parts Mfr
N.A.I.C.S.: 336390

Martinrea Developments de Mexico, S.A. de C.V. (1)
Antigua Carr A Arteaga No 2653, Saltillo, 25297, Mexico
Tel.: (52) 8444389250
Computer Peripheral Equipment Mfr
N.A.I.C.S.: 334118
David Rashid *(Gen Mgr)*

Martinrea Fabco (1)
19200 Glendale Ave, Detroit, MI 48223-3459
Tel.: (313) 272-8400
Web Site: http://www.martinrea.com
Sales Range: $25-49.9 Million
Emp.: 75
Prototypes for Automotive Industry
N.A.I.C.S.: 336370

Martinrea Fabco (1)
850 Division Rd, PO Box 1060, Windsor, N9A 6P7, ON, Canada
Tel.: (519) 969-9580
Web Site: http://www.tkafabco.com
Sales Range: $200-249.9 Million
Emp.: 1,000
Medium & Heavy Metal Stampings, Weldments, Assemblies & Systems & Tubular Fabrications
N.A.I.C.S.: 336211

Martinrea Fabco (1)
99 Golf Course Ln, Ridgetown, N0P 2C0, ON, Canada
Tel.: (519) 674-0711
Web Site: http://www.martinrea.com
Sales Range: $50-74.9 Million
Emp.: 240
Stamping of Automotive Parts
N.A.I.C.S.: 336370

Martinrea Fabco (1)
1 Fabco Dr, Springfield, TN 37172
Tel.: (615) 212-0586
Web Site: http://www.tkafabco.com
Sales Range: $50-74.9 Million
Emp.: 150
Motor Vehicle Parts & Accessories Mfr
N.A.I.C.S.: 336390
Mike Pope *(Plant Mgr)*

Martinrea Fabco Automative Structures (USA) Inc. (1)
1 Fabco Dr, Springfield, TN 37172-6843
Tel.: (615) 212-0586
Web Site: http://www.martinrea.com
Automotive Metal Steel Stamping Mfr
N.A.I.C.S.: 336370

Martinrea Fabco Hot Stampings Inc. (1)
19200 Glendale Ave, Detroit, MI 48223-3459
Tel.: (313) 272-8400
Web Site: http://www.martinrea.com
Automotive Metal Stamping Mfr
N.A.I.C.S.: 336390

Martinrea Heavy Stampings Inc. (1)
1000 Old Brunerstown Rd, Shelbyville, KY 40065
Tel.: (502) 633-5000
Automotive Metal Stamping Services
N.A.I.C.S.: 336370
Shawn Adelsberger *(Gen Mgr)*

Martinrea Honsel Germany GmbH (1)
Fritz-Honsel-Strasse 30, 59872, Meschede, Germany   (55%)
Tel.: (49) 291 2910
Web Site: https://www.honsel.com
Sales Range: $700-749.9 Million
Emp.: 3,500
Light Metal Product Mfr
N.A.I.C.S.: 332999

Martinrea Hopkinsville LLC (1)
1500 Frank Yost Ln, Hopkinsville, KY 42240-6818
Tel.: (270) 475-2000
Motor Vehicle Parts Distr
N.A.I.C.S.: 423120

Martinrea Industries, Inc. (1)
10501 MI State Rd 52, Manchester, MI 48158
Tel.: (734) 428-2400
Rev.: $175,000,000
Emp.: 300
Motor Vehicle Parts & Accessories
N.A.I.C.S.: 336390
Brad Jaekel *(CEO)*

Martinrea Jonesville LLC (1)
260 Gaige St, Jonesville, MI 49250-9431
Tel.: (517) 849-2195
Automotive Metal Parts Mfr
N.A.I.C.S.: 336390

Martinrea Metal Industries, Inc. (1)
2800 Livernois Rd Ste 450, Troy, MI 48083-1253
Tel.: (248) 823-5700
Web Site: http://www.martinrea.com
Emp.: 120
Automobile Parts Distr
N.A.I.C.S.: 423120

Rea International Inc (1)
3210 Martinrea Rd, Woodbridge, L4K 5B2, ON, Canada
Tel.: (416) 749-0314
Sales Range: $25-49.9 Million
Emp.: 70
Automobile Mfr
N.A.I.C.S.: 336110
Nick Orlando *(CEO)*

Subsidiary (Domestic):

2008788 Ontario Ltd. (2)
580 James St S, Saint Marys, N4X 1B3, ON, Canada
Tel.: (519) 349-2850
Web Site: http://www.martinrea.com
Sales Range: $25-49.9 Million
Emp.: 7
Iron & Steel Pipe Mfr
N.A.I.C.S.: 331210

INTERNATIONAL PUBLIC

Royal Automotive Group Ltd (1)
30 Aviva Park Dr, Woodbridge, L4L 9C7, ON, Canada
Tel.: (416) 749-0314
Automobile Parts Mfr
N.A.I.C.S.: 336390

Steelmatic Wire Inc. (1)
340 Carlingview Dr, Etobicoke, M9W 5G5, ON, Canada
Tel.: (416) 213-8877
Steel Pole Mfr
N.A.I.C.S.: 331222

Steelmatic Wire USA, Inc. (1)
300 Monroe St Ext, Sardis, MS 38666-9123
Tel.: (662) 487-3936
Sales Range: $25-49.9 Million
Emp.: 11
Steel Pole Mfr
N.A.I.C.S.: 331222

MARUBENI CONSTRUCTION MATERIAL LEASE CO., LTD.
2-4-1 Shibakoen, Minato-ku, Tokyo, 105-0011, Japan
Tel.: (81) 354048200
Web Site: https://www.mcml-maruken.com
Year Founded: 1968
9763—(TKS)
Rev.: $140,958,250
Assets: $215,089,400
Liabilities: $106,315,240
Net Worth: $108,774,160
Earnings: $7,674,210
Emp.: 302
Fiscal Year-end: 03/31/24
Construction Materials Leasing Services
N.A.I.C.S.: 532412
Tadashi Inoda *(Exec Mng Dir)*

Subsidiaries:

KOSHIN KOGYO CO., LTD. (1)
251-8 Nomura Hirooka, Nishi-ku, Shiojiri, 399-0702, Nagano, Japan
Tel.: (81) 263540208
Web Site: https://koshinkogyo.com
Construction Materials Distr
N.A.I.C.S.: 423390

KYOYU LEASE CO., LTD. (1)
106-38 Fujigaya Shinden, Kashiwa, 277-0932, Chiba, Japan
Tel.: (81) 471901212
Construction Materials Distr
N.A.I.C.S.: 423390

KYUSYU REPURO CO., LTD. (1)
3-1-1 Minami-futajima, Wakamatsu-ku Kita-Kyushu, Fukuoka, 808-0109, Japan
Tel.: (81) 937012114
Construction Materials Distr
N.A.I.C.S.: 423390

MARUKEN KISOKOJI CO., LTD. (1)
681-15 Wattsu, Kitahiroshima, 061-1264, Hokkaido, Japan
Tel.: (81) 118879638
Construction Materials Distr
N.A.I.C.S.: 423390

Marubeni Construction Material Lease Co., Ltd. - Asahikawa Plant (1)
14-gou Kita 9-sen, Pipu-cho Kamikawa, Hokkaido, 078-0329, Japan
Tel.: (81) 166852241
Construction Materials Mfr
N.A.I.C.S.: 332322

Marubeni Construction Material Lease Co., Ltd. - Gifu Plant (1)
2838 Shinkawahara Oyabu, Wanouchi-cho Anpachi, Gifu, 503-0202, Japan
Tel.: (81) 584694390
Construction Materials Mfr
N.A.I.C.S.: 332322

Marubeni Construction Material Lease Co., Ltd. - Ichihara Plant (1)
11-1 Yawata-kaigandori, Ichihara, 290-0067, Chiba, Japan
Tel.: (81) 436433311
Construction Materials Mfr

AND PRIVATE COMPANIES — MARUBENI CORPORATION

Marubeni Construction Material Lease Co., Ltd. - Ichihara Second Plant (1)
52-4 Yawata-kaigandori, Ichihara, 290-0067, Chiba, Japan
Tel.: (81) 436437611
Construction Materials Mfr
N.A.I.C.S.: 332322

Marubeni Construction Material Lease Co., Ltd. - Inazawa Plant (1)
1-1-1 Umesuga-cho, Inazawa, 492-8401, Aichi, Japan
Tel.: (81) 587361218
Construction Materials Mfr
N.A.I.C.S.: 332322

Marubeni Construction Material Lease Co., Ltd. - Nishihara Plant (1)
1021 Onaha, Nishihara-cho Nakagami, Okinawa, 903-0103, Japan
Tel.: (81) 989442200
Construction Materials Mfr
N.A.I.C.S.: 332322

Marubeni Construction Material Lease Co., Ltd. - Sapporo Plant (1)
681-15 Wattsu, Kitahiroshima, 061-1264, Hokkaido, Japan
Tel.: (81) 113762345
Construction Materials Mfr
N.A.I.C.S.: 332322

TOBAN KOGYO CO., LTD. (1)
17-2 Nijima, Harima-cho Kako, Hyogo, 675-0155, Japan
Tel.: (81) 794353847
Construction Materials Distr
N.A.I.C.S.: 423390

TOHOKU KOGYO CO., LTD. (1)
1-24-4 Minato, Miyagino-ku, Sendai, 983-0001, Miyagi, Japan
Tel.: (81) 222583492
Construction Materials Distr
N.A.I.C.S.: 423390

MARUBENI CORPORATION

4-2 Ohtemachi 1-chome, Chiyoda-ku, Tokyo, 100-8088, Japan
Tel.: (81) 332822111 JP
Web Site: https://www.marubeni.com
Year Founded: 1858
8002—(TKS)
Rev.: $47,925,904,150
Assets: $58,984,976,170
Liabilities: $35,434,564,110
Net Worth: $23,550,412,060
Earnings: $3,116,033,320
Emp.: 50,200
Fiscal Year-end: 03/31/24
Holding Company; Wholesale Trade Distr
N.A.I.C.S.: 551112
Jun Horie *(Mng Exec Officer)*

Subsidiaries:

AND Global Pte. Ltd. (1)
New Mind Building, Sukhbaatar District 5th Micro District, Ulaanbaatar, Mongolia
Tel.: (976) 77242244
Financial Services
N.A.I.C.S.: 522320
Anar Chinbaatar *(Co-Founder & Pres)*

Aguas Decima S.A. (1)
Arauco 434, Valdivia, Chile (100%)
Tel.: (56) 6004018000
Web Site: https://www.aguasdecima.cl
Water Treatment & Distribution Services
N.A.I.C.S.: 221310

Aircastle Limited (1)
201 Tresser Blvd Ste 400, Stamford, CT 06901
Tel.: (203) 504-1020
Web Site: https://www.aircastle.com
Rev.: $796,033,000
Assets: $7,266,851,000
Liabilities: $5,395,393,000
Net Worth: $1,871,458,000
Earnings: $62,759,000
Emp.: 115
Fiscal Year-end: 02/28/2023
Aircraft Leasing Services
N.A.I.C.S.: 532411
Takashi Kurihara *(Chm)*

Subsidiary (Non-US):

Aircastle Advisor (Ireland) Limited (2)
8 Fitzwilliam Place, Dublin, Ireland
Tel.: (353) 16650800
Web Site: http://www.aircastle.com
Sales Range: $100-124.9 Million
Emp.: 15
Aircraft Leasing Services
N.A.I.C.S.: 532411
Jane O'Callaghan *(Mng Dir)*

Subsidiary (Domestic):

Aircastle Advisor LLC (2)
300 First Stamford Pl 5th Fl, Stamford, CT 06902
Tel.: (203) 504-1020
Web Site: http://www.aircastle.com
Sales Range: $25-49.9 Million
Aircraft Leasing Services
N.A.I.C.S.: 532411

Subsidiary (Non-US):

Aircastle Singapore Pte. Limited (2)
501 Orchard Rd 07-03 Wheelock Place, Singapore, 238880, Singapore
Tel.: (65) 62639620
Commercial Jet Aircraft Rental & Leasing Services
N.A.I.C.S.: 532411

Merdeka Aircraft Leasing (Labuan) Limited (2)
Main Office Tower Financial Park, Labuan, 87000, Malaysia
Tel.: (60) 87451688
Aircraft Equipment Rental & Leasing Services
N.A.I.C.S.: 532411

Akita Offshore Wind Corporation (1)
Web Site: http://aow.co.jp
Wind Power Generation Services
N.A.I.C.S.: 221115
Keiji Okagaki *(Pres & CEO)*

Aroma Coffee (Shanghai) Co., Ltd. (1)
1088-east Boxue Rd Malu Town, Jiading District, Shanghai, 201801, China
Tel.: (86) 2169150498
Instant Coffee Mfr & Distr
N.A.I.C.S.: 311920

Azuri Technologies Ltd. (1)
Winship House Winship Road, Cambridge, CB24 6AP, United Kingdom
Tel.: (44) 1223228260
Web Site: https://www.azuri-group.com
Solar System Distr
N.A.I.C.S.: 221114
Alan Harper *(Chm)*

B-Quik Co., Ltd. (1)
No 256 2nd Floor Village No 3, Bang Khun Kong Subdistrict Bang Kruai District, Nonthaburi, 11130, Thailand
Tel.: (66) 20291000
Vehicle Equipment Mfr
N.A.I.C.S.: 336390

Benirei Corporation (1)
5F Shibaura Square Building 4-9-25 Shibaura, Minato-ku, Tokyo, 108-0023, Japan
Tel.: (81) 337690031
Emp.: 230
Seafood Products Warehousing Services & Whslr
N.A.I.C.S.: 493120

Chenya Energy Co., Ltd. (1)
302 19th Floor No 8 Ziqiang South Road E and Einstein Building, Hsinchu County, Zhubei, Taiwan
Tel.: (886) 35588685
Web Site: https://www.chenya-energy.com
Solar System Distr
N.A.I.C.S.: 221114

Creekstone Farms Premium Beef, LLC (1)
604 Goff Industrial Park Rd, Arkansas City, KS 67005
Tel.: (620) 741-3366
Poultry Processing Services
N.A.I.C.S.: 311615
Dennis Buhlke *(CEO)*

Distribuidora Automotriz Marubeni Ltda. (1)
Claudio Arrau 7050, Pudahuel, Santiago, Chile
Tel.: (56) 2 350 0400
Web Site: http://www.marubeni.cl
Sales Range: $75-99.9 Million
Emp.: 300
Automotive Distr
N.A.I.C.S.: 423110
Kenicharo Hoshika *(Gen Mgr)*

FUYO KANKO Co., Ltd. (1)
2320 Ohba, Fujisawa, 251-0861, Kanagawa, Japan
Tel.: (81) 466 34 8111
Web Site: http://www.cityfujisawa.ne.jp
Golf Club Operating Services
N.A.I.C.S.: 713910

Fukuyama Paper Co., Ltd. (1)
2-2-1 Kashima, Yodogawa-ku, Osaka, 532-0031, Japan
Tel.: (81) 663012131
Emp.: 130
Medium Board Mfr
N.A.I.C.S.: 322130

Gas Valpo SpA (1)
Camino Internacional 1420, Vina del Mar, Chile
Tel.: (56) 6006007000
Web Site: https://www.gasvalpo.cl
Gas Distr
N.A.I.C.S.: 221210

Gemsa Enterprises, LLC (1)
15610 Heron Ave, La Mirada, CA 90638
Tel.: (714) 521-1736
Web Site: http://www.gemsaoils.com
Sales Range: $1-9.9 Million
Emp.: 12
Edible Specialty Fats & Oil Mfr & Distr
N.A.I.C.S.: 311225
Emilio Viscomi *(Pres)*

IMT Corporation (1)
Ohdori Bus-Center Bldg No 1 4th Floor 5-1 Higashi 1-chome Minami 1-jo, Chuoku, Sapporo, Hokkaido, Japan
Tel.: (81) 11 207 7577
Web Site: http://www.marubeni.com
Investment Management Service
N.A.I.C.S.: 523999

JAL Business Aviation Co., Ltd. (1)
1-11-2 Haneda Airport, Ota-ku, Tokyo, 144-0041, Japan
Tel.: (81) 354605869
Web Site: https://www.jalba.co.jp
Aircraft Services
N.A.I.C.S.: 488190
Ryusuke Konto *(Pres & CEO)*

Jamaica Public Services Company Limited (1)
6 Knutsford Boulevard 5, Kingston, Jamaica
Tel.: (876) 8889355577
Web Site: https://www.jpsco.com
Electricity Distribution Services
N.A.I.C.S.: 221122
Michel Gantois *(Pres & CEO)*

Japan REIT Advisors Co., Ltd. (1)
Shiroyama Trust Tower 18F 4-3-1 Toranomon, Minato-ku, Tokyo, 105-6018, Japan (95%)
Tel.: (81) 354023680
Web Site: https://www.j-reitad.co.jp
Emp.: 84
Real Estate Manangement Services
N.A.I.C.S.: 531390
Norimasa Gaun *(Pres & CEO)*

Jiangmen Senkei Chemical Tank Storage Co., Ltd. (1)
Jiangyu Road 1st Jinguzhou, Xinhui, Jiangmen, 529141, China
Tel.: (86) 750 639 1788
Chemical Products Storage Services
N.A.I.C.S.: 493190

KM Distribucion De Maquinarias, S.A. de C.V. (1)
Carretera San Martin de las Flores 520 Edificio 3-C, Col La Nogalera, 44470, Tlaquepaque, Mexico
Tel.: (52) 33 3145 3336
Agricultural Machinery Dist
N.A.I.C.S.: 325320
Masato Inoshita *(Mng Dir)*

KOEI Co., Ltd. (1)
1215 Kamihonjo, Sanda, Hyogo, Japan
Tel.: (81) 795686311
Golf Course Operation Services
N.A.I.C.S.: 713910

KOYO LINE, LTD (1)
4-2 Ohtemachi 1-chome, Chiyoda-ku, Tokyo, 100-8088, Japan
Tel.: (81) 332824973
Web Site: https://www.mmsl.co.jp
Sales Range: $25-49.9 Million
Emp.: 43
Ship Operation & Management Services
N.A.I.C.S.: 488330
Kazunari Yamawaki *(Pres)*

Koa Kogyo Co., Ltd. (1)
1286-2 Hina, Fuji, 417-0847, Shizuoka, Japan
Tel.: (81) 545380123
Emp.: 262
Container Paper Board Mfr
N.A.I.C.S.: 322130

Kraft of Asia Paperboard & Packaging Co., Ltd. (1)
D2 Road Lot B7, Phu My 3 Specialized Industrial Park Phuoc Hoa Ward, Phu My, Ba Ria-Vung Tau, Vietnam
Tel.: (84) 2543891901
Web Site: https://kraftofasia.com
Emp.: 300
Container Board Mfr & Distr
N.A.I.C.S.: 322130

Kyoto Marubeni Co., Ltd (1)
369 Manjuji-dori Karasuma-dori Nishiri-Okuishi-cho, Shimogyo-ku, Kyoto, 600-8429, Japan
Tel.: (81) 753423330
Emp.: 80
Traditional Japanese Clothing Whslr
N.A.I.C.S.: 424350

MARUBENI AG Makina Ticaret Limited Sirketi (1)
Yukari Dudullu Serifail Ciftligi Miras Sokak No 30, Umraniye, 34775, Istanbul, Turkiye
Tel.: (90) 216 526 6474
Sales Range: $25-49.9 Million
Emp.: 20
Agricultural Machinery Distr
N.A.I.C.S.: 423820
Takashi Makano *(Gen Mgr)*

MM Capital Partners Co., Ltd. (1)
Nihonbashi Takashimaya Mitsui Building 10F 5-1 Nihonbashi 2 Chome, Chuo-ku, Tokyo, 103-6110, Japan
Tel.: (81) 355421025
Web Site: http://www.mmcp.co.jp
Bond Investment Services
N.A.I.C.S.: 523999
Tomohide Goto *(Pres & CEO)*

MMSL Pte. Ltd. (1)
182 Cecil Street 32-02 Frasers Tower, Singapore, 069547, Singapore
Tel.: (65) 62219918
Web Site: http://www.mmsl.com.sg
Marine Shipping Services
N.A.I.C.S.: 488510

MTJV (Thailand) Co., Ltd. (1)
The 9th Towers Grand Rama 9 TNB 01-02 23rd Floor Tower B, 33/4 Rama 9 Road Huay Khwang, Bangkok, 10310, Thailand
Tel.: (66) 27849700
Web Site: http://www.mtjv.co.th
Electrical System Distr
N.A.I.C.S.: 423610

MX Mobiling Co., Ltd. (1)
Toyosu Foresia Building 3-2-24 Toyosu, Koto-ku, Tokyo, 135-0061, Japan
Tel.: (81) 355323300
Web Site: https://www.mxmobiling.co.jp
Emp.: 4,417
Cellular Phone Software & Mobile Telecommunication Systems Mfr
N.A.I.C.S.: 517112
Tatsuya Abe *(Pres)*

MARUBENI CORPORATION

Marubeni Corporation—(Continued)

Subsidiary (Domestic):

NEC Facilities, Ltd. (2)
2-22-12 Shiba NEC Second Annex, Minato-Ku, Tokyo, 105-0014, Japan
Tel.: (81) 334551111
Web Site: https://www.necf.jp
Emp.: 4,012
Residential Remodeler
N.A.I.C.S.: 236118

NEC Saitama, Ltd. (2)
300-18 Motohara, Kamikawamachi, Saitama, Japan
Tel.: (81) 495773311
Sales Range: $150-199.9 Million
Emp.: 800
Electronic Components Mfr
N.A.I.C.S.: 334419
Takuni Kuki *(Pres)*

Marnix Corporation (1)
4-2 Ohtemachi 1-chome, Chiyoda-ku, Tokyo, 100-8088, Japan
Tel.: (81) 332827900
Web Site: https://marnix.co.jp
Insurance Brokerage Services
N.A.I.C.S.: 524210
Toru Komoguchi *(Pres & CEO)*

Marnix Reinsurance Brokers Pte. Ltd. (1)
138 Market Street 31-04 CapitaGreen, Singapore, 048946, Singapore
Tel.: (65) 62369150
Web Site: https://www.marnix.com.sg
Insurance Services
N.A.I.C.S.: 524210
Naoyuki Shimura *(CEO)*

Marubeni (China) Co., Ltd. (1)
6F Tower3 Jing An Kerry Centre 1228 Yan An Zhong Road, Jing An District, Shanghai, 200040, China
Tel.: (86) 2168411932
Chemical Products Mfr
N.A.I.C.S.: 325998
Yoshinori Ogawa *(Pres & CEO)*

Marubeni Aerospace Corporation (1)
1-1-3 Yurakucho, Chiyoda-ku, Tokyo, 100-0006, Japan **(100%)**
Tel.: (81) 35 157 7500
Web Site: https://www.marubeni-aerospace.co.jp
Emp.: 97
Aircraft & Aerospace Components Wholesale Trade Distr & Leasing Services
N.A.I.C.S.: 425120

Marubeni America Corporation (1)
90 Park Ave 6th Fl, New York, NY 10016 **(100%)**
Tel.: (212) 450-0100
Web Site: https://marubeniamerica.com
Sales Range: $450-499.9 Million
Emp.: 250
Industrial, Agricultural & Consumer Goods, Commodities & Natural Resources Trader; Financing, Leasing, Marketing, Logistics & Sales Services
N.A.I.C.S.: 424310
Koichi Mochizuki *(Pres & CEO)*

Joint Venture (Domestic):

Advanced Composites, Inc. (2)
1062 S 4th Ave, Sidney, OH 45365
Tel.: (937) 575-9800
Web Site: https://www.advcmp.com
Sales Range: $100-124.9 Million
Polypropylene Compounds Mfr & Sales; Owned 62.8% by Mitsui Chemicals America, Inc., 27% by Mitsui & Co., Ltd. & 10.2% by Marubeni America Corporation
N.A.I.C.S.: 325998

Subsidiary (Non-US):

Advanced Composites Mexicana S.A. de C.V. (3)
Avenida Japon 306 Parque Industrial San Francisco, San Francisco de los Romo, 20303, Aguascalientes, Mexico
Tel.: (52) 4499254010
Web Site: https://www.acpmex.com
Polypropylene Compounds Mfr & Sales
N.A.I.C.S.: 325998

Subsidiary (Domestic):

Columbia Grain International (2)
1300 SW 5th Ave Fl 29, Portland, OR 97201
Tel.: (503) 224-8624
Web Site: http://www.columbiagrain.com
Rev.: $600,000,000
Emp.: 35
Grain Storage & Shipping
N.A.I.C.S.: 115114
Jeff Van Pevenage *(Pres & CEO)*

Eastern Fish Company (2)
Glenpointe Ctr E 300 Frank W Burr Blvd Ste 30, Teaneck, NJ 07666
Tel.: (201) 801-0800
Web Site: https://easternfish.com
Sales Range: $350-399.9 Million
Emp.: 30
Fish & Seafood Product Distr
N.A.I.C.S.: 424460
Lee Bloom *(VP-Pur)*

Energy USA Inc. (2)
1776 I St NW Ste 725, Washington, DC 20006-3723
Tel.: (202) 785-9260
Web Site: http://www.marubeni-usa.com
Rev.: $4,071,968
Emp.: 7
Information Services Consumer
N.A.I.C.S.: 812990
Aki Tsuji *(Pres & CEO)*

Gavilon Agriculture Investment, Inc. (2)
1331 Capitol Ave, Omaha, NE 31411
Tel.: (402) 889-4000
Web Site: http://www.gavilonfertilizer.com
Grain Transport Services
N.A.I.C.S.: 484230

Gavilon Fertilizer, LLC (2)
12702 Westport Pkwy Ste 300, Omaha, NE 68138
Tel.: (402) 889-4390
Web Site: https://www.gavilonfertilizer.com
Emp.: 10
Fertilizer & Other Farm Chemicals & Supplies Distr & Whslr
N.A.I.C.S.: 424910

Gavilon Grain, LLC (2)
1331 Capitol Ave, Omaha, NE 68102-1106 **(100%)**
Tel.: (402) 889-4000
Sales Range: $200-249.9 Million
Emp.: 350
Agricultural Product Distribution, Merchandising & Trading Services
N.A.I.C.S.: 425120
Lew Batchelder *(Pres & CEO)*

Subsidiary (Domestic):

Gavilon Ag Service, LLC (3)
4100 N Mulberry Dr, Kansas City, MO 64116-1700
Tel.: (816) 421-8182
Web Site: http://www.gavilon.com
Sales Range: $25-49.9 Million
Emp.: 5
Farm Supplies Distr
N.A.I.C.S.: 424910

Subsidiary (Domestic):

Helena Agri-Enterprises, LLC (2)
225 Schilling Blvd, Collierville, TN 38017
Tel.: (901) 761-0050
Web Site: http://www.helenaagri.com
Chemical Product Mfr & Distr
N.A.I.C.S.: 325998

Helena Chemical Company (2)
225 Schilling Blvd Ste 300, Collierville, TN 38017-6937
Tel.: (901) 761-0050
Web Site: http://www.helenachemical.com
Emp.: 250
Pesticides & Agricultural Chemicals Mfr & Distr
N.A.I.C.S.: 325320
Jim Arnold *(Mgr-Adv & Pub Affairs)*

Intragrated Resources Holdings, Inc. (2)
300 Atlantic St, Stamford, CT 06901
Tel.: (203) 658-1200
Paper & Printing Services

N.A.I.C.S.: 424110

Long Island Automotive Group, Inc. (2)
1249 E Jericho Tpke Ste A, Huntington, NY 11743 **(100%)**
Tel.: (631) 264-2244
Web Site: http://www.jaguarhuntington.com
Emp.: 25
Holding Company; New & Used Car Dealerships
N.A.I.C.S.: 551112

Unit (Domestic):

Land Rover Huntington (3)
1249 E Jericho Tpke, Huntington, NY 11743-5611
Tel.: (631) 427-2222
Sales Range: $25-49.9 Million
Emp.: 100
New & Used Car Dealer
N.A.I.C.S.: 441110

Subsidiary (Domestic):

MCS Chassis Inc. (2)
450 Lexington Ave, New York, NY 10017-3911
Tel.: (212) 450-0635
Rev.: $170,000
Emp.: 3
Equipment Rental & Leasing
N.A.I.C.S.: 532490

Magellan Aviation Group LLLP (2)
2345 Township Rd Ste B, Charlotte, NC 28273
Tel.: (704) 504-9204
Web Site: https://www.magellangroup.net
Aircraft Services
N.A.I.C.S.: 488190
Michimoto Asano *(Chm, Interim Pres & Interim CEO)*

Marubeni Aerospace America Corporation (2)
700 S Flower St Ste1175, Los Angeles, CA 90017
Tel.: (213) 972-2782
Sales Range: $25-49.9 Million
Emp.: 15
Aircraft Equipment Distr
N.A.I.C.S.: 423860
Masashi Hasegawa *(Pres & CEO)*

Marubeni America Corporation - Los Angeles (2)
707 Wilshire Blvd Ste 3630, Los Angeles, CA 90017
Tel.: (213) 972-2700
Investment & Trading Services
N.A.I.C.S.: 523160

Marubeni Business Machines (America) Inc. (2)
6100 Blue Lagoon Dr Ste 370, Miami, FL 33126
Tel.: (305) 269-9292
Emp.: 11
Office Equipment Whslr
N.A.I.C.S.: 423420

Joint Venture (Domestic):

Marubeni Citizen-Cincom Inc. (2)
40 Boroline Rd Ste 6, Allendale, NJ 07401-1613
Tel.: (201) 818-0100
Sales Range: $25-49.9 Million
Emp.: 25
Mfr of Precision Industrial Machinery
N.A.I.C.S.: 423830
John Antignani *(Pres)*

Marubeni Itochu Pipe & Tube, Inc. (2)
750 Town & Country Blvd, Houston, TX 77024
Tel.: (281) 368-7000
Web Site: http://www.mitube.com
Sales Range: $25-49.9 Million
Emp.: 50
Steel Pipe & Tube Distr
N.A.I.C.S.: 423510
Mike Lamb *(CFO)*

Subsidiary (Domestic):

Marubeni Oil & Gas (USA) Inc. (2)

INTERNATIONAL PUBLIC

777 N Eldridge Pkwy Ste 900, Houston, TX 77079
Tel.: (832) 379-1100
Web Site: http://www.marubeni-usa.com
Oil & Gas Exploration Services
N.A.I.C.S.: 213112
Perry Murphree *(COO)*

Marubeni Plant Contractor, Inc. (2)
8777 Purdue Rd Ste 102, Indianapolis, IN 46268 **(100%)**
Tel.: (317) 684-3040
Sales Range: $25-49.9 Million
Emp.: 10
Industrial Buildings & Warehouses
N.A.I.C.S.: 236220

Marubeni Power International, Inc. (2)
375 Lexington Ave 7th Fl, New York, NY 10017
Tel.: (212) 450-0640
Web Site: http://www.marubeni-power.com
Electric Power Distribution Services
N.A.I.C.S.: 221122
Minako Wakayma *(Pres & CEO)*

Marubeni Specialty Chemicals Inc. (2)
10 Bank St Ste 740, White Plains, NY 10606-1952 **(100%)**
Tel.: (914) 428-8900
Web Site: http://www.marubenisci.com
Emp.: 40
Exporting & Importing Chemical
N.A.I.C.S.: 424690

Marubeni Steel Processing Inc. (2)
104 Western Dr, Portland, TN 37148-2017
Tel.: (615) 325-5454
Web Site: http://www.marubenisteel.com
Rev.: $9,000,000
Emp.: 80
Metals Service Center & Offices
N.A.I.C.S.: 423510

Marubeni Transport Service Corp. (2)
180 E Ocean Blvd, Long Beach, CA 90802-4708
Tel.: (562) 435-3722
Web Site: https://www.marubeni-trans.com
Sales Range: $25-49.9 Million
Emp.: 24
Customs House Brokers
N.A.I.C.S.: 488510

Midwest Railcar Corporation (2)
855 S Arbor Vitae, Edwardsville, IL 62025
Tel.: (618) 692-5575
Emp.: 15
General Freight Railcar Operating Services
N.A.I.C.S.: 483211
Richard Murphy *(Pres & CEO)*

Mieco Inc. (2)
Landmark Sq 111 W Ocean Blvd Ste 1600, Long Beach, CA 90802-4832 **(100%)**
Tel.: (562) 435-0085
Web Site: https://mieco.com
Sales Range: $25-49.9 Million
Emp.: 35
Electric Power Marketers
N.A.I.C.S.: 424720
Peter D'Anna *(VP)*

North Pacific Seafoods, Inc. (2)
4 Nickerson Ste 400, Seattle, WA 98109
Tel.: (206) 726-9900
Sales Range: $10-24.9 Million
Emp.: 30
Seafood Processing Services
N.A.I.C.S.: 311710

Subsidiary (Domestic):

North Pacific Seafoods, Inc. - Sitka Sound Seafoods Facility (3)
329 Katlian St, Sitka, AK 99835
Tel.: (907) 747-6662
Web Site: http://www.northpacificseafoods.com
Seafood Processing Services
N.A.I.C.S.: 311710
Robert Torres *(Gen Mgr)*

Subsidiary (Domestic):

Oak Creek Energy Systems Inc. (2)

AND PRIVATE COMPANIES

MARUBENI CORPORATION

500 La Terraza Blvd Ste 350, Escondido, CA 92025
Tel.: (760) 975-0910
Wind Energy Services
N.A.I.C.S.: 335929
Sheldon Greene *(CEO)*

PIC Group, Inc. (2)
1000 Parkwood Cir Ste 1000, Atlanta, GA 30339
Tel.: (770) 850-0100
Web Site: http://www.picworld.com
Emp.: 60
Global Power Generation Services
N.A.I.C.S.: 221118
Frank Avery *(Pres & CEO)*

PLM Trailer Leasing (2)
5722 Naylor Ave, Livermore, CA 94551 **(100%)**
Tel.: (925) 245-0056
Web Site: http://www.plmtrailer.com
Sales Range: $50-74.9 Million
Emp.: 2
Markets Trailers Owned & Managed by the Company on Short-Term Leases through a Network of Rental Facilities Nation Wide
N.A.I.C.S.: 532490
Don Durm *(VP-Customer Solutions)*

XL Parts LLC (2)
15701 NW Fwy, Houston, TX 77040
Tel.: (713) 983-1100
Web Site: https://www.xlparts.com
Automobile & Other Motor Vehicle Merchant Whslr
N.A.I.C.S.: 423110
Michael R. Odell *(Pres & CEO)*

Marubeni Arch-Log Co., Ltd. (1)
2F Hamamatsucho Rise Square 1-3-3 Shibaura, Minato-ku, Tokyo, 105-0023, Japan
Tel.: (81) 363817270
Web Site: https://m-arch-log.com
Building Materials Mfr
N.A.I.C.S.: 327120

Marubeni Argentina S.A. (1)
Av del Libertador 602/648 24F, 1001, Buenos Aires, Argentina
Tel.: (54) 1148112938
Chemical Products Distr
N.A.I.C.S.: 327910

Marubeni Asean Pte. Ltd. (1)
138 Market Street 31-01 CapitaGreen, Singapore, 048946, Singapore
Tel.: (65) 62204111
Chemical Products Mfr
N.A.I.C.S.: 325998
Takeshi Mamiya *(Pres & CEO)*

Marubeni Asian Power Singapore Pte. Ltd. (1)
111 Somerset Road 09-04 Tripleone Somerset, Singapore, 238164, Singapore
Tel.: (65) 6735 0046
Web Site: http://www.marubeni.com
Sales Range: $25-49.9 Million
Emp.: 5
Business Development Services
N.A.I.C.S.: 561499
Hidenobu Kashiwaya *(Mng Dir)*

Marubeni Asset Management Co., Ltd. (1)
Otemachi Building 5F 1-6-1 Otemachi, Chiyoda-ku, Tokyo, 100-0004, Japan
Tel.: (81) 362560200
Sales Range: $50-74.9 Million
Emp.: 57
Real Estate Manangement Services
N.A.I.C.S.: 531390

Marubeni Australia Ltd. (1)
Level 58 25 Martin Place, Royal Exchange, Sydney, 2000, NSW, Australia **(100%)**
Tel.: (61) 299312222
Web Site: https://www.marubeni.com
Sales Range: $50-74.9 Million
Emp.: 75
Trading Company
N.A.I.C.S.: 523160
Seiichi Kuwata *(Pres & CEO)*

Subsidiary (Domestic):

Marubeni Aluminium Australia Pty. Ltd. (2)
Suite 1703 Level 17 120 Collins Street, Melbourne, 3000, VIC, Australia
Tel.: (61) 396188188
Emp.: 7
Aluminum Ingots Distr
N.A.I.C.S.: 423510

Marubeni Coal Pty. Ltd. (2)
Suite 3705 Level 37 Riverside Centre 123 Eagle Street, Brisbane, 4000, QLD, Australia
Tel.: (61) 733186200
Web Site: http://www.marubeni.com
Investment Management Service
N.A.I.C.S.: 523999

Subsidiary (Non-US):

Marubeni New Zealand Ltd. (2)
Level 11 120 Albert Street, Auckland, 1010, New Zealand
Tel.: (64) 93793003
Web Site: http://www.marubenicorp.com
Sales Range: $50-74.9 Million
Emp.: 3
Trading Company
N.A.I.C.S.: 523160
Y. Kande *(Mng Dir)*

Subsidiary (Domestic):

Rangers Valley Cattle Station Pyt Ltd (2)
Valley Cattle Station, PO Box 63, Glen Innes, 2370, NSW, Australia
Tel.: (61) 26 734 4000
Web Site: https://www.rangersvalley.com.au
Sales Range: $10-24.9 Million
Emp.: 40
Livestock & Animal Farms Services
N.A.I.C.S.: 115116

Marubeni Auto Finance, Ltda (1)
Avda Vicuna Mackenna 3300 Macul, Casilla Correo 9816 Macul, Santiago, Chile
Tel.: (56) 226803300
Web Site: http://www.marubenicredit.cl
Automobile Financing Services
N.A.I.C.S.: 522220

Marubeni Auto Ltda (1)
Avda Vicuna Mackenna N 3300, Macul, Santiago, Chile
Tel.: (56) 223500400
Web Site: https://www.marubeni.cl
Emp.: 5
Automobile Sales & Repair Services
N.A.I.C.S.: 423110

Marubeni Automotive Corporation (1)
3-21 Kanda-nishiki-cho JPR Crest Takebashi Building 9F, Chiyoda-ku, Tokyo, 101-0054, Japan **(100%)**
Tel.: (81) 35 281 6555
Web Site: https://www.marubeni-automotive.co.jp
Emp.: 31
Automobile & Motor Vehicle Parts Wholesale Trade Distr
N.A.I.C.S.: 425120
Yutaka Sekine *(Pres)*

Marubeni Brasil S.A. (1)
Av Paulista 854 12F Bela Vista, Sao Paulo, 01310-913, Brazil
Tel.: (55) 1134661855
Chemical Products Distr
N.A.I.C.S.: 424690
Koichi Nagashima *(Pres & CEO)*

Marubeni CLS Corporation (1)
2nd Floor Toyama Builiding 1-7-13 Azuchimachi, Chuo-ku, Osaka, Japan
Tel.: (81) 6 6125 2011
Web Site: http://www.marubeni-cls.com
Rev.: $68,176,800
Emp.: 29
Leather Goods Distr
N.A.I.C.S.: 424990
Makoto Furukawa *(Pres)*

Marubeni Cement & Construction Materials Co., Ltd. (1)
Yasuda Green Park Bldg 9 Kanda-Nishikicho 2-chome Chiyoda-ku, Choyoda-ku, Tokyo, 101-0054, Japan
Tel.: (81) 3 3219 1781
Web Site: http://www.marubeni-cement.com
Emp.: 50
Cement & Construction Materials Distr
N.A.I.C.S.: 423390
Makoto Nakano *(Pres)*

Marubeni Chemix Corporation (1)
7th floor Sumitomo Realty and Development Kanda Building 7, Kanda Mitoshirocho Chiyoda-ku, Tokyo, 101-0053, Japan **(100%)**
Tel.: (81) 34 360 3400
Web Site: https://www.marubenichemix.co.jp
Emp.: 151
Chemical Wholesale Trade Distr
N.A.I.C.S.: 425120
Kanju Horikawa *(CEO)*

Marubeni Chile Limitada (1)
Edificio Del Pacifico Av Andres Bello 2687 Piso 4, Santiago, Chile
Tel.: (56) 227636335
Food Products Distr
N.A.I.C.S.: 424490

Marubeni Egg Corporation (1)
Sakura Muromachi Building 5F 4-5-1 Nihonbashi Muromachi, Chuo- ku, Tokyo, 103-0022, Japan
Tel.: (81) 368540650
Web Site: http://www.marubeniegg.jp
Egg Product Mfr & Distr
N.A.I.C.S.: 311999

Marubeni Ele-Next Co., Ltd. (1)
Dojima Avanza 1-6-20 Dojima, Kita-ku, Osaka, 530-0003, Japan
Tel.: (81) 663442111
Web Site: https://www.m-elenext.co.jp
Emp.: 153
Electronic Components Distr
N.A.I.C.S.: 423690
Hidetomo Naka *(Pres)*

Marubeni Eneble Corporation (1)
1-4-2 Otemachi, Chiyoda-ku, Tokyo, 100-8088, Japan
Tel.: (81) 120829859
Web Site: https://marubeni-eneble.com
Ecommerce Services
N.A.I.C.S.: 541611

Marubeni Energy Corporation (1)
Sumitomo Fudosan Chiyoda Fujimi building F11 12 8-19 Fujimi 1-chome, Chiyoda-ku, Tokyo, 102-8441, Japan **(66.6%)**
Tel.: (81) 36 261 8800
Web Site: https://www.marubeni-energy.co.jp
Emp.: 182
Petroleum Products Wholesale Trade Distr
N.A.I.C.S.: 425120
Tetsuya Takeshita *(Pres)*

Marubeni Ennex Corporation (1)
2-3-5 Shinminato, Mihama-ku, Chiba, 261-0002, Japan
Tel.: (81) 43 246 1100
Web Site: https://www.marubeni-ennex.co.jp
Oil & Gas Terminal Operator
N.A.I.C.S.: 424710

Marubeni Equipment Finance (Oceania) Pty. Ltd. (1)
Suite 12 03A Level 12 50 Margaret St, Locked Bag H1, Sydney, 2000, NSW, Australia
Web Site: http://www.marubenifinance.com.au
Financial Services
N.A.I.C.S.: 522320

Marubeni Europe plc (1)
95 Gresham Street, London, EC2V 7AB, United Kingdom **(100%)**
Tel.: (44) 2078268600
Web Site: http://www.europe.marubeni.com
Sales Range: $50-74.9 Million
Emp.: 100
Trading Company
N.A.I.C.S.: 523160

Subsidiary (Non-US):

Agrovista B.V. (2)
Handelstraat 6, Horst, 5961 PV, Limburg, Netherlands
Tel.: (31) 773999111
Emp.: 100
Specialty Chemicals Distr
N.A.I.C.S.: 424690

Subsidiary (Domestic):

Agrovista UK Limited (2)
Rutherford House, Nottingham Science and Technology Park University Boulevard, Nottingham, NG7 2PZ, Notts, United Kingdom
Tel.: (44) 1159390202
Emp.: 40
Chemical Distr
N.A.I.C.S.: 424690

Subsidiary (Non-US):

Axia Power Holdings, B.V. (2)
World Trade Center Tower-C 6th Floor Strawinskylaan 659, 1077 XX, Amsterdam, Netherlands
Tel.: (31) 203059730
Eletric Power Generation Services
N.A.I.C.S.: 221118

MarPless Communication Technologies (Pty) Ltd. (2)
Baobab House Eastwood Office Park 290a, Lizjohn Street Lynnwood Ridge, Centurion, 0081, Gauteng, South Africa
Tel.: (27) 12 657 0191
Web Site: http://www.marpless.co.za
Sales Range: $25-49.9 Million
Emp.: 30
Telecommunication Servicesb
N.A.I.C.S.: 517810
Kiyomasa Shirai *(CFO)*

Subsidiary (Domestic):

Marnix Europe Ltd (2)
95 Gresham Street, London, EC2V 7AB, United Kingdom
Tel.: (44) 2078268693
Sales Range: $50-74.9 Million
Emp.: 10
Insurance Brokerage Services
N.A.I.C.S.: 524210
Toru Komoguchi *(Mng Dir)*

Marubeni Auto Investment (UK) Ltd (2)
173 Cross Lane, Salford, M5 4AP, Manchester, United Kingdom
Tel.: (44) 1617422403
Web Site: https://www.marubeni-autouk.com
Sales Range: $50-74.9 Million
Emp.: 6
Automobile Financing Services
N.A.I.C.S.: 522220
Tony Cliff *(Mng Dir)*

Marubeni Energy Europe Limited (2)
95 Gresham Street, London, EC2V 7AB, United Kingdom
Tel.: (44) 2078268900
Web Site: http://www.marubeni.com
Petroleum Product Distr
N.A.I.C.S.: 424720

Branch (Non-US):

Marubeni Europe plc - Dusseldorf Branch (2)
Benratherstr 18-20, Dusseldorf, 40213, Germany **(100%)**
Tel.: (49) 21136710
Web Site: http://europe.marubeni.com
Emp.: 60
Trading Company
N.A.I.C.S.: 523160

Subsidiary (Domestic):

Marubeni Europower Ltd (2)
95 Gresham St, London, EC2V 7AB, United Kingdom
Tel.: (44) 207 826 8811
Web Site: https://marubeni-europower.com
Eletric Power Generation Services
N.A.I.C.S.: 221118

Subsidiary (Non-US):

Marubeni International (Europe) GmbH (2)
Benrather Strasse 18-20, PO Box 103664, 40213, Dusseldorf, Germany
Tel.: (49) 21136710
Chemical Products Distr
N.A.I.C.S.: 424690

Subsidiary (Domestic):

Marubeni North Sea Limited (2)
95 Gresham Street, London, EC2V 7AB, United Kingdom
Tel.: (44) 2077663636

MARUBENI CORPORATION

Marubeni Corporation—(Continued)
Emp.: 15
Oil & Gas Exploration Services
N.A.I.C.S.: 213112

Marubeni-Komatsu Ltd. (2)
Padgets Lane, Redditch, B98 0RT, Worcestershire, United Kingdom
Tel.: (44) 152 751 2512
Web Site: https://marubeni-komatsu.co.uk
Sales Range: $25-49.9 Million
Emp.: 100
Construction Equipment Distr
N.A.I.C.S.: 423810

Subsidiary (Non-US):

Mertens B.V. (2)
Handelstraat 6, 5961 PV, Horst, Netherlands
Tel.: (31) 773999111
Emp.: 100
Farm Product Distr
N.A.I.C.S.: 424590

Subsidiary (Domestic):

SmartestEnergy Ltd. (2)
The Columbus Building 7 Westferry Circus, London, E14 4HD, United Kingdom
Tel.: (44) 2074480900
Web Site: https://www.smartestenergy.com
Sales Range: $100-124.9 Million
Electric Power Distribution Services
N.A.I.C.S.: 221122
Robert Groves *(CEO)*

Marubeni Fashion Link, Ltd. (1)
JRE Yoyogi 1-chome Building 7th floor 22-1, Yoyogi 1-chome, Shibuya-ku, Tokyo, 151-0053, Japan
Tel.: (81) 368598119
Emp.: 260
Fashion Apparel Garments Whslr
N.A.I.C.S.: 424350

Marubeni Fashion Planning Corp. (1)
1-22-1 Yoyogi, Shibuya-ku, Tokyo, 151-0053, Japan
Tel.: (81) 35 333 5411
Web Site: https://www.mfp.jp
Sales Range: $25-49.9 Million
Emp.: 22
Fashion Design Services
N.A.I.C.S.: 541490
Yoshiyuki Matsumoto *(Pres)*

Marubeni Financial Service Corporation (1)
Tokyo Nihombashi Tower 7-1 Nihonbashi 2-Chome, Chiyoda-Ku, Tokyo, 100-8088, Japan
Tel.: (81) 3 3282 9584
Web Site: http://www.marubeni-mfs.com
Financial Management Services
N.A.I.C.S.: 523999

Marubeni Foods Corporation (1)
1-12-5 Kyobashi Kyobashi YS Building, Chuo-ku, Tokyo, 104-0031, Japan (99.99%)
Tel.: (81) 33 538 8800
Web Site: https://www.marubeni-foods.co.jp
Emp.: 100
Food & Beverage Products Wholesale Trade Distr
N.A.I.C.S.: 425120
Shigeto Shimizu *(CEO)*

Marubeni Footwear Inc. (1)
4F Nihonbashi Horidome-cho 2-chome Building, 2-4-3 Nihonbashi-Horidome-cho Chuo-ku, Tokyo, 103-0012, Japan
Tel.: (81) 336650135
Emp.: 154
Footwear Import & Distr
N.A.I.C.S.: 424340

Marubeni Footwear Resources Limited (1)
Unit 1615 16th Floor Tower 3 China-HongKong City 33 Canton Road, Tsimshatsui, Kowloon, China (Hong Kong)
Tel.: (852) 2730 3683
Web Site: http://www.marubeni.com
Footwear & Bags Mfr
N.A.I.C.S.: 316210

Marubeni Forest Linx Co., Ltd. (1)
4-2 Ohtemachi 1-chome, Chiyoda-ku, Tokyo, 100-8088, Japan
Tel.: (81) 362685211
Web Site: https://www.marubeni-flx.com
Emp.: 226
Paper Product Distr
N.A.I.C.S.: 424130
Naoki Obinata *(Pres & CEO)*

Marubeni Heavy Equipment Company Limited (1)
Lot 7 Quang Minh Industrial Zone, Me Linh, Hanoi, Vietnam
Tel.: (84) 2438430540
Web Site: http://www.mhe.vn
Machinery Equipment Distr
N.A.I.C.S.: 423830

Marubeni Holding Ltda. (1)
Claudio Arrau 7050, Pudahuel, Santiago, Chile
Tel.: (56) 23500400
Web Site: http://www.marubeni.com
Sales Range: $100-124.9 Million
Emp.: 200
Financial Management Services
N.A.I.C.S.: 523999

Marubeni Hospital Partners Corporation (1)
3-11 Kandanishikicho Senyo Bldg 4kai, Chiyoda-Ku, Tokyo, 101-0054, Japan
Tel.: (81) 352807072
Web Site: http://www.marubenihp.co.jp
Medical Equipment Distr
N.A.I.C.S.: 423450

Marubeni IT Solutions Inc. (1)
Ueno Frontier Tower Building 3-24-6 Ueno, Taito-ku, Tokyo, 110-0005, Japan
Tel.: (81) 345123000
Web Site: https://www.marubeni-itsol.com
Emp.: 398
Software Development Services
N.A.I.C.S.: 541511
Koji Tokuda *(Pres & CEO)*

Marubeni India Private Ltd. (1)
Unit No 01 3rd Floor Building A-2, Shaheed Jeet Singh Marg Qutab Institutional Area, New Delhi, 110 067, India
Tel.: (91) 1141295555
Web Site: https://www.marubeni.co.in
Food Products Distr
N.A.I.C.S.: 424490

Marubeni Information Systems Co., Ltd. (1)
Shinjuku Garden Tower 3-8-2, Okubo Shinjuku-ku, Tokyo, 169-0072, Japan (100%)
Tel.: (81) 342434000
Web Site: https://www.marubeni-sys.com
Emp.: 585
Information Technology Support Services
N.A.I.C.S.: 541519
Fumio Ueda *(Exec Officer)*

Subsidiary (US):

Marubeni Information Systems USA Corporation (2)
3945 Freedom Cir Ste 1020, Santa Clara, CA 95054-3014
Tel.: (408) 330-0605
Information Technology Support Services
N.A.I.C.S.: 541519

Marubeni International Petroleum (Singapore) Pte, Ltd (1)
8 Temasek Boulevard 30-03 Suntec Tower Three, Singapore, 38988, Singapore
Tel.: (65) 63368815
Web Site: http://www.marubeni.com
Sales Range: $25-49.9 Million
Emp.: 15
Petroleum Product Distr
N.A.I.C.S.: 424720
Andrew Chan *(Exec VP)*

Marubeni Intex Co., Ltd. (1)
29F Shin Daibiru Building 2-1 Dojimahama 1-chome, Kita-ku, Osaka, 530-0004, Japan
Tel.: (81) 663473500
Emp.: 140
Apparel Distr
N.A.I.C.S.: 424350
Takuya Yoda *(Mng Dir & Sls Mgr)*

Marubeni Iran Co., Ltd. (1)
Unit No 810 8th Floor No 18 West Corner of Sheikh Bahaei Sq, 1993873111, Tehran, Iran
Tel.: (98) 2188036022
Chemical Products Distr
N.A.I.C.S.: 424690

Marubeni Korea Corporation (1)
26F Mirae Asset Center1 West Tower 26 Eulji-ro 5-gil, Jung-gu, Seoul, Korea (South)
Tel.: (82) 23100114
Web Site: https://www.marubenikorea.co.kr
Chemical Products Distr
N.A.I.C.S.: 424690
Ryuichi Masatomi *(Pres & CEO)*

Marubeni Logistics Corporation (1)
Takebashi Yasuda Bldg 13 Kanda-nishikicho 3-chome, Chiyoda-ku, Tokyo, 101-0054, Japan
Tel.: (81) 332191511
Web Site: https://www.marubeni-logi.com
Sales Range: $50-74.9 Million
Emp.: 1,539
Warehousing & Logistics Services
N.A.I.C.S.: 493110
Moritsugu Hosoda *(Pres & CEO)*

Marubeni Maquinarias Mexico, S.A. de C.V. (1)
Miguel Aleman KM 15, Apodaca, 66600, Mexico
Tel.: (52) 81 8220 3109
Web Site: http://www.makomex.com
Construction Machinery Services
N.A.I.C.S.: 333120

Marubeni Metals Corporation (1)
4-1-7 Kudankita, Chiyoda-ku, Tokyo, 102-8250, Japan (100%)
Tel.: (81) 33 221 3811
Web Site: https://www.marumet.co.jp
Emp.: 78
Refined Metals & Metal Products Wholesale Trade Distr
N.A.I.C.S.: 425120
Masami Goto *(Pres)*

Marubeni Mexico S.A. de C.V. (1)
Blvd Manuel Avila Camacho 24 Piso 12 Col, 11000, Lomas de Chapultepec, Mexico
Tel.: (52) 5552027626
Web Site: http://www.marubeni.com.mx
Aluminum Metal Distr
N.A.I.C.S.: 423510

Marubeni Myanmar Fertilizer Co., Ltd. (1)
Thilawa Road, Banbwegon, Myanmar
Tel.: (95) 12309135
Web Site: https://mmf-myanmar.business.site
Fertilizer Mfr & Distr
N.A.I.C.S.: 325314

Marubeni Network Solutions Inc. (1)
Igarashi Building 2-11-5 Shibaura, Minato-ku, Tokyo, 108-0023, Japan
Tel.: (81) 354396543
Web Site: https://www.marubeni-network.com
Emp.: 302
Network Outsourcing Service
N.A.I.C.S.: 541613

Marubeni Nigeria Ltd. (1)
Nipost Towers Block A 10th Floor 1/3 Ologun Agbaje Street, Victoria Island, Lagos, Nigeria
Tel.: (234) 14536301
Food Products Distr
N.A.I.C.S.: 424490

Marubeni Nisshin Feed Co., Ltd. (1)
4-5-1 Nihonbashimuromachi, Chuo-ku, Tokyo, 103-0022, Japan (60%)
Tel.: (81) 35 201 3230
Web Site: https://www.mn-feed.com
Emp.: 504
Animal Feed Mfr & Distr
N.A.I.C.S.: 311119
Yoshiaki Mizumoto *(Pres)*

Marubeni Office Supply Co., Ltd. (1)
1-9-9 Shibadaimon Nomura Real Estate Shibadaimon Building 4th Floor, Minato-ku, Tokyo, 105-0012, Japan
Tel.: (81) 36 430 8760
Web Site: https://www.marubeni-os.com
Information Processing Paper Distr

N.A.I.C.S.: 424120

Marubeni Office Support Corporation (1)
1-4-2 Otemachi, Chiyoda-ku, Tokyo, 100-8088, Japan
Tel.: (81) 332827929
Office Support Services
N.A.I.C.S.: 561110

Marubeni Paper & Pulp Logistics Co., Ltd. (1)
5th Floor Nomura Building 9-9 Shibadaimon 1-Chome, Minato-ku, Tokyo, 105-0012, Japan
Tel.: (81) 3 6430 8750
Web Site: https://www.mppl.co.jp
Sales Range: $25-49.9 Million
Emp.: 36
Pulp Products Logistics Services
N.A.I.C.S.: 541614

Marubeni Paper Recycle Co., Ltd. (1)
1-4-2 Otemachi, Chiyoda-ku, Tokyo, 100-8088, Japan
Tel.: (81) 332824497
Emp.: 13
Waste Paper Distr
N.A.I.C.S.: 423840

Marubeni Personnel Management Corporation (1)
1-4-2 Otemachi, Chiyoda-ku, Tokyo, 100-8088, Japan
Tel.: (81) 3 3282 2069
Web Site: http://www.marubeni-mpm.com
Human Resource Consulting Services
N.A.I.C.S.: 541612

Marubeni Plant Engineering Corporation (1)
4-2 Ohtemachi 1-chome, Chiyoda-ku, Tokyo, 100-8088, Japan
Tel.: (81) 33 282 2111
Web Site: http://www.mapec.co.jp
Paper Plant Engineering & Consulting Services
N.A.I.C.S.: 541330
Toru Umezawa *(Pres & CEO)*

Marubeni Plax Corporation (1)
1-4-14 Koraku 9th floor Koraku Mori Building, Bunkyo-ku, Tokyo, 112-0004, Japan (100%)
Tel.: (81) 36 891 7700
Web Site: https://www.plax.jp
Emp.: 158
Plastic Resins & Products Wholesale Trade Distr
N.A.I.C.S.: 425120
Toshio Shinoda *(Pres)*

Marubeni Power Asset Management Ltd. (1)
15/F 8 Observatory Road, Tsim Sha Tsui, Kowloon, China (Hong Kong)
Tel.: (852) 2 106 5600
Web Site: https://www.mpam.marubeni.com
Sales Range: $50-74.9 Million
Emp.: 30
Asset Management Services
N.A.I.C.S.: 523940

Marubeni Power Retail Corporation (1)
Marubeni Building 1-4-2, Otemachi Chiyoda-ku, Tokyo, 100-8088, Japan
Tel.: (81) 332827480
Web Site: http://denki.marubeni.co.jp
Machinery Equipment Mfr & Distr
N.A.I.C.S.: 333248

Marubeni Power Systems Corporation (1)
Marubeni Tokyo Bldg 2F 4-2 Ohtemachi 1-chome, Chiyoda-ku, Tokyo, 100-8088, Japan (100%)
Tel.: (81) 332869000
Sales Range: $25-49.9 Million
Emp.: 75
Power Plant Engineering & Construction Services Contractor
N.A.I.C.S.: 237990
Ken Muroie *(Pres)*

Marubeni Protechs Corporation (1)
5F Kyobashi OM BLDG 19-8 Kyobashi 1-chome, Chuo-ku, Tokyo, 104-0031, Japan
Tel.: (81) 335380510
Web Site: https://www.m-protechs.com

AND PRIVATE COMPANIES

Emp.: 100
Environmental Consulting Services
N.A.I.C.S.: 541620
Kentaro Kai *(Pres & CEO)*

Marubeni Pulp & Paper Co., Ltd. (1)
4-2 Ohtemachi 1-chome, Chiyoda-ku, Tokyo, 100-8088, Japan
Tel.: (81) 362685211
Web Site: https://www.marubeni-flx.com
Emp.: 226
Paper Product Distr
N.A.I.C.S.: 424130

Marubeni Real Estate Co., Ltd. (1)
5-20-6 Shiba, Minato-ku, Tokyo, 108-0014, Japan
Tel.: (81) 3 5419 1980
Web Site: http://www.mfnet.co.jp
Real Estate Manangement Services
N.A.I.C.S.: 531390

Marubeni Real Estate Development Co., Ltd. (1)
1-4-2 Otemachi, Chiyoda - ku, Tokyo, 100-8088, Japan
Tel.: (81) 362685310
Web Site: https://www.mred.co.jp
Emp.: 91
Real Estate Services
N.A.I.C.S.: 531210

Marubeni Real Estate Management Co., Ltd. (1)
3rd / 4th Floor Shiba 520 Building 5-20-6 Shiba, Minato-ku, Tokyo, 108-0014, Japan
Tel.: (81) 354191980
Web Site: https://www.mfmc.co.jp
Emp.: 448
Real Estate Services
N.A.I.C.S.: 531210

Marubeni Safenet Co., Ltd. (1)
3F Kojimachi Square Nibancho 3, Chiyoda-ku, Tokyo, 102-0084, Japan
Tel.: (81) 352101610
Sales Range: $100-124.9 Million
Emp.: 137
Insurance Agency Services
N.A.I.C.S.: 524210
Hisashi Sunaoshi *(Pres & CEO)*

Marubeni Service Corporation (1)
Shindai Building 1-2-1 Dojimahama, Kita-ku, Osaka, 530-0004, Japan
Tel.: (81) 663472026
Sales Range: $25-49.9 Million
Emp.: 43
Facility Management Services
N.A.I.C.S.: 561210

Marubeni Taiwan Co., Ltd. (1)
16F-1 No168 Sec 3 Nanjing East Road, Taipei, 10488, Taiwan
Tel.: (886) 221735600
Chemical Product Mfr & Distr
N.A.I.C.S.: 325998

Marubeni Techno Rubber Corporation (1)
Tel.: (81) 356513881
Emp.: 50
Thermoplastic Rubber Import & Distr
N.A.I.C.S.: 423840
Kazutaka Sonomoto *(Pres)*

Marubeni Techno-Systems Corp (1)
Ochanomizu Kyoun Bldg 2-2 Kanda-Surugadai, Chiyada-ku, Tokyo, 101-0062, Japan
Tel.: (81) 3 5283 1200
Web Site: http://www.marubeni-techno.com
Rev.: $685,440,000
Emp.: 90
Industrial Machinery Distr
N.A.I.C.S.: 423830
Yasutaka Asada *(Mng Officer)*

Marubeni Telecom Co., Ltd. (1)
Toyosu Foresia 3-2-24 Toyosu, Koto-ku, Tokyo, 135-0061, Chiyoda, Japan
Tel.: (81) 351445480
Web Site: https://www.mtc.co.jp
Telecommunication Equipment Distr
N.A.I.C.S.: 423690

Marubeni Tetsugen Co., Ltd. (1)
Iidabashi Masumoto Bldg 6F 1-21 Agebacho, Shinjuku-ku, Tokyo, 162-0824, Japan (100%)
Tel.: (81) 33 513 1221
Web Site: https://www.marubeni-tetsugen.co.jp
Emp.: 60
Raw Metal & Material Wholesale Trade Distr
N.A.I.C.S.: 425120
Hiroshi Okado *(Pres)*

Marubeni Textile Asia Pacific Ltd. (1)
20F Tower 1 Admiralty Centre 18 Harcourt Road, Hong Kong, China (Hong Kong)
Tel.: (852) 2876 3600
Sales Range: $50-74.9 Million
Emp.: 10
Textile Products Import & Distr
N.A.I.C.S.: 424350
Paul Tester *(Gen Mgr)*

Marubeni Transport Engineering Co., Ltd. (1)
Nakoji New Bldg 6th Floor 2-5-16 Kanda-nishiki-cho, Chiyoda-ku, Tokyo, Japan
Tel.: (81) 3 5259 7501
Engineeering Services
N.A.I.C.S.: 541330

Marubeni Utility Services, Ltd (1)
1-1-1 Hitotsubashi Palace Side Building 2F, Chiyoda-ku, Tokyo, 100-0003, Japan
Tel.: (81) 332148481
Sales Range: $50-74.9 Million
Emp.: 54
Nuclear Power Generation Services
N.A.I.C.S.: 221113
Kazuaki Asami *(Pres & CEO)*

Marubeni Venezuela C.A. (1)
Torre La Castellana Nivel 3 Av Principal de la Castellana, Cruce Con Calle Jose Andel Lamas La Castellana, Caracas, 1060, Venezuela
Tel.: (58) 2122661677
Chemical Product Mfr & Distr
N.A.I.C.S.: 325998

Marubeni-Itochu Steel Inc. (1)
Nihonbashi 1-chome Bldg 4-1 Nihonbashi 1-chome 16-18F, Chuo-ku, Tokyo, 103-8247, Japan (50%)
Tel.: (81) 352043300
Web Site: https://www.benichu.com
Sales Range: $1-4.9 Billion
Emp.: 10,480
Iron & Steel Forging
N.A.I.C.S.: 332111
Tatsuhiko Toshita *(Pres & CEO)*

Subsidiary (Non-US):

Marubeni-Itochu Steel America, Inc. (2)
Tel.: (212) 660-6000
Sales Range: $25-49.9 Million
Emp.: 50
Steel Importer & Exporter; Steel Blanking, Cut-to-Length, Laser Welding & Stamping Services
N.A.I.C.S.: 425120
Toshio Namiki *(CEO)*

Subsidiary (Domestic):

ClarkWestern Building Systems, Inc. (3)
6510 General Dr, Riverside, CA 92509-0103
Tel.: (951) 360-3500
Web Site: http://www.clarkdietrich.com
Sales Range: $25-49.9 Million
Mfr & Developer of Metal Framing
N.A.I.C.S.: 332322

Marubeni-Itochu Tubulars America, Inc. (3)
750 Town and Country Blvd, Houston TX 77024
Tel.: (281) 368-7000
Web Site: https://www.mitube.com
Sales Range: $25-49.9 Million
Emp.: 50
Steel Tubes Supplier to the Oil & Gas Industry
N.A.I.C.S.: 423510
Taewoo Kim *(Mgr-Acctg)*

Subsidiary (Domestic):

Sooner Pipe LLC (4)
909 Fannin St Ste 3100, Houston, TX 77010
Tel.: (713) 759-1200
Oil Country Tubular Goods
N.A.I.C.S.: 423830
Joseph C. Ottaviani *(VP-Ops)*

Subsidiary (Domestic):

A-Z Terminal Corporation (5)
1919 Crosby Dayton Rd, Crosby, TX 77532
Tel.: (281) 328-4877
Web Site: http://www.soonerpipe.com
Sales Range: $1-9.9 Million
Emp.: 35
Oilfield Casing
N.A.I.C.S.: 237120
Joseph C. Ottaviani *(VP & Gen Mgr)*

Sooner Inc. (5)
909 Fannin St Ste 3100, Houston, TX 77010
Tel.: (888) 487-3557
Web Site: https://www.soonerpipe.com
Sales Range: $50-74.9 Million
Emp.: 93
Oil Tubular Products & General Oil Field Supplies Distr
N.A.I.C.S.: 423830
Dorinda J. Barker *(CFO)*

Subsidiary (Domestic):

CTAP LLC (6)
2585 Trailridge Dr E, Lafayette, CO 80026
Tel.: (844) 888-2827
Web Site: https://www.ctapllc.com
Industrial Machinery & Equipment Merchant Whslr
N.A.I.C.S.: 423830
Seth Merril *(Pres)*

Division (Domestic):

Marubeni-Itochu Steel Inc. - Osaka Division (2)
Nakanoshima Festival Tower 26F 2-3-18 Nakanoshima, Kita-ku, Osaka, 530-0005, Japan
Tel.: (81) 676384800
Web Site: http://www.benichu.com
Steel & Steel Products Whslr
N.A.I.C.S.: 423510

Marubeni-Mitsuhashi Rice, Inc. (1)
4-15-7 Nishi-Shinjuku, Shinjuku-ku, Tokyo, 160-0023, Japan (51%)
Tel.: (81) 35 302 7040
Web Site: https://www.mmrice.jp
Emp.: 60
Rice Distr
N.A.I.C.S.: 424490

Mascot-Chemical Paper Co., Ltd. (1)
1-3-30 Mikuriyahigashi, Higashi-osaka, 577-0033, Osaka, Japan
Tel.: (81) 6 6788 0394
Web Site: http://www.m-c-p.co.jp
Cash Register Paper Mfr & Distr
N.A.I.C.S.: 322230

Mg Leasing Corporation (1)
Hitotsubashi 2-chome 1-1 Josuikai Building, Chiyoda-ku, Tokyo, Japan (99%)
Tel.: (81) 332229345
Web Site: http://www.mgl.co.jp
Financial Services
N.A.I.C.S.: 523999
Masataka Kuramoto *(Pres & CEO)*

Mibugawa Power Company (1)
4-2 Ohtemachi 1-chome, Chiyoda-ku, Tokyo, Japan
Tel.: (81) 332827400
Web Site: http://www.mibuden.com
Electric Power Distribution Services
N.A.I.C.S.: 221122

Nacx Nakamura Co. Ltd. (1)
5th floor Shin-Osaka 3rd Doi Building 1-8-24 Nishinomiyahara, Yodogawa-ku, Osaka, Japan
Tel.: (81) 663945155
Emp.: 374
Frozen Food Whslr
N.A.I.C.S.: 424420
Soma Gihifuru *(Pres & CEO)*

Nippon Chunky Co., Ltd. (1)
1-30 Kuwada-cho Agricultural Mutual Aid Hall 5F, Kita-cho, Okayama, 700-0984, Japan
Tel.: (81) 868033660

MARUBENI CORPORATION

Emp.: 163
Poultry Farming Services
N.A.I.C.S.: 112990

Orffa International Holding B.V. (1)
Minervum 7032, 4817 ZL, Breda, Netherlands
Tel.: (31) 183447766
Web Site: https://orffa.com
Feed Additive Distr
N.A.I.C.S.: 424910

P.T. Marubeni Indonesia (1)
Menara Astra Lantai 51 Jl Jend Sudirman Kav 5-6, Jakarta, 10220, Indonesia
Tel.: (62) 2150842777
Emp.: 107
Chemical Product Mfr & Distr
N.A.I.C.S.: 325998
Shinji Kasai *(Pres)*

P.T. Matlamat Cakera Canggih (1)
Plaza BII Tower 2 12th Floor Jl M H Thamrin Kav 51, Jakarta, 10350, Indonesia
Tel.: (62) 21 3929236
Web Site: http://www.marubeni.com
Power Plant Construction Services
N.A.I.C.S.: 237130

P.T. Mega Auto Finance (1)
Gedung Wisma 76 Lt 12 23 Jl Letjen S Parman kav 76 Slipi, Jakarta, 11410, Indonesia
Tel.: (62) 2153666627
Web Site: https://www.maf.co.id
Vehicle Distr
N.A.I.C.S.: 423110

P.T. Megalopolis Manunggal Industrial Development (1)
MM2100 Industrial Town Cikarang Barat, Bekasi, 17520, West Java, Indonesia
Tel.: (62) 218981001
Web Site: https://mm2100.co.id
Emp.: 200
Property Development Services
N.A.I.C.S.: 531312

PROAVANCE Corporation (1)
5th floor Gotanda Chuo Building 2-3-5 Higashigotanda, Shinagawa-Ku, Tokyo, 141-0022, Japan
Tel.: (81) 357911400
Sales Range: $25-49.9 Million
Emp.: 35
Apparels & Fashion Accessories Distr
N.A.I.C.S.: 424350

PT Tanjungenim Lestari Pulp and Paper (1)
Ruko Blok I/29 Komplek PTC Mall Jl R Soekamto, Kab Muara Enim, Palembang, 30114, Sumatera Selatan, Indonesia
Tel.: (62) 711382409
Web Site: https://www.telpp.com
Sales Range: $300-349.9 Million
Emp.: 1,000
Wood Pulp Mfr & Distr
N.A.I.C.S.: 424990

Pacific Grain Terminal, Co., Ltd. (1)
11th floor Sumitomo Fudosan Kanda Building 7 Kanda Mitoyocho, Chiyoda-ku, Tokyo, 101-0053, Japan
Tel.: (81) 352835223
Emp.: 108
Grain Warehousing & Transportation Services
N.A.I.C.S.: 493130

Ravva Oil (Singapore) Pte. Ltd. (1)
138 Market Street Suite 31-01, Singapore, 48946, Singapore
Tel.: (65) 63368815
Web Site: http://www.marubeni.com
Oil & Gas Exploration Services
N.A.I.C.S.: 213112

San Roque Power Corporation (1)
36/F Tower 1 The Enterprise Center 6766 Ayala Avenue, Makati, 1200, Philippines
Tel.: (63) 28865300
Web Site: http://sanroquepower.ph
Hydro Power Services
N.A.I.C.S.: 221111

Seajacks International Limited (1)
Seajacks House South Denes Business Park South Beach Parade, Great Yarmouth, NR30 3QR, Norfolk, United Kingdom
Tel.: (44) 1493841400
Web Site: http://www.seajacks.com

MARUBENI CORPORATION

Marubeni Corporation—(Continued)
Gas Distribution Services
N.A.I.C.S.: 221210
Blair Ainslie (CEO)

Shanghai House Property Development Co., Ltd. (1)
Room 2102 Phase II Office Building Circular Trade Plaza, No 288 South Shaanxi Road, Shanghai, 200031, China
Tel.: (86) 216 467 2222
Web Site: https://www.shanghai-house.com
Property Development Services
N.A.I.C.S.: 531390

Shinko Chemical Terminal Co., Ltd. (1)
18 Sumiyoshihamacho, Higashinada-Ku, Kobe, 658-0042, Hyogo, Japan
Tel.: (81) 788112671
Web Site: https://www.shinkochemical.co.jp
Emp.: 48
Industrial, Agricultural & Consumer Goods; Commodities & Natural Resources Trader; Financing, Leasing, Marketing, Logistics & Sales Services
N.A.I.C.S.: 424310

Shinnihon Reiki Co., Ltd. (1)
1-4-1 Futsukaichi-Minami, Chikushino, 818-0057, Fukuoka, Japan
Tel.: (81) 929231161
Emp.: 87
Cooling Tower Mfr
N.A.I.C.S.: 333415

Sithe Fuel Co., Ltd. (1)
7-1 Wonjeong-ri, Posung-myon, Pyeongtaek, Gyeonggi-do, Korea (South)
Tel.: (82) 2 724 4800
Fuel Distr
N.A.I.C.S.: 457210

Sithe Yosu Cogeneration Co., Ltd. (1)
3 Lot 10 Block Yosu National Industrial Complex, Hwachi-dong, Yeosu, Chollanam-do, Korea (South)
Tel.: (82) 5 926 1703
Steam Distr
N.A.I.C.S.: 221330

Sumatra Pulp Corporation (1)
9th Floor Nishimoto Kosan Nishikicho Building 3-23 Kandanishiki-cho, Chiyoda-ku, Tokyo, Japan
Tel.: (81) 332191175
Investment Management Service
N.A.I.C.S.: 523999

Taiei Sangyo Co., Ltd. (1)
1 Taishi Taishi-cho, Minamikawachi-gun, Osaka, 583-0995, Japan
Tel.: (81) 721980888
Emp.: 30
Plastic Food Containers Mfr
N.A.I.C.S.: 322220

Temsa Is Makinalari Imalat Pazarlama Ve Satis A.S. (1)
Kucuk Camlica Mahallesi Sehit Ismail Moray Sokak No 2/1, Uskudar, 34696, Istanbul, Turkiye
Tel.: (90) 2165472400
Web Site: http://www.temsaismakinalari.com.tr
Construction Machinery Distr
N.A.I.C.S.: 423810

Tianjin Benny Trading Co., Ltd. (1)
Heping District, Tianjin, China
Tel.: (86) 22 8319 1696
Sales Range: $50-74.9 Million
Emp.: 6
Specialty Chemical Mfr & Distr
N.A.I.C.S.: 325180
Guoliang Liu (Gen Mgr)

Tokachi Grain Terminal Co., Ltd. (1)
6-5-1 Hiroo - cho Kaisho-mae, Hiroo - gun, Hokkaido, 089-2605, Japan
Tel.: (81) 155887700
Web Site: https://tokachi-grain-center.com
Emp.: 12
Grain Warehousing & Transportation Services
N.A.I.C.S.: 488999

Toyo Sugar Refining Co., Ltd. (1)
18-20 Koamicho Nihonbashi, Chuo-ku, Tokyo, 103-0016, Japan
Tel.: (81) 336687871
Web Site: https://www.toyosugar.co.jp
Rev.: $115,060,270
Assets: $90,530,560
Liabilities: $16,815,840
Net Worth: $73,714,720
Earnings: $10,000,930
Fiscal Year-end: 03/31/2024
Sugar Mfr & Distr
N.A.I.C.S.: 311314
Kazuhiro Endo (Mng Dir, Gen Mgr-Sugar Bus & Mgr-Sugar Sls)

Toyota Ghana Company Ltd. (1)
Ring Road West Industrial Area, PO Box 1644, Adjuma Linke, Accra, Ghana
Tel.: (233) 302 228813
Web Site: http://www.toyotaghana.com
Automotive Distr
N.A.I.C.S.: 423110
Takuya Kajiura (Mng Dir)

UNIMAC Rubber Co., Ltd. (1)
2nd Floor of Thai Union Rubber Office 59/11 Plempitak Road, Trang, 92000, Thailand
Tel.: (66) 75 212213
Web Site: http://www.marubeni.com
Natural Rubber Mfr & Distr
N.A.I.C.S.: 326299

Wellfam Foods Corporation (1)
7F Kudan Kaikan Terrace 1-6-5 Kudanminami, Chiyoda-ku, Tokyo, 102-0074, Japan
Tel.: (81) 335159000
Web Site: https://www.wellfam-foods.co.jp
Emp.: 1,254
Chicken Product Mfr
N.A.I.C.S.: 311615

Wonderful Saigon Garment Co., Ltd. (1)
14th Street Tan Thuan Export Processing Zone, District 7, Ho Chi Minh City, 08, Vietnam
Tel.: (84) 8 3770 1386
Emp.: 400
Uniforms Mfr
N.A.I.C.S.: 315250
Ryoji Nishida (Mng Dir)

Yamaboshiya Co., Ltd (1)
3rd floor Sakaisuji Inabata Building 1-15-14 Minamisenba, Chuo-ku, Osaka, 542-0081, Japan
Tel.: (81) 661252100
Emp.: 1,065
Confectionery Whslr
N.A.I.C.S.: 424450

ZAMine Service Peru S.A.C. (1)
Av La Encalada N 1420 Edifico Polo Hunt II Of 801, Surco, Lima, Peru
Tel.: (51) 14365442
Web Site: https://www.zamineperu.com
Machinery Equipment Distr
N.A.I.C.S.: 423830

i2ts, inc. (1)
5th floor Shinjuku 6-chome Building 6-24-16, Shinjuku-ku, Tokyo, 160-0022, Japan
Tel.: (81) 332071255
Emp.: 110
Web Hosting Services
N.A.I.C.S.: 518210

iSigma Capital Corporation
Otemachi 1st Square West Tower 2F 1-5-1, Otemachi Chiyoda-ku, Tokyo, 100-0004, Japan
Tel.: (81) 362063210
Web Site: https://www.i-sigma-capital.co.jp
Emp.: 29
Investment Business Services
N.A.I.C.S.: 523999
Akihiko Watanabe (CEO)

Subsidiary (Domestic):

Japan Foods Co., Ltd. (2)
203-1 Saraki Nagara-machi Chosei, Chiba, 297-0235, Japan (52.22%)
Tel.: (81) 475352211
Web Site: https://www.japanfoods.co.jp
Rev.: $92,695,680
Assets: $214,683,040
Liabilities: $144,106,160
Net Worth: $70,576,880
Earnings: $3,446,080
Emp.: 280
Fiscal Year-end: 03/31/2022
Soft Drinks, Juice & Alcoholic Beverages Mfr & Sales
N.A.I.C.S.: 312111
Tomio Hosoi (Pres, Pres & CEO)

Subsidiary (Domestic):

Japan Juice Processing Company (JJPC) (3)
203 1 Nagara Cho, 297 0235, Chiba, Japan
Tel.: (81) 475355710
Beverages & Soft Drinks Mfr
N.A.I.C.S.: 312111
Nakao Yoshiaki (Mgr)

iSigma Partners Corporation (1)
1-5-1 Otemachi 1st Square West Tower 2F, Otemachi Chiyoda-ku, Tokyo, 100-0004, Japan
Tel.: (81) 362063210
Web Site: http://www.isigma-p.jp
Investment Business Services
N.A.I.C.S.: 523999

iStrings Aviation Capital Co., Ltd. (1)
Vort Nihonbashi I 8F 2-9-4, Nihonbashi Chuo-ku, Tokyo, 103-0027, Japan
Tel.: (81) 332721135
Web Site: https://www.istrings.co.jp
Aircraft Services
N.A.I.C.S.: 488190
Saburo Koyama (CEO)

MARUBUN CORPORATION

8-1 Nihonbashi Odenmacho, Chuo-ku, Tokyo, 103-8577, Japan
Tel.: (81) 336399801
Web Site: https://www.marubun.co.jp
7537—(TKS)
Rev.: $1,563,198,900
Assets: $1,150,933,200
Liabilities: $777,911,070
Net Worth: $373,022,130
Earnings: $22,480,610
Emp.: 1,167
Fiscal Year-end: 03/31/24
Electronic Parts & Equipment Whslr
N.A.I.C.S.: 423690
Satoshi Fujino (Sr VP)

Subsidiaries:

FORESIGHT TECHNO CO., LTD (1)
3-4 Minamisuna 3-Chom, Koto-ku, Tokyo, 136-8580, Japan
Tel.: (81) 356659800
Web Site: http://www.foresight-t.co.jp
Sales Range: $75-99.9 Million
Emp.: 123
Electronic Parts Mfr
N.A.I.C.S.: 423690
Masahide Kato (Pres & CEO)

MARUBUN SEMICON CORPORATION (1)
Seio Bldg 2-1-28 Shiba, Minato-ku, Tokyo, 105-0014, Japan
Tel.: (81) 354396521
Web Site: http://www.marubun-semicon.co.jp
Sales Range: $25-49.9 Million
Emp.: 62
Semiconductors Design & Mfr & Whslr
N.A.I.C.S.: 334413
Shuji Aihara (CEO)

Subsidiary (Non-US):

Marubun Semicon (Shanghai) Co., Ltd (2)
D-302 Dong Fang Guoji Tower 85 Loushanguan Rd, Shanghai, 200336, China
Tel.: (86) 21 6208 5733
Web Site: http://www.marubun-semicon.co.jp
Emp.: 3
Electronic Equipments Mfr & Sales
N.A.I.C.S.: 423690

MARUBUN WEST CORPORATION (1)
2-2-3 Kaigandori, Chuo-ku, Kobe, 650-0024, Hyogo, Japan (100%)
Tel.: (81) 783314266
Web Site: http://www.marubun-west.co.jp

INTERNATIONAL PUBLIC

Sales Range: $25-49.9 Million
Emp.: 26
Electronic Parts Mfr
N.A.I.C.S.: 423690
Tadashi Fujiwara (Pres)

Marubun Taiwan, Inc. (1)
Room B 10Floor NO 133 Min Sheng East Road Sec 3, Taipei, 105, Taiwan
Tel.: (886) 227191168
Web Site: https://www.marubun.co.jp
Semiconductor Distr
N.A.I.C.S.: 423690

Marubun Tsusyo Co., Ltd. (1)
1-40 Matsushima, Kanazawa, 920-0385, Ishikawa, Japan
Tel.: (81) 762691880
Web Site: https://www.marubun-tsusyo.co.jp
Emp.: 337
Medical Equipment Distr
N.A.I.C.S.: 423450

Marubun/Arrow (Phils), Inc. (1)
2/F MDD Building 121 East Science Avenue Laguna Technopark, Special Economic Zone, Binan, 4024, Laguna, Philippines
Tel.: (63) 495413356
Cutting-edge Electronic Product Distr
N.A.I.C.S.: 423690

MARUC CO., LTD.

608 6-25-8 Jingumae, Shibuya-ku, Tokyo, 150-0001, Japan
Tel.: (81) 364271525
Web Site: https://www.maruc.jp
Year Founded: 2011
7056—(TKS)
Rev.: $4,702,320
Assets: $3,781,760
Liabilities: $3,333,920
Net Worth: $447,840
Earnings: $223,920
Emp.: 4
Fiscal Year-end: 08/31/24
Graphic Design Services
N.A.I.C.S.: 541430
Junya Kitano (Pres)

MARUCHIYO YAMAOKAYA CORPORATION

Higashi-Kari 7-jo 1-chome 4-32, Higashi Ward, Sapporo, 007-0827, Hokkaido, Japan
Tel.: (81) 117817170
Web Site: https://maruchiyo.yamaokaya.com
Year Founded: 1993
33990—(TKS)
Rev.: $129,352,020
Assets: $55,891,150
Liabilities: $39,586,890
Net Worth: $16,304,260
Earnings: $2,540,090
Fiscal Year-end: 01/31/20
Noodles Shop Operator
N.A.I.C.S.: 722511
Tadashi Yamaoka (Chm & Pres)

MARUDAI FOOD CO., LTD.

21-3 Midori-cho, Takatsuki, Osaka, Japan
Tel.: (81) 120338845
Web Site: https://www.marudai.jp
Year Founded: 1950
2288—(TKS)
Rev.: $1,512,420,880
Assets: $805,223,590
Liabilities: $390,439,480
Net Worth: $414,784,110
Earnings: ($62,226,540)
Emp.: 4,890
Fiscal Year-end: 03/31/24
Meat Product Mfr & Distr
N.A.I.C.S.: 333241
Tokuo Kudara (Pres)

Subsidiaries:

Marudai Meat Co., Ltd. (1)
5-2-28 Heiwajima, Ota-Ku, Tokyo, 143-0006, Japan

AND PRIVATE COMPANIES

MARUHA NICHIRO CORPORATION

Tel.: (81) 337628889
Meat Product Distr
N.A.I.C.S.: 424420

Toda Foods Co., Ltd. (1)
3-7-8 Hikawacho, Toda, 335-0027, Saitama, Japan
Tel.: (81) 484445518
Web Site: https://www.marudai.jp
Emp.: 159
Food Product Mfr & Distr
N.A.I.C.S.: 311991

Toraku Foods Co., Ltd. (1)
5-5-5 Koyocho-nishi, Higashinada-Ku, Kobe, 658-0033, Hyogo, Japan
Tel.: (81) 788571522
Web Site: http://www.toraku.co.jp
Desserts Mfr
N.A.I.C.S.: 311999

Umeya Co., Ltd. (1)
1-12-14 Bunri, Mizuhomachi, Tanabe, 646-0023, Wakayama, Japan
Tel.: (81) 739224785
Web Site: https://www.umeya.co.jp
Emp.: 120
Food Products Distr
N.A.I.C.S.: 424490

MARUFUJI SHEET PILING CO., LTD.

MFPR Nihonbashi-Honcho Bldg 3-7-2 Nihombashi Hon-cho, Chuo-ku, Tokyo, 103-0023, Japan
Tel.: (81) 336397641
Web Site: https://www.mrfj.co.jp
Year Founded: 1947
8046—(TKS)
Rev.: $228,329,230
Assets: $286,510,450
Liabilities: $89,446,520
Net Worth: $197,063,930
Earnings: $9,068,920
Fiscal Year-end: 03/31/24
Construction Material Mfr & Distr
N.A.I.C.S.: 333120
Koichi Shimura (Pres)

MARUHA NICHIRO CORPORATION

3-2-20 Toyosu, Koto-ku, Tokyo, 135-8608, Japan
Tel.: (81) 368330826   JP
Web Site: https://www.maruha-nichiro.com
Year Founded: 1943
1333—(TKS)
Rev.: $6,812,755,140
Assets: $4,440,604,610
Liabilities: $2,817,981,810
Net Worth: $1,622,622,800
Earnings: $137,838,330
Emp.: 12,531
Fiscal Year-end: 03/31/24
Holding Company; Marine Products Processing, Food Processing, Chemical Foodstuffs Mfr, Livestock Feed Mfr, Fish Hatcheries Operator & Fish Distr
N.A.I.C.S.: 551112
Shigeru Ito (Chm)

Subsidiaries:

AIXIA Corporation (1)
4F JRE Shiba 2-chome Daimon Building 2-3-3 Shiba, Minato-Ku, Tokyo, 105-0014, Japan
Tel.: (81) 334577811
Emp.: 74
Cat & Dog Food Mfr
N.A.I.C.S.: 311111
Kazuo Nagase (Pres)

Agrobest (M) Sdn. Bhd. (1)
Batu 20 Jalan Pekan-Nenasi, 26680, Pekan, Pahang Darul Makmur, Malaysia
Tel.: (60) 9 4211888
Shrimp Farming Services
N.A.I.C.S.: 112512

Alyeska Seafoods, Inc. (1)
3015 112th Ave NE Ste 100, Bellevue, WA 98004
Tel.: (206) 547-2100
Sales Range: $25-49.9 Million
Emp.: 250
Process & Export Surimi
N.A.I.C.S.: 311710
Theresa Koonce (Coord-Sls)

Austral Fisheries Pty. Ltd. (1)
Level 4 50 Oxford Close, West Leederville, 6007, WA, Australia
Tel.: (61) 892170100
Web Site: https://www.australfisheries.com.au
Frozen Seafood Distr
N.A.I.C.S.: 424460
David Carter (CEO)

Beppu Uoichi Co., Ltd. (1)
990-91 Kamegawa Hamada-Machi, Beppu, Oita, Japan
Tel.: (81) 977 67 3011
Food Products Mfr
N.A.I.C.S.: 311999

CIXI Young-Shin Foods Co., Ltd. (1)
No 2 Renmin North Rd Fangshi, Longshan Town, Cixi, 315318, Zhejiang, China
Tel.: (86) 5746 370 6300
Web Site: https://www.maruha-nichiro.co.jp
Frozen Seafood Processing Services
N.A.I.C.S.: 311710

Daikyo Gyorui Co., Ltd (1)
City-owned land Suzaku Bunkimachi, Shimogyo-ku, Kyoto, 600-8847, Japan
Tel.: (81) 753213100
Web Site: https://www.maruha-daikyo.co.jp
Frozen Seafood Whslr
N.A.I.C.S.: 424460

Daito Gyorui Co., Ltd. (1)
6-6-2 Toyosu, Koto-ku, Tokyo, Japan   (100%)
Tel.: (81) 355658112
Web Site: https://www.daitogyorui.co.jp
Rev.: $991,481,100
Assets: $209,204,460
Liabilities: $122,835,480
Net Worth: $86,368,980
Earnings: $2,364,660
Fiscal Year-end: 03/31/2019
Seafood Whslr
N.A.I.C.S.: 424460
Hiromi Amino (Pres)

Dalian Ohta Foods Co., Ltd. (1)
441 Hekou Village, Ganjingzi District, Dalian, China
Tel.: (86) 411 8479 4801
Fish Processing & Packaging
N.A.I.C.S.: 311710

Heilongjiang Rilubeida Foodstuffs Co., Ltd (1)
No 3 Yingbin Road Baoquanling Luobei County, Hegang, 154211, Heilongjiang, China
Tel.: (86) 4683779177
Web Site: http://www.maruha-nichiro.co.jp
Frozen Fruit Juice & Vegetable Mfr.
N.A.I.C.S.: 311411

Hokkaido Akebono Shokuhin, Co., Ltd. (1)
Takasago-cho Shikotuko-cho, Abuta-gun, Hokkaido, 049-5605, Japan
Tel.: (81) 142762225
Soft Drinks Mfr
N.A.I.C.S.: 312111

Kyushu Uoichi Co., Ltd. (1)
94-9 Nishi-minatomachi Kokura, Kita-Ku, Kitakyushu, 803-0801, Japan
Tel.: (81) 9 3583 2480
Processed Sea Food Whslr
N.A.I.C.S.: 424460

Maruha (N.Z.) Corporation Ltd. (1)
Level 13 Swanson House 12-26 Swanson Street, PO Box 2227, Auckland, 1140, New Zealand
Tel.: (64) 99854646
Sales Range: $50-74.9 Million
Emp.: 6
Fish & Seafood Whslr
N.A.I.C.S.: 424460
Tim Law (Mgr)

Maruha (Shanghai) Trading Corporation (1)
Room 2501 Shanghai International Trade Center No 2201 Yan an xi road, Wai Gao Qiao Bao Shui District, Shanghai, 200336, China
Tel.: (86) 2162753333
Web Site: https://www.maruha-nichiro.co.jp
Fish & Seafood Whslr
N.A.I.C.S.: 424460

Maruha Capital Investment, Inc. (1)
3015 112th Ave NE Ste 100, Bellevue, WA 98004
Tel.: (206) 382-0640
Web Site: https://www.maruhacap.com
Sales Range: $50-74.9 Million
Emp.: 50
Investment Management Service
N.A.I.C.S.: 523999

Maruha Holdings (Thailand) Co., Ltd (1)
No 3 Rajanakarn Building 19th Floor South Sathorn Road, Yannawa Sathorn, Bangkok, 10120, Thailand
Tel.: (66) 22863351
Web Site: http://www.maruha-nichiro-th.com
Sales Range: $25-49.9 Million
Emp.: 10
Seafood Whslr
N.A.I.C.S.: 424460

Subsidiary (Domestic):

KF Foods Co., Ltd. (2)
1 Moo 4 Baanplaiklongkru Road Tambol Nadee, Amphur Muang, Samut Sakhon, 74000, Thailand
Tel.: (66) 34 417 444
Web Site: http://www.maruha-nichiro-th.com
Fresh & Frozen Seafood Processing Services
N.A.I.C.S.: 311710

N&N Foods Company Ltd. (2)
5/7-8 5/10 Moo 4 Sai-Setthakij Road Tambon Nadee, Amphur Muang, Samut Sakhon, 74000, Thailand
Tel.: (66) 34425279
Web Site: https://www.nnfoods.co.th
Emp.: 700
Frozen Specialty Food Mfr
N.A.I.C.S.: 311412

Southeast Asian Packaging & Canning Ltd. (2)
233 Moo 4 Bangpoo Industrial Estate Praksa Muang, Samut Prakan, 10280, Thailand
Tel.: (66) 34419888
Web Site: http://www.maruha-nichiro-th.com
Food Products Packaging Services
N.A.I.C.S.: 561910

Maruha Nichiro Asset, Inc (1)
7-2-chome Higashi Shinbashi, Minato-Ku, Tokyo, 105-0021, Japan
Tel.: (81) 3 5777 2266
Web Site: http://www.maruha-nichiro-asset.co.jp
Real Estate Manangement Services
N.A.I.C.S.: 531390

Maruha Nichiro Logistics, Inc. (1)
Toyomi Promotion Building 6th floor 4-5 Toyomicho, Chuo-ku, Tokyo, 104-0055, Japan
Tel.: (81) 355481281
Emp.: 500
Logistics Consulting Servies
N.A.I.C.S.: 541614

Branch (Domestic):

Maruha Nichiro Logistics, Inc.-Kyusyu Branch (2)
Hakozaki Wharf 5-2-22, Higashi-ku, Fukuoka, 812-0051, Japan
Tel.: (81) 926418413
Web Site: http://www.logi.maruha-nichiro.co.jp
Emp.: 93
Refrigerated Warehousing & Storage Facilties
N.A.I.C.S.: 493120

Maruha Nichiro Meat & Products USA, Inc. (1)
2111 S 67th St Ste 300, Omaha, NE 68106
Tel.: (402) 509-1249
Veal Product Mfr

N.A.I.C.S.: 311612

Meihoku Uoichiba Co., Ltd. (1)
Hatsutan 107 Toyoba Toyoyama-Cho, Nishi-Kasugai-gun, Toyoyama, 480-0291, Aichi, Japan
Tel.: (81) 529035220
Web Site: https://www.meihoku-uoichiba.co.jp
Emp.: 71
Fresh & Frozen Seafood Distr
N.A.I.C.S.: 424460

Nichiro Chikusan Co., Ltd. (1)
18-1-1 Kita Nishimachi Nishi-ku, Sapporo-shi, Hokkaido, 063-8510, Japan
Tel.: (81) 116631131
Web Site: http://www.nichiro-ham.co.jp
Sales Range: $100-124.9 Million
Emp.: 556
Frozen Meat Whslr
N.A.I.C.S.: 424420
Tsutomu Umeki (Mng Dir)

Nichiro Fur Co., Ltd. (1)
4th floor Hatchobori FRONT Build No 20-9 2- Chome Hatchobori, Chuo - ku, Tokyo, 104-0032, Japan
Tel.: (81) 335530821
Web Site: https://nihon-mouton.co.jp
Sales Range: $25-49.9 Million
Emp.: 55
Mens & Boys Clothing & Furnishings Whslr
N.A.I.C.S.: 424350

Nichiro Seafoods Corporation (1)
3-13400-2 Wadacho, Hitachinaka, 311-1214, Ibaraki, Japan
Tel.: (81) 29 263 7771
Web Site: https://www.nichiroseafoods.co.jp
Cured Fish & Seafood Whslr
N.A.I.C.S.: 424460
Satashi Fujimori (Office Mgr)

Nichiro Tokachi Shokuhin Co., Ltd. (1)
194-5 Sarabetsu Sarabestu-mura, Kasai-gun, Hokkaido, 089-1501, Japan
Tel.: (81) 155522101
Fruit & Vegetable Canning
N.A.I.C.S.: 311421
Takao Suenaga (Pres)

Niigata Fresh Delica Co., Ltd. (1)
1-1027-1 Nanyo Nagaoka-shi, Niigata-Ken, 940-1194, Niigata, Japan
Tel.: (81) 258220377
Frozen Cakes Pies & Pastries Mfr
N.A.I.C.S.: 311813

Okhotsk Nichiro Corporation (1)
972 Aza-Omu Omu-machi, Monbetsu-gun, 098-1702, Hokkaido, Japan
Tel.: (81) 158842731
Seafood Canning
N.A.I.C.S.: 311710

P.T. Alfa Kurnia Fish Enterprise (1)
Graha Mik # 303 Taman Perkantoran Kuningan Jalan Setiabudi Selatan, Kavling 16-17, 12920, Jakarta, Indonesia
Tel.: (62) 2157941424
Web Site: http://www.maruha-nichiro.co.jp
Seafood Canning
N.A.I.C.S.: 311710

Peter Pan Seafoods, Inc. (1)
3015 112th Ave NE Ste 150, Bellevue, WA 98004
Tel.: (206) 728-6000
Sales Range: $10-24.9 Million
Emp.: 376
Canned & Frozen Salmon, Crab, Halibut, Cod, Pollock & Herring Mfr
N.A.I.C.S.: 311710

Premier Pacific Seafoods, Inc. (1)
333 1st Ave W, Seattle, WA 98119
Tel.: (206) 286-8584
Web Site: https://www.premierpacificseafoods.com
Fish & Seafood Whslr
N.A.I.C.S.: 424460
Joe Bersch (Pres & Sec)

Qingdao TAFCO Food Co., Ltd. (1)
Riviera Industrial Park, Jiaonan, Qingdao, China
Tel.: (86) 53288139651
Web Site: http://qd-tafco.com.cn
Food Mfr

MARUHA NICHIRO CORPORATION

Maruha Nichiro Corporation—(Continued)
N.A.I.C.S.: 311999

Rizhao Nichiro & Rongsense Foods Co., Ltd. (1)
Gao Ke Ji Gong Ye Yuan, Rizhao, Shandong, China
Tel.: (86) 633 2225588
Web Site: http://www.maruha-nichiro.co.jp
Seafood Distr
N.A.I.C.S.: 424460

Sai Gon Food Joint Stock Company (1)
Lot C24-24B/II C25/II - Street No 2F, Vinh Loc Industrial Park Vinh Loc A Ward Binh Chanh District, Ho Chi Minh City, Vietnam
Tel.: (84) 2837652061
Web Site: http://www.sgfoods.com.vn
Emp.: 300
Food Mfr
N.A.I.C.S.: 311999

Sakaiminato Uoichiba Co., Ltd. (1)
9-7 Showa Machi, Sakaiminato, 684-0034, Tottori, Japan
Tel.: (81) 859 42 2131
Web Site: http://www.maruha-nichiro.co.jp
Seafood Product Whslr
N.A.I.C.S.: 424420

Sakana del Peru S.A (1)
Sinchi Roca No 2751, Lince, Lima, Peru
Tel.: (51) 14222403
Sales Range: $25-49.9 Million
Emp.: 13
Finfish Fishing Services
N.A.I.C.S.: 114111
Marciano Corman (Gen Mgr)

Seafood Connection Holding B.V. (1)
Het Spijk 12, 8321 WT, Urk, Netherlands
Tel.: (31) 527687066
Web Site: http://www.seafoodconnection.nl
Frozen Seafood Distr
N.A.I.C.S.: 424460
Jan Kaptijn (CEO)

Shinko Gyorui Co., Ltd. (1)
1-1 Nakanoshima 1-Chome, Hyogo-Ku, Kobe, 652-0844, Japan
Tel.: (81) 78 672 7000
Web Site: http://www.maruha-shinko.co.jp
Emp.: 130
Frozen Seafood Distr
N.A.I.C.S.: 424460
H. Amino (Pres & CEO)

Sungourmet Corporation (1)
1284-63 Ketakachoshimosakamoto, Tottori, 689-0221, Japan
Tel.: (81) 857826633
Frozen Specialty Food Mfr
N.A.I.C.S.: 311412
Hiroyuki Umeki (Mgr)

Taiyo A&F Co., Ltd (1)
4-5 Toyomicho, Chuo-ku, Tokyo, 104-0055, Japan
Tel.: (81) 362201255
Sales Range: $75-99.9 Million
Emp.: 300
Fish Farming Services
N.A.I.C.S.: 112511
Nobuyuki Wakasa (Pres)

Subsidiary (Non-US):

Philippine Taiyo Aqua Farming Corp. (2)
Suite 701 Dasma Corporate Center 321 Dasmarinas, Saint Binondo, Manila, Philippines
Tel.: (63) 2 2445563
Emp.: 4
Aqua Farming Services
N.A.I.C.S.: 112511
Richard Sy (Pres)

Taiyo Namibia (Pty) Ltd. (2)
13th Road, PO Box 49, Walvis Bay, Namibia
Tel.: (264) 64212412
Fishing Services
N.A.I.C.S.: 114119

Subsidiary (Domestic):

Taiyo Shokuhin Co., Ltd. (2)
1-365 Takashima, Shimabara, 855-0801, Nagasaki, Japan
Tel.: (81) 957630333
Seafood Canning Services
N.A.I.C.S.: 311710

Taiyo Micronesia Corporation (1)
Kapwarsou St NFC Bldg Pohnpei, Kolonia, FM 96941
Tel.: (691) 320-2552
Fish Farming Services
N.A.I.C.S.: 112511

Tanabe Co., Ltd. (1)
1-4-15 Onohara Higashi, Minoo-Shi, Minoh, 562-0031, Osaka, Japan
Tel.: (81) 727286700
Web Site: https://www.rd-tanabe.com
Emp.: 170
Frozen Specialty Food Mfr
N.A.I.C.S.: 311412

Trans Ocean Products Inc. (1)
350 W Orchard Dr, Bellingham, WA 98225
Fresh & Frozen Seafood Processing Services
N.A.I.C.S.: 311710
Murry R. Park (Pres)

Westward Seafoods, Inc. (1)
3015 112th Ave NE Ste 100, Bellevue, WA 98004
Tel.: (206) 682-5949
Sales Range: $100-124.9 Million
Emp.: 50
Fish Processing
N.A.I.C.S.: 311710

Yantai Aqli Foodstuffs Co., Ltd. (1)
Longda Industrial Zone, Laiyang, Shandong, China
Tel.: (86) 535 7719801
Web Site: http://www.maruha-nichiro-th.com
Processed Food Mfr
N.A.I.C.S.: 311999

Yantai RiLuDa Foodstuffs Co., Ltd. (1)
Longda Industrial Zone, Laiyang, Shandong, China
Tel.: (86) 5357717093
Food Mfr
N.A.I.C.S.: 311999

Yayoi Sunfoods Co., Ltd. (1)
6F Shiba Daimon Center Building 1-10-11 Shiba Daimon, Minato-ku, Tokyo, 105-0012, Japan
Tel.: (81) 354001500
Web Site: https://www.yayoi-sunfoods.co.jp
Sales Range: $300-349.9 Million
Emp.: 1,712
Frozen Prepared Foods Mfr & Distr
N.A.I.C.S.: 311412
Satoshi Kuromoto (Pres)

Plant (Domestic):

Yayoi Sunfoods Co., Ltd. - Nagaoka Factory (2)
1-107-1 Nanyo, Nagaoka, 940-1194, Niigata, Japan
Tel.: (81) 258223800
Web Site: http://www.nichiro_sun.co.jp
Frozen Specialty Food Mfr
N.A.I.C.S.: 311412

Zhejiang Industrial Group Co., Ltd. (1)
No 1 Xingye Road, Ganlan Town Dinghai District, Zhoushan, 316000, Zhejiang, China
Tel.: (86) 5803696686
Seafood Mfr
N.A.I.C.S.: 311710

MARUHACHI HOLDINGS CO., LTD.

3-8-12 Shinyokohama, Kohoku-Ku, Yokohama, 222-0033, Kanagawa, Japan
Tel.: (81) 454710818
Web Site: https://maruhachi.co.jp
Year Founded: 1962
3504—(NGO)
Rev.: $124,473,580
Assets: $537,031,880
Liabilities: $120,897,280
Net Worth: $416,134,600
Earnings: $4,529,980
Fiscal Year-end: 03/31/20
Bedding & Living Product Distr
N.A.I.C.S.: 424930
Noriyuki Okamoto (Chm)

MARUHACHI SECURITIES CO., LTD.

4-4 Shin-Sakae-cho, Naka-ku, Nagoya, 460-0004, Aichi, Japan
Tel.: (81) 523070808
Web Site: https://www.maruhachi-sec.co.jp
Year Founded: 1944
8700—(TKS)
Sales Range: Less than $1 Million
Securities Brokerage Services
N.A.I.C.S.: 523150
Takuya Suzuki (Pres & CEO)

MARUHACHI WAREHOUSE COMPANY LIMITED

HF Monzen-Nakacho Building 4F 2-1-9 Tomioka, Koto-ku, Tokyo, 135-0047, Japan
Tel.: (81) 356200816
Web Site: https://www.maru8.co.jp
Year Founded: 1934
9313—(TKS)
Rev.: $35,251,480
Assets: $129,676,100
Liabilities: $51,005,460
Net Worth: $78,670,640
Earnings: $2,921,080
Fiscal Year-end: 11/30/23
Warehousing Services
N.A.I.C.S.: 493110

Subsidiaries:

Touhoku Maruhachi Unyu Company Ltd. (1)
4-1-11 Oroshimachihigashi, Wakabayashi-Ku, Sendai, 984-0002, Miyagi, Japan
Tel.: (81) 22 287 3528
Web Site: https://maru8-unyu.maru8.co.jp
Freight Transportation Services
N.A.I.C.S.: 484110

MARUHAN CORPORATION

231 Seiryu-cho Demachi Imadegawa Agaru, Kamigyo-Ku, Kyoto, 602-0822, Japan
Tel.: (81) 752520011 JP
Web Site: http://www.maruhan.co.jp
Year Founded: 1957
Rev.: $12,302,834,720
Assets: $7,255,285,840
Liabilities: $4,148,877,040
Net Worth: $3,106,408,800
Earnings: $140,379,360
Emp.: 10,570
Fiscal Year-end: 03/31/22
Entertainment Facilities
N.A.I.C.S.: 711310
Chang-Woo Han (Chm & CEO)

Subsidiaries:

MM International Co., Ltd (1)
Hulic Kandabashi Building 7F 1-21-1 Kanda Nishikicho, Chiyoda-ku, Tokyo, 101-0054, Japan
Tel.: (81) 332938686
Web Site: http://www.mmin-net.co.jp
Emp.: 1,697
Pachinko Prize Distr
N.A.I.C.S.: 423910

Taiheiyo Club, Inc. (1)
Bunka Hoso Nippon Cultural Broadcasting Media Plus 6F 1-31, Hamamatsu-cho Minato-Ku, Tokyo, 105-0013, Japan
Tel.: (81) 3 6430 2031
Web Site: http://www.taiheiyoclub.co.jp
Golf Club Operator
N.A.I.C.S.: 713910

Subsidiary (Domestic):

Taiheiyo Golf Service, K.K. (2)
477 Kamigokan, Annaka, 379-0108, Gunma, Japan
Tel.: (81) 273855811
Golf Club Operator
N.A.I.C.S.: 713910

Taiheiyo Golf Square, Inc. (2)
Sumitomoseisenshibaura Bldg 6f, Minato-Ku, Tokyo, 105-0023, Japan
Tel.: (81) 354461868
Golf Club Operator
N.A.I.C.S.: 713910

MARUHO CO., LTD.

1-5-22 Nakatsu, Kita-ku, Osaka, 531-0071, Japan
Tel.: (81) 6 6371 8876 JP
Web Site: http://www.maruho.co.jp
Year Founded: 1915
Sales Range: $650-699.9 Million
Emp.: 1,512
Pharmaceutical Mfr & Distr
N.A.I.C.S.: 325412
Koichi Takagi (Pres & CEO)

Subsidiaries:

Maruho Co., Ltd. - Hikone Plant (1)
2763 Takamiya-cho, Hikone, Shiga, Japan
Tel.: (81) 749 23 5541
Pharmaceuticals Product Mfr
N.A.I.C.S.: 325412

Maruho Co., Ltd. - Nagahama Plant (1)
1301-1 Tamura-cho, Nagahama, Shiga, Japan
Tel.: (81) 749 68 6800
Pharmaceuticals Product Mfr
N.A.I.C.S.: 325412

Maruho Deutschland GmbH (1)
Hemmelrather Weg 201, 51377, Leverkusen, Germany
Tel.: (49) 214 892201 0
Pharmaceutical Products Distr
N.A.I.C.S.: 424210

Maruho Hatsujyo Kogyo Co., Ltd. (1)
Kyoto Research Park 4th Floor 1 Bldg 134 Chudoji Minamimachi, Shimogyo-ku, Kyoto, 600-8813, Japan
Tel.: (81) 75 312 1661
Web Site: http://www.maruho-htj.co.jp
Emp.: 220
Packaging Machinery Mfr
N.A.I.C.S.: 333993
Ryohei Imai (Pres)

Plant (Domestic):

Maruho Hatsujyo Kogyo Co., Ltd. - Kameoka Factory (2)
12-1 Iwanoue Yoshida, Yoshikawa-cho, Kameoka, 621-0015, Kyoto, Japan
Tel.: (81) 771 22 1123
Packaging Machinery Mfr
N.A.I.C.S.: 333993

Maruho Hatsujyo Kogyo Co., Ltd. - Shinkouetsu Factory (2)
22 KyotoShinkouetsu-mura Uriuno, Sonobe-cho, Nantan, 622-0021, Kyoto, Japan
Tel.: (81) 771 63 5082
Packaging Machinery Mfr
N.A.I.C.S.: 333993

MARUI GROUP CO., LTD.

3-2 Nakano 4-chome, Nakano-ku, Tokyo, 164-8701, Japan
Tel.: (81) 333840101 JP
Web Site: https://www.0101maruigroup.co.jp
Year Founded: 1931
8252—(TKS)
Rev.: $1,554,850,470
Assets: $6,633,141,610
Liabilities: $4,956,660,530
Net Worth: $1,676,481,080
Earnings: $163,048,870
Emp.: 4,290
Fiscal Year-end: 03/31/24
Holding Company; Retail Stores Operator, Credit Card & Retail-Related Services

AND PRIVATE COMPANIES

MARUICHI STEEL TUBE LTD

N.A.I.C.S.: 551112
Yoshiaki Kogure *(Exec Officer)*

Subsidiaries:

AIM Create Co., Ltd. (1)
3-34-28 Nakano, Nakano-Ku, Tokyo, 164-0001, Japan
Tel.: (81) 353400101
Web Site: http://www.aim-create.co.jp
Sales Range: $75-99.9 Million
Emp.: 288
Advertising Services
N.A.I.C.S.: 541890

Epos Card Co., Ltd. (1)
4-3-2 Nakano, Nakano-ku, Tokyo, 164-8701, Japan
Tel.: (81) 345740101
Web Site: https://www.eposcard.co.jp
Financial Services
N.A.I.C.S.: 523210

Epos Small Amount & Short Term Insurance Co., Ltd. (1)
Marui Group South Exit Annex 3-34-28 Nakano, Nakano-ku, Tokyo, 164-0001, Japan
Tel.: (81) 345460101
Web Site: http://www.epos-ssi.co.jp
Insurance Services
N.A.I.C.S.: 523210

M & C Systems Co., Ltd. (1)
4-3-2 Nakano, Nakano-ku, Tokyo, 164-8701, Japan
Tel.: (81) 353430100
Web Site: https://www.m-and-c.co.jp
Emp.: 202
Software Development Services
N.A.I.C.S.: 541511

MRI Co., Ltd. (1)
3-34-28 Nakano, Nakano-ku, Tokyo, 164-8580, Japan
Tel.: (81) 345744700
Web Site: http://www.mri-s.co.jp
Financial Services
N.A.I.C.S.: 523210

Marui Co., Ltd. (1)
4-3-2 Nakano, Nakano-ku, Tokyo, 164-8701, Japan
Tel.: (81) 333840101
Web Site: http://www.0101.co.jp
Lifestyle Product Whslr
N.A.I.C.S.: 424590
Akira Iguchi *(Pres & CEO)*

Marui Facilities Co., Ltd. (1)
3-34-28 Nakano, Nakano-ku, Tokyo, 164-0001, Japan
Tel.: (81) 332290101
Web Site: https://www.marui-facilities.co.jp
Emp.: 467
Facility Management Services
N.A.I.C.S.: 561210

Marui Home Service Co., Ltd. (1)
34-28 Nakano 3-chome, Nakano-ku, Tokyo, 164-0001, Japan
Tel.: (81) 363610101
Web Site: https://www.marui-hs.co.jp
Emp.: 76
Facility Management Services
N.A.I.C.S.: 561210

Marui Kit Center Co., Ltd. (1)
2-5-1 Bijogihigashi Toda General Logistics Center No 2 Building 2F, Toda, 335-0032, Saitama, Japan
Tel.: (81) 484217351
Web Site: https://www.maruikitcenter.co.jp
Emp.: 62
Facility Management Services
N.A.I.C.S.: 561210
Atsuko Toida *(Pres)*

Mizonokuchishintoshi Co., Ltd. (1)
1-3-1 Mizoguchi, Takatsu-ku, Kawasaki, 213-0001, Kanagawa, Japan
Tel.: (81) 448147777
Web Site: https://www.nocty.jp
Insurance Services
N.A.I.C.S.: 523210

Moving Co., Ltd. (1)
2-5-1 Bijogihigashi, Shinjuku-Ku, Toda, 335-0032, Saitama, Japan **(93.2%)**
Tel.: (81) 482331000
Web Site: https://www.moving.co.jp

Sales Range: $450-499.9 Million
Emp.: 850
Merchandise Delivery
N.A.I.C.S.: 455219

Tsumiki Securities Co., Ltd. (1)
4-3-2 Nakano, Nakano-ku, Tokyo, Japan
Tel.: (81) 353430134
Web Site: https://www.tsumiki-sec.com
Emp.: 13
Financial Services
N.A.I.C.S.: 523210

Zero First Co., Ltd. (1)
5 49 4 Chuo Nakano ku, Tokyo, 164 8606, Japan
Tel.: (81) 333818111
Web Site: http://www.zero-first.co.jp
Sales Range: $25-49.9 Million
Emp.: 18
Credit Card-Related Businesses
N.A.I.C.S.: 326199

MARUI ORIMONO KK

15 Kunokiibe Nakanoto Town, Kashima, 929-1801, Ishikawa, Japan
Tel.: (81) 767 76 1337 JP
Web Site: https://www.maruig.co.jp
Year Founded: 1956
Emp.: 100
Textile Mfr
N.A.I.C.S.: 313310
Yoshio Miyamoto *(Pres)*

Subsidiaries:

Soko Seiren Co., Ltd. (1)
459 Minami Kobu-machi, Kanazawa, 920-0363, Japan **(55.78%)**
Tel.: (81) 762493131
Web Site: http://www.soko.co.jp
Rev.: $22,041,360
Assets: $28,304,320
Liabilities: $14,355,440
Net Worth: $13,948,880
Earnings: ($1,239,040)
Emp.: 160
Fiscal Year-end: 03/31/2022
Fiber Product Mfr & Whslr
N.A.I.C.S.: 314999

MARUICHI STEEL TUBE LTD

29th floor Namba SkyO 5-1-60 Namba, Chuo-ku, Osaka, 542-0076, Japan
Tel.: (81) 666430101
Web Site:
    https://www.maruichikokan.co.jp
5463—(TKS)
Rev.: $2,170,430,240
Assets: $3,582,355,040
Liabilities: $604,854,800
Net Worth: $2,977,500,240
Earnings: $268,716,800
Emp.: 2,383
Fiscal Year-end: 03/31/22
Steel Mfr & Sales
N.A.I.C.S.: 331110
Yoshinori Yoshimura *(Pres & COO)*

Subsidiaries:

Alpha Metal Co., Ltd. (1)
850 Inamitsu, Miyawaka, Fukuoka, 822-0144, Japan
Tel.: (81) 949523355
Emp.: 129
Automotive Parts Distr & Mfr
N.A.I.C.S.: 336390
Sumio Himuro *(Pres)*

Alphametal Mexico S.A. de C.V. (1)
Municipio de Tepezala 112 Parque Industrial del Valle de, Aguascalientes San Fco de los Romo, 20358, Aguascalientes, Mexico
Tel.: (52) 4491580301
Steel Tubing Mfr
N.A.I.C.S.: 331210

Hokkaido Maruichi Steel Tube Ltd. (1)
134-110 Aza Numanohata, Tomakomai, 059-1364, Hokkaido, Japan
Tel.: (81) 144553801
Web Site: http://www.maruichikokan.co.jp

Steel Tubes & Poles Products Mfr
N.A.I.C.S.: 331210

Plant (Domestic):

Hokkaido Maruichi Steel Tube Ltd. - Sapporo Pole Plant (2)
151-5 Kyoei, Kitahiroshima, 061-1112, Hokkaido, Japan
Tel.: (81) 113723136
Web Site: http://www.maruichikokan.co.jp
Steel Pole Mfr
N.A.I.C.S.: 331221

J-Spiral Steel Pipe Co., Ltd. (1)
Slope 47, Tam Phuoc Ward, Bien Hoa, Dong Nai, Vietnam
Tel.: (84) 2513511410
Web Site: https://jspiral.com
Emp.: 125
Steel Tubing Mfr
N.A.I.C.S.: 331210

KUMA Stainless Tubes Limited (1)
Plot No 27 Sector 2A, IMT Manesar, Gurgaon, 122 050, Haryana, India
Tel.: (91) 1244213056
Web Site: https://www.maruichikuma.com
Steel Tubes Whslr
N.A.I.C.S.: 331210

Kasuga Industry Ltd. (1)
3-2 7 Chome Kami-higashi, Hirano-ku, Osaka, 547-0002, Japan
Tel.: (81) 667914912
Steel Tube Processing Services
N.A.I.C.S.: 331210
Yoshinori Yoshimura *(Pres)*

Kyushu Maruichi Steel Tube Ltd. (1)
12 Meishihama Nagasu-cho, Tamana-gun, Kumamoto, 869-0111, Japan
Tel.: (81) 968783711
Sales Range: $25-49.9 Million
Emp.: 55
Steel Tube Mfr
N.A.I.C.S.: 331210
Fukio Okamoto *(Pres)*

Maruichi Kohan Ltd. (1)
29F Namba Skyo 1-60 5 Chome, Namba Chuo-ku, Osaka, 542-0076, Japan
Tel.: (81) 666438101
Sales Range: $25-49.9 Million
Emp.: 80
Steel Tubes Sales
N.A.I.C.S.: 331210
Hiroyuki Suzuki *(Chm & Pres)*

Maruichi Kuma Steel Tube Private Limited (1)
Plot No 27 Sector 2A IMT Manesar, Gurgaon, 122050, Haryana, India
Tel.: (91) 1244213056
Steel Tubing Mfr
N.A.I.C.S.: 331210

Maruichi Leavitt Pipe & Tube, LLC (1)
1717 W 115th St, Chicago, IL 60643
Tel.: (773) 729-7700
Steel Tube Mfr
N.A.I.C.S.: 331210
Pat Knutson *(Sls Mgr-Alabama)*

Plant (Domestic):

Leavitt Tube Company LLC - Jackson Plant (2)
211 Industrial Dr N, Madison, MS 39130-1186
Tel.: (601) 856-9051
Sales Range: $25-49.9 Million
Emp.: 6
Steel Tubes Whslr
N.A.I.C.S.: 331110

Maruichi Metal Product (Foshan) Co., Ltd. (1)
Huabao Nan Road Chengxi Industrial Park, Foshan National HI-TECH Industries Zone Chancheng District, Foshan, Guangdong, China
Tel.: (86) 75782108558
Steel Tubing Mfr
N.A.I.C.S.: 331210

Maruichi Metal Product (Tianjin) Co., Ltd. (1)
Zhongnan three street, west Tianjin eco-

nomic development zone area, Tianjin, China
Tel.: (86) 2259868898
Steel Tubing Mfr
N.A.I.C.S.: 331210

Maruichi Oregon Steel Tube, LLC (1)
8735 N Harborgate St, Portland, OR 97203
Tel.: (503) 737-1200
Steel Tubing Mfr
N.A.I.C.S.: 331210
Sho Morita *(Pres)*

Maruichi Philippines Steel Tube Inc. (1)
Phase 2B B3 L2-B Lima Technology Center, Brgy Bugtong na Pulo, Lipa, 4217, Batangas, Philippines
Tel.: (63) 9951707539
Steel Tubing Mfr
N.A.I.C.S.: 331210

Maruichi Stainless Tube Co., Ltd. (1)
13-1 Chofuminato-machi, Shimonoseki, 752-0953, Yamaguchi, Japan
Tel.: (81) 832463781
Steel Tubing Mfr
N.A.I.C.S.: 331210

Maruichi Steel Tube Ltd - Kashima Pole Plant (1)
3075-27 Shimasu, Itako, 311-2434, Ibaraki, Japan
Tel.: (81) 299646901
Web Site: http://www.maruichikokan.co.jp
Steel Pole Mfr
N.A.I.C.S.: 331221

Maruichi Steel Tube Ltd - Nagoya Plant (1)
14 Kanaoka, Ama-gun, Tobishima, 490-1445, Aichi, Japan
Tel.: (81) 567551101
Sales Range: $25-49.9 Million
Emp.: 100
Steel Tube Mfr
N.A.I.C.S.: 331210

Maruichi Steel Tube Ltd - Osaka Plant (1)
3-2 7 Chome Kami-higashi, Hirano-ku, Osaka, 547-0002, Japan
Tel.: (81) 667915551
Web Site: http://www.maruichikokan.co.jp
Sales Range: $25-49.9 Million
Emp.: 30
Steel Tube Mfr
N.A.I.C.S.: 331210
Yasuo Kawamura *(Sr Mng Officer)*

Maruichi Steel Tube Ltd - Pole Division (1)
125 2 Cho Ishihara-cho, Higashi-ku, Sakai, 599-8102, Osaka, Japan
Tel.: (81) 722581858
Web Site: http://www.maruichikokan.co.jp
Steel Poles Whslr
N.A.I.C.S.: 423510

Maruichi Steel Tube Ltd - Sakai Plant (1)
16 Ishizu-nishimachi, Nishi-ku, Sakai, 592-8332, Osaka, Japan
Tel.: (81) 722410301
Web Site: http://www.maruichikokan.co.jp
Steel Tube Mfr
N.A.I.C.S.: 334419

Maruichi Steel Tube Ltd - Sakai Pole Plant (1)
125 2 Cho Ishihara-cho, Higashi-ku, Sakai, 599-8102, Osaka, Japan
Tel.: (81) 72 258 1858
Web Site: http://www.maruichikokan.co.jp
Sales Range: $50-74.9 Million
Emp.: 150
Steel Tube Mfr
N.A.I.C.S.: 331210

Maruichi Steel Tube Ltd - Takuma Plant (1)
6883 Takuma Takuma-cho, Mitoyo, 769-1101, Kagawa, Japan
Tel.: (81) 875833301
Web Site: http://www.maruichikokan.co.jp
Sales Range: $25-49.9 Million
Emp.: 70
Steel Tube Mfr

Maruichi Steel Tube Ltd—(Continued)
N.A.I.C.S.: 331210

Maruichi Steel Tube Ltd - Tokyo Plant (1)
11 1Chome Shiohama, Ichikawa, 272-0127, Chiba, Japan
Tel.: (81) 47 395 1201
Web Site: http://www.maruichikokan.co.jp
Steel Tube Mfr
N.A.I.C.S.: 331210

Maruichi Sun Steel (Hanoi) Company Limited (1)
Binh Xuyen Industrial Zone, Huong Canh Town Binh Xuyen District, Binh Xuyen, Vinh Phuc, Vietnam
Tel.: (84) 2113582877
Steel Tubing Mfr
N.A.I.C.S.: 331210

Maruichi Sun Steel Joint Stock Company (1)
DT743 Road Dong Tac Quarter, Tan Dong Hiep Ward, Di An, Binh Duong, Vietnam
Tel.: (84) 2743742777
Web Site: https://maruichisunsteel.com
Emp.: 470
Steel Tubing Mfr
N.A.I.C.S.: 331210
Sakai Yasuyuki (Gen Dir)

Maruichimex S.A. de C.V. (1)
Circuito Japon 112 Parque Industrial San Francisco, PO 20304, San Francisco de los Romo, 20304, Aguascalientes, Mexico
Tel.: (52) 4499107040
Steel Tubing Mfr
N.A.I.C.S.: 331210

Metal One Sumisho Tubular Products Co., Ltd. (1)
Shin-Tokyo Building 5F 3-3-1 Marunouchi, Chiyoda-ku, Tokyo, 100-0005, Japan
Tel.: (81) 352200120
Emp.: 808
Steel Tubing Whslr
N.A.I.C.S.: 423510
Norio Naito (Chm)

Okinawa Maruichi Ltd. (1)
388-3 Ohira, Urasoe, 901-2113, Okinawa, Japan
Tel.: (81) 988761801
Steel Tubes Whslr & Distr
N.A.I.C.S.: 331210
Hajime Arita (Pres)

PT Indonesia Steel Tube Works (1)
Jln Rawa Sumur I no 1 kawasan Industri Pulogadung, Jakarta, 13940, Indonesia
Tel.: (62) 214600991
Web Site: https://www.istw.co.id
Sales Range: $125-149.9 Million
Emp.: 500
Pipes & Tubes Mfr
N.A.I.C.S.: 322219

Shikoku Maruichi Steel Tube Ltd. (1)
2112-48 Takuma, Takuma-cho, Mitoyo, 769-1101, Kagawa, Japan
Tel.: (81) 875834135
Steel Tube Mfr
N.A.I.C.S.: 331210
Yoshinori Yoshimura (Pres)

MARUKA FURUSATO CORPORATION
1-2-10 Minamishinmachi, Chuo-ku, Osaka, 540-0024, Japan
Tel.: (81) 669461600
Web Site: https://www.unisol-gr.com
Year Founded: 2021
7128—(TKS)
Rev.: $1,226,428,200
Assets: $853,224,780
Liabilities: $337,647,070
Net Worth: $515,577,710
Earnings: $33,308,820
Emp.: 1,951
Fiscal Year-end: 12/31/23
Holding Company; Machinery, Tools, Construction Materials & Internet Of Things Solutions Products & Services
N.A.I.C.S.: 551112
Ryohei Furusato (Pres)

Subsidiaries:

Furusato Industries, Ltd. (1)
1-2-10 Minamishin-machi, Chuo-ku, Osaka, 540-0024, Japan
Tel.: (81) 669469600
Web Site: http://www.furusato.co.jp
Rev.: $866,147,040
Assets: $643,836,160
Liabilities: $215,389,680
Net Worth: $428,446,480
Earnings: $18,730,800
Emp.: 495
Fiscal Year-end: 03/31/2021
Machinery & Tools Mfr & Sales
N.A.I.C.S.: 423810
Ryohei Furusato (Pres)

Subsidiary (Domestic):

G-net Corporation (2)
1-2-10 Minamishinmachi, Chuo-ku, Osaka, 540-0024, Japan
Tel.: (81) 669469618
Web Site: http://www.g-net.co.jp
Sales Range: $100-124.9 Million
Emp.: 460
Machine Tools & Housing Equipment Mfr
N.A.I.C.S.: 333517
Shinichiro Terada (Mng Dir)

Subsidiary (Non-US):

Retra Engineering (Thailand) Co., Ltd. (2)
No 33 2-3 Floor Sukhumvit 63 Ekkamai Klongton Nua, Wattana, Bangkok, 10110, Thailand
Tel.: (66) 381854923
Web Site: https://www.retra-co-th.com
Cutting Tool Distr
N.A.I.C.S.: 423830
Kazuhiro Soejima (Sls Mgr, Mng Dir & Chm)

Maruka Corporation (1)
2-28 Itsukaichimidori-machi, Ibaraki, 567-8520, Osaka, Japan
Tel.: (81) 726256721
Web Site: http://www.maruka.co.jp
Industrial Machinery Mfr
N.A.I.C.S.: 333248
Toshiaki Takeshita (Pres)

Subsidiary (US):

Industrial Tool, Inc. (2)
9210 52nd Ave N, Minneapolis, MN 55428
Tel.: (763) 533-7244
Web Site: http://www.industrial-tool.com
Sales Range: $1-9.9 Million
Emp.: 39
Machine Tool (Metal Cutting Types) Mfr
N.A.I.C.S.: 333517
Patrick Hjelm (Pres & CEO)

Subsidiary (Non-US):

MARUKA (M) SDN.BHD. (2)
No 4 Jalan Pju 1A/12 Taman Perindustrian Jaya, Ara Damansara, 47200, Petaling Jaya, Selangor, Malaysia
Tel.: (60) 378483251
Industrial Machinery Distr
N.A.I.C.S.: 423830

MARUKA ENTERPRISES, INC. (2)
Unit 401 & 402 La Fuerza Plaza I 2241 Don Chino Roces Ave, Makati, 1231, Philippines
Tel.: (63) 28120391
Web Site: http://www.maruka.com.ph
Industrial Machinery Distr
N.A.I.C.S.: 423830
Kunio Kobayashi (Gen Mgr)

Subsidiary (Non-US):

MARUKA TRADING GUANGZHOU LIMITED (3)
1605 Long Hui Bldg 5th Long, Tianhe, Guangzhou, 510635, China
Tel.: (86) 2087573055
Industrial Machinery Distr
N.A.I.C.S.: 423830

Subsidiary (Non-US):

MARUKA INDIA PVT LTD. (2)
Jmd Regent Square Office No 1003a/1003b/1004a/1004b 10th Floor, M G Road, Gurgaon, 122 002, Haryana, India
Tel.: (91) 1244285400
Industrial Machinery Distr
N.A.I.C.S.: 423830

MARUKA MACHINERY (THAILAND) CO., LTD. (2)
1st F1 Piarnsri Watana Building 29/9 Moo 14 Bangna-Trad Rd km 6, Bangkaew, Bang Phli, Samut Prakan, Thailand
Tel.: (66) 27430791
Industrial Machinery Distr
N.A.I.C.S.: 423830

MARUKA MACHINERY CORP. (2)
Fl 4-1 No 687 Sec 5 Chung Shan North Road, Taipei, Taiwan
Tel.: (886) 228361313
Industrial Machinery Distr
N.A.I.C.S.: 423830

MARUKA MEXICO S.A. de C.V. (2)
Boulevard Luis Donaldo Colosio No 248A Lomas Del Campestre 1, Seccion Aguascalientes, Aguascalientes, 20129, Mexico
Tel.: (52) 4491531491
Industrial Machinery Distr
N.A.I.C.S.: 423830

Subsidiary (US):

MARUKA USA INC. (2)
45 Route 46 E Ste 610, Pine Brook, NJ 07058
Tel.: (973) 487-3800
Web Site: http://www.marukausa.com
Industrial Machinery Mfr
N.A.I.C.S.: 333248
Kevin Bruce (Mgr-Sls-Natl)

Subsidiary (Non-US):

MARUKA VIETNAM CO., LTD. (2)
R 202 02nd Floor Techno Center Building Thang Long Industrial Park, Dong Anh, Hanoi, Vietnam
Tel.: (84) 439550164
Industrial Machinery Distr
N.A.I.C.S.: 423830

PT. MARUKA INDONESIA (2)
Sentra Niaga Kalimalang Blok A 7 No 5-6 Jl A Yani Margajaya, South Bekasi, Bekasi, 17141, Indonesia
Tel.: (62) 218891611
Industrial Machinery Distr
N.A.I.C.S.: 423830

PT. Unique Solutions Indonesia (2)
Jl Pinang Blok F23 No 15F Delta Silicon 3 Lippo Cikarang Desa, Cicau Kecamatan Cikarang Pusat, Bekasi, 17530, Jawa Barat, Indonesia
Tel.: (62) 2150915055
Engineeering Services
N.A.I.C.S.: 541330

Subsidiary (Domestic):

Sonoruka Engineering Co., Ltd. (2)
4-8-28 Torikaikami, Settsu, 566-0062, Osaka, Japan
Tel.: (81) 726547415
Industrial Machinery Equipment Distr
N.A.I.C.S.: 423830

MARUKOME CO., LTD.
883 Amori, Nagano, 380-0943, Japan
Tel.: (81) 352850111
Web Site: https://www.marukome.co.jp
Year Founded: 1854
Emp.: 458
Perishable Foods Mfg
N.A.I.C.S.: 311999
Aoki Tokio (Pres)

MARUMAE CO., LTD.
Takaono Nairiku Kogyo Danchi 3816-41 Okubo Takaono-machi, Izumi, 899-0401, Kagoshima, Japan
Tel.: (81) 996681152
Web Site: https://www.marumae.com
Year Founded: 1988
6264—(TKS)
Sales Range: $10-24.9 Million
Precision Machinery Equipment Mfr & Distr
N.A.I.C.S.: 332721
Toshikazu Maeda (Pres)

MARUO CALCIUM CO., LTD.
1455 Nishioka Uozumi-cho, Akashi, 674-0084, Hyogo, Japan
Tel.: (81) 789422112
Web Site: http://www.maruo-cal.co.jp
Year Founded: 1948
4102—(TKS)
Rev.: $85,196,290
Assets: $112,436,100
Liabilities: $46,422,030
Net Worth: $66,014,070
Earnings: $1,645,890
Emp.: 272
Fiscal Year-end: 03/31/24
Calcium Carbonate Mfr & Dsitr
N.A.I.C.S.: 325180
Tsunehisa Mori (Exec Officer, Deputy Gen Mgr-Production Div & Mgr-Plant-Tsuchiya)

Subsidiaries:

Kyushu Calcium Co., Ltd. (1)
152-1 Katsuyamamida, Miyako-machi, Miyako, 824-0811, Fukuoka, Japan
Tel.: (81) 930324446
Calcium Carbonate Mfr
N.A.I.C.S.: 325180

Maruo (Shanghai) Trading Co., Ltd. (1)
D310 Orient International Plaza 85 Loushanguan Road, Shanghai, 200336, China
Tel.: (86) 2162789872
Web Site: https://www.wanweigai.cn
Calcium Carbonate Distr
N.A.I.C.S.: 424690
Michihiro Tanii (Pres)

Maruo Calcium Co., Ltd. - Tsuchiura Plant (1)
5388 Amihara, Ami-machi, Inashiki, 300-0331, Ibaraki, Japan
Tel.: (81) 298870666
Calcium Carbonate Mfr
N.A.I.C.S.: 325180

Maruo Calcium Co., Ltd. - Tsuchiyama Plant (1)
2086 Nishifutami Futami-cho, Akashi, 674-0094, Hyogo, Japan
Tel.: (81) 789421881
Calcium Carbonate Mfr
N.A.I.C.S.: 325180

MARUSAN SECURITIES CO., LTD.
Kojimachi Front Bldg 3-3-6 Kojimachi, Chiyoda-ku, Tokyo, 102-0083, Japan
Tel.: (81) 332382200
Web Site: https://www.marusan-sec.co.jp
Year Founded: 1933
8613—(TKS)
Rev.: $122,998,880
Assets: $555,735,750
Liabilities: $208,552,110
Net Worth: $347,183,640
Earnings: $19,334,250
Fiscal Year-end: 03/31/24
Securities Brokerage Services
N.A.I.C.S.: 523150
Minoru Kikuchi (Pres)

MARUSAN-AI CO., LTD.
1 Arasita Aza Nikki cho, Okazaki, 444-2193, Aichi, Japan
Tel.: (81) 564273700
Web Site: https://www.marusanai.co.jp
Year Founded: 1952
25510—(NGO)
Rev.: $291,280,880
Assets: $251,321,840
Liabilities: $188,101,760
Net Worth: $63,220,080
Earnings: $1,713,360

Emp.: 444
Fiscal Year-end: 09/30/21
Soy Beans Mfr
N.A.I.C.S.: 311224
Watanabe Kuniyasu *(Chm & Pres)*
Subsidiaries:

Marusanai-tottori Co., Ltd. (1)
81-1 Nishientsuji Temple Kawahara-cho, Tottori, 680-1209, Tottori-shi, Japan
Tel.: (81) 858850310
Web Site: http://www.marusanai-tottori.co.jp
Grocery Product Mfr
N.A.I.C.S.: 311999

Tamai-miso Co., Ltd. (1)
561 Sakai Chikuhoku-mura, Higashichikuma-gun, Nagano, 399-7711, Japan
Tel.: (81) 120673024
Web Site: http://www.tamai-miso.net
Grocery Product Mfr
N.A.I.C.S.: 311999

MARUSHO HOTTA CO., LTD.
4-1-11 Nihombashi Muromachi, Chuo-ku, Tokyo, 103-0022, Japan
Tel.: (81) 335488121
Web Site: http://www.pearly-marusho.co.jp
Year Founded: 1933
8105—(TKS)
Rev.: $24,410,730
Assets: $25,137,830
Liabilities: $4,898,010
Net Worth: $20,239,820
Earnings: $125,590
Emp.: 272
Fiscal Year-end: 03/31/24
Apparel Product Whslr
N.A.I.C.S.: 424350
Masami Onishi *(Mng Dir)*

MARUTAI CO., LTD.
1042-1 Imajukuaoki, Nishi-Ku, Fukuoka, 819-0193, Japan
Tel.: (81) 928070711
Web Site: https://www.marutai.co.jp
Year Founded: 1947
2919—(FKA)
Sales Range: Less than $1 Million
Noodle Product Mfr
N.A.I.C.S.: 311824
Hiroyuki Miyamoto *(Mgr-Product Strategy Dept & Overseas Bus Dept)*

MARUTI INFRASTRUCTURE LIMITED
802 Surmount Building Opp Iscon Mega Mall S G Highway, Ahmedabad, 380015, Gujarat, India
Tel.: (91) 7940093482
Web Site: https://www.marutiinfra.in
531540—(BOM)
Rev.: $4,516,660
Assets: $4,940,412
Liabilities: $1,898,694
Net Worth: $3,041,718
Earnings: $96,866
Emp.: 22
Fiscal Year-end: 03/31/21
Construction & Engineering Services
N.A.I.C.S.: 541330
Nishit P. Patel *(Mgr-Project)*

MARUTI INTERIOR PRODUCTS LTD.
Plot No 13 Jai Kishan Industrial Estate Shapar Veraval, Rajkot, 360027, Gujarat, India
Tel.: (91) 8047640697
Web Site: https://www.everydaykitchen.in
Year Founded: 1997
543464—(BOM)
Car Rental Services
N.A.I.C.S.: 532111
Paresh P. Lunagaria *(Mng Dir)*

MARUTI SECURITIES LIMITED
Plot No 66 Parkview Enclave, Manovikas Nagar, Secunderabad, 500 009, Telangana, India
Tel.: (91) 4027756556
531319—(BOM)
Rev.: $156
Assets: $206,618
Liabilities: $4,794,262
Net Worth: ($4,587,644)
Earnings: ($20,890)
Fiscal Year-end: 03/31/21
Security Brokerage Services
N.A.I.C.S.: 523150
B. Srinivas *(Chm & Mng Dir)*

MARUTO SANGYO CO., LTD.
892-1 Higata, Ogori, 838-0112, Fukuoka, Japan
Tel.: (81) 942733845
Web Site: https://www.marutosangyo.co.jp
Year Founded: 1939
7894—(FKA)
Rev.: $162,323,920
Assets: $146,177,680
Liabilities: $67,924,560
Net Worth: $78,253,120
Earnings: $5,749,920
Fiscal Year-end: 02/28/22
Plastic Packaging Materials Mfr
N.A.I.C.S.: 326112
Taro Ozaki *(Pres)*

MARUWA CO., LTD.
3-83 Minamihonjigahara-cho, Owariasahi, 488-0044, Aichi, Japan
Tel.: (81) 561510841 JP
Web Site: https://www.maruwa-g.com
Year Founded: 1973
MAW—(LSE)
Rev.: $406,938,040
Assets: $809,824,150
Liabilities: $87,992,320
Net Worth: $721,831,830
Earnings: $100,577,760
Fiscal Year-end: 03/31/24
Circuit & Machinery Ceramics, Radio Frequency Products & Electronic Components Mfr
N.A.I.C.S.: 333310
Sei Kanbe *(Pres)*
Subsidiaries:

MARUWA Electronics Beijing Co., Ltd. (1)
No 116 Zizhuyuan Rd No 1117 Block C Jiahao International Ctr, Haidian Distric, Beijing, 100097, China
Tel.: (86) 10 5170 9187
Electronic Circuits Mfr
N.A.I.C.S.: 334419

Maruwa America Corporation (1)
360 N Sepulveda Blvd Ste 2060, El Segundo, CA 90245
Tel.: (310) 322-4700
Web Site: http://www.maruwa-america.com
Sales Range: $25-49.9 Million
Emp.: 5
Electronic Circuits Mfr
N.A.I.C.S.: 334419

Maruwa Electronics Hk Co., Ltd. (1)
No 122 Austin Rd Ste No B 17th Fl, Ritz Plz, Kowloon, China (Hong Kong)
Tel.: (852) 28851488
Web Site: http://www.maruwa.com.my
Electronic Circuits Mfr
N.A.I.C.S.: 334419

Maruwa Europe Ltd (1)
The Boulevard Orbital Park, Ashford, TN24 0GA, Kent, United Kingdom
Tel.: (44) 1233501555
Web Site: http://www.maruwa-g.com
Sales Range: $25-49.9 Million
Emp.: 15
Electronic Circuits Mfr
N.A.I.C.S.: 334419

Maruwa Korea Co., Ltd. (1)
1F Bisan-dong 470 Pyeongchon-daero, Dongan-gu, Anyang, 13915, Gyeonggi-do, Korea (South)
Tel.: (82) 313874060
Web Site: http://www.maruwa.co.kr
Sales Range: $25-49.9 Million
Emp.: 10
Electronic Circuits Mfr
N.A.I.C.S.: 334419

Maruwa Quartz Co., Ltd. (1)
7-1 Odaira Kumagami Miharu-cho, Tamura-gun, Kodaira, 963-7704, Fukushima, Japan
Tel.: (81) 247620012
Web Site: http://www.maruwa-quartz.com
Quartz Glass Products Mfr
N.A.I.C.S.: 327211
Makoto Kobe *(Pres)*

Maruwa Shanghai Trading Co., Ltd. (1)
Rm701 No 1 Lane 1628 Jinshajiang Rd, Shanghai, 200333, China
Tel.: (86) 2161453245
Web Site: http://www.maruwa-g.com
Electronic Circuits Mfr
N.A.I.C.S.: 334419

Maruwa Shomei Co., Ltd. (1)
Maruwa Bldg 3-16-13 Shiba, Minato-ku, Tokyo, 105-0014, Japan
Tel.: (81) 354846051
Web Site: http://www.maruwa-shomei.com
Sales Range: $25-49.9 Million
Emp.: 20
LED Lights & Peripheral Equipments Production Services
N.A.I.C.S.: 335139

Taiwan Maruwa Co Ltd (1)
1st Fl No 30 Sec 2, Chung Cheng Rd, Taipei, Taiwan
Tel.: (886) 228351100
Web Site: http://www.maruwa-g.com
Sales Range: $25-49.9 Million
Emp.: 8
Electronic Components Mfr
N.A.I.C.S.: 334419

MARUWN CORPORATION
7-2 Koamicho Nihonbashi, Chuo-ku, Tokyo, 103-8538, Japan
Tel.: (81) 368109452
Web Site: https://www.maruwn.co.jp
Year Founded: 1938
9067—(TKS)
Rev.: $297,397,120
Assets: $243,816,460
Liabilities: $78,540,020
Net Worth: $165,276,440
Earnings: $2,749,760
Emp.: 2,157
Fiscal Year-end: 03/31/24
Transportation Services
N.A.I.C.S.: 484110
Noriyuki Hagiya *(Exec Dir)*

MARUYAMA MFG. CO., INC.
3-4-15 Uchikanda, Chiyoda-ku, Tokyo, 101-0047, Japan
Tel.: (81) 332522271
Web Site: https://www.maruyama.co.jp
Year Founded: 1895
6316—(TKS)
Rev.: $293,710,340
Assets: $260,436,970
Liabilities: $122,423,030
Net Worth: $138,013,940
Earnings: $8,635,620
Emp.: 917
Fiscal Year-end: 09/30/23
Agricultural Machinery Mfr & Whslr
N.A.I.C.S.: 333111
Haruo Uchiyama *(Chm)*
Subsidiaries:

Asian Maruyama (Thailand) Co., Ltd. (1)
150/40 Moo 9 Pinthong Industrial Estate 2, T Nongkham A Sriracha, Chon Buri, 20110, Thailand
Tel.: (66) 3 304 6121
Web Site: https://asian-maruyama.co.th
Agricultural Machinery Equipment Distr
N.A.I.C.S.: 423820

MARUYAMA MFG (THAILAND) CO., LTD. (1)
Pinthong Industrial Estate 2 150/40 Moo 9 Tambol Nongkham, Amphur, Si Racha, 20110, Chonburi, Thailand
Tel.: (66) 38347 11721
Web Site: https://maruyama.co.th
Emp.: 90
Agricultural Machinery Mfr & Distr
N.A.I.C.S.: 333111

Maruyama (Shanghai) Trading Co., Inc. (1)
Room 307 Wanbao International Business Center No 664 Xinhua Road, Changning District, Shanghai, 200052, China
Tel.: (86) 216 282 4526
Web Site: https://www.maruyama.com.cn
Emp.: 10
Agricultural Machinery Distr
N.A.I.C.S.: 423820

Maruyama Excell Co., Ltd. - Chiba Factory (1)
1624-1 konumata, Togane, 283-0044, Chiba, Japan
Tel.: (81) 475520066
Fire Extinguisher Mfr
N.A.I.C.S.: 339999

Maruyama Logistics Co., Inc. (1)
60-1 Mukaihara Iitoyo, Tenei-mura Iwase-gun, Fukushima, 962-0512, Japan
Tel.: (81) 24 883 2031
Agricultural Machine Mfr & Distr
N.A.I.C.S.: 333111

Maruyama U.S. Inc. (1)
4770 Mercantile Dr Ste 100, Fort Worth, TX 76137
Tel.: (940) 383-7400
Agricultural Machinery Distr
N.A.I.C.S.: 423820

Nippon Kreis Co., Ltd. (1)
1662-11 konumata, Togane, 283-0044, Chiba, Japan
Tel.: (81) 475555771
Agricultural Equipment Mfr & Distr
N.A.I.C.S.: 333111

Seibu Maruyama Co., Ltd. (1)
150-2 Teramoto Kagamino-cho, Tomata-gun, Okayama, 708-0323, Japan
Tel.: (81) 868543122
Web Site: https://www.seibumaruyama.co.jp
Emp.: 40
Agricultural Machinery Mfr & Distr
N.A.I.C.S.: 333111
Jyunichi Sugimoto *(Pres)*

MARUYOSHI CENTER INC.
367-1 Kokubun, Kokubunji-cho, Takamatsu, 769-0198, Kagawa, Japan
Tel.: (81) 878745511
Web Site: http://ww2.maruyoshi-center.co.jp
Year Founded: 1970
7515—(TKS)
Rev.: $282,345,070
Assets: $114,822,550
Liabilities: $91,744,600
Net Worth: $23,077,950
Earnings: $957,150
Emp.: 2,157
Fiscal Year-end: 02/29/24
Supermarket Operator
N.A.I.C.S.: 445110
Hiromichi Kato *(Pres, CFO & COO)*

MARUZEN SHOWA UNYU CO., LTD.
2-15 Minami-nakadori, Naka-ku, Yokohama, 231-8419, Japan
Tel.: (81) 456715713
Web Site: https://www.maruzenshowa.co.jp
Year Founded: 1931
9068—(TKS)
Rev.: $926,682,340
Assets: $1,264,869,770

MARUZEN SHOWA UNYU CO., LTD.

Maruzen Showa Unyu Co., Ltd.—(Continued)

Liabilities: $419,179,760
Net Worth: $845,690,010
Earnings: $64,388,010
Emp.: 3,709
Fiscal Year-end: 03/31/24
Logistic Services
N.A.I.C.S.: 541614
Toshiyuki Asai (Chm & Pres)

Subsidiaries:

Jinri Container Service Co., Ltd. (1)
21 Terminal Xingang Tanggu, Tianjin, China
Tel.: (86) 22 2570 0566
Logistics Consulting Servies
N.A.I.C.S.: 541614

Kokusai Bulk Terminal Co., Ltd. (1)
3 Toyoura-cho, Naka-ku, Yokohama, 231-0814, Kanagawa, Japan
Tel.: (81) 456257000
Emp.: 80
Marine Cargo Services
N.A.I.C.S.: 488320
Shigeki Ito (Pres)

Kyoe Maruzen (Thailand) Co., Ltd. (1)
23/5 Sorachai Building 11st Floor Soi Sukhumvit 63 Sukhumvit Road, Klongtan-Nua Wattana, Bangkok, 10110, Thailand
Tel.: (66) 2 714 3141
Logistics Consulting Servies
N.A.I.C.S.: 541614

Maruzen Chubu Ryutsu Co., Ltd. (1)
4-2-12 Meieki, Nakamura-Ku, Nagoya, 450-0002, Aichi, Japan
Tel.: (81) 525811504
Logistics Consulting Servies
N.A.I.C.S.: 541614

Maruzen Densan Logistics (Pinghu) Corporation (1)
1730 The Ping Cheng Road Pinghu Economic Development Zone, Pinghu, Zhejiang, China
Tel.: (86) 573 8507 8880
Logistics Consulting Servies
N.A.I.C.S.: 541614

Maruzen Hokkaido Unyu Co., Ltd. (1)
2-13-1 Yonesato1jo, Shiroishi-Ku, Sapporo, 003-0871, Hokkaido, Japan
Tel.: (81) 118753177
Emp.: 10
Logistics Consulting Servies
N.A.I.C.S.: 541614
Tsuyoshi Sudo (Mgr)

Maruzen Ibaraki Ryutsu Co., Ltd. (1)
4-4-32 Kamisu, Kamisu, 314-0143, Japan
Tel.: (81) 299920900
Logistics Consulting Servies
N.A.I.C.S.: 541614

Maruzen Kansai Ryutsu Co., Ltd. (1)
3-3 Doyamacho, Kita-Ku, Osaka, 530-0027, Japan
Tel.: (81) 663157003
Logistics Consulting Servies
N.A.I.C.S.: 541614

Maruzen Kashima Butsuryu Co., Ltd. (1)
2774-23 Sunayama, Kamisu, 314-0255, Ibaraki, Japan
Tel.: (81) 479401105
Logistics Consulting Servies
N.A.I.C.S.: 541614

Maruzen Keiyo Butsuryu Co., Ltd. (1)
56 Anesakikaigan, Ichihara, 299-0107, Japan
Tel.: (81) 436614681
Emp.: 31
Logistics Consulting Servies
N.A.I.C.S.: 541614
Tetuotoumi Toriumi (Pres)

Maruzen Ryutsu Service Co., Ltd. (1)
4-11-11 Chojamachi, Naka-ku, Yokohama, 231-0033, Japan
Tel.: (81) 452506451

Emp.: 6
Logistics Consulting Servies
N.A.I.C.S.: 541614
Hattori Nasaharu (Pres)

Maruzen SH Logistics Sdn. Bhd. (1)
PLO162 Jalan Cyber 2 Kawasan Perindustrian Senai III, 81400, Senai, Johor, Malaysia
Tel.: (60) 75970220
Freight Truck Transport Services
N.A.I.C.S.: 484110

Maruzen Showa (Hong Kong) Ltd. (1)
Room 1205A Tung Ning Building 253 Des Voeux Road, Central, Hong Kong, China (Hong Kong)
Tel.: (852) 2541 3136
Logistics Consulting Servies
N.A.I.C.S.: 541614

Maruzen Showa (Taiwan) Co., Ltd. (1)
6F-1 No 20 Teh Hweist, Taipei, Taiwan
Tel.: (886) 2 2596 1446
Logistics Consulting Servies
N.A.I.C.S.: 541614

Maruzen Showa Korea Co., Ltd. (1)
12F 63 Jungang-daero, Jung-gu, Busan, Korea (South)
Tel.: (82) 519007766
Freight Truck Transport Services
N.A.I.C.S.: 484110

Maruzen Showa Logistics Co., Ltd. (1)
Middle Tower 912 Times Square No 28 Tian He North Road, Tian He District, Guangzhou, 510620, China
Tel.: (86) 20 3891 0691
Logistics Consulting Servies
N.A.I.C.S.: 541614

Maruzen Showa Singapore Pte Ltd. (1)
21 Jalan Buroh 07-00 Logistics 21, Singapore, 619478, Singapore
Tel.: (65) 6221 9373
Logistics Consulting Servies
N.A.I.C.S.: 541614

Maruzen Showa Unyu Co., Ltd. - Plant Engineering Division (1)
12-2 Minato-Cho, Kawasaki-Ku, Kawasaki, 210-0807, Japan
Tel.: (81) 44 244 5371
Engineeering Services
N.A.I.C.S.: 541330

Maruzen Sudamericana Ltda. (1)
Edif Maquisacruz PB Local 3 Av Ecuador No 2241, La Paz, Bolivia
Tel.: (591) 22420052
Freight Truck Transport Services
N.A.I.C.S.: 484110

Maruzen Transpack Co., Ltd. (1)
6 Kamomecho, Naka-Ku, Yokohama, 231-0813, Kanagawa, Japan
Tel.: (81) 456229913
Emp.: 6
Logistics Consulting Servies
N.A.I.C.S.: 541614
Minaguchi Mizuo (Mgr)

Maruzen of America, Inc. (1)
19640 Rancho Way, Rancho Dominguez, CA 90220
Tel.: (310) 637-8874
Web Site: https://www.mrzn.com
Logistics Consulting Servies
N.A.I.C.S.: 541614
Glenn A. Uriu (Dir-Marketing)

PT. Maruzen Samudera Taiheiyo (1)
Samudera Indonesia Building 4th Floor, Jl Letjen S Parman Kav 35, Jakarta, 11480, Indonesia
Tel.: (62) 21 2567 6919
Logistic Services
N.A.I.C.S.: 541614

Shanghai Kejian Apparel Inspection Co., Ltd. (1)
No 275 Shiyidong Road, Luodian Baoshan District, Shanghai, China
Tel.: (86) 21 5686 8023
Logistics Consulting Servies

N.A.I.C.S.: 541614

Showa Distribution K.K (1)
6F Mori Bldg 27-8 Hamamatsu-Cho 1-Chome, Minato-Ku, Tokyo, 108-8611, Japan
Tel.: (81) 3 3432 8331
Web Site: http://www.sbknet.co.jp
Emp.: 8
Logistics Consulting Servies
N.A.I.C.S.: 541614

TVL-Maruzen Global Logistics Co., Ltd. (1)
Room 9006 FuLiHaiYang office building No 11 Beichengtijanji Street, Jianbei District, Chongqing, 400020, China
Tel.: (86) 23 6789 5245
Logistics Consulting Servies
N.A.I.C.S.: 541614

United Thai Logistics Co., Ltd. (1)
25 Alma Link Building 11th Floor Soi Chitlom Phloenchit Road, Pathumwan, Bangkok, 10330, Thailand
Tel.: (66) 22531652
Logistics Consulting Servies
N.A.I.C.S.: 541614

United Thai Warehouse Co., Ltd. (1)
31/11 Moo 3 Tambol Bangsaothong, Amphur, Bang Sao Thong, 10540, Samutprakarn, Thailand
Tel.: (66) 2181 7028
Warehousing Services
N.A.I.C.S.: 493110

Unithai Maruzen Logistics (Vietnam) Corp. (1)
VietFracht Building 6th Floor 16-18 Nguyen Cong Tru, District 1, Ho Chi Minh City, Vietnam
Tel.: (84) 8 3914 6849
Logistics Consulting Servies
N.A.I.C.S.: 541614

Xuzhou Sinotrans Maruzen Transportation Co., Ltd. (1)
No 1 Long Hua si Road Development Zone, Xuzhou, Jiangsu, China
Tel.: (86) 516 8798 6711
Logistics Consulting Servies
N.A.I.C.S.: 541614

MARV JONES LTD.

20611 Lougheed Hwy, Maple Ridge, V2X 2P9, BC, Canada
Tel.: (604) 465-5464
Web Site:
https://www.marvjoneshonda.com
Year Founded: 1974
New & Used Car Dealers
N.A.I.C.S.: 441110
Lester Wong (Mgr-Parts)

MARVDASHT SUGAR COMPANY

Argentine Square Bayhaqi Street Building 10, Tehran, 15147 46717, Iran
Tel.: (98) 2188519184
Year Founded: 1935
Crop Farming Services
N.A.I.C.S.: 111998

MARVEL CAPITAL & FINANCE (INDIA) LIMITED

115B Shalimar Miracle Opp ICICI Bank, S V Road, Mumbai, 400062, India
Tel.: (91) 22 28781495
Year Founded: 1994
Assets: $1,839,013
Net Worth: $1,839,013
Earnings: ($738)
Fiscal Year-end: 03/31/16
Financial Management Services
N.A.I.C.S.: 523999

MARVEL DECOR LTD.

Plot No 210-211 G I D C Phase-II, Jamnagar, 361 004, Gujarat, India
Tel.: (91) 9512770707

INTERNATIONAL PUBLIC

Web Site:
https://www.marvellifestyle.com
MDL—(NSE)
Rev.: $6,288,172
Assets: $8,563,132
Liabilities: $2,856,292
Net Worth: $5,706,840
Earnings: $270,763
Emp.: 219
Fiscal Year-end: 03/31/23
Blind & Shade Mfr
N.A.I.C.S.: 337920
Ashok R. Paun (Chm & Mng Dir)

Subsidiaries:

Callistus Blinds Middle East (FZC) (1)
Q4- 118 SAIF Zone, PO Box 120723, Sharjah, United Arab Emirates
Tel.: (971) 521003262
Web Site: https://callistusblinds.ae
Window Covering Product Mfr
N.A.I.C.S.: 337920

Callistus UK Ltd. (1)
Magnolia House Spring Villa Park 11 Spring Villa Road, Edgware, HA8 7EB, United Kingdom
Tel.: (44) 1344595705
Web Site: https://www.callistusblinds.com
Window Covering Product Mfr
N.A.I.C.S.: 337920

MARVEL DISCOVERY CORP.

Suite 1903 -808 Nelson Street, Vancouver, V6Z 2H1, BC, Canada
Tel.: (604) 670-0019 BC
Web Site:
https://www.marveldiscovery.ca
Year Founded: 1987
MARVF—(OTCQB)
Rev.: $56,905
Assets: $1,588,039
Liabilities: $507,780
Net Worth: $1,080,260
Earnings: ($653,580)
Fiscal Year-end: 08/31/21
Uranium Exploration Services
N.A.I.C.S.: 212290
Geoff Balderson (CFO)

MARVEL VINYLS LTD.

G - 73 Connaught Circus, New Delhi, 110001, India
Tel.: (91) 1145306666
Web Site:
http://www.marvelvinyls.com
Textile Products Mfr
N.A.I.C.S.: 314999
Pavan Kumar Chawla (Chm)

MARVELL TECHNOLOGY GROUP LTD.

Victoria Pl 5th Fl 31 Victoria St, Hamilton, HM 10, Bermuda
Tel.: (441) 2948000 BM
Web Site: http://www.marvell.com
Year Founded: 1995
MRVL—(NASDAQ)
Rev.: $5,507,700,000
Assets: $21,228,500,000
Liabilities: $6,397,100,000
Net Worth: $14,831,400,000
Earnings: $933,400,000
Emp.: 6,577
Fiscal Year-end: 02/03/24
Semiconductor Product Mfr
N.A.I.C.S.: 334413
Richard S. Hill (Chm)

Subsidiaries:

Aquantia Corp. (1)
91 E Tasman Dr Ste 100, San Jose, CA 95134
Tel.: (408) 228-8300
Web Site: http://www.aquantia.com
Rev.: $120,784,000
Assets: $114,423,000
Liabilities: $21,201,000

AND PRIVATE COMPANIES — MARWEST APARTMENT REAL ESTATE INVESTMENT TRUST

Net Worth: $93,222,000
Earnings: ($9,772,000)
Emp.: 310
Fiscal Year-end: 12/31/2018
Ethernet Connectivity Solution Developing Services
N.A.I.C.S.: 334290
Ramin Farjadrad *(Sr VP-Tech Dev)*

Subsidiary (Non-US):

Aquantia B.V. (2)
High Tech Campus 41, 5656 AE, Eindhoven, Netherlands
Tel.: (31) 407470052
Electronic Security System Mfr
N.A.I.C.S.: 334290

Aquantia Semiconductor India Pvt. Ltd.
3rd Floor Salarpuria Premia Opp Cessna Business Park, Kadubeesanahalli Sarjapura Outer Ring Road, 560 103, Bengaluru, India
Tel.: (91) 8067206720
Electronic Security System Mfr
N.A.I.C.S.: 334290

Cavium LLC (1)
5488 Marvell Ln, Santa Clara, CA 95054
Tel.: (408) 222-2500
Semiconductor & Related Device Mfr
N.A.I.C.S.: 334413

Subsidiary (Non-US):

QLogic India Pvt. Ltd. (2)
1st Floor Tower C Tech Park One, Survey Number 191 Yerwada, Pune, 411 006, Maharashtra, India
Tel.: (91) 2025883361
Web Site: http://www.marvell.com
Data Processing & Storage Services
N.A.I.C.S.: 518210

Inphi Corporation (1)
110 Rio Robles, Santa Clara, CA 95134
Tel.: (408) 217-7300
Web Site: http://www.inphi.com
Rev.: $682,954,000
Assets: $1,008,236,000
Liabilities: $654,526,000
Net Worth: $353,710,000
Earnings: ($59,744,000)
Emp.: 1,086
Fiscal Year-end: 12/31/2020
Analog Semiconductor Mfr
N.A.I.C.S.: 334413
Oscar E. Agazzi *(VP-Engrg-Coherent DSP)*

Subsidiary (Domestic):

Clariphy Communications, Inc. (2)
7585 Irvine Ctr Dr Ste 100, Irvine, CA 92618
Tel.: (949) 861-3074
Web Site: http://www.clariphy.com
Rev.: $1,500,000
Emp.: 16
Commercial & Institutional Building Construction
N.A.I.C.S.: 236220

eSilicon Corporation (2)
2130 Gold St Ste 100, San Jose, CA 95002
Tel.: (408) 635-6300
Web Site: http://www.esilicon.com
Sales Range: $75-99.9 Million
Emp.: 92
Custom Semiconductor Chip Mfr
N.A.I.C.S.: 334413
Seth Neiman *(Chm)*

Marvell Accel Japan K.K. (1)
Nankai-nomura Building 1-10-4 Nanbanaka, Naniwa-ku, Osaka, 556-0011, Japan
Tel.: (81) 6 6633 0078
Web Site: http://www.acceltech.co.jp
Semiconductor Devices Mfr
N.A.I.C.S.: 334413

Marvell Asia Pte, Ltd. (1)
Tai Seng Center 3 Irving Road 10-01, Singapore, 369522, Singapore (100%)
Tel.: (65) 6756 1600
Web Site: http://www.marvell.com
Sales Range: $25-49.9 Million
Emp.: 100
Semiconductor & Related Device Whslr
N.A.I.C.S.: 423690

Marvell Hong Kong Limited (1)
To Yuen Mansion 39 To Yuen Street Kowloon Tong, Kowloon, China (Hong Kong)
Tel.: (852) 92292048
Web Site: http://www.marvell.com
Semiconductor & Related Device Whslr
N.A.I.C.S.: 423690

Marvell India Private Limited (1)
23 Airport Road II Floor Leela Galleria, Bengaluru, 560 008, India
Tel.: (91) 80 2502 6000
Emp.: 102
Semiconductor & Related Device Whslr
N.A.I.C.S.: 423690
Rakesh Yadav *(Gen Mgr)*

Marvell International Ltd. (1)
Argyle House 41A Cedar Avenue, Hamilton, HM 12, Bermuda
Tel.: (441) 2963230
Web Site: http://www.marvell.com
Semiconductor & Related Device Mfr
N.A.I.C.S.: 561499

Marvell Israel (M.I.S.L) Ltd. (1)
6 Hamada Street Mordot HaCarmel Industrial Park, Yokneam, 2069203, Israel
Tel.: (972) 4 909 1500
Web Site: http://www.marvell.com
Emp.: 194
Semiconductor & Related Device Whslr
N.A.I.C.S.: 423690

Marvell Italia S.r.l. (1)
Viale Della Republica 38, 27100, Pavia, Lombardy, Italy
Tel.: (39) 0382375511
Semiconductor & Related Device Whslr
N.A.I.C.S.: 423690

Marvell Japan K.K. (1)
4F Meguro Hilltop Walk 4-1-5 Kami-Osaki Shinagawa, Tokyo, 141-0021, Japan (100%)
Tel.: (81) 357409100
Web Site: http://www.marvell.co.jp
Sales Range: $25-49.9 Million
Emp.: 50
Semiconductor & Related Device Whslr
N.A.I.C.S.: 423690

Marvell Netherlands B.V. (1)
Laan van Diepenvoorde 4, Waalre, 5582LA, Netherlands
Tel.: (31) 40 2366690
Web Site: http://www.marvell.com
Semiconductor & Related Device Whslr
N.A.I.C.S.: 423690

Marvell Semiconductor Germany GmbH (1)
Siemensstrasse 23, Ettlingen, 76275, Germany
Tel.: (49) 7243502100
Web Site: http://www.marvell.com
Sales Range: $25-49.9 Million
Emp.: 60
Semiconductor & Related Device Whslr
N.A.I.C.S.: 423690

Marvell Semiconductor Israel, Ltd. (1)
Park Azorim Kyriat Arie, PO Box 692, Petach Tikva, 20692, Israel (100%)
Tel.: (972) 39703311
Web Site: http://www.marvell.com
Sales Range: $50-74.9 Million
Emp.: 250
Integrated Circuit Devices Mfr
N.A.I.C.S.: 334413

Marvell Semiconductor Korea, Ltd. (1)
19F Capital Tower 142 736-1 Youksam Dong Teheran-ro Gangnam-gu, Youksam-Dong Kangnam-Ku, Seoul, 06236, Korea (South)
Tel.: (82) 2 560 6700
Emp.: 50
Semiconductor & Related Device Whslr
N.A.I.C.S.: 423690

Marvell Semiconductor Sdn. Bhd. (1)
Plot 98 Hala Kampung Jawa Satu Non Free Industrial Zone, Bayan Lepas, 11900, Penang, Malaysia
Tel.: (60) 46159800
Web Site: http://www.marvell.com

Semiconductor & Related Device Whslr
N.A.I.C.S.: 423690

Marvell Semiconductor Technology Sarl (1)
Za La Piece 1-a5 A-one Business Center, 1180, Rolle, Switzerland
Tel.: (41) 218050521
Semiconductor Product Mfr
N.A.I.C.S.: 334413

Marvell Semiconductor, Inc. (1)
5488 Marvell Ln, Santa Clara, CA 95054
Tel.: (408) 222-2500
Web Site: http://www.marvell.com
Semiconductor & Related Device Whslr
N.A.I.C.S.: 423690

Marvell Sweden AB (1)
Bondevagen 15, 237 32, Stockholm, Sweden
Tel.: (46) 70 305 46 98
Web Site: http://www.marvell.com
Semiconductor Devices Mfr
N.A.I.C.S.: 334413

Marvell Switzerland Sarl (1)
Route de Pallatex 17, 1163, Etoy, Switzerland
Tel.: (41) 21 821 00 00
Web Site: http://www.marvell.com
Semiconductor & Related Device Whslr
N.A.I.C.S.: 423690

Marvell Taiwan Ltd. (1)
2FI No 1 Alley 20 Lane 407 Sec 2 Ti-Ding Blvd, Nei Hu District, Taipei, 00114, Taiwan
Tel.: (886) 2 8177 7071
Web Site: http://www.marvell.com
Semiconductor & Related Device Whslr
N.A.I.C.S.: 423690

Marvell Technology (Beijing), Ltd. (1)
Unit 407 Vision International Centre Tsinghua Science Park Building 9, No 1 Zhongguancun East Road Haidian District, Beijing, 100084, China
Tel.: (86) 10 8215 1511
Web Site: http://www.marvell.com
Semiconductor & Related Device Whslr
N.A.I.C.S.: 423690

Marvell Technology (Nanjing), Ltd. (1)
Room 310 Floor 3 Building 7 No 57 Andemen Road, Nanjing, Jiangsu, China
Tel.: (86) 2566089898
Semiconductor & Related Device Mfr
N.A.I.C.S.: 334413

Marvell Technology Japan Y.K. (1)
Shinjuku Center Bldg 44F 1-25-1 Nishi-Shinjuku, Shinjuku-ku, Tokyo, 163-0644, Japan
Tel.: (81) 3 5324 0355
Web Site: http://www.marvell.com
Semiconductor Devices Mfr
N.A.I.C.S.: 334413

Marvell Technology Sweden AB (1)
Olof Palmes G 29, Stockholm, 111 22, Sweden
Tel.: (46) 850625785
Semiconductor Device Distr
N.A.I.C.S.: 423690

Marvell Technology Vietnam Limited Liability Company (1)
5th Floor Block B Incubation Center Building Lot D 01 Tan Thuan Road, Tan Thuan Export Processing Zone Tan Thuan Dong Ward District 7, Ho Chi Minh City, Vietnam
Tel.: (84) 862884088
Semiconductor & Related Device Mfr
N.A.I.C.S.: 334413

Marvell Technology, Inc. (1)
1000 N W St Ste 1200, Wilmington, DE 19801
Tel.: (302) 295-4840
Web Site: https://www.marvell.com
Rev.: $5,507,700,000
Assets: $21,228,500,000
Liabilities: $6,397,100,000
Net Worth: $14,831,400,000
Earnings: ($933,400,000)
Emp.: 6,510
Fiscal Year-end: 02/03/2024
Mfr of Computer Products
N.A.I.C.S.: 551112

SysKonnect Inc. (1)
5488 Marvell Ln, Santa Clara, CA 95054
Tel.: (408) 222-2500
Mfr of Computer Products
N.A.I.C.S.: 423430

Xelerated AB (1)
Olof Palmes Gata 29, Stockholm, 111 22, Sweden
Tel.: (46) 8 50 62 57 00
Sales Range: $50-74.9 Million
Emp.: 150
Semiconductor Devices Mfr
N.A.I.C.S.: 334413

MARVELOUS INC.

Shinagawa Seaside East Tower 4-12-8 Higashishinagawa-Shinagawa, Shinagawa-ku, Tokyo, 140-0002, Japan
Tel.: (81) 357697447 JP
Web Site: https://www.marv.jp
Year Founded: 1997
7844—(TKS)
Rev.: $194,948,730
Assets: $228,296,180
Liabilities: $47,208,620
Net Worth: $181,087,560
Earnings: ($3,417,370)
Emp.: 397
Fiscal Year-end: 03/31/24
Audio & Video Equipment & Video Games Software Mfr
N.A.I.C.S.: 334310
Shuichi Motoda *(Pres)*

Subsidiaries:

Delfisound Inc. (1)
Central Daikanyama B1F 14-23 Daikanyama-cho, Shibuya-ku, Tokyo, 150-0034, Japan
Tel.: (81) 357283888
Music Recording Services
N.A.I.C.S.: 512250
Yukifumi Makino *(Pres)*

LINKTHINK INC. (1)
5F Shinagawa Seaside East Tower 4-12-8 Higashi-Shinagawa-ku, Tokyo, Japan
Tel.: (81) 3 5769 7447
Video Game Developers
N.A.I.C.S.: 339930

MAQL Europe Limited (1)
Third Floor Suite F Union House Eridge Road, Tunbridge Wells, TN4 8HF, United Kingdom
Tel.: (44) 1892513407
Web Site: http://www.maqleurope.com
Online Game Development Services
N.A.I.C.S.: 541511
Harry Holmwood *(CEO)*

XSEED JKS, Inc. (1)
3625 Del Amo Blvd Ste 205, Torrance, CA 90503
Tel.: (310) 792-8883
Web Site: https://www.xseedgames.com
Marketing Services Agency
N.A.I.C.S.: 541613

cavia inc. (1)
1 4 30 Roppongi Roppongi 25 Mori Bldg 18th Fl, Tokyo, 106 0032, Japan
Tel.: (81) 3 5575 3265
Video Game Software Development Services
N.A.I.C.S.: 449210

MARVIPOL S.A.

Ul Prosta 32, 00-838, Warsaw, Poland
Tel.: (48) 225365000
Web Site: https://www.marvipol.pl
Year Founded: 1996
MVP—(WAR)
Sales Range: Less than $1 Million
Real Estate Development Services
N.A.I.C.S.: 531390
Mariusz Wojciech Ksiazek *(CEO)*

MARWEST APARTMENT REAL ESTATE INVESTMENT TRUST

MARWEST APARTMENT REAL ESTATE INVESTMENT TRUST

Marwest Apartment Real Estate Investment Trust—(Continued)

500220 Portage Ave, Winnipeg, R3C 0A5, MB, Canada
Tel.: (204) 947-1200
Web Site: https://marwestreit.com
MAR.UN—(TSXV)
Sales Range: Less than $1 Million
Real Estate Development Services
N.A.I.C.S.: 531390
Cornelius W. V. Martens *(Principal)*

MARWYN INVESTMENT MANAGEMENT LLP

11 Buckingham Street, London, WC2N 6DF, United Kingdom
Tel.: (44) 20 7004 2700   UK
Web Site: http://www.marwyn.com
Year Founded: 2005
Privater Equity Firm
N.A.I.C.S.: 523999
James Corsellis *(Mng Partner)*

Subsidiaries:

Le Chameau SAS   (1)
Route de Bussy, 18130, Dun-sur-Auron, France   (83.7%)
Tel.: (33) 248666969
Web Site: http://www.lechameau.com
Sales Range: $75-99.9 Million
Emp.: 300
Rubber Boots & Footwear Mfr
N.A.I.C.S.: 316210
Charlotte Mazeau *(Mgr-Comm & PR)*

MARWYN VALUE INVESTORS LIMITED

Ugland House, PO Box 309, Georgetown, KY1 - 1104, Grand Cayman, Cayman Islands
Tel.: (345) 1534833000   GY
Web Site: https://www.marwynvalue.com
MVIR—(LSE)
Investment Fund Services
N.A.I.C.S.: 525910

MARZOCCHI POMPE S.P.A.

Via A Grazia 2, Zola Predosa, 40069, Bologna, Italy
Tel.: (39) 0516137511
Web Site: https://www.iubenda.com
Year Founded: 1949
MARP—(ITA)
Rev.: $53,497,338
Assets: $53,700,389
Liabilities: $30,883,569
Net Worth: $22,816,820
Earnings: $2,091,995
Emp.: 246
Fiscal Year-end: 12/31/22
Automotive Parts Mfr & Distr
N.A.I.C.S.: 336350
Paolo Marzocchi *(Pres)*

Subsidiaries:

Marzocchi (Shanghai) Trading Co., Ltd.   (1)
Room 051 7F 755 Wei Hai Road, Jing An District, Shanghai, 200040, China
Tel.: (86) 2163012989
Gear Pump Mfr & Distr
N.A.I.C.S.: 333996

Marzocchi Pumps USA Corp.   (1)
1355 Bowes Rd, Elgin, IL 60123
Tel.: (847) 923-9910
Gear Pump Mfr & Distr
N.A.I.C.S.: 333996

MARZOTTO S.P.A.

Largo Santa Margherita 1, Madleo, 36078, Valdagno, Italy
Tel.: (39) 0445429411
Web Site: http://www.marzottogroup.it
Sales Range: $50-74.9 Million
Emp.: 500
Clothing & Other Textile Product Mfr
N.A.I.C.S.: 313210
Antonio Favrin *(Chm)*

Subsidiaries:

Ambiente Energia S.r.l   (1)
Via Aiassa 15, 10070, Villanova Canavese, Torino, Italy
Tel.: (39) 011 9298509
Web Site: http://www.energiambiente.com
Textile Products Mfr
N.A.I.C.S.: 313210

Linificio e Canapificio Nazionale S.p.A.   (1)
Via A Ponti 6, Fara Gera D Adda, I 24045, Bergamo, Italy
Tel.: (39) 0363391111
Web Site: http://www.linificio.it
Sales Range: $100-124.9 Million
Emp.: 449
Fabric Mills
N.A.I.C.S.: 313210

Subsidiary (Non-US):

Filature de Lin Filin S.A.   (2)
BP 143 Naassen Chebedda, 1135, Ben Arous, Fouchana, Tunisia   (100%)
Tel.: (216) 71398408
Fabric Mills
N.A.I.C.S.: 313210

Marzotto S.p.A.   (1)
Largo Santa Margherita 1, 36078, Valdagno, Vicenza, Italy   (100%)
Tel.: (39) 0445 429411
Web Site: http://www.marzottogroup.it
Fabric Mill & Administrative Offices
N.A.I.C.S.: 313210

Marzotto S.p.A. - Estethia/ G.B Conte Division   (1)
Via Alessandro Rossi 54, 36013, Piovene Rocchette, Vicenza, Italy
Tel.: (39) 0445 693553
Textile Products Mfr
N.A.I.C.S.: 313210

Marzotto S.p.A. Division Marlane   (1)
Via Monticello 79A, I-13888, Mongrando, Biella, Italy   (100%)
Tel.: (39) 015 25 65200
Web Site: http://www.marlane.it
Sales Range: $50-74.9 Million
Emp.: 150
Fabrics for Elegant & Upper Casual Men's Wear
N.A.I.C.S.: 313210

Branch (Domestic):

Marzetto S.p,A Division Guabello   (2)
Via XXIV Maggio No 4, 13888, Mongrando, BI, Italy   (100%)
Tel.: (39) 0152565111
Web Site: http://www.guabello.it
Textile Mfr
N.A.I.C.S.: 313210
Ricardo Baietti *(Mgr)*

Marzotto Textile   (2)
via Largo St Margherita 1, I-36076, Valdagno, Italy   (100%)
Tel.: (39) 0445429682
Web Site: http://www.marzotto.it
N.A.I.C.S.: 313210
Jiordano Fella *(Mgr-Comml & Export Office)*

Marzotto Textile-Divisione Filati Lanerossi   (2)
Via A Rossi 50, Piovene Rocchette, I 36013, Vicenza, VI, Italy   (100%)
Tel.: (39) 0445693561
Web Site: http://www.marzotto.it
N.A.I.C.S.: 313210

Marzotto Textile-Divisione Tessuti Lanerossi   (2)
Largo S.Margherita 1, 36078, Valdagno, Italy   (100%)
Tel.: (39) 0445429411
Web Site: http://www.marzotto.it
N.A.I.C.S.: 313210

Marzotto Textile-Divisione Tessuti di Sondrio   (2)
Via Tonale 4, I 23100, Sondrio, Italy
Tel.: (39) 0342533111
Web Site: http://www.marzotto.it
N.A.I.C.S.: 313210

Marzotto Textiles (U.S.A.) Corp.   (1)
8 W 40th St, New York, NY 10018   (66.67%)
Tel.: (212) 944-0196
Web Site: http://www.tessutidisondrio.it
Textiles Mfr & Designer
N.A.I.C.S.: 313210

Nova Mosilana a.s   (1)
Charbulova 150, Cernovice, 657 35, Brno, Czech Republic
Tel.: (420) 548 136 111
Web Site: http://www.mosilana.cz
Textile Products Distr
N.A.I.C.S.: 424310

Sametex Spol. s.r.o   (1)
CSA 830, Kraslice, 358 01, Czech Republic
Tel.: (420) 352 686 313
Textile Products Distr
N.A.I.C.S.: 424310

Uab Lietlinen   (1)
Draugystes g 16, 51258, Kaunas, Lithuania
Tel.: (370) 37 490410
Emp.: 100
Textile Products Distr
N.A.I.C.S.: 424310
Favri Davide *(Chm)*

MAS ECONOMIC GROUP

PO Box 3955, Damascus, Syria
Tel.: (963) 116711900
Web Site: http://www.masgroup.net
Sales Range: $150-199.9 Million
Emp.: 600
Diversified Holding Company
N.A.I.C.S.: 551112
Firas Tlass *(Chm)*

Subsidiaries:

Al Akram for Metal Industries Ltd. Company   (1)
PO Box 3955, Damascus, Syria
Tel.: (963) 116711900
Metal Tank Mfr
N.A.I.C.S.: 332431

Al Fajr Coffee Roasting & Processing Company   (1)
PO Box 3955, Damascus, Syria
Tel.: (963) 116711900
Roasted Coffee Mfr
N.A.I.C.S.: 311920

Al Jabal Al Akhdar Conserve Company   (1)
PO Box 3955, Damascus, Syria
Tel.: (963) 116711900
Fruit & Vegetable Canning Services
N.A.I.C.S.: 311421

Golan Meat Industry Company   (1)
PO Box 3955, Damascus, Syria
Tel.: (963) 116711900
Processed Luncheon Meat
N.A.I.C.S.: 311613

MAS Distribution Company   (1)
PO Box 3955, Damascus, Syria
Tel.: (963) 116711900
Wholesale Trade Services
N.A.I.C.S.: 425120

MAS for Metal Ends Company   (1)
PO Box 3955, Damascus, Syria
Tel.: (963) 88282221
Web Site: http://www.masgroup.net
Metal Can Lids Mfr
N.A.I.C.S.: 332431

Syrian Meat Processing Company   (1)
PO Box 3955, Damascus, Syria
Tel.: (963) 116711900
Web Site: http://www.masgroup.net
Processed Luncheon Meat
N.A.I.C.S.: 311613

Syrian-Finnish Company for Dairy Products   (1)
Sehnaya Daraa Highway, PO Box 11850, Damascus, Syria
Tel.: (963) 116711905
Web Site: http://www.sfcdp.com

INTERNATIONAL PUBLIC

Sales Range: $25-49.9 Million
Emp.: 75
Dairy Products Processor
N.A.I.C.S.: 112120
Mohamed Mokadem *(Gen Mgr)*

MAS FINANCIAL SERVICES LIMITED

4th Floor Narayan Chambers B/h Patang Hotel Ashram Road, Ahmedabad, 380 009, India
Tel.: (91) 7941106500   In
Web Site: https://www.mas.co.in
Year Founded: 1995
540749—(BOM)
Rev.: $85,682,729
Assets: $741,144,591
Liabilities: $577,297,048
Net Worth: $163,847,543
Earnings: $19,705,154
Emp.: 719
Fiscal Year-end: 03/31/21
Financial Services
N.A.I.C.S.: 522220
Kamlesh C. Gandhi *(Co-Founder, Chm & Mng Dir)*

MAS GOLD CORP.

Unit 107 3239 Faithfull Avenue, Saskatoon, S7K 8H4, SK, Canada
Tel.: (306) 986-5722
Web Site: https://www.masgoldcorp.com
Year Founded: 1981
MSGCF—(OTCIQ)
Assets: $3,298,678
Liabilities: $833,760
Net Worth: $2,464,918
Earnings: ($1,515,486)
Fiscal Year-end: 09/30/23
Gold Exploration Services
N.A.I.C.S.: 212220
Ronald Kort Netolitzky *(Chm)*

MAS P.L.C

Part of the Second Floor Exchange House 54-62 Athol Street, Douglas, IM1 1JD, Isle of Man
Tel.: (44) 1624625000   IM
Web Site: https://www.masrei.com
Year Founded: 2008
MSP—(JSE)
Rev.: $89,617
Assets: $1,590,789
Liabilities: $549,718
Net Worth: $1,041,071
Earnings: $97,900
Fiscal Year-end: 06/30/23
Real Estate Development Services
N.A.I.C.S.: 531390
Martin Slabbert *(CEO)*

MASAFAT SPECIALIZED TRANSPORT COMPANY

Bayader Wadi Al-Sir, PO Box 144500, Amman, 11814, Jordan
Tel.: (962) 5814667
Web Site: https://www.masafat.jo
Year Founded: 2006
MSFT—(AMM)
Rev.: $24,938,433
Assets: $45,423,662
Liabilities: $14,412,305
Net Worth: $31,011,357
Earnings: $258,672
Emp.: 220
Fiscal Year-end: 12/31/20
Food Transportation Services
N.A.I.C.S.: 484230

MASAN CONSUMER CORP.

23 Le Duan street Ben Nghe, District 1, Ho Chi Minh City, Vietnam
Tel.: (84) 902662660
Web Site: https://www.masanconsumer.com
Rev.: $1,575,149,880

Assets: $2,583,144,520
Liabilities: $1,219,957,400
Net Worth: $1,363,187,120
Earnings: $224,860,200
Emp.: 9,135
Fiscal Year-end: 12/31/18
Investment Management Service
N.A.I.C.S.: 523999
Nguyen Dang Quang *(Member-Mgmt Bd)*

Subsidiaries:

Ma San Consumer Corporation (1)
12th Floor Kumho Asiana Plaza Saigon 39 Le Duan, Ben Nghe Ward District 1, Ho Chi Minh City, Vietnam
Tel.: (84) 862555660
Web Site: http://www.masanfood.com
Food Products Mfr
N.A.I.C.S.: 311999

Ma San Horizon Corporation (1)
No 17 Le Duan Street, Ben Nghe Ward District 1, Ho Chi Minh City, Vietnam
Tel.: (84) 862563862
Investment Advisory Services
N.A.I.C.S.: 523940

Vietnam National Chemical Group (1)
1A Trang Tien, Hoan Kiem District, Hanoi, Vietnam
Tel.: (84) 438240551
Web Site: http://www.vinachem.com.vn
Chemicals Mfr
N.A.I.C.S.: 325998
Chuyen Bui *(VP)*

Affiliate (Domestic):

Additives and Petroleum Products JSC (2)
Phu Thi Industrial Zone, Gia Lam District, Hanoi, Vietnam
Tel.: (84) 43 678 5060
Web Site: http://app.com.vn
Rev.: $7,987,969
Assets: $4,013,536
Liabilities: $1,963,183
Net Worth: $2,050,353
Earnings: $125,966
Emp.: 130
Fiscal Year-end: 12/31/2021
Petroleum Lubricants, Greases, Motor Oils, Brake Fluids, Cutting Oils, Hydraulic Fluids, Chemicals, Additives & Other Petroleum Products Mfr & Distr
N.A.I.C.S.: 324191
Trung Dung Hoang *(Vice Chm & Gen Dir)*

Subsidiary (Domestic):

Binh Dien Fertilizers Joint Stock Company (2)
C12/21 National Highway 1A, Tan Kien Commune Binh Chanh District, Ho Chi Minh City, Vietnam
Tel.: (84) 837561191
Web Site: https://www.binhdien.com
Fertilizer Distr
N.A.I.C.S.: 424690
Nguyen Van Thieu *(Chm)*

Can Tho Fertilizers and Chemicals Joint Stock Company (2)
Main Axis of Tra Noc 1 Industrial Park, Binh Thuy, Can Tho, Vietnam
Tel.: (84) 2923841043
Web Site: https://www.cfccobay.com
Fertilizer Mfr
N.A.I.C.S.: 325312

Chemical Engineering Joint Stock Corporation (2)
21A Cat Linh, Dong Da, Hanoi, Vietnam
Tel.: (84) 38 455 777
Web Site: http://www.ceco.com.vn
Fertilizer Distr
N.A.I.C.S.: 424690
Bo Hien Ngang *(Chm)*

Da Nang Rubber Joint Stock Company (2)
Lot - G Ta Quang Buu Street Lien Chieu Industrial Zone, Lien Chieu District, Da Nang, Vietnam
Tel.: (84) 511 377 1405
Web Site: http://www.drc.com.vn
Tire Mfr & Distr
N.A.I.C.S.: 336390

Ha Bac Nitrogenous Fertilizer and Chemical Limited Company (2)
Thoxuong Ward, Hanoi, Vietnam
Tel.: (84) 240 3854538
Web Site: http://www.damhabac.com.vn
Fertilizer Distr
N.A.I.C.S.: 424690

Hanoi Soap Joint Stock Company (2)
233B Nguyen Trai Street, Thanh Xuan district, Hanoi, Vietnam
Tel.: (84) 4 3858 7051
Web Site: http://www.haso.vn
Fertilizer & Pesticide Distr
N.A.I.C.S.: 424690

Net Detergent JSC (2)
D4 Street Loc An - Binh Son Industrial Zone, Long Thanh District, Bien Hoa, Dong Nai, Vietnam
Tel.: (84) 2513682102
Web Site: https://www.netcovn.com.vn
Rev.: $180,965,300
Assets: $89,381,400
Liabilities: $45,952,000
Net Worth: $43,429,400
Earnings: $17,843,500
Emp.: 730
Fiscal Year-end: 12/31/2023
Detergents Mfr
N.A.I.C.S.: 325611

Ninh Binh Phosphate Fertilizer Joint Stock Company (2)
Ninh An Commune, Hoa Lu District, Ninh Binh, Vietnam
Tel.: (84) 2293610863
Web Site: https://niferco.com.vn
Rev.: $72,655,000
Assets: $29,010,300
Liabilities: $8,498,000
Net Worth: $20,512,300
Earnings: $2,814,100
Fiscal Year-end: 12/31/2023
Phosphatic Fertilizer Mfr
N.A.I.C.S.: 325312

Paint and Plastic Joint Stock Company (2)
35 Dang Van Ngu 10th Ward, Phu Nhuan District, Ho Chi Minh City, Vietnam
Tel.: (84) 8 9 918 603
Web Site: http://www.ppc.com.vn
Packaging Bags Mfr
N.A.I.C.S.: 326199

The Southern Basic Chemicals JSC (2)
22 Ly Tu Trong Street, Ben Nghe ward District 1, Ho Chi Minh City, Vietnam
Tel.: (84) 8 3829 6620
Web Site: http://www.sochemvn.com
Chemical Products Distr
N.A.I.C.S.: 424690

Tiasang Battery Joint Stock Company (2)
Ton Duc Thang Avenue An Dong, An Duong District, Haiphong, Vietnam
Tel.: (84) 313857080
Web Site: https://www.tiasangbattery.com
Rev.: $7,204,538
Assets: $4,103,787
Liabilities: $930,063
Net Worth: $3,173,724
Earnings: $184,000
Emp.: 230
Fiscal Year-end: 12/31/2021
Battery Mfr
N.A.I.C.S.: 335910
Luong Van Tuyen *(Member-Mgmt Bd & Deputy Gen Dir)*

Van Dien Fused Magnesium Phosphate Joint Stock Company (2)
Phan Trong Tue Phan Hiep, Thanh Tri, Hanoi, Vietnam
Tel.: (84) 2436884489
Web Site: http://www.vandienfmp.vn
Fertilizer Mfr & Distr
N.A.I.C.S.: 325312

Viet Nam Chemical Import & Export Corporation (2)
4 Pham Ngu Lao, Hoan Kiem Dist, Hanoi, Vietnam
Tel.: (84) 38256333
Fertilizer Distr
N.A.I.C.S.: 424690

Viet Tri Chemical Joint Stock Company (2)
Song Thao Street Tho Son Ward, Viet Tri, Phu Tho, Vietnam
Tel.: (84) 2103911696
Web Site: https://www.vitrichem.vn
Rev.: $125,874,400
Assets: $75,463,900
Liabilities: $35,571,300
Net Worth: $39,892,600
Earnings: $6,765,700
Emp.: 370
Fiscal Year-end: 12/31/2023
Chemical Product Mfr & Whslr
N.A.I.C.S.: 325180
Van Dinh Hoan *(Member-Mgmt Bd & Gen Dir)*

Affiliate (Domestic):

Viet-Duc Welding Electrode Joint Stock Company (2)
Nhi Khe, Thuong Tin, Hanoi, Vietnam
Tel.: (84) 433853364
Web Site: http://www.viwelco.com.vn
Rev.: $11,111,800
Assets: $5,261,696
Liabilities: $1,432,135
Net Worth: $3,829,561
Earnings: $1,214,827
Emp.: 240
Fiscal Year-end: 12/31/2020
Welding Equipment Mfr
N.A.I.C.S.: 333992
Ngo Ba Viet *(Chm-Mgmt Bd)*

Subsidiary (Domestic):

Vietnam Pesticide Joint Stock Company (2)
102 Nguyen Dinh Chieu St, Da Kao Ward District 1, Ho Chi Minh City, Vietnam
Tel.: (84) 2838258853
Web Site: https://vipesco.com.vn
Fertilizer Mfr & Distr
N.A.I.C.S.: 325312
XuanDa Nguyen *(Accountant)*

VinaCafe Bien Hoa Joint Stock Company (1)
Bien Hoa Industrial Zone 1, Bien Hoa, Dong Nai, Vietnam **(98.49%)**
Tel.: (84) 2513836554
Web Site: https://www.vinacafebienhoa.com
Rev.: $235,252,100
Assets: $265,840,700
Liabilities: $54,562,200
Net Worth: $211,278,500
Earnings: $44,995,300
Fiscal Year-end: 12/31/2023
Coffee Mfr
N.A.I.C.S.: 311920

MASARU CORPORATION
Masaru Head Office Building 1-9-14 Saga, Koto-Ku, Tokyo, 135-8432, Japan
Tel.: (81) 336435859   JP
Web Site: https://www.masaru-co.jp
Year Founded: 1957
1795—(TKS)
Rev.: $59,114,618
Assets: $55,460,837
Liabilities: $22,821,269
Net Worth: $32,639,568
Earnings: $1,830,194
Fiscal Year-end: 03/31/24
Construction Services
N.A.I.C.S.: 541330
Jun Kariya *(Chm & Pres)*

MASAWARA PLC
Queensway House, Hilgrove Street, Saint Helier, JE4 9XY, Jersey
Tel.: (44) 20 7397 8900   JE
Web Site: http://www.masawara.com
Investment Holding Company
N.A.I.C.S.: 523999

Subsidiaries:

TA Holdings Limited (1)
17th Floor Joina City Cnr Julius Nyerere Way/Jason Moyo Ave, PO Box 3546, Harare, Zimbabwe
Tel.: (263) 4777348
Web Site: http://www.ta-holdings.com
Sales Range: $50-74.9 Million
Emp.: 762
Investment Holding Company
N.A.I.C.S.: 551112
Bothwell Patrick Nyajeka *(Dir-Fin)*

Affiliate (Domestic):

Aon Zimbabwe (Pvt) Ltd. (2)
Minerva House Kenilworth Gardens No 1 Kenilworth Rd Newlands, Borrowdale, Harare, Zimbabwe **(30.3%)**
Tel.: (263) 4883878
Web Site: http://www.minerva.com
Sales Range: $50-74.9 Million
Emp.: 100
Risk Consultancy & Insurance Broking Services
N.A.I.C.S.: 524210

Subsidiary (Non-US):

Botswana Insurance Company (Pty) Ltd (2)
BIC House Plot 50372 Gaborone Bus Park, PO Box 715, Gaborone Show Grounds, Gaborone, Botswana
Tel.: (267) 3600500
Web Site: http://www.bic.co.bw
Sales Range: $50-74.9 Million
Emp.: 85
Insurance Management Services
N.A.I.C.S.: 524298
Katrina O'Hare *(Mgr-Mktg)*

Cresta Hospitality Holdings (Pvt) Ltd. (2)
1Fl Block B 98 Albertine Ave, Wierda Valley, 2146, South Africa
Tel.: (27) 11 881 1200
Web Site: http://www.crestahotels.com
Sales Range: $10-24.9 Million
Emp.: 5
Home Management Services
N.A.I.C.S.: 721110
Glenn Stutchbury *(CEO)*

Subsidiary (Non-US):

Cresta Hospitality (Pvt) Ltd (3)
Amby, PO Box AY2, Harare, Zimbabwe
Tel.: (263) 4 446000
Home Management Services
N.A.I.C.S.: 721110

Subsidiary (Domestic):

Cresta Hotels (Pty) Ltd (3)
PO Box 650795, Benmore, Johannesburg, 2010, South Africa
Tel.: (27) 11 881 1200
Web Site: http://www.crestahotels.com
Sales Range: $10-24.9 Million
Emp.: 7
Home Management Services
N.A.I.C.S.: 721110
Glenn Stutchbury *(CEO)*

Joint Venture (Non-US):

Cresta Marakanelo (Pvt) Ltd (3)
Plot 50676 Fairground Office Park Phase 2 Block D Unit 2, Private Bag 00272, Gaborone, 00272, Botswana
Tel.: (267) 3912222
Web Site: http://www.crestamarakanelo.com
Emp.: 20
Hotel Owner & Operator
N.A.I.C.S.: 721110
Segomotso Banda *(Mgr-HR)*

Subsidiary (Domestic):

Grand Reinsurance (Pvt) Ltd (2)
Aon House Northridge Park, Borrowdale, Harare, Zimbabwe
Tel.: (263) 4 852039 44
Web Site: http://www.grandrei.co.zw
Sales Range: $50-74.9 Million
Emp.: 12
Insurance Management Services
N.A.I.C.S.: 524298

MASAWARA PLC

Masawara PLC—(Continued)

Sable Chemical Industries Ltd. (2)
Anne Newton Boulevard, PO Box 561,
Sherwood Block, Kwekwe,
Zimbabwe **(51%)**
Tel.: (263) 5523601
Sales Range: $250-299.9 Million
Emp.: 520
Chemical & Fertilizer Mfr
N.A.I.C.S.: 325311

Affiliate (Domestic):

United Refineries Ltd. (2)
Khami Road Extension, PO Box 873, Bulawayo, Zimbabwe **(20%)**
Tel.: (263) 9410561
Edible Oil & Soap Mfr
N.A.I.C.S.: 325620

Zimbabwe Fertilizer Company Limited (ZFC) (2)
35 Coventry Rd, Workington, Harare,
Zimbabwe **(22.5%)**
Tel.: (263) 4753882
Fertilizer Mfr & Distr
N.A.I.C.S.: 325311

Subsidiary (Domestic):

Zimnat Life Assurance Company Ltd. (2)
Zimnat House Nelson Corner Mandela Ave
& Third Street, Harare, 1155, Zimbabwe
Tel.: (263) 4 701176
Web Site: http://www.zimnatlife.co.zw
Fire Insurance Services
N.A.I.C.S.: 524113
Francis Masukusa (Dir-Ops)

MASCAREN INTERNATIONAL INC

500 Danforth Ave, Toronto, M4K 1P6,
ON, Canada
Tel.: (416) 465-6690
Web Site: http://www.mascaren.com
Sales Range: $50-74.9 Million
Emp.: 1,000
Cosmetic Product Whslr
N.A.I.C.S.: 456120

MASCHINENFABRIK BERTHOLD HERMLE AG

Industriestrasse 8-12, 78559, Gosheim, Germany
Tel.: (49) 7426950
Web Site: https://www.hermle.de
Year Founded: 1938
MBH3—(MUN)
Rev.: $587,258,840
Assets: $558,999,768
Liabilities: $154,011,942
Net Worth: $404,987,826
Earnings: $96,665,896
Emp.: 1,472
Fiscal Year-end: 12/31/23
Mailing Machine Mfr
N.A.I.C.S.: 333517
Dietmar Hermle (Chm-Supervisory Bd)

Subsidiaries:

Florian Konig (1)
Rofansiedlung 449 D, 6210, Wiesing, Austria
Tel.: (43) 524462373
Industrial Machinery Equipment Mfr
N.A.I.C.S.: 333248

Hermle (Schweiz) AG (1)
Tobelackerstrasse 6, Neuhausen am Rheinfall, 8212, Neuhausen, Schaffhausen, Switzerland
Tel.: (41) 526740040
Web Site: https://www.hermle-schweiz.ch
Sales Range: $25-49.9 Million
Emp.: 2
Specialty Trade Contractors
N.A.I.C.S.: 238990

Hermle + Partner Vertriebs GmbH (1)
Windhukstr 55, 42389, Wuppertal, Germany
Tel.: (49) 2027473990
Industrial Machinery & Equipment Whslr
N.A.I.C.S.: 423830

Hermle China Co Ltd. (1)
1 business owner territory bldg A place
1707 Rm, West Beijing Chaoyang, 100028,
Beijing, China
Tel.: (86) 1058220951
Web Site: http://www.hermle.com.cn
Sales Range: $25-49.9 Million
Emp.: 25
Industrial Machinery & Equipment Whslr
N.A.I.C.S.: 423830
D. Wang (Mng Dir)

Hermle Italia S.r.l. (1)
Via Papa Giovanni XXIII 9-b, 20053,
Rodano, MI, Italy
Tel.: (39) 0295327241
Web Site: https://www.hermle-italia.it
Sales Range: $25-49.9 Million
Emp.: 12
Industrial Machinery & Equipment Whslr
N.A.I.C.S.: 423830

Hermle Machine (Shanghai) Co. Ltd. (1)
Shanghai Industry Building Floor 21D No 18
Caoxi North Road, Xuhui District, Shanghai,
200030, China
Tel.: (86) 2164271891
Milling Machinery Mfr & Distr
N.A.I.C.S.: 333517

Hermle Machine Co (1)
5100 W Franklin Dr, Franklin, WI 53132-8847
Tel.: (414) 421-9770
Web Site: http://www.hermlemachine.com
Sales Range: $50-74.9 Million
Emp.: 10
Mfr of Toolroom Milling Machines
N.A.I.C.S.: 423830
Ken Merk (Mgr-Sls-Mid West)

Hermle Maschinenbau Gmbh (1)
Industriestrasse 8-12, 78559, Gosheim, Germany
Tel.: (49) 7426950
Web Site: https://www.hermle.de
Sales Range: $25-49.9 Million
Emp.: 2
Industrial Machinery Equipment Mfr & Whslr
N.A.I.C.S.: 333248

Hermle Mexiko S DE R.L. DE C.V. (1)
Av Monte Miranda Pte 15 Int 906 Monte
Miranda, 76240, El Marques, Mexico
Tel.: (52) 4422510723
Web Site: https://www.hermle.mx
High Precision Machine Tools Mfr
N.A.I.C.S.: 332721

Hermle Nederland B.V. (1)
Venloseweg 70d, 5961 JD, Horst, Netherlands
Tel.: (31) 773961761
Sales Range: $50-74.9 Million
Emp.: 10
Industrial Machinery & Equipment Whslr
N.A.I.C.S.: 423830

Hermle Nordic (1)
Faelledvej 1, 5000, Odense, Denmark
Tel.: (45) 66176950
Web Site: http://www.hermle-nordic.dk
Industrial Machinery Equipment Mfr
N.A.I.C.S.: 423830

Hermle Osterreich AG (1)
Sportplatzstrasse 31 2, Proleb, 8712, Leoben, Austria
Tel.: (43) 384283377
Industrial Machinery & Equipment Whslr
N.A.I.C.S.: 423830

Hermle SEA Co., Ltd. (1)
19 Moo 1 T Pong A Banglamung, Chon
Buri, 20150, Thailand
Tel.: (66) 38227364
Web Site: https://www.hermle-sea.com
High Precision Machine Tools Mfr
N.A.I.C.S.: 332721

Hermle Southeast Europe (1)
Komplex Gotze Deltschev Block 47 E
Magazin 2, 1404, Sofia, Bulgaria
Tel.: (359) 2 958 59 01
Web Site: http://www.hermle.bg
Emp.: 2
Industrial Machinery Equipment Mfr & Sales
N.A.I.C.S.: 333248

Hermle USA INC. (1)
5100 W Franklin Dr, Franklin, WI 53132
Tel.: (414) 421-9770
Web Site: https://www.hermleusa.net
High Precision Machine Tools Mfr
N.A.I.C.S.: 332721

Hermle WWE AG (1)
Zuger Strasse 72, 6340, Baar, Switzerland
Tel.: (41) 417685151
Web Site: http://www.hermle-wwe.com
Sales Range: $250-299.9 Million
Emp.: 900
Industrial Machinery & Equipment Whslr
N.A.I.C.S.: 423830

Hermle-Leibinger Systemtechnik GmbH (1)
Industriestrasse 8-12, D-78559, Gosheim,
Germany
Tel.: (49) 7426950
Web Site: http://www.hermle.de
Custom Computer Programming Services
N.A.I.C.S.: 541511
Rainer Kohler (Mng Dir)

OOO Hermle Vostok (1)
Ul Godovikova 9, 129085, Moscow, Russia
Tel.: (7) 495739641
Web Site: http://www.hermle-vostok.ru
Sales Range: $50-74.9 Million
Emp.: 70
Industrial Machinery & Equipment Whslr
N.A.I.C.S.: 423830

MASCHINENFABRIK GUSTAV EIRICH GMBH & CO KG

Walldurner Str 50, 74736, Hardheim,
Germany
Tel.: (49) 6283510
Web Site: http://www.eirich.com
Year Founded: 1863
Rev.: $178,715,940
Emp.: 650
Engineeering Services
N.A.I.C.S.: 541330
Ralf Rohmann (Co-Mng Dir)

Subsidiaries:

Eirich France SAS (1)
Parc Aktiland 1 rue Lombardie, 69800,
Saint-Priest-en-Jarez, France
Tel.: (33) 478931147
Engineeering Services
N.A.I.C.S.: 541330

Eirich Group China Ltd. (1)
Unit B&C Floor 7 Building D BENQ Commerce Plaza No 207 Songhong Rd, Chang-Ning, Shanghai, 200335, China
Tel.: (86) 2160431116
Web Site: http://www.eirichchina.com
Engineeering Services
N.A.I.C.S.: 541330

Eirich India Pvt. Ltd. (1)
119 ABC Govt Industrial Estate, Kandivli,
Mumbai, India
Tel.: (91) 2228679444
Engineeering Services
N.A.I.C.S.: 541330

Eirich Industrial Ltda. (1)
Estrada Velha de Itu n 1500, 06612-250,
Jandira, Brazil
Tel.: (55) 1146198900
Engineeering Services
N.A.I.C.S.: 541330

Eirich Machinery Jiangyin (EMJ) Co., Ltd. (1)
No 29 Naxiang Road, Jiangyin, 214422,
Jiangsu, China
Tel.: (86) 51086016188
Engineeering Services
N.A.I.C.S.: 541330

Eirich Machines Inc. (1)
4033 Ryan Rd, Gurnee, IL 60031
Tel.: (847) 336-2444
Engineeering Services
N.A.I.C.S.: 541330
Dino Chece (Mng Dir)

INTERNATIONAL PUBLIC

Nippon Eirich Co., Ltd. (1)
1210 Kichioka, Narita, 287-0225, Chiba,
Japan
Tel.: (81) 476 735251
Web Site: http://www.nippon-eirich.co.jp
Emp.: 100
Engineeering Services
N.A.I.C.S.: 541330
Stephan Eirich (Pres)

OOO Eirich Maschinentechnik (1)
ul Urzhumskaja 4 str 2, 129343, Moscow,
Russia
Tel.: (7) 4957716880
Engineeering Services
N.A.I.C.S.: 541330

OOO Eirich Maschinentechnik (1)
Startovaja 20, 49041, Dnepropetrovsk,
Ukraine
Tel.: (380) 567943145
Engineeering Services
N.A.I.C.S.: 541330

MASCHINENFABRIK HARRY LUCAS GMBH & CO. KG

Gadelander Strasse 24-26, 24539,
Neumunster, Germany
Tel.: (49) 432198770
Web Site: http://www.lucas-elha.de
Year Founded: 1942
Rev.: $11,035,200
Emp.: 50
Knitting Machine Mfr
N.A.I.C.S.: 315120
Thorsten Schatterny (Mgr-Factory)

Subsidiaries:

LUC-PRODUCT SP. Z O.O. (1)
ul J Cebuli 16, 46080, Chroscice, Poland
Tel.: (48) 774032415
Textile Machinery Mfr
N.A.I.C.S.: 333248

LUCAS America Inc. (1)
1841 B E Elisabeth Ave, Linden, NJ 07036
Tel.: (908) 925-4040
Textile Machinery Distr
N.A.I.C.S.: 423830

Lucas Textilmaschinen GmbH (1)
Berbisdorfer Strasse 73, Einsiedel, 09123,
Chemnitz, Germany
Tel.: (49) 372097192
Textile Machinery Mfr
N.A.I.C.S.: 333248

MASCHINENFABRIK HEID AKTIENGESELLSCHAFT

HEID-Werkstrasse 13, 2000, Stockerau, Austria
Tel.: (43) 226671262
Web Site: https://www.heid.info
Year Founded: 1883
HED—(VIE)
Sales Range: Less than $1 Million
Machine Tool Part Mfr
N.A.I.C.S.: 333515
Guenter Rothenberger (Member-Mgmt Bd)

MASCHINENFABRIK OTTO BAIER GMBH

Heckenwiesen 26, 71679, Asperg,
Germany
Tel.: (49) 714130320
Web Site: http://www.baier-tools.com
Year Founded: 1938
Rev.: $12,414,600
Emp.: 69
Power Tool Mfr
N.A.I.C.S.: 333991
Thomas Schwab (Mng Dir)

Subsidiaries:

BAIER S.A.R.L. (1)
48 rue du Docteur Leonce Basset, 93403,
Saint-Ouen, Cedex, France
Tel.: (33) 140128297
Web Site: http://www.baier.fr
Machine Tool Distr
N.A.I.C.S.: 423830

AND PRIVATE COMPANIES

BAIER Scandinavia ApS (1)
Topstykket 29, 3460, Birkerod, Denmark
Tel.: (45) 45942200
Web Site: http://www.baier.dk
Machine Tool Distr
N.A.I.C.S.: 423830

OTTO BAIER Italiana S.r.l. (1)
Via della Liberazione 21, San Giuliano Milanese, 20098, Milan, Italy
Tel.: (39) 0298280927
Web Site: http://www.ottobaier.it
Machine Tool Distr
N.A.I.C.S.: 423830

MASCHINENFABRIK WAGNER GMBH & CO. KG
Birrenbachshohe 17, 53804, Much, Germany
Tel.: (49) 2245620
Web Site: http://www.plarad.de
Year Founded: 1962
Sales Range: $25-49.9 Million
Emp.: 125
Torque Tools Mfr
N.A.I.C.S.: 333517
Klaus Rodemann *(Mng Dir)*

Subsidiaries:

PLARAD UK Ltd (1)
Unit 4 58/62 Walpole Road, BR2 9SF, Bromley, United Kingdom - England
Tel.: (44) 8456436978
Power Tool Distr
N.A.I.C.S.: 423830

Plarad Bolting Technology, LLC (1)
1517 W N Carrier Pkwy Ste 112, Grand Prairie, TX 75050-1288
Tel.: (469) 865-1649
Power Tool Distr
N.A.I.C.S.: 423830
Colby Jorden *(Dir-Service)*

Plarad Italy Srl (1)
Via della Vecchia Chimica 10, Cerro al Lambro, Milan, Italy
Tel.: (39) 029832954
Power Tool Distr
N.A.I.C.S.: 423830

Plarad Tork Anahtarlan ve Gerdirme Sistemleri San.Dis.Tic.Ltd.Sti. (1)
Tekstilkent Ticaret Merkezi A2 Blok Kat Girls D 22 Orucreis Mah, Barbaros Cad Esenler, Istanbul, Turkiye
Tel.: (90) 2126597776
Power Tool Distr
N.A.I.C.S.: 423830

MASHAER HOLDING COMPANY (K.S.C.P)
Ahmad Al-Jaber St Buliding 23 6th Floor, PO Box 23110, Al Sharq Safat, Kuwait, 13092, Kuwait
Tel.: (965) 22902666
Web Site: https://www.mashaerholding.com
Year Founded: 2000
MASHAER—(KUW)
Rev.: $10,484,234
Assets: $70,684,829
Liabilities: $13,457,340
Net Worth: $57,227,489
Earnings: $5,325,792
Emp.: 20
Fiscal Year-end: 12/31/23
Real Estate Services
N.A.I.C.S.: 531190

MASHHAD CARTON INDUSTRIES COMPANY
5th Fl Kaveh Bldg Sepahbod Gharani St Ferdosi Sq, Tehran, Iran
Tel.: (98) 21 88306813
Web Site: http://www.cartonmashhadco.com
Carton Mfr
N.A.I.C.S.: 322212
Masoud Matin Rad *(CEO)*

MASHONALAND HOLDINGS LIMITED
12th Floor ZB Towers 77 Jason Moyo Avenue, PO Box 717, Harare, Zimbabwe
Tel.: (263) 242253600
Web Site: https://www.mashholdings.co.zw
Year Founded: 1966
MASH—(ZIM)
Sales Range: $1-9.9 Million
Holding Company
N.A.I.C.S.: 551112
G. Mapfidza *(Exec Dir)*

Subsidiaries:

Willdale Limited (1)
195km Peg Lomagundi Road, Mount Hampden, Harare, Zimbabwe
Tel.: (263) 8677007150
Web Site: https://www.willdale.co.zw
Bricks Mfr
N.A.I.C.S.: 327331

MASHREQBANK P.S.C
Al Fattan Currency House Tower 1 Floor 1 Office 111, PO Box 1250, Deira, Dubai, United Arab Emirates
Tel.: (971) 44244444   AE
Web Site: http://www.mashreqbank.com
Year Founded: 1967
MASQ—(DFM)
Rev.: $3,610,102,933
Assets: $65,348,857,392
Liabilities: $56,820,744,220
Net Worth: $8,528,113,172
Earnings: $2,362,665,360
Emp.: 2,303
Fiscal Year-end: 12/31/23
Banking Services
N.A.I.C.S.: 522110
Ali Rashid Ahmed Lootah *(Vice Chm)*

Subsidiaries:

Mashreq Securities WLL (1)
Al Fattan Currency House Tower 1 Floor 1 Office 111, PO Box 1250, Dubai, United Arab Emirates
Tel.: (971) 43632222
Web Site: https://www.mashreqsecurities.com
Securities Brokerage Services
N.A.I.C.S.: 523150

Mashreqbank P.S.C - Mashreq Al Islami Division (1)
Umniyati Street off Al Asayel Street Burj Khalifa Community, PO Box 1250, Abu Dhabi, United Arab Emirates
Tel.: (971) 44244411
Web Site: https://www.mashreqalislami.com
Banking Services
N.A.I.C.S.: 522110

Mashreqbank P.S.C - New York (1)
50 Broadway Ste 1500, New York, NY 10004
Tel.: (212) 545-8200
Web Site: http://www.mashreqbank.com
Sales Range: $50-74.9 Million
Banking Services
N.A.I.C.S.: 522110

Mashreqbank P.S.C. - UK (1)
3rd Floor 48-54 Moorgate, 14-16 Finsbury Square, London, EC2R 6EJ, United Kingdom
Tel.: (44) 2073824000
Web Site: https://www.mashreqbank.com
Sales Range: $50-74.9 Million
Emp.: 10
Banking Services
N.A.I.C.S.: 522110

Mindscape Information Technology (1)
PO Box 99500, Dubai, United Arab Emirates
Tel.: (971) 42714333
Sales Range: $25-49.9 Million   (99%)
Emp.: 100
IT Services
N.A.I.C.S.: 541519

Sukoon Insurance PJSC (1)
Omar Bin Al Khattâb Street Next to Al Ghurair Mall Deira, PO Box 5209, Dubai, United Arab Emirates   (63.65%)
Tel.: (971) 42337777
Web Site: https://www.sukoon.com
Rev.: $1,264,546,140
Assets: $2,404,062,602
Liabilities: $1,650,127,991
Net Worth: $753,934,611
Earnings: $70,080,049
Emp.: 730
Fiscal Year-end: 12/31/2023
Life Insurance Carrier
N.A.I.C.S.: 524113
Abdul Aziz Abdulla Al-Ghurair *(Chm)*

Subsidiary (Domestic):

Sukoon Takaful PJSC (2)
PO Box 1993, Dubai, United Arab Emirates   (94.6%)
Tel.: (971) 42824403
Web Site: https://www.sukoontakaful.com
Rev.: $34,465,259
Assets: $101,539,699
Liabilities: $53,804,727
Net Worth: $47,734,971
Earnings: ($20,836,964)
Fiscal Year-end: 12/31/2023
Insurance Products & Services
N.A.I.C.S.: 524298
Ahmad Mohammed Amin Al Kazim *(Vice Chm & Mng Dir)*

MASHSTROY JSC
5 Acad A Balevski Str, PO Box 84, 5600, Troyan, Bulgaria
Tel.: (359) 670 66151
Web Site: http://www.mashstroy.bg
Year Founded: 1947
Metal Cutting Machinery Mfr
N.A.I.C.S.: 333517
Pavlin Minkov Pavlov *(Dir-IR)*

MASI AGRICOLA S.P.A.
Via Monteleone 26, sant Ambrogio di valpolicella, 37015, Verona, Italy
Tel.: (39) 0456832511
Web Site: https://www.masi.it
MASI—(ITA)
Sales Range: $75-99.9 Million
Emp.: 80
Wine Producer
N.A.I.C.S.: 312130
Sandro Boscaini *(Pres & Mng Dir)*

Subsidiaries:

Canevel Spumanti S.p.A. (1)
Via Recat e Ferrari 17, Valdobbiadene, 31049, Treviso, Italy
Tel.: (39) 0423975940
Web Site: http://www.canevel.it
Wine Product Mfr
N.A.I.C.S.: 312130

Masi Wine Bar Munich GmbH (1)
40 Maximilianstrasse, 80539, Munich, Germany
Tel.: (49) 8923032565
Winery Product Distr
N.A.I.C.S.: 424820

MASIMBA HOLDINGS LIMITED
44 Tilbury Road Willowvale, PO Box CY490, Causeway, Harare, Zimbabwe
Tel.: (263) 242611641
Web Site: https://www.masimbagroup.com
Year Founded: 1974
MSHL—(ZIM)
Rev.: $53,834,005
Assets: $85,784,666
Liabilities: $61,557,531
Net Worth: $24,227,135
Earnings: $7,550,472
Emp.: 2,088
Fiscal Year-end: 12/31/23
Holding Company
N.A.I.C.S.: 551112

MASKELIYA PLANTATIONS PLC

Gregory Sebborn *(Chm)*

MASINOPROJEKT KOPRING A.D.
Dobrinjska 8a, 11000, Belgrade, Serbia
Tel.: (381) 11 36 35 700
Web Site: http://www.masinoprojekt.co.rs
Year Founded: 1950
Sales Range: $1-9.9 Million
Emp.: 225
Engineering Consulting Services
N.A.I.C.S.: 541330

MASINSKI CENTAR A.D.
Kruzni put bb, 11309, Lestane, Serbia
Tel.: (381) 11 8035 897
Web Site: http://www.geosonda-mc.com
Year Founded: 1993
Sales Range: Less than $1 Million
Mining Machinery Mfr
N.A.I.C.S.: 333131

MASINSKI SERVIS UPP A.D.
Srbacki Put 140, 78418, Gradiska, Bosnia & Herzegovina
Tel.: (387) 51892279
MSRV-R-A—(BANJ)
Rev.: $31,916
Assets: $1,969,966
Liabilities: $668,904
Net Worth: $1,301,062
Earnings: ($22,354)
Emp.: 6
Fiscal Year-end: 12/31/12
Motor Vehicle Maintenance & Repair Services
N.A.I.C.S.: 811198
Dragan Cerovac *(Chm-Supervisory Bd)*

MASIVO SILVER CORP.
750 West Pender Street Suite 202, Vancouver, V6C 2T7, BC, Canada
Tel.: (602) 315-1231   BC
Year Founded: 2011
MASS—(TSXV)
Rev.: $1,115
Assets: $40,567
Liabilities: $330,317
Net Worth: ($289,750)
Earnings: ($265,769)
Fiscal Year-end: 03/31/24
Gold & Silver Exploration Company
N.A.I.C.S.: 212220
David Coburn *(Founder & CEO)*

MASK INVESTMENTS LIMITED
A-601/B International Trade Centre Majura Gate Ring Road, Surat, 395002, Gujarat, India
Tel.: (91) 2612463261
Web Site: https://www.maskinvestments.com
Year Founded: 1992
MASKINVEST—(NSE)
Rev.: $37,048
Assets: $11,875,586
Liabilities: $117,061
Net Worth: $11,758,525
Earnings: $7,069
Fiscal Year-end: 03/31/23
Investment Management Service
N.A.I.C.S.: 523940
Ayushi Manish Saboo *(CFO)*

MASKELIYA PLANTATIONS PLC
No 310 High Level Road Nawinna, Maharagama, Sri Lanka
Tel.: (94) 114310500
Web Site: https://www.stclairstea.com
MASK—(COL)
Rev.: $20,537,023

MASKELIYA PLANTATIONS PLC

Maskeliya Plantations PLC—(Continued)
Assets: $20,542,525
Liabilities: $14,712,034
Net Worth: $5,830,492
Earnings: $2,951,137
Emp.: 6,750
Fiscal Year-end: 03/31/23
Tea Mfr & Distr
N.A.I.C.S.: 111998
Sena Yaddehige *(Chm)*

MASLAVI CONSTRUCTION CO., LTD.
Moshe Aviv 1, Or Yehuda, 60371, Israel
Tel.: (972) 35339212   IL
Web Site: http://www.maslavi.co.il
Year Founded: 1977
MSLA—(TAE)
Rev.: $61,510,152
Assets: $152,585,161
Liabilities: $108,954,826
Net Worth: $43,630,335
Earnings: $5,505,180
Fiscal Year-end: 12/31/23
New Multifamily Housing Construction (except For-Sale Builders)
N.A.I.C.S.: 236116

MASON CAPITAL CORP
13F Jeonju Daewoo Bldg 213 Girindaero, Wansan-gu, Jeonju, Jeollabuk, Korea (South)
Tel.: (82) 632875305
Year Founded: 1989
Investment Management Service
N.A.I.C.S.: 523999

MASON GROUP HOLDINGS LIMITED
Portion 1 12/F The Center 99 Queens Road, Central, China (Hong Kong)
Tel.: (852) 22182888
Web Site: http://www.masonhk.com
0273—(HKG)
Rev.: $517,533,411
Assets: $619,974,357
Liabilities: $50,633,937
Net Worth: $569,340,420
Earnings: ($94,980,356)
Emp.: 115
Fiscal Year-end: 12/31/21
Investment Services
N.A.I.C.S.: 523940

Subsidiaries:

Blend & Pack Pty. Ltd.   (1)
24-26 Wedgewood Road, Hallam, 3803, VIC, Australia
Tel.: (61) 38 786 3637
Web Site:
   https://www.blendandpack.com.au
Dairy Products Mfr
N.A.I.C.S.: 311999

China United International Administrative Services Limited   (1)
32 Fl China United Ctr 28 Marble Rd, North Point, China (Hong Kong)
Tel.: (852) 31980111
Office Administrative Services
N.A.I.C.S.: 561110
Asiong Wong *(Mng Dir)*

Harris Fraser Group Limited   (1)
Portion 1 12/F The Center 99 Queen's Road, Central, China (Hong Kong)
Tel.: (852) 2 827 2278
Web Site: https://www.harris-fraser.com
Wealth Management Services
N.A.I.C.S.: 523940
Andy Lam *(CEO)*

Mason Privatbank Liechtenstein AG   (1)
Austrasse 51, 9490, Vaduz, Liechtenstein
Tel.: (423) 237 0707
Web Site: https://www.mason-privatbank.li
Banking Services

N.A.I.C.S.: 522110

MASON RESOURCES INC.
120 Adelaide Street West Suite 1410, Toronto, M5H 1T1, ON, Canada
Tel.: (416) 844-7365   ON
Web Site:
   https://masonresourcesinc.com
Year Founded: 2011
MGPHF—(OTCQX)
Rev.: $126,335
Assets: $20,738,588
Liabilities: $1,266,166
Net Worth: $19,472,421
Earnings: ($5,120,343)
Fiscal Year-end: 06/30/21
Graphite Mining Services
N.A.I.C.S.: 212390
Benoit Gascon *(Pres & CEO)*

MASOOD TEXTILE MILLS LIMITED
17/1 New Civil Lines Bilal Road, Faisalabad, Pakistan
Tel.: (92) 4126000176
Web Site:
   https://www.masoodtextile.com
Year Founded: 1984
MSOT—(LAH)
Rev.: $245,637,701
Assets: $266,625,358
Liabilities: $184,071,592
Net Worth: $82,553,766
Earnings: $9,566,689
Emp.: 14,161
Fiscal Year-end: 06/30/19
Textile Products Mfr
N.A.I.C.S.: 313310
Naseer Ahmad Shah *(Chm)*

Subsidiaries:

Masood Textile Mills Limited - Apparel Factory   (1)
Sargodha Road, Faisalabad, 38000, Punjab, Pakistan
Tel.: (92) 4187879314
Apparels Mfr
N.A.I.C.S.: 315210
Kamal Anjum *(Dir-Ops)*

Masood Textile Mills Limited - Apparel-III Factory   (1)
Masood Textile Mills Limited - Apparel-III Factory, Nishatabad, Faisalabad, 38000, Punjab, Pakistan
Tel.: (92) 418758435
Apparels Mfr
N.A.I.C.S.: 315210
Kamal Anjum *(Dir-Ops)*

Masood Textile Mills Limited - Falcon Factory   (1)
Rachna Town Satayana Road, Faisalabad, 38000, Punjab, Pakistan
Tel.: (92) 418722111
Apparels Mfr
N.A.I.C.S.: 313210

Masood Textile Mills Limited - Leopard Factory   (1)
Samana Pull, Faisalabad, 38000, Punjab, Pakistan
Tel.: (92) 41 8868433
Apparels Mfr
N.A.I.C.S.: 315210
Kamal Anjum *(Dir-Ops)*

Masood Textile Mills Limited - Panther Factory   (1)
Shaikhupura Road, Faisalabad, 38000, Punjab, Pakistan
Tel.: (92) 418757342
Web Site: http://www.masoodtextile.com
Apparels Mfr
N.A.I.C.S.: 315210

MASOVAL AS
Nordfroyveien 413, Sistranda, 7260, Froya, Norway
Tel.: (47) 72447070
Web Site: https://www.masoval.no
Year Founded: 1973

MAS—(OSL)
Rev.: $221,720,672
Assets: $476,649,824
Liabilities: $310,912,156
Net Worth: $165,737,669
Earnings: ($12,321,818)
Emp.: 315
Fiscal Year-end: 12/31/23
Fish Farming Services
N.A.I.C.S.: 112511
Gunnar Aftret *(CFO)*

Subsidiaries:

Pure Norwegian Seafood AS   (1)
Hendnesveien 99, 6533, Averoy, Norway
Tel.: (47) 71515290
Web Site: https://www.pns.no
Seafood Restaurant Operator
N.A.I.C.S.: 561599

MASRAF AL RAYAN (Q.S.C.)
69 Alad Al Sharqi Street, Lusail, Qatar
Tel.: (974) 44253333   QA
Web Site: https://www.alrayan.com
Year Founded: 2006
MARK—(QE)
Rev.: $2,621,557,110
Assets: $45,029,352,804
Liabilities: $38,226,528,452
Net Worth: $6,802,824,352
Earnings: $405,867,270
Emp.: 561
Fiscal Year-end: 12/31/23
Banking & Financial Investment Services
N.A.I.C.S.: 522110
Hussain Ali Al Abdulla *(Co/Co-Chm, Mng Dir & Mng Dir)*

Subsidiaries:

Al Khalij Commercial Bank (al khaliji) Q.S.C.   (1)
Al Jazi Tower Seventh Floor Asia Street 60 West Bay, PO Box 28000, Doha, Qatar
Tel.: (974) 44940494
Web Site: http://www.alkhaliji.com
Rev.: $577,276,128
Assets: $15,393,293,839
Liabilities: $13,344,079,116
Net Worth: $2,049,214,723
Earnings: $186,096,483
Emp.: 500
Fiscal Year-end: 12/31/2020
Banking Services
N.A.I.C.S.: 522110
Abdullah Nasser Al Misnad *(Vice Chm)*

Subsidiary (Non-US):

Al Khaliji France S.A.   (2)
49-51 Avenue George V, 75008, Paris, France
Tel.: (33) 149524952
Web Site: http://www.alkhaliji.ae
Mobile Banking Services
N.A.I.C.S.: 522110

Al Rayan Bank PLC   (1)
44 Hans Crescent, Knightsbridge, London, SW1X 0LZ, United Kingdom
Tel.: (44) 1298890137
Web Site: http://www.alrayanbank.co.uk
Rev.: $93,762,349
Assets: $2,947,558,680
Liabilities: $2,756,299,856
Net Worth: $191,258,824
Earnings: $8,015,188
Emp.: 335
Fiscal Year-end: 12/31/2019
Banking & Financial Services
N.A.I.C.S.: 523150
Ahmed Swaleh Abdisheikh *(Exec Dir-People & Tech)*

Al Rayan Investment L.L.C.   (1)
Masraf Al Rayan Bank 3rd Floor Grand Hamad Street, PO Box 28888, Doha, Qatar
Tel.: (974) 44235606
Web Site:
   http://www.alrayaninvestment.com
Investment Banking Services
N.A.I.C.S.: 523150
Nasser Jaralla Al-Marri *(Chm)*

INTERNATIONAL PUBLIC

MASS RESPONSE SERVICE GMBH
DC Tower 1 38 Stock Donau-City-Strasse 7, 1220, Vienna, Austria
Tel.: (43) 12702825
Web Site:
   http://www.massresponse.com
Telecommunication Servicesb
N.A.I.C.S.: 517810
Franz Pichler *(CEO)*

MASS TELECOM INNOVATION PLC
18 A Gerrard Road, Ikoyi, Lagos, Lagos, Nigeria
Tel.: (234) 1 8441666
Year Founded: 2001
Communication Equipment Mfr
N.A.I.C.S.: 334290

MASSARELLA CATERING GROUP LTD.
Thurcroft Hall Brookhouse, Laughton-en-le-Morthen, Sheffield, S25 1XZ, United Kingdom
Tel.: (44) 1909568891
Web Site:
   http://www.massarella.co.uk
Year Founded: 1860
Sales Range: $50-74.9 Million
Emp.: 2,000
Catering Services
N.A.I.C.S.: 722320
Mark Massarella *(Mng Dir)*

MASSIMO ZANETTI BEVERAGE GROUP SPA
Viale Felissent 53, Villorba, 31020, Treviso, Italy
Tel.: (39) 0422312611
Web Site: http://www.mzb-group.com
MZB—(ITA)
Rev.: $1,024,072,775
Assets: $1,049,342,416
Liabilities: $671,493,813
Net Worth: $377,848,603
Earnings: $17,147,296
Emp.: 3,585
Fiscal Year-end: 12/31/19
Holding Company
N.A.I.C.S.: 551112
Massimo Zanetti *(Chm & CEO)*

Subsidiaries:

Bean Alliance Group Pty. Ltd.   (1)
25 Kurnai Avenue, Reservoir, 3073, VIC, Australia
Tel.: (61) 394745555
Web Site: http://www.beanalliance.com.au
Roasting Plant Coffee Mfr & Distr
N.A.I.C.S.: 311920

Boncafe China Limited   (1)
Room 610-611 6/F Wantong Building No 3002 Sungang East Road, Luohu District, Shenzhen, 518028, China
Tel.: (86) 75525120839
Tea & Coffee Retailer
N.A.I.C.S.: 424490

Boncafe Vietnam Company Limited   (1)
No 384/1 Nam Ky Khoi Nghia Street, Ward 8 District 3, Ho Chi Minh City, Vietnam
Tel.: (84) 838468046
Tea & Coffee Retailer
N.A.I.C.S.: 424490

Brodie Melrose Drysdale & Co. Ltd.   (1)
Newhailes Industrial Estate Newhailes Road, Musselburgh, EH21 6SY, United Kingdom
Tel.: (44) 1316534010
Web Site: http://www.brodies1867.co.uk
Tea & Coffee Retailer
N.A.I.C.S.: 424490
Ann Hameda *(Natl Mgr-Retail-Sls)*

Massimo Zanetti Beverage Iberia S.A.   (1)

AND PRIVATE COMPANIES

Rua das Fontainhas n 70 Venda Nova, 2700-391, Amadora, Portugal
Tel.: (351) 214968500
Roasting Plant Coffee Mfr & Distr
N.A.I.C.S.: 311920

Massimo Zanetti Beverage Vietnam Company Ltd. (1)
Lot B 6E11 CN My Phuoc Industrial Park 3, Ben Cat Ward, Ho Chi Minh City, Binh Duong, Vietnam
Tel.: (84) 6502221584
Roasting Plant Coffee Mfr & Distr
N.A.I.C.S.: 311920

PT Bon Cafe Indonesia (1)
JI RS Fatmawati no 15A Gandaria Selatan, Cilandak, Jakarta Selatan, 12420, Indonesia
Tel.: (62) 217502025
Web Site: http://www.boncafeindonesia.com
Tea & Coffee Retailer
N.A.I.C.S.: 424490

SEGAFREDO ZANETTI SR spol.S.r.o. (1)
Trnavska cesta 50, 821 02, Bratislava, Slovakia
Tel.: (421) 244632341
Tea & Coffee Retailer
N.A.I.C.S.: 424490

Segafredo Zanetti Austria GmbH (1)
Hallwanger Landestrasse 10 Bei, Hallwang, 5300, Salzburg, Austria
Tel.: (43) 662661382
Tea & Coffee Retailer
N.A.I.C.S.: 424490

Segafredo Zanetti Belgium S.A. (1)
Chemin de la Praye 7G, 1420, Braine-l'Alleud, Belgium
Tel.: (32) 25220116
Tea & Coffee Retailer
N.A.I.C.S.: 424490

Segafredo Zanetti CR spol. s.r.o. (1)
Beranovych 707, 199 00, Prague, Czech Republic
Tel.: (420) 221969730
Tea & Coffee Retailer
N.A.I.C.S.: 424490

Segafredo Zanetti Croatia d.o.o. (1)
Jankomir 25, 10000, Zagreb, Croatia
Tel.: (385) 13794882
Tea & Coffee Retailer
N.A.I.C.S.: 424490

Segafredo Zanetti Hungaria Kft. (1)
1143 Budapest Stefania Street 101-103 Stefania Park Office House, 1062, Budapest, Hungary
Tel.: (36) 14733470
Tea & Coffee Retailer
N.A.I.C.S.: 424490

Segafredo Zanetti Poland Sp. Z o.o. (1)
Ul Partyzantow 7, 32-700, Bochnia, Poland
Tel.: (48) 146154100
Tea & Coffee Retailer
N.A.I.C.S.: 424490

MASSIVIT 3D PRINTING TECHNOLOGIES LTD.
11 Pesakh Lev St, Lod, 712936, Israel
Tel.: (972) 86519486
Web Site:
  https://www.massivit3d.com
Year Founded: 2013
MSVT—(TAE)
Rev.: $15,001,000
Assets: $32,776,000
Liabilities: $7,586,000
Net Worth: $25,190,000
Earnings: ($9,748,000)
Fiscal Year-end: 06/30/23
Printing Technology Engineering Mfr
N.A.I.C.S.: 333248
Yaron Yecheskel (Chm)

Subsidiaries:

Massivit 3D Europe BV (1)
Kalkoven 51, 1820, Melsbroek, Belgium
Tel.: (32) 2 306 8584

Automotive Products Mfr
N.A.I.C.S.: 336390

MASSULLO MOTORS LTD
4493 Joyce Ave, Powell River, V8A 3A8, BC, Canada
Tel.: (604) 485-7981
Web Site:
  http://www.massullomotors.com
Rev.: $11,221,695
Emp.: 25
New & Used Car Dealers
N.A.I.C.S.: 441110
Fabio Bombardir (Mgr-Svc)

MASSY HOLDINGS LTD.
63 Park Street, Port of Spain, Trinidad & Tobago
Tel.: (868) 6253426   TT
Web Site:
  https://www.massygroup.com
Year Founded: 1974
MASSY—(TRI)
Rev.: $2,094,688,348
Assets: $2,293,243,124
Liabilities: $1,170,514,697
Net Worth: $1,122,728,426
Earnings: $119,958,092
Emp.: 13,000
Fiscal Year-end: 09/30/23
Holding Company
N.A.I.C.S.: 551112
Elliot Gervase Warner (Pres & CEO-Grp)

Subsidiaries:

Automotive Components Limited (1)
O'Meara Road, Arima, Trinidad & Tobago
Tel.: (868) 6424236
Web Site:
  https://partsonline.massymotorstt.com
Automobile Parts Distr
N.A.I.C.S.: 423120
Debra Alexander (Mgr-HR)

Cargo Handlers Limited (1)
Brandons, Saint Michael, Bridgetown, Barbados
Tel.: (246) 430 4824
Emp.: 3
Cargo Handling Services
N.A.I.C.S.: 488320
Arlin Kellman (Gen Mgr)

Demerara Oxygen Company Limited (1)
Old Road Eccles East Bank, Demerara, Guyana
Tel.: (592) 2332728
Web Site: http://www.massygroup.com
Emp.: 90
Liquefied Petroleum Gas Distr
N.A.I.C.S.: 424720

Gas Products Limited (1)
236 Windward Road, Kingston, Jamaica
Tel.: (876) 92873019
Web Site:
  http://www.gasproductslimited.com
Liquefied Petroleum Gas Distr
N.A.I.C.S.: 424720

Huggins Shipping & Customs Brokerage Limited (1)
11 Charles Street, Port of Spain, Trinidad & Tobago
Tel.: (868) 623 8881
Web Site: http://www.huggins-shipping.com
Emp.: 60
Logistics Consulting Servies
N.A.I.C.S.: 541614
Shanta Ramlal (Mgr-Fin & Admin)

Illuminat (Barbados) Limited (1)
Whitepark Road, PO Box 872E, Saint Michael, Barbados
Tel.: (246) 431 5600
Web Site: http://www.massytechonlgies.com
Emp.: 60
Information Technology Consulting Services
N.A.I.C.S.: 541512
Keith Cuseale (CEO)

Illuminat (Jamaica) Limited (1)
28 Balmoral Avenue, Kingston, Jamaica

Tel.: (876) 926 3490
Information Technology Consulting Services
N.A.I.C.S.: 541512

Illuminat (Trinidad & Tobago) Limited (1)
155 Tragarete Road, PO Box 544, Port of Spain, Trinidad & Tobago
Tel.: (868) 622.7753
Information Technology Consulting Services
N.A.I.C.S.: 541990

Magna Rewards (Jamaica) Limited (1)
9 Molynes Road, Kingston, Jamaica
Tel.: (876) 968 9872
Web Site: http://magnarewards.com
Loyalty Program Services
N.A.I.C.S.: 561499

Magna Rewards (Trinidad) Limited (1)
Unit 3 Building 3 Fernandes Industrial Compound Eastern Main Road, Laventille, Trinidad & Tobago
Tel.: (868) 624 4455
Emp.: 100
Loyalty Program Services
N.A.I.C.S.: 561499
Mike Parris (Dir-Prism Svcs)

Massy Distribution (Barbados) Ltd. (1)
Mighty Grynner Highway, PO Box 1345, Saint Michael, BB11000, Barbados
Tel.: (246) 4178700
Web Site: https://massydistribution.com
General Merchandise Distr
N.A.I.C.S.: 424490
David Affonso (Chm)

Massy Distribution (Guyana) Inc. (1)
D4 Starlite Square Montrose, Demerara, Guyana
Tel.: (592) 2208198
Web Site:
  https://www.massydistribution.com
Supermarket Services
N.A.I.C.S.: 445110

Massy Distribution (St. Lucia) Ltd. (1)
Beausejour, PO Box BW 378, Gros Islet, Saint Lucia
Tel.: (758) 4518835
Web Site:
  https://www.massydistribution.com
Warehouse Services
N.A.I.C.S.: 493110

Massy Energy (Trinidad) Ltd. (1)
Web Site: http://www.massyenergy.com
Gas Product Mfr
N.A.I.C.S.: 325120
Navendra Dass (Gen Mgr)

Massy Energy Colombia S.A.S. (1)
Cra 45A No 93 - 64, Bogota, Colombia
Tel.: (57) 3158458684
Gas Product Mfr
N.A.I.C.S.: 325120

Massy Finance GFC Limited (1)
61-63 Edward Street, Port of Spain, Trinidad & Tobago
Tel.: (868) 6253683
Rev.: $5,574,619
Assets: $68,680,326
Liabilities: $51,042,770
Net Worth: $17,637,556
Earnings: $1,318,301
Emp.: 55
Fiscal Year-end: 09/30/2018
Financial Management Services
N.A.I.C.S.: 523999
Gilbert Sankar (CEO)

Massy Gas Products (Guyana) Ltd. (1)
Old Road Eccles, Demerara, Guyana
Tel.: (592) 233272830
Web Site: https://massygasproductsgy.com
Gas Product Mfr
N.A.I.C.S.: 325120

Massy Gas Products (Jamaica) Limited (1)
236 Windward Rd, Kingston, Jamaica
Tel.: (876) 9287301
Web Site: https://www.gasprojamaica.com

MASSY HOLDINGS LTD.

Gas Product Mfr
N.A.I.C.S.: 325120
Rohan Ambersley (CEO)

Massy Gas Products (Trinidad) Limited (1)
North Sea DrivePoint Lisas Industrial Estate, Savonetta, Trinidad & Tobago
Tel.: (868) 6363517
Web Site: https://massygasproducts.com
Gas Product Distr
N.A.I.C.S.: 424720
Kailashnath Maharaj (CEO)

Massy Machinery Limited (1)
Uriah Butler Highway, Chaguanas, Trinidad & Tobago
Tel.: (868) 6655555
Construction Equipment Rental Services
N.A.I.C.S.: 532412

Massy Motors Ltd. (1)
Lady Young Road, PO Box 1298, 674-4200, Morvant, Trinidad & Tobago
Tel.: (868) 6744200
Web Site: http://massymotors.com
New & Used Car Dealer
N.A.I.C.S.: 441110
David Jardim (CEO)

Massy Properties (Barbados) Ltd. (1)
2nd Floor Thomas Daniel Building Hincks Street, Bridgetown, Barbados
Tel.: (246) 4295686
Web Site:
  https://www.massypropertiesbb.com
Property Management Services
N.A.I.C.S.: 531311
Samuel Paynter Musson (Founder)

Massy Properties (Trinidad) Ltd. (1)
61 - 63 Edward Street, Port of Spain, Trinidad & Tobago
Tel.: (868) 627 3561
Web Site: http://www.massyoproperties.com
Emp.: 25
Property & Facility Management Services
N.A.I.C.S.: 531312

Massy Stores (Barbados) Ltd. (1)
Sargeants Village Christ Church, Bridgetown, Barbados
Tel.: (246) 4340482
Web Site: https://massystoresbb.com
Supermarket Services
N.A.I.C.S.: 445110

Massy Stores (Guyana) Inc. (1)
Block M Amazonia Mall Providence, Demerara, Guyana
Tel.: (592) 2227227
Web Site: https://massystoresgy.com
Supermarket Services
N.A.I.C.S.: 445110
Elizabeth Mason Hopkinson (Mgr-Store)

Massy Stores (SLU) Ltd. (1)
Choc Estate, Castries, Saint Lucia
Tel.: (758) 4572000
Web Site: https://massystoresslu.com
Supermarket Services
N.A.I.C.S.: 445110
Catherine Pascal (Mgr-Store)

Massy Stores (SVG) Ltd. (1)
Tel.: (784) 4571603
Web Site: http://massystoressvg.com
Supermarket Services
N.A.I.C.S.: 445110
Derek Winford (CEO)

Massy United Insurance Ltd. (1)
Lower Broad Street, Bridgetown, Barbados
Tel.: (246) 4301900
Web Site:
  http://www.massyunitedinsurance.com
Financial Services
N.A.I.C.S.: 541611
Randy Graham (CEO)

Melville Shipping Limited (1)
18-20 London Street, Port of Spain, Trinidad & Tobago
Tel.: (868) 625 4977
Web Site: http://www.melvilleshipping.com
Emp.: 45
Marine Cargo Handling Services
N.A.I.C.S.: 488320

NMH Trading & Distribution (Jamaica) Limited (1)

MASSY HOLDINGS LTD.

Massy Holdings Ltd.—(Continued)

3 Carifta Avenue, Kingston, Jamaica
Tel.: (876) 923 8481
Pharmaceutical Products Distr
N.A.I.C.S.: 424210

Pereira & Company Limited (1)
88 Queen Street, PO Box 434, Port of Spain, Trinidad & Tobago
Tel.: (868) 6253486
Web Site: https://pereira-company-ltd.woodme.com
Emp.: 102
Office Equipment Distr
N.A.I.C.S.: 423420

Pres-T-Con Limited (1)
52-54 Tumpuna Road, Arima, Trinidad & Tobago
Tel.: (868) 6432367
Web Site: https://www.prestcon2021.com
Concrete Products Mfr
N.A.I.C.S.: 327390

Seawell Air Services Limited (1)
Grantley Adams International Airport, Christ. Church, BB17089, Barbados
Tel.: (246) 428 0973
Emp.: 165
Aircraft Ground Handling Services
N.A.I.C.S.: 488190
Irvine Griffith *(Gen Mgr)*

T. Geddes Grant (Barbados) Limited (1)
109 Marcus Garvey Dr, Kingston, 11, Jamaica
Tel.: (876) 923 7311
Web Site: http://www.tgeddesgrant.com
Logistics Consulting Servies
N.A.I.C.S.: 541614

Three Sixty Communications Limited (1)
63 Tragarete Road, Port of Spain, Trinidad & Tobago
Tel.: (868) 609 2667
Web Site: http://www.360communications.biz
Emp.: 12
Telecommunication Servicesb
N.A.I.C.S.: 517810

Tobago Services Limited (1)
Northside Road Rockly Vale, Scarborough, Trinidad & Tobago
Tel.: (868) 639 2496
Emp.: 18
New Car Dealers
N.A.I.C.S.: 441110
Peter Aagaard *(Gen Mgr)*

Trading and Distribution Limited (1)
39a Wrightson Road, Port of Spain, Trinidad & Tobago
Tel.: (868) 627 7482
Logistics Consulting Servies
N.A.I.C.S.: 541614

MAST ENERGY DEVELOPMENTS PLC

2nd Floor Ludgate Hill, London, EC4M 7JW, United Kingdom UK
Web Site: https://www.med.energy
Year Founded: 2020
MAST—(LSE)
Rev.: $4,406
Assets: $10,360,066
Liabilities: $5,133,192
Net Worth: $5,226,874
Earnings: ($1,912,970)
Fiscal Year-end: 12/31/21
Natural Gas Extraction Services
N.A.I.C.S.: 211130
Pieter Krugel *(CEO)*

MAST INVESTMENTS LTD.

Roseneath The Grange, PO Box 665, Saint Peter Port, GY1 3SJ, Guernsey
Tel.: (44) 20 7199 3800
Web Site:
http://www.mastinvestments.com
Financial Software & Investment Services
N.A.I.C.S.: 513210

Darrel Krowitz *(CEO)*

MAST-JAGERMEISTER SE

Jagermeisterstrasse 7-15, 38296, Wolfenbuttel, Germany
Tel.: (49) 5331 810
Web Site:
http://www.jaegermeister.de
Liquor Mfr
N.A.I.C.S.: 424820
Michael Volke *(Chm)*

Subsidiaries:

Sidney Frank Importing Co., Inc. (1)
20 Cedar St, New Rochelle, NY 10801 (100%)
Tel.: (914) 637-7300
Web Site: http://www.sidneyfrank.com
Wine & Distilled Beverages Mfr & Whslr
N.A.I.C.S.: 312130
Jeffrey B. Popkin *(CEO)*

MASTEK LTD.

106 SDF IV, Seepz Andheri East, Mumbai, 400 096, India
Tel.: (91) 2267224200 In
Web Site: https://www.mastek.com
523704—(BOM)
Rev.: $315,323,616
Assets: $380,677,080
Liabilities: $165,606,468
Net Worth: $215,070,612
Earnings: $37,604,724
Emp.: 1,367
Fiscal Year-end: 03/31/23
Information Technology Services
N.A.I.C.S.: 541512
Ashank Desai *(Vice Chm & Mng Dir)*

Subsidiaries:

MST Solutions, LLC (1)
2195 W Chandler Blvd Ste 100, Chandler, AZ 85224
Web Site: http://www.mstsolutions.com
Sales Range: $10-24.9 Million
Emp.: 211
Information Technology Services
N.A.I.C.S.: 541512
Thiru Thangarathinam *(Founder & CEO)*

MajescoMastek Canada Ltd (1)
55 University Ave Ste 1700, Toronto, M5J 2H7, ON, Canada
Tel.: (647) 351-3926
Business Management Services
N.A.I.C.S.: 541611

MajescoMastek Software, Inc. (1)
105 Fieldcrest Ave Ste 208, Edison, NJ 08837
Tel.: (732) 590-6400
Web Site: http://www.majescomastek.com
Sales Range: $25-49.9 Million
Emp.: 15
Information Technology Services
N.A.I.C.S.: 541512
William S. McCarter *(Pres)*

Mastek (UK) Limited (1)
Crown House 1a High Street, Theale, Reading, RG7 5AH, Berkshire, United Kingdom
Tel.: (44) 118 930 1400
Software Development Consulting Services
N.A.I.C.S.: 541512

Mastek Digital Inc. (1)
10 Carlson Court Suite 610, Toronto, M9W6L2, ON, Canada
Tel.: (416) 619-0797
Information Technology Services
N.A.I.C.S.: 541511

Mastek Enterprise Solutions Private Limited (1)
Mastek Millennium Centre Millenium Business Park, Navi Mumbai, 400710, India
Tel.: (91) 2267914646
Digital Engineering & Market Services
N.A.I.C.S.: 541330

Mastek MSC (Thailand) Co. Ltd (1)
Level 41 Room 4138 United Center Building 323 Silom Road, Bangrak, 10500, Bangkok, Thailand

Tel.: (66) 2 630 4747
Software Development & Consulting Services
N.A.I.C.S.: 541611

Mastek MSC Sdn. Bhd. (1)
L3-I-7 E 12B Enterprise 4 Technology Park Malaysia Lebhuraya Puchong, Sungai Besi Bukit Jalil, Kuala Lumpur, 57000, Malaysia
Tel.: (60) 389926600
Sales Range: $25-49.9 Million
Emp.: 50
Software Development & Consulting Services
N.A.I.C.S.: 541512
Sudhakar Ram *(Pres)*

MASTER CHEMICALS LIMITED

2528 Plot No 209 Atlanta Building Jamnalal Bajaj Marg, Nariman Point, Mumbai, 400021, Maharashtra, India
Tel.: (91) 2242931800 In
Web Site:
https://www.masterchemicals.in
Year Founded: 1980
506867—(BOM)
Assets: $6,870,137
Liabilities: $10,969,836
Net Worth: ($4,099,699)
Earnings: ($3,235,822)
Fiscal Year-end: 03/31/23
Metal Product Mfr & Distr
N.A.I.C.S.: 332999
Subash Raju Kanumuri *(CFO)*

MASTER COMPONENTS LIMITED

D-10/A & D-10/B MIDC Ambad, Nashik, 422010, Maharashtra, India
Tel.: (91) 2536604938
Year Founded: 1999
MASTER—(NSE)
Rev.: $2,542,078
Assets: $2,017,552
Liabilities: $600,533
Net Worth: $1,417,018
Earnings: $207,976
Emp.: 120
Fiscal Year-end: 03/31/23
Plastic Component Mfr
N.A.I.C.S.: 325211
Akshada Bhase *(Sec)*

MASTER DRILLING GROUP LIMITED

4 Bosman Street, PO Box 902, Fochville, 2515, South Africa
Tel.: (27) 187718100 ZA
Web Site:
https://www.masterdrilling.com
Year Founded: 1986
MDI—(JSE)
Rev.: $123,141,882
Assets: $265,138,231
Liabilities: $88,988,842
Net Worth: $176,149,389
Earnings: $3,207,167
Emp.: 1,771
Fiscal Year-end: 12/31/20
Mineral Exploration Services
N.A.I.C.S.: 213115
Daniel Pretorius *(Founder & CEO)*

Subsidiaries:

Master Drilling Brasil Ltda (1)
Rua Nossa Senhora de Lourdes 209 Olhos D Agua, Belo Horizonte, 30390-530, Minas Gerais, Brazil
Tel.: (55) 3132867877
Drilling Contractor Services
N.A.I.C.S.: 213111

Master Drilling Changzhou Co., Ltd. (1)
No 585 Huanghe West Road, Xinbei District, Changzhou, 213133, Jiangsu, China
Tel.: (86) 51986926610
Drilling Contractor Services
N.A.I.C.S.: 213111

INTERNATIONAL PUBLIC

Master Drilling Chile SA (1)
Tel.: (56) 227991900
Drilling Contractor Services
N.A.I.C.S.: 213111

Master Drilling Egypt Limited (1)
90 Street 157 First New Cairo, Cairo, Egypt
Tel.: (20) 1288127742
Mining Services
N.A.I.C.S.: 212311

Master Drilling Europe AB (1)
Strandgatan 22, 931 31, Skelleftea, Sweden
Tel.: (46) 910415800
Web Site: https://www.masterdrilling.se
Mining Services
N.A.I.C.S.: 212811

Master Drilling Mexico SA de CV (1)
Antigua Carretera Torreon-San Pedro 752-4 Norte Col Ejido Ana, 27410, Torreon, Coahuila, Mexico
Tel.: (52) 8717928055
Drilling Contractor Services
N.A.I.C.S.: 213111

Master Drilling USA LLC (1)
2600 S Shore Blvd Ste 300, League City, TX 77573
Tel.: (271) 877-1810
Drilling Contractor Services
N.A.I.C.S.: 213111

MASTER STYLE PUBLIC COMPANY LIMITED

99/19 Sukhothai Road, Dusit, Bangkok, 10300, Thailand
Tel.: (66) 21054370
Web Site: https://www.master-plc.com
Year Founded: 2012
MASTER—(THA)
Rev.: $56,737,038
Assets: $106,177,866
Liabilities: $18,859,413
Net Worth: $87,318,453
Earnings: $12,152,601
Emp.: 756
Fiscal Year-end: 12/31/23
Health Care Srvices
N.A.I.C.S.: 621610
Jedsada Chokdamrongsuk *(Chm)*

MASTER TRUST LIMITED

SCO 19 Master Chambers, Feroze Gandhi Market, Ludhiana, 140001, India
Tel.: (91) 8069991111
Web Site:
https://www.mastertrust.co.in
511768—(BOM)
Rev.: $30,684,654
Assets: $107,239,314
Liabilities: $72,355,374
Net Worth: $34,883,940
Earnings: $4,691,642
Emp.: 14
Fiscal Year-end: 03/31/21
Financial Investment Services
N.A.I.C.S.: 523999
Harjeet Singh Arora *(Founder & Mng Dir)*

MASTER-PACK GROUP BERHAD

51-21-A Menara BHL Bank Jalan Sultan Ahmad Shah, 10050, Penang, Malaysia
Tel.: (60) 42108833
Web Site: https://www.master.net.my
MASTER—(KLS)
Rev.: $36,239,878
Assets: $43,385,068
Liabilities: $6,532,216
Net Worth: $36,852,852
Earnings: $5,357,205
Emp.: 190
Fiscal Year-end: 12/31/23
Industry Paper Packaging Services
N.A.I.C.S.: 322130

AND PRIVATE COMPANIES

Peng Loon Lee *(Co-Sec)*

Subsidiaries:

Master-Pack Sarawak Sdn. Bhd. (1)
Lot 1270-1271 Section 66, KTLD Bintawa Industrial Estate Jalan Keluli, 93450, Kuching, Sarawak, Malaysia
Tel.: (60) 8 233 9851
Web Site: https://www.master.net.my
Sales Range: $25-49.9 Million
Emp.: 80
Cartons & Paperboards Mfr
N.A.I.C.S.: 322130
Vincent Ting *(Gen Mgr)*

Master-Pack Sdn. Bhd. (1)
1574 Jalan Bukit Panchor, Seberang Perai Selatan, 14300, Nibong Tebal, Penang, Malaysia
Tel.: (60) 4 593 1550
Web Site: http://www.hunza.com.my
Sales Range: $75-99.9 Million
Emp.: 140
Cartons & Paperboards Mfr
N.A.I.C.S.: 322130
Chuah Hung Seong *(Mgr-Mktg)*

MASTERFLEX SE

Willy-Brandt-Allee 300, 45891, Gelsenkirchen, Germany
Tel.: (49) 209970770   De
Web Site: https://www.masterflex.de
Year Founded: 1987
MZX—(MUN)
Rev.: $111,623,334
Assets: $103,421,580
Liabilities: $40,236,062
Net Worth: $63,185,519
Earnings: $8,819,921
Emp.: 662
Fiscal Year-end: 12/31/23
Connector & Hose Systems Mfr
N.A.I.C.S.: 326220
Georg van Hall *(Chm-Supervisory Bd)*

Subsidiaries:

Fleima-Plastic GmbH (1)
Neustadt 2, 69483, Wald-Michelbach, Germany
Tel.: (49) 6207924120
Web Site: http://www.fleima-plastic.de
Sales Range: $25-49.9 Million
Emp.: 50
Plastic Connector Mfr
N.A.I.C.S.: 326199

Flexmaster USA, Inc. (1)
5235 Ted St, Houston, TX 77040
Tel.: (713) 462-7694
Web Site: https://www.flexmasterusa.com
Sales Range: $25-49.9 Million
Emp.: 60
Flexible Duct Mfr
N.A.I.C.S.: 332999

Masterduct Brazil LTDA (1)
Rua dos Estados 18 - Villa Industrial, Santana de Parnaiba, 06516-310, SP, Brazil
Tel.: (55) 1141515100
Web Site: https://www.masterduct.com.br
Hose Mfr
N.A.I.C.S.: 326220

Masterduct Inc. (1)
5235 Ted St, Houston, TX 77040
Tel.: (713) 462-5779
Web Site: https://www.masterduct.com
Technical Hose Mfr
N.A.I.C.S.: 326220

Masterflex Asia Pte. Ltd. (1)
2 Venture Drive 11-15 Vision Exchange, Singapore, 608526, Singapore
Tel.: (65) 68974585
Web Site: https://www.masterflex.asia
Emp.: 5
Hose Mfr
N.A.I.C.S.: 326220

Masterflex Cesko s. r. o. (1)
Prumyslova 917, 34815, Plana, Czech Republic
Tel.: (420) 374629469
Web Site: https://www.masterflex.cz
Emp.: 40

Plastic Tank Mfr
N.A.I.C.S.: 332996

Masterflex Handelsgesellschaft mbH (1)
Tel.: (49) 209970770
Web Site: http://www.masterflexgroupe.com
Emp.: 500
Plastics Product Mfr
N.A.I.C.S.: 326199
Anreas Bastin *(CEO)*

Masterflex Hoses (Kunshan) Co. Ltd. (1)
No 395 Jiande Rd, Zhangpu, Kunshan, 215321, Jiangsu, China
Tel.: (86) 51257952886
Web Site: https://www.masterflex-china.cn
Hose Mfr
N.A.I.C.S.: 326220

Masterflex Mobility GmbH (1)
Doncaster Platz 5, D 45699, Herten, Germany
Tel.: (49) 2366 18183 0
Fuel Cell, Electric Bikes & Electric Drive Mfr
N.A.I.C.S.: 336991

Subsidiary (Domestic):

Clean Air Bike GmbH (2)
Saarstr 14, D12161, Berlin, Germany
Tel.: (49) 30850739290
Web Site: http://www.cleanairbike.com
Electric Bicycle Mfr
N.A.I.C.S.: 336991

Masterflex Brennstoffzellentechnik GmbH (2)
Doncaster Platz 5, D 45699, Herten, Germany
Tel.: (49) 2366 18183 0
Fuel Cell Technology Developer
N.A.I.C.S.: 335999

Velodrive GmbH (2)
Konrad Adenauer Str 9 13, D 45699, Herten, Germany
Tel.: (49) 23 66 609 60 10
Web Site: http://www.velodrive.de
Electric Drive Mfr
N.A.I.C.S.: 335999

Masterflex RUS OOO (1)
Revolution Highway 102-2 1, 195279, Saint Petersburg, Russia
Tel.: (7) 812 3095313
Web Site: http://www.masterflex.ru
Emp.: 25
Plastic Hose Mfr
N.A.I.C.S.: 326220

Masterflex S.A.R.L. (1)
ZA des 2B, Belignence, 01360, Paris, France
Tel.: (33) 478060202
Web Site: https://www.masterflex.fr
Emp.: 10
Connector & Hose Systems Mfr
N.A.I.C.S.: 326220

Masterflex Scandinavia AB (1)
Kabelgatan 13, 43437, Kungsbacka, Sweden
Tel.: (46) 30017170
Web Site: https://www.masterflex.se
Sales Range: $25-49.9 Million
Emp.: 3
Connector & Hose Systems Mfr
N.A.I.C.S.: 326220

Masterflex Technical Hoses, Ltd. (1)
Prince of Wales Business Park Units G H Vulcan St, Oldham, OL1 4ER, United Kingdom
Tel.: (44) 1616268066
Web Site: https://masterflex-hose.co.uk
Emp.: 10
Connector & Hose Systems Mfr
N.A.I.C.S.: 326220

Masterflex Vertriebs GmbH (1)
Willy-Brandt-Allee 300, 45891, Gelsenkirchen, Germany
Tel.: (49) 2099707735
Hose Material Mfr
N.A.I.C.S.: 327910

Subsidiary (Domestic):

APT Advanced Polymer Tubing GmbH (2)

Borsigstrasse 13-15, 41469, Neuss, Germany
Tel.: (49) 21371097370
Web Site: http://www.aptubing.de
Plastic Product Whslr
N.A.I.C.S.: 424610
Mark Becks *(Co-CEO)*

Matzen & Timm GmbH (1)
Nordportbogen 2, 22848, Norderstedt, Germany
Tel.: (49) 408532120
Web Site: https://www.matzen-timm.de
Sales Range: $25-49.9 Million
Emp.: 100
Mandrel-Fabricated Hoses, Bellows, Shaped Parts & Sleeves Mfr
N.A.I.C.S.: 326220

Novoplast Schlauchtechnik GmbH (1)
In den Langen Stucken 6, 38820, Halberstadt, Germany
Tel.: (49) 394168690
Web Site: https://www.schlauchtechnik.de
Sales Range: $25-49.9 Million
Emp.: 70
Extruded Thermoplastic Hose & Profile Mfr
N.A.I.C.S.: 326220
Torsten Gebhardt *(Mgr-Bus Dev)*

MASTERKOOL INTERNATIONAL PUBLIC COMPANY LIMITED

12/16-17 20 thetsaban songkhro Road, Lat Yao Chatuchak, Bangkok, 10900, Thailand
Tel.: (66) 29538800
Web Site:
https://www.masterkool.com
Year Founded: 2002
Rev.: $23,698,655
Assets: $16,027,620
Liabilities: $9,472,185
Net Worth: $6,555,435
Earnings: $1,029,988
Fiscal Year-end: 12/31/19
Electrical Fan Mfr
N.A.I.C.S.: 333413

MASTERLIFT

2899 Plymouth Drive, Oakville, L6H 6G7, ON, Canada
Tel.: (905) 823-5222
Web Site: http://www.masterlift.com
Year Founded: 1971
Rev.: $12,353,098
Emp.: 60
Forklift Equipment Distr
N.A.I.C.S.: 423830
Gary Wilson *(Pres)*

MASTERPLAST NYRT.

Arpad utca 1, Magyarorszag, Sarszentmihaly, Hungary
Tel.: (36) 22801300
Web Site:
https://www.masterplastgroup.com
Year Founded: 1997
MASTERPLAST—(BUD)
Rev.: $235,194,080
Assets: $220,068,099
Liabilities: $160,665,199
Net Worth: $59,402,900
Earnings: $19,480,911
Emp.: 1,379
Fiscal Year-end: 12/31/21
Construction Products Mfr & Distr
N.A.I.C.S.: 327331

Subsidiaries:

Master Plast S.r.o. (1)
Velkoulanska Cesta 1339, 925 21, Sladkovicovo, Slovakia
Tel.: (421) 918410504
Web Site: https://www.masterplast.sk
Building Material Mfr & Distr
N.A.I.C.S.: 327120

Masterplast Hungaria Kft. (1)

Arpad u 1/A, 8143, Sarszentmihaly, Hungary
Tel.: (36) 22801300
Web Site: https://www.masterplast.hu
Emp.: 62
Building Material Mfr & Distr
N.A.I.C.S.: 327120

Masterplast International Kft. (1)
Arpad u 1/A, 8143, Sarszentmihaly, Hungary
Tel.: (36) 22801300
Web Site:
https://www.masterplastinternational.com
Construction Material Mfr & Distr
N.A.I.C.S.: 333120

Masterplast Italia S.R.L. (1)
Via Edison 17, Sant Ilario d Enza Loc, 42049, Calerno, RE, Italy
Tel.: (39) 05221215942
Web Site: https://www.masterplastitalia.it
Building Material Mfr & Distr
N.A.I.C.S.: 327120

Masterplast Medical Kft. (1)
Arpad u 1, 8143, Sarszentmihaly, Hungary
Tel.: (36) 22801300
Web Site:
https://www.masterplastmedical.com
Construction Material Mfr & Distr
N.A.I.C.S.: 333120

Masterplast Nonwoven GmbH (1)
Daimlerstrasse 3, 06449, Aschersleben, Germany
Tel.: (49) 3473221280
Web Site:
https://www.masterplastnonwoven.com
Nonwoven Product Mfr & Distr
N.A.I.C.S.: 313230

Masterplast Romania S.R.L. (1)
Sos Borsului Nr 45, 410605, Oradea, Romania
Tel.: (40) 728062587
Web Site: https://www.masterplastsrl.ro
Building Material Mfr & Distr
N.A.I.C.S.: 327120

Masterplast Sp. z o.o. (1)
Ul Kolejowa 23, 62-090, Rokietnica, Poland
Tel.: (48) 618145262
Web Site: https://www.masterplastgroup.pl
Building Material Mfr & Distr
N.A.I.C.S.: 327120

Masterplast YU D.o.o. (1)
Ferenca Bodrogvarija 172, 24000, Subotica, Serbia
Tel.: (381) 24625825
Web Site: https://www.masterplast.rs
Emp.: 900
Construction Material Mfr & Distr
N.A.I.C.S.: 333120

Masterplast d.o.o. (1)
Trg Hrvatske Mladezi 2, 31304, Dubosevica, Croatia
Tel.: (385) 31736512
Web Site: https://www.masterplast.hr
Construction Material Mfr & Distr
N.A.I.C.S.: 333120

MASTERWORK GROUP CO.,LTD.

No 30 Yonghe Road Beichen Economic and Technological Development Area, Tianjin, 300400, China
Tel.: (86) 2226976666
Web Site:
https://www.mkmchina.com
Year Founded: 1995
300195—(CHIN)
Rev.: $225,931,485
Assets: $881,517,880
Liabilities: $482,078,520
Net Worth: $399,439,360
Earnings: $5,733,665
Fiscal Year-end: 12/31/23
Printing & Packaging Machinery Mfr
N.A.I.C.S.: 333248
Li Li *(Chm & Pres)*

MASTRAD SA

32 rue Cambrai, 75019, Paris, France
Tel.: (33) 149269600

MASTRAD SA

Mastrad SA—(Continued)
Web Site: https://en.mastrad-paris.fr
Year Founded: 1994
ALMAS—(EUR)
Sales Range: $1-9.9 Million
Kitchen Utensil Mfr & Distr
N.A.I.C.S.: 332215
Mathieu Lion (Co-Founder & Pres)

MASTRONARDI PRODUCE LIMITED
2100 Rd 4 E, Kingsville, N9Y 2E5, ON, Canada
Tel.: (519) 326-1491
Web Site:
http://www.sunsetproduce.com
Sales Range: $200-249.9 Million
Emp.: 300
Vegetable Canning Services
N.A.I.C.S.: 311421

MAT CRAIOVA
Bld Decebal Nr 111, 200746, Craiova, Dolj, Romania
Tel.: (40) 251439294
Web Site: http://www.matcraiova.ro
Year Founded: 1878
MTCR—(BUC)
Rev.: $1,694,665
Assets: $6,840,283
Liabilities: $1,581,629
Net Worth: $5,258,654
Earnings: ($1,135,872)
Emp.: 89
Fiscal Year-end: 12/31/20
Agricultural Machine Repairing Services
N.A.I.C.S.: 333111

MATACHEWAN CONSOLIDATED MINES, LIMITED
Richmond Adelaide Centre Suite 1910 130 Adelaide St West, Box 18, Toronto, M5H 3P5, ON, Canada
Tel.: (416) 364-2173 Ca
Year Founded: 1933
MCM.A—(TSXV)
Rev.: $364,439
Assets: $5,960,402
Liabilities: $1,203,563
Net Worth: $4,756,838
Earnings: $99,228
Fiscal Year-end: 12/31/23
Financial Investment Services
N.A.I.C.S.: 523999
Richard D. McCloskey (Pres & CEO)

MATALAN RETAIL LTD.
Perimeter Road, Liverpool, L33 7SZ, United Kingdom
Tel.: (44) 3330044444 UK
Web Site: http://www.matalan.co.uk
Year Founded: 1985
Sales Range: $1-4.9 Billion
Emp.: 13,901
Retailer of Clothing for Men Women & Children Mfr
N.A.I.C.S.: 315990
John Hargreaves (Founder)

Subsidiaries:

Wolsey Ltd (1)
Abbey Meadows Mills, Abbey Meadows, Leicester, LE4 5AD, Leicestershire, United Kingdom (100%)
Tel.: (44) 1162626755
Web Site: http://www.wolsey.com
Mfr of Clothing for Men, Women & Children
N.A.I.C.S.: 315250

MATANG BERHAD
Unit 39 02 Level 39 Menara Multi-Purpose Capital Square, No 8 Jalan Munshi Abdullah, 50100, Kuala Lumpur, Malaysia
Tel.: (60) 326930189 MY

Web Site:
https://www.matangbhd.com
MATANG—(KLS)
Rev.: $3,032,193
Assets: $53,303,526
Liabilities: $1,070,199
Net Worth: $52,233,326
Earnings: $555,946
Emp.: 114
Fiscal Year-end: 06/30/23
Investment Holding Services
N.A.I.C.S.: 551112
Hooi Mooi Lim (Co-Sec)

MATAS A/S
Rormosevej 1, DK-3450, Allerod, Denmark
Tel.: (45) 48165555
Web Site:
https://www.matasgroup.com
MATAS—(CSE)
Rev.: $649,621,623
Assets: $908,712,072
Liabilities: $422,089,103
Net Worth: $486,622,969
Earnings: $40,615,821
Emp.: 2,124
Fiscal Year-end: 03/31/23
Health & Beauty Retailer
N.A.I.C.S.: 456120
Anders T. Skole-Sorensen (CFO)

Subsidiaries:

Andersen & Christensen Aalborg ApS (1)
Nytorv 27, Aalborg, 9000, Denmark
Tel.: (45) 98 13 42 00
Cosmetic Product Distr
N.A.I.C.S.: 456120

MHolding 3 A/S (1)
Vendersgade 25, Fredericia, 7000, Denmark
Tel.: (45) 75 92 01 80
Cosmetic Product Distr
N.A.I.C.S.: 456120

MHolding 5 ApS (1)
Jernbanepladsen 39-41, Hovedstaden, Kongens Lyngby, 2800, Denmark
Tel.: (45) 45879600
Cosmetic Product Distr
N.A.I.C.S.: 456120

MHolding 6 ApS (1)
Vesterbrogade 19, Gilleleje, 3250, Frederiksborg, Denmark
Tel.: (45) 48300555
Cosmetic Product Distr
N.A.I.C.S.: 456120

Matas Sverige AB (1)
Sodra forstadsgatan 21, 211 43, Malmo, Sweden
Tel.: (46) 40 12 12 20
Cosmetic Product Distr
N.A.I.C.S.: 456120

Materialisten Solrod/Centret ApS (1)
Solrod Center 45, Solrod Strand, Denmark
Tel.: (45) 56 14 23 29
Cosmetic Product Distr
N.A.I.C.S.: 456120

Miild A/S (1)
Hvedemarken 12, 3520, Farum, Denmark
Tel.: (45) 70605444
Web Site: https://miild.dk
Beauty Care Services
N.A.I.C.S.: 812112

MATASSA INCORPORATED
5335 Walker Road, Windsor, N0R 1L0, ON, Canada
Tel.: (519) 737-1506
Web Site:
http://www.matassainc.com
Year Founded: 1963
Construction Services
N.A.I.C.S.: 236220

MATCHES, INC.

c/o Suzhou Jinkai Textile Co Ltd, Yongle Development Zone, Huanjing Town, Taicang, Jiangsu, China
Tel.: (86) 512 5381 8777 WY
Year Founded: 2007
MTXS—(OTCIQ)
Sales Range: $75-99.9 Million
Emp.: 359
Online Dating Services
N.A.I.C.S.: 812990
Jinle Chen (Chm & CEO)

MATCHING SERVICE JAPAN CO., LTD.
2102 Fujimi Iidabashi Grand Bloom 4th floor, Chiyoda-ku, Tokyo, 102-0071, Japan
Tel.: (81) 332397373
Web Site: https://www.jmsc.co.jp
6539—(TKS)
Rev.: $30,234,140
Assets: $76,034,830
Liabilities: $7,733,700
Net Worth: $68,301,130
Earnings: $7,495,740
Emp.: 189
Fiscal Year-end: 03/31/24
Employment Placement Services
N.A.I.C.S.: 561311
Takahiro Arimoto (Founder)

MATCO FINANCIAL INC.
400 407 - 8th Avenue SW, Calgary, T2P 1E5, AB, Canada
Tel.: (403) 539-5740 AB
Web Site:
http://www.matcofinancialinc.com
Year Founded: 2006
Emp.: 13
Asset Management & Investment Advisory Services
N.A.I.C.S.: 523940
Ronald Mathison (Chm)

Subsidiaries:

Matco Investments Ltd. (1)
400 407 8th Avenue SW, Calgary, T2P 1E5, AB, Canada
Tel.: (403) 261-4653
Investment Holding Company
N.A.I.C.S.: 551112
Ronald P. Mathison (Pres & CEO)

MATCOR-MATSU GROUP INC.
7299 E Danbro Cres, Mississauga, L5N 6P8, ON, Canada
Tel.: (905) 819-9900
Web Site: https://www.matcor-matsu.com
Year Founded: 1991
Sales Range: $100-124.9 Million
Emp.: 4,200
Metal Component Manufacturing & Fabrication Services
N.A.I.C.S.: 336390
Scott Mawhinney (CEO)

Subsidiaries:

MATCOR Matsu (1)
401 S Steele St, Ionia, MI 48846-9401
Tel.: (616) 527-4050
Web Site: http://www.matcor-matsu.com
Sales Range: $25-49.9 Million
Emp.: 25
Technology, Managerial Services & Products for the Automotive & Transportation Industries
N.A.I.C.S.: 336370
Tim Oeschger (VP-HR)

Subsidiary (Domestic):

Brown Corporation of Moberly Inc. (2)
1755 Rte DD, Moberly, MO 65270 (100%)
Tel.: (660) 263-5082
Sales Range: $50-74.9 Million
Automotive Stampings
N.A.I.C.S.: 336370

INTERNATIONAL PUBLIC

MATCOR Metal Fabrication, Inc. (1)
7275 East Danbro Cres, Mississauga, L5N 6P8, ON, Canada
Tel.: (905) 814-7479
Web Site: https://www.matcormetalfab.com
Fabricated Metal Products Mfr
N.A.I.C.S.: 332999

Plant (US):

MATCOR Metal Fabrication, Inc. (2)
1021 W Birchwood St, Morton, IL 61550-0429
Tel.: (309) 266-7176
Web Site: http://www.matcor-matsu.com
Fabricated Metal Products Mfr
N.A.I.C.S.: 332999

MATCOR Metal Fabrication, Inc. (2)
2400 W Laurel St, Independence, KS 67301
Tel.: (620) 331-8737
Fabricated Metal Products Mfr
N.A.I.C.S.: 332999
Chris Britt (Gen Mgr)

MMG Manufacturas de Saltillo, S. de R.L. de C.V. (1)
Blvd Industria Automotriz No 3052, Ramos Arizpe, 25900, Coahuila, Mexico
Tel.: (52) 844 866 9444
Automobile Parts Mfr & Distr
N.A.I.C.S.: 336390

Matcor Automotive (Michigan) Inc. (1)
401 S Steele St, Ionia, MI 48846
Tel.: (616) 527-4050
Web Site: http://www.matcor-matsu.com
Emp.: 15
Automobile Parts Mfr & Distr
N.A.I.C.S.: 336390

Plant (Domestic):

Matcor Automotive (Michigan) Inc. - Michigan Plant (2)
314 S Steele St, Ionia, MI 48846
Tel.: (616) 527-1600
Automobile Parts Mfr
N.A.I.C.S.: 336390

Matcor Automotive (Mogreen) Inc. (1)
1927 N Theobald St Ext, Greenville, MS 38703
Tel.: (662) 344-0990
Automobile Parts Mfr & Distr
N.A.I.C.S.: 336390

Matcor Automotive Inc. (1)
1620 Steeles Ave E, Brampton, L6T 1A5, ON, Canada
Tel.: (905) 793-4035
Automobile Parts Mfr & Distr
N.A.I.C.S.: 336390
Glenn Mader (Dir-IT)

Matcor Metal Fabrication (Welcome) Inc. (1)
835 Salem Rd, Welcome, NC 27295
Tel.: (336) 731-5700
Automobile Parts Mfr & Distr
N.A.I.C.S.: 336390
Mike Barker (Engr-Welding)

Matsu Alabama Inc. (1)
9650 Kellner Rd SW, Huntsville, AL 35824
Tel.: (256) 772-5888
Automobile Parts Mfr & Distr
N.A.I.C.S.: 336390
Nick Milonopoulos (Mgr-Matls)

Matsu Barrie Inc. (1)
120 Mapleview Drive West, Barrie, L4N 9H6, ON, Canada
Tel.: (705) 734-1688
Automobile Parts Mfr & Distr
N.A.I.C.S.: 336390
Brent Mactavish (Asst Mgr)

Matsu Manufacturing (Barrie) Inc. (1)
120 Mapleview Dr West, Barrie, L4N 9H6, ON, Canada
Tel.: (705) 734-1688
Metal Products Mfr
N.A.I.C.S.: 332999

Matsu Ohio Inc. (1)

AND PRIVATE COMPANIES — MATICA TECHNOLOGIES AG

228 E Morrison St, Edgerton, OH 43517
Tel.: (419) 298-2394
Emp.: 300
Automobile Parts Mfr & Distr
N.A.I.C.S.: 336390
Kevin Moore *(Mgr-Production)*

MATEN PETROLEUM JSC
105 Bakhtygerei Kulmanov Street, 60011, Atyrau, Kazakhstan
Tel.: (7) 7122766666
Web Site: https://matenpetroleum.kz
Year Founded: 2010
MATN—(KAZ)
Rev.: $356,342,786
Assets: $549,722,245
Liabilities: $264,112,924
Net Worth: $285,609,321
Earnings: $83,321,639
Fiscal Year-end: 12/31/23
Petroleum Lubricating Oil Mfr
N.A.I.C.S.: 324191
Tian Kejian *(Gen Dir)*

MATERIALISE NV
Technologielaan 15, 3001, Leuven, Belgium
Tel.: (32) 16396611 BE
Web Site: https://www.materialise.com
Year Founded: 1990
MTLS—(NASDAQ)
Rev.: $276,415,929
Assets: $428,048,780
Liabilities: $172,713,145
Net Worth: $255,335,636
Earnings: $7,225,340
Emp.: 2,437
Fiscal Year-end: 12/31/23
Additive Manufacturing, Software & Services
N.A.I.C.S.: 339999
Wilfried Vancraen *(Co-Founder & CEO)*

Subsidiaries:

ACTech GmbH (1)
Halsbrucker Strasse 51, 09599, Freiberg, Germany
Tel.: (49) 37311690
Prototype Castings Mfr
N.A.I.C.S.: 331523

Subsidiary (US):

ACTech North America Inc. (2)
4343 Concourse Dr Ste 350, Ann Arbor, MI 48108-8802
Tel.: (734) 913-0091
Web Site: http://www.rapidcastings.com
Die-Cast Motor Vehicle Prototype Components Engineering & Mfr
N.A.I.C.S.: 336390

Materialise Iberia N.V. (1)
C/ Lleida 30 E-08339 Vilassar de Dalt, Barcelona, Spain
Tel.: (34) 629706385
3D Printing Services
N.A.I.C.S.: 541511

Materialise USA, LLC (1)
44650 Helm Ct, Plymouth, MI 48170
Tel.: (734) 259-6445
Emp.: 60
Additive Manufacturing, Software & Services
N.A.I.C.S.: 339999

Materialise Ukraine LLC (1)
Raisy Okipnoi Str 8a, 02002, Kiev, Ukraine
Tel.: (380) 445945610
Software Development Services
N.A.I.C.S.: 541511

RapidFit N.V. (1)
Technologielaan 15, 3001, Leuven, Belgium (83.33%)
Tel.: (32) 16396285
Additive Manufacturing Software & Services
N.A.I.C.S.: 339999
Filip Dehing *(CEO)*

MATERIALS ANALYSIS TECHNOLOGY INC.
1F No 262 Taiyuan St, Hsinchu, Zhubei, Taiwan
Tel.: (886) 36116678
Year Founded: 2002
3587—(TPE)
Rev.: $108,900,152
Assets: $156,985,065
Liabilities: $52,203,137
Net Worth: $104,781,928
Earnings: $13,697,189
Fiscal Year-end: 12/31/20
Electronic Components Mfr
N.A.I.C.S.: 337126
Yong-Fen Hsieh *(Chm & CEO)*

MATERIALS PETROLEUM JOINT STOCK COMPANY
COMECO Building 549 Dien Bien Phu, Ward 3 District 3, Ho Chi Minh City, Vietnam
Tel.: (84) 2838321111
Web Site: https://www.comeco.vn
Year Founded: 1975
COM—(HOSE)
Rev.: $178,904,326
Assets: $20,196,075
Liabilities: $2,101,653
Net Worth: $18,094,422
Earnings: $1,419,670
Fiscal Year-end: 12/31/23
Oil & Gas Trading Services
N.A.I.C.S.: 424710
Le Tan Thuong *(Exec Dir)*

MATERIALS TECHNOLOGIES
Route de la Borde, 60360, Crevecoeur-le-Grand, France
Tel.: (33) 3 44 46 42 42
Web Site: http://www.materials-technologies.com
Sales Range: $25-49.9 Million
Emp.: 130
Holding Company
N.A.I.C.S.: 551112
Yann Jaubert *(Dir Gen)*

Subsidiaries:

Adler SA (1)
Route de la Borde, 60360, Crevecoeur-le-Grand, France
Tel.: (33) 344464242
Web Site: http://www.alfi-technologies.com
Sales Range: $25-49.9 Million
Emp.: 70
Industrial Machinery & Equipment Mfr
N.A.I.C.S.: 333998
Yann Jaubert *(Dir-Publ)*

FIMEC Technologies (1)
Les Camandieres, F 49110, Le Pin-en-Mauges, France
Tel.: (33) 2 41 71 38 38
Web Site: http://www.fimec-technologies.com
Emp.: 80
Conveying Equipment Mfr
N.A.I.C.S.: 333922
Jaubert Yann *(Mng Dir)*

MATERIAUX COUPAL INC
870 Boul Iberville, St Jean sur Richelieu, Montreal, J2X 4A6, QC, Canada
Tel.: (450) 347-2391
Web Site: http://www.coupal.com
Sales Range: $100-124.9 Million
Emp.: 500
Roof Trusses & Prefabricated Walls Mfr
N.A.I.C.S.: 321992
Francois Doucet *(Pres)*

MATEX A.D.
Jevrejska I-L4, 78000, Banja Luka, Bosnia & Herzegovina
Tel.: (387) 51 218 262
Web Site: http://www.matexbl.com
Year Founded: 1969
MATE—(BANJ)
Sales Range: Less than $1 Million
Emp.: 4
Real Estate Property Renting Services
N.A.I.C.S.: 531190
Milinko Klincov *(Chm-Mgmt Bd)*

MATEX INTERNATIONAL LIMITED
1003 Bukit Merah Central 01-10 Inno Centre, Singapore, 159836, Singapore
Tel.: (65) 68610028 SG
Web Site: https://www.matex.com.sg
Year Founded: 1989
M15—(CAT)
Rev.: $5,569,946
Assets: $16,206,923
Liabilities: $6,931,758
Net Worth: $9,275,165
Earnings: ($3,060,668)
Emp.: 72
Fiscal Year-end: 12/31/23
Dyestuffs & Auxiliaries Mfr
N.A.I.C.S.: 325130
Alex Pang Kee Tan *(CEO & Mng Dir)*

Subsidiaries:

Amly Chemicals Co., Ltd. (1)
No 22 Zhanan Road Formerly No 8 Zhanan South Road, Taixing Economic Development Zone, Taixing, 225404, Jiangsu, China
Tel.: (86) 52387679500
Auxiliary & Textile Chemical Mfr & Distr
N.A.I.C.S.: 325130
Khoo Hai Hing *(Mgr)*

Dedot Trading (Shanghai) Co., Ltd. (1)
29F T2 Jiahui Square Â No 2601 Xietu RoadÂ , Shanghai, 200030, China
Tel.: (86) 2154248133
Auxiliary & Textile Chemical Mfr & Distr
N.A.I.C.S.: 325130

Matex Chemicals (Taixing) Co., Ltd. (1)
No 1 Binjiang South Road Taixing Economic Development Zone, Taixing, 225404, Jiangsu, China
Tel.: (86) 52387679652
Auxiliary & Textile Chemical Mfr & Distr
N.A.I.C.S.: 325130

Shanghai Matex Chemicals Co., Ltd. (1)
Sales Range: $25-49.9 Million
Emp.: 100
Dyestuffs Mfr & Whslr
N.A.I.C.S.: 325130

Unimatex Sdn. Bhd. (1)
18 Jln Perindustrian Silibin 1 Kawasan Perindustrian Ringan Silibin, 30100, Perak, Darul Ridzuan, Malaysia
Tel.: (60) 55279989
Sales Range: $25-49.9 Million
Emp.: 20
Dyestuffs Mfr & Whslr
N.A.I.C.S.: 325130

MATHESON VALVES
4060 Poirier, Ville Saint Laurent, H4R 2A5, QC, Canada
Tel.: (514) 337-1106
Web Site: http://www.mvfltd.com
Year Founded: 1981
Rev.: $16,296,717
Emp.: 25
Industrial Supplies Merchant Whslr
N.A.I.C.S.: 423840
Art Matheson *(Pres)*

MATHEW EASOW RESEARCH SECURITIES LIMITED
Rajkamal Building 128 Rashbehari Avenue 1st Floor, Kolkata, 700 029, India
Tel.: (91) 3340660354
Web Site: https://www.mersl.co.in
511688—(BOM)
Rev.: $299,536
Assets: $6,230,351
Liabilities: $4,335,008
Net Worth: $1,895,343
Earnings: $15,029
Emp.: 3
Fiscal Year-end: 03/31/21
Financial Assistance Services
N.A.I.C.S.: 522291
Beda Nand Choudhary *(Exec Dir)*

MATHIOS REFRACTORY S.A.
5 Epidavrou St, 18233, Athens, Greece
Tel.: (30) 2104913502
Web Site: https://mathios.com
Year Founded: 1880
MATHIO—(ATH)
Sales Range: Less than $1 Million
Emp.: 214
Refractory Material Mfr & Distr
N.A.I.C.S.: 327120
Mathios Nikolaou Dimitrio *(CEO)*

Subsidiaries:

BAU MARKET S.A. (1)
17o km NEO Athens-Corinth, Aspropyrgos, Greece
Tel.: (30) 2105580120
Web Site: http://www.baumarket.gr
Emp.: 2
Refractory Material Mfr & Distr
N.A.I.C.S.: 327120

MATHIOS AD (1)
Entr 1 Fl 4 Apt 13 45 Duhovno, Vazrazhdane, Ruse, Bulgaria
Tel.: (359) 878186555
Refractory Material Distr
N.A.I.C.S.: 423840

MATHS FOR MORE SL
Plaza de Gala Placidia 1 Escalera A Planta 15, 08006, Barcelona, Spain
Tel.: (34) 932 804 805
Web Site: http://www.wiris.com
Year Founded: 1999
Educational Software Developer Services
N.A.I.C.S.: 513210

Subsidiaries:

Design Science, Inc. (1)
140 Pine Ave 4th Floor, Long Beach, CA 90802
Tel.: (562) 432-2920
Web Site: http://www.dessci.com
Sales Range: $1-9.9 Million
Emp.: 30
Developer, Marketer & Supporting Software for Scientific & Technical Communication
N.A.I.C.S.: 513210
Paul R. Topping *(Pres & CEO)*

MATICA ENTERPRISES INC.
44 Victoria St Suite 1102, Toronto, M5C 1Y2, ON, Canada
Tel.: (416) 304-9935 BC
Web Site: http://www.maticaenterprises.com
Year Founded: 2007
MMJFF—(OTCQB)
Medicinal Product Mfr
N.A.I.C.S.: 325411
Boris Ziger *(Chm & CEO)*

MATICA TECHNOLOGIES AG
Theresienhohe 30, 80339, Munich, Germany
Tel.: (49) 89 5108 5880
Web Site: http://www.maticatech.com
Sales Range: $25-49.9 Million
Emp.: 95
Security Identification Solutions
N.A.I.C.S.: 561621

MATICA TECHNOLOGIES AG

Matica Technologies AG—(Continued)
Sandro Camilleri (Chm-Exec Bd & CEO)
Subsidiaries:

Matica Fintec S.p.A. (1)
Vicolo Omar N 33, 28066, Galliate, Novara, Italy
Tel.: (39) 03211828601
Web Site: https://www.maticafintec.com
Rev.: $25,876,111
Assets: $33,348,994
Liabilities: $17,327,601
Net Worth: $16,021,393
Earnings: $2,424,975
Emp.: 73
Fiscal Year-end: 12/31/2023
Software Development Services
N.A.I.C.S.: 541511
Sandro Camilleri (Chm)

MATICHON PUBLIC COMPANY LIMITED
12 Tethsabannarueman Road Prachanivate 1 Ladyao, Chatu Chak, Bangkok, 10900, Thailand
Tel.: (66) 25890020
Web Site: https://www.matichon.co.th
Year Founded: 2006
MATI—(THA)
Rev.: $21,660,150
Assets: $55,249,306
Liabilities: $10,169,315
Net Worth: $45,079,992
Earnings: $892,107
Fiscal Year-end: 12/31/23
Newspaper Publishing Services
N.A.I.C.S.: 513110
Parnbua Boonparn (Pres, Mng Dir & Mng Dir)

MATIN SPINNING MILLS LTD.
Capita South Avenue Tower 6th Floor House 50 Road 03 Gulshan Avenue, Gulshan 1, Dhaka, 1212, Bangladesh
Tel.: (880) 25881773536
Web Site: https://www.matinspinning.com
Year Founded: 2002
MATINSPINN—(CHT)
Rev.: $66,988,603
Assets: $100,235,224
Liabilities: $46,846,777
Net Worth: $53,388,447
Earnings: $3,896,181
Emp.: 2,355
Fiscal Year-end: 06/30/23
Textile Products Mfr
N.A.I.C.S.: 314999
Abdul Wahed (Chm)

MATISSART NORD SA
Zone Industrielle N 1, Labourse, 62113, France
Tel.: (33) 3 21 61 47 47
Web Site: http://www.matissart.com
Newspaper Publishers
N.A.I.C.S.: 541810
Subsidiaries:

Berg Lacquer Co. (1)
3150 E Pico Blvd, Los Angeles, CA 90023-3683
Tel.: (323) 261-8114
Web Site: http://www.ellispaint.com
Paints, Varnishes & Supplies
N.A.I.C.S.: 424950
Sandra Berg (CEO & Dir)

Seropa Industries SASU (1)
204 Bd de la Grande Delle, BP 84, F-14200, Herouville-Saint-Clair, France
Tel.: (33) 2 31 47 23 00
Web Site: http://www.seropaindustries.fr
Commercial & Service Industry Machinery Mfr
N.A.I.C.S.: 333310

MATO GMBH & CO., KG
Benzstrasse 16-24, 63165, Muhlheim, Germany
Tel.: (49) 61089060
Web Site: http://www.en.mato.de
Year Founded: 1906
Rev.: $63,503,438
Emp.: 150
Conveyor Belts Mfr
N.A.I.C.S.: 333922
Subsidiaries:

MATO Australia Pty. Ltd. (1)
Unit 2 / 152 Mitchell Ave, PO Box 448, Kurri Kurri, 2327, NSW, Australia
Tel.: (61) 1300850795
Web Site: http://www.mato.com.au
Conveyor Belt Distr
N.A.I.C.S.: 423840
Michael Haviland (Mgr-Sls & Svcs)

MATO Belt Maintenance Equipment (Langfang) Co., Ltd. (1)
Building No 36 of Tianshan International bussiness park, Yanjiao Develepoment Zone, Sanhe, 65201, Hebei, China
Tel.: (86) 316575997686
Web Site: http://www.mato.com.cn
Conveyor Belt Distr
N.A.I.C.S.: 423840

MATO France S.A.R.L. (1)
Z A Rue du 19 Mars 1962, 57490, L'Hopital, France
Tel.: (33) 387821215
Conveyor Belt Distr
N.A.I.C.S.: 423840

MATO Iberica S.L.U. (1)
Pol Ind Mora Garay C/ Marie Curie 36-38, 33211, Gijon, Spain
Tel.: (34) 985328900
Conveyor Belt Distr
N.A.I.C.S.: 423840

MATO Industries Ltd. (1)
Unit 1 Philips Road Whitebirk Industrial Estate, Blackburn, BB1 5PG, Lancashire, United Kingdom
Tel.: (44) 1254387638
Web Site: http://www.matoindustries.co.uk
Belt Fastener Distr
N.A.I.C.S.: 423710

MATO Products Pty. Ltd (1)
28 Forge Road Spartan, Johannesburg, 1620, South Africa
Tel.: (27) 119236285
Web Site: http://www.multotec.com
Fabricated Metal Mfr
N.A.I.C.S.: 332996

MATO Suisse GmbH (1)
Industriestrasse 53, Postfach 127, 6034, Inwil, Switzerland
Tel.: (41) 414490990
Web Site: http://www.mato.ch
Conveyor Belt Distr
N.A.I.C.S.: 423840

MATOMY MEDIA GROUP LTD.
6 Hanechoshet St, Tel Aviv, 6971070, Israel
Tel.: (972) 77 360 6060
Web Site: http://www.matomy.com
Year Founded: 2007
MTMY—(LSE)
Sales Range: $1-9.9 Million
Emp.: 400
Advertising Services
N.A.I.C.S.: 541890
Ofer Druker (Founder)

MATRA KAUSHAL ENTERPRISE LIMITED
702 E Al Karim Trade Centre, Ranigunj, Secunderabad, 500 033, India
Tel.: (91) 4066260041
Web Site: http://www.unistab.com
Rev.: $54,538
Assets: $3,604,132
Liabilities: $546,109
Net Worth: $3,058,022
Earnings: $5,057
Fiscal Year-end: 03/31/18
Electrical Equipment Mfr & Whslr
N.A.I.C.S.: 334413
Ramesh Chandra Partani (Chm & Mng Dir)

MATRA REALTY LIMITED
OFFICE No 103-HUBTOWN SOLARIS TELI GALI OFF NS PHADKE MARG, SAIWADI ANDHERI EAST, Mumbai, 400069, Maharashtra, India
Tel.: (91) 2226392219
Web Site: http://matrarealty.in
Year Founded: 1985
Assets: $201,385
Liabilities: $216,233
Net Worth: ($14,848)
Earnings: $859,268
Fiscal Year-end: 03/31/18
Real Estate Manangement Services
N.A.I.C.S.: 531390

MATRATZEN CONCORD GMBH
Horbeller Str 11, 50858, Cologne, Germany
Tel.: (49) 2234 96 44 100
Web Site: http://www.matratzen-concord.de
Emp.: 100
Mattress Retailer
N.A.I.C.S.: 459999

MATRICELF
Golda Meir 3, Ness Ziona, Israel
Tel.: (972) 504057353
Web Site: https://www.matricelf.com
Year Founded: 2019
MTLF—(TAE)
Assets: $8,344,799
Liabilities: $939,356
Net Worth: $7,405,443
Earnings: ($3,821,246)
Fiscal Year-end: 12/31/23
Biotechnology Research Services
N.A.I.C.S.: 541714
Doron Birger (Chm)

MATRIKS FINANSAL TEKNOLOJILER A.S.
Izzetpasa Mahallesi Yeni Yol Cad No 3 Nurol Tower Kat 18 D 125, Ofis 1808 Sisli, 34381, Istanbul, Turkiye
Tel.: (90) 2123545454
Web Site: https://www.matriksdata.com
Year Founded: 2003
MTRKS—(IST)
Rev.: $20,145,529
Assets: $12,345,715
Liabilities: $2,587,010
Net Worth: $9,758,705
Earnings: $3,323,205
Fiscal Year-end: 12/31/23
Software Development Services
N.A.I.C.S.: 541511
Reyha Gulerman (Chm)

MATRIMONY.COM LIMITED
No 94 TVH Beliciaa Towers Tower 2 5th Floor MRC Nagar, Raja Annamalaipuram, Chennai, 600 028, Tamil Nadu, India
Tel.: (91) 8144998877
Web Site: https://www.matrimony.com
Year Founded: 1997
MATRIMONY—(NSE)
Rev.: $53,963,036
Assets: $61,790,301
Liabilities: $25,850,261
Net Worth: $35,940,041
Earnings: $5,565,637
Emp.: 3,505
Fiscal Year-end: 03/31/21
Professional Dating Services
N.A.I.C.S.: 812990

INTERNATIONAL PUBLIC

Chandrasekar R. (CTO & Chief Infrastructure Officer)
Subsidiaries:

Bangladeshi Matrimony Private Limited (1)
House 15/A 1st Floor Road 5 Front Road 8 Block F Banani, Dhaka, 1213, Bangladesh
Tel.: (880) 18003000222
Web Site: https://www.bangladeshimatrimony.com
Marriage Matchmaking Services
N.A.I.C.S.: 812990

Consim Info USA Inc. (1)
220 Davidson Ave Ste 315, Somerset, NJ 08873-4148
Tel.: (732) 302-5806
Web Site: https://www.consim.com
Matrimony Services
N.A.I.C.S.: 624190

Matrimony DMCC (1)
No 903 Fortune Executive Tower Jumeirah Lake Towers, Dubai, United Arab Emirates
Tel.: (971) 45896090
Matrimony Services
N.A.I.C.S.: 624190

MATRITA SA
Nicolae Balcescu Street Number 5, Odorheiu Secuiesc, 535600, Harghita, Romania
Tel.: (40) 266 213550
Web Site: http://www.matrita.ro
Year Founded: 1975
Sales Range: $1-9.9 Million
Emp.: 285
Iron Casting Services
N.A.I.C.S.: 331511

MATRIX ASSET MANAGEMENT INC.
2600-1055 West Georgia Street, PO Box 11170 Royal Centre, Vancouver, V6E 3R5, BC, Canada
Tel.: (604) 895-7274
Web Site: http://www.matrixasset.ca
Sales Range: $10-24.9 Million
Emp.: 24
Asset & Wealth Management Services
N.A.I.C.S.: 523150
David Levi (Pres & CEO)
Subsidiaries:

ENSIS Management Inc. (1)
1120 - 200 Graham Ave, Winnipeg, R3C 4L5, MB, Canada
Tel.: (204) 949-3700
Sales Range: $25-49.9 Million
Emp.: 3
Asset Management Services
N.A.I.C.S.: 541618

GrowthWorks Ltd. (1)
Box 11170 Royal Centre 2600 1055 West Georgia Street, Vancouver, V6E 3R5, BC, Canada
Tel.: (604) 633-1418
Web Site: http://www.growthworks.ca
Venture Capital Management Services
N.A.I.C.S.: 523999

Subsidiary (Domestic):

GrowthWorks Atlantic Ltd. (2)
77 Westmorland St Ste 370, Fredericton, E3B 6Z3, NB, Canada
Tel.: (506) 444-0091
Investment Management Service
N.A.I.C.S.: 523999

GrowthWorks Capital Ltd. (2)
130 Kings St W Ste 2200, Toronto, M5X 1E3, ON, Canada
Tel.: (416) 934-7777
Web Site: http://www.growthworks.ca
Sales Range: $25-49.9 Million
Investment Management Service
N.A.I.C.S.: 523999

GrowthWorks WV Management Ltd. (2)

AND PRIVATE COMPANIES

MATSUKIYOCOCOKARA & CO.

130 King St W Ste 2200, PO Box 422, Toronto, M5X 1E3, ON, Canada
Tel.: (416) 934-7777
Web Site: http://www.growthworks.ca
Sales Range: $25-49.9 Million
Investment Management Service
N.A.I.C.S.: 523999

MATRIX COMPOSITES & ENGINEERING LIMITED
150 Quill Way, Henderson, 6166, WA, Australia
Tel.: (61) 894121200
Web Site: https://www.matrixengineered.com
Year Founded: 1999
MCE—(ASX)
Rev.: $56,782,852
Assets: $63,535,657
Liabilities: $42,825,855
Net Worth: $20,709,802
Earnings: $2,434,562
Emp.: 200
Fiscal Year-end: 06/30/24
Engineered Product Solutions, Composite Materials, Syntactic Foam Technology, Engineering & Elastomers;Precision & Custom Heavy Engineering & Equipment Solutions
N.A.I.C.S.: 325998
Aaron Paul Begley (CEO & Mng Dir)

Subsidiaries:

Begley International (1)
185 Camboon Rd, Malaga, 6090, WA, Australia
Tel.: (61) 92493300
Web Site: http://www.begley.com.au
Sales Range: $25-49.9 Million
Emp.: 74
Offshore Oil & Gas Machinery Mfr
N.A.I.C.S.: 333132

MATRIX CONCEPTS HOLDINGS BERHAD
Wisma Matrix No 57 Jalan Tun Dr Ismail, 70200, Seremban, Negeri Sembilan D K, Malaysia
Tel.: (60) 67642688
Web Site: http://mchb.com.my
Year Founded: 1997
MATRIX—(KLS)
Rev.: $235,567,831
Assets: $558,395,344
Liabilities: $137,685,291
Net Worth: $420,710,053
Earnings: $42,921,693
Emp.: 923
Fiscal Year-end: 03/31/23
Property Developer
N.A.I.C.S.: 237210
Mohamad Haslah Mohamad Amin (Chm)

Subsidiaries:

Matrix Concepts Sdn. Bhd. (1)
69 Impiana Avenue Jalan Seri Impian 1/2 Taman Seri Impian, Kluang, 86000, Johor, Malaysia
Tel.: (60) 77742688
Emp.: 13
Real Estate Development Services
N.A.I.C.S.: 531390
Tanseng Heng (Gen Mgr)

MATRIX DESIGN CO., LTD.
Room 1701 1702 17th Floor Rongchao Building No 4036 Jintian Road, Lianhua St Futian Center District Fuzhong Community Futian District, Shenzhen, 518045, Guangdong, China
Tel.: (86) 75583222578
Web Site: https://www.matrixdesign.cn
Year Founded: 2010
301365—(CHIN)
Rev.: $111,546,396
Assets: $281,509,020
Liabilities: $33,829,380
Net Worth: $247,679,640
Earnings: $23,191,272
Fiscal Year-end: 12/31/22
Architectural Services
N.A.I.C.S.: 541310
Guan Wang (Chm)

MATRIX GROUP (AUSTRALIA) PTY. LTD.
36 Bryants Rd, PO Box 3220, Loganholme, 4129, QLD, Australia
Tel.: (61) 738015999 AU
Web Site: http://www.matrix.com.au
Sales Range: $200-249.9 Million
Emp.: 180
Operative Builders & Construction Services
N.A.I.C.S.: 236117
John Davies (Mng Dir)

MATRIX HOLDINGS LIMITED
Suite 223-231 Tsimshatsui Centre 66 Mody Road Tsimshatsui East, Kowloon, China (Hong Kong)
Tel.: (852) 22681268
Web Site: http://www.matrix.hk.com
1005—(HKG)
Rev.: $125,726,985
Assets: $161,060,678
Liabilities: $29,000,640
Net Worth: $132,060,038
Earnings: $233,453
Emp.: 3,275
Fiscal Year-end: 12/31/22
Gifts & Novelties Mfr
N.A.I.C.S.: 332999
Sui Chuen Yu (Exec Dir)

Subsidiaries:

Fern-Howard Limited (1)
2 Newman Lane, Alton, GU34 2QR, Hampshire, United Kingdom
Tel.: (44) 1420470400
Web Site: http://www.fernhoward.com
Lighting Mfr
N.A.I.C.S.: 335139
Elke Hahmann (Mgr-Mktg)

Funrise, Inc. (1)
7811 Lemona Ave, Van Nuys, CA 91405
Tel.: (818) 883-2400
Web Site: http://www.funrise.com
Sales Range: $1-9.9 Million
Toy Mfr & Distr
N.A.I.C.S.: 339930
King Cheung Cheng (CEO)

Subsidiary (Domestic):

Funrise Distribution Company (2)
1450 E Mission Blvd, Ontario, CA 91761-2145
Tel.: (909) 923-8037
Toy Distr
N.A.I.C.S.: 423920

Subsidiary (Non-US):

Funrise International Limited (2)
1 Featherstone Rd, Milton Keynes, MK12 5TH, Buckinghamshire, United Kingdom
Tel.: (44) 1908555640
Web Site: http://www.funrise.com
Emp.: 7
Toy Distr
N.A.I.C.S.: 423920
James Dixon (CEO)

Matrix Manufacturing Vietnam Company Limited (1)
Hoa Khanh Industrial Area, Lien Chieu District, Da Nang, Vietnam
Tel.: (84) 511734440
Toy Mfr
N.A.I.C.S.: 339930

Viribright Lighting Inc. (1)
355 E Rincon St Ste 219, Corona, CA 92879
Web Site: http://www.viribright.us
Lighting Product Mfr & Distr
N.A.I.C.S.: 335139

MATSA RESOURCES LIMITED
Suite 11 139 Newcastle Street, Perth, 6000, WA, Australia
Tel.: (61) 892303555 AU
Web Site: https://www.matsa.com.au
MAT—(ASX)
Rev.: $490,796
Assets: $15,542,455
Liabilities: $6,817,012
Net Worth: $8,725,443
Earnings: ($3,073,842)
Emp.: 10
Fiscal Year-end: 06/30/24
Mineral Exploration Services
N.A.I.C.S.: 213114
Paul Poli (Founder & Chm)

MATSUDA SANGYO CO., LTD.
Shinjuku Nomura Building 6th Fl 1-26-2 Nishishinjuku, Shinjuku-ku, Tokyo, 163-0558, Japan
Tel.: (81) 353810001
Web Site: http://www.matsuda-sangyo.co.jp
7456—(TKS)
Rev.: $2,383,083,470
Assets: $984,473,570
Liabilities: $380,491,430
Net Worth: $603,982,140
Earnings: $48,160,460
Emp.: 1,624
Fiscal Year-end: 03/31/24
Metal Recycling
N.A.I.C.S.: 325998
Masayuki Waki (Exec Officer)

Subsidiaries:

Hokkaido Aoki Kagaku Co., Ltd. (1)
10-6-17 N Heiwa Dori, Shiroishi-ku, Sapporo, 003-0029, Hokkaido, Japan
Tel.: (81) 118626161
Metal Refining Services
N.A.I.C.S.: 331410

MATSUDA SANGYO Co. Ltd. - Iruma Plant (1)
3-5-10 Sayamadai, Iruma, 358-0033, Saitama, Japan
Tel.: (81) 429345672
Web Site: http://www.matsuda-sangyo.co.jp
Precious Metals Refining
N.A.I.C.S.: 331410

MATSUDA SANGYO Co. Ltd. - Iruma Plant II (1)
55-1 Higashisayama, Negishi, Iruma, 358-0034, Saitama, Japan
Tel.: (81) 429345767
Recycling Services
N.A.I.C.S.: 325612

MATSUDA SANGYO Co. Ltd. - Musashi Factory (1)
189-1 Sayamagahara, Iruma, 358-0032, Saitama, Japan
Tel.: (81) 429345357
Web Site: http://www.matsuda-sangyo.co.jp
Recycling Services
N.A.I.C.S.: 423920

MATSUDA SANGYO Co. Ltd. - Urban Recycle Business Dept. (1)
Shinjuku Nomura Bldg 6th Fl 1-26-2 Nishi-Shinjuku, Shinjuku-ku, Tokyo, 163-0558, Japan
Tel.: (81) 359095101
Web Site: http://www.matsuda-sangyo.co.jp
Recycling Services
N.A.I.C.S.: 562111

Matsuda Ecology Co., Ltd. (1)
Shinjuku Nomura Building 6th Fl 1-26-2 Nishi Shinjuku, Shinjuku-ku, Tokyo, 163-0558, Japan
Tel.: (81) 353229080
Web Site: http://www.matsuda-sangyo.co.jp
Convenience Food Stores
N.A.I.C.S.: 445131

Matsuda Ryutsu Co., Ltd. (1)
Shinjuku Nomura Building 6th Fl 1-26-2 Nishi Shinjuku, Shinjuku-ku, Tokyo, 163-0558, Japan
Tel.: (81) 333456025
Web Site: http://www.matsuda-sangyo.co.jp
Sales Range: $200-249.9 Million
Convenience Food Stores
N.A.I.C.S.: 445131

Matsuda Sangyo (Philippines) Corporation (1)
Lot 1 Block4 People's Technology Complex, Special Economic Zone, Carmona, 4116, Cavite, Philippines
Tel.: (63) 464302851
Web Site: http://www.matsuda-sangyo.co.jp
Sales Range: $25-49.9 Million
Emp.: 11
Scrap Materials Whslr
N.A.I.C.S.: 423390
Yoshiaki Matsuda (Pres)

Matsuda Sangyo (Singapore) Pte. Ltd. (1)
24 Techpark Crescent, Singapore, 638108, Singapore
Tel.: (65) 68611937
Web Site: http://www.matsuda-sangyo.co.jp
Sales Range: $25-49.9 Million
Metal Refineries
N.A.I.C.S.: 331410

Matsuda Sangyo (Thailand) Co., Ltd. (1)
Hitech Industrial Estate 148 Moo 1, Banlen, Bangpa-in, 13160, Ayutthaya, Thailand
Tel.: (66) 35729001
Web Site: http://www.matsuda-sangyothailand.com
Sales Range: $25-49.9 Million
Emp.: 60
Plastic Recycling Services
N.A.I.C.S.: 326199

Z.E.R.O. - Japan Co., Ltd. (1)
6F Shinjuku Nomura Building 1-26-2, Shinjuku-ku Nishi-Shinjuku, Tokyo, 163-0558, Japan
Tel.: (81) 359095106
Web Site: http://www.zero-japan.co.jp
Sales Range: $25-49.9 Million
Emp.: 15
Recyclable Devices Mfr & Sales
N.A.I.C.S.: 325991
Tetsuya Anzai (Pres)

MATSUI CONSTRUCTION CO., LTD.
1-17-22 Shinkawa, Chuo-Ku, Tokyo, 104-8281, Japan
Tel.: (81) 335531151
Web Site: https://www.matsui-ken.co.jp
Year Founded: 1939
1810—(TKS)
Rev.: $640,965,090
Assets: $512,698,040
Liabilities: $197,936,450
Net Worth: $314,761,590
Earnings: $7,674,210
Emp.: 767
Fiscal Year-end: 03/31/24
Construction Contractor Services
N.A.I.C.S.: 236116
Takahiro Matsui (Pres, CEO & Mng Dir)

MATSUI SECURITIES CO., LTD.
1-4 Kojimachi, Chiyoda-ku, Tokyo, 1028516, Japan
Tel.: (81) 352160606
Web Site: https://www.matsui.co.jp
Year Founded: 1918
8628—(TKS)
Sales Range: $200-249.9 Million
Emp.: 154
Securities Brokerage Services
N.A.I.C.S.: 523150
Michio Matsui (Pres & CEO)

MATSUKIYOCOCOKARA & CO.
7F MK Ochanomizu Bldg 1-8-2 Yushima, Bunkyo-ku, Tokyo, 113-0034, Chiba, Japan

MATSUKIYOCOCOKARA & CO.

MatsukiyoCocokara & Co.—(Continued)
Tel.: (81) 368450005
Web Site: https://www.matsukiyococokara.com
Year Founded: 2007
3088—(TKS)
Rev.: $6,758,929,910
Assets: $4,790,577,670
Liabilities: $1,385,264,310
Net Worth: $3,405,313,360
Earnings: $346,013,670
Fiscal Year-end: 03/31/24
Holding Company; Retail Drug Stores, Supermarkets, Home Centers & Other Stores Operator
N.A.I.C.S.: 551112
Namio Matsumoto (Chm)

Subsidiaries:

DARUMA DRUG STORE CO., LTD (1)
Sendai MKD Bld 3F 2-2-24 Chuo Aoba-ku, Sendai, 980-0021, Miyagi, Japan
Tel.: (81) 22 722 2574
Web Site: http://www.darumadrug.co.jp
Pharmaceutical Drug Retailer
N.A.I.C.S.: 456110
Keiichi Okano (Pres)

ITAYAMAMEDICO Co., Ltd. (1)
643-1 Sakurai-cho, Kofu, Yamanashi, Japan
Tel.: (81) 55 222 3456
Pharmaceutical Drug Retailer
N.A.I.C.S.: 456110
Kazumasa Itayama (Pres)

Koyo Yakuhin Co., Ltd. (1)
1 7 17 Katsuyama Kita, Ikuno-ku, Osaka, 544 0033, Japan
Tel.: (81) 6 6731 1351
Web Site: http://www.matsumotokiyoshi-hd.co.jp
Pharmaceutical Drug Mfr & Distr
N.A.I.C.S.: 456110

MatsumotoKiyoshi Co., Ltd. (1)
9-1 Shinmatsudohigashi, Matsudo, 270-8501, Chiba, Japan
Tel.: (81) 473445111
Web Site: http://www.matsukiyo.co.jp
Sales Range: $1-4.9 Billion
Emp.: 3,203
Retail Drugstores, Supermarkets, Home Centers & Other Stores Operator
N.A.I.C.S.: 456110
Nankai Matsumoto (Chm)

Matsumotokiyoshi Chu-Shikoku Co., Ltd. (1)
1-20-32 Fukutomi-Nishi, Minami-ku, Okayama, 702-8031, Japan
Tel.: (81) 862654161
Web Site: http://www.mkc.matsukiyo.co.jp
Pharmaceutical Drug Retailer
N.A.I.C.S.: 456110
Takashi Mori (Pres)

Matsumotokiyoshi East Co., Ltd. (1)
MKD Building 3rd Floor 2-2-24 Chuo, Aoba-ku, Sendai, 980-0021, Miyagi Prefecture, Japan
Tel.: (81) 222681780
Pharmacies & Drug Retailer
N.A.I.C.S.: 456110

Matsumotokiyoshi Kou-Shin-Etsu Co., Ltd. (1)
1393-3 Tsurugamidori-cho, Nagano, 380-0813, Japan
Tel.: (81) 262298490
Web Site: http://www.mk-koushinetsu.co.jp
Pharmaceutical Drug Retailer
N.A.I.C.S.: 456110

Matsumotokiyoshi Kyusyu Co., Ltd. (1)
6-24-20 Iikura, Sawara-ku, Fukuoka, 814-0161, Japan
Tel.: (81) 928711991
Web Site: http://www.mkq.matsukiyo.co.jp
Pharmaceutical Drug Retailer
N.A.I.C.S.: 456110

Matsumotokiyoshi Pharmacies Co., Ltd. (1)
9-1 Shinmatsudo-Higashi, Matsudo, 270-8501, Chiba, Japan
Tel.: (81) 473445150
Pharmaceutical Drug Retailer
N.A.I.C.S.: 456110
Tomiharu Otake (Pres)

Mogi Pharmaceutical Co., Ltd. (1)
4F 3-9-7 Nihonbashi Honmachi, Chuo-ku, Tokyo, 103-0023, Japan
Tel.: (81) 362649291
Web Site: http://www.mogiph.co.jp
Pharmaceutical Drug Retailer
N.A.I.C.S.: 456110

PAPASU Co., Ltd. (1)
4-8-3 Yokokawa, Sumida, Tokyo, 130-0003, Japan
Tel.: (81) 3 5610 8811
Web Site: http://www.papasu.co.jp
Pharmaceutical Drug Retailer
N.A.I.C.S.: 456110
Ryo Kouchi (Pres)

Sugiura Co., Ltd. (1)
170 Kawahigashi Wadacho, Konan, 483-8014, Japan
Tel.: (81) 587 54 1938
Web Site: http://www.s-healthbank.jp
Pharmaceutical Drug Retailer
N.A.I.C.S.: 456110

cocokara fine Inc. (1)
Innotech Bldg 3-17-6 Shin-Yokohama, Kohoku-ku, Yokohama, 222-0033, Kanagawa-ken, Japan
Tel.: (81) 455485929
Web Site: http://corp.cocokarafine.co.jp
Rev.: $3,629,064,540
Assets: $1,564,906,620
Liabilities: $703,472,760
Net Worth: $861,433,860
Earnings: $82,971,480
Fiscal Year-end: 03/31/2019
Holding Company; Pharmacy & Drug Store Owner & Operator; Nursing & Home Health Care Services; Online Healthcare Products Retailer
N.A.I.C.S.: 551112
Atsushi Tsukamoto (Pres)

Subsidiary (Domestic):

FINECARE Inc. (2)
2F 2-2-1 Bunzo, Minami-ku, Saitama, 336-0025, Saitama Prefecture, Japan
Tel.: (81) 487106750
Web Site: https://www.finecare.co.jp
Emp.: 602
Nursing & Home Health Care Services
N.A.I.C.S.: 621610
Kazushi Tsunefuji (Pres)

cocokara Healthcare Inc. (2)
Innotech Bldg 3-17-6 Shin-Yokohama, Kohoku-ku, Yokohama, 222-0033, Kanagawa, Japan
Tel.: (81) 45 548 5996
Web Site: http://www.cocokarafine.co.jp
Drugstore & Pharmacy Operator
N.A.I.C.S.: 456110

cocokarafine OEC Co., Ltd. (2)
Innotech Bldg 3-17-6 Shin-Yokohama, Kohoku-ku, Yokohama, 222-0033, Kanagawa, Japan
Tel.: (81) 45 548 5992
Web Site: http://www.shop.cocokarafine.co.jp
Online Healthcare Products Retailer
N.A.I.C.S.: 456110

MATSUMOTO INC.

1-2-1 Yashiro-no-ki, Moji-ku, Kitakyushu, 800-8555, Fukuoka, Japan
Tel.: (81) 933710298
Web Site: https://www.matsumoto-inc.co.jp
Year Founded: 1932
79010—(TKS)
Sales Range: Less than $1 Million
Commercial Printing Product Mfr
N.A.I.C.S.: 333248
Keizaburo Matsumoto (Pres & CEO)

MATSUMOTO YUSHI-SEIYAKU CO.,LTD

1-3 2-chome Shibukawa-cho, Yao-shi, Osaka, 581-0075, Japan
Tel.: (81) 729911001
Web Site: https://www.mtmtys.co.jp
4365—(TKS)
Rev.: $274,486,860
Assets: $591,674,320
Liabilities: $93,696,750
Net Worth: $497,977,570
Earnings: $49,601,440
Emp.: 500
Fiscal Year-end: 03/31/24
Plastics Product Mfr
N.A.I.C.S.: 326199
Naoki Kimura (Pres)

Subsidiaries:

Matsumoto Kosan Co., Ltd. (1)
247-1 Shimo-ogano, Ogano-machi, Chichibu, 368-0101, Saitama, Japan
Tel.: (81) 494750571
Web Site: https://www.mkknc.co.jp
Emp.: 95
Automobile Parts Mfr
N.A.I.C.S.: 336390

Matsumoto Yushi-Seiyaku Co.,Ltd - Osaka Factory (1)
1-6 Takasago, Takaishi, 592-0001, Osaka, Japan
Tel.: (81) 72 268 3210
Web Site: http://www.mtmtys.co.jp
Chemicals Mfr
N.A.I.C.S.: 325199
Naoki Kimura (Pres)

Matsumoto Yushi-Seiyaku Co.,Ltd - Shizuoka Factory (1)
2530 Yamashina, Fukuroi, 437-0066, Shizuoka, Japan
Tel.: (81) 538434170
Chemicals Mfr
N.A.I.C.S.: 325199

Matsumoto Yushi-Seiyaku Co.,Ltd - Yao Factory (1)
1-3 2-chome, Shibukawa-cho, Yao, 581-0075, Osaka, Japan
Tel.: (81) 729911001
Surface Active Agent & Polymer Mfr
N.A.I.C.S.: 325613

MATSUOKA CORPORATION, LTD.

4-14 Takaramachi, Fukuyama, 720-0045, Hiroshima, Japan
Tel.: (81) 849735188
Web Site: https://www.matuoka.co.jp
3611—(TKS)
Rev.: $397,763,360
Assets: $434,257,170
Liabilities: $195,893,960
Net Worth: $238,363,210
Earnings: $16,240,770
Emp.: 17,278
Fiscal Year-end: 03/31/24
Apparels Mfr
N.A.I.C.S.: 315250
Noriyuki Matsuoka (Pres)

Subsidiaries:

MK Apparels Limited (1)
Plot-60 Road-7 Ward-4 Block-4 Kumkumary Ashulia Savar, 1341, Dhaka, Bangladesh
Tel.: (880) 1730071333
Sewing Product Distr
N.A.I.C.S.: 424350
Manikur Rahman (Gen Mgr)

PT. Toray International Matsuoka Winner Industry (1)
Jl Raya Tegal Panas Jimbaran Desa Secang RT 01 Dusun, Samban Kec Bawen Kab, Semarang, Jawa Tengah, Indonesia
Tel.: (62) 298523720
Sewing Product Distr
N.A.I.C.S.: 424350

MATSUYA FOODS HOLDINGS CO., LTD.

1-14-5 Nakacho, Musashino-shi, Tokyo, 180-0006, Japan
Tel.: (81) 422381121
Web Site: https://www.matsuyafoods.co.jp
Year Founded: 1966
9887—(TKS)
Rev.: $843,508,710
Assets: $602,303,220
Liabilities: $312,302,670
Net Worth: $290,000,530
Earnings: $19,268,150
Emp.: 1,918
Fiscal Year-end: 03/31/24
Restaurant Operators
N.A.I.C.S.: 722511
Toshio Kawarabuki (Chm)

Subsidiaries:

Matsuya Foods, Co., Ltd. - Mt. Fuji Factory (1)
4242-4 Aza-Mine Oaza-Kitayama, Fujinomiya, 418-0112, Shizuoka, Japan
Tel.: (81) 544 59 1300
Food Products Mfr
N.A.I.C.S.: 311999

Matsuya Foods, Co., Ltd. - Ranzan Factory (1)
4-3 Hanamidai, Ranzan-machi, Hiki, 355-0204, Saitama, Japan
Tel.: (81) 493 61 1118
Food Products Mfr
N.A.I.C.S.: 311999
Yoshito Usui (Mng Dir)

Qingdao Matsuya Commercial Trade Co., Ltd. (1)
Room 1-903 No 123 Zhangzhou 2 Road, Shinan District, Qingdao, China
Tel.: (86) 532 8589 9025
Restaurant Operators
N.A.I.C.S.: 722511

Shanghai Matsuya F&B Management Co., Ltd. (1)
Room 1514 No 99 Huichuan Road, Changning District, Shanghai, China
Tel.: (86) 21 6235 0591
Restaurant Operators
N.A.I.C.S.: 722511

MATSUYA RESEARCH & DEVELOPMENT CO., LTD.

Tel.: (81) 779662096
Year Founded: 1982
7317—(TKS)
Rev.: $55,742,130
Assets: $65,584,420
Liabilities: $31,258,690
Net Worth: $34,325,730
Earnings: $6,299,330
Fiscal Year-end: 03/31/24
Industry Machinery Mfr & Distr
N.A.I.C.S.: 333248
Shoichi Tanaka (Auditor)

Subsidiaries:

Matsuya R&D (Vietnam) Co., Ltd. (1)
Plot No 404 Road 13, Amata Industrial Park Long Binh Ward, Bien Hoa, Dong Nai, Vietnam
Tel.: (84) 613936861
Automatic Sewing Machine Mfr & Distr
N.A.I.C.S.: 333248

Matsuya R&D Trading (Shanghai) Co., Ltd. (1)
Room 2801 Plaza Hyundai No 1 No 369 Xianxia Road, Changning Area, Shanghai, 200336, China
Tel.: (86) 2151727910
Automatic Sewing Machine Mfr & Distr
N.A.I.C.S.: 333248

MATTH. HOHNER AG

Andreas-Koch-Strasse 9, 78647, Trossingen, Germany
Tel.: (49) 7425200
Web Site: http://www.hohner.de
Year Founded: 1857
Sales Range: $75-99.9 Million
Emp.: 200
Musical Instrument Mfr

AND PRIVATE COMPANIES

N.A.I.C.S.: 339992
Matthias Hohner *(Founder)*

Subsidiaries:

Hohner Musikinstrumente GmbH & Co. KG **(1)**
Andreas-Koch-Strasse 9, 78647, Trossingen, Germany
Tel.: (49) 7425200
Web Site: http://www.hohner.de
Sales Range: $25-49.9 Million
Mfr of Musical Instruments
N.A.I.C.S.: 339992

Subsidiary (US):

Hohner, Inc./HSS **(2)**
1000 Technology Park Dr, Glen Allen, VA 23059-4500
Tel.: (804) 515-1900
Web Site: http://www.hohnerusa.com
Sales Range: $25-49.9 Million
Emp.: 40
Distr of Harmonicas, Melodicas, Diatonic & Piano Accordions, Recorders, Instruments for Music Education, Percussion Instruments, Musical Accessories, Electric & Acoustic Guitars, Cymbals & Drums
N.A.I.C.S.: 339992

Hohner S.A. **(1)**
Zone Industrielle, Semur-en-Auxois, 21140, Dijon, France **(100%)**
Tel.: (33) 380973300
Web Site: http://www.hohner.fr
Sales Range: $25-49.9 Million
Emp.: 30
Durable Goods Whslr
N.A.I.C.S.: 423990

Sonor GmbH & Co. KG **(1)**
Zum Heilbach 5, Bad Berleburg, Siegen, 57319, Germany
Tel.: (49) 2759790
Web Site: http://www.sonor.com
Sales Range: $25-49.9 Million
Emp.: 80
Musical Instrument Mfr
N.A.I.C.S.: 339992
Karl-Heinz Menzel *(Mng Dir)*

MATTHEW JOHNSON MARSHALL LTD.
Suite 3 80 Commercial Street, Edinburgh, EH6 6LX, United Kingdom
Tel.: (44) 1313225865 UK
Web Site: http://www.rmjm.com
Year Founded: 1956
Sales Range: $50-74.9 Million
Emp.: 200
Holding Company
N.A.I.C.S.: 551112
Peter Morrison *(CEO)*

Subsidiaries:

RMJM Ltd. **(1)**
80 Commercial Quay, Edinburgh, EH6 6LX, United Kingdom
Tel.: (44) 1312252532
Web Site: http://www.rmjm.com
Commercial & Residential Architectural Services
N.A.I.C.S.: 541310
Declan Thompson *(Grp Dir-Comml)*

Subsidiary (US):

RMJM Hillier Group, Inc. **(2)**
275 7th Ave 24th Fl, New York, NY 10001-6708
Tel.: (212) 629-4200
Web Site: http://www.hillier.com
Commercial & Residential Architectural Services
N.A.I.C.S.: 541310

Subsidiary (Domestic):

RMJM Hillier **(3)**
500 Alexander Pk, Princeton, NJ 08543-6395
Tel.: (609) 452-8888
Web Site: http://www.hillier.com
Sales Range: $100-124.9 Million
Emp.: 375

Commercial & Residential Architectural Services
N.A.I.C.S.: 541310

Subsidiary (Non-US):

RMJM Hong Kong Limited **(2)**
11Fl Walwick House W Taikoo Pl, 9 79 Kings Rd, Hong Kong, China (Hong Kong)
Tel.: (852) 25481698
Web Site: http://www.rmjm.com
Sales Range: $25-49.9 Million
Commercial & Residential Architectural Services
N.A.I.C.S.: 541310

Subsidiary (Domestic):

RMJM London Ltd. **(2)**
83 Paul Street, London, EC2A 4UT, United Kingdom
Tel.: (44) 2075498900
Web Site: http://www.rmjm.com
Sales Range: $25-49.9 Million
Commercial & Residential Architectural Services
N.A.I.C.S.: 541310

Subsidiary (Non-US):

RMJM Middle East Limited **(2)**
2th Fl H dubai Office Tower, PO Box 6126, 1 Sheikh Zayed Rd, Dubai, United Arab Emirates
Tel.: (971) 43296333
Web Site: http://www.rmjm.com
Commercial & Residential Architectural Services
N.A.I.C.S.: 541310
Raymond Park *(CEO)*

RMJM Singapore Pte. Ltd. **(2)**
137 Telok Ayer St 08 05, Singapore, 068802, Singapore
Tel.: (65) 63274681
Web Site: http://www.rmjm.com
Sales Range: $25-49.9 Million
Commercial & Residential Architectural Services
N.A.I.C.S.: 541310

MATTHEW WILLIAMSON LTD.
10-11 The Quadrant 135 Salusbury Road, London, NW6 6RJ, United Kingdom
Tel.: (44) 20 7491 6220
Web Site: http://www.matthewwilliamson.com
Sales Range: $1-9.9 Million
Emp.: 60
Clothing, Accessories & Fragrances Designer & Retailer
N.A.I.C.S.: 315990
Joseph Velosa *(Co-Founder & CEO)*

MATTING TECHNOLOGY CORPORATION
137 Martin Street, Granby, J2G 8B1, QC, Canada
Tel.: (450) 375-3542
Web Site: http://www.mattech.ca
Year Founded: 1987
Rev.: $11,500,000
Emp.: 80
Mat Mfr
N.A.I.C.S.: 337910
B. Randall Dobbs *(Pres)*

MATTONI 1873 A.S.
Horova 3, 360 21, Karlovy Vary, Czech Republic
Tel.: (420) 800111011 CZ
Web Site: https://www.mattoni1873.cz
Year Founded: 1873
Mineral & Spring Water Bottler
N.A.I.C.S.: 312112
Alessandro Pasquale *(CEO)*

Subsidiaries:

Knjaz Milos a.d. **(1)**
Industrijska zona BB, 34300, Arandelovac, Serbia
Tel.: (381) 34700700

Web Site: http://www.knjaz.co.rs
Bottled Water & Juice Mfr & Whslr
N.A.I.C.S.: 312112
Zorica Vukcevic-Kljajic *(Dir-Ops)*

MATTSSON METAL AB
Norvagen 6, Mora, 792 32, Sweden
Tel.: (46) 25039400 SE
Web Site: http://www.mmetal.se
Year Founded: 1945
Sales Range: $10-24.9 Million
Emp.: 110
Brass & Copper Hot-Forged Products Mfr
N.A.I.C.S.: 332112
Erik Eriksson *(Mng Dir)*

MATVAREEXPRESSEN AS
Spannavegen 152, 5535, Haugesund, Norway
Tel.: (47) 40001701
Web Site: https://www.mve.no
Year Founded: 2007
MVE—(EUR)
Online Shopping Site Operator
N.A.I.C.S.: 455219
Fredrik Engen *(CEO)*

MAUDORE MINERALS LTD.
123 Front Street W Suite 905, Toronto, M5J 2M2, ON, Canada
Tel.: (819) 797-9336
Web Site: http://www.maudore.com
Year Founded: 1996
MAOMF—(OTCIQ)
Sales Range: $1-9.9 Million
Gold Ore Mining Services
N.A.I.C.S.: 212220
George Fowlie *(Chm, Interim CEO & Interim CFO)*

MAUGHAN THIEM GROUP
1013 Port Road, Cheltenham, 5014, SA, Australia
Tel.: (61) 883001200
Web Site: http://www.maughanthiem.com.au
Year Founded: 1912
Automotive Retailer
N.A.I.C.S.: 441110
Daniel Thomas *(CEO)*

MAUI CAPITAL LTD.
Level 25 151 Queen Street, Auckland, New Zealand
Tel.: (64) 9 377 9377
Web Site: http://www.mauicapital.co.nz
Year Founded: 2008
Emp.: 11
Privater Equity Firm
N.A.I.C.S.: 523999
Paul Chrystall *(Mng Dir)*

Subsidiaries:

AB Equipment Limited **(1)**
101 Cryers Road, East Tamaki, Auckland, 2013, New Zealand **(100%)**
Tel.: (64) 92622709
Web Site: https://www.abequipment.co.nz
Sales Range: $50-74.9 Million
Emp.: 70
Material Handling Construction & Environmental Equipment Distr
N.A.I.C.S.: 423810
Natasha Wilson *(Branch Mgr)*

BJ Ball Group Ltd. **(1)**
121 Hugo Johnston Drive, Penrose, Auckland, 1061, New Zealand **(71%)**
Tel.: (64) 9 579 0050
Web Site: http://www.bjball.co.nz
Emp.: 100
Paper & Packaging Product Distr
N.A.I.C.S.: 424110
Craig Brown *(CEO)*

Subsidiary (Non-US):

BJ Ball Pty. Ltd. **(2)**

41-45 Mills Road, Braeside, 3195, VIC, Australia
Tel.: (61) 385873500
Web Site: http://www.bjball.com.au
Sales Range: $125-149.9 Million
Paper & Packaging Product Distr
N.A.I.C.S.: 424110

Subsidiary (Domestic):

BJ Ball **(3)**
3 White Ave, Athol Park, Adelaide, 5012, SA, Australia **(100%)**
Tel.: (61) 61884471377
Web Site: http://www.bjballpapers.com.au
Paper & Packaging Product Distr
N.A.I.C.S.: 424110

BJ Ball **(3)**
7-9 French Ave, Brendale, 4500, QLD, Australia **(100%)**
Tel.: (61) 733908444
Sales Range: $25-49.9 Million
Paper & Packaging Product Distr
N.A.I.C.S.: 424110

Freshmax Pty Ltd **(1)**
PO Box 132030, Auckland, 1644, New Zealand
Tel.: (64) 9 9171445
Web Site: http://www.freshmax.co.nz
Emp.: 100
Fruit Distr
N.A.I.C.S.: 424480
David Smith *(Chm)*

Subsidiary (Non-US):

De Luca Banana Marketing Pty Ltd **(2)**
PO Box 302, Brisbane, 4106, QLC, Australia
Tel.: (61) 7 3392 7596
Web Site: http://www.dbmco.com.au
Fruit Distr
N.A.I.C.S.: 424480
Patti Cooper *(Mgr-Quality)*

Freshmax Australia Pty Ltd **(2)**
44 Cambridge St 3032, Rocklea, 4106, QLD, Australia
Tel.: (61) 3 9688 5500
Web Site: http://www.freshmax.com.au
Emp.: 50
Fruit Distr
N.A.I.C.S.: 424480
Mark Leng *(Gen Mgr)*

VALLEYFRESH EXPORTS **(2)**
Av Velazco Astete 725 Ofc 301, San Borja, Lima, Peru
Tel.: (51) 987 523 555
Fruit Distr
N.A.I.C.S.: 424480
Jose Solf *(Mgr)*

Subsidiary (Domestic):

VALLEYFRESH NEW ZEALAND LIMITED **(2)**
32 Amelia Earheart Ave, Airport Oaks, Auckland, New Zealand
Tel.: (64) 9 436 0713
Fruit Distr
N.A.I.C.S.: 424480
Anton Masutti *(Gen Mgr)*

Subsidiary (Non-US):

Valley Fresh Australia Pty Ltd **(2)**
1-11 Bliss Court, Derrimut, 3030, VIC, Australia
Tel.: (61) 3 8368 2808
Web Site: http://www.valleyfresh.com.au
Fruit Distr
N.A.I.C.S.: 424480
Adam Carville *(Mgr-Ops-NSW)*

Subsidiary (US):

Valleyfresh North America, LLC **(2)**
3452 E Foothill Blvd Ste 500, Pasadena, CA 91107
Tel.: (626) 921-1400
Fruit Distr
N.A.I.C.S.: 424480

MAUM.AI, INC
4F Pangyo IT Center 30

MAUM.AI, INC

Maum.AI, Inc—(Continued)
Changeop-ro 40, Sujeong-gu, Seongnam, 13449, Gyeonggi-do, Korea (South)
Tel.: (82) 16613222
Web Site: https://www.maum.ai
Year Founded: 2014
377480—(KRS)
Rev.: $6,322,900
Assets: $28,983,798
Liabilities: $9,366,964
Net Worth: $19,616,834
Earnings: ($3,587,092)
Emp.: 144
Fiscal Year-end: 12/31/22
Software Development Services
N.A.I.C.S.: 541511
Taejoon Yoo *(CEO)*

MAUNA KEA TECHNOLOGIES SA
9 rue d Enghien, 75010, Paris, France
Tel.: (33) 148240345
Web Site: https://www.maunakeatech.com
Year Founded: 2000
ALMKT—(EUR)
Rev.: $8,753,507
Assets: $21,360,889
Liabilities: $42,864,235
Net Worth: ($21,503,346)
Earnings: ($12,065,616)
Emp.: 68
Fiscal Year-end: 12/31/22
Medical Imaging Equipment Mfr
N.A.I.C.S.: 339112
Sacha Loiseau *(Founder & Chm)*

Subsidiaries:

Biogene Pharma Ltd. (1)
86/2 West Dhanmondi 3rd Floor, Dhaka, 1209, Bangladesh
Tel.: (880) 29113954
Medical Equipment Mfr
N.A.I.C.S.: 339112
Mohammad Ali *(Mktg Mgr)*

Didr.Mehn-Andersen AS (1)
Ulsmagveien 29B, 5224, Nesttun, Norway
Tel.: (47) 55987700
Medical Equipment Mfr
N.A.I.C.S.: 339112

Imedex S.r.o. (1)
Kladska 1092/1a, 500 03, Hradec Kralove, Czech Republic
Tel.: (420) 495260286
Web Site: https://www.imedex.cz
Medical Device & Equipment Mfr
N.A.I.C.S.: 339112
Richard Uhlir *(Sls Mgr)*

Labord-Med-Aparelhagem de precisao Ltda. (1)
Alameda Sao Boaventura n 392 Fonseca, Niteroi, 24120-196, Rio de Janeiro, Brazil
Tel.: (55) 2137974900
Web Site: http://www.labor-med.com.br
Medical Equipment Mfr
N.A.I.C.S.: 339112

Mauna Kea Technologies Inc. (1)
660 Newtown-Yardley Rd Ste 107, Newtown, PA 18940
Tel.: (215) 478-6288
Web Site: http://www.maunakeatech.com
Medical Device Mfr
N.A.I.C.S.: 334510

Medical Scope, S.A.de C.V. (1)
Mount Irazu 189, 11000, Lomas de Chapultepec, Mexico
Tel.: (52) 5552022634
Web Site: http://www.medical-scope.com
Medical Device & Equipment Mfr
N.A.I.C.S.: 339112

Reinhard Di Lena GmbH (1)
Bahnstrasse 4 Top 001, 2340, Modling, Austria
Tel.: (43) 223628026
Web Site: http://www.fujinon.at

Endoscopy Device Mfr
N.A.I.C.S.: 334510

Scope Medical Co. (1)
80 Mohi El Din Abou El Ezz Mohandessin, Cairo, Egypt
Tel.: (20) 237601844
Web Site: https://www.scope-med.com
Medical Equipment Mfr & Distr
N.A.I.C.S.: 339112
Mohamed Hamza *(VP-Ops)*

MAUNA N.V.
Driebladhof 12, 5672 XH, Nuenen, Netherlands
Tel.: (31) 492 579 010
Holding Company
N.A.I.C.S.: 551112

Subsidiaries:

Mainetti SpA (1)
Via Casarette nr 58, Castelgomberto, Vicenza, 36070, Italy
Tel.: (39) 0445 428511
Web Site: http://www.mainetti.com
Garment Hangers Mfr & Packaging & Labeling Services
N.A.I.C.S.: 423990
Roberto Peruzzo *(CEO)*

Subsidiary (US):

The Star Group, Inc. (2)
80 A Industrial Rd, Lodi, NJ 07644
Tel.: (973) 778-8600
Web Site: http://www.thestargrp.com
Creative Branding & Packaging Services
N.A.I.C.S.: 541890
Michael Friedman *(Pres & CEO)*

MAURIA UDYOG LTD.
Sohna Road Sector-55, Faridabad, 121 015, Haryana, India
Tel.: (91) 1292477700
Web Site: http://www.mauria.com
539219—(BOM)
Rev.: $18,885,062
Assets: $64,683,473
Liabilities: $60,719,500
Net Worth: $3,963,974
Earnings: ($8,962,426)
Fiscal Year-end: 03/31/21
Steel Cylinder Mfr
N.A.I.C.S.: 332420
Sureka N. K. *(Exec Mng Dir)*

MAURICE LACROIX S.A.
Thurgauerstrasse 40, CH-8050, Zurich, Switzerland
Tel.: (41) 442091111   CH
Web Site: http://www.mauricelacroix.com
Year Founded: 1975
Sales Range: $75-99.9 Million
Emp.: 300
Watch Designer, Mfr & Distr
N.A.I.C.S.: 334519
Katrin Roth *(Mgr-Pub Rel-Intl)*

MAURITIUS FREEPORT DEVELOPMENT CO., LTD.
Freeport Zone 5 Mer Rouge, PO Box 303, Port Louis, Mauritius
Tel.: (230) 2062000
Web Site: http://www.mfd.mu
Year Founded: 1992
Sales Range: $10-24.9 Million
Logistics & Warehousing Services
N.A.I.C.S.: 541614
Rene Leclezio *(Chm)*

MAURITIUS OIL REFINERIES LIMITED
Quay Road, Port Louis, Mauritius
Tel.: (230) 2069800
Web Site: https://www.moroil.mu
Year Founded: 1968
MOR—(MAU)
Rev.: $47,252,922
Assets: $27,764,752

Liabilities: $18,299,753
Net Worth: $9,464,999
Earnings: $1,819,675
Emp.: 165
Fiscal Year-end: 06/30/23
Edible Oil Mfr
N.A.I.C.S.: 311224
G. Allain Doger de Speville *(Chm)*

MAURITIUS TELECOM LTD.
Telecom Tower Edith Cavell Street, Port Louis, 11302, Mauritius
Tel.: (230) 2037000   MU
Web Site: http://www.telecom.mu
Year Founded: 1992
Rev.: $278,740,533
Assets: $612,847,060
Liabilities: $366,597,295
Net Worth: $246,249,765
Earnings: $17,074,494
Emp.: 2,205
Fiscal Year-end: 12/31/19
Telecommunication Servicesb
N.A.I.C.S.: 517111

Subsidiaries:

Call Services Ltd. (1)
5th Floor my t Tower, Ebene, Mauritius
Tel.: (230) 2039000
Web Site: http://www.cslbpo.com
Sales Range: $100-124.9 Million
Telecommunications
N.A.I.C.S.: 517810
Vikraom Jayaraj *(Gen Mgr)*

Cellplus Mobile Communications Ltd. (1)
9th Floor Telecom Tower Edith Cavell Street, Port Louis, Mauritius (100%)
Tel.: (230) 2037500
Web Site: http://www.myt.mu
Mobile Communications Services
N.A.I.C.S.: 517112
Sarat Lallah *(CEO)*

MT Services Ltd (1)
10 Heather Close, Birmingham, B36 0RF, West Midlands, United Kingdom
Tel.: (44) 1827 62155
Human Resource Consulting Services
N.A.I.C.S.: 541612

Teleservices (Mauritius) Ltd. (1)
2nd Floor PCL Building 43 Sir William Newton St, 43 2nd Floor PCL Building, Port Louis, Mauritius
Tel.: (230) 2111288
Web Site: http://teleservices.yolasite.com
Sales Range: $25-49.9 Million
Telecommunications
N.A.I.C.S.: 517810
Rehman Mangou *(Mgr-Tele Svcs)*

MAURO DEMETRIO S.P.A.
Zona Industriale, 89018, Villa San Giovanni, Reggio Calabria, Italy
Tel.: (39) 09653333   IT
Web Site: http://www.caffemauro.com
Year Founded: 1949
Sales Range: $10-24.9 Million
Emp.: 55
Coffee Mfr
N.A.I.C.S.: 311920

MAUS FRERES S.A.
6 Rue Cornavin, PO Box 1880, 1211, Geneva, Switzerland
Tel.: (41) 229086600   CH
Web Site: http://www.maus.ch
Year Founded: 1927
Sales Range: $1-4.9 Billion
Emp.: 20,000
Holding Company Department Store Supermarket Franchise Restaurant Pharmacy Sporting Goods & Apparel Store Owner & Operator
N.A.I.C.S.: 551112
Didier Maus *(CEO)*

Subsidiaries:

AIGLE, S.A. (1)

INTERNATIONAL PUBLIC

ZI Ingrandes, BP 755, 86107, Chatellerault, Cedex, France (91.2%)
Tel.: (33) 549023800
Web Site: http://www.aigle.com
Sales Range: $200-249.9 Million
Emp.: 600
Outdoor Shoe & Clothing Retailer
N.A.I.C.S.: 458210

Devanlay SA (1)
23 25 rue de Provence, 75009, Paris, France (90%)
Tel.: (33) 0144826966
Web Site: http://www.lacosce.com
Sales Range: $1-4.9 Billion
Emp.: 3,600
Clothing Mfr & Retailer
N.A.I.C.S.: 458110

Fly Sitz Schweiz (1)
Bahnhofstrasse 85, CH-4622, Egerkingen, Switzerland
Tel.: (41) 623878900
Web Site: http://www.fly.fr
Sales Range: $25-49.9 Million
Emp.: 6
Interior Decor & Furniture Retailer
N.A.I.C.S.: 449110

Jumbo Markt AG (1)
Industriestrasse 34, PO Box 222, 8305, Dietlikon, Switzerland
Tel.: (41) 448056111
Web Site: http://www.jumbo.ch
Sales Range: $400-449.9 Million
Emp.: 1,500
Garden Supplies Retailer
N.A.I.C.S.: 444240
Gilg Jerome *(CEO)*

Lacoste S.A. (1)
8 Rue Castiglione, 75001, Paris, France (100%)
Tel.: (33) 44581212
Web Site: http://www.lacoste.com
Clothing, Perfume, Eyewear, Watches, Footwear & Leather Goods Mfr
N.A.I.C.S.: 315990
Veronique Mauduit *(Coord-External Rels)*

Manor AG (1)
Rebgasse 34, 4005, Basel, Switzerland
Tel.: (41) 616861111
Web Site: http://www.manor.ch
Sales Range: $200-249.9 Million
Emp.: 700
Department Store Owner & Operator
N.A.I.C.S.: 455110
Bergrand Jungo *(CIO)*

MyOne Services AG (1)
Birkenstrasse 21, 8306, Bruttisellen, Switzerland
Tel.: (41) 448055858
Web Site: http://www.myone.ch
Sales Range: $50-74.9 Million
Credit Card Services
N.A.I.C.S.: 522210

Restaurants Manora SA (1)
Rebgasse 34, CH-4005, Basel, Switzerland
Tel.: (41) 616861111
Web Site: http://www.manora.ch
Sales Range: $100-124.9 Million
Emp.: 700
Restaurant Owner & Operator
N.A.I.C.S.: 722511

MAVEN BRANDS INC.
32 - 100 Kalamalka Lake Rd, Vernon, V1T 9G1, BC, Canada
Tel.: (250) 275-6063   BC
Web Site: https://mavenbrands.ca
Year Founded: 2014
TRLFF—(OTCIQ)
Rev.: $162,678
Assets: $3,782,013
Liabilities: $4,915,880
Net Worth: ($1,133,868)
Earnings: ($1,838,846)
Fiscal Year-end: 03/31/22
Botanical Medicine Mfr
N.A.I.C.S.: 325411

MAVEN INCOME & GROWTH VCT 4 PLC
Kintyre House 205 West George

Street, Glasgow, G2 2LW, United Kingdom
Tel.: (44) 2031022750
Year Founded: 2004
MAV4—(LSE)
Rev.: $19,061,465
Assets: $112,132,604
Liabilities: $1,252,803
Net Worth: $110,879,801
Earnings: $12,649,269
Fiscal Year-end: 12/31/21
Investment Management Service
N.A.I.C.S.: 525990
William Robert Nixon *(Mgr-Fund)*

MAVEN INCOME & GROWTH VCT 5 PLC
6th Floor Saddlers House 44 Gutter Lane, London, EC2V 6BR, United Kingdom
Tel.: (44) 2031022750
Year Founded: 2000
MIG5—(LSE)
Rev.: $1,037,298
Assets: $81,779,549
Liabilities: $312,276
Net Worth: $81,467,273
Earnings: $4,032,428
Fiscal Year-end: 02/28/22
Investment Management Service
N.A.I.C.S.: 525990
Graham Miller *(Chm)*

MAVEN INCOME & GROWTH VCT PLC
6th Floor Saddlers House 44 Gutter Lane, London, EC2V 6BR, United Kingdom
Tel.: (44) 2031022750
Year Founded: 2000
MIG1—(LSE)
Rev.: $6,183,189
Assets: $81,135,833
Liabilities: $309,833
Net Worth: $80,826,000
Earnings: $4,000,887
Fiscal Year-end: 02/28/22
Investment Services
N.A.I.C.S.: 525910
John Pocock *(Chm)*

MAVEN WIRELESS SWEDEN AB
Torshamnsgatan 39B, 164 40, Kista, Sweden
Tel.: (46) 87604300
Web Site: https://www.mavenwireless.com
Year Founded: 2016
MAVEN—(OMX)
Rev.: $23,590,844
Assets: $18,003,852
Liabilities: $6,192,745
Net Worth: $11,811,107
Earnings: $3,874,362
Emp.: 34
Fiscal Year-end: 12/31/23
Telecommunication Equipment Distr
N.A.I.C.S.: 423690

MAVENS BIOTECH LIMITED
Room No 407 4th Floor Premises No 4 Clive Row, Kolkata, 700 001, India
Tel.: (91) 3322623056
Web Site: http://www.mavensbiotech.com
Rev.: $122,399
Assets: $2,889,706
Liabilities: $50,233
Net Worth: $2,839,473
Earnings: $12,392
Fiscal Year-end: 03/31/16
Biotechnology Software Development Services
N.A.I.C.S.: 541511
Ganga Sahai *(CFO)*

MAVERICK ADVERTISING & DESIGN
2nd Floor 21 St Thomas St, London, SE1 9RY, United Kingdom
Tel.: (44) 207 378 6969
Web Site: http://www.mavad.co.uk
Year Founded: 2002
Sales Range: $10-24.9 Million
Emp.: 55
Marketing & Advertising Agency Services
N.A.I.C.S.: 541613
Carron Edmonds *(Mng Dir)*

MAVERICK DRILLING & EXPLORATION LIMITED
Suite 2 24 Bolton Street, Newcastle, 2300, NSW, Australia
Tel.: (61) 249523659
Web Site: http://www.maverickdrilling.com
MAD—(ASX)
Sales Range: $10-24.9 Million
Emp.: 109
Oil & Gas Exploration & Mining Services
N.A.I.C.S.: 211120
Andrew James Crawford *(Sec)*

MAVI GIYIM SANAYI VE TICARET AS
Sultan Selim Mahallesi Eski Buyukdere Cad No 53, 34418, Istanbul, 34418, Turkiye
Tel.: (90) 2123712000
Web Site: https://www.mavi.com
MAVI—(IST)
Rev.: $327,157,913
Assets: $266,953,221
Liabilities: $182,570,030
Net Worth: $84,383,191
Earnings: $44,458,773
Emp.: 3,911
Fiscal Year-end: 12/31/22
Men & Women Clothing Retailer
N.A.I.C.S.: 458110
Savan Tuysuz *(Head-Ops)*

Subsidiaries:
Mavi Europe AG (1)
Seligenstadter Grund 19, 63150, Heusenstamm, Germany
Tel.: (49) 610468180
Web Site: https://eu.mavi.com
Clothing Whslr
N.A.I.C.S.: 424350

MAVSHACK AB
Tel.: (46) 705190516
Web Site: https://www.corp.mavshack.com
MAV—(OMX)
Rev.: $3,714,631
Assets: $3,468,300
Liabilities: $2,878,230
Net Worth: $590,070
Earnings: ($4,276,602)
Emp.: 45
Fiscal Year-end: 12/31/22
Media Distribution Services
N.A.I.C.S.: 541890
Tommy Carlstedt *(CEO)*

MAWDSLEY-BROOKS & CO. LTD.
Number Three South Langworthy Road, PO Box 18, Salford, M50 2PW, United Kingdom
Tel.: (44) 1617423300   UK
Web Site: http://www.mawdsleys.co.uk
Sales Range: $400-449.9 Million
Emp.: 680
Pharmaceutical Products Distr
N.A.I.C.S.: 424210

Subsidiaries:
Luto Research Limited (1)
103 Clarendon Road, Leeds, LS2 9DF, United Kingdom
Tel.: (44) 113 384 5900
Web Site: http://www.luto.co.uk
Pharmaceutical Research Services
N.A.I.C.S.: 541715
Claire Utting *(Sr Mgr-Bus Dev)*

MAWSON GOLD LIMITED
1305 - 1090 West Georgia Street, Vancouver, V6E 3V7, BC, Canada
Tel.: (604) 699-0202   BC
Web Site: https://www.mawsongold.com
Year Founded: 2004
MAW—(OTCIQ)
Rev.: $102,307
Assets: $42,995,900
Liabilities: $760,438
Net Worth: $42,235,462
Earnings: ($2,300,749)
Emp.: 13
Fiscal Year-end: 05/31/21
Uranium Mining & Exploration Services
N.A.I.C.S.: 212290
Michael Robert Hudson *(Chm & CEO)*

Subsidiaries:
Mawson Energi AB (1)
Kyrkgatan 41, Boden, 961 35, Sweden
Tel.: (46) 92150160
Web Site: http://www.mawsonresources.com
Sales Range: $50-74.9 Million
Emp.: 2
Uranium Exploration & Mining Services
N.A.I.C.S.: 212290
Folke Soderstrom *(CEO)*

Mawson Sweden AB (1)
Kanslihusvagen 5, 961 43, Boden, Sweden
Tel.: (46) 504488303
Web Site: http://mawsongold.com
Sales Range: $50-74.9 Million
Uranium Exploration & Mining Services
N.A.I.C.S.: 212290

MAWSON INFRASTRUCTURE GROUP INC.,
24 Hanagar Street, Hod Hasharon, 4527708, Israel
Tel.: (972) 722600536   DE
Web Site: http://www.wizepharma.com
Year Founded: 1999
MIGI—(NASDAQ)
Rev.: $84,385,407
Assets: $133,329,065
Liabilities: $57,162,945
Net Worth: $76,166,120
Earnings: ($52,762,308)
Emp.: 40
Fiscal Year-end: 12/31/22
Pharmaceutical Preparation Mfr
N.A.I.C.S.: 325412
Mark M. Sieczkarek *(Chm)*

MAWSON WEST LTD.
Level 1 1 Walker Avenue, West Perth, 6005, WA, Australia
Tel.: (61) 8 9485 9800   AU
Web Site: http://www.mawsonwest.com
Copper Exploration & Production Services
N.A.I.C.S.: 212230
Dennis Wilkins *(Sec)*

MAX 21 AG
Robert-Koch-Strasse 9, 64331, Weiterstadt, Germany
Tel.: (49) 61519067200
Web Site: http://www.max21.de
Year Founded: 2004

MA1—(DEU)
Sales Range: Less than $1 Million
Emp.: 22
Financial Investment Services
N.A.I.C.S.: 523940
Frank Wermeyer *(Member-Exec Bd)*

MAX ALERT SYSTEMS LIMITED
502 5th Floor Timmy Arcade Makwana Road Marol, Andheri West, Mumbai, 400059, India
Tel.: (91) 9969410171   In
Web Site: https://maxalert.in
Year Founded: 2004
534563—(BOM)
Rev.: $666,133
Assets: $312,187
Liabilities: $1,095,791
Net Worth: ($783,604)
Earnings: ($2,587,763)
Emp.: 16
Fiscal Year-end: 03/31/22
Security System Services
N.A.I.C.S.: 561621
Divya Vijay *(Officer-Compliance & Sec)*

MAX AUTOMATION SE
Breite Strasse 29-31, 40213, Dusseldorf, Germany
Tel.: (49) 211909910   De
Web Site: https://maxautomation.com
MXHN—(MUN)
Rev.: $438,644,822
Assets: $424,967,873
Liabilities: $298,177,364
Net Worth: $126,790,508
Earnings: $16,745,708
Emp.: 1,664
Fiscal Year-end: 12/31/23
Holding Company; Environmental Technology & Industrial Automation Products Mfr & Whslr
N.A.I.C.S.: 551112
Jens Kruse *(Deputy Chm-Supervisory Bd)*

Subsidiaries:
AIM Micro Systems GmbH (1)
Im Bresselsholze 8, 07819, Triptis, Germany
Tel.: (49) 3648214400
Web Site: http://www.aim-micro-systems.de
Electronic Components Mfr
N.A.I.C.S.: 334419

AIM-Assembly in Motion GmbH (1)
Dr Adolf Schneider Strasse 21, 73479, Ellwangen, Germany
Tel.: (49) 7961 877 0
Web Site: http://www.assemblyinmotion.com
Holding Company; Micro-Optic & Optoelectronic Components Mfr & Whslr
N.A.I.C.S.: 551112

Subsidiary (Domestic):
ELWEMA Automotive GmbH (2)
Dr-Adolf-Schneider-Strasse 21, 73479, Ellwangen, Germany
Tel.: (49) 79618770
Web Site: https://www.elwema.de
Emp.: 170
Automotive Electronic Components Mfr & Whslr
N.A.I.C.S.: 336320

Rohwedder Macro Assembly GmbH (2)
Kesselbachstrasse 1, 88697, Bermatingen, Germany
Tel.: (49) 75445020
Web Site: http://www.rohwedder.com
Industrial Automation Technologies Mfr
N.A.I.C.S.: 333248

IWM Automation GmbH (1)
Rehwinkel 9, 32457, Porta Westfalica, Germany
Tel.: (49) 573176080
Web Site: http://www.iwm-automation.de

MAX AUTOMATION SE

MAX Automation SE—(Continued)
Assembly & Testing Machinery Mfr
N.A.I.C.S.: 333998
Petra Pieper (CFO)

Mess- und Regeltechnik Jucker GmbH (1)
Dieselstr 52-54, 66763, Dillingen, Germany
Tel.: (49) 683190950
Web Site: https://www.juecker-germany.de
Instrument & Control System Mfr
N.A.I.C.S.: 334513

Micro automation LLC (1)
90 Bluegrass Vly Pkwy, Alpharetta, GA 30005
Web Site: https://www.micro-automation.us
Emp.: 200
Automation Engineering Services
N.A.I.C.S.: 541330

Micro automation LLP (1)
21 Tech Park Cres, Singapore, 638111, Singapore
Tel.: (65) 69503480
Web Site: https://www.micro-automation.com.sg
Emp.: 200
Industrial Machinery Mfr
N.A.I.C.S.: 333517

NSM Magnettechnik GmbH (1)
Lutzowstrasse 21, Olfen, 59399, Coesfeld, Germany
Tel.: (49) 2592880
Web Site: https://www.nsm-magnettechnik.de
Emp.: 200
Conveyor & Conveying Equipment Mfr
N.A.I.C.S.: 333922

Vecoplan AG (1)
Vor der Bitz 10, 56470, Bad Marienberg, Germany
Tel.: (49) 266162670
Web Site: http://www.vecoplan.com
Conveyor & Conveying Equipment Mfr
N.A.I.C.S.: 333922
Werner Berens (CEO)

Vecoplan Iberica S.L. (1)
Calle Camino Morgan 2A 2 planta A, 48014, Bilbao, Spain
Tel.: (34) 944536368
Conveyor & Conveying Equipment Mfr
N.A.I.C.S.: 333922

Vecoplan Limited (1)
Unit 1b Cofton Centre Groveley Lane Longbridge, Birmingham, B31 4PT, West Midlands, United Kingdom
Tel.: (44) 1212225489
Conveyor & Conveying Equipment Mfr
N.A.I.C.S.: 333922

Vecoplan Midwest LLC (1)
4005 Earnings Way, New Albany, IN 47150
Tel.: (812) 923-4992
Web Site: http://www.vecoplanmidwest.com
Pelleting Equipment Distr
N.A.I.C.S.: 423830
Ron King (VP-Sls)

bdtronic GmbH (1)
Ahornweg 4, 97990, Weikersheim, Germany
Tel.: (49) 79341040
Web Site: https://www.bdtronic.com
Industrial Machinery Mfr & Distr
N.A.I.C.S.: 333248
Andy Jorissen (Chief Comml Officer)

Subsidiary (US):

BARTEC Dispensing Technology Inc. (2)
2300 N Sweet Gum Ave, Broken Arrow, OK 74012
Tel.: (918) 250-6496
Web Site: https://www.bdtronic.com
Industrial Machinery Mfr & Distr
N.A.I.C.S.: 333248

Subsidiary (Non-US):

bdtronic BVBA (2)
Kempenstraat 157/A, 3590, Diepenbeek, Belgium
Tel.: (32) 11759689
Adhesive Dispenser Machine Mfr

bdtronic Italy S.r.l. (2)
Via della Genetica 15, 02100, Rieti, RI, Italy
Tel.: (39) 0746220990
Adhesive Dispenser Machine Mfr
N.A.I.C.S.: 333914
David Paolantoni (Mgr-Engrg)

bdtronic Ltd. (2)
10 Weymouth Road, Ashton under Lyne, OL6 9EP, Lancashire, United Kingdom
Tel.: (44) 1613445022
Adhesive Dispenser Machine Mfr
N.A.I.C.S.: 333914

bdtronic S.r.l. (2)
Via Bergamo 15, 20900, Monza, MI, Italy
Tel.: (39) 039389070
Adhesive Dispenser Machine Mfr
N.A.I.C.S.: 333914

bdtronic Suzhou Co., Ltd. (2)
4th Floor Building C East Suhong Road No 405, Suzhou Industrial Park, Suzhou, 215026, China
Tel.: (86) 51269360030
Adhesive Dispenser Machine Mfr
N.A.I.C.S.: 333914
Lili Zhao (Gen Mgr)

iNDAT Robotics GmbH (1)
Ginsheimer Str 8, 65462, Ginshelm-Gustavsburg, Germany
Tel.: (49) 613456480
Web Site: https://www.indat.net
Mechanical Engineering Services
N.A.I.C.S.: 541330
Martin Bottcher (CFO)

MAX CO., LTD.

6-6 Nihonbashi Hakozaki-cho, Chuo-ku, Tokyo, 103-8502, Japan
Tel.: (81) 336690311
Web Site: https://www.max-ltd.co.jp
Year Founded: 1942
6454—(TKS)
Rev.: $572,677,180
Assets: $804,549,370
Liabilities: $144,560,700
Net Worth: $659,988,670
Earnings: $68,975,350
Emp.: 168
Fiscal Year-end: 03/31/24
Industrial Equipment & Office Equipment Mfr
N.A.I.C.S.: 333248
Mitsuteru Kurosawa (Pres)

Subsidiaries:

MAX Business Co., Ltd. (1)
26 Tumbol Bang Mueang Amphoe, Mueang, Chon Buri, 10270, Samut Prakan, Thailand
Tel.: (66) 27404322
Gift Wares & Articles Mfr & Whslr
N.A.I.C.S.: 459420

Max Co (HK) Ltd. (1)
Unit B 7 F Chuan Kei Fty Bldg 15-23 Kin Hong St, Kwai Chung, New Territories, China (Hong Kong)
Tel.: (852) 24262106
Office Product Mfr
N.A.I.C.S.: 339940

Max Europe B.V. (1)
Tel.: (31) 365469669
Web Site: http://www.max-europe.com
Sales Range: $25-49.9 Million
Emp.: 15
Office Product Mfr
N.A.I.C.S.: 322230

Max Europe GmbH (1)
Oststr 22, 40211, Dusseldorf, Germany
Tel.: (49) 211 9365300
Office Product Mfr
N.A.I.C.S.: 322230

Max Fasteners (M) Sdn. Bhd. (1)
Lot 55 Kulim Indus Estate, PO Box 1, 09000, Kulim, Kedah, Malaysia
Tel.: (60) 44892001
Web Site: http://www.maxfasteners.com.my
Sales Range: $50-74.9 Million
Emp.: 220
Office Product Mfr
N.A.I.C.S.: 333310
Kenichi Yokosuka (Mng Dir)

Max Fastening Systems Co., Ltd. (1)
425 Fujigaoka Sekimotocho Kitaibaraki, Ibaraki, 319-1725, Japan
Tel.: (81) 293461770
Steel Wire Products Mfr
N.A.I.C.S.: 331222

Max Kuragano Co., Ltd. (1)
2644 Kuragano-machi, Takasaki, Gunma, 370-1201, Japan
Tel.: (81) 273462494
Web Site: http://www.max-ltd.co.jp
Nailers & Hand Driven Tools Mfr
N.A.I.C.S.: 333991

Max Thailand Co., Ltd. (1)
Eastern Seaboard Indust Estate 64167 Moo 4, Pluakdaeng Dist, Rayong, 21140, Thailand
Tel.: (66) 38959228
Sales Range: $25-49.9 Million
Emp.: 35
Office Product Mfr
N.A.I.C.S.: 459410
Atsushi Saito (Pres)

Max USA Corp. (1)
205 Express St, Plainview, NY 11803
Tel.: (516) 741-3151
Web Site: https://www.maxusacorp.com
Sales Range: $25-49.9 Million
Emp.: 20
Office Product Mfr
N.A.I.C.S.: 423420
Robbie Worrell (Mgr-Sls-Southeast)

Maxshinwa Co., Ltd. (1)
18-20 Maegami-cho Kawaguchi-shi, Saitama, Japan
Tel.: (81) 482663311
Heat Exchangers & Ventilators Mfr
N.A.I.C.S.: 332410

MAX FINANCIAL SERVICES LIMITED

L21 Max Towers Plot No C-001/A/1 Sector 16 B, Noida, 201301, Uttar Pradesh, India
Tel.: (91) 1149376000
Web Site:
https://maxfinancialservices.com
Year Founded: 1982
500271—(BOM)
Rev.: $3,809,444,084
Assets: $15,977,042,269
Liabilities: $15,496,060,481
Net Worth: $480,981,788
Earnings: $54,769,541
Emp.: 11
Fiscal Year-end: 03/31/23
Direct Life, Health & Medical Insurance Carriers
N.A.I.C.S.: 524114
Mohit Talwar (Mng Dir)

Subsidiaries:

Antara Senior Living Limited (1)
Antara Purukul Senior Living Antara Senior Living, Guniyal Gaon, Dehradun, 248 003, Uttarakhand, India
Tel.: (91) 9643000014
Web Site: https://www.antaraseniorcare.com
Emp.: 200
Fire Insurance Services
N.A.I.C.S.: 524113
Tara Singh Vachani (Chm)

Max Life Insurance Company Limited (1)
Plot No 90-C Udyog Vihar Sector 18, Jacaranda Marg DLF City Phase II, Gurgaon, 122015, India (87%)
Tel.: (91) 1244121500
Web Site: https://www.maxlifeinsurance.com
Insurance Services
N.A.I.C.S.: 524210
Prashant Tripathy (Mng Dir & CEO)

MAX HEALTHCARE INSTITUTE LIMITED

2nd Floor Capital Cyberscape Sector-

INTERNATIONAL PUBLIC

59, Sector-42 Golf Course Road, Gurgaon, 122 011, India
Tel.: (91) 1246207777
Web Site:
https://www.maxhealthcare.in
Year Founded: 2001
543220—(BOM)
Rev.: $563,735,987
Assets: $1,211,180,385
Liabilities: $322,793,598
Net Worth: $888,386,787
Earnings: $132,307,416
Emp.: 3,730
Fiscal Year-end: 03/31/23
Health Care Srvces
N.A.I.C.S.: 621610
Abhay Soi (Chm & Mng Dir)

MAX HEIGHTS INFRASTRUCTURE LIMITED

SD-65 Tower Appt Pitampura, New Delhi, 110034, India
Tel.: (91) 1127314646
Web Site:
https://www.maxheights.com
Year Founded: 1981
534338—(BOM)
Rev.: $875,252
Assets: $19,631,812
Liabilities: $15,747,309
Net Worth: $3,884,503
Earnings: ($205,050)
Emp.: 3
Fiscal Year-end: 03/31/22
Real Estate Development Services
N.A.I.C.S.: 531390
Naveen Narang (Mng Dir & CFO)

MAX HOLDER GMBH

Mahdenstr 8, 72768, Reutlingen, Germany
Tel.: (49) 71219307290
Web Site: http://www.max-holder.com
Sales Range: $50-74.9 Million
Emp.: 150
Agricultural Machinery & Equipment Mfr
N.A.I.C.S.: 333111
Andreas Vorig (CEO)

MAX INDIA LIMITED

Plot 167 Floor 1 Ready Money Mensin Dr Annie Besant Road Worli, Mumbai, 400018, Maharashtra, India
Tel.: (91) 1204696000
Web Site: https://www.maxindia.com
Year Founded: 2015
543223—(BOM)
Rev.: $25,592,578
Assets: $90,330,040
Liabilities: $25,333,313
Net Worth: $64,996,727
Earnings: $1,244,877
Emp.: 19
Fiscal Year-end: 03/31/23
Investment Banking Services
N.A.I.C.S.: 523150
Jatin Khanna (CFO)

Subsidiaries:

Antara Assisted Care Services Limited (1)
Max House 1 Dr Jha Marg Okhla Ind Area Phase 3, New Delhi, 110020, India
Tel.: (91) 1204954444
Care Home & Medicare Services
N.A.I.C.S.: 621610

Max Bupa Health Insurance Company Limited (1)
Samyak Tower 39 3rd Floor Pusa Road WEA Karol Bagh, New Delhi, 110005, India
Tel.: (91) 1161291900
Health Insurance Services
N.A.I.C.S.: 524114

MAX METAL CORPORATION PUBLIC COMPANY LIMITED

AND PRIVATE COMPANIES

90 CW Tower 22nd Floor B2202 Ratchadaphisek Rd, Huaykwang, Bangkok, 10310, Thailand
Tel.: (66) 168 301819
Web Site: http://www.maxmetalcorp.co.th
Year Founded: 1987
MAX—(THA)
Sales Range: $25-49.9 Million
Steel Product Distr
N.A.I.C.S.: 423510
Pipat Chanasongkram *(Chm)*

MAX PETROLEUM PLC
4th Floor Ergon House Dean Bradley Street, London, SW1P 2AL, United Kingdom
Tel.: (44) 2037134015
Year Founded: 2005
Oil & Gas Exploration Services
N.A.I.C.S.: 213112
Jim Jeffs *(Chm & CEO)*

MAX POWER MINING CORP.
550 Burrard Street Suite 2900, Vancouver, V6C 0A3, BC, Canada
Tel.: (778) 655-9266   BC
Web Site:
   https://www.maxpowermining.com
Year Founded: 2021
MAXX—(CNSX)
Assets: $8,120,953
Liabilities: $302,615
Net Worth: $7,818,338
Earnings: ($3,932,329)
Fiscal Year-end: 12/31/23
Mining Services
N.A.I.C.S.: 212210
Rav Mlait *(CEO)*

MAX RESOURCE CORP.
Suite 1570 - 200 Burrard St, Vancouver, V6C 3L6, BC, Canada
Tel.: (604) 365-1522
Web Site:
   https://www.maxresource.com
Year Founded: 1994
MAX—(TSXV)
Rev.: $340,210
Assets: $13,851,497
Liabilities: $941,966
Net Worth: $12,909,530
Earnings: ($5,597,524)
Fiscal Year-end: 12/31/23
Gold & Silver Exploration Services
N.A.I.C.S.: 212220
Brett Matich *(Pres & CEO)*

MAX SIGHT GROUP HOLDINGS LTD.
14/F McDonalds Building 48 Yee Wo Street, Causeway Bay, China (Hong Kong)
Tel.: (852) 28811780   Ky
Web Site:
   https://www.maxsightgroup.com
8483—(HKG)
Rev.: $3,984,758
Assets: $5,965,980
Liabilities: $3,069,945
Net Worth: $2,896,035
Earnings: ($1,578,833)
Emp.: 64
Fiscal Year-end: 12/31/22
Photographic Services
N.A.I.C.S.: 541921
Jamson Wing Chai Chan *(Chm & Exec Dir)*

Subsidiaries:

Fullwise International Limited (1)
Room 510-511A2 Nan Fung Tower 173 Des Voeux Road C, Hong Kong, China (Hong Kong)
Tel.: (852) 21527311
Web Site: http://www.full-wise.com

Semiconductor & Electronic Component Distr
N.A.I.C.S.: 423690

MAX STOCK LTD.
16 Hashita St, Caesarea, 3088900, Israel
Tel.: (972) 737695198
Web Site: https://www.maxstock.co.il
Year Founded: 2004
MAXO—(TAE)
Rev.: $303,442,330
Assets: $300,728,540
Liabilities: $238,680,386
Net Worth: $62,048,154
Earnings: $24,952,009
Emp.: 2,117
Fiscal Year-end: 12/31/23
Clothing Store Distr
N.A.I.C.S.: 458110
Shlomo Cohen *(Deputy CEO)*

MAX WEISHAUPT GMBH
Max-Weishaupt-Strasse 14, 88477, Biberach, Germany
Tel.: (49) 7353 830
Web Site: http://www.weishaupt.de
Year Founded: 1932
Sales Range: $650-699.9 Million
Emp.: 3,000
Heating Equipment Mfr
N.A.I.C.S.: 333414
Siegfried Weishaupt *(Mng Dir)*

Subsidiaries:

Andrew P.M. Petrides & Sons Ltd. (1)
Irinis 178, 3304, Limassol, Cyprus
Tel.: (357) 25 363347
Heating Equipment Mfr
N.A.I.C.S.: 333414

Arie Darma Enterprises (S) Pte. Ltd. (1)
338 Jalan Boon Lay, Singapore, 619526, Singapore
Tel.: (65) 62642076
Heating Equipment Mfr
N.A.I.C.S.: 333414

Baugrund Sud Gesellschaft fur Geothermie mbH (1)
Maybachstrasse 5, 88410, Bad Wurzach, Germany
Tel.: (49) 7564 93130
Heating Equipment Mfr
N.A.I.C.S.: 333414

Beauchem Thermtech Group, Inc. (1)
Beauchem Building No 02 Santol Street Mon-el Subdivision, Manila, 1707, Sucat, Philippines
Tel.: (63) 2 820820 2
Web Site: http://www.beauthermgroup.com
Emp.: 50
Heating Equipment Mfr
N.A.I.C.S.: 333414
Leonard Torres *(Gen Mgr)*

Casa-Mazout S.A.R.L. (1)
Parc Industriel CFCIM LOT N 1, 27182, Casablanca, Bouskoura, Morocco
Tel.: (212) 522 592230
Heating Equipment Mfr
N.A.I.C.S.: 333414

Denko Isi Kontrol Teknigi ve Servis A.S. (1)
Bulgurlu Cad No 80 Camlica, 34696, Istanbul, Turkiye
Tel.: (90) 216 54450 50
Heating Equipment Mfr
N.A.I.C.S.: 333414

Enviroburners Oy (1)
Hakamaenkuja 4-6, 01510, Vantaa, Finland
Tel.: (358) 207 871 524
Heating Equipment Mfr
N.A.I.C.S.: 333414

HSB Heizsysteme und Brenner AG (1)
Bruggstrasse 19, 4153, Reinach, Switzerland
Tel.: (41) 61 71696 96
Web Site: http://www.hsb.ch
Emp.: 30
Heating Equipment Mfr
N.A.I.C.S.: 333414
Dennis Geasspuler *(Mgr)*

Huynh Bang Trading & Engineering Service Co., Ltd. (1)
Room 505 Fideco Riverview Buildung 14 Thao Dien Street, Thao Dien Way 2, Ho Chi Minh City, Vietnam
Tel.: (84) 837 449 002
Web Site: http://www.huynhbang.com
Emp.: 15
Heating Equipment Mfr
N.A.I.C.S.: 333414
Khoa Huynh *(Mng Dir)*

Kalamarakis Sapounas SA (1)
Lonias & Neromilou Str, Chamomilos-Acharnes, 13678, Athens, Greece
Tel.: (30) 210 2406000
Heating Equipment Mfr
N.A.I.C.S.: 333414

Kvaliteettehnika OU (1)
Kadaka tee 84A, 12618, Tallinn, Estonia
Tel.: (372) 6779440
Web Site: http://www.kvaliteettehnika.ee
Emp.: 2
Heating Equipment Mfr
N.A.I.C.S.: 333414
Riva Kuusemets *(Owner)*

Max Weishaupt A/S (1)
Erhvervsvej 10, Glostrup, Denmark
Tel.: (45) 432763 00
Heating Equipment Mfr
N.A.I.C.S.: 333414

Middle East Marketing Corporation FZC (1)
Executive Suite Z3-75, Saif Zone, Sharjah, 123932, United Arab Emirates
Tel.: (971) 6 5455654
Web Site: http://www.menco-group.me
Emp.: 6
Heating Equipment Mfr
N.A.I.C.S.: 333414
Ziat Hariri *(Dir)*

Monarch-Nederland B.V. (1)
Verrijn-Stuartweg 43, 1112 AW, Diemen, Netherlands
Tel.: (31) 20 6997401
Heating Equipment Mfr
N.A.I.C.S.: 333414

Neuberger Gebaudeautomation GmbH (1)
Oberer Kaiserweg 6, 91541, Rothenburg, Germany
Tel.: (49) 9861 4020
Web Site: http://www.neuberger.net
Emp.: 420
Heating Equipment Mfr
N.A.I.C.S.: 333414
Klaus Lenkner *(Gen Mgr)*

P.A.N. Heating Systems Ltd. (1)
9 Hamashbir St Industrial Zone, Holon, Israel
Tel.: (972) 3 5500 151
Heating Equipment Mfr
N.A.I.C.S.: 333414

P.T. Arianto Darmawan (1)
Jalan Hegarmanah No 63-65, Bandung, 40141, Indonesia
Tel.: (62) 22 2030100
Heating Equipment Mfr
N.A.I.C.S.: 333414

Plameks Trejd doo Skopje (1)
Ulica Petar Acev Br 19 A, 1000, Skopje, North Macedonia
Tel.: (389) 2 2401 135
Heating Equipment Mfr
N.A.I.C.S.: 333414

Pyropac AG (1)
Heberrietstrasse, 9466, Sennwald, Switzerland
Tel.: (41) 81 7581011
Heating Equipment Mfr
N.A.I.C.S.: 333414

RCR Energy Limited (1)
Level 2 6 Albion Street, Napier, 4110, New Zealand
Tel.: (64) 6 872 7600
Heating Equipment Mfr
N.A.I.C.S.: 333414

RCR Energy Service P/L. (1)
11 Howleys Rd, Notting Hill, 3168, VIC, Australia
Tel.: (61) 395418600
Heating Equipment Mfr
N.A.I.C.S.: 333414

Rajni International (1)
405-406 Shapath-II Sarkhej-Gandhinagar Road Bodakdev, Bodakdev, Ahmedabad, 380 015, India
Tel.: (91) 79 2687160 5
Heating Equipment Mfr
N.A.I.C.S.: 333414

S.A. Weishaupt N.V. (1)
Boulevard Paepsemlaan 7, 1070, Anderlecht, Belgium
Tel.: (32) 2 3430900
Web Site: http://www.weishaupt.com
Heating Equipment Mfr
N.A.I.C.S.: 333414

Sedical, S.A. (1)
Poligono Industrial de Aveleda Nave C Travessa do Bairro N 40, 4485-010, Vila do Conde, Portugal
Tel.: (351) 22999 6220
Heating Equipment Mfr
N.A.I.C.S.: 333414

Shinko Shoji Co., Ltd. (1)
1-4-5 Toranomon Minatoku, Tokyo, 105. 0001, Japan
Tel.: (81) 3 350 26241
Heating Equipment Mfr
N.A.I.C.S.: 333414

Singhotex Co., Ltd. (1)
5th Fl No 56 Hsi-Ning N Road, Taipei, Taiwan
Tel.: (886) 2 2552
Heating Equipment Mfr
N.A.I.C.S.: 333414

WINN Burner Asia Sdn Bhd (1)
Unit D-08-1 Jalan SS7/13A Plaza, Kelana Jaya, Petaling Jaya, Malaysia
Tel.: (60) 3 78777901
Heating Equipment Mfr
N.A.I.C.S.: 333414

Walter Bosch GmbH & Co KG (1)
Industrie Nord, 6890, Lustenau, Austria
Tel.: (43) 5577 81310
Heating Equipment Mfr
N.A.I.C.S.: 333414

Weishaupt (South Africa) Pty. Ltd. (1)
52 Gerhardus Street, Randburg, 2125, South Africa
Tel.: (27) 11 7936 711
Web Site: http://www.weishaupt.de
Emp.: 4
Heating Equipment Mfr
N.A.I.C.S.: 333414
Ted Bolger *(Gen Mgr)*

Weishaupt (UK) Ltd (1)
Neachells Lane Willenhall, West Midlands, Willenhall, WV13 3RG, West Midlands, United Kingdom
Tel.: (44) 1902 609841
Heating Equipment Mfr
N.A.I.C.S.: 333414

Weishaupt AG (1)
Chrummacherstrasse 8, 8954, Geroldswil, Switzerland
Tel.: (41) 44 74929 29
Heating Equipment Mfr
N.A.I.C.S.: 333414

Weishaupt America Inc. (1)
2587 Millennium Dr Unit A, Elgin, IL 60124
Tel.: (847) 531-5800
Heating Equipment Mfr
N.A.I.C.S.: 333414

Weishaupt Corporation (1)
6280 Danville Road, Mississauga, L5T 2H7, ON, Canada
Tel.: (905) 564-0946
Heating & Cooling System Mfr

MAX WEISHAUPT GMBH

Max Weishaupt GmbH—(Continued)
N.A.I.C.S.: 333415

Weishaupt Hotechnikai Kft. (1)
Budai U 6, 2051, Biatorbagy, Hungary
Tel.: (36) 623 5308 80
Heating Equipment Mfr
N.A.I.C.S.: 333414

Weishaupt Italia S.p.A. (1)
Via Toti 5, 21040, Gerenzano, Italy
Tel.: (39) 02 9619961
Heating Equipment Mfr
N.A.I.C.S.: 333414

Weishaupt Luxemburg S.a.r.l. (1)
17A Rue de l industrie, 8069, Bertrange, Luxembourg
Tel.: (352) 3108511
Web Site: http://www.weishaupt.lu
Renewable Energy Services
N.A.I.C.S.: 221114

Weishaupt Norge AS (1)
Kongsvingervegen 37, 2040, Klofta, Norway
Tel.: (47) 225114 00
Web Site: http://www.weishaupt.no
Heating Equipment Mfr
N.A.I.C.S.: 333414

Weishaupt Partner MICAL sarl (1)
Lot 178 Azur et Mer Sbaa Amar, Algiers, Bordj el Bahri, Algeria
Tel.: (213) 21 202670
Heating Equipment Mfr
N.A.I.C.S.: 333414

Weishaupt Partner Mizami Ltd. (1)
Tafawa Balewa Square Complex Suite 21B, West Pavilion Entrance 1, Lagos, 12539, Nigeria
Tel.: (234) 805 1992790
Emp.: 10
Heating Equipment Mfr
N.A.I.C.S.: 333414
A. M. Anand *(Office Mgr)*

Weishaupt Partner Sarl MICAL (1)
Lot 178 Azur et Mer, Algiers, 16000, Algeria
Tel.: (213) 23806300
Renewable Energy Services
N.A.I.C.S.: 221114

Weishaupt Polska Sp. z o.o. (1)
Ul Bazancia 55, 02-892, Warsaw, Poland
Tel.: (48) 223369400
Web Site: http://www.weishaupt.pl
Renewable Energy Services
N.A.I.C.S.: 221114

Weishaupt Polska Sp. z.o.o. (1)
Biuras Lietuvoje, Smolensko G 6 308, LT-03201, Vilnius, Lithuania
Tel.: (370) 5 23380 87
Heating Equipment Mfr
N.A.I.C.S.: 333414

Weishaupt Romania S.R.L. (1)
Str Leordeni Nr 161T, 077160, Popesti-Leordeni, Romania
Tel.: (40) 31 106 97 38
Heating Equipment Mfr
N.A.I.C.S.: 333414

Weishaupt S.A. (1)
Bureau GDL Rue des trois Cantons Zone d acitivites Am Brill 2, 3961, Ehlerange, Luxembourg
Tel.: (352) 310851
Heating & Cooling System Mfr
N.A.I.C.S.: 333415

Weishaupt SAS (1)
21 rue Andre Kiener, 689012, Colmar, Cedex, France
Tel.: (33) 389 205050
Web Site: http://www.weishaupt.fr
Heating Equipment Mfr
N.A.I.C.S.: 333414

Weishaupt Spol. s r.o (1)
Stranicka 1C/3177, 102 00, Prague, 10, Czech Republic
Tel.: (420) 272652142
Heating Equipment Mfr
N.A.I.C.S.: 333414

Weishaupt Svenska AB (1)
Enhagsvagen 10 Box 601, 18726, Taby, Sweden
Tel.: (46) 8 76805 40

Heating Equipment Mfr
N.A.I.C.S.: 333414

Weishaupt d.o.o. (1)
Fra Andela Zvizdovica 1, 71000, Sarajevo, Bosnia & Herzegovina
Tel.: (387) 33 296384
Heating Equipment Mfr
N.A.I.C.S.: 333414

Weishaupt d.o.o. (1)
Teharje 1, 3000, Celje, Slovenia
Tel.: (386) 34257250
Heating & Cooling System Mfr
N.A.I.C.S.: 333415

Weishaupt de Mexico S. de R.L. de C.V. (1)
Prolongacion Bernardo Quintana Ext 2481 Int Modulo 31, Mexico, 76137, Queretaro, Mexico
Tel.: (52) 4421610635
Renewable Energy Services
N.A.I.C.S.: 221114
Francisco Mendoza Roldan *(Natl Sls Mgr)*

Weishaupt do Brasil Industria e Comercio Ltda. (1)
Av Visconde de Indaiatuba 1 801, 13338-010, Indaiatuba, Sao Paulo, Brazil
Tel.: (55) 1938019800
Heating & Cooling System Mfr
N.A.I.C.S.: 333415

Weishaupt doo (1)
Bulevar Mihajla Pupina 6, 11070, Belgrade, Serbia
Tel.: (381) 112200601
Heating & Cooling System Mfr
N.A.I.C.S.: 333415

Weishaupt s.r.o. (1)
Strasnicka 3177/1C, 102 00, Prague, Czech Republic
Tel.: (420) 272652142
Web Site: http://www.weishauptcz.cz
Renewable Energy Services
N.A.I.C.S.: 221114

Weishaupt spol. s r.o (1)
Rakos 8835/1, 96001, Zvolen, Slovakia
Tel.: (421) 455321665
Heating & Cooling System Mfr
N.A.I.C.S.: 333415

Weishaupt-Zagreb d.o.o (1)
Dragutina Golika 61, 10000, Zagreb, Croatia
Tel.: (385) 1 365507 3
Heating Equipment Mfr
N.A.I.C.S.: 333414

MAX'S GROUP, INC.

3rd Floor KDC Plaza 2212 Chino Roces Avenue, Barangay Pio del Pilar, Makati, 1230, Philippines
Tel.: (63) 28424280 PH
Web Site: https://www.maxsgroupinc.com
Year Founded: 2000
MAXS—(PHI)
Rev.: $165,069,133
Assets: $256,363,508
Liabilities: $159,729,275
Net Worth: $96,634,232
Earnings: $8,774,795
Emp.: 2,288
Fiscal Year-end: 12/31/23
Holding Company; Restaurants Owner, Operator & Franchisor
N.A.I.C.S.: 551112
Robert Ramon F. Trota *(Pres & CEO)*

MAX-ATLAS EQUIPMENT INTERNATIONAL INC.

371 Chemin Grand Bernier Nord, Saint-Jean-sur-Richelieu, J3B 4S2, QC, Canada
Tel.: (450) 346-8848
Web Site: http://www.max-atlas.com
Year Founded: 1962
Rev.: $12,333,000
Emp.: 100
Truck Trailer Mfr
N.A.I.C.S.: 336212

Tibor Varga *(Pres)*

MAXAM CAPITAL CORP.

1245-200 Granville St, Vancouver, BC, Canada
Tel.: (604) 685-0201
Web Site: http://www.maxamcapitalcorp.com
Investment Firm
N.A.I.C.S.: 523999
Johnny Ciampi *(Mng Dir)*

MAXAMCORP HOLDING, S.L.

Avda del Partenon 16, 28042, Madrid, Spain
Tel.: (34) 917220100
Web Site: http://www.maxam.net
Year Founded: 1872
Civil Explosive Mfr & Whslr
N.A.I.C.S.: 424690
Jose Fernando Sanchez-Junco Mans *(Chm & CEO)*

MAXBIZ CORPORATION BERHAD

2B Jalan Wawasan 2 Kawasan Perindustrian Sri Gading, Km 9 Jalan Kluang, 83300, Batu Pahat, Johor Darul Takzim, Malaysia
Tel.: (60) 74558733
Sales Range: $1-9.9 Million
Textile Dyeing & Chemicals Sales
N.A.I.C.S.: 313310
Jee Wai Leong *(Mng Dir & CEO)*

Subsidiaries:

M.K.K. Industries Sdn. Bhd. (1)
2B Jalan Wawasan 2 Kawasan Perindustrian Sri Gading, Batu Pahat, Johor, Malaysia
Tel.: (60) 74558733
Textile Dyeing Services
N.A.I.C.S.: 313310

MAXBURG CAPITAL PARTNERS GMBH

Promenadeplatz 8, D-80333, Munich, Germany
Tel.: (49) 89235135950 De
Web Site: https://maxburg.com
Investment Services
N.A.I.C.S.: 523999

MAXCLEAN HOLDINGS LTD

88 Yu Feng Road Shuo Fang Town New District, Wuxi, Jiangsu, China
Tel.: (86) 510 8526 1996
Web Site: http://www.maxclean.com
MAXAF—(OTCIQ)
Sales Range: $1-9.9 Million
Emp.: 241
Contamination Control Supplies & Cleaning Products Mfr
N.A.I.C.S.: 325612
Chunming Yu *(Chm)*

MAXCOM S.A.

Towarowa 23a, 43-100, Tychy, Poland
Tel.: (48) 323277089
Web Site: https://www.maxcom.pl
MXC—(WAR)
Rev.: $35,420,223
Assets: $21,334,858
Liabilities: $6,574,695
Net Worth: $14,760,163
Earnings: $156,250
Fiscal Year-end: 12/31/23
Household Appliance Mfr & Distr
N.A.I.C.S.: 335220
Arkadiusz Wilusz *(CEO)*

MAXELL, LTD.

2-16-2 Konan Taiyo-Life Shinagawa Building 21F, Minato-ku, Tokyo, 108-8248, Japan
Tel.: (81) 357157037 JP

INTERNATIONAL PUBLIC

Web Site: https://www2.maxell.co.jp
Year Founded: 1960
6810—(TKS)
Rev.: $853,608,790
Assets: $1,130,971,000
Liabilities: $487,771,730
Net Worth: $643,199,270
Earnings: $49,865,840
Emp.: 3,956
Fiscal Year-end: 03/31/24
Holding Company; Energy Products, Industrial Materials & Electronics Mfr & Whslr
N.A.I.C.S.: 551112
Kenichi Sano *(Exec Officer)*

Subsidiaries:

Maxell (Shanghai) Trading Co., Ltd. (1)
Room 3601 Building 1 Kerry Everbright City No 218 West Tianmu Road, Shanghai, 200070, China
Tel.: (86) 2133303377
Battery Mfr & Distr
N.A.I.C.S.: 335999

Maxell (Shenzhen) Trading Co., Ltd. (1)
No 04 22F Caiwuwei Jinglong Building, 139 Hongbao Road Laowei Community Guiyuan Street, Luohu District, Shenzhen, China
Tel.: (86) 75582805220
Web Site: http://www.maxell.cn
Primary Battery Mfr
N.A.I.C.S.: 335910

Maxell Asia (Singapore) Pte Ltd. (1)
160 Robinson Road #16-03 SBF Centre, 068914, Singapore, Singapore
Tel.: (65) 62209291
Audio Recording Media Mfr
N.A.I.C.S.: 334610

Maxell Asia, Ltd. (1)
Unit Nos 03B-06 13/F No 909 Cheung Sha Wan Road, Cheung Sha Wan, Kowloon, China (Hong Kong)
Tel.: (852) 27309243
Web Site: http://www.maxell.com.hk
Optical Recording Media & Consumer Electronic Component Mfr
N.A.I.C.S.: 334310

Maxell Canada (1)
10 Parr Blvd Unit 106, Bolton, L4K 4V3, ON, Canada
Tel.: (905) 669-8107
Web Site: http://www.maxellcanada.com
Emp.: 100
Audio & Video Equipment & Computer Storage Device Mfr
N.A.I.C.S.: 334310
Lynn Land *(Gen Mgr)*

Maxell Corporation of America (1)
3 Garret Mtn Plz 3rd Fl Ste 300, Woodland Park, NJ 07424-3352 (100%)
Tel.: (973) 653-2400
Web Site: https://www.maxell-usa.com
Emp.: 125
Marketer & Retailer of Audio & Video Recording Media, Computer Media, Accessories & Batteries
N.A.I.C.S.: 541512

Maxell Deutschland GmbH (1)
Am Seestern 18, 40547, Dusseldorf, Germany
Tel.: (49) 2115283239
Audio Equipment Distr
N.A.I.C.S.: 423620

Maxell Digital Products China Co., Ltd. (1)
No 8 Hutang Road, Jin'an District, Fuzhou, 350014, Fujian, China
Tel.: (86) 59187897666
Web Site: http://www.maxell-dm.cn
Optical Instrument & Len Mfr
N.A.I.C.S.: 333310

Maxell Europe Ltd. (1)
Ground Floor Block E Sefton Park Bells Hill Stoke Poges, Buckinghamshire, SL2 4HD, United Kingdom
Tel.: (44) 1628412012
Web Site: http://www.maxell.eu

AND PRIVATE COMPANIES

Audio & Video Storage Device Mfr
N.A.I.C.S.: 334310

Maxell Frontier Co., Ltd. (1)
134 Kobecho Hodogaya-ku, Yokohama
Business Park North Square III, Yokohama
240-0005, Kanagawa, Japan
Tel.: (81) 452797707
Web Site: http://www.frontier.maxell.co.jp
Plastic Mold Mfr
N.A.I.C.S.: 333511
Masahiko Umeda *(Pres)*

Maxell Hungary KFT (1)
Ipar utca 5, 1095, Budapest, Hungary
Tel.: (36) 14643800
Computer Peripheral Equipment Whslr
N.A.I.C.S.: 423690

Maxell Izumi Co., Ltd. (1)
3039 Sasaga, Matsumoto, 399-8721, Nagano, Japan
Tel.: (81) 26 358 4115
Web Site: https://www.izumi.maxell.co.jp
Emp.: 284
Hydraulic Tool & Hydraulic Equipment Mfr
N.A.I.C.S.: 333996
Koji Norimatsu *(Pres & CEO)*

Maxell Kureha Co., Ltd. (1)
Sakaisuji-Hommachi TF Bldg 9th Floor 4-27
2-chome, Kyutaro-machi Chuo-ku, Osaka,
541-0056, Japan
Tel.: (81) 66 271 8292
Web Site: https://www.kurehae.maxell.co.jp
Emp.: 275
Rubber Wheel Mfr
N.A.I.C.S.: 326299
Kazuhiro Kaizaki *(Pres)*

Maxell Latin America S.A. (1)
19th Floor Office 19-D Oceania Business
Plaza Tower 2000, Punta Pacifica, Panama,
Panama
Tel.: (507) 2696291
Web Site: https://www.maxell-latin.com
Digital Media Products Distr
N.A.I.C.S.: 423690

Maxell Spain S.A. (1)
Balmes 89 6-2a, 08008, Barcelona, Spain
Tel.: (34) 933237013
Sales Range: $25-49.9 Million
Emp.: 5
Computer Peripheral Equipment Mfr
N.A.I.C.S.: 334118
Joan Simon *(Gen Mgr)*

Maxell Taiwan, Ltd. (1)
14F No 111 Sung Chiang Road, Taipei,
104, Taiwan
Tel.: (886) 2 2516 5553
Web Site: http://www.maxell.com.tw
Sales Range: $25-49.9 Million
Emp.: 17
Battery Mfr & Whslr
N.A.I.C.S.: 423610
Shangsong Zhaofu *(Chm)*

MAXEON SOLAR TECHNOLOGIES, LTD.
8 Marina Boulevard 05-02, Marina
Bay Financial Centre, Singapore,
018981, Singapore
Tel.: (65) 63381888 SG
Web Site: https://www.maxeon.com
Year Founded: 2019
MAXN—(NASDAQ)
Rev.: $1,060,113,000
Assets: $1,260,418,000
Liabilities: $1,212,348,000
Net Worth: $48,070,000
Earnings: ($267,146,000)
Emp.: 5,344
Fiscal Year-end: 01/01/23
Solar Panel Mfr
N.A.I.C.S.: 334519
Bill Mulligan *(CEO)*

MAXFASTIGHETER I SVERIGE AB
Eskilstunavagen 34, 644 30, Torshalla, Sweden
Tel.: (46) 162006990
Web Site:
http://www.maxfastigheter.se

MAXF—(OMX)
Rev.: $15,577,160
Assets: $283,287,820
Liabilities: $189,974,901
Net Worth: $93,312,919
Earnings: $11,159,612
Emp.: 8
Fiscal Year-end: 12/31/19
Real Estate Manangement Services
N.A.I.C.S.: 531311
Hakan Karlsson *(Founder & CEO)*

MAXGROW INDIA LTD.
A/9 Parle Colony Co-Operative Housing Society Limited Sahakar Road,
Vile Parle East, Mumbai, 400057,
Maharashtra, India
Tel.: (91) 2226824197 In
Web Site: http://www.frontlinegroup.in
Rev.: $1,311,568
Assets: $3,455,020
Liabilities: $1,625,600
Net Worth: $1,829,420
Earnings: ($16,711)
Emp.: 8
Fiscal Year-end: 03/31/18
Holding Company; Human Resource
Services
N.A.I.C.S.: 551112
Roshni Rahul Saraf *(Chm & Mng Dir)*

MAXICITY HOLDINGS LIMITED
Room 1A 6/F Crystal Harbour Center
100 Granville Road, Tsim sha tsui,
Kowloon, China (Hong Kong)
Tel.: (852) 35982926 Ky
Web Site: http://www.maxicity.com.hk
Year Founded: 2013
2295—(HKG)
Rev.: $24,512,895
Assets: $26,386,508
Liabilities: $4,821,413
Net Worth: $21,565,095
Earnings: $1,845,563
Emp.: 137
Fiscal Year-end: 12/31/22
Holding Company
N.A.I.C.S.: 551112
Shing Kee Sieh *(Chm)*

MAXIGEN BIOTECH INC.
No 88 Keji 1st Rd, Guishan Dist,
Taoyuan, 333, Taiwan
Tel.: (886) 33287222
Web Site: https://mbi-bio.com
Year Founded: 1998
1783—(TAI)
Rev.: $20,344,517
Assets: $48,823,897
Liabilities: $4,312,862
Net Worth: $44,511,035
Earnings: $5,422,937
Emp.: 100
Fiscal Year-end: 12/31/23
Biomedical & Cosmeceutical Skincare
Products Mfr
N.A.I.C.S.: 325412
Sung-Ching Chen *(Pres & Head-Biomedical BU)*

MAXIGRAF, S.A.
Avenue Carlos Arosemena km 2,
Guayaquil, Ecuador
Tel.: (593) 42200136
Sales Range: $100-124.9 Million
Emp.: 350
Commercial Printing & Graphic Designing Services
N.A.I.C.S.: 323111
Juan Carlos Plaza *(CEO)*

MAXIM GLOBAL BERHAD
No 2D Jalan SS6/6 Kelana Jaya,
47301, Petaling Jaya, Selangor Darul
Ehsan, Malaysia
Tel.: (60) 378037008

Web Site:
https://maximglobal.com.my
Year Founded: 1968
MAXIM—(KLS)
Rev.: $25,446,670
Assets: $179,973,662
Liabilities: $66,621,028
Net Worth: $113,352,635
Earnings: $1,780,583
Emp.: 99
Fiscal Year-end: 12/31/23
Investment Holding Company
N.A.I.C.S.: 523999
Abdul Samad Alias *(Chm)*

MAXIM POWER CORP.
1800 715 - 5th Avenue SW, Calgary,
T2P 2X6, AB, Canada
Tel.: (403) 263-3021 AB
Web Site:
https://www.maximpowercorp.com
MXG—(TSX)
Sales Range: $1-9.9 Million
Emp.: 45
Electric Power Generation, Transmission & Distr
N.A.I.C.S.: 221122
M. Bruce Chernoff *(Chm)*

Subsidiaries:

Maxim Power (Austria) GmbH (1)
Grubenweg 5, Aldrans, Innsbruck, 6071,
Austria
Tel.: (43) 512346644
Electric Power Generation
N.A.I.C.S.: 221118

Maxim Power Europe BV (1)
Koningin Emmalaan 13, 1405 CJ, Bussum,
Netherlands
Tel.: (31) 356919285
Electric Power Generation
N.A.I.C.S.: 221118

Milner Power Inc. (1)
1210 715 - 5th Avenue S W, Calgary, T2P
2X6, AB, Canada **(100%)**
Tel.: (403) 263-3021
Web Site: https://milnerpower.com
Emp.: 50
Electric Power Generation
N.A.I.C.S.: 221118

Milner Power Limited Partnership (1)
715 5 Ave SW Ste 1210, Calgary, T2p 2x6,
AB, Canada
Tel.: (403) 750-9319
Thermal Coal Distr
N.A.I.C.S.: 423520

MAXIM RESOURCES INC.
Suite 1050 409 Granville Street, Vancouver, V6C 1T2, BC, Canada
Tel.: (604) 630-0280
Web Site:
http://www.maximresources.com
Year Founded: 1988
Sales Range: Less than $1 Million
Oil & Gas Exploration Services
N.A.I.C.S.: 213112

MAXIMAA SYSTEMS LIMITED
B-1 Yashkamal Tithal Road, Valsad,
396001, Gujarat, India
Tel.: (91) 2632222402
Web Site:
http://www.maximaasystems.com
Year Founded: 1991
Rev.: $1,685,346
Assets: $6,015,697
Liabilities: $3,505,497
Net Worth: $2,510,200
Earnings: ($33,879)
Emp.: 68
Fiscal Year-end: 03/31/19
Furniture Mfr
N.A.I.C.S.: 337215
Manoj Shah *(Co-Founder)*

MAXIMUM ENTERTAINMENT AB

Subsidiaries:

Maximaa Proyurveda Ltd. (1)
104 Shreeji Sharan Above ICICI Bank S M
Marg, Kandivali W, Mumbai, 400 067, India
Tel.: (91) 22 28076366
Web Site:
http://www.maximaaproyurveda.com
Pharmaceutical Product Mfr & Distr
N.A.I.C.S.: 325412
Mayur Shah *(Co-Mng Dir)*

MAXIMIZER SOFTWARE, INC.
208 W 1st Ave, Vancouver, V5Y 3T2,
BC, Canada
Tel.: (604) 601-8000
Web Site: http://wwwmaximizer.com
Sales Range: $10-24.9 Million
Emp.: 199
Customer & Contact Management
Software Solutions
N.A.I.C.S.: 541512
Terence Hui *(Chm)*

Subsidiaries:

Maximizer Asia Limited (1)
17th Fl Regent Ctr, 88 Queen's Rd, Central,
China (Hong Kong)
Tel.: (852) 25982888
Web Site: http://www.maximizer.com.hk
Business Software Solutions
N.A.I.C.S.: 541511

Maximizer Software Ltd. (1)
Apex House, London Road, Bracknell,
RG12 2XH, Berkshire, United Kingdom
Tel.: (44) 01628587777
Web Site: http://www.max.co.uk
Business Software Solutions
N.A.I.C.S.: 541511
Vivek Thomas *(Pres)*

**Maximizer Software Solutions Pty.,
Ltd.** (1)
815 Pacific Highway, Chatswood, 2067,
NSW, Australia
Tel.: (61) 299572011
Web Site: http://www.maximizer.com.au
Business Software Solutions
N.A.I.C.S.: 541511

MAXIMUM ENTERTAINMENT AB
Kungsgatan 64, 111 22, Stockholm,
Sweden
Tel.: (46) 706549541
Web Site: http://zordix.com
MAXENT.B—(OMX)
Rev.: $134,252,688
Assets: $153,999,347
Liabilities: $89,068,737
Net Worth: $64,930,610
Earnings: ($17,250,283)
Emp.: 233
Fiscal Year-end: 12/31/23
Game Developer & Publisher
N.A.I.C.S.: 513210
Malin Jonsson *(Chm)*

Subsidiaries:

Maximum Games LLC (1)
590 Ygnacio Valley Rd Ste 220, Walnut
Creek, CA 94596
Web Site: http://www.maximumgames.com
Sales Range: $10-24.9 Million
Emp.: 13
Entertainment Software Development Services
N.A.I.C.S.: 541511
Ally Davis *(Project Mgr)*

Subsidiary (Domestic):

Modus Games LLC (2)
590 Ygnacio Valley Rd Ste 220, Walnut
Creek, CA 94596
Tel.: (925) 478-2185
Web Site: http://modusgames.com
Electronic Games
N.A.I.C.S.: 713990
Christina Seelye *(CEO)*

MAXIMUS INTERNATIONAL LIMITED

Maximum Entertainment AB—(Continued)

MAXIMUS INTERNATIONAL LIMITED
504A OZONE Dr Vikram Sarabhai Marg Vadi-wadi, Vadodara, 390003, Gujarat, India
Tel.: (91) 2652345321
Web Site: https://www.maximusinternational.in
Year Founded: 2015
540401—(BOM)
Rev.: $12,143,325
Assets: $9,244,422
Liabilities: $4,366,908
Net Worth: $4,877,513
Earnings: $873,785
Emp.: 6
Fiscal Year-end: 03/31/23
Lubricant Product Mfr
N.A.I.C.S.: 333914

Subsidiaries:

Maximus Lubricant LLC (1)
Warehouse No A 03/04 Al Jazeera Al Hamra Opposite AIC, Ras al Khaimah, United Arab Emirates
Tel.: (971) 501897928
Web Site: https://www.motorollubes.com
Lubricant Oil Mfr
N.A.I.C.S.: 324191

Quantum Lubricants (E.A) Limited (1)
Broadway Warehouse Gate No 2 GD/No 20 Opp Nation Printing, PO Box 38981, Behind Med's Centre Mombasa Road, 00623, Nairobi, Kenya
Tel.: (254) 732200400
Lubricant Oil Whslr
N.A.I.C.S.: 811191

MAXIMUS RESOURCES LIMITED
Tel.: (61) 873243172
Web Site: http://www.maximusresources.com
MXR—(ASX)
Rev.: $363,196
Assets: $13,733,295
Liabilities: $256,228
Net Worth: $13,477,066
Earnings: ($824,908)
Emp.: 50
Fiscal Year-end: 06/30/22
Gold Mining & Exploration Services
N.A.I.C.S.: 212220
Rajita Alwis (Sec)

MAXINGVEST AG
Alter Wandrahm 17/18, 20457, Hamburg, Germany
Tel.: (49) 4052868696   De
Web Site: http://www.maxingvest.de
Year Founded: 1949
Sales Range: $15-24.9 Billion
Holding Company
N.A.I.C.S.: 551112
Reinhard D. Pollath (Chm-Supervisory Bd)

Subsidiaries:

Beiersdorf AG (1)
Beiersdorfstrasse 1-9, 22529, Hamburg, Germany   (50.46%)
Tel.: (49) 4049090
Web Site: https://www.beiersdorf.com
Rev.: $10,195,337,794
Assets: $13,629,397,798
Liabilities: $4,629,829,484
Net Worth: $8,999,568,314
Earnings: $808,331,535
Emp.: 21,958
Fiscal Year-end: 12/31/2023
Personal Care Product Distr
N.A.I.C.S.: 325620
Reinhard D. Pollath (Chm-Supervisory Bd)

Subsidiary (Non-US):

BDF Centro America S.A. (2)
Edificio Tikal Futura Torre Luna Nivel 10, Calzada Roosevelt 22 43, 01011, Guatemala, Guatemala
Tel.: (502) 3281111
Web Site: http://www.beiersdorf.com
Sales Range: $25-49.9 Million
Emp.: 60
Consumer Health Care Products Whslr
N.A.I.C.S.: 456199

BDF Corporativo, S.A. de C.V. (2)
Norte 35 No 695, 02300, Mexico, Mexico
Tel.: (52) 5557290200
Skin Care Products Distr
N.A.I.C.S.: 424210
Alexander Reindler (Gen Mgr)

BDF Costa Rica, S.A. (2)
Centro Corporativo Plaza Roble Boulevard Multiplaza contiguo al Hotel, San Jose, Costa Rica
Tel.: (506) 2201 8020
Web Site: http://www.beiersdorf.co.cr
Skin Care Products Distr
N.A.I.C.S.: 424210

BDF El Salvador S.A. de C.V. (2)
17 Avenida Sur No 1073 Urbanizacion San Jose Del Pino, Edificio Diszasa, San Salvador, Santa Tecla, El Salvador
Tel.: (503) 2288 8678
Web Site: http://www.beiersdorf.com
Sales Range: $25-49.9 Million
Emp.: 6
Pharmaceuticals & Toiletries Whslr
N.A.I.C.S.: 325412
Ronny Quan (Mng Dir)

BDF Mexico, S.A. de C.V. (2)
243 010 Colnia Cuauhtemoc, 6005, Mexico, Mexico
Tel.: (52) 55 5729 0200
Web Site: http://www.beiersdorf.com.mx
Skin Care Products Distr
N.A.I.C.S.: 424210

BDF NIVEA LTDA. (2)
Rua Alexandre Dumas 1711 Cond Edificio Birmann 11 - 6/7, Andar Chac Sto Antonio, Sao Paulo, Brazil
Tel.: (55) 11 5097 3800
Web Site: http://www.beiersdorf.com.br
Skin Care Products Distr
N.A.I.C.S.: 424210
Lucio Favari (Mgr-IT)

BDF Nivea S.A. (2)
Avenida De La Industria 31, E 28760, Tres Cantos, Madrid, Spain   (100%)
Tel.: (34) 918488200
Sales Range: $100-124.9 Million
Emp.: 300
Mfr of Toiletries
N.A.I.C.S.: 325620

BDF Panama S.A. (2)
Via Ricardo J Alfaro La Alameda, Calle 63 F No 26 Local B, Panama, Panama
Tel.: (507) 2368785
Web Site: http://www.beiersdorf.com.pa
Sales Range: $25-49.9 Million
Emp.: 5
Pharmaceuticals & Toiletries Whslr
N.A.I.C.S.: 325412

Beiersdorf (Malaysia) SDN. BHD. (2)
T1-12 Level 12 of Jaya 33 No 3 Jalan Semangat Sec 13, Petaling Jaya, 46200, Selangor, Malaysia
Tel.: (60) 3 7940 9668
Web Site: http://www.beiersdorf.my
Skin Care Products Distr
N.A.I.C.S.: 424210
Hock Guan Ng (Country Mgr)

Beiersdorf (Thailand) Co., Ltd. (2)
12 17 Floor Sathorn Thani Building I, 90 N Sathorn Road, Bangkok, 10500, Thailand   (100%)
Tel.: (66) 26657999
Web Site: http://www.beiersdorf.com
Sales Range: $50-74.9 Million
Emp.: 150
Silicone Release Paper Mfr
N.A.I.C.S.: 322120

Beiersdorf A/S (2)
Tevlingveien 23, 1081, Oslo, Norway   (100%)
Tel.: (47) 22907950
Web Site: http://www.beiersdorf.no
Sales Range: $25-49.9 Million
Emp.: 35
Cosmetics, Pharmaceuticals, Medical & Tesa Products
N.A.I.C.S.: 325620

Beiersdorf A/S (2)
Stdhavnjgae 16 2nd Fl, 2450, Copenhagen, Denmark   (100%)
Tel.: (45) 33450000
Web Site: http://www.beiersdorf.com
Sales Range: $25-49.9 Million
Emp.: 40
Pharmaceuticals & Toiletries Whslr
N.A.I.C.S.: 325412

Beiersdorf AB (2)
Gullbergs Strandgata 4, Gothenburg, 40124, Sweden   (100%)
Tel.: (46) 317990800
Web Site: http://www.beiersdorf.se
Sales Range: $100-124.9 Million
Emp.: 50
Cosmetics, Pharmaceuticals, Medical & Tesa Products
N.A.I.C.S.: 325620
Cornelius Becker (Mng Dir)

Beiersdorf Australia Ltd. (2)
4 Khartoum Rd, North Ryde, 2113, NSW, Australia   (100%)
Tel.: (61) 298880977
Web Site: http://www.beiersdorf.com.au
Sales Range: $25-49.9 Million
Emp.: 70
Pharmaceuticals & Cosmetics Mfr
N.A.I.C.S.: 325412

Beiersdorf Bulgaria EOOD (2)
Sofia Tower Al Stamboliiski Boulevard 103 5th floor, 1303, Sofia, Bulgaria
Tel.: (359) 2 923 16 00
Web Site: http://www.beiersdorf.bg
Emp.: 30
Skin Care Products Distr
N.A.I.C.S.: 424210
Maria Shtereva (Head-HR & Office Mgr)

Beiersdorf Canada Inc. (2)
2344 Alfred Nobel Blvd Suite 100A, Saint Laurent, H4S 0A4, QC, Canada   (100%)
Tel.: (514) 956-4330
Web Site: http://www.beiersdorf.ca
Sales Range: $25-49.9 Million
Emp.: 50
Pharmaceuticals & Toiletries Mfr
N.A.I.C.S.: 325412
Tobias Collee (Gen Mgr)

Beiersdorf Consumer Products (Pty.) Ltd. (2)
4th Floor Beacon Rock 21 Lighthouse Road, Umhlanga, 4319, South Africa
Tel.: (27) 31 267 85 00
Web Site: http://www.beiersdorf.co.za
Skin Care Products Distr
N.A.I.C.S.: 424210
Cindy Moodley (Mgr-Quality Assurance)

Beiersdorf Daily Chemical (Guangzhou) Co., Ltd. (2)
Fucong Road Economic & Technology Development, Conghua, Guangzhou, China
Tel.: (86) 20 61706666
Skin Care Products Distr
N.A.I.C.S.: 424210

Beiersdorf Daily Chemical (Hubei) Co., Ltd. (2)
No 1 Sibao Road, Xiantao, Hubei, China
Tel.: (86) 27 593 56 888
Skin Care Products Distr
N.A.I.C.S.: 424210

Beiersdorf Daily Chemical (Wuhan) Co., Ltd. (2)
C-BONS International Building No 512 Dongfeng Road Wuhan Economic, Technological Development Zone, 430056, Wuhan, Hubei, China
Tel.: (86) 27 593 56 689
Skin Care Products Distr
N.A.I.C.S.: 424210

Beiersdorf East Africa Ltd. (2)
Sasio Rd, PO Box 78273, Nairobi, 500507, Kenya   (100%)
Tel.: (254) 20530051

INTERNATIONAL PUBLIC

Web Site: http://www.beiersdorf.com
Sales Range: $50-74.9 Million
Emp.: 130
Pharmaceuticals & Toiletries Mfr
N.A.I.C.S.: 325412

Beiersdorf GmbH (2)
Laxenburger Str 151, 1100, Vienna, Austria
Tel.: (43) 1614000
Web Site: http://www.beiersdorf.com
Sales Range: $50-74.9 Million
Emp.: 250
Cosmetics, Pharmaceuticals & Medical Products Mfr
N.A.I.C.S.: 325620
Nitja Oqutancic (Mgr)

Subsidiary (Domestic):

Beiersdorf Hautpflege GmbH (2)
Wiesingerweg 25, 20253, Hamburg, Germany
Tel.: (49) 40 49 09 92 22
Skin Care Product Mfr
N.A.I.C.S.: 325620

Subsidiary (Non-US):

Beiersdorf Hellas AE (2)
Aghiou Nektariou Strasse 2 Geracas, Athens, 15344, Greece   (100%)
Tel.: (30) 2106600100
Web Site: http://www.beiersdorf.gr
Sales Range: $50-74.9 Million
Emp.: 250
Cosmetics, Pharmaceuticals, Medical Products Mfr
N.A.I.C.S.: 325620

Beiersdorf Holding B.V. (2)
De Passage 126-136, 1101 AX, Amsterdam, Netherlands
Tel.: (31) 885 440000
Holding Company
N.A.I.C.S.: 551112

Beiersdorf India Pvt. Ltd. (2)
Unit No 501-502 5th Floor Sej Plaza Off S V Roade Marve Road, Malad West, 400064, Mumbai, India
Tel.: (91) 832 2332034
Web Site: http://www.niveaindia.in
Skin Care Products Distr
N.A.I.C.S.: 424210

Beiersdorf Industria e Comercio Ltda. (2)
Estrada Municipal Bendito Antonio Regagnin Barrio dos Pintos 1470, Itatiba, Sao Paulo, Brazil
Tel.: (55) 11 5097 3800
Skin Care Products Distr
N.A.I.C.S.: 424210

Beiersdorf Ireland Ltd. (2)
First Floor Block 8 St John's Court, Santry, Dublin, Ireland
Tel.: (353) 1 844 2200
Web Site: http://www.beiersdorf.ie
Skin Care Products Distr
N.A.I.C.S.: 424210
Michelle Ryan (Mgr-Bus Dev)

Beiersdorf Kazakhstan LLP (2)
Office 903 136 Dostyc Av, 050051, Almaty, Kazakhstan
Tel.: (7) 727 313 0728 0
Web Site: http://www.nivea.kz
Emp.: 20
Skin Care Products Distr
N.A.I.C.S.: 424210
Burger Gewitt (Gen Mgr)

Beiersdorf Kft. (2)
Tartsay Vilmos Utca 3, HU 1126, Budapest, Hungary   (100%)
Tel.: (36) 4573900
Web Site: http://www.beierdorf.com
Sales Range: $25-49.9 Million
Emp.: 75
Pharmaceuticals & Cosmetics Mfr
N.A.I.C.S.: 325412

Beiersdorf Kimya Sanayi ve Ticaret A.S. (2)
Buyukdere Caddesi 185, Levent, 34394, Istanbul, Turkiye   (100%)
Tel.: (90) 2123717700
Web Site: http://www.beiersdorf.com.tr

AND PRIVATE COMPANIES — MAXINGVEST AG

Sales Range: $25-49.9 Million
Emp.: 50
Pharmaceuticals & Toiletries Mfr
N.A.I.C.S.: 325412
Coskun Beduk *(Gen Mgr)*

Beiersdorf Korea Ltd. (2)
Ace Tower 21F 1-170 Soonhwa-dong, chung-ku, Seoul, Korea (South)
Tel.: (82) 2 6742 0800
Web Site: http://www.beiersdorf.co.kr
Skin Care Products Distr
N.A.I.C.S.: 424210
Alexander Kruemke *(Bus Dir-Pharmacy Brands)*

Beiersdorf Manufacturing Argentona, S.L. (2)
Carretera de Mataro a Granollers KM 5 6, 08310, Barcelona, Spain
Tel.: (34) 93 7583 0
Skin Care Product Mfr
N.A.I.C.S.: 424210
Jordi Guijarro *(Mng Dir)*

Subsidiary (Domestic):

Beiersdorf Manufacturing Hamburg GmbH (2)
Troplowitzstr 10, 22529, Hamburg, Germany
Tel.: (49) 40 4909 0
Skin Care Product Mfr & Distr
N.A.I.C.S.: 325620
Joerg Schwartze *(Mng Dir)*

Beiersdorf Manufacturing Waldheim GmbH (2)
Am Eichberg, 04736, Waldheim, Germany
Tel.: (49) 34327 98 0
Skin Care Product Mfr
N.A.I.C.S.: 325620

Subsidiary (Non-US):

Beiersdorf Maroc S.A. (2)
Lotissement Attawfiq, Rue 1 Immeuble 29 3 Etage, Sidi Maarouf, Casablanca, 20190, Morocco
Tel.: (212) 22973636
Web Site: http://www.beiersdorf.com
Sales Range: $25-49.9 Million
Emp.: 65
Pharmaceuticals & Toiletries Mfr
N.A.I.C.S.: 325412

Beiersdorf Middle East FZCO (2)
1st Floor Zee Tower Dubai Media City, PO Box 502350, Dubai, United Arab Emirates
Tel.: (971) 4 367 1047
Web Site: http://www.beiersdorf.ae
Skin Care Products Distr
N.A.I.C.S.: 424210

Beiersdorf NV (2)
Bldg Amaliawolde, Amalialaan 126C, Baarn, 3743 KJ, Netherlands (100%)
Tel.: (31) 355440000
Web Site: http://www.beiersdorf.nl
Sales Range: $25-49.9 Million
Emp.: 80
Cosmetics, Pharmaceuticals & Medical Products Mfr
N.A.I.C.S.: 325620

Subsidiary (US):

Beiersdorf North America Inc. (2)
45 Danbury Rd, Wilton, CT 06897
Tel.: (203) 563-5800
Web Site: http://www.bdfusa.com
Sales Range: $450-499.9 Million
Emp.: 2,025
Holding Company
N.A.I.C.S.: 325620
Oliver Schrader *(Gen Mgr)*

Subsidiary (Domestic):

La Prairie, Inc. (3)
680 5th Ave 14th Fl, New York, NY 10019-5429
Tel.: (212) 506-0840
Web Site: http://www.laprairie.com
Sales Range: $25-49.9 Million
Emp.: 50
Skin Care Products Retailer
N.A.I.C.S.: 424210
Patrick Rasquinet *(CEO)*

Subsidiary (Non-US):

Beiersdorf OOO (2)
Zelmlyanoy Val Street 9, 105064, Moscow, Russia (100%)
Tel.: (7) 4952584022
Web Site: http://www.beiersdorf.ru
Sales Range: $50-74.9 Million
Emp.: 130
Pharmaceuticals & Toiletries Whslr
N.A.I.C.S.: 325412

Beiersdorf OU (2)
Sepise 18 20, EE 11415, Tallinn, Estonia (100%)
Tel.: (372) 6401360
Web Site: http://www.beiersdorf.com
Sales Range: $25-49.9 Million
Emp.: 15
Provider of Pharmaceuticals & Toiletries
N.A.I.C.S.: 325412

Beiersdorf Oy (2)
PO Box 91 20101, FIN 20780, Turku, Finland (100%)
Tel.: (358) 24103200
Web Site: http://www.beiersdorf.com
Sales Range: $25-49.9 Million
Emp.: 17
Cosmetics, Pharmaceuticals & Medical Products Mfr
N.A.I.C.S.: 325620
Leena Heino *(Office Mgr)*

Beiersdorf Personal Care (China) Co., Ltd. (2)
Floor 5 Wuhan Wanda Center No 96 Linjiang Avenue, Wuchang District, Wuhan, China
Tel.: (86) 27 59356888
Web Site: http://www.en.beiersdorf.cn
Skin Care Products Distr
N.A.I.C.S.: 424210

Beiersdorf Philippines Incorporated (2)
11th Floor Unit 4 Bench Tower 30th Street Corner Rizal Drive, Bonifacio Global City, 1634, Taguig, Philippines
Tel.: (63) 2 856 6556
Web Site: http://www.beiersdorf.ph
Skin Care Products Distr
N.A.I.C.S.: 424210
Alice Cayaban *(Mgr-HR)*

Beiersdorf Portuguesa Lda (2)
Rua Soeiro Pereira Gomes 59, Queluz, 2746-952, Portugal (100%)
Tel.: (351) 214368500
Web Site: http://www.beiersdorf.com
Sales Range: $50-74.9 Million
Emp.: 110
Cosmetics, Pharmaceuticals & Medical Products Mfr
N.A.I.C.S.: 325620

Beiersdorf Romania SRL (2)
Calea Serban Voda nr 133 Corp C et 2 Sector 4, 040205, Bucharest, Romania
Tel.: (40) 2 1 317 00 00
Web Site: http://www.beiersdorf.ro
Skin Care Products Distr
N.A.I.C.S.: 424210

Beiersdorf S.A. (2)
Calle 100 #19-54 Piso 10, Edificio Prime Tower, Bogota, D.C., Colombia (100%)
Tel.: (57) 1 644 7790
Web Site: http://www.beiersdorf.com.co
Sales Range: $50-74.9 Million
Emp.: 250
Cosmetics, Medical Products & Adhesive Tapes Mfr & Distr
N.A.I.C.S.: 325620
Rodrigo Guzman *(Gen Mgr)*

Beiersdorf S.A. (2)
118 Ave de France, 75013, Paris, France
Tel.: (33) 170373200
Web Site: http://www.beiersdorf.com
Sales Range: $200-249.9 Million
Emp.: 770
Cosmetics Mfr
N.A.I.C.S.: 325620

Beiersdorf S.A. (2)
Carretera de Mataro a Granollers C-1415 Km 5 6, PO Box 4, 08310, Argentona, Barcelona, Spain (100%)
Tel.: (34) 937583300

Web Site: http://www.beiersdorf.com
Sales Range: $100-124.9 Million
Emp.: 300
Medical & Tesa Products Mfr
N.A.I.C.S.: 325998
Mauricio Valdes *(Mng Dir)*

Beiersdorf S.A. (2)
Triunvirato 2902, 1427, Buenos Aires, Argentina (100%)
Tel.: (54) 1145530040
Web Site: http://www.beiersdorf.com
Sales Range: $25-49.9 Million
Emp.: 100
Industrial Adhesives, Cosmetics & Pharmaceutical Products Mfr
N.A.I.C.S.: 325412

Beiersdorf S.A. (2)
Camino Lo Espejo 501, Maipu, 13393, Chile (100%)
Tel.: (56) 23688800
Web Site: http://www.beiersdorf.com
Sales Range: $100-124.9 Million
Emp.: 300
Pharmaceuticals & Toiletries Mfr
N.A.I.C.S.: 325412

Beiersdorf S.A. (2)
Av Juan Panamericana Norte Km 7 1/2 Manuel Najas, No 134 y Juan de Selis, Quito, Ecuador (100%)
Tel.: (593) 22473473
Web Site: http://www.beiersdorf.ec
Sales Range: $25-49.9 Million
Emp.: 50
Pharmaceuticals & Toiletries Mfr
N.A.I.C.S.: 325412

Beiersdorf S.A. (2)
Av Mcal Lopez 3.794 esq Cruz del Chaco, Edificio Citibank Ctr Piso 10, Asuncion, Paraguay (100%)
Tel.: (595) 21621360
Web Site: http://www.beiersdorf.com.py
Sales Range: $25-49.9 Million
Emp.: 30
Toiletries & Pharmaceuticals Mfr
N.A.I.C.S.: 325412

Beiersdorf S.A. (2)
Av Brasil 2697, P 4 Apto 10, CP 11300, Montevideo, Uruguay (100%)
Tel.: (598) 27067108
Web Site: http://www.beiersdorf.com
Sales Range: $25-49.9 Million
Emp.: 8
Pharmaceuticals & Toiletries Mfr & Distr
N.A.I.C.S.: 325412
Jose Vazquez *(Gen Mgr)*

Beiersdorf S.A. (2)
Avenida Francisco de Miranda cruce con Avenida Libertador, Edificio KPMG Piso 4 Oficina 4, Municipio Chacao, Caracas, Venezuela
Tel.: (58) 212 5262411
Web Site: http://www.beiersdorf.com
Sales Range: $25-49.9 Million
Emp.: 30
Cosmetics & Toiletries Mfr
N.A.I.C.S.: 325620

Beiersdorf S.A.C. (2)
Edificio Torre Parque Mar Av Larco 1301 Piso 18, Miraflores, Lima, L 18, Peru (100%)
Tel.: (51) 6104848
Web Site: http://www.beiersdorf.com.pe
Sales Range: $50-74.9 Million
Emp.: 130
Pharmaceuticals & Toiletries Mfr
N.A.I.C.S.: 325412
Luis Leey *(Country Mgr)*

Beiersdorf S.R.L. (2)
Torre Enpresarial 710 Piso 16, Calle Cochabamba Esq Saavedra, Santa Cruz, 00591, Bolivia (100%)
Tel.: (591) 33376928
Web Site: http://www.beiersdorf.com
Sales Range: $25-49.9 Million
Emp.: 40
Pharmaceuticals & Cosmetics Mfr
N.A.I.C.S.: 325412
David Padilla *(Gen Mgr)*

Subsidiary (Domestic):

Beiersdorf Shared Services GmbH (2)

Quickbornstrasse 24, 20253, Hamburg, Germany
Tel.: (49) 40 4909 105
Information Technology Consulting Services
N.A.I.C.S.: 541512
Alexandra Striewski *(Mgr-HR & Comm)*

Subsidiary (Non-US):

Beiersdorf Singapore Pte. Ltd. (2)
101 Thomson Rd, No 31 03 05 United Sq, Singapore, 307591, Singapore (100%)
Tel.: (65) 62522288
Web Site: http://www.beiersdorf.com
Sales Range: $25-49.9 Million
Emp.: 25
Pharmaceuticals Product Mfr
N.A.I.C.S.: 325412
Ng Hock Guan *(Dir-Mktg)*

Beiersdorf Slovakia, s.r.o. (2)
Reznerova 5, SK 81101, Bratislava, Slovakia (100%)
Tel.: (421) 257101611
Web Site: http://www.beiersdorf.com
Sales Range: $10-24.9 Million
Emp.: 25
Pharmaceuticals & Toiletries Mfr
N.A.I.C.S.: 325412

Beiersdorf SpA (2)
Via Eraclito 30, 20128, Milan, Italy
Tel.: (39) 02257721
Web Site: http://www.beiersdorf.it
Sales Range: $200-249.9 Million
Emp.: 600
Cosmetics, Pharmaceuticals & Medical Products Mfr
N.A.I.C.S.: 325620

Plant (Non-US):

Beiersdorf Thailand Co. Ltd. (2)
163 Bang Plee Industrial Est, PO Box 24, Bangsaothong Bang Plee, Samut Prakan, 10540, Thailand (100%)
Tel.: (66) 231510435
Web Site: http://www.beiersdorf.com
Sales Range: $50-74.9 Million
Emp.: 150
Pharmaceuticals Product Mfr
N.A.I.C.S.: 325412

Subsidiary (Non-US):

Beiersdorf U.K. Limited (2)
2010 Solihull Parkway, Birmingham Business Park, Birmingham, B37 7YS, United Kingdom (100%)
Tel.: (44) 1213298800
Web Site: http://www.beiersdorf.co.uk
Sales Range: $50-74.9 Million
Emp.: 150
Pharmaceuticals & Toiletries Mfr
N.A.I.C.S.: 325412
Ralph Guskao *(Mng Dir)*

Beiersdorf UAB (2)
Eisiskiu Pl 8 A, 2038, Vilnius, Lithuania (100%)
Tel.: (370) 52159232
Web Site: http://www.beiersdorf.lt
Sales Range: $25-49.9 Million
Emp.: 40
Pharmaceuticals & Toiletries Mfr
N.A.I.C.S.: 325412

Beiersdorf Ukraine LLC (2)
27-T Degtyarivska Street 7th Floor, 04119, Kiev, Ukraine
Tel.: (380) 44 490 63 96
Web Site: http://www.beiersdorf.ua
Skin Care Products Distr
N.A.I.C.S.: 424210
Mikhail Kostenko *(Dir-Logistics)*

Beiersdorf Vietnam LLC (2)
Centec Tower 18th Floor 72-74 Nguyen Thi Minh Khai Str, District 3, Ho Chi Minh City, Vietnam
Tel.: (84) 8 39 393921
Web Site: http://www.NIVEA.com.vn
Skin Care Products Distr
N.A.I.C.S.: 424210

Beiersdorf d.o.o. (2)
Krizna 18, 10000, Zagreb, Croatia (100%)
Tel.: (385) 16001000
Web Site: http://www.beiersdorf.com

MAXINGVEST AG — INTERNATIONAL PUBLIC

maxingvest ag—(Continued)

Sales Range: $25-49.9 Million
Emp.: 45
Pharmaceuticals & Toiletries Mfr
N.A.I.C.S.: 325412
Branko Kotarac *(Gen Mgr)*

Beiersdorf d.o.o. (2)
Letaliska cesta 32, 1000, Ljubljana, Slovenia
Tel.: (386) 1 548 48 61
Web Site: http://www.beiersdorf.si
Skin Care Products Distr
N.A.I.C.S.: 424210

Beiersdorf d.o.o. (2)
Airport City Belgrade Omladinskih brigada 88 a, 11070, Novi Beograd, Serbia
Tel.: (381) 11 222 0 660
Web Site: http://www.beiersdorf.rs
Skin Care Products Distr
N.A.I.C.S.: 424210

Beiersdorf ehf (2)
Vegmuli2, 108, Reykjavik, Iceland
Tel.: (354) 533 1880
Web Site: http://www.beiersdorf.is
Skin Care Products Distr
N.A.I.C.S.: 424210

Beiersdorf spol. s.r.o. (2)
Walterovo Namesti 329/3, 158 00, Prague, Czech Republic **(100%)**
Tel.: (420) 222829600
Web Site: http://www.beiersdorf.cz
Sales Range: $25-49.9 Million
Emp.: 80
Pharmaceuticals & Cosmetics Mfr
N.A.I.C.S.: 325412

Beiersdorf, SRL (2)
Avenida Winston Churchill esquina Avenida Roberto Pastoriza Plaza Las, Americas local 311 Piantini, Santo Domingo, Dominican Republic
Tel.: (809) 566 1228
Web Site: http://www.beiersdorf.com.do
Skin Care Products Distr
N.A.I.C.S.: 424210

Subsidiary (Domestic):

Cosmed Produktions GmbH Berlin (2)
Franklinstrasse 1, Berlin, 10587, Germany **(100%)**
Tel.: (49) 30399825
Web Site: http://www.beiersdorf.com
Sales Range: $50-74.9 Million
Emp.: 170
Pharmaceutical Products
N.A.I.C.S.: 325412
Michael Frey *(Mng Dir)*

Subsidiary (Non-US):

NIVEA (Shanghai) Company Limited (2)
Floors 30-32 Tower1 Grand Gateway No 1 Hongqiao Road, Xuhui District, 200030, Shanghai, China
Tel.: (86) 21 39207900
Web Site: http://www.niveashanghai.cn
Skin Care Products Distr
N.A.I.C.S.: 424210

NIVEA (Taiwan) Ltd. (2)
6F No 31 Lane 258 Ruiguang Road, Nei Hu District, 00114, Taipei, Taiwan
Tel.: (886) 2 7733 3391
Web Site: http://www.nivea.com.tw
Skin Care Products Distr
N.A.I.C.S.: 424210
Eric Lin *(Mgr-Trade Mktg)*

Nivea Beiersdorf Turkey Kozmetik Sanayi ve Ticaret A.S. (2)
Kavacik ofis Ruzgarli Bahce Mahallesi Kavak Sokak No 20, Kavacik Beykoz, 34805, Istanbul, Turkiye **(100%)**
Tel.: (90) 216 333 79 00
Web Site: http://www.beiersdorf.com.tr
Sales Range: $25-49.9 Million
Emp.: 60
Nivea Cosmetic Products Mfr
N.A.I.C.S.: 325412

Nivea India Pvt. Ltd. (2)
301 - Hyde Park Opp Ansa Industrial Estate Saki Vihar Road, Andheri East, 400 072, Mumbai, India
Tel.: (91) 22 664 599 00
Web Site: http://www.nivea.in
Emp.: 300
Skin Care Products Distr
N.A.I.C.S.: 424210
Ashish Dewan *(Dir-Sls)*

Nivea Polska S.A. (2)
Ul Gniezienska 32, 61-021, Poznan, Poland **(100%)**
Tel.: (48) 618746200
Web Site: http://www.niveapolska.pl
Sales Range: $100-124.9 Million
Emp.: 250
Pharmaceutical & Toiletry Mfr
N.A.I.C.S.: 325412

Joint Venture (Non-US):

Nivea-Kao Co. Ltd. (2)
18-1 Shintomi 1-chome, Chuo-ku, Tokyo, 104-0041, Japan **(100%)**
Tel.: (81) 33 297 5350
Web Site: https://nivea-kao.jp
Sales Range: $25-49.9 Million
Emp.: 50
Cosmetics & Pharmaceuticals Mfr; Owned 50% by Beiersdorf Group & 50% by Kao Corporation
N.A.I.C.S.: 325620

Subsidiary (Non-US):

P.T. Beiersdorf Indonesia (2)
Gedung Bina Mulia II 3rd Floor, PO Box 4607, Kuningan, Jakarta, 12046, Indonesia **(100%)**
Tel.: (62) 215201971
Web Site: http://www.beiersdorf.com
Sales Range: $25-49.9 Million
Emp.: 75
Cosmetics, Pharmaceuticals & Packaging Tape Mfr
N.A.I.C.S.: 325620

S.A. Beiersdorf NV (2)
Boulevard Industriel 30, BE-1070, Brussels, Belgium
Tel.: (32) 25265211
Web Site: http://www.beiersdorf.com
Sales Range: $50-74.9 Million
Emp.: 135
Cosmetics, Pharmaceuticals & Medical Products Mfr
N.A.I.C.S.: 325412

Subsidiary (Domestic):

tesa SE (2)
Hugo Kirchberg Strasse 1, 22848, Norderstedt, Germany **(100%)**
Tel.: (49) 40888990
Web Site: http://www.tesa.com
Rev.: $1,225,708,092
Assets: $1,244,963,412
Liabilities: $578,515,392
Net Worth: $666,448,020
Earnings: $131,791,968
Emp.: 4,158
Fiscal Year-end: 12/31/2016
Mfr of Adhesive Labels
N.A.I.C.S.: 325520
Thomas Fuchs *(Member-Exec Bd-Exec VP-HR)*

Subsidiary (Non-US):

tesa A/S (3)
Klintehoj Vaenge 12, 3460, Birkerod, Denmark
Tel.: (45) 45 998 200
Web Site: http://www.tesa.dk
Adhesive Distr
N.A.I.C.S.: 424690
Steve Plastow *(Mgr)*

tesa AB (3)
PO Box 10275, 434 23, Kungsbacka, Sweden
Tel.: (46) 300 55 350
Web Site: http://www.tesa.se
Adhesive Distr
N.A.I.C.S.: 424690
Steve Plastow *(Mgr)*

tesa AS (3)
Karihaugveien 89, 1086, Oslo, Norway
Tel.: (47) 22 90 79 79
Web Site: http://www.tesatape.no
Adhesive Distr
N.A.I.C.S.: 424690
Steve Plastow *(Mgr)*

tesa BV (3)
Stationsplein 3-1, 1211 EX, Hilversum, Netherlands
Tel.: (31) 35 62 50 200
Web Site: http://www.tesa.nl
Adhesive Distr
N.A.I.C.S.: 424690
Ferdy Denie *(Mgr)*

tesa Bant Sanayi ve Ticaret A.S. (3)
Merdivenkoy Mah Bora Sokak No1 Nida Kule Goztepe K 4, Kadikoy, 34732, Istanbul, Turkiye
Tel.: (90) 216 578 9000
Web Site: http://www.tesabant.com.tr
Adhesive Distr
N.A.I.C.S.: 424690
Mete Konuralp *(Country Mgr)*

tesa Brasil Ltda. (3)
Rua Joao Gualberto 1259 - 18 andar, Centro Empresarial Lais Peretti Alto da Gloria, 80030-000, Curitiba, Parana, Brazil
Tel.: (55) 41 3021 8100
Web Site: http://www.tesatape.com.br
Adhesive Distr
N.A.I.C.S.: 424690
Antonio Marques *(Mgr)*

Subsidiary (Domestic):

tesa Converting Center GmbH (3)
Schnackenburgallee 160, 22525, Hamburg, Germany
Tel.: (49) 40 4909 908
Emp.: 300
Adhesive Mfr & Distr
N.A.I.C.S.: 325520
Philip Ortin *(Mgr)*

tesa Labtec GmbH (3)
Raiffeisenstr 4, 40764, Langenfeld, Germany
Tel.: (49) 2173 9735 0
Web Site: http://www.tesa-labtec.com
Adhesive Mfr & Distr
N.A.I.C.S.: 325520
Helge Lubenow *(Mng Dir)*

Subsidiary (Non-US):

tesa Oy (3)
Puutarhakatu 53, 20100, Turku, Finland
Tel.: (358) 2 2103 400
Web Site: http://www.tesa.fi
Adhesive Distr
N.A.I.C.S.: 424690

tesa Plant (Singapore) Pte. Ltd. (3)
164 Gul Circle, Singapore, 629621, Singapore
Tel.: (65) 68612026
Adhesive Distr
N.A.I.C.S.: 424690

tesa Plant Suzhou Co. Ltd. (3)
No 451 Zhongnan Street Suzhou Industrial Park, 215026, Suzhou, Jiangsu, China
Tel.: (86) 512 6258 7988
Adhesive Distr
N.A.I.C.S.: 424690
Marco Bornhoft *(Mgr)*

tesa Portugal, Lda (3)
Rua Soeiro Pereira Gomes 59 Queluz de Baixo Apartado 87, 2746-901, Queluz, Portugal
Tel.: (351) 21 434 96 00
Web Site: http://www.tesa.pt
Adhesive Distr
N.A.I.C.S.: 424690
Jordi Senespleda *(Mgr)*

tesa SpA (3)
Via L Cadorna 69, 20090, Vimodrone, Milano, Italy
Tel.: (39) 02 250 108 11
Web Site: http://www.tesaitalia.it
Emp.: 30
Adhesive Distr
N.A.I.C.S.: 424690
Matteo Martinelli *(Country Mgr)*

Plant (Domestic):

tesa SpA - Concagno Plant (4)
Via L Cadorna 27, 22070, Concagno, Italy
Tel.: (39) 031 995 111
Adhesive Mfr
N.A.I.C.S.: 325520
Roberto Moroni *(Mgr)*

Subsidiary (Non-US):

tesa Tape (Hong Kong) Limited (3)
Unit 3609 AIA Tower, 183 Electric Rd, North Point, China (Hong Kong) **(100%)**
Tel.: (852) 25839980
Web Site: http://www.tesa.com
Sales Range: $25-49.9 Million
Emp.: 3
Adhesive Label Mfr
N.A.I.C.S.: 325520

tesa Tape (Malaysia) Sdn. Bhd. (3)
No 49 Jalan P10/21 Taman Industri, Selaman Seksyen 10, 43650, Bandar Baru Bangi, Selangor, Malaysia **(100%)**
Tel.: (60) 3 8927 3010
Web Site: http://www.tesa.com
Sales Range: $1-9.9 Million
Emp.: 15
Adhesive Product Mfr
N.A.I.C.S.: 325520
Tanaka Takafumi *(Country Mgr)*

tesa Tape Australia Pty. Ltd. (3)
Unit 5 1 Foundation Place, Prospect, Sydney, 2148, Australia **(100%)**
Tel.: (61) 298493929
Web Site: http://www.tesa.com
Sales Range: $25-49.9 Million
Emp.: 50
Adhesive Tape Mfr
N.A.I.C.S.: 325520

tesa Tape Colombia Ltda (3)
Calle 67 Norte 7N-59 piso 3 Barrio Menga, Valle del Cauca, Cali, Colombia
Tel.: (57) 2 687 8484
Web Site: http://www.tesa.com.co
Adhesive Distr
N.A.I.C.S.: 424690
Juan Carlos Sarassa *(Mgr)*

Subsidiary (US):

tesa Tape Inc. (3)
5825 Carnegie Blvd, Charlotte, NC 28209-4633
Tel.: (704) 554-0707
Web Site: http://www.tesatape.com
Sales Range: $50-74.9 Million
Emp.: 230
Mfr of Tapes
N.A.I.C.S.: 322220
Steve Curiak *(Mgr-Market)*

Subsidiary (Non-US):

tesa Tape K.K. (3)
8F Shirokanetakanawa Station Bldg 1-27-6 Shirokane, Minato-ku, Tokyo, 108-0072, Japan **(100%)**
Tel.: (81) 368332300
Web Site: http://www.tesa.jp
Sales Range: $25-49.9 Million
Emp.: 60
Adhesive Product Mfr
N.A.I.C.S.: 325520
Andreas Walkembach *(Pres)*

tesa Tapes (India) Pvt. Ltd. (3)
703 7th Fl Hermes Atrium, PO Box 11, CBD Belapur, 400614, Navi Mumbai, India **(100%)**
Tel.: (91) 2227564139
Sales Range: $25-49.9 Million
Emp.: 30
Adhesive Tape Mfr
N.A.I.C.S.: 325520

tesa U.K. Limited (3)
Yeomans Dr, Blakelands, Milton Keynes, MK14 5LS, Bucks, United Kingdom
Tel.: (44) 1908211333
Web Site: http://www.tesa.com
Sales Range: $25-49.9 Million
Emp.: 30
Adhesive Tape Mfr
N.A.I.C.S.: 325520
Stephen Hauber *(Country Mgr)*

Subsidiary (Domestic):

tesa Werk Hamburg GmbH (3)
Heykenaukamp 10, 21147, Hamburg, Germany
Tel.: (49) 40 4909 904

AND PRIVATE COMPANIES

MAXINGVEST AG

Adhesive Mfr & Distr
N.A.I.C.S.: 325520
Torsten Sandgathe *(Mgr)*

tesa Werk Offenburg GmbH (3)
Kinzigstrasse 5, 77652, Offenburg, Germany
Tel.: (49) 781 801 0
Adhesive Mfr & Distr
N.A.I.C.S.: 325520
Thorsten Sandgathe *(Mgr)*

Subsidiary (Non-US):

tesa Western Europe B.V. (3)
UN Studio 6th floor Parnassusweg 813/A, 1082 LZ, Amsterdam, Netherlands
Tel.: (31) 20 3033500
Adhesive Distr
N.A.I.C.S.: 424690
Reinhold Zintgraf *(Mgr)*

tesa s.a.s. (3)
ZAC CARRE SENART-2 Allee de la mixite Batiment LA CROIX DU SUD, 77127, Lieusaint, France
Tel.: (33) 1 78 48 20 00
Web Site: http://www.tesa.fr
Adhesive Distr
N.A.I.C.S.: 424690
Bruno Derouet *(Mgr)*

tesa sa-nv (3)
Chaussee de Ruisbroek 76 Ruisbroeksesteenweg 76, 1180, Brussels, Belgium
Tel.: (32) 2 525 08 11
Web Site: http://www.tesa.be
Adhesive Distr
N.A.I.C.S.: 424690
Ferdy Denie *(Pres)*

Subsidiary (Domestic):

tesa scribos GmbH (3)
Sickingenstrasse 65, 69126, Heidelberg, Germany
Tel.: (49) 40 4909 6330
Web Site: http://www.tesa-scribos.com
Adhesive Mfr & Distr
N.A.I.C.S.: 325520
Christoph Dietrich *(Chm & Mng Dir)*

Subsidiary (Non-US):

tesa tape (Shanghai) Co., Ltd. (3)
No 1 2500 Lane Xiu Pu Road, Pudong, Shanghai, China
Tel.: (86) 21 68183110
Adhesive Distr
N.A.I.C.S.: 424690
Dick Li *(Mgr)*

tesa tape (Thailand) Limited (3)
1858/80 17th Floor Interlink Tower Bangna-Trad Road, Bangna, Bangkok, 10260, Thailand
Tel.: (66) 2 751 4025
Adhesive Distr
N.A.I.C.S.: 424690
Tanaka Takafumi *(Mgr)*

tesa tape AE (3)
2 Agiou Nektariou Str, 153 44, Pallini, Attiki, Greece
Tel.: (30) 210 6600 290
Web Site: http://www.tesa.gr
Adhesive Distr
N.A.I.C.S.: 424690

tesa tape Argentina S.R.L. (3)
Av Del Libertador 6966 5 B, C1429BMP, Buenos Aires, Argentina
Tel.: (54) 11 4781 1846
Adhesive Distr
N.A.I.C.S.: 424690
Henry Gonzalez *(Mgr)*

tesa tape Asia Pacific Pte. Ltd. (3)
9 North Buona Vista Drive 04-01 The Metropolis Tower 1, Singapore, 138588, Singapore
Tel.: (65) 6697 9888
Web Site: http://www.tesa-asia.com
Adhesive Distr
N.A.I.C.S.: 424690
Daniel Germain *(Mgr)*

tesa tape Centro America S.A. (3)
Diagonal 6 10-50 Zona 10 Edificio Interamericas WFC Torre Norte, nivel 12 oficina 1202, Guatemala, 1010, Guatemala
Tel.: (502) 22449100
Adhesive Distr
N.A.I.C.S.: 424690
Hector Robles *(Mgr)*

tesa tape Chile SA (3)
Av Presidente Riesco 5561 Oficina 1104, Las Condes, Santiago, Chile
Tel.: (56) 2 369 3600
Web Site: http://www.tesa.cl
Adhesive Distr
N.A.I.C.S.: 424690
David Paz *(Mgr)*

tesa tape Kft. (3)
Szabadsag ut 117, 2040, Budaors, Hungary
Tel.: (36) 23 814 154
Web Site: http://www.tesa.hu
Adhesive Distr
N.A.I.C.S.: 424690
Oliver Hoefs *(Mgr)*

tesa tape Korea Ltd. (3)
City Air Tower 159-9 Room 1805, Samseong-dong Gangnam-gu, Seoul, 135-973, Korea (South)
Tel.: (82) 2 569 84 51
Web Site: http://www.tesa.co.kr
Adhesive Distr
N.A.I.C.S.: 424690
Frank Kolmorgen *(Mgr)*

tesa tape Mexico SRL de CV (3)
Av Santa Fe No 170 P 7-4-14 Col Lomas de Santa Fe, 01210, Mexico, Mexico
Tel.: (52) 55 22827560
Web Site: http://www.tesatape.com.mx
Adhesive Distr
N.A.I.C.S.: 424690
Fernando Cruz *(Mgr)*

tesa tape SRL (3)
str Observatorului nr 113A etaj 1, Cluj-Napoca, 400363, Romania
Tel.: (40) 364 401 140
Web Site: http://www.tesatape.ro
Adhesive Distr
N.A.I.C.S.: 424690
Marius Alexik *(Mgr)*

tesa tape Schweiz AG (3)
Industriestrasse 19, 8962, Bergdietikon, Switzerland
Tel.: (41) 44 744 3444
Web Site: http://www.tesa.ch
Adhesive Distr
N.A.I.C.S.: 424690
Claus Grobe *(Mgr)*

tesa tape Sp. z.o.o. (3)
Grunwaldzka 184, 60-166, Poznan, Poland
Tel.: (48) 603857271
Web Site: http://www.tesa.pl
Emp.: 15
Adhesive Distr
N.A.I.C.S.: 424690
Tomasz Badyda *(Natl Dir)*

tesa tape posrednistvo in trgovina d.o.o. (3)
Pot k sejmiscu, Crnuce, 1231, Ljubljana, Slovenia
Tel.: (386) 1 560 24 10
Adhesive Distr
N.A.I.C.S.: 424690

tesa tape s.r.o. (3)
Walterovo namesti 329/3, 158 00, Prague, Czech Republic
Tel.: (420) 296824546
Web Site: http://www.tesa.com
Adhesive Distr
N.A.I.C.S.: 424690
Tomas Kuska *(Country Mgr)*

HMO Luxembourg S.a.r.l. (1)
5 BD Royal, 2449, Luxembourg, Luxembourg
Tel.: (352) 26 20 16 33
Emp.: 1
Financial Management Services
N.A.I.C.S.: 523999
Beatrice Neidercorn *(Office Mgr)*

La Prairie (Shanghai) Co. Ltd. (1)
Room 5503 Wheelock Square 1717 West Nanjing Road, Shanghai, 200040, China
Tel.: (86) 21 62 48 66 55
Skin Care Products Distr
N.A.I.C.S.: 424210
Roxanne Huang *(Gen Mgr)*

La Prairie (UK) Limited (1)
1st floor Kings House 10 Haymarket, London, SW1 Y4BP, United Kingdom
Tel.: (44) 207 968 68 88
Web Site: http://www.laprairie.co.uk
Skin Care Products Distr
N.A.I.C.S.: 424210
Philippe Despax *(Gen Mgr)*

La Prairie Group (RUS) LLC (1)
Paveletskaya Tower 24th floor Paveletskaya Square 2/2, 115054, Moscow, Russia
Tel.: (7) 4956604750
Skin Care Products Distr
N.A.I.C.S.: 424210
Laurence Chardiny-Kurchakov *(Gen Mgr)*

La Prairie Group Deutschland GmbH (1)
Lange Strasse 65, 76530, Baden-Baden, Germany
Tel.: (49) 72 21 683 800
Skin Care Products Distr
N.A.I.C.S.: 424210
Britta Bartholomae *(Gen Mgr)*

La Prairie Group France S.A.S. (1)
54 Ave Du General Leclerc, 92513, Boulogne, Cedex, France
Tel.: (33) 1 41 10 21 74
Skin Care Products Distr
N.A.I.C.S.: 424210
Laurent Leblond *(Gen Mgr)*

La Prairie Group Iberia S.A.U. (1)
Parque Empresarial La Moraleja Avd De Europa 22 3a Planta B, 28108, Madrid, Spain
Tel.: (34) 91 444 53 14
Skin Care Products Distr
N.A.I.C.S.: 424210
Alejandro Iraberri *(Gen Mgr)*

La Prairie Hong Kong Limited (1)
Suites 3210-12 32F One Island East 18 Westlands Road, Hong Kong, China (Hong Kong)
Tel.: (852) 2809 0100
Skin Care Products Distr
N.A.I.C.S.: 424210
Noelle Cheng *(Gen Mgr)*

La Prairie Japan K.K. (1)
1-8-8 Across Shinkawa Bld 2 Shinkawa, Chuo-ku, Tokyo, 104-0033, Japan
Tel.: (81) 3 5540 4301
Skin Care Products Distr
N.A.I.C.S.: 424210
Sachiko Awai *(Gen Mgr)*

La Prairie Korea Ltd (1)
20th floor Ace Tower 1-170 Sunwha-dong, Jung-gu, Seoul, 100-712, Korea (South)
Tel.: (82) 263 90 11 11
Skin Care Products Distr
N.A.I.C.S.: 424210
Allen Kim *(Gen Mgr)*

La Prairie Middle East (1)
Dubai Airport Free Zone Building 5W Block A 2nd Floor Office 219, PO Box 293758, Dubai, United Arab Emirates
Tel.: (971) 4 260 22 62
Skin Care Products Distr
N.A.I.C.S.: 424210
Alexandre Maureta *(Gen Mgr)*

SCS Skin Care Studio GmbH (1)
Gutenbergring 53, 22848, Norderstedt, Germany
Tel.: (49) 40 52868217
Web Site: http://www.nivea-spa.de
Skin Care Products Distr
N.A.I.C.S.: 424210
Pascal Zimmer *(Gen Mgr)*

Tchibo GmbH (1)
Uberseering 18, 22297, Hamburg, Germany **(100%)**
Tel.: (49) 4063870
Web Site: http://www.tchibo.de
Sales Range: $5-14.9 Billion
Emp.: 12,000
Coffee Mfr & Distr
N.A.I.C.S.: 311920
Michael Herz *(Chm-Supervisory Bd)*

Subsidiary (Non-US):

S.C. Tchibo Brands S.R.L. (2)
Str Calea Floreasca nr 55 etaj 3 sector 1, 014453, Bucharest, Romania
Tel.: (40) 21 318 97 06
Web Site: http://www.tchibo.com
Coffee Distr
N.A.I.C.S.: 424490

Tchibo (Schweiz) AG (2)
Industriestrasse 19, 8304, Wallisellen, Switzerland
Tel.: (41) 43 233 45 00
Web Site: http://www.tchibo.ch
Emp.: 50
Coffee Distr
N.A.I.C.S.: 424490

Tchibo Budapest Kft. (2)
Neumann Janos U 1, 2040, Budaors, Hungary
Tel.: (36) 23 502 000
Web Site: http://www.tchibo.com
Coffee Distr
N.A.I.C.S.: 424490
Zsolt Meszaros *(Mng Dir)*

Tchibo CIS LLC (2)
1-st Brestskaya St 29 13-th floor, 125047, Moscow, Russia
Tel.: (7) 495 730 07 00
Web Site: http://www.tchibo.ru
Coffee Distr
N.A.I.C.S.: 424490
Sergey Prigoda *(Mgr-Natl Sls)*

Tchibo Coffee International Ltd. (2)
Tchibo House Blenheim Road, Epsom, KT19 9BE, Surrey, United Kingdom
Tel.: (44) 845 600 8244
Web Site: http://www.tchibo-coffeeservice.co.uk
Coffee Distr
N.A.I.C.S.: 424490
Peter Simpkins *(Dir-Sls)*

Tchibo Coffee Nederland B.V. (2)
Bramengery 14 A K6, 3755 BZ, Eemnes, Utrecht, Netherlands
Tel.: (31) 35 628 9580
Coffee Distr
N.A.I.C.S.: 424490

Tchibo Coffee Service Polska Sp.z o.o. (2)
ul Fabryczna 5, 00-446, Warsaw, Poland
Tel.: (48) 22 383 11 40 47
Web Site: http://www.tchibo-coffeeservice.pl
Coffee Distr
N.A.I.C.S.: 424490
Pawel Tulinski *(Mng Dir)*

Tchibo Kahve Mamulleri Dagitim ve Pazarlama Ticaret Limited (2)
Barbaros Mah Cigdem Sk No 1-7, Atasehir, Istanbul, Turkiye
Tel.: (90) 216 575 44 11
Web Site: http://www.tchibo.com.tr
Coffee Distr
N.A.I.C.S.: 424490

Tchibo Manufacturing (Austria) GmbH (2)
Gadnergasse 71, 1110, Vienna, Austria
Tel.: (43) 1 76622
Coffee Mfr
N.A.I.C.S.: 311920
Harald Mayer *(Mgr)*

Tchibo Manufacturing Poland Sp.z o.o. (2)
ul Sloneczna 6, 05-270, Marki, Poland
Tel.: (48) 22 7711701
Coffee Mfr
N.A.I.C.S.: 311920

Tchibo Merchandising Hongkong LP (2)
7/F Tower 1 The Gateway 25 Canton Road, Tsim Sha Tsui, Kowloon, China (Hong Kong)
Tel.: (852) 2209 0300
Coffee Distr
N.A.I.C.S.: 424490
Christian Hellmund *(Dir-Textile Div)*

Tchibo Praha spol. s r.o. (2)
Zeletavska 1449/9, 140 00, Prague, Czech Republic
Tel.: (420) 224 001 264
Web Site: http://www.tchibo.cz
Coffee Distr
N.A.I.C.S.: 424490

maxingvest ag—(Continued)

Miroslav Zajic *(Brand Mgr-Natl Field Force & Depots)*

Tchibo Slovensko spol. s r.o. (2)
Prievozska 4, 821 09, Bratislava, Slovakia
Tel.: (421) 2 48 22 71 11
Web Site: http://www.tchibo.sk
Coffee Distr
N.A.I.C.S.: 424490
Zuzana Trvalikova *(Sr Brand Mgr)*

MAXIPARTS LIMITED
22 Efficient Drive, Derrimut, Truganina, 3029, VIC, Australia
Tel.: (61) 393687000 AU
Web Site: https://www.maxiparts.com.au
Year Founded: 1997
MXI—(ASX)
Rev.: $162,849,225
Assets: $141,742,120
Liabilities: $73,641,827
Net Worth: $68,100,294
Earnings: $3,743,323
Emp.: 450
Fiscal Year-end: 06/30/24
Holding Company; Truck Trailer & Parts Mfr, Sales, Rental & Support Services
N.A.I.C.S.: 551112
Peter Loimaranta *(CEO, Mng Dir & Gen Mgr-Intl Grp)*

Subsidiaries:

Colrain Pty Ltd (1)
22 Efficient Drive, Truganina, 3029, VIC, Australia
Tel.: (61) 3833681155
Web Site: http://www.colrain.com.au
Sales Range: $50-74.9 Million
Automotive Trailer Distr
N.A.I.C.S.: 423110
Peter Loimaranta *(Gen Mgr)*

Subsidiary (Domestic):

Colrain (Albury) Pty Ltd (2)
3/115 Catherine Crescent, Albury, 2641, NSW, Australia
Tel.: (61) 260401426
Web Site: http://www.colrainparts.com.au
Sales Range: $25-49.9 Million
Emp.: 6
Automotive Truck Parts Distr
N.A.I.C.S.: 423120

Colrain (Ballarat) Pty Ltd (2)
264 Park St, Ballarat, 3350, VIC, Australia
Tel.: (61) 353357305
Automotive Truck Parts Distr
N.A.I.C.S.: 423120

Hamelex White Pty Ltd (1)
175 South Gippsland Hwy, Dandenong, 3175, VIC, Australia
Tel.: (61) 387862100
Web Site: http://www.hamelexwhite.com.au
Sales Range: $25-49.9 Million
Emp.: 50
Tipping Trailer Mfr
N.A.I.C.S.: 336212

Lusty EMS Pty Ltd (1)
1773 Ipswich Rd, Rocklea, 4106, QLD, Australia
Tel.: (61) 732775511
Web Site: http://www.lustyems.com.au
Sales Range: $25-49.9 Million
Emp.: 90
Automotive Trailer Repair & Maintenance Services
N.A.I.C.S.: 811121

MaxiTRANS Australia Pty Ltd (1)
346 Boundary Rd, Derrimut, Derrimut, 3026, VIC, Australia
Tel.: (61) 383681100
Web Site: http://www.maxitrans.com.au
Sales Range: $50-74.9 Million
Emp.: 80
Trailing Transport Equipment Distr
N.A.I.C.S.: 423860
Stewart McMurtria *(Mgr-Mktg)*

MaxiTRANS Industries (N.Z.) Pty Ltd (1)
346 Boundary Rd, Derrimut, 3030, VIC, Australia
Tel.: (61) 383681100
Web Site: http://www.maxitrans.com.au
Sales Range: $25-49.9 Million
Emp.: 50
Trailing Transport Equipment Distr
N.A.I.C.S.: 423860

MaxiTRANS Services Pty Ltd (1)
346 Boundary Road, Derrimut, Derrimut, 3026, VIC, Australia
Tel.: (61) 383681100
Trailing Transport Equipment Distr
N.A.I.C.S.: 423860

MAXIS BERHAD
Level 21 Menara Maxis, Centre Off Jalan Ampang, 50088, Kuala Lumpur, Malaysia
Tel.: (60) 323307000
Web Site: https://www.maxis.com.my
Year Founded: 1995
MAXIS—(KLS)
Rev.: $2,277,742,500
Assets: $5,554,642,500
Liabilities: $3,890,205,000
Net Worth: $1,664,437,500
Earnings: $323,730,000
Emp.: 3,791
Fiscal Year-end: 12/31/21
Communications & Internet Technology Services
N.A.I.C.S.: 517112
Dipak Kaur *(Sec)*

Subsidiaries:

Aircel Limited (1)
5th Floor Building No 10A, DLF Cyber City DLF Phase II, Gurgaon, 122 002, India (74%)
Tel.: (91) 1247944800
Web Site: http://www.aircel.com
Mobile Telecommunications Services
N.A.I.C.S.: 517112
Shiraz Khanna *(Head-Revenue Assurance & Fin Shares Svcs & Controller-Fin)*

Dishnet Wireless Limited (1)
Royale Manor 2nd Floor, 48 ST Johns Rd, 560042, Bengaluru, India (74%)
Tel.: (91) 8065371567
Cellular & Wireless Telecommunications
N.A.I.C.S.: 517112

Maxis Broadband Sdn.Bhd. (1)
Lvl 18-23 Menara Maxis, Kuala Lumpur, 50088, Malaysia
Tel.: (60) 323307000
Web Site: http://www.maxis.com.my
Telephone Apparatus Mfr
N.A.I.C.S.: 334210

Maxis International Sdn. Bhd. (1)
Lvl 8-23 Menara Maxis, 50088, Kuala Lumpur, Malaysia (100%)
Tel.: (60) 323307000
Radio Television & Electronics Stores
N.A.I.C.S.: 449210
Ravindran Ambu *(Head)*

Maxis Mobile Sdn. Bhd. (1)
18th Fl Menara Maxis, Kuala Lumpur, 50088, Malaysia (100%)
Tel.: (60) 323307000
Cellular & Wireless Telecommunications
N.A.I.C.S.: 517112

MAXMIND PHARMACEUTICAL S.L.
Calle Copenhague N -12 Oficina 205 Edificio Tifan, Las Rozas, 28232, Madrid, Spain
Tel.: (34) 659405350
Web Site: https://www.maxmindpharma.es
Emp.: 100
Pharmaceutical Preparation Mfr
N.A.I.C.S.: 325412

MAXNERVA TECHNOLOGY SERVICES LTD.
23F Tower B Galaxy World No 1 Yabao Road, Longgang District, Shenzhen, China
Tel.: (86) 4008301359 BM
Web Site: http://www.maxnerva.com
Year Founded: 1980
1037—(HKG)
Rev.: $116,877,524
Assets: $101,977,996
Liabilities: $38,652,962
Net Worth: $63,325,033
Earnings: $3,907,332
Emp.: 588
Fiscal Year-end: 12/31/22
Telecommunication Products Mfr
N.A.I.C.S.: 334220
Mark Yi-Pin Chien *(Chm)*

Subsidiaries:

Daiwa Distribution (B.C.) Inc. (1)
165 - 4611 Viking Way, Richmond, V6V 2K9, BC, Canada
Tel.: (604) 244-9912
Web Site: http://www.daiwa.ca
Emp.: 20
Computer Peripheral Equipment Distr
N.A.I.C.S.: 423430

Elite Century Holdings Limited (1)
Rm C 3/f 1 - 3 Kai Hing Rd, Kowloon Bay, Hong Kong, China (Hong Kong)
Tel.: (852) 21872538
Holding Company
N.A.I.C.S.: 551112

MAXO TELECOMMUNICATIONS PTY. LTD.
Office 8/189-197 Anzac Ave, Harristown, 4350, QLD, Australia
Tel.: (61) 731235300 AU
Web Site: https://www.maxo.com.au
Year Founded: 2007
Telecommunication Servicesb
N.A.I.C.S.: 517810

MAXPRO CAPITAL ACQUISITION CORP.
5/F-4 No 89 Songren Road, Xinyi District, Taipei, 11073, Taiwan
Tel.: (886) 27 713 7952 DE
Year Founded: 2021
JMAC—(NASDAQ)
Investment Services
N.A.I.C.S.: 523999
Hong-Jung Chen *(CEO & Chm)*

MAXQ AI LTD.
76 Yigal Alon Street 5 th Floor, Tel Aviv, 6706701, Israel
Tel.: (972) 3 620 0028 II
Web Site: http://www.maxq.ai
Year Founded: 2013
Emp.: 18
Medical Application Software Development Services
N.A.I.C.S.: 513210
Gene Saragnese *(CEO)*

MAXRAY OPTICAL TECHNOLOGY CO. LTD.
5618 Tenth Line West Unit 9, Mississauga, L5M 7L9, ON, Canada
Tel.: (905) 824-6200 DE
Web Site: http://www.maxraytech.com
Year Founded: 2004
Sales Range: $50-74.9 Million
Emp.: 596
Plastic Film & Liquid Crystal Display Products Mfr
N.A.I.C.S.: 322220
Jack Chen *(Pres & CEO)*

MAXROTEC CO., LTD.
40 Seongseo-ro 71-gil, Dalseo-gu, Daegu, Korea (South)
Tel.: (82) 535846540
Web Site: http://www.maxrotec.com
Rev.: $32,092,877
Assets: $64,986,519
Liabilities: $40,767,162
Net Worth: $24,219,358
Earnings: ($8,677,504)
Emp.: 130
Fiscal Year-end: 12/31/19
Wireless Gantry Robot System Mfr
N.A.I.C.S.: 333248

Subsidiaries:

Maxrotec Co., Ltd. - Seongju Factory (1)
6BL/37BL/38BL Seongju General Industrial Complex, Haksan, Gyeongbuk, Korea (South)
Tel.: (82) 54 932 6540
Gantry Robot System Mfr
N.A.I.C.S.: 333248

MAXSCEND MICROELECTRONICS COMPANY LIMITED
11th Floor Building A3 No 777 West Jianshe Road, Binhu, Wuxi, 214072, Jiangsu, China
Tel.: (86) 51085106859
Web Site: https://www.maxscend.com
Year Founded: 2012
300782—(SSE)
Rev.: $516,319,596
Assets: $1,334,308,248
Liabilities: $114,925,824
Net Worth: $1,219,382,424
Earnings: $150,115,680
Fiscal Year-end: 12/31/22
Electronic Product Mfr & Distr
N.A.I.C.S.: 334419
Zhihan Xu *(Chm & Gen Mgr)*

MAXST CO., LTD.
2-3rd Floor STAY77 bldg Nambusunhwan-ro 351-gil, Gangnam-Gu, Seoul, Korea (South)
Tel.: (82) 25859566
Web Site: https://www.maxst.com
Year Founded: 2010
377030—(KRS)
Software Development Services
N.A.I.C.S.: 541511
Jaewan Park *(CEO)*

MAXTRAL INDUSTRY BERHAD
TB 324 2nd Floor Lot 21 Block 38 Fajar Complex, 91000, Tawau, Sabah, Malaysia
Tel.: (60) 89772122
Web Site: http://www.maxtral.com.my
Sales Range: Less than $1 Million
Veneer Plywood Mfr & Sale
N.A.I.C.S.: 321211
Ling Ling Beh Kim *(Chm)*

MAXVISION TECHNOLOGY CORP.
42F 43F and 45F Block A Xinhao e Du Caitian Road No 7018, Futian District, Shenzhen, 518000, Guangdong, China
Tel.: (86) 75583849888
Web Site: https://www.maxvision.com.cn
Year Founded: 1997
002990—(SSE)
Rev.: $138,878,064
Assets: $425,134,008
Liabilities: $131,022,684
Net Worth: $294,111,324
Earnings: $13,541,580
Fiscal Year-end: 12/31/22
Application Development Services
N.A.I.C.S.: 541511
Lei Qu *(Chm)*

MAXWAY INDUSTRIES, INC.

Area B Floor 6 Building 4 Huoju Road Xian High and New Technology, Development Area Eastern Area, Xi'an, 710043, Shaanxi, China
Tel.: (86) 29 82243655 NV
Year Founded: 2009
Digital Automobile Odometers Designer & Mfr
N.A.I.C.S.: 336399
Huang Xu *(Pres & CEO)*

MAXWELL ELECTRONICS LTD.
7th Fl Maxwell Industries Bldg, Kwun Tong, 2007, Kowloon, China (Hong Kong)
Tel.: (852) 27991111
Sales Range: $25-49.9 Million
Emp.: 200
Mfr of Photographic Equipment & Supplies
N.A.I.C.S.: 333310
Subsidiaries:

AIC Investment Ltd. (1)
1/F Maxwell Industrial Building, 350 Kwun Tong Road, Kwun Tong, 2007, Kowloon, China (Hong Kong)
Tel.: (852) 2791111
Holding Company
N.A.I.C.S.: 551112

Soligor GmbH (1)
Schulze Delitzsch Strasse 7, D 70771, Leinfelden, Germany **(100%)**
Tel.: (49) 711759040
Web Site: http://www.secure.soligor.com
Rev.: $11,000,000
Emp.: 15
Photographic Equipment Sales
N.A.I.C.S.: 423410

MAXWELL PAPER CANADA, INC.
435 College Street East, Belleville, K8N 5S7, ON, Canada
Tel.: (613) 962-7700
Web Site: http://www.maxwellpaper.ca
Year Founded: 1989
Rev.: $14,402,000
Emp.: 150
Paper Supplier
N.A.I.C.S.: 424130
Adrian Hilmi *(Pres & CEO)*

MAXXTEC AG
Bemannsbruch 16 18, 74909, Meckesheim, Germany
Tel.: (49) 6226929920
Web Site: http://www.maxxtec.com
Power & Heat Generation Equipment Mfr
N.A.I.C.S.: 332410
Rolf Schleicher *(CEO)*
Subsidiaries:

PT Maxxtec Teknologi Indonesia (1)
ITC Permata Hijau Lantai 3 C11 No 16, 12210, Jakarta, Indonesia
Tel.: (62) 21 53667587
Web Site: http://www.maxxtec.com
Emp.: 3
Plumbing & Heating Equipment Distr
N.A.I.C.S.: 423720
Suhandi Sutedja *(Dir Gen)*

MAY & BAKER NIGERIA PLC.
3/5 Sapara Street Industrial Estate, PMB 21049, Ikeja, Lagos, Nigeria
Tel.: (234) 8113681447
Web Site: https://may-baker.com
Year Founded: 1944
MAYBAKER—(NIGE)
Rev.: $10,605,753
Assets: $13,292,186
Liabilities: $7,189,508
Net Worth: $6,102,677
Earnings: $1,103,346

Emp.: 352
Fiscal Year-end: 12/31/22
Pharmaceuticals Product Mfr
N.A.I.C.S.: 325412
Nnamdi Okafor *(CEO & Mng Dir)*
Subsidiaries:

Biovaccines Nigeria Limited (1)
445 Herbert Macaulay Way, P M B 2010, Yaba, Lagos, Nigeria
Tel.: (234) 9063755237
Web Site: http://www.biovaccinesnig.com
Vaccines Mfr
N.A.I.C.S.: 325414
Oyewale Tomori *(Chm)*

Osworth Nigeria Limited (1)
3/5 Sapara Street, P M B 21049, Industrial Estate Ikeja, Lagos, Nigeria
Tel.: (234) 7890123
Web Site: https://www.osworthnigeria.com
Pharmaceuticals Mfr
N.A.I.C.S.: 325412
Ngozi Helen Chukelu *(COO)*

Tydipacks Nigeria Limited (1)
3/5 Sapara Street, Industrial Estate, Ikeja, Nigeria
Tel.: (234) 7098005296
Pharmaceuticals Mfr
N.A.I.C.S.: 325412

MAY+SPIES GMBH
Renkerstr 32, 52355, Duren, Germany
Tel.: (49) 242159070
Web Site: http://www.mayspies.com
Year Founded: 1920
Rev.: $28,990,000
Emp.: 159
Paper Product Mfr & Distr
N.A.I.C.S.: 322299
Heinrich Spies *(Mng Dir)*
Subsidiaries:

Kunzli Papier AG (1)
Moosmattstrasse 30, 8953, Dietikon, Switzerland
Tel.: (41) 447478947
Web Site: http://www.kuenzli-papier.ch
Paper Product Distr
N.A.I.C.S.: 424130

MAY+SPIES Gesellschaft m.b.H. + Co KG (1)
Felixdorfer Gasse 5, 2700, Wiener Neustadt, Austria
Tel.: (43) 262223143
Paper Product Distr
N.A.I.C.S.: 424130

MAYAGUEZ SA
Calle 22 Norte No 6AN-24 Oficina 701 Edificio Santa Monica Central, Santiago, Cali, Colombia
Tel.: (57) 26679562
Web Site: https://www.ingeniomayaguez.com
Year Founded: 1950
MAYAGUEZ—(COLO)
Sales Range: Less than $1 Million
Sugar Cane Mfr
N.A.I.C.S.: 311314
Mauricio Iragorri Rizo *(CEO & Principal)*

MAYAIR GROUP PLC
No 18 Jalan 6/2B Taman Industri Selesa Jaya, Seri Kembangan, 43300, Selangor, Malaysia
Tel.: (60) 3 8961 2908
Web Site: http://www.mayairgroup.com
Sales Range: $25-49.9 Million
Air Filtration & Clean Air Technology
N.A.I.C.S.: 333413
Wee Keong Yap *(CEO)*

MAYANOT TAMDA LTD.
19B HaLehi Street, Bnei Brak, 51200, Israel

Tel.: (972) 3 577 7989
Web Site: http://www.meyeden.co.il
Year Founded: 1976
Sales Range: $250-299.9 Million
Emp.: 516
Mineral Water Mfr
N.A.I.C.S.: 312112
Gilad Dahan *(CEO & CFO)*

MAYBERRY INVESTMENTS LTD.
1 1/2 Oxford Road, Kingston, 5, Jamaica
Tel.: (876) 9291908
Web Site: https://www.mayberryinv.com
Year Founded: 1985
MIL—(JAM)
Rev.: $10,302,232
Assets: $380,927,381
Liabilities: $219,976,509
Net Worth: $160,950,872
Earnings: ($9,529,892)
Emp.: 134
Fiscal Year-end: 12/31/23
Investment Banking & Securities Brokerage Services
N.A.I.C.S.: 523150
Christopher Berry *(Chm)*

MAYBERRY JAMAICAN EQUITIES LTD.
Suite 1 1st Floor Bourbon House Bourbon Street, Castries, Saint Lucia
Tel.: (758) 4532046
Web Site: https://www.mayberryinv.com
Year Founded: 2005
MJE—(JAM)
Rev.: $10,302,232
Assets: $262,369,413
Liabilities: $219,651,858
Net Worth: $42,717,555
Earnings: ($9,214,264)
Fiscal Year-end: 12/31/23
Financial Management Services
N.A.I.C.S.: 522320
Gary Peart *(CEO)*

MAYBERRY RESOURCES PLC
4188 Welwyn St, Vancouver, V5N 3Z2, BC, Canada
Tel.: (604) 367-2962
Web Site: http://www.mayberryresources.com
Gold & Copper Mining Services
N.A.I.C.S.: 212220
Benjamin Montanez *(Pres & CEO)*

MAYBOURNE HOTELS LIMITED
41-43 Brook Street Mayfair, London, W1K 4HJ, United Kingdom
Tel.: (44) 20 7107 8800 UK
Web Site: http://www.maybourne.com
Holding Company; Hotels Owner & Operator
N.A.I.C.S.: 551112
Paula Fitzherbert *(Dir-Comm)*
Subsidiaries:

Claridge's Hotel Limited (1)
Brook Street Mayfair, London, W1K 4HR, United Kingdom
Tel.: (44) 2076298860
Web Site: http://www.claridges.co.uk
Hotel Operator
N.A.I.C.S.: 721120
Thomas Kochs *(Gen Mgr)*

The Berkeley Hotel Limited (1)
Wilton Place Knightsbridge, London, SW1X 7RL, United Kingdom
Tel.: (44) 2072356000
Web Site: http://www.the-berkeley.co.uk
Hotel Operator
N.A.I.C.S.: 721120
Justin Pinchbeck *(Gen Mgr)*

The Connaught Hotel Limited (1)
Carlos Place Mayfair, London, W1K 2AL, United Kingdom
Tel.: (44) 2074997070
Web Site: http://www.the-connaught.co.uk
Hotel Operator
N.A.I.C.S.: 721120
Miguel Garcia Feliz *(Dir-Rooms)*

MAYEKAWA MFG. CO. LTD.
3-14-15 Botan, Koto-ku, Tokyo, 135-8482, Japan
Tel.: (81) 336428181
Web Site: http://www.mayekawa.com
Year Founded: 1937
Refrigeration Compressor Mfr
N.A.I.C.S.: 333912
Yoshiro Tanaka *(Pres)*
Subsidiaries:

MAYEKAWA HOLDING (THAILAND) CO., LTD (1)
2/3 Moo14 3rd Floor Bangna Tower Bldg Tower A Bangna-Trad Rd; K M 6 5 Bangkaew, Bang Phli, 10540, Samutprakarn, Thailand
Tel.: (66) 27519610
Holding Company
N.A.I.C.S.: 551112

MAYEKAWA SOUTH AFRICA (PTY) LTD. (1)
West End Unit 3 Prime Park Printers Way Montague Gardens, 7441, Cape Town, South Africa
Tel.: (27) 215511434
Compressor Distr
N.A.I.C.S.: 423740
Spiro Mitchell *(Gen Mgr)*

MAYEKAWA VIETNAM ONE MEMBER CO., LIMITED (1)
Room 305 3fl Tuoi Tre Tower 60a Hoang Van Thu Ward9, Phu Nhuan Dist, Ho Chi Minh City, Vietnam
Tel.: (84) 839975284
Web Site: http://www.mycomvietnam.com
Compressor Distr
N.A.I.C.S.: 423740

MAYEKAWA-SVEDAN sp. z o.o. (1)
ul Druskiennicka 8/10, 60-476, Poznan, Poland
Tel.: (48) 618420738
Web Site: http://www.svedan.com.pl
Air Conditioning System Distr
N.A.I.C.S.: 423730

Mayegawa Chile S.A.C. (1)
Cordillera 331, Modulo D14 Flex Center Puerto Vespucio, Santiago, Chile
Tel.: (56) 2 739 0202
Refrigeration Compressor Mfr
N.A.I.C.S.: 333912

Mayekawa (M) Sdn. Bhd. (1)
No 3 Jalan PJU 3/50 Sunway Damansaria Technology Park, 47810, Petaling Jaya, Malaysia
Tel.: (60) 3 78051406
Emp.: 12
Refrigeration Compressor Mfr
N.A.I.C.S.: 333912
Wee Keng Yip *(Gen Mgr)*

Mayekawa (Taiwan) Co. Ltd. (1)
8F NO 35 De Xing West Rd, Taipei, -11158, Taiwan
Tel.: (886) 2 28320168
Refrigeration Compressor Mfr
N.A.I.C.S.: 333912

Mayekawa (Thailand) Co. Ltd. (1)
23 Moo 14 9th Floor Bangna Tower Tower A, Bangna Trad Road K.M.6.5, Bangkok, 10540, Samutprakarn, Thailand
Tel.: (66) 2 751 9610
Refrigeration Compressor Mfr
N.A.I.C.S.: 333912

Mayekawa Argentina S.A. (1)
Lot 42Dr Jose Valetin Gomez 151, Heado-Partido de Moran, Buenos Aires, B1706FMA, Argentina
Tel.: (54) 11 4627 6660
Refrigeration Compressor Mfr
N.A.I.C.S.: 333912

MAYEKAWA MFG. CO. LTD.

Mayekawa Mfg. Co. Ltd.—(Continued)

Mayekawa Australia Pty. Ltd. (1)
Unit 2 44 McCauley St, Matraville, 2036, NSW, Australia
Tel.: (61) 2 9695 7000
Refrigeration Compressor Mfr
N.A.I.C.S.: 333912

Mayekawa Canada, Inc. (1)
12180 Riverside Way, Richmond, V6W 1K5, BC, Canada
Tel.: (604) 270-1544
Refrigeration Compressor Mfr
N.A.I.C.S.: 333912

Mayekawa Centroamerica S.A. (1)
Bodega 63 Condominio Comercial, Tuerro Dos El Cacique de Rio, Alajuela, 20109, Costa Rica
Tel.: (506) 2441 4464
Web Site: http://www.mayekawa.cr
Emp.: 9
Refrigeration Compressor Mfr
N.A.I.C.S.: 333912
Jose Garcia *(Gen Mgr)*

Mayekawa China Industries Co. Ltd. (1)
Room 3001 Nanzheng Building, 580 West Nanjing Rd, Shanghai, 200041, China
Tel.: (86) 21 5234 1988
Refrigeration Compressor Mfr
N.A.I.C.S.: 333912

Mayekawa Colombia S.A.S. (1)
Transversal 93 no 53-48, Interior 37, Bogota, Colombia
Tel.: (57) 1 430 9980
Web Site: http://www.mayekawa.com.com
Emp.: 50
Refrigeration Compressor Mfr
N.A.I.C.S.: 333912
Yasunori Hirasako *(Gen Mgr)*

Mayekawa Deutschland GmbH (1)
Unter Bahnhofstrasse 38A, 82110, Germering, Germany
Tel.: (49) 89 5527 989 0
Refrigeration Compressor Mfr
N.A.I.C.S.: 333912

Mayekawa Do Brasil Euipamentos Industriais Ltda. (1)
Rua Licatem 250, Jardim Fazenda Rincao Aruja, Sao Paulo, 07428-280, Brazil
Tel.: (55) 11 4654 8000
Web Site: http://www.mayekawa.com.br
Refrigeration Compressor Mfr
N.A.I.C.S.: 333912
Silvio Guglielmoni *(Comml Dir)*

Mayekawa Ecuador S.A. (1)
Calle 158 Y Av Guillermo Pareja, CC Stefany Local 4 Cola Solar 13, 1 MZ.28, Guayaquil, Ecuador
Tel.: (593) 4 262 9108
Web Site: http://www.mayekawa.com
Refrigeration Compressor Mfr
N.A.I.C.S.: 333912

Mayekawa France SARL (1)
9 Rue Michael Faraday, 78180, Yvelines, France
Tel.: (33) 1 30 58 2600
Refrigeration Compressor Mfr
N.A.I.C.S.: 333912

Mayekawa India Pvt. Ltd. (1)
602 6th Floor Welldone Techpark Sector 48 Sohna Road, Gurgaon, 122002, India
Tel.: (91) 12 4651 0181
Refrigeration Compressor Mfr
N.A.I.C.S.: 333912

Mayekawa Intertech A.G. (1)
Rosenbergstrasse 31, CH-6300, Zug, Switzerland
Tel.: (41) 41 726 8626
Refrigeration Compressor Mfr
N.A.I.C.S.: 333912

Mayekawa Italia S.R.L. (1)
Via Riccardo Lombardi 19/12, 20153, Milan, Italy
Tel.: (39) 02 489 29159
Refrigeration Compressor Mfr
N.A.I.C.S.: 333912

Mayekawa Mexico SA de CV (1)
Av Coyoacan 945, Col Del Valle Delegacion Benito Juarez, Mexico, 03100, Mexico
Tel.: (52) 55 5062 0870
Refrigeration Compressor Mfr
N.A.I.C.S.: 333912

Mayekawa Mfg. Co. Ltd. (China) (1)
No 643 Hanwei Plaza, No 7 Guanghua Road, Beijing, 100004, China
Tel.: (86) 10 6561 7811
Refrigeration Compressor Mfr
N.A.I.C.S.: 333912

Mayekawa Mfg. Co. Ltd. (Russia) (1)
Korovy Val 7 Office 228, 119049, Moscow, Russia
Tel.: (7) 499 230 01 76
Refrigeration Compressor Mfr
N.A.I.C.S.: 333912

Mayekawa Middle East FZCO, Dubai - U.A. E. (1)
PO BoxU RA08-UC05, Jebel Ali Free Zone, Dubai, United Arab Emirates
Tel.: (971) 4 888 6363
Web Site: http://www.mayekawa-me.com
Emp.: 30
Refrigeration Compressor Mfr
N.A.I.C.S.: 333912
Tepsuo Kozasa *(Gen Mgr)*

Mayekawa Philippines Corp. (1)
4F Unit A&B Suntree Tower 13 Meralco Ave Ortingas Ctr, Pasig, 1605, Philippines
Tel.: (63) 2 706 0473
Emp.: 35
Refrigeration Compressor Mfr
N.A.I.C.S.: 333912
Akihiro Watanabe *(Pres)*

Mayekawa S.L. (1)
Calle Montevideo 5 Nave 13, Industrial Camporroso, Madrid, 28806, Spain
Tel.: (34) 91 830 0392
Refrigeration Compressor Mfr
N.A.I.C.S.: 333912

Mayekawa Singapore Pte. Ltd. (1)
6 Tagore Ln, Singapore, 787470, Singapore
Tel.: (65) 6451 1565
Web Site: http://www.mayekawa.com
Emp.: 24
Refrigeration Compressor Mfr
N.A.I.C.S.: 333912
Yuji Ikeda *(Mng Dir)*

Mayekawa Turkey Sogutma Sanayi Ve Ticaret Limited Sirketi (1)
Istanbul Dunya Ticaret Merkezi, A-2 blok Kat 10 325, Istanbul, 34100, Yesilkoy, Turkiye
Tel.: (90) 212 4653631
Web Site: http://www.mayekawa.eu
Refrigeration Compressor Mfr
N.A.I.C.S.: 333912

Mayekawa U.S.A., Inc. (1)
130 Smart Park Dr, Lebanon, TN 37090
Tel.: (615) 773-2859
Refrigeration Compressor Mfr
N.A.I.C.S.: 333912
Kelly Sasaki *(VP)*

Mycom Chemical Process Corp. de Venezuela S.A. (1)
Calle 148 Centro Empresario, San Francisco Nivel 1 Local 5 Y6, Maracaibo, Venezuela
Tel.: (58) 261 418 1760
Refrigeration Compressor Mfr
N.A.I.C.S.: 333912

Mycom Korea Co., Ltd. (1)
Juyeon Building 2F, Seogye-Dong 209, Seoul, 140-710, Yongsan Ku, Korea (South)
Tel.: (82) 2 796 1766
Refrigeration Compressor Mfr
N.A.I.C.S.: 333912

Mycom North America, Inc. (1)
19475 Gramercy Pl, Torrance, CA 90501
Tel.: (310) 328-1362
Emp.: 30
Air-Conditioning & Warm Air Heating Equipment & Commercial & Industrial Refrigeration Equipment Mfr
N.A.I.C.S.: 333415

Mycom Peru S.A.C. (1)
Calle Luis Pasteur, Lima, 1490, Peru
Tel.: (51) 1 205 5400

Refrigeration Compressor Mfr
N.A.I.C.S.: 333912

Mycom Venezuela Sales & Service, C.A. (1)
Calle Los Mangos Edificio Selemar, Piso 8 Sabana Grande, Caracas, 1005, Venezuela
Tel.: (58) 212 216 6026
Refrigeration Compressor Mfr
N.A.I.C.S.: 333912
Jefferson Casas *(Mgr)*

N.V. Mayekawa Europe S.A. (1)
Leuvensesteenweg 605, 1930, Zaventem, Belgium
Tel.: (32) 2 757 9075
Refrigeration Compressor Mfr
N.A.I.C.S.: 333912

N.V. Mayekawa Europe S.A. (1)
16 Oakhurst Gardens, London, DA7 5JP, Bexleyheath, United Kingdom
Tel.: (44) 1322 433558
Refrigeration Compressor Mfr
N.A.I.C.S.: 333912

N.V. Mayekawa Europe S.A. (1)
24 Kaman Andreev 1303, Sofia, Bulgaria
Tel.: (359) 2 8910130
Refrigeration Compressor Mfr
N.A.I.C.S.: 333912

P.T. Mayekawa Indoneisa (1)
Graha Pratama Building, 9th Fl JI.M.T. Haryono Kav 15, Jakarta, 12810, Indonesia
Tel.: (62) 23 8370 9484
Refrigeration Compressor Mfr
N.A.I.C.S.: 333912

MAYER HOLDINGS LIMITED

21st Floor No 88 Lockhart Road, Wanchai, China (Hong Kong)
Tel.: (852) 35231116
Web Site: http://www.mayer.com.hk
Year Founded: 2011
Sales Range: $75-99.9 Million
Emp.: 350
Steel Pole Mfr
N.A.I.C.S.: 331210

Subsidiaries:

Guangzhou Mayer Corp., Limited (1)
No 38 Yonghe Rd Yonghe Econ Zone GETDD, Guangzhou, 511356, Guangdong, China
Tel.: (86) 2032221688
Web Site: http://www.mayer.com.cn
Steel Products Mfr & Distr
N.A.I.C.S.: 331110

MAYER MASCHINENBAUG-ESELLSCHAFT MBH

Kehlsteinstrasse 4, 84529, Traunstein, Germany
Tel.: (49) 868389840
Web Site: http://www.siloking.com
Year Founded: 1983
Rev.: $32,262,239
Emp.: 300
Animal Feed Machinery Mfr
N.A.I.C.S.: 333111
Richard Vogt *(Mgr-Mktg)*

MAYER STEEL PIPE CORPORATION

12th Floor No21 Section 3 Minquan East Road, Taipei, 104, Taiwan
Tel.: (886) 225091199
Web Site: https://www.mayer.com.tw
Year Founded: 1959
2020—(TAI)
Rev.: $229,223,870
Assets: $244,615,544
Liabilities: $111,440,396
Net Worth: $133,175,148
Earnings: $34,977,303
Fiscal Year-end: 12/31/23
Steel Pole Mfr
N.A.I.C.S.: 332996

Subsidiaries:

Grand Tech Precision Manufacturing (Thailand) Corporation Limited (1)

INTERNATIONAL PUBLIC

Eastern Seaboard Industrial Estate 300/26 Moo 1 Tasith Sub-District, Pluak Daeng, Rayong, Thailand
Tel.: (66) 38955633
Steel Pole Mfr
N.A.I.C.S.: 331210

Mayer International Corporation (1)
12F No 2-1 Sec 3 Minchuan E Rd, Taipei, 104, Taiwan
Tel.: (886) 225098678
Steel Pole Mfr
N.A.I.C.S.: 331210

Mayer Steel Pipe Corporation - Pu-Hsin Factory (1)
No 6 Youg Ping Road Yangmei Dist, Taoyuan, Taiwan
Tel.: (886) 34822821
Steel Pole Mfr
N.A.I.C.S.: 331210

Mayer Steel Pipe Corporation - Youth-Shih Factory (1)
No 6 Shih 1 Road You-Shih Industrial Park Young-Mei Dist, Taoyuan, Taiwan
Tel.: (886) 346425112
Steel Pole Mfr
N.A.I.C.S.: 331210

Vietnam Mayer Corp., Ltd. (1)
29 Dai Lo Huu Nghi, Thuan An, Binhduong, Vietnam
Tel.: (84) 6503711828
Steel Pole Mfr
N.A.I.C.S.: 331210

MAYER'S CARS & TRUCKS CO. LTD.

50 Hamasger St, PO Box 20193, Tel Aviv, 61201, Israel
Tel.: (972) 35689999
Web Site: http://www.mct.co.il
Year Founded: 1967
Rev.: $435,630,451
Emp.: 2,500
Automotive Importer & Whslr
N.A.I.C.S.: 423120
Israel Kass *(Co-Pres)*

Subsidiaries:

Kavim Public Transportation Ltd (1)
43 Second Aliyah St, PO Box 15074, Azor, 58001, Israel
Tel.: (972) 3 5570600
Public Transportation Services
N.A.I.C.S.: 485210

Mayer Ramot General Insurance Agency (2009) Ltd. (1)
26 HaMasger St, Tel Aviv, 67776, Israel
Tel.: (972) 3 7239999
General Insurance Services
N.A.I.C.S.: 524210

Merkavim Transportation Technologies Ltd. (1)
22 Granit Street The Industrial Park, 38900, Caesarea, Israel
Tel.: (972) 46176000
Web Site: http://www.merkavim.co.il
Sales Range: $100-124.9 Million
Emp.: 700
Bus Bodies Mfr
N.A.I.C.S.: 336211

MAYEX USA, INC.

Jozsef Attila U 1, H-1051, Budapest, Hungary
Tel.: (36) 12350882
Web Site: https://mayexusa.hu
Year Founded: 1998
MAYX—(OTCIQ)
Sales Range: Less than $1 Million
Packaging Services
N.A.I.C.S.: 561910
Kalman Schuszter *(Chm, Pres & CEO)*

MAYFAIR EQUITY PARTNERS LLP

8 Hanover Street, London, W1S 1YQ, United Kingdom
Tel.: (44) 203 058 2670

Web Site:
http://www.mayfairequity.com
Private Investment Firm
N.A.I.C.S.: 523999
Daniel Sasaki *(Founder & Mng Partner)*

Subsidiaries:

Nasstar Services Limited (1)
19-25 Nuffield Road, Poole, BH17 0RU, Dorset, United Kingdom
Tel.: (44) 8444434433
Web Site: http://www.nasstar.com
Software Services
N.A.I.C.S.: 513210
Wayne Churchill *(CEO)*

YO! Sushi Worlds (1)
95 Farringdon Road, London, EC1R 3BT, United Kingdom
Tel.: (44) 20 7841 0700
Web Site: http://www.yosushi.com
Sales Range: $10-24.9 Million
Emp.: 1,573
Restaurant Operators
N.A.I.C.S.: 722511
Robin Rowland *(CEO)*

MAYFAIR GOLD CORP.
489 McDougall St, Matheson, P0K 1N0, ON, Canada BC
Web Site: https://www.mayfairgold.ca
Year Founded: 2019
MFG—(TSXV)
Assets: $16,268,185
Liabilities: $1,869,358
Net Worth: $14,398,826
Earnings: ($13,598,089)
Fiscal Year-end: 12/31/22
Gold Exploration & Mining Services
N.A.I.C.S.: 212220
Howard Bird *(VP)*

MAYFAIR LUMBER SALES LTD
9516 44th Street SE, Calgary, T2C 2N4, AB, Canada
Tel.: (403) 236-3127
Web Site:
http://www.mayfairlumber.com
Sales Range: $50-74.9 Million
Lumber Distr
N.A.I.C.S.: 423310
Hank Dahl *(Pres & CEO)*

MAYFIELD CHILDCARE LIMITED
Suite 2 Ground Floor 207-213 Waverley Rd, PO Box 2214, Malvern, 3145, VIC, Australia
Tel.: (61) 395763156 AU
Web Site:
https://www.mayfieldchildcare.com
Year Founded: 2015
MFD—(ASX)
Rev.: $52,584,408
Assets: $160,553,020
Liabilities: $116,016,959
Net Worth: $44,536,061
Earnings: ($977,179)
Emp.: 950
Fiscal Year-end: 12/31/23
Child Care Services
N.A.I.C.S.: 624410
Michelle Clarke *(Exec Dir)*

MAYFIELD TOYOTA
10220 170th Street NW, Edmonton, T5S 1N9, AB, Canada
Tel.: (780) 479-7979
Web Site:
http://www.mayfieldtoyota.com
Year Founded: 1998
Sales Range: $50-74.9 Million
Emp.: 175
New & Used Car Dealers
N.A.I.C.S.: 441110
David Friesen *(Gen Mgr)*

MAYFLOWER ENGINEERING LTD
Coleridge Road, Sheffield, S9 5DA, South Yorkshire, United Kingdom
Tel.: (44) 1142441353
Web Site: http://www.mayflower-engineering.co.uk
Sales Range: $10-24.9 Million
Emp.: 90
Steel Mfrs
N.A.I.C.S.: 331221
Kevan Bingham *(Mng Dir)*

MAYFLOWER GMBH
Mannhardtstrasse 6, 80538, Munich, Germany
Tel.: (49) 89 24 20 54 0
Web Site: http://www.mayflower.de
Sales Range: $1-9.9 Million
Emp.: 70
Computer Programming
N.A.I.C.S.: 541511
Albrecht Gunther *(Mng Dir-HR)*

MAYHOOLA FOR INVESTMENTS LLC
36th Floor at Tornado Tower West Bay, Doha, Qatar
Tel.: (974) 40322222
Web Site: https://www.mayhoola.com
Financial Investment Services
N.A.I.C.S.: 523999

Subsidiaries:

Valentino Fashion Group S.p.A. (1)
Via Turati 16/18, 20121, Milan, Italy (70%)
Tel.: (39) 035996711
Web Site:
http://www.valentinofashiongroup.com
Sales Range: $500-549.9 Million
Clothing, Fashion Accessories & Footwear Mfr
N.A.I.C.S.: 315250
Jacopo Venturini *(CEO)*

MAYINGLONG PHARMACEUTICAL GROUP CO., LTD.
No 100 Nanhu Zhoujiawan Wuchang, Nanhu, Wuhan, 430064, Hubei, China
Tel.: (86) 2787389583
Web Site: http://www.mayinglong.cn
Year Founded: 1994
600993—(SHG)
Rev.: $495,946,012
Assets: $710,089,230
Liabilities: $202,001,132
Net Worth: $508,088,098
Earnings: $67,252,260
Fiscal Year-end: 12/31/22
Pharmaceutical Product Mfr & Distr
N.A.I.C.S.: 325412
Chen Ping *(Chm)*

MAYNARDS INDUSTRIES, LTD.
1837 Main Street, Vancouver, V5T 3B8, BC, Canada
Tel.: (604) 876-6787
Web Site: http://www.maynards.com
Year Founded: 1902
Sales Range: $25-49.9 Million
Emp.: 20
Auction Services
N.A.I.C.S.: 561990
Barry W. Scott *(Chm)*

Subsidiaries:

Maynards Europe GmbH (1)
Maximilianstrasse 4B, 82319, Starnberg, Germany
Tel.: (49) 8151 973420
Liquidation & Auction Services
N.A.I.C.S.: 459510
Daniel Kroeger *(Co-Mng Dir-Ops)*

MAYNE PHARMA GROUP LIMITED
1538 Main North Road, Salisbury, 5106, SA, Australia
Tel.: (61) 882092666 AU
Web Site:
https://www.maynepharma.com
HG6—(DEU)
Rev.: $325,475,213
Assets: $986,796,022
Liabilities: $559,936,249
Net Worth: $426,859,773
Earnings: ($209,897,751)
Emp.: 400
Fiscal Year-end: 06/30/22
Holding Company; Pharmaceutical Developer & Marketer
N.A.I.C.S.: 551112
Roger Campbell Corbett *(Chm)*

Subsidiaries:

Adelaide Apothecary LLC (1)
160 Moore Dr Ste 105, Lexington, KY 40503
Tel.: (859) 909-8520
Web Site:
https://www.adelaideapothecary.com
Pharmaceutical Products Distr
N.A.I.C.S.: 424210

Mayne Pharma Inc. (1)
3301 Benson Dr Ste 401, Raleigh, NC 27609
Tel.: (984) 242-1399
Pharmaceuticals Product Mfr
N.A.I.C.S.: 325412

Mayne Pharma International Pty. Ltd. (1)
1538 Main North Road, Salisbury, 5106, SA, Australia
Tel.: (61) 882092666
Web Site: http://www.maynepharma.com
Sales Range: $50-74.9 Million
Emp.: 150
Pharmaceuticals Mfr
N.A.I.C.S.: 325412

MAYOLY SPINDLER
6 avenue de l Europe, BP 51, 78401, Chatou, Cedex, France
Tel.: (33) 134805555
Web Site: http://www.mayoly-spindler.fr
Gastroenterology & Dermocosmetics Laboratory
N.A.I.C.S.: 621511
Olivier Vernin *(Chm-Supervisory Bd)*

MAYR-MELNHOF KARTON AG
Brahmsplatz 6, A-1041, Vienna, Austria
Tel.: (43) 150136910 AT
Web Site: https://www.mm-boardpaper.com
Year Founded: 1988
MMK—(VIE)
Rev.: $2,849,381,863
Assets: $2,713,032,189
Liabilities: $1,023,937,272
Net Worth: $1,689,094,917
Earnings: $213,018,649
Emp.: 10,014
Fiscal Year-end: 12/31/19
Recycled Fiber Based Cartonboard Mfr
N.A.I.C.S.: 322211
Peter J. Oswald *(Chm-Mgmt Bd & CEO)*

Subsidiaries:

Al-Ekbal Printing & Packaging Co. (1)
Na Our, PO Box 401, Amman, 11710, Jordan
Tel.: (962) 65728861
Web Site: http://www.ekbal.com
Sales Range: $50-74.9 Million
Emp.: 11
Packaging & Printing Materials Mfr

N.A.I.C.S.: 322220
Adel Abu Dargham *(Gen Mgr)*

Baiersbronn Frischfaser Karton GmbH (1)
Sagmuhleweg 18, Baiersbronn, Reutlingen, 72270, Germany
Tel.: (49) 74428310
Web Site: http://www.mm-karton.com
Emp.: 200
Paperboard Mills
N.A.I.C.S.: 322130
Daniel Wiktorn *(Mgr)*

Baiersbronn Frischfaser Karton Verwaltungs GmbH (1)
Sagmuhleweg 18, Baiersbronn, Baiersbronn, 72270, Germany
Tel.: (49) 74428310
Sales Range: $25-49.9 Million
Emp.: 180
Other Management Consulting Services
N.A.I.C.S.: 541618

C.P. Schmidt Verpackungs-Werk GmbH & Co. KG (1)
Merkurstrasse 22-26, 67663, Kaiserslautern, Germany
Tel.: (49) 63135370
Web Site: http://www.cpschmidt.de
Sales Range: $75-99.9 Million
Emp.: 300
Packaging & Labeling Services
N.A.I.C.S.: 561910

Ernst Schausberger & Co Gesellschaft m.b.H (1)
Heidestrasse 19, 4623, Gunskirchen, Austria
Tel.: (43) 724664930
Web Site: http://www.schausberger.com
Paperboard Mills
N.A.I.C.S.: 322130

FS-Karton GmbH (1)
Dusseldorferstrasse 182-184, 41460, Neuss, Germany
Tel.: (49) 21312370
Web Site: http://www.mm-karton.com
Sales Range: $125-149.9 Million
Emp.: 320
Setup Paperboard Box Mfr
N.A.I.C.S.: 322219

Industriewater Eerbeek B.V. (1)
Kanaalweg 8a, 6961 LW, Eerbeek, Netherlands
Tel.: (31) 313670470
Web Site: http://www.iweerbeek.nl
Sales Range: $25-49.9 Million
Emp.: 10
Water & Sewer Line & Structures Construction
N.A.I.C.S.: 237110

Keminer Remmers Spiehs Kartonhandels GmbH (1)
Obertsroter Str 9, D-76593, Gernsbach, Germany
Tel.: (49) 72249930
Web Site: https://www.keminer-remmers.de
Sales Range: $25-49.9 Million
Emp.: 100
Paper Idustry Machinery Mfr
N.A.I.C.S.: 333243
Gottfried Latzke *(Gen Mgr)*

Kolicevo Karton Proizvodnja kartona, d.o.o. (1)
Papirniska 1, Domzale, 1230, Slovenia
Tel.: (386) 1 7290 511
Web Site: http://www.mayr-melnhof.com
Sales Range: $125-149.9 Million
Emp.: 370
Cardboard Mfr
N.A.I.C.S.: 322130
Branko Rozie *(Mng Dir)*

MM CARTON - Austria Carton, S.A. (1)
Comte Borrell 205-207 Entr D, Barcelona, 8029, Spain
Tel.: (34) 934514114
Web Site: http://www.mm-karton.com
Sales Range: $25-49.9 Million
Emp.: 7
Corrugated & Solid Fiber Box Mfr
N.A.I.C.S.: 322211
Albeoca Antonio *(Mng Dir)*

MAYR-MELNHOF KARTON AG — INTERNATIONAL PUBLIC

Mayr-Melnhof Karton AG—(Continued)

MM Graphia Beteiligungs- und Verwaltungs GmbH (1)
Sagmuhleweg, Baiersbronn, 72270, Germany
Tel.: (49) 74428310
Paper Products Mfr
N.A.I.C.S.: 322299

MM Graphia Bielefeld GmbH (1)
Altenburger Strasse 9, 33649, Bielefeld, Germany
Tel.: (49) 52144880
Web Site: http://www.mm-graphia.com
Sales Range: $75-99.9 Million
Emp.: 350
Packaging & Labeling Services
N.A.I.C.S.: 561910

MM Graphia Dortmund GmbH (1)
Schleefstrasse 1, 44287, Dortmund, Germany
Tel.: (49) 231945001
Web Site: http://www.mm-graphia.com
Sales Range: $25-49.9 Million
Emp.: 85
Packaging & Labeling Services
N.A.I.C.S.: 561910

MM Graphia Innovaprint GmbH & Co KG (1)
Erpestrasse 15, 33649, Bielefeld, Germany
Tel.: (49) 521947130
Web Site: http://www.mm-packaging.com
Sales Range: $75-99.9 Million
Emp.: 300
Packaging & Labeling Services
N.A.I.C.S.: 561910
Martin Gatzka (Gen Mgr)

MM Graphia Trier GmbH (1)
Diedenhofener Strasse 20, 54294, Trier, Germany
Tel.: (49) 65182600
Sales Range: $25-49.9 Million
Emp.: 190
Packaging & Labeling Services
N.A.I.C.S.: 561910

MM Innovaprint Verwaltungs GmbH (1)
Irpestrasse 15, 33649, Bielefeld, Germany
Tel.: (49) 521947130
Web Site: http://www.mm-graphia.com
Sales Range: $150-199.9 Million
Emp.: 1,000
Administrative Management & General Management Consulting Services
N.A.I.C.S.: 541611

MM Karton Bulgaria EOOD (1)
Opalchenska Str 76, 1303, Sofia, Bulgaria
Tel.: (359) 29312294
Web Site: http://www.mm-karton.com
Sales Range: $25-49.9 Million
Emp.: 5
Corrugated & Solid Fiber Box Mfr
N.A.I.C.S.: 322211

MM Karton Praha S.r.o. (1)
Popovova 2089/19, 14300, Prague, 14300, Czech Republic
Tel.: (420) 24440196597
Sales Range: $25-49.9 Million
Emp.: 4
Corrugated & Solid Fiber Box Mfr
N.A.I.C.S.: 322211
Andrea Novakova (Office Mgr)

MM Kartonvertrieb GmbH (1)
Dusseldorferstrasse 182-184, 41460, Neuss, Germany
Tel.: (49) 2131 2370
Web Site: http://www.mm-Karton.com
Sales Range: $25-49.9 Million
Emp.: 30
Corrugated & Solid Fiber Box Mfr
N.A.I.C.S.: 322211

MM Packaging Behrens GmbH (1)
Fritz-Kunke-Str 8, 31061, Alfeld, Germany
Tel.: (49) 518180080
Folding & Tissue Box Mfr
N.A.I.C.S.: 322212

MM Packaging Caesar GmbH & Co KG (1)
Neue Strasse 23, Traben-Trarbach, 56841, Wiesbaden, Germany
Tel.: (49) 65417090
Web Site: https://www.mm-packaging.com
Sales Range: $25-49.9 Million
Emp.: 200
Packaging & Labeling Services
N.A.I.C.S.: 561910

Subsidiary (Domestic):

MM Packaging Caesar Verwaltungs GmbH (2)
Neue Strasse 23, 56841, Traben-Trarbach, Germany
Tel.: (49) 65417090
Web Site: http://www.mm-packaging.com
Sales Range: $25-49.9 Million
Commercial Packaging Services
N.A.I.C.S.: 561910

MM Packaging Colombia S.A.S. (1)
10 Street 20-650 Yumbo Valle, Arroyohondo, Yumbo, 760502, Colombia
Tel.: (57) 26698989
Web Site: http://www.mm-packaging.com.co
Emp.: 170
Folding & Corrugated Box Mfr
N.A.I.C.S.: 322211

MM Packaging France S.A.S. (1)
Zi Plaine des Isles, 89470, Moneteau, France
Tel.: (33) 386942300
Web Site: http://www.mmp-france.com
Sales Range: $50-74.9 Million
Emp.: 200
Folding Paperboard Box Mfr
N.A.I.C.S.: 322212

MM Packaging Polska Sp. z o.o. (1)
Elizy Orzeszkowej 5, Jozefow, 05-420, Otwock, Poland
Tel.: (48) 227800671
Packaging Products Mfr
N.A.I.C.S.: 326112

MM Packaging Schilling GmbH (1)
Knorrstrasse 10, 74074, Heilbronn, Germany
Tel.: (49) 71316330
Web Site: http://www.mm-packaging.com
Packaging & Labeling Services
N.A.I.C.S.: 561910

MM Packaging Ukraine LLC (1)
Marshala Krasovskogo Street 19a, 18015, Cherkassy, Ukraine
Tel.: (380) 472545901
Web Site: https://www.mm-packaging.com
Emp.: 300
Packaging & Labeling Services
N.A.I.C.S.: 561910
Poonar Ponomar (Mng Dir)

MM Packaging Vidon Limited Liability Company (1)
15-N3 Street Park 1, Song Than 3 Industrial Zone Phu Tan Ward, 75109, Thu Dau Mot, Binh Duong, Vietnam
Tel.: (84) 2743815977
Folding Box Mfr
N.A.I.C.S.: 322212

MM Polygrafoformlenie Packaging LLC (1)
Volkhonskoe shosse 4, Lomonosov municipal district Villozi village, 188508, Saint Petersburg, Leningrad, Russia
Tel.: (7) 8005506851
Web Site: http://www.mm-packaging.com
Special Commercial Printing
N.A.I.C.S.: 323111

MMP Neupack Polska Sp.z o.o. (1)
ul E Orzeszkowej 5, Jozefow, 05-420, Kielce, Poland
Tel.: (48) 227893996
Web Site: http://www.mmp-poland.com
Sales Range: $25-49.9 Million
Emp.: 200
Packaging & Labeling Services
N.A.I.C.S.: 561910
Olaf Kacperski (Mng Dir)

MMP Packetis S.A.S. (1)
Treille, 16380, Chazelles-sur-Lyon, France
Tel.: (33) 545957930
Folding Box Mfr
N.A.I.C.S.: 322212

MMP Premium Polska Sp. z o.o. (1)
Torunska 149 A, 85-880, Bydgoszcz, Poland
Tel.: (48) 523260110
Packaging Product Mfr & Distr
N.A.I.C.S.: 326112

MMP Premium Printing Center GmbH (1)
Diedenhofener Strasse 7, 54294, Trier, Germany
Tel.: (49) 65199463400
Packaging Product Mfr & Distr
N.A.I.C.S.: 326112

MMP Premium S.A.S. (1)
800 Rue du Tertre, 44150, Ancenis, France
Tel.: (33) 240092400
Packaging Product Mfr & Distr
N.A.I.C.S.: 326112

Marinetti S.A. (1)
Av Amerigo Vespucio Norte 1751, 1751, Renca, Santiago, Chile
Tel.: (56) 2 364 88 88
Web Site: http://www.mm-packaging.com
Sales Range: $125-149.9 Million
Emp.: 50
Packaging Paper Materials Mfr
N.A.I.C.S.: 322220
Marcelo Meneghello (Gen Mgr)

Mayr-Melnhof Cartonboard UK Limited (1)
Bourne House Bourne Close, Calcot, Reading, RG31 7BS, United Kingdom
Tel.: (44) 118 942 55 04
Emp.: 12
Packaging Cartonboard Distr
N.A.I.C.S.: 424130

Mayr-Melnhof Belgium N.V. / S.A. (1)
Leuvensesteenweg 643 bus 2, 1930, Zaventem, Belgium
Tel.: (32) 27252730
Sales Range: $50-74.9 Million
Emp.: 6
Lumber Plywood Millwork & Wood Panel Whslr
N.A.I.C.S.: 423310

Mayr-Melnhof Benelux B.V. (1)
Nijverheidsweg 37, 2102 LK, Heemstede, Netherlands
Tel.: (31) 235482787
Paper Mfr
N.A.I.C.S.: 322120

Mayr-Melnhof Cartonboard International GmbH (1)
Brahmsplatz 6, 1041, Vienna, Austria
Tel.: (43) 150136910
Web Site: http://www.mm-karton.com
Sales Range: $150-199.9 Million
Emp.: 500
Holding Company
N.A.I.C.S.: 551112

Mayr-Melnhof Cartonboard UK Limited (1)
Bourne House Bourne Close Calcot, Reading, RG31 7BS, United Kingdom
Tel.: (44) 118 942 55 04
Web Site: http://www.mm-karton.com
Sales Range: $25-49.9 Million
Emp.: 10
Cartonboard Mfr
N.A.I.C.S.: 322219
John Tomkins (Mng Dir)

Mayr-Melnhof Eerbeek B.V. (1)
Coldenhovenseweg 12, 6961ED, Eerbeek, Netherlands
Tel.: (31) 313675111
Web Site: http://www.mm-karton.com
Sales Range: $50-74.9 Million
Emp.: 180
Pulp Mill
N.A.I.C.S.: 322110
August Steinkellner (Mgr)

Mayr-Melnhof France Sarl (1)
62-64 Blvd Peireir, 75017, Paris, France
Tel.: (33) 144053460
Web Site: http://www.mm-karton.com
Sales Range: $25-49.9 Million
Emp.: 8
Paperboard Mills
N.A.I.C.S.: 322130

Mayr-Melnhof Gernsbach GmbH (1)
Obertsroter Strasse 9, 76593, Gernsbach, Germany
Tel.: (49) 72246410
Web Site: http://www.mm-karton.com
Sales Range: $50-74.9 Million
Emp.: 250
Paperboard Mills
N.A.I.C.S.: 322130
Hans-Joachim Stahl (Mng Dir)

Mayr-Melnhof Graphia Izmir Karton Sanayi ve Ticaret A.S. (1)
Tire Organize Sanayi Bolgesi, Izmir, 35900, Turkiye
Tel.: (90) 2325135252
Web Site: http://www.mm-packaging.com
Sales Range: $25-49.9 Million
Emp.: 100
Paper Mills
N.A.I.C.S.: 322120
Metin Taya (Gen Mgr)

Mayr-Melnhof Gravure GmbH (1)
Diedenhofener Strasse 7, Trier, 54294, Germany
Tel.: (49) 651994630
Sales Range: $25-49.9 Million
Emp.: 100
Packaging & Labeling Services
N.A.I.C.S.: 561910
Rainer Schmidt (Mng Dir)

Mayr-Melnhof Holdings N.V. (1)
Coldenhovenseweg 12, Eerbeek, 6961 ED, Netherlands
Tel.: (31) 313675111
Web Site: http://www.mm-karton.com
Sales Range: $25-49.9 Million
Emp.: 180
Packaging & Labeling Services
N.A.I.C.S.: 561910
August Steinkellner (Mng Dir)

Mayr-Melnhof Italia Srl (1)
Via Ressi 10, 20125, Milan, Italy
Tel.: (39) 026697666
Web Site: http://www.mm-karton.com
Sales Range: $50-74.9 Million
Emp.: 9
Lumber Plywood Millwork & Wood Panel Whslr
N.A.I.C.S.: 423310

Mayr-Melnhof Karton Gesellschaft m.b.H. (1)
Brahmsplatz 6, 1041, Vienna, Austria
Tel.: (43) 150136910
Web Site: http://www.mm-karton.com
Paperboard Mills
N.A.I.C.S.: 322130

Mayr-Melnhof Karton Gesellschaft m.b.H. (1)
Wannersdorf 80, 8130, Frohnleiten, Austria
Tel.: (43) 3126 2511 0
Web Site: http://www.mm-karton.com
Sales Range: $25-49.9 Million
Emp.: 200
Recycled Fiber-Based Cartonboard Mfr
N.A.I.C.S.: 322130

Mayr-Melnhof Karton Polska sp. z.o.o. (1)
ul Rooseveltta 18, Poznan, Poland
Tel.: (48) 618451045
Sales Range: $25-49.9 Million
Emp.: 6
Corrugated & Solid Fiber Box Mfr
N.A.I.C.S.: 322211

Mayr-Melnhof Karton Schweiz GmbH (1)
Bollstrasse 43, 3076, Worb, Switzerland
Tel.: (41) 9181263156
Web Site: http://www.mm-karton.com
Sales Range: $50-74.9 Million
Cartonboard Whslr
N.A.I.C.S.: 424130

Mayr-Melnhof Mediterra Sarl (1)
Carthage Ctr Rue du Lac de Constanca, 1053, Tunis, Tunisia
Tel.: (216) 71965064
Web Site: http://www.mm-karton.com
Corrugated & Solid Fiber Box Mfr
N.A.I.C.S.: 322211

Mayr-Melnhof Nederland B.V. (1)
Nijverheidsweg 37, PO Box 131, 2102 LK,

AND PRIVATE COMPANIES — MAYU GLOBAL GROUP BERHAD

Heemstede, Netherlands
Tel.: (31) 15306250
Sales Range: $25-49.9 Million
Emp.: 5
Corrugated & Solid Fiber Box Mfr
N.A.I.C.S.: 322211

Mayr-Melnhof Packaging Austria GmbH (1)
Scheydgasse 46, 1210, Vienna, Austria
Tel.: (43) 1277710
Web Site: http://www.mm-packaging.com
Sales Range: $100-124.9 Million
Emp.: 400
Packaging Machinery Mfr
N.A.I.C.S.: 333993
Wilhelm Hormanseder *(Pres)*

Mayr-Melnhof Packaging GmbH (1)
Merkurstr 22-26, Kaiserslautern, 67663, Germany
Tel.: (49) 74428310
Packaging Paper Products Mfr
N.A.I.C.S.: 322220

Mayr-Melnhof Packaging Iberica SL (1)
Ctra CV-50 Km 18-1, Alzira, 46600, Spain
Tel.: (34) 962455200
Web Site: http://www.mm-packaging.com
Sales Range: $50-74.9 Million
Emp.: 150
Sanitary Paper Product Mfr
N.A.I.C.S.: 322291
Miguel Ferrer *(Mng Dir)*

Mayr-Melnhof Packaging International GmbH (1)
Brahmsplatz 6, 1041, Vienna, Austria
Tel.: (43) 1502570
Web Site: http://www.mm-packaging.com
Sales Range: $50-74.9 Million
Emp.: 100
Holding Company
N.A.I.C.S.: 551112

Mayr-Melnhof Packaging Marinetti Limitada (1)
Americo Vespucio Norte 1751, Renca, Santiago, Chile
Tel.: (56) 223648805
Web Site: http://www.mmpackaging.cl
Corrugated Cardboard Product Mfr
N.A.I.C.S.: 322211

Mayr-Melnhof Packaging Romania SA (1)
Str DN 1 N 920 Blejoi jud, Prahova, Brasov, 107070, Romania
Tel.: (40) 244598107
Web Site: http://www.mm-packaging.com
Emp.: 200
Setup Paperboard Box Mfr
N.A.I.C.S.: 322219
Bogdan Pache *(Gen Mgr)*

Mayr-Melnhof Packaging UK Limited (1)
Fourth Avenue, Deeside Industrial Park, Deeside, CH5 2NR, Flintshire, United Kingdom
Tel.: (44) 1244289885
Packaging Product Mfr & Distr
N.A.I.C.S.: 326112

Mayr-Melnhof Papierresidu Verwerking B.V. (1)
Coldenhovensweg 12, 6961ED, Eerbeek, Netherlands
Tel.: (31) 313675111
Web Site: http://www.mm-karton.com
Sales Range: $25-49.9 Million
Emp.: 180
Packaging & Labeling Services
N.A.I.C.S.: 561910
August Steinkellner *(Dir-Tech)*

Mayr-Melnhof Printing & Packaging Tehran Company, Private Joint Stock (1)
No 21 Alborz St Opposite Mahdi Abad Old Qom, Tehran, 1818194718, Iran
Tel.: (98) 2155546050
Packaging Products Mfr
N.A.I.C.S.: 326112

Mayr-Melnhof UK Ltd. (1)
Bourne House Bourne Close, Reading, RG31 7BS, United Kingdom
Tel.: (44) 1189425504
Web Site: http://www.mm-karton.com
Sales Range: $25-49.9 Million
Emp.: 11
Corrugated & Solid Fiber Box Mfr
N.A.I.C.S.: 322211

MinPlus-CDEM Group B.V. (1)
Meander 251, 6825 MC, Arnhem, Netherlands
Tel.: (31) 26 3764542
Web Site: http://www.cdem.nl
Thermal Conversion Technology Producing Zero Carbon Green Energy & Mineral Products from Industrial Wastes
N.A.I.C.S.: 562998
A. de Wit *(Mng Dir)*

Neupack Gesellschaft m.b.H. (1)
Hirschwang 77, Reichenau, 2651, Vienna, Austria
Tel.: (43) 2666529510
Web Site: http://www.mm-packaging.com
Packaging & Labeling Services
N.A.I.C.S.: 561910

Neupack Polska Sp.z.o.o. (1)
Ul Rowna 2, 85846, Bydgoszcz, Poland
Tel.: (48) 523604630
Packaging & Labeling Services
N.A.I.C.S.: 561910

OOO TANN Nevskiy (1)
ul Leona Pozemskogo h 141, 180006, Pskov, Russia
Tel.: (7) 8112595800
Filter Paper Mfr.
N.A.I.C.S.: 322299

PacProject GmbH (1)
Borsteler Chaussee 55, 22453, Hamburg, Germany
Tel.: (49) 4080905390
Web Site: https://www.pacproject.com
Emp.: 30
Packaging Project Consulting Services
N.A.I.C.S.: 541690
Ole Bolling *(Mng Dir)*

Papyrus Altpapierservice Handelsgesellschaft m.b.H. (1)
Argentinierstrasse 41, 1040, Vienna, Austria
Tel.: (43) 15030664
Security System Services
N.A.I.C.S.: 561621

Papyrus Wertstoff Service GmbH (1)
Mozartstr 2, Bad Reichenhall, 83435, Germany
Tel.: (49) 8651718377
Law firm
N.A.I.C.S.: 541199

Parek Papierverwertungs Gesellschaft m.b.H. (1)
Industriestrasse West 9, Kapfenberg, 8605, Austria
Tel.: (43) 3862 335820
Paper Recycling Services
N.A.I.C.S.: 322130

Private Joint Stock Company (1)
2 Maksyma Zaliznyaka Str, 18015, Cherkassy, Ukraine
Tel.: (380) 472545901
Folding Box Mfr
N.A.I.C.S.: 322212

R + S Stanzformen GmbH (1)
Vilbeler Landstr 41, Frankfurt am Main, 60388, Germany
Tel.: (49) 6109 50160 0
Web Site: http://www.runds-stanzformen.de
Paper Industry Cutting Tool Mfr
N.A.I.C.S.: 333515

Stort Doonweg B.V. (1)
Kanaalweg 8-A, 6961LW, Eerbeek, Netherlands
Tel.: (31) 313670470
Packaging & Labeling Services
N.A.I.C.S.: 561910

Superpak Ambalaj sanayi ve ticaret anonim sirketi (1)
Bahcelievler Mh Izmir-Aydin Cd No 34, Torbali, 35875, Izmir, Turkiye
Tel.: (90) 2328538340
Sales Range: $50-74.9 Million
Emp.: 135
Folding Cartons Mfr
N.A.I.C.S.: 322212
Atila Callioglu *(Gen Mgr)*

TANN Germany GmbH (1)
Siemensstrasse 10a, 21509, Glinde, Germany
Tel.: (49) 407273720
Web Site: https://www.tanngermany.com
Emp.: 1,000
Flexible Packaging Material Mfr
N.A.I.C.S.: 326112

TANN Longyou Ltd. (1)
No 8 Guangzhi Road, Longyou, Quzhou, 324400, Zhejiang, China
Tel.: (86) 5707835088
Filter Paper Mfr & Distr
N.A.I.C.S.: 322299

TANN Paper Limited (1)
149 Heller Rd, Woodstock, E7M 1X3, NB, Canada
Tel.: (506) 325-9100
Filter Paper Mfr & Distr
N.A.I.C.S.: 322299

TANN Philippines, Inc. (1)
Barangay Sta Anastacia, First Philippine Industrial Park, Santo Tomas, 4234, Batangas, Philippines
Tel.: (63) 434055551
Filter Paper Distr
N.A.I.C.S.: 424130

TANN Shanghai Co., Ltd. (1)
No 216 Zhenchen Road, Shanghai, 200331, China
Tel.: (86) 2166276172
Filter Paper Mfr & Distr
N.A.I.C.S.: 322299

Tannpapier GmbH (1)
Fabrikstrasse 48a, 4050, Traun, Austria
Tel.: (43) 7229707000
Filter Paper Mfr & Distr
N.A.I.C.S.: 322299

Ukrainisch-Deutsche geschlossene Aktiengesellschaft (1)
Gromov Street 2, Cherkassy, 18015, Ukraine
Tel.: (380) 472 54 59 01
Web Site: http://www.mayr-melnhof
Flexible Packaging Materials Mfr
N.A.I.C.S.: 322220
Ponomar Volodymyr *(Chm)*

Varsity Packaging Limited (1)
10 Commerce Park Brunel Road Theale, Reading, RG74AB, Berkshire, United Kingdom
Tel.: (44) 1189425505
Web Site: https://www.varsitypackaging.co.uk
Sales Range: $50-74.9 Million
Emp.: 7
Cartonboard Distr
N.A.I.C.S.: 424130
Andrew Latimer *(Mng Dir)*

Vien Dong Investment Development Trading Corporation (1)
806 Au Co, Tan Binh Distrist, Ho Chi Minh City, Vietnam
Tel.: (84) 838428633
Web Site: https://www.vidon.com.vn
Rev.: $54,067,831
Assets: $51,614,042
Liabilities: $24,901,692
Net Worth: $26,712,350
Earnings: $1,569,020
Fiscal Year-end: 12/31/2023
Printing Services
N.A.I.C.S.: 323111
Tran Hoang Nghia *(Exec Dir)*

Wuro Papierverwertung GmbH & Co KG (1)
Winterhauser Str 108, Wurzburg, 97084, Germany
Tel.: (49) 931 61 00 50
Web Site: http://www.fischer-entsorgung.de
Corrugated & Solid Fiber Box Mfr
N.A.I.C.S.: 322211
Siegfried Fischer *(Co-Mng Dir)*

MAYTRONICS LTD.
Tel.: (972) 46598111
Web Site:
  https://www.maytronics.com
Year Founded: 1983
MTRN—(TAE)
Rev.: $522,051,380
Assets: $602,101,110
Liabilities: $370,886,304
Net Worth: $231,214,805
Earnings: $45,188,285
Emp.: 1,304
Fiscal Year-end: 12/31/23
Other Electronic Component Manufacturing
N.A.I.C.S.: 334419
Jonathan Basi *(Chm)*

Subsidiaries:

Bunger & Frese GmbH (1)
In den Ellern 1, 28832, Achim, Germany
Tel.: (49) 4214859115
Web Site: https://shop.schwimmbad-technik.de
Swimming Pool Product Whlsr
N.A.I.C.S.: 423910

Maytronics Australia Pty. Ltd. (1)
2/91 Rudd Street Entry off Boundary Road, Oxley, Brisbane, 4075, QLD, Australia
Tel.: (61) 1300693657
Web Site: https://www.maytronics.com.au
Swimming Pool Cleaning Services
N.A.I.C.S.: 561790

Maytronics US Inc. (1)
2221 Northmont Pkwy Ste 400, Duluth, GA 30096
Tel.: (770) 613-5050
Swimming Pool Cleaning Services
N.A.I.C.S.: 561790

MAYU GLOBAL GROUP BERHAD
No 15 & 17 Jalan Perusahaan Sungai Lokan 3 Taman Industri Sungai Lokan, 13800, Butterworth, Pulau Pinang, Malaysia
Tel.: (60) 46857324
Web Site:
  https://cms.mayuglobalgroupbhd.com
Year Founded: 1981
MAYU—(KLS)
Rev.: $40,099,616
Assets: $95,271,212
Liabilities: $10,637,396
Net Worth: $84,633,816
Earnings: $3,721,095
Emp.: 377
Fiscal Year-end: 06/30/23
Investment Holding Company
N.A.I.C.S.: 551112
R. Siva Raman *(Controller-Fin)*

Subsidiaries:

Duro Metal Industrial (M) Sdn. Bhd. (1)
Lot 717 Mukim Kapar 5 1/2 Miles Jalan Kapar, 42100, Klang, Selangor, Malaysia
Tel.: (60) 332918302
Web Site: https://www.duro.com.my
Metal Sheet Product Mfr
N.A.I.C.S.: 332322
Dhanabalan Pitchai Chetty *(Exec Dir)*

Metal Perforators (Malaysia) Sdn. Bhd. (1)
Lot 5 and 7 Jalan Tukang 16/4, PO Box 7045, 40700, Shah Alam, Selangor, Malaysia
Tel.: (60) 355191470
Web Site:
  https://www.metalperforators.com.my
Cable Ladder Product Mfr
N.A.I.C.S.: 332999

Sunrise Manner Sdn. Bhd. (1)
Lot 1146 Jalan Seladang Alam, 14000, Bukit Mertajam, Pulau Pinang, Malaysia
Tel.: (60) 45388388
Web Site: https://www.sunrisemanner.com
Real Estate Services
N.A.I.C.S.: 531390

Mayu Global Group Berhad—(Continued)

MAYUKH DEALTRADE LTD.
Office No 101 on 1st Floor Crystal Rose C H S Datta Mandir Road, Kandivali West Mahavir Nagar, Mumbai, 400067, India
Tel.: (91) 2228684491
Web Site: https://mayukh.co.in
539519—(BOM)
Rev.: $267,852
Assets: $1,979,196
Liabilities: $110,292
Net Worth: $1,868,904
Earnings: $59,388
Fiscal Year-end: 03/31/23
Textile Product Trading Services
N.A.I.C.S.: 523160
Tarun Mit Brambhatt *(Mng Dir)*

MAYUR FLOORINGS LIMITED
4 & 5 Near Advani Oeirlicon L B S Marg, Bhandup West, Mumbai, 400078, Maharashtra, India
Tel.: (91) 2225964268
Web Site: https://www.mayurfloorings.com
Year Founded: 1992
531221—(BOM)
Rev.: $365,566
Assets: $761,525
Liabilities: $210,647
Net Worth: $550,878
Earnings: $2,014
Fiscal Year-end: 03/31/23
Marble Product Mfr & Whslr
N.A.I.C.S.: 327991
Mahavir N. Sundrawat *(Chm & Mng Dir)*

MAYUR LEATHER PRODUCTS LTD.
B-5 Vrindavan Apartments Vrindavan Vihar Kings Road, Jaitpura, Jaipur, 302019, Rajasthan, India
Tel.: (91) 29988801
Web Site: http://www.mayurleather.com
531680—(BOM)
Rev.: $1,204,715
Assets: $2,352,710
Liabilities: $1,521,406
Net Worth: $831,303
Earnings: ($165,517)
Emp.: 38
Fiscal Year-end: 03/31/21
Footwear Mfr
N.A.I.C.S.: 316210
Rajendra Kumar Poddar *(CEO)*

MAYUR RESOURCES LTD.
Level 7 300 Adelaide Street, Brisbane, 4000, QLD, Australia
Tel.: (61) 731574400   SG
Web Site: https://www.mayurresources.com
MRL—(ASX)
Rev.: $1,337,578
Assets: $41,400,390
Liabilities: $11,728,080
Net Worth: $29,672,311
Earnings: ($3,624,486)
Fiscal Year-end: 06/30/24
Mineral Exploration & Development Services
N.A.I.C.S.: 213115
Paul Levi Mulder *(Mng Dir)*

MAYUR UNIQUOTERS LIMITED
Village Jaitpura Jaipur - Sikar Road, Jaipur, 303704, Rajasthan, India
Tel.: (91) 1423224001
Web Site: https://www.mayuruniquoters.com
MAYURUNIQ—(NSE)
Rev.: $92,385,780
Assets: $112,193,745
Liabilities: $15,666,979
Net Worth: $96,526,767
Earnings: $12,881,450
Emp.: 495
Fiscal Year-end: 03/31/22
Artificial Leather Products Mfr & Distr
N.A.I.C.S.: 315250
Rahul Joshi *(Compliance Officer & Sec)*

MAYWUFA COMPANY LIMITED
5F No 167 Fuxing North Road, Songshan Dist, Taipei, 105, Taiwan
Tel.: (886) 227136621
Web Site: https://www.maywufa.com.tw
Year Founded: 1976
1731—(TAI)
Rev.: $42,536,412
Assets: $92,614,896
Liabilities: $25,995,453
Net Worth: $66,619,442
Earnings: $5,529,873
Emp.: 209
Fiscal Year-end: 12/31/23
Hair Care, Skin Care & Pharmaceutical Mfr & Sales; Pharmacy Retail Store Owner
N.A.I.C.S.: 325620
Fred Y. J. Lai *(Gen Mgr)*

Subsidiaries:

Broadsound Corporation   (1)
5F No 31 Sintai Road, Hsinchu County, Zhubei, 30252, Taiwan
Tel.: (886) 3 553 9868
Web Site: https://www.broadsound.com.tw
Ultrasound Equipment Mfr & Distr
N.A.I.C.S.: 334510

PhytoHealth Corporation   (1)
5F-1 No 167 Fuxing North Road, Taipei, Taiwan
Tel.: (886) 225453697
Web Site: https://www.phytohealth.com.tw
Rev.: $5,313,745
Assets: $76,866,834
Liabilities: $2,611,236
Net Worth: $74,255,597
Earnings: ($2,424,769)
Emp.: 127
Fiscal Year-end: 12/31/2023
Pharmaceuticals Mfr
N.A.I.C.S.: 325412
Chen Chia Lee *(Chm)*

MAZAGON DOCK SHIPBUILDERS LIMITED
Dockyard Road, Mazagon, Mumbai, 400010, Maharashtra, India
Tel.: (91) 23762000
Web Site: https://www.mazagondock.in
Year Founded: 1979
MAZDOCK—(BOM)
Rev.: $630,892,080
Assets: $3,431,406,615
Liabilities: $2,962,978,200
Net Worth: $468,428,415
Earnings: $70,141,890
Emp.: 3,686
Fiscal Year-end: 03/31/21
Warship & Submarine Mfr
N.A.I.C.S.: 336611
Narayan Prasad *(Chm, Mng Dir & Dir-Corp Plng & Personnel)*

MAZARIN INC.
696 Rue Monfette East, Thetford Mines, G6G 7G9, QC, Canada
Tel.: (418) 338-3669   QC
Web Site: https://mazarin.ca
Year Founded: 1985
MZRNF—(OTCIQ)
Rev.: $3,939,461
Assets: $28,428,003
Liabilities: $22,923,933
Net Worth: $5,504,070
Earnings: $1,805,492
Fiscal Year-end: 12/31/23
Industrial Mineral Mining
N.A.I.C.S.: 212390
Guy Berard *(Pres)*

MAZARO N.V.
Bommelsrede 42, 9070, Destelbergen, Belgium
Tel.: (32) 92521480
Web Site: https://www.mazaro.eu
Year Founded: 2009
MLMAZ—(EUR)
Transmission Parts Mfr
N.A.I.C.S.: 336350
Filip De maziere *(Chm)*

MAZAYA QATAR REAL ESTATE DEVELOPMENT Q.S.C.
Qatar Tornado Tower Dafna Zone 60 Street 810-Building 17, PO Box 18132, Doha, Qatar
Tel.: (974) 40121212
Web Site: https://www.mazayaqatar.com
MRDS—(QE)
Rev.: $33,550,143
Assets: $659,834,135
Liabilities: $371,488,571
Net Worth: $288,345,564
Earnings: $8,141,296
Fiscal Year-end: 12/31/23
Real Estate Developers
N.A.I.C.S.: 236220
Rashid Fahad Al Naimi *(Chm)*

MAZDA LTD
650/1 Panchwati 2nd Lane, Ambawadi, Ahmedabad, 380 006, India
Tel.: (91) 7940007000
Web Site: https://www.mazdalimited.com
Year Founded: 1990
MAZDA—(NSE)
Rev.: $21,129,071
Assets: $23,620,789
Liabilities: $3,496,843
Net Worth: $20,123,946
Earnings: $2,228,895
Emp.: 219
Fiscal Year-end: 03/31/21
Automated Valve Packages Mfr
N.A.I.C.S.: 333611
Shanaya Mody Khatua *(Exec Dir)*

Subsidiaries:

Hitendra Nagar Sahakari Vasahat Ltd.   (1)
N H Road Naroda, Ahmedabad, 382 340, India
Tel.: (91) 7940266900
Pharmaceutical Chemical Mfr & Distr
N.A.I.C.S.: 325412

Mazda Ltd - Unit 1   (1)
Block No 11 & 12 Hitendra Nagar Sahakari Vasahat Ltd, N H Rd Naroda, Ahmedabad, 382 340, Gujarat, India
Tel.: (91) 79 22801670
Web Site: http://www.mazdalimited.com
Industrial Valve Mfr
N.A.I.C.S.: 332911

Mazda Ltd - Unit 2   (1)
C 1-39 13 16 G I D C, Naroda, Ahmedabad, 382 330, Gujarat, India
Tel.: (91) 7922821779
Web Site: http://www.mazdalimited.com
Sales Range: $50-74.9 Million
Emp.: 250
Industrial Valve Mfr
N.A.I.C.S.: 332911
Dharmesh Vyas *(Gen Mgr)*

MAZDA MOTOR CORPORATION
3-1 Shinchi Fuchu-cho, Aki-gun, Hiroshima, 730-8670, Japan
Tel.: (81) 822821111   JP
Web Site: https://www.mazda.com
Year Founded: 1920
MZA—(DEU)
Rev.: $31,910,845,820
Assets: $25,063,586,480
Liabilities: $13,447,317,900
Net Worth: $11,616,268,580
Earnings: $1,372,870,560
Emp.: 48,685
Fiscal Year-end: 03/31/24
Passenger & Commercial Vehicle Mfr
N.A.I.C.S.: 336110
Hiroyuki Matsumoto *(Exec Officer-Vehicle Dev & Product Plng)*

Subsidiaries:

AutoAlliance International Inc.   (1)
1 International Dr, Flat Rock, MI 48134-9401   (50%)
Tel.: (734) 782-0498
Automobile Manufacturing
N.A.I.C.S.: 336110
Rodney Haynes *(CFO & VP-Pur & Plng)*

Fukushima Mazda Co., Ltd.   (1)
1-8-21 Zukei, Koriyama, 963-8834, Fukushima, Japan
Tel.: (81) 249325420
Web Site: http://www.fukushima-mazda.co.jp
Car Dealing Services
N.A.I.C.S.: 441110

Hakodate Mazda Co., Ltd.   (1)
30-6 Miyamae-cho 2nd Floor Hakodate store, Hakodate, 040-0073, Japan
Tel.: (81) 138423124
Web Site: http://www.hakodatemazda.jp
Car Dealing Services
N.A.I.C.S.: 441110

Hokuriku Mazda Co., Ltd.   (1)
Yokomiya-cho 3-1, Nonoichi, 921-8817, Ishikawa Prefecture, Japan
Tel.: (81) 762481120
Web Site: http://www.hokuriku-mazda.jp
Car Dealing Services
N.A.I.C.S.: 441110

Kansai Mazda Co., Ltd.   (1)
1-3-25 Sakuragawa Yubinbango, Naniwa-ku, Osaka, 556-0022, Japan
Tel.: (81) 6 6568 8000
Web Site: http://www.kansai-mazda.co.jp
Emp.: 1,043
Automobile Dealers
N.A.I.C.S.: 441120

Kanto Mazda Co., Ltd.   (1)
3-12 Oyamanishi-cho, Itabashi-ku, Tokyo, 173-0033, Japan
Tel.: (81) 57 003 1261
Web Site: https://www.kanto-mazda.com
Emp.: 2,323
Automobile Dealers
N.A.I.C.S.: 441110

Keiji Mazda Co., Ltd.   (1)
1 Mukaidanishi-cho Kisshoin, Minami-ku, Kyoto, 601-8307, Kyoto Prefecture, Japan
Tel.: (81) 753151111
Web Site: http://website.keiji-mazda.jp
Car Dealing Services
N.A.I.C.S.: 441110

Kitakanto Mazda Co., Ltd.   (1)
2770-74 Senbacho, Mito, 310-0851, Japan
Tel.: (81) 292411141
Web Site: http://www.kitakanto-mazda.co.jp
Car Dealing Services
N.A.I.C.S.: 441110

Koushin Mazda Co., Ltd.   (1)
1-27-22 Nakagosho, Nagano, 380-0935, Nagano Prefecture, Japan
Tel.: (81) 262260294
Web Site: http://www.koushin-mazda.co.jp
Car Dealing Services
N.A.I.C.S.: 441110

Kurashiki Kako Co., Ltd.   (1)
4630 Yagara Tsurajima-cho, Kurashiki, 710-8555, Okayama, Japan   (75%)
Tel.: (81) 86 465 1111
Web Site: https://www.kuraka.co.jp
Emp.: 861
Automobile Parts Mfr
N.A.I.C.S.: 336330

AND PRIVATE COMPANIES

Hitoshi Takeshita (Chm)

Kyushu Mazda Co., Ltd. (1)
4-9-12 Higashihie, Hakata-ku, Fukuoka, 812-0007, Japan
Tel.: (81) 924822288
Web Site: http://q-mazda.jp
Emp.: 918
New & Used Car Dealers
N.A.I.C.S.: 441110

Mazda (Suisse) S.A. (1)
Avenue Des Morgines 12, 1213, Petit-Lancy, Switzerland (100%)
Tel.: (41) 227193300
Web Site: http://de.mazda.ch
Sales Range: $150-199.9 Million
Emp.: 38
Automobile Importer
N.A.I.C.S.: 423110
Jose Santamaria (Mng Dir)

Mazda Ace Co., Ltd. (1)
3-1 Shinchi Fuchu-cho, Aki-gun, Hiroshima, 735-0028, Japan
Tel.: (81) 825656563
Web Site: http://www.mazdaace.co.jp
Industrial Machinery & Equipment Mfr
N.A.I.C.S.: 333248

Mazda Australia Pty. Ltd. (1)
211 A Wellington Rd, Mulgrave, 3170, VIC, Australia (100%)
Tel.: (61) 80 003 4411
Web Site: https://www.mazda.com.au
Sales Range: $25-49.9 Million
Emp.: 130
Public Relations Services
N.A.I.C.S.: 541820
Alastair Doak (Mgr-Mktg)

Mazda Austria GmbH (1)
Ernst-Diez-Strasse 3 Worthersee, 9020, Klagenfurt, Austria (100%)
Tel.: (43) 4633888
Web Site: http://www.mazda.at
Rev.: $350,000,000
Emp.: 110
Automobile Importer
N.A.I.C.S.: 423110
Deimel Josef (Mgr-PR)

Mazda Automobiles France SAS (1)
34 rue de la Croix de Fer, CS 80131, 78105, Saint Germain-en-Laye, Cedex, France
Tel.: (33) 16 101 6565
Web Site: https://www.mazda.fr
Sales Range: $25-49.9 Million
Emp.: 47
Importer & Distr of Automobiles
N.A.I.C.S.: 336110

Mazda Automoviles Espana, S.A. (1)
C / Manuel Pombo Angulo 28, 28050, Madrid, Spain
Tel.: (34) 91 635 5922
Web Site: https://www.mazda.es
Importer & Distr of Automobiles
N.A.I.C.S.: 336110
Jose Maria Terol (Pres)

Mazda Canada, Inc. (1)
55 Vogell Road, Richmond Hill, L4B 3K5, ON, Canada (100%)
Tel.: (905) 787-7000
Web Site: http://www.mazda.ca
Sales Range: $50-74.9 Million
Emp.: 90
Automotive Distr
N.A.I.C.S.: 423110
Dave Klan (Pres & CEO)

Mazda Chuhan Co., Ltd. (1)
166 Nihookimachi, Minami-ku, Hiroshima, 734-0057, Japan
Tel.: (81) 822550211
Web Site: http://www.mazda-chuhan.co.jp
Car Dealing Services
N.A.I.C.S.: 441110

Mazda Colombia S.A.S. (1)
Carrera 7 N 75-66 Offices 601 and 602, Bogota, Colombia
Tel.: (57) 313073700
Web Site: http://www.mazda.com.co
Car Dealing Services
N.A.I.C.S.: 441110

Mazda Motor Europe GmbH (1)
Hitdorfer Strasse 73, 51371, Leverkusen, Germany (100%)
Tel.: (49) 2 173 9430
Web Site: https://www.mazda.eu
Sales Range: $700-749.9 Million
Emp.: 200
Automobile Importer
N.A.I.C.S.: 423110
Jeffrey Guyton (Pres & CEO)

Mazda Motor Italia S.p.A. (1)
Via Alessandro Marchetti 105, 00148, Rome, Italy
Tel.: (39) 0660 2971
Web Site: https://www.mazda.it
Sales Range: $25-49.9 Million
Emp.: 55
Importer & Distr of Automobiles
N.A.I.C.S.: 336110
Giovanni Barbiere (Dir-Fin)

Mazda Motor Logistics Europe N.V. (1)
Blaasveldstraat 162, 2830, Willebroek, Belgium (100%)
Tel.: (32) 38601231
Web Site: https://nl.mazda.be
Sales Range: $100-124.9 Million
Emp.: 350
Mfr of Aftermarket Automobile Parts
N.A.I.C.S.: 423110

Mazda Motor Russia, OOO (1)
Metropolis Business Center Leningradskoye Shosse 16A Building 2, 125171, Moscow, Russia
Tel.: (7) 84957881001
Web Site: https://www.mazda.ru
New Car Dealers
N.A.I.C.S.: 441110

Mazda Motor de Mexico, S. de R.L. de C.V. (1)
Mario Pani No 400 PB Col Santa Fe Cuajimalpa, Delegation of Morelos, 05348, Mexico, Mexico
Tel.: (52) 5568269351
Web Site: http://www.mazda.mx
Car Dealing Services
N.A.I.C.S.: 441110

Mazda Motor de Portugal Lda. (1)
Avenida Jose Malhoa 16 - Piso 3 - Fraccao B2, 1070-159, Lisbon, Portugal
Tel.: (351) 707222323
Web Site: http://www.mazda.pt
Automobile Dealers
N.A.I.C.S.: 441110
Luis Morays (Gen Mgr)

Mazda Motors (Deutschland) G.m.b.H (1)
Hitdorfer Strasse 73, 51371, Leverkusen, Germany
Tel.: (49) 21739430
Web Site: http://www.mazda.de
Automobile Dealers
N.A.I.C.S.: 441110

Mazda Motors UK Ltd. (1)
Victory Way Crossways Business Park, Dartford, DA2 6DT, Kent, United Kingdom
Tel.: (44) 345 748 4848
Web Site: https://www.mazda.co.uk
Sales Range: $50-74.9 Million
Emp.: 200
Automobile & Other Motor Vehicle Whslrs
N.A.I.C.S.: 336110
Jeremy Thomson (Mng Dir)

Mazda Motors of New Zealand Limited (1)
7 Westfield Pl Mount Wellington, PO Box 132057, Auckland, 1644, New Zealand (100%)
Tel.: (64) 92778700
Web Site: http://www.mazda.co.nz
Sales Range: $100-124.9 Million
Emp.: 25
Importer & Distributor of Automobiles & Repair Parts
N.A.I.C.S.: 336110
Andrew Clearwater (Mng Dir)

Mazda North American Operations (1)
7755 Irvine Ctr Dr, Irvine, CA 92618 (100%)
Tel.: (949) 727-1990
Web Site: https://www.mazdausa.com
Sales Range: $300-349.9 Million
Emp.: 750
Automobile Developer Marketer, Retailer & Servicer
N.A.I.C.S.: 423110
Robert T. Davis (Sr VP-Special Assignments)

Division (Domestic):

Mazda North American Operations (2)
200 Spectrum Ctr Dr, Irvine, CA 92618 (100%)
Tel.: (949) 727-1990
Web Site: https://www.mazdausa.com
Sales Range: $25-49.9 Million
Emp.: 42
Automobile Distribution
N.A.I.C.S.: 441110

Mazda North American Operations (2)
27100 International Dr, Flat Rock, MI 48134-2755
Tel.: (734) 782-6680
Web Site: http://www.mazdausa.com
Sales Range: $50-74.9 Million
Emp.: 120
Sales & Mfr of Mazda Cars
N.A.I.C.S.: 336110

Mazda North American Operations-Western Region (2)
200 Spectrum Center Dr Ste 100, Irvine, CA 92618-5004
Tel.: (949) 222-2699
Web Site: http://www.mazdausa.com
Sales Range: $25-49.9 Million
Emp.: 200
Automobile Distribution
N.A.I.C.S.: 541330
James O'Sullivan (Pres & CEO)

North America Mazda Information Bureau (2)
10 Corporate Park Ste 200, Irvine, CA 92606-5199
Information Services
N.A.I.C.S.: 561499

Mazda Parts Co., Ltd. (1)
1-13-20 Hikarimachi, Higashi-ku, Hiroshima, 732-0052, Japan
Tel.: (81) 825681200
Web Site: http://www.mazda-parts.co.jp
Automotive Parts Retailer
N.A.I.C.S.: 441330

Mazda Sales (Thailand) Co., Ltd. (1)
689 Bhiraj Tower at Emquartier 15th - 16th Floor Sukhumvit Road, Khlong Tan Nuea Wattana, Bangkok, 10110, Thailand
Tel.: (66) 2 030 5666
Web Site: https://www.mazda.co.th
Sales Range: $25-49.9 Million
Emp.: 50
Distr of Automobiles & Repair Parts
N.A.I.C.S.: 441330
Tadashi Miura (Pres)

Mazda Southern Africa (Pty.) Ltd. (1)
4 Travertine Ave N1 Business Park, Midrand, 0157, South Africa
Tel.: (27) 127607700
Web Site: http://www.mazda.co.za
Car Dealing Services
N.A.I.C.S.: 441110

Minami Kyushu Mazda Co., Ltd. (1)
4-4 Shineicho Shinei Store 2F, Kagoshima, 890-0072, Japan
Tel.: (81) 992553331
Web Site: http://www.minamikyusyu-mazda.dealer.mazda.co.jp
Car Dealing Services
N.A.I.C.S.: 441110

Nishi Shikoku Mazda Co., Ltd. (1)
793-1 Doi-cho, Matsuyama, 791-1115, Ehime Prefecture, Japan
Tel.: (81) 899691525
Web Site: http://www.nishi-shikoku-mazda.co.jp
Car Dealing Services
N.A.I.C.S.: 441110

Okinawa Mazda Sales Co., Ltd. (1)
4-1-5 Jitchaku, Urasoe, 901-2515, Okinawa Prefecture, Japan
Tel.: (81) 988776210
Web Site: http://www.okinawa-mazda.jp
Car Dealing Services
N.A.I.C.S.: 441110

PT. Mazda Motor Indonesia (1)
Menara Standard Chartered 17th Floor Jl Prof Dr Satrio No 164, Jakarta, 12930, Indonesia
Tel.: (62) 21 2553 2800
Web Site: http://www.mazda.co.id
Sales Range: $25-49.9 Million
Emp.: 50
Automobile Dealers
N.A.I.C.S.: 441110

Shizuoka Mazda Co., Ltd. (1)
1-20-28 Kuniyoshida, Suruga-ku, Shizuoka, 422-8006, Japan
Tel.: (81) 542611234
Web Site: http://www.shizuoka-mazda.co.jp
Car Dealing Services
N.A.I.C.S.: 441110

Tohoku Mazda Co., Ltd. (1)
1-3-23 Odawara, Miyagino-ku, Sendai, 983-0803, Miyagi Prefecture, Japan
Tel.: (81) 222972122
Web Site: http://www.tohoku-mazda.co.jp
Car Dealing Services
N.A.I.C.S.: 441110

Tokai Mazda Sales Co., Ltd. (1)
3-18 Futano-cho, Mizuho-ku, Nagoya, 467-0861, Aichi Prefecture, Japan
Tel.: (81) 528728131
Web Site: http://www.tokai-mazda.co.jp
Car Dealing Services
N.A.I.C.S.: 441110

MAZHAR ZORLU HOLDING A.S.

10003 Street No 6 Ataturk Organized Industrial, Cigli, Izmir, Turkiye
Tel.: (90) 2323768631
Web Site: https://www.mazharzorlu.com.tr
Year Founded: 1996
MZHLD—(IST)
Rev.: $50,572,950
Assets: $93,010,502
Liabilities: $20,983,236
Net Worth: $72,027,265
Earnings: $1,510,563
Fiscal Year-end: 12/31/23
Holding Company
N.A.I.C.S.: 551112
Kemal Zorlu (Chm)

MAZOR GROUP LIMITED

8 Monza Road Killarney Gardens, Cape Town, 7441, South Africa
Tel.: (27) 215561555
Web Site: http://www.mazor.co.za
MZR—(JSE)
Rev.: $26,063,823
Assets: $24,983,677
Liabilities: $10,014,756
Net Worth: $14,968,920
Earnings: ($2,002,933)
Emp.: 445
Fiscal Year-end: 02/29/20
Construction Service & Glass Mfr
N.A.I.C.S.: 327212
Monty Kaplan (Chm)

Subsidiaries:

Compass Glass (Pty) Ltd. (1)
Unit A6 Brackenright Bus Park Kruis Rd, Kruispad, Brackenfell, 7560, Western Cape, South Africa
Tel.: (27) 219817785
Sales Range: $75-99.9 Million
Emp.: 125
Laminated & Toughened Safety Glass Mfr & Distr
N.A.I.C.S.: 327215

Mazor Aluminium (Pty) Ltd. (1)
8 Monza Rd, Milnerton, Cape Town, 7441, Western Cape, South Africa
Tel.: (27) 215561555
Web Site: http://www.mazor.co.za
Aluminum Windows & Doors Distr

MAZOR GROUP LIMITED

Mazor Group Limited—(Continued)
N.A.I.C.S.: 423310

MAZU ALLIANCE LIMITED
Suite 2201 Level 22 Tower 2 101
Grafton St, Bondi Junction, 2022,
NSW, Australia
Tel.: (61) 2 8011 4099   AU
Investment Management Service
N.A.I.C.S.: 523940
Bingkun Huang *(Chm & CEO)*

MAZZUCCHELLI 1849 S.P.A.
Via S e P Mazzucchelli 7, 21043,
Castiglione Olona, Varese, Italy
Tel.: (39) 0331826111   IT
Web Site:
   http://www.mazzucchelli1849.it
Year Founded: 1849
Sales Range: $75-99.9 Million
Emp.: 375
Cellulose Acetate Mfr
N.A.I.C.S.: 325211
Luigi Landoni *(Mgr-Fin)*

Subsidiaries:

HUA YI Plastic Products (Shenzhen)
Co., Ltd.   (1)
Building No 4 Long Quan I Park, Hua Rong
Lu Dalang Baoan, Shenzhen, 518109,
China
Tel.: (86) 755 61162188
Plastics Product Mfr
N.A.I.C.S.: 326199

JEBSEN-MAZZUCCHELLI LTD   (1)
RM 303 3/F Shui Hing Centre 13 Sheung
Yuet Road, Kowloon Bay, Kowloon, China
(Hong Kong)
Tel.: (852) 29238499
Plastics Product Mfr
N.A.I.C.S.: 326199

Shanghai Da-shen Cellulose Plastics
Co., Ltd.   (1)
205 Xin Fei Road Songjiang, 201611,
Shanghai, China
Tel.: (86) 2167601849
Plastics Product Mfr
N.A.I.C.S.: 326199

Sic Plastics France S.A.   (1)
ZI Nord Rue De Tamas 16, PO Box 12,
01001, Oyonnax, France   **(100%)**
Tel.: (33) 474732660
Web Site: http://www.mazzucchelli1849.it
Sales Range: $25-49.9 Million
Emp.: 5
Mfr of Plastics
N.A.I.C.S.: 326199

MB HOLDING COMPANY LLC
PO Box 695, Muttrah, 114, Oman
Tel.: (968) 24580580   OM
Web Site:
   http://www.mbholdingco.com
Year Founded: 1982
Sales Range: $200-249.9 Million
Emp.: 4,000
Holding Company
N.A.I.C.S.: 551112
Mohammed Al-Barwani *(Founder, Owner & Chm-MB Grp & Chm)*

Subsidiaries:

Biogenomics Ltd.   (1)
First Floor Kothari Compound Opposite
Tiku-Ji-ni-Wadi, Thane, 400610, Maharashtra, India
Tel.: (91) 22 41617181
Web Site: http://www.biogenomics.co.in
Biotechnology Research & Development
Services
N.A.I.C.S.: 541714
R. M. Parakh *(Chm & Mng Dir)*

Century Drilling & Energy Services
(NZ) Ltd.   (1)
166 Karetoto Road, Wairakei, Taupo, 3377,
New Zealand
Tel.: (64) 7 376 0422
Web Site: http://www.mbcentury.co.nz

Oil & Gas Well Drilling Services
N.A.I.C.S.: 213111
Marcel Manders *(CEO)*

MB Century Drilling Pty Ltd.   (1)
49 Campbell Avenue, Wacol, 4076, QLD,
Australia
Tel.: (61) 37184444
Oil & Gas Well Drilling Services
N.A.I.C.S.: 213111

MB Informatics India Ltd.   (1)
802 A Signature Towers South City 1, Gurgaon, 122001, Haryana, India
Tel.: (91) 124 4936701
Web Site: http://www.mbinformatics.com
Finance & Accounting Services
N.A.I.C.S.: 541219
Dilip Hanumant Phadnis *(COO)*

MB Petroleum Services LLC   (1)
CPO Seeb, PO Box 695, Muscat, 111,
Oman
Tel.: (968) 245 80000
Web Site: http://www.mbpetroleum.com
Sales Range: $200-249.9 Million
Emp.: 1,900
Oil Field Services
N.A.I.C.S.: 213112
Salim Al-Harthy *(CEO)*

Subsidiary (Non-US):

Barwani Petroleum Services LLC   (2)
PO Box 2871, Tripoli, Libya
Tel.: (218) 21 335 1270
Petroleum Drilling Services
N.A.I.C.S.: 213111

Erdol-ErdgasWorkover GMBH & Co.
KG   (2)
Brietzer Weg 4, 29410, Salzwedel, Germany
Tel.: (49) 3901 83 520
Web Site: http://www.eegmbh.de
Oil & Gas Well Drilling Services
N.A.I.C.S.: 213111
Jorg W. Schulte *(Mng Dir)*

Koller Asset & Management GMBH &
Co. KG   (2)
Postfach 31 71, 29231, Celle, Germany
Tel.: (49) 51 41 9 89 80
Web Site: http://www.kollar.de
Emp.: 200
Asset Management Services
N.A.I.C.S.: 531390
Marijan Grahovac *(Pres)*

Koller Workover & Drilling GmbH   (2)
Nienhagener Str 35, 29336, Nienhagen,
Germany
Tel.: (49) 5144 49 55 20
Oil & Gas Well Drilling Services
N.A.I.C.S.: 213111

MB Century Drilling Limited   (2)
51Ffulcrum Street, Richlands, 4077, QLD,
Australia   **(51%)**
Tel.: (61) 737184444
Web Site: http://www.mbcentury.com
Sales Range: $50-74.9 Million
Emp.: 13
Drilling Oil & Gas Wells
N.A.I.C.S.: 213111

Subsidiary (Non-US):

PT Century Dinamik Drilling   (3)
Chase Plaza 14th Floor, J1 Jend Sudirman
Kav 21, 12920, Jakarta, Indonesia   **(100%)**
Tel.: (62) 215201518
Engineeering Services
N.A.I.C.S.: 541330

Subsidiary (Non-US):

MB Deutschland GMBH   (2)
Linprunstrasse 49, 80335, Munich, Germany
Tel.: (49) 8007237174
Web Site: http://www.mbcrusher.de
Construction Machinery Mfr
N.A.I.C.S.: 333120

Subsidiary (Domestic):

EEW GMBH   (3)
Untere Vorstadt 11, 71063, Sindelfingen,
Germany
Tel.: (49) 7031 79 67 0

Web Site: http://www.eew-gmbh.de
Real Estate Services
N.A.I.C.S.: 531210

Subsidiary (Non-US):

MB Drilling Co. Ltd.   (2)
Korosi u 43, Szolnok, 5002, Hungary
Tel.: (36) 56 424 033
Petroleum Drilling Services
N.A.I.C.S.: 213111

MB Drilling Overseas   (2)
Abu Remmaneh Al Hassan Street Building
No 21, Damascus, Syria
Tel.: (963) 11 3316419
Petroleum Drilling Services
N.A.I.C.S.: 213111

MB Drilling Overseas Ltd   (2)
Neocleous House 195 Archbishop Makarios
Iii Avenue, Limassol, 3030, Cyprus
Tel.: (357) 25110000
Oil & Gas Well Drilling Services
N.A.I.C.S.: 213111

MB Petroleum Deutschland
GmbH   (2)
Brietzer Weg 4, Salzwedel, 29410, Germany
Tel.: (49) 3901835210
Web Site: http://www.mbholdingco.com
Petroleum Services
N.A.I.C.S.: 211120

MB Petroleum Services LLC   (2)
PO Box 25299, Al Karama, Dubai, United
Arab Emirates
Tel.: (971) 4 8131411
Petroleum Drilling Services
N.A.I.C.S.: 213111

MB Petroleum Services LLC   (2)
A-202 Crystal Apartment Plot No 25 Sector
19, New Panvel, 410206, Navi Mumbai,
India
Tel.: (91) 22 27481335
Petroleum Drilling Services
N.A.I.C.S.: 213111

MB Petroleum Services LLC   (2)
PO Box 16924, Sana'a, Yemen
Tel.: (967) 1413835
Petroleum Drilling Services
N.A.I.C.S.: 213111

MB Petroleum Services LLC   (2)
PO Box 2678, Doha, Qatar
Tel.: (974) 4657246
Petroleum Drilling Services
N.A.I.C.S.: 213111

MB Petroleum Services Ltd.   (2)
PO Box 1969, Al Khobar, Saudi Arabia
Tel.: (966) 3 8117755
Petroleum Drilling Services
N.A.I.C.S.: 213111

RELLOK Cutting Solutions
GmbH   (2)
Industriestrasse 15, 29227, Celle, Germany
Tel.: (49) 5141 90 90 0
Web Site: http://www.rellok.com
Construction Machinery Mfr
N.A.I.C.S.: 333120

Mawarid Mining LLC   (1)
PO Box 2749, Ruwi, 112, Oman   **(100%)**
Tel.: (968) 24580530
Web Site: http://www.mawaridmining.com
Metal & Mineral Exploration, Development
& Mining Services
N.A.I.C.S.: 212290

Petrogas E&P LLC   (1)
PO Box 352, Ruwi, 112, Oman
Tel.: (968) 24561310
Petroleum Services
N.A.I.C.S.: 211120

Subsidiary (Non-US):

Petrogas E&P Netherlands B.V.   (2)
Appelgaarde 4, 2272 TK, Voorburg, Netherlands
Tel.: (31) 703572357
Emp.: 134
Oil & Gas Exploration, Drilling & Extraction
Services
N.A.I.C.S.: 211120
Nick Dancer *(Gen Mgr)*

INTERNATIONAL PUBLIC

Subsidiary (Domestic):

Petrogas LLC   (2)
Building No 1742 Way No 6826/ 18-Nov
Street, Azaiba, Muscat, Oman
Tel.: (968) 24527900
Petroleum Drilling Services
N.A.I.C.S.: 213111

Petrogas Rima LLC   (2)
Way No 46 Building No 585/ 18-Nov Street,
Azaiba, Muscat, Oman
Tel.: (968) 24584800
Petroleum Drilling Services
N.A.I.C.S.: 213111

United Engineering Services LLC   (1)
Seeb Airport, PO Box 2729, 111, Muscat,
Oman
Tel.: (968) 24561850
Web Site: http://www.uesoman.com
Industrial Machinery & Equipment Mfr
N.A.I.C.S.: 333998
Usama Al Barwani *(Mng Dir)*

Subsidiary (Non-US):

Hyspec Engineering Ltd   (2)
Rigg Street, Stewarton, KA3 5AJ, Ayrshire,
United Kingdom
Tel.: (44) 1560 483512
Web Site:
  http://www.hyspecengineering.co.uk
Emp.: 100
Precision Machine & Equipment Mfr
N.A.I.C.S.: 332721

Koller Maschinen und Anlagenbau
GmbH   (2)
Bruchkampweg 5, 29227, Celle, Germany
Tel.: (49) 5141 9898 0
Web Site: http://www.koller-celle.de
Emp.: 200
Industrial Machinery & Equipment Mfr
N.A.I.C.S.: 333998
Neville Storey *(CEO)*

UES International Sdn. Bhd.   (2)
No 1 Jalan TU43, Taman TasikUtama,
75450, Ayer Keroh, Melaka, Malaysia
Tel.: (60) 163292113
Industrial Machinery & Equipment Distr
N.A.I.C.S.: 423830

MB RAHASTOT OY
Bulevardi 1 A, 00100, Helsinki, Finland
Tel.: (358) 9 131011
Web Site: http://www.mbrahastot.fi
Capital Market Company
N.A.I.C.S.: 523150
Aapo Eskelinen *(Partner)*

Subsidiaries:

Raksystems Insinooritoimisto Oy   (1)
Vetotie 3 A, Vantaa, 01610, Finland
Tel.: (358) 207 495 500
Web Site: http://www.raksystems.fi
Hygiene, Pest Control, Safety & Fire Protection Services
N.A.I.C.S.: 561710
Marko Malmivaara *(Mng Dir)*

MB SHIPBROKERS K/S
Midtermolen 1, 2100, Copenhagen,
Denmark
Tel.: (45) 33441400
Web Site:
   http://www.maerskbroker.com
Year Founded: 1914
Sales Range: $100-124.9 Million
Emp.: 240
Freight Brokerage Services
N.A.I.C.S.: 488510
Claes Devantier *(Member-Exec Bd & Sr VP)*

Subsidiaries:

Maersk Broker Albis Schiffahrt
GmbH   (1)
Englische Planke 2, 20459, Hamburg, Germany
Tel.: (49) 40809060230
Ship Repair & Maintenance Services
N.A.I.C.S.: 336611

AND PRIVATE COMPANIES

Lars von Eitzen *(Gen Mgr)*

Maersk Broker America Inc (1)
10th Fl 177 Broad St, Stamford, CT 06901
Tel.: (203) 351-9859
Ship Repair & Maintenance Services
N.A.I.C.S.: 336611

Maersk Broker Hellas Limited (1)
44-46 Vouliagmenis Avenue, Voula, 16673, Athens, Greece
Tel.: (30) 2111048400
Ship Repair & Maintenance Services
N.A.I.C.S.: 336611

Maersk Broker Hong Kong Ltd (1)
Room 2307-11 23/F Leighton Centre, 77 Leighton Road, Causeway Bay, Hong Kong, China (Hong Kong)
Tel.: (852) 28372160
Ship Repair & Maintenance Services
N.A.I.C.S.: 336611

Maersk Broker Korea Co., Ltd (1)
Room 1521 15/F Gwanghwamun Officia Bldg 163 Shinmunno 1-ga, Jongno, Seoul, 110-999, Korea (South)
Tel.: (82) 27330540
Ship Repair & Maintenance Services
N.A.I.C.S.: 336611
Casper Ruaek Nielsen *(Pres)*

Maersk Broker Middle East DMC EST (1)
Gold and Diamond park bld 7 2nd floor office 204, PO Box 361003, Dubai, United Arab Emirates
Tel.: (971) 45016300
Ship Repair & Maintenance Services
N.A.I.C.S.: 336611
Rune Bonlokke *(Mgr-Sls & Pur)*

Maersk Broker UK Ltd (1)
New Loom House Suite 1 03 101 Back Church Lane, London, E1 1LU, United Kingdom
Tel.: (44) 2074816000
Ship Repair & Maintenance Services
N.A.I.C.S.: 336611
Ben Goss *(Mng Dir)*

MB WORLD GROUP BERHAD
Unit 5 01 Level 5 Plaza DNP No 59 Jalan Dato Abdullah Tahir, 80300, Johor Bahru, Johor, Malaysia
Tel.: (60) 7 330 5979   MY
Web Site: http://www.mbworld.com.my
Year Founded: 1995
MBWORLD—(KLS)
Rev.: $82,090,840
Assets: $153,813,139
Liabilities: $86,517,241
Net Worth: $67,295,898
Earnings: $13,209,301
Fiscal Year-end: 12/31/19
Geotechnical Engineering Services
N.A.I.C.S.: 541330
Simon Yow Yung Sim *(Exec Dir)*

Subsidiaries:

Emas Kiara Marketing Sdn. Bhd. (1)
Lot 13A Jalan RP 3 Rawang Industrial Estate, 48000, Rawang, Selangor, Malaysia   (100%)
Tel.: (60) 360929898
Emp.: 30
Geosynthetic Products Trading & Installation Services
N.A.I.C.S.: 423330

MB World Builders Sdn. Bhd. (1)
Unit 6-01 Level 6 Plaza DNP No 59 Jalan Dato Abdullah Tahir, 80300, Johor Bahru, Johor, Malaysia
Tel.: (60) 73305972
Property Development Services
N.A.I.C.S.: 531390

Mahabuilders Sdn. Bhd. (1)
Unit 5 01 Level 5 Plaza DNP No 59 Jalan Dato Abdullah Tahir, 80250, Johor Bahru, Johor, Malaysia
Tel.: (60) 7 330 5979
Web Site: http://www.mbgroup.com.my
Construction, Real Estate Development & Property Management Services
N.A.I.C.S.: 531390

MBB SE
Joachimsthaler Strasse 34, 10719, Berlin, Germany
Tel.: (49) 3084415330
Web Site: https://www.mbb.com
MBB—(DUS)
Rev.: $1,053,776,379
Assets: $1,268,368,707
Liabilities: $655,356,580
Net Worth: $613,012,127
Earnings: $13,412,020
Emp.: 3,645
Fiscal Year-end: 12/31/23
Investment Services
N.A.I.C.S.: 523999
Peter Niggemann *(Vice Chm)*

Subsidiaries:

Aumann AG (1)
Dieselstr 6, 48361, Beelen, Germany
Tel.: (49) 25868887800
Web Site: https://www.aumann.com
Rev.: $319,691,791
Assets: $389,368,065
Liabilities: $180,394,435
Net Worth: $208,973,630
Earnings: $10,575,075
Emp.: 870
Fiscal Year-end: 12/31/2023
Automotive Component Mfr & Distr
N.A.I.C.S.: 336320
Gert-Maria Freimuth *(Chm-Supervisory Bd)*

Aumann Beelen GmbH (1)
Dieselstrasse 6, 48361, Beelen, Germany   (100%)
Tel.: (49) 25868880
Web Site: http://www.claas-fertigungstechnik.com
Sales Range: $125-149.9 Million
Emp.: 270
Welding & Assembly Systems for Automotive Industry & Machine Tool Mfr
N.A.I.C.S.: 333517

Blomberger Holzindustrie GmbH (1)
Konigswinkel 2-6, 32825, Blomberg, Germany
Tel.: (49) 52359660
Web Site: https://www.delignit.de
Plywood Mfr
N.A.I.C.S.: 321211

CT Formpolster GmbH (1)
Borstelstrasse 113, 32584, Lohne, Germany
Tel.: (49) 573118040
Web Site: https://www.ct-formpolster.de
Polyurethane Flexible Foam Mfr
N.A.I.C.S.: 326150
Dennis Hanke *(Mng Dir)*

DHK Automotive GmbH (1)
Wustenbrander Str 11, Oberlungwitz, 09353, Zwickau, Germany
Tel.: (49) 372369460
Web Site: https://www.dhk-automotive.com
Molded & Milled Parts Mfr
N.A.I.C.S.: 333511

DTS Beteiligungen GmbH & Co. KG (1)
Schrewestrasse 2, Nordrhein-Westfalen, 32051, Herford, Germany
Tel.: (49) 52211011000
Web Site: http://www.dts.de
Sales Range: $50-74.9 Million
Emp.: 90
Investment Management Service
N.A.I.C.S.: 523940

Subsidiary (Domestic):

DTS Beteiligungen Verwaltungs GmbH (2)
Heidestr 38, 32051, Herford, Germany
Tel.: (49) 52211011000
Sales Range: $25-49.9 Million
Information Technology Consulting Services
N.A.I.C.S.: 541512

DTS IT AG (1)
Scherwestrasse 2, 32051, Herford, Germany
Tel.: (49) 52211013410
Web Site: https://www.dts-it-ag.de
N.A.I.C.S.: 531390

Subsidiary (Non-US):

DTS Cloud Security Monepe (2)
Omirou 8-5th Floor, 10564, Athens, 105 64, Greece
Tel.: (30) 2111040700
Software Support Services
N.A.I.C.S.: 541511

Subsidiary (Domestic):

DTS Systeme GmbH (2)
Schrewestrasse 2, 32051, Herford, Germany
Tel.: (49) 52211013000
Web Site: https://www.dts.de
Emp.: 400
Software Support Services
N.A.I.C.S.: 541511
Malte Ormann *(Head-Sls)*

DTS Systeme Munster GmbH (2)
Soester Strasse 13, 48155, Munster, Germany
Tel.: (49) 25160600
Software Support Services
N.A.I.C.S.: 541511

Subsidiary (Non-US):

DTS Systeme Wien GmbH (2)
Heiligenstadter Lande 29, 1190, Vienna, Austria
Tel.: (43) 1361441410
Software Support Services
N.A.I.C.S.: 541511

Subsidiary (Domestic):

ISL Internet Sicherheitslosungen GmbH (2)
Alte Wittener Str 70, 44803, Bochum, Germany
Tel.: (49) 2349766720
Web Site: https://www.isl.de
Security Management Services
N.A.I.C.S.: 561621

Friedrich Vorwerk SE & Co. KG (1)
Niedersachsenstrasse 19-21, Tostedt, 21255, Harburg, Germany
Tel.: (49) 418210470
Web Site: https://www.friedrich-vorwerk.de
Pipeline & Plant Technology Development Services
N.A.I.C.S.: 237120

Hanke Tissue Sp. z o.o. (1)
ul Fabryczna 1, 66-470, Kostrzyn, Poland
Tel.: (48) 957131300
Web Site: https://www.hanketissue.pl
Tissue Paper Mfr
N.A.I.C.S.: 322291
Robert Szczepkowski *(Pres)*

Huchtemeier Papier GmbH (1)
Gernotstrasse 18, Nordrhein-Westfalen, 44319, Dortmund, Germany
Tel.: (49) 23144940
Web Site: https://www.huchtemeier.com
Polyurethane Material Mfr
N.A.I.C.S.: 326150

Subsidiary (Domestic):

Huchtemeier Papier GmbH (2)
Gernotstrasse 18, Postfach 13 03 65, 44319, Dortmund, Germany
Tel.: (49) 2 314 4940
Web Site: https://www.huchtemeier.net
Sales Range: $25-49.9 Million
Emp.: 38
Paper Distribution Services
N.A.I.C.S.: 424130
Moritz Vosschulte *(CFO)*

OBO-Werke GmbH & Co. KG (1)
Am Bahnhof 5, 31655, Stadthagen, Germany
Tel.: (49) 57 217 8010
Web Site: https://www.obo-werke.de
Sales Range: $25-49.9 Million
Emp.: 65
Polyurethane Board & Block Materials Mfr
N.A.I.C.S.: 326150

MBCA BANK LIMITED
14th Fl Old Mutual Centre 3rd St Jason Moyo Ave, PO Box 3200, Harare, Zimbabwe
Tel.: (263) 4701636
Web Site: http://www.mbca.co.zw
Sales Range: $250-299.9 Million
Emp.: 282
Commericial Banking
N.A.I.C.S.: 522110
Joram Matsvimbo *(Head-Bus Dev & Institutional Banking)*

MBE WORLDWIDE S.P.A.
Viale Lunigiana 35/37, 20125, Milan, Italy
Tel.: (39) 02 67 625 777   IT
Web Site: http://www.mbeglobal.com
Year Founded: 1993
Holding Company; Mail Centers Owner, Operator & Franchisor
N.A.I.C.S.: 551112
Paolo Fiorelli *(Chm & CEO)*

Subsidiaries:

AlphaGraphics, Inc. (1)
143 Union Blvd Ste 650, Lakewood, CO 80228
Tel.: (800) 955-6246
Web Site: http://www.alphagraphics.com
Franchises; Commercial Printing Services
N.A.I.C.S.: 323111
Ryan Farris *(Pres, COO & CTO)*

Subsidiary (Domestic):

Sign Satisfaction, Inc. (2)
2325 Independence Dr, Austin, TX 78745
Tel.: (512) 266-6115
Marketing & Advertising Services; Signs, Banners, Vehicle Graphics, Floor Graphics, Window Graphics & Wall Graphics
N.A.I.C.S.: 541430
Dan Klopp *(Owner, Founder & Pres)*

PostNet International Franchise Corporation (1)
143 Union Blvd Ste 600, Lakewood, CO 80228
Tel.: (303) 771-7100
Web Site: http://postnetfranchise.com
Printing, Shipping, Graphic Design & Business Services
N.A.I.C.S.: 323111
Brian Spindel *(Pres & COO)*

Sistema Italia 93 S.r.l. (1)
Viale Lunigiana 35/37, 20125, Milan, Italy
Tel.: (39) 02 676251
Web Site: http://www.mbe.it
Private Mail Centers Operator & Franchisor
N.A.I.C.S.: 561431
Paolo Cominone *(Reg Mgr-Italy, France & Poland)*

MBF HOLDINGS BERHAD
Level 17 Menara MBf Jalan Sultan Ismail, Kuala Lumpur, 50250, Malaysia
Tel.: (60) 321678000   MY
Web Site: http://www.mbfh.com.my
Sales Range: $750-799.9 Million
Emp.: 11,000
Card & Payment Printing Services
N.A.I.C.S.: 323111
Siew Hoong Chong *(Head-Fin)*

Subsidiaries:

Carpenter Motors (Vanuatu) Ltd. (1)
Elluk Road Namba Tri, Port-Vila, Shefa, Vanuatu
Tel.: (678) 25444
Sales Range: $50-74.9 Million
Emp.: 80
Automotive Distr
N.A.I.C.S.: 423110

Carpenters Hardware Ltd. (1)
46 Matua Street, Walubay, Suva, Rewa, Fiji
Tel.: (679) 3313155
Web Site: http://www.carphardware.com.fj
Sales Range: $75-99.9 Million
Emp.: 180
Hardware Whslr
N.A.I.C.S.: 423710

MBF HOLDINGS BERHAD / INTERNATIONAL PUBLIC

MBf Holdings Berhad—(Continued)

Carpenters Properties Ltd. (1)
Carpenters Building 34 Rodwell Road, PO Box 299, Suva, Rewa, Fiji
Tel.: (679) 3313122
Web Site: http://www.carpproperties.com.fj
Property Management & Development Services
N.A.I.C.S.: 531210

Daltron (Vanuatu) Ltd. (1)
Orchid Building Father Lini Highway, PO Box 276, Port-Vila, 276, Shefa, Vanuatu
Tel.: (678) 22537
Web Site: http://www.daltron.com.vu
Emp.: 8
Software Development Services
N.A.I.C.S.: 541511

Industrial and Marine Engineering Ltd. (1)
Eliza Street Walu Bay, PO Box 296, Suva, 296, Rewa, Fiji
Tel.: (679) 3312133
Web Site: http://www.imel.com.fj
Sales Range: $50-74.9 Million
Emp.: 74
Vessel Docking & Ship Repair Services
N.A.I.C.S.: 488330
Inoke Seru (Mgr-Ops)

MBf Carpenters Shipping Ltd. (1)
Level 13A Menara MBf Jalan Sultan Ismail, 50250, Kuala Lumpur, Malaysia
Tel.: (60) 321678000
Web Site:
https://www.carpentersshipping.com
Shipping Services
N.A.I.C.S.: 488510

MBf Management Sdn. Bhd. (1)
Level 13 Menara MBF Jalan Sultan Ismail, 50250, Kuala Lumpur, Malaysia
Tel.: (60) 378612100
Investment Management Service
N.A.I.C.S.: 523940

MBf Printing Industry Sdn. Bhd. (1)
Lot 65931 Taman Perindustrian Sek 2 12, PO Box 93, 47100, Puchong, Selangor, Malaysia
Tel.: (60) 380644600
Web Site: http://www.mbfprinting.com.my
Sales Range: $150-199.9 Million
Emp.: 300
Commercial Printing Services & Packaging Products Mfr
N.A.I.C.S.: 323111

MBf Wood Terrace Capital Corporation (1)
404 Windsor Manor Ct, Johns Creek, GA 30097-5992
Tel.: (770) 476-4422
Housing Building Construction Services
N.A.I.C.S.: 236116

WRC Limited (1)
Pena Place Lot 4 Section 34, Mount Hagen, Western Highlands, Papua New Guinea
Tel.: (675) 5422700
Web Site: http://www.mbfh.com.my
Tea & Coffee Distr
N.A.I.C.S.: 311920

MBG GROUP JOINT STOCK COMPANY
No 906 Nguyen Khoai, Thanh Tri Ward Hoang Mai District, Hanoi, Vietnam
Tel.: (84) 436447655
Web Site: https://maxxbau.com
Year Founded: 2007
MBG—(HNX)
Rev.: $28,689,452
Assets: $31,358,508
Liabilities: $2,006,457
Net Worth: $29,352,052
Earnings: $1,149,237
Fiscal Year-end: 12/31/20
Lighting Equipment Mfr
N.A.I.C.S.: 335139
Pham Huy Thanh (Chm & Chm-Mgmt Bd)

MBH BANK NYRT.
Vaci u 38, 1056, Budapest, Hungary
Tel.: (36) 3278600 HU
Web Site: http://www.mkb.hu
Year Founded: 1950
MBHBANK—(BUD)
Rev.: $3,469,588,894
Assets: $31,988,520,381
Liabilities: $29,041,191,434
Net Worth: $2,947,328,947
Earnings: $527,590,864
Emp.: 8,838
Fiscal Year-end: 12/31/23
Commercial Banking Services
N.A.I.C.S.: 522110
Zsolt Barna (Chm & CEO)

Subsidiaries:

Budapest Bank (1)
Vaci ut 193, Budapest, Hungary
Tel.: (36) 80350350
Web Site: https://www.budapestbank.hu
Banking Services
N.A.I.C.S.: 522110

MKB - Euroleasing Autolizing Zrt. (1)
Lopotar u 24, 1134, Budapest, Hungary
Tel.: (36) 1 345 2424
Web Site: http://www.euroleasing.hu
Financial Management Services
N.A.I.C.S.: 523999

MKB Altalanos Biztosito Zrt. (1)
Vaci ut 76, Budapest, 1133, Hungary
Tel.: (36) 618866900
Web Site: http://www.mkbb.hu
Fire Insurance Services
N.A.I.C.S.: 524113

MKB Autopark OOD (1)
Dimitrov 16A fl 1, Sofia, Bulgaria
Tel.: (359) 28052786
Web Site: http://www.mkb-autopark.bg
Fleet Leasing & Management Services
N.A.I.C.S.: 485310
Zoltan Toth (CEO)

MKB Nyugdijpenztart es Egeszsegpenztart Kiszolgalo Kft. (1)
Szent Istvan ter 15, Budapest, Hungary
Tel.: (36) 12687001
Commercial Banking Services
N.A.I.C.S.: 522110

Nextebank S.A. (1)
Bulevardul Pipera nr 1B Voluntati Cubic Center etaj 7, judet Ilfov, Bucharest, 050525, Romania
Tel.: (40) 80 041 0310
Web Site: http://www.nextebank.ro
Commercial Banking Services
N.A.I.C.S.: 522110
Felicia Serbanescu (Head-Bancassurance Dept)

MBH CORPORATION PLC
7 Royal Victoria Patriotic Building John Archer Way, London, SW18 3SX, United Kingdom
Tel.: (44) 2088770266 UK
Web Site:
http://www.mbhcorporation.com
MBHCF—(OTCIQ)
Rev.: $180,313,052
Assets: $190,968,190
Liabilities: $100,470,841
Net Worth: $90,497,349
Earnings: $2,753,093
Emp.: 642
Fiscal Year-end: 12/31/22
Diversified Investment Holding Company
N.A.I.C.S.: 551112
Callum Laing (CEO)

Subsidiaries:

3 K'S Engineering Company Limited (1)
Embankment Road Machynys, Llanelli, SA15 2DN, United Kingdom
Tel.: (44) 1554750501
Web Site: https://www.3ksengineering.com
Heavy Machinery Mfr

N.A.I.C.S.: 333248

Acacia Training Ltd. (1)
Acacia House Trentham Business Quarter Bellringer Road, Trentham, Stoke-on-Trent, ST4 8GB, United Kingdom
Tel.: (44) 1782646346
Web Site: https://www.acaciatraining.co.uk
Educational Support Services
N.A.I.C.S.: 611710
Victoria Sylvester (CEO)

Academy 1 Sports Ltd. (1)
The Old Granary Dunton Road, Laindon, SS15 4DB, Essex, United Kingdom
Tel.: (44) 1375275052
Web Site: https://www.academy1group.com
Educational Support Services
N.A.I.C.S.: 611710

Cape Ltd. (1)
42 Fairfax Ave, Penrose, Auckland, 1061, New Zealand
Tel.: (64) 93744204
Web Site: https://www.cape.net.nz
Construction Services
N.A.I.C.S.: 236220
Dianne Weissenborn (Controller-Finance)

Driven by Riide Data Ltd. (1)
Unit 6 Block A Broomfield Business Park, Malahide, Dublin, KE36E398, Ireland
Tel.: (353) 1 533 7757
Web Site: https://www.drivenbyriidedata.ie
Taxi Service
N.A.I.C.S.: 485310

G.S. Contracts (Joinery) Ltd. (1)
GS House Moorside, Colchester, CO1 2TJ, Essex, United Kingdom
Tel.: (44) 1206793053
Web Site: https://www.gscontracts.com
Construction Contracting Services
N.A.I.C.S.: 236220
Gary Smith (Founder)

Gaysha Limited (1)
Work Life 4 Crown Place, Belgravia, London, EC2A 4BT, United Kingdom
Tel.: (44) 2038873623
Web Site: https://www.gaysha.co.uk
Construction Contracting Services
N.A.I.C.S.: 236220
Ian Elsey (CEO)

Guildprime Specialist Contracts Ltd. (1)
Guildprime Business Centre Southend Rd, Great Burstead, Billericay, CM11 2PZ, Essex, United Kingdom
Tel.: (44) 1277637888
Web Site: https://www.guildprime.com
Construction Contracting Services
N.A.I.C.S.: 236220
Kevin Potter (CEO)

Intercity Private Hire Limited (1)
82 Old Town Road Hanley, Stoke-on-Trent, ST1 2JT, United Kingdom
Tel.: (44) 1782855855
Web Site: https://intercity.taxi
Taxi Hire Services
N.A.I.C.S.: 541850

K S Training Ltd. (1)
Enterprise Centre 1 Hedingham Grove Chelmsley Wood, Chelmunds Cross, Birmingham, B37 7TP, United Kingdom
Tel.: (44) 333 307 0264
Web Site: https://www.kstraininggroup.com
Staff Training Services
N.A.I.C.S.: 611430

Learning Wings Pte Ltd (1)
Blk 15 Toa Payoh Lorong 8 05-08 Braddell Tech, Singapore, 319262, Singapore
Tel.: (65) 62942955
Web Site: https://www.learningwings.com.sg
Emp.: 238
Educational Support Services
N.A.I.C.S.: 611710

Logistica Training Limited (1)
Unit 5 Great Cliffe Court Great Cliffe Road, Dodworth, Barnsley, S75 3SP, United Kingdom
Tel.: (44) 1709966112
Web Site: https://www.logisticatraining.co.uk
Staff Training Services
N.A.I.C.S.: 611430

Meeting Of The Minds, Inc. (1)
PO Box 2915, Plainfield, NJ 07062
Tel.: (908) 369-1152
Web Site:
https://www.meetingsoftheminds.com
Concert Organizing Services
N.A.I.C.S.: 711310

Robinsons Caravans Limited (1)
Ringwood Road, Brimington, Chesterfield, S43 1DG, United Kingdom
Tel.: (44) 1246230000
Web Site:
http://www.robinsonscaravans.co.uk
Rev.: $16,920,750
Emp.: 76
New & Used Caravan Mfr
N.A.I.C.S.: 423860
Paul Seabridge (CEO)

Samuel Hobson House Limited (1)
20 Knutton Rd, Wolstanton, Newcastle-under-Lyme, ST5 0HU, United Kingdom
Tel.: (44) 1782620011
Web Site:
https://www.samuelhobsonhouse.co.uk
Aged Care Residential Services
N.A.I.C.S.: 623990
Vicky Smith (Mgr & Principal)

Victoria Gosden Travel Limited (1)
15 Kings Road, Fleet, GU51 3DH, Hampshire, United Kingdom
Tel.: (44) 1252613613
Web Site: https://www.vgtravel.co.uk
Taxi Service
N.A.I.C.S.: 485310

du Boulay Contracts Ltd. (1)
Studio 7 Royal Victoria Patriotic Building, John Archer Way, Wandsworth, London, SW18 3SX, United Kingdom
Tel.: (44) 2088770266
Web Site: https://www.duboulay.co.uk
Construction Contracting Services
N.A.I.C.S.: 236220

MBI & PARTNERS U.K. LIMITED
78-80 Wigmore Street, London, W1U 2SJ, United Kingdom
Tel.: (44) 20 7935 5859 UK
Web Site:
http://www.mbiinternational.com
Rev.: $9,000,000,000
Emp.: 9,000
Investment Holding Company
N.A.I.C.S.: 551112
Mohamed Issa Al Jaber (Founder, Chm & CEO)

Subsidiaries:

Houston Continentoil Inc. (1)
1800 West Loop S Ste 850, Houston, TX 77027
Tel.: (832) 426-5656
Oil & Gas Exploration Services
N.A.I.C.S.: 213112
Jean-Paul Chalot (CEO)

MBI International Holdings Limited (1)
78-80 Wigmore Street, London, W1U 2SJ, United Kingdom
Tel.: (44) 2079355859
Web Site: https://www.mbiinternational.com
Investment Institution Services
N.A.I.C.S.: 523150
Issa Al Jaber (Founder)

MBK CO., LTD.
6F SKY Nishiazabu Building 3-3-1 Nishiazabu, Minato-ku, Tokyo, 106-0031, Japan
Tel.: (81) 364345540
Web Site: https://www.mbkworld.co.jp
Year Founded: 1946
3121—(TKS)
Rev.: $10,904,420
Assets: $99,004,760
Liabilities: $70,446,240
Net Worth: $28,558,520
Earnings: $694,820
Fiscal Year-end: 10/31/23

AND PRIVATE COMPANIES

Investment Management Service
N.A.I.C.S.: 523940
Masatoshi Takasaki *(Pres & CEO)*

Subsidiaries:

Hotel System 21 Co., Ltd. (1)
800 Mizonokuchi, Kakogawa, 675-0064, Japan
Tel.: (81) 794218877
Web Site: http://www.kakogawa-hotel.com
Hotel Operator
N.A.I.C.S.: 721110

MBK PARTNERS LTD.

20th Floor Seoul Finance Center 84 Taepyung-ro 1-ka, Chung-ku, Seoul, 100-768, Korea (South)
Tel.: (82) 237068600 KR
Web Site:
   http://www.mbkpartnerslp.com
Year Founded: 2005
Privater Equity Firm
N.A.I.C.S.: 523999
Jay H. Bu *(Partner)*

Subsidiaries:

Accordia Golf Co., Ltd. (1)
Shinagawa Seaside Park Tower 9F 4-12-4 Higashi-shinagawa, Shibuya-ku, Tokyo, Japan
Tel.: (81) 3 66881500
Web Site: http://www.accordiagolf.co.jp
Rev.: $423,149,760
Emp.: 10,520
Fiscal Year-end: 03/31/2017
Golf Course Services, Golf Driving Range Management & Operation
N.A.I.C.S.: 713910
Takabumi Suzuki *(Mng Corp Officer)*

CAR Inc. (1)
No 118 East Zhongguancun Road, Haidian District, Beijing, 100098, PRC, China **(100%)**
Tel.: (86) 1058209888
Web Site: http://www.zuche.com
Car Rental & Leasing Services
N.A.I.C.S.: 532111
Yifan Song *(CEO)*

Connectwave Co., Ltd (1)
17th Floor 298 Beotkkot-ro, Geumcheon-gu, Seoul, 08510, Korea (South) **(86.93%)**
Tel.: (82) 216882470
Web Site: https://www.danawa.com
Rev.: $347,155,988
Assets: $750,150,105
Liabilities: $282,089,207
Net Worth: $468,060,898
Earnings: $16,295,466
Emp.: 779
Fiscal Year-end: 12/31/2022
Online Shopping Services
N.A.I.C.S.: 513140
Kim Yong Sung *(VP)*

Daesung Industrial Co., Ltd. (1)
662 Kyunginro, Guro-gu, Seoul, 152-888, Korea (South)
Tel.: (82) 221702160
Web Site: http://www.daesung.co.kr
Rev.: $1,435,291,537
Assets: $1,399,459,237
Liabilities: $918,487,210
Net Worth: $480,972,027
Earnings: ($7,397,233)
Emp.: 371
Fiscal Year-end: 12/31/2022
Petroleum Gas Distr
N.A.I.C.S.: 424720
Young Tae Kim *(Chm, Pres & CEO)*

Subsidiary (Domestic):

Daesung C&S Co., Ltd. (2)
606 Daesung D-polis B-dong 7th floor Seobu-saetgil, Geumcheon-gu, Seoul, Korea (South)
Tel.: (82) 2 2290 5500
Web Site: http://www.dsh21.co.kr
Detergents Mfr & Distr
N.A.I.C.S.: 325611
Kang Sung Yoon *(CEO)*

Daesung Celtic Co., Ltd. (2)
16F D-CUBE CITY Office Tower 692 Sindorim-Dong, Guro-gu, Seoul, Korea (South)
Tel.: (82) 2 732 3450
Web Site: http://www.celtic.co.kr
Gas Boiler Mfr & Distr
N.A.I.C.S.: 333414
Bong-Sick Ko *(CEO)*

Daesung Group Partners Co., Ltd. (2)
662 Kyunginro, Guro-gu, Seoul, Korea (South)
Tel.: (82) 2 170 2100
Web Site: http://www.daesung.co.kr
Industrial Gases & Related Tools & Appliances for Semiconductor Mfr & Sales
N.A.I.C.S.: 334413
Young Tae Kim *(Chm & CEO)*

Homeplus Co., Limited (1)
398 Hwagokoro, Gangseo-gu, Seoul, 135-080, Korea (South)
Tel.: (82) 234598000
Web Site: http://www.homeplus.co.kr
Hypermarkets, Supermarkets & Convenience Stores Operator & Franchisor
N.A.I.C.S.: 445110
Sang Hyun Kim *(CEO)*

Kuroda Electric Co., Ltd. (1)
5-17-9 Minami-Oi, Shinagawa-ku, Tokyo, 140-0013, Japan
Tel.: (81) 357645500
Web Site: http://www.kuroda-electric.co.jp
Electrical Equipment Whslr
N.A.I.C.S.: 423610
Koichi Hosokawa *(CEO & COO)*

Osstem Implant Co., Ltd. (1)
3 Magokjungang 12-ro, Gangseo-gu, Seoul, 153-759, Korea (South)
Tel.: (82) 220167000
Web Site: http://www.osstem.com
Rev.: $808,013,209
Assets: $1,052,570,092
Liabilities: $774,497,883
Net Worth: $278,072,209
Earnings: $105,950,894
Emp.: 2,143
Fiscal Year-end: 12/31/2022
Medical Appliances & Instruments Mfr
N.A.I.C.S.: 339113
Tae Kwan Uhm *(CEO)*

Subsidiary (Non-US):

Deutsche Osstem GmbH (2)
Mergenthalerallee 35-37, 65760, Eschborn, Germany
Tel.: (49) 61967775500
Dental Equipment & Device Mfr
N.A.I.C.S.: 339114

HIOSSEN Implant Canada Inc. (2)
122-8337 Eastlake Drive, Burnaby, V5A 4W2, BC, Canada
Tel.: (604) 324-0112
Web Site:
   https://www.hiossenimplantcanada.ca
Dental Equipment & Device Mfr
N.A.I.C.S.: 339114

Subsidiary (US):

HIOSSEN Inc. (2)
85 Ben Fairless Dr, Fairless Hills, PA 19030
Dental Equipment & Device Mfr
N.A.I.C.S.: 339114

Subsidiary (Non-US):

HIOSSEN de Mexico, S.A. de C.V. (2)
Chimalhuacan 3574-3B Edificio Torrvan Col Ciudad del Sol, 45450, Zapopan, Jalisco, Mexico
Tel.: (52) 3331215663
Dental Equipment & Device Mfr
N.A.I.C.S.: 339114

Hiossen Chile SpA (2)
Avda Providencia 2008 Oficina C, Santiago de, Providencia, Chile
Tel.: (56) 232451457
Dental Surgical Instruments Mfr & Distr
N.A.I.C.S.: 339114

Hiossen China Co., Ltd. (2)
Room 1-1403/1404 No 65 Dagu North Road Xiaobailou Street, Heping, Tianjin, China

Tel.: (86) 2227165021
Dental Surgical Instruments Mfr & Distr
N.A.I.C.S.: 339114

OSSTEM Philippines Inc. (2)
unit 203 2nd Floor Penensula Court Bldg 8735 Paceo de Roxas, Makati, Philippines
Tel.: (63) 9171283000
Web Site: http://www.ph.osstem.com
Dental Equipment & Device Mfr
N.A.I.C.S.: 339114
Christian Hizon *(Mgr-Product)*

Osstem Autralia Pty. Ltd. (2)
6A / 5 Talavera Road, Macquarie Park, 2113, NSW, Australia
Tel.: (61) 298892675
Web Site: http://au.osstem.com
Dental Equipment & Device Mfr
N.A.I.C.S.: 339114

Osstem Bangladesh Ltd. (2)
5FL House-13 Road-34 Gulshan-1, Dhaka, 1212, Bangladesh
Tel.: (880) 29898098
Web Site: http://bd.osstem.com
Dental Equipment & Device Distr
N.A.I.C.S.: 423450
Zillur Rahman *(Mgr-Sls)*

Osstem China Co., Ltd. (2)
Room 708-1B Zhubang 2000 No 100 Baizhuangxili, Chaoyang District, Beijing, 100025, China
Tel.: (86) 1085868702
Dental Equipment & Device Mfr
N.A.I.C.S.: 339114
Michael Lee *(Mgr-Mktg)*

Osstem Co., Ltd. (2)
3850/2 Theptarin Hospital 2 Bld 16FL Rama 4 Rd, phrakanong Klongtoey, Bangkok, 10110, Thailand
Tel.: (66) 26717988
Web Site: http://www.th.osstem.com
Dental Equipment & Device Mfr
N.A.I.C.S.: 339114

Osstem Corporation (2)
5F-2 No 131 Sec3 E Rd Nanjing E Rd, Jhongshan District, Taipei, Taiwan
Tel.: (886) 225471082
Web Site: http://www.tw.osstem.com
Dental Equipment & Device Mfr
N.A.I.C.S.: 339114

Osstem Hong Kong Ltd. (2)
Rm 2404 24/F Windsor House 311 Gloucester Road, Causeway Bay, China (Hong Kong)
Tel.: (852) 31129416
Web Site: http://www.hk.osstem.com
Dental Equipment & Device Mfr
N.A.I.C.S.: 339114

Osstem Implant Brasil Ltda. (2)
Rua De Rafael de Barros 210 - sala 81 e 82- Paraiso, Sao Paulo, 04003-041, SP, Brazil
Tel.: (55) 1132073107
Dental Equipment Mfr & Distr
N.A.I.C.S.: 339114

Osstem Implant LLP (2)
Office 808 Section-2 Abay Street 150/230 Bostandykskiy Region, Almaty, Kazakhstan
Tel.: (7) 87273115253
Dental Equipment & Device Mfr
N.A.I.C.S.: 339114

Osstem Implant Spain S.L. (2)
Avenida de Manoteras 32 Bloque B Primero B, 28050, Madrid, Spain
Tel.: (34) 910136949
Dental Equipment Mfr & Distr
N.A.I.C.S.: 339114

Osstem Implant Vina Co., Ltd. (2)
2nd Floor B14 C4-1 Hoang Van Thai Street Center of International, Trade Finance Phu My Hung Tan Phu Ward District 7, Ho Chi Minh City, Vietnam
Tel.: (84) 854130009
Web Site: http://vn.osstem.com
Dental Equipment & Device Mfr
N.A.I.C.S.: 339114

Osstem Implant dis Tic. A.S. (2)
Esentepe Mah Buyukdere Cd No 111 TEV Kocabas Ishani K 2, Sisli, 34394, Istanbul, Turkiye

Tel.: (90) 2123472097
Web Site: http://www.tr.osstem.com
Dental Equipment & Device Mfr
N.A.I.C.S.: 339114
Jeongwon Kim *(Mgr-HR & Fin)*

Osstem Implant india Pvt. Ltd. (2)
Office No 306 3rd Floor A Wing Sagar Tech Plaza Sakinaka Andheri Kurla, Road Andheri East, Mumbai, 400072, Maharashtra, India
Tel.: (91) 2267257111
Web Site: http://www.in.osstem.com
Dental Equipment & Device Mfr
N.A.I.C.S.: 339114
Mangesh Saroj *(Mgr-Product Trng)*

Osstem Japan Corp. (2)
B1F 4-5-37 Kamiosaki, Shinagawa-ku, Tokyo, 141-0021, Japan
Tel.: (81) 357479441
Dental Equipment & Device Mfr
N.A.I.C.S.: 339114

Osstem LLC (2)
8th Fl Ofc 1 Nagatino i-land 18/7 Andropova Prospect, 115432, Moscow, Russia
Tel.: (7) 4957399925
Web Site: http://www.osstem.ru
Dental Equipment & Device Mfr
N.A.I.C.S.: 339114

Osstem Malaysia Sdn. Bhd. (2)
B-07-12 Gateway Kiaramas Corporate Suite No 1 Jalan Desa Kiara, Mpnt kiara, 50480, Kuala Lumpur, Malaysia
Tel.: (60) 362110585
Web Site: http://my.osstem.com
Dental Equipment & Device Mfr
N.A.I.C.S.: 339114

Osstem Middle East FZCO (2)
Unit G23 inside Dubai Airport Free Zone, PO Box 371629, Dubai, United Arab Emirates
Tel.: (971) 43491922
Dental Equipment Mfr & Distr
N.A.I.C.S.: 339114

Osstem Mongol LLC (2)
201 Barilga MN Office 13th Microdistrict 6th Horoo 13373 Street 24-1, Bayanzurkh District, Ulaanbaatar, Mongolia
Tel.: (976) 70161599
Dental Equipment & Device Mfr
N.A.I.C.S.: 339114

Osstem New Zealand Limited (2)
Unit 10/6 Omega Street, Rosedale, Auckland, New Zealand
Tel.: (64) 96001500
Web Site: https://osstem.co.nz
Dental Equipment Mfr & Distr
N.A.I.C.S.: 339114

Osstem Singapore Pte. Ltd. (2)
Pico Creative Centre Level 3 PT 20 Kallang Avenue, Singapore, 339411, Singapore
Tel.: (65) 62701840
Web Site: https://www.sg.osstem.com
Dental Equipment & Device Mfr
N.A.I.C.S.: 339114
Tim T. H. Lee *(Mng Dir)*

Osstem South China Co., Ltd. (2)
Rm 01B 05-06 25F Centralcon Tower Jintian Road 3088, Futian District, Shenzhen, China
Tel.: (86) 75582046986
Dental Equipment & Device Mfr
N.A.I.C.S.: 339114

Osstem uah LLC (2)
Sumska str 1 office 903, 03022, Kiev, Ukraine
Tel.: (380) 675166500
Dental Equipment Mfr & Distr
N.A.I.C.S.: 339114

PT. Osstem Implant (2)
K-Link Office Tower 27 Jl Jend Gatot Subroto No 59A Kuningan Timur, Setiabudi Jakarta Selatan, Jakarta, 12950, Indonesia
Tel.: (62) 81113305574
Web Site: http://www.id.osstem.com
Dental Equipment & Device Mfr
N.A.I.C.S.: 339114

TASAKI & Co., Ltd. (1)
3-2 6-chome Minatojima Naka-machi, Chuo-ku, Kobe, 650-0046, Japan **(83%)**

MBK PARTNERS LTD.

MBK Partners Ltd.—(Continued)
Tel.: (81) 78 302 3321
Web Site: http://www.tasaki-global.com
Jewelry, Watch & Bag Mfr
N.A.I.C.S.: 423940
Toshikazu Tajima (Pres & CEO)

Subsidiary (Non-US):

MYANMAR TASAKI Co., Ltd. (2)
10 A Thukhawad di St, West Yankin, Yangon, Myanmar
Tel.: (95) 1660 962
Jewelry (Southsea Pearls) Mfr
N.A.I.C.S.: 339910
Thant Lwin (Gen Mgr)

TASAKI CHINA Co., Ltd (2)
3107-3108 31F Plaza 66 Tower 1 1266 Nanjing West Road, Shanghai, 200040, China
Tel.: (86) 2158356741
Web Site: http://www.tasaki.com.cn
Jewellery Distr
N.A.I.C.S.: 423940

TASAKI FRANCE S.A.S. (2)
7 Place Vendome, 75001, Paris, France
Tel.: (33) 53000000
Web Site: http://www.tasaki.fr
Jewellery Distr
N.A.I.C.S.: 423940
Takehiro Matsunaga (Gen Mgr)

TASAKI KOREA Co., Ltd. (2)
1402 14th floor Trade tower 51, Yeongdongdae-ro Gangnam-gu, Seoul, 06164, Korea (South)
Tel.: (82) 234615558
Web Site: http://www.tasaki.co.kr
Jewellery Distr
N.A.I.C.S.: 423940

TASAKI TAIWAN Co., Ltd. (2)
10F-2 318 Songjiang Road, Zhongshan Dist, Taipei, 10468, Taiwan
Tel.: (886) 225236636
Web Site: http://www.tasaki.com.tw
Jewellery Distr
N.A.I.C.S.: 423940

Tasaki Jewellery (Shanghai) Co., Ltd (2)
7000 Chuannanfeng Road, Pudong, Shanghai, 201312, China
Tel.: (86) 2158231010
Web Site: http://www.tasaki-global.com
Jewellery Distr
N.A.I.C.S.: 423940

UNIMAT Retirement Community Co., Ltd. (1)
Unimat Aoyama Bldg 2-12-14 Minami-Aoyama, Minato-Ku, Tokyo, 107-0062, Japan
Tel.: (81) 354138228
Web Site: http://www.unimat-rc.co.jp
Rev.: $526,651,440
Assets: $512,245,370
Liabilities: $360,215,940
Net Worth: $152,029,430
Earnings: $2,329,180
Fiscal Year-end: 03/31/2020
Nursing Care Services
N.A.I.C.S.: 621610
Shingo Heike (Chm)

WTT HK Limited (1)
9 Floor KITEC 1 Trademark Drive, Kowloon, China (Hong Kong)
Tel.: (852) 21121121
Web Site: http://www.wharftt.com
Telecommunications Network Operator
N.A.I.C.S.: 517810

MBK PUBLIC COMPANY LIMITED

8th Fl MBK Center 444 Phayathai Rd, Pathumwan, Bangkok, 10330, Thailand
Tel.: (66) 28539000
Web Site:
 https://investor.mbkgroup.co.th
Year Founded: 1974
MBK—(THA)
Rev.: $307,206,958
Assets: $1,765,278,004
Liabilities: $1,111,828,433
Net Worth: $653,449,571
Earnings: $47,503,901
Emp.: 3,630
Fiscal Year-end: 12/31/23
Shopping Center Operator
N.A.I.C.S.: 531120
Suphadej Poonpipat (Vice Chm)

Subsidiaries:

Apple Auto Auction (Thailand) Company Limited (1)
99/88 Village No 2, Bang Kadi Subdistrict Mueang Pathum Thani District, Pathumthani, Thailand
Tel.: (66) 21192299
Web Site: https://www.appleauction.co.th
Online Car Auction Services
N.A.I.C.S.: 561613

Ratchsima Rice Company Limited (1)
109 Moo 14 Mitraparp Road 90 Km Tumbol Lardbuakhow, Amphur Sikhio, Nakhon Ratchasima, Thailand
Tel.: (66) 25012175
Web Site: https://www.ratchasimarice.co.th
Packaged Rice Mfr & Distr
N.A.I.C.S.: 311212

Riverdale Golf & Country Club Company Limited (1)
123/5 Moo1 Tiwanon Road, Bang Kadi Sub-District Muang Pathum Thani District, Pathumthani, 12000, Thailand
Tel.: (66) 2 501 2789
Web Site: https://www.mbkgolf.com
Golf Course Development Services
N.A.I.C.S.: 713910

MBL INFRASTRUCTURES LTD

Baani Corporate One Tower 308 3rd Floor, Plot No 5 District Commercial Centre Jasola, New Delhi, 110 025, India
Tel.: (91) 1148593300
Web Site: https://www.mblinfra.com
Year Founded: 1995
MBLINFRA—(NSE)
Rev.: $35,554,114
Assets: $410,952,087
Liabilities: $296,777,672
Net Worth: $114,174,415
Earnings: $18,277
Emp.: 354
Fiscal Year-end: 03/31/22
Roads, Highways, Industrial Infrastructure Projects & Other Civil Engineering Services
N.A.I.C.S.: 237310
Anjanee Kumar Lakhotia (Chm & Mng Dir)

MBM RESOURCES BERHAD

23-01 Level 23 Menara MBMR 1 Jalan Syed Putra, 58000, Kuala Lumpur, Malaysia
Tel.: (60) 322738803 MY
Web Site: https://www.mbmr.com.my
MBMR—(KLS)
Rev.: $488,383,704
Assets: $535,151,534
Liabilities: $39,547,302
Net Worth: $495,604,233
Earnings: $65,623,069
Emp.: 2,040
Fiscal Year-end: 12/31/22
Motor Vehicles Mfr & Distr
N.A.I.C.S.: 336999
Peir Chyun Wong (Co-Sec)

Subsidiaries:

DMM Sales Sdn. Bhd. (1)
Lot 1 Jalan Keluli Section 15, 40200, Shah Alam, Selangor, Malaysia
Tel.: (60) 355109988
Web Site: https://dmms.com.my
Emp.: 300
Car Retailer
N.A.I.C.S.: 441110

A. Safwan (Officer-Sls Support)

Daihatsu (Malaysia) Sdn. Bhd. (1)
Lot 1 Jalan Keluli Section 15, 40200, Shah Alam, Selangor Darul Ehsan, Malaysia (51.5%)
Tel.: (60) 355109988
Web Site: https://www.daihatsu.com.my
Sales Range: $75-99.9 Million
Emp.: 200
Automotive Distr
N.A.I.C.S.: 423110

Federal Auto Holdings Berhad (1)
89A Jalan Sungai Pinang, 10150, Penang, Malaysia
Tel.: (60) 42817300
Web Site: https://www.federalauto.com.my
Car Retailer
N.A.I.C.S.: 441110

Hirotako Holdings Berhad (1)
No 18 Persiaran Sabak Bernam Seksyen 26, 40400, Shah Alam, Selangor Darul Ehsan, Malaysia
Tel.: (60) 351927223
Web Site: http://www.hirotako.com.my
Sales Range: $75-99.9 Million
Holding Company
N.A.I.C.S.: 551112

Joint Venture (Domestic):

Autoliv Hirotako Sdn. Bhd. (2)
Lebuh Taming, Jalan Balakong, 43300, Seri Kembangan, Selangor Darul Ehsan, Malaysia (51%)
Tel.: (60) 389612020
Web Site: http://www.hirotako.com.my
Sales Range: $125-149.9 Million
Emp.: 400
Automotive Restraint Systems Mfr
N.A.I.C.S.: 336360

Subsidiary (Domestic):

Autoliv Hirotako Safety Sdn. Bhd. (3)
Lot 1989 Lebuh Tanming Taman Tanming, Jalan Balakong, 43300, Seri Kembangan, Selangor Darul Ehsan, Malaysia
Tel.: (60) 389612020
Sales Range: $75-99.9 Million
Mfr of Automotive Airbags & Other Safety Systems
N.A.I.C.S.: 336390

Subsidiary (Domestic):

Autoliv Hirotako SRS Sdn. Bhd. (4)
Lot 1989 Lebuh Tanming Taman Tanming, Jalan Balakong, Seri Kembangan, 43300, Selangor Darul Ehsan, Malaysia
Tel.: (60) 389623576
Sales Range: $100-124.9 Million
Emp.: 400
Mfr of Automotive Safety Restraint Systems
N.A.I.C.S.: 336390
Looi Kokloon (Mng Dir)

Subsidiary (Domestic):

Hirotako Acoustics Sdn. Bhd. (2)
No 18 Persiaran Sabak Bernam Seksyen 26, 40400, Shah Alam, Selangor, Malaysia (100%)
Tel.: (60) 351927223
Sales Range: $50-74.9 Million
Emp.: 140
Automotive Acoustic Parts Mfr & Distr
N.A.I.C.S.: 336390
Lip Sung Thean (Gen Mgr)

Inai Benua Sdn. Bhd. (1)
12-01 Level 12 Menara MBMR No 1 Jalan Syed Putra, 58000, Kuala Lumpur, Malaysia
Tel.: (60) 322723388
Automobile Parts Mfr
N.A.I.C.S.: 336390

MBMI RESOURCES INC.

217-8787 Woodbine Avenue, Markham, L3R 5W9, ON, Canada
Tel.: (647) 299-9203 ON
Web Site:
 http://www.mbmiresources.com
Year Founded: 1987
Assets: $58,087
Liabilities: $5,673,974
Net Worth: ($5,615,886)
Earnings: ($569,629)
Fiscal Year-end: 01/31/19
Nickel Mining Services
N.A.I.C.S.: 212230
Joseph Shuen Chuen Chan (Pres & CEO)

MBP BELTING PHIL. CORPORATION

32 Mulawinan Road, Lawang Bato, Valenzuela, 1447, Metro Manila, Philippines
Tel.: (63) 24454105
Web Site: http://www.mbp.com.ph
Year Founded: 1984
Emp.: 200
Rubber Belt Mfr
N.A.I.C.S.: 326220
Manuel Ayroso (Gen Mgr)

MBS, INC.

1173-162 Nishikiba Ube City Yamaguchi Prefecture, Ube, Yamaguchi, 7550151, Japan
Tel.: (81) 836541414
Web Site:
 https://www.homemakeup.co.jp
1401—(TKS)
Housing & Building Renovation & Repairs
N.A.I.C.S.: 236118
Takashi Yamamoto (Pres)

MBV INTERNATIONAL LIMITED

No 58-66 Jalan Seroja 39 Taman Johor Jaya, Johor Bahru, 81100, Johor, Malaysia Ky
Year Founded: 1995
1957—(HKG)
Rev.: $30,477,606
Assets: $28,565,392
Liabilities: $1,999,084
Net Worth: $26,566,308
Earnings: $2,554,011
Emp.: 447
Fiscal Year-end: 12/31/22
Gift Product Distr
N.A.I.C.S.: 459420
Hoi Ki Lam (Sec)

Subsidiaries:

Oren Sport (Cheras) Sdn. Bhd. (1)
No 34G Jalan Pandan Indah 1/23A, 55100, Kuala Lumpur, Malaysia
Tel.: (60) 392741969
Garments Whslr
N.A.I.C.S.: 424310

Oren Sport (Kepong) Sdn. Bhd. (1)
No 41-1 Jalan Metro Perdana Timur 3, Taman Usahawan Kepong, 52100, Kuala Lumpur, Malaysia
Tel.: (60) 3625040018
Garments Whslr
N.A.I.C.S.: 424310

Oren Sport (Klang) Sdn. Bhd. (1)
No 1 Jalan Haji Abdul Karim 30/KS2, Taman Industri Sungai Jati, 41200, Klang, Selangor, Malaysia
Tel.: (60) 333821221
Garments Whslr
N.A.I.C.S.: 424310

Oren Sport (PJ) Sdn. Bhd. (1)
8 Jalan SS 25/34, Mayang Industrial Park, 47301, Petaling Jaya, Selangor, Malaysia
Tel.: (60) 378800911
Garments Whslr
N.A.I.C.S.: 424310

Oren Sport (S) Pte. Ltd. (1)
Blk 8 Lorong Bakar Batu 06-07, Kolam Ayer Industrial Estate, Singapore, 348743, Singapore
Tel.: (65) 62982526
Garments Whslr
N.A.I.C.S.: 424310

Oren Sport Sdn. Bhd. (1)
No 58-66 Jalan Seroja 39, Taman Johor Jaya, 81100, Johor Bahru, Johor, Malaysia
Tel.: (60) 73545222
Web Site: https://www.orensport.com
Sports Apparel Whslr
N.A.I.C.S.: 423910

MC BANK RUS JSC
30/1 Obrucheva Street Building 2 Krugozor Business Centre, 117485, Moscow, Russia
Tel.: (7) 4952870480
Web Site: http://www.mcbankrus.ru
Year Founded: 1994
Sales Range: Less than $1 Million
Automobile Financing Services
N.A.I.C.S.: 522220
Andrey Kochenkov *(Member-Mgmt Bd & Dir-Bus Dev)*

MC EDICIONES S.A.
Av Diagonal Numero 357, 8037, Barcelona, Spain
Tel.: (34) 93 254 1250 ES
Web Site:
  http://tienda.mcediciones.com
Magazine Publisher & Whslr
N.A.I.C.S.: 513120
Manuel Nunez *(Sls Mgr)*

MC GROUP PUBLIC COMPANY LIMITED
448 450 On-Nut Road, Prawet District, Bangkok, 10250, Thailand
Tel.: (66) 23291050
Web Site:
  https://www.mcgroupnet.com
Year Founded: 1975
MC—(THA)
Rev.: $101,527,480
Assets: $147,715,846
Liabilities: $45,374,245
Net Worth: $102,341,601
Earnings: $17,699,821
Emp.: 2,210
Fiscal Year-end: 06/30/23
Clothing Mfr & Retailer
N.A.I.C.S.: 315250
Sunee Seripanu *(Vice Chm, CEO & Mng Dir)*

Subsidiaries:

P.K. Garment (Import-Export) Co., Ltd. (1)
33/5-6 Sukhumvit Road Praves, Bangkok, 10250, Thailand
Tel.: (66) 23291050
Web Site: http://www.mcgroupnet.com
Emp.: 450
Apparels Mfr
N.A.I.C.S.: 315990
Korrakoch Phanomchoeng *(Production Mgr)*

Time Deco Corporation Limited (1)
9 Fl 5 Soi Ramintra 55/8 Ramintra Rd Tharang, Bangkhen, Bangkok, 10230, Thailand
Tel.: (66) 2374076263
Web Site: http://www.timedeco.co.th
Watch Distr
N.A.I.C.S.: 423940
Rujima Benjawatthananun *(Branch Mgr)*

MC INTERNATIONAL GROUP, INC.
10 Boulevard Des Freres Voisin, 92792, Issy-les-Moulineaux, Cedex 9, France
Tel.: (33) 1 41 46 88 88
Web Site:
  http://www.marieclairenational.com
Magazine Publisher
N.A.I.C.S.: 513120
Jean de Boisdeffre *(Exec Dir)*

MC MINING LIMITED
Block Arcade Suite 324 Level 3 96 Elizabeth Street, Melbourne, 3000, VIC, Australia
Tel.: (61) 893169100
Web Site:
  https://www.mcmining.co.za
MCM—(AIM)
Rev.: $23,511,000
Assets: $125,415,000
Liabilities: $48,279,000
Net Worth: $77,136,000
Earnings: ($20,835,000)
Emp.: 521
Fiscal Year-end: 06/30/22
Coal Exploration Services
N.A.I.C.S.: 212115
Tony Bevan *(Sec)*

Subsidiaries:

MC Mining Limited (1)
Ground Floor Greystone Building Fourways Golf Park Roos Street, Fourways, 2191, South Africa
Tel.: (27) 100038000
Web Site: https://www.mcmining.co.za
Sales Range: $50-74.9 Million
Emp.: 35
Coal Mining Services
N.A.I.C.S.: 213113

Magberg Manufacturing (Pty) Ltd (1)
Pinewood Ofc Park 33 Riley Rd, PO Box 1401, Woodmead, Sandton, 2199, Gauteng, South Africa
Tel.: (27) 118038247
Web Site: http://www.nimagrout.com
Sales Range: $25-49.9 Million
Emp.: 6
Magnesium Refining Services
N.A.I.C.S.: 331410

Metalloy Fibres (Pty) Ltd (1)
37 Lincoln St, Woodmead E, Sandton, Gauteng, South Africa
Tel.: (27) 11 803 8247
Sales Range: $25-49.9 Million
Emp.: 10
Stainless Steel Mfr
N.A.I.C.S.: 331110

MC-LINK S.P.A.
Via Carlo Perrier 4 9/a, 00157, Rome, Italy
Tel.: (39) 06 41892 1
Web Site: http://www.mclink.it
Sales Range: $25-49.9 Million
Information & Communications Technology
N.A.I.C.S.: 541512

MCAIRLAID'S VLIESSTOFFE GMBH & CO. KG
Munsterstrasse 61 65, 48565, Steinfurt, Germany
Tel.: (49) 255293340
Web Site: http://www.mcairlaids.net
Rev.: $17,932,200
Emp.: 150
Nonwoven Fabric Supplier
N.A.I.C.S.: 313230
Alexander Maksimow *(Pres, CEO & Mng Dir)*

Subsidiaries:

McAirlaid's Inc (1)
180 Corporate Dr, Rocky Mount, VA 24151
Tel.: (540) 352-5050
Sanitary Products Mfr
N.A.I.C.S.: 322291

McAirlaid's Nordic OU (1)
Laanemere tee 74, 13914, Tallinn, Estonia
Tel.: (372) 6311987
Sanitary Products Mfr
N.A.I.C.S.: 322291
Reet Truuts *(Mgr)*

MCALPINE FORD LINCOLN SALES
15815 Yonge Street, Aurora, L4G 1P4, ON, Canada
Tel.: (905) 841-0800
Web Site:
  http://www.mcalpineford.com
Rev.: $13,911,192
Emp.: 30
New & Used Car Dealers
N.A.I.C.S.: 441110
Mike Panza *(Mgr-Wholesale)*

MCAN MORTGAGE CORPORATION
200 King Street West Suite 600, Toronto, M5H 3T4, ON, Canada
Tel.: (416) 572-4880 Ca
Web Site: https://mcanfinancial.com
Year Founded: 1991
MKP—(TSX)
Rev.: $75,666,166
Assets: $1,667,718,907
Liabilities: $1,414,950,952
Net Worth: $252,767,955
Earnings: $36,956,501
Emp.: 98
Fiscal Year-end: 12/31/19
Mortgage Investment & Brokerage Services
N.A.I.C.S.: 523999
Susan Dore *(Co-Founder)*

Subsidiaries:

Xceed Mortgage Corporation (1)
600 - 200 Kings St W, Toronto, M5H 3T4, ON, Canada (100%)
Tel.: (416) 364-7944
Web Site: http://www.xceedmortgage.com
Sales Range: $10-24.9 Million
Emp.: 27
Mortgage Brokerage Services
N.A.I.C.S.: 522310
Melanie Lapointe *(Acct Mgr)*

MCAP INC
200 King St 400 W, Toronto, M5H 3T4, ON, Canada
Tel.: (416) 598-2665
Web Site: http://www.mcap.com
Sales Range: $25-49.9 Million
Emp.: 1,000
Loaning Services
N.A.I.C.S.: 522310
Tammy Oldenburg *(CFO & VP-Fin)*

MCB BANK LIMITED
MCB House 1st Floor 15 Main Jail Road Gulburg, Lahore, Pakistan
Tel.: (92) 111000622 PK
Web Site: https://www.mcb.com.pk
Year Founded: 1947
MCB—(PSX)
Rev.: $713,233,628
Assets: $9,518,617,323
Liabilities: $8,660,011,691
Net Worth: $858,605,631
Earnings: $231,817,136
Emp.: 16,354
Fiscal Year-end: 12/31/23
Banking Services
N.A.I.C.S.: 522110
Mian Mohammad Mansha *(Chm)*

Subsidiaries:

MCB - Arif Habib Savings & Investments Limited (1)
2nd Floor Adamjee House I I Chundrigar Road, Karachi, Pakistan
Tel.: (92) 21111147283
Web Site: https://www.mcbah.com
Investment Advice Services
N.A.I.C.S.: 523940

MCB Islamic Bank Limited (1)
59-T Commercial Phase II DHA, Lahore, Pakistan
Tel.: (92) 4234501000
Web Site: http://www.mcbislamicbank.com
Commercial Banking Services
N.A.I.C.S.: 522110
Raza Mansha *(Chm)*

MCB Non-Bank Credit Organisation Closed Joint Stock Company (1)
49B Tbilisi Ave, Baku, AZ1065, Azerbaijan
Tel.: (994) 125309999
Web Site: http://www.mcb.az
Construction Machinery Leasing Services
N.A.I.C.S.: 532412
Ramal Jafarov *(CEO)*

MCB Non-Bank Credit Organization Closed Joint Stock Company (1)
49B Tbilisi Ave, AZ1065, Baku, Azerbaijan
Tel.: (994) 125309999
Web Site: https://mcb.az
Real Estate Services
N.A.I.C.S.: 531190

MCB-Arif Habib Savings and Investments Limited (1)
2nd Floor Adamjee House I I Chundrigar Road, Karachi, Pakistan
Tel.: (92) 21111468378
Web Site: https://www.mcbfunds.com
Rev.: $4,319,391
Assets: $9,754,449
Liabilities: $3,492,240
Net Worth: $6,262,209
Earnings: $1,360,641
Emp.: 230
Fiscal Year-end: 06/30/2023
Asset Management Services
N.A.I.C.S.: 523940
Muhammad Saqib Saleem *(CEO)*

MCBRIDE PLC
Central Square 29 Wellington Street, Middleton, Leeds, LS1 4DL, United Kingdom
Tel.: (44) 1616539037
Web Site: https://www.mcbride.co.uk
MCB—(LSE)
Rev.: $1,181,496,459
Assets: $602,376,136
Liabilities: $522,244,691
Net Worth: $80,131,446
Earnings: $42,087,968
Emp.: 3,207
Fiscal Year-end: 06/30/24
Household Laundry, Cleaning & Personal Care Products
N.A.I.C.S.: 424690
Chris Smith *(CEO)*

Subsidiaries:

Chemolux S.A.R.L. (1)
Rue de l'industrie, Foetz, 3895, Luxembourg, Luxembourg
Tel.: (352) 5748491
Web Site: http://www.mcbride.eu
Sales Range: $150-199.9 Million
Emp.: 250
Cleaning & Maintenance Products Mfr
N.A.I.C.S.: 325998

Danlind A/S (1)
Laegaardvej 90 - 94, 7500, Holstebro, Denmark
Tel.: (45) 89872515
Laundry Product Mfr
N.A.I.C.S.: 325611

Fortune Laboratories Sdn Bhd (1)
Wisma Fortune No 4 Jalan 16/12 Section 16, 40200, Shah Alam, Selangor, Malaysia
Tel.: (60) 35 526 8000
Web Site: http://www.mcbridefortlab.com
Sales Range: $50-74.9 Million
Emp.: 200
Pharmaceuticals & Cosmetics Mfr
N.A.I.C.S.: 325412

Intersilesia McBride Polska Sp. Z.o.o. (1)
ul Matejki 2a, 47-100, Strzelce Opolskie, Opole, Poland
Tel.: (48) 774049100
Web Site: http://www.mcbride.pl
Sales Range: $150-199.9 Million
Emp.: 380
Household & Personal Care Products Mfr
N.A.I.C.S.: 325612
Wojciech Mazurek *(Mng Dir)*

McBride Australia Pty. Ltd. (1)
Suite 4 191-195 Riversdale Road, Hawthorn, 3122, VIC, Australia
Tel.: (61) 398180287
Laundry Product Mfr

MCBRIDE PLC

McBride plc—(Continued)
N.A.I.C.S.: 325611

McBride Denmark A/S (1)
Laegaardvej 90 - 94, DK-7500, Holstebro, Denmark
Tel.: (45) 89872515
Soap & Detergents Mfr
N.A.I.C.S.: 325611

McBride Hong Kong Holdings Limited (1)
Unit 2001-02 20th Floor Prosperity Place 6 Shing Yip Street, Kwun Tong, Kowloon, China (Hong Kong)
Tel.: (852) 27908480
Web Site: http://www.mcbride.co.hk
Sales Range: $50-74.9 Million
Emp.: 4
Investment Management Service
N.A.I.C.S.: 523940
Pasey Hui (Mgr-Comml)

McBride Malaysia Sdn. Bhd. (1)
2 Jalan Bestari 1/KU7 Taman Perindustrian Kapar Bestari, 42200, Klang, Selangor Darul Ehsan, Malaysia
Tel.: (60) 333962000
Web Site: https://mcbride.com.my
Household Products Mfr
N.A.I.C.S.: 335220

McBride S.A. (1)
6 Rue Moulin Masure, 7730, Estaimpuis, Hainaut, Belgium
Tel.: (32) 56482111
Cosmetics Distr
N.A.I.C.S.: 424690

McBride S.A.S. (1)
109-111 Rue Victor Hugo, 92532, Levallois-Perret, France
Tel.: (33) 147373804
Web Site: http://www.mcbride.eu
Sales Range: $50-74.9 Million
Emp.: 200
Household Cleaners Distr
N.A.I.C.S.: 424690

McBride S.A.U. (1)
Poligon Industrial I'lla, 08650, Sallent, Barcelona, Spain
Tel.: (34) 938372800
Laundry Product Mfr
N.A.I.C.S.: 325611

McBride plc - Barrow Factory (1)
Park Road, Barrow-in-Furness, LA14 4BN, Cumbria, United Kingdom
Tel.: (44) 1229814000
Web Site: http://www.mcbride.co.uk
Sales Range: $50-74.9 Million
Emp.: 130
Cosmetics Mfr
N.A.I.C.S.: 325620

McBride plc - Burnley Factory (1)
Windermere Ave, Burnley, BB10 2AF, Lancashire, United Kingdom
Tel.: (44) 1282872200
Sales Range: $125-149.9 Million
Emp.: 300
Household Cleaners Mfr
N.A.I.C.S.: 325612

McBride plc - Estaimpuis Factory (1)
4 Rue Moulin Masure, 7730, Estaimpuis, Hainaut, Belgium
Tel.: (32) 56482111
Sales Range: $125-149.9 Million
Emp.: 400
Household Cleaners Mfr
N.A.I.C.S.: 325612

McBride plc - Foetz Factory (1)
Rue de l'industrie Foetz, Mondercange, Esch-sur-Alzette, Luxembourg
Tel.: (352) 5748491
Sales Range: $50-74.9 Million
Emp.: 200
Household Cleaners Mfr
N.A.I.C.S.: 325612

McBride plc - Hull Factory (1)
Westcarr Lane Sutton Fields Industrial Estate, Hull, HU7 OBU, Yorkshire, United Kingdom
Tel.: (44) 1482 836 222
Sales Range: $125-149.9 Million
Emp.: 500
Household Products Mfr
N.A.I.C.S.: 321999

McBride plc - Middleton Factory (1)
Middleton Way, Middleton, M24 4DP, Manchester, United Kingdom
Tel.: (44) 1616539037
Web Site: http://www.mcbride.co.uk
Emp.: 400
Household & Personal Care Products Mfr
N.A.I.C.S.: 325612

McBride plc - Moyaux Factory (1)
20 Rue Gustave Flaubert, 14590, Moyaux, France
Tel.: (33) 231616161
Sales Range: $50-74.9 Million
Emp.: 110
Household Cleaners Mfr
N.A.I.C.S.: 325612

McBride plc - Rosporden Factory (1)
ZI De Dioulan, BP 21, 29140, Rosporden, France
Tel.: (33) 298669500
Web Site: http://www.mcbride.eu
Sales Range: $50-74.9 Million
Emp.: 140
Cosmetics Mfr
N.A.I.C.S.: 325620

McBride plc - St. Helens Factory (1)
Eurolink Lea Green, Saint Helens, WA9 4TT, Merseyside, United Kingdom
Tel.: (44) 1744 853 600
Personal Care Product Mfr
N.A.I.C.S.: 325620

Newlane Cosmetics Company Limited (1)
22 VSIPII Street 1, Vietnam Singapore Industrial Park II Hoa Phu Ward, Thu Dau Mot, Binh Duong, Vietnam
Tel.: (84) 650389536
Laundry Product Mfr
N.A.I.C.S.: 325611

Problanc S.A.S. (1)
55 Rue Deguingand, 92300, Levallois-Perret, Hauts-de-Seine, France
Tel.: (33) 147372844
Web Site: http://www.mcbride.co.uk
Sales Range: $25-49.9 Million
Emp.: 10
Cosmetics Distr
N.A.I.C.S.: 456120
Loungigne Marc (Pres)

Robert McBride Limited (1)
Middleton Way, Middleton, M24 4DP, Manchester, United Kingdom
Tel.: (44) 161 653 9037
Web Site: https://www.mcbride.co.uk
Sales Range: $150-199.9 Million
Emp.: 300
Household & Personal Care Products Whslr
N.A.I.C.S.: 424690
Colin McIntyre (Mng Dir)

Vitherm France S.A.S. (1)
Rue des Casernes, F-55400, Etain, France
Tel.: (33) 329878822
Home Furnishing Whslr
N.A.I.C.S.: 423220

Vitherm S.A.S. (1)
Rue des Casernes, 55400, Etain, France
Tel.: (33) 329878822
Web Site: http://www.vitherm.fr
Heat Exchanger Mfr
N.A.I.C.S.: 332410

MCC ENERGY PLC

Aurora House, 5-6 Carlos Place, London, W1K 3AP, United Kingdom
Tel.: (44) 2079079850
Year Founded: 1999
Sales Range: $25-49.9 Million
Emp.: 20
Investment Company
N.A.I.C.S.: 523150
David Wilson (Dir-Fin)

MCC GLOBAL NV

Keizersgracht 62-64, 1015 CS, Amsterdam, Netherlands
Tel.: (31) 20 520 6826 NI
Web Site: http://www.mccglobal.com
Privater Equity Firm
N.A.I.C.S.: 523999

MCC MEILI CLOUD COMPUTING INDUSTRY INVESTMENT CO., LTD.

Rouyuan Town, Shapotou District, Zhongwei, 755000, Ningxia, China
Tel.: (86) 9557679334
Web Site: http://www.china-meili.com
Year Founded: 1998
000815—(SSE)
Rev.: $154,501,776
Assets: $434,762,640
Liabilities: $165,690,252
Net Worth: $269,072,388
Earnings: ($32,624,748)
Fiscal Year-end: 12/31/22
Paper Products Mfr
N.A.I.C.S.: 322120
Yulu Liu (Chm)

MCCAIN FOODS LIMITED

8800 Main Street, Florenceville, E7L 1B2, NB, Canada
Tel.: (506) 392-5541 NB
Web Site: http://www.mccain.com
Year Founded: 1957
Sales Range: $5-14.9 Billion
Emp.: 30,000
Frozen Food Mfr
N.A.I.C.S.: 311412
Allison D. McCain (Chm)

Subsidiaries:

Ad van Geloven BV (1)
Kraaivenstraat 1, 5048 AB, Tilburg, Netherlands
Tel.: (31) 13 46 40 680
Web Site: http://www.vangeloven.com
Sales Range: $200-249.9 Million
Emp.: 900
Frozen Snack Food Mfr
N.A.I.C.S.: 311412
William Barker (Sls Mgr-Retail-Europe)

Beau Marais S.A. (France) (1)
483 Rue De Beau Marais, PO Box 147, 62403, Bethune, Cedex, France (100%)
Tel.: (33) 321646900
Web Site: http://www.beaumarais.com
Sales Range: $1-9.9 Million
Emp.: 300
Mfr of French Fries & Potato Flakes
N.A.I.C.S.: 311412

Charcuterie la Tour Eiffel, Inc. (1)
485 Dis Entrepreneurs, Quebec, G1M 2V2, QC, Canada (100%)
Tel.: (418) 687-2840
Web Site: http://www.toureiffel.ca
Sales Range: $25-49.9 Million
Emp.: 75
Veal Product Mfr
N.A.I.C.S.: 311612
Ken Garrier (Pres)

Day & Ross, Inc. (1)
398 Main Street, Hartland, E7P 1C6, NB, Canada (100%)
Tel.: (506) 375-4401
Web Site: https://dayross.com
Sales Range: $150-199.9 Million
Emp.: 1,000
Transportation: Courier Services, Air Freight Forwarding, Full Load Commodity Shipments, School Bus Operations, Air Cargo Shipments to & from Airports
N.A.I.C.S.: 492110
Laura Dickinson (VP-Safety & Compliance)

Subsidiary (US):

A&S Services Group, LLC (2)
883 E Tolna Rd, New Freedom, PA 17349
Tel.: (717) 759-3017
Web Site: http://www.askinard.com
Freight Trucking, Warehousing & Logistics Services
N.A.I.C.S.: 484110

Lutosa SA (1)
Zi du Vieux Pont 5, 7900, Leuze-en-Hainaut, Belgium
Tel.: (32) 69668211

INTERNATIONAL PUBLIC

Web Site: https://www.lutosa.com
Crispy Fry & Chips Distr
N.A.I.C.S.: 424450

McCain Alimentaire S.A. (1)
Zone Industrielle Notte Au Bois, PO Box 39, 62440, Harnes, France (100%)
Tel.: (33) 321087800
Web Site: http://www.mccain.fr
Sales Range: $150-199.9 Million
Emp.: 600
Mfr of French Fries & Potato Specialties
N.A.I.C.S.: 311412
Jean Bernou (Mng Dir)

McCain Alimentari (Italia) Srl (1)
Via G Zanchi 20, 24126, Bergamo, BG, Italy (100%)
Tel.: (39) 035 4526 111
Web Site: http://www.mccain.it
Sales of McCain Food Products
N.A.I.C.S.: 445298

McCain Argentina S.A. (1)
Ruta 226, Balcarce Km 61 5, Balcarce, 7620, Buenos Aires, Argentina (100%)
Tel.: (54) 2266439934
Web Site: http://www.maccain.com
Sales Range: $100-124.9 Million
Emp.: 300
N.A.I.C.S.: 311412

McCain Espana S.A. (Spain) (1)
Serano 240 4 Fl A, 28016, Madrid, Spain (100%)
Tel.: (34) 914430400
Web Site: http://www.mccain.es
Sales Range: $25-49.9 Million
Emp.: 45
Sales of French Fries & Potato Specialties
N.A.I.C.S.: 424450

McCain Fertilizers (1)
9109 Rte 130, PO Box 515, Florenceville, E7L 1YA, NB, Canada
Tel.: (506) 392-2810
Web Site: http://www.mccainsfoods.ca
Sales Range: $50-74.9 Million
Emp.: 10
Supplier of Fertilizers
N.A.I.C.S.: 424910

McCain Foods (Canada) Inc. (1)
8800 Main Street, Bristol, Florenceville, E7L 1B2, NB, Canada
Tel.: (506) 392-5541
Web Site: https://www.mccain.com
Sales Range: $150-199.9 Million
Emp.: 600
Frozen Food Mfr
N.A.I.C.S.: 311412

McCain Foods (GB) Limited (1)
Havers Hill, Eastfield, Scarborough, YO11 3BS, North Yorkshire, United Kingdom (100%)
Tel.: (44) 1723584141
Web Site: http://www.mccain.co.uk
Sales Range: $600-649.9 Million
Emp.: 21,000
Frozen French Frie Potato Specialties Pizza Products Value-Added Fish Product Cheese Mfr
N.A.I.C.S.: 424420
Bill Bartlett (Dir-Corp Affairs)

McCain Foods (India) Pvt. Ltd. (1)
C-11 Sda Commercial Complex, New Delhi, 110016, India
Tel.: (91) 11 26527181
Web Site: http://www.mccainindia.com
Frozen Food Distr
N.A.I.C.S.: 424420

McCain Foods (Japan) Limited (1)
Bois Hongo Building 3-42-5 Hongo Bunko-ku, Tokyo, 113, Japan (100%)
Tel.: (81) 3 5684 7811
Web Site: http://www.mccain.co.jp
Marketing & Distribution of Food Products
N.A.I.C.S.: 445298

McCain Foods Denmark (1)
Virkelyst 8 A, 4420, Regstrup, Denmark
Tel.: (45) 77206007
Web Site: http://www.mccain-nordic.com
Frozen Food Mfr
N.A.I.C.S.: 311412

McCain Foods Gmbh (1)

AND PRIVATE COMPANIES
MCDOWELL HOLDINGS LIMITED

Simmeringer Main Street 397, Vienna, 1110, Austria
Tel.: (43) 17684524
Web Site: http://www.mccain.at
Sales Range: $25-49.9 Million
Emp.: 15
Frozen Food Mfr
N.A.I.C.S.: 311412

McCain Foods Holland B.V. (1)
Siriusdreef 2, 2132 WT, Hoofddorp, Netherlands (100%)
Tel.: (31) 235584752
Web Site: http://www.mccain.nl
Sales Range: $25-49.9 Million
Emp.: 35
French Fries & Potato Specialties Mfr
N.A.I.C.S.: 311411
Aean Bernau *(Gen Mgr)*

McCain Foods Nordic (1)
Bryggavagen 100, Ekero, 17831, Sweden
Tel.: (46) 855611690
Web Site: http://www.mccain.se
Sales Range: $25-49.9 Million
Emp.: 5
Frozen Food Mfr
N.A.I.C.S.: 311412
Mats Thunblad *(Country Mgr)*

McCain Foods USA Inc. (1)
2275 Cabot Dr, Lisle, IL 60532-3653
Tel.: (630) 955-0400
Web Site: http://www.mccainusa.com
Sales Range: $100-124.9 Million
Emp.: 320
Pizza, Potato Product & Appetizer Mfr, Marketer & Distr
N.A.I.C.S.: 311411
Jeff DeLapp *(Pres-North America)*

Plant (Domestic):

McCain Foods USA (2)
1620 N 8th St, Colton, CA 92324
Tel.: (909) 825-8542
Sales Range: $75-99.9 Million
Emp.: 160
Packaged Frozen Goods
N.A.I.C.S.: 424420

McCain Foods USA Inc. (2)
801 Rockwell Ave, Fort Atkinson, WI 53538-2458 (100%)
Tel.: (920) 563-6625
Sales Range: $25-49.9 Million
Emp.: 130
Mfr of Onion Rings & Specialty Products
N.A.I.C.S.: 311411
Amy Griffith *(Head-Govt Rels & External Affairs)*

Subsidiary (Domestic):

McCain Snack Foods (2)
555 N Hickory Farm Ln, Appleton, WI 54914-3037
Tel.: (920) 997-2828
Web Site: http://www.mccain.com
Specialty Food Industry
N.A.I.C.S.: 484230
Wayne Lamont *(Mgr-HR)*

McCain-Ellios Food Inc. (2)
11 Gregg St, Lodi, NJ 07644-2704 (100%)
Tel.: (201) 368-0600
Web Site: http://www.mccainusa.com
Sales Range: $25-49.9 Million
Emp.: 100
Frozen Pizza Products
N.A.I.C.S.: 311412
Mary Rose *(Controller)*

McCain GmbH (Germany) (1)
Dusseldorfer Str 13, PO Box 5665, Eschborn, 65731, Germany (100%)
Tel.: (49) 6196900220
Web Site: http://www.mccain.de
Sales Range: $125-149.9 Million
Emp.: 55
Marketing & Distribution of Food Preparations
N.A.I.C.S.: 445298
Thomas Klein *(Mgr)*

McCain Poland Sp z.o.o. (1)
Chociwel 25, Strzelin, 57100, Poland
Tel.: (48) 713957100
Web Site: http://www.mccain.pl
Sales Range: $25-49.9 Million
Emp.: 250
Frozen Food Mfr

N.A.I.C.S.: 311412
Helga Hofmeiscer *(Gen Mgr)*

McCain Portugal Lda. (1)
Alameda dos Combatentes da Grande Guerra 247 Ed S Jose Esc 202, 2750 326, Cascais, Portugal
Tel.: (351) 21 4812330
Web Site: http://www.mccain.pt
Frozen Food Distr
N.A.I.C.S.: 424420

Valley Farms Limited (1)
107 Main Street, Florenceville, E7L 1B2, NB, Canada (100%)
Tel.: (506) 392-5541
Sales Range: $25-49.9 Million
Emp.: 20
Growing of Vegetables
N.A.I.C.S.: 111219

MCCAMBRIDGE LIMITED
Block D Greenogue Square, Dublin, Ireland
Tel.: (353) 14589744
Web Site: http://www.mccambridge.ie
Sales Range: $25-49.9 Million
Emp.: 200
Food Mfr
N.A.I.C.S.: 311812

MCCHIP RESOURCES INC.
Richmond Adelaide Centre Suite 1910 130 Adelaide St West, Toronto, M5H 3P5, ON, Canada
Tel.: (416) 364-2173   Ca
Year Founded: 1935
MCS—(TSXV)
Rev.: $1,840,370
Assets: $6,404,475
Liabilities: $650,492
Net Worth: $5,753,982
Earnings: $1,401,074
Fiscal Year-end: 12/31/20
Mineral Extraction Services
N.A.I.C.S.: 212290
Edward G. Dumond *(CFO & Sec)*

MCCLELLAN WHEATON CHEVROLET BUICK GMC LTD.
3850 48th Avenue, Camrose, T4V 3Z8, AB, Canada
Tel.: (780) 672-2355
Web Site: http://www.mcclellanwheaton.ca
Year Founded: 1988
Sales Range: $10-24.9 Million
Emp.: 40
Car Dealership
N.A.I.C.S.: 441110
Jarren Schultz *(Controller)*

MCCLELLAND OILFIELD RENTALS LIMITED
7901 99 Street, Clairmont, T8X 5B1, AB, Canada
Tel.: (780) 539-3656
Web Site: http://www.mdrentals.ca
Year Founded: 1981
Sales Range: $25-49.9 Million
Emp.: 16
Oil & Gas Drilling Services
N.A.I.C.S.: 213111
Dough Case *(VP-Sls)*

MCCOLL'S RETAIL GROUP PLC
McColl's House Ashwells Road, Pilgrims Hatch, Brentwood, CM15 9ST, Essex, United Kingdom
Tel.: (44) 1277372916
Web Site: http://www.mccolls.co.uk
Year Founded: 1901
MCLS—(LSE)
Rev.: $1,708,147,532
Assets: $763,445,956
Liabilities: $736,427,328
Net Worth: $27,018,628
Earnings: ($3,665,844)

Emp.: 15,309
Fiscal Year-end: 11/29/20
Retail Store Operator
N.A.I.C.S.: 445110

MCCONNELLS ADVERTISING SERVICE LTD.
Grand Mill Quay Barrow St, Dublin, 2, Leinster, Ireland
Tel.: (353) 14781544
Year Founded: 1916
Emp.: 110
Direct Marketing, Full Service, Production, Public Relations, Publicity/Promotions, Radio, T.V.
N.A.I.C.S.: 541810
Lawrence Keogh *(Dir-Creative)*

MCCONVILLE OMNI INSURANCE BROKERS LIMITED
685 Richmond Street Suite 300, London, N6A5M1, ON, Canada
Tel.: (519) 673-0880
Web Site: https://www.mcconvilleomni.ca
Year Founded: 1954
Insurance Agencies
N.A.I.C.S.: 524113

MCCOR MANAGEMENT
21 St Clair Avenue East Suite 500, Toronto, M4T 1L9, ON, Canada
Tel.: (647) 722-6472
Web Site: http://www.mccor.ca
Year Founded: 2014
Real Estate Development & Marketing Services
N.A.I.C.S.: 531390
Luc Corneli *(Founder & Principal)*

Subsidiaries:

McCOR Management - West (1)
330 Portage Ave Ste 1000, Winnipeg, R3C 0C4, MB, Canada
Tel.: (204) 947-2242
Web Site: http://www.mcor.ca
Sales Range: $50-74.9 Million
Emp.: 250
Real Estate Services
N.A.I.C.S.: 531390
T. J. Crowley *(COO-West)*

Unit (Domestic):

McCOR Management (2)
Suite 101 1933 - 18th Avenue NE, Calgary, T2E 7T8, AB, Canada
Tel.: (403) 263-0100
Emp.: 12
Real Estate Services
N.A.I.C.S.: 531390
Sheena Whitfield *(Gen Mgr)*

McCOR Management (2)
101 10320 - 102 Avenue, Edmonton, T5J 4A1, AB, Canada
Tel.: (780) 423-4400
Emp.: 28
Real Estate Services
N.A.I.C.S.: 531390
T. J. Crowley *(COO)*

McCOR Management (2)
2550 - 12th Avenue Suite 300, Regina, S4P 3X1, SK, Canada
Tel.: (306) 359-9799
Sales Range: $1-9.9 Million
Emp.: 30
Real Estate Services
N.A.I.C.S.: 531390
Laurie Ell *(Gen Mgr)*

MCCOWAN AND ASSOCIATES LTD.
158 Dunlop Street East Unit 201, Barrie, M4M 1B1, ON, Canada
Tel.: (705) 737-1057
Private Equity
N.A.I.C.S.: 523999
Ronald McCowan *(CEO)*

Subsidiaries:

Partners Real Estate Investment Trust (1)
249 Saunders Road Unit 3, Barrie, L4N 9A3, ON, Canada
Tel.: (705) 725-6020
Web Site: http://www.partnersreit.com
Rev.: $35,792,298
Assets: $211,604,165
Liabilities: $138,553,867
Net Worth: $73,050,298
Earnings: ($24,093,919)
Emp.: 24
Fiscal Year-end: 12/31/2018
Real Estate Investment Trust
N.A.I.C.S.: 525990
Jane Domenico *(Pres & CEO)*

MCCOY GLOBAL INC.
Suite 200 16011 116 Ave NW, Edmonton, T5M 3Y1, AB, Canada
Tel.: (780) 453-8451   AB
Web Site: https://www.mccoyglobal.com
Year Founded: 1996
MCCRF—(OTCIQ)
Rev.: $40,857,694
Assets: $45,631,261
Liabilities: $16,666,927
Net Worth: $28,964,334
Earnings: $178,301
Emp.: 126
Fiscal Year-end: 12/31/19
Field Equipment Trucking Services
N.A.I.C.S.: 336110
James W. Rakievich *(Pres & CEO)*

Subsidiaries:

3PS, Inc. (1)
1300 Arrow Point Dr, Cedar Park, TX 78613
Tel.: (512) 610-5200
Web Site: http://www.3psinc.com
Sensor System Mfr
N.A.I.C.S.: 334513
Kellie Warren *(Mgr-Sls & Mktg)*

McCoy Global Canada Corp. (1)
Suite 201 9910 39th Ave NW, Edmonton, T6E 5H8, AB, Canada (100%)
Tel.: (780) 453-8451
Web Site: https://www.mccoyglobal.com
Drilling Equipment Mfr, Distr & Sales
N.A.I.C.S.: 333132

McCoy Global S.a.r.l (1)
Warehouse No FZS1BJ03 Jebel Ali Free Zone, South Zone, Dubai, United Arab Emirates (100%)
Tel.: (971) 48036900
Web Site: http://www.mccoyglobal.com
Drilling Equipment Mfr, Distr & Sales
N.A.I.C.S.: 423830

McCoy Global USA, Inc. - Broussard (1)
4225 Hwy 90 E, Broussard, LA 70518
Tel.: (337) 837-8847
Web Site: http://www.mccoyglobal.com
Hydraulic Power Equipment Mfr
N.A.I.C.S.: 333611

Rebel Metal Fabricators Ltd (1)
225 Burnt Ridge Road, Red Deer, T4S 0K6, AB, Canada
Tel.: (403) 314-2265
Web Site: http://www.rebelvac.ca
Emp.: 25
Vacuum System Mfr
N.A.I.C.S.: 333310

MCDOWELL HOLDINGS LIMITED
UB Tower Level 12 UB City 24 Vittal Mallya Road, Bengaluru, 560001, India
Tel.: (91) 918046686000
Web Site: https://www.mcdowellholdings.co.in
532852—(BOM)
Rev.: $337,005
Assets: $109,041,592
Liabilities: $2,166,746
Net Worth: $106,874,845

4757

MCDOWELL HOLDINGS LIMITED

McDowell Holdings Limited—(Continued)
Earnings: ($155,146)
Emp.: 1
Fiscal Year-end: 03/31/21
Investment Management Service
N.A.I.C.S.: 523999

MCE ASCHERSLEBEN GMBH
Gustener Strasse 18, 06449, Aschersleben, Germany
Tel.: (49) 34738870   De
Web Site: http://www.mce-aschersleben.com
Year Founded: 1898
Sales Range: $1-9.9 Million
Emp.: 50
Large-Scale Plant Engineering Services
N.A.I.C.S.: 541330

MCE HOLDINGS BERHAD
No 2 and 4 Jalan Waja 7 Kawasan Perindustrian Pandan, 81100, Johor Bahru, Malaysia
Tel.: (60) 73553787
Web Site: https://www.multicode.com.my
Year Founded: 2015
7004—(KLS)
Rev.: $21,202,406
Assets: $29,394,910
Liabilities: $9,983,752
Net Worth: $19,411,158
Earnings: ($206,630)
Emp.: 380
Fiscal Year-end: 07/31/21
Automotive Electronics Parts Mfr
N.A.I.C.S.: 334419
Wee Hee Lee *(Co-Sec)*

Subsidiaries:

Multi-Code Electronics Industries (M) Berhad   (1)
No 2 and 4 Jalan Waja 7, kawasan Perinduastrian Pandan, 81100, Johor Bahru, Johor, Malaysia
Tel.: (60) 73553787
Automotive Equipment Mfr & Distr
N.A.I.C.S.: 336320

Subsidiary (Domestic):

Beaucar Accessories (M) Sdn. Bhd.   (2)
Lot 68745 Canang Emas 7 Off Jalan Telok Gong, 42000, Port Klang, Selangor, Malaysia
Tel.: (60) 331656298
Automotive Equipment Mfr & Distr
N.A.I.C.S.: 336320

Multi-Code Technologies (M) Sdn. Bhd.   (2)
Lot 68745 Canang Emas 7 Off Jalan Telok Gong, 42000, Port Klang, Selangor, Malaysia
Tel.: (60) 331656297
Automotive Equipment Mfr & Distr
N.A.I.C.S.: 336320

MCE TECHNOLOGIES (SUZHOU) CO., LTD
No 29 Dongfu Road Suzhou Industrial Park, Suzhou, 215123, Jiangsu, China
Tel.: (86) 51262653306
Year Founded: 2007
Metal Cabinets Mfr
N.A.I.C.S.: 332999

MCEWEN MINING INC.
150 King Street West Suite 2800, Toronto, M5H 1J9, ON, Canada   CO
Web Site: https://www.mcewenmining.com
MUX—(NYSE)
Rev.: $110,417,000
Assets: $528,719,000
Liabilities: $172,445,000
Net Worth: $356,274,000
Earnings: ($81,075,000)
Emp.: 520
Fiscal Year-end: 12/31/22
Holding Company; Gold Ore Exploration & Mining Services
N.A.I.C.S.: 551112
Robert Ross McEwen *(Chm)*

Subsidiaries:

Andes Corporacion Minera S.A.   (1)
Toranzo Sur 255, San Juan, Argentina
Tel.: (54) 2644267644
Gold Mining Services
N.A.I.C.S.: 212220

Las Yaretas S.A.   (1)
Calle Peru 930, M5500FAW, Mendoza, Argentina
Tel.: (54) 2614293737
Gold Mining Services
N.A.I.C.S.: 212220

Minera Andes S.A.   (1)
Toranzo Borjas Sur 255 5400, San Juan, Argentina
Tel.: (54) 2644234990
Gold Mining Services
N.A.I.C.S.: 212220

Timberline Resources Corporation   (1)
9030 N Hess St Ste 161, Hayden, ID 83835
Tel.: (208) 664-4859
Web Site: https://timberlineresources.co
Rev.: $551
Assets: $14,795,875
Liabilities: $358,095
Net Worth: $14,437,780
Earnings: ($2,180,344)
Emp.: 3
Fiscal Year-end: 09/30/2023
Gold Ore & Silver Ore Mining
N.A.I.C.S.: 212220
Leigh W. Freeman *(Chm)*

Tone Resources Limited   (1)
3374 West 19th Avenue, Vancouver, V6S 1C2, BC, Canada
Tel.: (604) 263-5614
Gold Mining Services
N.A.I.C.S.: 327910

Tonkin Springs LLC   (1)
1595 Meadow Wood Ln Ste 3, Reno, NV 89502
Tel.: (775) 825-8939
Gold Mining Services
N.A.I.C.S.: 212220

US Gold Canadian Acquisition Corporation   (1)
2900 Manulife Place 10180-101 Street, Edmonton, T5J 3V5, AB, Canada
Tel.: (780) 423-7100
Precious Metal Mining Services
N.A.I.C.S.: 212290

White Knight Resources Ltd.   (1)
510 West Hastings Street Suite 922, Vancouver, V6B 1L8, BC, Canada
Tel.: (604) 681-4462
Gold Mining Services
N.A.I.C.S.: 212220

MCF CORPORATE FINANCE GMBH
Emporio Tower Valentinskamp 70, 20355, Hamburg, Germany
Tel.: (49) 40 39803 0   De
Web Site: http://www.mcfcorpfin.com
Year Founded: 1987
Emp.: 60
Corporate Consulting Services
N.A.I.C.S.: 541611
Hans-Christoph Stadel *(Mng Partner & Mng Dir)*

Subsidiaries:

Keystone MCF Corporate Finance AB   (1)
Birger Jarlsgatan 18, 114 34, Stockholm, Sweden
Tel.: (46) 8 545 680 80
Web Site: http://www.keystone-mcf.com

Emp.: 9
Corporate Financial Consulting Services
N.A.I.C.S.: 541611
Andreas Per Lennart Stenback *(Partner & Head-Stockholm Office)*

MCF ENERGY LTD.
Tel.: (604) 685-4554   BC
Web Site: https://mcfenergy.com
Year Founded: 2007
MCF—(TSXV)
Assets: $72,014
Liabilities: $164,458
Net Worth: ($92,444)
Earnings: ($188,041)
Fiscal Year-end: 12/31/20
Oil & Gas Exploration
N.A.I.C.S.: 211120
James Hill P. Geo *(CEO)*

MCH GROUP AG
Messeplatz 10, 4005, Basel, Switzerland
Tel.: (41) 582002020
Web Site: https://www.mch-group.com
Year Founded: 1916
MCHN—(SWX)
Rev.: $436,862,528
Assets: $491,716,186
Liabilities: $366,155,211
Net Worth: $125,560,976
Earnings: ($9,987,805)
Emp.: 762
Fiscal Year-end: 12/31/22
Exhibition Organizing & Marketing Services
N.A.I.C.S.: 561920
Marco Gadola *(Vice Chm)*

Subsidiaries:

Expomobilia MCH Global Shanghai Ltd.   (1)
Room 805 Building 1 Unit 2 88 Keyuan Rd, Pudong, Shanghai, 201203, China
Tel.: (86) 2168812086
Event Arrangement Services
N.A.I.C.S.: 561920

MC2   (1)
3 Alpine Ct, Chestnut Ridge, NY 10977
Tel.: (800) 537-8073
Web Site: http://www.mc-2.com
Marketing Solutions Services, Exhibits, Events & Interactive Media Productions
N.A.I.C.S.: 541613
Gary Benson *(Chm)*

MCH Beaulieu Lausanne SA   (1)
Avenue des Bergieres 10, 1004, Lausanne, Switzerland
Tel.: (41) 216439999
Web Site: https://beaulieu-lausanne.com
Event Arrangement Services
N.A.I.C.S.: 561920

MCH Swiss Exhibition (Basel) Ltd.   (1)
Messeplatz 10, 4005, Basel, Switzerland
Tel.: (41) 58 200 2020
Event Arrangement Services
N.A.I.C.S.: 561920

MCH Swiss Exhibition (Zurich) Ltd.   (1)
Wallisellenstrasse 49, PO Box 8050, CH-8050, Zurich, Switzerland
Tel.: (41) 582065000
Web Site: https://www.messe-zurich.com
Event Arrangement Services
N.A.I.C.S.: 561920

MCH-US Corp.   (1)
15 E Midland Ave Ste 2B, Paramus, NJ 07652
Tel.: (551) 502-5000
Web Site: https://www.mc-2.com
Event Arrangement Services
N.A.I.C.S.: 561920

Masterpiece London Limited   (1)
21-23 Mossop Street, London, SW3 2LY, United Kingdom
Tel.: (44) 2074997470

Web Site: https://www.masterpiecefair.com
Fine Art Dealer Services
N.A.I.C.S.: 459920
Philip Hewat-Jaboor *(Chm)*

MCI CAPITAL ALTERNATYWNA SPOLKA INWESTYCYJNA S.A.
Warsaw Unit Rondo Ignacego Daszynskiego 1, 00-843, Warsaw, Poland
Tel.: (48) 226526030   PL
Web Site: https://www.mci.pl
Year Founded: 1999
MCI—(WAR)
Rev.: $4,197,860
Assets: $559,005,426
Liabilities: $77,614,430
Net Worth: $481,390,996
Earnings: $35,989,801
Emp.: 2,022
Fiscal Year-end: 12/31/22
Investment Management Firm
N.A.I.C.S.: 523999
Tomasz Czechowicz *(CEO, Member-Mgmt Bd, Mng Partner & Mgr-Fund)*

Subsidiaries:

ATM S.A.   (1)
Grochowska 21a, 04-186, Warsaw, Poland   (91.17%)
Tel.: (48) 225156800
Web Site: http://www.atm.com.pl
Rev.: $39,172,887
Assets: $154,529,707
Liabilities: $110,016,878
Net Worth: $44,512,829
Earnings: $1,580,900
Emp.: 200
Fiscal Year-end: 12/31/2019
Telecommunication Services
N.A.I.C.S.: 517112
Tomasz Galas *(Member-Mgmt Bd & VP)*

MCI Gandalf Aktywnej Alokacji SFIO   (1)
844 Miedzeszynski Wal St, 03 942, Warsaw, Poland
Tel.: (48) 226161407
Web Site: http://www.gandalf-fundusz.pl
Investment Fund Management Services
N.A.I.C.S.: 525910

Travelplanet.pl S.A.   (1)
ul Traugutta 45, 50-418, Wroolaw, Poland
Tel.: (48) 717717655
Web Site: http://www.travelplanet.pl
Travel Agency Operator
N.A.I.C.S.: 561510

MCI GROUP HOLDING SA
9 rue du Pre-Bouvier, Satigny, 1242, Geneva, Switzerland
Tel.: (41) 22 339 95 00
Web Site: http://www.mci-group.com
Year Founded: 1987
Sales Range: $150-199.9 Million
Emp.: 1,900
Holding Company
N.A.I.C.S.: 551112
Roger Tondeur *(Founder, Chm & Pres)*

Subsidiaries:

Network Media Partners, LLC   (1)
307 International Dr Ste 190, Hunt Valley, MD 21030
Tel.: (410) 584-1900
Web Site: http://www.networkmediapartners.com
Media Marketing & Advertising
N.A.I.C.S.: 541840
Carrie Hartin *(Pres)*

MCILROY & KING COMMUNICATIONS INC.
688 Richmond St West Ste 401, Toronto, M6J 1C5, ON, Canada
Tel.: (416) 516-5969
Web Site: http://www.mkmedia.biz
Year Founded: 2001

Sales Range: $1-9.9 Million
Emp.: 100
Media Buying Services
N.A.I.C.S.: 541810
Julie King (Partner)

MCINERNEY HOLDINGS PLC.
29 Kenilworth Sq Rathgar, 6, Dublin, Ireland
Tel.: (353) 14962010
Web Site: http://www.mcinerney.ie
Rev.: $579,200,000
Earnings: $48,700,000
Emp.: 200
Residential Construction
N.A.I.C.S.: 236115
Edmund F. Sullivan (Chm)

MCINTYRE GROUP OFFICE SERVICES INC.
406 Harmony Road RR 1, Ayr, N0B 1E0, ON, Canada
Tel.: (519) 740-7636
Web Site:
  http://www.mcintyregrp.com
Year Founded: 1986
Rev.: $11,688,210
Emp.: 150
Office Furniture Installation Services
N.A.I.C.S.: 811420
Dean L. Mcintyre (Pres)

MCJ CO., LTD.
Otemachi PLACE East Tower 6F 2-3-2, Otemachi Chiyoda-ku, Tokyo, 100-0004, Japan
Tel.: (81) 367393403
Web Site: https://www.mcj.jp
Year Founded: 1998
6670—(TKS)
Rev.: $1,239,077,550
Assets: $798,005,470
Liabilities: $273,528,410
Net Worth: $524,477,060
Earnings: $80,635,390
Emp.: 4,006
Fiscal Year-end: 03/31/24
Holding Company
N.A.I.C.S.: 551112
Yuji Takashima (Chm & CEO)

Subsidiaries:

Aiuto Co., Ltd. (1)
Yushima Bld 8F 3-14-9 Yushima, Bunkyo-ku, Tokyo, 113-0034, Japan
Tel.: (81) 367393937
Web Site: https://www.aiuto-jp.co.jp
Computer Peripheral Equipment Whslr
N.A.I.C.S.: 423430
Shinichi Watanabe (Pres)

Mouse Computer Co., Ltd. (1)
6th floor Otemachi Place East Tower 2-3-2 Otemachi, Chiyoda-ku, Tokyo, 100-0004, Japan
Tel.: (81) 367393811
Web Site: https://www.mouse-jp.co.jp
Personal Computer Mfr & Distr
N.A.I.C.S.: 334111

R-Logic International Pte. Ltd. (1)
Tel.: (65) 67484042
Web Site: http://www.r-logic.com
Computer Repair Services
N.A.I.C.S.: 811210

SolNac Corporation (1)
Shin-Yamamoto Building 1-1-25 Dojima, Kita-ku, Osaka, 530-0003, Japan
Tel.: (81) 647963233
Web Site: https://www.solnac.jp
Computer Peripheral Equipment Whslr
N.A.I.C.S.: 423430

Tekwind Co., Ltd. (1)
7th Floor Yushima First Bldg 3-19-11 Yushima, Bunkyo-ku, Tokyo, 113-0034, Japan
Tel.: (81) 343238606
Web Site: https://www.tekwind.co.jp
Computer Peripheral Equipment Whslr
N.A.I.C.S.: 423430

Wang Monchou (Pres)

UNIT.COM INC. (1)
4-16-1 Nihonbashi, Naniwa-ku, Osaka, 556-0005, Japan (100%)
Tel.: (81) 666470214
Web Site: https://www.unitcom.co.jp
Emp.: 859
Computer Parts Distr
N.A.I.C.S.: 423430

iiyama Benelux B.V. (1)
Wijkermeerstraat 8, 2131 HA, Hoofddorp, Netherlands
Tel.: (31) 204460404
Web Site: https://www.iiyama.com
Computer Peripheral Equipment Mfr
N.A.I.C.S.: 334118

MCKECHNIE ALUMINIUM SOLUTIONS LIMITED
Paraite Rd Bell Block, Private Bag 2007, New Plymouth, 4342, New Zealand
Tel.: (64) 67559900
Web Site:
  http://www.mckechnie.co.nz
Year Founded: 1951
Sales Range: $100-124.9 Million
Emp.: 250
Aluminum Extrusions Mfr
N.A.I.C.S.: 331318
Primod Khatri (Gen Mgr)

MCKEVITT TRUCKING LIMITED
1200 Carrick Street, Thunder Bay, P7B 5P9, ON, Canada
Tel.: (807) 623-0054
Web Site: http://www.mckevitt-trucking.com
Year Founded: 1948
Rev.: $16,701,973
Emp.: 165
General Trucking Services
N.A.I.C.S.: 484110

MCKINNON MICRO DISTRIBUTING LTD
107 3830 Jacombs Rd, Richmond, V6V 1Y6, BC, Canada
Tel.: (604) 279-9917
Web Site: http://www.mckinnon-micro.com
Year Founded: 1993
Rev.: $11,306,400
Emp.: 23
Computer Parts Supplier
N.A.I.C.S.: 423430
Tim J. McKinnon (Pres)

MCLAREN CONSTRUCTION GROUP
McLaren House 100 Kings Road, Brentwood, CM14 4EA, Essex, United Kingdom
Tel.: (44) 1277 205 800
Web Site:
  http://www.mclarengroup.com
Year Founded: 2001
Sales Range: $400-449.9 Million
Emp.: 620
Construction Engineering Services
N.A.I.C.S.: 541330
Kevin Taylor (Chm)

Subsidiaries:

Arthur Brett & Sons Limited (1)
103 Pimlico Road, London, SW1W 8PH, United Kingdom
Tel.: (44) 20 7730 7304
Web Site: http://www.arthurbrett.com
Household Furniture Mfr
N.A.I.C.S.: 337121
Abigail Reeve (Mgr-Showroom)

McLaren Construction Ltd. (1)
Unit 130 First Floor The Iridium Umm Suqeim Street, PO Box 27900, Al Barsha, Dubai, United Arab Emirates

Tel.: (971) 43417964
Construction Engineering Services
N.A.I.C.S.: 541330

McLaren Property BV (1)
Paasheuvelweg 16, 1105 BH, Amsterdam, Netherlands
Tel.: (31) 205646160
Holding Company
N.A.I.C.S.: 551112

MCLAREN RESOURCES INC.
30 Duncan Street Suite 606, Toronto, M5V 2C3, ON, Canada
Tel.: (416) 203-6784 ON
Web Site:
  https://www.mclarenresources.com
Year Founded: 1999
3ML—(DEU)
Assets: $129,633
Liabilities: $60,030
Net Worth: $69,603
Earnings: ($350,806)
Fiscal Year-end: 09/30/23
Petroleum Exploration Services
N.A.I.C.S.: 211120
John B. Heslop (Chm)

MCLAUGHLIN & HARVEY LTD.
15 Trench Road Mallusk, Newtownabbey, BT36 4TY, Northern Ireland, United Kingdom
Tel.: (44) 28 9034 2777
Web Site: http://www.mclh.co.uk
Year Founded: 1853
Sales Range: $300-349.9 Million
Emp.: 363
Construction Engineering Services
N.A.I.C.S.: 541330
Michael McSherry (Mgr-Contracts)

MCLEAN TECHNOLOGIES BERHAD
No 2 Woodlands Sector 1 01-22, Singapore, 738068, Singapore
Tel.: (65) 67538077
Web Site:
  https://www.mclean.com.sg
MCLEAN—(KLS)
Rev.: $11,084,193
Assets: $9,511,701
Liabilities: $4,135,098
Net Worth: $5,376,603
Earnings: ($692,209)
Emp.: 249
Fiscal Year-end: 12/31/22
Precision Cleaning & Plastic Injection Molding Services
N.A.I.C.S.: 561720
Hock Huat Yeo (Chm)

Subsidiaries:

DWZ Industries Sdn Bhd (1)
25 Jalan Maju 5 Taman Perindustrian Desa Cemerlang, Ulu Tiram, 81800, Johor Bahru, Malaysia
Tel.: (60) 78674557
Property Development Services
N.A.I.C.S.: 531390
Hasnul Zaidan (Mgr-Production)

MClean Technologies Pte Ltd (1)
2 Woodlands Sector 1 01-22, Singapore, 738068, Singapore (100%)
Tel.: (65) 67538077
Web Site: http://www.mclean.com.sg
Precision Cleaning & Surface Treatment Services
N.A.I.C.S.: 561720

Subsidiary (Domestic):

MClean Technologies Pte. Ltd. (2)
No 2 Woodlands Sector 1 01-22, Singapore, 738068, Singapore
Tel.: (65) 67538077
Emp.: 86
Industrial Cleaning Services
N.A.I.C.S.: 561720

MCLEOD RUSSEL INDIA LIMITED
4 Mango Lane Surendra Mohan Ghosh Sarani, Kolkata, 700001, India
Tel.: (91) 3322435391
Web Site:
  https://www.mcleodrussel.com
532654—(BOM)
Rev.: $168,057,593
Assets: $453,255,761
Liabilities: $384,252,310
Net Worth: $69,003,450
Earnings: ($128,049,194)
Emp.: 46,532
Fiscal Year-end: 03/31/23
Tea Mfr
N.A.I.C.S.: 311920
Rajeev Takru (Exec Dir)

Subsidiaries:

Borelli Tea Holdings Limited (1)
Woodlands 79 High Street, Greenhithe, DA9 9RD, Kent, United Kingdom
Tel.: (44) 1322374878
Tea Mfr
N.A.I.C.S.: 311920
Dilsher Sen (Sec)

McLeod Russel Africa Limited (1)
Tea House 1st Mezzanine Floor South Wing Off Nyerere Road, Mombasa, Kenya
Tel.: (254) 709749831
Tea Mfr
N.A.I.C.S.: 311920
Faith Amitta (Mktg Mgr)

McLeod Russel Middle East DMCC (1)
G-29 DMCC Tea Centre Jebel Ali Free Zone - South, Dubai, United Arab Emirates
Tel.: (971) 48807388
Tea Mfr
N.A.I.C.S.: 311920
Arjun Katyal (Gen Mgr)

McLeod Russel Uganda Limited (1)
PO Box 371, Fort Portal, Kampala, Uganda
Tel.: (256) 382420000
Tea Mfr
N.A.I.C.S.: 311920
Harpreet Singh Grewal (Gen Mgr)

MCLON JEWELLERY CO., LTD.
22F Building C Xingyao Science and Technology Innovation City No 1, Juye Road Binjiang District, Hangzhou, 310051, Zhejiang, China
Tel.: (86) 57189803195
Web Site: http://www.mclon.com
Year Founded: 2009
300945—(SSE)
Rev.: $226,095,948
Assets: $122,355,792
Liabilities: $8,575,632
Net Worth: $113,780,160
Earnings: $7,641,972
Fiscal Year-end: 12/31/22
Jewelry Product Distr
N.A.I.C.S.: 458310
Songhe Sun (Chm & Gen Mgr)

MCLOUD TECHNOLOGIES CORP.
600 777 Hornby Street, Vancouver, V6Z 1S4, BC, Canada
Tel.: (604) 669-9973 BC
Web Site:
  https://www.mcloudcorp.com
Year Founded: 2010
MCLD—(NASDAQ)
Rev.: $20,083,384
Assets: $56,574,720
Liabilities: $53,211,318
Net Worth: $3,363,402
Earnings: ($35,071,081)
Emp.: 300
Fiscal Year-end: 12/31/21
Cloud Services
N.A.I.C.S.: 513210

MCLOUD TECHNOLOGIES CORP.

mCloud Technologies Corp.—(Continued)
Russ McMeekin *(Co-Founder, Pres & CEO)*

Subsidiaries:

Agnity Global, Inc. (1)
42808 Christy St Ste 201, Fremont, CA 94538
Tel.: (510) 270-2669
Web Site: https://www.agnityglobal.com
Information Technology Services
N.A.I.C.S.: 541519
Sanjeev Chawla *(Pres, CEO & Founder)*

Kanepi Group Pty. Ltd. (1)
117 Stirling Hwy Nedlands, Perth, 6009, WA, Australia
Tel.: (61) 89 386 6317
Oil & Gas Machinery Equipment Mfr
N.A.I.C.S.: 333132

Kanepi Pte. Ltd. (1)
Suntec City Tower Two 9 Temasek Boulevard 07-01, Singapore, 038989, Singapore
Tel.: (65) 9 438 0704
Web Site: https://www.kanepi.com
Information Technology Services
N.A.I.C.S.: 541519

mCloud Technologies Services Inc. (1)
Suite 203 4208 97 Street Greystone 7 Building, Edmonton, T6E 5Z9, AB, Canada
Tel.: (825) 535-3912
Portfolio Management Services
N.A.I.C.S.: 523940

MCM ENTERTAINMENT GROUP LIMITED

21 31 Goodwood Street Level 4, Richmond, 3121, VIC, Australia
Tel.: (61) 396356600
Web Site:
http://www.authenticentertain.com
Year Founded: 1983
Sales Range: $25-49.9 Million
Emp.: 100
Radio, TV & Online Media Content Producer & Distr
N.A.I.C.S.: 516120
Ashley Leighton *(Controller-Fin)*

Subsidiaries:

Authentic Entertainment (1)
Level 1 355 Crown St Suite 103, Surry Hills, 2010, NSW, Australia
Tel.: (61) 2 8333 8800
Web Site:
http://www.authenticentertain.com.au
Sales Range: $25-49.9 Million
Emp.: 22
Digital Design & Website Development Services
N.A.I.C.S.: 541512
Claire Moylan *(Mgr-Admin)*

mcm entertainment Pty Ltd (1)
L 4 21-31 Goodwood St, Richmond, 3121, VIC, Australia
Tel.: (61) 396356600
Sales Range: $25-49.9 Million
Emp.: 75
Music & Entertainment Production Services
N.A.I.C.S.: 512230
Tony McGinn *(CEO)*

mcm media Pty Ltd (1)
L 4 21-31 Goodwood St, Richmond, 3121, VIC, Australia
Tel.: (61) 396356600
Web Site:
http://www.authenticentertain.com.au
Emp.: 45
Television Broadcasting Services
N.A.I.C.S.: 516120
Jonathan Hopkins *(Chief Strategy & Mktg Officer)*

MCM-MENEDZSER KERESKEDELMI ES SZOLGALTATO KORLATOLT FELELOSSEGU TARSASAG

Orczy Utca 6, Budapest, 1089, Hungary
Tel.: (36) 14644904
Web Site: http://www.novochem.hu
Sales Range: $25-49.9 Million
Emp.: 1
Holding Company
N.A.I.C.S.: 551112
Tamas Vomosi *(Deputy Mng Dir)*

Subsidiaries:

Novochem Ltd. (1)
Orczy Ut 6, 1089, Budapest, Hungary
Tel.: (36) 12101200
Web Site: http://www.novochem.hu
Sales Range: $25-49.9 Million
Chemical Trading Company
N.A.I.C.S.: 325998
Piry Laszlo *(Mng Dir)*

Subsidiary (Non-US):

Novochem Romania Co. Ltd. (2)
Str Gheorghe Doja nr 17 ap 4-5, 540342, Targu Mures, Mures, Romania
Tel.: (40) 365804830
Web Site: http://www.novochem.ro
Emp.: 14
Chemical Products Distr
N.A.I.C.S.: 424690
Jozsef Fogarasi *(Area Mgr-Sls)*

MCMILLAN SHAKESPEARE LIMITED

Level 21 360 Elizabeth Street, Melbourne, 3000, VIC, Australia
Tel.: (61) 390973000
Web Site: https://www.mmsg.com.au
MMS—(ASX)
Rev.: $347,901,975
Assets: $870,092,144
Liabilities: $784,058,490
Net Worth: $86,033,653
Earnings: $60,134,214
Emp.: 1,300
Fiscal Year-end: 06/30/24
Financial & Investment Services
N.A.I.C.S.: 561499
Mike Salisbury *(CEO & Mng Dir)*

Subsidiaries:

CLM Fleet Management Plc (1)
Corporate House Jenna Way, Newport Pagnell, MK16 9QB, United Kingdom
Tel.: (44) 190 821 0100
Web Site: https://www.clm.co.uk
Vehicle Rental Services
N.A.I.C.S.: 532111

MaxxiMe Pty Ltd (1)
8 Scania Court, Gepps Cross, 5094, SA, Australia
Tel.: (61) 88 262 1968
Web Site: https://www.maximtrading.com.au
Food Product Whslr
N.A.I.C.S.: 424490

Maxxia Fleet Limited (1)
Wellesley Street, PO Box 7337, Auckland, 1141, New Zealand
Tel.: (64) 9 903 0622
Asset Management Services
N.A.I.C.S.: 523940

Maxxia Ltd. (1)
Corporate House Jenna Way, Newport Pagnell, MK16 9QB, United Kingdom
Tel.: (44) 190 821 0100
Web Site: https://www.maxxia.co.uk
Asset Refinancing Services
N.A.I.C.S.: 522220

McMillan Shakespeare Australia Pty Limited (1)
Level 19 360 Eleizabeth Street, Melbourne, 3000, VIC, Australia
Tel.: (61) 390973000
Web Site: http://www.maxxia.com.au
Sales Range: $200-249.9 Million
Emp.: 300
Automobile Financing Services
N.A.I.C.S.: 525990
Michael Kay *(CEO)*

Plan Tracker Pty. Ltd. (1)
PO Box 92, Gosford, NSW, Australia
Tel.: (61) 1800549670
Web Site: https://www.plantracker.com.au
Disability Support Services
N.A.I.C.S.: 541990

MCMUNN & YATES BUILDING SUPPLIES LTD.

Highway 20 East, Box 610, Dauphin, R7N 2V4, MB, Canada
Tel.: (204) 638-5303
Web Site:
https://www.mcmunnandyates.com
Year Founded: 1971
Lumber Products & Building Materials Supplier
N.A.I.C.S.: 423310
Dave Krobel *(Mgr-Thompson Store)*

MCNALLY BHARAT ENGINEERING CO. LTD.

Ecospace Business Park Campus-2B 11F/12 Rajarhat New Town, Kolkata, 700 160, India
Tel.: (91) 3344591111
Web Site:
https://www.mcnallybharat.com
Year Founded: 1961
MBECL—(NSE)
Rev.: $72,598,194
Assets: $381,957,426
Liabilities: $385,649,369
Net Worth: $(3,691,943)
Earnings: $(5,938,241)
Emp.: 554
Fiscal Year-end: 03/31/21
Engineeering Services
N.A.I.C.S.: 541330
Srinivash Singh *(Mng Dir)*

Subsidiaries:

EWB Kornyezetvedelmi Kft (1)
Victor Hugo u 18-22, Budapest, H-1132, Hungary
Tel.: (36) 13496141
Web Site: http://www.ewb.hu
Sales Range: $25-49.9 Million
Emp.: 15
Pneumatic Conveying & Ash Handling Machinery Engineering
N.A.I.C.S.: 333248
Karoly Horvath *(Gen Mgr)*

MCNEX CO., LTD.

9fl Hanshin IT Tower II 47 Digitalro9gil, Geumcheon-gu, Seoul, Korea (South)
Tel.: (82) 220253600
Web Site: https://www.mcnex.com
Year Founded: 2004
097520—(KRS)
Rev.: $850,325,308
Assets: $413,328,638
Liabilities: $176,274,573
Net Worth: $237,054,065
Earnings: $17,620,634
Emp.: 430
Fiscal Year-end: 12/31/22
Mobile Camera Mfr
N.A.I.C.S.: 334220
Min Donguk *(CEO)*

MCNICHOLS PLC

No 7 9 Jeminat Laalu Street, Near Journalist Estate Kilometer 32 Lagos Ibadan Expressway, Lagos, Ogun, Nigeria
Tel.: (234) 7040921603
Web Site:
https://www.africanfinancials.com
Year Founded: 2005
MCNICHOLS—(NIGE)
Rev.: $617,338
Assets: $483,880
Liabilities: $202,282
Net Worth: $281,598
Earnings: $14,627
Emp.: 72

Fiscal Year-end: 12/31/22
Food & Beverage Product Mfr
N.A.I.C.S.: 311999
Olusegun Layode *(Chm)*

MCNULTY KOREA CO., LTD

42 Yeonamnyuleum-ro Seonghwan-eup, Seobuk-gu, Cheonan, Chungcheongnam-do, Korea (South)
Tel.: (82) 313761383
Web Site:
http://www.mcnultycoffee.com
Year Founded: 1997
222980—(KRS)
Rev.: $53,854,593
Assets: $68,432,216
Liabilities: $36,571,449
Net Worth: $31,860,767
Earnings: $(2,313,821)
Emp.: 151
Fiscal Year-end: 12/31/22
Coffee & Tea Mfr
N.A.I.C.S.: 311920

MCOT PUBLIC COMPANY LIMITED

63/1 Rama IX Road, Huay Kwang, Bangkok, 10310, Thailand
Tel.: (66) 22016000
Web Site: https://www.mcot.net
Year Founded: 2004
Television Broadcasting Services
N.A.I.C.S.: 516120
Teerapong Wongsiwawilas *(Chm)*

MCPHERSON'S LIMITED

105 Vanessa Street, Locked Bag 5018, Kingsgrove, 2208, NSW, Australia
Tel.: (61) 293708000
Web Site:
https://www.mcphersons.com.au
Year Founded: 1860
MCP—(ASX)
Rev.: $96,589,877
Assets: $98,090,945
Liabilities: $38,237,179
Net Worth: $59,853,766
Earnings: $(7,602,831)
Emp.: 264
Fiscal Year-end: 06/30/24
Holding Company; Household Consumer Products Mfr & Distr
N.A.I.C.S.: 551112
Brett Charlton *(CEO & Mng Dir)*

Subsidiaries:

McPherson's (UK) Limited (1)
Fisherton Garage, Aberlour, AB38 9LB, Banffshire, United Kingdom (100%)
Tel.: (44) 134 087 1401
Web Site: https://www.mcpherson.ltd.uk
Sales Range: $75-99.9 Million
Emp.: 200
Nondurable Goods Merchant Whslr
N.A.I.C.S.: 424990
David McPherson *(Mng Dir)*

McPherson's Consumer Products (NZ) Limited (1)
30 Highbrook Drive Highbrook, East Tamaki, Auckland, 2013, New Zealand (100%)
Tel.: (64) 9 265 4300
Web Site: http://www.mcpherson.co.nz
Sales Range: $25-49.9 Million
Emp.: 50
Housewares & Personal Care Products Whslr
N.A.I.C.S.: 423220
Paul Mitchell *(Gen Mgr)*

McPherson's Consumer Products Pte. Ltd. (1)
20 Toh Guan Road 03-00 CJ Korea Express Building, Singapore, 608839, Singapore (100%)
Tel.: (65) 65216820
Web Site: http://www.mcpher.com.au

Sales Range: $25-49.9 Million
Emp.: 32
Consumer Products Whslr
N.A.I.C.S.: 424310

McPherson's Consumer Products Pty. Ltd. (1)
105 Vanessa Street, Locked Bag 5018, Kingsgrove, 2208, NSW, Australia (100%)
Tel.: (61) 29 370 8000
Web Site: https://www.mcphersons.com.au
Sales Range: $150-199.9 Million
Emp.: 300
Houseware & Personal Care Products Whslr
N.A.I.C.S.: 423220
Paul J. Maguire (*CEO & Mng Dir*)

McPherson's Hong Kong Limited (1)
7 Fl Fook Cheong Building 63 Hoi Yuen Road, Kowloon, China (Hong Kong)
Tel.: (852) 23416604
Holding Company; Household Consumer Products Distr
N.A.I.C.S.: 551112

Subsidiary (Domestic):

McPherson's Consumer Products (HK) Limited (2)
Unit 201 New Bright Building 11 Shueng Yuet Road, Kowloon Bay, Kowloon, China (Hong Kong) (100%)
Tel.: (852) 23416604
Web Site: http://www.mcpher.com.au
Sales Range: $25-49.9 Million
Emp.: 35
Household Consumer Products Distr
N.A.I.C.S.: 423220

MCPHILLIPS (WELLINGTON) LTD
Horton House, Hortonwood 50, Telford, TF1 7FG, Shropshire, United Kingdom
Tel.: (44) 1952670440
Web Site: http://www.mcphillips.co.uk
Year Founded: 1963
Rev.: $44,126,332
Emp.: 250
Civil Engineering & Building Contractor Services
N.A.I.C.S.: 541330
Jim McPhillips (*Founder*)

MCPHILLIPS FORD LINCOLN SALES LTD.
2420 McPhillips Street, Winnipeg, R2V 4J6, MB, Canada
Tel.: (204) 339-9251
Year Founded: 1987
Rev.: $96,059,628
Emp.: 65
New & Used Car Dealers
N.A.I.C.S.: 441110
Glen Tamoto (*Gen Mgr*)

MCPHY ENERGY S.A.
1-3 All du Nanometre, La Motte Fanjas, 38000, Grenoble, France
Tel.: (33) 475711505 FR
Web Site: https://www.mcphy.com
Year Founded: 2008
MCPHY—(EUR)
Rev.: $14,515,210
Assets: $161,801,794
Liabilities: $78,366,335
Net Worth: $83,435,459
Earnings: ($62,236,737)
Emp.: 265
Fiscal Year-end: 12/31/23
Hydrogen Production Services
N.A.I.C.S.: 325998
Pascal Mauberger (*Founder*)

Subsidiaries:

McPhy Energy Deutschland GmbH (1)
Schwartzkopffstrasse 1, 15745, Wildau, Germany
Tel.: (49) 33754972100

Hydrogen Production & Storage Equipment Mfr
N.A.I.C.S.: 335999

McPhy Energy Italia Srl (1)
Via Ayrton Senna 22, 56028, San Miniato, Pl, Italy
Tel.: (39) 0571445811
Web Site: https://mcphy.com
Hydrogen Production & Storage Equipment Mfr
N.A.I.C.S.: 335999

MCROLLS OY
Tiilenpolttajankuja 4, 01720, Vantaa, Finland
Tel.: (358) 9 3508 100
Web Site: http://www.mcrolls.fi
Car Wash System & Garage Equipment Distr
N.A.I.C.S.: 423850
Rudi Steiner (*CEO & Mng Dir*)

Subsidiaries:

Balti Rehviseadmete A/S (1)
Parnu mnt 232E, 11314, Tallinn, Estonia
Tel.: (372) 6599545
Web Site: http://www.mcrolls.ee
Sales Range: $50-74.9 Million
Emp.: 5
Car Wash Equipment Sales
N.A.I.C.S.: 423850
Jaano Jarvsoo (*Mng Dir*)

MCS ET ASSOCIES, S.A.
256 Bis Pyrenees, 75116, Paris, France
Tel.: (33) 153301100
Web Site: http://www.mcsfr.com
Loan Management Services
N.A.I.C.S.: 522390
Jeremie Dyen (*Pres*)

MCS INTERNATIONAL GMBH
Karlstrasse 23 25, 46535, Dinslaken, Germany
Tel.: (49) 20644330
Web Site: http://www.mcs-int.de
Year Founded: 1887
Sales Range: $25-49.9 Million
Emp.: 250
Gas Cylinders & Pressure Vessels Mfr
N.A.I.C.S.: 331210
S.M. Yasini (*Mng Dir*)

MCS SERVICES LIMITED
Tel.: (61) 893012420 AU
Web Site: http://www.redgumresources.com
Year Founded: 2006
Sales Range: Less than $1 Million
Emp.: 6
Metal Mining
N.A.I.C.S.: 212290
Paul Simmons (*CEO & Mng Dir*)

MCVICAR INDUSTRIES INC.
11 Progress Avenue Unit 25, PO Box 19, Toronto, M1P 4S7, ON, Canada
Tel.: (416) 366-7420 ON
Web Site: http://www.mcvicar.ca
Year Founded: 2003
Sales Range: $25-49.9 Million
Holding Company; Specialty Chemical Research & Development, Mfr & Marketer
N.A.I.C.S.: 551112
Gang Chai (*Pres & CEO*)

Subsidiaries:

JITE Technologies Inc. (1)
Unit 25 11 Progress Avenue, Toronto, M1P 4S7, ON, Canada (100%)
Tel.: (416) 366-7420
Web Site: http://www.jite.com
Emp.: 4
Electronic & Electrical Connection Products Mfr & Whslr
N.A.I.C.S.: 335999

MD MALIND PROMET A.D.
Vojvode Stepe Stepanovica 22, 74480, Modrica, Bosnia & Herzegovina
Tel.: (387) 53811412
MLPR-R-A—(BANJ)
Rev.: $20,290
Assets: $2,697,816
Liabilities: $834,721
Net Worth: $1,863,095
Earnings: ($70,639)
Emp.: 4
Fiscal Year-end: 12/31/12
Soft Drinks Mfr
N.A.I.C.S.: 312111
Smiljka Maric (*Chm*)

MD MEDICAL GROUP INVESTMENT PLC
Dimitriou Karatasou 15 Anastasio Building 6th floor, Flat/Office 601 Strovolos, 2024, Nicosia, Cyprus
Tel.: (357) 22504000 CY
Web Site: http://www.mcclinics.com
Year Founded: 2010
MDMG—(LSE)
Rev.: $308,826,644
Assets: $462,007,135
Liabilities: $75,810,541
Net Worth: $386,196,594
Earnings: $87,431,580
Emp.: 7,992
Fiscal Year-end: 12/31/23
Health Care Srvices
N.A.I.C.S.: 621999
Mark Kurtser (*CEO*)

MD MEDICAL GROUP INVESTMENTS PLC
15 Dimitriou Karatasou Street Anastasio Building 6th Floor Office 601, Strovolos, 2024, Nicosia, Cyprus
Tel.: (357) 22504000
Web Site: https://www.mcclinics.com
Year Founded: 2006
14NY—(LSE)
Rev.: $339,709,130
Assets: $461,782,271
Liabilities: $150,663,095
Net Worth: $311,119,176
Earnings: $82,746,560
Emp.: 8,461
Fiscal Year-end: 12/31/21
Investment Management Service
N.A.I.C.S.: 523999
Vladimir Mekler (*Chm*)

Subsidiaries:

LLC Mother & Child Saint-Petersburg (1)
88 Srednyi Prospect, Saint Petersburg, Russia
Tel.: (7) 8007007001
Healtcare Services
N.A.I.C.S.: 524114

MDEX AG
Backerbarg 6, 22889, Tangstedt, Germany
Tel.: (49) 4109 555 444
Web Site: http://www.mdex.de
Year Founded: 1997
Telecommunication Servicesb
N.A.I.C.S.: 517112
Sebastian Hilberg (*Chm-Mgmt Bd*)

MDI ENERGIA SA
ul Wal Miedzeszynski 608, 03-994, Warsaw, Poland
Tel.: (48) 223766850
Web Site: https://mdienergia.pl
Eletric Power Generation Services
N.A.I.C.S.: 221118
Grzegorz Sochacki (*Co-Pres*)

MDI SOLUTIONS
155 University Ave Ste 1220, Toronto, M5H 3B7, ON, Canada
Tel.: (416) 255-5113
Web Site: http://www.mdisolutions.com
Sales Range: $50-74.9 Million
Emp.: 20
Data Integration & Interfacing Services
N.A.I.C.S.: 518210
Alan McLaren (*VP*)

MDJM LTD
Suite C-1505 Saidun Center Xikang Road, Heping District, Tianjin, China
Tel.: (86) 2283520851 Ky
Web Site: http://www.mdjhchina.com
Year Founded: 2002
MDJH—(NASDAQ)
Rev.: $450,634
Assets: $5,635,075
Liabilities: $705,944
Net Worth: $4,929,131
Earnings: ($2,154,084)
Emp.: 11
Fiscal Year-end: 12/31/22
Real Estate Development Services
N.A.I.C.S.: 531390
Siping Xu (*Chm & CEO*)

MDL DOORS INC.
42918 B Cranbrook Road, PO Box 297, Shediac, N0G 1H0, NB, Canada
Tel.: (519) 887-6974
Web Site: http://mdldoorsystems.com
Year Founded: 1983
Rev.: $23,660,619
Emp.: 102
Steel Door Mfr
N.A.I.C.S.: 332321
Mervin Lichty (*Pres & Gen Mgr*)

MDM CONSTRUCTION CO. LTD.
2-6285 205th Street, Langley, V2Y 1N7, BC, Canada
Tel.: (604) 533-4354
Web Site: https://www.mdmconstruction.ca
Year Founded: 1981
Sales Range: $10-24.9 Million
Emp.: 20
General Construction Services
N.A.I.C.S.: 236220
David L. G. Martens (*Co-Founder*)

MDR LIMITED
53 Ubi Crescent, Singapore, 408594, Singapore
Tel.: (65) 68418481
Web Site: https://www.m-dr.com
Year Founded: 2000
Y3D—(SES)
Rev.: $154,390,669
Assets: $134,574,718
Liabilities: $61,030,069
Net Worth: $73,544,649
Earnings: ($32,171,476)
Emp.: 230
Fiscal Year-end: 12/31/23
Mobile Communications & Electronic Equipment
N.A.I.C.S.: 334290
Ghim Choon Ong (*CEO*)

Subsidiaries:

Accord Customer Care Solutions (M) Sdn Bhd (1)
8 Jalan PJS 11/28, Bandar Sunway Metro, Petaling Jaya, 46150, Malaysia (100%)
Tel.: (60) 356211212
Sales Range: $25-49.9 Million
Emp.: 60
Communication Service
N.A.I.C.S.: 517112

Accord Customer Care Solutions (NSW) Pty. Ltd. (1)

MDR LIMITED

mDR Limited—(Continued)

Unit 4 199 Parramatta Road, Auburn, 2144, NSW, Australia
Tel.: (61) 297398400
Sales Range: $50-74.9 Million
Emp.: 120
Communication Service
N.A.I.C.S.: 517112

Accord Customer Care Solutions (SA) Pty Ltd (1)
2 Jackson Street, Toorak, 3142, VIC, Australia
Tel.: (61) 393898300
Communication Service
N.A.I.C.S.: 517112

Accord Customer Care Solutions FZ Co. (1)
Dubai Airport Free Zone C24, PO Box 54583, Dubai, 371905, United Arab Emirates
Tel.: (971) 42996288
Web Site: http://www.accs.ae
Sales Range: $25-49.9 Million
Emp.: 15
Communication Service
N.A.I.C.S.: 517112
Majdi Ayoub (Mng Dir)

After Market Solutions (CE) Pte. Ltd. (1)
20 Toh Guan Road, #07-00 Accord District Center, Singapore, 608839, Singapore
Tel.: (65) 6410 2600
Communication Service
N.A.I.C.S.: 517112

Golden Myanmar Sea Company Ltd. (1)
No 92 Seikkantha Street, Kyauktada Township, Yangon, Myanmar
Tel.: (95) 1398207
Web Site: http://www.myanmarworkers.com
Employment Agency Services
N.A.I.C.S.: 561311
Than Tin (Mng Dir)

Pixio Sdn. Bhd. (1)
No 32 Jalan 223 Seksyen 51/A DE, 46100, Petaling Jaya, Selangor, Malaysia
Web Site: http://www.pixio.com.my
HD Digital Printing Services
N.A.I.C.S.: 323111
Hari Kumar (Mgr-Bus Dev)

TCL & Alcatel Repair & Distribution Centre (Suzhou) (1)
Blk D 4F No 5 Xinghan St China-Singapore Suzhou, Industrial Park Suzhou, 215021, Suzhou, Jiangsu, China
Tel.: (86) 51267616022
Sales Range: $25-49.9 Million
Emp.: 50
Communication Service
N.A.I.C.S.: 517112

MDS TECH INC.

49 Daewangpangyo-ro 644beon-gil, Bundang-gu, Seongnam, 13493, Gyeonggi-do, Korea (South)
Tel.: (82) 316273000
Web Site: https://mdstech.co.kr
Year Founded: 1994
086960—(KRS)
Rev.: $117,751,179
Assets: $122,311,902
Liabilities: $39,826,719
Net Worth: $82,485,183
Earnings: ($5,465,821)
Emp.: 117
Fiscal Year-end: 12/31/22
Embedded Software Development
N.A.I.C.S.: 541511

Subsidiaries:

MDS Pacific Pte., Ltd. (1)
7030 Ang Mo Kio Avenue 5 08-93 Northstar AMK, 08-93 Northstar AMK, Singapore, 569880, Singapore
Tel.: (65) 6 297 2800
Web Site: https://www.mdspacific.com
Sales Range: $25-49.9 Million
Emp.: 4
Embedded Software Services

N.A.I.C.S.: 541511
Sunny Long (Mng Dir)

MDS Pacific Pty. Ltd. (1)
Suite 4 15 32 Delhi Road, North Ryde, 2113, NSW, Australia
Tel.: (61) 29 888 7715
Web Site: http://www.mdspacific.com
Sales Range: $25-49.9 Million
Emp.: 5
Embedded Software Development Solutions
N.A.I.C.S.: 541511
Sunny Long (Pres)

MDX PUBLIC COMPANY LIMITED

Floor 12A Column Tower Building No 199 Ratchadaphisek Road, Khlong Toei, Bangkok, 10110, Thailand
Tel.: (66) 23022300
Web Site: https://www.mdx.co.th
Year Founded: 1988
MDX—(THA)
Rev.: $8,344,878
Assets: $210,113,181
Liabilities: $12,680,549
Net Worth: $197,432,631
Earnings: $7,202,626
Fiscal Year-end: 12/31/23
Real Estate Development Services
N.A.I.C.S.: 531390
Pracha Hetrakul (Chm)

MDXHEALTH S.A.

CAP Business Center Rue d Abhooz 31, 4040, Herstal, Belgium
Tel.: (32) 43642070 BE
Web Site: https://www.mdxhealth.com
Year Founded: 2003
MDXH—(NASDAQ)
Rev.: $37,054,000
Assets: $119,135,000
Liabilities: $109,820,000
Net Worth: $9,315,000
Earnings: ($44,044,000)
Emp.: 252
Fiscal Year-end: 12/31/22
Gene Methylation Tests For Early Detection of Cancer
N.A.I.C.S.: 621511
Joseph Sollee (Gen Counsel & Exec VP-Corp Dev)

Subsidiaries:

MDxHealth B.V. (1)
Novio Tech Campus Transistorweg 5, 6534 AT, Nijmegen, Netherlands
Tel.: (31) 88 327 2727
Web Site: https://mdxhealth.com
Biotechnology Research Development Services
N.A.I.C.S.: 541714

MDxHealth, Inc. (1)
Venable Ctr 302 E Pettigrew St Ste 240, Durham, NC 27701 (100%)
Tel.: (919) 281-0980
Web Site: http://www.mdxhealth.com
Sales Range: $25-49.9 Million
Emp.: 5
Molecular Diagnostics for Cancer Assessments & Personalized Patient Treatments
N.A.I.C.S.: 325413

MDY HEALTHCARE LIMITED

31 Southampton Row, London, WC1B 5HJ, United Kingdom
Tel.: (44) 2076471800
Web Site: http://www.mdyhealthcare.com
Year Founded: 1993
Emp.: 4
Healthcare Investment Holding Company
N.A.I.C.S.: 523999
Grahame Cook (Chm)

ME CONSTRUCTION LTD.

3 Baden Place Crosby Row, London, SE1 1YW, United Kingdom
Tel.: (44) 20 7234 5967
Web Site: http://www.meconstruction.co.uk
Year Founded: 2007
Sales Range: $10-24.9 Million
Emp.: 25
Refurbishment Contractor
N.A.I.C.S.: 238990
Peter McCullagh (Dir-Estimating)

ME GROUP INTERNATIONAL PLC

Unit 3B Blenheim Road, Epsom, KT19 9AP, Surrey, United Kingdom
Tel.: (44) 1372453399 UK
Web Site: https://me-group.com
Year Founded: 1962
MEGP—(LSE)
Rev.: $294,122,916
Assets: $369,516,114
Liabilities: $219,329,784
Net Worth: $150,186,330
Earnings: $43,918,038
Emp.: 1,720
Fiscal Year-end: 10/31/22
Automatic Photo Booths Mfr & Operator; Photographic Development & Printing Equipment Mfr
N.A.I.C.S.: 333310
Serge Crasnianski (Deputy Chm & CEO)

Subsidiaries:

Animate Fotofixe e Maquinas Automaticas Lda (1)
Rua St Antonio do Zaire Bairro de Angola Lote 138 r/c, 2685-462, Camarate, Portugal (100%)
Tel.: (351) 219 476286
Web Site: http://www.animate.pt
Sales Range: $25-49.9 Million
Emp.: 17
Mfr of Automatic Photographic Machines
N.A.I.C.S.: 333310

Fotofix Schnellphotoautomaten GmbH (1)
Viersenerstrasse 47, PO Box 805, Krefeld, 10764, Germany (100%)
Tel.: (49) 215183980
Web Site: http://www.fotofix.com
Sales Range: $25-49.9 Million
Emp.: 70
Mfr of Automatic Photographic Machines
N.A.I.C.S.: 333310
Rene Graf-Zucht (Mng Dir)

Division (Domestic):

Fototronic Imager Division (2)
Viersenerstrasse 47, Krefeld, 100764, Germany (100%)
Tel.: (49) 2151376950
Sales Range: $25-49.9 Million
Whslr Photographic Machines
N.A.I.C.S.: 333310

Jolly Roger (Amusement Rides) Limited (1)
Heath Road Skegness Industrial Estate, Skegness, PE25 3SU, Lincolnshire, United Kingdom
Tel.: (44) 1754 896 800
Web Site: http://www.jolly-roger.co.uk
Sales Range: $25-49.9 Million
Emp.: 30
Amusement Park Rides Mfr
N.A.I.C.S.: 333310
Will Hennessy (Mgr-Production)

KIS S.A.S. (1)
7 Rue Jean-Pierre Timbaud, BP 309, Echirolles, 38130, France
Tel.: (33) 4 76 333 000
Web Site: http://www.kis.fr
Amusement Machine Whslr
N.A.I.C.S.: 423850

KIS USA (1)
3495 Piedmont Rd Bldg 11 Ste 350, Atlanta, GA 30305
Web Site: http://www.kisusa.com

INTERNATIONAL PUBLIC

Digital & Photo Imaging Solutions
N.A.I.C.S.: 812922

Nippon Auto Photo KK (1)
4-10-6 Utsutani Minami-ku, Yubinbango, Saitama, 336 0034, Japan (100%)
Tel.: (81) 48 861 1621
Web Site: http://www.pmi.co.jp
Sales Range: $25-49.9 Million
Emp.: 100
Mfr of Automatic Photographic Machines
N.A.I.C.S.: 333310

Nippon Auto-Photo Kabushiki Kaisha (1)
4-10-6 Uchiya, Minami-Ku, Saitama, 336-0034, Japan
Tel.: (81) 48 861 1621
Web Site: http://www.pmi.co.jp
Automatic Photographic Machinery Distr
N.A.I.C.S.: 423410

Photo Me Holding France S.A.S. (1)
7 Rue Jean-Pierre Timbaud, 38434, Echirolles, France
Tel.: (33) 4 76 33 30 00
Investment Management Service
N.A.I.C.S.: 523999
Jean Luc (Gen Mgr)

Photo-Me CR sro (1)
Papirenska, 16000, Praha 6, Bubenec, Czech Republic (76%)
Tel.: (420) 2 203 03 495
Mfr of Automatic Photographic Machines
N.A.I.C.S.: 333310

Photo-Me France / KIS (1)
7 Rue Jean Pierre Timbaud, PO Box 130, Echirolles, France (100%)
Tel.: (33) 476333000
Web Site: http://www.kis.fr
Sales Range: $50-74.9 Million
Emp.: 250
Mfr of Automatic Photographic Machines
N.A.I.C.S.: 333310
Ivan Semenoff (Pres)

Photo-Me Ireland Ltd (1)
33 Weatherwell Indus Est, Clondalkin, Dublin, 22, Ireland (100%)
Tel.: (353) 14572121
Web Site: http://www.photome.co.uk
Sales Range: $25-49.9 Million
Emp.: 15
Mfr of Automatic Photographic Machines
N.A.I.C.S.: 333310
Richard French (Gen Mgr)

Photo-Me Northern Ireland Ltd (1)
13 Falcon Rd, Adelaide Indus Est, Belfast, BT12 6RD, Down, United Kingdom (97%)
Tel.: (44) 2890881201
Web Site: http://www.photome.co.uk
Sales Range: $25-49.9 Million
Emp.: 10
Mfr of Automatic Photographic Machines
N.A.I.C.S.: 333310

Photo-Me Shanghai (1)
Room 1102 Tongyong Tower No 1346 Gong he Xin Road, Zhabei District, Shanghai, 200070, China
Tel.: (86) 21 66086328
Web Site: http://www.photomechina.com
Photography Studio Operating Services
N.A.I.C.S.: 541921

Photomatico (Singapore) Pte. Limited (1)
26 Sin Ming Lane 03-113, Midview City, Singapore, 573971, Singapore
Tel.: (65) 64582203
Sales Range: $25-49.9 Million
Emp.: 5
Commercial Photography Services
N.A.I.C.S.: 541922
Lily Tan (Mng Dir)

Photomaton S.A.S. (1)
4 Rue De La Croix Faron, Saint-Denis, Paris, 93 217, France
Tel.: (33) 1 49 46 17 20
Web Site: http://www.photomaton.fr
Sales Range: $75-99.9 Million
Emp.: 300
Commercial Photography Services
N.A.I.C.S.: 541922
Eric Mergui (Gen Mgr)

Photomaton SA (1)

4 Rue De La Croix Faron La Plaine, Saint Denis, Cedex, France **(100%)**
Tel.: (33) 1 49 46 1720
Web Site: http://www.photomaton.fr
Emp.: 300
Mfr of Automatic Photographic Machines
N.A.I.C.S.: 333310
Nathalie Pineau Villard *(Editor)*

Prontophot (Schweiz) AG **(1)**
Sonnentalstrasse 5, Dubendorf, CH 8600, Switzerland **(100%)**
Tel.: (41) 18018111
Web Site: http://www.prontophot.ch
Sales Range: $25-49.9 Million
Emp.: 30
Mfr of Automatic Photographic Machines
N.A.I.C.S.: 333310

Prontophot Austria GmbH **(1)**
Viktor Kaplanstrasse 9 B, Garasdorf, A2201, Austria **(95%)**
Tel.: (43) 17158334
Web Site: http://www.prontophot.at
Sales Range: $25-49.9 Million
Emp.: 10
Mfr of Automatic Photographic Machines
N.A.I.C.S.: 333310

Prontophot Holland BV **(1)**
Loonseweg 14, 5527 AC, Hapert, Netherlands **(100%)**
Tel.: (31) 497381377
Web Site: http://www.prontophot.nl
Sales Range: $25-49.9 Million
Emp.: 24
Mfr of Automatic Photographic Machines
N.A.I.C.S.: 333310

Prontophot SA **(1)**
Blvd De l Humanite 415, 1190, Forest, Belgium **(100%)**
Tel.: (32) 24630970
Web Site: http://www.prontophot.be
Mfr of Automatic Photographic Machines
N.A.I.C.S.: 333310

ME LIN STEEL JOINT STOCK COMPANY
Administrative Area No 8, Dong Da Ward, Vinh Yen, Vinh Phuc, Vietnam
Tel.: (84) 2435840545
Web Site: https://melinsteel.vn
Year Founded: 2003
MEL—(HNX)
Rev.: $27,637,990
Assets: $26,718,076
Liabilities: $16,368,842
Net Worth: $10,349,234
Earnings: $183,175
Emp.: 69
Fiscal Year-end: 12/31/23
Steel Products Mfr
N.A.I.C.S.: 331110

ME RENEWABLE POWER CORPORATION
Vista del yaque 13, La charcas, Santiago, Dominican Republic
Tel.: (809) 6087504857 NV
Year Founded: 2014
MEPW—(OTCIQ)
Liabilities: $75,532
Net Worth: ($75,532)
Earnings: ($20,460)
Fiscal Year-end: 12/31/20
Automatic Number Plate Recognition Software
N.A.I.C.S.: 513210
Karina Garcia Peralta *(Pres, CEO & CFO)*

ME THERAPEUTICS HOLDINGS INC.
177 Robson Street, Vancouver, V6B 0N3, BC, Canada
Tel.: (236) 516-7714 BC
Web Site: https://www.metherapeutics.com
Year Founded: 2021
METX—(CNSX)
Holding Company
N.A.I.C.S.: 551112

ME2ON CO., LTD
4F Chosun Refractories B/D 577 Seolleung-ro, Gangnam-gu, Seoul, 06143, Korea (South)
Tel.: (82) 25152864
Web Site: https://www.me2on.com
Year Founded: 2010
201490—(KRS)
Rev.: $85,913,242
Assets: $169,241,093
Liabilities: $23,777,981
Net Worth: $145,463,112
Earnings: $6,639,996
Emp.: 37
Fiscal Year-end: 12/31/22
Game Software Development Services
N.A.I.C.S.: 513210
Choi Won Seok *(Exec Dir)*

MEADE-KING ROBINSON & CO., LTD.
Tower Building 22 Water Street, Liverpool, L3 1BL, United Kingdom
Tel.: (44) 151 236 3191
Web Site: http://www.mkr.co.uk
Year Founded: 1867
Sales Range: $100-124.9 Million
Emp.: 32
Chemical Products Distr
N.A.I.C.S.: 424690
Philip Tarleton *(Mng Dir)*

MEADOW FOODS LIMITED
Marlston Court Marlston-Cum-Lache, Chester, CH4 9JS, Cheshire, United Kingdom
Tel.: (44) 1244 680 071
Web Site: http://www.meadowfoods.com
Year Founded: 1992
Sales Range: $500-549.9 Million
Emp.: 272
Dairy Product Whslr
N.A.I.C.S.: 424430
Simon Chantler *(Founder)*

Subsidiaries:

Nimbus Foods Ltd **(1)**
The Marian, Dolgellau, Gwynedd, LL40 1UU, United Kingdom
Tel.: (44) 1341423050
Web Site: http://www.nimbusfoods.co.uk
Bakery Products Decorations & Toppings Mfr
N.A.I.C.S.: 311352
Jack Proctor *(Comml Dir)*

MEARS GROUP PLC
1390 Montpellier Court Gloucester Business Park, Brockworth, Gloucester, GL3 4AH, United Kingdom
Tel.: (44) 1452634600 UK
Web Site: https://www.mearsgroup.co.uk
MER—(LSE)
Rev.: $1,192,648,402
Assets: $860,684,505
Liabilities: $587,731,191
Net Worth: $272,953,313
Earnings: $19,365,160
Emp.: 5,397
Fiscal Year-end: 12/31/21
Construction, Rehabilitation & Corrosion Control Services for the Pipeline Industry
N.A.I.C.S.: 333132
Andrew C. M. Smith *(Dir-Fin)*

Subsidiaries:

Haydon Mechanical And Electrical Limited **(1)**
City Reach 5 Greenwich View Place, Docklands, London, E14 9NN, United Kingdom
Tel.: (44) 2079873555
Web Site: http://www.haydonme.co.uk
Sales Range: $25-49.9 Million
Mechanical & Electrical Repair & Maintenance
N.A.I.C.S.: 811114
David Cutler *(Mng Dir)*

Mears Care Limited **(1)**
114b Power Road, London, W4 5PY, United Kingdom
Tel.: (44) 8001216525
Housing Care & Maintenance Services
N.A.I.C.S.: 624229

Mears Limited **(1)**
Roseville Road Unit 2, Leeds, LS8 5DR, West Yorkshire, United Kingdom **(100%)**
Tel.: (44) 1132002911
Web Site: http://www.mearsgroup.co.uk
Sales Range: $350-399.9 Million
Mechanical & Electrical Repair & Maintenance
N.A.I.C.S.: 811114

Mears New Homes Limited **(1)**
26-28 Hyde Way, Welwyn Garden City, AL7 3UQ, Hertfordshire, United Kingdom
Tel.: (44) 170 729 0100
Web Site: http://www.mearsnewhomes.co.uk
Housing Care & Maintenance Services
N.A.I.C.S.: 624229
Tim Carpenter *(Mng Dir)*

Morrison Facilities Services Limited **(1)**
Unit 5 Acton Lane, Hanover West Industrial Estate, London, NW10 7NB, United Kingdom
Tel.: (44) 2089639530
Emp.: 2,500
Financial & Investment Services
N.A.I.C.S.: 523999

Scion Group Limited **(1)**
1 Moorbrook Pk, OX11 7HP, Didcot, United Kingdom - England **(100%)**
Tel.: (44) 1235861931
Web Site: http://www.sciongroup.co.uk
Sales Range: $25-49.9 Million
Emp.: 20
Automotive Mechanical & Electrical Repair & Maintenance
N.A.I.C.S.: 811114

MEASAT GLOBAL BERHAD
Level 39 Menara Maxis Kuala Lumpur City Ctr, 50088, Kuala Lumpur, Malaysia
Tel.: (60) 323806688
Web Site: http://www.measat.com
Sales Range: $75-99.9 Million
Satellite Network Services
N.A.I.C.S.: 517111
Ali R. Ebadi *(Sr VP-Space Sys Dev)*

Subsidiaries:

MEASAT Broadband (International) Ltd **(1)**
Les Cascades Building Edith Cavell Street, Port Louis, Mauritius
Tel.: (230) 2105821
Wireless Telecommunication Services
N.A.I.C.S.: 517111

MEASAT Satellite Systems Sdn Bhd **(1)**
MEASAT Teleport and Broadcast Centre Jalan Teknokrat 1/ 2, 63000, Cyberjaya, Malaysia
Tel.: (60) 3 8213 2188
Satellite Communication Services
N.A.I.C.S.: 517410
Janice Boo *(Dir-Sls)*

MEATPAK AUSTRALIA PTY. LTD.
156 Churchill Rd N, Cavan, Cavan, 5094, SA, Australia
Tel.: (61) 881628400
Web Site: http://www.holcofinemeats.com.au
Sales Range: $50-74.9 Million
Emp.: 200
Meat Product Distr
N.A.I.C.S.: 424470
David Culbert *(Gen Mgr-Natl)*

MEBELSYSTEM AD
119 Alexander Stamboliyski Blvd, 4400, Pazardzhik, Bulgaria
Tel.: (359) 34451167
Web Site: https://www.mebelsistem.com
MSYS—(BUL)
Sales Range: Less than $1 Million
Office Furniture Mfr
N.A.I.C.S.: 337214

MEBUKI FINANCIAL GROUP, INC.
2-5-5 Minami-machi, Mito, 320-8610, Ibaraki, Japan
Tel.: (81) 293002869 JP
Web Site: https://www.mebuki-fg.co.jp
Year Founded: 2009
7167—(TKS)
Rev.: $2,049,549,480
Assets: $144,006,345,740
Liabilities: $137,466,418,350
Net Worth: $6,539,927,390
Earnings: $39,660
Emp.: 5,781
Fiscal Year-end: 03/31/24
Financial Investment Services
N.A.I.C.S.: 551111
Masanao Matsushita *(Exec VP)*

Subsidiaries:

Mebuki Lease Co., Ltd. **(1)**
3-4-12 Minamimachi Joyo Marine Building 7th Floor, Mito, 310-0021, Ibaraki, Japan
Tel.: (81) 29 231 3821
Web Site: https://www.mebuki-lease.co.jp
Leasing & Installment Services
N.A.I.C.S.: 522220

The Ashikaga Bank, Ltd. **(1)**
1-25 Sakura 4-Chome, Utsunomiya, 320-8610, Tochigi, Japan
Tel.: (81) 286220111
Commericial Banking
N.A.I.C.S.: 522110
Satoshi Fujisawa *(Chm)*

The Joyo Bank, Ltd. **(1)**
2-5-5 Minamimachi, Mito, 310-0021, Ibaraki, Japan **(100%)**
Tel.: (81) 292312151
Emp.: 3,303
Banking Services
N.A.I.C.S.: 522110
Tetsuya Akino *(Pres)*

Division (Non-US):

The Joyo Bank, Ltd. - Business Planning Division **(2)**
Room 1901 Shanghai International Trade Centre, 2201 Yan An Road West, Shanghai, 200336, China
Tel.: (86) 21 6209 0258
Web Site: http://www.joyobank.co.jp
Business Management Services
N.A.I.C.S.: 541618

Subsidiary (Domestic):

The Joyo Business Service Co., Ltd. **(2)**
2-5-5 Minamicho, Mito, Ibaraki, Japan
Tel.: (81) 292315901
Web Site: http://www.joyobank.co.jp
Administrative Management Services
N.A.I.C.S.: 541611

The Joyo Cash Service Co., Ltd. **(2)**
3-3 Shinhara chome - 1, Mito, Ibaraki, Japan
Tel.: (81) 292250481
Web Site: http://www.joyobank.co.jp
Automatic Teller Machines Management & Maintenance Services
N.A.I.C.S.: 238290

The Joyo Computer Service Co., Ltd. **(2)**

MEBUKI FINANCIAL GROUP, INC.

Mebuki Financial Group, Inc.—(Continued)
2-16-25 Nishihara, Mito, 310-0044, Ibaraki, Japan **(100%)**
Tel.: (81) 292534411
Web Site: https://www.joyonet.jp
Emp.: 197
Banking Software Development Services
N.A.I.C.S.: 541511
Akira Tsuruta (Pres)

The Joyo Credit Co., Ltd. (2)
3-4-12 Minamicho 4F Joyo Marine Building, Mito, 310-0021, Ibaraki, Japan
Tel.: (81) 29 227 7731
Web Site: http://www.joyocredit.co.jp
Emp.: 57
Loan Credit Guarantee Services
N.A.I.C.S.: 522292

The Joyo Credit Guarantee Co., Ltd. (2)
3-4-12 Minamicho, Mito, Ibaraki, Japan
Tel.: (81) 292263881
Web Site: http://www.joyobank.co.jp
Loan Credit Guarantee Services
N.A.I.C.S.: 522292

The Joyo Industrial Research Institute, Ltd. (2)
1-5-18 Sannomaru 4th floor Joyo Local Hall, Mito, 310-0011, Ibaraki, Japan
Tel.: (81) 292336731
Web Site: https://www.jir-web.co.jp
Emp.: 35
Business Consulting Services
N.A.I.C.S.: 541611
Chieki Chaya (Pres)

MEC COMPANY LTD.
3-4-1 Kuise Minamishimmachi, Amagasaki, 660-0822, Hyogo, Japan
Tel.: (81) 664018160
Web Site: https://www.mec-co.com
Year Founded: 1969
4971—(TKS)
Rev.: $99,401,800
Assets: $203,234,850
Liabilities: $27,565,920
Net Worth: $175,668,930
Earnings: $16,335,360
Emp.: 454
Fiscal Year-end: 12/31/23
PCB Chemicals Mfr
N.A.I.C.S.: 325998
Kazuo Maeda (Pres & CEO)

Subsidiaries:

MEC (HONG KONG) LTD. (1)
No 8 12/F Tower 3 China Hong Kong City
33 Canton Road, Tsimshatsui, Kowloon, China (Hong Kong)
Tel.: (852) 2 690 2255
Web Site: http://www.mec-co.com
Chemical Equipments Whslr
N.A.I.C.S.: 423830

Subsidiary (Non-US):

MEC FINE CHEMICAL (ZHUHAI) LTD. (2)
530 An Ji East Road, Sanzao Town Jinwan Qu, Zhuhai, 519040, Guangdong, China
Tel.: (86) 756 762 2328
Web Site: http://www.mec-co.com
Chemical Processing Equipments Whslr
N.A.I.C.S.: 424690

MEC COMPANY Ltd. - Nagaoka Factory (1)
221-36 Seiryo-cho, Nagaoka, 940-2045, Niigata, Japan
Tel.: (81) 25 847 2490
Web Site: http://www.mec-co.com
Sales Range: $75-99.9 Million
Emp.: 168
Chemicals Whslr
N.A.I.C.S.: 424690
Kazuo Maeda (Pres)

MEC COMPANY Ltd. - Nishinomiya Factory (1)
2-1-19 Naruohama, Nishinomiya, 663-8142, Hyogo, Japan
Tel.: (81) 798468588
Web Site: http://www.mec-co.com
Emp.: 20
Chemicals Whslr
N.A.I.C.S.: 424690

MEC China Specialty Products (Suzhou) Co., Ltd. (1)
31 Linjiang Road, Suzhou Industrial Park, Suzhou, 215121, Jiangsu, China
Tel.: (86) 5126 745 1990
Web Site: http://www.mec-co.com
Sales Range: $25-49.9 Million
Emp.: 24
Chemical Equipments Whslr
N.A.I.C.S.: 333248

MEC Europe N.V. (1)
Kaleweg 24-26, 9030, Gent, East Flanders, Belgium
Tel.: (32) 9 216 7272
Web Site: http://www.mec-co.com
Sales Range: $25-49.9 Million
Emp.: 15
Chemicals Whslr
N.A.I.C.S.: 424690

MEC Specialty Chemical (Thailand) Co., Ltd. (1)
31 Moo 1 Rojana Industrial Park, T Banchang A Uthai, Ayutthaya, 13210, Thailand
Tel.: (66) 3535585053
Chemical Material Mfr & Distr
N.A.I.C.S.: 325998

Mec Taiwan Company Ltd. (1)
No 3 Ziqiang 6th Rd, Zhongli Dist, Taoyuan, 32063, Zhongli, Taiwan
Tel.: (886) 3 434 3549
Web Site: http://www.mtw.com.tw
Sales Range: $25-49.9 Million
Emp.: 20
Production & Sales of Chemicals, Equipment & Related Materials in the Production of PCBs
N.A.I.C.S.: 325180

MEC HOLDING GMBH
Messer-Platz 1, 65812, Bad Soden am Taunus, Germany
Tel.: (49) 61967760555
Web Site: http://www.mec-holding.com
Sales Range: $550-599.9 Million
Emp.: 3,000
Holding Company
N.A.I.C.S.: 551112
Siegfried Schabel (CEO)

Subsidiaries:

BIT Analytical Instruments GmbH (1)
Am Kronberger Hang 3, 65824, Schwalbach am Taunus, Germany
Tel.: (49) 6196 806 100
Web Site: http://www.bit-instruments.com
Analytical Instrument Mfr
N.A.I.C.S.: 333248

BIT Japan Ltd. (1)
Level 28 Shinagawa Intercity Tower A 2-15-1, Minato-ku, Konan, 108-6028, Tokyo, Japan
Tel.: (81) 3 6717 2870
Medical Instrument Distr
N.A.I.C.S.: 423450

BIT MedTech, LLC (1)
15870 Bernardo Center Dr, San Diego, CA 92127
Tel.: (858) 613-1200
Web Site: http://www.bit-medtech.com
Analytical Instrument Mfr
N.A.I.C.S.: 333248
David K. Stelter (VP-Bus Dev)

Messer Cutting & Welding Co., Ltd. (1)
528 NanBang Rd, Kunshan, 215300, Jiangsu, China **(100%)**
Tel.: (86) 51257314949
Metal Plate Processing
N.A.I.C.S.: 333517

Messer Cutting Systems GmbH (1)
Otto-Hahn-Strasse 2-4, 64823, Gross-Umstadt, Germany
Tel.: (49) 60787870
Web Site: http://www.messer-cs.com

Cutting Machines & Welding Products Mfr & Sales
N.A.I.C.S.: 333517
John V. Emholz (Mng Dir)

Subsidiary (Non-US):

Castolin Eutectic International S.A. (2)
Swiss Market Centre, Ch. de la Venoge 7, CH-1025, Saint Sulpice, Switzerland
Tel.: (41) 800 300323
Web Site: http://www.castolin.com
Mfr Welding Products
N.A.I.C.S.: 333992

Subsidiary (Non-US):

Castolin AS (3)
Hammaren 13, Post Box 178, 4056, Tananger, Norway
Tel.: (47) 51 69 25 10
Web Site: http://www.castolin.com
Emp.: 30
Welding Machinery Mfr
N.A.I.C.S.: 333992
Erik Larsen (Gen Mgr)

Castolin Eutectic Ireland Ltd. (3)
36 Magna Avenue Magna Business Park, Citywest, Dublin, Ireland
Tel.: (353) 1 451 5833
Welding Machinery Mfr
N.A.I.C.S.: 333992
Madeleine Rushforth (Mgr-Quality)

Castolin Eutectic Ltd. (3)
Merse Road North Moons Moat, Redditch, B98 9HL, Worcestershire, United Kingdom
Tel.: (44) 1527 582200
Welding Machinery Mfr
N.A.I.C.S.: 333992

Castolin GmbH (3)
Gutenbergstrasse 10, 65830, Kriftel, Germany
Tel.: (49) 6192 403 0
Web Site: http://www.castolin.com
Welding Machinery Mfr
N.A.I.C.S.: 333992
Marco Klein Jr. (Product Mgr)

Castolin Iberica, s.a. (3)
P I de Alcobendas c/San Rafael 6, Alcobendas, 28108, Madrid, Spain
Tel.: (34) 914 900 300
Web Site: http://www.castolin.com
Emp.: 35
Welding Machinery Mfr
N.A.I.C.S.: 333992
Gose Picena (Gen Mgr)

Castolin Kaynak San. Ve Tic. Ltd. Sti. (3)
Yukari Dudulu Mahallesi Bostanci Yolu Sehit Sokak NO 53, 34775, Istanbul, Turkiye
Tel.: (90) 216 313 28 00
Web Site: http://www.castolin.com.tr
Welding Machinery Mfr
N.A.I.C.S.: 333992

Castolin Kft. (3)
Mohacsi u 14, Pecs, 7630, Hungary
Tel.: (36) 72 333 033
Web Site: http://www.cromatik.hu
Welding Machinery Mfr
N.A.I.C.S.: 333992

Castolin Scandinavia AB (3)
Transportgatan 37, Box 4193, 422 04, Hisings Backa, Sweden
Tel.: (46) 31 57 04 70
Web Site: http://www.castolin.se
Welding Machinery Mfr
N.A.I.C.S.: 333992
Lars Ersson (Key Acct Mgr)

Eutectic Canada Inc. (3)
428 rue Aime-Vincent, Vaudreuil-Dorion, J7V 5V5, QC, Canada
Tel.: (514) 695-7500
Web Site: http://www.eutectic.ca
Welding Machinery Mfr
N.A.I.C.S.: 333992
Michael Smolak (VP)

Subsidiary (US):

Eutectic Corporation (3)
N94 W14355 Garwin Mace Dr, Menomonee Falls, WI 53051

INTERNATIONAL PUBLIC

Tel.: (262) 532-4677
Web Site: http://www.eutectic.com
Welding Machinery Mfr
N.A.I.C.S.: 333992

Subsidiary (Non-US):

Eutectic Korea Ltd. (3)
Namdong Industrial Complex, Incheon, 405821, Korea (South)
Tel.: (82) 328175122
Web Site: http://www.eutectickorea.co.kr
Emp.: 19
Welding Machinery Mfr
N.A.I.C.S.: 333992
Jin Kim (CFO)

Eutectic Mexico, S.A. de C.V. (3)
Km 36 5 Autopista Mex Qro, 54730, Cuautitlan Izcalli, Mexico
Tel.: (52) 58721887
Web Site: http://www.eutectic.com.mx
Welding Machinery Mfr
N.A.I.C.S.: 333992

Subsidiary (US):

Eutectic USA (3)
N 94 W 14355 Garwin Mace Dr, Menomonee Falls, WI 53051
Tel.: (262) 255-5520
Web Site: http://www.eutectic-na.com
Sales Range: $25-49.9 Million
Emp.: 50
Nonferrous Metal Rolling, Drawing & Extruding Services
N.A.I.C.S.: 331491

Subsidiary (Non-US):

LLC Messer Eutectic Castolin (2)
str Kachalova 5, Kiev, 03126, Ukraine
Tel.: (380) 44 494 17 24
Web Site: http://www.castolin.com.ua
Emp.: 10
Machine Tool Equipment Mfr
N.A.I.C.S.: 333517
Igor Kuzmenko (CEO)

Messer Cutting Systems (China) Ltd. (2)
528 NanBang Road, Kunshan, 215300, Jiangsu, China
Tel.: (86) 51 257 314 949
Machine Tool Equipment Mfr
N.A.I.C.S.: 333517
Cauchy Ke (Head-Laser Dept)

Messer Cutting Systems India Private Ltd. (2)
No 199/2AB2 198/2A2A and 198/2A2B SNMV College Road, Malumichampatti, Coimbatore, 641 050, India
Tel.: (91) 422 7155521
Web Site: http://www.messer-cs.com
Emp.: 130
Machine Tool Equipment Mfr
N.A.I.C.S.: 333517
Narayanan Mani (Mng Dir)

Messer Cutting Systems Korea Ltd. (2)
624 Ocean Tower Bld 760-3 Woo 1-dong, Haeundae-Ku, Busan, 612-726, Korea (South)
Tel.: (82) 517470055
Machine Tool Equipment Mfr
N.A.I.C.S.: 333517

Messer Eutectic Castolin (S) Pte Ltd (2)
11 Tuas Avenue 5, Singapore, 639337, Singapore
Tel.: (65) 68626008
Emp.: 10
Machine Tools Mfr
N.A.I.C.S.: 333517
Vinay Paradkar (CEO)

Messer Eutectic Castolin Benelux nv/sa (2)
Rue des Ateliers 11, 7850, Enghien, Belgium
Tel.: (32) 2 888 24 51
Machine Tools Mfr
N.A.I.C.S.: 333517

Messer Eutectic Castolin Egypt LLC (2)
7 Palestine Street, New Maadi, Cairo, Egypt

AND PRIVATE COMPANIES — MECHEL PAO

Tel.: (20) 2 2518 7468
Machine Tool Equipment Mfr
N.A.I.C.S.: 333517
Ashish Walia *(Mng Dir)*

Messer Eutectic Castolin S.A.R.L. (2)
22 Avenue du Quebec ZA, BP 325, Courtaboeuf, 91958, France
Tel.: (33) 1 69 82 69 82
Web Site: http://www.castolin.fr
Machine Tools Mfr
N.A.I.C.S.: 333517
Vincent Martin *(Gen Mgr)*

Messer Eutectic Castolin Slovensko, s.r.o. (2)
Krajna 10, 821 04, Bratislava, Slovakia
Tel.: (421) 2 48 20 99 61
Web Site: http://www.messercutting.sk
Machine Tools Mfr
N.A.I.C.S.: 333517

Messer Eutectic Castolin Sp.z.o.o. (2)
Leonarda da Vinci 5, 44-109, Gliwice, Poland
Tel.: (48) 32 230 67 36
Web Site: http://www.castolin.pl
Machine Tool Equipment Mfr
N.A.I.C.S.: 333517

Messer Eutectic Castolin Switzerland S.A. (2)
Industriestrasse 34a, 8108, Dallikon, Switzerland
Tel.: (41) 44 847 17 17
Web Site: http://www.messer-castolin.ch
Machine Tools Mfr
N.A.I.C.S.: 333517

Messer Eutectic Castolin spol.s.r.o. (2)
Trojska 80/122, 182 00, Prague, Czech Republic
Tel.: (420) 283 090 077
Machine Tool Equipment Mfr
N.A.I.C.S.: 333517

Messer Eutectic South Africa (PTY) Ltd. (2)
Cnr Elsecar & Electron Close, Kya Sands, Johannesburg, Gauteng, South Africa
Tel.: (27) 11 708 1042
Web Site: http://www.messer-cs.co.za
Machine Tools Mfr
N.A.I.C.S.: 333517
Craig Bister *(Mgr-Sls)*

Messer Griesheim Ltd. (2)
Northumberland Business Park, West Dudley, Cramlington, Northumberland, United Kingdom
Tel.: (44) 191 250 4610
Web Site: http://www.messer-cw.co.uk
Machine Tools Mfr
N.A.I.C.S.: 333517
Alan Cardwell *(Gen Mgr)*

Messer Griesheim Saldatura S.r.l. (2)
Corso Semipone 44, 20154, Milan, Italy
Tel.: (39) 0236556700
Web Site: http://www.messer.it
Machine Tools Mfr
N.A.I.C.S.: 333517

Messer Cutting Systems, Inc. (1)
W141 N 9427 Fountain Blvd, Menomonee Falls, WI 53051
Tel.: (262) 255-5520
Web Site: http://www.messer-cs.com
Sales Range: $25-49.9 Million
Specialty Machine Tool Mfr
N.A.I.C.S.: 333515
Debbie Rector *(Controller)*

MEC RESOURCES LIMITED
Suite 2 Level 3 1111 Hay Street, West Perth, 6005, WA, Australia
Tel.: (61) 893288477
Web Site:
 https://www.mecresources.com.au
Rev.: $67,249
Assets: $9,982,832
Liabilities: $1,744,917
Net Worth: $8,237,915
Earnings: ($15,542,757)
Emp.: 2,000
Fiscal Year-end: 06/30/18
Investment Services for Exploration Companies
N.A.I.C.S.: 523999
David Breeze *(Mng Dir)*

Subsidiaries:

Advent Energy Limited (1)
14 View St, North Perth, 6006, Perth, Australia
Tel.: (61) 893288711
Web Site: http://www.adventenergy.com.au
Sales Range: $50-74.9 Million
Emp.: 7
Oil & Gas Exploration Services
N.A.I.C.S.: 213112
Tobias Foster *(Mgr-Corp Dev)*

MECACHROME INTERNATIONAL INC.
ZI de la Boitardiere Rue de Saint Regle CS 20300, 37403, Amboise, Cedex, France
Tel.: (33) 2 47 30 6740   Ca
Web Site:
 http://www.mecachrome.com
Year Founded: 1937
Sales Range: $400-449.9 Million
Emp.: 3,000
Aircraft & Automotive Component Mfr
N.A.I.C.S.: 336412
Arnaud de Ponnat *(Pres)*

Subsidiaries:

MK AERO Limited (1)
Zone Franche de Tanger Lot 25B Route de Rabat, 90100, Tangiers, Morocco
Tel.: (212) 539396800
Emp.: 198
Aircraft Engine Parts Mfr
N.A.I.C.S.: 336412

MK Atlantique, SA (1)
102 rue du Moulin des Landes, 44980, Sainte-Luce-sur-Loire, France
Tel.: (33) 240957200
Emp.: 196
Aircraft Engine Parts Mfr
N.A.I.C.S.: 336412

MK Automotive SAS (1)
ZI des Vignes Avenue Jean Monnet, 72300, Solesmes, France
Tel.: (33) 243620303
Emp.: 390
Aircraft Engine Parts Mfr
N.A.I.C.S.: 336412

Mecachrome Canada (1)
11 100 Rue Julien-Audette, Mirabel, J7N 3L3, QC, Canada   (100%)
Tel.: (450) 476-3939
Web Site: http://www.mecachrome.com
Emp.: 140
Aerostructure & Defense Production of Assemblies & Sub-Assemblies
N.A.I.C.S.: 336411
Jean Charles Raillat *(VP-Ops)*

Mecachrome Tangier (1)
Zone Franche de Tanger Lot 25B, Route de Rabat, Tangiers, 90100, Morocco   (100%)
Tel.: (212) 539 393813
Web Site: http://www.mecachrome.com
Sales Range: $25-49.9 Million
Emp.: 35
Aerostructure Finishing & Assembling
N.A.I.C.S.: 336412

Mecahers Aeronautica, Lda (1)
Aicep Global Parques, BlueBiz Parque Empresarial dal Peninsula de Setubal, 2910 845, Setubal, Portugal
Tel.: (351) 265249208
Emp.: 248
Aircraft Engine Parts Mfr
N.A.I.C.S.: 336412

MECAER S.P.A
Via per Arona 46, Borgomanero, 28041, Italy
Tel.: (39) 0322837173
Web Site: http://www.mecaer.com
Sales Range: $75-99.9 Million
Emp.: 300
Aircraft Part Mfr
N.A.I.C.S.: 336413
Alessandro Di Emidio *(Sec)*

Subsidiaries:

Mecaer America Inc. (1)
3205 Delaunay, Laval, H7L 5A4, QC, Canada
Tel.: (450) 682-7117
Web Site: http://www.mecaer.ca
Sales Range: $10-24.9 Million
Emp.: 100
Aircraft Part Mfr
N.A.I.C.S.: 336413

MECANICA FINA SA
Str Popa Lazar nr 5-25 Sector 2, Bucharest, Romania
Tel.: (40) 212520085
Web Site:
 https://www.mecanicafina.ro
Year Founded: 1923
MECE—(BUC)
Rev.: $4,117,936
Assets: $91,919,732
Liabilities: $54,193,135
Net Worth: $37,726,597
Earnings: $2,186,804
Emp.: 13
Fiscal Year-end: 12/31/22
Aircraft Mfr
N.A.I.C.S.: 336411
Sergio Mollo *(Pres)*

Subsidiaries:

Itagra SA (1)
Jud Ialomita, Boranesti, Bucharest, Romania
Tel.: (40) 212520085
Web Site: http://www.itagra.ro
Grain Farming Services
N.A.I.C.S.: 111199

MECARO CO., LTD.
89 Sandan-ro 121beon-gil, Pyeongtaek, 17745, Gyeonggi, Korea (South)
Tel.: (82) 316634476
Web Site:
 https://www.mecharonics.com
Year Founded: 2000
241770—(KRS)
Rev.: $41,411,021
Assets: $167,380,257
Liabilities: $19,960,402
Net Worth: $147,419,855
Earnings: $33,513,603
Emp.: 190
Fiscal Year-end: 12/31/22
Semiconductor Parts Mfr
N.A.I.C.S.: 333242
Jaejeong Lee *(Pres & CEO)*

MECASET N.V.
Vlamingstrat 7, Wevelgem, 8560, Belgium
Tel.: (32) 56412881
Web Site: http://www.sedac-meral.com
Sales Range: $250-299.9 Million
Emp.: 300
Holding Company
N.A.I.C.S.: 551112
Stefaan Gantois *(CEO)*

MECELEC COMPOSITES SA
rue des Condamines, BP 96, 07300, Tournon-sur-Rhone, France
Tel.: (33) 475078707   FR
Web Site: https://www.mecelec.fr
Year Founded: 1934
Rev.: $25,755,660
Earnings: $1,033,631
Emp.: 171
Fiscal Year-end: 12/31/18
Electrical Equipment Mfr & Distr
N.A.I.C.S.: 335999

MECHANICAL LLOYD COMPANY LTD.
No 2 Adjuma Crescent Ring Road West, PO Box 2086, South Industrial Area, Accra, Ghana
Tel.: (233) 30 2229312
Web Site: http://www.mechanical-lloyd.com
Year Founded: 1970
Rev.: $10,201,526
Assets: $13,270,448
Liabilities: $7,009,382
Net Worth: $6,261,066
Earnings: ($601,807)
Emp.: 149
Fiscal Year-end: 12/31/18
Automobile Distr & Retailer
N.A.I.C.S.: 423110
Terence Ronald Darko *(Mng Dir)*

MECHANICS CONSTRUCTION & FOODSTUFF JOINT STOCK COMPANY
No 29 Nguyen Thi Bay Street Ward 6, Tan An, Long An, Vietnam
Tel.: (84) 2723521212
Web Site:
 https://www.mecofood.com.vn
Year Founded: 2004
MCF—(HNX)
Rev.: $44,384,700
Assets: $16,933,500
Liabilities: $4,558,000
Net Worth: $12,375,500
Earnings: $1,086,400
Fiscal Year-end: 12/31/23
Packaging Products Mfr
N.A.I.C.S.: 322220

MECHATRONIC AG
Wittichstrasse 2, Darmstadt, 64295, Germany
Tel.: (49) 6151500310
Web Site: http://www.mechatronic.de
Year Founded: 1987
Rev.: $14,000,910
Emp.: 70
Medical Devices Services
N.A.I.C.S.: 334510
Thomas Ullmann *(CEO)*

MECHEL PAO
1 Krasnoarmeyskaya Ul, Moscow, 125993, Russia
Tel.: (7) 4952218888   RU
Web Site: http://www.mechel.com
MTL—(NYSE)
Rev.: $5,415,936,780
Assets: $3,199,529,100
Liabilities: $5,183,363,760
Net Worth: ($1,983,834,660)
Earnings: $1,112,877,930
Emp.: 51,414
Fiscal Year-end: 12/31/21
Coal & Steel Production & Mining
N.A.I.C.S.: 212115
Victor A. Trigubko *(Deputy CEO-Govt Rels & Member-Mgmt Bd)*

Subsidiaries:

Beloretsk Metallurgical Plant AO (1)
1 Blyukher str, the Republic of Bashkortostan, 453500, Beloretsk, Russia
Tel.: (7) 3479256980
Steel Wire & Rope Mfr
N.A.I.C.S.: 331222

Bratsk Ferroalloy Plant OOO (1)
Industrial district P 01 11/1, 665700, Bratsk, Russia
Tel.: (7) 3953495901
Ferrosilicon Mfr
N.A.I.C.S.: 325199

Chelyabinskiy Metallurgicheskiy Kombinat OAO (1)

MECHEL PAO

Mechel PAO—(Continued)
2-ya Paveletskaya st bldg 14, Chelyabinsk, 454047, Russia
Tel.: (7) 3517253066
Sales Range: Less than $1 Million
Steel Products Mfr
N.A.I.C.S.: 331110
Anton Grigorevich Levada (Chm)

Donetsk Electrometallurgical Plant PJSC (1)
122 l Tkachenko Str c, Donetsk, 83062, Ukraine
Tel.: (380) 62 332 23 53
Web Site: http://www.demz-ua.com
Steel Products Mfr
N.A.I.C.S.: 331513

Dynamic Energy, Inc. (1)
14055 Bicky Rd, Orlando, FL 32824
Tel.: (407) 851-1340
Marketing Consulting Services
N.A.I.C.S.: 541613

HBL Holding GmbH (1)
Freie-Vogel-Str 391, 44269, Dortmund, Germany
Tel.: (49) 231 79304 0
Web Site: http://www.hbl.de
Steel Product Distr
N.A.I.C.S.: 423510

Izhstal OAO (1)
ul Novoazhimova d 6 g, Udmurt Republic, Izhevsk, 426006, Russia
Tel.: (7) 3412910500
Web Site: https://www.izhstal.ru
Sales Range: Less than $1 Million
Rolled Steel Mfr
N.A.I.C.S.: 331221
Sergey M. Kozyonnov (Mng Dir & Gen Mgr)

Izhstal PAO (1)
Novoazhimova street 6, Udmurt Republic, 426006, Izhevsk, Russia
Tel.: (7) 3412910500
Rolled Steel Shape Mfr
N.A.I.C.S.: 331221

Korshunov Mining Plant OAO (1)
Ivashchenko St 9A/1, Zheleznogorsk-Ilimsky, 665651, Irkutsk, Russia
Tel.: (7) 395 66 3 26 05
Web Site: http://www.mechel.com
Iron Ore Mining Services
N.A.I.C.S.: 212210

Kuzbass Power Sales Company (1)
Lenin Prospect 90/4, Kemerovo Region, 650036, Kemerovo, Russia
Tel.: (7) 3847239233
Electric Power Distr
N.A.I.C.S.: 221122

Mechel Carbon AG (1)
Oberdorfstrasse 11, 6340, Baar, Switzerland
Tel.: (41) 41 768 45 00
Emp.: 15
Coal & Metal Mining Services
N.A.I.C.S.: 213113
Ilya Blagodarov (Gen Mgr)

Mechel Carbon Singapore Pte. Ltd. (1)
6 Temasek Boulevard 39-06, Suntec City Tower 4, Singapore, 038986, Singapore
Tel.: (65) 68076180
Metallurgical Coal Retailer
N.A.I.C.S.: 212115
Evgeniy Gorbunov (Gen Dir)

Mechel Coke OOO (1)
2 Paveletskaya St 14, 454047, Chelyabinsk, Russia
Tel.: (7) 3517254902
Coke Oven Battery Mfr
N.A.I.C.S.: 331110

Mechel Energo OOO (1)
2-ya Paveletskaya street 14, Chelyabinsk Region, 454047, Chelyabinsk, Russia
Tel.: (7) 3517254130
Power Sales Distribution Services
N.A.I.C.S.: 221122

Mechel Engineering OOO (1)
35 Ul Mishina, Moscow, 127083, Russia
Tel.: (7) 4952218888
Engineering Services

N.A.I.C.S.: 541330
Pavel Shtark (CEO)

Mechel Hardware OOO (1)
1 Krasnogvardeyskaya ul, 12167, Moscow, Russia (100%)
Tel.: (7) 4952218888
Web Site: http://www.mechel.com
Hardware Sales
N.A.I.C.S.: 423710

Mechel Materials OOO (1)
2-ya Paveletskaya street 14, Chelyabinsk Region, 454047, Chelyabinsk, Russia
Tel.: (7) 83517254922
Building Materials Mfr
N.A.I.C.S.: 327120

Mechel Mining OAO (1)
1 Krasnoarmeyskaya ul, Moscow, 125167, Russia
Tel.: (7) 4952218888
Web Site: http://www.mechel.com
Emp.: 1,000
Coal & Iron Ore Mining Services
N.A.I.C.S.: 213113

Mechel Mining Trading House OOO (1)
Krasnoarmeyskaya Street 1, Moscow, 125993, Russia
Tel.: (7) 495 221 50 01
Coal & Iron Ore Mining Services
N.A.I.C.S.: 213113

Mechel Service (1)
35 Mishina ul, 127083, Moscow, Russia (100%)
Tel.: (7) 4957399880
Web Site: http://www.mechel.com
Metallurgy Product Sales
N.A.I.C.S.: 332117

Mechel Service Global B.V. (1)
Parkstraat 20, 2514 JK, Hague, Netherlands
Tel.: (31) 70 844 0000
Web Site: http://www.mechel.com
Metal Products Services Center Operator & Distr
N.A.I.C.S.: 423510

Mechel Service Stahlhandel Austria GmbH (1)
Lunzerstrabe 105, 4021, Linz, Austria
Tel.: (43) 73269240
Web Site: http://www.ms-stahlhandel.at
Emp.: 1,500
Steel Mfrs
N.A.I.C.S.: 332312
Andreas Scheuchenpflug (Product Mgr)

Mechel Trading AG (1)
Oberdorfstrasse 11, 6340, Baar, Switzerland
Tel.: (41) 417684500
Steel Products Whslr
N.A.I.C.S.: 423510

Mechel Trading Ltd (1)
Oberdorfstrasse 11, 6340, Baar, Switzerland
Tel.: (41) 41 768 45 00
Steel Products Whslr
N.A.I.C.S.: 423510

Mechel Trading Ltd., Zug (1)
Im alten Riet 102, Schaan, 9494, Liechtenstein (100%)
Tel.: (423) 2355040
Sales Range: $50-74.9 Million
Emp.: 15
Metallurgy Product Sales
N.A.I.C.S.: 212390
Eduard Walther (Office Mgr)

Mechel Trans Auto OOO (1)
2-ya Paveletskaya street 14, Chelyabinsk Region, 454047, Chelyabinsk, Russia
Tel.: (7) 3517255995
Automobile Transport & Expedition Services
N.A.I.C.S.: 488490

Mechel-Steel Management OOO (1)
Krasnoarmeyskaya 1, Moscow, 125993, Russia
Tel.: (7) 4952218888
Web Site: http://www.mechel.com.ru
Steel Mfrs
N.A.I.C.S.: 331221

Mecheltrans Management OOO (1)
Krasnoarmeiskaya street 1, 125167, Moscow, Russia
Tel.: (7) 4959337347
Steel Mfrs
N.A.I.C.S.: 331221

Moscow Coke and Gas Plant OAO (1)
Belokamennoe Shosse 13, Vidnoye, Moscow, Russia
Tel.: (7) 495 541 13 39
Coke & Natural Gas Distr
N.A.I.C.S.: 221210

Port Kambarka OAO (1)
Nizhnekamskaya st 2, Kama Udmurt Republic, 427958, Kambarka, Russia
Tel.: (7) 3415338045
Transshipment Services
N.A.I.C.S.: 488320

Port Mechel Temryuk OOO (1)
the port of Temryuk, Temryuk, Russia
Tel.: (7) 8614858633
Coal Mining Services
N.A.I.C.S.: 213113

Port Posiet OAO (1)
Portovaya st 41, 692705, Posyet, Russia
Tel.: (7) 4233120321
Coal Mining Services
N.A.I.C.S.: 213113

Southern Kuzbass PJSC (1)
Yunosti street 6, Kemerovo region-Kuzbass, Mezhdurechensk, 652877, Russia (96.6%)
Tel.: (7) 3847572200
Sales Range: Less than $1 Million
Coal Product Mfr
N.A.I.C.S.: 324199
Andrey Ognev (Dir-Comml Activities)

Southern Kuzbass Power Plant PAO (1)
Komsomolskaya st 20, Kaltan, 652740, Kemerovo, Russia
Tel.: (7) 38471382968
Eletric Power Generation Services
N.A.I.C.S.: 221118

Southern Urals Nickel Plant OAO (1)
Prizavodskaya st 1, 462424, Orsk, Russia
Tel.: (7) 3537371130
Nickel Mining Services
N.A.I.C.S.: 212230

Tomusinsky Open Pit Mine OAO (1)
ul Gorkogo d 300, Mezhdurechensk, 652870, Kemerovskaya, Russia
Tel.: (7) 38475 7 31 79
Metal Mining Services
N.A.I.C.S.: 213114

Urals Stampings Plant OAO (1)
ul Dzerzhinskogo d 7, Chebarkul, 456440, Russia
Tel.: (7) 35168 9 23 24
Metal Stamping Mfr
N.A.I.C.S.: 332119

Vyartsilya Metal Products Plant (1)
Zavodskaya st 1, Vyartsilya, 186757, Sortavala, Russia
Tel.: (7) 8143032154
Hardware Mfr
N.A.I.C.S.: 332510

Yakutugol AO (1)
Lenin Prospect 3/1, The Republic of Sakha Yakutia Neryungri, 678960, Yuzhno-Sakhalinsk, Russia
Tel.: (7) 4114743874
Coke Coal Mining Services
N.A.I.C.S.: 212115

Yakutugol Holding Company OAO (1)
Lenin prospect 3/1, Neryungri, 678960, Russia
Tel.: (7) 41 147 96 125
Investment Management Service
N.A.I.C.S.: 523999
Igor V. Khafizov (CEO)

MECHEMA CHEMICALS INTERNATIONAL CORP.

No 1 Datong 1st Rd, Guanyin Dist, Taoyuan, 32849, Taiwan
Tel.: (886) 34833788
Web Site: https://www.mechema.com
4721—(TPE)
Rev.: $164,821,874
Assets: $78,262,296
Liabilities: $31,324,547
Net Worth: $46,937,748
Earnings: $11,922,740
Fiscal Year-end: 12/31/22
Chemical Product Mfr & Distr
N.A.I.C.S.: 325998
Yen-Lung Tsai (Chm & CEO)

MECHMAR CORPORATION (MALAYSIA) BERHAD

No 1 Jalan Perunding U1/17, Hicom-Glenmarie Industrial Pk, 40150, Shah Alam, Selangor Darul Ehsan, Malaysia
Tel.: (60) 3 5569 3688
Web Site: http://www.mechmar.com.my
Industrial Boiler & Pressure Vessel Mfr
N.A.I.C.S.: 334513
Kean Wan Tan (Chm)

Subsidiaries:

Independent Power Tanzania Limited (1)
Plot No 292/1 292/2 292/3 & 296 Block D Salasala Tegeta, PO Box 77173, Dar es Salaam, Tanzania
Tel.: (255) 222650750
Electric Power Generation & Distribution Services
N.A.I.C.S.: 238390

Mechmar (HK) Ltd. (1)
11th Floor Dah Sing Life Building 99 Des Voeux Road Central, Hong Kong, China (Hong Kong)
Tel.: (852) 25229115
Investment Management Service
N.A.I.C.S.: 523940

Mechmar Boilers Sdn. Bhd. (1)
Lot 14 Jalan Timah Pasir Gudang Ind Est, 81700, Pasir Gudang, Johor, Malaysia
Tel.: (60) 72511341
Emp.: 46
Industrial Boiler Mfr & Distr
N.A.I.C.S.: 332410
Liew Kaisiang (Mgr-Factory)

Mechmar Capital Sdn. Bhd. (1)
No 1 Jalan Perunding U1/17 Seksyen U1 Hicom-Glenmarie Industrial Park, 40150, Shah Alam, Selangor, Malaysia
Tel.: (60) 3 55692828
Sales Financing & Leasing Services
N.A.I.C.S.: 522220

Mechmar Cochran Boilers (M) Sdn. Bhd. (1)
No 1 Jalan Perunding U1/17 Seksyen U1 Hicom-Glenmarie Industrial Park, 40150, Shah Alam, Selangor, Malaysia
Tel.: (60) 3 55693688
Industrial Boilers Mfr & Distr
N.A.I.C.S.: 332410

Relau Estates Sdn Bhd (1)
1 Lebuh Relau 2 Taman Desa Relau, 11900, Bayan Lepas, Penang, Malaysia
Tel.: (60) 46424360
Emp.: 6
Real Estate Property Development Services
N.A.I.C.S.: 531210

MECO HOLDINGS CO. LTD.

Unit 3301 Citicorp Centre 18 Whitfield Road North Point, Hong Kong, China (Hong Kong)
Tel.: (852) 28918722
Web Site: http://www.meco.com
Sales Range: $25-49.9 Million
Emp.: 150
Holding Company; General Contractors
N.A.I.C.S.: 236220

AND PRIVATE COMPANIES

Reano Siragusa (CFO & Exec VP)
Subsidiaries:

Meco Engineering Ltd. (1)
Unit 3301 Citicorp Centre, 18 Whitfield,
North Point, China (Hong Kong) **(100%)**
Tel.: (852) 28918722
Web Site: http://www.meco-group.com
Sales Range: $25-49.9 Million
Emp.: 50
Installation of Air Conditioning, Electric & Plumbing
N.A.I.C.S.: 238220

Meco Holdings Co. Ltd. - Louisiana Plant (1)
68375 Compass Way E, Mandeville, LA 70471
Tel.: (985) 249-5500
Water Purification Equipment Mfr
N.A.I.C.S.: 333310

Meco Water Purification (Asia) Pte Ltd (1)
390 Havelock Road 03-06 King's Centre, Singapore, 169662, Singapore
Tel.: (65) 68367500
Water Purification Equipment Distr
N.A.I.C.S.: 423830
Jason Koh (Mgr-Bus Dev)

MECOM POWER & CONSTRUCTION LIMITED
Alameda Dr Carlos D Assumpcao No 258 Edf Kin Heng Long Plaza 6/Q-R-S, Macau, China (Macau)
Tel.: (853) 28238822 Ky
Web Site:
  http://www.mecommacau.com
Year Founded: 2000
1183—(HKG)
Rev.: $185,982,047
Assets: $135,260,439
Liabilities: $75,607,077
Net Worth: $59,653,362
Earnings: $691,781
Emp.: 129
Fiscal Year-end: 12/31/23
Civil Engineering Services
N.A.I.C.S.: 238120
Lam Sek Kuok (Founder & Chm)

Subsidiaries:

EHY Construction & Engineering Company Limited (1)
Alameda Dr Carlos D Assumpcao No 258 Edf Kin Heng Long Plaza 6/Q-R-S, Macau, China (Macau)
Tel.: (853) 28238822
Construction Contractor Services
N.A.I.C.S.: 236220
Anna Iu (Officer-Admin)

MED PAPER SA
Zone Industrielle Mghogha Route de Tetouan Lot 19, PO Box 400, Rabat, Morocco
Tel.: (212) 539362100
Web Site: https://www.med-paper.ma
Year Founded: 1948
MDP—(CAS)
Sales Range: $10-24.9 Million
Paper Products Mfr
N.A.I.C.S.: 322299
Mohsine Sefrioui (Chm, CEO & Mng Dir)

MED-EL GMBH
Furstenweg 77A, 6020, Innsbruck, Austria
Tel.: (43) 512288889
Web Site: http://www.medel.com
Year Founded: 1975
Sales Range: $25-49.9 Million
Emp.: 1,900
Cochlear Implant Mfr, Distr & Marketer
N.A.I.C.S.: 339112
Ingeborg Hochmair (Co-Founder & CEO)

Subsidiaries:

MED-EL Corporation (1)
2511 Old Cornwallis Rd, Durham, NC 27713
Tel.: (919) 572-2222
Web Site: http://www.medel.com
Sales Range: $25-49.9 Million
Emp.: 50
Cochlear Implant Distr
N.A.I.C.S.: 423450
Carla Anderson (Dir-HR & Facilities)

MED-EL Deutschland GmbH (1)
Moosstrasse 7, Starnberg, 82319, Germany
Tel.: (49) 815177030
Web Site: http://www.med-el.com
Sales Range: $25-49.9 Million
Emp.: 40
Cochlear Implant Mfr & Distr
N.A.I.C.S.: 339112

MED-EL GmbH (1)
Furstengasse 1, Vienna, 1090, Austria
Tel.: (43) 013172400
Sales Range: $25-49.9 Million
Emp.: 12
Cochlear Implant Distr & Marketer
N.A.I.C.S.: 423450
Inge Hochmair (Gen Mgr)

MED-EL Hearing Implant Technology Service Beijing Co. Ltd. (1)
Unit 901 Tower B SOHO New Town No 88 Jianguo Rd, Chaoyang District, 100022, Beijing, China
Tel.: (86) 10 85890330
Web Site: http://www.medel.com
Emp.: 40
Hearing Aid Distr
N.A.I.C.S.: 423450
Jade Ring (Gen Mgr)

MED-EL Implant Systems Australasia Pty Ltd (1)
Level 2 Suite 2 07 90-96 Bourke Road, Alexandria, Sydney, 2020, NSW, Australia
Tel.: (61) 2 9690 2455
Web Site: http://www.medel.com
Hearing Aid Distr
N.A.I.C.S.: 423450
Robyn Shakes (Gen Mgr)

MED-EL India Private Ltd. (1)
505 Pragati House 47-48 Nehru Place, New Delhi, 110 019, India
Tel.: (91) 11 4160 7171
Hearing Aid Distr
N.A.I.C.S.: 423450
Lokesh Jha (Mgr-Bus Dev & Svc)

MED-EL Latino America S.R.L. (1)
Viamonte 2146 3 piso, C1056A8H, Buenos Aires, Argentina
Tel.: (54) 11 4954 0404
Hearing Aid Distr
N.A.I.C.S.: 423450
Marcos Atkinson (Area Mgr)

MED-EL Middle East FZE (1)
Dubai Airport Free Zone East Wing 2 Ofc E1-215, PO Box 54320, Dubai, United Arab Emirates
Tel.: (971) 4 299 4700
Hearing Aid Distr
N.A.I.C.S.: 423450

MED-EL UK Ltd (1)
Bridge Mills Huddersfield Road, Holmfirth, HD9 3TW, United Kingdom
Tel.: (44) 01484686223
Sales Range: $50-74.9 Million
Emp.: 6
Cochlear Implant Distr
N.A.I.C.S.: 423450

VIBRANT MED-EL Hearing Technology (1)
400 avenue Roumanille Bat 6 - CS 70062, 06902, Sophia-Antipolis, France
Tel.: (33) 483 880 600
Hearing Aid Distr
N.A.I.C.S.: 423450

MEDA LIMITED
1575 Lauzon Rd, Windsor, N8S 3N4, ON, Canada
Tel.: (519) 944-7221
Web Site:
  http://www.medagroup.com
Year Founded: 1970
Sales Range: $10-24.9 Million
Emp.: 400
Engineeering Services
N.A.I.C.S.: 541330
David Lawn (Pres)

MEDACTA GROUP SA
Strada Regina, Castel San Pietro, 6874, Mendrisio, Switzerland
Tel.: (41) 916966060
Web Site: https://www.medacta.com
Year Founded: 1958
MOVE—(SWX)
Rev.: $471,748,327
Assets: $630,787,826
Liabilities: $334,376,214
Net Worth: $296,411,612
Earnings: $49,912,584
Emp.: 1,537
Fiscal Year-end: 12/31/22
Orthopaedic Product Mfr
N.A.I.C.S.: 339113
Francesco Siccardi (CEO)

Subsidiaries:

Knnex Health Inc. (1)
725 Cool Springs Blvd Ste 600, Franklin, TN 37067
Tel.: (615) 241-6142
Web Site: https://www.knnex.com
Medical Product Mfr & Distr
N.A.I.C.S.: 339113

Medacta Australia Pty Ltd (1)
Unit A1 16 Mars Road, Lane Cove West, Sydney, 2006, NSW, Australia
Tel.: (61) 1300361790
Web Site: https://www.medacta.com.au
Orthopaedic Product Mfr
N.A.I.C.S.: 339113
Dan Lawson (Mktg Dir)

Medacta Austria GmbH (1)
Dorf 25, Eugendorf, Austria
Tel.: (43) 622528428
Orthopaedic Product Mfr
N.A.I.C.S.: 339113
Bernhard Bauer (Gen Mgr)

Medacta Belgium Sprl (1)
Rue de l'Industrie 30/B, Nivelles, Belgium
Tel.: (32) 67555482
Web Site: https://www.medacta.be
Orthopaedic Product Mfr
N.A.I.C.S.: 339113

Medacta Canada Inc. (1)
31 Mcbrine Drive Unit 11, Kitchener, N2R 1J1, ON, Canada
Tel.: (519) 279-1934
Orthopaedic Product Mfr
N.A.I.C.S.: 339113
Tammy Jansen (Office Mgr)

Medacta Espana S.L. (1)
Av De Las Jacarandas 2 Edificio CREA Oficina, Burjassot, 920-921, Valencia, Spain
Tel.: (34) 963484688
Orthopedic Product Distr
N.A.I.C.S.: 423450

Medacta France SAS (1)
6 Rue du Commandant d'Estienne d'Orves, 92390, Villeneuve-la-Garenne, France
Tel.: (33) 147390722
Web Site: https://www.medacta.fr
Orthopaedic Product Mfr
N.A.I.C.S.: 339113

Medacta Germany GmbH (1)
Jahnstrasse 86, 73203, Goppingen, Germany
Tel.: (49) 7161504430
Orthopaedic Product Mfr
N.A.I.C.S.: 339113

Medacta Italia S.r.l. (1)
Via G Stephenson 94, Milan, Italy
Tel.: (39) 02390181
Orthopaedic Product Mfr
N.A.I.C.S.: 339113
Giorgio Gobitti (Mgr-Joint)

Medacta Japan Co. Ltd. (1)
Kojimachi-Nakata Bldg 2F 5-3-5, Kojimachi Chiyoda-ku, Tokyo, 102-0083, Japan
Tel.: (81) 362728797
Web Site: https://www.medacta.jp
Orthopaedic Product Mfr
N.A.I.C.S.: 339113
Akiyoshi Tanaka (Product Mgr)

Medacta UK Ltd. (1)
16 Greenfields Business Park Wheatfield Way, Hinckley, LE10 1BB, United Kingdom
Tel.: (44) 1455613026
Orthopaedic Product Mfr
N.A.I.C.S.: 339113
Olivia Punshon Symonds (Mgr-Logistics)

Medacta USA Inc (1)
6640 Carothers Pkwy Ste 420, Franklin, TN 37067
Tel.: (312) 896-9138
Web Site: https://www.medacta.us.com
Orthopaedic Product Mfr
N.A.I.C.S.: 339112
Eric Dremel (Pres)

MEDADVISOR LIMITED
Level 2 971 Burke Road, Camberwell, 3124, VIC, Australia
Tel.: (61) 390953036
Web Site:
  http://www.medadvisor.com.au
MDR—(ASX)
Rev.: $81,534,299
Assets: $65,960,635
Liabilities: $31,516,569
Net Worth: $34,444,066
Earnings: $528,935
Fiscal Year-end: 06/30/24
Pharmacy Support Services
N.A.I.C.S.: 561499
Richard Wade Ratliff (CEO & Mng Dir)

MEDALLION METALS LIMITED
Suite 1 11 Ventnor Avenue, West Perth, 6005, WA, Australia
Tel.: (61) 864248700 AU
Web Site:
  https://www.medallionmetals.com.au
Year Founded: 2015
MM8—(ASX)
Rev.: $1,978,221
Assets: $10,162,441
Liabilities: $3,762,067
Net Worth: $6,400,374
Earnings: ($3,319,911)
Fiscal Year-end: 06/30/23
Metal Exploration Services
N.A.I.C.S.: 213114

MEDALLION RESOURCES LTD.
Suite 410-325 Howe Street, Vancouver, V6C 1Z7, BC, Canada
Tel.: (604) 681-9558 BC
Web Site:
  http://www.medallionresources.com
MLLOF—(DEU)
Assets: $1,379,114
Liabilities: $100,362
Net Worth: $1,278,752
Earnings: ($780,137)
Emp.: 2
Fiscal Year-end: 03/31/22
Natural Resource Mining Services
N.A.I.C.S.: 212290
Mark Saxon (VP-Bus Dev)

MEDARO MINING CORP.
220-333 Terminal Avenue, Vancouver, V6A 4C1, BC, Canada
Tel.: (604) 800-0203 BC
Web Site:
  https://www.medaromining.com
Year Founded: 2020
MEDAF—(OTCIQ)
Mineral Exploration Services
N.A.I.C.S.: 213115
Faizaan Lalani (Pres)

MEDARTIS HOLDING AG

Medaro Mining Corp.—(Continued)

MEDARTIS HOLDING AG
Hochbergerstrasse 60E, 4057, Basel, Switzerland
Tel.: (41) 616333434   CH
Web Site: https://www.medartis.com
Year Founded: 1997
MED—(SWX)
Rev.: $251,968,149
Assets: $415,419,541
Liabilities: $112,401,950
Net Worth: $303,017,591
Earnings: $735,679
Emp.: 747
Fiscal Year-end: 12/31/23
Surgical & Medical Instrument Manufacturing
N.A.I.C.S.: 339112
Axel Maltzen *(Chief Production Officer & Member-Mgmt Bd)*

Subsidiaries:

Extera Importacao e Exportacao Ltda. (1)
Rua Sena Madureira 796, Sao Paulo, 04021-001, SP, Brazil
Tel.: (55) 1136247844
Medicinal Product Mfr
N.A.I.C.S.: 339112

Medartis Australia & New Zealand Pty. Ltd. (1)
64 Brooks Street, PO Box 311, Fortitude Valley, 4006, QLD, Australia
Tel.: (61) 733268700
Medicinal Product Mfr
N.A.I.C.S.: 339112
Kathryn Constance *(Gen Mgr)*

Medartis Co., Ltd. (1)
9F Gran Tokyo South Tower 1-9-2 Marunouchi, Chiyoda-ku, Tokyo, 100-6609, Japan
Tel.: (81) 345205048
Medicinal Product Mfr
N.A.I.C.S.: 339112

Medartis GmbH
Am Gansacker 10, 79224, Umkirch, Germany
Tel.: (49) 766598240
Medicinal Product Mfr
N.A.I.C.S.: 339112

Medartis GmbH (1)
Rheinstrasse 26, 6890, Lustenau, Austria
Tel.: (43) 557762776
Medicinal Product Mfr
N.A.I.C.S.: 339112

Medartis Iberia S.L. (1)
Calle Llull 321-329 Edificio Cinc, 08019, Barcelona, Spain
Tel.: (34) 931446087
Medical Equipment Mfr
N.A.I.C.S.: 339112

Medartis Inc. (1)
224 Vly Creek Blvd Ste 100, Exton, PA 19341
Tel.: (610) 961-6101
Medicinal Product Mfr
N.A.I.C.S.: 339112
Amar Gaurav Shah *(Mktg Mgr)*

Medartis Ltd. (1)
3 Pinnacle Way Pride Park, Derby, DE24 8ZS, United Kingdom
Tel.: (44) 1924476699
Medicinal Product Mfr
N.A.I.C.S.: 339112
Andrew Wilcher *(Gen Mgr)*

Medartis S.A. de C.V. (1)
Avenida Palmas 210 Piso 1 Oficina 101 Col Lomas de Chapultepec, Del Miguel Hidalgo, 11000, Mexico, Mexico
Tel.: (52) 5563887063
Medicinal Product Mfr
N.A.I.C.S.: 339112
Daniel Sommer *(Gen Mgr)*

Medartis S.a.r.l. (1)
Zac I Ilot des Sables 720 rue Le Chatelier, 38090, Vaulx-Milieu, France
Tel.: (33) 474999414

Medicinal Product Mfr
N.A.I.C.S.: 339112

Medartis Sp.z.o.o (1)
UI Legnicka 56, 54-204, Wroclaw, Poland
Tel.: (48) 713595618
Medicinal Product Mfr
N.A.I.C.S.: 339112

MEDASYS SA
22 Avenue Galilee, 92350, Le Plessis-Robinson, France
Tel.: (33) 175 60 91 00
Web Site: http://www.medasys.com
MED—(EUR)
Sales Range: $10-24.9 Million
Medical Imaging & Scientific Software
N.A.I.C.S.: 513210
Frederic Vaillant *(Chm & CEO)*

MEDAVAIL HOLDINGS, INC.
6665 Millcreek Dr Unit 1, Mississauga, L5N 5M4, ON, Canada
Tel.: (905) 812-0023   NV
Web Site: http://www.medavail.com
Year Founded: 2007
MDVL—(NASDAQ)
Rev.: $43,109,000
Assets: $33,132,000
Liabilities: $12,308,000
Net Worth: $20,824,000
Earnings: ($47,616,000)
Emp.: 279
Fiscal Year-end: 12/31/22
Therapeutic Products & Nutritional Supplements Mfr
N.A.I.C.S.: 325412
Robert Faulkner *(Chm)*

Subsidiaries:

MedAvail Technologies, Inc. (1)
6665 Millcreek Drive Unit 1, Mississauga, L5N 5M4, ON, Canada
Tel.: (905) 812-0023
Web Site: http://www.medavail.com
Healthcare Technology Services
N.A.I.C.S.: 621610
Mark Doerr *(CEO)*

MEDAVIE BLUE CROSS
Blue Cross Centre 644 Main St, PO Box 220, Moncton, E1C 8L3, NB, Canada
Tel.: (506) 853-1811
Web Site: http://www.medavie.bluecross.ca
Year Founded: 1943
Sales Range: $1-4.9 Billion
Emp.: 1,625
Life Health & Dental Insurance Services
N.A.I.C.S.: 524114
John P. Diamond *(CFO)*

Subsidiaries:

Emergency Medical Care (1)
5830 Lady Hammond Road, Halifax, B3K 5L6, NS, Canada
Tel.: (902) 484-0003
Ambulance Service Provider
N.A.I.C.S.: 621910

New Brunswick EMS (1)
210 John Street Suite 101, Moncton, E1C 0B8, NB, Canada
Tel.: (506) 872-6500
Web Site: http://www.smunbems.ca
Sales Range: $10-24.9 Million
Emp.: 100
Ambulance Service Provider
N.A.I.C.S.: 621910

MEDCAMP S.A.
ul Jeleniogorska 16 C/3, 60-179, Poznan, Poland
Tel.: (48) 795522055
Web Site: https://www.medcampsa.pl
Year Founded: 1998
Biotechnology Research & Development Services

N.A.I.C.S.: 541714
Tomasz Tylinski *(Chm)*

MEDCAP AB
Engelbrektsgatan 9-11, 11432, Stockholm, Sweden
Tel.: (46) 8347110
Web Site: https://www.medcap.se
MCAP—(OMX)
Rev.: $104,095,835
Assets: $133,870,953
Liabilities: $53,668,268
Net Worth: $80,202,684
Earnings: $11,014,639
Emp.: 474
Fiscal Year-end: 12/31/22
Investment Services
N.A.I.C.S.: 523150
Karl Tobieson *(Co-CEO)*

MEDCAW INVESTMENTS PLC
25 Ecclestone Place, London, SW1W 9NF, United Kingdom   UK
Web Site: https://medcaw-invest.com
Year Founded: 2020
MCI—(LSE)
Assets: $1,049,018
Liabilities: $303,849
Net Worth: $745,169
Earnings: ($244,895)
Fiscal Year-end: 12/31/22
Investment Management Service
N.A.I.C.S.: 523999
Sarah Cope *(Board of Directors & Chm)*

MEDCO HOLDINGS, INC.
31/F Rufino Pacific Tower 6784 Ayala Avenue, Makati, 1229, Philippines
Tel.: (63) 88110465
Web Site: https://www.medco.com.ph
MED—(PHI)
Rev.: $794
Assets: $836,825
Liabilities: $119,564
Net Worth: $717,261
Earnings: ($130,759)
Emp.: 2
Fiscal Year-end: 12/31/21
Investment Management Service
N.A.I.C.S.: 523940
Pauline C. Tan *(Asst Sec)*

Subsidiaries:

Medco Asia Investment Corp. (1)
31 Fl Rufino Pacific Tower 6784 Ayala Avenue, Makati, 1229, Philippines
Tel.: (63) 88110465
Web Site: http://www.medco.com.ph
Sales Range: $50-74.9 Million
Investment Banking Services
N.A.I.C.S.: 523150

MEDCOLCANNA ORGANICS, INC.
400 5th Avenue Southwest Suite 800, Calgary, T2P 0L6, AB, Canada
Tel.: (403) 971-9104
Web Site: http://www.ir.medcolcanna.com
Cannabis Product Mfr
N.A.I.C.S.: 325411
Felipe De La Vega *(CEO)*

MEDCOM TECH, S.A.
Viladecans Business Park-Edificio Brasil C/ Catalunya 83-85, Viladecans, 08840, Barcelona, Spain
Tel.: (34) 93 480 33 74
Web Site: http://www.medcomtech.es
MED—(MAD)
Sales Range: $1-9.9 Million
Emp.: 25
Medical Supplies & Equipment Distr
N.A.I.C.S.: 423450
Juan Sagales *(Pres & CEO)*

INTERNATIONAL PUBLIC

MEDEC SYSTEMS GMBH
Daimlerstr 11, 75334, Straubenhardt, Germany
Tel.: (49) 708292560
Web Site: http://www.medec.tv
Sales Range: $25-49.9 Million
Emp.: 10
Surgical & Medical Instrument Mfr
N.A.I.C.S.: 339112
Frank Lowas *(Mng Dir)*

MEDELA HOLDING AG
Lattichstrasse 4b, 6341, Baar, Switzerland
Tel.: (41) 848633352
Web Site: http://www.medela.ch
Year Founded: 1961
Sales Range: $125-149.9 Million
Emp.: 700
Infant Medical Care Equipment Mfr
N.A.I.C.S.: 339112
Michael Larsson *(Founder)*

Subsidiaries:

Medela Australia Pty Ltd. (1)
3 Arco Lane, Heatherton, 3202, VIC, Australia
Tel.: (61) 3 9552 8600
Web Site: http://www.medela.com
Emp.: 20
Medical Device Distr
N.A.I.C.S.: 423450
Jared Percy *(Mng Dir)*

Medela Benelux B.V. (1)
Uilenwaard 31, 5236 WB, 's-Hertogenbosch, Netherlands
Tel.: (31) 73 690 40 40
Medical Device Distr
N.A.I.C.S.: 423450

Medela Canada Inc (1)
4160 Sladeview Crescent Unit 8, Mississauga, L5L 0A1, ON, Canada
Tel.: (905) 608-7272
Medical Device Distr
N.A.I.C.S.: 423450
Anna Jankovic *(Acct Mgr)*

Medela Danmark (1)
Radhustorvet 5 2 sal, 3520, Farum, Denmark
Tel.: (45) 48 14 52 60
Medical Device Distr
N.A.I.C.S.: 423450

Medela Inc. (1)
1101 Corporate Dr, McHenry, IL 60050-7005
Tel.: (815) 363-1166
Web Site: http://www.medela.com
Medical & Hospital Equipment
N.A.I.C.S.: 423450

Medela India Private Limited (1)
Vatika Business Park First floor Tower 2 Sohna Road Sec 49, Gurgaon, 122018, Haryana, India
Tel.: (91) 124 4416965
Medical Device Distr
N.A.I.C.S.: 423450
Amit Raj Gogia *(Country Mgr)*

Medela Italia s.r.l. (1)
Via Turrini 13/15 Loc Bargellino, 40012, Calderara di Reno, Italy
Tel.: (39) 051 72 76 88
Medical Device Distr
N.A.I.C.S.: 423450

Medela Medical AB (1)
Mallslingan 18 A, Box 7266, 187 14, Taby, Sweden
Tel.: (46) 8 588 03 200
Medical Device Distr
N.A.I.C.S.: 423450
Milan Lexen *(Mng Dir)*

Medela Medical Norge Filial av Medela Medical AB (1)
Kjelsasveien 161, Pb 93, Kjelsas, Oslo, Norway
Tel.: (47) 24 05 66 10
Medical Device Distr
N.A.I.C.S.: 423450

AND PRIVATE COMPANIES

Medela Medizintechnik GmbH & Co Handels KG (1)
Georg-Kollmannsberger Strasse 2, 85386, Dietersheim, Germany
Tel.: (49) 89 31 97 59 0
Medical Device Distr
N.A.I.C.S.: 423450

Medela UK Ltd. (1)
Huntsman Drive Northbank Industrial Park, Irlam, Manchester, M44 5EG, United Kingdom
Tel.: (44) 161 776 0400
Medical Device Distr
N.A.I.C.S.: 423450

Medela s.a.r.l (1)
14 rue de la Butte Cordiere, Etampes, 91154, France
Tel.: (33) 1 69 16 10 30
Medical Device Distr
N.A.I.C.S.: 423450

Productos Medicinales Medela, S.L. (1)
c/ Manuel Fernandez Marquez 49, 8918, Badalona, Spain
Tel.: (34) 93 320 59 69
Medical Device Distr
N.A.I.C.S.: 423450

MEDEON BIODESIGN, INC.
7F 116 HouGang Street, Taipei, 11170, Taiwan
Tel.: (886) 228816686
Web Site: https://www.medeonbiodesign.com
Year Founded: 2012
6499—(TPE)
Rev.: $9,327,361
Assets: $126,317,825
Liabilities: $11,771,160
Net Worth: $114,546,665
Earnings: ($15,536,379)
Emp.: 142
Fiscal Year-end: 12/31/22
Pharmaceuticals Product Mfr
N.A.I.C.S.: 325412
Yue-The Jang (Chm & CEO)

Subsidiaries:

Medeologix, Inc. (1)
2F No 30 Baogao Rd, Xindian Dist, New Taipei City, 231029, Taiwan
Tel.: (886) 229112335
Medical Device Mfr & Distr
N.A.I.C.S.: 339112

MedeonBio, Inc. (1)
452 Oakmead Pkwy, Sunnyvale, CA 94085
Tel.: (650) 397-5100
Medical Device Mfr
N.A.I.C.S.: 339112

MediBalloon, Inc. (1)
32940 Alvarado-Niles Rd Ste 400, Union City, CA 94587
Tel.: (510) 431-3221
Medical Balloons Mfr
N.A.I.C.S.: 339112

Prodeon Medical, Inc. (1)
452 Oakmead Pkwy, Sunnyvale, CA 94085
Tel.: (669) 467-1100
Web Site: https://prodeonmedical.com
Special Clinic Center Services
N.A.I.C.S.: 621111

Second Source Medical LLC (1)
2200 Zanker Rd Ste F, San Jose, CA 95131
Tel.: (408) 432-6388
Web Site: https://www.secondsourcemed.net
Medical Device Mfr
N.A.I.C.S.: 339112

MEDESIS PHARMA S.A.
Avenue du Golf L 'Oree des Mas Bat Les Cypres, 34 670, Baillargues, France
Tel.: (33) 33467030396
Web Site: https://www.medesispharma.com
Year Founded: 2003
ALMDP—(EUR)
Biotechnology Research & Development Services
N.A.I.C.S.: 541714
Olivier Connes (Chm)

MEDEXUS PHARMACEUTICALS INC.
10 King Street East Suite 600, Toronto, M5C 1C3, ON, Canada
Tel.: (514) 762-2626
Web Site: https://www.medexus.com
Year Founded: 2013
MEDXF—(OTCQX)
Rev.: $108,096,000
Assets: $161,329,000
Liabilities: $138,881,000
Net Worth: $22,448,000
Earnings: $1,221,000
Emp.: 98
Fiscal Year-end: 03/31/23
Pediatric Pharmaceutical Products Mfr
N.A.I.C.S.: 325412
Sylvain Chretien (Founder)

Subsidiaries:

Medac Pharma, Inc. (1)
29 N Wacker Dr Ste 704, Chicago, IL 60606
Tel.: (312) 854-0500
Web Site: http://www.medacpharma.com
Pharmaceuticals Product Mfr
N.A.I.C.S.: 325412
Michael Adelman (Gen Mgr)

MEDFIRST HEALTHCARE SERVICES INC.
1 2F No 94 Fuxing 1st Rd, Guishan Dist, Taoyuan, 333, Taiwan
Tel.: (886) 33970761
Web Site: http://www.medfirst.com.tw
4175—(TPE)
Rev.: $225,872,589
Assets: $235,890,223
Liabilities: $193,088,266
Net Worth: $42,801,957
Earnings: $5,492,949
Fiscal Year-end: 12/31/22
Health Care Srvices
N.A.I.C.S.: 621610
Li-Ju Chen (Chm)

MEDGAZ, S.A.
Muelle de Poniente s/n Puerto de Almeria, 04002, Almeria, Spain
Tel.: (34) 950182900   ES
Web Site: http://www.medgaz.com
Year Founded: 2001
Emp.: 60
Deepwater Natural Gas Pipeline Construction & Transportation Services
N.A.I.C.S.: 486210
Juan Antonio Vera (Chm)

MEDGOLD RESOURCES CORP.
Suite 650-200 Burrard St, Vancouver, V6C 3L6, BC, Canada
Tel.: (604) 801-5432   BC
Web Site: https://marksmenergy.com
Year Founded: 1966
MED—(TSXV)
Rev.: $1,354
Assets: $1,160,732
Liabilities: $122,184
Net Worth: $1,038,548
Earnings: ($1,132,877)
Fiscal Year-end: 12/31/20
Mineral Exploration Services
N.A.I.C.S.: 212290
Simon Ridgway (Chm)

MEDHELP CARE AKTIEBOLAG
Marieviksgatan 19, 117 43, Stockholm, Sweden
Tel.: (46) 852852800
Web Site: https://www.medhelp.se
Year Founded: 1999
MEDHLP—(OMX)
Rev.: $8,346,735
Assets: $6,328,549
Liabilities: $3,671,055
Net Worth: $2,657,494
Earnings: ($1,092,978)
Emp.: 42
Fiscal Year-end: 12/31/23
Healthcare Technology Services
N.A.I.C.S.: 541511
Tobias Ekros (CEO)

MEDI ASSIST HEALTHCARE SERVICES PRIVATE LIMITED
IBC Knowledge Park 4/1 Bannerghatta Road Tower D, 4th Floor Bangalore, Karnataka, 560029, India
Tel.: (91) 8069190000
Web Site: https://www.mediassist.in
Year Founded: 2002
Hospitals & Health Care
N.A.I.C.S.: 621610
Satish Gidugu (CEO & Dir)

Subsidiaries:

Indian Health Organisation Private Limited (1)
213-B Okhla Industrial Estate Phase-III, New Delhi, 110020, India
Tel.: (91) 1149294466
Web Site: https://vhealth.io
Employee Benefit Insurance Services
N.A.I.C.S.: 525120

MEDI CAPS LTD.
Mhow Neemuch Road, Sector-1 Dist Dhar, Pithampur, 454775, Madhya Pradesh, India
Tel.: (91) 7292256205
Web Site: https://www.medicaps.com
523144—(BOM)
Rev.: $8,094,807
Assets: $15,672,761
Liabilities: $1,379,525
Net Worth: $14,293,236
Earnings: $1,519,113
Emp.: 5
Fiscal Year-end: 03/31/21
Gelatin Capsules Mfr
N.A.I.C.S.: 325412
Alok K. Garg (Mng Dir)

Subsidiaries:

MedGel Private Limited (1)
Special Economic Zone Plot No-19-20 Pharma Zone Phase-II Sector-III, Dist-Dhar, Pithampur, 454775, MP, India
Tel.: (91) 7292256205
Web Site: http://www.medgel.net
Soft Gelatin Mfr
N.A.I.C.S.: 325998
R. C. Mittal (Chm)

MEDI CINE MEDIENPRODUKTIONS GMBH
Bischheimer Weg 1, 55129, Mainz, Germany
Tel.: (49) 6131952960
Web Site: http://www.medi-cine.de
Year Founded: 1995
Sales Range: $50-74.9 Million
Emp.: 15
Television & Multimedia Production Services for Medical & Science Industries
N.A.I.C.S.: 516120
Frank Nadzeika (CEO)

MEDI GLASS LIMITED
119/6 Industrial Estate, Kotlakhpat, Lahore, Pakistan
Tel.: (92) 5120271
Ceramic Glass Mfr
N.A.I.C.S.: 327215

MEDI LIFESTYLE LIMITED

MEDI LIFESTYLE LIMITED
PKNS Block A Level 5 No 17 Jalan Yong Shook Lin, 46050, Petaling Jaya, Selangor Darul Ehsan, Malaysia
Tel.: (60) 379319921
Web Site: https://www.iev-group.com
Z4D—(CAT)
Rev.: $422,943
Assets: $176,643
Liabilities: $2,183,616
Net Worth: ($2,006,972)
Earnings: ($1,566,081)
Emp.: 14
Fiscal Year-end: 12/31/23
Offshore Oil & Engineering Services
N.A.I.C.S.: 213112
Christopher Nghia Do (Founder, Pres & CEO)

Subsidiaries:

Back to Life Sdn. Bhd. (1)
Unit 3015 129 Offices Block J2 Jaya One No 72, Jalan Prof Diraja Ungku Aziz, 46200, Petaling Jaya, Selangor, Malaysia
Tel.: (60) 129689701
Web Site: https://backtolife.asia
Chiropractic & Physical Therapy Medicine Services
N.A.I.C.S.: 621340

HealthPro Life Sdn. Bhd. (1)
43 Jalan SS2/3, 47300, Petaling Jaya, Selangor, Malaysia
Tel.: (60) 378768000
Health Care Srvices
N.A.I.C.S.: 621610

HealthPro Marketing Sdn. Bhd. (1)
100 3 015 129 Offices Block J Jaya One, 46200, Petaling Jaya, Selangor, Malaysia
Tel.: (60) 103394526
Ecommerce & Digital Marketing Services
N.A.I.C.S.: 541810

HealthPro Pharma Pte. Ltd. (1)
380 Jalan Besar 09-05 ARC 380, Singapore, 209000, Singapore
Tel.: (65) 62999881
Health Care Srvices
N.A.I.C.S.: 621610

IEV International Limited (1)
Level 19 Two International Finance Centre 8 Finance Street, Central, China (Hong Kong)
Tel.: (852) 2251-8674
Marine Engineering Services
N.A.I.C.S.: 541330

MEDI LIFESTYLE LIMITED
Dataran Hamodal Block B Level 2 No 4 Jalan Bersatu 13/4, 46200, Petaling Jaya, Selangor Darul Ehsan, Malaysia
Tel.: (60) 3 7960 9109
Year Founded: 2004
Sales Range: $25-49.9 Million
Emp.: 13
Offshore Engineering Services
N.A.I.C.S.: 541330
Juzer Noman (Mng Dir)

Subsidiaries:

IEV Energy Sdn. Bhd. (1)
Dataran Hamodal Block B Level 2 No 4 Jalan Bersatu 13/4, Petaling Jaya, 46200, Malaysia
Tel.: (60) 3 7960 9109
Natural Gas Transportation Services
N.A.I.C.S.: 486210

Subsidiary (Non-US):

PT IEV Gas (2)
Menara Era Suite 12A-05 Jalan Senen Raya No 135-137, Jakarta, 10410, Indonesia
Tel.: (62) 21 386 7801
Emp.: 15
Oil & Gas Exploration Services
N.A.I.C.S.: 213112

MEDI LIFESTYLE LIMITED

Medi Lifestyle Limited—(Continued)

Nicolaas Smit *(Gen Mgr)*

IEV Manufacturing Sdn. Bhd. (1)
No 13 Jln Tandang Seksyen 51, 46050, Petaling Jaya, Malaysia
Tel.: (60) 3 7782 8155
Sales Range: $25-49.9 Million
Oil Field Equipment Mfr
N.A.I.C.S.: 333132
Juzer Noman *(Deputy Gen Mgr)*

IEV Oil & Gas Technologies Co., Ltd. (1)
Floor 7 Abacus Building 58 Nguyen Dinh Chieu Street, Da Kao Ward District 1, Ho Chi Minh City, Vietnam
Tel.: (84) 8 3911 5614
Emp.: 10
Oil & Gas Exploration Services
N.A.I.C.S.: 213112
Le Quang Vinh *(Mng Dir)*

PT IEV Indonesia (1)
Menara Era Suite 12A-05 Jalan Senen Raya No 135-137, Jakarta, 10410, Indonesia **(95%)**
Tel.: (62) 21 386 7801
Sales Range: $25-49.9 Million
Emp.: 1
Offshore Engineering Services
N.A.I.C.S.: 541330
Sahrul Asturrachman *(Gen Mgr)*

MEDIA & INCOME TRUST PLC

Bow Bells House 1 Bread St, London, EC4M 9HH, United Kingdom
Tel.: (44) 2074636000
Investment Management Service
N.A.I.C.S.: 525990

MEDIA 6 SA

33 avenue du Bois de la Pie, 93290, Tremblay, France
Tel.: (33) 178783151 FR
Web Site: https://www.media6.com
EDI—(EUR)
Sales Range: $75-99.9 Million
Marketing Consulting Services
N.A.I.C.S.: 541613

Subsidiaries:

Aldige (1)
Zone Industrielle De La Seiglerie Rue Andre Marie Ampere, 44270, Machecoul, France
Tel.: (33) 240262526
Web Site: http://www.media6.com
Sales Range: $25-49.9 Million
Emp.: 20
Fitting Fixture Mfr
N.A.I.C.S.: 332999

Ateliers Normand SA (1)
5 avenue des Berthaudieres, 44680, Sainte-Pazanne, France
Tel.: (33) 240027940
Web Site: http://www.media6-ateliersnormand.fr
Emp.: 140
Advertising Services
N.A.I.C.S.: 541850

MEDIA6 Design (1)
33 avenue du Bois de la Pie, 93290, Tremblay, France
Tel.: (33) 1 78 78 31 51
Web Site: http://www.media6.com
Commercial Designing Services
N.A.I.C.S.: 541490

MEDIACOLOR SPAIN S.A (1)
Calle Carrasco I Formiguera 2 - 1, 8302, Mataro, Spain
Tel.: (34) 937587060
Web Site: http://www.mediacolorsp.com
Sales Range: $25-49.9 Million
Emp.: 24
Cosmetic Product Retailer
N.A.I.C.S.: 456120
Luis Sarle *(Gen Mgr)*

MEDIA BITES, UAB

Kestucio g 25, Vilnius, 08121, Lithuania
Tel.: (370) 52503415
Web Site: http://www.mediabites.lt
Year Founded: 2017
Media Channels & Publishing
N.A.I.C.S.: 541840
Martynas Basokas *(COO)*

MEDIA CENTRAL CORPORATION INC.

2455 Cawthra Road Suite 75, Mississauga, L5A 3P1, ON, Canada
Tel.: (647) 363-7717
Web Site: http://www.mediacentralcorp.com
Year Founded: 1999
FLYY—(CNSX)
Rev.: $1,490,243
Assets: $2,051,920
Liabilities: $1,936,925
Net Worth: $114,995
Earnings: ($3,567,197)
Emp.: 35
Fiscal Year-end: 12/31/20
Fiber Optic Sensor Mfr
N.A.I.C.S.: 335921
Brian Kalish *(CEO)*

Subsidiaries:

Marcon International Inc. (1)
2455 Cawthra Road Suite 75, Mississauga, L5A 3P1, ON, Canada
Tel.: (905) 275-7570
Web Site: http://www.marconintl.com
Industrial Equipment Distr
N.A.I.C.S.: 423830

MEDIA CHINESE INTERNATIONAL LIMITED

15/F Block A Ming Pao Industrial Centre, 18 Ka Yip Street, Chai Wan, China (Hong Kong)
Tel.: (852) 25953111
Web Site:
https://www.mediachinesegroup.com
MEDIAC—(KLS)
Rev.: $115,679,000
Assets: $233,631,000
Liabilities: $67,210,000
Net Worth: $166,421,000
Earnings: ($1,913,000)
Emp.: 2,917
Fiscal Year-end: 03/31/21
Newspaper Publishers
N.A.I.C.S.: 513110
Kiew Chiong Tiong *(CEO-Grp)*

Subsidiaries:

Beijing OMG M2U Advertising Company Limited (1)
19 F Tower A Full Link Plz No 18 Chaoyangmenwai Ave, Beijing, 100020, China
Tel.: (86) 1065889600
Newspaper Advertising Services
N.A.I.C.S.: 541840

Charming Holidays Limited (1)
Room 1632 Office Building Phase I Grand Plaza 639 Nathan Road, Mong Kok, Kowloon, China (Hong Kong)
Tel.: (852) 27811900
Web Site: http://www.charming-online.com
Travel & Tour Operating Agencies
N.A.I.C.S.: 561520

Delta Tour & Travel Services (Canada), Inc. (1)
1353 Huntingdon Drive, Scarborough, M1S 3J1, ON, Canada
Tel.: (416) 321-2133
Web Site: http://www.deltatours.ca
Sales Range: $25-49.9 Million
Emp.: 10
Travel & Tour Operating Agencies
N.A.I.C.S.: 561520

Delta Tour & Travel Services, Inc. (1)
3360 Flair Dr Ste 102, El Monte, CA 91731
Tel.: (626) 300-0033
Web Site: https://www.deltatours.com
Sales Range: $25-49.9 Million
Emp.: 25
Travel & Tour Operating Agencies
N.A.I.C.S.: 561520
Eric Lee *(Pres)*

Guang-Ming Ribao Sdn Bhd (1)
67 Jalan Macalister, 10400, Pulau Penang, Malaysia
Tel.: (60) 134846688
Web Site: http://guangming.com.my
Sales Range: $25-49.9 Million
Emp.: 70
Chinese Newspaper Publishing Services
N.A.I.C.S.: 513110

Media2U Company Limited (1)
16F Ming Pao Indus Ctr Block A 18 Ka Yip St, Chai Wan, China (Hong Kong)
Tel.: (852) 36053705
Magazine Advertising Services
N.A.I.C.S.: 541810

Ming Pao Education Publications Limited (1)
15th Floor Tower A Ming Pao Industrial Centre 18 Ka Yip Street, Ming Pao Industrial Centre, Chai Wan, China (Hong Kong)
Tel.: (852) 25155600
Web Site: https://www.mpep.com.hk
Textbook Publishing Services
N.A.I.C.S.: 513130

Ming Pao Holdings (Canada) Limited (1)
1355 Huntingwood Dr, Scarborough, M1S 3J1, ON, Canada
Tel.: (416) 321-0088
Web Site: http://www.mingpao.com
Investment Holding Services
N.A.I.C.S.: 523999

Ming Pao Holdings Limited (1)
15 F Ming Pao Indus Ctr Block A 18 Ka Yip St, Chai Wan, China (Hong Kong)
Tel.: (852) 25953111
Web Site: http://www.mingpal.com
Investment Holding Services
N.A.I.C.S.: 551112

Ming Pao Investment (USA) L.P. (1)
4331 33rd St Fl 2, Long Island City, NY 11101-2316
Tel.: (718) 786-2888
Sales Range: $25-49.9 Million
Emp.: 20
Newspaper Publishing Services
N.A.I.C.S.: 513110
Ping Huang *(Mgr-Fin)*

Ming Pao Magazines Limited (1)
16 Fl Ming Pao Indus Ctr Block A 18 Ka Yip St, Chai Wan, China (Hong Kong)
Tel.: (852) 36053705
Web Site: http://www.mingpaoweekly.com
Sales Range: $25-49.9 Million
Emp.: 100
Magazine Publishing Services
N.A.I.C.S.: 513120
Patrick Loam *(CEO)*

Ming Pao Newspapers (Canada) Limited (1)
5368 Parkwood Place, Richmond, V6V 2N1, BC, Canada
Tel.: (604) 231-8998
Web Site: http://www.mingpaocanada.com
Chinese Newspaper Publishing Services
N.A.I.C.S.: 513110

Ming Pao Newspapers Limited (1)
15-16 F Ming Pao Indus Ctr Block A 18 Ka Yip St, Chai Wan, China (Hong Kong)
Tel.: (852) 25155111
Web Site: http://www.mingpao.com
Newspaper Publishing Services
N.A.I.C.S.: 513110

Ming Pao Publications Limited (1)
15 F Ming Pao Indus Ctr Block A 18 Ka Yip St, Chai Wan, China (Hong Kong)
Tel.: (852) 25953111
Web Site: http://www.mingpao.com
Emp.: 50
Books Publishing Services
N.A.I.C.S.: 513130
Francis Tiong *(CEO)*

Mingpao.com Limited (1)
15th Floor Tower A Ming Pao Industrial Centre 18 Ka Yip Street, Chai Wan, China (Hong Kong)
Tel.: (852) 25953111
Web Site: https://www.mingpao.com
Web Hosting Services
N.A.I.C.S.: 518210
Woon Ting Kam *(COO)*

Nanyang Press Holdings Berhad (1)
2nd Floor Nanyang Siang Pau Building No 1 Jalan SS 7/2, PO Box 8565, 46793, Petaling Jaya, Selangor Darul Ehsan, Malaysia
Tel.: (60) 378726888
Web Site: http://www.nanyang.com
Newspaper & Magazine Publishing Services
N.A.I.C.S.: 513110

Nanyang Siang Pau Sdn Bhd (1)
No 1 Jalan SS 7/2, 47301, Petaling Jaya, Selangor, Malaysia
Tel.: (60) 378726888
Web Site: https://www.enanyang.my
Chinese Newspaper Publishing Services
N.A.I.C.S.: 513110

Sin Chew Media Corporation Berhad (1)
19 Jalan Semangat, 46200, Petaling Jaya, Selangor, Malaysia
Tel.: (60) 379658888
Web Site: http://www.sinchew.com.my
Newspaper Publishing Services
N.A.I.C.S.: 513110

The China Press Berhad (1)
80 Jalan Riong Off Jalan Bangsar, 59100, Kuala Lumpur, Malaysia
Tel.: (60) 322896363
Web Site: https://www.chinapress.com.my
Chinese Newspaper Publishing Services
N.A.I.C.S.: 513110

WAW Creation Limited (1)
15/F Block A 18 Ka Yip Street, Ming Pao Industrial Centre, Chai Wan, China (Hong Kong)
Tel.: (852) 25953111
Web Site: https://www.wawcreation.com
Content Marketing Services
N.A.I.C.S.: 541613

Yazhou Zhoukan Limited (1)
15th Floor Block A Ming Pao Industrial Centre 18 Ka Yip Street, Chai Wan, China (Hong Kong)
Tel.: (852) 25155836
Web Site: http://www.yzzk.com
Sales Range: $25-49.9 Million
Emp.: 30
Magazine Publishing Services
N.A.I.C.S.: 513120

MEDIA DO CO., LTD.

5F & 8F Palace Side Building 1-1-1 Hitotsubashi, Chiyoda-ku, Tokyo, 100-0003, Japan
Tel.: (81) 362125111 JP
Web Site: https://www.mediado.jp
Year Founded: 1999
3678—(TKS)
Rev.: $666,715,240
Assets: $365,929,080
Liabilities: $251,014,360
Net Worth: $114,914,720
Earnings: ($2,261,710)
Emp.: 250
Fiscal Year-end: 02/29/24
Book Publishers
N.A.I.C.S.: 513130
Yasushi Fujita *(Pres & CEO)*

Subsidiaries:

Digital Publishing Initiatives Japan Co., Ltd. (1)
Palace side Building 5/8th floor 1-1 Hitotsubashi 1, Chiyoda-ku, Tokyo, 100-0003, Japan **(70.52%)**
Tel.: (81) 368371850
Web Site: http://www.pubridge.jp
Digital Publishing Services
N.A.I.C.S.: 513130
Fujita Kyosugi *(Chm & Dir)*

MEDIA FIVE CO.

6th floor Yakuin Business Garden

AND PRIVATE COMPANIES

1-1-1 Yakuin, Chuo-ku, Fukuoka,
810-0022, Japan
Tel.: (81) 927620555
Web Site: https://www.media5.co.jp
Year Founded: 1996
3824—(FKA)
Rev.: $14,868,480
Assets: $6,534,000
Liabilities: $3,465,440
Net Worth: $3,068,560
Earnings: ($735,680)
Emp.: 229
Fiscal Year-end: 05/31/21
Business Consulting Services
N.A.I.C.S.: 541618
Eriya Ueno *(Pres)*

MEDIA KOBO INC.
12th Floor Sumitomo Shin-Akasaka
Building Akasaka 4-2-6, Minato-ku,
Tokyo, 107-0052, Japan
Tel.: (81) 355491766
Web Site: https://www.mkb.ne.jp
Year Founded: 1997
3815—(TKS)
Rev.: $12,514,640
Assets: $16,489,220
Liabilities: $9,989,320
Net Worth: $6,499,900
Earnings: ($1,679,400)
Fiscal Year-end: 08/31/24
Content Business Services
N.A.I.C.S.: 541810
Kahori Hasegawa *(Exec Officer)*

MEDIA LAB S.P.A.
Via Trieste 4, 19020, Follo, SP, Italy
Tel.: (39) 0187517775
Web Site: https://www.mlsw.com
Year Founded: 1994
MLLAB—(EUR)
Rev.: $1,497,053
Assets: $1,844,717
Liabilities: $704,636
Net Worth: $1,140,081
Earnings: $100,344
Fiscal Year-end: 12/31/23
Custom Computer Programming Services
N.A.I.C.S.: 541511
Massimo Ivani *(CEO)*

MEDIA LINKS CO., LTD.
Kawasaki Tech Center 18F 58016
Horikawacho, Saiwai-ku, Kawasaki,
212-0013, Kanagawa, Japan
Tel.: (81) 445893440
Web Site:
    https://www.medialinks.com
Year Founded: 1993
6659—(TKS)
Rev.: $20,563,710
Assets: $28,713,840
Liabilities: $10,965,990
Net Worth: $17,747,850
Earnings: ($1,606,230)
Emp.: 106
Fiscal Year-end: 03/31/24
Communication Equipment Mfr
N.A.I.C.S.: 334290
Harry Dale *(Gen Mgr-Technical Support-Americas)*

Subsidiaries:

ML AU Pty Ltd. (1)
2-12 Rokeby Street, Collingwood, 3066,
VIC, Australia
Tel.: (61) 394161513
Communication Equipment Mfr
N.A.I.C.S.: 334290

Media Links, Inc. (1)
431-C Hayden Station Rd, Windsor, CT
06095
Tel.: (860) 206-9163
Communication Equipment Maintenance
Services
N.A.I.C.S.: 811210

MEDIA MATRIX WORLDWIDE LIMITED
Plot No 38 4th Floor Sector 32, Gurgaon, 122001, India
Tel.: (91) 1244310000
Web Site:
    https://www.mmwlindia.com
Year Founded: 1985
512267—(BOM)
Rev.: $152,214,477
Assets: $38,521,929
Liabilities: $27,097,248
Net Worth: $11,424,681
Earnings: $536,214
Emp.: 5
Fiscal Year-end: 03/31/21
Video Production Services
N.A.I.C.S.: 512110
Gurvinder Singh Monga *(Sec)*

Subsidiaries:

DigiVive Services Private Limited (1)
Plot No 45-46 Udyog Vihar Phase - 1 Sector 20, Gurgaon, 122016, Haryana, India
Tel.: (91) 1244341200
Software Development Services
N.A.I.C.S.: 541511
Dushyant Kohli *(Head-Growth)*

MEDIA ONE GLOBAL ENTERTAINMENT LIMITED
Old No 1/38 New No 1/38 Mataji
Complex Flat no 32 Mount Road,
Chennai, 600002, India
Tel.: (91) 4445544028
Web Site:
    https://www.mediaoneglobal.net
Year Founded: 2002
503685—(BOM)
Rev.: $23,293
Assets: $4,784,410
Liabilities: $10,565,862
Net Worth: ($5,781,452)
Earnings: ($607,601)
Fiscal Year-end: 03/31/22
Digital Advertising Agency Services
N.A.I.C.S.: 541810

MEDIA PLUS A/S
Torggt 5, 0028, Oslo, Norway
Tel.: (47) 21 60 33 10
Web Site: http://www.mediaplus.no
Year Founded: 1968
Rev.: $24,000,000
Emp.: 20
N.A.I.C.S.: 541810
Reidar Larson *(Mng Dir)*

MEDIA PRIMA BERHAD
Sri Pentas No 3 Persiaran Bandar
Utama, 47800, Petaling Jaya, Selangor, Malaysia
Tel.: (60) 376213333
Web Site:
    https://www.mediaprima.com.my
MEDIA—(KLS)
Rev.: $279,691,335
Assets: $348,613,155
Liabilities: $194,020,695
Net Worth: $154,592,460
Earnings: $12,761,595
Emp.: 1,994
Fiscal Year-end: 12/31/21
Television & Radio Broadcasting Services
N.A.I.C.S.: 516210
Jessica Say Choon Tan *(Sec)*

Subsidiaries:

Big Tree Outdoor Sdn Bhd (1)
Second Floor Balai Berita Anjung Riong No
31 Jalan Riong, Bangsar, 59100, Kuala
Lumpur, Malaysia
Tel.: (60) 37 729 3889
Web Site: https://www.bigtree.com.my
Sales Range: $25-49.9 Million
Emp.: 98
Outdoor Advertising Services

N.A.I.C.S.: 541810
Mohamad Shukor Ariffin *(CEO)*

Ch-9 Media Sdn. Bhd. (1)
Sri Pentas No 3 Persiaran Bandar Utama
Bandar Utama, 47800, Petaling Jaya, Selangor, Malaysia
Tel.: (60) 377266333
Radio Broadcasting Services
N.A.I.C.S.: 516210

Gama Media International (BVI) Ltd. (1)
12th Road Kanda-Accra Opposite the
French Embassy, Accra, Ghana
Tel.: (233) 21 763458
Investment Management Service
N.A.I.C.S.: 523940

Kurnia Outdoor Sdn. Bhd. (1)
Lot 1 06 First Floor KPMG Tower 8 First
Avenue Bandar Utama, 47820, Petaling
Jaya, Selangor Darul Ehsen, Malaysia
Tel.: (60) 377271177
Sales Range: $25-49.9 Million
Emp.: 90
Outdoor Advertising Services
N.A.I.C.S.: 541850

Media Prima Digital Sdn. Bhd. (1)
3rd Floor North Wing Sri Pentas No 3 Persiaran Bandar Utama, 47800, Petaling
Jaya, Selangor, Malaysia
Tel.: (60) 377266333
Web Site:
    http://www.mediaprimadigital.com.my
Digital Marketing Services
N.A.I.C.S.: 541613
Rafiq Razali *(CEO)*

Metropolitan TV Sdn Bhd (1)
Sri Pentas No 3 Persiaran Bandar Utama,
Bandar Utama, 47000, Petaling Jaya, Selangor, Malaysia
Tel.: (60) 377288282
Web Site: http://www.mediaprima.com.my
Sales Range: $25-49.9 Million
Emp.: 47
Commercial Television Broadcasting Services
N.A.I.C.S.: 516120

Natseven TV Sdn Bhd (1)
Sri Pentas 2nd Floor North Wing No 3 Persiaran Bandar Utama, Bandar Utama,
47800, Petaling Jaya, Selangor, Malaysia
Tel.: (60) 377268777
Web Site: http://www.ntv7.com.my
Sales Range: $25-49.9 Million
Emp.: 40
Television Broadcasting Services
N.A.I.C.S.: 516120

Primeworks Studios Sdn Bhd (1)
North Wing Sri Pentas 3 Persiaran Bandar
Utama, 47800, Petaling Jaya, Selangor,
Malaysia
Tel.: (60) 377266333
Web Site: http://www.primeworks.com.my
Motion Picture & Film Production Services
N.A.I.C.S.: 512110

Rev Media Group Sdn. Bhd. (1)
3rd Floor Sri Pentas No 3 Persiaran Bandar
Utama, 47800, Petaling Jaya, Selangor,
Darul Ehsan, Malaysia
Tel.: (60) 376213333
Web Site: https://revmedia.my
Media Advertising Services
N.A.I.C.S.: 541840

Sistem Televisyen Malaysia Berhad. (1)
Sri Pentas No 3 Persiaran Bandar Utama
Bandar Utama, 47800, Petaling Jaya, Selangor Darul Ehsan, Malaysia
Tel.: (60) 377266333
Commercial Television Broadcasting Services
N.A.I.C.S.: 516120
Nurul Aini Abdul Bakar *(Gen Mgr)*

Synchrosound Studio Sdn. Bhd. (1)
PH North Wing Sri Pentas Persiaran Bandar Utama, 47800, Petaling Jaya, Selangor,
Malaysia
Tel.: (60) 377105022
Radio Broadcasting Services
N.A.I.C.S.: 516210

The New Straits Times Press (Malaysia) Berhad (1)

MEDIAHOLDING OAO

Balai Berita Bangsar 31 Jalan Riong,
59100, Kuala Lumpur, Malaysia
Tel.: (60) 320569499
Web Site: https://www.nstp.com.my
Sales Range: $150-199.9 Million
Emp.: 3,000
Newspaper & Internet Publisher
N.A.I.C.S.: 513110

Subsidiary (Domestic):

Berita Harian Sdn Berhad (2)
Balai Berita No 31, Jalan Riong, 59100,
Kuala Lumpur, Malaysia (100%)
Tel.: (60) 322822328
Web Site: http://www.bharian.com.my
Newspaper Publishers
N.A.I.C.S.: 513110

Berita Information System Sdn Bhd (2)
No 101 and 103 Kompleks Alor Setar Lebuh Raya Darul Aman, 05100, Alor Setar,
Kedah, Malaysia
Tel.: (60) 4 730 1812
Web Site: https://www.nstp.com.my
Online Newspaper Related Services
N.A.I.C.S.: 513110

NSTP e-Media Sdn Bhd (2)
Balai Berita No 31, Jalan Riong, 59100,
Kuala Lumpur, Malaysia (100%)
Tel.: (60) 322822328
Web Site: http://www.emedia.com.my
Newspaper Publishers
N.A.I.C.S.: 513110

MEDIA TIMES LIMITED
96-B Pace Mall Building M M Alam
Road Gulberg II, Lahore, Pakistan
Tel.: (92) 4235878614
Web Site:
    https://www.dailytimes.com.pk
MDTL—(LAH)
Rev.: $1,007,553
Assets: $1,815,389
Liabilities: $7,256,105
Net Worth: ($5,440,716)
Earnings: ($708,523)
Emp.: 87
Fiscal Year-end: 06/30/20
Newspaper Publishers
N.A.I.C.S.: 513110

MEDIA-MAKER S.P.A.
Via Privata Gioacchino Belli 14,
20127, Milan, Italy
Tel.: (39) 0287177406
Web Site: http://www.mmaker.it
Year Founded: 2017
ALKER—(EUR)
Sales Range: $25-49.9 Million
Outdoor Advertising Services
N.A.I.C.S.: 541850
Andrea Salice *(Chm)*

MEDIACAP SA
Ul Mangalia 2A, 02-758, Warsaw,
Poland
Tel.: (48) 22 463 99 70
Web Site: http://www.mediacap.pl
MCP—(WAR)
Media Advertising Services
N.A.I.C.S.: 541840
Jacek Olechowski *(Chm-Mgmt Bd)*

MEDIACLE GROUP AB
Tel.: (46) 812056015
Web Site: https://www.mediacle.com
Year Founded: 2013
Emp.: 80
Digital Marketing Services
N.A.I.C.S.: 541613
Santosh Jain *(CEO)*

MEDIAHOLDING OAO
Khoroshevskoe sh 12 bldg 1, Moscow, Russia
Tel.: (7) 495 800 20 02
Web Site: http://www.o2tv.ru
ODVA—(RUS)

4771

MEDIAHOLDING OAO

Mediaholding OAO—(Continued)
Sales Range: Less than $1 Million
Holding Company
N.A.I.C.S.: 551112

MEDIAHOUSE LIMITED
19 Elliott St, Hamilton, HM 10, Bermuda
Tel.: (441) 2951944
Web Site:
http://www.mediahouse.com
Year Founded: 1959
Sales Range: $25-49.9 Million
Emp.: 70
Commercial Printing & Web Media
N.A.I.C.S.: 513120
Warren Brown *(Deputy Chm)*

Subsidiaries:

Bermuda Sun Limited (1)
19 Elliott Street, Hamilton, HM10, Bermuda
Tel.: (441) 295 3902
Web Site: http://www.bermudasun.bm
Newspaper Publishers
N.A.I.C.S.: 513110
Lisa Beauchamp *(Gen Mgr)*

Bermuda.com Limited (1)
41 Victoria Street, Hamilton, HM 12, Bermuda
Tel.: (441) 2781870
Web Site: http://www.bermuda.com
Sales Range: $25-49.9 Million
Online Information Services
N.A.I.C.S.: 513199

Island Press Limited (1)
Elliot Street 19, Hamilton, Pembroke, HM 08, Bermuda
Tel.: (441) 2951944
Sales Range: $25-49.9 Million
Commercial Printing Services
N.A.I.C.S.: 323111
Jamie Petty *(Gen Mgr)*

MEDIAHUIS PARTNERS NV
Katwilgweg 2, 2050, Antwerp, Belgium
Tel.: (32) 32100210
Web Site: http://www.mediahuis.be
Year Founded: 2013
Investent Holding Company; Newspaper & Magazine Publishing
N.A.I.C.S.: 551112

Subsidiaries:

Mediahuis NV (1)
Katwilgweg 2, 2050, Antwerp, Belgium
Tel.: (32) 3 210 02 10
Web Site: http://www.mediahuis.be
Newspaper & Magazine Publishing Services
N.A.I.C.S.: 513110
Gert Ysebaert *(CEO)*

Subsidiary (Non-US):

Independent News & Media PLC (2)
Independent House 27-32 Talbot Street, Dublin, 1, Ireland
Tel.: (353) 14663200
Web Site: http://www.inmplc.com
Rev: $350,972,980
Assets: $245,321,728
Liabilities: $154,164,582
Net Worth: $91,157,146
Earnings: $14,973,250
Emp.: 845
Fiscal Year-end: 12/31/2017
International Newspaper & Magazine Publishing
N.A.I.C.S.: 513110
Ryan Preston *(CFO)*

Subsidiary (Non-US):

Abbey Communications (Netherlands) B.V. (3)
Locatellikade 1, Amsterdam, 1076 AZ, Netherlands
Tel.: (31) 205755600
Newspaper Publishing Services
N.A.I.C.S.: 513110

Subsidiary (Domestic):

Drogheda Independent Company Limited (3)
9 Shop St, Drogheda, Ireland
Tel.: (353) 419838658
Web Site: http://www.drogheda-independent.ie
Sales Range: $25-49.9 Million
Emp.: 30
Newspaper Publishers
N.A.I.C.S.: 513110

INM Securities (Ireland) Limited (3)
27-32 Talbot Street, Dublin, 1, Ireland
Tel.: (353) 1 466 3200
Web Site: http://www.inmplc.com
Emp.: 300
Newspaper Publishing Services
N.A.I.C.S.: 513110

Independent Colleges Limited (3)
60 - 63 Dawson Street, Dublin, Ireland
Tel.: (353) 1 6725058
Web Site: http://www.independentcolleges.ie
Education Development Services
N.A.I.C.S.: 611310
Padraig Hourigan *(Pres & CEO)*

Independent Communications Limited (3)
Independent House 27-32 Talbot Street, Dublin, 1, Ireland
Tel.: (353) 1 466 3200
Holding Company; Newspaper Publisher
N.A.I.C.S.: 551112
Robert Pitt *(CEO)*

Subsidiary (Domestic):

Independent Communications (Ireland) Limited (4)
3050 Lake Drive Citywest Digital Park, 24, Dublin, Ireland
Tel.: (353) 14112000
Sales Range: $25-49.9 Million
Emp.: 50
Newspaper Publishers
N.A.I.C.S.: 513110

Subsidiary (Domestic):

Independent Digital Limited (3)
2023 Bianconi Avenue, Dublin, Ireland
Tel.: (353) 1 466 3200
Web Site: http://www.independent.ie
Newspaper Publishing Services
N.A.I.C.S.: 513110

Independent Newspapers (Ireland) Limited (3)
27232 Talbot St, 27-32 Talbot St, Dublin, 1, Ireland
Tel.: (353) 17055333
Web Site: http://www.independent.ie
Sales Range: $100-124.9 Million
Emp.: 400
Newspaper Publishers
N.A.I.C.S.: 513110

Independent Newspapers Management Services Limited (3)
2023 Bianconi Ave Citywest Business Campus, Dublin, Ireland
Tel.: (353) 1 466 3200
Web Site: http://www.independent.ie
Business Management Consulting Services
N.A.I.C.S.: 541611

Joint Venture (Domestic):

Independent Star Limited (3)
Independent House, 27-32 Talbot Street, Dublin, 1, Ireland
Tel.: (353) 14901228
Web Site: http://www.thestar.ie
Sales Range: $25-49.9 Million
Emp.: 100
Newspaper Publishers
N.A.I.C.S.: 513110

Subsidiary (Domestic):

Internet Interaction Limited (3)
3050 Lake Drive Citywest Digital Park, Dublin, Ireland
Tel.: (353) 14112000
Sales Range: $25-49.9 Million
Emp.: 50
Newspaper Publishers
N.A.I.C.S.: 513110

Newspread Limited (3)
3050 Lake Drive Citywest Digital Pk Naas Rd, Dublin, 24, Ireland
Tel.: (353) 14537262
Web Site: http://www.newspread.ie
Sales Range: $25-49.9 Million
Emp.: 65
Whslr, Distr & Publisher of Newspapar & Magazines
N.A.I.C.S.: 513199

Sunday Newspapers Limited (3)
Independent House 27-32 Talbot Street, Dublin, 1, Ireland
Tel.: (353) 18849000
Web Site: http://www.sundayworld.com
Sales Range: $25-49.9 Million
Emp.: 70
Newspaper Publishers
N.A.I.C.S.: 513110

The Kerryman Limited (3)
9 - 10 Denny St, Tralee, Ireland
Tel.: (353) 667145560
Web Site: http://www.kerryman.ie
Sales Range: $25-49.9 Million
Emp.: 25
Newspaper Publishers
N.A.I.C.S.: 513199

Subsidiary (Non-US):

Mediahuis Nederland B.V. (2)
Basisweg 30, 1043 AP, Amsterdam, Netherlands
Tel.: (31) 888242222
Web Site: http://www.mediahuis.nl
Newspaper, Magazine, Internet & Mobile Applications Publisher; Radio Operations
N.A.I.C.S.: 513110
Koos Boot *(CFO)*

Subsidiary (Domestic):

Metro Holland B.V. (3)
Delfandlaan 4, NL 1062 EB, Amsterdam, Netherlands
Tel.: (31) 20 5114000
Web Site: http://www.metronieuws.nl
Newspaper Publishing
N.A.I.C.S.: 513110
Marshal Den Hoed *(Dir-Comm)*

Telegraaf Media Nederland (3)
Basisweg 30, 1043 AP, Amsterdam, Netherlands
Tel.: (31) 205859111
Web Site: http://www.telegraaf.nl
Media Holding Group
N.A.I.C.S.: 551112

Subsidiary (Domestic):

Nobiles Media BV (4)
Basisweg 30, Amsterdam, 1043 AP, Netherlands
Tel.: (31) 206231800
Web Site: http://www.speurders.nl
Online Information for Students
N.A.I.C.S.: 519290

MEDIALINK GROUP LIMITED
Suite 1001 10/F Tower 1 South Seas Centre 75 Mody Road, Tsim Sha Tsui East, Kowloon, China (Hong Kong)
Tel.: (852) 2 508 9767   Ky
Web Site:
http://www.medialink.com.hk
Year Founded: 1994
2230—(HKG)
Rev.: $43,232,032
Assets: $98,336,545
Liabilities: $32,255,576
Net Worth: $66,080,968
Earnings: $4,974,372
Emp.: 113
Fiscal Year-end: 03/31/21
Advertising Material Distribution Services
N.A.I.C.S.: 541870
Lovinia Chiu Siu Yin *(Co-Founder, Chm & CEO)*

MEDIAMAKER LTD.

INTERNATIONAL PUBLIC

Media House Padge Road, Nottingham, NG9 2RS, United Kingdom
Tel.: (44) 1159255440
Web Site:
http://www.mediamaker.co.uk
Sales Range: $10-24.9 Million
Emp.: 28
Event Planning & Production, New Media Development & Video Production Services
N.A.I.C.S.: 561499
Alison Glaves *(Mng Dir)*

MEDIAN DIAGNOSTICS, INC.
878 Sunhwan-daero Dongnae-myeon, Dongnae-myeon, Chuncheon, Gangwon-do, Korea (South)
Tel.: (82) 332440100
Web Site:
https://www.mediandiagnostics.com
Year Founded: 1999
233250—(KRS)
Biotechnology Research & Development Services
N.A.I.C.S.: 541714
Jin Sik Oh *(CEO)*

MEDIAN GROUP INC.
17 1 Level 17 Tower 2 Bank Rakyat Twin Tower, No 33 Jalan Rakyat, 50470, Kuala Lumpur, Malaysia
Tel.: (60) 3 2714 2020   TX
Web Site:
http://www.mediangroupinc.com
Year Founded: 2002
Sales Range: Less than $1 Million
Emp.: 12
Advertising & Telecommunications Services
N.A.I.C.S.: 541890
Andrew Hwan Lee *(Pres & CEO)*

MEDIAN TECHNOLOGIES SA
1800 Route des Cretes Les Deux Arcs, 6560, Valbonne, France
Tel.: (33) 493333777
Web Site:
https://www.mediantechnologies.com
Year Founded: 2002
ALMDT—(EUR)
Rev.: $25,146,263
Assets: $39,667,734
Liabilities: $51,029,915
Net Worth: ($11,362,181)
Earnings: ($25,369,246)
Emp.: 169
Fiscal Year-end: 12/31/23
Medical Imaging Software
N.A.I.C.S.: 513210
Yan Liu *(Chief Medical Officer)*

MEDIANA CO., LTD.
132 Donghwagongdan-ro Munmak-eup, Wonju, Gangwon-do, Korea (South)
Tel.: (82) 337425400
Web Site: https://www.mediana-global.com
Year Founded: 1993
041920—(KRS)
Rev.: $52,421,943
Assets: $79,342,566
Liabilities: $10,265,533
Net Worth: $69,077,033
Earnings: $8,128,605
Emp.: 159
Fiscal Year-end: 12/31/22
Electromedical & Electrotherapeutic Apparatus Mfr
N.A.I.C.S.: 334510
Min-Cheol Kwak *(CEO)*

Subsidiaries:

Mediana USA, Inc. (1)
Bldg 7/A 2799 152nd Ave NE, Redmond, WA 98052
Tel.: (425) 406-2262

AND PRIVATE COMPANIES — MEDIATEK INC.

Web Site: https://www.medianausa.com
Medical Equipment Mfr
N.A.I.C.S.: 334510
Yongshik Shin *(Pres)*

MEDIASET S.P.A.
via Paleocapa 3, 20121, Milan, Italy
Tel.: (39) 0225149588 IT
Web Site: http://www.mediaset.it
MFEB—(ITA)
Rev.: $3,074,290,761
Assets: $5,529,197,484
Liabilities: $2,356,661,884
Net Worth: $3,172,535,600
Earnings: $239,320,013
Emp.: 4,722
Fiscal Year-end: 12/31/23
Holding Company; Telecommunications & Broadcasting Services
N.A.I.C.S.: 551112
Pier Silvio Berlusconi *(Deputy Chm & CEO)*

Subsidiaries:

Mediaset Espana Comunicacion, S.A. (1)
Carretera de Fuencarral to Alcobendas n 4, 28049, Madrid, Spain **(55.69%)**
Tel.: (34) 913966300
Web Site: http://www.mediaset.es
Rev.: $1,027,603,311
Assets: $2,118,356,582
Liabilities: $752,664,244
Net Worth: $1,365,692,338
Earnings: $219,524,563
Emp.: 1,564
Fiscal Year-end: 12/31/2020
Television Broadcasting Services
N.A.I.C.S.: 516120
Alejandro Echevarria Busquet *(Chm)*

Mediaset Investment S.a.r.l. (1)
25 C Boulevard Royal, Luxembourg, 2449, Luxembourg **(100%)**
Tel.: (352) 2620421
Web Site: http://www.mediaset.it
Emp.: 2
Television Broadcasting Services
N.A.I.C.S.: 516120
Rovati Maurizio *(Gen Mgr)*

Publiespana S.A.U. (1)
Edificio Telecinco H C/ Federico Mompou 5 bis, 28049, Madrid, Spain
Tel.: (34) 91 395 9000
Web Site: https://www.publiesp.es
Provides Advertising Services
N.A.I.C.S.: 541890

Publitalia '80 S.p.A. (1)
Palazzo Cellini, Milan, 20090, Italy **(100%)**
Tel.: (39) 0221023345
Web Site: http://www.publitalia.it
Sales Range: $25-49.9 Million
Advertising Services
N.A.I.C.S.: 541890

Subsidiary (Domestic):

Digitalia '08 S.r.l. (2)
Palazzo Cellini-Milan 2, 20090, Segrate, Italy **(100%)**
Tel.: (39) 02 21024808
Web Site: http://www.digitalia08.it
Television Broadcasting Services
N.A.I.C.S.: 516120

Subsidiary (Non-US):

Publieurope Ltd. (2)
Ariel House 74 A Charlotte Street, London, W1T 4QJ, United Kingdom **(100%)**
Tel.: (44) 2079279800
Web Site: https://www.publieurope.com
Television Broadcasting Services
N.A.I.C.S.: 516120
Giuliano Adreani *(Chm)*

R.T.I. S.p.A. (1)
Largo del Nazareno 8, Rome, Italy **(100%)**
Tel.: (39) 0225141
Media Broadcast Management Services
N.A.I.C.S.: 516120

Subsidiary (Domestic):

BOING S.p.A. (2)
Viale Europa 46, 20093, Cologno Monzese, MI, Italy **(51%)**
Tel.: (39) 06 696651
Web Site: http://www.boingtv.it
Television Broadcasting Services
N.A.I.C.S.: 516120

Elettronica Industriale S.p.A. (2)
Viale Filippo Turati, IT-20851, Lissone, MB, Italy **(100%)**
Tel.: (39) 03973981
Holding Company; Television Broadcasting Towers & Other Telecommunication Infrastructure Construction & Support Services
N.A.I.C.S.: 551112
Vittadini Francesco *(Chm)*

Taodue S.r.l. (2)
Via Pompeo Magno 1, 00192, Rome, Italy **(100%)**
Tel.: (39) 063221813
Web Site: http://www.taodue.it
Television Program Production Services
N.A.I.C.S.: 512110

Videotime S.p.A. (2)
Piazza SS Giovanni e Paolo 8, 184, Rome, Italy **(99.01%)**
Tel.: (39) 06 77 08 62 70
Television Broadcasting Services
N.A.I.C.S.: 516120

Radio Studio 105 S.p.A. (1)
Largo Donegani 1, 20121, Milan, Italy
Tel.: (39) 02 659 6116
Web Site: https://www.105.net
Radio Network Services
N.A.I.C.S.: 516210

MEDIATEK INC.
No 1 Dusing 1st Rd, Hsinchu Science Park, Hsin-chu, 30078, Taiwan
Tel.: (886) 35670766 TW
Web Site: https://corp.mediatek.com
Year Founded: 1997
2454—(TAI)
Rev.: $11,458,732,793
Assets: $18,991,048,051
Liabilities: $5,649,294,129
Net Worth: $13,341,753,922
Earnings: $1,473,970,042
Emp.: 17,377
Fiscal Year-end: 12/31/20
Semiconductor Product Mfr
N.A.I.C.S.: 334413
Ming-Kai Tsai *(Chm)*

Subsidiaries:

Airoha Technology (Suzhou) Limited (1)
D304-1 1355 Jinjihu Avenue Suzhou Industrial Park, Jiangsu, China
Tel.: (86) 51289185858
Information Technology Services
N.A.I.C.S.: 541512

Airoha Technology Corp. (1)
5F No 6-5 Dusing Road Hsinchu Science Park, Hsinchu, 300, Taiwan
Tel.: (886) 36128800
Web Site: https://www.airoha.com
Emp.: 1,100
Wireless Communication Equipment Mfr
N.A.I.C.S.: 334210

Airotek (Chengdu) Inc. (1)
5F No 168 Tian Fu Five Street, Chengdu, PRC, China
Tel.: (86) 2885939000
Wireless Communication Equipment Mfr
N.A.I.C.S.: 334210

Airotek (Shenzhen) Inc. (1)
12F Block E China Resources Land Building No 18 Dachong 1st Road, Nanshan District, Shenzhen, 518052, China
Tel.: (86) 75582571180
Wireless Communication Equipment Mfr
N.A.I.C.S.: 334210

Alpha Imaging Technology Corporation (1)
5th Floor No 145 Shianjeng 9th Rd, Jubei, Hsin-chu, 302, Taiwan
Tel.: (886) 36560528
Web Site: http://www.a-i-t.com.tw

Sales Range: $50-74.9 Million
Emp.: 122
Development, Design, Manufacture & Sale of Integrated Circuits for Mobile Phones & Cameras
N.A.I.C.S.: 334413
Zhizhan Yan *(Gen Mgr)*

Chingis Technology Corporation (1)
3F No 2 Technology Road V Science Based Industrial Park, Hsin-chu, 30078, Taiwan
Tel.: (886) 35780333
Web Site: http://www.chingistek.com
Semiconductor Equipment Mfr
N.A.I.C.S.: 333242

EcoNet (Suzhou) Limited (1)
D304-1 1355 Jinjihu Avenue Suzhou Industrial Park, Jiangsu, China
Tel.: (86) 51289185858
Broadband Internet Providing Services
N.A.I.C.S.: 517111

ILI Technology Corp. (1)
8 10F No 1 Taiyuan 2nd Street, Zhubei, 302, Hsinchu, Taiwan
Tel.: (886) 3 560 0099
Web Site: https://www.ilitek.com
Semiconductor Devices Mfr
N.A.I.C.S.: 334413

MStar Semiconductor, Inc. (1)
4F-1 No 26 Tai-Yuan Street, ChuPei, Hsinchu, 302, Hsien, Taiwan
Tel.: (886) 3 5526006
Web Site: http://www.mstarsemi.com
Sales Range: $800-899.9 Million
Semiconductor Mfr
N.A.I.C.S.: 334413

MTK Wireless Limited (UK) (1)
Building 2010 Cambourne Business Park, Cambourne, Cambridge, CB23 6DW, Cambridgeshire, United Kingdom
Tel.: (44) 195 471 2000
Web Site: http://www.mediatek.com
Consumer Electronics Product Mfr
N.A.I.C.S.: 337126
Lawrence Loh *(Gen Mgr)*

MediaTek (Beijing) Inc. (1)
No 6 Park Jiuxianqiao Road Building 1-B, Chaoyang District, Beijing, 100180, China **(100%)**
Tel.: (86) 1056900888
Web Site: http://www.mediatek.com
Sales Range: $150-199.9 Million
Electronic Parts & Equipment Whslr
N.A.I.C.S.: 423690

MediaTek (Hefei) Inc. (1)
No 615 Wanshui Road, Hefei Hi-tech Industry Development Zone, Hefei, 230088, Anhui, China
Tel.: (86) 55165317511
Sales Range: $100-124.9 Million
Emp.: 400
Semiconductor Devices Mfr
N.A.I.C.S.: 334413

MediaTek (Shanghai) Inc. (1)
No 275 RuiPing Road 20F Building C Poly West Bund Center, Xuhui District, Shanghai, China
Tel.: (86) 2154519650
Fabless Semiconductor Mfr & Distr
N.A.I.C.S.: 334413

MediaTek (ShenZhen) Inc. (1)
Building No 4 Block No 1 No 22 Nanhuan Road, Shenzhen Bay ECO-Technology Park Nanshan District, Shenzhen, China
Tel.: (86) 7552 663 0099
Web Site: http://www.mediatek.com
Multimedia Integrated & Computer Peripheral Integrated Circuit Chip Mfr
N.A.I.C.S.: 334118

MediaTek Denmark ApS (1)
Alfred Nobels Vej 21a, Aalborg, Nordjyllands Amt, Denmark
Tel.: (45) 96326500
Sales Range: $25-49.9 Million
Emp.: 38
Consumer Electronics & Integrated Circuits Mfr
N.A.I.C.S.: 334418

MediaTek Germany GmbH (1)
Kesselstrasse 5-7, 40221, Dusseldorf, Germany

Tel.: (49) 2111645260
Technical Consulting Services
N.A.I.C.S.: 541519

MediaTek India Technology Pvt. Ltd. (1)
1A/1 3rd Floor SB Tower Sector-16A, Noida, 201301, Uttar Pradesh, India
Tel.: (91) 120 615 1000
Web Site: https://corp.mediatek.com
Fabless Semiconductor Mfr for Wireless Telecommunications
N.A.I.C.S.: 517112

MediaTek Japan Inc. (1)
Higashi Gotanda Square 9F 2-10-2 Higashi Gotanda, Shinagawa-ku, Tokyo, 141-0022, Kanagawa, Japan
Tel.: (81) 354476900
Consumer Electronics & Integrated Circuits Mfr
N.A.I.C.S.: 334413

MediaTek Korea Inc. (1)
4F Humax Village 216 Hwangsaeul-ro, Bundang-gu, Seongnam, Gyeonggi-do, Korea (South)
Tel.: (82) 317865400
Web Site: http://www.mediatek.com
Consumer Electronics & Integrated Circuits Mfr
N.A.I.C.S.: 334413

MediaTek Singapore Pte Ltd. (1)
No 1 Fusionopolis Walk 03-01 Solaris, Singapore, 138628, Singapore **(100%)**
Tel.: (65) 67735661
Web Site: http://www.mtk.com.tw
Sales Range: $25-49.9 Million
Emp.: 100
Semiconductor & Related Device Mfr
N.A.I.C.S.: 334413

MediaTek Sweden AB (1)
Teknikringen 10, Ostergotlands lan, 583 30, Linkoping, 583 30, Sweden
Tel.: (46) 13211500
Fabless Semiconductor Mfr & Distr
N.A.I.C.S.: 334413

MediaTek USA Inc. (1)
2840 Junction Ave, San Jose, CA 95134
Tel.: (408) 526-1899
Web Site: http://www.mediatek.com
Analog & Digital Semiconductors Mfr
N.A.I.C.S.: 334413
Patrick Wilson *(VP-Govt Affairs)*

Subsidiary (Domestic):

MediaTek Wireless, Inc. (2)
120 Presidential Way, Woburn, MA 01801
Tel.: (781) 503-8000
Web Site: http://www.mediatek.com
Wireless Handset Components Mfr
N.A.I.C.S.: 334220

MediaTek Wireless FZ-LLC (1)
Building No 17 Office No 156, PO Box 502337, Dubai, United Arab Emirates
Tel.: (971) 43625000
Fabless Semiconductor Mfr & Distr
N.A.I.C.S.: 334413

MediaTek Wireless Finland Oy (1)
Elektroniikkatie 16, 90590, Oulu, Finland
Tel.: (358) 207930700
Fabless Semiconductor Mfr & Distr
N.A.I.C.S.: 334413

Nephos (Hefei) Co., Ltd. (1)
No 615 Wanshui Road Hefei Hi-tech Industry Development Zone, Hefei, Anhui, China
Tel.: (86) 55165109118
Fabless Semiconductor Mfr & Distr
N.A.I.C.S.: 334413

Nephos (Taiwan) Inc. (1)
4F No 5 Dusing Rd Hsinchu Science Park, Hsinchu, 30078, Taiwan
Tel.: (886) 36667858
Fabless Semiconductor Mfr & Distr
N.A.I.C.S.: 334413

Nephos Inc. (1)
2840 Junction Ave, San Jose, CA 95134
Tel.: (408) 526-1899
Web Site: https://www.nephosinc.com
Fabless Semiconductor Mfr & Distr
N.A.I.C.S.: 334413
Ta Hsing Liu *(Dir-Technical)*

MEDIATEK INC.

MediaTek Inc.—(Continued)

Nephos Pte. Ltd. (1)
80 Robinson Road 02-00, Singapore, 068898, Singapore
Tel.: (65) 67735661
Fabless Semiconductor Mfr & Distr
N.A.I.C.S.: 334413

Ralink Technology Corp. (1)
5F 36 Tai-Yuen Street, Jhubei City, Hsinchu, 302, Hsien, Taiwan
Tel.: (886) 35600868
Web Site: http://www.ralinktech.com.tw
Sales Range: $200-249.9 Million
Emp.: 375
Wireless Local Area Network (LAN) Chipsets Developer, Designer, Mfr & Distr
N.A.I.C.S.: 334220

Subsidiary (Non-US):

Ralink Technology (Samoa) Corporation (China) (2)
Galaxycentury Bldg A Rm 2116 No 3069 CaiTain Rd, Shenzhen, GuanDong, China
Tel.: (86) 75533000580
Web Site: http://www.ralinktech.com
Chipset Mfr & Services
N.A.I.C.S.: 334413

Subsidiary (Domestic):

TrendChip Technologies Corp. (2)
5th Fl No 5 Tai-Yuen 1st St, Jhubei, 300, HsinGhu County, Taiwan
Tel.: (886) 36668066
Web Site: http://www.mediatek.com
Sales Range: $50-74.9 Million
Emp.: 170
Semiconductor Devices Mfr
N.A.I.C.S.: 334413

Richnex Microelectronics Corp. (1)
4F No 95 Minchiuan Road, Hsintien Dist, New Taipei City, 231-41, Taiwan
Tel.: (886) 286676161
Fabless Semiconductor Mfr & Distr
N.A.I.C.S.: 334413
Larry Huang (VP-Sls & Mktg)

MEDIATEL S.A.

ul Bitwy Warszawskiej 1920r 7A, 02-366, Warsaw, Poland
Tel.: (48) 223774044
Web Site: http://www.mediatel.pl
MTL—(WAR)
Sales Range: $50-74.9 Million
Emp.: 118
Telecommunication Servicesb
N.A.I.C.S.: 541618

MEDIAWAN SA

46 avenue de Breteuil, Paris, 75007, France
Tel.: (33) 018048040
Web Site: http://www.mediawan.fr
Year Founded: 2015
Emp.: 1,282
Audiovisual Content Editor, Producer & Distr
N.A.I.C.S.: 334310
Pierre Antoine Capton (CEO)

Subsidiaries:

Auteurs Associes SAS (1)
9 rue Beranger, 75003, Paris, France
Tel.: (33) 144117171
Web Site: http://www.auteursassocies.fr
Television & Film Production Services
N.A.I.C.S.: 512110

EGO Productions SASU (1)
3 rue des Dechargeurs, 75001, Paris, France
Tel.: (33) 144889400
Web Site: http://www.ego-productions.com
Television Services
N.A.I.C.S.: 516120
Pascale Breugnot (Pres)

Frenchkiss Pictures SAS (1)
2 rue de Choiseul, 75002, Paris, France
Tel.: (33) 44779510
Web Site: http://www.frenchkisspictures.com
Television Services

N.A.I.C.S.: 516120

Mon Voisin Productions SAS (1)
31 rue de Trevise, 75009, Paris, France
Tel.: (33) 177350723
Web Site: http://www.monvoisinproductions.com
Television Services
N.A.I.C.S.: 516120

ON Animation Studio Montreal SADC (1)
1257 Guy Street 2nd Floor, Montreal, H3H 2K5, QC, Canada
Tel.: (514) 375-1784
Web Site: https://www.onanimationstudios.com
Television Production Studio Services
N.A.I.C.S.: 512110
Alexis Vonarb (Founder)

Palomar S.p.A. (1)
via Guglielmo Imperiali di Francavilla 4, 00135, Rome, Italy (72%)
Tel.: (39) 063759681
Web Site: http://www.palomaronline.com
Television & Film Production
N.A.I.C.S.: 516120
Nicola Serra (CEO)

Storia Television SAS (1)
38 rue Jean Mermoz, 75008, Paris, France
Tel.: (33) 153302000
Web Site: http://www.storiatelevision.com
Television Services
N.A.I.C.S.: 516120

MEDIAZEN, INC.

1103 11th floor Kinstar Tower 8 Seongnam-daero 331, Jeongja-dong beon-gil Bundang-gu, Seongnam, Gyeonggi-do, Korea (South)
Tel.: (82) 264297100
Web Site: https://mediazen.co.kr
Year Founded: 2000
279600—(KRS)
Rev.: $13,795,813
Assets: $29,565,108
Liabilities: $13,253,747
Net Worth: $16,311,360
Earnings: $147,042
Emp.: 165
Fiscal Year-end: 12/31/21
Software Development Services
N.A.I.C.S.: 541511

MEDIAZEST PLC

Unit 9 Woking Business Park Albert Drive, Woking, GU21 5JY, Surrey, United Kingdom
Tel.: (44) 1483733300
Web Site: https://www.mediazest.com
MDZ—(AIM)
Rev.: $3,192,804
Assets: $4,223,106
Liabilities: $2,819,178
Net Worth: $1,403,928
Earnings: $11,322
Fiscal Year-end: 09/30/22
Investment Services
N.A.I.C.S.: 523999
Geoffrey Robertson (CEO)

Subsidiaries:

MediaZest (1)
Unit 9 Woking Business Park Albert Drive, Woking, GU21 5JY, Surrey, United Kingdom
Tel.: (44) 1483 733300
Web Site: http://www.mediazest.com
Sales Range: $50-74.9 Million
Emp.: 20
Technological Developments & Engineering Design Solutions
N.A.I.C.S.: 532490
Geoff Robertson (CEO)

MEDIBANK PRIVATE LIMITED

Tel.: (61) 386225780
Web Site: http://www.medibank.com.au

MPL—(ASX)
Rev.: $5,090,248,794
Assets: $3,128,628,996
Liabilities: $1,589,421,522
Net Worth: $1,539,207,474
Earnings: $331,466,136
Emp.: 3,220
Fiscal Year-end: 06/30/24
Health, Pet, Life & Travel Insurance
N.A.I.C.S.: 524114
Mike Wilkins (Chm)

Subsidiaries:

HealthStrong Pty Ltd (1)
Level 11 259 George Street, Sydney, 2000, NSW, Australia
Tel.: (61) 130 066 0086
Web Site: https://www.healthstrong.com.au
Rehabilitation & Home Care Services
N.A.I.C.S.: 621610

MHSI Pty. Ltd. (1)
78 Syed Amir Ali Avenue, Kolkata, West Bengal, India
Tel.: (91) 3335446247
Web Site: https://www.mhsi.edu.in
International Educational Services
N.A.I.C.S.: 611710

MEDIBIO LIMITED

Level 4 100 Albert Road, South Melbourne, 3205, VIC, Australia
Tel.: (61) 396927222
Web Site: http://www.medibio.com.au
TRI—(ASX)
Rev.: $596,494
Assets: $7,390,141
Liabilities: $783,922
Net Worth: $6,606,219
Earnings: ($957,943)
Fiscal Year-end: 06/30/24
Medicinal Product Mfr
N.A.I.C.S.: 339112
Melanie Leydin (Co-Sec)

Subsidiaries:

Medibio Limited (1)
8696 Eagle Creek Cir, Savage, MN 55378
Web Site: https://medibio.com.au
Mental Health Care Services
N.A.I.C.S.: 623220

MEDIC INTERNATIONAL LIMITED

4th Floor 1 Belle Vue Square Broughton Road, Skipton, BD23 1FJ, United Kingdom
Tel.: (44) 2080996947
Web Site: http://www.medicinternational.co.uk
Emp.: 70
Medical Recruitment Services
N.A.I.C.S.: 561311
Tracy Ward (Mng Dir)

MEDICA S.P.A.

Via Degli Artigiani 7, 41036, Medolla, MO, Italy
Tel.: (39) 053551159 IT
Web Site: https://www.medica-spa.com
Year Founded: 1985
MDC—(ITA)
Rev.: $94,093,918
Assets: $131,985,703
Liabilities: $71,931,853
Net Worth: $60,053,849
Earnings: $2,751,324
Emp.: 757
Fiscal Year-end: 12/31/23
Medical Equipment Mfr
N.A.I.C.S.: 339112
Luciano Fecondini (CEO)

MEDICA SUR, S.A.B. DE C.V.

Puente De Piedra 150, Colonia Toriello Guerra Alcaldia Tlalpan, 14050, Mexico, Mexico

INTERNATIONAL PUBLIC

Tel.: (52) 54247200
Web Site: https://medicasurmexico.com
Year Founded: 1981
MEDICA—(MEX)
Rev.: $243,327,501
Assets: $243,228,986
Liabilities: $123,196,510
Net Worth: $120,032,475
Earnings: $37,413,508
Emp.: 2,151
Fiscal Year-end: 12/31/23
Health Care Srvices
N.A.I.C.S.: 622110
Juan Carlos Griera Hernando (CEO)

MEDICAL CARE TECHNOLOGIES INC.

New World Tower 1 Suite 2302 18 Queen's Road, Central, China (Hong Kong)
Tel.: (852) 10 6407 0580 NV
Web Site: http://www.medicaretechinc.com
Year Founded: 2007
MDCE—(OTCIQ)
Childrens' Medical Clinics; Medical Management Software Systems; Pharmaceutical & Nutraceutical Products Distr
N.A.I.C.S.: 621498
Mark J. Langweiler (COO & Chief Medical Officer)

MEDICAL COMPRESSION SYSTEM (D.B.N) LTD.

12 Ha Ilan Street Or Akiva Industrial Park, PO Box 75, Or Akiva, 3060000, Israel
Tel.: (972) 4 626 6630
Web Site: http://www.mcsmed.com
Year Founded: 1997
Rev.: $1,256,726
Assets: $4,974,640
Liabilities: $1,757,082
Net Worth: $3,217,558
Earnings: $26,795
Emp.: 33
Fiscal Year-end: 12/31/18
Medical Device Mfr
N.A.I.C.S.: 334510

MEDICAL DATA VISION CO., LTD.

7 Kandamitoshirocho Sumitomo Real estate Kanda Building 10F, Chiyoda-ku, Tokyo, 1010053, Japan
Tel.: (81) 352836911
Web Site: https://www.mdv.co.jp
Year Founded: 2003
3902—(TKS)
Rev.: $45,510,710
Assets: $44,106,890
Liabilities: $13,499,360
Net Worth: $30,607,530
Earnings: $6,941,110
Emp.: 77
Fiscal Year-end: 12/31/23
Medical Data & Analysis
N.A.I.C.S.: 518210
Hiroyuki Iwasaki (Pres)

MEDICAL DEVELOPMENTS INTERNATIONAL LIMITED

4 Caribbean Drive, PO Box 9004, Scoresby, Melbourne, 3179, VIC, Australia
Tel.: (61) 395471888
Web Site: https://www.medicaldev.com
MVP—(ASX)
Rev.: $22,134,749
Assets: $39,503,873
Liabilities: $8,965,678
Net Worth: $30,538,194
Earnings: ($27,371,795)

AND PRIVATE COMPANIES

Emp.: 80
Fiscal Year-end: 06/30/24
Pain Relief & Respiratory Pharmaceuticals
N.A.I.C.S.: 325412
John Stewart Sharman (CEO)

MEDICAL DEVICES VENTURE SA
12 Rue Ampere, 91430, Igny, France
Tel.: (33) 16 933 1690
Web Site:
https://www.medicaldevices.com
MLMDV—(EUR)
Investment Services
N.A.I.C.S.: 523150
Loic Poirier (CEO & Chm)

MEDICAL FACILITIES CORPORATION
4576 Yonge Street Suite 701, Toronto, M2N 6N4, ON, Canada
Tel.: (416) 848-7380   ON
Web Site:
https://www.medicalfacilitiescorp.ca
MFCSF—(OTCIQ)
Rev.: $445,582,000
Assets: $354,885,000
Liabilities: $236,582,000
Net Worth: $118,303,000
Earnings: $43,999,000
Emp.: 1,529
Fiscal Year-end: 12/31/23
Medical Facility Management Services
N.A.I.C.S.: 622110
Jeffrey C. Lozon (Chm)

Subsidiaries:

Black Hills Surgical Hospital   (1)
216 Anamaria Dr, Rapid City, SD 57701   (51%)
Tel.: (605) 721-4700
Web Site: https://www.bhsc.com
Sales Range: $25-49.9 Million
Orthopaedic & Neurosurgical Procedure Services
N.A.I.C.S.: 622110

Oklahoma Spine Hospital, LLC   (1)
14101 Parkway Commons Dr, Oklahoma City, OK 73134   (51%)
Tel.: (405) 749-2700
Web Site: https://www.oklahomaspine.com
Sales Range: $25-49.9 Million
Emp.: 259
Specialty Spine Hospital
N.A.I.C.S.: 622110

Sioux Falls Specialty Hospital LLP   (1)
910 E 20th St, Sioux Falls, SD 57105   (51%)
Tel.: (605) 334-6730
Web Site: https://www.sfsh.com
Sales Range: $25-49.9 Million
Emp.: 250
Hospital Operations
N.A.I.C.S.: 622110
JoAnn Hirsch (Compliance Officer)

MEDICAL IKKOU CO., LTD.
36-25 Nishimarunouchi, Tsu, 514-0035, Mie, Japan
Tel.: (81) 592261193   JP
Web Site: https://www.m-ikkou.co.jp
Year Founded: 1985
3353—(TKS)
Rev.: $282,891,000
Assets: $224,462,310
Liabilities: $126,329,620
Net Worth: $98,132,690
Earnings: $7,366,510
Fiscal Year-end: 02/29/24
Holding Company; Pharmacies & Nursing Care Facilities Operator; Medical Supplies Wholesale Distr
N.A.I.C.S.: 551112
Toshihisa Minamino (Pres)

Subsidiaries:

Healthcare Ikkou Corporation   (1)
36-25 Nishimarunouchi, Tsu, 514-0035, Mie, Japan
Tel.: (81) 59 226 1900
Web Site: https://www.h-ikkou.co.jp
Emp.: 612
Nursing Care Facilities Operator
N.A.I.C.S.: 623110
Toshiharu Sakurai (Pres)

MEDICAL INTERNATIONAL TECHNOLOGY, INC.
1872 Rue Beaulac, Montreal, H4R 2E7, QC, Canada
Tel.: (514) 339-9355   CO
Web Site: https://mitneedlefree.com
MDLH—(OTCIQ)
Sales Range: Less than $1 Million
Emp.: 3
Needle-Free Jet Injector Products Researcher, Developer & Marketer
N.A.I.C.S.: 339112
Karim Menassa (Founder, Pres & CEO)

MEDICAL NET, INC.
1-34-14 Hatagaya, Shibuya-ku, Tokyo, 1510072, Japan
Tel.: (81) 357905261
Web Site: https://www.medical-net.com
Year Founded: 2001
3645—(TKS)
Rev.: $34,715,720
Assets: $26,367,290
Liabilities: $13,603,380
Net Worth: $12,763,910
Earnings: $33,050
Emp.: 179
Fiscal Year-end: 05/31/24
Medical Devices
N.A.I.C.S.: 621999
Dai Hirakawa (Pres)

MEDICAL PACKAGING COMPANY
124 Osman Abn Afan, Heliopolis, Cairo, Egypt
Tel.: (20) 2 26324708
Web Site: http://www.med-pack.com
Year Founded: 2006
MEPA.CA—(EGX)
Sales Range: Less than $1 Million
Pharmaceuticals Product Mfr
N.A.I.C.S.: 325412
Fawzy Foud Bakheet Nakhla Ibrahim (Chm)

MEDICAL PROGNOSIS INSTITUTE A/S
Venlighedsvej 1, 2970, Horsholm, Denmark
Tel.: (45) 2086 5206
Web Site: http://www.medical-prognosis.com
MPI—(CSE)
Medical Laboratories
N.A.I.C.S.: 621511
Ulla Hald Buhl (Officer-Comm)

MEDICAL SYSTEM NETWORK CO., LTD.
AKK Building 3-3 Kita 10-jo Nishi 24-chome, Chuo-ku, Sapporo, 060-0010, Hokkaido, Japan
Tel.: (81) 116121069   JP
Web Site: https://www.msnw.co.jp
Year Founded: 1999
4350—(TKS)
Rev.: $762,536,210
Assets: $450,464,890
Liabilities: $349,867,300
Net Worth: $100,597,590
Earnings: $12,294,600
Emp.: 3,619

Fiscal Year-end: 03/31/24
Pharmacy Services
N.A.I.C.S.: 456110
Inao Tajiri (Pres)

Subsidiaries:

Hokkaido Institute of Pahrmacy Benefit Co., Ltd.   (1)
10 Jonishi 24-2-1, Chuo Ward, Sapporo, 060-0010, Japan
Tel.: (81) 11 613 3577
Web Site: https://www.iyakusoken.jp
Real Estate Services
N.A.I.C.S.: 531210

Total Medical Service Co., Ltd.   (1)
4-17-22 Midorigahama Shingu-cho, Kasuya-gun, Fukuoka, 811-0119, Japan
Tel.: (81) 929629200
Web Site: https://www.tms-inc.co.jp
Sales Range: $50-74.9 Million
Emp.: 934
Pharmaceutical Retailer
N.A.I.C.S.: 456110

MEDICAL UNION PHARMACEUTICALS
36 Dr Mohammad Hassan El-Gamal St, PO Box 7010, 6th District Nasr City, Cairo, Egypt
Tel.: (20) 22709324
Web Site: http://www.mupeg.com
Year Founded: 1984
Sales Range: $150-199.9 Million
Emp.: 2,278
Pharmaceutical Preparation Mfr
N.A.I.C.S.: 325412
Mohamed Mahmoud (Chm)

MEDICALE CORP.
Otar Lortkifanidze 16, Tbilisi, Georgia
Tel.: (995) 17026054432   NV
Year Founded: 2020
Liabilities: $54,774
Net Worth: ($54,774)
Earnings: ($46,419)
Fiscal Year-end: 09/30/22
Dietary Supplement Mfr & Distr
N.A.I.C.S.: 325412
Borisi Alborovi (CEO)

MEDICALGORITHMICS S.A.
Al Jerozolimskie 81Central Tower Building 18th floor, 02-001, Warsaw, Poland
Tel.: (48) 228251249
Web Site: https://www.medicalgorithmics.pl
MDG—(WAR)
Rev.: $15,756,167
Assets: $27,316,485
Liabilities: $7,199,166
Net Worth: $20,117,319
Earnings: ($7,638,045)
Emp.: 228
Fiscal Year-end: 12/31/22
Medical Equipment Mfr
N.A.I.C.S.: 339112

Subsidiaries:

Medi-Lynx Cardiac Monitoring, LLC   (1)
6700 Pinecrest Dr Ste 200, Plano, TX 75024-4265   (75%)
Tel.: (855) 847-1009
Web Site: http://www.medi-lynx.com
Cardiac Monitoring Services
N.A.I.C.S.: 621999
Robyn Fees (Dir-HR)

MEDICALSYSTEM BIOTECHNOLOGY CO., LTD.
No 1228 Jinda South Road, Yinzhou District, Ningbo, 315104, Zhejiang, China
Tel.: (86) 57488178818
Web Site: http://www.nb-medicalsystem.com
Year Founded: 2003

MEDICENNA THERAPEUTICS CORP.

300439—(CHIN)
Rev.: $349,468,236
Assets: $503,148,672
Liabilities: $149,419,296
Net Worth: $353,729,376
Earnings: $27,873,612
Emp.: 770
Fiscal Year-end: 12/31/22
In-Vitro Diagnostic Products Mfr
N.A.I.C.S.: 325413
Zou Bingde (Chm)

MEDICALSYSTEM CO.,LTD
No 222 GuiJiaXiang SIP, Suzhou, 215000, China
Tel.: (86) 51262621210
Web Site: https://www.medicalsystem.com.cn
Year Founded: 2005
603990—(SHG)
Rev.: $42,893,225
Assets: $228,910,687
Liabilities: $38,017,849
Net Worth: $190,892,838
Earnings: $4,711,894
Fiscal Year-end: 12/31/22
Medical Software Development Services
N.A.I.C.S.: 541511
Weng Kang (Chm, Vice Chm & Gen Mgr)

MEDICAMEN BIOTECH LIMITED
1506 Chiranjiv Tower 43 Nehru Place, New Delhi, 110019, India
Tel.: (91) 1147589500
Web Site: https://www.medicamen.com
531146—(BOM)
Rev.: $15,488,673
Assets: $26,481,967
Liabilities: $8,342,544
Net Worth: $18,139,423
Earnings: $1,655,669
Emp.: 289
Fiscal Year-end: 03/31/21
Pharmaceutical Products Mfr & Distr
N.A.I.C.S.: 325412
Rajesh Madan (CEO)

MEDICAN CONSTRUCTION LTD
1870A 6th Ave SW, Medicine Hat, T1A 7X5, AB, Canada
Tel.: (403) 526-3477
Web Site: http://www.medican.com
Year Founded: 1974
Rev.: $13,119,890
Emp.: 80
Construction Services
N.A.I.C.S.: 236220
Ty Schneider (Chief Restructuring Officer)

MEDICANIMAL LIMITED
Unit 2 & 11 The Courtyard 100 Villiers Road Willesden, London, NW2 5PJ, United Kingdom
Tel.: (44) 844 585 7777
Web Site: http://www.medicanimal.com
Year Founded: 2007
Sales Range: $50-74.9 Million
Emp.: 300
Electronic Shopping Services
N.A.I.C.S.: 445298
Ivan Retzignac (Co-Founder & Dir-Strategic Dev)

MEDICENNA THERAPEUTICS CORP.
2 Bloor St W 7th Floor, Toronto, M4W 3E2, ON, Canada
Tel.: (416) 648-5555   AB

MEDICENNA THERAPEUTICS CORP.

Medicenna Therapeutics Corp.—(Continued)
Web Site:
https://www.medicenna.com
Year Founded: 2015
MDNA—(NASDAQ)
Rev.: $884,987
Assets: $14,134,668
Liabilities: $10,299,973
Net Worth: $3,834,696
Earnings: ($18,812,244)
Emp.: 16
Fiscal Year-end: 03/31/24
Financial Investment Services
N.A.I.C.S.: 523999
Humphrey A. R. Gardner (Chief Medical Officer)

MEDICINES DEVELOPMENT FOR GLOBAL HEALTH LIMITED
Level 1 18 Kavanagh Street, Southbank, 3006, VIC, Australia
Tel.: (61) 399122400
Web Site:
https://www.medicinesdevelop.com
Year Founded: 2005
Pharmaceuticals Product Mfr
N.A.I.C.S.: 325412

MEDICO INTERCONTINENTAL LIMITED
1-5th Floor Aditraj Arcade Nr Karma Shrestha Tower, 100 Ft Road Satellite, Ahmedabad, 380 015, Gujarat, India
Tel.: (91) 9898666178
Web Site:
https://www.medicolimited.com
539938—(BOM)
Rev.: $9,200,587
Assets: $7,059,481
Liabilities: $2,121,527
Net Worth: $4,937,953
Earnings: $432,612
Emp.: 25
Fiscal Year-end: 03/31/23
Finance Management Services
N.A.I.C.S.: 523150
Puneeta Sharma (Compliance Officer & Sec)

Subsidiaries:

Azillian Healthcare Private Limited (1)
109 1st Floor Safal Prelude Corporate Road Nr Hotel Ramada, Opp Prahalad Nagar Garden Anandnagar Road Satelliet, Ahmedabad, India
Tel.: (91) 9624226409
Web Site: https://www.azillian.in
Pharmaceuticals Product Mfr
N.A.I.C.S.: 325412

Evagrace Pharma Private Limited (1)
305 Aditraj Arcade Near Hetvee Tower Anand Nagar, Satellite, Ahmedabad, 380015, Gujarat, India
Tel.: (91) 9724338850
Web Site: https://www.evagracepharma.com
Pharmaceuticals Product Mfr
N.A.I.C.S.: 325412

Ritz Formulations Private Limited (1)
301 302 303 Aditraj Arcade Near Hetvi Tower 100 Feet Ring Road, Satellite, Ahmedabad, 380015, Gujarat, India
Tel.: (91) 8511143595
Web Site: https://www.ritzpharma.com
Pharmaceuticals Product Mfr
N.A.I.C.S.: 325412
Samir D. Shah (Mng Dir)

Sungrace Pharma Private Limited (1)
501-502 Aditraj Arcade Opp Titanium City Center 100 Feet Ring Road, Satellite, Ahmedabad, 380015, Gujarat, India
Tel.: (91) 7926742740
Web Site: http://www.sungracepharma.com

Pharmaceuticals Product Mfr
N.A.I.C.S.: 325412

MEDICO REMEDIES LIMITED
1105/1106 Hubtown Solaris N S Phadke Marg Opp teligali, Andheri East, Mumbai, 400 049, India
Tel.: (91) 2226701055
Web Site:
https://www.medicoremedies.com
Year Founded: 1994
540937—(BOM)
Rev.: $16,846,365
Assets: $10,322,205
Liabilities: $5,891,722
Net Worth: $4,430,483
Earnings: $353,761
Emp.: 107
Fiscal Year-end: 03/31/21
Pharmaceutical Preparation Mfr & Distr
N.A.I.C.S.: 325412
Harshit Haresh Mehta (Mng Dir)

MEDICON HELLAS S.A.
Melitona 5-7 Street, Gerakas, 15344, Athens, Greece
Tel.: (30) 2106606000
Web Site:
https://www.mediconsa.com
Year Founded: 1978
MEDIC—(ATH)
Sales Range: Less than $1 Million
Emp.: 153
Diagnostic Equipment Mfr & Distr
N.A.I.C.S.: 334510
Sotiria Mitropoulou (Vice Chm)

MEDICOVER AB
Riddargatan 12A, Stockholm, Sweden
Tel.: (46) 840017600
Web Site: http://www.medicover.com
Healtcare Services
N.A.I.C.S.: 621999
Stefan Stroe (Mgr-Ecommerce)

Subsidiaries:

NEOMEDIC S.A. (1)
al Generala Tadeusza Bora-Komorowskiego 25c, 31-476, Krakow, Poland
Tel.: (48) 122930963
Web Site: http://www.grupaneomedic.pl
Healtcare Services
N.A.I.C.S.: 621491

MEDICOVER HOLDING S.A.
20 rue Philippe II, 2340, Luxembourg, Luxembourg
Tel.: (352) 26203110
Web Site: http://www.medicover.com
Sales Range: $50-74.9 Million
Emp.: 3,000
Health Care Srvices
N.A.I.C.S.: 621999
Fredrik Ragmark (Grp CEO)

Subsidiaries:

Intersono Ltd. (1)
Antonovycha str 102, Kiev, 79057, Ukraine
Tel.: (380) 67 370 84 24
Web Site: http://www.intersono.ua
Health Care Srvices
N.A.I.C.S.: 621999
Shulhina Halyna (Dir-Quality)

Medicover Hungary (1)
Vaciut 22-24 Street 5, 1037, Budapest, Hungary
Tel.: (36) 0014653150
Web Site: http://www.medicover.hu
Sales Range: $100-124.9 Million
Emp.: 120
Health Care Srvices
N.A.I.C.S.: 524114

Medicover Rombel Srl (1)
Str Ion Campineanu 11 Etaj 4 Sector 1, Bucharest, Romania
Tel.: (40) 21310

Web Site: http://www.medicover.ro
Sales Range: $25-49.9 Million
Emp.: 111
Medical Laboratory & Diagnostic Testing Services
N.A.I.C.S.: 621511

Medicover Slovakia s.r.o. (1)
Heydukova 14, 81108, Bratislava, Slovakia
Tel.: (421) 2 32171211
Web Site: http://www.medicover.sk
Health Care Srvices
N.A.I.C.S.: 621999
Tatiana Harsova (Key Acct Mgr)

Medicover Sp z o o (1)
ul Bitwy Warszawskiej 1920 r 18, 02-366, Warsaw, Poland
Tel.: (48) 225927000
Web Site: http://www.medicover.pl
Health Care Srvices
N.A.I.C.S.: 524114

Medicover Srl (1)
Sergent Constantin Ghercu Street No 1A 1st Floor Sector 6, Bucharest, 11216, Romania
Tel.: (40) 213101699
Web Site: http://www.medicover.ro
Emp.: 22
Health Care Srvices
N.A.I.C.S.: 524114
Adrian Purcarea (Gen Mgr)

Synevo Bulgaria Ltd. (1)
ul Angel Kanchev 34 et 1, Sofia, 1000, Bulgaria
Tel.: (359) 29810241
Web Site: http://www.synevo.bg
Health Care Services
N.A.I.C.S.: 621999

Synevo Medical (Poland) Sp.z o.o (1)
Ul Dzika 4, 00-194, Warsaw, Poland
Tel.: (48) 226363782
Web Site: http://www.synevo.pl
Medical Laboratory & Diagnostic Testing Services
N.A.I.C.S.: 621511

Synevo Moldova (1)
Str Nicolae Testemitanu Nr 37, 2025, Chisinau, Moldova
Tel.: (373) 22 856990
Web Site: http://www.synevo.md
Health Care Srvices
N.A.I.C.S.: 621999
Andrei Sevcenco (Gen Dir)

Synevo Ukraine (1)
Street Shota Rustaveli 40, Kiev, Ukraine
Tel.: (380) 44 205 00 20
Web Site: http://www.synevo.ua
Health Care Srvices
N.A.I.C.S.: 621999

MEDICOX CO., LTD.
2nd and 3rd Floors Blue Pearl Building 549 Dosandaero, Gangnam-gu, Seoul, 06013, Korea (South)
Tel.: (82) 232189500
Web Site: https://www.c-ocean.co.kr
Year Founded: 1999
054180—(KRS)
Rev.: $16,733,719
Assets: $84,702,977
Liabilities: $36,198,081
Net Worth: $48,504,896
Earnings: ($32,688,484)
Emp.: 91
Fiscal Year-end: 12/31/22
LCE Display Panel Mfr
N.A.I.C.S.: 339999
Hyun Kyungsuk (CEO)

MEDICSKIN HOLDINGS LIMITED
21/F Tower 2 New World Tower 16-18 Queen s Road, Central, China (Hong Kong)
Tel.: (852) 2 526 9333
Web Site:
http://www.medicskinholdings.com
Year Founded: 2000

INTERNATIONAL PUBLIC

8307—(HKG)
Rev.: $6,490,532
Assets: $7,309,168
Liabilities: $5,480,360
Net Worth: $1,828,807
Earnings: $534,622
Emp.: 31
Fiscal Year-end: 03/31/22
Skin Care Treatment Services
N.A.I.C.S.: 812112
Kwok Leung Kong (Chm & CEO)

MEDICURE INC.
2-1250 Waverley Street, Winnipeg, R3T 6C6, MB, Canada
Tel.: (204) 487-7412
Web Site: https://www.medicure.com
Year Founded: 1997
MCUJF—(OTCIQ)
Rev.: $18,043,288
Assets: $23,388,607
Liabilities: $6,956,816
Net Worth: $16,431,791
Earnings: $1,067,812
Emp.: 48
Fiscal Year-end: 12/31/22
Pharmaceutical Company; Cardiovascular Drug Developer & Mfr
N.A.I.C.S.: 325411
Albert D. Friesen (Founder, Chm & CEO)

Subsidiaries:

Medicure International, Inc. (1)
1st Floor Limegrove Centre, Saint James, Barbados
Tel.: (246) 246 432 4000
Biotechnology Research Services
N.A.I.C.S.: 541713

Medicure Pharma, Inc. (1)
116 Village Blvd Ste 200, Princeton, NJ 08873-5800
Prescription Drugs Whlsr
N.A.I.C.S.: 424210

MEDICUS HOMECARE INC.
Waiblingerstrasse 34, 70372, Stuttgart, Germany
Tel.: (49) 157 894 69537
Year Founded: 2012
Investment Services
N.A.I.C.S.: 523999
Leon E. Nowek (CFO)

MEDIENART AG
Aurorastrasse 27, 5000, Aarau, Switzerland
Tel.: (41) 625449292
Web Site: http://www.medienart.ch
Advertising Company
N.A.I.C.S.: 541810
Jurg Rykart (Owner & Head-Sls & Fin)

MEDIENCE CO., LTD.
4 Nonhyeon-ro 64-gil, Gangnam-gu, Seoul, Korea (South)
Tel.: (82) 27088300
Web Site:
https://www.medience.co.kr
Year Founded: 1979
014100—(KRS)
Rev.: $54,780,680
Assets: $89,268,548
Liabilities: $27,168,464
Net Worth: $62,100,084
Earnings: ($8,994,133)
Emp.: 105
Fiscal Year-end: 12/31/22
Healthcare Product Development & Sales
N.A.I.C.S.: 339999
Lee Jin Seo (Dir)

Subsidiaries:

Boryung Co., Ltd. (1)
Boryung Bldg 136, Jongno-gu

Changgyeonggung-ro, Seoul, Korea (South)
Tel.: (82) 27088000
Web Site: http://www.boryung.co.kr
Pharmaceuticals Product Mfr
N.A.I.C.S.: 325412
Jae-Hyun Ahn (CEO)

Boryung Co., Ltd. - Ansan Factory (1)
1122-3 Shingil-dong, Danwon-gu, 425-839, Ansan, Gyeonggi-do, Korea (South)
Tel.: (82) 3149122716
Web Site: http://www.boryung.co.kr
Sales Range: $50-74.9 Million
Pharmaceuticals Product Mfr
N.A.I.C.S.: 325412

Soo & Soo, Ltd. (1)
5/F Boryung Bldg 66 - 21 Wonnam-Dong, Seoul, 110-750, Korea (South)
Tel.: (82) 27404210
Web Site: http://www.boryung.co.kr
Sales Range: $25-49.9 Million
Emp.: 30
Medical Device Mfr & Distr
N.A.I.C.S.: 423450

MEDIES
4 Fall Park Court, Leeds, LS13 2LP, West Yorkshire, United Kingdom
Tel.: (44) 7967396263　　WY
Year Founded: 2022
Video & Audio Streaming Services
N.A.I.C.S.: 518210
Kenneth Tindall (Pres, CEO, CFO, Principal Acctg Officer, Treas & Sec)

MEDIFARM A.D.
Bacvanska bb, Belgrade, Serbia
Tel.: (381) 112851538
Web Site: http://www.medifarm.rs
Year Founded: 1985
MDFR—(BEL)
Sales Range: $10-24.9 Million
Pharmaceutical Product Whslr
N.A.I.C.S.: 424210
Goran Mikic (Exec Dir)

MEDIGARD LIMITED
Suite 14 30 Tedder Avenue, Gold Coast, 4217, QLD, Australia
Tel.: (61) 7 55285640
Web Site:
　　http://www.medigard.com.au
Year Founded: 1999
Rev.: $28,639
Assets: $340,260
Liabilities: $853,482
Net Worth: ($513,222)
Earnings: ($479,727)
Fiscal Year-end: 06/30/18
Medical Instrument Mfr
N.A.I.C.S.: 339112
Patricia Mary Boero (CFO & Sec)

MEDIGEN BIOTECHNOLOGY CORP.
14F No 3 Park St, Nangang Dist, Taipei, 11503, Taiwan
Tel.: (886) 277361234
Web Site:
　　https://www.medigen.com.tw
Year Founded: 1999
Pharmaceuticals Product Mfr
N.A.I.C.S.: 325412
Stanley Chang (Chm & CEO)

MEDIGEN VACCINE BIOLOGICS CORP.
14F No 3 Park St, Nangang Dist, Taipei, 11503, Taiwan
Tel.: (886) 277361234
Web Site:
　　https://www.medigen.com.tw
6547—(TPE)
Chemical Research & Development Services
N.A.I.C.S.: 541715
Stanley Chang (CEO)

MEDIGENE AG
Lochhamer Str 11, 82152, Planegg, Germany
Tel.: (49) 892000330　　De
Web Site: https://www.medigene.com
Year Founded: 1994
MDG1—(OTCIQ)
Rev.: $10,745,872
Assets: $91,810,940
Liabilities: $26,525,071
Net Worth: $65,285,869
Earnings: ($35,465,430)
Emp.: 114
Fiscal Year-end: 12/31/20
Biopharmaceutical Mfr, Researcher & Developer
N.A.I.C.S.: 325412
Gerd Zettlmeissl (Chm-Supervisory Bd)

MEDIKA D.D.
Capraska 1, 10000, Zagreb, Croatia
Tel.: (385) 2412655
Web Site: https://www.medika.hr
Year Founded: 1922
MDKA—(ZAG)
Rev.: $671,526,283
Assets: $433,945,100
Liabilities: $331,986,686
Net Worth: $101,958,414
Earnings: $16,565,974
Emp.: 951
Fiscal Year-end: 12/31/22
Pharmaceutical Products Distr
N.A.I.C.S.: 424210
Ruzica Vadic (Chm)

MEDIKIT CO., LTD.
1-13-2 Yushima, Bunkyo-ku, Tokyo, 113-0034, Japan
Tel.: (81) 338390201
Web Site: https://www.medikit.co.jp
Year Founded: 1973
7749—(TKS)
Rev.: $144,367,320
Assets: $336,960,593
Liabilities: $45,398,071
Net Worth: $291,562,522
Earnings: $20,277,497
Emp.: 966
Fiscal Year-end: 03/31/24
Medical Device Mfr & Whslr
N.A.I.C.S.: 339112
Yoji Kageyama (Pres & CEO)

Subsidiaries:

Medikit Europe GmbH (1)
Gerbermuehlstrasse 7, 60594, Frankfurt am Main, Germany
Tel.: (49) 6987 006 6060
Web Site: https://www.medikit-europe.de
Medical Device Mfr & Distr
N.A.I.C.S.: 339112
Junko Takahashi (Mng Dir)

Medikit Vietnam Co., Ltd. (1)
Lot B3-D3 Nomura-Haiphong Industrial Park An Hai Dist, Haiphong, Vietnam
Tel.: (84) 313743160
Medical Equipment Distr
N.A.I.C.S.: 423450

PediaVascular Inc. (1)
7181 Chagrin Rd Ste 250, Chagrin Falls, OH 44023
Tel.: (216) 236-5533
Web Site: https://pediavascular.com
Medical Equipment Mfr & Distr
N.A.I.C.S.: 339112
Tim Moran (Founder)

MEDIKOMERC D.D. SARAJEVO
Marsala Tita 30/II, 71000, Sarajevo, Bosnia & Herzegovina
Tel.: (387) 33 226 562
Web Site: http://www.medikomerc.ba
MKOMRK1—(SARE)
Sales Range: Less than $1 Million

Emp.: 2
Medical Goods Whslr
N.A.I.C.S.: 424210
Licina Rifat (Exec Dir)

MEDILINES DISTRIBUTORS INCORPORATED
54 E Rodriguez Jr Avenue Backing F Pike St Bagong Ilog, Pasig, Philippines
Tel.: (63) 282517507　　PH
Web Site:
　　https://www.medilines.com.ph
Year Founded: 2002
MEDIC—(PHI)
Rev.: $12,275,558
Assets: $69,218,143
Liabilities: $30,390,459
Net Worth: $38,827,684
Earnings: $1,308,327
Emp.: 53
Fiscal Year-end: 12/31/23
Medical Equipment Distr
N.A.I.C.S.: 423450

MEDIMET PRECISION CASTING & IMPLANTS TECHNOLOGY GMBH
Ohle Ring 23-25 Wiepenkathen, 21684, Stade, Germany
Tel.: (49) 414180300　　De
Web Site: http://www.medimet.de
Year Founded: 1995
Sales Range: $50-74.9 Million
Emp.: 107
Medical Implants Mfr
N.A.I.C.S.: 339113
Reimund Dorschfeld (CEO)

MEDINAVI AG
Hirschbergstr 8, 80634, Munich, Germany
Tel.: (49) 17630414656
Web Site: http://www.medinavi.de
Medical Product Distr
N.A.I.C.S.: 423450
Rony Vogel (Vice Chm-Supervisory Bd)

MEDINCELL S.A.
3 Rue des Freres Lumiere, 34380, Jacou, France
Tel.: (33) 467021367
Web Site: https://www.medincell.com
MEDCL—(EUR)
Rev.: $14,877,122
Assets: $31,964,840
Liabilities: $78,044,154
Net Worth: ($46,079,313)
Earnings: ($34,874,895)
Emp.: 152
Fiscal Year-end: 03/31/23
Pharmaceutical Product Mfr & Distr
N.A.I.C.S.: 325412
Jaime Arango (CFO)

MEDINE LIMITED
4 Uniciti Office Park Riviere Noire Road, 90203, Bambous, 90203, Mauritius
Tel.: (230) 4016101
Web Site: https://www.medine.com
Year Founded: 1911
MSE—(MAU)
Rev.: $70,501,614
Assets: $664,215,669
Liabilities: $188,644,048
Net Worth: $475,571,620
Earnings: $25,656,649
Emp.: 920
Fiscal Year-end: 06/30/23
Property Development Services
N.A.I.C.S.: 531390
Thierry Sauzier (CEO)

Subsidiaries:

Casela Limited (1)
Royal Road, Cascavelle, 90203, Mauritius
Tel.: (230) 4016500
Web Site: https://www.caselaparks.com
Theme Park Services
N.A.I.C.S.: 713110

MEDINET CO., LTD.
9F TRC Center Building 1-1 Heiwajima 6-chome Ota, Tokyo, 143-0006, Japan
Tel.: (81) 366311201
Web Site: https://www.medinet-inc.co.jp
Year Founded: 1995
2370—(TKS)
Rev.: $6,611,440
Assets: $52,049,360
Liabilities: $4,598,000
Net Worth: $47,451,360
Earnings: ($8,160,240)
Emp.: 83
Fiscal Year-end: 09/30/21
Healthcare Services
N.A.I.C.S.: 621999
Yoshiji Kimura (Founder & Pres)

MEDINET GROUP LTD
Unit 3601 36/F Citicorp Centre, 18 Whitfield Road, Causeway Bay, China (Hong Kong)
Tel.: (852) 2 887 0099　　Ky
Web Site:
　　http://www.medinetgroup.com
8161—(HKG)
Rev.: $15,772,577
Assets: $8,829,971
Liabilities: $4,104,402
Net Worth: $4,725,569
Earnings: ($822,505)
Emp.: 98
Fiscal Year-end: 03/31/22
Dental Care Services
N.A.I.C.S.: 621210
Nelson Chi Wai Chan (Chm & Officer-Compliance)

Subsidiaries:

Medinet Health Centre Limited (1)
Room 601 10 Pottinger St, Central, China (Hong Kong)
Tel.: (852) 28105566
Medical Consulting Services
N.A.I.C.S.: 541611

MEDINEX LIMITED
111 North Bridge Road 23-04 Peninsula Plaza, Singapore, 179098, Singapore
Tel.: (65) 66046330　　SG
Web Site:
　　https://www.medinex.com.sg
Year Founded: 2009
OTX—(CAT)
Rev.: $9,607,601
Assets: $16,743,152
Liabilities: $3,565,996
Net Worth: $13,177,157
Earnings: $1,252,321
Emp.: 75
Fiscal Year-end: 03/31/23
Healtcare Services
N.A.I.C.S.: 621491
Jessie Mui Choo Low (CEO)

Subsidiaries:

AccTax Management Consultancy Private Limited (1)
Blk 165 Bukit Merah Central 06-3663, Singapore, 150165, Singapore
Tel.: (65) 65925130
Web Site: https://www.acctax.sg
Tax Investigation Services
N.A.I.C.S.: 561611

Medinex Professional Services Pte. Ltd. (1)

MEDINEX LIMITED

Medinex Limited—(Continued)

Blk 1003 Bukit Merah Central 06-13 Technopreneur Centre, Singapore, 159836, Singapore
Tel.: (65) 63245727
Web Site: http://www.patceljon.com
Tax Investigation Services
N.A.I.C.S.: 561611

Nex Healthcare Pte. Ltd. (1)
994 Bendemeer Road 03-02 B-Central, Singapore, 339943, Singapore
Tel.: (65) 63910271
Web Site: https://www.nexhealth.com.sg
Healtcare Services
N.A.I.C.S.: 621999

The Family Clinic @ Towner Pte. Ltd. (1)
101 Towner Road 01-202, Singapore, 322101, Singapore
Tel.: (65) 62950995
Web Site: http://www.tfctowner.com
Healtcare Services
N.A.I.C.S.: 621999

MEDINICE SA
ul Hankiewicza 2, 02-103, Warsaw, Poland
Tel.: (48) 725500051
Web Site: https://www.medinice.pl
Year Founded: 2012
ICE—(WAR)
Healtcare Services
N.A.I.C.S.: 621999
Joanna Bogdanska (Chm)

MEDINOTEC INC.
Northlands Deco Park 10 New Market Street Stand 299 Avant Garde Avenue, Northriding, Johannesburg, 2169, South Africa
Tel.: (27) 873302301 NV
Web Site:
  https://www.medinotecinc.com
Year Founded: 2021
MDNC—(OTCQX)
Rev.: $5,020,391
Assets: $4,804,279
Liabilities: $2,637,108
Net Worth: $2,167,171
Earnings: ($404,688)
Emp.: 35
Fiscal Year-end: 02/29/24
Medical Device Mfr & Distr
N.A.I.C.S.: 339112
Gregory Vizirgianakis (Founder)

Subsidiaries:

DISA Medinotec Proprietary Limited (1)
Northlands Business Park 171 Bush Telegraph, Northriding, 2169, South Africa
Tel.: (27) 117047837
Web Site: https://www.disamedinotec.com
Medical Device Mfr & Distr
N.A.I.C.S.: 339113

MEDIOBANCA S.P.A.
Piazzetta Enrico Cuccia 1, 20121, Milan, Italy
Tel.: (39) 0288291
Web Site:
  http://www.mediobanca.com
Rev.: $2,334,310,095
Assets: $88,412,571,847
Liabilities: $77,328,962,431
Net Worth: $11,083,609,416
Earnings: $672,343,787
Emp.: 5,010
Fiscal Year-end: 06/30/20
Financial Services
N.A.I.C.S.: 541611
Renato Pagliaro (Chm)

Subsidiaries:

Mbcredit Solutions S.P.A. (1)
Via Caldera 21, 20153, Milan, Italy
Tel.: (39) 0233222900
Web Site: https://www.mbcreditsolutions.it

Financial Investment Services
N.A.I.C.S.: 523999
Angelo Piazza (CEO)

Mediobanca International (Luxembourg) S.A. (1)
4 Boulevard Joseph II, L-1840, Luxembourg, Luxembourg
Tel.: (352) 2673031
Web Site: https://www.mediobancaint.lu
Fund Management Services
N.A.I.C.S.: 541611
Giovanni Mancuso (Chm)

Mediobanca Management Company (1)
2 Boulevard de la Foire Kansallis House, L1528, Luxembourg, Luxembourg
Tel.: (352) 27029921
Web Site:
  https://www.mediobancamanagement
  company.com
Fund Management Services
N.A.I.C.S.: 541611

RAM Active Investments (Europe) SA (1)
51 Avenue John F. Kennedy, 1855, Luxembourg, Luxembourg
Tel.: (352) 2856141
Financial Investment Services
N.A.I.C.S.: 523999

MEDIOBANCA-BANCA DE CREDITO FINANZIARIO S.P.A.
Piazzetta Enrico Cuccia 1, 20121, Milan, Italy
Tel.: (39) 0288291 IT
Web Site:
  https://www.mediobanca.com
Year Founded: 1946
MB—(ISE)
Rev.: $3,058,584,071
Assets: $98,898,136,197
Liabilities: $86,443,370,386
Net Worth: $12,454,765,810
Earnings: $1,108,132,959
Emp.: 5,031
Fiscal Year-end: 06/30/23
Financial Investment Services
N.A.I.C.S.: 523999
Francesco Saverio Vinci (Gen Mgr)

Subsidiaries:

Cairn Capital Limited (1)
62 Buckingham Gate, London, SW1E 6AJ, United Kingdom
Tel.: (44) 2072594800
Web Site: http://www.cairncapital.com
Emp.: 54
Fund Management Services
N.A.I.C.S.: 523940
Ansumana Bai-Marrow (Chief Compliance Officer)

Chebanca S.P.A. (1)
Viale Bodio 37 Palazzo, 20158, Milan, Italy
Tel.: (39) 0232004141
Web Site: https://www.chebanca.it
Asset Management Services
N.A.I.C.S.: 523940

Compass Banca S.P.A. (1)
Via Caldera 21, 20153, Milan, Italy
Tel.: (39) 02721321
Web Site: https://www.compass.it
Credit Financial Services
N.A.I.C.S.: 522299

Compass S.p.A. (1)
Via Caldera 21, 20153, Milan, Italy (100%)
Tel.: (39) 02721321
Web Site: https://compass.it
Commericial Banking
N.A.I.C.S.: 522110

MB Facta S.P.A. (1)
via Siusi 7, 20132, Milan, Italy
Tel.: (39) 022899911
Web Site: https://www.mbfacta.it
Financial Factoring Services
N.A.I.C.S.: 522299

Mediobanca SGR S.P.A. (1)
Foro Buonaparte 10, 20121, Milan, Italy
Tel.: (39) 0285961311

Web Site: https://www.mediobancasgr.com
Asset Management Services
N.A.I.C.S.: 523940

Mediobanca Securities USA LLC (1)
1450 Broadway, New York, NY 10018
Tel.: (212) 991-4744
Credit Financial Services
N.A.I.C.S.: 522299

Ram Active Investments S.A. (1)
8 Rue du Rhone, 1204, Geneva, Switzerland
Tel.: (41) 587268700
Web Site: http://ram-ai.com
Emp.: 40
Investment Management Service
N.A.I.C.S.: 523940
Robert Zito (Mng Dir & COO)

Ricerche e Studi R & S S.p.A. (1)
Foro Buonaparte n 10, 20121, Milan, Italy (100%)
Tel.: (39) 0286462348
Web Site: http://www.mbres.it
Sales Range: $25-49.9 Million
Emp.: 15
Management Consulting Services
N.A.I.C.S.: 541618
Gabriele Barbaresco (Mng Dir)

SPAFID Societa Per Amministrazioni Fiduciarie S.p.A. (1)
Via Filodrammatici 10, Milan, Italy (100%)
Tel.: (39) 02801451
Open-End Investment Funds
N.A.I.C.S.: 525910

Selmabipimme Leasing S.P.A. (1)
Via Siusi 7, 20132, Milan, Italy
Tel.: (39) 02748221
Web Site: https://www.selmabipiemme.it
Financial Lending Services
N.A.I.C.S.: 522220

Teleleasing S.p.A. (1)
Via Battistotti 11-A, 20133, Milan, Italy (80%)
Tel.: (39) 02700641
Web Site: http://www.teleleasing.it
Sales Range: $50-74.9 Million
Emp.: 100
General Rental Centers
N.A.I.C.S.: 532310

MEDIOLANUM FARMACEUTICI SPA
Via San Giuseppe Cottolengo, 15, Milan, Italy
Tel.: (39) 02891321
Web Site: http://www.mediolanum-
  farma.it
Year Founded: 1972
Pharmaceuticals Product Mfr
N.A.I.C.S.: 456110
Alessandro Del Bono (CEO)

Subsidiaries:

Elsalys Biotech SA (1)
317 Avenue Jean Jaures, 69007, Lyon, France
Tel.: (33) 437287300
Web Site: http://www.elsalysbiotech.com
Biotechnology Research & Development Services
N.A.I.C.S.: 541714
Christine Guillen (Founder & CEO)

MEDIOS AG
Heidestrabe 9, 10557, Berlin, Germany
Tel.: (49) 30232566800
Web Site: https://medios.group
ILM1—(MUN)
Rev.: $1,970,076,789
Assets: $656,526,682
Liabilities: $139,021,388
Net Worth: $517,505,295
Earnings: $20,763,795
Emp.: 512
Fiscal Year-end: 12/31/23
Investment Management Service
N.A.I.C.S.: 523940
Yann Samson (Chm-Supervisory Bd)

INTERNATIONAL PUBLIC

Subsidiaries:

Cas Central Compounding Baden-Wurttemberg GmbH (1)
Blumenstr 33/1, 71106, Magstadt, Germany
Tel.: (49) 7159806940
Web Site: https://www.casbw.de
Pharmaceuticals Product Mfr
N.A.I.C.S.: 325412

Cranach Pharma GmbH (1)
Luruper Chaussee 125 / Haus 6, Bahrenfeld, 22761, Hamburg, Germany
Tel.: (49) 4081955634
Web Site: https://cranach-pharma.de
Pharmaceuticals Distr
N.A.I.C.S.: 424210

Fortuna Herstellung GmbH (1)
Joseph-Meyer-Str 12, 68167, Mannheim, Germany
Tel.: (49) 62117828500
Web Site: https://www.fortunaherstellung.de
Medical Product Mfr & Distr
N.A.I.C.S.: 325412

Hvd medical GmbH (1)
Carl-Zeiss-Str 30, 66740, Saarlouis, Germany
Tel.: (49) 6831958380
Web Site: https://www.hvd-medical.com
Biopharmaceutical Product Mfr & Distr
N.A.I.C.S.: 325412

Kolsche Blister GmbH (1)
Siegburger Strasse 189a, 50679, Cologne, Germany
Tel.: (49) 22127328000
Web Site: https://www.koelsche-blister.de
Pharmaceuticals Product Mfr
N.A.I.C.S.: 325412

Medios Digital GmbH (1)
Heidestrase 9, 10557, Berlin, Germany
Tel.: (49) 30220132000
Web Site: http://www.mediosdigital.de
Pharmaceutical Drug Whslr
N.A.I.C.S.: 424210

Medios Individual GmbH (1)
Ringbahnstrasse 10-14, 12099, Berlin, Germany
Tel.: (49) 3075659020
Web Site: http://www.mediosindividual.de
Pharmaceutical Drug Whslr
N.A.I.C.S.: 424210

Medios Manufaktur GmbH (1)
Reuchlinstrasse 10, 10553, Berlin, Germany
Tel.: (49) 30992967000
Web Site: http://www.mediosmanufaktur.de
Pharmaceutical Drug Whslr
N.A.I.C.S.: 424210

Medios Pharma GmbH (1)
Reuchlinstrasse 10-11/F, 10553, Berlin, Germany
Tel.: (49) 302201327000
Web Site: http://www.mediospharma.de
Pharmaceutical Drug Whslr
N.A.I.C.S.: 424210
Mi-Young Miehler (COO & Member-Exec Bd)

NewCo Pharma GmbH (1)
Boveristr 2, 68309, Mannheim, Germany
Tel.: (49) 6214518020
Web Site: https://www.newco-pharma.de
Biopharmaceutical Product Mfr & Distr
N.A.I.C.S.: 325412

Onko Service GmbH & Co. KG (1)
Moserstr 52-54, 49074, Osnabruck, Germany
Tel.: (49) 54176028910
Web Site: https://www.onko-service.de
Biopharmaceutical Product Mfr & Distr
N.A.I.C.S.: 325412

Rhein Main Compounding GmbH (1)
Bodelwickelhstrasse 10a, 63739, Aschaffenburg, Germany
Tel.: (49) 60214207940
Web Site: https://www.rhein-main-compounding.de
Biopharmaceutical Product Mfr & Distr
N.A.I.C.S.: 325412

Rheinische Compounding GmbH (1)
Ernst-Robert-Curtius-Str 39, 53117, Bonn, Germany

Tel.: (49) 22818436600
Web Site: https://www.rheinische-compounding.de
Biopharmaceutical Product Mfr & Distr
N.A.I.C.S.: 325412

MEDIPAL HOLDINGS CORPORATION
3-1-1 Kyobashi, Chuo-ku, Tokyo, 104-8461, Japan
Tel.: (81) 335175171   JP
Web Site: https://www.medipal.co.jp
Year Founded: 1898
MEPDF—(OTCIQ)
Rev: $23,523,218,520
Assets: $11,892,229,470
Liabilities: $7,023,224,150
Net Worth: $4,869,005,320
Earnings: $274,143,140
Emp.: 13,075
Fiscal Year-end: 03/31/24
Holding Company
N.A.I.C.S.: 551112
Hisashi Tsutsu (Executives)

Subsidiaries:

ASTEC Co., Ltd. (1)
5F Shibahashi Building 14-3 Higashiarai, Tsukuba, 305-0033, Ibaraki, Japan
Tel.: (81) 29 855 2866
Web Site: https://www.astec-medical.co.jp
Medical Equipment Distr
N.A.I.C.S.: 423450

Atol Co., Ltd. (1)
2-5-1 Kashiihamafuto, Higashi-ku, Fukuoka, 813-8555, Japan (100%)
Tel.: (81) 92 665 7100
Web Site: https://www.atol-com.co.jp
Emp.: 1,365
Prescription & Pharmaceutical Products Wholesale Distr
N.A.I.C.S.: 424210
Shinjiro Watanabe (Pres)

Beijing Tianxingpuxin Bio-med Sinopharm Holding Co., Ltd. (1)
Block A Xinhua Shuangchuang Park Yard 8 Sixth Circle West Road, Huaxiang Fengtai District, Beijing, China
Tel.: (86) 108 368 1236
Web Site: https://www.bjtxpx.com.cn
Medical Equipment Distr
N.A.I.C.S.: 423450

Butsuryu 24, Inc. (1)
Tokimo Yushima Building 3-26-7 Yushima, Bunkyo-ku, Tokyo, 113-0034, Japan (100%)
Tel.: (81) 35 846 4821
Web Site: https://www.butsuryu24.co.jp
Emp.: 830
Management & Operation of Distribution Centers
N.A.I.C.S.: 493190
Kimihiko Tokushige (Pres)

Class A Network Co., Ltd. (1)
5-47-11 Jingumae, Shibuya-ku, Tokyo, 150-0001, Japan
Tel.: (81) 35 778 9388
Web Site: https://www.i-classa.com
Pharmacy Services
N.A.I.C.S.: 456110

Eiko Co., Ltd. (1)
411-18 Okura Wakayama-shi, Wakayama, 649-6261, Japan (100%)
Tel.: (81) 73 4770211
Cosmetics, OTC & Everyday Sundries Wholesale Distr
N.A.I.C.S.: 424210

Everlth Co., Ltd. (1)
5-2-10 Ozu, Minami-ku, Hiroshima, 732-0802, Japan (100%)
Tel.: (81) 82 286 3300
Web Site: https://www.everlth.co.jp
Wholesale Distribution of Prescription Pharmaceutical Products
N.A.I.C.S.: 424210
Hasegawa Takuro (Pres)

Haba Creation Co., Ltd. (1)
2-46 Honmachibashi PALTAC Headquarters 4th floor, Chuo-ku, Osaka, 540-0029, Japan
Tel.: (81) 64 793 0088
Web Site: https://www.habacreation.co.jp
Floor Creation Product Mfr & Distr
N.A.I.C.S.: 327120

Kuraya (USA) Corporation (1)
3625 Del Amo Blvd Ste 150, Torrance, CA 90503 (100%)
Tel.: (310) 542-4245
Web Site: https://www.kuraya-usa.com
Sales Range: $50-74.9 Million
Emp.: 3
Medical Training Seminars & Overseas Medical Information & Medical-Related Products
N.A.I.C.S.: 423450

Kuraya Kasei, Inc. (1)
917 Inaba Nagano-shi, Nagano, 380-0911, Japan (100%)
Tel.: (81) 262212005
Industrial Chemicals & Food Additives Sales
N.A.I.C.S.: 424690

MIC CO, LTD. (1)
3-37-4 Yushima HF Yushima Building 9F, Bunkyo-ku, Tokyo, 113-0034, Japan (100%)
Tel.: (81) 33 832 6214
Web Site: https://www.mic-kk.co.jp
Emp.: 15
Medical Management Consulting Services
N.A.I.C.S.: 611430
Nobutaka Ohashi (Auditor)

MM CORPORATION (1)
3-4-6 Hongo, Bunkyo-Ku, Tokyo, 113-0033, Japan
Tel.: (81) 33 816 3546
Web Site: https://www.mm-corp.co.jp
Emp.: 466
Medical Equipment Whslr
N.A.I.C.S.: 423450
Kazumi Takahashi (Chm)

MP Agro Co., Ltd. (1)
6-2-13 Omagari Kogyo Danchi, Kitahiroshima, 061-1274, Hokkaido, Japan
Tel.: (81) 11 376 3860
Web Site: https://www.mpagro.co.jp
Emp.: 504
Wholesale Distr of Animal Health & Feed Products
N.A.I.C.S.: 115210
Tomohiko Kimura (Pres)

MVC Co., Ltd. (1)
Kashiihamazu 2-5-1, Higashi-ku, Fukuoka, 813-8555, Japan
Tel.: (81) 92 663 1230
Web Site: https://www.mvc.jp
Medical Equipment Distr
N.A.I.C.S.: 423450

Mediceo Corporation (1)
2-7-15 Yaesu, Chuo-ku, Tokyo, 104-8464, Japan (100%)
Tel.: (81) 33 517 5050
Web Site: https://www.mediceo.co.jp
Emp.: 7,208
Pharmaceuticals & Medical Products & Reagents Wholesale Distr
N.A.I.C.S.: 424210

Mediceo Medical Co., Ltd. (1)
3 4 6 Hongo Bunkyo-ku, Tokyo, 113-003, Japan (100%)
Tel.: (81) 338163546
Web Site: http://www.e-truth.co.jp
Medical Equipment & Laboratory Instrument Sales
N.A.I.C.S.: 423450
Kazumi Takahashi (Pres & CEO)

Medie Co., Ltd. (1)
3F Shintomicho Building 3-10-9 Irifune, Chuo-ku, Tokyo, 104-0042, Japan
Tel.: (81) 33 537 1906
Web Site: https://www.medie.jp
Medical Equipment Distr
N.A.I.C.S.: 423450
Shinji Endo (Pres & CEO)

Medipal Foods Corporation (1)
17-1-4 Kita 10 West, Chuo-ku, Sapporo, 060-0010, Hokkaido, Japan
Tel.: (81) 11 611 7700
Web Site: https://www.medipalfoods.co.jp
Food Mfr & Distr
N.A.I.C.S.: 311999

Medipal Insurance Service Co., Ltd. (1)
3-1-7 Isobe Concordia Kobe 13F, Chuo-ku, Kobe, 651-0084, Japan
Tel.: (81) 78 230 5210
Web Site: https://www.medipal-hoken.co.jp
Non Life Insurance Agency Services
N.A.I.C.S.: 524210

NAKAZAWA UJIKE PHARMACEUTICAL CO., LTD. (1)
501 Itachino, Nankoku, 783-8585, Kochi, Japan
Tel.: (81) 88 802 5111
Web Site: https://www.nakazawaujike.com
Pharmaceutical Product Whslr
N.A.I.C.S.: 424210
Eiichiro Nakazawa (Pres)

OrphanPacific, Inc. (1)
Hamamatsucho Building Access 1-1-1, Shibaura Minato-ku, Tokyo, 105-0023, Japan
Tel.: (81) 36 779 8151
Web Site: https://www.orphanpacific.com
Medical Product Mfr & Distr
N.A.I.C.S.: 339112
Philippe Auvaro (Pres)

PRESUSCUBE Corporation (1)
4F DSakasaka Bldg 8-5-26, Akasaka Minato-ku, Tokyo, 107-0052, Japan
Tel.: (81) 354135171
Pharmacy Services
N.A.I.C.S.: 456110
Yuta Komori (Pres & CEO)

Paltac Corporation (1)
2-26 Honmachi-bashi, Chuo-ku, Osaka, 540-0029, Japan (100%)
Tel.: (81) 647931050
Web Site: https://www.paltac.co.jp
Sales Range: $5-14.9 Billion
Emp.: 2,221
Cosmetics & OTC Pharmaceutical Wholesale Distr
N.A.I.C.S.: 456120
Kunio Mikida (Chm)

SHIKOKU YAKUGYO CO. LTD. (1)
1828 Minamitakaimachi, Iyo-gun, Matsuyama, 791-1112, Ehime, Japan
Tel.: (81) 89 990 4175
Web Site: http://www.medipal.co.jp
Pharmaceutical Product Whslr
N.A.I.C.S.: 424210
Eiichiro Nakazawa (Pres)

SPLine Corporation (1)
2-7-15 Yaesu, Chuo-ku, Tokyo, 104-8461, Japan
Tel.: (81) 33 517 5508
Web Site: https://www.sp-line.co.jp
Pharmaceutical Products Distr
N.A.I.C.S.: 424210

Tokimo Co., Ltd. (1)
3-7-13 Kanda-Misakicho, Chiyoda-ku, Tokyo, 101-0061, Japan (100%)
Tel.: (81) 33 221 7381
Web Site: http://www.tokimo-bm.co.jp
Facility Management & Administration
N.A.I.C.S.: 541618

Toshichi Inc. (1)
4-1318 Setogoe, Chuo-ku, Sasebo, 857-0192, Nagasaki, Japan (100%)
Tel.: (81) 956410777
Web Site: https://www.toshichi.net
Emp.: 310
Pharmaceutical Product Whslr
N.A.I.C.S.: 424210
Kozo Azuma (Pres)

Trim Co., Ltd. (1)
3-1-7 Isobedori, Kobe, 651-0084, Hyogo, Japan (100%)
Tel.: (81) 782305210
Web Site: http://www.trim-insurance.co.jp
Non-Life Insurance Related Products
N.A.I.C.S.: 524298

YONYAKU CO., LTD. (1)
1828 Minamitakaimachi, Iyo-gun, Matsuyama, 791-1112, Ehime, Japan
Tel.: (81) 89 990 4141
Web Site: https://www.yonyaku.com
Emp.: 683
Pharmaceutical Product Whslr
N.A.I.C.S.: 424210

Yutaka Honda (Pres)

MEDIPHARM AB
Vickerkullavagen 6, 591 45, Motala, Sweden
Tel.: (46) 140384900   SE
Web Site: http://www.medipharm.se
Year Founded: 1987
Sales Range: $10-24.9 Million
Dairy Products Mfr
N.A.I.C.S.: 311511
Mikael Ulvan (CEO)

MEDIPHARM LABS CORP.
151 John Street, Barrie, L4N 2L1, ON, Canada
Tel.: (705) 719-7425
Web Site: https://www.medipharmlabs.com
MEDIF—(OTCQX)
Rev: $98,908,800
Assets: $129,195,469
Liabilities: $28,775,320
Net Worth: $100,420,149
Earnings: $865,486
Emp.: 230
Fiscal Year-end: 12/31/19
Biomedical Medicine Mfr
N.A.I.C.S.: 325411
Keith Strachan (Pres & Interim CEO)

Subsidiaries:

VIVO Cannabis Inc. (1)
126 Vanluven Road, Napanee, K7R 3L2, ON, Canada
Tel.: (855) 322-2266
Web Site: http://www.vivocannabis.com
Rev: $25,645,937
Assets: $158,033,336
Liabilities: $42,925,695
Net Worth: $115,107,642
Earnings: ($43,539,523)
Emp.: 200
Fiscal Year-end: 12/31/2020
Investment Services
N.A.I.C.S.: 523999
Paul Lucas (Chm)

Subsidiary (Non-US):

ABcann Germany GmbH (2)
Karl-Marx-Str 26, 12529, Schonefeld, Germany
Tel.: (49) 33792025442
Web Site: http://www.abcann.de
Medical Instrument Mfr
N.A.I.C.S.: 339112
Andreas Sander (Mng Dir)

Subsidiary (Domestic):

ABcann Medicinals Inc. (2)
PO Box 157, Napanee, K7R 3M3, ON, Canada
Tel.: (855) 322-2266
Web Site: http://www.abcann.ca
Pharmaceuticals Product Mfr
N.A.I.C.S.: 325412
Ken Clement (Founder)

Harvest Medicine Inc. (2)
Unit 480 5111 Northland Drive NW, Northland Village Mall, Calgary, T2L 2J8, AB, Canada
Tel.: (587) 356-3555
Web Site: http://www.hmed.ca
Pharmaceuticals Product Mfr
N.A.I.C.S.: 325412

Subsidiary (Domestic):

Trauma Healing Centers Inc. (3)
959 Cole Harbour Road, Dartmouth, B2V 1E6, NS, Canada
Tel.: (844) 429-6074
Web Site: http://www.traumahc.com
Health Care Srvces
N.A.I.C.S.: 621493
Kyle Atkinson (Founder)

MEDIPOST CO., LTD.
21 Daewangpangyo-ro 644, Bundang-gu, Seongnam, Gyeonggi-do, Korea (South)

MEDIPOST CO., LTD.

MEDIPOST Co., Ltd.—(Continued)
Tel.: (82) 234656677
Web Site: https://en.medi-post.co.kr
Year Founded: 2000
078160—(KRS)
Rev.: $49,241,881
Assets: $305,105,623
Liabilities: $165,068,470
Net Worth: $140,037,153
Earnings: $1,614,972
Emp.: 286
Fiscal Year-end: 12/31/22
Blood Banking Services
N.A.I.C.S.: 621991

Subsidiaries:

Evastem Co., Ltd. (1)
7th floor of Shirokanedai ST Building 4-7-4
Shirokanedai, Minato-ku, Tokyo, 108-0071, Japan
Tel.: (81) 354226273
Research & Development Services
N.A.I.C.S.: 541714

MEDIPOST Co., Ltd. - Cell Drug GMP Factory (1)
Unit 802 2nd Daeryung Post Tower 306 Digital-ro Guro-gu, Seoul, Korea (South)
Tel.: (82) 28667141
Stem Cell Drug Mfr
N.A.I.C.S.: 325412

Shandong Orlife Pharmaceutical Co., Ltd. (1)
2957 Beitianmen Street, High-Tech Zone, Tai'an, Shandong, China
Medical Device Mfr & Distr
N.A.I.C.S.: 339112

MEDIPOWER (OVERSEAS) PUBLIC CO. LIMITED

1 C Skokou 6th Fl, Nicosia, 1061, Cyprus
Tel.: (357) 32077237
Web Site: http://www.medipowergroup.com
MDPR—(TAE)
Rev.: $38,621,000
Assets: $416,570,000
Liabilities: $275,209,000
Net Worth: $141,361,000
Earnings: $8,219,000
Fiscal Year-end: 12/31/21
Other Activities Related to Real Estate
N.A.I.C.S.: 531390
Yair Goldfinger *(Chm)*

MEDIPURE HOLDINGS INC.

302-267 West Esplanade Ave, North Vancouver, V7M 1A5, BC, Canada
Tel.: (877) 264-0345   BC
Web Site: http://www.medipurepharma.com
Year Founded: 2014
Holding Company; Pharmaceuticals
N.A.I.C.S.: 551112
John Maynoard *(Dir-Medical)*

MEDIQON GROUP AG

Falkenried 29, 20251, Hamburg, Germany
Tel.: (49) 4020950269
Web Site: https://www.chaptersgroup.com
Year Founded: 1998
MCE—(DEU)
Rev.: $78,120,880
Assets: $247,211,686
Liabilities: $108,057,834
Net Worth: $139,153,852
Earnings: ($4,503,790)
Emp.: 952
Fiscal Year-end: 12/31/23
Pharmaceutical Product Mfr & Distr
N.A.I.C.S.: 325412

Subsidiaries:

BleTec Software GmbH (1)
Erbacher Strasse 72, 64380, Rossdorf, Germany
Tel.: (49) 6154801750
Web Site: https://www.bletec.de
Software Solutions Services
N.A.I.C.S.: 541511

Calmund & Riemer GmbH (1)
Moerser Str 282, 47228, Duisburg, Germany
Tel.: (49) 2065961620
Web Site: https://calmund-r.de
Cleaning Service
N.A.I.C.S.: 561740

CarMa Holding GmbH (1)
Entenmoorweg 9a, 27578, Bremerhaven, Germany
Tel.: (49) 6913360
Web Site: https://www.carma.de
Investment Services
N.A.I.C.S.: 523999

Carrierwerke GmbH (1)
Heinrich-Hertz-Strasse 11, 69190, Walldorf, Germany
Tel.: (49) 62278993737
Web Site: https://carrierwerke.de
Wireless Telecommunication Services
N.A.I.C.S.: 541618

Corporate Montage Europe GmbH (1)
Neugasse 15-19, 65183, Wiesbaden, Germany
Tel.: (49) 6117239770
Web Site: https://corporatemontage.de
Software Solutions Services
N.A.I.C.S.: 541511

Diamant Gebaudereinigungsdienst GmbH (1)
Stresemannstr 37, 28207, Bremen, Germany
Tel.: (49) 421444428
Web Site: https://diamant-bremen.de
Emp.: 400
Cleaning Service
N.A.I.C.S.: 561740

Elkom Solutions GmbH (1)
Karlstrasse 13, 78532, Tuttlingen, Germany
Tel.: (49) 7461966110
Web Site: https://elkomsolutions.de
Software Solutions Services
N.A.I.C.S.: 541511

Gelford GmbH (1)
Centrumstr 21, 45307, Essen, Germany
Tel.: (49) 201704800
Web Site: https://www.gelford.de
Emp.: 850
Building Cleaning Services
N.A.I.C.S.: 561740

Glasfaser Direkt GmbH (1)
Hohenzollernring 57, 50672, Cologne, Germany
Tel.: (49) 22171828282
Web Site: https://glasfaser-direkt.de
Telecommunication Servicesb
N.A.I.C.S.: 541618

Gripsware Datentechnik GmbH (1)
Albrecht-Durer-Str 2, 91334, Hemmoor, Germany
Tel.: (49) 7529974760
Web Site: https://gripsware.de
Software Solutions Services
N.A.I.C.S.: 541511

Interactive Network Communications GmbH (1)
Neue Mainzer Str 75, 60311, Frankfurt am Main, Germany
Tel.: (49) 6913360
Web Site: https://www.internet.de
Wireless Telecommunication Services
N.A.I.C.S.: 541618

Kaltehelden GmbH (1)
Offakamp 9d, 22529, Hamburg, Germany
Tel.: (49) 4080903770
Web Site: https://www.kaeltehelden.com
Refrigeration Equipment Repair & Maintenance Services
N.A.I.C.S.: 811310

Kunstschule Wandsbek GmbH (1)
Bowl Basket 15/16, 28195, Bremen, Germany
Tel.: (49) 42133659125
Web Site: https://www.kunstschule-wandsbek.de
Information Technology Services
N.A.I.C.S.: 541511

NGC Nachfolgekapital GmbH (1)
Franz-Joseph-Str 12, 80801, Munich, Germany
Tel.: (49) 1737195149
Web Site: https://nachfolge-kapital.com
Emp.: 690
Investment Services
N.A.I.C.S.: 523999

OPAS Software GmbH (1)
John F Kennedy Boulevard 3, 96052, Bamberg, Germany
Tel.: (49) 9519939120
Web Site: https://opas.eu
Emp.: 13
Software Solutions Services
N.A.I.C.S.: 541511

Ookam Software GmbH (1)
Leipziger Pl 15, 10117, Berlin, Germany
Tel.: (49) 17682092631
Web Site: https://www.ookam-software.com
Information Technology Services
N.A.I.C.S.: 541618

Parity Software GmbH (1)
Siemensstrasse 10, 71254, Ditzingen, Germany
Tel.: (49) 7156170260
Web Site: https://www.parity-software.com
Software Solutions Services
N.A.I.C.S.: 541511

SWH Softwarehaus Heider GmbH (1)
Am Kohlenschacht 10, 93077, Bad Abbach, Germany
Tel.: (49) 940595590
Web Site: https://atlantis-schulsoftware.de
Software Solutions Services
N.A.I.C.S.: 541511

Software24.com GmbH (1)
Eichbichlstr 1, 83071, Stephanskirchen, Germany
Tel.: (49) 80313044910
Web Site: https://www.software24.com
Software Solutions Services
N.A.I.C.S.: 541511

Speakeasy Berlin GmbH (1)
Warschauer Strasse 36, 10243, Berlin, Germany
Tel.: (49) 3060954149
Web Site: https://www.speakeasysprachzeug.de
Educational Support Services
N.A.I.C.S.: 611710

Voigt Software und Beratung AG (1)
Reinhold-Wurth-Str 19, 74360, Ilsfeld, Germany
Tel.: (49) 706291550
Web Site: https://voigtsoftware.com
Software Solutions Services
N.A.I.C.S.: 541511

WAREHaus GmbH (1)
Schorberger Strasse 66, 42699, Solingen, Germany
Tel.: (49) 212816236
Web Site: https://www.warehaus.de
Software Solutions Services
N.A.I.C.S.: 541511

MEDIROM HEALTHCARE TECHNOLOGIES INC.

Trade Pier Odaiba 16th Floor 231 Odaiba, Minato-ku, Tokyo, 135-0091, Japan
Tel.: (81) 367217364   JP
Web Site: https://www.medirom.co.jp
Year Founded: 2000
MRM—(NASDAQ)
Rev.: $32,346,853
Assets: $55,306,351
Liabilities: $50,550,983
Net Worth: $4,755,368
Earnings: ($5,219,166)
Emp.: 222
Fiscal Year-end: 12/31/20
Health Care Srvices
N.A.I.C.S.: 621610
Kouji Eguchi *(Founder & CEO)*

Subsidiaries:

Joyhands Wellness Inc. (1)
2-3-1 Daiba Tradepia Odaiba 16th floor, Minato-ku, Tokyo, 135-0091, Japan
Tel.: (81) 367217467
Web Site: http://www.joyhands-wellness.co.jp
Health & Wellness Services
N.A.I.C.S.: 621999

MEDIS, D.O.O.

Brnciceva 1, SI- 1231, Ljubljana, Slovenia
Tel.: (386) 1 589 69 00
Web Site: http://www.medis.si
Year Founded: 1989
Emp.: 200
Media Marketing Services
N.A.I.C.S.: 541613
Tone Strnad *(Gen Mgr-Medis)*

Subsidiaries:

Medis Adria d.o.o. (1)
Buzinska 58, 10000, Zagreb, Croatia
Tel.: (385) 12303446
Web Site: http://www.medisadria.hr
Marketing Consulting Services
N.A.I.C.S.: 541613
Igor Ralic *(Office Mgr)*

Medis GmbH (1)
St Veiter Strasse 34/3, 9020, Klagenfurt, Austria
Tel.: (43) 12363335
Web Site: http://www.medisaustria.at
Marketing Consulting Services
N.A.I.C.S.: 541613

Medis Hungary Kft. (1)
VIV Center Hosszuret u 1, 2045, Torokbalint, Hungary
Tel.: (36) 23801028
Web Site: http://www.medis.hu
Marketing Consulting Services
N.A.I.C.S.: 541613

Medis International d.o.o. (1)
Ahmeda Muratbegovica 2, 71000, Sarajevo, Bosnia & Herzegovina
Tel.: (387) 33559381
Marketing Consulting Services
N.A.I.C.S.: 541613

Medis Pharma d.o.o. (1)
Milutina Milankovica 11b 2 sprat, 11070, Novi Beograd, Serbia
Tel.: (381) 113122728
Marketing Consulting Services
N.A.I.C.S.: 541613

MEDISTA S.R.O.

Delnicka 12, 170 00, Prague, Czech Republic
Tel.: (420) 241444525   CZ
Web Site: http://www.medista.cz
Sales Range: $10-24.9 Million
Emp.: 19
Biochemical & Hematological Services
N.A.I.C.S.: 423450
Alexandra Kadlecova *(Gen Mgr)*

MEDISTIM ASA

Okernveien 94, 0579, Oslo, Norway
Tel.: (47) 23059660
Web Site: https://www.medistim.com
0OCD—(LSE)
Rev.: $45,440,329
Assets: $44,583,318
Liabilities: $10,619,619
Net Worth: $33,963,699
Earnings: $10,527,711
Emp.: 132
Fiscal Year-end: 12/31/22
Medical Equipment Mfr
N.A.I.C.S.: 339112

AND PRIVATE COMPANIES

MEDITERRANEAN SHIPPING COMPANY, S.A.

Haege J. K. Wetterhus *(VP-Mktg)*

Subsidiaries:

MediStim Deutschland GmbH (1)
Bahnhofstr 32, 82041, Deisenhofen, Germany
Tel.: (49) 8962819033
Web Site: https://www.medistim.com
Medical Equipments & Supplies Distr
N.A.I.C.S.: 423450

MediStim USA Inc. (1)
14000 25th Ave N Ste 108, Plymouth, MN 55447
Tel.: (763) 208-9852
Web Site: http://www.medistim.com
Medical Equipments & Consumables Distr
N.A.I.C.S.: 423450

Medistim Danmark Aps (1)
Sogade 16, 4100, Ringsted, Denmark
Tel.: (45) 23800333
Web Site: https://medistim.dk
Medical Device Distr
N.A.I.C.S.: 423450

Medistim Kirop AS (1)
okernveien 94, 0659, Oslo, Norway
Tel.: (47) 23035250
Web Site: http://www.medistim-kirop.com
Rev.: $8,948,945
Emp.: 18
Medical Equipments & Supplies Distr
N.A.I.C.S.: 423450

Medistim Norge AS (1)
Okernveien 94, PO Box 4744, Nydalen, 0579, Oslo, Norway
Tel.: (47) 23035250
Sales Range: $25-49.9 Million
Emp.: 17
Medical Equipments & Supplies Distr
N.A.I.C.S.: 423450

Medistim Spain S.L. (1)
Calle Balmes 173 4 2, 08006, Barcelona, Spain
Tel.: (34) 911238318
Medical Device Mfr & Distr
N.A.I.C.S.: 339112

Medistim UK Ltd. (1)
34 Nottingham South Wilford Ind Est Ruddington Lane, Wilford, Nottingham, NG11 7EP, United Kingdom
Tel.: (44) 1159810871
Medical Device Mfr & Distr
N.A.I.C.S.: 339112

MEDISUN PRECISION MEDICINE LTD.
Trust Company Complex Ajeltake Road, Majuro, MH96960, Marshall Islands
Tel.: (692) 93143718 MH
Year Founded: 2012
MPME—(OTCBB)
Medical Device Mfr
N.A.I.C.S.: 339112
Lisha Huang *(Chm)*

MEDITECNA S.R.L.
Camarones 1720, C1416ECH, Buenos Aires, Argentina
Tel.: (54) 1145857005
Web Site: http://www.meditecna.com.ar
Sales Range: $1-9.9 Million
Emp.: 25
Measuring & Controlling Device Mfr
N.A.I.C.S.: 334519

MEDITERRA CAPITAL MANAGEMENT LIMITED
Sehit Halil Ibrahim Cad No 39 Istinye, 34460 Sariyer, Istanbul, 34460, Turkiye
Tel.: (90) 212 323 54 00
Web Site: http://www.mediterracapital.com
Emp.: 12
Privater Equity Firm
N.A.I.C.S.: 523999

Ahmet Faralyali *(Co-Founder & Mng Partner)*

MEDITERRANEAN & GULF INSURANCE & REINSURANCE COMPANY S.J.S.C.
7731 King Saud Rd Al Murabba, PO Box 2302, Riyadh, 11451, Saudi Arabia
Tel.: (966) 114055588
Web Site: https://www.medgulf.com.sa
Year Founded: 1980
8030—(SAU)
Rev.: $567,965,605
Assets: $1,075,053,993
Liabilities: $903,060,925
Net Worth: $171,993,068
Earnings: ($84,043,728)
Emp.: 1,400
Fiscal Year-end: 12/31/22
Insurance & Reinsurance Products
N.A.I.C.S.: 524210
Mishal Al-Rasheed *(Gen Mgr-Client Care)*

Subsidiaries:

Prime Health for medical services SAE (1)
6 D / 5 El Laselky Str, New Maadi, Cairo, Egypt
Tel.: (20) 225173578
General Insurance Services
N.A.I.C.S.: 524298
Mina Refaat Habib *(Head-Audit Dept)*

The Mediterranean & Gulf Insurance & Reinsurance company s.a.l
Patriarche Howayek Street Medgulf Building, PO Box 113, Beirut Central District, 6320, Beirut, Lebanon
Tel.: (961) 1985000
Reinsurance Services
N.A.I.C.S.: 524130

MEDITERRANEAN MARITIME HUB FINANCE PLC
Xatt il-Mollijiet, Marsa, MRS 1152, Malta
Tel.: (356) 21491060
Web Site: http://www.mmh.com.mt
Year Founded: 2016
MM26A—(MAL)
Rev.: $1,077,934
Assets: $18,970,213
Liabilities: $18,388,531
Net Worth: $581,682
Earnings: $58,029
Fiscal Year-end: 12/31/21
Engineering Construction Services
N.A.I.C.S.: 237990
Paul Abela *(Chm)*

MEDITERRANEAN SHIPPING COMPANY, S.A.
S A Chemin Rieu 12-14, 1208, Geneva, Switzerland
Tel.: (41) 227038888
Web Site: https://www.msc.com
Year Founded: 1970
Sales Range: $100-124.9 Million
Emp.: 450
Freight Transportation Services
N.A.I.C.S.: 483111
Gianluigi Aponte *(Founder & Grp Chm)*

Subsidiaries:

Bollore Africa Logistics SAS (1)
Tour Bollore 31-32 quai de Dion Bouton, 92811, Puteaux, France
Tel.: (33) 146964433
Web Site: http://www.bollore-africa-logistics.com
Transportation & Logistics Services
N.A.I.C.S.: 488510
Philippe Labonne *(Pres)*

Gram Car Carriers A.S.A. (1)
Bryggegata 9 Aker Brygge, 0250, Oslo, Norway
Tel.: (47) 22017450
Web Site: https://gramcar.com
Rev.: $120,976,000
Assets: $609,741,000
Liabilities: $366,260,000
Net Worth: $243,481,000
Earnings: $23,877,000
Emp.: 16
Fiscal Year-end: 12/31/2022
Vehicle Freight Transportation Services
N.A.I.C.S.: 484230

MEDITERRANEAN SHIPPING COMPANY MEXICO SA DE CV (1)
Benjamin Franklin 204 Col Escandon, 11800, Mexico, Mexico
Tel.: (52) 55 5091 7070
Web Site: http://www.mscmexico.com
Deep Sea Freight Transportation Services
N.A.I.C.S.: 483111
Alonso Sopena *(Mng Dir)*

MSC (Angola) - Navegacao Logistica e Servicos Maritimos Lda (1)
43-5A E 5B Rua Guilherme Pereira Ingles, Largo Da Ingombota, Luanda, Angola
Tel.: (244) 222 333 073
Web Site: http://www.mscangola.com
Deep Sea Freight Transportation Services
N.A.I.C.S.: 483111
Rui Serafim *(Mgr-Ops & Logistics)*

MSC (Israel) Ltd. (1)
157 Yaffo street, PO Box 34004, Beit Arnot, Haifa, 31339, Israel
Tel.: (972) 46607000
Web Site: http://www.mscisrael.com
Deep Sea Freight Transportation Services
N.A.I.C.S.: 483111
Gianluigi Aponte *(Chm)*

MSC (Mauritius) Ltd (1)
MSC House Old Quay D Road, Port Louis, Mauritius
Tel.: (230) 202 6800
Web Site: http://www.msc.mu
Deep Sea Freight Transportation Services
N.A.I.C.S.: 483111
Alexander Lutchmun *(Mng Dir-Comml)*

MSC (PTY) LTD. (1)
MSC House 54 Dr Langalibalele Dube Street, PO Box 10687, 4001, Durban, South Africa
Tel.: (27) 31 360 7911
Web Site: http://www.mscsouthafrica.com
Deep Sea Freight Transportation Services
N.A.I.C.S.: 483111
Des Blankenberg *(Mgr-Grp IT)*

MSC (Tanzania) Ltd. (1)
Nelson Mandela Road Plot 296, PO Box 63039, Dar es Salaam, Tanzania
Tel.: (255) 22 285 1660
Web Site: http://www.msctanzania.com
Deep Sea Freight Transportation Services
N.A.I.C.S.: 483111
Johnson Maina *(Mgr-Liner)*

MSC AGENCY A.G. (1)
Steinentorstrasse 39, Basel, 4002, Switzerland
Tel.: (41) 61 555 6555
Web Site: http://www.mscswitzerland.com
Deep Sea Freight Transportation Services
N.A.I.C.S.: 483111

MSC Agency Pakistan (Pvt) Ltd (1)
3rd Floor Mackinnons Building II Chundrigar Road, Karachi, 74000, Pakistan
Tel.: (92) 21 32415200
Web Site: http://www.mscpakistan.com
Emp.: 100
Deep Sea Freight Transportation Services
N.A.I.C.S.: 483111
Muneera Khan *(Mgr-HR Dept)*

MSC Bahamas Ltd. (1)
24 Logwood Road, PO Box F-42183, Grand Bahama, Freeport, Bahamas
Tel.: (242) 351 1158
Web Site: http://www.mscbahamas.com
Deep Sea Freight Transportation Services
N.A.I.C.S.: 483111
Manuel Ruiz *(Mng Dir)*

MSC Belgium N.V. (1)
Noorderlaan 127A, 2030, Antwerp, Belgium

Tel.: (32) 3 543 2200
Web Site: http://www.mscbelgium.com
Emp.: 350
Deep Sea Freight Transportation Services
N.A.I.C.S.: 483111
Gert Dreesen *(CIO)*

MSC CANADA Inc. (1)
7 Saint Jacques West, Montreal, H2Y 1K9, QC, Canada
Tel.: (514) 844-3711
Web Site: https://www.msc.com
Deep Sea Freight Transportation Services
N.A.I.C.S.: 483111

MSC CRUCEROS, S.A.U. (1)
C/Arequipa 1-4, 28043, Madrid, Spain
Tel.: (34) 91 382 1660
Deep Sea Passenger Transportation Services
N.A.I.C.S.: 483112
Luigi Surace *(Mgr-Mktg)*

MSC CRUZEIROS DO BRASIL LTDA. (1)
Av Ibirapuera 2332-6th Floor-Tower 2, 04028-003, Sao Paulo, Brazil
Tel.: (55) 11 50538500
Web Site: http://www.msccruzeiros.com.br
Deep Sea Passenger Transportation Services
N.A.I.C.S.: 483112

MSC Crewing Services LLC (1)
92-V Lustdorfskaya Road, Odessa, 65088, Ukraine
Tel.: (380) 482 333 893
Deep Sea Passenger Transportation Services
N.A.I.C.S.: 483112
Andriy Udolatiy *(Mgr-Trng)*

MSC Crewing Services Pvt Ltd. (1)
MSC House 2nd & 3rd Floor Andheri-Kurla Road, Andheri East, Mumbai, 400059, India
Tel.: (91) 22 6752 2555
Web Site: http://www.msccs.com
Deep Sea Passenger Transportation Services
N.A.I.C.S.: 483112
Bhuvnesh Puri *(Deputy Gen Mgr)*

MSC Croatia d.o.o. (1)
Korzo 11 6th Floor, 51000, Rijeka, Croatia
Tel.: (385) 51 356 920
Web Site: http://www.msccroatia.com
Deep Sea Freight Transportation Services
N.A.I.C.S.: 483111
Zlatka Gulam *(Mgr-Comml)*

MSC Cruises (USA) Inc. (1)
6750 N Andrews Ave Ste 100, Fort Lauderdale, FL 33309
Tel.: (954) 772-6262
Web Site: http://www.msccruisesusa.com
Emp.: 80
Deep Sea Passenger Transportation Services
N.A.I.C.S.: 483112
Ileana Garcia *(Mgr-Mktg)*

MSC Cruises Scandinavia AB (1)
Forsta Hotorgshuset Sveavagen 17 13tr, 111 57, Stockholm, Sweden
Tel.: (46) 8 667 21 20
Web Site: http://www.msccruises.se
Deep Sea Passenger Transportation Services
N.A.I.C.S.: 483112
Dag Heimdal *(Acct Mgr)*

MSC DENMARK A/S (1)
Vandvejen 7 5th Floor, 8000, Arhus, Denmark
Tel.: (45) 8620 39 00
Web Site: http://www.msc.com
Deep Sea Freight Transportation Services
N.A.I.C.S.: 483111
Anders Munk Jensen *(Mgr-Sls-Trade)*

MSC De Nicaragua, S.A. de C.V. (1)
Frente Embajada de Canada Calle El Nogal No 30 Residencial Bolonia, Managua, Nicaragua
Tel.: (505) 22 862 673
Web Site: http://www.mscnicaragua.com
Deep Sea Freight Transportation Services
N.A.I.C.S.: 483111
Cristhiam Delgado *(CFO)*

MSC Dominicana S.R.L (1)

MEDITERRANEAN SHIPPING COMPANY, S.A.

Mediterranean Shipping Company, S.A.—(Continued)

Edificio Malaga VII Calle Rafael Augusto Sanchez No 38 Piso 2, Ensanche Naco, Santo Domingo, Dominican Republic
Tel.: (809) 381 1006
Web Site: http://www.mscdominicanrep.com
Deep Sea Freight Transportation Services
N.A.I.C.S.: 483111
Anny Saneaux (Mgr-Line-America Trade)

MSC EESTI AS (1)
Admirali House Ahtri 6A 8th Floor, EE-10151, Tallinn, Estonia
Tel.: (372) 666 3888
Web Site: http://www.msc.com
Emp.: 20
Deep Sea Freight Transportation Services
N.A.I.C.S.: 483111
Andres Nomkula (Mgr-Sls-Import)

MSC Finland Oy (1)
Ruoholahdenkatu 21, 00180, Helsinki, Finland
Tel.: (358) 9 4131 1500
Web Site: http://www.msc.com
Emp.: 50
Deep Sea Freight Transportation Services
N.A.I.C.S.: 483111
Kai Kronlund (Mgr-Import)

MSC France S.A. (1)
CHCI 182 Quai George V, BP 1339, 76065, Le Havre, Cedex, France
Tel.: (33) 23 274 6800
Web Site: http://www.mscfrance.com
Deep Sea Freight Transportation Services
N.A.I.C.S.: 483111

MSC GEMI ACENTELIGI AS. (1)
Sehitler Cad 1530 Sok No 1, Alsancak, 35230, Izmir, Türkiye
Tel.: (90) 232 488 62 00
Web Site: http://www.mscturkey.com
Deep Sea Freight Transportation Services
N.A.I.C.S.: 483111
Acar Ataseven (Mgr-IT & Pur)

MSC GREECE S.A. (1)
12 Akti Possidonos Street 7th Floor, Piraeus, 18531, Greece
Tel.: (30) 210 414 5500
Web Site: http://www.mscgreece.com
Deep Sea Freight Transportation Services
N.A.I.C.S.: 483111
Tilemachos Vassilakis (Mgr-Fin)

Subsidiary (Non-US):

Mediterranean Shipping Company Sh.p.k. (2)
European Trade Center 4th floor Office Number 456 Blv Bajram Curri, Tirana, Albania
Tel.: (355) 4 222 2 745
Web Site: http://www.mscalbania.com
Deep Sea Freight Transportation Services
N.A.I.C.S.: 483111
Nikos Kratimenos (Office Mgr)

MSC Germany GmbH (1)
Willy-Brandt-Str 49, 20457, Hamburg, Germany
Tel.: (49) 40 30 295 0
Web Site: http://www.msc.com
Deep Sea Freight Transportation Services
N.A.I.C.S.: 483111
Boris Wehmann (Deputy Mng Dir & Reg Dir-Fin)

MSC IRELAND LTD (1)
Apex Business Centre Blackthorn Road Sandyford Dublin 18, Dublin, 18, Ireland
Tel.: (353) 1 294 8704
Web Site: http://www.msc-ireland.com
Deep Sea Freight Transportation Services
N.A.I.C.S.: 483111
Paul Barton (CFO)

MSC Koper d.o.o. (1)
Ulica 15 Maja 2B, 6000, Koper, Slovenia
Tel.: (386) 5611 6240
Web Site: http://www.msc.com
Emp.: 24
Deep Sea Freight Transportation Services
N.A.I.C.S.: 483111

MSC Korea Ltd. (1)
Room 601 Marine Center Building 118 2-Ga Namdaemoon-ro, Chung-ku, Seoul, Korea (South)
Tel.: (82) 2 774 5566
Web Site: http://www.msc-korea.com
Deep Sea Freight Transportation Services
N.A.I.C.S.: 483111
Pill-Gwan Lee (Mgr-Sls)

MSC Kreuzfahrten AG (1)
Weisse Gasse 6, 4001, Basel, Switzerland
Tel.: (41) 61 260 01 01
Deep Sea Passenger Transportation Services
N.A.I.C.S.: 483112
Nicole Blom (Head-Mktg)

MSC Kreuzfahrten GmbH (1)
Neumarkter Strasse 63, 81673, Munich, Germany
Tel.: (49) 89 8563550
Web Site: http://www.msc-kreuzfahrten.de
Deep Sea Passenger Transportation Services
N.A.I.C.S.: 483112
Stefan Breitfeld (Head-ECommerce & IT)

MSC Krstarenja doo (1)
Sv Kriza 3, 20000, Dubrovnik, Croatia
Tel.: (385) 20 313 173
Deep Sea Passenger Transportation Services
N.A.I.C.S.: 483112

MSC LATVIA SIA (1)
Duntes Iela 17A, 1005, Riga, Latvia
Tel.: (371) 67 854 444
Web Site: http://www.msclatvia.com
Deep Sea Freight Transportation Services
N.A.I.C.S.: 483111
Atis Shulte (Mgr-Comml-Central Asia)

MSC Lanka (Private) Limited (1)
7th Floor 193 Dr Danister Silva Mawatha, Colombo 08, Colombo, 8, Sri Lanka
Tel.: (94) 11 452 9000
Web Site: http://www.mscsrilanka.com
Deep Sea Freight Transportation Services
N.A.I.C.S.: 483111
Arup Gupta (Mng Dir)

MSC Logistics (Pty) Ltd (1)
Plot 14415, Gaborone West, Gaborone, Botswana
Tel.: (267) 316 4672
Web Site: http://www.mscbotswana.com
Deep Sea Freight Transportation Services
N.A.I.C.S.: 483111

MSC MALAWI LIMITED (1)
PO Box 40059, Kanengo, Kanengo, Malawi
Tel.: (265) 1 710 562
Web Site: http://www.msc-malawi.com
Deep Sea Freight Transportation Services
N.A.I.C.S.: 483111
Frank Chirwa (Mgr-IT)

MSC Magyarorszag Kft (1)
30-32 Kozraktar Str 5th Floor, PO Box 905, 1093, Budapest, Hungary
Tel.: (36) 18009294
Web Site: http://www.msc.com
Deep Sea Freight Transportation Services
N.A.I.C.S.: 483111
Balazs Ersek (Mgr-Customer Svc)

MSC Mali S.A. (1)
Immeuble SOMAGEC, BP E1476, Korofina Sud - Route de Sotuba, Bamako, Mali
Tel.: (223) 20 21 99 61
Web Site: http://www.mscmali.com
Deep Sea Freight Transportation Services
N.A.I.C.S.: 483111

MSC Mediterranean Shipping Co. (Panama) S.A. (1)
Plaza La Boca 2nd Floor La Boca Trinidad & Tobago Street, Panama, Panama
Tel.: (507) 297 6700
Web Site: http://www.mscpanama.com
Deep Sea Freight Transportation Services
N.A.I.C.S.: 483111
Peter Bloam (Mgr)

MSC Mediterranean Shipping Company (Japan) K.K. (1)
Ark Mori Building 23F 1-12-32 Akasaka, Minato-Ku, Tokyo, 107-6023, Japan
Tel.: (81) 3 6685 7500
Web Site: http://www.msc-japan.com
Deep Sea Freight Transportation Services
N.A.I.C.S.: 483111

MSC Mediterranean Shipping Company Ghana Ltd. (1)
James Ahiadome Complex Meridian Street-Community One, PO Box 3010, Tema, Ghana
Tel.: (233) 303 211 839
Web Site: http://www.mscghana.com
Emp.: 90
Deep Sea Freight Transportation Services
N.A.I.C.S.: 483111
Andrew Lynch (Mng Dir)

MSC Mediterranean Shipping do Brasil Ltda (1)
Av Ana Costa 291 4th Floor, Gonzaga, 11060-917, Santos, Brazil
Tel.: (55) 13 3211 9500
Web Site: http://www.mscbrazil.com
Deep Sea Freight Transportation Services
N.A.I.C.S.: 483111
Elber Alves Justo (Mng Dir)

MSC NIGERIA LTD (1)
41 Creek Road, PO Box 4499, Apapa, Apapa, Nigeria
Tel.: (234) 909 3999 601
Web Site: http://www.mscnigeria.com
Deep Sea Freight Transportation Services
N.A.I.C.S.: 483111
Jeff Gosciniak (Mng Dir)

MSC Norway AS. (1)
Thunes Vei 2, PO Box 254, 0274, Oslo, Norway
Tel.: (47) 28 28 19 00
Web Site: http://www.mscnorway.com
Deep Sea Freight Transportation Services
N.A.I.C.S.: 483111
Arne Rognan (Mgr-Comml-CS Export)

MSC Poland Sp. z.o.o. (1)
Plac Kaszubski 17/208, 81-350, Gdynia, Poland
Tel.: (48) 58 666 1000
Web Site: http://www.msc.com
Deep Sea Freight Transportation Services
N.A.I.C.S.: 483111
Piotr Krajewski (Mgr-Intermodal)

MSC Romania SRL. (1)
70 Dr Iacob Felix Street Et 1 Sector 1, 011041, Bucharest, Romania
Tel.: (40) 21 206 9930
Web Site: http://www.msc.com
Emp.: 60
Deep Sea Freight Transportation Services
N.A.I.C.S.: 483111
Gabi Gazdaru (Mgr-IT)

MSC SENEGAL S.A. (1)
Hann Bel Air Route des Hydrocarbures, PO Box 4495, Dakar, Senegal
Tel.: (221) 33 859 0101
Web Site: http://www.mscsenegal.com
Deep Sea Freight Transportation Services
N.A.I.C.S.: 483111
Kader Lo (Deputy Mng Dir)

MSC SHIP MANAGEMENT (Cyprus) Ltd (1)
Cleovoulou Bldg 57 Omonias Avenue, PO Box 55705, CY-3780, Limassol, Cyprus
Tel.: (357) 25 835 300
Web Site: http://www.msccyprus.com
Deep Sea Freight Transportation Services
N.A.I.C.S.: 483111

MSC South East Asia (Singapore) Pte Ltd. (1)
61 Stamford Road /04-01, Singapore, 178892, Singapore
Tel.: (65) 6 505 9610
Web Site: http://www.msc.com
Emp.: 100
Deep Sea Freight Transportation Services
N.A.I.C.S.: 483111
Daren Foo (Gen Mgr)

Subsidiary (Non-US):

MSC Vietnam Company Limited (2)
3 Nguyen Luong Bang District 7 Parkson Paragon 10th Fl, District 7, Ho Chi Minh City, Vietnam
Tel.: (84) 8 5413 5253
Web Site: http://www.mscvietnam.com
Emp.: 90
Deep Sea Freight Transportation Services
N.A.I.C.S.: 483111
Hilary Tran (Mgr-Line)

INTERNATIONAL PUBLIC

MSC Ste Mauritanienne de Peche et de Navigation (1)
Avenue Du Sahel ZRB Nr 585, BP 40254, Nouakchott, Mauritania
Tel.: (222) 5 25 36 38
Web Site: http://www.mscmauritania.com
Deep Sea Freight Transportation Services
N.A.I.C.S.: 483111

MSC Sudan Ltd. (1)
MSC Building Commercial Zone Plot No 6, PO Box 07, Port Sudan, Sudan
Tel.: (249) 311 827 070
Web Site: http://www.mscsudan.com
Deep Sea Freight Transportation Services
N.A.I.C.S.: 483111
Mohammed Moharam (CFO)

MSC Sweden AB (1)
Gardavagen 1, PO Box 264, 401 24, Gothenburg, Sweden
Tel.: (46) 31 339 4900
Web Site: http://www.mscsweden.com
Deep Sea Freight Transportation Services
N.A.I.C.S.: 483111
Cecilia Forsheim (Mgr-Customer Svc)

MSC Syria Ltd. (1)
Al Akhawain Fliefel Ave 0602 Area No 1 Sheik Daher 1, PO Box 1133, Lattakia, 00960, Syria
Tel.: (963) 41 466 122
Web Site: http://www.mscsyria.com
Emp.: 50
Deep Sea Freight Transportation Services
N.A.I.C.S.: 483111
Gianluigi Aponte (Chm)

MSC TOGO, S.A. (1)
Zone Portuaire Route A3 d Akodessewa, BP 3547, Lome, Togo
Tel.: (228) 22 23 76 76
Web Site: http://www.msctogo.com
Deep Sea Freight Transportation Services
N.A.I.C.S.: 483111

MSC TUNISIE S.A.R.L. (1)
Imm MSC ZI-St Gobain, Megrine, Megrine, Tunis, Tunisia
Tel.: (216) 71 425 055
Web Site: http://www.msctunisia.com
Deep Sea Freight Transportation Services
N.A.I.C.S.: 483111
Aziz Bouzaiene (Mgr-IT)

MSC Vilnius UAB. (1)
Konstitucijos Av 7 21 Floor, 09308, Vilnius, Lithuania
Tel.: (370) 5 271 5160
Web Site: http://www.msc.com
Deep Sea Freight Transportation Services
N.A.I.C.S.: 483111
Evaldas Zvirblis (Country Mgr)

MSC Yemen Ltd. (1)
SISPIC Building 2nd floor Al-Kateeb Street, PO Box 4490, Hodeidah, Yemen
Tel.: (967) 3 219 130
Deep Sea Freight Transportation Services
N.A.I.C.S.: 483111

Mediterranean Shipping (Thailand) Co., Ltd. (1)
MSC Building 571 Sukhumvit 71 Road Soi Pridi Banomyong 25, Klongton-Nua Vadhana, Bangkok, 10110, Thailand
Tel.: (66) 20907000
Web Site: http://www.msc.com
Deep Sea Freight Transportation Services
N.A.I.C.S.: 483111
Tawatchai Chitsooksamrarn (Asst Mgr-Trade)

Mediterranean Shipping Company (Aust) Pty Limited (1)
16 McCabe St, Fremantle, 6159, WA, Australia
Tel.: (61) 893360500
Web Site: http://www.msc.com.au
Sales Range: $50-74.9 Million
Emp.: 175
Container Shipping ervices
N.A.I.C.S.: 488510
Kevin Clarke (Mng Dir)

Division (Domestic):

Mediterranean Shipping Company (Aust) Pty Limited (2)
Suite 532 5 Lime Street King Street Wharf,

AND PRIVATE COMPANIES

MEDITERRANEAN SHIPPING COMPANY, S.A.

Sydney, 2000, NSW, Australia
Tel.: (61) 282704000
Web Site: http://www.msc.com
Sales Range: $100-124.9 Million
Emp.: 50
Container Shipping ervices
N.A.I.C.S.: 488510
Kevin Clarke *(Mng Dir)*

Mediterranean Shipping Company (Aust) Pty Limited (2)
Suite 105-110 441 Docklands Drive Waterfront City, Docklands, Melbourne, 3008, VIC, Australia
Tel.: (61) 392541444
Web Site: http://www.msc.com
Sales Range: $25-49.9 Million
Emp.: 50
Container Shipping ervices
N.A.I.C.S.: 488510
Frank Mondo *(Mgr-Bus Applications Dev)*

Mediterranean Shipping Company (Aust) Pty Limited (2)
Unit 14 16 Metroplex Avenue, Murarrie, 4172, QLD, Australia
Tel.: (61) 739094666
Web Site: http://www.mscaustralia.com.au
Sales Range: $25-49.9 Million
Emp.: 16
Container Shipping ervices
N.A.I.C.S.: 488510
Paul Laps *(Gen Mgr)*

Mediterranean Shipping Company (Aust) Pty Limited (2)
19 Divett Street, Port Adelaide, 5015, SA, Australia
Tel.: (61) 883411644
Web Site: http://www.mscaustralia.com
Sales Range: $100-124.9 Million
Container Shipping ervices
N.A.I.C.S.: 488510
Terry Longbottom *(Gen Mgr)*

Division (Non-US):

Mediterranean Shipping Company New Zealand Limited (2)
Level 4 2 Commerce St, Auckland, 1010, New Zealand
Tel.: (64) 93029228
Web Site: http://www.mediterraneanshipping.com
Sales Range: $25-49.9 Million
Emp.: 8
Container Shipping ervices
N.A.I.C.S.: 488510
Steve Wright *(Gen Mgr)*

Mediterranean Shipping Company New Zealand Limited (2)
70 Gloucester St, Russley, 8053, Christchurch, New Zealand
Tel.: (64) 33743214
Web Site: http://www.mscnewzealand.com
Sales Range: $25-49.9 Million
Emp.: 100
Container Shipping Distr
N.A.I.C.S.: 488510
Kevin Inder *(Mgr-Southern Reg)*

Mediterranean Shipping Company New Zealand Limited (2)
78 Wharf St, Tauranga, 3110, New Zealand
Tel.: (64) 75776980
Web Site: http://www.mscnewzealand.com
Sales Range: $25-49.9 Million
Emp.: 12
Container Shipping ervices
N.A.I.C.S.: 488510

Mediterranean Shipping Company (Austria) GmbH (1)
Handelskai 92, 1200, Vienna, Austria
Tel.: (43) 1 369 6910
Web Site: http://www.msc.com
Emp.: 53
Deep Sea Freight Transportation Services
N.A.I.C.S.: 483111

Mediterranean Shipping Company (Hong Kong) Limited (1)
20/F Lee Garden 2 28 Yun Ping Road Causeway Bay, Hong Kong, China (Hong Kong)
Tel.: (852) 2902 5555
Web Site: http://www.msc.com
Deep Sea Freight Transportation Services

N.A.I.C.S.: 483111
Gianluigi Aponte *(Chm)*

Mediterranean Shipping Company (Lebanon) S.A.R.L.
Marine Tower - 10th Floor Gemaizeh - Saint Famille Street, Sainte Famille Street, Beirut, Lebanon
Tel.: (961) 1440600
Web Site: http://www.msc.com
Emp.: 65
Container Shipping Distr
N.A.I.C.S.: 483111
Khairallah El Zein *(Mng Dir)*

Mediterranean Shipping Company (Malaysia) Sdn. Bhd.
No 10-1-10-8 Level 10 Port Tech Tower Jalan Tiara 3/KU 01, Bandar Baru Klang, 41150, Klang, Selangor, Malaysia
Tel.: (60) 3 3002 8888
Web Site: http://www.mscmalaysia.com
Emp.: 100
Deep Sea Freight Transportation Services
N.A.I.C.S.: 483111
Lim Chee Peng *(Mgr-Depot)*

Mediterranean Shipping Company (Maroc) Sarl (1)
Youssra Center-3rd floor 213 Blvd de la Resistance, Casablanca, Morocco
Tel.: (212) 5 2229 5512
Web Site: http://www.mscmorocco.com
Deep Sea Freight Transportation Services
N.A.I.C.S.: 483111

Mediterranean Shipping Company (Netherlands) B.V. (1)
Westblaak 216-218, 3012 KP, Rotterdam, Netherlands
Tel.: (31) 102178600
Web Site: http://www.mscnetherlands.com
Sales Range: $50-74.9 Million
Emp.: 180
Container Shipping ervices
N.A.I.C.S.: 488510
Andre Oversluizen *(Mgr-Ops-Import & Vessel Coordination)*

Mediterranean Shipping Company (Portugal) S.A (1)
Empreendimento Alcantara-Rio Rua de Cascais N 32, 1300-120, Lisbon, Portugal
Tel.: (351) 21 3928410
Web Site: http://www.mscportugal.com
Deep Sea Freight Transportation Services
N.A.I.C.S.: 483111
Carlos Vasconcelos *(Co-Mng Dir)*

Mediterranean Shipping Company (Qatar), WLL. (1)
1st Floor Shaikh Bin Khalid Al Thani Bldg Umm Gwalina, PO Box 22726, Doha, Qatar
Tel.: (974) 4402 9888
Web Site: http://www.mscqatar.com
Emp.: 40
Deep Sea Freight Transportation Services
N.A.I.C.S.: 483111
Shinoj K. P. *(Mgr-Ops)*

Mediterranean Shipping Company (U.A.E.) L.L.C. (1)
Sharaf Building-4th Floor Al Mina Road, PO Box 50439, Dubai, 50439, United Arab Emirates
Tel.: (971) 4 352 4888
Web Site: http://www.mscae.com
Emp.: 120
Deep Sea Freight Transportation Services
N.A.I.C.S.: 483111
C. Rajmohan *(Asst Gen Mgr)*

Subsidiary (Non-US):

MEDITERRANEAN SHIPPING (KUWAIT) COMPANY W.L.L (2)
Laila Tower 8th Floor Salem Al Mubarak Str, PO Box 1319, Hawalli, 32014, Kuwait
Tel.: (965) 2572 3850
Web Site: http://www.msckuwait.com
Deep Sea Freight Transportation Services
N.A.I.C.S.: 483111
Vijayesh K. V. *(Asst Mgr-Fin)*

Mediterranean Shipping Company (UK) Ltd
Medite House 10 The Havens, Ipswich, IP3 9SJ, United Kingdom
Tel.: (44) 1473277777

Web Site: http://www.mscuk.com
Sales Range: $125-149.9 Million
Emp.: 400
Container Shipping ervices
N.A.I.C.S.: 488510
Daniel Everitt *(Mng Dir)*

Mediterranean Shipping Company (Zambia) Ltd. (1)
Corporate Park Stand No 20849 Alick Nkhata Rd, Lusaka, Zambia
Tel.: (260) 211 258 774
Web Site: http://www.msczambia.com
Emp.: 5
Deep Sea Freight Transportation Services
N.A.I.C.S.: 483111

Mediterranean Shipping Company Benin, S.A. (1)
Rue 135-ILOT 574-Parcelle A Zone Portuaire-Quartier Zongo Ehuzu 01, BP 132, Cotonou, Benin
Tel.: (229) 21 315 690
Web Site: http://www.mscbenin.com
Emp.: 40
Deep Sea Freight Transportation Services
N.A.I.C.S.: 483111
Gregory Krief *(Mng Dir)*

Mediterranean Shipping Company Bulgaria Ltd. (1)
6 Pliska Street, Varna, 9000, Bulgaria
Tel.: (359) 52 681 122
Web Site: http://www.mscbulgaria.com
Deep Sea Freight Transportation Services
N.A.I.C.S.: 483111
Milena Voinova *(Mgr-Import Dept)*

Mediterranean Shipping Company Cameroun S.A. (1)
Rue de la Base Navale, BP 1506, Douala, Cameroon
Tel.: (237) 33 439 148
Web Site: http://www.msccameroon.com
Deep Sea Freight Transportation Services
N.A.I.C.S.: 483111

Subsidiary (Non-US):

Mediterranean Shipping Company Bolivia (2)
1375 20th St Calacoto, La Paz, Bolivia
Tel.: (591) 22110000
Web Site: http://www.mscbolivia.com
Container Shipping ervices
N.A.I.C.S.: 488510
Carmen Flores *(Gen Mgr)*

Mediterranean Shipping Company Chile S.A. (1)
3120 Isidora Goyenechea Avenue 5th Floor, Las Condes, Santiago, Chile
Tel.: (56) 27291000
Web Site: http://www.mscchile.com
Sales Range: $50-74.9 Million
Emp.: 120
Container Shipping ervices
N.A.I.C.S.: 488510
Ricardo Klempau *(Mng Dir)*

Mediterranean Shipping Company Colombia Sa. (1)
World Trade Center Building Calle 100 No 8A-55 Office 1103 PH, Bogota, Colombia
Tel.: (57) 1 628 8800
Web Site: http://www.msccolombia.com
Deep Sea Freight Transportation Services
N.A.I.C.S.: 483111
Daniel Cundy *(Mng Dir)*

Mediterranean Shipping Company Costa Rica S.R.L (1)
Edificio Cerro Chato Pino N 2, La Uruca, San Jose, Costa Rica
Tel.: (506) 2291 5535
Deep Sea Freight Transportation Services
N.A.I.C.S.: 483111

Mediterranean Shipping Company Ltd. (1)
Villa Opp Ministry Of Foreign Affairs Km 5 Road, Mogadishu, Somalia
Tel.: (252) 616 549085
Web Site: http://www.mscsomalia.com
Deep Sea Freight Transportation Services
N.A.I.C.S.: 483111
Nour Eldiin *(Mgr-Logistics & Ops)*

Mediterranean Shipping Company MSC (Malta) LTD (1)

29 Lascaris WharfValletta, Valletta, VLT 1921, Malta
Tel.: (356) 21 226 816
Deep Sea Freight Transportation Services
N.A.I.C.S.: 483111
John Ripard *(Mng Dir)*

Mediterranean Shipping Company Madagascar S.A. (1)
Immeuble Madecasse 2eme Etage Ankorondrano Rue Ravoninahitriniarivo, PO Box 8063, 101, Antananarivo, Madagascar
Tel.: (261) 20 223 2130
Web Site: http://www.msc.com
Deep Sea Freight Transportation Services
N.A.I.C.S.: 483111
Sandeep Lodha *(CFO)*

Mediterranean Shipping Company Rus, LLC (1)
Moskovskiy prospekt 97 LIT A, 196084, Saint Petersburg, Russia
Tel.: (7) 8123465764
Web Site: http://www.mscrussia.com
Deep Sea Freight Transportation Services
N.A.I.C.S.: 483111
Tatyana Nazarova *(Mgr-Fin)*

Mediterranean Shipping Company S.R.L (1)
Via Francesco Ciampa 29, Piano Di Sorrento, 80063, Naples, Italy
Tel.: (39) 081 534 1270
Deep Sea Freight Transportation Services
N.A.I.C.S.: 483111
Marco Pica *(Project Mgr)*

Mediterranean Shipping Company Spain S.A. (1)
Avenida del Puerto 273, Edificio Puerto, 46011, Valencia, Spain
Tel.: (34) 963359100
Web Site: http://www.mscspain.com
Sales Range: $50-74.9 Million
Emp.: 200
Container Shipping ervices
N.A.I.C.S.: 488510
Francifco Lorente *(Mng Dir)*

Mediterranean Shipping Company Trinidad and Tobago Ltd (1)
2 Carlos Street, Port of Spain, Trinidad & Tobago
Tel.: (868) 623 1439
Web Site: http://www.msctrinidad.com
Deep Sea Freight Transportation Services
N.A.I.C.S.: 483111
Susan Mahabir *(Mgr-Documentation)*

Mediterranean Shipping Company USA Inc. (1)
420 5th Ave 8th Fl, New York, NY 10018-0222
Tel.: (212) 764-4800
Web Site: http://www.msc.us
Sales Range: $25-49.9 Million
Freight Transportation Arrangement Services
N.A.I.C.S.: 488510
Nicola Arena *(Chm & CEO)*

Mediterranean Shipping Company Uruguay SA (1)
1365 Andes Street-13th Floor, 11100, Montevideo, Uruguay
Tel.: (598) 2 902 2935
Web Site: http://www.mscuruguay.com
Deep Sea Freight Transportation Services
N.A.I.C.S.: 483111
Natalia Deleon *(Mgr-Acctg)*

Mediterranean Shipping Company W.L.L. (1)
4th Floor Amman Gate Building, Harem Bin Qutbah St Al-Sahel, Amman, Jordan
Tel.: (962) 6 581 3366
Web Site: http://www.mscjordan.com
Deep Sea Freight Transportation Services
N.A.I.C.S.: 483111
Fadi Ghawi *(CFO)*

Mediterranean Shipping Company de Venezuela C.A. (1)
Avenida Arturo Uslar Pietri Edificio Metalica Piso 15 Oficina A y B Ch, Caracas, 1060, Venezuela
Tel.: (58) 212 918 30 00
Web Site: http://www.msc-venezuela.com
Deep Sea Freight Transportation Services

MEDITERRANEAN SHIPPING COMPANY, S.A.

Mediterranean Shipping Company, S.A.—(Continued)
N.A.I.C.S.: 483111
Carolyn Blanco (Gen Mgr)

Mediterranean Shipping Company del Peru S.A.C. (1)
Avenida Alvarez Calderon 185-Piso 5 Lima 27, San Isidro, San Isidro, Peru
Tel.: (51) 1 221 7561
Web Site: http://www.mscperu.com
Deep Sea Freight Transportation Services
N.A.I.C.S.: 483111
Fernando Morales Draxl (Mgr-Ops, Agencies & Terminals)

Mediterranean Shipping Cruises Ltd. (1)
Queens House 55-56 Lincoln's Inn Fields, London, WC2A 3LJ, United Kingdom
Tel.: (44) 20 7092 2888
Web Site: http://www.msccruises.co.uk
Deep Sea Passenger Transportation Services
N.A.I.C.S.: 483112

SARL MSCA MEDITERRANEAN SHIPPING COMPANY (1)
Cooperative En-nahar No 11, Les Sources - Bir Mourad Rais, 16050, Algiers, Algeria
Tel.: (213) 21 563 531
Web Site: http://www.msc.com
Emp.: 40
Deep Sea Freight Transportation Services
N.A.I.C.S.: 483111
Benabdallah Mohamed Amine (Branch Mgr)

SAS Shipping Agencies Services SARL (1)
11B Blvd Joseph II, Luxembourg, L1840, Luxembourg
Tel.: (352) 26701621
Shipping Services
N.A.I.C.S.: 483111
Hugues Ronan Favard (CEO)

Total Terminals International LLC (1)
301 Hanjin Rd, Long Beach, CA 90802
Tel.: (562) 256-2622
Web Site: http://www.totalterminals.com
Boat Dealers
N.A.I.C.S.: 441222
James Kwon (Principal)

MEDITERRANEAN TOURISM INVESTMENT COMPANY
Four Seasons Hotel, PO Box 941654, Amman, 11194, Jordan
Tel.: (962) 5505180   JO
Year Founded: 1996
MDTR—(AMM)
Rev.: $5,393,552
Assets: $84,039,270
Liabilities: $17,035,977
Net Worth: $67,003,294
Earnings: ($5,147,546)
Emp.: 321
Fiscal Year-end: 12/31/20
Home Management Services
N.A.I.C.S.: 721110

MEDIUS HOLDINGS CO., LTD.
1-2-2 Yurakucho Tokyo Toho Hibiya Building, Chiyoda-ku, Tokyo, 100-0006, Japan
Tel.: (81) 368112958
Web Site: https://www.medius.co.jp
Year Founded: 2009
3154—(TKS)
Rev.: $1,615,887,580
Assets: $714,217,720
Liabilities: $591,453,580
Net Worth: $122,764,140
Earnings: $6,991,280
Emp.: 4,949
Fiscal Year-end: 06/30/24
Holding Company
N.A.I.C.S.: 551111
Yasuhiko Ikeya (Pres & CEO)

MEDIUS SVERIGE AB
Klarabergsviadukten 90, Stockholm, SE 111 64, Sweden
Tel.: (46) 13121630
Web Site: https://www.medius.com
Year Founded: 2001
Emp.: 100
Process Automation Services
N.A.I.C.S.: 541512
Anders Fohlin (CFO)

Subsidiaries:

Onpay Solutions, Inc. (1)
8382 Baymeadows Rd Ste 4, Jacksonville, FL 32256
Tel.: (904) 786-6369
Web Site: http://www.onpaysolutions.com
Mortgage & Nonmortgage Loan Brokers
N.A.I.C.S.: 522310
Juliet Negrete Anderson (Exec VP)

MEDIVAC LIMITED
Suite 6 Level 9 66 Hunter Street, Sydney, 2000, NSW, Australia
Tel.: (61) 3 9286 7500   AU
Sales Range: Less than $1 Million
Medical Device Mfr
N.A.I.C.S.: 339112
Kieran Patrick Honour (Chm)

MEDIVATE PARTNERS, LLC
15F Kwangil Plaza 331 Gangnam daero, Seocho gu, Seoul, 06627, Korea (South)
Tel.: (82) 2 536 0704
Web Site: http://www.medivatepartners.com
Privater Equity Firm
N.A.I.C.S.: 523999
Paul H Kim (CEO)

MEDIVIE THERAPEUTIC LTD.
1 The Willows Mark Road, Herts, Hemel Hempstead, HP2 7BN, United Kingdom
Tel.: (44) 8708 200 096
Web Site: http://www.medivie.com
Year Founded: 2012
MDVI—(TAE)
Rev.: $140,201
Assets: $3,891,884
Liabilities: $2,195,621
Net Worth: $1,696,262
Earnings: ($4,210,943)
Fiscal Year-end: 12/31/19
Medical Device Mfr
N.A.I.C.S.: 334510
Menachem Cohen (Chm & CEO)

MEDIVIR AB
Lunastigen 5 2nd Floor, PO Box 1086, SE 141 22, Huddinge, Sweden
Tel.: (46) 854683100
Web Site: https://www.medivir.se
Year Founded: 1988
MVIR—(OMX)
Rev.: $583,326
Assets: $21,935,336
Liabilities: $3,878,352
Net Worth: $18,056,984
Earnings: ($8,313,898)
Emp.: 9
Fiscal Year-end: 12/31/22
Pharmaceuticals Mfr
N.A.I.C.S.: 325412
Helena Levander (Chm)

Subsidiaries:

Medivir UK Ltd (1)
100 Fulbourn Rd, Cambridge, CB1 9PT, United Kingdom
Tel.: (44) 1799532100
Biotech Services
N.A.I.C.S.: 541714

MEDIVISION MEDICAL IMAGING LTD.
Hermon building Industrial Park, PO Box 45, 20692, Yokneam, Israel
Tel.: (972) 4 989 4884
Web Site: http://www.medivision.co.il
Medical Equipment Mfr & Distr
N.A.I.C.S.: 334510
Noam Allon (Chm & CEO)

MEDIVOLVE INC.
800-65 Queen Street W, Toronto, M5H 2M5, ON, Canada
Tel.: (416) 861-2267   BC
Web Site: http://www.copperone.com
Year Founded: 2006
4NCA—(DEU)
Rev.: $67,921,451
Assets: $46,385,619
Liabilities: $32,454,256
Net Worth: $13,931,362
Earnings: ($5,171,281)
Emp.: 237
Fiscal Year-end: 12/31/21
Copper Mining Services
N.A.I.C.S.: 212230
G. Scott Moore (Chm)

MEDIWELCOME HEALTHCARE MANAGEMENT & TECHNOLOGY INC.
10-12th Floor Parkview Place 6 North Road of East 6th Ring, Chaoyang, Beijing, China
Tel.: (86) 1056831999   Ky
Web Site: https://www.mediwelcome.com
Year Founded: 2000
2159—(HKG)
Rev.: $45,872,286
Assets: $29,674,070
Liabilities: $13,063,663
Net Worth: $16,610,407
Earnings: ($13,304,580)
Emp.: 335
Fiscal Year-end: 12/31/23
Health Care Srvices
N.A.I.C.S.: 621610
Siu Wai Tsoi (Sec)

MEDIZEN HUMANCARE INC.,
6F 6 Jeongui-ro 7-gil, Songpa-gu, Seoul, 135-847, Korea (South)
Tel.: (82) 25559806
Web Site: https://www.medizencare.com
Year Founded: 2012
Genetic Testing Services
N.A.I.C.S.: 621511
Shin Dong-Jik (CEO)

MEDLAB CLINICAL LIMITED
PO Box 6452, Alexandria, 2015, NSW, Australia
Tel.: (61) 281880311
Web Site: https://www.medlab.co
Year Founded: 2012
MDC—(ASX)
Rev.: $4,621,100
Assets: $8,708,978
Liabilities: $2,771,666
Net Worth: $5,937,311
Earnings: ($5,538,645)
Fiscal Year-end: 06/30/22
Biopharmaceutical Mfr
N.A.I.C.S.: 325412
Matt Hudson (Chm)

Subsidiaries:

Medlab Research Ltd. (1)
10 Orange Street Haymarket, London, WC2H 7DQ, United Kingdom
Tel.: (44) 2081380311
Healtcare Services
N.A.I.C.S.: 621610

MEDLEY, INC.
13F Roppongi Hills Mori Tower 6-10-1 Roppongi, Minato-ku, Tokyo, 106-6113, Japan
Tel.: (81) 345209823
Web Site: https://www.medley.jp
Year Founded: 2009
4480—(TKS)
Rev.: $145,571,880
Assets: $180,298,700
Liabilities: $55,252,370
Net Worth: $125,046,330
Earnings: $18,192,940
Emp.: 722
Fiscal Year-end: 12/31/23
Human Resource Recruitment Services
N.A.I.C.S.: 541612
Kohei Takiguchi (Pres & CEO)

Subsidiaries:

GCM Co., Ltd. (1)
Roppongi Hills Mori Tower 13F 6-10-1 Roppongi, Minato-ku, Tokyo, 106-6113, Japan
Tel.: (81) 120946275
Web Site: https://www.ginza-cm.com
Investment Fund Management Services
N.A.I.C.S.: 523940

MEDiPASS Co., Ltd. (1)
3rd floor RK Building 2-13-10 Shimomeguro, Meguro-ku, Tokyo, 153-0064, Japan
Tel.: (81) 364174066
Web Site: https://medipass.co.jp
Hospital Services
N.A.I.C.S.: 622110

NaCl Medical, Inc. (1)
2-12-5 Gakuenminami HOYO Parkside Building 2F, Matsue, 690-0826, Japan
Tel.: (81) 852289282
Web Site: http://www.nacl-med.co.jp
Hospital Services
N.A.I.C.S.: 622110

MEDLIFE S.A.
365 Calea Grivitei, District 1, 10719, Bucharest, Romania
Tel.: (40) 735300926
Web Site: https://www.medlifeinternational.com
Year Founded: 1996
M—(BUC)
Rev.: $482,555,979
Assets: $572,606,466
Liabilities: $465,269,088
Net Worth: $107,337,378
Earnings: ($904,597)
Emp.: 2,700
Fiscal Year-end: 12/31/23
Health Care Srvices
N.A.I.C.S.: 621610
Mihail Marcu (Chm & CEO)

Subsidiaries:

Badea Medical SRL (1)
Strada Rene Descartes Nr 27, Cluj-Napoca, 400486, Romania
Tel.: (40) 364140260
Web Site: https://www.badeamedica.ro
Medical Devices
N.A.I.C.S.: 622110

Biotest Med SRL (1)
Bdul Tomis 70-81 etaj III, Constanta, Romania
Tel.: (40) 241671166
Medical Equipment Mfr
N.A.I.C.S.: 339112

Centrul Medical Matei Basarab SRL (1)
45 Matei Basarab Street Sector 3, Bucharest, 30671, Romania
Tel.: (40) 213029434
Web Site: https://www.veridia.ro
Health Care Srvices
N.A.I.C.S.: 621610

Centrul Medical Micromedica SRL (1)
Str Petru Rares Nr 20, Piatra Neamt, Romania
Tel.: (40) 233222075
Medical Equipment Mfr
N.A.I.C.S.: 339112
Stefan Botez (Mgr-Clinic)

AND PRIVATE COMPANIES

MEDSERV P.L.C.

Centrul Medical Panduri SA (1)
Str Dr Ioan Atanasiu Nr 34 sector 5, Bucharest, Romania
Tel.: (40) 219901
Web Site: https://www.cmpanduri.ro
Health Care Srvices
N.A.I.C.S.: 621999
Andreea Stefanescu *(Mng Dir-Obstetrics & Gynecology)*

Dent Estet Clinic SA (1)
Bd Aviatorilor 27 Floor 1, District 1, Bucharest, Romania
Tel.: (40) 748358358
Web Site: https://www.dentestet.ro
Dental Clinic Services
N.A.I.C.S.: 621210
Andreea Necula *(Mgr-HR)*

Ghencea Medical Center SA (1)
Bulevardul Ghencea 43B, Bucharest, Romania
Tel.: (40) 756045204
Web Site:
https://www.ghenceamedicalcenter.ro
Medical Devices
N.A.I.C.S.: 622110

Micromedica Bacau SRL (1)
Bd ul Unirii 15, Bacau, Romania
Tel.: (40) 234286699
Medical Equipment Mfr
N.A.I.C.S.: 339112

Micromedica Roman SRL (1)
Strada Dobrogeanu Gherea nr 31, Roman, Romania
Tel.: (40) 233722777
Medical Equipment Mfr
N.A.I.C.S.: 339112

Micromedica Targu Neamt SRL (1)
Bd ul Marasesti nr 53, Targu Neamt, Romania
Tel.: (40) 233791333
Medical Equipment Mfr
N.A.I.C.S.: 339112

Oncoteam Diagnostic SA (1)
Str Splaiul Unirii nr 313A etajul 1 Sector 3, 030138, Bucharest, Romania
Tel.: (40) 312262020
Web Site: https://www.oncoteam.ro
Medical Devices
N.A.I.C.S.: 622110
Adina Balan *(Fin Mgr)*

Policlinica de Diagnostic Rapid SA (1)
Strada Turnului 2A, Brasov, Romania
Tel.: (40) 372875745
Medical Equipment Mfr
N.A.I.C.S.: 339112

Solomed Plus SRL (1)
Gavana-Aleea Spitalului Nr 28A, Pitesti, Romania
Tel.: (40) 733100188
Web Site: http://www.solomed.ro
Medical Equipment Mfr
N.A.I.C.S.: 339112

Stem Cells Bank SA (1)
B-dul Gen Ion Dragalina 37A, Timisoara, Romania
Tel.: (40) 256275640
Web Site: https://www.stemcellsbank.ro
Blood Bank Services
N.A.I.C.S.: 621991
Ioannis Kountouris *(Mgr)*

MEDLIVE TECHNOLOGY CO., LTD.
E1 No 1 Baijialou Chaoyang North Road, Red Manor International Bonded Innovation Park Chaoyang District, Beijing, China   Ky
Year Founded: 1996
2192—(HKG)
Rev.: $48,116,213
Assets: $705,260,715
Liabilities: $26,247,171
Net Worth: $679,013,544
Earnings: $19,368,961
Emp.: 605
Fiscal Year-end: 12/31/22
Information Technology Services
N.A.I.C.S.: 541512
Lijun Tian *(VP)*

MEDMEN ENTERPRISES, INC.
Hsbc Bldg Suite 2200 885 West Georgia St, Vancouver, V6C3E8, BC, Canada
Tel.: (604) 691-6100
Year Founded: 1991
MMEN—(CNSX)
Rev.: $140,811,689
Assets: $323,223,684
Liabilities: $641,736,420
Net Worth: ($318,512,736)
Earnings: ($195,186,605)
Emp.: 510
Fiscal Year-end: 06/25/22
Cannabis Distr
N.A.I.C.S.: 459999
Ana S. Bowman *(CFO)*

MEDMIRA INC.
155 Chain Lake Drive Suite 1, Halifax, B3S 1B3, NS, Canada
Tel.: (902) 450-1588   AB
Web Site: https://www.medmira.com
Year Founded: 1999
47M—(DEU)
Rev.: $191,082
Assets: $2,724,244
Liabilities: $13,937,859
Net Worth: ($11,213,615)
Earnings: ($1,996,041)
Fiscal Year-end: 07/31/23
Medical Equipment Mfr
N.A.I.C.S.: 334510
Hermes Chan *(Founder & CEO)*

Subsidiaries:

Maple Biosciences Inc. (1)
Suite 1 155 Chain Lake Drive, Halifax, B3S 1B3, NS, Canada
Tel.: (902) 450-1588
Sales Range: $25-49.9 Million
Emp.: 35
Medical Instrument Mfr
N.A.I.C.S.: 339112

MedMira Laboratories Inc. (1)
155 Chain Lake Dr Suite 1, Halifax, B3S 1B3, NS, Canada
Tel.: (902) 450-1588
Web Site: http://www.medmira.com
Emp.: 3
Medical Diagnostic Device Mfr
N.A.I.C.S.: 334510

MEDNATION AG
Graurheindorfer Strasse 137, Nettersheim, 53117, Bonn, Germany
Tel.: (49) 2289677820
Web Site: https://mednation.de
EIF—(MUN)
Rev.: $48,172,887
Assets: $79,699,414
Liabilities: $67,015,948
Net Worth: $12,683,466
Earnings: $2,483,708
Emp.: 452
Fiscal Year-end: 12/31/23
Health Care Srvices
N.A.I.C.S.: 621999
Markus-Michael Kuethmann *(Chm-Mgmt Bd)*

MEDONDO HOLDING AG
Tattenbachstrasse 6, 80538, Munich, Germany
Tel.: (49) 89997429010   De
Web Site:
https://holding.medondo.com
Year Founded: 2003
AMI—(MUN)
Rev.: $1,379,838
Assets: $20,344,324
Liabilities: $5,475,195
Net Worth: $14,869,129
Earnings: ($4,735,602)
Emp.: 29
Fiscal Year-end: 12/31/23
IT Services
N.A.I.C.S.: 541519
Thomas Kuhmann *(Chm-Supervisory Bd)*

Subsidiaries:

medondo AG (1)
Am Graswege 6, 30169, Hannover, Germany
Tel.: (49) 511 16 59 48 0
Web Site: http://www.medondo.com
Software Publisher
N.A.I.C.S.: 513210

MEDORA HOTELS & RESORTS LTD.
Mrkusica dvori 2, Podgora, 21327, Zagreb, Croatia
Tel.: (385) 21601701
Web Site:
https://www.medorahotels.com
HPDG—(ZAG)
Sales Range: Less than $1 Million
Hotel & Restaurant Operator
N.A.I.C.S.: 721110

MEDPACTO INC.
92 Myeongdal-ro, Seocho-gu, Seoul, 06668, Korea (South)
Tel.: (82) 269380200
Web Site: https://www.medpacto.com
Year Founded: 2013
235980—(KRS)
Rev.: $10,631,951
Assets: $82,596,070
Liabilities: $57,804,637
Net Worth: $24,791,432
Earnings: ($27,422,725)
Emp.: 66
Fiscal Year-end: 12/31/22
Biotechnology Research & Development Services
N.A.I.C.S.: 541714
Seong Jin Kim *(Founder)*

MEDPEER, INC.
4-20-3 Ebisu Garden Place Tower, Shibuya-ku, Tokyo, 150-6017, Japan
Tel.: (81) 364477961
Web Site: http://www.medpeer.co.jp
6095—(TKS)
Rev.: $103,088,600
Assets: $107,498,580
Liabilities: $46,616,750
Net Worth: $60,881,830
Earnings: $4,374,530
Fiscal Year-end: 09/30/23
Research & Information Services
N.A.I.C.S.: 519290
Akinobu Fukumura *(Exec Officer)*

MEDPLUS HEALTH SERVICES LIMITED
707 7th Floor 5-9-13 Taramandal Commercial Complex, Saifabad, Hyderabad, 500004, Telangana, India
Tel.: (91) 4067006700
Web Site:
https://www.medplusindia.com
Year Founded: 2006
543427—(BOM)
Pharmacy Retailer
N.A.I.C.S.: 456110
Gangadi Madhukar Reddy *(CEO & Mng Dir)*

MEDPRIN REGENERATIVE MEDICAL TECHNOLOGIES CO., LTD.
No 3 Yayingshi Road, Huangpu District, Guangzhou, 510663, Guangdong, China
Tel.: (86) 2032296118
Web Site: https://www.medprin.com
Year Founded: 2008

301033—(CHIN)
Rev.: $32,516,859
Assets: $110,840,704
Liabilities: $21,283,211
Net Worth: $89,557,493
Earnings: $5,757,380
Fiscal Year-end: 12/31/23
Medical Equipment Mfr & Distr
N.A.I.C.S.: 339112
Yuan Yuyu *(Chm)*

MEDRA CORP.
2480 Homer Watson Blvd Unit 3, Kitchener, N2P 2R5, ON, Canada
Tel.: (519) 895-2716
Electric Power Distribution Services
N.A.I.C.S.: 221122
Ronald Ilsley *(CFO & VP-Fin)*

MEDRX CO., LTD.
431-7 Nishiyama, Higashikagawa-city, Kagawa, 769-2712, Japan
Tel.: (81) 879233071
Web Site: https://www.medrx.co.jp
Year Founded: 2002
4586—(TKS)
Rev.: $205,610
Assets: $14,548,680
Liabilities: $907,520
Net Worth: $13,641,160
Earnings: ($6,607,880)
Emp.: 23
Fiscal Year-end: 12/31/23
Pharmaceuticals Mfr
N.A.I.C.S.: 325412
Yonehiro Matsumura *(Pres & CEO)*

Subsidiaries:

IL Pharma Inc. (1)
1 Broadway 14th Fl, Cambridge, MA 02142
Tel.: (617) 475-1546
Pharmaceutical Products Distr
N.A.I.C.S.: 424210
Yuji Kuwabara *(Pres & CEO)*

MEDRx USA Inc. (1)
2030 Main St Ste 1300, Irvine, CA 92614
Tel.: (949) 260-4788
Web Site: https://medrxusa.com
Pharmaceutical Drug Development System Mfr
N.A.I.C.S.: 325412
Yonehiro Matsumura *(Pres & CEO)*

MEDSCI HEALTHCARE HOLDINGS LIMITED
18F Bldg34 No 258 Xinzhuan Rd, Songjiang District, Shanghai, China
Tel.: (86) 2154480588   Ky
Web Site: https://ir.medsci.cn
Year Founded: 2012
2415—(HKG)
Health Care Srvices
N.A.I.C.S.: 621610
Fabao Zhang *(Founder)*

MEDSERV P.L.C.
Port of Marsaxlokk, Birzebbuga, BBG 3011, Malta
Tel.: (356) 22202000   Mt
Web Site: https://medservregis.com
Year Founded: 1974
MDS—(MAL)
Rev.: $72,241,701
Assets: $163,748,511
Liabilities: $98,610,908
Net Worth: $65,137,603
Earnings: $588,038
Emp.: 716
Fiscal Year-end: 12/31/22
Oil & Gas Support Services
N.A.I.C.S.: 213112
Anthony S. Diacono *(Chm-Grp)*

Subsidiaries:

Middle East Tubular Services (Gulf) Limited (1)
PC 322 Sohar Free Zone, PO Box 56, Falaj

MEDSERV P.L.C.

Medserv p.l.c.—(Continued)

Al Qabail, Oman
Tel.: (968) 98250805
Oilfield Logistic Services
N.A.I.C.S.: 486110

Middle East Tubular Services (Iraq) Ltd. (1)
Khor al Zubair Free Zone, Basrah, Iraq
Tel.: (964) 7706897777
Oilfield Logistic Services
N.A.I.C.S.: 486110

Middle East Tubular Services LLC (1)
Hamriyah Free Zone Phase II, PO Box 42122, Sharjah, United Arab Emirates
Tel.: (971) 65269099
Oilfield Logistic Services
N.A.I.C.S.: 486110

MEDSMART GROUP INC.
999 Wonderland Road, Building Tingxiang Suite 703, Nanchang, China
Tel.: (86) 866520370   NJ
Web Site: http://www.knsc.info
Year Founded: 2004
KNSC—(OTCIQ)
Sales Range: Less than $1 Million
Emp.: 4
Solar Powered Product Mfr
N.A.I.C.S.: 334419
Zoran Cvetojevic *(Chm & CEO)*

MEDTECH GLOBAL LIMITED
Level 2 99 Coventry Street Southbank, Melbourne, 3006, VIC, Australia
Tel.: (61) 3 9690 8666   AU
Web Site:
http://www.medtechglobal.com
Rev.: $16,927,541
Assets: $4,688,697
Liabilities: $6,325,883
Net Worth: ($1,637,186)
Earnings: ($804,083)
Fiscal Year-end: 03/31/18
Healthcare Technology Services
N.A.I.C.S.: 513210
Vino Ramayah *(Chm & CEO)*

Subsidiaries:

ConSova Corp. (1)
1667 Cole Blvd Ste 250, Lakewood, CO 80401 **(100%)**
Tel.: (303) 468-0320
Web Site: http://www.consova.com
Sales Range: $1-9.9 Million
Emp.: 30
Management Consulting Services
N.A.I.C.S.: 541618
John Cratin *(Sr VP-Bus Dev)*

Medtech Ltd. (1)
Medtech House Level 1 48 Market Place, Auckland, 1100, New Zealand **(100%)**
Tel.: (64) 93799166
Web Site: http://www.medtechglobal.com
Emp.: 60
Healthcare Technology Services
N.A.I.C.S.: 541519

MEDTECS INTERNATIONAL CORPORATION LIMITED
7B Counntry Space I Bldg 133 H V Dela Costa St, Makati, 1227, Philippines
Tel.: (63) 288179000
Web Site: https://www.medtecs.com
546—(CAT)
Rev.: $52,639,000
Assets: $166,767,000
Liabilities: $36,459,000
Net Worth: $130,308,000
Earnings: $22,488,000)
Emp.: 3,306
Fiscal Year-end: 12/31/23
Cut & Sew Apparel Manufacturing (except Contractors)
N.A.I.C.S.: 315250
Abdul Jabbar Karam Din *(Sec)*

Subsidiaries:

Context Corporation (1)
No 7 Argonaut Highway Cor Efficiency Ave Subic Bay Industrial Park, Phase 1 SBFZ, Subic, Philippines **(98.8%)**
Tel.: (63) 472527626
Trading of Hospital Textiles & Garments, Pillow Cases, Bed Sheets, Gowns & Apparel
N.A.I.C.S.: 423450

Hangzhou Jinchen Medical Supplies Manufacture Co., Ltd (1)
202 Zhangshan Road, Yuhang District, Hangzhou, 311107, China **(100%)**
Tel.: (86) 57186396888
Mfr & Trading of Woven & Non-Woven Medical Consumables
N.A.I.C.S.: 313230

Medtecs (Asia Pacific) Ptd. Ltd. (1)
138 Cecil Street 13-02 Cecil Court, Singapore, 069538, Singapore
Tel.: (65) 6 534 9222
Web Site: https://www.medtecs.com
Sale of Woven & Knitted Fabrics & Other Textile Products
N.A.I.C.S.: 313310

Medtecs (Cambodia) Corporation Limited (1)
No 52 Street 606 Corner Street 311, Village 8 Sangkat Boeng Kak 2 Khan Toul Kork, Phnom Penh, Cambodia **(100%)**
Tel.: (855) 23866659
Web Site: https://www.medtecs.com
Emp.: 12
Manufacture & Sales of Medical Consumables
N.A.I.C.S.: 315250

Medtecs (Taiwan) Corporation (1)
11F No 9 SongGao Rd, Xinyi Dist, Taipei, 110, Taiwan
Tel.: (886) 227392222
Web Site: https://www.medtecs.com.tw
Emp.: 40
Manufacturing, Leasing, Marketing & Distribution of Medical Consumables & Hospital Laundry Services
N.A.I.C.S.: 315210

Medtex Corporation (1)
7th Street Phase II BEZ Bataan Afab Marivelez, Marivelez, Bataan, 2106, Philippines **(100%)**
Tel.: (63) 479354287
Sales Range: $250-299.9 Million
Emp.: 650
Mfr & Sale of Elastic Bandages, Garters & Other Medical Garment Products
N.A.I.C.S.: 423450
Jianlang Duanmu *(Gen Mgr)*

Universal Weavers Corporation (1)
7th Street Phase II BEZ Bataan Export Processing Zone, Marivelez, Bataan, Philippines **(100%)**
Tel.: (63) 479354287
Web Site: http://www.medtecs.com
Emp.: 500
Mfr & Trading of Woven & Knitted Fabrics
N.A.I.C.S.: 313210

Zibo Liancheng Textiles & Garments Co., Ltd. (1)
Qinghe Economic Park, Gaoqing Country, Shangdong, 256301, China **(100%)**
Tel.: (86) 5336319988
Web Site: http://www.medtecs.com
Mfr & Trading of Woven Fabrics
N.A.I.C.S.: 313210

Zibo Lianhe Textiles Co., Ltd. (1)
Qinghe Economic Park, Gaoqing Country, Shangdong, 256301, China
Tel.: (86) 5336319988
Web Site: http://www.medtecs.com
Woven Fabrics Mfr & Distr
N.A.I.C.S.: 313210

MEDTEL PTY. LTD.
5 Orion Road, Lane Cove, 2066, NSW, Australia
Tel.: (61) 294136222   AU
Web Site: http://www.medtel.com.au
Year Founded: 1996
Sales Range: $25-49.9 Million
Emp.: 97
Medical Equipment, Devices & Clinical Software Whlsr
N.A.I.C.S.: 423450
Raymond Simkins *(CEO)*

MEDTRONIC PLC
20 On Hatch Lower Hatch Street, Dublin, 2, Ireland
Tel.: (353) 14381700   IE
Web Site: https://www.medtronic.com
Year Founded: 1949
MDT—(NYSE)
Rev.: $31,227,000,000
Assets: $90,948,000,000
Liabilities: $39,283,000,000
Net Worth: $51,665,000,000
Earnings: $3,758,000,000
Emp.: 95,000
Fiscal Year-end: 04/28/23
Holding Company; Medical Technologies Developer, Mfr & Whlsr
N.A.I.C.S.: 551112
Brett A. Wall *(Pres-Neuroscience Portfolio & Exec VP)*

Subsidiaries:

Aircraft Medical Ltd. (1)
10 Saint Andrew Square, Edinburgh, EH2 2AF, United Kingdom
Tel.: (44) 1383824326
Web Site: http://www.aircraftmedical.com
Medical Equipment Mfr
N.A.I.C.S.: 339112
Peter Inglis *(Head-Design)*

Airox (1)
Parc D activites Pau Pyrenees I echangeur, PO Box 833, Pau, 64008, France
Tel.: (33) 559140203
Medical Equipment Mfr
N.A.I.C.S.: 339112

Bellco Canada Inc. (1)
2900 Argentia Road Unit 10, Mississauga, L5N 7X9, ON, Canada
Tel.: (905) 821-1111
Web Site: http://www.bellcocanada.ca
Dialysis Center Operator
N.A.I.C.S.: 621492
Jed Dadson *(Sr Mgr-Bus & Quality Ops)*

Bellco Do Brasil (1)
Rua Sampaio Viana 277 9 Andar, 04004-000, Paraiso, Brazil
Tel.: (55) 1120391330
Therapy Treatment Services
N.A.I.C.S.: 622110

Bellco Hoxen Medical (Shanghai) Co. Ltd. (1)
9 Floor Room 906-909 No 333 Jiu Jiang Road, Shanghai, 2000000, China
Tel.: (86) 2163613366
Web Site: http://www.bellco-hoxen.com
Dialysis Equipment Mfr & Distr
N.A.I.C.S.: 334510

Bellco S.r.l. (1)
1 Via Camurana, 41037, Mirandola, Italy
Tel.: (39) 053529111
Emp.: 300
Medical Therapies & Systems Mfr
N.A.I.C.S.: 339112

Changzhou Kangdi Medical Stapler Co., Ltd (1)
No 16 Kunlun Road, Xinbei District, Changzhou, Jiangsu, China
Tel.: (86) 51985139869
Web Site: https://www.kangdi-med.com
Emp.: 270
Medical Equipment Mfr
N.A.I.C.S.: 339112

Comercial Kendall (Chile) Limitada (1)
Rosario Norte 532 piso 12, Las Condes, Chile
Tel.: (56) 226403200
Medical Equipment Mfr
N.A.I.C.S.: 339112

INTERNATIONAL PUBLIC

Covidien Hungary Kft. (1)
Mariassy u 7, 1095, Budapest, Hungary
Tel.: (36) 18807975
Medical Equipment Mfr
N.A.I.C.S.: 339112
Laszlo Makk *(Mgr-Market Dev)*

Covidien Limited (1)
20 On Hatch Lower Hatch Street, Dublin, 2, Ireland
Tel.: (353) 14381700
Web Site: http://www.covidien.com
Sales Range: $5-14.9 Billion
Emp.: 39,500
Pharmaceuticals Mfr
N.A.I.C.S.: 325412

Plant (Domestic):

Covidien (2)
Cornamaddy, Athlone, Westmeath, Ireland
Tel.: (353) 906441400
Sales Range: $150-199.9 Million
Emp.: 500
Medicinal Product Mfr
N.A.I.C.S.: 339112
Liam Hynes *(Dir-Mfg-Minimally Invasive Therapies Grp)*

Subsidiary (Non-US):

Covidien (Israel) Ltd. (2)
5 Shacham St, PO Box 3069, North Industrial Park, Caesarea, 38900, Israel
Tel.: (972) 6309423
Web Site: http://www.covidien.co.il
Healthcare Product Developer & Mfr
N.A.I.C.S.: 423450

Covidien (Thailand) Limited (2)
319 Chamchuri Square 17th Floor Unit 1-8 Phayatai Road, Pathumwan, Bangkok, 10330, Thailand
Tel.: (66) 22073100
Healthcare Product Developer & Mfr
N.A.I.C.S.: 424210

Covidien (UK) Commercial Limited (2)
Unit 2, Talisman Business Park, Bicester, OX26 6HR, Oxfordshire, United Kingdom
Tel.: (44) 1869328092
Sales Range: $25-49.9 Million
Emp.: 40
Medical Device & Hospital Equipment Supplies & Distr
N.A.I.C.S.: 423450

Covidien AG (2)
Victor von Bruns-Strasse 19, 8212, Neuhausen am Rheinfall, Switzerland
Tel.: (41) 525560600
Medical Equipment Mfr & Distr
N.A.I.C.S.: 339112

Covidien Argentina S.A. (2)
Aguero 351 Capital Federal - 1171 ABC, Buenos Aires, Argentina
Tel.: (54) 1148635300
Medical Equipment Whlsr
N.A.I.C.S.: 423450

Covidien Australia Pty Ltd (2)
52A Huntingwood Drive, Huntingwood, 2148, NSW, Australia
Tel.: (61) 1800350702
Medical Product Whlsr
N.A.I.C.S.: 423450

Covidien Austria GmbH (2)
Campus21 Europaring F09402, 2345, Brunn am Gebirge, Lower Austria, Austria
Tel.: (43) 2236378839
Medical Products Sales
N.A.I.C.S.: 423450

Covidien Belgium 2 NV (2)
Generaal De Wittelaan 9/5, 2800, Mechelen, Belgium
Tel.: (32) 15298137
Medical Equipment Whlsr
N.A.I.C.S.: 423450
Bob Moens *(Bus Mgr-Neurovascular)*

Covidien Deutschland GmbH (2)
Raffineriestr 18, 93333, Neustadt an der Donau, Germany
Tel.: (49) 9445959380
Medical Products Sales & Distr
N.A.I.C.S.: 423450

AND PRIVATE COMPANIES   MEDTRONIC PLC

Covidien ECE s.r.o. (2)
Galvaniho 7/a, 821 04, Bratislava, Slovakia
Tel.: (421) 248214573
Medical Equipment Whslr
N.A.I.C.S.: 423450

Covidien Healthcare India Private Limited (2)
Building No 9B 10th Floor DLF Cyber City Phase - III, Phase III, Gurgaon, 122002, Haryana, India
Tel.: (91) 1244709800
Sales Range: $75-99.9 Million
Emp.: 150
Medical Products Developer & Distr
N.A.I.C.S.: 423450

Covidien Healthcare International Trading (Shanghai) Co., Ltd. (2)
Part 102 Building 2 No 556 Fasai Road Pilot Free Trade Zone, ChaoHeJing-Tech Park, Shanghai, 200233, China
Tel.: (86) 2124125611
Medical Equipment Whslr
N.A.I.C.S.: 423450

Subsidiary (US):

Covidien Holding Inc. (2)
15 Hampshire St, Mansfield, MA 02048
Tel.: (508) 261-8000
Sales Range: $450-499.9 Million
Emp.: 1,700
Medical Devices & Products Mfr
N.A.I.C.S.: 339113
Douglas Hoekstra (Pres)

Plant (Domestic):

Covidien - Greenwood (3)
525 Emerald Rd N, Greenwood, SC 29646
Tel.: (864) 223-4281
Emp.: 500
Medical Equipment Whslr
N.A.I.C.S.: 423450
Jimmy Vickery (Plant Mgr & Dir-Mfg-Nursing Care)

Unit (Domestic):

Covidien GI Solutions (3)
540 Oakmead Pkwy, Sunnyvale, CA 94085
Tel.: (408) 328-7300
Medical Equipment Mfr
N.A.I.C.S.: 339112
Nga Van (Dir-Production)

Subsidiary (Domestic):

Nellcor Puritan Bennett LLC (3)
5920 Longbow Dr, Boulder, CO 80301
Tel.: (303) 305-2512
Ventilating Product Mfr
N.A.I.C.S.: 335210

Newport Medical Instruments, Inc. (3)
1620 Sunflower Ave, Costa Mesa, CA 92626
Tel.: (714) 427-5811
Ventilating Product Mfr
N.A.I.C.S.: 335210

ev3, Inc. (3)
15 Hampshire St, Mansfield, MA 02048
Tel.: (763) 398-7000
Sales Range: $400-449.9 Million
Emp.: 1,350
Catheter-Based & Endovascular Medical Devices Mfr
N.A.I.C.S.: 339112

Subsidiary (Domestic):

Micro Therapeutics, Inc. (4)
15 Hampshire St, Mansfield, MA 02048
Tel.: (949) 837-3700
Medical Device Mfr Specializing in Neurovascular Diseases & Disorders
N.A.I.C.S.: 339112
Paul R. Buckman (Co-Founder)

Subsidiary (Non-US):

ev3 Canada Inc. (4)
1920 Yonge St Suite 200, Toronto, M4S 3E2, ON, Canada
Tel.: (416) 572-7692
Surgical & Medical Instrument Mfr
N.A.I.C.S.: 339112

Subsidiary (Domestic):

superDimension, Inc. (3)
555 Long Wharf Dr, New Haven, CT 06511
Tel.: (763) 210-4000
Web Site: http://www.superdimension.com
Healthcare Product Developer & Mfr
N.A.I.C.S.: 339112

Subsidiary (Domestic):

Covidien Ireland Commercial Limited (2)
Block G Ground Floor Cherrywood Technology Park, Loughlinstown, Dublin, 18, Ireland
Tel.: (353) 14381613
Healthcare Product Developer & Mfr
N.A.I.C.S.: 423450
Evelyn Maguire (Controller)

Subsidiary (Non-US):

Covidien Israel Surgical Research Ltd. (2)
7 Hamarpe Street, Jerusalem, 9777407, Israel
Tel.: (972) 25899188
Medical Research
N.A.I.C.S.: 541715

Covidien Manufacturing Solutions, S.A. (2)
0 Zona Franca Coyol S A Ciudad Parque Industrial Estado, Alajuela, Costa Rica
Tel.: (506) 24365700
Medical Device Mfr
N.A.I.C.S.: 334510

Covidien Medical Products (Shanghai) Manufacturing L.L.C. (2)
Building 10 No 789 Puxing Road Caohejing EPZ, Pujiang Town Minhang District, Shanghai, 201114, China
Tel.: (86) 2124082408
Surgical & Medical Instrument Mfr
N.A.I.C.S.: 339112

Covidien Philippines, Inc. (2)
Hanston Square Building San Miguel Ave, Ortigas, Pasig, 1605, Philippines
Tel.: (63) 26338898
Medical Equipment Whslr
N.A.I.C.S.: 423450

Covidien Private Limited (2)
103 Penang Road 10-01 Visioncrest Commercial, Singapore, 238467, Singapore
Tel.: (65) 64820100
Sales Range: $50-74.9 Million
Emp.: 100
Medical Product Distr
N.A.I.C.S.: 423450
Jai Ganesh Chandra (Product Mgr-APAC Reg)

Covidien Pty Limited (2)
2 Alma Road, PO Box 2020, Macquarie Park, 2113, NSW, Australia
Tel.: (61) 294189611
Sales Range: $75-99.9 Million
Emp.: 299
Medical Products Developer & Sales
N.A.I.C.S.: 423450

Covidien Sendirian Berhad (2)
Level 12 Wisma Kelana Brem Tower 1 Jalan SS7/15 Jalan Stadium, Kelana Jaya, 47301, Petaling Jaya, Selangor Darul Ehsan, Malaysia
Tel.: (60) 374911900
Surgical & Medical Instrument Mfr
N.A.I.C.S.: 339112

Covidien Spain S.L. (2)
Servicio Tecnico World Trade Center Almeda Park Placa de la Pau, S/N Edif 7 - 3 Planta Cornella de Llobregat, 08940, Barcelona, Spain
Tel.: (34) 934758669
Sales Range: $50-74.9 Million
Emp.: 100
Medical Products Developer & Distr
N.A.I.C.S.: 423450

Covidien Taiwan Limited (2)
4F No 407 Rueiguang Rd, Neihu District, Taipei, 11492, Taiwan
Tel.: (886) 287978988
Medical Equipment Whslr
N.A.I.C.S.: 423450

Dendron GmbH (2)
Universitatsstrasse 142, Bochum, 44799, Germany
Tel.: (49) 23497061
Medical Products Developer, Mfr & Distr
N.A.I.C.S.: 423450

Ludlow Technical Products Canada, Ltd. (2)
215 Herbert Street, Gananoque, K7G 2Y7, ON, Canada
Tel.: (613) 382-4733
Surgical & Medical Instrument Mfr
N.A.I.C.S.: 339112
Tracy Ringrose (Mgr-HR)

MMJ, S.A. de C.V. (2)
Ave Henequen 1181 Desarrollo Salvarcar, 32573, Ciudad Juarez, Chihuahua, Mexico
Tel.: (52) 6566374100
Emp.: 2,000
Disposable Medical Products Mfr
N.A.I.C.S.: 339112

Mallinckrodt DAR Srl (2)
Via Bove n 2/4/6/8, Mirandola, 41037, MO, Italy
Tel.: (39) 0535617711
Sales Range: $100-124.9 Million
Emp.: 450
Mfr of Disposable Plastic Products for Anesthesia & Intensive Care
N.A.I.C.S.: 339112
Stefano Cavaliere (Plant Mgr)

Mediquip Sdn. Bhd. (2)
Batu 5 Padang Lati Jalan Santan, Kangar, 02450, Perlis, Malaysia
Tel.: (60) 49381411
Healthcare Product Developer & Mfr
N.A.I.C.S.: 424210

Medtronic Hong Kong Medical Limited (2)
Suite 1104-11 11/F Tower 1 The Gateway 25 Canton Road, Tsimshatsui, Kowloon, China (Hong Kong)
Tel.: (852) 29191300
Sales Range: $25-49.9 Million
Emp.: 40
Healthcare Product Developer & Mfr
N.A.I.C.S.: 424210

Nellcor Puritan Bennett Mexico, S.A. de C.V. (2)
Blvd Insurgentes 19030, Colonia Libramiento, 22225, Tijuana, Baja California, Mexico
Tel.: (52) 6646271100
Emp.: 3,000
Medical Equipment Whslr
N.A.I.C.S.: 423690
Moises Gutierrez (Gen Mgr)

Polysuture Industria e Comercio Ltda. (2)
Avenida Gabriel Ramos da Silva 245 Parque Industrial II, Sao Sebastiao do Paraiso, 37950-000, Minas Gerais, Brazil
Tel.: (55) 3535394750
Sales Range: $100-124.9 Million
Emp.: 300
Surgical & Medical Instrument Mfr
N.A.I.C.S.: 339112

Crospon Limited (1)
Galway Business Park, Dangan, Galway, H91 P2DK, Ireland
Tel.: (353) 91 519880
Web Site: http://www.crospon.com
Endoscopic Diagnostic Device Developer, Mfr & Whslr
N.A.I.C.S.: 339112

Diabeter B.V. (1)
Blaak 6, 3011 TA, Rotterdam, Netherlands
Tel.: (31) 882807277
Web Site: http://www.diabeter.nl
Diabetic Treatment Services
N.A.I.C.S.: 622110
Marja Buijs (Coord-Quality Improvement)

Floreane Medical Implants (1)
9 Boulevard Romain Rolland, 75014, Paris, France
Tel.: (33) 474089010
Medical Equipment Mfr & Distr
N.A.I.C.S.: 339112

Given Imaging (Los Angeles) LLC (1)
5860 Uplander Way, Culver City, CA 90230
Tel.: (310) 641-8492
Diagnostic Imaging Center Operator
N.A.I.C.S.: 621512

Given Imaging Vietnam Co., Ltd. (1)
No 6A 6th Floor Xuong Tieu Chuan Building Road 14 Tan Thuan Dong Ward, Tan Thuan Export Processing Zone 7 District, Ho Chi Minh City, Vietnam
Tel.: (84) 837700881
Medical Equipment Distr
N.A.I.C.S.: 423450
Minh Le (Gen Mgr)

Given Imaging do Brazil Ltda. (1)
Rua Cayowaa 225 Sala 20, Perdizes, 05018-000, Brazil
Tel.: (55) 1132211818
Diagnostic Imaging Center Operator
N.A.I.C.S.: 621512
Maurici Federicci (Mgr-Technical)

Haemopharm Biofluids S.r.l. (1)
Via dell'Industria 6, Tovo di Sant'Agata, 23030, Sondrio, Italy
Tel.: (39) 028055660
Web Site: http://www.hbiofluids.it
Pharmaceutical Product Mfr & Distr
N.A.I.C.S.: 325412

HeartWare International, Inc. (1)
Tel.: (508) 739-0950
Web Site: http://www.heartware.com
Holding Company; Medical Device Mfr
N.A.I.C.S.: 551112

Subsidiary (Non-US):

HeartWare Pty. Limited (2)
(100%)
Tel.: (61) 2 8078 6164
Web Site: http://www.heartware.com
Medical Device Mfr
N.A.I.C.S.: 339112

Intersect ENT, Inc. (1)
1555 Adams Dr, Menlo Park, CA 94025
Tel.: (650) 641-2100
Web Site: http://www.intersectent.com
Rev.: $106,748,000
Assets: $146,867,000
Liabilities: $215,936,000
Net Worth: ($69,069,000)
Earnings: ($159,635,000)
Emp.: 433
Fiscal Year-end: 12/31/2021
Medicinal Product Mfr
N.A.I.C.S.: 339112
Richard A. Meier (CFO & Exec VP)

Kendall, S.A. (1)
8th Floor Llano Bonito, Santa Maria Business District Corcione Business Plaza, Panama, Panama
Tel.: (507) 2717200
Emp.: 33
Medical Equipment Distr
N.A.I.C.S.: 423450

Mazor Robotics Ltd. (1)
5 Shacham Street, North Industrial Park, Caesarea, 3088900, Israel
Tel.: (972) 46187100
Web Site: http://www.mazorrobotics.com
Rev.: $64,947,000
Assets: $130,996,000
Liabilities: $17,233,000
Net Worth: $113,763,000
Earnings: ($12,419,000)
Emp.: 194
Fiscal Year-end: 12/31/2017
Surgical Device Mfr
N.A.I.C.S.: 339112
Sharon Levita (CFO & VP-Bus Ops)

Medicrea International SA (1)
5389 Route de Strasbourg, Vancia, 69140, Rillieux-la-Pape, France
Tel.: (33) 472018787
Web Site: http://www.medicrea.com
Rev.: $36,643,393
Assets: $74,246,548
Liabilities: $74,379,606
Net Worth: ($133,058)
Earnings: ($17,414,261)
Emp.: 184
Fiscal Year-end: 12/31/2019
Surgical Devices Designer & Mfr
N.A.I.C.S.: 339112
Denys Sournac (Founder, Chm & CEO)

MEDTRONIC PLC INTERNATIONAL PUBLIC

Medtronic, plc—(Continued)

Subsidiary (Non-US):

Medicrea Poland Sp. z.o.o. (2)
ul Kolejowa 1, 01-217, Warsaw, Poland
Tel.: (48) 221120111
Web Site: http://www.medicare.med.pl
Healtcare Services
N.A.I.C.S.: 621999

Subsidiary (Domestic):

Medicrea Technologies (2)
Z I Chef de Baie, 17000, La Rochelle, France
Tel.: (33) 546005555
Medical Devices
N.A.I.C.S.: 621491

Subsidiary (US):

Medicrea USA Corp. (2)
710 Medtronic Pkwy, Minneapolis, MN 55432
Tel.: (201) 222-3063
Sales Range: $10-24.9 Million
Emp.: 10
Medical Imaging Services
N.A.I.C.S.: 621512
Denys Sournac (Founder & CEO)

Medina Medical, Inc. (1)
710 Medtronic Pkwy, Minneapolis, MN 55432-5604
Tel.: (763) 514-4000
Web Site: https://www.medtronic.com
Medical Equipment Mfr
N.A.I.C.S.: 339112

Medtronic AG (1)
Talstrasse 9, 3053, Munchenbuchsee, Switzerland
Tel.: (41) 318680100
Emp.: 170
Medical Device Mfr & Distr
N.A.I.C.S.: 334510

Medtronic Bangladesh Pvt. Ltd. (1)
603 Level 6 Shanta Western Towers 186 Gulshan Tejgaon Link Road, Dhaka, 1208, Bangladesh
Tel.: (880) 28879263
Emp.: 12
Medical Device Distr
N.A.I.C.S.: 423450
Farrukh Alam (Country Mgr)

Medtronic Engineering & Innovation Center Private Limited (1)
3rd Floor Block-1 BSR IT / ITES SEZ, Nanakramguda Village Serilingampally Mandal Ranga Reddy, Hyderabad, 500008, Telangana, India
Tel.: (91) 4041331200
Emp.: 230
Engineering Research & Development Services
N.A.I.C.S.: 541715

Medtronic Holding B.V. (1)
Earl Bakkenstraat 10, 6422 PJ, Heerlen, Netherlands
Tel.: (31) 455668000
Holding Company
N.A.I.C.S.: 551112

Medtronic International Ltd. (1)
50 Pasir Panjang Road 04-51, Mapletree Business City, Singapore, 117384, Singapore
Tel.: (65) 68705300
Medical Equipment Mfr
N.A.I.C.S.: 339112

Medtronic Medical Appliance Technology & Service (Shanghai) Co., Ltd. (1)
Suite 1805-1812 E1 Tower Oriental Plaza No 1 East Chang An Ave, Dong Cheng District, Beijing, 100738, China
Tel.: (86) 1058698989
Medical Equipment Mfr
N.A.I.C.S.: 339112

Medtronic Medikal Teknolojileri San. Ve Tic. A.S. (1)
Saray Mah Dr Adnan Buyukdeniz Cad Akkom Ofis Park 2 Blok No 4 Kat 18, Umraniye, 34752, Istanbul, Turkiye
Tel.: (90) 2166361000

Medical Equipment Mfr
N.A.I.C.S.: 339112

Medtronic Romania SRL (1)
Baneasa Business & Technology Park Sos Bucharest-Ploiesti No 42-44, Building A A1 Wing 2nd floor, 013696, Bucharest, Romania
Tel.: (40) 372188000
Therapy Treatment Services
N.A.I.C.S.: 622110
Simona Brana (Mgr-Romania & Moldavia)

Medtronic Serbia d.o.o. (1)
Bul Zorana Dindica 64a, 1100, Belgrade, Serbia
Tel.: (381) 112095901
Medical Equipment Mfr
N.A.I.C.S.: 339112

Medtronic, Inc. (1)
710 Medtronic Pkwy, Minneapolis, MN 55432-5604
Tel.: (763) 514-4000
Sales Range: $15-24.9 Billion
Medical Technology Solutions & Medical Devices Mfr
N.A.I.C.S.: 339112
Claudia Napal Drayton (Executives)

Subsidiary (Domestic):

Ablation Frontiers L.L.C. (1)
2210 Faraday Ave Ste 100, Carlsbad, CA 92008
Tel.: (760) 827-0001
Cardiac Medical Devices Mfr
N.A.I.C.S.: 334510

Subsidiary (Non-US):

Biostar Biomedikal Muhendislik Anonim Sirketi (2)
Esnaf Caddesi 2 Umraniye, Atasehir, Istanbul, 34768, Turkiye
Tel.: (90) 2164492125
Web Site: http://www.biostar.biz.tr
Biotechnology Research & Development Services
N.A.I.C.S.: 541714

Subsidiary (Domestic):

CardioInsight Technologies Inc. (2)
710 Medtronic Pkwy, Minneapolis, MN 55432
Tel.: (216) 453-5950
Electrocardiographic Mapping Technology Mfr
N.A.I.C.S.: 339112
Patrick Wethington (Pres & CEO)

Subsidiary (Non-US):

Medtronic (Africa) (Proprietary) Limited (2)
Waterfall Distribution Campus Cnr Bridal Veil Rd K101 Pretoria Main Rd, Midrand, Johannesburg, 1682, Gauteng, South Africa
Tel.: (27) 112609300
Web Site: http://www.medtronic.co.za
Medical Equipment Mfr & Distr
N.A.I.C.S.: 339112

Medtronic (Shanghai) Management Co. Ltd. (2)
Floor 16 Building B The New Bund World Trade Center Phase I No 5, Lane 255 Dong Yu Road Pudong, Shanghai, 200126, China
Tel.: (86) 2120325888
Web Site: http://www.medtronic.com.hk
Medical Device Distr
N.A.I.C.S.: 423450

Medtronic (Taiwan) Ltd. (2)
2F No 2 Sec 1 Dunhua S Rd, SongShan Dist, Taipei, 105, Taiwan
Tel.: (886) 221836000
Web Site: http://www.medtronic.com.tw
Medical Device Distr
N.A.I.C.S.: 423450

Medtronic (Thailand) Limited (2)
319 Chamchuri Square Building 27th Floor Units 1-16 Phayathai Road, Pathumwan, Bangkok, 10330, Thailand
Tel.: (66) 22327400
Web Site: https://www.medtronic.com
Emp.: 401
Medical Device Mfr & Distr
N.A.I.C.S.: 339112

Subsidiary (Domestic):

Medtronic Ablation Frontiers LLC (2)
710 Medtronic Pkwy, Minneapolis, MN 55432
Tel.: (760) 827-0001
Web Site: http://www.ablationfrontiers.com
Electromedical & Electrotherapeutic Apparatus Mfr
N.A.I.C.S.: 334510

Subsidiary (Non-US):

Medtronic Adriatic d.o.o (2)
Folnegoviceva 1C, 10000, Zagreb, Croatia
Tel.: (385) 14881120
Web Site: http://adriatic.medtronic.com
Medical Equipment Distr
N.A.I.C.S.: 423450

Subsidiary (Domestic):

Medtronic Advanced Energy LLC (2)
180 International Dr, Portsmouth, NH 03801-6837
Tel.: (603) 742-1515
Web Site: http://www.salientsurgical.com
Surgical Devices Developer, Mfr & Sales
N.A.I.C.S.: 339113

Subsidiary (Non-US):

Medtronic Australasia Pty. Ltd. (2)
2 Alma Road, Macquarie Park, 2113, NSW, Australia **(100%)**
Tel.: (61) 298579000
Sales Range: $200-249.9 Million
Emp.: 450
Electronic Medical Devices & Supplies for Heart Treatment Sales & Distr
N.A.I.C.S.: 423450

Subsidiary (Non-US):

Medtronic New Zealand Limited (3)
Level 3 Building 5 666 Great South Road Penrose, Onehunga, Auckland, 1051, New Zealand
Tel.: (64) 99674600
Sales Range: $10-24.9 Million
Emp.: 15
Electromedical Apparatus Mfr
N.A.I.C.S.: 334510

Unit (Domestic):

Medtronic Cardiac Rhythm & Heart Failure Management (2)
8200 Coral Sea St NE, Mounds View, MN 55112
Tel.: (763) 514-4000
Sales Range: $5-14.9 Billion
Electronic Cardiac Pacemakers Mfr
N.A.I.C.S.: 339112

Subsidiary (Domestic):

Medtronic Care Management Services, LLC (2)
7980 Century Blvd, Chanhassen, MN 55317
Tel.: (952) 361-6467
Web Site: http://www.cardiocom.com
Disease Management & Patient Monitoring Services
N.A.I.C.S.: 621999
Sheri Louise Dodd (VP & Gen Mgr)

Subsidiary (Non-US):

Medtronic Chile SpA (2)
Rosario Norte 532 Piso 12, Las Condes, Santiago, Chile
Tel.: (56) 27833141
Emp.: 30
Medical Device Distr
N.A.I.C.S.: 423450

Medtronic China Kanghui Holdings (2)
1-8 Tianshan Road, Xinbei District, Changzhou, 213022, Jiangsu, China
Tel.: (86) 519 85195556
Web Site: http://www.kanghui.com
Emp.: 1,200
Holding Company; Orthopedic Implants Mfr & Sales
N.A.I.C.S.: 551112
Hongxin Nie (VP-Sls & Mktg-Beijing Libeier)

Subsidiary (Domestic):

Changzhou Kanghui Medical Innovation Co., Ltd. (3)
No 11 Changjiang North Road, Xinbei District, Changzhou, 213022, Jiangsu, China
Tel.: (86) 51985139851
Web Site: http://www.cn.kanghui-med.com
Medical Devices Mfr & Distr
N.A.I.C.S.: 339112

Subsidiary (Non-US):

Medtronic Comercial Ltda. (2)
Av Jornalista Roberto Marinho 85, Itaim Bibi, Sao Paulo, 04576-010, SP, Brazil
Tel.: (55) 1121829200
Web Site: https://www.medtronic.com
Emp.: 100
Medical Device Distr
N.A.I.C.S.: 423450

Unit (Domestic):

Medtronic Energy & Component Center (2)
6700 Shingle Creek Pkwy, Brooklyn Center, MN 55430
Tel.: (763) 514-1000
Emp.: 1,200
Mfr of Energy Components, Including Batteries & Capacitors, for Implantable Medical Devices
N.A.I.C.S.: 334419
Kirk Hauge (Sr Dir-Quality)

Subsidiary (Non-US):

Medtronic Europe Sarl (2)
Route du Molliau 31, 1131, Tolochenaz, Switzerland
Tel.: (41) 218027000
Web Site: http://www.medtronic.eu
Emp.: 800
Holding Company; Regional Managing Office; Medical Devices & Implants Mfr & Distr
N.A.I.C.S.: 551112
Robert ten Hoedt (Pres-EMEA & Exec VP)

Subsidiary (Non-US):

India Medtronic Private Limited (3)
Unit No 203 204 Vraj Complex Alembic -Gorwa main road, Baroda, 390016, Gujarat, India **(100%)**
Tel.: (91) 2653931838
Web Site: https://www.medtronic.com
Sales Range: $25-49.9 Million
Emp.: 1,100
Medical Equipment for Heart Disease Sales & Distr
N.A.I.C.S.: 423450

Invatec S.p.A. (3)
Via Martiri Della Liberta 7, Roncadelle, 25030, BS, Italy
Tel.: (39) 0302589311
Medical Devices Mfr & Distr
N.A.I.C.S.: 339112
Andrea Giarrizzo (Mng Dir & Dir-Mfg & Ops)

Subsidiary (Non-US):

Invatec Technology Center GmbH (4)
Hungerbuelstrasse 12, Frauenfeld, 8500, Switzerland
Tel.: (41) 522600660
Medical Equipment Mfr & Distr
N.A.I.C.S.: 339112

Subsidiary (Domestic):

Medtronic (Schweiz) AG (3)
Talstrasse 9, 3053, Munchenbuchsee, Switzerland
Tel.: (41) 318680100
Web Site: http://www.medtronic.ch
Emp.: 100
Medical Devices Marketing & Sales
N.A.I.C.S.: 423450

Subsidiary (Non-US):

Medtronic A/S (3)
Arne Jacobsens Alle 17, 2300, Copenhagen, Denmark
Tel.: (45) 32481800
Web Site: https://www.medtronic.com
Emp.: 130

AND PRIVATE COMPANIES — MEDTRONIC PLC

Electromedical Apparatus Mfr
N.A.I.C.S.: 334510

Subsidiary (Non-US):

Medtronic Aktiebolag (4)
Gustav IIIs Boulevard 42, 169 73, Solna, Sweden
Tel.: (46) 856858500
Web Site: https://www.medtronic.com
Sales Range: $50-74.9 Million
Emp.: 65
Medical Products Sales & Distr
N.A.I.C.S.: 423450
Marie Aabo (Country Dir)

Subsidiary (Domestic):

Medtronic Danmark A/S (4)
Arne Jacobsens Alle 17, 2300, Copenhagen, Denmark
Tel.: (45) 32481800
Emp.: 130
Medical Products Sales & Distr
N.A.I.C.S.: 423450

Subsidiary (Non-US):

Medtronic Norge AS (4)
Vollsveien 2 A, PO Box 458, 1327, Lysaker, Norway
Tel.: (47) 67103200
Web Site: https://www.medtronic.com
Medical Device Distr
N.A.I.C.S.: 423450

Subsidiary (Non-US):

Medtronic B.V. (3)
Earl Bakkenstraat 10, 6422 PJ, Heerlen, Netherlands (100%)
Tel.: (31) 455668000
Sales Range: $300-349.9 Million
Emp.: 1,100
Medical Products Sales
N.A.I.C.S.: 423450

Subsidiary (Domestic):

Medtronic Bakken Research Center B.V. (4)
Endepolsdomein 5, 6229 GW, Maastricht, Netherlands (100%)
Tel.: (31) 433566566
Web Site: https://www.medtronic.com
Sales Range: $50-74.9 Million
Emp.: 300
Medical Research Services
N.A.I.C.S.: 621511

Medtronic Trading NL BV (3)
Larixplein 4, 5616 VB, Eindhoven, Netherlands
Tel.: (31) 455668000
Emp.: 230
Medical Equipment Mfr & Distr
N.A.I.C.S.: 339112

Vitatron Holding B.V. (4)
Endepolsdomein 5, 6229 GW, Maastricht, Netherlands
Tel.: (31) 433566551
Web Site: https://www.vitatron.com
Sales Range: $50-74.9 Million
Emp.: 300
Electromedical & Electrotherapeutic Apparatus Mfr
N.A.I.C.S.: 334510

Subsidiary (Non-US):

Vitatron Belgium S.A./N.V. (5)
Avenue du Bourgmestre Etienne Demunter 5, 1090, Brussels, Belgium
Tel.: (32) 24560900
Electromedical Apparatus Mfr
N.A.I.C.S.: 334510

Subsidiary (Non-US):

Medtronic Belgium S.A./N.V. (3)
Burgemeester E Demunterlaan 5, 1090, Brussels, Belgium
Tel.: (32) 24560900
Web Site: https://www.medtronic.com
Sales Range: $50-74.9 Million
Emp.: 500
Medical Devices & Supplies Sales & Distr
N.A.I.C.S.: 423450

Subsidiary (Domestic):

Covidien Logistics BVBA (4)
Weg naar Zwartberg 239, 3660, Opglabbeek, Belgium
Tel.: (32) 89 36 54 00
Web Site: http://www.medtronic.be
Emp.: 300
Medical Product Distr
N.A.I.C.S.: 423450

Subsidiary (Non-US):

Medtronic Czechia s.r.o. (3)
Prosek Point Building B 6th floor, Prosecka 852/66, 190 00, Prague, Czech Republic
Tel.: (420) 233059111
Web Site: https://www.medtronic.com
Emp.: 140
Medical Products Sales & Distr
N.A.I.C.S.: 423450

Medtronic Finland Oy (3)
Lentajantie 3, 01530, Helsinki, Finland
Tel.: (358) 207281200
Web Site: https://www.medtronic.com
Emp.: 50
Medical Products Sales & Distr
N.A.I.C.S.: 423450

Medtronic France S.A.S. (3)
9 Boulevard Romain Rolland, 75014, Paris, France (100%)
Tel.: (33) 155381700
Web Site: https://www.medtronic.com
Sales Range: $150-199.9 Million
Emp.: 300
Electromedical Equipment & Supplies Sales & Distr
N.A.I.C.S.: 423450

Medtronic G.m.b.H. (3)
Earl-Bakken-Platz 1, 40670, Meerbusch, Germany (100%)
Tel.: (49) 215981490
Web Site: https://www.medtronic.com
Sales Range: $150-199.9 Million
Emp.: 400
Medical Devices & Products Distr
N.A.I.C.S.: 423450

Subsidiary (Domestic):

Medtronic Sofamor Danek Deggendorf GmbH (4)
Ulrichsberger Strasse 17, 94469, Deggendorf, Germany
Tel.: (49) 99138930
Web Site: https://www.medtronic.com
Emp.: 100
Medicinal Product Mfr
N.A.I.C.S.: 339112

Subsidiary (Non-US):

Medtronic Hungaria Kereskedelmi Kft (3)
Bocskai ut 134-146 C epulet 3 emelet, Dorottya Udvar, 1113, Budapest, Hungary
Tel.: (36) 18890600
Web Site: https://www.medtronic.com
Sales Range: $25-49.9 Million
Emp.: 20
Medical Products Sales & Distr
N.A.I.C.S.: 423450

Medtronic Iberica S.A. (3)
C/ Maria de Portugal 11, 28050, Madrid, Spain
Tel.: (34) 916250400
Web Site: https://www.medtronic.com
Sales Range: $75-99.9 Million
Emp.: 250
Medical Products Sales & Distr
N.A.I.C.S.: 423450
Maria Trenzado (Sr Mgr-Comm)

Subsidiary (Domestic):

Medtronic International Trading Sarl (3)
Route du Molliau 31, 1131, Tolochenaz, Switzerland (100%)
Tel.: (41) 218027000
Medical Products Wholesale Trade Distr
N.A.I.C.S.: 425120

Subsidiary (Non-US):

Medtronic Ireland Limited (3)
Ground Floor Block 3090-3094 Lake Drive, Citywest Business Campus, Dublin, 18, Ireland
Tel.: (353) 15111400
Web Site: http://www.medtronic.com
Emp.: 2,500
Medical Device Mfr
N.A.I.C.S.: 334510

Subsidiary (Domestic):

Medtronic Vascular Galway (4)
Parkmore Business Park West, Galway, Ireland
Tel.: (353) 91708000
Web Site: http://www.medtronic.ie
Medical Equipment Developer & Mfr
N.A.I.C.S.: 339112

Subsidiary (Non-US):

Medtronic Italia S.p.A. (3)
Via Varesina 162, Edificio Raimondi, 20156, Milan, MI, Italy
Tel.: (39) 02241371
Web Site: https://www.medtronic.com
Sales Range: $25-49.9 Million
Emp.: 20
Medical Product Distr
N.A.I.C.S.: 423450

Medtronic Limited (3)
Building 9 Croxley Park, Hatters Lane, Watford, WD18 8WW, Hertfordshire, United Kingdom
Tel.: (44) 1923212213
Web Site: https://www.medtronic.com
Sales Range: $100-124.9 Million
Emp.: 140
Medical Devices Sales & Distr
N.A.I.C.S.: 423450

Medtronic Oesterreich G.m.b.H. (3)
Millennium Tower Handelskai 94-96, 1200, Vienna, Austria
Tel.: (43) 1240440
Web Site: https://www.medtronic.com
Sales Range: $50-74.9 Million
Emp.: 180
Medical Devices & Supplies Sales & Distr
N.A.I.C.S.: 423450
Gerald Doubek (Mng Dir)

Medtronic Poland Sp. z o.o. (3)
Polna 11, 00-633, Warsaw, Poland
Tel.: (48) 222756999
Web Site: https://www.medtronic.com
Emp.: 800
Medical Devices Sales & Distr
N.A.I.C.S.: 423450

Medtronic Portugal, Lda (3)
Rua Tomas da Fonseca Tower E - 11th floor, 1600-209, Lisbon, Portugal
Tel.: (351) 217245100
Web Site: https://www.medtronic.com
Emp.: 150
Medical Device Distr
N.A.I.C.S.: 423450

Medtronic Slovakia s.r.o. (3)
CBC III Karadzicova 12, 821 08, Bratislava, Slovakia
Tel.: (421) 268206911
Web Site: https://www.medtronic.com
Medical Devices Sales & Distr
N.A.I.C.S.: 423450

Subsidiary (Domestic):

Medtronic International Technology, Inc. (2)
710 Medtronic Pkwy, Minneapolis, MN 55432
Tel.: (763) 514-4000
Medical Equipment Mfr
N.A.I.C.S.: 339112

Subsidiary (Non-US):

Medtronic International, Ltd. (2)
11/F Tower 1 the Gateway 25 Canton Road Suite 1106-11 Tsimshatsui, Kowloon, China (Hong Kong) (100%)
Tel.: (852) 29191300
Sales Range: $50-74.9 Million
Emp.: 100
Medical Devices & Supplies Sales & Distr
N.A.I.C.S.: 423450

Subsidiary (Non-US):

Medtronic Korea Ltd. (3)
17f Glass Tower 534 Teneran-ro, Gangnam-gu, Seoul, 06-181, Korea (South) (100%)
Tel.: (82) 234043600
Web Site: https://www.medtronic.com
Sales Range: $25-49.9 Million
Emp.: 60
Electronic Medical Devices & Supplies Sales & Distr
N.A.I.C.S.: 423450

Subsidiary (Domestic):

Medtronic Interventional Vascular Inc. (2)
35a Cherry Hill Dr, Danvers, MA 01923-5186 (100%)
Tel.: (978) 777-0042
Sales Range: $150-199.9 Million
Emp.: 650
Vascular Medical Devices Mfr
N.A.I.C.S.: 339112
Mark Chartier (Program Dir-Aortic & Peripheral Vascular)

Unit (Non-US):

Medtronic Israel (2)
10 Hamada St, Herzliya Pituach, 46733, Israel
Tel.: (972) 99724400
Web Site: https://www.medtronic.com
Sales Range: $25-49.9 Million
Emp.: 200
Medical Devices Research & Development, Mfr & Distr
N.A.I.C.S.: 339112
Judith Gal (CEO)

Subsidiary (Domestic):

Given Imaging Ltd. (3)
1 Kidama St, PO Box 258, Yokneam, 20692, Israel
Tel.: (972) 49097777
Sales Range: $150-199.9 Million
Emp.: 804
Medical Diagnostic Imaging Technology
N.A.I.C.S.: 423450

Subsidiary (Non-US):

Given Imaging (Asia) Company Limited (4)
1001 The Hennessy 256 Hennessy Road, Wanchai, China (Hong Kong)
Tel.: (852) 2989 0888
Medical Imaging Mfr
N.A.I.C.S.: 423410

Given Imaging GmbH (4)
Borsteler Chaussee 47, Hamburg, 22453, Germany
Tel.: (49) 405133000
Sales Range: $25-49.9 Million
Emp.: 35
Medical Diagnostic Imaging Technology
N.A.I.C.S.: 339112

Given Imaging K.K. (4)
1-2-70 Konan Shinagawa Season Terrace 22F, Minato-ku, Tokyo, 108-0075, Japan
Tel.: (81) 367744611
Sales Range: $25-49.9 Million
Emp.: 30
Medical Diagnostic Imaging Technology
N.A.I.C.S.: 423450
Kazem Samandari (Pres-Asia Pacific)

Given Imaging Pty. Ltd. (4)
2 Alma Road, North Ryde, 2113, NSW, Australia
Tel.: (61) 298579000
Emp.: 15
Medical Diagnostic Imaging Technology
N.A.I.C.S.: 423450

Subsidiary (Domestic):

Oridion Systems Ltd. (3)
Har Hotzvim Industrial Park 7 Hamarpe Street Building 5, Jerusalem, 97774, Israel
Tel.: (972) 25899159
Surgical Appliance Mfr
N.A.I.C.S.: 339113

Subsidiary (Non-US):

Medtronic Japan Co., Ltd. (2)
Shinagawa Season Terrace 1-2-70 Konan, Minato-ku, Tokyo, 108-0075, Japan
Tel.: (81) 367744611

MEDTRONIC PLC

Medtronic plc—(Continued)
Web Site: https://www.medtronic.com
Sales Range: $150-199.9 Million
Emp.: 1,525
Medical Devices & Products Mfr & Distr
N.A.I.C.S.: 339112

Medtronic Kazakhstan Limited Liability Partnership (2)
Abylai khan avenue 53 ABYLAI KHAN PLAZA 5th floor 5/07 office, Almaty, 050059, Kazakhstan
Tel.: (7) 7172508360
Emp.: 47
Medical Equipment Distr
N.A.I.C.S.: 423450
Raimbek Sissemaliev *(Mgr-Govt Affairs)*

Subsidiary (Domestic):

Medtronic Logistics LLC (2)
710 Medtronic Pkwy, Minneapolis, MN 55432
Tel.: (763) 505-2570
Supply Chain & Logistics Services
N.A.I.C.S.: 541614
Tammy Nelson *(Sr Dir-Global Supply Chain Operational Excellence)*

Subsidiary (Non-US):

Medtronic Mediterranean SAL (2)
St Charles City Centre - 6th Floor, PO Box 13-6572, Omar Daouk Street, 2020-0908, Beirut, Lebanon
Tel.: (961) 1370670
Web Site: http://www.medtronic.me
Emp.: 70
Medical Device Distr
N.A.I.C.S.: 423450

Medtronic Mexico S. de R.L. de C.V. (2)
Paseo Cucapah 10510 El Lag, 22210, Tijuana, Baja California, Mexico
Tel.: (52) 6649031100
Web Site: http://www.medtronic.com.mx
Emp.: 4,000
Medical Device Mfr
N.A.I.C.S.: 339112

Unit (Domestic):

Medtronic Microelectronics Center (2)
2343 W Medtronic Way, Tempe, AZ 85281
Tel.: (480) 968-6411
Sales Range: $500-549.9 Million
Emp.: 900
Microelectronics Mfr for Implantable Medical Devices
N.A.I.C.S.: 334510
Ron Wilson *(VP & Gen Mgr)*

Subsidiary (Domestic):

Medtronic MiniMed, Inc. (2)
18000 Devonshire St, Northridge, CA 91325-1219
Tel.: (818) 362-5958
Web Site:
http://www.medtronicdiabetes.com
Insulin Pumps Glucose Monitoring Systems Service
N.A.I.C.S.: 622210
Sean Salmon *(Pres & Exec VP)*

Medtronic Navigation, Inc. (2)
826 Coal Creek Cir, Louisville, CO 80027
Tel.: (720) 890-3200
Electromedical Apparatus Mfr
N.A.I.C.S.: 334510
Steve Hartmann *(Dir-Sys Engrg)*

Medtronic PS Medical, Inc. (2)
125 Cremona Dr, Goleta, CA 93117-5500
Tel.: (800) 468-9710
Neurosurgical & Critical Care Products Mfr
N.A.I.C.S.: 339112
Cliff Maher *(Sr Product Mgr)*

Medtronic Puerto Rico Operations Co. (2)
PR-149 KM 563, Villalba, PR 00766-6001
Tel.: (787) 847-3500
Sales Range: $450-499.9 Million
Emp.: 3,000
Medical Device Mfr
N.A.I.C.S.: 339112
Felix M. Negron *(VP-Ops & Gen Mgr)*

Subsidiary (Non-US):

Medtronic S.A.I.C. (2)
Av Madero 1020 5 Piso Ciudad Autonoma de, Buenos Aires, CP 1640, Argentina
Tel.: (54) 1148985700
Emp.: 40
Medical Devices & Supplies Distr
N.A.I.C.S.: 423450

Subsidiary (Domestic):

Medtronic Sofamor Danek USA, Inc. (2)
1800 Pyramid Pl, Memphis, TN 38132
Tel.: (901) 396-3133
Surgical Appliance & Supplies Mfr
N.A.I.C.S.: 339113

Medtronic Sofamor Danek, Inc. (2)
2600 Sofamor Danek Dr, Memphis, TN 38132-1719
Tel.: (901) 396-3133
Emp.: 600
Surgical Implants Mfr
N.A.I.C.S.: 339113
Pat Wilson *(VP-Spinal Therapies)*

Subsidiary (Non-US):

Medtronic Spine LLC (2)
Tel.: (901) 396-3133
Medical Device Mfr
N.A.I.C.S.: 339112

Subsidiary (Non-US):

Sanatis GmbH (3)
Tel.: (49) 6003935752
Orthopedic Biomaterials Mfr
N.A.I.C.S.: 325414

Unit (Domestic):

Medtronic Vascular (2)
3576 Unocal Pl, Santa Rosa, CA 95403 **(100%)**
Tel.: (707) 525-0111
Sales Range: $550-599.9 Million
Emp.: 2,000
Stent Systems & Percutaneous Transluminal Coronary Angioplasty Balloon Catheters Mfr
N.A.I.C.S.: 339112
Matt Birdsall *(VP-Res & Innovation)*

Subsidiary (Domestic):

Medtronic Xomed, Inc. (2)
4102 Southpoint Blvd, Jacksonville, FL 32216-6218
Tel.: (904) 296-9600
Web Site: http://www.xomed.com
Sales Range: $750-799.9 Million
Ear, Nose & Throat Surgical Products Developer, Mfr & Marketer
N.A.I.C.S.: 339112

Subsidiary (Non-US):

Medtronic of Canada Ltd. (2)
99 Hereford Street, Brampton, L6Y 0H3, ON, Canada **(100%)**
Tel.: (905) 460-3800
Web Site: http://www.medtronic.ca
Sales Range: $125-149.9 Million
Emp.: 260
Pacemakers Mfr & Distr
N.A.I.C.S.: 334510
Neil D. Fraser *(Pres)*

Subsidiary (Domestic):

Nobles Medical Technologies, Inc. (2)
17072 Newhope St, Fountain Valley, CA 92708
Tel.: (714) 427-0398
Emp.: 25
Medical Device Mfr
N.A.I.C.S.: 339112

Osteotech, Inc. (2)
710 Medtronic Pkwy LC 300, Minneapolis, MN 55432
Tel.: (732) 542-2800
Emp.: 297
Biologic Products Mfr
N.A.I.C.S.: 325414
Michele Levin-DeGeorge *(Sr Mgr-Matls)*

Sapheon LLC (2)
951 Aviation Pkwy Ste 900, Morrisville, NC 27560
Tel.: (919) 948-3967
Web Site: http://www.sapheoninc.com
Electromedical Device Mfr
N.A.I.C.S.: 334510

Sophono, Inc. (2)
5744 Central Ave Ste 100, Boulder, CO 80301
Tel.: (720) 407-5160
Web Site: http://www.sophono.com
Magnetic Hearing Implants Mfr
N.A.I.C.S.: 339112

SpinalGraft Technologies, LLC (2)
4340 Swinnea Rd Ste 39, Memphis, TN 38118
Tel.: (901) 396-3133
Electromedical & Electrotherapeutic Apparatus Mfr
N.A.I.C.S.: 334510

TYRX, Inc. (2)
1 Deer Park Dr Ste G, Monmouth Junction, NJ 08852
Tel.: (732) 246-8676
Web Site: http://www.tyrx.com
Medical Devices Mfr & Distr
N.A.I.C.S.: 339112

Visualase, Inc. (2)
826 Cole Creek Cir, Louisville, CO 80027
Tel.: (713) 275-2063
Surgical Laser Technologies Developer & Mfr
N.A.I.C.S.: 334510
Andre G. Marquette *(VP-Mktg)*

Zephyr Technology LLC (2)
1 Annapolis St Ste 200, Annapolis, MD 21401
Tel.: (443) 569-3603
Web Site: http://www.zephyranywhere.com
Electromedical Device Mfr
N.A.I.C.S.: 334510

N.G.C. Medical Srl (1)
Via Salvo D'Acquisto 8/14, 22078, Turate, CO, Italy
Tel.: (39) 02944791
Web Site: https://ngcmedical.it
Medical Equipment Mfr & Distr
N.A.I.C.S.: 339112

Nederlandse Obesitas Kliniek B.V. (1)
Amersfoortseweg 43, PO Box 601, Huis ter Heide, 3712 BA, Zeist, Netherlands
Tel.: (31) 888832444
Web Site: https://www.obesitaskliniek.nl
Obesity Clinic Operator
N.A.I.C.S.: 621111

Nederlandse Obesitas Kliniek West B.V. (1)
Amersfoortseweg 43, Huis ter Heide, 3712 BA, Zeist, Netherlands
Tel.: (31) 703204703
Obesity Clinic Operator
N.A.I.C.S.: 621111

Responsive Orthopedics, LLC (1)
5865 E State Rd 14, Columbia City, IN 46725
Tel.: (844) 822-5576
Medical Equipment Mfr
N.A.I.C.S.: 339112

Titan Spine, LLC (1)
6140 W Executive Dr Ste A, Mequon, WI 53092-4467
Tel.: (262) 242-7801
Web Site: http://www.titanspine.com
Surgical Appliance & Supplies Mfr
N.A.I.C.S.: 339113
Ragan E. Cheney *(Gen Counsel & Exec VP)*

ev3 Medical Devices (Beijing) Company, Ltd. (1)
Room 2501 Building B Chaowai MEN Tower No 26 Chao Yang Men Wai Street, Chaoyang District, Beijing, 100020, China
Tel.: (86) 1085654616
Medical Equipment Distr
N.A.I.C.S.: 423450
Li Judy *(Mgr-Mktg-Natl)*

MEDVIEW AIRLINE PLC

INTERNATIONAL PUBLIC

21 Olowu Street, Ikeja, Lagos, Nigeria
Tel.: (234) 07082543952
Web Site:
http://www.medviewairline.com
Year Founded: 2007
MEDVIEWAIR—(NIGE)
Sales Range: $10-24.9 Million
Flight Operations Services
N.A.I.C.S.: 488119

MEDX HEALTH CORP.

1495 Bonhill Road Unit 1, Mississauga, L5T 1M2, ON, Canada
Tel.: (905) 670-4428
Web Site:
https://www.medxhealth.com
Year Founded: 1999
MDXHF—(OTCIQ)
Rev.: $344,399
Assets: $520,739
Liabilities: $5,913,662
Net Worth: ($5,392,924)
Earnings: ($3,458,845)
Fiscal Year-end: 12/31/23
Medical Device Mfr
N.A.I.C.S.: 339112
Kenneth McKay *(Chm)*

Subsidiaries:

MedX Electronics Inc (1)
220 Superior Blvd, Mississauga, L5T 2L2, ON, Canada
Tel.: (905) 670-4428
Web Site: http://www.Medxhealth.com
Emp.: 10
Medical Equipment Mfr
N.A.I.C.S.: 339112

MEDY-TOX INC.

78 Gangni-gil Ochang-eup, Cheongwon-gu, Cheongju, Chungbuk, Korea (South) 363885,
Tel.: (82) 432171555
Web Site: http://www.medy-tox.co.kr
Year Founded: 2000
086900—(KRS)
Rev.: $149,638,801
Assets: $457,353,237
Liabilities: $124,770,068
Net Worth: $332,583,169
Earnings: $28,069,006
Emp.: 693
Fiscal Year-end: 12/31/22
Biopharmaceutical Mfr
N.A.I.C.S.: 325412
Ju Hee Seok *(VP)*

Subsidiaries:

MDT International Inc. (1)
10F Vort Shibadaimon 2-6-6 Shibadaimon, Minato-ku, Tokyo, 105-0012, Japan
Tel.: (81) 364529606
Web Site: https://www.medytox.jp
Pharmaceutical Preparation Mfr
N.A.I.C.S.: 325412

Medytox (Thailand) Co., Ltd. (1)
139 Sethiwan Tower Building 15B 15th floor Pan Rd Silom, Bang Rak, Bangkok, 10500, Thailand
Tel.: (66) 613612020
Pharmaceutical Product Mfr & Distr
N.A.I.C.S.: 325411

Medytox Korea Inc. (1)
1F 626 Teheran-ro Daechi-Dong Medytox Building, Gangnam-gu, Seoul, Korea (South)
Tel.: (82) 808502006
Web Site: https://www.medytoxkorea.com
Pharmaceutical Preparation Mfr
N.A.I.C.S.: 325412

MEEKA METALS LIMITED

Second Floor 46 Ventnor Avenue, West Perth, 6005, WA, Australia
Tel.: (61) 863882700
Web Site:
https://meekametals.com.au

AND PRIVATE COMPANIES

MEK—(ASX)
Rev.: $32,541
Assets: $23,670,110
Liabilities: $5,028,881
Net Worth: $18,641,229
Earnings: ($1,964,218)
Fiscal Year-end: 06/30/24
Metal Mining
N.A.I.C.S.: 212290
Harry Miller *(Sec)*

MEENAKSHI STEEL INDUSTRIES LIMITED
J-189 Basement J Block Saket, New Delhi, 110 017, India
Tel.: (91) 7303001011
Web Site:
https://www.meenakshisteel.in
Year Founded: 1985
512505—(BOM)
Rev.: $19,220,565
Assets: $402,104,976
Liabilities: $197,154,048
Net Worth: $204,950,928
Earnings: $6,079,710
Fiscal Year-end: 03/31/21
Investment Management Service
N.A.I.C.S.: 541611
Binita Sharad Gosalia *(Compliance Officer & Sec)*

MEERA INDUSTRIES LIMITED
2126 Road No 2 GIDC Sachin, Surat, 394 230, Gujarat, India
Tel.: (91) 2612399114
Web Site: https://www.meeraind.com
540519—(BOM)
Rev.: $2,498,114
Assets: $4,327,567
Liabilities: $1,323,068
Net Worth: $3,004,500
Earnings: ($166,323)
Fiscal Year-end: 03/31/23
Textile Machinery Mfr & Distr
N.A.I.C.S.: 333248
Dharmesh Vinodbhai Desai *(Chm & Mng Dir)*

MEERE COMPANY INC.
69-12 Jeongmunsongsang-ro, Yanggam-myeon, Hwaseong, Gyeonggi-do, Korea (South)
Tel.: (82) 316309999
Web Site:
https://www.meerecompany.com
Year Founded: 1984
049950—(KRS)
Rev.: $118,775,382
Assets: $131,116,842
Liabilities: $29,196,681
Net Worth: $101,920,161
Earnings: $22,468,287
Emp.: 321
Fiscal Year-end: 12/31/22
Electronic Components Mfr
N.A.I.C.S.: 334419
Jeon Min-joon *(Asst Mgr-QA Team)*

MEEZAN BANK LIMITED
Meezan House C-25 Estate Avenue SITE, Karachi, Pakistan
Tel.: (92) 21111331331
Web Site:
https://www.meezanbank.com
Year Founded: 1997
MEBL—(KAR)
Rev.: $367,257,866
Assets: $7,252,180,362
Liabilities: $6,847,871,069
Net Worth: $404,309,292
Earnings: $101,620,875
Emp.: 9,900
Fiscal Year-end: 12/31/19
Banking Services
N.A.I.C.S.: 522110
Irfan Siddiqui *(Pres & CEO)*

Subsidiaries:

Al Meezan Investment Management Limited (1)
Ground Floor Block B Finance and Trade Centre FTC, Sharah-e-Faisal, Karachi, 74400, Pakistan
Tel.: (92) 21111633926
Web Site: https://www.almeezangroup.com
Investment Management Service
N.A.I.C.S.: 523999
Mohammad Shoaib *(CEO)*

MEFCOM CAPITAL MARKETS LTD
5th Floor 77 Nehru Place Sanchi Building, New Delhi, 110 019, India
Tel.: (91) 1146500500
Web Site: https://www.mefcom.in
531176—(BOM)
Rev.: $8,031,912
Assets: $2,589,996
Liabilities: $880,688
Net Worth: $1,709,308
Earnings: ($682,635)
Fiscal Year-end: 03/31/23
Financial Management Services
N.A.I.C.S.: 523999
Vijay Mehta *(Chm & Mng Dir)*

MEFIN S.A.
Calea Bucuresti nr 5, Sinaia, Prahova, Romania
Tel.: (40) 244 307 000
Web Site: http://www.mefin.ro
Year Founded: 1892
Sales Range: $1-9.9 Million
Emp.: 13
Diesel Pump & Fuel Injection Systems Mfr
N.A.I.C.S.: 336310
Mariana Stoica *(Head-HR)*

MEG ENERGY CORP.
25th Floor - Main Floor Reception 21st Floor - Mail Room, 600 - 3 Avenue SW, Calgary, T2P 0G5, AB, Canada
Tel.: (403) 770-0446   AB
Web Site:
https://www.megenergy.com
Year Founded: 1999
MEGEF—(OTCIQ)
Rev.: $3,008,158,440
Assets: $6,019,377,840
Liabilities: $3,070,908,120
Net Worth: $2,948,469,720
Earnings: ($47,444,880)
Emp.: 516
Fiscal Year-end: 12/31/19
Oil Sands Exploration Services
N.A.I.C.S.: 211120
Derek W. Evans *(Pres & CEO)*

MEGA BANK NEPAL LIMITED
Rising Mall Kamaladi, Kathmandu, Nepal
Tel.: (977) 14169217
Web Site:
http://www.megabanknepal.com
MEGA—(NEP)
Rev.: $87,507,659
Assets: $1,307,410,708
Liabilities: $1,155,731,700
Net Worth: $151,679,008
Earnings: $13,477,375
Fiscal Year-end: 07/15/20
Commercial Banking Services
N.A.I.C.S.: 522110
Bhoj Bahadur Shah *(Chm)*

MEGA CENTER MANAGEMENT JSC
247a Rozybakiev st, A15T6C2, Almaty, Kazakhstan
Tel.: (7) 272322504
Web Site: http://www.mega.kz

MEGA—(KAZ)
Rev.: $32,191,643
Assets: $138,962,150
Liabilities: $108,283,163
Net Worth: $30,678,987
Earnings: $16,635,882
Fiscal Year-end: 12/31/19
Building Construction Services
N.A.I.C.S.: 236220
Seitzhan Esmagambetov *(Chm-Mgmt Bd & Gen Dir)*

MEGA CHEM (THAILAND) PUBLIC COMPANY LIMITED
25 Soi Chalongkrung 31, Ladkrabang Industrial Estate Soi G1/9, Bangkok, 10520, Thailand
Tel.: (66) 27396333
Web Site:
https://www.megachem.co.th
Year Founded: 1992
MGT—(THA)
Rev.: $28,493,698
Assets: $27,822,283
Liabilities: $10,229,742
Net Worth: $17,592,541
Earnings: $2,406,878
Fiscal Year-end: 12/31/23
Chemical Products Mfr
N.A.I.C.S.: 325998
Vitthaya Inala *(Chm & CEO)*

MEGA COPPER LTD.
Suite 600 666 Burrard Street, Vancouver, V6C 2X8, BC, Canada
Tel.: (604) 689-9600   BC
Year Founded: 2007
MCU.H—(TSXV)
Assets: $31,121
Liabilities: $255,799
Net Worth: ($224,678)
Earnings: ($118,909)
Fiscal Year-end: 12/31/23
Copper Mining Services
N.A.I.C.S.: 212230
Marilyn Miller *(CEO)*

MEGA CORPORATION LIMITED
Plot No 62 Upper Ground Floor, Okhla Industrial Area Phase-III, New Delhi, 110020, India
Tel.: (91) 1146557134   In
Web Site:
https://www.megacorpltd.com
Year Founded: 1985
531417—(BOM)
Rev.: $388,134
Assets: $6,209,921
Liabilities: $2,992,770
Net Worth: $3,217,150
Earnings: ($39,558)
Emp.: 4
Fiscal Year-end: 03/31/21
Aircraft Charter Services
N.A.I.C.S.: 481211
Surendra Chhalani *(CFO)*

MEGA FIN (INDIA) LIMITED
17th Floor A-Wing Mittal Tower Nariman Point, F Block Dr Annie Besant Road Worli, Mumbai, 400021, India
Tel.: (91) 2242305500
Web Site: https://www.megafin.in
532105—(BOM)
Rev.: $31,919
Assets: $288,952
Liabilities: $28,663
Net Worth: $260,289
Earnings: $9,107
Fiscal Year-end: 03/31/21
Investment Management Service
N.A.I.C.S.: 523999
Ajay S. Mittal *(Chm)*

MEGA FINANCIAL HOLDING CO., LTD.

MEGA FINANCIAL HOLDING CO., LTD.
Floors 14 17 20 21 No 123 Section 2 Zhongxiao East Road, Taipei, 100, Taiwan
Tel.: (886) 223578888
Web Site:
https://www.megaholdings.com.tw
Year Founded: 2002
2886—(TAI)
Rev.: $3,675,941,281
Assets: $137,409,411,031
Liabilities: $126,909,736,579
Net Worth: $10,499,674,452
Earnings: $1,039,520,276
Emp.: 9,786
Fiscal Year-end: 12/31/23
Holding Company
N.A.I.C.S.: 551112
Kuang-Hua Hu *(Pres)*

Subsidiaries:

Chung Kuo Insurance Co., Ltd. (1)
No 58 Sec 1 Wuchang St, Jhongjheng Dist, Taipei, 10044, Taiwan
Tel.: (886) 223812727
Web Site: http://www.cki.com.tw
Sales Range: $350-399.9 Million
Emp.: 25
Non-Life Insurance Services
N.A.I.C.S.: 524126

Mega Asset Management Co., Ltd. (1)
6F No 91 Hengyang Road, Taipei, Taiwan
Tel.: (886) 266326789
Web Site: http://www.megaholdings.com.tw
Asset Management Services
N.A.I.C.S.: 523999

Mega Bills Finance Co., Ltd. (1)
2 5F No 91 Hengyang Road, Taipei, Taiwan
Tel.: (886) 223831616
Web Site: http://www.chbfc.com.tw
Sales Range: $150-199.9 Million
Emp.: 222
Brokerage, Dealing & Underwriting Services
N.A.I.C.S.: 524210
Mei-Chu Liao *(Chm)*

Mega CTB Venture Capital Co., Ltd. (1)
91 Hengyang Road, 100, Taipei, Taiwan
Tel.: (886) 223140878
Web Site: http://www.megaholdings.com.tw
Emp.: 11
Venture Capital Investment Services
N.A.I.C.S.: 523999

Mega Capital (Asia) Co., Ltd (1)
Room 2213-2214 22nd Floor Cosco Tower 183 Queen's Road, Central Sheung Wan, Hong Kong, China (Hong Kong)
Tel.: (852) 2802 2022
Marketing Consulting Services
N.A.I.C.S.: 541613

Mega International Commercial Bank Co., Ltd. (1)
No 100 Chi-lin Rd, Taipei, 10424, Taiwan (100%)
Tel.: (886) 225633156
Web Site: http://www.megabank.com.tw
Rev.: $2,277,503,837
Assets: $110,865,239,989
Liabilities: $101,166,875,234
Net Worth: $9,698,364,755
Earnings: $819,442,127
Emp.: 6,762
Fiscal Year-end: 12/31/2019
Commercial Banking Services
N.A.I.C.S.: 522110
Yong-Yi Tsai *(Pres)*

Subsidiary (Non-US):

ICBC (Europe) N.V. (2)
World Trade Ctr Strawinskylaan 1203, Amsterdam, 1077 XX, Netherlands
Tel.: (31) 206621566
Sales Range: $50-74.9 Million
Emp.: 10
Banking Services
N.A.I.C.S.: 522110

Mega International Commercial Bank (Canada) (2)

MEGA FINANCIAL HOLDING CO., LTD.

Mega Financial Holding Co., Ltd.—(Continued)

1095 West Pender Street Suite 1250, Vancouver, V6E 2M6, BC, Canada **(100%)**
Tel.: (604) 689-5650
Web Site: http://www.megabank.com.tw
Sales Range: $50-74.9 Million
Emp.: 10
International Banking Services
N.A.I.C.S.: 522110

Mega International Commercial Bank Public Co., Ltd. (2)
36/12 P S Tower Asoke Sukhumvit 21 Road Klongtoengnua Wattana, Bangkok, 10110, Thailand
Tel.: (66) 22592000
Web Site: http://www.overseas.megebank.com.tw
Sales Range: $75-99.9 Million
Emp.: 150
Commercial Banking Services
N.A.I.C.S.: 522110

Mega International Investment Trust Co., Ltd. (1)
7 8F No 91 Hengyang Road, Taipei, Taiwan
Tel.: (886) 223815188
Web Site: http://www.megafunds.com.tw
Sales Range: $25-49.9 Million
Emp.: 90
Asset Management Services
N.A.I.C.S.: 541618

Mega Life Insurance Agency Co., Ltd. (1)
5F No 100 Jilin Road, Taipei, Taiwan
Tel.: (886) 225633156
Web Site: http://www.megaholdings.com.tw
Fire Insurance Services
N.A.I.C.S.: 524113

Mega Securities Co., Ltd. (1)
4th Floor No 95 Section 2 Zhongxiao East Road, Zhongzheng District, Taipei, 10058, Taiwan
Tel.: (886) 223278988
Web Site: https://www.emega.com.tw
Securities Brokerage Services
N.A.I.C.S.: 523150
Chih-Chuan Chen *(Pres)*

Mega Venture Capital Co., Ltd. (1)
7F No 91 Hengyang Road, Taipei, Taiwan
Tel.: (886) 223140878
Commercial Banking Services
N.A.I.C.S.: 522110

MEGA FIRST CORPORATION BERHAD

A-12 01 Level 12 Block A PJ8 23 Jalan Barat Seksyen 8, 46050, Petaling Jaya, Selangor Darul Ehsan, Malaysia
Tel.: (60) 379608818
Web Site: https://www.mega-first.com
MFCB—(KLS)
Rev.: $283,520,635
Assets: $907,729,735
Liabilities: $232,380,317
Net Worth: $675,349,418
Earnings: $100,682,963
Emp.: 1,106
Fiscal Year-end: 12/31/22
Limestone Quarrying Services
N.A.I.C.S.: 212311
Nan Kioh Goh *(Chm)*

Subsidiaries:

Anting Sendirian Berhad (1)
Lot 15588 Mukim Sungai Raya, Simpang Pulai, 31300, Ipoh, Perak Darul Ridzuan, Malaysia
Tel.: (60) 53574105
Holding Company Services
N.A.I.C.S.: 551112

Batamas Sdn. Bhd. (1)
Lot 138321 Jalan Changkat Larang, PO Box 15, 31007, Batu Gajah, Perak Darul Ridzuan, Malaysia
Tel.: (60) 53661654
Web Site: http://www.batamas.net
Sales Range: $25-49.9 Million
Emp.: 65
Investment Holding Services
N.A.I.C.S.: 523999
K. S. Yong *(Gen Mgr)*

Bloxwich (Malaysia) Sdn. Bhd. (1)
Lot 31 Seri Iskandar Technology Park Mukim Bota, Daerah Perak Tengah Bota, 32600, Ipoh, Perak, Malaysia
Tel.: (60) 53711516
Web Site: http://www.bloxwich.com.my
Sales Range: $25-49.9 Million
Automotive Components Mfr
N.A.I.C.S.: 336330

Don Sahong Power Company Ltd. (1)
Lao-Thai Friendship Avenue, 374/15 Vat Nak Village, Vientiane, Lao People's Democratic Republic
Tel.: (856) 621353532
Holding Company Services
N.A.I.C.S.: 551112
Kongher Herjalearn *(Mgr)*

Greentown Parking Sdn. Bhd. (1)
No 15A Persiaran Greentown 4A Greentown Avenue, 30450, Ipoh, Perak Darul Ridzuan, Malaysia
Tel.: (60) 52433092
Holding Company Services
N.A.I.C.S.: 551112

Hexachase Corporation Sdn. Bhd. (1)
No 6 and 8 Jalan Berkat 12, Taman Malim Jaya, 75250, Melaka, Malaysia
Tel.: (60) 63357472
Web Site: https://www.hexachase.com
Offset Printing Product Mfr
N.A.I.C.S.: 323111

Subsidiary (Domestic):

Hexachase Flexipack Sdn. Bhd. (2)
No 20 Jalan TTC 26 Taman Teknologi Cheng, 75250, Melaka, Malaysia
Tel.: (60) 63357472
Holding Company Services
N.A.I.C.S.: 551112

Idaman Harmoni Sdn. Bhd. (1)
Property Investment Services
N.A.I.C.S.: 523999

Mega First Housing Development Sdn. Bhd. (1)
No 34 & 36 Jalan Mawar 1B Taman Mawar Bandar Baru Salak Tinggi, 43900, Sepang, Selangor Darul Ehsan, Malaysia
Tel.: (60) 387060088
Sales Range: $50-74.9 Million
Emp.: 15
Property Development Services
N.A.I.C.S.: 531390

Mega First Power Industries Sdn. Bhd. (1)
A 12-01 Level 12 Block A PJ8 No 23 Jalan Barat Seksyen 8, 46050, Petaling Jaya, Selangor Darul Ehsan, Malaysia
Tel.: (60) 379608818
Web Site: http://www.mega-first.com
Sales Range: $50-74.9 Million
Emp.: 2
Investment Holding Services
N.A.I.C.S.: 523999

Mega First Power Services Sdn. Bhd. (1)
KM 6 Jalan Kuhara Muhibbah, 91000, Tawau, Sabah, Malaysia
Tel.: (60) 89711568
Sales Range: $10-24.9 Million
Emp.: 43
Power Plant Maintenance Services
N.A.I.C.S.: 561990
Lim Thian Soo *(Mng Dir)*

RCI Lime Sdn. Bhd. (1)
Lot 45157 45158 Gunung Panjang, PO Box 18, 31600, Gopeng, Perak, Malaysia
Tel.: (60) 53593188
Web Site: https://www.rci.com.my
Chemicals Mfr
N.A.I.C.S.: 325998

RCI Marketing Sdn. Bhd. (1)
A-12-01 Level 12 Block A PJ8 No 23 Jalan Barat Seksyen 8, 46050, Petaling Jaya, Selangor, Malaysia
Tel.: (60) 379609973
Chemicals Mfr
N.A.I.C.S.: 325998

Rock Chemical Industries (Malaysia) Sdn Berhad (1)
Lot 45157 45158 Gunung Panjang, PO Box 18, 31600, Gopeng, Perak Darul Ridzuan, Malaysia
Tel.: (60) 53593188
Limestone Processing & Distributing Services
N.A.I.C.S.: 212311

Serudong Power Sdn. Bhd. (1)
KM 6 Jalan Kuhara-Muhibbah Raya, Tawau, 91000, Sabah, Malaysia
Tel.: (60) 89711569
Sales Range: $10-24.9 Million
Emp.: 43
Plant Maintenance Services
N.A.I.C.S.: 561990
Nan Kioh Goh *(Chm)*

Syarikat Cheng Sun Quarry Sdn. Bhd. (1)
Lot 67887 Mukim Sg Raia, Keramat Pulai, 31300, Ipoh, Perak Darul Ridzuan, Malaysia
Tel.: (60) 53571502
Sales Range: $50-74.9 Million
Emp.: 43
Limestone Quarrying Services
N.A.I.C.S.: 212312
John Chu *(Mng Dir)*

MEGA GENOMICS LIMITED

401 Health Work North Garden Road, Haidian, Beijing, China
Web Site: https://www.megagenomics.cn
Year Founded: 2016
6667—(HKG)
Rev.: $20,948,715
Assets: $110,287,716
Liabilities: $21,006,175
Net Worth: $89,281,541
Earnings: $4,159,005
Emp.: 229
Fiscal Year-end: 12/31/23
Medical Laboratory Services
N.A.I.C.S.: 621511
Lin Lin *(Chm)*

MEGA INTERNATIONAL DEVELOPMENT CO LTD

2F No 112 Songjiang Rd, Zhongshan Dist, Taipei, 10457, Taiwan
Tel.: (886) 225423377
Web Site: https://mega-international.com.tw
Year Founded: 1970
5529—(TPE)
Rev.: $5,066,879
Assets: $99,610,543
Liabilities: $72,340,650
Net Worth: $27,269,893
Earnings: ($2,746,490)
Fiscal Year-end: 12/31/22
Building Construction Services
N.A.I.C.S.: 236210

MEGA INTERNATIONAL S.A.

9 avenue Rene Coty, 75014, Paris, France
Tel.: (33) 1 4275 4000 FR
Web Site: http://www.mega.com
Year Founded: 1991
Emp.: 500
Software Development Services
N.A.I.C.S.: 513210
Lucio de Risi *(Founder, Chm-Exec Bd & CEO)*

Subsidiaries:

MEGA NA, Inc. (1)
175 Paramount Dr Ste 302, Raynham, MA 02767
Tel.: (781) 784-7684
Web Site: http://www.mega.com
Computer Software Design & Development Services
N.A.I.C.S.: 513210

INTERNATIONAL PUBLIC

Frank Bernieri *(Sr VP & Mng Dir)*

MEGA LIFESCIENCES PUBLIC COMPANY LIMITED

909 Ample Tower 9th Floor Debaratna Road, Bangna Nuea, Bangkok, 10260, Thailand
Tel.: (66) 27694222
Web Site:
https://www.megawecare.com
Year Founded: 1982
MEGA—(THA)
Rev.: $460,540,517
Assets: $412,040,511
Liabilities: $140,491,581
Net Worth: $271,548,930
Earnings: $58,168,503
Emp.: 5,513
Fiscal Year-end: 12/31/23
Pharmaceutical & Nutraceutical Products Mfr & Distr
N.A.I.C.S.: 325412
Mechai Viravaidya *(Chm)*

Subsidiaries:

BiO-LiFE Marketing Sdn. Bhd. (1)
B-28-02 The Ascent Paradigm No 1 Jalan SS 7/ 26A, Kelana Jaya, 47301, Petaling Jaya, Selangor, Malaysia
Tel.: (60) 374997999
Web Site: https://www.biolife.com.my
Herbal Healthcare Product Mfr & Distr
N.A.I.C.S.: 325411

Mega Lifesciences (Australia) Pty. Limited (1)
60 National Avenue South Eastern Business Park, Pakenham, 3810, VIC, Australia
Tel.: (61) 359418599
Web Site: http://www.megawecare.com.au
Emp.: 33
Pharmaceuticals Product Mfr
N.A.I.C.S.: 325412

Mega Lifesciences Pty. Limited (1)
909 Ample tower 9th Floor Bangna-Trad Road, Bang Na, Bangkok, 10260, Thailand
Tel.: (66) 27694222
Pharmaceuticals Product Mfr
N.A.I.C.S.: 325412

Mega Lifesciences Sdn. Bhd. (1)
B-28-02 The Ascent Paradigm No 1 Jalan SS 7/ 26A, Kelana Jaya, 47301, Petaling Jaya, Selangor, Malaysia
Tel.: (60) 374997999
Web Site: https://www.megawecare.com.my
Pharmaceuticals Product Mfr
N.A.I.C.S.: 325412

MEGA NIRMAN & INDUSTRIES LIMITED

A6/343B, Paschim Vihar, New Delhi, 110 063, India
Tel.: (91) 1149879687
Web Site: https://www.mnil.in
Year Founded: 1983
539767—(BOM)
Rev.: $202,848
Assets: $1,386,733
Liabilities: $793,514
Net Worth: $593,220
Earnings: $1,451
Emp.: 6
Fiscal Year-end: 03/31/23
Real Estate Support Services
N.A.I.C.S.: 531390
Narayanjee Thakur *(Exec Dir)*

MEGA OR HOLDINGS LTD.

A T Shilot Beit Mega Or, PO 117, DN Center, Shilat, 73188, Israel
Tel.: (972) 89744880
Web Site: https://www.megaor.co.il
Year Founded: 2002
MGOR—(TAE)
Rev.: $67,058,432
Assets: $2,153,210,078
Liabilities: $1,389,895,544
Net Worth: $763,314,534
Earnings: $76,611,133

AND PRIVATE COMPANIES

Fiscal Year-end: 12/31/23
Offices of Other Holding Companies
N.A.I.C.S.: 551112
Zahi Nahmias *(Chm)*

MEGA SPRINT GUARD S.A
1st klm Lagkada-Soxou, Thessaloniki, Greece
Tel.: (30) 23940 25818
Web Site: http://www.megaguard.gr
Year Founded: 1994
Sales Range: $1-4.9 Billion
Emp.: 1,025
Security Guard Services
N.A.I.C.S.: 561612
Varvara Tachtaridou *(Pres, CEO & Mng Dir)*

MEGA URANIUM LTD.
217 Queen Street West Suite 401, Toronto, M5V 0R2, ON, Canada
Tel.: (416) 643-7630   ON
Web Site:
https://www.megauranium.com
Year Founded: 1990
MGA—(TSX)
Rev.: $187,484
Assets: $34,304,179
Liabilities: $486,693
Net Worth: $33,817,486
Earnings: ($4,537,873)
Emp.: 2
Fiscal Year-end: 09/30/19
Uranium Exploration & Mining
N.A.I.C.S.: 212290
Wendy Warhaft *(Gen Counsel)*

Subsidiaries:

Lake Maitland Pty Ltd   (1)
62 Havelock St, West Perth, Perth, 6005, WA, Australia
Tel.: (61) 892133000
Web Site: http://www.megauranium.com
Uranium Radium Vanadium Mining Services
N.A.I.C.S.: 212290

Maple Resources Inc.   (1)

Mega Hindmarsh Pty Ltd   (1)
105 Tusmore Ave, Tusmore, Adelaide, 5065, SA, Australia
Tel.: (61) 883048224
Sales Range: $50-74.9 Million
Uranium Mining Services
N.A.I.C.S.: 212290

Monster Copper Corporation   (1)
11 Rocksprings Avenue, Richmond Hill, L4S 1R2, ON, Canada
Tel.: (905) 780-8783
Gold & Copper Exploration Services
N.A.I.C.S.: 212220

Uranium Mineral Ventures Inc.   (1)
G 57 Havelock St, West Perth, Perth, 6005, WA, Australia
Tel.: (61) 892133000
Sales Range: $50-74.9 Million
Uranium Radium Vanadium Mining Services
N.A.I.C.S.: 212290

MEGA VIEW DIGITAL ENTERTAINMENT CORP.
30 Wertheim Court, Richmond Hill, L4B 1B9, ON, Canada
Tel.: (416) 226-7269
Entertainment Services
N.A.I.C.S.: 711130
Philip Chong *(Pres & CEO)*

MEGA-INFO MEDIA CO., LTD.
Lianmei Building Building No 1 Yard No 17 Guangqu Road, Chaoyang District, Beijing, 300308, China
Tel.: (86) 1065915208
Web Site:
https://www.zhaoxunmedia.com
Year Founded: 2007
301102—(SSE)
Rev.: $80,968,680
Assets: $507,006,864
Liabilities: $98,455,500
Net Worth: $408,551,364
Earnings: $26,938,548
Fiscal Year-end: 12/31/22
Digital Marketing Services
N.A.I.C.S.: 541810
Zhuangqiang Su *(Chm)*

MEGACABLE HOLDINGS, S. A. B. DE C. V.
Av Lazaro Cardenas No 1694 Del Fresno, 44900, Guadalajara, JA, Mexico
Tel.: (52) 3337500042
Web Site:
http://www.megacable.com.mx
Year Founded: 1978
MEGA—(MEX)
Rev.: $1,759,989,542
Assets: $4,035,133,204
Liabilities: $1,922,539,756
Net Worth: $2,112,593,448
Earnings: $177,297,328
Emp.: 30,663
Fiscal Year-end: 12/31/23
Telecommunication Servicesb
N.A.I.C.S.: 517111
Raymundo Fernandez *(Deputy Gen Dir)*

MEGACHEM LIMITED
11 Tuas link 1, Singapore, 638588, Singapore
Tel.: (65) 69339999
Web Site:
https://www.megachem.com.sg
Year Founded: 1988
5DS—(CAT)
Rev.: $106,499,140
Assets: $86,762,041
Liabilities: $41,011,462
Net Worth: $45,750,579
Earnings: $4,495,580
Emp.: 251
Fiscal Year-end: 12/31/22
Chemical Products Mfr
N.A.I.C.S.: 325998
Jeffrey Bock Chia Tan *(Exec Dir)*

Subsidiaries:

C.N. Chemicals Sdn. Bhd.   (1)
121 Jalan SS25/2 Taman Mewah, 47301, Petaling Jaya, Selangor, Malaysia
Tel.: (60) 3 7803 0795
Chemical Products Distr
N.A.I.C.S.: 424690

MG Chemicals (Australia) Pty Ltd   (1)
Suite 8 12 Pascoe Vale Road, Moonee Ponds, Melbourne, 3039, VIC, Australia
Tel.: (61) 3 9326 2882
Emp.: 4
Chemical Products Distr
N.A.I.C.S.: 424690

MGI Chemicals Private Limited   (1)
407 4th Floor Jaswanti Landmark LBS Marg Vikhroli, Hiranandani Garden Powai, Mumbai, 400076, India
Tel.: (91) 22 40260957
Web Site: http://www.megachem.com
Emp.: 9
Chemical Products Distr
N.A.I.C.S.: 424690

Megachem (Shanghai) Pte. Ltd.   (1)
11 Tuas Link 1, Singapore, 638588, Singapore
Tel.: (65) 69339999
Chemical Product Mfr & Distr
N.A.I.C.S.: 325998

Megachem (UK) Ltd   (1)
Castlegate Business Park, Caldicot, NP26 5AD, Monmouthshire, United Kingdom
Tel.: (44) 1291 422747
Emp.: 15
Chemical Products Distr
N.A.I.C.S.: 424690
Gary Foster *(Mng Dir)*

Megachem Australia Pty. Ltd.   (1)
Suite 2 34 Edgewater Boulevard, Maribyrnong, 3032, VIC, Australia
Tel.: (61) 393262882
Chemical Product Mfr & Distr
N.A.I.C.S.: 325998

Megachem International Trading (Beijing) Co. Ltd.
Room 2212 Building 7 Guancheng Mingdun Road Guangqumenwai Street, Dongcheng District, Beijing, 100022, China
Tel.: (86) 1087512969
Chemicals Mfr
N.A.I.C.S.: 325199

Megachem International Trading (Shanghai) Co., Ltd.   (1)
Room 1502 Yintong Building No 988 Dingxi Road, Changning District, Shanghai, 200050, China
Tel.: (86) 2152375028
Web Site: https://www.megachem.net.cn
Chemicals Mfr
N.A.I.C.S.: 325199

Megachem Manufacturing Pte Ltd   (1)
11 Tuas link 1, Singapore, 638588, Singapore
Tel.: (65) 69339999
Chemicals Mfr
N.A.I.C.S.: 325199

Megachem Middle East FZE   (1)
LIU 10 Unit AB03 South Zone Jebel Ali Free Zone, Dubai, United Arab Emirates
Tel.: (971) 48865458
Emp.: 8
Chemical Products Distr
N.A.I.C.S.: 424690

Megachem Phils., Inc   (1)
Greenlee Compound 143 M L Quezon Extension Street Brgy, Manggahan, Pasig, 1611, Philippines
Tel.: (63) 279140837
Emp.: 6
Chemical Products Distr
N.A.I.C.S.: 424690

Megachem Specialty Chemicals (I) Private Limited   (1)
702 & 703 Fairmount Plot No 4 & 6 Sanpada Palm Beach Road Sector 17, Navi Mumbai, 400705, India
Tel.: (91) 2240260957
Chemical Product Mfr & Distr
N.A.I.C.S.: 325998

Megachem Vietnam Company Limited   (1)
Unit 703 7th Floor 45 Dinh Tien Hoang Street, Ben Nghe Ward District 1, Ho Chi Minh City, Vietnam
Tel.: (84) 2839106638
Chemical Products Distr
N.A.I.C.S.: 424690

P.T. Mega Kemiraya   (1)
Tel.: (62) 215363189
Chemical Mfr & Distr
N.A.I.C.S.: 325199

MEGACHIPS CORPORATION
Shin-Osaka Hankyu Building 1-1-1 Miyahara, Yodogawa-ku, Osaka, 532-0003, Japan
Tel.: (81) 663992884   JP
Web Site:
https://www.megachips.co.jp
Year Founded: 1990
6875—(TKS)
Rev.: $382,996,620
Assets: $836,892,100
Liabilities: $158,223,570
Net Worth: $678,668,530
Earnings: $29,652,460
Emp.: 339
Fiscal Year-end: 03/31/24
LSI Electronic Device Designer, Mfr & Distr
N.A.I.C.S.: 334419
Masahiro Shindo *(Chm)*

Subsidiaries:

MegaChips LSI USA Corporation   (1)

MEGALIT SUMNIK A.D.

910 E Hamilton Ave Ste 120, Campbell, CA 95008
Tel.: (408) 570-0555
Electronic Components Mfr
N.A.I.C.S.: 334419
Ikuo Iwama *(CEO)*

MEGADO MINERALS LIMITED
Level 12 197 St Georges Terrace, Perth, 6000, WA, Australia
Tel.: (61) 861413260   AU
Web Site:
https://www.megadominerals.com
Year Founded: 2019
MEG—(ASX)
Rev.: $17,372
Assets: $6,130,057
Liabilities: $32,267
Net Worth: $6,097,790
Earnings: ($929,884)
Fiscal Year-end: 12/31/23
Other Nonmetallic Mineral Mining & Quarrying
N.A.I.C.S.: 212390
Aaron Bertolatti *(Sec)*

MEGAH PORT MANAGEMENT SDN. BHD.
W-2 Labuan Liberty Port Jalan Merdeka Wilayah Persekutuan, 87000, Labuan, Malaysia
Tel.: (60) 87424188   MY
Web Site:
https://www.staging.megahport.com
Port Facility Management Services
N.A.I.C.S.: 525110

MEGAIN HOLDING (CAYMAN) CO., LTD.
3/F Block A No 115 Huawei Road, Xiangzhou District, Zhuhai, 519000, Guangdong, China
Tel.: (86) 7566893518   Ky
Web Site:
https://www.megaincayman.com
Year Founded: 2016
6939—(HKG)
Rev.: $23,869,351
Assets: $54,027,609
Liabilities: $2,767,778
Net Worth: $51,259,831
Earnings: $3,213,890
Emp.: 154
Fiscal Year-end: 12/31/23
Holding Company
N.A.I.C.S.: 551112
Hsien-Wei Cheng *(Chm)*

MEGAL A.D.
Lopardinski put bb, 17520, Bujanovac, Serbia
Tel.: (381) 17651050
Web Site: http://www.megal.co.rs
Year Founded: 1979
MGAL—(BEL)
Rev.: $2,163,348
Assets: $4,021,948
Liabilities: $2,038,496
Net Worth: $1,983,452
Earnings: ($295,157)
Emp.: 120
Fiscal Year-end: 12/31/23
Heating Equipment Mfr
N.A.I.C.S.: 333414
Dragoljub Kostic *(Exec Dir)*

MEGALIT SUMNIK A.D.
Studenicka 4, Raska, 36350, Serbia
Tel.: (381) 36 736 344
Web Site: http://www.megalit-sumnik.rs
Year Founded: 2008
Sales Range: $10-24.9 Million
Emp.: 200
Construction Material Exploration Services
N.A.I.C.S.: 212321

MEGALIT SUMNIK A.D.

Megalit Sumnik a.d.—(Continued)

Srecko Minic (Exec Dir)

MEGANESUPER CO., LTD.
1-9-11 Nihonbashi Horidomecho
NEWS Nihonbashi Horidomecho 6F,
Chuo-ku, Tokyo, 103-0012, Japan
Tel.: (81) 46 5243611
Web Site:
http://www.meganesuper.co.jp
Year Founded: 1980
Eyeglass Retail Store Operator
N.A.I.C.S.: 456130
Naohiko Hoshizaki (Pres)

MEGAPORT LIMITED
Level 3 825 Ann St, Fortitude Valley,
4006, QLD, Australia
Tel.: (61) 730885999
Web Site: https://www.megaport.com
Year Founded: 2013
MP1—(ASX)
Rev.: $130,389,289
Assets: $143,364,716
Liabilities: $40,480,101
Net Worth: $102,884,615
Earnings: $6,414,263
Emp.: 280
Fiscal Year-end: 06/30/24
Software Development Services
N.A.I.C.S.: 513210
Bevan Slattery (Founder)

MEGARON S.A.
ul Pyrzycka 3e f, 70-892, Szczecin,
Poland
Tel.: (48) 914664540
Web Site:
https://www.megaron.com.pl
Year Founded: 2011
MEG—(WAR)
Rev.: $11,132,368
Assets: $8,527,185
Liabilities: $3,564,024
Net Worth: $4,963,161
Earnings: ($194,360)
Fiscal Year-end: 12/31/23
Plaster Coats, Gypsum Putty & Assembly Adhesives Mfr & Distr
N.A.I.C.S.: 325510
Piotr Andrzej Sikora (Chm & Chm-Mgmt Bd)

MEGASOFT LTD.
85 Kutchery Road Mylapore, Chennai, 600004, India
Tel.: (91) 4424616768
Web Site: https://www.megasoft.com
532408—(BOM)
Rev.: $5,312,572
Assets: $45,669,251
Liabilities: $22,237,400
Net Worth: $23,431,851
Earnings: $1,070,111
Emp.: 885
Fiscal Year-end: 03/31/23
Telecommunication Servicesb
N.A.I.C.S.: 517810
Kumar Venkataraman Gandarvakottai (Mng Dir)

Subsidiaries:

Megasoft Consultants Pte Ltd (1)
Level 30 Six Battery Road, Singapore,
049909, Singapore
Tel.: (65) 6550 9688
Sales Range: $25-49.9 Million
Emp.: 2
Software Consulting Services
N.A.I.C.S.: 541618

Megasoft Consultants Sdn Bhd (1)
Suite 18-3 D' Wangsa Jalan Wangsa Delima 11, 53300, Kuala Lumpur, Malaysia
Tel.: (60) 34 144 4562
Information Technology Services
N.A.I.C.S.: 541511

Velapan Systems Private Limited (1)

XIUS Corp. (1)
15 Tyngsboro Rd Unit 8C, North Chelmsford, MA 01863
Tel.: (781) 904-5000
Software Development Services
N.A.I.C.S.: 541511

XIUS S DE RL DE CV (1)
Pase o de la Reforma 505 piso 32 Col
Cuauhtemoc, 06500, Mexico, Mexico
Tel.: (52) 558 503 4200
Software Development Services
N.A.I.C.S.: 541511

XIUS-BCGI (1)
100 Crosby Dr, Bedford, MA 01730
Tel.: (781) 904-5000
Web Site: http://www.xius-bcgi.com
Sales Range: $100-124.9 Million
Emp.: 504
Roaming, Prepaid & Voice Service Systems
to Wireless Telephone Carriers
N.A.I.C.S.: 517112
Lola Levin (Dir-HR)

MEGASTAR FOODS LIMITED
Plot No 807 Industrial Area Phase-Ii,
Chandigarh, 160002, India
Tel.: (91) 1722653807
Web Site:
https://www.megastarfoods.com
Year Founded: 2011
541352—(BOM)
Rev.: $22,707,567
Assets: $11,744,597
Liabilities: $8,158,578
Net Worth: $3,586,019
Earnings: $571,512
Emp.: 99
Fiscal Year-end: 03/31/21
Wheat Flour Product Mfr & Distr
N.A.I.C.S.: 311211
Vikas Goel (Chm & Mng Dir)

MEGASTUDY CO., LTD.
24F 304 Hyoryeong-ro, Seocho-gu,
Seoul, Korea (South)
Tel.: (82) 269846811
Web Site: http://corp.megastudy.net
Year Founded: 2000
072870—(KRS)
Rev.: $93,267,672
Assets: $309,700,965
Liabilities: $48,511,427
Net Worth: $261,189,538
Earnings: $15,702,662
Emp.: 186
Fiscal Year-end: 12/31/22
Online Education School Services
N.A.I.C.S.: 611699
Lee Ju Ho (Gen Mgr)

Subsidiaries:

MegaMD Co., Ltd (1)
81 banpodae-ro, Seocho-gu, Seoul, Korea (South)
Tel.: (82) 269183505
Web Site: http://www.megamd.co.kr
Rev.: $49,446,992
Assets: $71,754,997
Liabilities: $21,331,116
Net Worth: $50,423,881
Earnings: $1,620,502
Emp.: 244
Fiscal Year-end: 12/31/2022
Educational Support Services
N.A.I.C.S.: 611710

MegaStudyEdu Co., Ltd. (1)
321 Hyoryeongro, Seochogu, Seoul, Korea (South)
Tel.: (82) 234898200
Web Site: http://www.megastudy.net
Rev.: $641,175,838
Assets: $693,913,177
Liabilities: $361,263,795
Net Worth: $332,649,382
Earnings: $76,360,552
Emp.: 1,966
Fiscal Year-end: 12/31/2022
Online Educational Support Services
N.A.I.C.S.: 611710

Lee Chang Seop (CFO)

MEGATECH SCIENTIFIC PTE. LTD.
52 Tuas Ave 9, Singapore, 639193,
Singapore
Tel.: (65) 65657211   SG
Web Site:
http://www.megatechsci.com
Year Founded: 1990
Sales Range: $1-9.9 Million
Emp.: 30
Micro-Contamination Control Facemasks & Apparel Mfr
N.A.I.C.S.: 315990
Xue Qing Liu (Owner)

MEGATRON ELEKTRONIK AG & CO.
Hermann Oberth Strasse 7, Putzbrunn, 85640, Munich, Germany
Tel.: (49) 89460940
Web Site: http://www.megatron.de
Rev.: $12,000,000
Emp.: 77
Sensor Mfr
N.A.I.C.S.: 334413
Peter A. Vizenetz (Founder)

Subsidiaries:

ELPAC Components (1)
Hermann Oberth Str 7, Putzbrunn, 85640,
Munich, Germany
Tel.: (49) 8946094400
Web Site: http://www.elpac.de
Electronic System Mfr
N.A.I.C.S.: 334511

MEGATRON S.a.r.l. (1)
451 route des Blaves, 74200, Allinges,
France
Tel.: (33) 450705454
Web Site: http://www.megatron.fr
Electronic System Mfr
N.A.I.C.S.: 334511

MEGATRON s.r.o (1)
Mrstikova 214/16, 100 00, Prague, Czech
Republic
Tel.: (420) 274780972
Web Site: http://www.megatron.cz
Electronic System Mfr
N.A.I.C.S.: 334511
Jan Svoboda (Gen Mgr)

Megatron Electronics & Controls Ltd (1)
12 Markoni st, PO Box 25205, Haifa,
3125101, Israel
Tel.: (972) 48410704
Web Site: http://www.megatron.co.il
Emp.: 50
Electronic System Mfr
N.A.I.C.S.: 334511

MEGAWATT LITHIUM AND BATTERY METALS CORP.
1500 1055 West Georgia Street, Vancouver, V6E 4N7, BC, Canada
Tel.: (604) 306-7821
Web Site:
https://www.megawattmetals.com
WALRF—(OTCQB)
Rev.: $65,236
Assets: $1,236,482
Liabilities: $360,236
Net Worth: $876,246
Earnings: ($823,062)
Fiscal Year-end: 09/30/23
Mineral Exploration Services
N.A.I.C.S.: 213115
David Thornley-Hall (CEO)

Subsidiaries:

Labrador Mineral Resources Inc. (1)

MEGAWIDE CONSTRUCTION CORPORATION
20 N Domingo Street Bgy Valencia,
Quezon City, 1112, Philippines

INTERNATIONAL PUBLIC

Tel.: (63) 286551111   PH
Web Site: https://megawide.com.ph
Year Founded: 2004
MWIDE—(PHI)
Rev.: $325,394,599
Assets: $1,771,673,880
Liabilities: $1,372,295,001
Net Worth: $399,378,880
Earnings: ($18,577,612)
Emp.: 1,731
Fiscal Year-end: 12/31/21
Residential & Industrial Building Construction
N.A.I.C.S.: 236116
Edgar B. Saavedra (Founder, Chm & CEO)

Subsidiaries:

Ferronoux Holdings, Inc. (1)
6th Floor Hanston Building F Ortigas Jr
Road, Ortigas Center, Pasig, Philippines
Tel.: (63) 88884762
Web Site:
https://www.ferronouxholdings.com
Rev.: $59,571
Assets: $2,786,335
Liabilities: $267,785
Net Worth: $2,518,550
Earnings: $17,524
Fiscal Year-end: 12/31/2023
Loan Financing
N.A.I.C.S.: 522310
Michael C. Cosiquien (Chm & Pres)

MEGAWIN TECHNOLOGY CO., LTD.
7F-1 No 8 Taiyuan 1st St, Jhubei,
30288, Taiwan
Tel.: (886) 35601501
Web Site:
https://www.megawin.com.tw
Year Founded: 1999
3122—(TPE)
Rev.: $15,975,487
Assets: $24,113,967
Liabilities: $8,411,969
Net Worth: $15,701,998
Earnings: $544,508
Fiscal Year-end: 12/31/22
Semiconductor Devices Mfr
N.A.I.C.S.: 334413
Kuo-Liang Wen (Chm & CEO)

Subsidiaries:

Megawin Technology (Shenzhen) Co., Ltd. (1)
Rm 905 9/F Block B HaiSong Building Tairan 9th Road, Chegongmiao Futian District,
Shenzhen, China
Tel.: (86) 75583435163
Semiconductor Product Mfr
N.A.I.C.S.: 334413

MEGGER GROUP LIMITED
Archcliffe Road, Dover, CT17 9EN,
Kent, United Kingdom
Tel.: (44) 1304 502 101   UK
Web Site: http://www.megger.com
Holding Company: Electrical Test & Measurement Equipment Designer,
Mfr & Distr
N.A.I.C.S.: 551112
Andrew Boughtwood (Mng Dir-Sls-UK & Intl)

Subsidiaries:

AVO Multi-Amp Corporation (1)
4271 Bronze Way, Dallas, TX 75237-1019
Tel.: (800) 723-2861
Web Site: http://us.megger.com
Electrical Test & Measurement Equipment
Designer, Mfr & Distr
N.A.I.C.S.: 334515
Larissa Sargent (Acct Mgr)

Plant (Domestic):

AVO Multi-Amp Corp. - Valley Forge (2)
Vly Forge Corporate Ctr 2621 Van Buren

Ave, Norristown, PA 19403
Tel.: (610) 676-8500
Web Site: http://www.megger.com
Sales Range: $25-49.9 Million
Emp.: 100
Electrical Test & Measurement Equipment Designer, Mfr & Distr
N.A.I.C.S.: 334515
Graeme Thomson *(VP-Sls)*

Megger (India) PVT Limited
211 Crystal Paradise Mall Off Veera Desai Road, Andheri, Mumbai, India
Tel.: (91) 22 2674 0468
Web Site: http://www.megger.com
Emp.: 11
Electrical Testing & Measuring Equipment Distr
N.A.I.C.S.: 423830
Ajay Goyal *(Mng Dir)*

Megger Canada Ltd.
Unit 106-55 Alden Road, Markham, L3R 6A8, ON, Canada
Tel.: (416) 298-6770
Electrical Testing & Measuring Equipment Mfr & Distr
N.A.I.C.S.: 334515
Carl Heathfield *(Mgr-Sls)*

Megger China (1)
Room 1108-28 11th Floor Langao Road 567, Shanghai, 200000, China
Tel.: (86) 10 6765 3379
Electrical Testing & Measuring Equipment Distr
N.A.I.C.S.: 423830

Megger Espana
Calle la Florida 1 Nave 16 Parque Empresarial Villapark, Villaviciosa de Odon, 28670, Madrid, Spain
Tel.: (34) 916 16 54 96
Web Site: http://www.megger.es
Electrical Testing & Measuring Equipment Distr
N.A.I.C.S.: 423830

Megger GmbH (1)
Obere Zeil 2, 61440, Oberursel, Germany
Tel.: (49) 6171 92987 0
Electrical Testing & Measuring Equipment Distr
N.A.I.C.S.: 423830

Megger Hong Kong Limited (1)
Workshop No 8 26/F Mega Trade Centre 1 - 6 Mei Wan St, Tsuen Wan, New Territories, China (Hong Kong)
Tel.: (852) 2618 9964
Electrical Testing & Measuring Equipment Distr
N.A.I.C.S.: 423830

Megger Indonesia (1)
Gedung Menara Karya 28th Floor Jalan HR Rasuna Said Blok X-5 Kav 1-2, Jakarta, 12950, Indonesia
Tel.: (62) 21 57895525
Electrical Testing & Measuring Equipment Distr
N.A.I.C.S.: 423830
Nito Septian *(Reg Mgr-Sls)*

Megger Instruments Limited (1)
Archcliffe Road, Dover, CT17 9EN, Kent, United Kingdom
Tel.: (44) 1304 502 101
Web Site: http://www.megger.com
Emp.: 300
Electrical Test & Measurement Equipment Designer & Mfr
N.A.I.C.S.: 334515
Stephen Drennan *(Mng Dir)*

Megger Limited (1)
Archcliffe Road, Dover, CT17 9EN, Kent, United Kingdom
Tel.: (44) 1304 502 101
Web Site: http://www.megger.com
Emp.: 200
Electrical Test & Measurement Equipment Distr
N.A.I.C.S.: 423610
Andrew Boughtwood *(Mng Dir)*

Megger Manama (1)
Millennium Tower 9th Floor Office No 142 Bldg No 398 Road 2803, King Mohammed IV Avenue Block No 428 Seef Area, Manama, Bahrain

Tel.: (973) 177 40 620
Electrical Testing & Measuring Equipment Distr
N.A.I.C.S.: 423830

Megger Middle East (1)
DIC13 Office 209 Bldg 14, PO Box 500503, Dubai, United Arab Emirates
Tel.: (971) 4 443 5489
Electrical Testing & Measuring Equipment Distr
N.A.I.C.S.: 423830

Megger Pakistan Limited (1)
H No 26 Rasheed Park Ex-Firdous Cinema Rajghar, Lahore, 54000, Pakistan
Tel.: (92) 321 8795555
Electrical Testing & Measuring Equipment Distr
N.A.I.C.S.: 423830

Megger Pty Limited (1)
Unit 1 11-21 Underwood Road, Homebush, 2140, NSW, Australia
Tel.: (61) 2 9397 5900
Web Site: http://www.megger.com
Electrical Testing & Measuring Equipment Distr
N.A.I.C.S.: 423830

Megger SA (1)
23 rue Eugene Henaff, 78190, Trappes, France
Tel.: (33) 1 30 16 08 90
Electrical Testing & Measuring Equipment Distr
N.A.I.C.S.: 423830

Megger South Africa (1)
PostNet Suite 242, Private Bag X3, Bloubergstrand, 7443, South Africa
Tel.: (27) 21 557 6572
Electrical Testing & Measuring Equipment Distr
N.A.I.C.S.: 423830

Megger Sweden AB (1)
Rinkebyvagen 19, 182 36, Danderyd, Sweden
Tel.: (46) 8 510 195 00
Electrical Testing & Measuring Equipment Distr
N.A.I.C.S.: 423830
Stina Flogell Ostlundh *(Mng Dir)*

PowerDB, Inc. (1)
3011 Earl Rudder Freeway Ste 200, College Station, TX 77845
Tel.: (979) 690-7925
Web Site: http://www2.powerdb.com
Software Development Services
N.A.I.C.S.: 541511
Douglas Sawyer *(Mgr-Software Dev)*

MEGH MAYUR INFRA LIMITED
MHB-11 A Wing 3rd floor No 302 Sarvodaya Co-Operative Housing Society, Limited Khernagar Bandra East, Mumbai, 400092, India
Tel.: (91) 2228993841
Web Site:
 https://www.meghmayurinfra.com
Year Founded: 1981
509003—(BOM)
Assets: $916,707
Liabilities: $140,982
Net Worth: $775,726
Earnings: ($12,360)
Fiscal Year-end: 03/31/23
Real Estate Development Services
N.A.I.C.S.: 531390
Rajendra Shah *(Exec Dir)*

MEGHE GROUP OF INSTITUTIONS
Atrey Layout, Pratap Nagar, Nagpur, 44022, India
Tel.: (91) 7122249462
Web Site: http://www.mginagpur.com
Educational Institutions
N.A.I.C.S.: 923110
Hemant Thakare *(Dir-Technical)*

Subsidiaries:

Ceinsys Tech Ltd. (1)

1601 Loadha Supremus SB Marg, Lower Parel West, Mumbai, 400013, Maharashtra, India
Tel.: (91) 2249472200
Web Site: https://www.ceinsys.com
Rev.: $26,604,760
Assets: $37,514,418
Liabilities: $13,738,613
Net Worth: $23,775,805
Earnings: $3,703,279
Emp.: 967
Fiscal Year-end: 03/31/2023
Geospatial Services
N.A.I.C.S.: 541360
Hemant Thakare *(COO)*

MEGHMANI FINECHEM LIMITED
Meghmani House B/H Safal Profitare Corporate Road Prahladnagar, Ahmedabad, 380015, Gujarat, India
Tel.: (91) 7929709600
Web Site:
 http://www.meghmanifinechem.com
Year Founded: 2007
MFL—(NSE)
Rev.: $263,339,560
Assets: $291,617,445
Liabilities: $163,435,657
Net Worth: $128,181,788
Earnings: $42,358,444
Emp.: 901
Fiscal Year-end: 03/31/23
Chemicals Mfr
N.A.I.C.S.: 325180
Maulik Patel *(Chm & Mng Dir)*

MEGHMANI ORGANICS LTD
Behind Safal Profitare Corporate Road, Prahlad Nagar, Ahmedabad, 380 015, Gujarat, India
Tel.: (91) 7929709600
Web Site: http://www.meghmani.com
Rev.: $304,174,674
Assets: $340,827,155
Liabilities: $175,510,114
Net Worth: $165,317,041
Earnings: $42,355,656
Emp.: 1,542
Fiscal Year-end: 03/31/19
Organic Limited & Pesticides Producer
N.A.I.C.S.: 325320
Jayanti Meghjibhai Patel *(Chm)*

Subsidiaries:

Meghmani Europe BVBA (1)
Grote Steen Weg 42- 44, 2600, Berchem, Belgium
Tel.: (32) 33375357
Web Site: http://www.meghmani.com
Sales Range: $25-49.9 Million
Emp.: 2
Pigment & Pesticide Products Mfr
N.A.I.C.S.: 325320

Meghmani Organics Ltd - Agro Division - I (1)
Plot No 402 403 404 & 452 Vlg Chharodi Taluka Sanand, Ahmedabad, Gujarat, India
Tel.: (91) 2717273251
Sales Range: $25-49.9 Million
Emp.: 100
Pesticide Mfr & Distr
N.A.I.C.S.: 325320

Meghmani Organics Ltd - Agro Division - II (1)
5001 B G I D C Ankleshwar, Bharuch, 393 002, Gujarat, India
Tel.: (91) 2646222971
Emp.: 400
Pesticide Mfr & Distr
N.A.I.C.S.: 325320
V. G. Patel *(Gen Mgr)*

Meghmani Organics Ltd - Agro Division - III (1)
Plot No CH 1 Plus 2 A GIDC Dahej Taluka Vagra, Bharuch, 392130, Gujarat, India
Tel.: (91) 2641256677
Pesticide Mfr & Distr
N.A.I.C.S.: 325320

Meghmani Organics Ltd - Pigment Blue Division (1)
Plot No 21 21 1 GIDC Panoli, Bharuch, 394116, Gujarat, India
Tel.: (91) 2646276352
Web Site: http://www.meghmani.com
Sales Range: $125-149.9 Million
Emp.: 400
Pigment Mfr
N.A.I.C.S.: 325130

Meghmani Organics Ltd - Power Plant (1)
Block No 398 Vlg Chharodi Sanand, Ahmedabad, 382170, Gujarat, India
Tel.: (91) 2717273252
Sales Range: $25-49.9 Million
Emp.: 55
Pigment & Pesticide Products Mfr
N.A.I.C.S.: 325320

MEGHNA CEMENT MILLS LIMITED
Plot 125/A Road 2 Block A Bashundhara R/A, Dhaka, 1229, Bangladesh
Tel.: (880) 28431024
Web Site:
 https://www.bashundharagroup.com
Year Founded: 1992
MEGHNACEM—(CHT)
Rev.: $32,143,837
Assets: $132,983,245
Liabilities: $119,102,517
Net Worth: $13,880,728
Earnings: $157,122
Emp.: 739
Fiscal Year-end: 06/30/23
Cement Mfr
N.A.I.C.S.: 327310
Khondoker Kingshuk Hossain *(CMO)*

MEGHNA CONDENSED MILK INDUSTRIES LIMITED
Navana tower 45 gulshsn Avenue 15th floor flat No 16/A Glushan 1, Dhaka, 1212, Bangladesh
Tel.: (880) 29882515
Web Site: https://www.mgoldbd.com
Year Founded: 2001
MEGCONMILK—(DHA)
Rev.: $758,473
Assets: $4,962,186
Liabilities: $14,565,919
Net Worth: ($9,603,733)
Earnings: ($1,443,276)
Fiscal Year-end: 06/30/19
Milk & Water Production Services
N.A.I.C.S.: 112120
Mohammed Zakaria *(Vice Chm)*

MEGHNA LIFE INSURANCE CO. LTD.
11/B & 11/D Toyenbee Circular Road Motijheel Commercial Area, Dhaka, 1000, Bangladesh
Tel.: (880) 223385393
Web Site:
 https://www.meghnalife.com
Year Founded: 1996
MEGHNALIFE—(CHT)
Rev.: $259,440
Assets: $5,547,035
Liabilities: $1,637,118
Net Worth: $3,909,917
Earnings: ($78,739)
Emp.: 1,313
Fiscal Year-end: 12/31/22
Insurance Services
N.A.I.C.S.: 524298
Hasina Nizam *(Vice Chm)*

MEGHNA PETROLEUM LIMITED
58-59 Agrabad C/A, Chittagong, 4100, Bangladesh
Tel.: (880) 31711897
Web Site: https://mpl.gov.bd
Year Founded: 1977

Meghna Petroleum Limited—(Continued)
MPETROLEUM—(CHT)
Rev.: $29,422,750
Assets: $993,460,535
Liabilities: $793,078,988
Net Worth: $200,381,547
Earnings: $41,396,196
Emp.: 373
Fiscal Year-end: 06/30/23
Petroleum Products Marketing Services
N.A.I.C.S.: 424720
Kazi Manowar Dilder *(Deputy Gen Mgr-A&F)*

MEGLIOQUESTO S.P.A.
Via Restelli 3/1, 20124, Milan, Italy
Tel.: (39) 0291430999 IT
Web Site:
https://www.meglioquesto.it
Year Founded: 2017
MQSPA—(EUR)
Management Consulting Services
N.A.I.C.S.: 541613
Jamie Torrents *(Chm)*

MEGLON INFRA-REAL (INDIA) LIMITED
W4/ 510 Usmansahebpet Stone House pet, Nellore, 524002, Andhra Pradesh, India
Tel.: (91) 2222631099
Web Site:
http://www.meglonindia.com
Year Founded: 1987
511367—(BOM)
Assets: $248,468
Liabilities: $9,330
Net Worth: $239,138
Earnings: ($1,024)
Fiscal Year-end: 03/31/20
Real Estate Development Services
N.A.I.C.S.: 531390
Inderjit K. Sharma *(Chm & Compliance Officer)*

MEGMILK SNOW BRAND CO., LTD.
5-1 Yotsuya-Honshio-cho, Shinjuku-ku, Tokyo, Japan
Tel.: (81) 332262124 JP
Web Site: https://www.meg-snow.com
Year Founded: 2009
2270—(TKS)
Rev.: $4,001,852,640
Assets: $2,850,377,420
Liabilities: $1,295,044,420
Net Worth: $1,555,333,000
Earnings: $128,432,300
Emp.: 275
Fiscal Year-end: 03/31/24
Holding Company; Dairy Products & Processed Food Production & Sales, Feedstuffs & Crop Seeds Mfr & Restaurant Operations
N.A.I.C.S.: 551112
Seiji Tobe *(Mng Exec Officer-R&D Center-Dairy Farming & Gen Mgr-R&D Center)*

Subsidiaries:
Chokuhan Haisou Co., Ltd. (1)
4F Odakyu Hatsudai Building 1-47-3, Hatsudai Shibuya- ku, Tokyo, 151-0061, Japan
Tel.: (81) 333736321
Web Site: https://www.chokuhanhaisou.com
Chilled Product Whslr
N.A.I.C.S.: 424420

Michinoku Milk Co., Ltd. (1)
60-1 Yahatamae, Shimonome Iwadeyama, Osaki, 989-6412, Miyagi Prefecture, Japan
Tel.: (81) 229722011
Web Site: https://www.michinoku-milk.com
Emp.: 124
Dairy Product Mfr & Distr

N.A.I.C.S.: 311511

Nichiraku Machinery Co., Ltd. (1)
1-2-6 Ryoke, Urawa-Ku, Saitama, 330-0072, Japan
Tel.: (81) 488836731
Web Site: https://www.nichiraku.co.jp
Emp.: 104
Food Product Machinery Mfr
N.A.I.C.S.: 333241

PT. Megmilk Snow Brand Indonesia (1)
Jl Science Boulevard Blok B1, A1 Kawasan Industri Jababeka V Jayamukti Cikarang Pusat, Bekasi, 17530, West Jawa, Indonesia
Tel.: (62) 2129574602
Web Site: https://www.megcheese.id
Cheese Mfr
N.A.I.C.S.: 311513

Snow Brand Australia Pty. Ltd. (1)
Level 10 IBM Centre 60 City Road, Southbank, 3006, VIC, Australia
Tel.: (61) 396862411
Web Site: https://www.snowbrand.com.au
Dairy Products Distr
N.A.I.C.S.: 424430

Snow Brand Hong Kong Co., Ltd. (1)
Unit C-D 7 F China Overseas Building 139 Hennessy Road, Wanchai, China (Hong Kong)
Web Site: http://www.snowbrand.com.hk
Powdered Milk Mfr
N.A.I.C.S.: 311514

Snow Brand Milk Products Co., Ltd. (1)
13 Horishio-cho, Shinjuku-ku, Tokyo, 160-8575, Japan
Tel.: (81) 332262111
Web Site: https://www.megmilk-snowbrand.co.jp
Sales Range: $1-4.9 Billion
Emp.: 2,870
Milk & Dairy Products Mfr & Distr
N.A.I.C.S.: 112120

Subsidiary (Domestic):

Snow Brand Milk Products Co., Ltd. (2)
1 1 Naebo Cho 6 Chome, Higashi Ku, Sapporo, 065 0043, Hokkaido, Japan
Tel.: (81) 117042311
Web Site: http://www.snowbrand.co.jp
Sales Range: $10-24.9 Million
Emp.: 27
Milk & Dairy Products; Agricultural, Biotech, Biochemical & Frozen Foods Mfr & Distr
N.A.I.C.S.: 311514

Snow Brand Seed Co., Ltd. (2)
13 Honshio Cho Shinjuku Ku, Tokyo, 160-8575, Japan
Tel.: (81) 332262286
Emp.: 1,500
Seeds & Feeds Distr & Mfr
N.A.I.C.S.: 111199
Yasushi Ohara *(Gen Mgr)*

Snow Brand Shoji Co., Ltd. (2)
13, Honshio-cho, Shinjuku, Tokyo, 160-003, Japan
Tel.: (81) 332262286
Web Site: http://www.snowbrand.co.jp
Sales Range: $300-349.9 Million
Emp.: 1,500
Marketing of Dairy Products & Other Food Products
N.A.I.C.S.: 311514
Hiroyuki Maruoka *(Mgr)*

Subsidiary (Non-US):

Snow Brand Siam Ltd (2)
1162 Wanit Bldg 2 Rm 1703, Bangkok, 10400, Thailand
Tel.: (66) 22545715
Web Site: http://www.snowbrand.co.th
Sales Range: $25-49.9 Million
Emp.: 33
Distribution of Dairy Products
N.A.I.C.S.: 424430

Snow Brand Trading Australia, Pty. (2)

4th Floor 50 Queen Street, Melbourne, 3000, VIC, Australia
Tel.: (61) 36141549
Distribution of Dairy Products
N.A.I.C.S.: 424430

Snow Brand Taiwan Co., Ltd. (1)
Room 1114 11th Floor International Trade Building No 333 Section 1, Keelung Road, Taipei, Taiwan
Tel.: (886) 227581011
Web Site: http://www.snowmilk.com.tw
Powdered Milk Mfr & Distr
N.A.I.C.S.: 311514

Yatsugatake Milk Co., Ltd. (1)
172 Chino, Chino, 391-8588, Nagano Prefecture, Japan
Tel.: (81) 266725600
Web Site: http://www.yatsugatakemilk.co.jp
Dairy Product Mfr & Distr
N.A.I.C.S.: 311511

MEGRISOFT LIMITED
SCO 80 Sector 47-D, Chandigarh, 160 047, India
Tel.: (91) 1722631550
Web Site: https://www.megrisoft.com
Year Founded: 1999
539012—(BOM)
Rev.: $331,954
Assets: $2,794,838
Liabilities: $51,242
Net Worth: $2,743,595
Earnings: $61,289
Emp.: 7
Fiscal Year-end: 03/31/21
Information Technology Services
N.A.I.C.S.: 541512
Rajnesh Sharma *(CFO)*

Subsidiaries:
MegriSoft Limited - Syracuse Branch (1)
4700 Onondaga Blvd, Syracuse, NY 13219
Tel.: (315) 703-9025
Software Development Services
N.A.I.C.S.: 513210

MEGROUP LTD.
50 Raffles Place 32-01 Singapore Land Tower, Singapore, 048623, Singapore
Tel.: (65) 390765361 SG
Web Site: https://www.me-grp.com
Year Founded: 2018
SJY—(SES)
Rev.: $97,067,072
Assets: $39,596,494
Liabilities: $28,363,157
Net Worth: $11,233,337
Earnings: $1,904,477
Fiscal Year-end: 03/31/24
Automotive Parts Mfr & Distr
N.A.I.C.S.: 336390
Abdul Razak Montel *(Head-Sls & Mfg)*

MEGUMAGOLD CORP.
Suite 1890 1075 West Georgia Street, Vancouver, V6E 3C9, BC, Canada
Tel.: (604) 687-2038 BC
Web Site: https://megumagold.com
Year Founded: 1989
NSAUF—(OTCEM)
Assets: $715,839
Liabilities: $1,272,063
Net Worth: ($556,224)
Earnings: ($1,505,696)
Fiscal Year-end: 03/31/24
Mineral Exploration Services
N.A.I.C.S.: 213114
Fred Antonio C. Tejada *(CEO)*

MEGUREIT ISRAEL LTD.
Migdal Sasson Hogi 10th floor Abba Hillel Silver 12, Ramat Gan, 5250606, Israel
Tel.: (972) 35007577 IL

Web Site: https://www.megureit.co.il
MGRT—(TAE)
Rev.: $15,896,118
Assets: $1,168,984,648
Liabilities: $748,740,146
Net Worth: $420,244,502
Earnings: $14,212,736
Fiscal Year-end: 12/31/23
Lessors of Other Real Estate Property
N.A.I.C.S.: 531190

MEHADRIN LTD.
Mivne Center, Be'erot Yitzhak, 6090500, Israel
Tel.: (972) 39371301
Web Site: https://www.mehadrin.co.il
Year Founded: 1951
MEDN—(TAE)
Rev.: $313,127,499
Assets: $364,128,189
Liabilities: $203,086,887
Net Worth: $161,041,302
Earnings: ($42,684,901)
Emp.: 380
Fiscal Year-end: 12/31/23
Fresh Fruit & Vegetable Merchant Wholesalers
N.A.I.C.S.: 424480

MEHAI TECHNOLOGY LIMITED
B-40 Sudarshanpura Industrial Area, Jaipur, 302 006, Rajasthan, India
Tel.: (91) 412212101
Web Site:
https://www.mehaitech.co.in
Year Founded: 2013
540730—(BOM)
Rev.: $1,065,967
Assets: $2,108,591
Liabilities: $494,503
Net Worth: $1,614,088
Earnings: $61,663
Emp.: 10
Fiscal Year-end: 03/31/23
Electric Equipment Mfr & Distr
N.A.I.C.S.: 335131
Sudhir Ostwal *(Chm & Mng Dir)*

MEHANIZACIJA CACAK A.D.
Brace Stanica 45, Cacak, Serbia
Tel.: (381) 32 376 227
Year Founded: 2003
Sales Range: Less than $1 Million
Emp.: 6
Building Construction Services
N.A.I.C.S.: 236220

MEHILAINEN OY
Pohjoinen Hesperiankatu 17 C, Helsinki, 00260, Finland
Tel.: (358) 010 414 0200
Web Site: http://www.mehilainen.fi
Health Care Service Provider
N.A.I.C.S.: 622110
Janne-Olli Jarvenpaa *(CEO)*

Subsidiaries:
Qvalitas Arstikeskus AS (1)
Parnu mnt 102c, 11312, Tallinn, Estonia
Tel.: (372) 6051500
Web Site: http://www.qvalitas.ee
Occupational Health Care Services
N.A.I.C.S.: 621999
Tonu Velt *(CEO)*

MEHOW INNOVATIVE LTD.
No 3 6th Baolong Road, Longgang, Shenzhen, 518116, China
Tel.: (86) 75583051518
Web Site: https://www.mehow.com
Year Founded: 2010
301363—(CHIN)
Rev.: $188,392,492
Assets: $496,235,238
Liabilities: $48,025,718

Net Worth: $448,209,520
Earnings: $44,126,845
Fiscal Year-end: 12/31/23
Medical Device Mfr & Distr
N.A.I.C.S.: 339112
Xiaochuan Xiong *(Chm)*

Subsidiaries:

MeHow Innovative (Huizhou) Ltd. (1)
No 318 3rd Longshan Road, West Subdistrict Dayawan, Huizhou, 516085, China
Tel.: (86) 7525533366
Medical Device Mfr
N.A.I.C.S.: 339112

Mehow Medical (M) Sdn. Bhd. (1)
No 1056 Jalan Perindustrian Bukit Minyak 8 Kawasan Perindustrian, Bukit Minyak, Malaysia
Tel.: (60) 45079116
Medical Device Equipment Mfr
N.A.I.C.S.: 339113

MEHR DASTGIR TEXTILE MILLS LIMITED
Mehr Dastgir Shaheed Yunus Dastgir Road, Multan, Pakistan
Tel.: (92) 4512092
Textile Mill Operator
N.A.I.C.S.: 314999

MEHR GOSTAR TAMIN DAROO
2th Floor Block 5 22th Avenue Mirzaye Shirazi Street, Motahhari Street, Tehran, Iran
Tel.: (98) 21 88912582
Web Site: http://www.mgtd.co
DTIP1—(THE)
Sales Range: Less than $1 Million
Personal Care & Cosmetic Product Mfr
N.A.I.C.S.: 325620
Ali Babaie *(Founder & CEO)*

MEHRABAD INDUSTRIAL CO.
No 314 Karimkhan Zand Avenue Valiasr Avenue, Tehran, 15938, Iran
Tel.: (98) 21 66692155
Web Site: http://www.mehrabad-co.net
Year Founded: 1959
Electric Equipment Mfr
N.A.I.C.S.: 335139
Ali Moslehi *(Mng Dir)*

MEHRAN SUGAR MILLS LIMITED
14th Floor Dolmen City Executive Tower, Marine Drive Block 4 Clifton, Karachi, 75600, Pakistan
Tel.: (92) 2135297814
Web Site: https://www.mehransugar.com
Year Founded: 1965
MRNS—(PSX)
Rev.: $45,559,410
Assets: $23,756,363
Liabilities: $9,801,419
Net Worth: $13,954,944
Earnings: $5,190,873
Emp.: 278
Fiscal Year-end: 09/30/23
Cane Sugar & Food Products Mfr
N.A.I.C.S.: 311314
Ahmed Ebrahim Hasham *(Mng Dir)*

Subsidiaries:

MFP Solar Sdn Bhd (1)
A-12-01 Level 12 Block A PJ8 No 23 Jalan Barat Seksyen 8, 46050, Petaling Jaya, Selangor, Malaysia
Tel.: (60) 379608818
Renewable Energy Services
N.A.I.C.S.: 221114

Mehran Sugar Mills Limited - Tando Allahyar Mill (1)
Deh Daro Sutha Tando Adam Road, Tando Allahyar, Sindh, Pakistan
Tel.: (92) 222414501
Sugar Products Mfr
N.A.I.C.S.: 311314

Stenta Films (Malaysia) Sendirian Berhad (1)
Lot No 10 Jalan P/10 Kawasan Perusahaan Seksyen 10, 43650, Bandar Baru Bangi, Selangor, Malaysia
Tel.: (60) 389243388
Web Site: https://www.stentafilms.com.my
Packaging Material Mfr & Distr
N.A.I.C.S.: 326112

MEHRCAM PARS COMPANY
Km 11 of Karaj Special Road, PO Box 174 13885, 1388836361, Tehran, 1388836361, Iran
Tel.: (98) 2144905176
Web Site: https://www.mehrcampars.com
Year Founded: 1990
MHKM1—(THE)
Sales Range: Less than $1 Million
Decorative Parts Mfr
N.A.I.C.S.: 332323

MEHTA HOUSING FINANCE LIMITED
Ground Floor Law Garden Apartment Scheme I, Opp Law Garden Ellisbridge, Ahmedabad, 380006, India
Tel.: (91) 7926565566
Web Site: http://www.mehtahousing.com
511740—(BOM)
Assets: $633,003
Liabilities: $19,671
Net Worth: $613,333
Earnings: ($23,549)
Emp.: 1
Fiscal Year-end: 03/31/23
Financial Investment Services
N.A.I.C.S.: 523999
Chirag D. Mehta *(Mng Dir & CFO)*

MEHTA INTEGRATED FINANCE LIMITED
03 Law Garden Appt Scheme-1 Opp Law Garden Ellisbridge, Ahmedabad, 380006, India
Tel.: (91) 7926565566
Web Site: https://mehtaintegratedfinance.com
Year Founded: 1985
511377—(BOM)
Rev.: $117,031
Assets: $1,969,064
Liabilities: $232,074
Net Worth: $1,736,990
Earnings: $65,024
Emp.: 5
Fiscal Year-end: 03/31/23
Financial Management Services
N.A.I.C.S.: 523999
Darshan V. Mehta *(Mng Dir)*

MEHTA SECURITIES LIMITED
Ground Floor Law Garden Appartment Scheme-1 Opp Law Garden, Ellisbridge, Ahmedabad, 380006, India
Tel.: (91) 7926565566
Web Site: https://www.mehtasecurities.com
511738—(BOM)
Rev.: $84,685
Assets: $1,757,465
Liabilities: $959,540
Net Worth: $797,924
Earnings: ($19,956)
Emp.: 5
Fiscal Year-end: 03/31/21
Financial Services
N.A.I.C.S.: 523999
Bhavna D. Mehta *(Mng Dir)*

MEI AH ENTERTAINMENT GROUP LIMITED
Mei Ah Centre 28 Chun Choi Street Tseung Kwan O Industrial Estate, Kowloon, China (Hong Kong)
Tel.: (852) 2 751 3388   BM
Web Site: http://www.meiah.com
Year Founded: 1984
0391—(HKG)
Rev.: $10,088,558
Assets: $97,663,140
Liabilities: $50,085,256
Net Worth: $47,577,884
Earnings: ($5,073,170)
Emp.: 93
Fiscal Year-end: 03/31/22
Television Broadcasting Services
N.A.I.C.S.: 516120
Kuo Hsing Li *(Founder & Chm)*

Subsidiaries:

Mei Ah (HK) Company Limited (1)
Metro Centre, Kowloon, China (Hong Kong)
Tel.: (852) 27542855
Electronic Equipment Distr
N.A.I.C.S.: 423690

Mei Ah Cineplex (1)
14/F China View Tower 1 No 2 Jia East Gongti Road, Chaoyang District, Beijing, China
Tel.: (86) 1085871866
Film Distribution Services
N.A.I.C.S.: 512120

Mei Ah Entertainment Development Inc. (1)
5/F No 293 Sec 2 Ti Ding Blvd, Neihu District, Taipei, Taiwan
Tel.: (886) 287519958
Web Site: http://www.meiah.com
Film Distribution Services
N.A.I.C.S.: 512120
Youning Lee *(Dir-Film)*

MEIBAN GROUP LTD.
Meiban Industrial Building 11 Ubi Road 1, Singapore, 408723, Singapore
Tel.: (65) 68919900
Web Site: http://www.meiban.com
Year Founded: 1987
Sales Range: $250-299.9 Million
Plastic Injection Molding Machine Mfr
N.A.I.C.S.: 333248
George Tiong Yong Goh *(Founder & CEO)*

Subsidiaries:

Meiban International Pte. Ltd. (1)
11 Ubi Road 1 Meiban Industrial Building, Singapore, 408723, Singapore
Tel.: (65) 68919921
Injection Molded Plastic Products Mfr
N.A.I.C.S.: 326121

Meiban Investment Pte Ltd (1)
Meiban Industrial Building 1 11 Ubi Road, Singapore, 408723, Singapore
Tel.: (65) 68919868
Web Site: http://www.meiban.com
Emp.: 300
Investment Management Service
N.A.I.C.S.: 523999
George Goh *(Chm)*

Meiban Technologies (Malaysia) Sdn. Bhd. (1)
No 20 Jalan Istimewa 7, Taman Perindustrian Cemerlang, 81800, Ulu Tiram, Johor, Malaysia
Tel.: (60) 78636111
Injection Molded Plastic Products Mfr
N.A.I.C.S.: 326121

Meiban Technologies (Zhongshan) Co., Ltd. (1)
Inside of Yixian Industrial Zone, Zhongshan, 528436, Guangdong, China
Tel.: (86) 76088296111
Injection Molded Plastic Products Mfr
N.A.I.C.S.: 326121

Meiban Technology Pte Ltd (1)
Meiban Industrial Building 1 11 Ubi Road, Singapore, 408723, Singapore
Tel.: (65) 68919868
Web Site: http://www.meiban.com
Sales Range: $125-149.9 Million
Emp.: 400
Injection Molded Plastic Products Mfr
N.A.I.C.S.: 326121

MEIDENSHA CORPORATION
ThinkPark Tower 2-1-1 Osaki, Shinagawa-ku, Tokyo, 141-6029, Japan
Tel.: (81) 364208400   JP
Web Site: https://www.meidensha.co.jp
Year Founded: 1897
6508—(TKS)
Rev.: $1,902,886,800
Assets: $2,212,942,070
Liabilities: $1,357,026,390
Net Worth: $855,915,680
Earnings: $74,065,050
Emp.: 22
Fiscal Year-end: 03/31/24
Electronic Equipment & Devices, Web-Based Live Video & Voice Communication System & Network Components Mfr; Engineering Services
N.A.I.C.S.: 333310
Yuji Hamasaki *(Chm)*

Subsidiaries:

Anotsugiken Co., Ltd. (1)
2630-1 Ano Ano-cho, Tsu, 514-2302, Mie, Japan
Tel.: (81) 592671588
Pharmaceutical Preparation Mfr & Distr
N.A.I.C.S.: 325412

HOKUTO DENKO CORPORATION (1)
4-22-13 Himonya, Meguro-ku, Tokyo, 152-0003, Japan
Tel.: (81) 337163235
Web Site: https://www.meidensha.com
Emp.: 93
Electrochemical Mfr & Distr
N.A.I.C.S.: 335999
Takashi Kodama *(Pres)*

Plant (Domestic):

HOKUTO DENKO CORPORATION - Atsugi Factory (2)
3028 Kamiechi, Uenohara, Atsugi, 243-0801, Kanagawa, Japan
Tel.: (81) 46 285 1014
Web Site: http://www.hokuto-denko.co.jp
Emp.: 100
Electrochemical Mfr
N.A.I.C.S.: 335999

Kofu Meidensha Electric Mfg Co., Ltd. (1)
825 Nakadate, Chuo, Yamanashi, 409-3894, Japan
Tel.: (81) 552747054
Electric Power Generation
N.A.I.C.S.: 221118
Keiji Kataoka *(Pres)*

M Winds Co., Ltd. (1)
2-1-1 Osaki ThinkPark Tower, Shinagawa-ku, Tokyo, 141-6029, Japan
Tel.: (81) 364208507
Wind Farm Services
N.A.I.C.S.: 221115

MEIDEN HANGZHOU DRIVE SYSTEMS CO., LTD. (1)
No 168 Hongxing Road, Xiaoshan Economic Technological Development Zone Qiaonan District, Hangzhou, 311231, Zhejiang, China
Tel.: (86) 57183696808
Web Site: http://www.meidensha.co.jp
Industrial Motor Mfr & Distr
N.A.I.C.S.: 335312

MEIDEN INDIA PVT. LTD. (1)
1st floor Tower C building No-10 DLF phase-2 Sector-24, Gurgaon, 122002, Haryana, India
Tel.: (91) 1244388916

MEIDENSHA CORPORATION

Meidensha Corporation—(Continued)
Web Site: https://www.meidensha.com
Electric Equipment Mfr
N.A.I.C.S.: 335999

MEIDEN KOREA CO., LTD. (1)
Room 1404 Dongwha Building 71
Yeouinararu-ro, Yeongdeungpo-gu, Seoul,
07327, Korea (South)
Tel.: (82) 27360231
Web Site: http://www.meidensha.com
Industrial Machinery Mfr & Distr
N.A.I.C.S.: 333248

MEIDEN SHANGHAI CO., LTD. (1)
Room 1806 Plaza 336 No 336 Xizang Road
Middle, Huangpu-District, Shanghai,
200001, China
Tel.: (86) 21 63860358
Electronic Components Distr
N.A.I.C.S.: 423610

MSA Co., Ltd. (1)
515 Kaminakamizo Higashimaka-aza, Shizuoka, 410-0058, Japan
Tel.: (81) 559294300
Surgical & Medical Instrument Mfr
N.A.I.C.S.: 339112

Meiden America Switchgear, Inc. (1)
2200 N Old Laurens Rd, Gray Court, SC 29645
Tel.: (864) 601-9090
Web Site: https://www.meidensha.com
Machinery & Equipment Whslr
N.A.I.C.S.: 423830
Minoru Kaneda (Pres)

Meiden America, Inc. (1)
15800 Centennial Dr, Northville, MI 48168
Tel.: (734) 656-1400
Web Site: http://www.meidenamerica.com
Sales Range: $25-49.9 Million
Emp.: 28
Engineeering Services
N.A.I.C.S.: 541330
Kirk Goodell (Sr Exec VP)

Meiden Aqua Business Company (1)
7th Floor Shiba / Taga Building 5-9-10
Shiba, Minato-ku, Tokyo, 108-0014, Japan
Tel.: (81) 364557414
Water Purification Services
N.A.I.C.S.: 221310

Meiden Asia Pte. Ltd. (1)
5 Jalan Pesawat, Singapore, 619363, Singapore
Tel.: (65) 62688222
Management Consulting Services
N.A.I.C.S.: 541618

Meiden Asia Pte. Ltd. (1)
Dubai Airport Free Zone DAFZA 6WA-606,
PO Box 54919, Dubai, United Arab Emirates
Tel.: (971) 42146692
Machinery & Equipment Whslr
N.A.I.C.S.: 423830

Meiden Ceramics Corporation (1)
146-4 Azaimaonawa Sawada, Numazu,
410-0052, Shizuoka, Japan
Tel.: (81) 55 929 4990
Web Site: http://www.m-cera.com
Ceramic Products Mfr & Distr
N.A.I.C.S.: 327120
Ken Iida (Mgr-Services)

Meiden Chemical Co., Ltd. (1)
515 Kaminakamizo Higashimaka-aza, Numazu, 410-0865, Shizuoka, Japan
Tel.: (81) 559230238
Web Site: http://www.chemical.meiden.co.jp
Measuring Displaying & Controlling Industrial Process Variables & Instruments & Related Products Mfr
N.A.I.C.S.: 334513
Tadashi Honna (Pres)

Meiden Engineering Corporation (1)
3-7-9 Osaki, Shinagawa-ku, Tokyo, 141-8607, Japan
Tel.: (81) 334907644
Web Site: http://www.meidensha.com
Machinery Equipment Mfr & Whslr
N.A.I.C.S.: 333248
Katsumi Kurihara (Pres)

Meiden Europe GmbH (1)
Carl-von-Linde-Str 38, 85716, Unterschleissheim, Germany
Tel.: (49) 89124148370
Web Site: https://www.meidensha.com
Electrical Equipment Whslr
N.A.I.C.S.: 423610

Meiden Facility Service Corporation (1)
2-8-1 Osaki, Shinagawa-ku, Tokyo, 141-0032, Japan
Tel.: (81) 364207940
Facility Services
N.A.I.C.S.: 561210

Meiden Foundry Industrial Co., Ltd. (1)
4 Nyogetsu Heisaka-cho, Nishio-shi, 444-0305, Nagoya, Japan
Tel.: (81) 563596181
Engineeering Services
N.A.I.C.S.: 541330

Meiden Kankyo Service Co., Ltd. (1)
Osaki Dekkan 2-2-15, Osaki Shinagawa-ku, 141-0032, Tokyo, Japan
Tel.: (81) 334900630
Sales Range: $300-349.9 Million
Emp.: 560
Commercial Air Rail & Water Transportation Equipment Rental & Leasing
N.A.I.C.S.: 532411
Tetsuo Kasuda (Pres)

Meiden Kiden Kogyo Co., Ltd. (1)
127 Nishishinmachi, Oota-shi, Ota, 373-0847, Gunma, Japan
Tel.: (81) 276206371
Web Site: https://www.meidensha.co.jp
Emp.: 111
Automotive Mechanical & Electrical Repair & Maintenance
N.A.I.C.S.: 811114

Meiden Kohsan Co., Ltd. (1)
5-5-5 Osaki, Shinagawa-ku, Tokyo, 141-8616, Japan
Tel.: (81) 334903737
Web Site: http://www.meidenkohsan.co.jp
Sales Range: $50-74.9 Million
Emp.: 210
Insurance Services
N.A.I.C.S.: 524298

Meiden Malaysia Sdn. Bhd. (1)
Unit A-12A-1 Level 12A Menara UOA Bangsar 5 Jalan Bangsar Utama 1, 59000, Kuala Lumpur, Malaysia
Tel.: (60) 322878188
Web Site: https://www.meidensha.com
Sales Range: $25-49.9 Million
Emp.: 30
Switchgear Apparatus Distr
N.A.I.C.S.: 423610
Masafumi Minami (Mng Dir)

Meiden Mediafront Corporation (1)
Maruki Building 13-7, Nishigotanda 1-Chome, 141-0031, Tokyo, Japan
Tel.: (81) 334904767
Web Site: http://www.meidensha.co.jp
Commercial Printing
N.A.I.C.S.: 323111

Meiden Metal Engineering Sdn. Bhd. (1)
Lot 6 Peringkat 3 Kawasan Perindustrian, 78000, Alor Gajah, Melaka, Malaysia
Tel.: (60) 65568790
Web Site: https://www.meidensha.com
Generator Transformer Mfr
N.A.I.C.S.: 335311

Meiden Pacific (China) Ltd. (1)
Unit 01-02A 16/F Tower 1 Ever Gain Plaza 88 Container Port Road, Kwai Chung, N.T, China (Hong Kong)
Tel.: (852) 25032468
Web Site: http://www.meidensha.com.cn
Sales Range: $25-49.9 Million
Emp.: 15
Engineeering Services
N.A.I.C.S.: 541330

Meiden Plant Engineering & Construction Co Ltd. (1)
Meiko Bldg 5-5, Oskai 5-chome Shinagawa-ku, 141-8616, Tokyo, Japan
Tel.: (81) 364207497

Sales Range: $25-49.9 Million
Emp.: 90
Management Consulting Services
N.A.I.C.S.: 541618

Meiden Plant Systems Corporation (1)
4F Gotanda NT Building 1-18-9 Nishi Gotanda, Shinagawa-Ku, Tokyo, 141-0031, Japan
Tel.: (81) 354876426
Web Site: https://www.meidensha.co.jp
Emp.: 202
Power Plant Construction Engineering Services
N.A.I.C.S.: 237130

Meiden Sheet Metal Products Corporation (1)
515 Kaminakamizo Higashimaka-aza, 410-0865, Numazu, Shizuoka, Japan
Tel.: (81) 559295541
Web Site: http://www.meidensha.co.jp
Metalworking Machines Mfr
N.A.I.C.S.: 333519
Shigeru Nakayama (Gen Mgr)

Meiden Shoji Co., Ltd. (1)
2-8-1 Osaki, Shinagawa-ku, Tokyo, 141-8565, Japan
Tel.: (81) 363846600
Web Site: https://www.meidensha.co.jp
Emp.: 80
Machinery Equipment Mfr & Whslr
N.A.I.C.S.: 333248

Meiden Singapore Pte Ltd. (1)
5 7 Jln Pesawat, Jurong Industrial Est, Singapore, 619363, Singapore
Tel.: (65) 62688222
Web Site: https://www.meidensha.co.jp
Sales Range: $25-49.9 Million
Emp.: 100
Engineeering Services
N.A.I.C.S.: 541330
Ko Yamamoto (Mng Dir)

Meiden Software Corporation (1)
515 Kaminakamizo Higashi-Makado, Numazu-shi, 410-8588, Shizuoka, Japan
Tel.: (81) 559234966
Web Site: http://www.meidensoftware.co.jp
Sales Range: $25-49.9 Million
Emp.: 200
Custom Computer Programming Services
N.A.I.C.S.: 541511

Meiden Syscon Co., Ltd. (1)
726-1 Osuwa, Numazu-shi, 410-0873, Shizuoka, Japan
Tel.: (81) 559244630
Web Site: http://www.meidensha.co.jp
Switchgear & Switchboard Apparatus Mfr
N.A.I.C.S.: 335313

Meiden System Engineering Co., Ltd. (1)
Meiko Buolding 5-5, Oskai 5-chome Shinagawa-ku, 141-8616, Tokyo, Japan
Tel.: (81) 354876500
Web Site: http://www.meidensha.co.jp
Engineeering Services
N.A.I.C.S.: 541330

Meiden System Manufacturing Corporation (1)
515 Kaminakamizo Higashinmonmon, Numazu, 410-0865, Shizuoka, Japan
Tel.: (81) 559294970
Web Site: https://www.meidensha.co.jp
Emp.: 267
Software Development Services
N.A.I.C.S.: 541511

Meiden System Solutions Corporation (1)
515 Kaminakamizo Higashimonmon, Numazu, 410-8588, Shizuoka, Japan
Tel.: (81) 559234966
Web Site: https://www.meidensha.co.jp
Emp.: 371
Software Development Services
N.A.I.C.S.: 541511

Meiden System Technology Co., Ltd. (1)
515 Kaminakamizo Higashimakado-aza, Numazu, 410-0865, Shizuoka, Japan
Tel.: (81) 55 923 1321
Electronic Components Mfr

N.A.I.C.S.: 334419

Meiden Techno System Co., Ltd. (1)
515 Kaminakamizo Higashinmanmon, Meidensha Numazu Office South Office Building, Numazu, 410-8588, Shizuoka, Japan
Tel.: (81) 559213272
Web Site: https://www.meidensha.co.jp
Emp.: 109
Maintenance Work Services
N.A.I.C.S.: 561790

Meiden Universal Service Ltd. (1)
127 Nishishinmachi, Ota, 373-0847, Gunma, Japan
Tel.: (81) 276327310
Web Site: https://www.meidensha.co.jp
Emp.: 59
Maintenance Work Services
N.A.I.C.S.: 561790

Meiden Zhengzhou Electric Co., Ltd. (1)
No 87 Hehuan Street, Zhengzhou Hi-Tech Industries Development Zone, Zhengzhou, 450001, Henan, China
Tel.: (86) 37156971963
Current-Carrying Wiring Device Mfr
N.A.I.C.S.: 335931

Meidensha (Shanghai) Corporate Management Co., Ltd. (1)
17A Global Harbor Office Tower B No 1188 Kai Xuan North Road, Putuo District, Shanghai, 200063, China
Tel.: (86) 2153062200
Management Consulting Services
N.A.I.C.S.: 541618

Meidensha Shoji Co., Ltd. (1)
ThinkPark Tower 29F 2-1-1, Osaki, Shinagawa-ku, Tokyo, 141-6029, Japan
Tel.: (81) 363846600
Web Site: http://www.meidensha.co.jp
Electrical Contractor
N.A.I.C.S.: 238210

PT Meiden Engineering Indonesia (1)
20th Floor Summitmas I Jl Jend Sudirman Kav 61-62, Jakarta, 12190, Indonesia
Tel.: (62) 215200612
Web Site: https://www.meidensha.com
Sales Range: $25-49.9 Million
Emp.: 30
Engineeering Services
N.A.I.C.S.: 541330
Yuji Ueda (Mng Dir)

Prime Meiden Limited (1)
1A Building No -10 Tower C, DLF Cyber City Phase 2, Gurgaon, 122 010, India
Tel.: (91) 1244549830
Web Site: http://www.primemeiden.com
Generator Transformer Mfr
N.A.I.C.S.: 335311
Hirdesh Kulshrestha (Co-CEO)

Shanghai Meiden Semiconductor Co Ltd. (1)
53-1A No 311 Fu Te Nan Lu, 200137, Shanghai, China
Tel.: (86) 2150483681
Engineeering Services
N.A.I.C.S.: 541330

Shanghai Meidensha Changcheng Switchgear Co. Ltd. (1)
No 885 Xingrong Rd, Industrial Zone Jiading, Shanghai, 201807, China
Tel.: (86) 2169169911
Cubicle-type Gas Mfr
N.A.I.C.S.: 333132

THAI MEIDENSHA CO., LTD. (1)
15th Floor Rasa Tower II 555 Phahol Yothin Road, Chatuchak Chatuchak, Bangkok, 10900, Thailand
Tel.: (66) 28215510
Web Site: http://www.meidensha.com
Electric Equipment Mfr
N.A.I.C.S.: 335999

Thai Meidensha Co., Ltd. (1)
0610 6th Floor Sakura Tower 339 Bogyoke Aung San Road, Kyauktada Township, Yangon, Myanmar
Tel.: (95) 9440733041
Engineeering Services
N.A.I.C.S.: 541330

Tridelta Meidensha GmbH (1)
Marie-Curie-Strasse 3, 07629, Hermsdorf, Germany
Tel.: (49) 366019328300
Web Site: https://www.tridelta-meidensha.de
Pharmaceutical Preparation Mfr & Distr
N.A.I.C.S.: 325412
Markus Jung *(Mng Dir)*

MEIDOH CO., LTD
4-5 Sangen-cho, Toyota, 471-0037, Aichi, Japan
Tel.: (81) 565310330
Web Site: https://www.meidoh.co.jp
Emp.: 100
Bolts, Nuts & Cold Forged Products Mfr
N.A.I.C.S.: 332722
Yasutaka Hasegawa *(Pres & CEO)*

Subsidiaries:

Pilgrim Screw Corporation (1)
2875 W Frye Rd, Chandler, AZ 85224
Web Site: http://www.pilgrimscrew.com
Bolt, Nut, Screw, Rivet & Washer Mfr
N.A.I.C.S.: 332722
Geoffrey Grove *(Pres & CEO)*

MEIDU ENERGY CORPORATION
4F Meidu Hengsheng Towers Metro No 70 Garden Bridge Road, Hangzhou, 310005, Zhejiang, China
Tel.: (86) 571 88301388
Web Site: http://www.chinameidu.com
Rev.: $766,780,110
Assets: $2,582,856,074
Liabilities: $1,094,843,785
Net Worth: $1,488,012,290
Earnings: ($184,707,269)
Fiscal Year-end: 12/31/18
Real Estate Development Services
N.A.I.C.S.: 531390
Zhanghua Wen *(Chm & Pres-Interim)*

MEIER CAPITAL AG
Bahnstrasse 24, 8603, Schwerzenbach, Switzerland
Tel.: (41) 44 806 49 00
Web Site: http://www.meiercapital.com
Asset Management Services
N.A.I.C.S.: 523999
Silvan G.-R. Meier *(Chm)*

Subsidiaries:

Meier Tobler Group AG (1)
Bahnstrasse 24, Nebikon, 8603, Schwerzenbach, Switzerland (72.7%)
Tel.: (41) 448064141
Web Site: https://www.meiertobler.ch
Sales Range: $450-499.9 Million
Holding Company; Climate Control Equipment Mfr & Distr.
N.A.I.C.S.: 551112
Martin Kaufmann *(CEO)*

Subsidiary (Domestic):

AxEnergy Ltd. (2)
Talstrasse 35-37, Pfaffikon, 8808, SZ, Switzerland
Tel.: (41) 55416 6670
Web Site: http://www.axenergy.com
Emp.: 120
Air Conditioning Equipment Mfr
N.A.I.C.S.: 333415
Oliver Zimmermann *(Gen Mgr)*

Condair Ltd. (2)
Talstrasse 35-37, Pfaffikon, 8808, SZ, Switzerland
Tel.: (41) 554166111
Web Site: http://www.condair.com
Sales Range: $50-74.9 Million
Emp.: 130
Air Conditioning Systems & Services
N.A.I.C.S.: 333415
Rolf Haupt *(Office Mgr)*

Subsidiary (Non-US):

Condair A/S (3)
Parallelvej 2, 8680, Ry, Denmark
Tel.: (45) 8788 2100
Web Site: http://www.mlsystem.com
Heating & Air Conditioning Equipment Mfr
N.A.I.C.S.: 333415

Condair SASU (3)
Le Parc aux Vignes 2 allee des'Arments, 77437, Marne-la-Vallee, France
Tel.: (33) 1 6095 8940
Emp.: 14
Heating & Air Conditioning Equipment Mfr
N.A.I.C.S.: 333415
Georges Simon *(Office Mgr)*

Subsidiary (Non-US):

Draabe Industrietechnik GmbH (2)
Schnackenburgallee 18, Hamburg, 22525, Germany
Tel.: (49) 4085 32770
Web Site: http://www.draabe.com
Emp.: 70
Humidifiers Mfr
N.A.I.C.S.: 333415
Tomas Kleitsch *(Gen Mgr)*

Eichler Hungaria Kft. (2)
Fehevari ut 44, 1119, Budapest, Hungary
Tel.: (36) 1 382 4580
Web Site: http://www.eichler.hu
Heating & Air Conditioning Equipment Mfr
N.A.I.C.S.: 333415

JS Humidifiers plc (2)
Artex Avenue Rustington, Littlehampton, BN16 3LN, W Sussex, United Kingdom
Tel.: (44) 1903 850200
Web Site: http://www.jshumidifiers.com
Emp.: 60
Heating & Air Conditioning Equipment Mfr
N.A.I.C.S.: 333415
Tim Scott *(Mng Dir)*

Subsidiary (US):

Nortec Humidity Inc. (2)
826 Proctor Ave, Ogdensburg, NY 13669-0698
Tel.: (315) 425-1255
Web Site: http://www.humidity.com
Sales Range: $25-49.9 Million
Emp.: 80
Air Conditioning Systems
N.A.I.C.S.: 333415
Namoi Cassidy *(Coord-Mktg)*

Subsidiary (Non-US):

Nortec Humidity Ltd. (2)
2740 Fenton Road, Ottawa, K1T 3T7, ON, Canada (100%)
Tel.: (613) 822-0335
Web Site: http://www.humidity.com
Sales Range: $25-49.9 Million
Emp.: 25
Air Conditioning Systems
N.A.I.C.S.: 333415

Walter Meier (Climate Beijing) Ltd. (2)
Beijing Opto Mechatronics Industrial Park Building 3 Section C, Tong Zhou District, Beijing, 101111, China
Tel.: (86) 10 8150 3008
Web Site: http://www.waltermeier.com
Sales Range: $25-49.9 Million
Emp.: 50
Air Conditioning Systems
N.A.I.C.S.: 333415
Kevin Chen *(Mgr-IT)*

Subsidiary (Domestic):

Walter Meier (Fertigungslosungen) AG (2)
Bahnstrasse 24, Schwerzenbach, 8603, Switzerland
Tel.: (41) 448064141
Web Site: http://www.waltermeier.com
Sales Range: $25-49.9 Million
Industrial Machining Systems Distr
N.A.I.C.S.: 423840

Subsidiary (Non-US):

Walter Meier (Klima Osterreich) GmbH (2)
Perfektastrasse 45, Vienna, 1230, Austria
Tel.: (43) 1 6033 1110
Web Site: http://www.condair.com
Emp.: 10
Heating & Air Conditioning Equipment Mfr
N.A.I.C.S.: 333415
Wolfgang Baumgartner *(Gen Mgr)*

Subsidiary (Domestic):

Walter Meier (Klima Schweiz) AG (2)
Bahnstrasse 24, 8603, Schwerzenbach, Switzerland
Tel.: (41) 18064141
Heating & Air Conditioning Equipment Distr
N.A.I.C.S.: 423730

Walter Meier (Services) AG (2)
Bahnstrasse 24, 8603, Schwerzenbach, Switzerland
Tel.: (41) 44 806 4141
Business Support Services
N.A.I.C.S.: 561499

MEIG SMART TECHNOLOGY CO., LTD.
Floor 32 Building B Shenzhen International Innovation Center, 1006 Shennan Avenue Futian District, Shenzhen, 518026, Guangdong, China
Tel.: (86) 75583218588
Web Site: https://www.meigsmart.com
Year Founded: 2007
002881—(SSE)
Rev.: $171,725,429
Assets: $149,925,178
Liabilities: $60,793,728
Net Worth: $89,131,450
Earnings: $4,204,082
Emp.: 1,000
Fiscal Year-end: 12/31/20
Electronic Parts Mfr & Distr
N.A.I.C.S.: 336320
Wang Ping *(Chm)*

MEIHAO MEDICAL GROUP CO., LTD.
197 Fuqian Street, Lucheng District, Wenzhou, Zhejiang, China
Tel.: (86) 57788298377 Ky
Web Site: https://www.meihaomedical.com
Year Founded: 2019
1947—(HKG)
Rev.: $19,520,180
Assets: $38,718,925
Liabilities: $11,485,694
Net Worth: $27,233,231
Earnings: $4,377,210
Emp.: 304
Fiscal Year-end: 12/31/22
Medical Device Mfr
N.A.I.C.S.: 339112
Xiaomin Wang *(Chm)*

MEIHO ENTERPRISE CO., LTD.
4F Meguro Yamate Place 2-10-11 Meguro, Meguro-ku, Tokyo, 1530063, Japan
Tel.: (81) 354347650
Web Site: https://www.meiho-est.com
Year Founded: 1968
8927—(TKS)
Rev.: $127,895,640
Assets: $174,806,880
Liabilities: $125,109,080
Net Worth: $49,697,800
Earnings: $8,552,500
Emp.: 154
Fiscal Year-end: 07/31/24
Real Estate Brokerage Services
N.A.I.C.S.: 531210
Yoshiaki Imoto *(Chm)*

Subsidiaries:

House Saison Enterprise Co., Ltd. (1)
2nd Floor House Saison Building 2-Sakaemachi-364, Kawaramachi Imadegawa Kudaru Kamigyo Ward, Kyoto, Japan
Tel.: (81) 752511900
Web Site: http://meiho-est.com
Real Estate Manangement Services
N.A.I.C.S.: 531210

MEIHO FACILITY WORKS LIMITED
JA Kyosai Bldg 6F 2-7-9 Hirakawa-cho, Chiyoda-ku, Tokyo, 102-0093, Japan
Tel.: (81) 352110066
Web Site: https://www.meiho.co.jp
Year Founded: 1980
1717—(TKS)
Sales Range: Less than $1 Million
Emp.: 237
Real Estate Manangement Services
N.A.I.C.S.: 531210
Takefumi Yoshikawa *(Sr Mng Dir)*

MEIHUA HOLDINGS GROUP CO., LTD.
No 66 Huaxiang Road Economic and Technical Development Area, Langfang, 065001, Hebei, China
Tel.: (86) 3162359999 CN
Web Site: https://www.meihuagrp.com
Year Founded: 2002
600873—(SHG)
Rev.: $3,922,376,253
Assets: $3,438,427,239
Liabilities: $1,540,762,110
Net Worth: $1,897,665,129
Earnings: $618,646,261
Emp.: 13,016
Fiscal Year-end: 12/31/22
Biological Fermented Products Mfr & Distr
N.A.I.C.S.: 325414
Wang Aijun *(Chm)*

Subsidiaries:

Shanxi Guangsheng Medicinal Capsule Co., Ltd (1)
No 5 Taixin East Street, Yushe County, Jinzhong, 031800, Shanxi Province, China
Tel.: (86) 354 663 7088
Web Site: https://www.gscapsule.com
Capsule Mfr
N.A.I.C.S.: 325998

MEIHUA INTERNATIONAL MEDICAL TECHNOLOGIES CO., LTD.
88 Tongda Road Touqiao Town, Guangling District, Yangzhou, 225000, China
Tel.: (86) 51487485999 Ky
Web Site: https://www.meihuamed.com
Year Founded: 2020
MHUA—(NASDAQ)
Rev.: $103,346,341
Assets: $163,577,579
Liabilities: $24,898,499
Net Worth: $138,679,080
Earnings: $6,242,969
Emp.: 626
Fiscal Year-end: 12/31/22
Holding Company
N.A.I.C.S.: 551112
Yongjun Liu *(Chm)*

MEIJI ELECTRIC INDUSTRIES CO., LTD.
2-13-8 Kamejima, Nakamura-ku, Nagoya, 453-8580, Japan
Tel.: (81) 524517661
Web Site: https://www.meijidenki.co.jp
Year Founded: 1958
3388—(TKS)
Rev.: $492,973,800

MEIJI ELECTRIC INDUSTRIES CO., LTD.

Meiji Electric Industries Co., Ltd.—(Continued)

Assets: $344,698,280
Liabilities: $126,151,850
Net Worth: $218,546,430
Earnings: $16,035,860
Emp.: 709
Fiscal Year-end: 03/31/24
Instrument Mfr
N.A.I.C.S.: 334515
Masahiro Hayashi *(Pres)*

Subsidiaries:

M.D Machinery Inc. **(1)**
2-1617 Fushiya, Nakagawa-ku, Nagoya, 454-0996, Aichi, Japan
Tel.: (81) 523556581
Electrical Component Mfr
N.A.I.C.S.: 334513

Subsidiary (Domestic):

M.D Machinery Inc. - Aichi Factory **(2)**
510 Shimaicho, Nakagawa-ku, Nagoya, 454-0974, Aichi, Japan
Tel.: (81) 524327146
Electrical Component Mfr
N.A.I.C.S.: 334513

Meiji (Thailand) Co., Ltd. **(1)**
1550 Thanapoom Tower 17th Floor New Petchburi Road, Makkasan Ratchathewi, Bangkok, 10400, Thailand
Tel.: (66) 2 652 7600
Web Site: https://meijithai.com
Industrial Machinery Distr
N.A.I.C.S.: 423830
Katsuhisa Naruse *(Mng Dir)*

Meiji Corporation **(1)**
150 Pierce Rd Ste 550, Itasca, IL 60143
Tel.: (847) 364-9333
Automation Component Distr
N.A.I.C.S.: 423830
Hiroki Sugiwaki *(Pres)*

Meiji Electric Industries (Shanghai) Co., Ltd. **(1)**
Room602 603 Hangtian South Building No 222 Caoxi Road, Xuhui District, Shanghai, 200233, China
Tel.: (86) 2134691388
Electrical Component Distr
N.A.I.C.S.: 423610

Meiji Electric Industries Co., Ltd. - Engineering Division **(1)**
Itabari48-1 Yamayashikicho, Chiryu, 472-0022, Aichi, Japan
Tel.: (81) 566828514
Electronic Components Mfr
N.A.I.C.S.: 334513

Meiji UK Ltd. **(1)**
26 Bartley Green Business Centre Kettleswood Drive Woodgate, Birmingham, B32 3DB, United Kingdom
Tel.: (44) 1214219330
Electrical Component Distr
N.A.I.C.S.: 423610
Satoru Okuyama *(Mng Dir)*

MEIJI HOLDINGS CO., LTD.

Tel.: (81) 332734001
Web Site: https://www.meiji.com
Year Founded: 2008
2269—(TKS)
Rev.: $7,307,315,340
Assets: $7,966,953,680
Liabilities: $2,759,641,950
Net Worth: $5,207,311,730
Earnings: $334,961,750
Fiscal Year-end: 03/31/24
Holding Company; Confectionery, Milk & Dairy Products & Pharmaceuticals Mfr & Distr
N.A.I.C.S.: 551112
Michiro Saza *(Sr Mng Exec Officer)*

Subsidiaries:

Chubu Meihan Co., Ltd. **(1)**
2-25 Uchikatacho, Mizuho-Ku, Nagoya, 467-0068, Aichi, Japan
Tel.: (81) 528521295
Dairy Products Mfr
N.A.I.C.S.: 311514

Joint Venture (Non-US):

Beghin-Meiji **(2)**
11 PRV de Rotterdam, 59777, Lille, Cedex, France
Tel.: (33) 388586060
Web Site: https://profeed.beghin-meiji.com
Confectionery Products; Joint Venture of Montedison S.p.A. & Meiji Seiki Kaisha, Ltd.
N.A.I.C.S.: 445292

Hokkaido Meihan Co., Ltd. **(1)**
14-2-1 Naebocho, Higashi-Ku, Sapporo, 065-0043, Hokkaido, Japan
Tel.: (81) 117421101
Web Site: http://www.meijimilk-st.jp
Dairy Products Mfr
N.A.I.C.S.: 311514

KM Biologics Co., Ltd. **(1)**
1-6-1 Okubo, Kita-ku, Kumamoto, 860-8568, Japan
Tel.: (81) 963441211
Web Site: https://www.kmbiologics.com
Emp.: 160
Biological Product Mfr
N.A.I.C.S.: 325414
Toshiaki Nagasato *(Pres)*

Kanazawa Meihan Co., Ltd. **(1)**
4-172 Horiuchi Nonoichimachi, Kanazawa, 921-8844, Ishikawa, Japan
Tel.: (81) 762487442
Dairy Products Mfr
N.A.I.C.S.: 311514

Kinki Meihan Co., Ltd. **(1)**
3-1-1 Tamagawa, Takatsuki, 569-0857, Osaka, Japan
Tel.: (81) 726780020
Dairy Products Mfr
N.A.I.C.S.: 311514

Kyushu Meinyu Hanbai Co., Ltd **(1)**
1-8-23 Higashinaka, Hakata-Ku, Fukuoka, 812-0892, Japan
Tel.: (81) 924756101
Dairy Products Mfr
N.A.I.C.S.: 311514

Medreich Limited **(1)**
Medreich House 12/8 Saraswati Ammal Street Maruthi Seva Nagar, Bengaluru, 560 033, Karnataka, India
Tel.: (91) 8040487100
Web Site: http://www.medreich.com
Pharmaceutical Product Mfr & Retailer
N.A.I.C.S.: 325412
Pankaj Garg *(Mng Dir)*

Meiji America Inc. **(1)**
PO Box 12002, York, PA 17402-0672
Tel.: (717) 848-6630
Web Site: https://meijiamerica.com
Confectionary Product Mfr & Whslr
N.A.I.C.S.: 311352

Meiji Business Support Co., Ltd. **(1)**
2-4-16 Kyobashi Meijikyobashi Bldg Nai, Chuo-ku, Tokyo, 104-0031, Japan
Tel.: (81) 332733488
Dairy Products Mfr & Distr
N.A.I.C.S.: 311514

Meiji Co., Ltd. **(1)**
2-10 Shinsuna 1-chrome, Koto-Ku, Tokyo, 136 8908, Japan
Tel.: (81) 356530300
Web Site: http://www.meiji.co.jp
Sales Range: $5-14.9 Billion
Emp.: 15,033
Mfr & Sale of Confectioneries, Milk & Dairy Products & Other Foods
N.A.I.C.S.: 311514
Kazuo Kawamura *(Pres)*

Subsidiary (Domestic):

Asahi Broiler Co., Ltd. **(2)**
5th floor Daini Yamaman Building 6-7 Koamicho Nihonbashi, Chou-Ku, Tokyo, 103-0016, Japan **(100%)**
Tel.: (81) 335273601
Emp.: 339
Livestock Services
N.A.I.C.S.: 424520
Shigeru Fujimaki *(Pres)*

Subsidiary (Non-US):

CP-Meiji Co., Ltd. **(2)**
1 CP Tower 2 30th Floor Ratchadapisek Road, Din Daeng Subdistrict Din Daeng District, Bangkok, 10400, Thailand
Tel.: (66) 26645291
Web Site: https://www.cpmeiji.com
Sales Range: $50-74.9 Million
Emp.: 200
Dairy Products, Ice Cream & Frozen Desserts Mfr
N.A.I.C.S.: 311520

Subsidiary (US):

D.F. Stauffer Biscuit Co., Inc. **(2)**
375 S Belmont St, York, PA 17403
Tel.: (717) 848-6630
Web Site: https://www.stauffers.com
Sales Range: $100-124.9 Million
Emp.: 300
Baked Goods Mfr
N.A.I.C.S.: 311340

Subsidiary (Domestic):

Donan Shokuhin Co., Ltd. **(2)**
14-32 Chiyogadaicho, Hakodate, 040-0013, Hokkaido, Japan
Tel.: (81) 138517187
Food Products Mfr
N.A.I.C.S.: 311999
Satushi Hanamura *(Mgr)*

Francais Co., Ltd. **(2)**
1-9-1 Marunouchi Tokyo Station Yaesu North Exit, Chiyoda-ku, Tokyo, 100-0005, Kanagawa, Japan
Tel.: (81) 368100221
Web Site: https://www.francais.jp
Confectionery Products Mfr & Whslr
N.A.I.C.S.: 311351

Fresh Network Systems Co. **(2)**
1-2-10 Shinsuna Meijitoyocho Bldg., Koto-Ku, Tokyo, 136-0075, Japan
Tel.: (81) 336407525
Dairy Products Mfr & Distr
N.A.I.C.S.: 311514

Subsidiary (Non-US):

Guangzhou Meiji Confectionery Co., Ltd. **(2)**
Fl 1 A 7 Bldg Beiwei Industrial One Zone, Guangzhou, China
Tel.: (86) 2082214446
Web Site: http://www.gzmeiji.com.cn
Sales Range: $25-49.9 Million
Emp.: 100
Confectionary Product Mfr
N.A.I.C.S.: 311352

Subsidiary (Domestic):

Kantou Seiraku Co., Ltd. **(2)**
426-2 Idoimachi, Maebashi, 379-2111, Gunma, Japan
Tel.: (81) 272807311
Dairy Products Mfr
N.A.I.C.S.: 311514

Subsidiary (US):

Laguna Cookie Company, Inc. **(2)**
4041 W Garry Ave, Santa Ana, CA 92704-6315
Tel.: (714) 259-1404
Baked Goods Mfr
N.A.I.C.S.: 311821

Subsidiary (Domestic):

Meiji Chewing Gum Co., Ltd. **(2)**
3-8 Asahi Nishibiwajima-cho, Kiyosu, 452-0064, Aichi, Japan
Tel.: (81) 525018291
Chewing Gum Mfr
N.A.I.C.S.: 311340
Ryuichi Sakagami *(Mng Dir)*

Subsidiary (Non-US):

Meiji Dairy Australasia Pty. Ltd **(2)**
Level 26 360 Collins Street, 360 Elizabeth St, Melbourne, 3000, VIC, Australia
Tel.: (61) 396545011
Sales Range: $25-49.9 Million
Emp.: 6
Ice Cream & Frozen Desserts Mfr

INTERNATIONAL PUBLIC

N.A.I.C.S.: 311520

Subsidiary (Domestic):

Meiji Feed Co., Ltd. **(2)**
1-2-10 Shinsuna, Koto-ku, Tokyo, 136-0075, Japan
Tel.: (81) 356531521
Emp.: 234
Animal Feed Mfr
N.A.I.C.S.: 311119
Yoshihito Hagawa *(Pres & CEO)*

Plant (Domestic):

Meiji Feed Co., Ltd. - Kakogawa Factory **(3)**
Hiraoka-Cho 192-2, Tsuchiyama, Kakogawa, 675-0104, Hyogo, Japan
Tel.: (81) 78 942 3737
Web Site: http://www.meijifeed.co.jp
Animal Feed Mfr
N.A.I.C.S.: 311119

Meiji Feed Co., Ltd. - Kashima Factory **(3)**
Oaza Higashi-Fukashiba 2-12, Kamisu, 314-0103, Ibaragi, Japan
Tel.: (81) 29 993 1511
Web Site: http://www.meijifeed.co.jp
Animal Feed Mfr
N.A.I.C.S.: 311119

Subsidiary (Domestic):

Meiji Food Materia Co., Ltd. **(2)**
2-4-16 Kyobashi, Chuo-ku, Tokyo, 104-0031, Japan
Tel.: (81) 332730360
Web Site: https://www.meijifm.co.jp
Sugar Mfr & Distr
N.A.I.C.S.: 424490

Meiji Food Material Corp. **(2)**
2-4-16 Kyobashi, Chuo-ku, Tokyo, 104-0031, Japan
Tel.: (81) 332730360
Web Site: https://www.meijifm.co.jp
Sales Range: $25-49.9 Million
Emp.: 100
Sugar & Foods Mfr
N.A.I.C.S.: 445298

Meiji Kenko Ham Co., Ltd. **(2)**
Meihi Toyo-Cho Building1-2-10, Shinsuna Koto-Ku, Tokyo, 136-0075, Japan
Tel.: (81) 356530620
Dairy Products Mfr
N.A.I.C.S.: 311514

Meiji Logitech Co., Ltd. **(2)**
6th floor Meiji Toyocho Building 1-2-10 Shinsuna, Koto-ku, Tokyo, 136-0075, Japan
Tel.: (81) 356530577
Refrigerated Transportation Services
N.A.I.C.S.: 488510

Meiji Oils & Fats Co., Ltd. **(2)**
1 1 11 Sanganda, 661 0024, Hyogo, Japan
Tel.: (81) 664280405
Sales Range: $25-49.9 Million
Emp.: 100
Dietary Fats Mfr
N.A.I.C.S.: 311225

Meiji Rice Delica Corporation **(2)**
2-28-1 Hiroshigashi, Sayama, 350-1320, Japan
Tel.: (81) 4 2954 8758
Web Site: http://www.meiji-rice.com
Sales Range: $100-124.9 Million
Emp.: 348
Processed Rice Mfr & Distr
N.A.I.C.S.: 311212

Subsidiary (Non-US):

Meiji Seika (Singapore) Pte. Ltd. **(2)**
36 Quality Road, Jurong Town, Singapore, 618806, Singapore
Tel.: (65) 62652411
Web Site: http://www.meiji.com.sg
Sales Range: $25-49.9 Million
Emp.: 150
Confections Mfr
N.A.I.C.S.: 311352

Meiji Seika Food Industry (Shanghai) Co., Ltd. **(2)**
No 1111 Xinfei Road Dongbu New Area Songjiang Industrial Zone, Shanghai,

AND PRIVATE COMPANIES

201611, China
Tel.: (86) 2167601212
Food Products Mfr
N.A.I.C.S.: 311999

Subsidiary (Domestic):

Meiji Shokuhin Kaisha, Ltd. (2)
Nagano 1544 Koshigoe, Ueda, 386-0403, Japan
Tel.: (81) 268 42 3151
Web Site: http://www.fd-meiji.co.jp
Sales Range: $25-49.9 Million
Emp.: 95
Convenience Foods Mfr
N.A.I.C.S.: 311999
Yoshihilo Kamo (Pres)

Meiji Techno-Service Inc. (2)
6-57-20 Kameido Kameidohigashiguchiekimae Bldg 7f, Koto-Ku, Tokyo, 136-0071, Japan
Tel.: (81) 356283900
Dairy Products Mfr & Distr
N.A.I.C.S.: 311514

Nihon Kanzume, Co., Ltd. (2)
9-1 Nishi 9 Jo Memurocho, Kasai, Hokkaido, 082-0039, Japan
Tel.: (81) 155627845
Health Care Products Mfr
N.A.I.C.S.: 325412

Nitto Co., Ltd. (2)
1-21-1 Nishishinjuku, Shinjuku-ku, Tokyo, 160-0023, Japan
Tel.: (81) 353396471
Web Site: http://www.aanitto.co.jp
Emp.: 80
Television Commercials Production Services
N.A.I.C.S.: 512110
Michihiko Shigenobu (Pres)

Okayamaken Shokuhin Co., Ltd. (2)
156 Eshi, Kasaoka, 714-0091, Okayama, Japan
Tel.: (81) 865 62 2124
Web Site: http://www.okashoku.co.jp
Convenience Foods Mfr
N.A.I.C.S.: 311999

Okinawa Meiji Milk Products Co., Ltd. (2)
1-65-1 Makiminato, Urasoe, 901-2502, Okinawa, Japan
Tel.: (81) 988775274
Emp.: 144
Dairy Products Mfr
N.A.I.C.S.: 311514

Shikoku Meiji Co., Ltd. (2)
3-5-11 Nakasuga, Matsuyama, 791-8078, Ehime, Japan
Tel.: (81) 899511126
Confectionery Mfr
N.A.I.C.S.: 311351

Shikoku Meiji Dairies Corporation (2)
1328-1 Saitakami Sita-cho, Mitoyo, 769-0401, Kagawa, Japan
Tel.: (81) 875 56 8800
Web Site: http://www.shikoku-meiji-dairy.co.jp
Sales Range: $25-49.9 Million
Emp.: 176
Milk, Dairy Products, Ice Cream & Other Foods Mfr
N.A.I.C.S.: 112120
Izumiya Shigeru (Pres & Dir)

Subsidiary (Non-US):

Thai Meiji Food Co., Ltd. (2)
252/95 Muang Thai-Phatra Complex Building Building 2 18th Floor, Units A and B Ratchadaphisek Road Huai Khwang, Bangkok, 10310, Thailand
Tel.: (66) 26943311
Convenience Foods Mfr
N.A.I.C.S.: 311999
Toshiyuki Aoyama (CEO)

Subsidiary (Domestic):

Tokai Meiji Co., Ltd. (2)
3001-1 Kuno, Fukuroi, 437-0061, Shizuoka, Japan
Tel.: (81) 538452727
Dairy Products Mfr
N.A.I.C.S.: 311514

Tokai Nuts Co., Ltd. (2)
2-10-10 Kajicho Akiyama Building 7th Floor, Chiyoda-Ku, Tokyo, 101-0044, Japan
Tel.: (81) 332548093
Emp.: 172
Canned Nuts Mfr
N.A.I.C.S.: 311911

Zao Shokuhin Kaisha, Ltd. (2)
4 16 Kyobashi 2 Chome, Chuo Ku, Tokyo, 104, Japan
Tel.: (81) 332726511
Chocolate & Caramels Mfr
N.A.I.C.S.: 311351

Meiji Dairies (Suzhou) Co., Ltd. (1)
No 189 Putuoshan Road High-tech Zone, Suzhou, China
Tel.: (86) 51266806111
Web Site: http://www.meiji-milk.cn
Dairy Product Retailer
N.A.I.C.S.: 424430

Meiji Ice Cream (Guangzhou) Co., Ltd. (1)
No 1 Xiayuan East Road, Guangzhou Economic and Technological Development Zone, Guangzhou, 510000, China
Tel.: (86) 2029080066
Web Site: https://www.meiji-icecream.com
Ice Cream Mfr
N.A.I.C.S.: 311520

Meiji India Private Limited (1)
703/A Polaris Off Marol Maroshi Road, Marol Naka Andheri-East, Mumbai, 400 059, India
Tel.: (91) 9136010696
Web Site: http://www.meijiindia.com
Confectionery Product Retailer
N.A.I.C.S.: 424450

Meiji Pharma Spain, S.A. (1)
Avda de Madrid 94, 28802, Alcala de Henares, Madrid, Spain
Tel.: (34) 918870980
Web Site: https://www.meiji.es
Pharmaceuticals Product Mfr
N.A.I.C.S.: 325412

Meiji Seika (Shanghai) Co., Ltd. (1)
No 555 Loushanguan Rd, Shanghai, 200051, China
Tel.: (86) 21 6219 3360
Emp.: 60
Confectionery Mfr
N.A.I.C.S.: 311351
Nakao Kiyoshi (Gen Mgr)

Meiji Seika Pharma Co., Ltd. (1)
Kyobashi Niyomeme 16th, Chuo-Ku, Tokyo, 104-8002, Japan
Tel.: (81) 332736030
Web Site: http://www.meiji-seika-pharma.co.jp
Sales Range: $1-4.9 Billion
Emp.: 5,759
Pharmaceuticals, Agricultural Chemicals & Veterinary Drugs Mfr & Sales
N.A.I.C.S.: 325412

Affiliate (Non-US):

Comercio e Industria Uniquimica Ltda. (2)
Avenida Casa Grande 574 Bairro Casa Grande, Diadema, CEP 09961 350, Sao Paulo, SP, Brazil
Tel.: (55) 1140666277
Web Site: http://www.uniquimica.com
Sales Range: $1-9.9 Million
Emp.: 30
Pharmaceutical Preparation Mfr
N.A.I.C.S.: 325412

Subsidiary (Domestic):

Meiji Sangyo Co., Ltd. (2)
1-1-12 Akasaka, Minato-ku, Tokyo, 107-0052, Japan
Tel.: (81) 35563887
Sales Range: $75-99.9 Million
Emp.: 352
Snack Food & Candy Mfr
N.A.I.C.S.: 311352

Ohkura Pharmaceutical Co., Ltd. (2)
66 Yanaginoshitacho Higashikujo, Minami-ku, Kyoto, 601-8025, Japan
Tel.: (81) 756611661

Pharmaceuticals Product Mfr
N.A.I.C.S.: 325412

Affiliate (Non-US):

P.T. Meiji Indonesian Pharmaceutical Industries (2)
Jl Prof Dr Soepomo No 40, Tebet, Jakarta Selatan, 12870, Pusat, Indonesia
Tel.: (62) 2121383388
Web Site: http://www.meiji.co.id
Sales Range: $25-49.9 Million
Emp.: 50
Pharmaceuticals Mfr
N.A.I.C.S.: 325412
Masanobu Sato (Pres)

Tedec-Meiji Farma S.A. (2)
Carretera M 300 Km 30 500, E 28802, Alcala de Henares, Madrid, Spain (80%)
Tel.: (34) 918870980
Web Site: http://www.tedecmeiji.com
Sales Range: $50-74.9 Million
Emp.: 300
Pharmaceuticals Mfr
N.A.I.C.S.: 325412

Thai Meiji Pharmaceutical Co., Ltd. (2)
193/106-107 Lake Rajada Office Complex 26th Floor Ratchadaphisek Road, Klongtoey, Bangkok, 10110, Thailand
Tel.: (66) 232607504
Sales Range: $50-74.9 Million
Emp.: 250
Pharmaceuticals & Nutritional Products Mfr
N.A.I.C.S.: 325412

Meito Warehouse Co., Ltd. (1)
1-5-3 Nihombashi Nihombashinishikawa Bldg, Chuo-Ku, Tokyo, 103-0027, Japan
Tel.: (81) 332815511
General Warehousing Services
N.A.I.C.S.: 493190

Multifood International Ltd. (1)
Shinsuna 1-2-10, Koto-ku, Tokyo, 136-8908, Japan
Tel.: (81) 332733391
Web Site: http://www.bruyerre.co.jp
Confectionery Mfr
N.A.I.C.S.: 311351
Shigetaro Asano (Pres)

Pharmazen Medicals Pte. Ltd. (1)
Tel.: (65) 67432017
Web Site: http://www.pharmazen-medicals.com
Pharmaceutical Product Retailer
N.A.I.C.S.: 456110

Sanofi-Aventis-Meiji Pharmaceuticals Co., Ltd. (1)
3-20-2 Nishishinjuku Tokyo Opera City Tower 47f, Shinjuku-Ku, Tokyo, 160-0023, Japan
Tel.: (81) 363014945
Pharmaceuticals Product Mfr
N.A.I.C.S.: 325412

Tohoku Meihan Co., Ltd. (1)
3-9-1 Izumichuo Keisen Bldg 2f, Izumi-Ku, Sendai, 981-3133, Miyagi, Japan
Tel.: (81) 227768871
Dairy Products Mfr
N.A.I.C.S.: 311514

Tokyo Meiji Foods Co., Ltd. (1)
1-2-14 Kawagishi, Toda, 335-0015, Saitama, Japan
Tel.: (81) 484445941
Dairy Products Mfr
N.A.I.C.S.: 311514

MEIJI MACHINE CO., LTD.

9F PMO Kanda Tsukasamachi Bldg 2-8-1 Kanda Tsukasamachi, Chiyoda-ku, Tokyo, 101-0048, Japan
Tel.: (81) 352953511
Web Site: https://www.meiji-kikai.co.jp
Year Founded: 1925
6334—(TKS)
Rev.: $32,362,560
Assets: $45,430,530
Liabilities: $24,417,340
Net Worth: $21,013,190
Earnings: $2,075,540

MEIJI SHIPPING CO., LTD.

Emp.: 179
Fiscal Year-end: 03/31/24
Industrial Machinery Mfr & Distr
N.A.I.C.S.: 333310
Masanori Takayama (Chm)

Subsidiaries:

Meiji Machine (Dezhou) Co., Ltd. (1)
18 pingguo yuan road, Dezhou, 253034, Shandong, China
Tel.: (86) 5342759555
Web Site: https://www.meiji-machine.com
Emp.: 28
Flour Milling Machinery Mfr
N.A.I.C.S.: 333241
Yamashita Hideki (Gen Mgr)

Yanagihara Seifunki Co., Ltd. (1)
412-3 Minaminagaike, Oaza, Nagano, 381-0024, Japan
Tel.: (81) 262660020
Web Site: http://www.yanagihara-seifunki.co.jp
Emp.: 10
Flour Milling Equipment Mfr
N.A.I.C.S.: 333241

MEIJI SHIPPING CO., LTD.

32 Akashi-machi, Chuo-ku, Kobe, 650-0037, Hyogo, Japan
Tel.: (81) 337920811 JP
Web Site: https://www.meiji-group.com
Year Founded: 1911
9115—(TKS)
Rev.: $429,768,980
Assets: $1,827,380,770
Liabilities: $1,289,240,840
Net Worth: $538,139,930
Earnings: $34,299,290
Emp.: 200
Fiscal Year-end: 03/31/24
Marine Transportation Services
N.A.I.C.S.: 488510
Kazuya Uchida (Chm & CEO)

Subsidiaries:

Hayakita Country Club Co., Ltd. (1)
671-1 Hayakitashinei, Abira-cho Yufutsu-gun, Hokkaido, 059-1431, Japan
Tel.: (81) 14 522 3010
Web Site: https://www.hayakitacc.com
Golf Course Services
N.A.I.C.S.: 713910

Hotel Annupuri Co., Ltd. (1)
480-1 Aza-niseko Niseko-cho, Abuta, 048-1511, Hokkaido, Japan
Tel.: (81) 136 58 3311
Web Site: http://www.niseko-ta.com
Emp.: 40
Home Management Services
N.A.I.C.S.: 721110
Hatsuyo Oshiro (Gen Mgr)

MMS Co., Ltd. (1)
Kamimeguro 1-18-12 Surfeel Nakameguro building, Meguro-ku, Tokyo, 153-0051, Japan
Tel.: (81) 337929812
Web Site: http://www.meiji-shipping.com
Sales Range: $25-49.9 Million
Emp.: 50
Ship Management Services
N.A.I.C.S.: 488510
M. Nishio (Mgr)

MMS Maritime (India) Private Ltd. (1)
401 Raheja Plaza 15/B Shah Industrial Estate Off Andheri Link Road, Andheri West, Mumbai, 400 053, Maharashtra, India
Tel.: (91) 2240620100
Web Site: https://www.mms-india.in
Sales Range: $25-49.9 Million
Emp.: 20
Shipping Recruitment Services
N.A.I.C.S.: 541612

MMSPhil Maritime Services Inc. (1)
Room 303 MMS Bacoor Bldg Old NIA Road Brgy Bayanan, Bacoor City, Cavite, 4102, Philippines
Tel.: (63) 464198132
Web Site: https://www.mmsphil.com.ph

MEIJI SHIPPING CO., LTD.

Meiji Shipping Co., Ltd.—(Continued)

Seafarer Recruitment & Training Services
N.A.I.C.S.: 611430

Maybaru Shipping & Trading Pte. Ltd. (1)
Singapore Post Centre 10 Eunos Road 8 12-05, Singapore, 408600, Singapore
Tel.: (65) 62255230
Sales Range: $25-49.9 Million
Emp.: 5
Shipping Finance & Commercial Management Services
N.A.I.C.S.: 541618
Takashi Himeno (Gen Mgr)

Meiji Real Estate Co., Ltd. (1)
3-2-1 Kajigaya, Takatsu-ku, Kawasaki, 213-0015, Kanagawa, Japan
Tel.: (81) 448650011
Web Site: http://www.mjf.co.jp
Sales Range: $50-74.9 Million
Emp.: 30
Real Estate Lending Services
N.A.I.C.S.: 531110
Shigeaki Era (CEO)

Meikai Kosan K.K. (1)
76-2 Kyo-machi, Chuo-ku, Kobe, 650-0034, Hyogo, Japan
Tel.: (81) 783921256
Building Management Services
N.A.I.C.S.: 561790

Multinational Maritime Inc. (1)
3/F Room 301 MMS Bacoor Bldg Old NIA Road Brgy Bayanan, Bacoor City, Manila, Philippines
Tel.: (63) 464198126
Web Site: http://www.mmi.com.ph
Sales Range: $10-24.9 Million
Emp.: 19
Seafarers Training Services
N.A.I.C.S.: 611430
Banny B. Briones (Pres & Gen Mgr)

Neom Maritime (Singapore) Pte. Ltd. (1)
Tel.: (65) 62275570
Web Site: http://www.meiji-group.com
Sales Range: $25-49.9 Million
Emp.: 40
Marine Shipping Services
N.A.I.C.S.: 488510
Praveen Jindel (Gen Mgr)

Tacty Corporation (1)
New SURFEEL Nakameguro Building 1-18-11 Kamimeguro, Meguro-ku, Tokyo, 153-0051, Japan
Tel.: (81) 337608033
Web Site: http://www.tacty.co.jp
Sales Range: $50-74.9 Million
Emp.: 10
Kitchen Cabinets Whslr
N.A.I.C.S.: 423990

The Windsor Hotels International Co., Ltd. (1)
Shimizu Toyako-cho, Abuta-gun, Hokkaido, 049-5722, Japan
Tel.: (81) 142731111
Hotel & Resort Operator
N.A.I.C.S.: 721110

Tohmei Shipping Co., Ltd. (1)
Shin Surseel Nakameguro bulding 1-18-11, Kamimeguro-Meguro-Ku, Tokyo, 1530051, Japan
Tel.: (81) 352504471
Web Site: http://www.meiji-shipping.com
Sales Range: $25-49.9 Million
Emp.: 9
Marine Shipping Services
N.A.I.C.S.: 488320
Masaru Nishikawa (Mgr)

MEIJI YASUDA LIFE INSURANCE COMPANY

1-1 Marunouchi 2-chome, Chiyoda-ku, Tokyo, 100-0005, Japan
Tel.: (81) 3 3283 8293
Web Site: http://www.meijiyasuda.co.jp
Year Founded: 2004
Rev.: $39,430,357,120
Assets: $412,502,513,280
Liabilities: $378,222,129,120
Net Worth: $34,280,384,160
Earnings: $2,011,968,640
Emp.: 48,385
Fiscal Year-end: 03/31/20
Fire Insurance Services
N.A.I.C.S.: 524113
Akio Negishi (Chm)

Subsidiaries:

MST Insurance Service Co., Ltd. (1)
Shinjuku L Tower 1-6-1 Nishi Shinjuku, Shinjuku-ku, Tokyo, 163-1522, Japan
Tel.: (81) 3 3340 3328
Web Site: http://www.mst-is.com
Emp.: 657
General Insurance Services
N.A.I.C.S.: 524210
Akihiko Minato (Chm)

Meiji Yasuda America, Inc. (1)
780 3rd Ave 42nd Fl, New York, NY 10017 (100%)
Tel.: (212) 332-4900
Sales Range: $50-74.9 Million
Emp.: 10
Health Insurance Services
N.A.I.C.S.: 524210
Nobutaka Yagi (Pres)

Meiji Yasuda Asia Ltd. (1)
Unit 2 18/F Tower 1 Admiralty Centre 18 Harcourt Road, Admiralty, 93162, Central, China (Hong Kong)
Tel.: (852) 25247021
Web Site: http://www.meijiyasuda.co.jp
Sales Range: $50-74.9 Million
Emp.: 10
Life Insurance
N.A.I.C.S.: 524113
Kazunari Takahashi (Mng Dir)

Meiji Yasuda Europe Ltd. (1)
125 Finsbury Pavement, London, EC2A 1NQ, United Kingdom (100%)
Tel.: (44) 2074488800
Web Site: http://www.meijiyasuda.co.jp
Sales Range: $75-99.9 Million
Emp.: 7
Insurance Services
N.A.I.C.S.: 524128

Meiji Yasuda General Insurance Co., Ltd. (1)
2-11-1 Tsukasa-machi Kanda, Chiyoda-ku, Tokyo, 101-0048, Japan
Tel.: (81) 3 3257 3111
General Insurance Services
N.A.I.C.S.: 524210

Meiji Yasuda Life Insurance Company - Beijing Office (1)
Room 6003 6th Floor Changfugong Office Building, 26 Jianguomen Wai Avenue Chaoyang District, Beijing, 100022, China (100%)
Tel.: (86) 1065139815
Web Site: http://www.meijiyasuda.co.jp
Sales Range: $75-99.9 Million
Emp.: 2
Life Insurance
N.A.I.C.S.: 524128

Meiji Yasuda Life Insurance Company - Frankfurt Office (1)
Goethestrasse 7, Frankfurt am Main, 60313, Germany (100%)
Tel.: (49) 69748000
Sales Range: $75-99.9 Million
Emp.: 1
Insurance Services
N.A.I.C.S.: 524128

Meiji Yasuda Life Insurance Company - Seoul Office (1)
Seoul Shinmun Daily Building 9th Floor 25 Taepyongno 1-ga, Chung-gu, Seoul, 100-745, Korea (South)
Tel.: (82) 27239111
Life Insurance
N.A.I.C.S.: 524210

Meiji Yasuda Realty USA Inc. (1)
780 3rd Ave 42nd Fl, New York, NY 10017
Tel.: (212) 332-4900
Sales Range: $50-74.9 Million
Emp.: 12
Insurance Services

N.A.I.C.S.: 524128
Haruo Mimori (Pres)

Meiji Yasuda System Technology Company Limited (1)
7-1-2 Touyou, Koutou-ku, Tokyo, 135-0016, Japan
Tel.: (81) 3 5665 0230
Information Technology Consulting Services
N.A.I.C.S.: 541512

Pacific Guardian Life Insurance Co., Ltd. (1)
Pacific Guardian Tower 1440 Kapiolani Blvd Ste 1700, Honolulu, HI 96814-3698
Tel.: (808) 955-2236
Web Site: http://www.pacificguardian.com
Sales Range: $100-124.9 Million
Emp.: 150
Life Insurance
N.A.I.C.S.: 524113
Alan M. Goda (Chm & Gen Counsel)

Branch (Domestic):

Pacific Guardian Life Insurance Co., Ltd. (2)
1440 Kapiolani Blvd Ste 1700, Honolulu, HI 96814-3698
Tel.: (213) 236-0660
Web Site: http://www.pacificguardian.com
Sales Range: $50-74.9 Million
Emp.: 9
Insurance Services
N.A.I.C.S.: 524128

StanCorp Financial Group, Inc. (1)
1100 S W 6th Ave, Portland, OR 97204 (100%)
Tel.: (971) 321-7000
Web Site: http://www.stancorpfinancial.com
Sales Range: $1-4.9 Billion
Emp.: 3,100
Holding Company; Financial & Insurance Products & Services
N.A.I.C.S.: 551112
J. Gregory Ness (Chm & CEO)

Subsidiary (Domestic):

Anthem Life Insurance Company (2)
6740 N High St Ste 200, Worthington, OH 43085-7500
Tel.: (614) 436-0688
Web Site: http://www.anthem.com
Sales Range: $1-9.9 Million
Emp.: 100
Group, Accidental Death & Dismemberment, Dependent Life, Short & Long Term Disability Insurance Services
N.A.I.C.S.: 524298

StanCorp Mortgage Investors, LLC (2)
19225 NW Tanasbourne Dr T3A, Hillsboro, OR 97124
Tel.: (971) 321-8573
Web Site: http://www.standard.com
Emp.: 78
Provider of Commercial Mortgage Loans
N.A.I.C.S.: 524128
Mark Fisher (Mng Dir & VP)

Standard Insurance Company (2)
1100 SW 6th Ave, Portland, OR 97204
Tel.: (775) 684-7000
Web Site: http://www.standard.com
Emp.: 2,321
Life & Disability Insurance; Retirement Plans; Dental Insurance
N.A.I.C.S.: 524113
J. Gregory Ness (Chm & CEO)

The Standard Life Insurance Company of New York (2)
360 Hamilton Ave Ste 210, White Plains, NY 10601
Tel.: (877) 241-4361
Web Site: http://www.standard.com
Emp.: 82
Insurance Brokerage Services
N.A.I.C.S.: 524210

MEIJIN ENERGY GROUP CO. LTD.

Meijin Group Building (Guanzhong Building) 2# Meijin North Street, Guangzhou, Qingxu, China
Tel.: (86) 3515798998
Web Site: http://www.meijingroup-e.com
Coal Mining & Coke Mfr
N.A.I.C.S.: 423520
Junliang Yao (Pres)

MEIKLES LIMITED

90 Speke Avenue, PO Box 3598, Harare, Zimbabwe
Tel.: (263) 4252068
Web Site: https://meiklesinvestor.com
Year Founded: 1892
MEIK—(ZIM)
Rev.: $2,184,871
Assets: $1,330,671
Liabilities: $634,107
Net Worth: $696,563
Earnings: $182,044
Fiscal Year-end: 03/31/19
Supermarkets, Hotels & Department Stores Owner & Operator
N.A.I.C.S.: 459999
John Ralph Thomas Moxon (Chm)

Subsidiaries:

Tanganda Tea Company (1)
194 Mutare Rd Msasa, Harare, Zimbabwe
Tel.: (263) 24 244 7523
Web Site: https://tangandatea.com
Tea Product Mfr & Distr
N.A.I.C.S.: 311920
Francis Chingono (Grp Mgr-Human Resources)

The Victoria Falls Hotel (1)
1 Mallett Drive, PO Box 10, Victoria Falls, Zimbabwe (50%)
Tel.: (263) 832844751
Web Site: http://www.victoriafallshotel.com
Sales Range: $50-74.9 Million
Emp.: 350
Hotel
N.A.I.C.S.: 721110
Farai Chimba (Gen Mgr)

Thomas Meikle Centre (Private) Limited (1)
99 Jason Moyo Avenue, PO Box 3598, Harare, Zimbabwe (100%)
Tel.: (263) 4252068
Web Site: http://www.meiklesinvestor.co.zw
Sales Range: $1-4.9 Billion
Emp.: 5,000
Store Retailers
N.A.I.C.S.: 459999
John Moxon (Chm)

MEIKO ELECTRONICS CO., LTD.

5-14-15 Ogami, Ayase, 252-1104, Kanagawa, Japan
Tel.: (81) 467766001
Web Site: https://www.meiko-elec.com
6787—(TKS)
Rev.: $1,186,217,380
Assets: $1,520,035,600
Liabilities: $822,958,220
Net Worth: $697,077,380
Earnings: $74,759,100
Emp.: 12,975
Fiscal Year-end: 03/31/24
Electric Circuit Components Mfr
N.A.I.C.S.: 334412
Yuichiro Naya (Pres & CEO)

Subsidiaries:

MD Systems Co., Ltd. (1)
Assorti atsugi Bldg 6F 4-9-14, Naka, Atsugi, 243-0018, Kanagawa, Japan
Tel.: (81) 462957851
Web Site: http://www.mdsystems.biz
Printed Circuit Board Mfr
N.A.I.C.S.: 334412

MDS Circuit Technology, Inc. (1)
9th Floor One/Neo 3rd Avenue cor 26th Street, Bonifacio Global City, Taguig, 1634, Philippines
Tel.: (63) 28180527
Web Site: https://www.mds-ct.com

AND PRIVATE COMPANIES   **MEILOON INDUSTRIAL CO., LTD.**

Printed Circuit Board Mfr
N.A.I.C.S.: 334412

Meiko Elec. Hong Kong. Co., Ltd. (1)
Unit 1616 Tower I Metroplaza 223 Hing Fong Road, Kwai Chung, China (Hong Kong)
Tel.: (852) 21918590
Web Site: http://www.meiko-elec.com
Printed Circuit Board Distr
N.A.I.C.S.: 423690
Shina T. *(Mng Dir)*

Meiko Electronics (Guangzhou Nansha) Co., Ltd. (1)
No 2 Guangsheng Road Nansha Economic and Technological Development Zon, Western Industrial District, Guangzhou, China
Tel.: (86) 2084980000
Printed Circuit Board Mfr
N.A.I.C.S.: 334418

Meiko Electronics (Wuhan) Co., Ltd. (1)
No 9 Shenlong Road Wuhan Economic and Technological, Development Zone, Wuhan, Hubei, China
Tel.: (86) 2784890000
Printed Circuit Board Mfr
N.A.I.C.S.: 334412

Meiko Electronics America, Inc. (1)
2975 Scott Blvd Ste 125, Santa Clara, CA 95054
Tel.: (650) 336-1400
Web Site: https://www.meiko-america.com
Printed Circuit Board Distr
N.A.I.C.S.: 423690

Meiko Electronics Co., Ltd. - Fukushima Factory (1)
1-2 Iwasawa Kamikitaba, Hirono-cho Futaba-gun, Fukushima, 979-0401, Japan
Tel.: (81) 240273970
Printed Circuit Board Mfr
N.A.I.C.S.: 334418

Meiko Electronics Co., Ltd. - Ishinomaki Factory (1)
8-5 Shigeyoshi-cho, Ishinomaki, 986-0844, Miyagi, Japan
Tel.: (81) 225988769
Web Site: http://www.meiko-elec.com
Printed Circuit Board Mfr
N.A.I.C.S.: 334418

Meiko Electronics Europe GmbH (1)
Am Soldnermoos 17, 85399, Hallbergmoos, Germany
Tel.: (49) 8960768340
Printed Circuit Board Distr
N.A.I.C.S.: 423690

Meiko Electronics Thang Long Co., Ltd. (1)
Lot J1-J2 Thang Long Industrial Park, Vong La Commune Dong Anh district, Hanoi, Vietnam
Tel.: (84) 2439591888
Emp.: 677
Printed Circuit Board Mfr
N.A.I.C.S.: 334412

Meiko Electronics Vietnam Co., Ltd. (1)
Lot CN9 Thach That -Quoc Oai Industrial Zone, Hanoi, Vietnam
Tel.: (84) 2433689888
Web Site: http://www.meiko-elec.com.vn
Printed Circuit Board Distr
N.A.I.C.S.: 423690

Meiko Tech Co., Ltd. (1)
Shin-Osaka Doi Bldg 10F 7-5-25 Nishinakajima, Yodogawa-ku, Osaka, 532-0011, Japan
Tel.: (81) 648067761
Printed Circuit Board Distr
N.A.I.C.S.: 423690

Meiko Techno Co., Ltd. (1)
1-14-1 Daikan, Yamato, 242-0025, Kanagawa, Japan
Tel.: (81) 462051766
Printed Circuit Board Mfr
N.A.I.C.S.: 334412

Meiko Towada Vietnam Co., Ltd. (1)
Plot C1 C2 Phuc Dien Industrial Zone, Cam Phunc Commune Cam Giang District, Hai Duong, Vietnam
Tel.: (84) 2203545777
Emp.: 801
Printed Circuit Board Mfr
N.A.I.C.S.: 334412

Yamagata Meiko Electronics Co., Ltd. (1)
250 Maki Yachi, Nishimurayama-gun, Kahoku, 999-3511, Yamagata, Japan
Tel.: (81) 237734515
Printed Circuit Board Mfr
N.A.I.C.S.: 334418

MEIKO NETWORK JAPAN CO., LTD.
29F/30F Sumitomo Fudosan Nishi-Shinjuku Bldg 7-20-1, Nishi-Shinjuku, Tokyo, 160-0023, Japan
Tel.: (81) 358602111   JP
Web Site: https://www.meikonet.co.jp
Year Founded: 1984
4668—(TKS)
Rev.: $140,441,380
Assets: $101,012,800
Liabilities: $33,314,320
Net Worth: $67,698,480
Earnings: $3,041,580
Emp.: 1,197
Fiscal Year-end: 08/31/24
Holding Company; Specialty Education & Test Preparation Services
N.A.I.C.S.: 551112
Hirotake Watanabe *(Founder & Chm)*

Subsidiaries:

Coco-Ro PTE LTD (1)
20 Devonshire Rd 01-01 / 02, Singapore, 239850, Singapore
Tel.: (65) 67361815
Web Site: https://www.coco-ro.org
School Operator
N.A.I.C.S.: 611110

MEIKO TRANS CO. LTD.
2-4-6 Irifune, Minato-ku, Nagoya, 455-8650, Japan
Tel.: (81) 526618111
Web Site: http://www.meiko-trans.co.jp
Sales Range: $600-649.9 Million
Emp.: 822
Marine Cargo Handling Services
N.A.I.C.S.: 488320
Jiro Takahashi *(Chm)*

Subsidiaries:

Meiko America, Inc. (1)
19600 Magellan Dr, Torrance, CA 90502
Tel.: (310) 483-7400
Web Site: http://www.meikoamerica.com
Sales Range: $25-49.9 Million
Emp.: 150
Freight Transportation Services
N.A.I.C.S.: 488510
Hisashi Kanamori *(Pres)*

Meiko Asia Co., Ltd. (1)
158/15-17 Moo 5 Nongkham, Si Racha, 20230, Chonburi, Thailand
Tel.: (66) 33046005
General Warehousing Services
N.A.I.C.S.: 493110

Meiko Euroexpress N.V. (1)
Haven 200 Schouwkensstraat 6, Antwerp, 2030, Belgium
Tel.: (32) 3545 9763
Web Site: http://www.meiko-europe.eu
Emp.: 40
Truck & Container Transportation Services
N.A.I.C.S.: 488510

Meiko Europe N.V. (1)
Haven 200 Schouwkensstraat 6, Antwerp, 2030, Belgium
Tel.: (32) 3545 9760
Web Site: http://www.meiko.be
Sales Range: $25-49.9 Million
Emp.: 16
Freight Transportation Arrangement
N.A.I.C.S.: 488510

Harry Cools *(Mng Dir-Transport)*

Meiko Kaiun Kosan Co., Ltd. (1)
9F Meiko Bldg 2-4-6 Irifune, Minato-ku, Nagoya, 455-0032, Japan
Tel.: (81) 526618141
General Insurance Services
N.A.I.C.S.: 524210

Meiko Logistics (India) Pvt., Ltd. (1)
No 86 Polyhose Towers Western Wing 3rd Floor Office-D AnnaÂ Salai, Guindy, Chennai, 600 032, Tamil Nadu, India
Tel.: (91) 4445040222
Logistics & Warehousing Services
N.A.I.C.S.: 493110
Siva Jampani *(Mgr)*

Meiko Rikuun Co., Ltd. (1)
24-10 Kitahama-cho, Chita, 478-0046, Aichi, Japan
Tel.: (81) 562551332
General Trucking Services
N.A.I.C.S.: 484121

Meiko Shanghai Trading Co., Ltd. (1)
Room 22H New Shanghai City Square No 33 South Henan Road, Huangpu District, Shanghai, 200002, China
Tel.: (86) 21 6337 5578
International Trade & Domestic Sales Services
N.A.I.C.S.: 561499

Meiko Trans (Guangzhou) Co., Ltd. (1)
Rm 1407 Ronghui Bldg No 302 Zhicheng Ave, 510730, Guangzhou, China
Tel.: (86) 2082068270
Web Site: http://www.meiko-trans.co.jp
Sales Range: $25-49.9 Million
Emp.: 5
Management Consulting Services
N.A.I.C.S.: 541618

Meiko Trans (Hong Kong) Co., Ltd. (1)
Unit 701 Tower 2 Enterprise Square Phase 1 No 9 Sheung Yuet Road, Kowloon Bay, Kowloon, China (Hong Kong)
Tel.: (852) 2735 3228
Web Site: http://www.meikoasia.com
Emp.: 13
Import, Export & Air-Freight Containerization Services
N.A.I.C.S.: 488510
Francesc Lloreta *(Gen Mgr)*

Meiko Trans (Singapore) Pte. Ltd. (1)
39 Keppel Road Blk 2 # 03-07/08, Tanjong Pagar Distripark, 089065, Singapore, Singapore
Tel.: (65) 62248633
Web Site: http://www.meiko-trans.co.jp
Sales Range: $25-49.9 Million
Emp.: 10
Freight Transportation Arrangement
N.A.I.C.S.: 488510

Meiko Trans (Thailand) Co., Ltd. (1)
16th Floor Unit A 216/67 LPN Twr, Nanglinchee Rd Chong Non See, 10120, Bangkok, Thailand
Tel.: (66) 22852890
Web Site: http://www.meiko.co.th
Sales Range: $25-49.9 Million
Emp.: 84
General Freight Trucking, Long-Distance, Truckload
N.A.I.C.S.: 484121
Osamu Kimizuka *(Mng Dir)*

Meiko Trans Co., Ltd. (1)
Room 44 9th Floor Maritime Bank Tower 180-192 Nguyen Cong Tru St, Nguyen Thai Binh Ward District 1, Ho Chi Minh City, Vietnam
Tel.: (84) 862884671
Air Freight Forwarding Services
N.A.I.C.S.: 481112

Meiko Trans De Mexico, S. de R.L. de C.V. (1)
Blvd Diaz Ordaz 1370 Int 701, Col Jardines De Irapuato, Irapuato, 36660, Guanajuato, Mexico
Tel.: (52) 4626244044
Freight Forwarding Services

N.A.I.C.S.: 488510

Meiko Trans Polska Sp. z o.o. (1)
Ul Wyczolkowskiego 121, Gliwice, 44-109, Poland
Tel.: (48) 327773880
Web Site: http://www.meiko-trans.co.jp
Sales Range: $25-49.9 Million
Emp.: 26
Freight Transportation Arrangement
N.A.I.C.S.: 488510
Takashi Nakagawa *(Mgr)*

Shanghai Meiko International Logistics Co., Ltd. (1)
22nd Floor New Shanghai City Square No 33, S Henan Rd Huangpu District, Shanghai, 200002, China
Tel.: (86) 2151082911
Web Site: http://www.meiko.co.th
Sales Range: $25-49.9 Million
Emp.: 20
Freight Transportation Arrangement
N.A.I.C.S.: 488510

MEILI AUTO HOLDINGS LIMITED
20/F Greenland Building Wangjing Hongtai Dong Street, Chaoyang District, Beijing, 100102, China
Tel.: (86) 1083030999   Ky
Year Founded: 2017
Rev.: $1,656,358,000
Assets: $5,883,592,000
Liabilities: $7,839,274,000
Net Worth: ($1,955,682,000)
Earnings: $320,472,000
Emp.: 5,343
Fiscal Year-end: 12/31/18
Holding Company
N.A.I.C.S.: 551112
Allen Chonglun Gu *(CEO)*

MEILLEURE HEALTH INTERNATIONAL INDUSTRY GROUP LIMITED
Unit 2906 Tower 1 Lippo Centre 89 Queensway Admiralty, Hong Kong, China (Hong Kong)
Tel.: (852) 25631500   BM
Web Site:
  http://www.meilleure.com.cn
2327—(HKG)
Rev.: $15,286,485
Assets: $218,185,778
Liabilities: $48,982,440
Net Worth: $169,203,338
Earnings: $2,266,950
Emp.: 97
Fiscal Year-end: 12/31/22
Pharmaceutical & Health Care Products Mfr
N.A.I.C.S.: 325412
Xuzhou Zhou *(Co-Chm & Exec Dir)*

Subsidiaries:

La Clinique de Paris (HK) Limited (1)
Rm 2822-2831 28/F Sun Hung Kai Ctr, Wanchai, China (Hong Kong)
Tel.: (852) 25281338
Web Site: https://www.lcdpi.net
Health Care Srvices
N.A.I.C.S.: 621498

Tech-Medi Development Limited (1)
Rm 2904 29/F Lippo Ctr Twr 1 Admiralty, Hong Kong, China (Hong Kong)
Tel.: (852) 28108991
Healthcare Product Distr
N.A.I.C.S.: 424210

MEILOON INDUSTRIAL CO., LTD.
No 99 Xing-fu Road, Taoyuan Dist, Taoyuan, Taiwan
Tel.: (886) 33261611
Web Site: https://www.meiloon.com
Year Founded: 1973

MEILOON INDUSTRIAL CO., LTD.

Meiloon Industrial Co., Ltd.—(Continued)
2477—(TAI)
Rev.: $76,219,625
Assets: $253,342,742
Liabilities: $113,109,744
Net Worth: $140,232,998
Earnings: $834,265
Emp.: 1,548
Fiscal Year-end: 12/31/23
Loudspeaker & Audio System Mfr
N.A.I.C.S.: 334310

MEINIAN ONEHEALTH HEALTHCARE HOLDINGS CO., LTD.
3rd Floor Building 9 Health Intelligence Valley, No 697 Lingshi Road Jing'an District, Shanghai, 200072, China
Tel.: (86) 4008008781
Web Site: https://health-100.cn
Year Founded: 2004
002044—(SSE)
Rev.: $1,198,012,140
Assets: $2,566,496,556
Liabilities: $1,415,670,048
Net Worth: $1,150,826,508
Earnings: ($74,852,856)
Fiscal Year-end: 12/31/22
Textile Products Mfr
N.A.I.C.S.: 314999
Rong Yu (Chm)

MEIRA, INC.
Meira Bldg 17 15 Tsubaki Cho, Nakamura Ku, Nagoya, 435 0015, Aichi, Japan
Tel.: (81) 524591271
Web Site: http://www.meira.co.jp
Year Founded: 1932
Sales Range: $1-9.9 Million
Emp.: 672
Bolts, Screws & Rivets Mfr
N.A.I.C.S.: 332722
Shin Ohashi (Pres & CEO)

Subsidiaries:

Rocknel Fastener, Inc. (1)
5309 11th St, Rockford, IL 61109-3657 (100%)
Tel.: (815) 873-4000
Web Site: http://www.rocknel.com
Automotive Fastener Mfr & Distr
N.A.I.C.S.: 339993
Ed Vaughn (Mgr-Pur)

MEISEI INDUSTRIAL CO., LTD.
Meisei Bldg 1-8-5 Kyomachibori, Nishi-ku, Osaka, 550-0003, Japan
Tel.: (81) 664470271
Web Site: https://www.meisei-kogyo.co.jp
Year Founded: 1944
1976—(TKS)
Rev.: $399,091,970
Assets: $558,095,520
Liabilities: $135,928,040
Net Worth: $422,167,480
Earnings: $41,266,230
Emp.: 9,810
Fiscal Year-end: 03/31/24
Chemical Products Mfr
N.A.I.C.S.: 326150
Yoshihisa Takase (Exec Officer)

Subsidiaries:

MEISEI MATSUYAMA KOJI Co., Ltd. (1)
35 2798 Minamiyoshida-machi, Matsuyama, 791-8042, Ehime, Japan
Tel.: (81) 899722804
Chemical Products Mfr
N.A.I.C.S.: 326150

Meisei International Co., Ltd. (1)
2 Jasmine Building 12th Floor Soi Sukhumvit 23 Prasarnmitr, Sukhumvit Road Klongtoey-nua Wattana, Bangkok, 10110, Thailand
Tel.: (66) 851526366
Insulation Material Distr
N.A.I.C.S.: 423330

Meisei International Pte. Ltd. (1)
2 International Business Park 10-05 in Tower 1 of The Strategy, Singapore, 609930, Singapore
Tel.: (65) 68612440
Insulation Material Distr
N.A.I.C.S.: 423330

Meisei Kenko Co., Ltd. (1)
2-13-22 Nagata, Joto-ku, Osaka, 536-0022, Japan
Tel.: (81) 669656000
Emp.: 43
Interior Design Services
N.A.I.C.S.: 541410

Meisei Nigeria Ltd. (1)
No 2B Evo Road G R A phase II, GRA Phase 3, Port Harcourt, Rivers, Nigeria
Tel.: (234) 84238495
Insulation Material Distr
N.A.I.C.S.: 423330

NIPPON KEICAL LIMITED (1)
Nakagawa Hosoe-cho, Kita-ku, Hamamatsu, 431-1304, Shizuoka, Japan
Tel.: (81) 535221911
Emp.: 61
Silicate Calcium Insulation Mfr
N.A.I.C.S.: 326150

P.T. Meisei Indonesia (1)
Wisma TTP 2nd Floor Jl Sultan Iskandar Muda No 33 Arteri Pondok Indar, Jakarta Selatan, 12240, Indonesia
Tel.: (62) 217269985
Insulation Material Distr
N.A.I.C.S.: 423330

SMI Global Sdn. Bhd. (1)
No 72 1st 2nd Floor Medan Jaya Commercial Centre Jalan Tun, Hussein Onn, 97000, Bintulu, Sarawak, Malaysia
Tel.: (60) 133200011
Insulation Material Distr
N.A.I.C.S.: 423330

MEISHENG CULTURAL & CREATIVE CORP., LTD.
Hi-Tech Park Xinchang Provincial, Shaoxing, 312500, Zhejiang, China
Tel.: (86) 57586280066
Web Site: http://www.chinarising.com.cn
002699—(SSE)
Rev.: $173,429,100
Assets: $253,777,212
Liabilities: $82,010,448
Net Worth: $171,766,764
Earnings: ($105,753,492)
Emp.: 860
Fiscal Year-end: 12/31/22
Apparels Mfr
N.A.I.C.S.: 315250
Xianmiao Yuan (Gen Mgr)

MEISTERLABS GMBH
Zugspitzstrasse 2, 85591, Vaterstetten, Germany
Tel.: (49) 8912135359
Web Site: http://www.mindmeister.com
Year Founded: 2007
Sales Range: $1-9.9 Million
Software Publisher
N.A.I.C.S.: 513210
Till Vollmer (Co-Founder & Mng Dir)

MEITAV INVESTMENT HOUSE LTD.
Zeev Jabotinsky 1, Bnei Brak, 5126380, Israel
Tel.: (972) 37903000
Year Founded: 1992
MTDS—(TAE)
Rev.: $323,192,885
Assets: $1,289,246,787
Liabilities: $1,089,149,178
Net Worth: $200,097,609
Earnings: $20,063,988
Emp.: 416
Fiscal Year-end: 12/31/22
Investment Management Service
N.A.I.C.S.: 523999
Ilan Raviv (CEO)

MEITEC CORPORATION
ORIX Ueno 1-chome Building 1-1-10 Ueno, Taito-ku, Tokyo, 110-0005, Japan
Tel.: (81) 503000582 JP
Web Site: https://www.meitec.co.jp
Year Founded: 1974
9744—(TKS)
Rev.: $1,037,115,200
Assets: $789,791,200
Liabilities: $351,413,040
Net Worth: $438,378,160
Earnings: $89,443,200
Emp.: 8,080
Fiscal Year-end: 03/31/22
Engineering Outsourcing Services
N.A.I.C.S.: 541330
Hideyo Kokubun (Pres, CEO, COO & Exec Officer-CSR Office)

Subsidiaries:

Apollo Giken Co., Ltd. (1)
4683-26 Higashiobokatacho, Isesaki, 3792204, Japan
Tel.: (81) 270631334
Machine Tool & Metal Forming Mfr
N.A.I.C.S.: 333517

Meitec Business Service Corporation (1)
Frontier Akihabara Building 7th Floor 5-8-5, Ueno Taito-ku, Tokyo, 110-0005, Japan
Tel.: (81) 367759472
Paper Product Mfr & Distr
N.A.I.C.S.: 322120

Meitec CAE Corporation (1)
8F ORIX Kyutaro-machi Bldg 3-3-9 Kyutaromachi, Chuo-ku, Osaka, 541-0056, Japan
Tel.: (81) 6 4963 9660
Web Site: http://www.meitec-cae.co.jp
Sales Range: $25-49.9 Million
Emp.: 80
Computer Software Programming Services
N.A.I.C.S.: 541511

Meitec Cast Inc. (1)
7th Floor Sakuradake Building 2-19 Sakuma-cho, Kanda Chiyoda-ku, Tokyo, 101-0025, Japan
Web Site: http://www.meitec-cast.co.jp
Paid Employment Agency Services
N.A.I.C.S.: 561311

Meitec Ex Corporation (1)
2-20-1 Koseitori Nagoya Techno Center 5th Floor, Nishi-ku, Nagoya, 451-0075, Aichi Prefecture, Japan
Tel.: (81) 525226711
Web Site: http://www.meitec-ex.co.jp
Worker Dispatch Services
N.A.I.C.S.: 561320

Meitec Fielders Inc (1)
Orix Ueno 1-chome Building 1-1-10 Ueno, Taito-ku, Tokyo, 110-0005, Japan
Tel.: (81) 5030005826
Web Site: https://www.m-fielders.co.jp
Emp.: 4,310
Help Supply Services
N.A.I.C.S.: 561320

Meitec Next Corporation (1)
ORIX Ueno 1-chome Building 7th Floor 1-1-10 Ueno, Taito-ku, Tokyo, 110-0005, Japan
Tel.: (81) 120964228
Web Site: http://www.m-next.jp
Sales Range: $10-24.9 Million
Emp.: 30
Employment Placement Agencies
N.A.I.C.S.: 561311

Three D Tec Inc. (1)
Ginzatowa Bldg 7th Fl, Chuo-Ku, Tokyo, 104-0061, Japan
Tel.: (81) 351480722
Web Site: http://www.3dtec.co.jp

INTERNATIONAL PUBLIC

Computer Programming Services
N.A.I.C.S.: 541511

MEITECH OFFSHORE ENGINEERING PTE. LTD.
No 15 Pandan Crescent, Singapore, 128470, Singapore
Tel.: (65) 62617888 SG
Year Founded: 2006
Oil & Gas Field Engineering Services
N.A.I.C.S.: 213112
Kah Hong Ang (Chm)

Subsidiaries:

PT. TWC Bintan (1)
JL Korindo Kp-Melayu Gunung Kijang, Bintan, Riau Islands, Indonesia
Tel.: (62) 771463747
Web Site: http://www.tiongwoon.com
Offshore Marine Engineering Services
N.A.I.C.S.: 541330

MEITO SANGYO CO., LTD.
2-41 Sasazuka-cho, Nishi-ku, Nagoya, 451-8520, ACH, Japan
Tel.: (81) 525217112
Web Site: https://www.meito-sangyo.co.jp
Year Founded: 1945
2207—(TKS)
Rev.: $161,231,120
Assets: $540,208,860
Liabilities: $202,649,380
Net Worth: $337,559,480
Earnings: ($4,646,830)
Emp.: 731
Fiscal Year-end: 03/31/24
Fine Chemical Product Mfr
N.A.I.C.S.: 325199
Masuo Miya (Pres & CEO)

MEITU INC.
Meitu Tower Building 2 Meifeng Innovation Valley No 2557, Binhai West Avenue Tongan, Xiamen, Fujian, China Ky
Web Site: https://www.meitu.com
Year Founded: 2008
1357—(HKG)
Rev.: $319,493,256
Assets: $766,716,157
Liabilities: $198,381,517
Net Worth: $568,334,640
Earnings: $2,894,290
Emp.: 2,057
Fiscal Year-end: 12/31/22
Software Development Services
N.A.I.C.S.: 541511
King Leung Gary Ngan (CFO)

MEITUAN
Tower C Hengjiweiye Building No 4 Wangjing East Road, Chaoyang District, Beijing, 100102, China
Tel.: (86) 1057376600
Web Site: https://www.about.meituan.com
3690—(HKG)
Rev.: $30,881,674,699
Assets: $34,325,159,357
Liabilities: $16,254,876,690
Net Worth: $18,070,282,667
Earnings: ($938,619,349)
Emp.: 91,932
Fiscal Year-end: 12/31/22
Online Platform Services
N.A.I.C.S.: 541511
Xing Wang (Chm & CEO)

MEIWA CORPORATION
3-1 Marunouchi 3-chome, Chiyoda-ku, Tokyo, 100-8311, Japan
Tel.: (81) 332409011
Web Site: https://www.meiwa.co.jp
Year Founded: 1947
8103—(TKS)
Rev.: $1,046,224,190

Assets: $564,196,550
Liabilities: $307,840,920
Net Worth: $256,355,630
Earnings: $18,203,940
Emp.: 518
Fiscal Year-end: 03/31/24
Chemicals Whslr
N.A.I.C.S.: 424690
Takashi Yoshida *(Pres & CEO)*

Subsidiaries:

Akahagi Flange Co. Ltd. (1)
4-2 Kamikamo, Sumoto, Hyogo, 656-0015, Japan
Tel.: (81) 799223811
Web Site: http://www.akahagiflange.com
Steel Product Mfr & Distr
N.A.I.C.S.: 332999

Juzen Corporation (1)
Ebara Bldg 4F 1-5-7 Kajicho, Chiyoda-ku, Tokyo, 101-0044, Japan
Tel.: (81) 332525731
Web Site: https://www.jc-jc.co.jp
Emp.: 57
Industrial Material Distr
N.A.I.C.S.: 423840
Hiroyuki Hisamoto *(Pres)*

Meiwa (Dalian) Corporation (1)
No 161 International Financial Tower No15 Renmin Road, Zhongshan Dist, Dalian, 116011, Liaoning, China
Tel.: (86) 41182507400
Metal Product Distr
N.A.I.C.S.: 423510
Fu Kun *(Pres)*

Meiwa (Shanghai) Corporation (1)
Room 1501-8 15th Floor, Jing'an District, Shanghai, 200070, China
Tel.: (86) 2164728063
Web Site: https://www.meiwa-sha.com.cn
Chemical Products Distr
N.A.I.C.S.: 424690
Koichi Fujii *(Pres)*

Meiwa (Thailand) Co., Ltd. (1)
Liberty Square Bldg 18F Unit 1805 287 Silom Road, Bangrak, Bangkok, 10500, Thailand
Tel.: (66) 22349761
Emp.: 10
Industrial Supplies Whslr
N.A.I.C.S.: 423840
Tomoyuki Sakai *(Pres)*

Meiwa Sales Co., Ltd. (1)
8-6 Imagawa Building 2-6 Kanda Izumicho, Chiyoda-ku, Tokyo, 101-0024, Japan
Tel.: (81) 358237511
Web Site: http://www.meiwasales.co.jp
Emp.: 20
Glass Product Distr
N.A.I.C.S.: 423220
Akira Iwai *(Pres)*

Meiwa Vietnam Co., Ltd. (1)
12F Saigon Centre 65 Le Loi Street, District 1, Ho Chi Minh City, Vietnam
Tel.: (84) 838296225
Chemical Products Distr
N.A.I.C.S.: 424690
Minoru Kuboaki *(Pres)*

PT. Meiwa Trading Indonesia (1)
Sentral Senayan II 16th Floor Jl Asia Afrika No 8, Tanah Abang, Jakarta, 10270, Indonesia
Tel.: (62) 2129655836
Industrial Supplies Whslr
N.A.I.C.S.: 423840
Gaku Ikeo *(Pres)*

SOKEN CORPORATION (1)
1-1 Kamiyoshi 651-193, Higashi Kamiyoshi, Kakogawa, 675-0057, Hyogo, Japan
Tel.: (81) 792966635
Web Site: http://www.soken-coltd.co.jp
Construction Materials Distr
N.A.I.C.S.: 423390
Tsutomu Aido *(Pres)*

Takeda Shoji Co., Ltd. (1)
2-20-6 Higashisumida, Sumida-ku, Tokyo, 131-0042, Japan
Tel.: (81) 336191306
Industrial Chemical Product Mfr & Distr
N.A.I.C.S.: 325998

Hiroshi Yasui *(Pres)*

Thai Meiwa Trading Co., Ltd. (1)
18F Liberty Square Bldg Unit 1805 287 Silom Road, Silom Bangrak, Bangkok, 10500, Thailand
Tel.: (66) 22349761
Domestic Consulting Services
N.A.I.C.S.: 541618
Katsumi Okamura *(Pres)*

Tokyo Glasron Co., Ltd. (1)
Akihabara Kato Building 2-15 Kanda Sakumacho, Chiyoda-ku, Tokyo, 101-0025, Japan
Tel.: (81) 358235270
Web Site: http://www.glasron.co.jp
Emp.: 60
Construction Materials Distr
N.A.I.C.S.: 423390

MEIWA ESTATE CO., LTD.
Meiwa Estate Shibuya Shinsen Building 9-6 Shinsen-cho, Shibuya-ku, Tokyo, 150-8555, Japan
Tel.: (81) 354890111
Web Site: https://www.meiwajisyo.co.jp
Year Founded: 1942
8869—(TKS)
Rev.: $470,962,500
Assets: $820,638,110
Liabilities: $609,296,580
Net Worth: $211,341,530
Earnings: $18,382,410
Emp.: 8,483
Fiscal Year-end: 03/31/24
Real Estate Manangement Services
N.A.I.C.S.: 531390
Hideaki Harada *(Pres)*

MEIWA INDUSTRY CO., LTD.
Rurie Hon-Atsugi 3-1-1 Kotobuki-cho, Atsugi, 243-0003, Kanagawa, Japan
Tel.: (81) 462237611
Web Site: https://www.meiwasangyo.co.jp
Year Founded: 1956
7284—(TKS)
Rev.: $148,024,340
Assets: $163,696,650
Liabilities: $90,880,890
Net Worth: $72,815,760
Earnings: ($2,016,050)
Emp.: 590
Fiscal Year-end: 03/31/24
Automotive Interior Parts Mfr & Whslr
N.A.I.C.S.: 336360
Kiyoshi Iizuka *(Pres)*

Subsidiaries:

MEIWA INDUSTRY (THAILAND) CO., LTD. (1)
888/ 50-51 Moo 9 Soi Rungcharoen Leabklongsongnam Suvarnabhumi Rd, Bang Pla, Bang Phli, 10540, Samut Prakan, Thailand
Tel.: (66) 26328255
Automobile Parts Distr
N.A.I.C.S.: 441330
Anothai Amnajsathit *(Coord-Sls)*

MEIWA INDUSTRY NORTH AMERICA, INC. (1)
1041 Veterans Dr, Lewisburg, TN 37091
Tel.: (931) 270-8930
Automobile Parts Distr
N.A.I.C.S.: 441330
Wanda Willis *(Coord-Quality Assurance)*

MEIWU TECHNOLOGY COMPANY LIMITED
No 743 Zhoushi Road Hangcheng Street 1602 Building C, Shenye Century Industrial Center, Shenzhen, 518102, China
Tel.: (86) 75585250400   VG
Year Founded: 2018
WNW—(NASDAQ)
Rev.: $10,977,429
Assets: $20,584,279
Liabilities: $11,568,372

Net Worth: $9,015,907
Earnings: ($16,312,705)
Emp.: 46
Fiscal Year-end: 12/31/23
Holding Company
N.A.I.C.S.: 551112
Xinliang Zhang *(Co-CEO)*

MEJERIANDELSLAGET MILKA MEIJERIOSUUSKUNTA
Riksattan 850, 66710, Kaitsor, Finland
Tel.: (358) 10381166   FI
Web Site: http://www.milka.net
Year Founded: 1918
Sales Range: $25-49.9 Million
Emp.: 220
Dairy & Cheese Products
N.A.I.C.S.: 311513
Pekka Laaksonen *(Mng Dir)*

MEKICS CO., LTD
21 Sangjiseok-gil, P'aju, Gyeonggi-do, Korea (South)
Tel.: (82) 7071192500
Web Site: https://www.mek-ics.com
Year Founded: 1998
058110—(KRS)
Rev.: $22,054,212
Assets: $66,544,316
Liabilities: $14,477,327
Net Worth: $52,066,989
Earnings: ($2,050,465)
Emp.: 133
Fiscal Year-end: 12/31/22
Medical Equipment Mfr
N.A.I.C.S.: 339112
Jong Cheol Kim *(CEO)*

MEKO AB
Klarabergsviadukten 70 C6 Box 19542 111 64 Stockholm, Stockholm, Sweden
Tel.: (46) 84640020   SE
Web Site: https://meko.com
MEKO—(OMX)
Rev.: $1,347,888,392
Assets: $1,477,329,137
Liabilities: $922,288,722
Net Worth: $555,040,415
Earnings: $44,676,726
Emp.: 5,324
Fiscal Year-end: 12/31/22
Automotive Parts Retailer
N.A.I.C.S.: 441330
Helena Skantorp *(Vice Chm)*

Subsidiaries:

BilXtra Autogarden Kongsberg AS (1)
Kobberbergveien 8, 3615, Kongsberg, Norway
Tel.: (47) 32723200
Web Site: http://www.autogarden.no
Automotive Repair Services
N.A.I.C.S.: 811111

BilXtra Kristiansund AS (1)
Industriveien 16, 6517, Kristiansund, Norway
Tel.: (47) 71565730
Auto Spare Parts & Accessory Distr
N.A.I.C.S.: 423120

BilXtra Skoyen AS (1)
Hovfaret 17, 0275, Oslo, Norway
Tel.: (47) 22520677
Auto Spare Parts & Accessory Distr
N.A.I.C.S.: 423120

Bileko Tires AB (1)
Stenaldersgatan 27, 213 76, Malmo, Sweden
Tel.: (46) 406488020
Web Site: https://www.bilekotires.se
Tire Distr
N.A.I.C.S.: 423130

Bilglascentralen AB (1)
Arods Industrivag 15, 422 43, Hisings Backa, Sweden

Tel.: (46) 3 123 4361
Web Site: https://www.bilglascentralen.se
Automotive Glass Services
N.A.I.C.S.: 811122

Bilutstyr Arendal AS (1)
Stoaveien 37, 4848, Arendal, Norway
Tel.: (47) 37058370
Web Site: http://bilutstyrarendal.no
Car Equipment Whslr
N.A.I.C.S.: 423120

CarPeople Danmark ApS (1)
Hvidkaervej 23D, 5250, Odense, Denmark
Tel.: (45) 65655015
Web Site: https://www.carpeople.dk
Automotive Component Maintenance Services
N.A.I.C.S.: 811198

DriveClever A/S (1)
Hvidkaervej 21, 5250, Odense, Denmark
Tel.: (45) 77898989
Web Site: https://www.driveclever.dk
Automotive Services
N.A.I.C.S.: 811111

FTZ Autodele & Vaerktoj A/S (1)
Hvidkaervej 21, 5250, Odense, Denmark
Tel.: (45) 65654000
Web Site: https://www.ftz.dk
Emp.: 3,000
Automobile Spare Parts Mfr
N.A.I.C.S.: 336390
Brian Steffensen *(Acct Mgr)*

Inter-Team Sp. z o.o. (1)
Ul Bialolecka 233, 03-253, Warsaw, Poland
Tel.: (48) 225060601
Web Site: http://www.inter-team.com.pl
Emp.: 1,500
Auto Spare Parts & Accessory Distr
N.A.I.C.S.: 423120

J&B Maskinteknikk AS (1)
Anolitveien 14, 1400, Ski, Norway
Tel.: (47) 63877799
Web Site: https://www.jbmaskin.no
Automotive Repair Services
N.A.I.C.S.: 811111

Lasingoo Norge AS (1)
Rosenholmveien 25, 1414, Trollasen, Norway
Tel.: (47) 6 967 6551
Web Site: https://www.lasingoo.no
Automotive Repair Services
N.A.I.C.S.: 811111

MECA Norway AS (1)
Kallerudsvingen 13, PO Box 1014, 2816, Gjovik, Norway
Tel.: (47) 6 113 1930
Web Site: https://www.meca.no
Auto Spare Parts & Accessory Distr
N.A.I.C.S.: 423120

MECA Scandinavia AB (1)
Stenaldergatan 27, Box 9509, 200 39, Malmo, Sweden
Tel.: (46) 40 671 60 60
Web Site: http://www.meca.se
Automobile Parts Retailer & Distr
N.A.I.C.S.: 441330

MECA Service AS (1)
Sommerroveien 3, 2816, Gjovik, Norway
Tel.: (47) 61109595
Auto Spare Parts & Accessory Distr
N.A.I.C.S.: 423120

MECA Verkstadsdrift AB (1)
Tunbytorpsgatan 8, 721 37, Vasteras, Sweden
Tel.: (46) 21840030
Auto Spare Parts & Accessory Distr
N.A.I.C.S.: 423120

Meca Bilverkstad Tunby AB (1)
Tunbytorpsgatan 8, 721 37, Vasteras, Sweden
Tel.: (46) 21840030
Auto Spare Parts & Accessory Distr
N.A.I.C.S.: 423120

Meko Service Nordic (1)
Solnavagen 4, Box 19542, SE-104 32, Stockholm, Sweden
Tel.: (46) 8 464 00 00
Web Site: http://mekonomen.com
Car Repair Shops Operator

MEKO AB

MEKO AB—(Continued)
N.A.I.C.S.: 811111

Mekonomen AS (1)
Rosenholmveien 25, 1414, Trollasen, Norway
Tel.: (47) 66805566
Web Site: http://www.mekonomen.no
Auto Spare Parts & Accessory Distr
N.A.I.C.S.: 423120

Mekonomen Alingsas AB (1)
Kristineholmsvagen 26 B, 441 39, Alingsas, Sweden
Tel.: (46) 322668500
Auto Spare Parts & Accessory Distr
N.A.I.C.S.: 423120

Mekonomen Arvika AB (1)
Akaregatan 8, 671 34, Arvika, Sweden
Tel.: (46) 57019830
Auto Spare Parts & Accessory Distr
N.A.I.C.S.: 423120

Mekonomen Backaplan AB (1)
Deltavagen 4, 417 05, Gothenburg, Sweden
Tel.: (46) 31235100
Auto Spare Parts & Accessory Distr
N.A.I.C.S.: 423120

Mekonomen BilLivet Backaplan AB (1)
Deltavagen 4, 417 05, Gothenburg, Sweden
Tel.: (46) 31235100
Auto Spare Parts & Accessory Distr
N.A.I.C.S.: 423120

Mekonomen BilLivet Bromma AB (1)
Ranhammarsvagen 18, 168 67, Bromma, Sweden
Tel.: (46) 851789400
Auto Spare Parts & Accessory Distr
N.A.I.C.S.: 423120

Mekonomen BilLivet Gardet AB (1)
Tegeluddsvagen 82, 115 28, Stockholm, Sweden
Tel.: (46) 856313131
Auto Spare Parts & Accessory Distr
N.A.I.C.S.: 423120

Mekonomen BilLivet Gavle AB (1)
Kryddstigen 1-3, 802 92, Gavle, Sweden
Tel.: (46) 26100110
Auto Spare Parts & Accessory Distr
N.A.I.C.S.: 423120

Mekonomen BilLivet Infra City AB (1)
Stockholmsvagen 37, 194 54, Upplands Vasby, Sweden
Tel.: (46) 859469920
Auto Spare Parts & Accessory Distr
N.A.I.C.S.: 423120

Mekonomen BilLivet Johanneshov AB (1)
Tradskolevagen 5-11 Globen, 121 62, Johanneshov, Sweden
Tel.: (46) 855930100
Auto Spare Parts & Accessory Distr
N.A.I.C.S.: 423120

Mekonomen BilLivet Katrinelund AB (1)
Celsiusgatan 38A, 212 14, Malmo, Sweden
Tel.: (46) 40295040
Auto Spare Parts & Accessory Distr
N.A.I.C.S.: 423120

Mekonomen BilLivet Sodertalje AB (1)
Forskargatan 17, 151 36, Sodertalje, Sweden
Tel.: (46) 840050048
Auto Spare Parts & Accessory Distr
N.A.I.C.S.: 423120

Mekonomen BilLivet Taby AB (1)
Stockholmsvagen 100-102, 187 30, Taby, Sweden
Tel.: (46) 86639351
Auto Spare Parts & Accessory Distr
N.A.I.C.S.: 423120

Mekonomen Billivet Albyberg AB (1)
Albybergsvingen 99, Osterhaninge, 137 69, Stockholm, Sweden
Tel.: (46) 87770170
Auto Spare Parts & Accessory Distr
N.A.I.C.S.: 423120

Mekonomen Billivet Almhult AB (1)
Torngatan 4, 343 34, Almhult, Sweden
Tel.: (46) 47615050
Auto Spare Parts & Accessory Distr
N.A.I.C.S.: 423120

Mekonomen Billivet Boras AB (1)
Enedalsgatan 11, 504 52, Boras, Sweden
Tel.: (46) 33124045
Auto Spare Parts & Accessory Distr
N.A.I.C.S.: 423120

Mekonomen Billivet Eklanda AB (1)
Arnegardsgatan 7, 431 49, Molndal, Sweden
Tel.: (46) 317104540
Auto Spare Parts & Accessory Distr
N.A.I.C.S.: 423120

Mekonomen Billivet Fosie AB (1)
Hornyxegatan 12, 213 76, Malmo, Sweden
Tel.: (46) 40927070
Auto Spare Parts & Accessory Distr
N.A.I.C.S.: 423120

Mekonomen Billivet Gislaved AB (1)
Enestromsgatan 7, 332 36, Gislaved, Sweden
Tel.: (46) 371799000
Auto Spare Parts & Accessory Distr
N.A.I.C.S.: 423120

Mekonomen Billivet Harnosand AB (1)
Industrigatan 2, 871 35, Harnosand, Sweden
Tel.: (46) 61124600
Auto Spare Parts & Accessory Distr
N.A.I.C.S.: 423120

Mekonomen Billivet Hedemora AB (1)
Ivarshyttevagen 1, 776 33, Hedemora, Sweden
Tel.: (46) 22514361
Auto Spare Parts & Accessory Distr
N.A.I.C.S.: 423120

Mekonomen Billivet Karlshamn AB (1)
Tubbatorg 2, 374 32, Karlshamn, Sweden
Tel.: (46) 45416650
Auto Spare Parts & Accessory Distr
N.A.I.C.S.: 423120

Mekonomen Billivet Kiruna AB (1)
Industrivagen 21-25, 981 38, Kiruna, Sweden
Tel.: (46) 980399000
Auto Spare Parts & Accessory Distr
N.A.I.C.S.: 423120

Mekonomen Billivet Lidingo AB (1)
Forradsvagen 4D, 181 41, Lidingo, Sweden
Tel.: (46) 87651908
Auto Spare Parts & Accessory Distr
N.A.I.C.S.: 423120

Mekonomen Billivet Ljungby AB (1)
Sparvagen 8, 341 31, Ljungby, Sweden
Tel.: (46) 37210666
Auto Spare Parts & Accessory Distr
N.A.I.C.S.: 423120

Mekonomen Billivet Nodinge AB (1)
Rodjans Vag 2, Nodinge, 449 34, Vastra Gotaland, Sweden
Tel.: (46) 30396460
Auto Spare Parts & Accessory Distr
N.A.I.C.S.: 423120

Mekonomen Billivet Norremark AB (1)
Erik Norbergs Vag 5, 352 45, Vaxjo, Sweden
Tel.: (46) 47018020
Auto Spare Parts & Accessory Distr
N.A.I.C.S.: 423120

Mekonomen Billivet Nybro AB (1)
Fagelvagen 2, 382 34, Nybro, Sweden
Tel.: (46) 48118666
Auto Spare Parts & Accessory Distr
N.A.I.C.S.: 423120

Mekonomen Billivet Skelleftea AB (1)
Tjarnvagen 36, 931 61, Skelleftea, Sweden
Tel.: (46) 910777416
Auto Spare Parts & Accessory Distr
N.A.I.C.S.: 423120

Mekonomen Billivet Stromstad AB (1)
Kilegatan 2, 452 33, Stromstad, Sweden
Tel.: (46) 52615111
Auto Spare Parts & Accessory Distr
N.A.I.C.S.: 423120

Mekonomen Billivet Varnamo AB (1)
Kavsjovagen 45, 331 35, Varnamo, Sweden
Tel.: (46) 37012304
Auto Spare Parts & Accessory Distr
N.A.I.C.S.: 423120

Mekonomen Billivet Vaxjo AB (1)
Marketenterivagen 25, 352 36, Vaxjo, Sweden
Tel.: (46) 47022659
Auto Spare Parts & Accessory Distr
N.A.I.C.S.: 423120

Mekonomen Bilverkstad AB (1)
Viktoriaesplanaden 7, 891 33, Ornskoldsvik, Sweden
Tel.: (46) 66016360
Auto Spare Parts & Accessory Distr
N.A.I.C.S.: 423120

Mekonomen Bollnas AB (1)
Verkstadsvagen 4, 821 43, Bollnas, Sweden
Tel.: (46) 27816500
Auto Spare Parts & Accessory Distr
N.A.I.C.S.: 423120

Mekonomen Eklanda AB (1)
Arnegardsgatan 7, 431 49, Gothenburg, Sweden
Tel.: (46) 31470910
Auto Spare Parts & Accessory Distr
N.A.I.C.S.: 423120

Mekonomen Enkoping AB (1)
Akerbygatan 2, 745 37, Enkoping, Sweden
Tel.: (46) 17138850
Auto Spare Parts & Accessory Distr
N.A.I.C.S.: 423120

Mekonomen Eskilstuna AB (1)
Gunborg Nymans Vag 1, 632 22, Eskilstuna, Sweden
Tel.: (46) 16136840
Auto Spare Parts & Accessory Distr
N.A.I.C.S.: 423120

Mekonomen Falkenberg AB (1)
Oktanvagen 2, 311 32, Falkenberg, Sweden
Tel.: (46) 34613995
Auto Spare Parts & Accessory Distr
N.A.I.C.S.: 423120

Mekonomen Falun AB (1)
Ryckepungsvagen 1, 791 77, Falun, Sweden
Tel.: (46) 2322030
Auto Spare Parts & Accessory Distr
N.A.I.C.S.: 423120

Mekonomen Flen AB (1)
Hantverkaregatan 5, 642 37, Flen, Sweden
Tel.: (46) 15712570
Auto Spare Parts & Accessory Distr
N.A.I.C.S.: 423120

Mekonomen Gavle AB (1)
Kryddstigen 1-3, 802 92, Gavle, Sweden
Tel.: (46) 26100110
Auto Spare Parts & Accessory Distr
N.A.I.C.S.: 423120

Mekonomen Hallsberg AB (1)
Kajsabacksvagen 5, 694 34, Hallsberg, Sweden
Tel.: (46) 58210402
Auto Spare Parts & Accessory Distr
N.A.I.C.S.: 423120

Mekonomen Harnosand AB (1)
Industrigatan 2, 871 53, Harnosand, Sweden
Tel.: (46) 61124600
Auto Spare Parts & Accessory Distr
N.A.I.C.S.: 423120

Mekonomen Jarfalla AB (1)
Nettovagen 11, 175 41, Jarfalla, Sweden
Tel.: (46) 858034440
Auto Spare Parts & Accessory Distr
N.A.I.C.S.: 423120

INTERNATIONAL PUBLIC

Mekonomen Kristianstad AB (1)
Jochums Vag 5, 291 59, Kristianstad, Sweden
Tel.: (46) 44219906
Auto Spare Parts & Accessory Distr
N.A.I.C.S.: 423120

Mekonomen Kungshamn AB (1)
Televerksvagen 8, 456 33, Kungshamn, Sweden
Tel.: (46) 52332390
Auto Spare Parts & Accessory Distr
N.A.I.C.S.: 423120

Mekonomen Mariestad AB (1)
Storegardsvagen 32, 542 35, Mariestad, Sweden
Tel.: (46) 50115175
Auto Spare Parts & Accessory Distr
N.A.I.C.S.: 423120

Mekonomen Mjolby AB (1)
Kungsvagen 31, 595 51, Mjolby, Sweden
Tel.: (46) 14215413
Auto Spare Parts & Accessory Distr
N.A.I.C.S.: 423120

Mekonomen Nordic (1)
Solnavagen 4, 113 65, Stockholm, Sweden
Tel.: (46) 8 464 0000
Web Site: https://www.mekonomen.se
Car Accessories, Repair & Maintenance Services
N.A.I.C.S.: 441330
David Larsson (*Acting Pres & CFO*)

Mekonomen Oy (1)
Hankasuontie 4, 00390, Helsinki, Finland
Tel.: (358) 103274600
Web Site: http://www.mekonomen.fi
Auto Spare Parts & Accessory Distr
N.A.I.C.S.: 423120

Mekonomen Skelleftea AB (1)
Tjarnvagen 36, 931 61, Skelleftea, Sweden
Tel.: (46) 910777416
Auto Spare Parts & Accessory Distr
N.A.I.C.S.: 423120

Mekonomen Sodertalje AB (1)
Forskargatan 17, 151 36, Sodertalje, Sweden
Tel.: (46) 840050048
Auto Spare Parts & Accessory Distr
N.A.I.C.S.: 423120

Mekonomen Solleftea AB (1)
Industrivagen 15, 881 35, Solleftea, Sweden
Tel.: (46) 62057750
Auto Spare Parts & Accessory Distr
N.A.I.C.S.: 423120

Mekonomen Stromstad AB (1)
Kilegatan 2, 452 33, Stromstad, Sweden
Tel.: (46) 52615111
Auto Spare Parts & Accessory Distr
N.A.I.C.S.: 423120

Mekonomen Sundsvall Birsta AB (1)
Larlingsvagen 1, 863 41, Sundsvall, Sweden
Tel.: (46) 60147030
Auto Spare Parts & Accessory Distr
N.A.I.C.S.: 423120

Mekonomen Tonsberg AS (1)
Kilengt 13, 3117, Tonsberg, Norway
Tel.: (47) 33359070
Auto Spare Parts & Accessory Distr
N.A.I.C.S.: 423120

Mekonomen Tranas AB (1)
Agatan 25, 573 31, Tranas, Sweden
Tel.: (46) 14014030
Auto Spare Parts & Accessory Distr
N.A.I.C.S.: 423120

Mekonomen Trollhattan AB (1)
Sandviksvagen 1, 461 70, Trollhattan, Sweden
Tel.: (46) 52080090
Auto Spare Parts & Accessory Distr
N.A.I.C.S.: 423120

Mekonomen Vanersborg AB (1)
Parallellgatan 56, 462 32, Vanersborg, Sweden
Tel.: (46) 52119880
Auto Spare Parts & Accessory Distr
N.A.I.C.S.: 423120

AND PRIVATE COMPANIES

Mekonomen Verkstadscenter Alvsjo AB (1)
Grossistvagen 1-5, 125 30, Alvsjo, Sweden
Tel.: (46) 850308494
Auto Spare Parts & Accessory Distr
N.A.I.C.S.: 423120

Mekonomen Vetlanda AB (1)
Vasterleden 60, 574 41, Vetlanda, Sweden
Tel.: (46) 38319350
Auto Spare Parts & Accessory Distr
N.A.I.C.S.: 423120

Mekster AB (1)
Medborgarplatsen 3, 118 26, Stockholm, Sweden
Tel.: (46) 105516080
Web Site: http://www.mekster.se
Auto Spare Parts & Accessory Distr
N.A.I.C.S.: 423120

Motor Norge AS (1)
Markveien 39, 9510, Alta, Norway
Tel.: (47) 7 844 9866
Web Site: https://www.motornorge.no
Motorcycle Equipment Distr
N.A.I.C.S.: 441227

Preqas AB (1)
Backstensgatan 11 C, 431 49, Molndal, Sweden
Tel.: (46) 317884200
Web Site: http://www.preqas.se
Car Repair Services
N.A.I.C.S.: 811111

Preqas AS (1)
Bolerveien 38, 2016, Frogner, Norway
Tel.: (47) 63877799
Web Site: http://www.preqas.no
Auto Spare Parts & Accessory Distr
N.A.I.C.S.: 423120

Promotor Akersberga AB (1)
Stationsvagen 30, 184 50, Akersberga, Sweden
Tel.: (46) 854065252
Auto Spare Parts & Accessory Distr
N.A.I.C.S.: 423120

Sorensen og Balchen AS (1)
Rosenholmveien 12, 1252, Oslo, Norway
Tel.: (47) 22 76 44 00
Web Site: http://www.sogb.no
Used Car Parts Whslr
N.A.I.C.S.: 423140
Andreas Hamdahl *(CFO)*

Speedy Bilservice Hogsbo AB (1)
EA Rosengrens Gata 13, 421 31, Vastra Frolunda, Sweden
Tel.: (46) 31472420
Car Repair Services
N.A.I.C.S.: 811111

Speedy Bilservice Ostermalm AB (1)
Valhallavagen 161, 115 53, Stockholm, Sweden
Tel.: (46) 86626065
Car Repair Services
N.A.I.C.S.: 811111

Speedy Bilservice pa Limhamn AB (1)
Hyllie Kyrkovag 35, 216 11, Malmo, Sweden
Tel.: (46) 40156100
Car Repair Services
N.A.I.C.S.: 811111

MEKONG FISHERIES JOINT STOCK COMPANY
Lot 24 Tra Noc Industrial Zone, Binh Thuy District, Can Tho, Vietnam
Tel.: (84) 2923841294
Web Site: https://www.mekongfish.vn
Year Founded: 1979
AAM—(HOSE)
Rev.: $5,634,636
Assets: $8,769,708
Liabilities: $421,105
Net Worth: $8,348,603
Earnings: $28,964
Emp.: 176
Fiscal Year-end: 12/31/23
Seafood Product Mfr
N.A.I.C.S.: 311710
Luong Hoang Manh *(Exec Dir)*

MEKOPRINT A/S
Mercurvej 1, 9530, Stovring, Denmark
Tel.: (45) 99365600 DK
Web Site: http://www.mekoprint.dk
Year Founded: 1954
Sales Range: $75-99.9 Million
Emp.: 500
Design, Serigraphy, Mechanical Processing, Surface Treatment & Mounting Services
N.A.I.C.S.: 332812
Esben Kold *(Vice Chm)*

Subsidiaries:

Mekoprint Chemigraphics (1)
Mercurvej 1-3, DK 9530, Stovring, Denmark
Tel.: (45) 99365600
Web Site: http://www.mekoprint.dk
Sales Range: $25-49.9 Million
Emp.: 50
Etched Sheet Metal Components Mfr
N.A.I.C.S.: 332322
Benny Albrektsen *(Bus Mgr-Chemigraphics Unit)*

Mekoprint Electronics (1)
Vibeholms Alle 15, 2605, Brondby, Denmark
Tel.: (45) 99365600
Web Site: http://www.mekoprint.dk
Sales Range: $100-124.9 Million
Emp.: 100
Electronic Interface Component Mfr
N.A.I.C.S.: 334418

Mekoprint Graphics (1)
Hermesvej 2, 9200, Stovring, Denmark
Tel.: (45) 99365600
Emp.: 100
Plastic Signs, Overlays & Transfers, Insulation Foils & Overlays Mfr
N.A.I.C.S.: 326199
Karsten Ries *(Mgr-Div)*

Mekoprint Mechanics (1)
Faborgvej 15, 9220, Aalborg, Denmark
Tel.: (45) 99365600
Sales Range: $25-49.9 Million
Emp.: 60
Chassis Parts, Instrument Panels & Front Panels Mfr
N.A.I.C.S.: 336370
Benny Albrektsen *(Mgr-Div Chemigraphics)*

MEL INVEST HOLDING AD
Gen Blvd Totleben 85-87, 1606, Sofia, Bulgaria
Tel.: (359) 28052020
Web Site: https://www.melinvest.bg
MELH—(BUL)
Sales Range: Less than $1 Million
Investment Management Service
N.A.I.C.S.: 525990
Valko Stoyanov Valev *(CEO)*

MELAMIN D.D.
Tomsiceva cesta 9, 1330, Kocevje, Slovenia
Tel.: (386) 18959300
Web Site: http://www.melamin.si
Year Founded: 1954
Sales Range: $25-49.9 Million
Emp.: 200
Chemical, Paint, Adhesive & Resin Mfr
N.A.I.C.S.: 325998
Srecko Stefanic *(Gen Mgr)*

Subsidiaries:

Futura DDB d.o.o. (1)
Poljanski Nasip 6, 1000, Ljubljana, Slovenia
Tel.: (386) 13004000
Web Site: http://www.futura.si
Sales Range: $25-49.9 Million
Emp.: 80
Advertising Services
N.A.I.C.S.: 541810
Marko Vicic *(Partner)*

Futura PR d.o.o. (1)
Poljanski Nasip 6, Ljubljana, Slovenia
Tel.: (386) 12801200
Web Site: http://www.futuraddb.si
Sales Range: $25-49.9 Million
Emp.: 10
Public Relations Services
N.A.I.C.S.: 541820

MELAT INVESTMENT COMPANY
Walyelasr Street Opposite Of Mellat Park Sayeh Street, Tehran, 19677 13914, Iran
Tel.: (98) 21 26217640
Year Founded: 1992
Investment Management Service
N.A.I.C.S.: 523999
Abutaleb Dibaei *(Chm)*

MELATI EHSAN HOLDINGS BERHAD
No 5 Jalan Titiwangsa, Wilayah Persekutuan, 53200, Kuala Lumpur, Malaysia
Tel.: (60) 340222177
Web Site: https://www.melatiehsan.com.my
MELATI—(KLS)
Rev.: $21,723,416
Assets: $85,368,979
Liabilities: $33,471,274
Net Worth: $51,897,704
Earnings: $3,557,079
Emp.: 51
Fiscal Year-end: 08/31/23
Construction Management Services
N.A.I.C.S.: 236118
Chee Yean Chan *(Co-Sec)*

MELBANA ENERGY LIMITED
Mezzanine Floor 388 George Street, Sydney, 2000, NSW, Australia
Tel.: (61) 283236600 AU
Web Site: https://www.melbana.com
Year Founded: 1994
MEOAF—(OTCIQ)
Rev.: $5,641,050
Assets: $64,335,836
Liabilities: $26,988,636
Net Worth: $37,347,201
Earnings: $2,176,656
Fiscal Year-end: 06/30/24
Crude Petroleum Extraction Services
N.A.I.C.S.: 211120
Andrew Gerard Purcell *(Chm)*

MELBOURNE ENTERPRISES LIMITED
Rm 2102-4 Melbourne Plaza 33 Queens Road, Central, China (Hong Kong)
Tel.: (852) 25239171 HK
Web Site: http://www.irasia.com 0158—(HKG)
Rev.: $20,691,359
Assets: $1,017,805,170
Liabilities: $9,499,635
Net Worth: $1,008,305,535
Earnings: $8,623,990
Emp.: 16
Fiscal Year-end: 09/30/21
Property Investment Services
N.A.I.C.S.: 523999
Ming Fai Chung *(Chm)*

MELBOURNE SYMPHONY ORCHESTRA
120-130 Southbank Blvd, Southbank, 3006, VIC, Australia
Tel.: (61) 396261111
Web Site: http://www.mso.com.au
Sales Range: $10-24.9 Million
Emp.: 130
Symphony Orchestra
N.A.I.C.S.: 711130
Raelene King *(Mgr-Personnel)*

MELBYE SKANDINAVIA AS

MELCO HOLDINGS INC.

Prost Stabelsvei 22, 2021, Skedsmokorset, Norway
Tel.: (47) 6387 0150 NO
Web Site: http://www.melbye.com
Year Founded: 1907
Sales Range: $200-249.9 Million
Emp.: 78
Holding Company; Energy & Fiber Networks Product Sales & Marketing Services
N.A.I.C.S.: 551112
Christian Aasheim *(Pres & CEO)*

Subsidiaries:

Melbye Skandinavia Norge AS (1)
Prost Stabelsvei 22, 2019, Skedsmokorset, Norway (100%)
Tel.: (47) 6387 0150
Web Site: http://www.melbye.com
Emp.: 35
Energy & Fiber Networks Product Sales & Marketing Services
N.A.I.C.S.: 423840
Christian Aasheim *(CEO & Mng Dir)*

Melbye Skandinavia Sverige AB (1)
Fordonsvagen 17, 553 02, Jonkoping, Sweden (100%)
Tel.: (46) 36 332 0700
Web Site: http://www.melby.com
Energy & Fiber Networks Product Sales & Marketing Services
N.A.I.C.S.: 423840
Lars Arberg *(Mng Dir)*

RS Technologies Inc. (1)
3553 31 Street NW, Calgary, T2L 2K7, AB, Canada
Tel.: (403) 219-8001
Web Site: http://www.groupsi.com
Sales Range: $1-9.9 Million
Advanced Composite Material Products Developer & Mfr
N.A.I.C.S.: 325211
David P. Werklund *(Chm)*

Subsidiary (Domestic):

RS Advanced Structures Inc. (2)
22 Industrial Park Rd, Tilbury, N0P 2L0, ON, Canada
Tel.: (519) 682-1110
Wood Products Mfr
N.A.I.C.S.: 321999

MELCHIONI SPA
Via Pietro Colletta 37 20135, Milan, Italy
Tel.: (39) 02 5794 1
Web Site: http://www.melchioni.it
Year Founded: 1955
Industrial Electronic Component Mfr
N.A.I.C.S.: 334419
Armando Melchioni *(Pres)*

MELCO HOLDINGS INC.
Akamon-dori Bldg 3-30-20 Ohsu, Naka-ku, Nagoya, 460-8315, Aichi, Japan
Tel.: (81) 522516891 JP
Web Site: https://melco-hd.jp
Year Founded: 1986
6676—(TKS)
Rev.: $963,559,530
Assets: $634,136,960
Liabilities: $211,612,540
Net Worth: $422,524,420
Earnings: $19,909,320
Emp.: 1,023
Fiscal Year-end: 03/31/24
Holding Company
N.A.I.C.S.: 551112
Hiroyuki Maki *(Pres)*

Subsidiaries:

BUFFALO DIRECT INC. (1)
Akamondori Building 3-30-20 Osu, Naka-ku, Nagoya, 460-8315, Aichi, Japan
Tel.: (81) 522496610
Web Site: https://www.buffalo.jp
Emp.: 648
Computer Peripherals Mfr & Sales

MELCO HOLDINGS INC.

Melco Holdings Inc.—(Continued)
N.A.I.C.S.: 423430

BUFFALO IT SOLUTIONS INC. (1)
1-11-1 Marunouchi Pacific Century Place Marunouchi 15th floor, Chiyoda-ku, Tokyo, 100-0005, Japan
Tel.: (81) 342131140
Web Site: https://buffalo-its.jp
Information Technology Services
N.A.I.C.S.: 541511

BUFFALO LEASE INC. (1)
Kayabacho Tower 21-2 Shinkawa 1-chome, Chuo-ku, Tokyo, 104-0033, Japan
Tel.: (81) 335233354
Web Site: http://www.melcoinc.com
Emp.: 1
Broadband Equipment Rental Services
N.A.I.C.S.: 532490
Hisashi Omattu *(Gen Mgr)*

Buffalo EU B.V. (1)
Saturnusstraat 17, 2132 HB, Hoofddorp, Netherlands
Tel.: (31) 235544632
Web Site: https://www.buffalo-technology.com
Sales Range: $25-49.9 Million
Emp.: 20
Wireless Network Services
N.A.I.C.S.: 517112

Buffalo Inc. (1)
Akamon-dori Building 30-30 Osu, Naka-ku, Nagoya, 460-8315, Aichi, Japan
Tel.: (81) 522496610
Web Site: https://www.buffalo.jp
Emp.: 648
Wireless Network Services
N.A.I.C.S.: 517112

Buffalo Logistics Inc. (1)
Chukyo Warehouse No 33 1-3 Mutsuno 2-chome, Atsuta-ku, Nagoya, 456-0023, Aichi, Japan
Tel.: (81) 528833035
Logistic Services
N.A.I.C.S.: 541614

Buffalo Technology (Taiwan) Inc. (1)
7F No 18 Ln 609 Sec 5 Chung Hsin Rd, San Chung, Taipei, Taiwan
Tel.: (886) 229999860
Web Site: https://www.buffalo-tech.com.tw
Sales Range: $25-49.9 Million
Emp.: 75
Networking Devices Mfr & Sales
N.A.I.C.S.: 334118

Buffalo Technology (USA) Inc. (1)
11000 Metric Blvd Ste 750, Austin, TX 78758
Tel.: (512) 794-8533
Web Site: http://www.buffalotech.com
Sales Range: $25-49.9 Million
Emp.: 50
Wireless Network Services
N.A.I.C.S.: 517112
Jay Pechek *(Mgr)*

Liberty Ship Inc. (1)
Kayabacho Tower 21-2 Shinkawa 1-Chome, Chuo-ku, Tokyo, 104-0033, Japan
Tel.: (81) 335233368
Web Site: http://www.liberty-ship.co.jp
Sales Range: $25-49.9 Million
Emp.: 3
Internet Content Management Services
N.A.I.C.S.: 541513

MELCO PERSONNEL SUPPORT INC. (1)
Kamiya Bldg 11-50 Ohsu 4-chome, Naka-ku, Nagoya, 460-0011, Aichi, Japan
Tel.: (81) 526197224
Recruitment Services
N.A.I.C.S.: 561311

Shimadaya Corporation (1)
1-33-11 Ebisunishi, Shibuya-ku, Tokyo, 150-0021, Japan
Tel.: (81) 354895595
Sales Range: $250-299.9 Million
Noodles Mfr & Whslr
N.A.I.C.S.: 311999
Norio Kinoshita *(Pres)*

MELCO INTERNATIONAL DEVELOPMENT, LTD.
37th Floor The Centrium 60 Wyndham Street, Central, China (Hong Kong)
Tel.: (852) 31513777
Web Site: https://www.melco-group.com
Year Founded: 1910
0200—(HKG)
Rev.: $1,347,121,268
Assets: $12,379,181,295
Liabilities: $10,672,458,008
Net Worth: $1,706,723,288
Earnings: ($1,273,382,918)
Emp.: 16,911
Fiscal Year-end: 12/31/22
Holding Company; Technology, Financial Services, Leisure & Entertainment
N.A.I.C.S.: 551112
Clarence Yuk Man Chung *(Exec Dir)*

Subsidiaries:

Aberdeen Restaurant Enterprises Limited (1)
Shum Wan Pier Drive Wong Chuk Hang, Aberdeen, China (Hong Kong) (86.68%)
Tel.: (852) 25539111
Web Site: https://www.jumbokingdom.com
Sales Range: $25-49.9 Million
Emp.: 200
Restaurant Management Services
N.A.I.C.S.: 722511

Entertainment Gaming Asia, Inc. (1)
37/F The Centrium 60 Wyndham Street, Central, China (Hong Kong) (100%)
Tel.: (852) 3147 6600
Web Site: http://www.egt-group.com
Rev.: $1,959,000
Assets: $39,428,000
Liabilities: $7,669,000
Net Worth: $31,759,000
Earnings: ($9,735,000)
Emp.: 60
Fiscal Year-end: 12/31/2016
Electronic Gaming Products Developer, Mfr & Distr
N.A.I.C.S.: 713290
Clarence Yuk Man Chung *(Chm, Pres & CEO)*

Melco Resorts & Entertainment Limited (1)
37/F The Centrium 60 Wyndham Stree, Central, China (Hong Kong) (51.3%)
Tel.: (852) 25983600
Web Site: https://www.melco-resorts.com
Rev.: $3,775,247,000
Assets: $8,335,072,000
Liabilities: $9,175,122,000
Net Worth: ($840,050,000)
Earnings: ($326,920,000)
Emp.: 20,209
Fiscal Year-end: 12/31/2023
Casino Gaming & Entertainment Resort Facilities Developer, Owner & Operator
N.A.I.C.S.: 721110
Lawrence Yau Lung Ho *(Chm & CEO)*

Melco Resorts and Entertainment (Philippines) Corporation (1)
City of Dreams Manila Asean Avenue cor, Roxas Boulevard Brgy Tambo, Paranaque, 1701, Philippines
Tel.: (63) 2 800 8080
Web Site: http://www.melco-resorts-philippines.com
Rev.: $655,104,340
Assets: $688,567,980
Liabilities: $580,251,620
Net Worth: $108,316,360
Earnings: $7,078,460
Emp.: 4,894
Fiscal Year-end: 12/31/2017
Hotel Operator
N.A.I.C.S.: 721120
Clarence Yuk Man Chung *(Chm & Pres)*

MELCOR DEVELOPMENTS LTD.
900 10310 Jasper Avenue NW, Edmonton, T5J 1Y8, AB, Canada
Tel.: (780) 423-6931 AB
Web Site: https://www.melcor.ca
Year Founded: 1923
F7G—(DEU)
Rev.: $238,043,274
Assets: $1,583,843,812
Liabilities: $670,467,272
Net Worth: $913,376,539
Earnings: $47,557,458
Emp.: 124
Fiscal Year-end: 12/31/23
Family & Commercial Real Estate Planning & Development
N.A.I.C.S.: 531312
Guy Pelletier *(VP-Red Deer)*

Subsidiaries:

Lewis Estates Golf Course (1)
260 Suder Greens Drive, Edmonton, T5T 4B7, AB, Canada
Tel.: (780) 489-4653
Web Site: https://www.lewisestatesgolf.com
Sales Range: $50-74.9 Million
Golf Course Owner & Operator
N.A.I.C.S.: 713910
Jerry Linquist *(Gen Mgr)*

Melcor Developments Arizona Inc. (1)
6930 E Chauncey Ln Ste 135, Phoenix, AZ 85054
Tel.: (480) 699-4687
Web Site: https://melcorusa.com
Real Estate Services
N.A.I.C.S.: 531390
Tim Melton *(Chm)*

The Links at Spruce Grove (1)
100 Links Rd, PO Box 4268, Spruce Grove, T7X 3B4, AB, Canada
Tel.: (780) 962-4653
Web Site: https://www.linksgolfcourse.com
Sales Range: $50-74.9 Million
Golf Course Operator & Owner
N.A.I.C.S.: 713910

MELCOR REAL ESTATE INVESTMENT TRUST
900 10310 Jasper Avenue NW, Edmonton, T5J 1Y8, AB, Canada
Tel.: (780) 423-6931 AB
Web Site: https://www.melcorreit.ca
Year Founded: 2013
MODVF—(OTCIQ)
Rev.: $55,803,368
Assets: $529,337,610
Liabilities: $378,851,255
Net Worth: $150,486,355
Earnings: $12,318,273
Fiscal Year-end: 12/31/23
Real Estate Investment Services
N.A.I.C.S.: 523999
Andrew J. Melton *(CEO)*

MELEWAR INDUSTRIAL GROUP BERHAD
15th Floor No 566 Jalan Ipoh, 51200, Kuala Lumpur, Selangor Darul Ehsan, Malaysia
Tel.: (60) 362506000 MY
Web Site: https://www.melewar-mig.com
Year Founded: 1969
MELEWAR—(KLS)
Rev.: $116,330,879
Assets: $159,079,101
Liabilities: $45,907,950
Net Worth: $113,171,150
Earnings: ($3,573,907)
Emp.: 547
Fiscal Year-end: 06/30/23
Steel Pole Mfr
N.A.I.C.S.: 331110
Leh Hong Soon *(Chief Treasury Officer)*

Subsidiaries:

3Bumi Oleo Sdn Bhd (1)
23 Jalan Cempaka Utama Taman Anugerah Suria, Sg Choh, 48000, Rawang, Selangor, Malaysia

INTERNATIONAL PUBLIC

Tel.: (60) 196638876
Web Site: https://www.3bumioleo.com
Palm Oil Mfr
N.A.I.C.S.: 311225

Jack Nathan Limited (1)
17 White Lion Road, Amersham, HP7 9HZ, Buckinghamshire, United Kingdom
Tel.: (44) 7495011803
Web Site: https://www.jacknathan.co.uk
Steel Tube Mfr
N.A.I.C.S.: 332999

Melewar Steel Mills Sdn Bhd (1)
Lot 717 Jalan Sungai Rasau Seksyen 16, 40200, Shah Alam, Selangor, Malaysia
Tel.: (60) 355191633
Web Site: https://www.melewar-mig.com
Emp.: 15
Steel Bar Mfr
N.A.I.C.S.: 331110
Teong Thuan Soo *(CEO)*

Melewar Steel Tube Sdn Bhd (1)
Lot 53 Persiaran Selangor, 40200, Shah Alam, Selangor, Malaysia
Tel.: (60) 355192455
Web Site: http://www.melewar-mig.com
Emp.: 180
Steel Products Mfr
N.A.I.C.S.: 331110

Mycron Steel Berhad (1)
Lot 717 Jalan Sungai Rasau Seksyen 16, 40706, Shah Alam, Selangor, Malaysia (54.8%)
Tel.: (60) 355106608
Web Site: https://www.mycronsteel.com
Rev.: $114,284,595
Assets: $149,444,819
Liabilities: $45,012,266
Net Worth: $104,432,553
Earnings: ($2,610,764)
Emp.: 427
Fiscal Year-end: 06/30/2023
Cold Rolled Steel Mfr
N.A.I.C.S.: 331221
Lily Kam May Yin *(Sec)*

Subsidiary (Domestic):

Mycron Steel CRC Sdn Bhd (2)
Lot 717 Jalan Sungai Rasau Seksyen 16, 40706, Shah Alam, Selangor, Malaysia
Tel.: (60) 355106608
Web Site: http://www.mycronsteel.com
Sales Range: $25-49.9 Million
Emp.: 150
Cold Rolled Steel Mfr
N.A.I.C.S.: 331221

Siam Power Generation Public Company Limited (1)
SSP Tower 1 18th Floor 555 Sukhumvit 63 Ekamai, Watthana, Bangkok, 10110, Thailand (70%)
Tel.: (66) 2711 5141
Web Site: http://www.sipco.co.th
Eletric Power Generation Services
N.A.I.C.S.: 221118

MELEXIS N.V.
Rozendaalstraat 12, 8900, Ieper, Belgium
Tel.: (32) 13670779
Web Site: https://www.melexis.com
MELE—(EUR)
Rev.: $902,393,136
Assets: $626,195,736
Liabilities: $105,924,604
Net Worth: $520,271,132
Earnings: $212,769,981
Emp.: 1,730
Fiscal Year-end: 12/31/22
Automotive Semiconductors Mfr
N.A.I.C.S.: 334413
Francoise Chombar *(CEO & Mng Dir)*

Subsidiaries:

K.K. Melexis (1)
Technical Research Center Yokohama Heiwa Bldg 9F 3-30-7 Honcho, Naka-ku, Yokohama, 231-0005, Japan
Tel.: (81) 45 226 5370
Semiconductor Product Mfr
N.A.I.C.S.: 334413

AND PRIVATE COMPANIES

Melefin NV (1)
Transportstraat 1 Poort West-Limburg 1371-1372, 3980, Tessenderlo, Limburg, Belgium
Tel.: (32) 13670780
Web Site: http://www.melexis.com
Sales Range: $50-74.9 Million
Emp.: 180
Semiconductor Devices Mfr & Distr
N.A.I.C.S.: 334413

Melexis Bulgaria Ltd (1)
2 Samokovsko Shosse, Gorublian, 1138, Sofia, Bulgaria
Tel.: (359) 24276029
Sales Range: $50-74.9 Million
Emp.: 200
Automotive Electronic Product Mfr
N.A.I.C.S.: 336320

Melexis Dresden GmbH (1)
Zur Wetterwarte 50 Haus 337 / Eingang A, 01109, Dresden, Germany
Tel.: (49) 35150193303
Semiconductor Product Mfr
N.A.I.C.S.: 334413

Melexis Electronic Technology Co.Ltd (1)
Room 607 Building B SOHO FuXing Plaza No 277 DanShui Road, HuangPu District, Shanghai, 200025, China
Tel.: (86) 21 580 6899
Web Site: https://www.melexis.com
Automotive Electronic Product Mfr
N.A.I.C.S.: 336320

Melexis France SAS (1)
10 rue des Roissys Hau, 91450, Ormoy, France
Tel.: (33) 169221650
Semiconductor Product Mfr
N.A.I.C.S.: 334413

Melexis GmbH (1)
Konrad-Zuse-Strasse 15, 99099, Erfurt, Germany
Tel.: (49) 36143026000
Sales Range: $50-74.9 Million
Emp.: 200
Integrated Semiconductor Devices Mfr
N.A.I.C.S.: 334413
Urfula Saremki *(Mgr-Global Qlty)*

Melexis Japan KK (1)
Yokohama Heiwa Bldg 9F 3-30-7 Honcho, Naka-ku, Yokohama, 231-0005, Kanagawa, Japan
Tel.: (81) 45 226 5370
Web Site: https://www.melexis.com
Emp.: 10
Integrated Semiconductor Devices Mfr
N.A.I.C.S.: 334413

Melexis Technologies SA (1)
Chemin de Buchaux 38, 2022, Bevaix, Neuchatel, Switzerland
Tel.: (41) 328470660
Emp.: 40
Automotive Electronic Systems Mfr
N.A.I.C.S.: 336320

Melexis Tessenderlo NV (1)
Transportstraat 1 Poort West-Limburg 1371-1372, 3980, Tessenderlo, Belgium
Tel.: (32) 13670780
Web Site: https://www.melexis.com
Sales Range: $50-74.9 Million
Emp.: 180
Integrated Circuits Mfr
N.A.I.C.S.: 334418

Melexis Ukraine (1)
4 Kotelnykova Street, 03115, Kiev, Ukraine
Tel.: (380) 444950700
Sales Range: $25-49.9 Million
Emp.: 70
Integrated Semiconductor Devices Mfr
N.A.I.C.S.: 334413

Melexis, Inc. (1)
15 Trafalgar Sq Ste 100, Nashua, NH 03063-1968
Tel.: (603) 223-2362
Web Site: http://www.melexis.com
Mfr of Automotive Semiconductors
N.A.I.C.S.: 334413

Sentron AG (1)
Baarermattstrasse 10, 6300, Zug, Switzerland
Tel.: (41) 417112170

Automotive Electronic Product Mfr
N.A.I.C.S.: 336320

MELFAS INC.
Melfas B/D 225-14 Pangyoyeok-ro, Bundang-gu, Seongnam, 463-400, Gyeonggi-do, Korea (South)
Tel.: (82) 317072280
Web Site: http://www.melfas.com
Year Founded: 2000
096640—(KRS)
Rev.: $8,072,352
Assets: $39,872,392
Liabilities: $18,182,779
Net Worth: $21,689,614
Earnings: ($11,337,701)
Emp.: 25
Fiscal Year-end: 12/31/22
Display Mfr
N.A.I.C.S.: 334419
Bae Sang Yeol *(CEO)*

Subsidiaries:

MELFAS Inc. - Anseong Plant (1)
143 Sinsohyeon-dong, Anseong, Gyeonggi-do, Korea (South)
Tel.: (82) 316716612
Technology Development Services
N.A.I.C.S.: 541714

MELHUS SPAREBANK
Tel.: (47) 72878000
Web Site: https://www.melhusbanken.no
Year Founded: 1840
MELG—(OSL)
Sales Range: Less than $1 Million
Commercial Banking Services
N.A.I.C.S.: 522110
Ragnar Torland *(CEO & Mgr)*

MELIA HOTELS INTERNATIONAL, S.A.
Gremio Toneleros 24 Poligono Son Castello, 7009, Palma de Mallorca, Spain
Tel.: (34) 971224400 ES
Web Site: https://www.meliahotels.com
Year Founded: 1986
MEL—(BAR)
Rev.: $1,826,044,679
Assets: $4,693,020,721
Liabilities: $4,211,853,011
Net Worth: $481,167,710
Earnings: $119,461,472
Emp.: 10,028
Fiscal Year-end: 12/31/22
Hotel Operator
N.A.I.C.S.: 721110
Gabriel Canaves Picornell *(Chief HR Officer)*

Subsidiaries:

Apartotel, S.A. (1)
Mauricio Legendre 16, Madrid, Spain (99.73%)
Tel.: (34) 915715040
Accounting Services
N.A.I.C.S.: 541219

Bisol Vallarta, S.A. De C.V. (1)
Paseo De La Marina Sur Lt No 7, Puerto Vallarta, Jalisco, Mexico (100%)
Tel.: (52) 3222210461
Web Site: https://www.bisolmelia.com
Sales Range: $50-74.9 Million
Emp.: 290
Hotels & Motels
N.A.I.C.S.: 721110

CADSTAR FRANCE, S. A. (1)
12 Rue du Mont Thabor, Paris, France
Tel.: (33) 155047667
Sales Range: $10-24.9 Million
Emp.: 30
Restaurant Operating Services
N.A.I.C.S.: 722511

Subsidiary (Domestic):

Hotel Colbert SAS (2)
4 rue Alfred Dauvergne, 36000, Chateauroux, France
Tel.: (33) 254357000
Web Site: https://www.lecolbert36.fr
Sales Range: $10-24.9 Million
Emp.: 34
Hotel Operator
N.A.I.C.S.: 721110

ROYAL ALMA BOUTIQUE SAS (2)
35 Rue Jean Goujon, 75008, Paris, France
Tel.: (33) 1 53936300
Home Management Services
N.A.I.C.S.: 721110
Aldja Benarbia *(Gen Mgr)*

TRYP FRANCOIS SAS (2)
3 Boulevard Montmartre, Paris, 75002, France
Tel.: (33) 1 42335153
Sales Range: $10-24.9 Million
Emp.: 20
Home Management Services
N.A.I.C.S.: 721110

Cala Formentor, S.A. De C.V. (1)
Blvd Kukulcan, Km 16 5 Zona Hotelera, 77500, Cancun, Mexico (92.4%)
Tel.: (52) 9988811100
Sales Range: $10-24.9 Million
Emp.: 100
Hotels & Motels
N.A.I.C.S.: 721110

Casino Tamarindos, S.A. (1)
Calle Las Retamas 3, San Bartolome De Tirajana, Las Palmas, Spain (100%)
Tel.: (34) 928762724
Casino
N.A.I.C.S.: 713210

Credit Control Riesgos, S.L. (1)
Gremio Herreros toneleros no 24 39 2 A, 07009, Palma de Mallorca, Spain (100%)
Tel.: (34) 971459020
Web Site: http://www.reisgos.com
Business Support Services
N.A.I.C.S.: 561499
Alfonso Plata *(Gen Mgr)*

Dock Telemarketing, S.A. (1)
Calle Orense 81, Madrid, Spain (100%)
Tel.: (34) 917460024
Travel Agencies
N.A.I.C.S.: 561510

Hotel Bellver, S.A. (1)
Paseo Maritimo 11, Palma de Mallorca, 7014, Spain (100%)
Tel.: (34) 971735142
Web Site: http://www.melia.com
Sales Range: $10-24.9 Million
Emp.: 65
Hotels & Motels
N.A.I.C.S.: 721110
Carolina Rosello *(Gen Mgr)*

Hotel Convento Extremadura, S.A. (1)
Pza Campillo 1, Caceres, Spain (77.63%)
Tel.: (34) 927320899
Hotels & Motels
N.A.I.C.S.: 721110

Hotel Madeleine Palace, S.A.S. (1)
33 Place de La Madeleine, 75008, Paris, France
Tel.: (34) 143129260
Web Site: https://www.hotel-madeleine-paris.fr
Hotel & Motel Services
N.A.I.C.S.: 721110

Hoteles Sol Melia, S.L. (1)
Calle Gremi De Boters 24, Palma de Mallorca, Spain (100%)
Tel.: (34) 971224400
Emp.: 400
Hotels & Motels
N.A.I.C.S.: 721110
Gabriel Escarrer *(Chm)*

Subsidiary (US):

VACATION CLUB SERVICES CO. (2)
4700 Millenia Blvd 240, Orlando, FL 32839-6013

MELIA HOTELS INTERNATIONAL, S.A.

Tel.: (407) 370-3666
Club Operating Services
N.A.I.C.S.: 713910

Impulse Hotel Development BV (1)
Strawinskylaan 915, 1077XX, Amsterdam, Netherlands (100%)
Tel.: (31) 205759194
Sales Range: $50-74.9 Million
Emp.: 1
Real Estate Investment Trust
N.A.I.C.S.: 525990

Lomondo, Ltd. (1)
Albany Street Regents Park, London, NW13UP, United Kingdom (100%)
Tel.: (44) 2073913000
Sales Range: $25-49.9 Million
Emp.: 250
Hotels & Motels
N.A.I.C.S.: 721110

MELIA LUXEMBOURG, S.A.R.L. (1)
1 Park Drai Eechelen 10 Rue Fort Thuengen, L 1499, Luxembourg, Luxembourg
Tel.: (352) 273331
Emp.: 60
Restaurant Operating Services
N.A.I.C.S.: 722511

Markserv, B.V. (1)
Strawinskylaan 915, 1077XX, Amsterdam, Netherlands (100%)
Tel.: (31) 205759194
Web Site: http://www.melia.com
Sales Range: $25-49.9 Million
Emp.: 2
Management Consulting Services
N.A.I.C.S.: 541618
Ewa Jerzak *(Mng Dir)*

Melia Inversiones Americanas, N.V. (1)
Strawinskylaan 915, 1077XX, Amsterdam, Netherlands
Tel.: (31) 205753440
Investment Advice
N.A.I.C.S.: 523940

Subsidiary (Non-US):

CARIBOTELS DE MEXICO, S. A. de C. V. (2)
Playa Santa Pilar Aptdo 9, Cozumel, Mexico
Tel.: (52) 9878729870
Emp.: 25
Restaurant Operating Services
N.A.I.C.S.: 722511

Melsol Management, B.V. (1)
Strawinskylaan 915, 1077 XX, Amsterdam, Netherlands (100%)
Tel.: (31) 205759194
Sales Range: $25-49.9 Million
Emp.: 1
Travel Agencies
N.A.I.C.S.: 561510

Moteles Andaluces, S.A. (1)
Calle Orense 81, Madrid, Spain (99.34%)
Tel.: (34) 913153246
Hotels & Motels
N.A.I.C.S.: 721110

Nyesa Melia Zaragoza S.L. (1)
Avenida Cesar Augusto 13, Zaragoza, 50004, Spain (50%)
Tel.: (34) 976430100
Web Site: http://www.melia.com
Sales Range: $10-24.9 Million
Emp.: 70
Hotels & Motels
N.A.I.C.S.: 721110
Luis Manuel Sachez *(Mgr)*

Parque San Antonio, S.A. (1)
carretera general puerto cruz las arenas S-N, 38400, Puerto de la Cruz, Canary Islands, Spain (79.59%)
Tel.: (34) 922384152
Sales Range: $10-24.9 Million
Emp.: 63
Hotels & Motels
N.A.I.C.S.: 721110

REALTUR, S. A. (1)
Calle Mauricio Legendre 16, Entreplanta, Madrid, Spain
Tel.: (34) 971224543
Restaurant Operating Services

MELIA HOTELS INTERNATIONAL, S.A.

Melia Hotels International, S.A.—(Continued)
N.A.I.C.S.: 722511

Rene Egli, S.L.U. (1)
Hotel Melia Fuerteventura Playa Sotavento,
Fuerteventura Canary Islands, 35628, Pajara, Spain
Tel.: (34) 928547483
Web Site: https://www.rene-egli.com
Windsurfing Services
N.A.I.C.S.: 713990

SECURISOL, S. A. (1)
Av Notari Alemany S / n, Magaluf, 7181, Calvia, Spain
Tel.: (34) 971130152
Safety & Security Services
N.A.I.C.S.: 561621

SOL MELIA FRANCE, S. A. S. (1)
20 Rue Du Sentier, 75002, Paris, France
Tel.: (33) 155047667
Restaurant Operating Services
N.A.I.C.S.: 722511

Subsidiary (Domestic):

Hotel Alexander, S.A.S. (2)
20 Rue du sentier, 75002, Paris, France
Tel.: (33) 156906100
Home Management Services
N.A.I.C.S.: 721110

SOL MELIA GREECE, HOTEL & TOURISTIC (1)
14 Halkokondyli & 28th Oktovriou, Athens, 10677, Greece
Tel.: (30) 2103320100
Tourism & Restaurant Operating Services
N.A.I.C.S.: 561520

Sol Group Corporation (1)
800 Brickell Ave Ste 601, Miami, FL 33131-3046
Tel.: (305) 350-9828
Web Site: https://www.sol-group.com
Sales Range: $10-24.9 Million
Emp.: 40
Hotel & Resort
N.A.I.C.S.: 561599

Sol Group, B.V. (1)
Strawinskylaan 915, Amsterdam, 1077XX, Netherlands **(100%)**
Tel.: (31) 205759194
Web Site: http://www.melia.com
Sales Range: $50-74.9 Million
Emp.: 2
Holding Company
N.A.I.C.S.: 551112
Toni Bagur *(Gen Mgr)*

Sol Maninvest, B.V. (1)
Strawinskylaan 915 WTC Toren A, 1077XX, Amsterdam, Netherlands **(100%)**
Tel.: (31) 205759194
Sales Range: $25-49.9 Million
Emp.: 2
Travel Agencies
N.A.I.C.S.: 561510

Sol Melia (1)
6 Battery Rd 18-07, Singapore, 049909, Singapore **(100%)**
Tel.: (65) 63343332
Hotel & Resort
N.A.I.C.S.: 721110

Sol Melia Balkans EAD (1)
Region de Primorski Golden-Sands-Varna Suite 13-1A1 13th Floor, 1000, Varna, Bulgaria
Tel.: (359) 52333222
Emp.: 300
Home Management Services
N.A.I.C.S.: 721110

Sol Melia Deutschland, GmbH (1)
Hahnstrasse 70, D-60528, Frankfurt, Germany **(100%)**
Tel.: (49) 69 47 86 50 28
Web Site: http://www.melia.com
Sales Range: $10-24.9 Million
Emp.: 15
Hotels & Motels
N.A.I.C.S.: 721110

Sol Melia Europe, B.V. (1)
Eduard Van Beinumstraat 40, 1077 CZ, Amsterdam, Netherlands **(100%)**
Tel.: (31) 205759194
Nondepository Credit Intermediation
N.A.I.C.S.: 522299

Sol Melia Hotel Manag. Shanghai Co., Ltd. (1)
No 1118 Gaojing Rd, Close to National Exhibition and Convention Center, Shanghai, 201702, China
Hotel & Motel Operator
N.A.I.C.S.: 721110

Sol Melia Investment, N.V. (1)
Strawinskylaan 915, 1077 XX, Amsterdam, Netherlands **(100%)**
Tel.: (31) 205759194
Sales Range: $25-49.9 Million
Emp.: 1
Management Consulting Services
N.A.I.C.S.: 541618
Toni Bagur *(Gen Mgr)*

Sol Melia Italia Srl (1)
Via Masaccio 19, Milan, 20149, Italy **(100%)**
Tel.: (39) 02444061
Web Site: https://www.melia.com
Sales Range: $25-49.9 Million
Emp.: 150
Hotels & Motels
N.A.I.C.S.: 721110

Sol Melia Travel S.A. (1)
Calle Gremi De Boters 24, Palma de Mallorca, Spain **(100%)**
Tel.: (34) 902194594
Travel Agencies
N.A.I.C.S.: 561510
Gabriel Escarrer *(Gen Mgr)*

Tenerife Sol, S.A. (1)
Avenida Rafael Puig 12, Playa de las Americas, 38650, Spain **(99.53%)**
Tel.: (34) 922790458
Web Site: https://www.melia.com
Emp.: 140
Hotels & Motels
N.A.I.C.S.: 721110
Gabriel Escarrer *(Gen Mgr)*

MELIAN
Avenue De La Caronniere, 73800, Montmelian, Savoie, France
Tel.: (33) 479265230
Sales Range: $10-24.9 Million
Emp.: 47
Supermarket
N.A.I.C.S.: 445110
Lionel Bridoux *(Pres)*

MELISRON LTD.
Beit Merkarim 2001 1 Abba Even Ave, Herzliya Pituach, Israel
Tel.: (972) 99565500
Web Site: https://www.melisron.co.il
Year Founded: 1987
MLSR—(TAE)
Real Estate Investment Services
N.A.I.C.S.: 531390
Yehuda Yuli Ofer *(Founder)*

MELITE FINANCE PLC
Level 3 Valletta Buildings South Street, Valletta, VLT 1103, Malta
Tel.: (356) 27200083
Web Site: http://www.meliteproperties.com
MT28A—(MAL)
Rev.: $1,927,419
Assets: $27,237,050
Liabilities: $25,610,839
Net Worth: $1,626,211
Earnings: ($5,202,028)
Fiscal Year-end: 12/31/20
Real Estate Manangement Services
N.A.I.C.S.: 531311
Paul Mercieca *(Chm)*

Subsidiaries:

Melite Properties s.r.l. (1)
Via Vittor Pisani 20, 20124, Milan, Italy
Tel.: (39) 0288210920
Real Estate Development Services
N.A.I.C.S.: 531390

Andrew Ganado *(Exec Dir)*

MELITRON CORPORATION
404 Silvercreek Parkway North, Guelph, N1H 1E8, ON, Canada
Tel.: (519) 763-6660
Web Site: http://www.melitron.com
Year Founded: 1995
Rev.: $12,020,360
Emp.: 90
Fabricated Metal Products Mfr
N.A.I.C.S.: 332999

MELITTA UNTERNEHMENSGRUPPE BENTZ KG
Marienstrasse 88, 32425, Minden, Germany
Tel.: (49) 57140460
Web Site: http://www.melitta-group.com
Year Founded: 1908
Sales Range: $800-899.9 Million
Emp.: 4,102
Coffee Mfr
N.A.I.C.S.: 311920
Stephan Bentz *(Co-Chm)*

Subsidiaries:

10X Innovation GmbH & Co. KG (1)
Mehringdamm 57, 10961, Berlin, Germany
Tel.: (49) 30700146300
Web Site: https://www.10xinnovation.de
Food Products Distr
N.A.I.C.S.: 424490
Rene Korte *(CEO)*

ACW-Film GmbH & Co. KG (1)
Ottostrasse 16-18, 26899, Rhede, Germany
Tel.: (49) 4964605260
Web Site: http://www.acw-film.de
Food Packaging Material Mfr
N.A.I.C.S.: 326111
Agnieszka Berndt *(Head-Sls)*

Celupa - Industrial Celulose e Papel Guaiba Ltda. (1)
Avenida Comendador Ismael Chaves Barcellos 150 Centro, 92500-000, Guaiba, Rio Grande do Sul, Brazil
Tel.: (55) 5121011100
Web Site: http://www.celupa.com.br
Paper Product Distr
N.A.I.C.S.: 424110

Cofresco Frischhalteprodukte Europa (1)
Ring Strasse 99, PO Box 1426, 32427, Minden, Germany **(100%)**
Tel.: (49) 57183966
Web Site: http://www.toppits.de
Sales Range: $25-49.9 Million
Emp.: 250
Mfr of Coffee; Household Foils & Wrappings; Filter Paper & Coffeemakers
N.A.I.C.S.: 311920

Cofresco PM S.A.S (1)
Rue d Hauteville 60, 75010, Paris, France
Tel.: (33) 148007300
Staple Food Product Mfr
N.A.I.C.S.: 311991

Cofresco Polska Sp.zo.o. (1)
Ul Sikorskiego 27, 87-300, Brodnica, Poland
Tel.: (48) 564933733
Staple Food Product Mfr
N.A.I.C.S.: 311991
Marcin Banasiak *(Production Mgr)*

Melitta Beratungs- und Verwaltungs GmbH & Co.KG (1)
Marienstrabe 88, Minden, 32423, North Rhine New Wese, Germany **(100%)**
Tel.: (49) 57140460
Web Site: http://www.melitta.info
Sales Range: $25-49.9 Million
Emp.: 50
Mfr of Coffee; Household Foils & Wrappings; Filter Paper & Coffeemakers
N.A.I.C.S.: 311920
Zeyen Markus *(Mng Dir)*

Melitta CR s.r.o. (1)

INTERNATIONAL PUBLIC

Radlicka 1/19, 150 00, Prague, Czech Republic
Tel.: (420) 222581713
Web Site: http://www.melitta.cz
Durable Good Product Whslr
N.A.I.C.S.: 423990
Nikola Marklova *(Mktg Mgr)*

Melitta Canada Inc. (1)
50 Ronson Drive Unit 150, Toronto, M9W 1B3, ON, Canada **(100%)**
Tel.: (905) 851-0429
Web Site: http://www.melitta.ca
Sales Range: $25-49.9 Million
Emp.: 8
Marketing of Coffee Filters & Small Electric Mfr
N.A.I.C.S.: 322299

Melitta France S.A.S. (1)
9 rue Saint Fiacre, Chezy-sur-Marne, 02570, Paris, France
Tel.: (33) 970805105
Web Site: http://www.melitta.fr
Coffee Product Retailer
N.A.I.C.S.: 445298

Melitta Ges.mbH (1)
Munchner Bundesstrasse 131, PO Box 62, 5020, Salzburg, Austria **(100%)**
Tel.: (43) 6624395110
Web Site: http://www.melitta.at
Sales Range: $25-49.9 Million
Emp.: 40
Sales of Coffee Mfr
N.A.I.C.S.: 311920
Amclad Konig *(CEO)*

Melitta GmbH (1)
Bahnhofstasse 47, CH 4622, Egerkingen, Switzerland **(100%)**
Tel.: (41) 623889830
Web Site: http://www.melitta.ch
Sales Range: $25-49.9 Million
Emp.: 12
Mfr& Sales of Coffee.
N.A.I.C.S.: 311920

Melitta Haushaltsprodukte GmbH & Co. KG (1)
Ring Strasse 99, Minden, 32427, North Rhine New Wese, Germany **(100%)**
Tel.: (49) 571860
Web Site: http://www.melitta.de
Mfr of Household Products
N.A.I.C.S.: 335220

Melitta Nordic A/S (1)
Maglekildevej 7, 4000, Roskilde, Denmark
Tel.: (45) 46353000
Web Site: http://www.melitta.dk
Food Products Mfr
N.A.I.C.S.: 311999

Melitta Nordic AB (1)
Garnisonsgatan 25A, 250 24, Helsingborg, Sweden
Tel.: (46) 426004700
Food Products Mfr
N.A.I.C.S.: 311999
Roger Nilsson *(Head-Sls-Nordic)*

Melitta Professional Coffee Solutions UK Ltd. (1)
Unit A / Enterprise House Waldeck Road, Maidenhead, SL6 8DR, Berkshire, United Kingdom
Tel.: (44) 1628829888
Web Site: http://www.melitta-professional.co.uk
Automatic Coffee Machine Equipment Mfr
N.A.I.C.S.: 333310

Melitta Professional Coffee Solutions USA Inc. (1)
2150 Pointe Blvd Ste 200, Elgin, IL 60123
Tel.: (847) 717-8900
Web Site: http://www.melitta-professional.com
Automatic Coffee Machine Equipment Mfr
N.A.I.C.S.: 333310

Melitta SystemService GmbH & Co. KG (1)
Zechenstrasse 60, Minden, 32429, Germany **(100%)**
Tel.: (49) 571 50 49 0
Web Site: http://www.melittasystemservice.de

Sales Range: $125-149.9 Million
Emp.: 300
Filter Coffee Machines & Automatic Coffee Machines Mfr & Marketer & Servicing
N.A.I.C.S.: 333310
Eric Martin-Vazquez *(Dir-Mktg & Intl Bus)*

Melitta USA Inc. (1)
13925 58th St N, Clearwater, FL 33760-3721
Tel.: (727) 535-2111
Web Site: http://www.melitta.com
Sales Range: $50-74.9 Million
Emp.: 191
Coffee Mfr; Coffee Filters, Coffee & Non-Electric Coffee Systems Sales & Marketing
N.A.I.C.S.: 311920
Marty Miller *(Pres & CEO)*

Melitta do Brasil Industria e Comercio Ltda. (1)
Av Paulista 854-6 Andar, Cerqueira Cesar, Sao Paulo, Brazil
Tel.: (55) 1131451200
Web Site: http://www.melitta.com.br
Sales Range: $250-299.9 Million
Emp.: 503
Marketing of Coffee & Coffee Products
N.A.I.C.S.: 424490

Melitta-Nederland B.V. (1)
Avelingen West 32, 4202 NL, Gorinchem, Netherlands (100%)
Tel.: (31) 183642626
Web Site: http://www.melitta.nl
Sales Range: $25-49.9 Million
Emp.: 13
Mfr of Coffee Filters
N.A.I.C.S.: 322299

Webo GmbH & Co. KG (1)
Hummelau 3, Amtzell, 88279, Ravensburg, Germany
Tel.: (49) 7520914950
Web Site: http://www.webo.de.com
Advertising Services
N.A.I.C.S.: 541810
Axel Wittig *(CEO)*

Wolf PVG GmbH & Co. KG (1)
Industriestrasse 15, Vlotho, 32602, Germany (100%)
Tel.: (49) 52289500
Web Site: http://www.wolf-pvg.de
Sales Range: $50-74.9 Million
Emp.: 200
Mfr Vacuum Cleaner Bags
N.A.I.C.S.: 326111
Lutwin Spix *(Mgr)*

MELKER SCHORLING AB
Birger Jarlsgatan 13, 111 45, Stockholm, Sweden
Tel.: (46) 8 407 36 60
Web Site: http://www.melkerschorlingab.se
Year Founded: 1987
Rev.: $66,514,560
Assets: $6,630,189,440
Liabilities: $2,941,120
Net Worth: $6,627,248,320
Earnings: $65,609,600
Emp.: 6
Fiscal Year-end: 12/31/16
Investment Management Service
N.A.I.C.S.: 523940
Mikael Ekdahl *(Chm)*

MELKIOR RESOURCES INC.
66 Brousseau Ave Suite 207, Timmins, P4N 5Y2, ON, Canada
Tel.: (226) 271-5170
Web Site: https://www.melkior.com
MKR—(OTCIQ)
Rev.: $142,412
Assets: $10,802,434
Liabilities: $25,013
Net Worth: $10,777,421
Earnings: $19,400
Fiscal Year-end: 08/31/21
Mineral Exploration Services
N.A.I.C.S.: 213114
Keith James Deluce *(CEO)*

MELLAT INSURANCE COMPANY
No 48 Haqhani Express Way Vanak Sq, 1517973913, Tehran, Iran
Tel.: (98) 2188878814
Web Site: https://www.melat.ir
General Insurance Services
N.A.I.C.S.: 524210

MELLBY GARD HOLDING AB
Anna Lindhs Plats 4, 211 19, Malmo, Sweden
Tel.: (46) 40 98 77 00
Web Site: http://www.mellby-gaard.se
Sales Range: Less than $1 Million
Holding Company Services
N.A.I.C.S.: 551112
Johan Andersson *(CEO)*

Subsidiaries:

Cale Group AB (1)
PO Box 1031, SE-164 21, Kista, Sweden
Tel.: (46) 87993700
Web Site: http://www.calegroup.se
Mfr & Distr of Products for Parking, Public Transport & Entry Fee Systems
N.A.I.C.S.: 423830
Henrik Mella *(Mng Dir)*

Subsidiary (Non-US):

Cale AS (2)
Nordasvn 15, Oslo, 1251, Norway
Tel.: (47) 22 62 10 00
Web Site: http://www.cale.as
Emp.: 10
Parking Meter Mfr
N.A.I.C.S.: 333310

Subsidiary (US):

Cale America, Inc. (2)
13808 Monroe's Bus Park, Clearwater, FL 33765
Tel.: (813) 405-3900
Web Site: http://www.caleamerica.com
Other Commercial Equipment Merchant Distr
N.A.I.C.S.: 423440
Andreas Jansson *(Mng Dir)*

Subsidiary (Non-US):

Cale BriParc Ltd (2)
Units C1 & C2 Cannon Park Transfesa Road, Paddock Wood, TN12 6UF, Kent, United Kingdom
Tel.: (44) 1892 839 489
Web Site: http://www.calebriparc.co.uk
Parking Meter Mfr
N.A.I.C.S.: 333310

Cale Danmark A/S (2)
Svovlhatten 3 St Th, Odense, 5220, Denmark
Tel.: (45) 24 29 35 70
Emp.: 3
Parking Meter Mfr
N.A.I.C.S.: 333310
Jens Thorup *(Area Mgr)*

Cale Deutschland GmbH (2)
Im Grunde 11, DE-31582, Nienburg, Germany
Tel.: (49) 5021 911 330
Parking Meter Mfr
N.A.I.C.S.: 333310

Cale Netherlands BV (2)
Postbus 2092, NL-3440 DB, Woerden, Netherlands
Tel.: (31) 34 843 17 92
Parking Meter Mfr
N.A.I.C.S.: 333310

Cale SAS (2)
passage du Genie, FR-75012, Paris, France
Tel.: (33) 1 45 89 95 06
Parking Meter Mfr
N.A.I.C.S.: 333310

Cale Systems Inc. (2)
9005 Boul du Quartier Unit E, Brossard, J4Y 0A8, QC, Canada
Tel.: (450) 444-4484
Parking Meter Mfr

N.A.I.C.S.: 333310
Edward Olender *(Pres)*

Eriksberg Vilt & Natur AB (1)
Guoviksvagen 353 Eriksberg Sateri, 374 96, Trensum, Sweden
Tel.: (46) 454 564300
Environmental Conservation Services
N.A.I.C.S.: 813312

Feralco AB (1)
Berga Alle 1, 254 52, Helsingborg, Sweden
Tel.: (46) 42 24 00 70
Web Site: http://www.feralco.com
Water Treatment Equipment Mfr
N.A.I.C.S.: 333310

Flash AB (1)
Faltspatvagen 1b, 224 78, Lund, Sweden
Tel.: (46) 46 12 43 40
Web Site: http://www.flashwoman.se
Apparel Distr
N.A.I.C.S.: 458110

Nikkarit AB (1)
Hyvelgatan 16, 74 171, Knivsta, Sweden
Tel.: (46) 18 34 50 40
Web Site: http://www.nikkarit.se
Building Construction Services
N.A.I.C.S.: 236220

Oscar Jacobson AB (1)
Vevgatan 1, 503 13, Boras, Sweden
Tel.: (46) 33233300
Web Site: http://www.oscarjacobson.com
Apparel Distr
N.A.I.C.S.: 458110

Roxtec AB (1)
Rombvagen 2, Box 540, 371 23, Karlskrona, Sweden
Tel.: (46) 455 36 67 00
Web Site: http://www.roxtec.com
Chemical Products Mfr
N.A.I.C.S.: 325520

Subsidiary (Non-US):

OOO Roxtec RU (2)
Novodanilovskaya embankment house 6 building 1 floor 2 apt XXVIII, room 1, 117105, Moscow, Russia
Tel.: (7) 4952216220
Web Site: http://www.roxtex.com
Chemical Products Mfr
N.A.I.C.S.: 325520

Rox Egypt (2)
19 Markaz El Maalomat St Sheraton, Heliopolis, 11361, Cairo, Egypt
Tel.: (20) 2 22669002
Chemical Products Mfr
N.A.I.C.S.: 325520

Roxtec AS (2)
Grini Naeringspark 15, 1361, Osteras, Norway
Tel.: (47) 6787 0850
Web Site: http://www.roxtec.com
Emp.: 15
Chemical Products Mfr
N.A.I.C.S.: 325520
Annette Birgerson *(Mgr-Brand & Corp Comm)*

Roxtec Africa (PTY) Ltd (2)
20 Park Road Richmond, PO Box 291910, Melville, Johannesburg, South Africa
Tel.: (27) 11 482 0088
Web Site: http://www.roxtec.co.za
Chemical Products Mfr
N.A.I.C.S.: 325520

Roxtec Australia Pty Ltd (2)
Unit 6 2-10 Claremont Avenue, PO Box 285, Greenacre, 2190, NSW, Australia
Tel.: (61) 2 9708 0055
Web Site: http://www.roxtec.com.au
Chemical Products Mfr
N.A.I.C.S.: 325520
Leo Konradsson *(Mng Dir)*

Roxtec BV (2)
Galvanistraat 10, 3846 AT, Harderwijk, Netherlands
Tel.: (31) 341 426 395
Chemical Products Mfr
N.A.I.C.S.: 325520

Roxtec CZ s.r.o (2)
Kotlaska 5/64, Prague, Czech Republic
Tel.: (420) 284 821 420

Web Site: http://www.roxtec.cz
Emp.: 5
Chemical Products Mfr
N.A.I.C.S.: 325520
Antonin Vejmelka *(Mng Dir)*

Roxtec Delegacion Norte (2)
Poligono Industrial Abendano, N 6 Oficina, 920800, Zarautz, Gipuzkoa, Spain
Tel.: (34) 943109743
Chemical Products Mfr
N.A.I.C.S.: 325520

Roxtec Denmark ApS (2)
Gydevang 4 B, 3450, Allerod, Denmark
Tel.: (45) 4918 4747
Chemical Products Mfr
N.A.I.C.S.: 325520
Lis Bendixen *(Mgr-Brand & Gen Mktg)*

Roxtec Finland Oy (2)
Kutomotie 6B, 00380, Helsinki, Finland
Tel.: (358) 10 271 3600
Web Site: http://www.roxtec.com
Emp.: 9
Chemical Products Mfr
N.A.I.C.S.: 325520
Henrik Hermansson *(Mng Dir)*

Roxtec France SAS (2)
91 rue Reaumur, 75002, Paris, France
Tel.: (33) 1 82 73 02 00
Chemical Products Mfr
N.A.I.C.S.: 325520

Roxtec GmbH (2)
Neuer Holtigbaum 1-3, 22143, Hamburg, Germany
Tel.: (49) 40 657398 0
Chemical Products Mfr
N.A.I.C.S.: 325520
Thomas Narr *(Mng Dir)*

Subsidiary (US):

Roxtec Inc (2)
10127 E Admiral Pl, Tulsa, OK 74116
Tel.: (918) 254-9872
Chemical Products Mfr
N.A.I.C.S.: 325520
Mark Nygren *(Pres)*

Subsidiary (Non-US):

Roxtec India Pvt Ltd (2)
D 64-65 Udyog Vihar, Phase V, 122 016, Gurgaon, India
Tel.: (91) 12 44 006 141
Web Site: http://www.roxtec.com
Chemical Products Mfr
N.A.I.C.S.: 325520
Ritesh Jha *(Fin Mgr)*

Roxtec Italia S.r.l. (2)
Via Leonardo Da Vinci 25, 20060, Cassina de' Pecchi, MI, Italy
Tel.: (39) 029590121
Chemical Products Mfr
N.A.I.C.S.: 325520
Massimiliano Urso *(Mgr-Regional Segment)*

Roxtec Japan K.K. (2)
Modulo Hamamatsucho 1F, 1-2-15 Hamamatsucho Minato-ku, Tokyo, 105-0013, Japan
Tel.: (81) 3 4550 0730
Web Site: http://www.roxtec.com
Emp.: 7
Chemical Products Mfr
N.A.I.C.S.: 325520
Roger Nin *(Mng Dir)*

Roxtec LTD (2)
Unit C 1 Waterfold Business Park, Bury, BL9 7BQ, United Kingdom
Tel.: (44) 161 7615280
Chemical Products Mfr
N.A.I.C.S.: 325520

Roxtec Latin America Ltda (2)
Av das Americas 3500-Toronto 3000, Sala 711-LeMonde OfficesBarra da Tijuca, 22620-140, Rio de Janeiro, Brazil
Tel.: (55) 21 3282 5160
Web Site: http://www.roxtec.com.br
Emp.: 11
Chemical Products Mfr
N.A.I.C.S.: 325520
Marcelo Campos *(Gen Mgr)*

Roxtec Middle East FZE (2)

MELLBY GARD HOLDING AB

Mellby Gard Holding AB—(Continued)

PO Box 17832, Dubai, United Arab Emirates
Tel.: (971) 4 8839655
Chemical Products Mfr
N.A.I.C.S.: 325520

Roxtec Poland Sp. z o. o. (2)
ul Obwodowa 50A, 84-240, Reda, Poland
Tel.: (48) 58 622 02 08
Chemical Products Mfr
N.A.I.C.S.: 325520

Roxtec RO s.r.l. (2)
Soseaua Industriala no 6, Logistic Park, 900147, Constanta, Romania
Tel.: (40) 341 445 294
Web Site: http://www.roxtec.com
Emp.: 7
Chemical Products Mfr
N.A.I.C.S.: 325520
Saulea Iulian *(Mgr-Energy Segment)*

Roxtec Sealing System(Shanghai)Co., Ltd. (2)
Rm 3005 China Insurance Building 166 Lujiazui East Road, Pudong, 200120, Shanghai, China
Tel.: (86) 21 68419977
Chemical Products Mfr
N.A.I.C.S.: 325520

Roxtec Singapore PTE Ltd (2)
No 16 Boon Lay Way, Trade Hub 21 01-46, 609965, Singapore, Singapore
Tel.: (65) 6863 1700
Chemical Products Mfr
N.A.I.C.S.: 325520
Roger Lim *(Mng Dir)*

Roxtec Sistemas Pasamuros SL (2)
C/Trigo 27 Nave 1 Pol Ind, Polvoranca, 289 14, Leganes, Spain
Tel.: (34) 916 882 178
Chemical Products Mfr
N.A.I.C.S.: 325520

Roxtec Yalitim Cozumleri San. ve Tic. Ltd. Sti. (2)
Girne Cad No 117 Omega Deniz Plaza 2, Kat.D 12 Girne Mahallesi, 34852, Istanbul, Turkiye
Tel.: (90) 216 474 50 26
Web Site: http://www.roxtec.com
Emp.: 7
Chemical Products Mfr
N.A.I.C.S.: 325520
Murat Ucer *(Gen Mgr)*

Roxtec bvba/sprl (2)
Wijmenstraat 21A/201, 9030, Mariakerke, Belgium
Tel.: (32) 9 281 1233
Web Site: http://www.roxtec.com
Emp.: 7
Chemical Products Mfr
N.A.I.C.S.: 325520
Michel Westelinck *(Mng Dir)*

Roxtec d.o.o. (2)
Franje Lucica 34, 10000, Zagreb, Croatia
Tel.: (385) 1 24 44 172
Chemical Products Mfr
N.A.I.C.S.: 325520

Roxtec de Mexico, S.A. de C.V. (2)
Av Ciudad Universitaria 286 Oficina 101A, Colonia Pedregal de San Angel Delg Alvaro Obregon, Mexico, Mexico
Tel.: (52) 55 55680630
Web Site: http://www.roxtec.com
Emp.: 10
Chemical Products Mfr
N.A.I.C.S.: 325520
Alfonso Guarneros Gurza *(Mng Dir)*

Smart Eyes International AB (1)
Vallgatan 38, 411 16, Gothenburg, Sweden
Tel.: (46) 31 725 76 00
Web Site: http://www.smarteyes.se
Optical Product Mfr
N.A.I.C.S.: 339115
Fredrik Wistrand *(CEO)*

Soderberg & Haak Maskin AB (1)
Industrivagen 2, PO Box 504, 245 25, Staffanstorp, Sweden
Tel.: (46) 46 25 92 00
Web Site: http://www.sodhaak.se
Agricultural Machinery Distr

N.A.I.C.S.: 423820

MELODIOL GLOBAL HEALTH LIMITED

Level 24 300 Barangaroo Avenue, Barangaroo, 2000, NSW, Australia
Tel.: (61) 893893100 AU
Web Site: http://www.cresopharma.com
Year Founded: 2015
ME1—(ASX)
Rev.: $5,800,776
Assets: $25,356,783
Liabilities: $10,473,309
Net Worth: $14,883,474
Earnings: ($21,885,263)
Fiscal Year-end: 12/31/22
Pharmaceuticals Product Mfr
N.A.I.C.S.: 325412
Miriam Halperin Wernli *(Co-Founder)*

Subsidiaries:

Health House International Limited (1)
243 Hay Street, Subiaco, 6008, WA, Australia
Tel.: (61) 1300835742
Web Site: http://www.velpic.com
Rev.: $6,517,536
Assets: $7,649,524
Liabilities: $2,446,765
Net Worth: $5,202,759
Earnings: ($4,066,397)
Fiscal Year-end: 06/30/2021
Investment Services
N.A.I.C.S.: 523999

MELROB LIMITED

1 Maidenbower Office Park Balcombe Road, Crawley, RH10 7NN, West Sussex, United Kingdom
Tel.: (44) 1293 880800
Web Site: http://www.melrob.com
Year Founded: 1995
Sales Range: $50-74.9 Million
Emp.: 53
Chemical Product Distribution Services
N.A.I.C.S.: 423830
Ian Melluish *(Mng Dir)*

Subsidiaries:

Melrob Europe GmbH (1)
Adenauerstrasse 18, 52146, Wurselen, Germany
Tel.: (49) 2405408650
Chemical Products Distr
N.A.I.C.S.: 424690

Melrob Iberia S.L.U (1)
C Sant Elies 29 Planta BP uerta 5, 08006, Barcelona, Spain
Tel.: (34) 944580164
Chemical Products Distr
N.A.I.C.S.: 424690

Melrob Korea Limited (1)
1807 KnK Digital Tower 220 Yeongsin-ro, Yeongdeungpo-gu, Seoul, 150-038, Korea (South)
Tel.: (82) 27855335
Chemical Products Distr
N.A.I.C.S.: 424690

Melrob Nutrition Limited (1)
Unit 1 Airfield Industrial Estate Cheddington Lane, Long Marston, Tring, HP23 4QR, United Kingdom
Tel.: (44) 1296663970
Chemical Products Distr
N.A.I.C.S.: 424690

Melrob Singapore Pte, Ltd (1)
110 Tuas South Avenue 2, West Point BizHub, 637160, Singapore, Singapore
Tel.: (65) 69339630
Chemical Products Distr
N.A.I.C.S.: 424690
Anny Siat Ni *(Office Mgr & Mgr-Admin)*

Melrob US Inc. (1)
6900 Philips Hwy Ste 32, Jacksonville, FL 32216
Tel.: (855) 635-7621

Chemical Products Distr
N.A.I.C.S.: 424690
Marc Jackson *(VP-Bus)*

Melrob-Chemiplus Limited (1)
Nihonbashi-Kakigara-Cho Tokyu Building 2F 1-29-4, Nihonbashi-Kakigara-Cho, Chuo, 103-0014, Tokyo, Japan
Tel.: (81) 362311361
Chemical Products Distr
N.A.I.C.S.: 424690
Satoshi Kato *(Mng Dir)*

Melrob-Eurolabs Limited (1)
Unit 12 John Bradshaw Court Alexandria Way, Congleton Business Park, Congleton, CW12 1LB, United Kingdom
Tel.: (44) 1260295510
Chemical Products Distr
N.A.I.C.S.: 424690
Matthew W. Roberts *(Mgr-Sls)*

MELROSE INDUSTRIES PLC

11th Floor The Colmore Building 20 Colmore Circus Queensway, West Midlands, Birmingham, B4 6AT, United Kingdom
Tel.: (44) 1212962800
Web Site: https://www.melroseplc.net
Year Founded: 2003
MRO—(LSE)
Rev.: $4,228,730,119
Assets: $8,746,528,654
Liabilities: $4,243,877,809
Net Worth: $4,502,650,846
Earnings: ($1,286,291,341)
Emp.: 13,492
Fiscal Year-end: 12/31/23
Industruial Equipmnt Mfr
N.A.I.C.S.: 333131
Christopher Miller *(Vice Chm)*

Subsidiaries:

Brush HMA B.V. (1)
Ringdijk 390B, 2983 GS, Ridderkerk, Netherlands
Tel.: (31) 180445500
Web Site: http://www.brush-hma.nl
Electrical Component Mfr
N.A.I.C.S.: 335999

Brush SEM s.r.o. (1)
Tr Edvarde Benese 56439, 30100, Plzen, Czech Republic
Tel.: (420) 378 210 555
Web Site: http://www.brush-sem.cz
High Voltage Generator Mfr
N.A.I.C.S.: 335312
Vratislav Turek *(Mgr-Sls)*

Brush Switchgear Limited (1)
Unit 3 Blackwood Business Park Newport Road, Blackwood, NP12 2XH, United Kingdom
Tel.: (44) 1495223001
AC & DC Medium Voltage Switchgear Mfr
N.A.I.C.S.: 335313
Duncan Crossland *(Mng Dir)*

Brush Transformers Ltd. (1)
Falcon Works, PO Box 20, Nottingham Road, Loughborough, LE11 1HN, United Kingdom
Tel.: (44) 1509611411
Sales Range: $25-49.9 Million
Emp.: 260
Transformer Mfr
N.A.I.C.S.: 335311

Eachairn Aerospace Holdings Limited (1)
Precision House Arden Road, Alcester, B49 6HN, United Kingdom
Tel.: (44) 1789 761020
Sales Range: $50-74.9 Million
Emp.: 14
Investment Management Service
N.A.I.C.S.: 523999

Ergotron Deutschland GmbH (1)
Teichhorn 4-6, Kronshagen, 24119, Rendsburg, Germany
Tel.: (49) 43154028780
Upholstered Furniture Mfr & Distr
N.A.I.C.S.: 337121
Frank Knaesche *(Country Mgr-DACH)*

INTERNATIONAL PUBLIC

Ergotron France SARL (1)
12 Quai du Commerce, 69009, Lyon, France
Tel.: (33) 975181830
Upholstered Furniture Mfr & Distr
N.A.I.C.S.: 337121
Mathieu Herbet *(Mgr-Territory)*

FKI Limited (1)
11th Floor Colmore Plaza 20 Colmore Circus Queensway, Birmingham, B4 6AT, United Kingdom
Tel.: (44) 17 8976 1036
Hardware Mfr & Distr
N.A.I.C.S.: 332510
David Roper *(CEO)*

Fokker Elmo (Langfang) Electrical Systems Co., Ltd. (1)
Langfang Economic and Technical Development Zone, Langfang, 065001, Hebei, China
Tel.: (86) 3165978600
Emp.: 1,000
Electrical Wiring Interconnection System Mfr
N.A.I.C.S.: 335932

Fokker Engineering Romania S.R.L. (1)
Bulevardul Pipera 1/VII Nord City Tower Etaj 4, Ilfov, Voluntari, Romania
Tel.: (40) 212048440
Aircraft Component Mfr & Distr
N.A.I.C.S.: 336413

Fokker Landing Gear B.V. (1)
Grasbeemd 28, 5705 DG, Helmond, Netherlands
Tel.: (31) 492575151
Emp.: 270
Landing Gear Component Mfr
N.A.I.C.S.: 336413

Fokker Services Asia Pte. Ltd. (1)
1800 W Camp Rd, Singapore, 797521, Singapore
Tel.: (65) 64811080
Aircraft Maintenance & Repair Services
N.A.I.C.S.: 488190

Fokker Services B.V. (1)
Hoeksteen 40, 2132 MS, Hoofddorp, Netherlands
Tel.: (31) 886280000
Web Site: http://www.fokkerservices.com
Emp.: 500
Aerospace Operation Services
N.A.I.C.S.: 488190
Manfred Hoogenboom *(Dir-e-Bus Dev)*

GKN Aerospace Engine Systems India Private Limited (1)
Unit 103 2nd and 3rd Floor Vaswani Augusta Embassy Golf Link Road, Chalaghatta, Bengaluru, 560 071, India
Tel.: (91) 8049618700
Aircraft Mfr & Distr
N.A.I.C.S.: 336411

GKN Aerospace Norway AS (1)
Kirkegardsveien 45, 3616, Kongsberg, Norway
Tel.: (47) 32728400
Aircraft Mfr & Distr
N.A.I.C.S.: 336411

GKN Aerospace Precision Machining, Inc. (1)
429 N W Rd, Wellington, KS 67152
Tel.: (620) 326-5952
Aerospace Engine Mfr
N.A.I.C.S.: 336412

GKN Aerospace Services Structures LLC (1)
1000 Corporate Row, Cromwell, CT 06416
Tel.: (860) 613-0236
Aerospace Engine Mfr
N.A.I.C.S.: 336412

GKN Aerospace Sweden AB (1)
Flygmotorvagen 1, 461 81, Trollhattan, Sweden
Tel.: (46) 52094000
Aircraft Engine Components Mfr
N.A.I.C.S.: 336412

GKN Aerospace Transparency Systems (Kings Norton) Limited (1)
Eckersall Road Kings Norton, Birmingham,

AND PRIVATE COMPANIES

B38 8SS, United Kingdom
Tel.: (44) 1216064100
Emp.: 220
Aerospace Toughened Glass Mfr & Distr
N.A.I.C.S.: 336413
Simon Aries (Gen Mgr)

GKN Aerospace Transparency Systems (Luton) Limited (1)
London Luton Airport, Luton, LU2 9PQ,
Bedfordshire, United Kingdom
Tel.: (44) 1582731441
Emp.: 400
Aerospace Parts & Component Mfr
N.A.I.C.S.: 336413
Steven Blair (Gen Mgr)

GKN Aerospace Transparency Systems (Thailand) Limited (1)
9/21 Moo 5 Phaholyothin Road, Klong Nueng Klong Luang, Pathumthani, 12120,
Thailand
Tel.: (66) 25161058
Emp.: 13
Aircraft Parts & Component Mfr
N.A.I.C.S.: 336413

GKN Aerospace, Inc. (1)
6031 Connection Dr Ste 600, Irving, TX 75039
Tel.: (972) 432-1900
Aerospace Engine Mfr
N.A.I.C.S.: 336412
Shawn Black (Pres-Defense)

GKN Automotive Bengaluru Private Limited (1)
Ground Floor Property Khata No 137, Bengaluru, 560037, India
Tel.: (91) 9845092784
Industrial Components & Consumer Products Mfr
N.A.I.C.S.: 339999

GKN Automotive Limited (1)
2100 The Crescent Birmingham Business Park, Birmingham, B37 7YE, West Midlands, United Kingdom
Tel.: (44) 1217884000
Web Site: http://www.gknautomotive.com
Automotive Parts Mfr & Distr
N.A.I.C.S.: 336390
Liam Butterworth (CEO)

GKN Hydrogen Corp. (1)
3246 Grey Hawk Ct, Carlsbad, CA 92010
Tel.: (760) 607-3001
Web Site: https://www.gknhydrogen.com
Renewable Energy Services
N.A.I.C.S.: 221111

GKN Sinter Istanbul Metal Sanayi Ve Ticaret Anonim Sirketi (1)
Yakuplumah Haramidere San Site Parlti SkJ Block No 106-107, Beylikduzu, Istanbul, Turkiye
Tel.: (90) 2128559500
Metal Additive Mfr
N.A.I.C.S.: 332117

GKN Zhongyuan Cylinder Liner Company Limited (1)
Xiguo Industrial Zone, Mengzhou, Henan, 454750, China
Tel.: (86) 3918518596
Web Site: http://en.gknzcylinderliners.com
Cylinder Liner Material Mfr & Distr
N.A.I.C.S.: 336310

Harrington Generators International (1)
Ravenstor Road, Wirksworth, Matlock, DE4 4FY, Derbyshire, United Kingdom
Tel.: (44) 1629824284
Web Site: http://www.harrington-international.co.uk
Sales Range: $25-49.9 Million
Emp.: 70
Petrol & Diesel Powered Generator Mfr
N.A.I.C.S.: 335312
Dan Clay (Mgr-Mktg)

Hawker Siddeley Switchgear Ltd (1)
Newport Rd, Blackwood, NP12 2XH, South Wales, United Kingdom
Tel.: (44) 1495223001
Web Site: http://www.hss-ltd.com
Sales Range: $100-124.9 Million
Emp.: 300

Electrical Switchgear & Overhead Line Equipment Mfr
N.A.I.C.S.: 335313
Barry Wilson (Mgr-Sls)

Subsidiary (Domestic):

Hawker Siddeley Switchgear Limited Technology Centre (2)
2 Broadfield Distribution Centre, Manchester, OL10 2TU, Heywood, United Kingdom
Tel.: (44) 1706674000
Web Site: http://www.hss-ltd.com
Sales Range: $25-49.9 Million
Emp.: 22
Electrical Switchgear & Overhead Line Equipment Mfr
N.A.I.C.S.: 335313

Unit (Non-US):

Hawker Siddeley Switchgear Ltd. South America (2)
Carrera 19 B No 86 A, Bogota, Colombia
Tel.: (57) 12564617
Switchgear & Switchboard Apparatus Mfr
N.A.I.C.S.: 335313

Subsidiary (Non-US):

Hawker Siddeley Switchgear Pty Australia (2)
2 Frawley Ave Narangba, PO Box 36, Brisbane, 4504, QLD, Australia
Tel.: (61) 738882333
Web Site: http://www.hss-ltd.com
Sales Range: $25-49.9 Million
Emp.: 40
Electrical Switchgear & Overhead Line Equipment Mfr
N.A.I.C.S.: 335313
Mark Hitchings (Gen Mgr)

Unit (US):

Whipp & Bourne Inc. (2)
2500 Alameda Ave Ste 115, Norfolk, VA 23513
Tel.: (757) 858-8972
Switchgear & Switchboard Apparatus Mfr
N.A.I.C.S.: 335313

IntelliVision Technologies Corp. (1)
6203 San Ignacio Ave Ste 112, San Jose, CA 95119
Tel.: (408) 754-1690
Web Site: http://www.intelli-vision.com
Software Services
N.A.I.C.S.: 541511
Vaidhi Nathan (CEO)

Linear Electronics (Shenzhen) Limited (1)
3/F Building A5 Hangcheng Ave, Anle Industrial Zone Xixiang Town Baoan District, Shenzhen, China
Tel.: (86) 75561195809
Web Site: http://www.linear-electronics.com
Electronic Products Mfr
N.A.I.C.S.: 334419

Melrose North America Inc (1)
1180 Peachtree St NE Ste, Atlanta, GA 30309
Tel.: (404) 941-2100
Web Site: http://www.melroseplc.net
Investment Management Service
N.A.I.C.S.: 523999

Subsidiary (Domestic):

Broan-NuTone, LLC (2)
926 W State St, Hartford, WI 53027-0140
Tel.: (262) 673-4340
Web Site: http://www.broan-nutone.com
Emp.: 2,500
Residential Ventilation Systems Mfr & Distr
N.A.I.C.S.: 335210
Frank Carroll (Pres & CEO)

Subsidiary (Non-US):

Venmar Ventilation ULC (3)
550 Lemire Blvd, Drummondville, J2C 7W9, QC, Canada (100%)
Tel.: (819) 477-6226
Web Site: http://www.venmar.ca
Whole House Air Exchangers
N.A.I.C.S.: 335210
Caroline Brunet (Mgr-Bus Dev)

Subsidiary (Domestic):

Generator & Motor Services of Pennsylvania LLC (2)
601 Braddock Ave, Turtle Creek, PA 15145-2073
Tel.: (412) 829-7500
Sales Range: $10-24.9 Million
Emp.: 45
Generator & Motor Maintenance Services
N.A.I.C.S.: 811310
Daryl Nelson (Mng Dir)

Harris Waste Management Group, Inc. (2)
200 Clover Reach, Peachtree City, GA 30269-1657
Tel.: (770) 631-7290
Web Site: http://www.harrisequip.com
Rev.: $60,000,000
Emp.: 500
Presses, Shears & Balers Mfr
N.A.I.C.S.: 333998
Jim Jagou (VP)

Nortek Air Solutions, LLC (2)
8000 Phoenix Pkwy OFallon, Saint Louis, MO 63368 (100%)
Tel.: (952) 358-6600
Web Site: http://www.nortekair.com
Large Capacity Commercial Air Conditioners, Heating & Cooling Coils, Air Handlers, Heat Pumps, V-Cubes & Roof-Top & Large Indoor HVAC Systems Mfr
N.A.I.C.S.: 333415
Russell E. Toney (Pres)

Subsidiary (Non-US):

Best S.p.A. (3)
Via Verdi 34, 60043, Cerreto d'Esi, Ancona, Italy
Tel.: (39) 07326921
Web Site: http://www.best-spa.com
Construction Materials Mfr
N.A.I.C.S.: 236118

Subsidiary (Domestic):

Nortek Security & Control LLC (2)
5919 Sea Otter Pl, Carlsbad, CA 92010
Tel.: (760) 438-7000
Web Site: http://www.nortekcontrol.com
Wireless Security & Control System Products Mfr & Distr
N.A.I.C.S.: 334419
Peggy McMillan (Mgr-Customer Svc)

Subsidiary (Domestic):

Magenta Research LTD (3)
621 Wilmer Ave B, Cincinnati, OH 45226
Tel.: (513) 666-4210
Web Site: http://www.magenta-research.com
Audio & Video Equipment Mfr
N.A.I.C.S.: 334310
Jonathan Begleiter (Mgr-Sls-Southeast Reg)

Panamax LLC (3)
1800 S McDowell Blvd Ste 20, Petaluma, CA 94954
Tel.: (707) 283-5900
Web Site: http://www.panamax.com
Power Management Product Mfr
N.A.I.C.S.: 335999

Zephyr Ventilation, LLC (3)
2277 Alameda St, Alameda, CA 94103
Tel.: (888) 880-8368
Web Site: http://www.zephyronline.com
Household Appliances Mfr
N.A.I.C.S.: 449210
Daniel Schaller (Mgr-Territory-Sls)

Nortek Global HVAC (UK) Limited (1)
Fens Pool Avenue, Brierley Hill, DY5 1QA, West Midlands, United Kingdom
Tel.: (44) 1384489250
Heating & Air Conditioning Equipment Mfr
N.A.I.C.S.: 333414

Nortek Global HVAC Belgium NV (1)
Robert Klingstraat 96A, 8940, Wervik, Belgium
Tel.: (32) 56529511
Oil Burner Mfr
N.A.I.C.S.: 333414

MELTON MOWBRAY BUILDING SOCIETY

Nortek Global HVAC France SAS (1)
Z I de Rosarge 230 rue de la Dombes Les Echets, Miribel, 01706, Lyon, Cedex, France
Tel.: (33) 472265050
Oil Burner Mfr
N.A.I.C.S.: 333414

Nortek Global HVAC, LLC (1)
8000 Phoenix Pkwy, O'Fallon, MO 63368
Web Site: http://www.nortekhvac.com
Heating & Cooling System Mfr
N.A.I.C.S.: 333415

MELSTACORP PLC
110 Norris Canal Road, 10, Colombo, 10, Sri Lanka
Tel.: (94) 115900300
Web Site: https://melstacorp.com
Year Founded: 1995
MELS—(COL)
Rev.: $823,079,235
Assets: $1,113,417,083
Liabilities: $611,461,999
Net Worth: $501,955,085
Earnings: $76,455,211
Emp.: 21,132
Fiscal Year-end: 03/31/23
Investment Advisory Services
N.A.I.C.S.: 523940
Harry Jayawardena (Chm)

Subsidiaries:

Bell Solutions (Pvt) Ltd. (1)
344 Galle Road, Colombo, Sri Lanka
Tel.: (94) 115339933
Telecommunication Servicesb
N.A.I.C.S.: 517810
D H S Jayawardena (Chm)

Bellvantage (Pvt) Ltd. (1)
No 46 Vauxhall Street, 02, Colombo, Sri Lanka
Tel.: (94) 115753753
Emp.: 500
Consulting Services
N.A.I.C.S.: 541618
Amitha Gooneratne (Chm)

Continental Insurance Lanka Limited (1)
79 Dr C W W Kannangara Mawatha, 07, Colombo, Sri Lanka
Tel.: (94) 112800200
Web Site: https://www.cilanka.com
Insurance Services
N.A.I.C.S.: 524210
Chaminda De Silva (Mng Dir)

Melsta Laboratories (Pvt) Ltd. (1)
1 Geethanjalee Place, 03, Colombo, Sri Lanka
Tel.: (94) 115660660
Laboratory Services
N.A.I.C.S.: 621511
Priyanka Perera (Head-Sls)

Melsta Technology (Pvt) Limited (1)
110 Norris Cannal Road, Colombo, Sri Lanka
Tel.: (94) 115900300
Web Site: https://www.melstatech.com
Database Management Services
N.A.I.C.S.: 518210

Periceyl (Pvt) Ltd. (1)
Norris Canal Rd, Colombo, 01000, Sri Lanka
Tel.: (94) 115635707
Web Site: http://www.periceyl.com
Foreign Liquor Mfr
N.A.I.C.S.: 312140

Splendor Media (Pvt) Ltd. (1)
Seagull Court No 5 8/1 Milagiriya Avenue, Colombo, Sri Lanka
Tel.: (94) 115625151
Web Site: https://www.splendor.lk
Radio Network Services
N.A.I.C.S.: 516110
Rossen Krause (CEO)

MELTON MOWBRAY BUILDING SOCIETY

MELTON MOWBRAY BUILDING SOCIETY

Melton Mowbray Building Society—(Continued)
Mutual House Leicester Road, Melton Mowbray, LE13 0DB, Leicestershire, United Kingdom
Tel.: (44) 1664 414141
Web Site: http://www.themelton.co.uk
Year Founded: 1875
Rev.: $15,197,509
Assets: $629,478,811
Liabilities: $576,369,504
Net Worth: $53,109,307
Earnings: $1,231,592
Emp.: 68
Fiscal Year-end: 12/31/19
Mortgage Lending & Other Financial Services
N.A.I.C.S.: 522310
Alan Leslie Craft *(Chm)*

MELTWATER N.V.
Singel 250, 1016, Amsterdam, Netherlands
Tel.: (31) 207400806 NI
Web Site: https://www.meltwater.com
Year Founded: 2001
MWTR—(EUR)
Rev.: $438,656,000
Assets: $401,783,000
Liabilities: $465,618,000
Net Worth: ($63,835,000)
Earnings: ($25,181,000)
Emp.: 2,354
Fiscal Year-end: 12/31/22
Software Development Services
N.A.I.C.S.: 541511
Aditya Jami *(CTO)*

Subsidiaries:

MW Emerald Ltd. (1)
O'Connell Bridge House 5th Floor D'Olier Street, Dublin, Ireland
Tel.: (353) 15136212
Information Technology Services
N.A.I.C.S.: 541511

Meltwater Australia Pty. Ltd. (1)
L9 50 Carrington Street, Sydney, 2000, NSW, Australia
Tel.: (61) 285997700
Information Technology Services
N.A.I.C.S.: 541511

Meltwater Deutschland GmbH (1)
Bruckenstrasse 6, 10179, Berlin, Germany
Tel.: (49) 30293692047
Information Technology Services
N.A.I.C.S.: 541511

Meltwater Finland OY (1)
Mikonkatu 15a, 100, Helsinki, Finland
Tel.: (358) 207551000
Information Technology Services
N.A.I.C.S.: 541511

Meltwater Japan KK (1)
Tokyu Fudosan Ebisu Bldg 5F 1-18-18 Ebisu, Shibuya-ku, Tokyo, 150-0013, Japan
Tel.: (81) 345207100
Information Technology Services
N.A.I.C.S.: 541511

Meltwater Singapore Pte. Ltd. (1)
60 Anson Road 18-03 Mapletree Anson, Singapore, 079914, Singapore
Tel.: (65) 31589493
Information Technology Services
N.A.I.C.S.: 541511

Meltwater South Africa (Pty.) Ltd. (1)
3 Dock Road V&A Waterfront, Cape Town, 8001, South Africa
Tel.: (27) 218385100
Information Technology Services
N.A.I.C.S.: 541511

Meltwater Sweden AB (1)
Brahegatan 10 7tr, 11437, Stockholm, Sweden
Tel.: (46) 858616801
Information Technology Services
N.A.I.C.S.: 541511

Meltwater The Netherlands B.V. (1)
Singel 250, 1016, Amsterdam, Netherlands

Tel.: (31) 207400806
Information Technology Services
N.A.I.C.S.: 541511

Owler Inc. (1)
465 California St Fl 11, San Francisco, CA 94104
Tel.: (650) 242-9253
Web Site: https://corp.owler.com
Information Technology Services
N.A.I.C.S.: 541511

MELUN AUTO
130 Route Nationale 6, 77240, Saint Denis, France
Tel.: (33) 164142240
Rev.: $22,900,000
Emp.: 28
New & Used Car Dealers
N.A.I.C.S.: 441110
Armand Chartier *(Dir-Mktg)*

MEMBERS CO., LTD.
Harumi Island Triton Square Tower X 37F 1-8-10 Harumi, Chuo-ku, Tokyo, 104-6034, Japan
Tel.: (81) 351440660
Web Site: https://www.members.co.jp
2130—(TKS)
Rev.: $135,286,870
Assets: $76,193,470
Liabilities: $36,969,730
Net Worth: $39,223,740
Earnings: $832,860
Emp.: 3,087
Fiscal Year-end: 03/31/24
Web Hosting Services
N.A.I.C.S.: 518210
Tadashi Kenmochi *(Pres)*

MEMEX INC.
3425 Harvester Rd Unit 200, Burlington, L7N 3M7, ON, Canada
Tel.: (905) 635-1540
Web Site:
   https://www.memexoee.com
OEE—(TSXV)
Rev.: $2,378,396
Assets: $1,227,336
Liabilities: $1,959,534
Net Worth: ($732,198)
Earnings: $129,817
Fiscal Year-end: 09/30/21
Technology Products Mfr
N.A.I.C.S.: 541519
David R. McPhail *(Pres & CEO)*

MEMG SECURITIES LTD.
N115 Manipal Center, Dickenson Road, Bengaluru, 560042, Karnataka, India
Tel.: (91) 8040197800 In
Web Site:
   http://www.memgsecurities.com
Year Founded: 1995
Investment Banking Services
N.A.I.C.S.: 523150

MEMIONTEC HOLDINGS LTD.
20 Woodlands Link 04-30/31, Woodlands East Industrial Estate, Singapore, 738733, Singapore
Tel.: (65) 67566989 SG
Web Site:
   https://www.memiontec.com
Year Founded: 1992
TWL—(SES)
Rev.: $50,632,432
Assets: $41,810,195
Liabilities: $25,403,317
Net Worth: $16,406,877
Earnings: $2,451,716
Emp.: 252
Fiscal Year-end: 12/31/23
Holding Company
N.A.I.C.S.: 551112
Tay Kiat Seng *(Chm & CEO)*

Subsidiaries:

MIT Water Technology Chengdu Co., Ltd. (1)
No 993 Baicao Road High-Tech Western Zone, Chengdu, 611130, Sichuan, China
Tel.: (86) 28879160508006
Wastewater Treatment Plant Services
N.A.I.C.S.: 562211

PT Memiontec Indonesia (1)
Jl Raya Cakung Cilincing Rukan Avenue Jakarta Garden City Blok F 8, No 136-137 Cakung, Jakarta Timur, Indonesia
Tel.: (62) 2122874199
Waste Water Treatment Services
N.A.I.C.S.: 562998

MEMORY-TECH CORPORATION
Akasaka Park Bldg 10F 5-2-20 Akasaka, Minato-ku, Tokyo, 107-0052, Japan
Tel.: (81) 3 5545 2700
Web Site: http://www.memory-tech.co.jp
Year Founded: 1985
Compact Discs, CD-ROMs & DVDs Mfr
N.A.I.C.S.: 334610
Yutaka Ueda *(Pres)*

Subsidiaries:

Pony Canyon Enterprise Inc. (1)
Noa Bldg 1st Floor 2-3-5 Azabudai, Minato-ku, Tokyo, 106-0041, Japan
Tel.: (81) 335856767
Web Site: http://www.pce.co.jp
Emp.: 116
Prerecorded Tape, Compact Disc & Record Stores
N.A.I.C.S.: 334610
Nishiya Yasuyuki *(Mng Dir)*

REAL-T Inc. (1)
4-38-19 Narita Higashi, Suginami-ku, Tokyo, 166-0015, Japan
Tel.: (81) 359291695
Web Site: http://www.real-t.co.jp
Animation Post-production Services
N.A.I.C.S.: 512191

MEMPHIS PHARMACEUTICAL & CHEMICAL INDUSTRIES
8 El Sawah - Amireya, Cairo, Egypt
Tel.: (20) 222829880
Web Site:
   https://www.memphis.com.eg
Year Founded: 1940
MPCI.CA—(EGX)
Sales Range: Less than $1 Million
Pharmaceuticals Product Mfr
N.A.I.C.S.: 325412
Ashraf Ibrahim Al Sayid Tantawi *(Head-Fin Sector)*

MEMSENSING MICROSYSTEMS SUZHOU CHINA CO., LTD.
No 8 Wangjiabang Lane, Suzhou Industrial Park, Suzhou, 215000, China
Tel.: (86) 51262386877
Web Site:
   https://www.memsensing.com
Year Founded: 2007
688286—(SHG)
Rev.: $41,088,088
Assets: $163,915,077
Liabilities: $19,365,948
Net Worth: $144,549,129
Earnings: ($7,712,720)
Fiscal Year-end: 12/31/22
Application Development Services
N.A.I.C.S.: 541511
Gang Li *(Chm & Gen Mgr)*

MEMSSTAR LIMITED
Starlaw Park Starlaw Road, Livingston, EH54 8SF, United Kingdom
Tel.: (44) 1506 409160

Web Site: http://www.memsstar.com
Year Founded: 2003
Sales Range: $10-24.9 Million
Emp.: 60
Semiconductor Manufacturing Equipment Mfr
N.A.I.C.S.: 333242
Tony McKie *(CEO)*

MEMSTAR TECHNOLOGY LTD.
11 Kian Teck Drive, Singapore, 628828, Singapore
Tel.: (65) 67752512 SG
Web Site:
   http://www.memstar.com.sg
Year Founded: 1979
Rev.: $11,925
Assets: $110,129
Liabilities: $989,760
Net Worth: ($879,631)
Earnings: ($162,037)
Fiscal Year-end: 06/30/17
Investment Holding Company
N.A.I.C.S.: 551112
Hailin Ge *(CEO-Mfg)*

Subsidiaries:

Jiangsu Memstar Membrane Material Technology Co., Ltd. (1)
No 5 Poyang Hu Road Sutong Science and Technology Park, Nantong, 226017, Jiangsu, China
Tel.: (86) 51380979922
Chemical Products Mfr
N.A.I.C.S.: 325199

Memstar (Mianyang) Co., Ltd. (1)
No 249 Pioneering Road Science & Technology Venture Park, Mianyang, 621000, Sichuan, China
Tel.: (86) 8168072777
Chemical Products Mfr
N.A.I.C.S.: 325199

Memstar USA, Inc. (1)
3655 Pollok Dr, Conroe, TX 77303
Web Site: http://www.memstarusa.com
Chemical Products Mfr
N.A.I.C.S.: 325199
Ge Hailin *(CEO-Mfg)*

MEMTECH INTERNATIONAL LTD
89 Short Street 04-01 Golden Wall Centre, Singapore, 188216, Singapore
Tel.: (65) 63390833
Web Site:
   http://www.memtechchina.com
Sales Range: $150-199.9 Million
Mobile Phones Components Mfr
N.A.I.C.S.: 334220
Jian Wang *(Gen Mgr-Nantong Plant)*

Subsidiaries:

Dongguan Memtech Electronic Products Co., Ltd. (1)
Zaoyi 1 Cun Wentang Industrial Estate, Dongcheng, Dongguan, Guangdong, China
Tel.: (86) 76988775555
Mobile Phone Key Pads Mfr & Distr
N.A.I.C.S.: 339999

Dongguan Memtech Lens Technologies Co., Ltd. (1)
Zao Yi 1 Wentang Industrial Estate, Dongcheng, Dongguan, Guangdong, China
Tel.: (86) 76988775555
Web Site: http://www.memtechchina.com
Mobile Window Lens Mfr
N.A.I.C.S.: 339999

Huzhou Memtech Electronic Industries Co., Ltd. (1)
No 6 328 Guangyuan Road Phoenix West Area, Huzhou, Zhejiang, China
Tel.: (86) 5722762222
Touch Panels Mfr
N.A.I.C.S.: 334118

Memtech Technologies Holdings Co., Ltd. (1)

AND PRIVATE COMPANIES — MENE INC.

5F C 2 No 191 Sec 2 Zhongyang Rd, Tucheng, 236, Taipei, Taiwan
Tel.: (886) 282629291
Investment Management Service
N.A.I.C.S.: 523999

MENA FOR TOURISTIC & REAL ESTATE INVESTMENT
Mena Garden City Compound, 6th of October City, Egypt
Tel.: (20) 238358826
Web Site: http://www.mena.com.eg
Year Founded: 1980
MENA.CA—(EGX)
Sales Range: Less than $1 Million
Real Estate Development Services
N.A.I.C.S.: 531390
Dawood Sulaiman Dawood Al Busairi *(Chm)*

MENA HYDROCARBONS INC.
1000 Bow Valley Square 2 205 - 5th Avenue SW, Calgary, T2P 2V7, AB, Canada
Tel.: (403) 930-7500   AB
Web Site: http://www.menahydrocarbons.com
Year Founded: 2010
MNH—(TSXV)
Sales Range: Less than $1 Million
Oil & Gas Exploration Services
N.A.I.C.S.: 213112
Leonard J. M. Julien *(Ops Mgr-Technical)*

MENA MANI INDUSTRIES LIMITED
4th Floor Karm Corporate House Opp Vikramnagar Nr Newyork Timber, Ambli-Bopal Road, Ahmedabad, 380059, Gujarat, India
Tel.: (91) 7926936006
Web Site: https://menamani.in
Year Founded: 1992
531127—(BOM)
Rev.: $847,275
Assets: $2,622,085
Liabilities: $2,734,285
Net Worth: ($112,200)
Earnings: $45,801
Emp.: 2
Fiscal Year-end: 03/31/23
Construction Engineering Services
N.A.I.C.S.: 541330
Swetank M. Patel *(Mng Dir)*

MENA REAL ESTATE COMPANY - KPSC
6th Floor Panasonic Tower Fahad Al Salem Street, PO Box 38381, Abdullah Al Salem District, 72254, Kuwait, 72254, Kuwait
Tel.: (965) 22245670
Web Site: https://www.mena-realestate.com
Year Founded: 2004
MENA—(KUW)
Rev.: $237,535
Assets: $60,923,241
Liabilities: $20,293,926
Net Worth: $40,629,315
Earnings: ($17,332,227)
Emp.: 13
Fiscal Year-end: 03/31/24
Real Estate Manangement Services
N.A.I.C.S.: 531390
Fawaz Adnan Al Rays *(Chief Investment Officer)*

MENAGE SELECTION VALNET S.A.S
Rue Pierre Magnol, 66600, Rivesaltes, France
Tel.: (33) 468 923 630
Web Site: http://www.msv-france.com
Year Founded: 1981
Bathroom Accessories Mfr
N.A.I.C.S.: 332999
Marcel Sobraques *(Pres)*
Subsidiaries:

Spirella SA   (1)
Tannenstrasse 98, 8424, Embrach, Switzerland
Tel.: (41) 44 866 24 24
Web Site: http://www.spirella-world.ch
Shower Curtains & Bathroom Decors & Accessory Mfr
N.A.I.C.S.: 423220
Ernst Kraft *(CEO)*

Subsidiary (Non-US):

Spirella France s.a.r.l.   (2)
4 Avenue Gutenberg, 31120, Portet-sur-Garonne, France
Tel.: (33) 56220 6560
Web Site: http://www.spirella.com
Shower Curtain & Bathroom Accessory Mfr
N.A.I.C.S.: 423220

Spirella GmbH   (2)
Burgbergweg 1, 56377, Nassau, Germany
Tel.: (49) 260494330
Web Site: http://www.spirella.ch
Shower Curtain & Bathroom Accessory Mfr
N.A.I.C.S.: 423220

MENANG CORPORATION (M) BERHAD
Wisma OZ No 11-1 Jalan Kuchai Maju 5 Kuchai Entrepreneurs Park, Jalan Kuchai Lama, 58200, Kuala Lumpur, Malaysia
Tel.: (60) 379711771
Web Site: https://www.menangcorporation.com
Year Founded: 1964
MENANG—(KLS)
Rev.: $18,734,392
Assets: $209,717,460
Liabilities: $106,924,233
Net Worth: $102,793,228
Earnings: $5,957,884
Fiscal Year-end: 06/30/23
Property Development & Leasing Services
N.A.I.C.S.: 531311
Kok Leng Too *(Vice Chm-Grp)*
Subsidiaries:

Menang Construction (M) Sdn. Bhd.   (1)
No 142 8th Floor Wisma SI Dredging Jln Ampang, 50450, Kuala Lumpur, Federal Territory, Malaysia
Tel.: (60) 321612361
Web Site: http://www.menangcorporation.com
Emp.: 50
Property Management & Leasing Services
N.A.I.C.S.: 531312
Youn Kim Wong *(Sec)*

Menang Development (M) Sdn. Bhd.   (1)
Seremban 3 Paradise Valley Golf Resort, Persiaran Seremban Eiga 2, Seremban, 70300, Negeri Sembilan, Malaysia
Tel.: (60) 66311711
Web Site: http://www.menangcorporation.com
Sales Range: $50-74.9 Million
Emp.: 10
Property Management & Leasing Services
N.A.I.C.S.: 531312
Abdul Mokhtar Ahmad *(Mng Dir)*

Seremban 3 Paradise Valley Golf Resort Sdn. Bhd.   (1)
Persiaran Seremban Tiga 2 Seremban 3, Seremban, Negeri Sembilan, Malaysia
Tel.: (60) 66335033
Sales Range: $50-74.9 Million
Emp.: 20
Golf Resort Management Services
N.A.I.C.S.: 713910

MENAPHI
Boulevard Du 14 Juillet, 27000, Evreux, Eure, France
Tel.: (33) 232287800
Rev.: $20,200,000
Emp.: 75
Miscellaneous General Merchandise Stores
N.A.I.C.S.: 444180
Pascal Bessonnard *(Dir)*

MENARA VENTURES
38 Habarzel St, Tel Aviv, Israel
Tel.: (972) 542277553
Web Site: http://www.menaraventures.com
MNRA—(TAE)
Assets: $12,953,999
Liabilities: $762,536
Net Worth: $12,191,463
Earnings: ($764,194)
Fiscal Year-end: 12/31/23
Financial Investment Services
N.A.I.C.S.: 523999
Eran Savir *(Co-Founder & CEO)*

MENCAST HOLDINGS LTD.
42E Penjuru Road Mencast Central, Singapore, 609161, Singapore
Tel.: (65) 62684331
Web Site: https://www.mencast.com.sg
Year Founded: 1981
5NF—(CAT)
Rev.: $35,386,954
Assets: $169,573,812
Liabilities: $150,800,728
Net Worth: $18,773,084
Earnings: $3,922,824
Emp.: 110
Fiscal Year-end: 12/31/20
Sterngear Equipment Mfr & Supplier
N.A.I.C.S.: 333248
Glenndle Soon Ngee Sim *(Chm & CEO)*
Subsidiaries:

Mencast Marine Pte. Ltd.   (1)
7 Tuas View Circuit, Singapore, 637642, Singapore
Tel.: (65) 62684155
Web Site: http://www.mencast.com.sg
Sales Range: $25-49.9 Million
Marine Engineering Services
N.A.I.C.S.: 541330

Recon Propeller & Engineering Pte. Ltd.   (1)
39 Tuas Ave 13, Singapore, 638999, Singapore
Tel.: (65) 68618406
Web Site: http://www.reconpropeller.com.sg
Sales Range: $25-49.9 Million
Emp.: 40
Marine Equipment Suppliers & Services
N.A.I.C.S.: 423690

MENDELSON INFRASTRUCTURES & INDUSTRIES LTD.
46 Hataasiya St, PO Box 232, Kiryat atta, Haifa, 2822767, Israel
Tel.: (972) 48464999
Web Site: https://www.mendelson.co.il
Year Founded: 1947
MNIN—(TAE)
Rev.: $292,633,785
Assets: $270,506,972
Liabilities: $144,566,098
Net Worth: $125,940,874
Earnings: $12,495,648
Fiscal Year-end: 12/31/23
Plumbing, Heating & Air-Conditioning Contractors
N.A.I.C.S.: 238220
Shaul Dancourt *(CEO)*

MENDERES TEKSTIL SANAYI VE TICARET AS
Adalet Mah Manas Bulv No 47 A Blok K 42, Bayrakli, 35530, Izmir, Turkiye
Tel.: (90) 2324350565
Web Site: https://www.menderes.com
Year Founded: 1958
MNDRS—(IST)
Rev.: $127,217,807
Assets: $236,936,179
Liabilities: $114,483,069
Net Worth: $122,453,110
Earnings: $32,368,023
Emp.: 3,477
Fiscal Year-end: 12/31/22
Textile Products Mfr
N.A.I.C.S.: 313310
Riza Akca *(Chm)*

MENDES JUNIOR TRADING E ENGENHARIA S.A.
Av Joao Pinheiro 39 - 14 Floor, 30130180, Belo Horizonte, Brazil
Tel.: (55) 3121219577
Web Site: http://www.mendesjunior.com.br
MEND3—(BRAZ)
Public Utilities Construction Services
N.A.I.C.S.: 237310
J. Murillo Valle Mendes *(Pres)*

MENDES MOTORS LIMITED
1811 Bank Street, Ottawa, K1V 7Z6, ON, Canada
Tel.: (613) 523-8666
Web Site: http://www.mendestoyota.ca
Year Founded: 1978
Sales Range: $10-24.9 Million
New & Used Car Dealers
N.A.I.C.S.: 441110
Ray Lacroix *(Mgr-Fixed Ops)*

MENDES SA
Z I Des Chanoux 19 Rue Paul Langevin, 93330, Neuilly-sur-Marne, Seine Saint Denis, France
Tel.: (33) 143008700
Web Site: http://www.mendes.com
Rev.: $24,800,000
Emp.: 40
Masonry & Other Stonework
N.A.I.C.S.: 238140
Jose Mendes *(Chm)*

MENDUS AB
Ostermalmstorg 5, 114 42, Stockholm, Sweden
Tel.: (46) 87328400
Web Site: https://www.immunicum.se
Year Founded: 2002
IMMU—(OMX)
Rev.: $2,773,610
Assets: $70,803,900
Liabilities: $4,797,831
Net Worth: $66,006,069
Earnings: ($9,517,829)
Emp.: 27
Fiscal Year-end: 12/31/23
Pharmaceuticals Product Mfr
N.A.I.C.S.: 325412
Alex Karlsson-Parra *(Chief Scientific Officer)*

MENE INC.
334 Adelaide Street West Suite 307, Toronto, M5V 1R4, ON, Canada
Tel.: (647) 494-0296   ON
Web Site: https://www.mene.com
Year Founded: 1980
MENE—(OTCIQ)
Rev.: $16,529,217
Assets: $25,773,045
Liabilities: $16,774,446
Net Worth: $8,998,600
Earnings: ($2,616,673)
Fiscal Year-end: 12/31/20
Mineral Exploration Services
N.A.I.C.S.: 213114

Mene Inc.—(Continued)

Roy Sebag *(Chm & CEO)*

MENHADEN RESOURCE EFFICIENCY PLC
25 Southampton Buildings, London, WC2A 1AL, United Kingdom
Tel.: (44) 2030084910
Web Site:
https://www.menhaden.com
Year Founded: 2014
MHN—(LSE)
Assets: $125,472,765
Liabilities: $409,530
Net Worth: $125,063,235
Earnings: ($24,740,430)
Fiscal Year-end: 12/31/22
Portfolio Management & Investment Advice
N.A.I.C.S.: 523940
Ian Cheshire *(Chm)*

MENICON CO., LTD.
3-21-19 Aoi, Naka-ku, Nagoya, 460-0006, Aichi, Japan
Tel.: (81) 529351515
Web Site: https://www.menicon.co.jp
Year Founded: 1951
7780—(TKS)
Rev.: $768,029,120
Assets: $1,188,557,320
Liabilities: $647,832,880
Net Worth: $540,724,440
Earnings: $29,996,180
Emp.: 1,023
Fiscal Year-end: 03/31/24
Contact Lenses & Lens Care Products Mfr
N.A.I.C.S.: 339112
Hidenari Tanaka *(Chm & CEO)*

Subsidiaries:

Fuji Contact Co., Ltd. (1)
Ikebukuro Higashiguchi Buld 5th Floor 1-41-7 Ikebukuro, Toshima-ku, Tokyo, 170-0013, Japan
Tel.: (81) 35 952 1081
Medical Equipment Mfr & Distr
N.A.I.C.S.: 339112

Itabashi Trading Co., Ltd. (1)
8F Tomizen Building 2-11-4 Ginza, Chuo-ku, Tokyo, 104-0061, Japan
Tel.: (81) 33 248 1006
Web Site: https://www.itabashi-trading.com
Medical Equipment Distr
N.A.I.C.S.: 423450

Meni-one Co., Ltd. (1)
Miyuki Business Park 4 390 Ichibagi-cho, Nishi-ku, Nagoya, 452-0805, Japan
Tel.: (81) 523253823
Contact Lens Mfr
N.A.I.C.S.: 339115

Menicon America, Inc. (1)
76 Treble Cove Rd Bldg 3, North Billerica, MA 01862
Tel.: (781) 609-2042
Web Site: https://www.meniconamerica.com
Contact Lens Distr
N.A.I.C.S.: 423460

Menicon Australia Pty Ltd. (1)
3 Lloyd Street, Saint Marys, 5042, SA, Australia
Tel.: (61) 882774545
Web Site: https://www.menicon.com.au
Contact Lens Distr
N.A.I.C.S.: 423460

Menicon B.V. (1)
Waanderweg 6, 7812 HZ, Emmen, Netherlands
Tel.: (31) 591610640
Contact Lens Mfr & Sales
N.A.I.C.S.: 339115

Menicon Business Assist Co., Ltd.
21-19 Aoi 3, Naka-ku, Nagoya, 460-0006, Japan
Tel.: (81) 52 979 3222

Medical Equipment Mfr & Distr
N.A.I.C.S.: 339112

Menicon Espana S.L. (1)
C/ Corcega N 329 5 2, 08037, Barcelona, Spain
Tel.: (34) 932721369
Web Site: https://www.menicon.es
Contact Lens Distr
N.A.I.C.S.: 423460

Menicon GmbH (1)
Heinrich-Krumm-Str 1-3, 63073, Offenbach, Germany
Tel.: (49) 6984000810
Web Site: https://www.menicon.de
Contact Lens Distr
N.A.I.C.S.: 423460

Menicon Korea Co., Ltd. (1)
Room 203 Ace High End Tower 2 61 Digital-ro 26-gil, Guro-gu, Seoul, Korea (South)
Tel.: (82) 27185123
Web Site: https://www.menicon.co.kr
Contact Lens Distr
N.A.I.C.S.: 423460

Menicon Ltd. (1)
Gatelodge Close Round Spinney, Northampton, NN3 8RJ, United Kingdom
Tel.: (44) 1604646216
Web Site: https://www.menicon.co.uk
Contact Lens Distr
N.A.I.C.S.: 423460

Menicon Nect Co., Ltd. (1)
Miyuki Business Park 4 390 Ichibagi-cho, Nishi-ku, Nagoya, 452-0805, Japan
Tel.: (81) 523257351
Contact Lens Mfr
N.A.I.C.S.: 339115

Menicon Pharma SAS (1)
Boulevard Sebastien Brant Parc d'Innovation, 67400, Illkirch-Graffenstaden, France
Tel.: (33) 388668130
Contact Lens Distr
N.A.I.C.S.: 423460

Menicon SAS (1)
13 Rue de la Perdrix, CS 20061, Roissy Ch de Gaulle, 95926, Villepinte, Cedex, France
Tel.: (33) 185731310
Web Site: https://www.menicon.fr
Contact Lens Distr
N.A.I.C.S.: 423460

Menicon Singapore Sales Pte. Ltd. (1)
8 International Business Park, Singapore, 609925, Singapore
Tel.: (65) 64114778
Web Site: https://www.menicon.sg
Contact Lens Distr
N.A.I.C.S.: 423460

W.I. System Inc. (1)
5th Floor Ikebukuro Aoyagi Building 2-43-1 Ikebukuro, Toshima-ku, Tokyo, 171-0014, Japan
Tel.: (81) 359791140
Contact Lens Mfr
N.A.I.C.S.: 339115

Wenzhou FocuSee Vision Care Technologies Co., Ltd. (1)
Room C-415 No 10, District Pioneer Park High-tech Industrial Park, Wenzhou, 325027, Zhejiang, China
Tel.: (86) 57788068885
Web Site: http://www.focusee.cn
Contact Lens Distr
N.A.I.C.S.: 423460

MENIF FINANCIAL SERVICES LTD.
Beit Oz 14 Abba Hillel St, Ramat Gan, 5250607, Israel
Tel.: (972) 36124005
Web Site: https://www.menif.co.il
Year Founded: 1999
MNIF—(TAE)
Rev.: $91,732,558
Assets: $719,292,156
Liabilities: $594,774,131
Net Worth: $124,518,025

Earnings: $34,399,502
Fiscal Year-end: 12/31/23
Miscellaneous Financial Investment Activities
N.A.I.C.S.: 523999

MENIVIM THE NEW REIT LTD.
3 HaEshel Street, Caesarea, Israel
Tel.: (972) 722506090
Web Site: https://www.menivim-reit.co.il
Year Founded: 2015
MNRT—(TAE)
Rev.: $55,417,875
Assets: $875,830,350
Liabilities: $438,509,456
Net Worth: $437,320,894
Earnings: $40,888,520
Fiscal Year-end: 12/31/23
Lessors of Other Real Estate Property
N.A.I.C.S.: 531190

MENNEN MEDICAL LTD.
6 Ha-Kishon Street, Yavne, Rehovot, 7610002, Israel
Tel.: (972) 89323333
Web Site:
http://www.mennenmedical.com
Year Founded: 1963
Sales Range: $10-24.9 Million
Emp.: 250
Medical Product Mfr & Distr
N.A.I.C.S.: 339112
Erez Nimrod *(Pres)*

Subsidiaries:

Charter Kontron Ltd (1)
Avant Business centre 21 Denbigh Road Denbigh West, Milton Keynes, MK1 1DT, United Kingdom
Tel.: (44) 1908646070
Web Site: http://www.charter-kontron.com
Medical Equipment Distr
N.A.I.C.S.: 423450
Nicholas Radwell *(Engr-Sls & Svc)*

Mennen Medical Corp. (1)
290 Andrews Rd, Feasterville Trevose, PA 19053 (100%)
Tel.: (215) 259-1020
Web Site: http://www.mennenmedical.com
Mfr of Medical Patient Monitoring Systems
N.A.I.C.S.: 334510
Angelia Adzic *(Pres)*

MENNICA POLSKA S.A.
ul Ciasna 6, 00-232, Warsaw, Poland
Tel.: (48) 226564200
Web Site:
https://www.mennica.com.pl
Year Founded: 1766
MNC—(WAR)
Rev.: $322,169,271
Assets: $242,962,116
Liabilities: $82,763,654
Net Worth: $160,198,463
Earnings: $8,151,284
Fiscal Year-end: 12/31/22
Collector Coin & Medals Mfr
N.A.I.C.S.: 459999
Piotr Sendecki *(Vice Chm-Supervisory Bd)*

Subsidiaries:

Mennica Invest Sp. z o.o. (1)
21 Pereca Street, Warsaw, 00-958, Masovian, Poland
Tel.: (48) 226564080
Building Construction & Supervision Services
N.A.I.C.S.: 236116

Mennica-Metale Szlachetne S.A. (1)
ul Pereca 21, 00-958, Warsaw, Masovian, Poland
Tel.: (48) 226564101
Web Site: http://www.mennica-metale.com.pl

Sales Range: $50-74.9 Million
Emp.: 108
Precious Metal Mining Services
N.A.I.C.S.: 331410

Skarbiec Mennicy Polskiej S.A. (1)
ul Walicow 11, 00-851, Warsaw, Masovian, Poland
Tel.: (48) 225668877
Web Site: http://www.skarbiecmennicy.pl
Sales Range: $25-49.9 Million
Emp.: 20
Coins & Medals Mfr & Distr
N.A.I.C.S.: 423940

MENON PISTONS LTD.
182 MIDC, Shiroli, Kolhapur, 416122, Maharashtra, India
Tel.: (91) 2302468041
Web Site:
https://www.menonpistons.com
531727—(BOM)
Rev.: $18,795,449
Assets: $16,649,478
Liabilities: $5,283,533
Net Worth: $11,365,946
Earnings: $1,219,709
Emp.: 368
Fiscal Year-end: 03/31/21
Automotive Piston Machinery Mfr
N.A.I.C.S.: 336310
Sachin Menon *(Chm & Mng Dir)*

Subsidiaries:

Menon Bearings Ltd. (1)
G-1 MIDC Gokul Shirgaon, Kolhapur, 416234, India
Tel.: (91) 2312672487
Web Site: https://www.menonbearings.in
Rev.: $27,027,519
Assets: $22,294,955
Liabilities: $15,285,666
Net Worth: $7,009,289
Earnings: $3,348,864
Emp.: 239
Fiscal Year-end: 03/31/2022
Automotive Bearing Mfr
N.A.I.C.S.: 332991
Ramesh Dattatraya Dixit *(Mng Dir)*

Menon Piston Rings Pvt Limited (1)
Sambhapur Kasarwadi Road, Toap, Kolhapur, 416 122, Maharashtra, India
Tel.: (91) 2302468041
Web Site: http://www.menonpistonrings.com
Piston Rings Mfr
N.A.I.C.S.: 327910
Milind Dhopessowarkar *(Gen Mgr)*

Menon Pistons Ltd. - Plant 2 (1)
H-1 MIDC Kupwad Block, Sangli, 416 436, India
Tel.: (91) 33 2345179
Piston Rings Mfr
N.A.I.C.S.: 336310

Menon Pistons Ltd. - Plant 3 (1)
B-58/59 MIDC, Shiroli, Kolhapur, 416 122, India
Tel.: (91) 230 2468103
Piston Rings Mfr
N.A.I.C.S.: 336310

Menon and Menon Limited (1)
Chandran Menon Road Shahu Market Yard, Kolhapur, 416005, Maharashtra, India
Tel.: (91) 9545273519
Cylinder Block & Cylinder Head Mfr
N.A.I.C.S.: 336310

Rapid Machining Technologies Private Limited (1)

MENORA MIVTACHIM HOLDINGS LTD.
Menora House 115 Allenby Street, PO Box 927, Tel Aviv, 61008, Israel
Tel.: (972) 37107801
Web Site:
https://www.menoramvt.co.il
Year Founded: 1935
MMHD—(TAE)
Rev.: $3,472,750,326

AND PRIVATE COMPANIES

Assets: $19,348,830,199
Liabilities: $17,520,400,334
Net Worth: $1,828,429,865
Earnings: $148,748,996
Emp.: 2,540
Fiscal Year-end: 12/31/23
Offices of Other Holding Companies
N.A.I.C.S.: 551112
Shai Kompel *(CFO)*

Subsidiaries:

Orot Life Insurance Agency (2005) Ltd. (1)
7 Jabotinsky, Ramat Gan, Israel
Tel.: (972) 36334010
Fire Insurance Services
N.A.I.C.S.: 524113

Shomera Insurance Company Ltd. (1)
13 Hasibim Street, PO Box 7634, Petach Tikva, 49170, Israel
Tel.: (972) 3 925 1111
Web Site: http://www.shomera.co.il
General Insurance Services
N.A.I.C.S.: 524210

MENSA SINAI TICARI VE MALI YATIRIMLAR AS

Merkez Mahallesi Inonu Caddesi No 104, Mimarsinan Buyukcekmec, Istanbul, Turkiye
Tel.: (90) 2122693600
Textile Products Mfr
N.A.I.C.S.: 313310
Mehmet Ulutas *(Chm)*

MENSCH UND MASCHINE SOFTWARE SE

Argelsrieder Feld 5, 82234, Wesseling, Germany
Tel.: (49) 81539330
Web Site: https://www.mum.de
MUM—(DEU)
Rev.: $345,862,292
Assets: $202,294,410
Liabilities: $109,750,701
Net Worth: $92,543,708
Earnings: $28,072,523
Emp.: 1,031
Fiscal Year-end: 12/31/22
Computer-Aided Design (CAD) & Computer-Aided Manufacturing (CAM) Software Solutions
N.A.I.C.S.: 513210
Adi Drotleff *(Founder, Chm & CEO)*

Subsidiaries:

DATAflor Software AG (1)
August-Spindler-Str 20, 37079, Gottingen, Germany
Tel.: (49) 551506650
Web Site: http://www.dataflor.de
Sales Range: $25-49.9 Million
Emp.: 15
Computer-Aided Design Software Developer
N.A.I.C.S.: 513210

EUKLID Software GmbH (1)
Calmbacher 43, PO Box 71034, Boblingen, Germany
Tel.: (49) 7031 685 99 97
Web Site: http://www.euklid-cadcam.com
Computer-Aided Design Software Developer
N.A.I.C.S.: 513210

Hummingbird Systems GmbH (1)
Frankenstr 152, 90461, Nuremberg, Germany
Tel.: (49) 9112379460
Web Site: https://www.hummingbird-systems.com
Software Development Services
N.A.I.C.S.: 541511

Man & Machine Software Sp. z o.o. (1)
Ul Zeromskiego 52, 90-626, Lodz, Poland
Tel.: (48) 422913333
Web Site: http://www.mum.pl
Computer Software Services
N.A.I.C.S.: 541519

Man & Machine Software s.r.l. (1)
Via Torri Bianche 1, 20871, Vimercate, MB, Italy
Tel.: (39) 039699941
Web Site: http://www.mum.it
Computer Software Services
N.A.I.C.S.: 541519

Man and Machine AB (1)
Fabriksgatan 13, Gothenburg, 41250, Sweden
Tel.: (46) 317628080
Web Site: http://www.manandmachine.se
Sales Range: $25-49.9 Million
Emp.: 7
Computer-Aided Design Software Developer
N.A.I.C.S.: 513210

Man and Machine Benelux NV (1)
Bergemeersenstraat 118, PO Box 9300, Aalst, Belgium
Tel.: (32) 53606969
Web Site: http://www.manandmachine.be
Sales Range: $25-49.9 Million
Emp.: 10
Computer-Aided Design Software Developer
N.A.I.C.S.: 513210

Man and Machine France S.A.R.L. (1)
168B -170 rue Raymond Losserand, 75014, Paris, France
Tel.: (33) 153728800
Web Site: https://www.manandmachine.fr
Software Development Services
N.A.I.C.S.: 541511

Man and Machine Ltd., (1)
Unit 8 Thame 40 Jane Morbey Road, Thame, OX9 3RR, Oxfordshire, United Kingdom
Tel.: (44) 1844263700
Web Site: https://www.manandmachine.co.uk
Sales Range: $25-49.9 Million
Computer-Aided Design Software Developer
N.A.I.C.S.: 513210

Man and Machine Romania SRL (1)
Remus 12, Sector 3, 030685, Bucharest, Romania
Tel.: (40) 312288088
Web Site: https://www.manandmachine.ro
Sales Range: $25-49.9 Million
Emp.: 998
Computer-Aided Design Software Developer
N.A.I.C.S.: 513210

Man and Machine S.a.r.l., (1)
168B-170 Rue Raymond Losserand, 75014, Paris, France
Tel.: (33) 153728800
Web Site: https://www.manandmachine.fr
Sales Range: $25-49.9 Million
Computer-Aided Design Software Developer
N.A.I.C.S.: 513210
Boubacar Likeng *(Country Mgr)*

Mensch und Maschine At Work GmbH (1)
Averdiekstr 5, 49078, Osnabruck, Germany
Tel.: (49) 541404110
Web Site: http://www.mum-os.de
Computer Software Services
N.A.I.C.S.: 541519
Sven Scherer *(Sls Mgr)*

Mensch und Maschine Austria GmbH (1)
Grosswilfersdorf 102/1, Grosswilfersdorf, 8263, Hartberg, Austria
Tel.: (43) 338566001
Web Site: https://www.mum.at
Information Technology Services
N.A.I.C.S.: 519290

Mensch und Maschine Deutschland GmbH (1)
Argelsrieder Feld 5, 82234, Wessling, Germany
Tel.: (49) 81539330
Web Site: http://www.mum.de

Sales Range: $25-49.9 Million
Emp.: 100
Computer-Aided Design Software Developer
N.A.I.C.S.: 513210
Adi Drotleff *(CEO)*

Mensch und Maschine Haberzettl GmbH (1)
Hallerweiherstrasse 5, 90475, Nuremberg, Germany
Tel.: (49) 911352263
Web Site: http://haberzettl.de
Computer Software Services
N.A.I.C.S.: 541519
Rainer Haberzettl *(Mng Dir)*

Mensch und Maschine Hungary Kft. (1)
Fenyves sor 7, 9400, Sopron, Hungary
Tel.: (36) 99796950
Web Site: https://www.mum.co.hu
Software Development Services
N.A.I.C.S.: 541511

Mensch und Maschine Infrastruktur GmbH (1)
Christophstrasse 7, 70178, Stuttgart, Germany
Tel.: (49) 7119334830
Computer Software Services
N.A.I.C.S.: 541519

Mensch und Maschine Scholle GmbH (1)
Rheinlandstrasse 24, 42549, Velbert, Germany
Tel.: (49) 20519890020
Web Site: https://www.scholle.de
Information Technology Services
N.A.I.C.S.: 519290

Mensch und Maschine Schweiz AG (1)
Zurichstrasse 25, Winkel, 8185, Zurich, Switzerland
Tel.: (41) 448641900
Web Site: http://www.mum.ch
Computer System Design Services
N.A.I.C.S.: 541512
Thomas J. Mueller *(Mng Dir)*

Mensch und Maschine Tedikon GmbH (1)
Memmingerstr 29, Weibenhorn, 89264, Neu-Ulm, Germany
Tel.: (49) 730992970
Computer Software Services
N.A.I.C.S.: 541519

Mensch und Maschine acadGraph GmbH (1)
Fritz-Hommel-Weg 4, 80805, Munich, Germany
Tel.: (49) 8930658960
Web Site: https://mum-acadgraph.de
Computer Software Services
N.A.I.C.S.: 541519

Mensch und Maschine benCon 3D GmbH (1)
Friesenweg 4 Haus 12, Bahrenfeld, 22763, Hamburg, Germany
Tel.: (49) 408980780
Computer Software Services
N.A.I.C.S.: 541519

OPEN MIND CAD-CAM Technologies India Private Ltd. (1)
No 610 611 6th Floor B Wing No6 Mittal Tower MG Road, Nr Saraswat Co-op Bank Jayanagar, Bengaluru, 560001, Karnataka, India
Tel.: (91) 8026766999
Computer Software Services
N.A.I.C.S.: 541519
Rajeev Vaidya *(Mng Dir)*

OPEN MIND Technologies AG (1)
Argelsrieder Feld 5, 82234, Wessling, Germany
Tel.: (49) 8153933500
Web Site: https://www.openmind-tech.com
Emp.: 300
CAM CAD Design Services
N.A.I.C.S.: 541512

Subsidiary (Non-US):

OPEN MIND Technologies China Co.Ltd (2)

Suite 1608 Zhong Rong International Plaza No 1088 South Pudong Road, Lucky Bldg, Shanghai, 200120, China
Tel.: (86) 2158876572
Web Site: http://www.openmind-tech.com
Sales Range: $25-49.9 Million
Emp.: 10
CAM CAD Design Services
N.A.I.C.S.: 541512

OPEN MIND Technologies France S.A.r.l., (2)
1 Rue du Baron Chouard, PO Box 50056, Saverne, 67701, Monswiller, Cedex, France
Tel.: (33) 388031795
Web Site: http://www.openmind-tech.com
Sales Range: $25-49.9 Million
Emp.: 6
CAM CAD Design Services
N.A.I.C.S.: 541512

OPEN MIND Technologies Italia s.r.l., (2)
Via Pome 14, Rho, 20017, Milan, Italy
Tel.: (39) 0293162503
Web Site: http://www.openmind-tech.com
CAM CAD Design Services
N.A.I.C.S.: 541512

OPEN MIND Technologies Japan Inc. (2)
Web Site: http://www.openmind-tech.com
Sales Range: $25-49.9 Million
Emp.: 10
CAM CAD Design Services
N.A.I.C.S.: 541512

OPEN MIND Technologies PTE Ltd. (2)
3791 Jalan Bukit Merah 04-08, 05-22 Ubi Techpark, Singapore, 159471, Singapore
Tel.: (65) 67429556
Web Site: http://www.openmind-tech.com
Sales Range: $25-49.9 Million
Emp.: 7
CAM CAD Designers
N.A.I.C.S.: 541512

OPEN MIND Technologies Schweiz GmbH (2)
Frauenfelderstrasse 37, Winkel, 9545, Wangi, Switzerland
Tel.: (41) 448603050
Web Site: http://www.openmind-tech.com
Emp.: 4
CAM CAD Design Services
N.A.I.C.S.: 541512

OPEN MIND Technologies Taiwan Inc. (2)
3F No 153 Huanbei Road, Zhongli District, Taoyuan, 32055, Taiwan
Tel.: (886) 34613125
Web Site: http://www.openmind-tech.com
Sales Range: $25-49.9 Million
Emp.: 9
CAM CAD Design Services
N.A.I.C.S.: 541512

OPEN MIND Technologies UK Limited (2)
Tel.: (44) 1869290003
Web Site: http://www.openmind-tech.com
CAM CAD Design Services
N.A.I.C.S.: 541512

Subsidiary (US):

OPEN MIND Technologies USA Inc. (2)
39111 W 6 Mile Rd, Livonia, MI 48152
Tel.: (781) 239-8095
Web Site: http://www.openmind-tech.com
CAM CAD Design Services
N.A.I.C.S.: 541512
Alan Levine *(Mng Dir)*

OPEN MIND Technologies Asia Pacific Ltd. (1)
MOVA Building 22 Jalan Kilang 03-00, Singapore, 159419, Singapore
Tel.: (65) 67429556
Web Site: https://www.openmind-tech.com
Mining Services
N.A.I.C.S.: 212210

OPEN MIND Technologies Benelux B.V. (1)
Titaniumlaan 86, 5221 CK, 's-

Mensch und Maschine Software SE—(Continued)

Hertogenbosch, Netherlands
Tel.: (31) 736480166
Software Development Services
N.A.I.C.S.: 541511

OPEN MIND Technologies Iberia S.L. (1)
Albufera Center Building Office 903 Plaza Alqueria de la Culla 4, Alfafar, 46910, Valencia, Spain
Tel.: (34) 960045502
Computer Software Services
N.A.I.C.S.: 541519
Roberto Villoslada Arriola *(Sls Mgr)*

OPEN MIND Technologies Portugal Unipessoal Lda. (1)
Edificio OPEN Rua da Belgica Lote 18, Zona Industrial Casal da Lebre, 2430-028, Marinha Grande, Portugal
Tel.: (351) 913852422
Computer Software Services
N.A.I.C.S.: 541519

OPEN MIND Technologies S.R.L. (1)
Via Pome 14, 20017, Rho, MI, Italy
Tel.: (39) 0293162503
Mining Services
N.A.I.C.S.: 212210

OPEN MIND Technologies Spain S.L. (1)
Albufera Center Building - Plaza Alqueria de la Culla 4 Office 903, 46910, Valencia, Spain
Tel.: (34) 961433880
Web Site: https://www.openmind-tech.com
Software Development Services
N.A.I.C.S.: 541511

Open Mind Technologia Brasil Ltda. (1)
Av Andromeda 885 SL2021 Alphaville Empresarial, Barueri, Sao Paulo, 06473-000, Brazil
Tel.: (55) 1124248580
Computer Software Services
N.A.I.C.S.: 541519
Rodrigo Zimerman *(CEO)*

SOFIN Consulting Ltd. (1)
Kivitie 4, 02240, Espoo, Finland
Tel.: (358) 405035608
Web Site: https://www.sofin.consulting
Bridge Design & Consulting Services
N.A.I.C.S.: 541611

Sofistik AG (1)
Flataustr 14, 90411, Nuremberg, Germany
Tel.: (49) 911399010
Web Site: https://www.sofistik.com
Emp.: 80
Software Development Services
N.A.I.C.S.: 541511
Frank Deinzer *(CEO)*

Subsidiary (Domestic):

Bimotion GmbH (2)
Flataustrasse 14, 90411, Nuremberg, Germany
Tel.: (49) 91139901800
Web Site: https://www.bimotion.de
Emp.: 6
Computer Software Services
N.A.I.C.S.: 541519

creaTa Software GmbH (1)
On Grenzweg 40, Hohenkirchen-Siegertsbrunn, Munich, 85635, Germany
Tel.: (49) 8102896357
Computer-Aided Design Software Developer
N.A.I.C.S.: 513210

customX GmbH (1)
In den Fritzenstucker 2, 65549, Limburg, Germany
Tel.: (49) 643149860
Web Site: https://www.customx.de
Emp.: 14
Computer Software Services
N.A.I.C.S.: 541519

MENTICE AB
Odinsgatan 10, 411 03, Gothenburg, Sweden
Tel.: (46) 203885601
Web Site: https://www.mentice.com
Year Founded: 1999
MNTC—(OMX)
Rev.: $25,768,636
Assets: $30,208,491
Liabilities: $15,318,778
Net Worth: $14,889,713
Earnings: ($263,846)
Emp.: 122
Fiscal Year-end: 12/31/23
Software Development Services
N.A.I.C.S.: 541511
Goran Malmberg *(Pres)*

MENTIGA CORPORATION BERHAD
Unit 30-01 Level 30 Tower A Vertical Business Suite Avenue 3, Bangsar South No 8 Jalan Kerinchi, 59200, Kuala Lumpur, Malaysia
Tel.: (60) 327839191 MY
Web Site: https://www.mentiga.com.my
Year Founded: 1970
MENTIGA—(KLS)
Rev.: $3,123,918
Assets: $58,295,015
Liabilities: $20,318,479
Net Worth: $37,976,536
Earnings: ($3,819,502)
Emp.: 50
Fiscal Year-end: 12/31/22
Investment Holding Services
N.A.I.C.S.: 551112
Kok Leong Yeap *(Co-Sec)*

Subsidiaries:

Mentiga Plantation Sdn Bhd (1)
Ladang Sg Lembing Sungai Lembing, Pahang, 26200, Malaysia
Tel.: (60) 95411945
Emp.: 13
Oil Palm Plantation Services
N.A.I.C.S.: 111120

MENTOR ONLINE AB
Tryffelslingan 10, PO Box 72001, 181 72, Lidingo, Sweden
Tel.: (46) 86704100
Web Site: http://www.mentoronline.se
Sales Range: $25-49.9 Million
Emp.: 80
Trade Journal Publisher; Web Portal Developer; E-Commerce & Business Information Services
N.A.I.C.S.: 513120
Mikael Heinig *(Co-CEO)*

Subsidiaries:

FRI Kopenskap Forlags AB (1)
Tryffelslingan 10, PO Box 72001, 181 72, Lidingo, Sweden (100%)
Tel.: (46) 854551333
Web Site: http://www.fri-kopenskap.se
EuroCommerce & Business Information Journal Publisher
N.A.I.C.S.: 513120
Maya Saksi *(Editor)*

MENTZENDORFF & CO LTD
Prince Consort House 27 29 Albert Embankment, London, SE1 7TJ, United Kingdom
Tel.: (44) 2078403600
Web Site: http://www.mentzendorff.co.uk
Year Founded: 1858
Rev.: $66,213,312
Emp.: 39
Wine Shipping Services
N.A.I.C.S.: 488390
Andrew Hawes *(Mng Dir)*

MENUISERIE G. DUBOIS
53 Rue De La Republique, 37800, Sepmes, Indre Et Loire, France
Tel.: (33) 247654465
Web Site: http://www.menuiserie-gdubois.com
Rev.: $13,000,000
Emp.: 88
Carpentry Services
N.A.I.C.S.: 238130
Guillaune D'Ocagne *(Pres)*

MENZIES CHRYSLER INC.
1602 Champlain Ave, Whitby, L1N 6A7, ON, Canada
Tel.: (905) 683-4100
Web Site: http://www.menzieschrysler.com
Year Founded: 1971
Sales Range: $100-124.9 Million
New & Used Car Dealers
N.A.I.C.S.: 441110
Todd Menzies *(Owner, Founder & Pres)*

MENZIES GROUP LIMITED
1-11 Glenferrie Road, Malvern, 3144, VIC, Australia
Tel.: (61) 383748100
Web Site: http://www.menziesgroup.com.au
Year Founded: 1969
Emp.: 2,000
Janitorial Services
N.A.I.C.S.: 561720
Tim Newton *(Chm)*

MEP INFRASTRUCTURE DEVELOPERS LTD
2102 Floor- 21st Plot-62 Kesar Equinox Sir Bhalchandra Road, Hindu Colony, Mumbai, 400014, India
Tel.: (91) 2224142776
Web Site: https://www.mepinfra.com
MEP—(NSE)
Rev.: $175,980,332
Assets: $650,452,271
Liabilities: $634,431,429
Net Worth: $16,020,841
Earnings: ($10,480,170)
Emp.: 1,524
Fiscal Year-end: 03/31/21
Road, Bridge, Highway & Toll Plaza Construction
N.A.I.C.S.: 237310
Jayant D. Mhaiskar *(Chm & Mng Dir)*

MEP TECHNOLOGIES, INC.
3100 Peugeot, Laval, H7L 5C6, QC, Canada
Tel.: (450) 682-0804
Web Site: http://www.meptec.com
Sales Range: $50-74.9 Million
Emp.: 350
Precision Metal Products Mfr
N.A.I.C.S.: 332999
Armand Afilalo *(Pres & CEO)*

MEPET METRO PETROL VE TESISLERI SANAYI TICARET AS
Ruzgarlibahce Sehit Er Cengiz Kircioglu Sok No 6 Kavacik Beykoz, 34810, Istanbul, 34810, Türkiye
Tel.: (90) 2162300828
Web Site: https://www.mepet.tr
MEPET—(IST)
Rev.: $56,268,549
Assets: $27,362,321
Liabilities: $9,949,262
Net Worth: $17,413,059
Earnings: $791,679
Fiscal Year-end: 12/31/22
Gas Station Refining Services
N.A.I.C.S.: 237120
Cagla Ozturk *(Chm & Gen Mgr)*

MER GROUP
5 Yahadut, Holon, 5885633, Israel
Tel.: (972) 35572555
Web Site: https://www.mer-group.com
Year Founded: 1948
CMER—(TAE)
Rev.: $116,523,872
Assets: $138,050,671
Liabilities: $112,227,517
Net Worth: $25,823,154
Earnings: ($8,887,082)
Emp.: 1,100
Fiscal Year-end: 12/31/20
Holding Company
N.A.I.C.S.: 551112
Aviad Lahav *(CFO)*

Subsidiaries:

Techmer Pvt. Ltd. (1)
11 Roma street, Sderot, 8714652, Israel
Tel.: (972) 35572555
Web Site: https://tech-mer.com
Information Technology Services
N.A.I.C.S.: 541519

MERAFE RESOURCES LIMITED
Building B Second Floor Ballyoaks Office Park 35 Ballyclare Drive, Bryanston, Johannesburg, 2191, South Africa
Tel.: (27) 117834780
Web Site: https://www.meraferesources.co.za
MRF—(JSE)
Rev.: $503,429,438
Assets: $362,774,071
Liabilities: $76,393,928
Net Worth: $286,380,143
Earnings: $95,466,419
Emp.: 6,260
Fiscal Year-end: 12/31/23
Ferrochrome Mfr
N.A.I.C.S.: 331110
Abiel Mngomezulu *(Chm)*

Subsidiaries:

Merafe Ferrochrome & Mining (Proprietary) Limited (1)
Corner Boshoek Sta & Rasimone Rd, Rustenburg, 0301, North West, South Africa
Tel.: (27) 117834780
Web Site: http://www.meraferesources.co.za
Sales Range: $200-249.9 Million
Emp.: 500
Iron & Chromium Mining Services
N.A.I.C.S.: 212210

MERCA LEASING GMBH & CO. KG
Westerbachstrasse 28, 61476, Kronberg, Germany
Tel.: (49) 6173 958 600
Web Site: http://www.merca-leasing.de
Sales Range: $25-49.9 Million
Emp.: 25
Automobile Leasing Services
N.A.I.C.S.: 532112
Ulrich Helmdach *(Mng Gen Partner)*

Subsidiaries:

KBC Lease (Deutschland) Verwaltungs GmbH (1)
Frankfurter Str 75, Kronberg, 61476, Germany
Tel.: (49) 617395860
Sales Range: $25-49.9 Million
Emp.: 3
Automobile Leasing Services
N.A.I.C.S.: 532112

KBC Vendor Finance (Deutschland) GmbH (1)
Frankfurter Str 75, Kronberg, 61476, Germany
Tel.: (49) 6173958810
Sales Range: $50-74.9 Million
Financial Management Services
N.A.I.C.S.: 523999
Ulrich Helmdach *(Mgr)*

KBC Vendor Lease (Deutschland) Service GmbH (1)
Frankfurter Str 75, Kronberg, 61476, Germany
Tel.: (49) 6173958600
Web Site: http://www.mercaleasing.de
Sales Range: $25-49.9 Million
Emp.: 3
Vehicle Leasing Services
N.A.I.C.S.: 532112

Protection One Service GmbH (1)
Frankfurter Str 75, Kronberg, 61476, Germany
Tel.: (49) 6173958600
Financial Management Services
N.A.I.C.S.: 523999

MERCADO ABIERTO ELECTRONICO S.A.
San Martin 344-18th Floor, C1004AAH, Buenos Aires, Argentina
Tel.: (54) 1145906600
Web Site: http://www.mae.com.ar
Sales Range: $10-24.9 Million
Emp.: 100
Electronic Components Mfr
N.A.I.C.S.: 334419
Hugo Dasani (Mgr-Mktg)

MERCADO DE VALORES DE BUENOS AIRES S.A.
25 De Mayo 359 8th Floor, Buenos Aires, 1002, Argentina
Tel.: (54) 1143166000
Web Site: http://www.merval.sba.com.ar
Securities & Commodity Exchanges
N.A.I.C.S.: 523210
Jorge Decarli (Gen Mgr)

MERCADOLIBRE, INC.
Av Caseros 3039 Floor 2, Parque Patricios, 1264, Buenos Aires, Argentina
Tel.: (54) 1146408000 DE
Web Site: https://www.mercadolibre.com
MELI—(NASDAQ)
Rev.: $14,473,000,000
Assets: $17,646,000,000
Liabilities: $14,575,000,000
Net Worth: $3,071,000,000
Earnings: $987,000,000
Emp.: 58,313
Fiscal Year-end: 12/31/23
Electronic Shopping, Payment Solutions & Advertising Services
N.A.I.C.S.: 522320

Subsidiaries:

Business Vision S.A. (1)
Hipolito Yrigoyen 1530 Ciudad Autonoma De, Buenos Aires, C1089AAD, Argentina
Tel.: (54) 1143785000
Web Site: http://www.bvision.com
Electronic Components Mfr
N.A.I.C.S.: 334419

Inmuebles Online SAPI de CV (1)
Mariano Escobedo 748 Piso 9 Col Anzures, Mexico, 11590, Mexico
Tel.: (52) 15536118150
Electronic Components Mfr
N.A.I.C.S.: 334419

MercadoLibre.com Atividades de Internet Ltda. (1)
Rua Arandu 281 9th Floor, Sao Paulo, 04562 030, Brazil
Tel.: (55) 1155082366
Web Site: http://www.mercadolivre.com.br
Electronic Trading
N.A.I.C.S.: 425120

MERCADONA, S.A.
Calle Valencia 5 Tavernes Blanques, 46016, Valencia, Spain
Tel.: (34) 963883333
Web Site: http://www.mercadona.es
Sales Range: $15-24.9 Billion
Emp.: 58,000
Supermarket Operator
N.A.I.C.S.: 445110
Juan Roig Alfonso (Chm & Pres)

MERCALIN AB
Marieholmsgatan 38, Box 13007, SE-402 51, Gothenburg, Sweden
Tel.: (46) 31 337 4170 SE
Web Site: http://www.mercalin.com
Year Founded: 2009
Sales Range: $1-9.9 Million
Marking Spray Products Mfr & Whslr
N.A.I.C.S.: 325510
Henrik Holmberg (Product Mgr)

MERCANTIL SERVICIOS FINANCIEROS INTERNACIONAL, S.A.
50th Street with 58th Street in Obarrio, Mercantil Tower 21st Floor, Bella Vista District, Panama City, Panama
Tel.: (507) 2825080
Web Site: https://mercantilsfi.com
Year Founded: 1925
MSFIA—(PAN)
Holding Company
N.A.I.C.S.: 551112

Subsidiaries:

Capital Bank, Inc. (1)
P H Global Plaza Building Lobby Level, PO Box 0823-05992, Panama, Panama
Tel.: (507) 209 7000
Web Site: http://www.capitalbank.com.pa
Emp.: 142
Commercial Banking Services
N.A.I.C.S.: 522110

MERCANTIL SERVICIOS FINANCIEROS, C.A.
Av Andres Bello Edif Mercantil Floor 25, Centro Comercial El Parque Segunda y Tercera Etapa P03 Chacao, Caracas, 1010, Venezuela
Tel.: (58) 2125031335 VE
Web Site: https://www.msf.com
Rev.: $205,814,028
Assets: $961,476,675
Liabilities: $569,885,427
Net Worth: $391,591,248
Earnings: $119,933,533
Emp.: 5,223
Fiscal Year-end: 12/31/18
Financial Holding Company
N.A.I.C.S.: 551111
Gustavo J. Vollmer Acedo (Pres)

Subsidiaries:

Mercantil Merinvest Casa de Bolsa, C.A. (1)
Avenida Andres Bello N 1 Edificio Mercantil 31st Floor, Caracas, 1050, Venezuela
Tel.: (58) 2125032066
Financial Investment Services
N.A.I.C.S.: 523999

Mercantil Seguros, C.A. (1)
Av Libertador con calle Isaias Latigo Chavez, Edificio Mercantil Seguros Chacao, Caracas, 1060, Venezuela
Tel.: (58) 212 276 2000
Web Site: http://www.mercantilseguros.com
Health, Title, Property & Casualty Insurance Products & Services
N.A.I.C.S.: 524298
Maria Silvia F. Rodriguez (Pres & CEO)

Mercantil Servicios de Inversion, C.A. (1)
Avenida Andres Bello N 1 Edificio Mercantil 22nd Floor, Caracas, 1050, Venezuela
Tel.: (58) 2125032714
Financial & Banking Services
N.A.I.C.S.: 522110

Mercantil Sociedad Administradora de Entidades de Inversion Colectiva, C.A. (1)
Avenida Andres Bello N 1 Edificio Mercantil 26th Floor, Caracas, 1050, Venezuela
Tel.: (58) 2125032020
Financial & Banking Services
N.A.I.C.S.: 522110

Mercantil, C.A. Banco Universal (1)
Avenida Andres Bello 1, Edificio Mercantil, Caracas, 1050, Venezuela
Tel.: (58) 212 503 1111
Web Site: http://www.mercantilbanco.com
Commercial Banking
N.A.I.C.S.: 522110
Nelson A. Pinto (Pres & CEO)

MERCANTILE BANK PLC
61 Dilkusha Commercial Area, Dhaka, 1000, Bangladesh
Tel.: (880) 9561213
Web Site: https://www.mblbd.com
MERCANBANK—(DHA)
Rev.: $55,362,708
Assets: $4,191,179,022
Liabilities: $3,904,589,561
Net Worth: $286,589,461
Earnings: $41,519,306
Emp.: 2,418
Fiscal Year-end: 12/31/20
Commercial Banking Services
N.A.I.C.S.: 522110
Mohd. Selim (Vice Chm)

Subsidiaries:

Mercantile Bank Securities Limited (1)
Shawdesh Tower 3rd and 4th Floor 41/6 Purana Palton, Dhaka, 1000, Bangladesh
Tel.: (880) 27122515
Banking Services
N.A.I.C.S.: 522110
Fahmida Haque (CEO)

Mercantile Exchange House (UK) Limited (1)
108 Whitechapel Road, London, E1 1JE, United Kingdom
Tel.: (44) 2036381919
Banking Services
N.A.I.C.S.: 522110
Khoyruzzaman Khan (CEO)

MERCANTILE INSURANCE COMPANY LIMITED
Red Crescent Bhaban 61 Motijheel C/A 1st Floor, Dhaka, 1000, Bangladesh
Tel.: (880) 2223387662 BD
Web Site: https://miiplc.com
Year Founded: 1996
MERCINS—(CSE)
Rev.: $604,643
Assets: $22,934,741
Liabilities: $15,152,578
Net Worth: $7,782,162
Earnings: $436,736
Emp.: 302
Fiscal Year-end: 12/31/23
Insurance Services
N.A.I.C.S.: 524298
Abdul Mannan Mazumder (Vice Chm)

MERCANTILE PORTS & LOGISTICS LIMITED
1st Floor Tudor House Le Bordage Rd, Saint Peter Port, GY1 1DB, Guernsey
Tel.: (44) 2037576880 GY
Web Site: https://www.mercpl.com
MPL—(AIM)
Rev.: $6,149,962
Assets: $182,110,578
Liabilities: $66,759,657
Net Worth: $115,350,921
Earnings: ($12,167,382)
Emp.: 44
Fiscal Year-end: 12/31/22
Logistics Consulting Servies
N.A.I.C.S.: 541614
Nikhil Gandhi (Partner)

Subsidiaries:

Karanja Terminal & Logistics Private Limited (1)
Office No 705 706 7th Floor Shelton Cubix Plot No 87 Sector 15, Belapur CBD, Navi Mumbai, 400614, India
Tel.: (91) 2261929000
Logistic Services
N.A.I.C.S.: 488510

MERCANTILE SHIPPING COMPANY PLC
108 Aluthmawatha Road, 15, Colombo, 15, Sri Lanka
Tel.: (94) 114489900
Web Site: https://www.mercmarine.net
MSL—(COL)
Rev.: $98,859
Assets: $10,210,891
Liabilities: $26,093,995
Net Worth: ($15,883,104)
Earnings: ($4,328,208)
Fiscal Year-end: 03/31/19
Hire Vessels & Cargo Services
N.A.I.C.S.: 488320
Chinthaka Parakrama Punyajith Gamalath Hapudeniya (Deputy Chm)

MERCANTILE VENTURES LIMITED
No 88 Mount Road, Guindy, Chennai, 600 032, Tamil Nadu, India
Tel.: (91) 4440432205
Web Site: https://www.mercantileventures.co.in
538942—(BOM)
Rev.: $6,039,497
Assets: $43,854,297
Liabilities: $2,486,156
Net Worth: $41,368,140
Earnings: $1,546,832
Emp.: 3
Fiscal Year-end: 03/31/21
Real Estate Prorperty Leasing Services
N.A.I.C.S.: 531190
E. N. Rangaswami (Exec Dir)

Subsidiaries:

Chitharanjan Developers LLP (1)

I3 Security Private Limited (1)
14 5th Cross Street R V Nagar, Anna Nagar-East, Chennai, 600102, India
Tel.: (91) 4426210003
Web Site: https://www.i3security.co.in
Security Services
N.A.I.C.S.: 561612

Walery Security Management Ltd. (1)
No 88 Mount Roa Guindy, Chennai, 600 032, India
Tel.: (91) 4440432205
Web Site: https://walerysecurity.com
Commercial Property Development Services
N.A.I.C.S.: 531210

MERCARI, INC.
Roppongi Hills Mori Tower 6-10-1, Minato-ku, Tokyo, 1066118, Japan
Tel.: (81) 368046907
Web Site: https://www.about.mercari.com
Year Founded: 2013
4385—(TKS)
Rev.: $1,165,671,540
Assets: $3,121,028,060
Liabilities: $2,672,286,160
Net Worth: $448,741,900
Earnings: $83,727,420
Fiscal Year-end: 06/30/24
Application Development Services
N.A.I.C.S.: 541511
Shintaro Yamada (CEO)

MERCARI, INC.

Mercari, Inc.—(Continued)

Subsidiaries:

Kashima Antlers F.C. Co., Ltd. (1)
2887 Aou Higashiyama, Kashima, 314-0021, Ibaraki, Japan
Tel.: (81) 29 984 6800
Web Site: https://www.antlers.co.jp
Football Club Operator
N.A.I.C.S.: 711211
Fumiaki Koizumi (Pres)

MERCATOR LIMITED

83-87 8th Floor Mittal Tower B-Wing, Nariman Point, Mumbai, 400021, India
Tel.: (91) 9166373333
Web Site: http://www.mercator.in
526235—(NSE)
Rev.: $5,818
Assets: $138,515,117
Liabilities: $301,765,457
Net Worth: ($163,250,340)
Earnings: ($297,667)
Emp.: 1
Fiscal Year-end: 03/31/23
Transport Shipping Services
N.A.I.C.S.: 488510
H. K. Mittal (Chm)

Subsidiaries:

Mercator International Pte. Ltd. (1)
9 Temasek Blvd 42 01B Suntec Tower 2, Singapore, 038989, Singapore
Tel.: (65) 62209320
Sales Range: $50-74.9 Million
Emp.: 20
Holding Company
N.A.I.C.S.: 551112
Shalabh Mittal (Mng Dir)

Mercator Oil & Gas Ltd. (1)
3rd Fl Mittal Tower B Wing Nariman Pt, Mumbai, 400021, Maharashtra, India
Tel.: (91) 2266373333
Web Site: http://www.mercator.in
Oil & Gas Field Exploration Services
N.A.I.C.S.: 213112

MERCATOR MEDICAL S.A.

Heleny Modrzejewskiej 30, 31-327, Krakow, Poland
Tel.: (48) 126655400
Web Site: https://en.mercatormedical.eu
Year Founded: 1993
MRC—(WAR)
Surgical & Medical Instrument Manufacturing
N.A.I.C.S.: 339112
Wieslaw Zyznowski (Chm-Mgmt Bd)

MERCATOR TRANSPORT GROUP CORPORATION

8200 Boul Decarie Suite 220, Montreal, H4T 1M4, QC, Canada
Tel.: (514) 874-1616
Web Site: http://www.corpgmt.com
Sales Range: $25-49.9 Million
Emp.: 124
Logistics Solutions Services
N.A.I.C.S.: 541614
Jean-Pierre Apelian (Pres & CEO)

Subsidiaries:

Mercator Argentina S.A. (1)
Bartolome Cruz 1528, Buenos Aires, 1638, Argentina
Tel.: (54) 1147977762
Freight Forwarding Services
N.A.I.C.S.: 488510

Mercator Canada Inc. (1)
8200 Decarie Blvd, Mount-Royal, H4P 2P5, QC, Canada
Tel.: (514) 738-6464
Sales Range: $25-49.9 Million
Emp.: 10
Logistics Consulting Servies
N.A.I.C.S.: 541614

Mercator Ghana Limited (1)
2nd Floor Gt Bank Building Community 1, PO Box C02106, Tema, Ghana
Tel.: (233) 303 203 115
Sales Range: $25-49.9 Million
Emp.: 32
Freight Forwarding Services
N.A.I.C.S.: 488510

Mercator Transport France Inc. (1)
12 Rue De Bruxelles Saint Quentin Fallavier, Paris, France
Tel.: (33) 474945050
Freight Forwarding Services
N.A.I.C.S.: 488510

Mercator Transport International Inc. (1)
8660 Ch Darnley Bureau 207, Mount-Royal, H4T 1M4, QC, Canada
Tel.: (514) 874-1616
Freight Forwarding Services
N.A.I.C.S.: 488510

MERCEDES SALAZAR JOYERIA S.A.

Carrera 18a #103-29, Bogota, 110111, Colombia
Tel.: (57) 1 6225533
Web Site: http://www.mercedessalazar.com
Year Founded: 2001
Sales Range: $1-9.9 Million
Emp.: 40
Jewelry Mfr & Retailer
N.A.I.C.S.: 339910
Diego Martinez Vargas (CEO)

MERCEDES-BENZ GROUP AG

Mercedesstr 120, 70372, Stuttgart, Germany
Tel.: (49) 711170 De
Web Site: https://group.mercedes-benz.com
Year Founded: 1994
MBG—(STU)
Rev.: $165,355,061,515
Assets: $283,857,112,022
Liabilities: $183,688,754,587
Net Worth: $100,168,357,436
Earnings: $15,682,063,458
Emp.: 166,056
Fiscal Year-end: 12/31/23
Automobiles, Trucks, Electric & Electronics, Aviation, Space Defense Technologies, Propulsion & Financial Services Mfr
N.A.I.C.S.: 336110
Olaf G. Koch (Executives, Supervisory Bd of Dirs)

Subsidiaries:

Anota Fahrzeug Service- und Vertriebsgesellschaft mbH (1)
Eichhornstr 3, Berlin, 10785, Germany
Tel.: (49) 3026942319
Motor Vehicle Distr
N.A.I.C.S.: 423110

Atlantis Foundries (Pty.) Ltd. (1)
11 William Gourlay Street, PO Box 1701, Dassenberg, Atlantis, 1701L7350, Western Cape, South Africa
Tel.: (27) 215737200
Web Site: http://www.daimler.com
Sales Range: $400-449.9 Million
Emp.: 1,172
Automotive Steel Casting Mfr
N.A.I.C.S.: 331511
Pieter Puplessis (Mng Dir)

Automotive Training GmbH (1)
Hauptstrasse 31, 70563, Stuttgart, Germany
Tel.: (49) 7111770402
Web Site: http://www.automotive-training-consulting.com
Sales Range: $25-49.9 Million
Emp.: 20
Automotive Training & Consulting Services
N.A.I.C.S.: 541618
Walter Konzmann (CEO & Co-Mng Dir)

CARS Technik und Logistik GmbH (1)
Junkersstrasse 3, 04509, Wiedemar, Germany
Tel.: (49) 34207922300
Web Site: https://www.cars-gmbh.de
Automotive Repair & Logistics Services
N.A.I.C.S.: 811198
Marc Stoesser (Mng Dir & Head-Ops-Vehicle Transport)

Circulo Cerrado S.A. de ahorro para fines determinados (1)
Azucena Villaflor 435, Buenos Aires, 1107, Argentina
Tel.: (54) 1148088820
Web Site: http://www.circulo.mercedes-benz.com.ar
Sales Range: $50-74.9 Million
Emp.: 12
Financial Management Services
N.A.I.C.S.: 523999

Columbia Freightliner, LLC (1)
1450 Bluff Rd, Columbia, SC 29201
Tel.: (803) 376-4455
Emp.: 50
Freight Liner Truck Distr
N.A.I.C.S.: 423110
Scott Witt (Gen Mgr)

Daimler AG - Mercedes-Benz Berlin Plant (1)
Daimlerstrasse 143, 12277, Berlin, 12277, Germany
Tel.: (49) 30 7491 0
Sales Range: $800-899.9 Million
Emp.: 2,628
Diesel Engine & Fuel System Mfr
N.A.I.C.S.: 333618

Daimler AG - Mercedes-Benz Bremen Plant (1)
Mercedesstrase 1, Bremen, 28190, Germany
Tel.: (49) 421 419 0
Web Site: http://www.daimler.com
Sales Range: $1-4.9 Billion
Emp.: 12,000
Automobile Mfr
N.A.I.C.S.: 336110
Andreas Kellerman (Plant Mgr)

Daimler AG - Mercedes-Benz Gaggenau Plant (1)
Hauptstrasse 107, 76568, Gaggenau, Germany
Tel.: (49) 722 561 0
Web Site: http://www.daimler.com
Sales Range: $1-4.9 Billion
Emp.: 6,212
Automobile Parts Mfr
N.A.I.C.S.: 336390

Daimler AG - Mercedes-Benz Hamburg Plant (1)
Tel.: (49) 3027 583 7857
Web Site: http://www.daimler.com
Sales Range: $800-899.9 Million
Emp.: 2,500
Axle & Light Weight Structural Component Mfr
N.A.I.C.S.: 336350
Werner Schalow (Mng Dir)

Daimler AG - Mercedes-Benz Kassel Plant (1)
Mercedesplatz 1, Kassel, 34127, Germany
Tel.: (49) 561 802 0
Web Site: http://www.daimler.com
Sales Range: $800-899.9 Million
Emp.: 2,893
Axle & Powertrain Component Mfr
N.A.I.C.S.: 336350
Ludwig Pauss (Gen. Mgr)

Daimler AG - Mercedes-Benz Mannheim Plant (1)
Hanns-Martin-Schleyer-Strasse 21-57, 68305, Mannheim, Germany
Tel.: (49) 621 393 0
Sales Range: $1-4.9 Billion
Emp.: 562
Automotive Engine Mfr
N.A.I.C.S.: 333618

Daimler AG - Mercedes-Benz Rastatt Plant (1)

INTERNATIONAL PUBLIC

Mercedesstrasse 1, Rastatt, 76437, Germany
Tel.: (49) 722 291 0
Sales Range: $1-4.9 Billion
Emp.: 6,168
Automobile Mfr
N.A.I.C.S.: 336110
Michael Goebel (Mng Dir)

Daimler AG - Mercedes-Benz Sindelfingen Plant (1)
Bela-Barenyi-Strasse, 71063, Sindelfingen, Germany
Tel.: (49) 7031 90 0
Emp.: 26,414
Commercial Vehicle Mfr
N.A.I.C.S.: 336110

Daimler AG - Mercedes-Benz Worth Plant (1)
Daimlerstrasse 1, 76744, Worth, Rheinland-Pfalz, Germany
Tel.: (49) 7271711
Sales Range: $1-4.9 Billion
Emp.: 11,645
Trucks Mfr
N.A.I.C.S.: 336120

Daimler Australia/Pacific Pty. Ltd. (1)
44 Lexia Place, Mulgrave, 3170, VIC, Australia
Tel.: (61) 395669266
Emp.: 2,000
Passenger Car & Commercial Vehicle Distr
N.A.I.C.S.: 423110
Horst Von Sanden (Mng Dir & CEO)

Daimler Belgium Financial Company S.A. (1)
Avenue Du Peage 68, Brussels, 1200, Belgium
Tel.: (32) 27241211
Web Site: http://www.mercedez.be
Sales Range: $50-74.9 Million
Emp.: 100
Financial Management Services
N.A.I.C.S.: 523999
De Haes Mark (CEO)

Daimler Buses GmbH (1)
Fasanenweg 10, 70771, Leinfelden-Echterdingen, Germany (100%)
Tel.: (49) 7311810
Web Site: https://www.daimlertruck.com
Sales Range: $1-4.9 Billion
Emp.: 8,000
Motor Vehicles & Passenger Car Bodies
N.A.I.C.S.: 336211
Till Oberworder (CEO)

Subsidiary (Non-US):

EvoBus Austria GmbH (2)
IZ NO-Sud Strasse 4 Objekt 18, 2355, Wiener Neudorf, Austria
Tel.: (43) 5770100
Web Site: https://www.evobus.com
Sales Range: $50-74.9 Million
Emp.: 120
Bus & Coach Mfr & Distr
N.A.I.C.S.: 336110
Roman Laczkovich (CFO)

EvoBus Portugal, S.A. (2)
Apartado 1 - Abrunheira, 2726-901, Mem Martins, Portugal
Tel.: (351) 21 925 7031
Web Site: https://www.evobus.com
Sales Range: $25-49.9 Million
Emp.: 22
Bus & Coach Mfr
N.A.I.C.S.: 336110
Gonzalo Rodriguez (Gen Mgr)

EvoBus Sverige AB (2)
Lasarettsgatan 30, Spanga, 574 40, Vetlanda, Sweden
Tel.: (46) 38319600
Web Site: https://www.evobus.com
Bus & Coach Mfr
N.A.I.C.S.: 336110
Gunter Klemt (Mgr)

Subsidiary (Domestic):

Mercedes-Benz Minibus GmbH (2)
Niedersachsenweg 20, 44309, Dortmund, Germany
Tel.: (49) 231 5182 0
Web Site: http://www.daimler.com

AND PRIVATE COMPANIES — MERCEDES-BENZ GROUP AG

Sales Range: $25-49.9 Million
Emp.: 249
Bus & Coach Mfr
N.A.I.C.S.: 336110

Daimler Buses North Carolina LLC (1)
6012 High Point Rd, Greensboro, NC 27407
Tel.: (336) 878-5400
Bus & Coach Mfr
N.A.I.C.S.: 336110

Daimler Canada Finance Inc (1)
1 Place Ville Marie 37th Floor, Montreal, H3B 3P4, QC, Canada
Tel.: (201) 573-0600
Fund Lending Services
N.A.I.C.S.: 522291

Daimler Colombia S. A. (1)
Centro Empresarial Usaquen Plaza Cra 7 120-20, Bogota, Colombia
Tel.: (57) 1 518 7474
Web Site: https://www.daimler.com.co
Sales Range: $100-124.9 Million
Emp.: 30
New Car Dealers
N.A.I.C.S.: 441110
Mathias Eduardo Held Kotietzkoc *(Gen Mgr)*

Daimler Espana Gestion Inmobiliaria, S.L. (1)
Avenida De Bruselas 30, Alcobendas, 28108, Madrid, Spain
Tel.: (34) 914846000
Real Estate Manangement Services
N.A.I.C.S.: 531390

Daimler Finance North America LLC (1)
1 Mercedes Dr, Montvale, NJ 07645
Tel.: (201) 573-2724
Financial Management Services
N.A.I.C.S.: 523940

Daimler Financial Services Mexico, S. de R.L. de C.V. (1)
Av Paseo De Los Tamarindos No 90 Piso 11, Mexico, 05120, Distrito Federal, Mexico
Tel.: (52) 5541552000
Web Site: http://www.daimlerfinancialservice.com.mx
Financial Management Services
N.A.I.C.S.: 523999
Victor Calderon *(Mng Dir-Fin Svcs)*

Daimler Fleet Management GmbH (1)
Siemensstrasse 7, 70469, Stuttgart, Germany (100%)
Tel.: (49) 7112 574 7326
Web Site: https://www.daimler-fleetmanagement.de
Fleet Management Services
N.A.I.C.S.: 532112
Dennis Thomann *(Acct Mgr-Fleet20plus)*

Daimler Fleet Services A.S. (1)
TEM Otoyolu Hadimkoy Cikisi Mercedes Caddesi, Bahcesehir, 34500, Istanbul, Turkiye
Tel.: (90) 212 866 65 65
Fleet Management Services
N.A.I.C.S.: 532112

Daimler FleetBoard GmbH (1)
Am Wallgraben 125, Stuttgart, 70565, Baden-Wurttemberg, Germany
Tel.: (49) 7 11 17 9 19 99
Web Site: http://www.fleetboard.com
Sales Range: $200-249.9 Million
Emp.: 800
Transportation Telematic Internet Services
N.A.I.C.S.: 517810
Ralf Forcher *(CEO)*

Subsidiary (Non-US):

Daimler FleetBoard UK Ltd. (2)
Victoria House Cygnet Drive, Tamworth, B79 7RU, Staffs, United Kingdom
Tel.: (44) 1827 311912
Web Site: http://www.fleetboard.com
Sales Range: $25-49.9 Million
Emp.: 15
Vehicle & Transportation Management Software Distr
N.A.I.C.S.: 423430

Daimler Group Services Madrid, S.A. (1)
Calle Isla De Graciosa 3 - 3 Planta, San Sebastian de los Reyes, 28703, Madrid, Spain
Tel.: (34) 914545311
Web Site: http://www.daimler.com
Sales Range: $200-249.9 Million
Emp.: 300
Financial Management Services
N.A.I.C.S.: 523999
Bernd Rumscheid *(Gen Mgr)*

Daimler IT Retail GmbH (1)
Hanns-Klemm 5, 71034, Boblingen, Germany
Tel.: (49) 7031 9046354
Web Site: http://www.daimler-itr.com
Sales Range: $25-49.9 Million
Emp.: 16
Information Technology Consulting Services
N.A.I.C.S.: 541512
Bettina Grimm *(Mng Dir)*

Daimler India Commercial Vehicles Private Limited (1)
Unit 301 & 302 3rd Floor Campus 3B RMZ Millennia Business Park No 143, Dr M G R Road Perungudi, Chennai, 600 096, India
Tel.: (91) 44 45996000
Web Site: http://www.daimler-indiacv.com
Sales Range: $450-499.9 Million
Emp.: 1,200
Light & Heavy Commercial Vehicles Mfr & Distr
N.A.I.C.S.: 336120
Aydogan Cakmaz *(VP-Product Engrg)*

Daimler Insurance Agency LLC (1)
36455 Corporate Dr, Farmington Hills, MI 48331
Tel.: (248) 991-6700
Web Site: http://www.daimlerinsurance.com
Commercial Vehicle Insurance Services
N.A.I.C.S.: 524210

Daimler Insurance Services GmbH (1)
Siemensstrasse 7, Stuttgart, 70469, Germany
Tel.: (49) 3025544600
Automobile Insurance Services
N.A.I.C.S.: 524126

Daimler Insurance Services UK Limited (1)
Burystead Ct Caldecotte Lake Dr Caldecott, Milton Keynes, MK15 8BA, Buckinghamshire, United Kingdom
Tel.: (44) 8708500845
General Insurance Services
N.A.I.C.S.: 524210

Daimler International Assignment Services USA, LLC (1)
36455 Corporate Dr, Farmington Hills, MI 48331
Tel.: (248) 991-6037
Automobile Parts Mfr
N.A.I.C.S.: 336390

Daimler International Finance B.V. (1)
Van Deventerlaan 50, Utrecht, 3528 AE, Netherlands
Tel.: (31) 306059316
Financial Management Services
N.A.I.C.S.: 523999

Daimler Manufactura, S.A. de C.V. (1)
Av Paseo De Los Tamarindos No 90 Piso 16 Bosques De Las Lomas, Cuajimalpa de Morelos, Mexico, 05120, Distrito Federal, Mexico
Tel.: (52) 5541552527
General Freight Trucking Services
N.A.I.C.S.: 484110

Daimler Meridian Corporation (1)
36455 Corporate Dr, Farmington Hills, MI 48331
Tel.: (248) 991-6700
Automobile Parts Mfr
N.A.I.C.S.: 336390

Daimler Middle East & Levant FZE (1)
Daimler Chrysler Street, PO Box 17880, Dubai, United Arab Emirates
Tel.: (971) 4 8833200
Web Site: http://www.mideast.mercedes-benz.com
Commercial Vehicle Distr
N.A.I.C.S.: 423110

Daimler Mitarbeiter Wohnfinanz GmbH (1)
Karl-Benz-Platz 1, Stuttgart, 70327, Baden-Wurttemberg, Germany
Tel.: (49) 7111776627
Financial Management Services
N.A.I.C.S.: 523999

Daimler Mobility AG (1)
Eichhornstrasse 3, 10875, Berlin, Germany (100%)
Tel.: (49) 3025540
Web Site: http://www.daimler-mobility.com
Sales Range: $75-99.9 Billion
Financial Services
N.A.I.C.S.: 522320
Yvonne Rosslenbroich *(Member-Mgmt Bd-Africa & Asia-Pacific Region)*

Subsidiary (Non-US):

Athlon Car Lease International B.V. (2)
Veluwezoom 4, 1327AG, Almere, Netherlands
Tel.: (31) 36 547 1100
Web Site: http://www.athlon.com
Car Lending Services
N.A.I.C.S.: 532112

Subsidiary (Non-US):

Athlon Belgium N.V. (3)
Peutiesesteenweg 115, 1830, Machelen, Belgium
Tel.: (32) 2 716 5611
Web Site: https://www.athlon.com
Car Lending Services
N.A.I.C.S.: 532112
Els Descamps *(Comml Dir)*

Athlon Car Lease Polska Sp. Z o.o. (3)
Al Jerozolimskie 142A, 02-305, Warsaw, Budynek West Station, Poland
Tel.: (48) 22 279 4646
Web Site: https://www.athlon.com
Car Lending Services
N.A.I.C.S.: 532112

Athlon France S.A. (3)
Immeuble le Mermoz 53 avenue Jean Jaures, CS60012-Le Mermoz, 93351, Le Bourget, Cedex, France
Tel.: (33) 156 63 23 02
Web Site: http://www.athlon.com
Car Lending Services
N.A.I.C.S.: 532112

Athlon Germany GmbH & Co. KG (3)
Am Seestern 24, Nordrhein-Westfalen, 40547, Dusseldorf, Germany
Tel.: (49) 21154018000
Web Site: http://www.athlon.com
Car Lending Services
N.A.I.C.S.: 532112

Athlon Italy Srl a Socio Unico (3)
Via Carlo Veneziani 56, 00148, Rome, Italy
Tel.: (39) 06412071
Web Site: https://www.athlon.com
Car Lending Services
N.A.I.C.S.: 532112

Athlon Luxembourg S.A. (3)
Ecoparc Windhof 22 Rue del Industrie, L-8399, Windhof, Luxembourg
Tel.: (352) 49 77 70 1
Web Site: http://www.athlon.com
Car Lending Services
N.A.I.C.S.: 532112

Athlon Portugal, Lda. (3)
Quinta da Fonte Rua dos Malhoes Edf D Pedro I Piso 2, paco de arcos, 2770-071, Oeiras, Portugal
Tel.: (351) 70 728 4566
Web Site: https://www.athlon.com
Car Lending Services
N.A.I.C.S.: 532112

Athlon Spain, S.A. (3)
Calle de la Calendula 93 Ed H Miniparc III, Alcobendas, 28109, Madrid, Spain
Tel.: (34) 93 477 6560
Web Site: https://www.athlon.com
Car Lending Services
N.A.I.C.S.: 532112

Athlon Sweden (3)
Agnesfridsvagen 185a, 21375, Malmo, Sweden
Tel.: (46) 4094 75 40
Web Site: http://www.athloncarlease.se
Car Lending Services
N.A.I.C.S.: 532112

Subsidiary (Domestic):

Daimler Export & Trade Finance GmbH (2)
Eichhornstr. 3, 10785, Berlin, Germany (100%)
Tel.: (49) 3025541634
Sales Range: $1-9.9 Million
Emp.: 30
Electrical Power Svcs
N.A.I.C.S.: 238210

Subsidiary (Non-US):

Mercedes-Benz Auto Finance Ltd. (2)
Tower C 6-9F Lei Shing Hong Plaza 8 Wangjing Street, Chaoyang District, Beijing, 100102, China
Tel.: (86) 4008981888
Web Site: http://www.mercedes-benz-finance.com.cn
Automotive Financial Leasing Services
N.A.I.C.S.: 522220
Emilio Escandon *(Mng Principal-New York)*

Subsidiary (Domestic):

Mercedes-Benz Bank AG (2)
Seimenstrasse 7, 70439, Stuttgart, Germany (100%)
Tel.: (49) 71125740
Web Site: http://www.mercedes-benz-bank.de
Sales Range: $150-199.9 Million
Emp.: 250
Automobile Mfr
N.A.I.C.S.: 336110

Subsidiary (Non-US):

Mercedes-Benz Financial Services Australia Pty. Ltd. (2)
Level 1 41 Lexia Place, Mulgrave, 3170, VIC, Australia
Tel.: (61) 3 8554 3000
Commercial Vehicle Financing Services
N.A.I.C.S.: 525990
Gero Goetzenberger *(Mng Dir)*

Mercedes-Benz Financial Services Austria GmbH (2)
Himmelreich 1, Salzburg, 5020, Austria
Tel.: (43) 662 4666 0
Web Site: http://www.mercedes-benz-financial.at
Financial Management Services
N.A.I.C.S.: 523999
Krista Kamsa *(Mgr-HR)*

Mercedes-Benz Financial Services BeLux N.V. (2)
Tollaan 68 Avenue du Peage, Brussels, 1200, Belgium
Tel.: (32) 2 254 6811
Web Site: http://www.mercedes-benz.be
Emp.: 500
Financial Management Services
N.A.I.C.S.: 523999
Eberhard Kern *(CEO)*

Mercedes-Benz Financial Services Canada (2)
2680 Matheson Blvd E Ste 500, Mississauga, L4W 0A5, ON, Canada
Tel.: (905) 813-6900
Web Site: http://www.mbfinancial.ca
Sales Range: $10-24.9 Million
Emp.: 70
Automotive Finance
N.A.I.C.S.: 522220

Mercedes-Benz Financial Services Ceska republika s.r.o. (2)
Daimlerova 2, Chodov, 149 45, Prague, Czech Republic

MERCEDES-BENZ GROUP AG

INTERNATIONAL PUBLIC

Mercedes-Benz Group AG—(Continued)
Tel.: (420) 271077666
Web Site: http://www.mercedes.cz
Sales Range: $50-74.9 Million
Emp.: 75
Automotive Financial Leasing Services
N.A.I.C.S.: 522220
Ralf Ewald *(CEO)*

Mercedes-Benz Financial Services Espana E. F. C., S.A.U. (2)
Avda de Bruselas 30 Poligono Arroyo de la Vega, Alcobendas, 28108, Madrid, Spain
Tel.: (34) 91 484 6000
Web Site: http://www.daimler.com
Motor Vehicle Financial Services
N.A.I.C.S.: 525990

Mercedes-Benz Financial Services France S.A. (2)
ZAC du Cournouiller 9 rue de Chaponval, 78870, Bailly, France
Tel.: (33) 1 30 80 84 00
Financial Management Services
N.A.I.C.S.: 523999

Mercedes-Benz Financial Services Hellas AE (2)
20 Odos Thivaidos, 14564, Kifissia, Greece
Tel.: (30) 210 8188800
Sales Range: $50-74.9 Million
Emp.: 3
Financial Management Services
N.A.I.C.S.: 523999
Stathis Skaris *(Mgr-IT)*

Mercedes-Benz Financial Services Hong Kong Ltd. (2)
59/F Central Plaza 18 Harbour Road, Wan-chai, China (Hong Kong)
Tel.: (852) 2594 8780
Web Site: http://www.daimler.com
Sales Range: $50-74.9 Million
Emp.: 10
Motor Vehicle Insurance Services
N.A.I.C.S.: 524126

Mercedes-Benz Financial Services Italia S.p.A (2)
Via Giulio Vincenzo Bona 110, 156, Rome, Italy
Tel.: (39) 06415951
Web Site: http://www.mercedes-benz-financialservices.it
Motor Vehicle Financial Services
N.A.I.C.S.: 525990

Mercedes-Benz Financial Services Nederland B.V. (2)
Ravenswade 4, 3439 LD, Nieuwegein, Netherlands
Tel.: (31) 306059820
Web Site: https://www.mercedes-benz-financialservices.nl
Sales Range: $100-124.9 Million
Emp.: 150
Automotive Financial Leasing Services
N.A.I.C.S.: 522220

Mercedes-Benz Financial Services New Zealand Ltd. (2)
9 Pacific Rise, Mount Wellington, Auckland, 1060, New Zealand
Tel.: (64) 9 573 3500
Sales Range: $25-49.9 Million
Emp.: 30
Automobile Financing Services
N.A.I.C.S.: 525990
Andrew Ernst *(Gen Mgr)*

Mercedes-Benz Financial Services Portugal - Instituicao Financeira de Credito S.A. (2)
Abrunheira - Apartado 6, 2726-901, Mem Martins, Portugal
Tel.: (351) 707210211
Web Site: http://www.mercedes-benz.pt
Automobile Financing Services
N.A.I.C.S.: 525990
Gerd Sailer *(Product Mgr)*

Mercedes-Benz Financial Services Rus OOO (2)
Leningradsky prospect 39A, 125167, Moscow, Russia
Tel.: (7) 4957975354
Web Site: https://www.mercedes-benz.ru
Financial Lending Services

N.A.I.C.S.: 522220
Christian Schueler *(CEO)*

Mercedes-Benz Financial Services Schweiz AG (2)
Bernstrasse 55, 8952, Schlieren, Switzerland
Tel.: (41) 447558000
Web Site: http://www.mercedes-benz-financialservices.ch
Emp.: 430
Automobile Financing Services
N.A.I.C.S.: 525990
Marcel Guerre *(CEO)*

Mercedes-Benz Financial Services Slovakia s.r.o. (2)
Tuhovska 29, 831 06, Bratislava, Slovakia
Tel.: (421) 249294600
Web Site: http://www.mbfs.sk
Sales Range: $50-74.9 Million
Emp.: 25
Automobile Financing Services
N.A.I.C.S.: 525990
Martin Pavelek *(Mng Dir)*

Mercedes-Benz Financial Services South Africa (Pty) Ltd. (2)
123 Wierda Road, Zwartkop, Centurion, 0046, South Africa
Tel.: (27) 86 132 4653
Web Site: https://www.mercedes-benz.co.za
Automobile Financing Services
N.A.I.C.S.: 525990

Mercedes-Benz Financial Services Taiwan Ltd. (2)
4F No 129 Min-Sheng East Road Sec 3, Taipei, 10596, Taiwan
Tel.: (886) 2 2547 8788
Web Site: http://www.mercedes-benz-financial.com.tw
Automobile Financing Services
N.A.I.C.S.: 522220

Mercedes-Benz Financial Services UK Limited (2)
Delaware Drive, Tongwell, Milton Keynes, MK15 8BA, United Kingdom
Tel.: (44) 870 847 0700
Automobile Financing Services
N.A.I.C.S.: 525990

Subsidiary (US):

Mercedes-Benz Financial Services USA LLC (2)
36455 Corporate Dr, Farmington Hills, MI 48331
Tel.: (248) 991-6700
Web Site: http://www.mbfs.com
Automobile Financing Services
N.A.I.C.S.: 525990
Janet Marzett *(VP-Ops-America)*

Subsidiary (Domestic):

Mercedes-Benz Leasing GmbH (2)
Siememstrasse 7, 70469, Stuttgart, Germany **(100%)**
Tel.: (49) 711257401
Web Site: http://www.mercedes-benz-bank.de
Sales Range: $25-49.9 Million
Emp.: 1,450
Car Lending Services
N.A.I.C.S.: 532112
Enten Mann *(CEO)*

Daimler North America Finance Corporation (1)
131 Continental Dr Ste 408, Newark, DE 19713
Tel.: (302) 292-6840
Financial Management Services
N.A.I.C.S.: 523999

Daimler Northeast Asia Parts Trading and Services Co., Ltd. (1)
Rm 901 9/F Daimler Mansion No 8 Yard Wangjing St, Chaoyang, Beijing, 100102, China
Tel.: (86) 1084173587
Automobile Part Whslr
N.A.I.C.S.: 423120

Daimler Parts Brand GmbH (1)
Epplestr 225, Stuttgart, 70567, Baden-Wurttemberg, Germany
Tel.: (49) 711170

Automobile Parts Mfr
N.A.I.C.S.: 336390

Daimler Purchasing Coordination Corp. (1)
36455 Corporate Dr, Farmington Hills, MI 48331
Tel.: (248) 991-6700
Automotive Distr
N.A.I.C.S.: 423110

Daimler Re Brokers GmbH (1)
Eichhornstr 3, Berlin, 10785, Germany
Tel.: (49) 3025540
Insurance Brokerage Services
N.A.I.C.S.: 524210

Daimler Re Insurance S.A. Luxembourg (1)
Rue De Bitbourg 53, Luxembourg, 1248, Luxembourg
Tel.: (352) 27 12 56 66
General Insurance Services
N.A.I.C.S.: 524210

Daimler Retail Receivables LLC (1)
36455 Corporate Dr, Farmington Hills, MI 48331
Tel.: (248) 991-6700
Automobile Parts Mfr
N.A.I.C.S.: 336110

Daimler Servicios Corporativos Mexico S. de R.L. de C.V (1)
Av Paseo De Los Tamarindos No 90 Piso 11, Mexico, 5120, Mexico
Tel.: (52) 5541552000
Business Management Consulting Services
N.A.I.C.S.: 541611

Daimler South East Asia Pte. Ltd. (1)
3 Temasek Avenue 29-01 Centennial Tower, Singapore, 39190, Singapore
Tel.: (65) 68 49 8 000
Sales Range: $150-199.9 Million
Emp.: 30
Commercial Vehicle Distr
N.A.I.C.S.: 423110
Wolfgang Erhard Huppenbauer *(Pres & CEO)*

Daimler TSS GmbH (1)
Wilhelm-Runge-Strasse 11, 89081, Ulm, Germany
Tel.: (49) 7 31 5 05 06
Web Site: http://www.daimler-tss.de
Sales Range: $75-99.9 Million
Emp.: 40
Software Development Services
N.A.I.C.S.: 541511
Gerhart Streit *(CEO)*

Daimler Trucks Canada Ltd. (1)
6733 Mississauga Rd Suite 404, Mississauga, L5N 6J5, ON, Canada
Tel.: (905) 812-6500
Web Site: http://www.daimler.com
Sales Range: $25-49.9 Million
Emp.: 6
Industrial Truck Mfr
N.A.I.C.S.: 333924
Brad Thiessen *(Gen Mgr)*

Daimler Trucks Korea Ltd. (1)
9th Fl Seoul Square Building 541 Namdaemunno 5-ga, Jung-gu, Seoul, 100-714, Korea (South)
Tel.: (82) 2 6456 2500
Web Site: http://www.daimler.com
Industrial Truck Mfr
N.A.I.C.S.: 333924

Daimler Trucks North America LLC (1)
4555 N Channel Ave, Portland, OR 97217
Tel.: (503) 745-8000
Web Site: https://northamerica.daimlertruck.com
Sales Range: $1-4.9 Billion
Emp.: 25,000
Heavy & Medium Duty Truck & Specialized Commercial Vehicle Mfr
N.A.I.C.S.: 336120
John O'Leary *(CFO)*

Branch (Domestic):

Daimler Trucks North America (2)
1400 Tulip Dr, Gastonia, NC 28052-1873

Tel.: (704) 868-5700
Web Site: http://www.daimler-trucksnorthamerica.com
Sales Range: $50-74.9 Million
Emp.: 1,000
Motor Vehicle Parts & Accessories Mfr
N.A.I.C.S.: 336390
John O'Leary *(Pres & CEO)*

Subsidiary (Domestic):

Detroit Diesel Corporation (2)
13400 Outer Dr W, Detroit, MI 48239
Tel.: (313) 592-5001
Web Site: http://www.detroitdiesel.com
Sales Range: $800-899.9 Million
Emp.: 2,600
Mfr & Designer of Diesel & Alternative Fuel Engines
N.A.I.C.S.: 333618
John F. Farmer *(Gen Counsel & VP)*

Subsidiary (Domestic):

Detroit Deisel Corporation (3)
13400 W Outer Dr, Detroit, MI 48239-1309
Tel.: (313) 592-5000
Sales Range: $450-499.9 Million
Emp.: 2,500
Industrial Machinery & Equipment
N.A.I.C.S.: 333618

Division (Domestic):

Detroit Diesel Corp. - Canton (3)
515 11th St SE, Canton, OH 44707-3811
Tel.: (330) 430-4300
Web Site: http://www.detroitdiesel.com
Sales Range: $50-74.9 Million
Emp.: 190
Distribution Center
N.A.I.C.S.: 423830
Jerry Reed *(Plant Mgr)*

Subsidiary (Domestic):

Detroit Diesel Corp. - Irvine (3)
7700 Irvine Ctr Dr Ste 875, Irvine, CA 92618
Tel.: (949) 753-7710
Sales Range: $25-49.9 Million
Emp.: 15
Diesel & Semi-Diesel or Dual-Fuel Engines
N.A.I.C.S.: 811111

Detroit Diesel Corp. - Laredo (3)
1109 Uniroyal Dr, Laredo, TX 78045-9406
Tel.: (956) 722-0906
Web Site: http://www.detroitdiesel.com
Sales Range: $50-74.9 Million
Emp.: 4
Diesel Engines & Parts
N.A.I.C.S.: 423830

Division (Domestic):

Detroit Diesel Overseas Distribution Corp. (3)
2277 Northwest 14th St, Miami, FL 33125-2101 **(100%)**
Tel.: (305) 637-1555
Web Site: http://www.detroitdiesel.com
Sales Range: $50-74.9 Million
Emp.: 5
Distr of Diesel Engines & Parts
N.A.I.C.S.: 423830
Pete Diaz *(Mgr)*

Subsidiary (Domestic):

Detroit Diesel Remanufacturing-Central (3)
840 Overlander Rd, Emporia, KS 66801-8900
Tel.: (620) 343-3790
Web Site: http://www.detroitdieselreman.com
Sales Range: $50-74.9 Million
Emp.: 180
Diesel Engine Rebuilding
N.A.I.C.S.: 333618

Division (Domestic):

Detroit Diesel Remanufacturing-East (3)
60703 Country Club Rd, Byesville, OH 43723
Tel.: (740) 439-7701
Web Site: http://www.detroitdiesel.com

AND PRIVATE COMPANIES   **MERCEDES-BENZ GROUP AG**

Sales Range: $150-199.9 Million
Emp.: 540
Diesel Engine Rebuilding
N.A.I.C.S.: 333618
Todd Moore *(Plant Mgr)*

Subsidiary (Domestic):

Detroit Diesel
Remanufacturing-West   (3)
PO Box 550, Tooele, UT 84074-0550
Tel.: (435) 843-6000
Web Site: http://www.detroitdiesel.com
Sales Range: $125-149.9 Million
Emp.: 400
Diesel Engine Rebuilding
N.A.I.C.S.: 333618
Bruce McCormack *(Engr-Safety & Environmental)*

Subsidiary (Non-US):

Detroit Diesel of Canada Ltd.   (3)
150 Dufferin Ave Ste 701, London, N6A
5N6, ON, Canada   (100%)
Tel.: (519) 661-0149
Web Site: http://www.detroitdiesel.com
Sales Range: $1-9.9 Million
Emp.: 19
Distr of Diesel Engine
N.A.I.C.S.: 333618

Subsidiary (Domestic):

Florida Detroit Diesel-Allison   (3)
2277 NW 14th St, Miami, FL 33125-2101
Tel.: (305) 638-5300
Web Site: http://www.fdda.com
Sales Range: $50-74.9 Million
Emp.: 80
Engines & Parts, Diesel
N.A.I.C.S.: 423830

Division (Domestic):

Florida Detroit Diesel-Allison   (3)
8411 Adamo Dr, Tampa, FL 33619-3517
Tel.: (813) 621-5651
Web Site: http://www.fpda.com
Sales Range: $25-49.9 Million
Emp.: 32
Sales of Automotive Parts
N.A.I.C.S.: 441330
Stanley Dale *(Mgr-HR)*

Florida Detroit Diesel-Allison   (3)
224 SW 52nd Ave, Ocala, FL
34474-9364   (100%)
Tel.: (352) 237-7977
Web Site: http://www.fdda.com
Sales Range: $25-49.9 Million
Emp.: 16
Sales & Services of Diesel Engines & Parts
N.A.I.C.S.: 423830

Subsidiary (Domestic):

Florida Detroit Diesel-Allison   (3)
2305 Rockfill Rd, Fort Myers, FL 33916-4819
Tel.: (239) 332-3100
Web Site: http://www.fdda.com
Sales Range: $50-74.9 Million
Emp.: 11
Engines & Parts Diesel
N.A.I.C.S.: 423830
Don Man *(CEO)*

Florida Detroit Diesel-Allison   (3)
3885 Selvitz Rd, Fort Pierce, FL 34981
Tel.: (772) 464-6006
Web Site: http://www.fdda.com
Sales Range: $25-49.9 Million
Emp.: 20
Sales & Services of Diesel Engines
N.A.I.C.S.: 423830
Fred Vedder *(Mgr-Svc)*

Florida Detroit Diesel-Allison Inc.   (3)
6850 Presidents Dr, Orlando, FL 32809-5699
Tel.: (407) 888-1700
Web Site: http://www.fdda.com
Sales Range: $25-49.9 Million
Emp.: 50
Diesel Engines & Parts
N.A.I.C.S.: 423830

Division (Domestic):

North America Fuel Systems Remanufacturing LLC   (3)
4232 Brockton Dr SE, Kentwood, MI 49512
Tel.: (616) 541-1100
Web Site: https://www.nafsreman.com
Sales Range: $50-74.9 Million
Emp.: 150
Fuel Injectors Remanufacturer
N.A.I.C.S.: 336310
Sanjiv Khurana *(Pres)*

Subsidiary (Domestic):

Outer Drive Holdings Inc.   (3)
13400 Outer Dr W, Detroit, MI 48239-1309
Tel.: (313) 592-5000
Web Site: http://www.detroitdiesel.com
Sales Range: $50-74.9 Million
Emp.: 1
Diesel Engines & Parts
N.A.I.C.S.: 423830

Subsidiary (Domestic):

Atlantic Detroit Diesel-Allison   (4)
281 Wolf Rd, Latham, NY 12110
Tel.: (518) 452-0000
Web Site:
    https://www.stewartandstevenson.com
Sales Range: $50-74.9 Million
Industrial Equipment
N.A.I.C.S.: 423830
Meredith Stonehouse *(Mgr-HR)*

Subsidiary (Domestic):

Freightliner LLC   (2)
4747 N Channel Ave, Portland, OR
97217-7613   (100%)
Tel.: (503) 745-8000
Web Site: http://www.freightliner.com
Diesel Trucks & Tractors Mfr
N.A.I.C.S.: 336120
Juergen Kritschgau *(CFO-Fin & Control)*

Subsidiary (Domestic):

Freightliner Custom Chassis   (3)
552 Hyatt St, Gaffney, SC 29341-2525
Tel.: (864) 487-1700
Web Site: http://www.freightlinerchassis.com
Sales Range: $150-199.9 Million
Emp.: 750
Assembly of Truck Tractors for Highway Use
N.A.I.C.S.: 336120
Gordon Tayllor *(Product Mgr)*

Subsidiary (Domestic):

Houston Freightliner Inc.   (4)
9550 N Loop E Fwy, Houston, TX 77029-1230
Tel.: (713) 672-4115
Web Site:
    https://www.houstonfreightliner.com
Sales Range: $125-149.9 Million
Emp.: 300
Commercial Trucks
N.A.I.C.S.: 423120
Rick Stuart *(Owner)*

Division (Domestic):

Beaumont Freightliner, Sterling, Western Star   (5)
7390 I-10, Beaumont, TX 77705-7209
Tel.: (409) 951-8300
Web Site: https://beaumontfreightliner.com
Sales Range: $100-124.9 Million
Emp.: 23
Personal Service Agents, Brokers & Bureaus
N.A.I.C.S.: 423110
Rick Stewart *(Pres)*

Subsidiary (Domestic):

Freightliner LLC   (3)
1800 N Main St, Mount Holly, NC 28120-9141
Tel.: (704) 822-7000
Web Site: http://www.freightliner.com
Sales Range: $100-124.9 Million
Emp.: 400
Trucks Mfr
N.A.I.C.S.: 339999
Jim Gaesey *(Mgr-HR)*

Freightliner LLC   (3)
3025 Evergreen Dr Ste 150, Duluth, GA
30096-2317
Tel.: (770) 623-5300

Web Site: http://www.freightliner.com
Sales Range: $25-49.9 Million
Emp.: 16
Trucks Commercial
N.A.I.C.S.: 493110

Freightliner LLC   (3)
9225 Indian Creek Pkwy, Overland Park, KS 66210-2009
Tel.: (913) 451-8626
Web Site: http://www.freightliner.com
Sales Range: $10-24.9 Million
Emp.: 28
North Central Retail Office
N.A.I.C.S.: 561110

Freightliner LLC   (3)
804 Mittel Dr, Wood Dale, IL 60191-1172
Tel.: (630) 350-3189
Web Site: http://www.freightliner.com
Sales Range: $50-74.9 Million
Emp.: 60
Automotive Supplies & Parts
N.A.I.C.S.: 423120

Freightliner LLC   (3)
5745 Challenge Dr, Memphis, TN
38115   (100%)
Tel.: (901) 367-8400
Web Site: http://www.freightliner.com
Sales Range: $50-74.9 Million
Emp.: 100
Distr of Motor Vehicle Supplies & New Parts
N.A.I.C.S.: 423120
Joe Hell *(Gen Mgr)*

Freightliner LLC   (3)
2078 Ctr Sq Rd, Logan Township, NJ 08085
Tel.: (856) 467-6000
Web Site: http://www.freightliner.com
Sales Range: $25-49.9 Million
Emp.: 20
Truck Parts & Accessories
N.A.I.C.S.: 423120

Freightliner Trucking L.L.C.   (3)
11550 Statesville Blvd, Cleveland, NC 27013
Tel.: (704) 645-5000
Web Site: http://www.freightlinertrucks.com
Sales Range: $700-749.9 Million
Emp.: 4,300
Training & Development Consultant
N.A.I.C.S.: 811111

Subsidiary (Non-US):

Freightliner of Canada, Ltd.   (3)
6733 Mississauga Rd Ste 404, Mississauga, L5N 6J5, ON, Canada   (100%)
Tel.: (905) 812-6500
Web Site: http://www.freightliner.com
Sales Range: $25-49.9 Million
Emp.: 12
Mfr of Diesel Trucks & Tractors
N.A.I.C.S.: 336211
Brad Thiessen *(Gen Mgr)*

Subsidiary (Domestic):

Freightliner of Grand Rapids, Inc.   (3)
5285 Clay Ave SW, Grand Rapids, MI 49548-5657
Tel.: (616) 284-5151
Web Site: https://www.ftlgr.com
Sales Range: $75-99.9 Million
Emp.: 140
Sales of Trucks
N.A.I.C.S.: 423110
Andy T. Einsley *(Office Mgr)*

Freightliner of Maine Inc.   (3)
422 Perry Rd, Bangor, ME
04401-6728   (100%)
Tel.: (207) 945-6451
Web Site:
    http://www.freightlinerofmaine.com
Sales Range: $50-74.9 Million
Emp.: 130
Provider of Automotive Goods & Services
N.A.I.C.S.: 423120
Tracy Thibodeau *(Controller)*

Freightliner of Southern Alabama   (3)
1507 Reeves St, Dothan, AL
36303-2843   (100%)
Tel.: (334) 793-4455
Web Site: http://www.freightliner.com

Sales Range: $25-49.9 Million
Emp.: 50
Mfr of Automotive Supplies & Parts
N.A.I.C.S.: 423120

Subsidiary (Non-US):

Globocam Anjou   (3)
8991 Boul Metropolitain East, Anjou, H1J
1K2, QC, Canada   (100%)
Tel.: (514) 353-4000
Web Site: https://www.globocam.ca
Sales Range: $10-24.9 Million
Emp.: 70
Dealers of Industrial Machinery & Equipments
N.A.I.C.S.: 423830
Gilles Beaudoin *(VP-Svcs)*

Subsidiary (Domestic):

Peach State Freightliner   (3)
5884 Frontage Rd, Forest Park, GA
30297-2882   (100%)
Tel.: (404) 366-8044
Web Site: http://www.peachstatetruck.com
Sales Range: $50-74.9 Million
Emp.: 250
Dealer of New & Used Trucks, Tractors & Trailers
N.A.I.C.S.: 441110
Rick Reynolds *(Owner)*

Subsidiary (Domestic):

Atlanta Freightliner Truck Sales & Service   (4)
333 Industrial Blvd, McDonough, GA
30253   (100%)
Tel.: (770) 957-1997
Web Site: http://www.peachstatetrucks.com
Sales Range: $10-24.9 Million
Emp.: 33
Dealer of New & Used Trucks, Tractors & Trailers
N.A.I.C.S.: 441110
Gary Conleay *(Branch Mgr)*

Freightliner Service Center   (4)
11710 Statesville Blvd, Cleveland, NC 27013
Tel.: (704) 278-3193
Web Site: http://www.freightliner-pdi.com
Sales Range: $10-24.9 Million
Emp.: 80
General Truck Repair
N.A.I.C.S.: 811111

Subsidiary (Domestic):

SelecTrucks of Cleveland L.L.C.   (3)
1244 Industrial Pkwy N, Brunswick, OH
44212   (100%)
Tel.: (330) 273-2142
Web Site: https://selectrucks.com
Sales Range: $25-49.9 Million
Emp.: 7
Sales of Trucks
N.A.I.C.S.: 441120

SelecTrucks of the Twin Cities   (3)
11152 Courthouse Blvd, Inver Grove Heights, MN 55077
Tel.: (651) 455-9775
Web Site: https://selectrucks.com
Sales Range: $25-49.9 Million
Emp.: 8
Truck Sales
N.A.I.C.S.: 441227

Sherwood Freightliner Sterling & Western Star   (3)
107 Monahan Ave, Dunmore, PA 18512
Tel.: (570) 343-9747
Web Site: http://www.freightlinertrucks.com
Sales Range: $25-49.9 Million
Emp.: 38
Dealers of New & Used Trucks, Tractors & Trailers
N.A.I.C.S.: 441110

Thomas Built Buses, Inc.   (3)
1408 Courtesy Rd, High Point, NC 27260-7248
Tel.: (336) 889-4871
Web Site: https://thomasbuiltbuses.com
Sales Range: $450-499.9 Million
Emp.: 1,600
Mfr of School & Commercial Buses
N.A.I.C.S.: 336211

MERCEDES-BENZ GROUP AG

Mercedes-Benz Group AG—(Continued)
Ken Hedgecock (VP-Sls & Mktg)

Western Star Trucks Inc. (3)
2477 Deerfield Dr, Fort Mill, SC
29715-6942 (100%)
Tel.: (313) 592-4200
Web Site: http://www.wstar.com
Sales Range: $350-399.9 Million
Emp.: 1,602
Mfr & Distributor of Truck Parts
N.A.I.C.S.: 336340
David Carson (Pres)

Subsidiary (Non-US):

Western Star Sales Thunder Bay Ltd. (4)
3150 arthur st w, PO Box 10039, Thunder Bay, P7E 3N1, ON, Canada
Tel.: (807) 939-2537
Rev.: $15,757,354
Emp.: 20
New & Used Car Dealer
N.A.I.C.S.: 441110
Lionel Boyer (Pres)

Subsidiary (Domestic):

Mitsubishi Fuso Truck of America, Inc. (2)
2015 Ctr Sq Rd, Logan Township, NJ 08085
Tel.: (856) 467-4500
Web Site: https://www.mitfuso.com
Sales Range: $200-249.9 Million
Emp.: 72
Class 3-7, Diesel Powered & Cab-Over Commercial Trucks Mfr
N.A.I.C.S.: 423110
Scott Coyle (VP-Svc Ops-North America)

Torc Robotics, Inc. (2)
405 Partnership Dr, Blacksburg, VA 24060
Tel.: (800) 530-9285
Web Site: http://www.torcrobotics.com
Search, Detection, Navigation, Guidance, Aeronautical & Nautical System & Instrument Mfr
N.A.I.C.S.: 334511
John Marinaro (VP-Fleet Ops)

Daimler Trucks Remarketing Corporation (1)
2477 Deerfield Rd, Fort Mill, SC 29715-6942
Tel.: (803) 578-3000
Automobile Mfr
N.A.I.C.S.: 336110

Daimler Trust Leasing LLC (1)
36455 Corporate Dr, Farmington Hills, MI 48331-3552
Tel.: (248) 991-6700
Automobile Parts Mfr
N.A.I.C.S.: 336390

Daimler UK Share Trustee Ltd. (1)
Delaware Drive Tongwell, Milton Keynes, MK15 8BA, Buckinghamshire, United Kingdom
Tel.: (44) 1908 301 570
Sales Range: $150-199.9 Million
Emp.: 1,000
Business Support Services
N.A.I.C.S.: 561499

Daimler Unterstutzungskasse GmbH (1)
Mercedesstr 137, Stuttgart, 70327, Germany
Tel.: (49) 711170
Automobile Mfr
N.A.I.C.S.: 336110
Ola Kallenius (CEO)

Daimler Vans Manufacturing, LLC (1)
8501 Palmetto Commerce Pkwy, Ladson, SC 29456
Tel.: (843) 695-5000
Web Site: http://www.daimler.com
Sales Range: $25-49.9 Million
Emp.: 93
Automobile Parts Mfr
N.A.I.C.S.: 336390
Marco Writz (Mgr)

Daimler Vans USA, LLC (1)
3 Mercedes Dr, Montvale, NJ 07645
Tel.: (877) 762-8267
Web Site: http://www.freightlinersprinterusa.com
Sprinter Van Mfr
N.A.I.C.S.: 336110

Daimler Vehicle Innovations USA, LLC (1)
1 Mercedes Dr, Montvale, NJ 07645
Tel.: (800) 762-7887
Automobile Parts Mfr
N.A.I.C.S.: 336390

Daimler Vehiculos Comerciales Mexico S. de R.L. de C.V. (1)
Av Paseo De Los Tamarindos 90, Bosques de las Lomas, 05120, Mexico, Mexico
Tel.: (52) 55 4155 2000
Web Site: http://www.daimler.com
Transportation Equipment Mfr
N.A.I.C.S.: 336999
Stefan Kurschner (Pres & CEO)

Daimler Vorsorge und Versicherungs-dienst GmbH (1)
Am Postbahnhof 16, 10243, Berlin, Germany
Tel.: (49) 711 174 4808
Web Site: https://www.daimler-vvd.com
Pension Fund & General Insurance Services
N.A.I.C.S.: 525110
Lutz Wieblitz (Mng Dir)

Daimler protics GmbH (1)
Gutenbergstrasse 19, 70771, Leinfelden-Echterdingen, Germany
Tel.: (49) 7111759660
Web Site: https://www.daimler-protics.com
Sales Range: $100-124.9 Million
Emp.: 400
Automotive Data Processing Services
N.A.I.C.S.: 518210

Daimler-Benz AG & Co. AMICITIA Grundstucksvermietung Potsdamer Platz OHG (1)
Lilienthalstr 6, Schonefeld, 12529, Germany
Tel.: (49) 711170
Real Estate Management Services
N.A.I.C.S.: 531390

Daimler-Benz AG & Co. EFFICIEN-TIA Grundstucksvermietung Potsdamer Platz OHG (1)
Lilienthalstr 6, Schonefeld, Germany
Tel.: (49) 711170
Real Estate Management Services
N.A.I.C.S.: 531390

Daimler-Benz AG & Co. LEGITIMA Grundstucksvermietung Potsdamer Platz OHG (1)
Lilienthalstr 6, Schonefeld, 12529, Germany
Tel.: (49) 711170
Web Site: http://www.daimler.com
Emp.: 10,000
Real Estate Management Services
N.A.I.C.S.: 531390
Pieter Zetsche (Mng Dir)

Daimler-Benz AG & Co. NEGOTIA Grundstucksvermietung Potsdamer Platz OHG (1)
Albert-Tanneur-Str 25, 14974, Ludwigsfelde, Brandenburg, Germany
Tel.: (49) 3378 337 8830
Real Estate Management Services
N.A.I.C.S.: 531390

Daimler-Benz AG & Co. NOBILITAS Grundstucksvermietung Potsdamer Platz OHG (1)
Hans Grade Allee 59, Schonefeld, 12529, Germany
Tel.: (49) 711170
Web Site: http://www.daimler.com
Real Estate Management Services
N.A.I.C.S.: 531390

Daimler-Benz AG & Co. PROSPERA Grundstucksvermietung Potsdamer Platz OHG (1)
Lilienthalstr 6, Schonefeld, 12529, Germany
Tel.: (49) 306331110
Real Estate Management Services
N.A.I.C.S.: 531390

Daiprodco Mexico S. de R.L. de C.V. (1)
Paseo De Los Tamarindos No 90 Torre 2 Piso 8 Bosques De Las Lomas, Cuajimalpa De Morelos, Mexico, 05120, Mexico
Tel.: (52) 5550817000
Business Management Consulting Services
N.A.I.C.S.: 541611

Daiya Shoji Co., Ltd. (1)
4-7-12 Nadakitadori, Nada-ku, Kobe, 657-0835, Japan
Tel.: (81) 78 861 1978
Data Processing Services
N.A.I.C.S.: 518210

Detroit Diesel Overseas Corporation (1)
13400 W Outer Dr, Detroit, MI 48239
Tel.: (313) 592-5000
Engine Equipment Mfr
N.A.I.C.S.: 333618

Detroit Diesel Realty, Inc. (1)
13400 W Outer Dr, Detroit, MI 48239
Tel.: (313) 592-5000
Real Estate Financial Services
N.A.I.C.S.: 531390

Detroit Diesel Remanufacturing Mexicana, S de R.L. de C.V. (1)
Carretera Villa Cuauhtemoc S/N Nave 5 Exhacienda Santin, Parque Ind Vesta Park, 50010, Toluca, Mexico
Tel.: (52) 7222622700
Motor Vehicle Parts Mfr
N.A.I.C.S.: 336390

Detroit Diesel-Allison de Mexico, S.A. de C.V. (1)
Av Santa Rosa No 58, San Juan Ixtacala, Tlalnepantla, 54160, Mexico, Mexico
Tel.: (52) 5553331826
Diesel Engine & Parts Mfr
N.A.I.C.S.: 333618

Deutsche Accumotive Verwaltungs-GmbH (1)
Neue Str 95, Kirchheim, 73230, Baden-Wurttemberg, Germany
Tel.: (49) 7021893546
Web Site: http://www.accumotive.de
Administrative Management Services
N.A.I.C.S.: 541611

Drivetest, Llc. (1)
812 Surrey Rd, Laredo, TX 78041
Tel.: (956) 725-1636
Sales Range: $1-9.9 Million
Emp.: 60
Automotive Testing Services
N.A.I.C.S.: 541380

EHG Elektroholding GmbH (1)
Epplestr 225, Stuttgart, 70567, Baden-Wurttemberg, Germany
Tel.: (49) 711170
Sales Range: $50-74.9 Million
Emp.: 1
Investment Management Service
N.A.I.C.S.: 523999

Eishin Jidosha Kogyo Co., Ltd. (1)
131-16 Kobukecho, Inage-Ku, Chiba, 263-0003, Japan
Tel.: (81) 432501233
Automobile Mfr
N.A.I.C.S.: 336110

EvoBus (Schweiz) AG (1)
Wieshofstrasse 120-122, 8408, Winterthur, Zurich, Switzerland
Tel.: (41) 581053535
Web Site: https://www.evobus.com
Emp.: 100
Bus & Coach Mfr
N.A.I.C.S.: 336110
Frank Scherhag (CEO)

EvoBus (UK) Ltd. (1)
Ashcroft Way, Cross Point Business Park, Coventry, CV2 2TU, United Kingdom
Tel.: (44) 247 662 6000
Web Site: https://www.evobus.com
Bus & Coach Mfr
N.A.I.C.S.: 336110
Mike Beagrie (Interim CEO, Mng Dir & Dir-Coach Sls)

EvoBus Belgium N.V. (1)
Z 4 Broekooi 270, 1730, Kobbegem, Belgium
Tel.: (32) 24540280

INTERNATIONAL PUBLIC

Web Site: https://www.evobus.com
Sales Range: $25-49.9 Million
Emp.: 6
Bus & Coach Mfr
N.A.I.C.S.: 336110
Hans Smits (Mng Dir)

EvoBus Danmark A/S (1)
Centervej 3, Koge, 4600, Roskilde, Denmark
Tel.: (45) 56370000
Web Site: http://www.evobus.dk
Motor Vehicle Distr
N.A.I.C.S.: 423110

EvoBus France SAS (1)
2 a 6 rue du Vignolle, BP 90134, Sarcelles, 95842, Sarcelles, France
Tel.: (33) 13 992 7737
Web Site: https://www.evobus.com
Bus & Coach Mfr
N.A.I.C.S.: 336110

EvoBus Iberica, S. A. (1)
Poligono Industrial de Vallegon s/n, Samano, 39709, Castro Urdiales, Spain
Tel.: (34) 942859200
Web Site: https://www.evobus.com
Sales Range: $100-124.9 Million
Emp.: 400
Bus & Coach Mfr
N.A.I.C.S.: 336110

EvoBus Italia S.p.A. (1)
Via Togliatti 7/11, Sorbara di Bomporto, 41030, Modena, Italy
Tel.: (39) 059810811
Web Site: https://www.evobus.com
Sales Range: $50-74.9 Million
Emp.: 15
Bus & Coach Mfr
N.A.I.C.S.: 336110
Holger Suffel (Pres)

EvoBus Nederland B.V. (1)
Handelsstraat 25, 3861 RR, Nijkerk, Netherlands
Tel.: (31) 332474247
Web Site: https://www.evobus.com
Sales Range: $25-49.9 Million
Emp.: 6
Bus & Coach Mfr
N.A.I.C.S.: 336110
Raimond Berle (Mgr-IT & Quality)

EvoBus Polska Sp. z o.o. (1)
Al Katowicka 46, 05-830, Wolica, Poland
Tel.: (48) 223560600
Web Site: https://www.evobus.com
Sales Range: $25-49.9 Million
Emp.: 5
Bus & Coach Mfr
N.A.I.C.S.: 336110

EvoBus Reunion S. A. (1)
72 Rue Paul Verlaine, Le Port, 97420, Reunion, France
Tel.: (33) 262425566
Car Mfr
N.A.I.C.S.: 336110

Gemini-Tur Excursoes Passagens e Turismo Ltda. (1)
65 Rua da Consolacao, 01301-000, Sao Paulo, Brazil
Tel.: (55) 11 21254999
Tour Operating Services
N.A.I.C.S.: 561520

Grundstucksverwaltungsgesellschaft Henne- Unimog GmbH & Co. OHG (1)
Lilienthalstr 6, Schonefeld, 12529, Germany
Tel.: (49) 3063313135
Real Estate Management Services
N.A.I.C.S.: 531390

Grundstucksverwaltungsgesellschaft Mercedes-Benz AG & Co. OHG (1)
Lilienthalstr 6, Schonefeld, 12529, Germany
Tel.: (49) 306331110
Real Estate Management Services
N.A.I.C.S.: 531390

Henne-Unimog GmbH (1)
Landsberger Strasse 382, Munich, 80687, Germany
Tel.: (49) 89 1206 0
Web Site: http://www.henne-unimog.de
New Car Dealers

AND PRIVATE COMPANIES

MERCEDES-BENZ GROUP AG

N.A.I.C.S.: 441110

Ilmore Engineering Ltd. (1)
Quarry Road, Brixworth, NN6 9UB, Northamptonshire, United Kingdom (100%)
Tel.: (44) 160 479 9100
Web Site: https://www.ilmor.co.uk
Emp.: 70
Automotive Engine Mfr
N.A.I.C.S.: 336310
Mario Illien *(Tech Dir)*

Jidosha Yuso Kogyo Co., Ltd. (1)
4-7-2 3jo Kikusuikamimachi, Shiroishi-Ku, Sapporo, 003-0813, Hokkaido, Japan
Tel.: (81) 118213171
Business Support Services
N.A.I.C.S.: 561499

Lapland Car Test Aktiebolag (1)
Skent, 930 90, Arjeplog, Norrbotten, Sweden
Tel.: (46) 96013280
Real Estate Manangement Services
N.A.I.C.S.: 531390

Legend Investments Ltd. (1)
Delaware Drive, Milton Keynes, MK15 8BA, Buckinghamshire, United Kingdom
Tel.: (44) 1908 668899
Investment Management Service
N.A.I.C.S.: 523940

MB GTC GmbH Mercedes-Benz Gebrauchtteile Center (1)
Morikestrasse 60-70, 73765, Neuhausen, Germany
Tel.: (49) 7111770000
Web Site: https://www.mbgtc.de
Emp.: 250
Motor Vehicle Parts Mfr
N.A.I.C.S.: 336390
Uwe Crossman *(Mng Dir)*

MDC Technology GmbH (1)
Rudolf-Carracciola-Str 1, Kolleda, 99625, Thuringen, Germany
Tel.: (49) 3635601190
Motor Vehicle Parts Mfr
N.A.I.C.S.: 336390

MILON Grundstucks-Verwaltungsgesellschaft mbH & Co. KG (1)
Tolzer Str 30, 82031, Grunwald, Germany
Tel.: (49) 89 641490
Real Estate Manangement Services
N.A.I.C.S.: 531390

Mercedes AMG High Performance Powertrains Limited (1)
Morgan Drive, Brixworth, NN6 9GZ, Northamptonshire, United Kingdom
Tel.: (44) 160 488 0100
Web Site: https://www.mercedes-amg-hpp.com
Sales Range: $100-124.9 Million
Emp.: 600
Automotive Engine Mfr
N.A.I.C.S.: 333618

Mercedes-AMG GmbH (1)
Daimlerstrasse 1, 71563, Affalterbach, Germany
Tel.: (49) 71443020
Web Site: https://www.mercedes-amg.com
Car & Engine Parts Mfr
N.A.I.C.S.: 336110

Mercedes-Benz (China) Ltd. (1)
16/F Daimler Tower No 8 Wangjing Commercial St, Chaoyang District, Beijing, 100102, China
Tel.: (86) 1084178887
Web Site: http://www.mercedes-benz.com.cn
New Car Dealers
N.A.I.C.S.: 441110
Klaus Maier *(Pres & CEO)*

Mercedes-Benz (Thailand) Limited (1)
AIA Sathorn Tower 20th Floor 11/1 South Sathorn Road, Yannawa Sathorn, Bangkok, 10120, Thailand
Tel.: (66) 2 034 1000
Web Site: https://www.mercedes-benz.co.th
New Car Dealers
N.A.I.C.S.: 441110

Alexander Paufler *(Pres & CEO)*

Mercedes-Benz - Aluguer de Veiculos, Unipessoal Lda. (1)
Abrunheira, Sintra, 2710-089, Portugal
Tel.: (351) 219257000
Web Site: http://www.mercedes-benz.pt
Emp.: 300
Passenger Car Rental Services
N.A.I.C.S.: 532111
Joerg Heinerman *(Gen Mgr)*

Mercedes-Benz AG (1)
Mercedesstrasse 120, 70372, Stuttgart, Germany
Tel.: (49) 711170
Web Site: http://www.mercedes-benz.com
New Car Dealers
N.A.I.C.S.: 441110
Ola Kallenius *(Chm)*

Mercedes-Benz AG & Co. Grundstucksvermietung Objekte Leipzig und Magdeburg KG (1)
Lilienthalstr 6, Schonefeld, 12529, Germany
Tel.: (49) 306331110
Web Site: http://www.daimler.com
Real Estate Manangement Services
N.A.I.C.S.: 531390

Mercedes-Benz Accessories GmbH (1)
Horizont 2 Building Am Wallgraben 125, 70565, Stuttgart, 70565, Germany
Tel.: (49) 7111795555
Web Site: http://www.mercedes-benz-accessories.com
Sales Range: $50-74.9 Million
Emp.: 20
Motor Vehicle Parts Mfr
N.A.I.C.S.: 336390
Christian Boucke *(CEO)*

Mercedes-Benz Advanced Design of North America, Inc. (1)
2250 Rutherford Rd, Carlsbad, CA 92008
Tel.: (619) 488-9360
Web Site: http://www.mbrdna.com
Automotive Research & Development
N.A.I.C.S.: 541420

Mercedes-Benz Argentina S.A. (1)
Lumina Panamericana - Edificio II Sargento Cabral 3770, Munro, B1605EFJ, Vicente Lopez, Argentina (100%)
Tel.: (54) 1148088700
Web Site: https://www.mercedes-benz.com.ar
Sales Range: $25-49.9 Million
Emp.: 100
Mfr of Automobiles
N.A.I.C.S.: 336110

Mercedes-Benz Asia GmbH (1)
Epplestr 225, Stuttgart, 70546, Germany
Tel.: (49) 711170
Web Site: http://www.daimler.com
Automotive Distr
N.A.I.C.S.: 423110

Mercedes-Benz Australia/Pacific Pty. Ltd. (1)
44 Lexia Place, Mulgrave, 3170, VIC, Australia (100%)
Tel.: (61) 38 554 3000
Web Site: https://www.mercedes-benz.com.au
Sales Range: $100-124.9 Million
Emp.: 400
Mercedes Benz Dealer
N.A.I.C.S.: 441110
Horst von Sanden *(Mng Dir)*

Mercedes-Benz Bank Polska S.A. (1)
Ul Gottlieba Daimlera 1, 02-460, Warsaw, Poland
Tel.: (48) 22 312 78 00
Web Site: http://www.daimler.com
Automobile Financing Services
N.A.I.C.S.: 525990

Mercedes-Benz Bank Rus OOO (1)
Leningradskij Prospekt 39, 125167, Moscow, Russia
Tel.: (7) 4957979911
Financial Management Services
N.A.I.C.S.: 523999
Christian Schuler *(CEO)*

Mercedes-Benz Bank Service Center GmbH (1)
Otto-Braun-Strasse 78, Berlin, 10249, Germany
Tel.: (49) 30 868755755
Commercial Banking Services
N.A.I.C.S.: 522110

Mercedes-Benz Banking Service GmbH (1)
Gewerbepark Eschberger Weg 3, Saarbrucken, 66121, Saarland, Germany
Tel.: (49) 71125740
Web Site: http://www.mercedes-benz-bank.com
Emp.: 2,000
Commercial Banking Services
N.A.I.C.S.: 522110
Klaus Entenmann *(CIO)*

Mercedes-Benz Belgium Luxembourg S.A. (1)
Avenue du Peage 68, 1200, Brussels, Belgium (100%)
Tel.: (32) 27241211
Web Site: https://www.mercedes-benz.be
Sales Range: $100-124.9 Million
Emp.: 350
Automobile Sales & Services
N.A.I.C.S.: 441110
Mark De Haes *(CEO)*

Mercedes-Benz Bordeaux SAS (1)
1 rue Port Arthur, 33130, Begles, France
Tel.: (33) 55 675 7600
Web Site: https://www.bordeaux.mercedes-benz.fr
New & Used Car Dealer
N.A.I.C.S.: 441110

Mercedes-Benz Broker Biztositasi Alkusz Hungary Kft. (1)
Karpat U 21, Budapest, 1133, Hungary
Tel.: (36) 18806081
Web Site: http://www.daimler.com
Sales Range: $50-74.9 Million
Emp.: 2
Insurance Brokerage Services
N.A.I.C.S.: 524210

Mercedes-Benz Canada Inc. (1)
2680 Matheson Blvd E Ste 400, Mississauga, L4W 0A5, ON, Canada (100%)
Tel.: (416) 425-3550
Web Site: https://www.mercedes-benz.ca
Sales Range: $800-899.9 Million
Emp.: 300
Sales & Service Company
N.A.I.C.S.: 441110
Christian Spelter *(VP-Fin)*

Subsidiary (Domestic):

Mercedes Benz Canada Inc. (2)
3650 Charles St, Vancouver, V5K 5A9, BC, Canada (100%)
Tel.: (604) 639-3310
Web Site: http://www.mercedes-benz.ca
Sales Range: $25-49.9 Million
Emp.: 20
Automobiles & Motor Vehicles
N.A.I.C.S.: 336390
Jim Rossitter *(Reg Mgr)*

Mercedes-Benz Canada Inc. (2)
761 Dundas Street East, Toronto, M5A 4N5, ON, Canada (100%)
Tel.: (416) 947-9000
Web Site: https://www.mercedes-benz.ca
Sales Range: $25-49.9 Million
Emp.: 100
Mfr of Automobiles & Other Motor Vehicles
N.A.I.C.S.: 336390
Mark Dube *(Gen Mgr)*

Mercedes-Benz Canada Inc. (2)
550 Terminal Avenue, Vancouver, V6A 0C3, BC, Canada (100%)
Tel.: (604) 736-7411
Web Site: https://www.mercedes-benz.ca
Sales Range: $25-49.9 Million
Emp.: 70
Automobiles & Other Motor Vehicles
N.A.I.C.S.: 336390
Mark Dube *(Gen Mgr)*

Mercedes-Benz Capital Services (Debis) UK Ltd. (1)
Burystead Court 120 Caldecotte Lake Drive, Milton Keynes, MK7 8ND, Buckinghamshire, United Kingdom
Tel.: (44) 8708405000
Investment Management Service
N.A.I.C.S.: 523999

Mercedes-Benz Ceska republika s.r.o. (1)
Daimlerova 2296/2, Prague, 149 45, Czech Republic
Tel.: (420) 271077111
Web Site: http://www.mercedes-benz.cz
Automotive Distr
N.A.I.C.S.: 423110
Karel Knap *(Mgr)*

Mercedes-Benz CharterWay Espana, S.A. (1)
Avenida De Bruselas 30, 28108, Alcobendas, Spain
Tel.: (34) 914846000
Passenger Car Rental Services
N.A.I.C.S.: 532111

Mercedes-Benz CharterWay GmbH (1)
English St 30, 10587, Berlin, Germany (100%)
Tel.: (49) 3026945455
Web Site: http://www.charterway.de
Sales Range: $25-49.9 Million
Emp.: 80
Motor Vehicles Mfr
N.A.I.C.S.: 336110
Bern Hard *(Mng Dir)*

Mercedes-Benz CharterWay Ltd. (1)
Delaware Drive, Tongwell, Milton Keynes, MK15 8BA, Great Britian, United Kingdom
Tel.: (44) 8702 403 135
Web Site: http://www.mbcharterway.co.uk
Emp.: 2,000
Automobile Insurance Services
N.A.I.C.S.: 524126

Mercedes-Benz CharterWay S.p.A. (1)
Via Giulio Vincenzo Bona 110, Rome, 00156, Italy
Tel.: (39) 06415951
Passenger Car Rental Services
N.A.I.C.S.: 532111

Mercedes-Benz CharterWay SAS (1)
Parc De Rocquencourt, Rocquencourt, 78150, Yvelines, France
Tel.: (33) 139235600
Commercial Truck Rental & Leasing Services
N.A.I.C.S.: 532120

Mercedes-Benz Comercial Valencia, S.A. (1)
Avenida La Pista 50, Massanassa, Valencia, 46470, Spain
Tel.: (34) 961 22 44 00
Web Site: http://www.valencia.mercedes-benz.es
Sales Range: $50-74.9 Million
Emp.: 185
New & Used Car Dealer
N.A.I.C.S.: 441110
Jose Luis Lopez-Schummer *(Pres)*

Mercedes-Benz Comercial, Lda. (1)
Abrunheira-Sintra Apartado 125, Mem Martins, 2726-901, Sintra, Portugal
Tel.: (351) 21 910 9400
Web Site: http://www.comercial.mercedes-benz.pt
Commercial Vehicle Mfr
N.A.I.C.S.: 336110

Mercedes-Benz Compania Financiera Argentina S.A. (1)
Boulevard Azucena Villaflor 435, Puerto Madero, C1107CII, Buenos Aires, Argentina
Tel.: (54) 11 4808 8900
Web Site: http://www.mbfonline.com.ar
Automotive Financial Leasing Services
N.A.I.C.S.: 522220

Mercedes-Benz Consult Graz GmbH (1)
Dr-Auner-Strasse 21, Raaba, 8072, Austria
Tel.: (43) 316 4115 0
Web Site: http://www.mercedes-benz-consult-graz.at
Automotive Repair Services

MERCEDES-BENZ GROUP AG — INTERNATIONAL PUBLIC

Mercedes-Benz Group AG—(Continued)
N.A.I.C.S.: 811114

Mercedes-Benz Danmark AS (1)
Digevej 114, 2300, Copenhagen, Denmark (100%)
Tel.: (45) 33785656
Web Site: https://www.mercedes-benz.dk
Sales Range: $25-49.9 Million
Emp.: 45
Mfr & Dealer of Automobiles, Trucks, Electric & Electronics, Aviation, Space Defense Technologies, Propulsion & Financial Service
N.A.I.C.S.: 336120
Laris Erve *(Dir-Comm)*

Mercedes-Benz Dealer Bedrijven B.V. (1)
Donau 42, 2491 BA, Hague, Netherlands
Tel.: (31) 703400300
Web Site: https://www.mbdb.nl
Emp.: 350
Used Car Dealers
N.A.I.C.S.: 441120
Jeroen van der Heiden *(Gen Mgr)*

Mercedes-Benz Desarrollo de Mercados, S. de R.L. de C.V. (1)
Paspo ve los Tamarindos No 90 Bosques de las Lomas, Mexico, 05120, Hidalgo, Mexico
Tel.: (52) 5541552566
Web Site: http://www.daimler.com.mx
Emp.: 400
New Car Dealers
N.A.I.C.S.: 441110
Stephan Kurschner *(Mgr)*

Mercedes-Benz Egypt S.A.E. (1)
28th Floor Sofitel Towers Cornich El-Nil, PO Box 1125, Maadi, Cairo, Egypt
Tel.: (20) 2 252 99 100
Web Site: http://www.mercedes-benz.com.eg
Sales Range: $25-49.9 Million
Emp.: 60
New & Used Car Dealer
N.A.I.C.S.: 441110
Thomas Zorn *(CEO)*

Mercedes-Benz Esch S.A. (1)
190 Route de Belvaux, Esch-sur-Alzette, 4026, Luxembourg
Tel.: (352) 552323 1
New & Used Car Dealer
N.A.I.C.S.: 441110

Mercedes-Benz Espana, S.A. (1)
Avenida de Bruselas 30, 28108, Alcobendas, Spain (100%)
Tel.: (34) 91 484 6000
Web Site: https://www.mercedes-benz.es
Sales Range: $100-124.9 Million
Emp.: 300
Mfr & Assembly of Automobiles
N.A.I.C.S.: 336110

Mercedes-Benz Finans Danmark A/S (1)
Tel.: (45) 3 378 8900
Web Site: http://www.dcsbilsalg.com
Fleet Management Services
N.A.I.C.S.: 532112

Mercedes-Benz Finans Sverige AB (1)
Dockgatan 1, 211 12, Malmo, Sweden
Tel.: (46) 406609260
Sales Range: $50-74.9 Million
Emp.: 7
Automobile Financing Services
N.A.I.C.S.: 525990

Mercedes-Benz Finansal Kiralama Turk A.S. (1)
Tem Otoyolu Hadimkoy Cikisi, 34500, Istanbul, Turkiye
Tel.: (90) 2128666565
Web Site: http://www.mercedes-benz-finansalhizmetler.com
Financial Lending Services
N.A.I.C.S.: 522220

Mercedes-Benz Finansman Turk A.S. (1)
TEM Otoyolu Hadimkoy Cikisi Mercedes Caddesi Bahcesehir, 34500, Istanbul, Turkiye
Tel.: (90) 212 866 6565
Web Site: http://www.mercedes-benz-finansalhizmetler.com
Financial Lending Services
N.A.I.C.S.: 522220

Mercedes-Benz Finanzierungsvermittlungs GmbH (1)
Schoemperlenstr 14, Karlsruhe, 76185, Germany
Tel.: (49) 72195650
Web Site: http://www.sug.de
Sales Range: $200-249.9 Million
Emp.: 46
Financial Intermediation Services
N.A.I.C.S.: 523910
Jens Thiemer *(Mng Dir)*

Mercedes-Benz Forsaljnings AB (1)
Bronsyxegatan 14, 213 75, Malmo, Sweden
Tel.: (46) 406717000
Web Site: https://www.mercedes-benz-malmo.se
Emp.: 100
Motor Vehicle Repair & Maintenance Services
N.A.I.C.S.: 811198
Lars Lieberg *(Gen Mgr)*

Mercedes-Benz France S.A. (1)
7 avenue Niepce, Montigny-le-Bretonneux, 78180, Molsheim, France (100%)
Tel.: (33) 17 749 3933
Web Site: https://www.mercedes-benz.fr
Sales Range: $150-199.9 Million
Emp.: 500
Sales & Service of Diesel Trucks & Tractors
N.A.I.C.S.: 423830
Klaus Fischenger *(Mng Dir)*

Mercedes-Benz GastroService GmbH (1)
Hauptstrasse 107, 76571, Gaggenau, Germany
Tel.: (49) 7225612674
Web Site: http://www.mb-gastro.com
Catering Services
N.A.I.C.S.: 722320

Mercedes-Benz Gent N.V. (1)
Afrikalaan 208, Gent, 9000, Oost-Vlaanderen, Belgium
Tel.: (32) 92500511
Web Site: http://www.gent.mercedes-benz.be
Emp.: 100
New Car & Used Car Dealer
N.A.I.C.S.: 441110
Mijnheer Koen Smet *(Mgr-After Sls)*

Mercedes-Benz Global Training Nederland B.V. (1)
Nijverheidsstraat 55, Nijkerk, 3861 RJ, Netherlands
Tel.: (31) 33 247 3333
Sales Range: $10-24.9 Million
Emp.: 17
Automotive Training Services
N.A.I.C.S.: 611692
Branko van Eerden *(Principal)*

Mercedes-Benz Grand Prix Ltd. (1)
Operations Centre, Brackley, NN13 7BD, Northamptonshire, United Kingdom
Tel.: (44) 1280 844000
Web Site: http://www.mercedesamgf1.com
Sales Range: $125-149.9 Million
Emp.: 500
Sporting Goods Retailer
N.A.I.C.S.: 459110
Toto Wolff *(Exec Dir)*

Mercedes-Benz Hellas S.A. (1)
20 Thivaidos, PO Box 51554, 145 64, Nea Kifissia, Greece (100%)
Tel.: (30) 2106296500
Web Site: https://www.mercedes-benz.gr
Sales Range: $50-74.9 Million
Emp.: 220
Motor Vehicles
N.A.I.C.S.: 336110
John Kalligeros *(Mng Dir)*

Mercedes-Benz Hong Kong Limited (1)
59th Floor Central Plaza 18 Harbour Road, Wanchai, China (Hong Kong)
Tel.: (852) 25948800
Web Site: http://www.mercedes-benz.com.hk
Emp.: 90
New Car Dealers
N.A.I.C.S.: 441110
Klaus Maier *(Pres)*

Mercedes-Benz India Private Limited (1)
E-3 MIDC Chakan-Phase III, Chakan Industrial Area Kuruli & Nighoje Khed, Pune, 410501, India
Tel.: (91) 2135673000
Web Site: http://www.mercedes-benz.co.in
Car Dealer
N.A.I.C.S.: 441110

Mercedes-Benz Insurance Broker SRL (1)
Bucharest North 50-23 Sector 1, 13981, Bucharest, Romania
Tel.: (40) 21 3060 700
Sales Range: $50-74.9 Million
Emp.: 2
Insurance Brokerage Services
N.A.I.C.S.: 524210
Cristina Staicu *(Gen Mgr)*

Mercedes-Benz Italia S.p.A. (1)
Via Giulio Vincenzo Bona 110, 00156, Rome, RM, Italy (97.2%)
Tel.: (39) 0641441
Web Site: https://www.mercedesbenz.it
Sales Range: $400-449.9 Million
Emp.: 1,000
Sales & Service Company
N.A.I.C.S.: 441110

Mercedes-Benz Japan Co., Ltd. (1)
Roppongi First Bldg 9-9 Roppongi 1-chome, Minato-ku, Tokyo, 106-8506, Japan (100%)
Tel.: (81) 355727200
Web Site: http://www.mercedes-benz.co.jp
Sales Range: $150-199.9 Million
Emp.: 457
Automobile & Other Motor Vehicle Mfr & Distr
N.A.I.C.S.: 423110

Subsidiary (Domestic):

Daimler Financial Services Japan Co., Ltd. (2)
Shin-Kawasaki Mitsui Bldg 890-12 Kashimada, Saiwai-ku, Kawasaki, 212-0058, Kanagawa, Japan
Tel.: (81) 44 542 1200
Web Site: http://www.daimler-financialservices.jp
Sales Range: $50-74.9 Million
Emp.: 150
Automotive Financial Leasing Services
N.A.I.C.S.: 522220
Hiroshi Hanai *(Pres & CEO)*

Mercedes-Benz Leasing (Thailand) Co., Ltd. (1)
20th Floor Rajanakarn Building 183 South Sathorn Road, Yannawa Sathorn, Bangkok, 10120, Thailand
Tel.: (66) 2614 8500
Web Site: http://www.mercedes-benz-leasing.co.th
Sales Range: $100-124.9 Million
Emp.: 120
Automotive Financial Leasing Services
N.A.I.C.S.: 522220

Mercedes-Benz Leasing Hrvatska d.o.o. (1)
Kovinska 5, 10090, Zagreb, 10090, Croatia
Tel.: (385) 1 3441 250
Web Site: http://www.mercedes-benz-leasing.hr
Sales Range: $50-74.9 Million
Emp.: 28
Automotive Financial Leasing Services
N.A.I.C.S.: 522220
Krunoslav Pavic *(Pres & Mng Dir)*

Mercedes-Benz Leasing IFN SA (1)
Bucharest 1523 swan office & technology park floor 3, Voluntari, 013981, Romania
Tel.: (40) 21 3060 700
Web Site: http://www.mercedes-benz-financial-services.ro
Sales Range: $50-74.9 Million
Emp.: 30
Automotive Financial Leasing Services
N.A.I.C.S.: 522220

Ones Taefun *(CEO)*

Mercedes-Benz Leasing Kft. (1)
Karpat U 21, 1133, Budapest, Hungary
Tel.: (36) 1 880 6066
Web Site: http://www.mercedes-benz-credit.hu
Automotive Financial Leasing Services
N.A.I.C.S.: 522220
Horst Wohlfart *(Mng Dir)*

Mercedes-Benz Leasing Polska Sp. z o.o. (1)
Ul Gottlieba Daimlera 1, 02-460, Warsaw, Poland
Tel.: (48) 223127802
Web Site: http://www.mercedes-benz-financialservices.pl
Automotive Financial Leasing Services
N.A.I.C.S.: 522220
Andrzeh Zyrek *(Mgr-Sls)*

Mercedes-Benz Leasing Treuhand GmbH (1)
Siemensstr 7, Stuttgart, 70469, Baden-Wurttemberg, Germany
Tel.: (49) 71511360
Automotive Financial Leasing Services
N.A.I.C.S.: 522220

Mercedes-Benz Leasing do Brasil Arrendamento Mercantil S.A. (1)
Rio Negro 585, Barueri, 06454-000, Sao Paulo, Brazil
Tel.: (55) 1168585800
Real Estate Lending Services
N.A.I.C.S.: 531190

Mercedes-Benz Leudelange S.A. (1)
Zone D'Activites Am Bann 16, Leudelange, 3372, Luxembourg
Tel.: (352) 2637261
New & Used Car Dealer
N.A.I.C.S.: 441110

Mercedes-Benz Lille SAS (1)
20 Rue Chappe, Villeneuve d'Ascq, 59650, Nord, France
Tel.: (33) 320723939
Web Site: http://www.lille.mercedes.fr
Sales Range: $50-74.9 Million
Emp.: 138
New & Used Car Dealer
N.A.I.C.S.: 441110
Gentile Hubert *(Gen Mgr)*

Mercedes-Benz Ludwigsfelde GmbH (1)
Zum Industriepark 10, 14974, Ludwigsfelde, Germany
Tel.: (49) 30275837857
Web Site: http://www.daimler.com
Sales Range: $400-449.9 Million
Emp.: 2,000
Automobile Mfr
N.A.I.C.S.: 336110

Mercedes-Benz Luxembourg S.A. (1)
Rue De Bouillon 45, Luxembourg, 1248, Luxembourg
Tel.: (352) 408011
Web Site: http://www.mercedes-benz.lu
New & Used Car Dealer
N.A.I.C.S.: 441110
Justin Mangen *(Mng Dir & Gen Mgr)*

Mercedes-Benz Luxembourg-Centre S.A. (1)
Rue De Bouillon 45, Luxembourg, 1248, Luxembourg
Tel.: (352) 408011
Sales Range: $50-74.9 Million
Emp.: 20
New & Used Car Dealer
N.A.I.C.S.: 441110

Mercedes-Benz Manufacturing Hungary Kft. (1)
Mercedes Ut 1, 6000, Kecskemet, Hungary
Tel.: (36) 76 30 1022
Web Site: http://www.mercedes-benz.hu
Sales Range: $400-449.9 Million
Emp.: 250
Automobile Mfr
N.A.I.C.S.: 336110

Mercedes-Benz Mexico, S. de R.L. de C.V. (1)
Twr 2 Lobbey No 1 11th Floor, Bosques de

AND PRIVATE COMPANIES — MERCEDES-BENZ GROUP AG

las Lomas, 5120, Mexico, Mexico
Tel.: (52) 55 4155 2000
Web Site: http://www.daimler.com
New & Used Car Dealer
N.A.I.C.S.: 441110

Mercedes-Benz Milano S.p.A. (1)
Via Gottlieb Wilhelm Daimler 1, Milan, 20151, Italy
Tel.: (39) 0230251
Web Site: http://www.milano.mercedes-benz.it
New & Used Car Dealer
N.A.I.C.S.: 441110

Mercedes-Benz Mitarbeiter-Fahrzeuge Leasing GmbH (1)
Service Center Berlin, Post Box 110706, 10837, Berlin, Germany
Tel.: (49) 711257402
Web Site: http://www.daimler.com
Passenger Car Rental Services
N.A.I.C.S.: 532111
Jurgen Hildebrand *(Mng Dir)*

Mercedes-Benz Molsheim SAS (1)
19 route industrielle de la Hardt, 67129, Molsheim, Cedex, France
Tel.: (33) 38 847 8800
Web Site: http://www.daimler.com
Sales Range: $200-249.9 Million
Emp.: 560
Automobile Mfr
N.A.I.C.S.: 336110

Mercedes-Benz Museum GmbH (1)
Mercedesstrasse 100, 70372, Stuttgart, Germany
Tel.: (49) 7111730000
Web Site: https://www.mercedes-benz.com
Museum Operating Services
N.A.I.C.S.: 712110
Michael Bock *(Chm)*

Mercedes-Benz Nederland B.V. (1)
 (100%)
Tel.: (31) 30 247 1911
Web Site: https://www.mercedes-benz.nl
Sales Range: $100-124.9 Million
Emp.: 300
Mfr & Dealer of Automobiles
N.A.I.C.S.: 336120

Mercedes-Benz New Zealand Ltd. (1)
9 Pacific Rise, Mount Wellington, 1062, Auckland, New Zealand
Tel.: (64) 9 573 0192
Web Site: http://www.mercedes-benz.co.nz
Sales Range: $25-49.9 Million
Emp.: 6
New & Used Car Dealer
N.A.I.C.S.: 441110

Mercedes-Benz Ninove N.V. (1)
Brakelsesteenweg 398, Ninove, 9406, East Flanders, Belgium
Tel.: (32) 54319229
Web Site: http://www.ninove.mercedes-benz.be
New & Used Car Dealer
N.A.I.C.S.: 441120
Johan de Ninove *(Mgr-After Sls)*

Mercedes-Benz Osterreich Vertriebsgesellschaft mbH (1)
Fasaneriestra 35, Salzburg, 5020, Austria (50%)
Tel.: (43) 66244780
Web Site: http://www.mercedes-benz.at
Sales Range: $50-74.9 Million
Emp.: 130
Automobile Mfr
N.A.I.C.S.: 336110
Corinna Widenmeyer *(Mng Dir)*

Mercedes-Benz Paris SAS (1)
10 rue de Saint-Germain, 78560, Le Port-Marly, France
Tel.: (33) 13 917 3117
Web Site: https://www.paris.mercedes-benz.fr
Used & New Car Dealer
N.A.I.C.S.: 441120

Mercedes-Benz Polska Sp. z.o.o. (1)
Ul Gottlieba Daimlera 1, 02-460, Warsaw, Poland
Tel.: (48) 22 354 4001

Web Site: https://www.mercedes-benz.pl
New & Used Car Dealer
N.A.I.C.S.: 441110

Mercedes-Benz Portugal, S.A. (1)
Apartado 1 - Abrunheira, 2726-911, Mem Martins, Portugal
Tel.: (351) 219257000
Web Site: http://www.mercedes-benz.pt
Emp.: 300
Commercial Vehicle Mfr
N.A.I.C.S.: 336110
Joerg Heinermann *(Mgr)*

Mercedes-Benz Portugal-Comercio de Automoveis, S.A. (1)
Industrial Abrunheira Ap 1, Abrunheira, 2725911, Portugal (100%)
Tel.: (351) 219257000
Web Site: http://www.mercedes-benz.com
Sales Range: $50-74.9 Million
Emp.: 200
Motor Vehicles & Passenger Cars
N.A.I.C.S.: 336110
Carstan Odar *(Mng Dir)*

Mercedes-Benz Project Consult GmbH (1)
Karl-Benz-Platz 1, Stuttgart, 70327, Germany
Tel.: (49) 7111721652
Business Management Consulting Services
N.A.I.C.S.: 541611
Claus-Peter Willi *(Mng Dir)*

Mercedes-Benz Renting, S.A. (1)
Avenida De Bruselas 30, 28108, Alcobendas, Spain
Tel.: (34) 91 484 60 00
Web Site: http://www.mercedes-benz.es
New & Used Car Dealer
N.A.I.C.S.: 441110

Mercedes-Benz Research & Development India Pvt Ltd. (1)
Pine Valley 3rd Floor Embassy Golf Links Business Park, Bengaluru, 530 071, India
Tel.: (91) 80 67685000
Sales Range: $75-99.9 Million
Emp.: 500
Information Technology Development Services
N.A.I.C.S.: 541511
Manu Saale *(CEO & Mng Dir)*

Mercedes-Benz Research & Development North America, Inc. (1)
850 Hansen Way, Palo Alto, CA 94304
Tel.: (650) 845-2500
Web Site: http://www.mbrdna.com
Automotive Research & Development Services
N.A.I.C.S.: 541715

Mercedes-Benz Retail Group UK Limited (1)
Delaware Drive Tongwell, Milton Keynes, MK15 8BA, Buckinghamshire, United Kingdom
Tel.: (44) 1908668899
Web Site: http://www.mercedes-benzretailgroup.co.uk
Emp.: 1,200
Commercial Vehicle Dealer
N.A.I.C.S.: 441227

Subsidiary (Domestic):

Mercedes-Benz Brooklands Limited (2)
Brooklands Drive, Weybridge, KT13 0SL, United Kingdom
Tel.: (44) 193 237 3000
Web Site: http://www.mercedes-benzbrooklands.co.uk
New & Used Car Dealer
N.A.I.C.S.: 441110

Mercedes-Benz Roma S.p.A. (1)
Via Zoe Fontana 220, 00131, Rome, Italy
Tel.: (39) 06451441
Web Site: https://www.roma.mercedes-benz.it
Emp.: 500
New Car Dealer
N.A.I.C.S.: 441110

Mercedes-Benz Romania S.R.L. (1)
Swan Office & Technology Park Cladirea Henley, Sos Bucuresti-Nord 15-23, 15-23

Soseaua Bucuresti-Nord, Voluntari, Romania
Tel.: (40) 31 130 5031
Web Site: https://www.mercedes-benz.ro
Emp.: 220
New Car Dealers; Passenger Car Mfr & Sales
N.A.I.C.S.: 336110
Radu Belu *(Mgr-Fleet Sls)*

Mercedes-Benz Schweiz AG (1)
Bernstrasse 55, 8952, Schlieren, Zurich, Switzerland
Tel.: (41) 447558000
Web Site: https://www.mercedes-benz.ch
Emp.: 500
Commercial Vehicle Mfr
N.A.I.C.S.: 336110
Marcel Joarry *(Gen Mgr)*

Mercedes-Benz Service Leasing SRL
Strada Bucharest Nr 23 Swan Bldg Voluntar Illfof, 13981, Bucharest, Romania
Tel.: (40) 21 3060 700
Sales Range: $25-49.9 Million
Emp.: 3
Passenger Car Leasing Services
N.A.I.C.S.: 532112
Roland Leitner *(CEO)*

Mercedes-Benz Services Correduria de Seguros, S.A. (1)
Avenida De Bruselas 30, Alcobendas, 28108, Madrid, Spain
Tel.: (34) 917214540
Web Site: http://www.mercedes-benzseguros.es
Insurance Brokerage Services
N.A.I.C.S.: 524210

Mercedes-Benz Servizi Assicurativi Italia S.p.A. (1)
Via Giulio Vincenzo Bona 110, Rome, 00156, Italy
Tel.: (39) 06 415951
Automobile Insurance Services
N.A.I.C.S.: 524126

Mercedes-Benz Sigorta Aracilik Hizmetleri A.S. (1)
Tem Otoyolu Hadimkoy Cikisi Mercedes Caddesi Bahcesehir, Istanbul, 34500, Turkiye
Tel.: (90) 212 867 30 00
Insurance Brokerage Services
N.A.I.C.S.: 524210

Mercedes-Benz Slovakia s.r.o. (1)
Einsteinova 33, 851 01, Bratislava, Slovakia
Tel.: (421) 80 060 1251
Web Site: https://www.mercedes-benz.sk
Automobile Vehicle Distr
N.A.I.C.S.: 423110
Zoltan Palinkas *(CIO)*

Mercedes-Benz Sosnowiec Sp. z o.o. (1)
Ul Gottlieba Daimlera 1, 41-209, Sosnowiec, Poland
Tel.: (48) 323684500
Web Site: https://www.sosnowiec.mercedes-benz.pl
Sales Range: $50-74.9 Million
Emp.: 30
New & Used Car Dealer
N.A.I.C.S.: 441110
Piotr Jankowski *(Mgr-Sls)*

Mercedes-Benz South Africa Ltd. (1)
Wierda Road R576/M10 West, Zwartkop, Centurion, 0046, South Africa
Tel.: (27) 12 677 1500
Web Site: https://www.mercedes-benz.co.za
New Car Dealers
N.A.I.C.S.: 441110

Mercedes-Benz Srbija i Crna Gora d.o.o. (1)
Omladinskih Brigada 33, Belgrade, 11070, Serbia
Tel.: (381) 11 3019000
Web Site: http://www.mercedes-benz.rs
Sales Range: $50-74.9 Million
Emp.: 25
New & Used Car Dealer
N.A.I.C.S.: 441110
Andreas Binder *(CEO & Gen Dir)*

Mercedes-Benz Sverige AB (1)

Dockgatan 1, Malmo, 21112, Sweden
Tel.: (46) 406718484
Web Site: https://www.mercedes-benz.se
New & Used Car Dealer
N.A.I.C.S.: 441110
Jorg Himmelmann *(Mgr)*

Mercedes-Benz Taiwan Ltd. (1)
13F No 129 Minsheng E Rd Section 3, Taipei, 10596, Taiwan
Tel.: (886) 2 2719 3488
Web Site: http://www.mercedes-benz.com.tw
Emp.: 300
Automobile Mfr
N.A.I.C.S.: 336110
Calvin Huang *(Gen Mgr)*

Mercedes-Benz Tamworth (1)
Mile Oak, Tamworth, B78 3PQ, Staffordshire, United Kingdom
Tel.: (44) 345 092 0244
Web Site: http://www.mercedes-benzretailgroup.co.uk
Emp.: 70
New Car Dealer Sales & Service
N.A.I.C.S.: 441110
Lesley Crombie *(Gen Mgr)*

Mercedes-Benz Tasit Ticaret ve Servis A.S. (1)
Akcaburgaz Mahallesi Mercedes Caddesi Number 6, Esenyurt, Istanbul, 34500, Turkiye
Tel.: (90) 212 867 43 00
Web Site: http://www.mercedes-benz-tasitticaret.com.tr
Sales Range: $25-49.9 Million
Emp.: 50
Automotive Repair & Maintenance Services
N.A.I.C.S.: 811198
Osman Nuri Aksoy *(Gen Mgr)*

Mercedes-Benz Technical Center Nederland B.V. (1)
Nijverheidsstraat 55, Nijkerk, 3861 RJ, Gelderland, Netherlands
Tel.: (31) 332473333
Automotive Body Repair & Maintenance Services
N.A.I.C.S.: 811121

Mercedes-Benz Trucks Osterreich GmbH (1)
Mercedes-Benz Platz 1, 5301, Eugendorf, Austria
Tel.: (43) 1360 277 3022
Web Site: https://www.mercedes-benz-trucks.com
Automobile Vehicle Distr
N.A.I.C.S.: 423110

Mercedes-Benz Turk A.S. (1)
Yilanli Ayazma Sok No 12, Davutpasa, Istanbul, 34 020, Turkiye (55%)
Tel.: (90) 2124843300
Web Site: http://www.mengarlar.com.tr
Sales Range: $50-74.9 Million
Emp.: 150
Mfr & Dealer of Automobiles
N.A.I.C.S.: 336110
John O'Leary *(Chief Transformation Officer)*

Mercedes-Benz UK Limited (1)
Delaware Drive Tongwell, Milton Keynes, MK15 8BA, United Kingdom (100%)
Tel.: (44) 207 660 9993
Web Site: https://www.mercedes-benz.co.uk
Sales Range: $200-249.9 Million
Emp.: 1,500
Car & Commercial Vehicle Importers
N.A.I.C.S.: 441110
Nick Andrews *(Dir)*

Mercedes-Benz USA, LLC (1)
1 Mercedes-Benz Dr, Sandy Springs, GA 30328 (100%)
Tel.: (201) 573-0600
Web Site: https://www.mbusa.com
Sales Range: $650-699.9 Million
Emp.: 1,600
Automotive Distr
N.A.I.C.S.: 423110
Tracey Matura *(Gen Mgr)*

Unit (Domestic):

Mercedes-Benz Credit (2)
111 Continental Dr, Newark, DE 19713-4306 (100%)

MERCEDES-BENZ GROUP AG

Mercedes-Benz Group AG—(Continued)
Tel.: (302) 368-2447
Web Site: http://www.mbcc.com
Sales Range: $25-49.9 Million
Emp.: 28
Car Division
N.A.I.C.S.: 444240

Subsidiary (Domestic):

Mercedes-Benz Customer Service Corp. (2)
3 Paragon Dr, Montvale, NJ 07645-1725
Tel.: (201) 476-6200
Web Site: http://www.mbusa.com
Sales Range: $25-49.9 Million
Emp.: 200
Automobile Maintenance Services
N.A.I.C.S.: 811198

Unit (Domestic):

Mercedes-Benz Financial (2)
PO Box 685, Roanoke, TX 76262 (100%)
Web Site: http://www.mbcredit.com
Sales Range: $50-74.9 Million
Emp.: 20
Provider of Financing Services of Dealers By Motor Vehicle Manufacturers
N.A.I.C.S.: 522299

Subsidiary (Domestic):

Mercedes-Benz Manhattan Inc. (2)
770 11th Ave, New York, NY 10019 (100%)
Tel.: (212) 629-1600
Web Site: https://www.mbmanhattan.com
Sales Range: $25-49.9 Million
Emp.: 200
Automobiles New & Used
N.A.I.C.S.: 441110

Mercedes-Benz Service Corp. (2)
3953 Research Park Dr, Ann Arbor, MI 48108-2219
Tel.: (734) 995-3066
Web Site: http://www.mbusa.com
Sales Range: $25-49.9 Million
Emp.: 22
Provider of Automotive Emissions Testing Without Repairs
N.A.I.C.S.: 811198

Mercedes-Benz U.S. International, Inc. (2)
1 Mercedes Dr, Tuscaloosa, AL 35490-2900
Tel.: (205) 507-3300
Web Site: http://www.mbusi.com
Motor Vehicles & Car Bodies Mfr
N.A.I.C.S.: 336110
Ian Dutfield (VP-HR)

Unit (Domestic):

Mercedes-Benz USA Inc. (2)
14613 Bar Harbor Rd, Fontana, CA 92336-1660
Tel.: (909) 428-4000
Sales Range: $50-74.9 Million
Emp.: 120
Automotive Supplies & Parts
N.A.I.C.S.: 423120

Mercedes-Benz USA Inc. (2)
400 Interpace Pkwy Bldg D, Parsippany, NJ 07054-1120
Tel.: (973) 331-5400
Web Site: http://www.mbusa.com
Sales Range: $25-49.9 Million
Emp.: 15
Automobile Sales
N.A.I.C.S.: 423110

Mercedes-Benz USA Inc. (2)
1 Mercedes Dr, Belcamp, MD 21017-1203
Tel.: (410) 272-6900
Web Site: http://www.mbusa.com
Sales Range: $25-49.9 Million
Emp.: 66
Automotive Body Shop
N.A.I.C.S.: 423110

Mercedes-Benz USA LLC (2)
13470 Intl Pkwy, Jacksonville, FL 32218 (100%)
Tel.: (904) 443-2100
Web Site: http://www.mbusa.com
Sales Range: $50-74.9 Million
Emp.: 60
Administrative Management
N.A.I.C.S.: 522220

Mercedes-Benz USA LLC (2)
100 New Canton Way, Trenton, NJ 08691-2345
Tel.: (609) 259-8778
Web Site: http://www.mbusa.com
Sales Range: $25-49.9 Million
Emp.: 70
Mfr of Automotive Supplies & Parts
N.A.I.C.S.: 423120
Niles Barlow (Gen Mgr-Fleet & Pre-Owned Ops)

Branch (Domestic):

Mercedes-Benz USA Los Angeles Regional Corporate Office (2)
650 Town Ctr Dr, Costa Mesa, CA 92626-1989 (100%)
Tel.: (714) 435-3100
Web Site: http://www.mbusa.com
Sales Range: $25-49.9 Million
Emp.: 30
Automotive Services
N.A.I.C.S.: 423110

Mercedes-Benz V.I. Lille SAS (1)
4 Rue De Seclin, Vendeville, 59175, Nord, France
Tel.: (33) 320161600
Web Site: http://www.lille.ul.mercedes.fr
Automobile Dealers
N.A.I.C.S.: 441110

Mercedes-Benz V.I. Lyon SAS (1)
Zac Les Grandes Terres 530 Rue Antoine Pinay, Genas, 69740, Rhone, France
Tel.: (33) 472473600
Automobile Dealers
N.A.I.C.S.: 441227

Mercedes-Benz V.I. Paris Ile de France SAS (1)
17 rue Marcelin Berthelot, 91320, Wissous, France
Tel.: (33) 16 013 8000
Web Site: https://www.paris-vi.mercedes-benz.fr
Automobile Dealers
N.A.I.C.S.: 441227
Herge Mouilleseaux (Office Mgr)

Mercedes-Benz V.I. Toulouse SAS (1)
65 Route De Paris, 31150, Fenouillet, France
Tel.: (33) 5 62 75 82 00
Web Site: http://www.toulouse.ul.mercedes.fr
Commercial Vehicle Services
N.A.I.C.S.: 488410

Mercedes-Benz Vertriebsgesellschaft mbH (1)
Muhlen Str 10, 10785, Berlin, Germany
Tel.: (49) 3026940
Web Site: http://wwwmercedesbenz.be
Motor Vehicle Distr
N.A.I.C.S.: 423110

Mercedes-Benz Warszawa Sp. z o.o. (1)
Ul Gottlieba Daimlera 1, 02-460, Warsaw, Poland
Tel.: (48) 223127000
Web Site: https://www.warszawa.mercedes-benz.pl
Emp.: 200
New & Used Car Dealer
N.A.I.C.S.: 441110

Mercedes-Benz Wavre S.A. (1)
Avenue Lavoisier 10, 1300, Wavre, Belgium
Tel.: (32) 10222888
Web Site: https://www.wavre.mercedes-benz.be
Automotive Repair & Maintenance Services
N.A.I.C.S.: 811198

Mercedes-Benz do Brasil S.A. (1)
Av Mercedes-Benz 679, 13054-750, Campinas, SP, Brazil (100%)
Tel.: (55) 19 3225 5418
Web Site: http://www.mercedes-benz.com.br
Mfr & Assembly of Automobiles
N.A.I.C.S.: 336110

Mercedes-Benz of South Africa (Pty.) Ltd. (1)
123 wierda road zwartkop centurian 0046, PO Box 1717, Pretoria, 1, South Africa (100%)
Tel.: (27) 126771500
Web Site: http://www.mercedesbenzsa.co.za
Sales Range: $400-449.9 Million
Emp.: 1,100
New Car Dealership
N.A.I.C.S.: 441110
Mpumelelo Zulu (Product Mgr)

Mercedes-Benz.io GmbH (1)
Breitscheidstrasse 10, 70174, Stuttgart, Germany
Tel.: (49) 71 118 4230
Web Site: https://www.mercedes-benz.io
Automobile Vehicle Distr
N.A.I.C.S.: 423110
Sophie Seiwald (Mng Dir)

MercedesService Card Beteiligungsgesellschaft mbH (1)
Mainparkstr 2-4, Kleinostheim, 63801, Germany
Tel.: (49) 60275090
Credit Card Operating Services
N.A.I.C.S.: 522320

MercedesService Card GmbH & Co. KG (1)
Mainparkstrasse 2, 63801, Kleinostheim, Germany
Tel.: (49) 602 750 9567
Web Site: https://www.mercedesservicecard.de
Sales Range: $50-74.9 Million
Emp.: 35
Automotive Credit Card Processing Services
N.A.I.C.S.: 522320
Juergen Beine (Mng Dir)

Mitsubishi Fuso Truck & Bus Corp. (1)
890 12 Kashimada, Saiwai ku, Kawasaki, 212 0058, Japan
Tel.: (81) 443307700
Web Site: http://www.mitsubishi-fuso.com
Sales Range: $1-4.9 Billion
Emp.: 15,400
Commercial Vehicle Mfr
N.A.I.C.S.: 336110
Kai-Uwe Seidenfuss (VP-Sls & Svc Intl)

Mitsubishi Fuso Truck Europe, S. A. (1)
Tramagal Plant Zona Industrial Casal da Coelheira, 2205-644, Tramagal, Portugal
Tel.: (351) 241 899800
Web Site: http://www.mitsubishifuso.com.pt
Sales Range: $100-124.9 Million
Emp.: 38
Trucks Mfr
N.A.I.C.S.: 336110
Antonio Jorge Lima Da Silva Rosa (Pres)

Mitsubishi Fuso Truck and Bus Australia Pty. Ltd. (1)
Level 1 Macarthur Point Business Centre 25 Solent Circuit, Norwest Business Park, Baulkham Hills, 2153, NSW, Australia
Tel.: (61) 2 8763 8700
Web Site: http://www.mitsubishi-trucks.com.au
Truck & Bus Distr
N.A.I.C.S.: 423110
Richard Eyre (Gen Mgr)

N.V. Mercedes-Benz Aalst (1)
Nachtegaalstraat 6, Aalst, 9320, Oost-Vlaanderen, Belgium
Tel.: (32) 5 385 95 95
Web Site: http://www.aalst.mercedes-benz.be
Emp.: 60
Automotive Repair & Maintenance Services
N.A.I.C.S.: 811198
Marcel van den Acker (Mgr-Fin & Admin)

N.V. Mercedes-Benz Mechelen (1)
Brusselsesteenweg 359, 2800, Mechelen, Antwerp, Belgium
Tel.: (32) 15401111
Web Site: https://mechelen.mercedes-benz.be
Automotive Repair & Maintenance Services

INTERNATIONAL PUBLIC

N.A.I.C.S.: 811198
Mevrouw Ilse Nauwelaerts (Mgr-Sls)

Nankyu Butsuryu Support Co., Ltd. (1)
2-5-7 Taniyamako, Kagoshima, 891-0131, Japan
Tel.: (81) 992623900
Business Support Services
N.A.I.C.S.: 561499

NuCellSys GmbH (1)
Neue Strasse 95 Industriepark Nabern, 73230, Kirchheim, 73230, Germany
Tel.: (49) 7021 89 3666
Web Site: http://www.nucellsys.com
Sales Range: $50-74.9 Million
Emp.: 200
Automotive Application Fuel Cell System Mfr
N.A.I.C.S.: 334413

P.T. DaimlerChrysler Indonesia (1)
Desa Wanaherang Gunung Putri, Bogor, 16965, Indonesia (33.3%)
Tel.: (62) 2186899350
Web Site: http://www.daimlerchrysler.com
Sales Range: $25-49.9 Million
Emp.: 100
Mfr & Assembly Company
N.A.I.C.S.: 336110

P.T. Mercedes-Benz Indonesia (1)
Desa Wanaherang, Gunung Putri, Bogor, 16965, West Java, Indonesia
Tel.: (62) 212 351 9108
Web Site: https://www.mercedes-benz.co.id
New Car Dealers
N.A.I.C.S.: 441110
Tina Hutani (Dir-Fin)

P.T. Star Engines Indonesia (1)
Desa Wanaherang Gunung Putri, Bogor, 16965, Indonesia
Tel.: (62) 2123519314
Automobile Parts Mfr
N.A.I.C.S.: 336390

PABCO Co., Ltd. (1)
456 Kashiwagaya, Ebina, 243-0402, Kanagawa, Japan
Tel.: (81) 46 231 2211
Web Site: https://www.pabco.co.jp
Emp.: 600
Automobile Parts Mfr
N.A.I.C.S.: 336390

PABCO Sendai Co., Ltd. (1)
2-4-11 Ogimachi, Miyagino-Ku, Sendai, 983-0034, Miyagi, Japan
Tel.: (81) 222322374
Automobile Mfr
N.A.I.C.S.: 336110

Porcher & Meffert Grundstucksgesellschaft mbH & Co. Stuttgart OHG (1)
Lilienthalstr 6, Schonefeld, 12529, Germany
Tel.: (49) 306331110
Web Site: http://www.daimler.com
Emp.: 35
Automobile Parts Mfr
N.A.I.C.S.: 336390
Holger Steinker (Gen Mgr)

Renting del Pacifico S.A.C. (1)
Av Nicolas Arriola 500, Lima, 1313, Peru
Tel.: (51) 17122000
Transportation Equipment Rental Services
N.A.I.C.S.: 532490

Ring Garage AG Chur (1)
Ringstrasse 5-9, Chur, 7000, Graubunden, Switzerland
Tel.: (41) 812871111
Web Site: http://www.ringgarage.mercedes-benz.ch
Emp.: 160
Passenger Car Rental Services
N.A.I.C.S.: 532111
Guido Amrein (CEO)

Russ & Janot GmbH (1)
Binderslebener Landstrasse 92, 99092, Erfurt, Germany
Tel.: (49) 36121500
Web Site: https://www.mercedes-benz-russ-janot.de
Automobile Dealers
N.A.I.C.S.: 441227

AND PRIVATE COMPANIES — MERCER INTERNATIONAL INC.

Ruth Verwaltungsgesellschaft mbH (1)
Metternichstr 7, Bochum, 44867, Germany
Tel.: (49) 2327 320414
Automobile Parts Mfr
N.A.I.C.S.: 336390

Saitama Rikuso Co., Ltd. (1)
5-23-15 Negishi, Minami-Ku, Saitama, 336-0024, Japan
Tel.: (81) 488611112
Business Support Services
N.A.I.C.S.: 561499

Sandown Motor Holdings (Pty.) Ltd. (1)
193 Bryanston Drive, Bryanston, Johannesburg, 2021, Gauteng, South Africa
Tel.: (27) 11 549 0200
Web Site: https://www.sandown.co.za
Commercial Vehicle Dealer
N.A.I.C.S.: 441227
Roy McAllister (CEO)

Sechste Vermogensverwaltungsgesellschaft DVB mbH (1)
Epplestr 225, Stuttgart, 70567, Germany
Tel.: (49) 7111795336
Investment Management Service
N.A.I.C.S.: 523999

SelecTrucks of America LLC (1)
4747 N Channel Ave, Portland, OR 97217
Tel.: (503) 745-8000
Automobile Whslr
N.A.I.C.S.: 423110

SelecTrucks of Toronto, Inc. (1)
1525 Britannia Road East, Mississauga, L4W 1S5, ON, Canada
Tel.: (905) 362-1302
Web Site: http://www.selectruckstoronto.com
Used Truck Dealer
N.A.I.C.S.: 441120

Siebte Vermogensverwaltungsgesellschaft DVB mbH (1)
Epplestr 225, Stuttgart, 70567, Germany
Tel.: (49) 7111795336
Investment Management Service
N.A.I.C.S.: 523940

Smart GmbH (1)
Leivnis Str 2, Postfach 2060, 71010, Boblingen, Germany **(100%)**
Tel.: (49) 18022802
Web Site: http://www.smart.com
Sales Range: $25-49.9 Million
Emp.: 50
Mfr & Dealer of Automobiles
N.A.I.C.S.: 336110

SteloTec GmbH (1)
Rudolf-Diesel-Str 48, 68169, Mannheim, Germany
Tel.: (49) 6213098380
Web Site: https://www.stelotec.de
Emp.: 50
Pipe & Pipe Fitting Mfr
N.A.I.C.S.: 326122
Hans-Martin Trefzger (Gen Mgr)

Suffolk Leasing, Inc. (1)
225 High Ridge Rd, Stamford, CT 06905
Tel.: (203) 975-3200
Automobile Leasing Services
N.A.I.C.S.: 522220

System Design GmbH (1)
Robert-Bosch-Str 9, Leonberg, 71229, Baden-Wurttemberg, Germany
Tel.: (49) 715297640
Web Site: http://www.system-design.com
Automotive Software Consulting Services
N.A.I.C.S.: 541512

T.O.C. (Schweiz) AG (1)
Kohlestrasse 6, 8952, Schlieren, Switzerland
Tel.: (41) 447554141
Web Site: https://www.toc-online.ch
Commercial Vehicle Dealer
N.A.I.C.S.: 441227
Hannelore Kastner (Mgr-Sls)

Taunus-Auto-Verkaufs GmbH (1)
Mainzer Strasse 82 - 92, 65189, Wiesbaden, Germany
Tel.: (49) 6117770
Web Site: https://www.taunus-auto.de
Automobile Dealers
N.A.I.C.S.: 441227

Troia Empreendimentos Imobiliarios Ltda. (1)
R Voluntarios de Sao Paulo 3361 Conj 41, San Jose, Brazil
Tel.: (55) 17 3234 6289
Automobile Leasing Services
N.A.I.C.S.: 522220

Vermogensverwaltungsgesellschaft Daimler Atlanta mbH (1)
Epplestr 225, Stuttgart, 70567, Germany
Tel.: (49) 711170
Web Site: http://www.diamler.com
Investment Management Service
N.A.I.C.S.: 523940
Tiger Zetcha (Mgr)

Western Star Trucks Sales, Inc. (1)
2477 Deerfield Dr, Fort Mill, SC 29715
Tel.: (803) 578-3300
Web Site: http://www.westernstartrucks.com
Emp.: 50
Motor Vehicle Parts Distr
N.A.I.C.S.: 336390
Scott Smith (Mgr-HR)

car2go GmbH (1)
Wilhelm-Runge-Str 11, 89081, Ulm, Germany
Tel.: (49) 180 573 11110
Web Site: http://www.car2go.com
Car Sharing Services
N.A.I.C.S.: 532111

Subsidiary (Non-US):

car2go Canada Ltd. (2)
45 Water Street, Vancouver, V6G 1Z3, BC, Canada
Tel.: (512) 497-5826
Web Site: http://www.car2go.com
Car Rental Services
N.A.I.C.S.: 532111

car2go France SAS (2)
2 Place Francfort, 69003, Lyon, France
Tel.: (33) 478186101
Web Site: http://www.car2go.com
Car Rental Services
N.A.I.C.S.: 532111

Subsidiary (US):

car2go North America LLC (2)
1717 W 6th St Ste 415, Austin, TX 78703
Tel.: (512) 480-0813
Web Site: http://www.car2go.com
Car Sharing Services
N.A.I.C.S.: 532111
Pete Alt (Supvr-Pur)

Subsidiary (Domestic):

RideScout LLC (3)
6122 Mordred Ln, Austin, TX 78739-1728
Tel.: (845) 325-2232
Web Site: http://www.ridescoutapp.com
Software Publisher
N.A.I.C.S.: 513210
Celite Milbrandt (VP-Product Dev)

Subsidiary (Domestic):

GlobeSherpa LLC (4)
2025 NW Overton St, Portland, OR 97209
Tel.: (503) 919-0766
Web Site: http://www.globesherpa.com
Custom Computer Programming Services
N.A.I.C.S.: 541511
Nat Parker (CEO)

Subsidiary (Non-US):

car2go Osterreich GmbH (2)
Ausstellungsstrasse 50 Stiege 3 2 Stock, 1020, Vienna, Austria
Tel.: (43) 1 267 7111
Web Site: https://www.share-now.com
Car Rental Services
N.A.I.C.S.: 532111

proceda Modellbau GmbH (1)
Im Neuenbuhl 23, Weissach, 71287, Baden-Wurttemberg, Germany
Tel.: (49) 7044900740
Web Site: http://www.proceda.de
Interior Design Services
N.A.I.C.S.: 541410

smart France SAS (1)
Europole de Sarreguemines, Hambach, 57913, France
Tel.: (33) 387 2820 00
Web Site: http://www.daimler.com
Sales Range: $200-249.9 Million
Emp.: 1,000
Automobile Mfr
N.A.I.C.S.: 336110
Bonnet Joelne (Gen Mgr)

smart Vertriebs gmbh (1)
Potsdamer Platz 1, Berlin, 10785, Germany
Tel.: (49) 30390170
New & Used Car Dealer
N.A.I.C.S.: 441110

trapoFit GmbH (1)
Werner-Seelenbinder-Str 11b, 09120, Chemnitz, Germany
Tel.: (49) 3714 007 5400
Web Site: https://chemnitz.trapofit.de
Car Rental Services
N.A.I.C.S.: 532111

MERCEDES-BENZ SURREY
15508-104th Ave, Surrey, V3R 1N8, BC, Canada
Tel.: (604) 581-7662
Web Site: http://www.mercedes-benz-surrey.ca
Year Founded: 1999
Sales Range: $10-24.9 Million
New & Used Car Retailer
N.A.I.C.S.: 441110
Stanley S. Shenker (Gen Mgr)

MERCELL HOLDING AS
Grensesvingen 6, 0663, Oslo, Norway
Tel.: (47) 21018800 NO
Web Site: http://www.mercell.com
Software Publisher
N.A.I.C.S.: 518210

Subsidiaries:

EU Supply PLC (1)
10 Queen Street Place, London, EC4R 1AG, United Kingdom
Tel.: (44) 2071274545
Web Site: http://www.eu-supply.com
Rev.: $6,520,784
Assets: $3,997,546
Liabilities: $4,124,540
Net Worth: ($126,993)
Earnings: $506,977
Emp.: 55
Fiscal Year-end: 12/31/2018
Electronic Tender Management & Contract Management Solutions
N.A.I.C.S.: 513210
Thomas Bo Beergrehn (CEO)

MERCER INTERNATIONAL INC.
Suite 1120 700 West Pender Street, Vancouver, V6C 1G8, BC, Canada
Tel.: (604) 684-1099 WA
Web Site: https://www.mercerint.com
Year Founded: 1968
MERC—(NASDAQ)
Rev.: $2,280,937,000
Assets: $2,725,037,000
Liabilities: $1,886,253,000
Net Worth: $838,784,000
Earnings: $247,039,000
Emp.: 3,320
Fiscal Year-end: 12/31/22
Pulp & Paper Mill Owner & Operator
N.A.I.C.S.: 322110
Uwe Bentlage (VP-Pulp Sls & Mktg-Europe)

Subsidiaries:

Alpha Santanol Pty. Ltd. (1)
17-21 Coulson Way, Canning Vale, Perth, 6155, WA, Australia
Tel.: (61) 892421594
Pulp & Solid Wood Product Mfr & Distr
N.A.I.C.S.: 321999

Daishowa-Marubeni International Ltd. (1)
Suite 700-510 Burrard Street, Vancouver, V6C 3A8, BC, Canada
Tel.: (604) 684-4326
Web Site: http://www.dmi.ca
Emp.: 600
Pulp & Paper Products Mfr & Distr
N.A.I.C.S.: 322110
Thomas Hamaoka (Exec VP)

Mercer Celgar Limited (1)
1921 Arrow Lakes Road, PO Box 1000, Castlegar, V1N 3H9, BC, Canada
Tel.: (250) 365-7211
Pulp & Solid Wood Product Mfr & Distr
N.A.I.C.S.: 321999

Mercer Forestry Services Ltd. (1)
2002C Dyffryn Road, PO Box 130, Lumby, V0E 2G0, BC, Canada
Tel.: (250) 547-6612
Pulp & Solid Wood Product Mfr & Distr
N.A.I.C.S.: 321999

Mercer Holz GmbH (1)
Hauptstr 16, 7366, Blankenstein, Germany
Tel.: (49) 3664282508
Web Site: http://www.mercer-holz.de
Portable Sawmill Whslr
N.A.I.C.S.: 321113
Wolfgang Beck (Mng Dir)

Mercer Mass Timber Llc (1)
19202 E Garland Ave, Spokane Valley, WA 99027
Tel.: (509) 866-5077
Pulp & Solid Wood Product Mfr & Distr
N.A.I.C.S.: 321999

Mercer Peace River Pulp Ltd. (1)
Courier Shipments 1 Pulp Mill Site Road, Postal Bag 4400, Peace River, T8S 1V7, AB, Canada
Tel.: (780) 624-7000
Pulp & Solid Wood Product Mfr & Distr
N.A.I.C.S.: 321999

Mercer Pulp Sales GmbH (1)
Charlottenstrasse 59, 10117, Berlin, Germany
Tel.: (49) 303064710
Sales Range: $25-49.9 Million
Emp.: 80
Pulp Mfr
N.A.I.C.S.: 322110
Uwe Bentlage (Mng Dir & VP-Sls & Mktg-Europe)

Mercer Stendal GmbH (1)
Goldbecker Strasse 1, 39596, Arneburg, Germany
Tel.: (49) 39321550
Pulp Mfr & Distr
N.A.I.C.S.: 322110

Mercer Timber Products GmbH (1)
Am Bahnhof 123, 7929, Saalburg-Ebersdorf, Germany
Tel.: (49) 36651800
Emp.: 300
Portable Sawmill Whslr
N.A.I.C.S.: 321113

Mercer Torgau GmbH & Co. KG (1)
Forstweg 1, 04860, Torgau, Germany
Tel.: (49) 342173830
Biofuel Mfr & Distr
N.A.I.C.S.: 325199

Zellstoff Celgar LP (1)
1921 Arrow Lakes Road, PO Box 1000, Castlegar, V1N 3H9, BC, Canada
Tel.: (250) 365-7211
Sales Range: $10-24.9 Million
Wood Pulp & Paper Mfr
N.A.I.C.S.: 322110

Zellstoff Celgar Limited (1)
1921 Arrow Lakes Road, PO Box 1000, Castlegar, V1N 3H9, BC, Canada
Tel.: (250) 365-7211
Web Site: http://www.mercerint.com
Sales Range: $125-149.9 Million
Emp.: 40
Kraft Pulp Mfr
N.A.I.C.S.: 322110
Kevin Anderson (Mng Dir)

Zellstoff Celgar Limited Partnership (1)

MERCER INTERNATIONAL INC.

Mercer International Inc.—(Continued)

1921 Arrow Lakes Road, PO Box 1000, Castlegar, V1N 3H9, BC, Canada
Tel.: (250) 365-7211
Web Site: http://www.celgar.com
Chemical Products Mfr
N.A.I.C.S.: 325998

Zellstoff Stendal GmbH (1)
Goldbecker Str 1, 39596, Arneburg, Germany
Tel.: (49) 39321550
Sales Range: $450-499.9 Million
Emp.: 592
Wood Pulp & Paper Mfr
N.A.I.C.S.: 322110

MERCHANT GROUP PTY LTD

Level 3 101 St Georges Terrace, Perth, 6000, WA, Australia
Tel.: (61) 8 6277 0050
Web Site:
   http://www.merchantfunds.com.au
Investment Holding Company
N.A.I.C.S.: 551112
Andrew Chapman (Mng Dir)

Subsidiaries:

Merchant Funds Management Pty Ltd (1)
Level 3 101 St Georges Terrace, Perth, 6000, WA, Australia
Tel.: (61) 8 6277 0050
Web Site: http://www.merchantfunds.com.au
Investment Services
N.A.I.C.S.: 523999
Andrew Chapman (Mng Dir)

MERCHANT HOUSE INTERNATIONAL LIMITED

First Floor 31 Cliff Street, Fremantle, 6160, WA, Australia
Tel.: (61) 894353200   BM
Web Site:
   https://www.lorettalee.com.hk
MHI—(ASX)
Rev.: $3,673,469
Assets: $21,877,812
Liabilities: $3,415,922
Net Worth: $18,461,890
Earnings: ($3,856,686)
Fiscal Year-end: 03/31/24
Footwear Mfr & Whslr
N.A.I.C.S.: 316210
Loretta Bic Hing Lee (Founder & Chm)

MERCHANTS PAPER COMPANY

975 Crawford Ave, PO Box 602, Windsor, N9A 6N4, ON, Canada
Tel.: (519) 977-9977
Web Site: http://www.merchants.ca
Year Founded: 1941
Rev.: $12,581,900
Emp.: 50
Disposable Products Distr
N.A.I.C.S.: 424130
Carl Cohen (Chm)

MERCHAVIA HOLDINGS AND INVESTMENTS LTD

BSR Tower No 4, Bnei Brak, Israel
Tel.: (972) 35788770
Web Site:
   https://www.merchavia.com
Year Founded: 1972
MRHL—(TAE)
Assets: $8,322,973
Liabilities: $338,997
Net Worth: $7,983,976
Earnings: ($4,484,321)
Fiscal Year-end: 12/31/23
Real Estate Investment Services
N.A.I.C.S.: 523999
Eli Arad (CEO)

MERCIA ASSET MANAGEMENT PLC

Forward House 17 High Street, Henley-in-Arden, B95 5AA, United Kingdom
Tel.: (44) 3302231430   UK
Web Site: https://www.mercia.co.uk
Year Founded: 1982
MERC—(AIM)
Rev.: $38,412,093
Assets: $258,659,942
Liabilities: $19,780,398
Net Worth: $238,879,544
Earnings: ($9,580,933)
Fiscal Year-end: 03/31/24
Investment Management Service
N.A.I.C.S.: 523940
Mark Payton (CEO)

Subsidiaries:

Northern 2 VCT Plc (1)
Forward House 17 High Street, Henley-in-Arden, B95 5AA, United Kingdom
Tel.: (44) 1912446000
Web Site: http://www.nvm.co.uk
Investment Services
N.A.I.C.S.: 523999
David Gravells (Chm)

Northern 3 VCT Plc (1)
Forward House 17 High Street, Henley-in-Arden, B95 5AA, United Kingdom
Tel.: (44) 1912446000
Web Site: http://www.nvm.co.uk
Investment Services
N.A.I.C.S.: 523999
James Ferguson (Chm)

Northern Venture Trust PLC (1)
Forward House 17 High Street, Henley-in-Arden, B95 5AA, United Kingdom
Tel.: (44) 1912446000
Web Site: http://www.nvm.co.uk
Investment Trust Services
N.A.I.C.S.: 523999
Simon Constantine (Chm)

MERCIALYS

16-18 rue du Quatre Septembre CS36812, 75082, Paris, cedex 02, France
Tel.: (33) 182827604
Web Site: https://www.mercialys.com
MERY—(EUR)
Rev.: $196,500,718
Assets: $2,374,076,609
Liabilities: $1,418,016,338
Net Worth: $956,060,272
Earnings: $51,584,060
Emp.: 168
Fiscal Year-end: 12/31/23
Asset Management & Marketing Services
N.A.I.C.S.: 541611
Eric Le Gentil (Chm)

MERCK KGAA

Frankfurter Strasse 250, 64293, Darmstadt, Germany
Tel.: (49) 6151720   De
Web Site:
   https://www.merckgroup.com
Year Founded: 1668
MRK—(OTCIQ)
Rev.: $20,511,243,200
Assets: $44,770,087,600
Liabilities: $20,777,874,600
Net Worth: $23,992,213,000
Earnings: $3,068,567,600
Emp.: 64,243
Fiscal Year-end: 12/31/22
Holding Company; Biopharmaceuticals, Consumer Health Products, Performance Materials & Life Science Tools Mfr
N.A.I.C.S.: 551112
Marcus Kuhnert (CFO & Member-Exec Bd)

Subsidiaries:

Allergopharma Joachim Ganzer Kg (1)
Hermann-Korner-Str 52, 21465, Hamburg, Germany
Tel.: (49) 40727650
Web Site: http://www.allergopharma.de
Sales Range: $125-149.9 Million
Emp.: 420
Pharmaceutical Preparation Manufacturing
N.A.I.C.S.: 325412
Marco Linari (CEO)

Biochrom GmbH (1)
Rahel-Hirsch-Str 10, 10557, Berlin, Germany
Tel.: (49) 307799060
Scientific Instrument Mfr & Distr
N.A.I.C.S.: 334516

Chemtreat Composites India Pvt Ltd (1)
1505 1506 Kesar Solitaire Plot no 5 Sector 19 off Palm Beach road, Sanpada, Navi Mumbai, 400 705, Maharashtra, India
Tel.: (91) 22 6619 5301
Chemical Products Mfr
N.A.I.C.S.: 325998
Nitin Mhatre (Acct Exec)

EMD Millipore Corporation (1)
400 Summit Dr, Burlington, MA 01803
Tel.: (978) 715-4321
Web Site: https://www.emdmillipore.com
Life Science Research, Drug Discovery & Development
N.A.I.C.S.: 334516

Subsidiary (Domestic):

Bioscience Research Reagents (2)
28820 Single Oak Dr, Temecula, CA 92590
Tel.: (951) 676-8080
Web Site: http://www.merckmillipore.com
Biological Products & Research
N.A.I.C.S.: 325414

EMD Biosciences, Inc. (2)
10394 Pacific Ctr Ct, San Diego, CA 92121-4340
Tel.: (858) 450-9600
Sales Range: $150-199.9 Million
Emp.: 352
Biochemical & Biological Reagents, Antibodies, Assays & Research Kits For Eye Research
N.A.I.C.S.: 424690

Subsidiary (Non-US):

Merck Chemicals GmbH (2)
Am Kronberger Hang 5, D 65824, Schwalbach, Hessen, Germany (100%)
Tel.: (49) 69 86798021
Web Site: http://www.merckmillipore.com
Sales Range: $10-24.9 Million
Emp.: 70
Mfr of Laboratory Instruments
N.A.I.C.S.: 334516

Merck Chemicals and Life Science, S.A. (2)
Maria de Molina 40, 28006, Madrid, Spain
Tel.: (34) 917454400
Web Site: https://www.merck.es
Laboratory Instruments Distr
N.A.I.C.S.: 423450

Merck Millipore (2)
885 Mountain Hwy Basewater, Bayswater, 3153, Vic, Australia (100%)
Tel.: (61) 3 9728 7600
Web Site: http://www.merckmillipore.com
Sales Range: $25-49.9 Million
Emp.: 50
Marketing & Sales of Laboratory Instruments
N.A.I.C.S.: 423450

Merck Millipore Ltd. (2)
Tullagreen, Carrigtohill, Cork, Ireland (100%)
Tel.: (353) 1890924645
Web Site: https://www.merckmillipore.com
Membrane Filtration & Chromatography Systems Mfr
N.A.I.C.S.: 334516

Millipore A/S (2)

INTERNATIONAL PUBLIC

Strandvejen 102 E, PO Box 84, 2900, Hellerup, Denmark (100%)
Tel.: (45) 70105645
Web Site: http://www.merckmillipore.com
Sales Range: $10-24.9 Million
Emp.: 6
Marketing & Sales of Laboratory Instruments
N.A.I.C.S.: 423450

Millipore AB (2)
Englundavagen 7, 17141, Solna, Sweden (100%)
Tel.: (46) 771200645
Web Site: http://www.millipore.com
Sales Range: $25-49.9 Million
Emp.: 50
Sales & Service of Laboratory Instruments
N.A.I.C.S.: 423450

Millipore AG (2)
Chamerstrasse 174, PO Box 148, CH 6301, Zug, Switzerland (100%)
Tel.: (41) 225675222
Web Site: http://www.millipore.com
Sales Range: $10-24.9 Million
Emp.: 3
Marketing & Sales of Laboratory Instruments
N.A.I.C.S.: 423450

Millipore B.V. (2)
Aarlerbjerwej 21-23 3rd Fl River Bldg, PO Box 23249, 1101 CH, Amsterdam, Netherlands (100%)
Tel.: (31) 205675559
Web Site: http://www.millipore.com
Sales Range: $50-74.9 Million
Emp.: 100
Marketing & Sales of Laboratory Instruments
N.A.I.C.S.: 423450

Millipore China Ltd. (2)
Rm 1401 Fubang Intl Twr, No 16 E 3rd Ring Rd, Beijing, 100022, China
Tel.: (86) 1051672330
Web Site: http://www.millipore.com.cn
Sales Range: $75-99.9 Million
Emp.: 200
Supplier of Laboratory Instruments
N.A.I.C.S.: 423450

Subsidiary (Domestic):

Millipore Cidra, Inc. (2)
Road 172 Kilometer 7.6 Barrio Certenejas Cidra, Cidra, PR 00739-1977
Tel.: (787) 273-8495
Web Site: http://www.millipore.com
Sales Range: $50-74.9 Million
Emp.: 400
Analytical Laboratory Instrument Mfr
N.A.I.C.S.: 334516

Division (Domestic):

Millipore Corporation - Bioscience Division (2)
17 Cherry Hill Dr, Danvers, MA 01923
Tel.: (978) 762-5100
Sales Range: $50-74.9 Million
Emp.: 250
Membrane Ultrafiltration & Chromatography Materials Devices & Systems Mfr
N.A.I.C.S.: 334516

Subsidiary (Non-US):

Millipore GmbH (2)
Hietzinger Hauptstrasse 145, A 1130, Vienna, Austria (100%)
Tel.: (43) 18778926
Web Site: http://www.millipore.com
Sales Range: $10-24.9 Million
Emp.: 14
Marketing & Sales of Laboratory Equipment
N.A.I.C.S.: 423450

Millipore Ireland B.V. (2)
Tullagreen Carrigtwohill, Cork, T45 KD29, Ireland (100%)
Tel.: (353) 214883666
Web Site: http://www.millipore.com
Sales Range: $75-99.9 Million
Emp.: 500
Mfr of Filtration Devices & Plastic Membrane Film
N.A.I.C.S.: 326113

Millipore Korea, Ltd. (2)

AND PRIVATE COMPANIES

MERCK KGAA

2nd Fl Paepong Bldg 999 -N6 Daechi Dong, 135 080, Seoul, Korea (South) (100%)
Tel.: (82) 230119600
Sales Range: $25-49.9 Million
Emp.: 30
Supplier of Laboratory Instruments
N.A.I.C.S.: 423450

Millipore Oy (2)
Pihatorma 1C, 02240, Espoo, Finland (100%)
Tel.: (358) 20305645
Web Site: http://www.millipore.com
Sales Range: $1-9.9 Million
Emp.: 10
Marketing & Sales of Laboratory Instruments
N.A.I.C.S.: 456199

Millipore S.A./N.V. (2)
Rue De La Fusee 60 Raketstraat, B 1130, Brussels, Belgium (100%)
Tel.: (32) 70225645
Web Site: http://www.millipore.com
Sales Range: $50-74.9 Million
Emp.: 30
Marketing & Sales of Laboratory Instruments
N.A.I.C.S.: 456199

Millipore S.A.S. (2)
39 Route Industrielle de la Hardt, 67120, Molsheim, France (100%)
Tel.: (33) 825045645
Sales Range: $25-49.9 Million
Emp.: 135
Mfr of Laboratory Instruments
N.A.I.C.S.: 334516

Millipore S.p.A. (2)
Via XI Febbraio 99, 20090, Vimodrone, Milan, Italy (100%)
Tel.: (39) 0848845645
Web Site: http://www.millipore.com
Sales Range: $25-49.9 Million
Emp.: 57
Marketing & Sales of Laboratory Instruments
N.A.I.C.S.: 423450

Millipore UK Ltd (2)
3 5 The Courtyard Hatter Lane, Watford, WD18 8YH, Herts, United Kingdom (100%)
Tel.: (44) 8709004645
Web Site: http://www.millipore.com
Sales Range: $25-49.9 Million
Emp.: 90
Mfr of Membrane Filtration & Chromatography Systems
N.A.I.C.S.: 334516

Subsidiary (Domestic):

Mirus Bio, LLC (2)
5602 Research Park Blvd Ste 210, Madison, WI 53719
Tel.: (608) 441-2852
Web Site: http://www.mirusbio.com
Sales Range: $10-24.9 Million
Emp.: 20
Biological Products Research & Development
N.A.I.C.S.: 541715
Scott Hayes *(VP-Scientific Ops)*

Subsidiary (Non-US):

Nihon Millipore K.K. (2)
Mita Kokusai Bldg 4 28 Mita 1 Chome, Mita Minato Ku, Tokyo, 108 0073, Japan (100%)
Tel.: (81) 354429782
Web Site: http://www.millipore.com
Sales Range: $125-149.9 Million
Mfr of Filters for Biomedical, Research & Industrial Applications
N.A.I.C.S.: 333310

Exelead Inc. (1)
6925 Guion Rd, Indianapolis, IN 46268
Tel.: (317) 347-2800
Web Site: https://www.exeleadbiopharma.com
Injection Medicine Mfr & Distr
N.A.I.C.S.: 325412

Intermolecular, Inc. (1)
3011 N First St, San Jose, CA 95134
Tel.: (408) 582-5700
Web Site: http://www.intermolecular.com
Rev.: $33,660,000
Assets: $43,393,000
Liabilities: $9,009,000
Net Worth: $34,384,000
Earnings: ($3,411,000)
Emp.: 88
Fiscal Year-end: 12/31/2018
Electronic Components Mfr
N.A.I.C.S.: 334419
Milind Weling *(Sr VP-Programs & Ops)*

Lamberts Healthcare Ltd. (1)
1 Lamberts Rd, Century Pl, Tunbridge Wells, TN2 3EH, United Kingdom (100%)
Tel.: (44) 1892554313
Web Site: http://www.lambertshealthcare.co.uk
Sales Range: $25-49.9 Million
Nutritional Supplements Mfr
N.A.I.C.S.: 325412

Merck Electronic Materials Ltd. (1)
50-14 Hyupdongdanji-gil, Miyang-myeon, Anseong, 17600, Gyeonggi-do, Korea (South)
Tel.: (82) 36708451
Web Site: https://www.merckgroup.com
Specialty Chemicals Mfr
N.A.I.C.S.: 325998

Merck Electronics KGaA (1)
Frankfurter Strasse 250, 64293, Darmstadt, Germany
Tel.: (49) 6151720
Electronic Equipment Mfr & Distr
N.A.I.C.S.: 334419

Merck Life Science (Pty.) Ltd. (1)
1 Friesland Drive Longmeadow Business Estate South, Modderfontein, Johannesburg, 1645, South Africa
Tel.: (27) 860063725
Electronic Equipment Mfr & Distr
N.A.I.C.S.: 334419

Merck Life Science AB (1)
Frosundaviks Alle 1, 169 70, Solna, Sweden
Tel.: (46) 856244500
Electronic Equipment Mfr & Distr
N.A.I.C.S.: 334419

Merck Life Science AS (1)
Tel.: (47) 81062645
Pharmaceutical & Chemical Mfr
N.A.I.C.S.: 325412

Merck Life Science B.V. (1)
Ildefonse Vandammestraat 5/7B, 1560, Hoeilaart, Belgium
Tel.: (32) 70225645
Pharmaceuticals Mfr
N.A.I.C.S.: 325412

Merck Life Science GmbH (1)
Lilienthalstrasse 16, 69214, Eppelheim, Germany
Tel.: (49) 6221759010
Pharmaceutical & Chemical Mfr
N.A.I.C.S.: 325412

Merck Life Science KGaA (1)
Frankfurter Strasse 250, 64293, Darmstadt, Germany
Tel.: (49) 6151720
Electronic Equipment Mfr & Distr
N.A.I.C.S.: 334419

Merck Life Science LLC (1)
Valovaya Street 35, Moscow, 115054, Russia
Tel.: (7) 4959373304
Electronic Equipment Mfr & Distr
N.A.I.C.S.: 334419

Merck Life Science N.V. (1)
Haarlerbergweg 21 A, North Holland, 1101 CH, Amsterdam, Netherlands
Tel.: (31) 786205411
Electronic Equipment Mfr & Distr
N.A.I.C.S.: 334419

Merck Life Science OY (1)
Tel.: (358) 20305645
Pharmaceutical & Chemical Mfr
N.A.I.C.S.: 325412

Merck Life Science S.r.l. (1)
Via Monte Rosa 93, 20149, Milan, Italy
Tel.: (39) 0800827018
Organic Chemical & Allied Product Whslr
N.A.I.C.S.: 424690

Merck Life Science Sp. z o o. (1)
Szelagowska 30, 61-626, Poznan, Poland
Tel.: (48) 618290100
Electronic Equipment Mfr & Distr
N.A.I.C.S.: 334419

Merck Life Science UK Limited (1)
The Old Brickyard New Rd, Gillingham, SP8 4XT, Dorset, United Kingdom
Tel.: (44) 800717181
Medical Equipment Mfr
N.A.I.C.S.: 339112

Merck Life Science spol. s r.o. (1)
Na Hrebenech II 1718/10, 14000, Prague, Czech Republic
Tel.: (420) 272084272
Electronic Equipment Mfr & Distr
N.A.I.C.S.: 334419

Merck Performance Materials (Suisse) S.A. (1)
Route de la Verrerie 6, 1267, Coinsins, Switzerland
Tel.: (41) 792513145
Pharmaceuticals Mfr
N.A.I.C.S.: 325412

Merck Performance Materials G.K. (1)
1-8-1 Shimomeguro, Meguro-ku, Tokyo, 153-8605, Japan
Tel.: (81) 354345270
Pharmaceuticals Mfr
N.A.I.C.S.: 325412

Merck Performance Materials Pvt. Ltd. (1)
8th Floor Godrej One Pirojshanagar Eastern Express Highway Vikhroli E, Mumbai, 400079, India
Tel.: (91) 2262109000
Pharmaceutical & Biotechnology Product Mfr
N.A.I.C.S.: 325412

Merck Pharma GmbH (1)
Alsfelder Str 17, D-64289, Darmstadt, Germany
Tel.: (49) 6151723100
Web Site: http://www.merck-pharma.de
Sales Range: $50-74.9 Million
Emp.: 100
Developer & Mfr of Pharmaceuticals & Chemicals
N.A.I.C.S.: 325412

Merck S.A. (1)
37 Rue Saint Romain, 69008, Lyon, Cedex, France (100%)
Tel.: (33) 472782525
Web Site: https://www.merckgroup.com
Holding Company; Biopharmaceuticals, Consumer Health Products, Performance Materials & Life Science Tools Mfr
N.A.I.C.S.: 551112

Merck S.R.L. (1)
Via Monte Rosa 93, 20149, Milan, Italy
Tel.: (39) 0238591445
Electronic Equipment Mfr & Distr
N.A.I.C.S.: 334419

Merck Serono S.A.S. (1)
37 Rue Saint-Romain, 69008, Lyon, France
Tel.: (33) 472782525
Electronic Equipment Mfr & Distr
N.A.I.C.S.: 334419

Merck Serono S.p.A. (1)
Via Casilina, 00176, Rome, Italy
Tel.: (39) 06703841
Pharmaceuticals Mfr
N.A.I.C.S.: 325412

Merck Serono SA (1)
9 Chemin Des Mines Case, Postale 54, 1200 01, CH-1211, Geneva, Switzerland
Tel.: (41) 224143000
Web Site: http://www.merckserono.com
Sales Range: $5-14.9 Billion
Emp.: 16,900
Holding Company
N.A.I.C.S.: 551112

Subsidiary (US):

EMD Serono Research Institute, Inc. (2)
1 Technology Pl, Rockland, MA 02370
Tel.: (781) 982-9000
Sales Range: $75-99.9 Million
Emp.: 500
Pharmaceutical Research Services
N.A.I.C.S.: 541715

EMD Serono, Inc. (2)
1 Technology Pl, Rockland, MA 02370
Tel.: (781) 982-9000
Web Site: http://www.emdserono.com
Sales Range: $150-199.9 Million
Pharmaceutical & Biological Research Services
N.A.I.C.S.: 541714

Subsidiary (Domestic):

EMD Serono Research & Development Institute (3)
45 A Middlesex Tpke, Billerica, MA 01821-3936
Tel.: (978) 294-1100
Web Site: http://www.emdserono.com
Commercial Biotechnical Research
N.A.I.C.S.: 541714

Subsidiary (Non-US):

Industria Farmaceutica Serono SpA (2)
Via Casilina 125, I-00176, Rome, Italy
Tel.: (39) 06703841
Web Site: http://www.serono.it
Sales Range: $50-74.9 Million
Emp.: 100
Pharmaceuticals Product Mfr
N.A.I.C.S.: 424210

Merck Serono GmbH (2)
Alsfelder Strasse 17, D-64289, Darmstadt, Germany
Tel.: (49) 615162850
Web Site: http://www.merckgroup.com
Sales Range: $500-549.9 Million
Emp.: 332
Pharmaceutical Sales
N.A.I.C.S.: 424210
Ernesto Bertarelli *(CEO)*

Merck Serono Israel Ltd. (2)
South Industrial Area 18 HaKishon St, Yavne, 81220, Israel
Tel.: (972) 893 82424
Web Site: http://www.merckserono.co.il
Sales Range: $25-49.9 Million
Emp.: 60
Biotechnology Research
N.A.I.C.S.: 541714

Serono France SA (2)
L'Arche du Parc 738 Rue Yves Kermen, F-92658, Boulogne-Billancourt, Cedex, France
Tel.: (33) 147611313
Web Site: http://www.serono.fr
Pharmaceuticals Product Mfr
N.A.I.C.S.: 424210

Serono Nordic AB (2)
Srosundaviks alle 1, Box 1803 stockholn, SE 19587, Stockholm, Sweden
Tel.: (46) 856244500
Web Site: http://www.merck.se
Sales Range: $25-49.9 Million
Emp.: 70
Pharmaceutical Sales
N.A.I.C.S.: 424210

Serono de Mexico SA de CV (2)
Calle 5 No 7 Frac Industrial Alce Blanco, Naucalpan de Juarez, 53370, Mexico, Mexico
Tel.: (52) 5521221600
Web Site: http://www.merck.com.mx
Pharmaceuticals Distr
N.A.I.C.S.: 424210

Merck Sp. z o.o. (1)
Al Jerozolimskie 142B, 02-305, Warsaw, Poland
Tel.: (48) 225359700
Electronic Equipment Mfr & Distr
N.A.I.C.S.: 334419

Merck Vietnam Company Limited (1)
106 Nguyen Van Troi Street 9th floor Centre Point Building, Phu Nhuan District, Ho Chi Minh City, Vietnam
Tel.: (84) 2838420100
Pharmaceuticals Mfr

MERCK KGAA

Merck KGaA—(Continued)
N.A.I.C.S.: 325412

Merck, S.L.U. (1)
Maria de Molina 40, 28006, Madrid, Spain
Tel.: (34) 917454400
Electronic Equipment Mfr & Distr
N.A.I.C.S.: 334419

MilliporeSigma Canada Ltd. (1)
2149 Winston Park Dr, Oakville, L6H 6J8, ON, Canada
Tel.: (905) 829-9500
Electronic Equipment Mfr & Distr
N.A.I.C.S.: 334419

Peer+ B.V. (1)
OTB Building Luchthavenweg 10, 5657 EA, Eindhoven, Netherlands (100%)
Tel.: (31) 612301120
Web Site: http://www.peerplus.nl
Emp.: 10
Liquid Crystal Windows Mfr
N.A.I.C.S.: 334419

Seven Seas Limited (1)
Hedon Road, Marfleet, Hull, HU9 5NJ, East Yorkshire, United Kingdom (100%)
Tel.: (44) 1482375234
Web Site: http://www.seven-seas.com
Sales Range: $125-149.9 Million
Emp.: 140
Mfr of Health Products
N.A.I.C.S.: 325411

Sigma-Aldrich Corporation (1)
3050 Spruce St, Saint Louis, MO 63103
Tel.: (314) 771-5765
Holding Company; Biochemicals & Organic Chemicals Developer, Mfr & Distr
N.A.I.C.S.: 551112

Subsidiary (Domestic):

Aldrich Chemical Co. LLC (2)
6000 N Teutonia Ave, Milwaukee, WI 53209
Tel.: (414) 438-3850
Fine Chemicals & Related Products Mfr
N.A.I.C.S.: 325199

Subsidiary (Non-US):

BioReliance KK (2)
Arco Tower 5F 1-8-1 Shimomeguro, Meguro-ku, Tokyo, 152-8927, Japan
Tel.: (81) 3 6758 3610
Web Site: http://www.bioreliance.com
Clinical Trial Support & Biosafety Testing Services
N.A.I.C.S.: 541380

Subsidiary (Domestic):

Cell Marque Corporation (2)
6600 Sierra College Blvd, Rocklin, CA 95677
Tel.: (916) 746-8900
Web Site: https://www.cellmarque.com
Medicinal & Botanical Mfr
N.A.I.C.S.: 325411

Cerilliant Corp. (2)
811 Paloma Dr Ste A, Round Rock, TX 78665
Tel.: (512) 238-9974
Web Site: https://www.cerilliant.com
Analytical Reference Standard & Components Mfr
N.A.I.C.S.: 424690

Research Organics LLC (2)
4353 E 49th St, Cleveland, OH 44125
Tel.: (216) 883-8025
Web Site: http://www.sigmaaldrich.com
Chemical Product & Preparation Mfr
N.A.I.C.S.: 325998

SAFC, Inc. (2)
645 Science Drive, Madison, WI 53711
Tel.: (608) 233-3115
Web Site: https://www.sigmaaldrich.com
Custom Manufacturing, Packaging & Raw Material Supply Services
N.A.I.C.S.: 325414

Subsidiary (Domestic):

BioReliance Corporation (3)
14920 Broschart Rd, Rockville, MD 20850-3349
Tel.: (301) 738-1000
Web Site: https://www.bioreliance.com
Biopharmaceutical Testing Services
N.A.I.C.S.: 541714

Subsidiary (Non-US):

BioReliance Ltd. (4)
Innovation Park, Hillfoots Rd, Stirling, FK9 4NF, United Kingdom
Tel.: (44) 1419469999
Web Site: https://www.bioreliance.com
Biosafety Testing Services
N.A.I.C.S.: 541714

Subsidiary (Domestic):

SAFC Biosciences, Inc. (3)
13804 W 107th St, Lenexa, KS 66215
Tel.: (913) 469-5580
Web Site: https://www.sigmaaldrich.com
Biopharmaceutical Cell Culture Reagents Developer & Mfr
N.A.I.C.S.: 325414

SAFC Carlsbad, Inc. (3)
6219 El Camino Real, Carlsbad, CA 92009
Tel.: (760) 710-6100
Web Site: https://www.sigmaaldrich.com
Biological Product Mfr
N.A.I.C.S.: 325414

SAFC Hitech, Inc. (3)
1429 Hilldale Ave, Haverhill, MA 01832-1300
Tel.: (978) 374-5200
Web Site: https://www.sigmaaldrich.com
Organic Chemical & Allied Product Whslr
N.A.I.C.S.: 424690

Subsidiary (Non-US):

Sigma-Aldrich (Switzerland) Holding AG (2)
Industriestrasse 25, 9471, Buchs, Switzerland (100%)
Tel.: (41) 817552511
Holding Company
N.A.I.C.S.: 551112

Subsidiary (Non-US):

Sigma-Aldrich BVBA/SPRL (3)
Brusselsesteenweg 288, 3090, Overijse, Belgium
Tel.: (32) 38991301
Organic Chemical & Allied Product Whslr
N.A.I.C.S.: 424690

Subsidiary (Non-US):

Sigma-Aldrich Chemie NV (4)
Stationsplein 4-E, 3331 LL, Zwijndrecht, Netherlands
Tel.: (31) 786205411
Organic Chemical & Allied Product Whslr
N.A.I.C.S.: 424690

Subsidiary (Non-US):

Sigma-Aldrich Canada Co. (3)
2149 Winston Park Drive, Oakville, L6H 6J8, ON, Canada
Tel.: (905) 829-9500
Organic Chemical & Allied Product Whslr
N.A.I.C.S.: 424690

Sigma-Aldrich Quimica Ltda. (3)
Providencia, 1981, Santiago, Chile
Tel.: (56) 800340200
Organic Chemical & Allied Product Whslr
N.A.I.C.S.: 424690

Sigma-Aldrich Sp. z.o.o. (3)
Szelagowska 30, 61-626, Poznan, Poland
Tel.: (48) 618290100
Organic Chemical & Allied Product Whslr
N.A.I.C.S.: 424690

Sigma-Aldrich Sweden AB (3)
Solkraftsvagen 14C, 135 70, Stockholm, Sweden
Tel.: (46) 87424200
Organic Chemical & Allied Product Whslr
N.A.I.C.S.: 424690

Sigma-Aldrich spol. s r.o. (3)
Na Hrebenech II 1718/10, 140 00, Prague, 4, Czech Republic
Tel.: (420) 246003200
Web Site: http://www.sigmaaldrich.com
Organic Chemical & Allied Product Whslr
N.A.I.C.S.: 424690

Marketa Kmentova (Mgr-Customer Svc)

Subsidiary (Non-US):

Sigma-Aldrich BV (2)
Stationsplein 4E, 3331 LL, Zwyndrecht, Netherlands
Tel.: (31) 786205411
Web Site: http://www.sigmaaldrich.com
Organic Chemical & Allied Product Whslr
N.A.I.C.S.: 424690

Subsidiary (Non-US):

Sigma-Aldrich Chemie Holding GmbH (3)
Eschenstr 5, Taufkirchen, 82024, Bayern, Germany
Tel.: (49) 8965130
Web Site: https://www.sigmaaldrich.com
Organic Chemical & Allied Product Whslr
N.A.I.C.S.: 424690
Bernd Krueger (Mng Dir)

Subsidiary (Domestic):

Sigma-Aldrich Biochemie GmbH (4)
Georg-Heyken-Strasse 14, 21147, Hamburg, Germany
Tel.: (49) 4079720250
Web Site: http://www.sigmaaldrich.com
Organic Chemical & Allied Product Whslr
N.A.I.C.S.: 424690

Subsidiary (Non-US):

Sigma-Aldrich Chemie GmbH (2)
Eschenstrasse 5, 82024, Taufkirchen, Germany
Tel.: (49) 8965130
Web Site: http://www.sigmaaldrich.com
Industrial Organic Chemicals Mfr
N.A.I.C.S.: 325199

Sigma-Aldrich Chimie S.a.r.l. (2)
80 Rue de Luzais L'Isle D'Abeau Chesnes, 38297, Saint-Quentin, Cedex, Fallavier, France
Tel.: (33) 474822888
Web Site: http://www.sigmaaldrich.com
Biological Chemicals & Products Mfr
N.A.I.C.S.: 325411

Sigma-Aldrich Chimie SNC (2)
80 Rue de Luzais L'Isle D'Abeau Chesnes, 38297, Saint-Quentin, Cedex, Fallavier, France
Tel.: (33) 474822888
Web Site: https://www.sigmaaldrich.com
Organic Chemical & Allied Product Whslr
N.A.I.C.S.: 424690

Sigma-Aldrich Co. Ltd. (2)
Fancy Rd, Poole, BH12 4QH, Dorset, United Kingdom
Tel.: (44) 1747833000
Web Site: http://www.sigmaaldrich.com
Medicinal Chemicals & Botanical Products Mfr
N.A.I.C.S.: 325411

Sigma-Aldrich Company Ltd. (2)
The Old Brickyard New Road, Gillingham, SP8 4XT, Dorset, United Kingdom
Tel.: (44) 1747833000
Web Site: http://www.sigmaaldrich.com
Industrial Organic Chemicals Mfr
N.A.I.C.S.: 325199

Sigma-Aldrich Grundstucks GmbH & Co. KG (2)
Riedstrasse 2, 89555, Steinheim, Germany
Tel.: (49) 7329970
Organic Chemical & Allied Product Whslr
N.A.I.C.S.: 424690

Sigma-Aldrich Ireland Ltd. (2)
Vale Rd Ballyraine Lower, Arklow, Y14EK18, Wicklow, Ireland
Tel.: (353) 40220370
Organic Chemical & Allied Product Whslr
N.A.I.C.S.: 424690

Sigma-Aldrich Israel, Ltd. (2)
3 Plaut St Park Rabin, Rehovot, 7670603, Israel
Tel.: (972) 89484222
Organic Chemical & Allied Product Whslr
N.A.I.C.S.: 424690

Sigma-Aldrich Japan G.K. (2)

INTERNATIONAL PUBLIC

Arko Tower 5F 1-8-1 Shimomeguro, Meguro-ku, Tokyo, 153-8927, Japan
Tel.: (81) 367568275
Web Site: https://www.sigma-aldrich.com
Emp.: 230
Industrial Organic Chemicals Mfr
N.A.I.C.S.: 325180

Subsidiary (Domestic):

Sigma-Aldrich Manufacturing LLC (2)
3300 S 2nd St, Saint Louis, MO 63118-3306
Tel.: (314) 286-6600
Web Site: https://www.sigmaaldrich.com
Organic Chemical & Allied Product Whslr
N.A.I.C.S.: 424690

Subsidiary (Non-US):

Sigma-Aldrich Oceania Pty. Limited (2)
PO Box 970, Castle Hill, 1765, NSW, Australia
Tel.: (61) 298410555
Web Site: https://www.sigmaaldrich.com
Organic Chemical & Allied Product Whslr
N.A.I.C.S.: 424690

Subsidiary (Domestic):

Sigma-Aldrich Pty. Limited (3)
PO Box 970, Castle Hill, 1765, NSW, Australia
Tel.: (61) 298410555
Web Site: https://www.sigmaaldrich.com
Organic Chemical & Allied Product Whslr
N.A.I.C.S.: 424690

Subsidiary (Non-US):

Sigma-Aldrich Production GmbH (2)
Industriestrasse 25, CH-9471, Buchs, Switzerland
Tel.: (41) 817552511
Organic Chemical & Allied Product Whslr
N.A.I.C.S.: 424690

Sigma-Aldrich Pte. Ltd. (2)
2 Science Park Drive #05-01/12 Ascent Building, Singapore, 118222, Singapore
Tel.: (65) 67791200
Organic Chemical & Allied Product Whslr
N.A.I.C.S.: 424690

Subsidiary (Non-US):

Sigma-Aldrich (M) Sdn. Bhd. (3)
Level 3 Menara Sunway Annexe Jalan Lagoon Timur, Bandar Sunway, 46150, Petaling Jaya, Selangor, Malaysia
Tel.: (60) 356353321
Organic Chemical & Allied Product Whslr
N.A.I.C.S.: 424690

Sigma-Aldrich Chemicals Private Ltd. (3)
Plot 12 Bommasandra-Jigani Link Road, Bengaluru, 560 100, India
Tel.: (91) 8066219400
Organic Chemical & Allied Product Whslr
N.A.I.C.S.: 325199

Subsidiary (Domestic):

Sigma-Aldrich RTC, Inc. (2)
2931 Soldier Springs Rd, Laramie, WY 82070
Tel.: (307) 742-5452
Web Site: https://www.sigmaaldrich.com
Pharmaceutical Products Mfr & Distr
N.A.I.C.S.: 325412

Supelco, Inc. (2)
595 N Harrison Rd, Bellefonte, PA 16823-6217
Tel.: (814) 359-3441
Organic Chemical & Allied Product Whslr
N.A.I.C.S.: 424690

Versum Materials, Inc. (1)
8555 S River Pkwy, Tempe, AZ 85284
Tel.: (602) 282-1000
Web Site: http://www.versummaterials.com
Rev: $1,372,300,000
Assets: $1,505,300,000
Liabilities: $1,292,900,000
Net Worth: $212,400,000
Earnings: $197,500,000
Emp.: 2,300

AND PRIVATE COMPANIES

Fiscal Year-end: 09/30/2018
Semiconductor Material Mfr
N.A.I.C.S.: 334413
Jeff White (Sr VP-Delivery Sys & Svcs)

Subsidiary (Non-US):

Versum Materials HYT Inc. (2)
283 Haebong-ro, Danwon-gu, Ansan, 15420, Gyeonggi-do, Korea (South)
Tel.: (82) 315008200
Semiconductor Material Mfr
N.A.I.C.S.: 334413

Versum Materials Korea Inc. (2)
5F Pangyo Silicon Park B, 35 Pango-ro 255beon-gil Bundang-gu, Seongnam, 13486, Korea (South)
Tel.: (82) 316964940
Semiconductor Material Mfr
N.A.I.C.S.: 334413

Versum Materials Netherlands B.V. (2)
Leidseveer 2-10, 3511 SB, Utrecht, Netherlands
Tel.: (31) 303072920
Semiconductor Material Mfr
N.A.I.C.S.: 334413

Versum Materials Singapore Pte. Ltd. (2)
2 Science Park Drive Ascent Building 05-01/12, Singapore, 118222, Singapore
Tel.: (65) 69091694
Semiconductor Material Mfr
N.A.I.C.S.: 334413

Versum Materials Taiwan Co. Ltd. (2)
15F No 223 Songjiang Rd, Zhongshan, Taipei, 10483, Taiwan
Tel.: (886) 221825800
Semiconductor Material Mfr
N.A.I.C.S.: 334413

eyrise B.V. (1)
De Run 5432, 5504 DE, Veldhoven, Netherlands
Tel.: (31) 402580503
Medical Equipment Mfr
N.A.I.C.S.: 339112

MERCK TBK
Jl TB Simatupang No 8 Pasar Rebo, Jakarta, 13760, Indonesia
Tel.: (62) 2128565600
Web Site: https://www.merckgroup.com
MERK—(INDO)
Rev.: $62,435,522
Assets: $62,200,448
Liabilities: $10,516,079
Net Worth: $51,684,369
Earnings: $11,574,906
Emp.: 372
Fiscal Year-end: 12/31/23
Health Care Srvices
N.A.I.C.S.: 621999

MERCOM CAPITAL PLC
190 High Street, Tonbridge, TN9 1BE, Kent, United Kingdom
Tel.: (44) 1732 366561   UK
Web Site: http://www.mercomoil.com
Year Founded: 2012
Emp.: 3
Investment Management Service
N.A.I.C.S.: 523940

MERCON HOLDING B.V.
Krinkelwinkel 6 8, 4202 LN, Gorinchem, Netherlands
Tel.: (31) 183668822
Web Site: http://www.mercon.com
Sales Range: $50-74.9 Million
Emp.: 115
Holding Company
N.A.I.C.S.: 551112
G. Willem Greffeoen (CEO & Mng Dir)

Subsidiaries:

Mercon Steel Structures B.V. (1)
Krinkelwinkel 6-8, 4202 LN, Gorinchem, Netherlands
Tel.: (31) 183634800
Web Site: http://www.mercon.nl
Offshore Drilling Rigs, Oil Tanks, Chemicals & Spheres, Desulphurization Plants, Power Stations, Heavy Steel Structures, Bridges, Lock Gates, Anti-Environmental Pollution Equipment
N.A.I.C.S.: 423830

MERCOR S.A.
Grzegorza z Sanoka 2, 80-408, Gdansk, Poland
Tel.: (48) 583414245
Web Site: https://www.mercor.com.pl
Year Founded: 1988
MCR—(WAR)
Rev.: $159,643,800
Assets: $113,734,248
Liabilities: $56,367,378
Net Worth: $57,366,870
Earnings: $11,996,443
Emp.: 910
Fiscal Year-end: 12/31/23
Fire Protection System Mfr
N.A.I.C.S.: 332323
Lucjan Myrda (Chm-Supervisory Bd)

Subsidiaries:

DFM Doors Sp. z o.o. (1)
Ul Antoniego Abrahama 1A, 80307, Gdansk, Poland
Tel.: (48) 58 380 3374
Web Site: https://www.dfm-europe.eu
Steel Fire Resistant Door Mfr & Distr
N.A.I.C.S.: 332321

Mercor Fire Protection Systems S.C. S.R.L. (1)
Drum Centura Chitila Mogosoaia No 3 Floor 4, Ilfov, Chitila, 077045, Romania
Tel.: (40) 37 132 4182
Web Site: https://mercor.ro
Smoke Evacuation System Distr
N.A.I.C.S.: 423620

Mercor Fire Protection Systems s.r.l. (1)
Drum Centura Chitila - Mogosoaia no 3 floor 4, Oras Chitila Ilfov, 077045, Bucharest, Romania
Tel.: (40) 371 324 182
Web Site: http://mercor.ro
Fire Prevention Equipment Sales
N.A.I.C.S.: 423850

Mercor Ukraina Sp. z o.o. (1)
Scheptyckich 26, 79-016, Lviv, Ukraine
Tel.: (380) 322403447
Web Site: http://www.mercor.com.ua
Fire Prevention, Security & Safety Equipment Distr
N.A.I.C.S.: 423990

Mercor-Proof LLC (1)
st Krasin 2 building 1 entrance number 3 floor 2, 123056, Moscow, Russia
Tel.: (7) 4951523232
Web Site: http://mercorproof.ru
Fire Prevention, Security & Safety Equipment Distr
N.A.I.C.S.: 423990

Tecresa Proteccion Pasiva, S.L. (1)
Margarita Salas n 26 PT Legatec, 28919, Leganes, Madrid, Spain
Tel.: (34) 914282260
Web Site: http://mercortecresa.com
Emp.: 40
Passive Fire Protection Products, Smoke Removal Products & Resistant Materials Mfr & Distr
N.A.I.C.S.: 332321

MERCUR SA
Tel.: (40) 345419919
Web Site: https://www.mercurcraiova.ro
MRDO—(BUC)
Rev.: $2,315,176
Assets: $20,615,369
Liabilities: $769,246
Net Worth: $19,846,123
Earnings: $461,999

Emp.: 32
Fiscal Year-end: 12/31/23
Shopping Center Operator
N.A.I.C.S.: 445110

MERCURIA ENERGY GROUP HOLDING SA
50 Rue du Rhone 6th Floor, 1204, Geneva, Switzerland
Tel.: (41) 225947000   CH
Web Site: http://www.mercuria.com
Year Founded: 2004
Emp.: 1,000
Holding Company; Oil & Energy Pricing, Logistics & Risk Management Trading Solutions
N.A.I.C.S.: 551112
Marco Dunard (CEO)

Subsidiaries:

Mercuria Energy Trading S.A. (1)
50 Rue du Rhone, 1204, Geneva, Switzerland
Tel.: (41) 22 594 70 00
Web Site: http://www.mercuria.com
Oil & Energy Pricing, Logistics & Risk Management Trading Solutions
N.A.I.C.S.: 425120
Marco Dunard (Pres & CEO)

Joint Venture (Non-US):

Henry Bath & Son Limited (2)
12 Princes Parade, Liverpool, L3 1BG, United Kingdom (49%)
Tel.: (44) 1512241800
Web Site: http://www.henrybath.com
Metal Wholesale Trade Broker
N.A.I.C.S.: 425120
Paul Wynne (CFO)

Subsidiary (Non-US):

Henry Bath B.V. (3)
Waalhaven Zuidzijde 21 Port Havens 2235, 3089 JH, Rotterdam, Netherlands
Tel.: (31) 102831000
Web Site: http://www.henrybath.com
Metal Wholesale Trade Broker
N.A.I.C.S.: 425120

Subsidiary (US):

Henry Bath LLC (3)
2400 Broening Hwy Ste 200, Baltimore, MD 21224
Tel.: (410) 633-7055
Web Site: http://www.henrybath.com
Metal Wholesale Trade Broker
N.A.I.C.S.: 425120

Subsidiary (Non-US):

Henry Bath Singapore Pte. Ltd. (3)
Warehouse SB8 Sembawang Wharves, 21 Deptford Road, Singapore, 759660, Singapore
Tel.: (65) 62662055
Web Site: http://www.henrybath.com
Sales Range: $25-49.9 Million
Emp.: 13
Metal Wholesale Trade Broker
N.A.I.C.S.: 425120
Sean Ginnane (CEO)

Subsidiary (US):

Mercuria Energy America, Inc. (2)
5 Greenway Plz, Houston, TX 77046
Tel.: (832) 209-2400
Energy & Petroleum Products Trading Solutions
N.A.I.C.S.: 425120

Subsidiary (Domestic):

Mercuria Energy Trading, Inc (3)
33 Benedict Pl 1st Fl, Greenwich, CT 06830
Tel.: (203) 413-3355
Oil & Energy Pricing, Logistics & Risk Management Trading Solutions
N.A.I.C.S.: 425120

MERCURIA HOLDINGS CO., LTD.
Uchisaiwaicho 1-3-3, Chiyoda-ku, Tokyo, 100-8560, Japan
Web Site: https://www.mercuria.jp
Year Founded: 2021
7347—(TKS)
Rev.: $41,419,780
Assets: $139,353,950
Liabilities: $10,025,260
Net Worth: $129,328,690
Earnings: $7,479,950
Emp.: 115
Fiscal Year-end: 12/31/23
Holding Company
N.A.I.C.S.: 551112
Toshihiro Toyoshima (CEO)

MERCURIA INVESTMENT CO., LTD.
Uchisaiwaicho 1-3-3 Chiyoda-ku, Tokyo, Japan
Tel.: (81) 33 500 9870
Web Site: http://www.mercuria.jp
Year Founded: 2005
Rev.: $43,264,060
Assets: $142,171,680
Liabilities: $25,318,370
Net Worth: $116,853,310
Earnings: $11,416,650
Emp.: 41
Fiscal Year-end: 12/31/19
Investment Management Service
N.A.I.C.S.: 523940
Toshihiro Toyoshima (CEO)

Subsidiaries:

Spring Asset Management Ltd. (1)
(80.4%)
Tel.: (852) 31000300
Emp.: 6
Asset Management Services
N.A.I.C.S.: 523940
Kevin Kwok Hoe Leung (Mng Dir)

MERCURIES & ASSOCIATES, HOLDING LTD.
3F No 236 Section 4 Xinyi Road, Taipei, Taiwan
Tel.: (886) 77198899
Web Site: https://www.mercuries.com.tw
2905—(TAI)
Rev.: $5,199,660,820
Assets: $48,542,011,475
Liabilities: $47,031,475,534
Net Worth: $1,510,535,941
Earnings: ($266,303,380)
Fiscal Year-end: 12/31/23
Holding Company
N.A.I.C.S.: 551112
Shiang Li Chen (Chm & Gen Mgr)

MERCURIES DATA SYSTEMS LTD.
3 F No 2 Lane 150 Sec 5 Xinyi Road, Xinyi District, Taipei, 110, Taiwan
Tel.: (886) 227225333
Web Site: https://www.mds.com.tw
2427—(TAI)
Rev.: $129,862,875
Assets: $219,356,380
Liabilities: $119,344,022
Net Worth: $100,012,358
Earnings: $8,234,344
Emp.: 872
Fiscal Year-end: 12/31/23
Banking Services
N.A.I.C.S.: 238290

MERCURIES LIFE INSURANCE CO., LTD.
Ste 58 Shitan Rd, Taipei, Taiwan
Tel.: (886) 80022258
Web Site: https://www.mli.com.tw
Year Founded: 1993
2867—(TAI)
Rev.: $2,538,805,392
Assets: $49,766,304,310

MERCURIES LIFE INSURANCE CO., LTD.

Mercuries Life Insurance Co., Ltd.—(Continued)
Liabilities: $48,460,147,618
Net Worth: $1,306,156,692
Earnings: ($311,193,585)
Emp.: 10,504
Fiscal Year-end: 12/31/23
Life Insurance
N.A.I.C.S.: 524113
Shiang-Jeh Chen *(Chm)*

MERCURITY FINTECH HOLDING INC.
Room 1112-2 Floor 11 No 15 Xinxi Road, Haidian District, Beijing, 100086, China
Tel.: (86) 2160151166   Ky
Web Site:
  https://mercurityfintech.com
Year Founded: 2011
MFH—(NASDAQ)
Rev.: $863,438
Assets: $18,893,082
Liabilities: $2,064,218
Net Worth: $16,828,864
Earnings: ($5,634,971)
Emp.: 9
Fiscal Year-end: 12/31/22
Third-Party E-Commerce Platforms
N.A.I.C.S.: 551112
Hua Zhou *(Chm & Co-CEO)*

MERCURIUS HEALTH SA
Taguspark Nucleo Central Expansao sala 290, 2740-122, Porto Salvo, Portugal
Tel.: (351) 217957641
Web Site:
  https://mercuriushealth.com
Year Founded: 1998
Medical & Health Care Services
N.A.I.C.S.: 622110
John Allen *(CEO)*
Subsidiaries:

Dr. Hoefer-Janker GmbH & Co. Klinik KG
Villenstrasse 8, 53129, Bonn, Nordrhein-Westfalen, Germany
Tel.: (49) 22853060
Web Site: http://www.robert-janker-klinik.com
Hospital Operations
N.A.I.C.S.: 622110
Frank Abele *(Mng Dir)*

MERCURY CAPITAL INVESTMENTS PTY LIMITED
Lawson Place Suite 303 Level 3 167 Phillip Street, Sydney, NSW, Australia
Tel.: (61) 282476700
Web Site:
  http://www.mercurycapital.com.au
Privater Equity Firm
N.A.I.C.S.: 523940
Ben Hawter *(Partner)*

MERCURY CAPITAL TRUST LTD
17 Barklaya Ul, Moscow, 121309, Russia
Tel.: (7) 4952237022
Web Site: http://www.mctrust.ru
Emp.: 100
Investment Management Service
N.A.I.C.S.: 525910
Maria Shvedova *(VP)*

MERCURY ENGINEERING LTD.
Mercury House Ravens Rock Road, Sandyford Industrial Estate, Dublin, D18 XH79, Ireland
Tel.: (353) 12163000
Web Site:
  http://www.mercuryeng.com
Year Founded: 1972
Sales Range: $700-749.9 Million

Emp.: 2,000
Engineeering Services
N.A.I.C.S.: 541330
Eoin Vaughan *(CEO)*
Subsidiaries:

MERCURY ENGINEERING SERVICES LLC   (1)
Offices No 1 & 2 Building No 1611 Street No 17 South Mawaleh, PO Box 189, Ruwi, Muscat, 112, Oman
Tel.: (968) 245 22323
Construction Engineering Services
N.A.I.C.S.: 541330

MERCURY INTERNATIONAL ELECTRO-MECHANICAL CONTRACTING LLC   (1)
Office 1204 Emirates National Investment Building Dalma Street, PO Box 114409, Al Nahyan Camp, Abu Dhabi, United Arab Emirates
Tel.: (971) 2 4438300
Sales Range: $75-99.9 Million
Emp.: 385
Construction Engineering Services
N.A.I.C.S.: 541330

MERCURY QATAR   (1)
Basement 1 Office No 3 Building No 346 C-Ring Road Street No 24, PO Box 37023, Al Muntazah, Doha, Qatar
Tel.: (974) 4455 0811
Construction Engineering Services
N.A.I.C.S.: 541330

Mercury Engineering Moscow   (1)
Krasnaya Presnya Bldg 24, Moscow, 123022, Russia
Tel.: (7) 495 739 4742
Sales Range: $25-49.9 Million
Emp.: 150
Construction Engineering Services
N.A.I.C.S.: 541330

Mercury Engineering Polska Sp. z o.o.   (1)
Ul Rzymowskiego 53, 02-697, Warsaw, Poland
Tel.: (48) 22 2122300
Web Site: http://www.mercurypol.pl
Sales Range: $25-49.9 Million
Emp.: 150
Construction Engineering Services
N.A.I.C.S.: 541330
Grzegorz Rychlik *(Gen Mgr)*

Mercury Engineering UK   (1)
Second Floor South High Holborn House 52-54 High Holborn, London, WC1V 6RL, United Kingdom
Tel.: (44) 207 8415260
Sales Range: $25-49.9 Million
Emp.: 15
Construction Engineering Services
N.A.I.C.S.: 541330

Mercury Middle East W.L.L   (1)
Unisono Tower 2nd Floor Building 614 Sanabis 410 Road 1011, PO Box 10739, Manama, Bahrain
Tel.: (973) 177 41404
Construction Engineering Services
N.A.I.C.S.: 541330
Sanjeev Kumar *(Mgr-HR)*

MERCURY INDUSTRIES BERHAD
Suite 11-1A Level 11 Menara Weld 76 Jalan Raja Chulan, 50200, Kuala Lumpur, Malaysia
Tel.: (60) 88401111
Web Site:
  https://www.mercury.com.my
MERCURY—(KLS)
Rev.: $1,380,462
Assets: $15,386,582
Liabilities: $4,239,222
Net Worth: $11,147,360
Earnings: ($1,512,656)
Fiscal Year-end: 12/31/22
Paints Mfr
N.A.I.C.S.: 325510
Chong Keat Yeoh *(Co-Sec)*

Subsidiaries:

Heap Seng Heng (M) Sdn. Bhd.   (1)
22 Jalan Chow Kit, 50350, Kuala Lumpur, Wilayah Persekutuan, Malaysia
Tel.: (60) 340414336
Paint Distr
N.A.I.C.S.: 424950
H. K. Lieu *(Mgr)*

Mercury Paints Factory Sdn. Bhd.   (1)
10 Jalan Perusahaan 4, Kawasan Industri Batu Caves, 68100, Batu Caves, Selangor, Malaysia
Tel.: (60) 36 188 7042
Web Site: https://www.mercurypaints.com
Sales Range: $50-74.9 Million
Emp.: 100
Paints Mfr & Distr
N.A.I.C.S.: 325510

MERCURY LABORATORIES LIMITED
2/13 & 2/14 P B NO 3001, BIDC Gorwa Estate Gorwa, Vadodara, 390 016, India
Tel.: (91) 2652477900
Web Site:
  https://www.mercurylabs.com
Year Founded: 1962
538964—(BOM)
Rev.: $9,484,257
Assets: $8,923,116
Liabilities: $3,887,010
Net Worth: $5,036,106
Earnings: $728,568
Emp.: 660
Fiscal Year-end: 03/31/21
Pharmaceuticals Product Mfr
N.A.I.C.S.: 325412
Rajendra R. Shah *(Chm & Mng Dir)*

MERCURY NZ LIMITED
33 Broadway Newmarket, PO Box 90399, Auckland, 1142, New Zealand
Tel.: (64) 80010180
Web Site:
  https://www.mightyriver.co.nz
MCY—(ASX)
Rev.: $1,339,900,000
Assets: $4,343,955,800
Liabilities: $1,974,342,650
Net Worth: $2,369,613,150
Earnings: $239,172,150
Emp.: 775
Fiscal Year-end: 06/30/19
Hydro Electric Services
N.A.I.C.S.: 221122
William Meek *(CFO)*
Subsidiaries:

Mercury Energy Limited   (1)
602 Great S Rd, Greenlane, Auckland, New Zealand   (100%)
Tel.: (64) 95803595
Web Site: http://www.mercury.co.nz
Sales Range: $250-299.9 Million
Emp.: 350
Electric Power Generation
N.A.I.C.S.: 221118
James Munro *(Gen Mgr)*

Rotokawa Geothermal Limited   (1)
Rapids Rd, Rotorua, New Zealand   (100%)
Tel.: (64) 93088200
Web Site: http://www.mightyriverpower.co.nz
Sales Range: $25-49.9 Million
Emp.: 35
Holding Company
N.A.I.C.S.: 551112
Fraser Whinnrey *(CEO)*

Tilt Renewables Limited   (1)
L23 535 Bourke Street, Melbourne, VIC, Australia
Tel.: (61) 1300660 623
Web Site: http://www.tiltrenewables.com
Rev.: $135,913,439
Assets: $1,077,877,332
Liabilities: $616,581,890
Net Worth: $461,295,443
Earnings: $8,564,516

INTERNATIONAL PUBLIC

Emp.: 200
Fiscal Year-end: 03/31/2019
Wind Electric Power Generation Services
N.A.I.C.S.: 221115
Steve Symons *(CFO & Sec)*

MERCY HEALTH SUPPORT SERVICES
Level 2, 12 Shelley Street, Richmond, VIC, Australia
Tel.: (61) 3 8416 7777
Web Site: http://www.mercy.com.au
Health Services
N.A.I.C.S.: 923130

MEREO BIOPHARMA GROUP PLC
4th Floor 1 Cavendish Place, London, W1G 0QF, United Kingdom
Tel.: (44) 3330237300   UK
Web Site:
  https://www.mereobiopharma.com
Year Founded: 2015
MREO—(NASDAQ)
Rev.: $944,973
Assets: $119,585,262
Liabilities: $35,585,841
Net Worth: $83,999,421
Earnings: ($46,428,593)
Emp.: 36
Fiscal Year-end: 12/31/22
Pharmaceutical Product Mfr & Distr
N.A.I.C.S.: 325412
Denise Scots-Knight *(CEO)*
Subsidiaries:

OncoMed Pharmaceuticals, Inc.   (1)
800 Chesapeake Dr, Redwood City, CA 94063
Tel.: (650) 995-8200
Web Site: http://www.oncomed.com
Rev.: $44,421,000
Assets: $65,078,000
Liabilities: $16,847,000
Net Worth: $48,231,000
Earnings: ($8,101,000)
Emp.: 22
Fiscal Year-end: 12/31/2018
Biopharmaceutical Mfr
N.A.I.C.S.: 325412
Yvonne Li *(CFO & Chief Acctg Officer)*

MERFORD HOLDING B.V.
Franklinweg 8, 4207 HZ, Gorinchem, Netherlands
Tel.: (31) 183643895
Web Site: https://www.merford.com
Year Founded: 1956
Industrial Machinery Mfr
N.A.I.C.S.: 333248
Subsidiaries:

Merford Acoustic Materials B.V.   (1)
Franklinweg 8, 4207 HZ, Gorinchem, Netherlands
Tel.: (31) 183643890
Noise Control Products Mfr
N.A.I.C.S.: 333248

Subsidiary (Domestic):

Akoestikon Geluidsisolatie B.V.   (2)
Schuilheuvelstraat 1, 4116 GA, Buren, Netherlands
Tel.: (31) 344579780
Construction Materials Whslr
N.A.I.C.S.: 423890

MERGE HOUSING BHD
No 2 Jalan Apollo CH U5/CH Seksyen U5, 40150, Shah Alam, Selangor Darul Ehsan, Malaysia
Tel.: (60) 378468068
Sales Range: $25-49.9 Million
Property Development Services
N.A.I.C.S.: 531312
Subsidiaries:

Selegie Tower Sdn. Bhd.   (1)
2 Jalan Apollo Ch U5/ch Section U5, Shah

Alam, 40150, Selangor, Malaysia
Tel.: (60) 378468068
Sales Range: $50-74.9 Million
Emp.: 100
Property Development & Investment Management Services
N.A.I.C.S.: 531390
Mei Lin Ng (Sec)

MERIAN GLOBAL INVESTORS
Millennium Bridge House 2 Lambeth Hill, London, EC4P 4WR, United Kingdom
Tel.: (44) 2073327500
Web Site: http://www.merian.com
Year Founded: 2018
Investment Management Service
N.A.I.C.S.: 523999
Warren Tonkinson (Mng Dir-Distri)

MERICSSON ACQUISITION CORPORATION
RM 1302 13/F Cheong K Building 84-86 Des Voeux Road, Central, China (Hong Kong)
Tel.: (852) 30622687   Ky
Year Founded: 2021
MLXAU—(NASDAQ)
Investment Services
N.A.I.C.S.: 523999
Andy Kwok (Chm & CEO)

MERIDA INDUSTRY CO., LTD.
Tel.: (886) 48526171
Web Site: https://www.merida-bikes.com
Year Founded: 1972
9914—(TAI)
Rev.: $891,497,955
Assets: $1,247,823,590
Liabilities: $542,426,579
Net Worth: $705,397,011
Earnings: $58,823,439
Emp.: 907
Fiscal Year-end: 12/31/23
Bicycle Mfr & Distr
N.A.I.C.S.: 336991
Wolfgang Renner (Co-CEO)

Subsidiaries:

Merida & Centurion Germany GmbH   (1)
Blumenstrasse 49-51, 71106, Magstadt, Germany
Tel.: (49) 71599459600
Web Site: https://www.mcg-parts.de
Bicycles Distr
N.A.I.C.S.: 423910

Merida Benelux B.V.   (1)
Laan van Westenenk 102, 7336 AZ, Apeldoorn, Netherlands
Tel.: (31) 555062200
Web Site: https://www.merida.nl
Bicycles Distr
N.A.I.C.S.: 423910

Merida Polska Sp. z o.o   (1)
Ul Marii Sklodowskiej-Curie 35, 41-800, Zabrze, Poland
Tel.: (48) 32 273 3232
Web Site: https://www.merida-bikes.com
Motor Cycle Parts Mfr & Distr
N.A.I.C.S.: 336390

Merida Sverige AB   (1)
Ovre Husargatan 32, 413 14, Gothenburg, Sweden
Tel.: (46) 31 742 8560
Web Site: https://www.merida.se
Motor Cycle Parts Mfr & Distr
N.A.I.C.S.: 336390

Miyata Cycle Co., Ltd.   (1)
2746-5 B1F Inokuchi Nakai-cho, Ashigarakami-gun, Tokyo, 259-0151, Kanagawa Prefecture, Japan   (70%)
Tel.: (81) 465800661
Web Site: https://www.miyatabike.com
Sales Range: $25-49.9 Million
Emp.: 60
Bicycles Mfr & Sales
N.A.I.C.S.: 336991

MERIDIA CO., LTD.
2-1-11 Nishiogikita, Suginami-ku, Tokyo, 167-0042, Japan
Tel.: (81) 359097211
Web Site: https://www.san-a.com
Year Founded: 1993
3228—(TKS)
Rev.: $1,297,468,480
Assets: $1,372,536,880
Liabilities: $856,408,960
Net Worth: $516,127,920
Earnings: $73,296,960
Emp.: 1,028
Fiscal Year-end: 08/31/21
Real Estate Services
N.A.I.C.S.: 531390
Kenta Kikuchi (Pres & CEO)

MERIDIAM INFRASTRUCTURE PARTNERS SAS
4, place de l'Opera, 75002, Paris, France
Tel.: (33) 1 53 34 96 96
Web Site: http://www.meridiam.com
Year Founded: 2005
Emp.: 300
Investment Management Service
N.A.I.C.S.: 523999
Thierry Deau (Founder & CEO)

Subsidiaries:

Allego N.V.   (1)
Westervoortsedijk 73 KB, 6827 AV, Arnhem, Netherlands   (89.4%)
Tel.: (31) 880333033
Web Site: https://www.allego.eu
Rev.: $156,974,962
Assets: $520,524,498
Liabilities: $606,129,937
Net Worth: ($85,605,439)
Earnings: ($119,017,915)
Fiscal Year-end: 12/31/2023
Holding Company; Electric Vehicle Charging Stations Operator
N.A.I.C.S.: 551112

Subsidiary (Domestic):

Allego B.V.   (2)
Industriepark Kleefse Waard, 6827 AV, Arnhem, Netherlands
Tel.: (31) 887500300
Web Site: http://www.allego.eu
Motor Vehicle Battery Charging Services
N.A.I.C.S.: 488490
Anja Van Niersen (Founder & Chm)

Autopista del Sol, Concesionaria Espanola, S.A.   (1)
Area de Peaje de San Pedro Pantano Roto s/n, 29670, Malaga, Spain   (85%)
Tel.: (34) 952799371
Web Site: http://www.autopistadelsol.com
Toll Motorway Construction & Management Services
N.A.I.C.S.: 237310

MERIDIAN A.D.
Branka Perduva bb, 78000, Banja Luka, Bosnia & Herzegovina
Tel.: (387) 51212184
Web Site:
    https://www.meridianbl.com
Year Founded: 1948
MRDN—(BANJ)
Sales Range: $1-9.9 Million
Emp.: 141
International Freight Transportation Services
N.A.I.C.S.: 488510
Andjelko Sobot (Chm-Mgmt Bd)

Subsidiaries:

Meridian BL d.o.o.   (1)
Letaliska cesta 33 M, 1000, Ljubljana, Slovenia
Tel.: (386) 59077110
Web Site:
    http://www.ljubljana.meridianbl.com
Cargo Transportation Services
N.A.I.C.S.: 488510

Meridian BL d.o.o.   (1)
Marsala Tita 206, Dobanovci Surcin, 11272, Belgrade, Serbia
Tel.: (381) 117848092
Web Site:
    http://www.beograd.meridianbl.com
Cargo Transportation Services
N.A.I.C.S.: 488510

MERIDIAN AUDIO LTD
Latham Road, Huntingdon, PE29 6YE, Cambridgeshire, United Kingdom
Tel.: (44) 1480445678
Web Site: http://www.meridian-audio.com
Year Founded: 1977
Rev.: $23,844,117
Emp.: 100
Audio & Video Home Entertainment Systems Mfr
N.A.I.C.S.: 334310
Bob Stuart (Co-Founder)

Subsidiaries:

Meridian America Inc.   (1)
110 Greene St Ste 407, New York, NY 10012
Tel.: (646) 666-0140
Audio & Video Equipment Distr
N.A.I.C.S.: 423990
Ken Forsythe (VP)

MERIDIAN BUSINESS SUPPORT LTD.
Trident 3 Trident Business Park Styal Road, Manchester, M22 5XB, United Kingdom
Tel.: (44) 1619293849
Web Site:
    http://www.meridianbs.co.uk
Year Founded: 1989
Sales Range: $150-199.9 Million
Emp.: 230
Employee Recruiting & Placement Services
N.A.I.C.S.: 561311
Derek Skelton (CEO)

MERIDIAN CAPITAL
Sadovaya Chernogryazskaya Ulitsa 13/3 Suite 8, Moscow, 105064, Russia
Tel.: (7) 4959375933
Web Site:
    http://www.meridiancapital.ru
Investment Consulting
N.A.I.C.S.: 541611
Yulia Leonova (Mng Partner)

MERIDIAN CO., LTD.
4F 196-35 Anyang-dong, Manan-gu, Anyang, 430-857, Gyeonngi-do, Korea (South)
Tel.: (82) 314637700   KR
Web Site: http://www.meridian.co.kr
MRBK—(NASDAQ)
Sales Range: $1-9.9 Million
Emp.: 15
Medical Device Mfr & Supplier
N.A.I.C.S.: 339112
In Beom Park (Pres & CEO)

MERIDIAN ENERGY LIMITED
Tel.: (64) 43811200
Web Site:
    http://www.meridianenergy.co.nz
MEZ—(ASX)
Rev.: $1,927,033,493
Assets: $5,994,019,139
Liabilities: $2,413,277,512
Net Worth: $3,580,741,627
Earnings: $56,818,182
Emp.: 878
Fiscal Year-end: 06/30/23
Holding Company; Renewable Resource Electric Power Generation & Distribution Services

N.A.I.C.S.: 551112
Peter Wilson (Deputy Chm)

Subsidiaries:

Dam Safety Intelligence Limited   (1)
Level 2 55 Lady Elizabeth Lane, Wellington, 6011, New Zealand
Tel.: (64) 43827590
Web Site: https://www.damsafety.co.nz
Dam Safety Management Services
N.A.I.C.S.: 237990
Dan Forster (Principal, Gen Mgr & Engr-Dam Safety)

DamWatch Services Ltd.   (1)
Level 3 88 The Terrace, Wellington, 6140, New Zealand   (100%)
Tel.: (64) 43811300
Web Site: https://www.damwatch.co.nz
Sales Range: $25-49.9 Million
Emp.: 30
Professional Scientific & Technical Services
N.A.I.C.S.: 541990
Patar Amos (Mng Dir)

Whisper Tech Limited   (1)
10 Magdala Place Middleton, Christchurch, 8024, New Zealand   (93.23%)
Tel.: (64) 33639293
Web Site: http://www.whispergen.co.nz
Sales Range: $25-49.9 Million
Emp.: 12
Heating & Energy Systems
N.A.I.C.S.: 333414

MERIDIAN MINING SE
c/o 1305-1090 West Georgia St, Vancouver, V6E 3V7, BC, Canada
Tel.: (778) 715-6410
Web Site:
    https://www.meridianmining.co
N2E—(DEU)
Rev.: $194,817
Assets: $17,451,208
Liabilities: $2,432,207
Net Worth: $15,019,001
Earnings: ($11,985,858)
Emp.: 69
Fiscal Year-end: 12/31/23
Mineral Exploration Services
N.A.I.C.S.: 213115
Adrian McArthur (Pres & CEO)

MERIDIAN PJSC
3rd Paveletsky proezd bldg 4, Moscow, 115114, Russia
Tel.: (7) 4957979653
Web Site: https://www.if-meridian.ru
MERF—(MOEX)
Sales Range: Less than $1 Million
Investment Management Service
N.A.I.C.S.: 525910
Vitaly Balanovich (Gen Dir)

MERIDIANA S.P.A.
Centro Direzionale Aeroporto Costa Smeralda Zona Industriale A, 07026, Olbia, Italy
Tel.: (39) 078952600   IT
Web Site: http://www.meridiana.it
Holding Company
N.A.I.C.S.: 551112
Franco Trivi (Chm)

Subsidiaries:

Eccelsa Aviation S.r.l.   (1)
Olbia Costa Smeralda Airport General Aviation Terminal, Via Dei Ricercatori 13/15, 07026, Olbia, Sardegna, Italy
Tel.: (39) 0789 563 480
Web Site: http://www.eccelsa.com
Airport Management Services
N.A.I.C.S.: 488119
Francesco Cossu (Gen Mgr)

Meridiana fly S.p.A.   (1)
Centro Direzionale Aeroporto Costa Smeralda, 07026, Olbia, Italy
Tel.: (39) 078952682
Web Site: http://www.meridiana.it

MERIDIANA S.P.A.

Meridiana S.p.A.—(Continued)
Sales Range: $400-449.9 Million
Airline Operator
N.A.I.C.S.: 481111
Franco Trivi (Vice Chm)

MERIDIE S.P.A.
Via Francesco Crispi 31, IT-80121, Naples, Italy
Tel.: (39) 081 684 9611
Web Site:
http://www.meridieinvestimenti.com
Year Founded: 2007
Sales Range: $1-9.9 Million
Emp.: 10
Corporate Management & Consulting Services
N.A.I.C.S.: 541611
Giovanni Lettieri (Pres)

Subsidiaries:

Atitech S.p.A. (1)
Aeroporto di Capodichino, 80144, Naples, Italy (75%)
Tel.: (39) 0813694006
Web Site: http://www.atitech.it
Commercial Aircraft Maintenance & Repair Services
N.A.I.C.S.: 488190

Equity Sud Advisor S.r.l. (1)
Via Francesco Crispi 31, 80121, Naples, Italy (100%)
Tel.: (39) 0816849611
Web Site: http://www.equitysudadvisor.com
Investment Advisory Services
N.A.I.C.S.: 523940

MedSolar S.p.A. (1)
Via GG Belli 39, IT-00139, Rome, Italy (99.4%)
Tel.: (39) 0632652745
Web Site: http://www.medsolar.eu
Photovoltaic Technologies Developer
N.A.I.C.S.: 334413

MERIEUX EQUITY PARTNERS
3 Rue Marcel Gabriel Riviere, 69002, Lyon, France
Tel.: (33) 478873700
Web Site: http://www.merieux-partners.com
Year Founded: 2018
Privater Equity Firm
N.A.I.C.S.: 523999
Jean-Francois Billet (Sr Partner)

MERIT CONTRACTORS NIAGARA
235 Martindale Road Suite 3, Saint Catharines, L2W 1A5, ON, Canada
Tel.: (905) 641-2374
Web Site:
http://www.meritcontractors.com
Rev.: $29,120,762
Emp.: 38
Industrial Building Construction
N.A.I.C.S.: 236210
Dennis Kowalchuk (CFO)

MERIT GROUP PLC
9th Floor The Shard 32 London Bridge Street, London, SE1 9SG, United Kingdom
Tel.: (44) 2075935500
Web Site:
https://www.meritgroupplc.com
Year Founded: 2001
MRIT—(AIM)
Rev.: $23,078,853
Assets: $56,280,860
Liabilities: $16,848,742
Net Worth: $39,432,117
Earnings: ($3,334,233)
Emp.: 977
Fiscal Year-end: 03/31/23
Global Political Information, Publishing, Training, Events & Communications Services

N.A.I.C.S.: 513120
Philip Machray (CEO & CFO)

Subsidiaries:

Fenman Limited (1)
Unit 2 e-space North, 181 Wisbech Road, Littleport, CB6 1RA, Cambridgeshire, United Kingdom
Tel.: (44) 1353865350
Web Site: http://www.fenman.co.uk
Sales Range: $25-49.9 Million
Emp.: 3
Materials & Information for Employee Training & Related Personnel Matters
N.A.I.C.S.: 513199

MERIT INTERACTIVE CO., LTD.
Daily Golden Plaza No 100 Jingda Road, Xihu District, Hangzhou, 310012, China
Tel.: (86) 57181061638
Web Site: https://ge.cn
Year Founded: 2010
300766—(CHIN)
Rev.: $60,553,302
Assets: $287,238,828
Liabilities: $51,842,505
Net Worth: $235,396,323
Earnings: ($7,032,838)
Fiscal Year-end: 12/31/23
Software Development Services
N.A.I.C.S.: 541511

MERIT PACKAGING LIMITED
Lakson Square Building No 2 Sarwar Shaheed Road, Karachi, 74200, Pakistan
Tel.: (92) 2135698000
Web Site: https://meritpack.com
Year Founded: 1982
MERIT—(KAR)
Rev.: $20,533,637
Assets: $33,194,568
Liabilities: $25,883,848
Net Worth: $7,310,720
Earnings: ($2,229,648)
Emp.: 257
Fiscal Year-end: 06/30/19
Printing & Packaging Materials Mfr
N.A.I.C.S.: 322220
Shahid Ahmed Khan (CEO)

MERIT TURIZM YATIRIM VE ISLETMELERI A.S.
Etiler Mahallesi 9 Bade Str Etiler, Besiktas, Istanbul, 34337, Marmara, Turkiye
Tel.: (90) 2123580444
Web Site:
https://www.meritturizm.com
Year Founded: 1988
MERIT—(IST)
Rev.: $3,504,515
Assets: $148,108,767
Liabilities: $7,825,297
Net Worth: $140,283,470
Earnings: $2,853,611
Fiscal Year-end: 12/31/23
Home Management Services
N.A.I.C.S.: 721110
Hande Tibuk (Chm)

MERITZ FINANCIAL GROUP INC.
28th floor Meritz Tower 382 Gangnam-daero, Gangnam-gu, Seoul, Korea (South)
Tel.: (82) 220186868
Web Site:
https://www.meritzgroup.com
138040—(KRS)
Sales Range: $15-24.9 Billion
Financial Investment Services
N.A.I.C.S.: 523999
Yong Bum Kim (CEO & CEO)

Subsidiaries:

Meritz Alternative Investment Management Co., Ltd. (1)
17 F Three IFC 10 Gukjegeumyung-ro, Yeoungdeungpo-gu, Seoul, 07326, Korea (South)
Tel.: (82) 263362900
Web Site: http://www.meritzaim.co.kr
Real Estate Investment Services
N.A.I.C.S.: 531390
Jun Hyun Shin (CEO)

Meritz Asset Management Co. Ltd. (1)
Gye-dong Building 104 Bukchon-ro, Jongno-gu, Seoul, 110-800, Korea (South)
Tel.: (82) 263203000
Web Site: http://www.meritzam.com
Investment Advice Services
N.A.I.C.S.: 523940
John Lee (CEO)

Meritz Fire & Marine Insurance Co., Ltd. (1)
382 Gangnam-daero, Gangnam-gu, Seoul, Korea (South) (100%)
Tel.: (82) 237862114
Web Site: http://www.meritzfire.com
Rev.: $6,454,549,709
Assets: $25,586,476,657
Liabilities: $22,689,974,373
Net Worth: $2,896,502,284
Earnings: $993,206,449
Fiscal Year-end: 12/31/2022
Non Life Insurance Agency Services
N.A.I.C.S.: 524210

PT.Meritz Korindo Insurance (1)
Wisma Korindo 1st Floor Jl M T Haryono Kav 62, Jakarta, 12780, Indonesia
Tel.: (62) 217975959
Web Site: http://www.meritzkorindo.co.id
General Insurance Services
N.A.I.C.S.: 524210
Park In Chul (Pres & Commissioner)

MERITZ SECURITIES CO., LTD.
Three IFC 10 Gukjegeumyung-ro, Yeongdeungpo-gu, Seoul, Korea (South)
Tel.: (82) 27856611
Web Site: https://home.imeritz.com
Year Founded: 1973
008560—(KRS)
Rev.: $35,218,365,825
Assets: $47,228,514,046
Liabilities: $42,701,998,892
Net Worth: $4,526,515,154
Earnings: $433,447,337
Emp.: 1,596
Fiscal Year-end: 12/31/23
Investment Management Service
N.A.I.C.S.: 523999
Hui-mun Choi (Exec Dir)

MERIVAARA OY
Puustellintie 2, 15150, Lahti, Finland
Tel.: (358) 33394611
Web Site: http://www.merivaara.com
Year Founded: 1901
Sales Range: $25-49.9 Million
Emp.: 140
Medical Equipment & Supplies
N.A.I.C.S.: 423450

Subsidiaries:

MERIVAARA AB (1)
Karlsbodavagen 41, PO Box 20126, 161 02, Bromma, Sweden
Tel.: (46) 8 6272950
Web Site: http://www.merivaara.se
Medical Device Mfr
N.A.I.C.S.: 334510

MERIVAARA AS (1)
Karoline Kristiansens Vej 6, Oslo, 0661, Norway
Tel.: (47) 22 88 04 60
Web Site: http://www.merivaara.no
Emp.: 120
Medical Device Mfr
N.A.I.C.S.: 334510

INTERNATIONAL PUBLIC

MERKANTI HOLDING PLC
Aragon House Business Centre Dragonara Road, Saint Julian's, STJ 3140, Malta
Tel.: (356) 23286000
Web Site:
http://www.merkantiholding.com
MR26A—(MAL)
Rev.: $4,729,000
Assets: $121,030,580
Liabilities: $58,377,510
Net Worth: $62,653,070
Earnings: $2,075,253
Emp.: 20
Fiscal Year-end: 12/31/23
Property Management Services
N.A.I.C.S.: 531311
Christopher Frendo (Exec Dir)

Subsidiaries:

Merkanti Bank Limited (1)
Aragon House Business Centre Dragonara Road, Saint Julian's, STJ 3140, Malta
Tel.: (356) 23286000
Web Site: http://www.merkantibank.com
Banking Services
N.A.I.C.S.: 522210
Samuel Morrow (CEO)

MERKBURN HOLDINGS LIMITED
302 1827 Woodward Drive, Ottawa, K2C 0P9, ON, Canada
Tel.: (613) 224-5464
Web Site: http://www.merkburn.com
Year Founded: 1969
Sales Range: $1-9.9 Million
Emp.: 120
Commercial Real Estate & Property Management Services
N.A.I.C.S.: 531312
Peter Dooher (Mng Partner)

MERKO GIDA SANAYI VE TICARET A.S.
Levent Mah Comert Sk Yapi Kredi Plaza Site B Block, No 1B Inner Door No 23 Besiktas, 34330, Istanbul, Turkiye
Tel.: (90) 8505600101
Web Site: https://www.merko.tr
Year Founded: 1982
MERKO—(IST)
Rev.: $45,122,520
Assets: $56,392,167
Liabilities: $27,795,664
Net Worth: $28,596,503
Earnings: $2,471,849
Fiscal Year-end: 12/31/22
Frozen Fruit & Vegetable Mfr
N.A.I.C.S.: 311411
Alistair Baran Blake (Chm)

MERKUR A.D.
Svetog Save 88, 74270, Teslic, Bosnia & Herzegovina
Tel.: (387) 53433596
Year Founded: 1983
MRKR-R-A—(BANJ)
Sales Range: Less than $1 Million
Bakery Products Mfr
N.A.I.C.S.: 311811

MERKUR BANK KGAA
Bayerstrasse 33, 80335, Munich, Germany
Tel.: (49) 89599980
Web Site: https://www.merkur-privatbank.de
Year Founded: 1959
MBK—(DEU)
Commercial Banking Services
N.A.I.C.S.: 522110
Marcus Lingel (Chm & CEO)

MERKUR D.D.

AND PRIVATE COMPANIES

Semizovac b b, 71 321, Semizovac, Bosnia & Herzegovina
Tel.: (387) 63692000
MRKSR—(SARE)
Rev.: $191,418
Assets: $9,828,553
Liabilities: $9,698,544
Net Worth: $130,010
Earnings: $347,491
Emp.: 1
Fiscal Year-end: 12/31/21
Real Estate Manangement Services
N.A.I.C.S.: 531210
Marko Kozelj *(Pres & Member-Mgmt Bd)*

MERKUR, D.D.
Cesta Na Okroglo 7, 4202, Naklo, Slovenia
Tel.: (386) 42588000 SI
Web Site: http://www.merkur.eu
Sales Range: $1-4.9 Billion
Emp.: 4,075
Home Improvement & Garden Products
N.A.I.C.S.: 444180
Jure Pisek *(Exec Dir-Pur)*

Subsidiaries:

Big Bang, d.o.o. (1)
Bulevar Mihajla Pupina 4, 11070, Belgrade, Novi Beograd, Serbia
Tel.: (381) 11 260 13 10
Web Site: http://www.bigbang.rs
Household Product Distr
N.A.I.C.S.: 449210

Bofex Beograd, d.o.o. (1)
Bulevar Mihajla Pupina 4, 11070, Belgrade, Serbia (100%)
Tel.: (381) 11 260 13 10
Power Equipment Stores
N.A.I.C.S.: 444230

Bofex, d.o.o. (1)
Smartinska cesta 152, 1000, Ljubljana, Slovenia (100%)
Tel.: (386) 13093700
Web Site: http://www.bigbang.si
Sales Range: $200-249.9 Million
Emp.: 520
Household Appliance Stores
N.A.I.C.S.: 443141

Intermerkur , d.o.o. (1)
Ul Safeta Zajke br 267 - Rajlovac, 71000, Sarajevo, Bosnia & Herzegovina (100%)
Tel.: (387) 33772800
Web Site: http://www.merkur.eu
Construction Materials Whslr
N.A.I.C.S.: 423390

Merkur Hrvatska, d. o. o. (1)
Ivana Keleka 18 A, 10 360, Zagreb, Croatia
Tel.: (385) 1 2009 333
Web Site: http://www.merkur.eu
Household Products Mfr
N.A.I.C.S.: 327110
Sasa Kirin *(Head-Product Grp)*

Merkur International Praha, Spol. S.r.o.
Slepa II 1007-15, 14200, Prague, Czech Republic (100%)
Tel.: (420) 261711405
Web Site: http://www.merkur.eu
Power Equipment Stores
N.A.I.C.S.: 444230

Merkur International, d.o.o. (1)
Partizanske Avijacije no 4, Novi Beograd, 11070, Novi Sad, Serbia (100%)
Tel.: (381) 113118965
Durable Goods Whslr
N.A.I.C.S.: 423990

Merkur MI Handels, GmbH (1)
Munchner Str 13, 85540, Haar, Germany (100%)
Tel.: (49) 89 99 02 260
Web Site: http://www.merkur.eu
Sales Range: $25-49.9 Million
Emp.: 60
Power Equipment Stores
N.A.I.C.S.: 444230

Merkur Nekretnine Zagreb, d.o.o. (1)
Kelekova 18a, 10360, Zagreb, Croatia (100%)
Tel.: (385) 12009333
Sales Range: $100-124.9 Million
Emp.: 300
Power Equipment Stores
N.A.I.C.S.: 444230

Merkur Osiguranje d.d. (1)
Ulica kneza Ljudevita Posavskog 31, 10300, Zagreb, Croatia (100%)
Tel.: (385) 16308333
Web Site: http://www.merkur.hr
Sales Range: $150-199.9 Million
Emp.: 500
Durable Goods Whslr
N.A.I.C.S.: 423990

Mersteel, d. o. o. (1)
Osijek Vukovarska 41 31 207 Tenja-Klisa, Osijek, Croatia
Tel.: (385) 31 515 900
Household Product Distr
N.A.I.C.S.: 449210
Kruno Skrapec *(Mgr-Comml)*

Subsidiary (Non-US):

Merkur Makedonija, d. o. o. (2)
Bulevar Edvard Kardelj br 12, 1000, Skopje, North Macedonia
Tel.: (389) 23 219 701
Household Product Distr
N.A.I.C.S.: 449210
Natasa Taseska *(Head-Acctg & Fin)*

Mersteel, d. o. o. (2)
Partizanske avijacije br 4, 11000, Belgrade, Novi Beograd, Serbia
Tel.: (381) 11 222 89 00
Household Product Distr
N.A.I.C.S.: 449210

Perles Merkur Italia, S.r.l. (1)
Via Aquileia 15-A, Villesse, 34070, Gorizia, Italy (100%)
Tel.: (39) 0481964611
Sales Range: $25-49.9 Million
Emp.: 10
Power Equipment Stores
N.A.I.C.S.: 444230
Davorin Adrer *(Mng Dir)*

Zelezokrivnica SCT - Merkur, d.o.o. (1)
Cesta na Okroglo 7, 4202, Naklo, Slovenia (45%)
Tel.: (386) 42588000
Sales Range: $25-49.9 Million
Emp.: 25
Power Equipment Stores
N.A.I.C.S.: 444230

MERLIN ENTERTAINMENTS PLC
Link House 25 West Street, Poole, BH15 1LD, Dorset, United Kingdom
Tel.: (44) 1202 666 900 UK
Web Site: http://www.merlinentertainments.biz
Rev.: $2,142,105,760
Assets: $4,780,398,340
Liabilities: $2,567,227,460
Net Worth: $2,213,170,880
Earnings: $291,874,600
Emp.: 21,123
Fiscal Year-end: 12/31/18
Holding Company; Amusement & Theme Park Owner & Operator
N.A.I.C.S.: 551112
Nick Varney *(CEO)*

Subsidiaries:

Amsterdam Dungeon B.V. (1)
Rokin 78, 1012 KW, Amsterdam, Netherlands
Tel.: (31) 205308500
Web Site: http://www.thedungeons.com
Amusement Park Services
N.A.I.C.S.: 713110

Gardaland S.r.l. (1)
Via Derna 4, Castelnuovo, 37014, Verona, Italy
Tel.: (39) 0456449777

Web Site: http://www.gardaland.it
Amusement Park Services
N.A.I.C.S.: 713110

Heide Park Soltau GmbH (1)
Heide Park 1, 29614, Soltau, Germany
Tel.: (49) 1806919101
Web Site: http://www.heide-park.de
Amusement Park Services
N.A.I.C.S.: 713110
Marcel Kafke *(Mgr-IT)*

LEGOLAND Deutschland Freizeitpark GmbH (1)
Legoland Allee 1, 89312, Gunzberg, Germany
Tel.: (49) 180670075701
Web Site: http://www.legoland.de
Amusement Park Services
N.A.I.C.S.: 713110
Frank Kilian *(Mgr-IT)*

LEGOLAND Discovery Center Arizona LLC (1)
5000 S Arizona Mills Cir Ste 135, Tempe, AZ 85282
Web Site: http://www.arizona.legolandcenter.com
Amusement Park Services
N.A.I.C.S.: 713110

LEGOLAND Discovery Center Columbus LLC (1)
157 Easton Town Ctr, Columbus, OH 43219
Tel.: (614) 407-7721
Web Site: http://www.columbus.legolandcenter.com
Amusement Park Services
N.A.I.C.S.: 713110
Jenna Maffei *(Mgr-Mktg)*

LEGOLAND Discovery Center Michigan LLC (1)
4240 Baldwin Rd, Auburn Hills, MI 48326
Tel.: (248) 409-6009
Web Site: http://www.michigan.legolandcenter.com
Amusement Park Services
N.A.I.C.S.: 713110
Joel Tellez *(Mgr-Retail)*

LEGOLAND Discovery Center Philadelphia LLC (1)
Plymouth Meeting Mall Unit 1055 500 W Germantown Pike, Plymouth Meeting, PA 19462
Tel.: (267) 245-9696
Web Site: http://www.philadelphia.legoland.com
Amusement Park Services
N.A.I.C.S.: 713110

LEGOLAND Discovery Center San Antonio LLC (1)
849 E Commerce St Ste 910, San Antonio, TX 78205
Tel.: (210) 610-1150
Web Site: http://www.sanantonio.legolandcenter.com
Amusement Park Services
N.A.I.C.S.: 713110
Jeremy Aguillen *(Gen Mgr)*

LEGOLAND Discovery Centre Deutschland GmbH (1)
Kehrwieder 5, 20457, Hamburg, Germany
Tel.: (49) 80666690110
Web Site: http://www.legolanddiscoverycentre.de
Amusement Park Services
N.A.I.C.S.: 713110

LEGOLAND Holidays Deutschland GmbH (1)
Legoland Allee 1, 89312, Gunzberg, Germany
Tel.: (49) 1806225789
Web Site: http://www.legolandholidays.de
Amusement Park Services
N.A.I.C.S.: 713110
Timothy De Young *(Mng Dir)*

Legoland ApS (1)
Nordmarksvej, 7190, Billund, Denmark
Tel.: (45) 75331333
Web Site: http://www.legoland.dk
Hotel Services
N.A.I.C.S.: 721110

Madame Tussaud Las Vegas LLC (1)

MERLIN ENTERTAINMENTS PLC

3377 S Las Vegas Blvd Ste 2001, Las Vegas, NV 89109
Tel.: (702) 862-7800
Amusement Park Services
N.A.I.C.S.: 713110
Gabriel Hewitt *(Gen Mgr)*

Madame Tussauds Amsterdam B.V. (1)
Dam 20, 1012 NP, Amsterdam, Netherlands
Tel.: (31) 205221010
Amusement Park Services
N.A.I.C.S.: 713110

Madame Tussauds Austria GmbH (1)
Riesenradplatz, 1020, Vienna, Austria
Tel.: (43) 18903366
Wedding Planning Services
N.A.I.C.S.: 812990

Madame Tussauds Deutschland GmbH (1)
Unter den Linden 74, 10117, Berlin, Germany
Tel.: (49) 1806545800
Amusement Park Services
N.A.I.C.S.: 713110

Madame Tussauds Orlando LLC (1)
8387 International Dr, Orlando, FL 32819
Tel.: (321) 209-9651
Amusement Park Services
N.A.I.C.S.: 713110
Jade Sparks *(Sr Mgr-Mktg)*

Madame Tussauds Washington LLC (1)
1001 F St, Washington, DC 20004
Tel.: (202) 942-7300
Amusement Park Services
N.A.I.C.S.: 713110
Taylor Spoelstra *(Mgr-Sls Trade)*

Merlin Entertainments Group Ltd. (1)
3 Market Close, Poole, BH15 1NQ, Dorset, United Kingdom
Tel.: (44) 1202666900
Web Site: http://www.merlinentertainments.biz
Sales Range: $1-4.9 Billion
Emp.: 13,000
Theme Park Operator
N.A.I.C.S.: 713110

Subsidiary (US):

LEGOLAND California LLC (2)
1 Legoland Dr, Carlsbad, CA 92008
Tel.: (760) 918-5346
Web Site: http://www.legoland.com
Sales Range: $50-74.9 Million
Theme Park Operator
N.A.I.C.S.: 713110
Rex Jackson *(Gen Mgr-LEGOLAND® Florida Resort)*

Subsidiary (Non-US):

Living and Leisure Australia Group (2)
Level 3 Northbank Place, 525 Flinders Street, Melbourne, 3000, VIC, Australia
Tel.: (61) 3 9415 4000
Sales Range: $125-149.9 Million
Owns & Operates Leisure Businesses & Assets
N.A.I.C.S.: 713990

Subsidiary (Domestic):

Oceanis Holdings Ltd. (3)
Cnr King & Flinders Streets, Melbourne, 3000, VIC, Australia
Tel.: (61) 3 9923 5900
Holding Company
N.A.I.C.S.: 551112

Subsidiary (Domestic):

Melbourne Underwater World Pty Ltd (4)
Melbourne Aquarium, Cnr King & Flinders Streets, Melbourne, 3000, VIC, Australia
Tel.: (61) 396200999
Web Site: http://www.melbourneaquarium.com.au
Sales Range: $75-99.9 Million
Emp.: 150
Aquarium Management Services

MERLIN ENTERTAINMENTS PLC

Merlin Entertainments plc—(Continued)
N.A.I.C.S.: 531312

Oceanis Australia Pty Ltd (4)
Cnr King & Flinders Streets, Melbourne, 3000, VIC, Australia
Tel.: (61) 3 9923 5900
Aquarium Construction & Management Services
N.A.I.C.S.: 236220

UnderWater World Sunshine Coast Pty Ltd. (4)
Parkyn Parade, Mooloolaba, 4557, QLD, Australia
Tel.: (61) 754586280
Web Site:
  http://www.underwaterworld.com.au
Sales Range: $50-74.9 Million
Emp.: 80
Aquarium Management Services
N.A.I.C.S.: 531312

Subsidiary (Domestic):

The Otway Fly Pty. Ltd. (3)
360 Phillips Track, Weeaproinah, 3237, VIC, Australia
Tel.: (61) 352359200
Web Site: http://www.otwayfly.com
Sales Range: $25-49.9 Million
Emp.: 30
Rainforest Adventure Activities
N.A.I.C.S.: 115310
Nathan Bridgeman (Gen Mgr)

Subsidiary (US):

Madame Tussauds Hollywood LLC (2)
6933 Hollywood Blvd Ste A, Los Angeles, CA 90028
Tel.: (323) 798-1670
Web Site: http://www.madametussauds.com
Beer, Wine & Liquor Stores
N.A.I.C.S.: 445320
Jenny Dempsey (Mgr-Events)

Unit (Domestic):

Thorpe Park (2)
Staines Road, Chertsey, KT16 8PN, Surrey, United Kingdom
Tel.: (44) 1932577123
Web Site: http://www.thorpepark.com
Sales Range: $25-49.9 Million
Amusement Park
N.A.I.C.S.: 713110

Pirate Adventure Golf Limited (1)
111A Old Dundonald Road, Dundonald, Belfast, BT1 1XT, United Kingdom
Tel.: (44) 2890480220
Web Site:
  http://www.piratesadventuregolf.com
Amusement Park Services
N.A.I.C.S.: 713110

SEA LIFE Deutschland GmbH (1)
Rheinallee 8, 53639, Konigswinter, Germany
Tel.: (49) 180666690101
Amusement Park Services
N.A.I.C.S.: 713110
Christine Leingang (Gen Mgr)

SEA LIFE Helsinki Oy (1)
Tivolitie 10, 00510, Helsinki, Finland
Tel.: (358) 95658200
Amusement Park Services
N.A.I.C.S.: 713110
Nora Sulander (Mgr-Mktg)

SEA LIFE Konstanz GmbH (1)
Hafenstrasse 9, 78462, Konstanz, Germany
Tel.: (49) 180666690101
Amusement Park Services
N.A.I.C.S.: 713110

MERLIN PROPERTIES, SOCIMI, S.A.

Paseo de la Castellana 257, 28046, Madrid, Spain
Tel.: (34) 917691900 ES
Web Site:
  https://www.merlinproperties.com
MRL—(BIL)
Rev.: $513,057,733
Assets: $13,318,700,741
Liabilities: $6,100,422,785
Net Worth: $7,218,277,957
Earnings: ($92,170,217)
Emp.: 256
Fiscal Year-end: 12/31/23
Real Estate Investment Trust
N.A.I.C.S.: 525990
Miguel Ollero (Mng Dir & COO)

Subsidiaries:

PK Hoteles, S.L. (1)
Paseo de la Castellana No 83-85, 28046, Madrid, Spain
Tel.: (34) 915767327
Home Management Services
N.A.I.C.S.: 721110

MERLION SP. Z O.O.

Ul Rozana 3, 75-212, Koszalin, Poland
Tel.: (48) 501329393 PL
Web Site: http://www.merlion.pl
Telecommunication Servicesb
N.A.I.C.S.: 517810

MERMER A.D.

Ivana Kosancica bb, Zagubica, Serbia
Tel.: (381) 62 1015193
Year Founded: 1974
MRMR—(BEL)
Sales Range: Less than $1 Million
Construction Stone Exploration Services
N.A.I.C.S.: 327991
Blagoje Antic (Exec Dir)

MERMEREN KOMBINAT AD

Lece Koteski No 60A, 7500, Prilep, North Macedonia
Tel.: (389) 48418940
Web Site:
  https://www.mermeren.com
Year Founded: 1946
MERM—(MAC)
Rev.: $40,476,447
Assets: $46,397,854
Liabilities: $3,301,613
Net Worth: $43,096,241
Earnings: $22,536,956
Emp.: 366
Fiscal Year-end: 12/31/19
White Marbles Mining Services
N.A.I.C.S.: 212319

MERO MICROFINANCE BITTIYA SANSTHA LTD.

Kupandol Jwagal, Post Box Number 220, Lalitpur, Patan, Nepal
Tel.: (977) 10561746
Web Site:
  https://www.meromicrofinance.com
MERO—(NEP)
Rev.: $16,968,118
Assets: $111,392,501
Liabilities: $96,973,181
Net Worth: $14,419,320
Earnings: $359,796
Fiscal Year-end: 07/16/23
Financial Consulting Services
N.A.I.C.S.: 541611
Ram Hari Dahal (CEO)

MERRION PHARMACEUTICALS PLC

3013 Lake Drive Citywest Business Campus, Dublin, 24, Ireland
Tel.: (353) 14693719 IE
Web Site:
  http://www.merrionpharma.com
Year Founded: 2004
3MP—(ISE)
Sales Range: Less than $1 Million
Emp.: 1
Oral Drug & Biotechnology Products Developer
N.A.I.C.S.: 325412
John S. Fox (CEO)

Subsidiaries:

Merrion Pharmaceuticals, LLC (1)
219 Racine Dr Ste D, Wilmington, NC 28403-8702
Tel.: (910) 799-1847
Web Site: http://www.merrionpharma.com
Sales Range: $50-74.9 Million
Oral Drug & Biotechnology Products Developer
N.A.I.C.S.: 325412

MERRITHEW CORPORATION

2200 Yonge Street Suite 500, Toronto, M4S 2C6, ON, Canada
Tel.: (416) 482-4050
Web Site: http://www.merrithew.com
Year Founded: 1988
Sales Range: $10-24.9 Million
Emp.: 60
Holding Company: Pilates Exercise Equipment, Training Videos, Yoga Products Mfr
N.A.I.C.S.: 551112
Tony Baylis (COO)

Subsidiaries:

Merrithew Health & Fitness Group (1)
500-2200 Yonge St, Toronto, M4S 2C6, ON, Canada (100%)
Tel.: (416) 482-4050
Web Site: http://www.merrithew.com
Health & Fitness Programs & Products
N.A.I.C.S.: 713940
Lindsay G. Merrithew (Pres & CEO)

MERRY ELECTRONICS CO., LTD.

No 22 23rd Road Taichung Industrial Park, Nantun Dist, Taichung, 408213, Taiwan
Tel.: (886) 423590811
Web Site: https://www.merry.com.tw
Year Founded: 1975
2439—(TAI)
Rev.: $1,199,855,509
Assets: $1,066,457,104
Liabilities: $625,555,750
Net Worth: $440,901,354
Earnings: $46,368,323
Emp.: 4,327
Fiscal Year-end: 12/31/23
Rechargeable Battery Mfr
N.A.I.C.S.: 335910
Chao-Te Chiang (VP-Bus Unit)

Subsidiaries:

Austar Hearing Science & Technology (Xiamen) Co., Ltd. (1)
Floor 3 Building B8 Biomedical Industrial Park, No 2064 Wengjiao West Road Haicang District, Xiamen, 361006, China
Tel.: (86) 592 590 0230
Web Site: https://www.austar-hearing.net
Hearing Aids Electronic Mfr & Distr
N.A.I.C.S.: 334510

Merry Electronics (HK) Co., Ltd. (1)
Room 10 2 F Block B Shatin Industrial Ctr 5-7 Yuen Shun Circuit, Sha Tin, New Territories, China (Hong Kong)
Tel.: (852) 26376877
Electric Equipment Mfr
N.A.I.C.S.: 334310

Merry Electronics (Shenzhen) Co., Ltd. (1)
48 MeiBao Rd, DaLang LongHua District, Shenzhen, 518109, Guangdong, China
Tel.: (86) 75528121888
Electro Acoustic Product Mfr
N.A.I.C.S.: 334510

Merry Electronics (Singapore) Pte, Ltd. (1)
21 Bukit Batok Crescent 21-79 WCEGA Tower, Singapore, 658065, Singapore
Tel.: (65) 6 659 9166
Electronic Components Mfr

INTERNATIONAL PUBLIC

N.A.I.C.S.: 334419

Merry Electronics North America Inc. (1)
174 West Besver Creek Rd 1st Floor, Richmond Hill, L4B 1B4, ON, Canada
Tel.: (905) 265-2060
Web Site: http://sonavox.ca
Consumer Electronics Mfr & Distr
N.A.I.C.S.: 334310

Merry Electronics USA (1)
15360 Valley Blvd, City of Industry, CA 91746
Tel.: (626) 333-8985
Web Site: http://www.merry.com.tw
Sales Range: $25-49.9 Million
Emp.: 5
Audio & Video Equipment Mfr
N.A.I.C.S.: 334310

Seas Fabrikker AS (1)
Ryggeveien 96, Moss, 1528, Norway
Tel.: (47) 9 400 2800
Web Site: https://seas.no
Speaker Mfr & Distr
N.A.I.C.S.: 334310

Sonavox Canada Inc. (1)
261 Milani Blvd Unit 100, Woodbridge, L4H 4E3, ON, Canada
Tel.: (905) 265-2060
Web Site: https://sonavox.com
Audio Product Mfr
N.A.I.C.S.: 334310

Xiamen Etimbre Hearing Technology Co. Ltd. (1)
1st Floor Building 9 No 71 Houxiang Road, Xiamen Biomedical Industry, Xiamen, China
Tel.: (86) 400 876 3558
Web Site: https://www.etimbre.cc
Hearing Aid Electronic Mfr & Distr
N.A.I.C.S.: 334510

MERSEN S.A.

Tour EQHO 2 avenue Gambetta, 92400, Courbevoie, France
Tel.: (33) 146915400 FR
Web Site: http://www.mersen.com
Year Founded: 1981
MRN—(EUR)
Sales Range: $1-4.9 Billion
Emp.: 6,917
Holding Company; Carbon & Graphite Products Mfr & Whslr
N.A.I.C.S.: 551112
Luc Themelin (CEO)

Subsidiaries:

AVO SA (1)
9 Rue des Imprimeurs, ZI de la Republique 1, 86000, Poitiers, France
Tel.: (33) 549622500
Sales Range: $75-99.9 Million
Emp.: 124
Electrical Appliance Television & Radio Set Whslr
N.A.I.C.S.: 423620

Mersen Benelux B.V. (1)
Mercuriusweg 4 - 6, 3113 AR, Schiedam, Netherlands (100%)
Tel.: (31) 102983030
Web Site: http://www.mersen.com
Sales Range: $25-49.9 Million
Emp.: 30
Carbon & Graphite Product Mfr
N.A.I.C.S.: 335991
Nico Vannuffelen (Mgr)

Mersen Canada Toronto Inc. (1)
6200 Kestrel Road, Mississauga, L5T 1Y9, ON, Canada (100%)
Tel.: (416) 252-9371
Web Site: http://www.mersen.com
Sales Range: $50-74.9 Million
Emp.: 105
Electrical Protection Solutions
N.A.I.C.S.: 335313
Bruce Brown (Sr VP & Gen Mgr)

Mersen Corporate Services SAS (1)
Immeuble Lafayette 2 Pl Des Vosges, 92051, Hauts-de-Seine, France
Tel.: (33) 146915400
Web Site: http://www.merson.com

Sales Range: $25-49.9 Million
Emp.: 14
Management Consulting Services
N.A.I.C.S.: 541618

Mersen France Amiens S.A.S. (1)
10 avenue Roger Dumoulin, 80084,
Amiens, France (100%)
Tel.: (33) 3 22 54 4500
Web Site: http://www.mersen.com
Sales Range: $150-199.9 Million
Emp.: 350
Electrical Specialties & Graphite Materials
N.A.I.C.S.: 335999

**Mersen France Gennevilliers
SAS** (1)
41 rue Jean Jaures, 92231, Gennevilliers,
France
Tel.: (33) 141854300
Web Site: http://www.mersen.com
Nonmetallic Mineral Product Mfr
N.A.I.C.S.: 327999

Mersen France Py SAS (1)
1 Rue Jules Ferry, 54530, Pagny-sur-
Moselle, France (100%)
Tel.: (33) 383816081
Web Site: http://www.mersen.com
Sales Range: $50-74.9 Million
Emp.: 250
Nonmetallic Mineral Product Mfr
N.A.I.C.S.: 327999

Mersen India Pvt. Ltd. (1)
98-5 Wheeler Rd Cooke Town, Bengaluru,
Karnataka, India
Tel.: (91) 8025471405
Web Site: http://www.mersen.co
Sales Range: $50-74.9 Million
Emp.: 150
Switchgear & Switchboard Apparatus Mfr
N.A.I.C.S.: 335313
V. I. Perumal *(Mng Dir)*

Mersen Italia S.p.A. (1)
Via Dei Missaglia 97 / B2, 20142, Milan,
Italy
Tel.: (39) 02 826 8131
Web Site: http://www.ilcarbonio.it
Carbon & Graphite Product Mfr
N.A.I.C.S.: 335991

Mersen Nordic AB (1)
Finlandsgatan 64, Kista, 164 74,
Sweden (100%)
Tel.: (46) 86296400
Web Site: http://www.mersen.com
Sales Range: $25-49.9 Million
Emp.: 20
Anticorrosion Materials
N.A.I.C.S.: 332117
Luc Themelin *(Mng Dir)*

Mersen Oceania Pty Ltd. (1)
75 Sparks Avenue, Fairfield, 3078, VIC,
Australia (100%)
Tel.: (61) 1300252007
Web Site: http://www.mersen.com
Sales Range: $25-49.9 Million
Emp.: 51
Carbon & Graphite Product Mfr
N.A.I.C.S.: 335991
Tom Petricca *(Mng Dir)*

Mersen South Africa Pty Ltd. (1)
Cnr Wright & Commando St, Johannesburg,
2093, South Africa (100%)
Tel.: (27) 114740000
Sales Range: $50-74.9 Million
Emp.: 150
Carbon & Graphite Product Mfr
N.A.I.C.S.: 335991
Eben Hattingh *(Gen Mgr)*

Mersen UK Holdings Ltd. (1)
South St, Portslade, Brighton, BN41 2LX,
East Sussex, United Kingdom
Tel.: (44) 1273415701
Web Site: http://www.mersen.co.uk
Sales Range: $50-74.9 Million
Emp.: 90
Holding Company
N.A.I.C.S.: 551112

Mersen USA Bn Corp. (1)
400 Myrtle Ave, Boonton, NJ
07005-1839 (100%)
Tel.: (973) 541-4720
Web Site: http://www.carbonebrush.com

Sales Range: $25-49.9 Million
Emp.: 100
Carbon & Graphite Product Mfr
N.A.I.C.S.: 335991

**Mersen USA Newburyport-MA
LLC** (1)
374 Merrimac St, Newburyport, MA
01950-1930 (100%)
Tel.: (978) 462-6662
Web Site: http://www.mersen.com
Sales Range: $75-99.9 Million
Emp.: 200
Mfr of Low & Medium Voltage Fuses, Fuse
Blocks, Power Distribution Blocks & Taylor
Wiring Duct for Commercial & Industrial
Applications
N.A.I.C.S.: 423610

Sofacel SA (1)
Ramon de Trincheria 39-41, Apartado N
1404, 08980, Barcelona, Spain
Tel.: (34) 936857800
Web Site: http://www.sofacel.es
Carbon & Graphite Product Mfr
N.A.I.C.S.: 335991

MERUS N.V.
Yalelaan 62, 3584 CM, Utrecht, Netherlands
Tel.: (31) 850162500
Web Site: https://www.merus.nl
Year Founded: 2003
MRUS—(NASDAQ)
Rev.: $41,586,000
Assets: $376,542,000
Liabilities: $129,487,000
Net Worth: $247,055,000
Earnings: ($131,194,000)
Emp.: 164
Fiscal Year-end: 12/31/22
Pharmaceuticals Product Mfr
N.A.I.C.S.: 325412
Anne van der Touw-Noordzij *(Sec)*

Subsidiaries:

Merus US, Inc. (1)
139 Main St, Cambridge, MA 02142
Tel.: (617) 401-4499
Clinical Services
N.A.I.C.S.: 621610

MERUS POWER OYJ
Pallotie 2, 33470, Ylojarvi, Finland
Tel.: (358) 207354320
Web Site:
https://www.meruspower.com
Year Founded: 2008
MERUS—(HEL)
Rev.: $32,046,584
Assets: $23,389,999
Liabilities: $10,041,947
Net Worth: $13,348,052
Earnings: ($880,892)
Emp.: 88
Fiscal Year-end: 12/31/23
Battery Mfr
N.A.I.C.S.: 335910
Kari Tuomala *(CEO)*

MERYLLION RESOURCES CORPORATION
217 Queen Street West Suite 310,
Toronto, M5V 0R2, ON, Canada
Tel.: (416) 842-9003 BC
Web Site: https://meryllionres.com
Year Founded: 2013
MYR—(CNSX)
Assets: $430,891
Liabilities: $60,903
Net Worth: $369,988
Earnings: ($289,276)
Fiscal Year-end: 09/30/22
Metal Mining
N.A.I.C.S.: 212290

MERZ PHARMA GMBH & CO. KGAA
Eckenheimer Landstrasse 100,
60318, Frankfurt am Main, Germany

Tel.: (49) 6915030
Web Site: http://www.merz.com
Sales Range: $750-799.9 Million
Emp.: 1,745
Pharmaceutical Research & Development Services
N.A.I.C.S.: 325412
Philip Burchard *(CEO)*

Subsidiaries:

Merz Aesthetics (1)
1875 S Grant St Ste 200, San Mateo, CA
94402
Tel.: (650) 286-4000
Web Site: http://www.merzaesthetics.com
Sales Range: $50-74.9 Million
Emp.: 310
Medical Aesthetics Products Mfr
N.A.I.C.S.: 325412
Gregory B. Bass *(VP-Managed Markets-North America)*

Merz Asia Pacific Pte. Ltd. (1)
21 Biopolis Road 06-03/04 North Tower
Nucleos, Singapore, 138567, Singapore
Tel.: (65) 6664 8633
Cosmetic Product Distr
N.A.I.C.S.: 424210

Merz Australia Pty Ltd (1)
Level 3 244 Coward St Mascot, Sydney,
2020, NSW, Australia
Tel.: (61) 2 80768120
Pharmaceutical Products Distr
N.A.I.C.S.: 424210

Merz North America (1)
4133 Courtney Rd Ste 10, Franksville, WI
53126
Tel.: (262) 835-3300
Web Site: http://www.merzusa.com
Sales Range: $25-49.9 Million
Emp.: 150
Medicinal Product Mfr
N.A.I.C.S.: 339112
Dean Erickson *(Gen Mgr-Ops)*

Merz Pharma (Schweiz) AG (1)
Hegenheimermattweg 57, 4123, Allschwil,
Switzerland
Tel.: (41) 61 486 3600
Web Site: http://www.merz.ch
Pharmaceutical Products Distr
N.A.I.C.S.: 424210

Merz Pharma Austria GmbH (1)
Guglgasse 17, 1110, Vienna, Austria
Tel.: (43) 1 869 16 04 0
Web Site: http://www.merz.co.at
Emp.: 30
Pharmaceutical Products Distr
N.A.I.C.S.: 424210
Karsten Schlemm *(CEO)*

Merz Pharma Benelux B.V. (1)
Hoevestein 36 D, 4903 SC, Oosterhout,
Netherlands
Tel.: (31) 162474800
Web Site: http://www.merzpharma.be
Sales Range: $25-49.9 Million
Emp.: 15
Medical Aesthetics Products Mfr
N.A.I.C.S.: 325412
Kristel Hectors *(Mng Dir)*

Merz Pharma Canada Ltd. (1)
5515 North Service Rd Suite 202, Burlington, L7L 6G4, ON, Canada
Tel.: (905) 315-1193
Web Site: http://www.merzcanada.com
Emp.: 40
Pharmaceutical Products Distr
N.A.I.C.S.: 424210
Bob Bennett *(Pres & Gen Mgr)*

Merz Pharma China Ltd. (1)
Suite 6083 6/F 21st Century Tower No.210
Century Avenue, Pudong New District,
Shanghai, China
Tel.: (86) 21 5172 0944
Pharmaceutical Products Distr
N.A.I.C.S.: 424210

Merz Pharma Espana S.L. (1)
Avenida de Bruselas 5 3a planta, 28108,
Madrid, Spain
Tel.: (34) 91 657 47 84
Web Site: http://www.merz.es
Pharmaceutical Products Distr

N.A.I.C.S.: 424210
Dusan Vaclav *(Mng Dir)*

Merz Pharma France S.A.S. (1)
Challenge 92 101 avenue Francois Arago,
92017, Nanterre, Cedex, France
Tel.: (33) 1 47 29 16 77
Pharmaceutical Products Distr
N.A.I.C.S.: 424210

Merz Pharma Italia S.r.l. (1)
Via Gustavo Fara 13, 20124, Milan, Italy
Tel.: (39) 02 66989111
Web Site: http://www.merz.it
Pharmaceuticals Product Mfr
N.A.I.C.S.: 325412

Merz Pharma UK Ltd. (1)
260 Centennial Park Elstree Hill South, Elstree, WD6 3SR, Hertfordshire, United
Kingdom
Tel.: (44) 208 236 0000
Web Site: http://www.merzpharma.co.uk
Pharmaceuticals Product Mfr
N.A.I.C.S.: 325412

Merz Pharma, S.A de C.V. (1)
Av Insurgentes Sur 1196 Piso 15 Torre de
los Parques Col Del Valle, 03200, Mexico,
Mexico
Tel.: (52) 55 9140 0650
Web Site: http://www.merz.com.mx
Pharmaceutical Products Distr
N.A.I.C.S.: 424210

Merz Pharmaceuticals LLC (1)
4215 Tudor Ln, Greensboro, NC 27410
Tel.: (336) 856-2003
Web Site: http://www.merzusa.com
Sales Range: $1-9.9 Million
Emp.: 10
Pharmaceutical Preparation Mfr
N.A.I.C.S.: 325412

Merz, Inc. (1)
6501 Six Forks Rd, Raleigh, NC 27615
Tel.: (919) 582-8000
Web Site: http://www.merzusa.com
Pharmaceuticals Product Mfr
N.A.I.C.S.: 325412
John Donofrio *(CFO & Head-Bus Dev)*

Ulthera, Inc. (1)
1840 S Stapley Dr Ste 200, Mesa, AZ
85204
Tel.: (480) 619-4069
Web Site: http://www.ulthera.com
Sales Range: $75-99.9 Million
Emp.: 175
Medical Device Mfr
N.A.I.C.S.: 339112
Robert F. Byrnes *(Chm)*

MESA PARTS GMBH
Im Gewerbegebiet 1, 79853, Lenzkirch, Germany
Tel.: (49) 76536830
Web Site: http://www.mesa-parts.com
Year Founded: 1896
Rev.: $37,789,002
Emp.: 500
Turned Parts Mfr
N.A.I.C.S.: 332721
Julian Meyer *(Mng Dir)*

MESB BERHAD
Lot 1903A 1st Floor Jalan Kpb 7 Kawasan Perindustrian Kg, Baru Balakong, 43300, Seri Kembangan, Selangor, Malaysia
Tel.: (60) 389618818 MY
Web Site: http://www.mesbbhd.com
Year Founded: 1995
MESB—(KLS)
Rev.: $49,128,255
Assets: $37,313,348
Liabilities: $14,959,148
Net Worth: $22,354,200
Earnings: $1,650,578
Emp.: 1,082
Fiscal Year-end: 06/30/22
Leatherware Product Whslr
N.A.I.C.S.: 316990
Saffie Bakar *(Chm)*

MESCO INC

MESB Berhad—(Continued)

MESCO INC
Arca East Bldg 3-2-1 Kinshi, Sumida-ku, Tokyo, 130-8531, Japan
Tel.: (81) 356107832
Web Site: http://www.mesco.co.jp
1737—(TKS)
Rev.: $238,215,120
Assets: $183,397,280
Liabilities: $47,857,920
Net Worth: $135,539,360
Earnings: $7,066,400
Emp.: 374
Fiscal Year-end: 03/31/21
Engineering & Piping Business Services
N.A.I.C.S.: 541330
Yoshihiko Koura *(Mng Dir & Mng Exec Officer)*

Subsidiaries:

MESCO (USA) INC. (1)
1237 S Shamrock Ave, Monrovia, CA 91016
Tel.: (626) 303-5680
Web Site: http://www.mescousa.com
Engineeering Services
N.A.I.C.S.: 541330
Linda Green *(Pres)*

MESCO Inc - Oita Pipe Plant (1)
843-18 Kasugaura Seike, Oita, 870-0011, Japan
Tel.: (81) 975382100
Web Site: http://www.mesco.co.jp
Sales Range: $25-49.9 Million
Emp.: 45
Construction Engineering Services
N.A.I.C.S.: 541330
Shoji Kawano *(Gen Mgr-Pipe & Materials Bus Unit)*

Mescoeng (M) Sdn. Bhd. (1)
Suite E406 4th Floor East Tower Wisma Consplant 1 No 2 Jalan SS 16/4, 47500, Petaling Jaya, Selangor, Malaysia
Tel.: (60) 358808880
Web Site: http://www.mesco.co.jp
Sales Range: $25-49.9 Million
Emp.: 6
Construction Engineering Services
N.A.I.C.S.: 541330

Siam Mesco Co., Ltd. (1)
622 Emporium Tower FL14th/5 Sukhumvit Road, Klongton Sub-district Klongtoey District, Bangkok, 10110, Thailand
Tel.: (66) 2 260 8441
Pipe Material Mfr & Distr
N.A.I.C.S.: 326122

Taiwan Mesco Co., Ltd. (1)
No 150 Cheng-Kung 3 Road, Nantou, Taiwan
Tel.: (886) 49 225 7701
Pipe Material Mfr & Distr
N.A.I.C.S.: 326122

MESCO PHARMACEUTICALS LIMITED
Upper Kesalton, Tallital, Nainital, 263 001, Uttarakhand, India
Tel.: (91) 9871862796
Web Site: http://www.mescopharma.com
Year Founded: 1986
500274—(BOM)
Assets: $24,959
Liabilities: $1,528,812
Net Worth: ($1,503,853)
Earnings: ($546)
Emp.: 3
Fiscal Year-end: 03/31/21
Pharmaceuticals Product Mfr
N.A.I.C.S.: 325412
Sameer Singh *(Mng Dir)*

MESHEK ENERGY-RENEWABLE ENERGIES LTD.
Geash Trading Zone, PO Box 322, Kibbutz Geash, Tel Aviv, 6095000, Israel
Tel.: (972) 97701555
Web Site: https://www.mske.co.il
Year Founded: 2016
MSKE—(TAE)
Rev.: $21,447,590
Assets: $899,501,654
Liabilities: $256,743,940
Net Worth: $642,757,714
Earnings: $268,966
Fiscal Year-end: 09/30/23
Energy Renewable Services
N.A.I.C.S.: 221114
Jon Cohen *(Chm)*

MESHULAM LEVINSTEIN CONSTRUCTING & ENGINEERING LTD.
Derech Menachem Begin 23Derech PetahTikva, Tel Aviv, Israel
Tel.: (972) 37100200
Web Site: https://www.levinstein.co.il
Year Founded: 1945
LEVI—(TAE)
Rev.: $170,008,010
Assets: $1,024,877,177
Liabilities: $566,167,970
Net Worth: $458,709,207
Earnings: $26,965,050
Fiscal Year-end: 12/31/23
New Multifamily Housing Construction (except For-Sale Builders)
N.A.I.C.S.: 236116

MESINIAGA BERHAD
1A Jalan SS16/1, 47500, Subang Jaya, Selangor Darul Ehsan, Malaysia
Tel.: (60) 356358828
Web Site: https://www.mesiniaga.com.my
MSNIAGA—(KLS)
Rev.: $61,993,439
Assets: $49,853,545
Liabilities: $24,860,741
Net Worth: $24,992,804
Earnings: $1,416,296
Emp.: 1,100
Fiscal Year-end: 12/31/22
Information Technology Services
N.A.I.C.S.: 541512
Keng Hoe Wong *(Dir-Sls)*

Subsidiaries:

Mesiniaga MSC Sdn. Bhd. (1)
5th Fl Menara Mesiniaga 1A Jalan SS16/1, 47500, Subang Jaya, Selangor Darul Ehsan, Malaysia
Tel.: (60) 356358828
Emp.: 100
Information & Communication Technology Services
N.A.I.C.S.: 541990
Fathil Sulaiman *(Dir)*

Mesiniaga Services Sdn. Bhd. (1)
2nd Floor Menara Mesiniaga 1A Jalan SS16/1, 47500, Subang Jaya, Selangor, Malaysia
Tel.: (60) 356358828
Sales Range: $75-99.9 Million
Emp.: 500
Information Technology Services
N.A.I.C.S.: 541519
Fathil Sulaiman *(Dir)*

Mesiniaga Techniques Sdn. Bhd. (1)
Menara Mesiniaga 1A Jalan SS 16/1, 47500, Subang Jaya, Selangor, Malaysia
Tel.: (60) 356358828
Web Site: http://www.mesiniaga.com.my
Sales Range: $200-249.9 Million
Emp.: 600
Computer Software Publisher
N.A.I.C.S.: 513210
Fitri Abdullah *(Gen Mgr)*

VA Dynamics Sdn. Bhd. (1)
11-2 2nd Floor Highway Centre Jalan 51/205, 46050, Petaling Jaya, Selangor Darul Ehsan, Malaysia
Tel.: (60) 377851152
Web Site: http://www.vadynamics.com.my
Sales Range: $50-74.9 Million
Emp.: 10
Communication System Distr
N.A.I.C.S.: 423690
Dan Pang *(Acct Mgr)*

MESNA INDUSTRIJA BRACA PIVAC D.O.O.
Tezacka 13, 21276, Dalmatia, Croatia
Tel.: (385) 21674433
Web Site: http://www.pivac.hr
Year Founded: 1952
Meat Product Distr
N.A.I.C.S.: 424470
Darko Markotic *(Mgr-Production)*

Subsidiaries:

Kras d.d. (1)
Ravnice 48, 10000, Zagreb, Croatia (50.39%)
Tel.: (385) 12396111
Web Site: http://www.kras.hr
Sales Range: $150-199.9 Million
Emp.: 150
Confectionary Product Mfr
N.A.I.C.S.: 311352
Darko Radisic *(Member-Mgmt Bd)*

Subsidiary (Non-US):

Kras Cz spol.s r.o. (2)
K Sokolovne 37, Prague, Czech Republic (100%)
Tel.: (420) 267711947
Web Site: http://www.kras.hr
Non-Durable Goods Whslr
N.A.I.C.S.: 424990

Kras Komerc d.o.o. (2)
Dame Gruev br.3, 1000, Skopje, North Macedonia (100%)
Tel.: (389) 23120286
Web Site: http://www.kras.mk
Sales Range: $25-49.9 Million
Emp.: 39
Chocolate & Confectionery Mfr
N.A.I.C.S.: 311351
Ilige Bisinov *(Mgr)*

Kras Slovakia s.r.o (2)
Stara Vajnorska 17, Bratislava, Slovakia (100%)
Tel.: (421) 22086864320
Web Site: http://www.krasslovakia.sk
Chocolate & Confectionery Mfr
N.A.I.C.S.: 311351

Subsidiary (Domestic):

Kras-Trgovina d.o.o. (2)
Ravnice 48, Zagreb, Croatia (100%)
Tel.: (385) 12329870
Web Site: http://www.kras.hr
Chocolate & Confectionery Retailer
N.A.I.C.S.: 424450

Subsidiary (Non-US):

Krascommerce d.o.o. (2)
Cesta Nabrdo 85, 1000, Ljubljana, Slovenia
Tel.: (386) 12344477
Cocoa & Biscuit Product Mfr
N.A.I.C.S.: 311352

Mira a.d. (2)
Ulica Kralja Aleksandra 3, 79101, Prijedor, Bosnia & Herzegovina (76.09%)
Tel.: (387) 52 232 211
Web Site: http://www.mira-prijedor.com
Sales Range: $1-9.9 Million
Emp.: 361
Biscuit Mfr
N.A.I.C.S.: 311821
Marica Vidakovic *(Chm-Mgmt Bd)*

MESNAC CO., LTD.
No 43 Zhengzhou Road, Qingdao, 266042, Shandong, China
Tel.: (86) 53284012387
Web Site: http://www.mesnac.com
Year Founded: 2000
002073—(SSE)
Rev.: $805,321,764
Assets: $1,927,011,060
Liabilities: $1,211,873,832

INTERNATIONAL PUBLIC

Net Worth: $715,137,228
Earnings: $28,452,060
Fiscal Year-end: 12/31/22
Application Software Development Services
N.A.I.C.S.: 513210
Guan Bingzheng *(Chm & Pres)*

Subsidiaries:

Fushun YIKESI New Material Co., Ltd. (1)
No 17 Qilong East Street, Dongzhou District, Fushun, 113000, Liaoning, China
Tel.: (86) 2453783610
Web Site: http://www.yikesi.com
Rubber Products Mfr
N.A.I.C.S.: 326299

Sichuan Deyang Zhenyun Plastics Co., Ltd. (1)
9073 Pleasantwood Ave, North Canton, OH 44720
Tel.: (888) 867-4872
Web Site: http://www.tmsi-usa.com
Automotive Parts Equipment Distr
N.A.I.C.S.: 423120

WYKO Tire Technology Ltd. (1)
Peartree Lodge Peartree Lane, Grazebrook Industrial Park, Dudley, DY2 0XW, West Midlands, United Kingdom
Tel.: (44) 1384844100
Web Site: https://wyko.com
Emp.: 3
Precision Tools Distr
N.A.I.C.S.: 423830

Subsidiary (US):

Wyko Tire Technology Inc (2)
6435 Hwy 411 S, Greenback, TN 37742
Tel.: (865) 856-2317
Web Site: https://www.wyko.com
Precision Tool Mfr
N.A.I.C.S.: 332721
Mike Evans *(Gen Mgr)*

MESOBLAST LIMITED
55 Collins Street Level 38, Melbourne, 3000, VIC, Australia
Tel.: (61) 396396036 AU
Web Site: https://www.mesoblast.com
Year Founded: 2004
MESO—(NASDAQ)
Rev.: $5,902,000
Assets: $669,153,000
Liabilities: $188,798,000
Net Worth: $480,355,000
Earnings: ($87,956,000)
Emp.: 73
Fiscal Year-end: 06/30/24
Bone & Joint Disease Therapy Developer
N.A.I.C.S.: 541715
Silviu Itescu *(CEO & Mng Dir)*

Subsidiaries:

Mesoblast, Inc. (1)
505 5th Ave Level 3, New York, NY 10017
Tel.: (212) 880-2060
Pharmaceuticals Product Mfr
N.A.I.C.S.: 325412

MESSAGEBIRD BV
Trompenburgstraat 2C, Amsterdam, 1079 TX, North Holland, Netherlands
Tel.: (31) 207009850
Web Site: http://www.messagebird.com
Year Founded: 2011
Telecommunication Servicesb
N.A.I.C.S.: 517810
Robert Vis *(Founder & CEO)*

Subsidiaries:

Message Systems, Inc. (1)
9160 Guilford Rd, Columbia, MD 21046
Tel.: (410) 872-4910
Web Site: https://www.sparkpost.com
Email Software Publisher
N.A.I.C.S.: 513210

AND PRIVATE COMPANIES

George Schlossnagle *(Pres)*

Subsidiary (Non-US):

Message Systems - Asia Pacific (2)
1 Fullerton Road One Fullerton 02-01, Singapore, 49213, Singapore
Tel.: (65) 68325550
Email Software Publisher
N.A.I.C.S.: 513210

Message Systems - China (2)
15/F China World Tower 3 Chalyang Dist, 1 Jianguomenwai Avenue, Beijing, 100004, China
Tel.: (86) 10 5737 2459
Web Site: http://www.messagesystems.com
Email Software Publisher
N.A.I.C.S.: 513210
Raymont Liu *(Mgr)*

Message Systems - EMEA (2)
90 Long Acre, London, WC2E 9RZ, United Kingdom
Tel.: (44) 207 849 3135
Email Software Publisher
N.A.I.C.S.: 513210

Message Systems - Japan (2)
1F Place Canada 7-3-37 Akasaka, Minato-ku, Tokyo, 107-0052, Japan
Tel.: (81) 3 6894 7462
Email Software Publisher
N.A.I.C.S.: 513210

MESSE ESANG CO LTD.
ES Tower 9 World Cup Bukro 58 Gil, Mapogu, Seoul, 03922, Korea (South)
Tel.: (82) 261216200 KR
Web Site: http://www.eng.messeesang.com
Exhibition Services
N.A.I.C.S.: 561920
Won Pyo Cho *(CEO)*

MESSE MUNCHEN GMBH
Messegelande, 81823, Munich, Germany
Tel.: (49) 89 949 20720
Web Site: http://www.messe-muenchen.de
Year Founded: 1964
Emp.: 1,100
Trade Fair Services
N.A.I.C.S.: 561920
Klaus Dittrich *(Chm & CEO)*

Subsidiaries:

AHK Aserbaidschan (1)
Nigar Rafibeyli Str 37, Baku, AZ1 005, Azerbaijan
Tel.: (994) 12 448 39 95
Trade Fair Services
N.A.I.C.S.: 561920
Tobias Baumann *(Mgr)*

Agora Turizm ve Ticaret Ltd. Sti. (1)
Halaskargazi Cad. No: 51, Misirli Plaza K-7 D-8, 34371, Istanbul, Türkiye
Tel.: (90) 212 2418171
Web Site: http://www.agoraturizm.com
Emp.: 10
Trade Fair Services
N.A.I.C.S.: 561920
Osman Genc *(Gen Mgr)*

Belimpex (1)
Antuna Strbana 18, Zagreb, Croatia
Tel.: (385) 1 3648276
Trade Fair Services
N.A.I.C.S.: 561920

Camara Chileno-Alemana de Comercio e Industria (1)
Av El Bosque Norte 0440 of 601, Santiago, Chile
Tel.: (56) 2 203 5320
Trade Fair Services
N.A.I.C.S.: 561920

Camara de Comercio e Industria Boliviano-Alemana (1)
Calle 15 Calacoto 7791 Torre Ketal of 311, La Paz, Bolivia
Tel.: (591) 2 2795151
Trade Fair Services
N.A.I.C.S.: 561920

Camara de Comercio e Industria Peruano-Alemana (1)
Camino Real no 348 Torre El Pilar, Piso 15 San Isidro, Lima, 27, Peru
Tel.: (51) 14 418616
Emp.: 18
Trade Fair Services
N.A.I.C.S.: 561920
Peter Andre *(Pres)*

Camara de Comercio e Industria Venezolano-Alemana (1)
Av San Felipe Centro Coinasa, Piso 4 Ofic 42 La Castellana, 1060, Caracas, Venezuela
Tel.: (58) 212 277 38 51
Trade Fair Services
N.A.I.C.S.: 561920

Camara de Industria y Comercio Argentino-Alemana (1)
Av Corrientes 327 piso 23, C1043AAD, Buenos Aires, Argentina
Tel.: (54) 11 5219 4000
Trade Fair Services
N.A.I.C.S.: 561920

Canada Unlimited Inc. (1)
9-6975 Meadowvale Town Centre Circle Suite 418, Mississauga, L5N 2V7, ON, Canada
Tel.: (905) 813-1051
Web Site: https://www.canada-unlimited.com
Trade Fair Services
N.A.I.C.S.: 561920

DEinternational DOOEL Skopje (1)
Bul Sv Kliment Ohridski 30/5, 1000, Skopje, North Macedonia
Tel.: (389) 2 3228 824
Trade Fair Services
N.A.I.C.S.: 561920

DIHA Deutsche Industrie- und Handelsvereinigung Albanien (1)
Rr Skenderbej 4/7, Tirana, Albania
Tel.: (355) 4 222 7146
Trade Fair Services
N.A.I.C.S.: 561920
Sabine Beck *(Dir-US Ops)*

De International Ltda. Filial de la Camara de Ind. y Com Colombo-Alemana (1)
Carrera 13 No 93-40 of 411, Bogota, Colombia
Tel.: (57) 1 6513777
Trade Fair Services
N.A.I.C.S.: 561920

De International de Mexico S. A. de C. V. (1)
Av Santa Fe 170 Piso 1 Oficina 4 - 12, Lomas de Santa Fe, 01210, Mexico, Mexico
Tel.: (52) 55 15 00 59 45
Trade Fair Services
N.A.I.C.S.: 561920

Deutsch-Baltische Handelskammer (1)
Strelnieku 1 1-4, 1010, Riga, Latvia
Tel.: (371) 6732 0718
Emp.: 12
Trade Fair Services
N.A.I.C.S.: 561920
Florian Schroeder *(CEO)*

Deutsch-Bulgarische Industrie- und Handelskammer (1)
F Joliot-Curie 25 A, Sofia, BG 1113, Bulgaria
Tel.: (359) 2 816 30 27
Trade Fair Services
N.A.I.C.S.: 561920
Mitko Vassilev *(Gen Mgr)*

Deutsch-Griechische Industrie- und Handelskammer (1)
Dorylaiou 10-12, 11521, Athens, Greece
Tel.: (30) 210 6419000
Trade Fair Services
N.A.I.C.S.: 561920

Deutsch-Malaysische Industrie- und Handelskammer (1)
Suite 47 01 Level 47 Menara AMBank, No 8 Jalan Yap Kwan Seng, 50450, Kuala Lumpur, Malaysia
Tel.: (60) 3 9235 1800
Trade Fair Services
N.A.I.C.S.: 561920

EXPO-Consult & Services spol. s.r.o. (1)
Prikop 4, Brno, Czech Republic
Tel.: (420) 5 4517 6158
Trade Fair Services
N.A.I.C.S.: 561920

ExpoService ApS (1)
Ornevej 63 4tv, Ulrike Mogelvang, 2400, Copenhagen, Denmark
Tel.: (45) 61 660098
Trade Fair Services
N.A.I.C.S.: 561920

Fairs & More, Inc. (1)
19 F Philippine Axa Life Centre, Sen Gil J Puyat Avenue cor Tindalo, Makati, 1200, Philippines
Tel.: (63) 2 759 6680
Trade Fair Services
N.A.I.C.S.: 561920

Firamunich, S.L. (1)
Avgda Corts Catalanes 2, La Planta Local 3, 08173, Barcelona, Spain
Tel.: (34) 93 488 1720
Trade Fair Services
N.A.I.C.S.: 561920

Fujan Rahbaran Co. (1)
Beheshti Ave Sarafraz Ave, Mowj Tower No 11 3rd Floor Unit 16, Tehran, Iran
Tel.: (98) 21 88500885
Trade Fair Services
N.A.I.C.S.: 561920

IMAG - Internationaler Messeund Ausstellungsdienst GmbH (1)
Am Messesee 2, 81829, Munich, Germany
Tel.: (49) 895529120
Web Site: http://www.imag.de
Trade Fair Management Services
N.A.I.C.S.: 561920
Peter Bergleiter *(CEO)*

Intermess Dorgeloh AG (1)
Obere Zaune 16, 8001, Zurich, Switzerland
Tel.: (41) 43 244 89 10
Trade Fair Services
N.A.I.C.S.: 561920

International Technology Exhibition and Events Joint Stock Company (1)
4th Floor ITEC Bldg No 6 107 Alley, Tran Duy Hung Str Trung Hoa Ward Cau, Hanoi, Giay, Vietnam
Tel.: (84) 4 3556 2292
Trade Fair Services
N.A.I.C.S.: 561920

JPO FairConsulting (1)
Katajanokanlaituri 5, 00160, Helsinki, Finland
Tel.: (358) 400 451667
Trade Fair Services
N.A.I.C.S.: 561920

Jing Mu International Exhibition Co. Ltd. (1)
China Intl Exhibition Center, 6 East Beisanhuan Rd, Beijing, Chaoyang, China
Tel.: (86) 10 84600553
Trade Fair Services
N.A.I.C.S.: 561920

KETIC Inc. (1)
302 Young-Jin Building 235-135, Seobinggo-Dong Yongsan-Gu, 140-240, Seoul, Korea (South)
Tel.: (82) 2 794 9044
Trade Fair Services
N.A.I.C.S.: 561920
Hyosun Jung *(Mng Dir)*

MAYA International GmbH (1)
Ungargasse 9, 1030, Vienna, Austria
Tel.: (43) 1 512 94 90
Trade Fair Services
N.A.I.C.S.: 561920

MMI (Shanghai) Co. Ltd. (1)
GC Tower, 11th floor No. 1088 Yuan Shen Road, Pudong New Area, GC Tower, 11th floor No. 1088 Yuan Shen Road, Pudong New Area, 200122, Shanghai, China
Tel.: (86) 21 2020 5500
Trade Fair Services
N.A.I.C.S.: 561920

MESSE MUNCHEN GMBH

MMI Asia (Hong Kong) Ltd. (1)
Room 2811 28th Floor Shui On Centre 6-8 Harbour Road, Wan Chai, Hong Kong, China (Hong Kong)
Tel.: (852) 25115199
Trade Fair Management Services
N.A.I.C.S.: 561920
Garman Chan *(Project Mgr)*

MMI Asia Pte. Ltd. (1)
20 Harbour Drive # 05-04 PSA Vista, 117612, Singapore, Singapore
Tel.: (65) 6236 0988
Trade Fair Services
N.A.I.C.S.: 561920

Subsidiary (Non-US):

bC Expo India Pvt. Ltd. Mumbai (2)
INIZIO 507 508 5th floor Cardinal Gracias Road, Opp P G building Chakala Andheri E, Mumbai, 400 099, India
Tel.: (91) 2267879800
Web Site: http://www.bcindia.com
Trade Fair Management Services
N.A.I.C.S.: 561920
Bhupinder Singh *(CEO & Member-Mgmt Bd)*

MMI Eurasia Fuarcilik Ltd. Sti. (1)
Halaskargazi Cad Misirli Plaza No 51-8, Sisli, 34371, Istanbul, Türkiye
Tel.: (90) 2122418171
Web Site: http://www.mmi-eurasia.com
Trade Fair Management Services
N.A.I.C.S.: 561920

MMI India Pvt Ltd. (1)
5th Floor Lalani Aura, 34th Road Khar West, 40052, Mumbai, India
Tel.: (91) 22 4255 4700
Trade Fair Services
N.A.I.C.S.: 561920

MMI South Africa (Pty) Ltd. (1)
Stonemill Office Park 300 Acacia Road Darrenwood, Randburg, 2194, South Africa
Tel.: (27) 11 476 8093
Trade Fair Services
N.A.I.C.S.: 561920

Mediators Marketing (1)
M-10&1 Mezzanine Floort, Progressive Plaza Beaumont Road Civil Line, Karachi, Pakistan
Tel.: (92) 21 35656113
Trade Fair Services
N.A.I.C.S.: 561920

Meplan GmbH (1)
Willy-Brandt-Allee 1, 81829, Munich, Germany
Tel.: (49) 8994924980
Web Site: http://www.meplan.com
Building Construction Services
N.A.I.C.S.: 236220
Carsten Michel *(Project Mgr)*

Messe Consult SRL (1)
Str Jean Monnet 1 Ap 5, 011955, Bucharest, Romania
Tel.: (40) 21 323 31 21
Trade Fair Services
N.A.I.C.S.: 561920

Messe Muenchen Japan Co., Ltd. (1)
Noahs Ark Toranomon 5F, 3-20-3 Toranomon Minato-ku, 105 0001, Tokyo, Japan
Tel.: (81) 3 6402 4583
Trade Fair Services
N.A.I.C.S.: 561920

Messe Reps. & Travel (1)
Unit 5 27 Mt Eden Road Eden Terrace, Auckland, New Zealand
Tel.: (64) 9 3031 000
Trade Fair Services
N.A.I.C.S.: 561920

Monacofiere Srl (1)
Via Bernardo Rucellai 10, 20126, Milan, Italy
Tel.: (39) 02 4070 83 01
Trade Fair Services
N.A.I.C.S.: 561920

MESSE MUNCHEN GMBH

Messe Munchen GmbH—(Continued)

MundiFeiras, Lda. (1)
Largo Maestro Miguel Angelo 8, Porto, Portugal
Tel.: (351) 22 616 4959
Trade Fair Services
N.A.I.C.S.: 561920

NurnbergMesse Brasil Ltda. (1)
Rua Verbo Divino 1547-7 Andar, Edificio Alianca - Chacara Santo Anton, 04719-002, Sao Paulo, Brazil
Tel.: (55) 11 3205 5025
Trade Fair Services
N.A.I.C.S.: 561920

OOO Messe Muenchen Consulting (1)
Gogolevskiy bl-d 17 Office 409, 119019, Moscow, Russia
Tel.: (7) 495 697 16 7
Trade Fair Services
N.A.I.C.S.: 561920

Pattern Limited (1)
2nd Floor 16 Blue Lion Place, SE1 4PU, London, United Kingdom - England
Tel.: (44) 20 3375 8230
Trade Fair Services
N.A.I.C.S.: 561920

Perkumpulan Ekonomi Indonesia Jerman (1)
Jl H Agus Salim No 115, 10310, Jakarta, Indonesia
Tel.: (62) 21 3155644
Trade Fair Services
N.A.I.C.S.: 561920

Promessa (1)
3 Rue de la Louviere, 78512, Rambouillet, France
Tel.: (33) 1 34 57 11 44
Trade Fair Services
N.A.I.C.S.: 561920

Saksa-Balti Kaubanduskoda Eestis (1)
Suurtuki 4b, Tallinn, Estonia
Tel.: (372) 6 27 69 42
Trade Fair Services
N.A.I.C.S.: 561920

Trade & Fairs Consulting (1)
Feldpreul 33, Nairobi, 61191, Kenya
Tel.: (254) 6003 826892
Trade Fair Services
N.A.I.C.S.: 561920

Trade Promotion Services Ltd. (1)
Szena ter 1/a, Budapest, 1173, Hungary
Tel.: (36) 1 224 7762
Trade Fair Services
N.A.I.C.S.: 561920

Trendset GmbH (1)
Ismaninger Strasse 63, 81675, Munich, Germany
Tel.: (49) 8946224650
Web Site: http://www.trendset.de
Trade Fair Management Services
N.A.I.C.S.: 561920
Anne Schmidthammer *(Project Mgr)*

Tysk-Svenska Handelskammaren (1)
Valhallavagen 185, 10252, Stockholm, Sweden
Tel.: (46) 8 6651820
Trade Fair Services
N.A.I.C.S.: 561920

Van Ekeris Expo Service B.V. (1)
Marsstraat 54, 2024 GE, Haarlem, Netherlands
Tel.: (31) 23 525 850
Trade Fair Services
N.A.I.C.S.: 561920

YONI Advertising Productions (Y.A.) Ltd. (1)
14 Raoul Wallenberg St, Tel Aviv, Israel
Tel.: (972) 3 6492050
Trade Fair Services
N.A.I.C.S.: 561920

bC Expo South Africa Prt. Ltd. (1)
PO Box 4367, Randburg, 2118, South Africa
Tel.: (27) 114768093
Web Site: http://www.bcafrica.com
Trade Fair Management Services
N.A.I.C.S.: 561920
Elaine Crewe *(CEO)*

MESSER GROUP GMBH
Messer-Platz 1, 65812, Bad Soden-Salmunster, Germany
Tel.: (49) 619677600   De
Web Site: http://www.messergroup.com
Year Founded: 1898
Sales Range: $1-4.9 Billion
Emp.: 5,211
Gas Mfr & Distr
N.A.I.C.S.: 325120
Stefan Messer *(CEO)*

Subsidiaries:

000 Elme Messer K (1)
Sudostroitelnaya 75, 236011, Kaliningrad, Russia
Tel.: (7) 4012395255
Web Site: http://www.elmemesser.ru
Industrial Gas Mfr
N.A.I.C.S.: 325120

Air Liquide CZ, s.r.o. (1)
Jinonicka 804/80, 158 00, Prague, Czech Republic
Tel.: (420) 257 290 384
Web Site: http://www.airliquide.cz
Sales Range: $25-49.9 Million
Emp.: 35
Industrial Gas Mfr
N.A.I.C.S.: 325120

Air Liquide Slovakia, s.r.o. (1)
Prievozska 4/A, Bratislava, 821 09, Slovakia
Tel.: (421) 2 5810 1051
Web Site: http://www.airliquide.sk
Sales Range: $25-49.9 Million
Emp.: 15
Industrial Gas Mfr
N.A.I.C.S.: 325120
Olivier Randet *(VP-Central Asia)*

Elme Messer Gaas A.S. (1)
Kopli 103, 11712, Tallinn, Estonia
Tel.: (372) 6102001
Web Site: http://www.elmemesser.ee
Industrial Gas Mfr
N.A.I.C.S.: 325120
Jaak Muug *(Mgr-Corp Sls)*

Elme Messer Metalurgs LSEZ SIA (1)
Brivibas iela 93, 3401, Liepaja, Latvia
Tel.: (371) 63424274
Industrial Gas Mfr
N.A.I.C.S.: 325120

Elme Messer Ukraine (1)
Autogena 10, 61046, Kharkiv, Ukraine
Tel.: (380) 577280111
Web Site: http://www.elmemesser.com.ua
Industrial Gas Mfr
N.A.I.C.S.: 325120

MG Odra Gas, spol. s.r.o. (1)
Na Popinci 1088, 739 32, Vratimov, Czech Republic
Tel.: (420) 595682186
Web Site: http://www.mgog.cz
Industrial Gas Mfr
N.A.I.C.S.: 325120
Rene Hmcarek *(Mng Dir & Head-Production & Engrg)*

Messer Albagaz SH.P.K. (1)
Autostrada Tirane-Durres KM 4 5, Tirana, Albania
Tel.: (355) 48200696
Web Site: http://www.messer.al
Industrial Gas Mfr
N.A.I.C.S.: 325120
Blertjan Braja *(Head-Quality Control)*

Messer Algerie SPA (1)
Lotissement RADI H Mida n 02, Cheraga, Algeria
Tel.: (213) 21367373
Industrial Nitrogen Mfr
N.A.I.C.S.: 325120

Messer Aligaz Sanayi Gazlari A.S. (1)
Hac Halim Mah Yeni Demiryolu Caddesi No 60, Kartepe, 41135, Kocaeli, Turkiye
Tel.: (90) 2623174900
Web Site: http://www.messer.com.tr
Industrial Gas Mfr
N.A.I.C.S.: 325120

Messer Austria GmbH (1)
Industriestrasse 5, 2352, Gumpoldskirchen, Austria
Tel.: (43) 506030
Web Site: http://www.messer.at
Industrial Gas Mfr
N.A.I.C.S.: 325120

Messer B.V. (1)
Middenweg 17 Havennummer M381, 4782, Moerdijk, Netherlands
Tel.: (31) 168384300
Web Site: http://www.messer.nl
Industrial Gas Mfr
N.A.I.C.S.: 325120
Jan Schaap *(Mgr-Sls)*

Messer Belgium N.V. (1)
Nieuwe Weg 1 Haven 1053, 2070, Zwijndrecht, Belgium
Tel.: (32) 35616111
Web Site: http://www.messer.be
Industrial Gas Mfr
N.A.I.C.S.: 325120
Marleen van Den Boom *(Mgr-HR)*

Messer Binh Phuoc Industrial Gases Co., Ltd. (1)
Hamlet 8, Minh Hung Commune, Bu Dang, Binh Phuoc Province, Vietnam
Tel.: (84) 6513972888
Industrial Gas Mfr
N.A.I.C.S.: 325120

Messer Bulgaria EOOD (1)
3A Dimitar Peshev Blvd, 1528, Sofia, Bulgaria
Tel.: (359) 28073232
Web Site: http://www.messer.bg
Industrial Gas Mfr
N.A.I.C.S.: 325120
Lussien Adam *(Dir-Sls)*

Messer Croatia Plin d.o.o. (1)
Industrijska 1, Postanski pretinac 81, 10290, Zapresic, Croatia
Tel.: (385) 13350777
Web Site: http://www.messer.hr
Industrial Gas Mfr
N.A.I.C.S.: 325120

Messer Danmark A/S (1)
Essen 9, 6000, Kolding, Denmark
Tel.: (45) 76320220
Web Site: http://www.messer.dk
Industrial Gas Mfr
N.A.I.C.S.: 325120

Messer Energo Gaz SRL (1)
Santierului nr 1 Mintia, 337532, Deva, Jud Hunedoara, Romania
Tel.: (40) 254236451
Web Site: http://www.messer.ro
Industrial Gas Mfr
N.A.I.C.S.: 325120

Messer France S.A.S. (1)
25 rue Auguste Blanche, 92816, Puteaux, Cedex, France
Tel.: (33) 140803300
Web Site: http://www.messer.fr
Industrial Gas Mfr
N.A.I.C.S.: 325120

Messer Gases del Peru S.A. (1)
Avenida Argentina, Callao, 2228, Lima, Peru
Tel.: (51) 4131000
Industrial Gas Mfr
N.A.I.C.S.: 325120

Messer Griesheim (China) Investment Co. Ltd. (1)
33 Floor Central Plaza 381 Huai Hai Zhong Road, Shanghai, China
Tel.: (86) 2123126666
Web Site: http://www.messergroup.cn
Industrial Gas Mfr
N.A.I.C.S.: 325120
May Huang *(Dir-HR & Admin)*

Messer Hungarogaz Kft. (1)
Vaci ut 117, 1044, Budapest, Hungary
Tel.: (36) 14351100
Web Site: http://www.messer.hu

INTERNATIONAL PUBLIC

Industrial Gas Mfr
N.A.I.C.S.: 325120

Subsidiary (Non-US):

Plin Sarajevo d.d. (2)
Rajlovacka b b, Rajlovac, 71122, Sarajevo, Bosnia & Herzegovina   (96.09%)
Tel.: (387) 33953100
Rev.: $87,906
Assets: $6,199,407
Liabilities: $2,445,772
Net Worth: $3,753,634
Earnings: ($88,766)
Emp.: 2
Fiscal Year-end: 12/31/2020
Industrial Gas Mfr
N.A.I.C.S.: 325120

Messer Iberica de Gases S.A. (1)
Autovia Tarragona-Salou km 3 8, Vilaseca, 43480, Tarragona, Spain
Tel.: (34) 977309500
Web Site: http://www.messer.es
Industrial Gas Mfr
N.A.I.C.S.: 325120

Messer Information Services GmbH (1)
Otto-Hahn-Strasse 2-4, 64823, Gross-Umstadt, Germany
Tel.: (49) 607839970
Web Site: http://www.messer-is.com
Industrial Gas Mfr
N.A.I.C.S.: 325120

Messer LLC (1)
200 Somerset Corporate Blvd Ste 7000, Bridgewater, NJ 08807
Web Site: http://www.messeramericas.com
Holding Company; Regional Managing Office
N.A.I.C.S.: 551112
Jens Luehring *(Pres & CEO)*

Joint Venture (Domestic):

Messer Industries USA, Inc. (2)
200 Somerset Corporate Blvd Ste 7000, Bridgewater, NJ 08807
Web Site: http://www.messer-us.com
Holding Company; Industrial Gas Mfr
N.A.I.C.S.: 551112

Subsidiary (Domestic):

Messer Gas LLC (3)
200 Somerset Corporate Blvd Ste 7000, Bridgewater, NJ 08807
Web Site: http://www.messer-us.com
Industrial Gas Mfr
N.A.I.C.S.: 325120

Subsidiary (Domestic):

Messer Gas Puerto Rico, Inc. (4)
Rd 869 Km 2 0 Esq Calle 19 Barrio Palmas, Catano, PR 00962
Tel.: (787) 641-7445
Web Site: http://www.messer-us.com
Industrial & Medical Gases, Specialty Gases, Cutting & Welding, Sales & Rent of Scaffolding & Construction Equipment, Safety Equipment & Accessories
N.A.I.C.S.: 424690

Messer Mostar Plin d.o.o (1)
Rodoc bb, 88000, Mostar, Bosnia & Herzegovina
Tel.: (387) 36352551
Web Site: http://www.messer.ba
Industrial Gas Mfr
N.A.I.C.S.: 325120

Messer Polska Sp. z o.o. (1)
ul Maciejkowicka 30, 41-503, Chorzow, Poland
Tel.: (48) 327726000
Web Site: http://www.messer.pl
Industrial Gas Mfr
N.A.I.C.S.: 325120

Messer Romania Gaz SRL (1)
Str Delea Veche nr 24, Corp A Etaj 3, 024102, Bucharest, Romania
Tel.: (40) 213273624
Web Site: http://www.messer.ro
Industrial Gas Mfr
N.A.I.C.S.: 325120

Messer Schweiz AG (1)

AND PRIVATE COMPANIES

META MATERIALS INC.

Seonerstrasse 75, 5600, Lenzburg, Switzerland
Tel.: (41) 628864141
Web Site: http://www.messer.ch
Industrial Gas Mfr
N.A.I.C.S.: 325120
Lussien Adam *(Dir-Sls)*

Messer Slovenija d.o.o. (1)
Jugova 20, 2342, Ruse, Slovenia
Tel.: (386) 26690300
Web Site: http://www.messer.si
Industrial Gas Mfr
N.A.I.C.S.: 325120

Messer Slovnaft s.r.o. (1)
Vlcie Hrdlo, 824 12, Bratislava, Slovakia
Tel.: (421) 245245283
Web Site: http://www.messer-slovnaft.sk
Industrial Gas Mfr
N.A.I.C.S.: 325120

Messer Tatragas s.r.o. (1)
Chalupkova 9, 819 44, Bratislava, Slovakia
Tel.: (421) 250254111
Web Site: http://www.messer.sk
Industrial Gas Mfr
N.A.I.C.S.: 325120

Messer Technogas s.r.o. (1)
Zeleny pruh 99, 140 02, Prague, Czech Republic
Tel.: (420) 241008100
Web Site: http://www.messer.cz
Industrial Gas Mfr
N.A.I.C.S.: 325120
Jirina Dalecka *(Mgr-HR)*

Messer Tehnogas AD (1)
Vuka Karadzica bb, 81400, Niksic, Montenegro
Tel.: (382) 77400040
Industrial Gas Mfr
N.A.I.C.S.: 325120

Messer Tehnoplin d.o.o. (1)
Rajlovacka bb, 71122, Sarajevo, Bosnia & Herzegovina
Tel.: (387) 33953100
Web Site: http://www.messer.ba
Industrial Gas Mfr
N.A.I.C.S.: 325120

Messer Vardar Tehnogas d.o.o.e.l. (1)
Istocna industriska zona bb, 1040, Skopje, North Macedonia
Tel.: (389) 22551418
Web Site: http://www.messer.com.mk
Industrial Gas Mfr
N.A.I.C.S.: 325120

Messer Vietnam Industrial Gases Co., Ltd. (1)
No 21 VSIP, Thuan An, Binh Duong, Vietnam
Tel.: (84) 650756700
Industrial Gas Mfr
N.A.I.C.S.: 325120

MesserGas, Distribuicao de Gases Industriais Lda (1)
Av Don Joao II Lote 1 02 2 2 -1 esquerdo, 1990-095, Lisbon, Portugal
Tel.: (351) 217942551
Web Site: http://www.messer.pt
Industrial Gas Mfr
N.A.I.C.S.: 325120

MESSER TEHNOGAS AD
Banjicki put 62, Belgrade, Serbia
Tel.: (381) 113537235
Web Site: https://www.messer.rs
Year Founded: 1997
TGAS—(BEL)
Rev.: $149,416,432
Assets: $249,658,980
Liabilities: $15,395,963
Net Worth: $234,263,017
Earnings: $24,133,140
Emp.: 361
Fiscal Year-end: 12/31/23
Industrial Gas Mfr
N.A.I.C.S.: 325120
Ernst Bode *(Mng Dir)*

MESTRO AB

Kungsgatan 10, 111 43, Stockholm, Sweden
Tel.: (46) 8302500
Web Site: https://www.mestro.com
Year Founded: 2005
MESTRO—(OMX)
Emp.: 42
Management Consulting Services
N.A.I.C.S.: 541618
Christine Berg *(Mng Dir)*

MESTRON HOLDINGS BERHAD
PT 50102 Jalan Meranti 1/9 Seksyen 10 Taman Perindustrian Meranti, Utama, 47120, Puchong, Selangor, Malaysia
Tel.: (60) 380691815　　MY
Web Site:
　https://www.mestron.com.my
Year Founded: 2002
MESTRON—(KLS)
Rev.: $23,737,712
Assets: $38,231,501
Liabilities: $15,680,208
Net Worth: $22,551,293
Earnings: $1,988,470
Emp.: 213
Fiscal Year-end: 12/31/22
Holding Company
N.A.I.C.S.: 551112
Lee Chun Heng *(Head-Sls & Mktg)*

META BIOMED CO., LTD.
270 Osongsaengmyeong1-ro Osong-eup, Heungdeok-gu, Cheongju, Chungbuk, Korea (South)
Tel.: (82) 432181981
Web Site: https://www.meta-biomed.com
Year Founded: 1990
059210—(KRS)
Rev.: $52,878,134
Assets: $92,862,524
Liabilities: $44,204,605
Net Worth: $48,657,919
Earnings: $2,761,189
Emp.: 250
Fiscal Year-end: 12/31/22
Surgical & Dental Equipment Mfr
N.A.I.C.S.: 339112
Suk Song Oh *(CEO)*

Subsidiaries:

Meta Biomed (Cambodia) Co., Ltd. (1)
Path Village Trapeng Tleng Sangkat Chaum Chao, Khan Porsenchey, Phnom Penh, Cambodia
Tel.: (855) 23969051
Medical Device & Equipment Mfr
N.A.I.C.S.: 339112

Meta Biomed Inc. (1)
3015 Advance Ln, Colmar, PA 18915
Tel.: (267) 282-5893
Web Site: https://metabiomedamericas.com
Medical Device & Equipment Mfr
N.A.I.C.S.: 339112
Jeen Kim *(Mgr-Ops)*

Meta Biomed Vina Co., Ltd. (1)
Lot N-1B Road No 4 Hamlet 3, Long Hau Commune Zone Expansion Long Hau Commune Can Giuoc Distric, Ho Chi Minh City, Long An, Vietnam
Tel.: (84) 836206672
Medical Device & Equipment Mfr
N.A.I.C.S.: 339112

Meta Ststems Co., Ltd. (1)
55 Galmachi-ro 281beon-gil, Jungwon-gu, Seongnam, 13209, Gyeonggi-do, Korea (South)
Tel.: (82) 317317377
Dental Equipment Mfr
N.A.I.C.S.: 339114

META BRIGHT GROUP BERHAD

V06-07-03A Signature 2 Lingkaran SV Sunway Velocity, Wilayah Persekutuan, 55100, Kuala Lumpur, Malaysia
Tel.: (60) 92012893
Web Site: https://mbgb.my
EASTLND—(KLS)
Rev.: $7,209,852
Assets: $67,598,528
Liabilities: $17,071,951
Net Worth: $50,526,577
Earnings: $1,843,192
Emp.: 205
Fiscal Year-end: 06/30/23
Investment Services
N.A.I.C.S.: 523999
Chin Hong Tan *(Exec Dir)*

Subsidiaries:

Discover Orient Holidays Sdn. Bhd. (1)
B-9-5 9th Floor Megan Avenue 1 Block B 189 Jalan Tun Razak, 50400, Kuala Lumpur, Malaysia
Tel.: (60) 32 166 2666
Web Site: https://discover-orient.com.my
Sales Range: $10-24.9 Million
Emp.: 15
Touring Support Services
N.A.I.C.S.: 561520

FBO Land (Setapak) Sdn. Bhd. (1)
No 24 Jalan 8/23e Danau Kota, 53300, Kuala Lumpur, Malaysia
Tel.: (60) 341498200
Web Site: http://www.eeb.com.my
Emp.: 10
Property Management & Development Services
N.A.I.C.S.: 531311

META CORPORATION PUBLIC COMPANY LIMITED
36th Floor 33/4 The Ninth Towers Tower A Rama 9 Road, Huai Khwang, Bangkok, 10310, Thailand
Tel.: (66) 201370967　　TH
Web Site:
　https://metacorporation.co.th
Year Founded: 1992
META—(THA)
Rev.: $2,467,916
Assets: $130,418,809
Liabilities: $70,144,232
Net Worth: $60,274,577
Earnings: ($3,357,325)
Emp.: 44
Fiscal Year-end: 12/31/23
Engineeering Services
N.A.I.C.S.: 541330
Soraj Rojanabenjakul *(Chm)*

META DATA LTD.
2161 North Zhongshan Road, Putuo District, Shanghai, 200333, China
Tel.: (86) 2122505999　　Ky
Web Site: http://www.onesmart.com
Year Founded: 2017
AIU—(NYSE)
Rev.: $524,500,646
Assets: $77,091,135
Liabilities: $785,112,082
Net Worth: ($708,020,946)
Earnings: ($764,145,140)
Emp.: 13,497
Fiscal Year-end: 08/31/21
Educational Service Provider
N.A.I.C.S.: 611210
Steve Xi Zhang *(Chm & CEO)*

META GROUP S.R.L.
Viale Umberto Tupini 116, 00144, Rome, RM, Italy
Tel.: (39) 07 4424 8220　　IT
Web Site: http://www.meta-group.com
Year Founded: 1993
Emp.: 18

Investment & Advisory Holding Company
N.A.I.C.S.: 551112
Andrea Di Anselmo *(Co-Founder-META Belgium (Brussels) & VP)*

Subsidiaries:

Zernike Meta - Ventures S.p.A. (1)
Viale Tupini Umberto 116, 144, Rome, RM, Italy
Tel.: (39) 07 4424 8220
Web Site:
　http://www.zernikemetaventures.com
Emp.: 15
Venture Capital Investment Firm
N.A.I.C.S.: 523999
Luigi Amati *(CEO)*

META HEALTH LIMITED
7500a Beach Road 12-303 The Plaza, Northstar AMK 08-85, Singapore, 199591, Singapore
Tel.: (65) 67595565
Web Site: https://metahealth.sg
Year Founded: 1987
5DX—(CAT)
Rev.: $3,561,425
Assets: $6,039,752
Liabilities: $6,413,383
Net Worth: ($373,631)
Earnings: ($2,522,433)
Fiscal Year-end: 12/31/23
Fixtures Mfr
N.A.I.C.S.: 333514
Kheng Choon Chua *(Founder & Sr VP-Engrg)*

Subsidiaries:

MCT (Thailand) Co., Ltd. (1)
282/9 Unit E 3rd Floor TC Green Office Building Rama 9 Rd, Huaykwang, Bangkok, 10310, Thailand
Tel.: (66) 2 105 3705
Web Site: https://www.mct.in.th
Music Book Publisher
N.A.I.C.S.: 512230
Siriyah Boonyatikarn *(Gen Mgr)*

Metal Component Technologies (Wuxi) Co., Ltd (1)
No 16 Area A No 1899 Jianghai East Rd, Wuxi, 214027, Jiangsu, China
Tel.: (86) 51082122218
Metal Component Mfr
N.A.I.C.S.: 332119

META MATERIALS INC.
60 Highfield Park Dr, Dartmouth, B3A 4R9, NS, Canada
Tel.: (902) 482-5729　　NV
Web Site:
　https://www.metamaterial.com
Year Founded: 2007
MMAT—(NASDAQ)
Rev.: $10,200,167
Assets: $408,917,982
Liabilities: $30,353,829
Net Worth: $378,564,153
Earnings: ($79,102,224)
Emp.: 239
Fiscal Year-end: 12/31/22
Oil & Gas Exploration Services
N.A.I.C.S.: 211120
Uzi Sasson *(Pres & CEO)*

Subsidiaries:

Cornes Technologies Ltd. (1)
Cornes House 5-1 Shiba 3-chome, Minato-ku, Tokyo, 105-0014, Japan
Tel.: (81) 35 427 7550
Web Site: https://www.cornestech.co.jp
Emp.: 190
Electrical Equipment Mfr & Distr
N.A.I.C.S.: 334419
Masahiko Yamaguchi *(Pres)*

Metamaterial Inc. (1)
82 Richmond Street East Suite 200, Toronto, M5C 1P1, ON, Canada
Tel.: (416) 970-3223

META MATERIALS INC.

Meta Materials Inc.—(Continued)
Web Site: http://www.czqminerals.com
Rev.: $37,219
Assets: $3,545,396
Liabilities: $18,267
Net Worth: $3,527,129
Earnings: ($370,489)
Fiscal Year-end: 05/31/2019
Uranium Exploration Services
N.A.I.C.S.: 212290
Efthymios Kallos (Chief Science Officer)

Subsidiary (Domestic):

Metamaterial Technologies Inc. (2)
1 Research Drive, Dartmouth, B2Y 4M9, NS, Canada
Tel.: (650) 993-9223
Web Site: http://www.metamaterial.com
Metamaterial Research & Production
N.A.I.C.S.: 541715
George Palikaras (Co-Founder & CEO)

Subsidiary (US):

Rolith, Inc. (3)
5880 W Las Positas Blvd Ste 51, Pleasanton, CA 94588
Tel.: (925) 548-6064
Web Site: http://www.rolith.com
Professional, Scientific & Technical Services
N.A.I.C.S.: 541990
Mukti Aryal (Engr-Process)

Nanotech Security Corp. (1)
Suite 505 - 3292 Production Way, Burnaby, V5A 4R4, BC, Canada
Tel.: (604) 678-5775
Web Site: http://www.nanosecurity.ca
Security System Services
N.A.I.C.S.: 561621
Doug Blakeway (Founder)

Division (Domestic):

Nanotech Security Corporation - Optical Thin Film Division (2)
350 Nash St rue Nash, Thurso, J0X 3B0, QC, Canada
Tel.: (819) 985-6400
Web Site: https://metamaterial.com
Emp.: 15
Optical Film Mfr
N.A.I.C.S.: 326199

Optodot Corporation (1)
100 Tradecenter Ste G-700, Woburn, MA 01801-1817
Tel.: (781) 569-5059
Web Site: http://www.optodot.com
Storage Battery Mfr
N.A.I.C.S.: 335910
Steve Carlson (Pres & CEO)

META MEDIA HOLDINGS LIMITED

7/F Global Trade Square 21 Wong Chuk Hang Road, Aberdeen, Hong Kong, China (Hong Kong)
Tel.: (852) 22509188
Web Site:
http://www.modernmedia.com.cn
Year Founded: 2001
0072—(HKG)
Rev.: $52,073,096
Assets: $100,621,872
Liabilities: $56,171,372
Net Worth: $44,450,500
Earnings: ($10,141,513)
Emp.: 420
Fiscal Year-end: 12/31/22
Magazine Publisher
N.A.I.C.S.: 513120
Zhong Shao (Founder, Chm, CEO & Chief Content Officer)

METAAGE CORPORATION

10th Floor No 516 Section 1 Neihu Road, Neihu District, Taipei, 114, Taiwan
Tel.: (886) 287978260
Web Site: https://www.metaage.tech
Year Founded: 1998

6112—(TAI)
Rev.: $647,951,838
Assets: $391,633,067
Liabilities: $218,481,401
Net Worth: $173,151,666
Earnings: $18,892,867
Emp.: 1,030
Fiscal Year-end: 12/31/23
Network Communication Services
N.A.I.C.S.: 517121
T. K. Young (Gen Mgr)

Subsidiaries:

Dkabio Co., Ltd. (1)
7F No 9 Aiguo W Rd, Zhongzheng, Taipei, 100006, Taiwan
Tel.: (886) 223315552
Web Site: https://www.dkabio.com
Healthcare Ecosystem Services
N.A.I.C.S.: 621999

Epic Cloud Co., Ltd. (1)
10th Floor No 516 Section 1 Neihu Road, Neihu District, Taipei, 114, Taiwan
Tel.: (886) 289796868
Web Site: https://www.epicloud.com.tw
Software Development Services
N.A.I.C.S.: 518210

Metaguru Corporation (1)
2F No 514 Section 1 Hu Road, Neihu, Taipei, Taiwan
Tel.: (886) 289796886
Web Site: https://www.metaguru.tech
Business Process Management Services
N.A.I.C.S.: 561110

METABOLIC EXPLORER S.A.

Biopole Clermont-Limagne 1 rue Emile Duclaux, 63360, Saint-Beauzire, France
Tel.: (33) 473334300
Web Site: https://www.metabolic-explorer.com
Year Founded: 1999
METEX—(EUR)
Sales Range: $1-9.9 Million
Chemical Intermediates Mfr
N.A.I.C.S.: 325998
Benjamin Gonzalez (Founder, Chm & CEO)

Subsidiaries:

METabolic Explorer S.A. (1)
Karl Heinz Beckurtsstrasse 13, Julich, 52425, Germany
Tel.: (49) 2461 690290
Chemical Compounds Production Services
N.A.I.C.S.: 541715

METACON AB

Drottninggatan 1B, 75310, Uppsala, Sweden
Tel.: (46) 19126800
Web Site: https://www.metacon.se
Year Founded: 2011
META—(OMX)
Rev.: $6,163,902
Assets: $17,444,566
Liabilities: $1,686,305
Net Worth: $15,758,261
Earnings: ($4,630,048)
Emp.: 31
Fiscal Year-end: 12/31/22
Renewable Energy Distribution Services
N.A.I.C.S.: 221210
Bo Carlsson (COO)

METAFRAX OJSC

Perm Region, Volga, 618250, Gubakha, Russia
Tel.: (7) 3424840898
Web Site: http://www.metafrax.ru
Year Founded: 1955
Methanol Producer
N.A.I.C.S.: 325998
Armen Garslyan (Chm)

Subsidiaries:

JSC Karbolit (1)
Dzerzhinskogo Str 34, Moscow region, Orekhovo-Zuyevo, Russia
Tel.: (7) 4964139971
Web Site: http://karbolit.metafraxgroup.com
Chemical Products Mfr
N.A.I.C.S.: 325199
Daut Vladimir Aleksandrovich (Chm & Gen Dir)

LLC Metadynea (1)
68/70 Butyrsky Val st bld 1, 127005, Moscow, Russia
Tel.: (7) 4957830052
Web Site: http://www.metadynea.ru
Chemical Products Mfr
N.A.I.C.S.: 325199
Ralph Peter Theuer (Mng Dir)

Subsidiary (Non-US):

Metadynea Trading S.A. (2)
366 route d Hermance, Anieres, 1247, Geneva, Switzerland
Tel.: (41) 227519010
Web Site: http://www.metadyneatrading.com
Chemical Products Distr
N.A.I.C.S.: 424690

Metadynea Austria GmbH (1)
Hafenstrasse 77, Krems, 3500, Austria (100%)
Tel.: (43) 27328990
Web Site: http://www.metadynea.com
Sales Range: $100-124.9 Million
Emp.: 150
Chemicals Mfr
N.A.I.C.S.: 325998
Ralph Peter Theuer (Mng Dir)

METAIR INVESTMENTS LIMITED

114 Oxford Road Oxford & Glenhove Building Suite 7 Houghton Estate, Johannesburg, 2198, South Africa
Tel.: (27) 107860800
Web Site: https://www.metair.co.za
Year Founded: 1948
MTA—(JSE)
Rev.: $863,542,594
Assets: $713,931,008
Liabilities: $412,610,581
Net Worth: $301,320,427
Earnings: $7,005,408
Emp.: 13,098
Fiscal Year-end: 12/31/23
Heating & Cooling Systems Mfr
N.A.I.C.S.: 333415
C. T. Loock (CEO)

Subsidiaries:

Climate Control Properties (Pty.) Ltd. (1)
42 Lavinia street, North End, Port Elizabeth, South Africa
Tel.: (27) 413734262
Web Site: https://www.climatecontrolsa.co.za
Emp.: 30
Air Conditioning & Refrigeration Distr
N.A.I.C.S.: 423730

Denso Sales South Africa (Pty.) Ltd. (1)
Isando Business Park E1A 10 Hulley Road, Kempton Park, 1609, Gauteng, South Africa
Tel.: (27) 800203027
Web Site: https://denso-sales.co.za
Emp.: 14
Automotive Component Mfr & Distr
N.A.I.C.S.: 336390

First National Battery Company (Pty) Ltd. (1)
64 Liverpool Road Industrial Sites, Benoni, 1501, South Africa (100%)
Tel.: (27) 117413600
Web Site: http://www.battery.co.za
Sales Range: $1-9.9 Million
Lead Acid Battery Production & Sales
N.A.I.C.S.: 335910

First National Battery Industrial (Pty) Ltd. (1)

INTERNATIONAL PUBLIC

64 Liverpool Road Industrial Sites, Benoni, South Africa, 1501, Gauteng, South Africa
Tel.: (27) 117413600
Web Site: http://www.battery.co.za
Sales Range: $100-124.9 Million
Automotive & Industrial Batteries Mfr
N.A.I.C.S.: 335910
Russell Bezuidenhout (CEO)

Hella Automotive South Africa (Pty) Ltd (1)
81 Nurburgring Street Zone 2 Coega SEZ Erf 229, Port Elizabeth, 6100, South Africa
Tel.: (27) 419965700
Web Site: https://www.hella.com
Emp.: 34
Automotive Lighting Equipment Mfr
N.A.I.C.S.: 335139
Theo Theuner (Mng Dir)

Hesto Harnesses (Pty) Ltd. (1)
11 Gledhow Mill Rd, Gledhow, Stanger, 4449, Kwazulu-Natal, South Africa
Tel.: (27) 32 437 6700
Web Site: https://www.hesto.com
Sales Range: $400-449.9 Million
Emp.: 2,100
Automotive Wire Harness Mfr
N.A.I.C.S.: 336320
John Chandler (Mng Dir)

Lumotech (Pty) Ltd. (1)
2 Fitzpatrick Street Cape Road Industrial, Uitenhage, 6229, Eastern Cape, South Africa
Tel.: (27) 419953111
Web Site: https://www.lumotech.co.za
Sales Range: $125-149.9 Million
Emp.: 600
Automotive & Commercial Lighting Products Mfr
N.A.I.C.S.: 335132
E. Wolfgang Ropertz (Mng Dir)

Metindustrial (Pty) Ltd. (1)
64 Liverpool Road, Benoni, 1502, South Africa
Tel.: (27) 117413600
Web Site: http://www.battery.co.za
Sales Range: $150-199.9 Million
Emp.: 350
Automotive Batteries Distr
N.A.I.C.S.: 423120

Subsidiary (Domestic):

Alfred Teves Brake Systems (Pty) Ltd. (2)
Cnr Kent All Black Rd, Boksburg North, Boksburg, 1460, South Africa
Tel.: (27) 118981832
Web Site: https://www.ate.co.za
Sales Range: $50-74.9 Million
Emp.: 136
Motor Vehicles Brake Systems Mfr & Distr
N.A.I.C.S.: 336340

Smiths Electric Motors (Pty) Ltd. (1)
10 Pineside Road, New Germany, 3610, South Africa
Tel.: (27) 317194911
Web Site: http://www.smiths.co.za
Emp.: 150
Electric Motor Mfr
N.A.I.C.S.: 335312

Smiths Manufacturing (Pty) Ltd (1)
10 Pineside Road, New Germany, New Germany, 3610, Kwazulu Natal, South Africa (100%)
Tel.: (27) 317194911
Web Site: https://www.smiths.co.za
Sales Range: $10-24.9 Million
Emp.: 300
Automotive Plastic, Air-Conditioning & Engine Cooling Component Mfr & Assembler
N.A.I.C.S.: 333618

Smiths Plastics (Pty) Ltd. (1)
2 Pineside Road, PO Box 181, New Germany, 3620, South Africa
Tel.: (27) 317194600
Web Site: http://www.smithsplastics.co.za
Sales Range: $200-249.9 Million
Resin Injection Molded Parts Mfr
N.A.I.C.S.: 336320
William Hilditch (Mng Dir)

Supreme Spring Holdings Ltd. (1)
45 Johnson Road Pretoriusstad, Pretori-

usstad, Nigel, 1490, Gauteng, South Africa (100%)
Tel.: (27) 117399200
Web Site: http://www.supremespring.co.za
Sales Range: $1-9.9 Million
Emp.: 509
Vehicle Suspension Components Designer, Developer & Mfr
N.A.I.C.S.: 336330

Unitrade 745 (Pty) Ltd. (1)
21 Bauhinia Road Moolla Industrial Area, Stanger, 4450, KwaZulu-Natal, South Africa
Tel.: (27) 325521275
Web Site: http://www.unitrade745.co.za
Sales Range: $25-49.9 Million
Automotive Cables Mfr & Distr
N.A.I.C.S.: 331420

METAL A.D.
Dositejeva 7, 78400, Gradiska, Republika Srpska, Bosnia & Herzegovina
Tel.: (387) 51813077
Web Site: https://www.metal-gradiska.com
Year Founded: 1957
METL—(BANJ)
Sales Range: $10-24.9 Million
Emp.: 230
Metal Products Mfr
N.A.I.C.S.: 332312
Marko Goncin (Dir)

METAL BANK LIMITED
Suite 506 Level 5 50 Clarence Street, Sydney, 2000, NSW, Australia
Tel.: (61) 290787669
Web Site: https://www.metalbank.com.au
MBK—(ASX)
Rev.: $2,022
Assets: $10,866,166
Liabilities: $420,779
Net Worth: $10,445,388
Earnings: ($1,484,834)
Emp.: 1
Fiscal Year-end: 06/30/24
Metal Mining Services
N.A.I.C.S.: 212290
Guy Robertson (Exec Dir)

METAL COATINGS (INDIA) LIMITED
912 Hemkunt Chambers 89 Nehru Place, New Delhi, 110019, India
Tel.: (91) 09899759632
Web Site: https://www.mcil.net
Year Founded: 1994
531810—(BOM)
Rev.: $20,707,311
Assets: $5,243,318
Liabilities: $765,439
Net Worth: $4,477,879
Earnings: $335,106
Emp.: 67
Fiscal Year-end: 03/31/23
Steel Pole Mfr
N.A.I.C.S.: 331110
Ramesh Chander Khandelwal (Chm)

Subsidiaries:

METAL COATINGS (INDIA) LIMITED - WORKS -I I (1)
Plot No 113 HSIIDC Industrial Estate Sector-59, Faridabad, 121004, India
Tel.: (91) 1292307602
Steel Pole Mfr
N.A.I.C.S.: 331110

METAL FABRICATORS AND WELDING LTD.
12509-124 Street, Edmonton, T5L 0N6, AB, Canada
Tel.: (780) 455-2186
Web Site: http://www.metalfab-ltd.com
Sales Range: $10-24.9 Million
Emp.: 40

Metal Components Fabricator
N.A.I.C.S.: 332312
Warren A. Schmitz (Pres & CEO)

METAL GAYRIMENKUL A.S.
Gokturk Merkez Mahallesi istanbul Caddesi Arcadiumlife II, Sitesi N26 K/2 EYUP, 34330, Istanbul, Turkiye
Tel.: (90) 212 322 65 65
Web Site: http://www.metalgayrimenkul.com
METAL—(IST)
Construction Engineering Services
N.A.I.C.S.: 236220
Akin Karali (Chm)

METAL HAWK LIMITED
Level 2 18 Kings Park Road, West Perth, 6005, WA, Australia
Tel.: (61) 478198665
Web Site: https://metalhawk.au
Year Founded: 2018
MHK—(ASX)
Rev.: $30,037
Assets: $5,929,823
Liabilities: $178,407
Net Worth: $5,751,416
Earnings: ($1,118,596)
Fiscal Year-end: 06/30/23
Metal Exploration Services
N.A.I.C.S.: 213114
Chris Marshall (Sec)

METAL RECLAMATION BHD.
Lot 6 8 9 Jalan Perigi Nanas 6/1, Pulau Indah Industrial Park West Port, 42920, Port Klang, Selangor Darul Ehsan, Malaysia
Tel.: (60) 33101 1198
Web Site: http://www.metalreclamation.com
Sales Range: $10-24.9 Million
Lead & Lead Alloy Sales
N.A.I.C.S.: 331491
May Peng Sin (Co-Sec)

Subsidiaries:

Metal Reclamation (Industries) Sdn. Bhd. (1)
Lot 6 8 & 9 Jalan Perigi Nanas 6/1 Pulau Indah Industrial Park, West Port, 42920, Port Klang, Selangor Darul Ehsan, Malaysia
Tel.: (60) 331011198
Web Site: http://www.metal-reclamation.com
Sales Range: $50-74.9 Million
Emp.: 200
Lead Alloys Mfr
N.A.I.C.S.: 332999

METAL SUPERMARKETS (CANADA) LTD.
520 Abilene Drive 2nd Floor, Mississauga, L5T 2H7, ON, Canada
Tel.: (905) 362-8226
Web Site: http://www.metalsupermarkets.com
Year Founded: 1985
Sales Range: $25-49.9 Million
Emp.: 20
Supplier & Retailer of Small Quantity Metals
N.A.I.C.S.: 423510
Stephen Schober (Pres & CEO)

METAL TIGER PLC
Weston Farm House Weston Down Lane Weston Colley, Winchester, SO21 3AG, United Kingdom
Tel.: (44) 20 3287 5349 UK
Web Site: http://www.metaltigerplc.com
MTR—(AIM)
Sales Range: $10-24.9 Million
Emp.: 16
Mining Investment Services
N.A.I.C.S.: 523999
Michael McNeilly (CEO)

METAL-QAYNAQ-SINAQ JSC
33A Babek Ave, AZ 1030, Baku, Azerbaijan
Tel.: (994) 12 4705105
Web Site: http://www.mqs.az
Year Founded: 1988
Sales Range: $150-199.9 Million
Emp.: 800
Metal Fabrication, Blast Furnaces, Testing & Training Services
N.A.I.C.S.: 333994
Elnar Allahverdiyev (Deputy Dir-Tech)

METALABS CO., LTD.
6-12 2nd floor Bongeunsa-ro 29-gil, Gangnam-gu, Seoul, Korea (South)
Tel.: (82) 221897700
Web Site: https://www.avista.co.kr
Year Founded: 2000
090370—(KRS)
Rev.: $17,379,485
Assets: $69,042,850
Liabilities: $8,536,234
Net Worth: $60,506,616
Earnings: ($3,141,499)
Emp.: 47
Fiscal Year-end: 12/31/22
Apparel Product Mfr & Distr
N.A.I.C.S.: 315250
Ha Ji-Seong (CEO)

METALAC A.D.
212 Kneza Aleksandra St, 32300, Gornji Milanovac, Serbia
Tel.: (381) 32770311
Web Site: https://www.metalac.com
Year Founded: 1959
MTLC—(BEL)
Rev.: $13,048,352
Assets: $36,133,367
Liabilities: $2,566,490
Net Worth: $33,566,878
Earnings: $2,347,410
Emp.: 2,000
Fiscal Year-end: 12/31/22
Investment Management Service
N.A.I.C.S.: 523940
Dragoljub Vukadinovic (Chm-Supervisory Bd)

Subsidiaries:

Metalac Bojler d.o.o. (1)
Ljubicska 1, 32300, Gornji Milanovac, Serbia (100%)
Tel.: (381) 32 717 432
Web Site: http://www.metalacbojler.com
Residential & Commercial Water Heaters Mfr
N.A.I.C.S.: 423440
Zoran Ognjanovic (Dir)

Metalac FAD d.o.o. (1)
Kneza Aleksandra 210, 32300, Gornji Milanovac, Serbia
Tel.: (381) 32 515 5200
Web Site: https://www.metalacfad.rs
Motor Vehicle Parts Mfr
N.A.I.C.S.: 336390

Metalac Inko Ltd (1)
Kneza Aleksandra 212, 32300, Gornji Milanovac, Serbia (100%)
Tel.: (381) 32 770 407
Web Site: http://www.metalacinko.com
Stainless Steel Sink Mfr
N.A.I.C.S.: 332999
Vladan Stojkovic (Dir)

Metalac Market Podgorica d.o.o. (1)
Kneza Aleksandra 212, 32300, Gornji Milanovac, Serbia (100%)
Tel.: (381) 32 770 336
Web Site: http://www.metalacmarket.me
Household Appliance Stores
N.A.I.C.S.: 449210
Sanja Dasic (Dir)

Metalac Market d.o.o (1)
Kneza Aleksandra 212, 32300, Gornji Milanovac, Serbia (100%)
Tel.: (381) 32 770 336
Web Site: http://www.metalacmarket.com

Household Products Retailer & Distr
N.A.I.C.S.: 449210
Stojan Slovic (Dir)

Metalac Posudje d.o.o. (1)
Kneza Aleksandra 212, Gornji Milanovac, Serbia (100%)
Tel.: (381) 32 770 311
Web Site: http://www.metalacposudje.com
Metal Cookware Products Mfr
N.A.I.C.S.: 332215
Aleksandar Markovic (Dir)

Metalac Print d.o.o. (1)
Kneza Aleksandra 212, 32300, Gornji Milanovac, Serbia
Tel.: (381) 3 277 0311
Web Site: https://www.metalacprint.com
Cardboard Box Mfr
N.A.I.C.S.: 322211

Metalac Trade d.o.o. (1)
Ljubicska 1, 32300, Gornji Milanovac, Serbia (100%)
Tel.: (381) 32 717 430
Web Site: http://www.metalactrade.co.rs
Household Appliance Whslr & Retailer
N.A.I.C.S.: 449210
Dragan Tomic (Dir)

Metrot d.o.o. (1)
Dmitry Ulyanov House 16 Bldg 2 Suite 272, 117292, Moscow, Russia (100%)
Tel.: (7) 495 937 50 36
Web Site: http://www.metrot.ru
Household Appliance Whslr & Distr
N.A.I.C.S.: 423620
Milan Vujovic (Dir Gen)

Promo Metal d.o.o. (1)
Obrtnicka 9, 10431, Sveta Nedelja, Croatia (100%)
Tel.: (385) 1 30 90 092
Web Site: http://www.prometal.hr
Metal Cookware & Other Household Products Whslr
N.A.I.C.S.: 449210
Aleksandar Jelic (Dir)

METALAC METALURGIJA A.D.
Bajci Zilinskog 11, 21000, Novi Sad, Serbia
Tel.: (381) 216612899
Web Site: https://www.metalac-metalurgija.co.rs
Year Founded: 1991
AGMT—(BEL)
Rev.: $531,929
Assets: $3,105,970
Liabilities: $841,054
Net Worth: $2,264,916
Earnings: $49,471
Emp.: 105
Fiscal Year-end: 12/31/22
Household Product Whslr
N.A.I.C.S.: 423220
Marko Sarenac (Mng Dir)

METALAC PROLETER A.D.
ul Rudnicke Vojske broj 18, 32300, Gornji Milanovac, Serbia
Tel.: (381) 32711894
Web Site: https://mojproleter.rs
Year Founded: 1946
PRGM—(BEL)
Rev.: $37,518,248
Assets: $13,056,131
Liabilities: $7,221,568
Net Worth: $5,834,563
Earnings: $703,049
Emp.: 413
Fiscal Year-end: 12/31/22
Retail Store Operator
N.A.I.C.S.: 445110
Jelena Lukovic (Dir Gen & Gen Mgr)

METALCOLOUR A/S
Agrovej 6, DK 4800, Nykobing, Denmark
Tel.: (45) 5484 9070 DK
Web Site: http://www.metalcolour.com
Year Founded: 1974

METALCOLOUR A/S

Metalcolour A/S—(Continued)
Sales Range: $10-24.9 Million
Emp.: 30
Laminated Sheet Metal & Aluminum
N.A.I.C.S.: 332999
Ingemar Forsberg *(CEO)*

Subsidiaries:

Dampa ApS (1)
Hojelokkevej 4A, 5690, Tommerup, Denmark
Tel.: (45) 63761300
Web Site: http://www.dampa.dk
Sales Range: $10-24.9 Million
Metal Ceilings
N.A.I.C.S.: 332323
Michael Nykjaer *(CEO)*

Metalcolour Asia Pte Ltd (1)
17 Tuas Avenue 4, Singapore, 639368, Singapore
Tel.: (65) 68982532
Laminated Sheet Mfr
N.A.I.C.S.: 326130
Quah Poh Keng *(Mng Dir)*

Metalcolour Sverige AB (1)
Emaljervagen 7, SE 372 30, Ronneby, Sweden
Tel.: (46) 457 781 00
Web Site: http://www.metalcolour.com
Laminated Sheet Metal & Aluminum Mfr
N.A.I.C.S.: 332999
Ingemar Forsberg *(CEO)*

METALCRAFT TECHNOLOGY INC.
273 Schoolhouse Street, Coquitlam, V3K 4Y1, BC, Canada
Tel.: (604) 515-1877
Web Site: http://www.metalcraft.ca
Year Founded: 1997
Sales Range: $10-24.9 Million
Emp.: 20
Metal Sheet Mfr
N.A.I.C.S.: 331221
Reh Abdulla *(Gen Mgr)*

METALES PELAZ, S.L.
Cantera Errepidea 2, 48950, Asua, Bizkaia, Spain
Tel.: (34) 944530603
Web Site:
http://www.metalespelazsl.com
Year Founded: 1946
Rev.: $10,885,778
Emp.: 26
Metal Scrap Distr
N.A.I.C.S.: 423930

METALEX VENTURES LTD.
203-1634 Harvey Ave, Kelowna, V1Y 6G2, BC, Canada
Tel.: (250) 860-8599
Web Site:
https://www.metalexventures.com
MTX—(TSXV)
Rev.: $3,368
Assets: $4,394,591
Liabilities: $1,591,526
Net Worth: $2,803,065
Earnings: $787,352
Fiscal Year-end: 04/30/21
Mineral Exploration Services
N.A.I.C.S.: 213114
Chad Ulansky *(Pres & CEO)*

METALFRIO SOLUTIONS S.A.
Av Abrahao Goncalves Braga 412, Vila Liviero, Sao Paulo, 04186-220, Brazil
Tel.: (55) 1126279000
Web Site:
https://www.metalfrio.com.br
Year Founded: 1960
FRIO3—(BRAZ)
Rev.: $392,209,991
Assets: $357,142,487
Liabilities: $422,983,947
Net Worth: ($65,841,460)
Earnings: $1,650,613
Fiscal Year-end: 12/31/23
Refrigerator Equipment Mfr
N.A.I.C.S.: 335220

Subsidiaries:

3L Locacoes e Servicos S.A. (1)
Rua Abrahao Goncalves Braga 412, Sacoma, Sao Paulo, 04186-220, Brazil
Tel.: (55) 1126279210
Web Site: http://www.3llocacoes.com.br
Refrigeration Equipment & Oven Rental Services
N.A.I.C.S.: 532210

METALICA SA
Str Independentei 13, Medgidia, Constanta, Romania
Tel.: (40) 241 814135
Sales Range: Less than $1 Million
Emp.: 78
Metal Structure Mfr
N.A.I.C.S.: 332312

METALICITY LIMITED
Level 14 QV1 Building 250 St Georges Terrace, Perth Airport, Perth, 6000, WA, Australia
Tel.: (61) 865000202 AU
Web Site:
https://www.metalicity.com.au
ARI—(ASX)
Rev.: $218,019
Assets: $6,483,486
Liabilities: $194,064
Net Worth: $6,289,422
Earnings: ($528,749)
Emp.: 1
Fiscal Year-end: 06/30/24
Mineral Exploration Services
N.A.I.C.S.: 212290
Neil Hackett *(Sec)*

METALINK LTD.
c/o Top Alpha Capital Ltd Haaliya 24, Beit-Yitzhak, Netanya, 4292000, Israel
Tel.: (972) 722117400
Year Founded: 1992
MTLK—(OTCIQ)
Rev.: $100,000
Assets: $1,969,000
Liabilities: $166,000
Net Worth: $1,803,000
Earnings: $62,000
Fiscal Year-end: 12/31/23
Wireless & Wireline Broadband Communication Solutions
N.A.I.C.S.: 517112
Joseph Winston *(Chm)*

METALITE RESOURCES INC
Suite 600-800 West Pender St, Vancouver, V6C 2V6, BC, Canada
Tel.: (778) 855-5001 Ca
Web Site:
http://www.metaliteresources.com
D68—(DEU)
Assets: $543,447
Liabilities: $93,778
Net Worth: $449,669
Earnings: ($1,601,623)
Fiscal Year-end: 12/31/22
Metal Mining & Exploration Services
N.A.I.C.S.: 213114
Michael Mulberry *(Pres & CEO)*

METALL ZUG AG
Industriestrasse 66, 6302, Zug, Switzerland
Tel.: (41) 587686050
Web Site: https://www.metallzug.ch
Year Founded: 1887
METN—(SWX)
Rev.: $716,120,843
Assets: $777,371,397
Liabilities: $202,756,098
Net Worth: $574,615,299
Earnings: $152,209,534
Emp.: 2,317
Fiscal Year-end: 12/31/22
Holding Company
N.A.I.C.S.: 551112
Martin Wipfli *(Chm)*

Subsidiaries:

Belimed AG (1)
Dorfstrasse 4, Ballwil, 6275, Switzerland (33%)
Tel.: (41) 417689600
Web Site: http://www.belimed.com
Sales Range: $50-74.9 Million
Emp.: 130
Cleaning, Disinfection & Sterilization Services
N.A.I.C.S.: 325412

Subsidiary (Non-US):

Belimed B.V. (2)
Energieweg 8, 6658, Amsterdam, Netherlands
Tel.: (31) 487 591 100
Cleaning, Disinfection & Sterilization Services
N.A.I.C.S.: 325412

Belimed GmbH (2)
Edisonstrasse 7a, 84453, Muhldorf, Germany
Tel.: (49) 863198960
Web Site: http://www.belimed.com
Sales Range: $50-74.9 Million
Emp.: 130
Cleaning, Disinfection & Sterilization Services
N.A.I.C.S.: 325412

Subsidiary (Domestic):

Belimed Deutschland GmbH (3)
Edisonstrasse 7a, Muhldorf, 84453, Germany
Tel.: (49) 863198960
Web Site: http://www.belimed.de
Sales Range: $25-49.9 Million
Emp.: 100
Cleaning, Disinfection & Sterilization Services
N.A.I.C.S.: 325412

Belimed Technik GmbH (3)
Edisonstrasse 7a, 84453, Muhldorf, Germany
Tel.: (49) 863198960
Web Site: http://www.belimed.com
Sales Range: $25-49.9 Million
Emp.: 100
Cleaning, Disinfection & Sterilization Services
N.A.I.C.S.: 325412

Subsidiary (US):

Belimed Inc. (2)
8351 Palmetto Commerce Pkwy Ste 101, Ladson, SC 29456
Tel.: (843) 216-7424
Web Site: http://www.belimed.us
Sales Range: $25-49.9 Million
Emp.: 50
Cleaning, Disinfection & Sterilization Services
N.A.I.C.S.: 325412

Subsidiary (Non-US):

Belimed Infection Control Kft. (2)
Aranykez u 6, 1052, Budapest, Hungary
Tel.: (36) 1 318 86 97
Disinfection & Sterilization System Distr
N.A.I.C.S.: 423850

Belimed Ltd. (2)
Unit 4 New Buildings Place, Dragons Green Road, Horsham, RH13 8GQ, West Sussex, United Kingdom
Tel.: (44) 1403738811
Sales Range: $25-49.9 Million
Emp.: 8
Cleaning, Disinfection & Sterilization Services
N.A.I.C.S.: 325412
Martin O'Hare *(Gen Mgr)*

INTERNATIONAL PUBLIC

Belimed Medical Equipment (Shanghai) Co., Ltd (2)
New Jinqiao Road 1299 1st Building 2nd Floor, Pudong, Shanghai, 201206, China
Tel.: (86) 215 137 0998
Web Site: http://www.belimed.com
Cleaning, Disinfection & Sterilization Services
N.A.I.C.S.: 325412

Belimed SAS (2)
Medical and Life Science Parc Espale 1 av Pierre Pflimlin, 68390, Sausheim, France
Tel.: (33) 38 963 6540
Web Site: https://www.belimed.com
Sales Range: $25-49.9 Million
Emp.: 45
Cleaning, Disinfection & Sterilization Services
N.A.I.C.S.: 325412

Subsidiary (Domestic):

Belimed Sauter AG (2)
Zelgstrasse 8, 8583, Bischofszell, Switzerland
Tel.: (41) 716448500
Web Site: http://www.sauterag.com
Sales Range: $50-74.9 Million
Cleaning, Disinfection & Sterilization Services
N.A.I.C.S.: 325412

Subsidiary (Non-US):

Belimed d.o.o. (2)
Kosovelova Cesta 2, 1290, Grosuplje, Slovenia
Tel.: (386) 17866010
Sales Range: $50-74.9 Million
Emp.: 130
Cleaning, Disinfection & Sterilization Services
N.A.I.C.S.: 325412

NV Belimed SA (2)
Rue de Clairvaux 8, 1348, Louvain-la-Neuve, Belgium
Tel.: (32) 10420240
Cleaning, Disinfection & Sterilization Services
N.A.I.C.S.: 325412

Sterifast Sterilization & Disinfection Systems, Lda. (2)
Praque Empresarial do Padrao Lote 11, 5460-343, Boticas, Portugal
Tel.: (351) 27 641 8287
Web Site: https://www.sterifast.com
Sterilization Equipment Mfr
N.A.I.C.S.: 332313

Belimed GmbH (1)
Triesterstrasse 238, 8073, Feldkirchen bei Graz, Austria
Tel.: (43) 3155 40699 0
Emp.: 13
Disinfection & Sterilisation Equipment Distr
N.A.I.C.S.: 423850
Andreas Pirs *(Mgr)*

Belimed Life Science AG (1)
Zelgstrasse 8, Sulgen, 8583, Weinfelden, Switzerland (33%)
Tel.: (41) 716448691
Medical Equipment Distr
N.A.I.C.S.: 423450

Haag-Streit Holding AG (1)
Gartenstadtstrasse 10, 3098, Koniz, Switzerland
Tel.: (41) 319780100
Web Site: http://www.haag-streit-holding.com
Ophthalmologists Instruments & Equipment, Optometrists & Opticians
N.A.I.C.S.: 333310

Subsidiary (Non-US):

Clement Clarke International Ltd. (2)
Edinburgh Way, Harlow, CM20 2TT, Essex, United Kingdom
Tel.: (44) 1279414969
Medical Instrument Mfr
N.A.I.C.S.: 339112

HS DOMS GmbH (2)
Langenschader Str 67 Saale, 07318, Saalfeld, Germany
Tel.: (49) 367154500

AND PRIVATE COMPANIES

Examination Unit & Patient Chair Mfr
N.A.I.C.S.: 339112

Subsidiary (Domestic):

Haag-Streit AG (2)
Gartenstadtstrasse 10, 3089, Koniz, Switzerland
Tel.: (41) 319780111
Web Site: http://www.haagstreit.com
Ophthalmic Goods Mfr
N.A.I.C.S.: 339115

Haag-Streit AG Verkauf Schweiz (2)
Gartenstadtstrasse 10, Koniz, 3089, Switzerland
Tel.: (41) 31 978 01 11
Web Site: http://www.haag-streit.ch
Medical Dental & Hospital Equipment & Supplies Whslr
N.A.I.C.S.: 423450

Subsidiary (Non-US):

Haag-Streit Deutschland GmbH (2)
Rosengarten 10, 22880, Wedel, Germany
Tel.: (49) 410370902
Web Site: http://www.haag-streit.de
Medical Dental & Hospital Equipment & Supplies Whslr
N.A.I.C.S.: 423450

Haag-Streit Far East Ltd. (2)
New Jinqiao Road 1299 1st Building 2nd Floor, Pudong, Shanghai, 201206, China
Tel.: (86) 2160793286
Optical & Mechanical Component Mfr
N.A.I.C.S.: 333310

Haag-Streit Surgical GmbH (2)
Rosengarten 10, 22880, Wedel, Germany
Tel.: (49) 410370904
Microscope & Equipment Mfr
N.A.I.C.S.: 333310
Alexandra Grosskopf (Mgr-Product)

Haag-Streit UK Ltd. (2)
Edinburgh Way, Harlow, CM20 2TT, Essex, United Kingdom
Tel.: (44) 1279883720
Medical Instrument Mfr
N.A.I.C.S.: 339112

Subsidiary (US):

Haag-Streit USA, Inc. (2)
3535 Kings Mills Rd, Mason, OH 45040
Tel.: (513) 336-7255
Web Site: https://www.haag-streit.com
Surgical Equipment & Supplies
N.A.I.C.S.: 423450

Subsidiary (Non-US):

John Weiss & Son Ltd. (2)
Unit A Edinburgh Way, Harlow, CM20 2TT, Essex, United Kingdom
Tel.: (44) 1279414969
Surgical Instrument Mfr & Distr
N.A.I.C.S.: 339112
Phil Martin (Reg Sls Mgr)

Moller-Wedel GmbH & Co. KG (2)
Rosengarten 10, 22880, Wedel, Germany
Tel.: (49) 410370901
Emp.: 100
Medical Equipment Mfr
N.A.I.C.S.: 339112

Moller-Wedel Optical GmbH (2)
Rosengarten 10, 22880, Wedel, Germany
Tel.: (49) 41039377610
Optical Measuring Instrument Mfr
N.A.I.C.S.: 334513

OptoMedical Technologies GmbH (2)
Maria-Goeppert-Strasse 9, 23562, Lubeck, Germany
Tel.: (49) 4511 608 6500
Web Site: http://www.opmedt.com
Surgical Instrument Distr
N.A.I.C.S.: 423450

Subsidiary (Domestic):

Spectros AG (2)
Lohweg 25, Ettingen, 4107, Arlesheim, Switzerland
Tel.: (41) 617262020
Optical & Mechanical Component Mfr
N.A.I.C.S.: 333310

Edgar Sporer (CEO)

Schleuniger Holding AG (1)
Bierigutstrasse 9, 3608, Thun, Switzerland
Tel.: (41) 333340333
Web Site: http://www.schleuniger.com
High Precision Wire Mfr
N.A.I.C.S.: 332618

Subsidiary (Non-US):

DiIT GmbH (2)
Justus-von-Liebig-Ring 11a, 82152, Krailling, Germany
Tel.: (49) 89 893 2500
Web Site: https://www.diit.de
Wire Harness Cable Mfr
N.A.I.C.S.: 335929

L W Solutions Ltd. (2)
Unit 12 Business Development Centre Main Avenue, Treforest Industrial Estate, Pontypridd, CF37 5UR, United Kingdom
Tel.: (44) 1443841738
Web Site: http://www.laserwiresolutions.com
Laser Wire Mfr
N.A.I.C.S.: 332618
Paul Taylor (Founder & CEO)

Subsidiary (Domestic):

Schleuniger AG (2)
Bierigutstrasse 9, 3608, Thun, Switzerland
Tel.: (41) 333340333
Web Site: http://www.schleuniger.com
Sales Range: $25-49.9 Million
Emp.: 160
High Precision Wire Mfr
N.A.I.C.S.: 332618
Christoph Schuepbach (CEO)

Subsidiary (Non-US):

Schleuniger GmbH (2)
Raiffeisenstrasse 14, 42477, Radevormwald, Germany
Tel.: (49) 21959290
High Precision Wire Mfr
N.A.I.C.S.: 332618

Schleuniger Japan Co., Ltd. (2)
Higashi-Naganuma 1726-15, Inagi, Tokyo, 206-0802, Japan
Tel.: (81) 424016581
Web Site: https://www.schleuniger.co.jp
High Precision Wire Mfr
N.A.I.C.S.: 332618

Schleuniger Machinery (Tianjin) Co., Ltd. (2)
A-101 and B-101 D9 Building No 1 Xuefu West Road, Xuefu Industrial Zone Xiqing Qu, Tianjin, 300392, China
Tel.: (86) 2283713090
Automotive Products Mfr
N.A.I.C.S.: 336110

Subsidiary (Domestic):

Schleuniger Solutions AG (2)
Gewerbestrasse 14, CH 6314, Zug, Switzerland
Tel.: (41) 417545353
Web Site: http://www.schleuniger.com
Sales Range: $25-49.9 Million
Emp.: 65
High Precision Wire Mfr
N.A.I.C.S.: 332618

Subsidiary (Non-US):

Schleuniger Test Automation GmbH (2)
Steinung 3 1, Jettingen, 71131, Germany
Tel.: (49) 74527406280
Automotive Products Mfr
N.A.I.C.S.: 336110

Schleuniger Trading (Shanghai) Co., Ltd. (2)
Room 108 BH Center No 7755 Zhongchun Road, Minhang Qu, Shanghai, 201101, China
Tel.: (86) 2162526677
Sales Range: $25-49.9 Million
Emp.: 29
High Precision Wire Mfr
N.A.I.C.S.: 332618

Subsidiary (US):

Schleuniger, Inc. (2)

---

87 Colin Dr, Manchester, NH 03103
Tel.: (603) 668-8117
Web Site: https://www.schleuniger-na.com
Sales Range: $25-49.9 Million
Emp.: 30
High Precision Wire Mfr
N.A.I.C.S.: 332618

Subsidiary (Non-US):

adaptronic Pruftechnik GmbH (2)
Karl Carstens Str 27, 97877, Wertheim, Germany
Tel.: (49) 9342858400
Web Site: https://adaptronic.com
Test Systems Mfr
N.A.I.C.S.: 333999
Andreas Kriegler (Mng Dir)

V-ZUG AG (1)
Industriestrasse 66, PO Box 6302, 6300, Zug, Switzerland
Tel.: (41) 587676767
Web Site: https://www.vzug.com
Household Appliances Mfr
N.A.I.C.S.: 335220
Heinz Buhofer (CEO)

Subsidiary (Domestic):

Gehrig Group AG (2)
Margrethenstrasse 6, 6275, Hochdorf, Switzerland
Tel.: (41) 414497777
Household Appliances Mfr
N.A.I.C.S.: 335220

Subsidiary (Non-US):

Hildebrand France S.A.R.L. (3)
1191 Route Nationale, 01120, Montluel, France
Tel.: (33) 472250759
Web Site: http://www.hildebrand.fr
Sales Range: $25-49.9 Million
Emp.: 1
Household Appliances Mfr
N.A.I.C.S.: 335220

Subsidiary (Domestic):

SIBIRGroup AG (2)
Bernstrasse 60, Schlieren, 8952, Switzerland
Tel.: (41) 448474811
Web Site: http://www.sibirgroup.ch
Sales Range: $25-49.9 Million
Emp.: 120
Household Appliances Mfr
N.A.I.C.S.: 335220

Subsidiary (Non-US):

V-ZUG (Shanghai) Domestic Appliance Co., Ltd. (2)
Block 1 and 2 No 1320 Yu Yuan Road, Shanghai, 200050, China
Tel.: (86) 2152371196
Home Appliance Mfr
N.A.I.C.S.: 335220

V-ZUG Australia Pty. Ltd. (2)
Suite 3/3990 Pacific Highway, Loganholme, QLD, Australia
Tel.: (61) 7 3209 6822
Household Appliance Distr
N.A.I.C.S.: 423620

V-ZUG Europe BVBA (2)
Evolis 102, Harelbeke, 8530, Kortrijk, Belgium
Tel.: (32) 56616000
Web Site: https://www.vzug.com
Home Appliance Mfr
N.A.I.C.S.: 335220

V-ZUG Hong Kong Co., Ltd. (2)
12/F 8 Russell Street Causeway Bay, Hong Kong, China (Hong Kong)
Tel.: (852) 27768808
Home Appliance Mfr
N.A.I.C.S.: 335220
Nelly Chan (Head-Fin & Controlling)

V-ZUG Singapore Pte. Ltd. (2)
2 Orchard Turn 02-07B ION Orchard, Singapore, 238801, Singapore
Tel.: (65) 69260878
Web Site: https://www.vzug.com
Home Appliance Mfr
N.A.I.C.S.: 335220

METALLIC GROUP OF COMPANIES

METALL- UND KUNSTST-OFFTECHNIK BARCHFELD GMBH
Im Vorwerk 14, 36456, Barchfeld, Germany
Tel.: (49) 36961 2390
Web Site: http://www.mkb-online.com
Year Founded: 1898
Sales Range: $10-24.9 Million
Stamping, Forming & Injection Moulding Tools & Devices Mfr & Developer
N.A.I.C.S.: 333511
Martin Zembsch (Mng Dir)

METALLA ROYALTY & STREAMING LTD.
Suite 501 543 Granville Street, Vancouver, V6C 1X8, BC, Canada
Tel.: (604) 696-0741   Ca
Web Site:
    https://www.metallaroyalty.com
Year Founded: 2000
MTA—(NYSEAMEX)
Rev.: $2,413,428
Assets: $130,889,238
Liabilities: $12,328,079
Net Worth: $118,561,159
Earnings: ($10,928,334)
Emp.: 5
Fiscal Year-end: 12/31/22
Investment Services
N.A.I.C.S.: 523999
Brett Heath (Pres & CEO)

Subsidiaries:

Nova Royalty Corp. (1)
Suite 501-543 Granville St, Vancouver, V6C 1X8, BC, Canada
Tel.: (416) 433-2801
Web Site: https://www.novaroyalty.com
Rev.: $1,489,487
Assets: $65,759,167
Liabilities: $8,542,159
Net Worth: $57,217,009
Earnings: ($5,890,586)
Emp.: 4
Fiscal Year-end: 12/31/2022
Mineral Mining Services
N.A.I.C.S.: 213115
Bill Tsang (CFO)

METALLIANCE SA
Zi La Saule, 71230, Saint Vallier, France
Tel.: (33) 385570134
Web Site: https://www.metalliance-tsi.com
MLETA—(EUR)
Sales Range: $25-49.9 Million
Emp.: 120
Industrial Machinery Mfr
N.A.I.C.S.: 333248
Jean-Claude Cothenet (CEO)

METALLIC GROUP OF COMPANIES
Suite 904 - 409 Granville Street, Vancouver, V6C 1T2, BC, Canada
Tel.: (604) 235-1982
Web Site: https://metallicgroup.ca
Holding Company
N.A.I.C.S.: 551112
Greg Johnson (Co-Founder & Chm)

Subsidiaries:

Granite Creek Copper Ltd. (1)
Suite 904 409 Granville Street, Vancouver, V6C 1T2, BC, Canada
Tel.: (604) 235-1982
Web Site: https://www.gcxcopper.com
Rev.: $233,150
Assets: $9,920,444
Liabilities: $2,120,300
Net Worth: $7,800,144
Earnings: ($1,674,818)
Fiscal Year-end: 05/31/2021
Gold, Copper & Molybdenum Mining
N.A.I.C.S.: 212220
Timothy Johnson (Pres & CEO)

METALLIC MINERALS CORP.

Metallic Group of Companies—(Continued)

METALLIC MINERALS CORP.
Suite 904 - 409 Granville Street, Vancouver, V6C 1T2, BC, Canada
Tel.: (604) 629-7800   BC
Web Site: https://metallic-minerals.com
Year Founded: 2007
MMNGF—(OTCQB)
Rev.: $577,436
Assets: $6,553,311
Liabilities: $198,363
Net Worth: $6,354,948
Earnings: ($5,860,857)
Fiscal Year-end: 07/31/21
Silver & Gold Mining Services
N.A.I.C.S.: 212220
Alicia Milne *(Sec)*

METALLINVESTBANK PJSC SCB
2/5/4 Slavyanskaya Square Building 3, Moscow, 109074, Russia
Tel.: (7) 4957279797
Web Site: http://www.metallinvestbank.ru
Sales Range: Less than $1 Million
Commercial Banking Services
N.A.I.C.S.: 522110

METALLIS RESOURCES INC.
604 - 850 West Hastings St, Vancouver, V6C 1E1, BC, Canada
Tel.: (604) 688-5077
Web Site: https://www.metallisresources.com
Year Founded: 2007
MTLFF—(OTCQB)
Rev.: $37,718
Assets: $6,787,270
Liabilities: $299,945
Net Worth: $6,487,325
Earnings: ($275,793)
Fiscal Year-end: 12/31/19
Metal Mining Services
N.A.I.C.S.: 212290
David Dupre *(VP-Exploration)*

METALLOINVEST JSC
28 Rublevskoye Roadway, Moscow, Russia
Tel.: (7) 4959815555
Web Site: http://www.metalloinvest.com
Year Founded: 2006
Sales Range: $5-14.9 Billion
Holding Company; Steel Mining
N.A.I.C.S.: 551112
Andrey Varichev *(CEO)*

Subsidiaries:

OAO Lebedinskiy Mining and Processing Works   (1)
Industrial Area Industrial Site of LGOK, Gubkin City, 309191, Belgorod, Russia
Tel.: (7) 4724154455
Iron Ore Mining Services
N.A.I.C.S.: 212210

OAO Mikhailovsky Mining and Processing Works   (1)
21 Lenina St, Zheleznogorsk, 307170, Kursk, Russia
Tel.: (7) 4714894105
Iron Ore Mining Services
N.A.I.C.S.: 212210

OAO Oskol Electrometallurgical Plant   (1)
Stary Oskol, 309515, Belgorod, Russia
Tel.: (7) 4725372707
Steel Products Mfr
N.A.I.C.S.: 331110

OAO Ural Steel   (1)
1 Zavodskaya St, Novotroitsk, Orenburg, 462353, Russia
Tel.: (7) 3537 66 21 53
Steel Products Mfr
N.A.I.C.S.: 331110

OOO Management Company METALLOINVEST   (1)
28 Rublevskoye Roadway, 121609, Moscow, Russia
Tel.: (7) 4959815555
Steel Products Mfr
N.A.I.C.S.: 331110

METALLUM RESOURCES INC.
1681 Chestnut Street Suite 400, Vancouver, V6J 4M6, BC, Canada
Tel.: (416) 953-5879   Ca
Web Site: https://www.metallumzinc.com
Year Founded: 1993
COPS—(TSXV)
Rev.: $410,909
Assets: $348,770
Liabilities: $4,286,573
Net Worth: ($3,937,803)
Earnings: ($5,642,414)
Fiscal Year-end: 12/31/19
Mineral Exploration Services
N.A.I.C.S.: 213114
Simon T. P. Ridgway *(Chm & CEO)*

Subsidiaries:

Minera Focus, S.A.C.   (1)
Av Guardia Civil 696, San Isidro, Lima, 27, Peru
Tel.: (51) 1 226 7152
Silver Ore Mining Services
N.A.I.C.S.: 212220

METALLURGICAL INDUSTRIES COMPANY (EJSC)
5 Athad Elmohameen Elarab Street, Cairo, Egypt
Tel.: (20) 27954844
Web Site: http://www.micor.com.eg
Sales Range: $150-199.9 Million
Emp.: 1,000
Holding Company
N.A.I.C.S.: 551112
Zaki A. Bassyoni *(Chm)*

Subsidiaries:

Egyptian Iron & Steel Company   (1)
Al-Tabbin, Helwan, Cairo, Egypt   (89.99%)
Tel.: (20) 27155491
Web Site: https://www.hadisolb.com
Sales Range: Less than $1 Million
Iron & Steel Product Mfr
N.A.I.C.S.: 331110

METALMAN INDUSTRIES LIMITED
JANAK 11 - New Palasia, Indore, 452001, MP, India
Tel.: (91) 731 4025522
Web Site: http://www.metalman-india.com
Year Founded: 1971
Sales Range: $50-74.9 Million
Pipes Mfr
N.A.I.C.S.: 331210
Rajiv Lochan Soni *(Chm & Mng Dir)*

METALNA INDUSTRIJA PRIJEDOR A.D.
Rudnicka bb, 79101, Prijedor, Bosnia & Herzegovina
Tel.: (387) 52 232 511
Web Site: http://www.mip.rs.ba
Year Founded: 1957
Emp.: 91
Welded Steel Structures & Components Mfr
N.A.I.C.S.: 333992
Boro Babic *(Gen Mgr)*

METALNRG PLC
107 Cheapside 9th Floor, London, EC2V 6DN, United Kingdom
Tel.: (44) 2077969060   UK
Web Site: https://www.metalnrg.com
MNRG—(LSE)
Rev.: $45,168
Assets: $2,577,881
Liabilities: $2,340,249
Net Worth: $237,632
Earnings: ($2,800,350)
Emp.: 4
Fiscal Year-end: 12/31/22
Financial Investment Services
N.A.I.C.S.: 523999
Rolf Ad Gerritsen *(CEO)*

Subsidiaries:

MetalNRG Eco Limited   (1)
1 Ely Place, London, EC1N 6RY, United Kingdom
Tel.: (44) 2077969060
Web Site: https://www.metalnrg.com
Investment Management Service
N.A.I.C.S.: 523999

METALO MANUFACTURING INC.
PO Box 14 535 Larry Uteck Blvd, Halifax, B3M 0E3, NS, Canada
Tel.: (902) 233-7255   AB
Web Site: https://www.metalo.ca
Year Founded: 2000
MMI—(CNSX)
Assets: $1,220,334
Liabilities: $9,685,683
Net Worth: ($8,465,350)
Earnings: ($1,124,537)
Fiscal Year-end: 06/30/22
Investment Services
N.A.I.C.S.: 523999
David J. Hennigar *(Chm)*

METALOPACK AD
Industrialna Zona, Karnobat, 8400, Bulgaria
Tel.: (359) 889322123
Web Site: https://www.metalopak.com
METK—(BUL)
Sales Range: Less than $1 Million
Packaging Product Mfr & Distr
N.A.I.C.S.: 326111

METALOPLASTIKA A.D.
Zlatiborska, 331310, Cajetina, Serbia
Tel.: (381) 313831386
Web Site: https://www.metaloplastika.rs
Year Founded: 1960
METL—(BEL)
Rev.: $7,970,600
Assets: $4,433,024
Liabilities: $1,987,351
Net Worth: $2,445,674
Earnings: $8,576
Emp.: 64
Fiscal Year-end: 12/31/22
Fabricated Metal Products Mfr
N.A.I.C.S.: 332999
Miroslav Gavrilovic *(Exec Dir)*

METALOPLASTIKA A.D.
Stopanja bb, 37242, Trstenik, Serbia
Tel.: (381) 37 727 659
Year Founded: 1960
Sales Range: $1-9.9 Million
Emp.: 46
Healtcare Services
N.A.I.C.S.: 621610
Radmila Stevanovic *(Exec Dir)*

METALOPRERADA A.D. UZICE
Krcagovo 29, 31000, Uzice, Serbia
Tel.: (381) 31 563 411
Web Site: http://www.metaloprerada.rs
Metal Products Mfr
N.A.I.C.S.: 332999
Aleksandar Katic *(Gen Mgr)*

INTERNATIONAL PUBLIC

METALORE RESOURCES LIMITED
PO Box 422, Simcoe, N3Y 4L5, ON, Canada
Tel.: (519) 428-2464
Web Site: https://www.metaloreresources.ca
MET—(TSXV)
Rev.: $318,640
Assets: $5,374,787
Liabilities: $745,038
Net Worth: $4,629,749
Earnings: ($635,704)
Emp.: 4
Fiscal Year-end: 03/31/24
Precious Metals & Hydrocarbons Explorer & Developer
N.A.I.C.S.: 213114
John Claire McVicar *(Chm)*

METALOTEHNA D.D. TUZLA
Husinskih rudara br 138, 75000, Tuzla, Bosnia & Herzegovina
Tel.: (387) 35 300 400
Web Site: http://www.metalotehna.ba
MTHNRK2—(SARE)
Rev.: $116,248
Assets: $1,842,712
Liabilities: $374,312
Net Worth: $1,468,400
Earnings: $32,247
Emp.: 1
Fiscal Year-end: 12/31/19
Metal Product Distr
N.A.I.C.S.: 423510

METALOTEHNA TRADE A.D.
Kralja Milutina 36, Belgrade, Serbia
Tel.: (381) 11 2656 033
Year Founded: 1992
MTTR—(BEL)
Sales Range: Less than $1 Million
Hardware Product Retailer
N.A.I.C.S.: 444140
Dragan Perkovic *(Dir)*

METALPHA TECHNOLOGY HOLDING LIMITED
Room 1803 Yintai International Building Kejiguan Road, Binjiang District, Hangzhou, Zhejiang, China
Tel.: (852) 85235652920   CN
Web Site: https://www.metalpha.net
Year Founded: 2014
MATH—(NASDAQ)
Rev.: $16,763,545
Assets: $174,718,509
Liabilities: $157,867,334
Net Worth: $16,851,175
Earnings: ($3,679,409)
Emp.: 19
Fiscal Year-end: 08/31/24
Fund Management Consulting Services
N.A.I.C.S.: 541611
Xiaohua Gu *(CFO)*

METALQUEST MINING INC
101-2148 West 38th Avenue, Vancouver, V6M 1R9, BC, Canada
Tel.: (613) 659-2773   BC
Web Site: https://www.elninoventures.com
Year Founded: 1989
ELN—(OTCIQ)
Rev.: $270
Assets: $798,096
Liabilities: $17,989
Net Worth: $780,107
Earnings: ($95,568)
Fiscal Year-end: 01/31/22
Copper Mining Exploration & Development Services
N.A.I.C.S.: 212230
Robert Guanzon *(CFO)*

AND PRIVATE COMPANIES

METALRAX GROUP PLC
Rectory Court Old Rectory Lane Alvechurch, Birmingham, B48 7SX, United Kingdom
Tel.: (44) 8450303300 UK
Web Site:
http://www.metalraxgroup.co.uk
Year Founded: 1964
Emp.: 469
Holding Company
N.A.I.C.S.: 551112

Subsidiaries:

Metalrax Engineering Support Services Limited (1)
Rectory Court Old Rectory Lane, Alvechurch, Birmingham, B48 7SX, W Midlands, United Kingdom (100%)
Tel.: (44) 1214 333444
Industrial Machinery & Equipment Whslr
N.A.I.C.S.: 423830

Metalrax Specialist Applications Limited (1)
Rectory Court Old Rectory Lane, Alvechurch, Birmingham, B48 7SX, W Midlands, United Kingdom (100%)
Tel.: (44) 1215583911
Specialty Fabricated Metal Products Mfr & Whslr
N.A.I.C.S.: 332999

METALS AUSTRALIA LIMITED
Level 1 8 Parliament Place, PO Box 1618, West Perth, 6005, WA, Australia
Tel.: (61) 894817833 AU
Web Site:
https://metalsaustralia.com.au
Year Founded: 1981
MLS—(ASX)
Rev.: $528,528
Assets: $24,819,378
Liabilities: $862,961
Net Worth: $23,956,417
Earnings: ($359,030)
Fiscal Year-end: 06/30/24
Mineral Exploration Services
N.A.I.C.S.: 212290
Martin Stein *(Sec)*

METALS CREEK RESOURCES CORP.
945 Cobalt Cres, Vancouver, P7B 5Z4, ON, Canada
Tel.: (807) 345-4990
Web Site:
https://www.metalscreek.com
Year Founded: 2004
M1C1—(DEU)
Rev.: $9,723
Assets: $6,812,252
Liabilities: $108,266
Net Worth: $6,703,986
Earnings: ($695,969)
Fiscal Year-end: 12/31/23
Gold Exploration Services
N.A.I.C.S.: 213114
Alexander Stares *(Pres & CEO)*

METALS EXPLORATION PLC
3843 Lincoln's Inn Fields, London, WC2A 3PE, United Kingdom
Tel.: (44) 2075397272 UK
Web Site:
https://www.metalsexploration.com
MTL—(AIM)
Rev.: $124,410,991
Assets: $120,605,467
Liabilities: $102,841,708
Net Worth: $17,763,759
Earnings: $8,753,956
Emp.: 791
Fiscal Year-end: 12/31/22
Metals Mining & Exploration Services
N.A.I.C.S.: 212290
Darren Patrick Bowden *(CEO)*

Subsidiaries:

FCF Minerals Corporation (1)
Unit 1407 Pacific Star Building Sen Gil Puyat Avenue corner, Makati Avenue, Makati, 1227, Metro Manila, Philippines
Tel.: (63) 28 659 5662
Web Site: http://www.fcfminerals.com
Metal Exploration Services
N.A.I.C.S.: 213114

MTL Philippines (1)
Unit 1407 Pacific Star Building Sen Gil Puyat Avenue cor Makati Avenue, Makati, 1227, Metro Manila, Philippines
Tel.: (63) 28944173
Gold & Copper Exploration Services
N.A.I.C.S.: 213114

METALS PLUS INCOME CORP.
141 Adelaide Street West Suite 1402, Toronto, M5H 3L5, ON, Canada
Tel.: (416) 364-8989 ON
Web Site:
http://faircourtassetmgt.com
Year Founded: 2011
Sales Range: Less than $1 Million
Investment Services
N.A.I.C.S.: 523999
Charles Taerk *(Pres & CEO)*

METALS X LIMITED
Tel.: (61) 892205700 AU
Web Site:
https://www.metalsx.com.au
MLX—(OTCIQ)
Rev.: $71,894,672
Assets: $140,518,480
Liabilities: $34,289,301
Net Worth: $106,229,179
Earnings: $66,811,002
Emp.: 467
Fiscal Year-end: 06/30/21
Metal Ore Exploration & Mining
N.A.I.C.S.: 212290
Fiona J. Van Maanen *(CFO & Sec)*

METALSGROVE MINING LIMITED
Suite 9 Level 2 389 Oxford Street, Hawthorn, 6016, WA, Australia
Tel.: (61) 893806789 AU
Web Site:
https://www.metalsgrove.com.au
Year Founded: 2021
MGA—(ASX)
Rev.: $33,644
Assets: $4,278,270
Liabilities: $86,402
Net Worth: $4,191,868
Earnings: ($2,236,547)
Fiscal Year-end: 06/30/24
Metal Exploration Services
N.A.I.C.S.: 213114
Anbarasan Sivasamy *(CEO)*

METALSTECH LIMITED
Unit 1 44 Denis Street, Subiaco, 6008, WA, Australia
Tel.: (61) 400408878 AU
Web Site: https://www.metalstech.net
Year Founded: 2016
MTC—(ASX)
Rev.: $1,826
Assets: $5,903,460
Liabilities: $1,556,380
Net Worth: $4,347,079
Earnings: ($1,511,386)
Fiscal Year-end: 06/30/24
Lithium Exploration Services
N.A.I.C.S.: 212390
Paul Fromson *(CFO & Sec)*

METALUL MESA SA
Str Gestului No 5, Bihor, Salonta, Romania
Tel.: (40) 259373175
Web Site: https://www.mesa.ro
Year Founded: 1991

MESA—(BUC)
Rev.: $2,179,866
Assets: $1,161,615
Liabilities: $613,128
Net Worth: $548,487
Earnings: $22,521
Emp.: 36
Fiscal Year-end: 12/31/23
Iron & Steel Forging Mfr
N.A.I.C.S.: 332111

METALUMEN MANUFACTURING INC
570 Southgate Dr, Guelph, N1G 4P6, ON, Canada
Tel.: (519) 822-4381
Web Site: http://www.metalumen.com
Year Founded: 1977
Rev.: $16,244,590
Emp.: 80
Lighting Equipment Mfr
N.A.I.C.S.: 335139
Martin F. Stocker *(Pres)*

METALURGICA DUQUE S.A.
R Engelberto Otto Hagemann 396, 89226185, Joinville, SC, Brazil
Tel.: (55) 47 3451 2000
Web Site: http://www.duque.com.br
Year Founded: 1955
Sales Range: $25-49.9 Million
Emp.: 1,000
Bicycle Parts Mfr
N.A.I.C.S.: 336991
Mario Hagemann *(Dir-IR)*

METALURGICA GERDAU S.A.
Av Farrapos 1811 Floresta, 90220 005, Porto Alegre, RS, Brazil
Tel.: (55) 5133232000 BR
Web Site: http://www.gerdau.com.br
Year Founded: 1961
GOAU3—(BRAZ)
Rev.: $13,743,433,443
Assets: $15,002,983,747
Liabilities: $5,116,965,400
Net Worth: $9,886,018,347
Earnings: $1,512,632,167
Emp.: 28,350
Fiscal Year-end: 12/31/23
Iron & Steel Product Mfr
N.A.I.C.S.: 551112
Gustavo Werneck da Cunha *(CEO)*

Subsidiaries:

Aceros Cox Comercial S.A. (1)
Camino Lo Ruiz 2901, Renca, Santiago, Chile
Tel.: (56) 2 498 1000
Web Site: http://www.aceroscox.cl
Sales Range: $25-49.9 Million
Emp.: 37
Steel Product Distr
N.A.I.C.S.: 423510

GTL Servicios Administrativos Mexico, S.A. de C.V. (1)
Pdte Masaryk No 111 Piso 3-302 Chapultepec Morales, Seccion Miguel Hidalgo, Mexico, 11570, Mexico
Tel.: (52) 5552627301
Sales Range: $25-49.9 Million
Emp.: 15
Administrative Management Services
N.A.I.C.S.: 561110

Gerdau Forestry (1)
Ave Farrapos 1811, Porto Alegre, 90220005, RS, Brazil (100%)
Tel.: (55) 5133232000
Web Site: http://www.gerdau.com
Sales Range: $1-4.9 Billion
Emp.: 400
Developer of Trees & Forests
N.A.I.C.S.: 113210
Andre Gerdau Johananpeter *(Pres)*

Gerdau S.A. (1)
Av Dra Ruth Cardoso 8 501 - 8 Floor, Pinheiros, Sao Paulo, 05425-070, SP, Brazil (74.94%)

METALURGICA GERDAU S.A.

Tel.: (55) 1130946600
Web Site: http://www.gerdau.com
Rev.: $13,743,433,443
Assets: $14,933,721,009
Liabilities: $5,114,424,369
Net Worth: $9,819,296,640
Earnings: $1,503,037,790
Emp.: 27,371
Fiscal Year-end: 12/31/2023
Steel Mfrs
N.A.I.C.S.: 327331
Guilherme Chagas Gerdau Johannpeter *(Chm)*

Subsidiary (Domestic):

Banco Gerdau (2)
Ave Farrapos 1811, Porto Alegre, 90220 005, RS, Brazil
Tel.: (55) 5133232000
Web Site: http://www.bancogerdau.com.br
Sales Range: $50-74.9 Million
Emp.: 25
Banking Services & Financing
N.A.I.C.S.: 522180
Murilo Osorio *(Gen Mgr)*

Subsidiary (Non-US):

Bogey Holding Company Spain S.L. (2)
Calle Portal De Gamarra 22, Vitoria, 1013, Alava, Spain
Tel.: (34) 945 16 46 00
Investment Management Service
N.A.I.C.S.: 523999

Subsidiary (Domestic):

Gerdau Acominas S.A. (2)
Rua Cenno Sbrighi 170 Ed II, 4 Andar Agua Branca, Sao Paulo, CEP 05036 010, SP, Brazil
Tel.: (55) 38744000
Sales Range: $25-49.9 Million
Emp.: 20
Steel Products Mfr
N.A.I.C.S.: 331110

Gerdau Acos Especiais S.A. (2)
Av Getulio Vargas 3200, 96705-000, Sao Paulo, Brazil
Tel.: (55) 5133232000
Web Site: http://www.gerdau.com.br
Sales Range: $350-399.9 Million
Emp.: 2,000
Steel Products Mfr
N.A.I.C.S.: 332111

Gerdau Acos Esticiais S.A. (2)
Ave Getulio Vargas 3200, Charqueadas, 96745000, RS, Brazil (100%)
Tel.: (55) 5133235824
Web Site: http://www.gerdau.com
Sales Range: $150-199.9 Million
Emp.: 1,500
Mfr of Steel
N.A.I.C.S.: 331110

Gerdau Acos Longos S.A. (2)
Avenida Farrapos 1811, 90220 005, Porto Alegre, RS, Brazil
Tel.: (55) 5133232000
Web Site: http://www.gerdau.com.br
Sales Range: $75-99.9 Million
Emp.: 300
Mfr of Steel Chains
N.A.I.C.S.: 331222
Jorge Johann Peter *(Pres)*

Gerdau Ameristeel Corporation (2)
Av Farrapos 1811 Floresta, Porto Alegre, 90220 005, Rio Grande do Sul, Brazil
Tel.: (55) 51 3323 2000
Sales Range: $350-399.9 Million
Emp.: 200
Steel Products Mfr
N.A.I.C.S.: 331513

Subsidiary (US):

Gerdau Long Steel North America (3)
4221 W Boy Scout Blvd Ste 600, Tampa, FL 33607
Tel.: (813) 286-8383
Web Site: http://www.gerdau.com
Sales Range: $1-4.9 Billion
Steel Mills, Scrap Recycling & Fabrication Facilities Owner & Operator

METALURGICA GERDAU S.A.

Metalurgica Gerdau S.A.—(Continued)
N.A.I.C.S.: 324199

Subsidiary (Domestic):

Gerdau Ameristeel Perth Amboy Inc. (4)
225 Elm St, Perth Amboy, NJ 08861
Tel.: (732) 442-1600
Web Site: http://www.gerdauameristeel.com
Emp.: 50
Steel Products Mfr
N.A.I.C.S.: 331110
Mike Woskey (Plant Mgr)

Division (Domestic):

Gerdau Perth Amboy Recycling Division (5)
225 Elm St, Perth Amboy, NJ 08862
Tel.: (732) 442-1600
Web Site: http://www.gerdau.com
Sales Range: $25-49.9 Million
Emp.: 5
Steel Mills
N.A.I.C.S.: 331110
Mark A. Quiring (VP & Gen Mgr-Perth Amboy & Sayreville Mills)

Subsidiary (Non-US):

Gerdau Cambridge Steel Mill (4)
160 Orion Pl, PO Box 1734, Cambridge, N1T 1R9, ON, Canada
Tel.: (519) 740-2488
Web Site: http://www.gerdau.com
Sales Range: $50-74.9 Million
Emp.: 200
Steel Mills
N.A.I.C.S.: 331110
Earl Weber (Mgr-Pur)

Plant (Domestic):

Gerdau Cartersville Steel Mill (4)
384 Old Grassdale Rd NE, Cartersville, GA 30121-5083
Tel.: (770) 387-3300
Web Site: http://www.gerdau.com
Sales Range: $125-149.9 Million
Emp.: 300
Steel Bar Mfr
N.A.I.C.S.: 331110

Gerdau Charlotte Steel Mill (4)
6601 Lakeview Rd, Charlotte, NC 28269
Tel.: (704) 596-0361
Web Site: http://www.gerdau.com
Sales Range: $100-124.9 Million
Emp.: 280
Steel Mills
N.A.I.C.S.: 331110

Gerdau Cincinnati Reinforcing Steel (4)
2175 Schlichter Dr, Hamilton, OH 45015
Tel.: (513) 869-7660
Web Site: http://www.gerdau.com
Sales Range: $25-49.9 Million
Emp.: 22
Structural Steel Fabrication
N.A.I.C.S.: 332312
Mike Gruber (Mgr-Sls)

Gerdau Joliet Steel Mill (4)
1 Industry Ave, Joliet, IL 60435-2653
Tel.: (815) 723-9335
Web Site: http://www.gerdau.com
Sales Range: $50-74.9 Million
Emp.: 200
Hot Rolled Steel Bar & Rebar Mfr
N.A.I.C.S.: 331110
Chuck Lamar (Mgr-Quality Assurance)

Subsidiary (Non-US):

Gerdau Manitoba Steel Mill (4)
27 Main St, PO Box 2500, Selkirk, R1A 2B4, MB, Canada (100%)
Tel.: (204) 482-3241
Sales Range: $100-124.9 Million
Emp.: 450
Mfr of Steel
N.A.I.C.S.: 331110
Gavin Tobin (VP & Gen Mgr)

Plant (Domestic):

Gerdau Midlothian Steel Mill (4)
300 Ward Rd, Midlothian, TX 76065-9801

Tel.: (972) 775-8241
Web Site: http://www.gerdau.com
Sales Range: $450-499.9 Million
Emp.: 1,450
Structural Steel Products Mfr & Scrap Steel Recycling
N.A.I.C.S.: 331110

Gerdau Muncie Reinforcing & Coating (4)
1810 S Macedonia Ave, Muncie, IN 47302
Tel.: (765) 286-5454
Web Site: http://www.gerdau.com
Sales Range: $25-49.9 Million
Emp.: 60
Mfr of Fabricated Structural Metal
N.A.I.C.S.: 332312
Mike Barrett (Div Mgr)

Gerdau Nashville Reinforcing Steel (4)
110 N 1st St, Nashville, TN 37213-1102
Tel.: (615) 256-3192
Web Site: http://www.gerdau.com
Sales Range: $75-99.9 Million
Emp.: 250
Concrete, Masonry & Other Building Materials Distr & Structural Steel Fabricator
N.A.I.C.S.: 444180
Ron Long (Reg Mgr)

Gerdau New Orleans Rebar Express (4)
325 Hord St, Harahan, LA 70123-4117 (100%)
Tel.: (504) 736-2110
Web Site: http://www.gerdau.com
Sales Range: $1-9.9 Million
Emp.: 8
Mfr of Welded Wire Fabric & Nails
N.A.I.C.S.: 331110

Gerdau Reinforcing Steel West (4)
3880 Murphy Canyon Rd, San Diego, CA 92123
Tel.: (858) 737-7700
Web Site: http://www.gerdauameristeel.com
Emp.: 150
Fabricated Structural Metal Mfr
N.A.I.C.S.: 332312
Nancy Erickson (Mgr-HR)

Subsidiary (Non-US):

Gerdau Whitby Steel Mill (4)
1801 Hopkins St S, Whitby, L1N 5T1, ON, Canada (100%)
Tel.: (905) 668-8811
Web Site: http://www.gerdau.com
Rev.: $658,400,000
Emp.: 600
Steel Bar, Structural Shapes & Flat Rolled Steel Mfr
N.A.I.C.S.: 331110

Plant (Domestic):

Lancaster Rail Products (4)
1888 Riverside Rd, Lancaster, SC 29720-8844 (100%)
Tel.: (803) 285-8444
Web Site: http://www.gerdau.com
Sales Range: $25-49.9 Million
Emp.: 45
Railroad Spikes
N.A.I.C.S.: 332111
Ron Ancevic (Gen Mgr)

Subsidiary (US):

Gerdau MacSteel Inc. (3)
5591 Morrill Rd, Jackson, MI 49201
Tel.: (800) 876-7833
Web Site: http://www.gerdaumacsteel.com
Steel Products Mfr & Distr
N.A.I.C.S.: 332999

Gerdau Special Steel North America (3)
5591 Morrill Rd, Jackson, MI 49201
Tel.: (517) 782-0415
Web Site: http://www.gerdau.com
Sales Range: $100-124.9 Million
Steel Bars & Billets Mfr
N.A.I.C.S.: 331110
Jack Finlayson (Pres)

Division (Domestic):

Gerdau Fort Smith Mill (4)

5225 Planters Rd, Fort Smith, AR 72915
Tel.: (479) 646-0223
Web Site: http://www.gerdau.com
Sales Range: $125-149.9 Million
Emp.: 350
Steel Bar Mfr
N.A.I.C.S.: 331110

Gerdau Monroe Mill (4)
3000 E Front St, Monroe, MI 48161
Tel.: (734) 243-2446
Web Site: http://www.gerdau.com
Sales Range: $100-124.9 Million
Steel Bars & Billets Mfr
N.A.I.C.S.: 331221
Tom Card (Supvr-Metallurgical Turn)

Gerdau Special Steel North America Nitro Steel - Pleasant Prairie Facility (4)
9955 80th Ave, Pleasant Prairie, WI 53158-2221
Tel.: (262) 947-0441
Web Site: http://www.gerdau.com
Sales Range: $25-49.9 Million
Emp.: 20
Nitrocarbonizing of Steel Tubing & Bars
N.A.I.C.S.: 331110

Gerdau Special Steel North America Quench & Temper Processes- Huntington Facility (4)
25 Commercial Rd, Huntington, IN 46750-8805
Tel.: (260) 356-9520
Web Site: http://www.gerdau.com
Sales Range: $25-49.9 Million
Emp.: 37
Heat Treating of Steel Tubing & Bars
N.A.I.C.S.: 332811

Subsidiary (Non-US):

Gerdau Steel Inc. (3)
160 Orion Place, Cambridge, N1T 1R9, ON, Canada
Tel.: (519) 740-2488
Sales Range: $75-99.9 Million
Emp.: 120
Steel Products Mfr
N.A.I.C.S.: 331110
Silvio Lemos (Gen Mgr)

Subsidiary (US):

TAMCO Steel, Inc. (3)
12459-B Arrow Route, Rancho Cucamonga, CA 91739-9601
Tel.: (909) 899-0660
Steel Bar Mfr
N.A.I.C.S.: 331110

Subsidiary (Domestic):

Gerdau Comercial De Acos S.A. (2)
Av dos Estados 1601, 90200-001, Porto Alegre, Brazil
Tel.: (55) 5133732500
Sales Range: $25-49.9 Million
Emp.: 35
Steel Products Mfr
N.A.I.C.S.: 332111

Subsidiary (Non-US):

Gerdau GTL Spain S.L. (2)
C/ Pedro de Vera 3 1A, Las Palmas de Gran Canaria, Las Palmas, Spain
Tel.: (34) 928380984
Steel Products Mfr
N.A.I.C.S.: 331110

Gerdau Laisa (2)
Camino Santos Dumont 2289, PO Box 15043, Montevideo, 12200, Uruguay (100%)
Tel.: (598) 25142727
Web Site: http://www.gerdaulaisa.com.uy
Sales Range: $75-99.9 Million
Emp.: 300
Mfr of Steel
N.A.I.C.S.: 331110

Subsidiary (Domestic):

Seiva S.A. - Florestas e Industrias (2)
Av Farrapos 1811 Floresta, Porto Alegre, 90220 005, Rio Grande do Sul, Brazil
Tel.: (55) 51 3323 2000

INTERNATIONAL PUBLIC

Timber Tract & Forestation Management Services
N.A.I.C.S.: 113110

Subsidiary (Non-US):

Sipar Aceros S.A. (2)
Route Nacional N 33 km 844, Santa Fe, 2121, Argentina
Tel.: (54) 3414958100
Web Site: http://www.sipar.com.ar
Sales Range: $75-99.9 Million
Emp.: 400
Steel Products Mfr
N.A.I.C.S.: 332111
Fernando Lombardo (Gen Mgr)

METALURGICA RIOSULENSE S.A.
Street Emilio Adami 700, 89164-910, Rio do Sul, SC, Brazil
Tel.: 4735314000
Web Site:
http://www.riosulense.com.br
Year Founded: 1946
RSUL4—(BRAZ)
Rev.: $61,034,481
Assets: $63,938,612
Liabilities: $30,133,175
Net Worth: $33,805,437
Earnings: $9,675,551
Fiscal Year-end: 12/31/23
Automobile Parts Mfr
N.A.I.C.S.: 336390

METALURGICA SA
Sos Iancului 46-48 S2, 21726, Bucharest, Romania
Tel.: (40) 212506666
Web Site: http://www.metalurgica.eu
MECA—(BUC)
Rev.: $954,763
Assets: $1,552,780
Liabilities: $80,903
Net Worth: $1,471,877
Earnings: $595
Emp.: 19
Fiscal Year-end: 12/31/23
Plastics Product Mfr
N.A.I.C.S.: 326199

METALURSKO KEMICNA INDUSTRIJA CELJE, D.D.
Kidriceva 26, 3001, Celje, Slovenia
Tel.: (386) 34276000
Web Site: http://www.cinkarna.si
Year Founded: 1873
Sales Range: $450-499.9 Million
Emp.: 1,000
Production & Marketing of Titanium Dioxide Pigments
N.A.I.C.S.: 325998
Tomaz Bencina (Pres-Mgmt Bd & Gen Mgr)

Subsidiaries:

Cinkarna Kvarc d. o. o. (1)
Ul 21 Decembar Bb, Tuzla, Bosnia & Herzegovina
Tel.: (387) 35286544
Chemical Products Mfr
N.A.I.C.S.: 325998

Kemija Mozirje (1)
Ljubija 11, 3330, Mozirje, Slovenia
Tel.: (386) 38370900
Web Site: http://www.cinkarna.si
Sales Range: $25-49.9 Million
Emp.: 40
Chemicals Mfr
N.A.I.C.S.: 325180

METALUS INC.
675 Rue Rocheleau, Drummondville, J2C 6L8, QC, Canada
Tel.: (819) 475-3114
Web Site: http://www.metalus.qc.ca
Year Founded: 1995
Rev.: $13,737,302
Emp.: 100

AND PRIVATE COMPANIES

Sheet Metal Transformation & Laser Cutting Services
N.A.I.C.S.: 423510
Sylvain Audet *(Pres)*

Subsidiaries:

Metalus inc. - Metal Grenier Division (1)
970 Pierre-Roux Est Blvd, Victoriaville, G6T 2H6, QC, Canada
Tel.: (819) 752-3807
Sheet Metal Cutting Services
N.A.I.C.S.: 423510

METAMEND SOFTWARE & DESIGN LTD.

3403 Seymour Place 2nd Floor, Victoria, V8X 1W4, BC, Canada
Tel.: (250) 381-6382
Web Site: http://www.metamend.com
Year Founded: 1998
Sales Range: $1-9.9 Million
Emp.: 10
Search Engine Marketing
N.A.I.C.S.: 541519
Todd Hooge *(Pres)*

METANET, INC.

10-2 Gwancheol-dong, Jongno-gu, Seoul, Korea (South)
Tel.: (82) 2 6001 8000   KR
Web Site: http://www.metanet.co.kr
Year Founded: 2000
Sales Range: $650-699.9 Million
Emp.: 9,000
Information Technology Consulting Services
N.A.I.C.S.: 541690
Young S. Choi *(Founder & Chm)*

Subsidiaries:

Vina Daewoo Information System Company Limited (1)
Ground Floor Rosana Tower 60 Nguyen Dinh Chieu st, Ward Da Kao Dist 1, Ho Chi Minh City, Vietnam
Tel.: (84) 344102067
Education Management Services
N.A.I.C.S.: 611430

METANOLSKO-SIRCETNI KOMPLEKS KIKINDA

Milosevacki put bb, 23300, Kikinda, Serbia
Tel.: (381) 230 423 050
Web Site: http://www.msk.co.rs
Emp.: 520
Organic Chemical Mfr
N.A.I.C.S.: 325199
Latinovic Mirko *(Gen Mgr)*

METAPS INC.

1-4-1 Mita Sumitomo Fudosan Azabu Juban Building 3F, Minato-ku, Tokyo, Japan
Tel.: (81) 353256280
Web Site: http://corp.metaps.com
6172—(TKS)
Rev.: $57,160,400
Assets: $272,124,160
Liabilities: $182,293,760
Net Worth: $89,830,400
Earnings: ($15,410,560)
Emp.: 231
Fiscal Year-end: 12/31/22
Business Software Developer
N.A.I.C.S.: 513210
Yuichiro Yamazaki *(CEO)*

Subsidiaries:

Metaps Pte Ltd. (1)
2 Marina Blvd Ste 38-01, The Sail Marina Bay, Singapore, 18987, Singapore
Tel.: (65) 62259792
Web Site: http://metaps.com
Emp.: 2
Software Development Services
N.A.I.C.S.: 541511

Wai Cheong Choy *(COO)*

Torchlight Inc. (1)
Ebisu Garden Place Tower 33rd floor 4-20-3, Ebisu Shibuya-ku, Tokyo, 150-6033, Japan
Tel.: (81) 35 447 7160
Web Site: https://www.torchlight.co.jp
Advertising Services
N.A.I.C.S.: 541810

METAREAL CORPORATION

23F Shinjuku Oak Tower 6-8-1 Nishi-Shinjuku, Tokyo, 163-6023, Japan
Tel.: (81) 366859570
Web Site: http://www.rozetta.jp
Year Founded: 1952
6182—(TKS)
Rev.: $29,614,930
Assets: $31,607,220
Liabilities: $19,688,930
Net Worth: $11,918,290
Earnings: $3,786,060
Fiscal Year-end: 02/29/24
Online Translation Service
N.A.I.C.S.: 541930
Junichi Goishi *(CEO)*

METAROCK GROUP LIMITED

Level 1 Riverside Plaza 45 River Street, PO Box 1671, MacKay, 4740, QLD, Australia
Tel.: (61) 749630400
Web Site:
    https://www.mastermyne.com.au
MYE—(ASX)
Rev.: $346,853
Assets: $229,208
Liabilities: $165,471
Net Worth: $63,737
Earnings: ($9,620)
Emp.: 1,962
Fiscal Year-end: 06/30/22
Underground Coal Mining
N.A.I.C.S.: 212115
Anthony Caruso *(CEO & Mng Dir)*

Subsidiaries:

Mynesight Pty Ltd (1)
45 River Street, PO Box 4449, MacKay, 4740, QLD, Australia
Tel.: (61) 1300447020
Web Site: https://www.mynesight.com.au
Mining Training Services
N.A.I.C.S.: 213113

Wilson Mining Services Pty Limited (1)
16 Metro Court, Gateshead, 2290, NSW, Australia
Tel.: (61) 249048222
Web Site: https://www.wilsonmining.com.au
Mining Services
N.A.I.C.S.: 213113

METATECH (AP), INC.

Rm 3 14F No 75 Sec 1 Xintai 5th Rd, Xizhi Dist, New Taipei City, 221, Taiwan
Tel.: (886) 226983466
Web Site:
    https://www.metatech.com.tw
Year Founded: 1998
3224—(TPE)
Rev.: $57,920,176
Assets: $109,265,579
Liabilities: $17,297,220
Net Worth: $91,968,358
Earnings: ($1,791,608)
Emp.: 183
Fiscal Year-end: 12/31/22
Semiconductor Component Distr
N.A.I.C.S.: 423840
Chun-Hua Chiu *(VP-Admin)*

Subsidiaries:

MetaTech (S) Pte. Ltd. (1)
60 Kaki Bukit Place 07-14 Eunos Techpark, Singapore, 415979, Singapore
Tel.: (65) 68467277

Web Site: http://www.metatech.com.sg
Marketing Services
N.A.I.C.S.: 541613

MetaTech Ltd. (1)
Room 2209 22 Floor Lemmi Centre No 50 Hoi Yuen Road, Kwun Tong, Kowloon, China (Hong Kong)
Tel.: (852) 21632000
Electronic Related Component Mfr
N.A.I.C.S.: 334419

Subsidiary (Non-US):

MetaTech (Shenzhen) Ltd. (2)
Room 305 Building G3 Echengg3 Tcl International No 1001, Zhongshanyuan Road Liuxiandong Xili Nanshan District, Shenzhen, 518055, China
Tel.: (86) 75588352800
Electronic Related Component Mfr
N.A.I.C.S.: 334419

METAVERSE CAPITAL CORP.

789 West Pender Street Suite 810, Vancouver, V6C 1H2, BC, Canada
Tel.: (604) 687-2038
Software Development Services
N.A.I.C.S.: 541511

METAVERSE YUNJI TECHNOLOGY GROUP COMPANY LIMITED

Room 701 Block D Building 4 Shenzhen Software Industry Base, Shenzhen, China
Tel.: (86) 75561363288   Ky
Web Site: http://www.zioncom.net
Year Founded: 1999
8287—(HKG)
Rev.: $79,189,485
Assets: $60,641,423
Liabilities: $42,812,715
Net Worth: $17,828,708
Earnings: $5,430,735)
Emp.: 850
Fiscal Year-end: 12/31/21
Electronic Equipment Mfr & Distr
N.A.I.C.S.: 334210
Byung Kwon Kim *(Founder & Chm)*

Subsidiaries:

Zioncom (Hong Kong) Technology Limited (1)
Room 1 6/F Fortune Commercial Building 362 Sha Tsui Road, Tsuen Wan, China (Hong Kong)
Tel.: (852) 24959788
Network Communication Product Mfr
N.A.I.C.S.: 334210

Zioncom Holdings Limited - Shenzhen Factory (1)
Blocks A1 & A2 B1 & B2 Lantian Technology Park Henggangxia, Xinqiao Town Shajing Subdistrict Bao'an District, Shenzhen, China
Tel.: (86) 75561363299
Network Communication Product Mfr
N.A.I.C.S.: 334210

METAWATER CO., LTD.

JR Kanda Manseibashi Building 25 Kanda Sudacho 1chome, Chiyoda-ku, Tokyo, 101-0041, Japan
Tel.: (81) 368537300
Web Site:
    https://www.metawater.co.jp
Year Founded: 2008
9551—(TKS)
Rev.: $1,094,358,210
Assets: $1,116,052,230
Liabilities: $615,833,870
Net Worth: $500,218,360
Earnings: $45,443,750
Emp.: 3,565
Fiscal Year-end: 03/31/24
Water, Wastewater & Solid Waste Treatment Systems Equipment Mfr & Construction
N.A.I.C.S.: 221310

Yasushi Nakamura *(Pres & CEO)*

Subsidiaries:

Akebono Engineering Co. (1)
7-8-17 Nishinakajima Yodogawa-Ku, Osaka, Japan
Tel.: (81) 668858181
Sewage Treatment Equipment Mfr
N.A.I.C.S.: 333310

Aqua Service Aichi Co. (1)
2-56 Sudacho Mizuho-Ku, Nagoya, Aichi, Japan
Tel.: (81) 528846896
Waste Water Treatment Services
N.A.I.C.S.: 221320

FUCHS Enprotec GmbH (1)
Stocktal 2, 56727, Mayen, Germany
Tel.: (49) 265180040
Web Site: https://www.fuchswater.com
Water Treatment & Purification System Mfr
N.A.I.C.S.: 333310

METAWATER Services Co., Ltd. (1)
25 1-chome Kanda Sudacho JR Kanda Manseibashi, Chiyoda-ku, Tokyo, 101-0041, Japan
Tel.: (81) 368537265
Web Site: http://metawaterservice.co.jp
Waste Treatment Services
N.A.I.C.S.: 221310

METAWATER TECH Co., Ltd. (1)
1-25 Kanda Sudacho JR Kanda Manseibashi Building, Chiyoda-ku, Tokyo, 101-0041, Japan
Tel.: (81) 368537621
Web Site: http://www.metawatertech.co.jp
Water Treatment & Purification System Mfr
N.A.I.C.S.: 333310

METAWATER USA, INC. (1)
301 Rte 17 N Ste 504, Rutherford, NJ 07070
Tel.: (201) 935-3436
Web Site: https://usa.metawater.com
Waste Water Treatment Services
N.A.I.C.S.: 221320

Subsidiary (Domestic):

Aqua-Aerobic Systems, Inc. (2)
6306 N Alpine Rd, Loves Park, IL 61111-7655
Tel.: (815) 654-2501
Waste Water Treatment Systems
N.A.I.C.S.: 333310
Peter G. Baumann *(Pres & CEO)*

Mecana Umwelttechnik GmbH (1)
Industriestrasse 39, 8864, Reichenburg, Switzerland
Tel.: (41) 554641200
Waste Water Treatment Services
N.A.I.C.S.: 221320

Rood Wit Blauw Holding B.V. (1)
Ambachtstraat 20, 7609 RA, Almelo, Netherlands
Tel.: (31) 546545020
Web Site: https://www.rwbwater.nl
Waste Water Treatment Services
N.A.I.C.S.: 221320

SIC Co., Ltd. (1)
6-3-1 Nishishinjuku Shinjuku-Ku, Tokyo, Japan
Tel.: (81) 353236753
Web Site: http://www.sicfuji.co.jp
Advertising Services
N.A.I.C.S.: 541810
Tetsuo Nakai *(Pres)*

Toriden-Shoji Co. (1)
153-36 Kumoyama, Tottori, 6800862, Tottori, Japan
Tel.: (81) 857234219
Waste Water Treatment Services
N.A.I.C.S.: 221320

Wigen Companies, Inc. (1)
Tel.: (952) 448-4884
Water Treatment & Purification System Mfr
N.A.I.C.S.: 333310

METCAP SP ZOO

Ul Hetmanska 120, Rzeszow, 35-078, Poland

METCAP SP ZOO

Metcap Sp zoo—(Continued)

Tel.: (48) 1 7 717 29 45
Iron & Steel Forging
N.A.I.C.S.: 332111

METCASH LIMITED
1 Thomas Holt Drive, Macquarie Park, 2113, NSW, Australia
Tel.: (61) 297413000
Web Site: https://www.metcash.com
MTS—(OTCIQ)
Rev.: $11,619,118,112
Assets: $3,984,877,571
Liabilities: $3,149,423,995
Net Worth: $835,453,576
Earnings: $189,325,549
Emp.: 8,017
Fiscal Year-end: 04/30/22
Convenience Retailer
N.A.I.C.S.: 445131
Scott Marshall *(CEO-Supermarkets & Convenience)*

Subsidiaries:

Alltools (Pakenham) Pty. Ltd. (1)
4 Livestock Way, Pakenham, 3810, VIC, Australia
Tel.: (61) 359416022
Electronic Tool Distr
N.A.I.C.S.: 423690

Australian Liquor Marketers Pty Limited (1)
14 Keane Street, Currajong, 4812, QLD, Australia
Tel.: (61) 1300881458
Web Site: http://portal.almliquor.com.au
Sales Range: $25-49.9 Million
Emp.: 20
Alcoholic Beverages Whslr
N.A.I.C.S.: 424820

Subsidiary (Domestic):

Australian Liquor Marketers (QLD) Pty. Ltd. (2)
4 Newington Road, Silverwater, 2128, NSW, Australia
Tel.: (61) 297417222
Web Site: http://www.metcash.com.au
Sales Range: $125-149.9 Million
Alcoholic Beverages Whslr
N.A.I.C.S.: 424820

Australian Liquor Marketers (WA) Pty. Ltd. (2)
218 Bannister Road, Canning Vale, 6155, WA, Australia
Tel.: (61) 894559000
Alcoholic Beverages Whslr
N.A.I.C.S.: 424820

Chelsea Heights Operations Pty Limited (1)
Corner Wells Road Spring Vale Road, Chelsea Heights, Melbourne, 3196, VIC, Australia
Tel.: (61) 397819500
Supermarkets Operation Services
N.A.I.C.S.: 445110

Clancy's Food Stores Pty. Ltd. (1)
591 Smollet Street, Albury, 2640, NSW, Australia
Tel.: (61) 260210580
Web Site: https://www.clancysfoodstore.com.au
Food Product Mfr & Distr
N.A.I.C.S.: 333241

Faggs Geelong Pty. Ltd. (1)
1-9 Barwon Terrace, Geelong, 3220, VIC, Australia
Tel.: (61) 352212899
Web Site: https://www.faggs.com.au
Hardware Products Distr
N.A.I.C.S.: 423710

Finlayson Timber & Hardware Pty. Ltd. (1)
135 Wellington Road, Brisbane, 4169, QLD, Australia
Tel.: (61) 733930588
Web Site: https://www.finlayson.com.au
Building Material Mfr & Distr
N.A.I.C.S.: 327120

Foodland Properties Pty. Ltd. (1)
50 Waterloo Road, Macquarie Park, Sydney, 2113, NSW, Australia
Tel.: (61) 297518200
Sales Range: $1-4.9 Billion
Supermarkets Operation Services
N.A.I.C.S.: 445110
Christopher Villani *(Mgr-Mktg)*

IGA Distribution Pty Limited (1)
50 Waterloo Road, Macquarie Park, Sydney, 2113, NSW, Australia
Tel.: (61) 297413000
Web Site: http://www.iga.net.au
Sales Range: $200-249.9 Million
Emp.: 700
Supermarkets Operation & Management Services
N.A.I.C.S.: 445110
Aiam Morrice *(Gen Mgr)*

Subsidiary (Domestic):

IGA Distribution (Vic) Pty Limited (2)
Lot 4 75-79 Fitzgerald Rd, Laverton N, Melbourne, 3026, VIC, Australia
Tel.: (61) 383686000
Web Site: https://www.iga.com.au
Sales Range: $125-149.9 Million
Emp.: 500
Convenience Food Distr
N.A.I.C.S.: 424420
Andrew Ritzer *(Mng Dir)*

IGA Distribution (WA) Pty Limited (2)
218 Bannister Road, Canning Vale, 6155, WA, Australia
Tel.: (61) 893116000
Web Site: https://www.metcash.com
Grocery Distr
N.A.I.C.S.: 445110
Paul Slaughter *(Gen Mgr)*

Independent Brands Australia Pty Limited (1)
4 Newington Road, Silverwater, 2128, NSW, Australia
Tel.: (61) 297417222
Web Site: https://www.iba.net.au
Alcoholic Beverages Retailer
N.A.I.C.S.: 424820
Fergus Collins *(CEO-Liquor Markets)*

K&B Timber and Hardware Pty. Ltd. (1)
Level 1 10 Ashwin Parade, Torrensville, 5031, SA, Australia
Tel.: (61) 883515211
Web Site: https://www.kbth.com.au
Truss Frame Mfr & Distr
N.A.I.C.S.: 332999

Liquor Traders Pty. Ltd. (1)
Unit 1 272 Selby Street, Wembley, 6014, WA, Australia
Tel.: (61) 893837666
Web Site: https://liquortraders.com.au
Alcoholic Beverages Whslr
N.A.I.C.S.: 424820

Metcash Holdings Pty. Ltd. (1)
50 Waterloo Road, Macquarie Park, Sydney, 2113, NSW, Australia
Tel.: (61) 297518200
Supermarkets Operation & Management Services
N.A.I.C.S.: 445110

Metcash Storage Pty Limited (1)
4 Newington Road, Silverwater, 2128, NSW, Australia
Tel.: (61) 297413000
Sales Range: $200-249.9 Million
Emp.: 600
Supermarkets Operation & Management Services
N.A.I.C.S.: 445110

Metcash Trading Africa (Pty) Ltd (1)
Cnr Crownwood Rd & Amethyst St, Theta Township Ext 1, Johannesburg, 2091, South Africa
Tel.: (27) 114902000
Web Site: http://www.metro.co.za
Sales Range: $5-14.9 Billion
Convenience Stores Owner & Operator
N.A.I.C.S.: 445131

Mirren (Australia) Pty. Ltd. (1)
11 Carisbrook Street, North Kellyville, 2155, NSW, Australia
Tel.: (61) 288145275
Web Site: https://www.mirren.com.au
Finance Investment Services
N.A.I.C.S.: 523999

Nu Fruit Pty. Ltd. (1)
90 Newman Street, PO Box 754, Wangaratta, 3677, VIC, Australia
Tel.: (61) 357237200
Web Site: https://nufruitonline.com
Sales Range: $25-49.9 Million
Emp.: 50
Fresh Produce Whslr
N.A.I.C.S.: 424480

Rennet Pty. Ltd. (1)
10 Oceanside Promenade, Mullaloo, Perth, 6027, WA, Australia
Tel.: (61) 894018411
Supermarkets Operation & Management Services
N.A.I.C.S.: 445110

Tasman Liquor Company Limited (1)
22 Ha Crescent Wiri, PO Box 76-206, Manukau, 2104, Auckland, New Zealand
Tel.: (64) 2633940
Web Site: https://www.tasmanliquor.co.nz
Emp.: 50
Alcoholic Beverages Retailer
N.A.I.C.S.: 424820

Timber and Hardware Exchange Pty. Ltd. (1)
10/435 Williamstown Road, Port Melbourne, 3004, VIC, Australia
Tel.: (61) 391351900
Web Site: https://www.timberhardware.com.au
Software Development Services
N.A.I.C.S.: 541511

Total Tools Moorabbin Store Pty. Ltd. (1)
Shop 7 / 430 Warrigal Road, Heatherton, 3202, VIC, Australia
Tel.: (61) 395512974
Electric Tool Distr
N.A.I.C.S.: 423610

Total Tools Preston Pty. Ltd. (1)
92 Bell Street, Preston, 3072, VIC, Australia
Tel.: (61) 394805277
Electric Tool Distr
N.A.I.C.S.: 423610

METCOR INC
560 Arthur Sauve Boulevard, Saint-Eustache, J7R 5A8, QC, Canada
Tel.: (450) 473-1884
Web Site: http://www.metcor.biz
Rev.: $10,456,579
Emp.: 80
Metal Heat Treating
N.A.I.C.S.: 332811
John Spencer *(CEO)*

METECH INTERNATIONAL LIMITED
2 Venture Drive 0810 Vision Exchange, Singapore, 118523, Singapore
Tel.: (65) 62504518 **SG**
Web Site: https://www.metechinternational.com
V3M—(SES)
Rev.: $3,873,596
Assets: $9,805,596
Liabilities: $1,127,080
Net Worth: $8,678,516
Earnings: ($1,924,193)
Fiscal Year-end: 06/30/22
Electronic Waste Recycling
N.A.I.C.S.: 562998
Simon Eng *(Chm)*

Subsidiaries:

Metech Recycling (Singapore) Pte. Ltd. (1)
100G Pasir Panjang Road 04-07 Interlocal Centre, Crescent, Singapore, 118523, Singapore
Tel.: (65) 6 250 4518
Web Site: https://www.metechinternational.com
Electronic Waste Recycling & Processing Services
N.A.I.C.S.: 562998

Metech Recycling, Inc. (1)
111 Adams Rd, Clinton, MA 01510
Tel.: (508) 795-1950
Web Site: https://www.metechrecycling.com
Electronic Waste Recycling Services
N.A.I.C.S.: 562998

Metech Recycling, Inc. (1)
6200 Engle Way, Gilroy, CA 95020
Tel.: (408) 848-3050
Web Site: https://www.metechrecycling.com
Electronic Waste Recycling Services
N.A.I.C.S.: 562998

Metech Reverslog Pte. Ltd. (1)
65 Tech Park Crescent, Singapore, 637787, Singapore
Tel.: (65) 62644338
Web Site: http://www.metechinternational.com
Software Services
N.A.I.C.S.: 541511

METECH RECYCLING (UK) LTD.
Unit 49 Hirwaun Ind Est Hirwaun, Aberdare, C44 9UP, Mid Glamorgan, United Kingdom
Tel.: (44) 1685814466
Web Site: http://www.metechrecycling.uk.com
Sales Range: $10-24.9 Million
Emp.: 38
Electronic Waste Recycling Services
N.A.I.C.S.: 562998
Graham Piteman *(Dir-Sls & Mktg)*

METECNO S.P.A.
Via Nazario Sauro 80, Travesio Loc Toppo, 33090, Pordenone, Italy
Tel.: (39) 0427591311
Web Site: http://www.metecnoitalia.it
Year Founded: 1961
Sales Range: $25-49.9 Million
Emp.: 80
Holding Company Industrial & Residential Construction Product Mfr
N.A.I.C.S.: 551112
Maurizio Morandi *(Pres)*

Subsidiaries:

METARCH ARCHITECTURAL PANELS S.A. (1)
Pol Ind de Lantaron C/El Pinar S/N, 01001, Lantaron, Alava, Spain
Tel.: (34) 945 332 049
Panel Mfr
N.A.I.C.S.: 332311

METECNO (INDIA) PVT LTD (1)
138/30 2nd floor Florida Towers Nelson Manickam Road, Chennai, India
Tel.: (91) 44 45608800
Web Site: http://www.metecno.in
Panel Mfr
N.A.I.C.S.: 332311
Anup Dave *(COO)*

Plant (Domestic):

METECNO (INDIA) PVT LTD - CHENNAI-SPR-FACTORY (2)
No E-11 Sipcot Industrial Park NH-4, Mambakkam Kancheepuram, Sriperumbudur, India
Tel.: (91) 44 27169038
Panel Mfr
N.A.I.C.S.: 332311

METECNO (THAILAND) LTD. (1)
25 Soi Watmahawong Moo 9 Poochaosamingpri Rd, Samrong Klang Prapradang, Samut Prakan, 10130, Thailand
Tel.: (66) 2 755 9265
Web Site: http://www.metecno.co.th

Panel Mfr & Distr
N.A.I.C.S.: 332311
Sudarshan B. T. *(Mng Dir)*

METECNO (VIETNAM) LTD (1)
Room no F34 40 Ba Huyen Thanh Quan Str Dist 3, Ho Chi Minh City, Vietnam
Tel.: (84) 8 39 300 962
Web Site: http://www.metecno.com.vn
Panel Mfr & Distr
N.A.I.C.S.: 332311
Sudarshan B. T. *(Gen Mgr)*

METECNO BAUSYSTEME GMBH (1)
Am Amselberg 1, 99444, Blankenhain, Germany
Tel.: (49) 36454560
Web Site: http://www.metecno.de
Panel Mfr
N.A.I.C.S.: 332311
Markus Haiden *(Mng Dir)*

METECNO BULGARIA AD (1)
Grivishko shosse 1, 5800, Pleven, Bulgaria
Tel.: (359) 64 882 900
Web Site: http://www.metecno.bg
Panel Mfr
N.A.I.C.S.: 332311
Chavdar Yotkov *(Reg Area Mgr-Sls)*

METECNO DE CHILE S.A. (1)
Avenida Nueva Industria numero 200, Santiago, Chile
Tel.: (56) 2 438 7500
Web Site: http://www.metecno.cl
Panel Mfr
N.A.I.C.S.: 332311

METECNO DE COLOMBIA S.A. (1)
Calle 94 No 15-32 of 403, Bogota, Colombia
Tel.: (57) 1 6165622
Web Site: http://www.metecnocolombia.com
Panel Mfr
N.A.I.C.S.: 332311

METECNO ESPANA S.A. (1)
Poligono Industrial de Bayas Parcelas 107-110E, 09200, Miranda de Ebro, Burgos, Spain
Tel.: (34) 947 330690
Web Site: http://www.metecno.es
Panel Mfr
N.A.I.C.S.: 332311

METECNO FRANCE S.A.R.L. (1)
2 rue stephenson, Saint-Quentin-en-Yvelines, 78181, France
Tel.: (33) 1 61084097
Panel Mfr
N.A.I.C.S.: 332311

METECNO PORTUGAL S.A. (1)
Lugar de Sa, Geme, Vila Verde, 4730-180, Portugal
Tel.: (351) 253 310 140
Panel Mfr
N.A.I.C.S.: 332311

METECNO TRADING GMBH (1)
Margaretnstrasse 72, 1050, Vienna, Austria
Tel.: (43) 1 585 26 18
Web Site: http://www.metecno.de
Emp.: 3
Panel Mfr
N.A.I.C.S.: 332311
Georg Dumpelnik *(Head-Sls)*

METECNO TRADING ROMANIA SRL (1)
Str 13 Decembrie nr 96, 500146, Brasov, Romania
Tel.: (40) 268 406 249
Web Site: http://www.metecno.ro
Panel Distr
N.A.I.C.S.: 332311
Manolescu Miorel *(Mgr-Sls)*

METECNO TRADING S.A. (1)
Corso San Gottardo 32, 6830, Chiasso, Switzerland
Tel.: (41) 91 6824114
Panel Mfr
N.A.I.C.S.: 332311

Metec Inc. (1)
405 Fentress Blvd, Daytona Beach, FL 32114
Tel.: (386) 255-5391
Web Site: http://www.alumashield.com
Rev.: $25,700,000
Emp.: 30
Sheet Metalwork
N.A.I.C.S.: 333415

Subsidiary (Domestic):

Aluma Shield Industries, Inc. (2)
725 Summerhill Dr, Deland, FL 32726
Tel.: (386) 626-6789
Sales Range: $25-49.9 Million
Mfr of Insulated Panels & Doors
N.A.I.C.S.: 333415
Kevin Kelly *(CEO)*

Benchmark Architectural Systems, Inc. (2)
720 Marion Rd, Columbus, OH 43207
Tel.: (614) 444-0110
Structural Shapes & Pilings, Steel
N.A.I.C.S.: 331110
Damon Reece *(Plant Mgr)*

Metecno International BV (1)
Driebladhof 12, 5672 XH, Nuenen, Netherlands
Tel.: (31) 492 57 90 10
Emp.: 1
Panel Mfr
N.A.I.C.S.: 332311

Metecno Lanka (Pvt.) Ltd. (1)
185 Korotota Road, Kaduwela, Sri Lanka
Tel.: (94) 115558190
Web Site: http://www.metecnolanka.com
Panel Mfr & Distr
N.A.I.C.S.: 332311
S. T. Nagendra *(Chm)*

ZHEJIANG METECNO NEW BUILDING PANELS, CO. Ltd. (1)
North of Jianshesan Lu West of Jinyi Lu Xiaoshan Economic, Hangzhou, Zhejiang, China
Tel.: (86) 571 826 08828
Web Site: http://www.metecno-zj.com
Panel Mfr
N.A.I.C.S.: 332311

METEHE OY
Voimakaari 17, 54100, Joutseno, Finland
Tel.: (358) 207 639 640
Web Site: http://www.metehe.fi
Emp.: 80
Metals Mfr
N.A.I.C.S.: 331110
Janne Stromberg *(Mng Dir)*

METEMTUR OTELCILIK VE TURIZM ISLETMELERI AS
Beyaz Karanfil Sokak No 13 3 Levent, Besiktas, 34330, Istanbul, Turkiye
Tel.: (90) 2122829787
Web Site: https://www.metemtur.com
Year Founded: 1985
METUR—(IST)
Rev.: $2,123,539
Assets: $6,501,106
Liabilities: $3,818,145
Net Worth: $2,682,961
Earnings: $410,183
Fiscal Year-end: 12/31/22
Hotel & Resort Management Services
N.A.I.C.S.: 721110
Koray Eti *(Chm)*

METEN INTERNATIONAL EDUCATION GROUP
No 2006 Xiangmei Road Floor 4 Tianjian Tianranju Commercial Center, Futian District, Shenzhen, 518045, Guangdong, China
Tel.: (86) 75582945250
Web Site: http://meten.com
Year Founded: 2006
MEDU—(NYSE)
Sales Range: $200-249.9 Million
Holding Company; Educational Services
N.A.I.C.S.: 551112

METEORIC RESOURCES NL
Level 1 35 Ventnor Avenue, West Perth, 6005, WA, Australia
Tel.: (61) 892262011 AU
Web Site: https://www.meteoric.com.au
MEI—(ASX)
Rev.: $192
Assets: $1,625,047
Liabilities: $326,139
Net Worth: $1,298,908
Earnings: ($4,256,456)
Fiscal Year-end: 06/30/22
Mineral Exploration Services
N.A.I.C.S.: 212290
Shastri Ramnath *(Dir-Technical)*

METEORITE CAPITAL, INC.
1 Place Ville-Marie Suite 3900, Montreal, H3B 4M7, QC, Canada
Tel.: (514) 878-8800
MTR.P—(TSX)
Assets: $476,054
Liabilities: $15,113
Net Worth: $460,940
Earnings: ($70,852)
Fiscal Year-end: 12/31/19
Asset Management Services
N.A.I.C.S.: 523940
Ivan Spector *(CEO)*

METER INSTRUMENTS CO., LTD.
No 5 Xiyan Road, Nanjing Jiangning Binjiang Economic Development Zone, Nanjing, 211178, Jiangsu, China
Tel.: (86) 2586981981
Web Site: https://www.metter.cn
Year Founded: 2006
301006—(SSE)
Rev.: $50,330,592
Assets: $185,420,664
Liabilities: $22,270,248
Net Worth: $163,150,416
Earnings: $15,326,064
Fiscal Year-end: 12/31/22
Measuring Instruments Mfr
N.A.I.C.S.: 334513
Weiguo Sun *(Chm & Gen Mgr)*

METGASCO LIMITED
Level 3 2 Elizabeth Plaza, North Sydney, 2060, NSW, Australia
Tel.: (61) 894632463 AU
Web Site: https://www.metgasco.com.au
Year Founded: 1999
MEL—(ASX)
Rev.: $1,585,302
Assets: $6,114,081
Liabilities: $6,308,921
Net Worth: ($194,840)
Earnings: ($8,810,844)
Emp.: 27
Fiscal Year-end: 06/30/24
Oil & Gas Exploration Services
N.A.I.C.S.: 211120
Philip Amery *(Chm)*

METHANEX CORPORATION
1800 Waterfront Centre 200 Burrard Street, Vancouver, V6C 3M1, BC, Canada
Tel.: (604) 661-2600
Web Site: https://www.methanex.com
MEOH—(NASDAQ)
Rev.: $4,311,188,000
Assets: $6,631,480,000
Liabilities: $4,202,023,000
Net Worth: $2,429,457,000
Earnings: $462,288,000
Emp.: 1,410
Fiscal Year-end: 12/31/22
Methanol Marketer & Mfr
N.A.I.C.S.: 325180

John N. Floren *(Pres & CEO)*

Subsidiaries:

Methanex Asia Pacific Limited (1)
3802 38/F The Lee Gardens 33 Hysan Avenue Causeway Bay, Hong Kong, China (Hong Kong)
Tel.: (852) 29181398
Sales Range: $25-49.9 Million
Emp.: 5
Methanol Mfr & Distr
N.A.I.C.S.: 325199

Methanex Chile S.A. (1)
Tel.: (56) 23744000
Web Site: http://www.methanex.com
Emp.: 22
Oil & Gas Exploration Services
N.A.I.C.S.: 213112

Methanex Europe SA/NV (1)
Waterloo Office Park - Building P Dreve Richelle 161, Box 31, 1410, Waterloo, Belgium
Tel.: (32) 23520670
Sales Range: $25-49.9 Million
Emp.: 25
Methanol Mfr & Distr
N.A.I.C.S.: 325199
Wade Wiggins *(VP)*

Methanex Japan Limited (1)
7th Floor Sumitomo Life Nishi-Shinbashi Bldg 1-10-2 Nishi-Shinbashi, Minato-ku, Tokyo, 105-0003, Japan
Tel.: (81) 368073920
Sales Range: $50-74.9 Million
Emp.: 3
Methanol Mfr & Distr
N.A.I.C.S.: 325199

Methanex New Zealand (1)
Level 3 36 Kitchener St, Auckland, 1140, New Zealand (100%)
Tel.: (64) 93569300
Web Site: http://www.methanex.com
Sales Range: $25-49.9 Million
Emp.: 5
Mfr of Methanol
N.A.I.C.S.: 325194

Subsidiary (Domestic):

Methanex Motunui Limited (2)
409 Main North Road SH3, Private Bag 2011, Motunui, New Plymouth, SH3, New Zealand
Tel.: (64) 67549700
Methanol Mfr & Distr
N.A.I.C.S.: 325199

Methanex Services (Shanghai) Co., Ltd. (1)
Unit 1102 - 1104 11F Tower 2 Jing An Kerry Center, 1539 West Nanjing Road, Shanghai, 200040, China
Tel.: (86) 2160231000
Methanol Distr
N.A.I.C.S.: 424690

Waterfront Shipping Company Limited (1)
1800 Waterfront Centre 200 Burrard Street, Vancouver, V6C 3M1, BC, Canada
Tel.: (604) 895-5300
Web Site: https://www.waterfront-shipping.com
Marine Transportation Services
N.A.I.C.S.: 488390
Paul Hexter *(Pres)*

METHANOL CHEMICALS COMPANY
Al Jubail Industrial City Road 251 Crossing 198, PO Box 2101, Jubail, 31471, Saudi Arabia
Tel.: (966) 133438801
Web Site: https://www.chemanol.com
Year Founded: 1989
2001—(SAU)
Rev.: $287,114,856
Assets: $478,889,574
Liabilities: $153,168,752
Net Worth: $325,720,822
Earnings: $55,040,261
Emp.: 500

METHANOL CHEMICALS COMPANY

Methanol Chemicals Company—(Continued)
Fiscal Year-end: 12/31/22
Chemical Product Mfr & Whslr
N.A.I.C.S.: 325199
Abullah Ali Al Sanea *(Chm)*

METHANOR SCA
24 Rue de Clichy, 75009, Paris, France
Tel.: (33) 140156177
Web Site: https://www.methanor.fr
ALMET—(EUR)
Sales Range: Less than $1 Million
Biogas Electric Power Generation Services
N.A.I.C.S.: 221117
Francois Gerber *(Mgr)*

METHAQ REAL ESTATE INVESTMENT P.L.C.
7th Circle-AL Hussini buliding, PO Box 2339, Amman, 11953, Jordan
Tel.: (962) 65857950 JO
Web Site:
https://www.methaqrealestate.com
Year Founded: 2006
MEET—(AMM)
Rev.: $11,137
Assets: $13,593,152
Liabilities: $2,453,625
Net Worth: $11,139,527
Earnings: ($1,758,940)
Emp.: 6
Fiscal Year-end: 12/31/20
Real Estate Investment Services
N.A.I.C.S.: 531390
Saleh Ahmad ALDabagh *(Chm)*

METHAQ TAKAFUL INSURANCE COMPANY P.S.C.
Liwa Tower M Floor ADNEC Area, PO Box 32774, Building Number C54, Abu Dhabi, United Arab Emirates
Tel.: (971) 26565333
Web Site: https://www.methaq.ae
Year Founded: 2008
METHAQ—(ABU)
Rev.: $89,171,734
Assets: $212,293,327
Liabilities: $185,417,150
Net Worth: $26,876,177
Earnings: $3,798,958
Fiscal Year-end: 12/31/22
Insurance Management Services
N.A.I.C.S.: 524298
Mohamed Abdullah Mohamed *(Mng Dir)*

METI CAPITAL SPA
Via Calabria 56, 00187, Rome, Italy
Tel.: (39) 0668760006
Web Site: http://www.meticapital.com
METI—(VIE)
Sales Range: Less than $1 Million
Real Estate Investment Services
N.A.I.C.S.: 531390

METI HOLDING SARL
8 Rue de Beggen, 1220, Luxembourg, Luxembourg
Tel.: (352) 270 2041 LU
Holding Company
N.A.I.C.S.: 551112
Flavio De Paulis *(Chm)*

Subsidiaries:

VDA Group S.p.A. (1)
Viale Lino Zanussi 3 33170, Pordenone, PN, Italy
Tel.: (39) 0434 516 111
Web Site: http://www.vdagroup.com
Hotel Integrated Solutions Services
N.A.I.C.S.: 541512
Flavio De Paulis *(Chm)*

METIA LIMITED
101 St Martin's Ln, London, WC2N 4AZ, United Kingdom
Tel.: (44) 20 3100 3500
Web Site: http://www.metia.com
Emp.: 200
Environmental, Local Marketing, New Technologies
N.A.I.C.S.: 541810
Steve Ellis *(Dir)*

METIS ENERGY LIMITED
133 New Bridge Road Chinatown Point 1801 02, Singapore, 059413, Singapore
Tel.: (65) 63930860 SG
Web Site: https://metisenergy.com
L02—(SES)
Rev.: $2,787,245
Assets: $102,667,575
Liabilities: $32,981,898
Net Worth: $69,685,677
Earnings: ($7,717,185)
Emp.: 43
Fiscal Year-end: 12/31/23
Investment Holding Services
N.A.I.C.S.: 551112
Yi Ngo Low *(CEO & Mng Dir)*

Subsidiaries:

PT. Jaya Pesona Abadi (1)
Wisma 46 BNI 41 JL Jenderal Sudirman Kavling 1 Karet Tengsin, Tanah Abang, dakarta, 10220, Indonesia
Tel.: (62) 215701837
Financial Holding Services
N.A.I.C.S.: 551112

METISA - METALURGICA TIMBOENSE S.A.
Rua Fritz Lorenz 2442 Distrito Industrial, PO Box 11, 89120-000, Timbo, 89120-000, SC, Brazil
Tel.: (55) 4732812222
Web Site: https://net.metisa.com.br
Year Founded: 1942
MTSA4—(BRAZ)
Rev.: $118,049,916
Assets: $113,404,304
Liabilities: $21,904,231
Net Worth: $91,500,074
Earnings: $17,986,198
Emp.: 1,200
Fiscal Year-end: 12/31/23
Industrial Machinery & Equipment Mfr
N.A.I.C.S.: 332216

METITO HOLDINGS LTD.
National Industries Park, PO Box 262335, Dubai, 262335, United Arab Emirates
Tel.: (971) 4 810 3333 AE
Web Site: http://www.metito.com
Year Founded: 1958
Emp.: 800
Waste Water Treatment Services
N.A.I.C.S.: 562910
Mutaz Ghandour *(Chm & CEO)*

Subsidiaries:

Berlinwasser Metito Technical Development Ltd (1)
Room 812 International Chamber of Commerce Tower No 168 Fuhua Road 3, Futian District, Shenzhen, 518 048, China
Tel.: (86) 75533367668
Engineeering Services
N.A.I.C.S.: 541330

Eurl Metito Algerie (1)
Micro Zone d-Activite Hydra Lot N-20 Dar Al Madina Bloc A 2eme Etage, Hydra, 16035, Algiers, Algeria
Tel.: (213) 23531138
Web Site: http://www.metito.com
Emp.: 40
Engineeering Services
N.A.I.C.S.: 541330

Metito (Overseas) Qatar WLL (1)
D Ring Road Building No 178 Al Hilal, PO Box 23616, Doha, Qatar
Tel.: (974) 4456 8650
Web Site: http://www.metito.com
Design & Supply of Water & Wastewater Treatments & Water Desalination Systems
N.A.I.C.S.: 924110
Walid Oraby *(Gen Mgr)*

Metito International, Inc. (1)
11931 Wickchester Ln Ste 100, Houston, TX 77043
Tel.: (281) 293-8500
Web Site: http://www.metito.com
Sales Range: $1-9.9 Million
Emp.: 15
Water Treatment Products & Systems for Water Desalination
N.A.I.C.S.: 333310

Metito LLC (1)
Al Sayegh Tower 3rd Floor Flat 035 Hamdan Street, PO Box 47881, Next to Gulf Air Building, Abu Dhabi, United Arab Emirates
Tel.: (971) 2 6333942
Engineeering Services
N.A.I.C.S.: 541330

Metito Libya General Contracting Co. (1)
Kornaish Road Beside Amlak El Dola Andalus 1, Tripoli, Libya
Tel.: (218) 214772003
Engineeering Services
N.A.I.C.S.: 541330

Metito Pollution Control India Pvt. Ltd (1)
B-9 Kings Corner Opp Victoria Church L J Road, Mahim, Mumbai, 400016, India
Tel.: (91) 22 24315566
Engineeering Services
N.A.I.C.S.: 541330

Metito Saudi Limited (1)
3rd Floor Office No 26 & 27 No 1 Salah-El-Din Street, Al Bait Development Building, Riyadh, 11312, Saudi Arabia
Tel.: (966) 11 4742277
Engineeering Services
N.A.I.C.S.: 541330
Mahmoud Kabeel *(Mgr-Sls)*

Metito Utilities Limited (1)
Technopark, PO 262335, Dubai, United Arab Emirates (100%)
Tel.: (971) 4 810 3333
Web Site: http://www.metito.com
Water & Wastewater Treatment Asset Investment
N.A.I.C.S.: 523999
Mutaz Ghandour *(Chm & CEO)*

Metito Water Treatment SAE (1)
Pyramids Heights Office Park Building 7 Km 22 Cairo, Alex Desert Road, Giza, 12577, Egypt
Tel.: (20) 235368100
Web Site: http://www.metito.com
Sales Range: $125-149.9 Million
Emp.: 200
Water Treatment System Services
N.A.I.C.S.: 221310
Salah Deghedy *(Gen Mgr)*

PT Metito Indonesia (1)
Jl Ampera Raya No 18A, Cilandak Timur - Ps Minggu, Jakarta, 12560, Indonesia
Tel.: (62) 217800394
Web Site: http://www.metito.com
Sales Range: $100-124.9 Million
Emp.: 400
Design & Supply of Water & Wastewater Treatment & Water Desalination Systems
N.A.I.C.S.: 333310

METIZI J.S.CO.
Industrial Area, PO Box 53, Roman, 3130, Vratsa, Bulgaria
Tel.: (359) 91232109
Web Site: https://www.metizi-co.com
METZ—(BUL)
Sales Range: $1-9.9 Million
Silo Mfr
N.A.I.C.S.: 332618
Vera Nanova *(Dir-IR)*

INTERNATIONAL PUBLIC

METKOMBANK PJSC
36 Oktyabrskaya Street, 623406, Kamensk-Uralsky, Russia
Tel.: (7) 3439378000
Web Site: http://eng.metcom.ru
Year Founded: 1993
Sales Range: Less than $1 Million
Commercial Banking Services
N.A.I.C.S.: 522110

METLEN ENERGY & METALS S.A.
8 Artemidos Str, Maroussi, 15125, Athens, Greece
Tel.: (30) 2106877300
Web Site:
https://www.metlengroup.com
Year Founded: 1990
MYTIL—(ATH)
Rev.: $6,806,034,967
Assets: $7,449,090,222
Liabilities: $5,052,088,280
Net Worth: $2,397,001,943
Earnings: $539,617,958
Emp.: 3,210
Fiscal Year-end: 12/31/22
Holding Company; Metallurgy, Energy & Defense Services
N.A.I.C.S.: 551112
Christos Gavalas *(Gen Mgr-Treasury)*

Subsidiaries:

Aluminium Of Greece Industrial & Commercial Societe Anonyme (1)
8 Artemidos Str, Maroussi, 151 25, Athens, Greece
Tel.: (30) 2103693000
Web Site: http://www.alhellas.com
Aluminium Products Mfr
N.A.I.C.S.: 331315

Aluminium de Greece S.A. (1)
8 Artemis Street, Maroussi, 15125, Athens, Greece (100%)
Tel.: (30) 2103693000
Web Site: http://www.alhellas.gr
Sales Range: $450-499.9 Million
Emp.: 1,300
Bauxite Mining & Aluminum Processing & Production
N.A.I.C.S.: 331313

Delfi Distomon A.M.E. (1)
Ano Kounouklias- Elaiona Fokidas, 331 00, Amfissa, Greece
Tel.: (30) 22650728704
Emp.: 100
Bauxite Mfr
N.A.I.C.S.: 331313
Georgios Fanourios Kontouzoglou *(Chm)*

Elemka S.A (1)
5-7 Patroklou str, Maroussi, 15125, Athens, Greece (83.5%)
Tel.: (30) 2108117000
Web Site: https://www.elemka.gr
Sales Range: $25-49.9 Million
Emp.: 20
Brick Stone & Construction Material Merchant Whslr
N.A.I.C.S.: 423320

Hellenic Vehicle Industry S.A. (1)
Sindos Industrial Area, Sindos, Thessaloniki, Greece (22.53%)
Tel.: (30) 2310798602
Automobile Mfr
N.A.I.C.S.: 336110

Kilkis Paleon Triethnes S.A. (1)
Artemidos 8, 151 25, Maroussi, Greece
Tel.: (30) 2103448300
Web Site:
https://www.kilkispalaiontriethnes.gr
Eletric Power Generation Services
N.A.I.C.S.: 221118

METKA EGN Mexico S. De.R.L. C.V. (1)
Hipolito Taine 244, Polanco, 11560, Mexico, Mexico
Tel.: (52) 5586235500
Solar Power Generation Services
N.A.I.C.S.: 221114

METKA Power West Africa Limited (1)
6th Floor The King's Court 3 Keystone Bank Crescent, Victoria Island, Lagos, Nigeria
Tel.: (234) 7083298129
Solar Power Generation Services
N.A.I.C.S.: 221114

METKA-EGM Chile SpA (1)
Av Manquehue Norte 151 of 906/907, Las Condes, Santiago, Chile
Tel.: (56) 2229295503
Solar Power Generation Services
N.A.I.C.S.: 221114

METKA-EGN Limited (1)
99 White Lion Street, London, N1 9PF, United Kingdom
Tel.: (44) 2080013341
Web Site: https://www.metka-egn.com
Solar Power Generation Services
N.A.I.C.S.: 221114
Nikos Papapetrou *(CEO)*

Metka Industrial - Construction S.A. (1)
8 Artemidos str, Maroussi, 15125, Athens, Greece
Tel.: (30) 210 270 9200
Web Site: https://www.metka.com
Sales Range: $450-499.9 Million
Industrial & Engineering Services
N.A.I.C.S.: 541330
Filippos Zotos *(Dir-Project)*

Subsidiary (Domestic):

GREEK STEEL INDUSTRY (SERVISTEEL) S.A. (2)
A Industrial Area, Volos, 38500, Magnesia, Greece
Tel.: (30) 2421095278
Steel Products Mfr
N.A.I.C.S.: 331110

Subsidiary (Non-US):

METKA BRAZI SRL (2)
53 Bucuresti Stefan Sanatescu, Bucharest, Romania
Tel.: (40) 722560201
Eletric Power Generation Services
N.A.I.C.S.: 221118

Subsidiary (Domestic):

RODAX S.A. (2)
62-66 Marinou Antypa Str, 8 marousi 15125, Iraklio, 14121 N, Athens, Greece
Tel.: (30) 2102709700
Web Site: http://www.rodax.gr
Sales Range: $25-49.9 Million
Emp.: 90
Electrical Design Services
N.A.I.C.S.: 335999

Moura Solar Farm Spv Pty Ltd. (1)
Level 5 461 Bourke Street, Melbourne, 3000, VIC, Australia
Tel.: (61) 458012491
Web Site: https://mourasolar.com.au
Solar Power Generation Services
N.A.I.C.S.: 221114

North Aegean Renewables A.E. (1)
Artemidos 8, 15125, Maroussi, Greece
Tel.: (30) 2103448300
Web Site:
https://www.northaegeanrenewables.gr
Eletric Power Generation Services
N.A.I.C.S.: 221118

Power Project Sanayi Insaat Ticaret Limited Sirketi (1)
Visnezade Mah Suleyman Seba Cad No 44 B 1 Blok D 9, Besiktas-Akaretler, 34357, Istanbul, Turkiye
Tel.: (90) 2123818100
Web Site: https://www.powerprojects.com.tr
Construction Contracting Services
N.A.I.C.S.: 236220
E. Kamaris *(Gen Mgr)*

S.C. Sometra S.A. Copsa Mica (1)
Fabricilor 1 St, Copsa Mica Sibiu County, 555400, Sibiu, Romania
Tel.: (40) 269840320
Web Site: https://sometra.ro
Rev.: $607,831

Assets: $14,209,665
Liabilities: $13,238,827
Net Worth: $970,838
Earnings: ($1,953,624)
Emp.: 6
Fiscal Year-end: 12/31/2023
Lead & Zinc Mining Services
N.A.I.C.S.: 212230
Christos Efstathiadis *(CEO)*

Servisteel S.A (1)
1st Industrial Area of Volos, Magnessia, TK 38500, Volos, Greece
Tel.: (30) 2421095148
Web Site: https://www.servisteel.gr
Fabricated Metal Products Mfr
N.A.I.C.S.: 332999

Sometra S.A (1)
Fabricilor 1 St, Copsa Mica, PO 555400, Sibiu, Romania   (87.96%)
Tel.: (40) 269840320
Web Site: https://sometra.ro
Metal Ore Mining
N.A.I.C.S.: 212290
Christos Efstathiadis *(CEO & Member-Mgmt Bd)*

METLIFECARE LIMITED
Level 4 20 Kent Street Newmarket, Auckland, 1023, New Zealand
Tel.: (64) 95398000
Web Site:
http://www.metlifecare.co.nz
Sales Range: $75-99.9 Million
Emp.: 1,108
Residential Buildings Owning & Maintenance Services
N.A.I.C.S.: 531110
Jan Martin *(Gen Mgr-Sls)*

Subsidiaries:

Metlifecare 7 Saint Vincent Limited (1)
7 Saint Vincent Avenue, Remuera, Auckland, 1050, New Zealand
Tel.: (64) 95241420
Sales Range: $50-74.9 Million
Emp.: 22
Retirement Villages Operation Services
N.A.I.C.S.: 531312

Metlifecare Bayswater Limited (1)
60 Maranui Street, Mount Maunganui, 3116, Tauranga, Bay of Plenty, New Zealand
Tel.: (64) 75474047
Emp.: 50
Retirement Villages Operation Services
N.A.I.C.S.: 531312
Alan Edwards *(CEO)*

Metlifecare Coastal Villas Limited (1)
Spencer Russell Drive, PO Box 27, Paraparaumu, 5032, North Island, New Zealand
Tel.: (64) 42966333
Web Site: http://www.metlifecare.co.nz
Sales Range: $25-49.9 Million
Emp.: 50
Retirement Villages Operation Services
N.A.I.C.S.: 531312
Alan Edwards *(CEO)*

Metlifecare Crestwood Limited (1)
38 Golf Rd, New Lynn, 0600, New Zealand
Tel.: (64) 98262000
Sales Range: $50-74.9 Million
Emp.: 55
Retirement Villages Operation Services
N.A.I.C.S.: 531312
Alan Edwards *(CEO)*

Metlifecare Greenwood Park Limited (1)
10 Welcome Bay Road, Welcome Bay, Tauranga, 3112, Bay of Plenty, New Zealand
Tel.: (64) 75447500
Emp.: 45
Retirement Villages Operation Services
N.A.I.C.S.: 531312
Glen Sowry *(CEO)*

Metlifecare Highlands Limited (1)
49 Aberfeldy Ave, Highland Park, Auckland, 2010, New Zealand
Tel.: (64) 95330600
Web Site: http://www.metlifecare.co.nz
Retirement Villages Operation Services

N.A.I.C.S.: 531312

Metlifecare Kapiti Limited (1)
1 Henley Way, Paraparaumu, 5032, North Island, New Zealand
Tel.: (64) 42961790
Web Site: http://www.metlifecare.co.nz
Sales Range: $50-74.9 Million
Emp.: 16
Retirement Villages Operation Services
N.A.I.C.S.: 531312
Alan Edwards *(CEO)*

Metlifecare Merivale Limited (1)
60 Browns Rd, Merivale, Christchurch, 8014, Canterbury, New Zealand
Tel.: (64) 3 375 4117
Web Site: http://www.metlifecare.co.nz
Retirement Villages Operation Services
N.A.I.C.S.: 531312

Metlifecare Oakwoods Limited (1)
357 Lower Queen Street, Richmond, Nelson, 7020, New Zealand
Tel.: (64) 35439700
Web Site: http://www.metlifecare.co.nz
Retirement Villages Operation Services
N.A.I.C.S.: 531312
Stepahan David *(CEO)*

Metlifecare Pakuranga Limited (1)
14 Edgewater Drive, Pakuranga, Auckland, 2010, New Zealand
Tel.: (64) 95771600
Retirement Villages Operation Services
N.A.I.C.S.: 531312

Metlifecare Pinesong Limited (1)
66 Avonleigh Road, Titirangi, Auckland, 0604, New Zealand
Tel.: (64) 98171800
Emp.: 50
Retirement Villages Operation Services
N.A.I.C.S.: 531312
Alan Edwards *(CEO)*

Metlifecare Pohutukawa Landing Limited (1)
8 Seventh View Ave, Beachlands, Auckland, 2018, New Zealand
Tel.: (64) 2 152 7545
Real Estate Services
N.A.I.C.S.: 531390
Jane Gregory *(Mgr)*

Metlifecare Powley Limited (1)
135 Connell Street blockhouse bay, Blockhouse Bay, Auckland, 0600, New Zealand
Tel.: (64) 96270700
Web Site: http://www.metlifecare.co.nz
Retirement Villages Operation Services
N.A.I.C.S.: 531312
Alan Edwards *(CEO)*

Metlifecare Somervale Limited (1)
33 Gloucester Road, Arataki, Mount Maunganui, 3116, Bay of Plenty, New Zealand
Tel.: (64) 75729020
Web Site: http://www.metlifecare.co.nz
Sales Range: $50-74.9 Million
Emp.: 60
Retirement Villages Operation Services
N.A.I.C.S.: 531312
Rhonda Howie *(Mgr)*

Metlifecare The Avenues Limited (1)
Cnr 10th Ave, Tauranga, 3110, Bay of Plenty, New Zealand
Tel.: (64) 75710400
Sales Range: $50-74.9 Million
Emp.: 9
Retirement Villages Operation Services
N.A.I.C.S.: 531312
Alan Edwards *(CEO)*

Metlifecare Wairarapa Limited (1)
140 Chapel Street, Masterton, 5810, Wellington, New Zealand
Tel.: (64) 63782577
Sales Range: $50-74.9 Million
Emp.: 60
Retirement Villages Operation Services
N.A.I.C.S.: 531312
Alan Edwards *(CEO)*

METNOR GROUP PLC
Metnor House Mylord Crescent, Killingworth, Newcastle upon Tyne, NE12 5YD, United Kingdom

Tel.: (44) 1912684000
Web Site: http://www.metnor.co.uk
Sales Range: $100-124.9 Million
Emp.: 281
Property Development, Construction & Electrical Services
N.A.I.C.S.: 236220
Stephen Rankin *(Chm & CEO)*

Subsidiaries:

Metnor (Great Yarmouth) Limited (1)
Edison Way Off Morton Peto Rd, Gapton Hall Industrial Estate, Great Yarmouth, NR31 0NG, Norfolk, United Kingdom
Tel.: (44) 1493441480
Web Site:
http://www.yarmouth.abacuspreview.co.uk
Sales Range: $50-74.9 Million
Emp.: 15
Hose Assemblies Sales & Rental Services
N.A.I.C.S.: 532289
Adrian Brooks *(CEO)*

Metnor Construction Limited (1)
Metnor House Mylord Crescent, Killingworth, Newcastle upon Tyne, NE12 5YD, Tyne & Wear, United Kingdom
Tel.: (44) 1912684000
Web Site: http://www.metnor.co.uk
Sales Range: $25-49.9 Million
Emp.: 50
Nonresidential Building Construction Services
N.A.I.C.S.: 236220
Joyce Wearn *(Office Mgr)*

METRAC- METALHANDELSGESELLSCHAFT IMPORT-EXPORT MBH
Friedrich Hoffmann Strasse 01, 39397, Groningen, Germany
Tel.: (49) 3940394180
Web Site: http://www.metrac-metalle.de
Year Founded: 1996
Rev.: $14,227,462
Emp.: 19
Nonferrous Metals Processing Services
N.A.I.C.S.: 331491
I. Hake-Winter *(CEO)*

METRANACO PUBLIC COMPANY LTD.
15 Ayion Omologiton, Nicosia, Cyprus
Tel.: (357) 22452600
Investment Services
N.A.I.C.S.: 523940

METRAWATT INTERNATIONAL GMBH
Sudwestpark 15, 90449, Nuremberg, Germany
Tel.: (49) 9112526610   De
Web Site: http://www.metrawatt-international.com
Year Founded: 2005
Sales Range: $10-24.9 Million
Emp.: 650
Holding Company; Industrial, Electrical & Medical Testing & Measurement Equipment Designer, Mfr & Distr
N.A.I.C.S.: 551112
Marcel Hutka *(Member-Mgmt Bd)*

Subsidiaries:

Camille Bauer AG (1)
Aargauerstrasse 7, 5610, Wohlen, Switzerland
Tel.: (41) 566182111
Web Site: http://www.camillebauer.com
Industrial Measurement Equipment Mfr & Distr
N.A.I.C.S.: 334513
Max Josef Ulrich *(Mng Dir)*

Electromediciones Kainos S.A. (1)
Carrer Energia 56, Cornella de Llobregat, 08940, Barcelona, Spain
Tel.: (34) 934 74 23 33
Web Site: http://www.kainos.com.es

METRAWATT INTERNATIONAL GMBH

METRAWATT International GmbH—(Continued)
Emp.: 12
Measuring Equipment Distr
N.A.I.C.S.: 423830
Santiago Ballus Lludrigas *(Dir-Comml)*

GMC merici technika s.r.o. (1)
Fugnerova 1a, 678 01, Blansko, Czech Republic
Tel.: (420) 516 482 611
Web Site: http://www.gmc.cz
Measuring Equipment Mfr
N.A.I.C.S.: 334519
Vladimir Sevcik *(Mgr)*

GMC-I Messtechnik GmbH (1)
Sudwestpark 15, 90449, Nuremberg, Germany
Tel.: (49) 91186020
Web Site: http://www.gossenmetrawatt.com
Measuring & Testing Equipment Mfr & Distr
N.A.I.C.S.: 334515
Marcel Hutka *(Mng Dir & Member-Mgmt Bd)*

GMC-I PROSyS Ltd. (1)
Allied Business Centre 1 Potter Place, West Pimbo, Skelmersdale, WN8 9PH, Lancs, United Kingdom **(100%)**
Tel.: (44) 1695567280
Web Site: http://www.i-prosys.com
Electrical Measurement Instruments Designer & Mfr
N.A.I.C.S.: 334515

GMC-I Service GmbH (1)
Thomas-Mann-Strasse 16-20, 90471, Nuremberg, Germany **(100%)**
Tel.: (49) 9118177180
Web Site: http://www.gmci-service.com
Commercial Electronic Products Calibration & Testing Services
N.A.I.C.S.: 811210

GMC-Instruments (Tianjin) Co., Ltd (1)
BLD M8-3-101 Green Industry Base No 6 Hai Tai Fa Zhan 6th Rd, Nan Kai District, 300384, Tianjin, China
Tel.: (86) 22 83726250
Web Site: http://www.gmci-china.cn
Measuring Equipment Distr
N.A.I.C.S.: 423830

GMC-Instruments Austria GmbH (1)
Richard-Strauss-Str 10/2, 1230, Vienna, Austria
Tel.: (43) 1 890 2287
Web Site: http://www.gmc-instruments.at
Measuring Equipment Distr
N.A.I.C.S.: 423830

GMC-Instruments France SAS (1)
3 rue Rene Cassin, 91349, Massy, Cedex, France **(100%)**
Tel.: (33) 169208949
Web Site: http://www.gmc-instruments.fr
Emp.: 10
Electronic Testing & Measurement Equipment Whslr
N.A.I.C.S.: 423490

GMC-Instruments Italia S.r.l. (1)
Via Romagna 4, Biassono, 20853, Milan, MB, Italy **(100%)**
Tel.: (39) 039248051
Web Site: http://www.gmc-instruments.it
Emp.: 10
Electronic Testing & Measurement Equipment Whslr
N.A.I.C.S.: 423490

GMC-Instruments Nederland B.V. (1)
Daggeldersweg 18, 3449 JD, Woerden, Netherlands **(100%)**
Tel.: (31) 348421155
Web Site: http://www.gmc-instruments.nl
Electronic Testing & Measurement Equipment Whslr
N.A.I.C.S.: 423490

GMC-Instruments Schweiz AG (1)
Glattalstrasse 63, 8052, Zurich, Switzerland **(100%)**
Tel.: (41) 443088080
Web Site: http://www.gmc-instruments.ch
Emp.: 9
Electronic Testing & Measurement Equipment Whslr

N.A.I.C.S.: 423490
Rene Weber *(Gen Mgr)*

Global Power Technology Inc. (1)
1000 New Durham Rd, Edison, NJ 08818
Tel.: (732) 287-3680
Web Site: http://www.dranetz.com
Holding Company; Measuring & Testing Equipment Mfr
N.A.I.C.S.: 551112
Bob Hart *(Pres)*

Subsidiary (Domestic):

Daytronic Corporation (2)
2566 Kohnle Dr, Miamisburg, OH 45342
Tel.: (937) 293-2566
Web Site: http://www.daytronic.com
Electronic Measurement & Control Instrument Mfr
N.A.I.C.S.: 334515
Matt Vagedes *(Gen Sls Mgr)*

Dranetz Technologies Inc. (2)
1000 New Durham Rd, Edison, NJ 08817
Tel.: (732) 287-3680
Web Site: http://www.dranetz.com
Mfr of Power Monitoring Equipment
N.A.I.C.S.: 334515
Bob Hart *(Pres)*

Electrotek Concepts, Inc. (2)
9040 Executive Park Dr Ste 222, Knoxville, TN 37923-4671
Tel.: (865) 470-9222
Web Site: http://www.electrotek.com
Power System Engineering Consultation Services
N.A.I.C.S.: 541690

MTP Messtechnik Produktions GmbH (1)
Thomas-Mann-Strasse 16-20, D-90471, Nuremberg, Germany
Tel.: (49) 9118177170
Web Site: http://www.mtp-manufacturing.com
Emp.: 120
Electronic Components & Systems Mfr
N.A.I.C.S.: 334419
Ralf Kraus *(Mng Dir)*

METRIC ASSET MANAGEMENT LP

20 Eglinton Avenue West Suite 1505, PO Box 2037, Toronto, M4R 1K8, ON, Canada
Tel.: (416) 640-4961
Web Site: http://www.metricasset.com
Investment & Asset Management Services
N.A.I.C.S.: 523940
Jason Marks *(Co-CEO & COO)*

METRIC CAPITAL PARTNERS LLP

33 Jermyn Street, London, SW1Y 6AD, United Kingdom
Tel.: (44) 20 3540 1550 UK
Web Site: http://www.metric-capital.com
Year Founded: 2011
Private Equity
N.A.I.C.S.: 523999
John Sinik *(Mng Partner & Chm-Investment Committee)*

Subsidiaries:

DSM Demolition Limited (1)
Arden House Arden Road Heartlands, Birmingham, B8 1DE, United Kingdom
Tel.: (44) 1213222225
Web Site: http://www.dsmdemolitiongroup.co.uk
Sales Range: $50-74.9 Million
Building Demolition Services
N.A.I.C.S.: 238910
Robin Powell *(Mng Dir)*

Less Mess Storage Inc. (1)
Suite 600-1090 West Georgia Street, Vancouver, V6E 3V7, BC, Canada
Tel.: (778) 999-7030
Web Site: http://www.lessmess-storage.com

Sales Range: $1-9.9 Million
Holding Company; Self-Storage Facilities Operator
N.A.I.C.S.: 551112
Peter Smith *(VP-Corp Dev)*

METRIC MOBILITY SOLUTIONS AG

Rotenburger Strasse 20, 30659, Hannover, Germany
Tel.: (49) 51161020
Web Site: http://www.metric-group.com
Sales Range: $100-124.9 Million
Emp.: 514
Hardware & Software Mfr
N.A.I.C.S.: 449210
Thomas Dibbern *(CEO & Member-Mgmt Bd)*

METRICS IN BALANCE N.V.

Zuiderlaan 1-3 box 8, 9000, Gent, Belgium
Tel.: (32) 497544558
Web Site: https://www.metricsinbalance.com
MLMIB—(EUR)
Sales Range: Less than $1 Million
Medical Device Distr
N.A.I.C.S.: 423450
Dirk Verstraete *(Mng Dir)*

METRICS MASTER INCOME TRUST

Level 18 Angel Place 123 Pitt Street, Sydney, 2000, NSW, Australia
Tel.: (61) 292299000 AU
MXT—(ASX)
Rev.: $19,112,610
Assets: $599,404,228
Liabilities: $3,315,304
Net Worth: $596,088,924
Earnings: $17,928,080
Fiscal Year-end: 06/30/22
Investment Trust Management Services
N.A.I.C.S.: 523940
Christopher Green *(Dir)*

METRIE CANADA LIMITED

3500 - 1055 Dunsmuir Street, Vancouver, V7X 1H3, BC, Canada
Tel.: (604) 691-9100
Web Site: https://www.metrie.com
Year Founded: 1926
Emp.: 100
Interior Finishings Mfr & Distr
N.A.I.C.S.: 541410
Kent Bowie *(Pres & CEO)*

Subsidiaries:

EL & EL Wood Products Corp. (1)
6011 Schaefer, Chino, CA 91710-7043
Tel.: (909) 591-0339
Web Site: http://www.elandelwoodproducts.com
Construction Materials Whslr
N.A.I.C.S.: 423390
Cathy Vidas *(Pres)*

Metrie, Inc. (1)
3801 S 20th Ave Ste 100, Euless, TX 76039
Tel.: (972) 241-7125
Millwork Mfr & Distr
N.A.I.C.S.: 423310

Subsidiary (Domestic):

Anderco, Inc (2)
540 Airpark Dr, Fullerton, CA 92833
Tel.: (714) 992-4162
Rev.: $7,100,000
Emp.: 40
Steel Foundries, except Investment
N.A.I.C.S.: 331513
Peter Johnson *(Pres)*

METRO AG

INTERNATIONAL PUBLIC

Metro-Strasse 1, 40235, Dusseldorf, Germany
Tel.: (49) 21168860 De
Web Site: https://www.metroag.de
Year Founded: 1964
MTTWF—(OTCIQ)
Rev.: $28,704,251,520
Assets: $14,773,193,120
Liabilities: $12,465,161,660
Net Worth: $2,308,031,460
Earnings: $515,135,600
Emp.: 768
Fiscal Year-end: 09/30/20
Department Store & Supermarket Operator
N.A.I.C.S.: 455110
Xaver Schiller *(Vice Chm-Supervisory Bd)*

Subsidiaries:

Avilo Marketing Gesellschaft m. b. H. (1)
Metro Platz 1, Voesendorf, 2331, Austria
Tel.: (43) 169080
Web Site: http://www.metro.ag
Super Market Stores Operating Services
N.A.I.C.S.: 445110
Mark Groenewoud *(Gen Mgr)*

Booq Software B.V. (1)
Platinastraat 25, 7554 NC, Hengelo, Netherlands
Tel.: (31) 880556677
Web Site: https://www.booqsolutions.com
Software Development Services
N.A.I.C.S.: 541511

CCG DE GmbH (1)
Isarstrasse 4, 65451, Kelsterbach, Germany
Tel.: (49) 61079812693
Web Site: https://www.ccg-logistics.com
Food Transportation Services
N.A.I.C.S.: 484230

Classic Fine Foods (Hong Kong) Limited (1)
Unit 401-406 Office Tower Hutchison Logistics Centre, 18 Container Port Road South, Kwai Chung, China (Hong Kong)
Tel.: (852) 26122066
Web Site: https://www.classicfinefoods.hk
Food & Restaurant Services
N.A.I.C.S.: 722511
Yannick Brooks *(Head-Food Svcs Div)*

Classic Fine Foods (Macau) Ltd. (1)
Tel.: (853) 28820540
Web Site: http://www.classicfinefoods.mo
Food & Restaurant Services
N.A.I.C.S.: 722511
Matthieu Gourgues *(Mgr)*

Classic Fine Foods (Singapore) Private Limited (1)
7A Chin Bee Drive, Singapore, 619858, Singapore
Tel.: (65) 65015555
Web Site: https://www.classicfinefoods.com.sg
Food & Restaurant Services
N.A.I.C.S.: 722511
Karen Tay *(Gen Mgr)*

Classic Fine Foods (Vietnam) Limited (1)
Lot Vb 17b-19-21a Street 22A Tan Thuan EPZ, Tan Thuan Dong Ward District 7, Ho Chi Minh City, Vietnam
Tel.: (84) 2837407104
Web Site: https://www.classicfinefoods.vn
Food & Restaurant Services
N.A.I.C.S.: 722511
Laurent Mouric *(Gen Mgr)*

Classic Fine Foods Japan Holdings (1)
TRC BE5-N 6-1-1 Heiwajima, Ota-ku, Tokyo, 143-0006, Japan
Tel.: (81) 368234141
Web Site: https://www.classicfinefoods.jp
Food & Restaurant Services
N.A.I.C.S.: 722511

Classic Fine Foods Philippines Inc. (1)
29th Floor Yuchengco Tower 1 RCBC Plaza

AND PRIVATE COMPANIES — METRO AG

Corner of Ayala and Sen, Gil Puyat Ave, Makati, Philippines
Tel.: (63) 288891676
Web Site: https://www.classicfinefoods.com.ph
Food & Restaurant Services
N.A.I.C.S.: 722511

Classic Fine Foods Sdn Bhd (1)
No 13 Jalan BK1/15 Taman Perindustrian, Bandar Kinrara KM 10 1/2, 47100, Puchong, Selangor, Malaysia
Tel.: (60) 380734388
Web Site: https://www.classicfinefoods.com.my
Food & Restaurant Services
N.A.I.C.S.: 722511

Classic Fine Foods UK Limited (1)
Westway Estate 18-20 Brunel Road Park Royal, London, W3 7XR, United Kingdom
Tel.: (44) 2076279666
Web Site: https://www.classicfinefoods.co.uk
Food & Restaurant Services
N.A.I.C.S.: 722511
Olivier Batel (Mng Dir)

Classic Fine Foodstuff Trading LLC (1)
Dubai Investment Park 2 Jebel Ali, PO Box 95118, Dubai, United Arab Emirates
Tel.: (971) 48702400
Web Site: https://www.classicfinefoods.ae
Bakery Product Distr
N.A.I.C.S.: 424490

Cool Chain Group Pl Sp. z o.o. (1)
Kamienna 10 PL, 31-403, Krakow, Poland
Tel.: (48) 124222329
Food Transportation Services
N.A.I.C.S.: 484230

DISH Plus GmbH (1)
Metro-Strasse 1, 40235, Dusseldorf, Germany
Tel.: (49) 2119699980
Web Site: https://www.dish.co
Digital Marketing Consulting Services
N.A.I.C.S.: 541613

Deepideas GmbH (1)
Metro-Strasse 1, 40235, Dusseldorf, Germany
Tel.: (49) 2119699980
Web Site: https://www.deepideas.digital
Software Development Services
N.A.I.C.S.: 541511

Deutsche SB-Kauf AG (1)
Hahnstrasse 72, 60528, Frankfurt am Main, Germany
Tel.: (49) 6966830
Sales of Food.
N.A.I.C.S.: 445298

Eijsink B.V. (1)
Platinastraat 25, 7554 NC, Hengelo, Netherlands
Tel.: (31) 880556677
Web Site: https://www.eijsink.nl
Software Development Services
N.A.I.C.S.: 541511

Fideco AG (1)
Langgasse 11, 3280, Murten, Switzerland
Tel.: (41) 266786000
Web Site: https://www.fideco.ch
Grocery Distr
N.A.I.C.S.: 445110

GKF Vermogensverwaltungsgesellschaft mbH & Co. Objekt Wiesbaden-Nordenstadt KG (1)
Standort Mainzer Str 180, 66123, Saarbrucken, Germany
Tel.: (49) 681810400
Super Market Stores Operating Services
N.A.I.C.S.: 445110

GKF Vermogensverwaltungsgesellschaft mit beschrankter Haftung (1)
Bertha-von-Suttner-Strasse 5, 66123, Saarbrucken, Germany
Tel.: (49) 681810400
Web Site: http://www.metrogroup.de
Super Market Stores Operating Services
N.A.I.C.S.: 445110

Heim & Buro Versand GmbH (1)
Zum Drahtzug 5, 57645, Nister, Germany
Tel.: (49) 2662948420
Web Site: http://www.heimundbuero.de
Trading Commodity Services
N.A.I.C.S.: 523160
Florian Detjen (Co-Founder)

Hermann Grosskuchentechnik Hotel- und Gastronomiebedarf GmbH (1)
360- Ausstatter der Profi-Gastronomie Burgstrasse 5, Allgau, 87509, Immenstadt, Germany
Tel.: (49) 832396500
Web Site: https://shop.hermann-gastro.de
Kitchen Appliance Distr
N.A.I.C.S.: 423620

Horten Verwaltungs GmbH & Co. Objekt Ingolstadt KG (1)
Mainzer Str 180-184, Saarbrucken, 66121, Germany
Tel.: (49) 68181040
Super Market Stores Operating Services
N.A.I.C.S.: 445110

Hospitality Digital GmbH (1)
Metro-Strasse 1, 40235, Dusseldorf, Germany
Tel.: (49) 2119699980
Web Site: https://www.hd.digital
Restaurant & Hospitality Services
N.A.I.C.S.: 722511
Volker Glaeser (CEO)

ICS METRO Cash & Carry Moldova S.R.L. (1)
Str Chisinau 5, Stauceni commune Chisinau Municipality, MD-4839, Chisinau, Moldova
Tel.: (373) 22405203
Web Site: https://www.metro.md
Food Product Whslr
N.A.I.C.S.: 424410
Ludmila Bordianu (Mgr-Invoice Control)

Inpakcentrale ICN B.V. (1)
Dijkgraaf 21, 6921 RL, Duiven, 6921 RL, Netherlands
Tel.: (31) 263193250
Super Market Stores Operating Services
N.A.I.C.S.: 445110

KUPINA Grundstucks-Verwaltungsgesellschaft mbH & Co. KG (1)
Tolzer Str 15, 82031, Grunwald, Germany
Tel.: (49) 89641430
Consumer Electronics Retail Store Operating Services
N.A.I.C.S.: 449210

Kaufhalle GmbH (1)
Mainzer Strasse 180, Saarbrucken, 66121, Germany
Tel.: (49) 68181042801
Real Estate Manangement Services
N.A.I.C.S.: 531390

Kaufhof Warenhaus Rostock GmbH (1)
Mainzer Str 180, Saarbrucken, 66121, Germany
Tel.: (49) 68181040
Consumer Electronics Retail Store Operating Services
N.A.I.C.S.: 449210
Jean-Christophe Bretxa (Mng Dir)

MAKRO Cash & Carry Belgium NV (1)
Nijverheidsstraat 70, 2160, Wommelgem, Belgium
Tel.: (32) 70222022
Sales Range: $800-899.9 Million
Emp.: 281
Super Market Stores Operating Services
N.A.I.C.S.: 445110

MAKRO Cash & Carry CR s.r.o. (1)
Chlumecka 2424, Horni Pocernice, 193 00, Prague, 9, Czech Republic
Tel.: (420) 281083083
Web Site: https://www.makro.cz
Sales Range: $800-899.9 Million
Emp.: 3,510
Super Market Stores Operating Services
N.A.I.C.S.: 445110

MCC Trading International GmbH (1)
Schlutestr 7a, 40235, Dusseldorf, Germany
Tel.: (49) 21168860
Super Market Stores Operating Services
N.A.I.C.S.: 445110

METRO Advertising GmbH (1)
Metro-Strasse 2, 40235, Dusseldorf, Germany
Tel.: (49) 2119693969
Web Site: https://www.metro-advertising.com
Advertising Services
N.A.I.C.S.: 541810
Clemens G. Hadtstein (CEO & Mng Dir)

METRO Beteiligungsmanagement Dusseldorf GmbH & Co. KG (1)
Metro Str 1, 40235, Dusseldorf, Germany
Tel.: (49) 21168860
Super Market Stores Operating Services
N.A.I.C.S.: 445110

METRO CASH & CARRY ROMANIA SRL (1)
Bdul Theodor Pallady no 51, District 3, 32258, Bucharest, Romania
Tel.: (40) 771360810
Web Site: http://www.metro.ro
Sales Range: $1-4.9 Billion
Emp.: 3,500
Super Market Stores Operating Services
N.A.I.C.S.: 445110
Frank Hammerle (Mgr-Fin)

METRO Cash & Carry Bulgaria EOOD (1)
Tsarigradsko shose blvd 7-11 km, 1784, Sofia, Bulgaria
Tel.: (359) 29762132
Web Site: https://www.metro.bg
Emp.: 150
Food Product Whslr
N.A.I.C.S.: 424410
Dimitar Vutkov (Head-Mktg)

METRO Cash & Carry China Holding GmbH (1)
Metro Platz 1, Voesendorf, 2331, Austria
Tel.: (43) 1690800
Investment Management Service
N.A.I.C.S.: 523999

METRO Cash & Carry Deutschland GmbH (1)
Metro-Strasse 8, 40235, Dusseldorf, Germany
Tel.: (49) 2119690
Web Site: https://www.metro.de
Sales Range: $1-4.9 Billion
Emp.: 14,725
Super Market Stores Operating Services
N.A.I.C.S.: 445110
Philippe Palazzi (Chief Customer & Mktg Officer)

METRO Cash & Carry France S.A.S. (1)
ZA du Petit Nanterre - 5 rue des Grands Pres, 92024, Nanterre, Cedex, France
Tel.: (33) 147866300
Web Site: https://www.metro.fr
Sales Range: $1-4.9 Billion
Emp.: 8,368
Food Product Retailer
N.A.I.C.S.: 445298
Gayrard Pascal (Gen Mgr)

METRO Cash & Carry France et Cie (1)
1 rue du Gabian Batiment le Thales 7th Floor Office 3, 98000, Monaco, Monaco
Tel.: (377) 97970327
Food Product Whslr
N.A.I.C.S.: 424410

METRO Cash & Carry International GmbH (1)
Metro-Strasse 1, 40235, Dusseldorf, Germany
Tel.: (49) 2119690
Web Site: http://www.metro.de
Sales Range: $25-49.9 Billion
Emp.: 400
Supermarket Operations
N.A.I.C.S.: 445110
Peter Wuebben (Head-Dept)

Subsidiary (Non-US):

Makro Cash & Carry Polska S.A. (2)
Al Krakowska 61, 02-183, Warsaw, Poland (60%)
Tel.: (48) 801066100
Web Site: https://www.makro.pl
Self-Service Wholesale Stores
N.A.I.C.S.: 424490

Makro Cash & Carry Portugal, S.A. (2)
Rua Quinta do Paizinho Portela de Carnaxide, Lisbon, 2790-236, Carnaxide, Portugal
Tel.: (351) 229051800
Web Site: http://www.makro.pt
Sales Range: $350-399.9 Million
Self-Service Wholesale Stores
N.A.I.C.S.: 445110
Isabel Caeiro (Comm Officer)

Makro Morocco S.A. (2)
Route Secondaire 1029, Municipalite de Sidi Maarouf, 20180, Casablanca, Morocco
Tel.: (212) 22639797
Self-Service Wholesale Stores
N.A.I.C.S.: 445110

METRO Cash & Carry International Holding B. V. (1)
Dalsteindreef 101-139, 1112 XC, Diemen, Netherlands
Tel.: (31) 203980917
Investment Management Service
N.A.I.C.S.: 523999

METRO Cash & Carry International Holding GmbH (1)
Metro-Platz 1, 2331, Voesendorf, Austria
Tel.: (43) 169080
Web Site: https://www.metro.at
Investment Management Service
N.A.I.C.S.: 523999

METRO Cash & Carry International Management GmbH (1)
Metro-Strasse 1, 40235, Dusseldorf, Germany
Tel.: (49) 2119694250
Web Site: https://www.hd.digital
Emp.: 4,000
Super Market Stores Operating Services
N.A.I.C.S.: 445110

METRO Cash & Carry Japan Holding GmbH (1)
Metro-Platz 1, Niederosterreich, 2331, Voesendorf, Austria
Tel.: (43) 169080
Web Site: https://www.metro.at
Emp.: 2,100
Investment Management Service
N.A.I.C.S.: 523999
Mark Croelewoug (Mng Dir)

METRO Cash & Carry Japan KK (1)
Omori Bellport D 7F 6-26-3 Minami-oi, Shinagawa-Ku, Tokyo, 140-0013, Japan
Tel.: (81) 357638400
Web Site: http://www.metro-cc.com
Sales Range: $200-249.9 Million
Emp.: 687
Super Market Stores Operating Services
N.A.I.C.S.: 445110

METRO Cash & Carry OOO (1)
Tel.: (7) 4955021009
Web Site: https://www.metro-cc.ru
Food Product Whslr
N.A.I.C.S.: 424410

METRO Cash & Carry Osterreich GmbH (1)
Metro-Platz 1, 2331, Voesendorf, Austria
Tel.: (43) 1 690 80
Web Site: http://www.metro.at
Rev.: $10,472,015,750
Emp.: 230
Super Market Stores Operating Services
N.A.I.C.S.: 445110
Akin Bayer (CEO)

METRO Cash & Carry SR s.r.o. (1)
Web Site: http://www.metro.sk
Super Market Stores Operating Services
N.A.I.C.S.: 445110

METRO Cash & Carry TOO (1)
st Saina 16g, 050000, Almaty, Kazakhstan
Tel.: (7) 7273302410
Web Site: http://www.metro.com.kz
Food Product Whslr
N.A.I.C.S.: 424410
Anastassiya Karyzhenskaya (Mgr-HR)

METRO AG

INTERNATIONAL PUBLIC

Metro AG—(Continued)

METRO Cash & Carry d.o.o. (1)
Jankomir 31, 10090, Zagreb, Croatia
Tel.: (385) 13444221
Web Site: https://www.metro-cc.hr
Sales Range: $400-449.9 Million
Emp.: 1,212
Super Market Stores Operating Services
N.A.I.C.S.: 445110

METRO Cash & Carry d.o.o. (1)
Zrenjaninski put br 11M, 11000, Belgrade, Serbia
Tel.: (381) 800222022
Web Site: https://www.metro.rs
Super Market Stores Operating Services
N.A.I.C.S.: 445110

METRO Central East Europe GmbH (1)
Riemergasse 14, Vienna, 1010, Austria
Tel.: (43) 51585103
Electronic Store Operating Services
N.A.I.C.S.: 449210

METRO Czestochowa Sp. z o.o. (1)
Wreczycka 11b, 42-200, Czestochowa, Poland
Tel.: (48) 884900922
Web Site: https://mtr-sp-z-o-o.business.site
General Merchandise Retailer
N.A.I.C.S.: 455219

METRO DOLOMITI Spa (1)
Via Maccani 112, 38100, Trento, Italy
Tel.: (39) 04618091
Web Site: http://www.metro.it
Super Market Stores Operating Services
N.A.I.C.S.: 445110

METRO Danmark Holding ApS (1)
Ejby Industrivej 111, Glostrup, 2600, Denmark
Tel.: (45) 43467700
Investment Management Service
N.A.I.C.S.: 523999

METRO Deutschland GmbH (1)
Metro-Strasse 8, 40235, Dusseldorf, Germany
Tel.: (49) 2119690
Web Site: https://www.metro.de
Food & Beverage Distr
N.A.I.C.S.: 424490

METRO Distributie Nederland B. V. (1)
Dalsteindreef 101-139, 1112 XC, Diemen, Netherlands
Tel.: (31) 203980200
Super Market Stores Operating Services
N.A.I.C.S.: 445110

METRO Finance B.V. (1)
Antoniuslaan 85b-C, Venlo, 5921 KB, Netherlands
Tel.: (31) 773961900
Sales Range: $50-74.9 Million
Emp.: 9
Financial Management Services
N.A.I.C.S.: 523999
Olaf Kruse *(Mng Dir)*

METRO Finance Ltd (1)
197 Ecclesall Road, Sheffield, S11 8HW, United Kingdom
Tel.: (44) 1142701444
Web Site: https://www.metrofinance.co.uk
Mortgage Loan Broking Services
N.A.I.C.S.: 522310

METRO Financial Services GmbH (1)
Metro-Strasse 1, 40235, Dusseldorf, Germany
Tel.: (49) 15115112233
Web Site: https://metro-fs.com
Financial Services
N.A.I.C.S.: 921130

METRO France S.A.S. (1)
ZA du Petit Nanterre - 5 rue des Grands Pres, 92024, Nanterre, France
Tel.: (33) 825090909
Web Site: https://www.metro.fr
Food & Restaurant Services
N.A.I.C.S.: 722511
Sylvain Bozoc *(Head-Omnichannel & E-commerce)*

METRO Global Business Services Private Limited (1)
3rd and 6th Floor Wing 2 Cluster D EON Tech Park, Kharadi, Pune, 411014, India
Tel.: (91) 2071001500
Web Site: http://www.metro-services.in
Business Management Services
N.A.I.C.S.: 541611
Sreeman Murthy *(Mng Dir)*

METRO Global Solution Center spolka z ograniczona odpowiedzialnoscia (1)
Pl Brama Portowa 1, 70-225, Szczecin, Poland
Tel.: (48) 914866600
Web Site: https://www.metro-gsc.pl
Accounting Services
N.A.I.C.S.: 541219

METRO Grosmarket Bakirkoy Alisveris Hizmetleri Ticaret Ltd. Sirketi (1)
15 July Mah Kocman Cad No 52 Bagcilar, 34212, Istanbul, Turkiye
Tel.: (90) 2124787000
Web Site: http://www.metro-tr.com
Food Product Whslr
N.A.I.C.S.: 424410

METRO Group Asset Management B.V. (1)
Antoniuslaan 85b C, Venlo, 5921 KB, Netherlands
Tel.: (31) 773961900
Sales Range: $50-74.9 Million
Emp.: 10
Property Management Services
N.A.I.C.S.: 531311
Olaf Schulze *(Gen Mgr)*

METRO Group Asset Management Ingatlan Kft. (1)
Malomko Utca 3, 2040, Budaors, Hungary
Tel.: (36) 23445630
Web Site: http://www.metro-properties.com
Sales Range: $25-49.9 Million
Emp.: 3
Shopping Center Management Services
N.A.I.C.S.: 531120

METRO Group Asset Management Services GmbH (1)
Mainzer Str 180, 66121, Saarbrucken, Germany
Tel.: (49) 681810401
Web Site: http://www.metro-properties.de
Real Estate Manangement Services
N.A.I.C.S.: 531390

METRO Group Retail Real Estate GmbH (1)
Neumannstr 8, 40235, Dusseldorf, Germany
Tel.: (49) 21168860
Real Estate Manangement Services
N.A.I.C.S.: 531390

METRO Group Wholesale Real Estate GmbH (1)
Neumannstr 8, Dusseldorf, 40235, Germany
Tel.: (49) 21168860
Real Estate Manangement Services
N.A.I.C.S.: 531390

METRO International AG (1)
Neuhofstrasse 4, 6340, Baar, Switzerland
Tel.: (41) 417687733
Food Whslr
N.A.I.C.S.: 424410
Werner Reichl *(Mgr-HR)*

METRO Italia Cash and Carry S. p. A. (1)
Via XXV Aprile 23, 20097, San Donato Milanese, Italy
Tel.: (39) 0251721
Web Site: https://www.metro.it
Sales Range: $800-899.9 Million
Emp.: 4,000
Super Market Stores Operating Services
N.A.I.C.S.: 445110

METRO Italia S.p.A (1)
Via XXV Aprile 23, 20097, San Donato Milanese, Italy
Tel.: (39) 0251721
Web Site: https://www.metro.it

Food & Beverage Distr
N.A.I.C.S.: 424490

METRO Jinjiang Cash & Carry Co., Ltd. (1)
1425 Zhen Bei Road, Putuo District, 200333, Shanghai, China
Tel.: (86) 2122078888
Web Site: http://www.metro.com.cn
Sales Range: $1-4.9 Billion
Emp.: 7,734
Super Market Stores Operating Services
N.A.I.C.S.: 445110

Subsidiary (Domestic):

Star Farm (Shanghai) Agriculture Information Consulting Company Limited (2)
Rm 2301 Suite C Fortune Plaza No 278 Suixi Rd, Hefei, 230041, China
Tel.: (86) 5515681367
Super Market Stores Operating Services
N.A.I.C.S.: 445110

METRO Kereskedelmi Kft. (1)
Keleti utca 3, 2040, Budaors, Hungary
Tel.: (36) 80509050
Web Site: https://www.metro.hu
Sales Range: $800-899.9 Million
Emp.: 2,872
Super Market Stores Operating Services
N.A.I.C.S.: 445110

METRO Leasing GmbH (1)
Mainzer Str 180-184, Saarbrucken, 66121, Germany
Tel.: (49) 6818104289
Financial Lending Services
N.A.I.C.S.: 522220

METRO Logistics Germany GmbH (1)
Schluterstr 1, 40235, Dusseldorf, Germany
Procurement Logistics Services
N.A.I.C.S.: 541614
Armin Koller *(CEO)*

METRO Markets GmbH (1)
Ria-Thiele-Strasse 2a, North Rhine-Westphalia, 40549, Dusseldorf, Germany
Tel.: (49) 21191194200
Web Site: https://www.metro-markets.de
Online Business Platform
N.A.I.C.S.: 561990
Philipp Blome *(CEO)*

METRO Pakistan (Pvt.) Limited (1)
Thokar Niaz Baig Multan Road, Lahore, 53700, Punjab, Pakistan
Tel.: (92) 42111786622
Web Site: https://www.metro.pk
Grocery Product Whslr
N.A.I.C.S.: 424410
Marek Andrzej Minkiewicz *(Mng Dir)*

METRO Properties CR s.r.o. (1)
Jeremiasova 1249/7, Prague, 155 00, Czech Republic
Tel.: (420) 220389111
Real Estate Manangement Services
N.A.I.C.S.: 531390

METRO Properties Gayrimenkul Yatirim A.S. (1)
Nisbetiye Caddesi No 22 Ozden Business Center Floor 1, Nisbetiye Mahallesi Besiktas, 34340, Istanbul, Turkiye
Tel.: (90) 2124510851
Web Site: https://www.metro-properties.com.tr
Real Estate Investment Services
N.A.I.C.S.: 531390
Osman Kocek *(COO)*

METRO SYSTEMS GmbH (1)
Metro-Strasse 12, Dusseldorf, 40235, Germany
Tel.: (49) 211 969 0
Web Site: http://www.metro.de
Sales Range: $75-99.9 Million
Emp.: 400
Information Technology Consulting Services
N.A.I.C.S.: 541512
Silvester Macho *(CEO)*

METRO Service GmbH (1)
Metro Platz 1, Voesendorf, 2331, Austria
Tel.: (43) 169080
Web Site: http://www.metro.at

Emp.: 30
Super Market Stores Operating Services
N.A.I.C.S.: 445110
Marc Groenewoud *(Gen Mgr)*

METRO Services PL spotka z ograniczonq odpowiedzialnosciq (1)
Ku Sloncu 67, 71-041, Szczecin, Poland
Tel.: (48) 914866600
Web Site: http://www.metro-services.pl
Accounting Services
N.A.I.C.S.: 541211
Marcin Renke *(Head-Div)*

METRO Sourcing (Shanghai) Co., Ltd. (1)
3/F Prona Plaza Building 1 Lane 2145 Jin Sha Jiang Road, Putuo District, Shanghai, 20033, China
Tel.: (86) 2122078888
Food Product Whslr
N.A.I.C.S.: 424410

METRO Sourcing International Limited (1)
1-9A and 11B 20/F Skyline Tower 39 Wang Kwong Road, Kowloon Bay, Kowloon, China (Hong Kong)
Tel.: (852) 27381388
Web Site: https://www.metro-sourcing.hk
Canned Food Product Distr
N.A.I.C.S.: 424490

METRO Systems Romania S.R.L. (1)
Sos Pipera Tunari 4C, 077190, Voluntari, Romania
Tel.: (40) 212438259
Web Site: http://www.metrosystems.ro
Emp.: 800
Information Technology Services
N.A.I.C.S.: 541511
Juergen Boekholt *(Mng Dir)*

METRO Warehouse Management (Hangzhou) Co. Ltd. (1)
No 1459 Moganshan Road, Jinjiadu, Hangzhou, 311112, China
Tel.: (86) 57188998888
Food Product Whslr
N.A.I.C.S.: 424410
Zhu Feng *(Mgr-Store)*

METRO Warehouse Management (Yantai) Co., Limited (1)
No 149 Zhichu Road, Zhifu, Yantai, 264000, China
Tel.: (86) 5352158888
Food Product Whslr
N.A.I.C.S.: 424410
Gao Wei *(Mgr-Store)*

METRO Warehouse Management (Zibo) Co., Ltd. (1)
No 102 Shanquan Road, Zhangdian, Zibo, 255051, China
Tel.: (86) 5337866888
Food Product Whslr
N.A.I.C.S.: 424410
Xiao Chi *(Mgr-Store)*

METRO Wholesale Myanmar Ltd. (1)
Lot No B-8 Zone A Thilawa Special Economic Zone, Thanlyin, Yangon, 11291, Myanmar
Tel.: (95) 9977203020
Web Site: http://www.metro-wholesale.com
Grocery Products Retailer
N.A.I.C.S.: 445110
Jens Michel *(CEO)*

METRO-nom GmbH (1)
Metro-Strasse 12, 40235, Dusseldorf, Germany
Tel.: (49) 2119690
Web Site: http://www.metronom.com
Food Product Whslr
N.A.I.C.S.: 424410
Timo Salzsieder *(CEO)*

MFM METRO Group Facility Management GmbH (1)
Dohrweg 25, 41066, Monchengladbach, Germany
Tel.: (49) 8005035418
Web Site: http://www.meinreal.de
Emp.: 400
Facility Management Services

AND PRIVATE COMPANIES **METRO AG**

N.A.I.C.S.: 561210
Christian Schrank *(CEO)*

MGA METRO GROUP Advertising Polska Sp. z o.o. (1)
Al Krakowska 61, 02-183, Warsaw, Poland
Tel.: (48) 225001450
Web Site: https://www.metro-advertising.pl
Consumer Electronics Retail Store Operating Services
N.A.I.C.S.: 449210

MGA METRO Group Advertising GmbH (1)
Metro-Strasse 2, 40235, Dusseldorf, Germany
Tel.: (49) 2119693969
Web Site: https://www.metro-advertising.com
Advertising Agency Services
N.A.I.C.S.: 541810

MGB METRO Group Buying HK Limited (1)
20/F Skyline Tower 39 Wang Kwong Road, Harbour City Tsim Sha Tsui, Kowloon, China (Hong Kong)
Tel.: (852) 27381388
Super Market Stores Operating Services
N.A.I.C.S.: 445110

MGI Metro Group Information Technology GmbH (1)
Metro-Strasse 12, 40235, Dusseldorf, Germany
Tel.: (49) 2119695000
Web Site: http://www.mgi.de
Sales Range: $25-49.9 Million
Emp.: 100
Information Technology Services
N.A.I.C.S.: 541519

Subsidiary (Non-US):

MGI METRO Group Information Technology Romania srl (2)
Construdava Business Center Soseau Pipera-Tunari nr 4C, Voluntari, Ilfov, 077190, Bucharest, Romania
Tel.: (40) 314138111
Web Site: http://www.mgi.de
Information Technology Services
N.A.I.C.S.: 541519

MGI METRO Group Information Technology Ukraine LLC (2)
43 Grygorenko Avenue, 2140, Kiev, Ukraine
Tel.: (380) 444921000
Web Site: http://www.mgi.de
Information Technology Services
N.A.I.C.S.: 541519

MGI Metro Group Iletisim ve Enformasyon Ticaret Limited Sirketi (2)
Kocman Cad, Gunesli, 34540, Istanbul, Turkiye
Tel.: (90) 2124787506
Web Site: http://www.metrosystems.de
Sales Range: $10-24.9 Million
Emp.: 17
Information Technology Services
N.A.I.C.S.: 541519

MGI Metro Group Information Technology LLC (2)
Leningradskoye Shosse 71G, 125445, Moscow, Russia
Tel.: (7) 4955021000
Information Technology Services
N.A.I.C.S.: 541519

MGL METRO Group Logistics GmbH (1)
Schlterstrasse 1, 40235, Dusseldorf, Germany
Tel.: (49) 21168860
Sales Range: $650-699.9 Million
Emp.: 3,800
Logistic Services
N.A.I.C.S.: 561499
Stephan Wohler *(CEO)*

MGL METRO Group Logistics Warehousing Beteiligungs GmbH (1)
Am Teinkamp 7, Sarstedt, 31157, Germany
Tel.: (49) 5066890
Logistics & Warehousing Services
N.A.I.C.S.: 541614

MGL METRO Group Logistics Warehousing GmbH (1)
Am Teinkamp 7, Sarstedt, 31157, Germany
Tel.: (49) 5066890
Logistics & Warehousing Services
N.A.I.C.S.: 541614

MIAG B.V. (1)
Antoniuslaan 85 B-C, Venlo, Blerick, 5921 KB, Netherlands
Tel.: (31) 77 396 19 19
Web Site: http://www.miag-bv.com
Supply Chain Financial Management Services
N.A.I.C.S.: 525990

MIB METRO Group Insurance Broker GmbH (1)
Metro Street 8, Dusseldorf, 40235, Germany
Tel.: (49) 21168860
Insurance Brokerage Services
N.A.I.C.S.: 524210

MIP METRO Group Intellectual Property GmbH & Co. KG (1)
Metro Str 1, 40235, Dusseldorf, Germany
Tel.: (49) 2119690
Web Site: http://www.metro.de
Emp.: 4,000
Super Market Stores Operating Services
N.A.I.C.S.: 445110
Olas Koch *(CEO)*

MMS Online Nederland B.V. (1)
Wilhelminakade 161, Rotterdam, 3063072ap, Netherlands
Tel.: (31) 102076500
Web Site: http://www.mediamart.com
Emp.: 400
Electronic Retail Stores Operating Services
N.A.I.C.S.: 449210
Rob Janssen *(CFO)*

MP Gayrimenkul Yonetim Hizmetleri Anonim Sirketi (1)
Karacaahmet Mh Sehit Omer Halisdemir Bulvari No 129, Sehitkamil, Gaziantep, Turkiye
Tel.: (90) 3423289560
Web Site: http://www.m1gaziantep.com.tr
Real Estate Rental Services
N.A.I.C.S.: 531110

MS E-Commerce GmbH (1)
SCS Burocenter Level B 4, Voesendorf, 2334, Austria
Tel.: (43) 1699070
Web Site: http://www.media-saturn.com
Super Market Stores Operating Services
N.A.I.C.S.: 445110
Sigrid Kuhn *(Mgr-PR)*

Makro Autoservicio Mayorista S. A. U. (1)
Poligono Industrial Las Mercedes C de Campezo 7, 28022, Madrid, Spain
Tel.: (34) 913219700
Web Site: https://www.makro.es
Emp.: 3,700
Food Products Distr
N.A.I.C.S.: 424490
Peter Gries *(CEO)*

Makro Cash & Carry Egypt LLC (1)
306 Corniche El Nil St 3rd Fl HSBC Office Bldg, Maadi, Cairo, Egypt
Tel.: (20) 227688200
Web Site: http://www.makro.com.eg
Sales Range: $100-124.9 Million
Emp.: 447
Super Market Stores Operating Services
N.A.I.C.S.: 445110

Makro Distribucion Mayorista, S.A.U. (1)
Paseo Imperial 40, 28005, Madrid, Spain
Tel.: (34) 900907503
Web Site: https://www.makro.es
Emp.: 3,800
Food Products Distr
N.A.I.C.S.: 424420

Meister feines Fleisch - feine Wurst GmbH (1)
Siedlerstrasse 1, 71126, Gaufelden, Germany
Tel.: (49) 70327830
Web Site: https://www.meister-wurst.de
Meat Product Whslr
N.A.I.C.S.: 424470

Metro Cash & Carry Nederland B.V. (1)
Spaklerweg 52, 1112 XC, Amsterdam, Netherlands
Tel.: (31) 203980200
Sales Range: $800-899.9 Million
Emp.: 300
Supermarket Operating Services
N.A.I.C.S.: 445110

Metro Group Asset Management GmbH & Co. KG (1)
Metro-Strasse 2, 40235, Dusseldorf, Germany
Tel.: (49) 21168864250
Web Site: https://www.metro-properties.de
Sales Range: $100-124.9 Million
Emp.: 120
Asset Management Services
N.A.I.C.S.: 523999

Subsidiary (Non-US):

Asset Ingatlan Management Kft. (2)
Malomko utca 7, 2040, Budaors, Hungary
Tel.: (36) 23445630
Web Site: https://asseting.hu
Sales Range: $50-74.9 Million
Emp.: 20
Asset Management Services
N.A.I.C.S.: 523999
Lasco Csici *(Gen Mgr)*

Cofalux Immobiliere S.A. (2)
2 route d'Arlon, 8008, Strassen, Luxembourg
Tel.: (352) 447803222
Web Site: http://www.metro-mam.pl
Asset Management Services
N.A.I.C.S.: 523999

Metro Group Asset Management Emlak Yonetim A.S. (2)
Cinar Caddesi Kavak Sokak Yalcinlar Plaza K 1, Yenibosna, 34197, Istanbul, Turkiye
Tel.: (90) 2124510851
Web Site: http://www.metro-mam.pl
Sales Range: $50-74.9 Million
Emp.: 100
Asset Management Services
N.A.I.C.S.: 523999

Metro Group Asset Management OOO (2)
Leningradskoye Shosse 71 G, 125445, Moscow, Russia
Tel.: (7) 4959813283
Web Site: http://www.metro-mam.ru
Asset Management Services
N.A.I.C.S.: 523999

Metro Group Asset Management Polska Sp. z o.o. (2)
Al Krakowska 61, 02183, Warsaw, Poland
Tel.: (48) 225000000
Web Site: http://www.metro-mam.pl
Asset Management Services
N.A.I.C.S.: 523999

Metro Group Settlement AG (1)
Aspermontstrasse 24, 7000, Chur, Switzerland
Tel.: (41) 813549060
Investment Management Service
N.A.I.C.S.: 523999

Metro Property Management (Changzhou) Co. Ltd. (1)
No 1297 Longcheng Av, Tianning Dist, Changzhou, 213001, China
Tel.: (86) 51985208888
Property Management Services
N.A.I.C.S.: 531312

Metro Reinsurance N.V. (1)
Dalsteindreef 101-139, Diemen, 1112 XC, Netherlands
Tel.: (31) 203980203
General Insurance Services
N.A.I.C.S.: 524210

Metro Warehouse Management (Taizhou) Co. Ltd. (1)
No 666 East of Shifu Avenue, Taizhou, 318001, China
Tel.: (86) 57683258888
Food Product Whslr
N.A.I.C.S.: 424410
Zhu Feng *(Mgr-Store)*

PT Classic Fine Foods Indonesia (1)
Kompleks Pergudangan BGR Jl Boulevard BGR no 1, Kelapa Gading Barat, Jakarta, 14240, Indonesia
Tel.: (62) 2145848040
Web Site: https://www.classicfinefoods.co.id
Gourmet Product Distr
N.A.I.C.S.: 424490
Thomas Pellegrini *(Mng Dir)*

PayRed Card Services AG (1)
Allmendstrasse 23, 8953, Dietikon, Switzerland
Tel.: (41) 447493636
Web Site: http://www.mediamat.ch
Sales Range: $25-49.9 Million
Emp.: 100
Super Market Stores Operating Services
N.A.I.C.S.: 445110
Karsten Sommer *(Pres)*

Pro A Pro Distribution Export SAS (1)
3 rue Voltaire, 82000, Montauban, France
Tel.: (33) 563214444
Web Site: https://www.proapro-export.com
Food Products Distr
N.A.I.C.S.: 424410

RUNGIS Express GmbH (1)
Am Hambuch 2 / Einfahrt Am Pannacker, 53340, Meckenheim, Germany
Tel.: (49) 22258830
Web Site: https://rungisexpress.com
Emp.: 700
Food Products Distr
N.A.I.C.S.: 424410
Kai D. Schneider *(Mng Dir)*

Remo Zaandam B.V. (1)
Kleine Tocht 14, 1507 CB, Zaandam, 1507 CB, Netherlands
Tel.: (31) 756123361
Electronic Retail Stores Operating Services
N.A.I.C.S.: 449210

Restu s.r.o. (1)
Jeremiasova 1249/7 Stodulky, 155 00, Prague, Czech Republic
Tel.: (420) 232000444
Web Site: http://www.restu.cz
Hotel Reservation Services
N.A.I.C.S.: 561599
Jiri Moskal *(CEO)*

Star Farm Pakistan Pvt. Ltd. (1)
Thokar Niaz Baig 2KM Multan Road, Lahore, 53700, Pakistan
Tel.: (92) 4237508012
Web Site: https://www.starfarm.pk
Emp.: 95,000
Farm Product Distr
N.A.I.C.S.: 424910
Marek Minikiewicz *(Mng Dir)*

Vierte real,- SB-Warenhaus GmbH (1)
Reyerhutte 51, 41065, Monchengladbach, Germany
Tel.: (49) 21614030
Web Site: http://www.real.de
Super Market Stores Operating Services
N.A.I.C.S.: 445110
Michael Blankenhagen *(Mgr-Category)*

Wirichs Immobilien GmbH (1)
Diessemer Bruch 59, 47805, Krefeld, Germany
Tel.: (49) 2151557930
Web Site: http://www.wirichs-immobilien.de
Real Estate Rental & Selling Services
N.A.I.C.S.: 531110

Zweite real,- SB-Warenhaus GmbH (1)
Huttenkreuzstrasse 8, 76275, Ettlingen, Germany
Tel.: (49) 724371090
Online Retail Store Operating Services
N.A.I.C.S.: 425120

cc delivery gmbh (1)
Am Hambuch 2, 53340, Meckenheim, Germany
Tel.: (49) 2225883234
Web Site: http://www.ccdelivery.com
Food Whslr & Retailer
N.A.I.C.S.: 424410
Joachim Bayer *(Acct Mgr)*

METRO AG

Metro AG—(Continued)

real,- Sp. z o.o. i Spolka spolka komandytowa (1)
Al Krakowska 61, 02-183, Warsaw, Poland
Tel.: (48) 225000000
Super Market Stores Operating Services
N.A.I.C.S.: 445110

real,- Digital Services GmbH (1)
Hansaallee 299, 40549, Dusseldorf, Germany
Tel.: (49) 22197597950
Web Site: http://www.real-digital.de
Ecommerce Services
N.A.I.C.S.: 541511
Gerald Schonbucher *(CEO)*

real,- Holding GmbH (1)
Friedrichstr 12, 55232, Alzey, Germany
Tel.: (49) 2119690
Investment Management Service
N.A.I.C.S.: 523999

real,- Hypermarket Romania S.R.L. (1)
Blvd Theodor Palady 51 N Sector 3, 032258, Bucharest, Romania
Tel.: (40) 314031000
Web Site: http://www.real-hypermarket.ro
Super Market Stores Operating Services
N.A.I.C.S.: 445110

real,- SB-Warenhaus GmbH (1)
Reyerhuette 51, 41065, Monchengladbach, Germany
Tel.: (49) 21614030
Web Site: http://www.real.com
Emp.: 80
Super Market Stores Operating Services
N.A.I.C.S.: 445110

METRO ALLIANCE HOLDINGS & EQUITIES CORP.
35th Floor One Corporate Center, Julia Vargas Ave cor Meralco Ave Ortigas Center, Pasig, 1605, Philippines
Tel.: (63) 27067888
Web Site:
 https://www.metroalliance.com
Year Founded: 1929
MAH—(PHI)
Rev.: $4,390,460
Assets: $12,731,879
Liabilities: $12,801,994
Net Worth: ($70,115)
Earnings: ($71,181)
Emp.: 326
Fiscal Year-end: 12/31/23
Holding Company
N.A.I.C.S.: 551112
Renato B. Magadia *(Chm & Pres)*

Subsidiaries:

Metro Combined Logistics Solutions, Inc. (1)
Unit 2002 20th Floor Antel Corporate Centre 121 Valero St Metro Manila, Salcedo Village, Makati, 1229, Philippines
Tel.: (63) 25532735
Web Site: https://www.metrocombined.com
Transportation Services
N.A.I.C.S.: 484110

METRO BANK HOLDINGS PLC
One Southampton Row, London, WC1B 5HA, United Kingdom
Tel.: (44) 2034028900   UK
Web Site:
 https://www.metrobankonline.co.uk
Year Founded: 2010
MTRO—(LSE)
Holding Company
N.A.I.C.S.: 551112
Daniel Frumkin *(CEO)*

METRO BRANDS LIMITED
LBS Marg CST Road Junction Kurla West Junction, Mumbai, 400070, Maharashtra, India
Tel.: (91) 2226547700

Web Site:
 https://www.metrobrands.com
543426—(BOM)
Rev.: $119,920,451
Assets: $226,499,350
Liabilities: $110,824,541
Net Worth: $115,674,809
Earnings: $8,820,726
Fiscal Year-end: 03/31/21
Footwear Retailer
N.A.I.C.S.: 424340
Rafique Malik *(Chm)*

METRO CHRYSLER LTD.
1047 Richmond Rd, Ottawa, K2B 6R1, ON, Canada
Tel.: (613) 596-1006
Web Site:
 http://www.metrochrysler.ca
Year Founded: 1981
Rev.: $23,408,000
Emp.: 50
New & Used Car Dealers
N.A.I.C.S.: 441110
Peter Pears *(Mgr-Sls)*

METRO GLOBAL HOLDINGS CORPORATION
Mezzanine Floor Renaissance Tower F, Meralco Avenue, Pasig, Philippines
Tel.: (63) 286336205
Web Site:
 https://metroglobalholdings.com
MGH—(PHI)
Rev.: $806,437
Assets: $80,032,558
Liabilities: $16,972,523
Net Worth: $63,060,035
Earnings: $37,418
Emp.: 11
Fiscal Year-end: 12/31/23
Holding Company
N.A.I.C.S.: 551112
Gilbert Raymund T. Reyes *(Sec)*

METRO HOLDINGS LIMITED
391A Orchard Road 19-00 Tower A, Ngee Ann City, Singapore, 238873, Singapore
Tel.: (65) 67333000
Web Site:
 https://www.metroholdings.com.sg
M01—(SES)
Rev.: $86,874,398
Assets: $1,738,315,672
Liabilities: $640,638,014
Net Worth: $1,097,677,658
Earnings: $18,780,289
Emp.: 364
Fiscal Year-end: 03/31/21
Property Development Services
N.A.I.C.S.: 531311
Ching Chek Tan *(Co-Sec)*

Subsidiaries:

Metro (Private) Limited (1)
12 Ang Mo Kio Street 65 05-01, Singapore, 569060, Singapore
Tel.: (65) 68353322
Web Site: https://www.metro.com.sg
Sales Range: $25-49.9 Million
Emp.: 100
Discount Department Stores Operation Services
N.A.I.C.S.: 455110
David Kai Kong Tang *(CEO)*

Metro China Holdings Pte Ltd (1)
391A Orchard Road 19-00 Tower A Ngee Ann City, Singapore, 238873, Singapore
Tel.: (65) 67333000
Web Site: http://www.metroholdings.sg
Investment Management Service
N.A.I.C.S.: 523999

Subsidiary (Non-US):

Crown Investments Ltd (2)
1944 Lincoln Rd, Fredericton, E3B 8M7, NB, Canada

Tel.: (506) 457-1905
Property Investment Services
N.A.I.C.S.: 531110

Metrobilt Construction Pte Ltd (1)
391A Orchard Rd Unit 19-00 Ngee Ann City Tower A, Singapore, 238873, Singapore
Tel.: (65) 67356177
Web Site: http://www.metroholdings.com
Sales Range: $25-49.9 Million
Emp.: 20
Commercial Building Construction Services
N.A.I.C.S.: 236220

Metrobilt Pte Ltd (1)
391A Orchard Rd 19-00 Ngee Ann City Tower A, Singapore, 238873, Singapore
Tel.: (65) 67356177
Web Site: http://www.metro.com.sg
Department Stores Operation Services
N.A.I.C.S.: 455110

Shanghai Huimei Property Co Ltd (1)
Room 903 Meiluo Mansion No 30 Tianyaoqiao Rd, Xuhui District, Shanghai, 200030, China
Tel.: (86) 2164268380
Residential Real Estate Management Services
N.A.I.C.S.: 531210

The Marketing Co Pte Ltd (1)
391a Orchard Road 17-01 Ngee Ann City Tower A, Singapore, 238873, Singapore
Tel.: (65) 63339014
Web Site: http://www.metro.com.sg
Sales Range: $75-99.9 Million
Emp.: 400
Outdoor Advertising Services
N.A.I.C.S.: 541850
David Tang *(CEO)*

METRO INC.
11 011 boul Maurice-Duplessis, Montreal, H1C 1V6, QC, Canada
Tel.: (514) 643-1000   Ca
Web Site: https://corpo.metro.ca
Year Founded: 1956
MTRAF—(OTCIQ)
Rev.: $14,302,425,240
Assets: $10,632,827,988
Liabilities: $5,616,222,804
Net Worth: $5,016,605,184
Earnings: $645,928,596
Emp.: 44,097
Fiscal Year-end: 09/25/21
Household Product Distr
N.A.I.C.S.: 551112
Simon Rivet *(Gen Counsel, Sec & VP)*

Subsidiaries:

Groupe Adonis Inc. (1)
1595 Daniel-Johnson Blvd 400, Laval, H7V 4C2, QC, Canada
Tel.: (450) 686-8099
Web Site: https://www.groupeadonis.ca
Emp.: 1,000
Grocery Products Retailer
N.A.I.C.S.: 445110

Groupe Premiere Moisson Inc. (1)
189 boul Harwood, Vaudreuil-Dorion, J7V 1Y3, QC, Canada
Tel.: (450) 455-2827
Web Site: https://premieremoisson.com
Bakery Products Mfr
N.A.I.C.S.: 311812

Pro Doc Ltee (1)
2925 Boul Industriel, Laval, H7L 3W9, QC, Canada
Tel.: (450) 668-9750
Web Site: http://www.prodoc.qc.ca
Pharmaceuticals Product Mfr
N.A.I.C.S.: 325412

The Jean Coutu Group (PJC) Inc. (1)
245 Jean Coutu Street, Varennes, J3X 0E1, QC, Canada
Tel.: (450) 646-9760
Web Site: https://www.jeancoutu.com
Pharmaceutical, Health & Beauty Cosmetics & Food Retailer

INTERNATIONAL PUBLIC

N.A.I.C.S.: 456110
Jean-Michel Coutu *(Pres)*

METRO INTER PLY CO LTD
72 Soi Nonthaburi 15 Nonthaburi 1 Road, Bang Kra Soa Mueng Nonthaburi, Nonthaburi, 11000, Thailand
Tel.: (66) 2 055 8555   TH
Web Site: http://www.metroply.com
Wood-Based Composite Panels, Veneers, Particle Board & Fiberboard Mfr
N.A.I.C.S.: 321219
Narong Piyasombatkul *(Pres)*

METRO LABEL GROUP, INC.
999 Progress Ave, Toronto, M1B 6J1, ON, Canada
Tel.: (416) 292-6600
Web Site:
 http://www.metrolabelgroup.com
Year Founded: 1974
Sales Range: $25-49.9 Million
Emp.: 130
Label Mfr
N.A.I.C.S.: 561910
Narinder Lal *(Chm)*

Subsidiaries:

Metro Jonergin, Inc. (1)
6200 Grande Alee, Saint-Hubert, J3Y 1B6, QC, Canada
Tel.: (514) 878-3961
Sales Range: $25-49.9 Million
Emp.: 75
Labels & Specialty Packaging Mfr
N.A.I.C.S.: 333993

Metro Label Pacific Ltd. (1)
20215- 97 Avenue, Langley, V1M 4B9, BC, Canada
Tel.: (604) 513-4119
Label Mfr
N.A.I.C.S.: 323111

Metropolis Label Corp. (1)
1901 N Kelly Rd, Napa, CA 94558-6221
Tel.: (800) 668-4405
Web Site: http://www.metrolabel.com
Sales Range: $10-24.9 Million
Emp.: 30
Labels & Specialty Packaging Mfr
N.A.I.C.S.: 561910

METRO LAND CORPORATION LTD.
17th floor Yintai Office Tower Beijing Yintai Centre, 2 Jianguomenwai Street, Beijing, 100022, China
Tel.: (86) 1065636688
Web Site: https://600683.com
600683—(SHG)
Rev.: $779,553,885
Assets: $7,695,755,716
Liabilities: $6,168,884,052
Net Worth: $1,526,871,664
Earnings: $28,388,080
Fiscal Year-end: 12/31/22
Residential Building Lessors & Department Store Operator
N.A.I.C.S.: 531110

METRO MINING LIMITED
Level 4 135 Wickham Terrace, GPO Box 10955, Brisbane, 4000, QLD, Australia
Tel.: (61) 730098000   AU
Web Site:
 https://www.metromining.com.au
MMI—(ASX)
Rev.: $160,643,008
Assets: $115,112,731
Liabilities: $108,333,220
Net Worth: $6,779,511
Earnings: ($9,183,298)
Emp.: 370
Fiscal Year-end: 12/31/23
Exploration & Mining Services
N.A.I.C.S.: 212390
Douglas Ritchie *(Chm)*

AND PRIVATE COMPANIES

METROFILE HOLDINGS LIMITED

METRO ORLEANS DODGE CHRYSLER JEEP RAM
1465 Youville Drive, Orleans, K1C 4R1, ON, Canada
Tel.: (613) 830-1777
Web Site:
  http://www.orleansdodge.ca
Year Founded: 2010
New & Used Car Dealers
N.A.I.C.S.: 441110
Guy Larochelle *(Mgr-Svc)*

METRO PACIFIC INVESTMENTS CORPORATION
10/F MGO Building Legaspi corner Dela Rosa Streets, Makati, 0721, Philippines
Tel.: (63) 28880888 PH
Web Site: http://www.mpic.com.ph
MPCFF—(OTCEM)
Rev.: $1,107,303,411
Assets: $12,948,000,239
Liabilities: $7,729,764,304
Net Worth: $5,218,235,935
Earnings: $475,886,969
Emp.: 17,543
Fiscal Year-end: 12/31/23
Holding Company; Investment & Management Services
N.A.I.C.S.: 551112
Manuel V. Pangilinan *(Chm)*

Subsidiaries:

Beacon Electric Asset Holdings, Inc. (1)
c/o MPI - 10/F MGO Bldg Legazpi cor Dela Rosa Streets, Makati, 0721, Philippines
Tel.: (63) 28880888
Rev.: $123,843,200
Fiscal Year-end: 12/31/2020
Investment Holding Company
N.A.I.C.S.: 551112
Manuel V. Pangilinan *(Chm)*

Metro Pacific Tollways Corporation (1)
7th flr L V Locsin Building 6752 Ayala Avenue cor Makati Avenue, Makati, 1200, Philippines (99.9%)
Tel.: (63) 288948700
Web Site: http://www.mptc.com.ph
Rev.: $266,180,816
Assets: $2,097,206,384
Liabilities: $1,418,923,667
Net Worth: $678,282,717
Earnings: $131,456,929
Fiscal Year-end: 12/31/2017
Toll Road Developer & Operator
N.A.I.C.S.: 488490
Rodrigo E. Franco *(Pres & CEO)*

Subsidiary (Non-US):

PT Nusantara Infrastructure Tbk (2)
Equity Tower 38th floor Sudirman Central Business District SCBD, Jl Jend Sudirman kav 52 - 53 Lot 9, Jakarta, 12190, Indonesia
Tel.: (62) 215150100
Web Site:
  https://www.nusantarainfrastructure.com
Rev.: $109,553,273
Assets: $280,491,625
Liabilities: $40,765,478
Net Worth: $239,726,146
Earnings: ($15,317,572)
Emp.: 272
Fiscal Year-end: 12/31/2023
Infrastrcuture Management Services
N.A.I.C.S.: 541618
M. Ramdani Basri *(Chm & CEO)*

METRO PERFORMANCE GLASS LIMITED
5 Lady Fisher Place Highbrook, PO Box 58-144, Auckland, 2163, New Zealand
Tel.: (64) 99273000
Web Site:
  https://www.metroglass.co.nz
MPG—(NZX)
Rev.: $169,729,297
Assets: $195,667,222
Liabilities: $134,171,871
Net Worth: $61,495,351
Earnings: ($330,021)
Emp.: 227
Fiscal Year-end: 03/31/22
Glass Mfr
N.A.I.C.S.: 327211
Andrew Dallison *(Gen Mgr-South Island)*

Subsidiaries:

Australian Glass Group Holding Pty. Ltd. (1)
81-83 Rushdale Street, Knoxfield, 3180, VIC, Australia
Tel.: (61) 397307400
Web Site: https://agg.com.au
Building Materials Mfr
N.A.I.C.S.: 332311

Christchurch Glass & Glazing Limited (1)
Unit 4 Somerford Business Park Wilverley Road, Christchurch, BH23 3RU, Dorset, United Kingdom
Tel.: (44) 7543164067
Web Site:
  https://www.christchurchglassglazing.com
Glass Products Mfr
N.A.I.C.S.: 327215

Hawkes Bay Glass & Glazing Limited (1)
52 Whakakake St, Tauriko, Tauranga, 3171, New Zealand
Tel.: (64) 75433361
Web Site: https://www.bayglaze.co.nz
Glass Product Distr
N.A.I.C.S.: 423390

METRO RETAIL STORES GROUP, INC.
Vicsal Building corner of C D Seno and W O Seno Streets Guizo, North Reclamation Area, Mandaue, Philippines
Tel.: (63) 322368390 PH
Web Site:
  https://www.metroretail.com.ph
Year Founded: 1982
MRSGI—(PHI)
Rev.: $652,783,366
Assets: $404,263,715
Liabilities: $234,259,121
Net Worth: $170,004,594
Earnings: ($6,616,506)
Fiscal Year-end: 12/31/21
Grocery Product Distr
N.A.I.C.S.: 445110
Frank S. Gaisano *(Chm & CEO)*

METRO SPINNING LIMITED
House No 17 Road No 06 Sector No 01 Uttara, Dhaka, 1230, Bangladesh
Tel.: (880) 8933612
Web Site:
  https://www.maksonsgroup.com.bd
Year Founded: 1993
METROSPIN—(CHT)
Rev.: $40,204,077
Assets: $97,793,563
Liabilities: $62,780,837
Net Worth: $35,012,726
Earnings: ($8,549,097)
Emp.: 2,221
Fiscal Year-end: 06/30/23
Yarn Mfr
N.A.I.C.S.: 313110
Mohammad Showkot Ali *(Mng Dir)*

METRO SUPPLY CHAIN GROUP INC.
2000 - 1002 Suite Sherbrooke West, Montreal, H3A 3L6, Canada
Tel.: (905) 738-5577
Web Site: https://www.metroscg.com
Emp.: 100
Logistics Services; Transportation Support & Warehousing Services
N.A.I.C.S.: 541614
Chris Fenton *(Pres & CEO)*

Subsidiaries:

SCI Group Inc. (1)
180 Attwell Drive Suite 600, Toronto, M9W 6A9, ON, Canada
Web Site: https://www.sci.ca
Logistics Consulting Servies
N.A.I.C.S.: 541614

METRO SYSTEMS CORPORATION PUBLIC COMPANY LIMITED
400 Chalermprakiat Rama IX Road Nong Bon, Prawet, Bangkok, 10250, Thailand
Tel.: (66) 20894000
Web Site:
  https://www.metrosystems.co.th
MSC—(THA)
Rev.: $222,907,542
Assets: $110,288,405
Liabilities: $45,589,373
Net Worth: $64,699,032
Earnings: $8,322,073
Emp.: 1,164
Fiscal Year-end: 12/31/23
Office Products Distr & Supplies
N.A.I.C.S.: 459410
Tavit Charuvajana *(CEO)*

Subsidiaries:

Metro Professional Products Co., Ltd. (1)
98/44 Moo 11 Soi Factory land 2Tumbol, Rai Khing Amphoe, Sam Phran, 74000, Nakhon Pathom, Thailand
Tel.: (66) 2 019 9399
Web Site: https://www.mpp.co.th
Computer System Design Services
N.A.I.C.S.: 541512

METRO TICARI VE MALI YATIRIMLAR HOLDING A.S.
Resadiye Caddesi Cumhuriyet Koyu No-18 Beykoz, Istanbul, Turkiye
Tel.: (90) 2123192875
Web Site:
  https://www.metroholding.com.tr
Year Founded: 1977
METRO—(IST)
Holding Company
N.A.I.C.S.: 551112
Galip Ozturk *(Co-Chm)*

METRO TOOL & DIE LIMITED
1065 Pantera Drive, Mississauga, L4W 2X4, ON, Canada
Tel.: (905) 625-8464
Web Site: https://www.mtdmetro.com
Year Founded: 1972
Rev.: $11,000,000
Emp.: 100
Stamping Industry Dies Supplier
N.A.I.C.S.: 332119
Andy Pantano *(Founder)*

METRO YATIRIM ORTAKLIGI AS
Buyukdere St No 171 Metrocity A Block Floor 17 1 Levent, Istanbul, Turkiye
Tel.: (90) 2123441685
Web Site: https://www.metroyo.com
Year Founded: 1999
MTRYO—(IST)
Sales Range: Less than $1 Million
Asset Management Services
N.A.I.C.S.: 523940
Levent Avni Ersalman *(Chm)*

METROD (MALAYSIA) BERHAD
No 3 Lengkuk Keluli 2 Bukit Raja Prime Industrial Park, 41720, Kelang, Selangor Darul Ehsan, Malaysia
Tel.: (60) 333413422
Web Site: http://www.metrod.com
Year Founded: 1981
Sales Range: $600-649.9 Million
Copper Product Mfr
N.A.I.C.S.: 331420
Rajan Mittal *(Pres & CEO)*

Subsidiaries:

Metrod (OFHC) Sdn Bhd (1)
3 Lengkuk Keluli 2 Bukit Raja Prime Industrial Park, Kelang, 41720, Selangor Darul Ehsan, Malaysia
Tel.: (60) 333413422
Sales Range: $50-74.9 Million
Emp.: 240
Copper Wires Mfr
N.A.I.C.S.: 331420
Ajay Kapadia *(Controller-Global Fin)*

Metrod Flat Products Sdn Bhd (1)
No 2 Slk Waja 1 Kaw 19 Kaw Perindustrian Bukit Raja, 41050, Kelang, Selangor, Malaysia
Tel.: (60) 333415327
Sales Range: $25-49.9 Million
Emp.: 100
Insulated & Non Insulated Copper Strips Mfr
N.A.I.C.S.: 331420
V. Krishnan *(Gen Mgr)*

METROD HOLDINGS BHD
No 3 Lengkuk Keluli 2, Bukit Raja Prime Industrial Park, 41720, Klang, Selangor Darul Ehsan, Malaysia
Tel.: (60) 333613422
Web Site: https://www.metrod.com
Year Founded: 1981
6149—(KLS)
Rev.: $877,597,023
Assets: $324,067,723
Liabilities: $224,054,879
Net Worth: $100,012,844
Earnings: $5,478,289
Emp.: 726
Fiscal Year-end: 12/31/22
Copper Wires Mfr
N.A.I.C.S.: 331420
Apurv Bagri *(Founder)*

METROFILE HOLDINGS LIMITED
1st Floor West Block 28 Fricker Road Illovo Boulevard, Johannesburg, 2196, Gauteng, South Africa
Tel.: (27) 100016380 ZA
Web Site: https://metrofile.com
Year Founded: 1983
MFL—(JSE)
Rev.: $66,843,362
Assets: $101,818,401
Liabilities: $62,389,921
Net Worth: $39,428,479
Earnings: $9,507,032
Emp.: 1,230
Fiscal Year-end: 06/30/22
Information & Rrecord Storage Management Services
N.A.I.C.S.: 541519
Paige Atkins *(Sec)*

Subsidiaries:

Cleardata (Pty) Ltd (1)
Linbro Business Park 5 Cosmic Street, Sandton, 2090, South Africa
Tel.: (27) 86 122 5327
Web Site: https://www.cleardata.co.za
Facility Services
N.A.I.C.S.: 561210
Rob Fedder *(Mng Dir)*

E-File Masters LLC (1)
Al Warsan 1, Dubai, United Arab Emirates (80%)
Tel.: (971) 600566220
Web Site: https://www.efileecm.com
Information Technology Services
N.A.I.C.S.: 541511

METROFILE HOLDINGS LIMITED

Metrofile Holdings Limited—(Continued)

Global Continuity (SA) (Pty) Ltd (1)
41 Wordsworth Avenue, Senderwood, Bedfordview, 2145, South Africa
Tel.: (27) 11 553 0000
Web Site: https://www.globalcontinuitysa.co.za
Information Technology Services
N.A.I.C.S.: 541511

IronTree Internet Services (Pty.) Ltd. (1)
Unit 1 Westlake Square, Westlake, Cape Town, South Africa
Tel.: (27) 879432278
Web Site: https://www.irontree.co.za
Information Technology Services
N.A.I.C.S.: 541511

Metrofile Mozambique Lda (1)
Av FPLM 1565, Maputo, Mozambique
Tel.: (258) 21462565
Facility Services
N.A.I.C.S.: 561210

Metrofile Records & Information Management Botswana (Pty) Ltd (1)
Plot 22033 West, Gaborone, Botswana
Tel.: (267) 3908062
Web Site: https://www.metrofilegroup.com
Facility Services
N.A.I.C.S.: 561210

Metrofile Records Management (Kenya) Ltd. (1)
PJ Park Enterprise Road, Box 78289, Industrial Area, 00507, Nairobi, Kenya
Tel.: (254) 27870940937
Web Site: https://kenya.metrofilecloud.com
Facility Services
N.A.I.C.S.: 561210

Metrofile Vysion (Pty.) Ltd. (1)
41 Wordsworth Avenue, Senderwood, Johannesburg, South Africa
Tel.: (27) 115530289
Web Site: https://www.metrofilevysion.com
Business Management Services
N.A.I.C.S.: 541611

Tidy Files (SA) (Pty) Ltd (1)
51 Main Service Road, Eikenhof, Johannesburg, Gauteng, South Africa
Tel.: (27) 11 943 4210
Web Site: https://www.tidyfiles.co.za
Facility Services
N.A.I.C.S.: 561210

METROGLOBAL LIMITED

506509 SHILP CG Road Opp Girish Cold drinks Navrangpura, Ahmedabad, 380 009, Gujarat, India
Tel.: (91) 7926468016
Web Site: https://www.metrogloballimited.com
500159—(BOM)
Rev.: $34,658,155
Assets: $47,162,142
Liabilities: $1,520,201
Net Worth: $45,641,942
Earnings: $972,945
Emp.: 16
Fiscal Year-end: 03/31/21
Holding Company
N.A.I.C.S.: 551112
Gautam M. Jain *(Chm & Mng Dir)*

METROHM AG

Ionenstrasse, Herisau, 9100, Switzerland
Tel.: (41) 71 353 8585
Web Site: http://www.metrohm.com
Year Founded: 1943
Chemical Analysis Instruments Mfr
N.A.I.C.S.: 334516
Christoph Fassler *(CEO)*

Subsidiaries:

Deutsche Metrohm GmbH & Co. KG (1)
In den Birken 3, 70794, Filderstadt, Germany
Tel.: (49) 711 77088 0
Web Site: http://www.metrohm.com
Sales, Training, Service of Analytical Lab Equipment
N.A.I.C.S.: 423490
Frank Ruckle *(Mng Dir)*

Deutsche Metrohm Prozessanalytik GmbH & Co. KG (1)
In den Birken 1, 70794, Filderstadt, Germany
Tel.: (49) 711 77088 900
Web Site: http://www.metrohm.com
Sales, Training & Service of Analytical Lab Equipment
N.A.I.C.S.: 423490
Michael Feige *(Mng Dir)*

Innovative Photonic Solutions, Inc. (1)
4250 US Hwy 1 Ste 1, Monmouth Junction, NJ 08852-1964
Tel.: (732) 355-9300
Web Site: http://www.ipslasers.com
Semiconductor & Related Device Mfr
N.A.I.C.S.: 334413
Dieter Strohm *(Pres & CEO)*

MEP Instruments Pty Ltd (1)
Unit 11 56 Buffalo Road, Gladesville, 2111, NSW, Australia
Tel.: (61) 2 8899 5200
Sales, Training & Service of Analytical Lab Equipment
N.A.I.C.S.: 423490

Metrohm Analytics Romania Srl (1)
Str Emil Racovita nr 25 et1 ap 4 sector 4, 041753, Bucharest, Romania
Tel.: (40) 214600361
Web Site: http://www.metrohm.ro
Chemical Analysis Instrument Distr
N.A.I.C.S.: 423830

Metrohm Applikon B.V. (1)
De Brauwweg 13, 3125 AE, Schiedam, Netherlands
Tel.: (31) 10 2983555
Web Site: http://www.metrohm.com
Chemical Analysis Instruments Mfr
N.A.I.C.S.: 334516
Timoer Frelink *(Mng Dir)*

Metrohm Autolab B.V. (1)
Kanaalweg 29-G, 3526 KM, Utrecht, Netherlands
Tel.: (31) 302893154
Web Site: http://www.metrohm-autolab.com
Chemical Analysis Instrument Distr
N.A.I.C.S.: 423830
Sef Coenen *(Mgr-Product Dev & Quality)*

Metrohm Belgium N.V. (1)
Blancefloerlaan 179G, B 2050, Antwerp, Belgium
Tel.: (32) 3 281 33 31
Web Site: http://www.metrohm.com
Emp.: 20
Sales, Training, Service of Analytical Lab Equipment
N.A.I.C.S.: 423830
Frank Hubrechts *(Mng Dir)*

Metrohm Canada, Inc. (1)
4160 Sladeview Crescent 6, Mississauga, L5L 0A1, ON, Canada
Tel.: (905) 569-0664
Web Site: https://www.metrohm.com
Emp.: 15
Analytical Laboratory Instruments Sales
N.A.I.C.S.: 423490

Metrohm France SAS (1)
13 avenue du Quebec, BP 90038, Villebon Courtaboeuf, 91942, Villebon-sur-Yvette, France
Tel.: (33) 1 6486 9700
Web Site: http://www.metrohm.fr
Analytical Laboratory Instruments Distr
N.A.I.C.S.: 423490
Herve Lacombe *(Gen Mgr)*

Metrohm Ireland Ltd (1)
Carlow Gateway Business Centre Athy Road, Carlow, Ireland
Tel.: (353) 14509616
Chemical Analysis Instrument Distr
N.A.I.C.S.: 423830

Metrohm Malaysia Sdn Bhd (1)
833 Lobby C Block A Kelana Centre Point Jalan SS7/19, 47301, Petaling Jaya, Selangor, Malaysia
Tel.: (60) 378807480
Web Site: http://www.metrohm.com.my
Chemical Analysis Instrument Distr
N.A.I.C.S.: 423830

Metrohm Middle East Fzc (1)
B2-21 SAIF Zone, PO Box 120747, Sharjah, United Arab Emirates
Tel.: (971) 65575991
Web Site: http://www.metrohm.ae
Industrial Machine Maintenance Services
N.A.I.C.S.: 561990
Amod Sarkale *(Mgr-Technical)*

Metrohm Nordic AB (1)
Fredsforsstigen 22-24, Bromma, 168 66, Sweden
Tel.: (46) 856484480
Chemical Analysis Instrument Distr
N.A.I.C.S.: 423830

Metrohm Nordic ApS (1)
Smedeland 7, 2600, Glostrup, Denmark
Tel.: (45) 70200561
Chemical Analysis Instrument Distr
N.A.I.C.S.: 423830

Metrohm Polska Sp. z o.o. (1)
ul Centralna 27, Opacz-Kolonia, 05-816, Warsaw, Poland
Tel.: (48) 227230291
Chemical Analysis Instrument Distr
N.A.I.C.S.: 423830
Wojciech Stokarski *(Mng Dir)*

Metrohm Siam Ltd. (1)
979/111-115 S M Tower 33rd Floor Phahonyothin Road Samsennai, Phya Thai, Bangkok, 10400, Thailand
Tel.: (66) 22980864
Chemical Analysis Instrument Distr
N.A.I.C.S.: 423830

Metrohm Singapore Pte Ltd (1)
31 Toh Guan Road East 06-08 LW Technocentre, Singapore, 608608, Singapore (100%)
Tel.: (65) 6872 2215
Web Site: http://www.metrohm.com
Sales, Training & Service of Analytical Lab Equipment
N.A.I.C.S.: 423490

Metrohm UK Ltd (1)
Metrohm House Evenwood Close Daresbury Court, Runcorn, WA7 1LZ, Cheshire, United Kingdom
Tel.: (44) 1928579600
Chemical Analysis Instrument Distr
N.A.I.C.S.: 423830

Metrohm USA Inc. (1)
6555 Pelican Creek Cir, Riverview, FL 33578
Tel.: (813) 316-4700
Web Site: http://www.metrohmusa.com
Analytical Laboratory Instruments Mfr & Distr
N.A.I.C.S.: 334516
Michael Melingo *(Pres & CEO)*

Division (Domestic):

Metrohm NIRSystems (2)
7703 Montpelier Rd Ste 1, Laurel, MD 20723
Tel.: (301) 680-9600
Web Site: http://www.metrohmusa.com
Sales Range: $25-49.9 Million
Emp.: 18
Analytical Instruments Mfr & Distr
N.A.I.C.S.: 334516
Denise Root *(Mgr-Mktg)*

PRIMALAB d.o.o. (1)
Petrovaradinska 1A-1B, 10000, Zagreb, Croatia
Tel.: (385) 17999658
Chemical Analysis Instrument Distr
N.A.I.C.S.: 423830
Andrea Gelemanovic *(Product Mgr)*

PRIMALAB d.o.o. (1)
Bul Zorana Dindica 123, New Belgrade, Belgrade, Serbia
Tel.: (381) 113120092
Chemical Analysis Instrument Distr
N.A.I.C.S.: 423830
Gordana Jovanovic *(Product Mgr)*

PRIMALAB d.o.o. (1)
Breg pri Polzeli Pod bregom 27, 3313, Polzela, Slovenia
Tel.: (386) 37050980
Web Site: http://www.primalab.eu
Chemical Analysis Instrument Distr
N.A.I.C.S.: 423830
Mojca Divjak Gulin *(Gen Mgr)*

PT. Metrohm Indonesia (1)
Menara Batavia Lt 3 JI K H Mas Mansyur Kav 126, Jakarta, 10220, Indonesia
Tel.: (62) 215727318
Web Site: http://www.metrohm.co.id
Chemical Analysis Instrument Distr
N.A.I.C.S.: 423830
Tenggara Kardinal *(Mng Dir)*

METROLAND AUSTRALIA LIMITED

Level 4 45 Murray Street, Pyrmont, 2009, NSW, Australia
Tel.: (61) 293958888
Web Site: http://www.metroland.com.au
Year Founded: 1997
Sales Range: $10-24.9 Million
Emp.: 16
Real Estate Development Services
N.A.I.C.S.: 531390
Eddie Lee *(Chm)*

Subsidiaries:

MetroBuild Associates Pty Limited (1)
No 33 Jihua Wu Rd, Foshan, China
Tel.: (86) 757 83125616
Property Development Services
N.A.I.C.S.: 531312

Stratawide Management Pty Limited (1)
4 45 Murray St, PO Box 306, Pyrmont, 2009, NSW, Australia
Tel.: (61) 293958811
Property Development Services
N.A.I.C.S.: 531312
Anthony Maroon *(Mgr)*

METRON TECHNOLOGY LTD.

2 Tangier Central Castle Street, Taunton, TA1 4AS, Somerset, United Kingdom
Tel.: (44) 1823 259231
Web Site: http://www.metron-athene.com
Capacity Management Solutions
N.A.I.C.S.: 513210
Andrew Smith *(CEO)*

Subsidiaries:

Metron-Athene, Inc. (1)
6320 Canoga Ave Ste 1500, Woodland Hills, CA 91367
Tel.: (818) 227-5019
Web Site: http://www.metron-athene.com
Capacity Management Solutions
N.A.I.C.S.: 513210

METRONIC GLOBAL BERHAD

No 2 Jalan Astaka U8 83 Seksyen U8 Bukit Jelutong, 40150, Shah Alam, Selangor Darul Ehsan, Malaysia
Tel.: (60) 378472111
Web Site: https://www.metronic-group.com
Year Founded: 1984
MTRONIC—(KLS)
Rev.: $9,798,164
Assets: $54,483,265
Liabilities: $26,529,522
Net Worth: $27,953,744
Earnings: ($1,822,085)
Emp.: 108
Fiscal Year-end: 06/30/22
Property Development Services
N.A.I.C.S.: 531312
Yuet Chyn Wong *(Sec)*

AND PRIVATE COMPANIES

Subsidiaries:

Metronic Engineering Sdn. Bhd. (1)
No 2 Jalan Astaka U8/83 Bukit Jelutong, Seksyen U8, 40150, Shah Alam, Selangor, Malaysia
Tel.: (60) 378472111
Web Site: https://www.metronic-group.com
Sales Range: $50-74.9 Million
Emp.: 100
Property Development Services
N.A.I.C.S.: 531390
Vincent Set *(Mng Dir)*

Metronic iCares Sdn. Bhd. (1)
No 2 Jalan Astaka U8/83 Seksyen U8 Bukit Jelutong, 40150, Shah Alam, Selangor, Darul Ehsan, Malaysia
Tel.: (60) 378469363
Web Site: http://www.micaresvc.com
Sales Range: $10-24.9 Million
Emp.: 100
Healthcare Management Consulting Services
N.A.I.C.S.: 621999

METROPOL GROUP OF COMPANIES

13 Bldg 1 Donskaya Str, 119049, Moscow, Russia
Tel.: (7) 495 933 3310
Web Site: http://www.metropolgroup.ru
Holding Company
N.A.I.C.S.: 551112
Aleksey Rodzyanko *(CEO-IFC Metropol)*

Subsidiaries:

JSC Zapsibgazprom (1)
Tyumen Street May Day 19, 625000, Tyumen, Russia **(76.48%)**
Tel.: (7) 3452544000
Web Site: http://www.zsgp.ru
Gas Exploration & Production Services
N.A.I.C.S.: 211120

METROPOL Investment Financial Company Ltd. (1)
13 bld 1 Donskaya str, 119049, Moscow, Russia
Tel.: (7) 4959333310
Web Site: http://www.metropol.com
Investment & Financial Services
N.A.I.C.S.: 523150
Aleksey Rodzyanko *(CEO)*

Metropol (Cyprus) Limited (1)
67 Spyros Araouzos str Ulysses House Karmazi office 101, 3036, Limassol, Cyprus
Tel.: (357) 25 817 220
Web Site: http://www.metropol-cyprus.com
Financial Investment Services
N.A.I.C.S.: 523999
Olga Kuznetsova *(Mng Dir)*

Metropol (UK) Limited (1)
LibertyHouse 222 Regent Street, London, W1B 5TR, United Kingdom
Tel.: (44) 20 7297 2467
Web Site: http://www.metropol-uk.com
Financial Investment Services
N.A.I.C.S.: 523999
Natalia Pastukhova *(Dir-Compliance)*

Putnik a.d. (1)
Palmira Toljatija 9, 11070, Belgrade, Serbia
Tel.: (381) 112259999
Web Site: https://www.putnik.com
Sales Range: $1-9.9 Million
Emp.: 55
Home Management Services
N.A.I.C.S.: 721110
Dmitry Razumov *(Gen Mgr)*

METROPOLE TELEVISION SA

89 Avenue Charles de Gaulle, 92575, Neuilly-sur-Seine, France
Tel.: (33) 141926666 FR
Web Site: https://www.groupem6.fr
Year Founded: 1987
MMT—(EUR)
Sales Range: $1-4.9 Billion
Emp.: 2,611
Holding Company; Television Broadcasting Stations Operator, Television Programming & Advertising Services
N.A.I.C.S.: 551112
Nicolas Abel Bellet de Tavernost *(Chm-Exec Bd)*

Subsidiaries:

C. Productions SA (1)
89 Avenue Charles de Gaulle, 92575, Neuilly-sur-Seine, Hauts-de-Seine, France
Tel.: (33) 141926666
Web Site: http://www.m6.fr
Emp.: 700
Television Program Production Services
N.A.I.C.S.: 512110
Ronan de Fressenel *(Dir-Mktg)*

Canal J (1)
26-28 ru Fracnois Premier, 75008, Paris, France
Tel.: (33) 156365555
Web Site: http://www.canalj.net
Sales Range: $25-49.9 Million
Emp.: 40
Children's Television Broadcasting Station
N.A.I.C.S.: 516120

Fun Radio (1)
22 Rue Bayard, 75008, Paris, France
Tel.: (33) 1 41 92 40 30
Web Site: http://www.funradio.fr
Radio Stations
N.A.I.C.S.: 516110

Girondins Horizons SAS (1)
9 Place Charles Gruet, 33000, Bordeaux, Gironde, France **(100%)**
Tel.: (33) 556446873
Travel & Tour Operating Agencies
N.A.I.C.S.: 561510
Jean-David Tregan *(Gen Mgr)*

Live Stage SAS (1)
89 Avenue Charles de Gaulle, 92200, Neuilly-sur-Seine, Hauts-de-Seine, France
Tel.: (33) 1419266666
Events Staging Services
N.A.I.C.S.: 711310

M6 Communication SAS (1)
89 Avenue Charles de Gaulle, 92575, Neuilly-sur-Seine, France
Tel.: (33) 141926666
Web Site: http://www.m6.fr
Emp.: 1,800
Music Publishers
N.A.I.C.S.: 512230
Christophe Foglio *(Mgr-HR)*

M6 Interactions SAS (1)
89 Avenue Charles de Gaulle, 92575, Neuilly-sur-Seine, France
Tel.: (33) 141926666
Web Site: http://www.m6.fr
Emp.: 1,200
Movie & Television Program Production Services
N.A.I.C.S.: 512110

M6 Web SAS (1)
89 Avenue Charles de Gaulle, 92575, Neuilly-sur-Seine, Cedex, France
Tel.: (33) 1 4192 6666
Web Site: http://www.m6.fr
Website Publisher
N.A.I.C.S.: 513199

M6-Thematique SAS (1)
89 Avenue Charles de Gaulle, Neuilly-sur-Seine, 92200, France
Tel.: (33) 141926666
Web Site: http://www.m6.fr
Sales Range: $100-124.9 Million
Emp.: 500
Television Broadcasting Services
N.A.I.C.S.: 516120
Nicolas Abel Bellet de Tavernost *(Mng Dir)*

MCM S.A (1)
28 rue Francois 1er, 75008, Paris, France
Tel.: (33) 1 56 36 53 00
Television Broadcasting Services
N.A.I.C.S.: 516120

Paris Premiere SAS (1)
89 Avenue Charles de Gaulle, Neuilly-sur-Seine, 92200, Hauts-de-Seine, France
Tel.: (33) 141925700
Web Site: http://www.paris-premiere.fr
Television Broadcasting Services
N.A.I.C.S.: 516120

RTL France Radio SASU (1)
56 Avenue Charles de Gaulle, F 75008, Neuilly-sur-Seine, France
Tel.: (33) 1 41 92 40 40
Web Site: http://www.rtl.fr
Radio Broadcasting
N.A.I.C.S.: 516110

Division (Non-US):

RTL AdConnect International, S.A. (2)
43 Boulevard Pierre Frieden, L-1543, Luxembourg, Luxembourg
Tel.: (352) 24 861
Web Site: http://www.rtl-adconnect.com
Media Advertising Services
N.A.I.C.S.: 541840
Stephane Coruble *(Mng Dir)*

Sedi TV SNC (1)
89 Ave Charles De Gaulle, 92575, Neuilly-sur-Seine, France **(100%)**
Tel.: (33) 141926666
Web Site: http://www.m6.fr
Sales Range: $25-49.9 Million
Emp.: 500
Operator of a Specialty Television Station
N.A.I.C.S.: 516120
Nicolas Gagernost *(Mng Dir)*

Studio 89 SAS (1)
114 Avenue Charles de Gaulle, 92200, Neuilly-sur-Seine, Hauts-de-Seine, France
Tel.: (33) 141926666
Web Site: http://www.societe.com
Sales Range: $400-449.9 Million
Emp.: 2,000
Motion Picture Production Services
N.A.I.C.S.: 512110
Dimitri Glineau *(Sls Mgr-Intl)*

METROPOLIS CAPITAL HOLDINGS LTD.

Room 7003A 887 Huai Hai Zhong Road, Huangpu District, Shanghai, 200020, China
Tel.: (86) 2164747900 Ky
Web Site: http://www.metropolis-leasing.com
Year Founded: 2009
8621—(HKG)
Rev.: $6,743,741
Assets: $53,790,672
Liabilities: $25,279,386
Net Worth: $28,511,286
Earnings: ($582,627)
Emp.: 78
Fiscal Year-end: 12/31/22
Motor Vehicle Financial Leasing Services
N.A.I.C.S.: 525990
David Chau *(Chm & CEO)*

METROPOLIS HEALTHCARE LTD.

4th Floor East Wing Plot254 B Nirlon House, Dr Annie Besant Road Worli, Mumbai, 400030, India
Tel.: (91) 8422801801
Web Site: https://www.metropolisindia.com
Year Founded: 1981
METROPOLIS—(NSE)
Rev.: $139,492,213
Assets: $180,038,247
Liabilities: $61,255,105
Net Worth: $118,783,142
Earnings: $17,192,494
Emp.: 4,289
Fiscal Year-end: 03/31/23
Laboratory Testing Services
N.A.I.C.S.: 541380
Sushil Kanubhai Shah *(Chm)*

Subsidiaries:

Amin's Pathology Laboratory Private Limited (1)
G-9 Tulsiani Chambers 212 Free Press Journal Marg, Nariman point, Mumbai, 400021, India
Tel.: (91) 40194545
Web Site: https://www.aminspathlab.com
Medical Testing Services
N.A.I.C.S.: 621511

Bokil Golwilkar Metropolis Healthcare Private Limited (1)
Ranade Chambers 8 Guruwar Peth Near Raj Laxmi Talkies, Satara, 415002, India
Tel.: (91) 2162237455
Chemical Pathology Services
N.A.I.C.S.: 541380

Ekopath Metropolis Lab Services Private Limited (1)
G S Road Christian Basti, Guwahati, 781005, Assam, India
Tel.: (91) 3612342595
Chemical Pathology Services
N.A.I.C.S.: 541380

Metropolis Bramser Lab Services (Mtius) Limited (1)
Ground Floor Lot 7 Moka Business Center, Moka, Mauritius
Tel.: (230) 4336740
Web Site: http://www.metropolismauritius.com
Chemical Pathology Services
N.A.I.C.S.: 541380

Metropolis Healthcare (Tanzania) Ltd. (1)
DSB Polyclinic Plot No 620 United Nations Road, PO Box 4737, Upanga, Dar es Salaam, Tanzania
Tel.: (255) 222150022
Chemical Pathology Services
N.A.I.C.S.: 541380

Metropolis Healthcare Ghana Ltd. (1)
1st Floor Pyramid Building Above Stanbic Bank, Near Nima Traffic Light Opp Nima Police Station Ring Road, Accra, Ghana
Tel.: (233) 543026795
Chemical Pathology Services
N.A.I.C.S.: 541380

Metropolis Healthcare Lanka (Pvt.) Limited (1)
25 Narahenpita Road, Nawala, Colombo, Sri Lanka
Tel.: (94) 114388388
Chemical Pathology Services
N.A.I.C.S.: 541380

Micron Metropolis Healthcare Private Limited (1)
Indira Complex Ground Floor Plot No 125/A-2, Near Dr Nadkarni Hospital Line Ali Panvel, Navi Mumbai, 410206, India
Tel.: (91) 2239467500
Chemical Pathology Services
N.A.I.C.S.: 541380

R.V. Metropolis Diagnostic & Health Care Center Private Limited (1)
No 76/10 15th Cross 4th Main, Malleshwaram, Bengaluru, 560003, India
Tel.: (91) 9321272715
Medical Testing Services
N.A.I.C.S.: 621511

METROPOLITAN BANK & TRUST COMPANY

19th Floor Metrobank Plaza Sen Gil Puyat Avenue, Makati, 1200, Philippines
Tel.: (63) 288575526
Web Site: http://www.metrobank.com.ph
Year Founded: 1962
MBT—(PHI)
Rev.: $2,011,103,005
Assets: $50,587,889,895
Liabilities: $44,750,093,415
Net Worth: $5,837,796,480
Earnings: $583,192,470
Emp.: 13,150
Fiscal Year-end: 12/31/22
Financial Investment Services
N.A.I.C.S.: 523999

METROPOLITAN BANK & TRUST COMPANY

Metropolitan Bank & Trust Company—(Continued)

Francisco C. Sebastian *(Vice Chm)*

Subsidiaries:

First Metro Securities Brokerage Corporation (1)
18F PSBank Center 777 Paseo de Roxas cor Sedeno St, Makati, 1226, Philippines
Tel.: (63) 288590600
Web Site: http://www.firstmetrosec.com.ph
Securities Brokerage Services
N.A.I.C.S.: 523150
Gonzalo G. Ordonez *(Pres)*

ORIX Metro Leasing and Finance Corporation (1)
21st Floor GT Tower International Ayala Avenue, Corner HV Dela Costa St, Makati, 1227, Philippines
Tel.: (63) 88588888
Web Site: https://www.orix.com.ph
Sales Range: $50-74.9 Million
Emp.: 1,106
Equipment Leasing & Hire-Purchase Services; Owned 60% by Metropolitan Bank & Trust Company & 40% by ORIX Corporation
N.A.I.C.S.: 532490
Fumihiko Sato *(Vice Chm)*

Philippine Savings Bank (1)
PSBank Center 777 Paseo de Roxas Avenue Corner Sedeno Street, Makati, 1226, Philippines (82.7%)
Tel.: (63) 288458888
Web Site: https://www.psbank.com.ph
Rev.: $298,787,192
Assets: $5,445,567,084
Liabilities: $4,719,770,280
Net Worth: $725,796,804
Earnings: $32,021,449
Emp.: 2,824
Fiscal Year-end: 12/31/2021
Banking Services
N.A.I.C.S.: 522292
Neil C. Estrellado *(Sr VP)*

METROPOLITAN EUROPEAN TRANSPORT LIMITED

One New Change, London, EC4M 9AF, United Kingdom
Tel.: (44) 20 7648 9000   UK
Web Site: http://www.metplc.com
Year Founded: 2011
Holding Company; Bus Transportation Services
N.A.I.C.S.: 551112
David Leeder *(CEO)*

Subsidiaries:

Andreas Bonifer, Spedition- und Verkehrsunternehmen Verwaltungs-GmbH (1)
Seligenstadter Strasse 129-137, Offenbach, 63073, Germany
Tel.: (49) 69 890020
Web Site: http://www.bonifer.de
Bus Operating Services
N.A.I.C.S.: 485210

BRH viabus GmbH (1)
Heinkelstrasse 25, 67346, Speyer, Germany
Tel.: (49) 6232 6709 0
Web Site: http://www.viabus.de
Bus Operating Services
N.A.I.C.S.: 485210
Lars Kongsbak *(Mng Dir)*

Kraus-Reisen Omnibusbetriebs GmbH (1)
Langgasse 65-71, Messel, 64409, Germany
Tel.: (49) 6159 54 54
Bus Operating Services
N.A.I.C.S.: 485210

Prumer Reiseburo Tucks Inh. M.A.T. GmbH (1)
Kalvarienbergstrasse 37, 54595, Prum, Germany (100%)
Tel.: (49) 6551 148690
Web Site: http://www.pruemer-reisebuero.de
Travel Agency
N.A.I.C.S.: 561510

METROPOLITAN POLICE SERVICE

Victoria Embankment, London, SW1A 2JL, United Kingdom
Tel.: (44) 2072301212
Web Site: https://www.met.police.uk
Protective Services
N.A.I.C.S.: 922120

METROPOLITAN STEEL CORPORATION LIMITED

Plot No HE -1/2 Landhi Industrial Area, Karachi, Pakistan
Tel.: (92) 2135656143
Web Site: http://www.metropolitansteel.com
Year Founded: 1955
MSCL—(PSX)
Rev.: $344,234
Assets: $3,226,975
Liabilities: $318,810
Net Worth: $2,908,165
Earnings: ($45,110)
Emp.: 14
Fiscal Year-end: 06/30/23
Steel Products Mfr
N.A.I.C.S.: 331221
Syed Asghar Jamil Rizvi *(CEO & Mng Dir)*

METROPOLITANA MILANESE S.P.A.

Via del Vecchio Politecnico 8, 20121, Milan, Italy
Tel.: (39) 0277471   IT
Web Site: http://www.mmspa.eu
Year Founded: 1955
Sales Range: $25-49.9 Million
Emp.: 231
Public Transportation & Infrastructure Services Distr
N.A.I.C.S.: 485119
Gianluigi Bozzi *(Dir-Contracting & Works Svc)*

Subsidiaries:

Metro Engineering Srl (1)
Via del Vecchio Politecnico 8, 20121, Milan, Italy
Tel.: (39) 02 77 471
Civil Engineering Construction Services
N.A.I.C.S.: 541330

METROVACESA, S.A.

C Puerto de Somport 23 building A, Parque via Norte, 28050, Madrid, Spain
Tel.: (34) 913183700   ES
Web Site: https://metrovacesa.com
Year Founded: 2016
MVC—(BIL)
Rev.: $476,443,989
Assets: $2,713,026,117
Liabilities: $764,450,680
Net Worth: $1,948,575,437
Earnings: ($25,336,715)
Emp.: 196
Fiscal Year-end: 12/31/22
Commercial Real Estate Investment, Development, Property Management & Leasing Services
N.A.I.C.S.: 531120
Ignacio Moreno Martinez *(Chm)*

METSALIITTO OSUUSKUNTA

Revontulenpuisto 2, 02100, Espoo, Finland
Tel.: (358) 104601   FI
Web Site: http://www.metsagroup.com
Year Founded: 1947
Rev.: $6,393,392,726
Assets: $7,719,642,924
Liabilities: $3,625,882,708
Net Worth: $4,093,760,216
Earnings: $686,138,222
Emp.: 9,310
Fiscal Year-end: 12/31/18
Holding Company; Forest Nursery & Timber Tract Operations; Wood & Wood-Based Products Mfr
N.A.I.C.S.: 551112
Vesa-Pekka Takala *(CFO & Exec VP)*

Subsidiaries:

Kumpuniemen Voima Oy (1)
Vaneritehtaankatu 1, Suolahti, 44200, Finland
Tel.: (358) 1046 57760
Electricity Power Generation Services
N.A.I.C.S.: 221118

Metsa Board Corporation (1)
Revontulenpuisto 2, FI-02100, Espoo, Finland
Tel.: (358) 104611
Web Site: https://www.metsagroup.com
Rev.: $2,676,019,858
Assets: $3,672,782,215
Liabilities: $1,238,938,053
Net Worth: $2,433,844,161
Earnings: $497,841,571
Emp.: 2,248
Fiscal Year-end: 12/31/2022
Chemical Forest Industry Products, Marketing, Packaging Raw Materials
N.A.I.C.S.: 322120
Mika Joukio *(CEO)*

Subsidiary (Domestic):

Antalis OY (2)
Paperitie 7, PO Box 24, FI-00390, Helsinki, Finland
Tel.: (358) 9348300
Web Site: http://www.mapsuomi.fi
Sales Range: $25-49.9 Million
Emp.: 80
Paper Whslr & Distr
N.A.I.C.S.: 424110
Jukka Silventola *(Mng Dir-Finland)*

M-Real Corporation Corporate Administration (2)
Revontulenpuisto 6, PO Box 20, Metsa, FIN 02120, Espoo, Finland (100%)
Tel.: (358) 0104611
Web Site: http://www.m-real.com
Sales Range: $25-49.9 Million
Emp.: 10
Paper Products Producer
N.A.I.C.S.: 322299

M-Real Corporation Packaging Group (2)
Keskuftori 5, PO Box 224, 33101, Tampere, Finland (100%)
Tel.: (358) 104633999
Sales Range: $25-49.9 Million
Emp.: 12
Paper & Packaging
N.A.I.C.S.: 322220

Division (Domestic):

M-Real Corporation, Board Division (3)
Halletuskatu 1, PO Box 208, 33101, Tampere, Finland
Tel.: (358) 0104633999
Web Site: http://www.m-real.com
Sales Range: $125-149.9 Million
Paperboard Producer
N.A.I.C.S.: 322220
Jukka Kettunen *(Sr VP-Production)*

Subsidiary (Domestic):

M-Real Finland (2)
Revontulentie 6 C, FIN 02100, Espoo, Finland (100%)
Tel.: (358) 000104611
Web Site: http://www.m-real.com
Sales Range: $25-49.9 Million
Emp.: 100
Paper Products Mfr
N.A.I.C.S.: 322299
Mikko Helander *(Gen Mgr)*

Subsidiary (US):

Price and Pierce International Inc. (3)

INTERNATIONAL PUBLIC

281 Tresser Blvd, Stamford, CT 06901-3239
Tel.: (203) 328-2080
Sales Range: $25-49.9 Million
Emp.: 20
Open Paper Brokers
N.A.I.C.S.: 322299

Subsidiary (Non-US):

M-Real S.A. (2)
ZI Du Clos Pre, FR 27460, Alizay, France
Tel.: (33) 235027272
Web Site: http://www.m_real.com
Sales Range: $125-149.9 Million
Emp.: 400
Hardwood Kraft Pulp Producer
N.A.I.C.S.: 322110

M-real France SAS (2)
11 Avenue Dubonnet Le Doublon, Batiment A 4th Floor, Courbevoie, 92407, France (100%)
Tel.: (33) 155612500
Web Site: http://www.m-real.com
Sales Range: $25-49.9 Million
Emp.: 50
Wholesale Wood Pulp & Specialty Papers
N.A.I.C.S.: 424990

Subsidiary (Domestic):

Metsa Board Aanekoski (2)
PO Box 400, 44101, Aanekoski, Finland (100%)
Tel.: (358) 1046 43999
Web Site: http://www.metsaboard.com
Sales Range: $50-74.9 Million
Emp.: 198
Produces Fully Coated Bleached Paperboards
N.A.I.C.S.: 322130
Jouko Wacklin *(VP & Mill Mgr)*

Subsidiary (Non-US):

Metsa Board Benelux b.v. (2)
Zam Bofhuhzensgraat 12, 1083 BA, Amsterdam, Netherlands (100%)
Tel.: (31) 205727000
Web Site: http://www.metsaboard.com
Sales Range: $25-49.9 Million
Emp.: 10
Paper Products Distr & Mfr
N.A.I.C.S.: 322299

Metsa Board Benelux n.v./s.a. (2)
Van Kerckhovenstraat 2, 2800, Mechelen, Belgium (100%)
Tel.: (32) 27727000
Web Site: http://www.metsaboard.com
Paperboards Whslr
N.A.I.C.S.: 424130
Young Mot *(Dir-Sls)*

Metsa Board Sweden AB (2)
Bruksvagen 90, 896 80, Husum, Sweden
Tel.: (46) 66318000
Web Site: http://www.metsaboard.com
Sales Range: $200-249.9 Million
Emp.: 800
Fine Paper Pulp Packaging & Paper
N.A.I.C.S.: 322110

Subsidiary (Non-US):

MoDo Merchants (3)
Tara St Holltov Industrial Estate Barbon, Coalville, LE67 1TW, Leicester, United Kingdom
Tel.: (44) 1530278140
Sales Range: $25-49.9 Million
Emp.: 100
Wholesale of Printing, Writing & Office Paper
N.A.I.C.S.: 424110

MoDo Paper SA (3)
Principe de Vergara 32, 2 Scha, E-280 01, Madrid, Spain
Tel.: (34) 917811171
Pulp & Paper Mills
N.A.I.C.S.: 322110

MoDo Van Gelder (3)
Joan Muyskenweg 32, PO Box 49000, NL 1009 CG, Amsterdam, Netherlands
Tel.: (31) 205605333
Web Site: http://www.modovangelder.nl

AND PRIVATE COMPANIES — METSO OYJ

Sales Range: $50-74.9 Million
Emp.: 170
Wholesales Paper
N.A.I.C.S.: 424130

Subsidiary (Domestic):

Metsa Group Financial Services
Ltd. (2)
Revontulenpuisto 2, PO Box 20, FIN 02020,
Espoo, Metsa, Finland (49%)
Tel.: (358) 1046011
Web Site: http://www.metsagroup.com
Sales Range: $25-49.9 Million
Emp.: 20
Paper Products Financial Services
N.A.I.C.S.: 322299

Subsidiary (Non-US):

Winpac Netherlands B.V. (2)
Papierbaan 50, PO Box 288, NL 9670 AG,
Winschoten, Netherlands (100%)
Tel.: (31) 597455555
Web Site: http://www.winpac.com
Sales Range: $25-49.9 Million
Emp.: 40
Paper & Paperboard Conversions
N.A.I.C.S.: 322120

Metsa Board Oyj (1)
METSA Revontulenpuisto 2, PO Box 20,
02100, Espoo, Finland
Tel.: (358) 104611
Wood Product Distr
N.A.I.C.S.: 423310

Metsa Forest Eesti AS (1)
Katusepapi 4, 11412, Tallinn, Estonia
Tel.: (372) 622 1460
Web Site: http://www.metsaforest.ee
Wood Procurement
N.A.I.C.S.: 423310

Metsa Forest Latvia SIA (1)
87e Vienibas Gatve, Riga, Latvia
Tel.: (371) 67804343
Web Site: http://www.metsaforest.lv
Wood Trade
N.A.I.C.S.: 423310

Metsa Forest Oy (1)
METSA Revontulenpuisto 2, PO Box 10,
02100, Espoo, Finland
Tel.: (358) 104601
Wood Product Distr
N.A.I.C.S.: 423310

Metsa Forest Sverige AB (1)
Husums Fabrik, Husum, 896 80, Vasternorrland, Sweden
Tel.: (46) 66318000
Wood Product Distr
N.A.I.C.S.: 423310
Setoo Puotanen *(Gen Mgr)*

Metsa Tissue Corporation (1)
Revontulenpuisto 2, 02100, Espoo, Finland
Tel.: (358) 104616
Web Site: http://www.metsatissue.com
Sales Range: $1-4.9 Billion
Emp.: 400
Paper Mills
N.A.I.C.S.: 322120
Juha Pilli-Sihvola *(CFO)*

Subsidiary (Non-US):

Metsa Tissue A/S (2)
orestads boulevard 73, 2630, Copenhagen, Denmark
Tel.: (45) 43713811
Web Site: http://www.metsatissue.com
Sales Range: $25-49.9 Million
Emp.: 22
Tissue & Cooking Paper Products Mfr
N.A.I.C.S.: 322220

Metsa Tissue Ltd. (2)
Marcar House 13 Parkshot, Richmond,
TW9 2RG, Surrey, United Kingdom
Tel.: (44) 2083322842
Web Site: http://www.metsatissue.com
Sales Range: $25-49.9 Million
Emp.: 12
Tissue & Cooking Paper Products Mfr
N.A.I.C.S.: 322220

Metsa Wood (1)
Tuulikuja 2, FI 02100, Espoo, Finland
Tel.: (358) 1046 05

Sales Range: $1-4.9 Billion
Emp.: 2,500
Wood Products Mfr
N.A.I.C.S.: 321999
Esa Kaikkonen *(Exec VP)*

Subsidiary (Non-US):

Metsa Wood Baco Production
S.R.L. (2)
Crinului Street 15, 605200, Bacau, Romania
Tel.: (40) 234374052
Web Site: http://www.scwejhofr.ro
Emp.: 500
Renewable Wood for Building & Construction
N.A.I.C.S.: 423310
Dan Banacu *(Gen Mgr)*

Metsa Wood CZ s.r.o. (2)
Skaly 215, PO Box 18, 763 62, Zlin, Czech Republic
Tel.: (420) 577 100 011
Wood Product Distr
N.A.I.C.S.: 423310

Metsa Wood Deutschland GmbH (2)
Louis Krages Strasse 30, 28237, Bremen, Germany
Tel.: (49) 421 6911 0
Wood Product Distr
N.A.I.C.S.: 423310

Metsa Wood Holland B.V. (2)
Schumanpark 9-C, 7336 AM, Apeldoorn, Netherlands
Tel.: (31) 55 538 6610
Web Site: http://www.metsawood.com
Wood Product Distr
N.A.I.C.S.: 423310

Metsa Wood Iberica S.L.U. (2)
P Castellana 140 Planta 17 pta dcha,
28046, Madrid, Spain
Tel.: (34) 91 563 6088
Wood Product Distr
N.A.I.C.S.: 423310

Metsa Wood Osterreich GesmbH (2)
Industriezentrum NO Sud Strasse 7 Obj 58
D2, A 2351, Wiener Neudorf, Austria
Tel.: (43) 2236 62 6400
Web Site: http://www.finnforest.at
Renewable Wood for Building & Construction
N.A.I.C.S.: 423310

Metsa Wood Schweiz AG (2)
3 Muhlebachstrasse 82, 8032, Zurich, Switzerland
Tel.: (41) 44 387 80 40
Wood Product Distr
N.A.I.C.S.: 423310

Metsa Wood Slovensko s.r.o. (2)
Vajnorska 135, 83237, Bratislava, Slovakia
Tel.: (421) 244259944
Web Site: http://www.finnforest.sk
Renewable Wood for Building & Construction
N.A.I.C.S.: 423310

Subsidiary (US):

Metsa Wood USA Inc. (2)
800 Military St Ste 200, Port Huron, MI 48060
Tel.: (810) 824-4890
Wood Product Distr
N.A.I.C.S.: 423310
Robert Loew *(Mng Dir)*

METSO OYJ
Rauhalanpuisto 9, 02230, Espoo, Finland
Tel.: (358) 20484100 FI
Web Site: https://www.metso.com
Year Founded: 1991
METSO—(HEL)
Rev.: $4,885,167,000
Assets: $6,231,240,400
Liabilities: $4,063,130,400
Net Worth: $2,168,110,000
Earnings: $277,702,600
Emp.: 16,705
Fiscal Year-end: 12/31/22
Holding Company; Aggregates, Mining & Metal Refining Industrial Technologies & Process Solutions

N.A.I.C.S.: 551112
Eeva Sipila *(Deputy CEO & CFO)*

Subsidiaries:

Ausiron Development Corporation
Pty. Ltd. (1)
15-19 Galli Ct, Dandenong, 3175, VIC, Australia
Tel.: (61) 397999922
Web Site:
  http://www.ausironindustries.com.au
Sales Range: $25-49.9 Million
Emp.: 6
Metal Products Mfr
N.A.I.C.S.: 332999

Edmeston AB (1)
Olof Asklunds gata 8, Vastra Frolunda,
Gothenburg, 42130, Sweden
Tel.: (46) 313356350
Web Site: http://www.edmeston.com
Sales Range: $10-24.9 Million
Emp.: 8
Sales of Steel-Belts & System Installations
for Automatic Processing, Handling & Sorting of Goods
N.A.I.C.S.: 424690

Kumpu GmbH (1)
Eschweilerstr 101-109, 52477, Alsdorf, Germany
Tel.: (49) 2404 670 80
Web Site: http://www.outotec.com
Industrial Machinery Mfr
N.A.I.C.S.: 333248

Larox India Private Ltd. (1)
116 Raiyan Arcade 1st Floor 1st Block 1st
Stage HBR Layout, Banaswadi, Bengaluru,
560 043, India
Tel.: (91) 80 4115 3783
Sales Range: $25-49.9 Million
Emp.: 16
Industrial Filter Mfr
N.A.I.C.S.: 333310

McCloskey International Ltd. (1)
47 Moor Road, Coalisland Co Tyrone, Dungannon, BT71 4QB, United Kingdom
Tel.: (44) 2887740926
Web Site:
  https://mccloskeyinternational.com
Waste Recycling Services
N.A.I.C.S.: 562998

Metso Brazil Industria e Comercio
Ltda. (1)
Avenida Independencia 2500, Bairro Iporanga, Sorocaba, CEP 18087-101, Sao Paulo, Brazil
Tel.: (55) 1521021300
Oil & Gas Mining Services
N.A.I.C.S.: 213112

Metso Bulgaria EOOD (1)
Ul Atanas Usunov Nr 21, 1505, Sofia, Bulgaria
Tel.: (359) 887201011
Mineral & Metal Distr
N.A.I.C.S.: 423520

Metso Maden Teknolojileri Anonim
Sirketi (1)
Macun Mah 179 Sk Yenimahalle, 06370,
Ankara, Turkiye
Tel.: (90) 3123873600
Metal Mining Services
N.A.I.C.S.: 212290

Metso Minerals Oy (1)
Fabianinkatu 9A, 00101, Helsinki, Finland
Tel.: (358) 20484100
Development & Marketing of Complete Systems & Turnkey Plants to the Construction,
Aggregate & Mining Industries
N.A.I.C.S.: 236220

Subsidiary (Non-US):

Metso Germany GmbH (2)
Kantstrasse 22-24, 44867, Bochum, Germany
Tel.: (49) 232754440
Web Site: https://www.metso.com
Sales Range: $10-24.9 Million
Emp.: 42
Mining Engineering Services
N.A.I.C.S.: 541330

Unit (Domestic):

Metso Germany GmbH -
Dusseldorf (3)
Grafenberger Allee 337a, 40235, Dusseldorf, Germany
Tel.: (49) 21121050
Crushing Equipment; Minerals Processing
N.A.I.C.S.: 236220
Mishaal Simon *(Mng Dir)*

Subsidiary (Non-US):

Metso India Private Ltd (2)
306 3rd Floor Barton Center MG Road,
Bengaluru, 560001, Karnataka, India
Tel.: (91) 8025580606
Web Site: http://contact.metso.com
Mining & Aggregates Services & Concrete Mfr
N.A.I.C.S.: 212312

Branch (Domestic):

Metso Minerals (India) Pvt. Ltd. -
Hyderabad (3)
2nd Floor Office No 202 Maheshwari Mayank Plaza D No 6-3-866/A, Greenlands
Road, Hyderabad, 5000016, Begumpet,
India
Tel.: (91) 40 40034236 8
Web Site: http://www.metso.com
Sales Range: $50-74.9 Million
Emp.: 15
Mining & Construction Services
N.A.I.C.S.: 212321

Metso Minerals (India) Pvt. Ltd. -
Kolkata (3)
19 A-2 Everest 46-C Jawaharlal Nehru Rd,
Kolkata, 700 071, India
Tel.: (91) 3322887987
Sales Range: $25-49.9 Million
Emp.: 14
N.A.I.C.S.: 236220

Subsidiary (Non-US):

Metso Minerals (Algerie) Eurl (2)
70 Route de Ain-Taya Lot N 01, Rouiba,
16012, Algeria
Tel.: (213) 21 85 52 24
Web Site: http://www.metso.com
Construction Machinery Whslr
N.A.I.C.S.: 423810

Metso Minerals (Argentina) S.A. (2)
Viamonte 783 5 Piso, Buenos Aires, Argentina
Tel.: (54) 114836 2006
Web Site: http://www.metso.com
Sales Range: $150-199.9 Million
Emp.: 500
Mineral Mining Services
N.A.I.C.S.: 212390

Metso Minerals (Australia)
Limited (2)
Level 2 1110 Hay Street, West Perth, 6005,
WA, Australia
Tel.: (61) 8 9420 5555
Sales Range: $25-49.9 Million
Emp.: 100
Sales & Service of Mining & Construction
Equipment
N.A.I.C.S.: 423810
Roof Warthstoon *(Gen Mgr)*

Subsidiary (Domestic):

Denver Equipment Pty., Ltd. (3)
1st Floor 40 Dickson Avenue, PO Box 365,
Artarmon, NSW, Australia
Tel.: (61) 2 439 6699
Sales Range: $25-49.9 Million
Emp.: 10
Mineral Recovery & Chemical Processing
Equipment
N.A.I.C.S.: 333248

Branch (Domestic):

Metso Minerals (Australia) Limited -
Arndell Park (3)
16 Lidco Street, Arndell Park, Sydney,
2148, NSW, Australia
Tel.: (61) 288251600
Web Site: http://www.metso.com

METSO OYJ — INTERNATIONAL PUBLIC

Metso Oyj—(Continued)
Sales Range: $25-49.9 Million
Emp.: 90
Mining & Construction
N.A.I.C.S.: 236220

Metso Minerals (Australia) Limited - Carrington (3)
17 Old Punt Road, Tomago, 2322, NSW, Australia
Tel.: (61) 249788100
Web Site: http://www.metso.com
Sales Range: $10-24.9 Million
Emp.: 50
N.A.I.C.S.: 236220
Jason Richard *(Acct Mgr)*

Metso Minerals (Australia) Limited - Eagle Farm (3)
1/8-10 Chapman Place, Eagle Farm, 4009, QLD, Australia
Tel.: (61) 7 3623 2999
Web Site: http://www.metso.com
Sales Range: $25-49.9 Million
Emp.: 60
Mining Machinery & Equipment Mfr
N.A.I.C.S.: 333131

Subsidiary (Non-US):

Metso Minerals (Brasil) Ltda. (2)
Avenida Independencia 2500 Iporanga, Sorocaba, 18087-101, SP, Brazil (100%)
Tel.: (55) 1530321400
Web Site: http://www.metso.com
Mining & Construction Services
N.A.I.C.S.: 236220

Unit (Domestic):

Metso Minerals (Brasil) Ltda. (3)
Av Regis Bittencourt 3180, 06793 900, Taboao da Serra, Brazil
Tel.: (55) 1179670999
N.A.I.C.S.: 236220

Subsidiary (Non-US):

Metso Minerals (Chile) SA (2)
Cerro El Plomo 5280 17th Floor, 7502, Santiago, Chile (100%)
Tel.: (56) 23702000
Web Site: http://www.metso.com
Sales Range: $25-49.9 Million
Emp.: 150
Environmental & Quality Solutions
N.A.I.C.S.: 236220
Eduardo Nilo *(Gen Mgr)*

Metso Minerals (Czech Republic) s.r.o (2)
Mezirka 1, Brno, 602 00, Czech Republic
Tel.: (420) 544425521
Web Site: http://www.metso.com
Emp.: 9
Industrial Machinery Sales & Maintenance Services
N.A.I.C.S.: 423830

Metso Minerals (Dordrecht) B.V. (2)
Bunsenstraat 19, 3316 GC, Dordrecht, Netherlands
Tel.: (31) 786186888
Sales Range: $25-49.9 Million
Emp.: 53
N.A.I.C.S.: 236220
Leun Temmink *(Gen Mgr)*

Metso Minerals (Italy) SpA (2)
Via Lucrezia Romana 65/N Int 10, 00043, Ciampino, Milan, Italy
Tel.: (39) 0694802360
Web Site: http://www.metso.com
Construction Machinery Whslr
N.A.I.C.S.: 423810

Metso Minerals (Johannesburg) (Pty) Ltd. (2)
64 Jet Pk Rd, PO Box X2006, 1469, Isando, South Africa (100%)
Tel.: (27) 113975090
Sales Range: $50-74.9 Million
Emp.: 200
N.A.I.C.S.: 236220

Metso Minerals (Mexico) SA de CV (2)
Salamanca Ote Eleya Fm Ed Industrial, 36541, Ciudad Juarez, Mexico
Tel.: (52) 4626225190

Web Site: http://www.metso.com
Sales Range: $25-49.9 Million
Emp.: 85
N.A.I.C.S.: 236220

Metso Minerals (Norway) AS (2)
Professor Birkelands vei 36 D, 1081, Oslo, Norway
Tel.: (47) 22903500
Web Site: http://www.metso.com
Emp.: 9
Mining & Construction Services
N.A.I.C.S.: 212290

Metso Minerals (Philippines) Inc. (2)
Room 304 Gaston Building 30, J Elizalde Street BF Homes, Paranaque, 1700, Philippines
Tel.: (63) 2 809 6165
Mineral Mining Services
N.A.I.C.S.: 212390

Metso Minerals (Poland) Sp. z o.o. (2)
Portelanavwa 12, 40 246, Katowice, Poland (100%)
Tel.: (48) 322530729
Web Site: http://www.metsominerals.pl
Sales Range: $25-49.9 Million
Emp.: 24
N.A.I.C.S.: 236220
Matiej Kostanski *(Gen Mgr-Sls)*

Metso Minerals (Portugal) Lda (2)
Rua Sebastiao e Silva Nos 71 -73 Zona Industrial de Massama, 2745-838, Sintra, Portugal
Tel.: (351) 21 438 8550
Web Site: http://www.metso.com
Construction Machinery Whslr
N.A.I.C.S.: 423810

Metso Minerals (Singapore) Pte Ltd (2)
180 Clemenceau Avenue 06-01 Haw Par Centre, Singapore, 229932, Singapore
Tel.: (65) 65089260
Web Site: http://www.metso.com
Sales Range: $50-74.9 Million
Emp.: 11
Mineral Mining Services
N.A.I.C.S.: 212390

Metso Minerals (South Africa) Pty. Ltd. (2)
ACSA Park 1 Jones Rd Jet Park, Boksburg, 1459, Johannesburg, South Africa (100%)
Tel.: (27) 119614000
Web Site: http://www.metso.com
Sales Range: $10-24.9 Million
Emp.: 50
Mfr of Abrasion-Resistant Rubber
N.A.I.C.S.: 326299

Metso Minerals (Sweden) AB (2)
Sjogatan 13, 852 34, Sundsvall, Sweden
Tel.: (46) 60140140
Web Site: http://www.metso.com
Sales Range: $50-74.9 Million
Emp.: 1,000
Mining & Construction Services
N.A.I.C.S.: 236220

Subsidiary (Domestic):

Armaturteknik i Osby AB (3)
Radiatorvagen, PO Box 65, 283 21, Osby, Sweden (100%)
Tel.: (46) 47917470
Web Site: http://www.armaturteknik.com
Sales Range: $1-9.9 Million
Emp.: 3
Mfr of Valves & Fittings
N.A.I.C.S.: 332919

Unit (Domestic):

Metso Minerals (Sweden) AB - Ersmark (3)
Fabriksvagen 1-3, 934 81, Ersmark, Sweden
Tel.: (46) 910584100
Sales Range: $25-49.9 Million
Emp.: 230
Produces Abrasion-Resistant Rubber for Use in Mining, Quarrying & Cement Industry; Technical Rubber for Hydraulic & Pneumatic Seals; Tracks for Military & Civil Cross Country Vehicles
N.A.I.C.S.: 326211

Metso Minerals (Sweden) AB - Kiruna (3)
Linbanevagen 9, 98128, Kiruna, Sweden
Tel.: (46) 980 75440
Mill Linings, Conveyor Belts, Hose Systems & Related Industrial Rubber Products
N.A.I.C.S.: 326220

Metso Minerals (Sweden) AB - Molnlycke (3)
Fibervagen 5, 435 33, Molnlycke, Sweden
Tel.: (46) 31807090
Web Site: http://www.metsomineral.com
Sales Range: $50-74.9 Million
Emp.: 200
N.A.I.C.S.: 236220

Subsidiary (Domestic):

Traryds Metall AB (3)
Gransvagen 4, PO Box 48, 287 34, Stromsnasbruk, Sweden (100%)
Tel.: (46) 43374880
Web Site: http://www.trarydsmetall.com
Sales Range: $25-49.9 Million
Emp.: 20
Mfrs. Castings of Copper Alloy
N.A.I.C.S.: 331420

Subsidiary (Non-US):

Metso Minerals (Thailand) Co. Ltd (2)
283/44 Soi Sukhumvit 55 Sukhumvit Rd, Khlong Tan Nua, 10110, Bangkok, Thailand
Tel.: (66) 27127241
Mineral Mining Services
N.A.I.C.S.: 212390

Metso Minerals (Tianjin) Co., Ltd. (2)
No 11 Bohai Road TEDA, Tianjin, 300457, China
Tel.: (86) 222532285
Web Site: http://www.metso.com
Construction Machinery Mfr
N.A.I.C.S.: 333120

Subsidiary (Domestic):

Metso Minerals (Tianjin) International Trade Co., Ltd. (3)
19/F Exchange Beijing Tower 4 China Merchants Ctr 118 Jian Guo Lu Yi, Chaoyang District, Beijing, 100022, China
Tel.: (86) 10 6566 6600
Mining Machinery Wholesale Trade Agency
N.A.I.C.S.: 425120

Subsidiary (Non-US):

Metso Minerals (UK) Ltd. (2)
Parkfield Road, Rugby, CV21 1QJ, Warks, United Kingdom
Tel.: (44) 1788532100
Rev.: $74,870,000
Emp.: 25
N.A.I.C.S.: 236220
Adrian Wood *(Gen Mgr)*

Unit (Domestic):

Metso Minerals (UK) Ltd. - Shepton Mallet (3)
23 Brewmaster Buildings, Charlton Trading Estate, Shepton Mallet, BA4 5QE, Somerset, United Kingdom
Tel.: (44) 1749 333555
Web Site: http://www.metso.com
Sales Range: $25-49.9 Million
Emp.: 20
Mining & Construction Services
N.A.I.C.S.: 236220

Subsidiary (Non-US):

Metso Minerals (Zambia) Ltd. (2)
Plot 1043 Blantyre Road Light Industrial Area, Kitwe, Zambia
Tel.: (260) 212 231177
Web Site: http://www.metso.com
Mineral Mining Services
N.A.I.C.S.: 212390

Metso Minerals (Zimbabwe) (Pty.) (2)
Falcon & Trojan St, AC 518, Bulawayo, Zimbabwe (100%)
Tel.: (263) 9469329

Sales Range: $25-49.9 Million
Emp.: 7
N.A.I.C.S.: 236220

Metso Minerals Austria (2)
Gosef-Pine gasse 3, 1230, Vienna, Austria (100%)
Tel.: (43) 0018136508
Web Site: http://www.metso.com
Sales Range: $25-49.9 Million
Emp.: 38
N.A.I.C.S.: 236220

Metso Minerals Canada Inc. (2)
30 Franklin St, PO Box 5900, Belleville, K8N 1A1, ON, Canada
Tel.: (613) 962-3411
Web Site: http://www.metso.com
Sales Range: $25-49.9 Million
Emp.: 14
Mfr of Rollers for Mineral Industries
N.A.I.C.S.: 333131

Unit (Domestic):

Metso Minerals Canada Inc. (3)
8319 Roper Rd, Edmonton, T6E 5C6, AB, Canada
Tel.: (780) 434-9317
Sales Range: $25-49.9 Million
Emp.: 3
N.A.I.C.S.: 236220

Metso Minerals Canada Inc. (3)
114 Airport Rd, Labrador City, A2V 2J7, NL, Canada
Tel.: (709) 282-3933
Sales Range: $25-49.9 Million
Emp.: 3
Marketing of Mineral Products
N.A.I.C.S.: 327999
Martin Dupont *(Gen Mgr)*

Subsidiary (Non-US):

Metso Minerals Dis Ticaret Limeted Sirketi (2)
64 Sok No 2/1, Ankara, Turkiye
Tel.: (90) 3123873600
Mineral Mining Services
N.A.I.C.S.: 212390

Metso Minerals Espana SA (2)
Calle Rivas 4, 28032, Madrid, Spain
Tel.: (34) 91 8255700
Web Site: http://www.metso.com
Sales Range: $25-49.9 Million
Emp.: 50
Construction Machinery & Equipment Whslr
N.A.I.C.S.: 423810

Subsidiary (Domestic):

Metso Minerals Finland Oy Ab (2)
Lokomonkatu 3-5, 33100, Tampere, Finland (100%)
Tel.: (358) 204845200
Sales Range: $10-24.9 Million
Emp.: 50
Produces Abrasion-Resistant Rubber
N.A.I.C.S.: 314910
Tapio Nurminen *(Gen Mgr)*

Subsidiary (Domestic):

Metso Minerals Finland Oy (3)
Hoylaamotie 2, Kello, 90820, Oulu, Finland (100%)
Tel.: (358) 204845340
Sales Range: $1-9.9 Million
Emp.: 12
Mining & Construction Equipment Distr
N.A.I.C.S.: 423810

Metso Minerals Finland Oy (3)
Kangaskatu 2, 76100, Pieksamaki, Finland (100%)
Tel.: (358) 204845360
Conveyor Belts Mfr
N.A.I.C.S.: 333922

Subsidiary (Non-US):

Metso Minerals France (2)
140 142 Rue Du Chevaleret, 75013, Paris, France
Tel.: (33) 145853028
Sales Range: $25-49.9 Million
Emp.: 10
Construction Services
N.A.I.C.S.: 236220

AND PRIVATE COMPANIES   METSO OYJ

Philippe Portevin *(Dir-Comml)*

Subsidiary (Domestic):

Metso Minerals CISA S.A. (3)
841 Boulevard Duhamel du Monceau, Olivet, 45160, France
Tel.: (33) 238 25 35 70
Web Site: http://www.metso.com
Sales Range: $25-49.9 Million
Mining & Construction Machinery Mfr
N.A.I.C.S.: 333131

Subsidiary (Non-US):

Metso Minerals Ghana Ltd. (2)
Bpa Heights 3Rd Floor No 11 Dodo Link, Airport West, Accra, 23321, Ghana **(100%)**
Tel.: (233) 30 277 0024
Web Site: http://www.metso.com
Sales Range: $50-74.9 Million
Emp.: 16
Mining & Construction Services
N.A.I.C.S.: 212290

Subsidiary (US):

Metso Minerals Industries, Inc. (2)
20965 Crossroads Cir, Waukesha, WI 53186-4083
Tel.: (262) 717-2500
Web Site: http://www.metso.com
Sales Range: $100-124.9 Million
Emp.: 300
Mfr of Specialized Machinery for Bulk Material Handling
N.A.I.C.S.: 333922
Todd Dillmann *(Gen Counsel & VP)*

Unit (Domestic):

Metso Copperstate Inc. (3)
4151 E Quartz Cir, Mesa, AZ 85215
Tel.: (480) 832-6500
Web Site: http://www.metso.com
Mineral Mining Services
N.A.I.C.S.: 212390
Steve Richardson *(Gen Mgr)*

Metso Minerals Industries, Inc. - Birmingham (3)
900 38th St N, Birmingham, AL 35222
Tel.: (205) 599-6600
Sales Range: $25-49.9 Million
Emp.: 10
Mineral Recovery & Chemical Processing Equipment
N.A.I.C.S.: 331110

Metso Minerals Industries, Inc. - Canonsburg (3)
4000 Town Center Blvd Ste 400, Canonsburg, PA 15317
Tel.: (412) 269-5000
Web Site: http://www.metso.com
Sales Range: $25-49.9 Million
Emp.: 100
Fabrication & Machine Shop
N.A.I.C.S.: 333922

Metso Minerals Industries, Inc. - Colorado Springs (3)
4820 Centennial Blvd Ste 115, Colorado Springs, CO 80919-3351
Tel.: (719) 471-3443
Sales Range: $50-74.9 Million
Emp.: 43
Mineral Recovery & Chemical Processing Equipment
N.A.I.C.S.: 333131

Metso Minerals Industries, Inc. - Danville (3)
350 Rail Rd St, Danville, PA 17821-1002
Tel.: (570) 275-3050
Web Site: http://www.metso.com
Sales Range: $50-74.9 Million
Emp.: 120
Engineering Consultation Services
N.A.I.C.S.: 541330

Metso Minerals Industries, Inc. - York (3)
2715 Pleasant Vly Rd, York, PA 17402
Tel.: (717) 843-8671
Web Site: http://www.metso.com
Sales Range: $125-149.9 Million
Emp.: 300
Mfr of Mining & Chemical Machinery
N.A.I.C.S.: 333131

Subsidiary (Non-US):

Metso Minerals Japan Co. Ltd (2)
Shin-yokohama Kaneko Bldg 4F 2-3-9 Shin-yokohama, Kouhoku-ku, Yokohama, 222-0033, Japan
Tel.: (81) 45 476 3935
Sales Range: $10-24.9 Million
Emp.: 13
Metal Waste Recycling Services
N.A.I.C.S.: 562920
Fumio Yokoyama *(Mng Dir-Admin)*

Metso Minerals S.A. (2)
Hofveld 5, 1702, Groot-Bijgaarden, Bijgaarden, Belgium **(100%)**
Tel.: (32) 24810960
Web Site: http://www.metso.com
Sales Range: $25-49.9 Million
Emp.: 100
N.A.I.C.S.: 236220

Metso Minerals s.r.o. (2)
Tovacovska 2910/17, Prerov, 75002, Czech Republic
Tel.: (420) 581 702711
Sales Range: $150-199.9 Million
Emp.: 200
Mineral Mining Services
N.A.I.C.S.: 212390
Ivo Dolezal *(Gen Mgr)*

PT. Metso Minerals Indonesia (2)
Prima 20th Floor, Jakarta, 12950, Indonesia
Tel.: (62) 21 573 7122
N.A.I.C.S.: 236220

ZAO Metso Minerals (CIS) (2)
11/1 Nikoloyamskaya Str, 109240, Moscow, Russia **(100%)**
Tel.: (7) 495 915 7364
Web Site: http://www.metso.com
Sales Range: $50-74.9 Million
Emp.: 15
Recycling Services & Sales of Treated Minerals
N.A.I.C.S.: 213115

Metso Mongolia LLC (1)
Ayud Tower 1603 Olympics Street 5, Sukhbaatar District 1st khoroo, Ulaanbaatar, 16607, Mongolia
Tel.: (976) 75776800
Metal Mining Services
N.A.I.C.S.: 212290

Metso Outotec Morocco LLC (1)
Sidi Maarouf-Lotissement la Colline, Immeuble California Garden Batiment B 4eme Etage, 20200, Casablanca, Morocco
Tel.: (212) 520493704
Oil & Gas Mining Services
N.A.I.C.S.: 213112

Metso Outotec New Material Technology (Shanghai) Co., Ltd. (1)
Floor 07 Tower T2 Everbright Anshi Center No 398 Huoshan Road, Yangpu, Shanghai, 200082, China
Tel.: (86) 2155083858
Metal Mining Services
N.A.I.C.S.: 212290

Metso Romania S.R.L. (1)
61-63 Ion Ionescu de la Brad Blv, District 1, 2951, Bucharest, Romania
Tel.: (40) 724223705
Mining & Mineral Processing Services
N.A.I.C.S.: 213112

OOO Outotec Norilsk (1)
Ul Ordzonikidze 6 a 5th Fl, Noril'sk, 662319, Russia
Tel.: (7) 3919220687
Emp.: 2
Metal Processing Machinery Mfr
N.A.I.C.S.: 333998
Olga Romashtina *(Mng Dir)*

Outkumpu - Minerals Processing (1)
40 Kings Park Road, West Perth, 6005, WA, Australia
Tel.: (61) 892112200
Web Site: http://www.outotec.com
Sales Range: $50-74.9 Million
Emp.: 96
Minerals Processing Plant
N.A.I.C.S.: 212290

Outokumpu Wenmec AB (1)
Gardesgatan 4, Kil, S 66532, Sweden
Tel.: (46) 55433210
Sales Range: $25-49.9 Million
Emp.: 25
Mfr of Equipment for Copper, Zinc & Nickel Smelters & Refineries
N.A.I.C.S.: 331410
Kurt Jonsson *(Gen Mgr)*

Outotec (Australasia) Pty. Ltd. (1)
72 Market St, South Melbourne, Melbourne, 3205, VIC, Australia
Tel.: (61) 3 9674 2301
Sales Range: $25-49.9 Million
Emp.: 5
Metal Processing Services
N.A.I.C.S.: 331492
Paul Abbott *(Mng Dir)*

Outotec (Ceramics) Oy (1)
Urusvuorenkatu 5, 20360, Turku, Finland
Tel.: (358) 20 529 211
Web Site: http://www.outotec.com
Emp.: 50
Ceramic Products Mfr
N.A.I.C.S.: 327120

Outotec (Chile) Ltda. (1)
Avda Vitacura 2939 Piso 9 Edificio Milenium, Las Condes, Santiago, 7550011, Chile
Tel.: (56) 23362000
Web Site: http://www.outotec.com
Sales Range: $50-74.9 Million
Emp.: 118
Mineral Processing & Services
N.A.I.C.S.: 327999

Outotec (Filters) GmbH (1)
Eschweiler Strasse 101 - 109, 52477, Alsdorf, Germany
Tel.: (49) 2404 670 80
Web Site: http://www.outotec.com
Sales Range: $25-49.9 Million
Emp.: 3
Industrial Filters Distr
N.A.I.C.S.: 423840

Outotec (Filters) Oy (1)
Tukkikatu 1, PO Box 29, 53900, Lappeenranta, Finland
Tel.: (358) 20 529 211
Metal Processing Services
N.A.I.C.S.: 423510
Markku Terasvasara *(Pres & CEO)*

Outotec (Finland) Oy (1)
Riihitontuntie 7 D, PO Box 86, 2201, Espoo, Finland
Tel.: (358) 20 529 211
Sales Range: $250-299.9 Million
Emp.: 100
Metal Processing Services
N.A.I.C.S.: 423510

Outotec (Ghana) Limited (1)
12 Asafouatse Afuah Street Airport West, PO Box AN 5733, Accra North, Accra, Ghana
Tel.: (233) 248390005
Metal Mining Services
N.A.I.C.S.: 213114

Outotec (Kazakhstan) LLP (1)
Baitursynova Street 19, Almaty, 050000, Kazakhstan
Tel.: (7) 727 278 1018
Web Site: http://www.outotec.com
Metal Processing Machinery Mfr
N.A.I.C.S.: 333248

Outotec (Mexico), S.A. de C.V. (1)
Homero #229-501, Colonia Chapultepec Morales, 11570, Mexico, DF, Mexico
Tel.: (52) 5552542776
Web Site: http://www.outotec.com
Sales Range: $50-74.9 Million
Emp.: 10
Mineral Processing
N.A.I.C.S.: 324199

Outotec (Norway) AS (1)
Ostensjoveien 34, PO Box 6305, Etterstad, Oslo, 667, Norway
Tel.: (47) 23 24 74 73
Sales Range: $50-74.9 Million
Emp.: 1
Metal Mining Services
N.A.I.C.S.: 213114
Sverre Nakkim *(Mgr-Design-Grinding Mills)*

Outotec (Perth) (1)
40 Kings Park Road, West Perth, 6005, WA, Australia
Tel.: (61) 892112200
Web Site: http://www.outotec.com
Sales Range: $50-74.9 Million
Emp.: 90
Base Metals Processing
N.A.I.C.S.: 212290

Outotec (Peru) S.A.C. (1)
Av El Derby N 055 Torre 2 Piso 10, Lima, 33, Peru
Tel.: (51) 17164444
Sales Range: $25-49.9 Million
Emp.: 40
Mineral & Metal Processing
N.A.I.C.S.: 324199
Felipe Viguera *(Gen Mgr)*

Outotec (Polska) Sp. z.o.o. (1)
Ul Graniczna 29, 40956, Katowice, Poland
Tel.: (48) 32 256 2305
Sales Range: $50-74.9 Million
Emp.: 5
Metal Processing Machinery Sales & Maintenance Services
N.A.I.C.S.: 423830
Witold Dybczak *(Gen Mgr)*

Outotec (RSA) (Pty) Ltd. (1)
Unit 28 Kyalami Crescent Kyalami Boulevard, PO Box 4197, Halfway House, Midrand, 1685, Gauteng, South Africa
Tel.: (27) 0117992410
Sales Range: $25-49.9 Million
Emp.: 90
Production Plant
N.A.I.C.S.: 324199

Outotec (Shanghai) Co. Ltd. (1)
Room 2308 Metro Plaza No 555 Loushanguan Road, Changning District, Shanghai, 200051, China
Tel.: (86) 21 6195 1122
Sales Range: $25-49.9 Million
Emp.: 7
Metal Processing Machinery Mfr
N.A.I.C.S.: 333248

Outotec (Sweden) AB (1)
Gymnasievagen 14, Box 745, 931 27, Skelleftea, Sweden
Tel.: (46) 910 87600
Web Site: http://www.outotec.com
Mineral & Metal Processing Machinery Mfr
N.A.I.C.S.: 333131

Outotec (Sydney) (1)
28 Rodborough Rd, French's Forest, 2086, NSW, Australia
Tel.: (61) 299842500
Web Site: http://www.outotec.com
Sales Range: $25-49.9 Million
Emp.: 50
Minerals Processing
N.A.I.C.S.: 324199

Outotec (USA) Inc. (1)
6100 Phillips Hwy, Jacksonville, FL 32216-5921
Tel.: (904) 353-3681
Web Site: https://www.outotec.com
Sales Range: $25-49.9 Million
Emp.: 50
Process Solutions, Technologies & Services for Mining & Metallurgical Industries
N.A.I.C.S.: 423810

Outotec (Zambia) Ltd. (1)
775 Lukasu Drive, Parklands, Kitwe, Zambia
Tel.: (260) 966688006
Web Site: https://www.outotec.com
Sales Range: $25-49.9 Million
Emp.: 21
Mining & Mineral Processing Equipment Distr
N.A.I.C.S.: 423830

Outotec Ausmelt Pty. Ltd. (1)
72 Market St, Melbourne, 3205, VIC, Australia
Tel.: (61) 396965766
Web Site: http://www.outotec.com
Sales Range: $10-24.9 Million
Emp.: 1
Smelting Technology Developer
N.A.I.C.S.: 333248

Outotec Deutschland GmbH (1)
Ludwig-Erhard-Str 21, Oberursel, 61440, Germany

METSO OYJ

Metso Oyj—(Continued)
Tel.: (49) 617196930
Mineral & Metal Processing Machinery Mfr
N.A.I.C.S.: 333131

Outotec Energy Products (1)
3568 W Industrial Loop, Coeur D'Alene, ID 83815-6016
Tel.: (208) 765-1611
Web Site: http://www.outotec.com
Emp.: 50
Electric Power Generation Services
N.A.I.C.S.: 221112

Outotec Filters Australia Pty. Ltd. (1)
20a Rodborough Rd Frenchs Forest, Sydney, 2086, NSW, Australia
Tel.: (61) 2 9910 6412
Sales Range: $50-74.9 Million
Emp.: 16
Industrial Filter Mfr
N.A.I.C.S.: 333998
Stuart Sneyd *(Gen Mgr)*

Outotec GmbH (1)
Ludwig-Erhard-Str 21, Oberursel, 61440, Germany
Tel.: (49) 61719693711
Sales Range: $200-249.9 Million
Emp.: 65
Mineral & Metal Processing Machinery Mfr
N.A.I.C.S.: 333131

Outotec Holding GmbH (1)
Ludwig-Erhard-Strasse 21, 61440, Oberursel, Germany
Tel.: (49) 617196930
Web Site: https://www.outotec.com
Investment Management Service
N.A.I.C.S.: 523999

Outotec India Private Ltd. (1)
South City Pinnacle 12th Floor Sector V Block EP, Salt Lake, Kolkata, 700 091, India
Tel.: (91) 3340140400
Web Site: https://www.outotec.com
Sales Range: $50-74.9 Million
Emp.: 80
Metal Mining Services
N.A.I.C.S.: 213114

Outotec Pty Ltd (1)
28 Rodborough Rd, French's Forest, 2086, NSW, Australia
Tel.: (61) 299842500
Web Site: https://www.outotec.com
Emp.: 500
Metal & Mineral Mining Services
N.A.I.C.S.: 213114

Outotec Pty Ltd. - Melbourne (1)
12 Kitchen Road, Dandenong South, Melbourne, 23175, VIC, Australia
Tel.: (61) 3 9566 5800
Web Site: http://www.outotec.com
Emp.: 60
Base Metal Processing
N.A.I.C.S.: 212290

Outotec St. Petersburg (1)
VO 7-th Line 76 Lit A, 199178, Saint Petersburg, Russia
Tel.: (7) 8002224300
Web Site: http://www.outotec.com
Sales Range: $50-74.9 Million
Emp.: 70
Mineral Engineering & Processing
N.A.I.C.S.: 213115

Outotec Tecnologia Brasil Ltda. (1)
Av Getulio Vargas 1300-20Th Floor Funcionarios, Conjunto 1007/1010 Funcionario, 30260 070, Belo Horizonte, MG, Brazil
Tel.: (55) 3132280700
Web Site: https://www.outotec.com
Sales Range: $50-74.9 Million
Emp.: 15
Metal & Mineral Processing
N.A.I.C.S.: 324199

Outotec Turula Oy (1)
Kuvernoorinkatu 2, FIN 83501, Outokumpu, Finland
Tel.: (358) 408644870
Web Site: http://www.outotec.com
Sales Range: $50-74.9 Million
Emp.: 150
Delivers Production Machinery Incorporating Mechanical, Electrical & Hydraulic Assemblies

N.A.I.C.S.: 333998

Shaorui Heavy Industries (Guangdong) Co. Ltd. (1)
Industrial Park of Wujiang, Shaoguan, Guangdong, China
Tel.: (86) 7518136739
Web Site: https://www.shaoruiheavy.com
Industrial Equipment Mfr
N.A.I.C.S.: 333248

Tedd Engineering Ltd. (1)
Unit 1 Tupton Way Holmewood Industrial Park, Chesterfield, S42 5BX, Derbyshire, United Kingdom
Tel.: (44) 1246690099
Web Site: https://www.teddengineering.com
Electronic Control System Mfr
N.A.I.C.S.: 334419

Tesab Engineering Ltd. (1)
Unit 9 Gortrush Industrial Estate, Omagh, BT78 5EJ, County Tyrone, United Kingdom
Tel.: (44) 2882252781
Web Site: https://tesab.com
Emp.: 80
Crusher & Screener Mfr
N.A.I.C.S.: 333131

ZAO Outotec (1)
V O 7-th Line 76 Lit A, Saint Petersburg, 199178, Russia
Tel.: (7) 8123325572
Emp.: 14
Mineral Mining Services
N.A.I.C.S.: 212390
Mark Rogers *(Mgr)*

METTEXIN SA
Str Rozelor Bl C 18 B, Constanta, Mangalia, Romania
Tel.: (40) 241751567
METT—(BUC)
Rev.: $597
Assets: $119,729
Liabilities: $107,974
Net Worth: $11,754
Earnings: ($15,329)
Emp.: 1
Fiscal Year-end: 12/31/23
Textile Product Whslr
N.A.I.C.S.: 424990
Iulian Claudiu Stefan *(Chm)*

MEVACO GMBH
Vordere Karlstrasse 12, 73033, Goppingen, Germany
Tel.: (49) 716150200
Web Site: http://www.mevaco.com
Year Founded: 1998
Sales Range: $50-74.9 Million
Emp.: 135
Metal & Perforated Sheet Mfr
N.A.I.C.S.: 332322
Stephan Geiger *(Mng Dir)*

MEVACO S.A.
Prari-Moustaki NATO Avenue, 19300, Aspropyrgos, Attica, Greece
Tel.: (30) 2105596623
Web Site: https://www.mevaco.gr
Year Founded: 1993
MEVA—(ATH)
Rev.: $31,439,755
Assets: $46,433,501
Liabilities: $16,511,314
Net Worth: $29,922,188
Earnings: $2,379,790
Emp.: 119
Fiscal Year-end: 12/31/21
Sheet Metal Processing & Metal Construction Products Mfr
N.A.I.C.S.: 332999
Dimitrios Kostopoulos *(Pres)*

Subsidiaries:

Venman S.A. (1)
12 Old National Road, PO Box 1091, 57022, Thessaloniki, Greece
Tel.: (30) 2310784684
Web Site: http://www.venman.gr

Sales Range: $25-49.9 Million
Emp.: 50
Solar & Thermal Systems & Heating Tanks Mfr
N.A.I.C.S.: 333415
Iordanis Kiopelis *(Gen Mgr)*

MEVANAH REAL ESTATE KD LTD.
Haaretz 7, Tel Aviv, Israel
Tel.: (972) 39070000
Web Site: https://www.mivnegroup.co.il
MVNE—(TAE)
Rev.: $329,990,878
Assets: $5,000,988,456
Liabilities: $2,760,156,332
Net Worth: $2,240,832,124
Earnings: $93,118,661
Fiscal Year-end: 12/31/23
Lessors of Other Real Estate Property
N.A.I.C.S.: 531190

MEWA S.A.
Ul Belwederska 23, 00-761, Warsaw, Poland
Tel.: (48) 84 688 11 00
Web Site: http://www.mewa.com.pl
Clothing Apparel Mfr & Distr
N.A.I.C.S.: 315990

MEWAH INTERNATIONAL INC.
5 International Business Park, Singapore, 609914, Singapore
Tel.: (65) 68295200
Web Site: https://www.mewahgroup.com
MV4—(SES)
Rev.: $4,123,796,000
Assets: $1,489,593,000
Liabilities: $703,103,000
Net Worth: $786,490,000
Earnings: $38,572,000
Emp.: 4,491
Fiscal Year-end: 12/31/23
Edible Fats & Oils Refining
N.A.I.C.S.: 311225
Abdul Jabbar Karam Din *(Sec)*

Subsidiaries:

Bremfield Sdn. Bhd. (1)
Lot 40A Jalan Sungai Pinang 5/1/KS11Section 4 Phase 2A, Pulau Indah Industrial Park, 42920, Pulau Indah, Selangor, Malaysia
Tel.: (60) 331693000
Palm Oil Refining Product Mfr
N.A.I.C.S.: 311225

Container Fabricator (M) Sdn Bhd (1)
Lot 40 Section 4 Fasa 2A Pulau Indah Industrial Park, Jalan Sungai Pinang 5/1, Pulau Indah, 42920, Selangor Darul Ehsan, Malaysia
Tel.: (60) 3 3101 1133
Palm Oil Mfr
N.A.I.C.S.: 311225

KRISPI OIL (TURKEY) LTD STI (1)
Atakoy 5 Kisim A-9 Blok Daire 3, Bakirkoy, 34158, Istanbul, Turkiye
Tel.: (90) 212 560 75 45
Edible Oil Mfr
N.A.I.C.S.: 311225

Krispi Oil Russia LLC (1)
Office 215 Vyborgskaya Naberezhnaya 61 Business Centre Aquatoria, Saint Petersburg, 197342, Russia
Tel.: (7) 812 448 5721
Sales Range: $25-49.9 Million
Emp.: 6
Edible Oil Mfr
N.A.I.C.S.: 311225
Tarun Saxena *(Gen Mgr)*

MOI International (Australia) Pty Ltd (1)
PO Box 483, Browns Plains, Logan, 4118, QLD, Australia (86%)

INTERNATIONAL PUBLIC

Tel.: (61) 7 3375 7012
Web Site: http://www.moiaust.com
Food Products Distr
N.A.I.C.S.: 424420
David Oldham *(Mgr-Sls-Northern Reg)*

MOI International (Singapore) Pte. Ltd. (1)
5 International Business Park Rd, Singapore, 609914, Singapore
Tel.: (65) 6 829 5296
Web Site: https://moigroup.com
Palm Oil Refining Product Mfr
N.A.I.C.S.: 311225
Subrajit Mahakul *(Mgr-Bus)*

Mewah Commodities Pte Ltd (1)
5 International Business Park 05-00 Informatics Building Jurong East, Singapore, 609914, Singapore
Tel.: (65) 68295291
Web Site: http://www.mewahgroup.com
Edible Oil Mfr
N.A.I.C.S.: 311225

Subsidiary (Non-US):

Krispi Oils Poland Sp. z.o.o. (2)
Al Jerozolimskie 44 lok 221, 00-024, Warsaw, Poland
Tel.: (48) 22 333 7331
Web Site: http://www.moigroup.com
Edible Oil Mfr
N.A.I.C.S.: 311225

Mewah Dairies Sdn Bhd (1)
Lot 86-95 Jalan Sungai Pinang 4/21 Section 4 Phase 2C, Pulau Indah Industrial Park, 42920, Pulau Indah, Selangor, Malaysia
Tel.: (60) 333222200
Palm Oil Refining Product Mfr
N.A.I.C.S.: 311225

Mewah Datu Sdn. Bhd. (1)
POIC Lahad Datu Phase 1 Lot 3A Miles 3 1/2 Jalan Kastam Baru Off, Jalan Minyak, 91110, Lahad Datu, Sabah, Malaysia
Tel.: (60) 89863521
Palm Oil Refining Product Mfr
N.A.I.C.S.: 311225

Mewah Marketing Pte Ltd. (1)
5 International Business Park, Singapore, 609914, Singapore
Tel.: (65) 68295200
Web Site: https://mewahgroup.com
Grocery Products Retailer
N.A.I.C.S.: 445110

Mewah Oils & Fats Pte Ltd (1)
5 International Business Park, Singapore, 609914, Singapore
Tel.: (65) 68295200
Emp.: 200
Palm Oil Mfr
N.A.I.C.S.: 311225
Cheo Tong Choon *(Chm)*

Mewah-Oils Sdn Bhd (1)
Lot 40 Jalan Sungai Pinang 5/1, Section 4 Phase 2A, Jalan Sungai Pinang 5/1, 42920, Pulau Indah, Selangor, Malaysia
Tel.: (60) 33 101 1133
Web Site: http://www.mewahgroup.com
Palm Oil Products Mfr & Distr
N.A.I.C.S.: 311225

Mewaholeo Industries Sdn Bhd (1)
PLO 283 Jalan Besi Satu Pasir Gudang Industrial Estate, 81700, Pasir Gudang, Johor, Malaysia
Tel.: (60) 72677111
Sales Range: $150-199.9 Million
Emp.: 400
Palm Oil Products Distr
N.A.I.C.S.: 424490
Cheo Tong Choon *(Chm)*

Mewaholeo Marketing Sdn Bhd (1)
Plo 283 Jalan Besi Satu Pasir Gudang Industrial Estate, Pasir Gudang, Pasir Gudang, 81700, Johor, Malaysia
Tel.: (60) 72677080
Web Site: http://www.mewahgroup.com
Sales Range: $150-199.9 Million
Emp.: 400
Palm Oil Products Distr
N.A.I.C.S.: 424490

Moi Foods Malaysia Sdn Bhd (1)

Tel.: (60) 331011133
Emp.: 800
Palm Oil Mfr
N.A.I.C.S.: 311225
Agnes Lim (Gen Mgr)

Ngo Chew Hong Edible Oil Pte Ltd (1)
231 Pandan Loop, Singapore, 128418, Singapore
Tel.: (65) 6 779 6800
Web Site: https://www.ngochewhong.com
Edible Oil Mfr & Distr
N.A.I.C.S.: 311225

Ngo Chew Hong Industries Pte Ltd (1)
231 Pandan Loop, Singapore, 128418, Singapore
Tel.: (65) 67783322
Web Site: http://www.ngochewhong.com
Edible Oil Mfr
N.A.I.C.S.: 311225

Ngo Chew Hong Oils & Fats (M) Sdn Bhd
23rd Mile Seremban Road Jalan Rinching Hulu, 43500, Semenyih, Selangor Darul Ehsan, Malaysia
Tel.: (60) 87237772
Sales Range: $75-99.9 Million
Emp.: 15
Palm Oil Distr
N.A.I.C.S.: 424490

MEWAR HI-TECH ENGINEERING LIMITED
1 Hawa Magri Industrial Area Sukher, Udaipur, 313 001, Rajasthan, India
Tel.: (91) 2942440234
Web Site: https://www.mewarhitech.com
Year Founded: 2006
540150—(BOM)
Rev.: $6,407,851
Assets: $7,461,696
Liabilities: $5,874,182
Net Worth: $1,587,513
Earnings: $46,278
Fiscal Year-end: 03/31/21
Construction Equipment Mfr & Distr
N.A.I.C.S.: 333131
Chatrsingh Harisingh Rathore (Chm & Mng Dir)

MEWAR POLYTEX LIMITED
207 A Mewar Industrial Area Road No 11, Madri, Udaipur, 313 003, Raj, India
Tel.: (91) 02942491036   In
Web Site: http://www.mewarpolytex.com
Year Founded: 1979
Fabric & Sack Mfr
N.A.I.C.S.: 314999
Sandeep Bapna (Mng Dir)

MEX HOLDINGS CO. LTD.
49 Mokotowska St, Warsaw, 00950, Poland
Tel.: (48) 226600222
Web Site: http://www.metalexport.pl
Sales Range: $75-99.9 Million
Emp.: 50
Investors & Manufacturers of Machine Tools & Tooling Accessories
N.A.I.C.S.: 333515
Piotr J. Buchner (Pres & Dir Gen)

Subsidiaries:

Italmex S.p.A. (1)
Via C Porta 9-10, Gorgonzola, Italy
Tel.: (39) 0295109154
Web Site: http://www.italmex.it
Metal Cutting Machine Tool Mfr
N.A.I.C.S.: 333517

Toolmex Corporation (1)
1075 Worcester Rd, Natick, MA 01760
Tel.: (508) 653-8897
Rev.: $31,447,362
Emp.: 28
Industrial Machinery & Equipment
N.A.I.C.S.: 423830

MEX POLSKA S.A.
ul POW 25, 90-248, Lodz, Poland
Tel.: (48) 426346730
Web Site: https://www.mexpolska.pl
Year Founded: 2007
MEX—(WAR)
Rev.: $24,244,156
Assets: $16,655,488
Liabilities: $12,427,083
Net Worth: $4,228,404
Earnings: $1,113,567
Emp.: 130
Fiscal Year-end: 12/31/23
Mexican Restaurant Operator
N.A.I.C.S.: 722511
Pawel Kowalewski (Pres)

MEXAN LIMITED
7th Floor Winland 800 Hotel Hotel 2 Rambler Crest No 1 Tsing Yi Road, Tsing Yi, New Territories, China (Hong Kong)
Tel.: (852) 2 129 7882   BM
Web Site: http://www.mexanhk.com
0022—(HKG)
Rev.: $3,548,885
Assets: $69,160,237
Liabilities: $14,583,640
Net Worth: $54,576,597
Earnings: ($5,752,895)
Emp.: 105
Fiscal Year-end: 03/31/22
Investment Management Service
N.A.I.C.S.: 523940
Edwin Yiu Kay Lun (Chm)

MEXCOMM SDN. BHD.
Suite 20 04 - 20 05 20th Floor Wisma Mca 163 Jalan Ampang, 50450, Kuala Lumpur, Malaysia
Tel.: (60) 321633228   MY
Web Site: http://www.mexcomm.net
Year Founded: 2007
Wireless Telecommunication Services
N.A.I.C.S.: 517112
Agnest Chan Wai Fong (Exec Dir)

MEXEDIA S.P.A.
Via di Affogalasino 105, 00148, Rome, Italy
Tel.: (39) 0694502581   IT
Web Site: https://www.mexedia.com
Year Founded: 2017
ALMEX—(EUR)
Software Development Services
N.A.I.C.S.: 541511
Elio Cosimo Catania (Chm)

Subsidiaries:

Matchcom Telecommunications Inc. (1)
1680 Michigan Ave Ste 700, Miami Beach, FL 33139
Tel.: (954) 456-3191
Web Site: https://matchcoms.com
Information Technology Services
N.A.I.C.S.: 541511

Phonetime Inc. (1)
1680 Michigan Ave Ste 700, Miami Beach, FL 33139
Tel.: (954) 456-3191
Web Site: https://www.phonetime.com
Telecommunication Servicesb
N.A.I.C.S.: 532490

MEXICAN GOLD MINING CORP.
1600 - 595 Burrard Street, Vancouver, V7X 1L4, BC, Canada
Tel.: (604) 558-6300   ON
Web Site: https://www.mexicangold.ca
Year Founded: 2006
MEX—(TSXV)
Rev.: $6,134
Assets: $169,570
Liabilities: $14,189
Net Worth: $155,381
Earnings: ($280,330)
Fiscal Year-end: 06/30/24
Mineral Exploration Services
N.A.I.C.S.: 213114
Shaun Drake (Sec)

MEYER APPAREL LTD
No 3&4 Mustil No 19 Killa No 5 Opposite Tata Consultancy, N H-8 Village Narsinph Pur, Gurgaon, 122 004, Haryana, India
Tel.: (91) 1242371812
Web Site: https://www.meyerapparel.com
Year Founded: 1993
531613—(BOM)
Rev.: $476,811
Assets: $1,049,509
Liabilities: $4,753,337
Net Worth: ($3,703,828)
Earnings: ($197,423)
Emp.: 23
Fiscal Year-end: 03/31/21
Men Wear Clothing Mfr
N.A.I.C.S.: 315250
R. K. Sharma (CFO & Sec)

MEYER BURGER TECHNOLOGY AG
Schorenstrasse 39, CH 3645, Thun, Switzerland
Tel.: (41) 41332212800
Web Site: https://www.meyerburger.com
Year Founded: 1953
MBTN—(SWX)
Rev.: $172,060,976
Assets: $798,716,186
Liabilities: $323,238,359
Net Worth: $475,477,827
Earnings: ($77,439,024)
Emp.: 521
Fiscal Year-end: 12/31/22
Industrial Machinery Mfr
N.A.I.C.S.: 333248
Franz Richter (Chm)

Subsidiaries:

AMB Apparate + Maschinenbau GmbH (1)
Gottlieb Daimler Str 4, D 86462, Langweid, Germany   (100%)
Tel.: (49) 8230 700 99 0
Web Site: http://www.amb-brain.de
Sales Range: $25-49.9 Million
Emp.: 50
Wafer Handling & Automation Technology Services
N.A.I.C.S.: 541330

Hennecke Systems GmbH (1)
Aachener Str 100, 53909, Zulpich, Germany   (100%)
Tel.: (49) 2252940801
Web Site: http://www.meyerburger.com
Sales Range: $25-49.9 Million
Wafer Measuring System Mfr
N.A.I.C.S.: 333242

MB Services Pte. Ltd (1)
20 Tuas South Avenue 14, 637312, Singapore, Singapore
Tel.: (65) 6686 2170
Electronic Components Distr
N.A.I.C.S.: 423690

MB Systems Co. Ltd (1)
10FL WooDuck B/D 330 Gangnam-daero, Seoul, 135-090, Gangnam-gu, Korea (South)
Tel.: (82) 2 3454 0701
Electronic Components Distr
N.A.I.C.S.: 423690

MBT Systems Ltd (1)
309 Route 94, Columbia, NJ 07832
Tel.: (908) 496-8999
Electronic Components Distr
N.A.I.C.S.: 423690

Meyer Burger AG (1)
Schorenstrasse 39, Gwatt, 3645, Thun, Switzerland
Tel.: (41) 334390505
Web Site: http://www.meyerburger.com
Emp.: 500
Solar, Semiconductor & Optical Technology Mfr
N.A.I.C.S.: 333242

Meyer Burger Automation GmbH (1)
Elisabeth Selbert Strasse 19, 40764, Langenfeld, Germany
Tel.: (49) 2173394550
Web Site: http://www.meyerburger.ch
Sales Range: $25-49.9 Million
Emp.: 8
Automation & Robotics Systems Mfr
N.A.I.C.S.: 334511

Meyer Burger Co. Ltd (1)
13F-1 No Zingiang Road, Jhubei, Hsin Chi, Taiwan
Tel.: (886) 3 6578612
Electronic Components Distr
N.A.I.C.S.: 423690
Daniel Buchmann (Gen Mgr)

Meyer Burger Global Ltd (1)
Schorenstrasse 39, 3645, Thun, Switzerland
Tel.: (41) 33 221 28 00
Industrial Machinery Mfr
N.A.I.C.S.: 333248

Meyer Burger India Private Ltd (1)
19B Commerce Avenue Mahaganesh Colony Paud Road, Pune, 411 038, India
Tel.: (91) 2069000208
Electronic Components Distr
N.A.I.C.S.: 423690

Meyer Burger KK (1)
Ishikawa Building 4F 2-5-5 Kudan Minami, Chiyoda-ku, Tokyo, 102-0074, Japan
Tel.: (81) 3 5211 2123
Industrial Machinery Maintenance Services
N.A.I.C.S.: 811310

Meyer Burger Trading (Shanghai) Co. Ltd. (1)
Room 2306 No 6088 Humin Road, Minhang District, Shanghai, 201100, China
Tel.: (86) 2122217225
Electronic Components Distr
N.A.I.C.S.: 423690
Heiko Schultz (Product Mgr)

Meyer Burger Trading Shanghai Co. Ltd. (1)
17F Building 1 Guoson Centre No5 Lane 388 Daduhe Road, Shanghai, 200 062, China
Tel.: (86) 21 2221 7333
Industrial Machinery Mfr
N.A.I.C.S.: 423830
Krain Zhang (Engr-Mechanical)

Pasan SA (1)
Rue Jaquet-Droz 8, 2000, Neuchatel, Switzerland
Tel.: (41) 323911600
Web Site: https://www.pasan.ch
Measurement Equipment Mfr
N.A.I.C.S.: 334515

Roth & Rau AG (1)
An der Baumschule 6-8, 09337, Hohenstein-Ernstthal, Germany   (95.11%)
Tel.: (49) 3723671234
Web Site: http://www.roth-rau.de
Sales Range: $100-124.9 Million
Emp.: 800
Plasma Enhanced Chemical Vapour Deposition Equipment Mfr
N.A.I.C.S.: 333248

Subsidiary (US):

Romaric Automation Design, Inc. (2)
8410 S 700 E Ste 201, Sandy, UT 84070
Tel.: (801) 561-5757
Web Site: http://www.romariccorp.com
Factory Automation Software & Services
N.A.I.C.S.: 513210

Subsidiary (Non-US):

Roth & Rau B.V. (2)

MEYER BURGER TECHNOLOGY AG

Meyer Burger Technology AG—(Continued)
Luchthavenweg 10, Eindhoven, 5657 EB, Netherlands
Tel.: (31) 402581581
Sales Range: $50-74.9 Million
Emp.: 150
Solar Machinery & Equipment Whslr
N.A.I.C.S.: 423830
Claus Lichtenberg *(Mng Dir)*

Somont GmbH (1)
Im Brunnenfeld 8, 79224, Umkirch, Germany
Tel.: (49) 7665 9809 7000
Web Site: http://www.somont.com
Soldering Systems Mfr
N.A.I.C.S.: 333992

MEYER PLC
No 32 Billings Way Oregun, PMB 21002, Ikeja, Lagos, Nigeria
Tel.: (234) 8020672366
Web Site: https://www.meyerpaints.com
Year Founded: 1960
MEYER—(NIGE)
Rev.: $1,062,208
Assets: $1,434,937
Liabilities: $362,805
Net Worth: $1,072,132
Earnings: $291,352
Emp.: 109
Fiscal Year-end: 12/31/22
Paint Mfr & Marketer
N.A.I.C.S.: 325510
Kayode Falowo *(Chm)*

MEYER WERFT GMBH
Industriegebiet Sud, 26871, Papenburg, Germany
Tel.: (49) 61 81 0
Web Site: http://www.meyerwerft.de
Year Founded: 1795
Emp.: 3,100
Shipbuilding
N.A.I.C.S.: 336611
Bernard Meyer *(Owner & Mng Dir)*

Subsidiaries:

AIP Innenprojekt GmbH (1)
Waldenburger Str 121, 09212, Limbach-Oberfrohna, Germany
Tel.: (49) 372240210
Web Site: http://www.aurich-aip.de
Interior Finishing & Design Services
N.A.I.C.S.: 541410
Peter Tesche *(Exec Dir)*

Engineering ENGnD Oy (1)
Tikkalantie 1, 26100, Rauma, Finland
Tel.: (358) 106708000
Web Site: http://www.engnd.com
Emp.: 200
Ship Building Mfr
N.A.I.C.S.: 336611
Heikki Malmi *(Mng Dir)*

Meyer Turku Oy (1)
Telakkakatu 1, 20101, Turku, Finland (70%)
Tel.: (358) 106700
Web Site: http://www.meyerturku.com
Sales Range: $700-749.9 Million
Shipbuilding
N.A.I.C.S.: 336611

Subsidiary (Domestic):

Piikkio Works Oy (2)
Kolamaenti 2, PO Box 65, 21500, Piikkio, Finland
Tel.: (358) 1067010
Web Site: http://www.meyerturku.com
Prefabricated Ship Cabin Mfr
N.A.I.C.S.: 336611
Ari Kumpulainen *(CEO & Mng Dir)*

NEPTUN WERFT GmbH & Co. KG (1)
Werftallee 13, 18119, Rostock, Germany
Tel.: (49) 3813841010
Web Site: http://www.neptunwerft.de
Emp.: 700
Ship Building Mfr

N.A.I.C.S.: 336611
Robert Laade *(Head-Project Mgmt Dept)*

MEYERS COLOUR COMPOUNDS LIMITED
900 Harrington Court, Burlington, L7N 3N4, ON, Canada
Tel.: (905) 633-9768
Web Site: https://www.meyerscolour.com
Year Founded: 1971
Rev.: $11,842,280
Emp.: 18
Plastics Product Mfr
N.A.I.C.S.: 326199
Tim Meyers *(Dir-Sls)*

MEYERS NORRIS PENNY LLP
Suite 2000 330 5th Avenue SW, Calgary, T2P 0L4, AB, Canada
Tel.: (403) 444-0150
Web Site: http://www.mnp.ca
Year Founded: 1958
Tax, Accounting & Business Services
N.A.I.C.S.: 541219
Trent Bester *(Sr VP-Consulting-Public Sector)*

Subsidiaries:

Next Digital, Inc. (1)
114 Avenue NW Suite 14505, Edmonton, T5M 2Y8, AB, Canada
Tel.: (780) 424-6398
Information Technology Services
N.A.I.C.S.: 519290

MEYERS TRANSPORT INC.
53 Grills Road, Belleville, K8N 4Z5, ON, Canada
Tel.: (613) 967-8440
Web Site: http://www.shipmts.com
Year Founded: 1927
Rev.: $33,432,722
Emp.: 475
Truckload & Logistics Services
N.A.I.C.S.: 484121
David Joyce *(VP-Admin, Fin & HR)*

Subsidiaries:

Mortrans, Inc. (1)
52 Grills Road, Belleville, K8N 5B6, ON, Canada
Tel.: (800) 267-2867
Freight Forwarding Services
N.A.I.C.S.: 484230
Paul-Erik Hansen *(Mgr-Ops)*

MEZZAN HOLDING CO KSC
3 Block A Street 176 173, PO Box 124, Shuwaikh Industrial Area 3, Kuwait, 13002, Kuwait
Tel.: (965) 22286444
Web Site: https://www.mezzan.com
MEZZAN—(KUW)
Rev.: $829,315,512
Assets: $884,321,275
Liabilities: $522,416,751
Net Worth: $361,904,524
Earnings: ($5,500,026)
Emp.: 8,800
Fiscal Year-end: 12/31/22
Food & Beverage Product Mfr
N.A.I.C.S.: 311999
Abdel Rahman Jassim Mohammad Al Wazzan *(Chm)*

Subsidiaries:

Conserved Foodstuffs Distributing Company W.L.L. (1)
Street No 2 Gate 94 Old Industrial Area, PO Box 5613, Doha, Qatar
Tel.: (974) 44524100
Web Site: https://www.khazanqatar.com
Mineral Water Mfr
N.A.I.C.S.: 312112

Emirates Star Services LLC (1)
11th Floor MQ Building 543 Sultan Bin Zayed The First St, Al Danah-Zone 1, Abu

Dhabi, United Arab Emirates
Tel.: (971) 26424888
Web Site: https://www.starservicesuae.com
Recruitment Consulting Services
N.A.I.C.S.: 561311

Jassim Al Wazzan Sons General Trading Company W.L.L. (1)
Building No 7 to 11 Block -1 Shuwaikh Industrial Area - 2, Near KGL or Behind Gulf Mart Shuwaikh, Kuwait, Kuwait
Tel.: (965) 24917504
Web Site: https://www.wazzan.com
Food Products Distr
N.A.I.C.S.: 424490

Kuwait Indo Trading Company W.L.L. (1)
First Floor Office No 1 Block No 11 Street 58 Ghadeer Commercial Bldg, Salman Dabbous Bldg Opp Ajial Mall, Fahaheel, 63011, Kuwait
Tel.: (965) 23925736
Web Site: https://kuwaitindo.com
Engineeering Services
N.A.I.C.S.: 541330

Mezzan Security W.L.L. (1)
Almana Petrol Station Near Midmac Round About Salwa Road, Doha, Qatar
Tel.: (974) 40354222
Web Site: https://www.mezzansecurityservices.com
Security System Services
N.A.I.C.S.: 561612

UNITRA International LLC (1)
Umm Ramool 28th B Street 12, PO Box 97108, Dubai, United Arab Emirates
Tel.: (971) 47024700
Web Site: https://www.mezzanuae.com
Food Products Distr
N.A.I.C.S.: 424490

MEZZION PHARMA CO., LTD.
7th floor Seokcheon Building 570 Samseong-ro, Gangnam-gu, Seoul, 6163, Korea (South)
Tel.: (82) 25608000
Web Site: https://www.mezzion.co.kr
140410—(KRS)
Rev.: $23,566,977
Assets: $41,434,752
Liabilities: $21,308,632
Net Worth: $20,126,121
Earnings: ($27,840,436)
Emp.: 47
Fiscal Year-end: 12/31/22
Pharmaceuticals Mfr
N.A.I.C.S.: 325412
Dean Park *(Founder & CEO)*

MF BANKA A.D.
Aleja Svetog Save 61, Banja Luka, Bosnia & Herzegovina
Tel.: (387) 51240300
Web Site: https://www.mfbanka.com
IEFB.R.A—(BANJ)
Rev.: $28,120,953
Assets: $430,919,218
Liabilities: $376,677,093
Net Worth: $54,242,125
Earnings: $5,042,805
Emp.: 334
Fiscal Year-end: 12/31/23
Banking Services
N.A.I.C.S.: 522110

MF INTERNATIONAL LIMITED
Unit 1801 Fortis Tower 77-79 Gloucester Road, Wanchai, China (Hong Kong)
Tel.: (852) 34266200
Year Founded: 2022
MFI—(NASDAQ)
Rev.: $4,091,554
Assets: $4,333,588
Liabilities: $2,830,236
Net Worth: $1,503,352
Earnings: $848,605
Emp.: 33
Fiscal Year-end: 12/31/23

INTERNATIONAL PUBLIC

Investment Management Service
N.A.I.C.S.: 523999

MF.1 ADVERTISING BRANDING STRATEGY
20 St Mary's Rd, Winnipeg, R2H 1H1, MB, Canada
Tel.: (204) 237-8514
Web Site: http://www.mf1.ca
Year Founded: 1989
Sales Range: $10-24.9 Million
Emp.: 20
N.A.I.C.S.: 541810
Ryan Hart *(Pres & Partner)*

MFC ASSET MANAGEMENT PUBLIC COMPANY LTD.
199 Coulumn Tower Ground Fl 21 & 23 Fl, Ratchadaphisek Road, Bangkok, 10110, Klongtoey, Thailand
Tel.: (66) 26492000
Web Site: http://www.mfcfund.net
Year Founded: 1975
Sales Range: $50-74.9 Million
Emp.: 150
Securities & Mutual Funds Management Services
N.A.I.C.S.: 523940
Narongchai Akrasanee *(Chm)*

MFC PATONG HERITAGE PROPERTY FUND
No 199 Column Tower building G/21-23 floor Ratchada Phisea Khlongtoei, Bangkok, Thailand
Tel.: (66) 26492000
M.PAT—(THA)
Rev.: $127,861
Assets: $18,409,040
Liabilities: $14,888
Net Worth: $18,394,152
Earnings: $62,179
Fiscal Year-end: 12/31/23
Investment Management Service
N.A.I.C.S.: 525990
Chokchai Aksaranan *(Vice Chm)*

MFEC PUBLIC COMPANY LIMITED
349 SJ Infinite One Business Complex VibhavadiRangsit Rd, Suanluang, Bangkok, 10250, Thailand
Tel.: (66) 28217999
Web Site: https://www.mfec.co.th
Year Founded: 1997
MFEC—(THA)
Rev.: $216,785,181
Assets: $215,497,295
Liabilities: $140,843,802
Net Worth: $74,653,494
Earnings: $21,232,552
Emp.: 1,370
Fiscal Year-end: 12/31/23
Network Computing & E-Business Solutions
N.A.I.C.S.: 541519
Siriwat Vongjarukorn *(Pres & CEO)*

Subsidiaries:

Advance Intelligence Modernity Company Limited (1)
333 Lao Peng Nguan Tower 21st Floor Soi Choeipuang, Vibhavadi Rangsit Road Chompol, Bangkok, 10900, Thailand
Tel.: (66) 2 618 8140
Web Site: http://www.aimadvance.com
Mobile Operating Services
N.A.I.C.S.: 517112

Modernform Integration Services Company Limited (1)
699 Modernform Tower 17th Floor Srinakarin Road, Suanluang, Bangkok, 10250, Thailand
Tel.: (66) 27228333
Web Site: http://www.misco.co.th
Information Technology Consulting Services
N.A.I.C.S.: 541512

AND PRIVATE COMPANIES

Subsidiary (Domestic):

M.I.S. Outsourcing Company Limited (2)
699 Modernform Tower 17th Floor Srinakarin Road, Suanluang, Bangkok, 10250, Thailand
Tel.: (66) 2 722 8333
Web Site: http://www.miso.co.th
Emp.: 30
Information Technology Consulting Services
N.A.I.C.S.: 541512

MFF CAPITAL INVESTMENTS LIMITED
Level 36 25 Martin Place, Sydney, 2000, NSW, Australia
Tel.: (61) 292354887 AU
Web Site:
https://www.mffcapital.com.au
MFF—(ASX)
Rev.: $445,108,171
Assets: $1,767,128,064
Liabilities: $384,222,087
Net Worth: $1,382,905,977
Earnings: $298,715,277
Fiscal Year-end: 06/30/24
Investment Management Service
N.A.I.C.S.: 523940
Chris Mackay *(Mng Dir & Portfolio Mgr)*

MFL INDIA LIMITED
UG 9 Well King Towers 94 4 Main Market Patparganj Mayur ViharPhase 1, Delhi, 110091, India
Tel.: (91) 1141425137
Web Site: https://mflindia.co.in
Year Founded: 1981
526622—(BOM)
Rev.: $1,252,423
Assets: $1,059,175
Liabilities: $1,234,132
Net Worth: ($174,956)
Earnings: $411,119
Fiscal Year-end: 03/31/21
Logistic Services
N.A.I.C.S.: 541614
Anil Thukral *(Mng Dir)*

MFM KOREA CO., LTD.
ADDRESS4F 5F Dong-sin Bldg 204 Dogok-ro, Gangnam-gu, Seoul, 06272, Korea (South)
Tel.: (82) 25587828
Web Site: https://mfmkorea.com
Year Founded: 2019
323230—(KRS)
Rev.: $115,096,169
Assets: $105,029,267
Liabilities: $80,619,701
Net Worth: $24,409,567
Earnings: ($440,414)
Emp.: 34
Fiscal Year-end: 12/31/22
Investment Services
N.A.I.C.S.: 523999
Hyunwook Kim *(CEO)*

MFO S.A.
Kozuszki Parcel 70 A, 96-500, Sochaczew, Poland
Tel.: (48) 607088825
Web Site: https://www.mfo.pl
Year Founded: 2000
Steel Products Mfr
N.A.I.C.S.: 331513
Marek Mirski *(Chm-Supervisory Bd)*

MFS INTERCORP LIMITED
Office No 5 1st Floor BLK B PKT 3 Se 34 Rohini Landmark NA, New Delhi, Delhi, 110042, India
Tel.: (91) 1121664020
513721—(BOM)
Rev.: $266,363
Assets: $671,351
Liabilities: $531,647
Net Worth: $139,704
Earnings: $40,405
Fiscal Year-end: 03/31/23
Mineral Mining Services
N.A.I.C.S.: 212210
Vishwakarma Kiran Bharatsingh *(Exec Dir)*

MFS TECHNOLOGY (S) PTE LTD
801 Toa Payoh Lorong 7 #02-01, Wearnes Building, Singapore, 319319, Singapore
Tel.: (65) 68613168 SG
Web Site: http://www.mfstech.com.sg
Year Founded: 1988
Flexible Circuits Designer, Mfr & Distr
N.A.I.C.S.: 334412
Geck Liang Cheng *(Chief Innovation Officer)*

Subsidiaries:

MFS Technology (Hunan) Co., Ltd. (1)
10 Dong Er Road, Xingsha, Changsha, 410100, Hunan, China
Tel.: (86) 73182870888
Electronic Chip Mfr
N.A.I.C.S.: 334413
Cheng Xing *(Product Mgr)*

MFS Technology (M) Sdn Bhd (1)
Lot 5 Batu Berendam Free Trade Zone Phase III, Batu Berendam, 75350, Melaka, Malaysia
Tel.: (60) 62810058
Electronic Chip Mfr
N.A.I.C.S.: 334413
Florence Lim *(Fin Mgr)*

MFS Technology (PCB) Co., Ltd. (1)
10 Dong Er Road Xingsha, Changsha, 410100, Hunan, China
Tel.: (86) 73182879960
Web Site: http://www.mfstech.com.sg
Printed Circuit Boards Mfr & Distr
N.A.I.C.S.: 334412

MFS Technology (Yiyang) Co., Ltd. (1)
33 Jin Gang Road Changchun Economic Development Zone, Ziyang, Yiyang, 430902, Hunan, China
Tel.: (86) 7372216666
Electronic Chip Mfr
N.A.I.C.S.: 334413

MFS Technology Europe UG (1)
Hasenbergsteige 14, 70178, Stuttgart, Germany
Tel.: (49) 1733647144
Electronic Chip Mfr
N.A.I.C.S.: 334413

MG BALTIC UAB
J Jasinskio g 16B, 03163, Vilnius, Lithuania
Tel.: (370) 52786219 LT
Web Site: http://www.mgbaltic.lt
Year Founded: 1992
Sales Range: $600-649.9 Million
Emp.: 3,716
Investment Services
N.A.I.C.S.: 523999
Darius Mockus *(Pres)*

Subsidiaries:

Apranga UAB (1)
Ukmerges g 362, Vilnius, Lithuania
Tel.: (370) 52390808
Web Site: https://aprangagroup.lt
Cloth Retailer
N.A.I.C.S.: 458110

Darnu Group UAB (1)
Aukstaiciu St 7, 11341, Vilnius, Lithuania
Tel.: (370) 52786170
Web Site: https://darnugroup.lt
Real Estate Services
N.A.I.C.S.: 531390
Sigita Survilaite-Mekioniene *(CEO)*

LNK Group (1)
7 Sporta Street, Riga, 1013, Latvia
Tel.: (371) 6733 4012
Web Site: http://www.lnk.lv
Holding Company
N.A.I.C.S.: 551112
Maksim Krivunec *(Mgr-Dev Dept)*

MG Baltic Investment (1)
Victoria Building J Jasinskio st 16B, 03163, Vilnius, Lithuania **(100%)**
Tel.: (370) 52786219
Web Site: http://www.mgbaltic.lt
Investment Services
N.A.I.C.S.: 523999

Subsidiary (Domestic):

APB Apranga (2)
Kirtimu str 51, 02244, Vilnius, Lithuania
Tel.: (370) 52390808
Web Site: http://www.apranga.lt
Sales Range: $50-74.9 Million
Emp.: 900
Clothing Retailer
N.A.I.C.S.: 458110
Rimantas Perveneckas *(Mng Dir)*

UAB Laisvas ir nepriklausomas kanalas (2)
Seskines Str 20, LT-07156, Vilnius, Lithuania
Tel.: (370) 52431058
Web Site: http://www.lnk.lt
Sales Range: $100-124.9 Million
Emp.: 280
Television Station
N.A.I.C.S.: 516120
Zita Sarakiene *(Mng Dir)*

UAB Mitnija (2)
Palemono Str 3, 52159, Kaunas, Lithuania
Tel.: (370) 37473291
Web Site: http://www.mitnija.lt
Sales Range: $25-49.9 Million
Emp.: 500
Construction Services
N.A.I.C.S.: 236210
Eulus Gemevlis *(Gen Mgr)*

UPG Baltic UAB (2)
Jonavos g 254a, LT 44132, Kaunas, Lithuania
Tel.: (370) 37763203
Web Site: http://www.upg.lt
Sales Range: $25-49.9 Million
Emp.: 19
Magazine Publisher
N.A.I.C.S.: 513120
Linas Krapavickas *(Gen Mgr)*

MV Group UAB (1)
Aukstaiciu St 7, 11341, Vilnius, Lithuania
Tel.: (370) 52786069
Web Site: https://mvgroup.eu
Alcoholic Beverage Mfr & Distr
N.A.I.C.S.: 312111

Mediafon, UAB (1)
Olimpieciu g 1-31, 09235, Vilnius, Lithuania
Tel.: (370) 52390901
Web Site: https://www.mediafon.com
Telecommunication Servicesb
N.A.I.C.S.: 513199

UAB MG Baltic Trade (1)
J Jasinskio g 16 B, 01112, Vilnius, Lithuania
Tel.: (370) 52786219
Web Site: http://www.mgbaltic.lt
Sales Range: $150-199.9 Million
Emp.: 1,500
Wholesale Trading Services
N.A.I.C.S.: 425120
Darius Mockus *(Pres)*

Subsidiary (Domestic):

AB Biofuture (2)
Silo 4, Silute, 99149, Lithuania
Tel.: (370) 44161121
Web Site: http://www.biofuture.lt
Sales Range: $25-49.9 Million
Emp.: 80
Bioethanol Producer
N.A.I.C.S.: 325998
Andrius Petruskevicius *(Mng Dir)*

UAB Mineraliniai vandenys (2)
J Jasinskio g 16 F, 03163, Vilnius, Lithuania
Tel.: (370) 852786069
Web Site: http://www.mv.lt
Sales Range: $125-149.9 Million
Emp.: 227

Consumer Goods Importer Producer Marketer & Distr
N.A.I.C.S.: 425120

Subsidiary (Non-US):

MV Eesti OU (3)
Kalmari 10, Lagedi Rae vald, 75327, Harjumaa, Estonia
Tel.: (372) 6 410 073
Alcoholic Beverages Whslr
N.A.I.C.S.: 424820
Peeter Peetsalu *(Key Acct Mgr)*

MV Latvia SIA (3)
Medus iela 7, Riga, 1048, Latvia
Tel.: (371) 679 30 211
Alcoholic Beverages Whslr
N.A.I.C.S.: 424820

MV Poland S.P.z.o.o. (3)
ul Belgijska 11, 02-511, Warsaw, Poland
Tel.: (48) 22 888 14 25
Alcoholic Beverages Whslr
N.A.I.C.S.: 424820

Subsidiary (Domestic):

UAB Stumbras (2)
K Bugos g 7, LT-44328, Kaunas, Lithuania
Tel.: (370) 37308800
Web Site: http://www.stumbras.lt
Emp.: 300
Alcohol Producer
N.A.I.C.S.: 312140

UAB Tromina (2)
VA Graiciuno Str 38, Vilnius, 02244, Lithuania
Tel.: (370) 52601929
Web Site: http://www.tromina.lt
Sales Range: $75-99.9 Million
Emp.: 385
Logistic Services
N.A.I.C.S.: 541614
Dainius Buknys *(Gen Mgr)*

UAB MG Valda (1)
J Jasinskio Str 16, 01112, Vilnius, Lithuania
Tel.: (370) 52786170
Web Site: http://www.mgvalda.lt
Sales Range: $50-74.9 Million
Emp.: 100
Real Estate Manangement Services
N.A.I.C.S.: 531390
Rolandas Vingilis *(Chm)*

MG INTERNATIONAL SA
ZI Athelia IV 163 Avenue des Tamaris, 13600, La Ciotat, Cedex, France
Tel.: (33) 442981490 FR
Web Site:
https://www.maytronics.com
Year Founded: 2002
ALMGI—(EUR)
Sales Range: $50-74.9 Million
Emp.: 75
Swimming Pool Maintenance Services
N.A.I.C.S.: 561790
David Alimi *(CEO-Interim)*

MG UNIT TRUST
Freshwater Place Level 15 2 Southbank Boulevard, Southbank, 3006, VIC, Australia
Tel.: (61) 390405840 AU
Web Site: http://www.mgc.com.au
Rev.: $18,204,422
Assets: $54,613,267
Net Worth: $54,613,267
Fiscal Year-end: 06/30/19
Investment Management Service
N.A.I.C.S.: 523940
John Spark *(Chm)*

MGAME CORP.
7th floor 3rd building Ace High-end Tower 145 Gasan Digital 1-ro, Geumcheon-gu, Seoul, 153-803, Korea (South)
Tel.: (82) 216440900
Web Site:
https://www.mgamecorp.com
Year Founded: 1997

Mgame Corp.—(Continued)
058630—(KRS)
Rev.: $56,492,810
Assets: $89,300,360
Liabilities: $17,873,662
Net Worth: $71,426,698
Earnings: $17,316,071
Emp.: 185
Fiscal Year-end: 12/31/22
Game Software Development Services
N.A.I.C.S.: 513210

MGC DERMA D.O.O
Emonska Cesta 8, Ljubljana, 1000, Slovenia
Tel.: (386) 17776565
Web Site: http://mgcderma.com
Cosmetic Product Mfr & Distr
N.A.I.C.S.: 325620

MGC PHARMACEUTICALS LTD.
1202 Hay Street, West Perth, 6005, WA, Australia
Tel.: (61) 863823390 AU
Web Site: http://www.mgcpharma.com.au
RGTLF—(OTCQB)
Rev.: $595,007
Assets: $7,203,112
Liabilities: $11,092,548
Net Worth: ($3,889,436)
Earnings: ($11,717,704)
Fiscal Year-end: 06/30/24
Pharmaceutical Product Mfr & Distr
N.A.I.C.S.: 325412
Nativ Segev (Co-Founder)

MGEN SOLUTIONS CO., LTD.
1117 Kolon Science Valley 2nd Complex 55 Digital-ro 34-gil, Guro-gu, Seoul, 06688, Korea (South)
Tel.: (82) 234128777
Web Site: https://www.mgensolutions.kr
Year Founded: 1973
032790—(KRS)
Rev.: $84,209,833
Assets: $58,259,406
Liabilities: $22,605,447
Net Worth: $35,653,959
Earnings: ($333,945)
Emp.: 75
Fiscal Year-end: 12/31/22
Mfr & Construction Services
N.A.I.C.S.: 333998
Sang-Hwan Cho (CEO)

MGF EASYBIKE SAS
49 Rue du Commandant Rollnad, 93350, Le Bourget, France
Tel.: (33) 1 41 69 71 20
Web Site: http://www.easybike.fr
Year Founded: 2004
Electric Bicycle Mfr
N.A.I.C.S.: 336991
Gregory Trebaol (Pres)

Subsidiaries:

Matra Manufacturing & Services SAS (1)
ZI du Parc de l'Espace-Bat H1 49bis rue du Commandant Rolland, 93 350, Le Bourget, France
Tel.: (33) 1 4169 7120
Web Site: http://www.matra
Electric Transport Solutions; Electric Bicycles, Scooters & Quads Mfr
N.A.I.C.S.: 336260

MGI DIGITAL TECHNOLOGY SA
4 Rue de la Meridienne, FR-94260, Fresnes, France
Tel.: (33) 145210660

Web Site: https://www.mgi-fr.com
Year Founded: 1982
ALMDG—(EUR)
Sales Range: $25-49.9 Million
Digital Printers & Related Products Designer, Mfr & Distr
N.A.I.C.S.: 333248

MGI-MINAS GERAIS PARTICIPACOES S.A.
Rodovia Papa Joao Paulo II N 4001/Predio Gerais 4 Andar, Cidade Administrativa Serra Verde, Belo Horizonte, 31630-901, MG, Brazil
Tel.: (55) 3139154878
Web Site: http://www.mgipart.com.br
Emp.: 100
Commercial Property Management Services
N.A.I.C.S.: 531312
Weverton Vilas Boas De Castro (CEO)

MGM FORD LINCOLN SALES LTD.
3010 50th Avenue, Red Deer, T4R 1M5, AB, Canada
Tel.: (403) 346-6621
Web Site: http://www.mgmfordlincoln.com
Year Founded: 1959
Rev.: $30,434,597
Emp.: 100
New & Used Car Dealers
N.A.I.C.S.: 441110
Wendy Price (Controller)

MGX MINERALS INC.
1111 Melville St 11th Floor, Vancouver, V6E 3V6, BC, Canada
Tel.: (604) 305-0078 BC
Web Site: https://www.mgxminerals.com
Year Founded: 2012
MGXMF—(OTCEM)
Rev.: $2,105,534
Assets: $8,917,423
Liabilities: $12,296,916
Net Worth: ($3,379,494)
Earnings: $18,398,513)
Fiscal Year-end: 07/31/20
Gold Mining
N.A.I.C.S.: 212220
Jared Lazerson (Chm)

Subsidiaries:

MGX Renewables Inc. (1)
1 - 8765 Ash Street, Vancouver, V6P 6T3, BC, Canada (60%)
Tel.: (604) 558-1406
Web Site: http://www.mgxrenewables.com
Eletric Power Generation Services
N.A.I.C.S.: 221117
John McLeod (COO)

MH CONNECTORS GROUP LIMITED
12 Fleming Close Park Farm North, Wellingborough, NN8 6UF, United Kingdom
Tel.: (44) 1536200963 UK
Web Site: http://www.mhsweden.se
Sales Range: $150-199.9 Million
Emp.: 527
Data-Communications & Telecommunication Component Supplier
N.A.I.C.S.: 334417
Graham McKee (Mng Dir)

Subsidiaries:

MH Sweden AB (1)
Rorkullsvagen 4, SE-302, Halmstad, Sweden (100%)
Tel.: (46) 35151390
Web Site: http://www.mhsweden.se
Sales Range: Less than $1 Million
Emp.: 25

Data-Communications & Telecommunication Component Supplier
N.A.I.C.S.: 334417
Henrik Olsen (Mng Dir)

MH ETHANOL CO., LTD.
25 Gwangnyeocheonnam-ro Naeseoeup, Masanhoewon-gu, Changwon, 51232, Gyeongsangnam-do, Korea (South)
Tel.: (82) 552310701
Web Site: https://www.mhethanol.com
Year Founded: 1978
023150—(KRS)
Rev.: $84,924,082
Assets: $343,186,790
Liabilities: $270,016,733
Net Worth: $73,170,057
Earnings: $9,131,784
Emp.: 48
Fiscal Year-end: 12/31/22
Alcohol Product Mfr
N.A.I.C.S.: 325193
Lee Bong Ki (Gen Mgr)

MH ROBOT & AUTOMATION CO., LTD.
No 1398 Shuntai Street, Zhucheng, Weifang, 262200, Shandong, China
Tel.: (86) 5366015555
Web Site: https://www.mhauto.cn
Year Founded: 2010
301199—(CHIN)
Rev.: $137,307,380
Assets: $463,241,055
Liabilities: $214,996,929
Net Worth: $248,244,126
Earnings: $3,981,197
Fiscal Year-end: 12/31/23
Software Development Services
N.A.I.C.S.: 541511
Jinping Wang (Chm)

MH-BETEILIGUNGS GMBH
Reichsstrasse 80, 58840, Plettenberg, Markischer Kreis, Germany
Tel.: (49) 23919550
Web Site: http://www.mh-b.eu
Privater Equity Firm
N.A.I.C.S.: 523999
Mattias Herfeld (Mng Dir)

MHC HOLDING, LTD.
Banistmo Tower 11th Floor Avenida Samuel Lewis, Panama, Panama
Tel.: (507) 264 4000
MHCH—(PAN)
Sales Range: Less than $1 Million
Holding Company
N.A.I.C.S.: 551112
Emanuel J. Gonzalez Revilla (Pres)

MHC JOINT STOCK COMPANY
18th Floor No 52 Le Dai Hanh Le Dai Hanh Ward, Hai Ba Trung District, Hanoi, Vietnam
Tel.: (84) 435770810
Web Site: https://www.marinahanoi.com
MHC—(HOSE)
Rev.: $5,420,560
Assets: $29,692,057
Liabilities: $7,346,537
Net Worth: $22,345,520
Earnings: $1,058,140
Emp.: 36
Fiscal Year-end: 12/31/23
Holding Company
N.A.I.C.S.: 551112
Hoang Duy Anh (Exec Dir)

MHC PLANTATIONS BHD
Tel.: (60) 54590001
Web Site: https://www.mhc.com.my
MHC—(KLS)
Rev.: $148,254,576

Assets: $178,515,163
Liabilities: $38,148,361
Net Worth: $140,366,802
Earnings: $19,058,893
Fiscal Year-end: 12/31/21
Palm Oil Cultivation Services
N.A.I.C.S.: 325998
King Seng Mah (Chm)

Subsidiaries:

Anson Oil Industries Berhad (1)
No 8 9 10 Medan Sri Intan Jalan Sekolah Teluk Intan, 36000, Teluk Intan, Perak, Malaysia
Tel.: (60) 56221722
Sales Range: $10-24.9 Million
Emp.: 26
Oil Palm Cultivation Services
N.A.I.C.S.: 115112
Mah King Thian (Mng Dir)

Telok Anson Hotel Sdn Berhad (1)
Jln Sekolah, 36000, Teluk Intan, Perak, Malaysia
Tel.: (60) 56226166
Web Site: http://www.mhc.com.my
Sales Range: $10-24.9 Million
Emp.: 11
Home Management Services
N.A.I.C.S.: 721110

Yew Lee Holdings Sdn Berhad (1)
No 7328 Jln Bidor Kampung Batu 12, 36020, Teluk Intan, Perak, Malaysia
Tel.: (60) 56561077
Sales Range: $25-49.9 Million
Emp.: 25
Oil Palm Cultivation Services
N.A.I.C.S.: 115112
Mah King Thiam (Mng Dir)

MHG GLASS PTY LTD
24 Mackey Street, North Geelong, 3215, VIC, Australia
Tel.: (61) 3 5279 6222
Web Site: http://www.mhgasiapacific.com
Emp.: 280
Motor Vehicle Parts Mfr
N.A.I.C.S.: 423140

Subsidiaries:

Flat Glass Industries Limited (1)
3 Moorebank Avenue, Moorebank, 2170, NSW, Australia
Tel.: (61) 298240999
Web Site: http://www.flatglass.com.au
Emp.: 200
Glass Processing Whslr
N.A.I.C.S.: 444180
Frank D'Urso (Mgr-Natl Procurement)

Subsidiary (Domestic):

Alternative Glass Supplies Pty Limited (2)
1 Hedderwick Rd, Bayswater N, Dandenong, 3174, VIC, Australia
Tel.: (61) 397617977
Web Site: http://www.altglass.com.au
Glass Mfr
N.A.I.C.S.: 327211

DLCO Australia Architectural Glass Fittings Pty. Ltd. (2)
PO Box 656, Moorebank, 2170, NSW, Australia
Tel.: (61) 298240999
Web Site: http://www.dlco.com.au
Sales Range: $25-49.9 Million
Emp.: 60
Frameless Glass Doors Mfr
N.A.I.C.S.: 327215
Nick O Connor (Mng Dir)

MHP SE
158 Ak Zabolotnogo Str, 03143, Kiev, Ukraine
Tel.: (380) 442070000
Web Site: http://www.mhp.com.ua
Agricultural Services
N.A.I.C.S.: 926140
Yuriy Kosyuk (CEO)

AND PRIVATE COMPANIES

Subsidiaries:

Perutnina Ptuj d.d. (1)
Potrceva 10, 2250, Ptuj, Slovenia
Tel.: (386) 27490100
Web Site: http://www.perutnina.eu
Poultry, Meat & Food Preparation
N.A.I.C.S.: 112390
Uros Ilic (Chm-Supervisory Bd)

Subsidiary (Domestic):

Agrokombinat Maribor d.d. (2)
Trzaska cesta 41 A, 2000, Maribor, Slovenia
Tel.: (386) 26544100
Web Site: http://www.agronatur.si
Sales Range: $10-24.9 Million
Emp.: 51
Hog & Pig Farming
N.A.I.C.S.: 112210
Franc Eersic (Mgr)

Gradbeni Remont d.o.o. (2)
Znidaricevo nabrezje 10, 2250, Ptuj, Slovenia
Tel.: (386) 27727931
Web Site: http://www.perutnina.si
Sales Range: $25-49.9 Million
Emp.: 19
Residential Construction
N.A.I.C.S.: 236115
Simone Eguer (Gen Mgr)

PP Nepremicnine d.o.o. (2)
Potrceva cesta 10, Ptuj, 2250, Slovenia
Tel.: (386) 27490100
Web Site: http://www.perutnina.com
Poultry Production
N.A.I.C.S.: 112390
Alojz Erlac (Exec Dir-Agriculture)

Subsidiary (Non-US):

Perutnina Ptuj-Pipo d.o.o. (2)
Ulica Rudolfa Steinera 7, Cakovec, 40000, Zagreb, Croatia
Tel.: (385) 40372888
Web Site: http://www.perutnina.com
Broilers & Meat Type Chicken Production
N.A.I.C.S.: 112320
Predrag Segovic (Mng Dir)

Subsidiary (Domestic):

Ptujska Klet d.o.o. (2)
Vinarski Trg 1, 2250, Ptuj, Slovenia
Tel.: (386) 27879810
Web Site: http://www.ptujska-klet.si
Sales Range: $25-49.9 Million
Emp.: 35
Wineries
N.A.I.C.S.: 312130
Vinko Mandl (Pres)

MHZ DESIGN COMMUNICATIONS INC.
171 E Liberty St Ste 340, Toronto, M6K 3P6, ON, Canada
Tel.: (416) 626-1777
Web Site: http://www.mhzdesign.com
Year Founded: 1998
Sales Range: $10-24.9 Million
Emp.: 15
Advertising Agencies
N.A.I.C.S.: 541810

MI MING MART HOLDINGS LIMITED
16th Floor Guangdong Tours Centre 18 Pennington Street, Hong Kong, China (Hong Kong) Ky
Web Site:
  https://www.mimingmart.com
Year Founded: 2009
8473—(HKG)
Rev.: $21,904,738
Assets: $22,666,173
Liabilities: $4,145,718
Net Worth: $18,520,454
Earnings: $2,650,581
Emp.: 87
Fiscal Year-end: 03/31/23
Holding Company
N.A.I.C.S.: 551112

Kwan Yau Mak (Sec)

MI TECHNOVATION BERHAD
No 20 Medan Bayan Lepas Technoplex MK 12 Tmn Perindustrian, 11900, Pulau Penang, Malaysia
Tel.: (60) 43738688
Web Site: https://mi-technovation.com
Year Founded: 2017
5286—(KLS)
Rev.: $56,678,511
Assets: $109,051,497
Liabilities: $12,953,029
Net Worth: $96,098,469
Earnings: $13,366,913
Emp.: 292
Fiscal Year-end: 12/31/20
Semiconductor Mfr
N.A.I.C.S.: 334413
Oh Kuang Eng (CEO)

Subsidiaries:

Accurus Scientific Co., Ltd. (1)
No 508-51 Section 1 Wen-Sien Road, Rende District, Tainan City, 717015, Taiwan
Tel.: (886) 63661288
Web Site: https://www.accurus.com.tw
Electrical & Electronics Appliances Mfr
N.A.I.C.S.: 334413

Mi Equipment (M) Sdn Bhd (1)
No 20 Medan Bayan Lepas Technoplex MK12, Tmn Perindustrian Bayan Lepas, 11900, Pulau Penang, Malaysia
Tel.: (60) 43738688
Web Site: https://www.mi-eq.com
WLCSP Sorting Machine Mfr & Whslr
N.A.I.C.S.: 333242
Evelyn Ng (Sr Mgr)

Mi Equipment Korea Co., Ltd. (1)
Dong Digital Empire2 88 Sinwon-ro, Yeongtong, 1107-101, Suwon, Gyeonggi-do, Korea (South)
Tel.: (82) 316957688
Web Site: https://www.mi-eq.com
WLCSP Sorting Machine Mfr & Whslr
N.A.I.C.S.: 333242

Mi International Pte Ltd (1)
Robinson Road Robinson Square 06-02, Singapore, 068908, Singapore
Tel.: (65) 63342679
WLCSP Sorting Machine Mfr & Whslr
N.A.I.C.S.: 333242
Chee Kheong Teo (Gen Mgr)

Subsidiary (Non-US):

Mi Equipment (Taiwan) Co., Ltd. (2)
No 20-1 Taiyuan St, Zhubei, 302082, Hsinchu, Taiwan
Tel.: (886) 35526001
WLCSP Sorting Machine Mfr & Whslr
N.A.I.C.S.: 333242

Suzhou Mi Equipment Co., Ltd. (2)
Plant 9 No 17 East Suhong Road, Suzhou Industrial Park Pilot Free Trade Zone Suzhou Area, Suzhou, 215021, Jiangsu, China
Tel.: (86) 51262964602
Web Site: https://www.mi-eq.com
WLCSP Sorting Machine Mfr & Whslr
N.A.I.C.S.: 333242
Ramon Liu (Sr Mgr-Customer Svc)

MI-PAY GROUP PLC
30 Crown Place Earl Street, London, EC2A 4ES, United Kingdom
Tel.: (44) 20 7112 2121
Web Site: http://www.mi-pay.com
Rev.: $4,234,751
Assets: $6,684,235
Liabilities: $6,278,002
Net Worth: $406,234
Earnings: ($298,646)
Emp.: 44
Fiscal Year-end: 12/31/18
Payment Solutions for E-Commerce Clients
N.A.I.C.S.: 561499
John Nicholas Beale (CFO)

Subsidiaries:

Autoclenz Services Limited (1)
Stanhope Road, Swadlincote, DE11 9BE, Derbyshire, United Kingdom
Tel.: (44) 1283 552272
Web Site: http://www.autoclenz.co.uk
Emp.: 20
Automotive Cleaning Services
N.A.I.C.S.: 811192

MIA DYNAMICS MOTORS LTD.
3 Walter Moses St Alon Towers, Tel Aviv, 6789204, Israel
Tel.: (972) 549279273 II
Web Site:
  https://www.miadynamics.com
Year Founded: 1991
MIA—(TAE)
Assets: $2,024,023
Liabilities: $615,748
Net Worth: $1,408,275
Earnings: ($15,355,187)
Fiscal Year-end: 12/31/22
Financial Services
N.A.I.C.S.: 523999
Yaniv Hevron (Chm)

MIAHELSA CORPORATION
3-10 Kawadacho, Shinjuku-Ku, Tokyo, 162-0054, Japan
Tel.: (81) 333412421
Web Site: http://www.merhalsa.jp
Year Founded: 1984
7688—(TKS)
Health Care Srvices
N.A.I.C.S.: 621610
Isamu Aoki (Founder & Pres)

MIAHELSA HOLDINGS CORPORATION
Ichigaya Nakano-cho 3-19, Shinjuku-ku, Tokyo, 162-0064, Japan
Tel.: (81) 333417205
Web Site: https://www.merhalsa-hd.jp
Year Founded: 2021
7129—(TKS)
Rev.: $150,192,420
Assets: $91,277,490
Liabilities: $69,424,830
Net Worth: $21,852,660
Earnings: $33,050
Fiscal Year-end: 03/31/24
Holding Company
N.A.I.C.S.: 551112

MIAN ELECTRONICS CORPORATION
Civil Club Market, Talagang Road, Chakwal, Pakistan
Tel.: (92) 543552419
Web Site:
  http://mianelectronics.alhaa.com
Sales Range: $25-49.9 Million
Emp.: 16
Home Appliances & Electronics Retailer
N.A.I.C.S.: 449210
Nouman Iftikhar (CEO)

MIANYANG FULIN PRECISION CO., LTD.
No 37 Fenghuang road High technicalindustrial park, Fucheng Disctrict, Mianyang, 621000, Sichuan, China
Tel.: (86) 8166800660
Web Site: https://www.fulinpm.com
Year Founded: 1997
300432—(CHIN)
Rev.: $1,031,480,892
Assets: $1,170,010,764
Liabilities: $491,873,148
Net Worth: $678,137,616
Earnings: $90,586,080
Emp.: 1,700
Fiscal Year-end: 12/31/22

Motor Vehicle Parts & Accessories Mfr
N.A.I.C.S.: 336390
Wang Zhihong (Chm)

MIAOJIAN PR (SINO PR) CONSULTING CO., LTD.
Office B405 Minghu Building No 24 Huangsi Avenue, Beijing, 100120, China
Tel.: (86) 10 6202 3966 CN
Emp.: 150
Communications, Consumer Marketing, Event Marketing, Financial, Government/Political/Public Affairs, Production, Public Relations
N.A.I.C.S.: 541820
Miao Jianmin (Pres)

MIAS OC SPOL. S R.O.
Krouna 322, Krouna, 539 43, Czech Republic
Tel.: (420) 469613300
Web Site: http://www.miasoc.cz
Year Founded: 1993
Sales Range: $10-24.9 Million
Emp.: 50
Office Furniture Mfr
N.A.I.C.S.: 337214
Ales Sokolik (Dir-Comml)

MIATA METALS CORP.
2133 1177 West Hastings Street, Vancouver, V6E 2K3, BC, Canada
Tel.: (778) 918-6528 BC
Web Site:
  https://www.miatametals.com
Year Founded: 2021
MMET—(CNSX)
Assets: $1,332,929
Liabilities: $89,203
Net Worth: $1,243,725
Earnings: ($979,784)
Fiscal Year-end: 06/30/24
Mineral Mining Services
N.A.I.C.S.: 213115
Jacob Verbaas (CEO)

Subsidiaries:

79North, Inc. (1)
Suit 306 82 Richmond St East, Toronto, M5C 1P1, ON, Canada
Tel.: (416) 786-6348
Web Site: http://www.79north.ca
Assets: $227,396
Liabilities: $98,312
Net Worth: $129,084
Earnings: ($1,370,429)
Fiscal Year-end: 11/30/2022
Mineral Exploration & Mining Services
N.A.I.C.S.: 213115
Carmelo Marrelli (CFO)

Miata Holdings Inc. (1)

MIBA AG
Dr Mitterbauer Strabe 3, 4663, Laarkirchen, Austria
Tel.: (43) 7613 2541 0
Web Site: http://www.miba.com
Year Founded: 1927
Emp.: 5,626
Holding Company; Engine & Automotive Products Mfr
N.A.I.C.S.: 551112
Wolfgang Litzlbauer (Deputy CEO)

Subsidiaries:

High Tech Coatings GmbH (1)
Parkring 3, 8712, Niklasdorf, Austria (100%)
Tel.: (43) 3842835310
Sales Range: $25-49.9 Million
Emp.: 5
Automotive Parts & Accessories Stores
N.A.I.C.S.: 441330
Gunter Hehenfelder (Mng Dir)

MIBA AG

Miba AG—(Continued)

Miba Automation Systems Ges.m.b.H. (1)
Aurachkirchen 45, Pinsdorf, 4812, Laakirchen, Austria **(100%)**
Tel.: (43) 761325412170
Web Site: http://www.miba.com
Sales Range: $75-99.9 Million
Emp.: 900
Automotive Repair & Maintenance Service
N.A.I.C.S.: 811198

Miba Bearings US LLC (1)
N State Rte 60, McConnelsville, OH 43756 **(100%)**
Tel.: (740) 962-4242
Web Site: http://www.miba.com
Sales Range: $25-49.9 Million
Emp.: 100
Ball & Roller Bearing Mfr
N.A.I.C.S.: 332991
Bernie Anderson (Pres)

Miba Deutschland GmbH (1)
Max-Eyth-Strasse 18, 70736, Fellbach, Germany
Tel.: (49) 71150530713
Web Site: http://www.miba.com
Sales Range: $25-49.9 Million
Emp.: 25
Metal Service Centers & Offices
N.A.I.C.S.: 423510

Miba Far East Pte Ltd (1)
3 Loyang Way 4, Singapore, 506956, Singapore **(100%)**
Tel.: (65) 65453869
Industrial Supplies Whslr
N.A.I.C.S.: 423840

Miba Frictec GmbH (1)
Peter-Mitterbauer-Str 1, Roitham, Gmunden, 4661, Austria **(100%)**
Tel.: (43) 76139020
Web Site: http://www.miba.com
Sales Range: $50-74.9 Million
Emp.: 250
Steel Wire Drawing
N.A.I.C.S.: 331222

Miba Gleitlager Austria GmbH (1)
Mitterbauer-Str 3, 4663, Laakirchen, Austria
Tel.: (43) 761325410
Engine Parts Mfr & Distr
N.A.I.C.S.: 336310

Miba Gleitlager GmbH (1)
Dr Mitterbauer Strasse 3, Laakirchen, 4663, Gmunden, Austria **(100%)**
Tel.: (43) 76132541
Web Site: http://www.miba.com
Sales Range: $400-449.9 Million
Emp.: 1,600
Motor Vehicle Parts Mfr
N.A.I.C.S.: 336390
Franz Peter Mitterbauer (CEO)

Miba Hydra Mechanica Corp. (1)
6625 Cobb Dr, Sterling Heights, MI 48312 **(100%)**
Tel.: (586) 939-0620
Web Site: http://www.miba.com
Sales Range: $25-49.9 Million
Emp.: 100
Fabricated Metal Products Mfr
N.A.I.C.S.: 332999
Boris Seipelt (Gen Mgr)

Miba Industrial Bearings Brasil Ltda. (1)
Av Manoel Inacio Peixoto 2147, Cataguases, 36771-000, MG, Brazil
Tel.: (55) 3234295302
Engine Parts Mfr & Distr
N.A.I.C.S.: 336310

Miba Industrial Bearings Germany GmbH (1)
Rolandsweg 16-20, 37520, Osterode am Hartz, Germany
Tel.: (49) 55229563200
Engine Parts Mfr & Distr
N.A.I.C.S.: 336310

Miba Industrial Bearings Germany Osterode GmbH (1)
Rolandsweg 16-20, 37520, Osterode am Hartz, Germany
Tel.: (49) 55229563200
Engine Parts Mfr & Distr

N.A.I.C.S.: 336310

Miba Precision Components (China) Co. Ltd. (1)
No 530 Xinglong Street Phase III, Industrial Park, 215024, Suzhou, China **(100%)**
Tel.: (86) 51262850900
Sales Range: $50-74.9 Million
Emp.: 130
Electronic Components Mfr
N.A.I.C.S.: 334419
Anthony Wang (Gen Mgr)

Miba Sinter Austria GmbH (1)
Dr Mitterbauer Strasse 1, Vorchdorf, 4655, Gmunden, Austria **(100%)**
Tel.: (43) 761465410
Metal Heat Treating
N.A.I.C.S.: 332811

Miba Sinter Brasil Ltda. (1)
Rodovia Santos Dumont KM 57 2, 13330-970, Indaiatuba, Brazil **(100%)**
Tel.: (55) 1938349902
Automotive Components Mfr
N.A.I.C.S.: 336390

Miba Sinter Holding GmbH & Co. KG (1)
Dr Mitterbauer Strasse 3, 4663, Laakirchen, Austria **(100%)**
Tel.: (43) 761325413161
Web Site: http://www.miba.com
Sales Range: $550-599.9 Million
Emp.: 17
Holding Company
N.A.I.C.S.: 551112
Harald Neubert (CEO-Miba Sinter Grp)

Miba Sinter Slovakia s.r.o. (1)
Nabrezie Oravy 2222, 02601, Dolny Kubin, Slovakia
Tel.: (421) 435802230
Engine Parts Mfr & Distr
N.A.I.C.S.: 336310

Miba Steeltec S.r.o. (1)
Hlavna 48, Vrable, 952 01, Slovakia **(100%)**
Tel.: (421) 372301575
Web Site: http://www.miba.com
Sales Range: $50-74.9 Million
Emp.: 240
Industrial Process Furnace & Oven Mfr
N.A.I.C.S.: 333994
Martin Leabl (Mng Dir)

MIBANCO-BANCO DE LA MICRO EMPRESA S.A.
Av Republica de Panama 4575 Interior 301, Surquillo, Peru
Tel.: (51) 5138000
Web Site: http://www.mibanco.com.pe
Year Founded: 1998
MIBANC1—(LIM)
Rev.: $4,460,349,767
Assets: $51,779,428,900
Liabilities: $45,254,711,607
Net Worth: $6,524,717,294
Earnings: $1,259,296,143
Fiscal Year-end: 12/31/23
Financial Services
N.A.I.C.S.: 561499
Luis Enrique Romero Belismelis (Chm)

MIC ELECTRONICS LIMITED
A-4/II Electronic Complex Kushaiguda ECIL Post, Hyderabad, 500 062, India
Tel.: (91) 4027122222
Web Site: http://www.micelectronics.com
Rev.: $389,505
Assets: $20,766,667
Liabilities: $39,241,918
Net Worth: ($18,475,251)
Earnings: ($3,267,224)
Emp.: 42
Fiscal Year-end: 03/31/20
Design, Development & Mfr of LED Video Displays, High-End Electronic & Telecommunication Equipment & Development of Telecom Software

N.A.I.C.S.: 334419
M. S. Murali Krishnan (Officer-Compliance & Sec)

Subsidiaries:

MIC Electronics Inc. (1)
4392 Miller Ave, Palo Alto, CA 94306
Tel.: (408) 980-2500
Light Emitting Diode Mfr
N.A.I.C.S.: 334413

MIC Technologies Australia (Pty.) Ltd. (1)
2/9 Carnegie Place, Blacktown, 2148, NSW, Australia
Tel.: (61) 411302583
Web Site: http://www.mictech.com.au
Telecommunications Equipment Mfr
N.A.I.C.S.: 334290

MICH RESOURCES LTD
3123-595 Burrard Street, Vancouver, V7X 1J1, BC, Canada
Tel.: (604) 609-6110
MICH—(CNSX)
Rev.: $15,504
Assets: $662,255
Liabilities: $139,764
Net Worth: $522,490
Earnings: ($1,114,309)
Fiscal Year-end: 11/30/22
Mineral Exploration Services
N.A.I.C.S.: 213115
Mark T. Brown (CFO)

MICHAEL HILL NEW ZEALAND LIMITED
Metroplex on Gateway 7 Smallwood Place, Murarrie, 4172, QLD, Australia
Tel.: (61) 731143500
Web Site: http://www.michaelhill.com
Year Founded: 1979
MHJ—(ASX)
Rev.: $430,641,692
Assets: $364,078,524
Liabilities: $252,646,233
Net Worth: $111,432,291
Earnings: ($319,845)
Emp.: 3,400
Fiscal Year-end: 06/30/24
Retail Jewelry Chain Operator
N.A.I.C.S.: 458310
Richard Michael Hill (Founder & Pres)

Subsidiaries:

Michael Hill International Inc. (1)
7 Smallwood Place, Murarrie, 4172, QLD, Australia
Tel.: (61) 733990200
Web Site: http://www.michaelhill.com.au
Sales Range: $50-74.9 Million
Emp.: 150
Jewelry Store Owner & Operator
N.A.I.C.S.: 458310

Michael Hill Jeweller (Australia) Pty Limited (1)
Shop N143 Crown Central Mall 200 Crown Street, Wollongong, 2500, NSW, Australia **(100%)**
Tel.: (61) 242257309
Web Site: http://www.michaelhill.com.au
Sales Range: $25-49.9 Million
Emp.: 10
Jewelry Stores
N.A.I.C.S.: 458310

Michael Hill Jeweller (Canada) Pty Limited (1)
6335 Edwards Blvd, Mississauga, ON, Canada
Web Site: https://www.michaelhill.ca
Jewellery & Watch Distr
N.A.I.C.S.: 423940

Michael Hill Jeweller Limited (1)
32900 South Fraser Way, Abbotsford, V2S 5A1, BC, Canada **(100%)**
Tel.: (604) 853-1205
Web Site: http://www.michaelhill.ca

INTERNATIONAL PUBLIC

Sales Range: $25-49.9 Million
Emp.: 9
Jewelry Stores
N.A.I.C.S.: 458310

MICHAEL HOERAUF MASCHINENFABRIK GMBH & CO. KG
Mozartstrasse 39-41, 73072, Donzdorf, Germany
Tel.: (49) 71629420
Web Site: http://www.hoerauf.com
Year Founded: 1938
Sales Range: $75-99.9 Million
Emp.: 250
Paper & Card Product Machinery Mfr
N.A.I.C.S.: 333243
Werner Stahlecker (Mng Dir-Sussen)

MICHAEL JACKSON MOTOR SALES LIMITED
480 Hume Street, Collingwood, L9Y 1W6, ON, Canada
Tel.: (705) 445-2222
Web Site: http://www.mikejacksongm.com
Rev.: $17,438,860
Emp.: 40
New & Used Car Dealers
N.A.I.C.S.: 441110
Michael Jackson (Principal)

MICHAEL WEINIG AG
Weinigstrasse 2/4, 97941, Tauberbischofsheim, Germany
Tel.: (49) 9341860
Web Site: http://www.weinig.com
Year Founded: 1905
Sales Range: $400-449.9 Million
Emp.: 2,155
Special Woodworking Machine Mfr
N.A.I.C.S.: 333243
Wolfgang Poschl (CEO)

Subsidiaries:

Frederic Colliou (1)
4 Allee Rigny Usse, ZAC La Maisonneraie, de la papoterie, F-37170, Chambray les Tours, France
Tel.: (33) 247480200
Web Site: http://www.weinig.de
Mfg Woodworking Machinery
N.A.I.C.S.: 333243

Holz-Her GmbH (1)
Plochinger Strasse 65, 72622, Nurtingen, Germany
Tel.: (49) 70227020
Web Site: http://www.holzherusa.com
Edging & Panel Material Mfr
N.A.I.C.S.: 326199
Frank Epple (Mng Dir)

Holz-Her Maschinenbau GmbH (1)
Grazer Vorstadt 110, 8570, Voitsberg, Austria
Tel.: (43) 314221751
Edging & Panel Material Mfr
N.A.I.C.S.: 326199

Josef Lageder (1)
Dantestrasse 12, 39031, Brüneck, Italy
Tel.: (39) 0474 441 208
Whslr Woodworking Machinery
N.A.I.C.S.: 423830

LuxScan Technologies S.a r.l. (1)
Z A R E Ouest, 4384, Ehlerange, Luxembourg
Tel.: (352) 540 416 1
Web Site: http://www.luxscan.com
Emp.: 14
Wood Products Mfr
N.A.I.C.S.: 321211
Voga Raphael (Gen Mgr)

MICHAEL WEINIG (YANTAI) Machinery Co Ltd. (1)
No 8 Nenjiang Rd Yantai Economic and Technological Development Zone, Yantai, Shandong, China
Tel.: (86) 5 35 6 38 35 35
Web Site: http://www.weinig.cn
Wood Processing Machine Mfr

AND PRIVATE COMPANIES

Michael Weinig (UK) Ltd. (1)
5 Blacklands Way Abingdon Business Park, Abingdon, OX14 1DY, United Kingdom **(100%)**
Tel.: (44) 235557600
Web Site: http://www.weinig.co.uk
Sales Range: $25-49.9 Million
Emp.: 20
Whslr of Woodworking Machinery.
N.A.I.C.S.: 423830

Michael Weinig AG (1)
Rorkullsvagen 7, 30107, Halmstad, Sweden
Tel.: (46) 35176700
Window & Door Mfr
N.A.I.C.S.: 321911

Michael Weinig Asia Pte. Ltd. (1)
11 Tampines Street 92 Tampines Biz-Hub 04-08, Singapore, 528872, Singapore
Tel.: (65) 67585178
Web Site: http://weinigasia.business.site
Panel Processing Machine Mfr
N.A.I.C.S.: 333517

Michael Weinig Australia Pty. Ltd. (1)
1B Widemere Rd, PO Box 6239, Wetherill Park, 2164, NSW, Australia **(100%)**
Tel.: (61) 296095911
Web Site: http://www.weinig.com.au
Sales Range: $25-49.9 Million
Emp.: 8
Mfr of Woodworking Machinery.
N.A.I.C.S.: 333243
Peter Joseph *(Controller-Fin)*

Michael Weinig SA (1)
2 Rte De Combe A l Ours, CH 2301, La Chaux-de-Fonds, Switzerland **(100%)**
Tel.: (41) 329269595
Web Site: http://www.weinig.ch
Sales Range: $25-49.9 Million
Emp.: 30
Mfr of Woodworking Machinery.
N.A.I.C.S.: 333243

Michael Weinig, Inc. (1)
124 Crosslake Pk Dr, Mooresville, NC 28117 **(100%)**
Tel.: (704) 799-0100
Web Site: http://www.weinigusa.com
Sales Range: $50-74.9 Million
Emp.: 90
Sale & Service for Special Woodworking Machine Distr
N.A.I.C.S.: 423830

NOVECO S.P.A. (1)
Via IV Novembre 47, 33044, Manzano, Italy **(100%)**
Tel.: (39) 0432754428
Web Site: http://www.noveco.it
Sales Range: $25-49.9 Million
Emp.: 5
Mfr of Woodworking Machinery.
N.A.I.C.S.: 333243

RAIMANN Holzoptimierung GmbH & Co. KG (1)
Weisserlenstrasse 11, 79108, Freiburg, Germany
Tel.: (49) 7 61 1 30 33 0
Wood Processing Machine Mfr
N.A.I.C.S.: 333243

WACO Jonsereds AB (1)
Skackelvagen 1, PO Box 283, Halmstad, 302 62, Sweden **(100%)**
Tel.: (46) 35176700
Web Site: http://www.waco.se
Sales Range: $400-449.9 Million
Emp.: 40
Mfr of Woodworking Machinery.
N.A.I.C.S.: 333243
Ebbe Johanson *(Mng Dir)*

WEINIG HOLZ-HER Schweiz AG (1)
Industriestrasse, 6034, Inwil, Switzerland
Tel.: (41) 41 449 90 90
Web Site: http://www.weinig.com
Wood Processing Machine Whslr
N.A.I.C.S.: 423830

Weinig Dimter GmbH & Co. KG (1)
Rudolf-Diesel-Strasse 16, 89257, Illertissen, Germany
Tel.: (49) 7303150
Window & Door Mfr
N.A.I.C.S.: 321911

Weinig France Sarl (1)
7 rue du Port, 25200, Montbeliard, France
Tel.: (33) 3 81 99 56 50
Web Site: http://www.weinig.fr
Wood Processing Machine Distr
N.A.I.C.S.: 423990

Weinig Grecon GmbH & Co. KG (1)
Hannoversche Strasse 58, 31061, Alfeld, Germany **(100%)**
Tel.: (49) 5181 939 0
Web Site: http://www.weinting.com
Sales Range: $50-74.9 Million
Emp.: 160
Production of Finger Jointing Lines
N.A.I.C.S.: 333243

Weinig Holz-Her Canada Inc. (1)
4317Autoroute des Laurentides, Laval, H7L 5W5, QC, Canada
Tel.: (450) 973-2397
Window & Door Mfr
N.A.I.C.S.: 321911

Weinig Holz-Her Espana S.L. (1)
Calle Marques del Turia num 4, 46930, Cuart de Poblet, Spain
Tel.: (34) 961 526336
Wood Processing Machine Distr
N.A.I.C.S.: 423990

Weinig Holz-Her France S.A.R.L. (1)
7 avenue de Strasbourg, Brunstatt Didenhiem, 68350, Mulhouse, France
Tel.: (33) 381995650
Window & Door Mfr
N.A.I.C.S.: 321911

Weinig Holz-Her Italia S.R.L. (1)
Via Giuseppe Di Vittorio Str 16, 39100, Bolzano, Italy
Tel.: (39) 0471058222
Window & Door Mfr
N.A.I.C.S.: 321911

Weinig Italia S.r.L. (1)
Via Fratelli Rosselli 16A, 50064, Incisa in Val d'Arno, Italy
Tel.: (39) 055 8335005
Web Site: http://www.weinig.com
Emp.: 3
Wood Processing Machine Distr
N.A.I.C.S.: 423990
Rossella Gaudenzi *(Office Mgr)*

Weinig Rus OOO (1)
Proezd Serebryakova d 6 floor 3, 129343, Moscow, Russia
Tel.: (7) 4997032433
Web Site: http://www.weinig.com.ru
Window & Door Mfr
N.A.I.C.S.: 321911

Weinig Vertrieb Und Service GmbH & Co. KG (1)
Weinigstrasse 2/4, 97941, Tauberbischofsheim, Germany
Tel.: (49) 9341860
Window & Door Mfr
N.A.I.C.S.: 321911

MICHANG OIL IND. CO., LTD.
35 gil Baumoe-ro, Seocho-gu, Seoul, Korea (South)
Tel.: (82) 25745115
Web Site: https://www.michang.co.kr
Year Founded: 1962
003650—(KRS)
Rev.: $321,211,692
Assets: $274,069,197
Liabilities: $27,751,207
Net Worth: $246,317,990
Earnings: $17,934,834
Emp.: 81
Fiscal Year-end: 12/31/22
Automotive Lubricant Oil Mfr
N.A.I.C.S.: 324191
Lee Jinsoo *(Mng Dir)*

MICHEL SEMEGEN HOLDINGS LTD.
75 Two Nations Crossing, Fredericton, E3A 0T3, NB, Canada
Tel.: (506) 450-8933
Web Site: http://www.canadiantire.ca
Year Founded: 1994
Rev.: $12,500,000
Emp.: 75
Auto Repair & Services
N.A.I.C.S.: 811198
Cindy Asher *(Office Mgr)*

MICHELL Y CIA. S.A.
Av Juan de la Torre 101, San Lazaro, Arequipa, Peru
Tel.: (51) 54202525
Web Site: http://www.michell.com.pe
Year Founded: 1931
MICHEI1—(LIM)
Rev.: $114,132,905
Assets: $172,670,083
Liabilities: $59,403,038
Net Worth: $113,267,046
Earnings: $8,174,961
Fiscal Year-end: 12/31/22
Wool & Yarn Product Mfr & Distr
N.A.I.C.S.: 313110
Michael W. Michell Stafford *(Chm)*

MICHELMERSH BRICK HOLDINGS PLC
Freshfield Lane, Danehill, Haywards Heath, RH17 7HH, Sussex, United Kingdom
Tel.: (44) 8449310022
Web Site: https://www.mbhplc.uk
MBH—(AIM)
Rev.: $98,459,234
Assets: $157,835,219
Liabilities: $39,643,400
Net Worth: $118,191,819
Earnings: $12,297,856
Fiscal Year-end: 12/31/23
Administrative Services
N.A.I.C.S.: 523991
Martin R. Warner *(Chm)*

Subsidiaries:

Blockleys Brick Ltd. (1)
Sommerfeld Rd Trench Lock, Telford, TF1 5RY, Shropshire, United Kingdom
Tel.: (44) 1952251933
Web Site: http://www.mbh.com
Sales Range: $25-49.9 Million
Emp.: 70
Facing & Stock Bricks Mfr
N.A.I.C.S.: 327120
Carl Duncan *(Mgr-IT)*

Charnwood Forest Brick Ltd. (1)
Old Sta Close, Shepshed, Loughborough, LE12 9NJ, Leicestershire, United Kingdom
Tel.: (44) 1509503203
Web Site: http://www.mbhplc.co.uk
Sales Range: $25-49.9 Million
Emp.: 50
Bricks Mfr
N.A.I.C.S.: 327120

Dunton Brothers Ltd. (1)
Blackwell Hall Ln Ley Hill, Chesham, HP5 1TN, Buckinghamshire, United Kingdom
Tel.: (44) 1494772111
Web Site: http://www.duntons.com
Sales Range: $25-49.9 Million
Emp.: 25
Mfr
N.A.I.C.S.: 327120

Fab-lite Building Solutions Limited (1)
Unit MD2 Skelmanthorpe Business Park Saville Road, Skelmanthorpe, Huddersfield, West Yorkshire, United Kingdom
Tel.: (44) 1484865572
Web Site: https://www.fab-lite.co.uk
Lightweight Arch Mfr
N.A.I.C.S.: 332999

Fab-lite Facades Limited (1)
82 Lime Pit Lane, Stanley, Wakefield, West Yorkshire, United Kingdom
Tel.: (44) 1924828362
Web Site: https://www.fab-lite-facades.co.uk
Pre-Fabrication Product Mfr
N.A.I.C.S.: 332311

FabSpeed UK Limited (1)

MICHMAN FINANCE LTD

Unit MD2 Skelmanthorpe Business Park Saville Road, Skelmanthorpe, Huddersfield, West Yorkshire, United Kingdom
Tel.: (44) 3301222123
Web Site: https://www.fabspeed.uk
Industrial Products Mfr
N.A.I.C.S.: 332311

Michelmersh Brick & Tile Company Ltd. (1)
Hill View Rd, Michelmersh, Romsey, SO51 0NN, Hampshire, United Kingdom
Tel.: (44) 1794368506
Web Site: http://www.mbhplc.co.uk
Sales Range: $25-49.9 Million
Emp.: 62
Bricks Mfr
N.A.I.C.S.: 327120

MICHELSON DIAGNOSTICS LIMITED
Eclipse House Eclipse Park Sittingbourne Road, Maidstone, ME14 3EN, Kent, United Kingdom
Tel.: (44) 20 8308 1695
Web Site: http://www.vivosight.com
Year Founded: 2006
Emp.: 10
Medical Device Mfr
N.A.I.C.S.: 339112
Jon Holmes *(Co-Founder & CTO)*

Subsidiaries:

Michelson Diagnostics Deutschland GmbH (1)
Life Science Centre Merowingerplatz 1, 40225, Dusseldorf, Germany
Tel.: (49) 80244772160
Scanner Distr
N.A.I.C.S.: 423450

Michelson Diagnostics Inc. (1)
1734 Lakeview Ave Ste 156, Dracut, MA 01826
Tel.: (888) 632-5305
Scanner Distr
N.A.I.C.S.: 423450

MICHINOKU COCA-COLA BOTTLING CO., LTD.
1-279 Hiromiyasawa Yahaba-cho, Shiwa-gun, Iwate, 028-3621, Japan
Tel.: (81) 19 698 3111 JP
Web Site: http://www.michinoku.ccbc.co.jp
Year Founded: 1962
Sales Range: $100-124.9 Million
Soft Drinks Mfr
N.A.I.C.S.: 312111
Hirokazu Yamura *(Pres)*

MICHLOL FINANCE LTD.
Masada 7 BSR 4 Bnei Brak 17th floor, Bnei Brak, Israel
Tel.: (972) 35178800 II
Web Site: https://www.michlol-fin.co.il
MCLL—(TAE)
Rev.: $50,427,683
Assets: $445,707,135
Liabilities: $374,321,586
Net Worth: $71,385,549
Earnings: $11,334,438
Fiscal Year-end: 12/31/23
Miscellaneous Financial Investment Activities
N.A.I.C.S.: 523999

MICHMAN FINANCE LTD
Bar Kochba 21, Bnei Brak, Israel
Tel.: (972) 39015606 II
Web Site: https://www.michman-loans.co.il
Year Founded: 2015
MCMN—(TAE)
Rev.: $38,016,300
Assets: $191,326,423
Liabilities: $153,133,027
Net Worth: $38,193,396
Earnings: $12,105,539
Fiscal Year-end: 12/31/23

MICHMAN FINANCE LTD

Michman Finance Ltd—(Continued)
Investment Management Service
N.A.I.C.S.: 523999

MICHONG METAVERSE (CHINA) HOLDINGS GROUP LIMITED
Unit B 13/F Winsan Tower 98 Thomson Road, Wanchai, China (Hong Kong) **Ky**
Web Site: https://www.metamichong.com
Year Founded: 2007
8645—(HKG)
Rev.: $16,836,045
Assets: $15,367,874
Liabilities: $5,875,752
Net Worth: $9,492,121
Earnings: $2,592,048
Emp.: 139
Fiscal Year-end: 06/30/23
Holding Company
N.A.I.C.S.: 551112

MICO BIOMED CO., LTD.
3 4th Floor 54 Changeop-ro Sujeong-gu, Gangnam-dong, Seongnam, 13449, Gyeonggi-do, Korea (South)
Tel.: (82) 70 5227 6000 **KR**
Web Site: http://www.micobiomed.com
Year Founded: 2009
Medical Equipment Mfr
N.A.I.C.S.: 423450
Sung-woo Kim *(CEO)*

MICO LTD.
Mosan-ro 8 79 Shinmosan-dong, Anseong, Gyeonggi-do, Korea (South)
Tel.: (82) 3180565800
Web Site: https://www.komico.com
Year Founded: 1996
059090—(KRS)
Rev.: $318,176,351
Assets: $560,794,417
Liabilities: $272,172,286
Net Worth: $288,622,131
Earnings: ($42,362,299)
Emp.: 153
Fiscal Year-end: 12/31/22
Semiconductor Product Mfr
N.A.I.C.S.: 334413
Choi Ha Yong *(CEO)*

Subsidiaries:

KoMiCo Equipment Parts Shenzhen Co., Ltd. (1)
No 5 Plant Hengsheng Industry Park Tantou Community Songgang Street, Baoan, Shenzhen, China
Tel.: (86) 75523001036
Electronic Products Mfr
N.A.I.C.S.: 334111

KoMiCo Ltd. (1)
8 Mosan-ro, Anseong, Gyeonggi-do, Korea (South)
Tel.: (82) 316705800
Web Site: https://komico.com
Electronic Products Mfr
N.A.I.C.S.: 334111

KoMiCo Technology Inc. (1)
201 Michael Angelo Way, Austin, TX 78728
Tel.: (512) 238-2400
Electronic Products Mfr
N.A.I.C.S.: 334111
James Jin *(COO)*

KoMiCo Technology Singapore Pte. Ltd. (1)
2 Woodlands Sector1 03-20 Woodlands Spectrum, Singapore, Singapore
Tel.: (65) 68928164
Electronic Products Mfr
N.A.I.C.S.: 334111

KoMiCo Technology Taiwan Ltd. (1)
No 14 Shijian Rd, Hukou Township, Hsinchu, 30352, Taiwan
Tel.: (886) 35972988
Electronic Products Mfr
N.A.I.C.S.: 334111

Mico Electronics (Wuxi) Ltd. (1)
No 9-5 Xinshuo Road, Xinwu District, Wuxi, Jiangsu, China
Tel.: (86) 51082241200
Electronic Products Mfr
N.A.I.C.S.: 334111

Micopower Co., Ltd. (1)
MiCoPower F2-dongm 23 Gongdan 2-ro, Anseong, 17567, Gyeonggi-do, Korea (South)
Tel.: (82) 316107940
Web Site: https://www.micopower.com
Hydrogen Energy Mfr
N.A.I.C.S.: 325120

MICREED CO., LTD.
2-3-1 Nishi-Shinjuku, Shinjuku-ku, Tokyo, 163-0904, Japan
Tel.: (81) 120917000
Web Site: https://www.micreed.co.jp
Year Founded: 1995
7687—(TKS)
Seafood Product Distr
N.A.I.C.S.: 424460
Reiko Katayama *(Pres)*

MICREX DEVELOPMENT CORPORATION
156 Laurier Drive, Edmonton, T5R 5P9, AB, Canada
Tel.: (780) 760-0921
Web Site: http://www.mixcorp.com
Year Founded: 1987
Mineral Exploration Services
N.A.I.C.S.: 213114
Stanley Marshall *(Founder, Pres & CEO)*

MICRO CONTACT SOLUTION CO., LTD.
15-21 Oh song 2gil Seonggeo-Eup, Seobuk-gu, Cheonan, 331-831, Chung-Nam, Korea (South)
Tel.: (82) 416214331
Web Site: https://www.mcsgroup.co.kr
Year Founded: 1999
098120—(KRS)
Rev.: $46,828,967
Assets: $43,985,996
Liabilities: $6,377,544
Net Worth: $37,608,452
Earnings: $5,404,407
Emp.: 157
Fiscal Year-end: 12/31/22
Electronic Components Mfr
N.A.I.C.S.: 334419
Sun-Mi Jung *(Deputy Gen Mgr)*

Subsidiaries:

MCS (Europe) Ltd. (1)
Kreuzhofstrasse 10D, 81476, Munich, Germany
Tel.: (49) 897557322
Electronic Components Distr
N.A.I.C.S.: 423690

MICRO FOCUS INTERNATIONAL PLC
The Lawn 22-30 Old Bath Road, Newbury, RG14 1QN, Berkshire, United Kingdom
Tel.: (44) 163 556 5200 **UK**
Web Site: http://www.microfocus.com
Year Founded: 1976
MFGP—(NYSE)
Rev.: $2,899,900,000
Assets: $10,346,600,000
Liabilities: $7,525,600,000
Net Worth: $2,821,000,000
Earnings: ($424,400,000)
Emp.: 11,782
Fiscal Year-end: 10/31/21
Legacy Development & Deployment Software
N.A.I.C.S.: 541512
Jane Smithard *(Chief Legal Officer & Gen Counsel)*

Subsidiaries:

GWAVA EMEA GmbH (1)
Von Braun Strasse 38a, 48683, Ahaus, Germany
Tel.: (49) 32211076466
Software Publishing Services
N.A.I.C.S.: 513210

Limited Liability Company Micro Focus (1)
Leningradskoye Shosse 16-A Block 3, 125171, Moscow, Russia
Tel.: (7) 4994034900
Software Publishing Services
N.A.I.C.S.: 513210

Micro Focus (US) Inc. (1)
700 King Farm Blvd Ste 400, Rockville, MD 20850
Tel.: (301) 838-5000
Web Site: http://www.microfocus.com
Rev.: $45,000,000
Emp.: 85
Software Developer
N.A.I.C.S.: 513210

Subsidiary (Domestic):

ArcSight, LLC (2)
Moffett Towers Bldg F 1140 Enterprise Way, Sunnyvale, CA 94089
Tel.: (801) 861-7000
Web Site: http://www.microfocus.com
Security & Compliance Management Solutions
N.A.I.C.S.: 541512

Subsidiary (Non-US):

ArcSight Hong Kong Limited (3)
21/F Henley Building 5, Queens Road Central, Hong Kong, China (Hong Kong)
Tel.: (852) 2588 5262
Web Site: http://www.microfocus.com
Security & Compliance Management Solutions
N.A.I.C.S.: 541511

Subsidiary (Domestic):

Borland Software Corporation (2)
8310 N Capital of Texas Hwy Bldg 2 Ste 100, Austin, TX 78731
Tel.: (512) 340-2200
Web Site: http://www.borland.com
Sales Range: $150-199.9 Million
Software Developer
N.A.I.C.S.: 513210

Subsidiary (Non-US):

Borland (Singapore) Pte. Ltd. (3)
3 Harbour Front Place, 09-02/04 Harbour Front Tower 2, Singapore, 099254, Singapore
Tel.: (65) 6510 4200
Web Site: http://www.borland.com.sg
Sales Range: $25-49.9 Million
Emp.: 100
Software Developer
N.A.I.C.S.: 513210

Borland Australia Pty Ltd. (3)
Darling Park, Tower 2 201 Sussex Street, Office Nos 3918 3928, Sydney, 2000, NSW, Australia
Tel.: (61) 290047181
Web Site: http://www.borland.com
Sales Range: $25-49.9 Million
Emp.: 65
Software Developer
N.A.I.C.S.: 513210

Borland Canada, Inc. (3)
445 Apple Creek Blvd Ste 203, Markham, L3R 9X7, ON, Canada
Tel.: (905) 968-2840
Sales Range: $25-49.9 Million
Emp.: 30
Software Developer
N.A.I.C.S.: 513210

Borland GmbH (3)
Robert-Bosch-Strasse 11, D-63225, Langen, Germany
Tel.: (49) 6103979150
Web Site: http://www.borland.com
Sales Range: $25-49.9 Million
Emp.: 50
Software & Microcomputers Developer
N.A.I.C.S.: 513210

Micro Focus (3)
Sumitomo Fudosan Roppongi-dori Bldg 9F, 7-18-18 Roppongi Minato-ku, Tokyo, 106 0032, Japan
Tel.: (81) 354134800
Web Site: http://www.microfocus.com
Sales Range: $25-49.9 Million
Emp.: 70
Software Developer
N.A.I.C.S.: 513210

Micro Focus Brazil (3)
Rua Joaquim Floriano 466-12 Andar Office Corporate, Sao Paulo, 04534-002, SP, Brazil
Tel.: (55) 11 2165 8000
Web Site: http://www.microfocus.com
Sales Range: $25-49.9 Million
Emp.: 40
Software Developer
N.A.I.C.S.: 513210

Branch (Domestic):

Micro Focus - Costa Mesa (2)
575 Anton Blvd Ste 510, Costa Mesa, CA 92626
Tel.: (714) 445-4400
Web Site: http://www.microfocus.com
Sales Range: $25-49.9 Million
Emp.: 37
Software Tools Developer
N.A.I.C.S.: 513210

Subsidiary (Domestic):

NetIQ (2)
515 Post Oak Blvd Ste 1200, Houston, TX 77027
Tel.: (713) 548-1700
Web Site: http://www.netiq.com
Emp.: 150
Developer of Integrated Systems & Security Management Products & Services
N.A.I.C.S.: 541512

Subsidiary (Non-US):

NetIQ - Australia (3)
Level 4 12-14 Claremont Street South Yarra, Melbourne, 3141, VIC, Australia
Tel.: (61) 3 9825 2300
Web Site: http://www.netiq.com
Performance & Availability Management, Security Management, Configuration & Vulnerability Management & Operational Change Control Services
N.A.I.C.S.: 513210

NetIQ - Japan (3)
Sumitomo Ichigaya Building 12F Ichigaya-honmura cho 1-1, Shinjuku-Ku, Tokyo, 162 0845, Japan
Tel.: (81) 3 5260 9300
Web Site: http://www.netiq.co.jp
Performance & Availability Management, Security Management, Configuration & Vulnerability Management & Operational Change Control Services
N.A.I.C.S.: 513210

NetIQ Ireland Limited (3)
2nd Floor Block 2 Parkmore East Business Park, Galway, Ireland
Tel.: (353) 91782600
Performance & Availability Management, Security Management, Configuration & Vulnerability Management & Operational Change Control Services
N.A.I.C.S.: 513210

NetIQ Nederlands (3)
Raoul Wallenberg 23, 2404 ND, Alphen aan den Rijn, Netherlands
Tel.: (31) 172505555
Web Site: http://www.netiq.com
Performance & Availability Management, Security Management, Configuration & Vulnerability Management & Operational Change Control Services
N.A.I.C.S.: 513210

AND PRIVATE COMPANIES

Subsidiary (Domestic):

Novell, Inc. (2)
1800 S Novell Pl, Provo, UT 84606
Tel.: (888) 321-4272
Web Site: http://www.novell.com
Networking & E-Business Software & Services
N.A.I.C.S.: 513210

Subsidiary (Non-US):

Microfocus Beijing (3)
Room 3603 Beijing Fortune Plaza Office Tower A No 7 Dongsanhuan, Zhongli Chaoyang District, Beijing, 100020, China
Tel.: (86) 10 6533 9000
Networking & E-Business Software & Services
N.A.I.C.S.: 513210

Microfocus Bengaluru (3)
Laurel Block D 65 2 Bagmane Tech Park, CV Raman Nagar Byrasandra Post, Bengaluru, 560093, India
Tel.: (91) 80 40022300
Networking & E-Business Software & Services
N.A.I.C.S.: 513210

Microfocus Malaysia (3)
Unit 501 Level 5 Uptown 1 1 Jalan SS21 58 Damansara Uptown, Petaling Jaya, 47300, Selangor, Malaysia
Tel.: (60) 376100214
Networking & E-Business Software & Services
N.A.I.C.S.: 513210

Microfocus Sydney (3)
Level 23 100 Miller St, Sydney, 2060, NSW, Australia
Tel.: (61) 282813400
Web Site: http://www.microfocus.com
Emp.: 30
Networking & E-Business Software & Services
N.A.I.C.S.: 513210

Microfocus Taiwan (3)
Room B 26th Fl 216 Tunn-Hwa S Rd Sec 2, Taipei, 106, Taiwan
Tel.: (886) 223760036
Networking & E-Business Software & Services
N.A.I.C.S.: 513210

Novell Canada (3)
1 Rue Holiday Street East Tower Ste 501, Pointe Calire, Montreal, H9R 5N3, QC, Canada
Tel.: (800) 453-1267
Web Site: http://www.novell.com
Networking & E-Business Software & Services
N.A.I.C.S.: 513210

Novell Chile S.A. (3)
Av Vitacura 2939 Piso 10 Las Condes, Santiago, Chile
Tel.: (56) 24315002
Web Site: http://www.novell.com
Networking & E-Business Software & Services
N.A.I.C.S.: 513210

Novell Finland Oy (3)
Linnoitustie 4A, Espoo, 02600, Finland
Tel.: (358) 9502951
Web Site: http://www.novell.fi
Networking & E-Business Software & Services
N.A.I.C.S.: 513210

Novell Ireland Software Limited (3)
Corrig Court Corrig Road Sandyford Industrial Industrial Estate, Sandiford, Dublin, 18, Ireland
Tel.: (353) 91782600
Web Site: http://www.novell.ie
Networking & E-Business Software & Services
N.A.I.C.S.: 513210

Novell Israel Software Limited (3)
Atidim, PO Box 58152, Tel Aviv, Israel
Tel.: (972) 35483759
Web Site: http://www.novell.com
Networking & E-Business Software & Services
N.A.I.C.S.: 513210

Novell Portugal Informatica Lda. (3)
Centro Empresarial Torres de R Tomas da Fonseca Torre G, Lisbon, 1600 209, Portugal
Tel.: (351) 217230630
Web Site: http://www.novell.com
Emp.: 4
Networking & E-Business Software & Services
N.A.I.C.S.: 513210
Michael Decastro *(Mng Dir)*

Novell Svenska AB (3)
Kronborgsgrand 1, 164 87, Kista, Sweden
Tel.: (46) 87522500
Web Site: http://www.novell.se
Networking & E-Business Software & Services
N.A.I.C.S.: 513210

Novell UK Limited (3)
The Lawn 22-30 Old Bath Road Newbury, Newbury, RG14 1QN, Berks, United Kingdom
Tel.: (44) 1635565200
Web Site: http://www.novell.co.uk
Networking & E-Business Software & Services
N.A.I.C.S.: 513210

Novell de Argentina S.A. (3)
Leandro N Alem 712 2nd Floor, Buenos Aires, C1001AAP, Argentina
Tel.: (54) 11 5258 8899
Web Site: http://www.novell.com
Networking & E-Business Software & Services
N.A.I.C.S.: 513210

Subsidiary (Domestic):

Novell de Puerto Rico, Inc. (3)
530 Ponce de Leon, San Juan, PR 00901-2304
Tel.: (582) 122-7780
Web Site: http://www.novell.com
Networking & E-Business Software & Services
N.A.I.C.S.: 513210

Subsidiary (Non-US):

Novell do Brasil Software Ltda (3)
Rua Joaquim Florino 466-12 Andar Office Corporate, Sao Paulo, 04534002, Brazil
Tel.: (55) 1121658000
Web Site: http://www.novell.com
Networking & E-Business Software & Services
N.A.I.C.S.: 513210

Subsidiary (Domestic):

Vertica Systems, LLC (2)
150 Cambridgepark Dr, Cambridge, MA 02140
Tel.: (617) 386-4400
Web Site: http://www.vertica.com
Data Management Solutions
N.A.I.C.S.: 513210

Micro Focus AS (1)
CJ Hambros Plass 2c, N-0164, Oslo, Norway
Tel.: (47) 21601605
Software Development Services
N.A.I.C.S.: 541511

Micro Focus B.V. (1)
Van Deventerlaan 31-51, 3528 AG, Utrecht, Netherlands
Tel.: (31) 308082600
Information Technology Services
N.A.I.C.S.: 541511

Micro Focus Czechia s.r.o. (1)
Za Brumlovkou 1559/5, 14000, Prague, Czech Republic
Tel.: (420) 220410540
Software Publishing Services
N.A.I.C.S.: 513210

Micro Focus GmbH (1)
Fraunhoferstrasse 7, 85737, Ismaning, Germany
Tel.: (49) 89420940
Software Development Services
N.A.I.C.S.: 541511

Micro Focus GmbH (1)
Wallisellen Business Park Richtistirasse 7, 8304, Wallisellen, Switzerland
Tel.: (41) 442004149
Software Publishing Services
N.A.I.C.S.: 513210

Micro Focus Holdings Limited (1)
The Lawn Old Bath Road, Newbury, RG14 1QN, Berkshire, United Kingdom
Tel.: (44) 163532646
Web Site: http://www.microfocus.com
Emp.: 30
Software Development Services
N.A.I.C.S.: 541511

Micro Focus Israel Limited (1)
Matam Advanced Technology Cntr 9 Andrei Sakharov St Building 5/1, Haifa, 31905, Israel
Tel.: (972) 48551755
Software Publishing Services
N.A.I.C.S.: 513210

Micro Focus KK (1)
Sumitomo Fudosan Roppongi-dori Bldg 9F 7-18-18 Roppongi, Minato-ku, Tokyo, 106-0032, Japan
Tel.: (81) 3 5413 4800
Web Site: http://www.microfocus.co.jp
Software Development Services
N.A.I.C.S.: 541511

Micro Focus Korea Limited (1)
15F 31 Gukjegeumyung-ro 8-gil, Yeongdeungpo-gu, Seoul, 07332, Korea (South)
Tel.: (82) 264845200
Software Publishing Services
N.A.I.C.S.: 513210

Micro Focus LLC (1)
Nimr Al Nakheel Centre Building A 1st Floor Imam Saud Bin, Abdulaziz Bin Muhammad Road, Riyadh, 11564, Saudi Arabia
Tel.: (966) 8018617000
Software Publishing Services
N.A.I.C.S.: 513210

Micro Focus Limited (1)
The Lawn 22-30 Old Bath Road, Newbury, RG14 1QN, Berkshire, United Kingdom
Tel.: (44) 163532646
Web Site: http://www.microfocus.com
Sales Range: $75-99.9 Million
Emp.: 400
Software Development Services
N.A.I.C.S.: 541511

Micro Focus Pte Limited (1)
3 Harbour Front Place 13-02/04 Harbour Front Tower 2, Singapore, 099254, Singapore
Tel.: (65) 6510 4200
Sales Range: $25-49.9 Million
Emp.: 40
Software Development Services
N.A.I.C.S.: 541511
Stephen McNulty *(Pres)*

Micro Focus Pty Limited (1)
Suite 1410 530 Little Collins Street, Melbourne, 3000, VIC, Australia
Tel.: (61) 3 9526 2901
Sales Range: $25-49.9 Million
Emp.: 7
Software Development Services
N.A.I.C.S.: 541511
Peter Fuller *(Mng Dir)*

Micro Focus SAS (1)
Tour Atlantique 22eme Etage 1 Place de la Pyramide, La Defense 9, 92911, Paris, France
Tel.: (33) 155703013
Web Site: http://www.microfocus.com
Software Development Services
N.A.I.C.S.: 541511

Micro Focus SL (1)
Paseo de la Castellana 42 5Floor, Madrid, 28046, Spain
Tel.: (34) 91 781 5004
Software Development Services
N.A.I.C.S.: 541511
Pedro Soldado *(Gen Mgr)*

Micro Focus Software (Ireland) Limited (1)
Corrig Court Corrig Road, Sandyford Industrial Estate Sandyford, Dublin, Ireland
Tel.: (353) 16058000
Software Publishing Services

N.A.I.C.S.: 513210

Micro Focus Software Denmark ApS (1)
World Trade Center Office 2 37 2 38 and 2 39-1 Borupvang 3, 2750, Ballerup, Denmark
Tel.: (45) 35256530
Software Publishing Services
N.A.I.C.S.: 513210

Micro Focus Software HK Limited (1)
21/F Henley Building 5 Queen's Road, Central, China (Hong Kong)
Tel.: (852) 30183711
Software Publishing Services
N.A.I.C.S.: 513210

Micro Focus Software Romania SRL (1)
3 George Constantinescu Street BOC Office Building 4 Floor, Entrance B 2nd District, 020339, Bucharest, Romania
Tel.: (40) 756061602
Software Publishing Services
N.A.I.C.S.: 513210

Micro Focus Software Solutions India Private Limited (1)
66/1 6th Floor Olympia Building Bagmane Tech Park Sir CV Raman Nagar, Byrasandra, Bengaluru, 560093, Karnataka, India
Tel.: (91) 8061454530
Software Publishing Services
N.A.I.C.S.: 513210

Micro Focus South Africa (Pty.) Ltd. (1)
Morningside Wedge Office Park 255 Rivonia Road, Morningside, Sandton, 2057, South Africa
Tel.: (27) 113228300
Software Publishing Services
N.A.I.C.S.: 513210

Micro Focus Sverige AB (1)
Kronborgsgrand 1, Kista, 164 46, Stockholm, Sweden
Tel.: (46) 844683430
Software Publishing Services
N.A.I.C.S.: 513210

Micro Focus Ukraine, LLC (1)
13 Pimonenko Street Building 6A/Office 61, Kiev, 04050, Ukraine
Tel.: (380) 445861282
Software Publishing Services
N.A.I.C.S.: 513210

MICRO LEASING PUBLIC COMPANY LIMITED

863/3 Petchkasem Road, Sanamchan Sub-District Mueang District, Nakhon Pathom, 73000, Thailand
Tel.: (66) 21055599   TH
Web Site: https://www.microleasingplc.com
Year Founded: 1994
MICRO—(THA)
Rev.: $26,835,431
Assets: $156,879,019
Liabilities: $94,655,202
Net Worth: $62,223,817
Earnings: ($2,337,099)
Emp.: 245
Fiscal Year-end: 12/31/23
Financial Investment Services
N.A.I.C.S.: 523999
Krit Umpote *(Chm)*

MICRO SYSTEMATION AB

Hornsbruksgatan 28, SE 117 34, Stockholm, Sweden
Tel.: (46) 87390270
Web Site: https://www.msab.com
Year Founded: 1984
MSAB.B—(OMX)
Rev.: $37,851,759
Assets: $23,039,670
Liabilities: $12,260,494
Net Worth: $10,779,176
Earnings: $1,985,265
Emp.: 202

MICRO SYSTEMATION AB

Micro Systemation AB—(Continued)

Fiscal Year-end: 12/31/20
Security Software Publisher
N.A.I.C.S.: 513210
Henrik Tjernberg (Chm)

Subsidiaries:

MSAB Incorporated (1)
241 18th St S Ste 202, Arlington, VA 22202
Tel.: (703) 750-0068
Forensic Analysis Services
N.A.I.C.S.: 541380

MSAB Japan K.K.
16th Floor Akasaka Ark Hills Building c/o
Business Sweden Office, Swedish Embassy, Tokyo, 107-6016, Japan
Tel.: (81) 355448516
Information Technology Services
N.A.I.C.S.: 541511

Micro Systemation (1)
30 rue Godot de Mauroy, 75009, Paris, France
Tel.: (33) 153307942
Security Software Publisher
N.A.I.C.S.: 513210

Micro Systemation Canada Inc. (1)
400 March Road Suite 420, Kanata, K2K 3H4, ON, Canada
Tel.: (519) 498-6780
Web Site: https://www.msab.com
Security Software Publisher
N.A.I.C.S.: 513210

Micro Systemation Inc. (1)
241 18th St S Ste 202, Arlington, VA 22202
Tel.: (703) 750-0068
Web Site: http://www.msab.com
Security Software Publisher
N.A.I.C.S.: 513210

Micro Systemation Ltd (1)
The Ashridge Business Centre 121 High Street, Berkhamsted, HP4 2DJ, Herefordshire, United Kingdom
Tel.: (44) 808 234 2450
Web Site: http://www.msab.com
Security Software Publisher
N.A.I.C.S.: 513210

MICRO-MECHANICS (HOLDINGS) LTD

No 31 Kaki Bukit Place Eunos Techpark, Singapore, 416209, Singapore
Tel.: (65) 67468800
Web Site: https://www.micro-mechanics.com
5DD—(SES)
Rev.: $49,664,315
Assets: $43,120,410
Liabilities: $8,706,145
Net Worth: $34,414,265
Earnings: $7,240,074
Emp.: 495
Fiscal Year-end: 06/30/23
Precision Tool Mfr
N.A.I.C.S.: 332216
Sumitri Mirnalini Menon (Chm)

Subsidiaries:

Micro-Mechanics Inc (1)
465 Woodview Ave, Morgan Hill, CA 95037
Tel.: (408) 779-2927
Precision Tools Mfr & Distr
N.A.I.C.S.: 332216

Micro-Mechanics Pte Ltd (1)
No 31 Kaki Bukit Place Eunos Techpark, Singapore, 416209, Singapore
Tel.: (65) 67468800
Sales Range: $25-49.9 Million
Emp.: 80
Precision Tools Mfr & Distr
N.A.I.C.S.: 332216
Christopher Borche (Mng Dir)

Micro-Mechanics Technology (Suzhou) Co. Ltd. (1)
8A Suchun Industrial Square No 428 Xinglong Street, Suzhou Industrial Park, Suzhou, 215126, China
Tel.: (86) 51287168800
Precision Tool Mfr

N.A.I.C.S.: 333515
Shen Zi Quan (Deputy Gen Mgr)

Micro-Mechanics Technology International, Inc. (1)
Lot B2-1C Carmelray Industrial Park II, Brgy Tulo, Calamba, 4027, Laguna, Philippines
Tel.: (63) 495457718
Sales Range: $25-49.9 Million
Emp.: 65
Precision Tool Mfr
N.A.I.C.S.: 332216

Micro-Mechanics Technology Sdn. Bhd. (1)
Lot P22 P23 Phase 4, Free Industrial Zone, 11900, Bayan Lepas, Penang, Malaysia
Tel.: (60) 46434648
Precision Tool Mfr
N.A.I.C.S.: 333515
Lay Chin Chuah (Mgr-GIT Section)

MICRO-STAR INTERNATIONAL CO., LTD.

No 69 Lide St, Zhonghe Dist, Taipei, 235, Taiwan
Tel.: (886) 232345599
Web Site: https://in.msi.com
Year Founded: 1986
2377—(TAI)
Rev.: $5,983,376,863
Assets: $2,960,326,060
Liabilities: $1,319,322,034
Net Worth: $1,641,004,026
Earnings: $246,342,121
Emp.: 3,107
Fiscal Year-end: 12/31/23
Computer Hardware Mfr & Distr
N.A.I.C.S.: 334118
Hsiang Hsu (Chm & Gen Mgr)

Subsidiaries:

Funtoro Inc. (1)
5F No 97 Lide St, Zhonghe, Taipei, Taiwan
Tel.: (886) 232341359
Electrical Goods Mfr
N.A.I.C.S.: 334111

MICRO-STAR NETHERLANDS HOLDING B.V. (1)
Przedstawicielstwo w Polsce Ul Cicha 5, Warsaw, 00-353, Poland
Tel.: (48) 717105200
Investment Holding Services
N.A.I.C.S.: 551112

Subsidiary (Non-US):

MSI COMPUTER (UK) LIMITED (2)
Unit 1 Canal Court Ground Floor, 152 - 154 High Street, Brentford, TW8 8JA, United Kingdom
Tel.: (44) 2036085252
Web Site: http://www.uk.msi.com
Computer Peripheral Equipment Distr
N.A.I.C.S.: 423430

MSI Computer SARL (2)
50 Boulevard Antoine Giroust, 77600, Bussy-Saint-Georges, France
Tel.: (33) 179867940
Web Site: http://fr.msi.com
Computer Peripheral Equipment Distr
N.A.I.C.S.: 423430

Mystar Computer B.V. (2)
Ekkersrijt 6050, 5692 GA, Son, Netherlands
Tel.: (31) 402676600
Electronic Device Distr
N.A.I.C.S.: 423430

MSI Computer (Australia) Pty. Ltd. (1)
40/7-9 Percy St, Auburn, 2144, NSW, Australia
Tel.: (61) 1300222688
Web Site: https://au.msi.com
Computer Peripheral Equipment Distr
N.A.I.C.S.: 423430

MSI Computer Europe B.V. (1)
Science Park 5706, Son, 5692 ER, Eindhoven, Netherlands
Tel.: (31) 402676100
Logistics Consulting Servies
N.A.I.C.S.: 541614

MSI Computer Japan Co., Ltd. (1)
Root Higashiueno Bldg 3F 1-11-4 Higashiueno, Taito-ku, Tokyo, 110-0015, Japan
Tel.: (81) 570093700
Web Site: https://www.jp.msi.com
Computer Peripheral Equipment Distr
N.A.I.C.S.: 423430

MSI ELECTRONICS (KUNGSHAN) CO., LTD. (1)
88 Qianjin East Road, Kunshan, 215300, China
Tel.: (86) 51257718888
Electrical Goods Mfr
N.A.I.C.S.: 334111

MSI Italy S.r.l (1)
Via Leopardi 7, 20123, Milan, Italy
Tel.: (39) 0294751570
Web Site: https://it.msi.com
Electronic Sales Support Services
N.A.I.C.S.: 541614

MSI Korea Co., Ltd. (1)
112 Cheongpa-ro Room 203 2nd floor 15-dong Najin Shopping Center, Yongsan-gu Hangang-ro 3-ga, Seoul, Korea (South)
Tel.: (82) 16444038
Electronic Components Distr
N.A.I.C.S.: 423690

MICRO-TECH (NANJING) CO., LTD.

No 10 Gaoke 3rd Road, High-tech Development Zone, Nanjing, 210032, Jiangsu, China
Tel.: (86) 2558648819
Web Site: http://www.micro-tech.com.cn
Year Founded: 2000
688029—(SHG)
Rev.: $278,012,147
Assets: $546,720,408
Liabilities: $86,985,368
Net Worth: $459,735,040
Earnings: $46,414,892
Fiscal Year-end: 12/31/22
Medical Equipment Mfr & Distr
N.A.I.C.S.: 339112
Xu Funing (Co-Founder)

Subsidiaries:

Canyon Medical Inc. (1)
Building 3 Phase 2 Accelerator No 11 Yaogu Avenue, Jiangbei New Area, Nanjing, 210032, Jiangsu, China
Tel.: (86) 4000258800
Web Site: http://www.en.canyonmedical.com.cn
Medical Device Mfr
N.A.I.C.S.: 339112

Micro-Tech Endoscopy USA Inc. (1)
2855 Boardwalk Dr, Ann Arbor, MI 48104
Web Site: https://www.mtendoscopy.com
Medical Device Mfr & Distr
N.A.I.C.S.: 339112

Micro-Tech Europe GmbH (1)
Mundelheimer Weg 36, 40472, Dusseldorf, Germany
Tel.: (49) 21173276260
Web Site: https://micro-tech-europe.com
Medical Device Mfr & Distr
N.A.I.C.S.: 339112
Daniel Kuhn (Mng Dir)

Micro-Tech Nederland B.V. (1)
Lage Mosten 49, 4822 NK, Breda, Netherlands
Tel.: (31) 767998691
Medical Device Distr
N.A.I.C.S.: 423450

MICRO-X LIMITED

A14 6 MAB Eastern Promenade, Adelaide, 5042, SA, Australia
Tel.: (61) 870993966   AU
Web Site: https://www.micro-x.com
Year Founded: 2011
MX1—(ASX)
Rev.: $10,164,263
Assets: $17,958,734
Liabilities: $8,436,164

INTERNATIONAL PUBLIC

Net Worth: $9,522,569
Earnings: ($6,520,433)
Fiscal Year-end: 06/30/24
Medical Product Development & Manufacturing
N.A.I.C.S.: 339112
Kingsley Hall (CEO, CFO & Sec)

Subsidiaries:

Virtual Observer Pty. Ltd. (1)
31 Affleck Rd, Perth International Airport, Perth, 6105, WA, Australia
Tel.: (61) 894791195
Web Site: http://www.virtualobserver.com.au
Web Development Services
N.A.I.C.S.: 518210
Neil Goodey (Founder)

MICRO2NANO INC.

43 Deokseong Industrial Complex 2-ro 50beongil, Idong-eup Cheoin-gu, Yongin, Gyeonggi-do, Korea (South)
Tel.: (82) 316597900
Web Site: https://www.micro2nano.com
Year Founded: 2000
424980—(KRS)
Emp.: 136
Semiconductor Components Mfr
N.A.I.C.S.: 333242
Kyu-Ho Hwang (CEO)

MICROALGO INC.

Unit 507 Building C Taoyuan Street Long Jing High and New Technology Jingu Pioneer Park, Nanshan District, Shenzhen, 518052, China
Tel.: (41) 75588600589
MLGO—(AIM)
Rev.: $87,132,230
Assets: $72,086,734
Liabilities: $5,075,274
Net Worth: $67,011,460
Earnings: ($6,963,546)
Emp.: 125
Fiscal Year-end: 12/31/22
Software Publr
N.A.I.C.S.: 513210
Min Shu (CEO)

MICROALLIANCE GROUP INC

No 1 Huabao Fubao China Street, Futian District, Shenzhen, 518000, Guangdong, China
Tel.: (86) 18566761769
FHAI—(NASDAQ)
Rev.: $37,393,802
Assets: $30,992,313
Liabilities: $2,746,306
Net Worth: $28,246,007
Earnings: $18,675,547
Emp.: 30
Fiscal Year-end: 12/31/21
Biological Product Mfr
N.A.I.C.S.: 325414

MICROBA LIFE SCIENCE LIMITED

Level 10 324 Queen Street, Brisbane, 4000, QLD, Australia
Tel.: (61) 1300974621   AU
Web Site: https://www.microba.com
Year Founded: 2017
MAP—(ASX)
Rev.: $3,592,393
Assets: $30,248,581
Liabilities: $4,553,477
Net Worth: $25,695,104
Earnings: ($8,788,528)
Fiscal Year-end: 06/30/22
Biotechnology Research & Development Services
N.A.I.C.S.: 541714
Luke Reid (CEO)

MICROBIO CO., LTD.

AND PRIVATE COMPANIES

14F-1 No 3 Yuan Qu St, Taipei, 115603, Taiwan
Tel.: (886) 226558558
Web Site:
https://www.twmicrobio.com
Year Founded: 2000
4128—(TPE)
Rev.: $53,836,351
Assets: $471,837,382
Liabilities: $33,843,511
Net Worth: $437,993,872
Earnings: $4,765,782
Fiscal Year-end: 12/31/22
Biotechnology Research & Development Services
N.A.I.C.S.: 541714
Hsien-Shou Kuo (Chm)

Subsidiaries:

Cotton Field Organic Co., Ltd. (1)
12th Floor No 236 Section 4 Xinyi Road, Daan District, Taipei, Taiwan
Tel.: (886) 227555268
Web Site: https://www.cotton-field.com.tw
Organic Food Mfr
N.A.I.C.S.: 325130

Sinew Pharma Co., Ltd. (1)
C516 Building C No 99 Ln 130 Sec 1 Academia Rd, Nangang Dist, Taipei, 11571, Taiwan
Tel.: (886) 227885365
Web Site: https://www.sinewpharma.com
Emp.: 23
Biotechnology Research & Development Services
N.A.I.C.S.: 541715
Kaimin Chu (Chm & CEO)

MICROBIX BIOSYSTEMS INC.
265 Watline Avenue, Mississauga, L4Z 1P3, ON, Canada
Tel.: (905) 361-8910
Web Site: https://www.microbix.com
Year Founded: 1988
MBX—(TSX)
Rev.: $14,544,901
Assets: $22,552,377
Liabilities: $8,036,276
Net Worth: $14,516,100
Earnings: $2,529,416
Emp.: 90
Fiscal Year-end: 09/30/21
Biological Product Mfr
N.A.I.C.S.: 325414
Martin Marino (Chm)

MICROCOSM TECHNOLOGY CO., LTD.
No 8 Nanke 9rd Rd, Shanhua District, Tainan City, Taiwan
Tel.: (886) 65050662
Web Site:
https://www.microcosm.com.tw
Year Founded: 1996
3354—(TPE)
Rev.: $4,860,113
Assets: $41,220,086
Liabilities: $10,100,866
Net Worth: $31,119,220
Earnings: ($662,696)
Fiscal Year-end: 12/31/22
Electronic Parts Mfr & Distr
N.A.I.C.S.: 334419
Tang-Chieh Huang (Chm & CEO)

MICRODATA
30 Boulevard Ibnou Sina, Casablanca, Morocco
Tel.: (212) 529009500
Web Site: https://www.microdata.ma
Year Founded: 1991
MIC—(CAS)
Sales Range: $50-74.9 Million
Computer Peripheral Equipment Whslr
N.A.I.C.S.: 423430
Hassane Amor (Chm & Mng Dir)

MICRODIGITAL CO., LTD.
15 Pangyo-ro 228beon-gil, Bundang-Gu, 13487, Seongnam, 13487, Gyeonggi-do, Korea (South)
Tel.: (82) 317012225
Web Site: https://www.md-best.com
Year Founded: 2002
305090—(KRS)
Rev.: $6,813,797
Assets: $21,788,586
Liabilities: $17,618,716
Net Worth: $4,169,870
Earnings: ($7,182,105)
Emp.: 84
Fiscal Year-end: 12/31/22
Dental Instrument Mfr & Distr
N.A.I.C.S.: 339114
Woo-Shik Choi (Mgr)

MICROELECTRONIC NH GMBH
Am Sandberg 1, Niederlauer, 97618, Munich, Germany
Tel.: (49) 9771 68867 0
Web Site: http://www.micro-nh.de
Emp.: 18
Microelectronics Mfr
N.A.I.C.S.: 334419
Karl Morgenthal (Mng Dir)

Subsidiaries:

SM Electronic GmbH (1)
Waldweg 2, Stapelfeld, D 22145, Hamburg, Germany (100%)
Tel.: (49) 40 67509 0
Web Site: http://www.sm-electronic.de
Sales Range: $10-24.9 Million
Electronic Reception Accessories Mfr, Including Satellite & Antenna Receivers
N.A.I.C.S.: 334419
Karl Morgenthal (Mng Dir)

MICROELECTRONICA S.A.
Str Erou Iancu Nicolae 126, Ilfov, 077190, Voluntari, Romania
Tel.: (40) 318241424
Web Site: http://www.microel.ro
Year Founded: 1981
Sales Range: $10-24.9 Million
Emp.: 14
Semiconductor Components Mfr
N.A.I.C.S.: 334413
Ioan Liviu Jalba (Chm & CEO)

MICROEMISSIVE DISPLAYS LTD.
Scottish Microelectronics Centre, West Mains Road, Edinburgh, EH9 3JF, United Kingdom
Tel.: (44) 131 650 7764
Year Founded: 1999
Sales Range: $25-49.9 Million
Emp.: 62
Microdisplays Mfr
N.A.I.C.S.: 334419
Paul van Eynde (Dir-Sls & Mktg)

MICROEQUITIES ASSET MANAGEMENT GROUP LIMITED
Suite 3105 Level 31 Governor Macquarie Tower 1 Farrer Place, Sydney, 2000, NSW, Australia
Tel.: (61) 290092900 AU
Web Site:
https://www.microequities.com.au
MAM—(ASX)
Rev.: $18,370,860
Assets: $15,855,301
Liabilities: $1,424,012
Net Worth: $14,431,288
Earnings: $10,986,473
Fiscal Year-end: 06/30/22
Asset Management Services
N.A.I.C.S.: 531390
Carlos Gil (Founder, CEO & Chief Investment Officer)

MICROFITS PTE LTD
Blk 25 Kallang Avenue 03-01 Kallang Basin Industrial Estate, Singapore, 339416, Singapore
Tel.: (65) 63095500
Industrial Machinery Mfr
N.A.I.C.S.: 333998

MICROGAMING SYSTEMS (UK) LTD.
Mgs House Circular Rd, Douglas, IM1 1BL, United Kingdom
Tel.: (44) 1624647777
Web Site:
http://www.microgaming.com
Year Founded: 1994
Sales Range: $25-49.9 Million
Emp.: 450
Developer of Internet Gaming Systems
N.A.I.C.S.: 522110
Kate Mughtin (Mgr-Mktg)

MICROLIFE CORPORATION
Burghardt Neihu Road 9th Floor No 431, Taipei, 114, Taiwan
Tel.: (886) 287971288
Web Site: http://www.microlife.com.tw
Year Founded: 1981
4103—(TAI)
Sales Range: $100-124.9 Million
Emp.: 2,620
Medical Diagnostic Equipment Mfr & Distr
N.A.I.C.S.: 339112
Jin Yuan Lin (Chm & Gen Mgr)

Subsidiaries:

Microlife AG Swiss Corporation (1)
Espenstrasse 139, Widnau, 9443, Saint Gallen, Switzerland
Tel.: (41) 717277000
Web Site: http://www.microlife.com
Sales Range: $25-49.9 Million
Emp.: 25
Surgical & Medical Instrument Mfr
N.A.I.C.S.: 339112

Microlife USA, Inc. (1)
1617 Gulf To Bay Blvd Ste 2, Clearwater, FL 33755-6419 (100%)
Tel.: (727) 451-0484
Web Site: http://www.microlifeusa.com
Sales Range: $25-49.9 Million
Emp.: 30
Surgical & Medical Instrument Mfr
N.A.I.C.S.: 339112
Mark Porter (Pres)

MICROLISE GROUP PLC
Farrington Way, Eastwood, Nottingham, NG16 3AG, Nottinghamshire, United Kingdom
Tel.: (44) 1773537000 UK
Web Site: https://www.microlise.com
Year Founded: 1982
SAAS—(AIM)
Rev.: $79,791,719
Assets: $159,222,419
Liabilities: $66,483,211
Net Worth: $92,739,207
Earnings: $1,707,902
Emp.: 661
Fiscal Year-end: 12/31/22
Software Development Services
N.A.I.C.S.: 541511

Subsidiaries:

Microlise S.A.S. (1)
Les Hauts de la Duranne 505 Avenue Galilee, 13290, Aix-en-Provence, France
Tel.: (33) 185650826
Transport Management Technology Services
N.A.I.C.S.: 541614

TruTac Limited (1)
Units 5 & 6 Westwood House Westwood Business Park, Coventry, CV4 8HS, United Kingdom
Tel.: (44) 2476690000
Web Site: https://www.trutac.co.uk
Software Development Services
N.A.I.C.S.: 541511

MICROMAX INFORMATICS LIMITED
Micromax House 90B Sector-18, Gurgaon, 122015, India
Tel.: (91) 124 4811000
Web Site:
http://www.micromaxinfo.com
Electronics Mfr
N.A.I.C.S.: 334290
Vikas Thapar (Sr VP-Fin)

MICROMEM TECHNOLOGIES INC.
121 Richmond Street West Suite 602, Toronto, M5H 2K1, ON, Canada
Tel.: (416) 364-6513 ON
Web Site:
https://www.micromeminc.com
MMTIF—(OTCQB)
Assets: $168,350
Liabilities: $5,009,554
Net Worth: ($4,841,204)
Earnings: ($2,691,670)
Emp.: 3
Fiscal Year-end: 10/31/23
Magnetic Random Access Memory (MRAM) Semiconductors Developer & Mfr
N.A.I.C.S.: 541511
Joseph Fuda (Pres & CEO)

MICRON MACHINERY CO., LTD.
5782 Zao Ueno, Yamagata, 990-2303, Japan
Tel.: (81) 236888111
Web Site: https://www.micron-grinder.co.jp
Year Founded: 1961
6159—(TKS)
Rev.: $29,227,780
Assets: $94,046,400
Liabilities: $12,035,700
Net Worth: $82,010,700
Earnings: $3,010,480
Emp.: 236
Fiscal Year-end: 08/31/24
Grinder Mfr
N.A.I.C.S.: 333991

Subsidiaries:

MICRON MACHINERY CO., LTD. - Miharashi Factory (1)
20-1 Miharashi-no-oka, Kaminoyama, Yamagata, 999-3107, Japan
Tel.: (81) 236958125
Emp.: 50
Grinder Mfr
N.A.I.C.S.: 333991
Makoto Sakakibara (Dir-Pur)

Micron Machinery (Thailand) Co., Ltd. (1)
No 641/1 Srinagarindra Rd, Suan Luang Sub-dist Suan Luang Dist, Bangkok, 10250, Thailand
Tel.: (66) 23215686
Grinder Distr
N.A.I.C.S.: 423830

Micron-U.S.A., Inc. (1)
5150 Falcon View Ave, Kentwood, MI 49512
Tel.: (616) 942-2007
Grinder Mfr
N.A.I.C.S.: 333991
Jerry Anderson (Pres)

MICRONICS JAPAN CO., LTD.
2-6-8 Kichijoji Hon-cho, Musashino-shi, Tokyo, 180-8508, Japan
Tel.: (81) 422212665
Web Site: https://www.mjc.co.jp
Year Founded: 1970

MICRONICS JAPAN CO., LTD.

MICRONICS JAPAN CO., LTD.—(Continued)
6871—(TKS)
Rev.: $271,490,280
Assets: $395,969,410
Liabilities: $103,861,410
Net Worth: $292,108,000
Earnings: $29,260,430
Emp.: 1,598
Fiscal Year-end: 12/31/23
Electronic Measuring Equipment Mfr
N.A.I.C.S.: 334419
Masayoshi Hasegawa (Pres & CEO)

Subsidiaries:

China MJC (SHANGHAI) CO., LTD. (1)
406 Room Building A No 168 Luoyang Road Meixia Building, Shanghai, 201104, China
Tel.: (86) 21 6410 8891
Semiconductor Device Whslr
N.A.I.C.S.: 423690

MEK Co., Ltd. (1)
28 Sinheung-ro 446beon-gil, Ojeong-gu, Bucheon, 144-52, Gyeonggi-do, Korea (South)
Tel.: (82) 326713103
Semiconductor Testing Device Mfr & Distr
N.A.I.C.S.: 334515

MICRONICS JAPAN CO., LTD. - Aomori Matsuzaki Plant (1)
41-1 Matsuzaki nishida, Hirakawa-shi, Aomori, 036-0114, Japan
Tel.: (81) 172 43 0060
Semiconductor Devices Mfr
N.A.I.C.S.: 334413

MICRONICS JAPAN CO., LTD. - Aomori Plant (1)
571-2 Machii minamida, Hirakawa, 036-0164, Aomori, Japan
Tel.: (81) 172 44 7277
Semiconductor Devices Mfr
N.A.I.C.S.: 334413

MJC Electronics Asia Pte. Ltd. (1)
60 Paya Lebar Road 10-54, Singapore, Singapore
Tel.: (65) 63861140
Web Site: https://www.mjc-test-socket.com
Electronic Instrument Distr
N.A.I.C.S.: 423690
Hiroshi Iwamitsu (Mng Dir)

MJC Electronics Corporation (1)
11004 Metric Blvd, Austin, TX 78758
Tel.: (512) 276-8951
Emp.: 15
Semiconductor Testing System Mfr & Distr
N.A.I.C.S.: 423690
Ryan Green (Controller)

MJC Europe GmbH (1)
Carl-von-linde-Str 10, 85716, Unterschleissheim, Germany
Tel.: (49) 89 3706 3290
Semiconductor Device Whslr
N.A.I.C.S.: 423690
Hiroshi Iwamitsu (Mng Dir)

MJC Microelectronics (Kunshan) Co., Ltd. (1)
No 6 Dexin Road, Zhangpu town, Kunshan, 215321, Jiangsu, China
Web Site: https://www.mmk.net.cn
Electronic Instrument Mfr & Distr
N.A.I.C.S.: 334515

MJC Microelectronics (Shanghai) Co., Ltd. (1)
B-4F 1618 Yishan RD, Minhang, Shanghai, 201103, China
Tel.: (86) 21 6401 8400
Semiconductor Testing System Mfr & Whslr
N.A.I.C.S.: 423690

Taiwan MJC Co., Ltd. (1)
No 36 Sec 2 Huanbei Rd, Jhubei, 302, Hsinchu, Taiwan
Tel.: (886) 3 551 8899
Web Site: http://www.twmjc.com.tw
Emp.: 85
Testing Equipment Mfr & Whslr
N.A.I.C.S.: 334515

MICRONX CO., LTD.
22 Maeyeo-ro 1-gil, Dong-gu, Daegu, 41059, Korea (South)
Tel.: (82) 536501000
Web Site: https://www.micronx.co.kr
Year Founded: 2001
448780—(KRS)
Medical Equipment Mfr & Distr
N.A.I.C.S.: 339112
Jong-Geon Lee (CEO)

MICROPOLE SA
91/95 Rue Carnot, 92300, Levallois-Perret, France
Tel.: (33) 174187418
Web Site: https://www.micropole.com
Year Founded: 1987
MUN—(EUR)
Sales Range: $125-149.9 Million
Emp.: 1,100
Business Intelligence, E-Business, Customer Relationship Management (CRM) & Enterprise Resource Planning Services
N.A.I.C.S.: 541519
Christian Poyau (Co-Founder & CEO)

Subsidiaries:

Conceptware (1)
Rue De La Decouverts, Immeuble Innopolis A,, 31670, Labege, France
Tel.: (33) 561392833
Sales Range: $25-49.9 Million
Emp.: 20
Business Consulting Services
N.A.I.C.S.: 541611
Schourtck Celins (Mng Dir)

Cross Systems Ingenierie (1)
34 Rue Viret, 69100, Villeurbanne, France
Tel.: (33) 472699444
Business Consulting Services
N.A.I.C.S.: 541611

Micropole Univers Consulting SAS (1)
100 Rue Lafayette, 75010, Paris, France
Tel.: (33) 142474447
Web Site: http://www.micropole-univers.com
Business Management Consulting Services
N.A.I.C.S.: 541611

Subsidiary (Domestic):

Apsalys SARL (2)
12 rue Jean Racine, 33600, Pessac, France
Tel.: (33) 556104773
Web Site: http:/apsalys.com
Business Consulting Services
N.A.I.C.S.: 541611

Micropole Univers Institut SA (1)
16 Rue D Athenes, Paris, 75009, France
Tel.: (33) 155078507
Business Training Services
N.A.I.C.S.: 541611
Lettoffe Therry (Gen Mgr)

Micropole Univers Suisse SA (1)
Avenue Gratta-Paille 2, 1018, Lausanne, Switzerland
Tel.: (41) 216411435
Sales Range: $25-49.9 Million
Emp.: 180
Business Consulting Services
N.A.I.C.S.: 541611

Subsidiary (Domestic):

Cross Systems Suisse SA (2)
Route des acacias 45b, les acacias, 1227, Geneva, Switzerland
Tel.: (41) 223084860
Web Site: http:/cross-systems.ch
Sales Range: $25-49.9 Million
Emp.: 120
Software Consulting Services
N.A.I.C.S.: 541512

Univers Informatique (1)
100 Rue La Fayette, 75010, Paris, France
Tel.: (33) 1 4247 4247
Business Consulting Services
N.A.I.C.S.: 541611

MICROPORT CARDIOFLOW MEDTECH CORP.
Zhangjiang Hi-Tech Park Zhangdong Road 1601, Shanghai, Pudong, 201203, China
Tel.: (86) 2138954600
Web Site: https://en.cardioflowmedtech.com
Year Founded: 2015
2160—(HKG)
Rev.: $46,551,700
Assets: $356,821,555
Liabilities: $33,540,790
Net Worth: $323,280,765
Earnings: ($65,287,716)
Emp.: 592
Fiscal Year-end: 12/31/23
Medical Device Mfr & Distr
N.A.I.C.S.: 339112
Jeffrey R. Lindstrom (Pres)

MICROPORT SCIENTIFIC CORPORATION
1601 Zhangdong Road ZJ Hi-Tech Park, Shanghai, 201203, China
Tel.: (86) 2138954600
Web Site: https://www.microport.com
Year Founded: 1998
MCRPF—(OTCIQ)
Rev.: $840,831,000
Assets: $3,994,085,000
Liabilities: $2,201,417,000
Net Worth: $1,792,668,000
Earnings: ($588,115,000)
Emp.: 9,435
Fiscal Year-end: 12/31/22
Medical Device Mfr
N.A.I.C.S.: 339112
Zhaohua Chang (Chm & CEO)

Subsidiaries:

Dongguan Kewei Medical Instrument Co., Ltd. (1)
Tongqing Road, Dongcheng District, Dongguan, 523127, Guangdong, China
Tel.: (86) 76939001000
Medical Equipment Mfr & Distr
N.A.I.C.S.: 339112

Fujian Kerui Pharmaceutical Co., Ltd. (1)
Yuanzai Industrial Village, Haikou, Fuqing, 350313, Fujian, China
Tel.: (86) 15960103919
Web Site: https://www.fjkerui.com
Pharmaceuticals Mfr
N.A.I.C.S.: 325412

Hemovent GmbH (1)
Pascalstr 59, 52076, Aachen, Germany
Tel.: (49) 2419901330
Web Site: https://www.hemovent.com
Medical Device Mfr
N.A.I.C.S.: 339112

Lombard Medical Limited (1)
Lombard Medical House 4 Trident Park, Basil Hill Road, Didcot, OX11 7HJ, Oxon, United Kingdom
Tel.: (44) 1235750800
Web Site: http://www.lombardmedical.com
Sales Range: $25-49.9 Million
Medical Device Mfr
N.A.I.C.S.: 334519

MicroPort CRM B.V. (1)
Paasheuvelweg 25 BP, 1105, Amsterdam, Netherlands
Tel.: (31) 205450100
Medical Device Mfr
N.A.I.C.S.: 339112

MicroPort CRM SARL (1)
4 Avenue Reaumur, 92140, Clamart, France
Tel.: (33) 146013333
Medical Device Equipment Mfr & Distr
N.A.I.C.S.: 339112
Dawn Sadlowski (Mgr-Plant)

MicroPort Cardiac Rhythm B.V. (1)
Paasheuvelweg 25, 1105 BP, Amsterdam, Netherlands
Tel.: (31) 205450100
Medical Equipment Mfr & Distr
N.A.I.C.S.: 339112

MicroPort Medical (Shanghai) Co., Ltd. (1)
501 Newton Road Z J Hi-Tech Park, Shanghai, 201203, China
Tel.: (86) 2138954600
Medical Equipment Mfr
N.A.I.C.S.: 334510

MicroPort Medical B.V. (1)
Kellensweg 4, 4004 JD, Tiel, Gelderland, Netherlands
Tel.: (31) 344636250
Sales Range: $25-49.9 Million
Emp.: 2
Medical Equipment Mfr
N.A.I.C.S.: 339112
H. Chang (Mgr)

MicroPort NeuroTech (Shanghai) Co., Ltd. (1)
Building 16 222 Guangdan Rd Shanghai Medical Zone, Shanghai, 201318, China
Tel.: (86) 2138954600
Medical Device Equipment Mfr & Distr
N.A.I.C.S.: 339112

MicroPort Orthopedics Japan K.K. (1)
10th floor Iino Building 2-1-1 Uchisaiwaicho, Chiyoda-ku, Tokyo, 100-0011, Japan
Tel.: (81) 367587263
Web Site: https://www.microportortho.jp
Emp.: 80
Orthomedical Equipment Whslr
N.A.I.C.S.: 423450

MicroPort Scientific GmbH (1)
Harkortstrasse 11-13, 40880, Ratingen, Germany
Tel.: (49) 2102102620
Web Site: http://www.microportortho.de
Orthomedical Equipment Whslr
N.A.I.C.S.: 423450

MicroPort Sorin CRM (Shanghai) Co., Ltd. (1)
15th Floor No 1601 Zhangdong Road, Pudong District, Shanghai, 201203, China
Tel.: (86) 2168862000
Medical Device Equipment Mfr & Distr
N.A.I.C.S.: 339112

Shanghai MicroPort CardioFlow Medtech Co., Ltd. (1)
No 501 Newton Road Zhangjiang Science City Pudong New Area, Shanghai, 201203, China
Tel.: (86) 2138954600
Medical Device Equipment Mfr & Distr
N.A.I.C.S.: 339112

Shanghai MicroPort EP MedTech Co., Ltd. (1)
Building 28 Lane 588 Tianxiong Road, Shanghai, 201318, China
Tel.: (86) 2138954600
Web Site: https://www.ep.microport.com
Medical Device Equipment Mfr & Distr
N.A.I.C.S.: 339112

Shanghai MicroPort Endovascular Medtech Co., Ltd. (1)
9F 5F Building 1 25 3399 Kangxin Rd, SIMZ Century Medicine Park, Shanghai, 201318, China
Tel.: (86) 2138139300
Web Site: https://www.endovastec.com
Emp.: 300
Medical Equipment Mfr & Distr
N.A.I.C.S.: 339112

Shanghai Microport Access Medtech Co., Ltd. (1)
501 Newton Rd ZJ Hi-Tech Park, Shanghai, 201203, China
Tel.: (86) 2138954600
Medical Device Equipment Mfr & Distr
N.A.I.C.S.: 339112

Sorin CRM S.A.S. (1)
Parc d Affaires NOVEOS 4 avenue Reaumur, 92140, Clamart, France
Tel.: (33) 146013333
Medical Equipment Mfr & Distr
N.A.I.C.S.: 334510

AND PRIVATE COMPANIES

Subsidiary (US):

MicroPort Orthopedics Inc. (2)
5677 Airline Rd, Arlington, TN 38002
Web Site: http://www.microportortho.com
Medical Device Equipment Mfr & Distr
N.A.I.C.S.: 339113
Paul Bryant (CTO)

Sorin CRM USA, Inc. (2)
14401 W 65th Way, Arvada, CO
80004-3503 (100%)
Tel.: (303) 425-5508
Web Site: http://www.sorin.com
Sales Range: $25-49.9 Million
Emp.: 40
Cardio-Medical Device Mfr & Distr
N.A.I.C.S.: 339112

Suzhou MicroPort Orthopedics Scientific (Group) Co., Ltd. (1)
No 151 Fengli St SIP, Suzhou, 215000, Jiangsu, China
Tel.: (86) 51265001777
Medical Device Equipment Mfr & Distr
N.A.I.C.S.: 339112

MICROQUAL TECHNO LTD.

B52 Neo Shine House Ground Floor,
Andheri West, Mumbai, 400053, India
Tel.: (91) 2240741515 In
Web Site: http://www.microqual.com
Year Founded: 1999
Sales Range: $25-49.9 Million
Emp.: 300
Communication Equipment Mfr
N.A.I.C.S.: 334220
Mahesh Choudhary (Founder & CEO)

MICROSAIC SYSTEMS PLC

GMS House Boundary Road, Woking, GU21 5BX, Surrey, United Kingdom
Tel.: (44) 1483751577
Web Site: https://www.microsaic.com
Year Founded: 2001
MSYS—(AIM)
Rev.: $1,978,916
Assets: $3,947,658
Liabilities: $515,117
Net Worth: $3,432,541
Earnings: $2,889,055
Emp.: 22
Fiscal Year-end: 12/31/22
Spectrometry Instruments Mfr
N.A.I.C.S.: 334516
Phil Bray (Dir-Ops)

MICROSERVE LTD.

4295 Dawson St, Burnaby, V5C 4B3, BC, Canada
Tel.: (604) 473-9883
Web Site: http://www.microserve.ca
Year Founded: 1987
Sales Range: $25-49.9 Million
Emp.: 300
IT Consulting, Integration, Design & Other Computer & Business Services
N.A.I.C.S.: 541519
Heather Schaan (VP)

MICROSKIN PLC

271a Rode Road, Wavell Heights, Brisbane, 4012, Australia
Tel.: (61) 7 32 60 6125
Web Site: http://www.microskin.com
Cosmetics Products Mfr
N.A.I.C.S.: 456120
Barry Amor (Chm)

MICROSOL INTERNATIONAL LL FZE

205 208 Fujairah Freezone Phase II, PO Box No 4940, Fujairah, United Arab Emirates
Tel.: (971) 9 228 2138
Web Site:
http://www.microsolinternational.com
Sales Range: $150-199.9 Million

Emp.: 300
Solar Energy Products Mfr
N.A.I.C.S.: 221114
Penubolu Suryanarayana (Dir-Bus Dev)

Subsidiaries:

Solon Energy GmbH (1)
Am Studio 16, 12489, Berlin, Germany
Tel.: (49) 30818790
Web Site: http://www.solon.com
Sales Range: $800-899.9 Million
Solar Cell Mfr
N.A.I.C.S.: 221114
Lars Podlowski (CTO)

Subsidiary (US):

SOLON Corporation (2)
6950 S Country Club Rd, Tucson, AZ 85706-7151
Tel.: (520) 807-1300
Sales Range: $25-49.9 Million
Emp.: 90
Photovoltaic Device Mfr
N.A.I.C.S.: 334413

Subsidiary (Domestic):

SOLON Investments GmbH. (2)
Emmy-Noether-Strasse 2, 79110, Freiburg, Baden-Wurttemberg, Germany
Tel.: (49) 7611563380
Sales Range: $150-199.9 Million
Solar Power Plants Construction & Installation Services
N.A.I.C.S.: 237130

SOLON Mobility GmbH (2)
Am Studio 16, 12489, Berlin, Germany
Tel.: (49) 3081879574
Web Site: http://www.solon.com
Sales Range: $100-124.9 Million
Emp.: 35
Renewable Energy Mobility Services
N.A.I.C.S.: 237130
Stefan Saeubereith (Mng Dir)

SOLON Nord GmbH. (2)
Siemensallee 1, 17489, Greifswald, Germany
Tel.: (49) 3834 810 2701
Web Site: http://www.solon-nord.com
Electrical Components & Photovoltaic Systems Mfr
N.A.I.C.S.: 334413

Subsidiary (Non-US):

SOLON S.p.A. (2)
Via dell'Industria e dell'Artigianato 2, 35010, Carmignano di Brenta, Padua, Italy
Tel.: (39) 049 945820 0
Web Site: http://www.solon.com
Emp.: 20
Solar Module Mfr
N.A.I.C.S.: 334419
Rolando Gennari (Mng Dir)

SOLON SAS (2)
120 Allee Jacques Monod, 69800, Saint Priest, France
Tel.: (33) 4 78 67 37 05
Web Site: http://www.solon.com
Solar Modules Sales
N.A.I.C.S.: 423720

MICROSPORE S.P.A.

Strada Satale 87 Km 204, 86035, Larino, Italy
Tel.: (39) 0874 824085
Web Site: http://www.microspore.com
Year Founded: 1981
Sales Range: $25-49.9 Million
Emp.: 52
Fertilizer & Other Agricultural Products Mfr & Distr
N.A.I.C.S.: 325314
Enrico Torzi (Founder)

MICROTEC S.R.L.

Via Julius-Durst Strabe 98, 39042, Bressanone, Italy
Tel.: (39) 0472 273 611
Web Site: http://www.microtec.eu
Year Founded: 1980

Wood Scanning & Optimization Systems & Products
N.A.I.C.S.: 321999
Frank Jost (CEO)

Subsidiaries:

Lucidyne Technologies, Inc. (1)
155 SW Madison Ave, Corvallis, OR 97333
Tel.: (541) 753-5111
Web Site: http://www.lucidyne.com
Sawmills & Wood Processing Services
N.A.I.C.S.: 321113
George Carman (Pres)

MICROTECH MEDICAL (HANGZHOU) CO., LTD.

No 108 Liuze Street Cangqian Street, Yuhang, Hangzhou, Zhejiang, China
Tel.: (86) 57185852073 CN
Web Site:
https://www.microtechmd.com
Year Founded: 2011
2235—(HKG)
Rev.: $35,061,415
Assets: $298,900,909
Liabilities: $13,526,994
Net Worth: $285,373,914
Earnings: ($17,309,464)
Emp.: 760
Fiscal Year-end: 12/31/23
Medical Device Mfr
N.A.I.C.S.: 339112
Fangling Xu (VP)

MICROTEK INTERNATIONAL, INC.

No 6 Industry East Road 3 Science-based Industrial Park, Hsin-chu, 30075, Taiwan
Tel.: (886) 35772155
Web Site: https://www.microtek.com
Year Founded: 1980
2305—(TAI)
Rev.: $18,833,414
Assets: $93,654,858
Liabilities: $20,723,339
Net Worth: $72,931,519
Earnings: $728,179
Emp.: 250
Fiscal Year-end: 12/31/23
Mfr of Innovative Scanners & Digital Imaging Solutions Products
N.A.I.C.S.: 334118

Subsidiaries:

Microtek Computer Technology (Wu Jiang) Co., Ltd (1)
No 499 JiangXing East Road, WuJiang Economic and Technological Development Zone, Suzhou, 215217, JiangSu, China
Tel.: (86) 51263401290
Web Site: http://www.microtekusa.com
Computer Peripheral Distr
N.A.I.C.S.: 423430

Microtek International Development Systems Division Inc (1)
Keegan Ave, Carson, CA 90746
Tel.: (310) 687-5800
Web Site: http://www.microtekintl.com
Sales Range: $50-74.9 Million
Emp.: 5
Computer Peripheral Distr
N.A.I.C.S.: 423430

Microtek Lab Inc (1)
9960 Bell Ranch Dr Unit 103, Santa Fe Springs, CA 90670
Tel.: (310) 687-5800
Web Site: http://www.microtekusa.com
Sales Range: $25-49.9 Million
Emp.: 5
Computer Peripheral Distr
N.A.I.C.S.: 334118

Shanghai Microtek Medical Device Co., Ltd (1)
Building 35 No 680 Guiping Rd, Shanghai, 200233, China
Tel.: (86) 216 485 6614

Photographic & Photocopying Equipment Mfr
N.A.I.C.S.: 333310

Shanghai Microtek Technology Co., Ltd (1)
Building 35 No 680 Guiping Road, Shanghai, 200233, China
Tel.: (86) 2164856614
Web Site: http://www.microtek.com.cn
Sales Range: $50-74.9 Million
Emp.: 100
Computer Peripheral Distr
N.A.I.C.S.: 423430

Shanghai Microtek Trading Co., Ltd (1)
Bldg 35 No 680 Guiping Rd, Shanghai, 200233, PRC, China
Tel.: (86) 2164856614
Web Site: http://www.microtek.com.cn
Sales Range: $50-74.9 Million
Emp.: 100
Computer Peripheral Distr
N.A.I.C.S.: 423430

MICROTIPS TECHNOLOGY INC.

12F No 31 Lane 169 Kang-Ning St, Hsi-Chih District, New Taipei City, 221, Taiwan
Tel.: (886) 226923889
Web Site:
https://www.microtips.com.tw
3285—(TPE)
Rev.: $26,821,499
Assets: $29,136,541
Liabilities: $10,577,369
Net Worth: $18,559,172
Earnings: ($283,338)
Fiscal Year-end: 12/31/22
Electronic Products Mfr
N.A.I.C.S.: 337126
Shyan-Tzeng Yang (Chm)

Subsidiaries:

Microtips Inc. (1)
Dong-Shen Road, Si-Ma Village Chang-Ping Town, Dongguan, 523570, Guangdong, China
Tel.: (86) 76983975888
Electronic Component Mfr & Distr
N.A.I.C.S.: 334419

Microtips Technology LLC (1)
3504 Lake Lynda Dr Ste 110, Orlando, FL 32817
Tel.: (407) 273-0204
Web Site: https://www.microtipsusa.com
Rev.: $9,000,000
Emp.: 6
Light Emitting Diode Module Mfr & Distr
N.A.I.C.S.: 334419
Nadim Rahman (Chief Technical Officer)

MICROWARE LIMITED

1/F Century Centre 44-46 Hung To Road Kwun Tong, Kowloon, China (Hong Kong)
Tel.: (852) 28565678 Ky
Web Site:
http://www.microware.com.hk
Year Founded: 1985
1985—(HKG)
Rev.: $143,719,447
Assets: $63,132,357
Liabilities: $34,650,993
Net Worth: $28,481,364
Earnings: $6,052,000
Emp.: 263
Fiscal Year-end: 03/31/21
Information Technology Support Services
N.A.I.C.S.: 541512
Ming Ho Chu (Chm & CEO)

MICROWAVE VISION SA

47 boulevard Saint Michel, 75005, Paris, France
Tel.: (33) 175775850

MICROWAVE VISION SA

Microwave Vision SA—(Continued)

Web Site:
http://www.microwavevision.com
Year Founded: 2008
ALMIC—(EUR)
Sales Range: $50-74.9 Million
Electromagnetic Field Measurement Systems Mfr
N.A.I.C.S.: 334515
Shawn Shadrokh *(Project Mgr)*

Subsidiaries:

Advanced ElectroMagnetics, Inc (1)
1320 Air Wing Rd Ste 101, San Diego, CA 92154
Tel.: (619) 449-9492
Web Site: http://www.aemi-inc.com
Sales Range: $25-49.9 Million
Emp.: 30
Measurement System Mfr & Sales
N.A.I.C.S.: 334513
Peter Deal *(Mgr-Mktg)*

ORBIT/FR, Inc. (1)
506 Prudential Rd, Horsham, PA 19044
Tel.: (215) 674-5100
Web Site: http://www.orbitfr.com
Rev.: $34,508,000
Assets: $31,838,000
Liabilities: $22,522,000
Net Worth: $9,316,000
Earnings: ($2,365,000)
Emp.: 141
Fiscal Year-end: 12/31/2015
N.A.I.C.S.: 334290

Satimo Industries, SA (1)
17 Avenue De Norvege, 91140, Villebon-sur-Yvette, Essonne, France
Tel.: (33) 169290247
Web Site: http://www.satimo.com
Sales Range: $25-49.9 Million
Emp.: 20
Electric Device Mfr
N.A.I.C.S.: 334515
Eric Beaumong *(Mgr-Mktg)*

MICS CHEMICAL CO.,LTD.

158-89 MorowaKitayama, AichigunTougou-tyou, Nagoya, 470-0151, Aichi, Japan
Tel.: (81) 56391211
Web Site: http://www.c-mics.com
Year Founded: 1959
7899—(TKS)
Rev.: $25,216,400
Assets: $37,451,920
Liabilities: $7,037,360
Net Worth: $30,414,560
Earnings: $300,080
Fiscal Year-end: 04/30/22
Food Products Mfr
N.A.I.C.S.: 311999
Shigeki Ohtsuka *(Pres)*

MICUBE SOLUTION, INC.

3F-5F 23 Hyoryeong-ro 55-gil, Seocho-gu, Seoul, 06654, Korea (South)
Tel.: (82) 25532171
Web Site: https://www.micube.co.kr
Year Founded: 2010
373170—(KRS)
Software Development Services
N.A.I.C.S.: 541511
Park Moon-Won *(Co-CEO)*

MICWARE CO. LTD.

1-1-3 Higashikawasaki-cho Kobe Crystal Tower 20F, Chuo-ku, Kobe, 650-0044, Japan
Tel.: (81) 78 366 5780 JP
Web Site: http://www.micware.co.jp
Year Founded: 2003
Navigation Software Development Services
N.A.I.C.S.: 334610
Kenji Narushima *(Pres & Dir)*

Subsidiaries:

HI Corporation (1)
Pacific Marks Shinjuku Park Side 2nd Floor 4-15-7 Nishi-shinjuku, Shinjuku-ku, Tokyo, 160-0023, Japan
Tel.: (81) 353337550
Web Site: http://www.hicorp.co.jp
Sales Range: $10-24.9 Million
Emp.: 28
Computer Software & 3D Content Developer & Distr
N.A.I.C.S.: 513210
Takeshi Sato *(Pres & CEO)*

Subsidiary (Non-US):

HI Korea & Co. (2)
2 19 Yeajang Dong Chung gu, Seoul, 100 250, Korea (South)
Tel.: (82) 222808154
Embedded Design Services
N.A.I.C.S.: 541490

MID COUNTIES CO-OPERATIVE

Co-operative House, Warwick Technology Park Gallows Hill, Warwick, CV34 6DA, United Kingdom
Tel.: (44) 1926 516000 UK
Web Site:
http://www.midcounties.coop
Year Founded: 1985
Rev.: $1,493,711,412
Assets: $894,934,477
Liabilities: $658,057,935
Net Worth: $236,876,542
Earnings: ($14,026,478)
Emp.: 4,473
Fiscal Year-end: 01/26/19
Retail Management Services
N.A.I.C.S.: 561499
Patrick Gray *(VP)*

Subsidiaries:

Countrystore (Maidenhead) Limited (1)
Station Road, Cookham, Maidenhead, SL6 9BT, Berkshire, United Kingdom
Tel.: (44) 1628522161
Web Site: http://www.cstore.co.uk
Grocery Product Whslr
N.A.I.C.S.: 424490

First Steps Childrens Nursery Limited (1)
25-27 Thanet Road, Margate, CT9 1UA, Kent, United Kingdom
Tel.: (44) 1843294256
Web Site:
http://www.firststepsnurserymargate.co.uk
Child Day Care Services
N.A.I.C.S.: 624410
Monique Chantler *(Supvr)*

Tavistock House Day Nursery Limited (1)
Tavistock House Borough Road, Sunderland, SR1 1PG, Tyne and Wear, United Kingdom
Tel.: (44) 1915140411
Web Site:
http://www.nurseriesinsunderland.co.uk
Child Day Care Services
N.A.I.C.S.: 624410

MID EUROPA PARTNERS LLP

South West House 11a Regent Street, London, SW1Y 4LR, United Kingdom
Tel.: (44) 2078863600 UK
Web Site: http://www.mideuropa.com
Year Founded: 2005
Rev.: $6,978,048,000
Emp.: 24
Privater Equity Firm
N.A.I.C.S.: 523999
Thierry Baudon *(Founder, Chm & Partner)*

Subsidiaries:

AeskuLab Holding, a.s. (1)

Evropska 2589/33b, Prague, Czech Republic
Tel.: (420) 255 775 200
Web Site: http://www.aeskulab.cz
Laboratory Testing Services
N.A.I.C.S.: 621511
Kamil Dolezel *(Gen Mgr)*

Diagnostyka Sp. z o.o. (1)
ul Prof Michala Zyczkowskiego 16, 31 864, Krakow, Poland
Tel.: (48) 122950100
Web Site: https://grupadiagnostyka.pl
Medical Laboratory Services
N.A.I.C.S.: 621511
Krzysztof Wojewoda *(Dir-Sls Dept)*

Energy 21 a.s. (1)
Building International Business Center Pobrezni 3, 186 00, Prague, Czech Republic
Tel.: (420) 267 997 784
Web Site: http://www.energy21.cz
Solar Power Generation Services
N.A.I.C.S.: 221114
Lubomira Stranska *(Accountant)*

Mid Europa Partners Kft (1)
Bank Center Citi Tower 2rd Floor Szabadsag ter 7, 1054, Budapest, Hungary
Tel.: (36) 14111270
Sales Range: $50-74.9 Million
Emp.: 9
Privater Equity Firm
N.A.I.C.S.: 523999
Thierry Baudon *(Gen Mgr)*

Holding (Domestic):

Invitel Holdings A/S (2)
Puskas Tivadar u 8-10, H-2040, Budaors, Hungary (91%)
Tel.: (36) 18011500
Web Site: http://english.invitel.hu
Sales Range: $1-9.9 Million
Emp.: 1,399
Holding Company; Communications Services
N.A.I.C.S.: 551112

Branch (US):

Invitel Holdings - U.S. Executive Office (3)
1201 3rd Ave Ste 3400, Seattle, WA 98101-3034
Tel.: (206) 654-0204
Executive Office
N.A.I.C.S.: 921110
Peter T. Noone *(Grp Gen Counsel & Sec)*

Subsidiary (Domestic):

Invitel Tavkozlesi Szolgaltato Zrt. (3)
Puskas Tivadar u 8-10, H-2040, Budaors, Hungary
Tel.: (36) 1 801 1500
Web Site: http://www.invitel.hu
Internet & Telecommunications Services
N.A.I.C.S.: 517111

Subsidiary (Non-US):

Euroweb Romania, S.A. (4)
Nouveau Ctr, Str Lipscani 102, Bucharest, Romania
Tel.: (40) 213076543
Web Site: http://www.euroweb.ro
Internet Services
N.A.I.C.S.: 517810
Ioneita Babi *(Mgr-IT)*

Mid Europa Partners Sp. z o.o. (1)
Warsaw Financial Center Fl 29, Ul. Emilii Plater 53, Warsaw, 113, Poland
Tel.: (48) 225407120
Web Site: http://www.mideuropa.com
Sales Range: $50-74.9 Million
Emp.: 9
Privater Equity Firm
N.A.I.C.S.: 523999
Zbigniew Rekusz *(Partner)*

Holding (Non-US):

UAB Bite Lietuva (2)
Uriekstes Iela 2A, Riga, LV-1005, Latvia
Tel.: (371) 25850600
Web Site: http://www.bite.lv
Sales Range: $100-124.9 Million
Mobile Communication & Internet Services
N.A.I.C.S.: 517112

INTERNATIONAL PUBLIC

Christopher Alan Robbins *(Chm-Mgmt Bd & CEO)*

MidEuropa Fund Management Limited (1)
Tudor House 2nd Floor Le Bordage, Saint Peter Port, GY1 1BT, Guernsey
Tel.: (44) 1481742300
Private Equity Services
N.A.I.C.S.: 523150

MidEuropa Fund Management Luxembourg Sarl (1)
2nd Floor 163 Rue du Kiem, Strassen, Luxembourg
Tel.: (352) 2812481
Private Equity Services
N.A.I.C.S.: 523150

MidEuropa SRL (1)
Charles de Gaulle Building 5th Floor, 15 Charles de Gaulle Plaza, 011857, Bucharest, Romania
Tel.: (40) 314337425
Private Equity Services
N.A.I.C.S.: 523150

MID INDIA INDUSTRIES LIMITED

401 Princess Centre 63 New Palasia, Indore, 452003, India
Tel.: (91) 7312433231
Web Site:
https://www.midindiaindustries.com
Year Founded: 1991
500277—(BOM)
Rev.: $1,761,610
Assets: $679,655
Liabilities: $1,169,280
Net Worth: ($489,625)
Earnings: $53,912
Emp.: 3
Fiscal Year-end: 03/31/23
Cotton Yarn Mfr
N.A.I.C.S.: 313110
Shailendra Agrawal *(Officer-Compliance & Sec)*

MID NORTH MOTORS (SUDBURY) LTD.

2100 Kingsway, Sudbury, P3B 2G2, ON, Canada
Tel.: (705) 560-2100
Web Site:
http://www.midnorthmitsubishi.com
Rev.: $24,142,860
Emp.: 65
New & Used Car Dealers
N.A.I.C.S.: 441110
Chris Scagnetti *(Gen Mgr)*

MID URBAN DEVELOPMENT CO., LTD.

1-4-4 Dojimahama Kita-ku, Osaka, 530-0004, Japan
Tel.: (81) 663469500
Web Site: http://www.mid.co.jp
Year Founded: 1999
Sales Range: $1-4.9 Billion
Emp.: 160
Real Estate Developement Services Focusing on Buildings & Residential Housing
N.A.I.C.S.: 236220
Isao Yamamoto *(Pres)*

MID WYND INTERNATIONAL INVESTMENT TRUST PLC

6th Floor Exchange Plaza 50 Lothian Road, Edinburgh, EH3 9BY, United Kingdom
Tel.: (44) 1312257300 UK
MWY—(LSE)
Assets: $588,114,394
Liabilities: $23,116,664
Net Worth: $564,997,730
Earnings: ($49,079,224)
Fiscal Year-end: 06/30/22
Investment Management Service

MID-TOWN FORD SALES LIMITED
100 1717 Waverley St, Winnipeg, R3T 6A9, MB, Canada
Tel.: (204) 284-7650
Web Site: http://www.midtown-ford.com
Sales Range: $25-49.9 Million
New & Used Car Dealers
N.A.I.C.S.: 441110
Dean Craig *(Sls Mgr-Used Vehicle)*

MIDA ASSETS PUBLIC CO,.LTD.
267 Charansanitwong Rd Bang-or, Bangplad, Bangkok, 10700, Thailand
Tel.: (66) 24342390
Web Site: https://www.midaassets.com
Year Founded: 1991
MIDA—(THA)
Rev.: $96,810,206
Assets: $307,493,324
Liabilities: $201,164,493
Net Worth: $106,328,832
Earnings: $8,522,304
Fiscal Year-end: 12/31/23
Electrical Appliances Repairing Services
N.A.I.C.S.: 811412
Wisood Ieosivikul *(Chm & Mng Dir)*

Subsidiaries:

Max Hotel Co., Ltd. (1)
29/67 Moo 9 Bangkrasor Muang, Nonthaburi, 11000, Thailand
Tel.: (66) 2591 7227
Web Site: http://www.midahotelngamwongwan.com
Home Management Services
N.A.I.C.S.: 721110

Mida Hotel and Resort Co., Ltd (1)
99/401-468 Soi Chaeng Wattana 10 Thung Song Hong Laksi, Bangkok, 10210, Thailand
Tel.: (66) 859565950
Web Site: https://www.mhg.co.th
Home Management Services
N.A.I.C.S.: 561110

Mida Leasing Public Company Limited (1)
48/1-5 Soi Chaeng Watthana 14 Chaeng Watthana Road, Thung Song Hong Subdistrict Lak Si, Bangkok, 10210, Thailand (60%)
Tel.: (66) 25746901
Web Site: https://www.mida-leasing.com
Rev.: $19,060,143
Assets: $137,512,994
Liabilities: $71,507,732
Net Worth: $66,005,263
Earnings: $3,287,705
Fiscal Year-end: 12/31/2020
Motor Vehicle Leasing Services
N.A.I.C.S.: 532112
Wisood Ieosivikul *(Chm & Pres)*

Mida Property Co., Ltd. (1)
267 Charansanitwong Road, Bang O Subdistrict Bang Phlat District, Bangkok, 10700, Thailand
Tel.: (66) 28855558
Web Site: https://www.midaproperty.com
Real Estate Services
N.A.I.C.S.: 531210

MIDAC HOLDINGS CO., LTD.
2163 Aritamaminamimachi, Chuo-ku, Hamamatsu, 431-3122, Shizuoka, Japan
Tel.: (81) 534719364
Web Site: https://www.midac.jp
Year Founded: 1952
6564—(NGO)
Rev.: $63,078,938
Assets: $177,740,287
Liabilities: $93,240,806
Net Worth: $84,499,481
Earnings: $12,599,930
Emp.: 350
Fiscal Year-end: 03/31/24
Waste Treatment & Disposal Services
N.A.I.C.S.: 562219
Keiko Kato *(Chm & Pres)*

Subsidiaries:

Midac Konan Co., Ltd. (1)
902-1 Magori-cho, Chuo-ku, Hamamatsu, 431-0203, Shizuoka, Japan
Tel.: (81) 535237788
Emp.: 32
General Waste Transport Services
N.A.I.C.S.: 562112

Midac Liner Co., Ltd. (1)
2163 Aritama minami-machi, Chuo-ku, Hamamatsu, 431-3122, Shizuoka, Japan
Tel.: (81) 534719380
Emp.: 44
General Waste Transport Services
N.A.I.C.S.: 562112

MIDAS AI CO., LTD.
A-1306 Woolimblue 9 Business Center 583 Yangcheon-ro, Gangseo-gu, Seoul, Korea (South)
Tel.: (82) 234978900
Year Founded: 2015
222810—(KRS)
Rev.: $89,382,316
Assets: $56,902,898
Liabilities: $34,448,771
Net Worth: $22,454,127
Earnings: ($31,217,151)
Emp.: 33
Fiscal Year-end: 12/31/22
Financial Investment Management Services
N.A.I.C.S.: 523940

MIDAS FINANCING LIMITED
MIDAS Center 10th 11th Floor House 05 Road 16 New 27 Old, Dhanmondi, Dhaka, 1209, Bangladesh
Tel.: (880) 9611221055
Web Site: https://www.mfl.com.bd
Year Founded: 1995
MIDASFIN—(CHT)
Rev.: $8,490,853
Assets: $109,394,694
Liabilities: $94,169,542
Net Worth: $15,225,153
Earnings: $56,774
Emp.: 197
Fiscal Year-end: 12/31/22
Financial Services
N.A.I.C.S.: 523999
Ahmed Ibne Mazid Khan *(Asst Gen Mgr-Internal Audit)*

Subsidiaries:

MIDAS Investment Ltd. (1)
MIDAS Centre 6th Floor House-05 Road-16 New 27 Old, Dhanmondi, Dhaka, 1209, Bangladesh
Tel.: (880) 9611221055
Web Site: https://www.midasinvbd.com
Financial Services
N.A.I.C.S.: 523999
Nazneen Sultana *(Chm)*

MIDAS GROUP (PTY) LTD
No 2 Gordon Ave Needo View Buissness, Meadowdale, Sandton, 2090, South Africa
Tel.: (27) 118796000
Web Site: http://www.midas.co.za
Sales Range: $75-99.9 Million
Emp.: 1,000
Automotive Parts
N.A.I.C.S.: 441330
Gordon Odgers *(Mng Dir)*

MIDAS INFRA TRADE LTD.
301 2633-2634 Bank Street Karol Bagh, New Delhi, 110005, India
Tel.: (91) 1142633934
Web Site: https://www.mitl.webresearch.com
Year Founded: 1994
531192—(BOM)
Rev.: $21,646,457
Assets: $4,537,301
Liabilities: $2,425,919
Net Worth: $2,111,382
Earnings: ($201,856)
Emp.: 32
Fiscal Year-end: 03/31/21
Financial Services
N.A.I.C.S.: 523999
Madhvi Gupta *(Exec Dir)*

MIDAS MINERALS LTD.
Level 2 8 Richardson St, West Perth, 6005, WA, Australia
Tel.: (61) 863836595 AU
Web Site: https://www.midasminerals.com
Year Founded: 2018
MM1—(ASX)
Rev.: $24,985
Assets: $4,162,622
Liabilities: $170,329
Net Worth: $3,992,293
Earnings: ($3,464,488)
Fiscal Year-end: 12/31/23
Mineral Exploration Services
N.A.I.C.S.: 212390
Carl Travaglini *(CFO)*

MIDASCO CAPITAL CORP.
605-815 Hornby St, Vancouver, V6Z 2E6, BC, Canada
Tel.: (604) 503-0986
Web Site: http://www.midascocapital.com
MGC—(TSXV)
Assets: $144,572
Liabilities: $4,191
Net Worth: $140,380
Earnings: ($57,906)
Fiscal Year-end: 12/31/21
Mineral Exploration Services
N.A.I.C.S.: 213114
William C. Pettigrew *(CEO)*

MIDDENDORP ELECTRIC CO., PTY. LTD.
L-1 372a Victoria St, PO Box 1, Brunswick, Melbourne, 3056, VIC, Australia
Tel.: (61) 393880000
Web Site: http://www.middys.com.au
Year Founded: 1928
Electrical Equipment Distr
N.A.I.C.S.: 423610
Nick Clark *(CEO)*

MIDDLE & WEST DELTA FLOUR MILLS
19 El Galaa St, PO Box 202, Tanta, Egypt
Tel.: (20) 403296810
Year Founded: 1967
WCDF.CA—(EGX)
Sales Range: Less than $1 Million
Agricultural Product Mfr
N.A.I.C.S.: 311211
Mohammed Abdul Ghaffar Mohammed Al Sabea *(Chm & Mng Dir)*

MIDDLE EAST AIRLINES AIR-LIBAN S.A.L.
MEA Head Office Airport Rd, PO Box 206, Beirut International Airport, Beirut, 0111, Lebanon
Tel.: (961) 1628888
Web Site: http://www.mea.com.lb
Year Founded: 1946
Sales Range: $200-249.9 Million
Emp.: 3,500
Provider of Airline Services
N.A.I.C.S.: 481111

Mohamad A. El Hout *(Chm & Dir Gen)*

Subsidiaries:

MASCO Mideast Aircraft Services Company (1)
Rafic Hariri International Airport - Boulevard MEA Headquarter - Masco, Beirut, 09-755, Lebanon
Tel.: (961) 1622350
Web Site: https://masco.com.lb
Aircraft Services
N.A.I.C.S.: 488190
Yassine Sabbagh *(Gen Mgr)*

Middle East Airline Ground Handing S.A.L. (1)
Rafic Hariri International Airport -MEA Headquarter, Beirut, Lebanon
Tel.: (961) 1622700
Web Site: https://meag.com.lb
Flying Field Services
N.A.I.C.S.: 488119
Richard Mujais *(Gen Mgr)*

Middle East Airports Services (MEAS) SAL (1)
Beirut Airport, PO Box 13 6225, Chouran, Beirut, Lebanon (100%)
Tel.: (961) 1628888
Web Site: http://www.measairports.com
Sales Range: $125-149.9 Million
Emp.: 350
Provider of Operational & Maintence Services for Facilities & Systems of Beirut International Airport
N.A.I.C.S.: 481111

MIDDLE EAST DIAMOND RESOURCES LIMITED
Kingsley Office Park Block A Ground Floor, 85 Protea Road Chislehurston, Sandton, South Africa
Tel.: (27) 11 326 5630 ZA
Year Founded: 2001
Sales Range: Less than $1 Million
Mineral Exploration Services
N.A.I.C.S.: 212290
Deon Botha *(Fin Dir)*

MIDDLE EAST GLASS MANUFACTURING
6 El-Mokhayam El-Daem St, 6th District, Nasr, Cairo, Egypt
Tel.: (20) 223814834
Web Site: https://www.meg.com.eg
Year Founded: 1979
MEGM.CA—(EGX)
Rev.: $129,847,105
Assets: $178,601,649
Liabilities: $132,041,978
Net Worth: $46,559,670
Earnings: $19,349,363
Emp.: 2,000
Fiscal Year-end: 12/31/23
Glass Mfr
N.A.I.C.S.: 327212
Abdulgalil Besher *(Chm)*

MIDDLE EAST HEALTHCARE CO
Al Batterjee Street, PO Box 2550, Al-Zahra District, Jeddah, 21461, Saudi Arabia
Tel.: (966) 122606000
Web Site: https://saudigermanhealth.com
Year Founded: 1988
4009—(SAU)
Rev.: $573,721,833
Assets: $1,199,581,641
Liabilities: $824,122,410
Net Worth: $375,459,231
Earnings: $19,091,418
Emp.: 9,000
Fiscal Year-end: 12/31/22
Health Care Srvices
N.A.I.C.S.: 621999
Sobhi Batterjee *(Chm)*

MIDDLE EAST INSURANCE CO. PLC

Middle East Healthcare Co—(Continued)

MIDDLE EAST INSURANCE CO. PLC
Zahran Street Building No 14, PO Box 1802, Amman, 11118, Jordan
Tel.: (962) 5005400
Web Site: http://www.meico.com.jo
Year Founded: 1962
Sales Range: $25-49.9 Million
Emp.: 142
Insurance Services
N.A.I.C.S.: 524298
Majed Smeirat *(Gen Mgr)*

MIDDLE EAST PAPER COMPANY
Prince Mohammed Bin Abdulaziz St Al Andalus Nojoud Center, PO Box 9249, 1st floor entrance A Unit No 45, Jeddah, 23326, Saudi Arabia
Tel.: (966) 126380111
Web Site: https://ir.mepco.biz
1202—(SAU)
Rev.: $316,492,680
Assets: $519,001,299
Liabilities: $203,767,031
Net Worth: $315,234,268
Earnings: $72,184,991
Emp.: 1,163
Fiscal Year-end: 12/31/22
Paperboard Container Mfr
N.A.I.C.S.: 322219
Ahmed El Fazary *(Chief Comml Officer)*

Subsidiaries:

Waste Collection & Recycling Co., Ltd. **(1)**
PO Box 54033, Jeddah, 21514, Saudi Arabia
Tel.: (966) 22897029
Web Site: https://www.wasco-sa.com
Emp.: 800
Waste Recycling Services
N.A.I.C.S.: 562920

MIDDLE EAST PRODUCING & MARKETING FISH
Al-Whda 15 St Nasser Helwa Building, Baghdad, Iraq
Tel.: (964) 17182629
Year Founded: 1994
AMEF—(IRAQ)
Sales Range: Less than $1 Million
Fish Farming Services
N.A.I.C.S.: 112511

MIDDLE EAST SPECIALIZED CABLES CO
Salah Uddin Street Al Bait Building 1Floor 1, PO Box 60536, Riyadh, 11555, Saudi Arabia
Tel.: (966) 112650555 SA
Web Site: https://www.mesccables.com
Year Founded: 1993
2370—(SAU)
Rev.: $247,056,662
Assets: $205,541,555
Liabilities: $104,884,484
Net Worth: $100,657,072
Earnings: $13,043,450
Emp.: 448
Fiscal Year-end: 12/31/23
Specialized Cables Mfr
N.A.I.C.S.: 335929
Yahya Ibraheem Alqunaibit *(Chm)*

MIDDLE ISLAND RESOURCES LIMITED
Suite 1 2 Richardson Street, West Perth, 6005, WA, Australia
Tel.: (61) 893221430
Web Site:
   http://www.middleisland.com.au
Rev.: $738,212

Assets: $4,700,350
Liabilities: $1,251,674
Net Worth: $3,448,676
Earnings: ($1,201,801)
Emp.: 60
Fiscal Year-end: 06/30/18
Gold Exploration Services
N.A.I.C.S.: 212220
Rick Yeates *(Mng Dir)*

MIDDLEFIELD CANADIAN INCOME PCC
199 Bishopsgate, London, EC2M 3TY, United Kingdom
Tel.: (44) 1481727111
MCC—(AIM)
Sales Range: Less than $1 Million
Investment Fund Services
N.A.I.C.S.: 525910
C. Orrico *(Mgr-Investments)*

MIDDLEFIELD GROUP LIMITED
First Canadian Place 58th Floor, PO Box 192, Toronto, M5X 1A6, ON, Canada
Tel.: (416) 362-0714
Web Site: http://www.middlefield.com
Year Founded: 1979
Sales Range: $75-99.9 Million
Emp.: 110
Holding Company; Investment Advisory, Fund Management & Real Estate Investment Services
N.A.I.C.S.: 551112
Robert F. Lauzon *(Mng Dir)*

Subsidiaries:

Middlefield Capital Corporation **(1)**
First Canadian Place 58th Floor, PO Box 192, Toronto, M5X 1A6, ON, Canada
Tel.: (416) 362-0714
Web Site: http://www.middlefield.com
Investment Advisory & Management Services
N.A.I.C.S.: 523940
Richard L. Faiella *(Mng Dir-Intl)*

Subsidiary (US):

Middlefield Financial Services Inc. **(2)**
1 Embarcadero Ctr Ste 500, San Francisco, CA 94111
Tel.: (415) 835-1308
Web Site: http://www.middlefield.com
Sales Range: $75-99.9 Million
Emp.: 3
Investment Advisory & Management Services
N.A.I.C.S.: 523940

Subsidiary (Non-US):

Middlefield International Limited **(2)**
288 Bishopsgate, London, EC2M 3TY, United Kingdom
Tel.: (44) 207 814 6644
Web Site: http://www.middlefield.co.uk
Sales Range: $50-74.9 Million
Emp.: 40
Investment Advisory & Management Services
N.A.I.C.S.: 523940
Richard L. Faiella *(Mng Dir)*

Middlefield Limited **(1)**
812 Memorial Drive NW, Calgary, T2N 3C8, AB, Canada
Tel.: (403) 269-2100
Web Site: http://www.middlefield.com
Open & Closed-End Investment Fund Management Services
N.A.I.C.S.: 523940

Affiliate (Domestic):

INDEXPLUS Income Fund **(2)**
812 Memorial Drive NW, Calgary, T2N 3C8, AB, Canada
Tel.: (403) 269-2100
Web Site: http://www.middlefield.com

Sales Range: $1-9.9 Million
Closed-End Investment Fund
N.A.I.C.S.: 525990

MBN Corporation **(2)**
812 Memorial Drive NW, Calgary, T2N 3C8, AB, Canada
Tel.: (403) 269-2100
Web Site: http://www.middlefield.com
Rev.: $1,626,495
Assets: $27,609,813
Liabilities: $379,223
Net Worth: $27,230,590
Earnings: $1,117,522
Fiscal Year-end: 12/31/2020
Gas & Oil Investment Trust
N.A.I.C.S.: 525990

Middlefield Can-Global REIT Income Fund **(2)**
812 Memorial Drive NW, Calgary, T2N 3C8, AB, Canada
Tel.: (403) 269-2100
Web Site: http://www.middlefield.com
Rev.: $2,283,314
Assets: $15,104,371
Liabilities: $912,997
Net Worth: $14,191,374
Earnings: ($2,567,504)
Fiscal Year-end: 12/31/2020
Real Estate Investment Trust
N.A.I.C.S.: 525990
Dean Orrico *(Pres & Chief Investment Officer)*

Middlefield REIT INDEXPLUS ETF **(2)**
812 Memorial Drive NW, Calgary, T2N 3C8, AB, Canada
Tel.: (403) 269-2100
Web Site: http://www.middlefield.com
Rev.: $2,103,661
Assets: $66,014,063
Liabilities: $462,550
Net Worth: $65,551,513
Earnings: $2,464,672
Fiscal Year-end: 12/31/2020
Closed-End Investment Fund
N.A.I.C.S.: 525990
Dean Orrico *(Pres & Chief Investment Officer)*

Middlefield Realty Services Limited **(1)**
First Canadian Place 58th Floor, PO Box 192, Toronto, M5X 1A6, ON, Canada
Tel.: (416) 362-0714
Real Estate Investment & Brokerage Services
N.A.I.C.S.: 531390
Henry Lee *(Pres)*

MIDEA GROUP CO., LTD.
Midea Headquarters Building No 6 Midea Street Beijiao Town, Shunde District, Foshan, 528311, Guangdong, China
Tel.: (86) 75722607708
Web Site: https://www.midea-group.com
Year Founded: 1968
000333—(SSE)
Rev.: $51,743,160,722
Assets: $67,295,938,192
Liabilities: $43,162,734,687
Net Worth: $24,133,203,506
Earnings: $4,668,799,153
Emp.: 166,000
Fiscal Year-end: 12/31/23
Electronics Appliance Mfr
N.A.I.C.S.: 551112
Hongbo Fang *(Chm & CEO)*

Subsidiaries:

Anhui Meizhi Compressor Co., Ltd. **(1)**
No 418 Caihong Rd Scientific City, Hefei, 230088, Anhui, China
Tel.: (86) 5515298890
Household Electronics Mfr & Distr
N.A.I.C.S.: 334419

Beijing Midea Commercial Air-conditioner Sales Co., Ltd **(1)**
Midea Industry City Beijiao, Foshan, 528311, Guangdong, China

INTERNATIONAL PUBLIC

Tel.: (86) 757 26333957
Household Electronic Products Distr
N.A.I.C.S.: 423620

Foshan Midea Material Supply Co., Ltd. **(1)**
Industrial Zone Penglai Road Beijiao Town, Shunde District, Foshan, 528000, Guangdong, China
Tel.: (86) 75726339592
Electrical Home Appliances Distr
N.A.I.C.S.: 423620

Guangdong Meizhi Precise Manufacture Co., Ltd **(1)**
High-Tech Industry Development Zone Ronggui Street, Shunde District, Foshan, 528305, Guangdong, China
Tel.: (86) 75728385889
Electronic Home Appliances Mfr
N.A.I.C.S.: 335220

Guangdong Meizhi Refrigeration Equipment Co., Ltd **(1)**
Shunfengshan Industrial Development Zone, Shunde, Foshan, 528333, Guangdong, China
Tel.: (86) 757 22329000
Refrigerator Equipment Mfr
N.A.I.C.S.: 333415

Guangdong Midea Refrigeration Equipment Co., Ltd. **(1)**
Midea Industrial City Penglai Rd Beijian Town, Shunde District, Foshan, 528311, Guangdong, China
Tel.: (86) 757 2633 8779
Electrical Home Appliance Mfr
N.A.I.C.S.: 335220

Guangzhou Hualing Air Conditioning Equipment Co., Ltd **(1)**
Dashi Panyu, Guangzhou, 511430, Guangdong, China
Tel.: (86) 2085512868
Home Appliance Mfr
N.A.I.C.S.: 335220

KUKA Aktiengesellschaft **(1)**
Zugspitzstrasse 140, 86165, Augsburg, Germany **(100%)**
Tel.: (49) 82179750
Web Site: https://www.kuka.com
Rev.: $3,575,265,036
Assets: $3,837,312,276
Liabilities: $2,327,069,080
Net Worth: $1,510,243,196
Earnings: $19,933,508
Emp.: 14,014
Fiscal Year-end: 12/31/2019
Holding Company; Automation Manufacturing & Assembly Equipment Mfr
N.A.I.C.S.: 551112
Wilfried Eberhardt *(CMO)*

Subsidiary (Non-US):

HLS Czech s. r. o. **(2)**
Pod Borkem 318, Mlada Boleslav, 293 01, Czech Republic
Tel.: (420) 326711011
Web Site: http://www.hls-group.com
Automotive Engineering Consulting Services
N.A.I.C.S.: 541330

Subsidiary (Domestic):

HLS Ingenieurburo GmbH **(2)**
Bgm-Wegele-Strasse 4, 86167, Augsburg, Bavaria, Germany
Tel.: (49) 82170070
Web Site: http://www.hls-group.com
Engineering Consulting Services
N.A.I.C.S.: 541330
Frank Klingemann *(Dir-Robotic Automation)*

Subsidiary (Non-US):

KUKA Slovakia s r.o. **(2)**
Sturova 1, 018 41, Dubnica nad Vahom, Slovakia
Tel.: (421) 4244 02204
Web Site: http://www.kukaenco.sk
Rev.: $11,586,400
Emp.: 170
Automotive Industry Large Pressing Tool Mfr
N.A.I.C.S.: 333514
Pavol Turna *(Exec Dir & Gen Mgr)*

AND PRIVATE COMPANIES

MIDEA GROUP CO., LTD.

Subsidiary (Domestic):

KUKA Systems GmbH (2)
Blucherstrasse 144, 86165, Augsburg, Germany
Tel.: (49) 8217970
Web Site: http://www.kuka-robotic.com
Automation Manufacturing Equipment
N.A.I.C.S.: 333248

Subsidiary (Non-US):

KUKA Systems GmbH - BOP France (2)
Tel.: (33) 130124500
Industrial Robots Whslr
N.A.I.C.S.: 423830

KUKA Systems UK Limited (2)
Hereward Rise, West Midlands, Halesowen, B62 8AN, United Kingdom
Tel.: (44) 1215850888
Welding Machineries Mfr
N.A.I.C.S.: 333992

Kuka Automation Equipment (Shanghai) Co., Ltd. (2)
No 388 Minshen Rd Songjiang Industrial Zone, Shanghai, China
Tel.: (86) 2167871808
Web Site: http://www.kuka.cn
Industrial Robots Mfr
N.A.I.C.S.: 333248

Kuka Automation Taiwan Ltd. (2)
Tel.: (886) 289781188
Web Site: http://www.kuka.com
Industrial Robots Mfr
N.A.I.C.S.: 333248

Kuka Automatisering + Robots N.V. (2)
Tel.: (32) 11516160
Web Site: http://www.kuka.be
Industrial Robots Mfr
N.A.I.C.S.: 811310

Kuka Automatisme + Robotique S.A.S. (2)
6 Rue du ParcTechvallee, 91140, Villebon-sur-Yvette, France
Tel.: (33) 169316600
Industrial Robots Whslr
N.A.I.C.S.: 423830
Bergerot Emmanuel *(Dir-Sls)*

Kuka Flexible Manufacturing Systems (Shanghai) Co., Ltd. (2)
No 388 Minshen Road Songjiang Industrial Zone, Shanghai, 201612, China
Tel.: (86) 2167871808
Web Site: http://www.kuka-systems.com
Sales Range: $50-74.9 Million
Emp.: 140
Industrial Automation System Mfr
N.A.I.C.S.: 334513

Kuka Hungaria Kft. (2)
Fo ut 140, 2335, Taksony, Pest, Hungary
Web Site: http://www.kuka-robotics.hu
Industrial Robots Mfr
N.A.I.C.S.: 333998

Kuka Nordic AB (2)
A Odhners gata 15, 42130, Vastra Frolunda, Sweden
Tel.: (46) 317266220
Web Site: http://www.kuka.se
Industrial Robots Whslr
N.A.I.C.S.: 423830

Kuka Robot Automation Malaysia Sdn. Bhd. (2)
No 5 Jalan PPU 2A, Taman Perindustrian Puchong Utama, 47100, Puchong, Selangor, Malaysia
Tel.: (60) 380660788
Web Site: http://www.kuka.com.my
Industrial Robot Distr
N.A.I.C.S.: 423830

Kuka Roboter Italia S. P. A. (2)
Via Leonardo da Vinci 3, 10095, Grugliasco, Italy
Tel.: (39) 0119595013
Web Site: http://www.kuka.it
Robot Systems Mfr
N.A.I.C.S.: 333248

Kuka Robotics (India) Pvt. Ltd. (2)
404 Good Earth Business Bay Sector 58, Gurgaon, 122002, Haryana, India
Tel.: (91) 1244748300
Web Site: http://www.kuka.com
Industrial Robots Whslr
N.A.I.C.S.: 423830

Kuka Robotics Canada Ltd. (2)
2865 Argentia Rd Units 4-5, Mississauga, L5N 8G6, ON, Canada
Tel.: (905) 858-5852
Web Site: https://www.kuka.com
Industrial Robots Whslr
N.A.I.C.S.: 423830

Subsidiary (US):

Kuka Robotics Corp. (2)
51870 Shelby Pkwy, Shelby, MI 48315-1787
Web Site: http://www.kuka-robotics.com
Industrial Robots Mfr
N.A.I.C.S.: 333248

Subsidiary (Non-US):

Kuka Robotics Japan KK (2)
YBP Technical Center 2F, 134 Godo cho, Yokohama, 135-0091, Hodogaya-ku, Japan
Tel.: (81) 457447531
Industrial Robots Mfr
N.A.I.C.S.: 333248

Kuka Robotics Russia OOO (2)
1 y Nagatinskiy pr d 2, 117105, Moscow, Russia
Tel.: (7) 495 357 01 00
Industrial Robots Whslr
N.A.I.C.S.: 423830

Kuka Robots Iberica, S.A. (2)
Pol Industrial Torrent de la Pastera Carrer Bages SN, 08800, Vilanova i la Geltru, Barcelona, Spain
Tel.: (34) 938142353
Industrial Robots Whslr
N.A.I.C.S.: 423830

Subsidiary (US):

Kuka Systems North America LLC (2)
6600 Center Dr, Sterling Heights, MI 48312-2666
Tel.: (586) 795-2000
Assembly & Welding Systems Distr
N.A.I.C.S.: 423440

Subsidiary (Domestic):

Kuka Assembly and Test Corp. (3)
5675 Dixie Hwy, Saginaw, MI 48601
Tel.: (989) 777-2111
Web Site: http://www.kuka-at.com
Automotive Components Assembling & Testing Services
N.A.I.C.S.: 336110
Scott Orendach *(Pres)*

Kuka Toledo Production Operations LLC (3)
3770 Stickney Ave, Toledo, OH 43608
Tel.: (419) 727-5599
Motor Vehicle Bodies Mfr
N.A.I.C.S.: 336211

Subsidiary (Non-US):

Kuka Systems de Mexico, S. de R. L. de C. V. (2)
114 Calle 2 Sur Parque Industrial Toluca 2000, 50223, Toluca, Mexico
Tel.: (52) 7222492310
Industrial Automation Machineries Mfr
N.A.I.C.S.: 334513

Kuka Systems do Brasil Ltda. (2)
Rua Rio de Janeiro 644, Casa Grande Diadema, Sao Paulo, 09961-730, Brazil
Tel.: (55) 1133822100
Web Site: http://www.kukasystems.com.br
Industrial Robots Mfr
N.A.I.C.S.: 334513

Kuka Systems do Braszil Ltda. (2)
Rua Rio de Janeiro 644, Casa Grande Diadema, Sao Paulo, 09961-730, Brazil
Tel.: (55) 1133822100
Web Site: https://www.kuka.com
Industrial Robots Testing & Maintenance Services

N.A.I.C.S.: 541380

Kuka de Mexico S. de R. L. de C. V. (2)
Eje 104 No 150-B Col Zona Industrial, CP 78395, San Luis Potosi, Mexico
Industrial Robots Mfr & Sales
N.A.I.C.S.: 333248

Swisslog Holding AG (2)
Webereiweg 3, 5033, Buchs, Switzerland (100%)
Tel.: (41) 628374141
Web Site: http://www.swisslog.com
Holding Company; Integrated Logistics Solutions
N.A.I.C.S.: 551112

Subsidiary (Non-US):

Swisslog (UK) Ltd. (3)
2 Brooklands Moons Moat Drive, Hurricane Court Heron Drive, Redditch, B98 9DW, United Kingdom
Tel.: (44) 1527551600
Warehousing & Distribution Services
N.A.I.C.S.: 493110

Swisslog AB (3)
Brodalsvagen 13B, 433 38, Partille, Sweden
Tel.: (46) 313366000
Web Site: http://www.swisslog.se
Logistics & Warehousing Services
N.A.I.C.S.: 541614

Swisslog AG (3)
(100%)
Tel.: (41) 628374141
Web Site: http://www.swisslog.com
Integrated Logistics Solutions
N.A.I.C.S.: 541614

Swisslog AS (3)
Ostre Aker vei 19, 0581, Oslo, Norway
Tel.: (47) 22789500
Warehouse & Distribution Services
N.A.I.C.S.: 493190

Swisslog Australia Pty. Ltd. (3)
Level 7 10 Herb Elliott Ave, Olympic Park, Sydney, 2127, NSW, Australia
Tel.: (61) 298695900
Logistics Consulting Servies
N.A.I.C.S.: 541614

Swisslog B.V. (3)
Tel.: (31) 345531188
Logistics Consulting Servies
N.A.I.C.S.: 541614

Swisslog Ergotrans B.V. (3)
Vissenstraat 14, Postbus 2165, 7302 EN, Apeldoorn, Gelderland, Netherlands
Tel.: (31) 553688888
Industrial Machinery Distr
N.A.I.C.S.: 423830

Swisslog Evomatic GmbH (3)
Gewerbepark Ost 6, 4621, Sipbachzell, Austria
Tel.: (43) 7240200750
Web Site: http://www.swisslog.com
Warehousing & Distribution Services
N.A.I.C.S.: 541614

Swisslog France SA (3)
28 quai Gallieni, 92150, Paris, France
Tel.: (33) 148096820
Logistics & Engineering Support Services
N.A.I.C.S.: 541614

Swisslog GmbH (3)
Tel.: (49) 2317589500
Web Site: http://www.swisslog.com
Logistics & Engineering Support Services
N.A.I.C.S.: 541614

Swisslog GmbH (3)
Martin-Schmeiber-Weg 6-8, 44227, Dortmund, 44227, Bayern, Germany
Tel.: (49) 2317589500
Logistics Consulting Servies
N.A.I.C.S.: 541614

Subsidiary (US):

Swisslog Healthcare North America (3)
11325 Main St, Broomfield, CO 80020 (100%)
Tel.: (303) 371-7770

Automated Material Transport Systems Pneumatic Tube Systems, Selective Vertical Conveyors & Electric Track Vehicle Systems Mfr
N.A.I.C.S.: 333922
Cory Kwarta *(Pres & CEO)*

Subsidiary (Non-US):

Swisslog Healthcare Canada (4)
2865 Argentia Road Units 4-5, Mississauga, L5N 8G6, ON, Canada
Tel.: (905) 629-2400
Web Site: https://www.swisslog-healthcare.com
Pneumatic Tube Systems Mfr
N.A.I.C.S.: 333922

Subsidiary (Non-US):

Swisslog Italia S.p.A. (3)
Via Taruffi 30/38, 41053, Maranello, Italy
Tel.: (39) 0536240311
Warehousing & Logistics Services
N.A.I.C.S.: 493190

Swisslog Logistics (Shanghai) Co., Ltd. (3)
Unit 08 Floor 18 76 Pu Jian Road You You International Plaza, Shanghai, 200127, China
Tel.: (86) 2150399928
Logistic Services
N.A.I.C.S.: 541614

Swisslog Logistics N.V. (3)
Prins Boudewijnlaan 43, 2650, Edegem, Belgium
Tel.: (32) 38303800
Logistics & Engineering Support Services
N.A.I.C.S.: 541614

Subsidiary (US):

Swisslog Logistics, Inc. (3)
161 Enterprise Dr, Newport News, VA 23603-1369
Tel.: (757) 820-3400
Automated Material Handling Systems
N.A.I.C.S.: 333922
Markus Schmidt *(Pres-Swisslog Logistics Automation Americas)*

Subsidiary (Non-US):

Swisslog Malaysia Sdn Bhd (3)
B-13-01 Menara Amfirst 2 Jalan SS 7/15 Jalan Stadium, Kelana Jaya, 47301, Petaling Jaya, Selangor Darul Ehsan, Malaysia
Tel.: (60) 374948500
Automated Warehousing & Distribution Systems Installation Services
N.A.I.C.S.: 238210

Swisslog Rohrpostsysteme GmbH (3)
Hansacker 5 7, Westerstede, 26655, Lower Saxony, Germany
Tel.: (49) 448883890
Logistics & Warehousing Services
N.A.I.C.S.: 541614

Swisslog Singapore Pte. Ltd. (3)
Tel.: (65) 62800600
Hospital Materials Transport & Automation System Installation Services
N.A.I.C.S.: 541614

Swisslog-Accalon AB (3)
Carl Tryggers vag 13, PO Box 135, 590 10, Boxholm, Ostergotland, Sweden
Tel.: (46) 14255500
Web Site: http://www.accalon.com
Logistics & Warehousing Services
N.A.I.C.S.: 541614

Midea America Corp. (1)
300 Kimball Dr Ste 201, Parsippany, NJ 07054
Tel.: (305) 591-8460
Web Site: http://www.midea.com
Sales Range: $50-74.9 Million
Emp.: 15
Household Appliance Distr
N.A.I.C.S.: 423620
John Tsen *(Pres)*

Subsidiary (Non-US):

Midea America (Canada) Corp. (2)
Unit 2 215 Shields Court, Markham, L3R

MIDEA GROUP CO., LTD.

Midea Group Co., Ltd.—(Continued)
8V2, ON, Canada
Tel.: (905) 305-6368
Household Appliance Distr
N.A.I.C.S.: 423620

Midea Europe GmbH (1)
Ludwig-Erhard-Strasse 14, 65760, Eschborn, Germany
Tel.: (49) 61 969 0200
Web Site: https://www.midea.com
Household Appliance Distr
N.A.I.C.S.: 423620

Midea Germany MHA Haushaltswaren GmbH (1)
Eiffestrasse 598, 20537, Hamburg, Germany
Tel.: (49) 4021985516
Household Appliance Distr
N.A.I.C.S.: 423620

Midea Refrigerating(Hong Kong) Co., Ltd. (1)
9 Canton Road Tsim Sha Tsui, Kowloon, China (Hong Kong)
Tel.: (852) 36694888
Emp.: 60
Electronic Home Appliances Mfr
N.A.I.C.S.: 335220
Simon Fong *(Gen Mgr)*

Servotronix Motion Control Ltd. (1)
21C Yagia Kapayim Street, POB 3919, Petah Tikva, 4913020, Israel
Tel.: (972) 3 927 3800
Web Site: https://www.servotronix.cn
Standard & Customized Motion Electronics Products Designer, Developer & Mfr
N.A.I.C.S.: 334513
Ilan Cohen *(Pres & CEO)*

Subsidiary (Non-US):

Servotronix Motion Technology Development Ltd. (2)
Room 605 Building B2 Kexing Science Park No 15 Keyuan Road, Nanshan District, Shenzhen, 518057, China
Tel.: (86) 7558 662 6603
Web Site: https://www.servotronix.cn
Electrical Products Distr
N.A.I.C.S.: 423610

Welling Holding Limited (1)
Xingye Road Beijiao Industrial Park Shunde, Foshan, 528311, Guangdong, China
Tel.: (86) 7572232 9000
Electric Motor Mfr
N.A.I.C.S.: 335312

Subsidiary (Non-US):

Welling International Hong Kong Ltd. (2)
Suite 3904 39/F Tower 6 The Gateway 9 Canton Road Harbour City, Tsim Sha Tsui, Kowloon, China (Hong Kong)
Tel.: (852) 3669 4888
Motor Mfr
N.A.I.C.S.: 335312

Subsidiary (Non-US):

Guangdong Welling Motor Manufacturing Co., Ltd. (3)
Xingye Road, Industrial Park Shunde, Foshan, Guangdong, China
Tel.: (86) 75726339911
Web Site: https://www.cccme.cn
Motor Mfr
N.A.I.C.S.: 335312

Wuxi Little Swan Company Limited (1)
No 18 South Changjiang Rd, New District, Wuxi, 214028, China
Tel.: (86) 51083704003
Sales Range: $15-24.9 Billion
Electric Appliances Mfr
N.A.I.C.S.: 335220

MIDEA REAL ESTATE HOLDING LTD.
34th Floor Midea Real Estate Plaza No 1 Chengde Road, Beijiao Town Shunde District, Foshan, 528311, Guangdong, China
Tel.: (86) 75726607122   Ky
Web Site: https://www.mideadc.com
Year Founded: 2004
3990—(HKG)
Rev.: $8,041,014,041
Assets: $43,474,022,962
Liabilities: $37,312,010,526
Net Worth: $6,162,012,435
Earnings: $739,314,549
Emp.: 15,252
Fiscal Year-end: 12/31/20
Holding Company
N.A.I.C.S.: 551112
Hengle Hao *(Chm & Pres)*

MIDEAST INTEGRATED STEELS LIMITED
Mesco Towers 3915 Lewis Road Kedar Gauri Square, Bhubaneswar, 751 014, Odisha, India
Tel.: (91) 6742432755   In
Web Site:
https://www.mescosteel.com
Year Founded: 1992
540744—(BOM)
Rev.: $64,835,043
Assets: $281,197,098
Liabilities: $234,117,156
Net Worth: $47,079,942
Earnings: ($13,604,682)
Emp.: 584
Fiscal Year-end: 03/31/20
Chemical Element Mfr & Distr
N.A.I.C.S.: 331110
Rita Singh *(Chm & Co-Mng Dir)*

MIDEAST PORTFOLIO MANAGEMENT LTD.
1/203 Vishal Complex Narsing Lane S V Road, Malad W, Mumbai, 400064, Maharashtra, India
Tel.: (91) 2228240444
Web Site:
https://www.mideastportfolio.com
526251—(BOM)
Rev.: $16,726
Assets: $385,838
Liabilities: $731
Net Worth: $385,107
Earnings: $6,714
Emp.: 6
Fiscal Year-end: 03/31/24
Financial Investment Services
N.A.I.C.S.: 523999
Kishor A. Shah *(Chm & Mng Dir)*

MIDFIELD MEAT INTERNATIONAL PTY. LTD.
Cnr Scott Street & McMeekin Road, PO Box 412, Warrnambool, 3280, VIC, Australia
Tel.: (61) 355634444
Web Site: http://www.midfield.com.au
Sales Range: $100-124.9 Million
Emp.: 1,500
Veal Product Mfr
N.A.I.C.S.: 112320
Colin McKenna *(Founder-Midfield Grp)*

Subsidiaries:

Meat Barns Australia Pty Ltd (1)
21 Scott Street, Warrnambool, 3280, VIC, Australia
Tel.: (61) 3 5560 5700
Web Site: http://www.themeatbarn.com.au
Meat Product Distr
N.A.I.C.S.: 445240

Midfield Co-Products Pty Ltd (1)
PO Box 556, Warrnambool, 3280, VIC, Australia
Tel.: (61) 3 5562 7775
Meat Byproduct Processing Services
N.A.I.C.S.: 311613
Ray Slade *(Mgr)*

Midfield Trading Pty Ltd (1)
247 Cormack Rd, Wingfield, Adelaide, 5013, SA, Australia
Tel.: (61) 8 82628888
Meat Product Whslr
N.A.I.C.S.: 424470

MIDI AUTO 19
Avenue Jean Charles Rivet, 19100, Brive-la-Gaillarde, Correze, France
Tel.: (33) 555889119
Web Site:
http://www.reseau.citroen.fr
Rev.: $36,200,000
Emp.: 48
N.A.I.C.S.: 441110
Nicolas Simon *(Dir)*

MIDI AUTO 56
Saint Laurent Route De Nantes, Sene, 56860, Morbihan, France
Tel.: (33) 297542274
Web Site:
http://www.reseau.citroen.fr
Rev.: $38,400,000
Emp.: 75
N.A.I.C.S.: 441110
Denis Aillet *(Mgr-DP)*

MIDI AUTO CAVAILLON
Route d'Avignon, 84300, Cavaillon, France
Tel.: (33) 8 99 024754
Rev.: $33,600,000
Emp.: 65
Citroen Automotive Concessionaire Services
N.A.I.C.S.: 441110
Michel Dubo *(Dir & Fin)*

MIDI P.L.C.
North Shore Manoel Island, Gzira, GZR3016, Malta
Tel.: (356) 20655500   Mt
Web Site: https://www.midimalta.com
Year Founded: 1992
MDI—(MAL)
Rev.: $4,493,751
Assets: $260,859,624
Liabilities: $178,351,231
Net Worth: $82,508,393
Earnings: ($1,676,077)
Emp.: 40
Fiscal Year-end: 12/31/23
Real Estate Development Services
N.A.I.C.S.: 531390
Alec A. Mizzi *(Chm)*

MIDLAND EXPLORATION INC.
Suite 4000 1 Place Ville Marie, Montreal, H3B 4M4, QC, Canada
Tel.: (450) 420-5977   QC
Web Site:
https://www.midlandexploration.com
Year Founded: 1995
MD—(TSXV)
Rev.: $237,840
Assets: $31,460,446
Liabilities: $1,421,132
Net Worth: $30,039,314
Earnings: $837,587
Fiscal Year-end: 09/30/23
Mineral Exploration Services
N.A.I.C.S.: 212390
Rene Branchaud *(Sec)*

MIDLAND HOLDINGS LIMITED
Room 2505-8 25/F World Wide House 19 Des Voeux Road C, Central, China (Hong Kong)
Tel.: (852) 25258383   BM
Web Site:
https://www.midlandholdings.com.hk
Year Founded: 1973
MTK—(DEU)
Rev.: $398,116,605
Assets: $488,889,798

INTERNATIONAL PUBLIC

Liabilities: $401,442,611
Net Worth: $87,447,186
Earnings: ($68,241,722)
Emp.: 4,994
Fiscal Year-end: 12/31/22
Real Estate Agency Services
N.A.I.C.S.: 531210
Freddie Kin Yip Wong *(Founder, Chm & Mng Dir)*

Subsidiaries:

Hong Kong Property Services (Agency) Ltd. (1)
Rooms 2505-8 25/F World-Wide House 19 Des Voeux Road, Central, China (Hong Kong)
Tel.: (852) 28448205
Web Site: https://en.hkp.com.hk
Real Estate Agent & Broker Services
N.A.I.C.S.: 531210

Midland Immigration Consultancy Limited (1)
14th Floor Midland Financial Building 33 Argyle Street, Mong Kok, China (Hong Kong)
Tel.: (852) 28448200
Web Site: http://www.mics.hk
Immigration Consulting Services
N.A.I.C.S.: 541618

Midland Macau Limited (1)
Rua Central Da Areia Preta No 716 La Baie Du Noble Shop Y, Macau, China (Macau)
Tel.: (853) 28762000
Web Site: https://www.midland.com.mo
Real Estate Agent & Broker Services
N.A.I.C.S.: 531210
Lily Hong *(Sls Dir)*

Midland Realty (Global) Limited (1)
17/F Overseas Trust Bank Building 160 Gloucester Road, Wanchai, China (Hong Kong)
Tel.: (852) 81031333
Web Site: https://www.midlandglobal.hk
Property Investment Services
N.A.I.C.S.: 531390

Midland Realty International Limited (1)
Shop C G/F Spring Garden Mansion 29-41 Spring Garden Lane, Wan Chai, Hong Kong, China (Hong Kong)
Tel.: (852) 96602572
Web Site: https://www.midland-realty-international-limited.business.site
Real Estate Agency Services
N.A.I.C.S.: 531210

MIDLAND MICROFIN LTD.
Gobind Niwas 2nd Floor 36 GT Road, Jalandhar, 144 001, Punjab, India
Tel.: (91) 181 508 5555
Web Site:
http://www.midlandmicrofin.com
Financial Services
N.A.I.C.S.: 525990
Amardeep Samra *(Mng Dir)*

MIDLOTHIAN CAPITAL PARTNERS LIMITED
Blackmoor Farm Ockham Lane, Cobham, KT11 1LZ, Surrey, United Kingdom
Tel.: (44) 20 3514 0897   UK
Web Site:
http://www.midlothiancapital.com
Year Founded: 2015
Privater Equity Firm
N.A.I.C.S.: 523999
Andrew Bracey *(Partner)*

Subsidiaries:

Dobbies Garden Centres Limited (1)
Melville Nursery, Lasswade, EH18 1AZ, United Kingdom
Tel.: (44) 1316631941
Web Site: http://www.dobbies.com
Garden Center Operator
N.A.I.C.S.: 444240
Matthew Bailey *(Mgr-Store)*

AND PRIVATE COMPANIES — MIDWICH GROUP PLC

Subsidiary (Domestic):

Dobbies Grovelands (2)
166 Hyde End Road, Shinfield, RG29ER,
Reading, United Kingdom
Tel.: (44) 01189684822
Web Site: http://www.dobbies.com
Nursery & Garden Centers
N.A.I.C.S.: 444240
Paul Hilliam (Mgr-Store)

Edinburgh Butterfly & Insect World (2)
Melville Nurseries, Lasswade, EH18 1AZ,
Midlothian, United Kingdom
Tel.: (44) 1316634932
Web Site: http://www.edinburgh-butterfly-world.co.uk
All Other Amusement & Recreation Industries
N.A.I.C.S.: 713990
Andrew McDonald (Gen Mgr)

MIDNIGHT SUN MINING CORP.
1205 - 789 West Pender Street, Vancouver, V6C 1H2, BC, Canada
Tel.: (604) 351-8850
Web Site: https://www.midnightsunmining.com
Year Founded: 2007
MDNGF—(OTCQB)
Rev.: $1,638
Assets: $16,252,538
Liabilities: $179,933
Net Worth: $16,072,605
Earnings: ($1,487,986)
Fiscal Year-end: 12/31/21
Mineral Exploration Services
N.A.I.C.S.: 212290
Allan J. Fabbro (Pres & CEO)

MIDPOINT & TRANSFER LTD.
22-25 Portman Close, London, W1H 6BS, United Kingdom
Tel.: (44) 2036870547   UK
Web Site: https://www.midpoint.com
Foreign Currency Exchange Services
N.A.I.C.S.: 522320
David S. Wong (CEO)

MIDSONA AB
Dockplatsen 16, Box 21009, 200 21, Malmo, Sweden
Tel.: (46) 406018200
Web Site: https://www.midsona.com
Year Founded: 1892
MSON.A—(OMX)
Rev.: $452,794,720
Assets: $625,904,160
Liabilities: $343,533,120
Net Worth: $282,371,040
Earnings: $21,486,080
Emp.: 820
Fiscal Year-end: 12/31/20
Holding Company; Healthcare Products Mfr & Distr
N.A.I.C.S.: 551112
Peter Asberg (Pres & CEO)

Subsidiaries:

Midsona Deutschland GmbH (1)
Zur Davert 7, 59387, Ascheberg, Germany
Tel.: (49) 259392800
Web Site: https://www.midsona.de
Food Products Distr
N.A.I.C.S.: 424490

Midsona Norge AS (1)
Lilleakerveien 8, PO Box 200, Lilleaker, 1326, Oslo, Norway
Tel.: (47) 93023564
Web Site: https://www.midsona.no
Food Product Mfr & Distr
N.A.I.C.S.: 311999

System Frugt A/S (1)
Blomstervej 8, Tilst, Arhus, 8381, Denmark
Tel.: (45) 87459595
Web Site: http://www.systemfrugt.dk
Sales Range: $50-74.9 Million
Emp.: 128
Packaged Dried Fruits, Nuts & Vegetables

N.A.I.C.S.: 311423
Steffen Molberg (CEO)

Vitamex AB (1)
Bergslagsgatan 9, 60116, Norrkoping, Sweden
Tel.: (46) 11230000
Web Site: http://www.vitamex.se
Sales Range: $50-74.9 Million
Nutritional Products Whslr
N.A.I.C.S.: 456191

MIDSUMMER AB
Elektronikhojden 6, 175 43, Jarfalla, Sweden
Tel.: (46) 852509610
Web Site: https://www.midsummer.se
Year Founded: 2002
MIDS—(OMX)
Rev.: $14,287,936
Assets: $42,353,215
Liabilities: $26,249,476
Net Worth: $16,103,740
Earnings: ($8,803,253)
Fiscal Year-end: 12/31/22
Solar Component Mfr & Distr
N.A.I.C.S.: 334413
Alex Witt (COO)

MIDT-NORSK HAVBRUK AS
Nyvegen 20, 7900, Rorvik, Norway
Tel.: (47) 908 44 800
Web Site: http://www.mnh.no
Year Founded: 1992
Aquaculture Industry
N.A.I.C.S.: 112519
Frank Oren (CEO)

MIDVALLEY ENTERTAINMENT LIMITED
9th Floor Gee Gee Emerald 312 Valluvar Kottam High Rd, Nungambakkam, Chennai, 600034, India
Tel.: (91) 4430632454
Web Site: http://www.mvel.in
Sales Range: $10-24.9 Million
Emp.: 50
Theater Owner & Operator; Film Producer, Distr & Exhibiter
N.A.I.C.S.: 512131
K. Ketheeswaran (Chm)

MIDWAY METALS PTY. LTD.
56 Business St, Yatala, 4207, QLD, Australia
Tel.: (61) 733829500
Web Site: http://www.midwaymetals.au
Stainless Steel Distr
N.A.I.C.S.: 423510
Shaun Stewart (Gen Mgr)

MIDWAY NISSAN
1300 Dundas Street East, Whitby, L1N 2K5, ON, Canada
Tel.: (905) 668-6828   ON
Web Site: http://www.midwaynissan.ca
Year Founded: 1965
New & Used Car Dealers
N.A.I.C.S.: 441110

MIDWAY PTY LTD
150 Corio Quay Rd, North Shore, 3215, VIC, Australia
Tel.: (61) 352779255
Sales Range: $25-49.9 Million
Emp.: 38
Wood Products; Wood Chips
N.A.I.C.S.: 321999
John Frederick (CEO)

MIDWEST GOLD LIMITED
No 8-2-684/3/25 26 Road no 12 Banjara Hills, Hyderabad, 500 034, India
Tel.: (91) 4023305194   In
Web Site: https://www.midwestgoldltd.com

Year Founded: 1990
526570—(BOM)
Rev.: $211,846
Assets: $943,109
Liabilities: $3,439,842
Net Worth: ($2,496,733)
Earnings: ($1,151,777)
Emp.: 9
Fiscal Year-end: 03/31/23
Gold Mining Services
N.A.I.C.S.: 212220
Baladari Satyanarayana Raju (Exec Dir)

Subsidiaries:

Midwest Granite Pvt Ltd (1)
No 8-2-684/3/25 and 26 Road No 12 Banjara Hills, Hyderabad, 500034, India
Tel.: (91) 4023305194
Granite Mining Services
N.A.I.C.S.: 212313

MIDWESTERN OIL & GAS COMPANY LIMITED
Plot 10 Block 12 Otunba Adedoyin Ogungbe Crescent Lekki Phase 1, PO Box 80024, Victoria Island, Lagos, Nigeria
Tel.: (234) 1 903 2530   NG
Web Site: http://www.midwesternog.com
Year Founded: 2001
Petroleum & Natural Gas Extraction Services
N.A.I.C.S.: 211120
Onajite P. Okoloko (Chm)

Subsidiaries:

NRG Drilling Nigeria Limited (1)
No 27B Prince Adelowo Adedeji Street Off Admiralty Way Lekki Phase 1, Lagos, Nigeria
Tel.: (234) 12711755
Web Site: http://www.nrgdrilling-ng.com
Oil & Gas Well Drilling Services
N.A.I.C.S.: 213111

MIDWICH GROUP PLC
Vinces Road, Diss, IP22 4YT, Norfolk, United Kingdom
Tel.: (44) 1379649200   UK
Web Site: https://www.midwichgroupplc.com
Year Founded: 1979
MIDW—(AIM)
Rev.: $1,519,880,081
Assets: $706,606,917
Liabilities: $537,288,563
Net Worth: $169,318,354
Earnings: $21,276,193
Emp.: 1,500
Fiscal Year-end: 12/31/22
Holding Company; Audio Visual, Film, Broadcast, Lighting & Document Solutions Distr for Trade Markets
N.A.I.C.S.: 551112
Stephen Fenby (Mng Dir)

Subsidiaries:

DVS Ltd. (1)
Unit 3 Neptune Point Vanguard Way, Cardiff, CF24 5PG, United Kingdom
Tel.: (44) 2920455512
Web Site: https://www.dvs.co.uk
Hardware Product Mfr & Distr
N.A.I.C.S.: 332510

Dutch Light Pro B.V. (1)
Kolenbranderstraat 10, 2984 AT, Ridderkerk, Netherlands
Tel.: (31) 180745833
Web Site: https://www.dutchlightpro.nl
Lighting Installation Services
N.A.I.C.S.: 238210
Rick ter Wee (Mng Dir)

Earpro S.A. (1)
Juan Ramon Jimenez 7 Nave 2 Poligono Industrial No 1, Sant Just Desvern, 08960, Barcelona, Spain

Tel.: (34) 934731143
Web Site: http://www.earpro.es
Audio & Video Equipment Distr
N.A.I.C.S.: 423690

Edge Electronics Trading LLC (1)
Edge Electronics Trading Misr Insurance Building Office-O-D-1, Building-226 Zone-25 Street-230 C- Ring Road, Doha, Qatar
Tel.: (974) 44980203
Web Site: https://edgeet.com
Audio & Video Equipment Distr
N.A.I.C.S.: 423690

Holdan Benelux B.V. (1)
Kolenbranderstraat 10, 2984 AT, Ridderkerk, Netherlands
Tel.: (31) 180728209
Web Site: http://www.holdan.nl
Motion Picture & Video Services
N.A.I.C.S.: 512110

Holdan Limited (1)
Brookfield House Peakdale Road, Brookfield Industrial Estate, Glossop, SK13 6LQ, Derbyshire, United Kingdom
Tel.: (44) 1457851000
Web Site: https://www.holdan.co.uk
Audio & Video Equipment Distr
N.A.I.C.S.: 423690

Invision UK Ltd. (1)
Vinces Road, Diss, IP22 4YT, Norfolk, United Kingdom
Tel.: (44) 135 927 0280
Web Site: https://www.invisionuk.com
Audio & Video Equipment Distr
N.A.I.C.S.: 423690
Peter Alloway (Head-Bus Dev)

Kern & Stelly Medientechnik GmbH (1)
Papenreye 61, 22453, Hamburg, Germany
Tel.: (49) 405720140
Web Site: https://www.kern-stelly.de
Audio & Video Equipment Distr
N.A.I.C.S.: 423690

Kern Und Stelly Medientechnik GmbH (1)
Sportallee 8, 22335, Hamburg, Germany
Tel.: (49) 405720140
Web Site: https://www.kern-stelly.de
Audio & Video Product Distr
N.A.I.C.S.: 423690

Midwich Australia Pty Limited (1)
Lot 4 Parklands Estate 23 South Street, Rydalmere, 2116, NSW, Australia
Tel.: (61) 130 066 6099
Web Site: https://www.midwich.com.au
Audio & Video Equipment Distr
N.A.I.C.S.: 423690

Midwich Limited (1)
Vinces Road, Diss, IP22 4YT, Norfolk, United Kingdom
Tel.: (44) 1379649200
Web Site: https://www.midwich.com
Audio & Video Equipment Distr
N.A.I.C.S.: 423690

MobilePro AG (1)
Europa-Strasse 19a, 8152, Glattbrugg, Switzerland
Tel.: (41) 448296550
Web Site: https://www.mobilepro.ch
Hardware Product Mfr & Distr
N.A.I.C.S.: 332510

NMK Middle East Trading LLC (1)
Warehouse No 8 Industrial Area 15, PO Box 3191, Sharjah, United Arab Emirates
Tel.: (971) 65332597
Electronic Equipment Mfr & Distr
N.A.I.C.S.: 335999

Prase Engineering SpA (1)
Via Nobel 10, 30020, Noventa Padovana, VE, Italy
Tel.: (39) 0421571411
Web Site: https://www.prase.it
Audio & Video Product Distr
N.A.I.C.S.: 423690

Sidev SAS (1)
183 avenue de l'industrie, 69140, Rillieux-la-Pape, France
Tel.: (33) 420100400
Web Site: https://www.sidev.fr
Audio & Video Equipment Distr

MIDWICH GROUP PLC

Midwich Group Plc—(Continued)
N.A.I.C.S.: 423690

Sound Technology Limited (1)
Letchworth Point Garden City, Letchworth, SG6 1ND, Hertfordshire, United Kingdom
Tel.: (44) 1462480000
Web Site: https://www.soundtech.uk
Musical Instrument Distr
N.A.I.C.S.: 459140

Starin Marketing, Inc. (1)
136 Venturi Dr, Chesterton, IN 46304
Tel.: (219) 929-4127
Web Site: https://www.starin.biz
Sales Range: $200-249.9 Million
Radio, Television & Other Electronics Stores
N.A.I.C.S.: 449210
Jim Starin (Founder)

Van Domburg Partners B.V. (1)
Kolenbranderstraat 10, 2984 AT, Ridderkerk, Netherlands
Tel.: (31) 180745888
Web Site: https://vandomburg.nu
Motion Picture & Video Services
N.A.I.C.S.: 512110
Gideon Steeds (COO)

MIE HOLDINGS CORPORATION
Suite 1501 Block C Grand Place 5 Hui Zhong Road, Chaoyang District, Beijing, 100101, China
Tel.: (86) 1051238111 Ky
Web Site:
http://www.mienergy.com.cn
1555—(HKG)
Rev.: $142,904,034
Assets: $317,963,178
Liabilities: $875,730,960
Net Worth: ($557,767,782)
Earnings: ($47,505,884)
Emp.: 1,005
Fiscal Year-end: 12/31/21
Holding Company; Oil & Gas Development & Production Services
N.A.I.C.S.: 551112
Zhang Ruilin (Chm & CEO)

Subsidiaries:

Emir Oil, LLP (1)
202 Dostyk Ave Business Center Forum 4th Floor, 050051, Almaty, Kazakhstan (100%)
Tel.: (7) 3272375124
Web Site: http://www.bmbmunai.com
Oil & Gas Exploration Services
N.A.I.C.S.: 211120

MIE KOTSU GROUP HOLDINGS, INC.
1-1 Chuo, Tsu, 514-0032, Mie, Japan
Tel.: (81) 592130351
Web Site: https://holdings.sanco.co.jp
Year Founded: 2006
3232—(TKS)
Rev.: $649,220,980
Assets: $1,198,346,730
Liabilities: $806,168,820
Net Worth: $392,177,910
Earnings: $31,397,500
Emp.: 5,387
Fiscal Year-end: 03/31/24
Transportation Related Services
N.A.I.C.S.: 488999
Yasushi Hara (Pres)

Subsidiaries:

Gozaisho Ropeway Co., Ltd. (1)
8625 Komono Komono-cho, Mie-gun, Mie, 510-1233, Japan
Tel.: (81) 593922261
Web Site: https://www.gozaisho.co.jp
Emp.: 46
Ski Lift Operator
N.A.I.C.S.: 713920
Tsuji Tomoyuki (CEO)

Happu Bus Co., Ltd. (1)
1604 Shinhori-Kita Kogaisuaza Oaza, Kuwana, Mie, Japan
Tel.: (81) 594226321
Web Site: http://www.happubus.sanco.co.jp
Emp.: 20
Bus Transportation Services
N.A.I.C.S.: 485510
Ando Sumito (CEO)

Kanko Pro Co., Ltd. (1)
Nagoya Sanco Building 9th Floor 3-21-7 Meieki Nakamura-Ku, Nagoya, Aichi, Japan
Tel.: (81) 525615100
Emp.: 20
Damage Insurance Services
N.A.I.C.S.: 524126
Beppu Michitaka (CEO)

Matsusaka Country Club Co., Ltd. (1)
2160 Shimomura-cho, Matsusaka, 515-0043, Mie, Japan
Tel.: (81) 598292911
Web Site: http://www.matsusakacc.com
Emp.: 11
Golf & Country Club Operator
N.A.I.C.S.: 713910
Ito Eiji (CEO)

Meihan Kintetsu Bus Co., Ltd. (1)
3-21-7 Meieki, Nakamura-ku, Nagoya, 450-0002, Aichi, Japan
Tel.: (81) 525414902
Web Site: https://www.mkb.co.jp
Emp.: 429
Bus Transportation Services
N.A.I.C.S.: 485510
Ogura Toshihide (Chm)

Meihan Kintetsu Travel Co., Ltd. (1)
Nagoya Sanco Bldg 6F 3-21-7 Meieki, Nakamura-ku, Nagoya, 450-0002, Aichi, Japan
Tel.: (81) 525637500
Web Site: https://www.kakopal.com
Emp.: 74
Travel Tour Operator
N.A.I.C.S.: 561520
Nishimura Masayuki (CEO)

Midori Services Co., Ltd. (1)
1-5 Nakagawacho, Ogaki, 503-0017, Gifu, Japan
Tel.: (81) 584753130
Web Site: https://www.midori-service.com
Emp.: 54
Landscape Gardening Services
N.A.I.C.S.: 561730
Nishimura Masayuki (CEO)

Mie Country Club Co., Ltd. (1)
7190 Chikusa Komono-cho, Mie, 510-1251, Japan
Tel.: (81) 593923163
Web Site: http://www.mie-cc.co.jp
Emp.: 80
Golf & Country Club Operator
N.A.I.C.S.: 713910
Iida Chikashi (CEO)

Mie Isuzu Motor Co., Ltd. (1)
505 Tarumi, Tsu, Mie, Japan
Tel.: (81) 592278111
Web Site: http://www.mie-isuzu.co.jp
Emp.: 211
Automotive Parts Mfr & Distr
N.A.I.C.S.: 336390
Kawamura Noriyuki (CEO)

Mie Kotsu Co., Ltd. (1)
1-1 Chuo, Tsu, 514-8635, Mie, Japan
Tel.: (81) 59 229 5511
Web Site: http://www.sanco.co.jp
Emp.: 1,310
Bus Transportation Services
N.A.I.C.S.: 485510
Ogura Toshihide (Chm)

Mie Kyuko Jidosha Co., Ltd. (1)
795-3 Otsu-Cho, Matsusaka, Mie, Japan
Tel.: (81) 598522113
Web Site: http://www.miekyuko.sanco.co.jp
Emp.: 21
Bus Transportation Services
N.A.I.C.S.: 485510
Ando Sumito (CEO)

Mieken Kanko Kaihatsu Co., Ltd. (1)
1-5-35 Shinmachi, Tsu, Mie, Japan
Tel.: (81) 592266752
Web Site: http://www.iseshimaskyline.com
Emp.: 97

Restaurant Operators
N.A.I.C.S.: 722511
Miyawaki Eiji (CEO)

Sanco Cogyo Co., Ltd. (1)
39 Hagiwara Seki-cho, Kameyama, 519-1114, Mie, Japan
Tel.: (81) 595978555
Web Site: http://www.sancocogyo.co.jp
Emp.: 73
Restaurant Operators
N.A.I.C.S.: 722511
Tsuji Takami (CEO)

Sanco Creative Life Co., Ltd. (1)
Gu Nishiki Third Street No 5 No 27 Nishiki Central Building 8F, Nagoya, Aichi, Japan
Tel.: (81) 528571561
Web Site: http://www.sanco-creative.co.jp
Emp.: 294
Door Distr
N.A.I.C.S.: 444140
Fujii Toshiaki (Pres)

Sanco Driving School Co., Ltd. (1)
3-7-6 Shinsei, Yokkaichi, 510-0064, Mie, Japan
Tel.: (81) 593523812
Web Site: https://sanco-ds.jp
Emp.: 93
Driving School Operator
N.A.I.C.S.: 611692
Ida Mitsuaki (CEO)

Sanco Inn Co., Ltd. (1)
21-7 Meieki 3 chome, Nakamura-ku, Nagoya, 450-0002, Aichi, Japan
Tel.: (81) 525641135
Web Site: https://www.sanco-inn.co.jp
Hotel Operator
N.A.I.C.S.: 721110

Sanco Iseshima Kotsu Co., Ltd. (1)
1500-1 Koda-Kushimoto-Cho, Ise, Mie, Japan
Tel.: (81) 596235134
Emp.: 172
Bus Transportation Services
N.A.I.C.S.: 485510
Muto Takayuki (CEO)

Sanco Oil Co., Ltd. (1)
574-3 Tarumi, Tsu, Mie, Japan
Tel.: (81) 592288101
Web Site: http://www.sanco-oil.co.jp
Emp.: 160
Petroleum Product Distr
N.A.I.C.S.: 424720
Umeyama Haruhisa (CEO)

Sanco Real Estate Appraisal Co., Ltd. (1)
3-21-7 Meieki Nakamura-Ku, Nagoya, Aichi, Japan
Tel.: (81) 525635531
Web Site: http://www.appraisal.sanco.co.jp
Emp.: 4
Real Estate Appraisal Services
N.A.I.C.S.: 531320
Yoshimura Mikio (CEO)

Sanco Real Estate Co., Ltd. (1)
9-18 Marunouchi, Tsu, Mie, Japan
Tel.: (81) 592275111
Web Site: http://re.sanco.co.jp
Emp.: 426
Residential Development Services
N.A.I.C.S.: 236117
Ogura Toshihide (Co-Pres)

Sanco Taxi Co., Ltd. (1)
3-3-6 Shinsho, Yokkaichi, 510-0064, Mie, Japan
Tel.: (81) 593532221
Web Site: http://www.sanco-taxi.co.jp
Emp.: 155
Taxi Transportation Services
N.A.I.C.S.: 485310
Nakajima Yoshihiro (Pres)

Toba Seaside Hotel Co., Ltd. (1)
1084 Arashima-Cho, Toba, 517-0021, Mie, Japan
Tel.: (81) 599255151
Web Site: http://www.tobaseasidehotel.co.jp
Emp.: 200
Hotel Operator
N.A.I.C.S.: 721110
Ibi Masahiro (CEO)

MIECO CHIPBOARD BERHAD

INTERNATIONAL PUBLIC

No 1 Block C Jalan Indah 2/6 Taman Indah, Batu 11 Cheras, 43200, Kuala Lumpur, Selangor Darul Ehsan, Malaysia
Tel.: (60) 390759991 MY
Web Site: https://www.mieco.com.my
Year Founded: 1972
MIECO—(KLS)
Rev.: $69,473,862
Assets: $134,705,608
Liabilities: $51,826,243
Net Worth: $82,879,365
Earnings: ($7,137,143)
Emp.: 640
Fiscal Year-end: 12/31/22
Chipboard Mfr
N.A.I.C.S.: 334413
Ah Chai Ng (Mng Dir)

Subsidiaries:

Mieco Manufacturing Sdn. Bhd. (1)
No 1 Block C Jalan Indah 2/6 Taman Indah Batu 11, 43200, Cheras, Selangor, Malaysia
Tel.: (60) 390759991
Particleboard Mfr
N.A.I.C.S.: 321219

Plant (Domestic):

Mieco Manufacturing Sdn. Bhd. - Pahang Factory (2)
Lot 74 Kawasan Perindustrian Gebeng, 26080, Kuantan, Pahang, Malaysia
Tel.: (60) 95835120
Particleboard Mfr
N.A.I.C.S.: 321219
Kevin Quek (Mgr-Domestic & Export)

Mieco Marketing Sdn Bhd (1)
No 1 Block C Jalan Indah 2/6 Taman Indah Cheras 11 Miles, 43200, Cheras, Selangor, Malaysia
Tel.: (60) 390759991
Web Site: https://www.mieco.com.my
Particleboard Mfr
N.A.I.C.S.: 321219

Seng Yip Furniture Sdn. Bhd. (1)
Lot 971 Kawasan Perindustrian Sungai Lalang Mukim Semenyih, Jalan Sungai Lalang, Semenyih, 43500, Selangor, Malaysia
Tel.: (60) 387234535
Web Site: http://www.sengyip.asiaep.com
Sales Range: $100-124.9 Million
Emp.: 450
Furniture Product Mfr
N.A.I.C.S.: 337122
Ng Ah Chai (CEO)

MIELE & CIE KG
Carl Miele-Strasse 29, PO Box 33325, Gutersloh, 5241, Germany
Tel.: (49) 5241890
Web Site: http://www.miele.com
Year Founded: 1899
Sales Range: $1-4.9 Billion
Emp.: 11
Major Household Appliance Mfr
N.A.I.C.S.: 335220
Markus Miele (Exec Dir)

Subsidiaries:

Miele & Cie KG - Arnsberg Plant (1)
Breddestr 53-55, Postfach 17 47, 59759, Arnsberg, Germany
Tel.: (49) 29 32 3 05 0
Emp.: 246
Steel Products Mfr
N.A.I.C.S.: 331513

Miele & Cie KG - Bielefeld Plant (1)
Mielestrasse 2, Postfach 10.01.07, 33611, Bielefeld, Germany
Tel.: (49) 521 807 0
Steel Mfrs
N.A.I.C.S.: 331513

Miele & Cie KG - Bunde Plant (1)
Miele-Strasse 1, 32257, Bunde, Germany
Tel.: (49) 52 23 4 81 0
Web Site: http://www.miele.com
Hob Units, Steam Ovens & Warmer Drawers Mfr
N.A.I.C.S.: 335220

AND PRIVATE COMPANIES

MIELE & CIE KG

Miele & Cie KG - Euskirchen Plant (1)
Roitzheimer Strasse 110, Postfach 11 67, 53879, Euskirchen, Germany
Tel.: (49) 2251 818 0
Electric Motor Mfr
N.A.I.C.S.: 335312

Miele & Cie KG - Lehrte Plant (1)
Industriestrasse 3, 31275, Lehrte, Germany
Tel.: (49) 5132 59 0
Web Site: http://www.miele.com
Emp.: 380
Electrical Appliance Mfr
N.A.I.C.S.: 335210

Miele & Cie KG - Oelde Plant (1)
Carl-Miele-Platz 1, 59302, Oelde, Germany
Tel.: (49) 5245 91 0
Steel Mfrs
N.A.I.C.S.: 331513

Miele & Cie KG -Burmoos Plant (1)
Miele Strasse 1, 5111, Burmoos, Austria
Tel.: (43) 62 74 63 44 0
Steel Mfrs
N.A.I.C.S.: 331513

Miele (Hong Kong) Ltd. (1)
41/F-4101 Manhattan Place 23 Wang Tai Road, Kowloon, China (Hong Kong)
Tel.: (852) 2610 1025
Web Site: http://www.miele.hk
Household Appliance Distr
N.A.I.C.S.: 423620
Kenny Lam *(Mng Dir)*

Miele (Pty) Ltd (1)
63 Peter Place, PO Box 69434, Sandton, 2194, South Africa
Tel.: (27) 11 875 9000
Web Site: http://www.miele.co.za
Household Appliance Distr
N.A.I.C.S.: 423620
Brennan Menday *(Mng Dir)*

Miele (Shanghai) Trading Ltd. (1)
1-3 Floor No 82 Shi Men Yi Road, Jing'An District, 200040, Shanghai, China
Tel.: (86) 21 61573500
Web Site: http://www.miele.com
Household Appliance Distr
N.A.I.C.S.: 423620

Miele A/S (1)
Erhvervsvej 2, 2600, Glostrup, Denmark
Tel.: (45) 43271310
Web Site: http://www.miele.dk
Household Appliance Distr
N.A.I.C.S.: 423620

Miele AB (1)
Industrivagen 20, Box 1397, 171 48, Solna, Sweden
Tel.: (46) 8 562 29 000
Web Site: http://www.miele.se
Household Appliance Distr
N.A.I.C.S.: 423620
Henrik von Bargen *(Product Mgr)*

Miele AG (1)
Limmatstr 4, 8957, Spreitenbach, Switzerland
Tel.: (41) 56 417 20 00
Web Site: http://www.miele.ch
Household Appliance Distr
N.A.I.C.S.: 423620

Miele AS (1)
Nesbruveien 71, 1394, Nesbru, Norway
Tel.: (47) 6717 3100
Web Site: http://www.miele.no
Household Appliance Distr
N.A.I.C.S.: 423620

Miele Appliances Ltd. (1)
Gold & Diamond Park Sheikh Zayed Road Office Nos 6-217, PO Box 114782, Dubai, United Arab Emirates
Tel.: (971) 4 3418444
Web Site: http://www.miele.ae
Household Appliance Distr
N.A.I.C.S.: 423620

Miele Appliances SRL (1)
Intrarea Narciselor 8, Otopeni, Jud Ilfov, Romania
Tel.: (40) 21 3520777
Household Appliance Distr
N.A.I.C.S.: 423620

Miele Australia Pty. Ltd. (1)
1 Gilbert Park Drive, Knoxfield, 3180, VIC, Australia
Tel.: (61) 3 97647 100
Web Site: http://www.miele.com.au
Household Appliance Distr
N.A.I.C.S.: 423620

Miele Company Limited (1)
Fairacres Marcham Road, Abingdon, OX14 1TW, United Kingdom
Tel.: (44) 1235 554455
Web Site: http://www.miele.co.uk
Household Appliance Distr
N.A.I.C.S.: 423620

Miele Electrodomesticos Ltda. (1)
Nueva Costanera 4055, 7630196, Vitacura, Santiago, Chile
Tel.: (56) 229570000
Web Site: http://www.miele.com
Household Appliance Distr
N.A.I.C.S.: 423620

Miele Elektrikli Aletler Dis Tic. ve Paz. Ltd. Sti (1)
Barbaros Mah Cigdem Sok My Office Is Merkezi No 13/A, Atasehir, 34746, Istanbul, Turkiye
Tel.: (90) 216 687 18 00
Web Site: http://www.miele.com.tr
Emp.: 10
Household Appliance Retailer
N.A.I.C.S.: 449210

Miele Ges.m.b.H. (1)
Mielestrasse 1, 5071, Wals-Siezenheim, Austria
Tel.: (43) 50 800 800
Web Site: http://www.miele.at
Household Appliance Distr
N.A.I.C.S.: 423620

Miele Hellas E.P.E. (1)
Mesogion 257, Psychiko, 15451, Athens, Greece
Tel.: (30) 210 6794 444
Web Site: http://www.miele.gr
Household Appliance Distr
N.A.I.C.S.: 423620

Miele Inc. (1)
9 Independence Way, Princeton, NJ 08540
Tel.: (609) 419-9898
Web Site: http://www.mieleusa.com
Sales Range: $75-99.9 Million
Emp.: 150
Major Household Appliances & Vacuums Sales & Services
N.A.I.C.S.: 423620
Jan Heck *(Pres & CEO)*

Miele India Pvt. Ltd. (1)
First Floor Copia Corporate Suites Commercial Plot No 9, Jasola, New Delhi, 110 025, India
Tel.: (91) 11 4690 0000
Web Site: http://www.miele.in
Household Appliance Distr
N.A.I.C.S.: 423620
R.P. Sing *(Mng Dir)*

Miele Ireland Ltd (1)
2024 Bianconi Avenue Citywest Business Campus, Dublin, Ireland
Tel.: (353) 1 4610710
Web Site: http://www.miele.ie
Household Appliance Distr
N.A.I.C.S.: 423620

Miele Italia S.r.l. (1)
Strada Di Circonvallazione 27, 39057, Appiano sulla Strada del Vino, Italy
Tel.: (39) 0471 666 111
Web Site: http://www.miele.it
Household Appliance Retailer
N.A.I.C.S.: 449210

Miele Japan Corp. (1)
Meguro Yamate Place 2F 2-10-11 Meguro, Meguro-ku, Tokyo, 153-0063, Japan
Tel.: (81) 3 5740 0030
Web Site: http://www.miele.co.jp
Household Appliance Distr
N.A.I.C.S.: 423620

Miele Kft. (1)
Also Torokvesz Ut 2, 1022, Budapest, Hungary
Tel.: (36) 1 8806 400
Web Site: http://www.miele.hu

Household Appliance Distr
N.A.I.C.S.: 423620

Miele Korea Limited (1)
Miele Haus 8 Fl 607-10 Yeoksam-dong, Gangnam-gu, Seoul, 135-080, Korea (South)
Tel.: (82) 2 34519 353
Web Site: http://www.miele.co.kr
Household Appliance Distr
N.A.I.C.S.: 423620

Miele LLC (1)
Zhylyanskaya Str 48 50A, 01033, Kiev, Ukraine
Tel.: (380) 44 4960300
Web Site: http://www.miele.ua
Household Appliance Distr
N.A.I.C.S.: 423620

Miele Limited (1)
161 Four Valley Drive, Vaughan, L4K 4V8, ON, Canada
Tel.: (905) 660-9936
Web Site: http://www.miele.ca
Household Appliance Distr
N.A.I.C.S.: 423620

Miele Nederland B.V. (1)
De Limiet 2, 4131 NR, Vianen, Netherlands
Tel.: (31) 347 378 911
Web Site: http://www.miele.nl
Household Appliance Distr
N.A.I.C.S.: 423620

Miele New Zealand Limited (1)
Level 2 10 College Hill Freemans Bay, Auckland, 1011, New Zealand
Tel.: (64) 9 5731269
Web Site: http://www.miele.co.nz
Emp.: 15
Household Appliance Distr
N.A.I.C.S.: 423620
Brian Scott *(Gen Mgr)*

Miele Oy (1)
Porttikaari 6, 01200, Vantaa, Finland
Tel.: (358) 9 87597 0
Web Site: http://www.miele.fi
Household Appliance Distr
N.A.I.C.S.: 423620
Esa Silver *(CEO)*

Miele Portuguesa, Lda (1)
Av Do Forte N 5, 2790-073, Carnaxide, Portugal
Tel.: (351) 21 4248 100
Web Site: http://www.miele.pt
Household Appliance Distr
N.A.I.C.S.: 423620

Miele Pte Ltd (1)
167 Penang Road Suite B1-01 Winsland House II, Singapore, 238462, Singapore
Tel.: (65) 6735 1191
Web Site: http://www.miele.sg
Household Appliance Distr
N.A.I.C.S.: 423620

Miele S.A.S. (1)
9 Ave Albert Einstein, Zone Industrielle Le Coudray, 93151, Le Blanc-Mesnil, France
Tel.: (33) 149394400
Web Site: http://www.miele.fr
Sales Range: $50-74.9 Million
Emp.: 220
Household Appliances Mfr
N.A.I.C.S.: 335220
Anne Lamoureux *(Mgr-Adv)*

Miele S.A.U. (1)
Avda De Bruselas 31, Alcobendas, 28108, Madrid, Spain
Tel.: (34) 902 398 398
Web Site: http://www.miele.es
Household Appliance Distr
N.A.I.C.S.: 423620

Miele SIA Eesti filiaal (1)
Kesk-Ameerika Tn 7-1, Harju, Tallinn, Estonia
Tel.: (372) 57880528
Web Site: http://www.miele.ee
Household Appliance Distr
N.A.I.C.S.: 423620

Miele Sdn Bhd (1)
G1-01-1 Menara Kencana Petroleum Solaris Dutamas No 1 Jalan Dutamas 1, 50480, Kuala Lumpur, Malaysia
Tel.: (60) 3 6205 3899

Web Site: http://www.miele.my
Household Appliance Distr
N.A.I.C.S.: 423620

Miele Sp. z o.o. (1)
Ul Gotarda 9, 02-683, Warsaw, Poland
Tel.: (48) 22 548 4000
Web Site: http://www.miele.pl
Household Appliance Distr
N.A.I.C.S.: 423620

Miele d.o.o. (1)
Brnciceva Ulica 41 G, Ljubljana, Slovenia
Tel.: (386) 1563 44 80
Web Site: http://www.miele.si
Household Appliance Distr
N.A.I.C.S.: 423620

Miele s.a r.l. (1)
20 Rue Christophe Plantin, 2339, Luxembourg, Luxembourg
Tel.: (352) 49711 20
Web Site: http://www.miele.lu
Household Appliance Distr
N.A.I.C.S.: 423620

Miele s.r.o. (1)
Plynarenska 1, 821 09, Bratislava, Slovakia
Tel.: (421) 258 103111
Web Site: http://www.miele.sk
Household Appliance Distr
N.A.I.C.S.: 423620

Miele trgovina i servis d.o.o. (1)
Buzinski Prilaz 32, 10000, Zagreb, Croatia
Tel.: (385) 1 6689 000
Web Site: http://www.miele.hr
Household Appliance Distr
N.A.I.C.S.: 423620

Miele, S.A. de C.V. (1)
Arquimedes 43 Polanco Chapultepec, 11560, Mexico, Mexico
Tel.: (52) 55 85039870
Web Site: http://www.miele.com.mx
Household Appliance Distr
N.A.I.C.S.: 423620

Miele, spol. s r.o. (1)
Holandska 4, 639 00, Brno, Czech Republic
Tel.: (420) 543553 111
Web Site: http://www.miele.cz
Household Appliance Distr
N.A.I.C.S.: 423620

N.V. Miele Belgie (1)
Z 5 Mollem 480, 1730, Mollem, Belgium
Tel.: (32) 24511616
Web Site: http://www.miele.be
Emp.: 200
Household Appliance Retailer
N.A.I.C.S.: 449210

OOO Miele CIS (1)
Leningradsky prospect 31A building 1 floor 8 room 1 room 1, 125284, Moscow, Russia
Tel.: (7) 4957458990
Web Site: http://www.miele.ru
Household Appliance Retailer
N.A.I.C.S.: 449210

SIA Miele (1)
Zaubes 9A-38, Riga, 1013, Latvia
Tel.: (371) 67889877
Web Site: http://www.miele.lv
Household Appliance Distr
N.A.I.C.S.: 423620

SIA Miele Lietuvos filialas (1)
Laisves Pr 125, 06118, Vilnius, Lithuania
Tel.: (370) 6 878 5450
Web Site: http://www.miele.lt
Household Appliance Distr
N.A.I.C.S.: 423620

Steelco S.p.A. (1)
Via Balegante, 27 Riese Pio X,, 31039, Treviso, Italy
Tel.: (39) 04237561
Web Site: https://www.steelcogroup.com
Machine Mfg
N.A.I.C.S.: 333248

Joint Venture (Non-US):

Belimed AG (2)
Dorfstrasse 4, Ballwil, 6275, Switzerland (67%)
Tel.: (41) 417689600
Web Site: www.belimed.com
Sales Range: $50-74.9 Million
Emp.: 130

MIELE & CIE KG

Miele & Cie KG—(Continued)
Cleaning, Disinfection & Sterilization Services
N.A.I.C.S.: 325412

Subsidiary (Non-US):

Belimed B.V. (3)
Energieweg 8, 6658, Amsterdam, Netherlands
Tel.: (31) 487 591 100
Cleaning, Disinfection & Sterilization Services
N.A.I.C.S.: 325412

Belimed GmbH (3)
Edisonstrasse 7a, 84453, Muhldorf, Germany
Tel.: (49) 863198960
Web Site: http://www.belimed.com
Sales Range: $50-74.9 Million
Emp.: 130
Cleaning, Disinfection & Sterilization Services
N.A.I.C.S.: 325412

Subsidiary (Domestic):

Belimed Deutschland GmbH (4)
Edisonstrasse 7a, Muhldorf, 84453, Germany
Tel.: (49) 863198960
Web Site: http://www.belimed.de
Sales Range: $25-49.9 Million
Emp.: 100
Cleaning, Disinfection & Sterilization Services
N.A.I.C.S.: 325412

Belimed Technik GmbH (4)
Edisonstrasse 7a, 84453, Muhldorf, Germany
Tel.: (49) 863198960
Web Site: http://www.belimed.com
Sales Range: $25-49.9 Million
Emp.: 100
Cleaning, Disinfection & Sterilization Services
N.A.I.C.S.: 325412

Subsidiary (US):

Belimed Inc. (3)
8351 Palmetto Commerce Pkwy Ste 101, Ladson, SC 29456
Tel.: (843) 216-7424
Web Site: http://www.belimed.us
Sales Range: $25-49.9 Million
Emp.: 50
Cleaning, Disinfection & Sterilization Services
N.A.I.C.S.: 325412

Subsidiary (Non-US):

Belimed Infection Control Kft. (3)
Aranykez u 6, 1052, Budapest, Hungary
Tel.: (36) 1 318 86 97
Disinfection & Sterilization System Distr
N.A.I.C.S.: 423850

Belimed Ltd. (3)
Unit 4 New Buildings Place, Dragons Green Road, Horsham, RH13 8GQ, West Sussex, United Kingdom
Tel.: (44) 1403738811
Sales Range: $25-49.9 Million
Emp.: 8
Cleaning, Disinfection & Sterilization Services
N.A.I.C.S.: 325412
Martin O'Hare (Gen Mgr)

Belimed Medical Equipment (Shanghai) Co., Ltd (3)
New Jinqiao Road 1299 1st Building 2nd Floor, Pudong, Shanghai, 201206, China
Tel.: (86) 215 137 0998
Web Site: https://www.belimed.com
Cleaning, Disinfection & Sterilization Services
N.A.I.C.S.: 325412

Belimed SAS (3)
Medical and Life Science Parc Espale 1 av Pierre Pflimlin, 68390, Sausheim, France
Tel.: (33) 38 963 6540
Web Site: https://www.belimed.com
Sales Range: $25-49.9 Million
Emp.: 45

Cleaning, Disinfection & Sterilization Services
N.A.I.C.S.: 325412

Subsidiary (Domestic):

Belimed Sauter AG (3)
Zelgstrasse 8, 8583, Bischofszell, Switzerland
Tel.: (41) 716448500
Web Site: http://www.sauterag.com
Sales Range: $50-74.9 Million
Cleaning, Disinfection & Sterilization Services
N.A.I.C.S.: 325412

Subsidiary (Non-US):

Belimed d.o.o. (3)
Kosovelova Cesta 2, 1290, Grosuplje, Slovenia
Tel.: (386) 17866010
Sales Range: $50-74.9 Million
Emp.: 130
Cleaning, Disinfection & Sterilization Services
N.A.I.C.S.: 325412

NV Belimed SA (3)
Rue de Clairvaux 8, 1348, Louvain-la-Neuve, Belgium
Tel.: (32) 10420240
Cleaning, Disinfection & Sterilization Services
N.A.I.C.S.: 325412

Sterifast Sterilization & Disinfection Systems, Lda. (3)
Praque Empresarial do Padrao Lote 11, 5460-343, Boticas, Portugal
Tel.: (351) 27 641 8287
Web Site: https://www.sterifast.com
Sterilization Equipment Mfr
N.A.I.C.S.: 332313

Joint Venture (Non-US):

Belimed Life Science AG (2)
Zelgstrasse 8, Sulgen, 8583, Weinfelden, Switzerland (67%)
Tel.: (41) 716448691
Medical Equipment Distr
N.A.I.C.S.: 423450

MIELE COSMED GROUP S.A.

Ul Wielkopolska 3, 26-600, Radom, Poland
Tel.: (48) 483845801
Web Site: https://dr-miele.eu
Year Founded: 1990
DMG—(WAR)
Cosmetic & Detergent Mfr & Distr
N.A.I.C.S.: 325611
Andreas Mielimonka (Chm)

Subsidiaries:

Global Cosmed Group S.A. (1)
ul Kuziennicza 15, Jawor, 59-400, Wroclaw, Poland
Tel.: (48) 768703031
Cosmetic Product Distr
N.A.I.C.S.: 456120
Magdalena Mielimonka (Pres)

MIEN DONG JOINT STOCK COMPANY

Road 1 - Bien Hoa 1 Industrial Park, Bien Hoa, Dong Nai, Vietnam
Tel.: (84) 2513836371
Web Site: https://miendong.com.vn
Year Founded: 1986
MDG—(HOSE)
Rev.: $11,412,524
Assets: $14,625,011
Liabilities: $9,423,223
Net Worth: $5,201,788
Earnings: ($1,503,388)
Emp.: 74
Fiscal Year-end: 12/31/23
Construction Services
N.A.I.C.S.: 236210

MIEN TRUNG POWER INVESTMENT & DEVELOPMENT JOINT STOCK COMPANY

No 10 Lam Son Phuoc Hoa, Nha Trang, Khanh Hoa, Vietnam
Tel.: (84) 583878092
Web Site: http://www.mientrungpid.com.vn
SEB—(HNX)
Rev.: $31,128,300
Assets: $70,888,700
Liabilities: $6,282,200
Net Worth: $64,606,500
Earnings: $15,597,800
Fiscal Year-end: 12/31/23
Electric Power Generation & Distribution Services
N.A.I.C.S.: 221111
Nguyen Hoai Nam (Member-Mgmt Bd & Gen Dir)

MIERKA DONAUHAFEN KREMS GESELLSCHAFT M.B.H. & CO KG

Karl Mierka Str 7-9, 3500, Krems, Austria
Tel.: (43) 2732 73571 0
Web Site: http://www.mierka.com
Emp.: 70
Logistic Services
N.A.I.C.S.: 488510
Hubert Mierka (Mng Dir)

Subsidiaries:

Danufert Handelsgesellschaft mbH (1)
Karl Mierka Strasse 7-9, 3500, Krems, Austria (40%)
Tel.: (43) 273273571
Web Site: http://www.mierka.com
Sales Range: $50-74.9 Million
Agricultural Product Whslr
N.A.I.C.S.: 424910

MIEV CO LTD

601 176 Heonleung-ro, Seocho-gu, Seoul, Korea (South)
Tel.: (82) 15771401
Web Site: http://www.miev.co.kr
Year Founded: 2003
Cosmetic Product Mfr & Distr
N.A.I.C.S.: 325620

MIEXACT LIMITED

5th Floor 10 Whitechapel High Street, London, United Kingdom
Tel.: (44) 2074900049 UK
Web Site: https://miexact.com
Emp.: 100
Management Consulting Services
N.A.I.C.S.: 541618
Polly Avgherino (Mng Dir)

MIG MEDIA NEURONS LIMITED

Shapath Hexa Sarkhej-Gandhinagar Highway Vishwas City 1 Sola, Ahmedabad, Gujarat, India
Tel.: (91) 9909903132
Web Site: http://www.madeingujarat.co
Year Founded: 2011
MMNL—(NSE)
Marketing Consulting Services
N.A.I.C.S.: 541613
Rushikesh Bhavsar (Founder & Chm)

MIGAO CORPORATION

1300-1500 West Georgia Street Suite 1500, Vancouver, V6G 2Z6, BC, Canada
Tel.: (647) 978-2108 ON
Year Founded: 1997
Potash Fertilizer Mfr
N.A.I.C.S.: 212390

INTERNATIONAL PUBLIC

Subsidiaries:

Guangdong Migao Chemical Co., Ltd. (1)
Qingzhou Dev Zone E Zone, Foshan, China
Tel.: (86) 75788869312
Inorganic Chemical Mfr
N.A.I.C.S.: 325180

Liaoning Migao Chemical Co., Ltd. (1)
Sitaizi Vlg, Lutun Town Bayuqua, Yingkou, Liaoning, China
Tel.: (86) 4177233798
Fertilizer Mfr
N.A.I.C.S.: 325311

Sichuan Migao Chemical Fertilizer Co., Ltd. (1)
No 35 Huangjin Rd, Dawn Town, Chengdu, China
Tel.: (86) 28 83603855
Chemical Fertiliser Mfr
N.A.I.C.S.: 325311

MIGDALOR ALTERNATIVE INVESTMENT

7 Gazit St, Petah Tikva, 4927987, Israel
Tel.: (972) 732225706
Web Site: http://www.migdalor-group.com
MGDA—(TAE)
Rev.: $10,772,870
Assets: $24,479,223
Liabilities: $7,702,138
Net Worth: $16,777,085
Earnings: $267,047
Fiscal Year-end: 06/30/22
Real Estate Investment Services
N.A.I.C.S.: 531390
Shlomi Elberg (Co-Founder)

MIGHTY CRAFT LIMITED

26 Cato Street, Hawthorn East, 3123, VIC, Australia
Tel.: (61) 394154000 AU
Web Site: https://www.mightycraft.com.au
Year Founded: 2017
MCL—(ASX)
Rev.: $73,456,347
Assets: $88,202,386
Liabilities: $44,381,561
Net Worth: $43,820,825
Earnings: $3,773,228
Emp.: 70
Fiscal Year-end: 06/30/23
Alcoholic Beverages Mfr
N.A.I.C.S.: 312140
Andrew Syme (CFO)

Subsidiaries:

Foghorn Brewery Pty. Ltd. (1)
218 King Street, Newcastle, 2300, NSW, Australia
Tel.: (61) 249294721
Web Site: https://foghornbrewery.com.au
Food & Beverage Services
N.A.I.C.S.: 624210

MIGWANG CONTACT LENS CO., LTD.

693 Namcheon-ro Namcheon-myeon, Gyeongsan, 712-881, Gyeongsangbukdo, Korea (South)
Tel.: (82) 538112262 KR
Web Site: http://www.migwang.com
Year Founded: 1980
Sales Range: $25-49.9 Million
Emp.: 183
Contact Lens Mfr & Distr
N.A.I.C.S.: 333310
Jong Gu Park (CEO)

Subsidiaries:

Clearlab SG Pte Ltd (1)
139 Joo Seng Rd Unit 01-01, Singapore, 368362, Singapore
Tel.: (65) 67491090

Web Site: http://www.clearlab.com
Mfr of Contact Lenses
N.A.I.C.S.: 333310
Park Haekyeung *(Mng Dir)*

MIHG MASCHINEN- INSTANDSETZUNGS- UND HANDELS GMBH
Orststeil Petschow Zum Dorfteich 4, 18196, Rostock, Germany
Tel.: (49) 382046070
Web Site: http://www.mihg.de
Agricultural Machinery Services
N.A.I.C.S.: 532490
Nando Schunemann *(Mng Dir)*

MIHIJAM VANASPATI LIMITED
Village Kangoi P O Mihijam, District Jamtara, Jamtara, 815 354, Jharkhand, India
Tel.: (91) 341 6460938
Web Site:
    http://www.mihijamvanaspati.com
Year Founded: 1989
Sales Range: $10-24.9 Million
Edible Oil Mfr
N.A.I.C.S.: 311225
Rajesh Agarwal *(Mng Dir)*

MIHIKA INDUSTRIES LTD.
3 Bentinck Street 2nd Floor, Kolkata, 700 001, West Bengal, India
Tel.: (91) 3322100875
Web Site:
    https://www.mihikaindustries.co.in
538895—(BOM)
Rev: $152,005
Assets: $2,647,347
Liabilities: $51,328
Net Worth: $2,596,019
Earnings: ($289,611)
Emp.: 6
Fiscal Year-end: 03/31/23
Fabric Product Trading Services
N.A.I.C.S.: 523160
Kuldeep Kumar Sethia *(Mng Dir)*

MIJEM NEWCOMM TECH INC.
820-44 Victoria Street, Toronto, M5C 1Y2, ON, Canada
Tel.: (647) 291-4673   Ca
Web Site: https://www.mijem.com
Year Founded: 2017
MJEM—(CNSX)
Assets: $17,530
Liabilities: $51,156
Net Worth: ($33,626)
Earnings: ($139,698)
Fiscal Year-end: 12/31/21
Software Development Services
N.A.I.C.S.: 541511
Phuong Dinh *(Founder)*

MIJIN SYSTEM CO. LTD.
6 Jungbu-daero 2565beon-gil, Yangji-myeon Cheoin-gu, Yongin, Gyeonggi-do, Korea (South)
Tel.: (82) 313358787   KR
Web Site: http://www.mijinsys.co.kr
Year Founded: 1976
Air Tool Spring Balancer & Electronic Driver Mfr
N.A.I.C.S.: 332912

MIJU CO., LTD.
1212 70 Gasan digital 1-ro, Geumcheon-gu, Seoul, Korea (South)
Tel.: (82) 220383999
Year Founded: 2013
351020—(KRS)
Rev: $14,816,152
Assets: $10,529,168
Liabilities: $8,235,639
Net Worth: $2,293,529
Earnings: $612,536
Emp.: 49
Fiscal Year-end: 12/31/22

Apparel Product Retailer
N.A.I.C.S.: 424350

MIKA ALAS A.D.
Save Kovacevica bb, Belgrade, Serbia
Tel.: (381) 11 332 88 66
Year Founded: 2005
Sales Range: Less than $1 Million
Emp.: 9
Fish Farming Services
N.A.I.C.S.: 112511

MIKE VAIL TRUCKING LTD.
4531 32nd Street SE, Calgary, T2B 3P8, AB, Canada
Tel.: (403) 272-5487
Web Site:
    http://www.mikevailtrucking.ab.ca
Year Founded: 1978
Rev: $14,172,027
Emp.: 125
Truck Transportation Services
N.A.I.C.S.: 484110
Mike Vail *(Pres & CEO)*

MIKI PULLEY CO., LTD.
10-41 Imaiminami-cho, Nakahara-ku, Kawasaki, 211-8577, Kanagawa, Japan
Tel.: (81) 447334371
Web Site: http://www.mikipulley.co.jp
Year Founded: 1939
Sales Range: $100-124.9 Million
Emp.: 824
Transmission Device Mfr & Distr
N.A.I.C.S.: 333613
Harukazu Miki *(Chm)*

Subsidiaries:

Inkok Industrial Co., Ltd.   (1)
1F EBiz Ctr 170 5 Guro Dong, Seoul, 152 050, Korea (South)   **(100%)**
Tel.: (82) 221082500
Web Site: http://www.inkok.co.kr
Sales Range: $50-74.9 Million
Emp.: 200
N.A.I.C.S.: 333612
Chang Caecon *(Mng Dir)*

Kaishin Industria E Comercio Ltda.   (1)
Rua Belchior Carneiro, 239 Lapa De Baixo, 05068-050, Sao Paulo, Brazil   **(40%)**
Tel.: (55) 1136116591
Web Site: http://www.kaishin.com.br
Sales Range: $25-49.9 Million
Emp.: 15
N.A.I.C.S.: 333612

MIKI PULLEY (EUROPE) AG   (1)
Rheinweg 5, 8200, Schaffhausen, Switzerland
Tel.: (41) 52 625 2424
Web Site: http://www.mikipulley.ch
Industrial Supplies Distr
N.A.I.C.S.: 423840

MIKI PULLEY (HONG KONG) CO., LTD.
Room 510 Cct Telecom Bldg 11 Wo Shing Street, Fotan, China (Hong Kong)
Tel.: (852) 2947 7508
Industrial Supplies Distr
N.A.I.C.S.: 423840

MIKI PULLEY (INDIA) PVT. LTD.   (1)
Plot B-29/2 Midc Taloja, Raigad, Mumbai, 410 208, India
Tel.: (91) 22 6565 2900
Web Site: http://www.mikipulley.co.in
Emp.: 20
Industrial Supplies Distr
N.A.I.C.S.: 423840
Riaz Mokashi *(Mng Dir)*

MIKI PULLEY (KOREA) CO., LTD   (1)
302-406 Bucheon Techno-Park 397 Seokcheon-Ro 397 Ssanyong 3rd 36-1, Samjeong-Dong Ojeong-Gu, Bucheon, 421-808, Gyeonggi-Do, Korea (South)
Tel.: (82) 32 624 1750

Web Site: http://www.mikipulley.kr
Industrial Supplies Distr
N.A.I.C.S.: 423840

Maschinenfabrik Moenninghoff GmbH & Co. KG   (1)
Hans-Lenze-Strasse 1, Aerzen, 31855, Germany   **(100%)**
Tel.: (49) 5154820
Sales Range: $25-49.9 Million
Emp.: 45
Drive & Automation Technology
N.A.I.C.S.: 333612
Erhard Tellbuscher *(Chm)*

Maschinenfabrik Moenninghoff GmbH & Co. KG   (1)
PO Box 101749, 44717, Bochum, Germany   **(100%)**
Tel.: (49) 23433350
Web Site: http://www.moenninghoff.de
Sales Range: $25-49.9 Million
Emp.: 100
N.A.I.C.S.: 333612
Kai Neubauer *(CEO)*

Miki Beltec Co., Ltd.   (1)
2 2 2819 Izumi Machi Yonezawa Shi, Yamagata, 992-0063, Japan   **(100%)**
Tel.: (81) 238383808
Web Site: http://www.mikipulley.co.jp
N.A.I.C.S.: 333612

Miki Power Control Co., Ltd.   (1)
461 Imai Minami Machi Nakahara Ku, Kawasaki, 211 8577, Japan   **(100%)**
Tel.: (81) 447334371
Sales Range: $25-49.9 Million
Emp.: 350
N.A.I.C.S.: 333612
Kazuhiro Tsukagoshi *(Mgr-Sls)*

Miki Pulley (Training) Co., Ltd.   (1)
No 2 Liao He Bei Dao, Bei Chen High Tech Park, Tianjin, 300410, China   **(100%)**
Tel.: (86) 2226303111
Web Site: http://www.mikipulley.co.jp
Sales Range: $50-74.9 Million
Emp.: 150
N.A.I.C.S.: 333612

Miki RA Hanbai Co., Ltd.   (1)
461 Imai Minami Machi Nakahara Ku, Kawasaki, 211 8577, Kanagawa, Japan   **(100%)**
Tel.: (81) 447115777
Web Site: http://www.mikipueuy.co.jp
Emp.: 3
N.A.I.C.S.: 333612
Mamoru Miki *(Pres)*

Miki Simpla Co., Ltd.   (1)
461 Imai Minami Machi Nakahara Ku, Kawasaki, 211 8577, Kanagawa, Japan   **(100%)**
Tel.: (81) 447334371
Web Site: http://www.mikipulley.com
Sales Range: $100-124.9 Million
Emp.: 300
N.A.I.C.S.: 333612

Naismith Engineering & Manufacturing Co Pty Ltd   (1)
149 Heidelberg Rd, Northcote, 3070, VIC, Australia
Tel.: (61) 394899811
Web Site: http://www.naismith.com.au
Sales Range: $25-49.9 Million
Emp.: 8
Power Transmission Product Mfr & Whslr
N.A.I.C.S.: 333612
Len Naismith *(Founder)*

Namsae International Trading Co., Ltd   (1)
32 34 Soi Srithammatirad Charoenkrung Rd, Pomprab, Bangkok, 10100, Thailand   **(60%)**
Tel.: (66) 22220072
Web Site: http://www.namsae.com
Sales Range: $25-49.9 Million
Emp.: 10
N.A.I.C.S.: 333612

PT. Himalaya Everest Jaya   (1)
Jl Daan Mogot Km 10 No 151 Pesing Poglar, Jakarta, 11710, Indonesia   **(100%)**
Tel.: (62) 215448965
Web Site: http://www.hej.co.id

Sales Range: Less than $1 Million
Emp.: 100
Electrical & Mechanical Mfr
N.A.I.C.S.: 333612

Rosta AG   (1)
Hauptstrasse 58, CH 5502, Hunzenschwil, Switzerland   **(100%)**
Tel.: (41) 628972421
Web Site: http://www.rosta.ch
Sales Range: $25-49.9 Million
Emp.: 60
Rubber Mfr
N.A.I.C.S.: 333612
Hanspeter Fischer *(CFO)*

Sing Huat Hardware & Machinery Pte., Ltd.   (1)
327-329 Jalan Besar, Singapore, 208981, Singapore
Tel.: (65) 62936861
Web Site: http://www.singhuat.com
Sales Range: $25-49.9 Million
Emp.: 35
Hardware Products Distr
N.A.I.C.S.: 423710

Sing Huat Hardware & Machinery Sdn. Bhd.   (1)
Lot 4 Jalan SS 13 4 Subang Jaya Industrial Estate, Subang Jaya, 47500, Petaling Jaya, Selangor, Malaysia
Tel.: (60) 356337655
Web Site: http://www.singhuat.com
Sales Range: $25-49.9 Million
Emp.: 25
Control & Piping Equipment Mfr
N.A.I.C.S.: 333612
Junn Wong *(Mgr)*

Zero-Max, Inc.   (1)
13200 6th Ave N, Plymouth, MN 55441   **(100%)**
Tel.: (763) 546-4300
Web Site: http://www.zero-max.com
Sales Range: $25-49.9 Million
Emp.: 77
Mfr & Market Mechanical Variable Speed Drives & Accessories, Couplings & Linear Actuators
N.A.I.C.S.: 333612
William Centner *(VP-Fin & Admin)*

MIKI TRAVEL LTD
Vintners Place 68 Upper Thames Street, London, EC4V 3BJ, United Kingdom
Tel.: (44) 2075075000
Web Site: http://www.miki.co.uk
Sales Range: $10-24.9 Million
Emp.: 60
Travel & Tour Agency
N.A.I.C.S.: 561510
Yoko Okano *(Mng Partner)*

Subsidiaries:

MIKI AGENCIA DE VIAGENS LDA   (1)
Rua Professor Mira Fernandes Lote 4LJB, Lisbon, 1900-385, Portugal
Tel.: (351) 21 845 1008
Travel Agency
N.A.I.C.S.: 561510

MIKI REISEN GMBH WARSZAWA SP.ZO.O   (1)
Bonifraterska 17, Warsaw, 00-203, Poland
Tel.: (48) 22 332 5892
Travel Agency
N.A.I.C.S.: 561510

MIKI Reisen GmbH   (1)
Kurfurstenstr 114, 10787, Berlin, Germany
Tel.: (49) 30 236253
Web Site: http://www.miki-reisen.de
Travel Agency
N.A.I.C.S.: 561510

MIKI TOURIST BELGIUM S.P.R.L.   (1)
5 Rue de la Tete d'Or, Brussels, 1000, Belgium
Tel.: (32) 2 2172826
Travel Agency
N.A.I.C.S.: 561510

MIKI TOURIST K.K.   (1)

MIKI TRAVEL LTD

Miki Travel Ltd—(Continued)
Aqua Dojima NBF Tower 4F Dojimahama 1-4-16, Kita-ku, Osaka, 530-0004, Japan.
Tel.: (81) 66 341 5791
Travel Agency
N.A.I.C.S.: 561510

MIKI TRAVEL AGENCY APS (1)
Gammel Koge Landevej 115-2 Valby, Copenhagen, 2500, Denmark
Tel.: (45) 36178810
Travel Agency
N.A.I.C.S.: 561510

MIKI TRAVEL AGENCY E.U.R.L (1)
22 Rue Caumartin, Paris, 75009, France
Tel.: (33) 1 4450 3100
Travel Agency
N.A.I.C.S.: 561510

MIKI TRAVEL AGENCY GMBH (1)
Wahringer Strasse 12/12 A-1090, Vienna, 1020, Austria
Tel.: (43) 1 31021880
Travel Agency
N.A.I.C.S.: 561510

MIKI TRAVEL AGENCY S.A. (1)
1-3 Rue de Chantepoulet, Geneva, 1201, Switzerland
Tel.: (41) 22 731 5144
Travel Agency
N.A.I.C.S.: 561510

MIKI TRAVEL AGENCY S.A.U. (1)
C/ Bruc 21 4-2, Barcelona, 08010, Spain
Tel.: (34) 93 3180266
Travel Agency
N.A.I.C.S.: 561510

MIKI TRAVEL HAWAII INC. (1)
Waikiki Shopping Plz Ste 403 5 2250 Kalakaua Ave, Honolulu, HI 96815
Tel.: (808) 675-2440
Travel Agency
N.A.I.C.S.: 561510

MIKI TRAVEL IDEGENFORGALMI KFT (1)
49 Batthyany Street, Budapest, 1015, Hungary
Tel.: (36) 6 1 4862550
Travel Agency
N.A.I.C.S.: 561510

MIKI TRAVEL LIMITED (1)
2106 Kuntai Int'l Building No 12 B Chao Wai St, Chaoyang Dist, Beijing, 100020, China
Tel.: (86) 10 5879 0128
Travel Agency
N.A.I.C.S.: 561510

MIKI TRAVEL PRAGUE SPOL S.R.O. (1)
2nd floor Narodni trida, Prague, 11000, Czech Republic
Tel.: (420) 22108 5279
Travel Agency
N.A.I.C.S.: 561510

Miki Tourist Nagoya (1)
NBF Nagoya-Hirokoji bldg 7F Sakae 2-3-6, Naka-ku, Nagoya, 4500002, Aichi, Japan
Tel.: (81) 52 218 3210
Travel Agency
N.A.I.C.S.: 561510
Tetsunori Dambara (Pres)

Miki Travel (Hong Kong) Limited (1)
Unit F-K King Palace Plaza 55 King Yip Street, Kwun Tong, Kowloon, China (Hong Kong)
Tel.: (852) 2526 0007
Web Site: http://www.mikitravel.hk
Travel Agency
N.A.I.C.S.: 561510

Miki Travel AS (1)
Lokketangen, Box 559, Sandvika, 1302, Norway
Tel.: (47) 6756 6180
Web Site: http://www.miki.no
Travel Agency
N.A.I.C.S.: 561510

Miki Travel Agency Italia srl (1)
Corso Italia 39a, 00198, Rome, Italy
Tel.: (39) 06 845711
Web Site: http://www.giapponeviaggi-miki.it

Travel Agency
N.A.I.C.S.: 561510

Miki Travel Consultancy Limited (1)
Room No 1602 United Power International Plaza No 1158 Jiangning Road, Shanghai, 200060, China
Tel.: (86) 21 6299 8021
Travel Agency
N.A.I.C.S.: 561510

Miki Travel Ltd (1)
5F No 138 Sec 2 Nanjing East Road, Taipei, Taiwan
Tel.: (886) 2 2502 0777
Web Site: http://www.miki.trabel.com
Emp.: 11
Travel Agency
N.A.I.C.S.: 561510
Jennifer Hui (Gen Mgr)

MIKIKOGYO CO., LTD.
951-1 Hojo, Himeji, 670-0947, Japan
Tel.: (81) 792815151
Web Site: https://www.mikikogyo.co.jp
Year Founded: 1962
1718—(TKS)
Rev.: $228,319,270
Assets: $213,536,620
Liabilities: $90,191,890
Net Worth: $123,344,730
Earnings: $5,948,510
Emp.: 267
Fiscal Year-end: 12/31/23
Civil Engineering Services
N.A.I.C.S.: 237990
Shoichiro Okada (Pres)

MIKIMOTO PEARL ISLAND CO., LTD.
1-7-1, Toba, 517-8511, Mie, Japan
Tel.: (81) 599252028
Web Site: http://www.mikimoto-pearl-museum.co.jp
Sales Range: $25-49.9 Million
Emp.: 100
Leisure Site & Museum
N.A.I.C.S.: 712110
Motohisa Matsuda (Pres)

MIKO INTERNATIONAL HOLDINGS LIMITED
No 168 Chong Rong Street Economic Technology Development Zone, Quanzhou, 362000, Fujian, China
Tel.: (86) 59524697165 Ky
Web Site: http://www.redkids.com
Year Founded: 1995
1247—(HKG)
Rev.: $19,995,066
Assets: $33,434,856
Liabilities: $13,656,708
Net Worth: $19,778,148
Earnings: ($1,449,068)
Emp.: 290
Fiscal Year-end: 12/31/22
Clothing Product Mfr & Distr
N.A.I.C.S.: 315250
Peiji Ding (Founder & Chm)

MIKO NV
Steenweg op Mol 177, B-2300, Turnhout, Belgium
Tel.: (32) 14462770
Web Site: https://www.mikogroup.be
Year Founded: 1801
MIKO—(EUR)
Rev.: $319,899,547
Assets: $344,561,210
Liabilities: $184,606,469
Net Worth: $159,954,741
Earnings: $2,701,181
Emp.: 1,421
Fiscal Year-end: 12/31/23
Coffee Industry Operator
N.A.I.C.S.: 311920
Frans Van Tilborg (CEO)

Subsidiaries:

Cornish Coffee Co Ltd. (1)
Unit 4 Barncoose Industrial Estate, Cornwall, Redruth, United Kingdom
Tel.: (44) 1209215555
Web Site: https://www.cornishcoffee.co.uk
Coffee Mfr & Distr
N.A.I.C.S.: 311920

Kaffebryggeriet AS (1)
Jogstadveien 21, 2007, Kjeller, Norway
Tel.: (47) 22322222
Web Site: https://www.kaffebryggeriet.no
Coffee Machinery Mfr & Distr
N.A.I.C.S.: 333241

Kaffekompaniet din Pauspartner AB (1)
Datavagen 20, Askim, Gothenburg, Sweden
Tel.: (46) 31289400
Web Site: https://www.kaffekompaniet.se
Coffee Bean & Coffee Machinery Distr
N.A.I.C.S.: 423440

Maas International B.V. (1)
Science Park Eindhoven 5051, 5692 EB, Son, Netherlands
Tel.: (31) 402644500
Web Site: https://maas.nl
Coffee Machinery Services
N.A.I.C.S.: 532490

Miko Cafe Service S.A.S. (1)
8 rue de l Angoumois, 95100, Argenteuil, France
Tel.: (33) 130257330
Web Site: https://miko-cafe.fr
Coffee Machinery Distr
N.A.I.C.S.: 424490

Miko Coffee (Scotland) Ltd. (1)
14 Flakefield East Kilbride, Glasgow, United Kingdom
Tel.: (44) 1355203270
Web Site: https://mikocoffee.co.uk
Coffee Mfr & Distr
N.A.I.C.S.: 311920

Miko Coffee Denmark ApS (1)
Horskaetten 18-20, DK-2630, Taastrup, Denmark
Tel.: (45) 70275265
Web Site: https://www.mikocoffee.com
Coffee Mfr & Distr
N.A.I.C.S.: 311920

Miko Kava s.r.o. (1)
Cesta polnohospodarov 30, 971 01, Prievidza, Slovakia
Tel.: (421) 903222925
Web Site: https://mikokava.sk
Coffee Machinery Mfr & Distr
N.A.I.C.S.: 333241

TIN Tea Import Network B.A. (1)
Bastion 26, 5509 MJ, Veldhoven, Netherlands
Tel.: (31) 402222954
Web Site: https://tin-tea.com
Tea Mfr & Distr
N.A.I.C.S.: 311920

MIKOBEAUTE INTERNATIONAL CO., LTD.
6F No 310 Sec 4 Zhongxiao E Rd, Da'an Dist, Taipei, 10694, Taiwan
Tel.: (886) 227755566
Web Site: https://mikobeaute.com
Year Founded: 2002
6574—(TPE)
Rev.: $21,300,285
Assets: $28,933,652
Liabilities: $7,889,973
Net Worth: $21,043,679
Earnings: $2,170,466
Fiscal Year-end: 12/31/22
Cosmetics Mfr
N.A.I.C.S.: 325620
Lu Qingsheng (Co-Founder, Chm, Pres & Gen Mgr)

MIKRO MSC BERHAD
3 Jalan Anggerik Mokara 31/48 Sek 31, Kota Kemuning, 40460, Shah Alam, Selangor, Malaysia

Tel.: (60) 355253863 MY
Web Site: https://itmikro.com.my
Year Founded: 1997
MIKROMB—(KLS)
Rev.: $11,704,272
Assets: $33,835,142
Liabilities: $4,633,207
Net Worth: $28,631,935
Earnings: $839,873
Emp.: 160
Fiscal Year-end: 06/30/23
Electrical Product Mfr & Distr
N.A.I.C.S.: 335314
Yuen Wah Yim (Co-Founder & Mng Dir)

Subsidiaries:

Mittric Systems Sdn. Bhd. (1)
5 Jalan Pemberita U1/49 Glenmarie, Temasya Industrial Park, 40150, Shah Alam, Selangor, Malaysia
Tel.: (60) 355693748
Web Site: https://www.mittric.com
Electrical Switchgear Product Distr
N.A.I.C.S.: 423610

MIKROELEKTRONIKA A.D.
Blagoja Parovica bb, Novakovici, 78000, Banja Luka, Bosnia & Herzegovina
Tel.: (387) 51389030
Web Site: https://www.mikroelektronika.net
Year Founded: 1975
CMEL—(BANJ)
Sales Range: $1-9.9 Million
Emp.: 51
Measuring Instruments Mfr
N.A.I.C.S.: 334513
Gordana Prastalo (Chm)

MIKROFIN OSIGURANJE A.D
Aleja Svetog Sava 61, 78000, Banja Luka, Bosnia & Herzegovina
Tel.: (387) 51225840
Web Site: https://www.mikrofinosiguranje.com
Year Founded: 2007
MKOS-R-A—(BANJ)
Food Transportation Services
N.A.I.C.S.: 488490
Radmila Bjeljac (Pres)

MIKRON HOLDING AG
Route du Vignoble 17 2017 Boudry, CH-2502, Biel, Switzerland
Tel.: (41) 323217200 CH
Web Site: https://www.mikron.com
Year Founded: 1908
MIKN—(SWX)
Rev.: $327,799,104
Assets: $339,785,166
Liabilities: $152,848,343
Net Worth: $186,936,823
Earnings: $19,263,315
Emp.: 1,327
Fiscal Year-end: 12/31/21
Holding Company; Industrial Manufacturing & Assembly Automation Equipment Mfr & Whslr
N.A.I.C.S.: 551112
Eduard Rikli (Vice Chm)

Subsidiaries:

Mikron Management AG (1)
Guterstrasse 20, 4900, Langenthal, Switzerland
Tel.: (41) 916106209
Web Site: http://www.mikron.com
Sales Range: $50-74.9 Million
Emp.: 6
Executive Offices; Industrial Manufacturing & Assembly Automation Equipment Mfr
N.A.I.C.S.: 921140

Subsidiary (Non-US):

Agie Charmilles China (H.K.) Ltd. (2)

Rm 507-508 5th Fl Iu Plz, 1 Mei Wing St, Tsuen Wan, China (Hong Kong) **(100%)**
Tel.: (852) 24152666
Web Site: http://www.mikron.com
N.A.I.C.S.: 333310

Mikron Assembly Technology (2)
Brunnenstrasse 4a Jules Ruckstuhl, CH9326, Horn, Germany
Tel.: (49) 718410533
Web Site: http://www.mikron-tg.com
Mfr of Industrial Machinery
N.A.I.C.S.: 333998

Mikron Assembly Technology-Nordic Reg. Office (2)
Skyllebakke Havn 47, DK 3600, Frederikssund, Denmark
Tel.: (45) 47388100
Web Site: http://www.mikron.com
Sales Range: $25-49.9 Million
Emp.: 1
Mfr of Industrial & Commercial Machinery & Equipment, NEC
N.A.I.C.S.: 333310

Mikron Assembly Technology-UK & Ireland (2)
74 Newland Lane, Ash Green, Coventry, CV7 9BA, West Midlands, United Kingdom **(100%)**
Tel.: (44) 2476366071
Sales Range: $125-149.9 Million
Industrial Machinery & Equipment Whslr
N.A.I.C.S.: 423830
Richard Krusts *(Mgr)*

Subsidiary (US):

Mikron Corp. Denver (2)
8100 S Potomac St, Englewood, CO 80112 **(100%)**
Tel.: (303) 364-5222
Web Site: http://www.mikron.com
Sales Range: $25-49.9 Million
Emp.: 100
Providers of Automation Products
N.A.I.C.S.: 333922

Mikron Corp. Monroe (2)
200 Main St, Monroe, CT 64608 **(100%)**
Tel.: (203) 261-3100
Web Site: http://www.ch.mikron-tg.com
Sales Range: $25-49.9 Million
Mfr of Automatic Machining Systems
N.A.I.C.S.: 335312

Subsidiary (Non-US):

Mikron GmbH (2)
Berner Feld 71, 78628, Rottweil, Germany **(100%)**
Tel.: (49) 74153800
Web Site: http://www.mikron.com
Sales Range: $25-49.9 Million
Emp.: 150
Sale of Transfer Machines
N.A.I.C.S.: 333519

Mikron Industrial Equipment (Shanghai) Co., Ltd. (2)
Building 4 No 2033 Husong Road, Song Jiang District, Shanghai, 201601, China
Tel.: (86) 2167679681
Emp.: 85
Automation System Mfr & Distr
N.A.I.C.S.: 335314

Mikron Machining Technology-India Office (2)
1010 Tenth Fl Brigade Towers, 135 Brigade Rd, Bengaluru, 560 025, India
Tel.: (91) 802279144
Web Site: http://www.mikron-tg.com
Industrial & Commercial Machinery & Equipment
N.A.I.C.S.: 333998

Division (Domestic):

Mikron S.A. Agno (2)
via ginnaseio, Casella Postale 115, 6903, Lugano, Switzerland **(100%)**
Tel.: (41) 916106111
Web Site: http://www.mikron-tg.com
Sales Range: $75-99.9 Million
Automatic Machining Systems, Transfer Machines, Flexible Manufacturing Systems & Cutting Tools
N.A.I.C.S.: 333517

Subsidiary (Domestic):

Mikron Tool S.A. Agno (3)
Via Campagna 1, 6982, Lugano, Agno, Switzerland **(100%)**
Tel.: (41) 916106500
Web Site: http://www.mikron-tg.com
Sales Range: $50-74.9 Million
Emp.: 110
Production of Tools
N.A.I.C.S.: 332216

Division (Domestic):

Mikron S.A. Boudry (2)
Rte du Vignoble 17, 2017, Boudry, Switzerland **(100%)**
Tel.: (41) 328431111
Web Site: http://www.mikron-tg.com
Sales Range: $75-99.9 Million
Automatic Assembly Lines & Feed Systems
N.A.I.C.S.: 333519

Subsidiary (Non-US):

Mikron SAS Nerviano (2)
Via S Ambrogio 16, Parabiago, 20015, Milan, Italy
Tel.: (39) 0331551222
Sales Range: $25-49.9 Million
Emp.: 2
Industrial Metal Equipment Distr
N.A.I.C.S.: 423830

Mikron Singapore Pte Ltd. (2)
61 Tai Seng Ave 05-11, Singapore, 534167, Singapore
Tel.: (65) 62991589
Web Site: http://www.mikron.com.sg
Emp.: 60
Precision Turned Product Mfr
N.A.I.C.S.: 332721

Mikron Tool (Shanghai) Co., Ltd. (2)
Building 4 No 2033 Husong Road, Song Jiang District, Shanghai, 201601, China
Tel.: (86) 15921577050
Cutting Tool Mfr & Distr
N.A.I.C.S.: 333515

Mikron Tunsberg AS (2)
Fjordgaten 2, N 3125, Tonsberg, Norway **(100%)**
Tel.: (47) 33018300
Web Site: http://www.mikron-tg.com
Sales Range: $25-49.9 Million
N.A.I.C.S.: 333310

Subsidiary (Domestic):

Step-Tec AG (2)
Industriestrasse 45, Luterbach, 4542, Switzerland **(95.45%)**
Tel.: (41) 326813535
Web Site: http://www.step-tec.ch
Sales Range: $25-49.9 Million
Development & Production of Spindles
N.A.I.C.S.: 333248

Subsidiary (Non-US):

UAB Mikron (2)
Talkos Pr 114L, LT-51142, Kaunas, Lithuania
Tel.: (370) 37395545
Emp.: 20
Automation System Mfr & Distr
N.A.I.C.S.: 335314

MIKUNI CORPORATION
Mikuni Building 6-13-11 Sotokanda Chiyoda-ku, Tokyo, 101-0021, Japan JP
Web Site: http://www.mikuni.co.jp
Year Founded: 1923
7247—(TKS)
Rev.: $660,610,010
Assets: $737,252,960
Liabilities: $468,900,180
Net Worth: $268,352,780
Earnings: $7,370,150
Emp.: 5,001
Fiscal Year-end: 03/31/24
Carburetors, Pumps, Heaters, Lawnmowers & General Industrial Machinery Mfr
N.A.I.C.S.: 336310
Masaki Ikuta *(Chm)*

Subsidiaries:

Asahi Air Supply, Inc. (1)
6th floor Mikuni Building 6-13-11 Sotokanda, Chiyoda-ku, Tokyo, 101-0021, Japan
Tel.: (81) 358755223
Web Site: https://www.asahiair.co.jp
Aircraft Parts Distr
N.A.I.C.S.: 423860

Eberspacher Mikuni Climate Control Systems Corporation (1)
2480 Kuno, Odawara, 250-0055, Kanagawa, Japan
Tel.: (81) 5038027612
Web Site: http://www.eberspaecher-mikuni.co.jp
Air Conditioning System & Related Product Distr
N.A.I.C.S.: 423730

Mikuni (Thailand) Co., Ltd. (1)
111 M 5 Banwha, Hi Tech Industial Estate Bang pa-in, Ayutthaya, 13160, Thailand
Tel.: (66) 3535005865
Web Site: http://www.mikuni.co.th
Emp.: 750
Automobile Product Mfr & Distr
N.A.I.C.S.: 336390
Shigeru Ikuta *(Mng Dir)*

Mikuni American Corporation (1)
8910 Mikuni Ave, Northridge, CA 91324-3496 **(100%)**
Tel.: (818) 885-1242
Web Site: http://supplier.mikuni.com
Rev.: $100,000,000
Emp.: 30
Importer of Carburetors & Associated Parts & Exporter of Aircraft Parts
N.A.I.C.S.: 423120

Mikuni Green Service Co., Ltd. (1)
Tani Building 5F 1-28-6 Kameido, Koto-ku, Tokyo, 136-0071, Japan
Tel.: (81) 368070262
Web Site: http://www.mikunigreen.jp
Golf Related Product Distr
N.A.I.C.S.: 423910

Mikuni India Private Limited (1)
SP2-19A 20 21 A, New Industrial Complex Majrakath Neemrana Tehsil Behror Distt, Alwar, 301705, Rajasthan, India
Tel.: (91) 1494246870
Web Site: https://www.mikuni.co.in
Automobile Component Parts Mfr & Distr
N.A.I.C.S.: 336110
Shigeru Ikuta *(Chm)*

Mikuni Life & Auto Co., Ltd. (1)
456-1 Frontage, Kazo, 349-1145, Saitama Prefecture, Japan
Tel.: (81) 480727221
Web Site: https://www.mikuni-la.co.jp
Emp.: 81
Wheelchair Vehicle Mfr & Distr
N.A.I.C.S.: 339113

Mikuni Partec Corporation (1)
500-1 Kasana, Makinohara, Shizuoka Prefecture, Japan
Tel.: (81) 548581620
Web Site: https://www.mikuni-partec.co.jp
Emp.: 233
Die Casting Product Mfr
N.A.I.C.S.: 331523

Mikuni Taiwan Corporation (1)
1F No 797 Jhongjheng Rd, Jhonghe District, New Taipei City, 235, Taiwan
Tel.: (886) 22 225 7392
Web Site: https://www.taiwanmikuni.com.tw
Emp.: 12
Engine Parts Mfr
N.A.I.C.S.: 336310
Masaki Ikuta *(Chm)*

Sunrise Medical Japan Co., Ltd. (1)
456-1 Makuchi, Kazo, 349-1145, Saitama Prefecture, Japan
Tel.: (81) 480316480
Wheelchair Vehicle Mfr & Distr
N.A.I.C.S.: 339113

MILA RESOURCES PLC
6th Floor 65 Gresham Street, London, EC2V 7NQ, United Kingdom
Tel.: (44) 3333001950 UK
Web Site:
   https://www.milaresources.com
Year Founded: 2015
MILA—(LSE)
Assets: $7,812,916
Liabilities: $395,024
Net Worth: $7,417,892
Earnings: ($693,622)
Emp.: 4
Fiscal Year-end: 06/30/23
Natural Gas Extraction Services
N.A.I.C.S.: 211130
Neil Hutchison *(Chief Technical Officer)*

MILAE BIORESOURCES CO., LTD.
506512 Ddong 26 Beopwonro 9gil, Songpa-gu, Seoul, Korea (South)
Tel.: (82) 222037397 KR
Web Site: https://www.milaebio.com
Year Founded: 2015
218150—(KRS)
Rev.: $58,012,292
Assets: $43,025,061
Liabilities: $11,704,747
Net Worth: $31,320,314
Earnings: $738,441
Emp.: 51
Fiscal Year-end: 12/31/22
Holding Company; Animal Feed Mfr & Distr
N.A.I.C.S.: 551112

Subsidiaries:

Milae Resources ML, Ltd. (1)
J-Tower 7F 7 Ogeum-ro 11-gil, Songpa-gu, Seoul, Korea (South)
Tel.: (82) 222037397
Web Site: http://www.milaebio.com
Animal Feed Mfr & Distr
N.A.I.C.S.: 311119
Seong-Jin Kim *(CEO)*

MILAN BLAGOJEVIC A.D.
Djure Strugara 20, 11300, Smederevo, Serbia
Tel.: (381) 26 633 600
Web Site: http://www.mbs.rs
Year Founded: 1998
Sales Range: $10-24.9 Million
Wood Kitchen Cabinet & Cooker Mfr
N.A.I.C.S.: 337110

MILAN BLAGOJEVIC INTER-TRANS A.D.
Radnicka bb, 32240, Lucani, Serbia
Tel.: (381) 32 818 790
Web Site:
   http://www.mbintertrans.co.rs
Year Founded: 2003
Sales Range: Less than $1 Million
Emp.: 6
Vehicle Insurance Services
N.A.I.C.S.: 524210

MILAN PREMASUNAC A.D.
Marsala Tita 2, Kacarevo, 26212, Serbia
Tel.: (381) 13 601 650
Web Site: http://www.utva-mp.com
Year Founded: 2003
Sales Range: $1-9.9 Million
Industrial Machinery Mfr
N.A.I.C.S.: 333998

MILAN STATION HOLDINGS LIMITED
Room 13 6/F Block A Hong Kong Industrial Centre 489-491 Castle Peak, Kowloon, Hong Kong, China (Hong Kong)
Tel.: (852) 27308037 Ky
Web Site:
   http://www.milanstation.com.hk
Year Founded: 2000

MILAN STATION HOLDINGS LIMITED

Milan Station Holdings Limited—(Continued)
1150—(HKG)
Rev.: $29,743,200
Assets: $17,924,205
Liabilities: $3,552,660
Net Worth: $14,371,545
Earnings: ($5,758,920)
Emp.: 63
Fiscal Year-end: 12/31/22
Women's Handbags & Apparel Accessories Retailer
N.A.I.C.S.: 458110
Tony Hon Leung Chan (CMO)

Subsidiaries:

Milan Station (Causeway Bay) Limited (1)
482 Jaffe Road, Causeway Bay, China (Hong Kong)
Tel.: (852) 2838 1618
Used Hand Bags Distr
N.A.I.C.S.: 459999

Milan Station (Tsuen Wan) Limited (1)
264 Castle Peak Road, Tsuen Wan, China (Hong Kong)
Tel.: (852) 24054038
Used Hand Bags Retailer
N.A.I.C.S.: 459999

Milan Station (Yuen Long) Limited (1)
Shop G003 G/F Kar Shing Building 15-19 Kau Yuk Road, Yuen Long, New Territories, China (Hong Kong)
Tel.: (852) 2475 8835
Used Hand Bags Retailer
N.A.I.C.S.: 459999

Milan Station Fashion (Causeway Bay) Limited (1)
Rm 1818 Nan Fung Commercial Centre, Kowloon Bay, Kowloon, China (Hong Kong)
Tel.: (852) 27308037
Used Hand Bags Distr
N.A.I.C.S.: 459999

Milan Station Fashion (Hong Kong) Limited (1)
Rm 4-6 G/F Cigna Twr 482 Jaffe Rd, Causeway Bay, Hong Kong, China (Hong Kong)
Tel.: (852) 28381618
Used Hand Bags Retailer
N.A.I.C.S.: 459999

Milan Station Fashion (TST) Limited (1)
G/f 46 Haiphone Rd, Hong Kong, China (Hong Kong)
Tel.: (852) 23660332
Used Hand Bags Retailer
N.A.I.C.S.: 459999

MILBON CO., LTD.
Kyobashi Edogrand 2-2-1 Kyobashi, Chuo-ku, Tokyo, 104-0031, Japan
Tel.: (81) 335173915
Web Site: https://milbon.com
Year Founded: 1960
4919—(TKS)
Rev.: $338,632,580
Assets: $378,542,190
Liabilities: $52,884,310
Net Worth: $325,657,880
Earnings: $28,367,090
Emp.: 1,140
Fiscal Year-end: 12/31/23
Hair Care Product Mfr & Whslr
N.A.I.C.S.: 325620
Ryuji Sato (Pres & CEO)

Subsidiaries:

MILBON (THAILAND) CO., LTD. (1)
7/380 Village No 6, Mapyangphon Subdistrict Pluak Daeng District, Rayong, 21140, Thailand
Tel.: (66) 266226123
Web Site: https://www.milbon.co.th
Hair Coloring Product Mfr & Distr
N.A.I.C.S.: 325620

MILBON USA, INC. (1)
568 Broadway Ste 606, New York, NY 10012
Tel.: (212) 431-8438
Web Site: http://www.milbon-usa.com
Hair Coloring Product Distr
N.A.I.C.S.: 424310

Milbon Co., Ltd. - Aoyama Plant (1)
758-30 Iseji, Iga, Mie, Japan
Tel.: (81) 595523321
Hair Coloring Product Mfr
N.A.I.C.S.: 325620

Milbon Co., Ltd. - Yumegaoka Plant (1)
7-7-5 Yumegaoka, Iga, 518-0131, Mie, Japan
Tel.: (81) 59 526 3838
Web Site: http://www.milbon.co.jp
Hair Coloring Product Mfr
N.A.I.C.S.: 325620

Milbon Europe GmbH (1)
Marienstrasse 33, 40210, Dusseldorf, Germany
Tel.: (49) 21115840344
Web Site: https://www.milbon.com.de
Cosmetic Product Mfr & Distr
N.A.I.C.S.: 326299

Milbon Korea Co., Ltd. (1)
4th and 5th floors Nobel Tech Building 115 Bongeunsa-ro, Gangnam-gu, Seoul, 06120, Korea (South)
Tel.: (82) 234487400
Web Site: https://www.milbon.co.kr
Hair Coloring Product Distr
N.A.I.C.S.: 424310

Milbon Malaysia Sdn. Bhd. (1)
S10-C-02 Wisma YNH No 8 Jalan Kiara Mont Kiara, 50480, Kuala Lumpur, Malaysia
Tel.: (60) 364122334
Web Site: https://www.milbon.com.my
Toilet Preparation Mfr
N.A.I.C.S.: 325620

Milbon Trading (Shanghai) Co., Ltd. (1)
Unit A1D2 25F Huaxin Haixin Bldg 666 Fuzhou Rd, Shanghai, 200001, China
Tel.: (86) 2163917017
Web Site: https://www.milbon.com
Hair Coloring Product Distr
N.A.I.C.S.: 424310

Milbon Vietnam Co., Ltd. (1)
7F Sai Gon View Office Building 117 Nguyen Cuu Vanst, Ward 17 Binh Thanh District, Ho Chi Minh City, Vietnam
Tel.: (84) 2838270139
Toilet Preparation Mfr
N.A.I.C.S.: 325620

MILDEF CRETE, INC.
7F No 250 Sec 3 Peishen Rd, Shen Keng District, New Taipei City, Taiwan
Tel.: (886) 226626074
Web Site: https://mildefcrete.com
Year Founded: 1990
3213—(TPE)
Rev.: $84,681,425
Assets: $103,669,512
Liabilities: $27,720,789
Net Worth: $75,948,723
Earnings: $7,359,535
Fiscal Year-end: 12/31/22
Hardware Product Mfr & Distr
N.A.I.C.S.: 332510
I-Tung Shen (Chm, Pres & CEO)

MILDEF GROUP AB
Muskotgatan 6, 254 66, Helsingborg, Sweden
Tel.: (46) 42250000
Web Site: https://www.mildef.com
Year Founded: 1997
MILDEF—(OMX)
Rev.: $67,821,840
Assets: $127,960,020
Liabilities: $55,630,800
Net Worth: $72,329,220
Earnings: $1,303,560
Emp.: 291
Fiscal Year-end: 12/31/22
Electronic Product Distr
N.A.I.C.S.: 423690
Bjorn Karlsson (Chm)

Subsidiaries:

HHCS Handheld USA Inc. (1)
2121 NE Jack London St Ste 100, Corvallis, OR 97330
Tel.: (541) 752-0313
Computer Equipment Whslr
N.A.I.C.S.: 423430

Handheld Germany GmbH (1)
Martin-Oberndorfer-Strasse 5, 83395, Freilassing, Germany
Tel.: (49) 8654779570
Computer Equipment Whslr
N.A.I.C.S.: 423430

Handheld Swiss GmbH (1)
Rohanstrasse 11, 7205, Zizers, Switzerland
Tel.: (41) 813300555
Computer Equipment Whslr
N.A.I.C.S.: 423430

MilDef AS (1)
Brynsengveien 2, 0667, Oslo, Norway
Tel.: (47) 23400310
Computer Equipment Mfr
N.A.I.C.S.: 334111

MilDef Integration Sweden AB (1)
Jarngatan 14, 195 72, Rosersberg, Sweden
Tel.: (46) 812105550
Information Technology Advisory Services
N.A.I.C.S.: 518210

MilDef Oy (1)
Lars Sonckin Kaari 14, 02600, Espoo, Finland
Tel.: (358) 400906100
Computer Equipment Mfr
N.A.I.C.S.: 334111

MilDef Sweden AB (1)
Gamla Varmdovagen 6 S, 131 37, Nacka, Sweden
Tel: (46) 42250000
Information Technology Advisory Services
N.A.I.C.S.: 518210

Mildef, Inc. (1)
630 W Lambert Rd, Brea, CA 92821
Tel.: (703) 224-8835
Computer Equipment Mfr
N.A.I.C.S.: 334111

Sysint AS (1)
Munkedamsveien 53B, 0250, Oslo, Norway
Tel.: (47) 23897325
Web Site: https://sysint.no
Management Consulting Services
N.A.I.C.S.: 541611

MILDEX OPTICAL, INC.
No 7 Luke 3rd Rd, Luzhu Dist, Kaohsiung, 821, Taiwan
Tel.: (886) 76955699
Web Site: https://www.mildex.com.tw
Year Founded: 2005
4729—(TPE)
Rev.: $42,734,703
Assets: $103,970,109
Liabilities: $62,100,116
Net Worth: $41,869,993
Earnings: $2,042,335
Emp.: 246
Fiscal Year-end: 12/31/22
Optical Lens Product Mfr
N.A.I.C.S.: 333310
Fang Ming-Tsung (Chm)

Subsidiaries:

Mildex Optical USA, Inc. (1)
2507 W Erie Dr Ste 101, Tempe, AZ 85282
Tel.: (480) 379-2817
Touch Screen Mfr & Distr
N.A.I.C.S.: 334419

MILEAGE COMMUNICATIONS PTE. LTD.
52B Club Street, Mileage House, 069429, Singapore, Singapore

Tel.: (65) 62221678 SG
Web Site: http://www.mileage.com.sg
Year Founded: 1992
N.A.I.C.S.: 541820
Yap Boh Tiong (Founder, Mng Dir & Dir-Overseas)

MILESTONE CAPITAL PARTNERS LLP
14 Floral Street, London, WC2E 9DH, United Kingdom
Tel.: (44) 2074208800 UK
Web Site: http://www.milestone-capital.com
Sales Range: $25-49.9 Million
Emp.: 10
Privater Equity Firm
N.A.I.C.S.: 523999
Erick Rinner (Mng Partner)

MILESTONE EHF.
Sudurlandsbraut 12, 108, Reykjavik, Iceland
Tel.: (354) 4141800 IS
Web Site: http://www.milestone.is
Year Founded: 1999
Sales Range: $400-449.9 Million
Emp.: 40
Private Investment Firm
N.A.I.C.S.: 551112
Karl E. Wernersson (Chm)

MILESTONE FURNITURE LIMITED
Level 4 DYNASTY Business Park A Wing Andheri-Kurla Raod J B Nagar, Met Village Opp Hp Petrol Pump, Mumbai, 400059, Maharashtra, India
Tel.: (91) 7738146226
Web Site: https://milestonefurniture.in
Year Founded: 2014
541337—(BOM)
Furniture Product Mfr & Distr
N.A.I.C.S.: 337122

MILESTONE GLOBAL LIMITED
54 - B Hoskote Industrial Area Chintamani Road, Bangalore Rural, Hoskote, 562114, Karnataka, India
Tel.: (91) 9945234594
Web Site: https://www.milestonegloballtd.com
Year Founded: 1991
531338—(BOM)
Rev.: $1,937,491
Assets: $1,206,849
Liabilities: $172,383
Net Worth: $1,034,466
Earnings: $76,732
Fiscal Year-end: 03/31/23
Granite Monument Mfr
N.A.I.C.S.: 327991
Alok Krishna Agarwal (Chm)

MILESTONE PHARMACEUTICALS INC.
1111 Dr Frederik-Philips Blvd Ste 420, Montreal, H4M 2X6, QC, Canada
Tel.: (514) 336-0444
Web Site: https://www.milestonepharma.com
Year Founded: 2003
MIST—(NASDAQ)
Rev.: $5,000,000
Assets: $74,483,000
Liabilities: $8,135,000
Net Worth: $66,348,000
Earnings: ($58,388,000)
Emp.: 39
Fiscal Year-end: 12/31/22
Biotechnology Research & Development Services
N.A.I.C.S.: 541714
Joseph Oliveto (Pres & CEO)

AND PRIVATE COMPANIES

MILFORD ASSET MANAGEMENT LIMITED
Level 17 41 Shortland Street, Auckland, 1140, New Zealand
Tel.: (64) 9 921 4700 NZ
Web Site: http://www.milfordasset.com
Year Founded: 2003
Investment & Wealth Management & Advisory Services
N.A.I.C.S.: 523940
Andrew Cross *(Chm)*

Subsidiaries:

Milford Australia Pty Ltd (1)
Level 57 MLC Centre 19-29 Martin Place, Sydney, 2000, NSW, Australia
Tel.: (61) 292386244
Financial Investment Services
N.A.I.C.S.: 523999

MILGREY FINANCE & INVESTMENTS LIMITED
31 Whispering Palms Shopping Center Lokhandwala Kandivali, Mumbai, 400101, India
Tel.: (91) 2226202230 In
Web Site: http://www.milgrey.in
Year Founded: 1983
511018—(BOM)
Rev.: $12
Assets: $3,973,155
Liabilities: $183,346
Net Worth: $3,789,809
Earnings: ($15,551)
Emp.: 1
Fiscal Year-end: 03/31/23
Investment Management Service
N.A.I.C.S.: 523150

MILIBOO SA
17 rue Mira - Parc Altais, 74650, Chavanod, France
Tel.: (33) 03098289300 FR
Web Site: https://www.miliboo.de
Year Founded: 2005
ALMLB—(EUR)
Sales Range: $25-49.9 Million
Home Furnishings Mfr & Distr
N.A.I.C.S.: 449129
Guillaume Lachenal *(Chm & CEO)*

MILITARY COMMERCIAL JOINT STOCK BANK
No 18 Le Van Luong, Trung Hoa ward Cau Giay district, Hanoi, Vietnam
Tel.: (84) 2462661088
Web Site: https://tuyendung.mbbank.com.vn
Year Founded: 1994
MBB—(HNX)
Rev.: $3,868,384,800
Assets: $94,495,364,000
Liabilities: $84,824,248,100
Net Worth: $9,671,115,900
Earnings: $2,105,379,200
Emp.: 16,234
Fiscal Year-end: 03/31/23
Commercial Banking Services
N.A.I.C.S.: 522110
Le Huu Duc *(Chm)*

Subsidiaries:

MB Securities Joint Stock Company (1)
21 Cat Linh, Dong Da District, Hanoi, Vietnam
Tel.: (84) 2473045688
Web Site: https://mbs.com.vn
Rev.: $37,750,704
Assets: $190,010,259
Liabilities: $123,216,810
Net Worth: $66,793,449
Earnings: $9,192,098
Fiscal Year-end: 12/31/2019
Financial Services
N.A.I.C.S.: 523999

Le Viet Hai *(Chm)*

MILK SPECIALITIES LTD.
S C O 158-159 IInd Floor Subcity Center Sector 34, Chandigarh, 160022, India
Tel.: (91) 172 2606497
Web Site: http://www.milktimeindia.com
Year Founded: 1993
Sales Range: $10-24.9 Million
Milk Production Services
N.A.I.C.S.: 112120
Dinesh Sood *(Sec & Gen Mgr-Fin)*

MILKILAND N.V.
Amsterdamse Bos Cuserstraat 93, 1081, Amsterdam, Netherlands
Tel.: (31) 208949651
Web Site: http://www.milkiland.nl
MLK—(WAR)
Rev.: $140,834,713
Assets: $199,120,067
Liabilities: $224,326,996
Net Worth: ($25,206,929)
Earnings: ($12,966,859)
Emp.: 2,729
Fiscal Year-end: 12/31/19
Dairy Products Including Milk, Cheese & Butter
N.A.I.C.S.: 112120
Olga Yurkevych *(Chief Production Officer)*

Subsidiaries:

LLC Bahmachregionpostach (1)
3 Tynytska St, Town Bakhmach, Chernigov, 15600, Ukraine
Tel.: (380) 463551968
Dairy Products Mfr
N.A.I.C.S.: 311511

LLC Milkiland RU (1)
Rustavely str 14, 127254, Moscow, Russia
Tel.: (7) 4956181086
Dairy Products Mfr
N.A.I.C.S.: 311511

LLC Milkiland Ukraine (1)
Office 303 9 Boryspilska Street, Kiev, Ukraine
Tel.: (380) 443695200
Dairy Products Mfr
N.A.I.C.S.: 311511

LLC Milkiland-Kazakhstan (1)
Zholdasbekov str 9 2 Business Center Eurasia of 608 md 1 samal, Almaty, Kazakhstan
Tel.: (7) 87051884919
Dairy Products Mfr
N.A.I.C.S.: 311511

Milkiland EU sp. z.o.o. (1)
Rzymowskiego str 53, 02-697, Warsaw, Poland
Tel.: (48) 224170800
Dairy Products Mfr
N.A.I.C.S.: 311511

Milkiland Intermarket (CY) Ltd. (1)
Strovolu 77 Strovolos Center 2nd Floor Flat Office 204, Strovolos, 2018, Nicosia, Cyprus
Tel.: (357) 22875111
Web Site: http://www.milkiland-intermarket.com
Dairy Products Mfr
N.A.I.C.S.: 311511

MILKYWAY CHEMICAL SUPPLY CHAIN SERVICE CO., LTD.
158 Jinkui Road, Pudong New Area, Shanghai, 201203, China
Tel.: (86) 4001510202
Web Site: https://www.mwclg.com
Year Founded: 1998
603713—(SHG)
Rev.: $1,625,216,402
Assets: $1,335,300,188
Liabilities: $788,593,258

Net Worth: $546,706,930
Earnings: $84,993,695
Fiscal Year-end: 12/31/22
Logistics & Warehousing Services
N.A.I.C.S.: 493110
Yinhe Chen *(Chm, Pres & Gen Mgr)*

MILL & TIMBER PRODUCTS LTD
12745-116th Avenue, Surrey, V3V 7H9, BC, Canada
Tel.: (604) 580-2781
Web Site: http://www.millandtimber.com
Year Founded: 1951
Sales Range: $50-74.9 Million
Emp.: 175
Sawmill Product Mfr
N.A.I.C.S.: 321113
Surinder Ghog *(Pres)*

Subsidiaries:

Flavelle Sawmill Company Ltd. (1)
2400 Murray Street, Port Moody, V3H 4H6, BC, Canada
Tel.: (604) 939-1141
Web Site: https://www.flavellesawmill.com
Sawmill Operator
N.A.I.C.S.: 321113

Mill & Timber Products Ltd - Port Hardy Division (1)
6565 Jensen Cove Road, PO Box 106, Port Hardy, V0N 2P0, BC, Canada
Tel.: (250) 949-6642
Web Site: https://www.millandtimber.com
Log Sorting Services
N.A.I.C.S.: 113310

Pan-Abode International Ltd. (1)
12745 116 Avenue, Surrey, V3V 7H9, BC, Canada
Tel.: (604) 582-8295
Web Site: https://www.panabode.com
Prefabricated Wood Building Mfr
N.A.I.C.S.: 321992

Smallwood Sawmill Ltd. (1)
10880 Dyke Road, Surrey, V3V 7P4, BC, Canada
Tel.: (604) 588-3580
Sawmill Operator
N.A.I.C.S.: 321113

MILLAT TRACTORS LIMITED
9KM Sheikhupura Road Shahdara, Lahore, Pakistan
Tel.: (92) 42111200786 PK
Web Site: https://www.millat.com.pk
Year Founded: 1964
MTL—(KAR)
Rev.: $229,982,286
Assets: $97,121,376
Liabilities: $48,790,290
Net Worth: $48,331,086
Earnings: $25,239,114
Emp.: 393
Fiscal Year-end: 06/30/19
Mfr & Marketer of Tractors & Related Parts
N.A.I.C.S.: 333112
Sikandar Mustafa Khan *(Chm)*

MILLCON STEEL PUBLIC COMPANY LIMITED
9 11 13 Soi Bang Kradee 32 Bang Kradee Road, Saem Dam Subdistrict Bang Khun Thian District, Bangkok, 10150, Thailand
Tel.: (66) 28964444
Web Site: https://www.millconsteel.com
Year Founded: 1998
MILL—(THA)
Rev.: $526,863,247
Assets: $642,111,520
Liabilities: $430,791,446
Net Worth: $211,320,075
Earnings: $12,627,115
Emp.: 545

MILLENNIUM GLOBAL HOLDINGS, INC.

Fiscal Year-end: 12/31/21
Steel Products Mfr & Distr
N.A.I.C.S.: 331110
Winai Phattiyakul *(Chm)*

Subsidiaries:

Millcon Eurapa Company Limited (1)
99 Moo 3 Tumbon Nikhom Phatthana, Amphoe Nikhorn hatthana, Rayong, 21180, Thailand
Tel.: (66) 3860 6041
Steel Mfrs
N.A.I.C.S.: 331221

World Wire Processing Co., Ltd. (1)
44/2 Group 2 Tivanont Road Bangadee, Muang Pathum Thani, Bangkok, 12000, Thailand (99.9%)
Tel.: (66) 25012020
Precast Concrete Products Transport & Installation Services
N.A.I.C.S.: 238120

Zentra-Wartung Engineering Company Limited (1)
52 Thaniya Plaza Building Floor 24 Silom Road, Surliyawongse Bangrak, Bangkok, 10500, Thailand
Tel.: (66) 2632 8283
Steel Mfrs
N.A.I.C.S.: 331221

MILLENMIN VENTURES INC.
66/F Central Plaza 18 Harbour Road, Wanchai, China (Hong Kong)
Tel.: (852) 25116016 Ca
Web Site: http://www.millenmin.com
Year Founded: 2009
MVM.P—(TSXV)
Rev.: $9
Assets: $63,853
Liabilities: $649,918
Net Worth: ($586,065)
Earnings: ($562,279)
Fiscal Year-end: 12/31/20
Investment Services
N.A.I.C.S.: 523999
Ching Fu Cheng *(CEO-Acting & CFO)*

MILLENNIAL POTASH CORP
885 West Georgia Street Suite 1328, Vancouver, V6C 3E8, BC, Canada
Tel.: (604) 288-8906
X0D—(DEU)
Rev.: $66,039
Assets: $5,165,995
Liabilities: $370,575
Net Worth: $4,795,420
Earnings: ($3,503,523)
Emp.: 15
Fiscal Year-end: 08/31/23
Asset Management Services
N.A.I.C.S.: 523940
Bob Meister *(Pres, CEO & Sec)*

MILLENNIUM GLOBAL HOLDINGS, INC.
Lot 9 Block 2 John St, Multinational Village, Paranaque, 1701, Philippines
Tel.: (63) 28537891
Web Site: https://www.millennium-globalholdingsinc.com
MG—(PHI)
Rev.: $18,089,319
Assets: $35,996,965
Liabilities: $24,031,349
Net Worth: $11,965,616
Earnings: ($39,556)
Fiscal Year-end: 12/31/23
Holding Company; Internet, Web Search Portals & Data Processing Services
N.A.I.C.S.: 551112
Michael Chi Jen Yang *(Chm, Pres & CEO)*

Subsidiaries:

IP E-Game Ventures Inc. (1)

MILLENNIUM GLOBAL HOLDINGS, INC.

Millennium Global Holdings, Inc.—(Continued)

1003 10th Floor Centerpoint Condominium Garnet Road cor Don Julia Varg, Ortigas Center Metro Manila, Pasig, 1605, Philippines
Tel.: (63) 2 976 4784
Web Site: http://www.e-games.com.ph
Rev.: $3,970,457
Assets: $70,766,277
Liabilities: $9,217,412
Net Worth: $61,548,865
Earnings: ($469,145)
Emp.: 113
Fiscal Year-end: 12/31/2015
Internet Game Portal
N.A.I.C.S.: 541511

Subsidiary (Domestic):

Digital Paradise, Inc. (2)
6/F Suntree Tower 27 Sapphire Road Cor Julia Vargas Avenue, Ortigas Center, Pasig, Philippines
Tel.: (63) 465 1100
Web Site: http://www.netopia.ph
Internet Service Provider
N.A.I.C.S.: 517111

Megamobile Inc. (1)
3F Media Resource Plaza Mola cor Pasong Tirad Sts, Makati, 1204, Philippines
Tel.: (63) 2 519 6298
Web Site: http://www.mymegamobile.com
Emp.: 30
Mobile Application Development Services
N.A.I.C.S.: 541511
Angelo Mendoca (Mgr-Bus Dev)

MILLENNIUM GROUP INTERNATIONAL HOLDINGS LIMITED

Flat B-C 1st Floor WangKwong Industrial Building 45 Hung ToRoad, Kwun Tong, Kowloon, 999077, China (Hong Kong)
Tel.: (852) 36195768   Ky
Web Site: https://www.millennium-gp.com
Year Founded: 1978
MGIH—(NASDAQ)
Rev.: $38,530,773
Assets: $43,637,106
Liabilities: $12,591,063
Net Worth: $31,046,043
Earnings: ($8,770,044)
Emp.: 498
Fiscal Year-end: 06/30/24
Holding Company
N.A.I.C.S.: 551112
Ming Hung Lai (Chm)

MILLENNIUM LIMITED

9U 175 Lower Gibbes Street, Chatswood, 2067, NSW, Australia
Tel.: (61) 403340917
Web Site: http://www.millenniumltd.com.au
Sales Range: Less than $1 Million
Fabrics, Apparel, Garments, Home Textiles & Home Decor Mfr & Distr
N.A.I.C.S.: 313210
Wei Huang (CEO)

MILLENNIUM MINERALS LIMITED

Unit 7 140 Abernethy Road, Belmont, 6104, WA, Australia
Tel.: (61) 892169011
Web Site: http://www.millenniumminerals.com
Rev.: $89,414,423
Assets: $85,837,143
Liabilities: $40,806,450
Net Worth: $45,030,693
Earnings: ($6,640,506)
Fiscal Year-end: 12/31/18
Gold Exploration & Mining Services
N.A.I.C.S.: 212220

MILLENNIUM ONLINE SOLUTIONS (INDIA) LIMITED

Flat No 53 5th Floor Wing No 11 Vijay Vilash Tores Building, Ghodbunder Road, Thane, 400615, India
Tel.: (91) 2266735330
Web Site: https://www.mosil.co
Year Founded: 1980
511187—(BOM)
Rev.: $391,681
Assets: $755,244
Liabilities: $210,126
Net Worth: $545,118
Earnings: ($52,111)
Fiscal Year-end: 03/31/23
Financial Investment Services
N.A.I.C.S.: 523999
Neeraj Gupta (Chm & Mng Dir)

MILLENNIUM PACIFIC GROUP HOLDINGS LTD

B3 YuCan Industrial Park Lanzhu West Road Export Processing Zone, Pingshan New District, Shenzhen, Guangdong, China
Tel.: (86) 75589595763   (1)
Web Site: http://www.mpgroup.hk
8147—(HKG)
Rev.: $8,370,885
Assets: $4,936,928
Liabilities: $4,799,355
Net Worth: $137,573
Earnings: ($2,743,163)
Emp.: 28
Fiscal Year-end: 12/31/22
GPS Navigation Devices, Mobile Internet Devices & Digital Video Recorders Mfr
N.A.I.C.S.: 334220

MILLENNIUM SILVER CORP.

20 Sixth Street, New Westminster, V3L 2Y8, BC, Canada
Tel.: (604) 527-8135   BC
Web Site: https://www.immc.ca
Year Founded: 1994
MSC—(TSXV)
Assets: $4,911,742
Liabilities: $249,975
Net Worth: $4,661,767
Earnings: ($144,265)
Fiscal Year-end: 12/31/22
Metal Mining & Exploration Services
N.A.I.C.S.: 212290
John A. Versfelt (Pres & CEO)

MILLER HUGHES FORD SALES

711 Pitt Street, Cornwall, K6J 3S1, ON, Canada
Tel.: (613) 932-2584
Web Site: http://www.millerhughesford.com
Rev.: $14,792,234
Emp.: 33
New & Used Car Dealers
N.A.I.C.S.: 441110
Gary Rose (Mgr-Fixed Ops)

MILLER LEASING MIETE GMBH

Louisenstrasse 145, 61348, Bad Homburg, Germany
Tel.: (49) 617248630
Web Site: http://www.miller-leasing.de
Year Founded: 1979
Rev.: $16,609,219
Emp.: 33
IT Systems Leasing Services
N.A.I.C.S.: 541519

MILLERS OILS LTD.

Hillside Oil Works, Brighouse, HD6 3DP, West Yorkshire, United Kingdom
Tel.: (44) 1484 713201
Web Site: http://www.millersoils.co.uk
Year Founded: 1887
Sales Range: $25-49.9 Million
Emp.: 117
Fuel Additive Whslr
N.A.I.C.S.: 457210
Jamie Ryan (Dir-Ops)

MILLERY ENTREPRISE

Parc Des Allies 70 Rue Pierre Corneille, 76140, Le Petit-Quevilly, Seine Maritime, France
Tel.: (33) 235651575
Rev.: $20,900,000
Emp.: 103
N.A.I.C.S.: 236220
Philippe Blondeau (Dir)

MILLET INNOVATION SA

ZA Champgrand, BP64, 26270, Loriol-sur-Drome, France
Tel.: (33) 475850190
Web Site: http://www.milletinnovation.com
Pharmaceuticals & Cosmetics Mfr
N.A.I.C.S.: 325412

MILLET MOUNTAIN GROUP SAS

21 rue du Pre Faucon Les Glaisins, 74943, Annecy-le-Vieux, Cedex, France
Tel.: (33) 450107250   FR
Men & Women Cloth Distr
N.A.I.C.S.: 458110

MILLFIELD GROUP

Shelley Road Newburn Industrial Estate, Newcastle upon Tyne, NE15 9RT, United Kingdom
Tel.: (44) 1912648541
Web Site: http://www.millfield-group.co.uk
Year Founded: 1963
Emp.: 200
Design, Mfr & Installation of Fiberglass Mouldings
N.A.I.C.S.: 327215
John Dodd (Mng Dir-Technical)

MILLHOUSE, INC. PLC

Nick Stretch Legal 530 Little Collins Street, Melbourne, 3000, VIC, Australia
Tel.: (61) 4 1118 5582
Web Site: http://www.millhouse.co
Investment Management Service
N.A.I.C.S.: 523999
David Millhouse (Deputy Chm & CEO)

MILLICOM INTERNATIONAL CELLULAR S.A.

2 rue du Fort Bourbon, L-1249, Luxembourg, L-1249, Luxembourg
Tel.: (352) 27759101   LU
Web Site: https://www.millicom.com
Year Founded: 1990
TIGO—(NASDAQ)
Rev.: $5,661,000,000
Assets: $14,516,000,000
Liabilities: $11,071,000,000
Net Worth: $3,445,000,000
Earnings: ($245,000,000)
Emp.: 16,527
Fiscal Year-end: 12/31/23
Holding Company; Cellular Communications & Specialized Mobile Radio Operations; Satellite Television Transmission
N.A.I.C.S.: 551112
Xavier Rocoplan (CIO, CTO & Exec VP)

Subsidiaries:

Airtel Ghana Limited (1)

INTERNATIONAL PUBLIC

AT Ghana Barnes Road PMB-TUC, Accra, Ghana   (50.05%)
Tel.: (233) 260000100
Web Site: https://www.at.com.gh
Telecommunication Servicesb
N.A.I.C.S.: 517410
Rosy Fynn (Mktg Dir)

Cable Onda, S.A. (1)
Building Cable Onda Hato Pintado Avenue, PO Box 0831-00593, Panama, Panama
Tel.: (507) 390 7555
Web Site: http://www.cableonda.com
Cable Broadcasting Network Services
N.A.I.C.S.: 516210

Edatel S.A. E.S.P. (1)
Cra 16 No 11A Sur 100, Los Balsos, Medellin, Colombia
Tel.: (57) 43251505
Web Site: http://www.edatel.com.co
Telecommunication Servicesb
N.A.I.C.S.: 517810

MIC Latin America BV (1)
Stockholm 26, 2993LM, Barendrecht, Netherlands   (100%)
Tel.: (31) 104048873
Trusts Estates & Agency Accounts
N.A.I.C.S.: 525920

MIC Tanzania Public Limited Company (1)
Tel.: (255) 716123103
Web Site: http://www.tigo.co.tz
Telecommunication Servicesb
N.A.I.C.S.: 517810

Millicom Holding BV (1)
Stockholm 26, 2993LM, Barendrecht, Netherlands   (100%)
Tel.: (31) 104048873
Trusts Estates & Agency Accounts
N.A.I.C.S.: 525920

Millicom Telecommunications BV (1)
Stockholm 26, 2993LM, Barendrecht, Netherlands   (100%)
Tel.: (31) 104048873
Real Estate Investment Trust
N.A.I.C.S.: 525990

MILLIMAGES S.A.

88 rue de la Folie Mericourt, 75011, Paris, France
Tel.: (33) 149294969
Web Site: http://www.millimages.com
Sales Range: $10-24.9 Million
Animated Films Production & Distr
N.A.I.C.S.: 512110
Jonathan Peel (Chm)

Subsidiaries:

The Picture Factory (1)
Maison Romaine 2 rue de Nancy, 88000, Epinal, France
Tel.: (33) 3 29 37 79 76
Web Site: http://www.thepicturefactory.fr
Emp.: 3
Online Picture Retailer
N.A.I.C.S.: 512120

MILLION CITIES HOLDINGS LIMITED

Room D 21/F Block 1 Tai Ping Industrial Center 57 Ting Kok Road, Tai Po, China (Hong Kong)
Tel.: (852) 26891999   Ky
Web Site: http://www.millioncities.com.cn
Year Founded: 2003
2892—(HKG)
Rev.: $80,194,093
Assets: $386,720,287
Liabilities: $181,730,812
Net Worth: $204,989,476
Earnings: $16,067,376
Emp.: 130
Fiscal Year-end: 12/31/22
Holding Company
N.A.I.C.S.: 551112
Ka Keung Lau (CEO)

MILLION HOPE INDUSTRIES

AND PRIVATE COMPANIES

HOLDINGS LIMITED
Office A 20/F Kings Wing Plaza 1 3
On Kwan Street, Shek Mun, Sha Tin,
New Territories, China (Hong Kong)
Tel.: (852) 2 693 0276 Ky
Web Site:
   http://www.millionhope.com.hk
Year Founded: 1990
1897—(HKG)
Rev.: $69,134,441
Assets: $86,757,752
Liabilities: $16,351,955
Net Worth: $70,405,797
Earnings: $5,022,481
Emp.: 253
Fiscal Year-end: 03/31/21
Holding Company
N.A.I.C.S.: 551112
Wai Ming Cheong *(Sr Mgr-Design)*
Subsidiaries:

Million Hope New-Tech Building Supplies (Huizhou) Limited (1)
Shang Xia Development Zone Shuikou office, Huicheng District, Huizhou, China
Tel.: (86) 7522077966
Web Site: http://www.millionhope.cn
Aluminum Alloy Door & Window Mfr
N.A.I.C.S.: 332321

MILLION STARS HOLDINGS LIMITED
Room 907B 9th Floor Empire Centre
68 Mody Road, Tsim Sha Tsui, Kowloon, China (Hong Kong)
Tel.: (852) 3589 6590
Web Site: http://www.millionstars.hk
Rev.: $34,764,311
Assets: $37,065,675
Liabilities: $10,116,910
Net Worth: $26,948,765
Earnings: ($4,700,576)
Emp.: 109
Fiscal Year-end: 06/30/19
Leather Product Mfr
N.A.I.C.S.: 316990
Yongjun Zhu *(Chm)*

MILLS ESTRUTURAS E SERVICOS DE ENGENHARIA, S.A.
Estrada do Guerengue no 1381
Taquara, Rio de Janeiro, 22713-002, Brazil
Tel.: (55) 2139248768 BR
Web Site: https://www.mills.com.br
Year Founded: 1952
MILS3—(BRAZ)
Rev.: $274,754,412
Assets: $546,496,161
Liabilities: $255,017,449
Net Worth: $291,478,712
Earnings: $55,481,504
Emp.: 2,141
Fiscal Year-end: 12/31/23
Construction, Building & Engineering Services
N.A.I.C.S.: 237990
Francisca Kjellerup Nacht *(Co-Chm)*

MILLSTREAM MINES LTD.
44 Victoria St Suite 712, Toronto, M5C 1Y2, ON, Canada
Tel.: (416) 368-9595
Web Site:
   http://www.millstreammines.com
Mineral Exploration Services
N.A.I.C.S.: 213114
W. Harrison *(Chm & CEO)*

MILLWALL HOLDINGS PLC
The Den Zampa Road, London, SE16 3LN, United Kingdom
Tel.: (44) 2072321222
Web Site:
   http://www.millwallholdingsplc.co.uk
Rev.: $23,306,821
Assets: $28,830,865
Liabilities: $26,639,268
Net Worth: $2,191,598
Earnings: ($890,852)
Emp.: 146
Fiscal Year-end: 06/30/19
Football Team Operator; Real Estate Services
N.A.I.C.S.: 531311
John G. Berylson *(Chm)*

MILMAN INDUSTRIES INC.
2502 Elm Street, Sudbury, P3E 4R6, ON, Canada
Tel.: (705) 682-9900
Web Site: http://www.milman.ca
Year Founded: 2011
Holding Company; Rail, Track, Locomotives, Waste Management & Environmental Services
N.A.I.C.S.: 551112
Milad Mansour *(Founder & Pres)*
Subsidiaries:

Diesel Electric Services (1)
1 Foundry Street, Sudbury, P3A 4R7, ON, Canada
Tel.: (705) 674-5626
Rail Equipment Maintenance Services
N.A.I.C.S.: 488210

Subsidiary (Domestic):

OWS Rail Car, Inc. (2)
100 Clifford St, Sarnia, N7T 8C4, ON, Canada
Tel.: (519) 332-5683
Web Site: http://www.owsrailcar.on.ca
Rev.: $1,330,337
Emp.: 18
Railroad Equipment Repair & Services
N.A.I.C.S.: 488210
John Brough *(Pres)*

MILNE AGRIGROUP PTY., LTD.
103 105 Welshpool Rd, Welshpool, 6106, WA, Australia
Tel.: (61) 893510700
Web Site: http://www.milne.com.au
Sales Range: $50-74.9 Million
Emp.: 100
Feed Mfr
N.A.I.C.S.: 311119
Graham Laitt *(Owner & Mng Dir)*
Subsidiaries:

Liveringa Pastoral Company (1)
Locked Bag 19, Welshpool, WA, WA, Australia
Tel.: (61) 893510799
Web Site: http://www.liveringa.com.au
Sales Range: $25-49.9 Million
Emp.: 55
Sheep Producer
N.A.I.C.S.: 112410

Mt Barker Chicken (1)
Locked Bag 19, Welshpool, 6896, WA, Australia
Tel.: (61) 894814166
Web Site:
   http://www.mtbarkerchicken.com.au
Chicken Producer
N.A.I.C.S.: 112320

MILNER CONSOLIDATED SILVER MINES LTD.
22 Lafontaine Road East, Tiny, L9M 0S2, ON, Canada
Tel.: (705) 533-3430
Year Founded: 1975
MCA.H—(TSXV)
Rev.: $11,327
Assets: $2,034
Liabilities: $345,813
Net Worth: ($343,779)
Earnings: ($63,349)
Fiscal Year-end: 12/31/23
Mineral Exploration Services
N.A.I.C.S.: 212290
Marilyn Miller *(CEO)*

MILOC GROUP LIMITED
8/F Sino Cheer Plaza 23 Jordan Road, Kowloon, China (Hong Kong)
Tel.: (852) 2110 4221
Web Site: http://www.miloc.com
Year Founded: 2009
ML—(AQSE)
Sales Range: Less than $1 Million
Pharmaceuticals Mfr
N.A.I.C.S.: 325412
Ching Fung Chow *(Co-Founder & Chm)*
Subsidiaries:

MiLOC Biotechnology Limited (1)
12 F Yue Xiu Building 160 Lockhart Road, Wanchai, China (Hong Kong) (100%)
Tel.: (852) 39955111
Pharmaceuticals Product Mfr
N.A.I.C.S.: 325412
Michael Ong *(Mng Dir)*

MILSY A.S.
Partizanska 224 / B, 957 01, Banovce nad Bebravou, Slovakia
Tel.: (421) 387623100
Web Site: http://www.milsy.eu
Year Founded: 1954
1MIL401E—(BRA)
Sales Range: Less than $1 Million
Dairy Products Mfr
N.A.I.C.S.: 311511
Bohuslav Siko *(Dir-Sls, Mktg & Logistics)*

MILTON CAPITAL PLC
The Scalpel 52 Lime Street 18th Floor, London, EC3M 7AF, United Kingdom
Tel.: (44) 2074690930 UK
Web Site: https://www.milton-capital.co.uk
Year Founded: 2021
MII—(LSE)
Asset Management Services
N.A.I.C.S.: 523999

MILTON CHRYSLER DODGE LIMITED
81 Ontario Street, Milton, L9T 2T2, ON, Canada
Tel.: (905) 878-8877
Web Site:
   http://www.miltonchrysler.ca
Year Founded: 1965
Sales Range: $10-24.9 Million
New & Used Car Dealers
N.A.I.C.S.: 441110
Rob Naidoo *(Gen Sls Mgr)*

MILTON INDUSTRIES LIMITED
1/2 Chitra-Ami Appartment Opp La Gajjar Chamber Ashram Road, Ahmedabad, 380009, India
Tel.: (91) 7926584193
Web Site:
   https://www.miltonindustries.in
Year Founded: 1985
MILTON—(NSE)
Rev.: $7,340,327
Assets: $8,882,705
Liabilities: $3,719,813
Net Worth: $5,162,892
Earnings: $343,996
Fiscal Year-end: 03/31/23
Laminate Product Mfr
N.A.I.C.S.: 334419

MILUX CORPORATION BERHAD
No 31 Lorong Jala 14KS10 Off Jalan Telok Gong, 42000, Klang, Malaysia
Tel.: (60) 331341254
Web Site: https://www.milux.com.my
MILUX—(KLS)
Gas & Electrical Home Appliances Mfr
N.A.I.C.S.: 335210
Chee How Tan *(Exec Dir)*
Subsidiaries:

Brightyield Sdn. Bhd. (1)
Lot 5100 No 19 Section B6 Jalan Kamunting 2 Bukit Beruntang, 48300, Rawang, Selangor, Malaysia
Tel.: (60) 360212126
Sales Range: $25-49.9 Million
Emp.: 40
Steam Cookers Mfr
N.A.I.C.S.: 335210

Enamel Products Sdn. Bhd. (1)
No 2605 Tkt Perusahaan Perai Kaw Perusahaan, 13600, Perai, Pulau Pinang, Malaysia
Tel.: (60) 43997700
Web Site: http://www.milux.com.my
Sales Range: $25-49.9 Million
Emp.: 10
Enamel Products Mfr
N.A.I.C.S.: 325998

Milux Home Appliances (India) Private Limited (1)
No 4 Mannurpet Manickam Pillai Street Ambattur Industrial Estate, 600058, Chennai, Tamil Nadu, India
Tel.: (91) 4426350075
Sales Range: $25-49.9 Million
Emp.: 40
Gas Stoves Mfr
N.A.I.C.S.: 333310

Milux Sales & Service Sdn. Bhd. (1)
No 31 Lorong Jala 14/KS10 Telok Gong, 42000, Port Klang, Selangor Darul Ehsan, Malaysia
Tel.: (60) 331341254
Web Site: https://milux.com.my
Household Electrical Appliances Distr
N.A.I.C.S.: 423620

T.H. Hin Home Tech Sdn. Bhd. (1)
Lot 100 1 Mukim 1 Tingkat Perusahaan 2A Kawasan Perusahaan, 13600, Perai, Pulau Pinang, Malaysia
Tel.: (60) 43993082
Web Site: http://www.milux.com.my
Emp.: 200
Commercial Electrical Appliances Mfr
N.A.I.C.S.: 335210
Lim Hock Seng *(Gen Mgr)*

MIMAKI ENGINEERING CO., LTD.
2182-3 Shigeno-Otsu, Tomi, 389-0512, Nagano, Japan
Tel.: (81) 268642281
Web Site: https://www.mimaki.com
6638—(TKS)
Rev.: $499,920,910
Assets: $500,495,980
Liabilities: $319,448,080
Net Worth: $181,047,900
Earnings: $24,503,270
Emp.: 2,044
Fiscal Year-end: 03/31/24
Computer Device Mfr
N.A.I.C.S.: 334118
Kazuaki Ikeda *(Pres)*
Subsidiaries:

Alpha Design Co., Ltd. (1)
2211-3 Shigeno-Kou, Tomi, 389-0511, Nagano Prefecture, Japan
Tel.: (81) 268640088
Web Site: http://www.alpha-design.co.jp
Automation Equipment Mfr & Distr
N.A.I.C.S.: 333998

GRAPHIC CREATION Co., Ltd. (1)
1333-3 Kazawa, Tomi, 389-0514, Nagano, Japan
Tel.: (81) 268646500
Web Site: http://www.graphic-creation.com
Digital Printing Services
N.A.I.C.S.: 323111

MIMAKI AUSTRALIA PTY LTD (1)
Unit 14 38-46 South Street, Rydalmere, 2116, NSW, Australia
Tel.: (61) 280364502
Web Site: http://www.mimakiaus.com.au

MIMAKI ENGINEERING CO., LTD.

MIMAKI ENGINEERING CO., LTD.—(Continued)
Inkjet Printer & Cutting Machine Mfr
N.A.I.C.S.: 334118
Tomomitsu Harada *(Mng Dir)*

MIMAKI BRASIL COMERCIO E IM-PORTACAO LTDA
Avenida Dr Luis Rocha Miranda 177, Jabaquara, Sao Paulo, 04344-010, Brazil
Tel.: (55) 1150790000
Web Site: https://www.brasil.mimaki.com
Inkjet Printer Distr
N.A.I.C.S.: 423430

MIMAKI DEUTSCHLAND GMBH (1)
Martin-Kollar-Str 10, 81829, Munich, Germany
Tel.: (49) 894374810
Web Site: https://www.mimaki.de
Inkjet Printer Distr
N.A.I.C.S.: 423430

MIMAKI ENGINEERING (TAIWAN) Co., Ltd. (1)
No 37 Section 3 Zhongshan Road, Tanzi District, Taichung, 42756, Taiwan
Tel.: (886) 425330101
Web Site: http://www.mimakitaiwan.com
Inkjet Printer Mfr
N.A.I.C.S.: 334118

MIMAKI ENGINEERING CO., LTD. - Kazawa Factory
1333-3 Kazawa, Tomi, 389-0514, Nagano, Japan
Tel.: (81) 268643411
Web Site: https://mimaki.com
Inkjet Printer Mfr
N.A.I.C.S.: 334118

MIMAKI EUROPE B.V. (1)
Stammerdijk 7E, 1112 AA, Diemen, Netherlands
Tel.: (31) 204627640
Web Site: https://www.mimakieurope.com
Inkjet Printer Distr
N.A.I.C.S.: 423430

MIMAKI IJ TECHNOLOGY (ZHEJIANG) CO., Ltd. (1)
1618 Xingpingyi Road, Economic Development Zone, Pinghu, 314200, Zhejiang, China
Tel.: (86) 57385280701
Inkjet Printer & Ink Mfr
N.A.I.C.S.: 325910

MIMAKI SINGAPORE PTE. LTD. (1)
31 Kaki Bukit Road 3 TechLink 02-03, Singapore, 417818, Singapore
Tel.: (65) 65082789
Web Site: https://www.singapore.mimaki.com
Inkjet Printer Distr
N.A.I.C.S.: 423430

MIMAKI USA, INC. (1)
150 Satellite Blvd NE Ste A, Suwanee, GA 30024
Tel.: (678) 730-0170
Web Site: http://www.mimakiusa.com
Inkjet Printer Distr
N.A.I.C.S.: 423430
Naoya Kawagoshi *(Pres)*

Mimaki (Thailand) Co., Ltd. (1)
1780 Teo Hong Bangna Building Ground Fl and 1st Fl Debaratna Rd, South Bangna Bangna, Bangkok, 10260, Thailand
Tel.: (66) 20126586
Web Site: http://www.thailand.mimaki.com
Printing Machinery Mfr & Distr
N.A.I.C.S.: 333248
Atsushi Nishida *(Mng Dir)*

Mimaki Bompan Textile S.r.l. (1)
Via Europa 10, 21049, Tradate, VA, Italy
Tel.: (39) 03311590120
Web Site: https://www.mimakibompan.it
Printing Machinery Mfr & Distr
N.A.I.C.S.: 333248
Hirokazu Hayashi *(CEO)*

Mimaki Eurasia Dijital Baski Teknolojileri Pazarlama Ve Ticaret Limited Sirketi
Beylikduzu OSB Mah 1 Cadde No 11/2, Beylikduzu, Istanbul, Turkiye
Tel.: (90) 2129999811

Web Site: http://www.mimaki.com.tr
Dye Jet Printing Machinery Mfr & Distr
N.A.I.C.S.: 333248

Mimaki India Private Limited (1)
DSM 332 and 333 3rd Floor DLF Tower Shivaji Marg, New Delhi, 110015, India
Tel.: (91) 1142822000
Web Site: http://www.india.mimaki.com
Inkjet Printer Mfr & Distr
N.A.I.C.S.: 333248
Yoshimoto Sugiyama *(Mng Dir)*

Mimaki Lithuania, UAB (1)
Baltosios Vokes Str 37A, Vilnius, Lithuania
Tel.: (370) 52059933
Printing Machine Product Mfr & Distr
N.A.I.C.S.: 333248

Mimaki Precision Co., Ltd. (1)
2182-3 Shigenootsu, Tomi, 389-0512, Nagano Prefecture, Japan
Tel.: (81) 268646066
Web Site: http://www.mimakiprecision.co.jp
Precision Sheet Metal Painting Parts Mfr
N.A.I.C.S.: 332322

PT. MIMAKI INDONESIA (1)
Jl Danau Sunter Barat Blok A3 No 13, Jakarta, 14350, Utara, Indonesia
Tel.: (62) 2165307942
Web Site: https://www.indonesia.mimaki.com
Computer Device Mfr & Distr
N.A.I.C.S.: 334118

SHANGHAI MIMAKI TRADING CO., LTD. (1)
1st Floor Building 45 555 Guiping Road, Shanghai, 200233, China
Tel.: (86) 2133676651
Web Site: http://www.shanghai.mimaki.com
Inkjet Printer & Cutting Plotter Distr
N.A.I.C.S.: 423430

WIZTEC Co., Ltd. (1)
MK3 Building 102 1-14-8 Myojincho, Hachioji, 192-0046, Tokyo, Japan
Tel.: (81) 426494682
Web Site: https://www.wiztec.co.jp
Emp.: 7
Inkjet Printer Mfr
N.A.I.C.S.: 334118

MIMECAST LTD.

1 Finsbury Avenue, London, EC2M 2PF, United Kingdom
Tel.: (44) 207 843 2300
Web Site: http://www.mimecast.com
MIME—(NASDAQ)
Rev.: $501,399,000
Assets: $934,707,000
Liabilities: $573,838,000
Net Worth: $360,869,000
Earnings: $29,745,000
Emp.: 1,765
Fiscal Year-end: 03/31/21
Cloud-Based Email Archiving, Continuity & Security Solutions
N.A.I.C.S.: 513210
Peter Bauer *(Chm & CEO)*

Subsidiaries:

Mimecast North America, Inc. (1)
480 Pleasant St, Watertown, MA 02472
Tel.: (781) 996-5340
Web Site: http://www.mimecast.com
Software Development Services
N.A.I.C.S.: 541511
David Raissipour *(Chief Tech & Product Officer)*

MIMEDIA HOLDINGS INC.

1066 West Hastings Street Suite 2300, Vancouver, V6E 3X2, BC, Canada
Tel.: (604) 805-6600
KH3—(DEU)
Rev.: $11,072
Assets: $1,958,223
Liabilities: $4,800,184
Net Worth: $(2,841,961)
Earnings: $(3,864,827)
Fiscal Year-end: 12/31/23
Business Consulting Services

N.A.I.C.S.: 522299
Eugene A. Hodgson *(CEO)*

MIMIR INVEST AB

Grev Turegatan 10 1tr, 114 46, Stockholm, Sweden
Tel.: (46) 739 86 36 37
Web Site: http://www.mimirinvest.com
Private Investment Firm
N.A.I.C.S.: 523999
Joakim Noto *(Mng Partner-Investments)*

Subsidiaries:

Puumerkki Oy (1)
Porvoontie 9, 04220, Kerava, Finland
Tel.: (358) 2074 50500
Web Site: http://www.puumerkki.fi
Sales Range: $150-199.9 Million
Building Materials Whslr
N.A.I.C.S.: 444180
Esko Mukkula *(Deputy CEO)*

Saint-Gobain Bockmann A/S (1)
Habornveien 50, Fredrikstad, 1630, Norway
Tel.: (47) 48 11 88 00
Web Site: http://www.bockmann.sggs.com
Glass Products Mfr
N.A.I.C.S.: 327215
Benoit Chatillon *(Gen Mgr)*

MIN AIK TECHNOLOGY CO., LTD.

12F-1 No 492-1 Sec 1 Wanshou Rd, Kuei Shan Dist, Taoyuan, Taiwan
Tel.: (886) 282001008
Web Site: https://www.minaik.com.tw
Year Founded: 1979
3060—(TAI)
Rev.: $86,841,555
Assets: $135,921,117
Liabilities: $53,531,507
Net Worth: $82,389,611
Earnings: $(7,644,527)
Emp.: 889
Fiscal Year-end: 12/31/23
Automation Services
N.A.I.C.S.: 541512
Tsan-Yung Sung *(Deputy COO)*

Subsidiaries:

MAP Technology Holdings Pte. Ltd. (1)
138 Cecil St #09-01A Cecil Ct, Singapore, 069538, Singapore
Tel.: (65) 65939700
Web Site: http://www.maptech.com.sg
Sales Range: $150-199.9 Million
Plastic Injection Mfr
N.A.I.C.S.: 333248

Subsidiary (Domestic):

Art Craft Technology Pte Ltd (2)
No 13 Loyang Lane, Singapore, Singapore
Tel.: (65) 62593900
Web Site: http://www.maptech.com.sg
Die Cut Components Mfr
N.A.I.C.S.: 333514

MAP Plastics Pte Ltd (2)
No 11/13 Loyang Lane Loyang Industrial Estate, Singapore, 508928, Singapore
Tel.: (65) 453268
Web Site: http://www.mapplasticspl.com
Sales Range: $50-74.9 Million
Emp.: 200
Injection Molded Plastic Products Mfr
N.A.I.C.S.: 326121
Loy Chit See *(Mng Dir)*

MATC Technology (M) Sdn. Bhd. (1)
Lot 4628 Kawasan Perindustrian, 78300, Masjid Tanah, Melaka, Malaysia
Tel.: (60) 6 3847099
Web Site: http://www.minaik.com.tw
Sales Range: $50-74.9 Million
Emp.: 233
Fabricated Metal Products Mfr
N.A.I.C.S.: 332312

Min Aik International Development Pte. Ltd. (1)

INTERNATIONAL PUBLIC

8 Burn Road 04-01 Trivex, Singapore, 369977, Singapore
Tel.: (65) 64880311
Electronic Components Mfr
N.A.I.C.S.: 334419

Min Aik Precision Industrial Co., Ltd. (1)
2 Guorui Road, Guanyin District, Taoyuan, 328, Taiwan
Tel.: (886) 34389966
Web Site: https://www.mapi.com.tw
Rev.: $68,285,226
Assets: $100,209,159
Liabilities: $39,279,014
Net Worth: $60,930,146
Earnings: $2,716,407
Emp.: 852
Fiscal Year-end: 12/31/2023
Metal Stamping Mfr
N.A.I.C.S.: 332119

Min Aik Technology (M) Sdn Bhd. (1)
ST 814 Kawasan Perindustrian, Masjid Tanah, Melaka, 78300, Malaysia
Tel.: (60) 63851268
Web Site: http://www.minaik.com.tw
Sales Range: $200-249.9 Million
Emp.: 509
Injection Molded Plastic Products Mfr
N.A.I.C.S.: 326130

Min Aik Technology (SuZhou) Co., Ltd. (1)
Datong Road, Suzhou New District on the 20th Export Processing Zone 1 No 78, Suzhou, 215151, Jiangsu, China
Tel.: (86) 51266729996
Web Site: http://www.minaik.com.tw
Emp.: 200
Hard Disk Drive Metal Parts Mfr
N.A.I.C.S.: 332999

Min Aik Technology (Thailand) Co., Ltd (1)
40/4 Moo 5 Rojana Industrial Park Zone E, Uthai, Phra Nakhon Si Ayutthaya, 13210, Thailand
Tel.: (66) 357415449
Hard Disk Drive Components Mfr
N.A.I.C.S.: 334118

Min Aik Technology USA Inc. (1)
1059 Bright Oak Pl, San Jose, CA 95120
Tel.: (408) 472-1447
Web Site: http://www.minaik.com.tw
Hard Disk Drive Mfr
N.A.I.C.S.: 334112

Min Aik Thailand(MATH) Co., Ltd. (1)
40/4 Rojana Industrial Estate Moo5 Tambol U Thai, Amphur U-Thai, Phra Nakhon Si Ayutthaya, Thailand
Tel.: (66) 35741544
Hard Disk Drive Components Mfr
N.A.I.C.S.: 334118

MIN FU INTERNATIONAL HOLDING LIMITED

Room 1509-1510 Jinying Building No 1 Jinying Road, Tianhe District, Guangzhou, 510600, Guangdong, China
Tel.: (86) 2032219108
Web Site: http://www.ztecgroup.com
Year Founded: 2008
8511—(HKG)
Rev.: $7,048,682
Assets: $10,178,547
Liabilities: $1,971,607
Net Worth: $8,206,940
Earnings: $402,951
Emp.: 25
Fiscal Year-end: 03/31/20
Measurement Instrument Mfr & Distr
N.A.I.C.S.: 334513

MIN XIN HOLDINGS LIMITED

Tel.: (852) 25215671 HK
Web Site: https://www.minxin.com.hk
Year Founded: 1980
0222—(HKG)
Sales Range: $125-149.9 Million

Emp.: 75
Real Estate & Investment Services
N.A.I.C.S.: 531312
Jin Guang Peng *(Chm)*

Subsidiaries:

Min Xin Insurance Company
Limited (1)
17 F Fairmont House 8 Cotton Tree Dr,
Central, China (Hong Kong)
Tel.: (852) 25215671
Web Site: http://www.mxic.com.hk
General Insurance Services
N.A.I.C.S.: 524210
Peter Kwok-Kwong Chan *(CEO)*

MINAEAN SP CONSTRUCTION CORP.

2050 - 1055 West Georgia Street, PO
Box 11121, Royal Centre, Vancouver,
V6E 3P3, BC, Canada
Tel.: (604) 684-2181   AB
Web Site: https://www.minaean.com
Year Founded: 1998
NJAN—(DEU)
Rev.: $6,498
Assets: $60,148
Liabilities: $635,265
Net Worth: ($575,116)
Earnings: ($706,679)
Emp.: 65,000
Fiscal Year-end: 03/31/23
Residential & Commercial Construction & Engineering
N.A.I.C.S.: 236220
Mervyn J. Pinto *(Pres & CEO)*

Subsidiaries:

Minaean (Ghana) Limited (1)
1 Quartey Papafio Avenue Patrice Lumumba Road, Accra, Ghana
Tel.: (233) 302770532
Construction Engineering Services
N.A.I.C.S.: 541330

Minaean Habitat India (PVT) Ltd. (1)
C 206 Plot No 55 2nd fl Sector 15 CBD Belapur, Mumbai, Maharastra, India (100%)
Tel.: (91) 2227570889
Web Site: http://www.minaeanindia.com
Development, Manufacturing & Construction of Cost-Effective Metal Buildings
N.A.I.C.S.: 332311
Sudhir Kumar Garg *(Mng Dir)*

Minaean Power Structures Inc. (1)
9331 NE Colfax St Ste 210, Portland, OR
97220 (100%)
Tel.: (503) 253-2970
Web Site: http://www.minaean.com
Light Gauge Steel Framing Supplier for
Commercial & Residential Buildings
N.A.I.C.S.: 332312
Mervyn J. Pinto *(Pres & CEO)*

MINAFIN SARL

224 Avenue de la Dordogne, 59640,
Dunkirk, France
Tel.: (33) 328607782   LU
Web Site: http://www.minafin.com
Year Founded: 2004
Sales Range: $200-249.9 Million
Holding Company; Fine & Specialty
Chemicals Mfr
N.A.I.C.S.: 551112

Subsidiaries:

Minakem SAS (1)
145 Chemin des Lilas, 59310, Beuvry-la-Foret, France
Tel.: (33) 3 2064 6830
Web Site: http://www.minakem.com
Holding Company; Fine Chemicals, Pharmaceutical Intermediates & Ingredients Mfr
N.A.I.C.S.: 551112
Laurence Jacques *(Dir Gen)*

Subsidiary (Domestic):

Minakem Beuvry Production
SASU (2)
145 Chemin des Lilas, 59310, Beuvry-la-Foret, France
Tel.: (33) 3 2064 6830
Web Site: http://www.minakem.com
Emp.: 150
Fine Chemicals, Pharmaceutical Intermediates & Ingredients Mfr & Whslr
N.A.I.C.S.: 325998
Laurence Jacques *(Mng Dir-Div)*

Subsidiary (Non-US):

Minakem High Potent (2)
Industrial Research Park Fleming, B 1348,
Louvain-la-Neuve, Belgium
Tel.: (32) 1048 3111
Web Site: http://www.omnichem.com
Emp.: 110
Pharmaceutical Industry Fine Chemicals &
Intermediates Mfr & Whslr
N.A.I.C.S.: 325998

Subsidiary (US):

Minakem, LLC (2)
411 Hackensack Ave 4th Fl Continental Plz,
Hackensack, NJ 07601
Tel.: (201) 546-1986
Web Site: http://www.minakem.com
Fine Chemicals, Pharmaceutical Intermediates & Ingredients Whslr
N.A.I.C.S.: 424690
Ioannis Valvis *(Pres)*

Minasolve SASU (1)
145 Chemin des Lilas, 59310, Beuvry-la-Foret, France
Tel.: (33) 3 2064 3182
Web Site: http://www.minasolve.com
Sales Range: $125-149.9 Million
Emp.: 150
Specialty Ingredients Mfr & Whslr
N.A.I.C.S.: 325998
Franco Manfre *(Dir Gen)*

Penn A Kem, LLC (1)
3324 Chelsea Ave, Memphis, TN 38108-1909
Tel.: (901) 320-4000
Web Site: http://www.pennakem.com
Sales Range: $10-24.9 Million
Specialty & Fine Chemicals Mfr & Whslr
N.A.I.C.S.: 325998
Barry Roberts *(Sls Mgr-North America)*

Pressure Chemical Co. (1)
3419 Smallman St, Pittsburgh, PA 15201
Tel.: (412) 682-5882
Web Site: http://www.presschem.com
Sales Range: $10-24.9 Million
Emp.: 43
Specialty Chemicals Mfr
N.A.I.C.S.: 325998
John Pannucci *(CEO)*

MINAL MEDICAL CENTRE LLC

Al Wasl Road Opposite Life Pharmacy, PO Box 293553, Dubai, United
Arab Emirates
Tel.: (971) 43420990
Year Founded: 1997
Skin & Hair Treatment Services
N.A.I.C.S.: 621111
Minal Patwardhan *(Partner)*

MINAMI KYUSHU COCA-COLA BOTTLING CO., LTD.

5-1 Minamitakae 3-chome, Kumamoto, 861-4106, Japan
Tel.: (81) 96 311 3100   JP
Web Site: http://www.minami-kyushu.ccbc.co.jp
Year Founded: 1962
Sales Range: $200-249.9 Million
Emp.: 1,449
Soft Drinks Mfr
N.A.I.C.S.: 312111

MINAPHARM PHARMACEUTICALS

El-Bardissi St 2T Takseem Asmaa
Fahmy St, Heliopolis, Cairo, Egypt
Tel.: (20) 224143170
Web Site:
  https://www.minapharm.com
Year Founded: 1986
MIPH.CA—(EGX)
Rev.: $125,925,328
Assets: $281,599,491
Liabilities: $167,798,460
Net Worth: $113,801,031
Earnings: $723,605
Emp.: 2,000
Fiscal Year-end: 12/31/23
Pharmaceutical Preparation Mfr
N.A.I.C.S.: 325412

MINASMAQUINAS S.A.

Br 381 Rod Fernao Dias Km 02
2211, Bandeirantes, Contagem,
322260536, MG, Brazil
Tel.: (55) 3133691814
Web Site:
  https://www.minasmaquinas.com.br
Year Founded: 1961
MMAQ4—(BRAZ)
Sales Range: Less than $1 Million
Automotive Retailer
N.A.I.C.S.: 441330
Bruno Silveira Kroeber Volpini *(Dir-Investor Relations)*

MINATO HOLDINGS INC.

6F Shimbashi Tokyu Building 4-21-3
Shimbashi, Minato-ku, Yokohama,
1050004, Kanagawa, Japan
Tel.: (81) 357331710
Web Site: https://www.minato.co.jp
Year Founded: 1956
6862—(TKS)
Rev.: $125,708,980
Assets: $111,193,420
Liabilities: $73,192,530
Net Worth: $38,000,890
Earnings: $9,802,630
Emp.: 360
Fiscal Year-end: 03/31/24
Mfr & Sales of Electronic Equipment
& Electronic Measurement Equipment
N.A.I.C.S.: 334519
Takehiko Wakayama *(Chm & Pres)*

Subsidiaries:

Creit Solutions Inc. (1)
6th Floor Shimbashi Tokyu Building 4-21-3
Shimbashi, Minato-ku, Tokyo, 105-0004,
Japan
Tel.: (81) 358437447
Web Site: https://www.creitsol.co.jp
Emp.: 180
System Engineering Services
N.A.I.C.S.: 541330

Japan Joint Solutions Co., Ltd. (1)
4-21-3 Shimbashi 6th floor Shimbashi Tokyu
Building, Minato-ku, Tokyo, 105-0004, Japan
Tel.: (81) 357331780
Web Site: https://www.jjss.co.jp
System Engineering Services
N.A.I.C.S.: 541330

Minato Advanced Technologies
Inc. (1)
4105 Minami Yamata-cho, Tsuzuki-ku, Yokohama, 224-0026, Kanagawa, Japan
Tel.: (81) 455915611
Web Site: https://www.minatoat.co.jp
Emp.: 90
Electronic Component Mfr & Distr
N.A.I.C.S.: 334419

Minato Financial Partners Inc. (1)
6th Floor Shimbashi Tokyu Building 4-21-3
Shimbashi, Minato-ku, Tokyo, 105-0004,
Japan
Tel.: (81) 357331770
Web Site: https://www.minato-fp.co.jp
Real Estate Brokerage Services
N.A.I.C.S.: 531210

Princeton Ltd. (1)
Shimbashi Tokyu Building 5F 4-21-3 Shimbashi, Minato-ku, Tokyo, 105-0004, Japan
Tel.: (81) 357331730
Web Site: https://www.princeton.co.jp
Emp.: 135
Computer Related Device Mfr & Distr
N.A.I.C.S.: 334418

SanMax Technologies Inc. (1)
5F Shimbashi Tokyu Building 4-21-3 Shimbashi, Minato-ku, Tokyo, 105-0004, Japan
Tel.: (81) 357331720
Web Site: https://3max.co.jp
System Board Mfr & Distr
N.A.I.C.S.: 334418

MINAURUM GOLD INC.

1570 200 Burrard Street, Vancouver,
V6C 3L6, BC, Canada
Tel.: (778) 330-0994   BC
Web Site: https://www.minaurum.com
Year Founded: 2007
MMRGF—(OTCQX)
Rev.: $14,498
Assets: $9,370,525
Liabilities: $398,748
Net Worth: $8,971,777
Earnings: ($5,883,275)
Fiscal Year-end: 04/30/21
Gold Mining Services
N.A.I.C.S.: 212220
Darrell A. Rader *(Pres & CEO)*

MINAXI TEXTILES LIMITED

Plot No 3311 Phase 4 GIDC Chhatral, Taluka Kalol, Gandhinagar, 382
729, Gujarat, India
Tel.: (91) 2764234008
Web Site:
  https://www.minaxitextiles.com
Year Founded: 1995
531456—(BOM)
Rev.: $3,507,667
Assets: $4,355,027
Liabilities: $3,644,614
Net Worth: $710,413
Earnings: ($744,895)
Emp.: 24
Fiscal Year-end: 03/31/23
Textile Products Mfr
N.A.I.C.S.: 313210
Bharatbhai P. Patel *(Exec Dir)*

MINBOS RESOURCES LIMITED

Unit 5 254 Rokeby Road, Subiaco,
6008, WA, Australia
Tel.: (61) 862197171
Web Site: https://www.minbos.com
MNB—(ASX)
Rev.: $72,479
Assets: $6,027,965
Liabilities: $239,857
Net Worth: $5,788,108
Earnings: ($3,187,585)
Fiscal Year-end: 06/30/21
Phosphate Mining Services
N.A.I.C.S.: 212390
Lindsay Reed *(CEO)*

MINCO CAPITAL CORP.

2060 1055 West Georgia Street, Vancouver, V6E 3R5, BC, Canada
Tel.: (604) 688-8002   BC
Web Site:
  https://www.mincocapitalcorp.com
Year Founded: 1982
MI5—(DEU)
Rev.: $44,706
Assets: $4,237,002
Liabilities: $170,442
Net Worth: $4,066,559
Earnings: ($1,037,003)
Fiscal Year-end: 12/31/23
Investment Services
N.A.I.C.S.: 523940
Ken Z. Cai *(Chm & CEO)*

Subsidiaries:

Minco Mining (China) Co. Ltd (1)
Suite 1706 Tower C Global Trade Centre 36
East Beisanhuan Road, Dongcheng District,
Beijing, 100013, China
Tel.: (86) 10 59575377

MINCO CAPITAL CORP.

Minco Capital Corp.—(Continued)
Gold Ore Mining Services
N.A.I.C.S.: 212220

MINCO SILVER CORPORATION
2060 - 1055 West Georgia Street, PO Box 11176, Vancouver, V6E 3R5, BC, Canada
Tel.: (604) 688-8002
Web Site: https://mincosilver.com
MSV—(OTCIQ)
Rev.: $1,328,131
Assets: $36,884,235
Liabilities: $1,082,976
Net Worth: $35,801,259
Earnings: ($946,598)
Emp.: 10
Fiscal Year-end: 12/31/20
Silver Ore Mining
N.A.I.C.S.: 212220
Ken Z. Cai (Chm, Pres & CEO)

MINCON GROUP PLC
Smithstown Industrial Estate, Shannon, V14 N993, Clare, Ireland
Tel.: (353) 61361099   IE
Web Site: https://www.mincon.com
Year Founded: 1977
MIO—(ISE)
Rev.: $173,232,145
Assets: $242,296,059
Liabilities: $72,022,298
Net Worth: $170,273,761
Earnings: $8,245,943
Emp.: 604
Fiscal Year-end: 12/31/23
Rock Drilling Tools & Related Products Mfr & Distr
N.A.I.C.S.: 333515
Thomas Purcell (COO)

Subsidiaries:

Attakroc Inc.   (1)
6330 Zephirin-Paquet Suite 300, Quebec, G2C 0M3, QC, Canada
Tel.: (418) 848-4844
Web Site: https://www.attakroc.com
Drilling Equipment Mfr
N.A.I.C.S.: 333131

Driconeq AB   (1)
Svetsarevagen 4, 686 33, Sunne, Sweden
Tel.: (46) 565184440
Web Site: https://driconeq.com
Drilling Equipment Mfr
N.A.I.C.S.: 333132
Christer Axelsson (Gen Mgr)

Driconeq Production AB   (1)
Svetsarevagen 4, 686 33, Sunne, Sweden
Tel.: (46) 565184440
Drilling Pipe & Equipment Mfr.
N.A.I.C.S.: 333131
Christer Axelsson (Gen Mgr-Technical)

Mincon Carbide Ltd.   (1)
Windsor Street, Sheffield, S4 7WB, United Kingdom
Tel.: (44) 1142752282
Web Site: https://www.hardmet.com
Tungsten Carbide Mfr
N.A.I.C.S.: 331492

Mincon Chile SA   (1)
Americo Vespucio 1385 Modulo 31, Quilicura, Santiago, Chile
Tel.: (56) 232239351
Drilling Equipment Mfr
N.A.I.C.S.: 333132

Mincon International Limited   (1)
Smithstown Industrial Estate, County Clare, Shannon, V14N993, Ireland
Tel.: (353) 61361099
Drilling Equipment Mfr
N.A.I.C.S.: 333132

Mincon Namibia Pty Ltd   (1)
Erf 198 Gold Street Plenarg Industrial Park Unit 3 Prosperita, Khomas, Windhoek, Namibia
Tel.: (264) 61230320

Drilling Equipment Mfr
N.A.I.C.S.: 333132

Mincon Sweden AB   (1)
Industrivagen 2-4 Ostergotlands Lan, 612-44, Finspang, Sweden
Tel.: (46) 12215480
Drilling Equipment Mfr
N.A.I.C.S.: 333132

Mincon West Africa SL   (1)
Calle Adolfo Alonso Fernandez S/N Parcela 16 Planta 2, Zona Franca Puerta 23 Puerto De La Luz Gran Canaria, 35008, Las Palmas, Spain
Tel.: (34) 928238026
Drilling Equipment Mfr
N.A.I.C.S.: 333132

MIND C.T.I. LTD.
2 HaCarmel St, Yoqne'am Illit, 2066724, Israel
Tel.: (972) 49936666   IL
Web Site: https://www.mindcti.com
Year Founded: 1995
MNDO—(NASDAQ)
Rev.: $21,551,000
Assets: $31,743,000
Liabilities: $7,936,000
Net Worth: $23,807,000
Earnings: $5,287,000
Emp.: 153
Fiscal Year-end: 12/31/22
Real-Time Mediation, Billing & Customer Care Solutions for Voice, Data, Video & Content Services
N.A.I.C.S.: 541511
Monica Iancu (Pres & CEO)

Subsidiaries:

MIND Software Srl   (1)
Str Ciurchi nr126-128 Tudor Office Center et 7, 700366, Iasi, Romania
Tel.: (40) 332413555
Sales Range: $25-49.9 Million
Emp.: 200
Real-Time, Mediation, Billing & Customer Care Solutions for Voice, Data, Video & Content Services
N.A.I.C.S.: 541511

Message Mobile GmbH   (1)
Stresemannstrasse 6, 21335, Luneburg, Germany
Tel.: (49) 413 124 4440
Web Site: https://www.message-mobile.com
Telecommunication Services
N.A.I.C.S.: 517810
Christof Ungerath (CEO)

MIND CANDY LTD.
Floor 4 15 Bonhill Street, London, EC2A 4DN, United Kingdom
Tel.: (44) 20 7501 1900
Web Site: http://www.mindcandy.com
Year Founded: 2004
Sales Range: $50-74.9 Million
Emp.: 234
Internet Application Development Services
N.A.I.C.S.: 541511
Darran Garnham (Chief Bus Dev Officer)

MIND CURE HEALTH, INC.
170 422 Richards Street, Vancouver, V6B 2Z4, BC, Canada
Web Site: https://www.mindcure.com
MCUR—(CNSX)
Sales Range: Less than $1 Million
Health & Wellness Product Distr
N.A.I.C.S.: 456199
Philip Tapley (Chm)

MIND GYM PLC
160 Kensington High Street, London, W8 7RG, United Kingdom
Tel.: (44) 2073685698   UK
Web Site: https://parentgym.com
Year Founded: 2000

MIND—(AIM)
Rev.: $66,077,517
Assets: $47,028,705
Liabilities: $20,382,093
Net Worth: $26,646,613
Earnings: $2,175,067
Emp.: 332
Fiscal Year-end: 03/31/22
Customer Relationship Management Services
N.A.I.C.S.: 541613
Octavius Black (Co-Founder & CEO)

Subsidiaries:

Mind Gym (USA) Inc.   (1)
475 Park Ave S Fl 2, New York, NY 10016
Tel.: (646) 649-4333
Professional Training & Coaching Services
N.A.I.C.S.: 812990

MIND MEDICINE (MINDMED) INC.
1055 West Hastings Street Suite 1700, Vancouver, V6E 2E9, BC, Canada
Tel.: (203) 648-5275   BC
Web Site: http://mindmed.co
Year Founded: 2010
MNMD—(NASDAQ)
Rev.: $4,664,000
Assets: $124,541,000
Liabilities: $46,407,000
Net Worth: $78,134,000
Earnings: ($95,732,000)
Emp.: 57
Fiscal Year-end: 12/31/23
Dicovery & Development of Psychedelic Medicine
N.A.I.C.S.: 541714
Miriam Halperin Wernli (Pres)

MINDA CORPORATION LIMITED
D 611 Sector 59, Noida, 201 301, Uttar Pradesh, India
Tel.: (91) 1204599300
Web Site: https://www.sparkminda.com
Year Founded: 1985
MINDACORP—(NSE)
Rev.: $517,462,982
Assets: $386,583,538
Liabilities: $195,851,568
Net Worth: $190,731,971
Earnings: $34,110,665
Emp.: 2,943
Fiscal Year-end: 03/31/23
Security Device Mfr
N.A.I.C.S.: 334290
Ashok Minda (Chm & Grp CEO)

Subsidiaries:

Minda KTSN Plastic Solutions GmbH & Co. KG.   (1)
Fabrikstrasse 2, 01796, Pirna, Germany
Tel.: (49) 35014900
Web Site: http://www.ktsn.de
Plastics Product Mfr
N.A.I.C.S.: 326199

Minda Management Services Limited   (1)
Plot No-68 Echelon Institutional Area Sector-32, Gurgaon, 122001, Haryana, India
Tel.: (91) 1244698400
Motor Vehicle Parts Mfr
N.A.I.C.S.: 336390

Minda Vietnam Automotive Company Limited   (1)
Binh Xuyen Industrial Park, Binh Xuyen District, 41361, Binh Xuyen, Vinh Phuc, Vietnam
Tel.: (84) 2113593010
Motor Vehicle Parts Mfr
N.A.I.C.S.: 336390

PT Minda Automotive, Indonesia   (1)
Jalan Permata Raya Lot CA-8, Kawasan

Industri KIIC, Karawang, 41364, West Java, Indonesia
Tel.: (62) 2678633190
Motor Vehicle Parts Mfr
N.A.I.C.S.: 336390

MINDA FINANCE LIMITED
37A Rajasthan Udyog Nagar GT Karnal Road, Near Jahangirpuri Metro Station, Delhi, 110 033, India
Tel.: (91) 1127691184
Web Site: http://www.mindafinance.com
Rev.: $701,912
Assets: $15,457,391
Liabilities: $3,718,950
Net Worth: $11,738,441
Earnings: $251,361
Emp.: 2
Fiscal Year-end: 03/31/18
Financial Support Services
N.A.I.C.S.: 523999
Pramod Kumar Garg (Exec Dir)

Subsidiaries:

Minda Nabtesco Automotive Pvt. Ltd.   (1)
B-64/1 Wazirpur Industrial Area North East, Delhi, 110052, India   (51%)
Tel.: (91) 7838885888
Commercial Vehicles Air Brake Systems Mfr
N.A.I.C.S.: 336340

MINDA INDUSTRIEANLAGEN GMBH
Hans-Bockler-Str 24, Minden, 1365, Germany
Tel.: (49) 57139970
Web Site: http://www.minda.de
Year Founded: 1979
Rev.: $33,105,600
Emp.: 200
Electronic Control Engineering Services
N.A.I.C.S.: 541830
Eberhard Falch (Mng Dir)

Subsidiaries:

Hohmeier Anlagenbau GmbH   (1)
Enzer Strasse 121, 31655, Stadthagen, Germany
Tel.: (49) 572197890
Web Site: http://www.hohmeier-anlagenbau.de
Automotive Components Mfr
N.A.I.C.S.: 336390

UNIVERSAL Corrugated B.V.   (1)
Konigweg 8, 7602 CX, Almelo, Netherlands
Tel.: (31) 546831111
Web Site: http://www.universal-corrugated.com
Industrial Equipment Mfr
N.A.I.C.S.: 333998
Uwe Leopold (Plant Mgr)

MINDAX LIMITED
Suite 3 Level 1 17 Ord Street, West Perth, 6005, WA, Australia
Tel.: (61) 893892111   AU
Web Site: https://www.mindax.com.au
Year Founded: 2003
MDX—(ASX)
Rev.: $1
Assets: $12,599,213
Liabilities: $178,623
Net Worth: $12,420,590
Earnings: ($3,630,576)
Fiscal Year-end: 06/30/23
Mineral Exploration Services
N.A.I.C.S.: 212290
Benjamin Chow (Chm)

MINDBIO THERAPEUTICS CORP.
Level 4 91-97 William Street, Melbourne, 3000, VIC, Australia

AND PRIVATE COMPANIES

Web Site:
https://www.mindbiotherapy.com
Year Founded: 2021
MBIO—(CNSX)
Assets: $1,270,739
Liabilities: $4,399,441
Net Worth: ($3,128,702)
Earnings: ($5,600,029)
Fiscal Year-end: 06/30/22
Biotechnology Research & Development Services
N.A.I.C.S.: 541714
Gavin Upiter *(Chm)*

MINDCHAMPS PRESCHOOL CHANGI BUSINESS PARK PTE. LTD.
51 Changi Business Park Central 2 01-16, Singapore, 486066, Singapore
Tel.: (65) 67816870
Preschool Services
N.A.I.C.S.: 624410

MINDCHAMPS PRESCHOOL LIMITED
6 Raffles Boulevard 04-100 Marina Square, Singapore, 039594, Singapore
Tel.: (65) 68282688
Web Site:
https://www.mindchamps.org
CNE—(SES)
Rev.: $45,606,521
Assets: $104,011,856
Liabilities: $53,399,037
Net Worth: $50,612,820
Earnings: $2,183,031
Emp.: 367
Fiscal Year-end: 12/31/22
Child Care Services
N.A.I.C.S.: 624410
David Chiem Phu An *(Co-Founder, Chm & CEO)*

Subsidiaries:

MindChamps Australia Corporate Pty. Limited (1)
Suite 1 Ground Floor 92-94 Norton Street, Leichhardt, 2040, NSW, Australia
Tel.: (61) 1300646324
Web Site: https://www.mindchamps.org
Educational Support Services
N.A.I.C.S.: 611710

MindChamps PreSchool Buangkok Private Limited (1)
15 Serangoon North Ave 5 02-00 Popular Building, Singapore, 554360, Singapore
Tel.: (65) 69559851
Education Services
N.A.I.C.S.: 611110

MindChamps PreSchool Paragon Pte. Limited (1)
290 Orchard Road Paragon 06-19/20, Singapore, 238859, Singapore
Tel.: (65) 67320087
Preschool Services
N.A.I.C.S.: 624410

MindChamps PreSchool TPY Pte. Limited (1)
490 Lorong 6 Toa Payoh HDB HUB Biz 3 05-12 Lift Lobby 2, Singapore, 310490, Singapore
Tel.: (65) 68282648
Preschool Services
N.A.I.C.S.: 624410

MindChamps PreSchool Woodlands Pte. Ltd. (1)
11 Woodlands Close 01-38/39 Woodlands 11, Singapore, 737853, Singapore
Tel.: (65) 63393296
Preschool Services
N.A.I.C.S.: 624410

MindChamps PreSchool Zhongshan Park Pte. Ltd. (1)
18 AH Hood Rd 05-51 Hiap Hoe Building AT Zhongshan Park, Singapore, 329983, Singapore

Tel.: (65) 67347702
Preschool Services
N.A.I.C.S.: 624410

Mindchamps Preschool @ Marina Square Pte. Limited (1)
04-100 6 Raffles Blvd Marina Square, Singapore, 39594, Singapore
Tel.: (65) 63330331
Preschool Services
N.A.I.C.S.: 624410

MINDFACTORY AG
Preussenstrasse 14 a-c, 26388, Wilhelmshaven, Germany
Tel.: (49) 44219131 0
Web Site: http://www.mindfactory.de
Sales Range: $75-99.9 Million
Emp.: 200
Computer Products & Electronic Equipment Retailer
N.A.I.C.S.: 423430
Fred Mielimonka *(Chm-Supervisory Bd)*

MINDFLAIR PLC
9th Floor 107 Cheapside, London, EC2V 6DN, United Kingdom
Tel.: (44) 2033688961   UK
Web Site: https://mindflair.tech
Year Founded: 1994
PIRI—(AIM)
Assets: $11,801,313
Liabilities: $1,927,544
Net Worth: $9,873,769
Earnings: ($462,005)
Fiscal Year-end: 12/31/22
Miscellaneous Financial Investment Activities
N.A.I.C.S.: 523999

MINDORO RESOURCES LTD.
Suite 1250 639 5th Avenue SW, Calgary, T2P 0M9, AB, Canada
Tel.: (780) 413-8187   AB
Web Site: http://www.mindoro.com
Year Founded: 1994
MIO—(ASX)
Gold Mining & Exploration Services
N.A.I.C.S.: 212220
Edsel Abrasaldo *(VP-Ops)*

MINDPOOL TECHNOLOGIES LTD.
3rd & 4th GK Mall Above Pantaloons, Near Konkane Chowk Pimple Saudager, Pune, 411027, India
Tel.: (91) 9972660966
Web Site:
https://www.mindpooltech.com
Year Founded: 2011
MINDPOOL—(NSE)
Rev.: $5,517,336
Assets: $2,685,624
Liabilities: $550,377
Net Worth: $2,135,247
Earnings: ($15,987)
Emp.: 270
Fiscal Year-end: 03/31/23
Information Technology Consulting Services
N.A.I.C.S.: 541519
Ritesh Sharma *(CEO & Mng Dir)*

MINDRAY MEDICAL INTERNATIONAL LTD.
Mindray Building Keji 12th Road South Hi Tech Industrial Park Nanshan, Shenzhen, 518057, China
Tel.: (86) 75581888666   Ky
Web Site: http://www.mindray.com
Year Founded: 1991
Sales Range: $1-4.9 Billion
Emp.: 8,300
Medical Device Mfr & Marketer
N.A.I.C.S.: 339112
Hang Xu *(Chm)*

Subsidiaries:

Hangzhou Optcla Medical Instrument Co., Ltd. (1)
No 88 West Baiyunyuan Rd Tongjun St, Tonglu, 311500, Hangzhou, China
Tel.: (86) 571 64239839
Web Site: http://www.hzguangdian.com.cn
Sales Range: $50-74.9 Million
Emp.: 13
Surgical Instrument Mfr & Distr
N.A.I.C.S.: 339112

Mindray (UK) Limited (1)
3 Percy Road St John's Park, Huntingdon, PE29 6SZ, Cambs, United Kingdom
Tel.: (44) 1480 416 840
Medical Equipment Mfr
N.A.I.C.S.: 339112

Mindray - Distribution and Commercialization of Medical Equipment Brazil Ltda. (1)
Rua Tavares Bastos 329 Perdizes, Sao Paulo, 05012-020, Brazil
Tel.: (55) 11 3124 8026
Web Site: http://www.mindray.com
Sales Range: $25-49.9 Million
Emp.: 3
Medical Equipment Distr
N.A.I.C.S.: 423450
Sergio Tamura *(Gen Mgr)*

Mindray Medical Canada Limited (1)
4250 Kingsway Suite 206, Burnaby, V5H 4T7, BC, Canada
Tel.: (604) 451-1199
Medical Equipment Distr
N.A.I.C.S.: 423450

Mindray Medical India Private Limited (1)
B-404 City Point Andheri Kurla Road, Andheri East, Mumbai, 400059, India
Tel.: (91) 22 4020 0000
Web Site: http://www.mindray.com
Sales Range: $25-49.9 Million
Emp.: 55
Medical Instrument Mfr
N.A.I.C.S.: 339112
Dean Zhang *(Mng Dir)*

Mindray Medical Mexico S de R. L. De C. V. (1)
Felix Parra No 175 Col San Jose Insurgentes, 3900, Mexico, Mexico
Tel.: (52) 55 5662 6620
Web Site: http://www.mindray.com
Emp.: 3
Medical Instrument Mfr
N.A.I.C.S.: 339112
Adam Beattie *(Office Mgr)*

Mindray Medical Netherlands B.V. (1)
Drs W van Royenstraat 8, 3871 AN, Hoevelaken, Netherlands
Tel.: (31) 33 25 44 911
Web Site: http://www.mindray.com
Emp.: 25
Medical Device Developer, Mfr & Marketer
N.A.I.C.S.: 339112
Laheber Peter *(Gen Mgr)*

Subsidiary (US):

Mindray DS USA, Inc. (2)
800 MacArthur Blvd, Mahwah, NJ 07430-0619
Tel.: (201) 995-8000
Web Site: http://www.mindray.com
Sales Range: $100-124.9 Million
Emp.: 400
Medical Monitoring & Life Support System Mfr
N.A.I.C.S.: 339112
Michael Thompson *(VP-Ultrasound Sls)*

Subsidiary (Non-US):

Mindray Medical Columbia SAS (2)
No 702 Torre UNIKA Carrera 9 No 77-67, Bogota, Colombia
Tel.: (57) 1 3130892
Medical Equipment Mfr
N.A.I.C.S.: 339112

Mindray Medical Espana S.L. (2)
Avenida Deburgoes 114 1St Fl, Madrid, 28050, Spain

MINDRAY MEDICAL INTERNATIONAL LTD.

Tel.: (34) 91 392 3754
Sales Range: $25-49.9 Million
Emp.: 12
Medical Instrument Mfr
N.A.I.C.S.: 339112

Mindray Medical France SARL (2)
Europarc Creteil 1 Allee des Cerisiers, 94035, Creteil, Cedex, France
Tel.: (33) 1 45 13 91 50
Sales Range: $25-49.9 Million
Emp.: 31
Medical Instrument Mfr
N.A.I.C.S.: 339112
Christophe Vergne *(Gen Mgr)*

Mindray Medical Germany GmbH (2)
Goebelstrasse 21, 64293, Darmstadt, Germany
Tel.: (49) 615139100
Sales Range: $25-49.9 Million
Emp.: 23
Medical Instrument Mfr
N.A.I.C.S.: 339112
Anders Bang *(Gen Mgr)*

Mindray Medical Sweden AB (2)
Rissneleden 136, Sundbyberg, Stockholm, 174 57, Sweden
Tel.: (46) 855554100
Web Site: http://www.artema.se
Sales Range: $25-49.9 Million
Emp.: 4
Medical Instrument Mfr
N.A.I.C.S.: 339112
Per Lindestam *(Mng Dir)*

Mindray Medical Technology Istanbul Limited Liability Company (2)
29 Ekim Cad Kuyumcukent 2 Nolu Plaza Kat 2 Daire 1 Yenibosna, Istanbul, 34520, Turkiye
Tel.: (90) 212 4820 877
Web Site: http://www.mindray.com
Sales Range: $25-49.9 Million
Emp.: 2
Medical Instrument Mfr
N.A.I.C.S.: 339112
Nilufer Goencue *(Mgr-Admin)*

Mindray Medical Rus Limited (1)
Olimpiyskiy prospect 16 building 5, 129110, Moscow, Russia
Tel.: (7) 4995536036
Web Site: http://www.mindray.com
Sales Range: $25-49.9 Million
Emp.: 35
Medical Instrument Mfr
N.A.I.C.S.: 339112
Guang Gao *(Gen Mgr)*

Mindray Medical Thailand Limited (1)
1768 Thai Summit Tower Room 407 4th Floor New Petchaburee Road, Kwaeng Bangkapi Khet Huai Khwang, Bangkok, 10320, Thailand
Tel.: (66) 26527288
Web Site: http://www.mindray.com
Medical Instrument Mfr
N.A.I.C.S.: 339112

Mindray Medical USA Corp. (1)
8650 154th Ave NE, Redmond, WA 98052
Tel.: (425) 881-0361
Web Site: http://www.mindray.com
Sales Range: $25-49.9 Million
Emp.: 10
Medical Device Developer, Mfr & Marketer
N.A.I.C.S.: 339112
Ronald Ede *(VP)*

Nanjing Mindray Bio-Medical Electronics Co., Ltd. (1)
No 666 Zheng Feng Middle Road, Nanjing, 211111, China
Tel.: (86) 2566082820
Sales Range: $100-124.9 Million
Emp.: 500
Medical Equipment Mfr
N.A.I.C.S.: 339112

PT Mindray Medical Indonesia (1)
The East 11th Floor Unit 08 Jl Lingkar Mega Kuningan Kav E 3 2 No 1, Jakarta, 12950, Indonesia
Tel.: (62) 21 576 2650
Web Site: http://www.mindray.com

MINDRAY MEDICAL INTERNATIONAL LTD.

Mindray Medical International Ltd.—(Continued)
Sales Range: $25-49.9 Million
Emp.: 16
Medical Instrument Mfr
N.A.I.C.S.: 339112

Shenzhen Mindray Bio-Medical Electronics Co. Ltd (1)
Mindray Building Keji 12th Road South High-tech Industrial Park, Nanshan, Shenzhen, 518057, China
Tel.: (86) 75581888997
Web Site: https://www.mindray.com
Rev.: $4,920,158,242
Assets: $6,752,349,437
Liabilities: $2,055,559,731
Net Worth: $4,696,789,706
Earnings: $1,631,356,546
Fiscal Year-end: 12/31/2023
Medical Equipment Mfr & Distr
N.A.I.C.S.: 334510

ZONARE Medical Systems, Inc. (1)
420 N Bernardo Ave, Mountain View, CA 94043-5209
Tel.: (650) 230-2800
Web Site: http://www.zonare.com
Sales Range: $50-74.9 Million
Emp.: 176
Compact Ultrasound Systems Developer, Mfr & Marketer
N.A.I.C.S.: 334510
Glen W. McLaughlin *(Founder & Pres)*

MINDS + MACHINES GROUP LIMITED

Craigmuir Chambers Road Town, Tortola, VG 1110, Virgin Islands (British)
Tel.: (284) 2078810180   VG
Web Site: http://www.mmx.co
MMX—(AIM)
Rev.: $16,829,000
Assets: $99,285,000
Liabilities: $23,316,000
Net Worth: $75,969,000
Earnings: $2,983,000
Emp.: 16
Fiscal Year-end: 12/31/20
Website Domain Registry & Consulting Services
N.A.I.C.S.: 518210
Deep Shah *(VP-Finance)*

Subsidiaries:

Bayern Connect GmbH (1)
Thierschstr 11, 80538, Munich, Germany
Tel.: (49) 899 580 7616
Web Site: https://nic.bayern
Domain Registry Services
N.A.I.C.S.: 518210
Caspar Von Veltheim *(Mng Dir)*

Minds + Machines (1)
3100 Donald Douglas Loop N Hngr 7, Santa Monica, CA 90405
Tel.: (310) 452-1491
Web Site: http://www.mindsandmachines.com
Application Software Development Services
N.A.I.C.S.: 541511
Antony Van Couvering *(CEO)*

MINDSPACE BUSINESS PARKS REIT

Raheja Tower Level 8 Block G C-30 Bandra Kurla Complex, Mumbai, 400051, India
Tel.: (91) 2226564000
Web Site:
https://www.mindspacereit.com
543217—(BOM)
Rev.: $157,862,250
Assets: $3,040,100,700
Liabilities: $690,471,600
Net Worth: $2,349,629,100
Earnings: $45,713,850
Emp.: 184
Fiscal Year-end: 03/31/21
Real Estate Investment Services
N.A.I.C.S.: 531190
Vinod Rohira *(CEO)*

MINDTECK INDIA LTD

A M R Tech Park Block-1 3rd Floor, 664 23/24 Hosur Main Road Bommanahalli, Bengaluru, 560 068, India
Tel.: (91) 8041548000
Web Site: https://www.mindteck.com
Year Founded: 1991
MINDTECK—(NSE)
Rev.: $40,904,023
Assets: $29,102,572
Liabilities: $6,245,429
Net Worth: $22,857,143
Earnings: $2,490,258
Emp.: 716
Fiscal Year-end: 03/31/23
Software Consulting
N.A.I.C.S.: 541512
Surjit Lahiri *(VP-Tech)*

Subsidiaries:

Mindteck Netherlands B.V. (1)
Schipholweg 103, 2316 XC, Leiden, Netherlands
Tel.: (31) 715249370
Web Site: http://www.mindteck.com
Sales Range: $25-49.9 Million
Emp.: 1
Software Services
N.A.I.C.S.: 513210

Mindteck Singapore Pte. Limited (1)
7 B Keppel Rd Unit No 05-09 PSA Tanjong Pagar Complex, Singapore, 89055, Singapore
Tel.: (65) 62254516
Sales Range: $25-49.9 Million
Emp.: 70
Software Programming Services
N.A.I.C.S.: 541511

Mindteck Software Malaysia SDN. BHD. (1)
Galleria Cyberjaya Unit 16-5 Jalan Tecknokrat 6 Cyber 5, 63000, Cyberjaya, Selangor Darul Ehsan, Malaysia
Tel.: (60) 383251365
Web Site: http://www.mindteck.com
Sales Range: $25-49.9 Million
Emp.: 100
Software Services
N.A.I.C.S.: 513210

MINDTELL TECHNOLOGY LIMITED

B-7-7 Sky Park Jalan USJ 25/1, One City, 47650, Subang Jaya, Selangor, Malaysia
Web Site:
https://www.mindtelltech.com
Year Founded: 2006
8611—(HKG)
Rev.: $3,085,583
Assets: $3,877,583
Liabilities: $1,578,060
Net Worth: $2,299,523
Earnings: ($1,667,160)
Emp.: 70
Fiscal Year-end: 11/30/22
Information Technology Services
N.A.I.C.S.: 541512
Yee Ping Chong *(Chm)*

Subsidiaries:

Tandem Advisory Sdn. Bhd. (1)
B-7-7 Sky Park One City Jalan USJ 25/1, 47650, Subang Jaya, Selangor, Malaysia
Tel.: (60) 350330661
Web Site: https://tandemasia.com
Consulting Services
N.A.I.C.S.: 541618

MINEBEA MITSUMI INC.

1-9-3 Higashi-shimbashi, Minato-ku, Tokyo, 105-0021, Japan
Tel.: (81) 367586711   JP
Web Site:
https://www.minebeamitsumi.com
Year Founded: 1951
6479—(TKS)
Rev.: $9,268,059,470
Assets: $9,360,566,420
Liabilities: $4,629,630,780
Net Worth: $4,730,935,640
Earnings: $357,171,350
Emp.: 83,886
Fiscal Year-end: 03/31/24
Machined Components, Rotary Components & Electronic Devices & Components Mfr
N.A.I.C.S.: 333248
Shigeru None *(Sr Mng Exec Officer)*

Subsidiaries:

Ablic Europe GmbH (1)
Frankfurter Strasse 227, 63263, Neu-Isenburg, Germany
Tel.: (49) 61023706300
Semiconductor Product Mfr & Distr
N.A.I.C.S.: 334413

Ablic Hong Kong Limited (1)
5F Wyler Centre 2 200 Tai Lin Pai Road N T, Kwai Chung, China (Hong Kong)
Tel.: (852) 24945111
Semiconductor Product Mfr & Distr
N.A.I.C.S.: 334413

Ablic Inc. (1)
1-9-3 Higashi-shimbashi, Minato-ku, Tokyo, 105-0021, Japan
Tel.: (81) 367586815
Web Site: https://www.ablic.com
Emp.: 950
Semiconductor Product Mfr & Distr
N.A.I.C.S.: 334413
Nobumasa Ishiai *(Pres & CEO)*

Ablic Korea Inc. (1)
11F TMAX Sunae Tower 29 Hwangsaeul-ro 258beon-gil, Bundang-gu, Seongnam, 13595, Gyeonggi, Korea (South)
Tel.: (82) 25658006
Semiconductor Product Mfr & Distr
N.A.I.C.S.: 334413

Ablic Shenzhen Inc. (1)
Room 2211-12 Office Tower Shun Hing Square Di Wang Commercial Centre, 5002 Shen Nan Dong Rd, Shenzhen, 518008, China
Tel.: (86) 75525110492
Semiconductor Product Mfr & Distr
N.A.I.C.S.: 334413

Ablic Taiwan Inc. (1)
14F No 102 Dunhua N Rd, Taipei, 105, Taiwan
Tel.: (886) 225635152
Semiconductor Product Mfr & Distr
N.A.I.C.S.: 334413

Ablic U.S.A. Inc. (1)
200 Pine Ave Ste 514, Long Beach, CA 90802
Tel.: (310) 517-7771
Semiconductor Product Mfr & Distr
N.A.I.C.S.: 334413

Access Mechanism L.L.C. (1)
Building - 1, Industrial zone Rzhavka village Kstovo area, 607684, Nizhniy Novgorod, Russia
Tel.: (7) 8314598369
Automotive Component Mfr & Distr
N.A.I.C.S.: 336390

Cerobear GmbH (1)
Kaiserstrasse 100, 52134, Herzogenrath, Germany
Tel.: (49) 240795560
Web Site: https://www.cerobear.com
Emp.: 130
Ceramic Rolling Bearing Mfr & Distr
N.A.I.C.S.: 332991
Bernd Reuter *(Gen Mgr-Aerospace-Europe)*

Cixi New MeiPeiLin Precision Bearing Co., Ltd. (1)
328 Sheng Shan Da Dao Xi Lu Cixi Shi, Ningbo, Zhejiang Sheng, China
Tel.: (86) 57463549687
Ball Bearing Mfr
N.A.I.C.S.: 332991

Daiichi Seimitsu Sangyo Co. (1)
3-28-23 Haginaka, Ota-ku, Tokyo, 144-0047, Japan
Tel.: (81) 337446371

INTERNATIONAL PUBLIC

Resin Injection Molding Mfr & Distr
N.A.I.C.S.: 325211

Dongguan Chengqu Daiichi Precision Mold Co., Ltd. (1)
Hi-Tech Park Shi Long Road Guan Long Road Section, Guan Cheng, Dongguan, Guangdong, China
Tel.: (86) 76922652155
Resin Injection Molding Mfr & Distr
N.A.I.C.S.: 325211

Honda Tsushin Kogyo Co., Ltd. (1)
Osaki MT Building 5-9-11 Kitashinagawa, Shinagawa-ku, Tokyo, 141-0001, Japan   (86.9%)
Tel.: (81) 368537150
Web Site: http://www.htk-jp.com
Rev.: $178,605,680
Assets: $157,406,480
Liabilities: $44,179,520
Net Worth: $113,226,960
Earnings: $6,708,240
Emp.: 960
Fiscal Year-end: 03/31/2022
Electronic Connector Mfr & Whslr
N.A.I.C.S.: 334417
Shinichiro Satani *(Pres)*

Subsidiary (Non-US):

HTK C&H (Thailand) Ltd. (2)
2/3 Bangna Tower A 2nd Floor Unit 204A 14 Bangna-Trad Road KM 6 5, Bangkok, Bang Phli, 10540, Samut Prakan, Thailand
Tel.: (66) 27519055
Emp.: 5
Connector Distr
N.A.I.C.S.: 423690
Toru Saijo *(Pres)*

HTK C&H Asia Pacific Pte Ltd. (2)
150 Kampong Ampat 06-02A KA Centre, Singapore, 368324, Singapore
Tel.: (65) 67459566
Web Site: https://www.honda-connectors.com.sg
Connector Distr
N.A.I.C.S.: 423690
Hiromasa Okamura *(Pres)*

HTK EUROPE LTD. (2)
Unit B1 Marston Gate South Marston Park, Swindon, SN3 4DE, United Kingdom
Tel.: (44) 1793836250
Emp.: 29
Connector Distr
N.A.I.C.S.: 423690
Yasuo Kumasaka *(Mng Dir)*

Subsidiary (Domestic):

HTK Engineering Co., Ltd. (2)
8 Higashida-cho 14th floor Paler Mitsui Building, Kawasaki-ku, Kawasaki, 210-0005, Kanagawa, Japan
Tel.: (81) 442211333
Web Site: https://www.minebea-ss.com
Emp.: 272
Software Development Services
N.A.I.C.S.: 541511
Nobuo Kobayashi *(Pres)*

Subsidiary (Non-US):

HTK HONG KONG LTD. (2)
16/F No 1 Chatham Road South, Tsim Sha Tsui, Kowloon, China (Hong Kong)
Tel.: (852) 27991700
Connector Distr
N.A.I.C.S.: 423690
Masami Yamamoto *(Pres)*

Japan 3d Devices Co., Ltd. (1)
7587-1 Oaza-yasuda, Kashiwazaki, 945-1352, Japan
Tel.: (81) 257233055
Electronic Device Mfr & Retailer
N.A.I.C.S.: 334419

Korea Mitsumi Co., Ltd. (1)
12F 29 Hwangsaeul-ro 258 beon-gil, Bundang-gu, Seongnam, 13595, Gyeonggi, Korea (South)
Tel.: (82) 234719734
Electronic Device Mfr & Retailer
N.A.I.C.S.: 334419

MIK Smart Lighting Network Corporation (1)
4106-73 Oaza Miyota Miyota-machi,

AND PRIVATE COMPANIES

MINEBEA MITSUMI INC.

Kitasaku-gun, Nagano, Japan **(51%)**
Tel.: (81) 3 6758 6703
Lighting Equipment Designer & Mfr
N.A.I.C.S.: 335139
Shinichi Yamamura *(Exec Officer & Dir)*

Mach Aero Bretigny Rectification S.A.S. (1)
2 Rue du Roussillon, 91220, Bretigny-sur-Orge, France
Tel.: (33) 169881111
Aerospace Spherical Bearing Component Mfr
N.A.I.C.S.: 336413

Minebea (Cambodia) Co., Ltd. (1)
Phnom Penh Special Economic Zone National Road 4, Sangkat Phleung Chhes Rotes Khan Posenchey, 12100, Phnom Penh, Cambodia
Tel.: (855) 23729371
Web Site: https://www.minebeacambodia.com
Emp.: 9,000
Ball Bearing Mfr
N.A.I.C.S.: 332991

Minebea (Hong Kong) Ltd. (1)
1010-11 10/F Mira Place Tower A 132 Nathan Road, Tsim Sha Tsui, Kowloon, China (Hong Kong)
Tel.: (852) 34232300
Industrial Bearings Distr
N.A.I.C.S.: 423840

Minebea (Shenzhen) Ltd. (1)
23/F Tower B Kingkey 100 No 5016 Shennan Road East, Luohu District, Shenzhen, 518001, China
Tel.: (86) 75582668846
Web Site: http://www.minebea.co.jp
Electronic Devices & Bearings Distr
N.A.I.C.S.: 423690

Minebea Access Solutions Inc. (1)
3700 Shimonaka, Sadowara-cho, Miyazaki, 880-0293, Japan **(100%)**
Tel.: (81) 985731211
Sales Range: $10-24.9 Million
Emp.: 1,103
Automobile Parts Mfr
N.A.I.C.S.: 336390

Minebea Electronic Devices (Suzhou) Ltd. (1)
No 1 Tong Sheng Road, Suzhou Industrial Park, Suzhou, 215126, China
Tel.: (86) 51262627086
LED Backlight Mfr
N.A.I.C.S.: 334413

Minebea Electronics & Hi-Tech Components (Shanghai) Ltd. (1)
No 8313 Hu Qing Ping Rd, Jinze Town Qingpu District, Shanghai, 201721, Qingpu, China **(100%)**
Tel.: (86) 2159290113
Web Site: https://www.minebeamitsumi.com
Sales Range: $400-449.9 Million
Emp.: 1,960
Mfr of Miniature Ball Bearings & Fan Motors
N.A.I.C.S.: 332991

Plant (Domestic):

Minebea Electronics & Hi-Tech Components (Shanghai) Ltd., - Shanghai Plant (2)
No 8313 Hu Qing Ping Rd, Jinze Town Qingpu District, Shanghai, 201721, China
Tel.: (86) 2159290113
Web Site: http://www.minebea.co.jp
Sales Range: $350-399.9 Million
Emp.: 1,960
Ball Bearing Mfr
N.A.I.C.S.: 332991

Subsidiary (Domestic):

Minebea Electronics & Hi-Tech Components (Shanghai) Ltd., - Xicen Plant (2)
No 5202 Lian Xi Rd, Jinze Town Qingpu District, Shanghai, 201721, China
Tel.: (86) 2159293680
Web Site: https://www.minebeamitsumi.com
Sales Range: $700-749.9 Million
Fan Motor & Measuring Component Mfr
N.A.I.C.S.: 334515

Minebea Electronics Motor (Malaysia) Sdn. Bhd. (1)
Lot 12 Jalan PKNK Utama Kawasan Perindustrian Sungai Petani, 08000, Sungai Petani, Kedah Darul Aman, Malaysia
Tel.: (60) 44411212
Web Site: https://www.minebeamitsumi.com
Emp.: 900
Electric Motor Mfr & Distr
N.A.I.C.S.: 335312
Yew Liang Khaw *(Sr Mgr-Mktg)*

Minebea Electronics Motor (Zhuhai) Co., Ltd. (1)
12 Pingdong 3rd Road Nanping Technology Park, Xiangzhou, Zhuhai, 519060, Guangdong, China
Tel.: (86) 7562511616
Web Site: https://www.minebeamitsumi.com
Sales Range: $1-4.9 Billion
Emp.: 6,106
Electric Motor Mfr
N.A.I.C.S.: 335312

Minebea Intec Aachen GmbH & Co. KG (1)
Am Gut Wolf 11, 52070, Aachen, Germany
Tel.: (49) 24118270
Industrial Weighing Product Mfr & Distr
N.A.I.C.S.: 334519

Minebea Intec Austria GmbH (1)
Leopold-Bohm-Strasse 12, 1030, Vienna, Austria
Tel.: (43) 166261160
Industrial Weighing Product Mfr & Distr
N.A.I.C.S.: 334519

Minebea Intec Belgium BVBA (1)
Z 3 Doornveld 33, 1731, Zellik, Belgium
Tel.: (32) 27560670
Industrial Weighing Product Mfr & Distr
N.A.I.C.S.: 334519

Minebea Intec Bovenden GmbH & Co. KG (1)
Leinetal 2, 37120, Bovenden, Germany
Tel.: (49) 551309830
Industrial Weighing Product Mfr & Distr
N.A.I.C.S.: 334519

Minebea Intec France S.A.S. (1)
283 Avenue du bois de la Pie ZI Paris Nord II CDG, 95941, Roissy-en-France, France
Tel.: (33) 148632046
Industrial Weighing Product Mfr & Distr
N.A.I.C.S.: 334519

Minebea Intec GmbH (1)
Meiendorfer Strasse 205 A, 22145, Hamburg, Germany
Tel.: (49) 4067960303
Web Site: http://www.minebea-intec.com
Industrial Weighing Product Mfr & Distr
N.A.I.C.S.: 334519
Jorg Hoffmann *(Mng Dir)*

Minebea Intec India Pvt. Ltd. (1)
No 26 D 2nd Phase, Peenya KIADB Industrial Area, Bengaluru, 560 058, India
Tel.: (91) 8067200200
Industrial Weighing Product Mfr & Distr
N.A.I.C.S.: 333998

Minebea Intec Industrial Weighing Equipment (Beijing) Co., Ltd. (1)
B411 Juhong Building No 9 Anqing Ave Tianzhu Airport Zone B, Shunyi District, Beijing, 101300, China
Tel.: (86) 4006699933
Industrial Weighing Product Mfr & Distr
N.A.I.C.S.: 333998

Minebea Intec Italy S.r.l. (1)
Via Alcide De Gasperi 20, 20834, Nova Milanese, MB, Italy
Tel.: (39) 036236141
Industrial Weighing Product Mfr & Distr
N.A.I.C.S.: 334519

Minebea Intec Netherlands B.V. (1)
Herikerbergweg 238, 1101 CM, Amsterdam, Netherlands
Tel.: (31) 306025030
Industrial Weighing Product Mfr & Distr
N.A.I.C.S.: 334519

Minebea Intec Poland Sp. z o.o. (1)
ul Wrzesinska 70, 62-025, Kostrzyn, Poland
Tel.: (48) 616560298

Industrial Weighing Product Mfr & Distr
N.A.I.C.S.: 334519

Minebea Intec Russia (1)
Obvodny canal emb 28, 192019, Saint Petersburg, Russia
Tel.: (7) 8126556444
Industrial Weighing Product Mfr & Distr
N.A.I.C.S.: 334519

Minebea Intec Spain S.L. (1)
C/Musgo 2 Edificio Europa II, 28023, Madrid, Spain
Tel.: (34) 915999440
Industrial Weighing Product Mfr & Distr
N.A.I.C.S.: 334519

Minebea Intec Switzerland AG (1)
Moosmattstrasse 36, 8953, Dietikon, Switzerland
Tel.: (41) 447465000
Industrial Weighing Product Mfr & Distr
N.A.I.C.S.: 334519

Minebea Intec UK Ltd. (1)
2670 Kings Court The Crescent Birmingham Business Park, Birmingham, B37 7YE, United Kingdom
Tel.: (44) 1217793131
Industrial Weighing Product Mfr & Distr
N.A.I.C.S.: 333998

Minebea Intec USA, Inc. (1)
1180 Lincoln Ave, Holbrook, NY 11741
Industrial Weighing Product Mfr & Distr
N.A.I.C.S.: 333998

Minebea Mitsumi Inc. - Fujisawa Plant (1)
1-1-1 Katase, Fujisawa, 251-8531, Kanagawa, Japan
Tel.: (81) 466 23 2131
Web Site: http://www.minebeamitsumi.com
Computer Peripheral Equipment Mfr
N.A.I.C.S.: 334419

Minebea Power Semiconductor Device, Inc (1)
5-2-2 Omikacho, Hitachi, 319-1221, Ibaraki, Japan
Tel.: (81) 294220330
Web Site: http://www.hitachi-power-semiconductor-device.co.jp
Emp.: 1,005
Semiconductor Component Mfr & Distr
N.A.I.C.S.: 334413
Masahiko Suzuki *(Pres)*

Minebea Precision Co., Ltd. (1)
4106-73 Oaza Miyoda Miyoda-cho, Kita-Saku-gun, Nagano, 389-0293, Japan
Tel.: (81) 425559111
Web Site: http://www.minebeaprecision.com
Aircraft Part Mfr
N.A.I.C.S.: 336413

Minebea Slovakia s.r.o. (1)
K Ietisku 1637, 040 17, Kosice, Slovakia
Tel.: (421) 557278111
Electronic Motor & Parts Mfr
N.A.I.C.S.: 336320
Jorg Hoffmann *(Mng Dir)*

Minebea Technologies Taiwan Co., Ltd. (1)
8F 28 Ching-Cheng Street Tong Tai Business Building, Taipei, 105, Taiwan
Tel.: (886) 227182363
Web Site: http://www.minebea.co.jp
Industrial Electronic Device Mfr & Distr
N.A.I.C.S.: 333248

Minebea Thai Limited (1)
1 Moo 7 Phaholyothin Road Km 51 Tambol Chiang Rak Noi, Amphoe, Bangpa-in, 13180, Ayutthaya, Thailand **(100%)**
Tel.: (66) 35361439
Web Site: http://www.minebea.co.th
Sales Range: $1-4.9 Billion
Emp.: 10,000
Mfr of Ball Bearings, Spherical Bearings, Keyboards, Rotary Components, Airmovers, Power Electronics & Audio Components
N.A.I.C.S.: 332991

Minebea Trading (Shanghai) Ltd. (1)
Room 303 K Wah Centre 1010 Middle Huai Hai Road, Xuhui District, Shanghai, 200031, China
Tel.: (86) 2154050707
Electronic Devices & Bearings Distr

N.A.I.C.S.: 423690

MinebeaMitsumi Technical Service (Suzhou) Ltd. (1)
1/F 11/F 12/F Kang Zhen Tower No 18 Lou Yang Road, Suzhou Industrial Park, Suzhou, 215126, China
Tel.: (86) 51269833793
Electronic Device Mfr & Retailer
N.A.I.C.S.: 334419

MinebeaMitsumi Technology Center Europe GmbH (1)
Minebea-Weg 1, 78052, Villingen-Schwenningen, Germany
Tel.: (49) 77219970
Motor Mfr
N.A.I.C.S.: 335312

Mitsumi (Shanghai) Electric Co., Ltd. (1)
Room 303 K Wah Centre 1010 Middle Huai Hai Road, Xuhui District, Shanghai, 200031, China
Tel.: (86) 2154050707
Electronic Device Mfr & Retailer
N.A.I.C.S.: 334419

Mitsumi Co., Ltd. (1)
Rm 1010-11 10/F Mira Place Tower A 132 Nathan Road, Tsim Sha Tsui, Kowloon, China (Hong Kong)
Tel.: (852) 23330163
Automotive Electrical Equipment Mfr & Distr
N.A.I.C.S.: 336320

Mitsumi Electric Co., Ltd. (1)
2-11-2 Tsurumaki, Tama, 206-8567, Tokyo, Japan
Tel.: (81) 42 310 5333
Web Site: https://www.mitsumi.co.jp
Emp.: 2,319
Integrated Electronics System Components, Tuners, Magnetic Heads, Capacitors, Coils & Switches Mfr
N.A.I.C.S.: 334310
Shigeru Moribe *(Chm)*

Subsidiary (Non-US):

Cebu Mitsumi, Inc. (2)
MRI Special Economiczone, Sabang Danao City, Cebu, 6004, Philippines
Tel.: (63) 324170001
Electronic Components Mfr
N.A.I.C.S.: 334419

Mitsumi (Thailand) Co., Ltd. (2)
10 Moo 3 Tambol Nong-Chark, Amphoe Ban-Bung, 20170, Chon Buri, Thailand
Tel.: (66) 38485000
Web Site: http://www.mitsumi.co.jp
Electric Equipment Mfr
N.A.I.C.S.: 334419

Mitsumi Automotive de Mexico, S.A. de C.V. (2)
Av Circuito Interior No 160 Parque Industrial, Millennium Zona Industrial del Potosi, 78395, Mexico, San Luis Potosi, Mexico
Tel.: (52) 4441440410
Electronic Components Distr
N.A.I.C.S.: 423690

Subsidiary (Domestic):

Mitsumi Electric Co., Ltd. - Akita Business Division (2)
95-2 Kamitsutsumishiki, Iitagawaiizuka, Katagami, 018-1504, Akita, Japan
Tel.: (81) 188777333
Electronic Components Mfr
N.A.I.C.S.: 334419

Mitsumi Electric Co., Ltd. - Atsugi Division (2)
1601 Sakai, Atsugi, 243-8533, Kanagawa, Japan
Tel.: (81) 462303333
Semiconductor Mfr
N.A.I.C.S.: 334413

Mitsumi Electric Co., Ltd. - Chitose Business Division (2)
1007-39 Izumisawa, Chitose, 066-8533, Hokkaido, Japan
Tel.: (81) 123283333
Electronic Components Mfr
N.A.I.C.S.: 334419

MINEBEA MITSUMI INC.

Minebea Mitsumi Inc.—(Continued)

Mitsumi Electric Co., Ltd. - Kyushu Business Division (2)
1049 Tateiwa, Iizuka, 820-8533, Fukuoka, Japan
Tel.: (81) 948229333
Electronic Components Mfr
N.A.I.C.S.: 334419

Division (Domestic):

Mitsumi Electric Co., Ltd. - Yamagata Business Division (2)
1-1059-5 Tachiyagawa, Yamagata, 990-2251, Japan
Tel.: (81) 236864113
Web Site: http://www.mitsumi.co.jp
Data Processing Services
N.A.I.C.S.: 518210

Subsidiary (Non-US):

Mitsumi Philippines, Inc. (2)
Luzon Avenue Phase 1, The Freeport Area of Bataan Mariveles, Bataan, 2106, Philippines
Tel.: (63) 479354011
Web Site: http://www.mitsumi.co.jp
Semiconductor Mfr
N.A.I.C.S.: 334413

Mitsumi Technology (M.) Sdn.Bhd. (2)
Batu 3 3/4 Parit Bilal, Batu Pahat, 83000, Johor, Malaysia
Tel.: (60) 74310111
Web Site: http://www.mitsumi.co.jp
Electrical Machinery Mfr
N.A.I.C.S.: 335999

Subsidiary (US):

NMB Technologies Corporation (2)
40000 Grand River Ave Technology Ctr Ste 200, Novi, MI 48375
Tel.: (248) 426-8448
Semiconductor Mfr
N.A.I.C.S.: 334413

Subsidiary (Non-US):

QINGDAO MITSUMI ELECTRONICS CO., LTD. (2)
No 10 Hongye Road Qingdao West Coast Comprehensive Bonded Zone, Qingdao Area China Pilot Free Trade Zone, Qingdao, 266426, Shandong, China
Tel.: (86) 53286897333
Web Site: http://www.mitsumi.co.jp
Electronic Components Distr
N.A.I.C.S.: 423690

Taiwan Mitsumi Co., Ltd. (2)
No 80 Chiang Shan Road, Taliao District, Kaohsiung, 83141, Taiwan
Tel.: (886) 77023911
Web Site: http://www.mitsumi.co.jp
Electronic Components Distr
N.A.I.C.S.: 423690

Tianjin Mitsumi Electric Co., Ltd. (2)
No 202 Weiguo Road, Dongli District, Tianjin, 300163, China
Tel.: (86) 2224371221
Web Site: http://www.mitsumi.co.jp
Electronic Components Mfr
N.A.I.C.S.: 334419

WUJIANG MITSUMI ELECTRONICS CO., LTD. (2)
No 969 Yunli Road Wujiang Economic and Technological Development Zone, Jiangsu, 215200, China
Tel.: (86) 51263401333
Web Site: http://www.mitsumi.co.jp
Electronic Components Distr
N.A.I.C.S.: 423690

Zhuhai Mitsumi Electric Co., Ltd. (2)
No 3043 Mingzhu South Road, Qianshan Xiangzhou District, Zhuhai, 519070, Guangdong, China
Tel.: (86) 7568613251
Web Site: http://www.mitsumi.co.jp
Electronic Components Mfr
N.A.I.C.S.: 334419

Myonic Holding GmbH (1)
Steinbeisstrasse 4, 88299, Leutkirch, Germany
Tel.: (49) 75619780
Web Site: https://www.minebeamitsumi.com
Emp.: 511
Ball Bearing Mfr & Distr
N.A.I.C.S.: 332991

Subsidiary (Non-US):

Myonic s.r.o. (2)
1 maje 2635, 756 61, Roznov pod Radhostem, Czech Republic
Tel.: (420) 57 651 1811
Web Site: http://www.myonic.com
Emp.: 190
Precision Ball Bearings Mfr & Distr
N.A.I.C.S.: 332991
Pavel Cibulec *(Mng Dir)*

Subsidiary (Domestic):

myonic GmbH (2)
Steinbeisstrasse 4, 88299, Leutkirch, Germany
Tel.: (49) 7 561 9780
Web Site: https://www.myonic.com
Sales Range: $100-124.9 Million
Emp.: 100
Miniature Ball Bearings
N.A.I.C.S.: 332991
Bernhard Bock *(Pres)*

Subsidiary (Non-US):

myonic Ltd. (2)
10 Warren Yard, Wolverton Mill, Milton Keynes, MK12 5NW, United Kingdom
Tel.: (44) 1908227123
Web Site: http://www.myonic.com
Sales Range: $25-49.9 Million
Emp.: 3
Miniature Ball Bearings Mfr
N.A.I.C.S.: 332991
David Griffiths *(Mng Dir)*

NMB (USA) Inc. (1)
9730 Independence Ave, Chatsworth, CA 91311-4323 (100%)
Tel.: (818) 341-3355
Web Site: http://www.nmbusa.com
Sales Range: $50-74.9 Million
Emp.: 200
Holding Company for North American Operations
N.A.I.C.S.: 332991

Joint Venture (Domestic):

C&A Tool Engineering, Inc. (2)
4100 N US 33, Churubusco, IN 46723 (51%)
Tel.: (260) 693-2167
Web Site: https://www.catool.com
Emp.: 650
Diamond Dies & Metalworking
N.A.I.C.S.: 333514
Jeff Herron *(Mgr-Ops)*

Subsidiary (Domestic):

NMB Corporation (2)
9730 Independence Ave, Chatsworth, CA 91311 (100%)
Tel.: (818) 341-3355
Web Site: http://www.nmbusa.com
Sales Range: $100-124.9 Million
Mfr & Distributor of Bearings, Motors, Other Electronic Devices & Machinery Components
N.A.I.C.S.: 332991

NMB Technologies Corporation (2)
39830 Grand River Ave Ste B-1, Novi, MI 48375-2140
Tel.: (248) 919-2250
Web Site: http://nmbtc.com
Sales Range: $150-199.9 Million
Emp.: 300
Ball Bearing Distr
N.A.I.C.S.: 423840
Richard LaPlace *(Pres)*

Division (Domestic):

NMB Technologies Corporation - Astro Division (3)
155 Lexington Dr, Laconia, NH 03246
Tel.: (603) 524-0004
Web Site: http://www.nhbb.com
Emp.: 450
Sleeve & Spherical Bearing Mfr
N.A.I.C.S.: 332991

NMB Technologies Corporation - HiTech Division (3)
175 Jaffrey Rd, Peterborough, NH 03458
Tel.: (603) 924-4100
Web Site: http://www.nhbb.com
Air Frame Ball Bearing Mfr
N.A.I.C.S.: 332991

NMB Technologies Corporation - Myonic USA Division (3)
9730 Independence Ave, Chatsworth, CA 91311
Tel.: (818) 341-3355
Web Site: http://www.nmb.com
Ball Bearing Mfr
N.A.I.C.S.: 332991

Subsidiary (Domestic):

New Hampshire Ball Bearings, Inc. (2)
175 Jaffrey Rd, Peterborough, NH 03458-1767
Tel.: (603) 924-4100
Web Site: http://www.nhbb.com
Sales Range: $100-124.9 Million
Emp.: 1,500
Precision Bearings & Bearing Products Mfr
N.A.I.C.S.: 332991

Division (Domestic):

New Hampshire Ball Bearings High Tech Div (3)
175 Jaffrey Rd, Peterborough, NH 03458-1767 (100%)
Tel.: (603) 924-4100
Web Site: http://www.nhbb.com
Sales Range: $75-99.9 Million
Domestic & Imported Precision Miniature Rod Ends & Sphericals, Journals & Bushings, Instrument Ball Bearings, Link Assemblies, Lined Parts & Composites
N.A.I.C.S.: 332991

Plant (Domestic):

New Hampshire Ball Bearings, Inc. - Chatsworth Plant (3)
9700 Independence Ave, Chatsworth, CA 91311
Tel.: (818) 407-9300
Web Site: http://www.nhbb.com
Sales Range: $75-99.9 Million
Emp.: 317
Ball Bearing Mfr
N.A.I.C.S.: 332991

New Hampshire Ball Bearings, Inc. - Laconia Plant (3)
155 Lexington Dr, Laconia, NH 03246
Tel.: (603) 524-0004
Web Site: http://www.minebea.com
Sales Range: $75-99.9 Million
Emp.: 411
Rod End & Spherical Bearing Mfr
N.A.I.C.S.: 332991

New Hampshire Ball Bearings, Inc. - Peterborough Plant (3)
175 Jaffrey Rd, Peterborough, NH 03458-1709
Tel.: (603) 924-4100
Web Site: http://www.nhbb.com
Emp.: 700
Aerospace Bearings Mfr
N.A.I.C.S.: 332991

NMB Italia S.r.l. (1)
Via A Grandi 39/41, Mazzo di Rho, 20017, Milan, Italy
Tel.: (39) 02939711
Web Site: http://www.nmbitalia.it
Sales Range: $25-49.9 Million
Emp.: 26
Sales of Ball Bearings, Spherical Bearings, Keyboards, Rotary Components, Airmovers, Power Electronics & Audio Components
N.A.I.C.S.: 425120

NMB Korea Co., Ltd. (1)
12F 29 Hwangsaeul-ro 258beon-gil, Bundang-gu, Seongnam, 13595, Gyeonggi, Korea (South) (100%)
Tel.: (82) 25574467
Web Site: http://www.nmbkorea.co.kr
Sales Range: $25-49.9 Million
Emp.: 32

INTERNATIONAL PUBLIC

Sales of Ball Bearings, Spherical Bearings, Keyboards, Rotary Components, Airmovers, Power Electronics & Audio Components
N.A.I.C.S.: 423840

NMB Minebea S.a.r.l. (1)
5 Avenue des Bosquets Les Ponts de Baillet, 95560, Baillet-en-France, France
Tel.: (33) 1 34083939
Web Site: http://www.nmb-minebea.fr
Keyboard Mfr
N.A.I.C.S.: 334118

NMB Precision Inc. (1)
1745 Bonhill Rd., Unit 1, East Unit #5, Mississauga, L5T 1C1, ON, Canada (100%)
Tel.: (905) 670-8138
Sales Range: $50-74.9 Million
Emp.: 6
Sale of Minebea Products
N.A.I.C.S.: 423840

NMB Sales Co., Ltd. (1)
1-8-15 Iwamotocho Itopia Iwamotocho 1-chome Building, Chiyoda-ku, Tokyo, 101-0032, Japan (100%)
Tel.: (81) 35 835 0371
Web Site: https://www.nmbhanbai.com
Electrical Equipment Parts Distr
N.A.I.C.S.: 423830
Kotobuki Sakamaki *(Pres & CEO)*

NMB Singapore Ltd. (1)
1 Chai Chee Avenue, Jurong Industrial Estate, Singapore, 469059, Singapore
Tel.: (65) 62411033
Web Site: http://www.minebea.co.jp
Bearing Mfr
N.A.I.C.S.: 332991

NMB Singapore Ltd. (1)
1 Chai Chee Avenue, Singapore, 469059, Singapore (100%)
Tel.: (65) 62411033
Sales Range: $300-349.9 Million
Emp.: 668
Sales of Ball Bearings, Spherical Bearings, Keyboards, Rotary Components, Airmovers, Power Electronics & Audio Components
N.A.I.C.S.: 423840

Holding (Non-US):

Minebea Technologies Pte. Ltd.-Hong Kong Branch (2)
1010-11, 10/F Mira Place Tower A 132 Nathan Road, Tsim Sha Tsui, Kowloon, China (Hong Kong) (100%)
Tel.: (852) 3 423 2300
Web Site: http://www.minebea.com.cn
Sales Range: $25-49.9 Million
Emp.: 50
Sales of Ball Bearings, Spherical Bearings, Keyboards, Rotary Components, Airmovers, Power Electronics & Audio Components
N.A.I.C.S.: 423840
Koichi Tsuta *(Gen Mgr)*

Minebea Technologies Taiwan Co., Ltd. Taipei Branch (2)
8F 28 Ching-Cheng Street Tong Tai Business Building, Taipei, 105, Taiwan (100%)
Tel.: (886) 227182363
Web Site: http://www.minebea.co.jp
Sales Range: $25-49.9 Million
Emp.: 38
Sales of Ball Bearings, Spherical Bearings, Keyboards, Rotary Components, Airmovers, Power Electronics & Audio Components
N.A.I.C.S.: 423840

NMB Thai Limited (1)
18 Moo 3 Asia Road Km Tambol Thanoo, Amphoe Uthai, Ayutthaya, 13210, Thailand
Tel.: (66) 35335309
Web Site: http://www.minebea.co.th
Sales Range: $400-449.9 Million
Emp.: 2,360
Mfr of Bearings
N.A.I.C.S.: 332991

NMB-Minebea India Private Ltd. (1)
Level-6 Regus JMD Regent Square M G Road, Gurgaon, 122002, Haryana, India
Tel.: (91) 1244883776
Electronic Device Mfr & Retailer
N.A.I.C.S.: 334419

NMB-Minebea Thai Ltd. (1)
19 th Floor Wave Place Building 55 Wire-

less Rd Lumpinee, Pathumwan, Bangkok, 10330, Thailand
Tel.: (66) 2253 4897
Web Site: http://www.minebea.co.th
Sales Range: $25-49.9 Million
Emp.: 50
Industrial Electronic Component Mfr
N.A.I.C.S.: 334419

Plant (Domestic):

Minebea Co., Ltd. - Bang Pa-in Plant (2)
1 Moo 7 Phaholyothin Road Km 51 Tambol Chiang Rak-Noi, Amphoe Bang Pa-in, Ayutthaya, 13180, Thailand
Tel.: (66) 35361439
Ball Bearing & Motor Mfr
N.A.I.C.S.: 332991

NMB-Minebea UK Ltd. (1)
Doddington Road, Sadler Road, Lincoln, LN6 3RA, Lincolnshire, United Kingdom (100%)
Tel.: (44) 1522500933
Web Site: https://www.minebeamitsumi.com
Sales Range: $50-74.9 Million
Emp.: 250
Mfr of Rod-End, Spherical, Instrument & Miniature Ball Bearings
N.A.I.C.S.: 332991
Mark Ftansfield (Mng Dir)

NMB-Minebea de Mexico, S. de R.L. de C.V. (1)
Av Armando Birlain 2001 Torre 1 Piso 2 Oficina 2A, 76090, Queretaro, Mexico
Tel.: (52) 4423371062
Electronic Device Mfr & Retailer
N.A.I.C.S.: 334419

NMB-Minebea do Brasil Importacao e Comercio de Componentes de Precisao Ltda. (1)
Rua Coronel Oscar Porto n 736 5 andar sala 53, Bairro Paraiso, Sao Paulo, 04003-003, Brazil
Tel.: (55) 1139390882
Electronic Device Mfr & Retailer
N.A.I.C.S.: 334419

NMB-Minebea-GmbH (1)
Siemensstrasse 30, PO Box 63225, 63225, Langen, Germany (100%)
Tel.: (49) 61039130
Web Site: http://www.minebeamitsumi.eu
Sales Range: $25-49.9 Million
Emp.: 130
Sales of Ball Bearings, Spherical Bearings, Keyboards, Rotary Components, Airmovers, Power Electronics & Audio Components
N.A.I.C.S.: 332991
Jens Richter (Mng Dir)

Pelmac Thai Limited (1)
1 Moo 7 Phaholyothin Rd, Km 51 Tambol Chiang Rak Noi Am, Bangpa-in, 13180, Ayutthaya, Thailand
Tel.: (66) 35361152
Sales Range: $200-249.9 Million
Emp.: 1,000
Mfr of Bearings
N.A.I.C.S.: 332991

Precision-Motors-Deutsche-Minebea GmbH (1)
(100%)
Tel.: (49) 77219970
Web Site: http://www.pmdm.de
Sales Range: $100-124.9 Million
Emp.: 260
Mfr of Spindle Motors
N.A.I.C.S.: 333248
Jorg Hoffmann (Mng Dir)

Sanwa Seisakusyo Ltd. (1)
Main office / factory 19 Sanjomachi, Nishiku, Saitama, 331-0056, Japan
Tel.: (81) 486207272
Web Site: https://www.sanwa-ss.com
Machine Tools Mfr
N.A.I.C.S.: 333517
Tadahiko Murakami (Pres)

U-SHIN LTD. (1)
3-9-6 Mita, Minato-ku, Tokyo, 108-8330, Japan (76.16%)
Tel.: (81) 36 758 6833
Web Site: http://www.u-shin-ltd.com

Sales Range: $1-4.9 Billion
Emp.: 7,656
Electronics Mfr
N.A.I.C.S.: 334419
Kizashi Masumori (Mng Exec Officer)

Subsidiary (Non-US):

ORTECH MALAYSIA SDN. BHD. (2)
No 5 7 Jalan Selat Selatan 21 Sobena Jaya, Pandamaran, 42000, Port Klang, Selangor Darul Ehsan, Malaysia
Tel.: (60) 331684835
Web Site: https://www.u-shin-ltd.com
Automotive Parts Mfr & Distr
N.A.I.C.S.: 336390
Kimihiko Sato (Mng Dir)

Subsidiary (Domestic):

Tokyo Sokuteikizai Co., Ltd. (2)
8-3-4 Shin-machi, Ome, 198-0024, Tokyo, Japan
Tel.: (81) 42 831 2321
Web Site: https://www.tosoku-inc.co.jp
Automobile Parts Mfr
N.A.I.C.S.: 336390
Daisuke Shirai (Pres)

Subsidiary (Non-US):

U-SHIN (HONG KONG) LIMITED (2)
1010-11 10/F Mira Place Tower A 132 Nathan Road, Tsim Sha Tsui, Kowloon, China (Hong Kong)
Tel.: (852) 23170318
Web Site: https://www.u-shin-ltd.com
Automobile Parts Distr
N.A.I.C.S.: 423120
Hong Wei Bao (Exec Dir)

U-SHIN (THAILAND) CO., LTD. (2)
WHA Eastern Seaboard Industrial Estate 500/24 Moo 3 Tambol Tasit, Amphur Pluakdaeng, Rayong, 21140, Thailand
Tel.: (66) 33659100
Web Site: https://www.u-shin-ltd.com
Emp.: 500
Automobile Parts Mfr
N.A.I.C.S.: 336390

Subsidiary (US):

U-SHIN AMERICA INC. (2)
40000 Grand River Ave Ste 105, Novi, MI 48375
Tel.: (248) 449-3155
Automobile Parts Distr
N.A.I.C.S.: 423120
Satoru Tsukui (VP & Gen Mgr)

Subsidiary (Non-US):

U-SHIN AUTOPARTS MEXICO,S.A. DE C.V. (2)
Calle Santiago 387 Centro Industrial De, 36835, Irapuato, 36835, Guanajuato, Mexico
Tel.: (52) 14625003000
Web Site: https://www.u-shin-ltd.com
Automobile Parts Mfr
N.A.I.C.S.: 336390
Satoru Tsukui (Mng Dir)

U-SHIN DEUTSCHLAND GMBH (2)
Waldstrasse 2, 85253, Erdweg, Germany
Tel.: (49) 813885220
Automobile Parts Mfr
N.A.I.C.S.: 336390
Shinichi Ueda (Co-Mng Dir)

U-SHIN EUROPE LTD. (2)
Batthyany puszta iparterulet 2, 2870, Kisber, Komarom-Esztergom, Hungary
Tel.: (36) 3 455 2520
Web Site: http://www.ushin.hu
Automobile Parts Mfr
N.A.I.C.S.: 336390
Tatsuya Mori (Co-Mng Dir)

U-SHIN INDIA PRIVATE LIMITED (2)
Unit No T2-1-16FL T2-2-16FL AIPL Business club Sector-62, Gurgaon, 122 102, Haryana, India
Tel.: (91) 1244043250
Web Site: https://www.u-shin-ltd.com
Emp.: 10
Automobile Parts Mfr
N.A.I.C.S.: 336390

Shusuke Tomita (Mng Dir)

U-SHIN INTERNATIONAL TRADING (SHANGHAI) LTD (2)
Room 1406 ShanghaiMart No 2299 YanAn Road West, Chang Ning, Shanghai, 200336, China
Tel.: (86) 2162368885
Web Site: https://www.u-shin-ltd.com
Automotive Part Whslr
N.A.I.C.S.: 423120
Hong Wei Bao (Exec Dir)

U-SHIN MANUFACTURING (SUZHOU) CO., LTD. (2)
No 12 Jingda Road Weiting Industrial Zone Suzhou Industrial Park, Suzhou, 215121, Jiangsu Province, China
Tel.: (86) 512 6275 2018
Automobile Parts Mfr
N.A.I.C.S.: 336390
Hong Wei Bao (Exec Dir)

U-SHIN MANUFACTURING (ZHONGSHAN) CO., LTD. (2)
No 10 Mao Nan Road Torch Development Zone, Zhongshan, 528437, Guangdong, China
Tel.: (86) 760 8533 6668
Web Site: http://www.u-shin-ltd.com
Automotive & Industrial Machinery Parts Mfr
N.A.I.C.S.: 336390

U-Shin Access Systems (Wuxi) CO., LTD. (2)
B11 Factory Building Xixie Road Wuxi High-Tech, Industrial Development Zone, Wuxi, 214112, Jiangsu, China
Tel.: (86) 106 800 3000
Automobile Parts Mfr
N.A.I.C.S.: 336390

U-Shin Deutschland Grundvermogen GmbH (2)
Englsatter Weg 18, 70567, Stuttgart, Germany
Tel.: (49) 711 7870600
Automobile Parts Mfr
N.A.I.C.S.: 336390

U-Shin Deutschland Zugangssysteme GmbH (2)
Waldstrasse 2, 85253, Erdweg, Germany
Tel.: (49) 813885220
Automobile Parts Mfr
N.A.I.C.S.: 336390

U-Shin France S.A.S. (2)
12 Rue Bernard Martel, 80100, Abbeville, France
Tel.: (33) 360329025
Web Site: https://www.minebeamitsumi.com
Automobile Parts Mfr
N.A.I.C.S.: 336390

U-Shin Holdings Europe BV (2)
Strawinskylaan 411, 1077 XX, Amsterdam, Netherlands
Tel.: (31) 205752727
Automobile Parts Mfr
N.A.I.C.S.: 336390

U-Shin Italia S.p.A. (2)
Via Torino 31, 10044, Pianezza, Italy
Tel.: (39) 0119684111
Automobile Parts Mfr
N.A.I.C.S.: 336390

U-Shin Slovakia s.r.o. (2)
K Ietuisc Budova 1329, 040 17, Kosice, Slovakia
Tel.: (421) 556133222
Web Site: https://www.u-shin.sk
Automobile Parts Distr
N.A.I.C.S.: 423120
Alexandra Suhyova (Engr-Quality)

U-Shin Spain S.L. (2)
Calle Francesc Layret No 13 Poligono Industrial Sant Armengol, Abrera, 08630, Barcelona, Spain
Tel.: (34) 931983005
Web Site: https://www.minebeamitsumi.com
Automobile Part Whslr
N.A.I.C.S.: 423120

U-Shin do Brasil Sistemas Automotivos Ltda. (2)
Estrada Velha Guarulhos Sao Miguel 4231 Jardim Araponga, Guarulhos, 07210-250,

Sao Paulo, Brazil
Tel.: (55) 112 138 31 11
Automobile Parts Mfr
N.A.I.C.S.: 336390

Subsidiary (Domestic):

U-shin Showa Ltd. (2)
17-35 Nakakahara-cho, Ibaraki, 567-0063, Osaka, Japan
Tel.: (81) 72 643 5657
Web Site: https://www.u-shin-showa.co.jp
Automobile Parts Mfr
N.A.I.C.S.: 336390
Hiroyuki Niiyama (Pres)

Subsidiary (Domestic):

U-shin Showa Ltd. - Kyoto Plant (3)
1-1 Iwanoue Yoshida Yoshikawa-cho, Kameoka-shi, Kyoto, 621-0015, Japan
Tel.: (81) 771225546
Web Site: https://www.u-shin-ltd.com
Automobile Parts Mfr
N.A.I.C.S.: 336390

Subsidiary (Domestic):

U-shin Transport Ltd. (2)
4-1-1 Tennoohama Kure-shi, Hiroshima, 737-8541, Japan
Tel.: (81) 823 30 0318
Freight Transportation Services
N.A.I.C.S.: 488510
Tsutomu Tominaga (Pres)

Subsidiary (Non-US):

YUHSHIN INDUSTRIAL CO., LTD. (2)
9F-3 No 220 Song Jiang Rd, Taipei, 10467, Taiwan
Tel.: (886) 225518490
Emp.: 10
Automobile Parts Mfr
N.A.I.C.S.: 336390
Kiyoshi Shimono (Pres)

Subsidiary (US):

YUHSHIN U.S.A. LIMITED (2)
2806 N Industrial Rd, Kirksville, MO 63501
Tel.: (660) 627-1655
Web Site: http://www.u-shin-ltd.com
Emp.: 12
Automotive Parts Mfr & Distr
N.A.I.C.S.: 336390
Kazunori Inoue (Mng Dir)

U-Shin Manufacturing (Wuxi) Co., Ltd. (1)
No 60 Gaodeng Road, Xishan Economic Technological Development Zone, Wuxi, 214110, Jiangsu, China
Tel.: (86) 51068003000
Industrial Machinery Mfr & Distr
N.A.I.C.S.: 333248

Yushshin Industrial Co., Ltd. (1)
9F-3 No 220 Song Jiang Road, Taipei, 10467, Taiwan
Tel.: (886) 225518490
Electronic Device Mfr & Retailer
N.A.I.C.S.: 334419

MINEHUB TECHNOLOGIES INC.
1030 West Georgia St Suite 918, Vancouver, V6E 2Y3, BC, Canada BC
Web Site: https://www.minehub.com
Year Founded: 2018
MHUBF—(OTCQB)
Rev.: $139,341
Assets: $1,179,753
Liabilities: $1,217,263
Net Worth: ($37,510)
Earnings: ($6,363,123)
Fiscal Year-end: 01/31/23
Mineral Exploration Services
N.A.I.C.S.: 213115
Andrea Aranguren (Pres)

MINEL KONCERN A.D.
Cara Lazara br 3, 11000, Belgrade, Serbia
Tel.: (381) 11 2631 435

MINEL KONCERN A.D.

MINEL Koncern A.D.—(Continued)
Web Site:
http://www.minelkoncern.com
Year Founded: 1948
MNHL—(BEL)
Sales Range: $1-9.9 Million
Emp.: 11
Electric Power Generation, Distribution & Transmission Services
N.A.I.C.S.: 221111
Milorad Markovic (Exec Dir)

MINEL RASTAVLJACI A.D.
Dimitrija Tucovica BB, 36300, Novi Pazar, Serbia
Tel.: (381) 20 313 866
Web Site: http://www.minel-rastavljaci.com
Year Founded: 1979
Sales Range: Less than $1 Million
Emp.: 67
Electricity Distribution & Control Equipment Mfr
N.A.I.C.S.: 335313

MINERA ALAMOS INC.
55 York Street Suite 402, Toronto, M5J 1R7, ON, Canada
Tel.: (416) 306-0990 ON
Web Site:
https://www.mineraalamos.com
Year Founded: 1934
MAI—(TSXV)
Assets: $26,096,125
Liabilities: $1,154,759
Net Worth: $24,941,365
Earnings: $4,774,605
Fiscal Year-end: 12/31/20
Metal Mining Services
N.A.I.C.S.: 212290
Chris Chadder (CFO)

Subsidiaries:

Minera Alamos de Sonora S.A. de C.V. (1)
Monterrey 190, Centro, Hermosillo, 83000, Sonora, Mexico
Tel.: (52) 662 2133864
Web Site: http://www.mineralamos.com
Mineral Mining Services
N.A.I.C.S.: 212390
Federico Alvarez (VP-Project Dev)

MINERA ANDINA DE EXPLORACIONES S.A.A.
Jr Arnaldo Alvarado Degregori No 392, Urb Pampas de Santa Teresa Monterrico Surco, Lima, Peru
Tel.: (51) 3450442
Web Site:
https://www.minandex.com.pe
Year Founded: 1996
ANDEXAC1—(LIM)
Rev.: $7,909,211
Assets: $7,197,258
Liabilities: $3,728,713
Net Worth: $3,468,545
Earnings: $3,879,578
Fiscal Year-end: 12/31/23
Mineral Mining Services
N.A.I.C.S.: 212390

MINERA FRISCO, S.A.B. DE C.V.
Av Paseo de Las Palmas No 781 Piso 7, Col Lomas De Chapultepec Iii Seccion Miguel Hidalgo, 11000, Mexico, Mexico
Tel.: (52) 21222600 MX
Web Site:
https://www.minerafrisco.com.mx
Year Founded: 2011
MFRISCO—(MEX)
Rev.: $516,036,279
Assets: $1,795,018,180
Liabilities: $1,452,663,508
Net Worth: $342,354,672
Earnings: ($44,629,217)
Emp.: 3,070
Fiscal Year-end: 12/31/23
Mineral Exploration Services
N.A.I.C.S.: 212290
Carlos Slim Helu (Pres)

Subsidiaries:

Compania San Felipe, S.A. de C.V. (1)
Km 123 Carr Mexicali-San Felipe, Baja California, Mexicali, 21850, Mexico
Tel.: (52) 5552837500
Mining Equipment Leasing Services
N.A.I.C.S.: 532412

Minera Real de Angeles, S.A. de C.V. (1)
Carretera Tepezala S/N, Aguascalientes, 20710, Mexico
Tel.: (52) 4969676000
Silver Ore Mining Services
N.A.I.C.S.: 212220

Minera San Francisco del Oro, S.A. de C.V. (1)
Domicilio Conocido, San Francisco del Oro, 33501, Chihuahua, Mexico
Tel.: (52) 628 525 0099
Zinc Ore Mining Services
N.A.I.C.S.: 212230

Minera Tayahua, S.A. de C.V. (1)
Domicilio Conocido S/n, Mazapil, 98238, Zacatecas, Mexico
Tel.: (52) 842 424 0056
Zinc Ore Mining Services
N.A.I.C.S.: 212230

MINERA IRL LIMITED
Tel.: (51) 14181230 JE
Web Site: https://www.minera-irl.com
Year Founded: 2003
DZX—(DEU)
Rev.: $36,993,000
Assets: $183,972,000
Liabilities: $121,425,000
Net Worth: $62,547,000
Earnings: ($15,999,000)
Emp.: 379
Fiscal Year-end: 12/31/22
Precious Metals Mining & Production
N.A.I.C.S.: 212290
Gerardo Perez Delgado (Chm)

MINERA VALPARAISO S.A.
Av Apoquindo 3846 piso 20, Las Condes, Santiago, Chile
Tel.: (56) 224216000 CL
Web Site: https://www.minera.cl
Year Founded: 1906
MINERA—(SGO)
Sales Range: Less than $1 Million
Eletric Power Generation Services
N.A.I.C.S.: 221111
Jorge Gabriel Larrain Bunster (Pres)

MINERACAO BURITIRAMA SA
Brigadeiro Faria Lima Avenue 15th Floor, 4300, Sao Paulo, Brazil
Tel.: (55) 11 5105 4343
Web Site: http://www.buritirama.com
Mining Services
N.A.I.C.S.: 212290
Joao Jose Oliveira de Araujo (Pres, COO & Member-Exec Bd)

MINERACAO RIO DO NORTE S.A.
Rua Rio Jari S N, Porto De Trombetas Oriximina, Para, 68 275 000, Brazil
Tel.: (55) 9335497743
Web Site: http://www.mrn.com.br
Year Founded: 1974
Emp.: 996
Prospecting, Exploration, Mining, Processing, Trading & Exporting of Bauxite
N.A.I.C.S.: 212290
Julio Cesar Ribeiro Sanna (Pres)

MINERAL & FINANCIAL INVESTMENTS LIMITED
One Nexus Way, Camana Bay, Georgetown, KY1-9005, Grand Cayman, Cayman Islands
Tel.: (345) 2072350422 Ky
Web Site:
https://mineralandfinancial.com
Year Founded: 2004
MAFL—(AIM)
Rev.: $150,215
Assets: $12,302,449
Liabilities: $407,725
Net Worth: $11,894,724
Earnings: $1,956,577
Fiscal Year-end: 06/30/23
Investment Management Service
N.A.I.C.S.: 523999
Jacques Vaillancourt (Pres & CEO)

MINERAL AND MECHANICAL JSC
No 2 - Dang Thai Than Street, Hoan Kiem, Hanoi, Vietnam
Tel.: (84) 438265106
Web Site: http://www.mimeco.vn
MIM—(HNX)
Rev.: $6,177,201
Assets: $4,963,455
Liabilities: $3,828,906
Net Worth: $1,134,549
Earnings: $275,039
Emp.: 210
Fiscal Year-end: 12/31/21
Manganese Ore Mining & Production Services
N.A.I.C.S.: 212290
Tang Nguyen Ngoc (Chm)

MINERAL COMMODITIES LIMITED
Level 2 161 Great Eastern Highway, Belmont, 6104, WA, Australia
Tel.: (61) 863738900 AU
Web Site:
https://www.mineralcommodity.com
MRC—(ASX)
Rev.: $28,571,711
Assets: $71,218,770
Liabilities: $28,328,216
Net Worth: $42,890,554
Earnings: ($10,062,526)
Emp.: 321
Fiscal Year-end: 12/31/23
Mineral Sand Development & Exploration Services
N.A.I.C.S.: 327999
Mark Victor Caruso (CEO)

Subsidiaries:

Skaland Graphite A.S. (1)
Bergsfjordveien 1668, Skaland, 9385, Tromso, Norway
Tel.: (47) 7 785 9600
Web Site: https://www.graphite.no
Flake Graphite Distr
N.A.I.C.S.: 424690

MINERAL GRINDING MILLS LIMITED
Suite-6 Second Floor Mitha Court Block 9, Karachi, Pakistan
Tel.: (92) 574815
Mineral Ore Mfr
N.A.I.C.S.: 212230

MINERAL HILL INDUSTRIES LTD.
422 Richards Street Suite 170, Vancouver, V6B 2Z4, BC, Canada
Tel.: (604) 617-6794
Web Site: https://mhi.mineralhill.com
Year Founded: 1987

INTERNATIONAL PUBLIC

MHIFF—(OTCIQ)
Rev.: $7
Assets: $181,332
Liabilities: $114,126
Net Worth: $67,206
Earnings: ($43,745)
Fiscal Year-end: 12/31/22
Mineral Exploration Services
N.A.I.C.S.: 213114
Dieter W. Peter (Pres & CEO)

MINERAL MIDRANGE S.A
Krakowiakow 50, 02-255, Warsaw, Poland
Tel.: (48) 228408500
Web Site:
https://www.mineralmidrange.com
Management Consulting Services
N.A.I.C.S.: 541618
Robert Andrzej Twarowski (Chm)

MINERAL MOUNTAIN RESOURCES LTD.
Suite 401- 1195 West Broadway, Vancouver, V6H 3X5, BC, Canada
Tel.: (604) 714-0111 BC
Web Site:
https://www.mineralmountain.com
MNRLF—(OTCQB)
Rev.: $1
Assets: $8,223,504
Liabilities: $994,165
Net Worth: $7,229,339
Earnings: ($711,829)
Fiscal Year-end: 03/31/23
Gold, Silver, Zinc, Lead & Copper Mining Services
N.A.I.C.S.: 212220
Bradley Baker (VP-Corp Dev)

MINERAL RESOURCES LIMITED
20 Walters Drive, Locked Bag 13, Canning Bridge LPO, Osborne Park, 6017, WA, Australia
Tel.: (61) 893293600 AU
Web Site:
https://www.mineralresources.com
MALRF—(OTCQX)
Rev.: $3,048,593,391
Assets: $4,484,433,451
Liabilities: $1,997,304,092
Net Worth: $2,487,129,359
Earnings: $971,299,063
Emp.: 3,268
Fiscal Year-end: 06/30/21
Mining Services
N.A.I.C.S.: 212290
Paul Brown (CEO)

Subsidiaries:

Crushing Services International Pty Ltd (1)
25 Wellard St, 6163, Bibra Lake, Western Australia, Australia
Tel.: (61) 894344422
Sales Range: $50-74.9 Million
Emp.: 40
Construction Material Mining Services
N.A.I.C.S.: 212390

Mesa Minerals Limited (1)
1 Sleat Road, Applecross, 6153, WA, Australia
Tel.: (61) 893293750
Web Site:
https://www.mesaminerals.com.au
Mineral Exploration Services
N.A.I.C.S.: 213114

Norwest Energy NL (1)
Level 2 30 Richardson Street, West Perth, 6005, WA, Australia (100%)
Tel.: (61) 892273240
Web Site: http://www.norwestenergy.com.au
Rev.: $443,222
Assets: $3,989,315
Liabilities: $477,263
Net Worth: $3,512,052
Earnings: ($341,150)

Emp.: 3
Fiscal Year-end: 06/30/2021
Hydrocarbon Resource Exploration Services
N.A.I.C.S.: 324110

PIHA Pty Ltd (1)
1 Sleat Rd, Applecross, Bibra Lake, 6153, Western Australia, Australia
Tel.: (61) 893293500
Web Site: http://www.piha.com.au
Sales Range: $25-49.9 Million
Emp.: 40
Pipeline Construction & Polyethylene Pipe Fittings Mfr
N.A.I.C.S.: 326122

MINERALBRUNNEN UBERKINGEN-TEINACH GMBH & CO.
Badstrasse 41, Bad Teinach-Zavelstein, D-75385, Calw, Germany
Tel.: (49) 70539262220
Web Site:
https://www.mineralbrunnen-kgaa.de
Year Founded: 1923
MUT3—(DEU)
Rev.: $162,600,051
Assets: $153,349,620
Liabilities: $77,613,100
Net Worth: $75,736,521
Earnings: $6,722,568
Emp.: 409
Fiscal Year-end: 12/31/23
Water & Soft Drink Bottling Services
N.A.I.C.S.: 312112

MINERALES Y PRODUCTOS DERIVADOS, S. A.
Avenida Algorta n 16, 48992, Getxo, Spain
Tel.: (34) 944255501
Web Site: https://www.minersa.com
Year Founded: 1942
MYD—(MAD)
Metal Mining Services
N.A.I.C.S.: 212290
Alberto Barrenechea Guimon *(Chm & CEO)*

MINERALOGY PTY. LTD.
Level 8 380 Queen Street, PO Box 1538, Brisbane, 4001, QLD, Australia
Tel.: (61) 738322044
Web Site:
http://www.mineralogy.com.au
Sales Range: $25-49.9 Million
Emp.: 8
Iron Ore Exploration & Mining Services
N.A.I.C.S.: 212210
Clive Mensink *(Sr Exec Officer)*

Subsidiaries:

Waratah Coal Limited (1)
Level 10 Santos House 60 Edward Street, Brisbane, 4000, QLD, Australia
Tel.: (61) 7 3303 0670
Web Site: http://www.waratahcoal.com
Coal Mining Services
N.A.I.C.S.: 212115
Clive Palmer *(Chm)*

MINERALS 260 LIMITED
Level 2 1292 Hay Street, West Perth, 6005, WA, Australia
Tel.: (61) 865566020   AU
Web Site:
https://www.minerals260.com.au
Year Founded: 2021
MI6—(ASX)
Rev.: $524,382
Assets: $11,425,772
Liabilities: $594,477
Net Worth: $10,831,295
Earnings: ($8,545,217)
Fiscal Year-end: 06/30/23
Mineral Exploration Services
N.A.I.C.S.: 212390

Curtis Abbott *(CFO)*

MINEROS SA
Cra 43 A No 14-109 Ed NovaTempo Piso 6, Medellin, Colombia
Tel.: (57) 6042665757
Web Site:
https://www.mineros.com.co
MINEROS—(COLO)
Rev.: $447,290,000
Assets: $493,757,000
Liabilities: $148,200,000
Net Worth: $345,557,000
Earnings: $17,214,000
Fiscal Year-end: 12/31/23
Mineral Exploration Services
N.A.I.C.S.: 213114
Eduardo Pacheco Cortes *(Chm)*

MINERS CONSTRUCTION CO.LTD.
440 Melville St, Saskatoon, S7J 4M2, SK, Canada
Tel.: (306) 934-4703
Web Site:
http://www.minersconstruction.com
Year Founded: 1911
Rev.: $10,259,504
Emp.: 30
General Contracting & Project Management Services
N.A.I.C.S.: 236220

MINERVA BUNKERING
10 Akti Kondili, Piraeus, 185 45, Athens, Greece
Tel.: (30) 210 458 6200   MH
Web Site: http://www.ampni.com
Rev.: $4,076,219,000
Assets: $1,600,933,000
Liabilities: $1,011,342,000
Net Worth: $589,591,000
Earnings: $51,871,000
Emp.: 991
Fiscal Year-end: 12/31/16
Marine Fuel Distr
N.A.I.C.S.: 457210
Tyler Baron *(CEO)*

Subsidiaries:

AMPN USA LLC (1)
299 Park Ave 2nd Fl, New York, NY 10171-0000
Tel.: (646) 369-6164
Petroleum Product Distr
N.A.I.C.S.: 424720

Aegean (Fujairah) Bunkering SA (1)
Fujairah, PO Box 2688, Fujairah, Dubai, United Arab Emirates
Tel.: (971) 92281600
Web Site: http://www.ampni.com
Sales Range: $50-74.9 Million
Emp.: 10
Suppliers of Refined Maritime Petroleum Products
N.A.I.C.S.: 424710
Nick Kachrilas *(Mng Dir & Station Mgr)*

Aegean Ace Maritime Company (1)
42 Hatzikyriakou Avenue, Piraeus, Athens, 18538, Greece
Tel.: (30) 210 458 6200
Refined Marine Fuel Distr
N.A.I.C.S.: 424720

Aegean Agency (Gibraltar) Limited (1)
Suite 2 1st Floor Watergardens 4, Gibraltar, GX111AA, Gibraltar
Tel.: (350) 200 50246
Web Site: http://www.ampni.com
Emp.: 4
Petroleum Product Distr
N.A.I.C.S.: 424720
Keith Nuza *(Mgr-Ops)*

Aegean Bunkering (C Verde) LDA (1)
Edificio Enacol Largo John Miller, Sao Vicente, 1359, Mindelo, Cape Verde
Tel.: (238) 231 93 20

Petroleum Product Distr
N.A.I.C.S.: 424720

Aegean Bunkering (Ghana) Ltd (1)
Community One, PO Box 1087, Tema, Ghana
Tel.: (233) 22214666
Web Site: http://www.ampni.com
Sales Range: $50-74.9 Million
Emp.: 6
Suppliers of Refined Maritime Petroleum Products
N.A.I.C.S.: 424710

Aegean Bunkering (Gibraltar) Limited (1)
Suite 2 Block 4 Water Gardens, Gibraltar, 35, Gibraltar
Tel.: (350) 200 502 45
Web Site: http://www.ampni.com
Emp.: 20
Petroleum Product Distr
N.A.I.C.S.: 424710
Spyros Maltezos *(Office Mgr)*

Aegean Bunkering (Hong Kong) Limited (1)
Unit 9/25th Floor Tower 2 Lipo Centre No 89 Queensway Str, Admiralty, Hong Kong, China (Hong Kong)
Tel.: (852) 2 801 7291
Web Site: http://www.ampni.com
Sales Range: $50-74.9 Million
Emp.: 1
Petroleum Product Distr
N.A.I.C.S.: 424720

Aegean Bunkering (Jam) Ltd (1)
Harbour Head Pen Rock Fort, Kingston, 2, Jamaica
Tel.: (876) 9387752
Web Site: http://www.ampni.com
Sales Range: $50-74.9 Million
Emp.: 8
Suppliers of Refined Maritime Petroleum Products
N.A.I.C.S.: 424710
Georgios Kontogeorgis *(Gen Mgr)*

Aegean Bunkering (Singapore) Pte Ltd. (1)
22 Jalan Kilang No 06-0 Mova Bldg, Singapore, 159419, Singapore
Tel.: (65) 10100
Web Site: http://www.ampni.com
Sales Range: $25-49.9 Million
Emp.: 20
Suppliers of Refined Maritime Petroleum Products
N.A.I.C.S.: 424710
Dennis Ho *(Gen Mgr)*

Aegean Bunkering (Trinidad) Ltd. (1)
3 French Street Woodbrook, Port of Spain, Trinidad & Tobago
Tel.: (868) 627 3005
Web Site: http://www.ampni.com
Petroleum Product Distr
N.A.I.C.S.: 424720

Aegean Marine Petroleum LLC (1)
Po Box 2688, Fujairah, United Arab Emirates
Tel.: (971) 9 2281600
Web Site: http://www.ampni.com
Sales Range: $25-49.9 Million
Emp.: 60
Petroleum Product Distr
N.A.I.C.S.: 424720
Danilo Lamadrid *(Safety Officer)*

Aegean Maritime Petroleum Inc. (1)
18001 Old Cutler Rd Ste 315 Palmetto Bay, Miami, FL 33157   **(100%)**
Tel.: (210) 458-6000
Web Site: http://www.ampni.com
Marine Petroleum Traders
N.A.I.C.S.: 424710

Aegean Maritime Petroleum Network Inc. (1)
20 Signal Rd, Stamford, CT 06902 **(100%)**
Tel.: (212) 763-5670
Web Site: http://www.ampni.com
Sales Range: $25-49.9 Million
Emp.: 25
Maritime Petroleum Traders
N.A.I.C.S.: 424710

Aegean North-West Europe (1)

7 Nijverheidsstraat, B-2960, Antwerp, Belgium
Tel.: (32) 3 65 20 608
Web Site: http://www.ampni.com
Sales Range: $50-74.9 Million
Emp.: 8
Refined Maritime Petroleum Products
N.A.I.C.S.: 424710
Tony Vertommen *(Mng Dir)*

Subsidiary (Non-US):

ICS Petroleum Ltd. (2)
Suite 1220- Oceanic Plaza 1066 West Hastings Street, Vancouver, V6E 3X1, BC, Canada
Tel.: (604) 685-6221
Web Site: http://www.icsgroup-vcr.com
Emp.: 20
Marine Fuel Distr
N.A.I.C.S.: 424720

Aegean Oil (USA) LLC (1)
299 Park Ave 2nd Fl, New York, NY 10171
Tel.: (212) 763-5600
Lubricant Oil Distr
N.A.I.C.S.: 424720

Aegean Ostria Maritime Company (1)
10 Akti Kondyli, 10845, Piraeus, Greece
Tel.: (30) 2104586000
Petroleum Product Distr
N.A.I.C.S.: 424720

Aegean Rose Maritime Company (1)
44 Hatzikiriakou Street, Piraeus, Greece
Tel.: (30) 210 458 6200
Web Site: http://www.ampny.com
Petroleum Product Distr
N.A.I.C.S.: 424720

Aegean Ship III Maritime Company (1)
42 Hatzikyriakou Avenue, Piraeus, Athens, 18538, Greece
Tel.: (30) 210 458 6200
Petroleum Product Distr
N.A.I.C.S.: 424720

Aegean Ship VIII Maritime Company (1)
Akti Kondyli 10, Piraeus, Athens, 18545, Greece
Tel.: (30) 210 458 6200
Petroleum Product Distr
N.A.I.C.S.: 424720

Aegean Ship XII Maritime Company (1)
42 Hatzikyriakou Avenue, Piraeus, Athens, 18538, Greece
Tel.: (30) 210 458 6200
Petroleum Product Distr
N.A.I.C.S.: 424720

Aegean Tiffany Maritime Company (1)
42 Hatzikyriakou Avenue, Piraeus, Athens, 18538, Greece
Tel.: (30) 210 458 6200
Petroleum Product Mfr
N.A.I.C.S.: 424720

ICS Bunkering Services Ltd. (1)
1066 West Hastings Street Suite 1450, Oceanic Plaza, Vancouver, V6E 3X1, BC, Canada
Tel.: (604) 685-6221
Petroleum Product Distr
N.A.I.C.S.: 424720
Gregg Carpenter *(Gen Mgr)*

ICS Petroleum (Montreal) Ltd. (1)
Suite 302 430 Ste-Helen Street, Montreal, H2Y 2K7, QC, Canada
Tel.: (514) 849-1223
Web Site: http://www.ampni.com
Petroleum Product Distr
N.A.I.C.S.: 424720

Jadaco BV (1)
Oost Kanaalweg 22, Postbus 15, 4424 NC, Wemeldinge, Netherlands
Tel.: (31) 113 621261
Petroleum Product Distr
N.A.I.C.S.: 424720

Maritime Dedicated Control N.V. (1)
Nijverheidsstraat 7, Brecht, 2960, Belgium
Tel.: (32) 36520608

MINERVA BUNKERING

Minerva Bunkering—(Continued)
Emp.: 21
Petroleum Product Distr
N.A.I.C.S.: 424720

Naxos Shipping (Pte.) Ltd. (1)
06-01 22 Jalan Kilang, Singapore, 159419, Singapore
Tel.: (65) 6501 0100
Marine Transportation Services
N.A.I.C.S.: 483111

Paros Shipping (Pte.) Ltd. (1)
06-01 22 Jalan Kilang, 159419, Singapore, Singapore
Tel.: (65) 6501 0100
Petroleum Product Distr
N.A.I.C.S.: 424720

Portland Bunkers International Ltd. (1)
The Old Guardhouse Incline Rd, Portland Port, Dorset, DT5 1PH, United Kingdom
Tel.: (44) 1305824620
Web Site: http://www.ampni.com
Sales Range: $25-49.9 Million
Emp.: 8
Suppliers of Refined Maritime Petroleum Products
N.A.I.C.S.: 424710
Roger Lawn (Mgr-Ops)

MINERVA BUNKERING PTE. LTD.
12 Marina View 26-01 Asia Square Tower 2, Singapore, 018961, Singapore
Tel.: (65) 64162080
Web Site:
http://www.minervabunkering.com
Marine Energy Mfr
N.A.I.C.S.: 488330
Tyler Baron (CEO)

Subsidiaries:

CEPSA PANAMA, S.A. (1)
50 Edificio Dresdner 6, Panama, Panama
Tel.: (507) 214 9601
Web Site: http://www.cepsa.com
Petroleum Product Distr
N.A.I.C.S.: 424710
Javier De La Rosa (Gen Mgr)

MINERVA GROUP HOLDING LIMITED
Units 3910-13 39/F COSCO Tower, 183 Queen's Road Central, Hong Kong, China (Hong Kong)
Tel.: (852) 22706600   BM
Web Site:
http://www.powerfinancial.com.hk
0397—(HKG)
Rev.: $9,304,695
Assets: $187,796,918
Liabilities: $6,865,748
Net Worth: $180,931,170
Earnings: ($21,838,583)
Emp.: 24
Fiscal Year-end: 12/31/22
Holding Company; Investment Services
N.A.I.C.S.: 551112
Danny Chun Chung Choi (Chm & CEO)

Subsidiaries:

Core Medical Technology Limited (1)
Rm 1a-1c 1F Hilton Plz Comml Ctr 3-9 Shatin Ctr St, Sha Tin, New Territories, China (Hong Kong)
Tel.: (852) 29489898
Diagnostic Equipments Sales
N.A.I.C.S.: 423450

E Cash Fintech Limited (1)
Room 107 1/F Energy Plaza No 92 Granville Road, Tsimshatsui East, Kowloon, China (Hong Kong)
Tel.: (852) 2 270 6636
Web Site: https://www.ecashfintech.com
Financial Investment Services
N.A.I.C.S.: 523999

Power Securities Company Limited (1)
Unit 1804 18/F Far East Finance Centre 16 Harcourt Road Admiralty, Tsim Sha Tsui East, Hong Kong, China (Hong Kong)
Tel.: (852) 37418000
Web Site: https://www.minervasec.hk
Financial Services
N.A.I.C.S.: 523999

MINERVA INSURANCE COMPANY PUBLIC LTD.
Tel.: (357) 77771414
MINE—(CYP)
Sales Range: $10-24.9 Million
Insurance Management Services
N.A.I.C.S.: 524298

MINERVA INTELLIGENCE INC.
810 - 1166 Alberni Street, Vancouver, V6E 3Z3, BC, Canada
Tel.: (604) 620-1051
Web Site:
https://www.minervaintelligence.com
QT7—(DEU)
Rev.: $39,961
Assets: $757,244
Liabilities: $222,237
Net Worth: $535,007
Earnings: ($1,223,677)
Emp.: 5
Fiscal Year-end: 12/31/23
Software Development Services
N.A.I.C.S.: 541511
Scott Tillman (CEO)

MINERVA KNITWEAR S.A.
6th Kilometer of the Thessaloniki Oraiokastro road, 564 29, Thessaloniki, Greece
Tel.: (30) 2310683110
Web Site: https://www.minerva.gr
Year Founded: 1974
MIN—(ATH)
Sales Range: Less than $1 Million
Emp.: 354
Innerwear Mfr
N.A.I.C.S.: 315250
Ladeni Anastasia (Pres & CEO)

MINERVAGRANDIR CO., LTD.
Oohori building 601 1-2-16 Shimoochiai, Shinjuku-ku, Tokyo, 161-0033, Japan
Tel.: (81) 359880298   JP
Year Founded: 2017
Financial Services
N.A.I.C.S.: 523999
Ryuhei Shinohara (Pres & CEO)

MINESTO AB
J A Wettergrens gata 14, 421 30, Vastra Frolunda, Sweden
Tel.: (46) 31290060
Web Site: https://www.minesto.com
Year Founded: 2007
MINEST—(OMX)
Rev.: $4,270,046
Assets: $51,714,575
Liabilities: $2,753,192
Net Worth: $48,961,383
Earnings: ($2,540,392)
Emp.: 58
Fiscal Year-end: 12/31/23
Eletric Power Generation Services
N.A.I.C.S.: 221115
Gustav Kvibling (CFO)

Subsidiaries:

Minesto UK Ltd. (1)
41-43 Market Street, Holyhead, LL65 1UN, Anglesey, United Kingdom
Tel.: (44) 1407762907
Aerospace Mfr
N.A.I.C.S.: 334511

MINETECH RESOURCES BERHAD
D-G-5 Block D Parklane Commercial Hub, No 21 Jalan SS7/26 Kelana Jaya, 47301, Petaling Jaya, Selangor Darul Ehsan, Malaysia
Tel.: (60) 378867848
Web Site:
https://www.minetech.com.my
Year Founded: 2012
MINETEC—(KLS)
Rev.: $26,195,050
Assets: $42,863,472
Liabilities: $25,369,033
Net Worth: $17,494,439
Earnings: ($2,182,270)
Emp.: 105
Fiscal Year-end: 03/31/23
Quarrying Services
N.A.I.C.S.: 212311
Leong Choy Chin (Exec Dir-Bus Dev & Ops)

Subsidiaries:

Minetech Korea Petroleum Industrial Sdn. Bhd. (1)
Lot 1414 Batu 29 Jalan KL Kuala Kubu Mukim Hulu Yam, Hulu Selangor, 44300, Serendah, Selangor, Malaysia
Tel.: (60) 360753933
Web Site: http://www.minetech.com.my
Sales Range: $25-49.9 Million
Emp.: 22
Bituminous Products Mfr
N.A.I.C.S.: 339999
Gilmore Kang (Mgr)

MINEXFOR SA
Str Titu Maiorescu Nr 2, Hunedoara, Deva, Romania
Tel.: (40) 721216893
Web Site:
https://www.perlaapusenilor.ro
MINX—(BUC)
Rev.: $310,783
Assets: $308,014
Liabilities: $227,013
Net Worth: $81,001
Earnings: ($54,189)
Fiscal Year-end: 12/31/22
Soft Drinks Mfr
N.A.I.C.S.: 312111

MINFENG SPECIAL PAPER CO., LTD.
No 70 Luli Street, Jiaxing, 314000, Zhejiang, China
Tel.: (86) 57382839083
Web Site:
https://www.mfspchina.com
Year Founded: 1923
600235—(SHG)
Rev.: $233,789,267
Assets: $339,602,222
Liabilities: $125,512,696
Net Worth: $214,089,526
Earnings: $8,933,675
Fiscal Year-end: 12/31/21
Paper Product Mfr & Distr
N.A.I.C.S.: 322299
Jiyou Han (Deputy Gen Mgr)

MING D.O.O.
Ulica Dvadesetdrugog oktobra 7/l, 11080, Zemun, Serbia
Tel.: (381) 113196782
Web Site: https://www.mingbgd.com
Year Founded: 1990
MING—(BEL)
Rev.: $8,459,887
Assets: $8,645,834
Liabilities: $2,536,679
Net Worth: $6,109,154
Earnings: ($56,802)
Emp.: 111
Fiscal Year-end: 12/31/23
Railway Car Parts Design & Mfr

INTERNATIONAL PUBLIC

N.A.I.C.S.: 339999
Predrag Madzarevic (Gen Mgr)

Subsidiaries:

MING Kovacnica ad (1)
Bul 12 februar 95, 18000, Nis, Serbia
Tel.: (381) 183100730
Fabricated Structural Metal Mfr
N.A.I.C.S.: 332312

MING FAI INTERNATIONAL HOLDINGS LIMITED
Unit D3 8/F TML Tower No 3 Hoi Shing Road, Tsuen Wan, New Territories, China (Hong Kong)
Tel.: (852) 24554888
Web Site:
http://www.mingfaigroup.com
3828—(HKG)
Rev.: $228,610,688
Assets: $223,056,278
Liabilities: $78,792,450
Net Worth: $144,263,828
Earnings: $8,904,855
Emp.: 4,700
Fiscal Year-end: 12/31/22
Travel & Private Label Amenities Industry Services
N.A.I.C.S.: 236220
Zigang Liu (Dir-Sls & Mktg)

Subsidiaries:

Ming Fai Asia Pacific Company Limited (1)
3 F Mai Kei Indus Bldg 5 Sun Hop Ln, Tuen Mun, New Territories, China (Hong Kong)
Tel.: (852) 24623303
Web Site: http://www.mingfai.com
Sales Range: $1-4.9 Billion
Emp.: 26
Bathroom Supplies Whslr
N.A.I.C.S.: 424210
Winnie Chan (Exec Dir)

Ming Fai Enterprise International Company Limited (1)
Rm F 6 F May Kay Indus Bldg 5 San Hop Ln, Tuen Mun, New Territories, China (Hong Kong)
Tel.: (852) 24623303
Bathroom Products Whslr
N.A.I.C.S.: 424210

Ming Fai Industrial (Shenzhen) Company Limited (1)
Ming Fai Industrial Estate Bainikeng, Pinghu, Longgang, Shenzhen, China
Tel.: (86) 75528802888
Hotel Supply & Equipment Distr
N.A.I.C.S.: 423850

Oriental Lotus Hotel Supplies Private Limited (1)
Villa 15 Phase 1 Chettinadd Enclave S Kolathur Main Road Narayanapuram, Pallikaranai, Chennai, 600 100, India
Tel.: (91) 7358776295
Hotel Supply & Equipment Distr
N.A.I.C.S.: 423850

Quality Amenities Supply Pte. Ltd (1)
8 Boon Lay Way Tradehub 21 Unit 07-04, Singapore, 609964, Singapore
Tel.: (65) 62736718
Web Site: http://www.q-amenities.com
Sales Range: $50-74.9 Million
Emp.: 10
Bathroom Products Whslr
N.A.I.C.S.: 424210
Seamus Mah (Mng Dir)

MING LE SPORTS AG
Ziegelhauser Landstrasse 3, 69120, Heidelberg, Germany
Tel.: (49) 62216492485
Web Site:
https://www.minglesports.de
ML2—(DEU)
Assets: $1,622,696
Liabilities: $44,155
Net Worth: $1,578,541

Earnings: $132,465
Emp.: 1
Fiscal Year-end: 12/31/23
Sportswear Mfr
N.A.I.C.S.: 315250
Hansjorg Plaggemars *(Member-Mgmt Bd)*

MING YANG SMART ENERGY GROUP LIMITED
Mingyang Industrial Park No 22 Huoju Avenue, Zhongshan Torch High-tech Industrial Development Zone, Zhongshan, 528437, Guangdong, China
Tel.: (86) 76028138666   CN
Web Site: https://www.myse.com
Year Founded: 2006
MYSE—(LSE)
Wind Electric Power Generation Services
N.A.I.C.S.: 221115
Chuanwei Zhang *(Chm)*

MING YUAN CLOUD GROUP HOLDINGS LIMITED
801 Tower A Gemdale Viseen Tower 16 Gaoxin South 10th Road, Gaoxin Community Yuehai Subdistrict Nanshan District, Shenzhen, China   Ky
Web Site:
  https://www.mingyuanyun.com
Year Founded: 1997
0909—(HKG)
Rev.: $227,022,043
Assets: $810,287,162
Liabilities: $127,140,701
Net Worth: $683,146,461
Earnings: ($81,280,876)
Emp.: 2,577
Fiscal Year-end: 12/31/23
Holding Company
N.A.I.C.S.: 551112
Junwen Ye *(Sec)*

MINGCHEN HEALTH CO., LTD.
Liannan Industrial Zone, Chenghai District, Shantou, 515834, Guangdong, China
Tel.: (86) 75485115109
Web Site:
  http://www.mingchen.com.cn
Year Founded: 1994
002919—(SSE)
Rev.: $132,734,160
Assets: $174,521,412
Liabilities: $70,730,712
Net Worth: $103,790,700
Earnings: $3,556,332
Fiscal Year-end: 12/31/22
Healthcare Product Mfr & Distr
N.A.I.C.S.: 325620
Chen Jianming *(Chm & Gen Mgr)*

MINGFA GROUP (INTERNATIONAL) COMPANY LIMITED
Unit 06-08 23/F South Twr Concordia Plaza 1 Science Museum Road, Tsim Sha Tsui, Kowloon, China (Hong Kong)
Tel.: (852) 2620 5885
Web Site: http://www.ming-fa.com
Year Founded: 1994
Sales Range: $350-399.9 Million
Emp.: 3,787
Commercial & Residential Property Developer
N.A.I.C.S.: 236220
Qingzhu Huang *(CEO)*

Subsidiaries:

Jiangsu Mingfa Industrial Raw Material Co., Ltd.   (1)
No 15 Fengji Rd, Yuhua Econ Dev Zone, Nanjing, Jiangsu, China
Tel.: (86) 2552885500

Sales Range: $25-49.9 Million
Emp.: 200
Logistic Center Development Services
N.A.I.C.S.: 541614

MingSheng (Xiamen) Investment & Management Co., Ltd.   (1)
No 78 Jia He Rd Fl 4 Ofc Bldg, Xiamen Mingfa Shopping Mall, Xiamen, 361009, Fujian, China
Tel.: (86) 5925314482
Web Site: http://www.ming-fa.com
Investments & Property Management Services
N.A.I.C.S.: 541618

Mingfa Group Company Limited   (1)
No 413 Lianqian E Rd Fl 16-17, Mingfa Hotel, Xiamen, Fujian, China
Tel.: (86) 5925028888
Web Site: http://www.ming-fa.com
Real Estate Services
N.A.I.C.S.: 531210

Mingfa Group Nanjing Real Estate Co., Ltd.   (1)
No 1 Binjiang Rd Taishan St, Pukou Dist, Nanjing, 210031, Jiangsu, China
Tel.: (86) 25 58855885
Web Site: http://www.mingfagroup.com
Property Development Services
N.A.I.C.S.: 531311

Xiamen Mingfa Hotel Co., Ltd.   (1)
413 Lianqian E Rd, Xiamen, Fujian, China
Tel.: (86) 5925978888
Home Management Services
N.A.I.C.S.: 541618

MINGTENG INTERNATIONAL CORPORATION INC.
Lvhua Village, Luoshe Town Huishan District, Wuxi, 214189, Jiangsu, China
Tel.: (86) 51083318500   Ky
Year Founded: 2021
MTEN—(NASDAQ)
Rev.: $8,225,911
Assets: $10,713,491
Liabilities: $3,266,640
Net Worth: $7,446,851
Earnings: $1,506,702
Emp.: 150
Fiscal Year-end: 12/31/23
Automotive Parts Mfr & Distr
N.A.I.C.S.: 336390

MINGXIN AUTOMOTIVE LEATHER CO., LTD.
No 188 Mingxin Road, Daqiao Town Nanhu, Jiaxing, 314006, Zhejiang, China
Tel.: (86) 57383675036
Web Site:
  https://www.mingxinleather.com
Year Founded: 2005
605068—(SHG)
Rev.: $120,119,501
Assets: $464,575,232
Liabilities: $195,426,888
Net Worth: $269,148,344
Earnings: $14,076,855
Fiscal Year-end: 12/31/22
Textile Product Mfr & Distr
N.A.I.C.S.: 313310
Junxin Zhuang *(Chm & Gen Mgr)*

MINGYANG SMART ENERGY GROUP LTD.
Mingyang Industrial Park No 22 HuoJu Road Torch Development Zone, Zhongshan Torch High-Tech Industrial Development Zone, Zhongshan, 528400, Guangdong, China
Tel.: (86) 76028138666
Web Site: https://www.myse.com.cn
Year Founded: 2006
601615—(SHG)
Rev.: $4,316,987,610
Assets: $9,679,207,576
Liabilities: $5,696,713,798

Net Worth: $3,982,493,778
Earnings: $485,026,893
Fiscal Year-end: 12/31/22
Energy Distribution Services
N.A.I.C.S.: 221122
Chuanwei Zhang *(Co-Pres & Co-CEO)*

Subsidiaries:

Beijing Jieyuan New Energy Investment Co., Ltd.   (1)
11th Floor Tower A COFCO Land Plaza No 208 Andingmenwai Street, Dongcheng District, Beijing, China
Tel.: (86) 1062660450
Web Site: http://www.jy-tz.cn
Investment Management Service
N.A.I.C.S.: 523940

MINGYUAN MEDICARE DEVELOPMENT COMPANY LIMITED
Room 2604 26/F West Tower Shun Tak Centre 200 Connaught Road, Central, China (Hong Kong)
Tel.: (852) 31023201
Web Site: http://www.mingyuan-hk.com
Sales Range: $50-74.9 Million
Medical Diagnostic Product Mfr
N.A.I.C.S.: 334510

MINGYUE OPTICAL LENS CO., LTD.
No 9 Yinxing Road, Development Zone, Danyang, 200333, Jiangsu, China
Tel.: (86) 2152660665
Web Site: https://www.mingyue.com
Year Founded: 2002
301101—(CHIN)
Rev.: $105,456,788
Assets: $246,865,337
Liabilities: $21,014,986
Net Worth: $225,850,351
Earnings: $22,189,155
Fiscal Year-end: 12/31/23
Ophthalmic Goods Mfr & Distr
N.A.I.C.S.: 339115
Gongwan Xie *(Chm)*

MINGZHU LOGISTICS HOLDINGS LIMITED
27F Yantian Modern Industry Service Center No 3018 Shayan Road, Yantian District, Shenzhen, 518081, Guangdong, China
Tel.: (86) 75525209839   Ky
Web Site: https://ir.szygmz.com
Year Founded: 2018
YGMZ—(NASDAQ)
Rev.: $89,002,243
Assets: $127,354,302
Liabilities: $82,797,349
Net Worth: $44,556,953
Earnings: ($9,579,760)
Emp.: 180
Fiscal Year-end: 12/31/23
Holding Company
N.A.I.C.S.: 551112
Jinlong Yang *(Founder, Chm & CEO)*

MINH HUU LIEN JSC
41-43 Road D1 Him Lam Residential Area, Tan Hung Ward District 7, Ho Chi Minh City, Vietnam
Tel.: (84) 2838770062
Web Site:
  http://www.minhhuulien.com
Year Founded: 2007
Sales Range: $1-9.9 Million
Furniture Mfr
N.A.I.C.S.: 337126
Tran Tuan Minh *(Chm-Mgmt Bd)*

MINH PHONG TRANSPORTATION JOINT STOCK COMPANY
135/17/19 Nguyen Huu Canh Street, Ward 22 Binh Thanh District, Ho Chi Minh City, Vietnam
Tel.: (84) 835125942   VN
Construction Materials Distr
N.A.I.C.S.: 423390
Vu Quang *(Gen Dir)*

MINH PHU SEAFOOD JOINT STOCK COMPANY
Industrial Zone Ward 8, Ca Mau, Vietnam
Tel.: (84) 7803 839391   VN
Web Site: http://www.minhphu.com
Year Founded: 1992
Rev.: $432,369,343
Assets: $272,908,895
Liabilities: $61,046,428
Net Worth: $211,862,467
Earnings: $26,009,283
Emp.: 6,480
Fiscal Year-end: 12/31/19
Seafood Whslr
N.A.I.C.S.: 424460
Le Van Quang *(Chm-Mgmt Bd & Gen Dir)*

Subsidiaries:

Minh Phat Seafood Processing Co., Ltd.   (1)
Thanh Dien, Ly Van Lam, Ca Mau, Ca Mau, Vietnam
Tel.: (84) 780838262
Food Products Mfr
N.A.I.C.S.: 311710

Minh Phu Biological Products Processing Co., Ltd.   (1)
Hamlet 1, Thoi Binh, Tri Phai, Ca Mau, Vietnam
Tel.: (84) 7803839391
Food Products Mfr
N.A.I.C.S.: 311710

Minh Phu Kien Giang Seafood Co., Ltd.   (1)
Cang Hamlet Hoa Die, Luong, Kien Giang, Vietnam
Tel.: (84) 773754099
Food Products Mfr
N.A.I.C.S.: 311710
Le Van Quang *(Chm)*

Minh Qui Seafood Processing Co., Ltd.   (1)
Industrial Zone of Ward 8, Ca Mau, Ca Mau, Vietnam
Tel.: (84) 780839391
Food Products Mfr
N.A.I.C.S.: 311710
Kara Dang *(Mgr-Sls)*

MINHO (M) BERHAD
Lot 6476 Lorong Sg Puluh Batu 6 Off Jalan Kapar, 42100, Klang, Selangor, Malaysia
Tel.: (60) 332911300
Web Site:
  https://www.minhomalaysia.com
MINHO—(KLS)
Rev.: $48,119,788
Assets: $105,621,587
Liabilities: $13,375,238
Net Worth: $92,246,349
Earnings: $2,384,762
Fiscal Year-end: 12/31/22
Molded Timber Products Mfr
N.A.I.C.S.: 423990
Choon Hian Tan *(Co-Sec)*

Subsidiaries:

Abadi Canggih Sdn. Bhd.   (1)
Jengka Timber Complex, 26400, Bandar Pusat Jengka, Pahang Darul Makmur, Malaysia
Tel.: (60) 94662181
Timber Product Mfr
N.A.I.C.S.: 321999
Jeff Loo *(Gen Mgr)*

MINHO (M) BERHAD

Minho (M) Berhad—(Continued)

Indah Paper Industries Sdn. Bhd. (1)
Lot 6503 Lorong Sungai Puluh Off Batu 6
Jalan Kapar, 42100, Klang, Selangor Darul Ehsan, Malaysia
Tel.: (60) 33 290 6018
Web Site: https://www.indahpaper.com
Sales Range: $25-49.9 Million
Emp.: 100
Paper Bag Mfr
N.A.I.C.S.: 322220
Vincent Ng (Mgr)

Lionvest Corporation (Pahang) Sdn. Bhd. (1)
Jengka Timber Complex, Bandar Pusat Jengka, 26400, Pahang, Malaysia
Tel.: (60) 94662181
Timber Product Mfr
N.A.I.C.S.: 321219

Lionvest Timber Industries Sdn. Bhd. (1)
Jengka Timber Complex, Bandar Pusat Jengka, 26400, Pahang Darul Makmur, Malaysia
Tel.: (60) 94664111
Sales Range: $25-49.9 Million
Emp.: 10
Timber Product Mfr
N.A.I.C.S.: 321999
Tan Kim Kee (Mgr)

My Squares Development Sdn. Bhd. (1)
2A Lintang Gelugor Off Persiaran Sultan Ibrahim, 42100, Klang, Selangor, Malaysia
Tel.: (60) 32906188
Timber Product Mfr
N.A.I.C.S.: 321219

Syarikat Minho Kilning Sdn Bhd (1)
Lot 6476 Lorong Sg Puloh Off 6th Miles
Jalan Kapar, 42100, Klang, Selangor Darul Ehsan, Malaysia
Tel.: (60) 33 291 1300
Web Site: http://www.minho.co.my
Sales Range: $25-49.9 Million
Emp.: 20
Chemical Preservatives Mfr
N.A.I.C.S.: 325998
K. P. Lim (Mgr-Factory)

Syarikat Vinco Timber Industries Sdn. Bhd. (1)
Jalan Kapar Batu 5 3/4 Sementa, 42200, Kelang, Selangor, Malaysia
Tel.: (60) 332912876
Emp.: 250
Investment Management Service
N.A.I.C.S.: 523999

Subsidiary (Domestic):

Costraco Sdn. Bhd. (2)
712 7th Floor Block B Kelana Square No 17 Jalan SS7/26, Kelana Jaya, 47301, Petaling Jaya, Selangor, Malaysia
Tel.: (60) 78802191
Web Site: http://www.costraco.com
Timber Product Mfr
N.A.I.C.S.: 321113
Henry Ng Kok Guan (Mng Dir)

Subsidiary (Domestic):

Indah Wood Products Sdn. Bhd. (3)
Unit 711 & 712 7th Floor Block B Kelana Square No 17 Jalan SS 7/26, Kelana Jaya, 47301, Petaling Jaya, Selangor, Malaysia
Tel.: (60) 78802191
Timber Product Mfr
N.A.I.C.S.: 321219

Subsidiary (Domestic):

Euro-CGA Sdn. Bhd. (2)
Unit 711 and 712 7th Floor Block B Kelana Square No 17 Jalan SS 7/26, Kelana Jaya, 47301, Petaling Jaya, Selangor Darul Ehsan, Malaysia
Tel.: (60) 37 880 2191
Web Site: http://www.costraco.com
Sales Range: $25-49.9 Million
Emp.: 25
Wood Products Mfr
N.A.I.C.S.: 321999

Victory Enterprise Sdn. Bhd. (1)
Lot 6466 Lorong Sg Puloh Off 6th Mile
Jalan Kapar, 42100, Klang, Selangor Darul Ehsan, Malaysia
Tel.: (60) 33 291 1300
Web Site: http://www.mtc.com.my
Sales Range: $50-74.9 Million
Emp.: 200
Wood Mouldings & Sawn Timber Mfr
N.A.I.C.S.: 321999
Ricky Yap (Mng Dir)

MINI DIAMONDS (INDIA) LIMITED
DE 8082 Bharat Diamond Bourse, Bandra Kurla Complex Bandra East, Mumbai, 400 051, India
Tel.: (91) 22 2367 1210
Web Site: http://www.minidiamonds.net
Year Founded: 1987
Rev.: $19,025,501
Assets: $20,126,181
Liabilities: $18,947,923
Net Worth: $1,178,259
Earnings: $47,188
Fiscal Year-end: 03/31/18
Jewelry Product Mfr & Distr
N.A.I.C.S.: 339910
Upendra N. Shah (Chm & Mng Dir)

MINI GEARS (STOCKPORT) LTD
Top Gear House Bletchley Road Heaton Mersey Industrial Estate, Stockport, SK4 3ED, Cheshire, United Kingdom
Tel.: (44) 1614320222
Web Site: http://www.minigears.co.uk
Rev.: $12,910,987
Emp.: 82
Metal Machined Components Mfr
N.A.I.C.S.: 332999
Nigel Walker (Mgr-Bus Dev)

MINIMEL A.D.
Carnojeviceva 12, Zrenjanin, Serbia
Tel.: (381) 23 541 056
Year Founded: 1992
Sales Range: Less than $1 Million
Technical & Science Research & Development Services
N.A.I.C.S.: 541990

MINING GREEN METALS LIMITED
Level 2 50 Kings Park Road, West Perth, 6005, WA, Australia
Tel.: (61) 893215594
Web Site: https://www.mininggreenmetals.com
Year Founded: 2021
MG1—(ASX)
Metal Exploration Services
N.A.I.C.S.: 213114
Matthew Edmondson (CFO)

MINISO GROUP HOLDING LIMITED
8/F M Plaza No 109 Pazhou Avenue, Haizhu District, Guangzhou, 510000, Guangdong, China
Tel.: (86) 2036228788
Web Site: https://ir.miniso.com
Year Founded: 2013
MNSO—(NYSE)
Rev.: $1,610,838,403
Assets: $1,888,058,905
Liabilities: $635,934,078
Net Worth: $1,252,124,827
Earnings: $250,168,792
Emp.: 3,696
Fiscal Year-end: 06/30/23
Holding Company
N.A.I.C.S.: 551112
Minxin Li (Exec VP)

MINITEL - SOCIEDADE DE FOMENTO DE APLICACOES INFORMATICAS, L.DA.
Travessa Legua da Povoa 1A, 1250-136, Lisbon, Portugal
Tel.: (351) 21 381 09 00
Web Site: http://www.minitel.pt
Sales Range: $1-9.9 Million
Emp.: 20
Computer Products Distr
N.A.I.C.S.: 423430
Joao Jose Martins Da Fonseca George (CEO)

MINKABU THE INFONOID, INC.
1-9-1 Higashi Shinbashi, Minato-ku, Tokyo, 105-7306, Japan
Tel.: (81) 368671531
Web Site: https://minkabu.co.jp
Year Founded: 2006
4436—(TKS)
Rev.: $65,571,200
Assets: $98,079,180
Liabilities: $57,202,940
Net Worth: $40,876,240
Earnings: ($7,799,800)
Emp.: 255
Fiscal Year-end: 03/31/24
Internet Media Publisher
N.A.I.C.S.: 516210
Ken Uryu (Chm & Pres)

Subsidiaries:

MINKABU Web3 Wallet, Inc. (1)
1-8-10 Kudankita, Chiyoda-ku, Tokyo, Japan
Tel.: (81) 362616754
Web Site: https://minkabu-web3wallet.co.jp
Software Development Services
N.A.I.C.S.: 541511

Robot Fund Co., Ltd. (1)
6F Tokyo Shiodome Building 1-9-1 Higashi-Shimbashi, Minato-ku, Tokyo, 105-0021, Japan
Tel.: (81) 358607565
Web Site: https://robotfund.co.jp
Robotic Solutions Services
N.A.I.C.S.: 541715

MINNOVA CORP.
217 Queen Street West Suite 401, Toronto, M5V 0R2, ON, Canada
Tel.: (647) 985-2785
Web Site: https://www.minnovacorp.ca
Year Founded: 1992
AGRDF—(OTCIQ)
Rev.: $3,279
Assets: $285,821
Liabilities: $3,302,021
Net Worth: ($3,016,200)
Earnings: ($1,318,104)
Fiscal Year-end: 03/31/23
Gold Exploration & Mining Services
N.A.I.C.S.: 212220
Gorden Glenn (CEO)

MINO CERAMIC CO., LTD.
1-17-28 Meiekiminami, Nakamura-ku, Nagoya, 450-0003, Aichi, Japan
Tel.: (81) 525519221
Web Site: https://www.mino-ceramic.co.jp
Year Founded: 1918
53560—(NGO)
Rev.: $93,551,371
Assets: $134,681,203
Liabilities: $44,876,115
Net Worth: $89,805,088
Earnings: $6,963,991
Emp.: 271
Fiscal Year-end: 03/31/24
Ceramic Products & Refractories Designer, Mfr & Whslr
N.A.I.C.S.: 327110
Shigetoshi Ohta (Pres)

INTERNATIONAL PUBLIC

Subsidiaries:

Bishu Kosan Co., Ltd. (1)
1-17-28 Meiekiminami, Nakamura-ku, Nagoya, 450-0003, Aichi, Japan
Tel.: (81) 525519400
Web Site: https://www.bishu-k.co.jp
Emp.: 53
Construction Material Mfr & Distr
N.A.I.C.S.: 327120
Shigetoshi Ohta (Exec Chm)

Biyo Bright Co., Ltd. (1)
1532 Yamaokachohara, Ena, 509-7605, Gifu, Japan
Tel.: (81) 573683107
Ceramic Product Retailer
N.A.I.C.S.: 444180

Japan Ceramic Engineering Co., Ltd. (1)
Koei Building 3F 1-7-4 Uchi-Kanda, Chiyoda-ku, Tokyo, 101-0047, Japan
Tel.: (81) 332916181
Engineering Consultancy Services
N.A.I.C.S.: 541330

Mino Ceramics Shoji Co., Ltd. (1)
868 Terakawado-cho, Mizunami, 509-6121, Gifu, Japan
Tel.: (81) 572683636
Ceramic Product Mfr & Distr
N.A.I.C.S.: 327120

MINOAN GROUP PLC
3rd Floor AMP House Dingwall Road, Croydon, CR0 2LX, Surrey, United Kingdom
Tel.: (44) 2082534305
Web Site: https://www.minoangroup.com
MIN—(AIM)
Assets: $69,820,751
Liabilities: $11,861,042
Net Worth: $57,959,709
Earnings: ($1,445,972)
Emp.: 7
Fiscal Year-end: 10/31/22
Management of Luxury Resort Development
N.A.I.C.S.: 721120
Christopher W. Egleton (Chm)

MINOLTA FINANCE LTD.
Unique Pearl BL-A Hatiara Roy Para, Kolkata, 700 157, West Bengal, India
Tel.: (91) 3322485794
Web Site: http://www.minolta.co.in
Year Founded: 1993
10023910—(KOL)
Rev.: $71,826
Assets: $1,548,557
Liabilities: $268,672
Net Worth: $1,279,884
Earnings: $6,163
Emp.: 6
Fiscal Year-end: 03/31/23
Financial Management Services
N.A.I.C.S.: 523999
Dinesh Kumar Patnia (Chm & Mng Dir)

MINOR INTERNATIONAL PCL
88 The Parq Building 12th Fl Ratchadaphisek Road, Klongtoey Subdistrict Klongtoey District, Bangkok, 10110, Thailand
Tel.: (66) 23657500
Web Site: https://www.minor.com
Year Founded: 1978
MINOF—(OTCIQ)
Rev.: $4,467,808,868
Assets: $10,485,636,618
Liabilities: $7,937,336,540
Net Worth: $2,548,300,078
Earnings: $177,719,954
Emp.: 78,094
Fiscal Year-end: 12/31/23
Hospitality & Leisure Services
N.A.I.C.S.: 721110

AND PRIVATE COMPANIES — MINOR INTERNATIONAL PCL

Paul Charles Kenny *(CEO-Minor Food)*

Subsidiaries:

Minor Corporation PCL (1)
Berli Jucker House 99 Soi Rubia, Sukhumvit 42 Road, Bangkok, 10110, Thailand
Tel.: (66) 23815151
Web Site: http://www.minorcorporation.com
Sales Range: $25-49.9 Million
Emp.: 100
Consumer Product Marketing, Retailing & Mfg
N.A.I.C.S.: 459999

Minor DKL Food Group Pty. Ltd. (1)
Level 13 199 Grey Street South, Brisbane, 4101, QLD, Australia
Tel.: (61) 1800975005
Web Site: https://minordkl.com.au
Food Restaurant Services
N.A.I.C.S.: 722511

Subsidiary (Domestic):

Nomad Coffee Group Pty. Ltd. (2)
16 River Street, Richmond, 3121, VIC, Australia
Tel.: (61) 1 326 3333
Web Site: https://www.nomadcoffeegroup.com.au
Coffee Product Mfr & Whslr
N.A.I.C.S.: 311920

Minor Food Group (Singapore) Pte. Ltd. (1)
2 Alexandra Road 05-04/05 Delta House, Singapore, 159919, Singapore
Tel.: (65) 62380525
Web Site: https://www.minorfoodsingapore.com
Online Food Services
N.A.I.C.S.: 722310

Minor Food Group PCL (1)
88 The Parq Building 11th Fl Ratchadaphisek Road, Klongtoey Subdistrict Klongtoey District, Bangkok, 10110, Thailand (100%)
Tel.: (66) 23656999
Web Site: https://www.minorfood.com
Emp.: 200
Restaurant Operators
N.A.I.C.S.: 722513

Minor Hotel Group Limited (1)
88 Ratchadaphisek, Klongtoey, Bangkok, 10110, Thailand (100%)
Tel.: (66) 23815151
Hotel Operator
N.A.I.C.S.: 721110
Dillip Rajakarier *(CEO)*

Mint Residential Pty. Ltd. (1)
4/420 Queen Street, PO Box 15427, Brisbane, 4000, QLD, Australia
Tel.: (61) 1300788270
Web Site: http://www.mintresidential.com.au
Hotel Operator
N.A.I.C.S.: 721110
Susan Tozer *(Sr Mgr-Property)*

NH Hotel Group, SA (1)
Santa Engracia 120 7th floor, 28003, Madrid, Spain (94.13%)
Tel.: (34) 914519718
Web Site: https://www.nh-hotels.com
Rev.: $2,383,259,742
Assets: $4,639,172,095
Liabilities: $3,524,565,626
Net Worth: $1,114,606,469
Earnings: $146,644,221
Emp.: 11,665
Fiscal Year-end: 12/31/2023
Holding Company; Luxury Hotel Owner & Operator
N.A.I.C.S.: 551112
Ramon Aragones *(Co-CEO)*

Subsidiary (Non-US):

Astron Kestrell, Ltd. (2)
33 Main Road N2, Plettenberg Bay, 6600, Western Cape, South Africa
Tel.: (27) 445333572
Sales Range: $10-24.9 Million
Emp.: 17
Restaurant Operating Services
N.A.I.C.S.: 722511

Serge Foulon *(Mng Dir)*

Atlantic Hotel Exploitatie, B.V. (2)
Deltaplein 200, Hague, 2554 EJ, Netherlands
Tel.: (31) 704482485
Restaurant Operating Services
N.A.I.C.S.: 722511
Jack den Heijer *(Gen Mgr)*

Chartwell de Nuevo Laredo, S.A. de C.V. (2)
Av Reforma No 5102 Lagos, Nuevo Laredo, 88290, Mexico
Tel.: (52) 8677114600
Restaurant Operating Services
N.A.I.C.S.: 722511

De Sparrenhorst, B.V. (2)
Eperweg 46, Nunspeet, 8072 DB, Netherlands
Tel.: (31) 341 25 59 11
Sales Range: $10-24.9 Million
Emp.: 50
Restaurant Operating Services
N.A.I.C.S.: 722511
Erik Werners *(Gen Mgr)*

Donnafugata Resort, S.r.l. (2)
Contrada Piombo, 97100, Ragusa, Italy
Tel.: (39) 0932 914 200
Web Site: http://www.donnafugatagolfresort.com
Sales Range: $25-49.9 Million
Emp.: 120
Resort Operating Services
N.A.I.C.S.: 721110

Expl. mij. Grand Hotel Krasnapolsky, B.V. (2)
Dam 9, 1012 JS, Amsterdam, Netherlands
Tel.: (31) 20 55 49 111
Web Site: http://www.nh-hotels.com
Restaurant Operating Services
N.A.I.C.S.: 722511

Expl. mij. Hotel Doelen, B.V. (2)
Nieuwe Doelenstraat 24, Amsterdam, 1012 CP, Netherlands
Tel.: (31) 205540600
Web Site: http://www.nh-hotels.com
Emp.: 5
Restaurant Operating Services
N.A.I.C.S.: 722511

Exploitatiemij. Tropenhotel, B.V. (2)
Linnaeusstraat 2c, Amsterdam, 1092 CK, Netherlands
Tel.: (31) 206925111
Web Site: http://www.amsterdamtropenhotel.com
Restaurant Operating Services
N.A.I.C.S.: 722511

Subsidiary (Domestic):

Explotaciones Hoteleras Condor, S.L. (2)
Calle VIA Augusta 127, 8006, Barcelona, Spain
Tel.: (34) 932094511
Restaurant Operating Services
N.A.I.C.S.: 722511

Gran Circulo de Madrid, S.A. (2)
Calle Alcala 15, 28014, Madrid, Spain
Tel.: (34) 915218700
Web Site: http://www.casinodemadrid.es
Casino Hotel Operating Services
N.A.I.C.S.: 721120

Subsidiary (Non-US):

Grande Jolly, S.p.A. (2)
Via Giovanni Battista Pergolesi 2 A, 20122, Milan, Italy (97.4%)
Tel.: (39) 027780721
Sales Range: $50-74.9 Million
Emp.: 70
Holding Company; Hotel Operator
N.A.I.C.S.: 551112
Gabriele Burgio *(Chm & Mng Dir)*

Subsidiary (Non-US):

JH Belgium, S.A. (3)
Rue Bodenbroekstraat 2-4, 1000, Brussels, Belgium (100%)
Tel.: (32) 25181100
Emp.: 70

Luxury Hotel Operator
N.A.I.C.S.: 721110

JH Deutschland GmbH (3)
Im Mediapark 8b, 50670, Cologne, Germany (100%)
Tel.: (49) 22127150
Emp.: 50
Luxury Hotel Operator
N.A.I.C.S.: 721110
Sabastian Kuehn *(Gen Mgr)*

JH Holland N.V. (3)
Vijzelstraat 4, 1017 HK, Amsterdam, Netherlands (100%)
Tel.: (31) 206222266
Web Site: http://www.nh-hotels.com
Luxury Hotel Operator
N.A.I.C.S.: 721110

Subsidiary (Non-US):

Grupo Hotelero Queretaro, S.A. de C.V. (2)
5 De Febrero No 1303, 76138, Queretaro, Mexico
Tel.: (52) 44 2238 4200
Web Site: http://www.nh-hotels.com
Home Management Services
N.A.I.C.S.: 721110

HEM Jaarbeursplein Utrecht, B.V. (2)
Jaarbeursplein 24, Utrecht, 3521 AR, Netherlands
Tel.: (31) 302977977
Web Site: http://www.nhhotels.com
Emp.: 75
Restaurant Operating Services
N.A.I.C.S.: 722511

Heiner Gossen Hotelbetrieb GmBH (2)
Friedrichstr 95, Berlin, 10117, Germany
Tel.: (49) 3020620713
Web Site: http://www.nh-hotels.com
Restaurant Operating Services
N.A.I.C.S.: 722511

Highmark Hoofddorp, B.V. (2)
Kruisweg 495, 2132 NA, Hoofddorp, Netherlands
Tel.: (31) 206550550
Web Site: http://www.nh-hotels.com
Restaurant Operating Services
N.A.I.C.S.: 722511

Hoteleira Brasil Ltda. (2)
Rua Haddock Lobo 347 - 14 Andar Conjunto 142, 01414 001, Cerqueira Cesar, Sao Paulo, Brazil
Tel.: (55) 11 3123 9600
Web Site: http://www.hotelariabrasil.com.br
Home Management Services
N.A.I.C.S.: 721110
Mauro Kaluf *(Gen Mgr)*

Hotelera de la Parra, S.A. de C.V. (2)
Liverpool No 155 Juarez, Cuauhtemoc, 06600, Mexico, Mexico
Tel.: (52) 5552289928
Web Site: http://hotelmexico.org
Restaurant Operating Services
N.A.I.C.S.: 722511

Subsidiary (Domestic):

Hoteles Hesperia, S.A. (2)
Mare de Deu de Bellvitge 3, L'Hospitalet de Llobregat, 08907, Barcelona, Spain
Tel.: (34) 932180300
Web Site: http://www.hesperia.com
Emp.: 150
Holding Company; Luxury Hotels Owner & Operator
N.A.I.C.S.: 551112

Subsidiary (Non-US):

Iberdrola Re, S.A. (2)
3 Avenue Monterey, 2163, Luxembourg, Luxembourg
Tel.: (352) 27 47 58
Electric Power Distribution Services
N.A.I.C.S.: 221122

Subsidiary (Domestic):

Inversores y Gestores Asociados, S.A. (2)

Calle Santa Engracia 130, Madrid, 28003, Spain
Tel.: (34) 914519718
Investment Management Service
N.A.I.C.S.: 523999

Subsidiary (Non-US):

Jan Tabak, N.V. (2)
Amersfoortsestraatweg 27, Bussum, 1401 CV, Netherlands
Tel.: (31) 356959911
Web Site: http://www.nh-hoteles.com
Home Management Services
N.A.I.C.S.: 721110

Koningshof, B.V. (2)
Karreveld 1a, Koudekerke, 4371 GA, Netherlands
Tel.: (31) 118555900
Restaurant Operating Services
N.A.I.C.S.: 722511

Krasnapolsky Belgian Shares, B.V. (2)
Noorderweg 68, 1221 AB, Hilversum, Netherlands
Tel.: (31) 35 6299299
Sales Range: $200-249.9 Million
Emp.: 35
Investment Management Service
N.A.I.C.S.: 523999

Krasnapolsky Hotels & Restaurants, N.V. (2)
Noorderweg 68, Hilversum, 1200 AP, Netherlands
Tel.: (31) 356 299 299
Restaurant Operating Services
N.A.I.C.S.: 722511

Krasnapolsky Hotels Ltd. (2)
Cnr Main Rd M9 Broadway Blvd R44, Somerset West, 7135, Western Cape, South Africa
Tel.: (27) 218551040
Restaurant Operating Services
N.A.I.C.S.: 722511
Serge Foulon *(Gen Mgr)*

Subsidiary (Domestic):

Latinoamericana de Gestion Hotelera, S.L. (2)
Calle Santa Engracia 120 - 7a, 28003, Madrid, Spain
Tel.: (34) 914519735
Web Site: http://www.nh-hotels.com
Home Management Services
N.A.I.C.S.: 721110

Subsidiary (Non-US):

Leeuwenhorst Congres Center, B.V. (2)
Langelaan 3, Noordwijkerhout, 2211 XT, Netherlands
Tel.: (31) 252378888
Sales Range: $25-49.9 Million
Emp.: 15
Restaurant Operating Services
N.A.I.C.S.: 722511
Michelle Aarts *(Mng Dir)*

Liberation Exploitatie, B.V. (2)
Bevrijdingsweg 1, Sprang-Capelle, 5161 BZ, Waalwijk, Netherlands
Tel.: (31) 416 674684
Sales Range: $10-24.9 Million
Emp.: 25
Restaurant Operating Services
N.A.I.C.S.: 722511

Museum Quarter, B.V. (2)
Hobbemakade 50, Amsterdam, 1071 XL, Netherlands
Tel.: (31) 205738200
Sales Range: $10-24.9 Million
Emp.: 38
Restaurant Operating Services
N.A.I.C.S.: 722511
Brinda Zaidom *(Gen Mgr)*

Subsidiary (Domestic):

NH Atardecer Caribeno, S.L. (2)
Calle de Santa Engracia 120, 28003, Madrid, Spain
Tel.: (34) 914519727
Real Estate Development Services
N.A.I.C.S.: 531390

MINOR INTERNATIONAL PCL

Minor International PCL—(Continued)

Unit (Domestic):

NH Balago (2)
28 Las Mieses St, 47009, Valladolid, Spain
Tel.: (34) 983363880
Web Site: http://www.nh-hoteles.com
Sales Range: $10-24.9 Million
Emp.: 15
Hotels & Motels
N.A.I.C.S.: 721110

Subsidiary (Domestic):

NH Barcelona Stadium hotel (2)
Travessera de les Corts 150-152, 8028, Barcelona, Spain
Tel.: (34) 913984661
Web Site: http://www.hotelnhrallye.hotelsearch.com
Emp.: 40
Restaurant Operating Services
N.A.I.C.S.: 722511
Sara Spray (Mng Dir)

Subsidiary (Non-US):

NH Belgium cvba (2)
Korenmarkt 22-24, 2800, Machelen, Belgium
Tel.: (32) 15420303
Web Site: http://www.nh-hotels.com
Restaurant Operating Services
N.A.I.C.S.: 722511

Unit (Non-US):

NH Berlin City Ost (2)
Rathausstr 2-3, 10367, Berlin, Germany
Tel.: (49) 30557570
Web Site: http://www.nh-hotels.com
Sales Range: $10-24.9 Million
Emp.: 15
Hotels & Motels
N.A.I.C.S.: 721110

NH Berlin City West (2)
Bundesallee 36-37, Berlin, 10717, Germany
Tel.: (49) 30860040
Web Site: http://www.nh-hoteles.com
Sales Range: $10-24.9 Million
Emp.: 20
Hotels & Motels
N.A.I.C.S.: 721110

Subsidiary (Non-US):

NH Caribbean Management, B.V. (2)
Noorderweg 68, Hilversum, 1221 AB, Netherlands
Tel.: (31) 356299299
Business Management Consulting Services
N.A.I.C.S.: 541611

NH Central Europe, GmbH & Co. KG (2)
Friedrichstrasse 76, 10117, Berlin, Germany
Tel.: (49) 30 20620727
Home Management Services
N.A.I.C.S.: 721110
Stephan Demmerle (Gen Mgr)

Unit (Non-US):

NH City & Tower (2)
Bolivar 160, Buenos Aires, 6069, Argentina
Tel.: (54) 1141216464
Emp.: 100
Hotels & Motels
N.A.I.C.S.: 721110
Patar Amado (Gen Mgr)

NH Danube City (2)
Wagramer Strasse 21, 1220, Vienna, Austria
Tel.: (43) 126 0200
Web Site: http://www.nh-hotels.com
Sales Range: $50-74.9 Million
Hotels & Motels
N.A.I.C.S.: 721110

Unit (Domestic):

NH Fuenlabrada (2)
Hungria 8, 28943, Fuenlabrada, Spain
Tel.: (34) 916002212
Web Site: http://www.nh-hoteles.es
Sales Range: $10-24.9 Million
Emp.: 15
Hotels & Motels
N.A.I.C.S.: 721110

Unit (Non-US):

NH Hamburg Mitte (2)
Schaferkampsallee 49, 20357, Hamburg, Germany
Tel.: (49) 40441150
Sales Range: $10-24.9 Million
Emp.: 20
Hotels & Motels
N.A.I.C.S.: 721110

Subsidiary (Domestic):

NH Hotel Ciutat de Reus, S.A. (2)
Avinguda Maria Fortuny 85, 43203, Reus, Spain
Tel.: (34) 913984664
Web Site: http://www.nh-hotels.com
Sales Range: $10-24.9 Million
Restaurant Operating Services
N.A.I.C.S.: 722511

Unit (Non-US):

NH Hotel De Ville (2)
Oude Boteringestraat 43-45, 9712 GD, Groningen, Netherlands
Tel.: (31) 503181222
Web Site: http://www.nh-hotels.com
Sales Range: $10-24.9 Million
Hotels & Motels
N.A.I.C.S.: 721110

Subsidiary (Non-US):

NH Hoteles Austria, GmbH (2)
Mariahilfer Strasse 32 - 34, Vienna, 1070, Austria
Tel.: (43) 1 52172 0
Home Management Services
N.A.I.C.S.: 722511
Christian Rothbauer (Gen Mgr)

NH Hoteles Deutschland, GmbH (2)
Leipziger Str 106-111, 10117, Berlin, Germany
Tel.: (49) 30 203760
Web Site: http://www.nh-hotels.com
Sales Range: $10-24.9 Million
Hotel Operating Services
N.A.I.C.S.: 721110

Subsidiary (Domestic):

NH Hoteles Espana, S.L. (2)
Santa Engracia 5, 28010, Madrid, Spain
Tel.: (34) 915940213
Web Site: http://www.nh-hotels.com
Restaurant Operating Services
N.A.I.C.S.: 722511

Subsidiary (Non-US):

NH Hoteles Switzerland GmbH (2)
Avenu De Mategnin 21, 1217, Meyrin, Geneva, Switzerland
Tel.: (41) 229899000
Web Site: http://www.nh-hotels.com
Sales Range: $10-24.9 Million
Restaurant Operating Services
N.A.I.C.S.: 722511

Subsidiary (US):

NH Hotels USA, Inc. (2)
9801 Westheimer Ste 302, Houston, TX 77042 (100%)
Tel.: (713) 952-7791
Web Site: http://www.nh-hotels.com
Holding Company; Hotel Operator
N.A.I.C.S.: 551112

Subsidiary (Non-US):

NH Hungary Hotel Management, Ltd. (2)
Vigszinhaz U 3, 1137, Budapest, Hungary
Tel.: (36) 18 14 00 00
Web Site: http://www.nh-hotels.com
Sales Range: $10-24.9 Million
Restaurant Operating Services
N.A.I.C.S.: 722511

Joint Venture (Non-US):

NH Italia S.r.l. (2)
Via Giovanni Battista Pergolesi 2 A, IT-20122, Milan, Italy
Tel.: (39) 027780721
Web Site: http://www.nh-hotels.it
Sales Range: $50-74.9 Million
Emp.: 70
Holding Company; Hotel Operator; Owned 52.5% by NH Hoteles, S.A. & 47.5% by Intesa Sanpaolo, S.p.A.
N.A.I.C.S.: 551112

Subsidiary (Non-US):

NH Italy Management, S.r.l. (2)
Via Pergolesi 2/A, Milan, 20124, Italy
Tel.: (39) 0262371
Sales Range: $10-24.9 Million
Emp.: 10
Restaurant Operating Services
N.A.I.C.S.: 722511

Unit (Non-US):

NH Kensington (2)
Cromwell Rd 202-220, London, SW5 0SW, United Kingdom
Tel.: (44) 2072441441
Web Site: http://www.nh-hotels.co.uk
Hotels & Motels
N.A.I.C.S.: 721110

Subsidiary (Domestic):

NH Las Palmas, S.A. (2)
Ferreras 1, 35008, Las Palmas, Spain
Tel.: (34) 913984661
Web Site: http://www.nh-hotels.com
Sales Range: $10-24.9 Million
Restaurant Operating Services
N.A.I.C.S.: 722511

NH Logrono, S.A. (2)
Avda Club Deportivo 98, 26007, Logrono, Spain
Tel.: (34) 94 1519270
Web Site: http://www.nh-hotels.com
Sales Range: $10-24.9 Million
Restaurant Operating Services
N.A.I.C.S.: 722511

Unit (Non-US):

NH Luxembourg (2)
1 Route de Treves, PO Box 1973, Senningerberg, 2633, Luxembourg, Luxembourg
Tel.: (352) 340571
Web Site: https://www.nh-hotels.com
Sales Range: $10-24.9 Million
Hotels & Motels
N.A.I.C.S.: 721110

Unit (Domestic):

NH Malaga (2)
Calle San Jacinto 2, 29007, Malaga, Spain
Tel.: (34) 91 398 4661
Web Site: https://www.nh-hotels.fr
Sales Range: $10-24.9 Million
Hotels & Motels
N.A.I.C.S.: 721110

Subsidiary (Non-US):

NH Rallye Portugal Lda. (2)
Avda Da Liberdade 180b, 1250-146, Lisbon, Portugal
Tel.: (351) 213514060
Web Site: http://www.nh-hotels.com
Restaurant Operating Services
N.A.I.C.S.: 722511

Unit (Non-US):

NH Santa Fe (2)
Juan Salvador Agraz 44, 5109, Mexico, Mexico
Tel.: (52) 5591777380
Web Site: http://www.nh-hoteles.com.mx
Sales Range: $10-24.9 Million
Emp.: 50
Hotels & Motels
N.A.I.C.S.: 721110

NH Santo Stefano (2)
Via Porta Palatina 19, 10122, Turin, Italy
Tel.: (39) 011 522 3311
Web Site: https://www.nh-hotels.com
Sales Range: $10-24.9 Million
Hotels & Motels
N.A.I.C.S.: 721110

INTERNATIONAL PUBLIC

Subsidiary (Domestic):

NH Sants Barcelona (2)
Numancia 74, 8029, Barcelona, Spain
Tel.: (34) 933224451
Web Site: http://www.nh-hotels.com
Sales Range: $10-24.9 Million
Emp.: 50
Hotels & Motels
N.A.I.C.S.: 721110

Subsidiary (Non-US):

NH The Netherlands, B.V. (2)
Noorderweg 68, Hilversum, 1221 AB, Netherlands
Tel.: (31) 356299299
Web Site: http://www.nh-hotels.com
Sales Range: $50-74.9 Million
Emp.: 60
Investment Management Service
N.A.I.C.S.: 523940

Unit (Non-US):

NH Timisoara (2)
Strada Pestalozzi 1/a, 300115, Timisoara, Romania
Tel.: (40) 25 640 7440
Web Site: https://www.nh-hotels.com
Sales Range: $10-24.9 Million
Hotels & Motels
N.A.I.C.S.: 721110

Subsidiary (Non-US):

NH Tortona, Srl. (2)
Via Tortona 35, 20144, Milan, Italy
Tel.: (39) 024898861
Web Site: http://www.nh-hotels.com
Sales Range: $10-24.9 Million
Restaurant Operating Services
N.A.I.C.S.: 722511

Unit (Non-US):

NH Waalwijk (2)
Bevrijdingsweg 1, 5161 BZ, Waalwijk, Netherlands
Tel.: (31) 41 667 4684
Web Site: http://www.nh-hotels.com
Sales Range: $10-24.9 Million
Hotel Accommodations
N.A.I.C.S.: 721110

Nhow Milano (2)
Via Tortona 35, 20144, Milan, Italy
Tel.: (39) 02 489 8861
Web Site: https://www.nhow-hotels.com
Hotels & Motels
N.A.I.C.S.: 721110

Subsidiary (Domestic):

Nuevos Espacios Hoteleros, S.L. (2)
Calle Alfonso Gomez 30 - 32, Madrid, 28037, Spain
Tel.: (34) 918099222
Sales Range: $10-24.9 Million
Emp.: 2
Restaurant Operating Services
N.A.I.C.S.: 722511
Mariano Perez Claver (Pres)

Subsidiary (Non-US):

OGBM Danny Kayelaan Zoetermeer BV (2)
Danny Kayelaan 20, 2719 EH, Zoetermeer, Netherlands
Tel.: (31) 793610202
Web Site: http://www.nh-hotels.com
Sales Range: $10-24.9 Million
Restaurant Operating Services
N.A.I.C.S.: 722511

Olofskapel Monumenten, B.V. (2)
Prins Hendrikkade 59-72, 1012 AD, Amsterdam, Netherlands
Tel.: (31) 20 5564564
Web Site: http://www.nh-hotels.com
Home Management Services
N.A.I.C.S.: 721110

Restaurant D'Vijff Vlieghen, B.V (2)
Spuistraat 294-302, 1012 VX, Amsterdam, Netherlands
Tel.: (31) 20 530 4060
Web Site: https://www.vijffvlieghen.nl
Restaurant Operating Services
N.A.I.C.S.: 722511

AND PRIVATE COMPANIES

Subsidiary (Domestic):

Retail Invest, S.L. (2)
Calle Santa Engracia 120, 28003, Madrid, Spain
Tel.: (34) 9 145 19718
Restaurant Operating Services
N.A.I.C.S.: 722511

Subsidiary (Non-US):

Servicios Chartwell de Nuevo Laredo, S.A. de C.V. (2)
Calle Reforma No 5102 Int-1 Patios Exaduana, Nuevo Laredo, 88290, Mexico
Tel.: (52) 8677114600
Sales Range: $10-24.9 Million
Emp.: 3
Restaurant Operating Services
N.A.I.C.S.: 722511
Marcoamtonao Dale *(Mgr)*

Servicios Corporativos Chartwell Monterrey, S.A. de C.V. (2)
Blvd Antonio L Rodriguez No 1880 Poniente Santa Maria, Monterrey, 64650, Mexico
Tel.: (52) 8181228000
Web Site: http://www.hiltongardeninnnmonterrey.com
Emp.: 43
Restaurant Operating Services
N.A.I.C.S.: 722511
Mirna Garcia *(Gen Mgr)*

Servicios Hoteleros Tlalnepantla, S.A. de C.V. (2)
Juan Salvador Agraz No 44 Piso 3 Santa Fe, Cuajimalpa De Morelos, Mexico, 05109, Mexico
Tel.: (52) 5552617704
Sales Range: $100-124.9 Million
Emp.: 700
Restaurant Operating Services
N.A.I.C.S.: 722511

Subsidiary (Domestic):

Sotogrande S.A. (2)
Avda de la Marina 1 Sotogrande, San Roque, Cadiz, Spain
Tel.: (34) 956 790 344
Web Site: http://www.sotogrande.com
Real Estate Development Services
N.A.I.C.S.: 531390
Marc Topiol *(Chm)*

NMT Limited (1)
60/158 Moo19 Soi17 Phaholyothin Road, Navanakorn Industrial Estate Klongnueng Klongluang, Pathumthani, 12120, Thailand
Tel.: (66) 2520363642
Web Site: https://www.nmtlimited.com
Personal Care & Pet Product Distr
N.A.I.C.S.: 459910

Oaks (M on Palmer) Management Pty. Ltd. (1)
81 Palmer Street, Townsville, 4810, QLD, Australia
Tel.: (61) 747532900
Hotel & Resort Management Services
N.A.I.C.S.: 721199

Oaks Hotels & Resorts (Carlyle Mackay) Pty. Ltd. (1)
23 Alfred Street, MacKay, 4740, QLD, Australia
Tel.: (61) 749636600
Hotel & Resort Management Services
N.A.I.C.S.: 721199

Oaks Hotels & Resorts (Mon Komo) Pty. Ltd. (1)
99 Marine Parade, Redcliffe, 4020, QLD, Australia
Tel.: (61) 732839300
Hotel & Resort Management Services
N.A.I.C.S.: 721199

Oaks Hotels & Resorts (Moranbah) Pty. Ltd. (1)
11 Bacon Street, Moranbah, 4744, QLD, Australia
Tel.: (61) 749415355
Hotel & Resort Management Services
N.A.I.C.S.: 721199

Oaks Hotels & Resorts (Rivermarque) Pty. Ltd. (1)

55-63 River Street, MacKay, 4740, QLD, Australia
Tel.: (61) 748627200
Hotel & Resort Management Services
N.A.I.C.S.: 721199

Oaks Hotels & Resorts Leasing (Collins) Pty. Ltd. (1)
480 Collins Street, Melbourne, 3000, VIC, Australia
Tel.: (61) 386106444
Hotel & Resort Management Services
N.A.I.C.S.: 721199

Oaks Hotels & Resorts Limited (1)
Bryant House Level 2 26 Duporth Avenue, Maroochydore, 4558, QLD, Australia
Tel.: (61) 732461700
Web Site: https://www.oakshotels.com
Sales Range: $100-124.9 Million
Hotel Operator
N.A.I.C.S.: 721110

Subsidiary (Domestic):

Calypso Plaza Management Pty. Ltd. (2)
99 Griffith St, PO Box 93, Coolangatta, Gold Coast, 4225, QLD, Australia
Tel.: (61) 755990000
Sales Range: $10-24.9 Million
Emp.: 10
Home Management Services
N.A.I.C.S.: 721110

Oaks Hotels & Resorts (VIC) Pty. Ltd. (2)
Bryant House Level 5 26 Duporth Ave, Maroochydore, 4558, QLD, Australia
Tel.: (61) 754796922
Web Site: http://www.oakshotelsresorts.com.au
Sales Range: $10-24.9 Million
Emp.: 80
Home Management Services
N.A.I.C.S.: 721110

Queensland Accommodation Corporation Pty. Ltd. (2)
Shop 4 19 Lear Jet Drv, Caboolture, Brisbane, 4510, QLD, Australia
Tel.: (61) 754957139
Web Site: http://www.qldaccommcorp.com.au
Sales Range: $10-24.9 Million
Emp.: 30
Home Management Services
N.A.I.C.S.: 721110

The Oaks Resort & Hotel Management Pty. Ltd. (2)
Level 5 26 Duporth Avenue, Maroochydore, 4558, QLD, Australia
Tel.: (61) 732461700
Web Site: http://www.oakshotels.com
Home Management Services
N.A.I.C.S.: 721110

The Hanger Limited (2)
Shop 4 10 Havelock Road Hawkes Bay, Havelock North, Hastings, 4130, New Zealand
Tel.: (64) 68770154
Web Site: http://www.thehanger.nz
Model Clothing Distr
N.A.I.C.S.: 458110

Zuma Bangkok Limited (1)
The St Regis Hotel ground floor 159 Ratchadamri Rd, Lumpini Pathumwan, Bangkok, Thailand
Tel.: (66) 21118999
Web Site: https://zumarestaurant.com
Restaurant Operators
N.A.I.C.S.: 722511

MINORI SOLUTIONS CO., LTD.
17F Shinjuku NS Bldg 2-4-1 Nishi-Shinjuku, Shinjuku-Ku, Tokyo, 163-0817, Japan
Tel.: (81) 3 33450601
Web Site: http://www.minori-sol.jp
Year Founded: 1980
Information Technology Services
N.A.I.C.S.: 541511

MINOS A.D.
Karadordeva 33, 32300, Gornji Milanovac, Serbia
Tel.: (381) 32 720 085
Year Founded: 2001
MNOS—(BEL)
Sales Range: Less than $1 Million
Railway Equipment Mfr
N.A.I.C.S.: 336510

MINOX INTERNATIONAL GROUP BERHAD
No 3 Jalan Industri PBP 11 Taman Industri Pusat Bandar Puchong, 47100, Puchong, Selangor, Malaysia
Tel.: (60) 380637450　　MY
Web Site: https://www.minox.biz
Year Founded: 2022
MINOX—(KLS)
Rev.: $9,778,282
Assets: $17,319,717
Liabilities: $6,584,192
Net Worth: $10,735,525
Earnings: $2,291,298
Emp.: 72
Fiscal Year-end: 12/31/22
Industrial Product Distr
N.A.I.C.S.: 423830

MINRAV GROUP LTD.
3 Habosem Street, Ashdod, Israel
Tel.: (972) 88516262
Web Site: http://www.minrav.co.il
Year Founded: 1969
MINRAV—(TAE)
Rev.: $399,272,401
Assets: $757,860,731
Liabilities: $594,098,966
Net Worth: $163,761,765
Earnings: ($21,487,465)
Emp.: 1,170
Fiscal Year-end: 12/31/22
Holding Company
N.A.I.C.S.: 551112

MINREX RESOURCES LIMITED
Level 2 7 Havelock Street, West Perth, 6008, WA, Australia
Tel.: (61) 894810389
Web Site: https://www.minrex.com.au
MRR—(ASX)
Rev.: $459,154
Assets: $9,886,024
Liabilities: $180,585
Net Worth: $9,705,439
Earnings: ($2,873,214)
Emp.: 1
Fiscal Year-end: 06/30/24
Gold Mining Services
N.A.I.C.S.: 212220
Simon Francis Durack *(Exec Dir)*

MINSHANG CREATIVE TECHNOLOGY HOLDINGS LIMITED
Unit 4203 42/F Tower one Lippo Centre 89 Queensway, Hong Kong, China (Hong Kong)
Tel.: (852) 2 682 3218　　Ky
Web Site: http://www.minshangct.com
1632—(HKG)
Rev.: $204,502,433
Assets: $72,197,458
Liabilities: $51,122,900
Net Worth: $21,074,558
Earnings: $3,289,893
Emp.: 118
Fiscal Year-end: 03/31/21
Restaurant Operators
N.A.I.C.S.: 722511

MINSHENG EDUCATION GROUP COMPANY LIMITED
No 301 3rd floor Building 9 East Third Ring Road Chaoyang District, Beijing, 100020, China

MINSUR S.A.

Tel.: (86) 1085911099　　Ky
Web Site: http://www.minshengedu.com
Year Founded: 2005
1569—(HKG)
Rev.: $330,496,686
Assets: $1,678,703,972
Liabilities: $971,492,886
Net Worth: $707,211,086
Earnings: $72,063,389
Emp.: 7,500
Fiscal Year-end: 12/31/22
Education Services
N.A.I.C.S.: 611310
Xuechun Li *(Founder & Chm)*

MINSHENG HOLDINGS CO., LTD.
15F Tower A Minsheng Financial Center No 28 Jianguomennei Avenue, Dongcheng District, Beijing, 100005, China
Tel.: (86) 1085259000
000416—(SSE)
Rev.: $2,758,860
Assets: $127,269,792
Liabilities: $3,782,376
Net Worth: $123,487,416
Earnings: ($4,012,632)
Fiscal Year-end: 12/31/22
Holding Company
N.A.I.C.S.: 551112
Zheng Yu *(Chm)*

MINSHENG SECURITIES CO., LTD.
16 Chaowai Street 1901 China Life Tower, Chaoyang, Beijing, China
Tel.: (86) 1085127999
Web Site: http://www.mszq.com
Securities Brokerage Services
N.A.I.C.S.: 523150

MINSTRELL RECRUITMENT LIMITED
Lowry Mil Lees Street, Swinton, Manchester, M27 6DB, United Kingdom
Tel.: (44) 1612364736
Web Site: http://www.minstrellrecruitment.com
Human Resources & Man Power Services
N.A.I.C.S.: 541612
Paul Leyshon *(Mgr-Engrg Acct)*

Subsidiaries:

Spectrum Contracting Services, Inc. (1)
108 Wind Haven Dr Ste B, Nicholasville, KY 40356
Web Site: http://www.spectrumcontract.com
Commercial & Institutional Building Construction
N.A.I.C.S.: 236220
Donnie E. Tucker *(Pres)*

MINSUD RESOURCES CORP.
340 Richmond Street West, Toronto, M5V 1X2, ON, Canada
Tel.: (416) 947-0464
Web Site: https://www.minsud.com
Year Founded: 2007
MSR—(TSXV)
Assets: $23,942,981
Liabilities: $20,187,849
Net Worth: $3,755,132
Earnings: ($7,478,388)
Emp.: 12
Fiscal Year-end: 12/31/23
Precious Metal Exploration Services
N.A.I.C.S.: 212290
Diego Bauret *(COO)*

MINSUR S.A.
Jr Lorenzo Bernini 149, San Borja, 27, Lima, 27, Peru
Tel.: (51) 2158330

MINSUR S.A.

MINSUR S.A.—(Continued)
Web Site: https://www.minsur.com
Year Founded: 1977
MINSUR1—(LIM)
Rev.: $611,808,490
Assets: $1,299,065,122
Liabilities: $638,994,683
Net Worth: $660,070,439
Earnings: $154,107,090
Emp.: 1,634
Fiscal Year-end: 12/31/23
Gold Ore Mining Services
N.A.I.C.S.: 212220
Juan-Luis Kruger Sayan *(CEO)*

MINT INCOME FUND
1 First Canadian Place Suite 5800, Toronto, M5X 1A6, ON, Canada
Tel.: (416) 362-0714
Year Founded: 1997
MICFF—(OTCIQ)
Rev.: $16,183,321
Assets: $96,818,841
Liabilities: $19,826,439
Net Worth: $76,992,402
Earnings: $14,051,913
Fiscal Year-end: 12/31/19
Investment Management Service
N.A.I.C.S.: 523999

MINT PAYMENTS LIMITED
Level 4 Unit 3 450 Victoria Road, Gladesville, 2111, NSW, Australia
Tel.: (61) 2 8752 7888
Web Site:
   http://www.mintpayments.com
Sales Range: Less than $1 Million
Mobile Payment Systems & Processing Services
N.A.I.C.S.: 522320
Andrew Teoh *(Mng Dir-Mint Payments Asia Pte Ltd)*

Subsidiaries:

Mint (Aust) Pty Limited (1)
Level 4 Ste 3 436-484 Victoria Rd, Gladesville, 2111, NSW, Australia
Tel.: (61) 287527888
Web Site: http://www.mintpayments.com
Emp.: 20
Electronic Payment Systems & Processing Services
N.A.I.C.S.: 522320

MINT SA
52 rue dOdin, 34965, Montpellier, Cedex, France
Tel.: (33) 499772140
Web Site: https://www.mint.eco
ALBUD—(EUR)
Telecommunication Servicesb
N.A.I.C.S.: 517810
Khaled Zourray *(Chm & CEO)*

MINTEL GROUP LTD.
11 Pilgrim Street, London, EC4V 6RN, United Kingdom
Tel.: (44) 20 7606 4533
Web Site: http://www.mintel.com
Year Founded: 1972
Sales Range: $10-24.9 Million
Emp.: 534
Marketing Consultancy Services
N.A.I.C.S.: 541613
Sian Brenchley *(Global Dir-Comm)*

Subsidiaries:

Mintel (Consulting) India Private Limited (1)
Level 8 Vibgyor Towers Bandra Kurla Complex, Mumbai, 400051, India
Tel.: (91) 2240907217
Marketing Consultancy Services
N.A.I.C.S.: 541613

Mintel (Consulting) Singapore Pte. Ltd. (1)
30 Raffles Place Chevron House 09-03, Singapore, 48622, Singapore
Tel.: (65) 66533600
Marketing Consultancy Services
N.A.I.C.S.: 541613

Mintel Consulting (Malaysia) Sdn. Bhd (1)
Unit 3 023 Jaya One Block B No 72A Jalan Universiti, Petaling Jaya, Kuala Lumpur, Malaysia
Tel.: (60) 362117500
Marketing Consultancy Services
N.A.I.C.S.: 541613

Mintel Germany GmbH (1)
Konrad-Zuse-Platz 8, 81929, Munich, Germany
Tel.: (49) 89207042153
Web Site: http://www.de.mintel.com
Marketing Consultancy Services
N.A.I.C.S.: 541613

Mintel Group Ltd (1)
Level 26 1 Bligh Street, Sydney, 2000, NSW, Australia
Tel.: (61) 282848100
Marketing Consultancy Services
N.A.I.C.S.: 541613

Mintel Group Ltd (1)
333 W Wacker Dr Ste 1100, Chicago, IL 60606
Tel.: (312) 932-0400
Marketing Consultancy Services
N.A.I.C.S.: 541613
Maria Guerrero *(Acct Mgr-Latin America)*

Mintel Group Ltd (1)
Level 26 1 Bligh Street, Sydney, 2000, NSW, Australia
Tel.: (61) 282848100
Marketing Consultancy Services
N.A.I.C.S.: 541613

Mintel Information Consulting (Shanghai) Co., Ltd (1)
25th Floor Broad Silver International Building 398 Huaihai Zhong Road, Shanghai, 200020, China
Tel.: (86) 2160327300
Marketing Consultancy Services
N.A.I.C.S.: 541613
Ailsa Beibei Gu *(Mgr-Insight)*

Mintel Japan Inc (1)
2-7-14 Kyobashi Burex Kyobashi 5F, Chuo, 104-0031, Tokyo, Japan
Tel.: (81) 362286591
Marketing Consultancy Services
N.A.I.C.S.: 541613

Mintel Pesquisas De Mercado Brasil Ltda (1)
R Br de Capanema 343 11, andar Jardins, Sao Paulo, 01411-011, Brazil
Tel.: (55) 1132301004
Web Site: http://www.brasil.mintel.com
Marketing Consultancy Services
N.A.I.C.S.: 541613

MINTH GROUP LIMITED
No 8 Dagang No 6 Road, Ningbo Economic and Technological Development Zone, Ningbo, 315800, China
Tel.: (86) 57486801018   Ky
Web Site: http://www.minthgroup.com
Year Founded: 2005
0425—(HKG)
Rev.: $2,429,817,577
Assets: $4,671,641,239
Liabilities: $2,186,825,332
Net Worth: $2,484,815,908
Earnings: $214,862,684
Emp.: 21,331
Fiscal Year-end: 12/31/22
Automobile Parts Mfr & Whslr
N.A.I.C.S.: 336211
Chiung Hui Huang *(Chief HR Officer)*

Subsidiaries:

CST GmbH (1)
Bakenroder Strasse 7, 38871, Ilsenburg, Germany
Tel.: (49) 394 524 8610
Web Site: https://www.cstgmbh.de
Aluminum Polishing Services
N.A.I.C.S.: 332813

Chongqing Changtai Auto Parts Co., Ltd. (1)
Xingke 4 Road High-Tech Zone, Yubei District, Chongqing, China
Tel.: (86) 2386046056
Auto Parts Mfr
N.A.I.C.S.: 336390

Constant Gain International Limited (1)
15/F City Indl Complex Blk C-D, Kwai Chung, New Territories, China (Hong Kong)
Tel.: (852) 24268168
Emp.: 50
Apparel Distr
N.A.I.C.S.: 424350
So Spencer *(Mgr-Gen Products Dev)*

Fuzhou Shintai Auto Parts Co., Ltd. (1)
Dongnan Auto City Qingkou Investment Zone, Minhou, Xiamen, Fujian, China
Tel.: (86) 59122778610
Auto Parts Mfr
N.A.I.C.S.: 336390

Guangzhou Minhui Auto Parts Co., Ltd. (1)
No 4 Yongshun Road Yonghe Development Zone, Economy and Technology Development Zone, Guangzhou, China
Tel.: (86) 2032221166
Auto Parts Mfr
N.A.I.C.S.: 336390

Huzhou Enchi Automotive Co., Ltd. (1)
2728 Maoergang Road, Wuxing District, Huzhou, 313000, Zhejiang, China
Tel.: (86) 4000572199
Web Site: http://www.enchiauto.com
Bus Parts Mfr
N.A.I.C.S.: 336120

Jiaxing Minth Machines Co., Ltd. (1)
No 786 Yazhong Rd, Jiaxing, Zhejiang, China
Tel.: (86) 57382586027
Automobile Parts Mfr
N.A.I.C.S.: 336390

MINTH Japan Ltd. (1)
6-90-1 Onoecho, Naka-Ku, Yokohama, Kanagawa, Japan
Tel.: (81) 456805881
Automobile Body Parts Distr
N.A.I.C.S.: 441330

Minth Aapico (Thailand) Co., Ltd. (1)
7/290 Moo 6 Amata City Industrial Estate Tambol Mabyangporn, Amphur Pluakdaeng, Rayong, 21140, Thailand
Tel.: (66) 38650865
Auto Parts Mfr
N.A.I.C.S.: 336390

Minth Automotive (UK) Company (1)
Hanover Place, Sunderland, SR4 6BY, United Kingdom
Tel.: (44) 7749166390
Auto Parts Mfr
N.A.I.C.S.: 336390

Minth GmbH (1)
Carl-von-Linde-Str 38, 85716, Unterschleissheim, Germany
Tel.: (49) 8917927726
Automotive Part Whslr
N.A.I.C.S.: 441330

Minth Mexico, S.A. DE C.V (1)
Arroyo de Los Arellano 214, 20283, Aguascalientes, Mexico
Tel.: (52) 4499295434
Rev.: $4,790,100
Emp.: 700
Automobile Body Parts Mfr
N.A.I.C.S.: 336211
Manuel Ando Camacho *(Plant Mgr)*

Minth North America, Inc. (1)
51331 Pontiac Trl, Wixom, MI 48393
Tel.: (248) 848-3580
Web Site: http://www.minthgroup.com
Emp.: 100
Automotive Part Whslr
N.A.I.C.S.: 441330

Ningbo Guohong Automotive Co., Ltd. (1)

INTERNATIONAL PUBLIC

NO 7 GangXi Road Ningbo Free Zone, 315800, Ningbo, Zhejiang, China
Tel.: (86) 574 86809522
Automotive Body Parts Mfr & Distr
N.A.I.C.S.: 336211

Wuhan Minhui Auto Parts Co., Ltd. (1)
41MD No 2 Fengshu Road Zhuankou Economy & Technology Development Zone, Wuhan, Hubei, China
Tel.: (86) 2784229218
Auto Parts Mfr
N.A.I.C.S.: 336390

MINTO APARTMENT REIT
200-180 Kent Street, Ottawa, K1P 0B6, ON, Canada
Tel.: (613) 230-7051
Web Site:
   https://www.mintoapartments.com
Year Founded: 1955
MI.UN—(TSX)
Rev.: $79,920,135
Assets: $1,568,971,572
Liabilities: $1,043,423,871
Net Worth: $525,547,701
Earnings: $15,278,782
Emp.: 147
Fiscal Year-end: 12/31/19
Real Estate Investment Services
N.A.I.C.S.: 531390
Jonathan Li *(Pres)*

MINTYE INDUSTRIES BHD.
No 175 Jalan Usaha 3 Air Keroh Industrial Area, 75450, Melaka, Malaysia
Tel.: (60) 62331188
Web Site: http://www.mintye.com
Sales Range: $10-24.9 Million
Brake Linings Mfr
N.A.I.C.S.: 335314
Kim Swee Yeo *(Chm)*

Subsidiaries:

Eurochain Manufacturer Sdn. Bhd. (1)
11B Kawasan Perusahaan Dioh, 72000, Kuala Pilah, Negeri Sembilan, Malaysia
Tel.: (60) 64817989
Sales Range: $25-49.9 Million
Emp.: 50
Motorcycle Roller Chains Mfr
N.A.I.C.S.: 336390

Mintye Chemicals Sdn. Bhd. (1)
19 Jalan Segambul Pusat, 51200, Kuala Lumpur, Malaysia
Tel.: (60) 362520004
Brake Fluid Blending Services
N.A.I.C.S.: 561990
Yeo Kin Soon *(Mng Dir)*

Mintye Metal Products Sdn. Bhd. (1)
Lot 4291 Ayer Keroh Industrial Estate Air Keroh, Air Keruh, 75450, Malacca, Malaysia
Tel.: (60) 62331111
Web Site: http://www.mintye.com
Sales Range: $25-49.9 Million
Emp.: 100
Sheet Metal Stamping & Fabrication Services
N.A.I.C.S.: 332119
Tan Kwee Kee *(Gen Mgr)*

MINUPAR PARTICIPACOES S.A.
Av Senador Alberto Pasqualini 1535, Sao Cristovao, Lajeado, 95913162, RS, Brazil
Tel.: (55) 5137149400
Web Site:
   https://www.minuano.com.br
Year Founded: 1946
MNPR3—(BRAZ)
Rev.: $65,795,390
Assets: $58,507,533
Liabilities: $116,456,978
Net Worth: ($57,949,445)
Earnings: $2,128,850

AND PRIVATE COMPANIES — MIRADA PLC

Fiscal Year-end: 12/31/23
Processed Meat Mfr & Distr
N.A.I.C.S.: 311991

MIOVISION TECHNOLOGIES, INC.
137 Glasgow St Suite 110, Kitchener, N2G 4X8, ON, Canada
Tel.: (519) 513-2407
Web Site: https://www.miovision.com
Year Founded: 2005
Software Development Services
N.A.I.C.S.: 513210
Kurtis McBride *(CEO)*

Subsidiaries:

C J Hensch & Associates, Inc. (1)
5215 Sycamore Ave, Pasadena, TX 77503-3949
Tel.: (214) 492-6300
Web Site: http://www.cjhensch.com
Scientific & Technical Consulting Services
N.A.I.C.S.: 541690
Roger Allen *(Pres)*

Global Traffic Technologies, LLC (1)
7800 3rd St N Bldg 100, Saint Paul, MN 55128-5441
Tel.: (651) 789-7333
Web Site: http://www.gtt.com
Traffic Control Equipment Mfr
N.A.I.C.S.: 334519
Terry Griffith *(Pres)*

MIP D.D.
Panovska cesta 1, 5000, Nova Gorica, Slovenia
Tel.: (386) 53304100
Sales Range: $150-199.9 Million
Emp.: 1,000
Meat & Poultry Products
N.A.I.C.S.: 311613
Marjan Velikonja *(Dir-Investment Projects)*

MIPCO SEAMLESS RINGS (GUJARAT) LIMITED
34 Corpus Techno Park 4th Block Avs Compound Koramangala, Bengaluru, 560 034, Karnataka, India
Tel.: (91) 8025520334   In
Web Site: http://www.mipco.co.in
Year Founded: 1980
Assets: $54,982
Liabilities: $112,220
Net Worth: ($57,237)
Earnings: ($16,380)
Mechanical Parts Mfr & Distr
N.A.I.C.S.: 332991
Sachendra Tummala *(Mng Dir)*

MIPIEN S.P.A
Via Anna Maria Adorni 1, Parma, 43121, Italy
Tel.: (39) 05212021
Web Site: http://www.pizzarotti.it
Holding Company
N.A.I.C.S.: 551112
Paolo Pizzarotti *(Pres)*

Subsidiaries:

Impresa Pizzarotti & C. S.p.A. (1)
Via Anna Maria Adorni 1, 43121, Parma, Italy
(92.41%)
Tel.: (39) 05212021
Web Site: http://www.pizzarotti.it
Sales Range: $1-4.9 Billion
Emp.: 1,718
Civil Engineering & Construction Services
N.A.I.C.S.: 236220
Bianchi Corrado *(Mng Dir)*

Subsidiary (Domestic):

Garboli S.p.A. (2)
Via Carlo Pesenti 121-123, 00156, Rome, Italy
Tel.: (39) 0323586773
Web Site: http://www.garboli.com
Sales Range: $250-299.9 Million
Emp.: 996

General Construction & Civil Engineering Contractor
N.A.I.C.S.: 237990

MIPOX CORPORATION
16F D-Tower Nishishinjuku 6-11-3 Nishishinjuku, Shinjuku-ku, Tokyo, 160-0023, Japan
Tel.: (81) 369112300
Web Site: http://www.mipox.co.jp
Year Founded: 1925
5381—(TKS)
Rev.: $61,803,749
Assets: $105,563,234
Liabilities: $56,114,950
Net Worth: $49,448,285
Earnings: ($2,695,738)
Fiscal Year-end: 03/31/24
Machine Tools Mfr
N.A.I.C.S.: 333517
Jun Watanabe *(Pres & CEO)*

Subsidiaries:

Mipox (Shanghai) Trading Co., Ltd. (1)
5968 Room 9F Taikang Insurance Centre 429 Nanquan North Road, Pudong district, Shanghai, 200120, China
Tel.: (86) 216 275 1212
Semiconductor Devices Mfr
N.A.I.C.S.: 334413

Mipox Abrasives India Pvt. Ltd. (1)
310 - 311/4 8th Cross Peenya Industrial Area 4th Phase, Bengaluru, 560058, India
Tel.: (91) 903 603 0898
Abrasive Product Mfr
N.A.I.C.S.: 327910

Mipox International Corp. (1)
1730 S Amphlett Blvd Ste 105, San Mateo, CA 94402
Tel.: (650) 638-9830
Web Site: https://www.mipox.co.jp
Abrasive Product Mfr
N.A.I.C.S.: 327910
Sam Murata *(Gen Mgr)*

Mipox Malaysia Sdn. Bhd. (1)
No 7 9 12 14 and 16 Lintang Bayan Lepas 2, Bayan Lepas Industrial Park Phase 4, 11900, Bayan Lepas, Penang, Malaysia
Tel.: (60) 4 642 8371
Semiconductor Devices Mfr
N.A.I.C.S.: 334413

Nihon Kenshi Co., Ltd. (1)
2-6-11, Kitahama, Chuo-ku, Osaka, 550-0041, Japan   (66.15%)
Tel.: (81) 647077110
Web Site: http://www.nihonkenshi.co.jp
Sales Range: $25-49.9 Million
Abrasive Product Mfr
N.A.I.C.S.: 327910
Kazunori Kaneyuki *(Pres)*

MIPS AB
Kemistvagen 1B, SE-183 79, Taby, Sweden
Tel.: (46) 709924042   SE
Web Site: https://www.mipscorp.com
Year Founded: 1996
MIPS—(OMX)
Rev.: $52,731,649
Assets: $71,838,677
Liabilities: $13,206,328
Net Worth: $58,632,349
Earnings: $16,390,832
Emp.: 100
Fiscal Year-end: 12/31/22
Sportswear Mfr & Distr
N.A.I.C.S.: 339920
Max Strandwitz *(CEO)*

MIQUEL Y COSTAS & MIQUEL, S.A.
Tuset 8-10 7 Planta, 08006, Barcelona, Spain
Tel.: (34) 932906100
Web Site: https://www.miquelycostas.com
Year Founded: 1879

MCM—(VAL)
Rev.: $215,118,077
Assets: $379,120,867
Liabilities: $126,664,878
Net Worth: $252,455,990
Earnings: $36,568,270
Emp.: 506
Fiscal Year-end: 12/31/23
Paper Mfr & Distr
N.A.I.C.S.: 322299

Subsidiaries:

Celulosa de Levante S.A. (1)
Carretera C-42 Km 8 5 Tortosa, 43500, Tarragona, Spain
Tel.: (34) 977449050
Web Site: http://www.celesa-pulp.com
Pulp Product Mfr
N.A.I.C.S.: 322299

Clariana, S.A. (1)
AvD Germany 48, 12540, Villarreal, Castellon, Spain
Tel.: (34) 964521950
Web Site: https://clariana.com
Paper Mfr
N.A.I.C.S.: 322291

MB Papeles Especiales S.A. (1)
Ctra del Carme Km 1, La Pobla de Claramunt, 08787, Barcelona, Spain
Tel.: (34) 938087100
Web Site: http://www.mbpapers.com
Sales Range: $25-49.9 Million
Filter & Absorbent Paper Mfr
N.A.I.C.S.: 339940

Miquel y Costas Argentina S.A. (1)
Presidente Sarmiento 1297, 1870, Avellaneda, Buenos Aires, Argentina
Tel.: (54) 1142053205
Web Site: http://www.smokingpaper.com.ar
Sales Range: $25-49.9 Million
Cigarette Paper & Rolling Paper Mfr
N.A.I.C.S.: 322120

Miquel y Costas Tecnologias S.A. (1)
Carrer de Tuset 10 7th Fl, 08006, Barcelona, Spain
Tel.: (34) 935054360
Technical Consulting Services
N.A.I.C.S.: 541690
Jorge Mercader Miro *(Pres)*

Papeles Anoia S.A. (1)
Tuset 8, 08006, Barcelona, Spain
Tel.: (34) 932375200
Web Site: http://www.papelesanoia.com
Sales Range: $25-49.9 Million
Specialty Papers & Related Products Mfr
N.A.I.C.S.: 322120

Sociedad Espanola Zig Zag S.A. (1)
Tuset 8, 08006, Barcelona, Spain
Tel.: (34) 932906100
Web Site: http://www.miquelycostas.com
Cigarette Paper & Rolling Paper Mfr
N.A.I.C.S.: 322120

Terranova Papers, S.A. (1)
Ctra de Carme Km 1, La Pobla de Claramunt, 08787, Barcelona, Spain
Tel.: (34) 938087100
Web Site: https://terranovapapers.com
Paper Mfr
N.A.I.C.S.: 322291

MIRACH ENERGY LIMITED
80 Robinson Road 02-00, Singapore, 068898, Singapore
Tel.: (65) 6536 8033   SG
Web Site: http://www.mirachenergy.com
AWO—(SES)
Sales Range: $1-9.9 Million
Oil & Gas Exploration & Production
N.A.I.C.S.: 211120
William Shut Li Chan *(Chm)*

MIRACLE AUTOMATION ENGINEERING CO., LTD.
No 288 Luo'ou Road Luoshe Town, Huishan District, Wuxi, 214081, Jiangsu, China

Web Site: http://www.chinaconveyor.com
002009—(SSE)
Rev.: $610,911,288
Assets: $1,019,426,148
Liabilities: $696,233,772
Net Worth: $323,192,376
Earnings: $27,866,592
Fiscal Year-end: 12/31/22
Engineering Machinery Mfr
N.A.I.C.S.: 333922
Huang Bin *(Chm & Gen Mgr)*

Subsidiaries:

Changchun Faw Miracle Technology Equipment Engineering Co. Ltd. (1)
1841 Jincheng Street, Automobile Industry Development Zone, Changchun, Jilin, China
Tel.: (86) 4318 590 7739
Web Site: https://www.faw-tq.com
Motor Vehicle Parts Mfr
N.A.I.C.S.: 336211

Hubei Lidi Machine Tool Co. LTD. (1)
No 2 Longxi Road Development Avenue, Xiling Economic Development Zone, Yichang, 443000, Hubei, China
Tel.: (86) 7176731227
Recycling Services
N.A.I.C.S.: 562920

MIRACLE INDUSTRIES LIMITED
99 Rupayan Golden Age 7th Floor Gulshan Avenue, Dhaka, 1212, Bangladesh
Tel.: (880) 258810353
Web Site: https://www.miracle.com.bd
Year Founded: 1993
MIRACLEIND—(CHT)
Assets: $13,554,402
Liabilities: $7,944,451
Net Worth: $5,609,950
Earnings: ($794,779)
Emp.: 33
Fiscal Year-end: 06/30/23
Kraft Paper Mfr
N.A.I.C.S.: 322120

MIRACLL CHEMICALS CO., LTD.
No 35 Changsha Road, Yantai, 264006, Shandong, China
Tel.: (86) 5353979898
Web Site: https://www.miracll.com
Year Founded: 2009
300848—(SSE)
Rev.: $207,098,424
Assets: $268,877,232
Liabilities: $100,484,280
Net Worth: $168,392,952
Earnings: $15,623,712
Fiscal Year-end: 12/31/22
Chemical Product Mfr & Distr
N.A.I.C.S.: 325520
Renhong Wang *(Chm & Gen Mgr)*

MIRACULUM S.A.
Ul Wschodu Slonca 8, 02-226, Warsaw, Poland
Tel.: (48) 222034885
Web Site: https://www.miraculum.pl
Year Founded: 1924
MIR—(WAR)
Rev.: $11,957,063
Assets: $15,132,876
Liabilities: $9,637,703
Net Worth: $5,495,173
Earnings: ($415,904)
Fiscal Year-end: 12/31/23
Cosmetic Product Distr
N.A.I.C.S.: 456120
Tomasz Sarapata *(Chm-Mgmt Bd)*

MIRADA PLC

MIRADA PLC

Mirada Plc—(Continued)

68 Lombard Street, London, EC3V 9LJ, United Kingdom
Tel.: (44) 2078682104
Web Site: http://www.mirada.tv
MIRA—(AIM)
Rev.: $11,134,000
Assets: $18,632,000
Liabilities: $10,734,000
Net Worth: $7,898,000
Earnings: ($2,992,000)
Emp.: 172
Fiscal Year-end: 03/31/21
Interactive Content & Services Developer & Supplier Via TV, the Web, Telephony & Mobile Phones
N.A.I.C.S.: 517112
Jose-Luis Vazquez (CEO)

Subsidiaries:

Fresh Interactive Technologies S.A (1)
Av de las Aguilas 2B, Pozuelo de Alarcon, 28044, Madrid, Spain
Tel.: (34) 917616400
Web Site: http://www.mirada.tv
Sales Range: $25-49.9 Million
Advertising Software Development Services
N.A.I.C.S.: 541511

YooMedia Enhanced Solutions (1)
Northumberland House, 155-157 Great Portland Street, London, W1W 6QP, United Kingdom
Tel.: (44) 2074620870
Sales Range: $25-49.9 Million
Emp.: 35
Interactive Content Supplier
N.A.I.C.S.: 513199

YooMedia Gambling & Games (1)
6 & 7 Prince Court, Wapping Lane, London, E1W 2DA, United Kingdom
Tel.: (44) 2079427942
Sales Range: $50-74.9 Million
Emp.: 27
Interactive Casino Games for TV, the Web & Mobile Phones
N.A.I.C.S.: 713290

MIRAE ASSET FINANCIAL GROUP

12F Tower 1 33 Jong-ro, Jongno-gu, Seoul, 03159, Korea (South)
Tel.: (82) 237742222
Web Site:
https://global.miraeasset.com
Year Founded: 1997
Sales Range: $5-14.9 Billion
Emp.: 12,578
Holding Company; Asset Management, Securities Brokerage, Investment Banking & Other Financial Products & Services
N.A.I.C.S.: 551112
Hyeon-Joo Park (Founder & Officer-Strategy-Global)

Subsidiaries:

Mirae Asset Global Investments Co., Ltd. (1)
East Tower 26F Mirae Asset CENTER1 67 Suha-dong, Jung-gu, Seoul, 100-210, Korea (South)
Tel.: (82) 3774 6644
Web Site:
http://investments.miraeasset.com
Rev.: $44,000,000,000
Asset Management Services
N.A.I.C.S.: 523940
Hyeon-Joo Park (Founder)

Subsidiary (Non-US):

Horizons ETFs Management (Canada) Inc. (2)
55 University Avenue Suite 800, Toronto, M5J 2H7, ON, Canada
Tel.: (416) 933-5745
Web Site: http://www.horizonsetfs.com
Emp.: 45
Fund Management Services

N.A.I.C.S.: 523940
Jasmit Bhandal (Pres)

Mirae Asset Global Investments (Brazil) Limited (2)
Olimpiadas 8194 Floor 12, CJ 122 Vila Nova Conceicao, São Paulo, 04551-000, Brazil
Tel.: (55) 11 2608 8500
Web Site:
http://www.investments.miraeasset.com.br
Emp.: 15
Asset Management Services
N.A.I.C.S.: 523940
Young Hwan Kim (Chief Investment Officer)

Mirae Asset Global Investments (China) (2)
5th Floor Mirae Asset Tower 166 Lujazui Ring Road, Pudong, Shanghai, 200120, China
Tel.: (86) 21 3135 2088
Investment Management Service
N.A.I.C.S.: 523940
Yangwen Shen (Mgr-Bus Dev)

Mirae Asset Global Investments (HK) Limited (2)
Level 15 Three Pacific Place, 1 Queens Road East, Hong Kong, China (Hong Kong)
Tel.: (852) 2295 1500
Web Site:
http://investments.miraeasset.com.hk
Asset Management Services
N.A.I.C.S.: 523940
Jung Ho Rhee (CEO)

Mirae Asset Global Investments (India) Pvt. Ltd. (2)
Unit No 606 6th Floor Windsor Building Off CST Road, Kalina Santacruz E, Mumbai, 400 098, India
Tel.: (91) 22 6780 0300
Web Site: http://www.miraeassetmf.co.in
Asset Management Services
N.A.I.C.S.: 523940
Puneet Bhatia (Head-Real Estate)

Mirae Asset Global Investments (UK) Ltd. (2)
4-6 Royal Exchange Buildings, London, EC3V 3NL, United Kingdom
Tel.: (44) 20 7715 9900
Emp.: 3
Asset Management
N.A.I.C.S.: 523940
Jose Morales (Chief Investment Officer)

Subsidiary (US):

Mirae Asset Global Investments (USA) LLC (2)
1350 Avenue of the Americas 33rd Fl, New York, NY 10019
Tel.: (212) 205-8300
Web Site: http://investments.miraeasset.us
Emp.: 38
Asset Management
N.A.I.C.S.: 523940
Robert P. Mulligan (Pres & Head-SIs & Distr)

Subsidiary (Domestic):

Multi Asset Global Investments Co., Ltd. (2)
16th Floor Mirae Asset Dawoo Bldg 56 Gukjegeumyung-ro, Yeongdeungpo-gu, Seoul, 150-716, Korea (South)
Tel.: (82) 2 3774 8000
Web Site: http://www.kdbasset.co.kr
Sales Range: $75-99.9 Million
Emp.: 70
Investment Advice
N.A.I.C.S.: 523940
Ki Cheon Nam (CEO)

Mirae Asset Securities Co., Ltd. (1)
Mirae Asset CENTER1 Bldg East Tower 26 Eulji-ro 5 gil, Jung-gu, Seoul, 100-210, Korea (South)
Tel.: (82) 15886800
Web Site:
https://english.securities.miraeasset.com
Rev.: $14,791,150,136
Assets: $93,120,817,234
Liabilities: $84,955,781,002
Net Worth: $8,165,036,232
Earnings: $245,453,698

Emp.: 3,470
Fiscal Year-end: 12/31/2023
Securities, Investment & Asset Management Services
N.A.I.C.S.: 523150
Hyeon-Joo Park (Founder & Officer-Strategy-Global)

Subsidiary (Non-US):

Mirae Asset Capital Markets (India) Pvt Ltd (2)
Tower 4,Equinox Business Park LBS Marg,1st Floor Off BKC,Kurla West Mumbai,, Maharashtra, 400070, India
Tel.: (91) 2262661300
Web Site: https://www.mstock.com
Emp.: 100
Financial Services
N.A.I.C.S.: 523999
Hyeon-Joo Park (Founder & Officer-Strategy-Global)

Subsidiary (US):

Mirae Asset Securities (USA) Inc. (2)
810 7th Ave 37th Fl, New York, NY 10019 (100%)
Tel.: (212) 407-1000
Web Site: http://miraeassetsecuritiesus.com
Securities, Investment & Management Services
N.A.I.C.S.: 523150
Jae Ryu (Pres)

MIRAE ASSET LIFE INSURANCE CO., LTD.

MiraeAssetSecurities Bldg 56 Gukjegeumyung-ro, Yeongdeungpo-gu, Seoul, 07330, Korea (South)
Tel.: (82) 15880220
Web Site:
https://www.life.miraeasset.com
Year Founded: 1988
085620—(KRS)
Sales Range: Less than $1 Million
Fire Insurance Services
N.A.I.C.S.: 524210
Jae Samg Byun (Pres & Co-CEO)

MIRAE ING CO., LTD.

648 Samsung-ro, Gangnam-gu, Seoul, Korea (South)
Tel.: (82) 234704400   KR
Web Site: http://www.miraeing.co.kr
Year Founded: 1971
007120—(KRS)
Sales Range: $1-9.9 Million
Communication Equipment Mfr
N.A.I.C.S.: 334220
Hak Su Kim (Pres)

MIRAE JOINT STOCK COMPANY

DT 743 Str Quarter 1B An Phu Ward, Thuan An, Binh Duong, Vietnam
Tel.: (84) 2743791038
Web Site: https://www.miraejsc.com
Year Founded: 2001
KMR—(HOSE)
Rev.: $20,339,575
Assets: $36,231,445
Liabilities: $9,820,473
Net Worth: $26,410,972
Earnings: $404,378
Emp.: 229
Fiscal Year-end: 12/31/23
Textile Products Mfr
N.A.I.C.S.: 314999
Young Sik Shin (CEO)

MIRAE SCI CO., LTD.

141Gwahaksaneop 4 ro Oksan-myeon, Heungdeok-gu, Cheongju, Korea (South)
Tel.: (82) 437100115
Web Site: http://miraesci.com
Year Founded: 1984
028040—(KRS)
Rev.: $12,726,280

Assets: $46,788,300
Liabilities: $32,239,680
Net Worth: $14,548,620
Earnings: $17,732,340
Fiscal Year-end: 12/31/19
Photoconductor Drum Mfr
N.A.I.C.S.: 334419
Jeong Oh Gong (CEO)

MIRAE TECHNOLOGY CO., LTD.

907 G-plus Kolon Digital Tower 123 Digital-ro 26-gil, Guro-gu, 08390, Seoul, Korea (South)
Tel.: (82) 28304474
Web Site: http://www.mirae-tech.co.kr
Year Founded: 1997
213090—(KRS)
Rev.: $22,696,074
Assets: $94,057,519
Liabilities: $26,069,116
Net Worth: $67,988,403
Earnings: $1,948,522
Emp.: 37
Fiscal Year-end: 12/31/20
Software Publishing Services
N.A.I.C.S.: 513210

MIRAEASSET NO. 3 SPECIAL PURPOSE ACQUISITION CO., LTD.

16F 26 Eulji-ro 5-gil, Jung-gu, Seoul, Korea (South)
Tel.: (82) 237743822
Year Founded: 2015
Investment Holding Company
N.A.I.C.S.: 551112
Kyung-Ha Lee (CEO)

MIRAI CORPORATION

101-0065 2-1 Nishikanda 3-chome, Chiyoda-ku, Tokyo, Japan
Tel.: (81) 366325960
Web Site: https://www.3476.jp
Year Founded: 2015
3476—(TKS)
Sales Range: Less than $1 Million
Real Estate Investment Services
N.A.I.C.S.: 531210
Michio Suganuma (Exec Dir)

MIRAI INDUSTRY CO., LTD.

1695-1 Niremata Wanochicho, Ampachi-Gun, Gifu, 503-0201, Japan
Tel.: (81) 584680010
Web Site: https://www.mirai.co.jp
Year Founded: 1965
7931—(TKS)
Rev.: $291,441,510
Assets: $419,959,740
Liabilities: $84,224,620
Net Worth: $335,735,120
Earnings: $33,816,760
Emp.: 1,252
Fiscal Year-end: 03/31/24
Electric Cable Pipe Mfr & Distr
N.A.I.C.S.: 335931
Masahiro Yamada (Board of Directors & Pres)

MIRAI WORKS, INC.

2F Prime Terrace KAMIYACHO 4-1-13 Toranomon, Minato-ku, Tokyo, 105-0001, Japan
Tel.: (81) 358601835
Web Site: https://www.mirai-works.co.jp
6563—(TKS)
Rev.: $59,336,210
Assets: $19,128,820
Liabilities: $10,968,230
Net Worth: $8,160,590
Earnings: $914,610
Emp.: 176
Fiscal Year-end: 09/30/23

AND PRIVATE COMPANIES

Human Resource Consulting Services
N.A.I.C.S.: 541612
Nagaharu Okamoto *(Pres)*

MIRAIAL CO., LTD.
Nissay Ikebukuro Building 1-24-1 Higashi-Ikebukuro, Toshima-ku, Tokyo, 170-0013, Japan
Tel.: (81) 339863782
Web Site: https://www.miraial.co.jp
Year Founded: 1968
4238—(TKS)
Rev.: $93,987,559
Assets: $188,109,831
Liabilities: $33,593,320
Net Worth: $154,516,511
Earnings: $7,267,445
Emp.: 313
Fiscal Year-end: 01/31/24
Semiconductor Product Mfr
N.A.I.C.S.: 334413
Masatoshi Hyobu *(Pres)*

Subsidiaries:

Miraial Tohoku Co., Ltd. (1)
1-1 Miyazawamae Okajima, Fukushima, 960-8201, Japan
Tel.: (81) 245724765
Web Site: https://miraial-tohoku.co.jp
Emp.: 34
Precision Machinery Metal Parts Mfr
N.A.I.C.S.: 332710

MIRAIT ONE CORPORATION
5-6-36 Toyosu, Koto-ku, Tokyo, 135-8111, Japan
Tel.: (81) 368073111
Web Site: https://www.mirait-one.com
Year Founded: 2010
1417—(TKS)
Rev.: $3,426,518,240
Assets: $3,436,935,600
Liabilities: $1,717,753,920
Net Worth: $1,719,181,680
Earnings: $82,856,350
Emp.: 16,985
Fiscal Year-end: 03/31/24
Holding Company; Engineering Services
N.A.I.C.S.: 551112
Toshiki Nakayama *(Pres & CEO)*

Subsidiaries:

Agility Rise Co., Ltd. (1)
430-1 Igusa Kawajima-cho, Hiki, 350-0158, Saitama Prefecture, Japan
Tel.: (81) 492997421
Cabling Infrastructure Services
N.A.I.C.S.: 517111

Appsilan Asia Pte. Ltd. (1)
8 Ayer Rajah Crescent, Singapore, 139939, Singapore
Tel.: (65) 65787101
Web Site: https://www.appsilan.com
Data Infrastructure & Management Services
N.A.I.C.S.: 518210

Ast-Eng Corp. (1)
3-9-10 Nagata, Joto-ku, Osaka, 536-0022, Japan
Tel.: (81) 642586140
Web Site: http://www.ast-eng.co.jp
Electrical Contracting Services
N.A.I.C.S.: 238210

Comlead Co., Ltd. (1)
2-2-13 Saiwai-cho, Naniwa-ku, Osaka, 556-0021, Japan
Tel.: (81) 666848335
Web Site: http://www.comlead.co.jp
Telecommunication Servicesb
N.A.I.C.S.: 517810

Cotonet Engineering Co., Ltd. (1)
5 Kamitobasugata-cho, Minami-ku, Kyoto, 601-8102, Japan
Tel.: (81) 756922511
Web Site: http://www.cotonet.jp
Civil Engineering Services
N.A.I.C.S.: 541330

Creist Inc. (1)
2-25-2 Nishigotanda, Shinagawa-ku, Tokyo, 141-0031, Japan
Tel.: (81) 358436295
Web Site: http://www.creist.co.jp
Infrastructure Construction Services
N.A.I.C.S.: 236220

Daimei SLK (Private) Limited (1)
No.125/4A Buthgamuwa Road, Kalapaluwawa Rajagiriya, Colombo, Sri Lanka
Tel.: (94) 112794009
Web Site: http://www.daimeislk.com
Telecom Design & Construction Services
N.A.I.C.S.: 237130
Kiyoshi Washizawa *(Chm)*

Daimei Tusan Co., Ltd. (1)
Mirait One Shinkiba Building 6th Fl 2-15-20 Shinkiba, Koto-ku, Tokyo, 136-0082, Japan
Tel.: (81) 362750150
Web Site: http://www.daimei-tusan.co.jp
Communication Control Equipment Mfr & Distr
N.A.I.C.S.: 334220

Ground Create Co., Ltd. (1)
3-3-15 Edobori, Nishi-ku, Osaka, 550-0002, Japan
Tel.: (81) 664463379
Web Site: http://www.gr-cr.com
Telecommunication Equipment Construction Services
N.A.I.C.S.: 238210

Hokubu Co., Ltd. (1)
2-60 Tomizukahigashi, Wakabayashi-ku, Sendai, 984-0824, Japan
Tel.: (81) 222863741
Telecommunication Equipment Construction Services
N.A.I.C.S.: 238210

Hope Net Co., Ltd. (1)
7F Yusen Awajicho Building 1-4-1 Kanda Awajicho, Chiyoda-ku, Tokyo, 101-0063, Japan
Tel.: (81) 352978004
Web Site: http://www.hope-net.co.jp
Employment Agency Services
N.A.I.C.S.: 561311

Katakura Construction Co., Ltd. (1)
5-31-12 Taishido, Setagaya-ku, Tokyo, 154-0004, Japan
Tel.: (81) 364508890
Web Site: http://www.kata-kura.com
Civil Engineering Services
N.A.I.C.S.: 541330

Lantro (Cambodia) Co., Ltd. (1)
WG119 St 06, Sangkat Toul Sangke Khan Russie Keo, Phnom Penh, Cambodia
Tel.: (855) 236850645
Cabling Infrastructure Services
N.A.I.C.S.: 517111

Lantro Myanmar Co., Ltd. (1)
No B-3 Kan Street Kan Yeik Mon Housing, Ward 10 Hlaing Township, Yangon, Myanmar
Tel.: (95) 9259166115
Cabling Infrastructure Services
N.A.I.C.S.: 517111

Lantrovision (S) Ltd (1)
8 Ayer Rajah Crescent LanTroVision Building, Singapore, 139939, Singapore
Tel.: (65) 67781668
Telecommunication Servicesb
N.A.I.C.S.: 334220

Subsidiary (Non-US):

Hangzhou Lantro Co., Ltd. (2)
Rm 213 Block 3 No 23 HuangGushan Road Xixi software zone, Hangzhou, 310003, Zhejiang, China
Tel.: (86) 57156830535
Web Site: http://www.lantro.com
Cables Mfr & Whslr
N.A.I.C.S.: 335921

Lantro (HK) Limited (2)
Unit 401-403 4/F Shui Hing Centre 13 Sheung Yuet Road, Kowloon Bay, China (Hong Kong)
Tel.: (852) 27893846
Web Site: http://www.lantro.com.hk
Computer Network Systems Integration Design Services
N.A.I.C.S.: 541512

Lantro (Malaysia) Sdn Bhd (2)
69 Jalan 3/32A Taman Danau Kota Off Jalan Genting Kelang, Setapak, 53300, Kuala Lumpur, Malaysia
Tel.: (60) 341436177
Computer Network Systems Integration Design Services
N.A.I.C.S.: 541512

Lantro (Penang) Sdn Bhd (2)
11-A Lorong Mayang Pasir 5 Taman Sri Tunas, 11950, Bayan Baru, Penang, Malaysia
Tel.: (60) 46435033
Computer Network Systems Integration Design Services
N.A.I.C.S.: 541512

Subsidiary (Domestic):

Lantro (S) Pte Ltd (2)
LanTroVision Building 8 Ayer Rajah Crescent, Singapore, 139 939, Singapore
Tel.: (65) 67781668
Computer Network Systems Integration Design Services
N.A.I.C.S.: 541512
Kenneth Ang *(Treasurer)*

Subsidiary (Non-US):

Lantro (Shanghai) Co., Ltd. (2)
Unit 1201-B Bldg 1 No 49 Lane 299 JiangChang W Rd, JingAn District, Shanghai, 200436, China
Tel.: (86) 2161421866
Web Site: http://www.lantro.com.cn
Network Systems Integration Design Services
N.A.I.C.S.: 541512

Lantro (Taiwan) Ltd. (2)
No 15 Lane 360 Neihu Road Section 1, Neihu, Taipei, 114, Taiwan
Tel.: (886) 226581047
Computer Network Systems Integration Design Services
N.A.I.C.S.: 541512

Lantro Technologies India Private Limited (2)
No 731 3rd Block Behind BDA Complex Koramangala, Bengaluru, 560 034, Karnataka, India
Tel.: (91) 8041264887
Cable Installation Services
N.A.I.C.S.: 238210

Lantrovision Korea Co. Ltd. (2)
Unit 503 Seokchon City Bldg 66-7 Bamgyee - Dong, Songpa-Gu, Seoul, 138-050, Korea (South)
Tel.: (82) 234318855
Computer Network Systems Integration Design Services
N.A.I.C.S.: 541512

Lapisnet Co., Ltd. (1)
3-1-10 Koyochonishi, Higashi-Nada-ku, Kobe, 658-0033, Hyogo Prefecture, Japan
Tel.: (81) 789404681
Web Site: http://www.lapisnet.co.jp
Electrical Contracting Services
N.A.I.C.S.: 238210

Libnet Co., Ltd. (1)
135 Otsu Kusube-cho, Ise, 516-0014, Mie Prefecture, Japan
Tel.: (81) 596257903
Web Site: http://www.libnet.co.jp
Library Management Services
N.A.I.C.S.: 519210

MIRAIT Corporation (1)
5-6-36 Toyosu, Koto-ku, Tokyo, 135-8112, Japan
Tel.: (81) 36 807 3700
Web Site: https://www.mrt.mirait.co.jp
Sales Range: $1-4.9 Billion
Emp.: 5,012
Telecommunication Engineering Services
N.A.I.C.S.: 541330
Masatoshi Suzuki *(Chm)*

Subsidiary (Domestic):

Kokko Systems Co., Ltd. (2)
4-11 Yotsuya, Shinjuku-ku, Tokyo, 160-0004, Japan
Tel.: (81) 333551051

MIRAIT ONE CORPORATION

Web Site: http://www.kokko-systems.co.jp
Telecommunication Equipment Construction Services
N.A.I.C.S.: 238210

Meisei Correspondence Co., Ltd. (2)
Chofu NK Building 301 4-20-2 Fuda, Chofu, 182-0024, Tokyo, Japan
Tel.: (81) 424413333
Web Site: https://www.meisei-c.co.jp
Emp.: 96
Communication Equipments Construction Services
N.A.I.C.S.: 334290
Masahiro Sakurai *(Chm)*

MIRAIT Technologies Australia Pty Limited (1)
Suite 9 Zenith Business Centre 6 Reliance Drive, Tuggerah, 2259, NSW, Australia
Tel.: (61) 243299900
Web Site: http://www.mirait.com.au
Emp.: 1,500
Telecommunication Infrastructure Services
N.A.I.C.S.: 517111
Kerry White *(CEO)*

MIRAIT Technologies Corporation (1)
3-3-15 Edobori, Nishi-ku, Osaka, 550-0002, Japan
Tel.: (81) 664463331
Web Site: http://www.miratec.co.jp
Sales Range: $700-749.9 Million
Emp.: 1,217
Communication Network Design Services
N.A.I.C.S.: 541330

Subsidiary (Domestic):

MIRAIT Information Systems Co., Ltd. (2)
1-20-10 Ebara, Shinagawa-ku, Tokyo, 142-0063, Japan
Tel.: (81) 35 843 6208
Web Site: https://www.miraitsystems.jp
Emp.: 360
Telecommunication Servicesb
N.A.I.C.S.: 517111
Mitsuyoshi Okamoto *(Pres & CEO)*

Subsidiary (Non-US):

MIRAIT PHILIPPINES INC. (2)
Unit 1205 Philippine Stock Exchange Building Exchange Road, Ortigas Center, Pasig, 1605, Metro Manila, Philippines
Tel.: (63) 276219583
Telecommunication Servicesb
N.A.I.C.S.: 517111
Hiroyuki Bamba *(Pres)*

MIRAIT-X Corporation (1)
4th Floor Premier Toyocho Building 3-23-21 Toya, Koto-ku, Tokyo, 135-0016, Japan
Tel.: (81) 362752010
Web Site: http://www.mirait-x.co.jp
Solar Power Generation Services
N.A.I.C.S.: 221114

MiratecDrone Corp. (1)
1-20-10 Ebara, Shinagawa-ku, Tokyo, 142-0063, Japan
Tel.: (81) 354965851
Web Site: http://www.miratecdrone.co.jp
Pilot Training Services
N.A.I.C.S.: 611512

Nippon Toyocom Co., Ltd. (1)
4F Milight Shinkiba Building 2-15-20 Shinkiba, Koto-ku, Tokyo, 136-0082, Japan
Tel.: (81) 362750200
Web Site: http://www.ntoyocom.co.jp
Building Comprehensive Maintenance Services
N.A.I.C.S.: 561790

Nishinihondenko Corporation (1)
2-3-39 Koda, Minami-ku, Kumamoto, 861-4108, Japan
Tel.: (81) 963340600
Web Site: http://www.nishinihondenko.jp
Electrical Contracting Services
N.A.I.C.S.: 238210

PT Lantro Technologies Indonesia (1)
CityLofts Sudirman 10-15 Jalan KH Mas Mansyur No 121, Jakarta Pusat, 10220, Indonesia

MIRAIT ONE CORPORATION

MIRAIT ONE Corporation—(Continued)
Tel.: (62) 2125558450
Cabling Infrastructure Services
N.A.I.C.S.: 517111

SOLCOM Co., Ltd. (1)
2-32 Minamisenda Higashimachi, Naka-ku, Hiroshima, 730-0054, Japan
Tel.: (81) 825043300
Web Site: https://www.solcom.co.jp
Sales Range: $350-399.9 Million
Construction Engineering Services
N.A.I.C.S.: 541330
Toshiyuki Hirahara *(Pres)*

STK Techno Corporation (1)
1-1-15 Minamidaimon-cho, Imabari, 794-0027, Ehime, Japan
Tel.: (81) 898232571
Telecommunication Equipment Construction Services
N.A.I.C.S.: 238210

Seikenkogyo Co., Ltd. (1)
3-5-15 Himejima, Nishiyodogawa-ku, Osaka, 555-0033, Japan
Tel.: (81) 664739174
Web Site: https://www.seikenkogyo.co.jp
Stainless Steel Product Mfr & Distr
N.A.I.C.S.: 331110
Hajime Kitahara *(CEO)*

Shanghai Changling Communication Equipment Co., Ltd. (1)
Unit 1201-B Bldg 1 No 49 Lane 299 JiangChang W Rd, JingAn District, Shanghai, 200436, China
Tel.: (86) 2161421866
Cabling Infrastructure Services
N.A.I.C.S.: 517111

Shikokutsuken Co., Ltd. (1)
1-1-15 Minamidaimon-cho, Imabari, 794-8601, Ehime, Japan
Tel.: (81) 898325555
Web Site: http://www.stk.co.jp
Telecommunication Equipment Construction Services
N.A.I.C.S.: 238210

Solcom Business Survice Corporation (1)
2-32 Minamisenda Higashimachi, Naka-ku, Hiroshima, 730-0054, Japan
Tel.: (81) 822583855
Web Site: http://www.solcom-bs.co.jp
Communication Equipment Rental Services
N.A.I.C.S.: 532490

Solcommeister Co., Ltd. (1)
2-1 Minamimyojinmachi Kaita-cho, Aki-gun, Hiroshima, 736-0055, Japan
Tel.: (81) 828211850
Web Site: http://www.solcom-m.co.jp
Electrical Contracting Services
N.A.I.C.S.: 238210

TTK Co., Ltd. (1)
1-2-23 Shintera, Wakabayashi-ku, Sendai, 984-8558, Miyagi, Japan
Tel.: (81) 222975111
Web Site: http://www.ttk-g.co.jp
Communication Equipment Design & Construction; Electrical Equipment Maintenance & Services
N.A.I.C.S.: 237130
Mikio Toi *(Pres & CEO)*

TTK ENG Akita Co., Ltd. (1)
1-1-7 Goshonoyumoto, Akita, 010-1415, Japan
Tel.: (81) 188267010
Telecommunication Equipment Construction Services
N.A.I.C.S.: 238210

TTK ENG Aomori Co., Ltd. (1)
354-9 Okuno Uramachi, Aomori, 030-0842, Aomori Prefecture, Japan
Tel.: (81) 177215881
Telecommunication Equipment Construction Services
N.A.I.C.S.: 238210

TTK ENG Fukushima Co., Ltd. (1)
1-5 Nakanouchi Oguraji, Fukushima, 960-8142, Fukushima Prefecture, Japan
Tel.: (81) 245201612
Telecommunication Equipment Construction Services
N.A.I.C.S.: 238210

TTK ENG Iwate Co., Ltd. (1)
11-501-9 Hiromiyasawa Yahaba-cho, Shiwa-gun, Iwate, 028-3621, Japan
Tel.: (81) 196372500
Telecommunication Equipment Distr
N.A.I.C.S.: 423690

TTK ENG Miyagi Co., Ltd. (1)
12-1 Rokuchonome Motomachi, Wakabayashi-ku, Sendai, 984-0014, Miyagi Prefecture, Japan
Tel.: (81) 223901225
Telecommunication Equipment Construction Services
N.A.I.C.S.: 238210

TTK ENG Yamagata Co., Ltd. (1)
2-8-2 Naneicho, Yamagata, 990-2445, Yamagata Prefecture, Japan
Tel.: (81) 236642260
Telecommunication Equipment Construction Services
N.A.I.C.S.: 238210

Todentsu Access Corporation (1)
590 Komagi, Nagareyama, 270-0132, Chiba Prefecture, Japan
Tel.: (81) 471782750
Web Site: http://www.todentsu-ac.co.jp
Telecommunication Equipment Maintenance Services
N.A.I.C.S.: 811210

Tokaikoei Inc. (1)
1-3-1 Toyosu, Koto-ku, Tokyo, 135-0061, Japan
Tel.: (81) 355482517
Web Site: http://www.tokai-koei.co.jp
Sewerage & Water Supply Construction Services
N.A.I.C.S.: 237110

Tsukada Electrical Construction Co., Ltd. (1)
47-19 Matsubara Kamiayashi, Aoba-ku, Sendai, Miyagi Prefecture, Japan
Tel.: (81) 223977192
Web Site: http://www.tsukadadenki.co.jp
Electrical Contracting Services
N.A.I.C.S.: 238210

VRnet (S) Pte. Ltd. (1)
8 Ayer Rajah Crescent, Singapore, 139939, Singapore
Tel.: (65) 67766618
Web Site: http://www.vrnet-inc.com
Network Consulting Services
N.A.I.C.S.: 541618

Yuwakogyo Corporation (1)
3-6 Minamikan-on-machi, Nishi-ku, Hiroshima, 733-0034, Aichi Prefecture, Japan
Tel.: (81) 822320281
Web Site: https://www.yuwa-kougyou.co.jp
Emp.: 17
Metal Products Mfr
N.A.I.C.S.: 332312

MIRAMAR RESOURCES LIMITED

Unit 1 22 Hardy St, South Perth, 6151, WA, Australia
Tel.: (61) 861666302 AU
Web Site: https://www.miramarresources.com
Year Founded: 2019
M2R—(ASX)
Rev.: $7,187
Assets: $5,932,096
Liabilities: $200,794
Net Worth: $5,731,302
Earnings: ($906,374)
Fiscal Year-end: 06/30/23
Exploration & Mining Services
N.A.I.C.S.: 213115
Allan Kelly *(Chm)*

MIRANDA MINERALS HOLDINGS LIMITED

The Greens Office Park Ground Floor Pecanwood Building, Charles de Gaulie Crescent Hig, Centurion, South Africa
Tel.: (27) 126654200
Web Site: http://www.mirandaminerals.com
Sales Range: Less than $1 Million
Mineral Exploration Service
N.A.I.C.S.: 333131
John Wallington *(Mng Dir)*

Subsidiaries:

Blue Moonlight Properties 215 (Pty) Ltd (1)
The Greens Ofc Park Ground Fl Pecanwood Highveld Technopark, Centurion, 0157, Gauteng, South Africa
Tel.: (27) 114873200
Property Management Services
N.A.I.C.S.: 531312

MIRARTH HOLDINGS, INC.

Tekko Building 16F 1-8-2 Marunouchi Chiyoda-ku, Tokyo, 100-0005, Japan
Web Site: http://www.leben.co.jp
8897—(TKS)
Rev.: $1,224,132,340
Assets: $2,230,524,670
Liabilities: $1,756,792,580
Net Worth: $473,732,090
Earnings: $54,056,580
Fiscal Year-end: 03/31/24
Leasing & Real Estate Services
N.A.I.C.S.: 531120
Masashi Yamamoto *(CFO & Mng Exec Officer)*

Subsidiaries:

Leben Clean Energy Co., Ltd. (1)
5th floor Iidabashi Building 1-18 Ageba-cho, Shinjuku-ku, Tokyo, 162-0824, Japan
Tel.: (81) 332332551
Web Site: https://www.leben-ce.com
Solar Power Generation Services
N.A.I.C.S.: 221114

Leben Community Co., Ltd. (1)
6-14 Sanbancho, Chiyoda-ku, Tokyo, 102-0075, Japan
Tel.: (81) 120901135
Web Site: https://www.l-community.co.jp
Emp.: 571
Business Research & Management Services
N.A.I.C.S.: 561499

Leben Home Build Co., Ltd. (1)
4-1-21 Nihonbashi Muromachi Kinsan Building 8F, Chuo-ku, Tokyo, 103-0022, Japan
Tel.: (81) 362621071
Web Site: https://www.leben-hb.co.jp
Commercial Building Construction Services
N.A.I.C.S.: 236220

Leben Zestock Co., Ltd. (1)
7F Yurakucho Building 1-10-1 Yurakucho, Chiyoda-ku, Tokyo, 100-0006, Japan
Tel.: (81) 362591733
Web Site: https://www.leben-zestock.co.jp
Real Estate Investment Services
N.A.I.C.S.: 531210

Takara Asset Management Co., Ltd. (1)
Otemachi Nomura Bldg 16F 2-1-1 Otemachi, Chiyoda-ku, Tokyo, 100-0004, Japan
Tel.: (81) 362626402
Web Site: https://www.takara-am.co.jp
Asset Management Services
N.A.I.C.S.: 531390

Takara Leben Realnet Co., Ltd. (1)
1-13-13 Nihonbashi Kayabacho Shippo Building 3F, Chuo-ku, Tokyo, 103-0025, Japan
Tel.: (81) 366619210
Web Site: https://www.leben-realnet.co.jp
Real Estate Brokerage Services
N.A.I.C.S.: 531210

Takara PAG Real Estate Advisory Ltd. (1)
1-14-15 Akasaka, Minato-ku, Tokyo, Japan
Tel.: (81) 364355264
Web Site: https://www.takara-pag.com
Real Estate Consulting Service
N.A.I.C.S.: 531210

INTERNATIONAL PUBLIC

MIRASOL RESOURCES LTD.

Suite 1150 - 355 Burrard Street, Vancouver, V6C 2G8, BC, Canada
Tel.: (604) 602-9989
Web Site: https://www.mirasolresources.com
Year Founded: 2003
MRZ—(OTCIQ)
Rev.: $480,905
Assets: $10,541,746
Liabilities: $894,809
Net Worth: $9,646,936
Earnings: ($4,664,410)
Fiscal Year-end: 06/30/21
Mineral Exploration Services
N.A.I.C.S.: 213114
Patrick Evans *(Chm)*

Subsidiaries:

Minera Mirasol Chile Limitada (1)
Avenida Nueva Providencia N 1881 Office 2004, Providencia, 7500520, Santiago, Chile
Tel.: (56) 223354293
Mineral Exploration Services
N.A.I.C.S.: 213114

MIRATECH LTD.

Premium Business Center 6-z Vatslava Havela Blvd, Kiev, 03124, Ukraine
Tel.: (380) 442064090
Web Site: http://www.miratechgroup.com
Year Founded: 1989
Sales Range: $75-99.9 Million
Emp.: 500
Information Technology Consulting Services
N.A.I.C.S.: 541611
Valeriy Kutsyy *(Chm)*

MIRATO S.P.A.

Strada Provinciale Est Sesia, Landiona, Novara, 28064, Italy
Tel.: (39) 0321827711 IT
Web Site: http://www.mirato.it
Sales Range: $150-199.9 Million
Emp.: 217
Personal Hygiene & Beauty Products Mfr & Distr
N.A.I.C.S.: 325620
Alberto Pollini *(Mgr-Comml)*

MIRATORG HOLDING

Prechistenskaya Embankment Dom 17 4th floor, 119034, Moscow, Russia
Tel.: (7) 4957750650
Web Site: http://www.miratorg.ru
Year Founded: 1995
Sales Range: Less than $1 Million
Food Products Distr
N.A.I.C.S.: 424490
Alexander Linnik *(Chm)*

MIRBUD S.A.

Unii Europejskiej 18, 96-100, Skierniewice, Poland
Tel.: (48) 468339828
Web Site: https://mirbud.pl
Year Founded: 2002
MRB—(WAR)
Rev.: $844,115,851
Assets: $580,233,992
Liabilities: $378,620,680
Net Worth: $201,613,312
Earnings: $34,403,963
Emp.: 846
Fiscal Year-end: 12/31/23
Real Estate Development Services
N.A.I.C.S.: 531390
Dariusz Jankowski *(Chm-Supervisory Bd)*

Subsidiaries:

Expo Mazury S.A. (1)

AND PRIVATE COMPANIES

Marywilska 44 Sp z o.o. ul Grunwaldzka 55, 14-100, Ostroda, Poland
Tel.: (48) 895065800
Web Site: http://www.expomazury.pl
Conference Hall Services
N.A.I.C.S.: 561920
Beata Maly-Kaczanowska (Pres)

Marywilska 44 Sp z o.o. (1)
ul Marywilska 44, 03-042, Warsaw, Poland
Tel.: (48) 603755015
Web Site: https://www.marywilska44.com
Shopping Mall Services
N.A.I.C.S.: 531120

MIRC ELECTRONICS LTD.
Onida House G-1 MIDC Mahakali Caves Road, Andheri E, Mumbai, 400 093, India
Tel.: (91) 2228200435
Web Site: https://www.onida.com
Year Founded: 1981
500279—(BOM)
Rev.: $104,836,122
Assets: $90,822,746
Liabilities: $60,314,300
Net Worth: $30,508,446
Earnings: $257,507
Emp.: 591
Fiscal Year-end: 03/31/21
Consumer Durables Mfr & Sales
N.A.I.C.S.: 423620
Gulu L. Mirchandani (Chm & Mng Dir)

MIRCH TECHNOLOGIES INDIA LIMITED
B-701 7th Floor Aurus Chambers, SS Amrutwar Marg Worli, Mumbai, 400 013, India
Tel.: (91) 7575872987
Web Site: https://mirchtechnologies.in
Year Founded: 1960
505336—(BOM)
Rev.: $254,972
Assets: $64,629
Liabilities: $25,537
Net Worth: $39,092
Earnings: $116,581
Emp.: 5
Fiscal Year-end: 03/31/21
Chemical Process Equipment Mfr
N.A.I.C.S.: 333248

MIRCOM TECHNOLOGIES LTD.
25 Interchange Way, Vaughan, L4K 5W3, ON, Canada
Tel.: (905) 660-4655   ON
Web Site: http://www.mircom.com
Year Founded: 1991
Fire Equipment Mfr
N.A.I.C.S.: 561621
Tony Falbo (Founder & CEO)

MIRELIS HOLDING SA
Rue de la Corraterie 12, 1204, Geneva, Switzerland
Tel.: (41) 223178600
Web Site: http://www.mirelis.ch
Year Founded: 1997
Asset Management Services & Investment Advice
N.A.I.C.S.: 523940
Alain Bruno Levy (Sec)

Subsidiaries:

Hyposwiss Private Bank Geneve SA (1)
Rue du General-Dufour 3, 1211, Geneva, Switzerland (100%)
Tel.: (41) 22 716 36 36
Web Site: http://www.hyposwiss.ch
Sales Range: $100-124.9 Million
Emp.: 175
Private Banking Services
N.A.I.C.S.: 522299
Thomas Stucki (Dir-Investment Center)

MIRGOR S.A.C.I.F.I.A.
Minones 2177 Belgrano Ciudad Autonoma de, C1428ART, Buenos Aires, Argentina
Tel.: (54) 1137527100   Ar
Web Site: https://mirgor.com
Year Founded: 1983
MIRG—(BUE)
Sales Range: Less than $1 Million
Holding Company; Motor Vehicle Parts, Home Electronic Appliances & Cell Phones Mfr
N.A.I.C.S.: 551112

Subsidiaries:

Electrotecnica Famar S.A.C.I.I.E. (1)
Rodney 70, Buenos Aires, C1427BNB, Argentina
Tel.: (54) 11 4858 8800
Automotive Repair & Maintenance Services
N.A.I.C.S.: 811198

Subsidiary (Domestic):

Famar Fueguina, S.A. (2)
Rodney 70 1427 Ciudad De, Buenos Aires, C1427BNB, Argentina
Tel.: (54) 1148588800
Motor Vehicle Electrical & Electronic Equipment Mfr
N.A.I.C.S.: 336320

MIRICOR ENTERPRISES HOLDINGS LIMITED
Room 1605 16th Floor Leighton Centre 77 Leighton Road, Causeway Bay, China (Hong Kong)
Tel.: (852) 2 864 4873   Ky
Web Site: http://www.miricor.com
1827—(HKG)
Rev.: $47,107,236
Assets: $61,499,470
Liabilities: $39,409,065
Net Worth: $22,090,405
Earnings: $3,273,770
Emp.: 366
Fiscal Year-end: 03/31/22
Medical Aesthetic Services
N.A.I.C.S.: 812112
Gigi Ka Yee Lai (Chm & CEO)

Subsidiaries:

Cos Max Limited (1)
39th and 40th floors 38 Russell Street, Golden Chaoyang Center, Causeway Bay, China (Hong Kong)
Tel.: (852) 39291888
Web Site: https://www.cosmax.com.hk
Skin Care Products Distr
N.A.I.C.S.: 424210

Cos Max Medical Centre (Central) Limited (1)
11/F Tower 2 New World Tower 16-18 Queen's Road Central, Central, China (Hong Kong)
Tel.: (852) 39291888
Medical Aesthetic Services
N.A.I.C.S.: 812112

Vitae Wellness Beauty Limited (1)
22/F Golden Chaoyang Centre 38 Russell Street, Causeway Bay, China (Hong Kong)
Tel.: (852) 39291838
Web Site: https://www.vitae.com.hk
Beauty Product Retailer
N.A.I.C.S.: 456120

MIRIS HOLDING AB
Danmarksgatan 26, 753 23, Uppsala, Sweden
Tel.: (46) 18146907
Web Site: https://www.mirissolutions.com
Year Founded: 2001
Medical Equipment Mfr & Distr
N.A.I.C.S.: 339112
Camilla Myhre Sandberg (CEO)

MIRLAND DEVELOPMENT CORPORATION PLC
Nicolaou Pentadromos Centre, Thessalonikis Street, 3025, Limassol, Cyprus
Tel.: (357) 25871785   CY
Web Site: http://www.mirland-development.com
Year Founded: 2004
Sales Range: $75-99.9 Million
Real Estate Management Services
N.A.I.C.S.: 531390
Roman Rozental (CEO)

MIRLE AUTOMATION CORPORATION
No 3 R&D Rd II Science Park, Hsinchu, 30076, Taiwan
Tel.: (886) 35783280
Web Site: https://www.mirle.com.tw
2464—(TAI)
Rev.: $288,195,908
Assets: $393,685,946
Liabilities: $254,998,323
Net Worth: $138,687,624
Earnings: $5,976,716
Emp.: 1,157
Fiscal Year-end: 12/31/23
Liquid Crystal Display Mfr
N.A.I.C.S.: 811310

Subsidiaries:

Mirle Automation (Kunshan) Co., Ltd. (1)
No 198 Dengta Road, Yushan Town, Kunshan, 215300, Jiangsu, China
Tel.: (86) 51236911988
Solar Equipment Mfr
N.A.I.C.S.: 333414

Mirle Automation Corporation - Taichung Factory (1)
No 311 Sec 2 Houke Rd Houli Dist, Taichung, 42152, Taiwan
Tel.: (886) 425218555
Solar Equipment Mfr
N.A.I.C.S.: 333414

Mirle Automation Corporation - Tainan Factory (1)
No 1-1 Nanke 1st Rd Tainan Science Park, Tainan City, 74147, Taiwan
Tel.: (886) 65053858
Solar Equipment Mfr
N.A.I.C.S.: 333414

Mirle Automation Inter Co., Ltd. (1)
Tel.: (66) 23995949
Solar Equipment Mfr
N.A.I.C.S.: 333414

Mirle Automation Technology (Shanghai) Co., Ltd. (1)
No 838 Yinglun Road China Pilot Free Trade Zone Waigaoqiao, Shanghai, 200131, China
Tel.: (86) 2150485800
Solar Equipment Mfr
N.A.I.C.S.: 333414

MIRLEX PTY. LTD.
114 126 Dandenong Valley Highway, Dandenong, 3164, VIC, Australia
Tel.: (61) 397936000
Sales Range: $25-49.9 Million
Emp.: 5
Plastics Product Mfr
N.A.I.C.S.: 326199
Nigel C. Chandler (Mng Dir)

Subsidiaries:

PolyPacific Pty. Ltd. (1)
114-126 Dandenong Valley Highway, Dandenong, 3175, VIC, Australia
Tel.: (61) 397936000
Web Site: http://www.polypacific.com.au
Sales Range: $25-49.9 Million
Polypropylene Compounds Mfr & Marketer; Owned 50% by Basell Australia (Holdings) Pty Ltd & 50% by Mirlex Pty Ltd
N.A.I.C.S.: 325998

MIRMIRE LAGHUBITTA BITTIYA SANSTHA LIMITED
Banepa-8, Kavrepalanchok, Dhulikhel, Nepal
Tel.: (977) 11662311
Web Site: https://www.nerudemirmire.com.np
MMFDB—(NEP)
Sales Range: Less than $1 Million
Investment Management Service
N.A.I.C.S.: 525990
Rajendra Prasad Neupane (Co-CEO-Acting)

MIROC A.D.
Kralja Aleksandra 1, Kladovo, Serbia
Tel.: (381) 19801397
Web Site: https://www.miroc.rs
Year Founded: 2005
MIRC—(BEL)
Rev.: $583,715
Assets: $1,879,165
Liabilities: $495,629
Net Worth: $1,383,536
Earnings: $124,962
Emp.: 10
Fiscal Year-end: 12/31/22
Departmental Store Operator
N.A.I.C.S.: 455110
Branimir Stefanovic (Exec Dir)

MIROKU CORPORATION
5371 Shinohara, Nankoku, 783-0006, Kochi, Japan
Tel.: (81) 888633310
Web Site: https://www.miroku-jp.com
Year Founded: 1946
7983—(TKS)
Rev.: $84,278,830
Assets: $148,209,360
Liabilities: $39,633,100
Net Worth: $108,576,260
Earnings: $3,410,290
Emp.: 620
Fiscal Year-end: 10/31/23
Hunting Rifle Mfr & Distr
N.A.I.C.S.: 332994
Yoshihiko Miroku (Pres)

Subsidiaries:

Miroku Machine Tool, Inc. (1)
836 Hie, Nankoku, 783-0054, Kochi, Japan
Tel.: (81) 888621136
Web Site: http://www.miroku-gd.co.jp
Emp.: 143
Gun Drill Machine Mfr & Distr
N.A.I.C.S.: 333515
Yoshihiko Miroku (Chm)

Miroku Machine Tool, Inc. (1)
110 Boggs Ln Ste 151, Cincinnati, OH 45246
Tel.: (513) 771-0666
Gun Drill Machine Mfr & Distr
N.A.I.C.S.: 333515

MIROKU JYOHO SERVICE CO., LTD.
4-29-1 Yotsuya, Shinjuku-ku, Tokyo, 160-0004, Japan
Tel.: (81) 353616369
Web Site: https://www.mjs.co.jp
Year Founded: 1977
9928—(TKS)
Rev.: $290,648,310
Assets: $304,178,980
Liabilities: $124,479,520
Net Worth: $179,699,460
Earnings: $28,013,180
Emp.: 2,168
Fiscal Year-end: 03/31/24
Software Development Services
N.A.I.C.S.: 541511
Nobuhiko Koreeda (Chm)

Subsidiaries:

MJS M&A Partners Co., Ltd. (1)
1-25-1 Shinjuku Center Building 48th Floor, Nishi-Shinjuku Shinjuku-ku, Tokyo, 163-0648, Japan
Tel.: (81) 35 324 0231

MIROKU JYOHO SERVICE CO., LTD.

Miroku Jyoho Service Co., Ltd.—(Continued)
Web Site: https://mmap.co.jp
Business Support Services
N.A.I.C.S.: 561499

Spice Inc. (1)
1-5-4 Higashiyama KDX Nakameguro Building, Meguro-ku, Tokyo, 153-0043, Japan
Tel.: (81) 35 708 5931
Web Site: https://www.spiceinc.jp
Administrative Management Services
N.A.I.C.S.: 541611

Transtructure Co., Ltd. (1)
JPR Kojimachi Building 5-4 Kojimachi, Chiyoda-ku, Tokyo, 102-0083, Japan
Tel.: (81) 35 213 3931
Web Site: https://www.transtructure.com
Human Resource Consulting Services
N.A.I.C.S.: 541612

Tribeck Inc. (1)
7-1-1 Akasaka Aoyama Yasuda Building 3rd Floor, Minato-ku, Tokyo, 107-0052, Japan
Tel.: (81) 35 414 2020
Web Site: https://www.tribeck.jp
Marketing Consulting Services
N.A.I.C.S.: 541613
Tsuyoshi Shirasu *(Mng Dir)*

MIRPURKHAS SUGAR MILLS LTD
Modern Motors House Beaumont Road, Karachi, 75530, Pakistan
Tel.: (92) 21111000009
Web Site: http://www.gfg.com.pk
MIRKS—(PSX)
Rev.: $27,986,671
Assets: $49,731,698
Liabilities: $35,010,665
Net Worth: $14,721,033
Earnings: $3,019,443
Emp.: 277
Fiscal Year-end: 09/30/23
Sugarcane Processor
N.A.I.C.S.: 311314
Wasif Khalid *(CFO & COO)*

Subsidiaries:

Mirpurkhas Sugar Mills Ltd - Mirpurkhas Factory (1)
Sub Post Office, Sugar Mill Jamrao Umerkot Road Mirpur Khas, Mirwah Gorchani, Sindh, Pakistan
Tel.: (92) 233517061
Sugar Mfr
N.A.I.C.S.: 311314

MIRRABOOKA INVESTMENTS LIMITED
Level 21 101 Collins Street, Melbourne, 3000, VIC, Australia
Tel.: (61) 396509911 AU
Web Site: https://www.mirra.com.au
Year Founded: 1999
MIR—(ASX)
Rev.: $8,099,626
Assets: $418,238,513
Liabilities: $52,473,958
Net Worth: $365,764,555
Earnings: $7,164,129
Fiscal Year-end: 06/30/24
Financial Investment Services
N.A.I.C.S.: 523999
Andrew J. B. Porter *(CFO & Co-Sec)*

MIRRIAD ADVERTISING PLC
96 Great Suffolk Street, London, SE1 0BE, United Kingdom
Tel.: (44) 2078842530 UK
Web Site: https://www.mirriadplc.com
Year Founded: 2015
MIRI—(AIM)
Rev.: $1,818,795
Assets: $17,790,465
Liabilities: $4,384,380
Net Worth: $13,406,085
Earnings: ($18,187,950)
Fiscal Year-end: 12/31/22
Media Advertising Services

N.A.I.C.S.: 541840
Stephan Beringer *(CEO)*

MIRVAC GROUP LTD.
Level 28 200 George St, Sydney, 2000, NSW, Australia
Tel.: (61) 290808000 AU
Web Site: https://www.mirvac.com
Year Founded: 1972
MGR—(ASX)
Rev.: $2,177,511,980
Assets: $13,182,298,950
Liabilities: $4,607,100,470
Net Worth: $8,575,198,480
Earnings: $694,934,330
Emp.: 1,550
Fiscal Year-end: 06/30/22
Offices of Other Holding Companies
N.A.I.C.S.: 551112
Brett Draffen *(Chief Investment Officer)*

Subsidiaries:

Mirvac Funds Management Limited (1)
Level 26 60 Margaret Street, Sydney, 2000, NSW, Australia
Tel.: (61) 290808000
Web Site: http://www.mirvac.com
Sales Range: $1-4.9 Billion
Investment Fund Management Services
N.A.I.C.S.: 523940

MIRZA INTERNATIONAL LTD
A-7 Mohan Cooperative Industrial Estate Mathura Road, New Delhi, 110044, India
Tel.: (91) 40959500
Web Site: https://www.mirza.co.in
MIRZAINT—(NSE)
Rev.: $78,895,750
Assets: $87,428,811
Liabilities: $23,475,811
Net Worth: $63,953,000
Earnings: $3,168,875
Emp.: 1,672
Fiscal Year-end: 03/31/23
Leather Integrated
N.A.I.C.S.: 313320
Rashid Ahmed Mirza *(Chm, CEO & Mng Dir)*

Subsidiaries:

Mirza UK Limited (1)
Mirza House Sherbourne Dr Tibrook, Milton Keynes, MK7 8HY, Buckinghamshire, United Kingdom
Tel.: (44) 1908365398
Leather Footwear Mfr
N.A.I.C.S.: 316210

MIRZA SUGAR MILLS LIMITED
10th Floor Portion B Lakson Square Building No 1, Sarwar Shaheed Road, Karachi, Pakistan
Tel.: (92) 2135680151
Web Site: http://www.mirzasugar.com
Emp.: 15
Cane Sugar Producer
N.A.I.C.S.: 311314

MISAWA & CO., LTD.
4-20-3 Ebisu, Shibuya-ku, Tokyo, 150-6025, Japan
Tel.: (81) 357935524
Web Site: https://www.unico-fan.co.jp
Year Founded: 1959
3169—(TKS)
Rev.: $102,465,580
Assets: $40,494,720
Liabilities: $24,823,190
Net Worth: $15,671,530
Earnings: $4,676,700
Emp.: 426
Fiscal Year-end: 01/31/20
Furniture Retailer
N.A.I.C.S.: 449110
Hiroyuki Suzuki *(Dir-Admin)*

MISAWA HABITA & CO., LTD.
47 Kita-machi, Isesaki, 372-0056, Japan
Tel.: (81) 270 221171
Web Site: http://www.habitacraft.com
Year Founded: 2010
Sales Range: $1-9.9 Million
Construction Engineering Services
N.A.I.C.S.: 541330
Kenichi Sagami *(Pres)*

MISEN ENERGY AB
Kungsportsavenyen 32, SE-411 36, Gothenburg, Sweden
Tel.: (46) 317595070
Web Site:
https://www.misenenergy.se
Year Founded: 2004
MISE—(OMX)
Assets: $972,211
Liabilities: $412,112
Net Worth: $560,098
Earnings: ($1,770,304)
Emp.: 2
Fiscal Year-end: 12/31/22
Oil & Gas Exploration Services
N.A.I.C.S.: 213112
Goran Wolff *(Mng Dir & CFO)*

Subsidiaries:

LLC Karpatygaz (1)
40-A Hlybochytska-str, 04050, Kiev, Ukraine
Tel.: (380) 445932233
Web Site: http://www.karpatygaz.com.ua
Natural Gas Distr
N.A.I.C.S.: 221210

MISH DESIGNS LIMITED
Gala No 4 Hathi Baug Mazgaon, Mumbai, 400010, India
Tel.: (91) 2223719478
Web Site: https://www.mishindia.com
Year Founded: 2017
544015—(BOM)
Online Shopping Services
N.A.I.C.S.: 425120

MISHIMA FOODS CO., LTD.
4 10 25 Hamadayama, Suginami Ku, Tokyo, 168 0065, Japan
Tel.: (81) 333171212
Web Site: http://www.mishima.co.jp
Year Founded: 1949
Sales Range: $75-99.9 Million
Emp.: 450
Seasonings & Prepared Foods
N.A.I.C.S.: 445110
Yutaka Mishima *(Pres)*

Subsidiaries:

Mishima Foods USA Inc. (1)
2340 Plz Del Amo Ste 105, Torrance, CA 90501-3451
Tel.: (310) 787-1533
Web Site: http://www.mishima.com
Sales Range: $50-74.9 Million
Emp.: 5
Mfr of Seasonings & Prepared Foods
N.A.I.C.S.: 424410
Yutaka Mishima *(Pres & Controller)*

MISHKA EXIM LIMITED
F14 First Floor Crossriver Mall CBD Ground Shahdara, Delhi, 110032, India
Tel.: (91) 1142111980
Web Site:
https://www.mishkaexim.com
539220—(BOM)
Rev.: $1,662,429
Assets: $2,793,478
Liabilities: $235,083
Net Worth: $2,558,396
Earnings: ($54,081)
Fiscal Year-end: 03/31/23
Wholesale Trade Agency
N.A.I.C.S.: 425120
Rajneesh Gupta *(Mng Dir)*

INTERNATIONAL PUBLIC

MISHKA FINANCE & TRADING LIMITED
Office No 63 1st Fl Shagun Arcade Premises, CHSL Gen AK Vadya Marg Malad East, Mumbai, 400 097, India
Tel.: (91) 28431998
Web Site:
http://www.mishkafinance.com
Year Founded: 1985
Sales Range: $1-9.9 Million
Security Brokerage Services
N.A.I.C.S.: 523150
Ankit Om Prakash Garodia *(CEO & Mng Dir)*

MISHO ECOLOGY AND LANDSCAPE CO., LTD.
Building 3 Zone B Shanshuicheng Science and Education Software Park, Binhu District, Wuxi, 214125, Jiangsu, China
Tel.: (86) 51082702530
Web Site: http://www.misho.com.cn
Year Founded: 2001
300495—(SSE)
Rev.: $18,661,968
Assets: $575,392,896
Liabilities: $475,721,532
Net Worth: $99,671,364
Earnings: ($96,453,396)
Fiscal Year-end: 12/31/22
Landscaping Services
N.A.I.C.S.: 561730
Wu Tianhua *(Chm & Sec)*

MISHORIM REAL ESTATE INVESTMENTS LTD.
11 Ben Gurion Vita Towers entrance A 6th floor, Bnei Brak, Israel
Tel.: (972) 37217800
Web Site: https://mishorim.com
Year Founded: 1990
MSHR—(TAE)
Rev.: $129,843,346
Assets: $907,519,256
Liabilities: $603,993,912
Net Worth: $303,525,344
Earnings: ($31,591,380)
Fiscal Year-end: 12/31/23
Real Estate Investment Services
N.A.I.C.S.: 531390
Alon Waxman *(CEO)*

MISHRA DHATU NIGAM LTD.
Kanchanbagh, Hyderabad, 500058, Telangana, India
Tel.: (91) 4024184000
Web Site: https://midhani-india.in
Year Founded: 1973
541195—(BOM)
Rev.: $109,072,933
Assets: $343,241,652
Liabilities: $189,126,671
Net Worth: $154,114,981
Earnings: $18,735,627
Emp.: 751
Fiscal Year-end: 03/31/23
Secondary Smelting Product Mfr
N.A.I.C.S.: 331492
Dinesh Kumar Likhi *(Chm)*

MISHTANN FOODS LTD.
B905 Empire Business Hub Opp Shakti Farm Science City Road, Ahmedabad, 380 060, India
Tel.: (91) 7940023116
Web Site: https://www.mishtann.com
539594—(BOM)
Rev.: $77,984,734
Assets: $30,937,807
Liabilities: $12,927,936
Net Worth: $18,009,871
Earnings: $5,985,561
Emp.: 9
Fiscal Year-end: 03/31/23
Food Products Mfr

AND PRIVATE COMPANIES

N.A.I.C.S.: 311212
Hiteshkumar Gaurishankar Patel *(Mng Dir)*

MISQUITA ENGINEERING LIMITED
182/1 Vaiginnim Vaddo, NachinolAldona, Goa, 403508, India
Tel.: (91) 8308848233
Web Site:
  https://www.misquitaengg.com
Year Founded: 2017
542801—(BOM)
Rev.: $948,825
Assets: $1,095,680
Liabilities: $352,282
Net Worth: $743,397
Earnings: $31,185
Emp.: 6
Fiscal Year-end: 03/31/21
Sheet Metal Work Mfg
N.A.I.C.S.: 332322
Pavan Kumar Gupta *(Sec & Compliance Officer)*

MISR BENI-SUEF CEMENT COMPANY
14 Marwah St Othman Towers Corniche Maadi, Cairo, Egypt
Tel.: (20) 25282464
Web Site:
  https://www.mbccegypt.com
Year Founded: 1997
MBSC.CA—(EGX)
Sales Range: Less than $1 Million
Cement Mfr
N.A.I.C.S.: 327310
Mohamed Shabaka *(Dir-PR & PR)*

MISR CEMENT COMPANY
8 km Qeft - Al Quseire Road, Qena, Egypt
Tel.: (20) 963420025
Web Site:
  https://www.misrcementgroup.com
Year Founded: 1997
MCQE.CA—(EGX)
Rev.: $130,370,140
Assets: $158,457,466
Liabilities: $94,674,832
Net Worth: $63,782,634
Earnings: $3,732,173
Fiscal Year-end: 12/31/23
Cement Mfr
N.A.I.C.S.: 327310
Mohammed Fahmi Abdul Rahman *(Sec & Head-Acctg)*

MISR HOTELS COMPANY
28 Hussein Wassf Street, Dokki, Giza, Egypt
Tel.: (20) 237612425
Web Site:
  https://www.misrhotels.com.eg
Year Founded: 1955
MHOT.CA—(EGX)
Sales Range: Less than $1 Million
Hotel & Restaurant Operator
N.A.I.C.S.: 721110
Amr Attia Ahmed Gomaa *(CEO & Mng Dir)*

MISR NATIONAL STEEL SAE
34 Damascus st Syria st, Mohandessin, Giza, Egypt
Tel.: (20) 37497246
Web Site: https://www.misrns.com
Year Founded: 1998
ATQA.CA—(EGX)
Sales Range: Less than $1 Million
Steel Bar Mfr
N.A.I.C.S.: 331110
Jamal Abdul Qader Abdul Basir *(Chm & Mng Dir)*

MISR OILS & SOAP
6 Adly Street, Cairo, Egypt
Tel.: (20) 223916188
Web Site: https://www.misroil.com
Year Founded: 1967
MOSC.CA—(EGX)
Sales Range: Less than $1 Million
Soap Mfr
N.A.I.C.S.: 325611
Hamed Abdul Salam Hassanein Saif *(Co-Chm & Mng Dir)*

MISR REFRIGERATION & AIR CONDITIONING
km 28 Cairo-Alex Desert Rd, 6th of October City, Egypt
Tel.: (20) 12 79182225
Web Site: http://www.miraco.com.eg
Year Founded: 1976
Air Conditioning Equipment Mfr
N.A.I.C.S.: 333415

MISSFRESH LTD.
3rd Floor Block A Vanke Times Center No. 9 Wangjing Street, Chaoyang District, Beijing, 100016, China
Tel.: (86) 1052665273   Ky
Year Founded: 2014
MF—(NASDAQ)
Rev.: $387,687,082
Assets: $25,476,422
Liabilities: $240,124,154
Net Worth: ($214,647,732)
Earnings: ($212,127,692)
Emp.: 57
Fiscal Year-end: 12/31/22
Online Shopping Services
N.A.I.C.S.: 445110
Zheng Xu *(Founder, Chm & CEO)*

MISSION DEVELOPMENT BANK LIMITED
Butwal-8, Durga Mandir, Nepal
Tel.: (977) 71551586
Web Site:
  http://www.missionbanknepal.com
Sales Range: Less than $1 Million
Commercial Banking Services
N.A.I.C.S.: 522110
Basudev Ghimire *(Chm)*

MISSION NEWENERGY LIMITED
Unit B9 431 Roberts Rd, Subiaco, 6008, WA, Australia
Tel.: (61) 863133975   AU
Web Site:
  http://www.missionnewenergy.com
Year Founded: 2006
MNELF—(OTCIQ)
Rev.: $165,152
Assets: $180,100
Liabilities: $173,170
Net Worth: $6,930
Earnings: $11,907
Emp.: 3
Fiscal Year-end: 06/30/19
Biodiesel Mfr; Wind Power Generation
N.A.I.C.S.: 324199
Nathan Mahalingam *(Chm & CEO)*

Subsidiaries:

Mission Biofuels India Private Limited (1)
Maa Gouri Complex 2nd Fl 191 Lewis Rd, Bhubaneswar, 751014, Orissa, India
Tel.: (91) 6742436744
Web Site:
  http://www.missionnewenergy.com
Biodiesel Mfr
N.A.I.C.S.: 324199

Mission Biotechnologies Sdn. Bhd. (1)
C-26-05 Dataran 32, No 2 Jalan 19 1, 46300, Petaling Jaya, Selangor Darul Ehsan, Malaysia
Tel.: (60) 379608770

Web Site:
  http://www.missionnewenergy.com
Biodiesel Mfr
N.A.I.C.S.: 324199

MISSION READY SOLUTIONS INC.
Suite 400-1681 Chestnut Street, Vancouver, V6J 4M6, BC, Canada   BC
Web Site: https://www.mrscorp.com
Year Founded: 2009
MSNVF—(OTCEM)
Rev.: $4,067,753
Assets: $1,984,355
Liabilities: $8,591,482
Net Worth: ($6,607,127)
Earnings: ($16,574,872)
Emp.: 27
Fiscal Year-end: 12/31/22
Investment Services
N.A.I.C.S.: 523999
Dong H. Shim *(CFO)*

Subsidiaries:

10-20 Services Inc. (1)
337 McMillan St, Fayetteville, NC 28301-5503
Tel.: (910) 491-0394
Web Site: http://www.10-20services.com
Emp.: 15
Military Equipment Repair & Maintenance Services
N.A.I.C.S.: 811310
Jeffery Schwartz *(Pres)*

PTF Manufacturing Inc. (1)
1202 McGhee Ln, Jacksboro, TN 37757-4112
Tel.: (423) 377-1186
Web Site: http://www.protecttheforce.com
Emp.: 30
Tactical & Armor Products Mfr
N.A.I.C.S.: 339999
Jeff Schwartz *(CEO)*

MISSISSAUGA TOYOTA INC
2215 Dundas Street East, Mississauga, L4X 2X2, ON, Canada
Tel.: (905) 625-3420
Web Site:
  https://www.mississaugatoyota.com
Year Founded: 1991
Sales Range: $10-24.9 Million
New & Used Car Dealers
N.A.I.C.S.: 441110
Stephen Gubasta *(Pres & COO)*

MISSONI S.P.A.
Via Salvini 1/A, Milan, 20122, Italy
Tel.: (39) 0276001479
Web Site: http://www.missoni.com
Sales Range: $75-99.9 Million
Emp.: 220
Clothing & Accessories Designer & Retailer
N.A.I.C.S.: 458110
Vittorio Missoni *(Owner)*

MISTANGO RIVER RESOURCES INC.
55 University Avenue Suite 1805, Box 546, Toronto, M5J 2H7, ON, Canada
Tel.: (416) 644-1567   Ca
Web Site: https://mistango.com
MIS—(CNSX)
Assets: $3,604,938
Liabilities: $870,044
Net Worth: $2,734,894
Earnings: $2,305,045
Fiscal Year-end: 12/31/22
Gold Mining Services
N.A.I.C.S.: 212220
Stephen Stewart *(Chm)*

MISTER SPEX SE
Hermann-Blankenstein-Strasse 24, 10249, Berlin, Germany
Tel.: (49) 32500050
Web Site: https://www.misterspex.de

MISUMI GROUP INC.

Year Founded: 2007
MRX—(DEU)
Rev.: $241,236,780
Assets: $302,637,600
Liabilities: $134,870,494
Net Worth: $167,767,106
Earnings: ($51,677,099)
Emp.: 1,079
Fiscal Year-end: 12/31/23
Optical Goods Retailer
N.A.I.C.S.: 456130
Maren Kroll *(Chief HR Officer)*

MISTRAL GAYRIMENKUL YATIRIM ORTAKLIGI AS
Cinarli Mah Ankara Asphalt Street Mistral Office Tower No 15 Floor, 20 D 202 Konak, Izmir, Turkiye
Tel.: (90) 2324215080
Web Site:
  https://www.mistralgyo.com.tr
Year Founded: 2012
MSGYO—(IST)
Sales Range: Less than $1 Million
Asset Management Services
N.A.I.C.S.: 523940
Serkan Ergunes *(Gen Mgr)*

MISUMI GROUP INC.
Iidabashi First Bldg 5-1 Koraku 2-chome, Bunkyo-ku, Tokyo, 112-8583, Japan
Tel.: (81) 358057050   JP
Web Site: http://www.misumi.co.jp
Year Founded: 1963
9962—(TKS)
Rev.: $2,430,159,890
Assets: $2,733,347,370
Liabilities: $435,189,180
Net Worth: $2,298,158,190
Earnings: $186,084,720
Emp.: 11,039
Fiscal Year-end: 03/31/24
Aluminum Frames & Other Related Products Mfr & Sales
N.A.I.C.S.: 331318
Tatsutaka Ohno *(Pres & CEO)*

Subsidiaries:

Anchor Lamina America, Inc. (1)
500 Progress Rd, Dayton, OH 45449
Tel.: (248) 489-9122
Web Site: https://www.daytonlamina.com
Sales Range: $50-74.9 Million
Emp.: 300
Die Components Mfr
N.A.I.C.S.: 333514

Dayton Progress Corporation (1)
500 Progress Rd, Dayton, OH 45449-0039
Tel.: (937) 859-5111
Web Site: http://www.daytonprogress.com
Sales Range: $100-124.9 Million
Emp.: 550
Metal Fabrication & Stamping Equipment Mfr
N.A.I.C.S.: 333514

Subsidiary (Non-US):

Dayton Progress Canada, Ltd. (2)
861 Rowntree Dairy Road, Woodbridge, L4L 5W3, ON, Canada
Tel.: (905) 264-2445
Web Site: https://www.daytonlamina.com
Sales Range: $1-9.9 Million
Emp.: 40
Metal Fabricating & Stamping Equipment Mfr
N.A.I.C.S.: 333514

Dayton Progress Corporation of Japan (2)
2 7 35 Hashimotodai, Mirodi-ku, Sagamihara, 252-0132, Kanagawa, Japan
Tel.: (81) 427740821
Web Site: http://www.dayton.co.jp
Sales Range: $25-49.9 Million
Emp.: 40
Metal Fabricating & Stamping Equipment Mfr
N.A.I.C.S.: 333514

MISUMI GROUP INC.

MISUMI Group Inc.—(Continued)
Satoshi Ojima (Pres)

Dayton Progress GmbH (2)
Adenaueralle 2, Postfach 1165, 61440, Oberursel, Germany
Tel.: (49) 6171924201
Web Site: http://www.daytonprogress.de
Sales Range: $25-49.9 Million
Emp.: 20
Metal Fabricating & Stamping Equipment Mfr
N.A.I.C.S.: 333514
Frederick C. Wilkinson (CEO)

Dayton Progress Ltd. (2)
Unit F8b Holly Farm Business Park, Honley, Kenilworth, CV8 1NP, Warwickshire, United Kingdom
Tel.: (44) 1926484192
Sales Range: $25-49.9 Million
Emp.: 7
Metal Fabricating & Stamping Equipment Mfr
N.A.I.C.S.: 333514

Dayton Progress Mexico, S. de R.L. de C.V. (2)
Avenida De Las Fuentes No 74 C, Parque Industrial Finsa El Marques, 76246, Queretaro, Mexico
Tel.: (52) 4422095114
Web Site: http://www.daytonlamina.com
Emp.: 50
Metal Fabricating & Stamping Equipment Mfr
N.A.I.C.S.: 333514

Dayton Progress Perfuradores Lda. (2)
ZI Casal da Areia Lote 17, 2460-392, Alcobaca, Portugal
Tel.: (351) 262540400
Web Site: https://www.daytonprogress.de
Emp.: 82
Metal Fabricating & Stamping Equipment Mfr
N.A.I.C.S.: 333514

Dayton Progress S.A.S (2)
105 Avenue de l Epinette Industrial Zone, BP 128, 77100, Meaux, France
Tel.: (33) 160247301
Web Site: https://www.daytonprogress.de
Sales Range: $25-49.9 Million
Emp.: 15
Metal Fabricating & Stamping Equipment Mfr
N.A.I.C.S.: 333514

Dayton Progress s.r.o. (2)
Prazska 707, 29471, Benatky nad Jizerou, Czech Republic
Tel.: (420) 326375911
Web Site: https://www.daytonprogress.de
Emp.: 7
Metal Fabricating & Stamping Equipment Mfr
N.A.I.C.S.: 333514

MISHIMA SEIKI CO., LTD. (1)
215 Metal Complex, Suntou-gun, Kakamigahara, 504-0957, Gifu, Japan
Tel.: (81) 583821245
Web Site: https://www.mishimaseiki.co.jp
Sales Range: $25-49.9 Million
Emp.: 51
Mechanical Component Mfr
N.A.I.C.S.: 333613
Sugiyama Atsushi (Mgr)

MISUMI Corporation (1)
KUDAN-KAIKAN TERRACE 6-5 Kudanminami 1-Chome, Chiyoda-ku, Tokyo, 102-8583, Japan
Tel.: (81) 367777800
Sales Range: $25-49.9 Million
Emp.: 100
Mechanical Component Mfr
N.A.I.C.S.: 334513

MISUMI E.A. HK Limited (1)
Suite 1207 12/F Tower 6 The Gateway Harbor City 9 Canton Road, Tsim Sha Tsui, Kowloon, China (Hong Kong)
Tel.: (852) 23332339
Web Site: http://www.misumi.com.hk
Automation Equipments & Cutting Tools Distr
N.A.I.C.S.: 423120

MISUMI Europa GmbH (1)
Franklinstrasse 61-63, 60486, Frankfurt am Main, Germany
Tel.: (49) 696681730
Web Site: http://de.misumi-ec.com
Sales Range: $25-49.9 Million
Emp.: 50
Mechanical Component Mfr
N.A.I.C.S.: 334513
Koichi Tsunematsu (Mng Dir)

Misumi (China) Precision Machinery Trading Co., Ltd. (1)
Building 10 No 999 Huancheng North Road, Fengxian District, Shanghai, China
Tel.: (86) 2167108701
Web Site: http://www.misumi.com.cn
Electronic Parts Mfr & Distr
N.A.I.C.S.: 334419

Misumi (Thailand) Co., Ltd. (1)
300/24 Moo 1 Eastern Seaboard Industrial Estate Soi 5 Ta Sit, A Pluakdaeng, Pluak Daeng, 21140, Rayong, Thailand
Tel.: (66) 38959200
Web Site: https://th.misumi-ec.com
Sales Range: $25-49.9 Million
Emp.: 100
Mechanical Component Mfr
N.A.I.C.S.: 334513

Misumi India Pvt Ltd (1)
Plot no 31 Electronic City Sector 18 Udyog Vihar - IV, Gurgaon, 122 016, Haryana, India
Tel.: (91) 1244688800
Web Site: http://in.misumi-ec.com
Sales Range: $25-49.9 Million
Emp.: 40
Mechanical Component Mfr
N.A.I.C.S.: 334513
Tsubasa Wada (Mng Dir)

Misumi Korea Corp. (1)
511 Yeongdong-daero, 159-1 Samseongdong Gangnam-gu Trade Center Rooms 1103 1404 3804 4201, Seoul, 06164, Korea (South)
Tel.: (82) 51093399
Web Site: https://kr.misumi-ec.com
Sales Range: $25-49.9 Million
Emp.: 100
Mechanical Component Mfr
N.A.I.C.S.: 334513

Misumi Malaysia Sdn. Bhd. (1)
BO2-C-08 Menara 3 KL Eco City No 3 Jalan Bangsar, 59200, Kuala Lumpur, Selangor, Malaysia
Tel.: (60) 378906399
Web Site: https://my.misumi-ec.com
Press Die Component Mfr & Distr
N.A.I.C.S.: 334513
Kazuhiro Fujikawa (Mng Dir)

Misumi Mexico S. de R.L. de C.V (1)
Av De las Fuentes 74 int B, Bernardo Quintana Industrial Park FinsaEl Marques, 76246, Queretaro, Mexico
Tel.: (52) 4426727661
Web Site: https://mx.misumi-ec.com
Press Die Component Mfr & Distr
N.A.I.C.S.: 334513

Misumi South East Asia Pte. Ltd. (1)
331 North Bridge Road 05-03 Odeon Towers, Singapore, 188720, Singapore
Tel.: (65) 67337211
Web Site: https://sg.misumi-ec.com
Sales Range: $25-49.9 Million
Emp.: 50
Press Die & Plastic Molds Distr
N.A.I.C.S.: 424610

Misumi Taiwan Corp. (1)
9th Floor-1 No.126 Section 4 Nanjing East Road, Taipei, 10595, Taiwan
Tel.: (886) 225703766
Web Site: http://www.misumi-ec.com
Sales Range: $25-49.9 Million
Emp.: 70
Mechanical Component Mfr
N.A.I.C.S.: 334513

Misumi USA, Inc. (1)
1475 E Woodfield Rd Ste 1300, Schaumburg, IL 60173
Tel.: (847) 843-9105
Web Site: http://us.misumi-ec.com
Mechanical Component Mfr
N.A.I.C.S.: 334513

Misumi Vietnam Co., Ltd. (1)
Lot No 15 TS11 Road, Tien Son Industrial Park Tien Du District, Hoan Son, Bac Ninh, Vietnam
Tel.: (84) 2223611555
Web Site: https://vn.misumi-ec.com
Press Die Component Mfr & Distr
N.A.I.C.S.: 334513
Yasuo Shimokura (Gen Dir)

P.C.S. Company (1)
34500 Doreka Dr, Fraser, MI 48026
Tel.: (586) 294-7780
Plastic Injection Molding & Die Casting Product Mfr
N.A.I.C.S.: 333511

PT. Misumi Indonesia (1)
Menara Karya LT 28 JL HR Rasuna Said Kav 1-2, Kuningan, Jakarta, 12950, Selatan, Indonesia
Tel.: (62) 2189840008
Web Site: https://id.misumi-ec.com
Press Die Component Mfr & Distr
N.A.I.C.S.: 334513

SP PARTS CO., LTD. (1)
3-2 Hoshinosato Ami-machi, Inashiki, 300-0326, Ibaraki, Japan
Tel.: (81) 298336700
Mechanical Component Mfr
N.A.I.C.S.: 334513

Plant (Domestic):

SP PARTS CO., LTD. - Kansai Plant (2)
2-3-2 Akamatsudai Kita-ku, Kobe, 651-1516, Hyogo, Japan
Tel.: (81) 789400113
Mechanical Component Mfr
N.A.I.C.S.: 334513

Saigon Precision Co., Ltd. (1)
Road 2 Saigon-LinhTrung E P Z, Thu Duc, Ho Chi Minh City, Vietnam
Tel.: (84) 8974387
Web Site: https://saigonprecision.talentnetwork.vn
Emp.: 2,500
Automation Component Mfr & Distr
N.A.I.C.S.: 335999

Suruga (Thailand) Co., Ltd. (1)
300/23 Moo 1 Eastern Seaboard Industrial Estate Soi 5 Tambol Tasith, Pluak Daeng, 21140, Rayong, Thailand
Tel.: (66) 38954936
Web Site: http://www.misumi.co.th
Mechanical Component Mfr
N.A.I.C.S.: 334513
Nobuyuki Ashida (Pres & Mng Dir)

Suruga India Pvt. Ltd. (1)
Plot no 31 Electronic City Sector 18 Udyog Vihar - IV, Gurgaon, 122016, Haryana, India
Tel.: (91) 1244688848
Configurable Component Distr
N.A.I.C.S.: 423690

Suruga Korea Co., Ltd. (1)
4Ma 714 Shiwa Industrial Complex 39 Byeolmang-ro, Danwon-gu, Ansan, 15415, Gyeonggi, Korea (South)
Tel.: (82) 314348357
Sales Range: $25-49.9 Million
Emp.: 11
Mechanical Component Mfr
N.A.I.C.S.: 334513

Suruga Polska Sp. z o.o. (1)
Slowackiego St 199A, 80-298, Gdansk, Pomeranian, Poland
Tel.: (48) 583406800
Web Site: http://www.misumi.co.jp
Sales Range: $25-49.9 Million
Emp.: 40
Precision Die Tools & Components Mfr
N.A.I.C.S.: 332216

Suruga Production Platform Co., Ltd. (1)
505 Nanatsushinya, Shimizu-ku, Shizuoka, 424-8566, Japan
Tel.: (81) 543440311
Web Site: https://www.suruga-g.co.jp
Sales Range: $150-199.9 Million
Emp.: 890
Mechanical Component Mfr
N.A.I.C.S.: 334513
Takumi Toya (Pres)

Division (Domestic):

Iwaki Fine Technology Co., Ltd. (2)
8-1 Yoshima Indus Complex Iwaki, Fukushima, 970-1144, Japan
Tel.: (81) 246366000
Web Site: http://www.suruga-g.co.jp
Sales Range: $25-49.9 Million
Emp.: 34
Mechanical Component Mfr
N.A.I.C.S.: 334513

Plant (Domestic):

Suruga Seiki Co., Ltd. - Kansai Plant (2)
Misumi Production Park 2-3-2 Akamatsudai, Kita-ku, Kobe, 651-1516, Hyogo, Japan
Tel.: (81) 789400281
Sales Range: $25-49.9 Million
Emp.: 848
Mechanical Component Mfr
N.A.I.C.S.: 334513
Ryusei Ono (Pres)

Suruga Seiki (Guangzhou) Co., Ltd. (1)
B No 9 American Indus Park 48 Hongmian Ave, Huadu Dist, Guangzhou, 510800, Guangdong, China
Tel.: (86) 20 3687 2889
Web Site: http://www.suruga-ost.com
Mechanical Component Mfr
N.A.I.C.S.: 334513

Suruga Seiki (Nantong) Co., Ltd. (1)
No 100 Tongda Road, Nantong Economic and Technological Development Area, Nantong, Jiangsu, China
Tel.: (86) 51380590000
Configurable Component Distr
N.A.I.C.S.: 423690

Suruga Seiki (Shanghai) Co.,Ltd. (1)
Sales Range: $100-124.9 Million
Emp.: 300
Precision Die Tools Mfr
N.A.I.C.S.: 334513

Suruga Seiki Sales & Trading (Shanghai) Co., Ltd. (1)
Room 007A Building 1 Library No 1 40 Wenshui Road, Jing'an District, Shanghai, China
Tel.: (86) 2162870630
Web Site: http://www.suruga-g.cn
Industrial Machinery Equipment Mfr & Distr
N.A.I.C.S.: 333248

Suruga USA Corp. (1)
40 S Addison Rd Ste 300, Addison, IL 60101
Tel.: (630) 628-4000
Web Site: http://www.suruga-g.co.jp
Sales Range: $25-49.9 Million
Emp.: 40
Tools & Dies Mfr
N.A.I.C.S.: 333515
Patrick Barger (Mgr-Production)

MISUNG POLYTECH CO., LTD.
196 3 Choonui Dong Wonmi Gu, 420-857, Bucheon, Gyeonggi Do, Korea (South)
Tel.: (82) 326652256
Web Site: http://www.mspt.co.kr
Year Founded: 1999
Sales Range: $50-74.9 Million
Emp.: 200
Cellular Phone Parts Mfr
N.A.I.C.S.: 334220
Jong Dal Kim (CEO)

MIT HOLDINGS CO., LTD.
24F World Business Garden Malibu West 2-6-1 Nakase, Mihama-ku, Chiba, 261-7124, Japan
Tel.: (81) 432397252
Web Site: https://www.mit-hd.co.jp
Year Founded: 2009

AND PRIVATE COMPANIES

4016—(TKS)
Rev.: $33,932,740
Assets: $16,122,660
Liabilities: $12,216,070
Net Worth: $3,906,590
Earnings: $333,230
Emp.: 15
Fiscal Year-end: 11/30/23
Holding Company
N.A.I.C.S.: 551112
Hiroshi Suzuki *(Chm & CEO)*

Subsidiaries:

Bigal Co., Ltd. (1)
World Business Garden Malibu West 24F 2-6-1 Nakase, Mihama-ku, Chiba, 261-7124, Japan
Tel.: (81) 432397450
Web Site: https://www.bigal.co.jp
Software Development Services
N.A.I.C.S.: 541511

NetValue Co., Ltd. (1)
2-1-61 Shiromi Twin 21 MID Tower 26F, Chuo-ku, Osaka, 540-6126, Japan
Tel.: (81) 669100830
Web Site: https://www.netvalue-io.com
Emp.: 117
Software Development Services
N.A.I.C.S.: 541511

System IO Co., Ltd. (1)
Tamachi Square 4th Floor 5-26-24, Shiba Minato-ku, Tokyo, 108-0014, Japan
Tel.: (81) 368094802
Web Site: https://www.systemio.co.jp
Emp.: 175
Computer System Consulting Services
N.A.I.C.S.: 541512

Vision Links Myanmar Co., Ltd. (1)
Unit 19 Room 101 PearlMon Housing, South Dagon Township, Yangon, Myanmar
Tel.: (95) 9455677603
Web Site: https://www.visionlinksm.com
Emp.: 22
Web Application Development Services
N.A.I.C.S.: 541511

MIT SIM S.P.A.
Palazzo Serbelloni Corso Venezia 16, Lombardia, 20121, Milan, Italy
Tel.: (39) 0230561270
Web Site: https://www.mitsim.it
MTS—(EUR)
Investment Management Service
N.A.I.C.S.: 523999
Gabriele Villa *(CEO)*

MITAC HOLDINGS CORPORATION
No 202 Wenhua 2nd Road, Guishan District, Taoyuan, 33383, Taiwan
Tel.: (886) 33289000
Web Site: https://www.mic-holdings.com
Year Founded: 1982
3706—(TAI)
Rev.: $1,162,105,094
Assets: $2,902,394,508
Liabilities: $893,570,521
Net Worth: $2,008,823,986
Earnings: $58,453,348
Emp.: 2,660
Fiscal Year-end: 12/31/23
Holding Company
N.A.I.C.S.: 551112
Matthew F. C. Miau *(Founder & Chm)*

Subsidiaries:

MiTAC Benelux N.V. (1)
Z5 Mollem 318, Asse, 1730, Mollem, Belgium
Tel.: (32) 24610799
Cloud Computing Product Mfr
N.A.I.C.S.: 334111

MiTAC Digital Technology Corporation (1)
No 200 Wenhua 2nd Rd, Guishan Dist, Taoyuan, 33383, Taiwan
Tel.: (886) 33961888
Web Site: https://www.mitacmdt.com
Cloud Computing Product Mfr
N.A.I.C.S.: 334111

Mitac Digital Corp. (1)
279 E Arrow Hwy Ste 201, San Dimas, CA 91773
Tel.: (408) 615-5100
Cloud Computing Product Mfr
N.A.I.C.S.: 334111

MITAC INTERNATIONAL CORP.
Yuan-Far 2nd Road Hsinchu Industrial Park, Hsin-chu, Taiwan
Tel.: (886) 035779250
Web Site: http://www.mitac.com
Year Founded: 1982
Sales Range: $25-49.9 Million
Emp.: 7,000
Microcomputers & Related Products Mfr, Design, Sales & Services
N.A.I.C.S.: 334111
Matthew F. C. Miau *(Chm & CEO)*

Subsidiaries:

Asia Union Electronic Chemical Corp. (1)
5th Fl 20 Ln 478 Jui Kuang Rd, Taipei, Taiwan
Tel.: (886) 226575555
Inorganic Chemical Mfr
N.A.I.C.S.: 325180

BOC Lien Hwa Industrial Gases Corp. (1)
6th Fl No 44 Chengteh Rd Sec 1, Taipei, Taiwan
Tel.: (886) 225552260
Web Site: http://www.boclh.com.tw
Industrial Gas Mfr
N.A.I.C.S.: 325120

Beijing Synnex Information Technologies Co , Ltd. (1)
6th Fl Ste B, China International Hi-Tech Co, Beijing, China
Tel.: (86) 1082012588
Web Site: http://www.synnex.com
Sales Range: $100-124.9 Million
Emp.: 500
Television Broadcasting
N.A.I.C.S.: 516120

GemTek Technology Co., Ltd. (1)
No 1 Jen-Ai Rd, HsinChu Industrial Park, Hsin-chu, Taiwan
Tel.: (886) 35985535
Computer Peripheral Equipment Mfr
N.A.I.C.S.: 334118

Getac Holdings Corporation (1)
5F Building A No 209 Sec 1 Nangang Road, Nangang District, Taipei, 11568, Taiwan **(33.97%)**
Tel.: (886) 227857888
Web Site: https://www.getac.com
Rev.: $1,137,792,462
Assets: $1,359,932,615
Liabilities: $586,970,611
Net Worth: $772,962,004
Earnings: $129,416,163
Emp.: 10,339
Fiscal Year-end: 12/31/2023
Research, Design, Development, Manufacture & Distribution of Computers & Related Products
N.A.I.C.S.: 334111

Subsidiary (Non-US):

Getac (UK) Ltd. (2)
Mitac House, Nedge Hill, Telford, TF3 3AH, Shropshire, United Kingdom
Tel.: (44) 1952207231
Web Site: http://en.getac.com
Sales Range: $25-49.9 Million
Emp.: 40
Electronic Components Mfr
N.A.I.C.S.: 334419

Subsidiary (US):

Getac Inc. (2)
43 Tesla, Irvine, CA 92618
Tel.: (949) 681-2900
Web Site: http://www.getac.com
Computer Equipment & Software Whslr

MITAC INTERNATIONAL CORP.

N.A.I.C.S.: 423430
Scott Shainman *(Pres-North America)*

Lien Jeh Transportation Co , Ltd. (1)
6th Fl 44 Cheng Te Rd Sec 1, Taipei, Taiwan
Tel.: (886) 225552260
Transportation Services
N.A.I.C.S.: 488999

MiTAC Australia Pty Ltd. (1)
Suite 2 408 Victoria Rd, Gladesville, 2111, NSW, Australia
Tel.: (61) 298799000
Web Site: http://www.mitac.com
Sales Range: $25-49.9 Million
Emp.: 30
Electric Equipment Mfr
N.A.I.C.S.: 335999

MiTAC Communications Co., Ltd. (1)
8F 187 Ti Ding Blvd Sec 2, Taipei, Taiwan
Tel.: (886) 226578000
Web Site: www.mitaccomm.com.tw
Computer System Design Services
N.A.I.C.S.: 541512

MiTAC Computer (Beijing) Ltd. (1)
Rm 5098 Haowei Bldg, No 25 Beitaipingzhuang Rd, 100088, Beijing, China
Tel.: (86) 1062381107
Emp.: 20
Electronic Computer Mfr
N.A.I.C.S.: 334111

MiTAC Computer (Kunshan) Ltd. (1)
No 269 2nd Road Export Processing Zone Changjiang South Road, Kunshan, Jiangsu, China
Tel.: (86) 512 57367777
Web Site: http://www.mitac.com
Electronic Components Mfr
N.A.I.C.S.: 334419

MiTAC Computer (Shanghai), Ltd. (1)
No 213 3rd Jiangchang San Rd, Zhabei District, Shanghai, 200436, China
Tel.: (86) 2161431188
Emp.: 400
Electronic Computer Mfr
N.A.I.C.S.: 334111

MiTAC Computers (Shunde) Ltd. (1)
No 1 Shunda Road Lunjiao Street, Shunde District, Foshan, 528308, Guangdong, China
Tel.: (86) 75727753168
Electronic Computer Mfr
N.A.I.C.S.: 334111

MiTAC Europe Ltd. (1)
Mitac House, Nedge Hill, Shifnal, TF3 3AH, Shropshire, United Kingdom
Tel.: (44) 1952207298
Web Site: http://www.syllex.com
Sales Range: $25-49.9 Million
Emp.: 100
Electronic Components Mfr
N.A.I.C.S.: 334419

MiTAC Inc. (1)
187 Tiding Blvd Sec 2, Taipei, Taiwan
Tel.: (886) 226576666
Web Site: http://www.mitac.com.tw
Computer Equipment & Software Whslr
N.A.I.C.S.: 423430

MiTAC International Corp. - Hsin-Chu Factory (1)
No 1 R&D Road 2 HsinChu Science Park, Hsin-chu, Taiwan
Tel.: (886) 33289000
Web Site: http://www.mitac.com
Communication Equipment Mfr
N.A.I.C.S.: 334290

MiTAC Japan Corp. (1)
Yasuda Shibaura 2nd Building 3F Kaigan 3-chome 2-12, Minato-ku, Tokyo, 108-0022, Japan
Tel.: (81) 337698311
Web Site: http://www.mic.com.tw
Sales Range: $50-74.9 Million
Durable Good Distr
N.A.I.C.S.: 423990

MiTAC Research (Shanghai) Ltd. (1)
No 213 Jiang Chang San Road, Shanghai, Zhabei, China

Tel.: (86) 2161431188
Computer System Design Services
N.A.I.C.S.: 541512

MiTAC Service (ShangHai) Co., Ltd. (1)
No 129 Fute North Road Waigaoqiao Free Trade Zone, Shanghai, 200131, China
Tel.: (86) 2158681198
Electronic Component Repair & Maintenance Services
N.A.I.C.S.: 811210

MiTAC Technology Corp. (1)
4th Floor 1 R & D 2nd Road, Hsinchu Science Park, Hsin-chu, Taiwan
Tel.: (886) 35782280
Electronic Components Mfr
N.A.I.C.S.: 334419

Mio Technology Benelux N.V. (1)
Z 5 Mollem 318 Asse, Asse, 1730, Vlaams Brabant, Belgium
Tel.: (32) 24610799
Web Site: http://www.eu.mio.com
Sales Range: $25-49.9 Million
Emp.: 34
Electronic Components Mfr
N.A.I.C.S.: 334419
Piet Deschuymer *(Gen Mgr)*

Mio Technology Corp. (1)
Building B No 209 Sec 1 NanGang Road, NanGang, Taipei, Taiwan
Tel.: (886) 2 2652 5888
Web Site: http://www.mio.com
Sales Range: $400-449.9 Million
Emp.: 1,700
Mobile Communication Equipment Mfr & Distr
N.A.I.C.S.: 334290
Billy Ho *(Pres)*

Mio Technology GMBH (1)
Fursterireder Strasse 279 a, 81377, Munich, Germany
Tel.: (49) 89 74 12 01 42
Web Site: http://eu.mio.com
Computer Peripheral Equipment Mfr
N.A.I.C.S.: 334118
Markus Bregler *(Gen Mgr)*

Mio Technology Korea (1)
7F Miso Bldg 890-47 Daechi-dong, Gangnam-gu, Seoul, 135-839, Korea (South)
Tel.: (82) 2 554 2654
Web Site: http://kr.mio.com
Electronic Components Mfr
N.A.I.C.S.: 334419

Mio Technology Ltd. (1)
Rm A 9/F Leader Industrial Center Ph 1 188 202 Texaco Rd, Tsuen Wan, New Territories, China (Hong Kong)
Tel.: (852) 24110726
Electronic Components Mfr
N.A.I.C.S.: 334419
Doris Sun *(Office Mgr)*

Tyan Computer (USA) Corporation (1)
3288 Laurelview Ct, Fremont, CA 94538
Tel.: (510) 651-8868
Web Site: http://www.tyan.com
Computer Equipment & Software Whslr
N.A.I.C.S.: 423430
Wei Chang *(Sr Dir-Sls)*

Tyan Computer Corporation (1)
7th Fl No 187 Tiding Blvd, Sec 2 Nei-Hu, Taipei, 115, Taiwan
Tel.: (886) 226525888
Web Site: http://www.tyan.com
Computer Equipment & Software Whslr
N.A.I.C.S.: 423430

Tyan Computer GmbH (1)
Einsteinstrasse 14, 85716, Unterschleissheim, Germany
Tel.: (49) 89318598000
Web Site: http://www.tyan.com
Computer Equipment & Software Whslr
N.A.I.C.S.: 423430

Union Material Technology Corp. (1)
27 Chien Yeh Rd, Taliao Hsiang, Kaohsiung, Taiwan
Tel.: (886) 77881167
Web Site: http://www.upc.com.tw
Plastics Material & Resin Mfr

MITAC INTERNATIONAL CORP.

MiTAC International Corp.—(Continued)
N.A.I.C.S.: 325211

United Industrial Gases Co, Ltd. (1)
12 Yen Hsin 1st Rd, Hsin-chu, Taiwan
Tel.: (886) 35783876
Industrial Gas Mfr
N.A.I.C.S.: 325120

MITACHI CO., LTD.
Mitachi Bldg 2-11-28 Iseyama, Naka-ku, Nagoya, 460-0026, Aichi, Japan
Tel.: (81) 523322512
Web Site: https://www.mitachi.co.jp
Year Founded: 1972
3321—(TKS)
Rev.: $257,122,390
Assets: $133,052,690
Liabilities: $37,293,620
Net Worth: $95,759,070
Earnings: $8,077,420
Emp.: 490
Fiscal Year-end: 05/31/24
Electronic Parts Whslr
N.A.I.C.S.: 423690
Kazuhiro Tachibana *(Pres)*

Subsidiaries:

M.A.Technology, Inc. (1)
Blk 15 Lot 6 Phase 3 CEZ, Rosario, 4106, Cavite, Philippines
Tel.: (63) 46 437 2020
Electronic Components Distr
N.A.I.C.S.: 423690

MITACHI (HK) CO., LTD. (1)
Unit 1303-4 13/F Railway Plaza No 39 Chatham Road South, Tsim Sha Tsui, Kowloon, China (Hong Kong)
Tel.: (852) 23693611
Emp.: 12
Electronic Components Distr
N.A.I.C.S.: 423690
T. Yamashige *(Pres)*

MITACHI (THAILAND) CO., LTD. (1)
1/38 Bangna Thani Building Room No 19A 19th Floor Soi Bangna-Trad 34, Debaratana Road Bangna Tai Bangna, Bangkok, 10260, Thailand
Tel.: (66) 21364360
Electronic Components Distr
N.A.I.C.S.: 423690

MITACHI ELECTRONICS (SH) CO., LTD. (1)
801-802 No 369 Xian Xia Road, Chang Ning District, Shanghai, China
Tel.: (86) 2151559955
Electronic Components Distr
N.A.I.C.S.: 423690

MITACHI ELECTRONICS (SZ) CO., LTD. (1)
Room 1313 Coastal Building East Block HaiDa 3 Road, Nanshan Qu, Shenzhen, China
Tel.: (86) 755 8627 1341
Electronic Components Distr
N.A.I.C.S.: 423690

Metech Co., Ltd. (1)
Gotanda NN Bldg 8F 2-12-19 Nishigotanda, Shinagawa-ku, Tokyo, 141-0031, Japan
Tel.: (81) 368878008
Web Site: https://www.mitachi.co.jp
Electronic Parts & Equipment Distr
N.A.I.C.S.: 423690

PT. MITACHI INDONESIA (1)
Mayapada Tower 19th floor Suite 05A Jl Jend Sudirman Kav 28, Jakarta, 12920, Indonesia
Tel.: (62) 215212025
Electronic Components Distr
N.A.I.C.S.: 423690

TAIWAN MITACHI CO., LTD. (1)
13F- 1 No 17 Sec 1 Chengde Rd, Datong District, Taipei, 10351, Taiwan
Tel.: (886) 225557295
Web Site: https://www.mitachi.co.jp
Electronic Components Distr
N.A.I.C.S.: 423690

MITAKE INFORMATION CORP.
11F No 39 Sec 2 Hsin Sheng N Rd, Taipei, Taiwan
Tel.: (886) 25639999
8284—(TPE)
Rev.: $77,468,311
Assets: $58,550,386
Liabilities: $20,105,462
Net Worth: $38,444,924
Earnings: $8,962,543
Fiscal Year-end: 12/31/22
Software Development Services
N.A.I.C.S.: 541511
Hung-Che Chiu *(Chm & CEO)*

MITANI CORPORATION
1-3-1 Toyoshima, Fukui-shi, Fukui, 910-8510, Japan
Tel.: (81) 776203111
Web Site: https://www.mitani-corp.co.jp
Year Founded: 1914
8066—(TKS)
Rev.: $2,146,736,310
Assets: $1,976,760,160
Liabilities: $750,565,500
Net Worth: $1,226,194,660
Earnings: $120,083,870
Emp.: 650
Fiscal Year-end: 03/31/24
Construction Materials Whslr
N.A.I.C.S.: 423320
Akira Mitani *(CEO)*

Subsidiaries:

Clean Gas Fukui Co., Ltd. (1)
1-17-25 Hanandohigashi, Fukui, Japan
Tel.: (81) 776355380
Web Site: http://www.cleangas.jp
Hydrocarbon Research & Exploration Services
N.A.I.C.S.: 211130

Dama Trading Pte. Ltd. (1)
Blk 3029A Ubi Road 3 01-98/99, Singapore, 408661, Singapore
Tel.: (65) 67436100
Web Site: https://dama.com.sg
Acrylic Product Mfr & Distr
N.A.I.C.S.: 326113

Fukui CableTV CO., LTD. (1)
1-6-1 Toshima Second Mitani Building, Fukui, 910-0857, Japan
Tel.: (81) 776203377
Web Site: https://www.fctv.jp
Cable Television Operator
N.A.I.C.S.: 561520

Fukui Energy CO., LTD. (1)
10-8-1 Kazuenakacho, Fukui, 918-8166, Japan
Tel.: (81) 776387833
Vehicle Leasing Services
N.A.I.C.S.: 532120

Fukui Seisakusho Co., Ltd. (1)
1-6 Shodaitajika, Hirakata, 573-1132, Osaka, Japan
Tel.: (81) 728574521
Web Site: http://www.fkis.co.jp
Emp.: 191
Steel Products Mfr
N.A.I.C.S.: 331210
Yo Fukui *(Pres)*

LFA Global Pte. Ltd. (1)
36 Gul Lane, Singapore, 629430, Singapore
Tel.: (65) 68619998
Web Site: https://lfaglobal.com
Emp.: 25
Marine Valve & Equipment Distr
N.A.I.C.S.: 423910

MJI Universal Pte. Ltd. (1)
133 Cecil Street 11-01A/B Keck Seng Tower, Singapore, 069535, Singapore
Tel.: (65) 62206676
Web Site: https://www.mjiuniversal.com
Animal Feed Ingredient Distr
N.A.I.C.S.: 424910

Mitani Computer Corp. (1)
7-1-13 Kumado Maruoka-cho, Sakai, 910-0393, Fukui, Japan
Tel.: (81) 776678000
Web Site: https://www.mtn.co.jp
Software Services
N.A.I.C.S.: 541511

Netz Toyota Fukui Co., Ltd. (1)
58-12 Imaichi-cho, Fukui, Japan
Tel.: (81) 120385812
Web Site: https://www.netzfukui.co.jp
Car Distr
N.A.I.C.S.: 441120

Nihon Bisoh Co., Ltd. (1)
4-15-33 Shibaura, Minato-ku, Tokyo, 108-0023, Japan
Tel.: (81) 958821925
Web Site: http://www.bisoh.co.jp
Emp.: 562
Industrial Machinery & Equipment Distr
N.A.I.C.S.: 423830

Son Ha Spice & Flavorings Co., LTD. (1)
Cassia Street Dinh Bang Industrial Zone, Tu Son, Vietnam
Tel.: (84) 2438784618
Web Site: https://www.sonhaspice.vn
Spice Product Mfr & Distr
N.A.I.C.S.: 311942

TsurumiSekiyu Co., Ltd. (1)
1-30-9 Shimosueyoshi, Tsurumi-ku, Yokohama, 230-0012, Kanagawa, Japan
Tel.: (81) 455724701
Web Site: https://www.tsuruseki.co.jp
Emp.: 39
Oil & Gas Services
N.A.I.C.S.: 213112

MITANI SANGYO CO., LTD.
1-5 Tamagawa-cho, Kanazawa, 920-8685, Ishikawa, Japan
Tel.: (81) 762332151
Web Site: https://www.mitani.co.jp
Year Founded: 1928
8285—(NGO)
Rev.: $633,346,370
Assets: $626,818,457
Liabilities: $315,249,334
Net Worth: $311,569,123
Earnings: $13,782,619
Emp.: 3,556
Fiscal Year-end: 03/31/24
Chemicals, Resins, Electronics, Information Systems, Air Conditioning Systems
N.A.I.C.S.: 325998
Tadateru Mitani *(Pres, CEO & & Officer-Organizational Strategy)*

Subsidiaries:

ACT-T Co., Ltd. (1)
4-11-11 Funakoshiminami, Aki-ku, Hiroshima, 736-0082, Japan
Tel.: (81) 828213362
Web Site: http://www.act-t.jp
Mechanical Device Jig Mfr & Distr
N.A.I.C.S.: 333511

Active Pharma Co., Ltd. (1)
2-36-1 Kanda Jimbocho Sumitomo Fudosan Chiyoda First Wing 6F, Reception 3F Chiyoda-ku, Tokyo, 101-0051, Japan
Tel.: (81) 335146050
Web Site: http://www.activepharma.co.jp
Pharmaceutical Product Mfr & Retailer
N.A.I.C.S.: 325412

Adonis Co., Ltd. (1)
1-5 Tamagawa-cho, Kanazawa, 920-0863, Ishikawa, Japan
Tel.: (81) 762338638
Web Site: http://www.e-adonis.co.jp
Office Supplies Distr
N.A.I.C.S.: 424120

Aureole Business Components & Devices Inc. (1)
Long Binh Industrial Zone, Long Binh Ward, Bien Hoa, Dong Nai, Vietnam
Tel.: (84) 2513991015
Web Site: https://www.mitani.co.jp
Emp.: 854
Precision Plastic Mold Mfr
N.A.I.C.S.: 333511
Osamu Miwa *(Gen Dir)*

INTERNATIONAL PUBLIC

Aureole Construction Software Development Inc. (1)
22 Floor AB Tower 76 Le Lai Street Dist 1, Ho Chi Minh City, Vietnam
Emp.: 250
Computer Aided Design Services
N.A.I.C.S.: 541512
Miura Shuhei *(Gen Dir)*

Aureole Expert Integrators Inc. (1)
7th Floor Technosoft Building, Cau Giay Industrial Zone Dich Vong Hau Ward Cau Giay District, Hanoi, Vietnam
Tel.: (84) 2437957390
Emp.: 15
Office Management Services
N.A.I.C.S.: 561110
Hiroyuki Yonezawa *(Gen Dir)*

Aureole Fine Chemical Products Inc. (1)
Lot D-4-2 Long Binh Techno park, Dong Nai, Vietnam
Tel.: (84) 618899436
Emp.: 35
Chemical Products Mfr
N.A.I.C.S.: 325998

Aureole Information Technology Inc. (1)
9th Floor Saigon Finance Center 9 Dinh Tien Hoang Street, District 1, Ho Chi Minh City, Vietnam
Tel.: (84) 2839110200
Emp.: 142
Software Development Services
N.A.I.C.S.: 541511
Munekatsu Okeyoshi *(Gen Dir)*

Aureole Mitani Chemical & Environment Inc. (1)
Lot D-4-1 Road No 2 Long Binh Industrial Zone, Bien Hoa, Dong Nai, Vietnam
Tel.: (84) 2513892222
Web Site: https://www.mitani.co.jp
Emp.: 52
Chemical Products Distr
N.A.I.C.S.: 424690
Masayuki Ado *(Chm)*

Aureole unit-Devices Manufacturing Service Inc. (1)
No 6A 17A Street Bien Hoa II Industrial Zone, An Binh Ward, Bien Hoa, Dong Nai, Vietnam
Tel.: (84) 2513835588
Web Site: https://www.mitani.co.jp
Emp.: 662
Mold Product Mfr
N.A.I.C.S.: 333511

Confidential Service Co., Ltd. (1)
2-6 Asahidai in Ishikawa Science Park, Nomi, Ishikawa Prefecture, Japan
Tel.: (81) 761515250
Data Center & Planning Services
N.A.I.C.S.: 518210

D-Circle Inc. (1)
Sumitomo Fudosan Chiyoda First Wing 2nd Floor 2-36-1 Kanda Jimbocho, Chiyoda-ku, Tokyo, 101-0051, Japan
Tel.: (81) 335146060
Web Site: http://www.d-circle.com
Software Development Services
N.A.I.C.S.: 541511

INFILL Co., Ltd. (1)
2-36-1 Kanda Jimbocho, Sumitomo Realty and Development Chiyoda First Wing Chiyoda-ku, Tokyo, 101-0051, Japan
Tel.: (81) 335146070
Web Site: http://www.infill.co.jp
Housing Equipment Retailer
N.A.I.C.S.: 449129

JAXSON Corporation (1)
1F 3-3-3 Akasaka, Minato-ku, Tokyo, 107-0052, Japan
Tel.: (81) 368264510
Web Site: https://jaxson.jp
Bathroom Equipment Mfr
N.A.I.C.S.: 332999

Mirai Kasei Inc. (1)
2473 Amemiya, Chikuma, 387-0001, Nagano Prefecture, Japan
Tel.: (81) 262747662
Web Site: http://www.miraikasei.com
Pharmaceutical & Medical Device Retailer

AND PRIVATE COMPANIES

N.A.I.C.S.: 456199

Mitani Sangyo Adonis Co., Ltd. (1)
1-5 Tamagawa-cho, Kanazawa, 920-0863, Ishikawa, Japan
Tel.: (81) 762338638
Web Site: https://www.e-adonis.co.jp
Emp.: 28
Computer & Office Equipment Distr
N.A.I.C.S.: 423430

Mitani Sangyo Constructions Co., Ltd. (1)
3-47 Mikyozuka, Nonoichi, 921-8801, Japan
Tel.: (81) 762699988
Web Site: https://www.mitani-cs.co.jp
Emp.: 82
Air-conditioning & Ventilation Equipment Distr
N.A.I.C.S.: 423730

Mitani Sangyo Ec Co., Ltd. (1)
Ambitious Hill 3-47 Okyozuka, Nonoichi, 921-8801, Ishikawa Prefecture, Japan
Tel.: (81) 762693214
Web Site: https://www.mitani-ec.co.jp
Emp.: 126
Petroleum Product Distr
N.A.I.C.S.: 424720

Nagano Saraya Syokai Inc. (1)
1-50 Arcs, Nagano, 380-0918, Japan
Tel.: (81) 262261570
Web Site: https://www.naganosaraya.co.jp
Water Treatment Chemical Distr
N.A.I.C.S.: 424690

Sagami Chemical Industry Co., Ltd. (1)
3-3-15 Asahimachi, Machida, 194-0023, Tokyo, Japan
Tel.: (81) 427236611
Web Site: http://www.sag-chem.co.jp
Pharmaceutical Product Mfr & Retailer
N.A.I.C.S.: 325412

Tama Kagaku Kogyo Co., Ltd. (1)
29 Shinmachi, Yashio, 340-0807, Saitama, Japan
Tel.: (81) 489361033
Web Site: https://tamakagaku.co.jp
Emp.: 106
Pharmaceutical Raw Material Distr
N.A.I.C.S.: 424210

Tesera Co., Ltd. (1)
Chiyoda First Building East Building 1 3-8-1, Nishi-Kanda Chiyoda-ku, Tokyo, 101-0065, Japan
Tel.: (81) 335146081
Web Site: https://tesera.jp
Housing Furniture Mfr & Distr
N.A.I.C.S.: 337122

MITANI SEKISAN CO., LTD.
Mitani Bldg 1-3-1 Toyoshima, Fukui, 910-8571, Japan
Tel.: (81) 776203333
Web Site: https://www.m-sekisan.co.jp
Year Founded: 1946
5273—(TKS)
Rev.: $549,396,760
Assets: $795,559,770
Liabilities: $235,448,200
Net Worth: $560,111,570
Earnings: $61,149,110
Emp.: 1,138
Fiscal Year-end: 03/31/24
Construction Material Mfr & Distr
N.A.I.C.S.: 327390
Shinji Mitani (Pres)

Subsidiaries:

Mitani Engineering CO., LTD. (1)
3-1-5 Chuo, Fukui, 910-0006, Japan
Tel.: (81) 776232255
Web Site: https://www.mitani-eng.jp
Silo Mfr
N.A.I.C.S.: 327390

MITCHEL-LINCOLN PACKAGING LTD
3737 Thimens Blvd, Ville Saint Laurent, H4R 1V1, QC, Canada
Tel.: (514) 332-3480
Web Site: http://www.mitchellincoln.ca
Year Founded: 1965
Sales Range: $75-99.9 Million
Emp.: 356
Corrugated Boxes
N.A.I.C.S.: 322211
David Garfinkle (Exec VP)

MITCHELL SERVICES LIMITED
112 Bluestone Circuit, Seventeen Mile Rocks, Brisbane, 4073, QLD, Australia
Tel.: (61) 737227222
Web Site: https://www.mitchellservices.com.au
MSV—(ASX)
Rev.: $158,138,777
Assets: $85,074,349
Liabilities: $41,250,999
Net Worth: $43,823,349
Earnings: $6,126,163
Emp.: 750
Fiscal Year-end: 06/30/24
Contract Drilling Services
N.A.I.C.S.: 238990
Todd Wild (Gen Mgr-Comml)

Subsidiaries:

Notch Holdings Pty Ltd (1)
133 Crocodile Crescent, Bohle, 4818, QLD, Australia
Tel.: (61) 747757299
Sales Range: $100-124.9 Million
Oil Well Drilling Services
N.A.I.C.S.: 213111

MITCHELL'S FRUIT FARMS LIMITED
72-FCC Gulberg IV, Lahore, Pakistan
Tel.: (92) 4235872392
Web Site: https://www.mitchells.com.pk
Year Founded: 1933
MFFL—(PSX)
Rev.: $9,802,950
Assets: $5,829,879
Liabilities: $5,312,751
Net Worth: $517,127
Earnings: ($212,963)
Emp.: 284
Fiscal Year-end: 06/30/23
Grocery & Confectionery Products Mfr
N.A.I.C.S.: 445110
Mehdi Mohsin (Exec Dir)

MITCHELLS & BUTLERS PLC
27 Fleet Street, Birmingham, B3 1JP, United Kingdom
Tel.: (44) 1214984000
Web Site: https://www.mbplc.com
Year Founded: 1898
MAB—(LSE)
Rev.: $1,445,971,800
Assets: $7,072,363,480
Liabilities: $4,215,720,600
Net Worth: $2,856,642,880
Earnings: ($88,251,800)
Emp.: 38,852
Fiscal Year-end: 09/25/21
Pub & Restaurant Operator
N.A.I.C.S.: 722511
Tim Jones (CFO)

Subsidiaries:

Miller & Carter Gaststatten Betriebsgesellschaft mbH (1)
Adolfstrasse 16, 65185, Wiesbaden, Germany
Tel.: (49) 61116050
Web Site: https://www.millerandcarter.de
Restaurant Services
N.A.I.C.S.: 722511

Mitchells & Butlers Germany GmbH (1)
Adolfstrasse 16, 65185, Wiesbaden, Germany
Tel.: (49) 61116050
Sales Range: $10-24.9 Million
Emp.: 43
Drinking Places
N.A.I.C.S.: 722410
Bernd Riegger (Mng Dir)

Mitchells & Butlers Leisure Retail Ltd. (1)
27 Fleet Street, Birmingham, B3 1JP, West Midlands, United Kingdom
Tel.: (44) 3031231113
Sales Range: $100-124.9 Million
Emp.: 700
Drinking Places
N.A.I.C.S.: 722410

Mitchells & Butlers Retail (No 2) Ltd. (1)
27 Fleet Street, Birmingham, B31JP, West Midlands, United Kingdom
Tel.: (44) 8706093000
Web Site: http://www.mbplc.com
Sales Range: $50-74.9 Million
Emp.: 500
Drinking Places
N.A.I.C.S.: 722410

Mitchells & Butlers Retail Ltd. (1)
27 Fleet Street, Birmingham, B3 1JP, West Midlands, United Kingdom
Tel.: (44) 1214984000
Sales Range: $100-124.9 Million
Emp.: 1,000
Drinking Places
N.A.I.C.S.: 722410

Standard Commercial Property Developments Ltd. (1)
27 Fleet St, Birmingham, B31JP, West Midlands, United Kingdom
Tel.: (44) 8706093000
Land Subdivision
N.A.I.C.S.: 237210

MITCON CONSULTANCY & ENGINEERING SERVICES LTD.
1st floor Kubera ChambersShivajinagar, Pune, 411005, Maharashtra, India
Tel.: (91) 2025534322
Web Site: https://www.mitconindia.com
Year Founded: 1982
MITCON—(NSE)
Rev.: $10,281,590
Assets: $29,698,112
Liabilities: $16,112,307
Net Worth: $13,585,804
Earnings: $455,201
Emp.: 165
Fiscal Year-end: 03/31/23
Management Consulting Services
N.A.I.C.S.: 541330
Pradeep Bavadekar (Mng Dir)

Subsidiaries:

Mitcon Trusteeship Services Limited (1)
402/1403 14th Floor Dalamal Tower B-Wing Free Press Journal Marg 211, Nariman Point, Mumbai, 400021, India
Tel.: (91) 2222828200
Web Site: http://www.mitcontrustee.com
Urban Infrastructure Services
N.A.I.C.S.: 925120
Ajit Guruji (CEO)

MITECH LIMITED
60 Cawley St, PO Box 11-813, Ellerslie, Auckland, 1542, New Zealand
Tel.: (64) 99155555 NZ
Web Site: http://www.mitech.co.nz
Year Founded: 1988
Sales Range: $10-24.9 Million
Emp.: 14
Coding & Marking Equipment Distr
N.A.I.C.S.: 423830
Peter Ayson (Mgr-Ops)

MITEKS A.D.
Pacirski put 69, Stara Moravica, Serbia
Tel.: (381) 24741069
Year Founded: 1960
MTKS—(BEL)
Sales Range: $1-9.9 Million
Emp.: 69
Textile Products Mfr
N.A.I.C.S.: 314999
Nikola Borkovic (Gen Mgr)

MITERI DEVELOPMENT BANK LTD.
Mahendra Path Dharan 12, Inaruwa, Nepal
Tel.: (977) 25536317
Web Site: https://www.miteribank.com.np
MDB—(NEP)
Rev.: $7,416,261
Assets: $61,384,338
Liabilities: $50,382,226
Net Worth: $11,002,112
Earnings: $1,219,499
Fiscal Year-end: 07/16/23
Commercial Banking Services
N.A.I.C.S.: 522110
Kishan Maskey (Chm)

MITHRA PHARMACEUTICALS S.A.
Rue Saint-Georges 5, 4000, Liege, Belgium
Tel.: (32) 43492822
Web Site: https://www.mithra.com
Year Founded: 1999
MITRA—(EUR)
Rev.: $72,304,123
Assets: $477,459,529
Liabilities: $441,104,036
Net Worth: $36,355,493
Earnings: ($64,342,758)
Emp.: 229
Fiscal Year-end: 12/31/22
Female Healthcare Product Mfr & Distr
N.A.I.C.S.: 325412
Jean-Manuel Fontaine (VP-External & Scientific Affairs)

Subsidiaries:

Mithra Pharmaceuticals CDMO SA (1)
Rue Saint-Georges 5, 4000, Liege, Belgium
Tel.: (32) 43492822
Web Site: https://www.mithra.com
Pharmaceuticals Product Mfr
N.A.I.C.S.: 325412

MITHRIL BERHAD
Suite 19 01 19th Floor Menara MAA, No 12 Jalan Dewan Bahasa, 50460, Kuala Lumpur, Malaysia
Tel.: (60) 321420366
Web Site: http://www.mithril.com.my
Sales Range: $1-9.9 Million
Polyurethane Rigid Foam Mfr
N.A.I.C.S.: 326150
Lily Kam May Yin (Sec)

Subsidiaries:

Mithril Saferay Sdn. Bhd. (1)
Lot 5930 Kawasan Perusahaan Kamunting, 34600, Kamunting, Perak, Malaysia
Tel.: (60) 58911128
Web Site: http://www.gaudidecor.com
Emp.: 200
Polyurethane Mouldings Mfr
N.A.I.C.S.: 326199
Aw Ken Wong (Dir-Ops)

MITHRIL RESOURCES LTD
The Block Arcade Suite 324 Level 3 96 Elizabeth St, Melbourne, 3000, VIC, Australia
Tel.: (61) 396927222

MITHRIL RESOURCES LTD

Mithril Resources Ltd—(Continued)

Web Site:
https://www.mithrilresources.com.au
MSG—(TSXV)
Rev.: $82,090
Assets: $21,984,281
Liabilities: $298,307
Net Worth: $21,685,974
Earnings: ($1,068,612)
Emp.: 9
Fiscal Year-end: 06/30/24
Nickel Explorer Company
N.A.I.C.S.: 325180
David Hutton (Mng Dir)

MITIE GROUP PLC

The Shard Level 12 32 London
Bridge Street, Southwark, London,
SE1 9SG, United Kingdom
Tel.: (44) 3306780710 UK
Web Site: https://www.mitie.com
Year Founded: 1987
MITFY—(OTCIQ)
Rev.: $4,898,901,000
Assets: $2,269,265,320
Liabilities: $1,745,598,260
Net Worth: $523,667,060
Earnings: $113,127,980
Emp.: 64,388
Fiscal Year-end: 03/31/23
Offices of Other Holding Companies
N.A.I.C.S.: 551112
Phil Bentley (CEO)

Subsidiaries:

Cole Motors Ltd. **(1)**
Redhill, Bristol, BS40 5TG, United
Kingdom **(100%)**
Tel.: (44) 1934862485
Web Site: http://www.mitie.com
Sales Range: $25-49.9 Million
Emp.: 15
Fluid Power Pump & Motor Mfr
N.A.I.C.S.: 333996
Justin Catterson (Gen Mgr)

Environmental Property Services
Ltd **(1)**
Riverside House 1 New Mill Road, Orpington, BR5 3QA, United Kingdom
Tel.: (44) 8456 080356
Web Site: http://www.epsplc.com
Property Management Services
N.A.I.C.S.: 531311
Peter Griffin (Gen Mgr)

Interserve (Facilities Management)
Ltd. **(1)**
Capital Tower 91 Waterloo Road, London,
SE1 8RT, United Kingdom **(100%)**
Tel.: (44) 2079022000
Sales Range: $150-199.9 Million
Emp.: 1,000
Facilities Management Services
N.A.I.C.S.: 561210

Subsidiary (Domestic):

Interserve (Facilities Services Slough)
Ltd. **(2)**
Petersfield Ave, Slough, SL2 5DN, United
Kingdom
Tel.: (44) 1753875474
Facility Management Services
N.A.I.C.S.: 561210

Interserve FS (UK) Ltd. **(2)**
Victoria House 1-3 College Hill, London,
EC4R 2RA, United Kingdom
Tel.: (44) 1276 607 444
Sales Range: $25-49.9 Million
Emp.: 25
Integrated Facilities Management Services
N.A.I.C.S.: 561210
Michael Peter Brown (Mng Dir)

Subsidiary (Domestic):

Interserve Catering Services
Limited **(3)**
Bridge House Mathisen Way, Colnbrook,
SL3 0HH, United Kingdom **(75%)**
Tel.: (44) 1753561730
Catering Services
N.A.I.C.S.: 722320

KBS Fire Protection Systems
Ltd. **(1)**
Kepler Lichfield Road, Industrial Estate,
Tamworth, B79 7XE, Staffordshire, United
Kingdom
Tel.: (44) 7768553411
Web Site: http://www.kbsfireprotection.co.uk
Sales Range: $50-74.9 Million
Emp.: 2
Fire Protection
N.A.I.C.S.: 922160

Linx International Group Ltd. **(1)**
Burgundy House 6 Snellings Road, Hersham, Walton-on-Thames, KT12 5JG, Surrey, United Kingdom
Tel.: (44) 1932225151
Web Site: http://www.linx-int.com
Risk Management Consulting Services
N.A.I.C.S.: 541618

Subsidiary (Domestic):

ARC Training International
Limited **(2)**
Unit 10 Claylands Road, Bishops Waltham,
Winchester, SO32 1QD, Hants, United
Kingdom
Tel.: (44) 1489896549
Web Site: http://www.arc-tc.com
Security Management Training Services
N.A.I.C.S.: 611430

MITIE Asset Management Ltd **(1)**
8 Monarch Court Brooms, Bristol, BS16
7FH, Avon, United Kingdom
Tel.: (44) 1179708800
Energy Asset Development Services
N.A.I.C.S.: 926130

MITIE Business Services Ltd. **(1)**
The Shard Level 12 32 London Bridge
Street, Southwark, London, SE1 9SG,
United Kingdom **(100%)**
Tel.: (44) 1173221322
Web Site: http://www.mitie.com
Sales Range: $250-299.9 Million
Emp.: 900
Business Support Services
N.A.I.C.S.: 561499

MITIE Catering Services Ltd. **(1)**
High Street South Cerney, Gloucester, GL7
5UG, United Kingdom **(100%)**
Tel.: (44) 1285861092
Sales Range: $10-24.9 Million
Emp.: 30
Food Service Contractor Services
N.A.I.C.S.: 722310

Branch (Domestic):

MITIE Catering Service (London)
Ltd. **(2)**
22 Shand St, London, SE1 2ES, United
Kingdom
Tel.: (44) 2031238760
Food Service Contractor Services
N.A.I.C.S.: 722310

MITIE Cleaning & Support Services
Limited **(1)**
Unit 9 Logman Center, Greenbank Crescent
East Tullos, Aberdeen, AB12 3BG, United
Kingdom **(95.89%)**
Tel.: (44) 1224245180
Web Site: http://www.mitie.com
Sales Range: $25-49.9 Million
Emp.: 30
Facility Cleaning & Support Services
N.A.I.C.S.: 561720

Subsidiary (Domestic):

MITIE Cleaning Services Ltd. **(2)**
5 Limehouse Court, 1 Lanark Square,
London, E14 9RH, United
Kingdom **(95.89%)**
Tel.: (44) 2079870811
Web Site: http://www.mitie.com
Sales Range: $25-49.9 Million
Contract Cleaning Services
N.A.I.C.S.: 561720
Rob Cattell (Mng Dir)

MITIE Services (Retail) Limited **(2)**
1st Floor 4 Brook Office Park Folly Brook
Road, Emersons Green, Bristol, BS16 7FH,
United Kingdom **(83.28%)**
Tel.: (44) 1179576670
Web Site: http://www.mitie.com
Sales Range: $100-124.9 Million
Retail Facility Cleaning & Support Services
N.A.I.C.S.: 561210

MITIE Transport Services
Limited **(2)**
Unit 3 Valmar Trading Estate, Valmar Road
Camberwell, London, SE5 9NW, United
Kingdom
Tel.: (44) 2073460160
Emp.: 200
Transportation Facility Cleaning & Support
Services
N.A.I.C.S.: 561210

MITIE Client Services Limited **(2)**
22 Shand Street, London, SE1 2ES, United
Kingdom **(91.3%)**
Tel.: (44) 2070892549
Telephone Answering, Reception, Event
Management, Training & Development Services
N.A.I.C.S.: 561421

MITIE Energy Ltd. **(1)**
Unit 1 Manaton Ct Manaton Close Matwood
Bus Pk, EX2 8PF, Exeter, United Kingdom -
England **(100%)**
Tel.: (44) 1392829999
Web Site: http://www.mitie.com
Sales Range: $25-49.9 Million
Emp.: 25
Plumbing Heating & Air-Conditioning Contractors
N.A.I.C.S.: 238220

MITIE Engineering Services Ltd. **(1)**
The Millennium Center, M4 Crosby Way,
Farnham, GU97XX, Surrey, United
Kingdom **(100%)**
Tel.: (44) 1252732400
Web Site: http://www.mitie.com
Sales Range: $25-49.9 Million
Emp.: 50
Engineeering Services
N.A.I.C.S.: 541330

Subsidiary (Domestic):

MITIE Engineering Maintenance
Ltd. **(2)**
The Counting House, 1st Floor 53 Tooley
Street, London, SE1 2QN, United
Kingdom **(100%)**
Tel.: (44) 2070228300
Electrical, Heating, Ventilation, Air Conditioning & Plumbing Contract Engineering
Maintenance Services
N.A.I.C.S.: 541330

Branch (Domestic):

MITIE Engineering Maintenance
(Caledonia) Ltd. **(3)**
MITIE House 35 Duchess Road, Rutherglen, Glasgow, G73 1AU, United
Kingdom **(57%)**
Tel.: (44) 1416137800
Web Site: http://www.mitie.co.uk
Sales Range: $25-49.9 Million
Emp.: 100
Electrical, Heating, Ventilation, Air Conditioning & Plumbing Contract Engineering
Maintenance Services
N.A.I.C.S.: 541330
John McCluskey (Mgr)

MITIE Engineering Maintenance
(North) Ltd. **(3)**
Vasbook House Talbot Road, Manchester,
M32 0FP, United Kingdom
Tel.: (44) 1618690500
Sales Range: $50-74.9 Million
Emp.: 140
Electrical, Heating, Ventilation, Air Conditioning & Plumbing Contract Engineering
Maintenance Services
N.A.I.C.S.: 541330
Ruby McGregor (CEO)

Subsidiary (Domestic):

MITIE Engineering Projects Ltd. **(2)**
104 Mere Grange off Elton Head Road Leaside St Helens, Merseyside, Liverpool, WA9
5GG, United Kingdom **(63%)**

INTERNATIONAL PUBLIC

Tel.: (44) 1515477300
Sales Range: $25-49.9 Million
Electrical, Heating, Ventilation, Air Conditioning & Plumbing Contract Engineering
Construction Services
N.A.I.C.S.: 541330
Ruby McGregor-Smith (CEO)

Branch (Domestic):

MITIE Engineering Services (Bristol)
Ltd. **(2)**
26-27 A Osprey Ct Hawkfield Bus Pk
Whitchurch, Bristol, BS14 0BB, United
Kingdom **(100%)**
Tel.: (44) 1179787900
Sales Range: $25-49.9 Million
Emp.: 3
Engineeering Services
N.A.I.C.S.: 541330

MITIE Engineering Services (Edinburgh) Ltd. **(2)**
35 Duchess Road, Rutherglen, Glasgow,
G73 1AU, United Kingdom **(54%)**
Tel.: (44) 1313335115
Web Site: http://www.mitie.com
Sales Range: $25-49.9 Million
Engineeering Services
N.A.I.C.S.: 541330

Subsidiary (Non-US):

MITIE Engineering Services (Guernsey) Ltd. **(2)**
Unit 2 Old Bakery Complex, Les Tracheries
L Islet, Saint Sampson's, GY2 4SN, Guernsey
Tel.: (44) 1481711184
Engineeering Services
N.A.I.C.S.: 541330

Branch (Domestic):

MITIE Engineering Services (North
East) Ltd. **(2)**
Unit 8 1st Floor, Vance Business Park Norwood, Gateshead, NE119NE, United
Kingdom **(83.14%)**
Tel.: (44) 1914606484
Engineeering Services
N.A.I.C.S.: 541330

MITIE Engineering Services (SE Region) Ltd. **(2)**
The Commodity Ctr, Braxted Park Rd,
Witham, CM83EW, Essex, United
Kingdom **(100%)**
Tel.: (44) 1621890804
Web Site: http://www.mitie.com
Sales Range: $10-24.9 Million
Emp.: 40
Engineeering Services
N.A.I.C.S.: 541330

MITIE Engineering Services (Scotland) Ltd. **(2)**
Seafield House Seafield Rd, Longman Industrial Estate, Inverness, IV11SG, United
Kingdom **(100%)**
Tel.: (44) 1463715233
Engineeering Services
N.A.I.C.S.: 541330

MITIE Engineering Services (South
East) Ltd. **(2)**
The Millennium Ctr, M4 Crosby Way, Farnham, GU9 7XX, Surrey, United
Kingdom **(100%)**
Tel.: (44) 1252732400
Web Site: http://www.mitie.com
Sales Range: $25-49.9 Million
Emp.: 50
Engineeering Services
N.A.I.C.S.: 541330

MITIE Engineering Services (South
West) Ltd. **(2)**
5 Hanover Ct Manaton Close, Matford Business Park, Devon, EX28PF, United Kingdom
Tel.: (44) 1392833186
Engineeering Services
N.A.I.C.S.: 541330

MITIE Engineering Services (Swansea) Ltd. **(2)**
Ste C Gr Floor Office Redwood Ct, Tawe
Business Village Phoenix, Swansea,

AND PRIVATE COMPANIES | MITRAJAYA HOLDINGS BERHAD

SA79LA, United Kingdom (100%)
Tel.: (44) 1792793663
Web Site: http://www.mitie.com
Sales Range: $25-49.9 Million
Emp.: 17
Engineeering Services
N.A.I.C.S.: 541330

MITIE Engineering Services (West Midlands) Ltd. (2)
unit 5 Meltex House Keplar Lichfield Rd Indus Est, Tamworth, B79 7XE, Staffordshire, United Kingdom
Tel.: (44) 1905756172
Web Site: http://www.mitie.com
Sales Range: $10-24.9 Million
Emp.: 40
Engineeering Services
N.A.I.C.S.: 541330

Subsidiary (Domestic):

MITIE Technology & Infrastructure Ltd. (2)
Planwell House Edington Way, Lefa Business Centre, Sidcup, DA14 5EF, Kent, United Kingdom (100%)
Tel.: (44) 2082699010
Sales Range: $25-49.9 Million
Emp.: 20
Technology & Infrastructure Engineering Services
N.A.I.C.S.: 541330

MITIE Facilities Services Ltd (1)
22 Shand St, London, SE1 2ES, United Kingdom
Tel.: (44) 20 7089 7150
Facilities Management Services
N.A.I.C.S.: 561210

MITIE Interiors Ltd. (1)
Counting House 1st Fl 53 Tooley St, London, SE1 2QN, United Kingdom (100%)
Tel.: (44) 2070228400
Web Site: http://www.mitie.com
Emp.: 15
Facility Interior Finishing & Refurbishment Services
N.A.I.C.S.: 238390

MITIE Lyndhurst Services Limited (1)
20 Ptarmigan Place, Attleborough Fields Industrial, Nuneaton, CV11 6RX, Warks, United Kingdom
Tel.: (44) 2476370504
Web Site: http://www.mitie.co.uk
Landscaping Services
N.A.I.C.S.: 561730

MITIE PFI Ltd. (1)
Mercury House Broadwater Road, Welwyn Garden City, AL7 3BQ, Herts, United Kingdom (100%)
Tel.: (44) 1707294500
Integrated School Facilities Management Services
N.A.I.C.S.: 561210

MITIE Property Services (UK) Ltd. (1)
Unit 4 Redesdale Court Whorlton Road, Riverside Park, Middlesbrough, TS21RL, Cleveland, United Kingdom
Tel.: (44) 1642247956
Web Site: http://www.mitie.com
Emp.: 10
Real Estate Property Lessors
N.A.I.C.S.: 531190
Ian Robson (Gen Mgr)

Branch (Domestic):

MITIE Property Services (Eastern) Ltd. (2)
Middleway Dales Manor Business Park, Cambridge, CB24TJ, United Kingdom (100%)
Tel.: (44) 1223830730
Real Estate Property Lessors
N.A.I.C.S.: 531190

MITIE Property Services (North East) Ltd. (2)
3 Redesdale Court Whorlton Road, Riverside Park, Middlesbrough, TS2 1RL, Cleveland, United Kingdom
Tel.: (44) 1388602763
Web Site: http://www.mitie.com

Sales Range: $800-899.9 Million
Painting & Wall Covering Contractors
N.A.I.C.S.: 238320
Terry Colling (Mgr-Ops)

MITIE Property Services (Scotland) Ltd. (2)
Unit 4 A West Telferton Industrial Estate, Edinburgh, EH76UL, United Kingdom
Tel.: (44) 1316573540
Real Estate Property Lessors
N.A.I.C.S.: 531190

MITIE Property Services - Airdrie (2)
Dalmacoulter Road, Stirling Road Industrial Estat, Airdrie, ML6 7UD, Lanarkshire, United Kingdom (65%)
Tel.: (44) 1236766777
Web Site: http://www.mitiepropertyservices.co.uk
Sales Range: $150-199.9 Million
Emp.: 400
Real Estate Property Lessors
N.A.I.C.S.: 531190
William Robson (Mng Dir)

MITIE Property Services - Cirencester (2)
Carted Barn High Street South Cerney, Cirencester, GL75UG, Gloucestershire, United Kingdom (100%)
Tel.: (44) 1285862300
Web Site: http://www.mitie.com
Sales Range: $50-74.9 Million
Emp.: 4
Real Estate Property Lessors
N.A.I.C.S.: 531190

MITIE Scotgate Ltd. (1)
Scotgate House Whitley Way, Northfields Industrial Estate, Peterborough, PE68AR, United Kingdom (100%)
Tel.: (44) 2082699010
Sales Range: $25-49.9 Million
Emp.: 30
Electrical Contractor
N.A.I.C.S.: 238210

MITIE Security Holdings Ltd (1)
4 Monarch Court Brooms, Bristol, BS16 7FH, United Kingdom
Tel.: (44) 117 957 6400
Investment Management Service
N.A.I.C.S.: 523999

MITIE Security Ltd. (1)
Security House 20 Milburn Ave, Oldbrook, Milton Keynes, MK6 2WX, United Kingdom (100%)
Tel.: (44) 1908671317
Sales Range: $10-24.9 Million
Emp.: 40
Security Guard Services
N.A.I.C.S.: 561612

Subsidiary (Domestic):

MITIE Aviation Security Ltd. (2)
202A Jubilee House Furlong Way Gatwick, East Gatwick Airport, London, RH60JW, Sussex, United Kingdom (100%)
Tel.: (44) 1293502661
Web Site: http://www.mitie.co.uk
Airport Security Guard Services
N.A.I.C.S.: 561612
Anthony Medhurst (Mng Dir)

Branch (Domestic):

MITIE Security (London) Ltd. (2)
22 Shand St, London, SE1 2ES, United Kingdom (100%)
Tel.: (44) 2074070063
Web Site: http://www.mitie.com
Security Guard Services
N.A.I.C.S.: 561612

MITIE Security (North) Ltd. (2)
Office 45-49 Sugar Mill, Huddersfield, LS11 7HL, United Kingdom
Tel.: (44) 1484448660
Web Site: http://www.mitie.co.uk
Sales Range: $10-24.9 Million
Emp.: 30
Security Guard Services
N.A.I.C.S.: 561612

MITIE Security (Scotland) Ltd. (2)
739 South Street, Emersons Green, Glasgow, G14 0BX, United Kingdom
Tel.: (44) 1419506000

Security Guard Services
N.A.I.C.S.: 561612

MITIE Security Systems Ltd. (1)
Elder House 3rd Floor 590-598 Elder Gate, Milton Keynes, MK9 1LR, Herts, United Kingdom (100%)
Tel.: (44) 8454516111
Web Site: http://www.mitie.com
Sales Range: $25-49.9 Million
Emp.: 100
Security System Services
N.A.I.C.S.: 561621
Venefa Coorden (Mgr-Sys)

Procius Limited (1)
Level 12 The Shard 32 London Bridge Street, London, SE1 9SG, United Kingdom
Tel.: (44) 1256487890
Web Site: http://www.procius.com
Background Screening & Criminality Checking Services
N.A.I.C.S.: 561611
Ashley Knight (Ops Mgr)

UK CRBS Limited (1)
GF11 The Square Basing View, Basingstoke, RG21 4EB, United Kingdom
Tel.: (44) 1256487889
Web Site: http://www.ukcrbs.co.uk
Online Criminality Check Services
N.A.I.C.S.: 561611

MITO SECURITIES CO., LTD.
7F Nihombashi Maruzen Tokyu Bldg 2-3-10 Nihombashi, Chuo-ku, Tokyo, 103-0027, Japan
Tel.: (81) 366363071
Web Site: https://www.mito.co.jp
Year Founded: 1947
8622—(TKS)
Sales Range: $125-149.9 Million
Securities Trading Services
N.A.I.C.S.: 523150
Kazuhiko Kobayashi (Pres)

MITON UK MICROCAP TRUST PLC
Beaufort House 51 New North Road, Exeter, EX4 4EP, United Kingdom
Tel.: (44) 2037141500 UK
Web Site:
   https://www.mitonukmicrocap.com
Year Founded: 2015
MINI—(LSE)
Assets: $75,756,744
Liabilities: $22,017,114
Net Worth: $53,739,630
Earnings: ($34,837,677)
Fiscal Year-end: 04/30/23
Investment Management Trust Services
N.A.I.C.S.: 523940
Gervais Williams (Mgr-Trust)

MITR PHOL SUGAR CORPORATION LIMITED
2 Ploenchit Center Building 3rd Floor Sukhumvit Road, Klongtoey, Bangkok, 10110, Thailand
Tel.: (66) 27941000
Web Site: http://www.mitrphol.com
Year Founded: 1956
Holding Company; Cane Sugar Farming, Refining & Distr
N.A.I.C.S.: 551112
Krisda Monthienvichienchai (Pres)

Subsidiaries:

MSF Sugar Limited (1)
47 Gordon Street, Gordonvale, 4865, QLD, Australia
Tel.: (61) 7 4043 3333
Web Site: http://www.msfsugar.com.au
Sales Range: $100-124.9 Million
Emp.: 760
Sugar Refining Services
N.A.I.C.S.: 311314
Trevor D. Crook (Gen Mgr-Agriculture)

Subsidiary (Domestic):

The Mulgrave Central Mill Co., Ltd. (2)
Gordon St, PO Box 21, Gordonvale, Cairns, 4865, QLD, Australia
Tel.: (61) 740433333
Web Site: http://www.mulgravemill.com.au
Sales Range: $25-49.9 Million
Emp.: 130
Raw Sugar Mfr
N.A.I.C.S.: 311313
Mike Barry (CEO)

Mitr Phol Sugarcane Research Centre Co., Ltd. (1)
399 Moo 1 Chumpae-Phukieo Road Khoksa-at, Chaiyaphum, Bangkok, 36110, Phukieo, Thailand
Tel.: (66) 2656 8488
Web Site: http://www.mitrphol.com
Sugarcane Biological Research & Development Services
N.A.I.C.S.: 541714

Panel Plus Co., Ltd. (1)
25th Floor Ploenchit Centre 2 Sukhumvit Road, Klongtoey, Bangkok, 10110, Thailand
Tel.: (66) 2656 8188
Web Site: http://www.panelplus.co.th
Particleboard Mfr
N.A.I.C.S.: 321219

MITRACO LIVESTOCK JOINT STOCK COMPANY
Vinh Cat Hamlet, Luu Vinh Son Thanh Ha, Ha Tinh, Vietnam
Tel.: (84) 393478456
Seafood Product Mfr
N.A.I.C.S.: 311710

MITRAJAYA HOLDINGS BERHAD
No 9 Block D Pusat Perdagangan Puchong Prima Persiaran Prima Utama, Taman Puchong Prima, 47150, Puchong, Selangor Darul Ehsan, Malaysia
Tel.: (60) 380609999
Web Site:
   https://www.mitrajaya.com.my
MITRA—(KLS)
Rev.: $89,080,937
Assets: $277,676,737
Liabilities: $85,045,003
Net Worth: $192,631,734
Earnings: $2,652,924
Emp.: 700
Fiscal Year-end: 12/31/20
Construction & Property Development Services
N.A.I.C.S.: 531312
Chek Lee Foo (Exec Dir)

Subsidiaries:

Kemajuan Sekim Baru Sdn. Bhd. (1)
1175 Site Office Kem Skim Baru Jalan Bukit Buluh Kampung Bukit Buluh, 81600, Pengerang, Johor, Malaysia
Tel.: (60) 78265611
Sales Range: $50-74.9 Million
Emp.: 1
Property Development Services
N.A.I.C.S.: 531390
Ong Teck Chong (Mgr)

Kina-Bijak Sdn. Bhd. (1)
C-7-1 Kiara 9 Residency 22 Jalan Kiara 3, Mont' Kiara, 50480, Kuala Lumpur, Malaysia
Tel.: (60) 380682888
Web Site: https://www.kiara9.com
Property Management Services
N.A.I.C.S.: 531311

Kyalami & Mitrajaya Builders (Pty) Ltd. (1)
54 Beauly Avenue Blue Valley Golf and Country Estate, Centurion, 0157, Gauteng, South Africa
Tel.: (27) 113181688
Property Development Services
N.A.I.C.S.: 531311

MITRAJAYA HOLDINGS BERHAD

Mitrajaya Holdings Berhad—(Continued)

Leo Vista Sdn. Bhd. (1)
D-01-07 Block D Jalan Prima 5/1 Persiaran Prima Utama, Taman Puchong Prima, 47100, Puchong, Selangor, Malaysia
Tel.: (60) 380682888
Web Site: http://www.mitrajaya.com.my
Sales Range: $50-74.9 Million
Emp.: 15
Property Development Services
N.A.I.C.S.: 531390

Maha-Mayang Sdn. Bhd. (1)
D-01-09 Ground Fl Blok D Jalan Prima 5/1 Taman Puchong Prima, 47100, Puchong, Selangor, Malaysia
Tel.: (60) 380609999
Web Site: http://www.mitrajaya.com.my
Sales Range: $25-49.9 Million
Emp.: 6
Building Construction Services
N.A.I.C.S.: 236116

Mitrajaya Development SA (Pty) Ltd. (1)
72 Beauty Avenue Blue Valley Golf Country Estate, PO Box 61, Halfway Kop, 1685, South Africa
Tel.: (27) 113181688
Web Site: http://www.mitrajaya.com.my
Property Management Services
N.A.I.C.S.: 531311

Mitrajaya Homes Sdn. Bhd. (1)
No 9 Block D Pusat Perdagangan Puchong Prima Persiaran Prima Utama, Taman Puchong Prima, 47150, Puchong, Selangor Darul Ehsan, Malaysia
Tel.: (60) 38 068 2888
Web Site: https://mitrajayaproperties.com
Sales Range: $25-49.9 Million
Emp.: 20
Building Construction Services
N.A.I.C.S.: 236210

Pembinaan Mitrajaya Sdn. Bhd. (1)
No 9 Block D Pusat Perdagangan Puchong Prima Persiaran Prima Utama, Taman Puchong Prima, 47150, Puchong, Selangor Darul Ehsan, Malaysia
Tel.: (60) 380609999
Web Site: http://www.mitrajaya.com.my
Sales Range: $50-74.9 Million
Construction & Civil Engineering Services
N.A.I.C.S.: 237990
Tan Eng Piow *(Founder)*

MITROSREM A.D.
Trg Svetog Dimitrija bb, Sremska Mitrovica, Serbia
Tel.: (381) 22 610 366
Web Site: http://www.mitrosremad.rs
Year Founded: 1971
Sales Range: $1-9.9 Million
Emp.: 435
Cereal Crop Farming Services
N.A.I.C.S.: 111998

MITSHI INDIA LIMITED
2 Juhu Adadhana CHS Ltd Ground Floor, Juhu Lane Andheri W, Mumbai, 400 058, Maharashtra, India
Tel.: (91) 2226481711
Web Site: https://mitshi.in
Year Founded: 1990
523782—(BOM)
Rev.: $925,835
Assets: $320,762
Liabilities: $13,308
Net Worth: $307,454
Earnings: $60,484
Fiscal Year-end: 03/31/23
Paints Mfr
N.A.I.C.S.: 325510
Kumar Vasantlal Shah *(Chm & Mng Dir)*

MITSIB LEASING PUBLIC COMPANY LIMITED
895-6 Village No 5 Srinakarin Road, Samrong Nuea Subdistrict Mueang District, Samut Prakan, 10270, Thailand
Tel.: (66) 27438787   TH
Web Site: https://www.mitsibleasing.com
Year Founded: 2003
MITSIB—(THA)
Rev.: $20,039,412
Assets: $55,175,451
Liabilities: $32,648,591
Net Worth: $22,526,859
Earnings: $1,023,762
Fiscal Year-end: 12/31/23
Financial Investment Services
N.A.I.C.S.: 523999

MITSIDES PUBLIC COMPANY LTD
Tel.: (357) 22572020   CY
Web Site: https://www.mitsidesgroup.com
Year Founded: 1932
MIT—(CYP)
Sales Range: Less than $1 Million
Flour & Pasta Production & Sales Services
N.A.I.C.S.: 311211
Constantinos P. Mitsides *(Chm & Mng Dir)*

Subsidiaries:

Larnaca Zenon Flourmills Ltd (1)
18 Iakovou Patatsou, 6304, Larnaca, Cyprus
Tel.: (357) 24530661
Sales Range: $25-49.9 Million
Emp.: 10
Flour Mfr & Distr
N.A.I.C.S.: 311211

MITSU CHEM PLAST LIMITED
329 Gala Complex 3rd Floor Din Dayal Upadhyay Marg Mulund W, Mumbai, 400 080, Maharashtra, India
Tel.: (91) 2225920055
Web Site: https://www.mitsuchem.com
Year Founded: 1990
540078—(BOM)
Rev.: $37,087,681
Assets: $21,223,800
Liabilities: $13,739,476
Net Worth: $7,484,323
Earnings: $1,415,335
Emp.: 391
Fiscal Year-end: 03/31/23
Plastic Product Mfr & Distr
N.A.I.C.S.: 326199
Jagdish Liladhar Dedhia *(Chm)*

MITSUBA CORPORATION
1-2681 Hirosawa-Cho, Kiryu, 376-8555, Gunma, Japan
Tel.: (81) 277520111   JP
Web Site: https://www.mitsuba.co.jp
Year Founded: 1946
7280—(TKS)
Rev.: $2,274,857,940
Assets: $2,363,022,120
Liabilities: $1,552,761,710
Net Worth: $810,260,410
Earnings: $90,828,010
Emp.: 3,205
Fiscal Year-end: 03/31/24
Transportation Equipment Business Services
N.A.I.C.S.: 926120
Katsuyoshi Kitada *(Pres & COO)*

Subsidiaries:

AMCO Corporation (1)
5-204-11 Aioi-cho, Kiryu, 376-0011, Gunma, Japan
Tel.: (81) 277522631
Web Site: http://www.amcocorporation.com
Automotive Accessories Mfr
N.A.I.C.S.: 423120

American Mitsuba Corporation (1)
2945 3 Leaves Dr, Mount Pleasant, MI 48858
Tel.: (989) 773-0377
Sales Range: $25-49.9 Million
Emp.: 27
Automotive Accessories Mfr
N.A.I.C.S.: 423120
Yoshimasa Kimura *(Pres)*

Plant (Domestic):

American Mitsuba Corp. - Indiana Plant (2)
21600 Monroeville Rd, Monroeville, IN 46773
Tel.: (260) 623-3700
Web Site: https://www.americanmitsuba.com
Emp.: 450
Automotive Accessories Mfr
N.A.I.C.S.: 423120

Subsidiary (Domestic):

Mitsuba Bardstown, Inc. (2)
901 Withrow Ct, Bardstown, KY 40004
Tel.: (502) 348-3100
Web Site: http://www.mitsuba.co.jp
Sales Range: $25-49.9 Million
Automotive Accessories Mfr
N.A.I.C.S.: 423120

Changzhou Shihlin Mitsuba Electric & Engineering Co., Ltd. (1)
No 9 Xin 4 Road, Electronics Park New District, Changzhou, Jiangsu, China
Tel.: (86) 51985485925
Automobile Parts Mfr
N.A.I.C.S.: 336390

Corporacion Mitsuba de Mexico, S.A. de C.V. (1)
Antiguo Camino a Huinala No 210, 66600, Apodaca, N L, Mexico
Tel.: (52) 81 1156 3100
Web Site: http://www.mitsuba.co.jp
Emp.: 1,200
Automotive Electronic Motors Mfr
N.A.I.C.S.: 336390

Subsidiary (Domestic):

Partes de Precision Mitsuba de Mexico S.A. DE C.V. (2)
Calle Energia No 110 Parque Indus La Silla Apodaca, Anillo Periferico, Apodaca, 66600, Nuevo Leon, Mexico
Tel.: (52) 8111563000
Web Site: http://www.mitsuba.co.jp
Sales Range: $25-49.9 Million
Emp.: 400
Diecast Component Mfr
N.A.I.C.S.: 333514
Ken Kokubo *(Mng Dir)*

Tokyo Electrica de Mexico S.A. de C.V. (2)
Av Industria Electrica Lt-10 M-6 Zona Parque Indus, Sabinas Hidalgo, 65260, Nuevo Leon, Mexico   (71.4%)
Tel.: (52) 8242424300
Web Site: http://www.mitsuba.co.jp
Automotive Accessories Mfr
N.A.I.C.S.: 336390

Corporacion Tatsumi de Mexico, S.A. de C.V. (1)
Eficiencia 111, Parque Industrial La Silla, 66648, Apodaca, Nuevo Leon, Mexico
Tel.: (52) 8110891100
Precisioned Machined Products Mfr
N.A.I.C.S.: 332721

Guangzhou Mitsuba Electric (Wuhan) Co., Ltd. (1)
Shamao Street, Xingfu Industrial Park Hannan District, Wuhan, Hubei, China
Tel.: (86) 2784398895
Automobile Parts Mfr
N.A.I.C.S.: 336390

Guangzhou Mitsuba Electric Co., Ltd. (1)
263 Lianguang Road Eastern Section of Getdd, Guangzhou, Guangdong, China
Tel.: (86) 2032020168
Automobile Parts Mfr
N.A.I.C.S.: 336390

Higashinihon Diecasting Industry Co., Ltd. (1)
1914-2 Ikuhara Misato-machi, Takasaki, 370-3102, Gunma, Japan

INTERNATIONAL PUBLIC

Tel.: (81) 273715821
Web Site: https://www.higashinihon-hd.co.jp
Emp.: 190
Aluminum Diecast Components Mfr
N.A.I.C.S.: 331523
Masaki Ishikura *(Pres)*

MITSUBA Corp. - Fukushima Plant (1)
100 Numanoshita Kitakanomata, Funehiki-machi, Tamura, 963-4433, Fukushima, Japan
Tel.: (81) 247820705
Web Site: http://www.mitsuba.co.jp
Sales Range: $50-74.9 Million
Emp.: 224
Automotive Electrical Motor & Motor Components Mfr
N.A.I.C.S.: 336320

MITSUBA Corp. - Niigata Plant (1)
950 Yamazakishinden Minami, Minami-Ku, Uonuma, 949-7226, Niigata, Japan
Tel.: (81) 257792800
Web Site: http://www.mitsuba.co.jp
Sales Range: $75-99.9 Million
Emp.: 168
Automotive Fluid Power Pump, Actuator & Electrical Motor Mfr
N.A.I.C.S.: 336390

MITSUBA Corp. - Niisato Plant (1)
598 No Niisato-Cho, Kiryu, 376-0122, Gunma, Japan
Tel.: (81) 277748211
Web Site: http://www.mitsuba.co.jp
Sales Range: $200-249.9 Million
Emp.: 775
Automotive Electrical Motor & Front Wiper Assemblies Mfr
N.A.I.C.S.: 336320

MITSUBA Corp. - Onishi Plant (1)
1351 Joboji, Fujioka, 370-1406, Gunma, Japan
Tel.: (81) 274523241
Sales Range: $75-99.9 Million
Emp.: 249
Automotive Fluid Power Pump, Relay & Regulator Mfr
N.A.I.C.S.: 336390

MITSUBA Corp. - Tomioka Plant (1)
1259-1 Tomioka, Tomioka, 370-2316, Gunma, Japan
Tel.: (81) 274627000
Web Site: http://www.mitsuba.co.jp
Emp.: 369
Automotive Electrical Motor & Motor Components Mfr
N.A.I.C.S.: 336320

MITSUBA Corp. - Tone Plant (1)
300 Oai Shirasawa-machi, Numata, 378-0124, Gunma, Japan
Tel.: (81) 278532311
Web Site: http://www.mitsuba.co.jp
Sales Range: $125-149.9 Million
Emp.: 237
Automotive Electrical Motor & Armature Assemblies Mfr
N.A.I.C.S.: 336320

Mitsuba Ability Staff Corporation (1)
2-1890-18 Tomoe-Cho, Kiryu, 376-0021, Gunma, Japan
Tel.: (81) 277208127
Staff Recruitment & Leasing Services
N.A.I.C.S.: 561330

Mitsuba Asia R&D Co., Ltd. (1)
789 / 6-7 Moo 9, Tambon Bangpla Amphoe Bangphli, Samut Prakan, 10540, Thailand
Tel.: (66) 21709430
Web Site: http://www.mitsuba.co.jp
Sales Range: $25-49.9 Million
Emp.: 11
Motor Vehicle Equipment Mfr
N.A.I.C.S.: 336390

Mitsuba Automotive Systems of Europe Kft. (1)
Patak utca 3-4, 3104, Salgotarjan, Nograd, Hungary
Tel.: (36) 32521420
Web Site: http://www.mitsuba.co.jp
Sales Range: $75-99.9 Million
Emp.: 150
Automotive Accessories Mfr
N.A.I.C.S.: 423120

AND PRIVATE COMPANIES — MITSUBA CORPORATION

Mitsuba Automotive Technology (Shanghai) Co., Ltd. (1)
Rm 808 Aetna Tower NO 107 Zunyi Road, Changning District, Shanghai, China
Tel.: (86) 2132230676
Marketing Services
N.A.I.C.S.: 541613

Mitsuba Autoparts do Brasil Industria Ltda. (1)
Avenida Japao No 1500, Nucleo Ayres Artur Nogueira, Sao Paulo, 13160-500, Brazil
Tel.: (55) 1938278800
Automobile Parts Mfr
N.A.I.C.S.: 336390

Mitsuba China (Hong Kong) Ltd. (1)
Room 1706 1707 17/F Olympia Plaza 255 King's Road, North Point, China (Hong Kong)
Tel.: (852) 25680124
Web Site: http://www.mitsuba.co.jp
Transportation Equipment Distr
N.A.I.C.S.: 423860

Mitsuba Electric (Dalian) Co., Ltd. (1)
31Northeast Third Street, Economic Technical Development Zone, Dalian, Liaoning, China (100%)
Tel.: (86) 41187618667
Web Site: http://www.mitsuba.co.jp
Power Windows & Sunroof Motors, Electric Power Steering Motors, Door Lock Actuators, Sensors & Power Seat Motors Mfr
N.A.I.C.S.: 336390

Mitsuba Environmental Analysis and Research Corporation (1)
Mitsuba Niisato Plant Site 598 No Niisato-Cho Kiryu, Gunma, 376-0122, Japan
Tel.: (81) 277745958
Web Site: http://www.t-clover.co.jp
Sales Range: $25-49.9 Million
Emp.: 12
Automotive Accessories Mfr
N.A.I.C.S.: 423120
Katsuo Ogawa (Pres)

Mitsuba Germany GmbH (1)
Otl-Aicher-Strasse 60-64, 80807, Munich, Germany
Tel.: (49) 8953886580
Web Site: http://www.mitsuba.co.jp
Sales Range: $25-49.9 Million
Emp.: 13
Transportation Equipments Marketing & Sales
N.A.I.C.S.: 423860

Mitsuba Harvest Co., Ltd. (1)
2-928-114 Aioi-cho, Kiryu, 376-0011, Gunma, Japan
Tel.: (81) 277555831
Web Site: http://www.mitsuba-harvest.co.jp
Tomato Farming Services
N.A.I.C.S.: 111219

Mitsuba India Pvt. Ltd. (1)
D-8 SIPCOT Industrial Complex, Gummidipoondi, 601 201, Tamil Nadu, India
Tel.: (91) 4427922558
Automobile Parts Mfr
N.A.I.C.S.: 336390

Mitsuba Italia S.p.A. (1)
Via Marco Biagi 12, 56025, Pontedera, PI, Italy
Tel.: (39) 058726901
Starter Motor Mfr
N.A.I.C.S.: 336320

Mitsuba Logistics Co., Ltd. (1)
19-161 Yoriaicho, Ota, 379-2303, Gunma, Japan
Tel.: (81) 277783511
Web Site: https://www.mitsuba-logistics.co.jp
Emp.: 323
Transport & Warehousing Services
N.A.I.C.S.: 493110

Mitsuba M-Tech Vietnam Co., Ltd. (1)
Lot D5-1 Long Binh Techno Park, Bien Hoa, Dong Nai, Vietnam
Tel.: (84) 613892224
Web Site: http://www.mitsuba.com
Sales Range: $400-449.9 Million
Emp.: 2,500
Automotive Accessories Mfr
N.A.I.C.S.: 336390

Mitsuba Manufacturing France S.A. (1)
Route de la Verrie Z I de la Gare, 85290, Saint-Laurent-sur-Sevre, France
Tel.: (33) 251646200
Web Site: http://www.mitsuba.co.jp
Sales Range: $25-49.9 Million
Emp.: 70
Automotive Accessories Mfr
N.A.I.C.S.: 336110

Mitsuba Manufacturing Morocco Sarl AU (1)
Lot 74 Zone Industrielle Sud-Ouest, 28810, Mohammedia, Morocco
Tel.: (212) 523315480
Automobile Parts Mfr
N.A.I.C.S.: 336390

Mitsuba Mitsuba Turkey Otomotiv A.S. (1)
GOSB2 MH 1500 SK No 1502/1, Cayirova, 41420, Kocaeli, Turkiye
Tel.: (90) 2627514122
Automobile Parts Mfr
N.A.I.C.S.: 336390

Mitsuba Philippines Corp. (1)
Lot1 Block14 Phase II Brgy Langkaan, First Cavite Industrial Estate, Dasmarinas, Cavite, Philippines
Tel.: (63) 464021203
Web Site: http://www.mitsuba.ph
Automotive Parts Mfr & Distr
N.A.I.C.S.: 336390

Mitsuba Philippines Technical Center Corporation (1)
14th Floor One Ayala Avenue Corporate Center Tower 2, EDSA Corner Ayala Ave Ayala Center, Makati, 1223, Metro Manila, Philippines
Tel.: (63) 9998877470
Web Site: https://mptc.ph
Sales Range: $25-49.9 Million
Emp.: 70
Automotive Components & Equipments Design & Mfr
N.A.I.C.S.: 811198
Susumu Aoki (Pres)

Mitsuba Rus LLC (1)
ul 3rd Promyshlennaya D 1, 425000, Volzhsky, Russia
Tel.: (7) 8363140288
Automobile Parts Mfr
N.A.I.C.S.: 336390

Mitsuba Sankowa Corporation (1)
3-3-4 Narimasu, Itabashi-ku, Tokyo, 175-0094, Japan
Tel.: (81) 339383201
Web Site: https://www.mitsuba.co.jp
Emp.: 52
Automobile Components Sales
N.A.I.C.S.: 423120

Mitsuba Shihlin Electric (Wuhan) Co., Ltd. (1)
513 Wubei Road Jinghe Street, Dongxihu Dis, Wuhan, Hubei, China
Tel.: (86) 2783249606
Automobile Parts Mfr
N.A.I.C.S.: 336390

Mitsuba Vietnam Co., Ltd. (1)
Lot D5-1 Long Binh Techno Park, Bien Hoa, Dong Nai, Vietnam
Tel.: (84) 2513892224
Electronic Products Mfr
N.A.I.C.S.: 334419

Mitsuba Vietnam Technical Center Co., Ltd. (1)
Zen Plaza Unit 1102 54-56 Nguyen Trai St, District 1, Ho Chi Minh City, Vietnam
Tel.: (84) 2839257466
Automobile Parts Mfr
N.A.I.C.S.: 336390

Mitsuba do Brasil Ltda. (1)
Av Max Teixeira No 334 Bairro Flores, Manaus, 69058-415, AM, Brazil
Tel.: (55) 9221238150
Web Site: http://www.mitsuba.co.jp
Sales Range: $150-199.9 Million
Emp.: 350
Automotive Accessories Mfr
N.A.I.C.S.: 423120

Miyazaki Mitsuba Corporation (1)
1-2 Imaichi Mitsumata-Cho, Kitamorokata-Gun, Miyazaki, 889-1905, Japan
Tel.: (81) 986521231
Web Site: http://www.mitsuba.co.jp
Motor Pumps Mfr
N.A.I.C.S.: 333914

Momimo Manufacturing Co., Ltd. (1)
3-136-1 Aioicho, Kiryu, 376-0011, Gunma, Japan
Tel.: (81) 277542345
Web Site: https://www.momimo.co.jp
Emp.: 127
Molding Component Mfr
N.A.I.C.S.: 333511

Nagano Mitsuba Corporation (1)
2713-1 Tagiri Iijima-Machi, Kamiina-gun, Nagano, 399-3701, Japan
Tel.: (81) 265863141
Web Site: http://www.mitsuba.co.jp
Sales Range: $25-49.9 Million
Emp.: 2
Motor Component Mfr
N.A.I.C.S.: 336390
Hiveo Wada (Pres)

Ochiai Manufacturing Co., Ltd. (1)
250-11 Uda, Tomioka, 370-2451, Gunma, Japan
Tel.: (81) 274623221
Web Site: http://www.mitsuba.co.jp
Sales Range: $25-49.9 Million
Emp.: 30
Spot Welding Products Mfr
N.A.I.C.S.: 333992

Office Advan Inc. (1)
1-2789 Hirosawacho, Kiryu, 376-0013, Gunma, Japan
Tel.: (81) 277520237
Web Site: https://www.o-advan.co.jp
Sales Range: $700-749.9 Million
Emp.: 3,000
Accounting Consignment Services
N.A.I.C.S.: 541211

P.T. Mitsuba Automotive Parts Indonesia (1)
Blok D-III No 3, Kawasan Industri Kota Bukit Indah, Purwakarta, 41181, Jawa Barat, Indonesia
Tel.: (62) 264350128
Automobile Parts Mfr
N.A.I.C.S.: 336390

P.T. Mitsuba Indonesia (1)
Jl Sliwangi Kelurahan Keroncong, Kecamatan Jatiuwung Kota, Tangerang, 15134, Banten, Indonesia
Tel.: (62) 215908020
Web Site: http://www.mitsuba.co.jp
Automotive Accessories Mfr
N.A.I.C.S.: 423120

PT. Tatsumi Indonesia (1)
Blok D-III No 3 Desa Dangdeur, Kawasan Industri Kota Bukit Indah Kecamatan Bungursari, Purwakarta, 41181, Jawa Barat, Indonesia
Tel.: (62) 2648302035
Automobile Parts Mfr
N.A.I.C.S.: 336390

RS Consultants CO., LTD. (1)
3-4025 Hirosawa-Cho Kiryu, 376-8502, Gunma, Japan
Tel.: (81) 277533740
Web Site: http://www.rs-c.co.jp
Sales Range: $25-49.9 Million
Emp.: 7
Business Consulting Services
N.A.I.C.S.: 541611

Ryomo Business Support Co., Ltd. (1)
2-2961 Hirosawacho, Kiryu, 376-0013, Gunma, Japan
Tel.: (81) 277706600
Web Site: https://www.rbs.co.jp
Emp.: 391
Information Technology Outsourcing Services
N.A.I.C.S.: 519290

Ryomo Internet Data Center Co., Ltd. (1)
3-4025 Hirosawa-cho, Kiryu, 376-8503, Gunma, Japan
Tel.: (81) 277 40 2090
Web Site: http://www.ridc.co.jp
Sales Range: $150-199.9 Million
Emp.: 700
internet Data Center Services & Agency Services
N.A.I.C.S.: 519290

Ryomo Philippines Information Corp. (1)
10th Floor Pacific Star Building Sen Gil Puyat Corner Makati Ave, Makati, 1200, Philippines
Tel.: (63) 28359813
Computer System Support & Operation Services
N.A.I.C.S.: 541519

Ryomo Systems Co., Ltd. (1)
3-4025 Hirosawa-cho, Kiryu, 376-8502, Gunma, Japan
Tel.: (81) 277533131
Web Site: https://www.ryomo.co.jp
System Integration Services
N.A.I.C.S.: 541512
Noboru Hino (Chm)

Ryomo Vietnam Solutions Co., Ltd. (1)
Saigon Riverside Office Center Unit 605-08 6th Floor, 2A-4A Ton Duc Thang St Ben Nghe Ward Dist 1, Ho Chi Minh City, Vietnam
Tel.: (84) 2838226524
Web Site: https://rvsc.ryomo-gr.com
Emp.: 86
Computer Networking Solutions
N.A.I.C.S.: 541511

Sanko Construction Co (1)
2-2961 Hirosawa-Cho, Kiryu, 376-0013, Gunma, Japan
Tel.: (81) 277533111
Electrical & Piping Engineering Services
N.A.I.C.S.: 541330
Masamichi Imoto (Pres)

Sanko Electric Co., Ltd. (1)
5-1167 Hirosawacho, Kiryu, 376-0013, Gunma, Japan
Tel.: (81) 277525816
Web Site: https://www.sanko-engineering.co.jp
Emp.: 105
Electric Device Mfr
N.A.I.C.S.: 334419

Santist Co., Ltd. (1)
3427-12 Miyako-Cho, Isesaki, 372-0801, Gunma, Japan
Tel.: (81) 270260100
Web Site: http://www.santist.co.jp
Sales Range: $25-49.9 Million
Emp.: 27
Automobile Components Sales
N.A.I.C.S.: 423120

Sun-You Corp. (1)
5-204-11 Aioi-cho, Kiryu, 376-0011, Gunma, Japan
Tel.: (81) 277532380
Automobile Parts Mfr
N.A.I.C.S.: 336390

Sunfield Internet Co., Ltd (1)
22961 Hirosawa-cho, Kiryu, 376-0013, Gunma, Japan
Tel.: (81) 120550520
Web Site: http://www.sunfield.ne.jp
Emp.: 55
Telecommunication Network Maintenance & Internet Services
N.A.I.C.S.: 517810

Tatsumi Corporation (1)
443 Minami Omachi, Ashikaga, 326-0836, Tochigi, Japan
Tel.: (81) 284713131
Web Site: https://www.tatsumi-ta.co.jp
Sales Range: $100-124.9 Million
Emp.: 306
Cold Forging Equipment Mfr
N.A.I.C.S.: 332111

Thai Summit Mitsuba Electric Manufacturing Co., Ltd. (1)
500/79 Moo 3 Hemaraj Eastern Seaboard Industrial Estate, Tambon Tasith Amphur

MITSUBA CORPORATION

MITSUBA Corporation—(Continued)

Pluak Daeng, Rayong, 21140, Thailand
Tel.: (66) 38698300
Automobile Parts Mfr
N.A.I.C.S.: 336390

Toyo Electric Manufacturing Co., Ltd. (1)
Tokyo Tatemono Yaesu Building 5F 1-4-16, Yaesu Chuou-ku, Tokyo, 103-0028, Gunma, Japan
Tel.: (81) 352028121
Web Site: https://www.toyodenki.co.jp
Emp.: 1,149
Motor Vehicle Accessories Mfr
N.A.I.C.S.: 336390

MITSUBISHI CHEMICAL GROUP CORPORATION

1-1 Marunouchi 1-chome, Chiyoda-ku, Tokyo, 100-8251, Japan
Tel.: (81) 367487300   JP
Web Site: https://www.mcgc.com
Year Founded: 2005
4188—(TKS)
Rev.: $28,999,510,980
Assets: $40,350,830,930
Liabilities: $25,309,808,980
Net Worth: $15,041,021,950
Earnings: $790,529,560
Emp.: 66,358
Fiscal Year-end: 03/31/24
Plastics Product Mfr
N.A.I.C.S.: 551112
Ken Fujiwara *(Chief Grp Compliance Officer & Mng Corp Exec Officer)*

Subsidiaries:

Lucite International Ltd (1)
Tel.: (44) 8702404620
Web Site: http://www.luciteinternational.com
Sales Range: $25-49.9 Million
Emp.: 14
Designer & Mfr of Acrylic Products
N.A.I.C.S.: 325211

Subsidiary (Non-US):

Kaohsiung Monomer Company Limited (2)
Tel.: (886) 73516651
Web Site: https://www.kmc.com.tw
Sales Range: $50-74.9 Million
Basic Inorganic Chemical Mfr
N.A.I.C.S.: 325180

Lucite International (China) Chemical Industry Co., Ltd. (2)
Tel.: (86) 2164268899
Web Site: http://www.lucite.com
Emp.: 100
Basic Organic Chemical Mfr
N.A.I.C.S.: 325199

Lucite International (Shanghai) Trading Co Limited (2)
Tel.: (86) 2164268899
Web Site: http://www.lucitechina.com
Chemical Product & Preparation Mfr
N.A.I.C.S.: 325998

Lucite International Asia Pacific Pte Limited (2)
Tel.: (852) 29237276
Chemical Product & Preparation Mfr
N.A.I.C.S.: 325998

Lucite International Canada Inc. (2)
Tel.: (905) 673-3345
Web Site: http://www.lucite.com
Sales Range: $50-74.9 Million
Emp.: 3
Plastics Materials & Basic Forms & Shapes Whslr
N.A.I.C.S.: 424610

Lucite International France SAS (2)
Tel.: (33) 384258114
Web Site: http://www.luciteinternational.com
Sales Range: $25-49.9 Million
Plastics Material & Resin Mfr
N.A.I.C.S.: 325211

Lucite International Holland B.V. (2)
Tel.: (31) 181233233

Web Site: https://lucitediakon.com
Sales Range: $25-49.9 Million
Chemical & Allied Products Merchant Whslr
N.A.I.C.S.: 424690

Lucite International Japan Limited (2)
Tel.: (81) 338654607
Web Site: http://www.lucite.com
Chemical Product & Preparation Mfr
N.A.I.C.S.: 325998

Lucite International Netherlands B.V. (2)
Tel.: (31) 181233272
Web Site: http://www.lucitesolutions.com
Sales Range: $25-49.9 Million
Chemical & Allied Products Merchant Whslr
N.A.I.C.S.: 424690

Lucite International Singapore Pte Limited (2)
Tel.: (65) 63250888
Chemical Product & Preparation Mfr
N.A.I.C.S.: 325998

Lucite International Speciality Polymers and Resins Limited (2)
Tel.: (44) 1325300990
Web Site: http://www.luciteinternational.com
Sales Range: $25-49.9 Million
Emp.: 50
Chemical & Allied Products Merchant Whslr
N.A.I.C.S.: 424690

Lucite International UK Limited (2)
Tel.: (44) 1254874444
Web Site: http://www.luciteinternational.com
Sales Range: $50-74.9 Million
Plastics Material & Resin Mfr
N.A.I.C.S.: 325211

Lucite International, Inc. (2)
Tel.: (901) 354-1000
Web Site: http://www.luciteinternational.com
Sales Range: $125-149.9 Million
Plastics & Resin Mfr
N.A.I.C.S.: 325211

Mitsubishi Chemical Advanced Materials AG (1)
Talstrasse 70, 8001, Zurich, Switzerland
Tel.: (41) 442136666
Specialty Plastics Mfr
N.A.I.C.S.: 325211

Subsidiary (US):

Mitsubishi Chemical Advanced Materials Inc. (2)
3837 Imperial Way, Stockton, CA 95215
Tel.: (209) 464-2701
Plastic Products & Resin Mfr
N.A.I.C.S.: 326199

Subsidiary (Non-US):

Polypenco Ltd. (2)
64 Gravelly Industrial Park Tyburn Road, Erdington, Birmingham, B24 8HZ, W Midlands, United Kingdom
Tel.: (44) 1213281748
Basic Shapes from High-Grade Engineering Plastics & Articles Machined from These
Basic Shapes, Pressure Hoses, High-Grade Injection Moulding Compounds
N.A.I.C.S.: 326121

Polytron GmbH (2)
An Der Zinkhutte 17, Postfach 200731, 51469, Bergisch Gladbach, Germany
Tel.: (49) 220210090
Web Site: http://www.polytron-gmbh.de
Sales Range: $75-99.9 Million
Emp.: 19
Plastics Products
N.A.I.C.S.: 326199

Quadrant B.V. (2)
Anthony Fokkerweg 2, PO Box 59, Almelo, 7602 PK, Netherlands
Tel.: (31) 546877777
Web Site: http://www.quadrantepp.com
Sales Range: $10-24.9 Million
Emp.: 80
Plastics Products
N.A.I.C.S.: 326199
Peter Bruijn *(Mng Dir)*

Subsidiary (Domestic):

Quadrant EPP AG (2)

Hardstrasse 5, CH 5600, Lenzburg, Switzerland
Tel.: (41) 628858150
Web Site: http://www.quadrantepp.com
Sales Range: $25-49.9 Million
Emp.: 100
Plastics Product Mfr
N.A.I.C.S.: 326199
Sven Welich *(CEO)*

Subsidiary (Non-US):

Quadrant CMS (3)
Galgenveldstraat 10, B 8700, Tielt, Belgium
Tel.: (32) 51423211
Web Site: http://www.quadrantplastics.com
Sales Range: $25-49.9 Million
Emp.: 200
Custom-Made High-Grade Injection Moulded Products of All Kinds of Thermoplasts for Consumer Electronics, Medical, Phtographic & Leisure-Time Applications
N.A.I.C.S.: 333248
Gohan Zangerwers *(Mng Dir)*

Quadrant EPP France Cestidur Division (3)
ZI Front De Bandiere, 01360, Balan, France
Tel.: (33) 472251787
Web Site: http://www.quadrantepp.com
Sales Range: $75-99.9 Million
Emp.: 52
Mfr of Basic Shapes from High-Grade Engineering Plastics & Articles
N.A.I.C.S.: 326199

Quadrant EPP Germany GmbH (3)
Tel.: (49) 72611550
Web Site: http://www.quadrantplastics.com
Sales Range: $50-74.9 Million
Emp.: 50
Plastics Product Mfr
N.A.I.C.S.: 326199
Juergen Zennekus *(Gen Mgr)*

Quadrant EPP S.A. (3)
ZI Front de Bandiere, 01360, Balan, France
Tel.: (33) 472931800
Web Site: http://www.quadrant.com
Sales Range: $75-99.9 Million
Emp.: 60
Mfr of Basic Shapes from High-Grade Engineering Plastics & Articles
N.A.I.C.S.: 326199
Francois Jean-Christophe *(Mgr-Sls)*

Quadrant EPP UK Ltd. (3)
Woodhouse Road, Todmorden, OL14 5TP, United Kingdom
Tel.: (44) 1706811000
Web Site: http://www.quadrantplastics.com
Sales Range: $75-99.9 Million
Emp.: 54
Mfr of Basic Shapes from High-Grade Engineering Plastics & Articles
N.A.I.C.S.: 326199
Joe Norwood *(Mgr-Site)*

Subsidiary (US):

Quadrant EPP USA, Inc. (3)
2120 Fairmont Ave, Reading, PA 19612-4235
Tel.: (610) 320-6600
Sales Range: $100-124.9 Million
Emp.: 350
Mfr of Basic Shapes from High-Grade Engineering Plastics & Articles
N.A.I.C.S.: 325220
Kress Schwartz *(Mgr-Mktg & Comm)*

Plant (Domestic):

Quadrant EPP USA, Inc. (4)
2710 American Way, Fort Wayne, IN 46809-3011
Tel.: (260) 479-4100
Web Site: http://www.quadrantplastics.com
Sales Range: $125-149.9 Million
Emp.: 90
Chemical Coating Mfr
N.A.I.C.S.: 325180
Dan Michalak *(Controller)*

Quadrant EPP USA, Inc. (4)
2530 N 4th St, Wytheville, VA 24382
Tel.: (276) 228-0100
Web Site: http://www.quadrantepp.com
Emp.: 100
Mfr of Plastic Products

INTERNATIONAL PUBLIC

N.A.I.C.S.: 326199

Subsidiary (Non-US):

Quadrant Kenkyo EPP Ltd. (3)
60 Ha Mei San Tsuen Ping Shan, Yuen Long, NT, China (Hong Kong)
Tel.: (852) 24702683
Web Site: http://www.quadrantplastics.com
Sales Range: $10-24.9 Million
Emp.: 11
Mfg Plastic Products
N.A.I.C.S.: 326199
Ho Wei *(Pres)*

Quadrant Polymer China Ltd. (3)
2906 Alexandra House, Central, China (Hong Kong)
Tel.: (852) 25265441
Sales of Polymers
N.A.I.C.S.: 424610

Subsidiary (Non-US):

Quadrant Plastic Composites Canada Inc. (2)
495 Laird Road, Guelph, N1G 3M1, ON, Canada
Tel.: (519) 837-1500
Web Site: http://www.quadrantepp.com
Sales Range: $75-99.9 Million
Emp.: 25
Mfrs. Nylon
N.A.I.C.S.: 325220
David Caberlin *(Mgr-Plant)*

Affiliate (Non-US):

Quadrant Polypenco Ltd. (2)
1-2-2 Nihonbashihongokucho, Chuo-ku, Tokyo, 103-0021, Japan (62%)
Tel.: (81) 3 3279 3201
Web Site: http://www.polypenco.co.jp
Sales Range: $75-99.9 Million
Emp.: 160
Engineering Plastics Mfr & Sales
N.A.I.C.S.: 326199

Subsidiary (Non-US):

Quadrant S.r.l. (2)
Via Trento 39, Milan, 20017, Italy
Tel.: (39) 029326131
Web Site: http://www.quadrantepp.com
Sales Range: $75-99.9 Million
Emp.: 36
Plastics Products
N.A.I.C.S.: 326199
Luca Introini *(Mgr-Fin)*

Mitsubishi Chemical Corporation (1)
Palace Building 1-1-1 Marunouchi, Chiyoda-ku, Tokyo, 100-8251, Japan (100%)
Tel.: (81) 367487300
Web Site: https://www.m-chemical.co.jp
Emp.: 42,127
Acrylic Fibers, Plastics & Resins Mfr
N.A.I.C.S.: 325199
Hitoshi Sasaki *(Mng Exec Officer & COO-MMA Bus Domain)*

Subsidiary (Domestic):

Acry Sunday Co., Ltd. (2)
2F Odagiri Building 2-5-7 Kotobuki, Taito-ku, Tokyo, 111-0042, Japan
Tel.: (81) 352463940
Web Site: https://www.acrysunday.co.jp
Emp.: 35
Acrylic Sheet Mfr
N.A.I.C.S.: 326113
Hiroyuki Umeda *(Pres)*

Alpolic Corp. (2)
Palace Building 1-1-1 Marunouchi, Chiyoda-ku, Tokyo, 100-8251, Japan
Tel.: (81) 367487349
Web Site: http://www.alpolic.com
Metal Surface & Resin Composite Materials Mfr
N.A.I.C.S.: 326199

Astro Corp. (2)
1-2-2 Nihonbashi Honishicho, Chuo-ku, Tokyo, 103-0021, Japan
Tel.: (81) 3 3279 3216
Web Site: http://www.astrocorp.co.jp
Artificial Turf & Water Treatment Products Mfr
N.A.I.C.S.: 326199

AND PRIVATE COMPANIES

DIA RIX CORPORATION (2)
2-1-30 Shiba, Minato-ku, Tokyo, 105-0014, Japan
Tel.: (81) 354455680
Web Site: https://www.diarix.co.jp
Sales Range: $150-199.9 Million
Emp.: 560
Real Estate Manangement Services
N.A.I.C.S.: 531390
Shinichi Torihara (CEO)

Dia Molding Co., Ltd. (2)
1700 Ochi-cho, Nagahama, 526-0243, Shiga, Japan
Tel.: (81) 749743560
Web Site: http://www.diamolding.co.jp
Injection Molding, Painting & Assembly of Plastic Products
N.A.I.C.S.: 326199

Subsidiary (Non-US):

Dia Moulding Slovakia s.r.o. (2)
Na Pasienkoch 10, 949 01, Nitra, Slovakia
Tel.: (421) 3761196203
Plastics Product Mfr
N.A.I.C.S.: 326199

Diapolyacrylate Co., Ltd. (2)
100/62 30th Fl Sathorn Nakorn Tower North Sathorn Rd, Khwaeng Silom Khet Bangrak, Bangkok, 10500, Thailand
Tel.: (66) 26367580
Polymethyl Methacrylate Pellet Mfr & Distr
N.A.I.C.S.: 325211

Subsidiary (Domestic):

Etsuryo Co., Ltd. (2)
1 Fukuda-cho, Joetsu, 942-0032, Niigata, Japan
Tel.: (81) 255433761
Emp.: 25
Light Metal Products, Industrial & Agricultural Materials Sales
N.A.I.C.S.: 423510

Subsidiary (US):

Hishi Plastics U.S.A., Inc. (2)
600 Ryerson Rd, Lincoln Park, NJ 07035 (51%)
Tel.: (973) 633-1230
Web Site: http://www.hishiplastics.com
Emp.: 50
Plastics Product Mfr
N.A.I.C.S.: 326199

Subsidiary (Domestic):

Hokuryo Mold Co., Ltd. (2)
205 Kanocho, Nagahama, 526-0051, Shiga, Japan
Tel.: (81) 749637731
Web Site: https://www.hokuryo-mold.co.jp
Sales Range: $25-49.9 Million
Emp.: 30
Special Die & Tool Die Set Jig & Fixture Mfr
N.A.I.C.S.: 333514

Subsidiary (Non-US):

Huizhou MMA Co., Ltd. (2)
No 8 Binhai 11th Road, PO Box 13, Daya Bay Petrochemical Industrial Park, Huizhou, 516082, Guangdong, China
Tel.: (86) 7525598300
Sales Range: $25-49.9 Million
Emp.: 80
Methyl Methacrylate Mfr
N.A.I.C.S.: 325211

Subsidiary (Domestic):

IFCO Japan Inc. (2)
New Pier Takeshiba North Tower 5th floor 1-11-1 Kaigan, Minato-ku, Tokyo, 105-0022, Japan
Tel.: (81) 354017431
Web Site: https://www.ifco-jpn.co.jp
Plastic Containers Leasing
N.A.I.C.S.: 532490
Kotaro Endo (Pres)

J-Film Corporation (2)
2-5-15 Higashi Kanda, Chiyoda-ku, Tokyo, 101-0031, Japan
Tel.: (81) 3 3862 8511
Web Site: http://www.jfilm.co.jp
Emp.: 737
Plastic Packaging Material Mfr & Distr

N.A.I.C.S.: 322220

Plant (Domestic):

J-Film Corporation - Narita Plant #1 (3)
179-93 Iwabe, Katori, 287-0102, Chiba-ken, Japan
Tel.: (81) 478 75 2222
Plastics Films Mfr
N.A.I.C.S.: 326112

J-Film Corporation - Narita Plant #2 (3)
2065-1 Iwabe, Katori, 287-0102, Chiba, Japan
Tel.: (81) 478 70 5700
Web Site: http://www.jfilm.co.jp
Laminating Film Mfr
N.A.I.C.S.: 322220

Subsidiary (Domestic):

J-Film Logistics, Inc. (3)
179-93 Iwabe, Katori, 287-0102, Chiba-ken, Japan
Tel.: (81) 478 70 5041
Web Site: http://www.jfilm.co.jp
Processing, Manufacture & Sale of Synthetic Resin Packaging Materials
N.A.I.C.S.: 541614

Subsidiary (Non-US):

J-Film Philippines, Inc. (3)
Lot 10 and 12 Block 14 Phase3 PEZA Rosari, Cavite, 4106, Philippines
Tel.: (63) 464371136
Emp.: 180
Plastics Films Mfr
N.A.I.C.S.: 326113

Subsidiary (Domestic):

Japan Polychem Corporation (2)
1-1-1 Marunouchi Palace Building, Chiyoda-ku, Tokyo, 100-8251, Japan
Emp.: 110
Developer & Mfr of Polyolefins
N.A.I.C.S.: 325110
Masahiko Tanaka (Pres)

Subsidiary (Domestic):

DIATEX Co., Ltd. (3)
7th Kanda Konyacho, Chiyoda-ku, Tokyo, 101-0035, Japan
Tel.: (81) 3 3254 3221
Web Site: http://www.diatex.co.jp
Emp.: 346
Yarn Products Mfr & Distr
N.A.I.C.S.: 313110
Takanobu Imaya (Pres)

Japan Polyethylene Corporation (3)
Palace Building 1-1-1 Marunouchi, Chiyoda-ku, Tokyo, 100-8251, Japan
Tel.: (81) 367487188
Web Site: https://www.j-polyethylene.com
Emp.: 551
Polyethylene Resin Mfr & Distr
N.A.I.C.S.: 325211
Youichi Shimizu (Exec Officer)

Japan Polypropylene Corporation (3)
Palace Building 1-1 Marunouchi 1-chome, Chiyoda-ku, Tokyo, 100-8251, Japan
Tel.: (81) 367487190
Web Site: https://www.j-polypropylene.com
Sales Range: $1-4.9 Billion
Emp.: 465
Polypropylene Resin Mfr & Distr
N.A.I.C.S.: 325211

Subsidiary (Non-US):

Kansai Coke and Chemicals Co., Ltd. (2)
Tel.: (81) 643005300
Web Site: http://www.tkcc.co.jp
Sales Range: $150-199.9 Million
Emp.: 402
Coke & Tar Derivatives Mfr & Distr
N.A.I.C.S.: 324199
Masanori Tsujikawa (Pres)

Affiliate (Domestic):

Kodama Chemical Industry Co., Ltd. (2)
2-25-16 Kanda Sudacho, Chiyoda-ku, Tokyo, 101-0041, Japan
Tel.: (81) 5036450121
Web Site: http://www.kodama-chemical.co.jp
Plastics Products Sales
N.A.I.C.S.: 423830

Subsidiary (Domestic):

M Commerce Co., Ltd. (2)
1-4-1 Shinkawa, Chuo-ku, Tokyo, 104-0033, Japan
Tel.: (81) 332061071
Web Site: http://www.mcomm.co.jp
Emp.: 50
Carbon Fiber & Chemical Products Mfr
N.A.I.C.S.: 335991

MC Humanets Corporation (2)
Mitsubishi Chemical Nihonbashi Building 1-2-2 Nihonbashi Honseki-cho, Chuo-ku, Tokyo, 103-0021, Japan
Tel.: (81) 368484210
Web Site: https://www.mchumanets.co.jp
Emp.: 70
Human Resource Consulting Services
N.A.I.C.S.: 541612

Subsidiary (Non-US):

MC Ionic Solutions UK, Ltd. (2)
Cassel Works New Road, Billingham, Stockton-on-Tees, TS23 1LE, United Kingdom
Tel.: (44) 1642734400
Sales Range: $25-49.9 Million
Emp.: 15
Chemical Products Mfr
N.A.I.C.S.: 325998
Hiroshi Izumikawa (Mng Dir)

Subsidiary (Domestic):

MC Partners Corporation (2)
2-1 Otemachi 2-chome, Chiyoda-ku, Tokyo, 100-0004, Japan
Tel.: (81) 335106175
Human Resource Consulting Services
N.A.I.C.S.: 541612
Koji Nakayama (Dir)

MCC Composite Products Co., Ltd. (2)
1-2 Ushikawa-dori 4-chome, Toyohashi, 440-8601, Aichi, Japan
Tel.: (81) 532642374
Carbon Fiber Composite Mfr
N.A.I.C.S.: 335991

Subsidiary (Non-US):

MCC PTA Asia Pacific Pte. Ltd. (2)
60 Anson Road 10-01, Mapletree Anson, Singapore, 79914, Singapore
Tel.: (65) 62205347
Web Site: http://www.mcap.biz
Sales Range: $25-49.9 Million
Emp.: 15
Specialty Chemicals Mfr
N.A.I.C.S.: 325199
Manabu Chikumoto (Mng Dir)

Subsidiary (Domestic):

MCC Unitec Co., Ltd. (2)
3-1-109 Koyo, Hachinohe, 031-0801, Aomori, Japan
Tel.: (81) 178 44 1112
Web Site: http://www.mcc-unitec.com
Functional Monomer Mfr
N.A.I.C.S.: 325998

Subsidiary (Non-US):

MCPP France S.A.S. (2)
Z I 2 route de la Gaubretiere, 85130, Tiffauges, France
Tel.: (33) 251657143
Sales Range: $150-199.9 Million
Emp.: 360
Thermoplastic Product Mfr
N.A.I.C.S.: 325211
Etienne Weil (Mng Dir)

Subsidiary (Non-US):

MCPP Poland Sp. z o.o. (3)
ul 15 Sierpnia 106, 96-500, Sochaczew, Poland
Tel.: (48) 468631360

MITSUBISHI CHEMICAL GROUP CORPORATION

Sales Range: $25-49.9 Million
Emp.: 50
Polyvinyl Chloride & Thermoplastic Elastomer Compounds Mfr
N.A.I.C.S.: 325991

Subsidiary (Domestic):

MEC Techno Co., Ltd. (2)
1-2-2 Nihonbashi Honseki-cho, Chuo-ku, Tokyo, 103-0021, Japan
Tel.: (81) 362620660
Web Site: https://www.mec-techno.co.jp
Emp.: 1,300
Painting & Waterproof Construction Services
N.A.I.C.S.: 238320

Subsidiary (Non-US):

MP International (Hong Kong) Ltd. (2)
Unit 2513 25th Floor Miramar Tower 132 Nathan Road TST, Kowloon, China (Hong Kong)
Tel.: (852) 25286198
Plastics Products Sales
N.A.I.C.S.: 326199

MRC Holdings, Ltd. (2)
100/63 Sathorn Nakorn Tower 30th Fl, North Shathorn Rd Khwaeng Silo, Bangkok, 10500, Thailand
Tel.: (66) 26367569
Web Site: http://www.umgabs.co.jp
Sales Range: $25-49.9 Million
Emp.: 20
Holding Company
N.A.I.C.S.: 551112

MRC Hong Kong Co., Ltd. (2)
Rm 3701 Tower 6 The Gateway Bldg, 9 Canton Rd Tsimshatsui, Kowloon, China (Hong Kong)
Tel.: (852) 23680121
Web Site: http://www.mrchk.com.hk
Sales Range: $25-49.9 Million
Emp.: 14
Provider of Sales & Information Services
N.A.I.C.S.: 519290
Yoshihiko Tsujeno (Mgr-Fin)

Subsidiary (Domestic):

Misuzu Erie Co., Ltd. (2)
3-8-13 Hinagahigashi, Yokkaichi, 510-0886, Mie, Japan
Tel.: (81) 593 45 8950
Web Site: http://www.misuzuerie.co.jp
Electrical Measuring Instrument Mfr & Distr
N.A.I.C.S.: 334515

Subsidiary (Non-US):

Mitsubishi Chemical (Thailand) Co., Ltd. (2)
100/62 30th Floor Sathorn Nakorn Tower North Sathorn Road, Kwang Silom Khet Bangrak, Bangkok, 10500, Thailand
Tel.: (66) 226718602
Sales Range: $25-49.9 Million
Emp.: 20
Mfr of Petrochemicals, Agrochemicals, Carbon Products, Information & Electronics Related Products, Pharmaceuticals, Plastic Based Products & Specialty Chemicals
N.A.I.C.S.: 325110
Eiju Zedeya (Mng Dir)

Subsidiary (Domestic):

Mitsubishi Chemical Agri Dream Co., Ltd. (2)
Mitsubishi Chemical Nihonbashi Building 1-2-2, Nihonbashi Hongokucho Chuo-ku, Tokyo, 103-0021, Japan
Emp.: 142
Agricultural Films & Irrigation Materials Mfr & Sales
N.A.I.C.S.: 326199
Shibamoto Katsutoshi (CEO)

Subsidiary (Non-US):

Mitsubishi Chemical China Commerce Limited (2)
Tel.: (86) 2154076161
Sales Range: $25-49.9 Million
Emp.: 10
Specialty Chemicals Mfr & Distr

MITSUBISHI CHEMICAL GROUP CORPORATION — INTERNATIONAL PUBLIC

Mitsubishi Chemical Group Corporation—(Continued)
N.A.I.C.S.: 325998

Subsidiary (Domestic):

Mitsubishi Chemical Cleansui Corporation (2)
Mitsubishi Chemical Nihonbashi Building
1-2-2, Nihonbashi Hongokucho Chuo-ku, Tokyo, 103-0021, Japan
Tel.: (81) 366339000
Web Site: http://www.cleansui.com
Sales Range: $25-49.9 Million
Emp.: 80
Water Purification Pumping Equipment Mfr & Distr
N.A.I.C.S.: 333914

Plant (Domestic):

Mitsubishi Chemical Corporation - Kashima Plant (2)
35 Towada, Kamisu, 314-0102, Ibaraki, Japan
Tel.: (81) 299963121
Web Site: http://www.m-kagaku.co.jp
Sales Range: $200-249.9 Million
Emp.: 800
Chemical Products Mfr
N.A.I.C.S.: 325998

Mitsubishi Chemical Corporation - Kurosaki Plant (2)
1-1 Shiroishi Kurosaki, Yahatanishi-ku, Kita-kyushu, 806-0004, Fukuoka, Japan
Tel.: (81) 93 643 2124
Sales Range: $400-449.9 Million
Emp.: 1,000
Chemical Products Mfr
N.A.I.C.S.: 325998
Nobuo Fukuda (Gen Mgr)

Mitsubishi Chemical Corporation - Mizushima Plant (2)
3-10 Mizushima Kaigandori, Kurashiki, 712-8525, Okayama, Japan
Tel.: (81) 864463822
Web Site: http://www.m-kagaku.co.jp
Chemical Products Mfr
N.A.I.C.S.: 325998
Tsutomu Hao (Gen Mgr-Kashima Plant)

Mitsubishi Chemical Corporation - Sakaide Plant (2)
1 Bannosu-cho, Sakaide, 762-8510, Kagawa, Japan
Tel.: (81) 877 46 8888
Sales Range: $200-249.9 Million
Emp.: 800
Chemical Products Mfr
N.A.I.C.S.: 325998
Kazutaka Akai (Gen Mgr)

Mitsubishi Chemical Corporation - Tsukuba Plant (2)
1000 Higashimamiana-cho, Ushiku, 300-1295, Ibaraki, Japan
Tel.: (81) 29 841 8111
Web Site: http://www.m-kagaku.co.jp
Industrial Chemicals Mfr
N.A.I.C.S.: 325998
Kazuki Yamaguchi (Gen Mgr)

Mitsubishi Chemical Corporation - Yokkaichi Plant (2)
1 Toho-cho, Yokkaichi, 510-8530, Mie, Japan
Tel.: (81) 59 345 7001
Emp.: 1,600
Industrial Chemicals Mfr
N.A.I.C.S.: 325998
Toru Mori (Gen Mgr)

Subsidiary (Domestic):

Mitsubishi Chemical Engineering Corporation (2)
1-2-2 Nihonbashi-Hongokucho, Chuo-ku, Tokyo, 103-0021, Japan
Tel.: (81) 362620011
Web Site: https://www.mec-value.com
Emp.: 1,200
Engineeering Services
N.A.I.C.S.: 541330
Hiroki Fujii (Pres)

Division (Domestic):

Mitsubishi Chemical Engineering Corporation - Kashima Division (3)
17-1 Towada, Kamisu, 314-0102, Ibaraki, Japan
Tel.: (81) 299 96 2501
Plant Maintenance Services
N.A.I.C.S.: 811310

Mitsubishi Chemical Engineering Corporation - Kurosaki Division (3)
1-2 Kurosakishiroishi, Yahatanishi-ku, Kita-kyushu, 806-0004, Fukuoka, Japan
Tel.: (81) 93 643 2702
Chemical Products Mfr
N.A.I.C.S.: 325998

Mitsubishi Chemical Engineering Corporation - Mizushima Division (3)
3-10 Ushiodori, Kurashiki, 712-8054, Okayama, Japan
Tel.: (81) 86 458 2750
Web Site: http://www.mec-value.com
Sales Range: $25-49.9 Million
Emp.: 120
Chemical Engineering Services
N.A.I.C.S.: 541330

Mitsubishi Chemical Engineering Corporation - Otake Division (3)
20-1 Miyuki-cho, Otake, 739-0693, Hiroshima, Japan
Tel.: (81) 827 53 5811
Sales Range: $125-149.9 Million
Emp.: 30
Chemical Products Mfr
N.A.I.C.S.: 325998
Shoji Masuyama (Gen Mgr)

Mitsubishi Chemical Engineering Corporation - Sakaide Division (3)
1 Bannosu-cho, Sakaide, 762-0064, Kagawa, Japan
Tel.: (81) 877 46 8893
Web Site: http://www.mec-value.com
Plant Maintenance Services
N.A.I.C.S.: 811310

Mitsubishi Chemical Engineering Corporation - Toyama Division (3)
3 Kaigandori, Toyama, 931-8601, Japan
Tel.: (81) 76 437 1526
Web Site: http://www.mec-value.com
Emp.: 80
Specialty Chemicals Mfr
N.A.I.C.S.: 325998

Mitsubishi Chemical Engineering Corporation - Toyohashi Division (3)
4-1-2 Ushikawadori, Toyohashi, 440-8601, Aichi, Japan
Chemical Products Mfr
N.A.I.C.S.: 325998

Mitsubishi Chemical Engineering Corporation - Yokkaichi Division (3)
1-30 Shiohama-cho, Yokkaichi, 510-0851, Mie, Japan
Tel.: (81) 59 345 7488
Web Site: http://www.mec-value.com
Industrial Chemicals Mfr
N.A.I.C.S.: 325998

Subsidiary (Non-US):

Mitsubishi Chemical Europe GmbH (2)
Willstatter Str 30, 40549, Dusseldorf, Germany
Tel.: (49) 211520540
Web Site: http://www.eu.mitsubishi-chemical.com
Sales Range: $25-49.9 Million
Emp.: 25
Mfr of Petrochemicals, Agrochemicals, Carbon Products, Information & Electronics Related Products, Pharmaceuticals, Plastic Based Products & Specialty Chemicals
N.A.I.C.S.: 325998

Mitsubishi Chemical Hong Kong Ltd. (2)
Suites 2905-6 29/F Tower 2 The Gateway Harbour City 25 Canton Rd, Tsimshatsui, Kowloon, China (Hong Kong)
Tel.: (852) 25227031
Web Site: http://www.m-chemical.com.hk
Sales Range: $50-74.9 Million
Emp.: 10
Mfr of Petrochemicals, Agrochemicals, Carbon Products, Information & Electronics Related Products, Pharmaceuticals, Plastic Based Products & Specialty Chemicals
N.A.I.C.S.: 325998

Mitsubishi Chemical India Private Ltd. (2)
3rd Floor Tower A Sushant Lok Phase 1, First India Place MG Road, Gurgaon, 122002, Haryana, India
Tel.: (91) 1244699800
Sales Range: $25-49.9 Million
Emp.: 8
Chemical Products Distr
N.A.I.C.S.: 424690
Ogata Tomohiko (Mng Dir)

Mitsubishi Chemical Infonics Pte Ltd (2)
103 Pioneer Road, Jurong, 639582, Singapore
Tel.: (65) 6863 8038
Web Site: http://www.m-kagaku.co.jp
Sales Range: $125-149.9 Million
Emp.: 50
Chemical Products Mfr & Distr
N.A.I.C.S.: 325998
Tomohiro Yamashita (Mng Dir)

Subsidiary (Domestic):

Mitsubishi Chemical Infratec Co., Ltd. (2)
1-1 Marunouchi 1-Chome, Chiyoda-ku, Tokyo, 100-8251, Japan
Tel.: (81) 366291272
Web Site: https://mchem-infratec.com
Plastic Products Export & Sales
N.A.I.C.S.: 561499
Katsuya Serizawa (Pres)

Mitsubishi Chemical Logistics Corporation (2)
1-30 Shibadaimon 1-chome, Minato-Ku, Tokyo, 105-0012, Japan (100%)
Tel.: (81) 3 5408 4500
Web Site: http://www.mclc.co.jp
Sales Range: $75-99.9 Million
Emp.: 1,112
Logistics Consulting Servies
N.A.I.C.S.: 541614
Nobuo Fukuda (Pres & CEO)

Mitsubishi Chemical Media Co., Ltd. (2)
Ogawamachi 3-20 second Ryumeikan building 8th floor, Chiyoda-ku, Tokyo, 101-0052, Japan
Tel.: (81) 3 5577 3090
Web Site: http://www.mcmedia.co.jp
Emp.: 510
Mfr & Marketer of Data Storage Devices & Recordable Media Products
N.A.I.C.S.: 334610

Subsidiary (Non-US):

Mitsubishi Chemical Singapore Pte. Ltd. (2)
9 Raffles Place 13-01/02 Republic Plaza, Singapore, 048619, Singapore
Tel.: (65) 62263707
Web Site: http://www.m-kagaku.co.jp
Sales Range: $25-49.9 Million
Emp.: 50
Mfr of Petrochemicals, Agrochemicals, Carbon Products, Information & Electronics Related Products, Pharmaceuticals, Plastic Based Products & Specialty Chemicals
N.A.I.C.S.: 325211
M. Waga (Mng Dir)

Subsidiary (Domestic):

Mitsubishi Chemical Systems, Inc. (2)
Tokyo Sky Tree East Tower 1-1-2 Oshiage, Sumida-ku, Tokyo, 131-0045, Japan
Tel.: (81) 3 6830 9800
Web Site: http://www.mitsubishichem-sys.co.jp
Emp.: 592
Information Technology Support Services
N.A.I.C.S.: 541513
Yoshio Katsuro (Pres)

Subsidiary (US):

Mitsubishi Chemical USA, Inc. (MCUSA) (2)
1 N Lexington Ave, White Plains, NY 10601-1712 (100%)
Tel.: (914) 286-3600
Web Site: http://www.mitsubishichemical.com
Sales Range: $10-24.9 Million
Emp.: 38
Intra-Company Marketing, Distribution & Administrative Services
N.A.I.C.S.: 561110

Subsidiary (Domestic):

Gelest Intermediate Holdings, Inc. (3)
11 E Steel Rd, Morrisville, PA 19067
Web Site: http://www.gelest.com
Holding Company
N.A.I.C.S.: 551112
Jonathan Goff (Pres)

Subsidiary (Domestic):

Bimax, Inc. (4)
281 Industrial Rd, Glen Rock, PA 17327
Tel.: (717) 227-1774
Web Site: http://www.bimax.com
Chemicals Mfr
N.A.I.C.S.: 325998

Gelest, Inc. (4)
11 E Steel Rd, Morrisville, PA 19067
Tel.: (215) 547-1015
Web Site: https://www.gelest.com
Plastics Material & Resin Mfr
N.A.I.C.S.: 325211
Jonathan Goff (CTO)

Subsidiary (Domestic):

MC Ionic Solutions US, Inc. (3)
2665 Fite Rd Ste 101, Memphis, TN 38127
Tel.: (901) 354-1111
Inorganic Chemical Mfr
N.A.I.C.S.: 325180
Barbara Rodas (Gen Mgr)

Mitsubishi Chemical Performance Polymers, Inc. (3)
2001 Hood Rd, Greer, SC 29650
Tel.: (864) 879-5806
Web Site: http://www.mcc-spd.com
Polymer Resin Mfr & Distr
N.A.I.C.S.: 325211
Mike Gragtmans (Exec Officer & Gen Mgr)

Subsidiary (Domestic):

Nordicus Partners Corporation (4)
280 S Beverly Dr Ste 505, Beverly Hills, CA 90212
Tel.: (424) 256-8560
Web Site: https://nordicuspartners.com
Rev.: $2,500
Assets: $1,807,573
Liabilities: $26,405
Net Worth: $1,781,168
Earnings: ($298,202)
Fiscal Year-end: 03/31/2024
Designs, Develops, Manufactures & Sells Medical Devices & Materials for Treatment of Cardiovascular & Other Diseases
N.A.I.C.S.: 339112
Bennett J. Yankowitz (CEO)

Subsidiary (Domestic):

Mitsubishi Kagaku Imaging Corporation (3)
401 Volvo Pkwy, Chesapeake, VA 23320-4611
Tel.: (757) 382-5700
Web Site: http://www.m-kagaku.co.jp
Mfr of Printer & Copy Machine Toner
N.A.I.C.S.: 333310

Mytex Polymers US Corporation (3)
1403 Port Rd, Jeffersonville, IN 47130
Tel.: (812) 280-2900
Web Site: https://www.mytexpolymers.com
Automotive Plastic Compound Mfr & Distr
N.A.I.C.S.: 326199
Mamoru Hirasawa (Exec VP-Sls & Mktg)

Subsidiary (Non-US):

Mitsubishi Plastics Asia Pacific Pte. Ltd. (2)
60 Anson Road 10-01 Mapletree Anson, Singapore, 079914, Singapore
Tel.: (65) 62261597
Web Site: http://www.alpolic.com

AND PRIVATE COMPANIES

MITSUBISHI CHEMICAL GROUP CORPORATION

Sales Range: $25-49.9 Million
Emp.: 7
Aluminum Composite Materials Sales
N.A.I.C.S.: 331318
May Chin Yong *(Gen Mgr)*

Subsidiary (US):

Mitsubishi Plastics Composites America, Inc. (2)
401 Volvo Pkwy, Chesapeake, VA 23320
Tel.: (757) 382-5750
Plastic Product Mfr & Distr
N.A.I.C.S.: 326199
Candice Rambo *(Mgr-Health & Safety Program)*

Subsidiary (Non-US):

Mitsubishi Plastics Euro Asia Ltd. (2)
Baglarbasi Kisikli Cad No 4 Sarkuysan-Ak Is Merkezi S-Blok Teras Kat, Altunizade, Istanbul, 34664, Turkiye
Tel.: (90) 216 651 8670
Web Site: http://www.alpolic.com
Sales Range: $50-74.9 Million
Emp.: 6
Plastic Product Distr
N.A.I.C.S.: 424610
Cem Kubat *(Gen Mgr)*

Mitsubishi Plastics Trading Shanghai Co., Ltd. (2)
No 4209 The Center 989 Chang Le Road, Shanghai, 200031, China
Tel.: (86) 2154076022
Emp.: 2
Plastic Product Distr
N.A.I.C.S.: 424610

Plant (Domestic):

Mitsubishi Plastics, Inc. - Azai Plant (2)
1700 Ochi-cho, Nagahama, 526-0243, Shiga, Japan
Tel.: (81) 749 74 3500
Web Site: http://www.mpi.co.jp
Sales Range: $200-249.9 Million
Emp.: 600
Plastics Product Mfr
N.A.I.C.S.: 326199

Mitsubishi Plastics, Inc. - Hanyu Plant (2)
2-22-35 Nishi, Hanyu, 348-0054, Saitama, Japan
Tel.: (81) 48 561 1712
Injection Molded Plastic Products Mfr
N.A.I.C.S.: 326199

Mitsubishi Plastics, Inc. - Koriyama Plant (2)
2-1 Machiikedai, Koriyama, 963-0215, Fukushima, Japan
Tel.: (81) 24 959 1900
Plastics Product Mfr
N.A.I.C.S.: 326199

Mitsubishi Plastics, Inc. - Mine Plant (2)
Higashibun 1133-1, Omine-cho, Mine, 759-2212, Yamaguchi, Japan
Tel.: (81) 837 52 2221
Web Site: http://www.mpi.co.jp
Plastics Product Mfr
N.A.I.C.S.: 326199

Mitsubishi Plastics, Inc. - Mizushima Plant (2)
4-6-1 Matsue, Kurashiki, 712-8052, Okayama, Japan
Tel.: (81) 86 455 0575
Sales Range: $25-49.9 Million
Emp.: 4
Plastics Product Mfr
N.A.I.C.S.: 326199
Yamagata Nobuyuki *(Plant Mgr)*

Mitsubishi Plastics, Inc. - Nagahama Plant (2)
5-8 Mitsuya-cho, Nagahama, 526-8660, Shiga, Japan
Tel.: (81) 749 65 5111
Sales Range: $900-999.9 Million
Emp.: 300
Plastics Product Mfr
N.A.I.C.S.: 326199
Yasuhiro Iwamoto *(Gen Mgr)*

Mitsubishi Plastics, Inc. - Sakaide Plant (2)
1 Bannosu-cho, Sakaide, 762-8510, Kagawa, Japan
Tel.: (81) 877 46 8812
Plastics Product Mfr
N.A.I.C.S.: 326199

Mitsubishi Plastics, Inc. - Santo Plant (2)
347 Inokuchi, Maibara, 521-0234, Shiga, Japan
Tel.: (81) 749 55 3000
Web Site: http://www.mpi.co.jp
Plastics Product Mfr
N.A.I.C.S.: 326199

Mitsubishi Plastics, Inc. - Tokyo Plant (2)
1-5-5 Suehiro-cho, Ome, 198-0025, Tokyo, Japan
Tel.: (81) 428 32 0781
Plastics Product Mfr
N.A.I.C.S.: 326199

Mitsubishi Plastics, Inc. - Tsukuba Plant (2)
1000 Higashimamiana-cho, Ushiku, 300-1295, Ibaraki, Japan
Tel.: (81) 298418111
Web Site: http://www.mpi.co.jp
Plastics Product Mfr
N.A.I.C.S.: 326199
Tokumei Kumiai *(CEO)*

Mitsubishi Plastics, Inc. - Ueda Plant (2)
2471-1 Fujiyama, Ueda, 386-1212, Nagano, Japan
Tel.: (81) 268 38 9511
Sales Range: $50-74.9 Million
Emp.: 20
Plastics Product Mfr
N.A.I.C.S.: 326199

Subsidiary (Non-US):

Mitsubishi Polyester Film GmbH (2)
Tel.: (49) 61196203
Plastics Product Mfr
N.A.I.C.S.: 326199
Ralph Vinzenz Meier *(Chm)*

Mitsubishi Polyester Film Suzhou Co., Ltd. (2)
No 99 Song Shan Road, Suzhou New District, Suzhou, Jiangsu, China
Tel.: (86) 51282286777
Polyester Film Mfr & Distr
N.A.I.C.S.: 326112

Subsidiary (US):

Mitsubishi Polyester Film, Inc. (2)
2001 Hood Rd, Greer, SC 29652
Tel.: (864) 879-5000
Web Site: https://www.m-petfilm.com
Sales Range: $125-149.9 Million
Emp.: 500
Mfr, Marketer & Research & Development of Polyester Film
N.A.I.C.S.: 326113

Subsidiary (Non-US):

Mitsubishi Rayon (Shanghai) Co., Ltd. (2)
Room 1601 Aetna Tower 107 Zunyi Road, Shanghai, 200051, China
Tel.: (86) 2162375868
Business Support Services
N.A.I.C.S.: 561499

Subsidiary (US):

Mitsubishi Rayon America, Inc. (2)
747 3rd Ave Fl 19, New York, NY 10017-4213
Tel.: (212) 223-3043
Web Site: http://www.mrany.com
Sales Range: $25-49.9 Million
Emp.: 8
Marketer & Distributor of Acrylic Fibers & Resins; Sales & Information Services
N.A.I.C.S.: 424690
Toru Ishii *(Gen Mgr)*

Subsidiary (Domestic):

Aldila, Inc. (3)
14145 Danielson St Ste B, Poway, CA 92064
Tel.: (858) 513-1801
Web Site: http://www.aldila.com
Graphite Golf Shafts Designer, Mfr & Marketer
N.A.I.C.S.: 339920
Scott M. Bier *(CFO)*

Dianal America, Inc. (3)
9675 Bayport Blvd, Pasadena, TX 77507-1403
Tel.: (713) 758-8100
Web Site: https://www.dianal.com
Sales Range: $25-49.9 Million
Mfr & Retailer of Coating Resins
N.A.I.C.S.: 325211
Hakaru Inaroka *(Pres)*

MRC Golf, Inc. (3)
5441 Avenida Encinas Ste B, Carlsbad, CA 92008
Tel.: (760) 929-0001
Web Site: http://www.mitsubishirayongolf.com
Sales Range: $25-49.9 Million
Golf Shaft Distr
N.A.I.C.S.: 423910
Yoichi Hoashi *(VP)*

Mitsubishi Rayon Carbon Fiber and Composites, Inc. (3)
5900 88th St, Sacramento, CA 95828
Web Site: http://www.mccfc.com
Carbon Fibers Retailer & Mfr
N.A.I.C.S.: 335991

Subsidiary (Domestic):

Evanston Carbon Fiber, LLC (4)
1375 Union Rd, Evanston, WY 82930-3018
Tel.: (307) 789-2499
Emp.: 45
Carbon Fiber Mfr
N.A.I.C.S.: 325180
Martin Kokoshka *(Gen Mgr)*

Subsidiary (Domestic):

Newport Adhesives & Composites, Inc. (3)
1822 Reynolds Ave, Irvine, CA 92614-5714
Tel.: (949) 253-5680
Web Site: http://www.newportad.com
Sales Range: $50-74.9 Million
Adhesives & Carbon Fiber Composites Producer & Retailer
N.A.I.C.S.: 325520

San Esters Corporation (3)
55 E 59th St Fl 19, New York, NY 10022-1112
Tel.: (212) 223-0020
Web Site: http://www.sanesters.com
Sales Range: $25-49.9 Million
Supplier of Methacrylate & Specialty Acrylate Monomers
N.A.I.C.S.: 424690

Subsidiary (Non-US):

Mitsubishi Rayon Co., Ltd. (2)
Rm 801 Twr 3 33 Canton Rd Tsimshatsui, Kowloon, (Hong Kong)
Tel.: (852) 23680121
Web Site: http://www.mrc.co.jp
Sales Range: $25-49.9 Million
Emp.: 10
Mfr of Synthetic Fibers
N.A.I.C.S.: 325220
Tatashi Iwasaki *(Mng Dir)*

Subsidiary (Non-US):

Wuxi MRC Origin Water Membrane Tech. Co., Ltd. (3)
No 26 Xinjin Road, Wuxi new district, Wuxi, Jiangsu, China
Tel.: (86) 51 81103557
Hollow Fiber Mfr & Distr
N.A.I.C.S.: 327999

Subsidiary (Non-US):

Mitsubishi Rayon Polymer Nantong Co., Ltd. (2)
No 6 Guangzhou Road Nantong Economic Technological Development Area, Nantong, 226009, Jiangsu, China
Tel.: (86) 51385928921

Web Site: http://www.mrpn.com.cn
Acrylic Molding Materials Mfr & Distr
N.A.I.C.S.: 326113

Subsidiary (Domestic):

Mitsubishi-Chemical Foods Corporation (2)
1-1 Marunouchi 1-chome, Chiyoda-ku, Tokyo, 100-8251, Japan
Tel.: (81) 3 6748 7424
Web Site: http://www.mfc.co.jp
Food Ingredients Mfr & Distr
N.A.I.C.S.: 311999

Subsidiary (Non-US):

Multi Risk Consultants (Thailand) Ltd. (2)
21st Fl Vongvanij Tower B 100/64-66 Rama 9 Rd, Huaykwang, Bangkok, 10310, Khet Bangrak, Thailand
Tel.: (66) 26450040
Web Site: https://www.mrc.co.th
Sales & Information Services
N.A.I.C.S.: 519290

Subsidiary (Domestic):

Nippon Rensui Co. (2)
Mitsubishi Chemical Nihonbashi Building 2-2, Nihonbashihongoku-cho 1-chome Chuo-ku, Tokyo, 103-0021, Japan
Tel.: (81) 368484220
Web Site: https://www.mcas.co.jp
Sales Range: $150-199.9 Million
Emp.: 472
Water Treatment Chemicals Distr & Plant Construction Services
N.A.I.C.S.: 424690
Masakatsu Yasuguchi *(Pres)*

Subsidiary (Non-US):

MRC Rensui Asia Pte Ltd (3)
82 Toh Guan Road East 02-13, Waterhub, Singapore, 608576, Singapore
Tel.: (65) 6220 2898
Emp.: 3
Water Treatment Plant Construction Services & Industrial Chemicals Distr
N.A.I.C.S.: 237110
Daisuke Kawabe *(Pres)*

NIPPON RENSUI ENGINEERING CO., LTD. (3)
11/F 8th Floor No 378 Section 1 Wenxin Road, Nantun District, Taichung, 40862, Taiwan
Tel.: (886) 4 2319 1885
Web Site: http://www.rensui.com.tw
Water Treatment Plant Construction Services & Industrial Chemicals Distr
N.A.I.C.S.: 237110
Ryuuichi Tamamoto *(Pres)*

Division (Domestic):

Nippon Rensui Co. - Specialty Plant & Materials Division (3)
Otsuka, Tohima-Ku, Tokyo, 170-0005, Japan
Tel.: (81) 3 5954 2723
Specialty Chemicals Mfr
N.A.I.C.S.: 325998

Nippon Rensui Co. - Water Treatment Division (3)
3-43-11 Minami Otsuka, Toshima-ku, Tokyo, 170-0005, Japan
Tel.: (81) 3 5954 2724
Water Treatment Plant Construction Services
N.A.I.C.S.: 237110

Subsidiary (Non-US):

RENSUI KOREA CO., LTD. (3)
1504 Samchang Plaza Bldg 173 Dowha-dong, Mapo-ku, Seoul, 121-745, Korea (South)
Tel.: (82) 2 6351 1001
Sales Range: $25-49.9 Million
Emp.: 6
Plant Construction Engineering Services & Specialty Chemicals Distr
N.A.I.C.S.: 237110
Ryuuichi Tamamoto *(Pres)*

MITSUBISHI CHEMICAL GROUP CORPORATION

Mitsubishi Chemical Group Corporation—(Continued)

Subsidiary (US):

Noltex LLC (2)
12220 Strang Rd, La Porte, TX 77571
Tel.: (281) 842-5000
Web Site: http://www.noltexllc.com
Copolymer of Ethylene & Vinyl Alcohol Mfr
N.A.I.C.S.: 325998

Subsidiary (Non-US):

P.T. Diachem Resins Indonesia (2)
Jl Tanah Abang III No 5-7, Jakarta, 10160, Indonesia
Tel.: (62) 213864790
Web Site: http://www.mrc.co.jp
Sales Range: $25-49.9 Million
Emp.: 20
Producer & Retailer of Coating Resins
N.A.I.C.S.: 325510
Toshinao Hirada (VP)

P.T. Mitsubishi Chemical Indonesia (2)
Gedung Setiabudi Atrium Suite 710 Setiabudi Office Park, Jl H R Rasuna Said Kuningan, Jakarta, 12920, Indonesia
Tel.: (62) 21 5207699
Industrial Chemical Mfr & Distr
N.A.I.C.S.: 325998

PT. MC Pet Film Indonesia (2)
17th Floor Unit D Jalan R A Kartini Kav 8, South Quarter Tower Cilandak Barat, Jakarta, 12430, Indonesia
Tel.: (62) 2122722172
Polyester Films Mfr & Sales
N.A.I.C.S.: 326199

Qingdao Anode Kasei Co., Ltd. (2)
No 15 Tonghui Yi Road Xiangdian Pingdu, Qingdao, 266700, Shangdong, China
Tel.: (86) 532 8330 2928
Anode Material Mfr & Distr
N.A.I.C.S.: 325998

Qingdao Lingtong Textile Co., Ltd. (2)
1201 Aetna Tower, 107 Zunyi Rd, 200051, Shanghai, China
Tel.: (86) 2162375868
Web Site: http://www.mrc.co.jp
Sales Range: $75-99.9 Million
Emp.: 400
Mfr & Retailer of Acrylic Yarn
N.A.I.C.S.: 313110

Subsidiary (Domestic):

Quadrant Polypenco Japan Ltd. (2)
1-2-2 Nihonbashihongoku-cho, Chuo-ku, Tokyo, 103-0021, Japan **(51%)**
Tel.: (81) 3 3279 3201
Web Site: http://www.polypenco.co.jp
Engineering Plastics & Associated Products Mfr
N.A.I.C.S.: 326199

Subsidiary (Non-US):

RESINDION S.R.L. (2)
Via Roma 55, 20082, Binasco, MI, Italy
Tel.: (39) 02900130223
Web Site: https://www.resindion.com
Sales Range: $25-49.9 Million
Emp.: 35
Polymer Resin Mfr & Distr
N.A.I.C.S.: 325211

Subsidiary (Domestic):

Rhombic Corporation (2)
191-1 Shiohama, Yokkaichi, 510-0863, Mie, Japan
Tel.: (81) 593468231
Web Site: https://www.rhombic.co.jp
Emp.: 568
Composite Resin Mfr
N.A.I.C.S.: 325211

Ryobi Techno Inc. (2)
1 Tsukigase-cho, Nagahama, Shiga, Japan **(100%)**
Tel.: (81) 749 73 3071
Plastics Product Mfr
N.A.I.C.S.: 326199

Ryoju Corporation (2)
5-6-10 Ueno Taito-ku, Tokyo, 110-0005, Japan **(100%)**
Tel.: (81) 338366080
Construction & Industrial Materials for Electronics Sales
N.A.I.C.S.: 424990

Ryoko Co., Ltd. (2)
14-1 Nihonbashi Koami-cho, Chuo-ku, Tokyo, 103-0016, Japan
Tel.: (81) 3 5651 0651
Web Site: http://www.kkryoko.co.jp
Sales Range: $50-74.9 Million
Emp.: 113
Plastic Products Mfr & Distr
N.A.I.C.S.: 326199

Subsidiary (Domestic):

Ryoko Plastic Co., Ltd. (3)
640-Naoe Yoro-cho Yoro-gun, Gifu, 503-1337, Japan
Tel.: (81) 52 32 3000
Plastics Products Mfr & Sales
N.A.I.C.S.: 326199

Ryoko Sizing Co., Ltd. (3)
1110 Washigashima, Oyabe, 932-8550, Toyama, Japan
Tel.: (81) 766 67 1580
Web Site: http://www.mitsubishi.com
Textile Products Mfr
N.A.I.C.S.: 314999

Ryoko Tekunika Co., Ltd. (3)
5-8 Mitsuya-cho, Nagahama, 526-0023, Shiga, Japan
Tel.: (81) 749655237
Contract & Temporary Employment Services
N.A.I.C.S.: 561320

Subsidiary (Domestic):

Ryouei Co., Ltd. (2)
58 Oshika, Maibara, 521-0214, Shiga, Japan
Tel.: (81) 749552891
Web Site: http://www.mpi.co.jp
Waste Sites Process, Management & Maintenance Services & PVC Compound Pellets Mfr & Whslr
N.A.I.C.S.: 423930

Subsidiary (Non-US):

Shanghai Baoling Plastics Co., Ltd. (2)
No 959 Xingqing Road, Jiading District, Shanghai, 201807, China **(77.4%)**
Tel.: (86) 2159163030
Web Site: https://www.sbp.com.cn
Plastics Product Mfr
N.A.I.C.S.: 326199

Suzhou MRC Opto-Device Co., Ltd. (2)
1315 Jinfengnan Road Mudu Town, Wuzhong District, Suzhou, Jiangsu, China
Tel.: (86) 512 6921 2701
Opto Electronic Component Mfr & Distr
N.A.I.C.S.: 334419
Norio Kawashima (Gen Mgr)

Tai Young Chemical Co., Ltd. (2)
No 42 Huazhong Road, Daliao District, Kaohsiung, 00831, Taiwan
Tel.: (886) 77871295
Web Site: https://www.diaion.com.tw
Ion Exchange Resin Mfr
N.A.I.C.S.: 325211

Tai Young High Tech Co., Ltd. (2)
No 62 Kuang Fu Road Hsihchu Industrial Park, Hsin-chu, Taiwan
Tel.: (886) 3 598 5987
Industrial Chemical Mfr & Distr
N.A.I.C.S.: 325998

Tai-Young Film Co., Ltd. (2)
No 23 Daye St, Daliao Dist, Kaohsiung, 831, Taiwan **(100%)**
Tel.: (886) 77877372
Web Site: http://www.mpi.co.jp
Unsupported Plastics Film & Sheet Mfr
N.A.I.C.S.: 326113

Thai MMA Co., Ltd. (2)
1 Siam Cememnt Rd, Bangsue, Bangkok, 10800, Thailand
Tel.: (66) 25865395

Web Site: http://www.mrc.co.jp
Sales Range: $25-49.9 Million
Emp.: 100
Mfr & Sales of MMA Monomer
N.A.I.C.S.: 325220

Subsidiary (Domestic):

The Nippon Synthetic Chemical Industry Co., Ltd. (2)
Osaka Fukoku Seimei Building 2-4 Komatsubara-cho, Kita-ku, Osaka, 530-0018, Japan **(100%)**
Tel.: (81) 6 7711 5400
Web Site: http://www.nichigo.co.jp
Chemical Mfr, Construction & Maintenance Logistics & Environmental Analysis Services
N.A.I.C.S.: 325211
Kazunori Takada (Exec Officer)

Subsidiary (US):

MSI Technology, L.L.C. (3)
3930 Ventura Dr Ste 300, Arlington Heights, IL 60004
Tel.: (847) 255-4888
Web Site: https://www.msitechnology.com
Adhesives & Sealants Distr
N.A.I.C.S.: 424690

NIPPON GOHSEI (U.S.A.) Co., Ltd. (3)
12220 Strang Rd, La Porte, TX 77571-9740
Tel.: (281) 842-5025
Web Site: http://www.nichigo.co.jp
Sales Range: $50-74.9 Million
Emp.: 2
Chemical Product Whslr
N.A.I.C.S.: 424690

Subsidiary (Non-US):

NIPPON GOHSEI (UK) Limited (3)
Soarnol House Saltend, Kingston upon Hull, HU12 8DS, E Yorkshire, United Kingdom
Tel.: (44) 1482333320
Web Site: http://www.nippon-gohsei.com
Sales Range: $25-49.9 Million
Emp.: 90
Ethylene Vinyl Alcohol Copolymer Mfr
N.A.I.C.S.: 326113
Peter Des Forges (Dir-Site)

NIPPON GOHSEI Europe GmbH (3)
Willstatterstrasse 30, 40549, Dusseldorf, Germany
Tel.: (49) 211520540
Web Site: https://eu.mitsubishi-chemical.com
Acetyl Chemicals Whslr
N.A.I.C.S.: 424690
Makoto Moritani (Mng Dir)

Subsidiary (US):

SOARUS L.L.C. (3)
3930 Ventura Dr Ste 300, Arlington Heights, IL 60004
Tel.: (847) 255-1211
Web Site: https://www.soarus.com
Sales Range: $25-49.9 Million
Emp.: 15
Plastics Materials Mfr & Whslr
N.A.I.C.S.: 326199

Plant (Domestic):

The Nippon Synthetic Chemical Industry Co., Ltd. - Kumamoto Plant (3)
221 Tsuigome-machi, Uto, 869-0408, Kumamoto, Japan
Tel.: (81) 964220850
Fine Chemicals Mfr
N.A.I.C.S.: 325199
Yoshiharu Nagao (Plant Mgr)

The Nippon Synthetic Chemical Industry Co., Ltd. - Mizushima Plant (3)
8-1 Matsue 4-chome, Kurashiki, 712-8052, Okayama, Japan
Tel.: (81) 864555211
Web Site: http://www.nichigo.co.jp
Sales Range: $50-74.9 Million
Emp.: 200
Industrial Chemicals Mfr
N.A.I.C.S.: 325199
Katsumi Kimura (Pres)

INTERNATIONAL PUBLIC

The Nippon Synthetic Chemical Industry Co., Ltd. - Ogaki Plant (3)
35 Kanda-cho 2-chome, Ogaki, 503-0917, Gifu, Japan
Tel.: (81) 584 81 4141
Emp.: 600
Industrial Chemicals Mfr
N.A.I.C.S.: 325411
Tadashi Miya (Plant Mgr)

Subsidiary (Domestic):

Toei Kasei Co., Ltd. (2)
3-8-3 Nihonbashi Honcho, Chuo-ku Toshiba Building, Tokyo, 103-0023, Japan
Tel.: (81) 3 5651 5811
Web Site: http://www.toeikasei.com
Industrial Chemicals Mfr & Distr
N.A.I.C.S.: 325998

Joint Venture (Domestic):

UMG ABS, Ltd. (2)
Shiodome Sumitomo Bldg 22F 1-9-2 Higashi-Shimbashi, Minato-ku, Tokyo, 105-0021, Japan **(50%)**
Tel.: (81) 3 6218 3880
Web Site: http://www.umgabs.co.jp
Holding Company; Resins Mfr
N.A.I.C.S.: 551112

Joint Venture (Domestic):

Techno-UMG Co., Ltd. (3)
Shiodome Sumitomo Building 22F 1-9-2 Higashi-Shimbashi, Minato, Tokyo, 105-0021, Japan **(49%)**
Tel.: (81) 362183880
Web Site: https://www.t-umg.com
Styrene Resin Mfr & Whslr
N.A.I.C.S.: 325211
Masaaki Mori (Exec VP)

Subsidiary (Non-US):

Techno-UMG (Shanghai) Co., Ltd. (4)
Room 2507-08 The Place Tower A 100 Zunyi Road, Shanghai, 200051, China
Tel.: (86) 2162953327
Web Site: http://www.t-umg.com
Synthetic Resin Sales
N.A.I.C.S.: 424690

Subsidiary (US):

Techno-UMG America, Inc. (4)
5405 Dupont Cir Ste E, Milford, OH 45150
Tel.: (513) 248-2033
Web Site: http://www.t-umg.com
Plastics Sales & Services
N.A.I.C.S.: 424610

Subsidiary (Non-US):

Techno-UMG Asia Co., Ltd. (4)
968 28th Floor U-Chuliang Foundation Building Rama 4 Road silom, Bangrak, Bangkok, 10500, Thailand
Tel.: (66) 26367569
Web Site: http://www.t-umg.com
Sales Range: $25-49.9 Million
Emp.: 20
Synthetic Resin Sales
N.A.I.C.S.: 424690
Takao Nagai (Mng Dir)

Techno-UMG Hong Kong Co., Ltd. (4)
Room 1002 10/F Tower 2 Lippo Centre 89 Queensway, Admiralty, Kowloon, China (Hong Kong)
Tel.: (852) 25217622
Web Site: http://www.t-umg.com
Chemical & Allied Products Merchant Whslr
N.A.I.C.S.: 424690
Louis Lo (Mng Dir)

Techno-UMG Shanghai Technical Center Co., Ltd. (4)
207 Zhongqing Road Maqiao, Minhang, Shanghai, 201111, China
Tel.: (86) 21 5457 0262
Synthetic Resin Research & Development
N.A.I.C.S.: 541715

Subsidiary (Domestic):

Yuka Denshi Company Limited (2)
4-1-23 Shiba, Minato-ku, Tokyo, 108-0014, Japan

AND PRIVATE COMPANIES
MITSUBISHI CHEMICAL GROUP CORPORATION

Tel.: (81) 3 5484 3952
Web Site: http://www.yukadenshi.co.jp
Electronic Chemicals Mfr
N.A.I.C.S.: 325998
Eiichi Sato *(Pres)*

Plant (Domestic):

Yuka Denshi Company Limited - Ibaraki Plant (3)
8-3-1 Cyuou Ami, Inashiki, 300-0332, Ibaraki, Japan
Tel.: (81) 593 75 5855
Plastic Materials Mfr
N.A.I.C.S.: 325211

Yuka Denshi Company Limited - Suzuka Plant (3)
5-14-3 Sumiyoshi, Suzuka, 513-0826, Mie, Japan
Tel.: (81) 593 75 5855
Web Site: http://www.yukadenshi.co.jp
Plastics Product Mfr
N.A.I.C.S.: 326199

Yuka Denshi Company Limited - Yokkaichi Plant (3)
3-3-17 Obata, Yokkaichi, 510-0875, Mie, Japan
Tel.: (81) 593 45 7018
Web Site: http://www.yukadenshi.co.jp
Plastics Product Mfr
N.A.I.C.S.: 326199

Mitsubishi Chemical Holdings (Beijing) Co., Ltd. (1)
Room 710 Beijing Fortune Building Dong San Huan Bei Lu 5, Chao Yang District, Beijing, 100004, China
Tel.: (86) 10 6590 8621
Sales Range: $50-74.9 Million
Emp.: 18
Investment Management Service
N.A.I.C.S.: 523940

Mitsubishi Chemical Holdings Europe GmbH (1)
Kasteler Strasse 45, 65203, Wiesbaden, Germany
Tel.: (49) 6119626923
Chemical Product Mfr & Distr
N.A.I.C.S.: 325998

Mitsubishi Engineering-Plastics Corporation (1)
Shiodome Sumitomo-Bldg 25F 1-9-2 Higashi-shinbashi, Minato Ward, Tokyo, 105-0021, Japan
Tel.: (81) 362749000
Emp.: 304
Chemical Product Mfr & Distr
N.A.I.C.S.: 325998
Takashi Komaya *(Pres & CEO)*

Mitsubishi Tanabe Pharma Corporation (1)
3-2-10 Dosho machi, Chuo-ku, Osaka, 541-8505, Japan (100%)
Tel.: (81) 662055085
Web Site: http://www.mt-pharma.co.jp
Rev.: $3,657,104,000
Assets: $10,195,944,000
Liabilities: $2,288,352,000
Net Worth: $7,907,592,000
Earnings: $489,808,000)
Emp.: 6,728
Fiscal Year-end: 03/31/2021
Pharmaceuticals Mfr
N.A.I.C.S.: 325412
Hiroaki Ueno *(Pres & CEO)*

Affiliate (Domestic):

Arkema Yoshitomi, Ltd. (2)
Palace Bldg 1-1 Marunouchi 1-Choume, Chiyoda-ku, Tokyo, 100-8251, Japan
Tel.: (81) 367487270
Web Site: http://www.a-yoshitomi.co.jp
Mfr of Organic Peroxides
N.A.I.C.S.: 325199

Subsidiary (Domestic):

BIPHA Corporation (2)
1007 124 Izumisawa Chitose, Hokkaido, 066 0051, Japan
Tel.: (81) 123288180
Web Site: http://www.bipha.co.jp
Sales Range: $25-49.9 Million
Pharmaceuticals Mfr
N.A.I.C.S.: 325412

Koji Yaku *(Pres)*

Benesis Corporation (2)
2 6 18 Kitahama Chuo-ku, Osaka, 541 8505, Japan
Tel.: (81) 662276050
Web Site: http://www.benesis.co.jp
Producer & Distr of Plasma Preparations
N.A.I.C.S.: 325412

Subsidiary (Non-US):

Guangdong Tanabe Pharmaceutical Co., Ltd. (2)
Room No B-2501/02 China International Center No 33 Zhongshansan Road, Yuexiu District, 510055, Guangzhou, China
Tel.: (86) 2083708900
Web Site: http://www.mt-pharma.co.jp
Pharmaceuticals Product Mfr
N.A.I.C.S.: 325412

Subsidiary (Domestic):

Hoshienu Pharmaceutical Co., Ltd. (2)
1380 Sugawacho, Gojo, 637-0014, Japan
Tel.: (81) 747232533
Web Site: http://www.hoshienu.com
Pharmaceuticals Product Mfr
N.A.I.C.S.: 325412
Toshiyuki Yoshimura *(Mgr)*

MP-Logistics Corporation (2)
2 6 9 Hiranomachi, Chuo-ku, Osaka, 541-0026, Japan
Tel.: (81) 662276412
Pharmaceutical Warehousing & Freight Transportation Services
N.A.I.C.S.: 493110

Subsidiary (Non-US):

Mitsubishi Pharma (Guangzhou) Co., Ltd. (2)
Jiaoyuan Rd GETDD, Guangzhou, Guangdong, China
Tel.: (86) 2082220238
Sales Range: $125-149.9 Million
Mfr of Pharmaceuticals
N.A.I.C.S.: 325412

Mitsubishi Pharma Deutschland GmbH (2)
Willstatterstrasse 30, 40549, Dusseldorf, Germany
Tel.: (49) 2115205440
Web Site: http://www.pharma-de.com
Sales Range: $25-49.9 Million
Emp.: 18
Pharmaceutical Products Mfr & Distr
N.A.I.C.S.: 325412
Andreas Wiegand *(Gen Mgr-Sls & Mktg)*

Mitsubishi Pharma Europe Ltd. (2)
Jupiter House Triton Ct, 14 Finsbury Sq, London, EC2A 1BR, United Kingdom
Tel.: (44) 70655000
Sales Range: $25-49.9 Million
Pharmaceutical Developer
N.A.I.C.S.: 541715

Mitsubishi Pharma Research & Development (Beijing) Co., Ltd. (2)
Room 1004 China Resources Bldg No 8 Jianguomenbei Avenue, Beijing, 100005, China
Tel.: (86) 1085191507
Web Site: http://www.mt-pharma.co.jp
Sales Range: $25-49.9 Million
Pharmaceutical Research & Development Services
N.A.I.C.S.: 541715

Subsidiary (US):

Mitsubishi Tanabe Pharma America, Inc. (2)
25 Independence Blvd Ste 202, Warren, NJ 07059
Tel.: (908) 604-6887
Web Site: http://www.mt-pharma-america.com
Pharmaceutical Products Research & Development Services
N.A.I.C.S.: 541715
Atsushi Fujimoto *(Pres)*

Subsidiary (Domestic):

Mitsubishi Tanabe Pharma Development America, Inc. (3)

525 Washington Blvd Ste 400, Jersey City, NJ 07310
Tel.: (908) 607-1950
Web Site: http://www.mt-pharma-development-america.com
Pharmaceutical Products Research & Development Services
N.A.I.C.S.: 541715
Hideki Kuki *(Pres)*

Mitsubishi Tanabe Pharma Holdings America, Inc. (3)
525 Washington Blvd Ste 400, Jersey City, NJ 07310
Tel.: (908) 607-1980
Web Site: http://www.mt-pharma.co.jp
Investment Management Service
N.A.I.C.S.: 523999

Tanabe Research Laboratories U.S.A., Inc. (3)
4540 Towne Centre Ct, San Diego, CA 92121-1900 (100%)
Tel.: (858) 622-7000
Web Site: http://www.trlusa.com
Pharmaceutical Research Services
N.A.I.C.S.: 325412
Eiji Tanaka *(Chm)*

Tanabe U.S.A., Inc. (3)
1849 Western Way, Torrance, CA 90501 (100%)
Tel.: (310) 783-0200
Web Site: http://www.tanabe-usa.com
Mfr of Pharmaceuticals
N.A.I.C.S.: 325412

Branch (Domestic):

Tanabe U.S.A. (4)
31 Schanck Rd Ste 1C, Freehold, NJ 07728
Tel.: (732) 845-1301
Web Site: http://www.tanabeusa.com
Sales Range: $25-49.9 Million
Emp.: 1
Provider of Marketing & Sales of Pharmaceuticals
N.A.I.C.S.: 424210

Subsidiary (Domestic):

Mitsubishi Tanabe Pharma Factory Ltd. (2)
17-10 Nihonbashi-Koamicho Chuo-ku, Tokyo, 103-8405, Japan
Tel.: (81) 367487700
Web Site: http://www.mt-pharma.co.jp
Pharmaceuticals Mfr
N.A.I.C.S.: 325412

Subsidiary (Domestic):

Yoshitomi Engineering, Ltd. (3)
955 Oaza Koiwai Yoshitomi Cho, Chikujo Gun, Fukuoka, 871 0801, Japan
Tel.: (81) 979220011
Sales Range: $10-24.9 Million
Emp.: 40
Provider of Construction Services
N.A.I.C.S.: 237120
Kuni Susa *(Gen Mgr)*

Subsidiary (Non-US):

Mitsubishi Tanabe Pharma Korea Co., Ltd. (2)
903 - 4 Sangsin-Ri Hyangnam-Eup, Hwaseong, 445-920, Korea (South)
Tel.: (82) 313536671
Sales Range: $50-74.9 Million
Pharmaceuticals Product Mfr
N.A.I.C.S.: 325412

NeuroDerm Ltd. (2)
3 Pekeris Street Ruhrberg Science Bldg Bell Entrance, Robin Science Park, Rehovot, 7670212, Israel
Tel.: (972) 89462729
Web Site: http://www.neuroderm.com
Pharmaceuticals Mfr
N.A.I.C.S.: 325412
Oded S. Lieberman *(CEO)*

P.T. Tanabe Indonesia (2)
Jl Tanah Abang III No 8, Jakarta, 10160, Indonesia
Tel.: (62) 213841842
Sales Range: $50-74.9 Million
Emp.: 145
Mfr & Sales of Pharmaceuticals

N.A.I.C.S.: 325412
Miesi Tanabe Indonesia *(CEO)*

Tai Tien Pharmaceuticals Co., Ltd. (2)
One of the 14th Floor No 8 Section 7 Shimin Avenue, Nangang District, Taipei, 115, Taiwan
Tel.: (886) 226518288
Web Site: http://www.tanabe.com.tw
Sales Range: $50-74.9 Million
Sales of Pharmaceuticals
N.A.I.C.S.: 424210

Taiwan Tanabe Seiyaku Co., Ltd. (2)
One of the 14th Floor No 8 Section 7 Shimin Avenue, Nangang District, Taipei, 115, Taiwan
Tel.: (886) 226518288
Web Site: http://www.tanabe.com.tw
Sales Range: $25-49.9 Million
Mfr & Sales of Pharmaceuticals
N.A.I.C.S.: 325412

Subsidiary (Domestic):

Tanabe R&D Service Co., Ltd. (2)
3-16-89 Kashima, Yodogawa-Ku, Osaka, 532-0031, Japan
Tel.: (81) 663002824
Web Site: http://www.tanabe-rds.co.jp
Research & Development Services
N.A.I.C.S.: 541715

Subsidiary (Non-US):

Tanabe Seiyaku (Malaysia) Sdn. Bhd. (2)
2 Jalan PJU 3 49 Swayma Damansara, 47810, Petaling Jaya, Selangor Darul Ehsan, Malaysia
Tel.: (60) 378036998
Web Site: http://www.pharmaforte.com.my
Sales Range: $25-49.9 Million
Exporter, Importer & Sales of Pharmaceuticals
N.A.I.C.S.: 424210

Tanabe Seiyaku Co., Ltd. (2)
CP House 97 107 Uxbridge Rd, Ealing, London, W5 5TL, United Kingdom
Tel.: (44) 2085660356
Web Site: http://www.tanabe.co.jp
Sales Range: $25-49.9 Million
Provider of Pharmaceuticals
N.A.I.C.S.: 325412

Subsidiary (Domestic):

Tanabe Total Service Co., Ltd. (2)
Tanabe Seiyaku 1st Bekkan 3-2-8 Hiranocho, Chuo-ku, Osaka, 541-0046, Japan
Tel.: (81) 662055535
Logistics Consulting Servies
N.A.I.C.S.: 541614

Yoshitomiyakuhin Corporation (2)
3-2-1-10 Doshomachi, Chuo Ku, Osaka, 541-8505, Japan
Tel.: (81) 662028455
Web Site: http://www.yoshitomi.jp
Sales Range: $50-74.9 Million
Emp.: 230
Pharmaceutical Sales Promotion & Marketing Services
N.A.I.C.S.: 424210

Nippon Sanso Holdings Corporation (1)
1-3-26 Koyama, Shinagawa-ku, Tokyo, 142-8558, Japan (50.57%)
Tel.: (81) 357888000
Web Site: http://www.tn-sanso.co.jp
Rev.: $8,296,085,410
Assets: $15,924,038,630
Liabilities: $9,670,238,310
Net Worth: $6,253,800,320
Earnings: $700,005,610
Emp.: 19,533
Fiscal Year-end: 03/31/2024
Holding Company; Industrial Gases & Gas Equipment Mfr & Distr
N.A.I.C.S.: 551112
Yujiro Ichihara *(Pres & CEO)*

Subsidiary (Non-US):

Air Products Industry Co., Ltd. (2)
282 Bangbon 3 Road, Nongkaem, Bangkok, 10160, Thailand
Tel.: (66) 22100283

MITSUBISHI CHEMICAL GROUP CORPORATION

Mitsubishi Chemical Group Corporation—(Continued)

Web Site: http://www.apithailand.com
Sales Range: $50-74.9 Million
Emp.: 301
Industrial Gas Mfr
N.A.I.C.S.: 325120

Crown Manufacturing Corp. (2)
8F-1 No 2 Section 1 Fu-Shing South Road, Taipei, 104, Taiwan
Tel.: (886) 2 8771 8696
Web Site: http://www.thermos.com.tw
Sales Range: $25-49.9 Million
Emp.: 20
Housewares Distr
N.A.I.C.S.: 326199

Dalian Taiyo Nippon Sanso Gas Co., Ltd. (2)
No 3 West Tieshan Road, Dalian Economic & Technical Development Zone, Dalian, 116022, China
Tel.: (86) 41187618331
Industrial Gas Mfr
N.A.I.C.S.: 325120

Ingasco, Inc. (2)
23rd Floor One Corporate Center Meralco corner Julia Vargas Ave, Ortigas Center, Pasig, Metro Manila, Philippines
Tel.: (63) 2 626 1500
Web Site: http://www.ingasco.com.ph
Sales Range: $25-49.9 Million
Emp.: 45
Industrial Gas Mfr
N.A.I.C.S.: 325120

Leeden National Oxygen Ltd. (2)
1 Shipyard Road, Singapore, 628128, Singapore
Tel.: (65) 62664868
Web Site: https://www.leedennox.com
Sales Range: $125-149.9 Million
Emp.: 1,585
Holding Company; Industrial Equipment, Hardware & Safety Products Distr & Industrial Gas Mfr & Distr
N.A.I.C.S.: 551112
Steven Weng Cheong Tham (CEO)

Subsidiary (Domestic):

Leeden Distribution Pte Ltd (3)
1 Shipyard Road, 628128, Singapore, 628128, Singapore
Tel.: (65) 6268 8333
Web Site: http://www.leedennox.com
Emp.: 100
Welding Products Distr & Welding Equipment Services
N.A.I.C.S.: 423840

Leeden International Pte. Ltd. (3)
1 Shipyard Road, Singapore, 628128, Singapore
Tel.: (65) 62664868
Emp.: 100
Administrative Management Services
N.A.I.C.S.: 561110

Subsidiary (Domestic):

Auweld International Pte Ltd (4)
1 Shipyard Road, Singapore, 628128, Singapore (100%)
Tel.: (65) 62626626
Web Site: https://www.auweld.com
Sales Range: $25-49.9 Million
Emp.: 100
Industrial Equipment Distr
N.A.I.C.S.: 423830

Subsidiary (Non-US):

Auweld Sdn Bhd (5)
PT 5075 Jalan Jangur 28/43 Seksyen 28, Hicom Industrial Estate, Shah Alam, 40400, Selangor Darul Ehsan, Malaysia
Tel.: (60) 3 5522 8333
Web Site: http://www.auweld.com
Sales Range: $25-49.9 Million
Emp.: 4
Industrial Equipment Distr
N.A.I.C.S.: 423830
Jeffrey Yap (Mgr)

Subsidiary (Domestic):

Eversafe Extinguisher Pte Ltd (4)
1 Shipyard Road, Singapore, 628128, Singapore (55%)
Tel.: (65) 62912611
Web Site: http://www.leedennox.com
Sales Range: $500-549.9 Million
Emp.: 1,500
Fire Extinguishers, Fire Fighting Appliances & Accessories Distr
N.A.I.C.S.: 423990

Subsidiary (Non-US):

Eversafe Extinguisher Sdn Bhd (4)
Lot 878 Jalan Subang 9 Taman Perindustrian Subang, 47500, Subang Jaya, Selangor Darul Ehsan, Malaysia
Tel.: (60) 380249898
Web Site: https://www.eversafe.net
Sales Range: $75-99.9 Million
Fire Extinguishers, Fire Fighting Appliances & Accessories Mfr & Distr
N.A.I.C.S.: 423990

Subsidiary (Domestic):

Eversafe System Sdn. Bhd. (5)
Lot 878 Jalan Subang 9 Taman Perindustrian Subang, Subang Jaya, Petaling Jaya, 47500, Selangor Darul Ehsan, Malaysia (100%)
Tel.: (60) 380249898
Web Site: http://www.eversafe.net
Fire Extinguishers, Fire Fighting Appliances & Accessories Distr
N.A.I.C.S.: 423990

Subsidiary (Non-US):

Leeden Philippines Inc. (4)
Unit 2-A Grand Hamptons Tower II 1st Ave Corner 31st Street, Crescent Park West, Bonifacio Global City, Taguig, 1634, Philippines
Tel.: (63) 2 846 2349
Sales Range: $50-74.9 Million
Emp.: 6
Welding & Safety Equipment Distr
N.A.I.C.S.: 423830

Leeden Powerweld Sdn Bhd (4)
No 168 Jalan Usaha 12 Kawasan Perindustrian, Ayer Keroh, 75450, Melaka, Malaysia (87.5%)
Tel.: (60) 62323288
Web Site: https://www.power-weld.com
Sales Range: $25-49.9 Million
Emp.: 20
Welding Equipment Mfr & Distr
N.A.I.C.S.: 333992

Leeden Sdn Bhd (4)
9 Jalan Api Api 26/1 Hicom Industrial Estate, 40400, Shah Alam, Selangor, Malaysia (100%)
Tel.: (60) 351016888
Sales Range: $25-49.9 Million
Emp.: 100
Safety Products Distr
N.A.I.C.S.: 423990

Leeden Welding Sdn Bhd (4)
Pt 5075 Jalan Jangur 28-43 Seksyen 28 Hicom Industrial Estate, 40400, Shah Alam, Malaysia (100%)
Tel.: (60) 3 5522 8333
Sales Range: $25-49.9 Million
Emp.: 100
Industrial Welding Equipment Distr
N.A.I.C.S.: 423830

NIG Industrial Gases Sdn Bhd (4)
PT 5074 & 5075 Jalan Jangur 28/43 Seksyen 28 Hicom Industrial Estate, 40400, Shah Alam, 40400, Malaysia (51%)
Tel.: (60) 355228222
Emp.: 30
Industrial Gas Mfr & Distr
N.A.I.C.S.: 325120
Tan Kean Hooi (Gen Mgr)

Subsidiary (Domestic):

NIG Gases Sdn Bhd (5)
PT 5074 & 5075 Jalan Jangur 28/43 Seksyen 28 Hicom Industrial Estate, 40400, Shah Alam, Selangor Darul Ehsan, Malaysia (57%)
Tel.: (60) 355228222
Sales Range: $25-49.9 Million
Industrial Gases Mfr & Distr
N.A.I.C.S.: 325120

Tan Kean Hooi (Gen Mgr)

Subsidiary (Domestic):

Leeden Hercules Sdn Bhd (6)
2249 Jalan IKS Bukit Minyak 1 Taman IKS Bukit Minyak, Seberang Perai Tengah, 14000, Bukit Mertajam, Penang, Malaysia
Tel.: (60) 45015555
Web Site: https www.leedenhercules.com
Industrial Gas Mfr & Sales
N.A.I.C.S.: 325120
Sam Cheang Fook (CEO)

Subsidiary (Domestic):

Hercules Machinery Gases Sdn Bhd (7)
No 2249 Jalan IKS Bukit Minyak 1 Taman IKS Bukit Minyak, 14000, Bukit Mertajam, Pulau Pinang, Malaysia
Tel.: (60) 4 501 5553
Web Site: http://www.myhercules.com.my
Industrial Gases & Equipment Whslr
N.A.I.C.S.: 424690
Fook Sam Cheang (Gen Mgr)

Subsidiary (Domestic):

NIG Gases Sdn Bhd (6)
Lot 295 Bandar Industri Gebeng Jaya, 26080, Kuantan, Pahang, Malaysia
Tel.: (60) 9 583 8218
Sales Range: $75-99.9 Million
Emp.: 11
Industrial Gas Distr
N.A.I.C.S.: 424690
Chong Porshen (Mgr-Sls)

Subsidiary (Non-US):

PT National Industrial Gases (4)
Jalan Brigjen Katamso Kawasan Bintang Industri II Lot No 1-3/20, Tanjong Uncang, Batam, 29422, Indonesia (100%)
Tel.: (62) 778 392 161
Web Site: http://www.leedenlimited.com
Industrial Gases Mfr & Distr
N.A.I.C.S.: 325120

Subsidiary (Domestic):

Leeden Investment Pte Ltd (3)
1 Shipyard Road, Singapore, 628128, Singapore (100%)
Tel.: (65) 62664868
Sales Range: $50-74.9 Million
Emp.: 200
Investment Holding & Leasing of Property
N.A.I.C.S.: 531110
Steven Tham (CEO)

Subsidiary (Non-US):

Matheson Gas Products Korea, Co, Ltd. (2)
94 Eumbongmyeon - ro, Eumbong - myeon, Asan, 336-834, Chungcheongnam - do, Korea (South)
Tel.: (82) 415397400
Web Site: https://mgpk.co.kr
Sales Range: $25-49.9 Million
Emp.: 75
Industrial Gas Mfr
N.A.I.C.S.: 325120

Subsidiary (US):

Matheson Tri-Gas, Inc. (2)
150 Allen Rd, Basking Ridge, NJ 07920
Tel.: (908) 991-9200
Web Site: https://www.mathesongas.com
Sales Range: $900-999.9 Million
Emp.: 4,500
Industrial, Medical & Specialty Gases, Gas Handling Equipment, Welding Equipment, Gas Detection & Purification Systems Distr
N.A.I.C.S.: 424690

Subsidiary (Domestic):

Continental Carbonic Products, Inc. (3)
3985 E Harrison Ave, Decatur, IL 62526
Tel.: (217) 428-2068
Web Site: http://www.continentalcarbonic.com
Sales Range: $100-124.9 Million
Emp.: 830
Dry Ice Mfr
N.A.I.C.S.: 325120

INTERNATIONAL PUBLIC

Subsidiary (Non-US):

Matheson K-Air India Private Limited (3)
G no 245 6 7 9 Plot no 2 Kharabwadi, Chakan, Pune, 410501, India (51%)
Tel.: (91) 2135 667700
Sales Range: $10-24.9 Million
Emp.: 100
Industrial Gas Supplier
N.A.I.C.S.: 424690
Kiran Karnawat (Mng Dir)

Nippon Gasses Euro-holding, S. L. (3)
Calle Orense 11, 28020, Madrid, Spain
Tel.: (34) 914533000
Web Site: https://nippongases.com
Industrial Gas Mfr
N.A.I.C.S.: 325120

Subsidiary (Non-US):

Dominion Gas Asia Pacific Pte Limited (4)
21 Tanjong King Rd, Singapore, 628047, Singapore
Tel.: (65) 66637222
Web Site: http://www.dominion-gas.com
Industrial Gas Distr
N.A.I.C.S.: 221210

Dominion Oilfield Services Limited (4)
Axim Road, Dixcovehill, Takoradi, Ghana
Tel.: (233) 3312023272
Industrial Gas Distr
N.A.I.C.S.: 221210

Dryce S.r.l. (4)
Via Aosta 6, 20063, Cernusco sul Naviglio, Italy
Tel.: (39) 02 92393501
Web Site: http://www.dryce.it
Natural Gas Distribution Services
N.A.I.C.S.: 221210

Magaldi Life S.r.l. (4)
Via Case Rosse 19/A, 84131, Salerno, Italy
Tel.: (39) 089383004
Web Site: https://www.magaldilife.it
Emergency Management Services
N.A.I.C.S.: 624230

Nippon Gases Belgium N.V. (4)
Lammerdries 29, B 2250, Olen, Belgium (100%)
Tel.: (32) 14250411
Web Site: http://www.nippongases.com
Producer & Retailer of Industrial Gases
N.A.I.C.S.: 221210

Branch (Domestic):

Nippon Gases Belgium N.V.-Schoten (5)
Metropoolstraat 17, 2900, Schoten, Belgium
Tel.: (32) 36418450
Web Site: http://nippongases.com
Producer & Retailer of Industrial Gases
N.A.I.C.S.: 221210

Subsidiary (Non-US):

Nippon Gases Norge AS (4)
Ringnesveien 50, PO Box 23, 0951, Oslo, Norway
Tel.: (47) 97774277
Emp.: 300
Industrial Gas Distr
N.A.I.C.S.: 424690

Subsidiary (Non-US):

Eiva-Safex AS (5)
Tel.: (47) 23051100
Web Site: http://www.eiva-safex.no
Lifting Equipment Mfr
N.A.I.C.S.: 333923

Subsidiary (Non-US):

Nippon Gases Offshore Tanks Limited (4)
Maersk House Crawpeel Rd Altens Industrial Estate, Portlethen, Aberdeen, AB12 3LG, Aberdeenshire, United Kingdom
Gas Tank Container Distr
N.A.I.C.S.: 423840

Nippon Gases Sverige AB (4)

AND PRIVATE COMPANIES

Volvogatan 14, PO Box 51, 731 36, Koping, Sweden
Tel.: (46) 775206500
Industrial Gas Distr
N.A.I.C.S.: 424690
Carina Bager *(Mgr-HR)*

Nippon Gasses UK Limited (4)
Gresley Way Immingham Dock, Immingham, DN40 2NT, NE Lincolnshire, United Kingdom
Tel.: (44) 1469554700
Industrial Gas Mfr
N.A.I.C.S.: 325120

Nippon Gasses Danmark A/S (4)
Rode Banke 120, 7000, Fredericia, Denmark
Tel.: (45) 76208800
Industrial Gas Distr
N.A.I.C.S.: 424690

Nippon Gasses Deutschland GmbH (4)
Hans-Bockler-Str 1, 40476, Dusseldorf, Germany (100%)
Tel.: (49) 21126000
Web Site: http://www.nippongases.com
Producer & Retailer of Industrial Gases
N.A.I.C.S.: 221210

Subsidiary (Domestic):

Nippon Gasses Espana S.L. (4)
Calle Orense 11, 28020, Madrid, Spain (100%)
Tel.: (34) 914533000
Web Site: http://nippongases.com
Metalworking Machinery
N.A.I.C.S.: 333519
Jose Ballester Ricart *(Dir-Safety, Environment & Quality)*

Subsidiary (Domestic):

OXIMESA, S.L. (5)
Orense 11 -5th floor, 28020, Madrid, Spain
Tel.: (34) 900212333
Web Site: http://www.oximesa.es
Various Health & Oxygen Therapies for Homecare Patients
N.A.I.C.S.: 621610

Oxigeno del Norte S.A. (5)
Shepherd Street, Barakaldo, Bilbao, 48903, Biscay, Spain
Tel.: (34) 944970644
Industrial Gas Mfr
N.A.I.C.S.: 325120

Subsidiary (Non-US):

Nippon Gasses Netherlands B.V. (4)
Beugsloepweg 3, 3133 KV, Vlaardingen, Netherlands (100%)
Tel.: (31) 104340455
Web Site: http://www.nippongases.com
Producer & Retailer of Industrial Gases
N.A.I.C.S.: 221210

Rivoira Refrigerant Gases SRL (4)
Via Benigno Crespi 19, Milan, Italy
Tel.: (39) 011208911
Web Site: http://www.rivoiragas.it
Atmospheric, Process & Specialty Gases Distr
N.A.I.C.S.: 221210

Subsidiary (Domestic):

RASIRC, Inc. (3)
7815 Silverton Ave, San Diego, CA 92126
Tel.: (858) 259-1220
Web Site: http://www.rasirc.com
Sales Range: $1-9.9 Million
Emp.: 26
Liquid & Gas Purification Equipment Mfr
N.A.I.C.S.: 333248
Jeffrey Spiegelman *(Founder & Pres)*

Western International Gas & Cylinders, Inc. (3)
7173 Hwy 159 E, Bellville, TX 77418
Tel.: (979) 413-2100
Web Site: https://www.westernintl.com
Industrial Gas Distr
N.A.I.C.S.: 424690

Subsidiary (Non-US):

Nippon Cutting & Welding Equipment Co., Ltd (2)
1/10 Moo 5 Tumbol Khanham Amphoe, Uthai Pranakhonsi Ayuttaya, Phra Nakhon Si Ayutthaya, 13210, Thailand
Tel.: (66) 35330127
Welding Equipment Mfr
N.A.I.C.S.: 333992

Nippon Gasses Euro-Holding, S.L.U. (2)
Calle Orense 11 - 9th andar, 28020, Madrid, Spain
Tel.: (34) 914537200
Web Site: http://www.nippongases.com
Holding Company; Industrial & Medical Gases Mfr
N.A.I.C.S.: 551112

Subsidiary (Domestic):

Andaluza de Gases S.A. (3)
Carretera A- 92, Alcala de Guadaira, Seville, 41500, Spain
Tel.: (34) 955631860
Sales Range: $25-49.9 Million
Emp.: 13
Industrial Gas Mfr
N.A.I.C.S.: 325120

Carbonorte S.L. (3)
Calle de Orense 11, Sa Planta, 28020, Madrid, Spain
Tel.: (34) 915535466
Industrial Gas Mfr
N.A.I.C.S.: 325120

Subsidiary (Non-US):

Domolife S.r.l. (3)
Via Aterno 56, 65218, Pescara, Italy
Tel.: (39) 0854311988
Web Site: https://www.domolife.it
Medical Gas Mfr & Distr
N.A.I.C.S.: 325120

Dryce Italia S.r.l. (3)
Via Aosta 6, 20063, Cernusco sul Naviglio, Milan, Italy
Tel.: (39) 0292393501
Web Site: https://www.dryce.eu
Emp.: 40
Industrial Gas Mfr
N.A.I.C.S.: 325120

Subsidiary (Domestic):

Ferrygas, S.A. (3)
Calle Carpinteros Pg Industrial Marife 22, Toledo, 45500, Talavera de la Reina, Spain
Tel.: (34) 925771177
Industrial Gas Mfr
N.A.I.C.S.: 325120

Subsidiary (Non-US):

General Medical S.r.l. (3)
Via Nazionale snc, Montefredane, 83030, Avellino, Italy
Tel.: (39) 0825607224
Web Site: http://www.gmitalia.eu
Medical & Indsutrial Gas Distr
N.A.I.C.S.: 221210

Medigas Italia S.r.l. (3)
Via Edison 6, 20057, Milan, Italy
Tel.: (39) 024888111
Web Site: https://www.medigas.it
Industrial Gas Mfr
N.A.I.C.S.: 325120

Praxair Gases Ireland Limited (3)
Unit 22 Airways Industrial Estate Viscount Avenue Santry, Dublin, D17 KC91, Ireland
Tel.: (353) 18547100
Industrial Gas Distr
N.A.I.C.S.: 424690

Praxair Gases UK Ltd. (3)
Gresley Way Immingham Dock, Immingham, DN40 2NT, United Kingdom
Tel.: (44) 1469554700
Industrial Gas Distr
N.A.I.C.S.: 424690
Lynn Bond *(Controller-Fin)*

Praxair PHP S.A.S. (3)
Mercus Garrabet, Ariege, 09400, France
Tel.: (33) 561024200
Web Site: http://www.praxair.com
Emp.: 37
Industrial Gas Distr
N.A.I.C.S.: 221210

Dr.Mazet Francis *(Gen Mgr)*

Praxair Portugal Gases S.A. (3)
E N 13ao Km 6 4, P-4470, Maia, Portugal
Tel.: (351) 229438320
Web Site: http://www.praxair.com
Sales Range: $25-49.9 Million
Emp.: 50
Industrial Gas Distr
N.A.I.C.S.: 423840

Rivoira Gas S.r.l. (3)
Via Benigno Crespi 19, 20159, Milan, Italy
Tel.: (39) 02771191
Web Site: http://www.rivoiragroup.it
Industrial Gas Distr
N.A.I.C.S.: 221210

Sauerstoff und Stickstoffrohrleitungs (3)
Futingsweg 34, 47805, Krefeld, Germany
Tel.: (49) 02151 3790
Sales Range: $25-49.9 Million
Emp.: 100
Industrial Gas Mfr
N.A.I.C.S.: 325120

Smeding B. V. (3)
Lage Traan 10 Industrieterrein leekstarveld, 9351 VL, Leek, Netherlands
Tel.: (31) 594612260
Web Site: http://www.smedingbv.nl
Industrial Gas Mfr
N.A.I.C.S.: 325120

Subsidiary (Non-US):

Shanghai Taiyo Nippon Sanso Gas Co., Ltd. (2)
No 1959 Zhuanxing Road, Xinzhuan Industry District, Shanghai, 201108, China
Tel.: (86) 2164422966
Industrial Gas Mfr
N.A.I.C.S.: 325120

Suzhou Taiyo Nippon Sanso Gas Co., Ltd (2)
229 Taishan Road, Suzhou New District, Suzhou, 215000, Jiangsu, China
Tel.: (86) 51268070596
Industrial Gas Mfr & Sales
N.A.I.C.S.: 325120

Taiyo Nippon Sanso Taiwan, Inc. (2)
TFC ONE Building No 1 Section 3 Gongdao 5th Road, East Dist, Hsin-chu, 30069, ROC, Taiwan
Tel.: (886) 35726588
Web Site: http://www.tnst.com.tw
Specialty Gases Distr
N.A.I.C.S.: 238990

Taiyo Nippon Sanso Trading (Shanghai) Co., Ltd (2)
Tel.: (86) 2158358700
Web Site: http://www.tn-sgas.com
Industrial Gas Mfr
N.A.I.C.S.: 325120

Joint Venture (Non-US):

Vietnam Japan Gas Joint Stock Company (2)
No 33 Road 3A Bien Hoa Industrial Zone 2, Bien Hoa, Dong Nai, Vietnam
Tel.: (84) 2513836706
Web Site: http://www.vijagas.vn
Sales Range: $25-49.9 Million
Emp.: 70
Industrial Gas Mfr
N.A.I.C.S.: 325120
Haruhiro Yasuga *(Gen Dir)*

The KAITEKI Institute, Inc. (1)
Palace Building 1-1 Marunouchi 1-chome, Chiyoda-ku, Tokyo, 100-8251, Japan
Tel.: (81) 3 6748 7170
Web Site: http://www.kaiteki-institute.com
Environmental Research & Development Services
N.A.I.C.S.: 541715
Yoshimitsu Kobayashi *(Chm)*

MITSUBISHI CORPORATION

MITSUBISHI CORPORATION
3-1 Marunouchi 2-Chome, Chiyoda-ku, Tokyo, 100-8086, Japan
Tel.: (81) 332102121
Web Site:
https://www.mitsubishicorp.com

Year Founded: 1954
8058—(TKS)
Rev.: $129,341,842,610
Assets: $155,067,770,920
Liabilities: $88,340,951,230
Net Worth: $66,726,819,690
Earnings: $6,372,264,740
Emp.: 80,037
Fiscal Year-end: 03/31/24
Holding Company
N.A.I.C.S.: 551112
Akira Murakoshi *(Exec Officer-Corp Comm & HR & Exec VP)*

Subsidiaries:

AMCK Aviation Holdings Ireland Limited (1)
First Floor 28-29 Sir John Rogerson's Quay, Dublin, D02 EY80, Ireland
Tel.: (353) 15170100
Web Site: http://www.amck.aero
Aircraft Leasing Services
N.A.I.C.S.: 532411
Paul Sheridan *(CEO)*

Agrex do Brasil S.A. (1)
AV T-63 No 1 296 New World 16th Floor Setor Bueno, Goiania, 74230-100, Brazil
Tel.: (55) 6230182700
Web Site: https://www.agrex.com.br
Fertilizer & Seed Mfr
N.A.I.C.S.: 325320

Agrex, Inc. (1)
8205 W 108th Terrace Ste 200, Overland Park, KS 66210
Tel.: (913) 851-6300
Web Site: http://www.agrexinc.com
Full-service Commodity Trading Company; Trading Grains, Oilseeds, Oils, Feed & Food Ingredients
N.A.I.C.S.: 523160

Ajoco Exploration Co., Ltd. (1)
2-3-1 Marunouchi Mitsubishishoji Bldg, Chiyoda-Ku, Tokyo, 100-0005, Japan
Tel.: (81) 332104174
Oil Exploration Services
N.A.I.C.S.: 213112

Ajoco'91 Exploration Co., Ltd. (1)
2-3-1 Marunouchi, Chiyoda-Ku, Tokyo, 100-0005, Japan
Tel.: (81) 332104174
Oil Exploration Services
N.A.I.C.S.: 213112

Alternative Investment Capital Ltd. (1)
6F Tekko Building 1-8-2 Marunouchi, Chiyoda-ku, Tokyo, 100-0005, Japan
Tel.: (81) 35 218 5230
Web Site: https://www.aicapital.co.jp
Sales Range: $50-74.9 Million
Emp.: 24
Asset Management Services
N.A.I.C.S.: 523940
Kiyoshi Shibano *(Principal)*

Amfine Chemical Corporation (1)
777 Terrace Ave Ste 602B, Hasbrouck Heights, NJ 07604
Tel.: (201) 818-0159
Web Site: https://www.amfine.com
Construction Materials Mfr
N.A.I.C.S.: 327320
John Mara *(Mgr-Technical & Mktg)*

Angola Japan Oil Co., Ltd. (1)
2-3-1 Marunouchi Mitsubishishoji Bldg, Chiyoda-Ku, Tokyo, 100-0005, Japan
Tel.: (81) 332104174
Emp.: 50
Oil Exploration Services
N.A.I.C.S.: 213112
Go Saitou *(Mgr-Admin)*

Anjo Isuzu Corporation (1)
16-1 Nishi Otsuka Imahon-machi, Anjo, 446-0008, Aichi, Japan
Tel.: (81) 566 98 1311
Steel Mfrs
N.A.I.C.S.: 331110

Asia Modified Starch Co., Ltd. (1)
130-132 Sindhorn Building Tower 1 2nd floor Wittayu Road, Lumpini Pathumwan, Bangkok, 10330, Thailand

MITSUBISHI CORPORATION

Mitsubishi Corporation—(Continued)

Tel.: (66) 26325447
Web Site: https://www.amsco.co.th
Emp.: 46
Tapioca Starch Mfr
N.A.I.C.S.: 311221

Astillas Exportaciones Limitada (1)
Valle Colcura s/n, Lota, Concepcion, Chile
Tel.: (56) 412408300
Web Site: http://www.astex.cl
Wood Chip Mfr
N.A.I.C.S.: 321113

Bell-Info-Tec Corporation (1)
Kishimoto Building 2-2-1 Marunouchi, Chiyoda-ku, Tokyo, 100-0005, Japan
Tel.: (81) 3 5219 5017
Web Site: http://www.isz.co.jp
Information Technology Consulting Services
N.A.I.C.S.: 541512

Bridgestone Sales (Thailand) Co., Ltd. (1)
990 Abdulrahim Rama IV Road, Silom, Bangkok, 10500, Thailand
Tel.: (66) 26361555
Web Site: http://www.bridgestone.co.th
Tiles Mfr
N.A.I.C.S.: 326211
Pech Panthong (Mgr-IT)

Brunei LNG Sdn. Bhd. (1)
Jalan Utara Panaga Seria KB 3534, Negara, 7082, Negara, Brunei Darussalam
Tel.: (673) 3236901
Sales Range: $200-249.9 Million
Emp.: 400
Liquified Natural Gas Mfr; Owned 50% by Government of Brunei, 25% by The Shell Petroleum Co. Ltd. & 25% by Mitsubishi Corporation
N.A.I.C.S.: 211120

Subsidiary (Domestic):

Brunei Shell Petroleum Co. Sdn. Bhd. (2)
Jalan Utara Panaga, Seria, KB2933, Negara, Brunei Darussalam
Tel.: (673) 3373999
Emp.: 3,500
Oil & Natural Gas Mfr
N.A.I.C.S.: 324110

CIMA Energy, Ltd. (1)
100 Waugh Dr Ste 500, Houston, TX 77007 **(100%)**
Tel.: (713) 209-1112
Web Site: http://www.cima-energy.com
Oil & Gas Marketing Services
N.A.I.C.S.: 424720
Michael D. Rupe (CFO & Exec VP)

Cape Flattery Silica Mines Pty., Ltd. (1)
Cairns Corporate Tower Level 15 15 Lake Street, PO Box 6212, Cairns, 4870, QLD, Australia
Tel.: (61) 74 051 5099
Web Site: https://www.cfsm.com.au
Sales Range: $50-74.9 Million
Emp.: 80
Silica Sand Mfr
N.A.I.C.S.: 212322
Garry Bartholdt (Gen Mgr)

Cermaq Group AS (1)
Dronning Eufemias gate 16, PO Box 144, Sentrum, 0102, Oslo, Norway
Tel.: (47) 23685000
Web Site: https://www.cermaq.com
Holding Company; Fish Farming & Fish Feed Mfr
N.A.I.C.S.: 551112
Geir Molvik (CEO)

Subsidiary (Non-US):

Cermaq Canada Ltd. (2)
203-919 Island Highway, Campbell River, V9W 2C2, BC, Canada
Tel.: (250) 286-0022
Web Site: https://www.cermaq.ca
Salmon Farming Services
N.A.I.C.S.: 112511
David Kiemele (Mng Dir)

Cermaq Chile S.A. (2)
Diego Portales 2000 Piso 10, 5480000, Puerto Montt, Chile
Tel.: (56) 652563250
Web Site: https://www.cermaq.cl
Salmon Farming Services
N.A.I.C.S.: 112511

Subsidiary (Domestic):

Cermaq Norway AS (2)
Gjerbakknes, 8286, Nordfold, Norway
Tel.: (47) 2368 5500
Web Site: http://www.cermaq.com
Sales Range: $50-74.9 Million
Emp.: 200
Fish Farming & Fish Whslr
N.A.I.C.S.: 112511
Snorre Jonassen (Reg Dir-Nordland)

Dai-Nippon Meiji Sugar Co., Ltd. (1)
Nishikawa Bldg 1-5-3 Nihonbashi, Chuo-ku, Tokyo, 103-0027, Japan
Tel.: (81) 3 3271 0101
Web Site: http://www.dmsugar.co.jp
Sales Range: $100-124.9 Million
Emp.: 349
Sugar Mfr
N.A.I.C.S.: 311314

Deccan Fine Chemicals (India) Pvt. Ltd. (1)
8-2-293/82/A/74A Road No 9, Jubilee Hills, Hyderabad, 500 033, Telangana, India
Tel.: (91) 404 345 9999
Web Site:
https://www.deccanchemicals.com
Chemical Products Mfr
N.A.I.C.S.: 325320
Jagan Buddharaju (COO)

Diamond Construction Equipment Corporation (1)
9th Floor Nishishinbashi 1-chome Kawate Building 5-8-8, Nishi-Shimbashi Minato-ku, Tokyo, 105-0003, Japan
Tel.: (81) 362057886
Web Site: http://www.diace.co.jp
Construction Machinery Rental Services
N.A.I.C.S.: 532490

Diamond Generating Asia, Limited (1)
Rm 6607-09 66 F Center 99 Queens Rd C, Central District, Hong Kong, China (Hong Kong)
Tel.: (852) 29801195
Power Generation Services
N.A.I.C.S.: 221118

Diamond Generating Corp. (1)
633 W 5th St 27th Fl, Los Angeles, CA 90071-1519 **(100%)**
Tel.: (213) 473-0080
Web Site: https://www.dgc-us.com
Turbine & Turbine Generator Set Units Mfr
N.A.I.C.S.: 333611
Shuhei Kurosawa (CEO)

Subsidiary (Domestic):

Boston Energy Trading and Marketing LLC (2)
1 International Pl 9th Fl, Boston, MA 02110
Tel.: (617) 912-6000
Web Site: http://betm.com
Electric Energy Services
N.A.I.C.S.: 221118
Reem Fahey (CEO)

Diamond Generating Corporation Mexico, S. DE R. L. DE C.V. (1)
Av Pasco de la Reforma 250 Capital Reforma Torre-B Piso 27, Col Juarez De ICuauhtemoc, 06600, Mexico, Mexico
Tel.: (52) 5526483000
Electricity Generation & Energy Services
N.A.I.C.S.: 221118
Patricia Briones (Mgr-Fin)

Diamond Generating Europe Limited (1)
Mid City Place 71 High Holborn, WC1V 6BA, London, United Kingdom - England
Tel.: (44) 2070253411
Web Site: http://www.dg-europe.com
Power Generation & Renewable Energy Services
N.A.I.C.S.: 221118
Keiichi Suzuki (CEO)

Subsidiary (Non-US):

Diamond Generating Europe BV (2)
WTC Tower H Level 13 Zuidplein-110, 1077 XV, Amsterdam, Netherlands
Tel.: (31) 205041591
Power Generation & Renewable Energy Services
N.A.I.C.S.: 221118

Diamond Realty Investments, Inc. (1)
515 S Flower St Ste 4860, Los Angeles, CA 90071-3037
Tel.: (213) 346-2100
Web Site:
http://www.diamondrealtyinvestement.com
Emp.: 20
Real Estate Manangement Services
N.A.I.C.S.: 531390
Zack Zaizen (Pres)

Diamond Realty Management Inc. (1)
10F Hirakawacho Mori Tower 16-1 Hirakawacho 2-Chome, Chiyoda-ku, Tokyo, 102-0093, Japan
Tel.: (81) 35 212 4811
Web Site: https://www.mc-dream.com
Emp.: 98
Real Estate Asset Management Services
N.A.I.C.S.: 531390
Katsumi Nakamoto (Pres & CEO)

Diamond Tanker Pte. Ltd. (1)
250 North Bridge Road 11-01 Raffles City Tower, Singapore, 179101, Singapore
Tel.: (65) 6338 2000
Web Site: http://www.d-tanker.com
Sales Range: $25-49.9 Million
Emp.: 15
Marine Transportation Services
N.A.I.C.S.: 488390
Yang Ho Lee (Gen Mgr & Head-Ops)

ElectroRoute Holdings Limited (1)
1st Floor Marconi House Digges Lane, Dublin, D02 TD60, Ireland
Tel.: (353) 16875700
Web Site: http://www.electroroute.com
Emp.: 75
Energy Trading Services
N.A.I.C.S.: 221122
Catherine Kelly (Dir-HR)

Foodlink Corporation (1)
1-2-3 Shibaura, Minato-Ku, Tokyo, 105-0023, Japan
Tel.: (81) 35 444 8655
Web Site: https://www.foodlink.co.jp
Emp.: 228
Meat & Meat Product Distr
N.A.I.C.S.: 424470
Jun Ishida (COO-Trading Grp & VP)

Gifu Isuzu Corporation (1)
1187-14 Fukagaya Sakahogi-cho, Kamogun, Gifu, 505-0077, Japan
Tel.: (81) 574 27 3221
Steel Mfrs
N.A.I.C.S.: 331110

Gourmet Delica Co., Ltd. (1)
12 3F 739 Shimotomi, Tokorozawa, 359-0001, Saitama, Japan
Tel.: (81) 429431001
Web Site: http://www.gourmet-delica.com
Food Products Mfr
N.A.I.C.S.: 311999

Gunma Isuzu Corporation (1)
3488 Oaza Shinozuka Ouramachi, Ouragun, Gunma, 370-0615, Japan
Tel.: (81) 276 88 3511
Web Site: http://www.isz.co.jp
Steel Products Mfr
N.A.I.C.S.: 331110

Plant (Domestic):

Gunma Isuzu Corporation - Takasaki Factory (2)
50-1 Oaza Kawai Tamamura-machi, Sawagun, Gunma, 370-1117, Japan
Tel.: (81) 270 65 6411
Web Site: http://www.isz.co.jp
Steel Mfrs
N.A.I.C.S.: 331110

HOGY Medical Asia Pacific Pte. Ltd. (1)
PSA Building 14-01A 460 Alexandra Road, Singapore, 119963, Singapore

INTERNATIONAL PUBLIC

Tel.: (65) 62590697
Web Site: http://www.hogymedical.com
Medical Related Product Mfr
N.A.I.C.S.: 339112

Hongling Financial Leasing Co., Ltd. (1)
96 Ying Chun Road, Pudong, Shanghai, 200127, China
Tel.: (86) 2150563050
Web Site: https://www.hongling.sh.cn
Financial Lending Services
N.A.I.C.S.: 522220

Human Link Corporation (1)
Marunouchi-Nakadori Bldg 8F 2-3 Marunouchi 2-chome, Chiyoda-ku, 100-0005, Japan
Tel.: (81) 33 210 8130
Web Site: https://www.humanlink.co.jp
Emp.: 209
Human Resource Consulting Services
N.A.I.C.S.: 541612
Takatoshi Wako (Pres & CEO)

I-communications Corporation (1)
Roppongi MY Bldg 4F 2-1-13 Roppongi, Minato-ku, Tokyo, 106-0032, Japan
Tel.: (81) 3 5563 0781
Web Site: http://www.icom1988.com
Corporate Training & Development Services
N.A.I.C.S.: 541618
Yayoi Usui (Gen Mgr)

I-willing Corporation (1)
Roppongi MY Bldg 4F 2-1-13 Roppongi, Minato-ku, Tokyo, 106-0032, Japan
Tel.: (81) 3 5563 0782
Web Site: http://www.i-willing.co.jp
Human Resource Consulting Services
N.A.I.C.S.: 541612

IT Frontier Corporation (1)
Harumi 1-8-10, Chuo-ku, Tokyo, 104-6032, Japan
Tel.: (81) 362217000
Web Site: http://www.itfrontier.co.jp
Rev.: $597,312,000
Emp.: 1,753
Information Technology Consulting Services
N.A.I.C.S.: 541512

ITC Corporation Co., Ltd. (1)
10th Floor Kishimoto Building 2-2-1 Marunouchi, Chiyoda-ku, Tokyo, 100-0005, Japan
Tel.: (81) 352195018
Web Site: https://www.itc-corporation.co.jp
Information Technology Consulting Services
N.A.I.C.S.: 541512

IVICT Europe GmbH (1)
Kennedydamm 19, 40476, Dusseldorf, Germany
Tel.: (49) 211 439 7500
Web Site: https://www.ivic-t.eu
Specialty Chemicals Mfr
N.A.I.C.S.: 325998
Tomohiko Ikeda (CEO)

Indiana Packers Corporation (1)
6755 W 100 N, Delphi, IN 46923
Tel.: (765) 564-3680
Web Site:
http://www.indianapackerscorp.com
Sales Range: $550-599.9 Million
Emp.: 1,700
Processed Pork Distr
N.A.I.C.S.: 424470
Russ Yearwood (Pres & COO)

Subsidiary (Domestic):

Specialty Foods Group, LLC (2)
6 Dublin Ln, Owensboro, KY 42301 **(100%)**
Tel.: (270) 926-2324
Web Site:
https://www.specialtyfoodsgroup.com
Processed Meat Mfr & Distr
N.A.I.C.S.: 311612

Division (Domestic):

Specialty Foods Group-Field Packing Div. (3)
6 Dublin Ln, Owensboro, KY 42301
Tel.: (270) 926-2324
Web Site:
http://www.specialtyfoodsgroup.com
Meat, Sausage & Smoked Meat Producer

AND PRIVATE COMPANIES — MITSUBISHI CORPORATION

N.A.I.C.S.: 311611
Keith Luedke (VP-Sls)

Isuzu Auto-Service Corporation (1)
3193-2 Aza Nishinone Oaza Shinozuka Ouramachi, Oura-gun, Gunma, 370-0615, Japan
Tel.: (81) 276 88 3933
Logistics Consulting Servies
N.A.I.C.S.: 541614

Isuzu Business Support Corporation (1)
10th floor Kishimoto Building 2-2-1 Marunouchi, Chiyoda-ku, Tokyo, 100-0005, Japan
Tel.: (81) 35 219 5013
Web Site: https://www.isz.co.jp
Emp.: 53
Steel Mfrs
N.A.I.C.S.: 331110
Junichiro Ushijima (Mgr)

Isuzu Chou Corporation (1)
1-4-14 Sakuramori, Yamato, 242-0028, Kanagawa, Japan
Tel.: (81) 46 263 8333
Web Site: http://www.isz.co.jp
Steel Mfrs
N.A.I.C.S.: 331110

Isuzu Malaysia Sdn. Bhd. (1)
501D Level 5 Tower D Uptown 5 No 5 Jalan SS21/39, Damansara Uptown, 47400, Petaling Jaya, Selangor, Malaysia
Tel.: (60) 377239777
Web Site: http://www.isuzu.net.my
Motor Vehicle Distr
N.A.I.C.S.: 423110

Isuzu Management Service Corporation (1)
Kishimoto Building 2-2-1, Chiyoda-ku, Tokyo, 100-0005, Japan
Tel.: (81) 3 5219 5061
Web Site: http://www.isz.co.jp
Business Consulting Services
N.A.I.C.S.: 541611

Isuzu Motors India Private Limited (1)
No 183 9th Floor Prestige Centre Court Office Block N S K Salai, The Forum Vijaya Mall Vadapalani, Chennai, 600 026, Tamil Nadu, India
Tel.: (91) 446 611 1700
Web Site: https://www.isuzu.in
Car Distr
N.A.I.C.S.: 441110
Daya Sankar Viswanath (VP & Mgr-Plant)

Isuzu Motors International Operations (Thailand) Co., Ltd. (1)
1010 Shinawatra Tower III 24th-25th Floor Vibhavadi Rangsit Road, Chatuchak, Bangkok, 10900, Thailand
Tel.: (66) 29662626
Web Site: https://www.imit.co.th
Motor Vehicles Mfr
N.A.I.C.S.: 336110

Isuzu Motors de Mexico S. de R.L. (1)
Paseo de la Reforma 350 Piso 18, Colonia Juarez Federal District, 06600, Mexico, Mexico (49%)
Tel.: (52) 800 644 7898
Web Site: https://www.isuzumex.com.mx
Sales Range: $1-9.9 Million
Emp.: 70
Import & Sales of Trucks
N.A.I.C.S.: 423110
Jun Narahashi (Pres)

Isuzu Sales Deutschland GmbH (1)
Schieferstein 11a, 65439, Florsheim, Germany
Tel.: (49) 6145 549 1100
Web Site: https://www.isuzu-sales.de
Import & Sales of Vehicles
N.A.I.C.S.: 423110

Isuzu UTE Australia Pty. Ltd. (1)
1000 Wynnum Rd, Cannon Hill, 4170, QLD, Australia
Tel.: (61) 1300147898
Web Site: https://www.isuzuute.com.au
Car Distr
N.A.I.C.S.: 441110

Isuzu Warehouse Corporation (1)
470-11 Oaza Yokokurashinden, Oyama, 323-0819, Tochigi, Japan
Tel.: (81) 285 27 3933
Steel Products Mfr
N.A.I.C.S.: 331110

JF Agri Ltd. (1)
152-2 Osaki-cho, Kanoya, 899-7307, Kagoshima, Japan
Tel.: (81) 994763381
Delicious & Safe Ingredient Food Product Mfr
N.A.I.C.S.: 311991

JF Chicken Co., Ltd. (1)
3887 Nosaki-cho, Osaki-cho, Nogata, 899-8313, Kagoshima, Japan
Tel.: (81) 994782211
Delicious & Safe Ingredient Food Product Mfr
N.A.I.C.S.: 311991

JF Foods Co., Ltd. (1)
3949 Kawanishi-Machi, Kanoya, 893-0032, Kagoshima, Japan
Tel.: (81) 994456425
Delicious & Safe Ingredient Food Product Mfr
N.A.I.C.S.: 311991

Japan Facility Solutions, Inc. (1)
17th floor Shin-Osaki Kogyo Building 1-6-4 Osaki, Shinagawa-ku, Tokyo, 141-0032, Japan (35%)
Tel.: (81) 363712500
Web Site: http://www.j-facility.com
Sales Range: $25-49.9 Million
Emp.: 200
Facilities Environmental Management Consulting Services
N.A.I.C.S.: 541620

Japan Space Imaging Corporation (1)
2-2-1 Kyobashi 20th Floor Kyobashi Edogrand, Chuo-Ku, Tokyo, 104-0031, Japan
Tel.: (81) 35 204 2711
Web Site: https://www.jsicorp.jp
Satellite Imagery Product Distribution Services
N.A.I.C.S.: 517410
Koji Ueda (Pres & CEO)

KIBIKASEI CO., LTD. (1)
8-2 Kandakonnyacho, Chiyoda-ku, Tokyo, 101-0035, Japan
Tel.: (81) 368597200
Web Site: https://www.kibikasei.co.jp
Emp.: 58
Adhesive Product Distr
N.A.I.C.S.: 424690

Kewpie Malaysia Sdn. Bhd. (1)
Plot 137-140, Serkam Industrial Estate Merlimau, 77300, Melaka, Malaysia
Tel.: (60) 62636188
Web Site: http://www.kewpie.com.my
Recipe & Sauce Mfr
N.A.I.C.S.: 311941

Kewpie Vietnam Co., Ltd. (1)
11 Vsip II-A Street No 14, Vietnam-Singapore II-A Industrial Park Vinh Tan Ward Tan Uyen District, Ho Chi Minh City, Binh Duong, Vietnam
Tel.: (84) 274 222 0266
Web Site: https://www.kewpie.com.vn
Spice Mfr
N.A.I.C.S.: 311942
Shinji Ono (Gen Dir)

Kohjin Co., Ltd. (1)
8th floor Kokuryu Shibakoen Building 2-6-15 Shibakoen, Minato-ku, Tokyo, 105-0011, Japan
Tel.: (81) 354052720
Web Site: https://www.kohjin.co.jp
Rev.: $382,597,920
Emp.: 665
Synthetic Resin Mfr
N.A.I.C.S.: 325211

Plant (Domestic):

Kohjin Co., Ltd - Saiki Factory (2)
1-6 Higashihama, Saiki, 876-8580, Oita, Japan
Tel.: (81) 97 222 1050
Pharmaceuticals Product Mfr
N.A.I.C.S.: 325412

Kohjin Co., Ltd.- Yatsushiro Factory (2)
1-1 Koukoukumachi, Yatsushiro, 866-8686, Kumamoto, Japan
Tel.: (81) 96 533 9752
Emp.: 200
Chemical Products Mfr
N.A.I.C.S.: 325998

Life Gear Corporation (1)
3rd Floor Ebisu SS Building 3-14 Ebisu, Shibuya-ku, Tokyo, 150-0013, Japan
Tel.: (81) 364325300
Web Site: http://www.lifegear.co.jp
Footwear Distr
N.A.I.C.S.: 458210

Lifetime Partners, Inc. (1)
2-9-11 Akasaka, Minato-ku, Tokyo, 107-0052, Japan
Tel.: (81) 3 5544 0170
Web Site: http://www.ltp.co.jp
Health Care Management Services
N.A.I.C.S.: 621999

MAC Funding Corporation (1)
85 NW Point Blvd, Elk Grove Village, IL 60007
Tel.: (630) 238-5600
Web Site: http://www.mac-funding.com
Financial Investment Services
N.A.I.C.S.: 523999

MC Agri Alliance Ltd. (1)
3-7 Otemachi 1-chome, Chiyoda-ku, Tokyo, 100-1004, Japan
Tel.: (81) 36 212 5121
Web Site: https://www.mc-agrialliance.com
Emp.: 67
Coffee & Edible Nut Mfr
N.A.I.C.S.: 311920
Susumu Isogai (Pres)

MC Autos del Peru S.A. (1)
Av Morro Solar 690, Santiago de Surco, Lima, Peru
Tel.: (51) 2117300
Web Site: http://www.mcautos.com.pe
Car Distr
N.A.I.C.S.: 441110

MC Aviation Partners Inc. (1)
18F Marunouchi Eiraku Building 4-1 Marunouchi 1-Chome, Chiyoda-ku, Tokyo, 100-0005, Japan
Tel.: (81) 3 6273 4933
Web Site: http://www.mcapgroup.com
Sales Range: $50-74.9 Million
Emp.: 64
Aircraft Leasing & Management Services
N.A.I.C.S.: 532411
Earl Sepulveda (Sr VP & Head-Technical Div)

MC Capital Inc. (1)
655 3rd Ave Fl 2, New York, NY 10017
Tel.: (212) 644-1840
Web Site: http://www.mitsubishicorp.com
Sales Range: $50-74.9 Million
Emp.: 10
Commercial Banking Services
N.A.I.C.S.: 522110
Ichiro Miyoshi (CEO)

MC Data Plus, Inc. (1)
7th Floor Ebisu First Square 1-14-14 Ebisu, Shibuya-ku, Tokyo, 150-0013, Japan
Tel.: (81) 364356262
Web Site: https://www.mcdata.co.jp
Emp.: 66
Cloud System Services
N.A.I.C.S.: 541519

MC Elevator (Myanmar) Ltd. (1)
2nd Floor Building No 9 MICT Park Thamine College Street, Hlaing Township, 11051, Yangon, Myanmar
Tel.: (95) 12305229
Elevator & Escalator Mfr
N.A.I.C.S.: 333921

MC Facilities Co., Ltd. (1)
2-1 Marunouchi 2-chome, Chiyoda-ku, Tokyo, 100-0005, Japan
Tel.: (81) 332109502
Web Site: https://www.mcfa.co.jp
Emp.: 126
Facility Management Services
N.A.I.C.S.: 561210

MC Ferticom Co., Ltd. (1)
4th Floor Kojimachi Koyo Building 10 Kojimachi 1-Chome, Chiyoda-ku, Tokyo, 102-0083, Japan
Tel.: (81) 33 263 8530
Web Site: https://www.mcferticom.jp
Emp.: 322
Fertilizer Mfr
N.A.I.C.S.: 325314
Yoshida Masahiro (Asst Gen Mgr)

MC Finance & Consulting Asia Pte. Ltd. (1)
1 Temasek Avenue 15-04 Millenia Tower, Singapore, 039192, Singapore
Tel.: (65) 64344314
Professional Services
N.A.I.C.S.: 541990

MC Machinery Systems, Inc. (1)
85 NW Point Blv, Elk Grove Village, IL 60007
Tel.: (630) 860-4210
Web Site: http://www.mitsubishi-world.com
Sales Range: $75-99.9 Million
Emp.: 150
Industrial Machinery Distr
N.A.I.C.S.: 423830
Bernardo Olguin (Reg Mgr-Sls)

MC Plastics Trading de Mexico SA (1)
Av Central No 211, Parque Industrial Toluca 2000, 50233, Toluca, Estado de Mexico, Mexico
Tel.: (52) 7222766570
Web Site: http://www.mcplasticos.com
Plastic Component Mfr
N.A.I.C.S.: 326199

MC Terminal Co., Ltd. (1)
2-10-1 Yurakucho Tokyo Kotsu Kaikan 5F, Chiyoda-Ku, Tokyo, 100-0006, Japan
Tel.: (81) 352227420
Financial Management Services
N.A.I.C.S.: 523999

MCAP EUROPE LIMITED (1)
46 St Stephens Green, Dublin, Ireland
Tel.: (353) 1 681 4320
Web Site: http://www.mcapgroup.com
Emp.: 9
Aircraft Equipment Leasing & Management Services
N.A.I.C.S.: 532411
Akihiro Miyamoto (Mng Dir)

MCE Bank GmbH (1)
Schieferstein 9, 65439, Florsheim, Germany
Tel.: (49) 6 145 5060
Web Site: https://www.mce-bank.eu
Sales Range: $200-249.9 Million
Emp.: 300
Automobile Financing Services
N.A.I.C.S.: 525990
Horst Sritz (Gen Mgr)

Subsidiary (Domestic):

ISUZU Bank GmbH (2)
Schieferstein 9, 65439, Florsheim, Germany
Tel.: (49) 614554500
Web Site: http://www.isd-bank.de
Vehicle Finance Services
N.A.I.C.S.: 522220

MCX Exploration (USA) Ltd. (1)
800 Gessner Ste 800, Houston, TX 77024-4276
Tel.: (713) 953-9292
Web Site: http://www.mcxusa.com
Sales Range: $50-74.9 Million
Emp.: 18
Oil & Gas Exploration Services
N.A.I.C.S.: 213112
Koji Maeda (Pres)

MMC Car Poland Sp. z o.o. (1)
street Cybernetics 10, 02-677, Warsaw, Poland
Tel.: (48) 224631800
Web Site: https://www.mitsubishi.pl
Automobile Dealers
N.A.I.C.S.: 441110

MPDC Gabon Co. Ltd (1)
3-1 Marunouchi 2-chome, Chiyoda-Ku, Tokyo, 100-0005, Japan (100%)
Tel.: (81) 332103192
Oil Exploration Services

MITSUBISHI CORPORATION

Mitsubishi Corporation—(Continued)
N.A.I.C.S.: 213112

MSK FARM MACHINERY CORPORATION (1)
Fendt 27-12 3 Chome Nishi Ikebukuro, Toshima-Ku, Tokyo, 171-0021, Japan
Tel.: (81) 3 3988 2282
Web Site: http://www.mskfm.co.jp
Agricultural Farm Machinery Distr
N.A.I.C.S.: 423820

Marunouchi Capital Inc. (1)
Kokusai Building 6F 3-1-1 Marunouchi, Chiyoda-ku, Tokyo, 100-0005, Japan
Tel.: (81) 36 212 6400
Web Site: https://www.marunouchi-capital.com
Emp.: 36
Investment Management Service
N.A.I.C.S.: 523940
Haruyasu Asakura (Pres & CEO)

Subsidiary (Domestic):

Nagatanien Holdings Co., Ltd. (2)
2-36-1 Nishi-Shimbashi, Minato-ku, Tokyo, 1058448, Japan **(85.09%)**
Tel.: (81) 334322514
Web Site: https://www.nagatanien-global.com
Rev.: $1,069,146,320
Assets: $935,233,200
Liabilities: $547,394,320
Net Worth: $387,838,880
Earnings: $30,143,520
Emp.: 1,933
Fiscal Year-end: 03/31/2023
Food Product Mfr & Distr
N.A.I.C.S.: 311999

Subsidiary (Non-US):

Chaucer Foods (Qingdao) Co. Limited (3)
8F Bandao International Mansion No 182-8 Haier Road, Qingdao, 266061, China
Tel.: (86) 53283895893
Food & Beverage Mfr
N.A.I.C.S.: 311421

Chaucer Foods Hong Kong Limited (3)
4/F Soho 77 77 Bonham Strand, Sheung Wan, China (Hong Kong)
Tel.: (852) 25441221
Food & Beverage Mfr
N.A.I.C.S.: 311421

Chaucer Foods Limited (3)
Freightliner Road, Hull, HU3 4UN, United Kingdom
Tel.: (44) 1482588088
Web Site: https://www.chaucerfoods.com
Food & Beverage Mfr
N.A.I.C.S.: 311421

Chaucer Foods S.A.S. (3)
110 Route de la Perriere, 49260, Bourgogne, France
Tel.: (33) 241535400
Food & Beverage Mfr
N.A.I.C.S.: 311421

Chaucer Foods UK Limited (3)
Melton Business Park 8 Redcliff Road, Melton, HU14 3RS, Yorkshire, United Kingdom
Tel.: (44) 1482588088
Food & Beverage Mfr
N.A.I.C.S.: 311421

Subsidiary (US):

Crunchies Natural Food Company LLC (3)
15910 Ventura Blvd 530, Encino, CA 91436
Web Site: https://www.crunchiesfood.com
Vegetable & Fruit Distr
N.A.I.C.S.: 424480

Subsidiary (Domestic):

Fujiwara Seimen Co., Ltd. (3)
Hokkaido 9-Jo-Dori 14-Chome Left 10, Asahikawa, 070-0039, Japan
Tel.: (81) 166265485
Web Site: https://www.fujiwara-seimen.co.jp
Emp.: 159
Noodles Mfr & Distr

Muginoho Co., Ltd. (3)
AS Building 2F 3-13-20 Nishitenma, Kita-ku, Osaka, 530-0047, Japan
Tel.: (81) 663617000
Web Site: https://www.muginoho.com
Emp.: 1,880
Shops & Restaurant Operators
N.A.I.C.S.: 722511

Nagatanien Foods Co., Ltd. (3)
2-36-1 Nishi-Shimbashi, Minato-ku, Tokyo, Japan
Tel.: (81) 334323105
Web Site: https://www.nagatanien-foods.co.jp
Food & Beverage Mfr
N.A.I.C.S.: 311421

Sunny Foods Co., Ltd. (3)
3-8-1 Nishi-Shimbashi Second Suzumaru Building 2F, Minato-ku, Tokyo, 105-0003, Japan
Tel.: (81) 357765828
Web Site: https://www.sunny-foods.com
Emp.: 79
Health Food Ingredients Mfr & Distr
N.A.I.C.S.: 311991

Marunouchi Infrastructure Inc. (1)
Hirakawacho Mori Tower 10F 2-1-1 Hirakawacho, Chiyoda-ku, Tokyo, Japan
Tel.: (81) 352124800
Web Site: http://www.marunouchi-infra.co.jp
Infrastructure Fund Services
N.A.I.C.S.: 523940

Meidi-ya Corporation (1)
4-11-7 Toyosu, Koto-ku, Tokyo, 135-0061, Japan
Tel.: (81) 3 3536 5002
Web Site: http://www.meidiya-corp.com
Food Products & Beverages Distr
N.A.I.C.S.: 424420

Metal One Corporation (1)
(60%)
Web Site: http://www.mtlo.co.jp
Sales Range: $200-249.9 Million
Emp.: 103
Iron & Steel Products Mfr & Whslr
N.A.I.C.S.: 331110
Daiju Mita (Exec Officer)

Subsidiary (US):

Alloy Tool Steel, Inc. (2)
13525 E Freeway Dr, Santa Fe Springs, CA 90670-5686
Tel.: (562) 921-8605
Web Site: https://www.alloytoolsteel.com
Sales Range: $25-49.9 Million
Emp.: 20
Mfr of Ferroalloy Tools
N.A.I.C.S.: 423510
Tetsu Watanabe (Pres & CEO)

Subsidiary (Domestic):

M.O.TEC Corporation (2)
Mita Kokusai Building 1-4-28 Mita, Minato-ku, Tokyo, 104-0032, Japan
Tel.: (81) 354457800
Web Site: http://www.motec-co.jp
Sales Range: $350-399.9 Million
Emp.: 290
Sale, Leasing, Processing, Construction & Transportation of Construction Scaffolding Materials
N.A.I.C.S.: 423390

Subsidiary (US):

Maruichi American Corp. (2)
11529 Greenstone Ave, Santa Fe Springs, CA 90670
Tel.: (562) 903-8600
Sales Range: $25-49.9 Million
Emp.: 85
Mfr of Steel Pipe
N.A.I.C.S.: 331210
Shelly Morita (Pres)

Plateplus, Inc. (3)
21 Waterway Ave Ste 525, The Woodlands, TX 77380-3129 **(100%)**
Tel.: (281) 298-0320
Web Site: https://www.plateplus.com
Hot-Rolled Coil, Sheet & Plate Steel Products Mfr & Whslr

N.A.I.C.S.: 332999
James Ralston (Pres & CEO)

Plant (Domestic):

Plateplus, Inc. - Houston (3)
8807 Liberty Rd, Houston, TX 77028-5730
Tel.: (713) 672-4200
Web Site: https://www.plateplus.com
Emp.: 50
Hot-Rolled Coil, Sheet & Plate Steel Products Mfr & Whslr
N.A.I.C.S.: 423510

Subsidiary (Domestic):

Stainless One Corporation (2)
9F NMF Kanda Iwamotocho Building 3-8-16 Iwamotocho, Chiyoda-ku, Tokyo, 101-0032, Japan
Tel.: (81) 3 5833 9671
Web Site: http://www.stnls1.co.jp
Emp.: 58
Stainless Steel Products Distr
N.A.I.C.S.: 423510
Jyun Takao (Pres)

Metal One Holdings America, Inc. (1)
6250 N River Rd, Rosemont, IL 60018-4247
Tel.: (847) 318-0019
Web Site: http://www.metaloneamerica.com
Emp.: 12
Sheet Metal Mfr
N.A.I.C.S.: 332322
Hitoshi Hattori (Pres)

Mitsubishi Australia Ltd. (1)
Level 36 120 Collins Street, Melbourne, 3000, VIC, Australia
Tel.: (61) 300793528
Web Site: http://www.mitsubishicorp.com
Sales Range: $50-74.9 Million
Emp.: 100
Consumer Goods Distr
N.A.I.C.S.: 424990
Hiromasa Yamamoto (CEO & Mng Dir)

Mitsubishi Company (Thailand), Ltd. (1)
968 24th-26th Floor U-Chuliang Foundation Building Rama 4 Road, Silom Bangrak, Bangkok, 10500, Thailand **(100%)**
Tel.: (66) 2 632 4100
Web Site: https://www.mitsubishicorp.com
Rev.: $28,560,000
Sales Range: $41330
Emp.: 230
Aircraft Engine Maintenance
N.A.I.C.S.: 541330
Minoru Furusawa (Gen Mgr)

Mitsubishi Corporation (China) Investment Co., Ltd. (1)
Mitsubishi Corporation Building No 96 Yingchun Road, Pudong New Area, Shanghai, 200127, China **(100%)**
Tel.: (86) 2168543030
Web Site: http://www.mitsubishicorp.com.cn
Sales Range: $200-249.9 Million
Emp.: 400
Investment Services
N.A.I.C.S.: 523940

Mitsubishi Corporation (Hong Kong) Ltd. (1)
15th Floor Tower 1 Admiralty Centre 18 Harcourt Road, Hong Kong, China (Hong Kong) **(100%)**
Tel.: (852) 25294381
Web Site: http://www.mitsubishicorp.com
Sales Range: $75-99.9 Million
Emp.: 120
Trading Services
N.A.I.C.S.: 425120

Mitsubishi Corporation (Korea) Ltd. (1)
22nd Floor State Tower Namsan 100 Toegye-ro, Jung-gu, Seoul, Korea (South)
Tel.: (82) 234555114
Web Site: http://www.mitsubishicorp.com
Sales Range: $50-74.9 Million
Emp.: 80
Trading Services
N.A.I.C.S.: 425120

Mitsubishi Corporation (Shanghai) Ltd. (1)
Mitsubishi Corporation Building No 96 Yingchun Road, Pudong New Area, Shanghai,

INTERNATIONAL PUBLIC

200127, China
Tel.: (86) 2168543030
Mineral Resource Trading Services
N.A.I.C.S.: 213114

Mitsubishi Corporation (Taiwan) Ltd. (1)
14F No 87 Songjiang Road, Taipei, 104, Taiwan **(100%)**
Tel.: (886) 22 507 3456
Web Site: https://www.mitsubishicorp.com
Sales Range: $50-74.9 Million
Emp.: 100
Trading Services
N.A.I.C.S.: 425120
Chiloy Chiang (Mgr)

Mitsubishi Corporation Asset Management Ltd. (1)
Hibiya Parkfront Bldg 7F 1-6 Uchisaiwaicho 2-Chome, Chiyoda-Ku, Tokyo, 100-0011, Japan
Tel.: (81) 365508600
Web Site: http://www.mcasset.com
Emp.: 49
Asset Management Services
N.A.I.C.S.: 523940
Toyota Watanabe (Pres & CEO)

Mitsubishi Corporation Capital Ltd. (1)
2-2-1 Marunouchi Kishimoto Bldg 1F, Chiyoda-Ku, Tokyo, 100-0005, Japan
Tel.: (81) 332184300
Web Site: http://www.mcashet.com
Emp.: 49
Financial Management Services
N.A.I.C.S.: 523999
Ichiro Miyoshi (Pres)

Mitsubishi Corporation Energy Co., Ltd. (1)
12th Floor Ote Center Building 1-1-3 Otemachi, Chiyoda-ku, Tokyo, 100-0004, Japan **(100%)**
Tel.: (81) 34 362 4200
Web Site: https://www.mc-ene.com
Emp.: 300
Petroleum Product Distr
N.A.I.C.S.: 424720
Koichi Minami (Pres & CEO)

Mitsubishi Corporation Financial & Management Services (Japan) Ltd. (1)
Tel.: (81) 332103021
Web Site: http://www.mcfj.co.jp
Sales Range: $200-249.9 Million
Emp.: 44
Financial Management Services
N.A.I.C.S.: 523999

Mitsubishi Corporation International (Europe) Plc. (1)
MidCity Place 71 High Holborn, London, WC1V 6BA, United Kingdom
Tel.: (44) 2070253000
Web Site: https://www.mitsubishicorp.com
Emp.: 150
Business Support Services
N.A.I.C.S.: 561499
Tetsuro Terada (Chm & Mng Dir)

Mitsubishi Corporation LT, Inc. (1)
10-1 Yurakucho 2-chome, Chiyoda-Ku, Tokyo, Japan
Tel.: (81) 36 267 2500
Web Site: https://www.mclogi.jp
Warehousing & Logistics Services
N.A.I.C.S.: 541614
Tatsuya Fujisaku (Pres & CEO)

Subsidiary (Non-US):

Mitsubishi Corporation LT Singapore Pte., Ltd. (2)
1 Temasek Avenue 19-00 Millenia Tower, Singapore, 039192, Singapore
Tel.: (65) 63393375
Transport Logistic Services
N.A.I.C.S.: 488510

Mitsubishi Corporation LT Taiwan Co., Ltd. (2)
2F-3 No 398 Huanbei Rd, Zhongli Dist, Taoyuan, 32070, Taiwan
Tel.: (886) 34259790
Transport Logistic Services
N.A.I.C.S.: 488510

AND PRIVATE COMPANIES

MITSUBISHI CORPORATION

Mitsubishi Corporation Life Sciences Holdings Limited (1)
1-1-3 Yurakucho Tokyo Takarazuka Building 14th Floor, Chiyoda-ku, Tokyo, 100-0006, Japan (100%)
Tel.: (81) 36 891 8060
Web Site: https://www.mclsltd.com
Holding Company
N.A.I.C.S.: 551112
Hiroshi Fujiki *(Pres & CEO)*

Subsidiary (Non-US):

MCLS Asia Co., Ltd. (2)
2 Phang Mung Chaphor 3-4 Road Tambon Huay Pong, Mueang Rayong, Rayong, 21150, Thailand
Tel.: (66) 38918200
Web Site: http://www.mclsasia.com
Savory Ingredient Mfr
N.A.I.C.S.: 311942

Subsidiary (Domestic):

Mitsubishi Corporation Life Sciences Limited (2)
1-1-3 Yurakucho Tokyo Takarazuka Building 14F, Chiyoda-ku, Tokyo, 100-0006, Japan (100%)
Tel.: (81) 36 891 7100
Web Site: https://www.mcls-ltd.com
Emp.: 1,308
Food Ingredient Mfr
N.A.I.C.S.: 311999
Hiroshi Fujiki *(Pres)*

Subsidiary (Domestic):

Mitsubishi Corporation Life Sciences Limited - Fuji Factory (3)
93 Nakagawara, Fuji, 417-0036, Shizuoka, Japan
Tel.: (81) 545526181
Food Products Mfr
N.A.I.C.S.: 311999

Subsidiary (Non-US):

PT. Centram (3)
Desa Carat Kee Gempole, Pasuruan, East Java, Indonesia
Tel.: (62) 343 851441
Food Ingredient Mfr
N.A.I.C.S.: 311999

Mitsubishi Corporation Machinery, Inc. (1)
4th floor Marunouchi 2-chome Building 2-5-1 Marunouchi, Chiyoda-ku, Tokyo, 100-0005, Japan
Tel.: (81) 368657800
Web Site: https://www.mcmachinery.co.jp
Sales Range: $150-199.9 Million
Emp.: 363
Industrial Machinery Parts Distr
N.A.I.C.S.: 423830

Mitsubishi Corporation Power Systems, Inc. (1)
Marunouchi Park Building 6-1 Marunouchi 2-Chome, Chiyoda-ku, Tokyo, 100-8086, Japan
Tel.: (81) 33 210 9300
Web Site: https://www.mcpower.co.jp
Emp.: 73
Power Plant Services
N.A.I.C.S.: 221118
Hisayoshi Nagamori *(Pres & CEO)*

Mitsubishi Corporation RtM (Middle East & Central Asia) (1)
Office 701 Level 7 Precinct Building 4 Dubai International, PO Box 34204, Financial Centre, Dubai, United Arab Emirates
Tel.: (971) 43076800
Metal & Mineral Resource Trading Services
N.A.I.C.S.: 213114

Mitsubishi Corporation RtM International Pte. Ltd. (1)
3 Temasek Avenue 32-01 Centennial Tower, Singapore, 039190, Singapore
Tel.: (65) 6 235 7372
Web Site: https://www.mitsubishicorprtm.com
Mineral Resource Trading Services
N.A.I.C.S.: 213114
Keiichi Shiobara *(Chm & CEO)*

Mitsubishi Corporation RtM Japan Ltd. (1)
7-2 Marunouchi 2-chome, Chiyoda-ku, Tokyo, 100-7027, Japan
Tel.: (81) 352211900
Web Site: http://www.mitsubishicorprtm.com
Rev.: $48,494,880,000
Emp.: 282
Seal Products Distr
N.A.I.C.S.: 423510
Kenichi Udagawa *(Exec Officer)*

Mitsubishi Corporation Technos (1)
Tamachi Station Tower S 13th Floor 1-21 Shibaura 3-Chome, Minato-ku, Tokyo, 108-0023, Japan
Tel.: (81) 334537441
Web Site: https://www.mmts.co.jp
Emp.: 316
Industrial Machinery & Equipment Distr
N.A.I.C.S.: 423830

Mitsubishi Corporation Technos Co., Ltd. (1)
Tamachi Station Tower S 13th Floor 1-21 Shibaura 3-Chome, Tokyo, 108-0023, Japan
Tel.: (81) 334537441
Web Site: https://www.mmts.co.jp
Emp.: 316
Automated Machinery & Equipment Distr
N.A.I.C.S.: 423830
Tomoki Yoda *(Pres)*

Subsidiary (Non-US):

MC Craftsman Machinery Pvt. Ltd. (2)
124 Sangothipalayam Road Arasur Post, Coimbatore, 641407, India
Tel.: (91) 9943988641
Web Site: https://mcmachinery.in
Emp.: 42
Industrial Machine & Machine Tool Mfr
N.A.I.C.S.: 333517
Ananth Iyer *(CEO & Mng Dir)*

MC Machinery Systems Do Brasil Ltda. (2)
Rua Amapa 191-Vila Invernada, Sao Paulo, 03191-160, Brazil
Tel.: (55) 1129663600
Industrial Machine & Machine Tool Mfr
N.A.I.C.S.: 333517

MC Machinery Systems de Mexico S.A. de C.V. (2)
Estatal State Innovation Technology Park 431 km 2 200, Hacienda La Machorra lot 62 nave 1, 76246, El Marques, Queretaro, Mexico
Tel.: (52) 4424286170
Web Site: http://www.mcmachinery.mx
Industrial Machine & Machine Tool Mfr
N.A.I.C.S.: 333517

MC Technos (Thailand) Co., Ltd. (2)
U-Chuliang Building 24th Floor 968 Rama 4 Road, Silom Bangrak, Bangkok, 10500, Thailand
Tel.: (66) 263242457
Web Site: http://www.mctechnos.co.th
Industrial Machine & Machine Tool Mfr
N.A.I.C.S.: 333517

PT. MC Technos Indonesia (2)
Jl Jawa Blok G No 1, Cikarang Barat, Bekasi, 17530, Indonesia
Tel.: (62) 218 998 3916
Web Site: https://www.mctechnos.co.id
Emp.: 10
Machine Tool & Industrial Machinery Whslr
N.A.I.C.S.: 423830
Thomas Tri Widagdo *(Asst Mgr)*

Ryosho Machinery (Shanghai) Co., Ltd. (2)
Room 2801 Innov Tower Block A 1801 HongMei Road, Shanghai, 200233, China
Tel.: (86) 2163513030
Web Site: http://www.ryosho.net.cn
Emp.: 35
Industrial Machine & Machine Tool Mfr
N.A.I.C.S.: 333517

Mitsubishi Corporation Urban Development, Inc. (1)
Yurakucho Denki Building Ninth Floor North 1-7-1 Yurakucho, Chiyoda-ku, Tokyo, 100-0006, Japan
Tel.: (81) 36 212 0610
Web Site: https://www.mcud.co.jp
Property Development Services
N.A.I.C.S.: 531390
Hiroki Itokawa *(Pres & CEO)*

Mitsubishi Development Pty Ltd (1)
Level 16 480 Queen Street, Brisbane, 4000, QLD, Australia
Tel.: (61) 732271000
Web Site: https://www.mdp.com.au
Investment Management Service
N.A.I.C.S.: 523999

Mitsubishi Elevator India Pvt. Ltd. (1)
Plot No 59-63 and 65-71 Vemagal Industrial Area, Shinegehalli Village Vemagal Hobli, Kolar, 563102, Karnataka, India
Tel.: (91) 8046480666
Web Site: https://www.mitsubishielevator.in
Elevator Distr
N.A.I.C.S.: 423830

Mitsubishi Espana S.A. (1)
Torre Picasso Planta 16 Oficina D Plaza Pablo Ruiz Picasso 1, 28020, Madrid, Spain
Tel.: (34) 915983950
Electrical System Mfr
N.A.I.C.S.: 335999

Mitsubishi Heavy Industries Compressor International Corporation (1)
14888 Kirby Dr, Pearland, TX 77047
Tel.: (832) 710-4700
Web Site: https://www.mhi.com
Centrifugal Compressor Mfr
N.A.I.C.S.: 333912

Mitsubishi Imaging (MPM), Inc. (1)
555 Theodore Fremd Ave, Rye, NY 10580
Web Site: https://www.mitsubishiimaging.com
Electronic Equipment Distr
N.A.I.C.S.: 423690

Mitsubishi International Corporation (1)
655 3rd Ave, New York, NY 10017
Tel.: (212) 605-2000
Web Site: http://www.mitsubishicorp.com
Sales Range: $300-349.9 Million
Emp.: 650
All Types of Commodities Exporter & Importer
N.A.I.C.S.: 423510
Jason Stevens *(Pres & CEO)*

Subsidiary (Domestic):

Chemtex International, Inc. (2)
1979 Eastwood Rd, Wilmington, NC 28403-7214 (90%)
Tel.: (910) 509-4400
Web Site: http://www.chemtex.com
Rev.: $100,000,000
Emp.: 100
Technical Engineers & Designers
N.A.I.C.S.: 541715
Pedro Losa *(CEO)*

Subsidiary (Domestic):

Chemtex Overseas, Inc. (3)
1979 Eastwood Rd, Wilmington, NC 28403-7214 (100%)
Tel.: (910) 509-4400
Web Site: http://www.chemtex.com
Engineering Services
N.A.I.C.S.: 541715

Subsidiary (Domestic):

Coil Plus-Illinois Inc. (2)
14023 Coil Plus Dr, Plainfield, IL 60544 (100%)
Tel.: (815) 436-3999
Web Site: https://www.coilplus.com
Sales Range: $25-49.9 Million
Emp.: 65
Processing of Steel Sheets
N.A.I.C.S.: 423510
Pat Soris *(Pres)*

Subsidiary (Non-US):

Mitsubishi Canada Limited (2)
2800-200 Granville Street, Vancouver, V6C 1G6, BC, Canada (100%)
Tel.: (604) 654-8000
Web Site: http://www.mitsubishi.ca
Sales Range: $550-599.9 Million
Emp.: 30
Importer & Exporter of Steel, Machinery, Metals, Food, Grains, Chemicals, Lumber & General Merchandise
N.A.I.C.S.: 325998

Mitsubishi Corporation Operations Limited (2)
71 High Holborn, London, WC1V 6BA, United Kingdom (100%)
Tel.: (44) 2070253286
Web Site: http://www.mitsubishicorp.com
Sales Range: $75-99.9 Million
Emp.: 150
Computer Consultants
N.A.I.C.S.: 425120

Joint Venture (Domestic):

TH Foods, Inc. (2)
2134 Harlem Rd, Loves Park, IL 61111 (50%)
Tel.: (815) 636-9500
Sales Range: $125-149.9 Million
Emp.: 355
Snack Food Mfr
N.A.I.C.S.: 311821

Mitsubishi International Food Ingredients, Inc. (1)
5080 Tuttle Crossing Blvd Ste 400, Dublin, OH 43016
Web Site: https://www.mifiusa.com
Nutritional & Pharmaceutical Product Distr
N.A.I.C.S.: 424210

Mitsubishi International G.m.b.H. (1)
Kennedydamm 19, 40476, Dusseldorf, Germany
Tel.: (49) 21143970
Web Site: https://www.mitsubishicorp.com
Sales Range: $75-99.9 Million
Emp.: 200
Industrial Products & Commodities Distr
N.A.I.C.S.: 423830

Mitsubishi International Polymer Trade Corporation (1)
2 Penn Plz E 11th Fl, Newark, NJ 07105
Tel.: (732) 357-2000
Web Site: http://www.micchem.com
Specialty Chemical & Industrial Resin Mfr
N.A.I.C.S.: 325998
James Bade *(Mgr-Credit & Collections)*

Mitsubishi Kakoki Kaisha, Ltd. (1)
2-1 Ohkawa-cho, Kawasaki-ku, Kawasaki, 210-8560, Kanagawa, Japan
Tel.: (81) 443335354
Web Site: https://www.kakoki.co.jp
Rev.: $315,786,140
Assets: $417,553,700
Liabilities: $188,999,730
Net Worth: $228,553,970
Earnings: $35,674,170
Emp.: 957
Fiscal Year-end: 03/31/2024
Industrial Machinery Mfr & Distr
N.A.I.C.S.: 333310
Toshikazu Tanaka *(Pres)*

Mitsubishi Motors Malaysia Sdn. Bhd. (1)
Level 6 Building A Dataran PHB Saujana Resort Seksyen U2, 40150, Shah Alam, Selangor, Malaysia
Tel.: (60) 376806688
Web Site: https://www.mitsubishi-motors.com.my
Motor Vehicle Distr
N.A.I.C.S.: 423110

Mitsubishi Motors Vietnam Co., Ltd. (1)
An Binh Ward, Di An District, Ho Chi Minh City, Binh Duong, Vietnam
Tel.: (84) 2838962181
Web Site: https://www.mitsubishi-motors.com.vn
Motor Vehicle Distr
N.A.I.C.S.: 423110
Tran Hoang Viet *(Mgr-Dealer Mktg)*

Mitsubishi Ore Transport Co., Ltd. (1)
New-Kokusai Building 5th Floor 3-4-1 Marunouchi, Chiyoda-ku, Tokyo, 100-0005, Japan
Tel.: (81) 33 211 2521

MITSUBISHI CORPORATION

Mitsubishi Corporation—(Continued)
Web Site: https://www.mot-tky.com
Emp.: 42
Marine Transportation Services
N.A.I.C.S.: 488390
Kazuyuki Suzuki (Pres)

Mitsubishi Shoji Agri-Service Corporation (1)
1-10 Sakaimachi 1st Floor Koyocho Koyo Building, Chiyoda-ku, Tokyo, 102-0083, Japan
Tel.: (81) 352755511
Web Site: https://www.mcagri.jp
Fertilizer Raw Material Distr
N.A.I.C.S.: 424910

Mitsubishi Shoji Chemical Corp. (1)
6-1 Kyobashi 1 chome, Chuo-ku, Tokyo, 104-0031, Japan
Tel.: (81) 33 562 8760
Web Site: https://www.mccml.co.jp
Emp.: 193
Chemical Products Distr
N.A.I.C.S.: 424690
Naritaka Maemoto (Sr VP)

Mitsubishi Shoji Construction Materials Corporation (1)
5-33-8 Sendagaya, Shibuya-ku, Tokyo, 151-0051, Japan
Tel.: (81) 3 5360 7211
Web Site: http://www.mckenzai.co.jp
Sales Range: $75-99.9 Million
Emp.: 220
Construction Materials Distr
N.A.I.C.S.: 423320

Mitsubishi Shoji Packaging Corporation (1)
3-10 Nihonbashi 2 chome, Chuo-ku, Tokyo, 103-0027, Japan
Tel.: (81) 3 3243 8200
Web Site: http://www.mcpackaging.co.jp
Rev.: $1,946,160,000
Emp.: 230
Packaging Paperboard Materials Distr
N.A.I.C.S.: 424130
Kimio Okano (Pres & CEO)

Mitsubishi Shoji Plastics Corp. (1)
Marunouchi Trust Tower Main 11F 1-8-3 Marunouchi, Chiyoda-ku, Tokyo, 100-8350, Japan
Tel.: (81) 3 6267 2600
Web Site: http://www.mcplas.co.jp
Rev.: $1,707,480,000
Emp.: 240
Injection Molding Machinery Distr & Rental Services
N.A.I.C.S.: 423830
Fujiko Watanabe (Pres)

Mitsubishi Shokuhin Co., Ltd. (1)
1-1 Koishikawa 1-chome, Bunkyo-ku, Tokyo, 112-8778, Japan
Tel.: (81) 345535111
Web Site: https://www.mitsubishi-shokuhin.com
Rev.: $13,724,878,410
Assets: $5,249,992,500
Liabilities: $3,902,418,410
Net Worth: $1,347,574,090
Earnings: $149,267,020
Emp.: 4,101
Fiscal Year-end: 03/31/2024
General Processed Foods Distr
N.A.I.C.S.: 424420
Toru Moriyama (Pres & CEO)

Subsidiary (Domestic):

Hokuriku Ryoshoku Ltd. (2)
4-6-4 Minato, Kanazawa, 920-0211, Ishikawa, Japan
Tel.: (81) 762672711
Food Product Whslr
N.A.I.C.S.: 424430

Nangoku RS Liquor Ltd. (2)
3337-1 Yamadacho, Kagoshima, Japan
Tel.: (81) 992753400
Sales Range: $25-49.9 Million
Emp.: 30
Alcoholic Beverages Whslr
N.A.I.C.S.: 424820
Toshio Sueta (Pres)

Ryoshoku Liquor Ltd. (2)
6-1-1 Heiwajima, Ota-Ku, Tokyo, 143-6560, Japan
Tel.: (81) 337674810
Web Site: http://www.rsliquor.co.jp
Liquor Whslr
N.A.I.C.S.: 424820

Muji U.S.A. Ltd. (1)
250 W39th St Ste 202, New York, NY 10018
Tel.: (917) 2227000
Web Site: http://www.muji.us
Household Apparel Distr
N.A.I.C.S.: 458110
Akita Toru (CEO)

Nexamp, Inc. (1)
101 Summer St 2nd Fl, Boston, MA 02110
Tel.: (617) 431-1440
Web Site: http://www.nexamp.com
Rev.: $4,795,000
Emp.: 45
Solar Energy Development Solutions
N.A.I.C.S.: 221114
Chris Clark (Chief Dev Officer)

Nikken Corporation Co., Ltd. (1)
Sanno Grand Building 14-2 Nagata-Cho 2-Chome, Chiyoda-Ku, Tokyo, 100-0014, Japan
Tel.: (81) 35 512 7311
Web Site: https://www.rental.co.jp
Emp.: 3,132
Construction Materials Rental Services
N.A.I.C.S.: 532412
Terutora Urano (Exec VP)

Subsidiary (US):

Americ Machinery Corporation (2)
690 Walnut Ave Ste 120, Vallejo, CA 94592
Tel.: (253) 236-8555
Web Site: http://www.americmachinery.com
Heavy Machinery Equipment Rental Services
N.A.I.C.S.: 532412

Subsidiary (Domestic):

Hokushin Kizai Co., Ltd. (2)
2-21-12 Yokogyocho, Mutsu, 035-0033, Aomori, Japan
Tel.: (81) 175228540
Web Site: https://www.hokushinkizai.co.jp
Civil Engineering & Construction Services
N.A.I.C.S.: 238910

Subsidiary (Non-US):

NDT (Thailand) Co., Ltd. (2)
Sovereign Plaza 16th Floor JL TB Simatupang kav 36, Cilandak, Jakarta Selatan, 12430, Indonesia
Tel.: (62) 2129400320
Construction Related Product Rental Services
N.A.I.C.S.: 532412

Subsidiary (Domestic):

NDT Corporation Ltd. (2)
8F Sanno Grand Bldg 14-2 Nagata-cho 2-Chome, Chiyoda-ku, Tokyo, 100-0014, Japan
Tel.: (81) 35 501 4811
Web Site: https://www.ndtcorp.co.jp
Heavy Construction Equipment Whslr
N.A.I.C.S.: 423810
Masashi Shikata (Pres)

NS Service Co., Ltd. (2)
282-1 Okubocho, Ashikaga, 326-0012, Tochigi, Japan
Tel.: (81) 284901650
Web Site: http://www.nss-corp.co.jp
Life Insurance Agency Services
N.A.I.C.S.: 524210

Nikken Real Estate Co., Ltd. (2)
282-1 Okubocho, Ashikaga, 326-0012, Tochigi, Japan
Tel.: (81) 284901235
Web Site: http://www.nf-corp.co.jp
Construction Related Product Rental Services
N.A.I.C.S.: 532412

Nikken Sangyo Co., Ltd. (2)
282-1 Okubocho, Ashikaga, 326-0012, Tochigi, Japan
Tel.: (81) 284901100
Web Site: https://www.ns-corp.co.jp
Emp.: 109
Construction Related Product Rental Services
N.A.I.C.S.: 532412

Seisan Gijyutsu Partners Co., Ltd. (2)
Toranomon Seiwa Building 1-2-3 Toranomon, Minato-ku, Tokyo, 105-0001, Japan
Tel.: (81) 362066441
Web Site: https://www.sg-partners.co.jp
Emp.: 130
Civil Engineering & Construction Services
N.A.I.C.S.: 238910

Ningbo Daling Seafood Processing Co., Ltd. (1)
No 10 Xingyesi Road East Area Of Ningbo Free Trade Zone, Ningbo, 315899, China
Tel.: (86) 57486821725
Agricultural Food Product Distr
N.A.I.C.S.: 424490

Ningbo Ocean Family Food Co., Ltd. (1)
No 812 East Baizhang Road, Yinzhou District, Ningbo, 315000, Zhejiang, China
Tel.: (86) 57487206989
Raw Seafood Product Distr
N.A.I.C.S.: 424460

Ningbo Today Food Co., Ltd. (1)
No 38 Zhongxing East Road, Xikou Fenghua, Ningbo, 315502, China
Tel.: (86) 57488847563
Web Site: https://www.todayfood.com.cn
Canned Meat Product Mfr
N.A.I.C.S.: 311422

Nissin Foods Singapore Pte. Ltd. (1)
1 Senoko Avenue 04-06, Singapore, 758297, Singapore
Tel.: (65) 62652447
Web Site: http://www.nissinfoods.com.sg
Instant Noodle Mfr
N.A.I.C.S.: 311991

Nitto-Fuji Flour Milling Co., Ltd. (1)
1-3-17 Shinkawa, Chuo-ku, Tokyo, 104-0033, Japan
Tel.: (81) 335538781
Web Site: https://www.nittofuji.co.jp
Rev.: $479,872,780
Assets: $424,626,400
Liabilities: $96,268,040
Net Worth: $328,358,360
Earnings: $28,013,180
Emp.: 403
Fiscal Year-end: 03/31/2024
Flour Product Mfr
N.A.I.C.S.: 311211
Yoshihisa Fujita (Pres & Chm)

Subsidiary (Domestic):

Masuda Flour Milling Co., Ltd. (2) (30.71%)
1-1-10 Umegako -cho, Nagata-ku, Kobe, 653-0021, Hyogo, Japan
Tel.: (81) 78 681 6701
Web Site: https://www.masufun.co.jp
Flour Milling Services
N.A.I.C.S.: 311211
Isamu Ito (Pres)

Nitto-Fuji International Vietnam Co., Ltd. (1)
No 49 Vsip Road 8 Vietnam-Singapore Industrial Park, Thuan An Town, Ho Chi Minh City, Binh Duong, Vietnam
Tel.: (84) 2743759074
Web Site: http://www.nittofuji.com.vn
Healthy Food Product Mfr
N.A.I.C.S.: 311999

Nosan Corporation (1)
46th Floor Yokohama Landmark Tower 2-2-1 Minatomirai, Nishi-ku, Yokohama, 220-8146, Kanagawa, Japan
Tel.: (81) 452243700
Web Site: http://www.nosan.co.jp
Sales Range: $100-124.9 Million
Emp.: 500
Food Producer
N.A.I.C.S.: 311230
Koji Okamoto (Pres & CEO)

Ome Isuzu Corporation (1)
3-5-11 Imai, Ome, 198-0023, Tokyo, Japan
Tel.: (81) 428 31 5941
Web Site: http://www.isz.co.jp
Steel Mfrs

INTERNATIONAL PUBLIC

N.A.I.C.S.: 331110

Onahama Petroleum Co., Ltd. (1)
1-1 Otsurugi Shimokawa Izumi -cho, Iwaki, 971-8183, Fukushima, Japan
Tel.: (81) 246564486
Web Site: https://www.onaseki.com
Oil Import & Storage Services
N.A.I.C.S.: 213112

PS Construction Co.,Ltd. (1)
18F Tokyo Shiodome Bldg 1-9-1 Higashi Shimbashi, Minato-ku, Tokyo, 105-7365, Japan
Tel.: (81) 363859342
Web Site: https://www.psc.co.jp
Rev.: $854,633,340
Assets: $807,199,980
Liabilities: $462,356,280
Net Worth: $344,843,700
Earnings: $33,406,940
Emp.: 1,110
Fiscal Year-end: 03/31/2024
Construction Engineering Services
N.A.I.C.S.: 541330
Mitsuo Sakurabayashi (Exec Officer)

PT Aplikasi Karya Anak Bangsa (1)
Web Site: http://www.gojek.com
Transport & Logistic Services
N.A.I.C.S.: 488510

PT Emina Cheese Indonesia (1)
Kawasan Industri Jl Jawa Blok G Desa Gandamekar, Cikarang Barat, Bekasi, 17520, Indonesia
Tel.: (62) 2122143770
Web Site: https://www.eminacheese.com
Cheese Mfr
N.A.I.C.S.: 311513

PT. Atri Distribusindo (1)
Alfa Tower Building 23rd Floor Jl Jalur Sutera Barat Kav, 7-9 Alam Sutera Pinang Kota Tangerang, Banten, 15143, Indonesia
Tel.: (62) 2180821466
Web Site: http://www.atri.co.id
Distribution & Logistic Services
N.A.I.C.S.: 541614

PT. Krama Yudha Tiga Berlian Motors (1)
Jl Jend A Yani Pulomas Project, Jakarta, 13210, Indonesia
Tel.: (62) 214891608
Web Site: https://www.ktbfuso.co.id
Motor Vehicle Distr
N.A.I.C.S.: 423110

PT. Mclogi-Ark Indonesia (1)
KTB Anex Building 5th Floor J1 Jend A Yani Proyek Pulomas, Jakarta Timur, 13210, Indonesia
Tel.: (62) 2122471101
Transport & Logistic Services
N.A.I.C.S.: 488510

PT. Mitsubishi Motors Krama Yudha Sales Indonesia (1)
Jl Jend A Yani Proyek Pulo Mas, Jakarta Timur, 13210, Indonesia
Tel.: (62) 21 475 9000
Web Site: https://www.mitsubishi-motors.co.id
Motor Vehicle Distr
N.A.I.C.S.: 423110
Metta Yunita (Head-Adv)

PT. Nissin Food Indonesia (1)
Jl Jababeka Raya Jababeka Industrial Estate No 1, Wangunharja Kec Cikarang Utara, Bekasi, 17530, Jawa Barat, Indonesia
Tel.: (62) 21 892 4130
Web Site: https://nissinfoods.co.id
Instant Noodle Mfr
N.A.I.C.S.: 311991
Rizal Rusevendi (Mgr-Pur)

Petro-Diamond Singapore (Pte) Ltd. (1)
250 North Bridge Road 11-01 Raffles City Tower, Singapore, 179101, Singapore
Tel.: (65) 63382000
Petroleum Product Distr
N.A.I.C.S.: 424720

Petro-Diamond, Inc. (1)
PO Box 19617, Irvine, CA 92623-9617
Tel.: (949) 553-0112
Web Site: http://www.petrodiamond.com

AND PRIVATE COMPANIES

Sales Range: $25-49.9 Million
Emp.: 50
Petroleum Marketing
N.A.I.C.S.: 424720
Andrew Hausig (Pres)

Philippine Resins Industries, Inc. (1)
Mezzanine Floor BDO Towers Paseo 8741
Paseo de Roxas Bel-Air, Makati, 1209, Philippines
Tel.: (63) 2 810 4956
Web Site: https://www.prii.com.ph
Sales Range: $25-49.9 Million
Emp.: 15
PVC Resin Mfr
N.A.I.C.S.: 325211
Remedios G. Herrera (VP-Fin)

Princes Limited (1)
Royal Liver Building, Pier Head, Liverpool, L3 1NX, United Kingdom
Tel.: (44) 151 966 7000
Web Site: https://www.princes.co.uk
Emp.: 470
Food & Drink Products Mfr & Distr
N.A.I.C.S.: 311999
Graham Breed (Dir-Mktg-Aqua Pura)

Riverina (Australia) Pty., Ltd. (1)
Level 7 303 Coronation Drive, Milton, 4064, QLD, Australia
Tel.: (61) 7 3007 6888
Web Site: http://www.riverina.com.au
Sales Range: $25-49.9 Million
Emp.: 30
Animal Feed Mfr
N.A.I.C.S.: 311119
Michael Greenwood (CFO-Fin & Acct)

SKYPORT SERVICE CORPORATION (1)
International Cargo Warehouse 3 1-2 Centrair, Tokoname, 479-0881, Aichi, Japan
Tel.: (81) 56 938 9700
Web Site: https://www.skyport.co.jp
Sales Range: $25-49.9 Million
Emp.: 26
Airport Ground Handling Services
N.A.I.C.S.: 488119
Eiichi Okamoto (Chm-Mgmt Bd)

San-Esu Inc. (1)
3-2-17 Kahei, Adachi-Ku, Tokyo, 121-8633, Japan
Tel.: (81) 336283333
Web Site: http://www.san-esu.co.jp
Sales Range: $150-199.9 Million
Emp.: 491
Snacks & Confectionery Distr
N.A.I.C.S.: 424450

Sanyo Foods Co., Ltd. (1)
1-1-1 Higashihama, Ichikawa, 272-0003, Chiba, Japan
Tel.: (81) 473290801
Web Site: https://www.sanyo-foods.co.jp
Emp.: 62
Food Products Mfr & Distr
N.A.I.C.S.: 311999

Sesaco Corporation (1)
530 S Main St, Hobart, OK 73651
Tel.: (580) 726-2570
Web Site: https://www.sesaco.com
Convenience Food Distr
N.A.I.C.S.: 445131
Jerry Riney (Gen Mgr-Production Div)

Seto Futo Co., Ltd. (1)
2767-24 Kojimashionasu, Kurashiki, 711-0934, Oka, Japan
Tel.: (81) 864750241
Web Site: https://setofuto.co.jp
Emp.: 69
General Port Transportation Services
N.A.I.C.S.: 483111

Shanghai Daling Food Co., Ltd. (1)
2626-3 Jungong Road, N0 2855 Jungong Road, Shanghai, 200030, China
Tel.: (86) 2154141318
Agricultural Food Product Distr
N.A.I.C.S.: 424490

Sinar Berlian Sdn. Bhd. (1)
Level 18 Tower 3 Petronas Persiaran KLCC, Kuala Lumpur, 50088, Malaysia (100%)
Tel.: (60) 321611255
Sales Range: $50-74.9 Million
Emp.: 80
Trading Services

N.A.I.C.S.: 425120
Kenji Otha (Gen Mgr)

TCV Stevedoring Company, S.A. (1)
Muelle de Levante s/n, Valencia, 46024, Spain
Tel.: (34) 963241680
Port Terminal Services
N.A.I.C.S.: 488310

Thai Kurabo Co., Ltd. (1)
525/1 Moo2 Sukhumvit Road, Bangpoomai Samuthprakarn, Bangkok, 10330, Thailand
Tel.: (66) 232325147
Cotton & Synthetic Yarn Mfr
N.A.I.C.S.: 313110

Thai MC Company Ltd. (1)
968 24th-26th Floor U-Chuliang Foundation Building Rama 4 Road, Silom Bangrak, Bangkok, 10500, Thailand
Tel.: (66) 2 632 4100
Web Site: https://www.mitsubishicorp.com
Sales Range: $50-74,9 Million
Emp.: 200
Industrial Machinery Mfr
N.A.I.C.S.: 333248
Minoru Furusawa (Pres)

The Colt Car Company Ltd. (1)
Watermoor, Cirencester, GL7 1LF, Gloucestershire, United Kingdom
Tel.: (44) 1285655777
Web Site: http://www.mitsubishi-motors.co.uk
Car Retailer
N.A.I.C.S.: 327910
Rob Lindley (Mng Dir)

Toyo Reizo Co., Ltd. (1)
2-37-28 Eitai, Koto-Ku, Tokyo, 135-0034, Japan
Tel.: (81) 3 5620 3200
Web Site: http://www.toyoreizo.com
Sea Food Products Distr
N.A.I.C.S.: 424490

Tredia China Co., Ltd. (1)
Bund Center 8F Office Tower 222 Yan An Rd E, Shanghai, 200002, China
Tel.: (86) 2163350700
Web Site: http://www.tredia.com
Household Apparel Distr
N.A.I.C.S.: 458110

Tredia Fashion Co., Ltd. (1)
Suites1506-09 15/F Tower 1 China Hong Kong City 33 canton Road, Tsim Tsa Tsui, Kowloon, China (Hong Kong)
Tel.: (852) 27393321
Web Site: http://www.tredia.hk
Sales Range: $25-49.9 Million
Emp.: 20
Knitted Fabric Mfr
N.A.I.C.S.: 313240
Shingo Nishida (Pres & Mng Dir)

Tredia Vietnam Co., Ltd. (1)
Saigon Centre 5th Floor 65 Le Loi Boulevard, District 1, Ho Chi Minh City, Vietnam
Tel.: (84) 2838294770
Web Site: http://www.tredia-hcm.com
Emp.: 56
Apparel Garment & Accessory Mfr
N.A.I.C.S.: 315990

Tri Petch Isuzu Leasing Co., Ltd. (1)
1088 Service Center Building 5th Floor Vibhavadi Rangsit Road, Chatuchak, Bangkok, 10900, Thailand
Tel.: (66) 1366
Web Site: https://www.isuzuleasing.com
Emp.: 600
Car Lending Services
N.A.I.C.S.: 532112
Kittima Surattisittikorn (Mgr)

Triland Metals Ltd. (1)
MidCity Place 71 High Holborn, London, WC1V 6BA, United Kingdom
Tel.: (44) 207 061 5612
Web Site: https://www.triland.com
Sales Range: $50-74.9 Million
Emp.: 70
Non Ferrous Metal Sales
N.A.I.C.S.: 423510
Martin Pratt (COO)

Subsidiary (US):

Triland Metals Americas Inc. (2)
151 W 42nd St, New York, NY 10036
Tel.: (646) 434-1300
Web Site: https://www.triland.com
Metal Trading Services
N.A.I.C.S.: 213114

Subsidiary (Non-US):

Triland Metals Singapore Pte. Ltd. (2)
3 Temasek Avenue 33-03 Centennial Tower, Singapore, 039190, Singapore
Tel.: (65) 69227850
Web Site: https://www.triland.com
Metal Trading Services
N.A.I.C.S.: 213114

Triland Metals Tokyo Ltd. (2)
7-2 Marunouchi 2-Chome, Chiyoda-ku, Tokyo, 100-7027, Japan
Tel.: (81) 332872500
Web Site: https://www.triland.com
Metal Trading Services
N.A.I.C.S.: 213114

Triland USA Inc. (1)
655 3rd Ave 2nd Fl, New York, NY 10017
Tel.: (646) 434-1250
Commodity Brokerage Services
N.A.I.C.S.: 523160
Deirdre Anderson (Mgr-Acctg)

Umm Al Houl Power Company (1)
1st Floor Al Emadi Financial Square Building No 2, PO Box 37804, Muntaza Signal C Ring Road, Doha, Qatar
Tel.: (974) 44964300
Web Site: http://www.ummalhoul.net
Electricity Distribution Services
N.A.I.C.S.: 221118

WaterCell Inc. (1)
Higuchi I/H Building 2-11-13 Higuchi, Chuo-ku, Niigata, 950-0911, Japan
Tel.: (81) 252457766
Web Site: https://www.water-cell.jp
Emp.: 32
Agriculture Information & Development Services
N.A.I.C.S.: 926140

Xiamen Daling Seafood Co., Ltd. (1)
No 29 North Donggang Road Xiamen Area of Fujian Free-Trade, Experiment Zone, Xiamen, 361006, China
Tel.: (86) 5925221982
Pre-Packed Food Distr
N.A.I.C.S.: 424420

Xian Daling Seafood Co., Ltd. (1)
No 11 Building Meigui Mansion No 3 Gaioxin Road, High-Tech District, Xi'an, 710077, Shanxi, China
Tel.: (86) 2988210488
Pre-Packed Food Distr
N.A.I.C.S.: 445298

Yokohama Akarenga Inc. (1)
1-1 Shinko, Naka-ku, Yokohama, 231-0001, Kanagawa Prefecture, Japan (51%)
Tel.: (81) 45 211 1515
Web Site: https://www.yokohama-akarenga.jp
Emp.: 19
Commercial Facilities Management Services
N.A.I.C.S.: 531120
Uematsu Seno Hide (Pres & CEO)

Zhejiang North Supreme Seafood Co., Ltd. (1)
No 46 Jianshesan Road Xiaoshan Economic Development Zone, Hangzhou, 311200, China
Tel.: (86) 57182831933
Aquatic Product Distr
N.A.I.C.S.: 445298

Zhoushan Daling Seafood Co., Ltd. (1)
No 770 Haiyin Road, Donggang Sub-District Putuo District, Zhoushan, 316000, Zhejiang, China
Tel.: (86) 5803063066
Pre-Packed Food Distr
N.A.I.C.S.: 445298

MITSUBISHI ELECTRIC CORPORATION

Tokyo Building 2-7-3 Marunouchi, Chiyoda-ku, Tokyo, 100-8310, Japan
Tel.: (81) 332182111   JP
Web Site: https://www.mitsubishielectric.com
Year Founded: 1921
6503—(TKS)
Rev.: $34,754,811,540
Assets: $40,766,117,400
Liabilities: $15,209,094,420
Net Worth: $25,557,022,980
Earnings: $1,883,512,890
Emp.: 149,134
Fiscal Year-end: 03/31/24
Semiconductor Product Mfr
N.A.I.C.S.: 334413
Kei Uruma (Pres & CEO)

Subsidiaries:

AG Melco Elevator Co. L.L.C. (1)
Dubai Municipality Building 1st Floor, PO Box 11058, Adjacent to Muraqqabat Police Station Deira, Dubai, United Arab Emirates
Tel.: (971) 42795000
Web Site: http://www.agmelco.com
Emp.: 3,000
Elevator Mfr & Distr
N.A.I.C.S.: 333921
M. Kalimullah (CEO)

DB Seiko Co., Ltd. (1)
Mizoguchi 1127, Himeji, 679-2161, Hyogo, Japan
Tel.: (81) 792321245
Web Site: http://www.dbseiko.co.jp
Emp.: 1,090
Engine Electrical Equipment Mfr
N.A.I.C.S.: 336320
Michiyasu Nampo (Pres)

DeLclima S.p.A. (1)
Via Lodovico Seitz 47, 31100, Treviso, TV, Italy
Tel.: (39) 0422 413023
Web Site: http://www.del-clima.com
Industrial Refrigeration Equipment Mfr
N.A.I.C.S.: 333415
Carlo Grossi (Vice Chm & Mng Dir)

Subsidiary (Domestic):

Climaveneta S.p.A. (2)
Via Caduti di Cefalonia 1, 36061, Bassano del Grappa, VI, Italy
Tel.: (39) 0424 509 500
Web Site: http://www.in.climaveneta.com
Industrial Refrigeration Equipment Mfr
N.A.I.C.S.: 333415
Maurizio Marchesini (Mng Dir)

Subsidiary (Non-US):

Climaveneta Deutschland GmbH (3)
Mitsubishi-Electric-Platz 1, 40882, Ratingen, Germany (100%)
Tel.: (49) 2102 486 8710
Web Site: http://de.climaveneta.com
Industrial Refrigeration Equipment Distr
N.A.I.C.S.: 423740
Martin Altenbokum (Mng Dir)

Climaveneta France (3)
Mitsubishi Electric 2 rue de l'Union, 92565, Rueil-Malmaison, Cedex, France
Tel.: (33) 155685568
Web Site: https://fr.climaveneta.com
Industrial Refrigeration Equipment Distr
N.A.I.C.S.: 423740

Climaveneta Polska Sp. z o.o. (3)
ul Sienkiewicza 13A, 05-120, Legionowo, Poland
Tel.: (48) 22 766 34 55
Web Site: http://pl.climaveneta.com
Industrial Refrigeration Equipment Distr
N.A.I.C.S.: 423740

Subsidiary (Domestic):

RC Group S.p.A (2)
via Roma 5, Valle Salimbene, 27010, Pavia, Italy
Tel.: (39) 0 382 433 811
Web Site: http://www.rcgroup.it
Industrial Refrigeration Equipment Mfr
N.A.I.C.S.: 333415
Fabio Silini (Mgr-IT)

MITSUBISHI ELECTRIC CORPORATION

Mitsubishi Electric Corporation—(Continued)

Subsidiary (Non-US):

Topclima - Climaveneta Spain (2)
c Londres n 67, 08036, Barcelona, Spain
Tel.: (34) 934195600
Web Site: http://es.climaveneta.com
Emp.: 60
Industrial Refrigeration Equipment Distr
N.A.I.C.S.: 423740

Hitachi Mitsubishi Hydro Corporation (1)
Tamachi Nikko Bldg 29-14 Shiba 5-chome, Minato-ku, Tokyo, 108-0014, Japan
Tel.: (81) 337698005
Web Site: http://www.hm-hydro.com
Emp.: 450
Eletric Power Generation Services
N.A.I.C.S.: 221118
Susumu Amakasu *(Pres)*

ICONICS, Inc. (1)
100 Foxborough Blvd, Foxborough, MA 02035
Tel.: (508) 543-8600
Web Site: http://www.iconics.com
Computer Software Publisher
N.A.I.C.S.: 513210
Mark Hepburn *(Sr VP-Worldwide Sls)*

Internacional de Elevadores, S.A. de C.V.
Km 20 6 Carretera Libre Tiajuana-Ensenada, Rosarito, 22710, Baja Cfa, Mexico **(100%)**
Tel.: (52) 6616120080
Web Site: http://www.mitsubishielectric.com
Sales Range: $75-99.9 Million
Emp.: 140
Holding Company
N.A.I.C.S.: 551112
Ramon Aguilar *(Mgr-Production)*

Iplanet Inc. (1)
1-1-1 Minami-Aoyama Shin-Aoyama Building West Building, Minato-ku, Tokyo, 107-8619, Japan
Tel.: (81) 334753151
Web Site: https://www.iplanet-inc.com
Emp.: 461
Strategic Planning & Management Services
N.A.I.C.S.: 541611

Kang Yong Electric Public Company Limited (1)
67 Moo 11 Bangna-Trad K M 20 Bangplee, Samut Prakan, 10540, Thailand **(41.15%)**
Tel.: (66) 23372900
Web Site: http://www.mitsubishi-kye.com
Rev.: $251,898,128
Assets: $277,210,349
Liabilities: $50,190,633
Net Worth: $227,019,715
Earnings: $4,586,362
Emp.: 2,005
Fiscal Year-end: 03/31/2022
Electrical Products Mfr
N.A.I.C.S.: 335999
Praphad Phodhivorakhun *(Chm)*

Melco Display Technology Inc. (1)
1576-1 Sumiyoshi Shisuimachi, Kikuchi, 861-1203, Kumamoto, Japan
Tel.: (81) 968386900
Web Site: https://www.mitsubishi.com
Computer Peripheral Equipment Mfr
N.A.I.C.S.: 334118

Melco Power Device Corporation (1)
216 Hikamicho Sajiki, Tanba, 669-3652, Hyogo Prefecture, Japan
Tel.: (81) 795826855
Web Site:
https://www.melcopowerdevice.co.jp
Emp.: 1,164
Electric Semiconductor Product Mfr
N.A.I.C.S.: 334413

Melco Semiconductor Engineering Corporation (1)
1-1-1 Imajuku Higashi, Nishi-ku, Fukuoka, 819-0192, Japan
Tel.: (81) 928053802
Web Site: http://www.msec-melco.co.jp
Electric Semiconductor Product Mfr
N.A.I.C.S.: 334413

Meldas System Engineering Corporation (1)

1-19-30 Aoi, Higashi-Ku, Nagoya, 461-0004, Aichi, Japan
Tel.: (81) 529795311
Web Site: https://www.memt.co.jp
Sales Range: $50-74.9 Million
Emp.: 148
Industrial Automation Products Mfr
N.A.I.C.S.: 333998
Shotaro Fukuda *(Pres)*

Mitsubishi Electric & Electronics (Shanghai) Co., Ltd. (1)
29th Floor Shanghai Maxdo Center No 8 Xing Yi Road, Chang Ning, Shanghai, 200336, China
Tel.: (86) 2152082030
Semiconductor & Electronic Device Mfr
N.A.I.C.S.: 334413

Mitsubishi Electric & Electronics USA, Inc. (1)
5900-A Katella Ave, Cypress, CA 90630 **(100%)**
Tel.: (714) 220-2500
Web Site: http://us.mitsubishielectric.com
Sales Range: $1-4.9 Billion
Emp.: 4,000
Holding Company; Operation & Exporting Electric & Electronic Parts
N.A.I.C.S.: 423690
Bruce Brenizer *(VP-HR)*

Subsidiary (Domestic):

Mitsubishi Digital Electronics America, Inc. (2)
9351 Jeronimo Rd, Irvine, CA 92618-1904
Tel.: (949) 465-6000
Web Site: http://www.mitsubishi-tv.com
Sales Range: $100-124.9 Million
Emp.: 360
Upgradeable Projection Televisions, VCRs & Audio Products for Complete Home Theater Systems Mfr
N.A.I.C.S.: 334310

Mitsubishi Electric Automation, Inc. (2)
500 Corporate Woods Pkwy, Vernon Hills, IL 60061-3108
Tel.: (847) 478-2100
Web Site: http://www.meau.com
Sales Range: $50-74.9 Million
Emp.: 200
Automation Equipment Mfr
N.A.I.C.S.: 333998
Scott Rohlfs *(Sr Dir-Bus Dev)*

Unit (Domestic):

Mitsubishi Electric Automation, Inc. - Industrial Sewing Equipment (3)
1000 Nolen Dr Ste 200, Grapevine, TX 76051
Tel.: (817) 416-9767
Sales Range: $1-9.9 Million
Emp.: 15
Industrial Machinery & Equipment Merchant Whslr
N.A.I.C.S.: 423830
Barry Spruell *(Mgr-Svc)*

Subsidiary (Domestic):

Mitsubishi Electric Automotive America, Inc. (2)
Starter/Alternator Manufacturing HQ 4773 Bethany Rd, Mason, OH 45040-8344 **(100%)**
Tel.: (513) 398-2220
Web Site: http://www.meaa-mea.com
Sales Range: $100-124.9 Million
Emp.: 400
Mfr & Sale of Electronic & Automotive Parts
N.A.I.C.S.: 336320

Mitsubishi Electric Finance America, Inc. (2)
5900-A Katella Ave, Cypress, CA 90630
Tel.: (714) 220-2500
Sales Range: $50-74.9 Million
Emp.: 2
Cash Management & Financial Services for Affiliated Mitsubishi Companies
N.A.I.C.S.: 522291
Takamasa Hirai *(Pres)*

Mitsubishi Electric Research Laboratories (2)

201 Broadway 8th Fl, Cambridge, MA 02139-1955
Tel.: (617) 621-7500
Web Site: http://www.merl.com
Sales Range: $500-549.9 Million
Emp.: 80
Provider of Research & Development
N.A.I.C.S.: 541715
Richard C. Waters *(Pres & CEO)*

Mitsubishi Electric Visual Solutions America, Inc. (2)
9351 Jeronimo Rd, Irvine, CA 92618
Tel.: (949) 465-6000
Web Site: http://www.mevsa.com
Display Products Mfr & Distr
N.A.I.C.S.: 334413
Vigil White *(Mgr-Consumer Rels)*

NEC-Mitsubishi Electronics (2)
3250 Lacey Rd Ste 500, Downers Grove, IL 60515
Tel.: (630) 467-3000
Web Site: http://www.necdisplay.com
Computer Terminals, Monitors & Components Mfr
N.A.I.C.S.: 334118

Affiliate (Domestic):

Powerex Inc. (2)
173 Pavillion Ln, Youngwood, PA 15697-1806
Tel.: (724) 925-7272
Web Site: http://www.pwrx.com
Sales Range: $25-49.9 Million
Emp.: 250
Mfr of Power Semiconductors, Rectifiers, Thyristors, Bipolar Power Transistors
N.A.I.C.S.: 334413

Mitsubishi Electric (H.K.) Ltd. (1)
20/F 1111 King's Road, Taikoo Shing, China (Hong Kong)
Tel.: (852) 2510 0555
Web Site: http://hk.mitsubishielectric.com
Electronic Component Mfr & Distr
N.A.I.C.S.: 334419

Mitsubishi Electric (Malaysia) Sdn. Bhd. (1)
Plo 32 Kawasan Perindustrian, 81400, Senai, Johor, Malaysia
Tel.: (60) 75996062
Emp.: 558
Printer & Video Copy Processor Mfr & Distr
N.A.I.C.S.: 334118
Higuchi Takashi *(Mng Dir)*

Mitsubishi Electric Air Conditioning & Refrigeration Systems Co., Ltd. (1)
Tel.: (81) 364041020
Web Site: http://www.mitsubishi.com
Emp.: 300
Air Conditioning Equipment Mfr & Distr
N.A.I.C.S.: 333415

Subsidiary (Domestic):

Mitsubishi Electric Air Conditioning & Refrigeration Equipment Sales Co., Ltd. (2)
2-15-9 Uchikanda Uchikanda282 Bldg, Chiyoda-Ku, Tokyo, 101-0047, Japan
Tel.: (81) 3 3258 0211
Air Conditioning Equipment Distr
N.A.I.C.S.: 423730

Mitsubishi Electric Air Conditioning Systems Europe Ltd. (1)
Nettlehill Road, Houstoun Industrial Estate, Livingston, EH54 5EQ, United Kingdom
Tel.: (44) 1506445500
Sales Range: $200-249.9 Million
Emp.: 54
Air Conditioning Equipment Mfr
N.A.I.C.S.: 333415
Atsuhiro Yabu *(Pres)*

Mitsubishi Electric Asia Pte. Ltd. (1)
307 Alexandra Road Mitsubishi Electric Building, Singapore, 159943, Singapore
Tel.: (65) 6473 2308
Web Site:
http://www.mitsubishielectric.com.sg
Emp.: 20
Household Electronic Appliance Mfr
N.A.I.C.S.: 335220

Mitsubishi Electric Australia Pty. Ltd. (1)

348 Victoria Road, Rydalmere, 2116, NSW, Australia
Tel.: (61) 296847777
Web Site:
http://www.mitsubishielectric.com.au
Electronic Product Mfr & Distr
N.A.I.C.S.: 335999

Mitsubishi Electric Automation (China) Ltd. (1)
Mitsubishi Electric Automation Center 1386 Hongqiao Road, Changning District, Shanghai, 200336, China
Tel.: (86) 2123223030
Web Site: http://www.mitsubishielectric-fa.cn
Electrical Product Whslr
N.A.I.C.S.: 423610

Mitsubishi Electric Automation (Hong Kong) Ltd. (1)
10th Floor Manulife Tower 169 Electric Road North Point, Chang Ning Zone, Shanghai, China
Tel.: (86) 28878870
Web Site: http://www.meah.com.hk
Emp.: 30
Industrial Machinery Whslr
N.A.I.C.S.: 423830

Mitsubishi Electric Automation (Thailand) Co., Ltd. (1)
Bang-Chan Industrial Estate 111 Soi Serithai 54 T Kannayao, A Kannayao, Bangkok, 10230, Thailand
Tel.: (66) 2 517 1326
Web Site: https://www.meath-co.com
Emp.: 2,400
Motor & Electricity Monitoring Equipment Mfr
N.A.I.C.S.: 335999
Somchin Leelaket *(Chm, Pres & Dir-Sls & Admin)*

Mitsubishi Electric Automation Korea Co., Ltd. (1)
7F to 9F Gangseo Hangang Xi-tower A 401, Yangcheon-ro Gangseo-Gu, Seoul, 157-200, Korea (South)
Tel.: (82) 261039460
Web Site: https://kr.mitsubishielectric.com
Sales Range: $50-74.9 Million
Emp.: 12
Factory Automation Equipment Mfr
N.A.I.C.S.: 333998
Se Woong Oh *(Gen Mgr)*

Mitsubishi Electric Automotive (China) Co., Ltd. (1)
No 88 Lushan Road, New and Hi-tech Industrial Development Zone, Changshu, 215500, Jiangsu, China
Tel.: (86) 51252133030
Electric Power Steering Equipment Mfr & Distr
N.A.I.C.S.: 336390

Mitsubishi Electric Automotive Czech s.r.o. (1)
Politickych Veznu 1564, 274 01, Slany, Czech Republic
Tel.: (420) 31 250 0111
Web Site: https://www.mitsubishielectric.cz
Emp.: 750
Electrical Rotating & Automotive Electronic Component Mfr & Whslr
N.A.I.C.S.: 336320
Shigeru Shiroyama *(Pres)*

Plant (Domestic):

Mitsubishi Electric Automotive Czech s.r.o. - Automation Factory (2)
Polityckyhch Veznu 1516, 158 00, Slany, Czech Republic
Tel.: (420) 251551470
Emp.: 300
Automotive Electronic Component Mfr
N.A.I.C.S.: 336320
Shijeru Shiroyama *(Pres)*

Mitsubishi Electric Automotive India Pvt. Ltd. (1)
167-170 Sector 5 IMT Manesar, Gurgaon, 122050, Haryana, India
Tel.: (91) 1242290123
Sales Range: $125-149.9 Million
Emp.: 40
Automotive Electronic Equipment Mfr & Whslr

MITSUBISHI ELECTRIC CORPORATION

N.A.I.C.S.: 336320
Yoshito Inaya *(Mng Dir)*

Mitsubishi Electric Business Systems Co., Ltd (1)
1-32-2 Honmachi Harmony Tower 16th 25th 26th floors, Nakano-ku, Tokyo, 164-0012, Japan
Tel.: (81) 353090600
Web Site: https://www.mdsol.co.jp
Emp.: 1,006
Electronic Parts & Equipment Distr
N.A.I.C.S.: 423690

Mitsubishi Electric Consumer Products (Thailand) Co., Ltd. (1)
700/406 Amata City Moo 7 Tambon Don Hua Roh, Chonburi Industrial Estate, Amphur Muang, 20000, Chonburi, Thailand
Tel.: (66) 38265800
Web Site: https://th.mitsubishielectric.com
Electronic Product Mfr & Distr
N.A.I.C.S.: 335999
Yasumasa Yamane *(Pres & Mng Dir)*

Mitsubishi Electric Control Software Corporation (1)
6-1-2 Hamayama-dori, Kobe, 652-0871, Hyogo, Japan
Tel.: (81) 78 651 7361
Electrical Software Development Services
N.A.I.C.S.: 541511

Mitsubishi Electric Dalian Industrial Products Co., Ltd. (1)
Dongbei 3-5 Dalian Economic & Technical Development Zone, Dalian, 116600, Liaoning, China
Tel.: (86) 41187613072
Web Site: http://www.mdidl.com
Sales Range: $200-249.9 Million
Emp.: 1,000
Machine Tools Mfr
N.A.I.C.S.: 333517

Mitsubishi Electric Engineering Co., Ltd. (1)
Hulic Kudan Building 1-13-5 Kudankita, Chiyoda-ku, Tokyo, 102-0073, Japan
Tel.: (81) 332881101
Web Site: https://www.mee.co.jp
Emp.: 5,459
Electronic Power Conditioner Mfr & Whslr
N.A.I.C.S.: 334419

Mitsubishi Electric Europe B.V. (1)
Harman House George Street, Uxbridge, UB8 1QQ, Middlesex, United Kingdom (100%)
Tel.: (44) 1895276600
Web Site: https://emea.mitsubishielectric.com
Sales Range: $25-49.9 Million
Emp.: 30
Holding Company; Importer & Distr of Electric & Electronic Consumer Goods & Office Products
N.A.I.C.S.: 551112
Kei Uruma *(Pres & CEO)*

Mitsubishi Electric Finance Europe PLC (1)
Harman House George Street, Uxbridge, UB8 1QQ, Middlesex, United Kingdom
Tel.: (44) 189 527 6600
Web Site: https://gb.mitsubishielectric.com
Sales Range: $50-74.9 Million
Emp.: 36
Trade Financing Services
N.A.I.C.S.: 522299
Hirouyuki Omoda *(Pres)*

Mitsubishi Electric Home Appliance Co., Ltd. (1)
1728-1 Omaeda, Fukaya, 369-1295, Saitama, Japan
Tel.: (81) 485841231
Web Site: http://www.mitsubishi.com
Emp.: 1,000
Household Appliances Mfr & Distr
N.A.I.C.S.: 335220

Mitsubishi Electric Hong Kong Group Ltd. (1)
24 City Plaza 1 1111 Kings Road Tai Koo Shing, Hong Kong, China (Hong Kong)
Tel.: (852) 2887 8870
Web Site: http://www.mehkg.com
Escalator Distr

N.A.I.C.S.: 423830

Mitsubishi Electric India Pvt. Ltd. (1)
3rd Floor Tower A Global Gateway MG Road, Gurgaon, 122 002, Haryana, India
Tel.: (91) 124 673 9300
Web Site: https://www.mitsubishielectric.in
Sales Range: $75-99.9 Million
Emp.: 130
Electrical & Electronic Equipment Distr
N.A.I.C.S.: 423620
Rajeev Sharma *(Head-Corp Svcs & Strategic Plng)*

Mitsubishi Electric Information Network Corporation (1)
Tamachi First Building 4-6-8 Shibaura, Minato-ku, Tokyo, 108-0023, Japan
Tel.: (81) 36 414 8000
Web Site: https://www.mind.co.jp
Emp.: 3,391
Telecommunication Software Development Services
N.A.I.C.S.: 541511
Takeo Ikeda *(Pres)*

Mitsubishi Electric Information Systems Corporation (1)
MS Shibaura Building 4-13-23 Shibaura, Minato-ku, Tokyo, 108-0023, Japan
Tel.: (81) 354457504
Web Site: https://www.mdis.co.jp
Emp.: 1,247
Information Technology Services
N.A.I.C.S.: 541511

Mitsubishi Electric Kang Yong Watana Co., Ltd. (1)
28 Krungthep Kreetha Rd, Hua mak Bangkapi, Bangkok, 10240, Thailand
Tel.: (66) 27637000
Web Site: https://www.mitsubishi-kyw.co.th
Air Conditioning System & Consumer Electronics Whslr
N.A.I.C.S.: 532210

Subsidiary (Domestic):

MELCO Trading (Thailand) Co., Ltd. (2)
No 1 MD Tower 21st Floor Room C3 E F Soi Bangna-Trad 25 Debaratna Road, Bangna Nuea, Bangkok, 10260, Thailand (51%)
Tel.: (66) 23618070
Sales Range: $25-49.9 Million
Emp.: 66
Electronic & Electric Component Whslr
N.A.I.C.S.: 423690
Kimiya Goto *(Mng Dir)*

Mitsubishi Electric Life Network Co., Ltd. (1)
Tokyo Fashion Town Bldg Higashi-Kan 7f, Koto-Ku, Tokyo, 135-0063, Japan
Tel.: (81) 335706811
Household Electrical Appliances Distr
N.A.I.C.S.: 423620

Mitsubishi Electric Life Service Corporation (1)
7th floor Shiba Park Building B 2-4-1 Shiba Koen, Minato-ku, Tokyo, 105-0011, Japan
Tel.: (81) 364026001
Web Site: https://www.mdlife.co.jp
Emp.: 3,791
Real Estate Manangement Services
N.A.I.C.S.: 531390

Mitsubishi Electric Lighting Co., Ltd. (1)
2-14-4 ofuna, Kamakura, 247-0056, Kanagawa, Japan
Tel.: (81) 467412701
Web Site: https://www.mitsubishi.com
Sales Range: $125-149.9 Million
Emp.: 50
Lighting Fixture Mfr & Whslr
N.A.I.C.S.: 335139
Mori Toru *(Office Mgr)*

Mitsubishi Electric Micro-Computer Application Software Co., Ltd. (1)
2-5-1 Inadera, Amagasaki, 661-0981, Hyogo, Japan
Tel.: (81) 6 6494 5061
Web Site: http://www.mms.co.jp
Sales Range: $150-199.9 Million
Emp.: 779

Communication Software Development Services & Electrical Machinery Mfr
N.A.I.C.S.: 541511
Yasushi Tagami *(Pres)*

Mitsubishi Electric Plant Engineering Corporation (1)
5-24-8 Higashiueno Sumitomo Real Estate Ueno Building No 6, Taito-ku, Tokyo, 110-0015, Japan
Tel.: (81) 358276311
Web Site: http://www.mpec.co.jp
Emp.: 2,664
Expanded Infrastructure-Related Business Services
N.A.I.C.S.: 541330

Mitsubishi Electric Ryoden Air-Conditioning & Visual Information Systems (Hong Kong) Ltd. (1)
9/F Skyline Tower 39 Wang Kwong Road, Kowloon Bay, Kowloon, China (Hong Kong)
Tel.: (852) 2510 1505
Web Site: http://www.mitsubishi-ryoden.com.hk
Sales Range: $50-74.9 Million
Emp.: 90
Projector & Air Conditioning Equipment Distr
N.A.I.C.S.: 423690
Markus Krenzlin *(Mng Dir)*

Mitsubishi Electric Sales Canada, Inc. (1)
8061 Lougheed Highway Unit 120, Burnaby, V5A 1W9, BC, Canada (100%)
Tel.: (604) 415-6487
Web Site: http://www.mitsubishielectric.ca
Sales Range: $25-49.9 Million
Emp.: 50
Distribution & Sales of Electronic Products
N.A.I.C.S.: 334419

Mitsubishi Electric System & Service Co., Ltd. (1)
20F Carrot Tower 4-1-1 Taishido, Setagaya-ku, Tokyo, 154-8520, Japan
Tel.: (81) 354317750
Web Site: https://www.melsc.co.jp
Emp.: 2,012
Electrical Software Development Services & Equipment Mfr
N.A.I.C.S.: 541511

Mitsubishi Electric TOKKI Systems Corporation (1)
1-15-9 Osaki, Shinagawa-ku, Tokyo, 141-0032, Japan
Tel.: (81) 357459141
Web Site: https://www.medstec.co.jp
Emp.: 1,150
Electrical Component Mfr
N.A.I.C.S.: 335999

Mitsubishi Electric Taiwan Co., Ltd. (1)
11th Floor No 90 Sec 6 Chung Shan N Road, Taipei, 111, Taiwan
Tel.: (886) 228319357
Web Site: https://tw.mitsubishielectric.com
Sales Range: $50-74.9 Million
Emp.: 150
Electronic Components Distr
N.A.I.C.S.: 423690

Mitsubishi Electric Thai Auto-Parts Co., Ltd. (1)
Siam Eastern Industrial Park 60/16 Moo 3 T Mabyangporn A, Pluak Daeng, 21140, Rayong, Thailand
Tel.: (66) 3889123441
Web Site: http://www.meta.co.th
Sales Range: $25-49.9 Million
Emp.: 5
Automotive Electronic Equipment Mfr & Distr
N.A.I.C.S.: 336320

Mitsubishi Electric Trading Corporation (1)
Meiji-Seimei-kan 3F 1-1 Marunouchi 2-chome, Chiyoda-ku, Tokyo, 100-0005, Japan
Tel.: (81) 35 220 7301
Web Site: https://www.melco-trading.net
Emp.: 748
Electrical & Electronic Equipment Mfr & Whslr
N.A.I.C.S.: 335999

Kenji Nishimura *(Pres)*

Mitsubishi Electric Vietnam Company Limited (1)
11th 12th Floor Tower B Viettel Building 285 Cach Mang Thang 8 Street, Ward 12 District 10, Ho Chi Minh City, Vietnam
Tel.: (84) 839105945
Web Site: https://www.mitsubishi-electric.vn
Sales Range: $25-49.9 Million
Emp.: 5
Household Appliance Distr
N.A.I.C.S.: 423620
Takashi Egawa *(Mng Dir)*

Mitsubishi Electric de Mexico S.A. de C.V. (1)
Mariano Escobedo No 69, Industrial Zone, 54030, Tlalnepantla, Mexico
Tel.: (52) 5591717600
Web Site: https://melmex.mx
Sales Range: $25-49.9 Million
Emp.: 100
Elevators, Escalators & Electrical Railroad Equipment Mfr & Distr
N.A.I.C.S.: 333921

Plant (Domestic):

Mitsubishi Electric de Mexico S.A. de C.V. - San Juan Del Rio Factory (2)
Km 4 Carretera, Tequisquiapan, San Juan del Rio, 54030, Edo de Queretaro, Mexico
Tel.: (52) 427 272 1045
Web Site: http://www.mitsubishielectric.com
Electrical Transportation Equipment Mr
N.A.I.C.S.: 336320

Mitsubishi Elevator (Singapore) Pte Ltd (1)
No 11 Kaki Bukit Crescent Kaki Bukit Techpark 1, Singapore, 416241, Singapore
Tel.: (65) 68425678
Elevator Installation Services & Distr
N.A.I.C.S.: 238290
Kaori Takahashi *(Mng Dir)*

Mitsubishi Elevator (Thailand) Co., Ltd. (1)
9th - 10th 12th Fl Bangna Towers A 2/3 Moo 14 Debaratna Road, Bangkaew, Bang Phli, 10540, Samutprakarn, Thailand
Tel.: (66) 23120707
Web Site: http://www.mitsubishielevator.co.th
Sales Range: $250-299.9 Million
Emp.: 1,000
Elevator & Escalator Distr
N.A.I.C.S.: 423830

Mitsubishi Elevator Asia Co., Ltd. (1)
700/86 Amata Nakorn Industrial Estate Moo 6 Bangna-Trad Rd, Tambon Don Hua Roh Muang District, Chon Buri, 20000, Thailand
Tel.: (66) 38213170
Elevator & Escalator Mfr
N.A.I.C.S.: 333921

Mitsubishi Elevator Europe B.V. (1)
Schietboom 20, 3905 TD, Veenendaal, Netherlands
Tel.: (31) 318586586
Web Site: https://www.mitsubishi-elevators.com
Sales Range: $25-49.9 Million
Emp.: 115
Elevator & Escalator Repair & Maintenance Services & Mfr
N.A.I.C.S.: 811210
Evert Fischer *(Gen Mgr)*

Mitsubishi Elevator Hong Kong Co., Ltd. (1)
36/F Lee & Man Commercial Center 169 Electric Road, North Point, China (Hong Kong)
Tel.: (852) 2 510 1030
Web Site: https://www.hmecg.com
Sales Range: $300-349.9 Million
Emp.: 700
Escalator & Elevator Installation Services & Distr
N.A.I.C.S.: 423830
Masafumi Nishiyama *(Mng Dir)*

Mitsubishi Elevator Korea Co., Ltd. (1)
01 Jisikgiban-ro Songdo-dong, Yeonsu-gu, Incheon, 21991, Korea (South)

MITSUBISHI ELECTRIC CORPORATION

Mitsubishi Electric Corporation—(Continued)
Tel.: (82) 325855311
Web Site:
http://www.mitsubishielevator.co.kr
Elevator Mfr & Distr
N.A.I.C.S.: 333921

Mitsubishi Elevator Malaysia Sdn. Bhd. (1)
No 42 Jalan Penchala, 46050, Petaling Jaya, Selangor Darul Ehsan, Malaysia
Tel.: (60) 377883003
Sales Range: $25-49.9 Million
Emp.: 10
Elevator Installation Services & Distr
N.A.I.C.S.: 238290
Yoshimi Hirayama *(Mng Dir)*

Mitsubishi Precision Co., Ltd. (1)
Shibaura Crystal Shinagawa 8th floor
1-6-41 Konan, Minato-ku, Tokyo, 135-0063, Japan
Tel.: (81) 367123740
Web Site: https://www.mpcnet.co.jp
Emp.: 837
Navigation Radar & Inertial Device Mfr
N.A.I.C.S.: 334511
Seiji Fujimoto *(Pres & CEO)*

Mitsubishi Space Software Co., Ltd. (1)
WTC Bldg 2-4-1 Hamamatsu-cho, Minato-ku, Tokyo, 105-5129, Japan
Tel.: (81) 33 435 4726
Web Site: https://www.mss.co.jp
Sales Range: $200-249.9 Million
Emp.: 943
System Integration Services
N.A.I.C.S.: 541511
Yasunori Kamochi *(Pres)*

Miyoshi Electronics Corporation (1)
Miyoshi Electronics Building 3-13-21 Kuyo, Kawanishi, 666-0024, Hyogo, Japan
Tel.: (81) 727561331
Web Site: https://www.miyoshi.elec.co.jp
Emp.: 132
Telecommunication Device Mfr
N.A.I.C.S.: 334290
Yasuhisa Maekawa *(Pres & COO)*

Motum AB (1)
Ranhammarsvägen 29 Bromma, Stockholm, 161 11, Sweden
Tel.: (46) 20520052
Web Site: http://www.motum.se
Emp.: 350
Industrial Supplies Whslr
N.A.I.C.S.: 423830

P.T. Mitsubishi Jaya Elevator and Escalator (1)
Gedung Jaya 10th Floor Jl M H Thamrin No 12, PO Box 2584, Jakarta Pusat, 10025, Jakarta, Indonesia
Tel.: (62) 21 319 28100
Web Site: http://www.mitsubishielectric.asia
Elevator & Escalator Mfr & Distr
N.A.I.C.S.: 333921

RYO-SA BUILWARE Co., Ltd. (1)
1-7-7 Nishiikebukuro 3rd floor Nishiikebukuro Building, Toshima-ku, Tokyo, 171-0021, Japan **(100%)**
Tel.: (81) 3 5396 2806
Web Site: http://www.ryo-sa.co.jp
Emp.: 681
Energy & Electric Systems Sales & Installation Services
N.A.I.C.S.: 221118
Akio Yamamoto *(Mng Dir)*

Ryoden Elevator Construction, Ltd. (1)
2-4 Ichigaya Sadoharacho, Shinjuku-Ku, Tokyo, 162-0842, Japan
Tel.: (81) 332359201
Web Site: https://www.mitsubishi.com
Construction Machinery Distr
N.A.I.C.S.: 423810

Ryowa Corporation (1)
6-12-1 Minamise, Fukushima-Ku, Kurashiki, 712-8055, Okayama, Japan
Tel.: (81) 864555151
Web Site: https://www.mitsubishi.com
Automotive Electronic Component Distr
N.A.I.C.S.: 423120

Setsuyo Astec Corporation (1)
1-29 Minamimorimachi 2-chome, Kita-ku, Osaka, 530-0054, Japan
Tel.: (81) 661300154
Web Site: https://www.setsuyo.co.jp
Emp.: 300
Electrical Equipment Distr
N.A.I.C.S.: 423610
Motokazu Inaba *(Pres & CEO)*

Setsuyo Enterprise Co., Ltd. (1)
No 105 Wugong 3rd Road, Wugu District, New Taipei City, 248019, Taiwan
Tel.: (886) 222992499
Web Site: https://www.setsuyo.com.tw
Automation & Semiconductor Electronic Product Distr
N.A.I.C.S.: 423690

Shanghai Mitsubishi Elevator Co., Ltd. (1)
No 811 Jiangchuan Road, Minhang, Shanghai, 200245, China
Tel.: (86) 2164303030
Web Site: https://www.smec-cn.com
Elevator Mfr & Distr
N.A.I.C.S.: 333921
Shen Danye *(Reg Mgr)*

Siam Compressor Industry Co., Ltd. (1)
G Tower Level 33 9 Rama 9 Road, Huaykwang, Bangkok, 10310, Chon Buri, Thailand **(100%)**
Tel.: (66) 38490900
Web Site: https://www.siamcompressor.com
Sales Range: $400-449.9 Million
Emp.: 2,350
Rotary & Scroll Compressors Mfr
N.A.I.C.S.: 333912

Tada Electric Co., Ltd. (1)
8-1-1 Tsukaguchi-Honmachi, Amagasaki, 661-0001, Hyogo, Japan
Tel.: (81) 66 496 2291
Web Site: https://www.tadadenki.jp
Emp.: 319
Heat Exchanger Mfr & Distr
N.A.I.C.S.: 332410
Hiroyuki Nakano *(Mng Dir & Gen Mgr-Heat Exchanger Works)*

Unit (Domestic):

Tada Electric Co., Ltd. - Heat Exchanger Works (2)
488 Shimogasaka, Oku-cho, Setouchi, 701-4247, Okayama, Japan
Tel.: (81) 869 22 0157
Web Site: http://www.tadadenki.jp
Emp.: 333
Heat Exchanger Mfr
N.A.I.C.S.: 333414

Taiwan Mitsubishi Elevator Co., Ltd. (1)
Chung-Ling Building No 363 Sec 2 Fu-Hsing S Rd, Taipei, Taiwan
Tel.: (886) 227335353
Elevator & Escalator Machinery Mfr
N.A.I.C.S.: 333921

Toshiba Mitsubishi-Electric Industrial Systems Corporation (1)
Square Garden 3-1-1, Kyobashi Chuo-ku, Tokyo, 104-0031, Japan
Tel.: (81) 332775511
Sales Range: $600-649.9 Million
Emp.: 1,943
N.A.I.C.S.: 238210

Toyo Electric Corporation (1)
2-156 Ajiyoshi-cho, Kasugai, 486-8585, Aichi Prefecture, Japan
Tel.: (81) 568314191
Web Site: http://www.toyo-elec.co.jp
Emp.: 454
Electronic Control Device Mfr
N.A.I.C.S.: 335999
Shoko Matsuo *(Pres)*

MITSUBISHI ESTATE CO., LTD.
Otemachi Park Building 1-1 Otemachi 1-chome, Chiyoda-ku, Tokyo, 100-8133, Japan
Tel.: (81) 332875100 JP
Web Site: https://www.mec.co.jp
Year Founded: 1937
MES—(DEU)
Rev.: $9,945,981,070
Assets: $50,128,574,280
Liabilities: $32,780,014,550
Net Worth: $17,348,559,730
Earnings: $1,113,335,520
Emp.: 11,045
Fiscal Year-end: 03/31/24
Real Estate Development, Sales & Leasing Services
N.A.I.C.S.: 531190
Hirotaka Sugiyama *(Chm)*

Subsidiaries:

Chelsea Japan Co., Ltd. (1)
3 2 3 Marunouchi Chiyoda Ku, Tokyo, 100 0005, Japan
Tel.: (81)332147155
Web Site: http://www.premiumoutlets.co.jp
Sales Range: $10-24.9 Million
Emp.: 40
Leases & Manages Fashion-Oriented Outlet Centers; Joint Venture of Chelsea Property Group (40%) & Mitsubishi Estate Co., Ltd. (60%)
N.A.I.C.S.: 531190
Yoshimura Hidetoshi *(Pres)*

Grand Parking Center Co., Ltd. (1)
2-6-2 Otemachi Nippon Bldg B2f, Chiyoda-Ku, Tokyo, 100-0004, Japan
Tel.: (81) 332414020
Automobile Parking Services
N.A.I.C.S.: 812930

Higashinihon Kaihatsu Co., Ltd. (1)
1442-23 Yosawa, Sunto-gun Oyamacho, Shizuoka, 410-1326, Japan
Tel.: (81) 550 78 3211
Web Site: http://www.mitsubishi.com
Travel Agency Services
N.A.I.C.S.: 561510

Hokuryo City Service Co., Ltd. (1)
4-1 Kita2jonishi Hokkaido Bldg, Chuo-Ku, Sapporo, 060-0002, Hokkaido, Japan
Tel.: (81) 112427411
Real Estate Management Services
N.A.I.C.S.: 531390

IMS Co., Ltd. (1)
3-14 Kamisoneshimmachi, Kokuraminami-Ku, Kitakyushu, 800-0215, Fukuoka, Japan
Tel.: (81) 934747221
Property Management Services
N.A.I.C.S.: 531311

Izumi Park Town Service Co., Ltd. (1)
1-25-17 Teraoka, Izumi-ku, Sendai, 981-3204, Miyagi, Japan
Tel.: (81) 22 3780022
Property Management Services
N.A.I.C.S.: 531311

Japan Real Estate Asset Management Co., Ltd. (1)
3-3-1 Marunouchi, Chiyoda-Ku, Tokyo, 100-0005, Japan **(63%)**
Tel.: (81) 332117921
Real Estate Management Services
N.A.I.C.S.: 531390

MEC Design International Corporation (1)
Inui-Building Kachidoki 7F 1-13-1 Kachidoki, Chuo-ku, Tokyo, 104-0054, Japan
Tel.: (81) 36 704 0100
Web Site: https://www.mecdesign.co.jp
Sales Range: $25-49.9 Million
Emp.: 60
Interior Design & Supervision of Construction & Facilities
N.A.I.C.S.: 541410
Satoshi Okamoto *(Sr Mng Officer & Gen Mgr-Bus Promo & Project Mgmt Div)*

MEC Human Resources, Inc. (1)
Otemachi Bldg, Chiyoda-Ku, Tokyo, 100-0004, Japan
Tel.: (81) 332875221
Human Resource Consulting Services
N.A.I.C.S.: 541612

MEC Information Development Co., Ltd. (1)
Otemachi Bldg 7f, 242, Chiyoda-Ku, Tokyo, 100-0004, Japan
Tel.: (81) 3 3214 9300
Web Site: http://www.mec.co.jp
Software Development Services
N.A.I.C.S.: 541511
Fumihiko Sato *(Gen Mgr)*

MT Community Staff Co., Ltd. (1)
3-7-4 Hatchobori Kyobashi Park Bldg, Chuo-ku, Tokyo, 104-0032, Japan
Tel.: (81) 362227127
Property Management Services
N.A.I.C.S.: 531311

Marunouchi Direct Access Co., Ltd. (1)
Shin-Kokusai Building 8F 4-1 Marunouchi, Chiyoda-ku, Tokyo, 100-0005, Japan
Tel.: (81) 33 214 4881
Web Site: https://www.directaccess.co.jp
Sales Range: $1-9.9 Million
Emp.: 10
Telecommunication Servicesb
N.A.I.C.S.: 517810

Marunouchi Heat Supply Co., Ltd. (1)
1-6-5 Marunouchi Marunouchi Kitaguchi Building, Chiyoda-ku, Tokyo, 100-0005, Japan
Tel.: (81) 3 3287 2288
Web Site: http://www.marunetu.co.jp
Emp.: 151
Heat Supply Utility Consulting Services
N.A.I.C.S.: 541690

Marunouchi Hotel Co., Ltd. (1)
1-6-3 Marunouchi, Chiyoda-ku, Tokyo, 100-0005, Japan **(100%)**
Tel.: (81) 332171111
Web Site: http://www.marunouchi-hotel.co.jp
Emp.: 112
Home Management Services
N.A.I.C.S.: 721110
Toshiyuki Watanabe *(Pres)*

Minato Mirai 21 D.H.C. Co., Ltd. (1)
1-45 Sakuragicho 1-chome, Naka-ku, Yokohama, 231-0062, Kanagawa, Japan
Tel.: (81) 452210321
Web Site: http://www.mm21dhc.co.jp
Emp.: 62
Heating & Cooling System Installation Services
N.A.I.C.S.: 238220
Shigeru Uchida *(Pres)*

Mitsubishi Estate Building Management Co., Ltd. (1)
2-5-1 Marunouchi, Chiyoda-ku, Tokyo, 100-0005, Japan
Tel.: (81) 3 3287 4111
Real Estate Management Services
N.A.I.C.S.: 531390

Mitsubishi Estate Housing Components Co., Ltd. (1)
228-4 Shimminato, Mihama-ku, Chiba, 261-0002, Japan
Tel.: (81) 432429031
Manufacture, Processing & Sales of Construction Materials
N.A.I.C.S.: 236220

Mitsubishi Estate New York, Inc. (1)
1221 Avenue of the Americas, New York, NY 10020
Tel.: (212) 698-2200
Sales Range: $25-49.9 Million
Emp.: 5
Real Estate Development
N.A.I.C.S.: 237210
Tetsuya Masuda *(Pres)*

Mitsubishi Estate Parks Co., Ltd. (1)
3F Sanbancho, Chiyoda-ku, Tokyo, 102-0075, Japan
Tel.: (81) 352151720
Web Site: http://www.mec-p.co.jp
Real Estate Investment Services
N.A.I.C.S.: 531390

Mitsubishi Jisho Community Co., Ltd. (1)
6-1 Sanbancho Mitsubishi Estate Community Building, Chiyoda-ku, Tokyo, 102-0075, Japan
Tel.: (81) 352136100
Web Site: http://www.mec-c.com
Emp.: 5,497
Real Estate Management Services

AND PRIVATE COMPANIES / MITSUBISHI ESTATE CO., LTD.

N.A.I.C.S.: 531390

Mitsubishi Jisho House Net Co., Ltd. (1)
Osaka Station 4th Building 20F 11-11-2000
Osaka Station, Kita-ku, Osaka, 530-0001, Japan
Tel.: (81) 664563502
Web Site: http://www.mec-h.com
Real Estate Manangement Services
N.A.I.C.S.: 531390

Mitsubishi Jisho Investment Advisors, Inc.
Marunouchi Kitaguchi Building 19F 1-6-5
Marunouchi, Chiyoda-ku, Tokyo, 100-0005, Japan
Tel.: (81) 33 218 0031
Web Site: https://www.mecinvest.com
Sales Range: $50-74.9 Million
Emp.: 50
Real Estate & Investment Advisory Services
N.A.I.C.S.: 531390
Masaki Sakagawa *(Sr Exec Dir)*

Mitsubishi Jisho Property Management Co., Ltd. (1)
Marunouchi Nakadori Bldg 2-2-3
Marunouchi, Chiyoda-ku, Tokyo, 100-0005, Japan
Tel.: (81) 332874111
Web Site: https://www.mjpm.co.jp
Sales Range: $75-99.9 Million
Emp.: 260
Real Estate, Land Development & Property Management Services
N.A.I.C.S.: 531390

Mitsubishi Jisho Residence Co., Ltd. (1)
1-9-2 Otemachi Otemachi Financial City Grand Cube, Chiyoda-ku, Tokyo, 100-8189, Japan
Tel.: (81) 362818000
Web Site: http://www.mec-r.com
Emp.: 1,094
Commercial Condominium Management Services
N.A.I.C.S.: 531311

Mitsubishi Jisho Retail Property Management Co., Ltd. (1)
1-7-1 Daiba, Minato-ku, Tokyo, 135-8707, Japan
Tel.: (81) 3 3528 4151
Web Site: http://www.mitsubishi.com
Real Estate Manangement Services
N.A.I.C.S.: 531390

Mitsubishi Jisho Sekkei Inc. (1)
Marunouchi 2-chome Building 2-5-1
Marunouchi, Chiyoda-ku, Tokyo, 100-0005, Japan
Tel.: (81) 33 287 5555
Web Site: https://www.mj-sekkei.com
Sales Range: $125-149.9 Million
Emp.: 450
Lessors of Other Real Estate Property
N.A.I.C.S.: 531190

Mitsubishi Jisho Towa Community Co., Ltd. (1)
1-8-8 Shinkawa Chuo-ku, Tokyo, Japan
Tel.: (81) 362227108
Web Site: http://www.mjtc.co.jp
Sales Range: $200-249.9 Million
Real Estate, Land Development & Property Management Services
N.A.I.C.S.: 531390

Mitsubishi Real Estate Services Co., Ltd. (1)
2-2-1 Otemachi Shinotemachi Bldg, Chiyoda-Ku, Tokyo, 100-0004, Japan
Tel.: (81) 3 3510 8011
Real Estate Manangement Services
N.A.I.C.S.: 531390

Mitsubishi Real Estate Strategies (1)
1-9-2 Otemachi, Chiyoda Ku, Tokyo, 100-0004, Japan (100%)
Tel.: (81) 33 510 8011
Web Site: https://www.mecyes.co.jp
Sales Range: $150-199.9 Million
Emp.: 633
Real Estate Services
N.A.I.C.S.: 531390

Rockefeller Group, Inc. (1)
1271 Avenue of the Americas 24th Fl, New York, NY 10020
Tel.: (212) 282-2000
Web Site: https://www.rockefellergroup.com
Sales Range: $75-99.9 Million
Emp.: 120
Real Estate, Real Estate Services & Telecommunications Services
N.A.I.C.S.: 531390
Vincent E. Silvestri *(COO & VP)*

Subsidiary (Domestic):

MEC USA, Inc. (2)
1221 Ave of the Americas, New York, NY 10020 (100%)
Tel.: (212) 698-2200
Sales Range: $25-49.9 Million
Emp.: 5
Holding Company
N.A.I.C.S.: 237210
Tetsuya Masuda *(Pres)*

Subsidiary (Non-US):

MEC UK Limited (3)
17 Floor 88 Wood Street, London, EC2V 7DA, United Kingdom (100%)
Tel.: (44) 2077766900
Sales Range: $50-74.9 Million
Development of Office Buildings & Retail Stores
N.A.I.C.S.: 531120
Naoki Umeda *(Gen Mgr)*

Subsidiary (Domestic):

Rockefeller Group International, Inc. (2)
1271 Avenue of the Americas 24th Fl, New York, NY 10020-1001 (100%)
Tel.: (212) 282-2000
Web Site: https://www.rockefellergroup.com
Real Estate Development, Sales & Leasing; Telecommunications Services
N.A.I.C.S.: 531120
Atsushi Nakajima *(Acting Pres & CEO)*

Subsidiary (Non-US):

Europa Capital Partners Limited (3)
15 Sloane St, London, SW1W 8ER, United Kingdom (75%)
Tel.: (44) 20 7881 6800
Web Site: http://www.europacapital.com
Sales Range: $50-74.9 Million
Emp.: 40
Real Estate Investment Trust
N.A.I.C.S.: 525990
Robert J. W. Martin *(Co-Founder, Principal & Head-Central Europe)*

Joint Venture (Non-US):

Sandpiper CI Limited (4)
1 L Avenue le Bas, Longueville, Saint Saviour, JE4 8NB, Jersey
Tel.: (44) 1534508508
Web Site: https://www.sandpiperci.com
Holding Company; General Retail, Liquor & Convenience Stores & Supermarket Franchises Operator; Owned by Duke Street Capital Limited & by Europa Capital Partners Limited
N.A.I.C.S.: 551112
Tony O'Neill *(CEO)*

Subsidiary (Domestic):

Sandpiper CI Retail Limited (5)
1 L'Avenue le Bas, Longueville, Saint Saviour, JE4 8NB, Jersey
Tel.: (44) 153 450 8508
Web Site: https://www.sandpiperci.com
Sales Range: $600-649.9 Million
Holding Company; General Retail, Liquor & Convenience Stores & Supermarket Franchises Operator
N.A.I.C.S.: 551112
Tony O'Neill *(CEO)*

Subsidiary (Domestic):

Rockefeller Group Development Corporation (3)
1271 Avenue of the Americas, New York, NY 10020-1513 (100%)
Tel.: (212) 282-2000
Web Site: https://www.rockefellergroup.com
Sales Range: $50-74.9 Million
Emp.: 100
Real Estate Development, Construction & Management
N.A.I.C.S.: 237210
Kevin R. Hackett *(Pres & CEO)*

Subsidiary (Domestic):

TA Realty LLC (2)
1 Federal St 17th Fl, Boston, MA 02110
Tel.: (617) 476-2700
Web Site: https://www.tarealty.com
Real Estate Investment & Management Services
N.A.I.C.S.: 523999
Scott W. Amling *(Partner)*

Royal Park Hotel Management Co., Ltd. (1)
1-6-1 Otemachi Otemachi Bldg 5f, Chiyoda-Ku, Tokyo, 100-0004, Japan
Tel.: (81) 352246200
Web Site: http://www.rph-the.co.jp
Home Management Services
N.A.I.C.S.: 721110
Naoki Okajima *(Pres)*

Royal Park Hotels & Resorts Co., Ltd. (1)
Otemachi Building 1-6-1 Otemachi, Chiyoda-ku, Tokyo, 100-0004, Japan (100%)
Tel.: (81) 362123800
Web Site: http://www.royalparkhotels.co.jp
Sales Range: $10-24.9 Million
Emp.: 13
Operation of Royal Park Hotels; Consulting & Consignment of Hotel Management Activities
N.A.I.C.S.: 721110

Subsidiary (Domestic):

Royal Park Hotel Co., Ltd. (2)
2-1-1 Nihonbashi-Kakigara-cho, Chuo-ku, Tokyo, 103-8520, Japan
Tel.: (81) 336671111
Web Site: https://www2.rph.co.jp
Emp.: 604
Hotel Operations
N.A.I.C.S.: 721110

Royal Park Inn Nagoya Co., Ltd. (2)
3-27-5 Meieki, Nakumura-ku, 450-0002, Nagoya, Aichi, Japan
Tel.: (81) 525814411
Web Site: http://www.royalpark-nagoya.com
Sales Range: $10-24.9 Million
Hotel Operations
N.A.I.C.S.: 721110

Royal Park Shiodome Tower Co., Ltd. (2)
1-6-3 Higashishimbashi, Minato-Ku, 105-8433, Japan
Tel.: (81) 362531111
Web Site: http://www.rps-the.co.jp
Sales Range: $10-24.9 Million
Hotel Operations
N.A.I.C.S.: 721110
Kaname Ebata *(Pres)*

Tohoku Royal Park Hotel Co., Ltd. (2)
6-2-1 Teraoka, Izumi-Ku, Sendai, 981-3204, Miyagi, Japan
Tel.: (81) 22 377 1111
Web Site: http://www.srph.co.jp
Sales Range: $10-24.9 Million
Emp.: 10
Home Management Services
N.A.I.C.S.: 721110
Kazuhisa Hara *(Pres & Chief Privacy Officer)*

Ryoei Life Service Co., Ltd. (1)
3-33-13 Okusawa, Setagaya-Ku, Tokyo, 158-0083, Japan
Tel.: (81) 120265056
Web Site: http://www.ryoeilife.jp
Property Management Services
N.A.I.C.S.: 531311
Masahiko Aikawa *(CEO)*

Sunshine BS Corporation (1)
3-1-3 Higashiikebukuro World Import Mart Bldg 9f, Toshima-Ku, Tokyo, 170-8630, Japan
Tel.: (81) 339893378

Sales Range: $25-49.9 Million
Emp.: 65
Commercial Building Maintenance Services
N.A.I.C.S.: 561730

Sunshine City Corporation (1)
3-1-1 Higashi-Ikebukuro, Toshima-Ku, Tokyo, 170-8630, Japan
Tel.: (81) 3 3989 3321
Web Site: http://www.sunshinecity.co.jp
Emp.: 133
Offices & Shopping Center Leasing Services
N.A.I.C.S.: 531120

Sunshine Enterprise Corporation (1)
3-1-3 Higashiikebukuro World Import Mart 9, Toshiima-Ku, Tokyo, 170-0013, Japan
Tel.: (81) 339893460
Commercial Building Management Services
N.A.I.C.S.: 236220

Tokyo Garage Co., Ltd. (1)
2-14-2 Nagatacho Sanno Grand Building 4F, Chiyoda-Ku, Tokyo, 100-0014, Japan
Tel.: (81) 3 3504 0610
Web Site: http://www.tokyo-garage.co.jp
Emp.: 204
Automobile Parts & Products Sales & Parking Services
N.A.I.C.S.: 812930
Takehiko Mino *(Pres)*

Tokyo Kotsu Kaikan Co., Ltd. (1)
2-10-1 Yurakucho Tokyokotsukaikan, Chiyoda-Ku, Tokyo, 100-0006, Japan
Tel.: (81) 332122931
Commercial Building Leasing Services
N.A.I.C.S.: 531120

Towa Real Estate Development Co., Ltd. (1)
2-3-13 Yaesu, Chuo-ku, Tokyo, 104 8484, Japan
Tel.: (81) 332726331
Sales Range: $1-4.9 Billion
Emp.: 629
Sale, Brokerage & Lease of Real Estate & Contract Building Construction
N.A.I.C.S.: 531390

Subsidiary (Domestic):

Towa Real Estate Brokerage Co., Ltd. (2)
Towa Hatano Building 2-4-4 Hongo, Bunkyo-ku, Tokyo, 113 0033, Japan
Tel.: (81) 338153101
Sales Range: $50-74.9 Million
Emp.: 272
Real Estate Agents & Managers
N.A.I.C.S.: 531210

URBAN LIFE Co., Ltd. (1)
14th floor Higashinada Center Building 8-6-26 Motoyama Minamimachi, Higashinada-ku, Kobe, 658-0015, Japan (96.89%)
Tel.: (81) 78 452 0668
Web Site: https://www.urbanlife.co.jp
Real Estate Related Services
N.A.I.C.S.: 531390
Yoshitaka Morishita *(Pres)*

Yokohama Royal Park Hotel Co., Ltd. (1)
2-2-1-3 Minatomirai, Nishi-ku, Yokohama, 220-8173, Kanagawa, Japan
Tel.: (81) 45 221 1111
Web Site: https://www2.yrph.com
Sales Range: $100-124.9 Million
Emp.: 580
Hotel Operations
N.A.I.C.S.: 721110

Yokohama Sky Building Co., Ltd. (1)
2-19-12 Takashima, Nishi-ku, Yokohama, Japan
Tel.: (81) 454411221
Real Estate Lending Services
N.A.I.C.S.: 531390
Kenichi Iwata *(Pres)*

Yuden Building Kanri Co., Ltd. (1)
1-7-1 Yurakucho Yurakucho Denki Bldg, Chiyoda-Ku, Tokyo, 100-0006, Japan
Tel.: (81) 332117833
Property Management Services
N.A.I.C.S.: 531311

MITSUBISHI ESTATE LOGISTICS REIT INVESTMENT CORPORATION

Mitsubishi Estate Co., Ltd.—(Continued)

MITSUBISHI ESTATE LOGISTICS REIT INVESTMENT CORPORATION
165 Marunouchi, Chiyoda-ku, Tokyo, 100-8150, Japan
Tel.: (81) 332180030
Web Site: https://www.mel-reit.co.jp
Year Founded: 2016
3481—(TKS)
Sales Range: Less than $1 Million
Real Estate Investment Services
N.A.I.C.S.: 531210
Ken Takanashi *(Exec Dir)*

MITSUBISHI GAS CHEMICAL COMPANY, INC.
Mitsubishi Building 5-2 Marunouchi 2-chome, Chiyoda-ku, Tokyo, 100-8324, Japan
Tel.: (81) 332835000   JP
Web Site: https://www.mgc.co.jp
Year Founded: 1918
4182—(TKS)
Rev.: $5,376,686,370
Assets: $7,059,546,100
Liabilities: $2,532,806,580
Net Worth: $4,526,739,520
Earnings: $256,586,980
Emp.: 7,918
Fiscal Year-end: 03/31/24
N.A.I.C.S.: 325199
Toshikiyo Kurai *(Chm)*

Subsidiaries:

AGELESS (THAILAND) CO., LTD. (1)
700/323 Moo 6 Tumbol Don Hua Lor, Amata City Chonburi Industrial Estate, Chon Buri, 20000, muang chonburi, Thailand
Tel.: (66) 38458351
Web Site: http://www.mgc.co.jp
Chemical Products Mfr
N.A.I.C.S.: 325199

AGELESS Service Center Co., Ltd. (1)
3-6-1 Kanda Surugadai Ryowa Building, Chiyoda-ku, Tokyo, 101-0062, Japan
Tel.: (81) 3 3251 0761
Web Site: http://www.mgc.co.jp
Business Support Services
N.A.I.C.S.: 561499

Appi Geothermal Energy Corporation (1)
129-1 Osuke 18th Chiwari, Hachimantai, 028-7111, Japan
Tel.: (81) 195687332
Web Site: https://www.appige.co.jp
Geothermal Electric Power Mfr
N.A.I.C.S.: 335311

Brunei Methanol Company Sdn. Bhd. (1)
Sungai Liang Industrial Park Spark Kg, Sungai Liang Daerah Belait, KC1135, Negara, Brunei Darussalam
Tel.: (673) 3229300
Web Site: http://www.brunei-methanol.com
Methanol Mfr & Distr
N.A.I.C.S.: 325199
Kaneshige Kubushiro *(CEO)*

CG Ester Corporation (1)
2-16-13 Nihonbashi Landic Nihonbashi Building 8F, Chuo-ku, Tokyo, 103-0027, Japan
Tel.: (81) 352032860
Plasticizer Product Mfr & Distr
N.A.I.C.S.: 325199

Dia Aqua Solutions Co., Inc. (1)
6F Ryowa Building 3-6-1 Kanda Surugadai, Chiyoda-ku, Tokyo, 101-0062, Japan
Tel.: (81) 352244871
Web Site: https://www.mitsubishi.com
Waste Treatment Services
N.A.I.C.S.: 221310

Du Pont-MGC Co., Ltd. (1)
2-5-2 Marunouchi 2-chome, Chiyoda-ku, Tokyo, 100-8324, Japan
Tel.: (81) 3 3283 4723
Emp.: 2
Chemical Products Mfr
N.A.I.C.S.: 325180

EIWA Chemical Ind. Co., Ltd. (1) **(100%)**
Web Site: http://www.eiwa-chem.co.jp
Emp.: 132
Mfr & Sales of Blowing Agents for Rubber Products
N.A.I.C.S.: 326299
Kuniaki Jinnai *(Pres)*

Fudow Company Limited (1)
2-15-16 Shin-Yokohama, Kohoku-ku, Yokohama, 222-0033, Japan **(100%)**
Tel.: (81) 455484210
Web Site: https://fudow.co.jp
Emp.: 202
Mfr & Sales of Molding Resin Compounds
N.A.I.C.S.: 325991

Fuel DME Production Co., Ltd. (1)
86-51 Ichiban-cho Higashi Nakadori, Niigata, 951-8116, Kita-ku, Japan **(100%)**
Tel.: (81) 332834824
Web Site: http://www.fueldme.com
Mfr & Sales of Dimethyl Ether Chemicals
N.A.I.C.S.: 325180
Akira Ishiwada *(Pres)*

Fuji Boring Co., Ltd. (1)
4039-11 Manohara Shinden, Fujinomiya, 418-0001, Japan
Tel.: (81) 544581473
Web Site: https://fuji-b.co.jp
Natural Gas Well Drilling Services
N.A.I.C.S.: 213111

Global Polyacetal Co., Ltd. (1)
5-2 Marunouchi 2-chome, Chiyoda-ku, Tokyo, 100-8324, Japan
Tel.: (81) 332834949
Plastic Product Mfr & Distr
N.A.I.C.S.: 325211

Granopt Co., Ltd. (1)
4-4 Ougibuchi Aza Ougida, Noshiro, 016-0122, Akita Prefecture, Japan
Tel.: (81) 185701800
Web Site: http://www.granopt.jp
Emp.: 90
Faraday Rotator Mfr
N.A.I.C.S.: 339999

Hachimantai Green Energy Corporation (1)
181-1 Aza Akabuchi Hachimantai, Kazuno, 018-5141, Akita, Japan
Tel.: (81) 186224445
Geothermal Power Energy Services
N.A.I.C.S.: 221116

Hubei Lingyong Electronic Materials Co., Ltd. (1)
No 7 Huaxiang 1st Road Yanhua Industrial Park, Yunmeng County, Xiaogan, 432500, China
Tel.: (86) 7124222990
Pigment Mfr & Distr
N.A.I.C.S.: 325130

J-Chemical, Inc. (1)
3F Seiwa Bld 3-31-1 Hong, Bunkyo-ku, Tokyo, 113-0033, Japan
Tel.: (81) 351487131
Web Site: https://jchemical.com
Wood Adhesive & Formalin Distr
N.A.I.C.S.: 424690

JSP Corporation (1)
Shin Nisseki Bldg 4-2 3-chome Marunouchi, Chiyoda-ku, Tokyo, 100-0005, Japan **(51%)**
Tel.: (81) 362126306
Web Site: https://www.co-jsp.co.jp
Rev.: $892,687,110
Assets: $1,002,109,050
Liabilities: $340,652,960
Net Worth: $661,456,090
Earnings: $42,244,510
Emp.: 3,008
Fiscal Year-end: 03/31/2024
Plastic Packaging Products Mfr
N.A.I.C.S.: 326140
Yukio Sakai *(Pres)*

Subsidiary (Non-US):

JSP Foam Products Pte. Ltd. (2)
19 Tuas Link 2, Jurong Industrial Estate, Singapore, 638564, Singapore
Tel.: (65) 68632826
Web Site: http://www.co-jsp.co.jp
Plastic Foam Products Mfr & Sales
N.A.I.C.S.: 326140

Subsidiary (US):

JSP International Group Ltd. (2)
1285 Drummers Ln Ste 301, Wayne, PA 19087
Tel.: (610) 651-8600
Plastic Packaging Products Mfr
N.A.I.C.S.: 326140

Subsidiary (Non-US):

JSP International S.A.R.L. (2)
Industrielle Le Bois Zone Chevalier, Route de Francieres, 60 190, Estrees-St. Denis, Oise, France
Tel.: (33) 344917000
Web Site: http://www.co-jsp.co.jp
Polypropylene Mfr & Sales
N.A.I.C.S.: 325211
Alain Litzler *(Sls Mgr)*

Subsidiary (Non-US):

JSP International s.r.o. (3)
Prumyslovy park11/158, CZ-350 02, Cheb, Czech Republic
Tel.: (420) 354401811
Web Site: http://www.co-jsp.co.jp
Polystyrene Foam Products Mfr & Sale
N.A.I.C.S.: 326140

Subsidiary (Non-US):

JSP Plastics (Shanghai) Co., Ltd. (2)
Room 102 Floor 4 WeWork No 627 Huaihai Middle Road, Huangpu District, Shanghai, 200020, China
Tel.: (86) 2163404500
Web Site: https://www.jsp-china.com
Plastic Product Distr
N.A.I.C.S.: 424610

Subsidiary (Domestic):

JSP molding Ltd. (2)
5 Satsuki-cho, Kanuma, 322-0014, Tochigi, Japan
Tel.: (81) 289766301
Web Site: http://www.co-jsp.co.jp
Molded Products Mfr & Sales
N.A.I.C.S.: 333511

Subsidiary (Non-US):

KOSPA Corporation (2)
Seoul Sales Office 4th floor Beautiful Tower 246 Dangsan-ro, Yeongdeungpo-gu, Seoul, 152-842, Korea (South)
Tel.: (82) 28682900
Web Site: https://www.kospa.co.kr
Polystyrene Foam Products Mfr & Sale
N.A.I.C.S.: 326140

KP Co. Ltd. (2)
Tel.: (81) 289763281
Food Containers Mfr
N.A.I.C.S.: 322219
Masayuki Suzuki *(Dir)*

Subsidiary (Domestic):

Seihoku Package Co., Ltd. (2)
3102-6 Nakazato, Noda, 270-0237, Chiba, Japan
Tel.: (81) 471278111
Web Site: https://www.seihoku-pk.co.jp
Emp.: 92
Industrial Packaging Materials Mfr
N.A.I.C.S.: 326112
Tadaharu Mukai *(Mng Dir)*

Subsidiary (Non-US):

Taiwan JSP Chemical Co., Ltd. (2)
No 10 Lane 452 Section 2 Jianxing Road, Xinfeng, Hsinchu, 304, Taiwan
Tel.: (886) 35573168
Web Site: https://www.tjsp.com.tw
Polypropylene Products Mfr & Sales
N.A.I.C.S.: 326140

Subsidiary (US):

ViewRay, Inc. (2)

INTERNATIONAL PUBLIC

1099 18th St Ste 3000, Denver, CO 80202
Tel.: (440) 703-3210
Web Site: https://investors.viewray.com
Rev.: $102,206,000
Assets: $271,397,000
Liabilities: $189,155,000
Net Worth: $82,242,000
Earnings: ($107,330,000)
Emp.: 295
Fiscal Year-end: 12/31/2022
Radiation Therapy Systems Design & Mfr
N.A.I.C.S.: 334516
Daniel Jeffrey Moore *(Chm)*

Subsidiary (Domestic):

Yuka Sansho Kenzai Co., Ltd. (2)
Matsunaga Bldg 2F 2-1-17 Hamamatsucho, Minato-ku, Tokyo, 105-0013, Japan **(100%)**
Tel.: (81) 354056730
Web Site: http://www.yukasansho.com
Emp.: 32
Polystyrene Foam Mfr & Sales
N.A.I.C.S.: 326140
Makoto Taga *(Pres & CEO)*

Japan DME Co.,Ltd. (1)
5-2 Marunouchi 2-chome, Chiyoda-ku, Tokyo, 100-8324, Japan
Tel.: (81) 3 3283 4824
Web Site: http://www.mgc.co.jp
Business Support Services
N.A.I.C.S.: 561499

Japan Finechem Company, Inc. (1)
9F Uchisaiwaicho Tokyu Building 1-3-2 Uchisaiwaicho, Chiyoda-ku, Tokyo, 100-0011, Japan **(100%)**
Tel.: (81) 355114600
Web Site: http://www.jfine.co.jp
Sales Range: $125-149.9 Million
Emp.: 287
Mfr & Sales of Fine Chemicals & Electronic Products
N.A.I.C.S.: 325180

Japan Methyl Ether Co., Ltd. (1)
5-2 Marunouchi 2-chome, Chiyoda-ku, Tokyo, 100-8324, Japan
Tel.: (81) 3 3283 4825
Dimethyl Ether Mfr & Whslr
N.A.I.C.S.: 325199

Japan Pionics Co., Ltd. (1)
1-3 Nishi-Shinbashi 1-chome Minato-ku, Tokyo Sakurada Bldg, Tokyo, 105 0003, Japan **(75%)**
Tel.: (81) 335068801
Web Site: http://www.japan-pionics.co.jp
Sales Range: $1-9.9 Million
Emp.: 160
Mfr & Sales of Gas Generators & Gas Purifiers & Mfr of Disposable Body Warmers
N.A.I.C.S.: 333611
Ryoichi Takahashi *(Pres)*

Japan Saudi Arabia Methanol Company, Inc. (1)
Hibiya Kokusai Building 2-2-3 Uchisaiwaicho, Chiyoda-ku, Tokyo, 100-0011, Japan
Tel.: (81) 335933541
Business Administration Services
N.A.I.C.S.: 561110

Japan Trinidad Methanol Company, Inc. (1)
5-2 Marunouchi 2-chome, Chiyoda-ku, Tokyo, 100-8324, Japan
Tel.: (81) 332834832
Investment Services
N.A.I.C.S.: 523999

Japan U-Pica Company Ltd. (1)
Madre Matsuda Bldg 4-13 Kioi-cho, Chiyoda-ku, Tokyo, 102-0094, Japan **(100%)**
Tel.: (81) 368500251
Web Site: https://www.u-pica.co.jp
Emp.: 121
Resin Material Mfr
N.A.I.C.S.: 325211
Yoshihiro Yamane *(Pres)*

Subsidiary (Domestic):

Japan U-Pica Company Ltd. - Mine Factory (2)
3058-21 Higashibun Ikejiri Omine-cho, Mine, 759-2212, Yamaguchi, Japan

AND PRIVATE COMPANIES

Tel.: (81) 837521901
Resin Mfr
N.A.I.C.S.: 325211

Japan U-Pica Company Ltd. - Shonan Factory (2)
5-3-3 Higashi Yawata, Hiratsuka, 254-0016, Kanagawa, Japan
Tel.: (81) 463221984
Resin Mfr
N.A.I.C.S.: 325211

Subsidiary (Non-US):

U-Pica Resin (Changshu) Co., Ltd. (2)
Changchun Road Riverside Industrial Park Economic Development Zone, Jiangsu, 215537, China
Tel.: (86) 51252367584
Resin Mfr & Distr
N.A.I.C.S.: 325211
Kazuo Tsukada *(Chm)*

KAGAKU UNYU CO., LTD. (1)
1-11 Mizushima-nakadori 3-chome, Kuraishiki, 712-8072, Okayama, Japan
Tel.: (81) 864483655
Transportation Services
N.A.I.C.S.: 488999

Kinoe Terminal Co., Inc. (1)
1-3 Nishi-shinbashi 1-chome, Minato-ku, Tokyo, 105 0003, Japan
Tel.: (81) 335933663
Web Site: http://www.mgc.co.jp
Sales Range: $25-49.9 Million
Methanol Products Storage Services
N.A.I.C.S.: 493190

Kokuka Sangyo Co., Ltd. (1)
1-16-4 Shinbashi Resona Shimbashi Building 5F, Minato-ku, Tokyo, 105-0004, Japan
Tel.: (81) 335933663
Web Site: https://www.kokuka.co.jp
Sales Range: $25-49.9 Million
Emp.: 103
Marine Transportation of Chemical Products
N.A.I.C.S.: 483111
Yutaka Katada *(Pres)*

Korea Engineering Plastics Co., Ltd. (1)
14th Floor OCI Bldg 94 Sogong-ro, Jung-gu, Seoul, 04532, Korea (South)
Tel.: (82) 27287499
Chemical Product Mfr & Distr
N.A.I.C.S.: 325998
David M. Postolowski *(CEO)*

Korea Polyacetal Co., Ltd. (1)
14F 94 Sogong-ro, Jung-gu, Seoul, Korea (South)
Tel.: (82) 27287406
Web Site: https://www.gpac-kpac.com
Chemical Resin Mfr & Distr
N.A.I.C.S.: 325211

Kyoudou Kasankasuiso Corporation (1)
35 Higashi Wada, Kamisu, 314-0102, Ibaraki, Japan
Tel.: (81) 299 97 0785
Web Site: http://www.mgc.co.jp
Hydrogen Peroxide Mfr
N.A.I.C.S.: 325180

M.G.C ENGINEERING CO., INC. (1)
1318 Tayuhama, Kita-ku, Niigata, 950-3112, Japan
Tel.: (81) 25 259 7187
Engineeering Services
N.A.I.C.S.: 541330

MGC Advance Co., Ltd. (1)
1383 Tayuhama, Kita-ku, Niigata, 950-3112, Japan
Tel.: (81) 252593255
Web Site: http://www.mgc-adv.co.jp
Chemical Product Mfr & Distr
N.A.I.C.S.: 325998

MGC Advanced Polymers, Inc. (1)
1100 Port Walthall Dr, Colonial Heights, VA 23834
Tel.: (804) 520-7800
Web Site: https://www.mapnylon.com
Plastic Polymer Mfr
N.A.I.C.S.: 325211

MGC Ageless Co., Ltd. (1)
3-6-1 Kanda Surugadai, Chiyoda-ku, Tokyo, 101-0062, Japan
Tel.: (81) 332510761
Web Site: http://www.home.mgc-ageless.co.jp
Optical Product Mfr
N.A.I.C.S.: 333310

MGC Computer Service Co., Ltd. (1)
5-2 Marunouchi 2-chome, Chiyoda-ku, Tokyo, 100-8324, Japan
Tel.: (81) 3 3283 4845
Web Site: http://www.mgc.co.jp
Computer System Services
N.A.I.C.S.: 541512

MGC Electrotechno (Thailand) Co., Ltd. (1)
500/128 Moo3 Tambol Tasit, Pluak Daeng, 21140, Rayong, Thailand
Tel.: (66) 38950470
Chemical Product Mfr & Distr
N.A.I.C.S.: 325998

MGC Electrotechno Co., Ltd. (1)
9-41 Sugiyama Saigo-mura, Nishishirakawa-gun, Fukushima, 961-8031, Japan
Tel.: (81) 248255000
Web Site: http://www.mgcet.jp
Laminate Plastic Plate Product Mfr
N.A.I.C.S.: 326130

MGC Energy Company Limited (1)
2-5-2 Marunouchi, Chiyoda-ku, Tokyo, 100-8324, Japan
Tel.: (81) 332835135
Web Site: https://energy.mgc.co.jp
Electric Power Distribution Services
N.A.I.C.S.: 221122

MGC Farmix Co., Ltd. (1)
1-8 Toyoyohi yanaigoya, Shirakawa, 961-0005, Fukushima, Japan
Tel.: (81) 248249007
Web Site: https://mgc-farmix.co.jp
Vegetable Distr
N.A.I.C.S.: 424480

MGC Filsheet Co., Ltd. (1)
4-2242 Mikajima, Tokorozawa, 359-1164, Saitama, Japan
Tel.: (81) 429482151
Web Site: https://www.mgcfs.jp
Emp.: 405
Polycarbonate Films & Sheets Mfr
N.A.I.C.S.: 326113
Tsuneaki Iwakiri *(Pres)*

MGC Insurance Service, Inc. (1)
15F Kanda Square 2-1 Kandanishikicho 2-chome, Chiyoda-ku, Tokyo, 101-0054, Japan
Tel.: (81) 366263370
Web Site: https://www.mgc-hoken.co.jp
Insurance Services
N.A.I.C.S.: 524210

MGC Logistics Service Mizushima Co., Ltd. (1)
3-10 Mizushima Kaigandori, Kurashiki, 712-8525, Okayama, Japan
Tel.: (81) 86 446 3825
Transportation & Storage Services
N.A.I.C.S.: 488999

MGC Logistics Yamakita Co., Ltd. (1)
950 Kishi Yamakita-machi, Yamakita, 258-0112, Kanagawa, Japan
Tel.: (81) 465 75 2635
Logistics & Transportation Services
N.A.I.C.S.: 541614

MGC NIIGATA SERVICE CO., LTD. (1)
3500 Matsuhamacho, Kita-ku, Niigata, 950-3121, Japan
Tel.: (81) 25 259 6293
Web Site: http://www.mgc.co.jp
Transportation & Storage Services
N.A.I.C.S.: 488999

MGC Pure Chemicals America, Inc. (1)
6560 S Mountain Rd, Mesa, AZ 85212-9716
Tel.: (480) 987-9100
Web Site: https://www.mgcpure.com

Chemical Products Distr
N.A.I.C.S.: 424690

MGC Pure Chemicals Singapore Pte. Ltd. (1)
29 Tuas West Road, Singapore, 638388, Singapore
Tel.: (65) 68978971
Specialty Chemicals Mfr & Distr
N.A.I.C.S.: 325180

MGC Pure Chemicals Taiwan, Inc. (1)
No 12 Jing 1st Rd, Wuqi Dist, Taichung, 435, Taiwan
Tel.: (886) 426584466
Web Site: https://www.mpct.com.tw
Sales Range: $25-49.9 Million
Emp.: 47
Specialty Chemicals Mfr & Distr
N.A.I.C.S.: 325199
Hirokozu Serizawa *(Gen Mgr)*

MGC Specialty Chemicals Netherlands B.V. (1)
Theemsweg 5 3197 KM Botlek, Rotterdam, Netherlands
Tel.: (31) 103216400
Web Site: https://www.msc-n.nl
Chemical Product Mfr & Distr
N.A.I.C.S.: 325998

MGC TRADING (THAILAND) LTD. (1)
18th Floor Unit 1810 Empire Tower No 1 South Sathorn Rd, Yannawa Sathorn, Bangkok, 10120, Thailand
Tel.: (66) 26703417
Web Site: http://www.mgc.co.jp
Emp.: 8
Chemical Product Whslr
N.A.I.C.S.: 424690
Yoshihiro Kawamoto *(Mng Dir)*

MGC Terminal Company, Inc. (1)
7F Hibiya Kokusai Building 2-2-3 Uchisaiwaicho, Chiyoda-ku, Tokyo, 100-0011, Japan
Tel.: (81) 335933035
Web Site: http://www.mgc-terminal.jp
Chemical Products Distr
N.A.I.C.S.: 424690

MGC Woodchem Corporation (1)
8F Ryowa Building 3-6-1 Kanda Surugadai, Chiyoda-ku, Tokyo, 101-0062, Japan
Tel.: (81) 362852817
Web Site: https://www.mgcwoodchem.com
Wood Adhesive Mfr & Distr
N.A.I.C.S.: 325520

MITSUBISHI GAS CHEMICAL EUROPE GMBH (1)
Immermannstr 14-16, 40210, Dusseldorf, Germany
Tel.: (49) 211363080
Web Site: https://www.mgc-europe.de
Sales Range: $50-74.9 Million
Emp.: 9
Chemical Products Distr
N.A.I.C.S.: 424690

MITSUBISHI GAS CHEMICAL SHANGHAI COMMERCE LTD. (1)
2110A Westgate Mall 1038 Nanjing Road W, Shanghai, 200041, China
Tel.: (86) 2162184081
Web Site: http://www.mgc-sh.com
Emp.: 12
Chemical Product Whslr
N.A.I.C.S.: 424690

MT Optics Inc. (1)
Mitsubishi Building 5-2 Marunouchi 2-Chome, Chiyoda-ku, Tokyo, 100-8324, Japan
Tel.: (81) 332834933
Pigment Mfr & Distr
N.A.I.C.S.: 325130

Meihan Shinku Kogyo Co., Ltd. (1)
106-1 Koyama Kanan-cho, Minamikawachi-gun, Osaka, 585-0034, Japan
Tel.: (81) 721903223
Web Site: http://www.msk-japan.co.jp
Plastic Sheet Mfr
N.A.I.C.S.: 326112
Nissho Iwamoto *(Pres)*

Mitsubishi Engineering-Plastics Corporation (1)

MITSUBISHI GAS CHEMICAL COMPANY, INC.

Shiodome Sumitomo-Bldg 25F 1-9-2 Higashi-shinbashi, Minato Ward, Tokyo, 105-0021, Japan
Tel.: (81) 362749000
Emp.: 304
Chemical Product Mfr & Distr
N.A.I.C.S.: 325998
Takashi Komaya *(Pres & CEO)*

Mitsubishi Gas Chemical America, Inc. (1)
655 3rd Ave 19th Fl, New York, NY 10017
Tel.: (212) 687-9030
Web Site: https://www.mgc-a.com
Chemical Product Mfr & Distr
N.A.I.C.S.: 325998
Susumu Kagiwada *(Pres)*

Mitsubishi Gas Chemical Company, Inc. - Kashima Plant (1)
35 Towada, Kamisu, 314-0102, Ibaraki, Japan
Tel.: (81) 299963121
Chemical Products Mfr
N.A.I.C.S.: 325199

Mitsubishi Gas Chemical Company, Inc. - Mizushima Plant (1)
3-10 Mizushima Kaigandori, Kurashiki, 712-8525, Okayama, Japan
Tel.: (81) 864463822
Chemical Products Mfr
N.A.I.C.S.: 325199

Mitsubishi Gas Chemical Company, Inc. - Naniwa Plant (1)
3-27 Funamachi 1-chome, Taisho-ku, Osaka, 551-0022, Japan
Tel.: (81) 665513371
Chemical Products Mfr
N.A.I.C.S.: 325199

Mitsubishi Gas Chemical Company, Inc. - Niigata Plant (1)
3500 Matsuhamacho, Kita-ku, Niigata, 950-3121, Japan
Tel.: (81) 25 258 3474
Web Site: http://www.mgc.co.jp
Chemical Products Mfr
N.A.I.C.S.: 325199

Mitsubishi Gas Chemical Company, Inc. - Yamakita Plant (1)
950 Kishi Yamakita-machi, Ashigarakami-gun, Yamakita, 258-0112, Kanagawa, Japan
Tel.: (81) 465 75 1111
Web Site: http://www.mgc.co.jp
Chemical Products Mfr
N.A.I.C.S.: 325199

Mitsubishi Gas Chemical Company, Inc. - Yokkaichi Plant (1)
4-16 Hinagahigashi 2-chome, Yokkaichi, 510-0886, Mie, Japan
Tel.: (81) 593458800
Chemical Products Mfr
N.A.I.C.S.: 325199

Subsidiary (Domestic):

Mitsubishi Gas Chemical Company, Inc. - Saga Plant (2)
681-45 Kamikumakawa Fuji-cho, Saga, 840-0512, Japan
Tel.: (81) 952642400
Chemical Products Mfr
N.A.I.C.S.: 325199

Mitsubishi Gas Chemical Engineering-Plastics (Shanghai) Co., Ltd. (1)
No 55 Mu Hua Road, Shanghai Chemical Industry Park, Shanghai, 201507, China
Tel.: (86) 2131273366
Chemical Product Mfr & Distr
N.A.I.C.S.: 325998

Mitsubishi Gas Chemical Singapore Pte. Ltd. (1)
4 Shenton Way 28-01 SGX Centre 2, Singapore, 068807, Singapore
Tel.: (65) 62240059
Web Site: https://www.mgcs.com.sg
Sales Range: $50-74.9 Million
Emp.: 13
Natural Gas Extraction Services
N.A.I.C.S.: 211130

Mitsubishi Gas Chemical Trading, Inc. (1)

MITSUBISHI GAS CHEMICAL COMPANY, INC.

Mitsubishi Gas Chemical Company, Inc.—(Continued)
Kanda Square 15F 2-2-1 Kanda-nishikicho, Chiyoda-ku, Tokyo, 101-0054, Japan
Tel.: (81) 366263350
Web Site: https://www.mgctrading.co.jp
Emp.: 444
Chemical Products Distr
N.A.I.C.S.: 424690
Otsuka Hiroyuki (Pres)

Mizushima Kasozai Co., Ltd. (1)
5-2 Marunouchi 2-chome, Chiyoda-ku, Tokyo, 100-8324, Japan
Tel.: (81) 332834733
Emp.: 2
Special Plasticizer Mfr & Distr
N.A.I.C.S.: 325180

Mizushima Paraxylene Co., Ltd. (1)
2-6-3 Otemachi, Chiyoda-ku, Tokyo, 100-8161, Japan
Tel.: (81) 362755109
Chemical Product Mfr & Distr
N.A.I.C.S.: 325998

Nisshin Coloring Co., Ltd. (1)
2500-6 Oaza ogohara, Komono-cho, Mie, 510-1222, Japan
Tel.: (81) 593943100
Web Site: http://www.mgc.co.jp
Plastics Material & Resin Mfr
N.A.I.C.S.: 325211

Nisshin Unyu Co., Ltd. (1)
1318 Tayuhama, Kita-ku, Niigata, 950-3112, Japan
Tel.: (81) 25 259 3255
Web Site: http://www.mgc.co.jp
Transportation & Storage Services
N.A.I.C.S.: 488999

Osaka Naigai Ekiyu Co., Ltd. (1)
2-2-3 Umemachi Konohana-Ku, Konohana-ku, Osaka, 554-0032, Japan
Tel.: (81) 6 6468 4501
Transportation Services
N.A.I.C.S.: 488999

Oshika Formalin Co., Ltd. (1)
5-2 Marunouchi 2-chome, Chiyoda-ku, Tokyo, 100-8324, Japan
Tel.: (81) 332834832
Web Site: http://www.mgc.co.jp
Specialty Chemicals Distr
N.A.I.C.S.: 424690

PT Peroksida Indonesia Pratama (1)
Graha Purna Bakti Building Jl Jend A Yani No 39, PO Box 53, Cikampek, Karawang, 41373, West-Java, Indonesia
Tel.: (62) 264313383
Web Site: http://www.ptpip.co.id
Chemical Product Mfr & Distr
N.A.I.C.S.: 325998
Norikazu Okuda (Pres)

PTM ENGINEERING PLASTICS (NANTONG) CO., LTD. (1)
No171 Minxing Road NETDA, Nantong, 226009, Jiangsu, China
Tel.: (86) 51385922000
Web Site: http://www.mgc.co.jp
Polyacetal Mfr & Distr
N.A.I.C.S.: 325211

Polyols Asia Company, Inc. (1)
5-2 Marunouchi 2-chome, Chiyoda-ku, Tokyo, 100-8324, Japan
Tel.: (81) 332834832
Chemical Product Mfr & Distr
N.A.I.C.S.: 325998

RYODEN KASEI CO., LTD (1)
2-6-1 Miwa, Sanda, 669-1513, Hyogo, Japan
Tel.: (81) 795626803
Web Site: http://www.ryoka.co.jp
Laminate Plastic Products Mfr & Whslr
N.A.I.C.S.: 326130

RYOKO LOGISTICS CO., LTD (1)
2-81 Kamisucho, Toyonaka, 561-0873, Osaka, Japan
Tel.: (81) 6 6331 2453
Web Site: http://www.ryoko-logistics.co.jp
Emp.: 273
Logistics Consulting Services
N.A.I.C.S.: 541614

Ryoko Chemical Co., Ltd. (1)
4-12-20 Nihonbashi-Honcho PMO Nihonbashi-Honcho, chuo-ku, Tokyo, 103-0023, Japan (100%)
Tel.: (81) 368610050
Web Site: http://www.ryoko.co.jp
Sales Range: $75-99.9 Million
Emp.: 130
Industrial Chemicals & Resin Sales
N.A.I.C.S.: 424690

Ryowa Enterprise Co., Ltd. (1)
5-2 Marunouchi 2-chome, Chiyoda-ku, Tokyo, 100-8324, Japan
Tel.: (81) 332834945
Web Site: http://www.mgc.co.jp
Property Management Services
N.A.I.C.S.: 531311

Ryoyo Trading Co., Ltd. (1)
Tokyo Sakurada Bldg 1-3 Nishi-shimbashi 1-chome, Minato-ku, Tokyo, 105 0003, Japan (100%)
Tel.: (81) 335063750
Web Site: http://www.ryoyotrading.com
Sales Range: $300-349.9 Million
Emp.: 49
Insurance Agency & Sales & Distribution of Industrial Chemicals
N.A.I.C.S.: 524210
Shuichi Murai (Pres)

Subsidiary (Non-US):

Shanghai Ryoto Trading Co., Ltd. (2)
2701 Westgate Tower 1038 Nanjing W Road, Jing-an District, Shanghai, 200041, China (100%)
Tel.: (86) 2152280585
Web Site: http://www.ryoyotrading.com
Emp.: 20
Insurance Business Services
N.A.I.C.S.: 524210

Ryoyu Industrial Corp. (1)
192-5 Inamasu, Itakura-ku, Joetsu, 944-0101, Niigata, Japan
Tel.: (81) 255782945
Web Site: https://www.ryoyu-k.co.jp
Heating Equipment Mfr
N.A.I.C.S.: 333414
Hiroyuki Hirayama (Pres)

SHINSANSO KAGAKU CO. (1)
148-58 Aza Yufutsu, Tomakomai, 059-1371, Hokkaido, Japan
Tel.: (81) 144 55 7337
Web Site: http://www.mgc.co.jp
Specialty Chemicals Mfr
N.A.I.C.S.: 325199

Samyoung Pure Chemicals Co., Ltd. (1)
22 1-ro 5-sandan Seongnam-myeon, Dongnam-gu, Cheonan, 31245, Chungcheongnam-do, Korea (South)
Tel.: (82) 415208000
Chemical Product Mfr & Distr
N.A.I.C.S.: 325998
Jeong Kwon (CEO)

Saudi Methanol Company (1)
PO Box 10065, Al-Sinaiyah, Jubail, 31961, Saudi Arabia
Tel.: (966) 33577810
Chemical Product Mfr & Distr
N.A.I.C.S.: 325998

THAI POLYCARBONATE CO., LTD. (1)
Padaeng Industrial Estate 1/1 Padaeng Rd Map-Ta-Phut, Muang, Rayong, 21150, Thailand
Tel.: (66) 38684816
Web Site: https://www.tpcc-tpac.com
Polycarbonate Resin Mfr
N.A.I.C.S.: 325211

Tai Hong Circuit Ind. Co., LTD. (1)
No 81 Guangfu Road, Hsinchu Expanded Industrial Zone, Hukou, 303, Hsinchu, Taiwan
Tel.: (886) 35985111
Web Site: https://www.tci.com.tw
Sales Range: $100-124.9 Million
Emp.: 1,100
Circuit Printing Board; Owned by Changchun Group, Mitsubishi Gas Chemical Company, Inc & Japan Printed Circuit Ind Co

Taixing Lingsu Specialty Materials Co., Ltd. (1)
No 1003 1 Futai Road, Taixing Economic Development Zone, Taixing, Jiangsu, China
Tel.: (86) 52387188006
Chemical Product Mfr & Distr
N.A.I.C.S.: 325998

Taixing Mgc Lingsu Co., Ltd. (1)
No 30 Shugang West Road, Binjiang, Taixing, 225400, China
Tel.: (86) 52387188006
Pigment Mfr & Distr
N.A.I.C.S.: 325130

Thai Polyacetal Co., Ltd. (1)
Emporium Tower Floor 24/4-8 622 Sukhumvit Road, Klongton Klongtoey, Bangkok, 10110, Thailand
Tel.: (66) 22619260
Web Site: http://www.tpcc-tpac.com
Chemical Product Mfr & Distr
N.A.I.C.S.: 325998

Tokyo Shokai, Ltd. (1)
3-6-1 Kanda Surugadai, Chiyoda-ku, Tokyo, 101 0062, Japan
Tel.: (81) 332510171
Web Site: http://www.tokyoshokai.co.jp
Sales Range: $25-49.9 Million
Emp.: 100
Whslr of Compound Resins & Other Industrial Products
N.A.I.C.S.: 325991
Katsushige Hayashi (Pres)

Toyo Kagaku Co., Ltd (1)
1008 Oaza Terajiri hino-cho, Gamo, 529-1606, Shiga, Japan
Tel.: (81) 748 52 5000
Web Site: http://www.toyokagaku.com
Pharmaceutical Products Mfr & Distr
N.A.I.C.S.: 325412
Koichi Oka (CEO)

Yamada Kasei Company., Ltd. (1)
Yamada Bldg 2-8-4, Uchikanda Chiyoda-ku, Tokyo, 101-0047, Japan
Tel.: (81) 332567861
Emp.: 20
Chemical Products Mfr & Whslr
N.A.I.C.S.: 325199
Yoshihiro Yamada (Pres)

Yonezawa DIA Electronics Co., Ltd. (1)
446-3 Hachimanbara 3-chome, Yonezawa, 992-1128, Yamagata, Japan (100%)
Tel.: (81) 238281345
Web Site: http://www.mgc.co.jp
Sales Range: Less than $1 Million
Emp.: 90
Manufacture & Processing of Mass Molding Laminates
N.A.I.C.S.: 322220

Yutaka Chemicals Corporation (1)
1 Akashicho 8-chome, Chuo-ku, Tokyo, 104-0044, Japan
Tel.: (81) 3 5148 7134
Web Site: http://www.mgc.co.jp
Formalin Mfr
N.A.I.C.S.: 325998

Yuzawa Geothermal Power Copration (1)
135-4 Aza Sekinokuchi, Akinomiya, Yuzawa, 019-0321, Akita, Japan
Tel.: (81) 183552555
Thermal Power Distribution Services
N.A.I.C.S.: 221118

MITSUBISHI HC CAPITAL INC.

5-1 Marunouchi 1-chome, Chiyoda-ku, Tokyo, 100-6525, Japan
Tel.: (81) 368653000   JP
Web Site: http://www.mitsubishi-hc-capital.com
Year Founded: 1971
8593—(TKS)
Rev.: $8,657,230,560
Assets: $58,175,164,080
Liabilities: $50,225,618,960
Net Worth: $7,949,545,120
Earnings: $535,594,400
Emp.: 5,563

INTERNATIONAL PUBLIC

Fiscal Year-end: 03/31/21
Equipment Leasing & Financial Services
N.A.I.C.S.: 532490
Tsuyoshi Nonoguchi (Sr Mng Dir)

Subsidiaries:

Bangkok Mitsubishi HC Capital Co., Ltd. (1)
26th Fl Asia Centre Tower 173/35 South Sathorn Road, Thungmahamek Sathorn, Bangkok, 10120, Thailand
Tel.: (66) 20334488
Web Site: http://www.th.mitsubishi-hc-capital.com
Auto Financing & Leasing Services
N.A.I.C.S.: 522220
Toru Iwasawa (Pres)

Bangkok Mitsubishi UFJ Lease Co., Ltd. (1)
26th Fl Asia Centre Tower 173/35 South Sathorn Road, Thungmahamek Sathorn, Bangkok, 10120, Thailand
Tel.: (66) 20334488
Web Site: https://www.th.mitsubishi-hc-capital.com
Sales Range: $1-9.9 Million
Emp.: 100
Financial Lending Services
N.A.I.C.S.: 522299

Beacon Intermodal Leasing, LLC (1)
111 Huntington Ave Ste 500, Boston, MA 02199
Tel.: (617) 345-5600
Web Site: http://www.beaconintermodal.com
Emp.: 70
Container Leasing Services
N.A.I.C.S.: 531130
Katherine McCabe (Pres & CEO)

CL Solution Management Co., Ltd (1)
22-24 Marunouchi 3 Chome, Naka-ku, Nagoya, 460-0002, Aichi, Japan
Tel.: (81) 528579217
Web Site: http://www.lf.mufg.jp
Equipment Leasing Services
N.A.I.C.S.: 532490

CLE Capital Inc. (1)
2200 de la Sidbec Sud Street, Trois Rivieres, G8Z 4H1, QC, Canada
Tel.: (819) 373-8000
Web Site: http://www.clecapital.ca
Business Financing Services
N.A.I.C.S.: 522291

Capital Insurance Corporation (1)
Sumitomo Real Estate Kudan Building 1-8-10, Kudankita Chiyoda-ku, Tokyo, 102-0073, Japan
Tel.: (81) 120777970
Web Site: https://www.capital-sonpo.co.jp
Emp.: 89
Insurance Services
N.A.I.C.S.: 524210

Center Point Development Inc. (1)
Otemachi Financial City Grand Cube 19F Otemachi 1-9-2, Chiyoda-ku, Tokyo, 100-0004, Japan
Tel.: (81) 362061275
Web Site: http://www.centerpoint.jp
Asset Management Services
N.A.I.C.S.: 523940
Eiji Kosuda (Partner)

Chukyo General Lease Co., Ltd (1)
Marunouchi 1-15-15, Naka-ku, 460-0002, Nagoya, Aichi, Japan
Tel.: (81) 522185001
Investment Banking Services
N.A.I.C.S.: 523150

DRS Company Limited (1)
1-9-2 Otemachi Otemachi Financial City Grand Cube 19th floor, Chiyoda-ku, Tokyo, 100-0004, Japan (100%)
Tel.: (81) 368601200
Web Site: https://www.drs.co.jp
IT Equipment, Machine Tools & Measurement Equipment Rental
N.A.I.C.S.: 532420

Diamond Asset Finance Company Limited (1)
Web Site: http://www.dia-asset.co.jp

AND PRIVATE COMPANIES — MITSUBISHI HC CAPITAL INC.

Real Estate Lease, Real Estate Finance & Loans
N.A.I.C.S.: 525990

Diamond Asset Service Company Limited (1)
8-17 Yaesu 1-chome, Chuo-ku, Tokyo, 103-0028, Japan
Tel.: (81) 3 3276 8605
Web Site: http://www.lf.mufg.jp
Administrative Management Services
N.A.I.C.S.: 561110

Engine Lease Finance Corporation (1)
Building 156 Shannon Free Zone, Shannon, Co Clare, Ireland
Tel.: (353) 61363555
Web Site: http://www.elfc.com
Spare Engine Financing & Leasing Services
N.A.I.C.S.: 522220
Yuichiro Noguchi (Chm)

Engs Commercial Finance Co. (1)
1 Pierce Pl, Itasca, IL 60143 (90%)
Tel.: (630) 256-8432
Web Site: http://www.engsfinance.com
Specialized Lease & Loan Solutions to Truck, Trailer & Related Equipment Dealers, Manufacturers & Operators
N.A.I.C.S.: 525990
Mark M. Rosinski (VP-Accts-Natl)

Global Asset Solution Company Limited (1)
5-1 Marunouchi 1 Chome, Chiyoda-ku, Tokyo, 100-6525, Japan
Tel.: (81) 3 6865 3041
Web Site: http://www.lf.mufg.jp
Emp.: 8
Equipment Leasing Services
N.A.I.C.S.: 532420
Mikio Uozaki (Pres)

HSE Ltd. (1)
3-2-2 Saiwaicho, Hitachi, 317-0073, Ibaraki, Japan
Tel.: (81) 294557808
Web Site: http://www.h-sustainable-energy.co.jp
Renewable Energy Power Generation Services
N.A.I.C.S.: 221118

Healthcare Management Partners, Inc. (1)
15F Shiodome Building 1-2-20 Kaigan, Minato-ku, Tokyo, 105-0022, Japan
Tel.: (81) 368605501
Web Site: https://www.hcmp.jp
Health Care Management Services
N.A.I.C.S.: 541611

Hirogin Auto Lease Co. Ltd (1)
7-19 Hondori, Naka-ku, Hiroshima, 730-0035, Japan
Tel.: (81) 825453728
Web Site: http://www.lf.mufg.jp
Industrial Equipments Leasing Services
N.A.I.C.S.: 532490

Hitachi Capital (UK) PLC (1)
Novuna House Thorpe Road, Staines-upon-Thames, TW18 3HP, Surrey, United Kingdom (100%)
Tel.: (44) 01784227322
Web Site: http://www.hitachicapital.co.uk
Rev.: $902,653,926
Assets: $7,513,613,616
Liabilities: $6,709,308,740
Net Worth: $804,304,876
Earnings: $126,521,294
Emp.: 1,365
Fiscal Year-end: 03/31/2019
Leasing & Credit Services
N.A.I.C.S.: 523999
Nat Sims (Sec & Dir-Legal)

Division (Domestic):

Hitachi Capital (UK) - Business Finance Division (2)
Thorpe Road, Staines-upon-Thames, TW18 3HP, Surrey, United Kingdom
Tel.: (44) 1784 227 322
Web Site: http://www.hitachicapital.co.uk
Vehicle Finance Services
N.A.I.C.S.: 532112
Robert Gordon (CEO)

Hitachi Capital (UK) - Consumer Finance Division (2)
2 Apex View, Leeds, LS11 9BH, West Yorkshire, United Kingdom
Tel.: (44) 344 375 5500
Web Site: http://www.hitachicapital.co.uk
Financial Management Services
N.A.I.C.S.: 523999

Hitachi Capital (UK) - Invoice Finance Division (2)
5 Hollinswood Court Stafford Park 1, Telford, TF3 3DE, Shropshire, United Kingdom
Tel.: (44) 8082399368
Web Site: http://www.hitachicapital.co.uk
Factoring Services
N.A.I.C.S.: 522299
Andy Dodd (Mng Dir)

Subsidiary (Non-US):

Hitachi Capital Vehicle Solutions Ltd (2)
Tel.: (44) 3444632900
Web Site: http://www.hitachicapitalvehicle.co.uk
Automobile Leasing Services
N.A.I.C.S.: 522220

Division (Domestic):

Hitachi Capital Vehicle Solutions Ltd. - Commercial Vehicle Services Division (3)
Hakuba House White Horse Business Park, Trowbridge, BA14 0FL, Wilts, United Kingdom
Tel.: (44) 1225 777710
Web Site: http://www.hitachicapital.co.uk
Automobile Leasing Services
N.A.I.C.S.: 522220

Hitachi Capital Auto Lease Corporation (1)
1-3-1 Nishi-Shinbashi Square 8th Floor, Nishi-Shinbashi Minato-ku, Tokyo, 105-0003, Japan
Tel.: (81) 335037401
Web Site: http://www.hitachi-capital-auto.co.jp
Automobile Financing & Leasing Services
N.A.I.C.S.: 522220

Hitachi Capital Canada Corp. (1)
3390 South Service Rd Ste 301, Burlington, L7N 3J5, ON, Canada
Web Site: http://www.hitachicapital.ca
Equipment Financing Services
N.A.I.C.S.: 522220

Hitachi Capital Corporation (1)
Nishi-Shinbashi Square 3-1 Nishi Shimbashi 1-chome, Minato-ku, Tokyo, 105-0003, Japan
Tel.: (81) 335032111
Web Site: http://www.hitachi-capital.co.jp
Sales Range: $1-4.9 Billion
Emp.: 5,558
Personal Credit & Leasing Services
N.A.I.C.S.: 525990
Seiji Kawabe (Pres, CEO & Exec Officer)

Subsidiary (Non-US):

Hitachi Capital (Thailand) Co., Ltd. (2)
17th floor CRC Tower All Seasons Place 87/2 Wireless Road, Lumpini Phatumwan, Bangkok, 10330, Thailand
Tel.: (66) 2 685 3490
Web Site: http://www.hitachi-capital.co.th
Industrial & Communication Equipment Leasing Services
N.A.I.C.S.: 532490

Hitachi Capital Asia Pacific Pte Ltd. (2)
111 Somerset Road 14-05 Triple One Somerset, Singapore, 238164, Singapore
Tel.: (65) 6734 1222
Web Site: http://www.hitachi-capital.com.sg
Financial Management Services
N.A.I.C.S.: 523999

Subsidiary (Domestic):

Hitachi Capital Insurance Corp. (2)
1-8-10 Kudan-kita, Chiyoda Ku, Tokyo, 102-0073, Japan (79.4%)
Tel.: (81) 352761391
Web Site: http://www.hitachi-ins.co.jp
Rev.: $41,349,840
Assets: $148,774,260
Liabilities: $85,046,220
Net Worth: $63,728,040
Earnings: $3,460,920
Emp.: 91
Fiscal Year-end: 03/31/2019
Disability Insurance Services
N.A.I.C.S.: 524128
Keijiro Yodo (Pres)

Subsidiary (Non-US):

Hitachi Capital Leasing (China) Co., Ltd. (2)
Room 1509 Beijing Development Building 5 East Third Ring North Road, Chaoyang District, Beijing, 100004, China
Tel.: (86) 10 6590 9667
Web Site: http://www.hitachi-capital.cn
Financial Lending Services
N.A.I.C.S.: 522220

Subsidiary (Domestic):

Hitachi Capital NBL Corporation (2)
9th Floor Nishi-Shimbashi Square 1-3-1 Nishi-Shimbashi, Minato-ku, Tokyo, 105-0003, Japan
Tel.: (81) 5038162188
Web Site: http://www.hitachi-capital-nbl.co.jp
Emp.: 400
Business Equipment Leasing Services
N.A.I.C.S.: 532420
Takashi Nakamura (Pres)

Subsidiary (US):

Mitsubishi HC Capital America, Inc. (2)
800 Connecticut Ave, Norwalk, CT 06854 (100%)
Tel.: (203) 956-3000
Web Site: https://www.mhccna.com
Financial Management Services
N.A.I.C.S.: 523999
Terry Hatfield (Exec VP-Operational Excellence)

Subsidiary (Domestic):

Global Technology Finance, LLC (3)
4041 MacArthur Blvd 290, Newport Beach, CA 92660
Tel.: (949) 955-1866
Sales Range: $1-9.9 Million
Emp.: 16
Nondepository Credit Intermediation
N.A.I.C.S.: 522299

Hitachi Capital Malaysia Sdn. Bhd. (1)
D-29-3A Menara Suezcap 1 KL Gateway 2 Jalan Kerinchi, 59200, Kuala Lumpur, Malaysia
Tel.: (60) 379412830
Web Site: http://www.hitachi-capital.my
Emp.: 100
Business Financing Services
N.A.I.C.S.: 522291
Masao Nishida (Chm)

Jackson Square Aviation Ireland Limited (1)
Tel.: (353) 15518883
Aircraft Leasing Services
N.A.I.C.S.: 532411
Chris Dailey (Pres & Chief Comml Officer)

Jackson Square Aviation, LLC (1)
909 Montgomery St Ste 500, San Francisco, CA 94133
Tel.: (415) 821-8300
Web Site: https://www.jsa.com
Emp.: 74
Aircraft Leasing Services
N.A.I.C.S.: 532411
Kevin McDonald (CEO)

Japan Infrastructure Initiative Company Limited (1)
10F Meiji Yasuda Life Building 2-1-1, Marunouchi Chiyoda-ku, Tokyo, 100-0005, Japan
Tel.: (81) 368657460
Web Site: http://www.japaninfra.com
Emp.: 26
Investment Services
N.A.I.C.S.: 523999

Hiroaki Odajima (Pres & CEO)

Japan Medical Lease Corporation (1)
1-3-8 Nishigotanda, Shinagawa-ku, Tokyo, 141-0031, Japan
Tel.: (81) 334908641
Web Site: https://www.nichii-lease.com
Emp.: 174
Hospital Equipments Leasing Services
N.A.I.C.S.: 423450

Just Automobile Leasing Co., Ltd (1)
1-1-1 Hayabuchi, Tsuzuki-ku, Yokohama, 224-0025, Kanagawa, Japan
Tel.: (81) 455937774
Web Site: http://www.justauto.co.jp
Sales Range: $100-124.9 Million
Emp.: 134
Automobile Leasing Services
N.A.I.C.S.: 522220

M-CAST, Inc (1)
Tel.: (81) 366759925
Web Site: https://www.e-mcast.com
Sales Range: $25-49.9 Million
Emp.: 34
Medical Equipment Distr
N.A.I.C.S.: 423450

MHC Eco Solutions Co., Ltd. (1)
Nishi-Shinbashi Square 1-3-1 Nishi-Shinbashi, Minato-ku, Tokyo, 105-0003, Japan
Tel.: (81) 335037333
Web Site: https://www.mhc-eco-solutions.co.jp
Global Warming Services
N.A.I.C.S.: 813312

MHC Mobility B.V. (1)
Trondheimweg 5, 9723 TX, Groningen, Netherlands
Tel.: (31) 882828400
Web Site: https://www.mhcmobility.nl
Automobile Financing & Leasing Services
N.A.I.C.S.: 522220
Mark Feddes (COO)

MHC Mobility GmbH (1)
Perfektastrasse 87, 1230, Vienna, Austria
Tel.: (43) 18690001
Web Site: http://www.mhcmobility.at
Automobile Financing & Leasing Services
N.A.I.C.S.: 522220

MHC Mobility Sp. z o.o. (1)
ul Franciszka Klimczaka 1, 02-797, Warsaw, Poland
Tel.: (48) 222236060
Web Site: https://www.mhcmobility.pl
Transportation Leasing Services
N.A.I.C.S.: 532411

MHC Reuse Services Corporation (1)
Nishi-Shinbashi Square 1-3-1, Nishi-Shinbashi Minato-ku, Tokyo, 105-0003, Japan
Tel.: (81) 335037333
Web Site: https://www.mhc-reuse-service.co.jp
Emp.: 92
Household Appliance Whslr
N.A.I.C.S.: 423620

MHC Triple Win Corporation (1)
Nishi-Shinbashi Square 1-3-1, Nishi-Shinbashi Minato-ku, Tokyo, 105-0003, Japan
Tel.: (81) 335037360
Web Site: https://www.mhc-triplewin.co.jp
Accounting Outsourcing Services
N.A.I.C.S.: 541219

MUL Business Company Limited (1)
Tel.: (81) 352171923
Web Site: http://www.lf.mufg.jp
Equipment Leasing Services
N.A.I.C.S.: 532490

MUL Eco-Business Co., Ltd (1)
12-4 Minamisuna 7-chome, Koto-ku, Tokyo, 136-0076, Japan
Tel.: (81) 363889306
Web Site: http://www.lf.mufg.jp
Sales Range: $10-24.9 Million
Emp.: 30
Document Processing Services
N.A.I.C.S.: 561410

MITSUBISHI HC CAPITAL INC.

INTERNATIONAL PUBLIC

Mitsubishi HC Capital Inc.—(Continued)

MUL Energy Investment Company Limited (1)
Jinbocho Mitsui Building 1-105, Kanda Jimbocho Chiyoda-ku, Tokyo, 101-0051, Japan
Tel.: (81) 368959272
Web Site: http://www.mul-ei.co.jp
Renewable Energy Power Generation Services
N.A.I.C.S.: 221118

MUL Insurance Company Limited (1)
9-2 Otemachi 1-chome, Chiyoda-ku, Tokyo, 100-0004, Japan
Tel.: (81) 368601386
Web Site: http://www.lf.mufg.jp
Insurance Consulting Services
N.A.I.C.S.: 524298

MUL Principal Investments Company Limited (1)
5-1 Marunouchi 1-chome, Chiyoda-ku, Tokyo, 100-6525, Japan
Tel.: (81) 3 6865 3022
Web Site: http://www.lf.mufg.jp
Sales Range: $50-74.9 Million
Emp.: 5
Investment Banking Services
N.A.I.C.S.: 523150

MUL Property Co., Ltd. (1)
3-22-24 Marunouchi Nagoya Sakuradori Building, Naka-ku, Nagoya, 460-0002, Aichi, Japan **(100%)**
Tel.: (81) 528579211
Web Site: http://www.mul-property.jp
Sales Range: $125-149.9 Million
Emp.: 44
Property Leasing Services
N.A.I.C.S.: 531190
Tetsuo Kasuya (Chm)

MUL Railcars, Inc. (1)
121 SW Morrison St Ste 1525, Portland, OR 97204
Tel.: (503) 208-9295
Web Site: http://www.mul-railcars.com
Railcar Leasing Services
N.A.I.C.S.: 532411
Andy Vestergaard (CEO)

MUL Realty Advisers Company Limited (1)
2-2-1 Otemachi, Chiyoda-ku, Tokyo, 100-0004, Japan
Tel.: (81) 368609864
Web Site: http://www.mul-ra.co.jp
Asset Management Services
N.A.I.C.S.: 523940

MUL Realty Investment Company Limited (1)
Marunouchi Eiraku Building 1-4-1, Marunouchi Chiyoda-ku, Tokyo, 100-0005, Japan
Tel.: (81) 367759280
Web Site: http://www.mul-ri.co.jp
Real Estate Investment Services
N.A.I.C.S.: 531390
Hidekazu Tanaka (Pres)

MUL Utility Innovation Company Limited (1)
1-5-1 Marunouchi, Chiyoda-ku, Tokyo, 100-6525, Japan
Tel.: (81) 368653096
Web Site: http://www.mul-ui.co.jp
Solar Power Generation Services
N.A.I.C.S.: 221114

Mitsubishi Auto Leasing Corporation (1)
Tamachi Center Bldg 5-34-7 Shiba, Minato-ku, Tokyo, 108-8411, Japan
Tel.: (81) 354760112
Web Site: https://www.mitsubishi-autolease.com
Emp.: 1,084
Financial Management Services
N.A.I.C.S.: 522320

Mitsubishi Electric Credit Corporation (1)
1-6-3 Osaki, Shinagawa-ku, Tokyo, 141-8505, Japan
Tel.: (81) 120505485
Web Site: https://www.mefs.co.jp
Emp.: 383
Consumer Lending Services
N.A.I.C.S.: 522291

Mitsubishi Electric Financial Solutions Corporation (1)
1-6-3 Osaki, Shinagawa-ku, Tokyo, 141-8505, Japan
Tel.: (81) 354965421
Web Site: https://www.mefs.co.jp
Emp.: 383
Credit Purchase Brokerage Services
N.A.I.C.S.: 524126

Mitsubishi HC Business Lease Corporation (1)
1-3-1 Nishi-Shimbashi Nishi-Shimbashi Square, Minato-ku, Tokyo, 105-0003, Japan
Tel.: (81) 5038162157
Web Site: https://www.mitsubishi-hc-bl.co.jp
Emp.: 554
Real Estate Lending Services
N.A.I.C.S.: 531110

Mitsubishi HC Capital (Hong Kong) Limited (1)
16/F Wai Fung Plaza No 664 Nathan Road, Mongkok, Kowloon, China (Hong Kong)
Tel.: (852) 23903481
Web Site: https://www.mitsubishi-hc-capital.com.hk
Loan & Financing Services
N.A.I.C.S.: 522291
Keiichi Sato (Mng Dir)

Mitsubishi HC Capital (Thailand) Co., Ltd. (1)
173/35 26th Fl Asia Centre Tower South Sathorn Road, Thungmahamek Sathorn, Bangkok, 10120, Thailand
Tel.: (66) 20334411
Web Site: https://www.mitsubishi-hc-capital.co.th
Financial Services
N.A.I.C.S.: 523999

Mitsubishi HC Capital Asia Pacific Pte. Ltd. (1)
111 Somerset Road 14-05 TripleOne Somerset, Singapore, 238164, Singapore
Tel.: (65) 67341222
Web Site: https://www.mitsubishi-hc-capital.com.sg
Loan & Financing Services
N.A.I.C.S.: 522291

Mitsubishi HC Capital Canada, Inc. (1)
1100 Burloak Drive Suite 401, Burlington, L7L 6B2, ON, Canada
Web Site: https://www.mhccna.com
Financial Services
N.A.I.C.S.: 523999

Mitsubishi HC Capital Community Corporation (1)
Nishi-Shinbashi Square 1-3-1, Nishi-Shimbashi Minato-ku, Tokyo, 105-0003, Japan
Tel.: (81) 335037322
Web Site: http://www.mitsubishi-hc-capital-community.co.jp
Real Estate Lending Services
N.A.I.C.S.: 531110

Mitsubishi HC Capital Energy Inc. (1)
Jimbocho Mitsui Building 1 105 Kanda Jimbocho, Chiyoda-ku, Tokyo, 101-0051, Japan
Tel.: (81) 368959272
Web Site: https://www.mhc-energy.com
Emp.: 59
Energy Development Services
N.A.I.C.S.: 926110

Mitsubishi HC Capital Estate Plus Inc. (1)
1-6-5 Marunouchi North Exit Building, 14th floor, Tokyo, 100-0005, Japan
Tel.: (81) 368601171
Web Site: https://www.mitsubishi-hc-capital-estateplus.jp
Real Estate Services
N.A.I.C.S.: 531210

Mitsubishi HC Capital Malaysia Sdn. Bhd. (1)
Level D 29 3A Menara Suezcap 1 KL Gateway No 2 Jalan Kerinchi, Gerbang Kerinchi Lestari, 59200, Kuala Lumpur, Malaysia
Tel.: (60) 379412830
Web Site: https://mitsubishi-hc-capital.my
Emp.: 100
Leasing & Financial Services
N.A.I.C.S.: 532120

Mitsubishi HC Capital Management (China) Limited (1)
12/F Wai Fung Plaza 664 Nathan Road, Mongkok, Kowloon, China (Hong Kong)
Tel.: (852) 23903481
Web Site: https://www.mitsubishi-hc-capital-mc.com.hk
Loan & Financing Services
N.A.I.C.S.: 522291
Keiichi Sato (Mng Dir)

Mitsubishi HC Capital Property Inc. (1)
14th Floor Marunouchi North Exit Building 1-6-5 Marunouchi, Chiyoda-ku, Tokyo, 100-0005, Japan
Tel.: (81) 368601171
Web Site: https://www.mitsubishi-hc-capital-property.jp
Real Estate Lending Services
N.A.I.C.S.: 531110

Mitsubishi HC Capital Servicer Corporation (1)
1-3-1 Nishi-Shimbashi Square 9th Floor, Nishi-Shimbashi Minato-ku, Tokyo, 105-0003, Japan
Tel.: (81) 335037390
Web Site: https://www.mitsubishi-hc-servicer.co.jp
Investment Services
N.A.I.C.S.: 523999

Mitsubishi HC Capital Trust Corporation (1)
Nishi-Shinbashi Square 11F 1-3-1, Nishi-Shimbashi Minato-ku, Tokyo, 105-0003, Japan
Tel.: (81) 335032205
Web Site: http://www.mitsubishi-hc-capital-trust.co.jp
Money Lending Services
N.A.I.C.S.: 522390

Mitsubishi HC Capital UK PLC (1)
Novuna House Thorpe Road, Staines-upon-Thames, TW18 3HP, United Kingdom
Tel.: (44) 3433519171
Emp.: 2,200
Vehicle Leasing Financial Services
N.A.I.C.S.: 522320

Mitsubishi UFJ Lease & Finance (China) Co., Ltd. (1)
Room 1004 AZIA Center No 1233 Lujiazui Ring Road, Pudong New District, Shanghai, China
Tel.: (86) 2168880050
Web Site: http://www.cn.lf.mufg.jp
Financial Services
N.A.I.C.S.: 522220

Mitsubishi UFJ Lease & Finance (Hong Kong) Limited (1)
Room 402 Far East Finance Centre 16 Harcourt Road, Hong Kong, China (Hong Kong)
Tel.: (852) 25277620
Web Site: http://www.hk.lf.mufg.jp
Auto & Equipment Financing Services
N.A.I.C.S.: 522220

Mitsubishi UFJ Lease & Finance (Ireland) Limited (1)
Custom House Plaza 3 Harbour Master Pl IFSX, Dublin, Leinster, Ireland
Tel.: (353) 1 670 1822
Sales Range: $50-74.9 Million
Emp.: 2
Equipment Leasing Services
N.A.I.C.S.: 532490

Mitsubishi UFJ Lease (Singapore) Pte. Ltd (1)
7 Straits View 23-01 Marina One East Tower, Singapore, 018936, Singapore
Tel.: (65) 62202515
Web Site: http://www.lf.mufg.jp
Sales Range: $50-74.9 Million
Emp.: 20
Financial Lending Services
N.A.I.C.S.: 522320

Mobility Mixx B.V. (1)
PJ Oudweg 4 ch, 1314, Almere, Netherlands
Tel.: (31) 885272800
Web Site: https://mobilitymixx.com
Information Technology Consulting Services
N.A.I.C.S.: 541512

P.T. Mitsubishi HC Capital and Finance Indonesia (1)
MidPlaza 2 9th Floor Jalan Jenderal Sudirman Kav 10 - 11, Jakarta, 10220, Indonesia
Tel.: (62) 215735905
Web Site: https://www.id.mitsubishi-hc-capital.com
Investment Financing Services
N.A.I.C.S.: 522320

PNW Railcars, Inc. (1)
121 SW Morrison St Ste 900, Portland, OR 97204
Tel.: (503) 208-9295
Web Site: https://www.pnwrailcars.com
Railcar Leasing Services
N.A.I.C.S.: 532411

PT. Arthaasia Finance (1)
Kencana Tower 5 and 6 Floor Jl Raya Meruya Ilir No 88, Business Park Kebon Jeruk, Jakarta, 11620, Indonesia
Tel.: (62) 2158908189
Web Site: https://www.aaf.co.id
Automobile Financing & Leasing Services
N.A.I.C.S.: 522220

PT. Mitsubishi UFJ Lease & Finance Indonesia (1)
MidPlaza 2 9th Floor Jalan Jenderal Sudirman Kav 10 - 11, Jakarta, 10220, Indonesia
Tel.: (62) 215735905
Web Site: http://www.id.lf.mufg.jp
Loan & Financing Services
N.A.I.C.S.: 522291
Isao Someya (Pres)

PT. Takari Kokoh Sejahtera (1)
Jl Arjuna Utara No 131, Kec Tj Duren Selatan Kel Grogol Petamburan, Jakarta Barat, 11470, Indonesia
Tel.: (62) 215640101
Web Site: https://www.takari.co.id
Loan & Financing Services
N.A.I.C.S.: 522291
Saphira Devi Karjono (Pres)

Sekisui Leasing Co., Ltd. (1)
2F KDX Kobayashi Doshomachi Building 4-4-10 Doshomachi, Chuo-ku, Osaka, 541-0045, Japan
Tel.: (81) 667343600
Web Site: https://www.sekisui-lease.co.jp
Loan Services
N.A.I.C.S.: 522390

The Casio Lease Company Limited (1)
6-2 Honmachi 1-chome, Shibuya-ku, Tokyo, 151-8543, Japan
Tel.: (81) 3 5334 4855
Web Site: https://www.casio-lease.co.jp
Investment Banking Services
N.A.I.C.S.: 523150
Hiroyuki Kimishima (Pres & Dir)

U-Machine (China) Co., Ltd. (1)
Unit 1601-02 Phase I Qiantan Oriental Plaza, No 512 Haiyang West Road and 38 Qianmao Road Pudong New District, Shanghai, China
Tel.: (86) 2161096065
Web Site: https://www.u-machine.co.jp
Used Machine Distr
N.A.I.C.S.: 423830

U-Machine (Thailand) Co., Ltd. (1)
173/35 Asia Centre Tower 26th Floor South Sathorn Road, Thungmahamek Sathorn, Bangkok, 10120, Thailand
Tel.: (66) 21636424
Used Machine Distr
N.A.I.C.S.: 423830

U-Machine Inc (1)
Nagoya Sakura-dori Building 3-22-24 Marunouchi, Naka-ku, Nagoya, 460-0002, Aichi, Japan
Tel.: (81) 528579213
Web Site: https://www.u-machine.co.jp

AND PRIVATE COMPANIES — MITSUBISHI HEAVY INDUSTRIES, LTD.

Emp.: 40
Industrial Equipment Sales
N.A.I.C.S.: 423830

MITSUBISHI HEAVY INDUSTRIES, LTD.
2-3 Marunouchi 3-chome, Chiyoda-ku, Tokyo, 100-8332, Japan
Tel.: (81) 362756200   JP
Web Site: https://www.mhi.com
Year Founded: 1950
MHVYF—(OTCIQ)
Rev.: $30,783,741,670
Assets: $41,353,871,990
Liabilities: $25,749,949,050
Net Worth: $15,603,922,940
Earnings: $1,467,572,030
Emp.: 77,778
Fiscal Year-end: 03/31/24
Ships, Steel Structures, Power Systems, Nuclear & Other Plants, Machinery for Industrial & General Use, Aerospace Systems & Airconditioning & Refrigeration Systems
N.A.I.C.S.: 333120
Takashi Mikogami *(Pres/CEO-Logistics, Thermal & Drive Sys & Exec VP)*

Subsidiaries:

Aomori Daiya Co., Ltd. (1)
1-1, Keyaki 1-chome, Aomori, 030-0918, Japan
Tel.: (81) 17 726 6600
Marine Engine Parts Distr & Installation Services
N.A.I.C.S.: 423860

Artemis Intelligent Power Ltd.
Unit 3 Edgefield Industrial Estate, Loanhead, EH20 9TB, Midlothian, United Kingdom
Tel.: (44) 7976730264
Web Site: http://www.digitaldisplacement.com
Hydraulic Pump Product Mfr
N.A.I.C.S.: 333996

Breaker Electrical Pty. Ltd. (1)
19 Lang Parade, Milton, 4064, QLD, Australia
Tel.: (61) 738780888
Thermal Power Generation Product Distr
N.A.I.C.S.: 423840

C.D.P.A. – LD3E Co., Ltd. (1)
Z l du Bignon Erbray, BP 107, 44 143, Chateaubriant, France
Tel.: (33) 2 40 28 27 85
Agricultural Machinery Distr
N.A.I.C.S.: 423820

CBC Industrias Pesadas S.A. (1)
Rod Dom Gabriel Paulino Bueno Couto SN - Km 68 - Medeiros, Caixa Postal 820, Jundiai, 13212-240, SP, Brazil
Tel.: (55) 1144313900
Web Site: https://www.cbcsa.com.br
N.A.I.C.S.: 336611

Caterpillar Japan Ltd. (1)
1106-4 Shimizu Uozumi-cho Akashi-city, Hyogo, 674-8686, Japan
Tel.: (81) 357171121
Web Site: http://www.cat.com
Sales Range: $100-124.9 Million
Emp.: 350
Mfr, Sales & Marketing of Construction Equipment & Engines; Joint Venture of Caterpillar Inc. & Mitsubishi Heavy Industries, Ltd.
N.A.I.C.S.: 333120

Subsidiary (Domestic):

Caterpillar Operator Training Ltd. (2)
3700 Tana, Sagamihara, 252-5292, Kanagawa, Japan
Tel.: (81) 427637130
Web Site: http://cot.jpncat.com
Industrial Machinery Operating Training Services
N.A.I.C.S.: 611513

Changzhou Baoling Heavy & Industrial Machinery Co., Ltd. (1)
41 Xinye Road, Changzhou, Jiangsu, China (100%)
Tel.: (86) 5198 325 8150
Web Site: https://www.cblhi.com
Sales Range: $100-124.9 Million
Emp.: 500
Design & Manufacturing of Various Types of Steel-Making Machines (Including Spare Parts) & Industrial Machinery
N.A.I.C.S.: 333248

Chiba Eco-Creation Co., Ltd. (1)
727-1 Sankaku-cho, Hanamigawa-ku, Chiba, 262-0011, Japan
Tel.: (81) 43 286 3932
Environmental Consulting Services
N.A.I.C.S.: 541620

Choryo Designing Co., Ltd. (1)
1-1 Akunoura-machi, Nagasaki, 850-8610, Japan
Tel.: (81) 95 828 4121
Web Site: http://www.medis.co.jp
Shipping Marine Equipment Mfr
N.A.I.C.S.: 336999

Choryo Senpaku Kouji Co., Ltd. (1)
1-1 Akunoura-machi, Nagasaki, 850-8610, Japan
Tel.: (81) 95 864 1080
Web Site: http://www.mhi.co.jp
Marine Component Mfr & Distr
N.A.I.C.S.: 332999
Masataka Nakamura *(Mng Dir)*

Chubu Jukan Operation Co., Ltd. (1)
22-9 Meieki 2-chome, Nishi-ku, Nagoya, 451-0045, Japan
Tel.: (81) 52 541 3900
Waste Treatment Equipment Maintenance Services
N.A.I.C.S.: 811310

Churyo Engineering Co., Ltd. (1)
3-18-1 Sakae, Naka-ku, Nagoya, 460-0008, Aichi, Japan
Tel.: (81) 528 665 9800
Web Site: http://www.churyo.co.jp
Emp.: 1,060
Aircraft Equipment Mfr
N.A.I.C.S.: 336413

Commercial Airplane Company (1)
2-3 Uchi-saiwai-cho 2-chome, Chiyoda-ku, Tokyo, 100-0011, Japan
Tel.: (81) 3 3503 3221
Commercial Airplane Mfr
N.A.I.C.S.: 336411

Concast (India) Ltd. (1)
47-48 Jolly Maker Chambers II, Nariman Point, Mumbai, 400 021, India
Tel.: (91) 2222020414
Web Site: http://www.concastindia.com
Slab & Billet Casting Product Mfr
N.A.I.C.S.: 331110

Concentric, LLC (1)
1621 W Crosby Rd, Carrollton, TX 75006 (100%)
Tel.: (972) 242-2779
Web Site: http://www.concentricusa.com
Facilities Services
N.A.I.C.S.: 561210
John Shea *(Pres)*

Subsidiary (Domestic):

All Battery Sales & Service, Inc. (2)
727 134th St SW, Everett, WA 98204-6305
Tel.: (425) 743-7677
Web Site: http://www.allbatterysalesandservice.com
Hazardous Waste Collection
N.A.I.C.S.: 562112
Jack R. Bradbury *(Gen Mgr)*

Indy Power Grid LLC (2)
3950 Culligan Ave Ste G, Indianapolis, IN 46218
Tel.: (317) 547-4743
Web Site: http://www.indypowergrid.com
Rev.: $4,606,000
Emp.: 7
Electrical Apparatus & Equipment, Wiring Supplies & Related Equipment Merchant Whslr
N.A.I.C.S.: 423610

Jantech Services, Inc. (2)
5004A W Linebaugh Ave, Tampa, FL 33624
Tel.: (919) 872-4556
Web Site: http://www.jantechups.com
Computer & Office Machine Repair & Maintenance
N.A.I.C.S.: 811210
Jay A. Nizborski *(Founder, Pres & CFO)*

STANGCO Industrial Equipment Inc. (2)
3330 W Castor St, Santa Ana, CA 92704-3908
Web Site: http://www.stangco.com
Industrial Machinery & Equipment Merchant Whslr
N.A.I.C.S.: 423830
Gregory Brandt *(Mgr-Ops)*

Daiya Building Service Co., Ltd. (1)
4-11-1 Shiba TB Tamachi Building, Minato-ku, Tokyo, 108-0014, Japan
Tel.: (81) 33 454 2761
Web Site: https://www.dybs.jp
Emp.: 261
Building Maintenance Services
N.A.I.C.S.: 561730

Daiya Logistics Co., Ltd. (1)
5-29 Sakuragi-cho, Nishi-ku, Yokohama, 220-0021, Japan
Tel.: (81) 452013732
Transportation Services
N.A.I.C.S.: 485999

Daiya PR Co., Ltd. (1)
16-5 Konan 2-chome, Minato-ku, Tokyo, 108-0075, Japan
Tel.: (81) 3 6716 5299
Web Site: http://www.daiya-pr.co.jp
Online Advertising Services
N.A.I.C.S.: 541810

Dia Ecotech Hiroshima Co., Ltd. (1)
5-1 Ebaoki-machi, Naka-ku, Hiroshima, 730-0837, Japan
Tel.: (81) 82 235 3058
Plastic Containers Packaging & Storage Services
N.A.I.C.S.: 561910

Diamond Air Service Incorporation. (1)
1 Toyoba Toyoyama-cho, Nishikasugai-gun, Komaki, 480-0293, Aichi, Japan
Tel.: (81) 56 829 0020
Web Site: https://www.das.co.jp
Sales Range: $50-74.9 Million
Emp.: 150
Aircraft Maintenance Services
N.A.I.C.S.: 488190
Toru Fujita *(Pres)*

Diamond F.C. Partners, Co., Ltd. (1)
2-3 Marunouchi 3-chome, Chiyoda-ku, Tokyo, 100-8332, Japan
Tel.: (81) 5037799188
Thermal Power Generation Product Distr
N.A.I.C.S.: 423840

Diamond GT Service Europe S.r.l. (1)
Via Valle Di Sotto 3/G, Cremella, 23894, Lecco, Italy
Tel.: (39) 0399210427
Thermal Power Generation Product Distr
N.A.I.C.S.: 423840

Diamond Office Service Co., Ltd. (1)
17-12 Shibaura 3-chome, Minato-ku, Tokyo, 108-0023, Japan
Tel.: (81) 354275611
Office & Business Product Services
N.A.I.C.S.: 561499

Diamond Travel Co., Ltd. (1)
6-22 Kan-on-shin-machi 2-chome, Nishi-ku, Hiroshima, 733-0036, Japan
Tel.: (81) 82 292 8880
Web Site: http://www.dtc-h.co.jp
Travel Management Services
N.A.I.C.S.: 561599

Diamond WTG Engineering & Services, Inc. (1)
Riviera Plz Ste 500 1618 SW 1st Ave, Portland, OR 97201
Tel.: (971) 361-2267
Wind Power Generation Services
N.A.I.C.S.: 221115

Diastein Co., Ltd. (1)
4711-3 Kamitonno, Nogata, 822-0011, Fukuoka, Japan
Tel.: (81) 949 29 0003
Web Site: http://www.mhi.co.jp
Wind Turbine Gear Mfr & Distr
N.A.I.C.S.: 333612

E-Techno Ltd. (1)
1-1-1 Wadasaki-cho, Hyogo-ku, Kobe, 652-8585, Japan
Tel.: (81) 78 672 4050
Web Site: https://www.techno-denshi.jp
Electronic Components Mfr
N.A.I.C.S.: 334419

Energis Co., Ltd. (1)
1-1 Wadasakicho 1-Chome, Hyogo-ku, Kobe, 652-0854, Japan
Tel.: (81) 78 672 4990
Web Site: http://www.energis.co.jp
Emp.: 60
Nuclear Energy Consulting Services
N.A.I.C.S.: 541690
Takao Nakagawa *(CEO)*

Global Component Technologies Corporation (1)
1-15-9 Osaki, Shinagawa-ku, Tokyo, 141-0032, Japan
Tel.: (81) 366369000
Web Site: http://www.gctengine.co.jp
Emp.: 306
Engine Parts Mfr & Retailer
N.A.I.C.S.: 336310
Hiroshi Narukawa *(Pres & CEO)*

Higashi Chugoku Ryoju Estate Co., Ltd. (1)
11-20 Itosaki 2-chome, Mihara, 729-0324, Hiroshima, Japan
Tel.: (81) 848 62 6111
Web Site: http://www.eryoko.co.jp
Civil Engineering Construction Services
N.A.I.C.S.: 237990

Hiroji Center Co., Ltd. (1)
10-17 Kan-on-shin-machi 2-chome, Nishi-ku, Hiroshima, 733-0036, Japan
Tel.: (81) 82 232 6418
Web Site: http://www.mhi.co.jp
Driving School Operation Services
N.A.I.C.S.: 611692

Hiroshima Ryoju Engineering Co., Ltd. (1)
6-22 Kan-on-shin-machi 4-chome, Nishi-ku, Hiroshima, 733-8553, Japan
Tel.: (81) 822319181
Web Site: http://www.mhi.co.jp
Packaging Machinery Mfr & Distr
N.A.I.C.S.: 333993

Hokkaido Service Engineering Co., Ltd. (1)
789 Herokaruusu Horikappu-mura-aza Tomari-mura, Furuu-gun, Hokkaido, 045-0201, Japan
Tel.: (81) 135 75 2523
Nuclear Power Generation Services
N.A.I.C.S.: 221113

JR West Properties Co., Ltd. (1)
34-6 Shiba 5-chome, Minato-ku, Tokyo, 108-0014, Japan
Tel.: (81) 366869380
Thermal Power Generation Product Distr
N.A.I.C.S.: 423840

Japan Casting & Forging Corporation (1)
46-59 Sakinohama Nakabaru, Tobata-ku, Kitakyushu, 804-8555, Japan
Tel.: (81) 93 884 0011
Web Site: http://www.jcf.co.jp
Sales Range: $200-249.9 Million
Emp.: 650
Steel Casting Mfr
N.A.I.C.S.: 331513
Tomiyoshi Masuda *(Pres & CEO)*

Jukan Operation Co., Ltd. (1)
14th floor Yokohama Blue Avenue Building 4-2 Minatomirai 4-chome, Nishi-ku, Yokohama, 220-0012, Kanagawa, Japan
Tel.: (81) 45 227 1250
Environmental Equipment Maintenance Services
N.A.I.C.S.: 811310

Jyuukan Urban Facilities Service Co., Ltd. (1)

MITSUBISHI HEAVY INDUSTRIES, LTD.

INTERNATIONAL PUBLIC

Mitsubishi Heavy Industries, Ltd.—(Continued)
4-1 Wadamiya-dori 5-chome, Hyogo-ku,
Kobe, 652-0863, Hyogo, Japan
Tel.: (81) 78 686 1060
Web Site: http://www.mhi.co.jp
Industrial Machinery Maintenance Services
N.A.I.C.S.: 811310

Kagoshima Daiya Co., Ltd. (1)
5-9 Taniyama-ko 2-chome, Kagoshima,
891-0131, Japan
Tel.: (81) 99 284 2010
Hydraulic Fishing Equipment Distr & Maintenance Services
N.A.I.C.S.: 423830

Kaliakra Wind Power AD (1)
114 Vasil Levski Blvd, 1527, Sofia, Bulgaria
Tel.: (359) 29433060
Web Site: http://www.kwp.bg
Emp.: 14
Wind Power Generation Services
N.A.I.C.S.: 221115

Kanmon Dock Service, Ltd. (1)
16-1 Hikoshima-enoura-machi 6-chome,
Shimonoseki, 750-8505, Yamaguchi, Japan
Tel.: (81) 83 266 8311
Industrial Equipment Maintenance Services
N.A.I.C.S.: 811310

Konan Kucyou Co., Ltd. (1)
4-97 Uedahigashi-machi, Nishinomiya, 663-8133, Hyogo, Japan
Tel.: (81) 798 40 4092
Web Site: http://www.konankuchou.co.jp
Emp.: 10
Air Conditioning & Refrigeration Equipment Distr
N.A.I.C.S.: 423730
Hiromi Miyazaki *(Office Mgr)*

Koryo Engineering Co., Ltd. (1)
8-19 Arai-cho Shinhama 2-chome,
Takasago, 676-0008, Hyogo, Japan
Tel.: (81) 79 442 3868
Web Site: http://www.koryo.co.jp
Nuclear Equipment Mfr
N.A.I.C.S.: 334517

Kouza Eco-Creation Co., Ltd. (1)
3-8-10 Kokubuminami, Ebina, 243-0405,
Kanagawa, Japan
Tel.: (81) 462310235
Thermal Power Generation Product Distr
N.A.I.C.S.: 423840

Kowa Kogyo Co., Ltd. (1)
3-10 Dejima-machi, Nagasaki, 850-0862,
Japan
Tel.: (81) 95 824 3638
Ship Building Services
N.A.I.C.S.: 336611
Toshihiro Ide *(Pres)*

Kyushu Jukan Operation Co., Ltd. (1)
8-27 Hakataeki-chuogai, Hakata-ku, Fukuoka, 812-0012, Japan
Tel.: (81) 92 471 7953
Web Site: http://www.mhi.co.jp
Environmental Equipment Maintenance Services
N.A.I.C.S.: 811310

Logisnext Chubu Co., Ltd. (1)
1-52 Shinyoshi-cho, Nakagawa-ku, Nagoya,
454-0822, Aichi Prefecture, Japan
Tel.: (81) 523690558
Handling Equipment Mfr
N.A.I.C.S.: 333924

Logisnext Chugoku Co., Ltd. (1)
4-6-61 Kanonshinmachi, Nishi-ku, Hiroshima, 733-0036, Japan
Tel.: (81) 825032342
Handling Equipment Mfr
N.A.I.C.S.: 333924

Logisnext Hokkaido Co., Ltd. (1)
6-3-1 Ryutsu Center, Shiroishi-ku, Sapporo,
003-0030, Hokkaido, Japan
Tel.: (81) 118924149
Handling Equipment Mfr
N.A.I.C.S.: 333924

Logisnext Kinki Co., Ltd. (1)
2-3-13 Chibune, Nishiyodogawa-ku, Osaka,
555-0013, Japan
Tel.: (81) 664775584

Handling Equipment Mfr
N.A.I.C.S.: 333924

Logisnext Kyushu Co., Ltd. (1)
1-38-24 Kanenokuma, Hakata-ku, Fukuoka,
812-0863, Japan
Tel.: (81) 925033310
Handling Equipment Mfr
N.A.I.C.S.: 333924

Logisnext Manufacturing (Thailand) Co., Ltd. (1)
7/353Moo 6 Temboi Map Yang Phon,
Amata City Industrial Estate, Pluak Daeng,
Thailand
Tel.: (66) 38650961
Handling Equipment Mfr
N.A.I.C.S.: 333924

Logisnext Shikoku Co., Ltd. (1)
1645-1 Mimaya-cho, Takamatsu, 761-8042,
Kagawa, Japan
Tel.: (81) 878135252
Handling Equipment Mfr
N.A.I.C.S.: 333924

Logisnext Shinetsu Co., Ltd. (1)
1-8-19 Akebono-cho, Konan-ku, Niigata,
950-0134, Japan
Tel.: (81) 253811081
Handling Equipment Mfr
N.A.I.C.S.: 333924

Logisnext Shizuoka Co., Ltd. (1)
7-8-1 Magarikane, Suruga-ku, Shizuoka,
422-8006, Japan
Tel.: (81) 542831215
Handling Equipment Mfr
N.A.I.C.S.: 333924

Logisnext Tohoku Co., Ltd. (1)
3-2-8 Oroshimachi-Higashi, Wakabayashi-ku, Sendai, 984-0002, Miyagi Prefecture,
Japan
Tel.: (81) 222880911
Handling Equipment Mfr
N.A.I.C.S.: 333924

Logisnext Tokyo Co., Ltd. (1)
6-1-1 Heiwajima, Ota-ku, Tokyo, 143-0006,
Japan
Tel.: (81) 337673381
Handling Equipment Mfr
N.A.I.C.S.: 333924

Logisnext UniCarriers Co., Ltd. (1)
35-2 Dainichihigashimachi, Moriguchi, 570-0016, Osaka, Japan
Tel.: (81) 669021133
Handling Equipment Mfr
N.A.I.C.S.: 333924

MCO Saudi Arabia Limited (1)
Al khobar Gate Tower Al Sheikh Tower 7th
Floor Office No 073, Khobar -Dammam
Highway King Fahd Road Al Bandariyah, Al
Khobar, Saudi Arabia
Tel.: (966) 138965354
Gas Compressor Mfr & Distr
N.A.I.C.S.: 333912

MH Power Systems Korea, Ltd. (1)
9F West Tower Mirae Asset Center 1 26
Eulji-ro 5-gil, Jung-gu, Seoul, 04539, Korea
(South)
Tel.: (82) 221870200
Thermal Power Distribution Services
N.A.I.C.S.: 221118

MH Power Systems Middle East, LLC (1)
Plot 96NR27, PO Box 52309, Industrial City
of Abu Dhabi III, Abu Dhabi, United Arab
Emirates
Tel.: (971) 25501504
Thermal Power Generation Product Distr
N.A.I.C.S.: 423840

MHI Accounting Service, Ltd. (1)
16-5 Konan 2-chome, Minato-ku, Tokyo,
108-0075, Japan
Tel.: (81) 36 716 2781
Web Site: http://www.mhi.co.jp
Financial Contracting Services
N.A.I.C.S.: 523910

MHI Aero Engine Service Co., Ltd. (1)
1200 Higashitanaka, Komaki, 485-0826,
Aichi, Japan
Tel.: (81) 56 878 0300

Web Site: http://www.mhi-aes.co.jp
Sales Range: $150-199.9 Million
Emp.: 175
Aircraft Engine Parts Distr & Maintenance Services
N.A.I.C.S.: 423860
Yojiro Kakuma *(Pres)*

MHI Aerospace Logitem Co., Ltd. (1)
10 Oye-cho, Minato-ku, Nagoya, 455-0024,
Japan
Tel.: (81) 52 322 2630
Web Site: http://www.mhiasl.co.jp
Logistics Consulting Servies
N.A.I.C.S.: 541614

MHI Aerospace Production, Ltd. (1)
10 Oe-cho, Minato-ku, Nagoya, 455-0024,
Japan (100%)
Tel.: (81) 52 611 9591
Web Site: http://www.mitsubishi-map.co.jp
Emp.: 1,000
Aircraft & Space Equipment Mfr
N.A.I.C.S.: 336413

MHI Aerospace Systems Corp. (1)
10 Oe-cho, Minato-ku, Nagoya, 455-8515,
Japan
Tel.: (81) 52 614 2488
Web Site: https://www.masc.co.jp
Emp.: 213
Aerospace Control System Software Development Services
N.A.I.C.S.: 541511

MHI Aerospace Vietnam Co., Ltd. (1)
Plot No N-8 Thang Long Industrial Park,
Dong Anh District, Hanoi, Vietnam
Tel.: (84) 4 3959 0130
Emp.: 400
Civil Airline Component Assembling Services
N.A.I.C.S.: 488190
Yoshiki Ito *(Gen Dir)*

MHI Airport Environment Co., Ltd. (1)
1 Senshu Kuko-minami, Sennan, 549-0021,
Osaka, Japan
Tel.: (81) 72 456 6185
Web Site: http://www.mhi.co.jp
Airport Environmental Consulting Services
N.A.I.C.S.: 541620

MHI Australia, Pty. Ltd. (1)
Level 29 Chifley Tower 2 Chifley Square,
Sydney, 2000, NSW, Australia
Tel.: (61) 292388078
Engineering Electrical Equipment Mfr
N.A.I.C.S.: 335999

MHI Automotive Capital LLC (1)
16-5 Konan 2-chome, Minato-ku, Tokyo,
108-0075, Japan
Tel.: (81) 367162030
Engineering Electrical Equipment Mfr
N.A.I.C.S.: 335999

MHI Business Risk Support, Ltd. (1)
34-7 Shiba 5-chome, Minato-ku, Tokyo,
108-0014, Japan
Tel.: (81) 354439824
Thermal Power Generation Product Distr
N.A.I.C.S.: 423840

MHI Canada Aerospace, Inc. (1)
6390 Northwest Drive, Mississauga, L4V
1S1, ON, Canada
Tel.: (905) 612-6781
Web Site: http://www.mhi.co.jp
Aircraft Part Mfr
N.A.I.C.S.: 336413

MHI Capital America, Inc. (1)
20 E Greenway Plz Ste 830, Houston, TX
77046
Tel.: (346) 308-8871
Thermal Power Generation Product Distr
N.A.I.C.S.: 423840

MHI Capital Asia Pacific Pte. Ltd. (1)
150 Beach Road 29-00 Gateway West, Singapore, 189720, Singapore
Tel.: (65) 63055200
Thermal Power Generation Product Distr
N.A.I.C.S.: 423840

MHI Compressor do Brazil Ltda. (1)
Avenida Doutor Morato 190 Sala 01 Vila

Rezende, Piracicaba, 13405-260, Sao
Paulo, Brazil
Tel.: (55) 1925342003
Gas Compressor Mfr & Distr
N.A.I.C.S.: 333912

MHI Diesel Service Engineering Co., Ltd. (1)
1-1 Wadasaki-cho 1-chome, Hyogo-ku,
Kobe, 652-8585, Japan
Tel.: (81) 78 672 4072
Web Site: http://www.mhi-dse.co.jp
Emp.: 100
Material Handling Equipment Distr
N.A.I.C.S.: 423830
Yutaka Sakai *(Mgr-Sls)*

MHI Energy & Service Co., Ltd. (1)
8-1 Sachiura 1-chome, Kanazawa-ku, Yokohama, 236-8515, Japan
Tel.: (81) 45 771 3003
Electric Power Distr
N.A.I.C.S.: 221122
Komiyama Masahito *(Mgr-Tech)*

MHI Engine System (Shenzhen) Co., Ltd. (1)
No 7 Building No 18 South Huanguan Road
Guanlan, Baoan District, Shenzhen, Guangdong, China
Tel.: (86) 755 3388 3030
Web Site: http://www.mhi.co.jp
Diesel Power Generation Parts Distr
N.A.I.C.S.: 423830

MHI Engine System Hong Kong Ltd. (1)
Suite 11218 11/F Ocean Centre Harbour
City, Tsim Tsa Tsui, Kowloon, China (Hong Kong)
Tel.: (852) 2375 1816
Diesel Power Generation Parts Distr
N.A.I.C.S.: 423120

MHI Engine System Middle East FZE (1)
Q4-44 Sharjah Airport International Free
Zone Saif Zone, PO Box 121801, Sharjah,
United Arab Emirates
Tel.: (971) 65489295
Power Generator Parts Distr
N.A.I.C.S.: 423610

MHI Engine System Philippines, Inc. (1)
24 Warehouse 4C Sunblest Compound KM
23 West Service Road BO, Cupang,
Muntinlupa, 1700, Metro Manila, Philippines
Tel.: (63) 2 775 0209
Diesel Power Generating Equipment Sales
& Installation Services
N.A.I.C.S.: 423440

MHI Engine System Vietnam Co., Ltd. (1)
39 Dai Lo Huu Nghi, Vietnam Singapore
Industrial Park, Thuan An, Binh Duong,
Vietnam
Tel.: (84) 2743769251
Power Generator Parts Distr
N.A.I.C.S.: 423610

MHI Engineering & Industrial Projects India Private Limited (1)
Unit No 907 Unitech Signature Towers
Tower-B 9th Floor South City-I, Gurgaon,
122 001, Haryana, India
Tel.: (91) 1244989000
Web Site: http://www.mhieip.com
Industrial & General Machinery Mfr
N.A.I.C.S.: 333998
Debraj Sen *(Head-Bus Dev)*

MHI Equipment Alsace S.A.S (MEA) (1)
26 rue Francois Spoerry, 68100, Mulhouse,
France
Tel.: (33) 38 936 6565
Web Site: http://www.mhi.co.jp
Emp.: 85
Diesel Engine Mfr & Distr
N.A.I.C.S.: 336310
Ichiro Ichihashi *(Pres)*

MHI Equipment Europe B.V. (1)
Damsluisweg 2, PO Box 30101, 1332 EC,
Almere, Netherlands (100%)
Tel.: (31) 365388311
Web Site: http://www.mhimee.nl

AND PRIVATE COMPANIES — MITSUBISHI HEAVY INDUSTRIES, LTD.

Sales Range: $200-249.9 Million
Emp.: 914
N.A.I.C.S.: 336611
Takashi Kado (Pres)

MHI Executive Experts Co., Ltd. (1)
4-36 Hon-machi, Naka-ku, Yokohama, 231-0005, Kanagawa, Japan
Tel.: (81) 452227628
Construction & Engineering Services
N.A.I.C.S.: 541330

MHI Facility Service Co., Ltd. (1)
34-6 Shiba 5-chome, Minato-ku, Tokyo, 108-0014, Japan
Tel.: (81) 334511172
Thermal Power Generation Product Distr
N.A.I.C.S.: 423840

MHI Finance Co., Ltd. (1)
16-5 Konan 2-chome, Minato-ku, Tokyo, 108-0075, Japan
Tel.: (81) 3 6716 2690
Web Site: http://www.mhi-global.com
Industrial Machinery Leasing Services
N.A.I.C.S.: 532490

MHI General Services Co., Ltd. (1)
1-1 Wadasaki-cho 1-chome, Kobe, 652-0854, Hyogo, Japan
Tel.: (81) 78 671 4425
Web Site: http://www.mgs-web.jp
Factories Utility Services
N.A.I.C.S.: 561990

MHI Haseg Co., Ltd. (1)
261 Yamanobe, Katori, 287-0042, Chiba, Japan
Tel.: (81) 478585330
Web Site: http://www.mhi-haseg.com
Industrial Machinery Products Mfr
N.A.I.C.S.: 333248

MHI Information Systems Co., Ltd. (1)
1-1 Akunoura-machi, Nagasaki, 850-8610, Japan
Tel.: (81) 95 862 5550
Emp.: 900
Computer Software Development Services
N.A.I.C.S.: 541511
Shuji Karafuda (Mgr)

MHI International Investment B.V. (1)
Atrium Strawinskyluan 3105, 10772X, Amsterdam, Netherlands
Tel.: (31) 20 6465996
Investment Management Service
N.A.I.C.S.: 523999

MHI Logitec Company Limited (1)
1200 Oaza Higashitanaka, Komaki, 485-0826, Aichi Prefecture, Japan
Tel.: (81) 568790710
Aircraft Part Mfr
N.A.I.C.S.: 336413

MHI Machine Tool Engineering Co., Ltd (1)
130 Roku-jizo, Ritto, 520-3017, Shiga, Japan
Tel.: (81) 77 554 3260
Web Site: http://www.mme-e.co.jp
Machine Tools & Peripheral Equipment Mfr
N.A.I.C.S.: 333515

MHI Marine Engineering, Ltd. (1)
Tamachi Center Bldg 6F 34-7 Shiba 5-chome, Minato-ku, Tokyo, 108-0014, Japan
Tel.: (81) 3 3798 5941
Rev.: $118,397,520
Emp.: 37
Marine Engineering Services
N.A.I.C.S.: 541330

MHI Maritech, Co., Ltd. (1)
1-1 Akunoura-machi, Nagasaki, 850-8610, Japan
Tel.: (81) 95 828 7782
Shipping Design Software Development Services
N.A.I.C.S.: 541511

MHI NS Engineering Co., Ltd. (1)
1-1-1 Wadasaki-cho, Hyogo-ku, Kobe, 652-8585, Japan
Tel.: (81) 786712321
Web Site: http://www.mhi-nseng.co.jp
Software Development Services

N.A.I.C.S.: 541511
Kosuke Yasuda (Pres & CEO)

MHI Nuclear Engineering Co. Ltd. (1)
Mitsubishijuko Yokohama Bldg 3-1 Minatomirai 3-chome, Nishi-ku, Yokohama, 220-8401, Kanagawa, Japan
Tel.: (81) 45 200 6450
Web Site: http://www.mnec.co.jp
Emp.: 1,000
Nuclear Power Plant Construction Services
N.A.I.C.S.: 237130
Yukio Nishihara (Gen Mgr)

MHI Oceanincs Co., Ltd. (1)
53 Tsukuba-machi 6-chome, Isahaya, 854-0065, Nagasaki, Japan
Tel.: (81) 958287110
Thermal Power Generation Product Distr
N.A.I.C.S.: 423840

MHI Personnel, Ltd. (1)
16-5 Konan 2-chome, Minato-ku, Tokyo, 108-8215, Japan
Tel.: (81) 3 6716 2417
Payroll Processing Services
N.A.I.C.S.: 541214

MHI Plant Corporation (1)
4-6-22 Kanonshinmachi, Nishi-ku, Hiroshima, 733-0036, Japan
Tel.: (81) 82 294 5111
Web Site: https://www.mhiplant.co.jp
Emp.: 187
Industrial Machinery Mfr
N.A.I.C.S.: 333248
Tetsuo Murata (Pres)

MHI Power America Latina EIRELI (1)
Alameda Santos 415 6 oandar Conj 62, Cerqueira Cesar, Sao Paulo, Brazil
Tel.: (55) 1133863500
Project Management Services
N.A.I.C.S.: 541611

MHI Power Control Systems Co., Ltd. (1)
12 Nishiki-cho, Naka-ku, Yokohama, 231-8715, Japan
Tel.: (81) 452850114
Web Site: http://www.power.mhi.com
Environmental Equipment Mfr & Distr
N.A.I.C.S.: 334512
Katsuhiko Toda (Pres)

MHI Power Engineering Co., Ltd. (1)
12 Nishiki-cho, Naka-ku, Yokohama, 231-8715, Japan
Tel.: (81) 452850120
Thermal Power Generation Product Distr
N.A.I.C.S.: 423840

MHI Power Middle East for Manufacturing Parts & Machinery, LLC (1)
Plot 96NR27, PO Box 52309, Industrial City of Abu Dhabi III, Abu Dhabi, United Arab Emirates
Tel.: (971) 25501504
Engineering Electrical Equipment Mfr
N.A.I.C.S.: 335999

MHI Power Project (Thailand) Co., Ltd. (1)
87/2 CRC Tower All Seasons Place 45th Floor Wireless Road Lumpini, Pathumwan, Bangkok, 10330, Thailand
Tel.: (66) 20160121
Gas Turbine Mfr & Distr
N.A.I.C.S.: 333611

MHI Power Romania SRL (1)
Str Marius Emanoil Buteica 18-20 Sector 3, 031823, Bucharest, Romania
Tel.: (40) 314370620
Turbine Product Distribution Services
N.A.I.C.S.: 221115

MHI Power Systems Inspection Technologies, Ltd. (1)
12 Nishiki-cho, Naka-ku, Yokohama, 231-8715, Japan
Tel.: (81) 45 629 1269
Web Site: http://www.mitec-ndt.co.jp
Inspection & Measurement Services
N.A.I.C.S.: 541990

MHI Power Technical Services Corporation (1)

27th Floor Robinsons Cybergate Center Tower 3 Pioneer Street, Mandaluyong, 1550, Philippines
Tel.: (63) 277940220
Web Site: http://www.mts.power.mhi.com
Thermal Power Distribution Services
N.A.I.C.S.: 221118

MHI Pro Staff Corporation (1)
4-36 Hon-machi, Naka-ku, Yokohama, 231-0005, Kanagawa, Japan
Tel.: (81) 45 222 7628
Electrical Engineering Services
N.A.I.C.S.: 541330

MHI Residential Air-conditioners (Shanghai) Co., Ltd. (1)
2299 Yan An Xi Lu, HongQiao Changning Qu, Shanghai, China
Tel.: (86) 2162363030
Engineering Electrical Equipment Mfr
N.A.I.C.S.: 335999

MHI Russia LLC (1)
Office 1602 12 Krasnopresnenskaya nab, 123610, Moscow, Russia
Tel.: (7) 4952581471
Market Research Services
N.A.I.C.S.: 541910

MHI Sagami High-tech Ltd. (1)
3000 Tana, Chuo-ku, Sagamihara, 252-5293, Kanagawa, Japan
Tel.: (81) 42 761 3152
Web Site: https://www.mhi.com
Industrial Machinery Mfr & Distr
N.A.I.C.S.: 333248

MHI SeaTec Ltd. (1)
1-1 Wadasaki-cho 1-chome, Hyogo-ku, Kobe, 652-8585, Japan
Tel.: (81) 78 672 4063
Web Site: http://www.mhi-seatec.co.jp
Marine Engineering Services
N.A.I.C.S.: 541330

MHI Shenyang Pump Engineering Co., Ltd. (1)
408 Room Feng Da Building Yin Zun No 19-1 Huahai Road, Shenyang, China
Tel.: (86) 24 2580 0788
Engineering Consulting Services
N.A.I.C.S.: 541330

MHI Solution Technologies Co., Ltd. (1)
1-1 Shinhama 2-chome Arai-cho, Nishi-ku, Takasago, 676-8686, Hyogo, Japan
Tel.: (81) 79 445 6786
Web Site: https://www.mhi.com
Emp.: 715
Industrial Machinery Mfr
N.A.I.C.S.: 333248

MHI SpaceJet America, Inc. (1)
1601 E Valley Rd Ste 300, Renton, WA 98057
Tel.: (206) 513-7700
Civil Aircraft Parts Distr
N.A.I.C.S.: 423860

MHI Special Vehicles Parts Supply & Technical Service Co., Ltd. (1)
4-3 Kata-machi, Shinjuku, Tokyo, 160-0001, Japan
Tel.: (81) 332265191
Engineering Electrical Equipment Mfr
N.A.I.C.S.: 335999

MHI Steel Machinery Engineering & Service Co., Ltd. (1)
6-22 Kan-on-shin-machi 4-chome, Nishi-ku, Hiroshima, 733-0036, Japan
Tel.: (81) 82 291 2746
Web Site: http://www.mhises.co.jp
Casting Equipment Mfr & Distr
N.A.I.C.S.: 333248
Hiroshi Okuno (Pres)

MHI Sul Americana Distribuidora de Motores Ltda (1)
Avenida Paulista 1274- 8 Conj 23 Sala C, Sao Paulo, 01310-100, SP, Brazil
Tel.: (55) 1135157890
Web Site: http://www.msamotores.com.br
Sales Range: $50-74.9 Million
Emp.: 6
Automotive Engine Distr
N.A.I.C.S.: 423120

MHIEC Environment (Beijing) Co., Ltd. (1)
Room No 1516 Pacific Century Tower A No 2A Workers Stadium North Road, Chaoyang District, Beijing, 100027, China
Tel.: (86) 1065393296
Environmental Equipment Product Distr
N.A.I.C.S.: 423830

MHIRJ Aviation Inc. (1)
2400 Aviation Way, Bridgeport, WV 26330
Aircraft Equipment Mfr
N.A.I.C.S.: 336413
Don Nolan (Sls Dir-Bus Dev)

MHIRJ Aviation ULC (1)
3655 Avenue des Grandes Tourelles Suite 110, Boisbriand, J7H 0E2, QC, Canada
Tel.: (450) 497-0555
Web Site: http://www.mhirj.com
Aircraft Components Mfr
N.A.I.C.S.: 336413
Michael Descent (Sls Mgr-Parts & Svcs)

MHPS (Hangzhou) Environmental Equipment Co., Ltd. (1)
No 367 XingZhong Rd, Yuhang Economix Development Zone Yuhang District, Hangzhou, Zhejiang, China
Tel.: (86) 57189272255
Environmental Equipment Mfr
N.A.I.C.S.: 334519

MHPS Dalian Electricity Equipment Co., Ltd. (1)
Room 1101 Block A Zhongnan Building No 18 West China Road, Ganjingzi District, Dalian, Liaoning, China
Tel.: (86) 41184951690
Thermal Power Generation Product Mfr & Distr
N.A.I.C.S.: 335999

MI LNG Company, Ltd. (1)
5-1 Shinbashi 4-chome, Minato-ku, Tokyo, 105-0004, Japan
Tel.: (81) 357332006
Engineering Electrical Equipment Mfr
N.A.I.C.S.: 335999

MLP Canada Limited (1)
1250B Reid St Unit 4-6, Richmond Hill, L4B 1G3, ON, Canada (100%)
Tel.: (905) 793-3555
Web Site: http://www.mlpcanada.com
Sales Range: $25-49.9 Million
Emp.: 7
Sales & Services of Lithographic Presses
N.A.I.C.S.: 333248

MLP Hong Kong Ltd. (1)
Rm 1211 Kodak House II 321 Java Rd, North Point, China (Hong Kong) (100%)
Tel.: (852) 28873200
Web Site: http://www.mlphongkong.com
Sales Range: $25-49.9 Million
Emp.: 40
N.A.I.C.S.: 336611

MLP UK Ltd. (1)
Unit 12B Riverside South, Accomodation Rd, Leeds, LS9 0RQ, United Kingdom (100%)
Tel.: (44) 113 235 9829
Web Site: http://www.mhi.co.jp
Sales Range: $25-49.9 Million
Emp.: 30
Engineering, Manufacturing & Construction Heavy Equipment
N.A.I.C.S.: 336120

MPS-CT LLC (1)
628 Hebron Ave Ste 400, Glastonbury, CT 06033
Engineering Electrical Equipment Mfr
N.A.I.C.S.: 335999

Maintenance Partners, NV (1)
Vitshoekstraat 6, Zwijndrecht, 2070, Zwijndrecht, Belgium
Tel.: (32) 35417140
Web Site: https://www.maintenancepartners.com
Sales Range: $25-49.9 Million
Emp.: 7
Mechanical Maintenance & Mechanical Maintenance & Engineering Services
N.A.I.C.S.: 541330

Masuda Eco Creation (1)

MITSUBISHI HEAVY INDUSTRIES, LTD.

Mitsubishi Heavy Industries, Ltd.—(Continued)
1082-7 Tada-cho, Masuda, 698-0031, Shimane, Japan
Tel.: (81) 85 631 4153
Web Site: http://www.mhi.co.jp
Waste Treatment & Recycling Services
N.A.I.C.S.: 221320

Mechanical Dynamics & Analysis LLC (1)
19 British American Blvd, Latham, NY 12110
Tel.: (518) 399-3616
Web Site: http://www.mdaturbines.com
Power Generator Product Distr
N.A.I.C.S.: 423840
Mark Crittenden *(Mgr-Generator Repairs Engrg Div)*

Meeraner Dampfkesselbau GmbH (1)
Zwickauer Strasse 94-98, 08393, Meerane, Germany
Tel.: (49) 3764530
Web Site: http://www.mdkb.de
Power Boiler & Heat Exchanger Mfr
N.A.I.C.S.: 332410
Bernd Klein *(CEO)*

Mhphils Realty Corporation (1)
AG and P Special Economic Zone Barangay San Roque, Bauan, Batangas, 4201, Philippines
Tel.: (63) 437271117
Engineering Electrical Equipment Mfr
N.A.I.C.S.: 335999

Mitsubishi Agricultural Machinery Co., Ltd. (1)
667-1 Iya-machi, Higashiizumo, 699-0195, Shimane, Japan
Tel.: (81) 852 52 2111
Web Site: http://www.mam.co.jp
Sales Range: $200-249.9 Million
Emp.: 706
Agricultural Machinery Mfr & Distr
N.A.I.C.S.: 333111

Subsidiary (Non-US):

ENTREPOSTO MAQUINAS Comercio de equipamento agricola e industrial s.a. (2)
Quinta das Areias Lote 34 e 35 h 99, Castanheira do Ribatejo, Portugal
Tel.: (351) 263 287 800
Web Site: http://www.entrepostomaquinas.pt
Agricultural Equipment Distr
N.A.I.C.S.: 423820

Master Farm Services (GB) Ltd. (2)
Bures Park Colne Road, Bures, CO8 5DJ, Suffolk, United Kingdom
Tel.: (44) 178 722 8450
Web Site: https://www.masterfarm.co.uk
Emp.: 12
Agricultural & Horticultural Equipment Distr
N.A.I.C.S.: 423820
Garry Ingram *(Mng Dir)*

Mitsubishi FBR Systems, Inc. (1)
34-17 Jingu-mae 2-chome, Shibuya-ku, Tokyo, 150-0001, Japan
Tel.: (81) 36 439 4333
Web Site: http://www.mfbr.co.jp
Fast Breeder Reactor Research & Development Services
N.A.I.C.S.: 561990

Mitsubishi Heavy Industries (Changshu) Machinery Co., Ltd. (1)
Huangpujiang Road, Southeast Kaiyu District, Changshu, 215500, Jiangsu, China
Tel.: (86) 51252303030
Engineering Electrical Equipment Mfr
N.A.I.C.S.: 335999

Mitsubishi Heavy Industries (China) Co., Ltd. (1)
6th Floor Changfu Palace Office Building No 26 Jianguomenwai Street, Chaoyang District, Beijing, 100022, China
Tel.: (86) 106 512 4291
Web Site: http://www.mhi.com.cn
Industrial Machinery Distr
N.A.I.C.S.: 423820

Mitsubishi Heavy Industries (Shanghai) Co., Ltd. (1)
26th Floor HSBC Tower 1000 Lujiazui Ring Road, Pudong New Area, Shanghai, 200120, China
Tel.: (86) 216 841 3030
Web Site: http://www.mhi.com.cn
Emp.: 100
Air Conditioning Parts Distr
N.A.I.C.S.: 423730

Mitsubishi Heavy Industries (Thailand) Ltd (1)
Nos 173/31 173/34 Asia Centre Building 25th Floor South Sathorn Road, Thungmahamek Sathorn, Bangkok, 10120, Thailand **(100%)**
Tel.: (66) 2 679 0600
Web Site: https://www.mhit.co.th
Sales Range: $25-49.9 Million
Emp.: 50
N.A.I.C.S.: 336611

Mitsubishi Heavy Industries Aero Engines, Ltd. (1)
1200 Higashi-tanaka, Komaki, 485-0826, Aichi Prefecture, Japan
Tel.: (81) 568794123
Emp.: 620
Aircraft Mfr
N.A.I.C.S.: 336411
Katsuyuki Shimauchi *(Pres & CEO)*

Mitsubishi Heavy Industries Air-Conditioning & Refrigeration Corporation (1)
15th Floor Igarashi Building 2-11-5, Shibaura Minato-ku, Tokyo, 108-0023, Japan
Tel.: (81) 368914440
Refrigeration Equipment Distr
N.A.I.C.S.: 423740

Mitsubishi Heavy Industries Air-Conditioning & Thermal Systems Corporation (1)
25-5 Nishi-gotanda 7-chome, Shinagawa-ku, Tokyo, 141-0031, Japan
Tel.: (81) 3 5745 8870
Web Site: http://www.mhi.co.jp
Air Conditioning & Heating Equipment Distr
N.A.I.C.S.: 423730

Mitsubishi Heavy Industries Air-Conditioning Europe Ltd. (1)
5 The Square Stockley Park, Uxbridge, UB11 1ET, United Kingdom
Tel.: (44) 2087564200
Web Site: http://www.mhiae.com
Air Conditioning Product Mfr
N.A.I.C.S.: 333415

Mitsubishi Heavy Industries Air-conditioners (Shanghai) Co., Ltd. (1)
2903-2906 Shanghaimart 2299 Yan An Road West, Shanghai, 200336, China
Tel.: (86) 2162363030
Engineering Electrical Equipment Mfr
N.A.I.C.S.: 335999

Mitsubishi Heavy Industries America, Inc. (1)
20 Greenway Plz Ste 830, Houston, TX 77046 **(100%)**
Tel.: (346) 308-8800
Web Site: http://www.mitsubishitoday.com
Holding Company; Regional Managing Office
N.A.I.C.S.: 551112
Mashiko Arihara *(CEO)*

Subsidiary (Domestic):

Crystal Mover Services, Inc. (2)
815 NW 57th Ave Ste 222, Miami, FL 33126
Tel.: (786) 476-5985
Web Site: http://www.crystal-mover.com
Sales Range: $25-49.9 Million
Emp.: 8
Automated People Mover Maintenance Services
N.A.I.C.S.: 811198
Michio Koizumi *(Pres & CEO)*

Subsidiary (Non-US):

Daily Equipment Company (2)
Tel.: (601) 932-6011
Web Site: http://www.dailyeq.com
Sales Range: $25-49.9 Million
Emp.: 40
Whslr of Lift Trucks & Parts
N.A.I.C.S.: 423830
Bryant Consin *(Branch Mgr)*

Subsidiary (Domestic):

FMS Equipment Rental Inc. (2)
10795 Hammerly Blvd Ste 350, Houston, TX 77043
Tel.: (713) 365-7600
Web Site: http://www.mhi.co.jp
Forklift Machinery Sales & Leasing Services
N.A.I.C.S.: 423830

Federal Broach & Machine Company (2)
1961 Sullivan Dr, Harrison, MI 48625
Tel.: (989) 539-7420
Web Site: https://www.federalbroach.com
Sales Range: $10-24.9 Million
Emp.: 75
Cutting Machine Tool Accessories Mfr
N.A.I.C.S.: 333517
Joe Witer *(Pres)*

Intercontinental Jet Service Corp. (2)
3322 N 74th E Ave, Tulsa, OK 74115
Tel.: (918) 834-8888
Web Site: https://www.ijetservice.com
Emp.: 30
Aircraft Engine Maintenance Services
N.A.I.C.S.: 811198
Mark T. James *(Pres)*

MHI Machine Tool U.S.A. Inc. (2)
520 Thomas Dr, Bensenville, IL 60106
Tel.: (630) 693-4880
Web Site: http://www.mhimex.com
Sales Range: $25-49.9 Million
Emp.: 30
N.A.I.C.S.: 336611

Division (Domestic):

MHIA Inc Corrugating Machinery Division (2)
11204 McCormick Rd, Hunt Valley, MD 21031-1101 **(100%)**
Tel.: (410) 584-7990
Web Site: https://www.mhicorrugating.com
Sales Range: $25-49.9 Million
Emp.: 20
Mfr of Corrugating Machines
N.A.I.C.S.: 423830

Subsidiary (Domestic):

MLP U.S.A. Inc. (3)
600 Barclay Blvd, Lincolnshire, IL 60069-4328
Tel.: (847) 634-9100
Sales Range: $25-49.9 Million
Mfr of Printing Presses
N.A.I.C.S.: 423830
Mike Stock *(Dir-Sheetfed & Web Offset Sls)*

Subsidiary (Domestic):

Mitsubishi Aircraft Corporation America, Inc. (2)
4951 Airport Pkwy Ste 500, Addison, TX 75001
Tel.: (469) 916-7920
Web Site: http://www.mrj-japan.com
Sales Range: $25-49.9 Million
Emp.: 10
Civil Aircraft Information Gathering Services
N.A.I.C.S.: 519290
Hirofumi Takahashi *(Pres)*

Mitsubishi Engine North America Inc (2)
1250 Greenbriar Dr Ste E, Addison, IL 60101-1098
Tel.: (630) 268-0780
Web Site: http://www.mitsubishi-engine.com
Sales Range: $25-49.9 Million
Emp.: 35
Distribution of Turbo Charges
N.A.I.C.S.: 423830

Division (Domestic):

Mitsubishi Heavy Industries America, Inc. - Aircraft Product Support Division (2)

INTERNATIONAL PUBLIC

4951 Airport Pkwy Ste 530, Addison, TX 75001-6041
Tel.: (972) 934-5480
Web Site: http://www.mhi.com
Aircraft Part Mfr
N.A.I.C.S.: 336412

Mitsubishi Heavy Industries America, Inc. - Environmental Systems Division (2)
9301 Amberglen Blvd, Austin, TX 78729
Tel.: (512) 219-2340
Web Site: http://www.mhi.co.jp
Industrial Machinery Mfr
N.A.I.C.S.: 333248

Mitsubishi Heavy Industries America, Inc. - Injection Molding Machinery Division (2)
1051 Ardmore Ave, Itasca, IL 60143
Tel.: (630) 693-4880
Web Site: http://www.mhiinj.com
Injection Molding Machine Mfr
N.A.I.C.S.: 333248
Kiyoshi Ikuta *(VP & Gen Mgr)*

Mitsubishi Heavy Industries America, Inc. - Machine Tool Division (2)
46992 Liberty dr, Wixom, MI 48393
Tel.: (248) 669-6136
Web Site: http://www.mhi.co.jp
Emp.: 25
Machine Tools Mfr
N.A.I.C.S.: 333515

Subsidiary (Domestic):

Mitsubishi Heavy Industries Climate Control Inc. (2)
1200 N Mitsubishi Pkwy, Franklin, IN 46131-7560
Tel.: (317) 346-5000
Web Site: http://www.mhi.co.jp
Sales Range: $100-124.9 Million
Emp.: 300
N.A.I.C.S.: 336611

Mitsubishi Nuclear Energy Systems, Inc. (2)
6210 Ardrey Kell Rd Ste 350, Charlotte, NC 28277
Tel.: (704) 945-2600
Web Site: https://mnes-us.com
Nuclear Power Generation Services
N.A.I.C.S.: 221113
Shinya Toiguchi *(Pres & CEO)*

Mitsubishi Power Americas, Inc. (2)
400 Colonial Ctr Pkwy, Lake Mary, FL 32746
Tel.: (407) 688-6100
Web Site: https://power.mhi.com
Eletric Power Generation Services
N.A.I.C.S.: 221118

Mitsubishi Power Systems Inc. (2)
400 Colonial Ctr Pkwy, Lake Mary, FL 32746
Tel.: (407) 688-6100
Web Site: http://www.mpshq.com
Sales Range: $50-74.9 Million
Emp.: 300
N.A.I.C.S.: 336611
Koji Hasegawa *(Pres)*

PW Power Systems, Inc. (2)
628 Hebron Ave Ste 400, Glastonbury, CT 06033
Tel.: (860) 368-5900
Web Site: http://www.pwps.com
Sales Range: $50-74.9 Million
Emp.: 380
Gas Turbine Mfr
N.A.I.C.S.: 333611
Lucia Maffucci *(Mktg Mgr)*

Joint Venture (Domestic):

Wood Group Pratt & Whitney Industrial Turbine Services, LLC (3)
1460 Blue Hills Ave, Bloomfield, CT 06002
Tel.: (860) 286-4600
Web Site: https://www.wgpw.com
Sales Range: $10-24.9 Million
Emp.: 85
Industrial & Aero Turbine Overhaul & Technical Support Services; Owned 51% by United Technologies Corporation & 49% by John Wood Group PLC

AND PRIVATE COMPANIES — MITSUBISHI HEAVY INDUSTRIES, LTD.

N.A.I.C.S.: 811310
George T. Gaudette (Pres)

Subsidiary (Domestic):

Pacific Engine Development & Consulting, Inc. (2)
PMBLB 13 PO Box 1001, Saipan, MP 96950
Tel.: (670) 233-7332
N.A.I.C.S.: 336611

Division (Domestic):

Paper Machinery Group (2)
1155 Prairie Hill Rd, Rockton, IL 61072
Tel.: (608) 363-9215
N.A.I.C.S.: 336611

Tire Machinery Division (2)
600 Cherry Fork Ave, Leetonia, OH 44431-1277
Tel.: (330) 427-8900
Web Site: http://www.mhi.co.jp
Sales Range: $50-74.9 Million
Emp.: 200
Tire Manufacturing
N.A.I.C.S.: 326291

Mitsubishi Heavy Industries Asia Pacific Pte. Ltd. (1)
150 Beach Road 29-00 Gateway West, Singapore, 189202, Singapore
Tel.: (65) 6 305 5200
Web Site: https://www.mhi.com
Emp.: 251
Industrial Engineering Services
N.A.I.C.S.: 541330

Mitsubishi Heavy Industries Australia, Pty. Ltd. (1)
Level 6 160 Queen St, Melbourne, 3000, VIC, Australia
Tel.: (61) 396709799
Sales Range: $25-49.9 Million
Emp.: 3
Industrial Machinery Sales & Maintenance Services
N.A.I.C.S.: 811310

Subsidiary (Domestic):

Mitsubishi Heavy Industries Air-Conditioners Australia, Pty. Ltd. (2)
Block E 391 Park Road, Regents Park, 2143, NSW, Australia
Tel.: (61) 28 774 7500
Web Site: https://www.mhiaa.com.au
Sales Range: $25-49.9 Million
Air Conditioning Equipment Distr
N.A.I.C.S.: 423730

Subsidiary (Domestic):

Dai-Ei Australia Pty. Ltd. (3)
1 Remington Dr, Dandenong, 3175, VIC, Australia
Tel.: (61) 3 8795 5200
Web Site: http://www.daieiaust.com.au
Sales Range: $25-49.9 Million
Emp.: 15
Paper Converting Machinery Product Suppliers
N.A.I.C.S.: 423830

Graphic Controls Pty. Ltd. (3)
9D Lakewood Boulvard, Braeside, 3195, VIC, Australia
Tel.: (61) 3 9588 0035
Web Site: http://www.mhiau.com.au
Printing Machinery Mfr
N.A.I.C.S.: 333248

Division (Domestic):

Mitsubishi Heavy Industries Ltd.-Air-Conditioning & Refrigeration Division (2)
9 C Comml Road Kingsjrovee 2208, Sydney, 2216, NSW, Australia (100%)
Tel.: (61) 295977977
Web Site: http://www.mhi.net.au
Sales Range: $25-49.9 Million
N.A.I.C.S.: 336611

Mitsubishi Heavy Industries BFG Gas Turbine Service (Nanjing) Co., (1)
19/F Jianwei Building 88 North Zhongshan Road, Nanjing, China
Tel.: (86) 25 83242711
Gas Turbine Maintenance Services
N.A.I.C.S.: 811310

Mitsubishi Heavy Industries Compressor Corporation (1)
4-6-22 Kan-on-shin-machi, Nishi-ku, Hiroshima, 733-8553, Japan
Tel.: (81) 82 291 2200
Web Site: http://www.mhicompressor.com
Sales Range: $125-149.9 Million
Emp.: 906
Compressor & Industrial Equipment Mfr & Distr
N.A.I.C.S.: 333912

Mitsubishi Heavy Industries Dongfang Gas Turbine (Guangzhou) Co., Ltd. (1)
No 52 Guangxing Road, Nansha District, Guangzhou, 511458, China
Tel.: (86) 2084989430
Gas Turbine Mfr & Distr
N.A.I.C.S.: 333611

Mitsubishi Heavy Industries Engine & Turbocharger, Ltd. (1)
3000 Tana, Chuo-ku, Sagamihara, 252-5293, Kanagawa, Japan
Tel.: (81) 427621973
Emp.: 5,500
Turbocharger Mfr
N.A.I.C.S.: 333611
Takeshi Kajino (Pres & CEO)

Mitsubishi Heavy Industries Engine System Asia Pte. Ltd. (1)
No 3 Tuas Avenue 12, Singapore, 639024, Singapore (100%)
Tel.: (65) 6 862 2202
Web Site: https://mhiesa.com.sg
Sales Range: $50-74.9 Million
Emp.: 75
Diesel Generators
N.A.I.C.S.: 335312
Shujiro Shiohara (Mng Dir)

Mitsubishi Heavy Industries Engine System Asia Pte. Ltd. (1)
No 3 Tuas Avenue 12, Singapore, 639024, Singapore (100%)
Tel.: (65) 6 862 2202
Web Site: https://www.mhiesa.com.sg
Emp.: 74
Diesel Generator & Engine Distr
N.A.I.C.S.: 423860
Motoi Kawashima (Mng Dir)

Mitsubishi Heavy Industries Engine Systems Co., Ltd. (1)
6-21 Nishi-gotanda 3-chome, Shinagawa-ku, Tokyo, 141-0031, Japan
Tel.: (81) 35 745 8850
Web Site: http://www.mhi-eng.com
Emp.: 600
Gas Engine Power Generation System Installation Services
N.A.I.C.S.: 238210

Mitsubishi Heavy Industries Engineering, Ltd. (1)
3-1 Minatomirai 3-chome, Nishi-ku, Yokohama, 220-8401, Kanagawa, Japan
Tel.: (81) 452009600
Chemical Products Mfr
N.A.I.C.S.: 325998
Kenji Terasawa (Pres & CEO)

Mitsubishi Heavy Industries Environmental & Chemical Engineering Co., Ltd. (1)
Yokohama Blue Avenue Bldg 4-4-2 Minatomirai, Nishi-ku, Yokohama, 220-0012, Kanagawa, Japan
Tel.: (81) 45 227 1280
Web Site: https://www.mhiec.co.jp
Emp.: 590
Environmental Control Equipment Installation Services
N.A.I.C.S.: 238210
Takayuki Hishinuma (Pres & CEO)

Division (Domestic):

Mitsubishi Heavy Industries Environmental & Chemical Engineering Co., Ltd. - Engineering Division (2)
3-1 Minatomirai 3-chome, Nishi-ku, Yokohama, 220-8401, Japan
Tel.: (81) 45 200 9850
Automotive Engineering Services
N.A.I.C.S.: 541330
Hiroshi Ohira (CEO)

Mitsubishi Heavy Industries Environmental & Chemical Engineering Co., Ltd. - O&M Division (2)
Yokohama Blue Avenue Bldg 4-4-2 Minatomirai, Nishi-ku, Yokohama, 220-0012, Kanagawa, Japan
Tel.: (81) 45 227 1280
Web Site: https://www.mhiec.co.jp
Emp.: 594
Construction Machinery Mfr
N.A.I.C.S.: 333120
Hiroki Morimoto (Mgr)

Mitsubishi Heavy Industries Environmental & Chemical Engineering Co., Ltd. - Plant Engineering Division (2)
17th Floor Yokohama Blue Avenue Building 4-2 Minatomirai 4-chome, Nishi-ku, Yokohama, 220-0012, Kanagawa, Japan
Tel.: (81) 45 227 1286
Web Site: http://www.mhiec.co.jp
Plant Construction & Engineering Services
N.A.I.C.S.: 237990

Mitsubishi Heavy Industries Europe, Ltd. (1)
Building 11 Chiswick Park 566 Chiswick High Road, London, W4 5YA, United Kingdom (100%)
Tel.: (44) 2034807500
Web Site: http://www.mhie.com
Sales Range: $25-49.9 Million
Emp.: 35
N.A.I.C.S.: 336611

Division (Non-US):

Mitsubishi Heavy Industries Europe, Ltd. - Corrugating Machinery Division (2)
Splijtbakweg 115, 1333 HJ, Almere, Netherlands
Tel.: (31) 36 8000000
Sales Range: $25-49.9 Million
Emp.: 10
Corrugating Machinery Mfr
N.A.I.C.S.: 333243
H. Kikumoro (Gen Mgr)

Mitsubishi Heavy Industries Food & Packaging Machinery Co., Ltd. (1)
1 Iwatsuka-machi-aza-takamichi, Nakamura-ku, Nagoya, 453-0862, Japan
Tel.: (81) 52 412 1200
Web Site: http://www.mhisk.com
Food Packaging Machinery Mfr & Distr
N.A.I.C.S.: 333993

Mitsubishi Heavy Industries Forklift & Engine Turbocharger Holdings, Ltd. (1)
Marunouchi Nijubashi Bldg 2-3 Marunouchi 3-Chome, Chiyoda-ku, Tokyo, 100-8332, Japan
Tel.: (81) 362756580
Turbocharger Mfr
N.A.I.C.S.: 333611

Mitsubishi Heavy Industries Forklift (Dalian) Co., Ltd. (1)
No 99 Tianshou Jie, Dalian Development Area, Dalian, 116630, China
Tel.: (86) 41139213030
Forklift Mfr & Distr
N.A.I.C.S.: 333924

Mitsubishi Heavy Industries France S.A.S. (1)
32 rue de Monceau, 75008, Paris, France
Tel.: (33) 142676075
Aircraft Product Distr
N.A.I.C.S.: 423860

Mitsubishi Heavy Industries India Private Ltd. (1)
402 4th Floor Worldmark 2, Asset Area 8 Aerocity Hospitality District, New Delhi, 110037, India
Tel.: (91) 114 102 1234
Web Site: http://www.mhiindia.com
Sales Range: $25-49.9 Million
Emp.: 50
Industrial Machinery Procurement & Sales
N.A.I.C.S.: 423830

Subsidiary (Domestic):

Mitsubishi Heavy Industries India Precision Tools, Ltd. (2)
Plot No 2 Sipcot Industrial Complex, Ranipet, Vellore, 632 403, Tamil Nadu, India
Tel.: (91) 4172244361
Web Site: http://www.mhi-ipt.in
Sales Range: $25-49.9 Million
Gear Cutting Tool Mfr
N.A.I.C.S.: 333515
P. Sinharoy (Head-Sls-Jamshedpur)

Division (Domestic):

Mitsubishi Heavy Industries India Private Ltd. - Power Systems Engineering Division (2)
5th Floor Cristsu Complex 41/7 Lavelle Road, Bengaluru, 560 001, India
Tel.: (91) 80 40197197
Industrial Machinery Distr
N.A.I.C.S.: 423830

Mitsubishi Heavy Industries Korea Ltd. (1)
4/F Samtan Bldg 947 7 Daechi-Dong, Gangnam-Gu, Seoul, 135280, Korea (South)
Tel.: (82) 25660821
Web Site: http://www.mhik.com
Industrial Machinery Mfr & Distr
N.A.I.C.S.: 333248

Mitsubishi Heavy Industries Machine Tool Co., Ltd. (1)
130 Rokujizo, Ritto, 520-3080, Shiga, Japan
Tel.: (81) 775533300
Emp.: 840
Machine Tool Mfr & Distr
N.A.I.C.S.: 333517
Kenichi Wakabayashi (Pres & CEO)

Mitsubishi Heavy Industries Machine Tool Sales Co., Ltd. (1)
130 Roku-jizo, Ritto, 520-3080, Shiga, Japan
Tel.: (81) 77 553 2033
Web Site: http://www.mhi.co.jp
Industrial Machine Tool Distr
N.A.I.C.S.: 423830

Mitsubishi Heavy Industries Machinery Systems, Ltd. (1)
1-1 Wadasaki-cho 1-chome, Hyogo-ku, Kobe, 652-8585, Japan
Tel.: (81) 786724600
Web Site: http://www.mhi-ms.com
Heavy Industrial Machinery Mfr & Distr
N.A.I.C.S.: 333248
Naoaki Ikeda (Pres)

Mitsubishi Heavy Industries Machinery Technology Corporation (1)
6-22 Kan-on-shin-machi 4-Chome, Nishi-ku, Hiroshima, 733-8553, Japan
Tel.: (81) 822942339
Industrial Machinery Mfr
N.A.I.C.S.: 333248

Mitsubishi Heavy Industries Marine Machinery & Equipment Co., Ltd. (1)
1-1 Akunoura-machi, Nagasaki, 850-8610, Japan
Tel.: (81) 5038484200
Web Site: http://www.mhi-mme.com
Emp.: 199
Marine Equipment Mfr & Distr
N.A.I.C.S.: 332410
Toshiaki Hori (Pres & CEO)

Mitsubishi Heavy Industries Marine Structure, Co., Ltd. (1)
180 Koyagi-machi, Nagasaki, 851-0393, Japan
Tel.: (81) 958734430
Marine Construction Product Mfr
N.A.I.C.S.: 336612
Kunio Shiiba (Pres & CEO)

Mitsubishi Heavy Industries Mechatronics Systems, Ltd. (1)
1-16 Komatsu-dori 4-chome, Hyogo-ku, Kobe, 652-0865, Japan
Tel.: (81) 78 672 4600
Web Site: http://www.mhi-ms.co.jp
Industrial Equipment Mfr
N.A.I.C.S.: 333248

MITSUBISHI HEAVY INDUSTRIES, LTD.

Mitsubishi Heavy Industries, Ltd.—(Continued)

Mitsubishi Heavy Industries Meiki Engines Co., Ltd. (1)
1 Aza Takamichi Iwatsuka-cho, Nakamura-ku, Nagoya, 453-8515, Aichi Prefecture, Japan
Tel.: (81) 524121144
Engineering Electrical Equipment Mfr
N.A.I.C.S.: 335999

Mitsubishi Heavy Industries Netherlands (1)
Damsluisweg 2, PO Box 30101, Almere, 1303 AC, Netherlands
Tel.: (31) 365388311
Web Site: http://www.mtee.eu
Sales Range: $200-249.9 Million
Emp.: 700
N.A.I.C.S.: 336611
Ichi Hashi (Pres)

Mitsubishi Heavy Industries Philippines, Inc. (1)
3rd Floor Republic Glass Building 196 Salcedo Street, Legaspi Village, Makati, 1229, Metro Manila, Philippines
Tel.: (63) 2 889 3500
Web Site: http://www.mhi.co.jp
N.A.I.C.S.: 336611

Mitsubishi Heavy Industries Precision Casting Co., Ltd. (1)
1-17 Hiraide Industrial Park, Utsunomiya, 321-0905, Tochigi, Japan
Tel.: (81) 28 661 4151
Web Site: http://www.mitsubishicast.co.jp
Sales Range: $100-124.9 Million
Emp.: 300
Precision Casting Mfr & Distr
N.A.I.C.S.: 331523
Hiroyuki Fukunishi (Pres)

Mitsubishi Heavy Industries Printing & Packaging Machinery, Ltd. (1)
1-1-1 Itosakiminami, Mihara, 729-0393, Hiroshima, Japan
Tel.: (81) 84 867 2068
Web Site: https://www.mhi-ppm.com
Sales Range: $250-299.9 Million
Emp.: 660
Printing & Packaging Machinery Sales
N.A.I.C.S.: 423830
Masami Shimizu (Pres)

Mitsubishi Heavy Industries Singapore Private Ltd. (1)
150 Beach Rd 29-00 Gateway West, Singapore, 189720, Singapore
Tel.: (65) 62936552
Web Site: http://www.mies.com.sg
Sales Range: $50-74.9 Million
Emp.: 100
Industrial Machinery Distr
N.A.I.C.S.: 423830
Yoshio Nakayama (Mng Dir)

Mitsubishi Heavy Industries Thermal Systems, Ltd. (1)
3-1 Asahi Nishi-biwajima-cho, Kiyosu, 452-8561, Aichi Prefecture, Japan
Tel.: (81) 525039200
Web Site: http://www.mhi-mth.co.jp
Air Conditioning Product Mfr
N.A.I.C.S.: 333415
Kaoru Kusumoto (Pres)

Mitsubishi Heavy Industries Thermal Transport Europe GmbH (1)
Hannoversche Strasse 49, 49084, Osnabruck, Germany
Tel.: (49) 541800050
Web Site: http://www.mhi-tte.com
Refrigeration Equipment Distr
N.A.I.C.S.: 423740
Bjorn Reckhorn (Mng Dir-Sls & After Sls)

Mitsubishi Heavy Industries Transportation & Construction Engineering, Ltd. (1)
Mitsubishijuko Yokohama Bldg 3-1 Minatomirai 3-chome, Nishi-ku, Yokohama, Japan
Tel.: (81) 452009800
Thermal Power Generation Product Distr
N.A.I.C.S.: 423840

Mitsubishi Heavy Industries Transportation Equipment Engineering & Service Co., Ltd. (1)
1-1 Itosakiminami 1-chome, Mihara, 729-0393, Hiroshima, Japan
Tel.: (81) 848 67 7340
Web Site: http://www.mhi-tes.co.jp
Industrial Transportation Equipment Maintenance Services
N.A.I.C.S.: 811114

Mitsubishi Heavy Industries de Mexico, S.A. de C.V. (1)
Paseo de la Reforma No 265 Piso18, Col Cuauhtemoc, 06500, Mexico, Mexico
Tel.: (52) 5555114193
Web Site: http://www.mhi-global.com
Market Research, Public Relations & Sales Services
N.A.I.C.S.: 541910

Mitsubishi Heavy Industries, (Hong Kong) Ltd. (1)
Unit 2201 22/F Mira Place Tower A 132 Nathan Road, Tsim Sha Tsui, Kowloon, China (Hong Kong) **(100%)**
Tel.: (852) 2 525 5262
Web Site: http://www.mhi.com
Sales Range: $25-49.9 Million
Emp.: 20
N.A.I.C.S.: 336611
Y. Oba (Mng Dir)

Subsidiary (Domestic):

Mitsubishi Heavy Industries Ltd (2)
Rm 809 World Peace Center, 55 Wo Tong Tsui St, Kwai Chung, Hong Kong, China (Hong Kong) **(100%)**
Tel.: (852) 24250650
Web Site: http://www.mhi.co.jp
N.A.I.C.S.: 336611

Mitsubishi Heavy Industries, Ltd. - Eba Plant (1)
5-1 Eba Okimachi, Naka-ku, Hiroshima, 730-8642, Japan
Tel.: (81) 82 291 2112
Web Site: http://www.mhi.co.jp
Industrial Machinery Mfr
N.A.I.C.S.: 333248

Mitsubishi Heavy Industries, Ltd. - Futami Plant (1)
1 Minami-Futami Futami-cho, Akashi, 674-0093, Hyogo, Japan
Tel.: (81) 78 672 4312
Industrial Shipyard Machinery Mfr
N.A.I.C.S.: 333248

Mitsubishi Heavy Industries, Ltd. - Hiroshima Machinery Works (1)
6-22 Kan-on-shin-machi 4-chome, Nishi-ku, Hiroshima, 733-8553, Japan
Tel.: (81) 82 291 2112
Industrial Machinery Mfr
N.A.I.C.S.: 333248

Mitsubishi Heavy Industries, Ltd. - Honmoku Plant (1)
12 Nishikicho, Naka-ku, Yokohama, 231-8715, Kanagawa, Japan
Tel.: (81) 45 629 1600
Industrial Machinery Mfr
N.A.I.C.S.: 333248

Mitsubishi Heavy Industries, Ltd. - Isahaya Plant (1)
53 Tsukubamachi 6-chome, Isahaya, 854-0065, Nagasaki, Japan
Tel.: (81) 957 25 0845
Web Site: http://www.mhi.co.jp
Industrial Machinery Mfr
N.A.I.C.S.: 333248

Mitsubishi Heavy Industries, Ltd. - Iwanai Plant (1)
476-24 Azana Ohama Iwanai-cho, Iwanai-gun, Hokkaido, 045-0001, Japan
Tel.: (81) 135 61 2109
Air Conditioning & Refrigerator Mfr
N.A.I.C.S.: 333415

Mitsubishi Heavy Industries, Ltd. - Iwatsuka Plant (1)
1 Aza Takamichi Iwatsuka-cho, Nakamura-ku, Nagoya, 453-8515, Aichi, Japan
Tel.: (81) 52 412 1110
Industrial Machinery Mfr
N.A.I.C.S.: 333248

INTERNATIONAL PUBLIC

Mitsubishi Heavy Industries, Ltd. - Komaki Minami Plant (1)
1 Oaza Toyoba Toyoyama, Nishikasugai District, Komaki, 480-0296, Japan
Tel.: (81) 568 28 1112
Aerospace System Mfr
N.A.I.C.S.: 334511

Mitsubishi Heavy Industries, Ltd. - Matsusaka Plant (1)
22 Koyocho, Matsusaka, 515-0053, Mie, Japan
Tel.: (81) 598 29 4511
Air Conditioning & Refrigerator Mfr
N.A.I.C.S.: 333415

Mitsubishi Heavy Industries, Ltd. - Mihara Machinery Works (1)
6-22 Kan-on-shin-machi 4-chome, Nishi-ku, Hiroshima, 733-8553, Japan
Tel.: (81) 848 67 2065
Industrial Machinery Mfr
N.A.I.C.S.: 333248

Mitsubishi Heavy Industries, Ltd. - Nagoya Air-Conditioning & Refrigeration Machinery Works (1)
3-1 Asahi Nishi-biwajima-cho, Kiyosu, 452-8561, Aichi, Japan
Tel.: (81) 52 503 9200
Industrial Machinery Mfr
N.A.I.C.S.: 333248

Mitsubishi Heavy Industries, Ltd. - Nagoya Guidance & Propulsion Systems Works (1)
1200 O-aza Higashi Tanaka, Komaki, 485-8561, Aichi, Japan
Tel.: (81) 568 79 2113
Emp.: 2,000
Industrial Machinery Mfr
N.A.I.C.S.: 333248
Sakurai Keiji (Gen Mgr)

Mitsubishi Heavy Industries, Ltd. - Ritto Machinery Works (1)
130 Roku-jizo, Ritto, 520-3080, Shiga, Japan
Tel.: (81) 77 553 3300
Emp.: 900
Industrial Machinery Mfr
N.A.I.C.S.: 333248
Seiji Seijirao (Gen Mgr)

Mitsubishi Heavy Industries, Ltd. - Sagamihara Machinery Works (1)
3000 Tana, Chuo-ku, Sagamihara, 252-5293, Kanagawa, Japan
Tel.: (81) 42 761 1101
Web Site: http://www.mhi.co.jp
Industrial Machinery Mfr
N.A.I.C.S.: 333248

Mitsubishi Heavy Industries, Ltd. - Saiwaimachi Plant (1)
12 Saiwaimachi 6-chome, Nagasaki, 850-0046, Japan
Tel.: (81) 95 824 3336
Web Site: http://www.mhi.co.jp
Industrial Machinery Mfr
N.A.I.C.S.: 333248

Mitsubishi Heavy Industries, Ltd. - Takasago Plant (1)
1-1 Shinhama 2-chome Arai-cho, Takasago, 676-8686, Hyogo, Japan
Tel.: (81) 79 445 6652
Air Conditioning & Refrigeration System Mfr,
N.A.I.C.S.: 333415

Mitsubishi Heavy Industries, Ltd. - Tobishima Plant (1)
5 Kanaoka Tobishima-cho, Ama-gun, Tobishima, 490-1445, Aichi, Japan
Tel.: (81) 567 55 1211
Aerospace System Mfr
N.A.I.C.S.: 334511

Mitsubishi Heavy Industries, Ltd. - Yamatomachi Plant (1)
16-1 Higashi Yamatomachi 2-chome, Shimonoseki, 750-8505, Yamaguchi, Japan
Tel.: (81) 83 267 8335
Web Site: http://www.mhi-global.com
Industrial Shipyard Machinery Mfr
N.A.I.C.S.: 333248

Mitsubishi Heavy Industries-Haier (Qingdao) Air-Conditioners Co., Ltd. (1)
No157-1 Tianshan 2nd Road, Jimo, Qingdao, 266101, China **(100%)**
Tel.: (86) 53288938520
Web Site: http://www.mq.co.jp
Sales Range: $25-49.9 Million
Emp.: 50
Shipbuilding
N.A.I.C.S.: 336611

Mitsubishi Heavy Industries-Jinling Air-Conditioners Co., Ltd. (1)
No 162 Jiangcui Road Hushan, Jianghai District, Jiangmen, 529040, Guangdong, China **(100%)**
Tel.: (86) 750 386 3000
Web Site: https://www.mja.com.cn
Sales Range: $200-249.9 Million
Emp.: 800
Air Conditioner Mfr
N.A.I.C.S.: 333415

Mitsubishi Heavy Industries-Mahajak Air Conditioners Co., Ltd (1)
Soi Chalongkrung 31 Kwang Lamplatiew, 220 Lad Krabang Industrial Estate Free Zone 3 khet Lad Krabang, Bangkok, 10520, Thailand **(100%)**
Tel.: (66) 2 326 0401
Web Site: http://mhi-air.maco.co.th
Sales Range: $450-499.9 Million
Emp.: 2,000
N.A.I.C.S.: 336611

Mitsubishi Heavy Industries-Vst Diesel Engines Private Limited (1)
Plot No 305, Hebbal Industrial Area Metagalli, Mysore, 570016, Karnataka, India
Tel.: (91) 8214003400
Diesel Engine Mfr
N.A.I.C.S.: 336310

Mitsubishi Hitachi Power Systems (China) Co., Ltd. (1)
3302 K Wah Centre 1010 Middle Huaihai Road, Xuhui District, Shanghai, 200031, China
Tel.: (86) 2154923222
Thermal Power Generation Product Distr
N.A.I.C.S.: 423860

Mitsubishi Hitachi Power Systems Gas Turbine Service (Nanjing) Co., Ltd. (1)
16F No 3 Building No 68 Aoti Street New Town SCI-Tech Park, Jianye District, Nanjing, Jiangsu, China
Tel.: (86) 2583242711
Gas Turbine Maintenance Services
N.A.I.C.S.: 811310

Mitsubishi Hitachi Power Systems Jieneng (Qingdao) Steam Turbine Co., Ltd. (1)
16F D and D Cai fu Building No182-6 Haier Road, Laoshan-District, Qingdao, 266100, China
Tel.: (86) 53255730797
Steam Turbine Distr
N.A.I.C.S.: 423860

Mitsubishi Industrias Pesadas do Brasil Ltda. (1)
Rua Pamplona 145 10oandar Cjs1001, Sao Paulo, 01405-900, SP, Brazil
Tel.: (55) 1131709201
Web Site: http://www.mhib.com.br
Industrial Machinery Distr
N.A.I.C.S.: 423830

Mitsubishi Logisnext Asia Pacific Pte. Ltd. (1)
No 1 Tuas West Street, Singapore, 637444, Singapore
Tel.: (65) 65716237
Web Site: http://www.logisnext.com.sg
Forklift Mfr & Distr
N.A.I.C.S.: 333924

Mitsubishi Logisnext Co., Ltd. (1)
2-1-1 Higashikotari, Nagaoka, 617-8585, Kyoto, Japan
Tel.: (81) 759517171
Web Site: https://www.logisnext.com
Rev: $4,638,699,700
Assets: $3,513,181,950
Liabilities: $2,737,610,820
Net Worth: $775,571,130
Earnings: $181,907,200

AND PRIVATE COMPANIES

MITSUBISHI HEAVY INDUSTRIES, LTD.

Emp.: 12,043
Fiscal Year-end: 03/31/2024
Material Handling Equipment Distr & Mfr
N.A.I.C.S.: 423830
Takashi Mikogami *(Chm)*

Subsidiary (US):

Mitsubishi Caterpillar Forklift America Inc. (2)
2121W Sam Houston Pkwy N, Houston, TX 77043-2421
Tel.: (713) 365-1000
Web Site: http://www.mcfa.com
Sales Range: $250-299.9 Million
Emp.: 800
Manufacturing, Sales & Servicing of Forklift Trucks
N.A.I.C.S.: 333924
Ken Barina *(Pres)*

Subsidiary (Non-US):

Caterpillar Shanghai Engine Company, Ltd. (3)
2336 Jun Gong Road, 200432, Shanghai, China (55%)
Tel.: (86) 2165745656
Construction Machinery Mfr
N.A.I.C.S.: 333120

Subsidiary (Non-US):

Mitsubishi Caterpillar Forklift Asia Pte. Ltd. (2)
No 1 Tuas W St, Singapore, 637244, Singapore (100%)
Tel.: (65) 65716237
Web Site: http://www.mcfs.com.sg
Sales Range: $25-49.9 Million
Emp.: 25
Joint Venture of Mitsubishi Heavy Industries Ltd. (80%) & Caterpillar Inc. (20%)
N.A.I.C.S.: 333120

Mitsubishi Caterpillar Forklift Europe B.V. (2)
Hefbrugweg 77, 1332 AM, Almere, Netherlands (100%)
Tel.: (31) 365494411
Web Site: http://www.mcfe.com
Sales Range: $200-249.9 Million
Emp.: 550
Joint Venture of Mitsubishi Heavy Industries Ltd. (80%) & Caterpillar Inc. (20%)
N.A.I.C.S.: 333120

NICHIYU SINGAPORE PTE. LTD. (2)
6 Tuas Avenue 1, Singapore, 639491, Singapore
Tel.: (65) 68633263
Industrial Vehicle Parts Mfr
N.A.I.C.S.: 336390

Nichiyu Asia (Thailand) Co., Ltd. (2)
888/9-10 Moo 9 Soi Roongcharoen Lieb Klong Suvarnabhumi Rd, Bangpla Bangplee, Bangkok, 10540, Samutprakarn, Thailand
Tel.: (66) 218 167 1721
Web Site: https://www.nichiyu.co.th
Supplier of Forklift Trucks Accessories & Parts
N.A.I.C.S.: 423830

Nichiyu Asia Pte. Ltd. (2)
No 6 Tuas Ave 1, 639491, Singapore, Singapore
Tel.: (65) 68619725
Web Site: http://www.nichiyu.com.sg
Sales Range: $25-49.9 Million
Emp.: 30
Automobile & Motor Vehicle Whslr
N.A.I.C.S.: 423110

Subsidiary (Non-US):

NICHIYU FORKLIFTS INDIA PVT. LTD (3)
No 61 Velachery Road, Saidapet, Chennai, 600 015, India
Tel.: (91) 442 235 4213
Web Site: https://www.nichiyu.in
Emp.: 6
Electric Forklift Truck Mfr
N.A.I.C.S.: 333924

Subsidiary (Non-US):

Nichiyu Asialift Philippines, Inc. (2)
No 9 M Flores Street Barangay Sto Rosario, Silangang Pateros, Manila, 1621, Philippines
Tel.: (63) 28 640 1088
Web Site: https://www.nichiyuasialift.com.ph
Industrial Machinery & Equipment Whslr
N.A.I.C.S.: 423830

Nichiyu Forklift (Shanghai) Co., Ltd. (2)
Hua Du Mansion Room I 11th Floor No 838 Zhangyang Road, Pudong, Shanghai, 200122, China
Tel.: (86) 2150588600
Web Site: http://www.nichiyu.com.cn
Conveyor & Conveying Equipment Mfr
N.A.I.C.S.: 333922

Nichiyu Forklift (Shenzhen) Co., Ltd. (2)
Room 706 Block A Business Center, Longhua New District, Shenzhen, 518109, China
Tel.: (86) 75583480091
Web Site: http://www.nmf.co.jp
Sales Range: $25-49.9 Million
Emp.: 20
Automobile & Motor Vehicle Whslr
N.A.I.C.S.: 423110

Nichiyu Forklift Europe SAS (2)
ZI Mi-Plaine, 4 rue Georges Besse, 69740, Genas, France
Tel.: (33) 478900101
Electronic Parts & Equipment Whslr
N.A.I.C.S.: 423690

Nichiyu Hong Kong Co., Ltd. (2)
No 19 2 / F On Wui Center 25 Lok Yip Road, Fanling, NT, China (Hong Kong)
Tel.: (852) 2 719 9202
Web Site: https://www.nichiyu.com.hk
Sales Range: $25-49.9 Million
Emp.: 4
Hardware Stores
N.A.I.C.S.: 444140

Shanghai Nichiyu Forklift Manufacturing Co., Ltd. (2)
No 150 Xun Ye Road Sheshan Branch, Songjiang Industrial Zone, Shanghai, 201602, China
Tel.: (86) 215 779 2111
Web Site: http://www.sowellsoft.net
Electronic Parts & Equipment Whslr
N.A.I.C.S.: 423690

Subsidiary (Domestic):

UniCarriers Corporation (2)
1-2 Shin-Ogura, Saiwai-ku, Kawasaki, 212-0031, Kanagawa, Japan (100%)
Tel.: (81) 44 330 9000
Web Site: http://www.unicarriers.co.jp
Sales Range: $1-4.9 Billion
Emp.: 5,813
Forklifts, Container Carriers, Transfer Cranes & Other Material Handling Machinery Mfr & Distr
N.A.I.C.S.: 333924

Subsidiary (US):

UniCarriers Americas Corporation (3)
240 N Prospect St, Marengo, IL 60152
Tel.: (815) 568-0061
Web Site: http://www.unicarriersamericas.com
Forklift Trucks Mfr & Distr
N.A.I.C.S.: 423830
Dale Mark *(VP-Mfg Ops)*

Subsidiary (Domestic):

Capital Equipment & Handling, Inc. (4)
1100 Cotton wood Ave, Hartland, WI 53029
Tel.: (262) 369-5500
Web Site: http://www.cehwi.com
Emp.: 200
Industrial Equipment Distr
N.A.I.C.S.: 423830

New England Industrial Truck, Inc. (4)
220 Ballardvale St Ste J, Wilmington, MA 01887
Tel.: (781) 935-9105
Web Site: http://www.neit.com

Emp.: 75
Forklift, Industrial Truck & Other Materials Handling Machinery Dealer
N.A.I.C.S.: 423830

Subsidiary (Non-US):

UniCarriers Europe AB (3)
Metallvagen 9, 435 33, Molnlycke, Sweden
Tel.: (46) 3 198 4000
Web Site: https://www.unicarrierseurope.com
Holding Company; Regional Managing Office; Forklifts & Other Material Handling Machinery Mfr & Distr
N.A.I.C.S.: 551112

Subsidiary (Non-US):

UniCarriers Denmark A/S (4)
Greve Main 19, 2670, Greve, Denmark
Tel.: (45) 72210210
Web Site: http://www.unicarrierseurope.com
Forklift Distr
N.A.I.C.S.: 423830
Steen Junge *(Sls Dir)*

UniCarriers France SAS (4)
3 avenue des Gros Chevaux, CS 27081 95053, Cergy-Pontoise, 95310, Saint-Ouen-l'Aumone, CEDEX, France
Tel.: (33) 13 440 3200
Web Site: https://www.unicarrierseurope.com
Emp.: 200
Forklift Distr
N.A.I.C.S.: 423830

UniCarriers Germany GmbH (4)
Lessingstrasse 14, 46149, Oberhausen, Germany
Tel.: (49) 208 6567 0
Web Site: http://www.unicarrierseurope.com
Emp.: 200
Forklift Distr
N.A.I.C.S.: 423830
Daniel Matas *(Mng Dir)*

UniCarriers Manufacturing Spain, S.A. (4)
Soto Grande s/n, 31110, Noain, NavarraNoain, Spain
Tel.: (34) 948 298810
Web Site: http://www.unicarriersspain.com
Forklift Mfr
N.A.I.C.S.: 333924
Jorge Garcia Orejana *(Gen Mgr-Comml)*

UniCarriers Netherlands B.V. (4)
IJzersteden 28, 7547 TB, Enschede, Netherlands
Tel.: (31) 882053000
Web Site: http://www.unicarrierseurope.com
Emp.: 500
Forklift & Other Material Handling Machinery Distr
N.A.I.C.S.: 423830

UniCarriers UK Limited (4)
Jane Morbey Road, Thame, OX9 3RR, Oxon, United Kingdom
Tel.: (44) 1844215501
Web Site: http://www.unicarrierseurope.com
Forklift Distr
N.A.I.C.S.: 423830
Mark Gibb *(Mng Dir)*

Mitsubishi Logisnext Forklift (Shanghai) Co., Ltd. (1)
11F Hua Do Bldg No 838 Zhang Yang Rd, Pudong, Shanghai, 200122, China
Tel.: (86) 2150588600
Engineering Electrical Equipment Mfr
N.A.I.C.S.: 335999

Mitsubishi Power (Philippines) Inc. (1)
AG and P Special Economic Zone, Barangay San Roque Bauan, Batangas, 4201, Philippines
Tel.: (63) 439802432
Web Site: http://www.phl.mhps.com
Emp.: 646
Power Boiler Mfr
N.A.I.C.S.: 332410
Yukio Nakata *(Pres)*

Mitsubishi Power (Thailand) Ltd. (1)
87/2 CRC Tower All Seasons Place 45th Floor Wireless Road Lumpini, Pathumwan,

Bangkok, 10330, Thailand
Tel.: (66) 20160100
Thermal Power Generation Product Distr
N.A.I.C.S.: 423840
Koji Nishikawa *(Pres & Mng Dir)*

Mitsubishi Power Aero (1)
Gasheka ul D 7 Str 1, 123056, Moscow, Russia
Tel.: (7) 4957558385
Engineering Electrical Equipment Mfr
N.A.I.C.S.: 335999

Mitsubishi Power Asia Pacific Pte. Ltd. (1)
150 Beach Road 33-03/04 Gateway West, Singapore, 189720, Singapore
Tel.: (65) 62935352
Thermal Power Generation Product Distr
N.A.I.C.S.: 423840
Osamu Ono *(CEO & Mng Dir)*

Mitsubishi Power Australia Pty. Ltd. (1)
Unit 2153/2155 North Tower level 21 459 Collins Street, Melbourne, 3000, VIC, Australia
Tel.: (61) 386303355
Thermal Power Generation Product Distr
N.A.I.C.S.: 423840

Mitsubishi Power Canada, Ltd. (1)
460-10655 Southport Road S W, Calgary, T2W 4Y1, AB, Canada
Tel.: (403) 278-1881
Web Site: http://www.mitsubishipower.ca
Thermal Power Generation Product Mfr & Distr
N.A.I.C.S.: 335999

Mitsubishi Power Egypt, L.L.C. (1)
2nd Floor egID Building Block 72 off 90 Axis City Center, 5th Settlement, New Cairo, Egypt
Tel.: (20) 226145045
Engineering Electrical Equipment Mfr
N.A.I.C.S.: 335999

Mitsubishi Power Environmental Solutions, Ltd. (1)
1-8 Sakuragicho 1-Chome, Naka-Ku, Yokohama, Japan
Tel.: (81) 452324948
Engineering Electrical Equipment Mfr
N.A.I.C.S.: 335999
Shoichi Onishi *(Pres)*

Mitsubishi Power India Private Limited (1)
5th Floor Pride Hulkul No 116 Lal Bagh Main Rd SGN Layout, Vinobha Nagar Sudhama Nagar, Bengaluru, 560027, Karnataka, India
Tel.: (91) 8067187187
Thermal Power Generation Product Distr
N.A.I.C.S.: 423840
Tatsuto Nagayasu *(Chm, CEO & Mng Dir)*

Mitsubishi Power Industries Co., Ltd. (1)
KDX Yokohama Kannai Bldg 3-56-1 Aioicho, Naka-ku, Yokohama, 231-0012, Japan
Tel.: (81) 452274950
Thermal Power Generation Product Mfr & Distr
N.A.I.C.S.: 335999

Mitsubishi Power Maintenance Service Co., Ltd. (1)
8-25 Shinhama 2-chome Arai-cho, Takasago, 676-0008, Hyogo, Japan
Tel.: (81) 794459810
Emp.: 194
Thermal Power Generation Product Distr
N.A.I.C.S.: 423840
Naoya Kagawa *(Pres & CEO)*

Mitsubishi Power Precision Casting Co., Ltd. (1)
1-17 Hiraide Industrial Park, Utsunomiya, 321-0905, Tochigi, Japan
Tel.: (81) 286614151
Thermal Power Generation Product Distr
N.A.I.C.S.: 423840
Tetsuya Fukumoto *(Pres & CEO)*

Mitsubishi Power Saudi Arabia Limited, Co. (1)
Dammam 2nd Industrial City Street No 95, PO Box 9222, Dammam, Saudi Arabia

MITSUBISHI HEAVY INDUSTRIES, LTD.

Mitsubishi Heavy Industries, Ltd.—(Continued)
Tel.: (966) 138141114
Engineering Electrical Equipment Mfr
N.A.I.C.S.: 335999

Mitsubishi Power Systems (Asia Pacific) Pte Ltd. (1)
150 Beach Road 28-03 Gateway West, Singapore, 189720, Singapore
Tel.: (65) 6293 5352
Web Site: http://www.mhi.co.jp
Power Equipment Parts Distr
N.A.I.C.S.: 423610
Hiroyuki Iwase *(Gen Mgr)*

Subsidiary (Non-US):

Mitsubishi Power Systems (Thailand) Ltd. (2)
CRC Tower All Seasons Place Unit 1 and 7 45th Floor 87/2 Wireless Road, Lumpini Phatumwan, Bangkok, 10330, Thailand
Tel.: (66) 20160100
Web Site: http://www.mps-t.com
Power Generation Equipment Distr
N.A.I.C.S.: 423830

Mitsubishi Power Systems Europe, Ltd. (1)
The Point 37 North Wharf Road, London, W2 1AF, United Kingdom
Tel.: (44) 207 535 0500
Web Site: http://www.emea.mhps.com
Sales Range: $25-49.9 Million
Emp.: 90
Power Generating Equipment Mfr
N.A.I.C.S.: 333611

Mitsubishi Power de Mexico, S.A. de C.V. (1)
Paseo de la Reforma No 265 Piso 18, Col Cuauhtemoc, Mexico, Mexico
Tel.: (52) 5555114193
Thermal Power Generation Product Distr
N.A.I.C.S.: 423840

Mitsubishi Power, Ltd. (1)
Mitsubishijuko Yokohama Bldg 3-1 Minatomirai 3-chome, Nishi-ku, Yokohama, 220-8401, Kanagawa, Japan
Tel.: (81) 45 200 6100
Web Site: https://power.mhi.com
Boilers, Chemical Plant Equipment & Operational Support Systems Mfr
N.A.I.C.S.: 332410
Yasuo Fujitani *(Sr VP)*

Subsidiary (Non-US):

Babcock-Hitachi (Philippines) Inc. (2)
AG&P Special Economic Zone Barangay San Roque Bauan, Batangas, 4201, Philippines
Tel.: (63) 43 727 1027
Web Site: http://www.bhpi.com.ph
Emp.: 900
Mfr of Boilers, Chemical Plant Equipment & Operational Support Systems
N.A.I.C.S.: 332410
Clara Evelyn Fider *(Mgr-HR)*

Babcock-Hitachi Dongfang Boiler Co., Ltd. (2)
No 4 Bridge Chengnan Road, Jiaxing, 314001, Zhejiang, China
Tel.: (86) 573 8262 5132
Sales Range: $100-124.9 Million
Emp.: 40
Heat Boiler Mfr & Distr
N.A.I.C.S.: 333414

Mitsubishi Hitachi Power Systems Europe GmbH (1)
Schifferstrasse 80, 47059, Duisburg, Germany
Tel.: (49) 20380380
Web Site: http://www.emea.mhps.com
Metalworking Machines Mfr
N.A.I.C.S.: 333513
Rainer Kiechl *(CEO)*

Subsidiary (Non-US):

Mitsubishi Hitachi Power Systems Africa (Pty) Ltd. (3)
Building 30 The Woodlands Office Park 20 Woodlands Drive, Woodmead, 2054, Sandton, South Africa

Tel.: (27) 11 260 4300
Web Site: http://www.za.mhps.com
Eletric Power Generation Services
N.A.I.C.S.: 221111
Kiyoshi Okazoe *(Chm-Mgmt Bd)*

Mitsubishi Shipbuilding Co., Ltd. (1)
Mitsubishijuko Yokohama Bldg 3-1 Minatomirai 3-chome, Nishi-ku, Yokohama, 220-8401, Kanagawa, Japan
Tel.: (81) 452006611
Passenger Ship Building Services
N.A.I.C.S.: 336611
Toru Kitamura *(Pres & CEO)*

Mitsubishi Turbocharger & Engine America, Inc. (1)
2 Pierce Pl Ste 1100, Itasca, IL 60143
Tel.: (630) 268-0750
Web Site: http://www.mtea-us.com
Turbo Engine Mfr & Distr
N.A.I.C.S.: 333611

Mitsubishi Turbocharger & Engine Europe B.V. (1)
Damsluisweg 2, 1332 EC, Almere, Netherlands
Tel.: (31) 365388311
Turbine Generator Set Mfr
N.A.I.C.S.: 333611

Mitsubishi Turbocharger Asia Co., Ltd. (1)
700/803 Moo1 T Panthong A, Panthong, Chon Buri, 20160, Thailand
Tel.: (66) 38 932 800
Turbocharger Parts Mfr & Distr
N.A.I.C.S.: 333611

Mitsubishi-Hitachi Metals Machinery, Inc. (1)
Shintamachi Bldg 34-6 Shiba 5-chome, Minato-ku, Tokyo, 108-0014, Japan (55.7%)
Tel.: (81) 3 5765 5231
Web Site: http://www.m-hmm.co.jp
Metal Rolling & Processing Machinery Mfr
N.A.I.C.S.: 333519
Kazunari Haraguchi *(Exec VP)*

Subsidiary (Non-US):

MHPS Plant Services Pty Ltd. (2)
Level 7 19 Lang Parade, PO Box 1559, Milton, 4064, QLD, Australia
Tel.: (61) 738780888
Web Site: http://www.anz.mhps.com
Fabricated Wire Product Mfr
N.A.I.C.S.: 332618

Mitsubishi-Hitachi Metals Machinery (Shanghai), Inc. (2)
Room 1707 Tower A 69 Dongfang Road, Shanghai, 200120, China
Tel.: (86) 21 6859 8835
Web Site: http://www.m-hmm.co.jp
Metal Rolling & Processing Machinery Mfr
N.A.I.C.S.: 333519

Subsidiary (US):

Mitsubishi-Hitachi Metals Machinery USA, Inc. (2)
500 Cherrington Pkwy, Coraopolis, PA 15108-4744
Tel.: (412) 269-6630
Web Site: http://www.m-hmm.co.jp
Metal Rolling & Processing Machinery Mfr & Distr
N.A.I.C.S.: 333519
Kathy Uebelacher *(Office Mgr)*

Subsidiary (Domestic):

MHCG, Inc. (3)
N53 W24900 S Corporate Cir, Sussex, WI 53089
Tel.: (262) 691-0400
Web Site: http://www.gfg-peabody.com
Sales Range: $25-49.9 Million
Metal Roll Coating, Electrostatic Oiling & Coil Coating Equipment Mfr & Distr
N.A.I.C.S.: 333519
Linda Taylor *(Controller)*

Mohawk Labor Services, LLC (1)
82 Rotterdam Industrial Park, Schenectady, NY 12306
Tel.: (518) 831-1090

Web Site: http://www.mohawklaborservices.com
Turbine & Generator Set Mfr
N.A.I.C.S.: 333611

NAFAS JENTERA SDN BHD (1)
Lot 1 Jalan Teknologi 3/5 Taman Sains Selangor 1, Kota Damansara, 47810, Petaling Jaya, Selangor, Malaysia
Tel.: (60) 361441200
Web Site: http://www.nafas.com.my
Agricultural Machinery & Fertilizer Distr
N.A.I.C.S.: 423820

NICHIDAI (THAILAND) LTD. (1)
700/882 Moo 5 Tb Nhongkakha, AP Phanthong, Phan Thong, 20160, Chonburi, Thailand
Tel.: (66) 3 818 5245
Web Site: https://www.nichidai.jp
Car Metallic Parts Mfr & Sales
N.A.I.C.S.: 336390

Nagasaki Nishi Eco-Creation Co., Ltd. (1)
3-526-23 Kaminoshimamachi, Nagasaki, 850-0078, Japan
Tel.: (81) 958659753
Industrial Electrical Equipment & Component Mfr
N.A.I.C.S.: 335999

Nihon Kensetsu Kogyo Co., Ltd. (1)
4-12-5 Tsukishima, Chuo-ku, Tokyo, 104-0052, Japan
Tel.: (81) 33 532 7151
Web Site: https://www.nikkenko.co.jp
Emp.: 465
Nuclear Power Plant Construction Services
N.A.I.C.S.: 237130

Nishinihon-JKO Co., Ltd. (1)
2-21 Kozen-cho, Nagasaki, 850-0032, Japan
Tel.: (81) 958256381
Engineering Electrical Equipment Mfr
N.A.I.C.S.: 335999

Nuclear Development Corporation (1)
622-12 Funaishikawa, Tokai-mura Nakagun, Ibaraki, 319-1111, Japan
Tel.: (81) 29 282 9111
Web Site: http://www.ndc-tokai.co.jp
Sales Range: $25-49.9 Million
Emp.: 70
Nuclear Fuel Research & Development Services
N.A.I.C.S.: 541715

Nuclear Plant Service Engineering Co., Ltd. (1)
1-1-1 Wadazakicho Kobe Shipyard, Hyogo-ku, Kobe, 652-8585, Japan
Tel.: (81) 78 672 4180
Web Site: http://www.nusec.co.jp
Emp.: 398
Nuclear Plant Engineering Services
N.A.I.C.S.: 541330

Nuclear Power Training Center, Ltd. (1)
129-1-1 Kutsumi, Tsuruga, 914-0823, Fukui, Japan
Tel.: (81) 77 023 9090
Web Site: https://www.jntc.co.jp
Sales Range: $10-24.9 Million
Emp.: 50
Industrial Training Services
N.A.I.C.S.: 611430
Hiroaki Higuchi *(Pres)*

PT. MHI Engine System Indonesia (1)
302 Bld Cilandak Commercial Estate CCE, PO Box 7510, Cilandak, Jakarta, Indonesia
Tel.: (62) 217890191
Diesel Engine Mfr
N.A.I.C.S.: 333618

PT. MPS Indonesia (1)
Sentral Senayan II 12th Floor JL Asia Afrika No 8 Senayan, Gelora Bung Karno, Jakarta, 10270, Indonesia
Tel.: (62) 21 5797 4441
Web Site: http://www.mhps.com
Sales Range: $25-49.9 Million
Emp.: 30
Industrial Machinery Mfr & Distr
N.A.I.C.S.: 333248

INTERNATIONAL PUBLIC

Shinichi Ueki *(Pres)*

PT. Mitsubishi Heavy Industries Indonesia (1)
12th Floor Sentral Senayan II JI Asia Afrika No 8 Gelora Bung Karno, Senayan, Jakarta, 10270, Indonesia
Tel.: (62) 2157974430
Engineering Electrical Equipment Mfr
N.A.I.C.S.: 335999

PT. Mitsubishi Power Indonesia (1)
Sentral Senayan II 12th Floor Jl Asia Afrika No 8 Gelora Bung Karno, Jakarta Pusat, 10270, Indonesia
Tel.: (62) 2180668900
Thermal Power Generation Product Distr
N.A.I.C.S.: 423840

Power Generation Services, Inc. (1)
1160 McKinley St, Anoka, MN 55303
Rev.: $7,333,333
Emp.: 20
Thermal Power Generation Services
N.A.I.C.S.: 221116
Scott Hughes *(Mgr-Customer Svc)*

Pratt & Whitney Power Systems CIS LLC (1)
Hasek Street D7 Ctp1 5th Floor, 123056, Moscow, Russia
Tel.: (7) 4957558385
Industrial Electrical Equipment & Component Mfr
N.A.I.C.S.: 335999

Primetals International Trading (Shanghai) Ltd. Inc. (1)
369 Shenfu Road, Xinzhuang Industrial Park Minhang District, Shanghai, 201108, China
Tel.: (86) 2161968688
Iron & Steel Product Mfr
N.A.I.C.S.: 331110

Primetals Technologies (Shanghai), Inc. (1)
Room 1707 Tower A 69 Dongfang Road, Shanghai, 200120, China
Tel.: (86) 2168598835
Non-Ferrous Metal Equipment Whslr
N.A.I.C.S.: 423510

Primetals Technologies Austria GmbH (1)
Turmstrasse 44, 4031, Linz, Austria
Tel.: (43) 73265920
Web Site: https://www.primetals.com
Iron & Steel Product Mfr
N.A.I.C.S.: 331110

Primetals Technologies Belgium S.A./N.V. (1)
W A Mozartlaan 4 Building Amadeus, 1620, Drogenbos, Belgium
Tel.: (32) 471401010
Iron & Steel Product Mfr
N.A.I.C.S.: 331110

Primetals Technologies Brazil Ltda. (1)
Rua Joao XXIII s/n, Santa Cruz do Sul, 23560-352, Rio de Janeiro, Brazil
Tel.: (55) 2131984711
Iron & Steel Product Mfr
N.A.I.C.S.: 331110

Primetals Technologies Czech Republic s.r.o. (1)
28 rijna 2663/150, 702 00, Ostrava, Czech Republic
Tel.: (420) 597400660
Iron & Steel Product Mfr
N.A.I.C.S.: 331110

Primetals Technologies France S.A.S. (1)
41 Route de Feurs, BP 99, 42600, Savigneux, France
Tel.: (33) 477966300
Iron & Steel Product Mfr
N.A.I.C.S.: 331110

Primetals Technologies Germany GmbH (1)
Bunsenstrasse 43, 91058, Erlangen, Germany
Tel.: (49) 913198860
Iron & Steel Product Mfr
N.A.I.C.S.: 331110

AND PRIVATE COMPANIES — MITSUBISHI HEAVY INDUSTRIES, LTD.

Primetals Technologies India Private Ltd. (1)
Godrej Waterside Tower No II Unit Nos 706 and 707 7th Floor Plot No 5, Block DP Sector-V Salt Lake City, Kolkata, 700091, India
Tel.: (91) 3366291000
Iron & Steel Product Mfr
N.A.I.C.S.: 331110

Primetals Technologies Italy S.r.l. (1)
Via Luigi Pomini 92, Marnate, Italy
Tel.: (39) 0331741211
Iron & Steel Product Mfr
N.A.I.C.S.: 331110

Primetals Technologies Japan, Ltd. (1)
6-22 Kannon Shinmachi 4-Chome, Nishi-ku, Hiroshima, 733-8553, Japan
Tel.: (81) 822912181
Industrial Rolling Equipment Mfr & Distr
N.A.I.C.S.: 333519

Primetals Technologies Korea Limited (1)
Jaehwa Square 16th Floor 311 Dongmak-ro, Mapo-gu, 04156, Seoul, Korea (South)
Tel.: (82) 231498003
Iron & Steel Product Mfr
N.A.I.C.S.: 331110

Primetals Technologies Mexico, S.R.L. de C.V. (1)
Miguel Aleman Km 26, Parque Industrial Milimex, 66637, Apodaca, Nuevo Leon, Mexico
Tel.: (52) 8181960909
Iron & Steel Product Mfr
N.A.I.C.S.: 331110

Primetals Technologies Poland Sp. z o.o. (1)
Ul Stefana Korbonskiego 14, 30-443, Krakow, Poland
Tel.: (48) 122114300
Iron & Steel Product Mfr
N.A.I.C.S.: 331110

Primetals Technologies Russia LLC (1)
Gilyarovskogo Str 10 bld 1 floor 4, 129090, Moscow, Russia
Tel.: (7) 4951145518
Iron & Steel Product Mfr
N.A.I.C.S.: 331110

Primetals Technologies USA LLC (1)
5895 Windward Pkwy, Alpharetta, GA 30005
Tel.: (770) 740-3800
Iron & Steel Product Mfr
N.A.I.C.S.: 331110

Primetals Technologies Ukraine LLC (1)
4-B Mykoly Hrinchenka Str, 03038, Kiev, Ukraine
Tel.: (380) 442337200
Iron & Steel Product Mfr
N.A.I.C.S.: 331110

Primetals Technologies, Limited (1)
566 Chiswick High Road Building 11 Chiswick Park, London, W4 5YA, United Kingdom
Tel.: (44) 2089964300
Web Site: http://www.primetals.com
Metal Mfr & Distr
N.A.I.C.S.: 332312
Satoru Iijima (Chm & CEO)

Primetals Teknoloji Sanayi ve Ticaret A.S. (1)
Yakacik Cad No 111, 34870, Istanbul, Turkiye
Tel.: (90) 2164593160
Iron & Steel Product Mfr
N.A.I.C.S.: 331110

RedsLand Corporation (1)
1771 Shimookubo, Saitamashisa kura-ku, Saitama, 338-0825, Japan
Tel.: (81) 488401541
Industrial Electrical Equipment & Component Mfr
N.A.I.C.S.: 335999

Rimas ApS (1)
Falstervej 2, Logstor, 9670, Denmark
Tel.: (45) 96 66 03 99
Web Site: http://www.rimas.dk
Construction Machinery Mfr
N.A.I.C.S.: 333120

Rocla Oyj (1)
Jampankatu 2, PO Box 88, 04401, Jarvenpaa, Finland
Tel.: (358) 2077811
Web Site: http://www.rocla.com
Sales Range: $100-124.9 Million
Emp.: 400
Electric Warehouse Truck Mfr & Distr
N.A.I.C.S.: 336320
Tapio Rummukainen (Pres & CEO)

Rokkasho Reprocessing Plant Maintenance Service Co., Ltd. (1)
1-45 Obuchi-aza-iyasakadaira Rokkasyomura, Aomori, 039-3212, Japan
Tel.: (81) 175 73 3050
Web Site: http://www.mhi-global.com
Fuel Reprocessing Plant Management Services
N.A.I.C.S.: 457210

Ryoju Cold Chain Co., Ltd. (1)
Miyako Building 1-5-4 Kanda, Chiyoda-ku, Tokyo, 101-0047, Japan
Tel.: (81) 35 259 2051
Web Site: https://www.rccc.co.jp
Emp.: 176
Refrigeration Equipment Distr & Rental Services
N.A.I.C.S.: 423740

Ryoju Estate Co., Ltd. (1)
34-6 Shiba 5-chome, Minato-ku, Tokyo, 108-0014, Japan
Tel.: (81) 3 3451 1172
Web Site: http://www.rje.co.jp
Civil Engineering Construction Services
N.A.I.C.S.: 237990
Kenichi Okubo (Pres)

Unit (Domestic):

Hiroshima Ryoju Estate Co., Ltd. (2)
8-4 Kan-on-shin-machi 4-chome, Nishi-ku, Hiroshima, 733-0036, Japan
Tel.: (81) 82 294 5100
Web Site: http://www.h-rk.co.jp
Civil Engineering Construction Services
N.A.I.C.S.: 237990
Kazi Hiroki (Pres)

Kinki Ryoju Estate Co., Ltd. (2)
2-19 Kasamatsu-dori 9-chome, Hyogo-ku, Kobe, 652-0864, Japan
Tel.: (81) 78 672 4718
Civil Engineering Construction Services
N.A.I.C.S.: 237990

Nagoya Ryoju Estate Co., Ltd. (2)
6-16 Oye-cho, Minato-ku, Nagoya, 455-0024, Japan
Tel.: (81) 52 612 1886
Web Site: http://www.nrkk.co.jp
Civil Engineering Construction Services
N.A.I.C.S.: 237990

Nishinihon Ryoju Estate Fukuoka Co., Ltd. (2)
5-3 Akunoura-machi, Nagasaki, 850-8677, Japan
Tel.: (81) 95 861 6540
Web Site: http://www.ryoko-fukuoka.jp
Civil Engineering Construction Services
N.A.I.C.S.: 237990

Ryonetsu Co., Ltd. (1)
1-8-13 Hakataeki Minami Hakataeki Minami R Building, Hakata-ku, Fukuoka, 812-8553, Japan
Tel.: (81) 92 411 5741
Web Site: https://www.ryonetsu.co.jp
Emp.: 292
Air Conditioning & Refrigeration System Mfr & Maintenance Services
N.A.I.C.S.: 333415

Ryonichi Engineering Co., Ltd. (1)
8-1 Sachiura 1-chome, Kanazawa-ku, Yokohama, 236-8515, Japan
Tel.: (81) 45 772 5011
Web Site: http://www.ryonichi.co.jp
Marine Steel Products Mfr
N.A.I.C.S.: 331221

Ryosei Service Co., Ltd. (1)
1-2 Sawatari, Yokohama, Yokohama, 221-0844, Japan
Tel.: (81) 45 311 6941
Cleaning Equipment Maintenance Services
N.A.I.C.S.: 811310

Ryosen Engineers Co., Ltd. (1)
4-31 Minami Kan-on 6-chome, Nishi-ku, Hiroshima, 733-0035, Japan
Tel.: (81) 82 291 4573
Web Site: http://www.ryosen.com
Compressor & Conveyance System Mfr
N.A.I.C.S.: 333912

Ryoyu System Engineering Co., Ltd. (1)
1-6 Komatsu-dori 5-chome, Hyogo-ku, Kobe, 652-0865, Japan
Tel.: (81) 78 672 4058
System Engineering Services
N.A.I.C.S.: 541330

Sagami Logistics & Service Co., Ltd. (1)
3000 Tana, Chuo-ku, Sagamihara, 252-5293, Kanagawa, Japan
Tel.: (81) 42 761 4733
Logistics Consulting Services
N.A.I.C.S.: 541614

Saudi Factory for Electrical Appliances Company Ltd. (1)
Industrial City Phase I, PO Box 34833, Jeddah, 21478, Saudi Arabia
Tel.: (966) 26378417
Sales Range: $50-74.9 Million
Emp.: 145
Air Conditioning Equipment Mfr
N.A.I.C.S.: 333415

Seibu Jukan Operation Co.,Ltd. (1)
1-24 Sakae-cho-dori 1-chome, Chuo-ku, Kobe, 650-0023, Japan
Tel.: (81) 78 334 0286
Sewage Waste Treatment & Management Services
N.A.I.C.S.: 221320

Seiryo Engineering Co., Ltd. (1)
1-14 Wadamiya-dori 7-chome, Hyogo-ku, Kobe, 652-0863, Hyogo, Japan
Tel.: (81) 78 671 2321
Web Site: http://www.seiryo-eng.co.jp
Marine & Nuclear Equipment Mfr
N.A.I.C.S.: 334517

Seo Koatsu Kogyo Co., Ltd. (1)
Mitsubishi Juko Osaka Bldg 5th Floor 1-3-20 Tosabori, Nishi-ku, Osaka, 550-0001, Japan
Tel.: (81) 66 225 2338
Web Site: https://www.seo-koatsu.co.jp
Sales Range: $50-74.9 Million
Emp.: 310
Steel Forged Products Mfr & Distr
N.A.I.C.S.: 332111
Toshiyuki Osada (Pres)

Plant (Domestic):

Seo Koatsu Kogyo Co., Ltd. - Ichikawa Works (2)
869-20 Aza Kanzaki Ichikawa-cho, Kanzaki-gun, Hyogo, 679-2333, Japan
Tel.: (81) 790 28 0590
Steel Forged Products Mfr
N.A.I.C.S.: 332111

Seo Koatsu Kogyo Co., Ltd. - Kaizuka Works (2)
1-20 Nishikikita-cho, Kaizuka, 597-0092, Osaka, Japan
Tel.: (81) 72 437 6921
Web Site: https://www.seo-koatsu.co.jp
Industrial Machinery Mfr
N.A.I.C.S.: 333248

Seo Koatsu Kogyo Co., Ltd. - Mikkaichi Works (2)
9-10 Nishikatasoe-cho, Kawachinagano, 586-0047, Osaka, Japan
Tel.: (81) 72 163 5081
Web Site: https://www.seo-koatsu.co.jp
Industrial Machinery Mfr
N.A.I.C.S.: 333248

Shanghai MHI Turbocharger Co., Ltd. (1)
No 338 Xinke Road, Qingpu District, Shanghai, 201701, China (40%)
Tel.: (86) 216 921 0030
Web Site: https://www.smtc.sh.cn
Sales Range: $50-74.9 Million
Emp.: 200
Turbo Chargers Mfr & Distr
N.A.I.C.S.: 336310

Shimonoseki Ryoju Engineering Co., Ltd. (1)
16-1 Hikoshima Enoura-cho 6-chome, Shimonoseki, 750-8505, Japan
Tel.: (81) 83 267 1903
Web Site: http://www.sekiryo.co.jp
Telecommunication Construction Services
N.A.I.C.S.: 237130
Hisaaki Hashimoto (Gen Mgr)

Shinryo Corporation (1)
Comore Yotsuya/Yotsuya Tower 5th Floor 1-6-1 Yotsuya, Shinjuku-ku, Tokyo, 160-8510, Japan
Tel.: (81) 33 357 2151
Web Site: https://www.shinryo.com
Sales Range: $350-399.9 Million
Emp.: 2,251
Building Engineering Services
N.A.I.C.S.: 541330
Takeshi Kagami (Pres & CEO)

Subsidiary (Non-US):

GMP Technical Solutions Private Limited (2)
309-316 3rd Floor Swastik Disa Business Park, Behind Wadhani Industrial Estate L B S Marg Ghatkopar W, Mumbai, 400 086, Maharashtra, India
Tel.: (91) 2249716529
Web Site: https://www.gmptech.net
Emp.: 1,222
Engineeering Services
N.A.I.C.S.: 541330

Shunjusha Co., Ltd. (1)
34-7 Shiba 5-chome, Minato-ku, Tokyo, 108-0014, Japan
Tel.: (81) 3 5443 0022
Web Site: http://www.shunju.co.jp
Fire & Casualty Insurance Handling Services
N.A.I.C.S.: 524298

SpaceJet Montreal Center, Inc. (1)
3655 Avenue des Grandes Tourelles Suite 110, Boisbriand, J7H 0E2, QC, Canada
Tel.: (438) 476-2405
Industrial Electrical Equipment & Component Mfr
N.A.I.C.S.: 335999

Sunlex Co., Ltd (1)
3-12 Tonya-cho 3-chome, Kumagaya, 360-0024, Saitama, Japan
Tel.: (81) 48 527 2071
Web Site: http://www.mhi.co.jp
Storage & Packaging Services
N.A.I.C.S.: 493190

TES Philippines, Inc. (1)
Edsa Mrt Depot North Ave cor Edsa, Metro Manila, Quezon City, Philippines
Tel.: (63) 2 920 0232
Web Site: http://www.mhi.co.jp
Sales Range: $25-49.9 Million
Emp.: 250
Transportation System Maintenance Services
N.A.I.C.S.: 811114

Tamachi Building Co., Ltd. (1)
34-7 Shiba 5-chome, Minato-ku, Tokyo, 108-0014, Japan
Tel.: (81) 3 3451 1131
Real Estate Manangement Services
N.A.I.C.S.: 531390

Tarumi Golf Co., Ltd. (1)
2-1 Shiomigaoka 2-chome, Tarumi-ku, Kobe, 665-0005, Hyogo, Japan
Tel.: (81) 786725839
Industrial Electrical Equipment & Component Mfr
N.A.I.C.S.: 335999

Techno Data Engineering Co., Ltd. (1)
1-1 Wadasaki-cho 1-chome, Hyogo-ku, Kobe, 652-8585, Japan
Tel.: (81) 78 672 4981
Industrial Engineering Services
N.A.I.C.S.: 541330

MITSUBISHI HEAVY INDUSTRIES, LTD.

Mitsubishi Heavy Industries, Ltd.—(Continued)

Thai Compressor Manufacturing Co., Ltd. (1)
33/3 Moo 21 Suwinthawong Rd Saladang Bangnumprieo, Chachoengsao, 24000, Thailand
Tel.: (66) 38 593 0623
Web Site: https://www.thacom.co.th
N.A.I.C.S.: 336611

Tokiwa Machinery Works Ltd. (1)
47 Suzukawa, Isehara, 259-1146, Kanagawa, Japan
Tel.: (81) 463 94 2300
Diesel Engine Mfr
N.A.I.C.S.: 333618

Tokyo Environment Operation Ltd. (1)
Aomi 3-chome, Koto-ku, Tokyo, 135-0064, Japan
Tel.: (81) 3 3527 5755
Waste Treatment Plant Maintenance Services
N.A.I.C.S.: 562211

Toyo CR Sdn. Bhd. (1)
No 16 Jalan Serendah 26/41 Seksyen 26, 40400, Shah Alam, Selangor, Malaysia
Tel.: (60) 351920788
Industrial Electrical Equipment & Component Mfr
N.A.I.C.S.: 335999

Turboden S.p.A. (1)
Via Cernaia 10, 25124, Brescia, Italy
Tel.: (39) 0303552001
Web Site: http://www.turboden.com
Renewable Energy Services
N.A.I.C.S.: 221118
Paolo Bertuzzi *(CEO & Mng Dir)*

Turboden Turkey ORC Turbo Jeneratör Sanayi Anonim Sirketi (1)
Barbaros Mahallesi Billur Sk No 23/8, Cankaya, Ankara, Turkiye
Tel.: (90) 5330435890
Renewable Energy Services
N.A.I.C.S.: 221118

UniCarriers Forklift (Anhui) Co., Ltd. (1)
158 Woyun Rd, Hefei Economic and Technological Development Area, Hefei, 230601, Anhui, China
Tel.: (86) 55163680660
Industrial Electrical Equipment & Component Mfr
N.A.I.C.S.: 335999

Urawa Red Diamonds Co., Ltd. (1)
2-1 Nakanoda, Midori-ku, Saitama, Japan
Tel.: (81) 488121001
Industrial Electrical Equipment & Component Mfr
N.A.I.C.S.: 335999

WiLans GmbH (1)
Am Klopp 18, 66687, Wadern, Germany
Tel.: (49) 1738742550
Web Site: http://www.wilans.de
Agricultural Machinery Distr
N.A.I.C.S.: 423820

Yamagata Eco-Creation Co., Ltd. (1)
11-19 Matsumicho, Yamagata, 990-2431, Japan
Tel.: (81) 236748510
Industrial Electrical Equipment & Component Mfr
N.A.I.C.S.: 335999

Zhangjiagang Nan-Ling-Cheng Steel Structure Co., Ltd. (1)
Nansha Town, Zhangjiagang, Jiangsu, China **(100%)**
Tel.: (86) 5208390067
Web Site: http://www.mhie-prague.com
Sales Range: $25-49.9 Million
Emp.: 100
N.A.I.C.S.: 336611

Zhejiang Feida MHPS High Efficiency Flue Gas Cleaning Systems Engineering Co., Ltd. (1)
Room 1009 New Building 88 Wangyun Road, Zhuji, 311800, Zhejiang, China
Tel.: (86) 57587189312
Flue Gas Cleaning Services

N.A.I.C.S.: 561790

MITSUBISHI LOGISTICS CORPORATION

19-1 Nihonbashi 1-Chome, Chuo-ku, Tokyo, 103-0027, Japan
Tel.: (81) 332786611   JP
Web Site: https://www.mitsubishi-logistics.co.jp
Year Founded: 1887
9301—(TKS)
Rev.: $2,489,986,400
Assets: $5,441,970,160
Liabilities: $2,075,663,040
Net Worth: $3,366,307,120
Earnings: $173,194,560
Emp.: 4,732
Fiscal Year-end: 03/31/22
Warehousing, Intermodal Transport, Real Estate Rental & Leasing Services
N.A.I.C.S.: 493110
Masao Fujikura *(Chm, Pres, Pres & CEO)*

Subsidiaries:

Beijing Global Express Co., Ltd. (1)
No 11 Rongshang 6th Road, Majuqiaozhen Tongzhou District, Beijing, 101102, China
Tel.: (86) 1060593056
Logistic Services
N.A.I.C.S.: 541330

Dia Logistics (M) Sdn. Bhd. (1)
No 9B Jalan Batu Unjur 8, Taman Bayu Perdana, Port Klang, 41200, Selangor Darul Ehsan, Malaysia **(100%)**
Tel.: (60) 333230309
Sales Range: $25-49.9 Million
Emp.: 5
Supply Chain Management, Logistics & General Warehousing & Storage
N.A.I.C.S.: 541614

Dia Systems Corporation (1)
Tokyo Dia Building 3 1-28-25 Shinkawa, Chuo-ku, Tokyo, 104-0033, Japan
Tel.: (81) 335536315
Web Site: https://www.dia-systems.co.jp
Sales Range: $50-74.9 Million
Emp.: 88
Computer Software Equipments Sales
N.A.I.C.S.: 423430

Fuji Logistics Co., Ltd. (1)
3-10-1 Mita, Minato-ku, Tokyo, 108-0073, Japan
Tel.: (81) 334548411
Web Site: https://www.fujibuturyu.co.jp
Emp.: 1,027
Logistics Management, Consulting & Storage Systems
N.A.I.C.S.: 541614
Tsuneo Shinozuka *(Mng Dir)*

Subsidiary (Non-US):

Fuji Logistics (Dalian FTZ) Co. Ltd. (2)
B-416 Taihua Building Dalian Free Trade Zone, Taihua Mansion Dalian Free Tra, Dalian, 116600, China **(100%)**
Tel.: (86) 41187327980
Web Site: http://www.fujibuturyu.co.jp
General Warehousing & Logistics
N.A.I.C.S.: 493110

Fuji Logistics (H.K.) Co, Limited (2)
18/F Phase 3 YKK Bldg 7 San Ping Circuit, Tuen Mun, New Territories, China (Hong Kong)
Tel.: (852) 26361611
Freight Transportation Arrangement
N.A.I.C.S.: 488510

Fuji Logistics (Shenzhen) Co, Ltd (2)
No 5 Taohua Rd, Futian Free Trade Zone, Shenzhen, China
Tel.: (86) 75583580416
General Warehousing & Storage
N.A.I.C.S.: 493110

Fuji Logistics Europe B.V. (2)
Warmonderweg 12-B, 2171 AH, Sassenheim, Netherlands

Tel.: (31) 25240160
Web Site: https://www.fuji-logistics.com
Sales Range: $25-49.9 Million
Emp.: 20
General Freight Trucking, Local
N.A.I.C.S.: 484110
M. Takeda *(Mng Dir)*

Subsidiary (Domestic):

Fuji Logistics Operations Co, Ltd (2)
3-10-1 Mita, Tokyo, Japan
Tel.: (81) 354768677
Sales Range: $25-49.9 Million
Emp.: 100
General Warehousing & Storage
N.A.I.C.S.: 493110

Fuji Logistics Support Co ,Ltd (2)
Urban-net Mita building 3-10-1 Mita, Minato-ku, Tokyo, 108-0073, Japan
Tel.: (81) 354768064
Web Site: http://www.fujibuturyu.co.jp
Sales Range: $10-24.9 Million
Emp.: 20
General Warehousing & Storage
N.A.I.C.S.: 493110

SII Logistics Inc. (2)
1-8 Nakase, Mihama-ku, Chiba, 261-8507, Japan
Tel.: (81) 432111798
Web Site: http://www.fujibuturyu.co.jp
International Trade Financing
N.A.I.C.S.: 522299

Hakuryo Koun Co.,Ltd. (1)
1-5-13 Hakozaki-futo, Higashi-ku, Fukuoka, 812-0051, Japan
Tel.: (81) 926335490
Web Site: http://www.hakuryo-koun.co.jp
Marine Transportation Services
N.A.I.C.S.: 488320

Hanryo Kigyo Co.,Ltd. (1)
2-15-8 Fujinosato, Ibaraki, 567-0054, Japan
Tel.: (81) 726435221
Freight Forwarding Services
N.A.I.C.S.: 488510

Jupiter MLC Logistics (Myanmar) Limited (1)
Room 8D Penthouse Floor No 24/26 Race Course Condominium, South Race Course Road Tamwe Township, Yangon, Myanmar
Tel.: (95) 1542725
Logistic Services
N.A.I.C.S.: 541330
Arthur Myo Win *(Project Mgr)*

Keihin Naigai Forwarding Co.,Ltd. (1)
Mitsubishi Soko Echizenbori Building 1-29-8 Shinkawa, Chuo-ku, Tokyo, 104-0033, Japan
Tel.: (81) 355661751
Web Site: https://www.keihinnaigai-fwd.co.jp
Sales Range: $25-49.9 Million
Emp.: 50
Cargo Handling Services
N.A.I.C.S.: 488320

Kinko Service Co.,Ltd. (1)
17F Yokohama Dia Building 1-7 Kinko-cho, Kanagawa-ku, Yokohama, 221-0056, Kanagawa, Japan
Tel.: (81) 452112660
Web Site: http://www.fujibuturyu.co.jp
Sales Range: $25-49.9 Million
Emp.: 69
Freight Transportation Services
N.A.I.C.S.: 483211

Kobe Diamaintenance Co.,Ltd. (1)
1-8-5 Higashikawasaki-cho, Chuo-ku, Kobe, 650-0044, Hyogo, Japan **(100%)**
Tel.: (81) 783601000
Web Site: http://www.kobe-dmc.co.jp
Emp.: 236
Building Management & Maintenance Services
N.A.I.C.S.: 561790

Kyokuryo Warehouse Co.,Ltd. (1)
2-4-1 Goryo, Daito, 574-0064, Osaka, Japan
Tel.: (81) 728713221
Web Site: http://www.kyokuryo.co.jp
General Warehousing Services
N.A.I.C.S.: 493110

Kyushu Ryoso Transportation Co.,Ltd. (1)

INTERNATIONAL PUBLIC

6-10 Okihamamachi, Hakata-ku, Fukuoka, 812-0031, Japan
Tel.: (81) 922832733
Sales Range: $25-49.9 Million
Emp.: 50
Freight Forwarding Services
N.A.I.C.S.: 488510

MLC ITL Logistics Co., Ltd. (1)
E Town 1 Building 6th Floor Room 6 1 364 Cong Hoa St, Ward 13 Tan Binh Dist, Ho Chi Minh City, Vietnam
Tel.: (84) 838126500
Web Site: https://www.mlc-itl.com
Transportation Services
N.A.I.C.S.: 485999
D. Tamy *(Mgr-Airfreight)*

Meiryo Kigyo Co.,Ltd. (1)
2-67-4 Kiba, Tobishima Village, Ama, 490-1444, Aichi, Japan
Tel.: (81) 567572272
Web Site: https://www.meiryo-kigyo.com
Emp.: 90
Freight Transportation Services
N.A.I.C.S.: 483211

Mitsubishi Logistics America Corp. (1)
48 Wall St Ste 401, New York, NY 10005 **(100%)**
Tel.: (212) 968-0610
Web Site: http://www.mitsubishi-logistics-america.com
Sales Range: $25-49.9 Million
Emp.: 22
Freight Forwarding
N.A.I.C.S.: 488510

Mitsubishi Logistics China Co., Ltd. (1)
Room807 UC Tower 500 Fushan Road, Pudongxin District, Shanghai, 200122, China
Tel.: (86) 2166287351
Web Site: https://www.mitsubishi-logistics-cn.com
Transportation Services
N.A.I.C.S.: 485999
Kenji Kaneko *(Chm)*

Mitsubishi Logistics Europe B.V. (1)
Ridderhaven 17, Ridderkerk, 2984 BT, Rotterdam, Netherlands **(100%)**
Tel.: (31) 104954144
Web Site: https://www.mitsubishi-logistics.de
Sales Range: $1-9.9 Million
Emp.: 10
General Warehousing & Storage
N.A.I.C.S.: 493110
L. Huisman *(Asst Gen Mgr)*

Mitsubishi Logistics Hong Kong Ltd. (1)
Unit 02-03 05-06 Level 13 Tower 1 Kowloon Commerce Centre, 51 Kwai Cheong Road, Kwai Chung, 51, New Territories, China (Hong Kong) **(100%)**
Tel.: (852) 28908866
Web Site: https://www.mitsubishi-logistics.com.hk
Sales Range: $25-49.9 Million
Emp.: 23
General Warehousing & Storage
N.A.I.C.S.: 493110
Yamamoto Junji *(Mgr)*

Mitsubishi Logistics Singapore Pte. Ltd. (1)
10 Jalan Kilang 07-04/05 Sime Darby Enterprise Centre, Singapore, 159410, Singapore **(100%)**
Tel.: (65) 62621511
Sales Range: $25-49.9 Million
Emp.: 10
General Warehousing & Storage
N.A.I.C.S.: 493110
Tomite Akira *(Gen Mgr)*

Mitsubishi Logistics Thailand Co., Ltd. (1)
16th Floor Sethiwan Tower 139 Pan Road, Silom Bangrak, Bangkok, 10500, Thailand **(100%)**
Tel.: (66) 22379272
Web Site: https://www.mitsubishi-logistics.co.th
Sales Range: $25-49.9 Million
Emp.: 100
General Warehousing & Storage

AND PRIVATE COMPANIES

MITSUBISHI MATERIALS CORPORATION

N.A.I.C.S.: 493110
Yoichi Furukawa *(Mng Dir)*

Mitsubishi Warehouse California Corp. (1)
3040 E Victoria St, Compton, CA 90221-5617
Tel.: (310) 886-5500
Web Site: http://www.mwc-corp.com
Sales Range: $10-24.9 Million
Emp.: 50
General Warehousing & Storage
N.A.I.C.S.: 493110

Monryo Transport Corporation (1)
1-5 Honmachi Fukuoka Port Moji Ichibankan 3rd floor, Moji-ku, Kitakyushu, 801-0834, Japan
Tel.: (81) 933218331
Web Site: http://www.monryo.co.jp
Sales Range: $50-74.9 Million
Emp.: 129
Freight Forwarding Services
N.A.I.C.S.: 488510
Minoru Kakei *(Pres)*

Nagata Lines Co.,Ltd. (1)
2323 Shiga, Suwa, 392-0012, Japan
Tel.: (81) 266581800
Freight Forwarding Services
N.A.I.C.S.: 488510

Nagoya Dia Buil-Tech Co.,Ltd. (1)
Meieki Third Street No 16 No 22, Nakamura-ku, Nagoya, 450-0002, Aichi, Japan
Tel.: (81) 525655158
Web Site: http://www.nagoya-dbtec.co.jp
Commercial Property Rental Services
N.A.I.C.S.: 531120

Naigai Forwarding Co., Ltd. (1)
6-1 Shinkocho, Chuo-ku, Kobe, 650-0041, Japan
Tel.: (81) 783925700
Web Site: http://www.naigai-fwd.co.jp
Emp.: 93
Freight Forwarding Services
N.A.I.C.S.: 488510

Osaka Dia Buil-Tech Co.,Ltd. (1)
3-14-24 Fukushima Hanshin Dia Building 1F, Fukushima-ku, Osaka, 553-0003, Japan
Tel.: (81) 664548700
Real Estate Manangement Services
N.A.I.C.S.: 531390

P.T. Dia-Jaya Forwarding Indonesia (1)
Gajah Mada Tower 19th Floor Room 06 Jl Gajah Mada 19-26, Jakarta Pusat, 10130, Indonesia
Tel.: (62) 216340469
Logistic Services
N.A.I.C.S.: 541330

P.T. Mitsubishi Logistics Indonesia (1)
Kawasan Industri MM-2100 Blok G, Cikarang Barat, Bekasi, 17520, Jawa Barat, Indonesia
Tel.: (62) 2122143306
General Warehousing & Storage
N.A.I.C.S.: 493110

Ryoso Transportation Co.,Ltd. (1)
1-18-8 Saga Sagacho MD Building, Kotoku, Tokyo, 135-0031, Japan
Tel.: (81) 336425041
Web Site: https://www.ryoso-trans.com
Emp.: 212
General Cargo Transportation Services
N.A.I.C.S.: 488320

Sairyo Service Co.,Ltd. (1)
3-3 Nishibukuro, Yashio, 340-0833, Saitama, Japan
Tel.: (81) 489240345
Warehousing & Freight Trucking Services
N.A.I.C.S.: 484110

Seiho Kaiun Kaisha Ltd (1)
Fukuoka Parking Building 1-17 Tsunabamachi, Hakata-ku, Fukuoka, 812-0024, Japan
Tel.: (81) 933215061
Sales Range: $25-49.9 Million
Freight Forwarding Transportation Services
N.A.I.C.S.: 484121

Shanghai Linghua Logistics Co., Ltd. (1)
333 Keyuan Road Zhangjiang Hi-Tech Park, Pudong New Area, Shanghai, 201203, China **(100%)**
Tel.: (86) 2150800108
Web Site: http://www.linghua-logistics.com
Sales Range: $25-49.9 Million
Emp.: 100
General Warehousing & Storage
N.A.I.C.S.: 493110

Shanghai Lingyun Global Forwarding Co., Ltd. (1)
333 Keyuan Road Pudong Pilot Free Trade Zone, Shanghai, 200080, China
Tel.: (86) 2163508811
Web Site: https://www.mitsubishi-logistics-cn.com
Transportation Services
N.A.I.C.S.: 485999

Shanghai Puling Transportation & Warehouse Co., Ltd. (1)
333 Keyuan Road Zhangjiang Hi-Tech Park, Pudong New Area, Shanghai, 201203, China
Tel.: (86) 2150801103
Web Site: http://www.puling.com.cn
Sales Range: $25-49.9 Million
Emp.: 100
General Warehousing & Storage
N.A.I.C.S.: 493110

Shanghai Qingke Warehouse Management Co., Ltd. (1)
No 89 Xin Tao Road, Zhong Gu Town Qingpu, Shanghai, 201707, China
Tel.: (86) 2159793472
Logistic Services
N.A.I.C.S.: 541330

Shenzhen Lingyang Global Forwarding Co., Ltd. (1)
Room 17A12 Baoneng Huigu Building No 3038 Baoan North Road, Luohu District, Shenzhen, 518022, China
Tel.: (86) 75525951705
Logistic Services
N.A.I.C.S.: 541330

Shinryo Koun Co.,Ltd. (1)
6-21 Onohama-cho, Chuo-ku, Kobe, 651-0082, Hyogo, Japan
Tel.: (81) 783211681
Emp.: 230
Freight Trucking Services
N.A.I.C.S.: 484121

Tokyo Dia Service Co., Ltd. (1)
Echizenbori Building 1-29-8 Shinkawa, Chuo-ku, Tokyo, 104-0033, Japan
Tel.: (81) 335525801
Computer Processing Services
N.A.I.C.S.: 541513

Touryo Kigyo Co.,Ltd. (1)
Echizenbori Building 1-29-8 Shinkawa, Chuo-ku, Tokyo, 104-0033, Japan
Tel.: (81) 335518988
Sales Range: $50-74.9 Million
Emp.: 200
Cargo Handling Services
N.A.I.C.S.: 488320

Yokohama Dia Building Management Corporation (1)
1-10 Kinkocho, Kanagawa-ku, Yokohama, 221-0056, Kanagawa, Japan
Tel.: (81) 455778123
Web Site: http://www.yokohama-bayquarter.com
Building Management Consulting Services
N.A.I.C.S.: 236220
Haruka Sugino *(Mgr-Sls)*

MITSUBISHI MATERIALS CORPORATION

3-2-3 Marunouchi Chiyoda-ku, Tokyo, 100-8117, Japan
Tel.: (81) 352525206   JP
Web Site: http://www.mmc.co.jp
Year Founded: 1871
5711—(TKS)
Rev.: $10,183,643,620
Assets: $14,328,021,080
Liabilities: $9,796,053,050
Net Worth: $4,531,968,030
Earnings: $196,931,730
Emp.: 18,323
Fiscal Year-end: 03/31/24
Holding Company; Cement, Metals, Advanced Materials, Electronic Materials & Components Mfr & Distr
N.A.I.C.S.: 551112
Akira Takeuchi *(Chm)*

Subsidiaries:

Dia Plaza Co., Ltd. (1)
No 36 Ibarashima 4-chome, Akita, Japan
Tel.: (81) 188645111
Web Site: https://www.diaplaza.co.jp
Athletic Club & Driving School Management Services
N.A.I.C.S.: 611699

Diamet Corporation (1)
3-1-1 Kogane-cho, Higashi-ku, Niigata, 950-8640, Japan
Tel.: (81) 252750111
Web Site: https://www.diamet.co.jp
Powder Metallurgical Products Mfr & Distr
N.A.I.C.S.: 325998

Diamet Klang (Malaysia) Sdn. Bhd. (1)
Lot 26 Leboh Sultan Mohamed 1 Bandar Sultan, Suleiman, 42000, Port Klang, Selangor Darul Ehsan, Malaysia
Tel.: (60) 331764245
Powder Metallurgy Product Mfr
N.A.I.C.S.: 332117

Diasalt Corp. (1)
Shimokawabata Redevelopment Building 11F 3-1 Shimokawabata-cho, Hakata-ku, Fukuoka, 812-0027, Japan
Tel.: (81) 924021393
Web Site: https://diasalt.co.jp
Food Products Mfr & Distr
N.A.I.C.S.: 311999

Goto Mfg Co., Ltd. (1)
1-17 Kita Industrial Park, Kitakami, 024-0002, Iwate Prefecture, Japan
Tel.: (81) 197666051
Web Site: https://group.mmc.co.jp
Semiconductor Parts Mfr
N.A.I.C.S.: 334413

Gotoh Philippines Corp. (1)
118 Excellence Avenue Corner Competence Drive, Camelray Industrial Park 1, Calamba, 4037, Laguna, Philippines
Tel.: (63) 495497856
Web Site: http://www.gotohphils.com
Electronic Component & Material Mfr
N.A.I.C.S.: 334419
Norida Urzo *(Asst Mgr-Sls)*

Guangdong Diamet Powder Metallurgy Co., Ltd. (1)
No 6-1 Keyuan 3 Rd XiaoHuangPu, Ronggui Shunde District, Foshan, 528305, Guangdong, China
Tel.: (86) 75722119470
Powder Metallurgy Product Mfr
N.A.I.C.S.: 332117

Hachimantai Geothermal Corporation (1)
Kaminakajima 140 Hanawa, Kazuno, 018-5201, Akita, Japan **(77%)**
Tel.: (81) 186233861
Web Site: http://www.mmc.co.jp
Environmental Consulting Services
N.A.I.C.S.: 541620
Mitsutaka Bamba *(Pres)*

Hosokura Metal Mining Co., Ltd. (1)
48 Nangoaracho Uguisawa, Kurihara, 989-5402, Miyagi Prefecture, Japan
Tel.: (81) 228553143
Web Site: https://www.hosokura.co.jp
Lead Mfr
N.A.I.C.S.: 331314

Japan New Metals Co., Ltd. (1)
1-6-64 Sennaricho, Toyonaka, 561-0829, Osaka, Japan **(89%)**
Tel.: (81) 663331171
Web Site: http://www.jnm.co.jp
Sales Range: $50-74.9 Million
Emp.: 200
Mfr & Refiner of Tungsten Carbide & Molybdenum Powders & Fine Chemical Materials
N.A.I.C.S.: 332117

Yoshikazu Okada *(Pres)*

Luvata Pori Oy (1)
Kuparitie 5, PO Box 60, 28330, Pori, Finland
Tel.: (358) 26266111
Web Site: http://www.luvata.com
Emp.: 350
Copper & Copper Alloy Semi-Products Mfr
N.A.I.C.S.: 331420
Jussi Helavirta *(Pres & CEO)*

Subsidiary (US):

Luvata Appleton LLC (2)
553 Carter Ct, Kimberly, WI 54136
Tel.: (920) 738-8119
Web Site: http://www.mmluvata.com
Copper Alloy Wire Mfr
N.A.I.C.S.: 331420
Thomas Jacques *(Dir-Sls & Mktg)*

Subsidiary (Non-US):

Luvata Malaysia Sdn Bhd (2)
PLO 573 Jalan Keluli 10 Kawasan Perindustrian, 81700, Pasir Gudang, Johor, Malaysia
Tel.: (60) 72526688
Web Site: http://www.mmluvata.com
Petroleum Product Mfr
N.A.I.C.S.: 324199
Michael Nordgren *(Mng Dir)*

Subsidiary (US):

Luvata Ohio, Inc. (2)
1376 Pittsburgh Dr, Delaware, OH 43015
Tel.: (740) 363-1981
Web Site: http://www.mmluvata.com
Resistance Welding Cap Electrode Mfr
N.A.I.C.S.: 333992

Luvata Waterbury, Inc (2)
2121 Thomaston Ave, Waterbury, CT 06704
Tel.: (203) 753-5215
Web Site: http://www.mmluvata.com
Emp.: 100
Niobium Tin & Niobium Titanium Superconducting Wire Mfr
N.A.I.C.S.: 335929
Hem Kanithi *(VP-Bus Dev)*

Subsidiary (Non-US):

Luvata Welyn Garden Ltd. (2)
Centrapark Bessemer Road, Welwyn Garden City, AL7 1HT, Herts, United Kingdom
Tel.: (44) 1707379789
Web Site: http://ww.mmluvata.com
Resistance Welding Cap Electrode Mfr
N.A.I.C.S.: 333992
Ian Virnuls *(Sls Mgr)*

MA Packaging Co., Ltd. (1)
8F JRE-Shiba-Nichome-Daimon-Building 2-3-3 Shiba, Minato-ku, Tokyo, Japan
Tel.: (81) 337697260
Web Site: https://www.mapackaging.co.jp
Emp.: 242
Aluminum Container Mfr
N.A.I.C.S.: 332431
Takashi Yatabe *(Pres)*

MA Trading Co., Ltd. (1)
Shiba 2-chome Daimon Building 2-3-3, Minato-ku, Tokyo, 105-0014, Japan
Tel.: (81) 352320741
Web Site: http://www.mat-de-akinai.com
Aluminium Products Mfr
N.A.I.C.S.: 331315

MALC-Thai Co., Ltd. (1)
15th Floor 139 Sethiwan Tower Pan Road, Silom Bangrak, Bangkok, 10500, Thailand
Tel.: (66) 22666304
Emp.: 9
Aluminium Products Mfr
N.A.I.C.S.: 331315

MMC Electronic Materials Taiwan Co., Ltd. (1)
8F-1 No 35 Kan-Ku Street, Datong Dist, Taipei, 10343, Taiwan
Tel.: (886) 225582895
Sputtering & Alpha Solder Pastes Mfr
N.A.I.C.S.: 333992

MMC Electronics (Bangkok) Co., Ltd. (1)
129/2 Moo 17 Bangplee industrial Estate

MITSUBISHI MATERIALS CORPORATION

Mitsubishi Materials Corporation—(Continued)

Debaratana Rd, Bangsaothong, Samut Prakan, 10570, Thailand
Tel.: (66) 23151536
Web Site: http://www.mmeth.co.th
Sales Range: $50-74.9 Million
Emp.: 150
Sales of Electronic Parts
N.A.I.C.S.: 449210

MMC Electronics (M) Sdn. Bhd. (1)
Plot 8 Kinta Free Industrial Zone Jalan Kuala Kangsar, 31200, Chemor, Perak, Malaysia
Tel.: (60) 52913981
Web Site: http://www.mmem.com.my
Sales Range: $100-124.9 Million
Emp.: 400
Ceramic Electronic Component Mfr
N.A.I.C.S.: 334419

MMC Electronics Korea Inc. (1)
suite 1102 Trade Tower 511 Yeongdong-daero, Gangnam-Gu, Seoul, 06164, Korea (South)
Tel.: (82) 260000777
Web Site: https://mmckorea.com
Electronic Parts Mfr & Distr
N.A.I.C.S.: 334419

MMC Electronics Lao Co., Ltd. (1)
Km 22 Specific Economic and Trade Park, Noonthong Villiage Saithany District, Vientiane, Lao People's Democratic Republic
Tel.: (856) 21737020
Emp.: 877
Electronic Components Mfr
N.A.I.C.S.: 334419

MMC Hard Metal U.K. Ltd. (1)
Mitsubishi House Galena Close, Amington Heights, Tamworth, B77 4AS, United Kingdom
Tel.: (44) 1827312312
Sales Range: $25-49.9 Million
Emp.: 15
Fabricated Metal Product Distr
N.A.I.C.S.: 423510

MMC Hardmetal (Holdings) Europe GmbH
Comeniusstr 2, Meerbusch, 40670, Germany
Tel.: (49) 215991890
Investment Management Service
N.A.I.C.S.: 523999
Tanaka Yutaka *(Pres)*

MMC Hardmetal India PVT. Ltd. (1)
Prasad Enclave 118/119 1st Floor 2nd Stage 5th main, BBMP Ward 11 New 38 Industrial Suburb Yeshwanthpura, Bengaluru, 560 022, Karnataka, India
Tel.: (91) 8022043600
Web Site: http://www.mitsubishicarbide.com
Seal Products Distr
N.A.I.C.S.: 423510

MMC Hardmetal OOO (1)
Electrozavodskaya str 24 building 3, 107023, Moscow, Russia
Tel.: (7) 4957255885
Cutting Tool Mfr
N.A.I.C.S.: 333515

MMC Hardmetal Poland, Sp.zo.o (1)
Al Armii Krajowej 61, 50-541, Wroclaw, Poland
Tel.: (48) 713351620
Cutting Tool Mfr
N.A.I.C.S.: 333515

MMC Hardmetal Russia Ltd. (1)
ul Bolschaya Semenovskaya 11 Building 5, 107023, Moscow, Russia
Tel.: (7) 495 725 58 85
Sales Range: $25-49.9 Million
Emp.: 3
Seal Products Distr
N.A.I.C.S.: 423510

MMC Hardmetal Thailand Co., Ltd. (1)
622 Emporium Tower Floor 22/1-4 Sukhumvit Road, Klongton Klongtoey, Bangkok, 10110, Thailand
Tel.: (66) 26618170
Web Site: https://www.mmc-carbide.com
Sales Range: $25-49.9 Million
Emp.: 2
Hard Metal Products Distr
N.A.I.C.S.: 423510

MMC Hartmetall GmbH (1)
Comeniusstrasse 2, 40670, Meerbusch, Germany
Tel.: (49) 215991890
Web Site: https://www.mmc-hardmetal.com
Emp.: 70
Fabricated Metal Product Distr
N.A.I.C.S.: 423510

MMC Italia S.R.L. (1)
Viale Certosa 144, 20156, Milan, Italy
Tel.: (39) 029377031
Web Site: https://mmc-hardmetal.com
Hand Tools Distr
N.A.I.C.S.: 423830
Marco Rimoldi *(Gen Mgr)*

MMC Metal France S.A.R.L. (1)
6 rue Jacques Monod, 91400, Orsay, Cedex, France
Tel.: (33) 169355353
Web Site: https://mmc-hardmetal.com
Sales Range: $25-49.9 Million
Emp.: 34
Seal Products Distr
N.A.I.C.S.: 423510
Jean-Yves Lebacle *(Gen Mgr)*

MMC Metal Singapore Pte. Ltd. (1)
10 Arumugam Rd 04 00 Lion Industrial Bldg, Singapore, 409957, Singapore
Tel.: (65) 67439370
Web Site: http://www.mitsubishicarbide.com
Sales Range: $25-49.9 Million
Emp.: 20
Sales of Hard-Metal Products
N.A.I.C.S.: 423510

MMC Metal de Mexico S.A. (1)
Av La Canada No 16 Parque Industrial Bernardo Quintana El Arques, 76246, Queretaro, Mexico
Tel.: (52) 4421926800
Web Site: http://www.wrt.mitsubishicarbide.com
Hand Tool Equipment Distr
N.A.I.C.S.: 423830
Georges Ghorayeb *(Gen Mgr)*

MMC Shanghai Co., Ltd. (1)
Unit 2107B Raffles City Changning office Tower 1, No 1133 Changning Road, Shanghai, 200051, China
Tel.: (86) 2162472951
Web Site: http://www.mmc.co.jp
Electronic Parts & Component Distr
N.A.I.C.S.: 423690

MMC Taishin Tool Co., Ltd. (1)
1 8F No 35 Gangu Street, Datong District, Taipei, 10343, Taiwan
Tel.: (886) 225582818
Web Site: https://www.mmctaishin.com.tw
Drill Bit & Cutting Tool Mfr
N.A.I.C.S.: 333515

MMC Tooling Co., Ltd. (1)
179-1 Kanegasaki Nishioike, Uozumi-cho, Akashi, 674-0071, Hyogo, Japan
Tel.: (81) 789361749
Web Site: https://www.mmctooling.co.jp
Cutting Tool Mfr
N.A.I.C.S.: 333515

MMC Tools (Thailand) , Co., Ltd. (1)
508/1 Moo2 Tambol Klongjig Amphur, Bangpa-in, Phra Nakhon Si Ayutthaya, 13160, Changwat, Thailand
Tel.: (66) 35258024
Web Site: https://www.mmct.co.th
Emp.: 1,747
Cutting Tool Mfr
N.A.I.C.S.: 333515

MUE Materials Taiwan Co., Ltd. (1)
20-1 Jianguo Rd, Tanzih Township, Taichung, Taiwan
Tel.: (886) 425320173
Electronic Parts Mfr & Distr
N.A.I.C.S.: 334419

Material Business Support Corp. (1)
1-600 Kitabukurocho, Omiya Ward, Saitama, 330-8508, Japan
Tel.: (81) 486415777
Web Site: https://group.mmc.co.jp
Office Work Support Services
N.A.I.C.S.: 561990

Materials Eco Recycle Co., Ltd. (1)
4054 Naoshima-cho, Kagawa, 761-3110, Kagawa-ken, Japan
Logistic Services
N.A.I.C.S.: 541614

Materials Eco-Refining Co., Ltd. (1)
KDX Kajicho Building 2F 3-5-2 Kandakajicho, Chiyoda-ku, Tokyo, 101-0045, Japan
Tel.: (81) 352894001
Web Site: https://www.mercompany.co.jp
Emp.: 172
Nonferrous & Precious Metal Mfr
N.A.I.C.S.: 331410
Koji Iwami *(Pres)*

Materials Tohoku Corporation (1)
50 Hanebori Nagasaka, Higashiyama-cho, Ichinoseki, 029-0302, Iwate, Japan
Tel.: (81) 191484745
Web Site: https://www.material-tohoku.com
Emp.: 90
Limestone Mining Services
N.A.I.C.S.: 212312

Materials' Finance Co., Ltd. (1)
1-3-2 Otemachi Otemachi First Square Bldg Keidanrenkaikan, Chiyoda-Ku, Tokyo, 100-0004, Japan
Tel.: (81) 352525234
Financial Management Services
N.A.I.C.S.: 523999

Mitsubishi Aluminum Co., Ltd. (1)
3-3 Shiba 2-Chome, Minato-ku, Tokyo, 105-8546, Japan **(88%)**
Tel.: (81) 337690111
Web Site: http://www.malco.co.jp
Sales Range: $200-249.9 Million
Emp.: 1,000
Production & Sales of Aluminum & Aluminum Alloy Mill Products & Fabricated Products
N.A.I.C.S.: 331318

Mitsubishi Cable Industries, Ltd. (1)
New Kokusai Building 3-4-1 Marunouchi, Chiyoda-ku, Tokyo, 100-8303, Japan
Tel.: (81) 332161551
Web Site: https://www.mitsubishi-cable.co.jp
Sales Range: $900-999.9 Million
Emp.: 515
Cable, Fiberscopes, Optical Cable, Automotive Components & O-Rings Mfr
N.A.I.C.S.: 332618

Subsidiary (US):

Mitsubishi Cable America, Inc. (2)
2975 Bowers Ave Ste 307, Santa Clara, CA 95051 **(100%)**
Tel.: (408) 486-9915
Web Site: http://www.mcausa.com
Sales Range: $25-49.9 Million
Cable, Fiberscopes, Optical Cable, Automotive Components & O-Rings Mfr
N.A.I.C.S.: 332618

Mitsubishi Cement Corporation (1)
151 Cassia Way, Henderson, NV 89014 **(67%)**
Tel.: (702) 932-3900
Web Site: https://www.mitsubishicement.com
Sales Range: $25-49.9 Million
Production & Sales of Cement
N.A.I.C.S.: 327310

Mitsubishi Hitachi Tool Engineering, Ltd. (1)
Hulic Ryogoku Bldg 8F 4-31-11 Ryogoku, Sumida-ku, Tokyo, 130-0026, Japan **(51%)**
Tel.: (81) 3 6890 5101
Web Site: http://www.mmc-hitachitool.co.jp
Sales Range: $200-249.9 Million
Industrial Tools & Machine Tools Mfr
N.A.I.C.S.: 333517
Teruhiko Masuda *(Pres)*

Subsidiary (Non-US):

MMC Hitachi Tool Engineering (Shanghai) Ltd. (2)
11F Chuang Xing Financial Center, 288 Nanjing Rd West, Shanghai, 200003, China
Tel.: (86) 21 3366 3058
Industrial Machinery & Tool Distr
N.A.I.C.S.: 423830

INTERNATIONAL PUBLIC

MMC Hitachi Tool Engineering Europe GmbH (2)
Itterpark 12, 40724, Hilden, Germany
Tel.: (49) 210324820
Web Site: https://www.moldino.eu
Machine Tools Mfr
N.A.I.C.S.: 333517
Toru Yamaguchi *(Pres)*

Branch (Non-US):

MMC Hitachi Tool Engineering Europe (3)
EPIC Eliot Park, Barling Way, Nuneaton, CV10 7RH, United Kingdom
Tel.: (44) 24 7679 6500
Web Site: http://www.mmc-hitachitool-eu.com
Industrial Machinery Sales
N.A.I.C.S.: 423830
Hiroshi Nitta *(CEO)*

Mitsubishi Materials (Australia) Pty. Ltd. (1)
Se 802 L 8 46-48 Market St, Sydney, 2000, NSW, Australia
Tel.: (61) 292624992
Emp.: 3
Coal Mining Services
N.A.I.C.S.: 213113
Reiner Lenz *(Mng Dir)*

Mitsubishi Materials (Shanghai) Corp. (1)
2101 Tower 1 Raffles City 1133 Changning road, Changning District, Shanghai, 200051, China
Tel.: (86) 2162890022
Web Site: http://www.mmsc-carbide.com.cn
Machine Tools Mfr
N.A.I.C.S.: 333515

Mitsubishi Materials Corporation - Akashi Plant (1)
179-1 Nishioike Kanagasaki, Uozumi-cho, Akashi, 674-0071, Hyogo, Japan
Tel.: (81) 789361551
Cutting Tool Mfr
N.A.I.C.S.: 333415

Mitsubishi Materials Corporation - Gifu Plant (1)
1528-1 Yokoi Nakashinden, Godo-cho Anpachi-gun, Gifu, 503-2394, Japan
Tel.: (81) 584 27 4330
Web Site: http://www.carbide.mmc.co.jp
Tungsten Carbide Cutting Tool Mfr
N.A.I.C.S.: 333515

Mitsubishi Materials Corporation - Tsukuba Plant (1)
1511 Furumagi, Joso, 300-2795, Ibaraki, Japan
Tel.: (81) 297421111
Machine Tools Mfr
N.A.I.C.S.: 333517

Mitsubishi Materials Electronic Chemicals Co., Ltd. (1)
3-1-6 Barajima, Akita, 010-8585, Japan
Tel.: (81) 18 864 6011
Web Site: http://www.mmc-ec.co.jp
Emp.: 300
Chemical Products Mfr & Distr
N.A.I.C.S.: 325998

Plant (Domestic):

Mitsubishi Materials Electronic Chemicals Co., Ltd. - Kashima Plant (2)
19-1 Higashi-Fukashiba, Kamisu, 314-0103, Ibaragi, Japan
Tel.: (81) 299 92 2121
Chemical Products Mfr
N.A.I.C.S.: 325998

Mitsubishi Materials Espana S.A. (1)
Emperor Street 2, 46136, Museros, Valencia, Spain
Tel.: (34) 961441711
Web Site: https://www.mmc-hardmetal.com
Cutting Tool Mfr & Distr
N.A.I.C.S.: 333515

Mitsubishi Materials Kenzai Corporation (1)
2-3-10 Shinjuku, Shinjuku-ku, Tokyo, 160-0022, Japan **(100%)**

AND PRIVATE COMPANIES

MITSUBISHI MATERIALS CORPORATION

Tel.: (81) 353652332
Production & Sales of Concrete Products & Other Building Materials
N.A.I.C.S.: 327331

Mitsubishi Materials Southeast Asia Co., Ltd. (1)
622 Emporium Tower 22nd Floor Room 1-4 Sukhumvit Road, Klongtoey, Bangkok, 10110, Thailand
Tel.: (66) 226209235
Web Site: https://www.mmsea.co.th
Emp.: 11
Automotive Products Mfr
N.A.I.C.S.: 336390

Mitsubishi Materials Techno Corporation (1)
1-30-7 Taito, Taito-ku, Tokyo, 110-0016, Japan
Tel.: (81) 366287970
Web Site: http://www.mmtec.co.jp
Sales Range: $400-449.9 Million
Emp.: 1,021
Design, Construction & Maintenance of Environmentally Sound Machinery
N.A.I.C.S.: 334512

Mitsubishi Materials Trading Corp. (1)
17F Nihonbashi Hamacho F-Tower 3-21-1 Nihonbashi Hama-cho, Chuo-ku, Tokyo, 103-0007, Japan
Tel.: (81) 336601682
Web Site: https://www.mmtc.co.jp
Automotive Products Mfr
N.A.I.C.S.: 336390

Mitsubishi Materials U.S.A. Corporation (1)
3535 Hyland Ave Ste 200, Costa Mesa, CA 92626 (100%)
Tel.: (714) 352-6100
Web Site: http://www.mmus.com
Sales & Distr of Carbide Tool Products
N.A.I.C.S.: 332999

Division (Domestic):

Mitsubishi Materials USA Corporation - Electronic Components (2)
300 N Martingale Rd Ste 500, Schaumburg, IL 60173 (100%)
Tel.: (847) 252-6360
Web Site: http://www.mmea.com
Sales Range: $50-74.9 Million
Electronic Components Distr
N.A.I.C.S.: 423690

Subsidiary (Non-US):

MMC Electronics (HK) Ltd. (3)
17th Floor Willy Plaza 48 Hoi Yuen Road, Kwun Tong, Kowloon, China (Hong Kong) (75%)
Tel.: (852) 23054296
Web Site: http://www.mmc.co.jp
Sales Range: $25-49.9 Million
Wholesale of Electronic Parts & Equipment
N.A.I.C.S.: 423690

Subsidiary (Domestic):

MMC Electronics America Inc. (3)
17401 Eastman, Irvine, CA 92614-5523
Tel.: (408) 562-0000
Wholesale of Electronic Parts & Equipment
N.A.I.C.S.: 423690

Subsidiary (Non-US):

MUE Materials Taiwain Co., Ltd. (3)
No 20-1 Jianguo Rd Tanzih Township, Tantzu, Taichung, ROC, Taiwan
Tel.: (886) 425320173
Web Site: http://www.mmc.co.jp
Electronic Parts & Equipment Sales
N.A.I.C.S.: 423690

Subsidiary (Domestic):

RFM Inc. (2)
190 Summit St, Brighton, MI 48116-2466
Tel.: (810) 229-4567
Emp.: 15
Metalworking Tool Mfr
N.A.I.C.S.: 333519
Rudy Meffert *(VP-HR & IT)*

Mitsubishi Nuclear Fuel Co., Ltd. (1)
622-1 Funaishikawa, Tokai Village Naka District, Naka, 319-1197, Ibaraki, Japan (66%)
Tel.: (81) 292822011
Web Site: https://www.mhi.com
Sales Range: $25-49.9 Million
Emp.: 100
Production & Sales of Nuclear Fuels for Power Generation
N.A.I.C.S.: 221113
Kenji Umeda *(Pres & CEO)*

Mitsubishi Polysilicon America Corporation (1)
7800 Mitsubishi Ln, Theodore, AL 36582
Tel.: (251) 443-6440
Web Site: https://www.mpsac.com
Emp.: 400
Polysilicon Production
N.A.I.C.S.: 541519

Mitsubishi Shindoh Co., Ltd. (1)
3-4-1 Marunouchi, Chiyoda-ku, Tokyo, 100-0005, Japan (100%)
Tel.: (81) 366295850
Web Site: http://www.mitsubishi-shindoh.com
Sales Range: $450-499.9 Million
Emp.: 60
Mfr & Sales of Copper & Copper Alloy Sheets & Tubes
N.A.I.C.S.: 331420
Hori Kazumasa *(Pres)*

Nevada Ready Mix Corp. (1)
151 Cassia Way, Henderson, NV 89014
Tel.: (702) 457-1115
Web Site: https://www.nevadareadymix.com
Ready Mixed Concrete & Aggregate Mfr
N.A.I.C.S.: 327320

OTEC (Thailand) Co., Ltd. (1)
258 Moo 2 Tambol Klongjig Amphur Bang Pa-in Changwat, Phra Nakhon Si Ayutthaya, 13160, Thailand
Tel.: (66) 352583212
Emp.: 170
Rock Drilling Tool Mfr
N.A.I.C.S.: 333131

Onahama Smelting And Refining Co., Ltd. (1)
1-1 Nagisa Onahama, Chiyoda-ku, Iwaki, 971-8101, Fukushima, Japan (55.7%)
Tel.: (81) 246545333
Web Site: https://group.mmc.co.jp
Sales Range: $100-124.9 Million
Emp.: 475
Copper Refinery & Smelting Process
N.A.I.C.S.: 331410
Takahiro Yamada *(Pres)*

PT. MMC Metal Fabrication (1)
Cikarang Industrial Estate I Jl Jababeka XIIB Blok W 26, Cikarang, Bekasi, West Java, Indonesia
Tel.: (62) 218936733
Web Site: http://www.mmf.co.id
Weld Assembly Products Mfr
N.A.I.C.S.: 333992

PT. Ryoko Sangyo Indonesia (1)
Luna 1 Room Delonix Hotel Komplex Sedana, Sukaluyu Teluk Jambe, Karawang, 41361, West java, Indonesia
Tel.: (62) 2678458543
Emp.: 6
Automotive Products Mfr
N.A.I.C.S.: 336390

PT. Smelting (1)
Capital Place Office Tower 3rd Floor Unit C Jend Gatot Subroto Kav 18, Jl Jendral Gatot Subroto Kav 9-11, Jakarta, 12710, Indonesia (60.5%)
Tel.: (62) 2127939997
Web Site: http://www.ptsmelting.com
Smelting, Refining & Sales of Copper
N.A.I.C.S.: 331410

Prime Conduit, Inc. (1)
23240 Chagrin Blvd Ste 405, Cleveland, OH 44122
Tel.: (216) 464-3400
Web Site: http://www.primeconduit.com
Sales Range: $25-49.9 Million
PVC Pipe Mfr
N.A.I.C.S.: 326122

Plant (Domestic):

Prime Conduit, Inc. (2)
6500 Interpace St, Oklahoma City, OK 73135
Tel.: (405) 670-2266
Web Site: http://www.primeconduit.com
Sales Range: $25-49.9 Million
Emp.: 80
Thermoplastic Conduit & Pipe Mfr
N.A.I.C.S.: 326122
Jeremy Zeliff *(Mgr-Quality)*

Robertson's Ready Mix, Ltd. (1)
200 S Main St Ste 200, Corona, CA 92882
Tel.: (951) 685-4600
Web Site: https://www.rrmca.com
Sales Range: $100-124.9 Million
Emp.: 60
Ready Mixed Concrete
N.A.I.C.S.: 327320

Ryoen Corp. (1)
1517-3 Kami Yokoura Sakito-cho, Saiki, 857-3101, Nagasaki, Japan
Web Site: http://www.ryouen.co.jp
Salt Mfr & Whslr
N.A.I.C.S.: 311942

Ryoko Lime Industry Co., Ltd. (1)
10-2 Kanda Toyama-cho Ascend Kanda Building 2F, Chiyoda-ku, Tokyo, 101-0043, Japan (100%)
Tel.: (81) 352899221
Web Site: https://www.ryokolime.co.jp
Emp.: 127
Production & Sales of Limestone
N.A.I.C.S.: 212312
Yukio Shimoda *(Gen Mgr)*

Ryoko Sangyo (Thailand) Co., Ltd. (1)
45/13 Moo1 TPARK Bangplee 1 Bangna-Trad Rd Km 22 Srisa Jorrake Yai, Bang Sao Thong, 10570, Samutprakarn, Thailand
Tel.: (66) 2136421719
Automotive Components Mfr
N.A.I.C.S.: 336390
Atsuo Kajiwara *(Pres)*

Ryoko Sangyo Corp. (1)
17th Floor Nihonbashi Hamacho F-Tower 3-21-1 Nihonbashi Hamacho, Chuo-ku, Tokyo, 103-0007, Japan
Tel.: (81) 336601682
Industrial Machinery Distr
N.A.I.C.S.: 423830
Toshio Hiratsuka *(Pres)*

Ryoko Service Corporation (1)
3-21-1 Nihonbashi Hamacho Nihonbashi Hamacho F Tower 13th floor, Chuo-ku, Tokyo, 103-0007, Japan
Tel.: (81) 336601365
Web Site: https://www.ryoukou.co.jp
Non Life Insurance Agency Services
N.A.I.C.S.: 524210

Ryosei Amagasaki Electric Wire Co., Ltd. (1)
16-4 Kitahatsushima-cho, Amagasaki, 660-0834, Hyogo, Japan
Tel.: (81) 664817360
Electric Wire & Cable Mfr
N.A.I.C.S.: 335929

Ryosei Kiko Co., Ltd. (1)
1008 Shinbori, Kumagaya, 360-0841, Saitama, Japan
Tel.: (81) 485332971
Web Site: https://www.mitsubishi-cable.co.jp
Emp.: 96
Electric Wire & Cable Mfr
N.A.I.C.S.: 335929

Ryosei Systems, Ltd. (1)
16-4 Kitahatsushima-cho, Amagasaki, 660-0834, Hyogo, Japan
Tel.: (81) 671678000
Web Site: https://www.ryosys.com
Emp.: 217
Civil & Electrical Construction Services
N.A.I.C.S.: 237130

Ryoshindo Manufacturing Sdn. Bhd. (1)
PLO520 Jln Keluli 3, Kaw Perindustrian Pasir Gudang, 81700, Pasir Gudang, Johor, Malaysia
Tel.: (60) 72515802
Web Site: http://www.ryoshindoh.com
Copper & Copper Alloy Mfr
N.A.I.C.S.: 331420

Sambo Metals Corp. (1)
1-4-6 Aramoto Nishi, Higashi, Osaka, 577-0024, Japan
Tel.: (81) 666184520
Web Site: https://www.sambo-metals.co.jp
Emp.: 40
Copper Product & Electric Wire Whslr
N.A.I.C.S.: 423610

Tachibana Metal Manufacturing Co., Ltd. (1)
OAP Tower 10F 1-8-30 Temmabashi, Kita-Ku, Osaka, 530-0042, Japan
Tel.: (81) 6 6354 2700
Fabricated Aluminum Products Mfr & Distr
N.A.I.C.S.: 332999

Tachibana Metal Mfg Co., Ltd. (1)
Web Site: http://www.tachibana-metal.co.jp
Emp.: 147
Extruded Aluminum Products Mfr
N.A.I.C.S.: 331318

Tamagawa Engineering Co., Ltd. (1)
128-7 Ogimachi, Aizuwakamatsu, 965-0025, Fukushima Prefecture, Japan
Tel.: (81) 242227153
Web Site: http://www.tama-eng.co.jp
Industrial Automation Device Mfr
N.A.I.C.S.: 334512

Tianjin Tianling Carbide Tools Co., Ltd. (1)
No 3 9th Xinghua Branch Road, Xiqing Economic Development Area, Tianjin, 300385, China
Tel.: (86) 2223974860
Web Site: http://www.mmsc-carbide.com.cn
Production & Sales of Carbide Cutting Tools
N.A.I.C.S.: 333515

Tokyo Hoso Kogyo Co., Ltd. (1)
2116 Ikeda Nagase Moroyamamachi, Iruma, 350-0443, Saitama, Japan
Tel.: (81) 492946131
Industrial Gas Pipe Mfr
N.A.I.C.S.: 332996

Tokyo Ryoko Concrete Co., Ltd. (1)
No 8-20 Konan 5-Chome, Minato-ku, Tokyo, 108-0075, Japan
Tel.: (81) 334717040
Web Site: https://www.trcc.co.jp
Emp.: 22
Ready Mixed Concrete & Aggregate Mfr
N.A.I.C.S.: 327320

UBE-Mitsubishi Cement Corporation (1)
Iino Building 2-1-1 Uchisaiwaich, Chiyoda-ku, Tokyo, 1010062, Japan (50%)
Tel.: (81) 36 275 0330
Web Site: https://www.mu-cc.com
Emp.: 8,000
Cement Mfr
N.A.I.C.S.: 327310

Universal Can Corp. (1)
1-4-25 Kouraku, Bunkyo-ku, Tokyo, 112-8525, Japan
Tel.: (81) 3 38687470
Web Site: http://www.unicam.co.jp
Sales Range: $200-249.9 Million
Emp.: 900
Metal Can Mfr & Distr
N.A.I.C.S.: 332439
Tatsuya Hanafusa *(Pres)*

Subsidiary (Domestic):

Universal Can Corp. - Fuji-oyama Plant (2)
1500 Suganuma Oyama-cho, Sunto-gun, Shizuoka, 410-1392, Japan
Tel.: (81) 550763211
Emp.: 200
Can Ends Mfr
N.A.I.C.S.: 332431
Tomohiro Hayachi *(Mgr-Gen Dept)*

Plant (Domestic):

Universal Can Corp. - Gunma Plant (2)
906-2 Nobe-cho, Tatebayashi, 374-0047, Gunma, Japan
Tel.: (81) 276 74 8500
Metal Container Mfr
N.A.I.C.S.: 332439

MITSUBISHI MATERIALS CORPORATION

Mitsubishi Materials Corporation—(Continued)

Subsidiary (Domestic):

Universal Can Corp. - Okayama Plant (2)
150 Minamigata Seto-cho, Higashi-ku, Okayama, 709-0844, Japan
Tel.: (81) 869531511
Metal Container Mfr
N.A.I.C.S.: 332439

Universal Can Corp. - Shiga Plant (2)
681 Furuta Zaiji Koura-cho, Inukami-gun, Shiga, 522-0244, Japan
Tel.: (81) 749382001
Metal Tank Mfr
N.A.I.C.S.: 332431

Universal Can Corp. - Yuki Plant (2)
1-1 Shintsutsumi Nakadori, Yuki, 307-0016, Ibaraki, Japan
Tel.: (81) 296333811
Aluminium Container Mfr
N.A.I.C.S.: 332439

MITSUBISHI MOTORS CORPORATION
1-21 Shibaura 3-chome, Minato-ku, Tokyo, 108-8410, Japan
Tel.: (81) 334561111
Web Site: https://www.mitsubishi-motors.com
Year Founded: 1970
MMO—(DEU)
Rev.: $18,439,183,290
Assets: $16,224,046,700
Liabilities: $9,320,192,540
Net Worth: $6,903,854,160
Earnings: $1,022,626,490
Emp.: 28,982
Fiscal Year-end: 03/31/24
Motor Vehicles, Associated Components & Industrial Engines Mfr
N.A.I.C.S.: 336110
Hitoshi Inada (Sr Exec Officer-Corp Governance)

Subsidiaries:

Asian Transmission Corp. (1)
Calmelray Industrial Park 1 Canlubang, Calamba, Laguna, Philippines (90%)
Tel.: (63) 495491666
Web Site: http://www.asian-transmission.com.ph
Sales Range: $150-199.9 Million
Emp.: 600
Automobile Parts Distr
N.A.I.C.S.: 423120
Takashi Minagawa (Pres & CEO)

Car Research & Development Center (1)
1 Nakashinkiri Hashime Cho, Okazaki, 444 8501, Aichi, Japan (100%)
Tel.: (81) 564313100
Web Site: http://www.mitsubishi-motors.co.jp
Sales Range: $1-4.9 Billion
Emp.: 7,000
N.A.I.C.S.: 336110

Higashi Nihon Mitsubishi Motors Sales Co., Ltd. (1)
4-1-11 Higashihayadori, Konan-Ku, Niigata, 950-0148, Japan
Tel.: (81) 253821021
Automotive Part Whslr
N.A.I.C.S.: 423140

Hokkaido Mitsubishi Motor Sales Co., Ltd. (1)
10 1 15 Minami 10 West, Chuo-ku, Sapporo, 064-0810, Japan
Tel.: (81) 115113111
Web Site: http://www.hokkaido-mitsubishi.com
Car Whslr
N.A.I.C.S.: 423110

Kanto Mitsubishi Motors Sales Co., Ltd. (1)
1-4-7 Takaban Meguro ku, Meguro-Ku, Tokyo, 152-0004, Japan
Tel.: (81) 337143211
Motor Vehicle Parts Whslr
N.A.I.C.S.: 423140

MMC Diamond Finance Corporation (1)
6F Nittamachi Building 5-34-6 Shiba, Minato-ku, Tokyo, 108-8407, Japan
Tel.: (81) 3 6722 5111
Web Site: http://www.mmc-dia-finance.com
Automobile Financing Services
N.A.I.C.S.: 522220

MMC Holding (Thailand) Co., Ltd. (1)
69 69 13 Moo Paholyothin Rd, Khlong Luang, Bangkok, Thailand
Tel.: (66) 29088000
Automobile Sales
N.A.I.C.S.: 425120

MMTh Engine Co., Ltd. (1)
199/9 Moo 3 Laemchabang Industrial Estate, Si Racha, Chon Buri, 20210, Thailand
Tel.: (66) 38498500
Web Site: http://www.mitsubishi-motors.co.th
Automotive Engine Mfr
N.A.I.C.S.: 336390

Mitsubishi Automotive Accessories & Products Co., Ltd. (1)
5-33-8 Shiba Daiichitamachi Bldg 6f, Minato-Ku, Tokyo, 108-0014, Japan
Tel.: (81) 3 5445 0830
Web Site: http://www.mitsubishi-motors-carlife.com
Automobile Parts Distr
N.A.I.C.S.: 423120

Mitsubishi Automotive Logistics Technology Co., Ltd. (1)
Shimosakunobe 6-chome No 32 No 1 Tsuda Mountain Auto Square, Mitsubishi Motors the central office 2F Takatsu-ku, Kawasaki, 213-0033, Kanagawa, Japan
Tel.: (81) 448204800
Web Site: http://www.mmc-mlt.co.jp
Emp.: 590
Automobile Storage Services
N.A.I.C.S.: 493110

Mitsubishi Motor Europe B.V. (1)
Beach Ave 150, 1119 PR, Schiphol, Netherlands (82%)
Tel.: (31) 204468111
Sales Range: $75-99.9 Million
Emp.: 200
Wholesale Distribution of Automobiles
N.A.I.C.S.: 425120

Mitsubishi Motor Sales Netherlands B.V. (1)
Bovenkerkerweg 6-8, 1185 XE, Amstelveen, Netherlands
Tel.: (31) 20 4056800
Web Site: http://www.mitsubishi-motors.nl
Motor Vehicle Distr
N.A.I.C.S.: 423110

Mitsubishi Motor Sales of Canada, Inc. (1)
2090 Matheson Blvd East, Mississauga, L4W 5P8, ON, Canada
Tel.: (905) 214-9000
Web Site: https://www.mitsubishi-motors-pr.ca
Motor Vehicle Distr
N.A.I.C.S.: 423110
Paul Simmonds (VP-Sls & Mktg)

Mitsubishi Motors (Thailand) Co., Ltd. (1)
FYI Center Tower 1 9th Floor 2525 Rama IV Rd, Klong Toei, 10110, Bangkok, Thailand
Tel.: (66) 2 079 9000
Web Site: https://www.mitsubishi-motors.co.th
Emp.: 500
Automotive Distr
N.A.I.C.S.: 423110
Egathi Rattana-Aree (Exec VP-Domestic Sls Unit & After Sls Unit)

Mitsubishi Motors Australia Ltd. (1)
1284 South Road, PO Box 8, Clovelly Park, 5039, SA, Australia (100%)
Tel.: (61) 1300131211
Web Site: http://www.mitsubishi-motors.com.au
Sales Range: $1-4.9 Billion
Emp.: 150
Car Mfr
N.A.I.C.S.: 336110

Mitsubishi Motors Belgium NV (1)
Prins Boudewijnlaan 30 2nd Floor, 2550, Kontich, Belgium
Tel.: (32) 32808484
Web Site: http://www.mitsubishi-motors.be
Sales Range: $25-49.9 Million
Emp.: 40
Automobile Parts Mfr
N.A.I.C.S.: 336390

Mitsubishi Motors Corporation - Power Train Plant (1)
2-1 Kosuna-cho Kosei-cho Koka-gun, Shiga, 520 3212, Japan (100%)
Tel.: (81) 748753131
Power Train Mfr
N.A.I.C.S.: 336350

Mitsubishi Motors Danmark A/S (1)
Hovedvejen 1, 2600, Glostrup, Denmark (100%)
Tel.: (45) 47270027
Web Site: http://www.mitsubishi-motors.dk
Sales Range: $25-49.9 Million
Emp.: 20
Automobile Whslr
N.A.I.C.S.: 423110

Mitsubishi Motors Deutschland GmbH (1)
Stahlstr 42-44, Russelsheim, 65428, Germany
Tel.: (49) 614292040
Web Site: http://www.mitsubishi-motors.de
Sales Range: $25-49.9 Million
Emp.: 100
Automobile Parts Mfr
N.A.I.C.S.: 336390
Werner Frey (Gen Mgr)

Mitsubishi Motors Europe B.V. (1)
Beech Ave 150, 6121 SG, Born, Netherlands
Tel.: (31) 464819500
Web Site: http://www.mitsubishi-motors-europe.com
Sales Range: $150-199.9 Million
Emp.: 400
Motor Vehicle Distr
N.A.I.C.S.: 423110
Eric Wepierre (Pres & CEO)

Mitsubishi Motors France S.A.S (1)
1 Avenue du Fief, BP 30479, Saint Ouen l' Aumone, 95005, Cergy-Pontoise, Cedex, France
Tel.: (33) 134306060
Web Site: http://www.mitsubishi-motors.fr
Sales Range: $25-49.9 Million
Emp.: 40
Automobile Parts Mfr
N.A.I.C.S.: 336390

Mitsubishi Motors Middle East & Africa FZE (1)
Jebel Ali Freezone Street N512, Dubai, United Arab Emirates
Tel.: (971) 48818222
Web Site: http://mitsubishi-motors-middle-east-and-africa.business.site
Car Whslr
N.A.I.C.S.: 423110
Shadab Ahmed (Asst Mgr)

Mitsubishi Motors New Zealand Ltd. (1)
Todd Pk Heriot Dr, PO Box 50914, Porirua, 5022, New Zealand (100%)
Tel.: (64) 42370109
Web Site: http://www.mmnz.co.nz
Sales Range: $250-299.9 Million
Emp.: 55
Automobile Sales
N.A.I.C.S.: 425120
Warren Brown (Gen Mgr-Sls & Mktg)

Mitsubishi Motors North America, Inc. (1)
6400 Katella Ave, Cypress, CA 90630-5208 (97.2%)
Tel.: (714) 372-6000
Web Site: http://www.mitsubishicars.com
Sales Range: $1-4.9 Billion
Emp.: 1,590
Cars & Trucks Distr
N.A.I.C.S.: 423110
Gayu Uesugi (Chm)

Subsidiary (Domestic):

Mitsubishi Motor Sales of Caribbean Inc. (2)
Carretera No 2 Km 201 Barrio Candelaria, Toa Baja, PR 00949 (100%)
Tel.: (787) 251-8715
Sales Range: $50-74.9 Million
Emp.: 38
Automobile Sales
N.A.I.C.S.: 425120
Tsuhiro Oshikiri (Pres & CEO)

Mitsubishi Motors Credit of America, Inc. (2)
PO Box 9940, Mobile, AL 36691 (100%)
Tel.: (714) 799-4730
Web Site: http://www.mitsubishicredit.com
Sales Range: $100-124.9 Million
Emp.: 150
Automotive Finance
N.A.I.C.S.: 522291
Dan Booth (Pres)

Branch (Domestic):

Mitsubishi Motors North America, Inc. (2)
PO Box 689040, Franklin, TN 37068 (100%)
Tel.: (309) 888-8000
Web Site: http://www.mitsubishicars.com
Sales Range: $400-449.9 Million
Emp.: 1,500
Passenger Car Production
N.A.I.C.S.: 336110
Daniel Ball (VP-Aftersales)

Subsidiary (Domestic):

Mitsubishi Motors R&D of America, Inc. (2)
3735 Varsity Dr, Ann Arbor, MI 48108-2223
Tel.: (734) 973-4441
Automobile Research & Testing Services
N.A.I.C.S.: 541715
Bradley Heuft (Engr-Res)

Mitsubishi Motors Parts Sales Co., Ltd. (1)
297 Akibacho, Totsuka-Ku, Yokohama, 245-0052, Kanagawa, Japan
Tel.: (81) 458101300
Motor Vehicle Parts Whslr
N.A.I.C.S.: 423140

Mitsubishi Motors Philippines Corporation (1)
No 1 Auto Park Ave, Greenfield Automotive Park Special Economic Zone, Santa Rosa, 4026, Laguna, Philippines (100%)
Tel.: (63) 498 530 9999
Web Site: https://www.mitsubishi-motors.com.ph
Sales Range: $350-399.9 Million
Emp.: 712
Automobile Mfr
N.A.I.C.S.: 336110
Mutsuhiro Oshikiri (Pres)

Mitsubishi Motors R&D Europe GmbH (1)
Diamant Str 1, 65468, Trebur, Germany (100%)
Tel.: (49) 614791410
Web Site: http://www.mitsubishi.com
Sales Range: $25-49.9 Million
Emp.: 60
N.A.I.C.S.: 336110
Osamu Masuko (Pres)

Mitsubishi Motors de Portugal, S.A. (1)
Rua Dr Jos- Espirito Santo 38, 1950 097, Lisbon, Portugal (50%)
Tel.: (351) 218312100
Web Site: https://www.mitsubishi-motors.pt
Sales Range: $150-199.9 Million
Emp.: 17
Automobile Mfr
N.A.I.C.S.: 425120
Paulo Cabrita (Mng Dir)

Nagoya Plant (1)
1 Nakashinkiri, Hashime Cho, Okazaki, 444 8501, Aichi, Japan (100%)
Tel.: (81) 564313100

AND PRIVATE COMPANIES

Web Site: http://www.mitsubishi-motor.co.jp
Sales Range: $1-4.9 Billion
Emp.: 7,300
N.A.I.C.S.: 336110

P.T. Mitsubishi Krama Yudha Motors & Manufacturing (1)
Petukangan III Raya Bekasi Km 22 J1, Pulogadung, Jakarta, 13920, Timur, Indonesia
Tel.: (62) 214602908
Web Site: http://www.btmkn.co.id
Sales Range: $50-74.9 Million
Emp.: 25
Automobile Mfr
N.A.I.C.S.: 425120

Pajero Manufacturing Co., Ltd. (1)
2079 Sakakura Sakahogicho, Kamo-Gun, Gifu, 505-8505, Japan
Tel.: (81) 574285100
Web Site: http://www.pajero.co.jp
Emp.: 1,355
Automobile Parts Mfr
N.A.I.C.S.: 336390

Suiryo Plastics Co., Ltd. (1)
1424 Mizue Funao-cho, Kurashiki, 710-0262, Okayama, Japan
Tel.: (81) 86 552 3153
Web Site: https://www.suiryo.co.jp
Emp.: 665
Automotive Plastic Product Mfr
N.A.I.C.S.: 326199

Tokyo Plant-Kawasaki (1)
10 Okura Cho, Kawasaki, 211 8522, Kanagawa Nakahara Ku, Japan
Tel.: (81) 445872000
Sales Range: $1-4.9 Billion
Emp.: 4,000
N.A.I.C.S.: 336110

Tri Petch Isuzu Sales Co., Ltd. (1)
1088 Vibhavadi Rangsit Rd, Chatuchak, Bangkok, 10900, Thailand
Tel.: (66) 2 966 2111
Web Site: https://www.isuzu-tis.com
Sales Range: $75-99.9 Million
Emp.: 500
Commercial Vehicles & Pickup Trucks Whslr
N.A.I.C.S.: 423110

MITSUBISHI PAPER MILLS LIMITED

2-10-14 Ryogoku, Sumida-ku, Tokyo, 130-0026, Japan
Tel.: (81) 356001488
Web Site: https://www.mpm.co.jp
Year Founded: 1898
3864—(TKS)
Rev.: $1,278,783,820
Assets: $1,555,861,800
Liabilities: $954,655,860
Net Worth: $601,205,940
Earnings: $27,563,700
Emp.: 2,832
Fiscal Year-end: 03/31/24
Paper Products Mfr
N.A.I.C.S.: 322120
Kunio Suzuki *(Chm)*

Subsidiaries:

Diamic Co., Ltd. (1)
Ryogoku City Core 12F 2-10-14 Ryogoku, Sumida-ku, Tokyo, 130-0026, Japan
Tel.: (81) 356001540
Emp.: 131
Printing Plate Material Services
N.A.I.C.S.: 323120

Hachinohe Paper Processing Co., Ltd. (1)
1-2 Aomoriyachi, Kawaragi, Hachinohe, Japan
Tel.: (81) 178292511
Paper Processing & Logistics Services
N.A.I.C.S.: 561910

KJ Specialty Paper Co., Ltd. (1)
Fuji Mill 7-1 Shimbashi-cho, Fuji, 417-0004, Shizuoka, Japan
Tel.: (81) 545524075
Web Site: http://www.kjsp.co.jp
Emp.: 182
Paper Products Mfr
N.A.I.C.S.: 322299
Takeshi Sunakawa *(Pres & CEO)*

Kitakami Hitec Paper Corp. (1)
35 Sasanagane, Aisari-Cho, Kitakami, 024-0051, Iwate, Japan
Tel.: (81) 197673211
Emp.: 100
Pulp & Paper Mfr
N.A.I.C.S.: 322120

MP Juarez LLC (1)
Ave Valle del Cedro 1551 Paraq Ind Intermex, Juarez, Chihuahua, 32690, Mexico
Tel.: (52) 6566816977
Emp.: 100
Paper Mfr
N.A.I.C.S.: 322120

Mitsubishi HiTec Paper Bielefeld GmbH (1)
Bielefeld Mill Niedernholz 23, 33699, Bielefeld, Germany
Tel.: (49) 52120910
Web Site: http://www.mitsubishi-paper.com
Sales Range: $25-49.9 Million
Emp.: 450
Paper Mfr
N.A.I.C.S.: 322120
Andreas Jastrzembowski *(Gen Mgr)*

Mitsubishi HiTec Paper Europe GmbH (1)
Niedernholz 23, 33699, Bielefeld, Germany
Tel.: (49) 52120910
Web Site: https://www.mitsubishi-paper.com
Emp.: 700
Communication Paper Mfr & Distr
N.A.I.C.S.: 339940

Mitsubishi HiTec Paper Flensburg GmbH (1)
Flensburg Mill Husumer Str 12, 24941, Flensburg, Germany
Tel.: (49) 46186950
Web Site: http://www.mitsubishi-paper.com
Paper Mfr
N.A.I.C.S.: 322120

Mitsubishi Paper Engineering Co., Ltd. (1)
3 Aomori Yachi, Kawaragi, Hachinohe, 039-1197, Japan
Tel.: (81) 178292571
Web Site: https://www.mpec-mpm.co.jp
Emp.: 210
Industrial Engineering Services
N.A.I.C.S.: 541330

Mitsubishi Paper GmbH (1)
Am Albertussee 1, 40549, Dusseldorf, Germany
Tel.: (49) 21153596200
Web Site: http://www.mitsubishi-paper.com
Emp.: 2,000
Paper Mfr
N.A.I.C.S.: 322120

Mitsubishi Paper Holding (Europe) GmbH (1)
On Albertussee 1, Dusseldorf, 40549, Germany
Tel.: (49) 21153596202
Web Site: http://www.mitsubishi-paper.com
Paper Mfr
N.A.I.C.S.: 322120
Yutaka Ashie *(Mng Dir)*

Ryoshi Co., Ltd. (1)
Ryogoku City Core 2-10-14 Ryogoku, Sumida-ku, Tokyo, Japan
Tel.: (81) 356001341
Web Site: https://www.ryoshico.com
Emp.: 51
Real Estate Services
N.A.I.C.S.: 531390

Ryoukou Co.,Ltd. (1)
105 Sakae-cho Takasago-cho, Takasago, Japan
Tel.: (81) 794420367
Web Site: https://ryoukou-mpm.com
Paper & Pulp Mfr
N.A.I.C.S.: 322299

Toho Tokushu Pulp Co., Ltd. (1)
Ryogoku City Core 2-10-14 Ryogoku, Sumida-ku, Tokyo, 130-0026, Japan
Tel.: (81) 356001490
Web Site: https://www.ttp.bz
Pulp Product Mfr
N.A.I.C.S.: 322110

Zhuhai MPM Filter Ltd. (1)
No 17 Yijing Lane, Pingsha Town, Zhuhai, China
Tel.: (86) 7568895033
Web Site: https://www.mpmzhuhai.com.cn
Paper & Pulp Mfr
N.A.I.C.S.: 322299

MITSUBISHI PENCIL CO., LTD.

5-23-37 Higashi-Ohi, Shinagawa, Tokyo, 140-8537, Japan
Tel.: (81) 334586221
Web Site: https://www.uniball.com
Year Founded: 1887
7976—(TKS)
Rev.: $530,339,090
Assets: $1,035,189,630
Liabilities: $206,652,230
Net Worth: $828,537,400
Earnings: $72,076,940
Emp.: 2,708
Fiscal Year-end: 12/31/23
Stationery Product Mfr & Whslr
N.A.I.C.S.: 339940
Eiichiro Suhara *(Chm)*

Subsidiaries:

Hobbyra Hobbyre Corporation (1)
5-23-37 Higashioi, Shinagawa, Tokyo, 140-0011, Japan
Tel.: (81) 570037030
Web Site: https://www.hobbyra-hobbyre.com
Fabric Knitting Mfr & Distr
N.A.I.C.S.: 313240

Mitsubishi Pencil (Taiwan) Co., Ltd. (1)
8th Floor No 111 Songjiang Road, Zhongshan District, Taipei, Taiwan
Tel.: (886) 225023030
Web Site: http://www.mpuni.com.tw
Writing Instrument Mfr & Distr
N.A.I.C.S.: 339992

Mitsubishi Pencil (thailand) Co., Ltd. (1)
29/1 Piya Place Langsuan Building Floor 7th Unit 7C, Soi Langsuan Ploenchit Road Lumpini Patumwan, Bangkok, 10330, Thailand
Tel.: (66) 211793145
Web Site: https://www.mp-uni.com
Writing Instrument Mfr & Distr
N.A.I.C.S.: 339992

Mitsubishi Pencil Co. U.K. Ltd. (1)
Unit C Knowlhill Business Park Roebuck Way, Knowlhill, Milton Keynes, MK5 8GB, United Kingdom
Tel.: (44) 1908328832
Web Site: https://uniball.co.uk
Plastic Packaging Mfr & Distr
N.A.I.C.S.: 326112

Mitsubishi Pencil Co., Ltd. - Gunma Factory (1)
1091 Tateishi Fugioka, Gunma, 375-8501, Japan
Tel.: (81) 274421275
Stationery Product Mfr
N.A.I.C.S.: 339940

Mitsubishi Pencil Co., Ltd. - Yamagata Factory (1)
1654 Kamikomatsu Kawanishi-Machi Higashiokitama-Gun, Yamagata, 999-0192, Japan
Tel.: (81) 234421275
Stationery Product Mfr
N.A.I.C.S.: 339940

Mitsubishi Pencil Co., Ltd. - Yokohama Factory (1)
2-5-12 Ire Kanagawa-Ku, Yokohama, 221-8550, kanagawa, Japan
Tel.: (81) 454211324
Stationery Product Mfr
N.A.I.C.S.: 339940

Mitsubishi Pencil Corp. Of America (1)
3838 W Carson St Ste 380, Torrance, CA 90503

MITSUBISHI RESEARCH INSTITUTE, INC.

Tel.: (310) 316-6001
Stationery Product Distr
N.A.I.C.S.: 424120

Mitsubishi Pencil Espana S.A. (1)
Avda Can Roses s/n Nave 3 Rubi, 08191, Barcelona, Spain
Tel.: (34) 936990611
Web Site: https://www.uni-ball.es
Stationery Product Distr
N.A.I.C.S.: 424120

Mitsubishi Pencil France SA (1)
32 Avenue Pierre Grenier, 92517, Boulogne-Billancourt, Cedex, France
Tel.: (33) 146943333
Web Site: https://www.uniballfrance.eu
Stationery Product Distr
N.A.I.C.S.: 424120

Mitsubishi Pencil Korea Sales Co., Ltd. (1)
1141 Daeyoung Building Yeouido-dong 11 Gukjegeumyung-ro 8-gil, Yeongdeungpo-gu, Seoul, Korea (South)
Tel.: (82) 278620813
Web Site: https://www.uniball.co.kr
Stationery Product Distr
N.A.I.C.S.: 424120

Mitsubishi Pencil Vietnam Co., Ltd. (1)
C7 Thang Long Industrial Park Dong Anh Dist, Hanoi, Vietnam
Tel.: (84) 48811092
Stationery Product Distr
N.A.I.C.S.: 424120

Nagae Inshoh Do Co., Ltd. (1)
250-63 Yatacho, Matsue, 690-0021, Shimane, Japan
Tel.: (81) 852607066
Web Site: https://www.nagae-hanko.com
Stamp Mfr & Distr
N.A.I.C.S.: 339940

Uni Industry Co., Ltd. (1)
5-4-93 Toy Town Mibu-cho, Shimotsuga-gun, Tochigi, 321-0202, Japan
Tel.: (81) 282861511
Web Site: https://www.unikougyou.co.jp
Adhesive Mfr & Distr
N.A.I.C.S.: 325520

Uni Polymer Co., Ltd. (1)
970-2 Kamikawara Hondo, Fujioka, 375-0051, Gunma, Japan
Tel.: (81) 274509011
Web Site: https://unip.mpuni.co.jp
Stationery Product Distr
N.A.I.C.S.: 424120

Uni Yazi Gerecleri Kirtasiye ve San. Tic. A.S. (1)
Nishistanbul A Blok No 67-68 Cobancesme, 34196, Bahcelievler, Istanbul, Turkiye
Tel.: (90) 2126036161
Web Site: http://www.uniball.com.tr
Stationery Product Distr
N.A.I.C.S.: 424120

Yamagata Mitsubishi Pencil Precision Co., Ltd. (1)
4026-1 Kamikomatsu, Kawanishi-machi, Higashimatsuyama, 999-0121, Yamagata, Japan
Tel.: (81) 238462101
Web Site: https://seiko.mpuni.co.jp
Writing Instruments Mfr
N.A.I.C.S.: 339940

MITSUBISHI RESEARCH INSTITUTE, INC.

10-3 Nagatacho 2-Chome, Chiyoda-Ku, Tokyo, 100-8141, Japan
Tel.: (81) 351572111
Web Site: https://www.mri.co.jp
Year Founded: 1970
3636—(TKS)
Rev.: $802,919,520
Assets: $833,334,720
Liabilities: $301,778,640
Net Worth: $531,556,080
Earnings: $34,820,880
Emp.: 4,428
Fiscal Year-end: 09/30/24
IT Consulting, Services & Solutions

MITSUBISHI RESEARCH INSTITUTE, INC.

Mitsubishi Research Institute, Inc.—(Continued)
N.A.I.C.S.: 541519
Takashi Morisaki *(Chm & Pres)*

Subsidiaries:

HR Solution DCS Co., Ltd. (1)
Shinagawa Seaside West Tower 4-12-2
Higashi-Shinagawa, Shinagawa-ku, Tokyo, 140-0002, Japan
Tel.: (81) 334588250
Web Site: http://www.hrdcs.co.jp
Personnel Management & Development Services
N.A.I.C.S.: 541612

IT-One Co., Ltd. (1)
Tipco Tower 21st - 22nd Floor 118/1 Rama 6 Road, Phayathai, Bangkok, 10400, Thailand
Tel.: (66) 22715191
Web Site: https://www.itone.co.th
Emp.: 400
Information Technology Consulting Services
N.A.I.C.S.: 541512
Matthew Edward Zavadil *(CEO)*

MD Business Partner Co., Ltd. (1)
2-17-12 Kiba, Koto-ku, Tokyo, 135-0042, Japan
Tel.: (81) 338205251
Emp.: 242
Temporary Staffing Services
N.A.I.C.S.: 561320

MRI Research Associates, Inc. (1)
Tokyu Capitol Tower 2-10-3 Nagatacho, Chiyoda-ku, Tokyo, 100-0014, Japan
Tel.: (81) 335188430
Web Site: https://www.mri-ra.co.jp
Emp.: 164
Information Technology Consulting Services
N.A.I.C.S.: 541512
Kazuyoshi Nagasaka *(Mgr-Technical)*

Nippon Care Communications Co., Ltd. (1)
14-17 Nihombashi Odemmacho, Chuo-ku, Tokyo, 103-0011, Japan
Tel.: (81) 336623490
Web Site: https://www.care.com.co.jp
Information Technology Consulting Services
N.A.I.C.S.: 541512

OPT JAPAN Co., Ltd. (1)
Nishiyokencyo Building 1-1 Nishigokencyo, Shinjyuku-ku, Tokyo, 162-0812, Japan
Tel.: (81) 352619791
Web Site: http://www.optjapan.com
Information Technology Consulting Services
N.A.I.C.S.: 541512

Touhoku Diamond Computer Service Co., Ltd. (1)
2-2-1 Central Miyagi Sendai Mitsubishi Building 5F, Aoba-ku, Sendai, 980-0021, Japan
Tel.: (81) 22 224 0435
Web Site: https://www.tdcs.co.jp
Emp.: 52
Software Development Services
N.A.I.C.S.: 541511

MITSUBISHI STEEL MFG. CO., LTD.

Daiwa Tsukishima Bldg 16-13 Tsukishima 4-chome, Chuo-ku, Tokyo, 104-8550, Japan
Tel.: (81) 335363111
Web Site: https://www.mitsubishisteel.co.jp
Year Founded: 1917
5632—(TKS)
Rev.: $1,123,323,230
Assets: $972,139,310
Liabilities: $655,969,790
Net Worth: $316,169,520
Earnings: ($6,405,090)
Emp.: 4,076
Fiscal Year-end: 03/31/24
Fabricated Steel Product Mfr
N.A.I.C.S.: 332111
Motoyuki Sato *(Chm, Pres, Pres & CEO)*

Subsidiaries:

MSM (Thailand) Co., Ltd. (1)
38/8 Moo5 Laemochabang Industrial Estate, T Thungsukhla A Siracha, Chon Buri, 20230, Thailand
Tel.: (66) 384919607
Web Site: https://www.msm.co.th
Emp.: 936
Cast Magnets & Precision Castings Mfr & Distr
N.A.I.C.S.: 331511
Yoshio Takita *(Pres)*

MSM Cebu, Inc. (1)
5th St PEZA-Mactan Pusok, Lapu-Lapu, 6015, Mactan Island Cebu, Philippines
Tel.: (63) 323401687
Web Site: http://www.mitsubishisteel.co.jp
Emp.: 1,062
Precision Springs & Assemblies Mfr & Distr
N.A.I.C.S.: 332613

MSM NINGBO CO., LTD. (1)
Workshop No 12 Southern Zone NFTZ, Ningbo, Zhejiang, China
Tel.: (86) 574 8682 2299
Web Site: http://www.mitsubishisteel.co.jp
High Precision Assemblies Mfr & Whslr
N.A.I.C.S.: 334419

MSM Ningbo Spring Co., Ltd. (1)
25 JiuLongShan Road, South Zone NFTZ, Ningbo, Zhejiang, China
Tel.: (86) 57486823510
Web Site: http://www.mitsubishisteel.co.jp
Sales Range: $50-74.9 Million
Emp.: 163
Automotive Coil Springs Mfr & Whslr
N.A.I.C.S.: 332613

MSM Spring India Pvt. Ltd. (1)
139 Karanai Village Perambakkam Post, Sriperumbudur Thiruvallur District, Chennai, 631 402, India
Tel.: (91) 4467602500
Automotive Coil Spring Mfr & Distr
N.A.I.C.S.: 332613

MSSC Ahle GmbH (1)
Oberleppe 2, Karlsthal Lindlar, 51789, Karlsruhe, Germany
Tel.: (49) 22669080
Web Site: https://www.ahle-federn.com
Automotive Spring Mfr
N.A.I.C.S.: 332613
Gotz Peter Ander *(Mng Dir)*

MSSC Canada Inc. (1)
201 Park Avenue East, Chatham, N7M 3V7, ON, Canada
Tel.: (519) 354-1100
Web Site: http://www.msscna.com
Emp.: 280
Mfr & Sales of Automotive Coil Springs, Torsion & Stabilizer Bars & Assemblies
N.A.I.C.S.: 336390
Gino Negri *(Pres)*

MSSC Inc. (1)
2040 Crooks Rd Ste A, Troy, MI 48084
Tel.: (248) 502-8000
Suspension Coil Spring Mfr
N.A.I.C.S.: 332613

MSSC US Inc. (1)
102 Bill Bryan Blvd, Hopkinsville, KY 42240
Tel.: (270) 887-3000
Automotive Coil Spring Mfr & Distr
N.A.I.C.S.: 332613

Meritor Suspension Systems Company (1)
6401 W Fort St, Detroit, MI 48209
Tel.: (313) 551-2735
Web Site: http://www.mitsubishisteel.co.jp
Sales Range: $10-24.9 Million
Emp.: 6
Automotive Coil Springs, Torsion Bars, Stabilizer Bars & Automobile Assemblies
N.A.I.C.S.: 336340

Mitsubishi Nagasaki Machinery Mfg. Co., Ltd (1)
1-2-1 Fukahori-cho, Nagasaki, 851-0301, Japan
Tel.: (81) 958716106
Web Site: https://www.mnm.co.jp
Sales Range: $100-124.9 Million
Emp.: 350
Rolling Mill Machinery & Equipment Mfr

N.A.I.C.S.: 333519

Mitsubishi Steel Muroran Inc. (1)
12 Nakamachi, Muroran, 050-0087, Hokkaido, Japan **(70%)**
Tel.: (81) 143412800
Steel Mfrs
N.A.I.C.S.: 331110

PT. Jatim Taman Steel Mfg. (1)
Jl Raya Taman No 1 Throughout, Sepanjang, Sidoarjo, 61257, East Java, Indonesia
Tel.: (62) 317881139
Web Site: https://jts.co.id
Steel Mfrs
N.A.I.C.S.: 331110
Hiroshi Sekine *(Pres)*

PT. MSM INDONESIA (1)
Ruko No 7 Ruko Gresik Prima JL Mayjend Sungkono No 1, Desa Segromadu, Gresik, 61123, Kebonas, Indonesia
Tel.: (62) 313991119
Sales Range: $50-74.9 Million
Emp.: 4
Automotive & Precision Parts Distr
N.A.I.C.S.: 423120
Bramandida Kurniayawan *(Mgr-Exports)*

MITSUBISHI UFJ FINANCIAL GROUP, INC.

7-1 Marunouchi 2-chome, Chiyoda-ku, Tokyo, 100-8330, Japan
Tel.: (81) 332408111
Web Site: https://www.mufg.jp
Year Founded: 2001
MUFG—(NYSE)
Rev.: $65,904,553,730
Assets: $2,625,942,185,119
Liabilities: $2,503,859,543,386
Net Worth: $122,082,641,734
Earnings: $9,124,721,594
Emp.: 112,500
Fiscal Year-end: 03/31/24
Bank & Financial Services Holding Company
N.A.I.C.S.: 551111
Masahiro Kuwahara *(Chief Risk Officer)*

Subsidiaries:

ACOM Co., Ltd. (1)
Tokyo Shiodome Bldg 1-9-1 Higashi-Shinbashi, Minato-ku, Tokyo, Japan **(36.88%)**
Tel.: (81) 368650001
Web Site: https://www.acom.co.jp
Rev.: $1,948,165,300
Assets: $9,369,033,830
Liabilities: $4,912,737,080
Net Worth: $4,456,296,750
Earnings: $350,931,510
Emp.: 2,121
Fiscal Year-end: 03/31/2024
Loan & Financial Services
N.A.I.C.S.: 525990
Makoto Kondo *(Exec Mng Officer-Corp Risk Mgmt Dept)*

Subsidiary (Domestic):

IR Loan Servicing, Inc. (2)
Trusty Kojimachi Building 7F 3-4 Kojimachi, Chiyoda-ku, Tokyo, 1020083, Japan
Tel.: (81) 352156511
Web Site: https://www.irservicing.co.jp
Sales Range: $200-249.9 Million
Emp.: 132
Loan Servicing
N.A.I.C.S.: 525990

BOT Lease Co., Ltd. (1)
Tokyo Sumitomo Twin Building East Building 2-27-1 Shinkawa, Chuo-ku, Tokyo, 104-0033, Japan
Tel.: (81) 335378051
Web Site: https://www.botlease.co.jp
Emp.: 622
Financial Lending Services
N.A.I.C.S.: 522220

BTMU Lease (Deutschland) GmbH (1)
Breite Strasse 34, 40213, Dusseldorf, Germany
Tel.: (49) 211366783

INTERNATIONAL PUBLIC

Financial Lending Services
N.A.I.C.S.: 522220

BTMU Participation (Thailand) Co., Ltd. (1)
898 Ploenchit Tower 9th Floor Zone B1 Ploenchit Road, Lumpini Pathumwan, Bangkok, 10330, Thailand
Tel.: (66) 22630856
Financial Management Services
N.A.I.C.S.: 523999

Bank Nusantara Parahyangan Tbk (1)
Jl Ir H Juanda No 95, Bandung, 40132, Jawa Barat, Indonesia
Tel.: (62) 22 82560100
Web Site: http://www.bankbnp.com
Rev.: $57,742,982
Assets: $530,672,214
Liabilities: $451,022,828
Net Worth: $79,649,386
Earnings: $4,176,300
Emp.: 1,137
Fiscal Year-end: 12/31/2017
Commercial Banking Services
N.A.I.C.S.: 522110
Eiichiro Sakai *(Dir-Credit, Fin & IT)*

DVB Bank SE (1)
Platz der Republik 6, 60325, Frankfurt, Germany
Tel.: (49) 69975040
Web Site: http://www.dvbbank.com
Rev.: $378,297,920
Assets: $12,481,989,000
Liabilities: $11,472,007,248
Net Worth: $1,009,981,752
Earnings: ($378,543,568)
Emp.: 329
Fiscal Year-end: 12/31/2020
Transport Finance Services
N.A.I.C.S.: 523999
Wolfgang Kohler *(Chm-Supervisory Bd)*

Subsidiary (Non-US):

DVB Bank N.V. (2)
WTC Schiphol Tower F 6th floor Schiphol Boulevard 255, 1118 BH, Amsterdam, Netherlands
Tel.: (31) 88 399 7900
Web Site: http://www.dvbbank.com
Sales Range: $50-74.9 Million
Emp.: 50
Commericial Banking
N.A.I.C.S.: 522110
Martin Hessels *(Gen Mgr)*

Subsidiary (US):

DVB Capital Markets LLC (2)
609 5th Ave, New York, NY 10017
Tel.: (212) 858-2623
Web Site: http://www.dvbbank.com
Sales Range: $50-74.9 Million
Emp.: 6
Investment Banking & Securities Dealing
N.A.I.C.S.: 523150

Subsidiary (Non-US):

DVB Group Merchant Bank (Asia) Ltd (2)
77 Robinson Road 30-02, Singapore, 068896, Singapore
Tel.: (65) 65113433
Web Site: http://www.dav.com
Sales Range: $50-74.9 Million.
Emp.: 55
Commericial Banking
N.A.I.C.S.: 522110

DVB Transport Finance Ltd (2)
Ark Hills Sengokuyama Mori Tower 26F 2609 9-10 Roppongi 1-chome, Minato-ku, Tokyo, 106-0032, Japan **(100%)**
Tel.: (81) 351141880
Web Site: http://www.dvb-bank.com
Sales Range: $25-49.9 Million
Emp.: 4
All Other Support Activities for Transportation
N.A.I.C.S.: 488999
Kinichi Yuki *(Mng Dir)*

Subsidiary (Domestic):

LogPay Financial Services GmbH (2)

AND PRIVATE COMPANIES

MITSUBISHI UFJ FINANCIAL GROUP, INC.

Schwalbacher Str 72, 65760, Eschborn, Germany
Tel.: (49) 61968012701
Web Site: http://www.logpay.de
Sales Range: $50-74.9 Million
Emp.: 50
Other Activities Related to Credit Intermediation
N.A.I.C.S.: 522390

Defined Contribution Plan Consulting of Japan Co., Ltd. (1)
2-10-1 Yurakucho, Chiyoda-ku, Tokyo, 100-0006, Japan
Tel.: (81) 3 3287 0251
Web Site: http://www.dcj-net.co.jp
Emp.: 100
Investment Banking & Security Services
N.A.I.C.S.: 523150

Japan Electronic Monetary Claim Organization (1)
15th floor Wateras Tower 2-101 Kanda-Awajicho, Chiyoda-ku, Tokyo, 101-0063, Japan
Tel.: (81) 352950007
Web Site: https://www.jemc.jp
Securities Brokerage Services
N.A.I.C.S.: 523150

KOKUSAI Asset Management Co., Ltd. (1)
Shin-Yurakucho Bldg 1-12-1 Yurakucho, Chiyoda-ku, Tokyo, 100-0006, Japan
Tel.: (81) 352216200
Web Site: https://www.am.mufg.jp
Sales Range: $200-249.9 Million
Emp.: 793
Asset Management Services
N.A.I.C.S.: 523940
Sunao Yokokawa *(Pres & CEO)*

Kabu.com Securities Co., Ltd. (1)
24F Kasumigaseki Building 3-2-5 Kasumigaseki, Chiyoda-ku, Tokyo, 100-6024, Japan **(52.96%)**
Tel.: (81) 120390390
Web Site: https://www.kabu.com
Sales Range: $150-199.9 Million
Emp.: 203
Financial Investment Management Services
N.A.I.C.S.: 523150
Masakatsu Saito *(Pres & CEO)*

Ling Zheng Investment Consulting (Shanghai) Co., Ltd. (1)
Unit 3106 Azia Center 1233 Lujiazui Ring Road, Pudong New Area, Shanghai, 200120, China
Tel.: (86) 2168413018
Commercial Banking Services
N.A.I.C.S.: 522110

MU Business Engineering, Ltd. (1)
3-1-8 Nihombashi, Chuo-Ku, Tokyo, 103-0027, Japan
Tel.: (81) 335237766
Engineeering Services
N.A.I.C.S.: 541330

MU Investments Co., Ltd. (1)
2-3-11 Kanda Surugadai, Chiyoda-ku, Tokyo, 101-0062, Japan
Tel.: (81) 352021801
Web Site: https://www.mu-iv.co.jp
Emp.: 103
Financial Investment Services
N.A.I.C.S.: 523999

MUFG Bank (China), Ltd. (1)
16F New Bund Times Square No399 Haiyang West Road, Pudong New District, Shanghai, 200126, China
Tel.: (86) 2168881666
Commercial Banking Services
N.A.I.C.S.: 522110

MUFG Bank Ltd. (1)
1-4-5 Marunouchi, Chiyoda-ku, Tokyo, 100-8388, Japan **(100%)**
Tel.: (81) 332401111
Web Site: https://www.bk.mufg.jp
Sales Range: $15-24.9 Billion
Emp.: 31,796
Banking Services
N.A.I.C.S.: 522110
Kanetsugu Mike *(Pres & CEO)*

Subsidiary (Non-US):

AO MUFG Bank (Eurasia) (2)
Building 2 Romanov per 4, 125009, Moscow, Russia
Tel.: (7) 4952258999
Web Site: http://www.bk.mufg.jp
Sales Range: $50-74.9 Million
Emp.: 70
Banking Services
N.A.I.C.S.: 522110

Affiliate (Non-US):

Asia Financial Holdings Limited (2)
16th Floor Worldwide House 19 Des Voeux Road Central, Hong Kong, China (Hong Kong)
Tel.: (852) 36069200
Web Site: https://www.afh.hk
Holding Company
N.A.I.C.S.: 551111

Subsidiary (Non-US):

Asia Insurance Company Limited (3)
19 C and D Block-L Gulberg-III, Lahore, Pakistan
Tel.: (92) 4235865575
Web Site: https://www.asiainsurance.com.pk
Rev.: $2,820,031
Assets: $10,329,631
Liabilities: $4,045,305
Net Worth: $6,284,325
Earnings: $39,859
Emp.: 161
Fiscal Year-end: 12/31/2019
General Insurance Services
N.A.I.C.S.: 524126
Ihtsham ul Haq Qureshi *(CEO)*

Subsidiary (US):

BTMU Leasing & Finance, Inc. (2)
1251 Avenue of the Americas, New York, NY 10020-1104
Tel.: (212) 782-4000
Web Site: http://www.bk.mufg.jp
Sales Range: $350-399.9 Million
Emp.: 1,000
Leasing & Financial Services
N.A.I.C.S.: 522291

Subsidiary (Non-US):

Banco de Tokyo-Mitsubishi UFJ Brasil S/A (2)
Av Paulista 1274, Bela Vista, Sao Paulo, 01310-925, SP, Brazil
Tel.: (55) 1132680308
Web Site: https://www.br.bk.mufg.jp
Sales Range: $10-24.9 Million
Banking Services
N.A.I.C.S.: 522110

Bank of Ayudhya Public Company Limited (2)
1222 Rama III Road Bang Phongphang, Yan Nawa, Bangkok, 10120, Thailand **(76.88%)**
Tel.: (66) 22962000
Web Site: http://www.krungsri.com
Rev.: $4,065,007,249
Assets: $80,811,981,497
Liabilities: $69,968,516,989
Net Worth: $10,843,464,508
Earnings: $967,198,626
Emp.: 13,952
Fiscal Year-end: 12/31/2023
Banking Services
N.A.I.C.S.: 522110
Noriaki Goto *(Vice Chm)*

Subsidiary (Domestic):

Ayudhya Capital Auto Lease Plc (3)
Krungsri Ploenchit Tower 16th Floor 550 Ploenchit Road, Lumpini Pathumwan, Bangkok, 10330, Thailand
Tel.: (66) 27407400
Web Site: http://www.krungsriauto.com
Automobile Lease & Purchase Services
N.A.I.C.S.: 532112

Ayudhya Capital Services Company Limited (3)
Krungsri Ploenchit Tower 550 Ploenchit Road, Lumpini Pathumwan, Bangkok, 10330, Thailand
Tel.: (66) 26278000
Commercial Banking Services
N.A.I.C.S.: 522110

Ayudhya Development Leasing Co., Ltd. (3)
Krungsri Ploenchit Tower 14th Floor 550 Ploenchit Road, Lumpini Pathumwan, Bangkok, 10330, Thailand **(99.99%)**
Tel.: (66) 22082300
Web Site: http://www.krungsrileasing.com
Sales Range: $75-99.9 Million
Emp.: 33
Leasing & Financing Services
N.A.I.C.S.: 522390
Chandrashekar Subramanian Krishooindmangalam *(Chm)*

Subsidiary (Non-US):

Home Credit Indonesia PT (3)
Plaza Oleos 8th Floor Jl No 53A, TB Simatupang, South Jakarta, Indonesia **(75%)**
Tel.: (62) 2129539600
Web Site: https://www.homecredit.co.id
Financial Payment Services
N.A.I.C.S.: 522320
Animesh Narang *(CEO)*

Subsidiary (Domestic):

Krungsri Asset Management Co., Ltd. (3)
1st-2nd Zone A 12th 18th Zone B Floor Ploenchit Tower 898, Ploenchit Road Lumpini Pathumwan, Bangkok, 10330, Thailand **(77%)**
Tel.: (66) 26575757
Web Site: https://www.krungsriasset.com
Sales Range: $50-74.9 Million
Emp.: 90
Asset Management Services
N.A.I.C.S.: 525910
Prasert Impornrugee *(Chief IT Officer)*

Krungsri Ayudhya AMC Ltd. (3)
Floor 11 1222 Rama III Road, Bang Phongphang Yan Nawa, Bangkok, 10120, Thailand **(99.99%)**
Tel.: (66) 22964100
Web Site: http://www.krungsriproperty.com
Emp.: 200
Real Estate Services
N.A.I.C.S.: 531390

Krungsri Factoring Co., Ltd. (3)
1222 Bank of Ayudhya Building Floor 21 Rama 3 Road, Bangpongpang Yannawa, Bangkok, 10120, Thailand **(99.99%)**
Tel.: (66) 22082849
Web Site: https://www.krungsrinimble.com
Sales Range: $50-74.9 Million
Emp.: 40
Credit Intermediation Services
N.A.I.C.S.: 522390

Krungsri General Insurance Broker Limited (3)
Krungsri Ploenchit Office 550 Ploenchit Road, Lumphini Pathumwan, Bangkok, 10330, Thailand
Tel.: (66) 26278029
Insurance Services
N.A.I.C.S.: 524210

Krungsri Life Assurance Broker Limited (3)
Krungsri Ploenchit Office 550 Ploenchit Road, Lumphini Pathumwan, Bangkok, 10330, Thailand **(99.99%)**
Tel.: (66) 26278028
Sales Range: $50-74.9 Million
Emp.: 13
Insurance Management Services
N.A.I.C.S.: 524298

Krungsri Securities Public Company Limited (3)
898 Ploenchit Tower Building 3rd Floor, Ploenchit Road Lumpini Pathumwan, Bangkok, 10330, Thailand **(86.33%)**
Tel.: (66) 26597000
Web Site: https://www.krungsrisecurities.com
Sales Range: $10-24.9 Million
Emp.: 300
Investment Banking & Securities Dealing
N.A.I.C.S.: 523150

Krungsriayudhya Card Co., Ltd. (3)
Krungsri Ploenchit Tower Building 550 Ploenchit Road, Lumpini Pathumwan, Bangkok, 10330, Thailand
Tel.: (66) 26463000
Web Site: https://www.krungsricard.com
Credit Card Services
N.A.I.C.S.: 561499

Siam Realty and Services Co., Ltd. (3)
Bank of Ayudhya Plc Head Office Tower C Floor 5A 1222 Rama III Road, Bang Phongphang Yan Nawa, Bangkok, 10120, Thailand
Tel.: (66) 22963435
Sales Range: $650-699.9 Million
Emp.: 1,800
Real Estate Services
N.A.I.C.S.: 531390

Subsidiary (Non-US):

Bank of Tokyo-Mitsubishi UFJ (Canada) Ltd. (2)
Royal Bank Plaza South Tower 200 Bay Street Suite 1800, Toronto, M5J 2J1, ON, Canada
Tel.: (416) 865-0220
Web Site: https://www.bk.mufg.jp
Sales Range: $50-74.9 Million
Emp.: 60
Banking Services
N.A.I.C.S.: 522110
Yoshio Furuheshi *(Pres)*

Bank of Tokyo-Mitsubishi UFJ (China), Ltd. (2)
17-20F New Bund Times Square No399 Haiyang West Road, Pudong New District, Shanghai, 200126, China
Tel.: (86) 2168881666
Sales Range: $50-74.9 Million
Emp.: 60
Banking Services
N.A.I.C.S.: 522110

Bank of Tokyo-Mitsubishi UFJ (Malaysia) Berhad (2)
Level 9 Menara IMC, No 8 Jalan Sultan Ismail, 50250, Kuala Lumpur, Malaysia
Tel.: (60) 320348000
Sales Range: $150-199.9 Million
Emp.: 280
Banking Services
N.A.I.C.S.: 522110

Bank of Tokyo-Mitsubishi UFJ (Mexico) S.A. (2)
Avenida Paseo de la Reforma No 250 Piso 11, Colonia Juarez Delegacion Cuauhtemoc, 06600, Mexico, DF, Mexico
Tel.: (52) 5511028300
Banking Services
N.A.I.C.S.: 522110

Subsidiary (US):

Bank of Tokyo-Mitsubishi UFJ Trust Company (2)
1251 Ave of the Americas, New York, NY 10020-1104
Web Site: http://www.bk.mufg.jp
Assets: $4,533,000,000
Emp.: 376
Banking Services
N.A.I.C.S.: 523991

Representative Office (Non-US):

Bank of Tokyo-Mitsubishi UFJ, Ltd. - Bangkok (2)
898 Ploenchit Tower 9th Floor Zone B1 Ploenchit Road, Lumpini Pathumwan, Bangkok, 10330, Thailand
Tel.: (66) 22630856
Assets: $24,000,000
Emp.: 600
Banking Services
N.A.I.C.S.: 522110

Bank of Tokyo-Mitsubishi UFJ, Ltd. - Brussels (2)
Boulevard Louis Schmidt 29, 1040, Brussels, Belgium
Tel.: (32) 25514411
Web Site: http://www.bk.mufg.jp
Sales Range: $50-74.9 Million
Emp.: 25
Banking Services
N.A.I.C.S.: 522110

MITSUBISHI UFJ FINANCIAL GROUP, INC.

Mitsubishi UFJ Financial Group, Inc.—(Continued)

Branch (US):

Bank of Tokyo-Mitsubishi UFJ, Ltd. - Chicago (2)
227 West Monroe St, Chicago, IL 60606-5055
Tel.: (312) 696-4500
Web Site: http://www.bk.mufg.jp
Sales Range: $50-74.9 Million
Emp.: 80
Banking Services
N.A.I.C.S.: 522110

Representative Office (Non-US):

Bank of Tokyo-Mitsubishi UFJ, Ltd. - Dusseldorf (2)
Breite Strasse 34, 40213, Dusseldorf, Germany
Tel.: (49) 21136670
Sales Range: $100-124.9 Million
Emp.: 180
Banking Services
N.A.I.C.S.: 522110

Branch (US):

Bank of Tokyo-Mitsubishi UFJ, Ltd. - Los Angeles (2)
445 S Figueroa St Ste 2700, Los Angeles, CA 90071-5800
Tel.: (213) 488-3700
Web Site: http://www.bk.mufg.jp
Sales Range: $50-74.9 Million
Emp.: 65
Banking Services
N.A.I.C.S.: 522110

Representative Office (Non-US):

Bank of Tokyo-Mitsubishi UFJ, Ltd. - Madrid (2)
Jose Ortega y Gasset 29 3rd floor, 28006, Madrid, Spain
Tel.: (34) 914328500
Sales Range: $50-74.9 Million
Emp.: 70
Banking Services
N.A.I.C.S.: 522110
Takuya Araki (Gen Mgr)

Bank of Tokyo-Mitsubishi UFJ, Ltd. - Milano (2)
Via Filippo Turati 9, 20121, Milan, Italy
Tel.: (39) 02669931
Sales Range: $50-74.9 Million
Emp.: 50
Banking Services
N.A.I.C.S.: 522110
Greg Lynn (Gen Mgr)

Branch (US):

Bank of Tokyo-Mitsubishi UFJ, Ltd. - New York (2)
1251 Avenue of The Americas, New York, NY 10020-1104
Tel.: (212) 782-4000
Web Site: http://www.bk.mufg.jp
Sales Range: $350-399.9 Million
Emp.: 1,000
Banking Services
N.A.I.C.S.: 522110

Representative Office (Non-US):

Bank of Tokyo-Mitsubishi UFJ, Ltd. - Paris (2)
Le Centorial 18 rue du Quatre Septembre, PO Box 2101, 75002, Paris, France
Tel.: (33) 149264927
Web Site: http://www.bk.mufj.jp
Sales Range: $50-74.9 Million
Emp.: 16
Banking Services
N.A.I.C.S.: 522110

Bank of Tokyo-Mitsubishi UFJ, Ltd. - Seoul (2)
14 Sejong-daero Grand Central 26F, Jung-gu, Seoul, Korea (South)
Tel.: (82) 27512700
Sales Range: $50-74.9 Million
Emp.: 150
Banking Services
N.A.I.C.S.: 522110

Bank of Tokyo-Mitsubishi UFJ, Ltd. - Singapore (2)
7 Straits View 23-01 Marina One East Tower, Singapore, 018936, Singapore
Tel.: (65) 65383388
Sales Range: $50-74.9 Million
Emp.: 50
Banking Services
N.A.I.C.S.: 522110
Peter Heidinger (Head-Corp Banking-Asia & Oceania)

Bank of Tokyo-Mitsubishi UFJ, Ltd. - Sydney (2)
Level 25 Gateway, 1 Macquarie Place, Sydney, 2000, NSW, Australia
Tel.: (61) 292961111
Sales Range: $50-74.9 Million
Emp.: 150
Banking Services
N.A.I.C.S.: 522110

Subsidiary (US):

MUFG Americas Holdings Corporation (2)
1251 Ave of the Americas, New York, NY 10020-1104 (65.4%)
Tel.: (212) 782-6800
Web Site: https://www.mufgamericas.com
Rev.: $6,957,000,000
Assets: $167,846,000,000
Liabilities: $150,567,000,000
Net Worth: $17,279,000,000
Earnings: $166,000,000
Emp.: 13,900
Fiscal Year-end: 12/31/2020
Bank Holding Company
N.A.I.C.S.: 551111
Stephen E. Cummings (Pres & CEO)

Subsidiary (Non-US):

MUFG Bank (Europe) N.V. (2)
World Trade Center Tower I 5th Floor, Strawinskylaan 1887, 1077 XX, Amsterdam, Netherlands
Tel.: (31) 205737737
Web Site: https://www.nl.bk.mufg.jp
Sales Range: $50-74.9 Million
Emp.: 160
Banking Services
N.A.I.C.S.: 522110
Mark A. B. Selles (CFO & Member-Mgmt Bd)

Branch (Non-US):

Bank of Tokyo-Mitsubishi UFJ (Holland) N.V. - Prague (3)
Klicperova 3208/12, Prague, 150 00, Czech Republic
Tel.: (420) 257257911
Web Site: http://www.btmholland.com
Sales Range: $50-74.9 Million
Emp.: 9
Banking Services
N.A.I.C.S.: 522110

Bank of Tokyo-Mitsubishi UFJ (Holland) N.V. - Vienna (3)
Schwarzenbergplatz 5/3 2, 1030, Vienna, Austria
Tel.: (43) 150262
Web Site: http://www.nl.bk.mufg.jp
Sales Range: $50-74.9 Million
Emp.: 9
Banking Services
N.A.I.C.S.: 522110

Subsidiary (Non-US):

Mitsubishi UFJ Global Custody S.A. (2)
287 289 Route D Arlon, L1150, Luxembourg, Luxembourg
Tel.: (352) 4451801
Web Site: http://www.bk.mufg.jp
Sales Range: $75-99.9 Million
Emp.: 110
Banking Services
N.A.I.C.S.: 522110
Hirokati Ahada (Mng Dir)

Joint Venture (Non-US):

PT BRI Multifinance Indonesia (2)
Brilliant Tower Fl 121 and 22 Jl Gatot Subroto Kav 64 No 117A, Menteng Dalam Tebet, Jakarta, 10220, Indonesia
Tel.: (62) 215745333
Web Site: https://www.brifinance.co.id
Financial Lending Services
N.A.I.C.S.: 522220

Subsidiary (Non-US):

PT Bank Danamon Indonesia Tbk (2)
Jl HR Rasuna Said Blok C No 10, Karet Setiabudi, Jakarta, 12920, Indonesia (94.1%)
Tel.: (62) 2180645000
Web Site: https://www.danamon.co.id
Rev.: $1,312,459,869
Assets: $14,371,516,308
Liabilities: $11,127,154,950
Net Worth: $3,244,361,358
Earnings: $237,553,442
Emp.: 23,238
Fiscal Year-end: 12/31/2023
Banking Services
N.A.I.C.S.: 522110
Herry Hykmanto (Dir-Syariah & Ops)

Subsidiary (Domestic):

PT Adira Dinamika Multi Finance Tbk (3)
Graha Adira 10th-12th Floor, Jl Menteng Raya No 21, 10340, Jakarta, Indonesia (76%)
Tel.: (62) 213918686
Financial Investment
N.A.I.C.S.: 523999
Hafid Hadeli (Pres)

Representative Office (Non-US):

The Bank of Tokyo-Mitsubishi UFJ, Ltd. - London (2)
Ropemaker Place 25 Ropemaker Street, London, EC2Y 9AN, United Kingdom
Tel.: (44) 2075771000
Web Site: http://www.uk.bk.mufg.jp
Sales Range: $300-349.9 Million
Emp.: 700
Banking Services
N.A.I.C.S.: 522110

MUFG Bank Mexico, S.A. (1)
Avenida Paseo de la Reforma No 250 Piso 11 Torre A, Colonia Juarez Delegacion Cuauhtemoc, 06600, Mexico, Mexico
Tel.: (52) 5511028300
Web Site: http://cms.mx.bk.mufg.jp
Commercial Banking Services
N.A.I.C.S.: 522110

MUFG Bank Turkey Anonim Sirketi (1)
Fatih Sultan Mehmet Mahallesi Poligon Caddesi Buyaka 2 Sitesi 2 Blok, No 8B Ic Kapi No 82 Umraniye, 34771, Istanbul, Turkiye
Tel.: (90) 2166003000
Web Site: https://www.tu.bk.mufg.jp
Commercial Banking Services
N.A.I.C.S.: 522110
Ali Vefa Celik (Co-Chm)

MUFG Bank, Ltd. (1)
Royal Bank Plaza South Tower 200 Bay Street Suite 1800, Toronto, M5J 2J1, ON, Canada
Tel.: (416) 865-0220
Commercial Banking Services
N.A.I.C.S.: 522110
Hironori Kamezawa (Deputy Pres)

MUFG Investor Services FinTech Limited (1)
1st Floor Office No 11 Emelle Building 135 Arch Makarios III Avenue, 3021, Limassol, Cyprus
Tel.: (357) 25028241
Commercial Banking Services
N.A.I.C.S.: 522110

MUFG Lux Management Company S.A. (1)
287-289 route d'Arlon, 1150, Luxembourg, Luxembourg
Tel.: (352) 445180907
Portfolio Management Services
N.A.I.C.S.: 523940

MUFG Participation (Thailand) Co., Ltd. (1)
898 Ploenchit Tower 9th Floor Zone B1 Ploenchit Road Lumpini, Pathumwan, Bangkok, 10330, Thailand
Tel.: (66) 22630856
Commercial Banking Services
N.A.I.C.S.: 522110

MUFG Securities (Canada), Ltd. (1)
Royal Bank Plaza South Tower Suite 2940 200 Bay Street, Toronto, M5J 2J1, ON, Canada
Tel.: (647) 475-4455
Securities & Brokerage Services
N.A.I.C.S.: 523150

MUFG Securities Asia Limited (1)
AIA Central 1 Connaught Road, Central, China (Hong Kong)
Tel.: (852) 28601500
Commercial Banking Services
N.A.I.C.S.: 522110

Mitsubishi UFJ Asset Management Co., Ltd. (1)
Shin-Yurakucho Bldg 1-12-1 Yurakucho, Chiyoda-ku, Tokyo, 100-0006, Japan
Tel.: (81) 352216200
Web Site: https://www.am.mufg.jp
Emp.: 818
Asset Management Services
N.A.I.C.S.: 523940

Mitsubishi UFJ Capital Co., Ltd (1)
Nihonbashi Plaza Building 7F 2-3-4 Nihonbashi, Chuo-ku, Tokyo, 103-0027, Japan
Tel.: (81) 352058581
Web Site: https://www.mucap.co.jp
Emp.: 60
Portfolio Management Services
N.A.I.C.S.: 523999
Takashi Hasegawa (Mng Dir)

Mitsubishi UFJ Factors Limited (1)
2-101 Kanda Awajicho Wateras Tower, Chiyoda-ku, Tokyo, 101-8637, Japan
Tel.: (81) 332518351
Web Site: https://www.muf.bk.mufg.jp
Emp.: 611
Investment Banking & Security Services
N.A.I.C.S.: 523150

Mitsubishi UFJ Information Technology, Ltd (1)
Nakano Central Park South 4-10-2 Nakano, Nakano-ku, Tokyo, 164-0001, Japan
Tel.: (81) 333191111
Web Site: https://www.it.mufg.jp
Emp.: 3,000
Information Technology Consulting Services
N.A.I.C.S.: 541512

Mitsubishi UFJ Investment Services (HK) Limited (1)
8F AIA Central 1 Connaught Road, Central, China (Hong Kong)
Tel.: (852) 28236666
Commercial Banking Services
N.A.I.C.S.: 522110

Mitsubishi UFJ Investor Services & Banking (Luxembourg) S.A. (1)
287-289 route d'Arlon, 1150, Luxembourg, Luxembourg
Tel.: (352) 4451801
Web Site: http://www.lu.tr.mufg.jp
Investment Fund Administration Services
N.A.I.C.S.: 525910

Mitsubishi UFJ Loan Business (1)
4-11-1 Kotobashi Kinshicho Daiya Bldg 7f, Sumida-Ku, Tokyo, 130-0022, Japan
Tel.: (81) 336342801
Mortgage Loan Brokerage Services
N.A.I.C.S.: 522310

Mitsubishi UFJ NICOS Co., Ltd. (1)
3-33-5 Hongo, Bunkyo-ku, Tokyo, 113-8411, Japan
Tel.: (81) 337701177
Web Site: http://www.nicos.co.jp
Sales Range: $1-4.9 Billion
Emp.: 5,588
Credit Card Services
N.A.I.C.S.: 522210

Mitsubishi UFJ Personal Financial Advisers Co., Ltd. (1)
1-7-17 Nihonbashi, Chuo-ku, Tokyo, 103-0027, Japan
Tel.: (81) 3 3548 2121
Web Site: http://www.mupfa.co.jp

AND PRIVATE COMPANIES

MITSUBISHI UFJ FINANCIAL GROUP, INC.

Financial Consulting Services
N.A.I.C.S.: 541611

Mitsubishi UFJ Real Estate Services Co., Ltd. (1)
2nd floor Iwanami Jimbocho Building 2-1 Kanda Jimbocho, Chiyoda-ku, Tokyo, 101-0051, Japan
Tel.: (81) 343304718
Web Site: https://www.sumai1.com
Emp.: 854
Real Estate Development Services
N.A.I.C.S.: 531390

Mitsubishi UFJ Research and Consulting Ltd (1)
Holland Hills Mori Tower 5-11-2 Toranomon, Minato-ku, Tokyo, 105-8501, Japan
Tel.: (81) 367331000
Web Site: https://www.murc.jp
Sales Range: $150-199.9 Million
Emp.: 1,300
Financial Management Consulting Services
N.A.I.C.S.: 541618
Satoshi Murabayashi *(Co-Pres)*

Subsidiary (Non-US):

PT. MU Research and Consulting Indonesia (2)
MidPlaza 2 18th Floor Jl Jend Sudirman Kav 10-11, Jakarta, 10220, Indonesia
Tel.: (62) 215749518
Web Site: https://www.murc.jp
Sales Range: $25-49.9 Million
Emp.: 8
Financial Management Consulting Services
N.A.I.C.S.: 541618
Toshiya Hatta *(Chm)*

Mitsubishi UFJ Securities Holdings Co., Ltd. (1)
Otemachi Financial City Grand Cube 1-9-2 Otemachi, Chiyoda-ku, Tokyo, 100-8127, Japan
Tel.: (81) 362132550
Web Site: http://www.hd.sc.mufg.jp
Rev.: $3,400,409,760
Assets: $307,094,950,800
Liabilities: $297,370,529,280
Net Worth: $9,724,421,520
Earnings: $350,609,600
Fiscal Year-end: 03/31/2022
Securities Brokerage Services
N.A.I.C.S.: 523150
Takashi Nagaoka *(Chm)*

Subsidiary (Domestic):

MU Hands-on Capital Co., Ltd. (2)
Ishikawa Building 7F 8-16 Nihombashi-Honcho 4chome, Chuo-ku, Tokyo, 103-0023, Japan
Tel.: (81) 3 3245 8300
Web Site: http://www.hands-on.sc.mufg.jp
Sales Range: $50-74.9 Million
Emp.: 22
Investment Management Service
N.A.I.C.S.: 523999
Haruo Adachi *(Gen Mgr-Investment Bus Plng & Admin Dept)*

Subsidiary (US):

MUFG Securities Americas Inc. (2)
1221 Ave of the Americas, New York, NY 10020-1001
Tel.: (212) 405-7000
Web Site: http://www.us.sc.mufg.jp
Securities Brokerage Services
N.A.I.C.S.: 523150

Affiliate (Domestic):

Mitsubishi UFJ Merrill Lynch PB Securities Co., Ltd. (2)
4-1 Nihonbashi, Chuo-ku, Tokyo, 103-8242, Japan (50.98%)
Tel.: (81) 3 6225 8300
Web Site: http://www.muml-pb.co.jp
Asset Management Services
N.A.I.C.S.: 523940

Joint Venture (Domestic):

Mitsubishi UFJ Morgan Stanley Securities Co., Ltd. (2)
Otemachi Financial City Grand Cube 1-9-2, Otemachi Chiyoda-ku, Tokyo, 100-8127, Japan

Tel.: (81) 362138500
Web Site: https://www.sc.mufg.jp
Sales Range: $1-4.9 Billion
Emp.: 5,630
Securities Brokerage Services
N.A.I.C.S.: 523150
Haruo Nakamura *(Deputy Pres)*

Subsidiary (Non-US):

Mitsubishi UFJ Securities (HK), Limited (2)
AIA Central 1 Connaught Road, Central, China (Hong Kong)
Tel.: (852) 28601500
Web Site: http://www.mufj.com.jp
Sales Range: $50-74.9 Million
Emp.: 55
Securities Brokerage Services
N.A.I.C.S.: 523150

Mitsubishi UFJ Securities International PLC (2)
Ropemaker Place 25 Ropemaker Street, London, EC2Y 9AN, United Kingdom
Tel.: (44) 2076285555
Web Site: http://www.int.sc.mufg.jp
Sales Range: $350-399.9 Million
Emp.: 650
Securities Brokerage Services
N.A.I.C.S.: 523150

Mitsubishi UFJ Trust & Banking Corporation (1)
4-5 Marunouchi 1-Chome, Chiyoda-ku, Tokyo, 100-8212, Japan (100%)
Tel.: (81) 332121211
Web Site: https://www.tr.mufg.jp
Sales Range: $5-14.9 Billion
Emp.: 6,218
Trust & Banking Services
N.A.I.C.S.: 523991

Subsidiary (Non-US):

First Sentier Investors (Australia) IM Ltd. (2)
Darling Park Tower 1 201 Sussex Street, Sydney, 2000, NSW, Australia
Tel.: (61) 2 9273 3000
Web Site: http://www.firststateinvestments.com
Investment Management Service
N.A.I.C.S.: 523940
Mark Steinberg *(CEO)*

Holding (Non-US):

Igneo Infrastructure Partners (3)
First Sentier Investors Finsbury Circus House 15 Finsbury Circus, London, EC2M 7EB, United Kingdom
Tel.: (61) 29010 5200
Web Site: https://www.igneoip.com
Rev.: $15,000,000,000
Financial Investment Services
N.A.I.C.S.: 523999
John DiMarco *(Mng Dir)*

Subsidiary (US):

US Signal Company, LLC (4)
20 Monroe Ave NW, Grand Rapids, MI 49503
Tel.: (616) 988-7422
Web Site: http://www.ussignalcom.com
Data Processing, Hosting & Related Services
N.A.I.C.S.: 518210
Joanna Shaw *(CFO)*

Subsidiary (Domestic):

ONENECK IT SOLUTIONS LLC (5)
8401 Greenway Blvd, Middleton, WI 53562
Tel.: (480) 315-3000
Web Site: https://www.oneneck.com
Information Technology Consulting Services
N.A.I.C.S.: 541512
Hank Koch *(Sr VP-Data Centers-Managed Svcs)*

Holding (US):

Patriot Rail Company LLC (3)
10752 Deerwood Park Blvd Ste. 300, Jacksonville, FL 32256
Tel.: (904) 423-2540
Web Site: http://patriotrailandports.com
Activities Related to Real Estate

N.A.I.C.S.: 531390
John E. Fenton *(CEO)*

Subsidiary (Domestic):

Columbia & Cowlitz Railway Company, LLC (4)
3401 Industrial Way, Longview, WA 98632-9285
Tel.: (360) 355-6881
Web Site: https://patriotrail.com
Freight Rail Transportation Services
N.A.I.C.S.: 482111

DeQueen & Eastern Railroad Company, LLC (4)
412 E Lockesburg Ave, De Queen, AR 71832
Tel.: (870) 279-5081
Web Site: https://patriotrail.com
Railroad Transportation Services
N.A.I.C.S.: 482111

Delta Southern Railroad, Inc. (4)
469 Port Rd Madison Parish Port, Tallulah, LA 71282
Tel.: (318) 600-4489
Web Site: http://deltasouthern.net
Sales Range: $1-9.9 Million
Emp.: 34
Line-Haul Railroads
N.A.I.C.S.: 482111
Linda Wainwright *(VP)*

Golden Triangle Railroad, LLC (4)
4335 Carson Rd, Columbus, MS 39701
Tel.: (904) 676-3983
Web Site: https://patriotrail.com
Track Miles Operator
N.A.I.C.S.: 482111

Hobo Corp. (4)
64 Railroad St, Lincoln, NH 03251
Tel.: (603) 745-2135
Web Site: http://www.hoborr.com
Sales Range: $1-9.9 Million
Emp.: 50
Scenic & Sightseeing Transportation, Land
N.A.I.C.S.: 487110
Brenda Clark *(CEO)*

Subsidiary (Non-US):

Link Administration Holdings Limited (2)
Level 12 680 George Street, Sydney, 2000, NSW, Australia
Tel.: (61) 282807100
Web Site: www.linkgroup.com
Rev.: $900,525,327
Assets: $3,020,445,869
Liabilities: $1,864,164,022
Net Worth: $1,156,281,847
Earnings: ($51,772,224)
Emp.: 7,169
Fiscal Year-end: 06/30/2022
Holding Company
N.A.I.C.S.: 551112
Michael Carapiet *(Chm)*

Subsidiary (Non-US):

BCMGlobal ASI Limited (3)
Block C Maynooth Business Campus, County Kildare, Maynooth, Ireland
Tel.: (353) 16548800
Loan & Asset Management Services
N.A.I.C.S.: 531390

BCMGlobal Mortgage Services Limited (3)
Crown House Crown Street Ipswich DX 141240 13, Ipswich, United Kingdom
Tel.: (44) 1473283800
Loan & Asset Management Services
N.A.I.C.S.: 531390

FlexFront B.V. (3)
Bison track 3002 - B301, 3605 LT, Maarssen, Netherlands
Tel.: (31) 306005120
Web Site: https://www.flexfront.nl
Emp.: 130
Mortgage Loan Services
N.A.I.C.S.: 522310

Subsidiary (Domestic):

Link Advice Pty Limited (3)
Level 1 1A Homebush Bay Drive, Rhodes, 2138, NSW, Australia

Tel.: (61) 1300734007
Web Site: http://www.linkadvice.com.au
Financial Advice Services
N.A.I.C.S.: 523940
Duncan McPherson *(CEO)*

Subsidiary (Non-US):

Link Asset Services (France) SAS (3)
21 Boulevard Haussmann, 75009, Paris, France
Tel.: (33) 180956874
Financial Services
N.A.I.C.S.: 523999

Subsidiary (Domestic):

Link DigiCom Pty Limited (3)
Unit 1 15 Percy Street, Auburn, 2144, NSW, Australia
Tel.: (61) 290262400
Web Site: https://www.linkdigicom.com.au
Communication Service
N.A.I.C.S.: 517810

Link Digital Solutions Pty Limited (3)
Level 12 680 George Street, Sydney, 2000, NSW, Australia
Tel.: (61) 282806000
Web Site: https://www.linkdigitalsolutions.com
Software Development Services
N.A.I.C.S.: 541511

Link Fund Solutions Pty Limited (3)
Level 12 680 George Street, Sydney, 2000, NSW, Australia
Tel.: (61) 287671114
Web Site: http://www.linkfundsolutions.com
Administrative & Registry Management Services
N.A.I.C.S.: 541611

Subsidiary (Non-US):

Link Intime India Private Limited (3)
C 101 247 Park LBS Marg, Vikhroli West, Mumbai, 400083, India
Tel.: (91) 2249186000
Web Site: https://linkintime.co.in
Corporate Registry, Transfer & Other Related Investor Legal Services
N.A.I.C.S.: 541199

Subsidiary (Domestic):

TSR Consultants Private Limited (4)
C-101 1st Floor 247 Park Lal Bahadur Shastri Marg, Vikhroli, Mumbai, India
Tel.: (91) 2266568484
Web Site: https://www.tcplindia.co.in
Fixed Deposit Management Services
N.A.I.C.S.: 523999

Universal Capital Securities Pvt Ltd (4)
21 Shakti Niwas Opp Satya Saibaba Temple Mahakali Caves Road, Andheri (East), Mumbai, 400 023, India
Tel.: (91) 2228207203
Capital Market & Share Transfer Services
N.A.I.C.S.: 524292

Subsidiary (Non-US):

Link Market Services (Frankfurt) GmbH (3)
Mergenthalerallee 15-21, 65760, Eschborn, Germany
Tel.: (49) 61968870500
Web Site: https://www.linkmarketservices-ffm.de
Registry Management Services
N.A.I.C.S.: 541611

Link Market Services (Hong Kong) Pty Limited (3)
Suite 1601 16/F Central Tower 28 Queen's Road, Central, China (Hong Kong)
Tel.: (852) 37072600
Web Site: https://www.linkmarketservices.hk
Administrative & Registry Management Services
N.A.I.C.S.: 541611

Link Market Services GmbH (3)
Landshuter Allee 10, 80637, Munich, Germany
Tel.: (49) 89210270
Web Site: http://www.linkmarketservices.de

MITSUBISHI UFJ FINANCIAL GROUP, INC.

Mitsubishi UFJ Financial Group, Inc.—(Continued)
Registry Management Services
N.A.I.C.S.: 541611

Link Market Services Limited (3)
65 Gresham Street, London, EC2V 7NQ, United Kingdom
Tel.: (44) 2072047570
Registry Management Services
N.A.I.C.S.: 541611

Orient Capital Limited (3)
65 Gresham Street, London, EC2V 7NQ, United Kingdom
Tel.: (44) 2077767574
Web Site: https://www.orientcap.com
Investor Relation Services
N.A.I.C.S.: 561990
Liz Long (Head-Client Rels)

Subsidiary (Domestic):

Synchronised Software Pty Limited (3)
Tower 4 727 Collins Street, Docklands, 3008, VIC, Australia
Tel.: (61) 390705295
Web Site: https://www.syncsoft.com.au
Software Development Services
N.A.I.C.S.: 541511

Subsidiary (US):

MUFG Investor Services (US), LLC (2)
805 King Farm Blvd Ste 600, Rockville, MD 20850
Tel.: (240) 614-4800
Web Site: http://www.mufg-investorservices.com
Fiduciary & Fund Administration Services
N.A.I.C.S.: 523991

Subsidiary (Domestic):

MUFG Capital Analytics, LLC (3)
325 N St Paul St Ste 4700, Dallas, TX 75201
Tel.: (214) 765-1800
Investment Services
N.A.I.C.S.: 523150

Branch (US):

Mitsubishi UFJ Trust & Banking Corporation, New York Branch (2)
1221 Ave of the Americas 10th Fl, New York, NY 10020
Tel.: (212) 838-7700
Web Site: http://www.tr.mufg.jp
Banking Services
N.A.I.C.S.: 522299

Subsidiary (Non-US):

Mitsubishi UFJ Trust International Limited (2)
24 Lombard St, London, EC3V 9AJ, United Kingdom
Tel.: (44) 2079292866
Web Site: https://www.tr.mufg.jp
Sales Range: $75-99.9 Million
Emp.: 150
Banking Services
N.A.I.C.S.: 522210
Ray Paul Winters (CEO & Mng Dir)

Mitsubishi UFJ Trust Investment Technology Institute (1)
Mitsubishi UFJ Trust and Banking Corporation Bldg 22F 4-, Marunouchi 1-Chome Chiyoda-ku, Tokyo, 100-0005, Japan
Tel.: (81) 366657286
Web Site: https://www.mtec-institute.co.jp
Emp.: 46
Investment Management Service
N.A.I.C.S.: 523999

PT U Finance Indonesia (1)
Anz Tower 21 Floor Jalan Jenderal Sudirman Kav 33A, Jakarta, 10220, Indonesia
Tel.: (62) 215711109
Web Site: http://www.ufinance.co.id
Financial Management Services
N.A.I.C.S.: 523999

Ryoshin DC Card Company, Ltd. (1)
2-19-12 Shibuya, Tokyo, 151-0064, Japan
Tel.: (81) 334983591
Web Site: https://www.ryoshindc.co.jp
Investment Banking & Security Services
N.A.I.C.S.: 523150

The Master Trust Bank of Japan, Ltd. (1)
2-11-3 Hamamatsucho MTBJ Building, Minato-ku, Tokyo, 105-8579, Japan
Tel.: (81) 354035100
Web Site: https://www.mastertrust.co.jp
Commercial Banking Services
N.A.I.C.S.: 522110
Ken Iiyama (Mng Dir)

Tokyo Credit Services, Ltd. (1)
2-6-3 Hitotsubashi, Chiyoda-ku, Tokyo, 101-0003, Japan
Tel.: (81) 352757600
Web Site: https://www.tokyo-card.co.jp
Investment Banking & Securities Services
N.A.I.C.S.: 523150

MITSUBOSHI BELTING LTD.
4-1-21 Hamazoe-dori, Nagata-ku, Kobe, 653-0024, Japan
Tel.: (81) 786715071
Web Site: https://www.mitsuboshi.com
Year Founded: 1919
5192—(TKS)
Rev.: $555,332,540
Assets: $896,494,470
Liabilities: $247,081,800
Net Worth: $649,412,670
Earnings: $46,944,220
Emp.: 4,471
Fiscal Year-end: 03/31/24
Belts & Building Material Mfr
N.A.I.C.S.: 315250
Masayoshi Nakajima (Sr Mng Exec Officer)

Subsidiaries:

MBL (USA) Corporation (1)
601 Dayton Rd, Ottawa, IL 61350-9535
Tel.: (815) 434-1282
Web Site: http://www.mblusa.com
Polyurethane Rubber Mfr
N.A.I.C.S.: 326150

MBL Antriebstechnik Deutschland GmbH. (1)
Hansemannstrasse 63, 41468, Neuss, Germany
Tel.: (49) 2131740940
Web Site: https://www.mitsuboshi.de
Sales Range: $75-99.9 Million
Emp.: 20
Power Transmission Services
N.A.I.C.S.: 221121
Yoshinori Tsugawa (Gen Mgr)

MBL Shanghai International Trading Co., Ltd. (1)
F8 NO 601 Tianshan Road, Shanghai, 200383, China
Tel.: (86) 2132573802
Web Site: http://www.mitsuboshi.co.jp
Power Transmission Belt Mfr
N.A.I.C.S.: 326220

MOI Tech Hong Kong Ltd. (1)
Unit 3 20/F Kowloon Plaza 485 Castle Peak Road, 11, Wo Shing St Sakin, Kowloon, New Territories, China (Hong Kong)
Tel.: (852) 24035978
Web Site: http://www.mitsuboshi.com
Emp.: 64
Power Transmission Belt Mfr
N.A.I.C.S.: 326220

Mitsuboshi Belting Europe GmbH (1)
Hansemannstrasse 63, 41468, Neuss, Germany
Tel.: (49) 2131740940
Web Site: http://www.mitsuboshi.de
Power Transmission Belt Mfr
N.A.I.C.S.: 326220
Atsushi Morita (Mng Dir)

Mitsuboshi Belting Ltd. - Kobe Plant (1)
4-1-21 Hamazoe-dori, Nagata-ku, Kobe, 653-0024, Japan
Tel.: (81) 786715071
Web Site: http://www.mitsuboshi.co.jp
Conveyor Belts Mfr
N.A.I.C.S.: 326220

Mitsuboshi Belting Ltd. - Nagoya Plant (1)
1818 Ohaza-Nishinoshima, Komaki, 485-0077, Aichi, Japan
Tel.: (81) 568724121
Transmission Belt Mfr
N.A.I.C.S.: 326220

Mitsuboshi Belting Ltd. - Shiga Plant (1)
100-2 Terakubo Makino-cho, Takashima, 520-1834, Shiga, Japan
Tel.: (81) 740270133
Web Site: http://www.mitsuboshi.com
Power Transmission Belt Mfr
N.A.I.C.S.: 326220

Mitsuboshi Belting Ltd. - Shikoku Plant (1)
2893 Tsuda Tsuda-machi, Kagawa, 769-2401, Sanuki, Japan
Tel.: (81) 879423181
Web Site: http://www.mitsuboshi.com
Belts Mfr
N.A.I.C.S.: 316990

Mitsuboshi Belting Vietnam Co., Ltd. (1)
Room No 1511 15th Floor ICON4 Tower No 243A De La Thanh St, Dong Da Dist, Hanoi, Vietnam
Tel.: (84) 2437606625
Power Transmission Belt Mfr
N.A.I.C.S.: 326220

Mitsuboshi Belting-India Private Limited (1)
Plot No R 672 Rabale MIDC, TTC Industrial Area, Navi Mumbai, 400 701, Maharashtra, India
Tel.: (91) 2227600016
Power Transmission Belt Mfr
N.A.I.C.S.: 326220

Mitsuboshi Overseas Headquarters Private Limited (1)
14 Jurong Port Road, Singapore, 619091, Singapore
Tel.: (65) 68564360
Web Site: http://www.mitsuboshi.com
Sales Range: $50-74.9 Million
Emp.: 200
Rubber Belt Mfr
N.A.I.C.S.: 326220

Mitsuboshi Poland Sp. z o.o. (1)
Budynek B8 ul 3-go Maja 8, 05-800, Pruszkow, Masovian, Poland
Tel.: (48) 227383930
Sales Range: $25-49.9 Million
Emp.: 16
Industrial Belts Mfr
N.A.I.C.S.: 326220

P.T. Mitsuboshi Belting Indonesia (1)
Jl Industri Raya Blok D No 4, Pasir Jaya Jatiuwung, Tangerang, 15135, Banten, Indonesia
Tel.: (62) 215902070
Web Site: http://www.mitsuboshi-mbi.com
Industrial Belts Mfr
N.A.I.C.S.: 326220

P.T. Seiwa Indonesia (1)
JL Lombok I Blok M2-2 Kawasan Industri MM2100 Cikarang Barat, Bekasi, 17520, West Java, Indonesia
Tel.: (62) 218980324
Industrial Belt Mfr
N.A.I.C.S.: 333248

PT. Mitsuboshi Belting Sales Indonesia (1)
Wisma 77 Tower 1 Lantai 2 Jl Letnan Jenderal S Parman RT/RW 006/003, Kel Slipi Kec Palmerah, Jakarta Barat, 11410, Indonesia
Tel.: (62) 215363033
Power Transmission Belt Mfr
N.A.I.C.S.: 326220

Stars Technologies Industrial Limited (1)
64/40 Moo 4, Eastern Seaboard Industrial Estate Tambon Pluakdaeng Amphur Pluak-daeng, Rayong, 21140, Thailand
Tel.: (66) 38954738
Power Transmission Belt Mfr
N.A.I.C.S.: 326220

Suzhou Mitsuboshi Belting Co., Ltd. (1)
277 Liangang Road, Suzhou New District, Jiangsu, 215129, China
Tel.: (86) 51266658880
Power Transmission Belt Mfr
N.A.I.C.S.: 326220

MITSUBOSHI CO., LTD.
5F Eslead Building Honmachi 1-4-8 Honmachi, Chuo-ku, Osaka, 541-0053, Japan
Tel.: (81) 662618881
Web Site: https://www.kk-mitsuboshi.co.jp
5820—(TKS)
Rev.: $68,274,690
Assets: $83,999,880
Liabilities: $40,387,100
Net Worth: $43,612,780
Earnings: $813,030
Emp.: 159
Fiscal Year-end: 03/31/24
Electric Wire & Cable Mfr
N.A.I.C.S.: 335921
Ryoichi Kisoi (Pres)

Subsidiaries:

Mitsuboshi Philippines Corporation (1)
Lot11 Block12 First Cavite Industrial Estate Brgy Langkaan, Dasmarinas, 4114, Cavite, Philippines
Tel.: (63) 464020552
Electric Wire Mfr & Distr
N.A.I.C.S.: 335931
Mitsoboshi Laconico (Supvr-HR)

MITSUCHI CORPORATION
1203 Ushiyama-Cho, Kasugai, 486-0901, Aichi, Japan
Tel.: (81) 568356350
Web Site: https://www.mitsuchi.co.jp
Year Founded: 1963
3439—(TKS)
Rev.: $81,774,340
Assets: $102,319,000
Liabilities: $40,230,960
Net Worth: $62,088,040
Earnings: $2,606,180
Emp.: 513
Fiscal Year-end: 06/30/24
Automobile Fasteners Mfr & Sales
N.A.I.C.S.: 336390
Kazushi Nakamura (Pres)

Subsidiaries:

Mitsuchi Corporation of America (1)
190 Waldron Rd, La Vergne, TN 37086
Tel.: (615) 793-2552
Web Site: http://www.mitsuchi.co.jp
Emp.: 24
Pins & Fasteners Distr
N.A.I.C.S.: 423710

Mitsuchi Manufacturing, Inc (1)
1203 Ushiyama-cho, Moriyama-ku, Kasugai, 486-0901, Aichi, Japan
Tel.: (81) 568356350
Emp.: 60
Automobile Fasteners Mfr
N.A.I.C.S.: 336110

Mitsuchi Seisakusho Co., Ltd. (1)
159-3 Mukogayumi Iinan-cho, Matsusaka, 515-1412, Mie, Japan
Tel.: (81) 598322200
Web Site: http://www.mitsuchi.co.jp
Sales Range: $25-49.9 Million
Emp.: 60
Motor Vehicle Parts & Accessories Mfr
N.A.I.C.S.: 336390

Mitsuchi Suzhou Corporation (1)
Factory 158-7 Jingshajiang Road, Huqui District, Suzhou, 215151, Jiangsu, China
Tel.: (86) 5126 807 8826
Motor Vehicle Parts Mfr

AND PRIVATE COMPANIES — MITSUI & CO., LTD.

N.A.I.C.S.: 336390

Thai Mitchi Corporation Ltd. (1)
60/71 Moo 19 Phaholyothin Rd, Klong Nueng, Khlong Luang, 12120, Pathumthani, Thailand
Tel.: (66) 2 909 4880
Web Site: http://www.mitsuchi.co.jp
Sales Range: $50-74.9 Million
Motor Vehicle Parts & Accessories Mfr
N.A.I.C.S.: 336390

MITSUI & CO., LTD.
2-1 Otemachi 1-chome, Chiyoda-ku, Tokyo, 100-8631, Japan
Tel.: (81) 332851111   JP
Web Site: https://www.mitsui.com
Year Founded: 1947
MITSF—(OTCIQ)
Rev.: $88,077,866,620
Assets: $111,705,708,220
Liabilities: $60,346,384,990
Net Worth: $51,359,323,230
Earnings: $7,030,951,240
Emp.: 53,602
Fiscal Year-end: 03/31/24
Holding Company
N.A.I.C.S.: 551112
Tatsuo Yasunaga *(Chm)*

Subsidiaries:

ARAMARK Uniform Services Japan Corporation (1)
Tornare Nihonbashi Hamacho 8Floor 3-3-2 Nihonbashi Hamacho, Chuo-ku, Tokyo, 103-0007, Japan
Tel.: (81) 358470930
Web Site: https://www.aramark-uniform.co.jp
Emp.: 1,506
Uniform Rentals, Sales & Cleaning Services
N.A.I.C.S.: 812331
Akihiro Nishimura *(Pres)*

Accountable Healthcare Holdings Corp. (1)
999 Yamato Rd Ste 210, Boca Raton, FL 33431
Tel.: (561) 235-7810
Web Site: http://www.ahcstaff.com
Holding Company; Healthcare Staffing Solutions
N.A.I.C.S.: 551112
Jeff Yesner *(CFO)*

Holding (Domestic):

Accountable Healthcare Staffing, Inc. - Phoenix (2)
3800 N Central Ave Ste 800, Phoenix, AZ 85012
Tel.: (480) 499-4501
Web Site: http://www.ahcstaff.com
Healthcare Staffing Services
N.A.I.C.S.: 621610

Aglobis AG (1)
Grienbachstrasse 17, 6300, Zug, Switzerland
Tel.: (41) 417683700
Web Site: https://www.aglobis.com
Chemical Products Distr
N.A.I.C.S.: 424690
Beat Heller *(CEO)*

Aim Services Co., Ltd. (1)
Ark Hills Front Tower 2-23-1, Akasaka Minato-ku, Tokyo, 107-0052, Japan   (50%)
Tel.: (81) 362357500
Web Site: http://www.aimservices.co.jp
Sales Range: $10-24.9 Million
Emp.: 200
Food & Support Services; Joint Venture by Aramark Corporation & by Mitsui & Co., Ltd
N.A.I.C.S.: 445132

Atlatec Holdings, S.A. de C.V. (1)
Privada San Alberto 301 Residencial Santa Barbara, Garza Garcia, 66266, Mexico
Tel.: (52) 81 8 133 3200
Investment Management Service
N.A.I.C.S.: 523999

B Food Science Co., Ltd. (1)
17th Floor Tokyo Sankei Bldg 1-7-2 Otemachi, Chiyoda-ku, Tokyo, 100-0004, Japan
Tel.: (81) 362022131
Web Site: http://www.bfsci.co.jp
Emp.: 239
Chemical Product Mfr & Distr
N.A.I.C.S.: 325998
Masami Yokoyama *(Pres & CEO)*

BUSSAN REAL ESTATE CO., LTD. (1)
1-1-15 Nishishimbashi Bussan Bldg, Minato-Ku, Tokyo, 105-0003, Japan
Tel.: (81) 335031221
Web Site: http://www.mitsui.com
Real Estate Sales, Leasing & Management Development Services
N.A.I.C.S.: 531390
Masami Iijima *(Pres & CEO)*

Bangkok Coil Center Co., Ltd. (1)
102/1 102/3 102/4 102/5 Moo 1 Wat Daowadoeng Road Tambol Bangkadi, Mueang Pathum Thani, Pathumthani, 12000, Thailand
Tel.: (66) 20216000
Web Site: http://www.bcc.co.th
Rolled Steel Coil & Sheet Mfr
N.A.I.C.S.: 331221
Yoshihiro Ito *(Pres)*

Plant (Domestic):

Bangkok Coil Center Co., Ltd. - Amata Nakorn Factory (2)
700/508 M 2 T Bankao, A Panthong, Chon Buri, 20160, Thailand
Tel.: (66) 3845 4730
Rolled Steel Coil Mfr
N.A.I.C.S.: 331221
Yoshihiro Ito *(Pres)*

Bussan Food Materials Co., Ltd. (1)
2-7-8 Nihonbashibakurocho, Chuo-ku, Tokyo, 103-0002, Japan
Tel.: (81) 356526725
Web Site: http://www.tkj.co.jp
Emp.: 100
Fruit Juice Product Mfr & Distr
N.A.I.C.S.: 311411
Hiroshi Fujii *(Pres & CEO)*

Bussan Logistics Solutions Co., Ltd. (1)
1-1-1 Nishi-Shimbashi Hibiya Fort Tower 20F, Minato-ku, Tokyo, 105-0003, Japan   (100%)
Tel.: (81) 36 775 7412
Web Site: https://www.blsc.biz
Emp.: 1,581
Logistics Consulting Servies
N.A.I.C.S.: 541614
Sugiyama Yasushi *(Pres & CEO)*

Bussan Sumisho Carbon Energy Co., Ltd. (1)
8F Glass City Koraku 1-1-7 Koraku, Bunkyo-ku, Tokyo, 112-0004, Japan
Tel.: (81) 358042050
Web Site: http://www.bscarbon.co.jp
Coal Distr
N.A.I.C.S.: 423520
Jun Miyamoto *(Pres & CEO)*

Coral Bay Nickel Corporation (1)
Rio Tuba, Batarasa, Palawan, Philippines
Tel.: (63) 27501536
Web Site: http://www.smm.co.jp
Sales Range: $50-74.9 Million
Emp.: 200
Nickel & Cobalt Products Mfr; Joint Venture Owned 54% by Sumitomo Metal Mining Co., Ltd. & 18% by Mitsui & Co., Ltd. & 18% by Nissho Iwai Corp. & 10% by Rio Tuba Nickel Mining Corp.
N.A.I.C.S.: 331491

Daiichi Tanker Co., Ltd. (1)
PMO Kandatsukasamachi 6F 2-8-1 Kandatsukasamachi, Chiyoda-ku, Tokyo, 101-0048, Japan
Tel.: (81) 35 209 1181
Web Site: https://www.ititan.co.jp
Cargo Transportation Services
N.A.I.C.S.: 484110
Tomohisa Kitamura *(Pres)*

Deeside Power (UK) Limited (1)
Weighbridge Road Zone 4, Deeside Industrial Park, Deeside, CH5 2UL, Flintshire, United Kingdom   (25%)
Tel.: (44) 1244286000
Web Site: http://www.deesidepower.com
Sales Range: $50-74.9 Million
Emp.: 60
Electric Power Generator & Distr
N.A.I.C.S.: 221112

Euro-Mit Staal B.V. (1)
Duitslandweg 7, 4389 PJ, Ritthem, Netherlands
Tel.: (31) 118422500
Web Site: http://www.euro-mit-staal.com
Electrical Steel Coil Distr
N.A.I.C.S.: 423690
Mariko Hara *(Mng Dir)*

Fertilizantes Mitsui S.A. Industria e Comercio (1)
Estacao Bauxita S/N Bauxita, Pocos de Caldas, 37701-970, Brazil
Tel.: (55) 35 3729 1800
Fertilizer Mfr & Distr
N.A.I.C.S.: 325314

GRI Renewable Industries, S.L. (1)
Ombu Street 3 Floor 2 and 11, 28045, Madrid, Spain
Tel.: (34) 913791900
Web Site: http://www.gri.com.es
Emp.: 3,500
Wind Turbine Mfr
N.A.I.C.S.: 333611
Andre Aparicio *(Mng Dir & COO)*

HANAE MORI Associates Co., Ltd (1)
16F Roppongi Hills North Tower 2-31 Roppongi 6-chome, Minato-ku, Tokyo, 106-0032, Japan
Tel.: (81) 3 5413 6590
Web Site: http://www.hanae-mori.com
Emp.: 1
Clothing Apparel & Accessories Mfr
N.A.I.C.S.: 315990
Tsuro Sato *(Pres & CEO)*

HOUSE DEPOT PARTNERS CO., LTD. (1)
1-1-8 Nihonbashihoncho 9th floor Nihonbashihoncho 1-chome Building, Chuo-Ku, Tokyo, 103-0023, Japan
Tel.: (81) 335171100
Web Site: http://www.housedepot-p.co.jp
Home Loan Mortgage Services
N.A.I.C.S.: 522299

Hans Kissle Company, LLC (1)
9 Creek Brook Dr, Haverhill, MA 01832   (80%)
Tel.: (978) 556-4500
Web Site: http://www.hanskissle.com
Perishable Prepared Food Mfr
N.A.I.C.S.: 311991

Human Associates Holdings, Inc. (1)
1-3-3 Minamiaoyama, Minato-Ku, Tokyo, 107-0062, Japan
Tel.: (81) 357652231
Web Site: http://www.humanassociates.com
Rev.: $24,122,560
Assets: $24,016,080
Liabilities: $13,687,520
Net Worth: $10,328,560
Earnings: ($1,026,080)
Fiscal Year-end: 03/31/2021
Holding Company
N.A.I.C.S.: 551112
Akihabe Watanabe *(Chm & Pres)*

ITC Rubis Terminal Antwerp N.V. (1)
Blikken Haven 1662, Doel, 9130, Beveren, Belgium
Tel.: (32) 32100900
Web Site: http://www.itcrubis.com
Liquefied Gas & Petroleum Product Distr
N.A.I.C.S.: 424710
Filip Masquillier *(CEO)*

Japan Alternative Investment Co., Ltd. (1)
19th Floor KDDI Otemachi Bldg 1-8-1 Otemachi, Chiyoda-ku, Tokyo, 100-0004, Japan
Tel.: (81) 3 3510 0961
Web Site: http://www.j-alternative.co.jp
Sales Range: $50-74.9 Million
Emp.: 43
Investment Management Service
N.A.I.C.S.: 523999
Hiroyuki Kobayashi *(CFO, Chief Admin Officer & Mng Dir)*

Joy Global (Peru) S.A.C. (1)
Av Jorge Basadre 592, San Isidro, Lima, 27, Peru   (60%)
Tel.: (51) 14406541
Mining Machinery & Equipment Mfr
N.A.I.C.S.: 333131

Komatsu-Mitsui Maquinarias Peru S.A. (1)
Calle Dean Valdivia 148 Pisos 13-14, San Isidro, Lima, Peru
Tel.: (51) 16158400
Web Site: http://www.kmmp.com.pe
Construction Machinery Distr
N.A.I.C.S.: 423810

MBK Nigeria Ltd. (1)
2 Fl Plot 1261 Adeola Hopewell St, PO Box 2764, Victoria Island, Lagos, Nigeria   (100%)
Tel.: (234) 12612341
Sales Range: $50-74.9 Million
Emp.: 10
Trading & Investments
N.A.I.C.S.: 425120

MIT POWER CANADA LP INC. (1)
20 Adelaide St E Suite 1400, Toronto, M5C 2T6, ON, Canada
Tel.: (416) 362-0978
Investment Management Service
N.A.I.C.S.: 523999

MITSUI & CO., (MIDDLE EAST) B.S.C.(c) (1)
Al-Rossais Tower Office No 92 9th Floor Bldg No 283 Road 1704, PO Box 20262, Diplomatic Area 317, Manama, 20262, Bahrain
Tel.: (973) 17540340
Sales Range: $25-49.9 Million
Emp.: 2
Power Plant Construction Engineering Services
N.A.I.C.S.: 237130

MITSUI BUSSAN KOZAI HANBAI CO., LTD. (1)
1-5-7 Kameido Koto, Tokyo, 136-0071, Japan
Tel.: (81) 3 5628 1820
Web Site: http://www.mbkkh.co.jp
Steel Product Distr
N.A.I.C.S.: 423510

MITSUI BUSSAN MACHINE TEC Co., Ltd. (1)
Room 1208 Building B Far East International Plaza 317 Xianxia Road, Shanghai, 200051, China
Tel.: (86) 21 6235 0101
Web Site: http://www.mmknet.com
Sales Range: $75-99.9 Million
Emp.: 118
Machine Tool Distr
N.A.I.C.S.: 423830
Atsushi Tanimoto *(Pres)*

Subsidiary (Non-US):

MMK MACHINERY (THAILAND) CO., LTD. (2)
173/18 Asia Centre 17th Floor South Sathorn Road, Thungmahamek Sathorn, Bangkok, 10120, Thailand
Tel.: (66) 2163 6310
Web Site: http://www.mmknet.com
Industrial Machinery Distr
N.A.I.C.S.: 423830

MITSUI BUSSAN METALS CO., LTD. (1)
19 20F Yaesu First Financial Building 3-7 Yaesu 1-chome, Chuuo-ku, Tokyo, 103-0028, Japan
Tel.: (81) 3 5202 3200
Web Site: http://www.mitsui-metals.com
Rev.: $2,469,280,000
Emp.: 240
Non Ferrous Metal Products Mfr & Distr
N.A.I.C.S.: 331491
Masahiro Yamazawa *(Auditor)*

Division (Domestic):

MITSUI BUSSAN METALS CO., LTD. - CHUBU NON-FERROUS METALS SALES DIVISION (2)

MITSUI & CO., LTD.

Mitsui & Co., Ltd.—(Continued)

5F Reception 8F Nagoya Mitsui Bussan Bldg 16-21 Meieki Minami 1-chome, Nakamura-Ku, Nagoya, 450-0003, Japan
Tel.: (81) 52 584 2307
Web Site: http://www.mitsui-metals.com
Sales Range: $25-49.9 Million
Emp.: 10
Nonferrous Metal Products Mfr
N.A.I.C.S.: 331410
Masaki Nagahama (Branch Mgr)

MITSUI BUSSAN METALS CO., LTD. - CHUGOKU AND SHIKOKU BUSINESS DIVISION
14F Hiroshima Train Vert Bldg 2-22 Kamiyacho 1-chome, Naka-ku, Hiroshima, 730-0031, Japan
Tel.: (81) 82 246 2119
Seal Products Distr
N.A.I.C.S.: 423510

MITSUI BUSSAN METALS CO., LTD. - HOKKAIDO BUSINESS DIVISION (2)
11F Nippon Life Sapporo Bldg 1-1 Nishi 4-chome Kita-3-jo, Chuo-ku, Sapporo, 060-0003, Hokkaido, Japan
Tel.: (81) 11 213 3224
Metal Products Mfr
N.A.I.C.S.: 332999

MITSUI BUSSAN METALS CO., LTD. - HOKURIKU BUSINESS DIVISION (2)
10F Urban-place Bldg 18-7 Ushijimacho, Sakurabashidori, Toyama, 930-0858, Japan
Tel.: (81) 76 445 2720
Web Site: http://www.mitsui-metals.com
Metal Products Mfr
N.A.I.C.S.: 332999

Unit (Domestic):

MITSUI BUSSAN METALS CO., LTD. - IRON MAKING RAW MATERIALS UNIT (2)
22F Mitsui & Co Bldg 2-1 Ohtemachi 1-chome, Chiyoda-ku, Tokyo, 100-0004, Japan
Tel.: (81) 3 3285 2326
Web Site: http://www.mitsui-metals.com
Emp.: 3
Metal Raw Material Mfr
N.A.I.C.S.: 331491
Masaaki Shibata (Gen Mgr)

Division (Domestic):

MITSUI BUSSAN METALS CO., LTD. - IRON ORE DIVISION (3)
22F Mitsui & Co Bldg 2-1 Ohtemachi 1-chome, Chiyoda-ku, Tokyo, 100-0004, Japan
Tel.: (81) 33 285 2326
Web Site: http://www.mitsui-metals.com
Sales Range: $50-74.9 Million
Emp.: 2
Iron Ore Mining Services
N.A.I.C.S.: 212210
Isao Sato (Gen Mgr)

MITSUI BUSSAN METALS CO., LTD. - METALLURGICAL COAL DIVISION (3)
22F Mitsui & Co Bldg 2-1 Ohtemachi 1-chome Cheodac, Chiyoda-ku, Tokyo, 100-0004, Japan
Tel.: (81) 3 3285 2262
Sales Range: $100-124.9 Million
Metallurgical Coke Mfr
N.A.I.C.S.: 331110

Division (Domestic):

MITSUI BUSSAN METALS CO., LTD. - KYUSHU BUSINESS DIVISION (2)
8F Hakata Mitsui Bldg No 2 1-35 Tenyamachi Hakata-ku, Fukuoka, 812-0025, Japan
Tel.: (81) 92 271 8180
Metal Product Whslr
N.A.I.C.S.: 423510

MITSUI BUSSAN METALS CO., LTD. - NIIGATA BUSINESS DIVISION (2)
4F Coi Niigata Bldg 4-2 1-chome Higashi-Odori, Chuo-ku, Niigata, 950-0087, Japan
Tel.: (81) 25 246 8616
Metal Product Distr
N.A.I.C.S.: 423510

MITSUI BUSSAN METALS CO., LTD. - OSAKA NON-FERROUS METALS SALES DIVISION (2)
17F Osaka Mitsui Bussan Bldg 3-33 Nakanoshima 2-chome, Kita-ku, Osaka, 530-0005, Japan
Tel.: (81) 6 6226 3242
Non Ferrous Metal Mfr
N.A.I.C.S.: 331491

MITSUI BUSSAN METALS CO., LTD. - OSAKA SCRAP & FERRO ALLOY DIVISION (2)
17F Osaka Mitsui Bussan Bldg 3-33 Nakanoshima 2-chome, Kita-ku, Osaka, 530-0005, Japan
Tel.: (81) 6 6226 9620
Web Site: http://www.mitsui-metals.com
Sales Range: $25-49.9 Million
Emp.: 20
Scrap & Ferrous Alloy Metal Mfr
N.A.I.C.S.: 331110

Unit (Domestic):

Mitsui Bussan Metals Co., Ltd.- Sakai Works (2)
6 Ohamanishimachi, Sakai-ku, Sakai, 590-0977, Osaka, Japan
Tel.: (81) 722218567
Web Site: https://www.mitsui-metals.com
Sales Range: $25-49.9 Million
Emp.: 30
Metal Products Mfr
N.A.I.C.S.: 332999

MITSUI BUSSAN PACKAGING CO., LTD (1)
3-3-3 Akasaka, Minato-ku, Tokyo, 107-0052, Japan
Tel.: (81) 3 3286 6300
Web Site: https://www.mbk-packaging.com
Emp.: 120
Packaging Paper Products Mfr
N.A.I.C.S.: 322220
Aki Hiraga (Pres & CEO)

MITSUI BUSSAN STEEL TRADE CO., LTD. (1)
11 F Marunouchi Trust Tower North 1-8-1 Marunouchi, Chiyoda-Ku, Tokyo, 100-0005, Japan
Tel.: (81) 3 3286 7300
Web Site: http://www.m-s-t.biz
Sales Range: $25-49.9 Million
Emp.: 44
Steel Product Distr
N.A.I.C.S.: 423510
Ichizo Kutsukake (Pres)

MITSUI BUSSAN TECHNO PRODUCTS CO., LTD. (1)
Osaka Mitsui-Bussan Bldg 3-33 Nakanoshima 2-chome, Kita-ku, Osaka, 530-0005, Japan
Tel.: (81) 662263111
Web Site: http://www.mitsuibussan-technoproducts.com
Sales Range: $50-74.9 Million
Emp.: 90
Functional Textile & Industrial Materials Distr
N.A.I.C.S.: 424310
Tetsuo Nonomura (Pres & CEO)

MRCE Dispolok GmbH (1)
Landsberger Strasse 290, Munich, D-80687, Germany
Tel.: (49) 89818867100
Web Site: http://www.dispolok.com
Sales Range: $50-74.9 Million
Emp.: 29
Locomotive Leasing Services
N.A.I.C.S.: 532411
Dirk Steffes (COO & Mng Dir)

Micro Biopharm Japan Co., Ltd. (1)
1-3-1 Kyobashi, Chuo-ku, Tokyo, 104-0031, Japan
Tel.: (81) 36 265 1761
Web Site: https://www.microbiopharm.com
Emp.: 344
Pharmaceuticals Product Mfr
N.A.I.C.S.: 325412

Masanobu Suzuki (Pres)

Subsidiary (Domestic):

MBJ Chemical Corporation (2)
3-3-6 Nihombashihoncho, Chuo-Ku, Tokyo, 103-0023, Japan
Tel.: (81) 3 3510 6810
Web Site: http://www.microbiopharm.com
Chemical Products Mfr
N.A.I.C.S.: 325998

Subsidiary (Non-US):

Shenzhen Main Luck Pharmaceuticals Inc. (2)
Main Luck Building Lanzhu Road East, Pingshan District, Shenzhen, 518029, China
Tel.: (86) 7552 584 3999
Web Site: https://www.wanle.com.cn
Pharmaceuticals Product Mfr
N.A.I.C.S.: 325412
Guo Caiwang (Gen Mgr)

Subsidiary (Domestic):

Shunan Finechem Incorporated (2)
4980 Kaiseicho, Shunan, 746-0006, Yamaguchi, Japan
Tel.: (81) 834 63 4845
Web Site: http://www.microbiopharm.com
Emp.: 4
Chemical Products Mfr
N.A.I.C.S.: 325998
Takeshi Sonoba (Mgr)

Mitsiam International, Ltd. (1)
15th - 17th Floor Sathorn City Tower 175 South Sathorn Road, PO Box 870, Tungmahamek Sathorn, Bangkok, 10120, Thailand
Tel.: (66) 23442222
Web Site: http://www.mitsui.co
Sales Range: $200-249.9 Million
Emp.: 300
Head Office; General Import & Export Trading
N.A.I.C.S.: 212210
Takeo Kato (Pres)

Mitsiam Motors Co., Ltd. (1)
88 Moo 5 Bangna-Trad Rd Km 56 Tambon Klong-Tamru, Amphoe Mueang, Chon Buri, 20000, Thailand
Tel.: (66) 2784 5256
Web Site: http://www.mitsiammotors.co.th
Sales Range: $75-99.9 Million
Emp.: 25
Bus & Truck Distr
N.A.I.C.S.: 423110
Komut Kasettham (Mgr-Sls)

Mitsui & Co. (Argentina) S.A. (1)
710 Bouchard Piso 12, C1106ABL, Buenos Aires, Argentina
Tel.: (54) 1143174900
International Trade Financing Services
N.A.I.C.S.: 522299

Mitsui & Co. (Asia Pacific) Pte. Ltd. (1)
12 Marina View 31-01 Asia Square Tower 2, Singapore, 018961, Singapore
Tel.: (65) 63213111
International Trade Financing Services
N.A.I.C.S.: 522299
Koji Nagatomi (Pres & CEO)

Subsidiary (Non-US):

ACI Motors Limited (2)
ACI Centre 245, Tejgaon Industrial Area, Dhaka, 1208, Bangladesh
Tel.: (880) 16533
Web Site: https://acimotors-bd.com
Farm Machinery Distr
N.A.I.C.S.: 423820

Mitsui & Co. (Asia Pacific) Pte. Ltd. - Kuala Lumpur Branch (1)
Level 29 Menara Hap Seng 2 Plaza Hap Seng No 1 Jalan P Ramlee, 50250, Kuala Lumpur, Malaysia
Tel.: (60) 321168000
Web Site: http://www.mitsui.com
Sales Range: $100-124.9 Million
Emp.: 200
General Import & Export Trading
N.A.I.C.S.: 212210

INTERNATIONAL PUBLIC

Mitsui & Co. (Asia Pacific) Pte. Ltd. - Manila Branch (1)
36th Floor GT Tower International 6815 Ayala Avenue, PO Box 2116, Bel-Air, Makati, 1209, Philippines
Tel.: (63) 288197777
Web Site: http://www.mitsui.com
Sales Range: $50-74.9 Million
Emp.: 100
General Import & Export Trading Company
N.A.I.C.S.: 425120

Mitsui & Co. (Australia) Ltd. (1)
Level 15 120 Collins Street, Melbourne, 3000, VIC, Australia
Tel.: (61) 396058800
Web Site: http://www.mitsui.com
Sales Range: $50-74.9 Million
Trading & Investments
N.A.I.C.S.: 425120
Masato Sugahara (CEO & Chm)

Branch (Domestic):

Mitsui & Co. (Australia) Ltd. (2)
Level 24 480 Queen Street, Brisbane, 4000, QLD, Australia
Tel.: (61) 730328800
Web Site: http://www.mitsui.com.au
Sales Range: $50-74.9 Million
Emp.: 10
Trading & Investments
N.A.I.C.S.: 425120

Mitsui & Co. (Australia) Ltd. (2)
Level 16 Exchange Tower 2 The Esplanade, Number 2 The Esplanade, Perth, 6000, WA, Australia
Tel.: (61) 894762333
Web Site: http://www.mitsui.com.au
Sales Range: $50-74.9 Million
Emp.: 25
Trading & Investments
N.A.I.C.S.: 425120

Mitsui & Co. (Australia) Ltd. (2)
Suite 37 02 Level 37 100 Miller Street, Sydney, 2000, NSW, Australia
Tel.: (61) 292569500
Web Site: http://www.mitsui.com.au
Sales Range: $25-49.9 Million
Emp.: 12
Metal Products Mfr
N.A.I.C.S.: 332999

Subsidiary (Domestic):

Mitsui Bussan Woodchip Oceania Pty. Ltd. (2)
Level 40 120 Collins Street, Melbourne, 3000, VIC, Australia
Tel.: (61) 3 9605 8800
Web Site: http://www.mitsui.com.au
Sales Range: $25-49.9 Million
Emp.: 9
Woodchips Whslr
N.A.I.C.S.: 423310
Lachlan Cook (Mgr-Dev)

Mitsui & Co. (Beijing), Ltd. (1)
34th Fl CWTC Tower 1 1 Jianguomenwai St, Beijing, 100004, China
Tel.: (86) 65053331
Sales Range: $100-124.9 Million
Emp.: 110
General Import & Export Trading
N.A.I.C.S.: 212210

Mitsui & Co. (Brasil) S.A. (1)
Avenida Paulista 1842 23 andar Edificio Cetenco Plaza, Torre Norte, Sao Paulo, 01310-923, Brazil (100%)
Tel.: (55) 1133719700
Web Site: http://www.mitsui.com
Emp.: 110
General Import & Export Trading
N.A.I.C.S.: 522299
Yuki Kodera (Pres)

Branch (Domestic):

Mitsui & Co. (Brasil) S.A. (2)
Ave do Contorno 6 321 7 andar Edificio Concorde, Savassi, Belo Horizonte, 30110-039, MG, Brazil
Tel.: (55) 3132841250
Web Site: http://www.mitsuibr.com.br
General Import & Export Trading

AND PRIVATE COMPANIES

MITSUI & CO., LTD.

N.A.I.C.S.: 212210

Mitsui & Co. (Brasil) S.A. (2)
Praia do Flamengo 200 14 andar Flamengo, Rio de Janeiro, 22210-901, RJ, Brazil (100%)
Tel.: (55) 2132359700
Web Site: http://www.mitsui.com
Sales Range: $25-49.9 Million
Emp.: 45
Global Business Investments
N.A.I.C.S.: 425120
Toshiya Asahi *(VP-Brazil)*

Mitsui & Co. (Canada) (1)
800 Rene Levesque W Ste 1520, Montreal, H3B 1X9, QC, Canada (100%)
Tel.: (514) 866-4321
Web Site: http://www.mitsui.com
Sales Range: $50-74.9 Million
Emp.: 3
Import & Export Trading of Metals, Machinery, Chemicals, Foodstuffs & Other Goods
N.A.I.C.S.: 423830

Mitsui & Co. (Canada) (1)
Suite 3200 Four Bentall Centre 1055 Dunsmuir Street, PO Box 49046, Vancouver, V7X 1E6, BC, Canada
Tel.: (604) 331-3100
Web Site: http://www.mitsui.com
Sales Range: $25-49.9 Million
Emp.: 12
Import & Export Trading of Metals, Machinery, Textiles, Chemicals & Other Goods
N.A.I.C.S.: 423830
Fumiaki Miyamoto *(Pres)*

Mitsui & Co. (Canada) (1)
Suite 2100 Dome Tower 333 - 7th Avenue SW, Calgary, T2P 2Z1, AB, Canada (100%)
Tel.: (403) 264-3571
Web Site: http://www.mitsui.com
Sales Range: $25-49.9 Million
Emp.: 14
Import & Export Trading in Metals, Machinery, Textiles & Other Goods
N.A.I.C.S.: 423830

Mitsui & Co. (Canada) Ltd. (1)
TD Bank Tower 66 Wellington Street West Suite 3510, PO Box 306, Toronto, M5K 1K2, ON, Canada (100%)
Tel.: (416) 365-3800
Web Site: http://www.mitsui.com
Sales Range: $50-74.9 Million
Emp.: 62
Import & Export Trading of Metals, Machinery, Textiles, Foodstuffs & Other Goods
N.A.I.C.S.: 423830

Mitsui & Co. (Chile) Ltda. (1)
Av Andres Bello 2711, Las Condes, Santiago, Chile
Tel.: (56) 22906200
International Trade Financing Services
N.A.I.C.S.: 522299
Yoshinori Takase *(Pres)*

Mitsui & Co. (Colombia) Ltda. (1)
Carrera 7 No 71-52 Torre A Piso 13 Oficina 1302, Bogota, 110111, Colombia
Tel.: (57) 13123088
International Trade Financing Services
N.A.I.C.S.: 522299

Mitsui & Co. (Guangdong) Ltd. (1)
17th Floor No 8 Zhujiang West Road, Tianhe District, Guangzhou, Guangdong, China
Tel.: (86) 20 3813 1888
Sales Range: $50-74.9 Million
Emp.: 35
General Import & Export Trading
N.A.I.C.S.: 212210

Mitsui & Co. (Italia) S.p.A. (1)
Piazza del Liberty 2, 20121, Milan, Italy
Tel.: (39) 0262231
Web Site: http://www.mitsui.com
Sales Range: $250-299.9 Million
Emp.: 43
Textiles, Clothing, Chemical Products, Plastic Products, Iron Products, Steel Products, Metals & Jewelry Importer & Exporter
N.A.I.C.S.: 425120

Mitsui & Co. (Malaysia) Sdn. Bhd. (1)
Level 28 Menara Hap Seng 2 Plaza Hap Seng No 1 Jalan P Ramlee, 50250, Kuala Lumpur, Malaysia
Tel.: (60) 321168000
International Trade Financing Services
N.A.I.C.S.: 522299

Mitsui & Co. (N.Z.) Ltd. (1)
Level 17 55 Shortland Street, PO Box 6141, Auckland, 1010, New Zealand (100%)
Tel.: (64) 93033639
Web Site: http://www.mitsui.com
Sales Range: $100-124.9 Million
Emp.: 12
Trading & Investments
N.A.I.C.S.: 522299
Masato Sugahara *(Chm)*

Mitsui & Co. (Peru) S.A. (1)
Av Javier Prado Este 444 Torre Prado Oficina 701, San Isidro, Lima, Peru
Tel.: (51) 12211040
International Trade Financing Services
N.A.I.C.S.: 522299

Mitsui & Co. (Shanghai) Ltd. (1)
40-41st Floor Shanghai World Financial Center No 100 Century Avenue, Pudong New Area, Shanghai, 200120, China
Tel.: (86) 213 850 0500
Web Site: https://www.mitsui.com
Electronic Parts & Equipment Distr
N.A.I.C.S.: 423690
Nobuhiro Shimizu *(Gen Mgr)*

Mitsui & Co. (Taiwan), Ltd. (1)
21st Fl No 97 SEC 2 Tun Hua S Rd, Taipei, 106, Taiwan (100%)
Tel.: (886) 223262543
Web Site: https://www.mitsui.com
Sales Range: $100-124.9 Million
Emp.: 146
General Import & Export Trading
N.A.I.C.S.: 212210

Branch (Domestic):

Mitsui & Co. (Taiwan), Ltd. (2)
14th Fl C Room Cathay Life Chung Cheng Bldg No 2 Chung Cheng 3 Road, Kaohsiung, 80027, Taiwan (100%)
Tel.: (886) 72132888
Web Site: http://www.mitsui.com
Sales Range: $50-74.9 Million
Emp.: 20
General Import & Export Trading Company
N.A.I.C.S.: 212210
Tomofumi Osaki *(Chm & CEO)*

Mitsui & Co. (Thailand) Ltd. (1)
15th - 17th Floor Sathorn City Tower 175 South Sathorn Road, PO Box 865, Tungmahamek Sathorn, Bangkok, 10120, Thailand
Tel.: (66) 23442222
Web Site: http://www.mitsui.co.jp
Sales Range: $100-124.9 Million
Emp.: 200
General Import & Export Trading
N.A.I.C.S.: 212210
Takeo Kato *(Pres)*

Mitsui & Co. (Tianjin) Ltd. (1)
Tianjin International Building 2410A 75 Nanjing Road, Tianjin, 300050, China
Tel.: (86) 2258095678
Web Site: http://www.mitsui.co.jp
Sales Range: $50-74.9 Million
Emp.: 14
General Import & Export Trading
N.A.I.C.S.: 212210

Mitsui & Co. (Turkey) Ltd. (1)
Is Kuleleri Kule 2 Kat 7 4 Levent, PO Box 212, Sisli, 34330, Istanbul, Turkiye
Tel.: (90) 212 319 4000
Sales Range: $25-49.9 Million
Emp.: 2
Chemical Products Distr
N.A.I.C.S.: 424690
Takeshi Hokari *(Gen Mgr)*

Mitsui & Co. (U.S.A.), Inc. (1)
200 Park Ave, New York, NY 10166-0005 (100%)
Tel.: (212) 878-4000
Web Site: https://www.mitsui.com
Sales Range: $5-14.9 Billion
Emp.: 349
Investment

N.A.I.C.S.: 523999
Kota Odagiri *(Sr VP)*

Joint Venture (Domestic):

Advanced Composites, Inc. (2)
1062 S 4th Ave, Sidney, OH 45365
Tel.: (937) 575-9800
Web Site: https://www.advcmp.com
Sales Range: $100-124.9 Million
Polypropylene Compounds Mfr & Sales; Owned 62.8% by Mitsui Chemicals America, Inc., 27% by Mitsui & Co., Ltd. & 10.2% by Marubeni America Corporation
N.A.I.C.S.: 325998

Subsidiary (Non-US):

Advanced Composites Mexicana S.A. de C.V. (3)
Avenida Japon 306 Parque Industrial San Francisco, San Francisco de los Romo, 20303, Aguascalientes, Mexico
Tel.: (52) 4499254010
Web Site: https://www.acpmex.com
Polypropylene Compounds Mfr & Sales
N.A.I.C.S.: 325998

Subsidiary (Domestic):

Certis USA LLC (2)
9145 Guilford Rd Ste 175, Columbia, MD 21046 (100%)
Tel.: (301) 604-7340
Web Site: http://www.certisusa.com
Sales Range: $50-74.9 Million
Emp.: 100
Mfr & Developer of Pest Control & Crop Protection Compounds
N.A.I.C.S.: 424910
Remi Lohse *(Mgr-Sls-Specialty Ag-Southwest)*

Game Changer Holdings Inc. (2)
200 Park Ave Fl 36, New York, NY 10166-0005
Tel.: (212) 878-4295
Investment Management Service
N.A.I.C.S.: 523999

Hydro Capital Corporation (2)
200 Park Ave Fl 36, New York, NY 10166
Tel.: (212) 682-5005
Sales Range: $50-74.9 Million
Emp.: 3
Investment Management Service
N.A.I.C.S.: 523999
Stephen Zoota *(Mng Dir)*

Branch (Domestic):

Mitsui & Company (U.S.A.), Inc. - Seattle Office (2)
1201 3rd Ave Ste 1560, Seattle, WA 98101-3025
Tel.: (206) 223-5604
Web Site: http://www.mitsui.com
Business Investment, Project Development & Management
N.A.I.C.S.: 523940

Subsidiary (Domestic):

Mitsui E&P USA LLC (2)
1300 Post Oak Blvd Ste 1800, Houston, TX 77056
Tel.: (713) 960-0023
Sales Range: $25-49.9 Million
Emp.: 40
Oil & Gas Exploration Services
N.A.I.C.S.: 213112
Frank Saenz *(Mgr-HR)*

Mitsui Rail Capital Holdings, Inc. (2)
71 S Wacker Dr Ste 1800, Chicago, IL 60606-4637
Tel.: (312) 803-8880
Freight Car Leasing & Management Services
N.A.I.C.S.: 532120
Jeff Rasmussen *(Dir-Sls & Mktg)*

Mitsui Seiki USA Inc. (2)
563 Commerce St, Franklin Lakes, NJ 07417-1309
Tel.: (201) 337-1300
Web Site: https://www.mitsuiseiki.com
Sales Range: $25-49.9 Million
Emp.: 6
Mfr of Industrial Machinery & Equipment
N.A.I.C.S.: 423830

Scott Walker *(Chm)*

Paul Stuart, Inc. (2)
Madison Ave and 45th St, New York, NY 10017
Tel.: (212) 682-0320
Web Site: http://www.paulstuart.com
Sales Range: $100-124.9 Million
Emp.: 200
Retail Apparel Specialty Store
N.A.I.C.S.: 458110
Mona Reilly *(Dir-PR)*

Road Machinery Company (2)
926 S 7th St, Phoenix, AZ 85034
Tel.: (602) 252-7121
Web Site: https://www.roadmachinery.com
Sales Range: $150-199.9 Million
Emp.: 345
Sales & Renter of Off-Highway Trucks & Construction Equipment
N.A.I.C.S.: 423810
Steve Branson *(Pres & COO)*

Steel Technologies Inc. (2)
700 N Hurstbourne Pkwy Ste 400, Louisville, KY 40222
Tel.: (502) 245-2110
Web Site: http://www.steeltechnologies.com
Sales Range: $800-899.9 Million
Emp.: 1,194
Flat Rolled Steel Processing
N.A.I.C.S.: 331110
Patrick M. Carroll *(Exec VP-Automotive)*

Joint Venture (Domestic):

Delaco Kasle LLC (3)
25225 Hall Rd, Woodhaven, MI 48183-5111
Tel.: (734) 692-8000
Web Site: http://www.delacosteel.com
Sales Range: $100-124.9 Million
Emp.: 100
Supplier of Automotive Steel Blanks; Owned 49% by Steel Technologies, Inc & 51% by Delaco Steel Corporation
N.A.I.C.S.: 331110
Ivan Brillhart *(Gen Mgr)*

Ferrolux Metals Co. LLC (3)
36263 Michigan Ave, Wayne, MI 48184
Tel.: (734) 727-6161
Web Site: http://www.ferrolux.com
Sales Range: $150-199.9 Million
Steel Processing; Joint Venture Between Ferragon (51%) & Steel Technologies (49%)
N.A.I.C.S.: 331221
Eduardo Gonzalez *(Pres)*

Branch (Domestic):

Steel Technologies Inc. (3)
1801 Alabama Ave, Flint, MI 48505-3985
Tel.: (810) 767-4300
Web Site: http://www.steeltechnologies.com
Sales Range: $25-49.9 Million
Emp.: 100
Automotive Steel Products
N.A.I.C.S.: 331110

Steel Technologies Inc. (3)
2220 Joseph Lloyd Pkwy, Willoughby, OH 44094
Tel.: (440) 946-8666
Sales Range: $25-49.9 Million
Emp.: 100
Steel Processing
N.A.I.C.S.: 331110

Steel Technologies LLC (3)
3301 Mallard Fox Dr, Decatur, AL 35601
Tel.: (256) 350-5025
Web Site: http://www.steeltechnologies.com
Sales Range: $25-49.9 Million
Emp.: 3
Mfr of Flat-Rolled Steel Products
N.A.I.C.S.: 331221
Tad Carroll *(VP-Sls-Southern Reg)*

Subsidiary (Non-US):

Steel Technologies de Mexico, S.A. de C.V. (3)
Federalismo 204 Fraccionamiento Industrial La Silla, 67199, Guadalupe, Mexico
Tel.: (52) 8181275070
Web Site: http://www.steeltechnologies.com.mx
Sales Range: $50-74.9 Million
Emp.: 150
Steel Processing

MITSUI & CO., LTD.

Mitsui & Co., Ltd.—(Continued)
N.A.I.C.S.: 331210

Subsidiary (Domestic):

SunWize Technologies, Inc. (2)
11 W Saint John St Ste 1200, San Jose, CA 95113
Tel.: (408) 510-5170
Web Site: http://www.sunwize.com
Solar Electric Power Distribution Services
N.A.I.C.S.: 221122
David Kaltsas *(Pres & COO)*

Mitsui & Co. Alternative Investments Limited (1)
11th Floor Chiyoda First Bldg South Wing 3-2-1, Nishikanda Chiyoda-ku, Tokyo, 101-0065, Japan
Tel.: (81) 363610420
Web Site: http://www.mitsui-ai.com
Securities Brokerage Services
N.A.I.C.S.: 523150
Takateru Mitsui *(Pres & CEO)*

Mitsui & Co. Asset Management Holdings S.A. (1)
2-1 Nishi-Kanda 3-chome, Chiyoda-ku, Tokyo, 101-0065, Japan
Tel.: (81) 366294680
Web Site: http://www.mitsui-am.com
Real Estate Asset Management Services
N.A.I.C.S.: 531390
Tamotsu Hagino *(Pres & CEO)*

Mitsui & Co. Benelux S.A./N.V. (1)
Rue Belliard 65 / Belliardstraat 65, PO Box 1, 1040, Brussels, Belgium **(100%)**
Tel.: (32) 26782111
Web Site: http://www.mitsui.com
Sales Range: $25-49.9 Million
Emp.: 34
International Trading House Services
N.A.I.C.S.: 425120
Yoshiyuki Morishita *(Pres & CEO)*

Mitsui & Co. Commodity Risk Management Ltd. (1)
5th Floor St Martins Court 10 Paternoster Row, London, EC4M 7BB, United Kingdom
Tel.: (44) 207 489 6600
Web Site: http://www.mcrm.com
Sales Range: $50-74.9 Million
Emp.: 5
Commodities Trading Services
N.A.I.C.S.: 523160
Peter Allan *(Mng Dir)*

Mitsui & Co. Deutschland GmbH (1)
Herzogstrasse 15, 40217, Dusseldorf, Germany **(100%)**
Tel.: (49) 21193860
Web Site: http://www.mitsui
Sales Range: $100-124.9 Million
Emp.: 179
General Import & Export Trading
N.A.I.C.S.: 425120

Branch (Non-US):

Mitsui & Co. Deutschland GmbH-Bucharest Office (2)
Inter-Continental Hotel 2nd Floor, 4 Blvd N Balcescu Sector 1, Bucharest, Romania
Tel.: (40) 213113111
Web Site: http://www.mitsui.co.jp
Sales Range: $50-74.9 Million
Emp.: 9
Trading & Investments
N.A.I.C.S.: 425120

Mitsui & Co. Deutschland GmbH - Czech Republic Office (2)
Prague City Center, Klimentska 46, 110 02, Prague, Czech Republic
Tel.: (420) 222101900
Web Site: http://www.mitsui.eu
Sales Range: $100-124.9 Million
Emp.: 10
Trading & Logistic Services
N.A.I.C.S.: 425120

Mitsui & Co. Deutschland GmbH - Hungary Office (2)
XIII Vaci Ut 22-24, West-End Business Center 5F, 1132, Budapest, Hungary
Tel.: (36) 14502940
Web Site: http://www.mitsui.co.jp
Sales Range: $50-74.9 Million
Emp.: 6
Trading & Investments
N.A.I.C.S.: 425120

Mitsui & Co. Deutschland GmbH-Warsaw (2)
LIM Center 12th fl Al Jerozolimskie 65/79, 00-697, Warsaw, Poland **(100%)**
Tel.: (48) 226293211
Web Site: http://www.mitsui.de
Sales Range: $50-74.9 Million
Emp.: 20
Trade Brokers
N.A.I.C.S.: 425120

Mitsui & Co. Energy Marketing & Services (USA), Inc. (1)
1300 Post Oak Blvd Ste 1900, Houston, TX 77056
Tel.: (346) 230-4839
Web Site: http://www.mems-usa.com
Commodity Trading & Investment Services
N.A.I.C.S.: 523160
Eiji Yanagawa *(Pres & CEO)*

Mitsui & Co. Europe (Espana) S.A. (1)
Paseo de la Castellana 7 10th Floor, 28046, Madrid, Spain **(100%)**
Tel.: (34) 915981561
Web Site: http://www.mitsui.com
Sales Range: $1-9.9 Million
Emp.: 23
Head Office
N.A.I.C.S.: 212210
Node Modi *(Mng Dir)*

Mitsui & Co. Europe (Espana) S.A. (1)
Avenida Diagonal 613 6B, Barcelona, 08028, Spain **(100%)**
Tel.: (34) 933638750
Sales Range: $50-74.9 Million
Emp.: 8
Trading & Investments
N.A.I.C.S.: 425120

Mitsui & Co. Europe (Portugal) Lda. (1)
Rua Castilho 165 3 Fl, 1070 050, Lisbon, Portugal **(100%)**
Tel.: (351) 213828240
Sales Range: $50-74.9 Million
Emp.: 7
General Import & Export Trading
N.A.I.C.S.: 425120

Mitsui & Co. Europe PLC (1)
8th and 9th Floors 1 St Martin's Le Grand, London, EC1A 4AS, United Kingdom **(100%)**
Tel.: (44) 2078220321
Web Site: http://www.mitsui.com
Sales Range: $200-249.9 Million
Emp.: 272
Global Business Investments
N.A.I.C.S.: 425120

Subsidiary (Domestic):

Mitsui & Co. Europe Holdings PLC (2)
8 & 9 Fl 1 St Martin's Le Grand, London, EC1A 4AS, United Kingdom
Tel.: (44) 20 7822 0321
Emp.: 20
Investment Management Service
N.A.I.C.S.: 523999

Branch (Non-US):

Mitsui & Co. Europe PLC - Athens Branch (2)
73 Possidonos Ave Paleon Faliron, 175 62, Athens, Greece
Tel.: (30) 2109856811
Web Site: http://www.mitsui.com
General Import & Export Trading
N.A.I.C.S.: 238990

Mitsui & Co. Europe PLC - Dublin Branch (2)
Molesworth House 1-2 South Frederick Street, Dublin, 2, Ireland
Tel.: (353) 14744810
Web Site: http://www.mitsui.com
Sales Range: $50-74.9 Million
Emp.: 3
Import & Export Services

Mitsui & Co. Europe PLC - Istanbul Branch (2)
Is Kuleleri Kule 2 Kat 7, Levent, 34330 4, Istanbul, Turkiye
Tel.: (90) 2123194000
Sales Range: $50-74.9 Million
Emp.: 25
Business Services
N.A.I.C.S.: 425120

Mitsui & Co. Europe Plc (1)
Regus Les Pins Maritime 22nd Algeria Business Centre 11th Floor, Les Pins Maritime Mo, Algiers, Algeria
Tel.: (213) 144017000
International Trade Financing Services
N.A.I.C.S.: 522299

Mitsui & Co. Europe Plc (1)
8th and 9th Floors 1 St Martin's Le Grand, London, EC1A 4AS, United Kingdom **(100%)**
Tel.: (44) 207 822 0321
Web Site: https://www.mitsui.com
Emp.: 272
Business Management, Trading & Investment Services
N.A.I.C.S.: 425120
Atsushi Kume *(COO & Sr Exec Mng Officer)*

Mitsui & Co. Europe S.A. (1)
112 Avenue Kleber, 75116, Paris, France **(100%)**
Tel.: (33) 144017000
Web Site: http://www.mitsui.com
Sales Range: $350-399.9 Million
Emp.: 40
Trading & Investments
N.A.I.C.S.: 425120

Mitsui & Co. Financial Services (Asia) Ltd. (1)
80 Robinson Road 25-00, Singapore, 068898, Singapore
Tel.: (65) 64219254
Web Site: http://www.mitsu.com
Sales Range: $50-74.9 Million
Emp.: 7
Financial Management Services
N.A.I.C.S.: 523999
Takashi Manabe *(Gen Mgr)*

Mitsui & Co. Global Investment Ltd. (1)
2-1 Otemachi 1-Chome, Chiyoda-ku, Tokyo, 100-8631, Japan
Tel.: (81) 33 285 1111
Web Site: https://www.mitsui-global.com
Sales Range: $50-74.9 Million
Emp.: 16
Investment Management Service
N.A.I.C.S.: 523999
Katsuhiko Oizumi *(Pres & CEO)*

Mitsui & Co. Global Logistics (Asia) Pte. Ltd. (1)
12 Marina View Asia Square Tower 2 31-01, Singapore, 018961, Singapore
Tel.: (65) 64210488
Emp.: 18
Integrated Transportation Services
N.A.I.C.S.: 541614
Ng Teng Hua Hua Raymond *(Mng Dir)*

Mitsui & Co. Global Logistics, Ltd. (1)
2-14-1 Higashishimbashi, Minato-ku, Tokyo, 105-0021, Japan
Tel.: (81) 356751130
Real Estate Lending Services
N.A.I.C.S.: 531110
Kazuya Takemori *(Pres & CEO)*

Mitsui & Co. India Pvt. Ltd. (1)
4th Floor Worldmark 3 Asset 7 Aerocity NH-8, District Centre Saket, New Delhi, 110037, India **(100%)**
Tel.: (91) 1143531111
Web Site: http://www.mitsui.com
Sales Range: $50-74.9 Million
Emp.: 150
Trading & Investments
N.A.I.C.S.: 425120
Masaharu Okubo *(Chm)*

Branch (Domestic):

Mitsui & Co. India Pvt. Ltd. (2)

INTERNATIONAL PUBLIC

2 Upper Woods Street 2nd Floor, Kolkata, 700016, India **(100%)**
Tel.: (91) 3340021333
Web Site: http://www.mitsui-india.com
Sales Range: $50-74.9 Million
Emp.: 15
Trading & Investments
N.A.I.C.S.: 425120

Mitsui & Co. India Pvt. Ltd. (2)
PLATINA Unit No 704 7th Floor Plot No C-59 G- Block, Bandra Kurla Complex Bandra East, Mumbai, 400051, India **(100%)**
Tel.: (91) 2267742222
Web Site: http://www.mitsui-india.com
Sales Range: $50-74.9 Million
Emp.: 60
Trading & Investments
N.A.I.C.S.: 425120

Mitsui & Co. India Pvt. Ltd.-Chennai Branch (2)
7th Floor SPIC Annexe Building No 88 Mount Road, Guindy, Chennai, 600 032, India **(100%)**
Tel.: (91) 4442917400
Web Site: http://www.mitsui.com
Sales Range: $50-74.9 Million
Emp.: 25
Trading, Iron & Steel, Nonferrous Metals, Machinery, Chemicals, Energy, Petroleum, Foodstuffs, Textiles, Services & General Merchandise
N.A.I.C.S.: 425120

Mitsui & Co. Kuwait W.L.L. (1)
Al Sahab Tower 3rd Floor Mohammed Thunayan Al Ghanim Street, Salhiya, Kuwait, 13034, Kuwait
Tel.: (965) 2424257
Web Site: http://www.mitsui.com
Sales Range: $50-74.9 Million
Emp.: 18
Trading & Investments
N.A.I.C.S.: 425120

Mitsui & Co. Ltd. Korea (1)
33rd Floor East Tower CENTER1 26 Euljiro 5-gil, Jung-gu, Seoul, 04539, Korea (South) **(100%)**
Tel.: (82) 234200601
Web Site: http://www.mitsui.co.jp
Sales Range: $50-74.9 Million
Emp.: 111
General Import & Export Trading
N.A.I.C.S.: 212210
Tomoyuki Moriyama *(Pres & CEO)*

Mitsui & Co. Machine Tech Ltd. (1)
Shiodome City Center 34th Floor 1-5-2, Higashi-Shimbashi Minato-ku, Tokyo, 105-7134, Japan
Tel.: (81) 367573700
Web Site: http://www.mmknet.com
Machine Tools Mfr
N.A.I.C.S.: 333517
Takeo Arai *(Pres)*

Mitsui & Co. Moscow LLC (1)
16th floor Naberezhnaya Tower Block B 10 Presnenskaya Naberezhnaya, 123112, Moscow, Russia
Tel.: (7) 4959569600
Web Site: http://www.mitsui.com
Emp.: 95
Trading & Investments
N.A.I.C.S.: 425120
Meguro Hiroshi *(Pres, CEO & Gen Dir)*

Mitsui & Co. Norway A/S (1)
Klingenberggaten 7 B, Vika, 0161, Oslo, Norway **(100%)**
Tel.: (47) 23114340
Web Site: http://www.mitsui.com
Sales Range: $50-74.9 Million
Emp.: 16
Global Business Investments
N.A.I.C.S.: 425120

Mitsui & Co. Plant Systems, Ltd. (1)
Shiodome Sumitomo Bldg 26F 1-9-2 Higashi-Shimbashi, Minato-ku, Tokyo, 105-0021, Japan
Tel.: (81) 36 218 3000
Web Site: https://www.plantsystems.mitsui.co.jp
Emp.: 275
Power Plant Construction Engineering Services
N.A.I.C.S.: 237130

AND PRIVATE COMPANIES
MITSUI & CO., LTD.

Naosuje Senvaki *(Pres & CEO)*

Mitsui & Co. Plastics Ltd. (1)
JA Building 6/7/8F 1-3-1 Otemachi, Chiyoda-ku, Tokyo, 100-6808, Japan
Tel.: (81) 363285000
Web Site: http://www.mitsui-plastics.com
Emp.: 589
Chemical Products Distr
N.A.I.C.S.: 424690
Katsunori Mori *(Pres & CEO)*

Mitsui & Co. Power & Infrastructure Development Ltd. (1)
1-2-1 Otemachi, Chiyoda-ku, Tokyo, 100-8631, Japan
Tel.: (81) 332854360
Web Site: https://www.mpid.co.jp
Emp.: 25
Power Plant Construction Engineering Services
N.A.I.C.S.: 237130

Mitsui & Co. Scandinavia AB (1)
World Trade Ctr, 10136, Stockholm, Sweden **(100%)**
Tel.: (46) 86792300
Sales Range: $50-74.9 Million
Emp.: 15
Head Office
N.A.I.C.S.: 212210

Mitsui & Co. Steel Ltd. (1)
35F Akasaka Biz Tower 5-3-1 Akasaka, Minato-ku, Tokyo, 107-6335, Japan
Tel.: (81) 35 544 5001
Web Site: https://www.mitsui-steel.com
Emp.: 299
Iron & Steel Products Mfr & Distr
N.A.I.C.S.: 331110
Keiji Kasamatsu *(VP)*

Division (Domestic):

Mitsui & Co. Steel Ltd. (2)
4F Denryoku Buildingg 1-3-7-1, Aoba-ku, Sendai, 980-0811, Miyagi, Japan
Tel.: (81) 22 264 5054
Web Site: http://www.mitsui-steel.com
Emp.: 2
Metal Products Mfr
N.A.I.C.S.: 332999
Alain Poublon *(Gen Mgr)*

Mitsui & Co. Venezuela C.A. (1)
Edificio Cavendes Piso 10 Avenida Francisco de Miranda, Cruce Con Primera Avenida de Los Palos Grandes, Caracas, Venezuela
Tel.: (58) 2122850011
International Trade Financing Services
N.A.I.C.S.: 522299

Mitsui & Co., (Egypt) S.S.C. (1)
Nile Tower Bldg 19th Floor 21-23 Giza St Giza A R E, PO Box 48, 11511, Cairo, Egypt
Tel.: (20) 235702012
International Trade Financing Services
N.A.I.C.S.: 522299

Mitsui & Co., (Hong Kong) Ltd. (1)
25th and 26th Floors Far East Finance Centre 16 Harcourt Road, Hong Kong, China (Hong Kong) **(100%)**
Tel.: (852) 28238777
Web Site: http://www.mitsui.com
Sales Range: $100-124.9 Million
Emp.: 116
General Import & Export Trading Company
N.A.I.C.S.: 212210

Mitsui & Co., (Panama International, S.A.) (1)
Diagnoal 6 10 65 Zona 10 Centro Genecial Las Margaritas 9 Nivel, Oficina 901 B, Guatemala, Guatemala **(100%)**
Tel.: (502) 3316775
General Import & Export Trading
N.A.I.C.S.: 212210

Mitsui & Co., Iran Ltd. (1)
4Th Floor No 37 East Atefi alley Nelson Mandela Blvd, Tehran, 19177 97498, Iran **(100%)**
Tel.: (98) 2126290341
Sales Range: $50-74.9 Million
Emp.: 60
General Import & Export Trading
N.A.I.C.S.: 212210

Mitsui & Co., Logistics Partners Ltd. (1)
Chiyoda First Bldg 13th Floor South Wing 3-2-1 Nishikanda, Chiyoda-ku, Tokyo, 101-0065, Japan **(70%)**
Tel.: (81) 33 238 7171
Web Site: https://www.m-lp.net
Sales Range: $50-74.9 Million
Emp.: 30
Real Estate Investment Trust Management Services
N.A.I.C.S.: 523940
Takayuki Kawashima *(Pres & CEO)*

Mitsui & Co., Ltd (1)
Casablanca Marina Boulevard Sidi Mohammed Ben Abdellah, Building A5-1 Crystal 1 Office No 17 10th Floor, 20000, Casablanca, Morocco **(100%)**
Tel.: (212) 522276970
Sales Range: $50-74.9 Million
Emp.: 10
Trading & Investments
N.A.I.C.S.: 425120

Mitsui & Co., Ltd (1)
Av 4 De Fevereiro No 84 3 Andar Porta 5 6 7, 2945, Luanda, Angola **(100%)**
Tel.: (244) 222391480
Sales Range: $50-74.9 Million
Emp.: 2
Trading & Investments
N.A.I.C.S.: 425120

Mitsui & Co., Ltd (1)
8 Ct Rd, PO Box 4052, cnr 2nd St Robert Mugabe Rd, Harare, Zimbabwe
Tel.: (263) 4496416
Trading & Investments
N.A.I.C.S.: 425120

Mitsui & Co., Ltd (1)
Cnr Stella Street Sandown 1st Floor 138 West Street, Sandton, 2196, South Africa **(100%)**
Tel.: (27) 117838835
Web Site: http://www.mitsui.com
Sales Range: $25-49.9 Million
Emp.: 30
Importer of Metals, Food, Machinery & Chemicals
N.A.I.C.S.: 423510

Mitsui & Co., Ltd (1)
Zamil House 12th floor 2200 Prince Turkey Street, Cornishe, Al Khobar, 34413, Saudi Arabia **(100%)**
Tel.: (966) 138496001
Web Site: http://www.mitsui.com.jp
Sales Range: $50-74.9 Million
Emp.: 20
Trading & Investments
N.A.I.C.S.: 425120

Mitsui & Co., Ltd (1)
Block B/ Building 1 1st floor-Office No 400 The Boulevard, PO Box 3077, Al Abdali, Amman, 11190, Jordan
Tel.: (962) 65673649
Web Site: http://www.mitsui.com
Sales Range: $50-74.9 Million
Emp.: 5
Trading & Investments
N.A.I.C.S.: 425120

Mitsui & Co., Ltd (1)
Nile Tower Bldg 19th Floor 21-23 Giza St, Giza, ARE, Egypt **(100%)**
Tel.: (20) 235702012
Sales Range: $50-74.9 Million
Emp.: 15
Trading & Investments
N.A.I.C.S.: 425120

Mitsui & Co., Ltd (1)
2nd Floor B Block Finance & Trade Centre Shahrah-e-Faisal, PO Box 74400, Karachi, Pakistan **(100%)**
Tel.: (92) 2135205118
Web Site: http://www.mitsui.com
Sales Range: $50-74.9 Million
Emp.: 30
Trading & Investments
N.A.I.C.S.: 425120

Mitsui & Co., Ltd (1)
Office No 20 2nd Floor Park Lane Tower 172 Tufail Road, PO Box 1151, Lahore, 54810, Pakistan **(100%)**
Tel.: (92) 4236066800

Web Site: http://www.mitsui.co.jp
Sales Range: $50-74.9 Million
Emp.: 10
Trading & Investments
N.A.I.C.S.: 425120

Mitsui & Co., Ltd (1)
Office No 209 2nd Floor Islamabad Stock Exchange Tower 52-B, PO Box 1366, Jinnah Avenue, 44000, Islamabad, Pakistan **(100%)**
Tel.: (92) 512072700
Sales Range: $50-74.9 Million
Emp.: 3
Trading & Investments
N.A.I.C.S.: 425120

Mitsui & Co., Ltd (1)
Bay's Edgewater 2nd Floor Plot NE N-12 North Avenue, Gulshan, Dhaka, 1212, Bangladesh
Tel.: (880) 29884833
Sales Range: $50-74.9 Million
Emp.: 30
Trading & Investments
N.A.I.C.S.: 425120

Mitsui & Co., Ltd (1)
Chamber House 4th Floor Agrabad, PO Box 667, Chittagong, 4000, Bangladesh
Tel.: (880) 31723222
Web Site: http://www.gewater.com
Sales Range: $50-74.9 Million
Emp.: 45
Trading & Investments
N.A.I.C.S.: 425120

Mitsui & Co., Ltd (1)
No 44 Pyidaungsu Yeiktha Rd Dagon Township, Yangon, Myanmar
Tel.: (95) 1228036
Sales Range: $50-74.9 Million
Emp.: 10
Trading & Investments
N.A.I.C.S.: 425120

Mitsui & Co., Ltd. (1)
33rd Floor East Tower CENTER1 26 Euljiro 5-gil, PO Box 1928, Jung-gu, Seoul, 04539, Korea (South)
Tel.: (82) 234200601
Web Site: https://www.mitsui.com
Sales Range: $50-74.9 Million
Emp.: 111
General Import & Export Trading
N.A.I.C.S.: 425120
Tomoyuki Moriyama *(Pres & CEO)*

Mitsui & Co., Ltd. (1)
19 Floor Dalian Senmao Building 147 Zhongshan Rd, Dalian, 116011, Zhongshan Lu, China
Tel.: (86) 41182372006
Web Site: http://www.mitsui.com
Sales Range: $50-74.9 Million
Emp.: 10
General Import & Export Trading
N.A.I.C.S.: 212210

Mitsui & Co., Ltd. - Indonesia (1)
Menara BCA 51st Floor Grand Indonesia Jl M H Thamrin No 1, PO Box 3456, Jakarta, 10310, Indonesia
Tel.: (62) 2129856234
Web Site: http://www.mitsui.com
Sales Range: $50-74.9 Million
Emp.: 100
General Import & Export Trading
N.A.I.C.S.: 212210

Mitsui & Co., Middle East Ltd. (1)
6th Floor East Wing DIFC Gate Building, PO Box 9710, Deira, Dubai, United Arab Emirates
Tel.: (971) 4 404 7100
Web Site: http://www.mitsui.co.jp
Sales Range: $50-74.9 Million
Emp.: 67
Trading & Investments
N.A.I.C.S.: 425120

Branch (Domestic):

Mitsui & Co., Middle East Ltd. (2)
Suite No 1002 10th Floor Al-Masaood Tower Sh Hamdan Street, PO Box 2999, Abu Dhabi, United Arab Emirates **(100%)**
Tel.: (971) 26322119
Web Site: http://www.mitsui.com
Sales Range: $50-74.9 Million
Emp.: 12
Financing & Infrastructure Logistics

N.A.I.C.S.: 425120

Branch (Non-US):

Mitsui & Co., Middle East Ltd. (2)
5th floor Bait Al Reem Building Al Thaqafa Road, PO Box 3014, Al Khuwair Muscat, Ruwi, 112, Oman **(100%)**
Tel.: (968) 24602340
Web Site: http://www.mitsui.com
Sales Range: $25-49.9 Million
Emp.: 7
Network & Information Resources
N.A.I.C.S.: 517810

Mitsui & Co., Principal Investments Ltd. (1)
Otemachi Financial City Grand Cube 19F 9-2 Otemachi 1-Chome, Chiyoda-ku, Tokyo, 100-0004, Japan
Tel.: (81) 33 285 3260
Web Site: https://www.mcpi.co.jp
Sales Range: $50-74.9 Million
Emp.: 17
Investment Management Service
N.A.I.C.S.: 523999
Masami Kawahara *(Pres & CEO)*

Mitsui & Co., Realty Management Ltd. (1)
3-2-1 Nishikanda 13th floor Chiyoda First Building South Building, Chiyoda-ku, Tokyo, 101-0065, Japan
Tel.: (81) 352108940
Web Site: https://www.mbrm.co.jp
Real Estate Manangement Services
N.A.I.C.S.: 531390

Mitsui & Co., Vietnam Ltd. (1)
The Times Square Building 12th Floor 57-69F Dong Khoi Street, Ben Nghe Ward District 1, Ho Chi Minh City, Vietnam
Tel.: (84) 2838292604
Web Site: http://www.mitsui.com
Emp.: 70
Petroleum & Food Products Distr
N.A.I.C.S.: 424720

Mitsui AgriScience International SA/NV (1)
Boulevard de la Woluwe 60 Woluwedal 60, Brussels, 1200, Belgium
Tel.: (32) 2 331 38 94
Sales Range: $25-49.9 Million
Emp.: 12
Agricultural Chemical Mfr & Distr
N.A.I.C.S.: 325320
Toru Tanaka *(Mng Dir)*

Mitsui Alimentos Ltda. (1)
Rua Xv De Novembro 62, Santos, 11010 150, Sao Paulo, Brazil
Tel.: (55) 1332194226
Web Site: http://www.mitsuialimentos.com.br
Emp.: 2
Food Products Mfr & Distr
N.A.I.C.S.: 311999
Wilson Carvalho *(Mng Dir)*

Mitsui Argentina S.A. (1)
710 Bouchard Piso 12, Buenos Aires, C1106ABL, Argentina **(100%)**
Tel.: (54) 1143174900
Web Site: http://www.mitsui.com
Sales Range: $50-74.9 Million
Emp.: 25
Global Business Investments
N.A.I.C.S.: 425120

Mitsui Bussan Aerospace Co., Ltd. (1)
Shuwa-Shiba Park Building A-12F 4-1 Shiba-Koen 2-Chome, Minato-ku, Tokyo, 105-0011, Japan
Tel.: (81) 3 3437 8770
Web Site: http://www.aerospace.mitsui.co.jp
Aerospace & Defense Products Distr
N.A.I.C.S.: 423860

Subsidiary (US):

Mitsui Bussan Aerospace Corporation (2)
600 E Las Colinas Blvd Ste 1230, Irving, TX 75039
Tel.: (972) 869-7519
Emp.: 5
Aerospace & Defense Products Distr
N.A.I.C.S.: 423860

MITSUI & CO., LTD.

Mitsui & Co., Ltd.—(Continued)

Mitsui Bussan Agro Business Co., Ltd. (1)
Nihombashi Talk Building 3-5 Nihombashi Hongoku-Cho 3-Chome, Chuo-Ku, Tokyo, 103-0021, Japan
Tel.: (81) 3 5200 3800
Web Site: http://www.mitsui-agro.co.jp
Emp.: 8
Fertilizer & Agricultural Products Distr
N.A.I.C.S.: 424910

Mitsui Bussan Automotive (Thailand) Co., Ltd. (1)
19/4 Moo 14 King Kaew Road, Racha Thewa Subdistrict, Bang Phli, 10540, Samut Prakan, Thailand
Tel.: (66) 21306464
Web Site: http://www.mitsiammotors.co.th
Truck Dealing Services
N.A.I.C.S.: 441110

Mitsui Bussan Automotive Inc. (1)
Shiodome City Center 34F 5-2 Higashi Shimbashi 1-Chome, Minato-ku, Tokyo, Japan
Tel.: (81) 33 571 9550
Web Site: https://www.mitsuibussan-automotive.jp
Emp.: 50
Automobile Parts Distr
N.A.I.C.S.: 423120
Takao Hayakawa (Corp Auditor)

Mitsui Bussan Business Partners Co., Ltd. (1)
1-2-1 Otemachi Mitsuibussan Bldg, Chiyoda-Ku, Tokyo, 100-0004, Japan
Tel.: (81) 3 3512 7038
Web Site: http://www.mitsui-mbp.co.jp
Emp.: 20
Human Resource Consulting Services
N.A.I.C.S.: 541612
Josef Klasek (Gen Mgr)

Mitsui Bussan Chemicals Co., Ltd. (1)
JA Building 11F 3-1 Otemachi 1-Chome, Chiyoda-ku, Tokyo, 100-6811, Japan
Tel.: (81) 367595000
Web Site: http://www.mb-chemicals.co.jp
Emp.: 231
Industrial Chemical Distr
N.A.I.C.S.: 424690
Seiichi Yanagisawa (Pres & CEO)

Mitsui Bussan Commodities Ltd. (1)
6th Floor 1 St Martin's Le Grand, London, EC1A 4BB, United Kingdom
Tel.: (44) 207 489 6600
Web Site: https://www.mitsuibussancommodity.com
Sales Range: $50-74.9 Million
Emp.: 5
Commodity Brokerage & Risk Management Services
N.A.I.C.S.: 523160
Peter Allan (CEO)

Mitsui Bussan Copper Investment & Co., Ltd. (1)
1-2-1 Otemachi, Chiyoda-Ku, Tokyo, 100-0004, Japan
Tel.: (81) 3 3285 3377
Investment Management Service
N.A.I.C.S.: 523999
Yasunaga Tatsuo (Pres)

Mitsui Bussan Credit Consulting Co., Ltd. (1)
1-14-8 Nihombashiningyocho Tt1 Bldg 5kai, Chuo-Ku, Tokyo, 103-0013, Japan
Tel.: (81) 3 5962 3001
Web Site: http://www.mitsui-credit.com
Emp.: 30
Credit Consulting Services
N.A.I.C.S.: 522390
Toshiya Matsui (Pres)

Mitsui Bussan Financial Management Ltd. (1)
1-2-1 Otemachi Mitsuibussan Bldg, Chiyoda-Ku, Tokyo, 100-0004, Japan
Tel.: (81) 332858167
Web Site: http://www.webmfm.jp
Financial Management Services
N.A.I.C.S.: 523999

Mitsui Bussan Frontier Co., Ltd. (1)
3-3-1 Nishishimbashi Ts Bldg 6f, Minato-Ku, Tokyo, 105-0003, Japan
Tel.: (81) 3 6860 0150
Web Site: http://www.mbk-frontier.com
Sales Range: $25-49.9 Million
Emp.: 4
Electronic Device Distr
N.A.I.C.S.: 423690

Mitsui Bussan Inter-Fashion Ltd. (1)
Hulic Aoyama Building 6-12 Kita-aoyama 3-chome, Minato-ku, Tokyo, 107-0061, Japan
Tel.: (81) 3 5467 6064
Web Site: http://www.mif-ltd.co.jp
Rev.: $1,217,549,260
Emp.: 382
Textile Apparel & Fashion Accessories Mfr & Distr
N.A.I.C.S.: 315990
Y. Okuno (Gen Mgr)

Mitsui Bussan Plastics Trade Co., Ltd. (1)
Kayaba-cho First Bldg 9F & 10F 17-21 Shinkawa 1-chome, Chuo-ku, Tokyo, 104-0033, Japan
Tel.: (81) 3 6328 5000
Web Site: http://www.mbptrade.com
Rev.: $3,374,770,000
Emp.: 583
Plastic & Resin Products Distr
N.A.I.C.S.: 424610
Akio Yamamoto (Pres & CEO)

Subsidiary (Non-US):

Mitsui Bussan E-Film (Hong Kong) Mfg. Co. Ltd. (2)
Unit A G/F Century Centre No 1 Ping Ha Road Ping Shan, Yuen Long, New Territories, China (Hong Kong)
Tel.: (852) 2616 9672
Web Site: http://www.mef.com.hk
Industrial Film Distr
N.A.I.C.S.: 423840

Mitsui Bussan Precious Metals (Hong Kong) Limited (1)
Two Exchange Square Suite 1306 8 Connaught Place, Central, China (Hong Kong)
Tel.: (852) 28992065
Sales Range: $25-49.9 Million
Emp.: 14
Precious Metal Distr
N.A.I.C.S.: 423510
Hisashi Nagato (Gen Mgr)

Mitsui Bussan Secure Directions, Inc. (1)
Yusen Suitengumae Building 6F 1-14-8 Nihonbashi Ningyo-Cho, Chuo-ku, Tokyo, 103-0013, Japan
Tel.: (81) 35 649 1961
Web Site: https://www.mbsd.jp
Sales Range: $25-49.9 Million
Emp.: 264
Internet Security & Information Technology Consulting Services
N.A.I.C.S.: 561621
Toshio Kanki (CEO)

Mitsui Bussan Trade Services Ltd. (1)
1-2-1 Otemachi Mitsuibutsusan Bldg, Chiyoda-Ku, Tokyo, 100-0004, Japan
Tel.: (81) 3 3285 8480
Web Site: http://www.webmts.co.jp
Cargo Handling Services
N.A.I.C.S.: 488320

Mitsui Chili Ltda.
Torre de la Constanera Avenida Andres Bello 2711 Floor 11, Piso 11 Las Condes, Santiago, Chile (100%)
Tel.: (56) 22906200
Sales Range: $50-74.9 Million
Emp.: 30
General Import & Export Trading
N.A.I.C.S.: 212210

Mitsui Coal Holdings Pty. Ltd. (1)
Level 12 240 Queen Street, Brisbane, 4000, QLD, Australia
Tel.: (61) 7 3032 8875
Sales Range: $50-74.9 Million
Emp.: 22
Coal Mining Services
N.A.I.C.S.: 213113

Mitsui Concrete Industries Co., Ltd. (1)
10-1, Uchi-Kanda 1-chome, Chiyoda-ku, Tokyo, 101, Japan
Tel.: (81) 032953136
Sales Range: $50-74.9 Million
Emp.: 200
Mfr & Sale of Cement Products
N.A.I.C.S.: 327310

Mitsui E&P Australia Pty. Limited (1)
Level 22 Exchange Plaza 2 The Esplanade, Perth, 6000, WA, Australia
Tel.: (61) 8 6364 4777
Sales Range: $50-74.9 Million
Emp.: 32
Oil & Gas Exploration Services
N.A.I.C.S.: 213112

Mitsui Electronics Inc. (1)
Shiba Park Building A-10F 4-1 Shibakoen 2-chome, Minato-ku, Tokyo, 105-0011, Japan
Tel.: (81) 3 6403 5900
Web Site: http://www.mbel.co.jp
Rev.: $435,202,000
Emp.: 21
Electronic Parts Distr
N.A.I.C.S.: 423690
Makoto Ichikawa (Pres & CEO)

Mitsui Foods Co., Ltd. (1)
1-1-1 Nishi-Shimbashi, Minato-ku, Tokyo, 105-8466, Japan
Tel.: (81) 367007100
Web Site: http://www.mitsuifoods.co.jp
Sales Range: $400-449.9 Million
Emp.: 1,029
Food Products Mfr & Distr
N.A.I.C.S.: 311999

Mitsui Gas e Energia do Brasil Ltda. (1)
Praia de Botafogo - 300 13th Floor Room 1301, Botafogo, Rio de Janeiro, 22250-040, Brazil
Tel.: (55) 21 3138 3600
Web Site: http://www.mitsuigas.com.br
Natural Gas Distribution Services
N.A.I.C.S.: 221210

Joint Venture (Domestic):

Petrobras Gas S.A. (2)
Av Hemmilque Valagaes No 28 18th Floor, Parte-Centro, 20231030, Rio de Janeiro, RJ, Brazil (49%)
Tel.: (55) 2132241000
Web Site: http://www.gaspetro.petrobras.com.br
Sales Range: $100-124.9 Million
Emp.: 101
Natural Gas Pipeline Transportation Services
N.A.I.C.S.: 486210
Jose Formigle (Dir-Exploration & Production)

Mitsui Iron Ore Development Pty. Ltd. (1)
L 26 2 The Esplanade, Perth, 6000, WA, Australia
Tel.: (61) 894762333
Iron Ore Mining Services & Distr
N.A.I.C.S.: 212210

Mitsui Knowledge Industry Co., Ltd. (1)
Atago Green Hills MORI Tower 2-5-1, Atago Minato ku, Tokyo, 105 6215, Japan (94.33%)
Tel.: (81) 363761000
Web Site: http://www.mki.co.jp
Sales Range: $350-399.9 Million
Emp.: 2,162
Development & Production of Computer Systems; Establishment of Information Network; Consulting on Effective Utilization of Computing Power
N.A.I.C.S.: 334118
Kengo Asano (Pres & CEO)

Subsidiary (Non-US):

MKI (U.K.), LTD (2)
8th and 9th floors 1 St Martin's Le Grand, London, EC1A 4AS, United Kingdom
Tel.: (44) 207 822 0382
Web Site: http://www.mki.co.jp

INTERNATIONAL PUBLIC

Sales Range: $25-49.9 Million
Emp.: 4
Information Technology Consulting Services
N.A.I.C.S.: 541512
Masayuki Tobe (Mng Dir)

Subsidiary (Domestic):

MKI Technologies Co., Ltd. (2)
2-7-14 Higashinakano, Nakano-ku, Tokyo, 164-0003, Japan
Tel.: (81) 332275711
Web Site: http://www.mkitec.co.jp
Sales Range: $300-349.9 Million
Emp.: 457
Communication Equipment Repair & Maintenance Services
N.A.I.C.S.: 811210

Mitsui Lumber Co., Ltd. (1)
4-14, Toyo 2-chome, Koto-ku, Tokyo, 135, Japan
Tel.: (81) 3 3649 3151
Sales Range: $200-249.9 Million
Emp.: 800
Mfr of Building Materials & Housing; Lumber Industry Consultants
N.A.I.C.S.: 337122

Mitsui Miike Machinery Co., Ltd. (1)
5F Mitsui Building No 2 Nihonbashi-Muromachi 2-1-1, Chuo-ku, Tokyo, 103-0022, Japan (15%)
Tel.: (81) 332702001
Web Site: http://www.mitsuimiike.co.jp
Sales Range: $150-199.9 Million
Emp.: 533
Mining, Chemical & Construction Machinery Mfr
N.A.I.C.S.: 325998
Yukitomo Hirakawa (Chm)

Mitsui Mining & Smelting Co., Ltd. (1)
Gate City Ohsaki West Tower 19F 1-11-1 Osaki, Shinagawa-ku, Tokyo, 141-8584, Japan (100%)
Tel.: (81) 35 437 8028
Web Site: https://www.mitsui-kinzoku.com
Sales Range: $50-74.9 Million
Emp.: 200
Mfr of Zinc, Lead, Copper & Other Nonferrous Metals, Die-Cast Products, Rolled Copper & Zinc, Chemicals & Materials for Electronics
N.A.I.C.S.: 325180
Sadao Senda (Pres)

Subsidiary (US):

Oak-Mitsui Inc. (2)
80 1st St, Hoosick Falls, NY 12090
Tel.: (518) 686-4961
Web Site: http://www.oakmitsui.com
Sales Range: $25-49.9 Million
Emp.: 30
Copper Foil
N.A.I.C.S.: 332999
John J. Blaber (VP-Sls-Mktg)

Mitsui Mutual Life Insurance Company (1)
2-3 Otemachi 1-chome, Chiyoda-ku, Tokyo, 100-8123, Japan (100%)
Tel.: (81) 332116111
Sales Range: $1-4.9 Billion
Emp.: 10,000
Life Insurance
N.A.I.C.S.: 524113

Mitsui Norin Co., Ltd. (1)
1-2-9 Nishi-Shimbashi, Minato-ku, Tokyo, 160-0023, Japan
Tel.: (81) 335000611
Web Site: http://www.mitsui-norin.co.jp
Emp.: 525
Tea Mfr & Distr
N.A.I.C.S.: 311920

Mitsui Oil & Gas Co., Ltd. (1)
1 Chome 32 2 Harmony Tower Hon Machi, Nakano Ku, Tokyo, 164 8723, Japan
Tel.: (81) 332937111
Sales Range: $125-149.9 Million
Emp.: 300
Distribution & Marketing of Automotive Fuels, Kerosene, Heavy Oils & Liquefied Petroleum Gas
N.A.I.C.S.: 324110

AND PRIVATE COMPANIES

MITSUI & CO., LTD.

Mitsui Oil Exploration Co., Ltd. (1)
Otemachi One Mitsui Co Building 14F 2-1
Otemachi 1-chome, Chiyoda-ku, Tokyo,
100-0004, Japan **(90.26%)**
Tel.: (81) 35 208 5717
Web Site: https://www.moeco.com
Emp.: 140
Oil & Gas Exploration Services
N.A.I.C.S.: 213112
Mitsuo Hidaka *(Chm & CEO)*

Subsidiary (Domestic):

Moeco Southwest Vietnam Petroleum Co., Ltd. (2)
1-2-9 Nishishimbashi, Minato-Ku, Tokyo, 105-0003, Japan
Tel.: (81) 335025786
Sales Range: $75-99.9 Million
Emp.: 15
Oil & Gas Exploration Services
N.A.I.C.S.: 213112

Mitsui Plastics Trading (Shanghai) Co., Ltd. (1)
15F Tower A Central Towers 555 Langao Road, Putuo District, Shanghai, 200333, China
Tel.: (86) 2122236666
Web Site: http://www.mitsuiplastics-shanghai.com
Chemical Products Distr
N.A.I.C.S.: 424690
Jun Hiyama *(Chm, Pres & CEO)*

Mitsui Plastics, Inc. (1)
10 Bank St Ste 1010, White Plains, NY 10606
Tel.: (914) 287-6800
Web Site: http://www.mitsuiplastics.com
Polymer Material Distr
N.A.I.C.S.: 424610
Teruya Mogi *(Pres & CEO)*

Mitsui Power Ventures Limited (1)
Fl 8 & 9 No 1 St Martin Le Grand, London, EC1A AS, United Kingdom
Tel.: (44) 2078220321
Eletric Power Generation Services
N.A.I.C.S.: 221118

Mitsui Rail Capital Participacoes Ltda. (1)
Rua Frei Caneca 1380, Sao Paulo, 01307-002, Brazil
Tel.: (55) 1121055400
Freight Car Leasing Services
N.A.I.C.S.: 532120

Mitsui de Colombia S.A. (1)
Carrera 7 No 71-52 Torre A Piso 13 Oficina 1302, Bogota, 110111, Colombia **(100%)**
Tel.: (57) 13123088
Web Site: http://www.mitsui.com
Sales Range: $1-9.9 Million
Emp.: 35
General Import & Export Trading
N.A.I.C.S.: 212210

Mitsui de Mexico, S. de R.L. de C. V. (1)
Av Ricardo Margain 575 Suites 5643 Torre IOS, Santa Engracia N L San Pedro Garza Garcia, 66267, Monterrey, Mexico
Tel.: (52) 8110017560
General Import & Export Trading
N.A.I.C.S.: 212210

Mitsui de Mexico, S.A.R.L. de C.V. (1)
Av Paseo de la Reforma 505 Piso 33 Torre Mayor, 06500, Mexico, Mexico **(100%)**
Tel.: (52) 5552840500
Web Site: https://www.mitsui.com
Sales Range: $50-74.9 Million
Emp.: 95
Head Office; General Import & Export Trading
N.A.I.C.S.: 212210
Michihiro Nose *(Pres)*

Mitsui de Venezuela C.A. (1)
Edificio Cavendes Piso 10 Avenida Francisco de Miranda, Cruce Con Primera Avenida de Los Palos Grandes, Caracas, Venezuela
Tel.: (58) 2122850011
Web Site: http://www.mitsui.co
Sales Range: $50-74.9 Million
Emp.: 23
General Import & Export Trading

N.A.I.C.S.: 212210

Mitsui del Peru S.A. (1)
Avenida Ricardo Rivera Navarrete No 501 Edificio Capital Oficina 10-B, San Isidro, Lima, 27, Peru
Tel.: (51) 1 221 1040
Emp.: 15
Industrial Machinery Distr
N.A.I.C.S.: 423830
Akio Ushio *(Gen Mgr)*

Mitsui& Co. Korea Ltd. (1)
33rd Floor East Tower Center1 26 Euljiro 5-gil, Jung-gu, Seoul, 04539, Korea (South)
Tel.: (82) 234200601
International Trade Financing Services
N.A.I.C.S.: 522299
Tomoyuki Moriyama *(Pres & CEO)*

Mitsuibussan Insurance Co., Ltd. (1)
1-1-1 Kanda Sudacho Kanda Sudacho Square Building 11th floor, Chiyoda-ku, Tokyo, 101-0041, Japan
Tel.: (81) 3 5297 6221
Web Site: http://www.insurance.ne.jp
General Insurance Services
N.A.I.C.S.: 524210
Taku Matsumoto *(Pres)*

NISSO BASF Agro Co., Ltd. (1)
Shinko Building 1-11-4 Kudan-Kita, Chiyoda-ku, Tokyo, 102 0073, Japan
Tel.: (81) 332370655
Herbicide Mfr
N.A.I.C.S.: 325320

Next Capital Company Limited (1)
163 Ocean Insurance Building Floor 15 Thanon Surawong, Suriya Wong Bang Rak, Bangkok, 10500, Thailand
Tel.: (66) 23429699
Web Site: http://www.nextcapital.co.th
Automotive Financial Leasing Services
N.A.I.C.S.: 522220

Nippon Amazon Aluminium Co., Ltd. (1)
Nihonbashi-Muromachi Plaza Building 8th Floor, 4-7 Nihonbashi-Muromachi 3 Chome Chuo-ku, Tokyo, 103-0022, Japan
Tel.: (81) 332788831
Web Site: http://www.amazon-aluminium.jp
Project Management Services
N.A.I.C.S.: 541611
Kenji Kobayashi *(Pres)*

Nippon Unisys, Limited (1)
1-1 Toyosu 1-chome Koto-ku, Tokyo, 135-8560, Japan **(28%)**
Tel.: (81) 3 5546 4111
Web Site: http://www.unisys.co.jp
Sales Range: $1-4.9 Billion
Emp.: 8,820
Sale & Leasing of UNIVAC Computer Systems; Joint Venture with Sperry Corporation (34.68%) & Mitsui & Co., Ltd.
N.A.I.C.S.: 541512

Nishi Nippon Electric Wire & Cable Co., Ltd. (1)
Kasugaura, Oita shi, Oita, 870-0011, Oita Prefecture, Japan **(19.21%)**
Tel.: (81) 975375552
Web Site: https://www.nnd.co.jp
Wire & Cable Mfr
N.A.I.C.S.: 334220
Toshihide Kanai *(Pres)*

Novus International, Inc. (1)
20 Research Park Dr, Saint Charles, MO 63304 **(80%)**
Tel.: (314) 576-8886
Web Site: https://www.novusint.com
Products & Services to the Animal & Agricultural Industry
N.A.I.C.S.: 311119
Francois Fraudeau *(Pres & CEO)*

Subsidiary (Domestic):

Agrivida, Inc. (2)
78E Olympia Ave, Woburn, MA 01801
Tel.: (781) 391-7813
Web Site: http://www.agrivida.com
Pharmaceutical & Biotechnology Mfr
N.A.I.C.S.: 325412
Dan Meagher *(CEO)*

BioResource International, Inc. (2)
4222 Emperor Blvd Ste 460, Durham, NC 27703
Tel.: (919) 993-3389
Web Site: https://www.briworldwide.com
Sales Range: $10-24.9 Million
Emp.: 30
Animal Feed Enzyme Product Development Services
N.A.I.C.S.: 541715

Subsidiary (Non-US):

Novus Argentina, S.A. (2)
Juncal 615 11th Fl A, 1062, Buenos Aires, Argentina **(100%)**
Tel.: (54) 143140900
Web Site: http://www.novusint.com
Sales Range: $10-24.9 Million
Emp.: 3
N.A.I.C.S.: 115116

Novus Chile Ltda. (2)
Ave Ergolf 99 Office 401, Santiago, Chile
Tel.: (56) 22355161
Web Site: http://www.novuschile.cl
Sales Range: $10-24.9 Million
Emp.: 1
N.A.I.C.S.: 115116

Novus Europe NV (2)
Leuvensesteenweg 643, 1930, Zaventem, Belgium **(100%)**
Tel.: (32) 27781441
Web Site: https://www.novusint.com
Farm Management Services
N.A.I.C.S.: 115116

Novus International Pte. Ltd. (2)
51 Golvhill Plz, Singapore, 308900, Singapore **(100%)**
Tel.: (65) 62520688
Farm Management Services
N.A.I.C.S.: 115116

Novus International Trading (Shanghai) Co. Ltd. (2)
Room 1001 Litong Plaza 1350 North Sichuan Road, Hongkou District, Shanghai, 200080, China
Tel.: (86) 2160809288
Web Site: https://www.novusint.com
Livestock & Wholesome Food Agricultural Services
N.A.I.C.S.: 115116

Novus International de Mexico (2)
Av 5 de Febrero 1351 Sequoia 202 Zona Industrial B Juarez 4, CP 76116, Queretaro, Mexico **(100%)**
Tel.: (52) 4429800679
Web Site: https://www.novusint.com
Farm Management Services
N.A.I.C.S.: 115116

Novus Italiana S.r.l. (2)
Via Adriano Bernareggi 4, 24123, Bergamo, Italy
Tel.: (39) 0354128057
Farm Management Services
N.A.I.C.S.: 115116

Novus Spain S.A. (2)
Calle Claudio Coello 76-1 AB, 28001, Madrid, Spain **(100%)**
Tel.: (34) 902158367
Web Site: http://www.novusint.com
Sales Range: $10-24.9 Million
Emp.: 6
N.A.I.C.S.: 115116

Novus de Colombia Ltda. (2)
Calle 100 N 8 A 55, Ofca 607 World Trade Ctr, A251071, Bogota, Colombia **(100%)**
Tel.: (57) 16210029
Web Site: https://www.novusint.com
Farm Management Services
N.A.I.C.S.: 115116

Novus do Brasil Comercio e Importacao Ltda. (2)
Avenida Presidente Vargas 2921 14 Andar, Indaiatuba, Sao Paulo, 13338-705, Brazil
Tel.: (55) 1939368591
Web Site: https://www.novusint.com
Farm Management Services
N.A.I.C.S.: 115116

OMC SHIPPING PTE. LTD. (1)
12 Marina View 12-03 Asia Square Tower 2, Singapore, 018961, Singapore
Tel.: (65) 6 557 2678

Web Site: https://www.omcs.com.sg
Sales Range: $25-49.9 Million
Emp.: 3
Marine Shipping Services
N.A.I.C.S.: 488330
Akhil Dalakoti *(Gen Mgr-Ship Mgmt)*

Orient Marine Co., Ltd. (1)
Marunouchi Trust Tower North 18th Floor 1-8-1 Marunouchi, Chiyoda-ku, Tokyo, 100-0005, Japan
Tel.: (81) 3 6665 9000
Web Site: http://www.toyosenpaku.com
Sales Range: $75-99.9 Million
Emp.: 158
Shipping Machinery & Equipment Distr
N.A.I.C.S.: 423860
Hidekuni Nebashi *(Pres)*

P.T. Mitsui Indonesia (1)
Menara BCA 51st-52nd Floor Grand Indonesia JI M H Thamrin No 1, Jakarta, 10310, Indonesia
Tel.: (62) 2129856111
Sales Range: $100-124.9 Million
Emp.: 120
General Import & Export Trading
N.A.I.C.S.: 212210

P.T. Petnesia Resindo (1)
Jl Moch Toha Km 1 Pabuaran Tumpeng, Tangerang, 15112, Banten, Indonesia
Tel.: (62) 215533083
N.A.I.C.S.: 325220

P.T. Standard Toyo Polymer (1)
Plaza Bank Index 7th Floor JI M H Thamrin No 57, Jakarta, 10350, Indonesia **(50%)**
Tel.: (62) 213903132
Web Site: https://www.statomer.com
Sales Range: $25-49.9 Million
Emp.: 135
PVC Resin Mfr
N.A.I.C.S.: 325211
Toshiharu Nakagima *(Pres)*

PRI Foods Co., Ltd. (1)
2-6-30 Kitahakusandai, Hachinohe, 039-1114, Aomori Prefecture, Japan
Tel.: (81) 178705506
Web Site: http://www.prifoods.jp
Feed Ingredient Mfr & Distr
N.A.I.C.S.: 311119

PT Yamaha Indonesia Motor Manufacturing (1)
JI Dr Krt Radjiman Widyodiningrat RT/RW 009-06 Rawa Terate, Cakung, East Jakarta, 13920, Indonesia
Tel.: (62) 2124575555
Web Site: http://www.yamaha-motor.co.id
Motorcycle Mfr & Distr
N.A.I.C.S.: 336991

PT. Bussan Auto Finance (1)
Jalan Raya Tanjung Barat No 121 RT 14/RW 4 Kelurahan Tanjung Barat, Kecamatan Jagakarsa, Jakarta, 12530, Indonesia
Tel.: (62) 1500750
Web Site: http://www.baf.id
Auto Financing Services
N.A.I.C.S.: 522220
Lynn Ramli *(Co-Pres)*

Penske Truck Leasing Company, L.P. (1)
2675 Morgantown Rd, Reading, PA 19607
Tel.: (610) 775-6000
Web Site: http://www.pensketruckleasing.com
Commercial & Consumer Truck Leasing, Contract Maintenance & Rental Services
N.A.I.C.S.: 532120
Don Metcalf *(Dir-Product Mktg)*

Subsidiary (Domestic):

Decarolis Truck Rental Inc. (2)
333 Colfax St, Rochester, NY 14606-3107
Tel.: (585) 254-1169
Web Site: http://www.decarolis.com
Sales Range: $400-449.9 Million
Emp.: 500
Truck Rental & Leasing
N.A.I.C.S.: 532120
Paul DeCarolis *(Chm)*

Subsidiary (Domestic):

Monroe School Transportation Inc. (3)

MITSUI & CO., LTD.

Mitsui & Co., Ltd.—(Continued)
970 Emerson St, Rochester, NY 14606-2708
Tel.: (585) 458-3230 **(100%)**
Web Site: http://www.nellc.com
Sales Range: $25-49.9 Million
Emp.: 300
School Buses & Transportation
N.A.I.C.S.: 485410

Subsidiary (Domestic):

Kris-Way Truck Leasing Inc. (2)
43 Hemco Rd Ste 1, South Portland, ME 04106
Tel.: (207) 799-8593
Web Site: http://www.kris-way.com
Sales Range: $25-49.9 Million
Emp.: 150
Truck Leasing Services
N.A.I.C.S.: 532120
Thomas Keefer *(Pres)*

Division (Domestic):

Penske Truck Rental (2)
2675 Morgantown Rd, Reading, PA 19607
Tel.: (610) 775-6000
Web Site: http://www.pensketruckrental.com
Sales Range: $125-149.9 Million
Truck Rental Services
N.A.I.C.S.: 532120
Brian Hard *(Pres & CEO)*

Subsidiary (Domestic):

Star Truck Rentals Inc. (2)
3940 Eastern Ave SE, Grand Rapids, MI 49508
Tel.: (616) 243-7033
Web Site: http://www.starlease.com
Sales Range: $25-49.9 Million
Emp.: 130
Provider of Tranportation Services
N.A.I.C.S.: 532120
David Bylenga *(Exec VP)*

Portek International Pte. Ltd. (1)
237 Pandan Loop 02-01, Westech Building, Singapore, 128424, Singapore
Tel.: (65) 68731114
Web Site: https://www.portek.com
Ports Operating Services
N.A.I.C.S.: 483113
Kok Leong Liew *(Chief Technical Officer)*

Subsidiary (Non-US):

Gabon Port Management S.A. (2)
Zone Portuaire d'Owendo, BP 394, Libreville, Gabon
Tel.: (241) 703274
Web Site: http://www.portek.com
Sales Range: $50-74.9 Million
Port Operation Services
N.A.I.C.S.: 488310

Hanggu Cranetek Co., Ltd. (2)
Startowers Officetel 1221 76-1 Sangnam-Dong, Changwon, 641-831, Gyeongsangnam-do, Korea (South)
Tel.: (82) 552816623
Crane Rental Services
N.A.I.C.S.: 238990

PT. Indo Log
Gedung Menara Satu Sentra Kelapa Gading Lt 6 Unit 0601, Jl Boulevard Blok LA 3 No 1 Kelapa Gading Timur Kelapa Gading, Jakarta, 14240, Indonesia
Tel.: (62) 2129385827
Web Site: http://www.portek.com
Marine Cargo Handling Services
N.A.I.C.S.: 488320

PT. Portek Indonesia (2)
Ruko Sentra Bisnis Artha Gading Blok A6-A No 17, Jalan Boulevard Artha Gading, Jakarta, 14240, Indonesia
Tel.: (62) 2129629992
Web Site: http://www.portek.com
Marine Cargo Handling Services
N.A.I.C.S.: 488320

Portek China Ltd. (2)
Unit 2602-03 26/F BEA Tower Millennium City 5 418 Kwun Tong Road, Kwun Tong, New Territories, China (Hong Kong)
Tel.: (852) 2648 2113
Web Site: http://www.portek.com

Sales Range: $50-74.9 Million
Emp.: 10
Industrial Machinery Leasing Services
N.A.I.C.S.: 532412

Subsidiary (Domestic):

Portek Engineering Holdings Pte Ltd (2)
237 Pandan Loop Unit 02-01 Westech Building, Singapore, 128424, Singapore
Tel.: (65) 68731114
Investment Management Service
N.A.I.C.S.: 523999

Subsidiary (Domestic):

Port Technology Pte Ltd (3)
235 Pandan loop Unit 02-01, Singapore, 128424, Singapore
Tel.: (65) 68731114
Port Management & Equipment Leasing Services
N.A.I.C.S.: 532412

Subsidiary (Domestic):

Petrosahara Pte Ltd (4)
20 Harbour Drive 02-01 PSA Vista, Singapore, 117612, Singapore
Tel.: (65) 68731114
Port Management & Equipment Leasing Services
N.A.I.C.S.: 532412

Subsidiary (Domestic):

Portek Systems & Equipment Pte Ltd (3)
20 Harbour Drive 02-01 PSA Vista, Singapore, 117612, Singapore
Tel.: (65) 68731114
Crane Rental Services
N.A.I.C.S.: 532412

Subsidiary (Non-US):

Portek North Asia Limited (2)
Unit C 15/F Chinabest Intl Centre No 8 Kwai On Road, Kwai Chung, New Territories, China (Hong Kong)
Tel.: (852) 26482113
Web Site: http://www.portek.com
Sales Range: $25-49.9 Million
Emp.: 6
Marine Cargo Handling & Port Services
N.A.I.C.S.: 488320
Aline Wong *(Mgr-Corp Comm)*

Regency Steel Asia Pte Ltd. (1)
8 Jurong Town Hall Road 24-03/04 The JTC Summit, Singapore, 609434, Singapore
Tel.: (65) 6 221 0018
Web Site: https://www.regencysteelasia.com
Sales Range: $50-74.9 Million
Emp.: 80
Steel Product Distr
N.A.I.C.S.: 423510
Takayuki Saito *(COO)*

San-ei Sucrochemical Co., Ltd. (1)
24-5 Kitahamacho, Chita, 478-8503, Aichi, Japan **(70%)**
Tel.: (81) 56 255 5111
Web Site: https://www.sanei-toka.co.jp
Emp.: 268
Pharmaceutical Glucose Mfr
N.A.I.C.S.: 325412
Noriyuki Naito *(Pres & Dir)*

Sanki Engineering Co., Ltd. (1)
2-1-1 Nihonbashi Muromachi, Tokyo, 100 8331, Japan **(100%)**
Tel.: (81) 33 27 16 665
Web Site: http://www.sanki.co.jp
Sales Range: $1-4.9 Billion
Emp.: 600
Air-Conditioning & Heating Equipment Mfr
N.A.I.C.S.: 333415

Seikei Steel Column Corp. (1)
3-2 Sakae-cho, Sano, 327-0816, Tochigi, Japan
Tel.: (81) 283 22 4425
Web Site: https://www.seikeicolumn.co.jp
Steel Tube Mfr & Distr
N.A.I.C.S.: 331210

Shanghai Mitsui Plastic Compounds Ltd. (1)
No 511 Yutang Rd, Songjiang Industrial Zone, Shanghai, 201600, China **(33%)**
Tel.: (86) 2157741111
Web Site: http://www.shmpc.com.cn
Sales Range: $1-9.9 Million
Emp.: 150
Plastics Compounding Mfr
N.A.I.C.S.: 325211

Shark Bay Salt Pty. Ltd. (1)
Level 16 Exchange Tower 2 The Esplanade, Perth, 6000, WA, Australia
Tel.: (61) 892658000
Web Site: http://www.salt.com.au
Salt Mfr
N.A.I.C.S.: 325998
Ben Knight *(Gen Mgr-Mktg & Shipping)*

Sumitomo Mitsui Construction Co., Ltd.
2-1-6 Tsukuda, Chuo-ku, Tokyo, 104-0051, Japan
Tel.: (81) 345823171
Web Site: https://www.smcon.co.jp
Sales Range: $900-999.9 Million
Emp.: 2,771
General Contractor; Architectural & Civil Engineering, Including Industrial Plant Installation
N.A.I.C.S.: 236220

Subsidiary (Domestic):

Sumiken Mitsui Road Co., Ltd. (2)
13-27 Yochocho, Shinjuku-ku, Tokyo, 162-0055, Japan
Tel.: (81) 353681660
Web Site: https://www.smrc.co.jp
Rev.: $204,334,930
Assets: $183,057,340
Liabilities: $92,811,010
Net Worth: $90,246,330
Earnings: $3,880,070
Emp.: 440
Fiscal Year-end: 03/31/2024
Civil Engineering Construction Services
N.A.I.C.S.: 237990
Takayuki Matsui *(Chm)*

TRI-NET LOGISTICS (ASIA) PTE. LTD. (1)
80 Robinson Road 19-01, Singapore, 68898, Singapore
Tel.: (65) 64210488
Sales Range: $25-49.9 Million
Emp.: 4
Logistics Consulting Servies
N.A.I.C.S.: 541614

Taiyokenki Rental Co., Ltd. (1)
2-26 Otsubo-cho, Suruga-ku, Shizuoka, 422-8507, Japan
Tel.: (81) 542843111
Web Site: http://www.taiyokenki.co.jp
Construction Equipment Rental Services
N.A.I.C.S.: 532412

Toho Bussan Kaisha, Ltd. (1)
Shiba Park Building A 8F Shiba Koen 2-4-1, Minato-ku, Tokyo, 105-8547, Japan
Tel.: (81) 3 3438 5711
Web Site: http://www.tohob.co.jp
Sales Range: $75-99.9 Million
Emp.: 163
Agricultural Supplies Distr
N.A.I.C.S.: 424910
Takashi Yokoyama *(Mng Officer)*

Tokyo International Air Cargo Terminal Ltd. (1)
6-3 Haneda Airport 2-Chome, Ota-ku, Tokyo, 144-0041, Japan
Tel.: (81) 35 757 7502
Web Site: https://www.tiact.co.jp
Emp.: 236
Air Cargo Handling Services
N.A.I.C.S.: 488119
Hiroshi Yokoyama *(Pres & CEO)*

Toyota Canada, Inc. (1)
1 Toyota Place, Toronto, M1H 1H9, ON, Canada
Tel.: (416) 438-6320
Web Site: https://www.toyota.ca
Sales Range: $250-299.9 Million
Emp.: 575
CBU Vehicle Import & Sales; Joint Venture of Mitsui & Co., Ltd. (50%) & Toyota Motor Corporation (50%)
N.A.I.C.S.: 423120
Stephen Beatty *(VP-Corp)*

Toyota Turkiye Motorlu Araclar A.S. (1)
Gulsuyu Mevkii Ankara Asfalti, 34846, Istanbul, Turkiye **(10%)**
Tel.: (90) 2164585858
Web Site: http://www.toyotasa.com.tr
Sales Range: $50-74.9 Million
Emp.: 150
Automobiles Mfr; Joint Venture of Haci Omer Sabanci Holding A.S., Toyota Motor Corp. & Mitsui & Co., Ltd.
N.A.I.C.S.: 336110

Trinet Logistics Co., Ltd. (1)
7-2 Honcho 1-Chome Nihonbashi, Chuo-ku, Tokyo, Japan
Tel.: (81) 3 5299 8851
Web Site: http://www.trinet-logi.com
Rev.: $370,052,000
Emp.: 180
Storage & Logistics Consulting Services
N.A.I.C.S.: 493110
Akio Yamada *(Sr Mng Officer)*

VENDOR SERVICE CO., LTD. (1)
Hibiya Fort Tower 1-1-1Nishi-Shimbashi, Minato-ku, Tokyo, 105-0003, Japan **(100%)**
Tel.: (81) 36 362 6000
Web Site: https://www.vsk.co.jp
Emp.: 375
Food Ingredients & Foods Packaging Materials Distr
N.A.I.C.S.: 311999
Takeshi Egawa *(Pres & CEO)*

Veloce Logistica SA (1)
Av Luigi Papaiz 239 Administrative Block 1st Floor, Diadema, Campanario, 09931-610, Sao Paulo, Brazil
Tel.: (55) 1139057000
Web Site: http://www.velocelog.com.br
Logistic Services
N.A.I.C.S.: 541614

World Hi-Vision Channel, Inc. (1)
6-25-14 Jingumae Jingumae Media Square Building, Shibuya-Ku, Tokyo, 150-0001, Japan
Tel.: (81) 364511202
Web Site: https://www.twellv.co.jp
Television Broadcasting Services
N.A.I.C.S.: 516120

MITSUI AUTO FINANCE PERU S.A.

Av Juan de Arona 151 Interior 201, San Isidro, Lima, Peru
Tel.: (51) 16308500 Pe
Web Site: https://www.mafperu.com
Year Founded: 1998
MITSUFC1—(LIM)
Sales Range: Less than $1 Million
Auto Sales Financing Services
N.A.I.C.S.: 522220
Jorge Fernando Chavez Alvarez *(Chm)*

MITSUI CHEMICALS, INC.

Yaesu Central Tower 2-2-1 Yaesu, Chuo-ku Tokyo Midtown Yaesu, Tokyo, 104-0028, Japan
Tel.: (81) 368807500 JP
Web Site: https://jp.mitsuichemicals.com
Year Founded: 1997
4183—(TKS)
Rev.: $11,565,801,230
Assets: $14,646,563,590
Liabilities: $8,136,995,930
Net Worth: $6,509,567,660
Earnings: $330,493,390
Emp.: 19,861
Fiscal Year-end: 03/31/24
Chemical Products Mfr
N.A.I.C.S.: 325110
Tsutomu Tannowa *(Chm)*

Subsidiaries:

ACOMON AG (1)
Weinbergstrasse 5, Zug, 6300, Switzerland
Tel.: (41) 41 726 1400
Web Site: http://www.acomon.com
Optical Monomers Distr

AND PRIVATE COMPANIES

MITSUI CHEMICALS, INC.

N.A.I.C.S.: 423460
Eckehard Mielke *(CEO)*

ARRK Corporation (1)
10F Tatsuno Minami Hommachi Building
2-2-9 Minami Hommachi, Chuo-ku, Osaka,
541-0054, Japan **(81.03%)**
Tel.: (81) 66 260 1801
Web Site: https://jp.arrk.com
Emp.: 785
Industrial Design Model Mfr
N.A.I.C.S.: 541420
Jiro Sakano *(Gen Mgr-Asia Bus Div & Exec Officer)*

Chiba Phenol Company, Limited (1)
1-5-2 Higashi-Shimbashi, Minato-ku, Tokyo,
105-7122, Japan
Tel.: (81) 3 6253 3287
Web Site: http://www.mitsuichem.co.jp
Sales Range: $1-4.9 Billion
Emp.: 10,000
Phenol Mfr & Distr
N.A.I.C.S.: 325998

Chiba Polyol Corporation (1)
1-5-2 Higashi-Shimbashi, Minato-ku, Tokyo,
105-7117, Japan
Tel.: (81) 3 6253 4085
Web Site: http://www.mitsuichem.com
Sales Range: $250-299.9 Million
Emp.: 1,000
Chemical Products Mfr & Distr
N.A.I.C.S.: 325998

Cosmo Polyurethane (Malaysia) Sdn, Bhd (1)
Suite E-06-16 Plaza Mont'Kiara No 2, Jalan
Kiara Mont'Kiara, 50480, Kuala Lumpur,
Malaysia
Tel.: (60) 362033223
Web Site: https://kemicalinfo.com
Polyurethane Chemical Distr
N.A.I.C.S.: 424690
Cliff Chan *(Gen Mgr)*

Cosmos Corporation (1)
3 Chigusa-kaigan, Ichihara, Chiba, 299-
0108, Japan **(100%)**
Tel.: (81) 436629758
Cargo Handling & Accident Prevention Services
N.A.I.C.S.: 488320

Dentca, Inc. (1)
357 Van Ness Way 250, Torrance, CA
90501
Web Site: http://www.dentca.com
3D Printable Denture Material Mfr
N.A.I.C.S.: 333248
Sun Kwon *(Pres & CEO)*

DuPont Mitsui Fluorochemicals Co., Ltd. (1)
1-5-18 Sarugaku-cho Chiyoda-ku, Tokyo,
101-0064, Japan **(50%)**
Tel.: (81) 352815800
Web Site: http://www.md-fluoro.co.jp
Sales Range: $150-199.9 Million
Fluorocarbon Compounds & Resins Mfr
N.A.I.C.S.: 325211

DuPont Mitsui Polychemicals Co., Ltd. (1)
1-5-2 Siodome City Center Higashi-
Shimbashi, Minato-ku, Tokyo, 105-7117,
Japan **(50%)**
Tel.: (81) 362534000
Web Site: http://www.mdp.jp
Polyolefin Resins, Coating Resins & Foam Sheeting Mfr
N.A.I.C.S.: 325211

Evolue Japan Co., Ltd. (1)
Tokyo Midtown Yaesu Yaesu Central Tower
2-2-1 Yaesu, Chuo-ku, Tokyo, 104-0028,
Japan
Tel.: (81) 362534750
Polyethylene Mfr & Distr
N.A.I.C.S.: 325998

Foshan Mitsui Chemicals & SKC Polyurethanes Co., Ltd. (1)
No 51 C Zone, Sanshui Industrial Park Leping Town Sanshui District, Foshan, Guangdong, China
Tel.: (86) 75787662850
Polyurethane Mfr & Distr
N.A.I.C.S.: 326150

Grand Siam Composites Co., Ltd. (1)
1 Siam Cement Road, Bangsue, Bangkok,
10800, Thailand
Tel.: (66) 25862500
Sales Range: $125-149.9 Million
Polypropylene Compounds Mfr & Sales;
Owned 48% by Mitsui Chemicals, Inc. &
46% by SCG Chemicals Co., Ltd.
N.A.I.C.S.: 325998
Kazunori Asami *(Mng Dir)*

Heraeus Kulzer GmbH (1)
(100%)
Sales Range: $450-499.9 Million
Emp.: 1,420
Dental, Medical & Laboratory Technology Services
N.A.I.C.S.: 811210

Subsidiary (Non-US):

Heraeus Dental Korea Co., Ltd. (2)
Room 501 Namsung Plaza Bldg 345-30
Gasan-dong, Geumcheon-gu, Seoul, 153-
782, Korea (South)
Tel.: (82) 2 709 30701
Web Site: http://www.heraeus-dental.kr
Dental Equipment Distr
N.A.I.C.S.: 423450

Heraeus Kulzer Austria GmbH (2)
Andromeda Tower Donau - City - Strasse 6
Top 2 OG/ 1, 1220, Vienna, Austria
Tel.: (43) 14080941
Web Site: https://kulzer.de
Dental Equipment Distr
N.A.I.C.S.: 423450

Heraeus Kulzer Benelux B.V. (2)
Fustweg 5, 2031 CJ, Haarlem, Netherlands
Tel.: (31) 235434250
Web Site: http://www.heraeus-kulzer.com
Dental Equipment Distr
N.A.I.C.S.: 423450

Heraeus Kulzer Dental Ltd. (2)
1585 Gu Mei Rd, Shanghai, 200233, China
Tel.: (86) 2123526200
Web Site: http://www.heraeus-kulzer.com
Dental Equipment Distr
N.A.I.C.S.: 423450
Maik Walther *(Pres)*

Heraeus Kulzer Hungary Kft. (2)
Stefania ut 101-103, 1143, Budapest, Hungary
Tel.: (36) 18880822
Web Site: https://www.mykulzer.hu
Dental Equipment Distr
N.A.I.C.S.: 423450

Heraeus Kulzer Iberia (2)
Marie Curie 19 Bajo Ofic 5, Rivas Vaciamadrid, 28521, Madrid, Spain
Tel.: (34) 912967292
Web Site: https://kulzer.es
Dental Equipment Distr
N.A.I.C.S.: 423450

Heraeus Kulzer Japan Kabushiki Kaisha (2)
2nd floor TSK Building 4-8-13 Hongo,
Bunkyo-ku, Tokyo, 113 0033, Japan
Tel.: (81) 358032151
Web Site: https://kulzer.co.jp
Sales Range: $25-49.9 Million
Emp.: 27
Dental Equipment Distr
N.A.I.C.S.: 423450

Subsidiary (US):

Heraeus Kulzer LLC (2)
4315 S Lafayette Blvd, South Bend, IN
46614-2517 **(100%)**
Tel.: (574) 291-0661
Web Site: https://kulzerus.com
Sales Range: $25-49.9 Million
Emp.: 80
Dental Equipment Distr
N.A.I.C.S.: 423450
Sandy Wisler *(Dir-HR)*

Subsidiary (Non-US):

Heraeus Kulzer Ltd. (2)
Unit 58 Tempus Business Centre Kingsclere Road, Albert Road/Northbrook Street, Basingstoke, RG21 6XG, Berks, United Kingdom

Tel.: (44) 163530500
Web Site: https://www.kulzer.com
Dental Equipment Distr
N.A.I.C.S.: 423450

Heraeus Kulzer Mexico S.A. de C.V. (2)
Homero 527 floor 3 Col PolancoAlc Miguel
Hidalgo, 11550, Mexico, Mexico
Tel.: (52) 5555315549
Web Site: https://kulzer.mx
Dental Equipment Distr
N.A.I.C.S.: 423450

Heraeus Kulzer Nordic AB (2)
Florettgatan 18, SE 250 24, Helsingborg,
Sweden
Tel.: (46) 424530700
Web Site: http://www.heraeus-kulzer.se
Dental Equipment Distr
N.A.I.C.S.: 423450
Kjell Carlsson *(Mng Dir)*

Heraeus Kulzer S.r.l. (2)
Via Console Flaminio 5/7, 20134, Milan,
Italy
Tel.: (39) 022100941
Web Site: http://www.heraeus-kulzer.com
Dental Equipment Distr
N.A.I.C.S.: 423450

Heraeus Kulzer South America Ltda. (2)
Rua Cenno Sbrighi 27 - Sala 42 - Agua
Branca, Sao Paulo, 05036 010, SP, Brazil
Tel.: (55) 8007717723
Web Site: https://kulzer.com.br
Dental Equipment Distr
N.A.I.C.S.: 423450

Hokkaido Mitsui Chemicals, Inc. (1)
1 Toyonuma-cho, Sunagawa, Hokkaido,
073-0138, Japan **(100%)**
Tel.: (81) 12 554 3131
Web Site: https://www.hmci.co.jp
Sales Range: $25-49.9 Million
Emp.: 50
Wood Adhesives, Paper Resins, Foliar Activators & Chemical Products Mfr & Sales
N.A.I.C.S.: 325520
Hiroshi Ishimoto *(Pres)*

Subsidiary (Domestic):

Isikari Co., Ltd. (2)
17-1-33 Higashi-Ichijyo-minami, Sunagawa,
Hokkaido, 073-0131, Japan **(100%)**
Tel.: (81) 125 54 4141
Petroleum Products Sales; Insurance Services
N.A.I.C.S.: 424720

Image Polymers Company (1)
384 Lowell St Unit 206, Wakefield, MA
01880
Tel.: (781) 587-1096
Web Site: http://www.image-polymers.com
Toner Resin Mfr & Distr
N.A.I.C.S.: 325211
Ken Spatola *(VP-Sls & Mktg)*

Japan Composite Co., Ltd. (1)
Advantech Nihonbashi Building 2F 3-2-13
Nihonbashi Honcho, Chuo-ku, Tokyo, 103-
0023, Japan
Tel.: (81) 33 516 3002
Web Site: https://www.j-comp.co.jp
Sales Range: $50-74.9 Million
Emp.: 120
Unsaturated Polyester Resins Mfr & Distr
N.A.I.C.S.: 325211
Nobuyuki Matsubara *(Mng Dir)*

KATSUZAI CHEMICAL CORPORATION (1)
3-8-3 Nihonbashi Honcho Nihonbashi Life
Science Building 3, Chuo-ku, Tokyo, 103-
0023, Japan **(54.5%)**
Tel.: (81) 35 623 3181
Web Site: https://www.katsuzai.co.jp
Synthetic Resins & Chemical Products Mfr
N.A.I.C.S.: 325211
Hidenori Hayashi *(Gen Mgr-Sls)*

KOC Solution Co., Ltd. (1)
10-26 Exporo 339beon-gil, Yuseong-gu,
Daejeon, Korea (South)
Tel.: (82) 429335267
Plastic Len Monomer Mfr & Distr
N.A.I.C.S.: 339115

KYODO CARBON CO., LTD. (1)
1-1-7 Motowanishi-cho, Muroran, 050-0065,
Hokkaido, Japan
Tel.: (81) 143 55 3074
Web Site: http://www.mitsuichem.com
Liquid Carbon Gas Mfr & Distr
N.A.I.C.S.: 325120

KYUSHU INDUSTRIAL GAS, INC. (1)
20-2 Oura-machi, Omuta, 836-0824, Fukuoka, Japan
Tel.: (81) 944522603
Web Site: http://www.mitsuichem.com
Emp.: 3
Industrial Gas Mfr & Distr
N.A.I.C.S.: 325120

Kulzer Dental Ltd. (1)
No 1585 Gumei Road, Xuhui District,
Shanghai, 200233, China
Tel.: (86) 2123526200
Dental Equipment Mfr & Distr
N.A.I.C.S.: 339114

Kulzer GmbH (1)
Leipziger Strasse 2, 63450, Hanau, Germany
Tel.: (49) 61814139999
Web Site: http://www.kulzer.de
Dental Material Mfr & Distr
N.A.I.C.S.: 339114

Kulzer Japan Co., Ltd. (1)
2nd floor TSK Building 4-8-13, Hongo
Bunkyo-ku, Tokyo, 113-0033, Japan
Tel.: (81) 358032151
Web Site: https://kulzer.co.jp
Emp.: 27
Dental Product Mfr
N.A.I.C.S.: 339114

Kyowa Industrial Co., Ltd. (1)
711 Glenn Ave, Wheeling, IL 60090
Tel.: (847) 459-3500
Chemical Products Mfr
N.A.I.C.S.: 325998

Kyowa Industrial Co., Ltd. (1)
4-18-18 Suguecho, Sanjo, Niigata Prefecture, Japan
Tel.: (81) 256344441
Web Site: https://www.kyowa-ind.co.jp
Injection Mold Die Mfr
N.A.I.C.S.: 333514
Yusuke Kumagai *(Pres)*

MC Business Support, Ltd. (1)
2-4-1 Higashi-Shimbashi, Minato-ku, Tokyo,
105-0021, Japan
Tel.: (81) 354083900
Web Site: http://www.mitsuichem.com
Business Support Services
N.A.I.C.S.: 561499

MC Industries, Ltd. (1)
14-1 Komagoekitamachi, Shimizu-ku, Shizuoka, 424-8710, Japan
Tel.: (81) 543 34 1221
Web Site: http://www.mitsuichem.com
Synthetic Resin Compounds & Wood Preservatives Mfr
N.A.I.C.S.: 325998

MC Operation Support, Ltd. (1)
3 Chikusa Kaigan, Ichihara, 299-0108,
Chiba, Japan
Tel.: (81) 436629677
Web Site: https://www.mcos.co.jp
Emp.: 649
Business Support Services
N.A.I.C.S.: 561499

MC RYOKKA CO., LTD. (1)
1-9-1 Nihonbashi-honcho, Chuo-ku, Tokyo,
103-0023, Japan
Tel.: (81) 352902956
Web Site: https://www.mc-ryokka.com
Agricultural Chemical Product Mfr
N.A.I.C.S.: 325320

MC Tohcello (Malaysia) Sdn. Bhd. (1)
A-07-06 Empire Tower Empire Subang
SS16/1, 47500, Subang Jaya, Selangor,
Malaysia
Tel.: (60) 356314597
Solar Encapsulant Material Distr
N.A.I.C.S.: 423330

MCNS Polyurethanes Malaysia Sdn. Bhd. (1)

4981

MITSUI CHEMICALS, INC.

Mitsui Chemicals, Inc.—(Continued)
Suite E-06-16 Plaza Mont'Kiara No 2 Jalan Kiara, Mont'Kiara, 50480, Kuala Lumpur, Malaysia
Tel.: (60) 362033223
Polyurethane Mfr & Distr
N.A.I.C.S.: 326150

Miike Dyes Works, Ltd. (1)
30 Asamuta-machi, Omuta, Fukuoka, 836-0817, Japan (100%)
Tel.: (81) 944518181
Dyestuffs, Pigments & Intermediates Mfr & Sales
N.A.I.C.S.: 325130

Mitsui Advanced Composites (Zhongshan) Co., Ltd.
18 Haojiang Road, Zhongshan Torch Hi-Tech Industrial Development Zone, Zhongshan, 528437, Guangdong, China (100%)
Tel.: (86) 7602 389 5888
Web Site: http://www.mitsuichem.com
Polypropylne Compounds Mfr & Sales
N.A.I.C.S.: 325998
Sotoyeme Toshiti *(Gen Mgr)*

Mitsui Chemical Analysis & Consulting Service, Inc. (1)
580-32 Nagaura, Sodegaura, 299-0265, Chiba, Japan (100%)
Tel.: (81) 43 864 2400
Web Site: https://www.mcanac.co.jp
Emp.: 500
Chemical Analysis, Measuring & Safety Testing
N.A.I.C.S.: 541380
Tsukasa Iida *(Pres)*

Mitsui Chemical Logistics, Inc. (1)
7-13-10 ginza, Chuo-ku, Tokyo, 104-0061, Japan
Tel.: (81) 335475951
Logistics, Freight Transportation & Packaging Services
N.A.I.C.S.: 541614

Subsidiary (Domestic):

MCI Logistics (East), Inc. (2)
7-13-10 Ginza, Chuo-ku, Tokyo, 104-0061, Japan (100%)
Tel.: (81) 3 3547 5970
Trucking & Warehousing Services
N.A.I.C.S.: 484121

MCI Logistics (West), Inc. (2)
2-17 Rinkai-cho, Izumiotsu, Osaka, 595-0075, Japan (100%)
Tel.: (81) 725214388
Web Site: http://www.mcil-west.co.jp
Sales Range: $25-49.9 Million
Trucking & Warehousing Services
N.A.I.C.S.: 484121

Mitsui Chemicals & SKC Polyurethanes Inc. (1)
Shiodome City Center 5-2 Higashi-Shimbashi 1-chome, Minato-ku, Tokyo, Japan
Tel.: (81) 362534120
Web Site: http://www.mcnskc.com
Polyurethane Material Mfr & Distr
N.A.I.C.S.: 325211
E. J. Lim *(Co-CEO)*

Mitsui Chemicals (Shanghai) Co., Ltd. (1)
21F Capital Square 268 Hengtong Road, Jing'an District, Shanghai, 200070, China (100%)
Tel.: (86) 2158886336
Web Site: http://www.cn.mitsuichem.com
Sales Range: $50-74.9 Million
Chemical Marketer
N.A.I.C.S.: 424690

Mitsui Chemicals (Thailand) Co., Ltd. (1)
33/4 Unit TNA01 Floor 33 Tower A The 9th Towers Grand Rama 9, Rama 9 Road Kwaeng Huay Kwang Khet Huay Kwang, Bangkok, 10310, Thailand
Tel.: (66) 20263242
Chemical Product Mfr & Distr
N.A.I.C.S.: 325998

Mitsui Chemicals Agro, Inc. (1)
Nihonbashi Dia Building 1-19-1 Nihonbashi, Chuo-ku, Tokyo, 103-0027, Japan (100%)
Tel.: (81) 35 290 2700
Web Site: https://www.mitsui-agro.com
Emp.: 450
Pesticide & Other Agricultural Chemical Products Developer, Mfr & Distr
N.A.I.C.S.: 325320
Takero Katakura *(Sr Mng Exec Officer)*

Mitsui Chemicals America, Inc. (1)
800 Westchester Ave Ste S306, Rye Brook, NY 10573 (100%)
Tel.: (914) 253-0777
Web Site: http://www.mitsuichemicals.com
Sales Range: $25-49.9 Million
Emp.: 40
Chemical Products & Plastics Developer & Mfr
N.A.I.C.S.: 325998

Joint Venture (Domestic):

Advanced Composites, Inc. (2)
1062 S 4th Ave, Sidney, OH 45365
Tel.: (937) 575-9800
Web Site: https://www.advcmp.com
Sales Range: $100-124.9 Million
Polypropylene Compounds Mfr & Sales; Owned 62.8% by Mitsui Chemicals America, Inc., 27% by Mitsui & Co., Ltd. & 10.2% by Marubeni America Corporation
N.A.I.C.S.: 325998

Subsidiary (Non-US):

Advanced Composites Mexicana S.A. de C.V. (3)
Avenida Japon 306 Parque Industrial San Francisco, San Francisco de los Romo, 20303, Aguascalientes, Mexico
Tel.: (52) 4499254010
Web Site: https://www.acpmex.com
Polypropylene Compounds Mfr & Sales
N.A.I.C.S.: 325998

Subsidiary (Domestic):

Anderson Development Company (2)
1415 E Michigan St, Adrian, MI 49221-3499 (100%)
Tel.: (517) 263-2121
Web Site: http://www.andersondevelopment.com
Sales Range: $50-74.9 Million
Specialty Chemicals Mfr & Sales
N.A.I.C.S.: 325998
Mark Kramer *(Pres & CEO)*

SDC Technologies, Inc. (2)
45 Parker Ste 100, Irvine, CA 92618
Tel.: (714) 939-8300
Web Site: http://www.sdctech.com
Coating Product Mfr
N.A.I.C.S.: 325510

Mitsui Chemicals Asia Pacific, Ltd. (1)
3 HarbourFront Place 10-01 HarbourFront Tower 2, Singapore, 099254, Singapore
Tel.: (65) 6 534 2611
Web Site: https://www.ap.mitsuichemicals.com
Sales Range: $25-49.9 Million
Emp.: 100
Semiconductors & Polyethylene Products Mfr
N.A.I.C.S.: 333242
Ikunori Sakai *(CEO & Mng Dir)*

Mitsui Chemicals Do Brasil Comercio Ltda. (1)
Avenida Paulista 91 6 andar Conjunto 602, Bela Vista, Sao Paulo, 01311-000, SP, Brazil
Tel.: (55) 1130164000
Web Site: http://www.mitsuichemicalsbrasil.com
Emp.: 9
Chemical Products Mfr
N.A.I.C.S.: 325998

Mitsui Chemicals Engineering Co., Ltd. (1)
1-7-6 Shimbashi, Minato-ku, Tokyo, 105-0005, Japan (100%)
Tel.: (81) 335758111
Web Site: http://www.mcec.co.jp
Sales Range: $125-149.9 Million
Emp.: 419
Engineering, Plant Construction & Machine Maintenance Services
N.A.I.C.S.: 541330

Mitsui Chemicals Europe GmbH (1)
Oststr 34, 40211, Dusseldorf, Germany (100%)
Tel.: (49) 211173320
Sales Range: $25-49.9 Million
Emp.: 48
Polypropylene Compounds Mfr & Sales
N.A.I.C.S.: 325998
Toru Morita *(Pres & CEO)*

Mitsui Chemicals Functional Composites (Shanghai) Co., Ltd. (1)
No 736 Huachuang Road, Jinshanwei Town Jinshan District, Shanghai, 201512, China
Tel.: (86) 2167321999
Milastomer & Admer Product Mfr & Distr
N.A.I.C.S.: 325211

Mitsui Chemicals India, PVT. LTD. (1)
3rd Floor B-Wing Prius Platinum D3, District Center Saket, New Delhi, 110017, India
Tel.: (91) 1141204200
Web Site: https://in.mitsuichemicals.com
Sales Range: $25-49.9 Million
Emp.: 55
Industrial Chemical Whslr
N.A.I.C.S.: 424690

Mitsui Chemicals Industrial Products Ltd (1)
3-39-10 Yushima, Bunkyo-ku, Tokyo, 113-0034, Japan
Tel.: (81) 338370281
Fabricated Construction Material Mfr & Distr
N.A.I.C.S.: 327120

Mitsui Chemicals Korea, Inc. (1)
15F Building-B pine avenue 100 Eulji-ro, Jung-gu, Seoul, 04551, Korea (South)
Tel.: (82) 260310200
Polyurethane Mfr & Distr
N.A.I.C.S.: 326150

Mitsui Chemicals MC, Ltd. (1)
14-1 Komagoshi Kitamachi, Shimizu-ku, Shizuoka, 424-0906, Japan
Tel.: (81) 543341221
Web Site: https://www.mck.co.jp
Emp.: 191
Polyurethane Resin Mfr & Distr
N.A.I.C.S.: 325211

Mitsui Chemicals Operation Services Co., Ltd. (1)
Tel.: (81) 436629677
Web Site: http://www.mcos.co.jp
Chemical Products Mfr
N.A.I.C.S.: 325998

Mitsui Chemicals Scientex Sdn. Bhd. (1)
S11-06 First Subang Jalan SS15/4G, 47500, Subang Jaya, Selangor, Malaysia
Tel.: (60) 356217798
Urethane Prepolymer Mfr & Distr
N.A.I.C.S.: 326150

Mitsui Chemicals Singapore R&D Centre Pte. Ltd. (1)
50 Science Park Road 06-08 The Kendall Singapore Science Park II, Singapore, 117406, Singapore
Tel.: (65) 65705730
Chemical Product Research & Development Services
N.A.I.C.S.: 541715

Mitsui Chemicals Sun Alloys Co., Ltd. (1)
580-271 Nagaura, Sodegaura, 299-0265, Chiba Prefecture, Japan
Tel.: (81) 438640251
Web Site: https://www.sunalloys.com
Emp.: 151
Synthetic Resin Compound Product Mfr
N.A.I.C.S.: 325211

Mitsui Chemicals Tohcello, Inc. (1)
Sumitomo Fudosan Kanda Bldg 7 Kanda Mitoshiro-cho, Chiyoda-ku, Tokyo, 101-8485, Japan
Tel.: (81) 36 895 9300
Web Site: https://mc-tohcello.co.jp
Emp.: 1,058
Packaging Silicon Coated Film & Sheet Mfr

INTERNATIONAL PUBLIC

N.A.I.C.S.: 322220
Takeshi Kaide *(CEO)*

Subsidiary (Domestic):

Mitsui Chemicals Tohcello, Inc. - Anjo Works (2)
174-3 Dando Jogairi-cho, Anjo, 444-1202, Aichi, Japan
Tel.: (81) 566921165
Foam Molded Hard Sheets Mfr
N.A.I.C.S.: 326130

Division (Domestic):

Mitsui Chemicals Tohcello, Inc. - Functional Sheet Business Division (2)
Sumitomo Fudosan Kanda Bldg 7 Kanda Mitoshiro-cho, Chiyoda-ku, Tokyo, 101-8485, Japan
Tel.: (81) 3 6895 5722
Packaging Functional Sheet Mfr
N.A.I.C.S.: 322220

Subsidiary (Domestic):

Mitsui Chemicals Tohcello, Inc. - Hamamatsu Works (2)
2253-3 Ono, Hamakita-ku, Hamamatsu, 434-0002, Shizuoka, Japan
Tel.: (81) 535822253
Deposition Films Mfr
N.A.I.C.S.: 325992

Unit (Domestic):

Mitsui Chemicals Tohcello, Inc. - Ibaraki Works (2)
9 Kitatone, Koga, 306-0213, Ibaraki, Japan
Tel.: (81) 280921562
Web Site: http://www.mc-tohcello.co.jp
Silicon Coated & Polypropylene Film Mfr
N.A.I.C.S.: 327910

Subsidiary (Domestic):

Mitsui Chemicals Tohcello, Inc. - Industrial Film Business Division (2)
Sumitomo Fudosan Kanda Bldg 7 Kanda Mitoshiro-cho, Chiyoda-ku, Tokyo, 101-8485, Japan
Tel.: (81) 368955710
Packaging Silicon Coated Film & Sheet Mfr
N.A.I.C.S.: 322220

Mitsui Chemicals Tohcello, Inc. - Katsuta Works (2)
148-27 Kouya, Hitachinaka, 312-0002, Ibaraki, Japan
Tel.: (81) 292851023
Packaging Functional Sheet Mfr
N.A.I.C.S.: 322220

Unit (Domestic):

Mitsui Chemicals Tohcello, Inc. - Koga Works (2)
3 Okasato, Koga, 306-0206, Ibaraki, Japan
Tel.: (81) 280 98 1115
Web Site: http://www.mc-tohcello.co.jp
Polypropylene & Multiple Layer Film Mfr
N.A.I.C.S.: 322220

Mitsui Chemicals Tohcello, Inc. - Nagoya Works (2)
Nagoya Works 2-1 Tango-dori, Minami-ku, Nagoya, 457-0801, Aichi, Japan
Tel.: (81) 52 614 2131
Web Site: http://www.mc-tohcello.co.jp
Photovoltaic Encapsulants & Semiconductor Tapes Mfr
N.A.I.C.S.: 325998

Division (Domestic):

Mitsui Chemicals Tohcello, Inc. - Packaging Film Business Division (2)
Sumitomo Fudosan Kanda Bldg 7 Kanda Mitoshiro-cho, Chiyoda-ku, Tokyo, 101-8485, Japan
Tel.: (81) 3 6895 5700
Packaging Silicon Coated Film & Sheet Mfr
N.A.I.C.S.: 322220

Mitsui Chemicals, Inc. - Elastomers Division (1)
Shiodome City Center 5-2 Higashi-Shimbashi 1-chome, Minato-ku, Tokyo, 105-

AND PRIVATE COMPANIES — MITSUI CHEMICALS, INC.

7122, Japan
Tel.: (81) 3 6253 3425
Web Site: http://www.mitsuichem.com
Polymeric Materials Mfr
N.A.I.C.S.: 325998

Mitsui Chemicals, Inc. - Fine & Performance Chemicals Division (1)
Shiodome City Center 5-2 Higashi-Shimbashi 1-chome, Minato-ku, Tokyo, 105-7117, Japan
Tel.: (81) 3 6253 3815
Specialty Chemicals Mfr
N.A.I.C.S.: 325998

Mitsui Chemicals, Inc. - Functional Film Division (1)
Shiodome City Center 5-2 Higashi-Shimbashi 1-chome, Minato-ku, Tokyo, 105-7117, Japan
Tel.: (81) 3 6253 3883
Fabricated Chemical Products Mfr
N.A.I.C.S.: 325998

Mitsui Chemicals, Inc. - Health Care Materials Division (1)
Shiodome City Center 5-2 Higashi-Shimbashi 1-chome, Minato-ku, Tokyo, 1057122, Japan
Tel.: (81) 3 6253 3858
Health Care Functional Chemicals Mfr
N.A.I.C.S.: 325998

Mitsui Chemicals, Inc. - Ichihara Works (1)
3 Chigusa-kaigan, Ichihara, 299-0108, Chiba, Japan
Tel.: (81) 436623221
Chemical Products Mfr
N.A.I.C.S.: 325998

Mitsui Chemicals, Inc. - Industrial Chemicals Div. (1)
Shiodome City Center 5-2 Higashi-Shimbashi 1-chome, Minato-ku, Tokyo, 105-0122, Japan
Tel.: (81) 3 6253 3290
Web Site: http://www.mitsuichem.com
Chemical Products Mfr
N.A.I.C.S.: 325998

Mitsui Chemicals, Inc. - Iwakuni-Ohtake Works (1)
1-2 Waki 6-chome Waki-cho, Kuga-gun, Yamaguchi, 740-0061, Japan
Tel.: (81) 827539010
Chemical Products Mfr
N.A.I.C.S.: 325998

Mitsui Chemicals, Inc. - Licensing Division (1)
Shiodome City Center 5-2 Higashi-Shimbashi 1-chome, Minato-ku, Tokyo, 105-7122, Japan
Tel.: (81) 368807431
Functional Chemical Products Mfr
N.A.I.C.S.: 325998

Mitsui Chemicals, Inc. - Mobara Branch Factory (1)
1900 Togo, Mobara, 297-8666, Chiba, Japan
Tel.: (81) 475 23 0111
Web Site: http://www.mitsuichem.com
Chemical Products Mfr
N.A.I.C.S.: 325998

Mitsui Chemicals, Inc. - Nagoya Works (1)
1 Tangodori 2-chome, Minami-ku, Nagoya, 457-8522, Japan
Tel.: (81) 526142111
Web Site: http://www.mitsuichem.com
Chemical Products Mfr
N.A.I.C.S.: 325998

Mitsui Chemicals, Inc. - Nonwovens Fabric Division (1)
Shiodome City Center 5-2 Higashi-Shimbashi 1-chome, Minato-ku, Tokyo, 105-7122, Japan
Tel.: (81) 3 6253 3620
Fabricated Chemical Products Mfr
N.A.I.C.S.: 325998

Mitsui Chemicals, Inc. - Omuta Works (1)
30 Asamuta-machi, Omuta, 836-8610, Fukuoka, Japan
Tel.: (81) 944 51 8111
Web Site: http://www.mitsuichem.com
Chemical Products Mfr
N.A.I.C.S.: 325998

Mitsui Chemicals, Inc. - Osaka Works (1)
6 Takasago 1-chome, Takaishi, 592-8501, Osaka, Japan
Tel.: (81) 722683502
Chemical Products Mfr
N.A.I.C.S.: 325998

Mitsui Chemicals, Inc. - PTA PET Division (1)
Shiodome City Center 5-2 Higashi-Shimbashi 1-chome, Minato-ku, Tokyo, 105-7122, Japan
Tel.: (81) 3 6253 3220
Web Site: http://www.mitsuichem.com
Chemical Products Mfr
N.A.I.C.S.: 325998

Mitsui Chemicals, Inc. - Performance Compound Division (1)
Shiodome City Center 5-2 Higashi-Shimbashi 1-chome, Minato-ku, Tokyo, 105-7117, Japan
Tel.: (81) 3 6253 3456
Web Site: http://www.mitsuichem.com
Polymeric Materials Mfr
N.A.I.C.S.: 325998
Tsutomu Tannowa (Pres & CEO)

Mitsui Chemicals, Inc. - Performance Polymers Division (1)
Shiodome City Center 5-2 Higashi-Shimbashi 1-chome, Minato-ku, Tokyo, 105-7117, Japan
Tel.: (81) 3 6253 3695
Web Site: http://www.mitsuichem.com
Polymeric Materials Mfr
N.A.I.C.S.: 325998

Mitsui Chemicals, Inc. - Petrochemical Feedstocks Division (1)
1-5-2 Shiodome City Center Higashi-Shimbashi 1-chome, Minato-ku, Tokyo, 105-7122, Japan
Tel.: (81) 3 6253 3020
Petrochemical Mfr
N.A.I.C.S.: 325110

Mitsui Chemicals, Inc. - Phenols Division (1)
1-5-2 Shiodome City Center Higashi-Shimbashi 1-chome, Minato-ku, Tokyo, 105-7117, Japan
Tel.: (81) 362533260
Chemical Products Mfr
N.A.I.C.S.: 325998

Mitsui Chemicals, Inc. - Planning & Coordination Division (1)
1-6-3 Higashi-Shinbashi, Minato-ku, Tokyo, 105-8333, Japan
Tel.: (81) 368807458
Chemical Products Mfr
N.A.I.C.S.: 325998

Mitsui Chemicals, Inc. - Polyurethane Division (1)
Shiodome City Center 5-2 Higashi-Shimbashi 1-chome, Minato-ku, Tokyo, 105-7117, Japan
Tel.: (81) 3 6253 4120
Web Site: http://www.mitsuichem.com
Polyurethane Chemicals Mfr
N.A.I.C.S.: 325998

Mitsui Chemicals, Inc. - Tokuyama Branch Factory (1)
3-1 Tokuyama Minatomachi, Shunan, 745-0045, Yamaguchi, Japan
Tel.: (81) 834315880
Chemical Products Mfr
N.A.I.C.S.: 325998

Mitsui Elastomers Singapore Pte Ltd (1)
3 Harbour Front Place 10-01 Harbour Front Tower 2, Singapore, 99254, Singapore
Tel.: (65) 6532 0403
Web Site: http://www.mitsuichem.com
Sales Range: $50-74.9 Million
Emp.: 100
Chemical Products Mfr & Distr
N.A.I.C.S.: 325998

Mitsui Fine Chemicals, Inc. (1)
4-3-18 Nihonbashi-muromachi, Chuo-ku, Tokyo, 103-0022, Japan
Tel.: (81) 3 368 4289
Web Site: http://www.mkf.co.jp
Inorganic Chemical Products Mfr & Distr
N.A.I.C.S.: 325180

Mitsui Hygiene Materials (Thailand) Co., Ltd. (1)
64/45 Moo 4 Pluakdaeng Eastern Seaboard Industrial Estate, Rayong, 21140, Thailand
Tel.: (66) 3 368 4289
Web Site: https://www.mhm.co.th
Emp.: 220
Polypropylene Spunbond Mfr & Distr
N.A.I.C.S.: 313230
Hiroshi Ishii (Pres)

Mitsui Prime Advanced Composites India Pvt Ltd. (1)
Plot No SP2-54 55 56, New Industrial Area Complex Majrakath Neemrana, Alwar, 301 705, Rajasthan, India
Tel.: (91) 1494246577
Web Site: http://www.mitsuichem.com
Polypropylene Compound Mfr & Distr
N.A.I.C.S.: 325211

Mitsui Prime Advanced Composites do Brasil Industria e Comercio de Compostos Plasticos S.A. (1)
Rua Juraci Aletto 224-C, Bairro Sertaozinho, Maua, 09370-813, Sao Paulo, Brazil
Tel.: (55) 1145468700
Polypropylene Compound Mfr & Distr
N.A.I.C.S.: 325211

Mitsui Takeda Chemicals, Inc. (1)
1-52-2 Higashi-Shinbashi, Minato-ku, Tokyo, 105-7117, Japan
Tel.: (81) 362534100
Web Site: http://www.takeda.com
Sales Range: $200-249.9 Million
Emp.: 900
Urethane Raw Materials & Derivatives & Organic Acids Mfr & Sales; Owned 51% by Mitsui Chemicals, Inc. & 49% by Takeda Pharmaceutical Company Limited
N.A.I.C.S.: 325199

Joint Venture (Non-US):

Croslene Chemical Industries, Ltd. (2)
11F No 22 Nanjing W Rd, Datong Dist, Taipei, 103, Taiwan
Tel.: (886) 225556661
Web Site: http://www.croslene.com.tw
Synthetic Resins Mfr & Sales; Owned 50% by Mitsui Takeda Chemicals, Inc. & 48% by Lidye Co., Ltd.
N.A.I.C.S.: 325211

Kumho Mitsui Chemicals, Inc. (2)
Floor 11th East Bldg Signature Tower 100 Cheonggyecheon-ro, Joong-gu, Seoul, Korea (South)
Tel.: (82) 269613750
Web Site: https://www.kmci.co.kr
Emp.: 248
MDI Mfr & Sales
N.A.I.C.S.: 325998

Nippon A&L, Inc. (1)
Sumitomo Bldg 5-33 Kitahama 4-Chome, Chuo-ku, Osaka, 541-8550, Japan
Tel.: (81) 662203656
Web Site: https://www.n-al.co.jp
Sales Range: $125-149.9 Million
Emp.: 350
Resins & Latexes Mfr & Sales; Owned 85% by Sumitomo Chemical Company, Ltd. & 15% by Mitsui Chemicals, Inc.
N.A.I.C.S.: 325211
Toshiro Kojima (Chm)

Nippon Alkyl Phenol Co., Ltd. (1)
1-5-2 Higashi-Shimbashi, Minato-ku, Tokyo, 105-7117, Japan
Tel.: (81) 362533283
Web Site: http://www.mitsuichem.com
Alkylphenol Mfr & Distr
N.A.I.C.S.: 325998

Nippon Aluminum Alkyls, Ltd. (1)
16F Fukoku Seimei Bldg 2-2 Uchisaiwai-cho 2-chome, Chiyoda-ku, Tokyo, 100-0011, Japan
Tel.: (81) 335040811
Web Site: https://www.naa.co.jp
Sales Range: $25-49.9 Million
Emp.: 50
Organic Compounds such as Alkylaluminum & Their Derivatives Mfr & Sales; Owned 50% by Mitsui Chemicals, Inc. & Albemarle Corporation
N.A.I.C.S.: 325199
Masanobu Itaya (Pres)

Nippon Epoxy Resin Manufacturing Co., Ltd. (1)
1-5-2 Higashi-Shimbashi, Minato-ku, Tokyo, 105-7117, Japan
Tel.: (81) 3 6253 3283
Web Site: http://www.mitsuichem.com
Epoxy Resin Mfr & Sales
N.A.I.C.S.: 325211

Nippon Tensar Ltd. (1)
3-39-10 Yushima, Bunkyo-ku, Tokyo, 113-0034, Japan
Tel.: (81) 338370281
Plastic Product Mfr & Distr
N.A.I.C.S.: 326199

Osaka Petrochemical Industries, Ltd. (1)
1-5-2 Higashi-Shimbashi, Minato-ku, Tokyo, 105-7122, Japan (100%)
Tel.: (81) 362533026
Web Site: http://www.mitsuichem.com
Sales Range: $25-49.9 Million
Emp.: 100
Ethylene, Propylene & Other Basic Petrochemical Products Mfr & Sales
N.A.I.C.S.: 325110

P.T. Cosmo Polyurethane Indonesia (1)
Wisma Kyoei Prince 17th Floor Jl Jend Sudirman Kav 3, Jakarta, 10220, Indonesia
Tel.: (62) 215723101
Urethane Premixture Mfr & Distr
N.A.I.C.S.: 325998

P.T. MCNS Polyurethanes Indonesia (1)
Wisma Keiai Lt 17 Jl Jend Sudirman Kav 3, Jakarta, 10220, Indonesia
Tel.: (62) 215723101
Polyurethane Mfr & Distr
N.A.I.C.S.: 326150

P.T. Petnesia Resindo (1)
Jl Moch Toha Km 1 Pabuaran Tumpeng, Tangerang, 15112, Banten, Indonesia
Tel.: (62) 215533083
N.A.I.C.S.: 325220

Prime Evolue Singapore Pte. Ltd. (1)
3 Harbourfront Place 10-01 Harbourfront Tower 2, Singapore, 099254, Singapore
Tel.: (65) 65342612
Chemical Product Mfr & Distr
N.A.I.C.S.: 325998

Prime Polymer Co., Ltd. (1)
Shiodome City Center 19th floor 1-5-2 Higashi-Shimbashi, Minato-ku, Tokyo, 105-7122, Japan
Tel.: (81) 36 253 4500
Web Site: https://www.primepolymer.co.jp
Emp.: 684
Polyolefin Mfr & Sales; Owned 65% by Mitsui Chemicals, Inc. & 35% by Idemitsu Kosan Co., Ltd.
N.A.I.C.S.: 325110
Kensuke Fujimoto (Pres & Gen Mgr-Plng & Admin Div)

SDC Technologies Asia Pacific, Pte. Ltd. (1)
27 Tuas South Street 1, Singapore, 638035, Singapore
Tel.: (65) 62106355
Coating Product Mfr
N.A.I.C.S.: 325510
Loh Boon Chye (Pres)

San-Business Services, Ltd. (1)
1-5-2 Higashi-Shimbashi, Minato-ku, Tokyo, 105-7117, Japan (100%)
Tel.: (81) 3 6253 4300
Travel & General Damage Insurance Services
N.A.I.C.S.: 524298

Sanseikaihatsu Co., Ltd. (1)
30 Asamuta-machi, Omuta, Fukuoka, 836-

MITSUI CHEMICALS, INC.

Mitsui Chemicals, Inc.—(Continued)
0817, Japan **(100%)**
Tel.: (81) 944528411
Web Site: http://www.mitsuichem.com
Cargo Handling & Accident Prevention Services
N.A.I.C.S.: 488320

Saxin Corporation **(1)**
4-2-1 Sekinotsu, Otsu, 520-2277, Shiga, Japan
Tel.: (81) 775463121
Web Site: http://www.saxin.jp
Chemical Products Mfr
N.A.I.C.S.: 325998

Shikoku Tohcello Co., Ltd. **(1)**
37 Tadatsu Yoshinari-aza Ojin-cho, Tokushima, 771-1153, Japan
Tel.: (81) 886411221
Web Site: https://www.shikoku-tohcello.co.jp
Emp.: 123
Synthetic Resin Film Mfr & Sales
N.A.I.C.S.: 325211

Shimonoseki Mitsui Chemicals, Inc. **(1)**
7-1-1 Hikoshima-sakomachi, Shimonoseki, 750-0092, Yamaguchi, Japan **(100%)**
Tel.: (81) 832661122
Web Site: https://www.shimonoseki-mci.co.jp
Phosphoric Acid & Fertilizers Mfr & Sales
N.A.I.C.S.: 325312

Siam Tohcello Co., Ltd. **(1)**
No 1 Siam Cement Road, Bang Sue Subdistrict Bang Sue District, Bangkok, 10800, Thailand
Tel.: (66) 210538123
Web Site: https://www.siamtohcello.com
LLDPE Film Mfr
N.A.I.C.S.: 326113

Sun Alloys Co., Ltd. **(1)**
580-271 Nagaura Sodegaura, Chiba, 299-0265, Japan **(100%)**
Tel.: (81) 438640251
Web Site: http://www.mitsui-chem.co.jp
Compounded Polymers Mfr & Sales
N.A.I.C.S.: 325991

Sunrex Industry Co., Ltd. **(1)**
1 Asake-cho, Yokkaichi, 512-8501, Mie, Japan **(100%)**
Tel.: (81) 593362200
Web Site: https://www.sun-rex.jp
Spunbonded Nonwoven Fabrics & Plastic Film Mfr & Sales
N.A.I.C.S.: 313230

Taiwan Mitsui Chemicals, Inc. **(1)**
7F - 2 No 4 Section 1 Zhongxiao West Road, Taipei, 100405, Taiwan **(100%)**
Tel.: (886) 223617887
Web Site: https://tw.mitsuichemicals.com
Sales Range: $50-74.9 Million
Emp.: 10
Electronics & Information Materials Sales
N.A.I.C.S.: 423690

Taiwan Tohcello Functional Sheet, Inc. **(1)**
No 55 Beiling 6th Road, Luzhu District, Kaohsiung, 82151, Taiwan
Tel.: (886) 76955355
Semiconductor Tape Mfr & Distr
N.A.I.C.S.: 334413

Thai Mitsui Specialty Chemicals Co., Ltd. **(1)**
No 92/28-29 Sathorn Thani Building 2 12th Floor North Sathorn Road, Silom, Bangrak, 10500, Bangkok, Thailand **(52%)**
Tel.: (66) 2 236 8898
Web Site: https://www.tmsc.co.th
Sales Range: $125-149.9 Million
Emp.: 290
Specialty Chemicals Mfr & Sales
N.A.I.C.S.: 325998
Sumon Suwanpatra (Chm)

Thai PET Resin Co., Ltd. **(1)**
138 Boonmitr Building 8th Floor Silom Road, Suriyawongse Bangrak, Bangkok, 10500, Thailand
Tel.: (66) 26345894
Polyethylene Terepthalate Resin Mfr & Sales; Owned 40% by Mitsui Chemicals, Inc., 40% by Toray Industries, Inc. & 20% by SCG Chemicals Co., Ltd.
N.A.I.C.S.: 325211

Tianjin Cosmo Polyurethane Co., Ltd. **(1)**
No 28 Huashan Road, Tianjin Economical Development Area Hangu Modern Industrial Park, Tianjin, 300480, China
Tel.: (86) 2267162206
Polyurethane Mfr & Distr
N.A.I.C.S.: 326150

Tohcello Logistics Co., Ltd. **(1)**
142-1 Oaza Nogi Nogimachi, Shimotsuga-gun, Tochigi, 329-0114, Japan
Tel.: (81) 280579100
Warehousing Services
N.A.I.C.S.: 493110

Tohcello Slitter Co., Ltd. **(1)**
142-1 Oaza Nogi Nogimachi, Shimotsuga-gun, Tochigi, 329-0114, Japan
Tel.: (81) 280552496
Plastic Film Slitting Product Mfr
N.A.I.C.S.: 326112

Toyo Beauty Supply Corporation **(1)**
3-3-10 Nihonbashi-hongokucho, Chuo-ku, Tokyo, 103-0021, Japan
Tel.: (81) 332411410
Web Site: http://www.mitsuichem.com
Cosmetics Mfr
N.A.I.C.S.: 325620

Toyo Phosphoric Acid, Inc. **(1)**
7-1-1 Hikoshima-sakomachi, Shimonoseki, 750-0092, Yamaguchi, Japan
Tel.: (81) 832661122
Phosphoric Acid Mfr & Distr
N.A.I.C.S.: 325312

Utsunomiya Chemical Industry Co., Ltd **(1)**
1215 Iwazo-machi, Utsunomiya, 321-0973, Tochigi, Japan
Tel.: (81) 28 661 4361
Agricultural Insecticide Mfr
N.A.I.C.S.: 325320

Yamamoto Chemicals, Inc. **(1)**
1-43 Yugecho-Minami, Yao, 581-0034, Osaka, Japan
Tel.: (81) 72 949 4561
Web Site: https://www.yamamoto-chemicals.co.jp
Emp.: 90
Industrial Chemical Dye Pigments Mfr & Distr
N.A.I.C.S.: 325998
Masayuki Okabe (Pres & CEO)

Yoncello Sangyo Co., Ltd. **(1)**
37 Tadatsu Yoshinari-aza Ojin-cho, Tokushima, 771-1153, Japan
Tel.: (81) 886411221
Chemical Products Mfr
N.A.I.C.S.: 325998

Yongsan Mitsui Chemicals, Inc. **(1)**
9F Yongsan B/D 273 Hangang-daero 04321, Yongsan-gu, Seoul, 140-150, Korea (South)
Tel.: (82) 232749191
Web Site: https://yongsan-mitsui.com
Sales Range: $25-49.9 Million
Emp.: 6
Acrylamide Mfr & Sales; Owned 50% by Yongson Chemicals, Inc. & 50% by Mitsui Chemicals, Inc.
N.A.I.C.S.: 325998

Zhang Jia Gang Free Trade Zone Mitsui Link-Upon Advanced Materials, Inc. **(1)**
No 18 Gangao Road Zhang Jia Gang Free Trade Zone, Zhangjiagang, 215634, Jiangsu, China
Tel.: (86) 512 5832 2088
Web Site: http://www.mitsuichem.com
Engineering Plastic Compound Mfr
N.A.I.C.S.: 326199

MITSUI DM SUGAR HOLDINGS CO LTD

Mita S-Garden 5-26-16 Shiba, Minato-ku, Tokyo, Japan
Tel.: (81) 364536161
Web Site: https://www.msdm-hd.com
Year Founded: 1947
2109—(TKS)
Rev.: $1,128,816,140
Assets: $1,265,339,080
Liabilities: $489,721,680
Net Worth: $775,617,400
Earnings: $55,821,450
Fiscal Year-end: 03/31/24
Sugar Refining & Sales
N.A.I.C.S.: 311314
Taku Morimoto (Pres & Co-CEO)

MITSUI E&S HOLDINGS CO., LTD.

6-4 Tsukiji 5-chome, Chuo-ku, Tokyo, 104-8439, Japan
Tel.: (81) 335443133   JP
Web Site: https://www.mes.co.jp
Year Founded: 1917
MU1—(DEU)
Rev.: $1,995,393,750
Assets: $3,087,795,400
Liabilities: $2,119,364,300
Net Worth: $968,431,100
Earnings: $165,587,110
Emp.: 5,952
Fiscal Year-end: 03/31/24
Holding Company; Ship & Industrial Construction Services
N.A.I.C.S.: 551112
Taketsune Matsumura (CFO, CIO & Chief Information Security Officer)

Subsidiaries:

ADMAP Inc. **(1)**
3-16-2 Tamahara, Tamano, 706-0014, Okayama, Japan
Tel.: (81) 863 23 3333
Semiconductor Parts Mfr
N.A.I.C.S.: 334413
Koichi Okayama (Auditor)

Division (Domestic):

ADMAP Inc. - Sales Division **(2)**
Nittetsu ND Tower 5-7 1-chome Kameido, Kohto-ku, Tokyo, 136-0071, Japan
Tel.: (81) 3 5626 7341
Semiconductor Device Distr
N.A.I.C.S.: 423690

Azuma Machinery Co., Ltd. **(1)**
1-155 Hongo Minogo-cho, Onomichi, 722-0212, Hiroshima Prefecture, Japan
Tel.: (81) 848382770
Diesel Engine Part Maintenance Services
N.A.I.C.S.: 811111

BWSC Lanka (Private) Ltd. **(1)**
103/8 Galle Road, Colombo, Sri Lanka
Tel.: (94) 114 721 900
Diesel Engine Mfr
N.A.I.C.S.: 336310

BWSC Malta Ltd. **(1)**
Delimara Power Station Power Station Road, Marsaxlokk, MXK1320, Malta
Tel.: (356) 21 654 120
Ship Building Services
N.A.I.C.S.: 336611

BWSC Mindanao Inc **(1)**
Daruma Industries Corp Building KM7 Lanang, PO Box 81142, 8000, Davao, Philippines
Tel.: (63) 82 234 2247
Web Site: http://www.bwsc.com
Diesel Engine Mfr
N.A.I.C.S.: 336310

Burmeister & Wain Scandinavian Contractor A/S **(1)**
Gydevang 35, 3450, Allerod, Denmark
Tel.: (45) 48140022
Web Site: https://www.bwsc.com
Rev.: $192,790,849
Assets: $197,664,766
Liabilities: $84,864,737
Net Worth: $108,800,029
Earnings: $9,826,016
Emp.: 642
Fiscal Year-end: 12/31/2023
Diesel Engine Mfr
N.A.I.C.S.: 333618
Jens Peter Koch (CEO)

INTERNATIONAL PUBLIC

Subsidiary (Non-US):

BWSC (Mauritius) Ltd. **(2)**
1st Floor Manor House Corner Saint George/De Chazal Streets, Port Louis, Mauritius
Tel.: (230) 211 32 98
Web Site: http://www.bwsc.com
Power Plant Construction Services
N.A.I.C.S.: 237130

Colombo Power (Private) Limited **(1)**
103/8 Galle Road, Colombo, Sri Lanka
Tel.: (94) 114 721666
Emp.: 60
Eletric Power Generation Services
N.A.I.C.S.: 221118
Kazuki Mashimo (Chm)

DASH Engineering Philippines Inc. **(1)**
3rd Floor PPC 24 Building The North Park United Nation Avenue, Alang-alang, Mandaue, 6014, Cebu, Philippines
Tel.: (63) 32 888 2000
Web Site: https://www.dash.com.ph
Sales Range: $75-99.9 Million
Emp.: 500
Shipbuilding & Engineering Services
N.A.I.C.S.: 541330
Takuya Aramaki (Pres)

DPS Bridge Works Co., Ltd. **(1)**
N1-W6-2, Chue-ku, Sapporo, 060-0001, Hokkaido, Japan
Tel.: (81) 11 221 2055
Web Site: http://www.mes.co.jp
Design, Production & Sale of Prestressed Concrete Products & General Civil & Architectural Construction
N.A.I.C.S.: 327390

Engineers and Constructors International, Inc. **(1)**
2638 S Sherwood Forest Blvd 100, Baton Rouge, LA 70816 **(100%)**
Tel.: (225) 293-7768
Web Site: https://ecigrouponline.com
Engineering Consulting & Construction Management Services
N.A.I.C.S.: 541330
Charles Beals (Co-Founder)

Green Power Ichihara Co., Ltd. **(1)**
1 Yawatakaigandori, Ichihara, 290-8531, Chiba, Japan
Tel.: (81) 436 41 1220
Web Site: http://www.mes.co.jp
Emp.: 30
Biomass Power Generation Services
N.A.I.C.S.: 221118

Kaji Technology Corporation **(1)**
6 Bodai, Mihara-ku, Sakai, 587-0064, Osaka, Japan **(51%)**
Tel.: (81) 723610881
Web Site: https://www.kajitech.com
Rev.: $58,491,560
Assets: $80,547,492
Liabilities: $24,704,063
Net Worth: $55,843,429
Earnings: $2,329,143
Fiscal Year-end: 03/31/2020
Gas & Air Compressor Mfr
N.A.I.C.S.: 333912
Yoshiyuki Ishihara (Mng Dir)

MES (Thailand) Ltd. **(1)**
Prime Building 15th Floor UnitB 24 Sukhumvit 21 Rd Asoke, Khlongtoey Nua Wattana, Bangkok, 10110, Thailand
Tel.: (66) 26617450
Marine Engineering Services
N.A.I.C.S.: 541330

MES AFTY Corporation **(1)**
2-35-2 Hyoe, Hachioji, 192-0918, Tokyo, Japan
Tel.: (81) 42 632 8840
Web Site: http://www.jsw-afty.co.jp
Emp.: 40
Industrial Machinery Mfr
N.A.I.C.S.: 333248
Nobuhisa Kobasyashi (Pres)

MES Ferrotec China Co., Ltd. **(1)**
No 365 Yuanguang Rd, Baoshan City Industrial Park, Shanghai, China
Tel.: (86) 2136316860
Induction Heater Mfr & Distr

AND PRIVATE COMPANIES

MITSUI E&S HOLDINGS CO., LTD.

N.A.I.C.S.: 333414

MES Shipping Co., Ltd. (1)
6-4 Tsukiji 5-chome, Chuo-ku, Tokyo, 104-8439, Japan
Tel.: (81) 335443578
Marine Equipment Distr
N.A.I.C.S.: 423910

MES TECHNOSERVICE (SHANGHAI) Co., Ltd. (1)
Room 2106 Dongfang Road 877 Jiaxing Bldg, Pudong, Shanghai, 200122, China
Tel.: (86) 21 61940144
Sales Range: $25-49.9 Million
Emp.: 9
Diesel Engine Maintenance Services
N.A.I.C.S.: 811198

MES Techno Service Co., Ltd. (1)
1-1 Tama 3-chome, Tamano, 706-8651, Okayama, Japan
Tel.: (81) 863 23 2391
Web Site: http://www.techno.mes.co.jp
Sales Range: $25-49.9 Million
Emp.: 194
Industrial Machinery Repair & Maintenance Services
N.A.I.C.S.: 811310

MES Technoservice Machinery Construction Logistics Industry & Trade Corporation (1)
1245 Sokak No 25, Ostim Yenimahalle, Ankara, Turkiye
Tel.: (90) 3124361362
Ship Building Services
N.A.I.C.S.: 336611

MES Technoservice Middle East W.L.L (1)
PO Box 24945, Doha, Qatar
Tel.: (974) 44882511
Rotating Machine Maintenance Services
N.A.I.C.S.: 811310

MES Testing & Research Center Co., Ltd. (1)
3-1-1 Tama, Tamano, Okayama, 706-8651, Japan (100%)
Tel.: (81) 863232620
Web Site: http://www.mestrc.co.jp
Sales Range: Less than $1 Million
Emp.: 20
Apparatus Analysis & Testing Services
N.A.I.C.S.: 541380
Matsuyama Tadashi *(CEO)*

MES Tokki & Engineering Co., Ltd. (1)
3-1-1 Tama, Tamano, 706-8651, Okayama, Japan
Tel.: (81) 863232700
Steel Structure Equipment Mfr
N.A.I.C.S.: 332312

MES-KHI Yura Dock Co., Ltd. (1)
193-13 Ajiro Yuracho, Hidaka-gun, Wakayama, 649 1112, Japan (100%)
Tel.: (81) 738651112
Web Site: http://www.mes.co.jp
Repairing of Ships; Production & Installation of Steel Structures
N.A.I.C.S.: 336611

MODEC International, Inc. (1)
15011 Katy Fwy Ste 500, Houston, TX 77094
Tel.: (281) 529-8100
Web Site: http://www.modec.com
Oil & Gas Offshore Floating Platforms Mfr
N.A.I.C.S.: 336611
Bruce Beever *(CFO)*

MODEC, Inc. (1)
Nihonbashi Maruzen Tokyu Building 4th & 5th Floors, 3-10 Nihonbashi 2-chome Chuo-ku, Tokyo, 103-0027, Japan (50.1%)
Tel.: (81) 352901200
Web Site: https://www.modec.com
Rev.: $3,594,849,790
Assets: $3,909,589,070
Liabilities: $2,868,528,920
Net Worth: $1,041,060,150
Earnings: $97,069,190
Emp.: 6,333
Fiscal Year-end: 12/31/2023
Design, Construction, Installation Leasing & Operation of Marine Structures, Including Offshore Petroleum Production/Storage Facilities

N.A.I.C.S.: 237990
Yasuhiro Takano *(Exec Mng Officer)*

Subsidiary (US):

MODEC International LLC (2)
14741 Yorktown Plz Dr, Houston, TX 77040
Tel.: (281) 529-8100
Web Site: http://www.modec.com
Sales Range: $100-124.9 Million
Emp.: 277
Marine Floating Production System Operation, Maintenance & Construction
N.A.I.C.S.: 236210
Rick Hall *(Pres)*

Subsidiary (Non-US):

MODEC Management Services Pte Ltd. (2)
9 North Buona Vista Drive 04-05 The Metropolis Tower 1, Singapore, 138588, Singapore
Tel.: (65) 6 496 4000
Web Site: https://www.modec.com
Sales Range: $25-49.9 Million
Emp.: 25
Marine Floating Production System Operation, Maintenance & Construction
N.A.I.C.S.: 236210

MODEC Management Services Pte Ltd. (2)
Level 7 225 St Georges Terrace, Perth, 6000, WA, Australia
Tel.: (61) 89 278 8400
Web Site: https://www.modec.com
Sales Range: $25-49.9 Million
Emp.: 35
Marine Floating Production System Operation, Maintenance & Construction
N.A.I.C.S.: 236210

MODEC Management Services Pte Ltd. (2)
No 2 Phan Dinh Phung Street, Ward 1, Vung Tau, 780000, Ba Ria - Vung Tau, Vietnam
Tel.: (84) 254 351 5500
Web Site: https://www.modec.com
Marine Floating Production System Operation, Maintenance & Construction
N.A.I.C.S.: 236210

MODEC Offshore Production Systems (Singapore) Pte Ltd. (2)
9 North Buona Vista Drive 21-01 The Metropolis Tower 1, Singapore, 138588, Singapore
Tel.: (65) 6 496 4000
Web Site: https://www.modec.com
Sales Range: $100-124.9 Million
Emp.: 500
Marine Floating Production System Operation, Maintenance & Construction
N.A.I.C.S.: 236210

MODEC Servicos de Petroleo do Brasil Ltda (2)
Praia do Flamengo 66 - 4 ao 12 andar, Rio de Janeiro, 22210-903, Brazil
Tel.: (55) 213 545 8000
Web Site: https://www.modec.com
Sales Range: $25-49.9 Million
Emp.: 35
Marine Floating Production System Operation, Maintenance & Construction
N.A.I.C.S.: 236210

Subsidiary (US):

SOFEC, Inc. (2)
15011 Katy Fwy Ste 500, Houston, TX 77094 (51%)
Tel.: (713) 510-6600
Web Site: https://www.sofec.com
Sales Range: $50-74.9 Million
Emp.: 140
Marine Terminal & Mooring System Developer & Mfr
N.A.I.C.S.: 236210
Brent Konstanzer *(Pres & CEO)*

Minami Nippon Shipbuilding Co., Ltd. (1)
1179-3 Shitanoe, Usuki, 875-0002, Oita, Japan
Tel.: (81) 972 67 2116
Ship Building & Repairing Services
N.A.I.C.S.: 336611

Osmu Tomimura *(Gen Mgr)*

Mitsui E&S (China) Co., Ltd. (1)
Room 2512 Shanghai International Trade Centre 2201 Yan An Road West, Shanghai, 200336, China
Tel.: (86) 2162089201
Marine Engineering Services
N.A.I.C.S.: 541330

Mitsui E&S Asia Pte. Ltd. (1)
No 2 International Business Park The Strategy Tower 1 FL No 02/03-05, Singapore, 609930, Singapore
Tel.: (65) 67771677
Diesel Engine Part Maintenance Services
N.A.I.C.S.: 811111

Mitsui E&S Business Service Co., Ltd. (1)
6-4 Tsukiji 5-chome, Chuo-ku, Tokyo, 104-8439, Japan
Tel.: (81) 335443133
Emp.: 119
Administrative Management Services
N.A.I.C.S.: 561110
Takeshi Iizuka *(Pres)*

Mitsui E&S Engineering Co., Ltd. (1)
6-4 Tsukiji 5-chome, Chuo-ku, Tokyo, 104-8439, Japan
Tel.: (81) 433519020
Emp.: 190
Biomass Plant Construction Services
N.A.I.C.S.: 237130
Shigeru Tokumaru *(Pres)*

Mitsui E&S Machinery Co., Ltd. (1)
6-4 Tsukiji 5-Chome, Chuo-ku, Tokyo, 104-8439, Japan
Tel.: (81) 335443951
Web Site: https://www.mitsuimachinery.com
Emp.: 2,700
Reciprocating Compressor Mfr
N.A.I.C.S.: 333912

Mitsui E&S Machinery Europe Limited (1)
80 Coleman Street, London, EC2R 5BJ, United Kingdom
Tel.: (44) 2071042280
Marine Engineering Services
N.A.I.C.S.: 541330

Mitsui E&S Power Systems Inc. (1)
7 Kanda Konyacho Kanda System Building 3rd Floor, Chiyoda-ku, Tokyo, 101-0035, Japan
Tel.: (81) 368061075
Web Site: http://www.mesps.co.jp
Diesel Engine Equipment Mfr & Distr
N.A.I.C.S.: 333618

Mitsui E&S Shipbuilding Co., Ltd. (1)
6-4 Tsukiji 5-chome, Chuo-ku, Tokyo, 104-8439, Japan
Tel.: (81) 335443318
Emp.: 1,388
Ship Building Services
N.A.I.C.S.: 336611
Isamu Funatsu *(Pres)*

Subsidiary (Domestic):

Akishima Laboratories (Mitsui Zosen) Inc. (2)
1-1-50 Tsutsujigaoka, Akishima, 196-0012, Tokyo, Japan
Tel.: (81) 425453111
Web Site: https://akishima-labo.co.jp
Sales Range: $25-49.9 Million
Emp.: 65
Marine Engineering Research, Development & Consulting Services
N.A.I.C.S.: 541715

Mitsui E&S Systems Research Inc. (1)
1-3-D-9 Nakase, Mihama-ku, Chiba, 261-8501, Chiba Prefecture, Japan
Tel.: (81) 432746162
Web Site: http://www.msr.co.jp
Emp.: 643
Computer Peripheral Product Mfr & Distr
N.A.I.C.S.: 334118
Toshifumi Morishige *(Pres & CEO)*

Mitsui E&S Technical Research Co., Ltd. (1)
3-1-1 Tama ball 3 -chome 1, Tamano, 706-

0012, Okayama Prefecture, Japan
Tel.: (81) 863232620
Web Site: http://www.mestrc.co.jp
Non-Destructive Inspection Services
N.A.I.C.S.: 541380

Mitsui Meehanite Metal Co., Ltd. (1)
111 Kaminokawa Oka-cho, Okazaki, 444-0005, Aichi, Japan
Tel.: (81) 56 455 6638
Web Site: https://www.m-meehanite.co.jp
Industrial Machinery & Steel Cast Goods Mfr & Distr
N.A.I.C.S.: 332111

Mitsui Thang Long Steel Construction Co., Ltd. (1)
Xam Duong Village, Ninh So Commune Thuong Tin District, Hanoi, Vietnam
Tel.: (84) 436860112
Web Site: http://www.mtsc.com.vn
Steel Structure Mfr & Distr
N.A.I.C.S.: 332312

Mitsui Zosen (U.S.A.) Inc. (1)
25503 Whitesell St, Hayward, CA 94545
Tel.: (510) 780-9585
Web Site: http://www.mes.co.jp
Engineering Consulting Services
N.A.I.C.S.: 541330

Mitsui Zosen Chiba Kiko Engineering Inc. (1)
1 Kaigandori, Yawata, Ichihara, 290-8531, Chiba, Japan
Tel.: (81) 436 41 5811
Industrial Machinery Mfr
N.A.I.C.S.: 333248

Mitsui Zosen Environment Engineering Corporation (1)
4-6 Nishikasai 8-chome, Edogawa-ku, Tokyo, 134-0088, Japan
Tel.: (81) 3 3675 2038
Kitchen Garbage Recycling Plant Management Services
N.A.I.C.S.: 562920

Mitsui Zosen Europe Limited (1)
Level 16 City Tower, 40 Basinghall Street, London, EC2V 5DE, United Kingdom
Tel.: (44) 2072567171
Web Site: http://www.mes.co.jp
Sales Range: $25-49.9 Million
Emp.: 8
Sales Support & Marketing Information & Services, Including Technical Assistance in Procurement of Equipment & Materials for Industrial Facilities
N.A.I.C.S.: 561499
Isao Yaoshino *(Mng Dir)*

Mitsui Zosen Plant Engineering Inc. (1)
4-6 Nishikasai 8-chome, Edogawa-ku, Tokyo, 134-0088, Japan
Tel.: (81) 3 3675 8162
Web Site: http://www.mes.co.jp
Plant Construction & Engineering Services
N.A.I.C.S.: 237990

Mitsui Zosen Systems Research Inc. (1)
1-3-D9 Nakase, Mihama-ku, Chiba, 261 8501, Japan
Tel.: (81) 43 274 6162
Web Site: http://www.msr.co.jp
Sales Range: $100-124.9 Million
Emp.: 622
Development & Design of Computer Software Packages; Development, Production & Sales of Computer Peripherals
N.A.I.C.S.: 513210
Toshifumi Morishige *(Pres & CEO)*

Mitsuizosen Technoservice Hongkong Limited (1)
Unit Nos 1309-1312 Level 13 Metro Plaza Tower 1 223 Hing Fong Road, Kwai Fong, New Territories, China (Hong Kong)
Tel.: (852) 2610 1282
Sales Range: $25-49.9 Million
Emp.: 13
Industrial Equipment Repair & Maintenance Services
N.A.I.C.S.: 811310
Youichi Kudou *(Mng Dir)*

Mitsuizosen Technoservice Taiwan Co., Ltd. (1)

MITSUI E&S HOLDINGS CO., LTD.

Mitsui E&S Holdings Co., Ltd.—(Continued)

No 6 19th Floor Ming quan 2nd Rd, Chien-Chen District, Kaohsiung, 806, Taiwan
Tel.: (886) 7 331 2801
Sales Range: $50-74.9 Million
Emp.: 10
Diesel Engine Parts Distr & Maintenance Services
N.A.I.C.S.: 423120

NGH Japan Co., Ltd. (1)
6-4 Tsukiji 5-chome, Chuo-ku, Tokyo, 104 8439, Japan **(80%)**
Tel.: (81) 335443555
Web Site: http://www.nghjapan.mes.co.jp
Emp.: 25
Technology & Business Development of Natural Gas Hydrate (NGH) & Production, Transportation, Re-Gasification & Sales of NGH; Owned 20% by Mitsui & Co., Ltd.
N.A.I.C.S.: 221210

Nigata Shipbuilding & Repair, Inc. (1)
4-3776 Irifune-cho, Niigata, 951-8011, Japan
Tel.: (81) 25 222 6121
Web Site: http://www.mes.co.jp
Ship Building & Repairing Services
N.A.I.C.S.: 336611

PT MES Machinery Indonesia (1)
7th Floor Nusantara Building JL MH Thamrin No 59, Jakarta, 10350, Indonesia
Tel.: (62) 2131922910
Crane Mfr
N.A.I.C.S.: 333923

Paceco Corp. (1)
25503 Whitesell St, Hayward, CA 94545
Tel.: (510) 264-9288
Web Site: http://www.pacecocorp.com
Crane Mfr
N.A.I.C.S.: 333923

Sanzo Business Creative Co., Ltd. (1)
18th Floor Nittetsu ND Tower 5-7 Kameido 1-chome, Koto-ku, Tokyo, 136-0071, Japan
Tel.: (81) 3 5626 7112
Office Administrative Services
N.A.I.C.S.: 561110

Sanzo Enterprise Co., Ltd. (1)
7-17-8 Ginza, Chuo-ku, Tokyo, 104-0061, Japan
Tel.: (81) 3 3544 3575
Ship Equipment Distr & Leasing Services
N.A.I.C.S.: 532411

Sanzo Kosan Co., Ltd. (1)
5-6-4 Tsukiji, Chuo-ku, Tokyo, 104 8439, Japan
Tel.: (81) 3 3544 3797
Web Site: http://www.mes.co.jp
Construction, Sale of Imported Houses, Real Estate, Insurance Agency Activities & Freighting Services
N.A.I.C.S.: 531390

Sanzo Manufacturing & Construction Co., Ltd. (1)
1 Nishinosu, Oita, 870-0902, Japan
Tel.: (81) 97 558 3339
Boiler & Pressure Vessels Mfr
N.A.I.C.S.: 332410

Shanghai Hudong Sanzo Marine Machinery Co., Ltd. (1)
2789 Pudong Dado 12F 1204Rm Donghua Science & Technology Mansion, Shanghai, 200129, China
Tel.: (86) 21 5871 3610
Ship Building Services
N.A.I.C.S.: 336611

Tamano Engineering Co., Ltd. (1)
1-1 Tama 3-chome, Okayama, 706-8651, Tamano, Japan
Tel.: (81) 863232010
Web Site: http://www.tamano.or.jp
Sales Range: $50-74.9 Million
Emp.: 200
Design Drawings of Ships, Ship Machinery, Land Machinery & Systems & Plant Engineering
N.A.I.C.S.: 333248

Techno-Seaways Inc. (1)
2-2-15 606 Hamamatsucho, Minato-ku, Tokyo, 105-0013, Japan
Tel.: (81) 3 5402 6261
Techno Super Liner Leasing Services
N.A.I.C.S.: 532411

Toyo Electronics Corp. (1)
1-35-22 Ookayama Nikkan Building, Meguro-ku, Tokyo, 152-0033, Japan
Tel.: (81) 33 723 6211
Web Site: https://www.sd.toyonics.co.jp
Emp.: 111
Electronic Machinery Mfr & Distr
N.A.I.C.S.: 333248

Western Biomass Operating Company Ltd (1)
Western Wood Energy Plant 1 Longlands Lane, Margam, Port Talbot, SA13 2NR, United Kingdom
Tel.: (44) 1 639 861 810
Power Plant Construction Management Services
N.A.I.C.S.: 237130
Colin Jones *(Gen Mgr)*

MITSUI FUDOSAN CO., LTD.

1-1 Nihonbashi-Muromachi 2 chome, Chuo-ku, Tokyo, 103-0022, Japan
Tel.: (81) 332463168 **JP**
Web Site:
https://www.mitsuifudosan.co.jp
Year Founded: 1941
8801—(TKS)
Rev.: $15,753,540,290
Assets: $62,725,773,470
Liabilities: $41,344,697,310
Net Worth: $21,381,076,160
Earnings: $1,484,916,670
Emp.: 2,049
Fiscal Year-end: 03/31/24
Real Estate Development & Management Services
N.A.I.C.S.: 531390
Hiromichi Iwasa *(Chm)*

Subsidiaries:

Cany Corporation (1)
Tokyo Opera City Tower 17th floor 3-20-2, Nishi-Shinjuku Shinjuku-ku, Tokyo, 163-1477, Japan
Tel.: (81) 362762410
Web Site: http://www.cany.co.jp
Emp.: 877
Restaurant Operating Services
N.A.I.C.S.: 721110

Celestine Hotel Co., Ltd. (1)
3-23-1 Shiba, Minato-ku, Tokyo, 105-0014, Japan
Tel.: (81) 354414111
Web Site: http://www.celestinehotel.com
Sales Range: $25-49.9 Million
Emp.: 100
Home Management Services
N.A.I.C.S.: 561110
Mitsudu Atachi *(Pres)*

Daiichi Engei Co., Ltd. (1)
MGL Katsushima Building No 20 5F 1-5-21 Katsushima, Shinagawa-ku, Tokyo, 140-0012, Japan
Tel.: (81) 364041530
Web Site: http://www.daiichi-engei.jp
Real Estate Services
N.A.I.C.S.: 531390
Noboru Ito *(Pres)*

First Facilities Challenged Co., Ltd. (1)
1-6-2 Nihonbashi Muromachi 162 Building 7F, Chuo-ku, Tokyo, 103-0022, Japan
Tel.: (81) 335162266
Web Site: http://www.1st-f.co.jp
Rev.: $258,960
Emp.: 10
Employment Guidance & Support Services
N.A.I.C.S.: 561311

First Facilities Chiba Co., Ltd. (1)
1-11-1 Chuo, Chuo-ku, Chiba, 260-0013, Japan
Tel.: (81) 43 202 1150
Web Site: http://www.1st-f-chiba.co.jp
Sales Range: $75-99.9 Million
Emp.: 300
Building Management Services
N.A.I.C.S.: 561720

First Facilities Co., Ltd. (1)
2-6-7 Kuramae, Taito-ku, Tokyo, 111-8605, Japan
Tel.: (81) 358203040
Web Site: http://www.1st-f.co.jp
Rev.: $2,978,040
Emp.: 3,326
Building Management Services
N.A.I.C.S.: 238990

First Facilities Gunma Co., Ltd. (1)
17-17 Shinmaebashi-cho, Maebashi, 371-0843, Gunma, Japan
Tel.: (81) 27 254 2400
Web Site: http://www.1st-f-gunma.co.jp
Sales Range: $25-49.9 Million
Emp.: 88
Building Management Services
N.A.I.C.S.: 561110

First Facilities West Co., Ltd. (1)
24 Sumitomo Life Bldg Hikaru Honcho 2 2 Chuo-ku 4 Chome, Osaka, 541-0053, Japan
Tel.: (81) 6 6245 3181
Web Site: http://www.1st-f-west.co.jp
Emp.: 929
Building Management Services
N.A.I.C.S.: 541618
Kulakane Hidemi *(Pres)*

Haimurubushi Co., Ltd. (1)
Tel.: (81) 980853111
Web Site: http://www.haimurubushi.co.jp
Room & Accommodation Services
N.A.I.C.S.: 721110

Halekulani Corporation (1)
2199 Kalia Rd, Honolulu, HI 96815
Tel.: (808) 923-2311
Web Site: https://www.halekulani.com
Sales Range: $50-74.9 Million
Emp.: 15
Real Estate Services
N.A.I.C.S.: 531390
Ulrich Krauer *(Gen Mgr)*

Kyusin Kaihatsu Inc. (1)
2950-1 Yoshiono, Usuki, 875-0071, Oita, Japan
Tel.: (81) 972653131
Resort Management Services
N.A.I.C.S.: 721120

La Tours, Inc. (1)
Lalaport Mitsui Building 2-1-1 Hamacho, Funabashi, 273-0012, Chiba, Japan
Tel.: (81) 47 434 7055
Web Site: http://www.latours.co.jp
Travel & Tour Operating Agencies
N.A.I.C.S.: 561510

LaLaport Management Co., Ltd. - LaLaport KASHIWANOHA Facility (1)
175 Wakashiba, Kashiwa, 277-8518, Chiba, Japan
Tel.: (81) 471681588
Web Site: http://www.lalaport.co.jp
Sales Range: $1-4.9 Billion
Emp.: 3,000
Shopping Mall Management Services
N.A.I.C.S.: 531120

LaLaport Management Co., Ltd. - LaLaport SHIN MISATO Facility (1)
3-1-1 Shin Misato LalaCity, Misato, 341-8550, Saitama, Japan
Tel.: (81) 489501515
Shopping Mall Management Services
N.A.I.C.S.: 531120

LaLaport Management Co., Ltd. - LaLaport TOKYO-BAY Facility (1)
2-1-1 Hamamachi, Funabashi, 273-8530, Chiba, Japan
Tel.: (81) 474339800
Sales Range: $300-349.9 Million
Emp.: 673
Commercial Property Management & Rental Services
N.A.I.C.S.: 531312

LaLaport Management Co., Ltd. - LaLaport YOKOHAMA Facility (1)
4035-1 Ikebe, Tsuzuki-ku, Yokohama, 224-0053, Kanagawa, Japan
Tel.: (81) 459311000
Sales Range: $25-49.9 Million
Emp.: 30
Commercial Facility Management Services

INTERNATIONAL PUBLIC

N.A.I.C.S.: 531120

LaLaport Management Co., Ltd. - MITSUI OUTLET PARK Iruma Facility (1)
3169-1 Miyadera, Iruma, 358-0014, Saitama, Japan
Tel.: (81) 429351616
Sales Range: $300-349.9 Million
Emp.: 1,000
Shopping Mall Management Services
N.A.I.C.S.: 531120

LaLaport Management Co., Ltd. - MITSUI OUTLET PARK Jazz Dream Nagashima Facility (1)
368 Urayasu Nagashima-cho, Kuwana, 511-1135, Mie, Japan
Tel.: (81) 594458700
Web Site: http://www.mitsui-shopping-park.com
Shopping Mall Management Services
N.A.I.C.S.: 531120

LaLaport Management Co., Ltd. - MITSUI OUTLET PARK Marine Pier Kobe Facility (1)
12-2 Kaigan-dori, Tarumi-ku, Kobe, 650-0024, Hyogo, Japan
Tel.: (81) 787094466
Sales Range: $300-349.9 Million
Emp.: 600
Shopping Mall Management Services
N.A.I.C.S.: 531120

LaLaport Management Co., Ltd. - MITSUI OUTLET PARK Sendai Minato Facility (1)
123 Miyagino Ward Nakano-Ideka, Sendaishi, Miyagi, 980-8671, Japan
Tel.: (81) 22 355 8800
Shopping Mall Management Services
N.A.I.C.S.: 531120
Tadashi Ando *(Pres)*

LaLaport Management Co., Ltd. - MITSUI OUTLET PARK Yokohama Bayside Facility (1)
5-2 Shiraho, Kanazawa-ku, Yokohama, 236-8666, Kanagawa, Japan
Tel.: (81) 457754446
Web Site: http://mitsui-shopping-park.com
Shopping Mall Management Services
N.A.I.C.S.: 531120

LaLaport Management Co., Ltd. - URBAN DOCK LaLaport TOYOSU Facility (1)
2-4-9 Toyosu, Koutou-ku, Tokyo, 135-8614, Japan
Tel.: (81) 570077732
Web Site: http://mitsui-shopping-park.com
Commercial Facility Management Services
N.A.I.C.S.: 531312

LaLaport Management Co., Ltd. - MITSUI OUTLET PARK Tama Minami Osawa Facility (1)
1-600 Minami Osawa, Hachioji, Tokyo, 192-0364, Japan
Tel.: (81) 426705777
Sales Range: $50-74.9 Million
Emp.: 10
Commercial Facility Management Services
N.A.I.C.S.: 531312

MF Housing Service Chugoku Co., Ltd. (1)
Nakamachi Mitsui Building 9-12 Nakamachi, Naka-ku, Hiroshima, 730-0037, Japan
Tel.: (81) 822401150
Sales Range: $50-74.9 Million
Emp.: 60
Property Management Services
N.A.I.C.S.: 531210

MF Housing Service Kyushu Co., Ltd. (1)
Hakata Mitsui Building 10-1 Kami Gofukumachi, Hakata-ku, Fukuoka, 812-0036, Japan
Tel.: (81) 92 262 5522
Residential Property Development Services
N.A.I.C.S.: 236115

Mitsui Fudosan (Asia) Malaysia Sdn. Bhd. (1)
Lot 21-02 21st Floor Menara Hap Seng 2 Plaza Hap Seng, No 1 Jalan P Ramlee,

AND PRIVATE COMPANIES

MITSUI FUDOSAN CO., LTD.

50250, Kuala Lumpur, Malaysia
Tel.: (60) 320221116
Real Estate Services
N.A.I.C.S.: 531390
Wykeen Lum *(Mgr-Bus Dev)*

Mitsui Fudosan (Asia) Pte. Ltd. (1)
16 Raffles Quay No 40-01 Hong Leong Building, Singapore, 048581, Singapore
Tel.: (65) 62208158
Web Site: http://www.mitsuifudosan-asia.com
Sales Range: $50-74.9 Million
Emp.: 12
Real Estate Services
N.A.I.C.S.: 531390
Jiro Ueda *(Mng Dir)*

Mitsui Fudosan (Shanghai) Consulting Co., Ltd. (1)
Unit2112 One ICC Shanghai International Commerce Center, 999 Middle Huaihai Road Xuhui District, Shanghai, 200031, China
Tel.: (86) 2153966969
Web Site: http://www.mituifudosan.co.sg
Sales Range: $25-49.9 Million
Emp.: 40
Residential Property Development Services
N.A.I.C.S.: 531210

Mitsui Fudosan (U.K.) Ltd. (1)
6th Floor Cassini House 57-58 St James's Street, London, SW1A 1LD, United Kingdom (100%)
Tel.: (44) 2073184370
Web Site: https://www.mitsuifudosan.co.uk
Sales Range: $50-74.9 Million
Emp.: 4
Real Estate Services
N.A.I.C.S.: 531390
David Height *(Dir-Plng & Engrg)*

Mitsui Fudosan Accommodations Fund Management Co., Ltd. (1)
Nihonbashi 1-chome Mitsui Building 1-4-1, Nihonbashi Chuo-ku, Tokyo, 103-0027, Japan
Tel.: (81) 332463677
Sales Range: $50-74.9 Million
Emp.: 31
Investment Management Service
N.A.I.C.S.: 523940
Tateyuki Ikura *(Pres & CEO)*

Mitsui Fudosan America, Inc. (1)
1251 Avenue of the Americas Ste 800, New York, NY 10020-1104 (100%)
Tel.: (212) 403-5600
Web Site: https://www.mfamerica.com
Sales Range: $50-74.9 Million
Emp.: 24
Real Estate Sales
N.A.I.C.S.: 531390
John E. Westerfield *(CEO)*

Mitsui Fudosan Architectural Engineering CO., LTD. (1)
3-2-1 Nihonbashi Muromachi, Chuo - ku, Tokyo, 104-0061, Japan
Tel.: (81) 332463197
Web Site: https://www.mf-engineering.co.jp
Emp.: 135
Architectural Design Services
N.A.I.C.S.: 541310

Mitsui Fudosan Asia (Thailand) Co., Ltd. (1)
388 Exchange Tower 33rd Floor Unit 3301 Sukhumvit Road, Klongtoey, Bangkok, 10110, Thailand
Tel.: (66) 22584033
Real Estate Services
N.A.I.C.S.: 531390

Mitsui Fudosan Australia Pty. Ltd. (1)
Level 15 175 Pitt Street, Sydney, 2000, NSW, Australia
Tel.: (61) 291591848
Real Estate Services
N.A.I.C.S.: 531390

Mitsui Fudosan Building Management Co., Ltd. (1)
2-1-1 Nihonbashi Muromachi, Chuo-ku, Tokyo, 103-0022, Japan
Tel.: (81) 362141400
Web Site: https://www.mfbm.co.jp

Emp.: 1,806
Administrative Management & Building Rental Services
N.A.I.C.S.: 531120

Mitsui Fudosan Co., Ltd. (1)
20/F One International Finance Centre 1 Harbour View Street, Central, China (Hong Kong)
Tel.: (852) 28556974
Real Estate Services
N.A.I.C.S.: 531390

Mitsui Fudosan Consulting (Beijing) Co., Ltd. (1)
12th Floor Unit 05 China World Office 1 No 1 Jianguomenwai Avenue, Beijing, 100004, China
Tel.: (86) 1065053101
Real Estate Services
N.A.I.C.S.: 531390

Mitsui Fudosan Consulting (Guangzhou) Co., Ltd. (1)
Room 1405 R and F Centre No 10 Huaxia Road, Zhujiang New Town, Guangzhou, 510623, China
Tel.: (86) 2028023188
Real Estate Services
N.A.I.C.S.: 531390

Mitsui Fudosan Engineering Advisors Inc. (1)
3-2-1 Nihonbashi Muromachi Nihonbashi Muromachi Mitsui Tower, Chuo, Tokyo, Japan
Tel.: (81) 332463197
Web Site: https://www.mf-engineering.co.jp
Emp.: 135
Civil Engineering & Construction Services
N.A.I.C.S.: 541330

Mitsui Fudosan Facilities Co., Ltd. (1)
Toranomon Mitsui Building 3-8-1 Kasumigaseki, Chiyoda- ku, Tokyo, 100-0013, Japan
Tel.: (81) 335288640
Web Site: https://www.mitsui-fc.co.jp
Emp.: 3,921
Building Maintenance & Repair Services
N.A.I.C.S.: 561790

Mitsui Fudosan Frontier REIT Management Inc. (1)
6th Floor Kojun Bldg 6-8-7, Ginza Chuo-Ku, Tokyo, 104-0061, Japan
Tel.: (81) 332890440
Web Site: https://www.f-reit.co.jp
Sales Range: $50-74.9 Million
Emp.: 21
Investment Management Service
N.A.I.C.S.: 523940
Hiroshi Matsumoto *(Compliance Officer)*

Mitsui Fudosan Hotel Management Co., Ltd. (1)
2F Nihonbashi Honcho 2-chome Bldg 2-2-5 Nihonbashi-Honcho, Chuo-ku, Tokyo, 103-0023, Japan
Tel.: (81) 335480328
Web Site: https://www.gardenhotels.co.jp
Sales Range: $75-99.9 Million
Emp.: 336
Home Management Services
N.A.I.C.S.: 561110

Mitsui Fudosan Housing Lease Co., Ltd. (1)
Shinjuku Mitsui Building 2-1-1 Nishi Shinjuku, Shinjuku-ku, Tokyo, 163-0405, Japan
Tel.: (81) 353811031
Web Site: http://mfhl.mitsui-chintai.co.jp
Sales Range: $300-349.9 Million
Emp.: 827
Property Management & Leasing Services
N.A.I.C.S.: 531190
Yoshihito Tsunoda *(Chm)*

Mitsui Fudosan Housing Service Kansai Co.,Ltd. (1)
4-25 Honmachi 4-chome, Chuo-ku, Osaka, 541-0053, Japan
Tel.: (81) 662056701
Sales Range: $25-49.9 Million
Emp.: 40
Property Development Services
N.A.I.C.S.: 531311
Yasuhiko Yamashiro *(Mgr)*

Mitsui Fudosan Investment Advisors, Inc. (1)
Nihonbashi 1-chome Mitsui Building 1-4-1, Nihonbashi Chuo-Ku, Tokyo, 103-0027, Japan
Tel.: (81) 332463920
Sales Range: $50-74.9 Million
Emp.: 82
Investment Management Service
N.A.I.C.S.: 523940
Shuji Tomikawa *(Pres & CEO)*

Mitsui Fudosan Logistics REIT Management Co., Ltd. (1)
8-7 Ginza 6-chome, Chuo-ku, Tokyo, 104-0061, Japan
Tel.: (81) 363275160
Web Site: https://www.mflp-m.co.jp
Investment Management Service
N.A.I.C.S.: 523940
Yukio Yoshida *(Pres & CEO)*

Mitsui Fudosan Realty Co., Ltd. (1)
9th floor Kasumigaseki Building 3-2-5 Kasumigaseki, Chiyoda-ku, Tokyo, 100-6019, Japan (100%)
Tel.: (81) 367584060
Web Site: https://www.mf-realty.jp
Sales Range: $200-249.9 Million
Emp.: 5,391
Sales of Real Estate & Land Development Services
N.A.I.C.S.: 237210

Subsidiary (Domestic):

Car Sharing Japan Co., Ltd. (2)
Kasumigaseki 3-chome No 2 No 5 Kasumigaseki Building 19th Floor, Chiyoda-ku, Tokyo, 100-6019, Japan (100%)
Tel.: (81) 335803101
Web Site: http://www.careco.jp
Car Sharing Services
N.A.I.C.S.: 532111
Shingo Kurokawa *(Pres & CEO)*

Mitsui Fudosan Residential Co., Ltd. (1)
3-2-1 Nihonbashi Muromachi, Chuo-ku, Tokyo, 103-0022, Japan
Tel.: (81) 332463600
Web Site: https://www.mfr.co.jp
Sales Range: $650-699.9 Million
Emp.: 1,957
Property Development Services
N.A.I.C.S.: 531311

Mitsui Fudosan Residential Lease Co., Ltd. (1)
Shinjuku Mitsui Building 2-1-1 Nishi-Shinjuku, Shinjuku-ku, Tokyo, 163-0405, Japan
Tel.: (81) 353811031
Web Site: https://mfhl.mitsui-chintai.co.jp
Emp.: 827
Real Estate Services
N.A.I.C.S.: 531390

Mitsui Fudosan Residential Service Chugoku Co., Ltd. (1)
730-0037 Nakamachi Mitsui Building 9-12 Nakamachi, Naka Ward, Hiroshima, Japan
Tel.: (81) 822401150
Web Site: https://www.mitsuikanri-chugoku.co.jp
Insurance Agency Services
N.A.I.C.S.: 524210

Mitsui Fudosan Residential Service Co., Ltd. (1)
NBF Toyosu Canal Front 5-6-52 Toyosu, Koto-ku, Tokyo, 135-0061, Japan
Tel.: (81) 335343458
Web Site: http://www.mitsui-kanri.co.jp
Emp.: 2,892
Property Management Services
N.A.I.C.S.: 531210
Kiyotaka Fujibayashi *(Chm)*

Mitsui Fudosan Residential Service Co., Ltd. (1)
NBF Toyosu Canal Front 5-6-52 Toyosu, Koto-ku, Tokyo, 135-0061, Japan
Tel.: (81) 335343101
Web Site: http://www.mitsui-kanri.co.jp
Property Management Services
N.A.I.C.S.: 531311
Shigeru Takamatsu *(Chm)*

Mitsui Fudosan Residential Service Kansai Co., Ltd. (1)
4-4-25 Honmachi, Chuo-ku, Osaka, 541-0053, Japan
Tel.: (81) 662536233
Web Site: http://www.mitsuikanri-kansai.co.jp
Emp.: 613
Residential Apartment Services
N.A.I.C.S.: 531110

Mitsui Fudosan Residential Service Kyushu Co., Ltd. (1)
Hakata Mitsui Building 10-1 Kamigofukumachi, Hakata, Fukuoka, 812-0036, Japan
Tel.: (81) 922625522
Web Site: https://www.mitsuikanri-kyushu.co.jp
Insurance Agency Services
N.A.I.C.S.: 524210

Mitsui Fudosan Residential Service Tohoku Co., Ltd. (1)
Sendai Honmachi Mitsui Building 2-4-6 Honmachi, Aoba-ku, Sendai, 980-0014, Miyagi, Japan
Tel.: (81) 222629531
Web Site: https://www.mitsuikanri-tohoku.co.jp
Property Management Services
N.A.I.C.S.: 531210

Mitsui Fudosan Residential Wellness Co., Ltd. (1)
Nihonbashi Muromachi Mitsui Tower 3-2-1 Nihonbashi Muromachi, Chuo, Tokyo, 103-0022, Japan
Tel.: (81) 332463969
Web Site: https://www.mfrw.co.jp
Residential Services
N.A.I.C.S.: 531110

Mitsui Fudosan Retail Management Co., Ltd. - LaLaport Koshien (1)
1-100 Koushien-8-bancho, Nishinomiya, 663-8178, Hyogo, Japan
Tel.: (81) 798444321
Web Site: http://www.mf-shogyo.co.jp
Shopping Mall Management Services
N.A.I.C.S.: 531120

Mitsui Fudosan Retail Management Co., Ltd. - MITSUI OUTLET PARK Makuhari (1)
2-6-1 Hibino, Mihama-ku, Chiba, 261-0013, Japan
Tel.: (81) 359279321
Web Site: http://www.mitsui-shopping-park.com
Sales Range: $25-49.9 Million
Emp.: 200
Shopping Mall Management Services
N.A.I.C.S.: 541618

Mitsui Fudosan Taiwan Co., Ltd. (1)
21st Floor No 66 Section 1 Zhongxiao West Road, Zhongzheng District, Taipei, 10018, Taiwan
Tel.: (886) 223615631
Web Site: http://www.mftw-consulting.com
Real Estate Services
N.A.I.C.S.: 531390
Airi Y. *(Project Mgr)*

Mitsui Home Co., Ltd. (1)
53rd floor Shinjuku Mitsui Building 1-1-1 Nishi-Shinjuku, Shinjuku-ku, Tokyo, 163-0453, Japan (100%)
Tel.: (81) 333464411
Web Site: https://www.mitsuihome.co.jp
Sales Range: $1-4.9 Billion
Emp.: 2,580
Housing Design, Construction & Sale; Housing Materials Import, Production & Processing
N.A.I.C.S.: 236118
Akira Ikeda *(Pres & CEO)*

Subsidiary (Domestic):

Mitsui Designtec Co., Ltd. (2)
6-chome Ginza 6-17-1 Ginza SQUARE, Chuo-ku, Tokyo, 104-0061, Japan
Tel.: (81) 363663131
Web Site: https://www.mitsui-designtec.co.jp
Emp.: 796
Construction Management & Interior Design Services
N.A.I.C.S.: 236118

MITSUI FUDOSAN CO., LTD.

Mitsui Fudosan Co., Ltd.—(Continued)

Atsushi Hinokida (Sr Exec Officer)

Mitsui Home Estate Co., Ltd. (1)
6th floor Apple Building 2-3-11 Fujimi, Chiyoda-ku, Tokyo, 102-0071, Japan
Tel.: (81) 352263733
Web Site: https://www.mhe.co.jp
Emp.: 286
Real Estate Services
N.A.I.C.S.: 531390

Mitsui Home Remodeling Co., Ltd. (1)
Shinjuku Mitsui Building 35F 2-1-1 Nishi Shinjuku, Shinjuku, 163-0435, Tokyo, Japan
Tel.: (81) 363673831
Web Site: http://www.mitsui-reform.com
Emp.: 347
Residential Remodeling Services
N.A.I.C.S.: 236118

Mitsui-No-Mori Co., Ltd. (1)
10411 Higashidake, Toyohira, Chino, Nagano, Japan
Tel.: (81) 266762388
Web Site: https://www.mitsuinomori.co.jp
Emp.: 122
Real Estate Services
N.A.I.C.S.: 531390

NBF Office Management Co., Ltd. (1)
2-1-1 6th floor Mitsui Building No 2 Nihonbashi Muromachi, Chuo-ku, Tokyo, 103-0022, Japan
Tel.: (81) 332463607
Web Site: http://www.nbf-om.com
Residential Land & Building Rental Services
N.A.I.C.S.: 531110

Nippon Building Fund Management Ltd. (1)
Muromachi Furukawa Mitsui Building 16th Floor 3-1 2-chome, Nihonbashi Muromachi Chuo-ku, Tokyo, 103-0022, Japan
Tel.: (81) 335163370
Web Site: https://www.nbf-m.com
Emp.: 33
Asset Management Services
N.A.I.C.S.: 523940

Resident First Co., Ltd. (1)
Aoyama Tower Place 4F 4-14 Akasaka 8-Chome, Minato-ku, Tokyo, 107-0052, Japan
Tel.: (81) 357729927
Web Site: https://www.resident-chintai.co.jp
Sales Range: $75-99.9 Million
Emp.: 110
Residential Property Leasing Services
N.A.I.C.S.: 531110
Yasuhiro Takehara (Pres)

Sunlife Creation Co., Ltd. (1)
4-6-7 Nihonbashi Honkoku Nihonbashi Nigin-dori Building 2F, Chuo, Tokyo, 103-0021, Japan
Tel.: (81) 362140810
Web Site: https://www.slc-mh.co.jp
Emp.: 301
Real Estate Brokerage Services
N.A.I.C.S.: 531190

Tokyo Dome Corporation (1)
1-3-61 Koraku, Bunkyo-ku, Tokyo, 112-8575, Japan **(84.82%)**
Tel.: (81) 338112111
Web Site: http://www.tokyo-dome.jp
Rev.: $839,577,690
Assets: $2,790,889,500
Liabilities: $1,795,458,490
Net Worth: $995,431,010
Earnings: $73,378,340
Emp.: 888
Fiscal Year-end: 01/31/2020
Arts Event & Exhibition Organizer
N.A.I.C.S.: 711310
Akira Nishikatsu (Sr Mng Dir)

Subsidiary (Domestic):

Matsudo Kousan Co., Ltd. (2)
8-3 Honmachi, Matsudo, 271-0091, Japan
Tel.: (81) 473662121
Web Site: https://www.matsudokousan.co.jp
Emp.: 28
Real Estate Management Services
N.A.I.C.S.: 531390

Olympia Kogyo Co., Ltd. (2)
7-33-28 Fujimi-cho, Tachikawa, 190-0013, Tokyo, Japan
Tel.: (81) 425277985
Emp.: 45
Industrial Machinery & Equipment Mfr
N.A.I.C.S.: 333998

TOKYO DOME HOTEL CORPORATION (2)
1-3-61 Koraku, Bunkyo-ku, Tokyo, 112-8562, Japan
Tel.: (81) 358052111
Web Site: https://www.tokyodome-hotels.co.jp
Emp.: 433
Hotel Operator
N.A.I.C.S.: 721110

Tokyo Midtown Management Co., Ltd. (1)
9-7-1 Akasaka, Minato-ku, Tokyo, 107-0052, Japan
Tel.: (81) 334753100
Web Site: https://en.tokyo-midtown.com
Emp.: 170
Real Estate Services
N.A.I.C.S.: 531390
Goro Toyama (Pres)

Uniliving Co., Ltd. (1)
NBF Shin Urayasu Tower 11F 5-2 Irifune 1 Chome, Mihama-Ku, Urayasu, 279-0012, Chiba, Japan
Tel.: (81) 473046370
Web Site: http://www.uniliv.co.jp
Rev.: $38,239,760
Emp.: 1,863
Hardware Retailer
N.A.I.C.S.: 444140

MITSUI FUDOSAN LOGISTICS PARK, INC.
8-7 Ginza 6-chome Chuo-ku, Tokyo, 104-0061, Japan
Tel.: (81) 363275160
Web Site: http://www.mflp-r.co.jp
Year Founded: 2016
3471—(TKS)
Sales Range: Less than $1 Million
Real Estate Investment Services
N.A.I.C.S.: 531210
Anne L. Mariucci (Gen Partner)

MITSUI HIGH-TEC INC.
2-10-1 Komine, Yahatanishi-ku, Kitakyushu, 807-8588, Fukuoka, Japan
Tel.: (81) 936141111
Web Site: https://www.mitsui-high-tec.com
6966—(TKS)
Rev.: $1,388,796,290
Assets: $1,387,484,640
Liabilities: $699,804,270
Net Worth: $687,680,370
Earnings: $110,214,050
Emp.: 4,864
Fiscal Year-end: 01/31/24
Machine Tools Mfr
N.A.I.C.S.: 333517
Yasunari Mitsui (Pres)

Subsidiaries:

Mitsui High-Tec (Canada), Inc. (1)
60 Fen Ridge Court, Brantford, N3V 1G2, ON, Canada
Tel.: (519) 750-5788
Motor Core Mfr & Retailer
N.A.I.C.S.: 336390

Mitsui High-Tec (Europe) Sp. z o.o. (1)
Ul Technologiczna 1, Skarbimierz, 49-318, Brzeg, Poland
Tel.: (48) 774449360
Motor Core Mfr & Retailer
N.A.I.C.S.: 336390

Mitsui High-Tec (Shanghai) Co., Ltd. (1)
No 2001 Xinjinqiao Rd Pilot Free Trade Zone, Shanghai, 201206, China
Tel.: (86) 2158996160
Lead Frame & Motor Core Mfr & Retailer
N.A.I.C.S.: 336390

Mitsui High-tec (Guang Dong) Co., Ltd. (1)
10 Lian Xin Road, Shang Jiao Village Chang An Town, Dongguan, 523878, Guangdong, China
Tel.: (86) 76938956866
Web Site: http://www.mitsui-high-tec.com
Integrated Circuit Lead Frames & Motor Cores Mfr
N.A.I.C.S.: 335999

Mitsui High-tec (Hong Kong), Ltd. (1)
Unit 2506-7 25/F Yen Sheng Centre 64 Hoi Yuen Road, Kwun Tong, Kowloon, China (Hong Kong)
Tel.: (852) 23896354
Web Site: http://www.mitsui-high-tec.com
Integrated Circuit Lead Frames & Motor Cores Mfr & Sales
N.A.I.C.S.: 335999

Mitsui High-tec (Malaysia) Sdn. Bhd. (1)
Lot 11-A Jalan Ragum 15/17, 40000, Shah Alam, Selangor, Malaysia
Tel.: (60) 351639000
Web Site: http://www.mitsui-high-tec.com
Precision Fabrication Surface Grinder Mfr
N.A.I.C.S.: 332999

Mitsui High-tec (Philippines), Inc. (1)
3rd Floor Unit 3E The Calamba Executive Center, Brgy Uno Crossing, Calamba, 4027, Laguna, Philippines
Tel.: (63) 495023881
Web Site: http://www.mitsui-high-tec.com
Lead Frames Mfr & Supplier
N.A.I.C.S.: 332999

Mitsui High-tec (Singapore) Pte. Ltd. (1)
37 Tuas Avenue 8, Singapore, 639249, Singapore
Tel.: (65) 68978900
Sales Range: $100-124.9 Million
Emp.: 295
Precision Tool Mfr
N.A.I.C.S.: 332216
Amy Wong (Dir-Sls)

Mitsui High-tec (Taiwan) Co., Ltd. (1)
1 South 5th Rd, Cian Jhen Technology Industrial Park, Kaohsiung, Taiwan
Tel.: (886) 78215300
Web Site: http://www.mitsui-high-tec.com
Sales Range: $50-74.9 Million
Lead Frames Mfr & Supplier
N.A.I.C.S.: 334412

Mitsui High-tec (Thailand) Co., Ltd. (1)
125 Moo 1 Hi-tech Industrial Estate, Tambol Baan Lane Amphur Bang Pa-in, Ayutthaya, 13160, Thailand
Tel.: (66) 35351660
Web Site: http://www.mitsui-high-tec.com
Sales Range: $50-74.9 Million
Lead Frames Mfr
N.A.I.C.S.: 334412

Mitsui High-tec (Tianjin) Co., Ltd. (1)
No 61 6th avenue, Teda, Tianjin, 300457, China
Tel.: (86) 2266202186
Web Site: http://www.mhttj.com
Lead Frames Mfr & Supplier
N.A.I.C.S.: 334419

Mitsui High-tec (USA), Inc. (1)
64 W Seegers Rd, Arlington Heights, IL 60005
Tel.: (847) 593-1634
Web Site: http://www.mitsui-high-tec.com
Sales Range: $25-49.9 Million
Dies & Stamping Products Mfr
N.A.I.C.S.: 332721

Mitsui High-tec Inc. - IC Plant (1)
2-10-1 Komine, Yahatanishi-ku, Kitakyushu, 807-8588, Fukuoka, Japan
Tel.: (81) 936141111
Web Site: http://www.mitsui-high-tec.com
Semiconductor Assembling Services
N.A.I.C.S.: 334413

Mitsui High-tec Inc. - Kibita Plant (1)
410-10 Oaza shimozakai, Nogata, 822-0007, Fukuoka, Japan
Tel.: (81) 949280600
Lead Frames Mfr
N.A.I.C.S.: 332999

Mitsui High-tec Inc. - Kumamoto Plant (1)
312-8 Oaza Toriko Nishihara-mura, Aso-gun, Kumamoto, 861-2401, Japan
Tel.: (81) 962793353
Lead Frames Mfr & Supplier
N.A.I.C.S.: 339940

Mitsui High-tec Inc. - Nogata Plant (1)
965 1 Oaza Nakaizumi, Nogata, 822-0011, Fukuoka, Japan
Tel.: (81) 949222500
Lead Frames Mfr
N.A.I.C.S.: 332999

Mitsui High-tec Inc. - Tooling Plant (1)
864-8 Oaza Nobu, Yahatanishi-ku, Kitakyushu, 807-1262, Fukuoka, Japan
Tel.: (81) 936190050
Web Site: http://www.mitsui-high-tec.com
Sales Range: $100-124.9 Million
Stamping Die Mfr
N.A.I.C.S.: 333514

Mitsui High-tec Trading Co., Ltd. (1)
No 2001 Xinjinqiao Rd Pilot Free Trade Zone, Pudong, Shanghai, 201206, China
Tel.: (86) 2158996160
Lead Frames Mfr & Whslr
N.A.I.C.S.: 334412

Mitsui Stamping Co., Ltd. (1)
2145-2 Aza Nishikukioka Oaza Maeda, Yahatahigashi-ku, Kitakyushu, 805-0058, Fukuoka, Japan
Tel.: (81) 936726331
Motor Core Stamping Product Mfr
N.A.I.C.S.: 336370

MITSUI MATSUSHIMA HOLDINGS CO., LTD.
Otemom Pine Bldg 11F 1-1-12 Otemon, Chuo-ku, Fukuoka, 810-8527, Japan
Tel.: (81) 927712171
Web Site: https://www.mitsui-matsushima.co.jp
Year Founded: 1913
1518—(FKA)
Rev.: $451,010,560
Assets: $656,662,160
Liabilities: $312,664,000
Net Worth: $343,998,160
Earnings: $52,233,280
Emp.: 1,305
Fiscal Year-end: 03/31/22
Holding Company
N.A.I.C.S.: 551112
Shinichiro Kushima (Chm)

MITSUI O.S.K. LINES, LTD.
Shosen Mitsui Building 1-1 Toranomon 2-Chome, Minato-ku, Tokyo, 105-8688, Japan
Tel.: (81) 335877015 JP
Web Site: https://www.mol.co.jp
Year Founded: 1964
9104—(TKS)
Rev.: $10,760,498,320
Assets: $27,236,848,720
Liabilities: $11,573,250,700
Net Worth: $15,663,598,020
Earnings: $1,729,513,110
Emp.: 9,795
Fiscal Year-end: 03/31/24
Marine Freight Transportation & Logistics Services
N.A.I.C.S.: 483111
Takeshi Hashimoto (Pres)

Subsidiaries:

Asahi Tanker Co., Ltd. (1)
1-2-2 Uchisaiwaicho, Chiyoda-Ku, Tokyo, 100-0011, Japan
Tel.: (81) 335081631

AND PRIVATE COMPANIES

MITSUI O.S.K. LINES, LTD.

Web Site: https://www.asahi-tanker.com
Emp.: 298
Ship Equipment Distr
N.A.I.C.S.: 423860
Kazunori Nakai *(Pres & CEO)*

Bangpoo Intermodal Systems Co., Ltd. (1)
596 Moo 4 Bangpoo Industrial Estate Soi 13B Pathana 1 Rd, Phraeksa Muang, Samut Prakan, 10280, Thailand
Tel.: (66) 23240790
Sales Range: $25-49.9 Million
Emp.: 100
Warehousing & Marine Cargo Handling Services
N.A.I.C.S.: 488320
Waki Ikemoto *(Mng Dir)*

Blue Highway Service K.K. (1)
2-10-2 Higashigotanda Higashigotanda Square 4F, Shinagawa-ku, Tokyo, 141-0022, Japan
Tel.: (81) 368538009
Sales Range: $25-49.9 Million
Emp.: 10
General Freight Trucking Services
N.A.I.C.S.: 484110

Chugoku Shipping Agencies Ltd. (1)
Sales Range: $25-49.9 Million
Emp.: 34
Shipping Services
N.A.I.C.S.: 488510

Daibiru Corporation (1)
3-6-32 Nakanoshima, Kita-ku, Osaka, 530-0005, Japan **(82.6%)**
Tel.: (81) 664411932
Web Site: http://www.daibiru.co.jp
Rev.: $415,359,120
Assets: $3,813,223,040
Liabilities: $2,193,313,760
Net Worth: $1,619,909,280
Earnings: $81,670,160
Emp.: 2,457
Fiscal Year-end: 03/31/2021
N.A.I.C.S.: 531120
Takeo Yada *(Exec Officer)*

Subsidiary (Non-US):

Daibiru CSB Co., Ltd. (2)
16 Phan Chu Trinh Street, Hoan Kiem District, Hanoi, Vietnam
Tel.: (84) 942122255
Building Leasing Services
N.A.I.C.S.: 531110

Daibiru Saigon Tower Co., Ltd. (2)
29 Le Duan Boulevard, Ben Nghe Ward District 1, Ho Chi Minh City, Vietnam
Tel.: (84) 2838234000
Web Site: http://www.saigontower.com
Building Leasing Services
N.A.I.C.S.: 531110

Subsidiary (Domestic):

MOL Kosan Co., Ltd (2)
3-3-6 Nihonbashimoto -cho, Chuo-ku, Tokyo, 103-0023, Honcho, Japan
Tel.: (81) 33 517 5300
Web Site: https://www.mo-kosan.co.jp
Sales Range: $100-124.9 Million
Emp.: 2,253
Building Maintenance & Management Services
N.A.I.C.S.: 561790
Yoichi Ibayashi *(Pres & CEO)*

Subsidiary (Domestic):

Kosan Kanri Service West Co., Ltd. (3)
2-4 Tosabori 2-chomeNishi-ku, Osaka, 550-0001, Japan
Tel.: (81) 664416491
Office Space Rental & Real Estate Management Services
N.A.I.C.S.: 531210

Subsidiary (Domestic):

Nowatec Co., Ltd. (2)
975-1 Nagazaike, Fukaya, 369-1101, Saitama, Japan
Tel.: (81) 485835892
Web Site: https://www.nowa-tec.jp
Electrical Equipment Retailer
N.A.I.C.S.: 423610

Santo Tatemono Service Co., Ltd. (2)
3-6-32 Nakanoshima, Kita-ku, Osaka, 530-0005, Japan **(100%)**
Tel.: (81) 6 6441 1936
Web Site: http://www.daibiru.co.jp
Other Services to Buildings & Dwellings
N.A.I.C.S.: 561790

Tanshin Building Services Co., Ltd. (2)
164 Higashihagocho, Fukuchiyama, 620-0933, Kyoto, Japan
Tel.: (81) 773244602
Web Site: http://www.mo-kosan.co.jp
Emp.: 138
Firefighting Equipment Inspection Services
N.A.I.C.S.: 922160

Diamond Line K.K. (1)
5-7-11 Ikushi, Oita, 870-0003, Japan
Tel.: (81) 975338811
Marine Transportation Services
N.A.I.C.S.: 483111

Euro Marine Carrier B.V. (1)
Corsicaweg 10-14, 1044 AB, Amsterdam, Noord-Holland, Netherlands
Tel.: (31) 205060860
Web Site: http://www.nissancarrier.co.jp
Sales Range: $25-49.9 Million
Emp.: 21
Marine Transportation Services
N.A.I.C.S.: 483113

Euromol B.V. (1)
Hofhoek 7, 3176 PD, Poortugaal, Zuid-Holland, Netherlands
Tel.: (31) 102013294
Emp.: 1
Finance & Insurance Services
N.A.I.C.S.: 522291

Ferry Sunflower Limited (1)
3-1-1 Koyocho Higashi, Higashinada-ku, Kobe, 658-0031, Hyogo, Japan **(100%)**
Tel.: (81) 788571988
Web Site: https://www.ferry-sunflower.co.jp
Ferry Passenger Transportation Services
N.A.I.C.S.: 483114
Atsushi Igaki *(Pres & Dir)*

Ferry Sunflower, Ltd. (1)
3-21 Koyocho Higashi, Higashinada-ku, Kobe, 658-0031, Hyogo, Japan
Tel.: (81) 788575470
Web Site: https://www.ferry-sunflower.co.jp
Sales Range: $25-49.9 Million
Emp.: 11
Ferry Passenger Transportation Services
N.A.I.C.S.: 483114
Akihito Okimura *(Pres)*

Green Kaiji Kaisha, Ltd. (1)
3-5 Hama 2-chome, Minato-ku, Nagoya, 455-0036, Aichi, Japan
Tel.: (81) 526542249
Web Site: http://www.mol.co.jp
Tugboat Operation Services
N.A.I.C.S.: 488330

Green Shipping Ltd. (1)
1-5 Minatomachi, Moji-Ku, Kitakyushu, 801-0852, Fukuoka, Japan
Tel.: (81) 933214262
Sales Range: $50-74.9 Million
Emp.: 134
Marine Shipping Services
N.A.I.C.S.: 488510
Hirochi Ueshima *(Pres)*

Hokuso Kohatsu K.K. (1)
1-1 Toranomon 2-chome, Minato-ku, Tokyo, 105-0001, Japan
Tel.: (81) 3 3587 7111
Web Site: http://www.mol.co.jp
Sales Range: $50-74.9 Million
Emp.: 3
Office Space Rental & Real Estate Management Services
N.A.I.C.S.: 531120
Idhiro Osako *(Mgr)*

Ikuta & Marine Co., Ltd. (1)
5 Kaigan-dori, Chuo-ku, Kobe, 650-0024, Hyogo, Japan
Tel.: (81) 783922437
Web Site: http://www.mol.co.jp
Marine Shipping Services
N.A.I.C.S.: 488510

International Container Transport Co., Ltd. (1)
22-14 Toranomon 1-chome, Minato-ku, Tokyo, 105-0001, Japan
Tel.: (81) 3 3539 1131
Web Site: http://www.ict-corp.co.jp
Marine Cargo Handling & Container Trucking Services
N.A.I.C.S.: 484110

Japan Express Co., Ltd. (1)
8-1 Shinko-cho, Chuo-ku, Kobe, 650-0041, Hyogo, Japan
Tel.: (81) 78 321 2151
Web Site: https://www.japan-express.co.jp
Emp.: 111
Warehousing & Freight Forwarding Services
N.A.I.C.S.: 488310
Junzo Murakami *(Pres)*

Japan Express Co., Ltd. (1)
8-1 Shinko-cho, Chuo-ku, Kobe, 650-0041, Japan
Tel.: (81) 783212151
Emp.: 111
Harbor Operation & Customs Clearance Services
N.A.I.C.S.: 488310

Japan Express Packing & Transport Co., Ltd. (1)
18 Daikokufuto, Tsurumi-Ku, Yokohama, 230-0054, Kanagawa, Japan
Tel.: (81) 455049721
Sales Range: $25-49.9 Million
Emp.: 40
Freight Transportation Services
N.A.I.C.S.: 488510
Kojima Ichiro *(Pres)*

Japan Hydrographic Charts & Publications Co.,Ltd. (1)
6-85 Bentendori Utoku Building 5th floor, Naka-ku, Yokohama, 231-0007, Kanagawa, Japan
Tel.: (81) 452288808
Sales Range: $25-49.9 Million
Emp.: 20
Nautical Charts Sales & Publications Services
N.A.I.C.S.: 561990
Yasuhiko Ito *(Pres & CEO)*

Kosan Kanri Service Co.,Ltd. (1)
3-6 Nihonbashihoncho 3-Chome, Chuo-Ku, Tokyo, 103-0023, Japan
Tel.: (81) 335175207
Web Site: http://www.mo-kosan.co.jp
Sales Range: $75-99.9 Million
Emp.: 150
Office Rental & Real Estate Services
N.A.I.C.S.: 531210

Kusakabe Maritime Engineering Co., Ltd. (1)
5-1-14 Hamabe-dori, Chuo-Ku, Kobe, 651-0083, Hyogo, Japan
Tel.: (81) 782227761
Web Site: https://www.kusakabe-eng.co.jp
Sales Range: $25-49.9 Million
Emp.: 40
Marine Engineering Services
N.A.I.C.S.: 541330
Satoshi Akita *(Pres)*

M.O. Engineering Co., Ltd. (1)
1-1-2 Yashio, Shinagawa-ku, Tokyo, 140-0003, Japan
Tel.: (81) 357552600
Web Site: http://www.mo-eng.co.jp
Sales Range: $25-49.9 Million
Emp.: 21
Marine Engineering Services
N.A.I.C.S.: 541330
Takashi Shiotsu *(Pres)*

M.O. Tourist Co., Ltd. (1)
17th floor Arca Central 1-2-1 Kinshi, Sumida-ku, Tokyo, 130-0013, Japan **(100%)**
Tel.: (81) 362841251
Web Site: https://www.mo-tourist.co.jp
Sales Range: $25-49.9 Million
Emp.: 200
Travel Agency
N.A.I.C.S.: 561510

M.O.Air Logistics, Inc. (1)
Prologis Park Narita 1-B 78-7 Minamisanri-zuka, Narita, 286-0113, Chiba Prefecture, Japan
Tel.: (81) 476356170
Web Site: http://www.moal.co.jp
Custom Clearance Services
N.A.I.C.S.: 488510

MOL (America) Inc. (1)
700 E Butterfield Rd Ste 150, Lombard, IL 60148 **(100%)**
Tel.: (925) 688-2600
Web Site: http://www.molpower.com
Sales Range: $50-74.9 Million
Emp.: 100
Freight Transportation Services
N.A.I.C.S.: 483111
Richard Craig *(Pres & CEO)*

MOL (Brasil) Ltda. (1)
Alameda Santos 787 - 9 andar - Conjunto 92 Cerqueira Cesar, Sao Paulo, 01419-001, Brazil
Tel.: (55) 1131453999
Sales Range: $25-49.9 Million
Emp.: 120
Marine Transportation Services
N.A.I.C.S.: 483111
Peter Duifhuizen *(Mng Dir)*

MOL (China) Co., Ltd. (1)
Room 1602-1604 17/F Hongyi Plaza No 288 Jiujia, 200001, Shanghai, China
Tel.: (86) 2123206000
Web Site: http://www.molcn.com.cn
Sales Range: $125-149.9 Million
Emp.: 360
Marine Shipping Services
N.A.I.C.S.: 488320
Akimitsu Ashida *(Chm)*

MOL (Europe) Ltd. (1)
Enterprise House Ocean Way Ocean Village, Southampton, SO 14 3XB, Hampshire, United Kingdom
Tel.: (44) 2380714500
Web Site: http://www.molpower.com
Sales Range: $25-49.9 Million
Emp.: 55
Marine Shipping Services
N.A.I.C.S.: 488510
Dawn Trotman *(Gen Mgr)*

MOL Accounting Co., Ltd. (1)
2-1-1 Toranomon, Minato-ku, Tokyo, 105-0001, Japan
Tel.: (81) 335877640
Web Site: https://www.mol.co.jp
Emp.: 49
Accounting Services
N.A.I.C.S.: 541219

MOL Adjustment , Ltd. (1)
2-1-1 Toranomon 2-chome, Minato-ku, Tokyo, 105-0001, Japan
Tel.: (81) 335877650
Web Site: http://www.molgroup.com
Sales Range: $25-49.9 Million
Emp.: 20
Marine Engineering Services
N.A.I.C.S.: 541330
Shinjiko Kawasaki *(Mgr)*

MOL Auto Carrier Express South Africa (Pty.) Ltd. (1)
1st Floor 49 Richefond Circle Ridgeside, Umhlanga, 4320, South Africa
Tel.: (27) 315802200
Oil & Gas Transportation Services
N.A.I.C.S.: 484230

MOL Business Support, Ltd. (1)
2-1-1 Toranomon, Minato-ku, Tokyo, 105-0001, Japan
Tel.: (81) 335876451
Human Resource Development Services
N.A.I.C.S.: 541612

MOL Chemical Tankers Pte. Ltd. (1)
5 Shenton Way 15-01 UIC Building, Singapore, 068808, Singapore
Tel.: (65) 63495800
Web Site: https://www.molchemtankers.com
Emp.: 133
Oil & Gas Transportation Services
N.A.I.C.S.: 484230
Akio Mitsuta *(CEO & Mng Dir)*

Subsidiary (US):

Fairfield Chemical Carriers, Inc (2)
5 River Rd 25, Wilton, CT 06897

4989

MITSUI O.S.K. LINES, LTD.   INTERNATIONAL PUBLIC

Mitsui O.S.K. Lines, Ltd.—(Continued)
Tel.: (203) 761-1147
Web Site: http://www.fairfieldchemical.com
Rev.: $7,072,000
Emp.: 13
Business to Business Electronic Markets
N.A.I.C.S.: 425120
Arty Allen (VP-Chartering)

Subsidiary (Non-US):

MOL Nordic Tankers A/S (2)
Tuborg Havnevej 15, 2900, Hellerup, Denmark
Tel.: (45) 39109000
Web Site: https://www.nordictankers.com
Chemical Shipping Services
N.A.I.C.S.: 483111
Bjorn Nilsson (Chm)

Subsidiary (Non-US):

Nordic Tankers Marine SIA (3)
Duntes Str 17A 2nd Floor, LV-1005, Riga, Latvia
Tel.: (371) 6785 4944
Web Site: http://www.nordictankers.dk
Sales Range: $25-49.9 Million
Emp.: 9
Marine Shipping Services
N.A.I.C.S.: 488510
Yuriy Lipskiy (Mgr-HR-Marine)

Subsidiary (Domestic):

Nordic Tankers Trading A/S (3)
Tuborg Havnevej 15, 2900, Hellerup, Denmark
Tel.: (45) 39109000
Emp.: 100
Cargo Handling Services
N.A.I.C.S.: 488320
Peter Jamieson (Mng Dir)

Subsidiary (Non-US):

Nordic Tankers (Colombia) Ltda. (4)
Carrera 7 No 71-52 Oficina 503/Torre A Edificio Carrera Septima, PO Box 75641, 110231, Bogota, Colombia (51%)
Tel.: (57) 6013120193
Web Site: http://www.nordictankers.dk
Emp.: 6
Commercial Management Services
N.A.I.C.S.: 541618
William Fraser (Gen Mgr)

MOL Consolidation Service Limited (1)
Room 1601 Hongyi Plaza 288 Jiujiang Road, Shanghai, China
Tel.: (86) 2153689100
Warehousing & Logistics Services
N.A.I.C.S.: 493110

MOL Consolidation Service Limited (1)
27th Floor Ever Gain Plaza Tower 1 88 Container Port Road, Kwai Chung, New Territories, China (Hong Kong)
Tel.: (852) 28236800
Logistics & Warehousing Services
N.A.I.C.S.: 493110

MOL Container Center (Thailand) Co., Ltd. (1)
96/11 Moo 10, T Nongkham, Si Racha, 20230, Chonburi, Thailand
Tel.: (66) 655162145
Web Site: http://www.molcct.com
Cargo Container Inspection Services
N.A.I.C.S.: 811310

MOL Dohle Worldwide Logistics GmbH (1)
Alter Wall 55, 20457, Hamburg, Germany
Tel.: (49) 405005810
Web Site: https://www.mol-doehle.com
Freight Transportation Services
N.A.I.C.S.: 483111
Daniel Schmidt (Mng Dir)

MOL Drybulk Ltd. (1)
8th Floor Mitsui OSK Line 2-1-1, Toranomon Minato-ku, Tokyo, 105-0001, Japan
Tel.: (81) 335876010
Web Site: http://www.moldrybulk.co.jp
Transportation Machinery & Equipment Leasing Services
N.A.I.C.S.: 532490

MOL Ferry Co., Ltd. (1)
Akihabara Daibiru Building 11F 1-18-13 Sotokanda, Chiyoda-ku, Tokyo, 101-0021, Japan
Tel.: (81) 368667307
Sales Range: $200-249.9 Million
Emp.: 600
Ferry Passenger Transportation Services
N.A.I.C.S.: 483114

MOL Information Technology Asia Limited (1)
Unit B-D 11/F KC 100 100 Kwai Cheong Road, Kwai Chung, China (Hong Kong)
Tel.: (852) 28236468
Information Technology Services
N.A.I.C.S.: 541511

MOL Information Technology India Private Limited (1)
Eco Centre Business Tower 18th Floor EM 4 EM Block Sector V, Salt Lake, Kolkata, 700 091, West Bengal, India
Tel.: (91) 3340008500
Web Site: https://www.mol-it.com
Information Technology Services
N.A.I.C.S.: 541511
Tsuyoshi Yoshida (Pres)

MOL LNG Transport Co., Ltd. (1)
2-1-1 Toranomon Commercial Ship Mitsui Building, Minato-ku, Tokyo, 105-0001, Japan
Tel.: (81) 33 587 7635
Web Site: https://www.mol.co.jp
Sales Range: $10-24.9 Million
Emp.: 82
Ship Management Services
N.A.I.C.S.: 561990

MOL Liner, Ltd. (1)
Units B-D 11/F KC100 100 Kwai Cheong Road, Kwai Chung, New Territories, China (Hong Kong)
Tel.: (852) 28236800
Web Site: https://mol-hongkong.com
Emp.: 400
Marine Shipping Services
N.A.I.C.S.: 488320
Junichiro Ikeda (Chm)

MOL Logistics (Cambodia) Co., Ltd. (1)
Canadia Tower No 315 18th Floor Preah Monivong Blvd Corner St, Preah Ang Duong Phum 1 Sangkat Wat Phnom Khan Daun Penh, Phnom Penh, Cambodia
Tel.: (855) 23962397
Ocean Freight Services
N.A.I.C.S.: 488510
Yoshitomi Hirano (Mng Dir)

MOL Logistics (Czech) s.r.o. (1)
Jakubska 647/2, 110 00, Prague, Czech Republic
Tel.: (420) 373731314
Web Site: http://www.mol-logistics.cz
Logistic Services
N.A.I.C.S.: 541614
Kazushige Tanioka (Mng Dir)

MOL Logistics (Deutschland) GmbH (1)
Wahlerstrasse 20, 40472, Dusseldorf, Germany
Tel.: (49) 21 141 8830
Web Site: https://www.mol-logistics.de
Sales Range: $25-49.9 Million
Emp.: 46
Warehousing & Logistics Services
N.A.I.C.S.: 493110
Jun Kaneko (Mng Dir)

MOL Logistics (H.K.) Ltd. (1)
Unit 01-03 05-11 19-21 21/F Metropole Square 2 On Yiu Street, Sha Tin, N T, China (Hong Kong)
Tel.: (852) 26862388
Logistics & Freight Forwarding Services
N.A.I.C.S.: 488510
A. Noto (Gen Mgr-Air, Warehouse, Transportation & Distr Div)

MOL Logistics (India) Pvt. Ltd. (1)
Unit No 53B 5th Floor Kalpataru Square Kondivita Lane, Off Andheri Kurla Road Andheri East, Mumbai, 400 059, India
Tel.: (91) 2240714500
Emp.: 60
Ocean Freight Services

N.A.I.C.S.: 488510
Yukio Matsunaga (Mng Dir)

MOL Logistics (Japan) Co., Ltd. (1)
Mitsui Sumitomo Insurance Surugadai Annex Building, 2F 11 Kanda Surugadai 3-chome, Chiyoda-ku, Tokyo, 101-8527, Japan (59.74%)
Tel.: (81) 352821200
Sales Range: $550-599.9 Million
Emp.: 1,200
Logistics & Freight Transportation Services
N.A.I.C.S.: 541614

Subsidiary (Non-US):

M.O. Air International (Taiwan) Co.,Ltd. (2)
6F No 5 Shaoxing N Street, Taipei, 10049, Taiwan
Tel.: (886) 266306780
Sales Range: $10-24.9 Million
Emp.: 27
Warehousing & Logistics Services
N.A.I.C.S.: 493110

Subsidiary (US):

MOL Logistics (USA) Inc. (2)
380 N Broadway Ste 202, Jericho, NY 11753 (100%)
Tel.: (516) 403-2100
Sales Range: $25-49.9 Million
Emp.: 10
Freight Forwarding Services
N.A.I.C.S.: 488510
Yofhihiro Okada (Pres)

MOL Logistics (Kyushu) Co., Ltd. (1)
10-28 Enokida 2-chome, Hakata-ku, Fukuoka, 812-0004, Japan
Tel.: (81) 924146284
Ocean Freight Services
N.A.I.C.S.: 488510

MOL Logistics (Malaysia) Sdn. Bhd. (1)
12th Floor The Lighthouse No 1 One Logistics Hub, Persiaran Sungai Hampar Seksyen 32, 40460, Shah Alam, Selangor, Malaysia
Tel.: (60) 351611000
Ocean Freight Services
N.A.I.C.S.: 488510

MOL Logistics (Myanmar) Co., Ltd. (1)
No 62 Mahabandoola Housing Complex B Room No 803-804, 8th Floor Tawatsintha Street Pazundaung Township, Yangon, Myanmar
Tel.: (95) 1200150
Ocean Freight Services
N.A.I.C.S.: 488510

MOL Logistics (Netherlands) B.V. (1)
Tel.: (31) 13 537 3373
Web Site: https://www.mol-logistics.nl
Emp.: 180
Warehousing & Logistics Services
N.A.I.C.S.: 488510
John Appels (Mgr-Acctg)

MOL Logistics (Philippines) Inc. (1)
ECH Plaza No 8006 Dr A Santos Ave Brgy BF, Sucat, Paranaque, Manila, Philippines
Tel.: (63) 288535424
Ocean Freight Services
N.A.I.C.S.: 488510

MOL Logistics (Shizuoka), Inc. (1)
Tel.: (81) 542871010
Web Site: http://www.mlg-shizuoka.jp
Freight Forwarding Services
N.A.I.C.S.: 488510

MOL Logistics (Singapore) Pte. Ltd. (1)
15 Changi Business Park Crescent 04-10 Haite Building, Singapore, 528729, Singapore
Tel.: (65) 65458010
Web Site: https://www.mol-logistics.com.sg
Sales Range: $25-49.9 Million
Emp.: 50
Warehousing & Logistics Services
N.A.I.C.S.: 493110
Cyrus Chan (Deputy Mng Dir)

MOL Logistics (Taiwan) Co., Ltd. (1)
6F No 71 Sec 2 Nanjing E Rd, Taipei,

10457, Taiwan
Tel.: (886) 225670155
Ocean Freight Services
N.A.I.C.S.: 488510

MOL Logistics (Thailand) Co., Ltd. (1)
163 Thai Samut Building 11th - 12th floor Surawongse Road, Suriyawongse Sub-District Bangrak District, Bangkok, 10500, Thailand
Tel.: (66) 22877878
Sales Range: $25-49.9 Million
Emp.: 102
Warehousing & Logistics Services
N.A.I.C.S.: 493110

MOL Logistics (UK) Ltd. (1)
Unit 6 Crown Business Centre Horton Road, West Drayton, UB7 8HP, Middlesex, United Kingdom
Tel.: (44) 1895459700
Web Site: https://mol-logistics.uk
Sales Range: $25-49.9 Million
Emp.: 10
Warehousing & Logistics Services
N.A.I.C.S.: 493110
Tsutomu Ono (Mng Dir)

MOL Logistics (Vietnam) Inc. (1)
E-Town Building Rm 2 5A Second Floor 364 Cong Hoa St, Tan Binh Dist, Ho Chi Minh City, Vietnam
Tel.: (84) 2838121349
Web Site: http://www.mol-logistics.com.vn
Emp.: 164
Freight Forwarding Services
N.A.I.C.S.: 488510

MOL Logistics (WBLZ) Co., Ltd. (1)
C2-1 Warehouse No 166 Shenfei Road, China Shanghai Pilot Free Trade Zone, Shanghai, 200137, China
Tel.: (86) 2133665566
Ocean Freight Services
N.A.I.C.S.: 488510

MOL Logistics Lanka (Private) Ltd. (1)
123 Level 8 Bauddhaloka Mawatha, Colombo, Sri Lanka
Tel.: (94) 112304721
Emp.: 7
Custom Clearance Services
N.A.I.C.S.: 488510
Yasuhisa Matsuno (Mng Dir)

MOL Marine & Engineering Co., Ltd. (1)
Tel.: (81) 335876011
Web Site: http://www.molmec.com
Emp.: 111
Marine Engineering Services
N.A.I.C.S.: 541330
Takashi Nakashima (Pres)

MOL Marine Consulting, Ltd. (1)
Pier City Shibaura Building 11F 18-1 Kaigan 3-chome, Minato-ku, Tokyo, 108-0022, Japan
Tel.: (81) 354431011
Web Site: http://www.momc.co.jp
Sales Range: $25-49.9 Million
Emp.: 30
Marine Consulting Services
N.A.I.C.S.: 541330

MOL Maritime (India) Pvt. Ltd. (1)
Unit No 52 Kalpataru Square Kondivita Lane Next to Hotel Vits, Off Andheri Kurla Road Andheri East, Mumbai, 400 059, India
Tel.: (91) 2261507000
Web Site: http://www.molmi.info
Shipping Services
N.A.I.C.S.: 488510

MOL Naikou, Ltd. (1)
16-12 Ginza 6-chome, Chuo-ku, Tokyo, 104-0061, Japan
Tel.: (81) 351482170
Web Site: http://www.mol-naikou.co.jp
Sales Range: $25-49.9 Million
Emp.: 20
Ferry Passenger Transportation Services
N.A.I.C.S.: 483114
Hiroshi Tanaka (Pres)

MOL Netherlands Bulkship B.V. (1)
Hofhoek 7, 3176 PD, Poortugaal, Zuid-Holland, Netherlands

AND PRIVATE COMPANIES

Tel.: (31) 105031029
Ship Management Services
N.A.I.C.S.: 488510

MOL Ship Management Co., Ltd. (1)
1-1 Toranomon 2-chome, Minato-ku, Tokyo, 105-0001, Japan
Tel.: (81) 335876130
Emp.: 70
Ship Management Services
N.A.I.C.S.: 488510

MOL Ship Tech Inc. (1)
Tel.: (81) 335877087
Marine Consulting Services
N.A.I.C.S.: 541330

MOL South Afica (Proprietary) Limited (1)
17th Floor Standard Chartered Bank Building, Heerengracht, Cape Town, 8001, Western Cape, South Africa
Tel.: (27) 214412200
Web Site: http://www.molpower.com
Sales Range: $25-49.9 Million
Emp.: 80
Marine Shipping Services
N.A.I.C.S.: 488510
Frederic Malevialle *(Mng Dir)*

MOL Tankship Management Pte. Ltd. (1)
5 Shenton Way 17-02/03 UIC Building, Singapore, 068808, Singapore
Tel.: (65) 62496899
Web Site: http://www.mol-tankship.com
Freight Forwarding Services
N.A.I.C.S.: 488510
Ikutoshi Kato *(Mng Dir)*

MOL Techno-Trade, Ltd. (1)
Yaesu Daibiru Building 6F 1-1 1-Chome Kyobashi, Chuo-ku, Tokyo, 104-0031, Japan
Tel.: (81) 3 6367 5300
Web Site: http://www.motech.co.jp
Rev.: $593,450,000
Emp.: 120
Marine Equipments & Supplies Distr
N.A.I.C.S.: 423860
Shugo Aoto *(Pres)*

MVG Dinh Vu Co., Ltd. (1)
Lot CN5 3l, Dinh Vu Industrial Park Dong Hai 2 Ward Hai An District, Haiphong, Vietnam
Tel.: (84) 936512269
Web Site: http://www.mvgdinhvu.com.vn
Custom Clearance Services
N.A.I.C.S.: 488510

Magsaysay MOL Marine, Inc. (1)
5th and 6th Floor Magsaysay Building 520 T M Kalaw Street, Ermita, Manila, 1000, Philippines
Tel.: (63) 285268888
Web Site: http://www.magmol.com
Crew Manning Services
N.A.I.C.S.: 488390
Rene G. Juntado *(Pres)*

Meimon Taiyo Ferry Co., Ltd. (1)
2F Higobashi Union Bldg 1-9-6, Edobori Nishi-ku, Osaka, 550-0002, Japan
Tel.: (81) 664497155
Web Site: http://www.cityline.co.jp
Emp.: 219
Ticket Booking Services
N.A.I.C.S.: 561599

Minami Kyushu Marine Service Co., Ltd. (1)
3269-2 Shibushi Shibushi-cho, Shibushi, 899-7103, Kagoshima, Japan
Tel.: (81) 994724179
Shipping Services
N.A.I.C.S.: 488510

Mitsui Kinkai Kisen Co., Ltd. (1)
21-1 Toranomon 2-Chome, Minato-ku, Tokyo, 105-0001, Japan
Tel.: (81) 335876757
Web Site: http://www.mol.co.jp
Ship Management Services
N.A.I.C.S.: 541618

Mitsui O.S.K. Bulk Shipping (Asia Oceania) Pte Ltd. (1)
200 Cantonment Road 02-07 Southpoint, Singapore, 089763, Singapore
Tel.: (65) 63231303
Sales Range: $25-49.9 Million
Emp.: 15
Marine Cargo Handling Services
N.A.I.C.S.: 488320
Toshiyuki Sonobe *(Mng Dir)*

Mitsui O.S.K. Bulk Shipping (Europe) Ltd. (1)
3 Thomas Moore Square, London, E1W 1WY, United Kingdom
Tel.: (44) 2037648000
Web Site: http://www.mol.co.jp
Sales Range: $50-74.9 Million
Emp.: 200
Marine Shipping Services
N.A.I.C.S.: 488510

Mitsui O.S.K. Career Support Ltd. (1)
1-1 Toranomon 2-Chome Minato-Ku, Minato-Ku, Tokyo, 105-0001, Japan
Tel.: (81) 3 3587 7638
Web Site: http://www.molcs.co.jp
Employment Support Services
N.A.I.C.S.: 561311

Mitsui O.S.K. Holdings (Benelux) B.V. (1)
Hofhoek 7, 3176 PD, Poortugaal, Zuid-Holland, Netherlands
Tel.: (31) 10 2013294
Emp.: 1
Marine Shipping Services
N.A.I.C.S.: 488510

Mitsui O.S.K. Kinkai, Ltd. (1)
Tel.: (81) 335876010
Sales Range: $25-49.9 Million
Emp.: 80
Marine Shipping Services
N.A.I.C.S.: 488510
Shiro Aeachi *(Pres)*

Mitsui O.S.K. Lines (Australia) Pty .Ltd. (1)
Level 18 No 1 York St, Sydney, 2000, NSW, Australia
Tel.: (61) 293201600
Sales Range: $25-49.9 Million
Emp.: 30
Marine Cargo Handling Services
N.A.I.C.S.: 488320
Mark Austin *(Mng Dir)*

Mitsui O.S.K. Lines (Japan) Ltd. (1)
1-1 Toranomon 2-Chome, Minato-ku, Tokyo, 105-8688, Japan
Tel.: (81) 335877684
Web Site: http://www.moljapan.co.jp
Sales Range: $50-74.9 Million
Emp.: 120
Shipping Services
N.A.I.C.S.: 488510

Mitsui O.S.K. Passenger Line, Ltd. (1)
5th floor of Sankaidou Building 1-9-13 Akasaka, Minato-ku, Tokyo, 107-8532, Japan
Tel.: (81) 351145200
Web Site: https://www.nipponmaru.jp
Emp.: 115
Marine Passenger Transportation Services
N.A.I.C.S.: 483112
Koide Fumitaka *(Mgr-Sls)*

Nihon Tug-Boat Co., Ltd. (1)
Mitsui O S K Lines Building 5 Kaigandori, Chuo-ku, Kobe, 650-0024, Hyogo, Japan
Tel.: (81) 783313625
Emp.: 103
Tugboat Operation Services
N.A.I.C.S.: 488330
Shigeshi Omori *(Pres)*

Nissan Motor Car Carrier Co., Ltd. (1)
Hibiya Daibiru Bldg 1-2-2 Uchisaiwai-cho, Chiyoda-ku, Tokyo, 100-0011, Japan
Tel.: (81) 343346600
Web Site: https://www.nissancarrier.co.jp
Sales Range: $25-49.9 Million
Emp.: 59
Marine Shipping Services
N.A.I.C.S.: 541618
Ken Fujii *(Mng Dir)*

Subsidiary (US):

World Logistics Service (U.S.A.), Inc. (2)
111 W Ocean Blvd Ste 1040, Long Beach, CA 90802
Tel.: (562) 437-8005
Web Site: http://www.wls-usa.com
Marine Shipping Services
N.A.I.C.S.: 488510
Mike Miyake *(Sr Mgr)*

Ocean Network Express Holdings, Ltd. (1)
11F W Building, 1-8-15 Kohnan Minato-ku,, Tokyo, 108-0075, Japan (31%)
Tel.: (65) 62200196
Web Site: https://holdco.one-line.com
Marine transportation
N.A.I.C.S.: 713930

Subsidiary (Non-US):

Ocean Network Express Pte. Ltd. (2)
7 Straits View, #16-01 Marina One East Tower,, Singapore, 018936, Singapore
Tel.: (65) 62200196
Web Site: https://www.one-line.com
Container Shipping Businesses
N.A.I.C.S.: 488330
Jeremy Nixon *(CEO)*

Subsidiary (US):

TraPac, LLC (3)
920 West Harry Bridges Blvd, Wilmington, CA 90744
Tel.: (310) 830-2000
Web Site: http://www.trapac.com
Rev.: $7,000,000
Emp.: 50
Freight Transportation Arrangement
N.A.I.C.S.: 488510
Scott Axelson *(VP-Bus Dev)*

Yusen Terminals, LLC (3)
701 New Dock St, Terminal Island, CA 90731
Tel.: (310) 548-8000
Web Site: http://www.yti.com
Marine Cargo Terminal Operating Services
N.A.I.C.S.: 488310
Alan McCorkle *(CEO)*

Orange P.R. Ltd. (1)
2-1-1 Toranomon 2-chome, Minato-ku, Tokyo, 105-8688, Japan
Tel.: (81) 335877665
Sales Range: $25-49.9 Million
Emp.: 15
Advertising Services
N.A.I.C.S.: 541810

Osaka Shipping Co., Ltd. (1)
1-25-13 Edobori, Nishi-Ku, Osaka, 550-0002, Japan
Tel.: (81) 664432821
Emp.: 15
Real Estate Rental Services
N.A.I.C.S.: 531110
Morio Kotani *(Pres)*

PKT Logistics Group Sdn. Bhd. (1)
The Lighthouse Campus No 1 One Logistics Hub Persiaran Sungai Hampar, Section 32, 40460, Shah Alam, Selangor, Malaysia
Tel.: (60) 351618111
Web Site: http://www.pktgroup.com
Transportation Logistics Services
N.A.I.C.S.: 488510

PT. MOL Logistics Warehouse (1)
Centennial Tower 15th FL Jl Jend Gatot Subroto Kav 24-25, Jakarta Selatan, 12930, Indonesia
Tel.: (62) 2122958266
Ocean Freight Services
N.A.I.C.S.: 488510
Hiroshi Arita *(Pres)*

Phoenix Tankers Pte. Ltd. (1)
5 Shenton Way UIC Building 16-06, Singapore, 068808, Singapore
Tel.: (65) 64998940
Web Site: https://www.molenergia.com
Tanker Chartering Services
N.A.I.C.S.: 483111
Daisuke Watanabe *(Mng Dir)*

Rotterdam World Gateway B.V. (1)
Amoerweg 50, Maasvlakte, 3199 KD, Rotterdam, Netherlands
Tel.: (31) 107422000
Web Site: http://www.rwg.nl

MITSUI O.S.K. LINES, LTD.

Port Terminal Operation Services
N.A.I.C.S.: 488310

Shanghai HuaGuo Transportation Co., Ltd. (1)
6th Floor Enterprise Centre Tower 2 Kerry Everbright City, No 209 Gonghe Road, Shanghai, 200070, China
Tel.: (86) 2133665566
Ocean Freight Services
N.A.I.C.S.: 488510

Shanghai HuaJia Int'l Freight Forwarding Co., Ltd. (1)
6th Floor Enterprise Centre Tower 2 Kerry Everbright City, No 209 Gonghe Road, Shanghai, 200070, China
Tel.: (86) 2152035600
Ocean Freight Services
N.A.I.C.S.: 488510

Shanghai Longfei International Logistics Co., Ltd. (1)
Room 1506 Hongkou SOHO No 575 Wu song Road, Hongkou District, Shanghai, 200080, China
Tel.: (86) 2123560728
Web Site: http://www.longfei.sh.cn
Freight Forwarding Services
N.A.I.C.S.: 488510

Shinyo Kaiun Corporation (1)
Tel.: (81) 722381161
Web Site: http://www.shin-yo.co.jp
Freight Forwarding Services
N.A.I.C.S.: 488510
Tetsushi Inaba *(Pres)*

Shosen Koun Co., Ltd. (1)
9-10 Minatojima, Chuo-Ku, Kobe, 650-0045, Hyogo, Japan
Tel.: (81) 783041200
Sales Range: $25-49.9 Million
Emp.: 96
Marine Shipping Services
N.A.I.C.S.: 488510
Takao Furukawa *(Pres)*

Tan Cang - Cai Mep International Terminal Co., Ltd. (1)
7th Floor Saigon Newport Building, Tan Phuoc Ward, Phu My, Ba Ria-Vung Tau, Vietnam
Tel.: (84) 2543938555
Web Site: http://www.tcit.com.vn
Port Terminal Operation Services
N.A.I.C.S.: 488310

Tan Cang - Cai Mep Towage Services Co., Ltd. (1)
No 26 My Phu 2C Phu My Hung Zone, Tan Phu Ward Dist 7, Ho Chi Minh City, Vietnam
Tel.: (84) 854170596
Web Site: https://www.tcts.com.vn
Towage Services
N.A.I.C.S.: 488330
Pham Duc Phuong *(Gen Dir)*

Tan Cang Hai Phong International Container Terminal Co., Ltd. (1)
Don Luong Area, Cat Hai Town Cat Hai District, Haiphong, Vietnam
Tel.: (84) 2253765499
Web Site: https://hict.net.vn
Containers Handling Services
N.A.I.C.S.: 488320

Thai Intermodal Systems Co., Ltd. (1)
890 Lasalle Road, Bangna, Bangkok, 10260, Thailand
Tel.: (66) 239875224
Web Site: http://www.timco.co.th
Warehouse Management Services
N.A.I.C.S.: 493110
Dai Tatsumi *(Mng Dir)*

Tokyo Marine Co., Ltd. (1)
8th Floor METLIFE Nihonbashi-Honcho Building 1-1-1 Nihonbashi-Honcho, Chuo-Ku, Tokyo, 103-0023, Japan
Tel.: (81) 332417711
Web Site: http://www.tokyomarine.net
Rev.: $499,577,000
Emp.: 115
Marine Shipping Services
N.A.I.C.S.: 488510

Subsidiary (Non-US):

TM Manila Shipmanagement Inc. (2)

MITSUI O.S.K. LINES, LTD.

INTERNATIONAL PUBLIC

Mitsui O.S.K. Lines, Ltd.—(Continued)

Ste 804 Ermita Center Bldg 1350 Roxas Blvd Ermita, Manila, Philippines
Tel.: (63) 25365169
Sales Range: $25-49.9 Million
Emp.: 13
Marine Shipping Services
N.A.I.C.S.: 488510

TM Shipmanagement Co., Ltd. (2)
Room 1104 Korea Express Building 1211-1 Choryang 1-Dong, Dong-Ku, Busan, 601-714, Korea (South)
Tel.: (82) 514666401
Sales Range: $25-49.9 Million
Emp.: 22
Marine Shipping Services
N.A.I.C.S.: 488510
Mancig Jeong *(Mng Dir)*

Tokyo Marine Asia Pte., Ltd. (2)
20 McCallum Street 13-01 Tokio Marine Centre, Singapore, 069046, Singapore
Tel.: (65) 6 372 2988
Web Site: https://www.tokiomarine.com
Sales Range: $25-49.9 Million
Emp.: 73
Marine Shipping Services
N.A.I.C.S.: 488510

Ube Port Service Co., Ltd. (1)
5-5 Minatocho 1-Chome, Ube, 755-0027, Yamaguchi, Japan
Tel.: (81) 836313710
Sales Range: $25-49.9 Million
Emp.: 20
Tugboat Operation Services
N.A.I.C.S.: 488330
Nakato Nattori *(Pres)*

Utoc Corporation (1)
6-85 Benten-dori, Naka-ku, Yokohama, 231-0007, Kanagawa, Japan **(66.87%)**
Tel.: (81) 452016931
Web Site: http://www.utoc.co.jp
Rev.: $471,628,960
Assets: $443,363,360
Liabilities: $112,491,280
Net Worth: $330,872,080
Earnings: $7,966,640
Emp.: 1,661
Fiscal Year-end: 03/31/2021
Warehousing & Harbor Transportation Services
N.A.I.C.S.: 488310
Masahiro Tanabe *(Pres)*

Subsidiary (Non-US):

SR-UTOC INTERNATIONAL TRANSPORTATION LOGISTICS (TIANJIN) INC. (2)
No 156 Xin Gang Road Tianjin Port Free Trade Zone, Tianjin, 300461, China
Tel.: (86) 22 2576 4719
Web Site: http://www.sr-utoc.com
Logistics Consulting Servies
N.A.I.C.S.: 541614

UTOC (Thailand) Co., Ltd. (2)
71 Radniyom Road Tambon Tapma, Ampur Muang, Rayong, 21000, Thailand
Tel.: (66) 38918900
Logistics Consulting Servies
N.A.I.C.S.: 541614

Subsidiary (US):

UTOC America, Inc. (2)
23332 Hawthorne Blvd Ste 206, Torrance, CA 90505
Tel.: (310) 373-0110
Logistics Consulting Servies
N.A.I.C.S.: 541614

Subsidiary (Non-US):

UTOC Engineering Pte. Ltd. (2)
352 Jalan Boon Lay, Singapore, 619531, Singapore
Tel.: (65) 68610566
Plant Construction Service
N.A.I.C.S.: 236210

MITSUI-SOKO HOLDINGS CO., LTD.
3-20-1 Nishi-shimbashi, Minato-ku, Tokyo, 105-0003, Japan
Tel.: (81) 364008000 JP
Web Site: https://www.mitsui-soko.com
Year Founded: 1909
9302—(TKS)
Rev.: $1,722,519,730
Assets: $1,742,019,230
Liabilities: $943,346,150
Net Worth: $798,673,080
Earnings: $80,027,270
Emp.: 7,882
Fiscal Year-end: 03/31/24
Warehousing, Cargo Handling & Other Logistics Services
N.A.I.C.S.: 493110
Hirobumi Koga *(Pres & CEO)*

Subsidiaries:

AW Rostamani Logistics LLC (1)
Jebel Ali Free Zone, PO Box 17605, Dubai, United Arab Emirates
Tel.: (971) 4 811 9999
Web Site: https://www.awrostamanilogistics.com
Freight Forwarding Services
N.A.I.C.S.: 488510
Abdul Wahid Al Rostamani *(Chm)*

Co-next Inc. (1)
19-21 Nihonbashi-hakozaki-cho, Chuo-Ku, Tokyo, 103-0015, Japan
Tel.: (81) 364008778
Warehousing Transport Services
N.A.I.C.S.: 485999

Hakata Sanso-Butsuryu Co., Ltd. (1)
1-5-5 Hakozakifuto, Higashi-ku, Fukuoka, 812-0051, Japan
Tel.: (81) 926315385
Web Site: https://www.mitsui-soko.com
Warehousing Transport Services
N.A.I.C.S.: 485999

IM Express Co., Ltd. (1)
4-6-21 Aomi, Koto-ku, Tokyo, 135-0064, Japan
Tel.: (81) 335201636
Web Site: https://www.mitsui-soko.com
Warehousing Transport Services
N.A.I.C.S.: 485999

Joint Venture Sunrise Logistics Co., Ltd. (1)
27B National Highway 1A, Linh Xuan Ward Thu Duc City, Ho Chi Minh City, Vietnam
Tel.: (84) 283 724 5996
Web Site: https://www.jvsunriselog.com
Freight Forwarding Services
N.A.I.C.S.: 488510
Chu Thi Ngoc Hugen *(Gen Mgr)*

Key Logistics AB (1)
Forsta Langgatan 30, 413 27, Gothenburg, Sweden
Tel.: (46) 317041436
Web Site: http://www.keylogistics.se
Warehousing Transport Services
N.A.I.C.S.: 485999
Stefan Hansson *(Mng Dir)*

Kobe Sunso Koun Co., Ltd. (1)
6-6 Shinko-cho, Chuo-ku, Kobe, 650-0041, Hyogo, Japan
Tel.: (81) 783326531
Web Site: https://www.mitsui-soko.com
Warehousing Transport Services
N.A.I.C.S.: 485999

MS Logistics Co., Ltd. (1)
3-4-41 Iinozaka, Natori, 981-1225, Miyagi, Japan
Tel.: (81) 223842332
Warehousing Transport Services
N.A.I.C.S.: 485999

MS North Star Logistics Co., Ltd. (1)
Phutthamonthon Sai 5 Transport Center No 133 Moo 1 Building 2, Bang Toei Subdistrict Sampran District, Nakhon Pathom, 73210, Thailand
Tel.: (66) 28894646
Web Site: https://msnorthstar-logistics.com
Warehousing Transport Services
N.A.I.C.S.: 485999

MSC Trading (Shanghai) Co., Ltd. (1)
4/F Block 1 No 65 SongYuan Road, Changning District, Shanghai, China
Tel.: (86) 2133765372
Warehousing Transport Services
N.A.I.C.S.: 485999

MSE China (Beijing) Co., Ltd. (1)
Room No 308 Tianrui Mansion 1-1 Tianzhu Zhen-Fu-Qian Street, Shunyi-District, Beijing, 101312, China
Tel.: (86) 1064584492
Web Site: https://www.mitsui-soko.com
Warehousing Transport Services
N.A.I.C.S.: 485999

MSE Do Brasil Logistica Ltda. (1)
Av Fagundes Filho 134 - Cj 63, Sao Paulo, 04304-000, SP, Brazil
Tel.: (55) 1122768889
Warehousing Transport Services
N.A.I.C.S.: 485999

MSE Europe Tasimacilik, Organizasyon Lojistik Limited Sirketi (1)
Akcaburgaz Mahallesi 3108 Sokak No 3/1 Kat 1, Kirac Esenyurt, 34522, Istanbul, Turkiye
Tel.: (90) 2129161057
Warehousing Transport Services
N.A.I.C.S.: 485999

MSE Express Mexico, S.A. DE C.V. (1)
Tel.: (52) 5541695790
Freight Forwarding Services
N.A.I.C.S.: 488510

Mitex (Tianjin) Co., Ltd. (1)
Room1917 Binjiang International Hotel 105 Jiangshe Road, Heping District, Tianjin, 300042, China
Tel.: (86) 2223891958
Warehousing Transport Services
N.A.I.C.S.: 485999

Mitex International (H.K.) Ltd. (1)
Units 01-02 8/F Ever Gain Plaza Tower 1 88 Container Port Road, Kwai Chung, NT, China (Hong Kong)
Tel.: (852) 2366 4378
Web Site: http://www.mitex-intl.com
Emp.: 101
Logistics & Freight Transportation Services
N.A.I.C.S.: 488510

Subsidiary (Domestic):

Mitex Multimodal Express Ltd. (2)
1st Floor Gateway TS 8 Cheung Fai Road, Tsing Yi, New Territories, China (Hong Kong)
Tel.: (852) 2765 6328
Web Site: http://www.mitex-intl.com
Cargo Tracking & Forwarding
N.A.I.C.S.: 481112

Noble Business International Ltd. (2)
Unit 6-10 10/F Tower II Ever Gain Plaza, 88 Container Port Road, Kwai Chung, New Territories, China (Hong Kong)
Tel.: (852) 02489 0338
Web Site: http://www.mitex-intl.com
Cargo Forwarding
N.A.I.C.S.: 488510

Mitex International (Hong Kong) Ltd. (1)
Units 1-2 8/F Ever Gain Plaza Tower 1 88 Container Port Road, Kwai Chung, NT, China (Hong Kong)
Tel.: (852) 23664378
Web Site: https://www.mitex-intl.com
Emp.: 80
Warehousing Transport Services
N.A.I.C.S.: 485999

Mitex Logistics (Shanghai) Co., Ltd. (1)
4/F Block 1 No 65 SongYuan Road, Changning District, Shanghai, China
Tel.: (86) 2161275177
Warehousing Transport Services
N.A.I.C.S.: 485999

Mitex Shenzhen Logistics Co., Ltd. (1)
Room 1311-1313 Changping Commercial Building Honghua Road 99, Futian Free Trade Zone, Shenzhen, China
Tel.: (86) 75582712138
Warehousing Transport Services
N.A.I.C.S.: 485999

Mits Transport (Thailand) Co., Ltd. (1)
287 Liberty Square Building 11th Floor Silom Road, Silom Bangrak, Bangkok, 10500, Thailand
Tel.: (66) 20124900
Warehousing Transport Services
N.A.I.C.S.: 485999

Mitsui Warehouse Terminal Service Co., Ltd. (1)
1-3-87 Nankonaka, Suminoe-ku, Osaka, 559-0033, Japan
Tel.: (81) 676681070
Web Site: https://www.mitsui-soko.com
Warehousing Transport Services
N.A.I.C.S.: 485999

Mitsui-Soko (Europe) s.r.o. (1)
Prosecka 855/68 Building C, 190 00, Prague, Czech Republic
Tel.: (420) 242419000
Warehousing Transport Services
N.A.I.C.S.: 485999

Mitsui-Soko (Korea) Co., Ltd. (1)
Kyung-Gi B/D Samgak-Dong 13F 9 Namdaemun-ro 10-gil, Choong-gu, Seoul, 04540, Korea (South)
Tel.: (82) 27353399
Warehousing Transport Services
N.A.I.C.S.: 485999

Mitsui-Soko (Malaysia) Sdn. Bhd. (1)
Lot 4 Lebuh Sultan Muhamed 2 Kawasan 21, Bandar Sultan Suleiman, 42000, Port Klang, Selangor, Malaysia
Tel.: (60) 3 3176 1522
Web Site: http://www.mitsui-soko.com.my
Freight Forwarding, Warehousing & Transport
N.A.I.C.S.: 541614

Mitsui-Soko (Singapore) Pte. Ltd. (1)
No 2 Pioneer Sector Lane, Singapore, 628321, Singapore
Tel.: (65) 62276935
Web Site: https://www.mitsui-soko.com.sg
Warehousing Transport Services
N.A.I.C.S.: 485999

Mitsui-Soko (Taiwan) Co., Ltd. (1)
10th Floor No 80 Songjiang Road, Zhongshan District, Taipei, 104, Taiwan
Tel.: (886) 225619260
Web Site: https://www.mitsui-soko.com.tw
Emp.: 60
Warehousing Transport Services
N.A.I.C.S.: 485999

Mitsui-Soko (Thailand) Co., Ltd. (1)
287 Liberty Square Building 11th Floor Silom Road Silom, Bangrak, Bangkok, 10500, Thailand
Tel.: (66) 2 012 4900
Web Site: http://www.mitsui-soko.co.th
Emp.: 276
Freight Transport, Warehousing & Forwarding
N.A.I.C.S.: 541614
Katsuhiko Norioka *(Mng Dir)*

Subsidiary (Domestic):

MITS Logistics (Thailand) Co., Ltd. (2)
11th Floor Liberty Square Building 287 Silom Road Silom, Bangrak, Bangkok, 10500, Thailand
Tel.: (66) 20124900
Web Site: http://www.mitsui-soko.co.th
Logistics & Warehousing
N.A.I.C.S.: 541614

Mitsui-Soko (Chiangmai) Co., Ltd. (2)
199 Mahidol Road T Haiya, A Muang, Chiang Mai, 50100, Thailand
Tel.: (66) 539049067
Web Site: http://www.mitsui-soko.co.th
Freight Forwarding, Warehousing & Transport
N.A.I.C.S.: 541614

Mitsui-Soko (U.S.A.) Inc. (1)
1651 E Glenn Curtiss St, Carson, CA 90746
Tel.: (310) 639-3060

AND PRIVATE COMPANIES

MITSUUROKO GROUP HOLDINGS CO., LTD.

Web Site: https://www.mitsui-soko-usa.com
Emp.: 30
International Combined Transport/Warehousing/Cargo Forwarding
N.A.I.C.S.: 483111

Branch (Domestic):

Mitsui-Soko (U.S.A.) Inc. (2)
5250 Old Louisville Rd Bldg 1, Pooler, GA 31322
Tel.: (912) 748-0578
Web Site: http://www.mitsui-soko-usa.com
Emp.: 10
Freight Transportation Arrangement & Warehousing
N.A.I.C.S.: 488510

Mitsui-Soko Agencies (Malaysia) Sdn. Bhd.
Lot 4 Lebuh Sultan Muhamed Kawasan 21 Perusahaan Selat Kelang Utara, Bandar Sultan Suleiman, 42000, Port Klang, Selangor Darul Ehsan, Malaysia
Tel.: (60) 331761522
Warehousing Transport Services
N.A.I.C.S.: 485999

Mitsui-Soko Business Partners Co., Ltd. (1)
3-22-23 Kaigan, Minato-ku, Tokyo, 108-0022, Japan
Tel.: (81) 364008601
Web Site: https://www.mbp-co.net
Emp.: 243
Warehousing Transport Services
N.A.I.C.S.: 485999

Mitsui-Soko Express Co., Ltd. (1)
3-20-1 Nishi-Shimbashi, Minato-ku, Tokyo, 105-0003, Japan (64.2%)
Tel.: (81) 35 776 5100
Web Site: http://www.mitsui-soko-exp.co.jp
Emp.: 500
Cargo Forwarding; Customs Broker
N.A.I.C.S.: 488510
Takanobu Kubo *(Pres & CEO)*

Subsidiary (Non-US):

MS Express South Africa (Pty) Ltd.
97 9th Avenue, Morningside, Durban, 4001, South Africa
Tel.: (27) 31 314 9500
Emp.: 25
Air & Ocean Freight Transport & Logistics Services
N.A.I.C.S.: 488510
Garth Botha *(CEO)*

MSE China (Guangzhou) Co., Ltd. (2)
Tel.: (86) 2084986771
Air & Ocean Freight Transport & Logistics Services
N.A.I.C.S.: 488510

MSE Express (Thailand) Co., Ltd. (2)
12/20-21 Moo 5 Soi Kingkeaw 44 Kingkeaw Road Tambon Rachatheva, Amphur Bangplee, Bangkok, 10540, Thailand
Air & Ocean Freight Transport & Logistics Services
N.A.I.C.S.: 488510

Subsidiary (US):

MSE Express America, Inc. (2)
2700 Delta Ln, Elk Grove Village, IL 60007
Tel.: (847) 238-2600
Emp.: 30
Freight Transportation Arrangement
N.A.I.C.S.: 488510
Tom Casey *(Mgr-Natl Sls)*

Subsidiary (Non-US):

MSE Forwarders India Pvt. Ltd. (2)
971-471 Ground Floor Prestige Terminus 1 Airport Exit Road, Bengaluru, 560 017, India
Tel.: (91) 80 4115 1563
Air & Ocean Freight Transport & Logistics Services
N.A.I.C.S.: 488510

PT. Puninar MSE Indonesia (2)

Air & Ocean Freight Transport & Logistics Services
N.A.I.C.S.: 488510

Mitsui-Soko Kyushu Co., Ltd. (1)
Hakataekimae Daiichi Seimei Building 1-4-1 Hakataekimae, Hakata-ku, Fukuoka, 812-0011, Japan
Tel.: (81) 924816730
Web Site: https://www.mitsui-soko.com
Warehousing Transport Services
N.A.I.C.S.: 485999

Mitsui-Soko Logistics Co., Ltd. (1)
MSC Onarimon Bldg 4th Floor 3-20-1 Nishi-Shinbashi, Tokyo, 105-0003, Japan
Tel.: (81) 3 6400 8057
Web Site: http://www.mitsui-soko-lg.com
Emp.: 350
Cargo Forwarding & Warehousing
N.A.I.C.S.: 488510
Kenta Yasuhara *(Gen Mgr-Sls)*

Mitsui-Soko Supply Chain Solutions, Inc. (1)
5432 Toyoshina, Azumino, 399-8282, Nagano, Japan
Tel.: (81) 263729089
Warehousing Transport Services
N.A.I.C.S.: 485999

Subsidiary (Domestic):

Logistics Operation Service Co., Ltd. (2)
325 Gambara, Kami-machi Kami-gun, Miyagi, 981-4263, Japan
Tel.: (81) 229632395
Warehousing Transport Services
N.A.I.C.S.: 485999

Subsidiary (Non-US):

MS Supply Chain Solutions (Thailand) Ltd. (2)
2126 Krommadit Building 5th Floor New Petchburi Road, Bangkapi Huay Kwang, Bangkok, 10310, Thailand
Tel.: (66) 27156500
Web Site: https://www.mscs.co.th
Warehousing Transport Services
N.A.I.C.S.: 485999

Mitsui-Soko Transport Co., Ltd. (1)
2-4-9 Tosabori, Nishi-ku, Osaka, 550-0001, Japan
Tel.: (81) 677111070
Web Site: https://www.mitsui-soko.com
Warehousing Transport Services
N.A.I.C.S.: 485999

Subsidiary (Non-US):

AMT Co., Ltd. (2)
311 DMC Hi-Tech Industry Center 330 Seongamro, Mapo-Gu, Seoul, Korea (South)
Tel.: (82) 220621074
Web Site: http://www.amtsaw.com
Dielectric Product Mfr
N.A.I.C.S.: 333994

Subsidiary (Domestic):

Marukyo Transportation Co., Ltd. (2)
3-6-10 Nagata, Higashi, Osaka, 577-0015, Japan
Tel.: (81) 66 788 9690
Web Site: https://www.marukyo.jp
Warehousing Transport Services
N.A.I.C.S.: 485999
Satoshi Watanabe *(Pres)*

Subsidiary (Non-US):

Shanghai Marukyo Transportation Co., Ltd. (2)
Room 202B No 1 Building No 641 Tianshan Road, Changning, Shanghai, China
Tel.: (86) 2152068085
Warehousing Transport Services
N.A.I.C.S.: 485999

Mitsui-Soko Vietnam Co., Ltd. (1)
Lot CN2 10 Minh Phuong IP, Dong Hai 2 Ward Hai An, Haiphong, Vietnam
Tel.: (84) 2256274333
Web Site: https://www.mitsui-soko.com
Warehousing Transport Services
N.A.I.C.S.: 485999

Mitsunori Corporation (1)
1307 Kida-cho, Fukui, 918-8106, Japan
Tel.: (81) 776206111
Web Site: https://www.mitsui-soko.com
Warehousing Transport Services
N.A.I.C.S.: 485999

N.V. MSE Europe S.A. (1)
Brucargo Vliegveld 749, 1820, Steenokkerzeel, Belgium
Tel.: (32) 27535575
Warehousing Transport Services
N.A.I.C.S.: 485999

Nantong Sinavico International Logistics Co., Ltd. (1)
Suite 2506 of Nantong International Trade Center 88 Chongchuan Road, Chongchuan District, Nantong, Jiangsu, China
Tel.: (86) 51385701790
Warehousing Transport Services
N.A.I.C.S.: 485999

PST CLC, a.s. (1)
Prazska 180, Zdiby, 250 66, Prague, Czech Republic
Tel.: (420) 286000208
Web Site: https://www.pst-clc.cz
Freight Forwarding, Warehousing & Customs Services
N.A.I.C.S.: 541614
Jiri Bradna *(Vice Chm & Dir-Logistics)*

PST Hungary Kft. (1)
Varga J ter 1, 2537, Nyergesujfalu, Hungary
Tel.: (36) 202785854
Web Site: https://www.pst-hungary.hu
Warehousing Transport Services
N.A.I.C.S.: 485999

PT. Mitsui-Soko Indonesia (1)
JL Rorotan No 8 Kawasan Industri Cakung Cilincing, Jakarta Utara, Jakarta, 14140, Indonesia
Tel.: (62) 214 485 0123
Web Site: http://www.mitsui-soko.co.id
Emp.: 215
Warehousing, Seaport Operations & Cargo Forwarding
N.A.I.C.S.: 493190
Kiyotaka Imai *(Chm)*

Prime Cargo (H.K.) , Ltd. (1)
Room 623 Nan Fung Commercial Centre 19 Lam lok street, Kowloon Bay, China (Hong Kong)
Tel.: (852) 27566800
Warehousing Transport Services
N.A.I.C.S.: 485999

Prime Cargo Poland Sp. Z o.o. (1)
Ul Prosta 16, Lozienica, 72-100, Goleniow, Poland
Tel.: (48) 918811730
Warehousing Transport Services
N.A.I.C.S.: 485999

Prime Cargo Shanghai Ltd. (1)
Room 908 Spring International Plaza No 699 Zhaohua Road, Shanghai, 200050, China
Tel.: (86) 2152340098
Warehousing Transport Services
N.A.I.C.S.: 485999

Sanko Trucking Co., Ltd. (1)
30 Shinmei, Nakanogo, Kitanagoya, 481-0045, Aichi, Japan
Tel.: (81) 568240305
Web Site: https://www.mitsui-soko.com
Warehousing Transport Services
N.A.I.C.S.: 485999

Sanso K.K. (1)
Mitsui-Soko Hakozaki Annex 4F 1-21, Nihonbashi-hakozaki-cho Chuo-Ku, Tokyo, 103-0015, Japan
Tel.: (81) 336390471
Warehousing Transport Services
N.A.I.C.S.: 485999

Sanso Kouun Co., Ltd. (1)
1-1-1 Kinjofuto, Minato-ku, Nagoya, 455-0848, Aichi, Japan
Tel.: (81) 528758501
Web Site: https://www.mitsui-soko.com
Warehousing Transport Services
N.A.I.C.S.: 485999

Sanyu Service Co., Ltd. (1)
Mitsui-Soko Tosabori Annex 3F 2-5-4 Tosabori, Nishi-ku, Osaka, 550-0001, Japan
Tel.: (81) 664483391
Web Site: https://www.mitsui-soko.com
Warehousing Transport Services
N.A.I.C.S.: 485999

Seiyu Koun Co., Ltd. (1)
12-1 Tachinourakaigan, Moji-ku, Kitakyushu, 801-0805, Fukuoka, Japan
Tel.: (81) 933210681
Web Site: https://www.mitsui-soko.com
Warehousing Transport Services
N.A.I.C.S.: 485999

Shanghai Jinjiang Mitsui-Soko International Logistics Co., Ltd. (1)
No 6 Lane 251 Shendong Road, Pudong New Area, Shanghai, China
Tel.: (86) 2158876568
Warehousing Transport Services
N.A.I.C.S.: 485999

Toko Maruraku Transportation Co., Ltd. (1)
32 Nishiki-cho, Naka-ku, Yokohama, 231-0812, Kanagawa, Japan
Tel.: (81) 456296235
Web Site: https://www.mitsui-soko.com
Warehousing Transport Services
N.A.I.C.S.: 485999

MITSUMURA PRINTING CO., LTD.

1-15-9 Osaki, Shinagawa-ku, Tokyo, 141-8567, Japan
Tel.: (81) 334921181
Web Site:
  https://www.mitsumura.co.jp
Year Founded: 1936
7916—(TKS)
Rev.: $97,167,000
Assets: $197,896,790
Liabilities: $71,216,140
Net Worth: $126,680,650
Earnings: $370,160
Emp.: 661
Fiscal Year-end: 03/31/24
Commercial Printing Services
N.A.I.C.S.: 323111
Shigeo Abe *(Chm & Mng Dir)*

MITSUUROKO GROUP HOLDINGS CO., LTD.

Tokyo Square Garden 3-1-1 Kyobashi, Chuo-ku, Tokyo, 104-0031, Japan
Tel.: (81) 332756300
Web Site:
  https://www.mitsuuroko.com
Year Founded: 1926
8131—(TKS)
Rev.: $2,043,051,850
Assets: $1,195,524,260
Liabilities: $535,198,480
Net Worth: $660,325,780
Earnings: $60,197,270
Emp.: 1,767
Fiscal Year-end: 03/31/24
Holding Company
N.A.I.C.S.: 551112
Kohei Tajima *(Pres & CEO-Grp)*

Subsidiaries:

Logitri Holdings Co., Ltd. (1)
3-1-1 Kyobashi, Chuo-ku, Tokyo, 104-0031, Japan
Tel.: (81) 332756329
Logistic Services
N.A.I.C.S.: 541614

Mitsuuroko Beverage Co., Ltd. (1)
3-1-1 Kyobashi, Chuo-ku, Tokyo, 104-0031, Japan
Tel.: (81) 332756382
Emp.: 65
Food & Beverage Product Mfr
N.A.I.C.S.: 311999

Mitsuuroko Co., Ltd. (1)
3-1-1 Marunouchi, Chiyoda-ku, Tokyo, 100-0005, Japan
Tel.: (81) 343164334
Emp.: 39

MITSUUROKO GROUP HOLDINGS CO., LTD.

INTERNATIONAL PUBLIC

Mitsuuroko Group Holdings Co., Ltd.—(Continued)
Real Estate Lending Services
N.A.I.C.S.: 531110

Mitsuuroko Creative Solutions Co., Ltd. (1)
1-8-1 Shitamachi Omiyashitamachi 1-chome Building, Omiya Ward, Saitama, 330-0844, Japan
Tel.: (81) 486509991
Web Site: https://www.mitsuuroko-creativesolutions.com
Software Development Services
N.A.I.C.S.: 541511

Mitsuuroko Energy Force Co., Ltd. (1)
3-1-1 Kyobashi, Chuo-ku, Tokyo, 104-0031, Japan
Tel.: (81) 332756366
Web Site: https://www.mitsuuroko-energyforce.com
LP Gas & Petroleum Product Whslr
N.A.I.C.S.: 424720

Mitsuuroko Green Energy Co., Ltd. (1)
Taiyo Seimei Nihonbashi Building 14F
2-11-2 Nihonbashi, Chuo-ku, Tokyo, 103-0027, Japan
Tel.: (81) 367586311
Web Site: https://www.mitsuurokogreenenergy.com
Wind Electric Power Generation Services
N.A.I.C.S.: 221115

Mitsuuroko Lease Co., Ltd. (1)
3-1-1 Kyobashi, Chuo-ku, Tokyo, 104-0031, Japan
Tel.: (81) 362029280
Finance Leasing Services
N.A.I.C.S.: 522220

Mitsuuroko Vessel Co., Ltd. (1)
3-1-1 Kyobashi, Chuo-ku, Tokyo, 104-0031, Japan
Tel.: (81) 332756360
Emp.: 364
LP Gas & Petroleum Product Distr
N.A.I.C.S.: 457210

Mitsuuroko Voyagers Co., Ltd. (1)
3-1-1 Kyobashi Tokyo Square Garden, Chuo-ku, Tokyo, 104-0031, Japan
Tel.: (81) 332756380
Food & Beverage Product Mfr
N.A.I.C.S.: 311999

Triforce Corporation (1)
3-1-1 Kyobashi, Chuo-ku, Tokyo, 104-0031, Kanagawa, Japan
Tel.: (81) 332756373
Web Site: https://www.triforce-corporation.com
Real Estate Manangement Services
N.A.I.C.S.: 531320

MITSUWA ELECTRIC CO., LTD.
6-7-9 Minamishinagawa, Shinagawa-ku, Tokyo, 140-0004, Japan
Tel.: (81) 334743682
Web Site: http://www.mitsuwa-elec.co.jp
Year Founded: 1933
Emp.: 70
Electric Device Mfr
N.A.I.C.S.: 334419
Hiroshi Miyazaki *(Chm)*

Subsidiaries:

Mitsuwa Electric Co., Ltd. - Mobara Plant (1)
646 Mobara, Chiba, Mobara, 297-0026, Japan
Tel.: (81) 475235534
Electric Device Mfr
N.A.I.C.S.: 334419

MITSUWA ELECTRIC INDUSTRY CO., LTD.
7-720 Konda Habikino, Osaka, 5838550, Japan
Tel.: (81) 729542381

Web Site: http://www.mitsuwa-ec.co.jp
Electric Device Mfr
N.A.I.C.S.: 334419
Hiroshi Yamada *(Pres)*

Subsidiaries:

Thai Mitsuwa Public Company Limited (1)
31 Moo 2 Banchang, A Muang, Pathumthani, 12000, Thailand **(56.69%)**
Tel.: (66) 25815558
Web Site: https://www.thaimitsuwa.com
Rev.: $111,630,543
Assets: $111,188,716
Liabilities: $22,681,669
Net Worth: $88,507,046
Earnings: $15,169,132
Emp.: 2,261
Fiscal Year-end: 03/31/2024
Plastic Components & Plastic Injection Molds Mfr
N.A.I.C.S.: 326199
Hiroshi Yamada *(Mng Dir)*

MITTAL LIFE STYLE LTD.
Unit No 8/9 Ravi Kiran Estate Company Link Road, Near Monginis Opp Citi Mall Andheri West, Mumbai, 400053, Maharastra, India
Tel.: (91) 2226741792
Web Site: https://www.mittallifestyle.in
Year Founded: 2005
MITTAL—(NSE)
Rev.: $7,652,982
Assets: $4,031,185
Liabilities: $315,988
Net Worth: $3,715,197
Earnings: $63,030
Emp.: 12
Fiscal Year-end: 03/31/23
Textile Products Mfr
N.A.I.C.S.: 314999
Brijesh Kumar Mittal *(Mng Dir)*

MITTEL S.P.A.
Via Borromei 5, 20123, Milan, Italy
Tel.: (39) 02721411   IT
Web Site: https://www.mittel.it
Year Founded: 1885
MIT—(ITA)
Sales Range: $200-249.9 Million
Bank Holding Company
N.A.I.C.S.: 551111
Pietro Santicoli *(COO)*

Subsidiaries:

Disegno Ceramica Srl (1)
Via del Bocciodromo snc, Gallese Scalo Viterbo, 01035, Rome, Italy
Tel.: (39) 076 149 6725
Web Site: https://www.disegnoceramica.com
Pottery Product Mfr
N.A.I.C.S.: 327110

FD Group Srl (1)
Via D Biancolelli 47A/49A, 40132, Bologna, BO, Italy
Tel.: (39) 051 014 4155
Web Site: https://www.fd-group.eu
Automotive Industrial Design Services
N.A.I.C.S.: 541420

Gruppo Zaffiro Srl (1)
via della Vecchia Filatura 26/1, Martignacco, 33035, Udine, Italy
Tel.: (39) 043 240 7311
Web Site: https://www.gruppozaffiro.it
Physiotherapy Services
N.A.I.C.S.: 621340

Mittel Advisory SpA (1)
Via Orefici 2, 20123, Milan, Italy
Tel.: (39) 02 7223601
Web Site: http://www.mittel-advisory.it
Sales Range: $50-74.9 Million
Emp.: 14
Financial Advisory, Mergers & Acquisitions & Debt Restructuring Services
N.A.I.C.S.: 523940

Mittel Generale Investimenti S.p.A. (1)
Piazza Armando Diaz 7, 20123, Milan, Italy **(100%)**
Tel.: (39) 02721411
Web Site: http://www.mgispa.it
Sales Range: $50-74.9 Million
Emp.: 5
Merchant Banking & Investment Services
N.A.I.C.S.: 523150
Eugenio Volonte *(CEO)*

Subsidiary (Domestic):

Ma-Tra Fiduciaria Srl (2)
Piazza Armando Diaz 7, 20123, Milan, Italy **(81%)**
Tel.: (39) 02721411
Web Site: http://www.mettel.it
Sales Range: $25-49.9 Million
Emp.: 40
Financial Services
N.A.I.C.S.: 523991

Mittel Capital Markets SpA (2)
Piazza Armando Diaz 7, 20123, Milan, Italy
Tel.: (39) 02721411
Web Site: http://www.mittel.it
Investment Services
N.A.I.C.S.: 523999

Mittel Investimenti Immobiliari Srl (1)
Piazza Armando Diaz 7, 21023, Milan, Italy
Tel.: (39) 02721411
Web Site: http://www.mittel.it
Sales Range: $50-74.9 Million
Emp.: 100
Investment Services
N.A.I.C.S.: 523999

Subsidiary (Domestic):

Mittel S.p.A. (2)
Piazza Armando Diaz 7, 20123, Milan, Italy
Tel.: (39) 02721411
Web Site: http://www.mittel.it
Investment Services
N.A.I.C.S.: 523999

Mittel Partecipazioni Stabili SRL (2)
Piazza Armando Diaz 7, Milan, 20123, Italy
Tel.: (39) 0272141239
Real Estate Investment Management Services
N.A.I.C.S.: 531390

MITTELBRANDENBURGISCHE SPARKASSE IN POTSDAM
Saarmunder Str 61, 14478, Potsdam, Germany
Tel.: (49) 331898989
Web Site: http://www.mbs.de
Bank Holding Company
N.A.I.C.S.: 551111
Gerhard Zepf *(Member-Mgmt Bd)*

Subsidiaries:

Weberbank AG (1)
Hohenzollerndamm 134, 14199, Berlin, Germany
Tel.: (49) 30897980
Web Site: http://www.weberbank.de
Sales Range: $250-299.9 Million
Emp.: 200
Banking Services
N.A.I.C.S.: 522110
Walter Fehubert *(Vice Chm)*

MITULA GROUP LIMITED
Calle Enrique Granados, Edif 2 planta 2, 28224, Madrid, Pozuelo de Alarcon, Spain
Tel.: (34) 917082147
Web Site: http://www.mitulagroup.com
Year Founded: 2009
Website Operator
N.A.I.C.S.: 513199
Gonzalo del Pozo *(CEO, Exec Dir & Co-Founder)*

MIURA CO., LTD.
7 Horie-cho, Matsuyama, 799-2696, Ehime, Japan
Tel.: (81) 899791111   JP

Web Site: https://www.miuraz.co.jp
Year Founded: 1927
6005—(TKS)
Rev.: $1,055,583,950
Assets: $1,592,758,820
Liabilities: $392,944,670
Net Worth: $1,199,814,150
Earnings: $128,022,480
Emp.: 6,135
Fiscal Year-end: 03/31/24
Industrial Steam Boilers Mfr
N.A.I.C.S.: 332410
Daisuke Miyauchi *(Pres & CEO)*

Subsidiaries:

Korea Miura Co., Ltd. (1)
701-1 3-dong 775 Gyeongin-ro, Yeongdeungpo-gu, Seoul, 150-834, Korea (South) **(100%)**
Tel.: (82) 226712410
Web Site: https://www.miura.co.kr
Sales Range: $100-124.9 Million
Emp.: 270
Fabricated Plate Work
N.A.I.C.S.: 332313

MIURA SOUTH EAST ASIA Pte. Ltd. (1)
No 3 Soon Lee Street 03-36 Pioneer Junction, Singapore, 627606, Singapore
Tel.: (65) 64651147
Web Site: http://www.miuraz.co.jp
Sales Range: $25-49.9 Million
Emp.: 22
Industrial Steam Boiler Mfr
N.A.I.C.S.: 332410

Maruse Engineering (V) Co., Ltd. (1)
No 78 Nam Phuc - Le Jardin Phu My Hung, Tan Phu Ward District 7, Ho Chi Minh City, Vietnam
Tel.: (84) 2854101836
Web Site: https://www.marusevn-boiler.com
Boiler Mfr & Distr
N.A.I.C.S.: 332410

Miura America Co., Ltd. (1)
2200 Steven B Smith Blvd, Rockmart, GA 30153
Tel.: (678) 685-0929
Web Site: https://miuraboiler.com
Industrial Steam Boiler Mfr
N.A.I.C.S.: 332410

Subsidiary (Domestic):

MIURA MANUFACTURING AMERICA Co., Ltd. (2)
2200 Steven B Smith Blvd, Rockmart, GA 30153
Tel.: (678) 685-0929
Web Site: http://www.miuraz.co.jp
Industrial Steam Boiler Mfr
N.A.I.C.S.: 332410
Duy Vuong Nguyen *(Engr-Electrical)*

Miura Bangladesh Co., Ltd. (1)
Level 11 Sanmar Tower 2 Plot 38A Road 35, Gulshan 2, Dhaka, 1212, Bangladesh
Tel.: (880) 248810577
Industrial Boiler Mfr & Distr
N.A.I.C.S.: 332410

Miura Boiler Brazil Ltd. (1)
Rua Jose Capretz 361 Parque Industrial, Jundiai, Sao Paulo, 13213-095, Brazil
Tel.: (55) 1133797434
Web Site: http://miuraboiler.com.br
Boiler Mfr & Distr
N.A.I.C.S.: 332410

Miura Boiler Co., Ltd. (1)
8 Copernicus Boulevard, Brantford, N3P 1Y4, ON, Canada **(100%)**
Tel.: (519) 758-8111
Web Site: http://www.miuraboiler.com
Sales Range: $25-49.9 Million
Emp.: 40
Mfr of Boilers
N.A.I.C.S.: 332313
Tatsuya Fujiwara *(Pres)*

Miura Boiler Co., Ltd. (1)
2F No 99 Ruihu Street, Neihu District, Taipei, 114067, Taiwan **(100%)**
Tel.: (886) 227991683
Web Site: https://www.miuraz.com.tw

Sales Range: $25-49.9 Million
Emp.: 108
Fabricated Plate Work
N.A.I.C.S.: 332313

Miura Boiler Malaysia Sdn. Bhd. (1)
Tel.: (60) 322423335
Web Site: http://www.miura.com.my
Boiler Mfr & Distr
N.A.I.C.S.: 332410
Keiichi Murakami *(Mng Dir)*

Miura Boiler Mexico S.A. De C.V. (1)
Boulevard Manuel Avila Camacho number 685 Fraccionamiento, Industrial Alce Blanco Torre Norte Office 302 Naucalpan de Juarez, 53370, Mexico, Mexico
Tel.: (52) 5553605939
Web Site: http://miuraboiler.mx
Boiler Mfr & Distr
N.A.I.C.S.: 332410

Miura Boiler West Inc. (1)
5420 Newport Dr Ste 59, Rolling Meadows, IL 60008-3723
Tel.: (847) 465-0001
Web Site: http://www.miuraboiler.com
Sales Range: $50-74.9 Million
Emp.: 4
Sales & Service of Boilers
N.A.I.C.S.: 423720

Miura Canada Co., Ltd. (1)
4025 Sladeview Crescent Unit 5 6, Mississauga, L5L 5Y1, ON, Canada
Web Site: https://www.miuraboiler.ca
Boiler Mfr & Distr
N.A.I.C.S.: 332410

Miura Environmental Management Co. Ltd (1)
7 Horie-cho, Matsuyama, 799-2696, Japan
Pump & Pumping Equipment Mfr
N.A.I.C.S.: 333914

Miura Industries (Suzhou) Co., Ltd. (1)
Power Boiler & Heat Exchanger Mfr
N.A.I.C.S.: 332410

Miura Industries (China) Co., Ltd. (1)
No 8 Nanqian Lane Suzhou Industrial Park, Suzhou, China
Tel.: (86) 51288168892
Web Site: http://www.miura-cn.com
Emp.: 680
Boiler Mfr & Distr
N.A.I.C.S.: 332410

Miura Industries (Thailand) Co., Ltd. (1)
84/2 moo9 bangwua, Bangpakong, Chachoengsao, 24130, Thailand
Tel.: (66) 38134400
Web Site: https://www.miura.co.th
Emp.: 43
Boiler Mfr & Distr
N.A.I.C.S.: 332410
Yuji Kido *(Pres)*

Miura Institute of Research & Development (1)
7 Horie Cho, Matsuyama, 7992696, Japan (100%)
Tel.: (81) 899797107
Web Site: http://www.miuraz.co.jp
Sales Range: $800-899.9 Million
Fabricated Plate Work
N.A.I.C.S.: 332313
Yasuo Ochi *(Gen Mgr)*

Miura Kouki Co. Ltd. (1)
4020 Kakio, Seiyo- shi, Shirakawa, Ehime, Japan
Tel.: (81) 894821155
Web Site: http://www.miuraz.co.jp
Sales Range: $25-49.9 Million
Emp.: 60
Pump & Pumping Equipment Mfr
N.A.I.C.S.: 333914
Motoyuki Yoshida *(Pres)*

Miura Machine Co Ltd (1)
7 Horie-cho, Matsuyama, 799-2696, Ehime, Japan
Tel.: (81) 899797037
Metal Container Mfr
N.A.I.C.S.: 332439

Miura Machine Vider Co., Ltd. (1)
2797 Minami Yoshida Cho, Matsuyama, 791 8042, Ehime, Japan (100%)
Tel.: (81) 899712234
Web Site: http://www.miuramachine.com
Sales Range: $25-49.9 Million
Emp.: 40
Fabricated Plate Work
N.A.I.C.S.: 332313
Syunji Inai *(Pres)*

Miura Netherlands B.V. (1)
Buitenveldertselaan106, 1081 AB, Amsterdam, Netherlands
Tel.: (31) 206616372
Industrial Boiler Mfr
N.A.I.C.S.: 332410

Miura Seiki Co., Ltd. (1)
2380 Oaza-Sunouchi-Otsu, Toon, 791 0321, Ehime, Japan
Tel.: (81) 899665557
Fabricated Plate Work
N.A.I.C.S.: 332313

Miura Singapore Co Pte. Ltd. (1)
No 3 Soon Lee Street 03-36 Pioneer Junction, Singapore, 627606, Singapore
Tel.: (65) 64651147
Web Site: http://miurasingapore.com.sg
Boiler Mfr & Distr
N.A.I.C.S.: 332410
Keiichi Murakami *(Mng Dir)*

Miura Taiwan Eng Co., Ltd. (1)
2F No 99 Ruihu St, Neihu Dist, Taipei, Taiwan
Tel.: (886) 227991683
Web Site: http://www.miuraz.com.tw
Boiler Mfr & Distr
N.A.I.C.S.: 332410

Miura Techno Co., Ltd. (1)
864-1 Hojotsuji Matsuyama, Hojo, 799 2430, Ehime, Japan (100%)
Tel.: (81) 899932800
Sales Range: $25-49.9 Million
Emp.: 50
Fabricated Plate Work
N.A.I.C.S.: 332313

Miura Turkey Heating Systems Industry Co., Ltd. (1)
Tel.: (90) 2122176088
Web Site: http://miura.com.tr
Boiler Mfr & Distr
N.A.I.C.S.: 332410

PT. Miura Indonesia (1)
Jl harapan Raya Lot KK 10 Karawang International Industrial City KIIC, Karawang, 41361, Jawa Barat, Indonesia
Tel.: (62) 2129369977
Web Site: https://www.miura.co.id
Sales Range: $25-49.9 Million
Emp.: 74
Industrial Steam Boiler Mfr
N.A.I.C.S.: 332410

Sunchemi Co., Ltd. (1)
864-1 Hojotsuji, Matsuyama, 799 2430, Ehime, Japan
Tel.: (81) 899602207
Web Site: http://www.miuraz.co.jp
Sales Range: $25-49.9 Million
Emp.: 13
Fabricated Plate Work
N.A.I.C.S.: 332313

MIURA PRINTING CORPORATION
1111, Sumida-ku, Tokyo, 130-8588, Japan
Tel.: (81) 0336321111   JP
Web Site: http://www.miura.com
Year Founded: 1931
Commercial Printing Services
N.A.I.C.S.: 323111

MIVTACH SHAMIR HOLDINGS LTD.
Or Torwer A Habarzel 27, Tel Aviv, 6971039, Israel
Tel.: (972) 37684949   IL
Web Site: https://msgroup.co.il
Year Founded: 1958

MISH—(TAE)
Rev.: $92,155,269
Assets: $1,121,428,080
Liabilities: $659,743,601
Net Worth: $461,684,480
Earnings: $55,899,985
Emp.: 6,100
Fiscal Year-end: 12/31/23
Holding Company
N.A.I.C.S.: 551112
Yehezkel Dovrat *(Chm)*

MIWON CHEMICALS CO., LTD.
325-1 Seoksu 2-Dong, Manan-Gu, Anyang, 430-806, Gyeonggi-do, Korea (South)
Tel.: (82) 314799200
Web Site:
  https://www.miwonchemicals.com
Year Founded: 2011
134380—(KRS)
Rev.: $180,371,991
Assets: $113,411,715
Liabilities: $11,624,222
Net Worth: $101,787,493
Earnings: $12,471,815
Emp.: 211
Fiscal Year-end: 12/31/22
Chemical Products Mfr
N.A.I.C.S.: 325998
Ho Tae Kim *(Pres)*

MIWON COMMERCIAL CO., LTD.
464 Anyang-ro, Manan-gu, Anyang, 13967, Gyeonggi-do, Korea (South)
Tel.: (82) 314799120
Web Site: https://www.mwc.co.kr
Year Founded: 1959
002840—(KRS)
Rev.: $336,090,199
Assets: $318,780,022
Liabilities: $56,582,172
Net Worth: $262,197,849
Earnings: $55,389,311
Emp.: 653
Fiscal Year-end: 12/31/22
Chemical Products Mfr
N.A.I.C.S.: 325998
Eung-ju Son *(Pres)*

Subsidiaries:

Asia Stabilizers Co., Ltd. (1)
22-21 Segyosandan Road, Pyeongtaek, 17843, Korea (South)
Tel.: (82) 31 6502000
Web Site: http://www.ascl.co.kr
Emp.: 90
Polymer Stabilizer Mfr
N.A.I.C.S.: 325998
Peter Richard Smith *(Co-CEO)*

Miwon Commercial Co Ltd - Banwol Factory (1)
7-Block-12 Banwol Indus Zone 405-3 Moknae-Dong, Danwon-Gu, Ansan, 425-100, Korea (South)
Tel.: (82) 2 325 2013
Web Site: http://www.mwc.co.kr
Chemical Products Mfr
N.A.I.C.S.: 325998

Taekwang Fine Chemical Co., Ltd. (1)
Miwon Gwanggyo Center 2nd Floor 20, Poeun-daero 59 beon-gil, Siheung, 16864, Gyeonggi, Korea (South)
Tel.: (82) 3180848585
Web Site: https://www.corebond.kr
Emp.: 40
Chemical Products Mfr
N.A.I.C.S.: 325180
Young Man Lee *(Pres)*

MIWON HOLDINGS CO.,LTD.
20 Poeun-daero 59 beon-gil, Suji-gu, Yongin, 16864, Gyeonggi, Korea (South)
Tel.: (82) 314799313
Web Site: http://www.miramer.com

Year Founded: 1983
107590—(KRS)
Rev.: $394,441,803
Assets: $383,850,262
Liabilities: $181,370,347
Net Worth: $202,479,915
Earnings: $21,015,817
Emp.: 20
Fiscal Year-end: 12/31/22
Specialty Chemicals Mfr
N.A.I.C.S.: 325998
Hyung Woong Kim *(CEO)*

Subsidiaries:

Miwon (Shenzhen) Chemical Co., Ltd. (1)
Room 1402 Block A Xinian Center 6021 Shennan Avenue, Futian, Shenzhen, Guangdong, China
Tel.: (86) 75525337781
Chemical Products Mfr
N.A.I.C.S.: 325998

Miwon Austria GmbH (1)
Parking 18 A, 8074, Grambach, Austria
Tel.: (43) 31640095710
Chemical Products Mfr
N.A.I.C.S.: 325998

Miwon Europe GmbH (1)
Zeppelinstrasse 26 DE, 47638, Straelen, Germany
Tel.: (49) 28349446710
Chemical Products Mfr
N.A.I.C.S.: 325998

Miwon Guangzhou Chemical Co., Ltd. (1)
Room 1515 E Tower Greenland Central Plaza No 48 Kexue Avenue, Huangpu District, Guangzhou, China
Tel.: (86) 2031603024
Chemical Distr
N.A.I.C.S.: 424690

Miwon Nantong Chemical Co., Ltd. (1)
No 249 Gongyuannan Road, Qidong, 226200, Jiangsu, China
Tel.: (86) 51383692488
Chemical Products Mfr
N.A.I.C.S.: 325998

Miwon North America Inc. (1)
Ste 104 100 Arrandale Blvd, Exton, PA 19341
Tel.: (484) 872-8711
Chemical Products Mfr
N.A.I.C.S.: 325998

Miwon Spain SLU (1)
C/Pons i Enrich 22 N22-24, Barcelona, 08243, Manresa, Spain
Chemical Products Mfr
N.A.I.C.S.: 325998

Miwon Specialty Chemical India Pvt. Ltd. (1)
6A109 Wework Spectrum Tower Mindspace, Malad West, Mumbai, 400064, Maharashtra, India
Tel.: (91) 2250023717
Chemical Products Mfr
N.A.I.C.S.: 325998

Miwon Specialty Chemical USA, Inc. (1)
1700 Longwood Rd, Columbia, SC 29209
Tel.: (803) 610-4346
Chemical Distr
N.A.I.C.S.: 424690

MIXCOR AGGREGATES INC.
6303-43 Street, Leduc, T9E 0G8, AB, Canada
Tel.: (780) 986-6721
Web Site: http://www.mixcor.ca
Year Founded: 1969
Construction Materials Supplier
N.A.I.C.S.: 423390
Terry Mix *(Pres)*

MIXI, INC.
Shibuya Scramble Square 36F

MIXI, INC.

mixi, Inc.—(Continued)
2-24-12 Shibuya, Shibuya ku, Tokyo, 150-6136, Japan
Tel.: (81) 357385900
Web Site: https://www.mixi.co.jp
Year Founded: 1999
MIXIF—(OTCIQ)
Rev.: $1,053,036,390
Assets: $1,594,041,570
Liabilities: $278,611,860
Net Worth: $1,315,429,710
Earnings: $37,004,370
Emp.: 1,556
Fiscal Year-end: 03/31/23
Social Networking Website Operator
N.A.I.C.S.: 516210
Kenji Kasahara *(Founder & Dir)*

Subsidiaries:

Chariloto Co., Ltd.
1-14-10 Sumitomo Mitsui Banking Corporation Gotanda Building 7th Floor, Shinagawa-ku, Tokyo, Japan
Tel.: (81) 357891262
Web Site: http://www.chariloto.jp
Emp.: 214
Bicycle Race Ticket Sale Services
N.A.I.C.S.: 711219

TOKYO FOOTBALL CLUB Co., Ltd. (1)
1-2-3 Shimoishiwara, Chofu, 182-0034, Japan
Tel.: (81) 424442630
Web Site: https://www.fctokyo.co.jp
Football Club Services
N.A.I.C.S.: 711211

MIYAIRI VALVE MFG. CO., LTD.

1-2 Ginza-Nishi, Chuo-ku, Tokyo, 104-0061, Japan
Tel.: (81) 335355575
Web Site: https://www.miyairi-valve.co.jp
Year Founded: 1949
6495—(TKS)
Sales Range: Less than $1 Million
Industrial Valve Mfr
N.A.I.C.S.: 332911
Naoki Fukuoka *(Mgr-Factory)*

Subsidiaries:

Miyairi Valve Mfg. Co., Ltd. - Kofu Factory (1)
1588 Mujina, Minami-Alps, Yamanashi, Japan
Tel.: (81) 55 285 0111
Industrial Valve Mfr
N.A.I.C.S.: 332911

MIYAJI ENGINEERING GROUP INC.

9-19 Nihonbashi-tomizawacho, Chuo-ku, Tokyo, 103-0006, Japan
Tel.: (81) 356490111
Web Site: https://www.miyaji-eng.com
Year Founded: 2000
3431—(TKS)
Rev.: $458,502,650
Assets: $490,105,060
Liabilities: $181,880,760
Net Worth: $308,224,300
Earnings: $28,779,940
Fiscal Year-end: 03/31/24
Engineering Services
N.A.I.C.S.: 541330
Shigetoshi Aota *(Chm & Pres)*

Subsidiaries:

MM Bridge Co., Ltd. (1)
1-20-24 Kanonshinmachi Hiroshima Ryoko Center Building 7F, Nishi-ku, Hiroshima, 733-0036, Japan
Tel.: (81) 82 292 1111
Web Site: http://www.mm-bridge.com
Emp.: 160 (51%)

Bridge Steel Structures Mfr & Installation Services
N.A.I.C.S.: 331110
Miyami Yu *(Pres)*

MIYAKO, INC.

1-6-7 Temma, Kita-ku, Osaka, Japan
Tel.: (81) 872 3091
Web Site: http://www.miyako-inc.jp
Piping Material Mfr
N.A.I.C.S.: 332913
Masaru Tsukada *(Pres)*

MIYAKOSHI HOLDINGS INC.

23-1 Omorikita, Ota-ku, Tokyo, 143-0016, Japan
Tel.: (81) 332987111
Web Site: https://www.miyakoshi-holdings.com
6620—(TKS)
Rev.: $7,515,570
Assets: $183,156,490
Liabilities: $7,026,430
Net Worth: $176,130,060
Earnings: $3,542,960
Emp.: 800
Fiscal Year-end: 03/31/24
Holding Company; Electrical, Audio, Video, Household & Medical Equipment Mfr & Sales
N.A.I.C.S.: 551112
Kunimasa Miyakoshi *(Chm & Pres)*

MIYOSHI LIMITED

26 Boon Lay Way Tradehub 21 No 01-80, Singapore, 609970, Singapore
Tel.: (65) 62655221
Web Site: https://www.miyoshi.biz
M03—(CAT)
Rev.: $32,433,494
Assets: $38,089,663
Liabilities: $16,220,082
Net Worth: $21,869,581
Earnings: $(1,282,697)
Emp.: 659
Fiscal Year-end: 08/31/23
Metal Stamping Mfr
N.A.I.C.S.: 332119
Karen Yoke Fong Gan *(VP-Corp Dev)*

Subsidiaries:

Miyoshi Hi-Tech Co., Ltd. (1)
38 Moo 1 Hi-Tech Industrial Estate BanPo, Band Pa-In, Ayutthaya, 13160, Thailand
Tel.: (66) 35314031
Metal Stamping Mfr
N.A.I.C.S.: 332119

Miyoshi Precision (Malaysia) Sdn. Bhd. (1)
No 4 Jalan Wira 3 Taman Tan Sri Yaacob, Skudai, 81300, Johor Bahru, Johor, Malaysia
Tel.: (60) 75111855
Sales Range: $50-74.9 Million
Emp.: 150
Metal Stamping Mfr
N.A.I.C.S.: 332119

Miyoshi Precision (Thailand) Co., Ltd. (1)
66 Moo 5 Bangna-Trad Km 37 T Bangsamak, Bang Pakong, 24180, Chachoengsao, Thailand
Tel.: (66) 38 842 741
Web Site: http://www.miyoshi.biz
Precision Tools & Dies Mfr
N.A.I.C.S.: 332216

Miyoshi Precision Huizhou Co., Ltd. (1)
Jin Chuan Road, Tong Qiao Industrial Park Huicheng District, Huizhou, 516032, Guangdong, China
Tel.: (86) 7119926
Integrated Engineering Services
N.A.I.C.S.: 541330

Miyoshi Technologies Phils., Inc. (1)
Lot B1-5 Road 6 Brgy Milagrosa, Carmelray Industrial Park II, Calamba, 4027, Laguna, Philippines

Tel.: (63) 495081388
Integrated Engineering Services
N.A.I.C.S.: 541330

OE Aquitech (M) Sdn. Bhd. (1)
No 4 Jalan Wira 3 Taman Tan Sri Yaacob, 81300, Skudai, Johor, Malaysia
Tel.: (60) 75111855
Hydroponic Production Services
N.A.I.C.S.: 111419

OE Aquitech (Singapore) Pte. Ltd. (1)
26 Boon Lay Way 01-80 Tradehub 21, Singapore, 609970, Singapore
Tel.: (65) 97580381
Web Site: https://www.openandeat.com
Hydroponic Production Services
N.A.I.C.S.: 111419

Wuxi Miyoshi Precision Co., Ltd. (1)
No 108 Hongda Road, Hongshan Town, Wuxi, Jiangsu, China
Tel.: (86) 51085300128
Integrated Engineering Services
N.A.I.C.S.: 541330

MIYOSHI OIL & FAT CO., LTD.

4-66-1 Horikiri, Katsushika-ku, Tokyo, 124-8510, Japan
Tel.: (81) 336031111
Web Site: https://www.miyoshi-yushi.co.jp
Year Founded: 1937
4404—(TKS)
Rev.: $398,713,240
Assets: $442,720,870
Liabilities: $242,392,920
Net Worth: $200,327,950
Earnings: $14,725,930
Fiscal Year-end: 12/31/23
Vegetable Oil Mfr & Distr
N.A.I.C.S.: 311225

MIYUKI BUILDING CO., LTD

3-20-27 Nishiki, Naka-ku, Nagoya, 460-0003, Aichi, Japan
Tel.: (81) 522030231
Web Site: https://www.miyuki-re.jp
Year Founded: 1978
Emp.: 100
Construction Management Services
N.A.I.C.S.: 236220

MIZIA-96 AD

7 Balgarska aviatsia Str, 5800, Pleven, Bulgaria
Tel.: (359) 64800581
Web Site: https://www.mizia96ad.eu
Year Founded: 1950
MIZA—(BUL)
Sales Range: Less than $1 Million
Emp.: 820
Leather Jacket Mfr
N.A.I.C.S.: 316990

MIZKAN HOLDINGS CO., LTD.

2-6 Nakamura-cho, Handa, 475-8585, Aichi, Japan
Tel.: (81) 569213331 JP
Web Site: http://www.mizkan.net
Year Founded: 1923
Sales Range: $750-799.9 Million
Emp.: 2,410
Holding Company; Sauces, Marinades & Other Food Products Mfr & Whslr
N.A.I.C.S.: 311941
Kazuhide Matazaemon Nakano VIII *(Chm & CEO)*

Subsidiaries:

Mizkan (Thailand) Co.,Ltd. (1)
Rojana Industrial Park, 53 Moo 9 Tambol Thanu Amphur U, 13210, Ayutthaya, Thailand
Tel.: (66) 35330580
Web Site: http://www.mizkan.net
Sales Range: $75-99.9 Million
Emp.: 150
Grocery Product Whslr

N.A.I.C.S.: 424490

Mizkan Americas, Inc. (1)
1661 Feehanville Dr Ste 300, Mount Prospect, IL 60056 (100%)
Tel.: (847) 590-0059
Web Site: http://www.mizkan.com
Sales Range: $25-49.9 Million
Emp.: 100
Liquid Condiments Mfr
N.A.I.C.S.: 311941
Craig Smith *(Pres & CEO)*

Division (Domestic):

Mizkan Americas, Inc. - Border Products Division (2)
1750 Valley View Ln Ste 350, Farmers Branch, TX 75234
Tel.: (972) 406-3300
Web Site: http://www.borderfoodsinc.com
Green Chile Peppers Processor & Sauce Mfr
N.A.I.C.S.: 311999

Unit (Domestic):

Mizkan Americas, Inc. - Border Foods Plant (3)
4065 J St SE, Deming, NM 88030
Tel.: (575) 546-8863
Web Site: http://www.borderfoodsinc.com
Green Chile Peppers Processor & Sauce Mfr
N.A.I.C.S.: 311999

Mizkan Asia Pacific Pte. Ltd (1)
No 2 Pioneer Sector Lane, Singapore, 628321, Singapore
Tel.: (65) 68616063
Web Site: http://www.mizkan.net
Sales Range: $50-74.9 Million
Emp.: 2
Grocery Product Whslr
N.A.I.C.S.: 424490
Sekiguchi Toshikazu *(COO)*

Mizkan China Co., Ltd. (1)
7th Fl No 88 ShuangJing Baiziwan S 2 Rd Chaoyang Dist, Beijing, China
Tel.: (86) 1062002275
Grocery Product Whslr
N.A.I.C.S.: 424490

Mizkan Co., Ltd. (1)
2-6 Nakamura-cho, Handa, 475-8585, Aichi, Japan (100%)
Tel.: (81) 569213331
Web Site: http://www.mizkan.co.jp
Sauces, Marinades & Other Food Products Mfr & Whslr
N.A.I.C.S.: 311941

Mizkan Euro Ltd. (1)
2nd Floor Building 10 Chiswick Park 566, Chiswick High Road, London, W4 5X5, United Kingdom
Tel.: (44) 2036752220
Web Site: http://www.mizkan.co.uk
Emp.: 60
Food Products Mfr
N.A.I.C.S.: 311999

MIZRAHI TEFAHOT BANK LTD.

7 Jabotinsky Street, PO Box 3450, Ramat Gan, 5252007, Israel
Tel.: (972) 37559000 IL
Web Site: https://www.mizrahi-tefahot.co.il
Year Founded: 1923
MZTF—(TAE)
Rev.: $6,508,594,979
Assets: $121,523,778,537
Liabilities: $113,741,391,465
Net Worth: $7,782,387,072
Earnings: $1,331,272,708
Emp.: 7,106
Fiscal Year-end: 12/31/23
Commercial Banking Services
N.A.I.C.S.: 522110
Israel Engel *(Exec VP & Head-Retail Div)*

Subsidiaries:

ETGAR Portfolio Management of Mizrahi Tefahot Bank Ltd. (1)

123 Hashmonaim Street, Tel Aviv, 6713329, Israel
Tel.: (972) 35631520
Commercial Banking Services
N.A.I.C.S.: 522110
Kobi Yosef (CEO)

Etgar Investment Portfolio Management Company of the Mizrahi Tefahot Group Ltd. (1)
105 Allenby St, Tel Aviv, 65134, Israel
Tel.: (972) 35649731
Web Site: http://www.etgar.com
Emp.: 23
Portfolio Management Services
N.A.I.C.S.: 523940

Mizrahi Capital Markets (1)
7 Jabotinsky Street, 52520, Ramat Gan, 52520, Israel
Tel.: (972) 37559207
Web Site: http://www.umtb.co.il
Sales Range: $400-449.9 Million
Emp.: 600
Underwriting for IPOs & Investment Banking Advice
N.A.I.C.S.: 523940
Eldid Frasger (CEO)

Mizrahi Tefahot Bank Ltd. - Los Angeles (1)
800 Wilshire Blvd Ste 1410, Los Angeles, CA 90017
Tel.: (213) 362-2999
Web Site: https://www.umtbusa.com
Sales Range: $50-74.9 Million
Emp.: 30
Banking Services
N.A.I.C.S.: 522110

Mizrahi Tefahot Trust Company Ltd. (1)
123 Hachashmonaim St, Tel Aviv, 6713329, Israel
Tel.: (972) 35630733
Commercial Banking Services
N.A.I.C.S.: 522110
Yonatan Rothem (Chief Operating & Control Officer)

Mizrahi-Tefahot Factoring Ltd. (1)
7 Jabotinsky, Ramat Gan, 52520, Israel
Tel.: (972) 37559557
Sales Range: $50-74.9 Million
Emp.: 5
Equipment Leasing Services
N.A.I.C.S.: 522220

Mizrahi Tefahot Technology Division Ltd (1)
15 Lincoln St, Tel Aviv, 6713407, Israel
Tel.: (972) 35634333
Web Site: http://www.mizrahitefahot.co.il
Sales Range: $200-249.9 Million
Emp.: 450
Banking Services
N.A.I.C.S.: 523150

Mizrhai Tefahot Technology Division Ltd. (1)
15 Lincoln St, Tel Aviv, 6713407, Israel
Tel.: (972) 35634333
Commercial Banking Services
N.A.I.C.S.: 522110

Tefahot Insurance Agency (1989) (1)
113 Allenby, Jaffa, Tel Aviv, 65817, Israel
Tel.: (972) 37106321
General Insurance Services
N.A.I.C.S.: 524210

UMB (Switzerland) Ltd. (1)
Nuschelerstrasse 31, 8021, Zurich, Switzerland
Tel.: (41) 2268686
Web Site: http://www.mizrahi-tefahot.co.il
Investment Banking
N.A.I.C.S.: 523150

Union Bank of Israel Ltd. (1)
6-8 Ahuzat Bayit Street, Tel Aviv, 65143, Israel
Tel.: (972) 35191539
Web Site: http://www.unionbank.co.il
Banking Services
N.A.I.C.S.: 522110
Benny Gurevitz (CIO & Deputy Gen Mgr)

United Mizrahi Bank (Switzerland) Ltd. (1)
Nuschelerstrasse 31, 8001, Zurich, Switzerland
Tel.: (41) 442268686
Web Site: http://www.umbzh.ch
Private Banking Services
N.A.I.C.S.: 522110

MIZUHO CAPITAL CO., LTD.
1-2-1 Uchisaiwaicho, Chiyoda-ku, Tokyo, 100-0011, Japan
Tel.: (81) 3 3596 1300
Web Site: http://www.mizuho-vc.co.jp
Year Founded: 1983
Sales Range: $50-74.9 Million
Emp.: 75
Venture Capital Services
N.A.I.C.S.: 523910
Yutaka Suzuki (Mng Dir)

MIZUHO FINANCIAL GROUP, INC.
Otemachi Tower 1-5-5 Otemachi, Chiyoda-ku, Tokyo, 100-8176, Japan
Tel.: (81) 368386101   JP
Web Site: https://www.mizuhogroup.com
Year Founded: 2003
MFG—(NYSE)
Rev.: $52,943,883,392
Assets: $1,693,145,630,888
Liabilities: $1,628,254,885,551
Net Worth: $64,890,745,337
Earnings: $7,452,516,553
Emp.: 52,307
Fiscal Year-end: 03/31/24
Financial Holding Company
N.A.I.C.S.: 551111
Jun Kawada (Mng Dir & Mng Dir)

Subsidiaries:

AO Mizuho Bank (Moscow) (1)
5th floor 20 bld 1 Ovchinnikovskaya nab, 115035, Moscow, Russia
Tel.: (7) 4952120333
Web Site: http://www.mizuhobank.com
Financial Insurance Services
N.A.I.C.S.: 524210
Tadao Hayashi (Pres)

Asset Management One Co., Ltd. (51%)
Tekko Building 1-8-2 Marunouchi, Chiyoda-ku, Tokyo, 100-0005, Japan
Tel.: (81) 36 774 5000
Web Site: https://www.am-one.co.jp
Asset Management Services
N.A.I.C.S.: 523940
Akira Sugano (Pres & CEO)

Subsidiary (Non-US):

Asset Management One Hong Kong Limited (2)
12/F K11 Atelier 18 Salisbury Road Tsim Sha Tsui, Hong Kong, China (Hong Kong)
Tel.: (852) 29189030
Asset Management Services
N.A.I.C.S.: 523940

Asset Management One Singapore Pte. Ltd. (2)
2 Shenton Way 12-01 SGX Centre I, Singapore, 068804, Singapore
Tel.: (65) 65325470
Asset Management Services
N.A.I.C.S.: 523940

Asset Management One International Ltd. (1)
Mizuho House 30 Old Bailey, London, EC4M 7AU, United Kingdom
Tel.: (44) 2073293777
Web Site: http://www.am-one-int.co.uk
Asset Management Services
N.A.I.C.S.: 523940

Greenhill & Co., Inc. (1)
1271 Ave of the Americas, New York, NY 10020
Tel.: (212) 389-1500
Web Site: https://www.greenhill.
Rev.: $258,454,000
Assets: $552,789,000
Liabilities: $471,825,000
Net Worth: $80,964,000
Earnings: $3,274,000
Emp.: 382
Fiscal Year-end: 12/31/2022
Bank Holding Company; Investment Banking & Advisory Services
N.A.I.C.S.: 551111
David A. Wyles (Pres-London)

Subsidiary (Non-US):

Greenhill & Co. Asia (Singapore) Pte. Ltd. (2)
8 Marina View 15 10 Asia Square Tower 1, Singapore, 018960, Singapore
Tel.: (65) 98623763
Investment Banking Services
N.A.I.C.S.: 523150
Crystal Siah (Office Mgr)

Greenhill & Co. Australia Pty Limited (2)
Level 43 Governor Phillip Tower 1 Farrer Place, Sydney, 2000, NSW, Australia
Tel.: (61) 292291410
Web Site: http://www.greenhill.com
Investment Banking Services
N.A.I.C.S.: 523150
Roger Feletto (Mng Dir & Head)

Greenhill & Co. Canada Ltd. (2)
79 Wellington Street West Suite 3403, PO Box 333, Toronto, M5K 1K7, ON, Canada
Tel.: (416) 601-2576
Web Site: http://www.greenhill.com
Sales Range: $75-99.9 Million
Emp.: 9
Investment Banking & Advisory Services
N.A.I.C.S.: 523150
Steve Mayer (Pres)

Group (Non-US):

Greenhill & Co. International LLP (2)
Lansdowne House 57 Berkeley Square, London, W1J 6ER, United Kingdom
Tel.: (44) 2071987400
Web Site: http://www.greenhill.com
Sales Range: $25-49.9 Million
Emp.: 75
Holding Company; Regional Managing Office
N.A.I.C.S.: 551112

Subsidiary (Domestic):

Greenhill & Co. Europe LLP (3)
Berkeley Square House, London, W1J 6BY, United Kingdom
Tel.: (44) 2071987400
Web Site: http://www.greenhill.com
Sales Range: $125-149.9 Million
Emp.: 70
Investment Banking & Advisory Services
N.A.I.C.S.: 523150

Subsidiary (Non-US):

Greenhill & Co. Japan Ltd. (2)
Marunouchi Building 2-4-1 Marunouchi, Chiyoda-ku, Tokyo, 100-6333, Japan
Tel.: (81) 345205100
Web Site: http://www.greenhill.com
Investment Banking & Advisory Services
N.A.I.C.S.: 523150

Greenhill & Co. Sweden AB (2)
Biblioteksgatan 8, 111 46, Stockholm, Sweden
Tel.: (46) 84021370
Investment Banking Services
N.A.I.C.S.: 523150
Jacob Spens (Mng Dir)

Greenhill & Co. do Brasil Assessoria Ltda. (2)
Av Brigadeiro Faria Lima 2277 19, Sao Paulo, 01452-000, Brazil
Tel.: (55) 1120390600
Web Site: http://www.greenhill.com
Investment Banking Services
N.A.I.C.S.: 523150

Subsidiary (Domestic):

Greenhill & Co., LLC (2)
1271 Avenue of the Americas, New York, NY 10020
Tel.: (212) 389-1500
Web Site: http://www.greenhill.com

Sales Range: $50-74.9 Million
Emp.: 125
Investment Banking & Advisory Services
N.A.I.C.S.: 523150

Greenhill Cogent (2)
2101 Cedar Springs Rd, Dallas, TX 75201
Tel.: (214) 871-5400
Web Site: http://www.greenhill.com
Sales Range: $25-49.9 Million
Emp.: 46
Investment Banking & Financial Advisory Services
N.A.I.C.S.: 523150

Subsidiary (Non-US):

Greenhill Germany GmbH (2)
Neue Mainzer Strasse 52, 60311, Frankfurt am Main, Germany
Tel.: (49) 6927227200
Management Consulting Services
N.A.I.C.S.: 541618

Japan Fund Management (Luxembourg) S.A. (1)
1B rue Gabriel Lippmann, Schuttrange, 5365, Munsbach, Luxembourg
Tel.: (352) 2769201
Web Site: http://www.jfml.lu
Fund Management Services
N.A.I.C.S.: 523940
Hiroshi Kageyama (Chm)

Mizuho Alternative Investments, LLC (1)
1114 Ave Of The Americas, New York, NY 10036
Tel.: (212) 282-4420
Web Site: http://www.mizuhocbk.com
Sales Range: $50-74.9 Million
Emp.: 30
Investment Management Service
N.A.I.C.S.: 523999
Chris Crawford (COO)

Mizuho Bank Europe N.V. (1)
Atrium Amsterdam 3rd Floor Strawinskylaan 3053, 1077 ZX, Amsterdam, Netherlands
Tel.: (31) 205734343
Financial Management Services
N.A.I.C.S.: 523940
Izabella Nagy (Assoc Mgr-Operational Risk & Strategic Plng)

Mizuho Bank Europe N.V. (1)
Avenue Louise 480, 1050, Brussels, Belgium
Tel.: (32) 26455280
Financial Management Services
N.A.I.C.S.: 523940

Mizuho Bank, Ltd. (1)
1-1-5 Uchisaiwaicho Chiyoda ku, Chiyoda-Ku, Tokyo, 100 0011, Japan (100%)
Tel.: (81) 335961111
Web Site: http://www.mizuhobank.co.jp
Sales Range: $5-14.9 Billion
Emp.: 16,090
Individual & Small Business Financial Services
N.A.I.C.S.: 522110
Koji Fujiwara (Pres & CEO)

Subsidiary (US):

Mizuho Americas LLC (2)
1271 Ave of the Americas, New York, NY 10020
Tel.: (212) 282-3000
Corporate & Investment Banking
N.A.I.C.S.: 523150
Bill Featherston (Mng Dir & Head-Americas Res)

Subsidiary (Domestic):

Capstone Partners LP (3)
13355 Noel Rd Ste 1600, Dallas, TX 75240
Tel.: (972) 980-5800
Web Site: http://www.capstonepartnerslp.com
Rev.: $2,412,000
Emp.: 6
Investment Banking & Securities Dealing
N.A.I.C.S.: 523150

Subsidiary (Non-US):

Mizuho Bank (Canada) (2)
100 Yonge Street Suite 1102, Toronto, M5C

MIZUHO FINANCIAL GROUP, INC. — INTERNATIONAL PUBLIC

Mizuho Financial Group, Inc.—(Continued)
2W1, ON, Canada
Tel.: (416) 874-0222
Web Site: http://www.mizuhobank.com
International Banking Services
N.A.I.C.S.: 522299

Mizuho Bank (Switzerland) Ltd. (2)
Loewenstrasse 32, Zurich, 8001, Switzerland
Tel.: (41) 44 216 91 11
Web Site: http://www.mizuho.ch
Sales Range: $50-74.9 Million
Emp.: 25
International Banking
N.A.I.C.S.: 522299
Bignia Vieli *(Vice Chm)*

Mizuho Capital Markets (HK) Limited (2)
16th Fl 2 Pacific Pl 88 Queensway, Central, China (Hong Kong) **(100%)**
Tel.: (852) 25373818
Sales Range: $75-99.9 Million
Emp.: 30
N.A.I.C.S.: 522299
Shuichi Kanehila *(Mng Dir)*

Mizuho Capital Markets (UK) Limited (2)
River Plate House 7-11 Finsbury Circus, London, EC2M 7DH, United Kingdom
Tel.: (44) 2079729900
Sales Range: $25-49.9 Million
Emp.: 40
Provider of Financial Services
N.A.I.C.S.: 522320

Subsidiary (US):

Mizuho Capital Markets Corporation (2)
1440 Broadway 25 Fl, New York, NY 10018-2301
Tel.: (212) 547-1500
Sales Range: $25-49.9 Million
Emp.: 100
Swaps & Derivatives Services
N.A.I.C.S.: 541618

Mizuho Corporate Bank of California (2)
350 S Grand Ave Ste 1500, Los Angeles, CA 90071-3043
Tel.: (213) 612-2700
Sales Range: $25-49.9 Million
Emp.: 50
Banking Services
N.A.I.C.S.: 522110

Subsidiary (Non-US):

Mizuho Securities Singapore Pte. Limited (2)
1 Raffles Quay N Tower Ste 32-02, Singapore, 48583, Singapore **(100%)**
Tel.: (65) 66035688
Web Site: http://www.mizuho-sc.com
Sales Range: $50-74.9 Million
Emp.: 20
Financial Futures Markets Operations
N.A.I.C.S.: 523160

P.T. Bank Mizuho International Indonesia (2)
Plaza BII Menara 2 24th Floor, Jakarta, 10350, Indonesia **(100%)**
Tel.: (62) 213925222
Sales Range: $75-99.9 Million
Emp.: 200
Financial Services
N.A.I.C.S.: 522299

ZAO Mizuho Corporate Bank (Moscow) (2)
37 Bolshaya Ordynka, 119017, Moscow, Russia
Tel.: (7) 4957295858
Web Site: http://www.mizuho.com
Sales Range: $25-49.9 Million
Emp.: 50
Banking Services
N.A.I.C.S.: 522110

Mizuho Bank, Ltd. (1)
Suite 201-202 Entrance 4 2nd Floor Manama Center, Manama, Bahrain
Tel.: (973) 17224522
Financial Management Services
N.A.I.C.S.: 523940
Aldo J. Polak *(Mng Dir)*

Mizuho Capital Partners Co., Ltd. (1)
3rd Floor Yusen Building 2-3-2 Marunouchi, Chiyoda-ku, Tokyo, 100 0005, Japan
Tel.: (81) 3 3284 1632
Web Site: http://www.mizuho-cp.co.jp
Financial Investment
N.A.I.C.S.: 523999
Tadashi Miyazaki *(Mng Dir & Head-Mezzanine Funds)*

Mizuho Corporate Bank (China), Ltd (1)
23rd Floor Shanghai World Financial Center 100 Century Avenue, Pudong New Area, Shanghai, 200120, China
Tel.: (86) 21 3855 8888
Emp.: 70
Commercial Banking Services
N.A.I.C.S.: 522110
Hiroyuki Shimo *(CEO)*

Mizuho Corporate Bank Nederland N.V. (1)
Apollolaan 171, 1077 AS, Amsterdam, Netherlands
Tel.: (31) 20 5734343
Commercial Banking Services
N.A.I.C.S.: 522110

Mizuho Corporate Bank-BA Investment Consulting GmbH (1)
Landhausgasse 4/7, 1010, Vienna, Austria
Tel.: (43) 1 5355868
Web Site: http://www.mizuhocbk.com
Investment Management Service
N.A.I.C.S.: 523999

Mizuho Credit Guarantee Co., Ltd. (1)
3-13 Kanda-Nishiki-cho, Chiyoda-ku, Tokyo, 101-0054, Japan
Tel.: (81) 3 5217 1811
Sales Range: $200-249.9 Million
Emp.: 33
Credit Guarantee Services
N.A.I.C.S.: 522299
Yvan Rivaux *(Pres)*

Mizuho Factors, Limited (1)
Shin-Marunouchi Center Bldg 1-6-2 Marunouchi, Chiyoda-ku, Tokyo, 100-0005, Japan **(100%)**
Tel.: (81) 3 3286 2200
Web Site: http://www.mizuho-factor.co.jp
Emp.: 199
Domestic Factoring & Local Collection Services
N.A.I.C.S.: 522299
Hideki Tajiri *(Mng Exec Officer)*

Mizuho Financial Strategy (1)
1-1-5 Uchisaiwaicho Chiyoda-ku, Tokyo, 100 0011, Japan
Tel.: (81) 352241111
Web Site: http://www.mizuhobank.jp
Sales Range: $5-14.9 Billion
Emp.: 36,535
Advisory Services
N.A.I.C.S.: 525990

Mizuho Information & Research Institute Inc. (1)
2-3 Kanda-Nishikicho, Chiyoda-ku, Tokyo, 101-8443, Japan **(91.5%)**
Tel.: (81) 3 5281 7548
Web Site: http://www.mizuho-ir.co.jp
Emp.: 4,700
Market Research & Consulting Services
N.A.I.C.S.: 541910
Toyonori Takashima *(Sr Mng Dir)*

Mizuho International plc (1)
Bracken House One Friday Street, London, EC4M 9JA, United Kingdom
Tel.: (44) 20 7236 1090
Web Site: http://www.uk.mizuho-sc.com
Emp.: 80
Securities Brokerage Services
N.A.I.C.S.: 523150
Christoph Seibel *(CEO-Mizuho Securities Europe GmbH)*

Mizuho Investment Consulting (Shanghai) Co., Ltd. (1)
23rd Floor Shanghai World Financial Center No 100 Century Avenue, Pudong New Area, Shanghai, China
Tel.: (86) 21 6877 5888
Web Site: http://www.mizuho-sc.com
Investment Management Consulting Services
N.A.I.C.S.: 541611

Mizuho Private Wealth Management Co., Ltd. (1)
1-1-5 Uchisaiwaicho, Chiyoda-Ku, Tokyo, 100-0011, Japan
Tel.: (81) 335968000
Commercial Banking Services
N.A.I.C.S.: 522110

Mizuho Research Institute Ltd. (1)
1-2-1 Uchisaiwaicho, Chiyoda-Ku, Tokyo, 100-0011, Japan
Tel.: (81) 335918800
Web Site: http://www.mizuho-ri.co.jp
Sales Range: $200-249.9 Million
Emp.: 290
Investment Banking
N.A.I.C.S.: 523150
Motonori Wakabayashi *(Pres & CEO)*

Mizuho Securities (Singapore) Pte. Ltd. (1)
One Raffles Quay North Tower Unit 32-02, Singapore, 048583, Singapore
Tel.: (65) 6603 5688
Securities Brokerage Services
N.A.I.C.S.: 523150

Mizuho Securities Co., Ltd. (1)
Otemachi 1-5-1 First Sq, Chuo-ku, Tokyo, 100-0004, Japan
Tel.: (81) 352083210
Web Site: http://www.mizuho-sc.com
Security Brokers
N.A.I.C.S.: 523150

Subsidiary (Non-US):

Gainwell Securities Co .Ltd. (2)
Unit 2302 Pea Harbor Way Ctr 56 Gloucester Rd, Wanchai, China (Hong Kong) **(100%)**
Tel.: (852) 28101822
Web Site: http://www.gainwell.com.hk
Sales Range: $10-24.9 Million
Emp.: 15
Security Brokers, Dealers & Flotation Companies
N.A.I.C.S.: 561621

Subsidiary (Domestic):

Mitsui Securities Co., Ltd. (2)
Nisseifukui Building Fukui, Fukui, Japan **(80%)**
Tel.: (81) 776222680
Securities Brokerage
N.A.I.C.S.: 523150

Subsidiary (Non-US):

Mizuho Saudi Arabia Company (2)
North Lobby 1st Floor Al Faisaliah Tower King Fahd Road, Olaya District, Riyadh, 11544, Saudi Arabia
Tel.: (966) 1 273 4111
Web Site: http://www.mizuho-sc.com
Business Support Services
N.A.I.C.S.: 561499

Mizuho Securities Asia Limited (2)
12th Floor Chater House 8 Connaught Road, Central, China (Hong Kong)
Tel.: (852) 2685 2000
Web Site: http://www.mizuho-sc.com
Sales Range: $75-99.9 Million
Emp.: 200
Securities Brokerage Services
N.A.I.C.S.: 523150

Subsidiary (Domestic):

Mizuho Securities Property Management Co., Ltd (2)
1-20-6 Nihombashi Chuo-Ku, 103-0027, Tokyo, Japan
Tel.: (81) 352550721
Sales Range: $25-49.9 Million
Emp.: 20
Nonresidential Buildings Lessors
N.A.I.C.S.: 531120

Subsidiary (US):

Mizuho Securities USA Inc. (2)
320 Park Ave, New York, NY 10022
Tel.: (212) 209-9300
Web Site: http://www.mizuhosecurities.com
Securities Brokerage Services
N.A.I.C.S.: 523150
Matthew DeSalvo *(Exec Mng Dir & Head-Equities)*

Subsidiary (Domestic):

Nippon Securities Technology Co., Ltd. (2)
Tokyo Dia Building 5go-Kan 5th Floor, Chuo-Ku, Tokyo, Japan
Tel.: (81) 332978691
Custom Computer Programming Services
N.A.I.C.S.: 541511

Shin-Wako Securities Investment Trust & Management Co., Ltd. (2)
1 12 2 Kayaba Cho Nihonbashi, Chuo-Ku, Tokyo, 103, Japan
Tel.: (81) 336676131
Security Brokers, Dealers & Flotation Companies
N.A.I.C.S.: 561621

Shinko Commerce Co., Ltd. (2)
Shinkoshoken Bldg Nigo-Kan Chuo-Ku, Tokyo, Japan
Tel.: (81) 332771873
Non-Durable Goods Whslr
N.A.I.C.S.: 424990

Shinko Investment Trust Management Co., Ltd. (2)
17-10 Nihonbashi 1-Chome Chuo-ku, Tokyo, 103-0027, Japan
Tel.: (81) 332771811
Web Site: http://www.shinkotoushin.co.jp
Open-End Investment Funds
N.A.I.C.S.: 525910

Shinko Principal Investment Co., Ltd (2)
2-8-1 Kyobashi Chuo-Ku, Tokyo, Japan
Tel.: (81) 352032280
Investment Advice
N.A.I.C.S.: 523940

Shinko Securities Business Services Co., Ltd (2)
8-4-6 Nishikasai Edogawa-Ku, Tokyo, 227-0036, Japan
Tel.: (81) 356969100
Web Site: http://www.shinko-sbs.co.jp
Business Services
N.A.I.C.S.: 561499

Mizuho Securities Europe GmbH (1)
TaunusTurm 34th Floor Taunustor 1, 60310, Frankfurt am Main, Germany
Tel.: (49) 69427293000
Financial Management Services
N.A.I.C.S.: 523940
Christoph Seibel *(CEO)*

Mizuho Securities India Private Limited (1)
Unit No 141 9th Floor Free Press House 215 Free Press Journal Marg, Nariman Point, Mumbai, 400 021, India
Tel.: (91) 22 6747 7600
Web Site: http://uk.mizuho-sc.com
Financial Management Services
N.A.I.C.S.: 523999

Mizuho Trust & Banking Co., Ltd. (1)
2-1 Yaesu 1-Chome Chuo-ku, Tokyo, 103 8670, Japan
Tel.: (81) 332788111
Web Site: http://www.mizuho-tb.co.jp
Sales Range: $1-4.9 Billion
Emp.: 3,700
Banking & Trust Services
N.A.I.C.S.: 522110
Hiroaki Ehara *(Mng Exec Officer)*

Subsidiary (Non-US):

Mizuho Trust & Banking (Luxembourg) S.A. (2)
1B Rue Gabriel Lippmann, L 5365, Munsbach, Luxembourg **(100%)**
Tel.: (352) 4216171
Web Site: http://www.mizuho.lu
Sales Range: $50-74.9 Million
Emp.: 100
Commercial & Investment Banking
N.A.I.C.S.: 522110

AND PRIVATE COMPANIES

Hiroshi Takahashi *(Exec VP)*

MIZUHO LEASING COMPANY, LIMITED
2-6 Toranomon 1-chome, Minato-ku, Tokyo, 105-0001, Japan
Tel.: (81) 352536511
Web Site: https://www.mizuho-ls.co.jp
Year Founded: 1969
8425—(TKS)
Rev.: $4,336,999,470
Assets: $22,231,650,960
Liabilities: $20,051,672,960
Net Worth: $2,179,978,000
Earnings: $232,804,200
Emp.: 2,176
Fiscal Year-end: 03/31/24
Equipment & Vehicle Leasing Services
N.A.I.C.S.: 532490
Shinichiro Maruyama *(Sr Mng Dir & CFO)*

Subsidiaries:

Affordable Car Leasing Pty. Ltd. (1)
10/10 Cloyne Rd, Southport, 4215, QLD, Australia
Tel.: (61) 300227562
Web Site: https://affordablecarloans.com.au
Car Loans Payment Services
N.A.I.C.S.: 541611

Aircastle Limited (1)
201 Tresser Blvd Ste 400, Stamford, CT 06901
Tel.: (203) 504-1020
Web Site: http://www.aircastle.com
Rev.: $796,033,000
Assets: $7,266,851,000
Liabilities: $5,395,393,000
Net Worth: $1,871,458,000
Earnings: $62,759,000
Emp.: 115
Fiscal Year-end: 02/28/2023
Aircraft Leasing Services
N.A.I.C.S.: 532411
Michael J. Inglese *(CEO)*

Subsidiary (Non-US):

Aircastle Advisor (Ireland) Limited (2)
8 Fitzwilliam Place, Dublin, Ireland
Tel.: (353) 16650800
Web Site: http://www.aircastle.com
Sales Range: $100-124.9 Million
Emp.: 15
Aircraft Leasing Services
N.A.I.C.S.: 532411
Jane O'Callaghan *(Mng Dir)*

Subsidiary (Domestic):

Aircastle Advisor LLC (2)
300 First Stamford Pl 5th Fl, Stamford, CT 06902
Tel.: (203) 504-1020
Web Site: http://www.aircastle.com
Sales Range: $25-49.9 Million
Aircraft Leasing Services
N.A.I.C.S.: 532411

Subsidiary (Non-US):

Aircastle Singapore Pte. Limited (2)
501 Orchard Rd 07-03 Wheelock Place, Singapore, 238880, Singapore
Tel.: (65) 62639620
Commercial Jet Aircraft Rental & Leasing Services
N.A.I.C.S.: 532411

Merdeka Aircraft Leasing (Labuan) Limited (2)
Main Office Tower Financial Park, Labuan, 87000, Malaysia
Tel.: (60) 87451688
Aircraft Equipment Rental & Leasing Services
N.A.I.C.S.: 532411

Dai-ichi Leasing Co., Ltd. (1)
4-14 Akasaka 8-chome, Minato-ku, Tokyo, 107-0052, Japan (90%)
Tel.: (81) 3 3501 5711
Web Site: http://group.dai-ichi-life.co.jp
Financial Lending Services
N.A.I.C.S.: 522220
Katsuhiko Yoshida *(Pres)*

IBJ Auto Lease Company, Limited (1)
3-19 Kyobashi 2-chome, Chuo-ku, Tokyo, 104-8360, Japan (98.71%)
Tel.: (81) 352057080
Sales Range: $50-74.9 Million
Emp.: 17
Auto Leasing Services
N.A.I.C.S.: 532112

IBJ Leasing (UK) Ltd. (1)
Mizuho House 30 Old Bailey, London, EC4M 7AU, United Kingdom (100%)
Tel.: (44) 2072362222
Web Site: http://www.ibjl.co.jp
Sales Range: $25-49.9 Million
Emp.: 8
Financial Services
N.A.I.C.S.: 561499

IBJ Leasing America Corp. (1)
150 E 52nd St 7th Fl, New York, NY 10022 (100%)
Tel.: (212) 750-1800
Financial Services
N.A.I.C.S.: 561499

Krungthai Mizuho Leasing Company Limited (1)
98 Sathorn Square Office Tower 33rd Floor Unit 3307-3313, North Sathorn Road Silom Bangrak, Bangkok, 10500, Thailand
Tel.: (66) 20090888
Web Site: https://ktmizuho.co.th
Financial Lending Services
N.A.I.C.S.: 533110

Marunouchi & Co., Ltd. (1)
23-19 Kyobashi, Chuo-ku, Tokyo, 104-8360, Japan (100%)
Tel.: (81) 352051320
Sales Range: $25-49.9 Million
Emp.: 10
Used Equipment Sales
N.A.I.C.S.: 459510

Mizuho Leasing (China) Ltd. (1)
Room 08-10 20F Metro Plaza No 555 Loushanguan Road, Changning District, Shanghai, 200051, China
Tel.: (86) 2162290022
Industrial Machinery Leasing Services
N.A.I.C.S.: 532490

Mizuho Leasing (Singapore) Pte. Ltd. (1)
80 Robinson Road 10-01A, Singapore, 068898, Singapore
Tel.: (65) 64206255
Industrial Machinery Leasing Services
N.A.I.C.S.: 532490

Mizuho Leasing (UK) Limited (1)
Mizuho House 30 Old Bailey, London, EC4M 7AU, United Kingdom
Tel.: (44) 2072362222
Industrial Machinery Leasing Services
N.A.I.C.S.: 532490

Mizuho Marubeni Leasing Corporation (1)
10F Tokyu Bancho Building 6 Yonbancho, Chiyoda-ku, Tokyo, 102-0081, Japan
Tel.: (81) 332229345
Web Site: https://www.mm-leasing.com
Emp.: 140
Leasing & Financial Services
N.A.I.C.S.: 523999

Mizuho-Toshiba Leasing Company, Limited (1)
1-2-6 Toranomon, Minato-ku, Tokyo, 105-0001, Japan
Tel.: (81) 352536700
Web Site: http://www.toshiba-lease.co.jp
Financial Lending Services
N.A.I.C.S.: 522220

Nippon Steel Kowa Real Estate Co., Ltd. (1)
AKASAKA INTERCITY AIR 1-8-1 Akasaka, Minato Ward, Tokyo, Japan
Tel.: (81) 367748000
Web Site: https://www.nskre.co.jp
Emp.: 557
Real Estate Investment Services

N.A.I.C.S.: 531210

Nissan Leasing Co., Ltd. (1)
3-19 Kyobashi 2-Chome, Chuo-ku, Tokyo, 104-8360, Japan (90%)
Tel.: (81) 352051286
Equipment Leasing Services
N.A.I.C.S.: 532490

PLM Fleet, LLC (1)
100 Mulberry St 3 Gateway Ste 1100, Newark, NJ 07102
Tel.: (862) 229-6473
Web Site: https://www.plmfleet.com
Refrigerated Trailer Rental Services
N.A.I.C.S.: 532120
Kenji Funaki *(Chm & Chief Strategy officer)*

PNB-Mizuho Leasing & Finance Corporation (1)
PNB Makati Center 5th Floor 6754 Ayala Ave cor Legaspi St, Makati, 1226, Metro Manila, Philippines
Tel.: (63) 28925555
Web Site: http://www.pnb-ibjlleasing.com.ph
Financial Lending Services
N.A.I.C.S.: 522220
Florencia G. Tarriela *(Chm)*

Universal Leasing Co., Ltd. (1)
5-3 Kachidoki 6-chome, Chuo-ku, Tokyo, 104-0054, Japan
Tel.: (81) 335393981
Equipment Leasing Services
N.A.I.C.S.: 532490

Vietnam International Leasing Company Limited (1)
Room 902 Centeo Tower 72-74, Nguyen Thi Minh Khai District 3, Ho Chi Minh City, Vietnam
Tel.: (84) 2838232788
Web Site: http://www.vinaleasing.com
Financial Lending Services
N.A.I.C.S.: 522220

MIZUHO MEDY CO., LTD.
5-4 Fujinoki-machi, Tosu, 841-0048, Saga, Japan
Tel.: (81) 942850303
Web Site: https://www.mizuho-m.co.jp
Year Founded: 1977
4595—(TKS)
Pharmaceutical Manufacture & Sales
N.A.I.C.S.: 325412
Fuminari Karakawa *(Chm & Pres)*

MIZUNO CORPORATION
1-12-35 Nanko-kita, Suminoe-ku, Osaka, 559-8510, Japan
Tel.: (81) 666148110 JP
Web Site: https://corp.mizuno.com
Year Founded: 1906
8022—(TKS)
Rev.: $1,518,389,710
Assets: $1,362,658,110
Liabilities: $423,608,460
Net Worth: $939,049,650
Earnings: $94,595,710
Emp.: 3,584
Fiscal Year-end: 03/31/24
Mfr, Whslr & Retailer of Sporting Goods; Designer & Builder of Sports Facilities
N.A.I.C.S.: 339920
Akito Mizuno *(Pres)*

Subsidiaries:

MIZUNO CORPORATION (GERMANY) (1)
Bayerwaldstr 9, 81737, Munich, Germany
Tel.: (49) 89450500
Sports Products Mfr & Distr
N.A.I.C.S.: 339920

Mizuno (China) Corporation (1)
Room 207 2nd Floor No 501 Jiujiang Road, Huangpu District, Shanghai, 200001, China
Tel.: (86) 2163290066
Web Site: http://www.mizuno.com.cn
Sports Product Distr
N.A.I.C.S.: 423910

Mizuno (Taiwan) Corporation (1)

MIZUNO CORPORATION

9F No 49 Sec 3 Minsheng E Rd, Taipei, 104, Taiwan (80%)
Tel.: (886) 225095100
Web Site: http://www.mizuno.tw
Sales Range: $25-49.9 Million
Emp.: 70
Import & Export; Sales of Sporting Goods
N.A.I.C.S.: 459110

Mizuno Canada Limited (1)
5206 Timberlea Blvd, Mississauga, L4W 2S5, ON, Canada
Tel.: (905) 629-0500
Web Site: http://www.mizunocda.com
Sport Products Mfr & Distr
N.A.I.C.S.: 339920
Mark M. O'Brien *(Chm)*

Mizuno Corporation (1)
Rivium Quadrant 205, 2909 LC, Capelle aan den IJssel, Netherlands
Tel.: (31) 108991800
Sports Equipment Mfr
N.A.I.C.S.: 339920

Mizuno Corporation (1)
Mizuno House 612 Reading Road, Winnersh, Wokingham, RG41 5HE, Berkshire, United Kingdom
Tel.: (44) 1189362100
Sports Equipment Mfr
N.A.I.C.S.: 339920

Mizuno Corporation (1)
Bayerwaldstr 9, 81737, Munich, Germany
Tel.: (49) 89450500
Sports Equipment Mfr
N.A.I.C.S.: 339920

Mizuno Corporation (UK) Ltd. (1)
Mizuno House 3 Oaklands Business Centre, Oaklands Park, Wokingham, RG41 2FD, Berkshire, United Kingdom
Tel.: (44) 1189362100
Web Site: http://www.mizuno.eu
Sales Range: $25-49.9 Million
Sports Goods Mfr & Distr
N.A.I.C.S.: 339920

Mizuno Corporation Australia Pty, Ltd. (1)
17 Anzed Court, Mulgrave, Melbourne, 3170, VIC, Australia
Tel.: (61) 392397100
Sales Range: $25-49.9 Million
Emp.: 25
Sports Products Mfr & Distr
N.A.I.C.S.: 339920

Mizuno Corporation France (1)
Tel.: (33) 141158711
Web Site: http://www.mizuno.com
Sales Range: $25-49.9 Million
Emp.: 15
Marketing of Golf Goods
N.A.I.C.S.: 459110

Mizuno Corporation Niederlassung Deutschland (1)
Bahnof Str 1616 Hhfchen, 81671, Munich, Germany (100%)
Tel.: (49) 89450500
Web Site: http://wwwmizunoeurope.com
Sales Range: $25-49.9 Million
Emp.: 30
Marketing of Sporting Goods
N.A.I.C.S.: 459110
Wolf Giehl *(Gen Mgr)*

Mizuno Corporation of Hong Kong Ltd. (1)
Room 1202 On Hong Commercial Building 145 Hennessy Road, Wanchai, China (Hong Kong) (100%)
Tel.: (852) 25986089
Web Site: http://www.mizuno.co.jp
Sales Range: $25-49.9 Million
Retail Footwear Mfr & Sales
N.A.I.C.S.: 339920

Mizuno Iberia S.L. (1)
calle Sant Elies 29-35 local 4o 2a Escalera B, 08006, Barcelona, Spain
Tel.: (34) 900933431
Sports Equipment Mfr
N.A.I.C.S.: 339920

Mizuno Italia S.r.l. (1)
Viale risorgimento 20, Beinasco, 10092, Turin, Italy

MIZUNO CORPORATION

Mizuno Corporation—(Continued)
Tel.: (39) 0113494811
Sports Equipment Mfr
N.A.I.C.S.: 339920
Mark Kaiway *(Pres)*

Mizuno Korea Ltd. (1)
13F YTN News Square 76 Sangamsan-ro, Mapo-gu, Seoul, Korea (South)
Tel.: (82) 231431288
Web Site: http://www.mizuno.co.kr
Sports Equipment Mfr
N.A.I.C.S.: 339920
Jinhyun Ryu *(Asst Mgr)*

Mizuno Norge AS (1)
Narviga 5, 4633, Kristiansand, 4633, Norway
Tel.: (47) 48055400
Sports Equipment Mfr
N.A.I.C.S.: 339920
Aleksander Poulsen *(Sls Mgr)*

Mizuno Singapore Pte Ltd (1)
51 Changi Business Park Central 2 06-01 The Signature, Singapore, 486066, Singapore
Tel.: (65) 65899488
Sports Equipment Mfr
N.A.I.C.S.: 339920
Masakatsu Mitsuoka *(Mktg Dir)*

Mizuno Sports Service Co. Ltd. (1)
1-12-35 Nankokita, Suminoe-ku, Osaka, 559-8510, Japan
Tel.: (81) 666148136
Web Site: http://www.mizuno-sports-service.co.jp
Sports Equipment Mfr
N.A.I.C.S.: 339920

Mizuno USA, Inc. (1)
3155 Northwoods Pkwy, Peachtree Corners, GA 30071-1571 (100%)
Tel.: (770) 441-5553
Web Site: https://www.mizunousa.com
Sales Range: $75-99.9 Million
Footwear, Equipment & Apparel Mfr for Baseball, Softball, Running, Track & Field, Volleyball, Court Sports, Soccer & Golf
N.A.I.C.S.: 423910
Mark M. O'Brien *(Pres)*

Senoh Corporation
250 Matsuhidai, Matsudo, 270-2214, Chiba, Japan
Tel.: (81) 473865807
Web Site: https://www.senoh.jp
Emp.: 364
Sports Equipment Mfr
N.A.I.C.S.: 339920

Shanghai Mizuno Corporation Ltd. (1)
No 505 Shen Zhuan Road Shen Lane, Zhujiajiao Town Qingpu, Shanghai, 201714, China
Tel.: (86) 2159835888
Web Site: http://www.mizuno.com.cn
Sales Range: $50-74.9 Million
Sporting Goods
N.A.I.C.S.: 339920

Thai Mizuno Co., Ltd (1)
571 RSU Tower Unit 802 8th floor Soi Sukhumvit 31 Sukhumvit Road, Klongton Nua Wattana, Bangkok, 10110, Thailand
Tel.: (66) 22613258
Sports Equipment Mfr
N.A.I.C.S.: 339920

MJ GLEESON PLC

3 Europa Court Sheffield Business Park, Sheffield, S9 1XE, United Kingdom
Tel.: (44) 1142612900
Web Site: https://gleesonhomes.co.uk
Year Founded: 1903
GLE—(LSE)
Rev.: $436,482,557
Assets: $477,814,711
Liabilities: $101,497,725
Net Worth: $376,316,986
Earnings: $24,400,910
Emp.: 743
Fiscal Year-end: 06/30/24

Home Construction Services
N.A.I.C.S.: 236116
Dermot Gleeson *(Chm)*

Subsidiaries:

GL Plant Limited (1)
Drake Rd, Mitcham, CR44HQ, United Kingdom
Tel.: (44) 1264781178
Office Machinery & Equipment Rental & Leasing
N.A.I.C.S.: 532420

Gleeson Developments Limited (1)
Hollinsbrook Park Little 66, Off Roach Bank Rd, Bury, BL98RN, United Kingdom
Tel.: (44) 1617618100
Web Site: http://www.gleeson-homes.co.uk
Sales Range: $25-49.9 Million
Emp.: 8
Heavy & Civil Engineering Construction
N.A.I.C.S.: 237990

Gleeson Homes Ltd. (1)
5 Europa Court, Sheffield Business Park, Sheffield, S9 1XE, Hampshire, United Kingdom
Tel.: (44) 1142612900
Web Site: https://gleesonhomes.co.uk
Sales Range: $50-74.9 Million
Emp.: 15
Real Estate Agents & Brokers
N.A.I.C.S.: 531210
Jolyon Harrison *(Mgr-Site)*

Gleeson Land Limited (1)
Sentinel House Harvest Crescent, Ancells Business Park, Fleet, GU51 2UZ, Hampshire, United Kingdom (100%)
Tel.: (44) 1252360300
Web Site: https://www.gleesonland.co.uk
Sales Range: $50-74.9 Million
Emp.: 15
Real Estate Agents & Brokers
N.A.I.C.S.: 531210
Keiron Coulter *(Dir-Fin)*

Gleeson Regeneration Limited (1)
Hollinsbrook Park Little 66, Off Roach Bank Rd, Bury, BL98RN, United Kingdom
Tel.: (44) 1617618100
Web Site: http://www.gleeson-homes.com
Sales Range: $25-49.9 Million
Emp.: 20
Heavy & Civil Engineering Construction
N.A.I.C.S.: 237990
Jolyon Harrison *(Mng Dir)*

MJ HUDSON GROUP PLC

Forum 4 Grenville Street, PO Box 246, Saint Helier, JE4 8TQ, Jersey
Tel.: (44) 1534712900
Web Site: http://www.mjhudson.com
Year Founded: 2010
MJH—(LSE)
Rev.: $54,068,484
Assets: $113,823,098
Liabilities: $63,310,484
Net Worth: $50,512,615
Earnings: ($7,331,688)
Emp.: 233
Fiscal Year-end: 06/30/21
Asset Management Services
N.A.I.C.S.: 523940
Matthew Hudson *(Founder & CEO)*

Subsidiaries:

MJ Hudson Allenbridge Holdings Limited (1)
1 Frederick's Pl, London, EC2R 8AE, United Kingdom
Tel.: (44) 2070791000
Web Site: http://www.mjhudson-allenbridge.com
Investment Advisory Services
N.A.I.C.S.: 523940
Odi Lahav *(CEO)*

Meyler LLC (1)
380 Lexington Ave Ste 1700, New York, NY 10168
Tel.: (914) 299-1706
Web Site: http://www.meylercapital.com
Marketing Services
N.A.I.C.S.: 541613

David Allison *(Dir-Brand Strategy)*

MJ ROOFING & SUPPLY LTD.

862 Dufferin Avenue, Winnipeg, R2X 0A3, MB, Canada
Tel.: (204) 586-8411
Web Site: http://www.mjroofing.net
Year Founded: 1959
Rev.: $12,921,952
Emp.: 110
Roofing Contractors
N.A.I.C.S.: 238160

MJL BANGLADESH LIMITED

Mobil House CWS A 13/A Gulshan Avenue Bir Uttam Mir Shawkat Sarak, Dhaka, 1212, Bangladesh
Tel.: (880) 258813661
Web Site: https://www.mobilbd.com
MJLBD—(CHT)
Rev.: $302,438,710
Assets: $339,286,425
Liabilities: $192,703,796
Net Worth: $146,582,628
Earnings: $25,257,724
Emp.: 440
Fiscal Year-end: 06/30/23
Lubricants & Grease Marketing Services
N.A.I.C.S.: 811191
Farhana Afreen Mahmood *(Sec)*

Subsidiaries:

Omera Cylinders Limited (1)
Mobil House CWS 13/A Gulshan Avenue Bir Uttam Mir Shawkat Sarak, Gulshan, Dhaka, 1212, Bangladesh
Tel.: (880) 1755605259
Web Site: https://www.omeracylinders.com
Steel Gas Cylinder Mfr & Distr
N.A.I.C.S.: 332420

MK ELECTRON CO., LTD.

316-2 kumeu-ri Pogok-eup, Cheoin-gu, Yongin, Gyeonggi, Korea (South)
Tel.: (82) 313301900
Web Site: http://www.mke.co.kr
Year Founded: 1982
033160—(KRS)
Rev.: $784,801,821
Assets: $1,664,403,167
Liabilities: $884,018,655
Net Worth: $780,384,512
Earnings: $2,396,708
Emp.: 292
Fiscal Year-end: 12/31/22
Semiconductor Material Mfr
N.A.I.C.S.: 335999
Charlie Hyun *(CEO)*

Subsidiaries:

MK Electron (Kunshan) Co., LTD. (1)
Tel.: (86) 512501064
Semiconductor Material Mfr
N.A.I.C.S.: 335999

MK EXIM (INDIA) LTD.

G 1/150 Garment Zone EPIP RIICO Industrial Area, Sitapura Sanganer, Jaipur, 302022, Rajasthan, India
Tel.: (91) 1413937501
Web Site: https://www.mkexim.com
538890—(BOM)
Rev.: $12,972,860
Assets: $9,692,206
Liabilities: $1,315,941
Net Worth: $8,376,265
Earnings: $2,016,332
Emp.: 46
Fiscal Year-end: 03/31/23
Jewellery Products Mfr & Distr
N.A.I.C.S.: 339910
Manish Murlidhar Dialani *(Mng Dir)*

MK GROUP DOO

INTERNATIONAL PUBLIC

Bulevar Mihajla Pupina 115e, 11070, Belgrade, Serbia
Tel.: (381) 11 3539 539   RS
Web Site: http://www.mkgroup.rs
Year Founded: 2005
Holding Company
N.A.I.C.S.: 551112
Miodrag Kostic *(Pres)*

Subsidiaries:

AIK banka a.d. (1)
Nikole Pasica BR 42, 18000, Nis, Serbia
Tel.: (381) 18507401
Web Site: http://www.aikbanka.rs
Rev.: $84,130,844
Assets: $1,991,226,861
Liabilities: $1,448,602,289
Net Worth: $542,624,572
Earnings: $54,398,019
Emp.: 100
Fiscal Year-end: 12/31/2018
Banking Services
N.A.I.C.S.: 523150
Nikola Litvinenko *(Member-Mgmt Bd)*

MK KASHIYAMA CORP.

1119 Otai, Saku-city, Nagano, 385-0009, Japan
Tel.: (81) 267661755
Web Site: http://www.mkg.co.jp
Year Founded: 1960
Disc Brake Pads & Brake Shoes Store & Mfr
N.A.I.C.S.: 333248
Tsuyoshi Kashiyama *(Pres)*

Subsidiaries:

Tokai Material Co., Ltd. (1)
1095-6 Yoshihashi, Yachiyo, 276-0047, Chiba, Japan
Tel.: (81) 474508511
Web Site: http://www.tokai-material.co.jp
Sales Range: $50-74.9 Million
Emp.: 120
Brake Pad Mfr
N.A.I.C.S.: 336340

MK RESTAURANT GROUP PUBLIC COMPANY LIMITED

1200 Debaratana Road, Bangna, Bangkok, 10260, Thailand
Tel.: (66) 28361000
Web Site: https://www.mkrestaurant.com
Year Founded: 1962
M—(THA)
Rev.: $495,491,404
Assets: $593,976,376
Liabilities: $179,615,863
Net Worth: $414,360,513
Earnings: $49,837,446
Emp.: 14,315
Fiscal Year-end: 12/31/23
Restaurant Owner & Operator
N.A.I.C.S.: 722511
Rit Thirakomen *(Chm & CEO)*

Subsidiaries:

International Food Supply Company Limited (1)
29/35 Soi Saimai 58 Saimai Area, Or-Ngern District, Bangkok, 10220, Thailand
Tel.: (66) 299185867
Web Site: https://www.ifs.co.th
Food Products Distr
N.A.I.C.S.: 311999
Kunnikar Nilapant *(Founder & Mng Dir)*

Laem Charoen Seafood Company Limited (1)
555/235 Prachautis 17 Prachautis Rd Huai Khwang Sam Sen Nok, Bangkok, Thailand
Tel.: (66) 26902555
Web Site: https://www.laemcharoenseafood.com
Seafood Distr
N.A.I.C.S.: 424460

MK SEIKO CO., LTD.

1825 Amenomiya, Chikuma, 387-8603, Nagano, Japan
Tel.: (81) 262720601
Web Site: https://www.mkseiko.co.jp
Year Founded: 1956
5906—(TKS)
Rev.: $188,213,140
Assets: $176,995,970
Liabilities: $77,641,060
Net Worth: $99,354,910
Earnings: $4,712,930
Emp.: 834
Fiscal Year-end: 03/31/24
Automotive Equipment Mfr & Distr
N.A.I.C.S.: 336390
Shoichi Maruyama *(Pres)*

Subsidiaries:

AZx Inc. (1)
6F Kishimoto Building 2-2-1 Marunouchi, Chiyoda-ku, Tokyo, 100-0005, Japan
Tel.: (81) 36 551 2991
Web Site: https://www.azx-inc.co.jp
Information Technology Services
N.A.I.C.S.: 541511

MK Denshi Co., Ltd. (1)
6598 Shinonoishiozaki, Nagano, 388-8014, Japan
Tel.: (81) 26 292 2043
Printed Circuit Assembly Mfr
N.A.I.C.S.: 334418

MK Kosan Co., Ltd. (1)
975 Minamichitosemachi, Nagano, 380-0822, Japan
Tel.: (81) 26 226 5084
Automobile Mfr
N.A.I.C.S.: 336110

MK Seiko (Vietnam) Co., Ltd. (1)
14th Street Tan Thuan Export Processing Zone, Dist 7, 700000, Ho Chi Minh City, Vietnam
Tel.: (84) 837701141
Web Site: https://vn.mkseiko.co.jp
Emp.: 207
Household Appliance Mfr & Distr
N.A.I.C.S.: 335210

Metal Star Kogyo Co., Ltd. (1)
2-6-34 Yutaka, Higashi-ku, Niigata, 950-0812, Nigata, Japan
Tel.: (81) 25 274 1947
Automobile Mfr
N.A.I.C.S.: 336110

MK-KLINIKEN AG
Sportallee 1, 22335, Hamburg, Germany
Tel.: (49) 40514590 De
Web Site: http://www.marseille-kliniken.com
Year Founded: 1984
Sales Range: $250-299.9 Million
Emp.: 4,850
Health Care Srvices
N.A.I.C.S.: 621399
Dieter Wopen *(Member-Mgmt Bd)*

Subsidiaries:

ALGOS Fachklinik Bad Klosterlausnitz GmbH, (1)
Herrmann-Sachse-Strasse 36, 07639, Bad Klosterlausnitz, Germany
Tel.: (49) 36601870
Web Site: http://www.algos-fachklinik.de
Nursing Care & Rehabilitation Services
N.A.I.C.S.: 623110

AMARITA Buxtehude GmbH (1)
Bertha-von-Suttner-Allee 8, 21614, Buxtehude, Germany
Tel.: (49) 41 61 74 75 98
Web Site: http://www.amarita-buxtehude.de
Nursing Care & Rehabilitation Services
N.A.I.C.S.: 623110
Doreen Gjardy *(Mgr)*

AMARITA Datteln GmbH (1)
Friedrich-Ebert-Strasse 72, 45711, Datteln, Germany
Tel.: (49) 800 47 47 201
Web Site: http://www.amarita-datteln.de
Sales Range: $10-24.9 Million
Emp.: 82
Nursing Care & Rehabilitation Services
N.A.I.C.S.: 623110
Matthias Brzeszniak *(Mgr-Facilities)*

AMARITA Hamburg Mitte PLUS GmbH (1)
Sportallee 1, 22335, Hamburg, Germany
Tel.: (49) 4055500
Web Site: http://www.medina-pflege-hamburg.de
Nursing Care & Rehabilitation Services
N.A.I.C.S.: 623110

AMARITA Oldenburg GmbH (1)
Clausewitzstr 5, 26125, Oldenburg, Germany
Tel.: (49) 44193320
Web Site: http://www.amarita-oldenburg.de
Nursing Care & Rehabilitation Services
N.A.I.C.S.: 623110

Astor Park Wohnanlage Langen GmbH (1)
Debstedter Str 26-302, 27607, Langen, Germany
Tel.: (49) 800 47 47 201
Nursing Care & Rehabilitation Services
N.A.I.C.S.: 623110

Betrium Nr 53 Vermogensverwaltungs-GmbH (1)
Freyensteiner Chaussee 3 a, Pritzwalk, 16928, Brandenburg, Germany
Tel.: (49) 800 47 47 202
Nursing Care & Rehabilitation Services
N.A.I.C.S.: 623110

Gotthard Schettler Klinik GmbH (1)
Professor Mueller-Schmidt-Strasse 4, 76669, Bad Schonborn, Germany
Tel.: (49) 72538010
Web Site: http://www.gotthard-schettler-klinik.com
Nursing Care & Rehabilitation Services
N.A.I.C.S.: 623110

Karlsruher Sanatorium Aktiengesellschaft (1)
Alsterkrugchaussee 283, 22297, Hamburg, Germany
Tel.: (49) 800 47 47 204
Nursing Care & Rehabilitation Services
N.A.I.C.S.: 623110

Klinik Bad Herrenalb GmbH (1)
Promenade 42, 76332, Bad Herrenalb, Germany
Tel.: (49) 8004747204
Nursing Care & Rehabilitation Services
N.A.I.C.S.: 623110

MHCC - Marseille Health Care Consulting GmbH, (1)
Sportallee 1, 22335, Hamburg, Germany
Tel.: (49) 40514590
Nursing Care & Rehabilitation Services
N.A.I.C.S.: 623110

MK IT-Entwicklungs GmbH (1)
Sportallee 1, 22335, Hamburg, Germany
Tel.: (49) 40514590
Web Site: http://www.mk-kliniken.com
Nursing Care & Rehabilitation Services
N.A.I.C.S.: 623110

MK-Delta GmbH (1)
Sportallee 1, 22335, Hamburg, Germany
Tel.: (49) 40514590
Web Site: http://www.marseille-kliniken.com
Nursing Care & Rehabitation Services
N.A.I.C.S.: 623110

Marseille-Klinik Omega GmbH (1)
Sportallee 1, 22335, Hamburg, Germany
Tel.: (49) 40514590
Web Site: http://www.mk-kliniken.de
Nursing Care & Rehabilitation Services
N.A.I.C.S.: 623110

Medina Belzig GmbH (1)
Hans-Marchwitza-Str 23, Belzig, 14806, Brandenburg, Germany
Tel.: (49) 33841445133
Web Site: http://www.medina-belzig.de
Nursing Care & Rehabilitation Services
N.A.I.C.S.: 623110

Medina Soziale Behindertenbetreuung GmbH (1)
Breitenfelder Weg 8, 38486, Klotze, Germany
Tel.: (49) 800 4 74 72 03
Web Site: http://www.medina-pflege.de
Nursing Care & Rehabilitation Services
N.A.I.C.S.: 623110

PRO F&B Gastronomische Dienstleistungsgesellschaft mbH (1)
Sportallee 1, 22335, Hamburg, Germany
Tel.: (49) 40 51 45 90
Web Site: http://www.marseille-kliniken.de
Catering Services
N.A.I.C.S.: 722320

PROMINT Dienstleistungsgruppe Neuruppin GmbH (1)
Gerhart-Hauptmann-Str 39, Neuruppin, 16816, Brandenburg, Germany
Tel.: (49) 49339168490
Nursing Care & Rehabilitation Services
N.A.I.C.S.: 623110

Psychosomatische Fachklinik Gengenbach GmbH (1)
Wolfsweg 12, 77723, Gengenbach, Germany
Tel.: (49) 78038080
Web Site: https://www.celenus-kliniken.de
Nursing Care & Rehabilitation Services
N.A.I.C.S.: 623110

Reha-Klinik Sigmund Weil GmbH (1)
Prof-Kurt-Sauer-St 4, 76669, Bad Schonborn, Germany
Tel.: (49) 72538010
Web Site: https://www.celenus-kliniken.de
Nursing Care & Rehabilitation Services
N.A.I.C.S.: 623110

SFS Dienstleistungs GmbH (1)
Freyensteiner Chaussee 3 a, Pritzwalk, 16928, Brandenburg, Germany
Tel.: (49) 800 47 47 202
Nursing Care & Rehabilitation Services
N.A.I.C.S.: 623110

Senioren Wohnpark Aschersleben GmbH (1)
Askanierstr 40, 06449, Aschersleben, Germany
Tel.: (49) 34739610
Web Site: http://www.senioren-wohnpark-aschersleben.de
Nursing Care & Rehabilitation Services
N.A.I.C.S.: 623110

Senioren Wohnpark Bad Langensalza GmbH, (1)
Gutenbergstr 35 D, Bad Langensalza, 99974, Germany
Tel.: (49) 3603 821 0
Nursing Care & Rehabilitation Services
N.A.I.C.S.: 623110
Simona Scholce *(Mng Dir)*

Senioren Wohnpark Coswig GmbH (1)
Berliner Str 36, 06869, Coswig, Germany
Tel.: (49) 34903450
Web Site: http://www.senioren-wohnpark-coswig.de
Nursing Care & Rehabilitation Services
N.A.I.C.S.: 623110

Senioren Wohnpark Klausa GmbH (1)
Am Leinawald 47 48, 04 603, Nobitz, Thuringia, Germany
Tel.: (49) 34494780
Nursing Care & Rehabilitation Services
N.A.I.C.S.: 623110

Senioren Wohnpark Langen GmbH (1)
Sportallee 1, 22335, Langen, Germany
Tel.: (49) 4051459555
Web Site: http://www.senioren-wohnpark.com
Nursing Care & Rehabilitation Services
N.A.I.C.S.: 623110

Senioren Wohnpark Meerbusch GmbH (1)
Helen-Keller-Str 7, 40670, Meerbusch, Germany
Tel.: (49) 8004747202
Nursing Care & Rehabilitation Services
N.A.I.C.S.: 623110

Senioren Wohnpark Neuruppin GmbH (1)
Artur-Becker-Str 31, 16816, Neuruppin, Germany
Tel.: (49) 800 47 47 202
Nursing Care & Rehabilitation Services
N.A.I.C.S.: 623110

Senioren Wohnpark Stutzerbach GmbH (1)
Auerhahnstr 11 D, 98 714, Stutzerbach, Germany
Tel.: (49) 36784550
Emp.: 55
Nursing Care & Rehabilitation Services
N.A.I.C.S.: 623110

Senioren Wohnpark Tangerhutte GmbH (1)
Heinrich Rieke-Ring 8, 39517, Tangerhutte, Germany
Tel.: (49) 800 47 47 202
Nursing Care & Rehabilitation Services
N.A.I.C.S.: 623110

Senioren Wohnpark Thale GmbH (1)
4 Goetheweg, 06502, Thale, Germany
Tel.: (49) 800 47 47 202
Nursing Care & Rehabilitation Services
N.A.I.C.S.: 623110

Senioren Wohnpark Treuenbrietzen GmbH (1)
Berliner Chaussee 43, 14929, Treuenbrietzen, Germany
Tel.: (49) 4051459555
Web Site: http://www.senioren-wohnpark.com
Nursing Care & Rehabilitation Services
N.A.I.C.S.: 623110

Senioren Wohnpark Wolmirstedt GmbH, (1)
Julius-Bremer-Str 8, 39326, Wolmirstedt, Germany
Tel.: (49) 8004747202
Nursing Care & Rehabilitation Services
N.A.I.C.S.: 623110

Senioren-Wohnpark Arnsberg GmbH (1)
Klosterstr 15, 59821, Arnsberg, Germany
Tel.: (49) 8004747202
Nursing Care & Rehabilitation Services
N.A.I.C.S.: 623110

Senioren-Wohnpark Cottbus SWP GmbH (1)
Peitzer Str 26a, 03 042, Cottbus, Germany
Tel.: (49) 3557536599
Web Site: http://www.senioren-wohnpark-cottbus-swp.de
Nursing Care & Rehabilitation Services
N.A.I.C.S.: 623110
Monika Schommel *(Mgr)*

Senioren-Wohnpark Dusseldorf Volksgarten GmbH (1)
Industriestrape 9, 40227, Dusseldorf, Germany
Tel.: (49) 4051459555
Web Site: http://www.senioren-wohnpark.com
Nursing Care & Rehabilitation Services
N.A.I.C.S.: 623110

Senioren-Wohnpark Erkner GmbH (1)
Gerhart-Hauptmann-Str 12, 15537, Erkner, Germany
Tel.: (49) 800 47 47 202
Nursing Care & Rehabilitation Services
N.A.I.C.S.: 623110

Senioren-Wohnpark Friedland GmbH (1)
Riemannstrasse 104, Friedland, 17098, Brandenburg, Germany
Tel.: (49) 800 47 47 202
Nursing Care & Rehabilitation Services
N.A.I.C.S.: 623110

Senioren-Wohnpark Friedland SWP GmbH (1)
Riemannstrabe 104, Friedland, 17098, Gottingen, Germany
Tel.: (49) 8004747202
Nursing Care & Rehabilitation Services

MK-KLINIKEN AG

MK-Kliniken AG—(Continued)
N.A.I.C.S.: 623110

Senioren-Wohnpark Hennigsdorf GmbH (1)
Friedrich-Wolf-Strasse 11, 16761, Hennigsdorf Berlin, Germany
Tel.: (49) 3302870880
Web Site: http://www.senioren-wohnpark-hennigsdorf.de
Nursing Care & Rehabilitation Services
N.A.I.C.S.: 623110
Volker Feldkamp (Mng Dir)

Senioren-Wohnpark Klotze GmbH (1)
Schutzenstr 25, 38486, Klotze, Germany
Tel.: (49) 8004747202
Web Site: http://www.senioren-wohnpark.com
Nursing Care & Rehabilitation Services
N.A.I.C.S.: 623110

Senioren-Wohnpark Kreuztal Krombach GmbH (1)
Big Book 10, Kreuztal - Krombach, 57223, Kreuztal, Germany
Tel.: (49) 8004747202
Web Site: http://www.senioren-wohnpark.com
Nursing Care & Rehabilitation Services
N.A.I.C.S.: 623110

Senioren-Wohnpark Landshut GmbH (1)
Professor Mueller-Schmidt-Strabe 1, 84034, Landshut, Germany
Tel.: (49) 87114370
Sales Range: $10-24.9 Million
Emp.: 80
Nursing Care & Rehabilitation Services
N.A.I.C.S.: 623110

Senioren-Wohnpark Leipzig Am Kirschberg GmbH, (1)
Karlsruher St 31, 04209, Leipzig, Germany
Tel.: (49) 341426590
Nursing Care & Rehabilitation Services
N.A.I.C.S.: 623110

Senioren-Wohnpark Leipzig Eutritzscher Markt GmbH, (1)
Grafe St 1, 04129, Leipzig, Germany
Tel.: (49) 8004747202
Nursing Care & Rehabilitation Services
N.A.I.C.S.: 623110

Senioren-Wohnpark Leipzig Stadtpalais GmbH, (1)
Sebastian-Bach-St 51, 04109, Leipzig, many
Tel.: (49) 34114910
Web Site: http://www.marseille-kliniken.com
Nursing Care & Rehabilitation Services
N.A.I.C.S.: 623110

Senioren-Wohnpark Lemwerder GmbH (1)
Wiesenstr 1b, Lemwerder, 27809, Langen, Germany
Tel.: (49) 800 4 74 72 02
Web Site: http://www.senioren-wohnpark-lemwerder.de
Nursing Care & Rehabilitation Services
N.A.I.C.S.: 623110
Maximilian Kramer (Deputy Mgr-Facility)

Senioren-Wohnpark Lessingplatz GmbH (1)
Industriestrasse 7, 40227, Dusseldorf, Germany
Tel.: (49) 800 47 47 202
Nursing & Rehabilitation Services
N.A.I.C.S.: 623110

Senioren-Wohnpark Lichtenberg GmbH (1)
Mollendorffstr 102/103, D 10367, Berlin, Germany
Tel.: (49) 800 4747202
Web Site: http://www.senioren-wohnpark.com
Nursing Care & Rehabilitation Services
N.A.I.C.S.: 623110
Helvi Morgenstem (Exec Dir)

Senioren-Wohnpark Montabaur GmbH (1)
Joseph Kehrein-Str 1, 56410, Montabaur, Germany
Tel.: (49) 800 47 47 202
Nursing Care & Rehabilitation Services
N.A.I.C.S.: 623110

Senioren-Wohnpark Neuruppin SWP GmbH (1)
Artur-Becker-St 31, Neuruppin, 16816, Brandenburg, Germany
Tel.: (49) 33915180
Nursing Care & Rehabilitation Services
N.A.I.C.S.: 623110

Senioren-Wohnpark Radensleben GmbH (1)
Dorfstr 97, 16818, Radensleben, Germany
Tel.: (49) 3 39 25 8 49 99
Web Site: http://www.senioren-wohnpark-radensleben.de
Nursing Care & Rehabilitation Services
N.A.I.C.S.: 623110

Senioren-Wohnpark soziale Altenbetreuung GmbH (1)
Peitz Str 26, 03042, Cottbus, Germany
Tel.: (49) 355756450
Nursing Care & Rehabilitation Services
N.A.I.C.S.: 623110

Spezial-Pflegeheim Hennigsdorf GmbH (1)
Fontanesiedlung 17, 16761, Hennigsdorf Berlin, Germany
Tel.: (49) 8004747203
Web Site: http://www.spezial-pflegeheim-hennigsdorf.de
Nursing Care & Rehabilitation Services
N.A.I.C.S.: 623110

Sport und Rehabilitationszentrum Harz GmbH (1)
Michael Stein 18, 38889, Blankenburg, Germany
Tel.: (49) 3944944106
Web Site: http://www.sport-rehabilitationszentrum.com
Nursing Care & Rehabilitation Services
N.A.I.C.S.: 623110

TURK BAKIM EVI Pflegeeinrichtung Berlin Kreuzberg GmbH, (1)
Methfessel 43, 10965, Berlin, Germany
Tel.: (49) 800 47 47 207
Nursing Care & Rehabilitation Services
N.A.I.C.S.: 623110

Teufelsbad Fachklinik Blankenburg GmbH (1)
Michael Stein 18, 38889, Blankenburg, Germany
Tel.: (49) 39449440
Web Site: https://www.celenus-kliniken.de
Nursing Care & Rehabilitation Services
N.A.I.C.S.: 623110

Teufelsbad Residenz Blankenburg GmbH (1)
Michael Stein 18, 38889, Blankenburg, Germany
Tel.: (49) 39449440
Nursing Care & Rehabilitation Services
N.A.I.C.S.: 623110

Villa Auenwald Seniorenheim GmbH (1)
Barnecker St 3, 04178, Leipzig, Germany
Tel.: (49) 34144760
Sales Range: $10-24.9 Million
Emp.: 78
Nursing Care & Rehabilitation Services
N.A.I.C.S.: 623110

MKANGO RESOURCES LTD.

550 Burrard Street Suite 2900, Vancouver, V6C 0A3, BC, Canada
Tel.: (403) 444-5979   AB
Web Site: https://www.mkango.ca
Year Founded: 2007
MKA—(AIM)
Assets: $7,015,065
Liabilities: $5,097,060
Net Worth: $1,918,005
Earnings: ($3,156,402)
Fiscal Year-end: 12/31/23
Mineral Exploration Services
N.A.I.C.S.: 213114

Derek Linfield (Chm)

Subsidiaries:

HyProMag GmbH (1)
Tiefenbronnerstrasse 59, 75175, Pforzheim, Germany
Tel.: (49) 7231286498
Web Site: https://hypromag.de
Magnet Component Recycling Services
N.A.I.C.S.: 562920

MKH BERHAD

5th Floor Wisma MKH Jalan Semenyih, 43000, Kajang, Selangor Darul Ehsan, Malaysia
Tel.: (60) 387378228
Web Site:
https://www.mkhberhad.com
MKH—(KLS)
Rev.: $225,701,621
Assets: $830,321,975
Liabilities: $403,527,850
Net Worth: $426,794,125
Earnings: $16,401,026
Emp.: 4,300
Fiscal Year-end: 09/30/20
Property Development & Management Services
N.A.I.C.S.: 531312
Fook Wah Chen (Deputy Mng Dir)

Subsidiaries:

AA Meat Shop Sdn. Bhd. (1)
No 22 Jalan Hujan Rahmat Taman Overseas Union, Kuala Lumpur, 58200, Malaysia
Tel.: (60) 3 7783 1800
Sales Range: $25-49.9 Million
Emp.: 40
Meat Products Retailer
N.A.I.C.S.: 445240

Aliran Perkasa Sdn. Bhd. (1)
G 03 Ground Floor Wisma Metro Kajang Jalan Semenyih, 43000, Kajang, Selangor, Malaysia
Tel.: (60) 387372323
Web Site: http://www.mkhberhad.com
Sales Range: $75-99.9 Million
Emp.: 250
Property Development Services
N.A.I.C.S.: 531390
Alyz Yeap (Mgr)

Dapat Jaya Builder Sdn. Bhd. (1)
Suite 1 5th Floor Wisma MKH Metro Kajang Jalan Semenyih, 43000, Kajang, Selangor, Malaysia
Tel.: (60) 387378228
Web Site: http://www.mkhberhad.com
Sales Range: $150-199.9 Million
Emp.: 300
Property Development Services
N.A.I.C.S.: 531390

Global Retreat (MM2H) Sdn. Bhd. (1)
Suite 4 07 4th Floor Wisma MKH Jalan Semenyih, 43000, Kajang, Selangor, Malaysia
Tel.: (60) 387378228
Sales Range: $75-99.9 Million
Emp.: 300
Tourism Services
N.A.I.C.S.: 561520
Chong Yun Han (Mgr)

Kajang Resources Corporation Sdn. Bhd. (1)
5th Fl Wisma Metro Kajang Jalan Semenyih, 43000, Kajang, Selangor, Malaysia
Tel.: (60) 387233272
Residential Property Development Services
N.A.I.C.S.: 236116

MKH Building Materials Sdn. Bhd. (1)
4th Floor Wisma MKH Jalan Semenyih, 43000, Kajang, Selangor Darul Ehsan, Malaysia
Tel.: (60) 387378228
Building Materials Distr
N.A.I.C.S.: 423220

Maha Usaha Sdn. Bhd. (1)
3rd Floor Seksyen 7 Jalan Tun Abdul Aziz,

43000, Kajang, Selangor, Malaysia
Tel.: (60) 387337333
Business Management Services
N.A.I.C.S.: 561499
K. K. Ng (Mgr)

Metro Kajang Construction Sdn. Bhd. (1)
Tkt 5 Wisma Metro Kajang Jalan Semenyih, Kajang, 43000, Selangor, Malaysia
Tel.: (60) 387378228
Sales Range: $50-74.9 Million
Emp.: 150
Residential Building Construction Services
N.A.I.C.S.: 236116
Eddie Chen (Mng Dir)

Pelangi Semenyih Sdn. Bhd. (1)
Taman Pelangi 1 No 5&7, 43500, Semenyih, Selangor, Malaysia
Tel.: (60) 387247668
Web Site: http://www.mkh.com
Real Estate Property Development Services
N.A.I.C.S.: 531390

Srijang Indah Sdn. Bhd. (1)
F18 First Floor Metro Point Complex Jalan Jelok 8, 43000, Kajang, Selangor, Malaysia
Tel.: (60) 387373759
Web Site:
http://www.metropointcomplex.com
Sales Range: $50-74.9 Million
Emp.: 20
Property Development & Management Services
N.A.I.C.S.: 531390

Srijang Kemajuan Sdn. Bhd. (1)
5th Floor Wisma Metro Kajang Jalan Semenyih, Kajang, 43000, Selangor, Malaysia
Tel.: (60) 387378228
Web Site: http://www.mkhberhad.com
Sales Range: $100-124.9 Million
Emp.: 300
Residential Property Development Services
N.A.I.C.S.: 236116

Tip Top Meat Sdn. Bhd. (1)
Lot PT 17840 Off Jalan Rawang Batang Berjuntal Mukim Serendah, 48000, Rawang, Selangor, Malaysia
Tel.: (60) 361041031
Livestock Breeding Services
N.A.I.C.S.: 115210

Vast Furniture Manufacturing (Kunshan) Co. Ltd. (1)
No 588 Airport Road, Shipu Qiandeng Town, Kunshan, 215343, Jiangsu, China
Tel.: (86) 51257405975
Web Site: http://www.vastcn.com
Sales Range: $50-74.9 Million
Emp.: 116
Household Furniture Mfr
N.A.I.C.S.: 337121

MKP MOBILITY LIMITED

Bangalore Roadchallekere Challekere, PO Box 9, Challakere, 577 522, Karnataka, India
Tel.: (91) 8195222258
Web Site:
https://www.chitraspinltd.com
Year Founded: 1990
521244—(BOM)
Assets: $145,461
Liabilities: $1,883
Net Worth: $143,578
Earnings: ($10,584)
Fiscal Year-end: 03/31/21
Business Support Services
N.A.I.C.S.: 561499
S. Vishwanath (Mng Dir)

MKSYSTEM CORPORATION

2-4-12 Nakazakinishi Kita-ku, Osaka, 530-0015, Japan
Web Site: http://www.mks.jp
3910—(TKS)
Rev.: $17,443,790
Assets: $16,908,380
Liabilities: $11,514,620
Net Worth: $5,393,760
Earnings: ($4,415,480)
Emp.: 118

AND PRIVATE COMPANIES

Fiscal Year-end: 03/31/24
Insurance Services
N.A.I.C.S.: 524114

MKT PRINT D.D.
Dunajska 123, 1113, Ljubljana, Slovenia
Tel.: (386) 15608200
Web Site: http://www.mkt-print.com
Sales Range: $25-49.9 Million
Emp.: 300
Printing, Bookbinding & Text Preparation Services
N.A.I.C.S.: 323111
Jure Sumi *(CEO)*

Subsidiaries:

Euroadria d.o.o. (1)
Dunajska 123, 1113, Ljubljana, Slovenia
Tel.: (386) 1 560 82 00
Sales Range: $50-74.9 Million
Emp.: 240
Printing Services
N.A.I.C.S.: 323120

MKT PRINT Netherlands b.v. (1)
Weerterbeekweg 8, 6001, Weert, Netherlands
Tel.: (31) 495 45 00 06
Printing Services
N.A.I.C.S.: 323120

MKVENTURES CAPITAL LIMITED
Express Towers Ramnath Goenka Marg Nariman Point, Mumbai, 400021, Maharashtra, India
Tel.: (91) 2262673701
Web Site: https://mkventurescapital.com
Year Founded: 1991
514238—(BOM)
Rev.: $1,872,667
Assets: $2,115,795
Liabilities: $3,063
Net Worth: $2,112,732
Earnings: $623,168
Emp.: 1
Fiscal Year-end: 03/31/22
Securities Dealing Services
N.A.I.C.S.: 523150
Ankita Phophaliya *(Officer-Compliance & Sec)*

ML DYEING LTD.
House 11 Floor 6-A Road 12 Block F Niketon Gulshan-1, Dhaka, Bangladesh
Tel.: (880) 248810050
Web Site: https://www.mldyeing.com
Year Founded: 2001
MLDYEING—(DHA)
Rev.: $1,410,703
Assets: $44,641,250
Liabilities: $3,720,437
Net Worth: $40,920,812
Earnings: $1,161,261
Fiscal Year-end: 06/30/22
Sweater & Knit Yarn Mfr
N.A.I.C.S.: 313110
Golam Azam Chowdhury *(Mng Dir)*

ML SYSTEM SA
Zaczernie 190 G, Zaczernie, 36-062, Rzeszow, Poland
Tel.: (48) 177788266
Web Site: https://www.mlsystem.pl
MLS—(WAR)
Rev.: $49,101,880
Assets: $147,021,341
Liabilities: $96,739,329
Net Worth: $50,282,012
Earnings: ($1,179,624)
Fiscal Year-end: 12/31/23
Solar Energy Equipment Mfr & Distr
N.A.I.C.S.: 335999
Dawid Cycon *(Pres)*

MLABS SYSTEMS BERHAD
Lot 4 1 4th Floor Menara Lien Hoe No 8 Persiaran, Tropicana Golf and Country Resort, 47410, Petaling Jaya, Selangor Darul Ehsan, Malaysia
Tel.: (60) 378872896   MY
Web Site: https://www.mlabs.com
Year Founded: 1997
MLAB—(KLS)
Rev.: $4,760,458
Assets: $28,632,487
Liabilities: $1,562,748
Net Worth: $27,069,739
Earnings: ($1,860,981)
Emp.: 82
Fiscal Year-end: 06/30/23
Software Development Services
N.A.I.C.S.: 541511
Tee Kein Ong *(Exec Dir)*

Subsidiaries:

Ikhlas Al Dain Sdn. Bhd. (1)
Unit 4 1 Level 4 Menara Lien Hoe Persiaran Tropicana, Tropicana Golf and Country Resort, 47410, Petaling Jaya, Selangor, Malaysia
Tel.: (60) 376881014
Web Site: https://www.ikhlasaldain.com
Financial Services
N.A.I.C.S.: 523999

MLADINSKA KNJIGA ZALOZBA, D.D.
Slovenska cesta 29, 1000, Ljubljana, Slovenia
Tel.: (386) 12413000
Web Site: http://www.mladinska.com
Year Founded: 1945
Sales Range: $75-99.9 Million
Emp.: 900
Books, Audio Tapes, CD-ROMs & Magazines Publisher
N.A.I.C.S.: 513130
Andrej Gogala *(Mgr-Buying Rights)*

Subsidiaries:

Cankarjeva Zalozba - Zaloznistvo d.o.o. (1)
Slovenska cesta 29, Ljubljana, 1000, Slovenia
Tel.: (386) 1 241 32 50
Web Site: http://www.mladinska.com
Sales Range: $25-49.9 Million
Book Publishers
N.A.I.C.S.: 513130
Peter Tomsic *(Gen Mgr)*

Mladinska Knjiga Beograd (1)
Omladinskih brigada 102, 11070, Belgrade, Serbia
Tel.: (381) 11 225 70 00
Web Site: http://www.mladinska.rs
Book Publishers
N.A.I.C.S.: 513130

Mladinska Knjiga Sarajevo (1)
Muhameda Kantardzica 3, Sarajevo, 71000, Bosnia & Herzegovina
Tel.: (387) 33 957 600
Web Site: http://www.ladinska.ba
Sales Range: $25-49.9 Million
Emp.: 30
Book Publishers
N.A.I.C.S.: 513130
Adnan Catovic *(Mng Dir)*

Mladinska Knjiga Skopje (1)
Ul Ljubljanska Br 5, 1000, Skopje, North Macedonia
Tel.: (389) 2 30 72 544
Web Site: http://www.mkskopje.com
Book Publishers
N.A.I.C.S.: 513130

Mladinska Knjiga Trgovina, d.o.o. (1)
Brnciceva ul 41e, Ljubljana, 1000, Slovenia
Tel.: (386) 1 560 54 00
Book & Stationery Retailer
N.A.I.C.S.: 459210

Mozaik Knjiga Zagreb (1)
Karlovacka cesta 24 A, Zagreb, 10000, Croatia
Tel.: (385) 1 631 51 24
Web Site: http://www.mozaik-knjiga.hr
Sales Range: $25-49.9 Million
Emp.: 100
Book Publishers
N.A.I.C.S.: 513130
Vidmar Bojan *(Gen Mgr)*

MLADOST A.D.
Omladinska 106, 37230, Aleksandrovac, Serbia
Tel.: (381) 37751195
Year Founded: 2002
MLAL—(BEL)
Rev.: $1,175,546
Assets: $438,386
Liabilities: $147,317
Net Worth: $291,069
Earnings: $10,570
Emp.: 84
Fiscal Year-end: 12/31/23
Building Construction Services
N.A.I.C.S.: 236220
Miljko Miljkovic *(Dir)*

MLADOST A.D.
Nikole Pasica 10, Pozega, Serbia
Tel.: (381) 31713265
Year Founded: 1996
MLDP—(BEL)
Sales Range: Less than $1 Million
Emp.: 7
Innerwear Mfr
N.A.I.C.S.: 315250
Milos Milovic *(CEO)*

MLAVA A.D.
Cara Dusana 27, Zagubica, Serbia
Tel.: (381) 12 443 125
Year Founded: 2003
Sales Range: Less than $1 Million
Emp.: 7
Fish Farming Services
N.A.I.C.S.: 112511

MLD SA
9 Rue Anatole de la forge, FR-75017, Paris, France
Tel.: (33) 1 34 08 27 46
Web Site: http://www.arthurmaury.fr
MLAMY—(EUR)
Sales Range: Less than $1 Million
Numismatics & Stamp Collecting Services
N.A.I.C.S.: 459999
Idalina Pereira *(Chm & CEO)*

MLEKARA LOZNICA A.D.
Ulica Prvog Maja bb, Loznica, 15300, Serbia
Tel.: (381) 15 871 824
Web Site: http://www.mlekaraadloznica.com
Year Founded: 1980
Sales Range: $1-9.9 Million
Emp.: 85
Dairy Products Mfr
N.A.I.C.S.: 112120

MLEKARA PLANA A.D.
28 Oktobra br 1, Velika Plana, 11320, Serbia
Tel.: (381) 26 521 121
Web Site: http://www.mlekaraplana.co.rs
Year Founded: 1949
Sales Range: $1-9.9 Million
Emp.: 62
Dairy Products Mfr
N.A.I.C.S.: 311513

MLG OZ LIMITED
10 Yindi Way, PO Box 1484, Kalgoorlie, 6433, WA, Australia
Tel.: (61) 890211011   AU

MLO MARITIME LOGISTICS UND OPERATIONS GMBH

Web Site: https://www.mlgoz.com.au
Year Founded: 2001
MLG—(ASX)
Rev.: $250,273,578
Assets: $160,496,671
Liabilities: $83,481,639
Net Worth: $77,015,032
Earnings: $527,916
Emp.: 874
Fiscal Year-end: 06/30/23
Metal Mining Services
N.A.I.C.S.: 213114
Murray Leahy *(Mng Dir)*

MLIN A.D.
Ekstravilan bb, Bela Crkva, Serbia
Tel.: (381) 13 851 232
Year Founded: 1929
Sales Range: Less than $1 Million
Emp.: 20
Food Products Mfr
N.A.I.C.S.: 311212

MLIN I PEKARA D.D.
Ljubace bb, 75 214, Tuzla, Bosnia & Herzegovina
Tel.: (387) 35808540
Web Site: http://www.mpljubace.ba
Year Founded: 1950
MLHRRK3—(SARE)
Rev.: $5,791,702
Assets: $14,934,035
Liabilities: $2,965,060
Net Worth: $11,968,974
Earnings: ($566,006)
Emp.: 128
Fiscal Year-end: 12/31/20
Bakery Product Distr
N.A.I.C.S.: 424940
Ibric Samir *(Pres)*

MLINOVI A.D.
Zeleznicka bb, Curug, Serbia
Tel.: (381) 21 833 015
Year Founded: 2001
MLIN—(BEL)
Sales Range: $1-9.9 Million
Emp.: 71
Food Products Mfr
N.A.I.C.S.: 311212
Dragan Kovacevic *(Exec Dir)*

MLINPEK D.D. BUGOJNO
Gornjevakufska 35, 70230, Bugojno, Bosnia & Herzegovina
Tel.: (387) 3 025 2002
Web Site: http://www.mlinpek.net
MLPBR—(SARE)
Rev.: $7,544,838
Assets: $8,995,424
Liabilities: $1,025,091
Net Worth: $7,970,334
Earnings: $775,308
Emp.: 51
Fiscal Year-end: 12/31/20
Grain Mill Product Mfr
N.A.I.C.S.: 333519

MLINPEK-ZITAR D.D.
Bravnice bb, 70101, Jajce, Bosnia & Herzegovina
Tel.: (387) 3 065 7983
MZTJR—(SARE)
Rev.: $5,239,472
Assets: $6,186,058
Liabilities: $508,439
Net Worth: $5,677,619
Earnings: $520,438
Emp.: 73
Fiscal Year-end: 12/31/20
Bakery Products Mfr
N.A.I.C.S.: 311919

MLO MARITIME LOGISTICS UND OPERATIONS GMBH
Schlachte 41, 28195, Bremen, Germany

MLO MARITIME LOGISTICS UND OPERATIONS GMBH

MLO Maritime Logistics und Operations GmbH—(Continued)
Tel.: (49) 421165700
Web Site: http://www.mlo.de
Year Founded: 1996
Rev.: $28,967,400
Emp.: 8
Road & Water Transportation Services
N.A.I.C.S.: 488490
Andreas Harder *(Mng Dir)*

MLP GROUP S.A.
Ul 3 Maja 8, 05-800, Pruszkow, Poland
Tel.: (48) 227383010
Web Site: https://www.mlp.pl
MLG—(WAR)
Rev.: $51,035,061
Assets: $1,293,096,541
Liabilities: $684,451,218
Net Worth: $608,645,324
Earnings: ($13,226,118)
Emp.: 50
Fiscal Year-end: 12/31/23
Industrial Building Construction
N.A.I.C.S.: 236210
Michael Shapiro *(Vice Chm-Mgmt Bd)*

Subsidiaries:

MLP Business Park Poznan Sp. z o.o. (1)
Wolczynska 18, Poznan, Poland
Tel.: (48) 227383010
Real Estate Services
N.A.I.C.S.: 531390

MLP SAGLIK HIZMETLERI AS
Otakcilar Cd Flatofis Istanbul No 78 Kat 3 D Blok No 103, Eyup, 34050, Istanbul, Turkiye
Tel.: (90) 2122275555
MPARK—(IST)
Rev.: $303,839,273
Assets: $260,559,960
Liabilities: $204,746,305
Net Worth: $55,813,655
Earnings: $500,160,615
Fiscal Year-end: 12/31/22
Health Care Srvices
N.A.I.C.S.: 621498
Deniz Can Yuçel *(Dir-Strategy & Investor Relations)*

MLP SE
Alte Heerstrasse 40, D-69168, Wiesloch, Germany
Tel.: (49) 62223080   De
Web Site: https://www.mlp.de
MLP—(DUS)
Rev.: $1,038,874,134
Assets: $4,324,366,570
Liabilities: $3,729,899,459
Net Worth: $594,467,111
Earnings: $53,626,005
Emp.: 2,338
Fiscal Year-end: 12/31/23
Various Financial Services
N.A.I.C.S.: 522299
Uwe Schroeder-Wildberg *(Chm-Exec Bd & CEO)*

Subsidiaries:

DI Deutschland.Immobilien AG (1)
Georgstr 44, 30159, Hannover, Germany
Tel.: (49) 5119209240
Web Site: https://www.deutschland.immobilien
Real Estate Manangement Services
N.A.I.C.S.: 531210

DOMCURA Aktiengesellschaft (1)
Theodor-Heuss-Ring 49, 24113, Kiel, Germany
Tel.: (49) 431546540
Web Site: https://www.domcura.de
Financial Services
N.A.I.C.S.: 523999

Dr. Schmitt GmbH (1)
Versicherungsmakler Dieselstrasse 2-8, 97082, Wurzburg, Germany
Tel.: (49) 931450750
Web Site: https://www.dsv-wzbg.de
Insurance Brokerage Services
N.A.I.C.S.: 524210

FERI Trust (Luxembourg) S.A. (1)
18 Boulevard de la Foire, 1528, Luxembourg, Luxembourg
Tel.: (352) 2704480
Web Site: https://www.feri.lu
Emp.: 250
Financial Services
N.A.I.C.S.: 522320

Jahn & Sengstack GmbH (1)
Glockengiesserwall 2, 20095, Hamburg, Germany
Tel.: (49) 403038780
Web Site: https://jahn-sengstack.de
Insurance Services
N.A.I.C.S.: 523999

MLP Banking AG (1)
Alte Heerstrasse 40, D-69168, Wiesloch, Germany
Tel.: (49) 622231690
Banking & Financial Services
N.A.I.C.S.: 541611

MLP Finanzberatung SE (1)
Alte Heerstrasse 40, D-69168, Wiesloch, Germany
Tel.: (49) 62223080
Web Site: https://www.mlp.de
Banking & Financial Services
N.A.I.C.S.: 541611

NORDVERS GmbH (1)
Theodor-Heuss-Ring 49, 24113, Kiel, Germany
Tel.: (49) 43154654510
Web Site: https://www.nordvers.de
Insurance Services
N.A.I.C.S.: 524210

RISConsult GmbH (1)
Arbachtalstrasse 22, 72800, Eningen, Germany
Tel.: (49) 71219230
Web Site: https://www.risconsult.de
Risk Managemeng Srvices
N.A.I.C.S.: 541611

RVM Versicherungsmakler GmbH (1)
Arbachtalstrasse 22, 72800, Eningen, Germany
Tel.: (49) 71219230
Web Site: https://www.rvm.de
Emp.: 230
Insurance Services
N.A.I.C.S.: 524210

TPC THE PENSION CONSULTANCY GmbH (1)
Speicherstadt, Alter Wandrahm 10, 20457, Hamburg, Germany
Tel.: (49) 403287090
Web Site: http://www.tpc-pension.com
Pension & Operational Provisions Consultant
N.A.I.C.S.: 524292
Joerg Huesing *(Mng Dir)*

Vertrieb Deutschland.Immobilien GmbH (1)
Georgstr 44, 30159, Hannover, Germany
Tel.: (49) 5119209240
Web Site: https://www.deutschland.immobilien
Real Estate Manangement Services
N.A.I.C.S.: 531390

ZSH GmbH (1)
Langer Anger 3-5, 69115, Heidelberg, Germany
Tel.: (49) 62218370
Web Site: https://www.zsh.de
Financial Services
N.A.I.C.S.: 523999

MLS CO., LTD.
No 1 Mulinsen Avenue, Xiaolan Town, Zhongshan, 528415, Guangdong, China
Tel.: (86) 76089828888

Web Site: https://www.mlsledlights.com
Year Founded: 1997
002745—(SSE)
Rev.: $2,851,944,398
Assets: $4,408,294,477
Liabilities: $2,370,114,269
Net Worth: $2,038,180,208
Earnings: $177,568,858
Emp.: 12,600
Fiscal Year-end: 12/31/21
LED Lighting Diodes Mfr
N.A.I.C.S.: 334419
Sun Qinghuan *(Chm & Gen Mgr)*

MLS INNOVATION INC.
Vepe Texnopoli, 55535, Pylaia, Greece
Tel.: (30) 2310929090
Web Site: http://www.mls.gr
Year Founded: 1995
MLS—(ATH)
Sales Range: $10-24.9 Million
Emp.: 157
Interactive Media Product Mfr
N.A.I.C.S.: 334210
John N. Kamatakis *(Chm & CEO)*

MLT AIKINS LLP
1500 Hill Center I 1874 Scarth Street, Regina, S4P 4E9, SK, Canada
Tel.: (306) 347-8000   Ca
Web Site: http://www.mltaikins.com
Year Founded: 1920
Emp.: 240
Law firm
N.A.I.C.S.: 541110
Milad Alishahi *(Partner)*

MM CONFERENCES
ul Stawki 2, 00-193, Warsaw, Poland
Tel.: (48) 223792900
Web Site: https://mmcpolska.com
Year Founded: 2008
Asset Management Services
N.A.I.C.S.: 523940
Piotr Zesiuk *(CEO)*

MM FORGINGS LIMITED
A24/25 SVK Towers 8th Floor Guindy Industrial Estate, Chennai, 600 032, Tamilnadu, India
Tel.: (91) 4471601000
Web Site: https://www.mmforgings.com
Year Founded: 1946
522241—(BOM)
Rev.: $176,718,686
Assets: $199,043,259
Liabilities: $118,308,782
Net Worth: $80,734,476
Earnings: $15,339,440
Emp.: 1,941
Fiscal Year-end: 03/31/23
Automobile Parts Mfr
N.A.I.C.S.: 336110
N. Srinivasan *(Chm)*

Subsidiaries:

DVS Industries Private Limited (1)
Plot No 49 Sec-24, Faridabad, 121005, India
Tel.: (91) 1294323505
Web Site: http://www.dvsindustries.co.in
Industrial Alloy Mfr
N.A.I.C.S.: 331110

MM GROUP INDUSTRIAL & INTERNATIONAL TRADE
18 El-Obour Buildings Salah Salem Street, Cairo, Egypt
Tel.: (20) 224010040
Web Site: https://www.mti-mmgroup.com
Year Founded: 1996
MTIE.CA—(EGX)
Rev.: $218,429,254

INTERNATIONAL PUBLIC

Assets: $93,779,624
Liabilities: $31,034,567
Net Worth: $62,745,057
Earnings: $14,748,019
Emp.: 1,800
Fiscal Year-end: 12/31/23
Consumer Electronics Distr
N.A.I.C.S.: 423620
Gamal Mahmoud *(Founder)*

MM RUBBER COMPANY LIMITED
Empire Infantry 3rd Floor 29 Infantry Road, Bengaluru, 560 001, Karnataka, India
Tel.: (91) 7669568709
Web Site: https://mmfoam.com
Year Founded: 1957
509196—(BOM)
Rev.: $3,814,941
Assets: $2,778,226
Liabilities: $1,198,041
Net Worth: $1,580,185
Earnings: ($511,711)
Fiscal Year-end: 03/31/21
Latex Foam Rubber Mfr
N.A.I.C.S.: 326299
Roy Mammen *(Mng Dir)*

MM2 ASIA LTD.
1002 Jalan Bukit Merah 07-08, Singapore, 159456, Singapore
Tel.: (65) 63760177
Web Site: https://www.mm2asia.com
1B0—(SES)
Rev.: $99,507,225
Assets: $318,000,000
Liabilities: $250,118,562
Net Worth: $67,881,438
Earnings: ($17,349,389)
Emp.: 290
Fiscal Year-end: 03/31/23
Movies, TV & Online Content Producer & Distr
N.A.I.C.S.: 512110

Subsidiaries:

AsiaOne Online Pte. Ltd. (1)
1002 Jalan Bukit Merah 04-17, Singapore, 159456, Singapore
Tel.: (65) 66943842
Web Site: http://www.asiaone.com
News Agency Services
N.A.I.C.S.: 516210

UnUsUaL Limited (1)
45 Kallang Pudding Road 01-01 Alpha Building, Singapore, 349317, Singapore
Tel.: (65) 68414555
Web Site: https://www.unusual.com.sg
Rev.: $55,152,622
Assets: $45,976,272
Liabilities: $8,636,869
Net Worth: $37,339,403
Earnings: $5,733,634
Fiscal Year-end: 03/31/2024
Event Management Services
N.A.I.C.S.: 711310
Leslie Chin Soon Ong *(CEO & Exec Dir)*

Subsidiary (Non-US):

UnUsUaL Productions (M) Sdn. Bhd. (2)
Lot 834-A01 Ground Floor Office Jalan Kusta, Kawasan Industri Kampung Jaya, 47000, Sungai Buloh, Selangor, Malaysia
Tel.: (60) 361505554
Sound & Lighting Equipment Rental Services
N.A.I.C.S.: 532490

mm2 Entertainment Hong Kong Limited (1)
Workshop No 2 1 Floor International Plaza No 20 Sheung Yuet Rd, Kowloon Bay, China (Hong Kong)
Tel.: (852) 23513981
Film Production Services
N.A.I.C.S.: 512110

mm2 Entertainment Sdn. Bhd. (1)

AND PRIVATE COMPANIES / MML CAPITAL PARTNERS LLP

B 06 03 Menara Bata PJ Trade Centre No 8 Jalan PJU 8/8A, Bandar Damansara Perdana, 47820, Petaling Jaya, Selangor, Malaysia
Tel.: (60) 377278388
Film Production Services
N.A.I.C.S.: 512110

mm2 Entertainment USA, Inc. (1)
12 E 49th St 11th Fl, New York, NY 10017
Tel.: (917) 951-7770
Film Production Services
N.A.I.C.S.: 512110
Claudia Pak *(Dir-Dev)*

mm2 Screen Management Sdn. Bhd. (1)
Menara Bata PJ Trade Center No 8 Jalan PJU 8/8A, Bandar Damansara Perdana, 47820, Petaling Jaya, Selangor, Malaysia
Tel.: (60) 350383217
Web Site: https://www.mmcineplexes.com
Cinema Management & Operation Services
N.A.I.C.S.: 711110

MMA OFFSHORE LIMITED
Level 10 12-14 The Esplanade, Perth, 6000, WA, Australia
Tel.: (61) 894317431   AU
Web Site: https://www.mmaoffshore.com
MRM—(ASX)
Rev.: $217,418,672
Assets: $410,660,218
Liabilities: $149,581,741
Net Worth: $261,078,476
Earnings: $25,920,208
Emp.: 1,100
Fiscal Year-end: 06/30/22
Offices of Other Holding Companies
N.A.I.C.S.: 551112
David Ross *(Mng Dir)*

Subsidiaries:

MMA Offshore Asia Pte. Ltd (1)
9 Raffles Place 15-02 Republic Plaza, Singapore, 048619, Singapore   (100%)
Tel.: (65) 62651010
Web Site: http://www.mma.com.au
Water Transportation Support Services
N.A.I.C.S.: 488390

Subsidiary (Domestic):

Java Marine Lines Pte. Ltd. (2)
13 Tuas Crescent, Singapore, 638707, Singapore
Tel.: (65) 68645599
Ship Chartering Services
N.A.I.C.S.: 488390

MMA Offshore Shipyard And Engineering Services Pte. Ltd. (2)
13 Tuas Crescent, Singapore, 638707, Singapore
Tel.: (65) 62651010
Ship Engineering & Building Services
N.A.I.C.S.: 336611

Mermaid Marine Vessel Operations Pty. Ltd. (1)
Endeavour Shed 1 Mews Road, Fremantle, 6160, WA, Australia
Tel.: (61) 8 9431 7431
Web Site: http://www.mma.com.au
Harbor Support Vessels Operator
N.A.I.C.S.: 488390

Mermaid Supply Base Pty. Ltd. (1)
Mermaid Road, Dampier, 6713, WA, Australia
Tel.: (61) 8 9183 6600
Web Site: http://www.mma.com.au
Sales Range: $25-49.9 Million
Emp.: 50
Marine Shore Facilities Operator
N.A.I.C.S.: 488390

MMAG HOLDINGS BERHAD
No 3 Jalan TP 2 Taman Perindustrian UEP, 47600, Subang Jaya, Selangor, Malaysia
Tel.: (60) 378903535   MY
Web Site: https://www.mmag.com.my

MMAG—(KLS)
Rev.: $89,332,424
Assets: $126,665,103
Liabilities: $95,279,596
Net Worth: $31,385,507
Earnings: ($18,918,985)
Fiscal Year-end: 03/31/23
Information & Communication Technology Services
N.A.I.C.S.: 517810
Eng Su Wong *(Mng Dir)*

Subsidiaries:

Line Clear Express & Logistics Sdn. Bhd. (1)
3 Jln TP 2 Taman Perindustrian Uep, Bayan Lepas, 47600, Subang Jaya, Selangor, Malaysia   (80.75%)
Tel.: (60) 165015050
Web Site: https://www.lineclearexpress.com
Courier Service
N.A.I.C.S.: 492110
Adam Khoo Teow Beng *(COO)*

Line Clear Express (KT) Sdn. Bhd. (1)
No 3 Jalan TP 2 Taman Perindustrian UEP, 47600, Subang Jaya, Selangor Darul Ehsan, Malaysia
Tel.: (60) 165015050
Freight Forwarding Services
N.A.I.C.S.: 488510

MMAG Digital Sdn. Bhd. (1)
Menara Persoft 12th Floor 6B Persiaran Tropicana, Tropicana Golf and Country Resort, 47410, Petaling Jaya, Selangor, Malaysia
Tel.: (60) 376889888
Web Site: http://www.ingens.com.my
Computer Peripheral Equipment Distr
N.A.I.C.S.: 423430
Howie Tan *(Head-Mobile)*

MMC CORPORATION BERHAD
Ground Floor Wisma Budiman, Persiaran Raja Chulan, 50200, Kuala Lumpur, Malaysia
Tel.: (60) 320711000   MY
Web Site: http://www.mmc.com.my
2194—(KLS)
Rev.: $1,111,955,130
Assets: $6,461,588,678
Liabilities: $3,912,963,120
Net Worth: $2,548,625,558
Earnings: $110,346,390
Emp.: 15,327
Fiscal Year-end: 12/31/20
Infrastructure Holding Company
N.A.I.C.S.: 551112
Mabel Khuan Eoi Lee *(Dir-Treasury-Grp)*

Subsidiaries:

Johor Port Berhad (1)
PO Box 151, 81707, Pasir Gudang, Johor, Malaysia
Tel.: (60) 7 253 5888
Web Site: https://www.johorport.com.my
Logistic Services
N.A.I.C.S.: 488510
Shahrull Allam Shah Abdul Halim *(CEO)*

Subsidiary (Domestic):

Seaport Worldwide Sdn. Bhd. (2)
LC06 & LC07 Senai Cargo Building Senai International Airport, 81250, Johor Bahru, Johor, Malaysia
Tel.: (60) 75951114
Web Site: http://www.sww.com.my
Oilhub Services
N.A.I.C.S.: 213112

Kontena Nasional Berhad (1)
Batu 9 Jalan Klang Lama Seri Setia, 46000, Petaling Jaya, Selangor, Malaysia
Tel.: (60) 378761933
Web Site: http://www.kn.com.my
Emp.: 600
Comprehensive Logistic Services
N.A.I.C.S.: 488510
Vera Ann Villenguez *(Acting Head-Ops)*

MMC Engineering & Construction Sdn. Bhd. (1)
Unit 7-02 Level 7 Wisma Zelan Jalan Tasik Permaisuri 2 Wilayah, Persekutuan Bandar Tun Razak, 56000, Kuala Lumpur, Malaysia
Tel.: (60) 391721711
Engineeering Services
N.A.I.C.S.: 541330

MMC Engineering Sdn. Bhd. (1)
Level 23 Wisma Zelan Jalan Tasik Permaisuri 2, Bandar Tun Razak, 56000, Cheras, Wilayah Persekutuan, Malaysia
Tel.: (60) 39 172 1711
Web Site: https://www.mmce.com.my
Engineeering Services
N.A.I.C.S.: 541330
Mohd Abdul Fatah Endut *(CEO)*

MMC Oil & Gas Engineering Sdn. Bhd. (1)
Level 22 Menara Tokio Marine Life 189 Jalan Tun Razak, 50400, Kuala Lumpur, Malaysia
Tel.: (60) 32 161 6000
Web Site: https://www.mmcog.com
Oil & Gas Operator Services
N.A.I.C.S.: 213112
Aiman Halim *(Sr Engr-Project)*

MMC Saudi Arabia Limited (1)
Business Park Office 1202, Jeddah, Saudi Arabia
Tel.: (966) 544470702
Web Site: https://www.mmcsaudi.com
Strategic Advisory Services
N.A.I.C.S.: 541611
Ahmad Mahfoud *(Mng Dir)*

Malakoff Corporation Berhad (1)
Level 12 Block 4 Plaza Sentral Jalan Stesen Sentral 5, 50470, Kuala Lumpur, Malaysia   (51%)
Tel.: (60) 322633388
Web Site: https://www.malakoff.com.my
Rev.: $2,191,566,138
Assets: $4,652,662,222
Liabilities: $3,235,557,884
Net Worth: $1,417,104,339
Earnings: $81,672,593
Emp.: 3,113
Fiscal Year-end: 12/31/2022
Holding Company; Electric & Water Utility Services
N.A.I.C.S.: 551112
Mohd Nazersham Mansor *(CFO)*

Joint Venture (Non-US):

Hidd Power Company BSC (2)
Hidd Power Station, Hidd Industrial Area, Hidd, Bahrain   (40%)
Tel.: (973) 1 767 9479
Web Site: https://www.hpc.com.bh
Water & Electric Utility Services
N.A.I.C.S.: 221112
Radhakrishnan Kaiparambath *(Mgr-Engrg, Plng & Performance)*

Northport (Malaysia) Bhd. (1)
Jalan Pelabuhan Pelabuhan Utara, 42000, Port Klang, Malaysia
Tel.: (60) 33 169 8888
Web Site: https://www.northport.com.my
Comprehensive Logistic Services
N.A.I.C.S.: 488510
Azman Shah Mohd Yusof *(CEO)*

Pelabuhan Tanjung Pelepas Sdn. Bhd. (1)
Block A Wisma PTP Jalan Pelabuhan Tanjung Pelepas TST 507, 81560, Gelang Patah, Johor, Malaysia
Tel.: (60) 7 504 2222
Web Site: https://www.ptp.com.my
Port Services
N.A.I.C.S.: 488510
Marco Neelsen *(CEO)*

Penang Port Sdn. Bhd. (1)
Level 5 5130 Terminal Penang Sentral, Jalan Bagan Dalam, 12100, Butterworth, Malaysia
Tel.: (60) 4 375 2400
Web Site: https://www.penangport.com.my
Port Services
N.A.I.C.S.: 488510
Sasedharan Vasudevan *(CEO)*

Senai Airport Terminal Services Sdn. Bhd. (1)
Senai International Airport Darul Tazim, 81250, Johor Bahru, Johor, Malaysia
Tel.: (60) 7 599 4500
Web Site: https://www.senaiairport.com
Airport Services
N.A.I.C.S.: 488119
Md Derick Basir *(CEO)*

MMC LIMITED
Level 25 QBE Centre 125 Queen Street, Auckland, 1010, New Zealand
Tel.: (64) 9 309 89 26
Web Site: http://mmcnz.co.nz
Financial Services
N.A.I.C.S.: 523999
Robert Moss *(Mng Dir)*

Subsidiaries:

AEGIS Limited (1)
ASB North Wharf 12 Jellicoe Street, Auckland Central, Auckland, 1010, New Zealand
Tel.: (64) 9 487 9006
Web Site: http://www.aegis.co.nz
Investment Management Service
N.A.I.C.S.: 523999

MMC SANAYI VE TICARI YATIRIMLAR AS
Kavacik Mah Orhan Veli Kanik Cad, Istanbul, 34810, Turkiye
Tel.: (90) 2164133330
Web Site: http://www.mmcsanayi.com
MMCAS—(IST)
Rev.: $42,081
Assets: $229,437
Liabilities: $151,583
Net Worth: $77,854
Earnings: ($77,509)
Fiscal Year-end: 12/31/23
Transportation Services
N.A.I.C.S.: 485999
Selim Sayilgan *(Chm)*

MMG CANADA, LTD.
10 Vansco Road, Toronto, M8Z 5J4, ON, Canada
Tel.: (416) 251-2831
Web Site: http://www.mmgca.com
Year Founded: 1952
Sales Range: $25-49.9 Million
Emp.: 40
Iron Powder Component Mfr
N.A.I.C.S.: 331221
Paul Marques *(Pres)*

MML CAPITAL PARTNERS LLP
Grand Buildings 1-3 Strand, London, WC2N 5HR, United Kingdom
Tel.: (44) 2070242200   UK
Web Site: http://www.mmlcapital.com
Year Founded: 1988
Equity Investment Firm
N.A.I.C.S.: 523999
Rory Brooks *(Co-Founder)*

Subsidiaries:

MML Capital France Sarl (1)
12-14 Rond-Point des Champs-Elysees, 75008, Paris, France
Tel.: (33) 1 5353 1488
Web Site: http://www.mmlcapital.com
Equity Investment Firm
N.A.I.C.S.: 523999
Henry-Louis Merieux *(Mng Partner)*

MML Capital Partners LLC (1)
333 Ludlow St 2nd Fl N Tower, Stamford, CT 06902
Tel.: (203) 323-9118
Web Site: http://www.mmlcapital.com
Equity Investment Firm
N.A.I.C.S.: 523999

Vanguard Healthcare Solutions Ltd. (1)
Unit 1411 Charlton Ct Gloucester Bus Pk, Gloucester, GL3 4AE, United Kingdom
Tel.: (44) 1452651850
Web Site: http://www.vanguardhealthcare.co.uk

MML CAPITAL PARTNERS LLP

MML Capital Partners LLP—(Continued)
Sales Range: $10-24.9 Million
Emp.: 15
Mobile Healthcare Services
N.A.I.C.S.: 622110
Mary Smallbone *(Mng Dir-Europe)*

MMP INDUSTRIES LTD.
B-24 Hingna Midc Area, Hingna, Nagpur, 440016, India
Tel.: (91) 7104668000
Web Site: https://www.mmpil.com
Year Founded: 1983
MMP—(NSE)
Rev.: $64,609,999
Assets: $42,920,664
Liabilities: $12,090,774
Net Worth: $30,829,890
Earnings: $2,556,286
Emp.: 452
Fiscal Year-end: 03/31/23
Metal Products Mfr
N.A.I.C.S.: 332312
Anil K. Jain *(Gen Mgr)*

Subsidiaries:

Star Circlips & Engineering Ltd. (1)
B-24 MIDC Hingna Road, Nagpur, 440 016, Maharashtra, India
Tel.: (91) 710 464 6427
Web Site: https://www.starcirclips.com
Aluminium Products Mfr
N.A.I.C.S.: 331315

MMS VENTURES BERHAD
Plot 84A Lintang Bayan Lepas 9 Bayan Lepas Industrial Park Phase 4, 11900, Penang, Malaysia
Tel.: (60) 46460888 MY
Web Site: https://mmsis.com
Year Founded: 2004
MMSV—(KLS)
Rev.: $11,188,823
Assets: $16,523,829
Liabilities: $1,248,453
Net Worth: $15,275,376
Earnings: $1,914,731
Fiscal Year-end: 12/31/22
Investment Holding Services
N.A.I.C.S.: 551112
Teik Keat Sia *(CEO)*

MMTC LIMITED
Core-1 SCOPE COMPLEX 7 Institutional Area Lodhi Road, New Delhi, 110003, India
Tel.: (91) 112 436 2200
Web Site: http://mmtclimited.com
Year Founded: 1963
MMTC—(BOM)
Rev.: $4,097,612,610
Assets: $747,181,890
Liabilities: $726,706,890
Net Worth: $20,475,000
Earnings: ($107,736,720)
Emp.: 702
Fiscal Year-end: 03/31/21
Trading Services
N.A.I.C.S.: 522299
Ved Prakash *(Chm & Mng Dir)*

Subsidiaries:

Indian Commodity Exchange Ltd. (1)
1st Floor Office - 109 Blue Diamond Nodh No 1158 to 63/65/9 Hat Faliyu, Mahidharpura, Surat, 395003, Gujarat, India
Tel.: (91) 2612609960
Web Site: http://www.icexindia.com
Stock Exchange Services
N.A.I.C.S.: 523210
Vijay Kumar Sharma *(Chm)*

MMTC Transnational Pte. Ltd. (1)
3 Raffles Place, 08-01 Bharat Building, Singapore, 048617, Singapore
Tel.: (65) 6 538 5313
Web Site: https://www.mtpl.com.sg
Sales Range: $550-599.9 Million
Emp.: 5
Commodity Trading Services
N.A.I.C.S.: 523160
Ved Prakash *(Chm)*

MMTEC, INC.
AF 16/F Block B Jiacheng Plaza 18 Xiaguangli, Chaoyang District, Beijing, 100027, China
Tel.: (86) 1056172312 VG
Web Site: http://www.51mm.com
Year Founded: 2015
MTC—(NASDAQ)
Rev.: $1,099,133
Assets: $11,415,507
Liabilities: $2,031,156
Net Worth: $9,384,351
Earnings: ($5,645,376)
Emp.: 55
Fiscal Year-end: 12/31/22
Holding Company
N.A.I.C.S.: 551112
Xiangdong Wen *(Chm)*

MN HOLDINGS BERHAD
F-07-01 Garden Shoppe One City Jalan USJ 25/1B, 47650, Subang Jaya, Selangor, Malaysia
Tel.: (60) 351150008
Web Site: https://mnholdings.com.my
Year Founded: 2007
MNHLDG—(KLS)
Rev.: $35,719,117
Assets: $31,893,016
Liabilities: $16,453,302
Net Worth: $15,439,714
Earnings: $2,019,271
Emp.: 100
Fiscal Year-end: 06/30/23
Holding Company
N.A.I.C.S.: 551112
Loy Siong Hay *(Mng Dir)*

MN TECHNOLOGIES SAS
Cra 67 102a - 25, Bogota, Colombia
Tel.: (57) 18054433 Co
Web Site: http://www.mnt.com.co
Analytical Measurement Device Mfr
N.A.I.C.S.: 334516

MN-FUND PJSC
Dmitrovskiy per d 4 str 1, Moscow, 107031, Russia
Tel.: (7) 4956212839
Real Estate Manangement Services
N.A.I.C.S.: 522299
Alexander Ivanovich Orlov *(Gen Dir)*

MNC MEDIA INVESTMENT LTD
39 MacTaggart Road Asia Media Centre, Singapore, 368084, Singapore
Tel.: (65) 68481212 Ky
Web Site: http://www.mncmi.com
Year Founded: 1999
MIH—(ASX)
Rev.: $19,315,104
Assets: $96,768,061
Liabilities: $16,558,998
Net Worth: $80,209,063
Earnings: ($1,623,748)
Emp.: 130
Fiscal Year-end: 12/31/21
Interactive Entertainment Products
N.A.I.C.S.: 518210
Hary Tanoesoedibjo *(Chm & CEO)*

MNC WIRELESS BERHAD
100-3 011 129 Offices Jaya One No 72A Jalan Profesor Diraja Ungku Aziz, 46200, Petaling Jaya, Selangor, Malaysia
Tel.: (60) 374911880 MY
Web Site: http://www.mnc.com.my
Year Founded: 2002
MNC—(KLS)
Rev.: $2,631,874
Assets: $18,583,679
Liabilities: $2,056,367
Net Worth: $16,527,312
Earnings: ($1,406,276)
Fiscal Year-end: 04/30/23
Mobile Application Development Services
N.A.I.C.S.: 541511
Christopher Chor How Tan *(CEO)*

MNI S.A.
Ul Plac Trzech Krzyzy 3, 00-535, Warsaw, Poland
Tel.: (48) 22 583 37 44
Web Site: http://www.mni.pl
Telecommunication Servicesb
N.A.I.C.S.: 517810

MNP PETROLEUM CORPORATION
Bahnhofstr 9, 6341, Baar, Switzerland
Tel.: (41) 44 718 1030 NV
Web Site: http://www.mnppetroleum.com
Year Founded: 1998
MNP—(OTCIQ)
Sales Range: Less than $1 Million
Emp.: 30
Gas & Oil Exploration Services
N.A.I.C.S.: 211120
Heinz Juergen Klaus Scholz *(Chm)*

Subsidiaries:

Manas Petroleum AG (1)
Bahnhofstrasse 9, PO Box 155, 6340, Baar, Zug, Switzerland
Tel.: (41) 447181030
Web Site: http://www.mnppetroleum.com
Emp.: 8
Oil & Field Exploration Services
N.A.I.C.S.: 213112

MNRB HOLDINGS BERHAD
12th Floor Bangunan Malaysian Re No 17 Lorong Dungun, Damansara Heights, 50490, Kuala Lumpur, Malaysia
Tel.: (60) 320968000
Web Site: https://www.mnrb.com.my
Year Founded: 1972
MNRB—(KLS)
Rev.: $701,633,016
Assets: $2,615,361,481
Liabilities: $2,068,785,185
Net Worth: $546,576,296
Earnings: $25,285,291
Emp.: 1,042
Fiscal Year-end: 03/31/23
Reinsurance Carrier Services
N.A.I.C.S.: 524130
Norazman Hashim *(CFO-Grp, Co-Sec & Exec VP)*

Subsidiaries:

MMIP Services Sdn. Bhd. (1)
6th Floor Bangunan Malaysian Re No 17 Lorong Dungun Damansara Heights, 50490, Kuala Lumpur, Malaysia
Tel.: (60) 320806000
Web Site: http://www.mnrb.com.my
Sales Range: $50-74.9 Million
Emp.: 9
Insurance Services
N.A.I.C.S.: 524298

MNRB Retakaful Berhad (1)
9th Floor Bangunan Malaysian Re No 17 Lorong Dungun Damansara Heights, Kuala Lumpur, 50490, Malaysia
Tel.: (60) 320967007
Web Site: http://www.mnrb-retakaful.com.my
Sales Range: $50-74.9 Million
Emp.: 12
Financial Security Services
N.A.I.C.S.: 523999
Sharkawi Alis *(Chm)*

INTERNATIONAL PUBLIC

Malaysian Re (Dubai) Ltd. (1)
Unit 101 Level 1 Gate Village 4 Dubai International Financial Centre, PO Box 506571, The Gate District, Dubai, United Arab Emirates
Tel.: (971) 43230388
Web Site: http://www.mnrb.com.my
Sales Range: $50-74.9 Million
Emp.: 5
Reinsurance Services
N.A.I.C.S.: 524130
Ahmad Saiful Bahri Mohamed *(Exec Officer)*

Malaysian Reinsurance Berhad (1)
12th Floor Bangunan Malaysian Re No 17 Lorong Dungun Damansara Heights, 50490, Kuala Lumpur, Malaysia
Tel.: (60) 320968000
Web Site: http://www.malaysian-re.com.my
Sales Range: $200-249.9 Million
Emp.: 300
Reinsurance Services
N.A.I.C.S.: 524130
Mohammad Redzal Abdul Samah *(VP & Head-Technical Acctg & Underwriting Admin)*

Takaful Ikhlas Family Berhad (1)
9th Floor IKHLAS Point Tower 11A Avenue 5 Bangsar South No 8, Jalan Kerinchi, 59200, Kuala Lumpur, Malaysia
Tel.: (60) 327239999
Web Site: https://www.takaful-ikhlas.com.my
Insurance Services
N.A.I.C.S.: 524210
Johar Mat *(Chm)*

Takaful Ikhlas General Berhad (1)
5th Floor Bangunan Malaysian Re No 17 Lorong Dungun, Damansara Heights, 50490, Kuala Lumpur, Malaysia
Tel.: (60) 327239999
Insurance Services
N.A.I.C.S.: 524210
Ahmad Fariman Yunus *(Sr VP & Head-Underwriting)*

Takaful Ikhlas Sdn. Bhd. (1)
Ikhlas Point Tower 11A Avenue 5 Bangsar South No 8 Jalan Kerinchi, 59200, Kuala Lumpur, Wilayah Persekutuan, Malaysia
Web Site: http://www.takaful-ikhlas.com.my
Sales Range: $200-249.9 Million
Emp.: 400
Financial Protection & Insurance Services
N.A.I.C.S.: 523999

MNTECH CO, LTD.
16 Gwahaksaneop 1-ro Oksanmyeon, Heungdeok-gu, Cheongju, Chungcheongbuk-Do, Korea (South)
Tel.: (82) 437101100
Web Site: http://www.mntech.co.kr
Year Founded: 2002
Sales Range: $125-149.9 Million
Emp.: 350
Optical Film Mfr
N.A.I.C.S.: 326112
Kim Chul Young *(CEO)*

MO-BRUK S.A.
Niecew 68, 33-322, Korzenna, Poland
Tel.: (48) 184417048
Web Site: https://www.mobruk.pl
Year Founded: 1985
MBR—(WAR)
Rev.: $60,216,763
Assets: $85,985,219
Liabilities: $29,636,179
Net Worth: $56,349,040
Earnings: $20,035,887
Emp.: 250
Fiscal Year-end: 12/31/23
Waste Management
N.A.I.C.S.: 562998
Jozef Tadeusz Mokrzycki *(Chm-Mgmt Bd)*

MOA BREWING COMPANY LIMITED
Suite 3 Level 1 152 Quay Street, Auckland, New Zealand

AND PRIVATE COMPANIES

Tel.: (64) 93679472
Web Site: http://www.moabeer.com
Beer Mfr
N.A.I.C.S.: 312120
Stephen Smith *(CEO)*

MOAB MINERALS LIMITED
Level 1 2A/300 Fitzgerald Street, Perth, 6006, WA, Australia
Tel.: (61) 861669107   AU
Web Site:
   https://www.moabminerals.com.au
MOM—(ASX)
Rev.: $70,171
Assets: $4,694,797
Liabilities: $139,738
Net Worth: $4,555,059
Earnings: ($860,021)
Fiscal Year-end: 06/30/24
Adult Product Sales
N.A.I.C.S.: 339930
Malcolm Day *(Mng Dir)*

Subsidiaries:

Calvista Australia Pty Ltd.   (1)
Building 41 9 Ashley Street, Braybrook, 3019, VIC, Australia
Tel.: (61) 396955858
Web Site: https://www.calvista.com.au
Sales Range: $25-49.9 Million
Emp.: 40
Adult Toys & Videos & Novelties Whslr
N.A.I.C.S.: 423920

Calvista New Zealand Limited   (1)
15 Gundry St, Newton, Auckland, New Zealand
Tel.: (64) 93095496
Web Site: http://www.calvista.co.nz
Sales Range: $50-74.9 Million
Emp.: 5
Adult Toys Whslr
N.A.I.C.S.: 423920

MOADATA CO., LTD.
222 223 42 Changeop-ro, Sujeong-gu, Seongnam, Gyeonggi-do, Korea (South)
Tel.: (82) 7040995131
Web Site: https://www.moadata.co.kr
Year Founded: 2014
288980—(KRS)
Rev.: $16,654,445
Assets: $42,805,184
Liabilities: $14,368,867
Net Worth: $28,436,316
Earnings: $1,376,383
Emp.: 48
Fiscal Year-end: 12/31/22
Software Development Services
N.A.I.C.S.: 541511

MOARA CIBIN S.A.
Sos Alba Iulia nr 70, Sibiu, Romania
Tel.: (40) 269229651
Web Site: https://www.moaracibin.ro
Year Founded: 1991
MOIB—(BUC)
Rev.: $67,488,666
Assets: $44,668,548
Liabilities: $24,168,647
Net Worth: $20,499,901
Earnings: $1,916,885
Emp.: 419
Fiscal Year-end: 12/31/22
Grain Mill Product Mfr
N.A.I.C.S.: 311230

MOATABLE, INC.
4/F Tower D Building 15 No 5 Jiangtai Road, Chaoyang District, Beijing, 100015, China
Tel.: (86) 1084176807   Ky
Web Site: http://www.renren-inc.com
MTBL—(NYSE)
Rev.: $45,808,000
Assets: $94,708,000
Liabilities: $28,942,000
Net Worth: $65,766,000
Earnings: ($75,244,000)
Emp.: 601
Fiscal Year-end: 12/31/22
Social Networking Website Operator
N.A.I.C.S.: 516210
Joseph Chen *(Chm & CEO)*

MOATECH CO., LTD.
Tel.: (82) 328109000
Web Site: http://www.moatech.co.kr
Year Founded: 1985
033200—(KRS)
Rev.: $28,543,289
Assets: $71,547,565
Liabilities: $5,264,972
Net Worth: $66,282,592
Earnings: ($1,297,402)
Emp.: 87
Fiscal Year-end: 03/31/22
Electronic Components Mfr
N.A.I.C.S.: 334419
Je-Hee Lee *(CEO)*

Subsidiaries:

DONGGUAN DONGMA ELECTRONIC COMPANY   (1)
Lingxia Management Area, LiagBu Town, Dongguan, Guang Dong, China
Tel.: (86) 769 8330 8523
Industrial Equipment Mfr
N.A.I.C.S.: 333248

MOATECH HONG KONG LIMITED   (1)
Unit 706 7/F South Seas Centre Tower 2 No 75 Mody Road, Tsimshatsui, Hong Kong, China (Hong Kong)
Tel.: (852) 2170 1963
Industrial Equipment Mfr
N.A.I.C.S.: 333248

MOATECH PHILIPPINES INC.   (1)
Lot 1 Phase 1-A First Philippine Industrial Park FPIP Brgy Sta Anasta, Santo Tomas, 4234, Batangas, Philippines
Tel.: (63) 43 405 5021
Emp.: 830
Industrial Equipment Mfr
N.A.I.C.S.: 333248

Moatech Co., Ltd. - Incheon Factory   (1)
405-817 74B-16L Namdong Estate 644-15 koJan-Dong, NamDong-Gu, Incheon, Korea (South)
Tel.: (82) 32 816 9482
Industrial Equipment Mfr
N.A.I.C.S.: 333248

MOBA MOBILE AUTOMATION AG
Kapellenstrasse 15, 65555, Limburg, Germany
Tel.: (49) 643195770
Web Site: http://www.moba-automation.com
Year Founded: 1972
Rev.: $37,050,684
Emp.: 280
Construction Machinery Mfr
N.A.I.C.S.: 333120
Volker Harms *(Pres, CEO & Member-Mgmt Bd)*

Subsidiaries:

MOBA (Dalian) Mobile Automation Co., Ltd.   (1)
No 10 Fuquan North Road Central Industrial Park ETDZ, 116600, Dalian, China
Tel.: (86) 41139269388
Construction Machinery Distr
N.A.I.C.S.: 423810

MOBA Corporation   (1)
Kenwood Business Park 180 Walter Way Ste 102, Fayetteville, GA 30214
Tel.: (678) 817-9646
Construction Machinery Distr
N.A.I.C.S.: 423810

MOBA Electronic S.r.l.   (1)
Via Germania 12/A, 37069, Villafranca di Verona, Italy
Tel.: (39) 0456300761
Web Site: http://www.moba.it
Construction Machinery Distr
N.A.I.C.S.: 423810

MOBA France   (1)
10 Rue de Derriere la Montagne Parc des Tuileries, 77500, Chelles, France
Tel.: (33) 164266190
Construction Machinery Distr
N.A.I.C.S.: 423810

MOBA Mobile Automation (I) PVT. LTD.   (1)
B 210-211 GIDC Electronics Estate Sector 25, Gandhinagar, Gujarat, India
Tel.: (91) 7932910900
Construction Machinery Distr
N.A.I.C.S.: 423810
Hardik Rathod *(Asst Mgr-Dev)*

MOBA Mobile Automation Ltd.   (1)
10a-10b Pegasus Way Haddenham Business Park, Haddenham, HP17 8LJ, Buckinghamshire, United Kingdom
Tel.: (44) 1844293220
Construction Machinery Distr
N.A.I.C.S.: 423810
Ian Lewis *(Mng Dir)*

MOBA-ISE Mobile Automation SL   (1)
Poligono Industrial Pla de la Bruguera C/ Bergueda 6, Castellar del Valles, 8211, Barcelona, Spain
Tel.: (34) 937158793
Web Site: http://www.moba-ise.com
Construction Machinery Distr
N.A.I.C.S.: 423810
Ernest Montull Martinez *(Dir-Comml)*

MOBASE CO., LTD.
73 Dongtancheomdansaneop 1-ro, Hwaseong, Gyeonggi-do, Korea (South)
Tel.: (82) 325294200
Web Site: http://www.mobase.com
Year Founded: 1999
101330—(KRS)
Rev.: $1,017,721,596
Assets: $761,065,995
Liabilities: $448,648,491
Net Worth: $312,417,504
Earnings: $18,709,699
Emp.: 50
Fiscal Year-end: 12/31/22
Injection Molding Products Mfr
N.A.I.C.S.: 333248

Subsidiaries:

Mobase Electronics Co., Ltd.   (1)
100 Saneop-ro 156 ben-gil, Gwonseon-gu, Suwon, Gyeonggi-do, Korea (South)
Tel.: (82) 3151743000
Web Site: https://www.seoyonelec.com
Rev.: $707,334,024
Assets: $537,955,087
Liabilities: $383,194,126
Net Worth: $154,760,961
Earnings: $5,213,875
Emp.: 1,165
Fiscal Year-end: 12/31/2022
Automotive Parts Mfr & Distr
N.A.I.C.S.: 336320
Lee Kwang Yoon *(CEO)*

Subsidiary (Non-US):

Guizhou Huachang Automobile Electrics Co., Ltd.   (2)
No 81 Huanghe Ease Road Xiaohe District, Guiyang, Guizhou, China
Tel.: (86) 7082608131
Web Site: http://www.gzhuachang.com.cn
Automobile Parts Distr
N.A.I.C.S.: 423120

Seoyon Electronics Poland Sp. z o.o.   (2)
Ul Antonio Gaudiego 6a, 44-109, Gliwice, Poland
Web Site: http://www.seoyonelec.pl
Automobile Parts Mfr
N.A.I.C.S.: 336320

Plant (Domestic):

Seoyon Electronics co., ltd. - Cheonan Factory   (2)
369 Hwabok-ro Sunam-ri Dong myeon Dongnam-gu, Cheonan, Chungcheongnam-do, Korea (South)
Tel.: (82) 415505813
Automobile Parts Mfr
N.A.I.C.S.: 336320

Seoyon Electronics co., ltd. - Mg Factory   (2)
149 Byeolmang-ro Danwon-gu, Ansan, Gyeonggi-do, Korea (South)
Tel.: (82) 313624000
Automobile Parts Mfr
N.A.I.C.S.: 336320

Subsidiary (Domestic):

Shinchang Connector Co., Ltd.   (2)
706 Baeksuk-Dong Seobuk-Gu, Cheonan, Chungnam, Korea (South)
Tel.: (82) 415647370
Web Site: http://www.sc-connector.co.kr
Steering Product Mfr & Distr
N.A.I.C.S.: 336330
Hwan-Young Yeo *(CEO)*

Subsidiary (Non-US):

Suzhou Seoyon Die Casting Ltd   (2)
48 Yingchunnanlu Road Wuzhong Economic Development Zone, Suzhou, Jiangsu, China
Tel.: (86) 8513831815
Automobile Parts Distr
N.A.I.C.S.: 423120

Suzhou Seoyon Electronics Ltd.   (2)
185 Shanxing Road Guoxiang, Wuzhong Development Zone, Suzhou, Jiangsu, China
Tel.: (86) 51265966881
Automobile Parts Distr
N.A.I.C.S.: 423120

Subsidiary (Domestic):

WOOCHANG Precision Co., Ltd.   (2)
632-7 Sungkog-Dong Danwon-Ku, Ansan, kyungki-Province, Korea (South)
Tel.: (82) 31 491 9437
Web Site: http://www.woo-chang.com
Automobile Parts Mfr & Distr
N.A.I.C.S.: 336320
Song In Myeong *(Pres)*

MOBCAST HOLDINGS, INC.
Step Roppongi 4F 6-8-10 Roppongi, Tokyo, 106-0032, Japan
Tel.: (81) 357151523
Web Site: https://mobcast.co.jp
Year Founded: 2004
3664—(TKS)
Rev.: $23,907,480
Assets: $17,689,550
Liabilities: $14,917,360
Net Worth: $2,772,190
Earnings: ($2,694,200)
Emp.: 40
Fiscal Year-end: 12/31/23
Mobile Entertainment Platform
N.A.I.C.S.: 517112
Koki Yabu *(Pres & CEO)*

MOBERG PHARMA AB
Gustavslundsvagen 42, 167 51, Bromma, Sweden
Tel.: (46) 852230700   SE
Web Site:
   https://www.mobergpharma.com
Year Founded: 2006
MOB—(OMX)
Assets: $63,010,703
Liabilities: $2,383,207
Net Worth: $60,627,495
Earnings: ($2,093,931)
Emp.: 9
Fiscal Year-end: 12/31/23
Pharmaceuticals Mfr
N.A.I.C.S.: 325412
Peter Wolpert *(Founder & Chm)*

MOBEST SA
Intrarea Heliade Intre Vii 8, Bucharest, Romania
Tel.: (40) 212524740

MOBEST SA

Mobest SA—(Continued)
Web Site: https://mobest.ro
MOBE—(BUC)
Rev.: $5,347,618
Assets: $17,391,367
Liabilities: $423,990
Net Worth: $16,967,377
Earnings: $228,292
Emp.: 19
Fiscal Year-end: 12/31/23
Warehousing & Storage Services
N.A.I.C.S.: 493110

MOBETIZE CORP.
1150-510 Burrard Street, Vancouver,
V6C 3A8, BC, Canada
Tel.: (778) 588-5563 NV
Web Site: http://www.mobetize.com
Year Founded: 2012
Rev.: $438,281
Assets: $154,113
Liabilities: $1,167,242
Net Worth: ($1,013,129)
Earnings: $1,444,586
Emp.: 5
Fiscal Year-end: 03/31/18
Investment Services
N.A.I.C.S.: 523999
Ajay Hans *(CEO)*

MOBEUS EQUITY PARTNERS LLP
30 Haymarket Street, London, SW1Y 4EX, United Kingdom
Tel.: (44) 20 7024 7600 UK
Web Site:
  http://www.mobeusequity.co.uk
Emp.: 27
Equity Investment Firm
N.A.I.C.S.: 523999
Mark Wignall *(Mng Partner)*

Subsidiaries:

ATG Media Ltd (1)
The Harlequin Building 65 Southwark Street, London, SE1 0HR, United Kingdom
Tel.: (44) 203 725 5500
Web Site: http://www.atgmedia.com
Online Auction Services
N.A.I.C.S.: 541850
Colin Tenwick *(Chm)*

Subsidiary (US):

BidSpotter, Inc. (2)
3006 Judson St Ste 201, Gig Harbor, WA 98335
Tel.: (253) 858-6777
Web Site: http://www.bidspotter.com
Online Auction Services
N.A.I.C.S.: 517122
Richard LeMieux *(Sr VP-Ops-North America)*

Automated Systems Group Ltd (1)
Technology House 20 Trafalgar Way, Bar Hill, Cambridge, CB23 8SQ, United Kingdom
Tel.: (44) 845 207 7000
Web Site: http://www.asl-group.co.uk
Emp.: 130
Printer Distr
N.A.I.C.S.: 423430
Andrew Keates *(Mgr-Corp Acct)*

Creative Graphics International Ltd. (1)
6-8 Singer Way Woburn Road Industrial Estate, Kempston, Bedford, MK42 7AW, Bedfordshire, United Kingdom
Tel.: (44) 1234 846 000
Web Site: http://www.cgi-visual.com
Emp.: 50
Commercial Sign Mfr & Distr
N.A.I.C.S.: 339950
Peter Owen *(Mgr)*

Motorclean Ltd. (1)
25 Hornsby Square, Southfields, Laindon, SS16 5SD, Essex, United Kingdom
Tel.: (44) 1268 540 200
Web Site: http://www.motorclean.net
Vehicle Inspection Services

N.A.I.C.S.: 811198
Steve McBrierty *(CEO)*

Veritek Global Ltd (1)
Franklin House Chaucer Business Park Dittons Road, Polegate, Eastbourne, BN26 6QH, East Sussex, United Kingdom
Tel.: (44) 1323 500200
Web Site: http://www.veritekglobal.com
Emp.: 299
Mechanical Engineering Services
N.A.I.C.S.: 541330
Jim Edgar *(CEO)*

Subsidiary (Non-US):

Veritek Australasia Pty Ltd (2)
3A/8 Mowbray Terrace, Brisbane, 4169, QLD, Australia
Tel.: (61) 4 4760 0052
Mechanical Engineering Services
N.A.I.C.S.: 541330
Tim Pilgrim *(Mng Dir)*

Veritek Benelux BV (2)
Weidehek 83, 4824 AT, Breda, Netherlands
Tel.: (31) 76 711 4823
Mechanical Engineering Services
N.A.I.C.S.: 541330
Andrew Light *(Gen Mgr)*

Veritek Czech Republic s.r.o. (2)
Pristavni 24, 170 00, Prague, Czech Republic
Tel.: (420) 296837105
Mechanical Engineering Services
N.A.I.C.S.: 541330
Jiri Rach *(Engr-Svc)*

Veritek GmbH (2)
Hanns-Martin-Schleyer-Strasse 9A, 47877, Willich, Germany
Tel.: (49) 2154 81451 0
Mechanical Engineering Services
N.A.I.C.S.: 541330
Andrew Light *(Gen Mgr)*

Veritek Iberia S.L. (2)
Calle San Maximo 31 Planta 4 Nave 3, 28041, Madrid, Spain
Tel.: (34) 91 708 1559
Mechanical Engineering Services
N.A.I.C.S.: 541330
Rene Spang *(Gen Mgr)*

Veritek Italy srl (2)
Via Francesco Parigi n 30, Chivasso, 10034, Turin, Italy
Tel.: (39) 011 9196172
Web Site: http://www.veritekglobal.eu
Mechanical Engineering Services
N.A.I.C.S.: 541330
Vanni Chiesa *(Gen Mgr)*

MOBEUS INCOME & GROWTH VCT PLC
5 New Street Square, London, EC4A 3TW, United Kingdom UK
Web Site: https://www.migvct.co.uk
Year Founded: 2004
MIX—(LSE)
Rev.: $3,267,937
Assets: $127,012,530
Liabilities: $383,031
Net Worth: $126,629,499
Earnings: ($23,720,155)
Fiscal Year-end: 12/31/22
Investment Management Service
N.A.I.C.S.: 523999
Clive Boothman *(Chm)*

MOBI DEVELOPMENT CO., LTD.
Mobi Building 7 Langshan First Road Science and Technology Park, Nanshan District, Shenzhen, Guangdong, China
Tel.: (86) 75586186100 Ky
Web Site: http://www.mobi-
  antenna.com
0947—(HKG)
Rev.: $96,454,800
Assets: $183,956,713
Liabilities: $104,631,556
Net Worth: $79,325,158

Earnings: ($32,258,444)
Emp.: 1,791
Fiscal Year-end: 12/31/22
Wireless Communication Antennas
N.A.I.C.S.: 334220
Xiang Hu *(Chm & CEO)*

MOBI724 GLOBAL SOLUTIONS INC.
1275 Avenue des Canadiens-de-Montreal WeWork Suite 500, Montreal, H3B 0G4, QC, Canada
Tel.: (514) 394-5200 AB
Web Site: https://www.mobi724.com
Year Founded: 2005
MOBIF—(OTCIQ)
Rev.: $285,703
Assets: $761,250
Liabilities: $9,863,999
Net Worth: ($9,102,749)
Earnings: ($3,873,482)
Fiscal Year-end: 12/31/22
Mobile Payment Systems
N.A.I.C.S.: 513210
Marcel Vienneau *(Co-Founder & CEO)*

Subsidiaries:

Vault Acquiring Solutions LLC (1)
5699 Kanan Rd, Agoura Hills, CA 91301
Tel.: (818) 477-3922
Software Development Services
N.A.I.C.S.: 541511

MOBICO GROUP PLC.
National Express House Mill Lane, Digbeth, Birmingham, B5 6DD, United Kingdom
Tel.: (44) 8450130130 UK
Web Site:
  https://www.mobicogroup.com
Year Founded: 1972
MCG—(LSE)
Rev.: $2,946,659,716
Assets: $5,826,112,292
Liabilities: $3,859,862,188
Net Worth: $1,966,250,104
Earnings: $110,789,952
Emp.: 44,500
Fiscal Year-end: 12/31/21
Offices of Other Holding Companies
N.A.I.C.S.: 551112
Jorge Cosmen *(Deputy Chm)*

Subsidiaries:

A1A Transportation, Inc. (1)
4749 Orange Dr, Davie, FL 33314
Tel.: (954) 584-5877
Sales Range: $1-9.9 Million
School Bus Transportation Services
N.A.I.C.S.: 485410
Enrique Hernandez *(Pres)*

Agreda Bus, S.L. (1)
Avda Manuel Rodriguez Ayuso 110 Antigua Ctra de Madrid Km 3157, 50012, Zaragoza, Spain
Tel.: (34) 976300818
Web Site: http://www.agredabus.es
Transportation Services
N.A.I.C.S.: 484110

AlpyBus S.a.r.l. (1)
8 Chemin de Morglas, Verbier, 1214, Geneva, Switzerland
Tel.: (41) 227232984
Web Site: http://www.alpybus.com
Transport Services
N.A.I.C.S.: 484110

Alsa Grupo, S.L.U. (1)
Calle Miguel Fleta 4, 28037, Madrid, Spain
Tel.: (34) 82059478
Transportation Services
N.A.I.C.S.: 484110

Autos Rodriguez Eocar, S.L. (1)
Requiande 1-Cedofeita, Ribadeo, 27711, Lugo, Spain
Tel.: (34) 982137458
Web Site: http://www.eocar.es
Transportation Services

INTERNATIONAL PUBLIC

N.A.I.C.S.: 484110

Chicagoland Coach Lines LLC (1)
2005 W 43 St, Chicago, IL 60609
Tel.: (312) 206-3666
Web Site:
  http://www.chicagolandcoachlines.com
Travel Agency Services
N.A.I.C.S.: 561510
Chris Pellegrino *(Gen Mgr)*

Coliseum Coaches Limited (1)
Broadcut, Wallington, Fareham, PO16 8TB, Hampshire, United Kingdom
Tel.: (44) 2380472377
Web Site:
  http://www.coliseumcoaches.co.uk
Transportation Services
N.A.I.C.S.: 532289

Eggmann Frey AG (1)
Rue du Mont Blanc 14, 1201, Geneva, Switzerland
Tel.: (41) 227169120
Web Site: http://eurolines.ch
Travel Agency Services
N.A.I.C.S.: 561510

Fox Bus Lines Inc. (1)
3 Silver Fox Dr, Millbury, MA 01527
Tel.: (508) 865-6000
Web Site: http://www.silverfoxcoach.com
School Bus Transportation Services
N.A.I.C.S.: 485410
William Fox *(Pres)*

GVA Transfers.com SARL (1)
8 Chemin de Morglas, 1214, Vernier, Switzerland
Tel.: (41) 224201533
Web Site: http://www.gvatransfers.com
Travel Agency Services
N.A.I.C.S.: 561510

Gatwick Express Ltd (1)
3rd Floor 41-51 Grey Street, Newcastle upon Tyne, NE1 6EE, United Kingdom (100%)
Tel.: (44) 3458501530
Web Site: http://www.gatwickexpress.co.uk
Train Service
N.A.I.C.S.: 482111

Guaguas Gumidafe, S.L. (1)
C / Pedro Arguello 10, Galdar, 35460, Las Palmas, Spain
Tel.: (34) 928552279
Web Site: http://www.gumidafe.com
Shipping Company Services
N.A.I.C.S.: 492110

Kiessling Transit, Inc. (1)
101 Constitution Blvd Ste A, Franklin, MA 02038
Tel.: (508) 384-5701
Web Site: https://www.kiesslingtransit.com
School Bus Transportation Services
N.A.I.C.S.: 485410
Lars Kiessling *(CEO)*

London Eastern Railway Limited (1)
Floor One Oliver's Yard, 55 City Road, London, EC1Y 1HQ, United Kingdom
Tel.: (44) 20 7549 5900
Web Site: http://www.onerailway.com
Railway Transportation Services
N.A.I.C.S.: 485112

Lucketts Travel Limited (1)
Broadcut, Wallington, Fareham, PO16 8TB, Hampshire, United Kingdom
Tel.: (44) 1329242617
Web Site: http://www.lucketts.co.uk
Emp.: 380
Transportation Services
N.A.I.C.S.: 485510

Mortons Travel Limited (1)
Berry Court Business Park, Little London, Tadley, RG26 5AT, United Kingdom
Tel.: (44) 1256592310
Web Site: http://www.mortonstravel.com
Transportation Services
N.A.I.C.S.: 485510

Movelia Tecnologias, S.L. (1)
Calle Santa Leonor 65 Avalon Business Park Building A, 28037, Madrid, Spain
Tel.: (34) 902646428
Web Site: http://www.movelia.es
Computer Support & Services

AND PRIVATE COMPANIES

N.A.I.C.S.: 811210

National Express Corporation (1)
4300 Weaver Pkwy Ste 100, Warrenville, IL 60555-3920
Tel.: (630) 435-8000
Web Site: http://www.nationalexpressgroup.com
Sales Range: $25-49.9 Million
Emp.: 50
Contract Bus Transportation Services
N.A.I.C.S.: 485510

Subsidiary (Domestic):

Diamond Transportation Services Inc. (2)
7307C Highland St, Springfield, VA 22150-3610 (100%)
Tel.: (703) 339-9625
Web Site: http://www.diamondtransportation.us
Emp.: 200
Special Needs Transportation
N.A.I.C.S.: 485991
Robert M. Werth (Pres)

Durham School Services, L.P. (2)
4300 Weaver Prkwy, Warrenville, IL 60555
Tel.: (630) 435-8000
Web Site: http://www.durhamschoolservices.com
School Bus & Local Bus Charter Service
N.A.I.C.S.: 485410

Subsidiary (Domestic):

Durham School Services (3)
109 Aldene Rd Ste 9, Roselle, NJ 07203
Tel.: (908) 298-0045
Web Site: http://www.durhamschoolservices.com
Sales Range: $25-49.9 Million
Emp.: 100
School Bus & Rental Bus Services
N.A.I.C.S.: 485410

Branch (Domestic):

Durham School Services, Regional Office (3)
2713 River Ave, Rosemead, CA 91770-3303 (100%)
Tel.: (626) 573-3769
Web Site: http://www.durhamschoolservices.com
Sales Range: $25-49.9 Million
Emp.: 7
Bus Charter Services
N.A.I.C.S.: 485410

Subsidiary (Non-US):

Stock Transportation Limited (2)
60 Columbia Way Suite 800, Markham, L3R 0C9, ON, Canada
Tel.: (905) 940-9977
Web Site: http://www.stocktransportation.com
Transportation Services
N.A.I.C.S.: 485410
Mark Hannah (COO & Sr VP)

National Express LLC (1)
2601 Navistar Dr, Lisle, IL 60532
Tel.: (800) 950-0485
Web Site: https://nellc.com
Transportation Services
N.A.I.C.S.: 488490

Subsidiary (Domestic):

WeDriveU, Inc. (2)
700 Airport Blvd Ste 250, Burlingame, CA 94010 (60%)
Tel.: (650) 645-6800
Web Site: http://www.wedriveu.com
Transportation Management & Staffing Services
N.A.I.C.S.: 541614
Dennis Carlson (Exec Chm)

National Express Limited (1)
Fl 12 No 1 Hagley Rd, Edgbaston, Birmingham, B16 8TG, United Kingdom (100%)
Tel.: (44) 1216251122
Web Site: http://www.nationalexpress.com
Sales Range: $50-74.9 Million
Emp.: 200
Coach Service
N.A.I.C.S.: 485510

Subsidiary (Domestic):

Airlinks Airport Services Limited (2)
Heathrow Coach Centre, Sipson Road, West Drayton, UB7 0HN, Middx, United Kingdom
Tel.: (44) 20 8990 6300
Web Site: http://www.airlinks.co.uk
Sales Range: $100-124.9 Million
Transportation Services
N.A.I.C.S.: 485113

Eurolines (UK) Limited (2)
Albany House, 4 Cardiff Road, Luton, LU1 1PB, Bedfordshire, United Kingdom
Tel.: (44) 1582415841
Web Site: http://www.eurolines.co.uk
Scheduled Bus Transportation Services
N.A.I.C.S.: 485113

Unit (Domestic):

National Express West Midlands (2)
51 Bordesley Green, Bordesley, Birmingham, B9 4BZ, United Kingdom (100%)
Tel.: (44) 1212547272
Web Site: http://www.nationalexpress.com
Sales Range: $50-74.9 Million
Bus Services
N.A.I.C.S.: 485113
Peter Coates (Mng Dir)

National Express Manchester Metrolink Limited (2)
51 Bordesley Green, Birmingham, B9 4BZ, United Kingdom
Tel.: (44) 1215022006
Contract Bus Transportation Services
N.A.I.C.S.: 485999

Northern Rail Limited (1)
Northern House, 9 Rougier St, York, YO1 6HZ, United Kingdom (100%)
Tel.: (44) 8450000125
Web Site: http://www.northernrail.org
Train Service
N.A.I.C.S.: 488210

Odier Excursions, S.A. (1)
Ch des Aulx 9, 1228, Plan-les-Ouates, Switzerland
Tel.: (41) 223314545
Web Site: http://www.odier-excursions.ch
Travel Agency Services
N.A.I.C.S.: 561510

Queen City Transportation, LLC (1)
211 Township Ave, Cincinnati, OH 45216
Tel.: (513) 941-8700
Web Site: http://www.queencitytransportation.com
Sales Range: $1-9.9 Million
Bus Transportation Services
N.A.I.C.S.: 485410
Elaine Sheaks (Gen Mgr)

SARL Chamexpress.com (1)
498 Avenue des Alpages, 74310, Les Houches, France
Tel.: (33) 1743817305
Web Site: http://www.chamexpress.com
Airport Services
N.A.I.C.S.: 485999

Smith Bus Service, Inc. (1)
1890 Bucklina Ave, Odenton, MD 21113
Tel.: (410) 672-2836
Transport Services
N.A.I.C.S.: 484110

Solent Coaches Limited (1)
Unit 72 Basepoint Business Centre Aviation Park West, Hurn, Christchurch, BH23 6NX, United Kingdom
Tel.: (44) 1425473188
Web Site: http://www.solentcoaches.co.uk
Transportation Services
N.A.I.C.S.: 485510

Tayside Public Transport Co Limited (1)
44-48 East Dock Street Angus, Dundee, DD1 3JS, United Kingdom
Tel.: (44) 1382201121
Sales Range: $125-149.9 Million
Emp.: 380
Local Bus Charter Service
N.A.I.C.S.: 485510

The Kings Ferry Limited (1)
Travel Centre Eastcourt Lane, Gillingham, ME8 6HW, Kent, United Kingdom
Tel.: (44) 8452579845
Web Site: http://www.thekingsferry.co.uk
Sales Range: $25-49.9 Million
Hire Coach & Commuter Services
N.A.I.C.S.: 481111

Transportes Unidos de Asturias, S.L. (1)
Poligono Espiritu Santo s / n, Asturias, 33010, Oviedo, Spain
Tel.: (34) 985969699
Web Site: http://www.tua.es
Transportation Services
N.A.I.C.S.: 485510

Transportes Urbanos de Guadalajara, S.L. (1)
C/ Livorno 55 Poligono Industrial del Henares, Marchamalo, 19180, Guadalajara, Spain
Tel.: (34) 900813338
Web Site: http://urbanos.guadalajara.es
Transport Services
N.A.I.C.S.: 484110

Travel Coventry (1)
2 Ford St, Coventry, CV1 5WT, W Midlands, United Kingdom (100%)
Tel.: (44) 2476817000
Web Site: http://www.nationalexpress.co.uk
Sales Range: $125-149.9 Million
Emp.: 500
Bus Services
N.A.I.C.S.: 485510

Travel Dundee Ltd (1)
44 48 E Dock St, Dundee, DD1 3JS, Scotland, United Kingdom (100%)
Tel.: (44) 1382201121
Web Site: http://www.traveldundee.co.uk
Sales Range: $125-149.9 Million
Emp.: 350
Bus Services
N.A.I.C.S.: 485510

West Midlands Travel Limited (1)
51 Bordesley Green, Birmingham, B9 4BZ, United Kingdom
Tel.: (44) 1212547272
Web Site: http://www.nxbus.co.uk
Bus & Coach Operating Services
N.A.I.C.S.: 485210

Wise Coaches, Inc. (1)
540 Collins Park Dr, Antioch, TN 37013
Tel.: (615) 391-3505
Web Site: https://www.wisecoachesofnashville.com
Bus Transportation Services
N.A.I.C.S.: 485410
Alan Wise (Pres)

Woods Coaches Limited (1)
223 Gloucester Crescent, Wigston, Leicester, LE18 4YR, United Kingdom
Tel.: (44) 1183224655
Web Site: http://www.stewartstours.co.uk
Transportation Services
N.A.I.C.S.: 485510

Worthing Coaches Limited (1)
Spencer Road, Lancing, BN15 8UA, West Sussex, United Kingdom
Tel.: (44) 1903505805
Web Site: http://www.worthing-coaches.co.uk
Transportation Services
N.A.I.C.S.: 485510

MOBICON GROUP LIMITED

Clarendon House 2 Church Street, Hamilton, HM 11, Bermuda
Tel.: (441) 2951422 BM
Web Site: http://www.mobicon.com
Year Founded: 1983
1213—(HKG)
Rev.: $52,451,979
Assets: $40,908,022
Liabilities: $18,840,211
Net Worth: $22,067,811
Earnings: $673,380
Emp.: 386
Fiscal Year-end: 03/31/23
Holding Company
N.A.I.C.S.: 551112

Measure Kim Fung Hung (Co-Founder & Chm)

Subsidiaries:

A Plus 2 Computer Limited (1)
7/F New Trend Centre 704 Prince Edward Road East, San Po Kong, Kowloon, China (Hong Kong)
Tel.: (852) 23529092
Computer Peripheral Mfr & Distr
N.A.I.C.S.: 332510

A Power Limited (1)
23rd Floor New Trend Center, 704 Prince Edward Rd E San Po, Kowloon, China (Hong Kong)
Tel.: (852) 23448890
Web Site: http://www.mobicon.com
Sales Range: $25-49.9 Million
Emp.: 35
Electronic Components Mfr
N.A.I.C.S.: 334419
Yeung Beryl (Gen Mgr)

AESI (HK) Limited (1)
23/F New Trend Centre 704 Prince Edward Road East, San Po Kong, Kowloon, China (Hong Kong)
Tel.: (852) 23813189
Web Site: http://www.aesi.com.hk
Sales Range: $25-49.9 Million
Information Technology Consulting Services
N.A.I.C.S.: 541512

APower Holdings Limited (1)
7/F New Trend Centre 704 Prince Edward Road East, San Po Kong, Kowloon, China (Hong Kong)
Tel.: (852) 64019916
Web Site: https://3c.apowerhk.com
Electronic Accessories Distr
N.A.I.C.S.: 423690

Create Tech Software Systems Ltd. (1)
23/F New Trend Centre 704 Prince Edward Road East, San Po Kong, Kowloon, China (Hong Kong)
Tel.: (852) 23448890
Web Site: https://createtech.com
Sales Range: $25-49.9 Million
Electronic Components Mfr
N.A.I.C.S.: 334419

DV Power Limited (1)
7/F New Trend Centre 704 Prince Edward Road East, San Po Kong, Kowloon, China (Hong Kong)
Tel.: (852) 28979718
Web Site: http://www.dvpower.com.hk
Sales Range: $50-74.9 Million
Electronic Parts & Equipment Whslr
N.A.I.C.S.: 423690

MCU Power Limited (1)
7/F New Trend Centre 704 Prince Edward Road East, San Po Kong, Kowloon, China (Hong Kong)
Tel.: (852) 23259228
Web Site: http://www.mcupower.com.hk
Sales Range: $75-99.9 Million
Electronic Parts & Equipment Whslr
N.A.I.C.S.: 423690
Ka-Fai Ng (CEO)

Mantech Electronics (Cape) (Proprietary) Limited (1)
24 Mail Street Western Province Park, Epping, 7460, South Africa (51%)
Tel.: (27) 215353150
Web Site: http://www.mantech.co.za
Sales Range: $25-49.9 Million
Electronic Components Mfr
N.A.I.C.S.: 334419

Mantech Electronics (KZN) (Proprietary) Limited (1)
900 - 914 Umgeni Road Morning Side, Durban, 4001, South Africa (51%)
Tel.: (27) 313097686
Web Site: http://www.mantech.co.za
Sales Range: $25-49.9 Million
Electronic Parts & Equipment Whslr
N.A.I.C.S.: 423690
Manny Moutinho (CEO)

Mantech Electronics (Pty) Ltd. (1)
32 Laub Street New Centre, Johannesburg, 2001, South Africa

MOBICON GROUP LIMITED

Mobicon Group Limited—(Continued)
Tel.: (27) 114939307
Web Site: https://www.mantech.co.za
Sales Range: $25-49.9 Million
Electronic Component Mfr & Distr
N.A.I.C.S.: 334419
Mina Moutinho (Mng Dir)

Mobicon (BVI) Limited (1)
7/F New Trend Centre 704 Prince Edward Road East, Kowloon, San Po Kong, China (Hong Kong)
Tel.: (852) 23978218
Web Site: http://www.mobicon.com
Sales Range: $50-74.9 Million
Emp.: 100
Holding Company; Electronics
N.A.I.C.S.: 551112

Subsidiary (Domestic):

Mobicon Holdings Limited (2)
7/F New Trend Centre 704 Prince Edward Road East, San Po Kong, Kowloon, China (Hong Kong)
Tel.: (852) 23978218
Sales Range: $50-74.9 Million
Emp.: 250
Distribution of Electronic Components, Automation & Equipment
N.A.I.C.S.: 423690
Beryl Yeung Man Yi (CEO)

Mobicon (Taiwan) Limited (1)
7/F No 586 Rui Guang Road, Nei-Hu District, Taipei, 114, Taiwan (100%)
Tel.: (886) 226579336
Web Site: http://www.mobicon.com
Sales Range: $25-49.9 Million
Electronic Connector Mfr
N.A.I.C.S.: 334417

Mobicon Electronic Trading (Shenzhen) Limited (1)
Rm 203-204 Building 6A International Business Trading Center, Hong Hua Road Futian Free Trade Zone, Shenzhen, 518000, Guangdong, China (100%)
Tel.: (86) 75583593687
Web Site: http://www.mobicon.com
Industrial Machinery & Equipment Whslr
N.A.I.C.S.: 423830

Mobicon-Mantech Holdings Limited (1)
32 Laub Street New Centre, Johannesburg, 2001, South Africa (61%)
Tel.: (27) 114939307
Web Site: http://www.mantech.co.za
Sales Range: $50-74.9 Million
Electronic Components Mfr
N.A.I.C.S.: 334419

Mobicon-Remote Electronic Pte Ltd. (1)
50 Ubi Ave 3 02-06 Frontier, Singapore, 408866, Singapore (100%)
Tel.: (65) 67477472
Web Site: https://www.mobicon.com.sg
Sales Range: $25-49.9 Million
Electronic Parts & Equipment Whslr
N.A.I.C.S.: 423690

Mobicon-Remote Electronic Sdn. Bhd. (1)
19 Jalan PJS 3/59 Taman Sri Manja, 46000, Petaling Jaya, Selangor, Malaysia (50.1%)
Tel.: (60) 377832257
Web Site: https://www.mobicon.com.my
Sales Range: $25-49.9 Million
Electrical Apparatus & Equipment Wiring Supplies & Construction Material Whslr
N.A.I.C.S.: 423610

Switch Technique KZN Proprietary Limited (1)
369 Magwaza Maphalala Str, Umbilo, Durban, 4013, South Africa
Web Site:
  https://www.switchtechniquekzn.co.za
Electrical Equipment Mfr & Distr
N.A.I.C.S.: 335999

Videocom Technology (HK) Limited (1)
7/F New Trend Centre 704 Prince Edward Road East, San Po Kong, Kowloon, China (Hong Kong)

Tel.: (852) 23529092
Web Site: https://www.videocom.com.hk
Sales Range: $50-74.9 Million
Emp.: 3
Computer Peripheral & Accessories Distr
N.A.I.C.S.: 423430

MOBIDAYS, INC.
417 Eonju-ro, Gangnam-gu, Seoul, Korea (South)
Tel.: (82) 220521620
Web Site: https://www.mobidays.com
Year Founded: 2014
363260—(KRS)
Advertising Agency Services
N.A.I.C.S.: 541810

MOBIIS CO., LTD.
Room 203 2nd floor Building C Innovalley 253 Pangyo-ro, Bundang-gu, Seongnam, 13486, Gyeonggi-do, Korea (South)
Tel.: (82) 3180188484
Web Site: http://www.mobiis.com
Year Founded: 2000
250060—(KRS)
Rev.: $15,083,135
Assets: $59,272,086
Liabilities: $25,128,281
Net Worth: $34,143,805
Earnings: ($4,751,795)
Emp.: 39
Fiscal Year-end: 12/31/22
Precision Control Equipment Mfr
N.A.I.C.S.: 334519
Jee-hun Kim (CEO)

MOBILA SA
Str G-Ral Cerchez Nr 10, Barlad, Vaslui, Romania
Tel.: (40) 235 417190
Sales Range: Less than $1 Million
Furniture Mfr
N.A.I.C.S.: 337214
Doina Gherache (Pres)

MOBILE ACCOUNT SOLUTIONS LIMITED
Suckling Yard Church Street, Ware, SG12 9EN, Hertfordshire, United Kingdom
Tel.: (44) 1920 466 466
Web Site:
  http://www.mobileaccount.co.uk
Year Founded: 2006
Sales Range: $75-99.9 Million
Emp.: 14
Telecommunication Servicesb
N.A.I.C.S.: 517112
Danny Cox (Mng Dir)

MOBILE APPLIANCE INC.
Daeryung Techno Town 1701 1706-ho 401 Simin-daero, Dongan-gu, Anyang, Gyeonggi-do, Korea (South)
Tel.: (82) 314218071
Web Site:
  https://www.mobileappliance.co.kr
Year Founded: 2004
087260—(KRS)
Rev.: $40,245,464
Assets: $55,268,593
Liabilities: $19,937,200
Net Worth: $35,331,394
Earnings: $1,618,510
Emp.: 62
Fiscal Year-end: 12/31/22
Car Infotainment System Distr
N.A.I.C.S.: 423120

MOBILE COMPUTING CORPORATION
6300 Northwest Dr Unit #1, Mississauga, L4V 1J7, ON, Canada
Tel.: (905) 676-8900

Web Site:
  https://www.mobilecom.com
Year Founded: 1984
Sales Range: $10-24.9 Million
Emp.: 30
Workforce Automation Software Solutions
N.A.I.C.S.: 334610
Camille S. Peters (Pres & CEO)

MOBILE DIGITAL COMMUNICATIONS LTD.
36/2 Internatsionalnaya Ave, Minsk, Belarus
Tel.: (375) 3303030
Web Site: http://www.velcom.by
Telecommunication Servicesb
N.A.I.C.S.: 517810
Helmut Duhs (CEO)

MOBILE FACTORY INC.
8F Higashi-Gotanda 1-chome Building 1-24-2 Higashi - Gotanda, Shinagawa-ku, Tokyo, 141-0022, Japan
Tel.: (81) 334471181
Web Site:
  https://www.mobilefactory.jp
3912—(TKS)
Rev.: $23,893,300
Assets: $27,438,300
Liabilities: $6,139,940
Net Worth: $21,298,360
Emp.: 85
Fiscal Year-end: 12/31/23
Mobile Applications
N.A.I.C.S.: 513210
Miyajima Yuji (Founder & CEO)

MOBILE INTERNET (CHINA) HOLDINGS LIMITED
Hong Sheng Industrial Park Fengxin Industrial Zone, Yichun, Jiangxi, China
Tel.: (86) 7954588155
Web Site: http://www.hs-pack.com
1439—(HKG)
Rev.: $25,630,441
Assets: $34,169,429
Liabilities: $83,655,936
Net Worth: ($49,486,507)
Earnings: ($26,666,734)
Emp.: 300
Fiscal Year-end: 12/31/21
Packaging Products Mfr
N.A.I.C.S.: 322212
Hong Cai Chen (Chm)

MOBILE STREAMS PLC
125 Wood Street, London, EC2V 7AW, United Kingdom
Tel.: (44) 2036035255
Web Site:
  http://www.mobilestreams.com
MOS—(AIM)
Rev.: $2,265,043
Assets: $1,317,550
Liabilities: $655,670
Net Worth: $661,879
Earnings: ($4,705,180)
Emp.: 6
Fiscal Year-end: 06/30/23
Mobile Content & Messaging Products
N.A.I.C.S.: 517112
Simon D. Buckingham (Founder)

Subsidiaries:

Mobile Streams De Argentina S.R.L. (1)
San Martin 323 Piso 17, Buenos Aires, C1004 AAG, Argentina
Tel.: (54) 1148110213
Emp.: 40
Mobile Application Design Services
N.A.I.C.S.: 513210

INTERNATIONAL PUBLIC

Mobile Streams Inc (1)
909 3rd Ave 28th Fl, New York, NY 10022
Tel.: (212) 223-0795
Mobile Content Distr
N.A.I.C.S.: 321991
Simon Buckingham (CEO)

MOBILE TELECOMMUNICATIONS COMPANY K.S.C.
Tel.: (965) 24644444
Web Site: https://www.zain.com
Year Founded: 1983
ZAIN—(KUW)
Rev.: $6,204,108,031
Assets: $16,236,133,771
Liabilities: $9,865,322,240
Net Worth: $6,370,811,531
Earnings: $945,064,838
Emp.: 7,900
Fiscal Year-end: 12/31/23
Telecommunication Servicesb
N.A.I.C.S.: 517112
Bader Nasser Al-Kharafi (Vice Chm & Grp CEO)

Subsidiaries:

Mobile Telecommunications Company Saudi Arabia (1)
Granada Business Park - Building A3, PO Box 295814, Ash Shuhada, Riyadh, 11351, Saudi Arabia
Tel.: (966) 592448888
Web Site: https://www.sa.zain.com
Rev.: $2,419,723,237
Assets: $7,560,548,194
Liabilities: $4,947,598,454
Net Worth: $2,612,949,740
Earnings: $146,558,059
Fiscal Year-end: 12/31/2022
Mobile Telecommunications
N.A.I.C.S.: 517112

Zain Bahrain B.S.C (Closed) (1)
Zain Bahrain Tower Road 2806 Building 401 Block 428, PO Box 266, Manama, Bahrain
Tel.: (973) 36031000
Web Site: http://www.bh.zain.com
Telecommunication Servicesb
N.A.I.C.S.: 517112

MOBILE TELESYSTEMS PUBLIC JOINT STOCK COMPANY
Vorontsovskaya street Bldg 4, 109147, Moscow, Russia
Tel.: (7) 4957660055   RU
Web Site: http://ir.mts.ru
Year Founded: 1993
MBT—(NYSE)
Rev.: $7,198,408,410
Assets: $13,683,068,460
Liabilities: $13,486,352,580
Net Worth: $196,715,880
Earnings: $854,981,310
Emp.: 57,843
Fiscal Year-end: 12/31/21
Mobile Cellular Communication Services
N.A.I.C.S.: 517112
Ruslan S. Ibragimov (Member-Mgmt Bd & VP-Govt Rels & PR)

Subsidiaries:

Comstar United TeleSystems JSC (1)
Petrovsky blv 12/3, 127051, Moscow, Russia (62%)
Tel.: (7) 4959560000
Web Site: http://www.comstar.ru
Sales Range: $1-4.9 Billion
Telecommunication Servicesb
N.A.I.C.S.: 517111

Subsidiary (Domestic):

Moscow City Telephone Network JSC (2)
12 Petrovskiy Boulevard Bldg 3, Moscow, 127994, Russia
Tel.: (7) 4959500000
Web Site: http://www.mgts.ru

AND PRIVATE COMPANIES

Sales Range: $600-649.9 Million
Emp.: 18,022
Telecommunications & Data Transmission Services
N.A.I.C.S.: 517111

Mobile TeleSystems B.V. (1)
Prins Bernhardplein 200, 1097JB, Amsterdam, Netherlands
Web Site: http://ir.mts.ru
Wireless Telecommunication Services
N.A.I.C.S.: 517112

Subsidiary (Non-US):

PJSC MTS Bank (2)
Andropova Avenue 18 Building 1, 115432, Moscow, Russia (94.7%)
Tel.: (7) 4957770001
Web Site: http://www.mtsbank.ru
Commericial Banking
N.A.I.C.S.: 522110
Ilya Valentinovich Filatov *(Chm-Mgmt Bd & CEO)*

Multiregional TransitTelecom OJSC (1)
Marksistskaya st 22 bldg 1, 109147, Moscow, Russia (100%)
Tel.: (7) 4997090101
Web Site: http://en.mtt.ru
Telecommunication Servicesb
N.A.I.C.S.: 517112
Evgeny Vasiliev *(CEO)*

Ukrainian Mobile Communications (1)
Leiptsigska 15, 06101, Kiev, Ukraine
Tel.: (380) 442300257
Web Site: http://www.mps.com.ua
Provider of Telephone Services
N.A.I.C.S.: 517111

MOBILE WORLD INVESTMENT CORPORATION
Lot T2-1 2 D1 Street High-Tech Park Tan Phu Ward, Thu Duc, Ho Chi Minh City, Vietnam
Tel.: (84) 2838125960
Web Site: https://mwg.vn
Year Founded: 2004
MWG—(HOSE)
Rev.: $13,472,224,889
Assets: $5,583,409,561
Liabilities: $3,190,151,410
Net Worth: $2,393,258,152
Earnings: $409,976,303
Emp.: 74,008
Fiscal Year-end: 12/31/22
Investment Services
N.A.I.C.S.: 523999
Nguyen Duc Tai *(Chm)*

Subsidiaries:

Tran Anh Digital World Joint Stock Company (1)
No 1174 Lang Street Lang Thuong Ward Dong Da District, Dong Da District, Hanoi, Vietnam (99.33%)
Tel.: (84) 437666666
Web Site: https://www.trananh.com.vn
Sales Range: $125-149.9 Million
Consumer Electronics & Home Appliances Retailer
N.A.I.C.S.: 449210

MOBILE-HEALTH NETWORK SOLUTIONS
2 Venture Drive 07-06/07 Vision Exchange, Singapore, 608526, Singapore
Tel.: (65) 62225223   Ky
Year Founded: 2009
MNDR—(NASDAQ)
Rev.: $13,968,535
Assets: $7,950,615
Liabilities: $3,811,162
Net Worth: $4,139,453
Earnings: ($15,602,792)
Emp.: 73
Fiscal Year-end: 06/30/24
Health Care Srvices
N.A.I.C.S.: 621610

MOBILE-TECHNOLOGIES CO., LTD.
193/49-50 12A Floor Lake Rajada Office Complex Rachadapisek Road, Klongtoey, Bangkok, 10110, Thailand
Tel.: (66) 2661 8858
Web Site: http://www.mobile-technologies.com
Information Technology Services
N.A.I.C.S.: 541511
Eli Hem Jensen *(CEO)*

MOBILETRON ELECTRONICS CO., LTD.
85 Sec 4 Chung-Ching Rd, Ta-Ya District, Taichung, 428, Taiwan
Tel.: (886) 425683366
Web Site: https://www.more.com.tw
1533—(TAI)
Rev.: $130,927,592
Assets: $274,697,429
Liabilities: $185,391,471
Net Worth: $89,305,958
Earnings: ($7,240,165)
Emp.: 865
Fiscal Year-end: 12/31/23
Electronic Control System Mfr
N.A.I.C.S.: 336320
Y. C. Kim Tsai *(Chm & Pres)*

Subsidiaries:

Mobiletron Comecio de Autopecas e Ferramentas Ltda (1)
Rua Salviano da Silva No 445 Quadra 1 Lote 08, Sao Jose dos Campos, 12238-573, Sao Paulo, Brazil
Tel.: (55) 12 3903 9500
Web Site: http://www.more.com.tw
Automobile Electronic Product Mfr
N.A.I.C.S.: 334310

Mobiletron Electronics (Ningbo) Co., Ltd. (1)
C6 Zonea Far East Industry, Yuyao, Zhejiang, China
Tel.: (86) 574 62760669
Web Site: http://www.more.com.tw
Automobile Electronics Tools Mfr & Distr
N.A.I.C.S.: 332216

Mobiletron U.K. LTD (1)
Unit 80 Roman Way Roman Way Industrial Estate, Longridge Road, Preston, PR2 5BE, Lancashire, United Kingdom
Tel.: (44) 1772693780
Sales Range: $25-49.9 Million
Emp.: 20
Automobile Electronic Components Mfr
N.A.I.C.S.: 336320
Ian Uttley *(Mng Dir)*

MOBILEWAVE GROUP PLC
71 Gloucester Place, London, W1U 8JW, United Kingdom
Tel.: (44) 2081445898
Web Site: http://www.mobilewave.com
Electronic Products Developer, Mfr & Marketer
N.A.I.C.S.: 335999
Rory M. Stear *(Founder, Chm & CEO)*

MOBILEWEBADZ LTD.
5-11 Lavington Street Europoint, London, SE1 0NZ, United Kingdom
Tel.: (44) 207 928 8128
Web Site: http://www.mobilewebadz.com
Year Founded: 2002
Sales Range: $25-49.9 Million
Emp.: 60
Mobile Advertising Services
N.A.I.C.S.: 541810
Kieran O'Keeffe *(Chm)*

MOBILEZONE HOLDING AG
Suurstoffi 22, 6343, Rotkreuz, Switzerland
Tel.: (41) 584002424
Web Site: https://www.mobilezoneholding.ch
Year Founded: 1999
MOZN—(SWX)
Rev.: $1,111,641,907
Assets: $418,412,417
Liabilities: $370,391,353
Net Worth: $48,021,064
Earnings: $60,462,306
Emp.: 921
Fiscal Year-end: 12/31/22
Cellular Telephone Services
N.A.I.C.S.: 517112
Markus Bernhard *(Co-CEO)*

Subsidiaries:

Mobiletouch AG (1)
Spinnerei-Lettenstrasse Zweidlen, 8192, Zurich, Switzerland
Tel.: (41) 840303303
Web Site: http://www.mobiletouch.ch
Emp.: 113
Portable Electronic Device Repair Services
N.A.I.C.S.: 811210

Mobiletouch Austria GmbH (1)
Lembockgasse 49 Haus 1 Stiege A1, Zufahrt mit dem Auto uber Talpagasse 1 / 3 OG, 1230, Vienna, Austria
Tel.: (43) 1866490
Web Site: https://www.mobiletouch.at
Portable Electronic Device Repair Services
N.A.I.C.S.: 811210
Martin Hammerschmid *(Mng Dir)*

SH Telekommunikation Deutschland GmbH (1)
Porschestrasse 7, 44809, Bochum, Germany
Tel.: (49) 22196070002
Web Site: http://www.sh.de
Telecommunication Servicesb
N.A.I.C.S.: 517810

TPHCom GmbH (1)
Bergiusstrasse 1a, 48165, Munster, Germany
Tel.: (49) 25019184891
Web Site: http://www.tphcom.de
Smartphone & Telecommunication Equipment Distr
N.A.I.C.S.: 423690
Carsten Stuwe *(Mgr-Key Account)*

TalkTalk AG (1)
Suurstoffi 22, 6343, Rotkreuz, Switzerland
Tel.: (41) 800300250
Web Site: https://www.talktalk.ch
Telecommunication Servicesb
N.A.I.C.S.: 517810

einsAmobile GmbH (1)
Samerwiesen 6, 63179, Obertshausen, Germany
Tel.: (49) 610440570
Web Site: http://www.einsamobile.de
Sales Range: $600-649.9 Million
Emp.: 40
Mobile Phone Whslr
N.A.I.C.S.: 423690
Murat Ayhan *(Founder & Mng Dir)*

mobilezone ag (1)
Suurstoffi 22, 6343, Rotkreuz, Zurich, Switzerland
Tel.: (41) 584002424
Web Site: https://www.mobilezone.ch
Sales Range: $50-74.9 Million
Emp.: 70
Cellular Telephones Sls
N.A.I.C.S.: 423690
Markus Bernhard *(CEO)*

mobilezone business ag (1)
Bahnweg 4, 9107, Urnasch, Switzerland
Tel.: (41) 71 364 11 13
Sales Range: $25-49.9 Million
Emp.: 30
Cellular Telephone Services
N.A.I.C.S.: 517112

MOBILIARIA MONESA S.A.
Av Diagonal 429, Barcelona, 08036, Spain
Tel.: (34) 933662727
Web Site: http://www.mobiliariamonesa.com
Sales Range: Less than $1 Million
Financial Investment Services
N.A.I.C.S.: 523999
Francisco De Paula Guinart Villaret *(Chm)*

MOBILICOM LTD.
1 Rakefet Steet Shoham, Azor, 6083705, Israel
Tel.: (972) 777103060
Web Site: https://www.mobilicom.com
MOB—(NASDAQ)
Rev.: $1,782,969
Assets: $16,248,014
Liabilities: $2,563,165
Net Worth: $13,684,848
Earnings: ($261,630)
Emp.: 24
Fiscal Year-end: 12/31/22
Mobile Wireless Telecommunication Services
N.A.I.C.S.: 517112
Yossi Segal *(Co-Founder & VP-R&D)*

MOBILITAS SA
14, rue Denis Papin, 95250, Beauchamp, France
Tel.: (33) 17766686
Web Site: https://www.mobilitas.org
Year Founded: 1974
Emp.: 4,500
International Trade & Development
N.A.I.C.S.: 522299

Subsidiaries:

Santa Fe Holdings Ltd. (1)
18/F C C Wu Bldg 302 - 308 Hennessy Rd, Wanchai, China (Hong Kong)
Tel.: (852) 25746204
Investment Management Service
N.A.I.C.S.: 523940
Samuel Mergui *(CEO)*

MOBILITYONE LIMITED
2-3 Incubator 2 Technology Park Malaysia, Bukit Jalil, 57000, Kuala Lumpur, Malaysia
Tel.: (60) 389963600   JE
Web Site: https://www.mobilityone.com.my
Year Founded: 2007
MBO—(AIM)
Rev.: $307,668,941
Assets: $19,985,231
Liabilities: $15,829,328
Net Worth: $4,155,903
Earnings: ($1,792,657)
Emp.: 127
Fiscal Year-end: 12/31/23
Electronic Transaction & Payment Services
N.A.I.C.S.: 522320
Rizal A. Rahman *(CEO)*

Subsidiaries:

M1 Pay Sdn. Bhd. (1)
Wisma LMS No 6 Jalan Abdul Rahman Idris, Kampung Baru, 50300, Kuala Lumpur, Malaysia
Tel.: (60) 392130669
Web Site: https://www.m1pay.com.my
Commercial Banking Services
N.A.I.C.S.: 522110
Muhammad Afiq *(Mgr)*

MOBILUM TECHNOLOGIES INC.
700-838 W Hastings Street, Vancouver, V6C 0A6, BC, Canada
Tel.: (778) 990-8985   BC
Web Site: https://mobilum.com
Year Founded: 2010
MBLM—(CNSX)
Rev.: $1,084,558
Assets: $13,338,691
Liabilities: $3,144,095

MOBILUM TECHNOLOGIES INC.

Mobilum Technologies Inc.—(Continued)
Net Worth: $10,194,596
Earnings: ($31,795,990)
Fiscal Year-end: 02/28/22
Software Publisher
N.A.I.C.S.: 513210

MOBIMO HOLDING AG
Rutligasse 1, CH-6000, Lucerne, Switzerland
Tel.: (41) 412494980 CH
Web Site: https://www.mobimo.ch
Year Founded: 1999
MOBN—(SWX)
Rev.: $300,192,905
Assets: $4,274,365,854
Liabilities: $2,162,647,450
Net Worth: $2,111,718,404
Earnings: $150,008,869
Emp.: 160
Fiscal Year-end: 12/31/22
Holding Company
N.A.I.C.S.: 551112
Daniel Crausaz *(Vice Chm)*

Subsidiaries:

BSS&M Real Estate AG (1)
Seestrasse 59, 8700, Kusnacht, Switzerland
Tel.: (41) 442895030
Web Site: https://www.projektkontor.ch
Property Management Services
N.A.I.C.S.: 531311

Mobimo FM Service AG (1)
Seestrasse 59, CH-8700, Kusnacht, Switzerland
Tel.: (41) 444654411
Web Site: https://www.mobimofmservice.ch
Property Management Services
N.A.I.C.S.: 531311
Daniel Wermuth *(Mng Dir)*

Mobimo Management AG (1)
Seestrasse 59, 8700, Kusnacht, Switzerland
Tel.: (41) 443971111
Web Site: https://www.mobimo.ch
Property Management Services
N.A.I.C.S.: 531311
Daniel Ducrey *(CEO)*

Projektkontor AG (1)
Muhlebachstrasse 23, 8008, Zurich, Switzerland
Tel.: (41) 442895030
Web Site: https://www.projektkontor.ch
Real Estate Services
N.A.I.C.S.: 531390

MOBIO TECHNOLOGIES INC.
1080 Mainland St Suite 205, Vancouver, V6B 2T4, BC, Canada
Tel.: (604) 428-7050
Web Site: https://www.mobio.net
Year Founded: 1998
MBO—(TSXV)
Rev.: $6,310
Assets: $31,532
Liabilities: $587,649
Net Worth: ($556,117)
Earnings: ($170,248)
Fiscal Year-end: 07/31/22
Software Solutions
N.A.I.C.S.: 513210
Laurie Baggio *(CEO)*

MOBIRIX CORPORATION
604-607 Jayplatz 186 Gasan Digital 1-ro, Geumcheon-Gu, Seoul, 8502, Korea (South)
Tel.: (82) 220285700
Web Site: https://www.mobirix.com
Year Founded: 2007
348030—(KRS)
Rev.: $52,180,455
Assets: $74,054,109
Liabilities: $6,338,923
Net Worth: $67,715,186
Earnings: $9,148,999

Emp.: 104
Fiscal Year-end: 12/31/21
Software Development Services
N.A.I.C.S.: 541511
Sang-Hyun Yoo *(Gen Mgr)*

MOBIUS ECOCAPITAL PLC
2015 Victoria Street Suite 200, Saint-Lambert, J4S 1H1, QC, Canada
Tel.: (450) 923-9381 UK
Web Site:
http://www.mobiusecocapital.com
Year Founded: 2010
Investment Services; Carbon
N.A.I.C.S.: 523999
Yves Gauthier *(Chm)*

Subsidiaries:

Carbonfolio (1)
2206 Maryse Bastie, Montreal, H4R 3C5, QC, Canada
Tel.: (514) 953-5412
Web Site: http://www.carbonfolio.com
Sales Range: $50-74.9 Million
Emp.: 2
Financial Support Services
N.A.I.C.S.: 523999

L2I - Financial Solutions Inc. (1)
2015 Victoria Ave Ste 200, Saint-Lambert, J4S 1H1, QC, Canada
Tel.: (450) 923-9381
Web Site: http://www.solutionsl2i.com
Financial Support Services
N.A.I.C.S.: 561990

MOBIUS INVESTMENT TRUST PLC
25 Southampton Buildings, London, WC2A 1AL, United Kingdom
Tel.: (44) 2038298500 UK
Web Site:
https://www.mobiusinvestment.com
Year Founded: 2018
MMIT—(LSE)
Sales Range: Less than $1 Million
Portfolio Management & Investment Advice
N.A.I.C.S.: 523940
Mark Mobius *(Founder)*

MOBIUS KNOWLEDGE SERVICES PVT. LTD.
1st Floor Block A1 Gateway Office Parks, Perungalathur, Chennai, 600 063, India
Tel.: (91) 4449085800 In
Web Site:
http://www.mobiusservices.com
Year Founded: 2002
Emp.: 1,000
Outsourced Data Aggregation, Information Processing & Other Value-Added Services
N.A.I.C.S.: 519290
Karthik Karunakaran *(Co-Founder & CEO)*

Subsidiaries:

Mobius365 Data Services Private Limited (1)
Block No 1168/4-7 3rd & 4th Floor Samsurya Constructions Behind Airtel, Building Avinashi Road PN Palayam, Coimbatore, 641037, Tamil Nadu, India
Tel.: (91) 422 2240348
Web Site: http://www.mobius365.com
Emp.: 320
Data Service Provider
N.A.I.C.S.: 518210
Karthik Karunakaran *(CEO)*

Mobius365 Knowledge Services Incorporated (1)
48 Wall St 11th Fl, New York, NY 10005
Tel.: (646) 664-1983
Web Site: http://www.mobius365.com
Data Service Provider
N.A.I.C.S.: 518210
Karthik Karunakaran *(CEO)*

Subsidiary (Domestic):

365 Media, Inc. (2)
1820 Gateway Dr Ste 170, San Mateo, CA 94404
Tel.: (650) 286-4108
Web Site: http://www.365media.com
Sales Range: $25-49.9 Million
Emp.: 300
Technology Solutions for the Publishing Industry
N.A.I.C.S.: 541519
John Tilly *(CEO)*

MOBIVENTURES, INC.
1st Floor Offies 3 Anchor Business Center, Swindon, ENG SN5 842, United Kingdom
Tel.: (44) 7740611413
Year Founded: 2005
MBLV—(OTCIQ)
Sales Range: Less than $1 Million
Software Development Services
N.A.I.C.S.: 513210

MOBIVIA GROUPE SA
511/589 Rue des Seringats, 59262, Sainghin-en-Melantois, France
Tel.: (33) 3 20 60 74 74
Web Site: http://www.mobivia.com
Sales Range: $1-4.9 Billion
Emp.: 10,600
Holding Company Services
N.A.I.C.S.: 551112
Christophe Ribault *(Chm)*

Subsidiaries:

A.T.U Auto-Teile-Unger GmbH & Co. KG (1)
Dr-Kilian-Strasse 11, 92637, Weiden, Germany
Tel.: (49) 96163186650
Web Site: http://www.atu.de
Sales Range: $1-4.9 Billion
Emp.: 10,000
Automotive Parts & Accessories Retailer & Repair Services
N.A.I.C.S.: 811111
Markus Meissner *(Head-Corp Comm)*

Norauto SA (1)
511/589 rue des Seringats, 59262, Sainghin-en-Melantois, France
Tel.: (33) 320607474
Web Site: http://www.norauto.fr
Sales Range: $1-4.9 Billion
Emp.: 8,067
Automotive Care Services
N.A.I.C.S.: 811198
Fabien Derville *(Mng Dir)*

Subsidiary (Non-US):

Norauto Hungary Kft (2)
Bocskai ut 134-146, 1113, Budapest, Hungary
Tel.: (36) 18806200
Motor Vehicle Supplies & New Parts Whslr
N.A.I.C.S.: 423120

Norauto Italia Spa (2)
Via Bologna 94 F, Turin, Italy
Tel.: (39) 0112445611
Automotive Parts & Accessories Stores
N.A.I.C.S.: 441330

Norauto Polska Sp. z o.o. (2)
ul Jubilerska 10 04-190 Warszawa, Warsaw, 04 190, Poland
Tel.: (48) 225151000
Motor Vehicle Supplies & New Parts Whslr
N.A.I.C.S.: 423120
Christian Michelet *(Gen Mgr)*

Norauto Portugal - PeCas E Acessorios, Lda (2)
Avenida Dos Cavaleiros 49A, Carnaxide, 2794 057, Portugal (100%)
Tel.: (351) 214250800
Sales Range: $25-49.9 Million
Emp.: 41
Automotive Parts & Accessories Stores
N.A.I.C.S.: 441330
Carlos Grossinho *(Gen Mgr)*

Norauto Sherry SL (2)

Cuatro Caminos, Jerez De La Frontera, Cadiz, Spain
Tel.: (34) 956312815
Automobile & Motor Vehicle Whslr
N.A.I.C.S.: 423110

MOBVISTA, INC.
43/F-44/F Tianying Plaza No 222-3 Xingmin Road, Zhujiang New Town Tianhe District, Guangzhou, Guangdong, China
Tel.: (86) 2037039010 Ky
Web Site: http://www.mobvista.com
Year Founded: 2013
1860—(HKG)
Rev.: $894,405,000
Assets: $602,074,000
Liabilities: $354,035,000
Net Worth: $248,039,000
Earnings: $10,190,000
Emp.: 777
Fiscal Year-end: 12/31/22
Mobile Application Development Services
N.A.I.C.S.: 541511
Wei Duan *(Co-Founder & Co-Chm)*

MOCHE INVERSIONES S.A.
Av Manuel Olguin 335 Oficina 1405, Santiago de Surco, Lima, Peru
Tel.: (51) 640 8101
Web Site: http://www.moche.pe
Year Founded: 2006
Telecommunication Servicesb
N.A.I.C.S.: 517810

MOCHIDA PHARMACEUTICAL CO., LTD.
7 Yotsuya 1-chome, Shinjuku-ku, Tokyo, 160-8515, Japan
Tel.: (81) 333587211
Web Site: https://www.mochida.co.jp
Year Founded: 1913
45340—(TKS)
Rev.: $996,991,600
Assets: $1,566,136,880
Liabilities: $337,028,560
Net Worth: $1,229,108,320
Earnings: $83,122,160
Emp.: 1,558
Fiscal Year-end: 03/31/21
Pharmaceutical Product Mfr & Distr
N.A.I.C.S.: 325412
Yoichi Kono *(Exec Mng Dir)*

Subsidiaries:

Mochida International Co., Ltd. (1)
YS Building 9 San-eicho, Shinjuku-Ku, Tokyo, 160-0008, Japan
Tel.: (81) 332250901
Pharmaceuticals Product Mfr
N.A.I.C.S.: 325412

Mochida Pharmaceutical Plant Co., Ltd. (1)
431 Nakadawara, Otawara, 324-0062, Tochigi, Japan (100%)
Tel.: (81) 28 724 1111
Web Site: https://mpp.mochida.co.jp
Emp.: 336
Pharmaceuticals Product Mfr
N.A.I.C.S.: 325412

Technofine Co., Ltd. (1)
342 Gensuke, Fujieda, 426-8640, Shizuoka, Japan
Tel.: (81) 54 636 7032
Pharmaceuticals Product Mfr
N.A.I.C.S.: 325412

Technonet Co., Ltd. (1)
4-7-17 Chuo, Nakano-ku, Tokyo, 164-0011, Japan
Tel.: (81) 367460080
Web Site: https://www.technonet.co.jp
Pharmaceuticals Product Mfr
N.A.I.C.S.: 325412

MODA BAGNO - N. VARVERIS S.A.

AND PRIVATE COMPANIES

50 Anapafseos Str, 152 35, Vrilissia, Greece
Tel.: (30) 2108036700
Web Site: https://www.modabagno.gr
Year Founded: 1980
MODA—(ATH)
Sales Range: Less than $1 Million
Emp.: 200
Home Furnishings Retailer
N.A.I.C.S.: 449129
Nikolaos E. Varveris *(Chm & CEO)*

MODA INC.
Trust Tower 13F 60 Mabang-ro Seocho-gu, Seoul, 137-739, Korea (South)
Tel.: (82) 2 523 7677
Web Site: http://web.modacom.co.kr
Year Founded: 1991
Sales Range: $10-24.9 Million
Emp.: 105
High Speed Mobile Communication Device Mfr
N.A.I.C.S.: 334220
Jong-Sei Kim *(Pres & CEO)*

MODA-INNOCHIPS CO., LTD.
769-12 Wonsi-dong Danwon-gu, Ansan, Gyeonggi-do, Korea (South)
Tel.: (82) 3180400000
Web Site: http://www.innochips.co.kr
Year Founded: 2000
080420—(KRS)
Rev.: $315,457,907
Assets: $772,869,436
Liabilities: $482,690,818
Net Worth: $290,178,618
Earnings: ($47,045)
Emp.: 442
Fiscal Year-end: 12/31/22
Electronic Components Mfr
N.A.I.C.S.: 334419
Oh Yil Gwon *(CEO)*

MODALIS THERAPEUTICS CORPORATION
3-11-5 Nihonbashi-Honcho Nihonbashi-Lifescience-Bldg 2 7F, Chuo-ku, Tokyo, 103-0023, Japan
Tel.: (81) 368224584
Web Site: https://www.modalistx.com
Year Founded: 2016
4883—(TKS)
Assets: $14,357,250
Liabilities: $4,573,050
Net Worth: $9,784,200
Earnings: ($16,952,190)
Emp.: 27
Fiscal Year-end: 12/31/23
Pharmaceuticals Product Mfr
N.A.I.C.S.: 325412
Tetsuya Yamagata *(CTO & Sr VP)*

MODE...INFORMATION GMBH
Pilgerstrasse 20, 51491, Overath, Germany
Tel.: (49) 220660070
Web Site: http://www.modeinfo.com
Year Founded: 1957
Rev.: $30,898,560
Emp.: 67
Fashion Consulting Service
N.A.I.C.S.: 541490
Yann Menard *(Mng Dir)*

MODEL RESTAURANTS COMPANY PLC
Almadinah Almunawara Street Al Haytham Building 5th Floor, PO Box 2975, Amman, 11181, Jordan
Tel.: (962) 5539307
Year Founded: 2007
FOOD—(AMM)
Sales Range: $1-9.9 Million
Emp.: 6
Restaurant Operators

N.A.I.C.S.: 722511
Amer Al Kawthar *(Gen Mgr)*

MODELLA WOOLLENS LIMITED
4-C Vulcan Insurance Building Veer Nariman Road, Churchgate, Mumbai, 400 020, India
Tel.: (91) 2222047424
Web Site: https://www.modellawoollens.com
Year Founded: 1961
503772—(BOM)
Rev.: $195,376
Assets: $59,147
Liabilities: $63,072
Net Worth: ($3,926)
Earnings: $187,339
Emp.: 3
Fiscal Year-end: 03/31/23
Fabric Material Whslr
N.A.I.C.S.: 424310
Sandeep P. Shah *(Chm)*

MODERN ANIMAL & AGRICULTURAL PRODUCTION
Nedal Street Raeden Architecture, Baghdad, Iraq
Tel.: (964) 1 5559987
Year Founded: 1991
Animal Production Services
N.A.I.C.S.: 112990

MODERN AVENUE GROUP CO., LTD.
No 23 Guangpu Middle Road, Huangpu Road West Tianhe District, Guangzhou, Guangdong, China
Tel.: (86) 2083963777
Web Site: https://www.modernavegroup.com
002656—(SSE)
Rev.: $32,276,556
Assets: $110,962,332
Liabilities: $39,804,804
Net Worth: $71,157,528
Earnings: ($5,812,560)
Emp.: 800
Fiscal Year-end: 12/31/22
Men's Clothing Mfr & Retailer
N.A.I.C.S.: 315250

MODERN CHEMICAL INDUSTRIES CO.
Sec 925 St 8 Bld 28 Behind Bata, Baghdad, Iraq
Tel.: (964) 1 7783358
Year Founded: 1946
IMCI—(IRAQ)
Sales Range: Less than $1 Million
Chemical Products Mfr
N.A.I.C.S.: 325998

MODERN CHINESE MEDICINE GROUP COMPANY LIMITED
88 Jinwei Road, Longhua County, Chengde, China
Tel.: (86) 3147162222   Ky
Web Site: http://www.cdysjdyy.com
Year Founded: 1986
1643—(HKG)
Medical Instrument Mfr
N.A.I.C.S.: 339112
Wei Xie *(Chm)*

MODERN CONSTRUCTION MATERIALS INDUSTRY CO.
Al-Garmah Al-Enbar, Fallujah, Iraq
Tel.: (964) 24662196
Year Founded: 1976
Construction Materials Mfr
N.A.I.C.S.: 327390

MODERN DAIRIES LTD.
136 km GT Road, P Box 3, Karnal, 132001, Haryana, India

Tel.: (91) 1745242901
Web Site: https://www.milkplus.com
Year Founded: 1992
519287—(BOM)
Rev.: $83,324,446
Assets: $10,162,684
Liabilities: $25,601,735
Net Worth: ($15,439,051)
Earnings: ($4,741,287)
Emp.: 398
Fiscal Year-end: 03/31/21
Dairy Products Mfr
N.A.I.C.S.: 311514
Krishnan Kumar Goyal *(Chm & Mng Dir)*

MODERN DENIM LTD.
10 KM Mile Stone Sarkhej-Bavla N H 8 A Ta Sanand, Village Moraiya, Ahmedabad, 382210, Gujarat, India
Tel.: (91) 2717251361
Web Site: http://www.moderndenim.com
Year Founded: 1991
Fabrics Mfr
N.A.I.C.S.: 313310
Sachin Ranka *(Chm & Mng Dir)*

MODERN DENTAL GROUP LIMITED
Units 1708-16 17/F CEO Tower 77 Wing Hong Street, Cheung Sha Wan Kowloon, Hong Kong, China (Hong Kong)
Tel.: (852) 3766 0777
Web Site: http://www.moderndentalgp.com
Emp.: 91
Dental Prosthetics
N.A.I.C.S.: 339114
Ngai Shing Kin *(CEO)*

Subsidiaries:

MicroDental, Inc.   (1)
5601 Arnold Rd, Dublin, CA 94568
Tel.: (925) 829-3611
Web Site: http://www.microdental.com
Full Service Dental Laboratories
N.A.I.C.S.: 339116
Mike Gerard *(CEO)*

MODERN EKONOMI SVERIGE HOLDING AB
Munkgatan 7, 722 12, Vasteras, Sweden
Tel.: (46) 854512110
Web Site: http://www.modernekonomi.se
ME—(OMX)
Rev.: $12,952,688
Assets: $6,907,286
Liabilities: $5,781,709
Net Worth: $1,125,578
Earnings: ($31,741)
Emp.: 113
Fiscal Year-end: 09/30/20
Business Management Consulting Services
N.A.I.C.S.: 541611
Frans Blom *(CEO)*

MODERN ENGINEERING AND PROJECTS LIMITED
103/4 Plot -215 Free Press House Fl-10 Free Press Journal Marg, Nariman Point, Mumbai, 400021, India
Tel.: (91) 2266666007   In
Web Site: https://mep.ltd
Year Founded: 1946
539762—(BOM)
Rev.: $10,975
Assets: $419,799
Liabilities: $1,388
Net Worth: $418,412
Earnings: ($6,822)
Fiscal Year-end: 03/31/21
Cultivation Services

MODERN LAND (CHINA) CO., LTD.

N.A.I.C.S.: 111339
Yash Kishore Saraogi *(Mng Dir)*

MODERN HEALTHCARE TECHNOLOGY HOLDINGS LIMITED
6/F Sino Industrial Plaza 9 Kai Cheung Road, Kowloon Bay, Kowloon, China (Hong Kong)
Tel.: (852) 28662377   Ky
Web Site: http://www.modernbeautysalon.com
0919—(HKG)
Rev.: $45,864,127
Assets: $73,642,808
Liabilities: $44,853,311
Net Worth: $28,789,497
Earnings: ($8,861,442)
Emp.: 904
Fiscal Year-end: 03/31/22
Beauty & Wellness Services
N.A.I.C.S.: 812112
Kai Wing Yip *(CTO)*

MODERN INDIA LTD
1 Mittal Chambers 228 Nariman Point, Mumbai, 400021, India
Tel.: (91) 226744 4200
Web Site: http://www.modernindia.co.in
Rev.: $29,548,889
Assets: $33,642,687
Liabilities: $28,700,090
Net Worth: $4,942,596
Earnings: ($460,443)
Emp.: 32
Fiscal Year-end: 03/31/19
Real Estate Services
N.A.I.C.S.: 531312
Vijay Kumar Jatia *(Chm & Mng Dir)*

Subsidiaries:

Indian Institute of Jewellery Limited   (1)
Mod Ctr Sane Guruji Marg Mahalaxmi, Mumbai, 400 011, Maharashtra, India
Tel.: (91) 2266661102
Web Site: http://www.iij.net.in
Sales Range: $25-49.9 Million
Emp.: 40
Jewellery Educational Services
N.A.I.C.S.: 458310
Renu Kapoor *(Gen Mgr)*

Modern India Property Developers Ltd.   (1)
Mod Ctr Sane Guruji Marg Mahalaxmi, Mumbai, 400 011, Maharashtra, India
Tel.: (91) 2266624181
Real Estate Manangement Services
N.A.I.C.S.: 531390
Vijaykumar Jatia *(Chm & Dir)*

MODERN INSULATORS LTD.
Talheti Abu Road, Sirohi, 307 026, Rajasthan, India
Tel.: (91) 2974228044
Web Site: http://www.moderninsulators.com
Insulator Mfr
N.A.I.C.S.: 327110
Sachin Ranka *(Chm & Mng Dir)*

MODERN LAND (CHINA) CO., LTD.
4F Building 10 Mega Hall No 1 Xiangheyuan Road, Dongcheng District, Beijing, 100028, China
Tel.: (86) 1084407008
Web Site: http://www.modernland.hk
1107—(HKG)
Rev.: $2,411,606,448
Assets: $12,549,717,756
Liabilities: $10,867,829,395
Net Worth: $1,681,888,361
Earnings: $171,133,272
Emp.: 2,387
Fiscal Year-end: 12/31/20

MODERN LAND (CHINA) CO., LTD.

Modern Land (China) Co., Ltd.—(Continued)
Real Estate Developers
N.A.I.C.S.: 237210
Lei Zhang (Chm)

Subsidiaries:

America Modern Green Development (Houston), LLC (1)
11233 Shadow Creek Pkwy Ste 289, Pearland, TX 77584
Tel.: (281) 741-3837
Real Estate Manangement Services
N.A.I.C.S.: 531390

Crown Point Regional Center, LLC (1)
11233 Shadow Creek Pkwy Ste 289, Pearland, TX 77584
Tel.: (281) 741-3837
Web Site: http://www.crownpointus.com
Investment & Immigration Consulting Services
N.A.I.C.S.: 541618
Tingfu Qiao (Exec VP)

MODERN MALLEABLES LIMITED

Malleable House 53-B Mirza Ghalib Street, Kolkata, 700016, India
Tel.: (91) 3322264904
Web Site:
https://www.modernmalleables.com
Year Founded: 1982
23035—(CSE)
Line Fitting Mfr
N.A.I.C.S.: 332913
Vinay Jha (Compliance Officer, Sec & Sr VP)

MODERN MOBILITY AIDS, INC.

79 Bramsteele Road, Brampton, L6W3K6, ON, Canada
Tel.: (416) 254-2581   NV
Year Founded: 2007
MDRM—(OTCIQ)
Assets: $133,000
Liabilities: $799,000
Net Worth: ($666,000)
Earnings: ($408,000)
Emp.: 7
Fiscal Year-end: 06/30/21
Personal Care Product Distr
N.A.I.C.S.: 456199
Tito DiMarco (CEO)

MODERN PAINTS INDUSTRIES CO.

Al Zafaraniya - Industrial complex, Baghdad, Iraq
Tel.: (964) 7734960745
Web Site: https://mpicoating.com
Year Founded: 1976
Paints Mfr
N.A.I.C.S.: 325510

MODERN PHARMACEUTICAL COMPANY LLC

Dubai Healthcare City Building No 71, PO Box 1586, District 1, Dubai, United Arab Emirates
Tel.: (971) 43834444   AE
Web Site:
http://www.mpchealthcare.com
Year Founded: 1969
Pharmaceuticals Product Mfr
N.A.I.C.S.: 325412

MODERN SEWING CO.

Al-Wezearia Sec 203 St 10 Buld 2, Baghdad, Iraq
Tel.: (964) 1 4253324
Year Founded: 1988
IMOS—(IRAQ)
Sales Range: Less than $1 Million
Apparels Mfr
N.A.I.C.S.: 314999

MODERN SHARES & STOCK BROKERS LTD.

Wankhede Stadium North Stand Staircase No13 D Road, Churchgate, Mumbai, 400020, India
Tel.: (91) 2268252400
Web Site:
https://www.modernshares.com
Year Founded: 1939
509760—(BOM)
Rev.: $355,878
Assets: $1,991,188
Liabilities: $536,599
Net Worth: $1,454,589
Earnings: $21,953
Emp.: 19
Fiscal Year-end: 03/31/23
Financial Services
N.A.I.C.S.: 523999
Anil S. Manghnani (Exec Dir)

MODERN STEELS LIMITED

G T Road, Mandi Gobindgarh, 147301, Punjab, India
Tel.: (91) 1722609001
Web Site:
https://www.modernsteels.com
Year Founded: 1973
513303—(BOM)
Rev.: $29,657,600
Assets: $15,772,400
Liabilities: $32,237,800
Net Worth: ($16,465,400)
Earnings: ($6,916,000)
Emp.: 255
Fiscal Year-end: 03/31/20
Steel Products Mfr
N.A.I.C.S.: 331210
Krishan Kumar Goyal (Chm & Mng Dir)

MODERN SYNTEX (INDIA) LTD.

A-4 Vijay Path Tilak Nagar, Jaipur, 302004, Rajasthan, India
Tel.: (91) 1412623431
500281—(BOM)
Textile Products Mfr
N.A.I.C.S.: 314999
H. S. Ranka (Chm & Mng Dir)

MODERN THREADS (INDIA) LTD.

A-4 Vijay Path Tilak Nagar, Jaipur, Rajasthan, India
Tel.: (91) 1414113645
Yarn & Sewing Thread Mfr
N.A.I.C.S.: 313110

MODERN TIMES GROUP MTG AB

Skeppsbron 18, Box 2094, 111 30, Stockholm, Sweden
Tel.: (46) 856200050   SE
Web Site: https://www.mtg.com
Year Founded: 1987
MTGB—(OMX)
Rev.: $647,756,480
Assets: $2,128,586,880
Liabilities: $917,187,040
Net Worth: $1,211,399,840
Earnings: ($55,424,320)
Emp.: 1,460
Fiscal Year-end: 12/31/21
Media & Communications Services Including TV Broadcasting, Radio, Publishing, Electronic Retailing & Media Services
N.A.I.C.S.: 516120
Maria Redin (Pres & CEO)

Subsidiaries:

DreamHack Sports Games A/S (1)
Lindgreens alle 12 S, 2300, Copenhagen, Denmark
Tel.: (45) 40778833
Web Site:
http://www.dreamhacksportsgames.com
Sports Organizing Services
N.A.I.C.S.: 711310
Roger Lodewick (CEO)

InnoGames GmbH (1)
Friesenstrasse 13, 20097, Hamburg, Germany
Tel.: (49) 4078893350
Web Site: https://www.innogames.com
Emp.: 350
Game Publisher
N.A.I.C.S.: 513210
Hendrik Klindworth (Co-Founder & CEO)

Kongregate Inc. (1)
10680 Treena St Ste 155, San Diego, CA 92131
Tel.: (415) 618-0087
Web Site: https://www.kongregate.com
Online Gambling Services
N.A.I.C.S.: 541511
Emily Greer (Founder)

MTG A/S Danmark (1)
Strandlodsvej, 1408, Copenhagen, Denmark
Tel.: (45) 77305503
Web Site: http://www.tv3.dk
Emp.: 20
Television Broadcasting Services
N.A.I.C.S.: 516120

Subsidiary (Domestic):

Strix Television A/S Danmark (2)
Vermundsgade 40 B St, 2100, Copenhagen, Denmark
Tel.: (45) 39 16 57 00
Web Site: http://www.strix.dk
Emp.: 5
Television Broadcasting Services
N.A.I.C.S.: 516120
Fredrik Hillerbrand (Country Mgr)

TV3 A/S Danmark (2)
Strandlodsvej 30, 1408, Copenhagen, Denmark
Tel.: (45) 77305500
Web Site: http://www.tv3.dk
Sales Range: $50-74.9 Million
Emp.: 20
Television Broadcasting Services
N.A.I.C.S.: 516120

Viasat Denmark (2)
Wildersgade 8, PO Box 4050, DK 1408, Copenhagen, Denmark
Tel.: (45) 70134050
Web Site: http://www.viasat.dk
Television Programming Subscription & Distribution Services
N.A.I.C.S.: 517111

MTG AS Norge (1)
Ingvald Ystegaards veg 7B, Trondheim, 7047, Norway
Tel.: (47) 73900822
Web Site: http://www.mtg.no
Television Broadcasting Services
N.A.I.C.S.: 516120

Subsidiary (Domestic):

P4 Radio hele Norge (2)
Storgaten 129, N2626, Lillehammer, Norway (40%)
Tel.: (47) 61248444
Web Site: http://www.p4.no
Sales Range: $25-49.9 Million
Emp.: 100
N.A.I.C.S.: 812990
Kalle Lisberg (Mng Dir)

P5 Radio Halve Norge AS (2)
Akersgata 73, 0180, Oslo, Norway
Tel.: (47) 23000000
Radio Broadcasting Services
N.A.I.C.S.: 516210

Strix Televisjon AS (2)
Karl Johansgt 12b Entrance From Kirkegt 34, 0154, Oslo, Norway
Tel.: (47) 22 40 17 20
Web Site: http://www.strix.no
Sales Range: $25-49.9 Million
Emp.: 100
Television Broadcasting Services
N.A.I.C.S.: 516120

INTERNATIONAL PUBLIC

TV3 AS Norge (2)
Akersgata 73, PO Box TV3 Youngstorget, Oslo, 0028, Norway
Tel.: (47) 22 99 00 33
Web Site: http://www.tv3.no
Sales Range: $25-49.9 Million
Emp.: 50
Television Broadcasting Services
N.A.I.C.S.: 516120
Vaiva Roscinaite (Controller-Inventory)

TV3 Norway (2)
Akers Gaten 73, Youngstorget, 0180, Oslo, Norway (100%)
Tel.: (47) 22990033
Web Site: http://www.tv3.no
Sales Range: $25-49.9 Million
Emp.: 47
N.A.I.C.S.: 812990
Morten Micalsen (Gen Mgr)

TV4 AS Norge (2)
Hammersborg Torg 1, 0179, Oslo, Norway
Tel.: (47) 22990033
Television Broadcasting Services
N.A.I.C.S.: 516120

Viasat AS Norge (2)
Youngstorget, PO Box 8873, 0028, Oslo, Norway (100%)
Tel.: (47) 22990150
Web Site: http://www.viasat.no
Sales Range: $25-49.9 Million
Emp.: 25
Television Programming Subscription & Distribution Services
N.A.I.C.S.: 517111
Vegard Drogseth (Mng Dir)

MTG Accounting AB (1)
Ringvagen 52, 118 67, Stockholm, Sweden
Tel.: (46) 8 562 086 00
Investment Management Service
N.A.I.C.S.: 523999

MTG Broadcast Centre Stockholm AB (1)
Positionen 2, 115 74, Stockholm, Sweden
Tel.: (46) 856209000
Television Broadcasting Services
N.A.I.C.S.: 516120
Jorgen Madsen (Gen Mgr)

MTG Broadcasting AB (1)
Skeppsbron 18, 103 13, Stockholm, Sweden
Tel.: (46) 856200050
Television Broadcasting Services
N.A.I.C.S.: 516120

MTG Broadcasting Holding AB (1)
Ringvagen 52, Stockholm, 11867, Sweden
Tel.: (46) 8 56 20 00 50
Web Site: http://www.mtg.com
Emp.: 900
Investment Management Service
N.A.I.C.S.: 523999
Jorgen Madsen (CEO)

MTG Financing Partners HB (1)
Ringvagen 52, 820 46, Stockholm, Sweden
Tel.: (46) 856200050
Web Site: http://www.mtg.com
Emp.: 1,000
Financial Management Services
N.A.I.C.S.: 523999
Anders Jensen (Mng Dir)

MTG Holding AB (1)
Skeppsbron 18, Stockholm, Sweden
Tel.: (46) 8 562 000 50
Investment Management Service
N.A.I.C.S.: 523999

MTG Modern Services AB (1)
Ringvagen 52, 11867, Stockholm, Sweden
Tel.: (46) 8 562 000 00
Web Site: http://www.mtg.com
Television Broadcasting Services
N.A.I.C.S.: 516120

MTG Modern Studios Holding AB (1)
Lumaparksvagen 11, Stockholm, 120 31, Sweden
Tel.: (46) 856208731
Investment Management Service
N.A.I.C.S.: 523999

Subsidiary (Domestic):

Strix Drama AB (2)

AND PRIVATE COMPANIES

Frihamnsgatan 28 Magasin 3, Box 27022,
102 51, Stockholm, Sweden
Tel.: (46) 8 522 595 00
Sales Range: $25-49.9 Million
Emp.: 10
Motion Picture Production Services
N.A.I.C.S.: 512110

MTG Online AB (1)
Soder Malarstrand 43, 118 25, Stockholm,
Sweden
Tel.: (46) 8 562 025 95
Online Television Broadcasting Services
N.A.I.C.S.: 516210

MTG Publishing AB (1)
Ringvagen 52, 111 60, Stockholm, Sweden
Tel.: (46) 856200050
Web Site: http://www.mtg.com
Newspaper Publishing Services
N.A.I.C.S.: 513110
Yorgen Madsen *(CEO)*

MTG Radio AB (1)
Ringvagen 52, Stockholm, 17115, Sweden
Tel.: (46) 8 562 720 00
Web Site: http://www.mtgradio.se
Radio Broadcasting & Networking Services
N.A.I.C.S.: 516210
Lotta Carlson *(Mgr-Natl Sls)*

MTG Radio Sales AB (1)
Ringvagen 52, Box 17115, 104 62, Stockholm, Sweden
Tel.: (46) 856272000
Radio Broadcasting Services
N.A.I.C.S.: 516210

MTG TV Online AB (1)
Soder Malarstrand 43, Box 17179, Stockholm, 104 62, Sweden
Tel.: (46) 8 562 327 16
Television Broadcasting Services
N.A.I.C.S.: 516120

Metro Mordyc Sweden (1)
Ringvagen 52, PO Box 45075, SE 11867,
Stockholm, Sweden **(100%)**
Tel.: (46) 84022030
Web Site: http://www.metro.se
Sales Range: $25-49.9 Million
Emp.: 100
N.A.I.C.S.: 812990

Modern Entertainment Ltd (1)
6740 Hayvenhurst Ave, Van Nuys, CA
91406-5772 **(100%)**
Tel.: (818) 909-9683
Sales Range: $50-74.9 Million
Emp.: 11
International Film Distributors
N.A.I.C.S.: 711190

Modern Times Group (1)
Skeppsbron 18, Box 2094, 111 30, Stockholm, Sweden **(100%)**
Tel.: (46) 856200050
Web Site: http://www.nordicartist.se
Sales Range: $75-99.9 Million
Emp.: 850
N.A.I.C.S.: 812990
Jorgen Madsen *(Mng Dir)*

**Nova Televizia First Private Channel
EAD** (1)
41 Christopher Columbus Blvd Porsche
Business Centre, 1592, Sofia, Bulgaria
Tel.: (359) 280 500 00
Web Site: http://www.mtg.com
Television Broadcasting Services
N.A.I.C.S.: 516120
Didier Stoessel *(CEO)*

OY Viasat Finland Ab (1)
PO Box 3000, 40101, Jyvaskyla, Finland
Tel.: (358) 9 424 999 99
Television Broadcasting Services
N.A.I.C.S.: 516120

RIX FM (1)
Ringvagen 52, Stockholm, 17115,
Sweden **(100%)**
Tel.: (46) 856272000
Web Site: http://www.rixfm.com
Sales Range: $25-49.9 Million
Emp.: 200
N.A.I.C.S.: 812990
Ana Bergeren *(Gen Mgr)*

Redaktorerna i Stockholm AB (1)
Ringvagen 52, Stockholm, Sweden

Tel.: (46) 8 562 086 90
Web Site: http://www.redaktorerna.se
Sales Range: $25-49.9 Million
Emp.: 14
Magazine Publishing Services
N.A.I.C.S.: 513120
Pia Constenius *(Dir-Art)*

**Societe Europeene de
Communication** (1)
75 Rte De Longwy, LU 8080, Bertrange,
Luxembourg **(100%)**
Tel.: (352) 27750101
Sales Range: $25-49.9 Million
Emp.: 100
N.A.I.C.S.: 812990

Strix Television AB (1)
Magasin 3 Frihamnsgatan 28, 115 56,
Stockholm, Sweden **(100%)**
Tel.: (46) 852259500
Web Site: http://strix.se
Sales Range: $25-49.9 Million
Emp.: 100
Television Production Services
N.A.I.C.S.: 512191

Subsidiary (Domestic):

Strix International (2)
Frihamnsgatan 28 Magasin 3, 11556,
Stockholm, Sweden
Tel.: (46) 8 522 595 00
Television Broadcasting Services
N.A.I.C.S.: 516120

Strix Television bv (1)
Meeuwenlaan 98-100, 1021 JL, Amsterdam, Netherlands
Tel.: (31) 20 31 22 900
Web Site: http://www.strix.no
Emp.: 30
Television Broadcasting Services
N.A.I.C.S.: 516120
Marjolein van Westerloo *(Mgr)*

TV3 (1)
Ringvagen 52, SE 10462, Stockholm,
Sweden **(100%)**
Tel.: (46) 856202300
Web Site: http://www.tv3.se
Sales Range: $75-99.9 Million
Emp.: 260
N.A.I.C.S.: 812990

TV3 Sweden (1)
Ringvagen 52, PO Box 54, SE 104 62,
Stockholm, Sweden **(100%)**
Tel.: (46) 856202300
Web Site: http://www.tv3.se
Sales Range: $125-149.9 Million
Emp.: 13
N.A.I.C.S.: 812990
Manfred Aronsson *(CEO)*

TV6 Sweden (1)
Ring Road Vagen, PO Box 54, Stockholm,
11867, Sweden **(100%)**
Tel.: (46) 856202300
Web Site: http://www.tv6.se
Sales Range: $25-49.9 Million
Emp.: 50
N.A.I.C.S.: 812990
Anders Nielsson *(Exec VP)*

TV8 Sweden (1)
Ringvagen 52, SE 11867, Stockholm,
Sweden **(100%)**
Tel.: (46) 856202300
Web Site: http://www.tv8.se
Sales Range: $25-49.9 Million
Emp.: 1,000
N.A.I.C.S.: 812990
Anders Nielsson *(CEO-MTG Online)*

TV8 redaktion (1)
Ringvagen 52, SE 104 62, Stockholm,
Sweden **(100%)**
Tel.: (46) 856201280
Web Site: http://www.tv8.se
Sales Range: $25-49.9 Million
Emp.: 25
N.A.I.C.S.: 812990

Tele 2 AB (1)
Borkarsgord Sgatan 16, PO Box 62, 16494,
Kista, Sweden **(100%)**
Tel.: (46) 856264000
Sales Range: $150-199.9 Million
Emp.: 1,000
N.A.I.C.S.: 812990

Thomas Ekman *(CEO)*

Televisionsaktiebolaget TV8 AB (1)
Soder Malarstrand 43, 118 25, Stockholm,
Sweden
Tel.: (46) 8 562 023 00
Television Broadcasting Services
N.A.I.C.S.: 516120

Titan Television (1)
Magasin 3 Frihamnsgatan 28, 115 56,
Stockholm, Sweden **(100%)**
Tel.: (46) 852801100
Web Site: http://www.titan.se
Sales Range: $1-9.9 Million
Emp.: 90
TV Production
N.A.I.C.S.: 516120
Thomas Hedberg *(CEO)*

Viasat Broadcasting G Ltd (1)
25/8 Abafun Crescent, PMB 74, Labone
Osu, Accra, Ghana
Tel.: (233) 302 760 515
Web Site: http://www.viasat1.com.gh
Sales Range: $25-49.9 Million
Emp.: 48
Television Programming Subscription & Distribution Services
N.A.I.C.S.: 517111

Viasat Global LLC (1)
Building 19 Leninskaya Sloboda Str, Moscow, 115280, Russia
Tel.: (7) 495 225 7301
Web Site: http://www.viasat.su
Emp.: 50
Television Programming Subscription & Distribution Services
N.A.I.C.S.: 517111
Ekaterina Kuzyakova *(Office Mgr)*

Viasat Sweden (1)
Ringvagen 52, PO Box 170 54, Stockholm,
11867, Sweden **(100%)**
Tel.: (46) 856202300
Web Site: http://www.viasat.se
Sales Range: $25-49.9 Million
Emp.: 20
Television Programming Subscription & Distribution Services
N.A.I.C.S.: 517111
Jorgen Madsen *(Gen Mgr)*

Subsidiary (Domestic):

Viasat Broadcasting AB (2)
Ring Vagen 52, 11867, Stockholm, Sweden
Tel.: (46) 856208600
Web Site: http://www.viasat.se
Sales Range: $25-49.9 Million
Emp.: 45
Broadcasting
N.A.I.C.S.: 517410

Viasat Film AB (2)
Soder Malarstrand 43, Stockholm, 118 25,
Sweden
Tel.: (46) 8 562 025 00
Web Site: http://www.viasat.se
Emp.: 200
Television Broadcasting Services
N.A.I.C.S.: 516120
Madeline Philander *(Gen Mgr)*

Viasat Sport/TV3 Sport (2)
Hangovagen 25 Hus 8, 115 74, Stockholm,
Sweden
Tel.: (46) 856209070
N.A.I.C.S.: 812990

Viasat Ukraine LLC (1)
Polovetskaya 3/42, Kiev, 4107, Ukraine
Tel.: (380) 44 490 36 00
Television Programming Subscription & Distribution Services
N.A.I.C.S.: 517111

Viasat World Ltd (1)
Chiswick Green 610 Chiswick High Road,
London, W4 5RU, United Kingdom
Tel.: (44) 2088345992
Web Site: http://www.viasatworld.com
Television Programming Subscription & Distribution Services
N.A.I.C.S.: 517111

Unit (Domestic):

Viasat Broadcasting U.K. (2)
Viasat Broadcast Centre Horton Rd, West

Drayton, UB7 8JD, Middlesex, United
Kingdom **(100%)**
Tel.: (44) 895433433
Web Site: http://www.viasat.co.uk
Sales Range: $50-74.9 Million
Emp.: 160
Television Programming Subscription & Distribution Services
N.A.I.C.S.: 517111

MODERNFORM PUBLIC COMPANY LIMITED

Modernform Tower Floor 1 - 4 699
Srinakarindr Road Phattanakan, Suanluang, Bangkok, 10250, Thailand
Tel.: (66) 20949999
Web Site:
http://www.modernform.co.th
Year Founded: 1978
MODERN—(THA)
Rev.: $75,035,926
Assets: $95,609,938
Liabilities: $28,255,121
Net Worth: $67,354,818
Earnings: $1,755,560
Emp.: 1,375
Fiscal Year-end: 12/31/23
Office Furniture Mfr
N.A.I.C.S.: 449110
Chareon Usanachitt *(Chm)*

Subsidiaries:

**MODERNFORM PUBLIC COMPANY
LIMITED - Production 1 Plant** (1)
33/2 33/5 Bangna-trad Highway Tambon
Bangchalong, Amphoe Bangplee, Samut
Prakan, 10540, Thailand
Tel.: (66) 2337 0222
Furniture Mfr
N.A.I.C.S.: 337121

**MODERNFORM PUBLIC COMPANY
LIMITED - Production 2A Plant** (1)
5 Bangkhuntien Road Kwang Sa-Mae-Dam,
Khet Bangkhuntien, Bangkok, 10150, Thailand
Tel.: (66) 2416 9802
Furniture Mfr
N.A.I.C.S.: 337121

**MODERNFORM PUBLIC COMPANY
LIMITED - Production 2B Plant** (1)
622 Bangkhuntien Road Kwang Ta-Kam,
Khet Bangkhuntien, Bangkok, 10150, Thailand
Tel.: (66) 2897 2201
Furniture Mfr
N.A.I.C.S.: 337121

MODETOUR NETWORK INC.

5th floor Baeknam Building 16 Euljiro, Jung-gu, Seoul, Korea (South)
Tel.: (82) 15445252
Web Site:
https://www.modetournetwork.com
Year Founded: 1989
080160—(KRS)
Rev.: $36,635,642
Assets: $207,400,727
Liabilities: $139,152,429
Net Worth: $68,248,298
Earnings: $(14,183,951)
Emp.: 598
Fiscal Year-end: 12/31/22
Travel Arrangement Services
N.A.I.C.S.: 561510
Intae Yu *(CEO)*

Subsidiaries:

Mode Tour Real Estate Investment
Trust Inc. (1)
701 7F Seoul Center B/D 116 Sogong-ro
Jung-Gu, Seoul, 04533, Korea
(South) **(42.16%)**
Tel.: (82) 262535911
Web Site: http://www.modetourreit.com
Rev.: $4,051,887
Assets: $79,193,333
Liabilities: $37,823,377
Net Worth: $41,369,956
Earnings: $8,054,133

MODETOUR NETWORK INC.

MODETOUR Network Inc.—(Continued)
Emp.: 10
Fiscal Year-end: 12/31/2022
Hospitality Real Estate Investment Trust
N.A.I.C.S.: 525990
Dong-Ju Choi *(Chm & CEO)*

Modetour International Inc. (1)
5th floor Chungjeong Building 135 Tongil-ro, Seodaemun-gu, Seoul, 03735, Korea (South)
Tel.: (82) 237884800
Web Site: https://www.modetourint.com
Emp.: 40
Travel & Ticketing Services
N.A.I.C.S.: 561510

MODEX INTERNATIONAL SECURITIES LTD.
507 Padma Tower-II 22 Rajendra Place, New Delhi, 110 001, India
Tel.: (91) 1147451800
Web Site: http://www.modexindia.com
Rev.: $3,559,419
Assets: $15,145,840
Liabilities: $12,987,833
Net Worth: $2,158,007
Earnings: $183,432
Emp.: 62
Fiscal Year-end: 03/31/19
Securities Brokerage Services
N.A.I.C.S.: 523150
Dharmendra Kumar Arora *(Exec Dir)*

MODI NATURALS LIMITED
Bisalpur Road, Pilibhit, 262001, Uttar Pradesh, India
Tel.: (91) 9568009891
Web Site: https://www.modinaturals.com
Year Founded: 1974
519003—(BOM)
Rev.: $60,965,836
Assets: $16,546,335
Liabilities: $7,283,570
Net Worth: $9,262,765
Earnings: $1,435,431
Emp.: 573
Fiscal Year-end: 03/31/21
Edible Oil Mfr
N.A.I.C.S.: 311224
Akshay Modi *(Exec Dir)*

MODI RUBBER LIMITED
Modi Nagar, Civil Lines, Ghaziabad, 201204, Uttar Pradesh, India
Tel.: (91) 1126848416
Web Site: https://www.modirubberlimited.com
500890—(BOM)
Rev.: $2,291,212
Assets: $61,518,814
Liabilities: $4,581,472
Net Worth: $56,937,342
Earnings: ($326,480)
Emp.: 26
Fiscal Year-end: 03/31/20
Tiles Mfr
N.A.I.C.S.: 326211
Vinay Kumar Modi *(Chm)*

Subsidiaries:

Gujarat Guardian Ltd. (1)
State Highway- 13 Village Kondh Valia Road, Ankleshwar, 393001, Gujarat, India
Tel.: (91) 2643 275106
Web Site: http://www.gujaratguardianglass.com
Flat Glass Mfr
N.A.I.C.S.: 327215
Vinay Kumar Modi *(Chm)*

Uniglobe Mod Travels Pvt. Ltd. (1)
Unit 1008 Barton Centre 84 MG Road, Bengaluru, 560001, Karnataka, India
Tel.: (91) 8049388100
Web Site: https://www.uniglobemodtravel.com
Travel Management Services
N.A.I.C.S.: 561510

MODI'S NAVNIRMAAN LIMITED
Shop No-1 Rashmi Heights Bldg M G Road Opp Kamala Nagar, Kandivali West, Mumbai, 400067, India
Tel.: (91) 9819989100
Web Site: https://www.modisnirman.com
Year Founded: 2010
543539—(BOM)
Rev.: $5,270,535
Assets: $7,123,698
Liabilities: $3,256,399
Net Worth: $3,867,298
Earnings: $691,050
Fiscal Year-end: 03/31/23
Construction Services
N.A.I.C.S.: 236210

MODIIN ENERGY LIMITED PARTNERSHIP
3 Azrieli Center Triangle Tower 42nd floor, Tel Aviv, 6702301, Israel
Tel.: (972) 36075155
Web Site: http://www.modiin-energy.com
Year Founded: 1992
MDIN—(TAE)
Rev.: $27,033,000
Assets: $106,086,000
Liabilities: $66,154,000
Net Worth: $39,932,000
Earnings: $2,115,000
Fiscal Year-end: 12/31/23
Crude Petroleum Extraction
N.A.I.C.S.: 211120
Ron Maor *(Deputy Chm & CEO)*

MODIPON LIMITED
Hapur Road, Modinagar, 201 204, Uttar Pradesh, India
Tel.: (91) 9582388706
Web Site: https://www.modipon.net
Year Founded: 1965
503776—(BOM)
Assets: $918,950
Liabilities: $11,769,582
Net Worth: ($10,850,632)
Earnings: ($73,029)
Emp.: 4
Fiscal Year-end: 03/31/23
Real Estate Manangement Services
N.A.I.C.S.: 531210
Manish Kumar Modi *(Mng Dir)*

MODISON METALS LTD.
33 Nairman Bhavan 227 - Nariman Point, Mumbai, 400021, India
Tel.: (91) 2222026437
Web Site: https://www.modison.com
Year Founded: 1965
MODISONLTD—(NSE)
Rev.: $46,573,650
Assets: $29,238,327
Liabilities: $5,242,719
Net Worth: $23,995,608
Earnings: $1,997,091
Emp.: 257
Fiscal Year-end: 03/31/22
Switchgear Mfr & Distr
N.A.I.C.S.: 335313
Girdharilal Modi *(Co-Mng Dir)*

MODRICA MPI A.D.
Riste Mikicica 90, 74480, Modrica, Bosnia & Herzegovina
Tel.: (387) 53 811 105
Year Founded: 1998
MPIM—(BANJ)
Sales Range: Less than $1 Million
Emp.: 5
Grain Mill Product Mfr
N.A.I.C.S.: 311230
Marko Rasic *(Chm-Mgmt Bd)*

MODULAT INC.
2F Hulic Mita Bldg 5-25-11 Shiba, Minato-ku, Tokyo, 108-0014, Japan
Tel.: (81) 3 34542061
Web Site: http://www.modulat.com
Year Founded: 2000
Computer Installation Services
N.A.I.C.S.: 541519
Tatsuro Furusawa *(Chm)*

MODULIGHT CORPORATION
Hermiankatu 22, 33720, Tampere, Finland
Tel.: (358) 207439000
Web Site: https://www.modulight.com
Year Founded: 2000
MODU—(HEL)
Rev.: $4,343,838
Assets: $69,028,707
Liabilities: $8,887,330
Net Worth: $60,141,377
Earnings: ($12,800,561)
Emp.: 70
Fiscal Year-end: 12/31/23
Medical Device Mfr
N.A.I.C.S.: 339112
Anca Guina *(CFO)*

MODUS THERAPEUTICS AB
Olof Palmes gata 29 IV, 11122, Stockholm, Sweden
Tel.: (46) 850249253
Web Site: https://www.modustx.com
Year Founded: 2011
MODTX—(OMX)
Assets: $1,034,678
Liabilities: $1,271,981
Net Worth: ($237,303)
Earnings: ($1,681,776)
Emp.: 2
Fiscal Year-end: 12/31/22
Holding Company
N.A.I.C.S.: 551112
Claes Lindblad *(CFO)*

MOELVEN INDUSTRIER ASA
PO Box 134, 2391, Moelv, Norway
Tel.: (47) 6234 7000
Web Site: http://www.moelven.com
Rev.: $1,169,281,125
Assets: $626,568,900
Liabilities: $357,659,790
Net Worth: $268,909,110
Earnings: $21,392,820
Emp.: 3,399
Fiscal Year-end: 12/31/19
Holding Company; Building Materials & Systems
N.A.I.C.S.: 551112
Morten Kristiansen *(Pres & CEO)*

Subsidiaries:

Moelven Are AS (1)
Spydebergveien 143, 1820, Spydeberg, Norway
Tel.: (47) 69836710
Wood Products Distr; Wood Planing & Coating Services
N.A.I.C.S.: 423990
Morten Tunby *(Mng Dir)*

Moelven Arjangs Sag AB (1)
Kyrkerudsvagen 5, 672 32, Arjang, Sweden
Tel.: (46) 101225530
Web Site: http://www.moelven.com
Sales Range: $25-49.9 Million
Emp.: 39
Sawmills
N.A.I.C.S.: 321113
Per Anders Jonas Andersson *(Mng Dir)*

Moelven Bioenergi AS (1)
Strandsagvegen 4, 2383, Brumunddal, Norway
Tel.: (47) 62347000
Sawmill Product Mfr & Distr
N.A.I.C.S.: 333243

Moelven ByggModul AB (1)
Brovagen 27, 661 93, Saffle, Sweden
Tel.: (46) 10 122 5800
Web Site: http://www.moelven.com
Prefabricated Wood Building Mfr
N.A.I.C.S.: 321992
Johan Samuelsson *(CEO)*

Moelven ByggModul AS (1)
Industrivegen 12, 2390, Moelv, Norway
Tel.: (47) 6234 7166
Web Site: http://www.moelven.com
Prefabricated Wood Building Mfr
N.A.I.C.S.: 321992
Lars Brede Aandstad *(Dir-Admin)*

Moelven Component AB (1)
Skarevagen 60, Box 8060, 650 08, Karlstad, Sweden
Tel.: (46) 10 122 5370
Web Site: http://www.moelven.com
Emp.: 31
Wood Planing & Engineered Component Mfr
N.A.I.C.S.: 321912
Maria Hutchinson *(Mgr-Market)*

Moelven Dalatra AB (1)
Industrivagen 2, 785 42, Mockfjard, Sweden
Tel.: (46) 10 122 5600
Web Site: http://www.moelven.com
Sales Range: $25-49.9 Million
Emp.: 53
Sawmills
N.A.I.C.S.: 321113
Rolf Peter Funk *(CEO & Mng Dir)*

Moelven Danmark A/S (1)
Herstedostervej 27-29C, 2620, Albertslund, Denmark
Tel.: (45) 43434800
Web Site: http://www.moelven.com
Lumber & Wood Products Distr
N.A.I.C.S.: 423310
Mads Ambus *(Mgr-Economy & Admin)*

Moelven Deutschland GmbH (1)
Steintwietenhof 2, 20459, Hamburg, Germany
Tel.: (49) 4041919101
Sawmill Product Mfr & Distr
N.A.I.C.S.: 333243
Thorsten Bar *(Sls Dir)*

Moelven Edanesagen AB (1)
Arvid Olofssonsv, Edane, 671 70, Arvika, Sweden
Tel.: (46) 10 122 5170
Web Site: http://www.moelven.com
Sales Range: $25-49.9 Million
Emp.: 92
Sawmill & Planing Mill
N.A.I.C.S.: 321113
Sven Jorgen Olofsson *(CEO)*

Moelven Eidsvoll AS (1)
Myhrersvingen 9, 2080, Eidsvoll, Norway
Tel.: (47) 63924880
Web Site: http://www.moelven.com
Wood Moulding Mfr
N.A.I.C.S.: 321912
Bjornar Berge *(Dir)*

Moelven Langmoen AS (1)
Strandsagvegen 4, 2383, Brumunddal, Norway
Tel.: (47) 62332700
Web Site: http://www.moelven.com
Finished Wood Products Distr
N.A.I.C.S.: 423310

Moelven Limtre AS (1)
Lundemoveien 1, 2390, Moelv, Norway
Tel.: (47) 6233 4000
Web Site: http://www.moelven.com
Sales Range: $25-49.9 Million
Emp.: 120
Glulam Beams Mfr
N.A.I.C.S.: 321113
Rune Abrahamsen *(CEO)*

Moelven List AB (1)
Lovene, 531 96, Lidkoping, Sweden
Tel.: (46) 10 122 5210
Web Site: http://www.moelven.com
Wood Flooring & Paneling Mfr
N.A.I.C.S.: 321918
Magnus Ingves *(CEO)*

Moelven Modus AS (1)
Asfaltveien 1, 2069, Jessheim, Norway
Tel.: (47) 6050
Web Site: http://www.moelven.com

AND PRIVATE COMPANIES

Emp.: 290
Commercial Wood Interior Product Mfr
N.A.I.C.S.: 321918
Trygve Andreas Toften *(Mng Dir)*

Moelven Notnas AB (1)
Notnasvagen 9, 685 33, Torsby, Sweden
Tel.: (46) 10 1225300
Web Site: http://www.moelven.com
Sales Range: $25-49.9 Million
Emp.: 70
Sawmills
N.A.I.C.S.: 321113
Peter Broberg *(Mng Dir)*

Moelven Notnas Ransby AB (1)
Notnasvagen 9, 685 00, Torsby, Sweden
Tel.: (46) 101225300
Sawmill Product Mfr & Distr
N.A.I.C.S.: 333243
Peter Broberg *(Mng Dir)*

Moelven Notnas Wood AB (1)
Notnasvagen 9, 685 33, Torsby, Sweden
Tel.: (46) 56016800
Emp.: 23
Wood Products Mfr
N.A.I.C.S.: 321912
Magnus Goran Ingves *(Mng Dir)*

Moelven Pellets AS (1)
Nordmoveien 60, 3534, Sokna, Norway
Tel.: (47) 62347000
Sawmill Product Mfr & Distr
N.A.I.C.S.: 333243

Moelven Ransbysagen AB (1)
Branasvagen 35, Syssleback, 680 60, Torsby, Sweden
Tel.: (46) 10 122 5560
Web Site: http://www.moelven.com
Sales Range: $10-24.9 Million
Emp.: 32
Sawmills
N.A.I.C.S.: 321113
Sven Peter Broberg *(Mng Dir)*

Moelven Skog AB (1)
Skarevagen 60, Box 8006, 650 08, Karlstad, Sweden
Tel.: (46) 10 122 6500
Web Site: http://www.moelven.com
Timber Tract & Logging Operations
N.A.I.C.S.: 113110

Moelven Timber AS (1)
PO Box 164, 2391, Moelv, Norway
Tel.: (47) 62347000
Web Site: http://www.moelven.com
Holding Company; Sawmills Operator & Lumber Whslr
N.A.I.C.S.: 551112

Subsidiary (Domestic):

Moelven Eidsvoll Vaerk AS (2)
Sagvegen 10, 2074, Eidsvoll, Norway
Tel.: (47) 9511 9415
Web Site: http://www.moelven.com
Sawmill & Planing Mill
N.A.I.C.S.: 321113
Nils Anton Haehre *(Mng Dir)*

Moelven Loten AS (2)
Rokosjovegen 525, 2340, Loten, Norway
Tel.: (47) 62547500
Web Site: http://www.moelven.com
Sales Range: $1-9.9 Million
Emp.: 30
Sawmills
N.A.I.C.S.: 321113
Lars Grotta *(Dir-Mktg & Mgr-Sls)*

Moelven Mjosbruket AS (2)
Industrivegen 35, 2836, Biri, Norway
Tel.: (47) 61145200
Web Site: http://www.moelven.com
Sales Range: $10-24.9 Million
Emp.: 38
Sawmills
N.A.I.C.S.: 321113
Sturla Westrum *(Mng Dir)*

Moelven Numedal AS (2)
Fv40 14, 3620, Flesberg, Norway
Tel.: (47) 32295000
Web Site: http://www.moelven.com
Sales Range: $10-24.9 Million
Emp.: 35
Sawmills
N.A.I.C.S.: 321113

Rune Frogner *(Mng Dir)*

Moelven Osterdalsbruket AS (2)
Industriveien 133, 2480, Koppang, Norway
Tel.: (47) 62462900
Web Site: http://www.moelven.com
Sales Range: $10-24.9 Million
Emp.: 52
Sawmill & Planing Mill
N.A.I.C.S.: 321113
Anders Gronli *(Gen Mgr)*

Moelven Soknabruket AS (2)
Nordmoveien 48, 3534, Sokna, Norway
Tel.: (47) 32144500
Web Site: http://www.moelven.com
Sales Range: $25-49.9 Million
Emp.: 70
Sawmill & Planing Mill
N.A.I.C.S.: 321113
Atle Nilsen *(Mng Dir)*

Moelven Telemarksbruket AS (2)
Rotebergv 21, 3800, Bo, Midt-Telemark, Norway (51%)
Tel.: (47) 35954400
Web Site: http://www.moelven.com
Sales Range: $1-9.9 Million
Emp.: 26
Sawmills
N.A.I.C.S.: 321113
Ole Einar Lefebvre Grimsgaard *(Mng Dir)*

Moelven Valer AS (2)
Fv491 900, 2435, Braskereidfoss, Norway
Tel.: (47) 62428000
Web Site: http://www.moelven.com
Sales Range: $25-49.9 Million
Emp.: 64
Sawmills
N.A.I.C.S.: 321113

Moelven Van Severen AS (2)
Pinavegen 5, 7800, Namsos, Norway
Tel.: (47) 74213300
Web Site: http://www.moelven.com
Sales Range: $25-49.9 Million
Emp.: 85
Sawmill & Planing Mill
N.A.I.C.S.: 321113
Knut Johan Dreier *(Mng Dir)*

Moelven Toreboda AB (1)
Bruksgatan 8, Box 49, 545 21, Toreboda, Sweden
Tel.: (46) 10 122 6200
Web Site: http://www.moelven.com
Glulam Beams Mfr
N.A.I.C.S.: 321113
Johan Niclas Ake Ahlen *(CEO)*

Moelven Treinterior AS (1)
Nordre Kongsveg 56, 2372, Brottum, Norway
Tel.: (47) 62359777
Web Site: http://www.moelven.com
Wood Flooring Mfr
N.A.I.C.S.: 321918

Moelven Trysil AS (1)
Slettmov 34, 2420, Trysil, Norway
Tel.: (47) 62452100
Sawmill Product Mfr & Distr
N.A.I.C.S.: 333243
Runar Pettersen *(Mng Dir)*

Moelven Valasen AB (1)
Korvagen, 691 52, Karlskoga, Sweden
Tel.: (46) 10 1225400
Web Site: http://www.moelven.com
Sales Range: $50-74.9 Million
Emp.: 86
Sawmill Mfr
N.A.I.C.S.: 321113

Moelven Valasen Wood AB (1)
Valasen, Industriomradet, 691 94, Karlskoga, Sweden
Tel.: (46) 10 122 5140
Sales Range: $25-49.9 Million
Wood Products Mfr
N.A.I.C.S.: 321912
Manuel Jesus Sandoval Gonzalez *(Mng Dir)*

Moelven Varmlands Tra AB (1)
Fabriksgatan 8, 661 30, Saffle, Sweden
Tel.: (46) 533691060
Web Site: http://www.moelven.com
Emp.: 25
Interior Wood Panel & Pressure-Treated Lumber Mfr

N.A.I.C.S.: 321912
Magnus Goran Ingves *(Mng Dir)*

Moelven Virke AS (1)
Industrivegen 2, 2390, Moelv, Norway
Tel.: (47) 62347000
Web Site: https://www.moelven.com
Prefabricated Wood Building Mfr
N.A.I.C.S.: 321992

Moelven Wood AB (1)
PO Box 8006, 650 08, Karlstad, Sweden
Tel.: (46) 5453 6400
Wood Building & Interior Products Mfr & Whslr
N.A.I.C.S.: 321912

Moelven Wood AS (1)
Sagvegen 10, 2074, Eidsvoll, Norway
Tel.: (47) 63959750
Web Site: http://www.moelven.com
Wood Building & Interior Products Mfr
N.A.I.C.S.: 321912

Moelven arjang Sag AB (1)
Kyrkerudsvagen 5, 672 32, Arjang, Sweden
Tel.: (46) 101225530
Sawmill Product Mfr & Distr
N.A.I.C.S.: 333243
Christer Hagberg *(Mng Dir)*

UJ-Trading AB (1)
Gransnaret 17, Gusselby, 711 95, Lindesberg, Sweden
Tel.: (46) 58150200
Sawmill Machinery Wholesale Trade Broker
N.A.I.C.S.: 425120
Hans Jansson *(Mng Dir)*

MOF TECHNOLOGIES LIMITED
63 University Road, Belfast, BT9 5PX, United Kingdom
Tel.: (44) 28 9503 0101   UK
Web Site:
  http://www.moftechnologies.com
Metal-Organic Framework Materials Mfr
N.A.I.C.S.: 325998
Paschal McCloskey *(CEO)*

MOFFITT DODGE CHRYSLER LTD.
205 Route 170, Oak Bay, E3L 3X7, NB, Canada
Tel.: (888) 339-2711
Web Site: http://www.moffittdodge.ca
Year Founded: 1975
Sales Range: $1-9.9 Million
Emp.: 20
Full Service Automotive Dealership
N.A.I.C.S.: 441110
Andrew Moffitt *(Bus Mgr, Dealer & Principal)*

MOG HOLDINGS LIMITED
No 1-2 1st & 2nd Floor Jalan Kajang Indah 1 Taman Kajang Indah, Sg Chua, Kajang, Selangor, Malaysia
Tel.: (60) 387399178   Ky
Web Site: http://www.mog.com.my
Year Founded: 1996
1942—(HKG)
Rev.: $48,946,667
Assets: $67,159,365
Liabilities: $39,497,989
Net Worth: $27,661,376
Earnings: $2,644,656
Emp.: 514
Fiscal Year-end: 03/31/22
Holding Company
N.A.I.C.S.: 551112
Kwang Hua Ng *(Founder & Chm)*

MOGO, INC.
516 - 409 Granville St, Vancouver, V6C 1T2, BC, Canada
Tel.: (604) 659-4380
Web Site: https://www.mogo.ca
MOGO—(NASDAQ)
Rev.: $53,937,424
Assets: $173,270,326

Liabilities: $86,526,426
Net Worth: $86,743,900
Earnings: ($129,606,586)
Emp.: 261
Fiscal Year-end: 12/31/22
Mortgage Broker Services
N.A.I.C.S.: 522310
Gregory Feller *(Co-Founder, Pres & CFO)*

MOGU INC.
Huanglong Wanke Center 23/F Building No G No 77 Xueyuan Road, Xihu District, Hangzhou, 310012, China
Tel.: (86) 57185308201   Ky
Web Site: http://www.mogu-inc.com
Year Founded: 2011
MOGU—(NYSE)
Rev.: $22,200,930
Assets: $129,923,848
Liabilities: $44,847,696
Net Worth: $85,076,152
Earnings: ($9,271,018)
Emp.: 308
Fiscal Year-end: 03/31/24
Online Shopping Services
N.A.I.C.S.: 459999
Qi Chen *(Co-Founder & Chm)*

MOGUL GAMES GROUP LTD
Suite 4 Level 10 221 Queen Street, Melbourne, 3000, VIC, Australia
Tel.: (61) 396025564
Web Site:
  http://www.esportmogul.com
Year Founded: 2011
MGG—(ASX)
Rev.: $66,520
Assets: $2,484,463
Liabilities: $383,260
Net Worth: $2,101,202
Earnings: ($2,417,709)
Emp.: 3
Fiscal Year-end: 12/31/22
Sports Media Services
N.A.I.C.S.: 516210
George Lazarou *(Sec)*

MOH NIPPON PLC
71-75 Shelton Street Covent Garden, London, WC2H 9JQ, United Kingdom   UK
Web Site: https://mohnippon.com
Year Founded: 2021
MOH—(LSE)
Assets: $12,848
Liabilities: $33,181
Net Worth: ($20,333)
Earnings: ($88,219)
Fiscal Year-end: 04/30/22
Asset Management Services
N.A.I.C.S.: 523999
Xiaochen Zhao *(Sec)*

MOHAMED N. AL-HAJERY & SONS LTD.
PO Box 152, Kuwait, 13002, Kuwait
Tel.: (965) 4831000
Web Site: http://www.hajery.com
Year Founded: 1946
Rev.: $5,119,122
Emp.: 700
Pharmaceuticals, Consumer Goods, Perfumes & Cosmetics, Food Products, Medical Equipment & Salon & Beauty Equipment Distr
N.A.I.C.S.: 424210
Naser Al Hajery *(Chm)*

MOHAMMAD FAROOQ TEXTILE MILLS LIMITED
PlotNos 6&7 Sector 21, Korangi Industrial Area, Karachi, 75180, Sindh, Pakistan
Tel.: (92) 215011571   PK
Year Founded: 1967
Sales Range: $100-124.9 Million

MOHAMMAD FAROOQ TEXTILE MILLS LIMITED

Mohammad Farooq Textile Mills Limited—(Continued)
Emp.: 930
Textile Products Mfr & Distr
N.A.I.C.S.: 313210
Mohammad F. Sumar (Chm & CEO)

MOHAMMED ABDULMOHSIN AL-KHARAFI & SONS WLL
PO Box 886, Safat, Kuwait, 13009, Kuwait
Tel.: (965) 4813622
Web Site: http://www.makharafi.net
Year Founded: 1956
Sales Range: $400-449.9 Million
Emp.: 15,000
Engineeering Services
N.A.I.C.S.: 541330
Mohsen Kamel (Mng Dir)

Subsidiaries:

ABJ Engineering & Contracting co. (KSC)
Plot No-20 Mina Abdulla Industrial Area, PO Box 10331, Shuaiba, 65454, Kuwait
Tel.: (965) 22259522
Web Site: http://www.abjengineering.com
Fabricated Structural Metal Mfr
N.A.I.C.S.: 332312
K. Viswanathan (Mgr-Ops-Fabrication Svcs)

ADMAK General Contracting Company W.L.L. (1)
PO Box 650, Abu Dhabi, United Arab Emirates
Tel.: (971) 2 6264626
Web Site: http://www.makahara.net
Emp.: 1,000
Highway & Bridge Construction Services
N.A.I.C.S.: 237310
Naser Hakim (Exec Dir)

Al Nasser Real Estate Company S.A.R.L. (1)
BLOM Bank Building-3rd Floor, PO Box 446, Beirut Damascus Highway Hazmie, Beirut, Lebanon
Tel.: (961) 5 957405
Real Estate Management Services
N.A.I.C.S.: 531110

Credit Andorra Private Bankers (1)
Mali i Robit Golem, Kavaje, Albania
Tel.: (355) 694055558
Web Site: http://www.malirobitresort.com
Home Management Services
N.A.I.C.S.: 721110

Lebanese Real Estate Commercial Company S.A.R.L. (1)
BLOM Bank Building-3rd Floor Beirut Damascus Highway Hazmieh, PO Box 446, Beirut, Lebanon
Tel.: (961) 5 957405
Real Estate Management Services
N.A.I.C.S.: 531390

M.A. Kharafi & Sons Co. (The Gambia) Ltd. (1)
128A Kairaba Avenue, PO Box 3330, Serrekunda, Gambia
Tel.: (220) 4494156
Investment Management Service
N.A.I.C.S.: 523940
M. Nagaty (Area Mgr)

M.A. Kharafi Construction (Pty) Ltd (1)
1311 Church Street, PO Box 53, Hatfield, Pretoria, South Africa
Tel.: (27) 12 342 5210
Civil Engineering Services
N.A.I.C.S.: 541330

MAK Bulgaria Ltd. (1)
16 Frederik Joliat Courie Street Building 155 Apt 22 5th Floor, 1113, Sofia, Bulgaria
Tel.: (359) 2 971 9292
Real Estate Lending Services
N.A.I.C.S.: 531110

MAK Contracting S.A.R.L. (1)
MAK Centre 2nd Floor Al-Sham Road, PO Box 182, Hazmieh, Beirut, 182, Lebanon
Tel.: (961) 5 950480

Sales Range: $25-49.9 Million
Emp.: 50
Building Finishing & Contracting Services
N.A.I.C.S.: 238390

Mohammed Abdulmohsin Al-Kharafi & Sons Co. W.L.L. (1)
Shuwaikh Industrial Area, PO Box 886, Kuwait, 13009, Kuwait
Tel.: (965) 24813622
Civil Engineering Services
N.A.I.C.S.: 541330
Hussein Azmi (Mgr-Mktg)

Mohammed Abdulmohsin Al-Kharafi & Sons Company W.L.L. (1)
MAK Centre 1st Floor Al-Sham Road, PO Box 182, Hazmieh, Beirut, 29022411, Lebanon
Tel.: (961) 5 950987
Web Site: http://www.makharafi.net
Emp.: 5,000
Civil Engineering Services
N.A.I.C.S.: 541330
George Ramses (Exec Dir)

Mohammed Abdulmohsin Al-Kharafi & Sons.
Mikocheni Industrial Area Plot No 113 Opp Kwanza Bottlers, PO Box 6164, Dar es Salaam, 6164, Tanzania
Tel.: (255) 22 2780792
Emp.: 30
Civil Engineering Services
N.A.I.C.S.: 541330
Mohammed Bahy (Gen Mgr)

MOHAMMED ENTERPRISES TANZANIA LIMITED
20Th Floor Golden Jubilee Towers Ohio Street, PO Box 20660, Dar es Salaam, Tanzania
Tel.: (255) 222122830
Web Site: http://www.metl.net
Year Founded: 2002
Sales Range: $50-74.9 Million
Emp.: 450
Agricultural Exporter Importer Product Distr & Mfr
N.A.I.C.S.: 333241
Mohammed G. Dewji (Pres & CEO)

Subsidiaries:

21st Century Food and Packaging Ltd (1)
Kiwalani Metl Complex Nyerere Road, Dar es Salaam, 6667, Tanzania
Tel.: (255) 222123316
Sweetener Mfr
N.A.I.C.S.: 325199
Lmirajart Sing (Mgr)

21st Century Textiles Ltd (1)
Kihonda Industrial Area 5 Block E, PO Box 269, Morogoro, Tanzania
Tel.: (255) 23 2601900
Cotton Yarn Mfr
N.A.I.C.S.: 313110

Afritex Ltd (1)
Gofu Chini Industrial Area Plot No 8-9, PO Box 835, Tanga, Tanzania
Tel.: (255) 27 2646421
Household Linen Mfr
N.A.I.C.S.: 313220

East Coast Oils and Fats Ltd (1)
Kurasini Industrial Area Plot No 234-235 Zamcargo Rd, PO Box 50054, Dar es Salaam, Tanzania
Tel.: (255) 22 2850860
Soap, Edible Oil & Fat Mfr
N.A.I.C.S.: 325611

Mo Cashew Ltd (1)
Mbagala Rangi Tatu Plot No 141/10 & 141/11, PO Box 20660, Dar es Salaam, Tanzania
Tel.: (255) 22 2118930
Cashew Nut Whslr
N.A.I.C.S.: 424590
Babu Raj (Gen Mgr)

Royal Soap and Detergent Industries (1)
Mabibu Industrial Area Plot No 1A Mandela Rd, PO Box 22196, Dar es Salaam, Tanzania
Tel.: (255) 22 2850860
Soap & Detergent Mfr
N.A.I.C.S.: 325611

TPM (1998) Ltd (1)
Kihonda Industrial Complex Plot No 6 Block E, PO Box 239, Morogoro, Tanzania
Tel.: (255) 23 2604860
Web Site: http://www.metl.com
Sisal Bag Mfr
N.A.I.C.S.: 313110

MOHAMMED JALAL & SONS WLL
Po Box-113, PO Box 113, Manama, Bahrain
Tel.: (973) 17533311
Web Site: http://wwwjalal.com
Year Founded: 1947
Sales Range: $1-4.9 Billion
Emp.: 3,500
Holding Company
N.A.I.C.S.: 551112
Mohammed Jalal (Chm)

Subsidiaries:

Airmech WLL (1)
PO Box 20137, Manama, Bahrain
Tel.: (973) 17593013
Web Site: http://www.airmech.net
Sales Range: $150-199.9 Million
Emp.: 850
Mechanical, Electrical & Steel Fabrication Engineers & Contractors
N.A.I.C.S.: 541330

Data Capture Systems (1)
PO Box 113, Manama, Bahrain
Tel.: (973) 17535503
Web Site: http://www.dcsme.ae
Business Solutions for Bar Coding, Radio Frequency Systems & Scanning Devices
N.A.I.C.S.: 334418

Gulf Trading Stores (1)
PO Box 113, Manama, Bahrain
Tel.: (973) 17223347
Web Site: http://www.jalal.com
Sales Range: $50-74.9 Million
Emp.: 10
Building Materials Whslr
N.A.I.C.S.: 423320
Mohammed Jalal (Chm)

Kontra (1)
Al samaha Bldg 1572 Road 5647 Alsalihiya 356, PO Box 1618, Manama, Bahrain
Tel.: (973) 17255729
Sales Range: $350-399.9 Million
Emp.: 1,250
Interior Designer
N.A.I.C.S.: 541410
M. Gelal (Mng Dir)

Mechanical Contracting & Services Co. WLL (1)
Bldg 317 Rd 4110 Block 941 East Riffa, PO Box 5238, Manama, Bahrain
Tel.: (973) 17623723
Web Site: http://www.mcscwll.com
Sales Range: $400-449.9 Million
Emp.: 2,500
Engineering Services Specializing in Refinery Shutdown, Construction & Maintenance Work
N.A.I.C.S.: 541330
William Abu Hamad (CEO & Mng Dir)

Mohammed Jalal & Sons WLL - Ideal Home Division (1)
PO Box 2754, Manama, Bahrain
Tel.: (973) 17 405 545
Sanitary Ware Mfr
N.A.I.C.S.: 332999
Saeed Ansari (Mgr)

Mohammed Jalal & Sons WLL - Mohammed Jalal Engineering & Technology Division (1)
PO Box 747, Manama, Bahrain
Tel.: (973) 17 252 921
Web Site: http://www.mjtechbas.com
Emp.: 50
Engineeering Services
N.A.I.C.S.: 541330

INTERNATIONAL PUBLIC

Nevin Megchiani (Gen Mgr)

Mohammed Jalal Catering W.L.L. (1)
PO Box 1335, Manama, Bahrain
Tel.: (973) 17 274 800
Catering Services
N.A.I.C.S.: 722320
Rakesh Sharma (Area Mgr)

MOHAN MEAKIN LTD.
Mohan Nagar, Ghaziabad, 201007, India
Tel.: (91) 1202657001
Web Site: http://www.mohanmeakin.com
Brewery
N.A.I.C.S.: 312120
P. D. Goswami (Fin Dir)

MOHAWK FORD SALES
930 Upper James St, Hamilton, L9C3A5, ON, Canada
Tel.: (905) 388-1711
Web Site: http://www.mohawkford.dealer.com
Rev.: $22,259,925
Emp.: 46
New & Used Car Dealers
N.A.I.C.S.: 441110

MOHENZ CO., LTD.
Namgwan-ri 195 Pungse-myeon, Dongnam-gu, Cheonan, Chungcheongnam-do, Korea (South)
Tel.: (82) 25713011
Web Site: http://www.imohenz.com
006920—(KRS)
Rev.: $69,124,756
Assets: $43,083,395
Liabilities: $17,885,851
Net Worth: $25,197,544
Earnings: $1,757,486
Emp.: 78
Fiscal Year-end: 12/31/22
Readymix Concrete Mfr
N.A.I.C.S.: 327320
Oh Joon Youp (Gen Mgr)

MOHIB EXPORTS LIMITED
8th Kilometer Manga Raiwind Road Mouzapura, Kasur, Pakistan
Tel.: (92) 4951 383601
Textile Products Mfr
N.A.I.C.S.: 313210

MOHINDRA FASTENERS LIMITED
304 Gupta Arcade Inder Enclave Rohtak Road, New Delhi, 110 087, India
Tel.: (91) 11 46200400
Web Site: http://www.mohindra.asia
Year Founded: 1996
Rev.: $19,433,927
Assets: $13,893,065
Liabilities: $6,435,319
Net Worth: $7,457,746
Earnings: $1,305,499
Emp.: 361
Fiscal Year-end: 03/31/19
Fastener Mfr
N.A.I.C.S.: 339993
Deepak Arneja (Chm, CEO & Mng Dir)

Subsidiaries:

Mohindra Fasteners Limited Haryana Plant (1)
60th K M Stone Delhi Rohtak Road, Kharawar, Rohtak, 124 001, Haryana, India
Tel.: (91) 1262666630
Fastener Mfr
N.A.I.C.S.: 339993

MOHINI HEALTH & HYGIENE LTD.
Plot No 109 Sector III Industrial Area,

AND PRIVATE COMPANIES

MOL MAGYAR OLAJ- ES GAZIPARI NYRT.

Pithampur Dist, Dhar, Madhya Pradesh, India
Tel.: (91) 7292426665
Web Site:
https://www.mohinihealth.com
Year Founded: 2009
MHHL—(NSE)
Rev.: $23,780,577
Assets: $16,594,341
Liabilities: $5,840,285
Net Worth: $10,754,056
Earnings: $813,273
Emp.: 207
Fiscal Year-end: 03/31/23
Textile Products Mfr
N.A.I.C.S.: 313310
Sarvapriya Bansal *(Chm)*

MOHIT INDUSTRIES LTD.
Office No 908 9th Floor Rajhans Montessa Dumas Road Magdalla Choryasi, Surat, 395007, Gujarat, India
Tel.: (91) 2612463262
Web Site:
https://www.mohitindustries.com
Year Founded: 1991
MOHITIND—(NSE)
Rev.: $20,638,638
Assets: $15,277,968
Liabilities: $7,966,983
Net Worth: $7,310,985
Earnings: $93,799
Emp.: 250
Fiscal Year-end: 03/31/21
Cotton Yarn Mfr
N.A.I.C.S.: 313110
Naresh Sitaram Saboo *(Co-Mng Dir)*

MOHIT PAPER MILLS LIMITED
15A/13 Upper Ground Floor East Patel Nagar, New Delhi, 110008, India
Tel.: (91) 1125886798
Web Site: https://www.mohitpaper.in
Year Founded: 1992
530169—(BOM)
Rev.: $11,393,751
Assets: $14,801,091
Liabilities: $10,546,823
Net Worth: $4,254,268
Earnings: ($469,000)
Emp.: 180
Fiscal Year-end: 03/31/21
Paper Mfr & Whlsr
N.A.I.C.S.: 322120
Sandeep Jain *(Chm & Mng Dir)*

MOHITE INDUSTRIES LIMITED
RS No 347 Ambapwadi Phata NH-4, Vadgaon Taluka Hatkanangale, Kolhapur, 416112, Maharashtra, India
Tel.: (91) 2302471230
Web Site: https://www.mohite.com
Year Founded: 1966
532140—(BOM)
Rev.: $10,409,304
Assets: $28,215,754
Liabilities: $15,109,778
Net Worth: $13,105,977
Earnings: $802,266
Emp.: 287
Fiscal Year-end: 03/31/23
Cotton Yarn Mfr
N.A.I.C.S.: 313110
Shivaji R. Mohite *(Chm & Co-Mng Dir)*
Subsidiaries:

Abhishek Corporation Ltd. (1)
Gat No 148 Tamgaon Kolhapur Hupari Road, Taluka Karveer, Kolhapur, 416 234, Maharashtra, India
Tel.: (91) 2312676191
Web Site:
https://www.abhishekcorporation.com
Rev.: $12,211,222
Assets: $12,211,222
Liabilities: $131,442,893

Net Worth: ($119,231,672)
Earnings: ($2,791,548)
Fiscal Year-end: 03/31/2021
Yarn Product Mfr
N.A.I.C.S.: 313110
Anjali Anasaheb Mohite *(CFO)*

MOHO RESOURCES LTD.
3/9 Loftus Street, West Leederville, 6007, WA, Australia
Tel.: (61) 894810389
Web Site:
https://www.mohoresources.com.au
MOH—(ASX)
Assets: $3,435,137
Liabilities: $590,706
Net Worth: $2,844,430
Earnings: ($3,949,344)
Fiscal Year-end: 06/30/24
Mineral Exploration Services
N.A.I.C.S.: 213114
Shane B. Sadleir *(Mng Dir)*

MOHOTA INDUSTRIES LTD
Block No 15 3rd Floor Gate No 2 DevKaranMansion 63 Princess Street, Mumbai, 400002, India
Tel.: (91) 2222084711
Web Site:
http://www.mohotaindustries.com
Year Founded: 1898
530047—(BOM)
Rev.: $16,001,227
Assets: $41,903,994
Liabilities: $17,149,321
Net Worth: $24,754,673
Earnings: ($4,311,162)
Emp.: 772
Fiscal Year-end: 03/31/20
Fiber Yarn Mfr
N.A.I.C.S.: 313110
Vinod Kumar Mohota *(Chm & Mng Dir)*

MOHR GMBH
Nordring 12, 76473, Rastatt, Germany
Tel.: (49) 722930490
Web Site: http://moplexhamburg.com
Sales Range: $10-24.9 Million
Emp.: 21
Tower Mobile & Used Crane Distr
N.A.I.C.S.: 423810
Matthias Mohr *(Mng Dir-New Crane Trade)*

MOHSIN HAIDER DARWISH LLC
PO Box 880, Muscat, 112, Oman
Tel.: (968) 24703777
Web Site: http://www.mhdoman.com
Year Founded: 1921
Sales Range: $50-74.9 Million
Emp.: 500
Consumer Products Importer & Distr
N.A.I.C.S.: 425120
Lujaina Mohsin Darwish *(Chm)*

MOI CORPORATION
Bunkyo Ward, Chiyoda-ku, Tokyo, 113-0033, Japan
Tel.: (81) 335271471
Web Site: https://www.about.moi.st
Year Founded: 2012
5031—(TKS)
Emp.: 38
Software Development Services
N.A.I.C.S.: 541511

MOIL LIMITED
MOIL BHAWAN 1A Katol Road, Nagpur, 440013, Maharashtra, India
Tel.: (91) 7122591661
Web Site: https://www.moil.nic.in
Year Founded: 1962
533286—(BOM)
Rev.: $174,699,989

Assets: $462,778,789
Liabilities: $77,862,289
Net Worth: $384,916,500
Earnings: $24,110,091
Emp.: 5,866
Fiscal Year-end: 03/31/21
Manganese Ore Mining Services
N.A.I.C.S.: 212290
Mukund P. Chaudhari *(Chm & Mng Dir)*

MOISELLE INTERNATIONAL HOLDINGS LIMITED
Units 1-5 11th Floor Kodak House 2 39 Healthy Street East, North Point, China (Hong Kong)
Tel.: (852) 2 396 4259
Web Site: http://www.moiselle.com.hk
0130—(HKG)
Rev.: $17,867,083
Assets: $92,196,581
Liabilities: $25,796,000
Net Worth: $66,400,581
Earnings: ($5,281,344)
Emp.: 300
Fiscal Year-end: 03/31/22
Fashion Apparel & Accessories Mfr
N.A.I.C.S.: 313220
Elaine Lin Pang *(COO & Sec)*
Subsidiaries:

Moiselle Singapore Pte. Ltd. (1)
Shop 01-26 The Shoppes at Marina Bay Sands 2 Bayfront Avenue, Singapore, Singapore
Tel.: (65) 66887788
Women Clothing Distr
N.A.I.C.S.: 458110

MOJ S.A.
ul Tokarska 6, 40-859, Katowice, Poland
Tel.: (48) 326040900
Web Site: http://www.moj.com.pl
Year Founded: 1913
MOJ—(WAR)
Rev.: $20,174,035
Assets: $19,824,441
Liabilities: $10,493,140
Net Worth: $9,331,301
Earnings: $625,254
Fiscal Year-end: 12/31/23
Mining Tool Mfr
N.A.I.C.S.: 333131
Marian Bak *(Chm-Mgmt Bd)*

MOJAVE BRANDS INC
1055 West Georgia StSuite 2050, PO Box 11121, Royal Centre, Vancouver, V6E 3P3, BC, Canada
Tel.: (416) 453-4708
Web Site:
http://www.highhampton.com
Year Founded: 2010
MOJO—(CNSX)
Rev.: $15,887
Assets: $516,337
Liabilities: $42,420
Net Worth: $473,917
Earnings: ($51,368)
Fiscal Year-end: 08/31/23
Investment Services
N.A.I.C.S.: 523999

MOKSH ORNAMENTS LTD.
B-405/1 B-405/2 4th floor 99 Mulji Jetha Bldg Kalbadevi Road, Vitthalwadi, Mumbai, 400002, India
Tel.: (91) 2261834395
Web Site:
https://www.mokshornaments.com
Year Founded: 2012
MOKSH—(NSE)
Rev.: $53,618,428
Assets: $9,531,599
Liabilities: $3,417,217
Net Worth: $6,114,382

Earnings: $735,483
Emp.: 13
Fiscal Year-end: 03/31/23
Golden Jewellery Product Distr
N.A.I.C.S.: 458310
Amrit J. Shah *(Mng Dir)*

MOL GLOBAL, INC.
Lot 07-03 08-03 Level 7 & 8, Berjaya Times Square No 1 Jalan Imbi, 55100, Kuala Lumpur, Malaysia
Tel.: (60) 3 2082 1251
Web Site: http://www.mol.com
Sales Range: $50-74.9 Million
Emp.: 507
Online & Mobile Payment Systems
N.A.I.C.S.: 522320
Preecha Praipattarakul *(CEO)*

MOL MAGYAR OLAJ- ES GAZIPARI NYRT.
Dombovari ut 28, 1117, Budapest, Hungary
Tel.: (36) 12090000
Web Site: https://molgroup.info
Year Founded: 1991
MOL—(BUD)
Rev.: $25,974,606,292
Assets: $22,315,953,125
Liabilities: $10,156,340,261
Net Worth: $12,159,612,864
Earnings: $1,645,217,888
Emp.: 24,912
Fiscal Year-end: 12/31/23
Holding Company; Oil & Natural Gas Production, Refining & Distribution
N.A.I.C.S.: 551112
Zoltan Aldott *(Chm-Supervisory Bd)*
Subsidiaries:

ALTEO Energiaszolgaltato Nyrt (1)
Korhaz utca 6-12, 1055, Budapest, Hungary (73.79%)
Tel.: (36) 12368050
Web Site: https://www.alteo.hu
Rev.: $268,306,741
Assets: $249,390,390
Liabilities: $157,597,668
Net Worth: $91,792,722
Earnings: $34,603,451
Emp.: 454
Fiscal Year-end: 12/31/2023
Electric Power Distr
N.A.I.C.S.: 221122
Attila Chikan *(CEO)*

Subsidiary (Domestic):

Alte-go Kft. (2)
Korhaz Utca 6-12, 1033, Budapest, Hungary
Tel.: (36) 205799999
Web Site: https://altego.hu
Electrical Charging Equipment Distr
N.A.I.C.S.: 423610

Alteo-therm Kft. (2)
Korhaz utca 6-12, 1033, Budapest, Hungary
Tel.: (36) 12368050
Web Site: https://www.alteo.hu
Electricity Production Services
N.A.I.C.S.: 221114

Eco-first Kft. (2)
Korhaz Utca 6-12, 1033, Budapest, Hungary
Tel.: (36) 12368050
Web Site: https://ecofirst.hu
Waste Management Services
N.A.I.C.S.: 562998

Fe-group Invest Zrt. (2)
Sirkert U 2-4, 1108, Budapest, Hungary
Tel.: (36) 12643585
Web Site: https://fegroup.hu
Waste Recycling Services
N.A.I.C.S.: 562920

Aurora Kunststoffe GmbH (1)
Max-Eyth-Str 14-16, 74632, Neuenstein, Germany
Tel.: (49) 794291420
Web Site: https://www.aurora-kunststoffe.de
Plastic Grinding Material Mfr & Distr

MOL MAGYAR OLAJ- ES GAZIPARI NYRT.   INTERNATIONAL PUBLIC

MOL Magyar Olaj- es Gazipari Nyrt.—(Continued)
N.A.I.C.S.: 333248

Balatongaz Kft., Ltd. (1)
Orgonalty Utca 1, H 8243, Kossuth Lajostelep, Hungary (75%)
Tel.: (36) 87444206
Sales Range: $75-99.9 Million
Emp.: 3
Natural Gas Supplier
N.A.I.C.S.: 221210

Dalby A.S. (1)
Vlcie hrdlo 1, 824 12, Bratislava, Slovakia
Tel.: (421) 240552331
Web Site: https://www.dalby.sk
Diesel Fuel Whslr
N.A.I.C.S.: 424720

FER Tuzoltosag es Szolgaltato Kft. (1)
Olajmunkas Ut 2, H-2443, Szazhalombatta, Hungary
Tel.: (36) 23551115
Web Site: https://www.fer.hu
Sales Range: $50-74.9 Million
Emp.: 210
Fire Protection Services
N.A.I.C.S.: 922160

FGSZ Foldgazszallito Zrt. (1)
Tanacshaz U 5, 8600, Siofok, Hungary
Tel.: (36) 84 505 117
Web Site: http://fgsz.hu
Sales Range: $200-249.9 Million
Natural Gas Transmission
N.A.I.C.S.: 486210

Plant (Domestic):

FGSZ Foldgazszallito Zrt - Gellenhaza Natural Gas Transmission Plant (2)
Pf 8, Ipartelep, 8981, Gellenhaza, Hungary
Tel.: (36) 92 366 332
Natural Gas Transmission Services
N.A.I.C.S.: 486210

FGSZ Foldgazszallito Zrt - Kecskemet Natural Gas Transmission Plant (2)
Szolnoki Hegy 232 Pf 61, 6000, Kecskemet, Hungary
Tel.: (36) 204249486
Web Site: http://fgsz.hu
Natural Gas Transmission Services
N.A.I.C.S.: 486210

FGSZ Foldgazszallito Zrt - Vecses Natural Gas Transmission Plant (2)
Pf 2, 2221, Vecses, Hungary
Tel.: (36) 1 8805 316
Web Site: http://www.fgsz.hu
Natural Gas Transmission Services
N.A.I.C.S.: 486210

Subsidiary (Domestic):

Magyar Gaz Tranzit Zrt. (2)
Zahony u 7 Graphisoft Park B Building 2 em, 1031, Budapest, Hungary
Tel.: (36) 13042343
Web Site: http://www.gaztranzit.hu
Gas Pipeline Implementation Distr
N.A.I.C.S.: 486210

Fonte Viva Kft. (1)
Vasut utca 1, 8698, Somogyvar, Hungary
Tel.: (36) 85540900
Web Site: https://www.fonteviva.hu
Mineral Water Mfr & Distr
N.A.I.C.S.: 312112

Fresh Corner Restaurants Kft. (1)
Oktober huszonharmadika u 14, 1117, Budapest, Hungary
Tel.: (36) 18865006
Web Site: https://www.freshcorner.hu
Catering Services
N.A.I.C.S.: 722320

GES Geofizikai Szolgaltato Kft. (1)
Szantofold Ut 7 9 Levelcim, 1601, Budapest, Hungary
Tel.: (36) 1 305 2611
Web Site: http://www.ges.hu
Sales Range: $100-124.9 Million
Emp.: 324
Data Processing & Management Services
N.A.I.C.S.: 518210

GES Kft. (1)
Szantofold Ut 7 9, 1151, Budapest, Hungary (100%)
Tel.: (36) 13052600
Web Site: http://www.ges.hu
Sales Range: $100-124.9 Million
Emp.: 500
Provider of Geophysical/Seismic, Measuring & Computer-Aided Data Processing Services to Oil Companies, for the Purpose of Oil Exploration
N.A.I.C.S.: 333132
Imre Szilagyi (Mng Dir)

Geoinform Kft. (1)
Korosi ut 43, 5000, Szolnok, Hungary
Tel.: (36) 309448053
Web Site: https://www.geoinform.hu
Hydrocarbon Research & Exploration Services
N.A.I.C.S.: 213112
Attila Czafit (CFO)

IES - Italiana Energia e Servizi spa (1)
Strada Cipata 79, 46100, Mantua, Italy
Tel.: (39) 03763781
Web Site: http://www.iesitaliana.com
Sales Range: $125-149.9 Million
Emp.: 40
Petroleum Refinery Services
N.A.I.C.S.: 324110
Ferenc Horvath (Chm)

Subsidiary (Domestic):

Melies SRL (2)
Strada Cipata 79, Mantua, 46100, Italy
Tel.: (39) 0376378271
Sales Range: $125-149.9 Million
Petroleum Product Distr
N.A.I.C.S.: 424720

Panta Distribuzione SPA (2)
Regione Pozzetti, 15040, Valmacca, Italy
Tel.: (39) 0142411490
Petroleum Product Distr
N.A.I.C.S.: 424720

ISO-SZER Kft. (1)
HRSZ 4703/59, Ipari Park, 7030, Paks, Hungary
Tel.: (36) 75510177
Web Site: https://www.isoszer.hu
Construction Services
N.A.I.C.S.: 236220

ITK Holding Plc. (1)
Istvantelki ut 8, 1045, Budapest, Hungary
Tel.: (36) 14221650
Web Site: https://www.itkholding.hu
Public Transport Services
N.A.I.C.S.: 926120

Kalegran Ltd. (1)
Chapo Central 20 Spyrou Kyprianou Street 3rd Floor, Nicosia, 1075, Cyprus
Tel.: (357) 22749000
Oil & Gas Exploration Services
N.A.I.C.S.: 213112
Irina Zodiatou (Gen Mgr)

MOL & INA d.o.o. (1)
Ulica 15 Maja 19, 6000, Koper, Slovenia (67%)
Tel.: (386) 56633300
Web Site: https://www.omv.si
Sales Range: $75-99.9 Million
Emp.: 70
Petroleum Services
N.A.I.C.S.: 541330
Vanja Lombar (Dir Gen)

MOL Austria GmbH. (1)
Walcherstrasse 11a, 1020, Vienna, Austria
Tel.: (43) 1211200
Web Site: https://molaustria.at
Petroleum Product Distr
N.A.I.C.S.: 424720

Subsidiary (Domestic):

Roth Heizole GmbH. (2)
Conrad Von Hotzendorf Str. 160, 8010, Graz, Austria
Tel.: (43) 316 4722120
Emp.: 121
Petroleum Product Distr
N.A.I.C.S.: 424720

MOL Austria Handels GmbH (1)
Walcherstrasse 11a 7, 1020, Vienna, Austria (100%)
Tel.: (43) 1 21120 1100
Web Site: http://www.molaustria.at
Energy Products Mfr & Whslr
N.A.I.C.S.: 425120
Bela Horvat (Mng Dir)

MOL Campus Kft. (1)
Dombovari ut 28, 1117, Budapest, Hungary
Tel.: (36) 18865000
Web Site: https://www.molcampus.hu
Emp.: 2,500
Real Estate Development Services
N.A.I.C.S.: 531390

MOL Ceska Republika s.r.o. (1)
Quadrio Building 5th Floor Purkynova 2121/3, 110 00, Prague, 1, Czech Republic
Tel.: (420) 241080800
Web Site: https://molcesko.cz
Oil & Gas Operation Services
N.A.I.C.S.: 424720

MOL GBS Slovensko s.r.o. (1)
Wolf's Throat 1, 824 12, Bratislava, Slovakia
Tel.: (421) 240558841
Administrative Services
N.A.I.C.S.: 561110

MOL Germany GmbH (1)
Ottostr 5, D-80333, Munich, Germany
Tel.: (49) 8953886260
Web Site: https://molgermany.de
Emp.: 7
Petroleum Product Distr
N.A.I.C.S.: 424720
Zoltan Szanto (Mng Dir)

MOL IT & Digital GBS Slovensko, s.r.o. (1)
Vlcie Hrdlo 1, 824 12, Bratislava, Slovakia
Tel.: (421) 240558766
IT Support Services
N.A.I.C.S.: 541519

MOL Norge AS (1)
Trelastgata 3, Oslo Area, 0191, Oslo, Norway
Tel.: (47) 22003050
Web Site: https://www.molnorge.no
Oil & Natural Gas Exploration Services
N.A.I.C.S.: 213112

MOL Racing Kft. (1)
Ipartelep Hrsz 2704/1, 2443, Szazhalombatta, Hungary
Tel.: (36) 23553839
Web Site: https://www.molracing.hu
Chemical Mfr & Distr
N.A.I.C.S.: 325998

MOL Romania PP s.r.l. (1)
Str Danielopolu 4-6 Et2 Sector 1, 014134, Bucharest, Romania
Tel.: (40) 212048500
Web Site: https://www.molgroupchemicals.com
Sales Range: $50-74.9 Million
Lubricants & Fuel Whslr
N.A.I.C.S.: 424720

MOL Romania Petrochemicals (1)
Str Danielopolu 4 6 Et2 Sector 1, 014 134, Bucharest, Romania
Tel.: (40) 212048500
Emp.: 2
Petrochemical Product Distr
N.A.I.C.S.: 424690
Eugen Matei (Head-Petchem Ops-Romania & Moldavia)

MOL Romania Petroleum Products Srl (1)
Bd 21 Decembrie 1989 Nr 77 Room C 1 1 Cd The Office Building Fl 1, Cluj-Napoca, 400604, Romania (100%)
Tel.: (40) 264407600
Web Site: http://www.molromania.ro
Sales Range: $100-124.9 Million
Emp.: 170
N.A.I.C.S.: 213112

MOL Serbia (Intermol) d.o.o. (1)
Omladinskih brigada 88/V, Novi Beograd, Serbia
Tel.: (381) 112096900
Web Site: https://molserbia.rs
Lubricating Oil Mfr
N.A.I.C.S.: 324191

MOL Serbia d.o.o. (1)
Omladinskih Brigada 88/V, 11070, Belgrade, Serbia
Tel.: (381) 112 096 900
Web Site: http://www.molserbia.rs
Fuel & Lubricant Distr
N.A.I.C.S.: 424720

MOL Slovenia d.o.o. (1)
Ulica arhitekta Novaka 6, SI-9000, Murska Sobota, Slovenia
Tel.: (386) 25303332
Diesel Fuel Whslr
N.A.I.C.S.: 424720

MOL Slovenija d.o.o. (1)
Lendavska Ulica 24a, Murska Sobota, 9000, Slovenia
Tel.: (386) 2 530 33 10
Web Site: http://www.mol.si
Petroleum Product Whslr
N.A.I.C.S.: 424720

MOL Slovensko spol. s.r.o. (1)
Vlcie hrdio 1, 824 12, Bratislava, Slovakia (100%)
Tel.: (421) 240551111
Web Site: http://www.slovnaft.sk
Wholesale Trading in Lubricants & Fuels
N.A.I.C.S.: 324191

MOL Ukraine LLC (1)
Street Sichovykh Striltsiv 50 Office 5-B, 04053, Kiev, Ukraine
Tel.: (380) 444860083
Web Site: https://www.mol-ukraine.com.ua
Lubricant Product Mfr & Distr
N.A.I.C.S.: 324191

MOL-CEZ European Power Hungary Kft. (1)
Olajmunkas Utca 2, Szazhalombatta, Hungary
Tel.: (36) 1 464 0768
Heat Electric Generation & Distribution Services
N.A.I.C.S.: 221330

MOL-GAZ Trading Ltd. (1)
Oktober huszonharmadika u 18, 1117, Budapest, Hungary (59%)
Tel.: (36) 12090000
Web Site: http://www.mol.hu
Gas Supplier
N.A.I.C.S.: 221210

MOL-LUB Kft. (1)
Fo Ut 21, 2931, Almasfuzito, Hungary
Tel.: (36) 34526330
Web Site: https://mollubricants.com
Sales Range: $75-99.9 Million
Emp.: 200
Petroleum Product Distr
N.A.I.C.S.: 424720

MOL-RUSS OOO. (1)
Kosmodamianskaya Nab 52 bld 4 floor 8, Moscow, Russia
Tel.: (7) 4959676805
Sales Range: $25-49.9 Million
Emp.: 150
Petroleum Product Distr
N.A.I.C.S.: 424720

MOL-Trans Kft. (1)
Petroleumkikoto U 5 7, 1211, Budapest, Hungary
Tel.: (36) 1 420 7498
Sales Range: $75-99.9 Million
Emp.: 23
Petroleum Product Distr
N.A.I.C.S.: 424720

MOLTRADE-Mineralimpex (1)
Benczur U 13, 1068, Budapest, Hungary (100%)
Tel.: (36) 014625300
Web Site: http://www.moltrade.hu
Sales Range: $25-49.9 Million
Emp.: 10
Export, Import, Trading, Wholesale Retailing & Retail Trading of Motor Vehicle Fuels, Other Fuels & Forwarding
N.A.I.C.S.: 457210
Sandor Sagi (Dir-Fin)

MOLTRANS (1)
Petroleumkikoto Ut 5 7, Budapest, 361420, Hungary (100%)
Tel.: (36) 14207498

Sales Range: $200-249.9 Million
Emp.: 300
Mineral Oil Products
N.A.I.C.S.: 212390
Laslo Bago *(Mng Dir)*

Multipont Program Zrt. (1)
Tel.: (36) 618865000
Web Site: https://www.multipont.hu
Card Application Services
N.A.I.C.S.: 518210

Nelsa S.r.l. (1)
Via Varesina 118, 22075, Lurate Caccivio, CO, Italy
Tel.: (39) 0314430361
Web Site: https://nelsalubrificanti.it
Heating Fuel Distr
N.A.I.C.S.: 424710

Nitrogenmuvek Rt. (1)
14 Hosok Sqr, 8105, Petfurdo, Hungary (100%)
Tel.: (36) 88620100
Web Site: http://www.nitrogen.hu
Sales Range: $125-149.9 Million
Emp.: 300
Nitrogenous Fertilzer Producer
N.A.I.C.S.: 325311

OT Industries Zrt. (1)
44 Galvani Str, Budapest, 1117, Hungary (100%)
Tel.: (36) 1453 6300
Web Site: http://www.otindustries.hu
Holding Company
N.A.I.C.S.: 551112
Gabriel Racka *(CEO)*

Subsidiary (Domestic):

OT Industries Engineering Co. Ltd. (2)
44 Galvani Str, 1117, Budapest, Hungary
Tel.: (36) 14536300
Web Site: http://www.otindustries.hu
Engineeering Services
N.A.I.C.S.: 541330

OT Industries-DKG Machine Manufacturing Co. Ltd. (2)
9 Var str, 8800, Nagykanizsa, Hungary
Tel.: (36) 93 310 159
Web Site: http://www.otindustries.hu
Oil & Gas Equipment Mfr
N.A.I.C.S.: 333132

OT Industries-KVV Contractor Co. Ltd. (2)
Bajcsy-Zs u 207, 8600, Siofok, Hungary
Tel.: (36) 84 310 310
Steel Pole Mfr
N.A.I.C.S.: 331210

Panfora Oil & Gas S.r.l. (1)
The Office Bulevardul 21 Decembrie 1989 nr 77 Etaj 1 Camera C 1 2, Cladirea C-D, RO-400603, Cluj-Napoca, Romania
Tel.: (40) 264407646
Web Site: https://www.panfora.ro
Mineral Exploration Services
N.A.I.C.S.: 213115

Petrolszolg Kft. (1)
Olajmunkas Ut 2, H-2440, Szazhalombatta, Hungary
Tel.: (36) 23551217
Web Site: https://petrolszolg.hu
Oil & Gas Exploration Services
N.A.I.C.S.: 213112

ReMat Hulladekhasznosito Zrt. (1)
TVK Ipartelep 2096/3 2096/8 hrsz, 3580, Tiszaujvaros, Hungary
Tel.: (36) 49521664
Washing Equipment Mfr & Distr
N.A.I.C.S.: 335220

SHM Seven Investments Ltd. (1)
City Forum 11 Florinis Street 7th Floor, 1065, Nicosia, Cyprus
Tel.: (357) 22749000
Investment Management Service
N.A.I.C.S.: 523999

SWS s.r.o. (1)
Vojany 332, 076 72, Michalovce, Slovakia
Tel.: (421) 566395334
Web Site: http://www.sws.sk
Liquid Gas Transloading Services
N.A.I.C.S.: 488210

Nora Jencsoova *(Head-Bus Support)*

Slovnaft A.S. (1)
Vlcie hrdlo 1, 824 12, Bratislava, Slovakia
Tel.: (421) 240551111
Oil Refining
N.A.I.C.S.: 324110
Oszkar Vilagi *(Chm & CEO)*

Slovnaft Ceska republika spol sro (1)
Olbrachtova 9, 140 00, Prague, 4, Czech Republic
Tel.: (420) 241 080 811
Web Site: http://www.slovnaft.cz
Fuel Retailer
N.A.I.C.S.: 457120

Slovnaft Mobility Services, s.r.o. (1)
Vlcie hrdlo 1, 824 12, Bratislava, Slovakia
Tel.: (421) 259505950
Web Site: https://www.slovnaftbajk.sk
Bicycle Rental Services
N.A.I.C.S.: 532284

Slovnaft Polska S.A. (1)
Ul Wadowicka 6 Entrance 8, Buma Square Business Park, 30-415, Krakow, Poland
Tel.: (48) 122991000
Web Site: https://www.slovnaft.pl
Fuel Distr
N.A.I.C.S.: 424710

Slovnaft Trans A.S. (1)
Vlcie hrdlo, 824 20, Bratislava, Slovakia
Tel.: (421) 45520041
Vehicle Repair & Maintenance Services
N.A.I.C.S.: 811198

The Kiskungaz Co., Ltd. (1)
Gubacsi ut 30, 1097, Budapest, Hungary
Tel.: (36) 1 280 5254
N.A.I.C.S.: 213112

Tifon d.o.o. (1)
Zadarska ulica 80, HR-10000, Zagreb, Croatia
Tel.: (385) 16160600
Web Site: https://tifon.hr
Sales Range: $250-299.9 Million
Emp.: 500
Petroleum Bulk Station Operating Services
N.A.I.C.S.: 424710

Vurup A.S. (1)
Vlcie Hrdlo, PO Box 50, 820 03, Bratislava, Slovakia
Tel.: (421) 240555134
Web Site: https://www.vurup.sk
Testing Laboratory Services
N.A.I.C.S.: 541380
Zdena Simcakova *(Asst Mng Dir)*

MOLAN STEEL COMPANY
Eastern Ring Road Exit No 16 Palladium Center Complex, PO Box 7090, AlFarouq, Riyadh, 14323, Saudi Arabia
Tel.: (966) 112255601
Web Site: https://www.molansteel.com
Year Founded: 2015
9553—(SAU)
Rev.: $23,918,296
Assets: $14,194,555
Liabilities: $6,173,169
Net Worth: $8,021,386
Earnings: ($1,276,233)
Emp.: 32
Fiscal Year-end: 12/31/23
Steel Fabrication Product Mfr
N.A.I.C.S.: 331110
Abdul Rahman Ibrahim Suleiman Al-Odhaibi *(Chm)*

MOLD-TEK PACKAGING LIMITED
8229382A700 Road No 36
8229382A700 Road No 36 Jubliee Hills, Jubliee Hills, Hyderabad, 500033, Telangana, India
Tel.: (91) 4040300300
Web Site: https://www.moldtekpackaging.com

MOLDTECH—(NSE)
Rev.: $65,494,120
Assets: $59,580,394
Liabilities: $24,642,372
Net Worth: $34,938,021
Earnings: $6,546,021
Emp.: 563
Fiscal Year-end: 03/31/21
Packaging Plastic Products Mfr
N.A.I.C.S.: 322220
J. Lakshmana Rao *(Chm & Mng Dir)*

MOLD-TEK TECHNOLOGIES LIMITED
8-2-293/82/A/700 Plot No 700 Road No 36, Jubliee Hills, Hyderabad, 500033, Telangana, India
Tel.: (91) 4040300300
Web Site: https://www.moldtekgroup.com
MOLDTECH—(NSE)
Rev.: $18,034,924
Assets: $15,674,251
Liabilities: $3,096,987
Net Worth: $12,577,263
Earnings: $3,547,221
Emp.: 1,107
Fiscal Year-end: 03/31/23
Information Technology Consulting Services
N.A.I.C.S.: 541512
J. Lakshmana Rao *(Chm & Mng Dir)*

Subsidiaries:

RMM Global, Inc. (1)
2841 Riviera Dr Ste 306, Akron, OH 44333
Tel.: (330) 867-4505
Web Site: http://www.moldtekindia.com
Emp.: 4
Engineering Consulting Services
N.A.I.C.S.: 541330
Prasad Raju *(Pres)*

MOLE VALLEY FARMERS LTD
Exmoor House Lime Way Pathfields Business Park, South Molton, Devon, EX36 3LH, United Kingdom
Tel.: (44) 1769573431
Web Site: http://www.molevalleyfarmers.com
Year Founded: 1960
Rev.: $649,732,538
Assets: $199,478,621
Liabilities: $139,589,653
Net Worth: $59,888,968
Earnings: $582,350
Emp.: 2,073
Fiscal Year-end: 09/30/19
Farming & Agricultural Products Distr
N.A.I.C.S.: 112410
Graeme M. Cock *(Chm)*

Subsidiaries:

Cox & Robinson (Agricultural) Ltd (1)
The Creamery Brackley Road, Buckingham, MK18 1JD, Buckinghamshire, United Kingdom
Tel.: (44) 1280816011
Web Site: http://www.coxandrobinson.co.uk
Livestock Feed Distr
N.A.I.C.S.: 424910
Peter Hunt *(Mgr-Admin)*

D&I Bridgman and Son Ltd (1)
Down View Newton St Petrock, Torrington, EX38 8LS, Devon, United Kingdom
Tel.: (44) 1409261321
Web Site: http://www.bridgmans.co.uk
Farm Machinery & Equipment Distr
N.A.I.C.S.: 423820

Mole Valley Farmers Ltd - Feed Supplements Plant (1)
The Market Site Bath Road, Bridgwater, TA6 4NT, Somerset, United Kingdom
Tel.: (44) 1278420481
Livestock Feed Mfr
N.A.I.C.S.: 311119
Dean Fury *(Mgr)*

Mole Valley Farmers Ltd - Lifton Feed Mill (1)
Spry Mill, Lifton, Devon, PL16 0BA, United Kingdom
Tel.: (44) 1566780261
Livestock Feed Mfr
N.A.I.C.S.: 311119
James Trebble *(Mgr)*

Mole Valley Farmers Ltd - Porte Marsh Mill (1)
Porte Marsh Trading Estate, Calne, SN11 9BW, Wiltshire, United Kingdom
Tel.: (44) 1278444829
Livestock Feed Mfr
N.A.I.C.S.: 311119
James Trebble *(Mgr-Site)*

Mole Valley Farmers Ltd Witheridge Engineering Division (1)
The Forge Church Street, Witheridge, Tiverton, EX16 8AP, Devon, United Kingdom
Tel.: (44) 1884860478
Livestock Feed Mfr
N.A.I.C.S.: 311119
Kim Turner *(Mgr)*

Molecare Veterinary Services Ltd. (1)
Exmoor House Lime Way, Pathfields Business Park South Molton, Devon, EX36 3LH, United Kingdom
Tel.: (44) 1392347240
Web Site: https://www.molecarevetservices.com
Veterinary Services
N.A.I.C.S.: 541940

Three Counties Feeds Ltd (1)
Unit 2 Ground Floor Oaklands Court, Tiverton Business Park, Tiverton, EX16 6TG, Devon, United Kingdom
Tel.: (44) 1884256256
Web Site: http://www.threecountiesfeeds.co.uk
Livestock Feed Mfr
N.A.I.C.S.: 311119

MOLECULAR DATA INC.
11/F Building 15 2177 Shenkun Road, Minhang District, Shanghai, 201106, China
Tel.: (86) 2154365166   Ky
Web Site: http://investor.molbase.com
Year Founded: 2018
MKD—(NASDAQ)
Rev.: $1,163,846,283
Assets: $104,921,425
Liabilities: $109,192,767
Net Worth: ($4,271,342)
Earnings: ($50,252,420)
Emp.: 189
Fiscal Year-end: 12/31/20
Holding Company
N.A.I.C.S.: 551112
Dongliang Chang *(Co-Founder & Chm)*

MOLECULAR ENERGIES PLC
Carrwood Park Selby Road, Leeds, LS15 4LG, United Kingdom
Tel.: (44) 2070167950   UK
Web Site: https://www.molecularenergies.com
PPC—(AIM)
Rev.: $34,147,000
Assets: $129,872,000
Liabilities: $61,031,000
Net Worth: $68,841,000
Earnings: $4,579,000
Emp.: 66
Fiscal Year-end: 12/31/21
Crude Petroleum Extraction
N.A.I.C.S.: 211120
Peter Levine *(Chm & CEO)*

Subsidiaries:

Green House Capital Limited (1)
5 Carrwood Park Selby Road, Leeds, LS15 4LG, United Kingdom
Tel.: (44) 1133372210

Molecular Energies PLC—(Continued)
Web Site: https://ghcplc.com
Agricultural Product Whslr
N.A.I.C.S.: 424590

MOLECULAR PARTNERS AG
Wagistrasse 14, 8952, Zurich, Schlieren, Switzerland
Tel.: (41) 447557700
Web Site:
https://www.molecularpartners.com
MOLN—(NASDAQ)
Rev.: $214,716,312
Assets: $296,999,317
Liabilities: $30,680,877
Net Worth: $266,318,440
Earnings: $133,464,987
Emp.: 175
Fiscal Year-end: 12/31/22
Biopharmaceutical Mfr & Researcher
N.A.I.C.S.: 325412
Patrick Amstutz (Co-Founder, CEO & Member-Mgmt Bd)

MOLENWIJCK B.V.
Looaenbeemd 18, Eindhoven, 5652 BH, Netherlands
Tel.: (31) 402518331
Web Site: http://www.molenwijck.nl
Sales Range: $25-49.9 Million
Emp.: 5
Holding Company
N.A.I.C.S.: 551112
Josephus G. L. M. Reijers (CEO)

Subsidiaries:

Copaco N.V. (1)
Wekkerstraat 25, 5652 AN, Eindhoven, AN, Netherlands
Tel.: (31) 402513340
Web Site: http://www.copaco.nl
Information Technology Products Mfr
N.A.I.C.S.: 519290

MOLIBDENOS Y METALES S.A.
Camino Nos a los Morros N 66, San Bernardo, Santiago, Chile
Tel.: (56) 229376600
Web Site: https://molymet.com
MOLYMET—(SGO)
Rev.: $2,475,078,000
Assets: $1,968,980,000
Liabilities: $1,104,897,000
Net Worth: $864,083,000
Earnings: $24,816,000
Emp.: 1,276
Fiscal Year-end: 12/31/23
Molybdenum Concentrates Producer
N.A.I.C.S.: 331491
Gonzalo Concha Parada (VP-Engrg)

Subsidiaries:

MOLYMET Germany GmbH (1)
Niels-Bohr-Str 5, Wolfen, 6749, Bitterfeld, Germany
Tel.: (49) 349360400
Web Site: https://www.chemiemetall.de
Molybdenum Metal Powders Mfr
N.A.I.C.S.: 331492
Klaus Andersson (CEO)

MOLYMET Services Ltd. (1)
1 Milkhouse Gate, PO Box 1622, Woking, Guildford, GU1 3EZ, Surrey, United Kingdom
Tel.: (44) 1483302203
Sales Range: $25-49.9 Million
Emp.: 5
Metal Products Mfr
N.A.I.C.S.: 332999
Javier Guevara (Mng Dir)

MOLYMEX S.A. de C.V. (1)
Blvd Luis Donaldo Colosio No 450 Torre 1 Nivel 5 Local 1 Entre, Calle Real Del Arco y Blvd Solidaridad Colonia Metrocentro, 83250, Hermosillo, Sonora, Mexico
Tel.: (52) 6622893640
Web Site: https://www.molymex.com.mx

Sales Range: $50-74.9 Million
Emp.: 141
Molybdenum Chemicals Mf
N.A.I.C.S.: 325411

Molymet Belgium (1)
Langerbruggekaai 13, Havennummer 8120, 9000, Gent, East Flanders, Belgium
Tel.: (32) 92540511
Web Site: https://www.molymetbelgium.be
Sales Range: $50-74.9 Million
Emp.: 130
Ferromolybdenum Chemicals Mfr
N.A.I.C.S.: 331110
Guido Provoost (Gen Mgr)

Molymet Corporation (1)
401 E Pratt St Ste 2415, Baltimore, MD 21202 (100%)
Tel.: (410) 234-9944
Sales Range: $50-74.9 Million
Emp.: 200
Metal Products Mfr
N.A.I.C.S.: 332999

Molymet Germany GmbH (1)
Niels-Bohr-Str 5, 06749, Bitterfeld-Wolfen, Germany
Tel.: (49) 349360400
Web Site: http://www.molymet.de
Molybdenum Mfr
N.A.I.C.S.: 331110

MOLINEL SA
18 Rue Du Pont Rouge, 59236, Frelinghien, Nord, France
Tel.: (33) 320387000
Web Site: http://www.molinel.com
Rev.: $31,600,000
Emp.: 88
N.A.I.C.S.: 315250
Beno T. Dupre (Dir)

MOLINOS RIO DE LA PLATA S.A.
Uruguay 4075 Victoria, B1644HKG, Buenos Aires, Argentina
Tel.: (54) 1143401100
Web Site:
https://www.molinos.com.ar
Year Founded: 1902
MOLI—(BUE)
Rev.: $468,998,365
Assets: $390,193,365
Liabilities: $209,040,205
Net Worth: $181,153,161
Earnings: $50,712,155
Emp.: 5,000
Fiscal Year-end: 12/31/23
Soybean Oil & Other Food Products
N.A.I.C.S.: 311225
Guillermo Nelson Garcia Abal (Vice Chm)

Subsidiaries:

La Saltena S.A. (1)
1804 1607 Villa Adelina, Buenos Aires, Argentina
Tel.: (54) 800 888 2727
Web Site: http://www.lasaltena.com.ar
Emp.: 500
Dough & Flour Mixes Mfr
N.A.I.C.S.: 311824

Molinos International S.A. (1)
Edificio 1 Oficina 007 Zonamerica, Montevideo, 91600, Uruguay
Tel.: (598) 25182055
Food Products Mfr & Distr
N.A.I.C.S.: 311224

Molinos USA Corp. (1)
1441 Brickell Ave Ste 1410, Miami, FL 33131-3136
Tel.: (305) 358-1123
Web Site: http://www.molinos.com
Sales Range: $50-74.9 Million
Emp.: 6
Food Products Distr
N.A.I.C.S.: 424410
Fede Nino (Reg Mgr)

PCA International S.A. (1)
Ruta 8 Kilometro 17 500 Zona Franca Edificio, Montevideo, 91600, Uruguay

Tel.: (598) 25182055
Sales Range: $25-49.9 Million
Emp.: 6
Soyabean & Sunflower Seed Mfr
N.A.I.C.S.: 111110

MOLITEC STEEL CO., LTD.
18-31 Tanimachi 6-chome, Chuo-ku, Osaka, 542-0012, Japan
Tel.: (81) 667625643   JP
Web Site: https://www.molitec.co.jp
Year Founded: 1943
5986—(TKS)
Rev.: $335,616,140
Assets: $246,057,250
Liabilities: $152,347,280
Net Worth: $93,709,970
Earnings: $2,062,320
Emp.: 685
Fiscal Year-end: 03/31/24
Cold Rolled Steel Processing & Sales; Machinery Tools, Steel Parts, Plastic Products & Parts Mfr & Distr
N.A.I.C.S.: 331221
Takashi Kado (Pres)

Subsidiaries:

Juthawan Molitec (Thailand) Co., Ltd. (1)
150/67 Moo9 Tambon, Nongkham Amphur, Si Racha, 20110, Chon Buri, Thailand
Tel.: (66) 38 296900
Web Site: http://www.molitec.co.jp
Steel Products Mfr
N.A.I.C.S.: 331221

Molitec Steel (Vietnam) Co., Ltd. (1)
Factory E Road B2 Section B Pho Noi A IP, Lac Hong Commune Van Lam Dist, Hanoi, Hung Yen, Vietnam
Tel.: (84) 2213587985
Steel Products Mfr
N.A.I.C.S.: 331221

Molitec Steel Mexico, S.A. de C.V. (1)
Circuito Progreso No 118 Parque Industrial Logistica Automotriz, 20340, Aguascalientes, Mexico
Tel.: (52) 4499227840
Steel Products Whslr
N.A.I.C.S.: 423510

PT. Molitec Steel Indonesia (1)
Sentral Senayan II 16th Floor Jl Asia Afrika No 8 Kav 1/RW 3 Gelora, Tanah Abang, Jakarta, 10270, Pusat, Indonesia
Tel.: (62) 2129655875
Steel Products Mfr
N.A.I.C.S.: 331221

Shanghai Molitec Steel Co., Ltd. (1)
Zhao Yi Techno Park East 306 No 18 Tianshan Road, No 18 Tianshan Road, Shanghai, 200336, China
Tel.: (86) 2162902777
Emp.: 10
Steel Products Mfr
N.A.I.C.S.: 331221

MOLLERGRUPPEN AS
Frysjaveien 31, PO Box 6671, Oslo, Norway
Tel.: (47) 24033300
Web Site: http://www.moller.no
Year Founded: 1936
Sales Range: $1-4.9 Billion
Emp.: 4,000
Car Importer, Dealership Operator & Financing Services
N.A.I.C.S.: 441227
Pal Syversen (Pres & CEO)

Subsidiaries:

Harald A. Moller AS (1)
PO Box 46, Kjelsaas, Oslo, Norway (100%)
Tel.: (47) 24033300
Web Site: http://www.mollerbil.no
Sales Range: $150-199.9 Million
Emp.: 270
Automobile & Motor Vehicle Whslr
N.A.I.C.S.: 423110

Moller Baltikum AS (1)
PO Box 46, Oslo, Norway (100%)
Tel.: (47) 24033300
Web Site: http://www.moller.no
Sales Range: $150-199.9 Million
Emp.: 3,000
Automobile & Motor Vehicle Whslr
N.A.I.C.S.: 423110
Ketil B. Dorre (Mng Dir)

Moller BilFinans AS (1)
PO Box 6672, Etterstad, Oslo, 609, Norway
Tel.: (47) 24033300
Web Site: http://www.kunzeservice.no
Sales Range: $25-49.9 Million
Emp.: 38
Automobile & Motor Vehicle Whslr
N.A.I.C.S.: 423110
Steimlvam Solbakkem (Gen Mgr)

Moller Bil AS (1)
Frysjaveien 31, 0884, Oslo, Norway (100%)
Tel.: (47) 91504444
Web Site: http://www.mollerbil.no
Sales Range: $50-74.9 Million
Emp.: 130
New Car Dealers
N.A.I.C.S.: 441110

MOLOGEN AG
Fabeckstr 30, D-14195, Berlin, Germany
Tel.: (49) 308417880
Web Site: http://www.mologen.com
MGNK—(DEU)
Rev.: $4,721,565
Assets: $10,702,443
Liabilities: $11,783,325
Net Worth: ($1,080,882)
Earnings: ($13,591,657)
Emp.: 50
Fiscal Year-end: 12/31/18
Biotechnology Company
N.A.I.C.S.: 541714
Oliver Krautscheid (Chm-Supervisory Bd)

MOLOPO ENERGY LIMITED
Suite 3 Level 2 470 Collins Street, Melbourne, 3000, VIC, Australia
Tel.: (61) 384592200
Web Site:
http://www.molopoenergy.com
Year Founded: 1986
Rev.: $317,152
Assets: $9,739,597
Liabilities: $483,815
Net Worth: $9,255,782
Earnings: ($29,526,098)
Emp.: 2
Fiscal Year-end: 12/31/18
Energy Resource Development Services
N.A.I.C.S.: 213113
Roger Corbett (Chm)

MOLTEN METALS CORPORATION
600-1090 West Georgia Street, Vancouver, V6E 3V7, BC, Canada
Tel.: (778) 918-2261   BC
Web Site:
https://www.moltenmetalscorp.com
Year Founded: 2020
MLTNF—(OTCIQ)
Assets: $703,358
Liabilities: $54,830
Net Worth: $648,528
Earnings: ($257,266)
Fiscal Year-end: 12/31/23
Mineral Exploration Services
N.A.I.C.S.: 213115
Brooklyn Reed (Sec)

MOLTEN VENTURES PLC
20 Garrick Street, London, WC2E 9BT, United Kingdom
Tel.: (44) 2079318800   UK

AND PRIVATE COMPANIES

Web Site:
https://www.moltenventures.com
GROW—(LSE)
Assets: $1,718,256,372
Liabilities: $139,485,255
Net Worth: $1,578,771,117
Earnings: ($51,249,786)
Fiscal Year-end: 03/31/24
Investment Management Service
N.A.I.C.S.: 523940
Ben Wilkinson *(CFO)*

MOLTEN VENTURES VCT PLC
20 Garrick Street, London, WC2E 9BT, United Kingdom
Tel.: (44) 2079318800   UK
Web Site:
http://www.draperesprit.com
MVCT—(LSE)
Rev.: $26,918,936
Assets: $141,504,704
Liabilities: $458,920
Net Worth: $141,045,784
Earnings: $24,139,192
Fiscal Year-end: 03/31/22
Asset Management Services
N.A.I.C.S.: 523940
David Brock *(Chm)*

Subsidiaries:

Forward Partners Group Plc (1)
Huckletree Shoreditch Alphabeta Building 18 Finsbury Square, London, EC2A 1AH, United Kingdom
Web Site: https://www.forwardpartners.com
Rev.: $642,515
Assets: $123,124,211
Liabilities: $1,104,519
Net Worth: $122,019,692
Earnings: ($54,342,338)
Emp.: 34
Fiscal Year-end: 12/31/2022
Asset Management Services
N.A.I.C.S.: 523999

Subsidiary (Domestic):

Forward Partners Management Company Limited (2)
WeWork 1 Mark Square, London, EC2A 4EG, United Kingdom
Tel.: (44) 2030210684
Financial Investment Services
N.A.I.C.S.: 523999

Forward Partners Venture Advance Ltd. (2)
Huckletree Shoreditch 18 Finsbury Square, London, EC2A 1AH, United Kingdom
Tel.: (44) 2030210684
Web Site:
https://www.forwardadvances.com
Financial Investment Services
N.A.I.C.S.: 523999

Molten Ventures Growth SP GP LLP (1)
20 Garrick Street, London, WC2E 9BT, United Kingdom
Tel.: (44) 2079318800
Web Site: https://www.moltenventures.com
Financial Investment Services
N.A.I.C.S.: 523999

MOM'S TOUCH & CO.
24 25 Floor 1077 Cheonho-daero, Gangdong-gu, Seoul, Korea (South)
Tel.: (82) 24188884
Web Site:
https://www.haimarrow.co.kr
Year Founded: 2015
220630—(KRS)
Rev.: $246,800,213
Assets: $102,224,224
Liabilities: $34,222,443
Net Worth: $68,001,782
Earnings: $23,798,544
Fiscal Year-end: 12/31/22
Financial Investment Management Services
N.A.I.C.S.: 523940

Subsidiaries:

MOM'S Touch Vietnam Limited Liability Company (1)
47-49-51 Phung Khac Khoan St, Dakao Wards Dist 1, Ho Chi Minh City, Vietnam
Tel.: (84) 838277164
Restaurant Services
N.A.I.C.S.: 722511

MoM's Touch Taiwan Co., Ltd. (1)
2nd Floor 8-Hao Nantai St, Yongkang District, Tainan City, Taiwan
Tel.: (886) 62545888
Restaurant Services
N.A.I.C.S.: 722511

MOMENT GROUP AB
Tradgardsgatan 2, 41108, Gothenburg, Sweden
Tel.: (46) 317336700
Web Site:
https://www.momentgroup.com
Year Founded: 1987
MOMENT—(OMX)
Rev.: $80,020,980
Assets: $103,519,814
Liabilities: $99,695,599
Net Worth: $3,824,215
Earnings: $4,201,673
Emp.: 386
Fiscal Year-end: 12/31/22
Entertainment Event Prodction Services
N.A.I.C.S.: 711320
Martin du Hane *(CFO-Interim)*

MOMENTOUS HOLDINGS CORP.
32 Curzon Street, London, W1J 7WS, United Kingdom
Tel.: (44) 2038713051   NV
Web Site:
http://www.momentouscorp.com
Year Founded: 2015
MMNT—(OTCIQ)
Rev.: $238,792
Assets: $124,636
Liabilities: $633,356
Net Worth: ($508,720)
Earnings: ($392,013)
Emp.: 3
Fiscal Year-end: 05/31/20
Holding Company
N.A.I.C.S.: 551112
Andrew Eddy *(Pres, CEO, CFO, Treas & Sec)*

Subsidiaries:

V Beverages Limited (1)
32 Curzon Street, London, W1J 7WS, United Kingdom
Tel.: (44) 2038713051
Web Site: http://www.vbeverages.com
Alcoholic Beverages Mfr
N.A.I.C.S.: 312140
Andrew Eddy *(CEO)*

MOMENTUM FINANCIAL HOLDINGS LIMITED
Room 2407 24th Floor China Resources Bldg 26 Harbour Road, Wanchai, China (Hong Kong)
Tel.: (852) 3691 8480
Web Site: http://www.1152.com.hk
Year Founded: 1995
Investment Holding Company
N.A.I.C.S.: 551112
Qiang Zheng *(Exec Dir)*

MOMENTUM GROUP LIMITED
268 West Avenue, Centurion, 0157, Gauteng, South Africa
Tel.: (27) 126718911   ZA
Web Site:
https://www.momentumgroup.co.za
Year Founded: 1989
MMTHF—(OTCIQ)
Rev.: $5,740,947,640
Assets: $39,246,507,900
Liabilities: $37,577,142,120
Net Worth: $1,669,365,780
Earnings: $218,605,440
Emp.: 15,821
Fiscal Year-end: 06/30/24
Holding Company; Insurance & Financial Services
N.A.I.C.S.: 551112
Jeanette Cilliers Marais *(CEO)*

Subsidiaries:

Anthemis Exponential Ventures LLP (1)
3rd Floor 25 Soho Square, London, W1D 3QR, United Kingdom
Tel.: (44) 2036530100
Financial Services
N.A.I.C.S.: 523999

Metropolitan Card Operations (Pty) Ltd. (1)
PO Box 2212, 7535, Bellville, South Africa
Tel.: (27) 219405129
Sales Range: $150-199.9 Million
Emp.: 800
Business Services
N.A.I.C.S.: 561499

Metropolitan Collective Investments Ltd. (1)
268 West Avenue, PO Box 925, Centurion, 0157, South Africa (100%)
Tel.: (27) 219405981
Web Site: http://www.momentum.co.za
Sales Range: $50-74.9 Million
Emp.: 30
Direct Property & Casualty Insurance Carriers
N.A.I.C.S.: 524126
Leon Greyling *(Mng Dir)*

Metropolitan Health (Pty) Ltd. (1)
0A Carl Cronje Dr Stellenbosch University, Cape Town, 7530, South Africa
Tel.: (27) 21 480 4511
Web Site:
https://momentumhealthsolutions.co.za
Health Solution Business Services
N.A.I.C.S.: 621999

Metropolitan Health Corporate (Pty) Ltd. (1)
0A Carl Cronje Dr Stellenbosch University, Cape Town, 7530, South Africa (100%)
Tel.: (27) 214804511
Web Site: http://www.mhg.co.za
Sales Range: $200-249.9 Million
Emp.: 2,000
Ambulatory Health Care Services
N.A.I.C.S.: 621999

Metropolitan Health Corporate (Pty) Ltd. (1)
0A Carl Cronje Dr Stellenbosch University, Cape Town, 7530, South Africa (100%)
Tel.: (27) 214804511
Web Site: http://www.mhg.co.za
Sales Range: $200-249.9 Million
Emp.: 2,000
Ambulatory Health Care Services
N.A.I.C.S.: 621999

Metropolitan Health Corporate (Pty) Ltd. (1)
0A Carl Cronje Dr Stellenbosch University, Cape Town, 7530, South Africa (100%)
Tel.: (27) 214804511
Web Site: http://www.mhg.co.za
Sales Range: $200-249.9 Million
Emp.: 2,000
Ambulatory Health Care Services
N.A.I.C.S.: 621999

Metropolitan Health Corporate (Pty) Ltd. (1)
0A Carl Cronje Dr Stellenbosch University, Cape Town, 7530, South Africa (100%)
Tel.: (27) 214804511
Web Site: http://www.mhg.co.za
Sales Range: $200-249.9 Million
Emp.: 2,000
Ambulatory Health Care Services
N.A.I.C.S.: 621999

Metropolitan Health Group (Pty) Ltd. (1)
Parc du Cap 7 Mispel Road, Cape Town, 7535, South Africa (100%)
Tel.: (27) 214804511
Web Site: http://www.mhg.co.za
Sales Range: $1-4.9 Billion
Emp.: 5,000
Health & Welfare Funds
N.A.I.C.S.: 525120
Dylan Garnett *(CEO)*

Metropolitan Health Holdings (Pty) Ltd. (1)
Parc du Cap 7 Mispel Road, PO Box 2212, 7535, Bellville, South Africa (100%)
Tel.: (27) 219405911
Web Site: http://www.metropolitan.co.za
Sales Range: $450-499.9 Million
Emp.: 3,000
Emergency & Relief Services
N.A.I.C.S.: 624230
Wilhelm van Zyl *(CEO)*

Metropolitan Lesotho Ltd. (1)
Metropolitan Building Kingsway Street, Maseru, 100, Lesotho (100%)
Tel.: (266) 22222300
Web Site: https://www.metropolitan.co.ls
Sales Range: $200-249.9 Million
Emp.: 300
Direct Life Insurance Carriers
N.A.I.C.S.: 524113
Mamello Phomane *(Mng Dir)*

Metropolitan Lesotho Ltd. (1)
Metropolitan Building Kingsway Street, Maseru, 100, Lesotho (100%)
Tel.: (266) 22222300
Web Site: https://www.metropolitan.co.ls
Sales Range: $200-249.9 Million
Emp.: 300
Direct Life Insurance Carriers
N.A.I.C.S.: 524113
Mamello Phomane *(Mng Dir)*

Metropolitan Lesotho Ltd. (1)
Metropolitan Building Kingsway Street, Maseru, 100, Lesotho (100%)
Tel.: (266) 22222300
Web Site: https://www.metropolitan.co.ls
Sales Range: $200-249.9 Million
Emp.: 300
Direct Life Insurance Carriers
N.A.I.C.S.: 524113
Mamello Phomane *(Mng Dir)*

Metropolitan Lesotho Ltd. (1)
Metropolitan Building Kingsway Street, Maseru, 100, Lesotho (100%)
Tel.: (266) 22222300
Web Site: https://www.metropolitan.co.ls
Sales Range: $200-249.9 Million
Emp.: 300
Direct Life Insurance Carriers
N.A.I.C.S.: 524113
Mamello Phomane *(Mng Dir)*

Metropolitan Life (Namibia) Ltd. (1)
PO Box 3785, Windhoek, Namibia
Tel.: (264) 612973000
Web Site: http://www.metropolitan.com.na
Sales Range: $100-124.9 Million
Emp.: 150
Direct Life Insurance Carriers
N.A.I.C.S.: 524113

Metropolitan Life Insurance Ghana Ltd. (1)
Omnipotent House 10 Dzorwulu Extension N1 Road Cantonments, PMB CT456, Accra, Ghana
Tel.: (233) 302633933
Web Site: https://www.metropolitan.com.gh
Insurance Services
N.A.I.C.S.: 524210
Philip Du Preez *(Co-CEO)*

Metropolitan Life Insurance Kenya Limited (1)
PO Box 46783, Nairobi, Kenya
Tel.: (254) 20243158
Web Site: http://www.metropolitan.co.ke
Direct Life Insurance Carriers
N.A.I.C.S.: 524113

Metropolitan Life Ltd. (1)
Parc du Cap 6 Mispel Road, PO Box 2212, Bellville, 7530, South Africa (100%)
Tel.: (27) 219405911
Web Site: http://www.metropolitanlife.co.za

MOMENTUM GROUP LIMITED

Momentum Group Limited—(Continued)
Sales Range: $50-74.9 Million
Emp.: 15
Insurance Agencies & Brokerages
N.A.I.C.S.: 524210
Nicolaas Kruger *(CEO)*

Metropolitan Life of Botswana Ltd. (1)
Plot 54352 East Tower, Zambezi Towers, Private Bag 00231, CBD, Gaborone, 09267, Botswana
Tel.: (267) 3624400
Web Site: https://metropolitan.co.bw
Direct Life Insurance Carriers
N.A.I.C.S.: 524113
Frikkie Augustyn *(Mng Dir)*

Metropolitan Odyssey Ltd. (1)
PO Box 4045, Tyger Vallei, 7536, Cape Town, South Africa **(100%)**
Tel.: (27) 219173372
Web Site: http://www.odysseylife.co.za
Insurance Agencies & Brokerages
N.A.I.C.S.: 524210

Momentum Life Botswana Ltd. (1)
Plot 54352 East Tower Zambezi Towers, CBD Private Bag, 00231, Gaborone, Botswana
Tel.: (267) 362 4400
Web Site: https://metropolitan.co.bw
Insurance Related Services
N.A.I.C.S.: 524298

Momentum Metropolitan Life Ltd. (1)
268 West Avenue, Centurion, 0157, Gauteng, South Africa **(100%)**
Tel.: (27) 126718911
Web Site: https://www.momentum.co.za
Life Insurance Products & Services
N.A.I.C.S.: 524113

Subsidiary (Domestic):

Momentum Africa Investments Limited (2)
4 High Street, Melrose, 2076, South Africa
Tel.: (27) 117153000
Investment Management Service
N.A.I.C.S.: 523999

Momentum Medical Scheme Administrators (Pty) Ltd. (2)
201 uMhlanga Ridge Blvd Cornubia, Durban, 4339, South Africa
Tel.: (27) 315734000
Web Site: https://momentummedicalscheme.co.za
Sales Range: $300-349.9 Million.
Emp.: 600
Pension Fund Administration Services
N.A.I.C.S.: 524292

Subsidiary (Non-US):

Momentum Wealth International Ltd. (2)
La Plaiderie House La Plaiderie, Saint Peter Port, GY1 1WF, Guernsey
Tel.: (44) 126845008
Web Site: https://www.momentum.co.gg
Administrative Management Services
N.A.I.C.S.: 541611

MOMINA KREPOST PLC
23 Magistralna str, 5000, Veliko Tarnovo, Bulgaria
Tel.: (359) 885047666
Web Site: https://www.mkrepost-bg.com
Year Founded: 1966
MKR—(BUL)
Sales Range: Less than $1 Million
Rubber & Plastic Product Mfr
N.A.I.C.S.: 326299
Emanuil Tsvetkov *(Exec Dir)*

MOMO S.R.L.
via Winkelmann 2, 20146, Milan, Italy
Tel.: (39) 02424112
Web Site: http://www.momo.com
Sales Range: $75-99.9 Million
Emp.: 400
Automotive Safety Product
N.A.I.C.S.: 339999

Subsidiaries:

MOMO Automotive Accessories (1)
22412 Gilberto Unit B, Rancho Santa Margarita, CA 92688
Tel.: (949) 749-6666
Web Site: http://www.momousa.com
Automotive Accessories Mfr & Distr
N.A.I.C.S.: 441330

MOMO.COM INC.
4F No 96 Zhouzi St, Neihu District, Taipei, 11493, Taiwan
Tel.: (886) 221626688
Web Site: https://corp.momo.com.tw
Year Founded: 2004
8454—(TAI)
Rev.: $3,572,481,568
Assets: $926,176,720
Liabilities: $593,269,542
Net Worth: $332,907,179
Earnings: $118,669,409
Emp.: 6,551
Fiscal Year-end: 12/31/23
Electronic Shopping
N.A.I.C.S.: 455219
C. F. Lin *(Chm)*

MON COURTIER ENERGIE GROUPE S.A.
22-26 Quai de, Bacalan, 33000, Bordeaux, France
Tel.: (33) 557991577
Web Site: https://www.moncourtierenergy.com
Year Founded: 2017
ALMCE—(EUR)
Emp.: 130
Electricity Distribution Services
N.A.I.C.S.: 237990
Charlie Evrard *(Chm)*

MON COURTIER ENERGIE SAS
22-26 Quai de Bacalan, 33300, Bordeaux, France
Web Site: https://www.moncourtierenergy.com
Year Founded: 2017
O4Z—(DEU)
Insurance Brokerage Services
N.A.I.C.S.: 524210
Charlie Evrard *(Pres)*

MON SPACE NET, INC.
100 3 041 129 Offices Block Jaya 1 72 A Jalan Universiti, Petaling Jaya, 46200, Malaysia
Tel.: (60) 322820888
Media Advertising Services
N.A.I.C.S.: 541840

MON-ASAR JOINT STOCK COMPANY
12th Khoroo, Bayangol District, Ulaanbaatar, Mongolia
Tel.: (976) 11 364269
Year Founded: 1997
Building Construction Services
N.A.I.C.S.: 236220

MONADELPHOUS GROUP LIMITED
59 Albany Highway, Victoria Park, 6100, WA, Australia
Tel.: (61) 893161255
Web Site: https://www.monadelphous.com.au
MND—(OTCIQ)
Rev.: $1,344,082,678
Assets: $595,380,965
Liabilities: $292,290,758
Net Worth: $303,090,206
Earnings: $37,134,165
Emp.: 7,559
Fiscal Year-end: 06/30/21

Holding Company; Engineering & Construction Services
N.A.I.C.S.: 551112
Calogero Giovanni Battista Rubino *(Chm)*

Subsidiaries:

MAQrent S.p.A. (1)
Ruta del Cobre 320 Sitio 8, Antofagasta, Chile
Tel.: (56) 963202050
Web Site: http://www.maqrent.cl
Construction Machinery Rental Services
N.A.I.C.S.: 532412

Monadelphous Engineering Associates Pty. Ltd. (1)
59 Albany Highway, Victoria Park, 6100, WA, Australia
Tel.: (61) 8 9316 1255
Web Site: http://www.monadelphous.com.au
Emp.: 500
Engineering & Construction Services
N.A.I.C.S.: 541330

SinoStruct Pty. Ltd. (1)
59 Albany Highway, Victoria Park, Perth, 6100, WA, Australia
Tel.: (61) 893337006
Web Site: http://www.sinostruct.com
Fabricated Steel Mfr & Distr
N.A.I.C.S.: 332312
Martin Cauble *(Ops Mgr)*

MONAGHAN MIDDLEBROOK MUSHROOMS UNLIMITED COMPANY
, Tyholland, H18 FW95, Monaghan, Ireland
Tel.: (353) 47 38200
Web Site: http://www.monaghan-mushrooms.com
Year Founded: 1999
Sales Range: $150-199.9 Million
Emp.: 1,500
Holding Company; Mushroom Production
N.A.I.C.S.: 551112
Ronnie Wilson *(Founder & CEO)*

Subsidiaries:

Monaghan Belgium B.V.B.A (1)
Industrieterrein Jagersborg 1608, 3680, Maaseik, Belgium
Tel.: (32) 89651760
Mushroom Distr
N.A.I.C.S.: 424420

Monaghan Champignons B.V. (1)
Hamweg 5, 5961 PS, Horst, Netherlands
Tel.: (31) 773235252
Web Site: http://www.monaghan-champignons.com
Mushroom Distr
N.A.I.C.S.: 424420
Magda van Dieten *(Mgr-HR)*

Monaghan Mushrooms Ireland Unlimited Company (1)
, Tyholland, H18 FW95, Monaghan, Ireland
Tel.: (353) 47 38200
Web Site: http://www.monaghan-mushrooms.com
Mushroom Production
N.A.I.C.S.: 111411
Ronnie Wilson *(Founder & CEO)*

Monaghan Mushrooms Limited (1)
Stock Lane, Langford, Somerset, BS40 5ES, United Kingdom
Tel.: (44) 1934 854 108
Mushroom Distr
N.A.I.C.S.: 424420
Przemyslaw Migacz *(Coord-Product)*

Monaghan Mushrooms Ltd. (1)
7345 Guelph Line, PO Box 58, Campbellville, L0P 1B0, ON, Canada **(100%)**
Tel.: (905) 878-9375
Sales Range: $25-49.9 Million
Emp.: 300
Mushroom Producer
N.A.I.C.S.: 111411
Kirsten Penderell *(Mgr-HR)*

INTERNATIONAL PUBLIC

Monaghan Pilze GmbH (1)
Carl-Zeiss Str 36, 89150, Laichingen, Germany
Tel.: (49) 7333 953100
Web Site: http://www.monaghan-pilze.com
Mushroom Distr
N.A.I.C.S.: 424420

Walkro International BV (1)
Columbusweg 22, 5928 LC, Venlo, Netherlands
Tel.: (31) 77 387 6000
Web Site: http://www.walkro.nl
Emp.: 235
Mushroom Farming Services
N.A.I.C.S.: 111411

Subsidiary (Non-US):

Walkro Belgie NV (2)
Kringloopstraat 5, 3630, Maasmechelen, Belgium
Tel.: (32) 896 500 52
Web Site: http://www.walkro.eu
Emp.: 80
Mushroom Distr
N.A.I.C.S.: 424420
Freddy Hermans *(Branch Mgr)*

Subsidiary (Domestic):

Walkro Blitterswijck BV (2)
Veerweg 11, 5863 AR, Blitterswijck, Netherlands
Tel.: (31) 478 538 181
Web Site: http://www.walkro.nl
Emp.: 50
Mushroom Farming Services
N.A.I.C.S.: 111411
Erik Hoogen *(Mng Dir)*

Subsidiary (Non-US):

Walkro Deutschland & Co, KG (2)
Pilzhof Muhlgebreite 4, 06528, Wallhausen, Germany
Tel.: (49) 34656613
Mushroom Distr
N.A.I.C.S.: 424420

MONALISA CO., LTD.
21F Korea Construction Financial Cooperative Bldg 15 Boramae-ro 5-gil, Dongjak-gu, Seoul, 156-714, Korea (South)
Tel.: (82) 28298800
Web Site: http://www.monarisa.co.kr
Year Founded: 1977
012690—(KRS)
Rev.: $92,707,362
Assets: $75,008,287
Liabilities: $15,477,415
Net Worth: $59,530,872
Earnings: $1,791,161
Emp.: 198
Fiscal Year-end: 12/31/22
Sanitary Paper Mfr
N.A.I.C.S.: 322291
Se-Hoon Park *(CEO)*

MONALISA GROUP
12th Floor Monalisa Tower Building T2 Poly Center Wenhua Road, Lecong Town Shunde District, Foshan, 528211, Guangdong, China
Tel.: (86) 75786808730
Web Site: https://www.fs-monalisa.com
Year Founded: 1992
002918—(SSE)
Rev.: $745,190,459
Assets: $1,161,284,305
Liabilities: $610,443,796
Net Worth: $550,840,509
Earnings: $86,778,144
Emp.: 1,700
Fiscal Year-end: 12/31/20
Ceramic Product Mfr & Distr
N.A.I.C.S.: 327120
Xiao Libiao *(Chm & Pres)*

MONAMI CO., LTD.
Monami Building SonGok-Ro 17,

Suji-gu, Yongin, Gyeonggi-do, Korea (South)
Tel.: (82) 312705172
Web Site: https://www.monami.com
Year Founded: 1960
005360—(KRS)
Rev.: $114,691,205
Assets: $167,537,822
Liabilities: $85,768,414
Net Worth: $81,769,409
Earnings: $2,411,354
Emp.: 212
Fiscal Year-end: 12/31/22
Stationery Product Mfr
N.A.I.C.S.: 339940

MONARCA MINERALS INC.
18 King Street East Suite 902, Toronto, M5C 1C4, ON, Canada
Tel.: (647) 401-9292   Ca
Web Site:
  https://monarcaminerals.com
OSI2—(DEU)
Assets: $77,436
Liabilities: $2,677,885
Net Worth: ($2,600,450)
Earnings: ($876,933)
Fiscal Year-end: 11/30/22
Mineral Exploration & Mining Services
N.A.I.C.S.: 327999
Michael R. Smith *(Exec VP-Exploration & Qualified Person)*

MONARCH HOLDINGS PLC
Prospect House Prospect Way, London Luton Airport, Luton, LU2 9NU, Bedfordshire, United Kingdom
Tel.: (44) 8712250250
Web Site: http://www.monarch.co.uk
Year Founded: 1967
Sales Range: $650-699.9 Million
Emp.: 2,830
Oil Transportation Services
N.A.I.C.S.: 481111
Richard Mintern *(COO, Mng Dir-Aircraft Engrg & Dir-Tech-Airlines)*

MONARCH NETWORTH CAPITAL LTD.
Monarch House Opp Prahladbhai Patel Garden Near Ishwar Bhuvan, Commerce Six Road Navrangpura, Ahmedabad, 380009, India
Tel.: (91) 7926666500
Web Site:
  https://www.mnclgroup.com
Year Founded: 1993
511551—(BOM)
Rev.: $14,071,470
Assets: $56,631,944
Liabilities: $41,913,018
Net Worth: $14,718,926
Earnings: $3,322,942
Emp.: 518
Fiscal Year-end: 03/31/21
Investment Services
N.A.I.C.S.: 523999
Vaibhav Jayantilal Shah *(Mng Dir)*

Subsidiaries:

Networth SoftTech Ltd.   (1)
Office 901 /902 9th Fl Atlanda Center Opp Udhyoh Bhavan, Mumbai, 400 063, Maharashtra, India
Tel.: (91) 2230641600
Sales Range: $25-49.9 Million
Emp.: 450
Software Consulting Services
N.A.I.C.S.: 541618
Vaibhav Shah *(Mng Dir)*

Networth Wealth Solutions Ltd   (1)
7 Pushpa Kunj Complex 26 Farmland, Central Bazaar Rd, Ramdaspeth, Nagpur, 440010, Maharashtra, India
Tel.: (91) 712 6500301
Web Site: http://www.networthdirect.com

Financial Consulting Services
N.A.I.C.S.: 525990

MONARQUES GOLD CORPORATION
68 Avenue de la Gare Office 205, Saint-Sauveur-des-Monts, J0R 1R0, QC, Canada
Tel.: (514) 840-9709   Ca
Web Site:
  http://www.monarquesgold.com
MQR—(OTCIQ)
Rev.: $24,222,041
Assets: $55,539,126
Liabilities: $20,964,203
Net Worth: $34,574,923
Earnings: $371,834
Fiscal Year-end: 06/30/19
Gold Mining Operations
N.A.I.C.S.: 212220
Jean-Marc Lacoste *(Pres & CEO)*

MONASH ABSOLUTE INVESTMENT COMPANY LIMITED
Level 12 Grosvenor Place 225 George Street, Sydney, 2000, NSW, Australia
Tel.: (61) 292378862
Web Site:
  http://www.monashinvestors.com
MA1—(ASX)
Rev.: $3,736,667
Assets: $37,792,094
Liabilities: $3,821,531
Net Worth: $33,970,563
Earnings: $1,488,040
Fiscal Year-end: 06/30/20
Portfolio Management Services
N.A.I.C.S.: 523940

MONASH IVF GROUP LIMITED
Level 1 510 Church St, Cremorne, 3121, VIC, Australia
Tel.: (61) 394208235
Web Site:
  https://www.monashivfgroup.com.au
MVF—(ASX)
Rev.: $170,245,726
Assets: $339,523,236
Liabilities: $174,820,379
Net Worth: $164,702,857
Earnings: ($3,972,356)
Emp.: 997
Fiscal Year-end: 06/30/24
Assisted Reproductive & Ultrasound Services; Reproduction Supportive Medications
N.A.I.C.S.: 621511
Michael Knaap *(CEO & Mng Dir)*

Subsidiaries:

Hobart IVF Pty. Ltd.   (1)
Level 4 81 Elizabeth Street, Hobart, 7000, TAS, Australia
Tel.: (61) 361691111
Web Site: https://fertilitytasmania.com.au
Fertility Clinic Operator
N.A.I.C.S.: 621410

Monash Ultrasound Pty. Ltd.   (1)
Pelaco Building Level 1 21-31 Goodwood Street, Richmond, 3121, VIC, Australia
Tel.: (61) 394299188
Web Site: http://monashultrasound.com.au
Medical & Diagnostic Services
N.A.I.C.S.: 621511

MONBAT AD
32 A Cherni vrah blvd Fl 4, 1407, Sofia, Bulgaria
Tel.: (359) 29621150
Web Site: https://www.monbat.com
Year Founded: 1959
5MB—(BUL)
Rev.: $214,887,430
Assets: $272,705,551
Liabilities: $150,199,205
Net Worth: $122,506,346

Earnings: $2,180,223
Emp.: 1,307
Fiscal Year-end: 12/31/22
Battery Mfr
N.A.I.C.S.: 335910
Florian Huth *(Deputy Chm)*

Subsidiaries:

START AD   (1)
20 Sveshtenik Pavel Atanasov Str, 9300, Dobrich, Bulgaria
Tel.: (359) 58822501
Power Battery Mfr & Distr
N.A.I.C.S.: 335910

MONCEAU ASSURANCES MUTUELLES ASSOCIEES
65, rue Monceau, Paris, 75008, france, France
Tel.: (33) 1 49 95 79 79
Insurance Services
N.A.I.C.S.: 524298
Frederic Channac *(Head-Life, Property & Casualty Insurance Ops)*

Subsidiaries:

Vitis Life S.A.   (1)
52 Boulevard Marcel Cahen, 1311, Luxembourg, Luxembourg   **(100%)**
Tel.: (352) 262 046 500
Web Site: www.vitislife.com
Sales Range: $250-299.9 Million
Life Insurance Products & Services
N.A.I.C.S.: 524113
Nicolas Limbourg *(CEO)*

MONCLER S.P.A.
Via Enrico Stendhal 47, 20144, Milan, Italy
Tel.: (39) 0242203500
Web Site: http://www.moncler.com
MONC—(ITA)
Rev.: $3,220,609,756
Assets: $5,387,459,529
Liabilities: $1,918,401,684
Net Worth: $3,469,057,846
Earnings: $660,373,408
Emp.: 7,203
Fiscal Year-end: 12/31/23
Clothing Mfr
N.A.I.C.S.: 315250
Marco Diego De Benedetti *(Vice Chm)*

Subsidiaries:

Industries S.p.A.   (1)
Via Venezia 1, Trebaseleghe, 35010, Padua, Italy
Tel.: (39) 0499323111
Web Site: http://www.industries-group.com
Apparel Product Mfr & Distr
N.A.I.C.S.: 315990

Subsidiary (Non-US):

Moncler Brasil Comercio de moda e acessorios Ltda.   (2)
Av Presidente Juscelino Kubitschek 2041, Sao Paulo, 04543-011, Brazil
Tel.: (55) 1131526262
Apparel Product Mfr
N.A.I.C.S.: 315990

Moncler Denmark ApS   (2)
Ostergade 36, 1100, Copenhagen, Denmark
Tel.: (45) 33111183
Apparel Product Mfr
N.A.I.C.S.: 315990

Moncler Holland B.V.   (2)
Pc Hooft Straat 90, 1071 CC, Amsterdam, Netherlands
Tel.: (31) 204904790
Apparel Product Mfr
N.A.I.C.S.: 315990

Moncler Hungary KFT   (2)
Andrassy Ut 23, 1061, Budapest, Hungary
Tel.: (36) 614132680
Men Apparel Product Mfr
N.A.I.C.S.: 315250

Moncler Norway AS   (2)
Nedre Slottsgate 15, 0157, Oslo, Norway
Tel.: (47) 21984004
Apparel Product Mfr
N.A.I.C.S.: 315990

Moncler Prague s.r.o.   (2)
Parizska Street 127/20, 11000, Prague, Czech Republic
Tel.: (420) 222311489
Apparel Product Mfr
N.A.I.C.S.: 315990

Moncler Ukraine LLC   (2)
Khreschatyk Passage 15, 01001, Kiev, Ukraine
Tel.: (380) 893202400
Apparel Product Mfr
N.A.I.C.S.: 315990

White Tech S.p.zo.o.   (2)
Bracka 9, 00-501, Warsaw, Poland
Tel.: (48) 223107211
Apparel Product Mfr
N.A.I.C.S.: 315990

MONCOA MEDICAL RESEARCH INC.
1125 Howe Street Suite 900, Vancouver, V6Z 2K8, BC, Canada
Tel.: (604) 689-5610
Web Site: https://www.moncoa.com
Sales Range: Less than $1 Million
Emp.: 15
Gold Mining Services
N.A.I.C.S.: 212220

MONDAY.COM LTD.
6 Yitzhak Sadeh St, Tel Aviv, 6777506, Israel
Tel.: (972) 559397720   Il
Web Site: https://www.monday.com
Year Founded: 2012
MNDY—(NASDAQ)
Rev.: $729,695,000
Assets: $1,275,656,000
Liabilities: $462,148,000
Net Worth: $813,508,000
Earnings: ($1,877,000)
Emp.: 1,854
Fiscal Year-end: 12/31/23
Software Development Services
N.A.I.C.S.: 541511
Roy Mann *(Co-Founder & Co-CEO)*

MONDE NISSIN CORPORATION
20th and 21st Floors 6750 Office Tower Ayala Avenue, Makati, 1200, Philippines
Tel.: (63) 27597500   PH
Web Site:
  http://www.mondenissin.com
Bakery Products Retailer
N.A.I.C.S.: 311811
Henry Soesanto *(CEO)*

Subsidiaries:

Marlow Foods Ltd.   (1)
Station Road, Stokesley, TS9 7AB, North Yorkshire, United Kingdom
Tel.: (44) 8456029000
Web Site: http://www.quorn.co.uk
Mycoproteins Mfr
N.A.I.C.S.: 325414
Kevin Brennan *(CEO)*

MONDE SANS FRONTIERES
9 Rue Du Delta, 75009, Paris, France
Tel.: (33) 156026161
Web Site: http://www.msftravel.com
Rev.: $20,300,000
Emp.: 38
N.A.I.C.S.: 561510
Leon Sarkis *(Mng Dir)*

MONDI PLC
Ground Floor Building 5 The Heights, Brooklands, Weybridge, KT13 0NY, Surrey, United Kingdom

MONDI PLC — INTERNATIONAL PUBLIC

Mondi plc—(Continued)
Tel.: (44) 1932826300 UK
Web Site:
https://www.mondigroup.com
Year Founded: 2007
MNDI—(JSE)
Rev.: $7,910,641,053
Assets: $10,753,291,604
Liabilities: $4,174,401,036
Net Worth: $6,578,890,568
Earnings: ($144,614,720)
Emp.: 21,773
Fiscal Year-end: 12/31/23
Packaging Product Mfr & Distr
N.A.I.C.S.: 322220
Shay Gonen *(CFO)*

Subsidiaries:

Dipeco AG (1)
Bruhlstrasse 5, 4800, Zofingen, Switzerland
Tel.: (41) 62 785 3200
Web Site: https://www.dipeco.com
Flexible Packaging Mfr
N.A.I.C.S.: 326112

EURO WASTE A.S. (1)
Litomericka 272, 411 08, Steti, Czech Republic
Tel.: (420) 41 680 3750
Web Site: https://www.eurowaste.cz
Recycling Paper Product Distr
N.A.I.C.S.: 423930
Jaroslav Tymich *(Mng Dir)*

LLC Mondi Aramil (1)
25 Klubnaya Str, Aramil, 624000, Sverdlovskaya, Russia
Tel.: (7) 3433611530
Bag Product Mfr
N.A.I.C.S.: 326111

LLC Mondi Pereslavl (1)
Mendeleeva sq 2-G bld 55, Pereslavl-Zalesskiy, 152025, Moscow, Russia
Tel.: (7) 4853566000
Printed Equipment Mfr
N.A.I.C.S.: 333248

Mondi AG (1)
Marxergasse 4A, 1030, Vienna, Austria
Tel.: (43) 179 0130
Packaging Paper Product Mfr & Distr
N.A.I.C.S.: 322220

Mondi Aberdeen Limited (1)
Ground Floor Building 5 The Heights Brooklands, Weybridge, KT13 0NY, United Kingdom
Tel.: (44) 193 282 6384
Paper Product Distr
N.A.I.C.S.: 424130

Mondi Akrosil, LLC (1)
7201 108th St, Pleasant Prairie, WI 53158-2912
Tel.: (262) 997-3000
Tiles Mfr
N.A.I.C.S.: 339113

Mondi Ascania GmbH (1)
Daimlerstrasse 8, 06449, Aschersleben, Germany
Tel.: (49) 347 387 6311
Non Woven Fabric Material Mfr
N.A.I.C.S.: 313230

Mondi Bad Rappenau GmbH (1)
Wilhelm-Hauff-Strasse 41, 74906, Bad Rappenau, Germany
Tel.: (49) 706 6290
Corrugated Board Mfr & Distr
N.A.I.C.S.: 322211

Mondi Bags Hungaria Kft. (1)
Tunde u2, 4400, Nyiregyhaza, Hungary
Tel.: (36) 4 259 9240
Paper Bag Mfr
N.A.I.C.S.: 322220

Mondi Bags Iberica S.L. (1)
Autovia A-2 Km 582, Abrera, 08630, Barcelona, Spain
Tel.: (34) 93 770 0176
Bag Product Mfr
N.A.I.C.S.: 326111

Mondi Bags Mielec Sp. z o.o. (1)
Wojska Polskiego 12, 39-300, Mielec, Poland
Tel.: (48) 1758 182 4144
Valve Bag Mfr
N.A.I.C.S.: 322220

Mondi Bags Steti A.S. (1)
Litomericka 272, 411 08, Steti, Czech Republic
Tel.: (420) 41 680 2951
Paper Bag Mfr
N.A.I.C.S.: 322220

Mondi Bags Swiecie Sp. z o.o (1)
Bydgoska 12, 86-100, Swiecie, Poland
Tel.: (48) 52 332 4102
Paper Bag Mfr
N.A.I.C.S.: 322220

Mondi Bags USA, LLC (1)
Tel.: (870) 727-9570
Bag Product Mfr
N.A.I.C.S.: 326111

Mondi Bangkok Company, Limited (1)
789/10 Moo 9, Bang Pla Sub-District Bang Phli District, 10540, Samut Prakan, Thailand
Tel.: (66) 213 052 3639
Packaging Products Mfr
N.A.I.C.S.: 326199

Mondi Bekescsaba Kft. (1)
Tevan Andor u 2, 5600, Bekescsaba, Hungary
Tel.: (36) 6 654 0300
Printed Barrier Laminate Paper Mfr
N.A.I.C.S.: 322220

Mondi Bucharest S.R.L. (1)
Filderman Wilhelm 4 3rd Floor Apt 19 District 3, 030866, Bucharest, Romania
Tel.: (40) 21 351 2250
Bag Product Mfr
N.A.I.C.S.: 326111

Mondi Bupak s.r.o. (1)
Papirenska 41, 370 52, Ceske Budejovice, Czech Republic
Tel.: (420) 38 773 3111
Corrugated Box Mfr
N.A.I.C.S.: 322211

Mondi Cartagena SAS (1)
Zona Franca La Candelaria Km 9-Cr A Mamonal, Cartagena, Colombia
Tel.: (57) 320 400 0790
Paper Sack Mfr
N.A.I.C.S.: 322220

Mondi Coating (Thailand) Co. Ltd. (1)
888/100-101 M 19, T Bangpleeyai A Bangplee, 10540, Samut Prakan, Thailand
Tel.: (66) 217 471 5258
Engineering Material Services
N.A.I.C.S.: 541330

Mondi Coating Steti A.S. (1)
Litomericka 272, 411 08, Steti, Czech Republic
Tel.: (420) 41 680 2643
Extrusion Coated Material Mfr
N.A.I.C.S.: 322220

Mondi Coating Zeltweg GmbH (1)
Bahnhofstrasse 3, 8740, Zeltweg, Austria
Tel.: (43) 35 779 0010
Coated & Laminated Composite Packaging Product Mfr
N.A.I.C.S.: 322220

Mondi Consumer Bags & Films Benelux B.V. (1)
Productieweg 82 2nd Floor, 3481 MH, Harmelen, Netherlands
Tel.: (31) 34 874 1838
Plastics Bag Mfr
N.A.I.C.S.: 322220

Mondi Consumer Packaging International AG (1)
Airport Center at Muenster Osnabrueck Airport, Greven, 48268, Germany
Tel.: (49) 257191910
Sales Range: $800-899.9 Million
Emp.: 4,000
Flexible Packaging Mfr
N.A.I.C.S.: 322220
Ralph Landwehr *(CEO)*

Mondi Corrugated Swiecie Sp. z o.o (1)
Bydgoska 1, 86-100, Swiecie, Poland
Tel.: (48) 52 567 0900
Corrugated Box Mfr
N.A.I.C.S.: 322220

Mondi Deeside (1)
Parkway Deeside Industrial Park, Deeside, CH5 2NS, United Kingdom
Tel.: (44) 1244 833230
Web Site: http://www.mondigroup.com
Packaging Products Mfr
N.A.I.C.S.: 326112

Mondi Dorohusk Sp. z o.o. (1)
Brzezno 1, Brzezno Dorohusk, 22-174, Lublin, Poland
Tel.: (48) 82 562 7100
Corrugated Board Mfr & Distr
N.A.I.C.S.: 322211

Mondi Eschenbach GmbH (1)
Am Stadtwald 14, 92676, Eschenbach, Germany
Tel.: (49) 9 645 9300
Emp.: 190
Corrugated Board Mfr & Distr
N.A.I.C.S.: 322211

Mondi Glossop Ltd. (1)
Etherow Works Woolley Bridge, Glossop, SK13 2NU, United Kingdom
Tel.: (44) 1457892300
Web Site: http://www.mondigroup.com
Sales Range: $25-49.9 Million
Emp.: 100
Siliconized-Release Papers & Films Mfr
N.A.I.C.S.: 322220

Mondi Gournay Sarl (1)
5 Rue Vernet, 75008, Paris, France
Tel.: (33) 68 011 1842
Plastic Bag & Pouch Mfr
N.A.I.C.S.: 326111

Mondi Gradisca S.r.l. (1)
Via Dell Industria 11, Gradisca d'Isonzo, 34072, Gorizia, GO, Italy
Tel.: (39) 048 196 0530
Paper Valve Sack & Open Mouth Sack Mfr
N.A.I.C.S.: 322220

Mondi Gronau GmbH (1)
Jobkesweg 11, 48599, Gronau, Germany
Tel.: (49) 2 562 9190
Packaging & Engineered Material Mfr
N.A.I.C.S.: 326111

Mondi Halle GmbH (1)
Wielandstrasse 2, 33790, Halle, Germany
Tel.: (49) 5 201 7090
Polyethylene Film Mfr
N.A.I.C.S.: 326113

Mondi Hammelburg GmbH (1)
Thuringenstrasse 1-3, Hammelburg, 97762, Bad Kissingen, Germany
Tel.: (49) 9732 787 8700
Paper Bag Mfr
N.A.I.C.S.: 322220

Mondi Heerlen B.V. (1)
Imstenraderweg 15, NL-6422 PM, Heerlen, Lymburg, Netherlands
Tel.: (31) 455437878
Sales Range: $25-49.9 Million
Emp.: 87
Silicone-Coated Release Papers & Films Mfr
N.A.I.C.S.: 322220

Mondi Inncoat GmbH (1)
Angererstrasse 25, 83064, Raubling, Germany
Tel.: (49) 8 035 9010
Coated Paper Mfr
N.A.I.C.S.: 322220

Mondi Istanbul Ambalaj Limited Sti (1)
Yilmaz Alpaslan Cd 12/A, 59850, Corlu, Tekirdag, Turkiye
Tel.: (90) 282 685 4246
Industrial Bag Mfr
N.A.I.C.S.: 322220

Mondi Italia S.r.l. (1)
Via Balilla 32, Romano di Lombardia, 24058, Bergamo, Italy
Tel.: (39) 036 391 6111

Paper Bag Mfr
N.A.I.C.S.: 322220

Mondi Jackson LLC (1)
14591 State Hwy 177, Jackson, MO 63755
Tel.: (573) 335-4900
Bag Product Mfr
N.A.I.C.S.: 326111

Mondi Julich GmbH (1)
Rathausstrasse 29, 52428, Julich, Germany
Tel.: (49) 2 461 6230
Coated Paper Mfr
N.A.I.C.S.: 322220

Mondi Kale Nobel Ambalaj Sanayi Ve Ticaret A.S. (1)
Bloklari A-2 Kat 6 No 229-230 Yesilkoy Dunya Ticaret Mrk, Bakirkoy, 34149, Istanbul, Turkiye
Tel.: (90) 212 465 7460
Ice Cream Pack Mfr
N.A.I.C.S.: 311412

Mondi Korneuburg GmbH (1)
Stockerauer Strasse 110, 2100, Korneuburg, Austria
Tel.: (43) 22 627 2093
Printed Barrier Laminate Paper Mfr
N.A.I.C.S.: 322220

Mondi Kuala Lumpur Sdn. Bhd. (1)
Lot Nos PT 5034 and 5036 Jalan Teluk Datuk 28/40, 40000, Shah Alam, Selangor, Malaysia
Tel.: (60) 35 191 5133
Valve Bag Mfr
N.A.I.C.S.: 322220

Mondi Lebanon SAL (1)
7th Floor Bloc C Kassis Building Antelias Highway, Antelias, Beirut, Lebanon
Tel.: (961) 452 2990
Valve Bag Mfr
N.A.I.C.S.: 322220

Mondi Lohja Oy (1)
Kotkantie 5, 08100, Lohja, Finland
Tel.: (358) 20744611
Web Site: http://www.mondigroup.com
Sales Range: $125-149.9 Million
Emp.: 445
Siliconized-Release & Specialty Papers Mfr
N.A.I.C.S.: 322220
Kari Kalliala *(Mng Dir)*

Mondi Maastricht N.V. (1)
Fort Willemweg 1, 6219 PA, Maastricht, Netherlands
Tel.: (31) 43 329 9352
Valve Bag Mfr
N.A.I.C.S.: 322220

Mondi Mexico S. de R.L. de C.V. (1)
Calle Pino No 3100, Zona Industrial Nombre de Dios, 31110, Chihuahua, Mexico
Tel.: (52) 614 893 0373
Valve Bag Mfr
N.A.I.C.S.: 322220

Mondi Minneapolis, Inc. (1)
Main St Exchange Bldg 123 Main St W, Waconia, MN 55387
Tel.: (763) 574-2636
Shipping Services
N.A.I.C.S.: 492110

Mondi Moss AS (1)
Radmann Sirasvei 1, 1712, Gralum, Norway
Tel.: (47) 9 288 5101
Paper Bag Distr
N.A.I.C.S.: 424130

Mondi Neusiedler GmbH (1)
Theresienthalstrasse 50, 3363, Ulmerfield-Hausmening, Austria
Tel.: (43) 7 475 5000
Uncoated Fine Paper Mfr
N.A.I.C.S.: 322120

Mondi Orebro AB (1)
Pappersbruksallen 3A, 70130, Orebro, Sweden
Tel.: (46) 1 935 4500
Industrial Coating Material Mfr
N.A.I.C.S.: 325510

Mondi Packaging Akrosil, LLC (1)
206 Garfield Ave, Menasha, WI 54952-3318
Tel.: (920) 722-6404
Web Site: http://www.mondi.com

AND PRIVATE COMPANIES

Sales Range: $50-74.9 Million
Emp.: 178
Silicone-Coated Liners, Papers, Polykrafts & Films Mfr
N.A.I.C.S.: 322220

Plant (Domestic):

Mondi Packaging Akrosil, LLC (2)
3165 Wilson Rd, Lancaster, OH 43130-8144
Tel.: (740) 687-6968
Web Site: http://www.mondigroup.com
Sales Range: $25-49.9 Million
Emp.: 50
Silicone-Coated Liners, Papers, Polykrafts & Films Mfr
N.A.I.C.S.: 322220

Mondi Packaging Bags Ukraine LLC (1)
Fabrychna 20, Zhydachiv, 81700, Lviv, Ukraine
Tel.: (380) 32 259 0501
Packaging Products Mfr.
N.A.I.C.S.: 326199

Mondi Packaging Limited (1)
Old Whieldon Rd, Stoke-on-Trent, ST44HW, United Kingdom
Tel.: (44) 1782747574
Web Site: http://www.mondipackaging.com
Sales Range: $50-74.9 Million
Emp.: 200
Packaging Solutions
N.A.I.C.S.: 423930

Plant (Domestic):

Mondi Packaging Ltd. (2)
Mugiemoss Road, Bucksburn, Aberdeen, AB2 19ND, United Kingdom
Tel.: (44) 1224712881
Web Site: http://www.mondipackaging.com
Sales Range: $50-74.9 Million
Emp.: 60
Multi-Wall Paper Sack Mfr
N.A.I.C.S.: 322220

Mondi Packaging Paper Sales Asia Pte. Ltd. (1)
350 Orchard Road 18-04 Shaw House, Singapore, 238868, Singapore
Tel.: (65) 6 732 8106
Packaging Paper Distr
N.A.I.C.S.: 424130

Mondi Packaging Services GmbH (1)
Kelsenstrasse 7, A-1030, Vienna, Austria
Tel.: (43) 1795230
Web Site: http://www.mondipackaging.com
Sales Range: $125-149.9 Million
Emp.: 400
Packaging Solutions
N.A.I.C.S.: 339991

Mondi Padova S.r.l. (1)
Via Mazzini 21, San Pietro in Gu, 35010, Padua, Italy
Tel.: (39) 049 945 8411
Paper Sack & Bag Mfr
N.A.I.C.S.: 322220

Mondi Paper Sales Deutschland GmbH (1)
Oberbaumbrucke 1, 20457, Hamburg, Germany
Tel.: (49) 40 300 9170
Offset Printing Paper Distr
N.A.I.C.S.: 424110

Mondi Paper Sales France Sarl (1)
121 Rue d Aguesseau, 92100, Boulogne-Billancourt, France
Tel.: (33) 15 560 1820
Offset Printing Paper Mfr
N.A.I.C.S.: 323111

Mondi Paper Sales GmbH (1)
Marxergasse 4A, 1030, Vienna, Austria
Tel.: (43) 179 0130
Uncoated Fine Paper Mfr
N.A.I.C.S.: 322120

Mondi Paper Sales Netherlands B.V. (1)
Van Heuven Goedhartlaan 13D, 1181 LE, Amstelveen, Netherlands
Tel.: (31) 20 333 2000

Corrugated Paper Distr
N.A.I.C.S.: 424130

Mondi Poperinge N.V. (1)
Nijverheidslaan 11, 8970, Poperinge, Belgium
Tel.: (32) 5 733 3688
Paper Bag Mfr
N.A.I.C.S.: 322220

Mondi Powerflute Oy (1)
Selluntie 142, 70420, Kuopio, Finland
Tel.: (358) 106606999
Paper & Packaging Products Mfr & Distr
N.A.I.C.S.: 322130
Antero Putkonen *(Dir-Production)*

Mondi Poznan Sp. z o.o. (1)
Ul Wyzwolenia 34/36, 62-070, Dopiewo, Poland
Tel.: (48) 61 849 5000
Plastics Films Mfr
N.A.I.C.S.: 326112

Mondi Romeoville LLC (1)
1140 Arbor Dr, Romeoville, IL 60446
Tel.: (630) 378-9886
Bag Product Mfr
N.A.I.C.S.: 326111

Mondi SCP, A.S. (1)
Tatranska Cesta 3, 03417, Ruzomberok, Slovakia
Tel.: (421) 44 436 2222
Paper Products Mfr
N.A.I.C.S.: 322299

Mondi Sabac d.o.o. (1)
Nova 9, 15000, Sabac, Serbia
Tel.: (381) 15 719 5108
Bag Product Mfr
N.A.I.C.S.: 326111

Mondi Solec Sp. z o.o. (1)
Solec 143, 05-532, Baniocha, Poland
Tel.: (48) 22 701 9000
Printed Laminate & Film Mfr
N.A.I.C.S.: 326112

Mondi South Africa (Pty) Limited (1)
Merebank Mill Travancore Drive, Merebank, 4052, South Africa
Tel.: (27) 314512157
Web Site: http://www.mondigroup.com
Paper & Packaging Product Mfr & Distr
N.A.I.C.S.: 322220
Vivien McMenamin *(CEO & CEO)*

Mondi South Africa Ltd. (1)
, 1st floor no3 Melrose Boulevar, Johannesburg, 2076, South Africa
Tel.: (27) 0116384586
Paper & Packaging Producer & Distr
N.A.I.C.S.: 322220
David Hathorn *(CEO)*

Mondi Stambolijski E.A.D (1)
Zavodska Str 1, Stambolijski, 4210, Plovdiv, Bulgaria
Tel.: (359) 3 290 9281
Kraft Paper Mfr
N.A.I.C.S.: 322121

Mondi Steti A.S. (1)
Litomericka 272, 411 08, Steti, Czech Republic
Tel.: (420) 41 680 1111
Paper & Pulp Product Mfr
N.A.I.C.S.: 322110

Mondi Styria GmbH (1)
Bahnhofstrasse 3, 8740, Zeltweg, Austria
Tel.: (43) 35 779 0010
Packaging Film Mfr
N.A.I.C.S.: 326112

Mondi Swiecie S.A. (1)
Ul Bydgoska 1, 86 100, Swiecie, Kujawsko-Pomorskie, Poland (100%)
Tel.: (48) 523321501
Web Site: http://www.mondigroup.pl
Emp.: 1,023
Paper Mill; Production of Corrugated Board & High Quality Printed Boxes
N.A.I.C.S.: 322130

Mondi Szada Kft. (1)
Vasut u 13, Szada, 2111, Budapest, Hungary
Tel.: (36) 2 850 2502
Printed Barrier Laminate Paper Mfr
N.A.I.C.S.: 322220

Mondi Szczecin Sp. z o.o. (1)
Sloneczna 20, Kliniska Wielkie, 72123, Goleniow, Poland
Tel.: (48) 91 469 8701
Cardboard Mfr
N.A.I.C.S.: 322130

Mondi TSP Company Limited (1)
10 Moo 3 T Nongchumpol Neau Amphor Khowyoi, 76140, Phetchaburi, Thailand
Tel.: (66) 3 256 6038
Food & Beverage Mfr
N.A.I.C.S.: 311991

Mondi Tekkote LLC (1)
580 Willow Tree Rd, Leonia, NJ 07605-2211
Tel.: (201) 585-8875
Tiles Mfr
N.A.I.C.S.: 339113

Mondi Thessaloniki A.E. (1)
Block G Y Phase A, Industrial Zone of Sindos, 57022, Thessaloniki, Greece
Tel.: (30) 231 072 3280
Packaging Product Distr
N.A.I.C.S.: 424130

Mondi Tire Kutsan Kagit Ve Ambalaj Sanayi A.S. (1)
Toki Mahallesi Hasan Tahsin Caddesi No 28, Tire, 35900, Izmir, Turkiye
Tel.: (90) 232 512 1156
Paper Product Distr
N.A.I.C.S.: 424130

Mondi Tire Kutsan Kagit Ve Ambalaj Sanayii AS (1)
Hasan Tahsin Street No 28 Tire, Toki District, 35900, Izmir, Turkiye
Tel.: (90) 2325121156
Web Site: http://www.mondigroup.com.tr
Sales Range: Less than $1 Million
Paper & Cardboard Box Mfr
N.A.I.C.S.: 322212
Joseph Hubertus Anna Raymundus Schoonbrood *(Chm)*

Mondi Tokyo KK (1)
Plaza Mikado Bldg 7F 2-14-5, Akasaka Minato-ku, Tokyo, 107-005, Japan
Tel.: (81) 36 230 3221
Paper Bag Mfr
N.A.I.C.S.: 322220

Mondi Tolentino S.r.l. (1)
Via G Falcone 1, 62029, Tolentino, MC, Italy
Tel.: (39) 073 395 5011
Valve Paper Bag Mfr
N.A.I.C.S.: 322220

Mondi Trebsen GmbH (1)
Erich-Hausmann-Strasse 1, Trebsen, 04687, Leipzig, Germany
Tel.: (49) 9732 787 8100
Paper Bag Mfr
N.A.I.C.S.: 322220

Mondi Warszawa Sp. z o.o. (1)
Ul Tarczynska 98, 96-320, Mszczonow, Poland
Tel.: (48) 46 857 2780
Box Mfr
N.A.I.C.S.: 322211

Mondi Wellpappe Ansbach GmbH (1)
Robert-Bosch-Str 3, 91522, Ansbach, Germany
Tel.: (49) 981 1880
Packaging Paper Product Mfr & Distr
N.A.I.C.S.: 322220

Mondi Wierzbica Sp. z o.o. (1)
Kolonia Rzeczkow 76, 26-680, Wierzbica, Poland
Tel.: (48) 48 629 2942
Bag Product Mfr
N.A.I.C.S.: 326111

Mondi Zimele Proprietary Limited (1)
Mondi House 380 Old Howick Road, Hilton, Pietermaritzburg, 3245, South Africa
Tel.: (27) 33 329 5506
Web Site: https://www.mondizimele.co.za
Forestry Services
N.A.I.C.S.: 115310
Nelly Ndlovu *(Gen Mgr)*

Natro Tech S.R.L. (1)

MONDO TV S.P.A.

Via Balilla 32, Romano di Lombardia, 24058, Bergamo, Italy
Tel.: (39) 036 391 6130
Dry Mortar Filling Equipment Mfr
N.A.I.C.S.: 333993

OJSC Mondi Syktyvka (1)
2 Bumazhnikov pr, 167026, Syktyvkar, Russia
Tel.: (7) 8212699555
Pulp & Paper Product Mfr
N.A.I.C.S.: 322299

OOO Mondi Sales CIS (1)
Business Center Four Winds 1-ya Tverskaya-Yamskaya 21 5th floor, 125047, Moscow, Russia
Tel.: (7) 4959264884
Printing Paper Mfr
N.A.I.C.S.: 323111

Olmuksan International Paper Ambalaj Sanayi ve Ticaret Anonim Sirketi (1)
Esentepe Mahallesi Harman 1 Sk Nidakule Levent Apt N 7/9/54 Sisli, Istanbul, Turkiye (90.38%)
Tel.: (90) 2123711020
Web Site: http://www.olmuksan-ipaper.com
Rev.: $172,759,320
Assets: $134,083,663
Liabilities: $96,078,543
Net Worth: $38,005,120
Earnings: ($15,482,430)
Emp.: 833
Fiscal Year-end: 12/31/2019
Paper & Packaging Materials Mfr
N.A.I.C.S.: 322211
Tamer Parla *(Gen Mgr-Izmir Plant)*

Pap Sac Maghreb SA (1)
Route d El Jadida Km 16, 20150, Casablanca, Morocco
Tel.: (212) 52 044 4400
Valve Bag Mfr
N.A.I.C.S.: 322220

Powerflute International S.L. (1)
Calle Joaquin Costa 36A-2, 28002, Madrid, Spain
Tel.: (34) 91 781 7235
Corrugated Paper Distr
N.A.I.C.S.: 424130

Siyaqhubeka Forests Proprietary Limited (1)
Mondi Richard's Bay Mill 7 Western Arterial, Richards Bay, 3900, Alton, South Africa
Tel.: (27) 35 902 2111
Web Site: https://www.siyaqhubeka.co.za
Forestry Services
N.A.I.C.S.: 115310
Sanele Zuma *(Mgr)*

Slovpaper Recycling s.r.o. (1)
Tatranska Cesta 3, 03417, Ruzomberok, Slovakia
Tel.: (421) 44 436 2248
Web Site: https://www.slovpaper.sk
Recycle Paper Distr
N.A.I.C.S.: 423930

Suez Bags Company S.A.E. (1)
K30 Maadi/Ein Sokhna Road, Cairo, Egypt (98.3%)
Tel.: (20) 225222056
Paper Products Mfr
N.A.I.C.S.: 322130

MONDO FOODS COMPANY LTD.

40 Otter Street, Winnipeg, R3T 4J7, MB, Canada
Tel.: (204) 453-7722
Web Site:
https://www.mondofoods.com
Rev.: $23,214,302
Emp.: 100
Food Products Distr
N.A.I.C.S.: 722310
Maria De Nardi *(Co-Founder)*

MONDO TV S.P.A.

Via Brenta 11, 00198, Rome, Italy
Tel.: (39) 0686323293
Web Site: https://www.mondotv.it

MONDO TV S.P.A.   INTERNATIONAL PUBLIC

Mondo TV S.p.A.—(Continued)
MTV—(ITA)
Rev: $31,122,373
Assets: $126,075,151
Liabilities: $40,908,990
Net Worth: $85,166,162
Earnings: $5,364,952
Emp.: 53
Fiscal Year-end: 12/31/20
Animated Cartoon TV & Film Production & Distribution Services
N.A.I.C.S.: 512110

Subsidiaries:

Mondo Entertainment GmbH (1)
Planckstrase 7A, 22765, Hamburg, Germany
Tel.: (49) 4041304141
Sales Range: $25-49.9 Million
Emp.: 5
Television Network Broadcasting Services
N.A.I.C.S.: 516120

Mondo Home Entertainment S.p.A. (1)
Via Melchiorre Gioia 72, 20125, Milan, Italy
Tel.: (39) 026679791
Web Site: http://www.mondohe.it
Sales Range: $25-49.9 Million
Television Network Broadcasting Services
N.A.I.C.S.: 516120

Mondo TV France SA (1)
52 rue Gerard, 75013, Paris, France (99.7%)
Tel.: (33) 158100405
Web Site: https://www.mondotv-france.com
Sales Range: Less than $1 Million
Animated Cartoon Production & Distribution
N.A.I.C.S.: 512110
Sylvie Mahe (CEO)

Mondo TV Iberoamerica SA (1)
Calle 3 1/32Ivarez de Baena No 4 Esc 2 Planta 2 Puerta 4A, Madrid, 28006, Spain
Tel.: (34) 913992710
Web Site: http://mondotviberoamerica.com
Sales Range: Less than $1 Million
Film Production Services
N.A.I.C.S.: 512110

Mondo TV Spain S.L. (1)
Rios Rosas 36 3 Izq, 28003, Madrid, Spain
Tel.: (34) 913992710
Web Site: http://www.mondotvspain.es
Sales Range: $25-49.9 Million
Emp.: 3
Animated Cartoon Production Services
N.A.I.C.S.: 512110
Luiana Do Amaral (Mgr-Mktg)

Mondo TV Suisse SpA (1)
Piazza Degli Affari N 6, 20123, Milan, Italy
Tel.: (39) 068 632 3293
Web Site: http://ch.mondotvgroup.com
Sales Range: Less than $1 Million
Media Advertising Services
N.A.I.C.S.: 541840
Yvano D'Andrea (Chm & CEO)

Moviemax Italia S.R.L. (1)
Via Giandomenico Romagnosi 20, Rome, 00196, Italy
Tel.: (39) 0636006760
Web Site: http://www.moviemax.it
Sales Range: $25-49.9 Million
Emp.: 15
Television Network Broadcasting Services
N.A.I.C.S.: 516120

MONDRAGON CORPORATION
P Jose M Arizmendiarrieta n 5, Mondragon, 20500, Guipuzcoa, Spain
Tel.: (34) 943779300
Web Site: http://www.mondragon-corporation.com
Year Founded: 1956
Sales Range: $5-14.9 Billion
Emp.: 81,837
Financial, Industrial & Distribution Services
N.A.I.C.S.: 561499
Inigo Ucin (Pres)

Subsidiaries:

AOTEK S. COOP. (1)
Barrio San Andres 19 - Apdo 2, 20500, Arrasate, Gipuzkoa, Spain
Tel.: (34) 943 039805
Web Site: http://www.aotek.es
Automation & Optical Engineering Services
N.A.I.C.S.: 237990

Alecop S. Coop. (1)
Loramendi Kalea 11, 20500, Arrasate, Gipuzkoa, Spain
Tel.: (34) 943 712 405
Web Site: http://www.alecop.com
Industrial Machinery Mfr
N.A.I.C.S.: 333310

Alkargo S Coop (1)
Aritz Bidea 83, 48100, Munguia, Bizkaia, Spain
Tel.: (34) 94 674 00 04
Web Site: http://www2.alkargo.com
Electronic Transformer Mfr
N.A.I.C.S.: 334416
Javier Egido (Gen Mgr)

Aurrenak S. Coop. (1)
Vitorialanda 15 C Ali-Gobeo, 1010, Vitoria, Alava, Spain
Tel.: (34) 945 24 48 50
Web Site: http://www.aurrenak.com
Emp.: 100
Aluminium Casting & Molding Services
N.A.I.C.S.: 336370
Javier Alvarez (Dir)

Subsidiary (Non-US):

AURRENAK Service S.A. de C.V. (2)
2023 c/Industrial Siderurgica Parque Industrial Saltillo-Ramos Arizpe, Ramos Arizpe, 25900, Coahuila, Mexico
Tel.: (52) 945 00 34 70
Aluminium Casting & Molding Services
N.A.I.C.S.: 336370

Auzo Lagun S.coop. (1)
Uribarri etorbidea 35 - Apdo 140, 20500, Madrid, Gipuzkoa, Spain
Tel.: (34) 943 79 46 11
Web Site: http://www.ausolan.com
Refurbishment & Cleaning Services
N.A.I.C.S.: 561720

Barrenetxe S. Coop (1)
Okerra 7, 48270, Markina, Bizkaia, Spain
Tel.: (34) 94 6168143
Web Site: http://www.barrenetxe.com
Vegetable Farming Services
N.A.I.C.S.: 111211

Batz, S. Coop. (1)
Torrea Auzoa 32, 48140, Igorre, Bizkaia, Spain
Tel.: (34) 94 630 50 00
Web Site: http://www.batz.com
Automotive System Engineering Services
N.A.I.C.S.: 237990

Behi-Alde S. Coop. (1)
Barrio Olaeta S/N, Olaeta, Alava, Spain
Tel.: (34) 945 45 01 00
Dairy Milk Production Services
N.A.I.C.S.: 311119

Beijing Fagor Automation Equipment Co., Ltd. (1)
Room 912 Chengshimaibo Building No 16 Dayelu Apartado, 610100, Chengdu, Sichuan, China
Tel.: (86) 2 866 132 081
Automation System Engineering Services
N.A.I.C.S.: 237990

Biurrarena S. Coop. (1)
Pol Bidebitarte Donostia Ibilbidea 28 - Apdo 887, 20115, Astigarraga, Gipuzkoa, Spain
Tel.: (34) 943 55 43 50
Web Site: http://www.biurrarena.com
Emp.: 16
Construction Machinery Mfr
N.A.I.C.S.: 333120
Darvis Lopez (Mng Dir)

CS Centro Stirling S. Coop. (1)
Avda Alava 3 E, 20550, Aretxabaleta, Guipuzcoa, Spain
Tel.: (34) 943 037 948
Web Site: http://www.centrostirling.com
Industrial Machinery Mfr
N.A.I.C.S.: 333310

Coinalde, S. Coop. (1)
Zurrupitieta 17 Pl Jundiz, 1015, Vitoria, Araba, Spain
Tel.: (34) 945 292 319
Web Site: http://www.coinalde.es
Nails & Wire Mfr
N.A.I.C.S.: 314994

Subsidiary (Non-US):

COINALDE POLSKA SP. Z.O.O. (2)
ul Japonska 3 Lg, Jelcz, 55-220, Laskowice, Poland
Tel.: (48) 71 3811266
Nails & Wire Mfr
N.A.I.C.S.: 314994

Copreci S.Coop. (1)
Av de Alava 3, 20550, Aretxabaleta, Gipuzkoa, Spain
Tel.: (34) 943719499
Web Site: http://www.copreci.com
Kitchen Utensil Mfr
N.A.I.C.S.: 326199

Subsidiary (Domestic):

COPRECI - ALTSASUKO S.COOP. (2)
Txunkai Auzoa Ibarrea 2 Industrialdea, 31800, Alsasua, Navarra, Spain
Tel.: (34) 948 563 172
Home Appliance Mfr
N.A.I.C.S.: 335210

Subsidiary (Non-US):

COPRECI CZ, S.R.O. (2)
Komenskeho 274, 79368, Dvorce, Czech Republic
Tel.: (420) 554 773 420
Home Appliance Mfr
N.A.I.C.S.: 335210

COPRECI DE MEXICO, SA DE CV (2)
C/ Uno n 736 Z I Guadalajara, Guadalajara, 44940, Jalisco, Mexico
Tel.: (52) 33 3881 1170
Home Appliance Mfr
N.A.I.C.S.: 335210

COPRECI DO BRASIL, LTDA. (2)
Rua Dr Pedro Costa 483 Sala 22 - 2 Andar Edificio Agata, 12010-160, Taubate, Sao Paulo, Brazil
Tel.: (55) 12 3622 1541
Home Appliance Mfr
N.A.I.C.S.: 335210

COPRECI SYSTEMS, S.R.L. (2)
Via G Galilei 12, Mareno di Piave, Treviso, Italy
Tel.: (39) 0438492531
Home Appliance Mfr
N.A.I.C.S.: 335210

COPRECI TR.LTD.STI. (2)
Geposb Cumhuriyet Caddesi 6 cadde, Gebze, Kocaeli, Turkiye
Tel.: (90) 262 751 42 55
Kitchen Utensil Mfr
N.A.I.C.S.: 326199

Czech LANA, s.r.o. (1)
Chrudimska 584, Zdirec nad Doubravou, 582 63, Czech Republic
Tel.: (420) 569 430 060
Web Site: http://www.leartiker.com
Wood Processing Services
N.A.I.C.S.: 321114
Robert Micka (Mgr-Fin)

DOMUSA CALEFACCION, S.COOP. (1)
Barrio San Esteban s/n - Apdo 95, 20737, Errezil, Gipuzkoa, Spain
Tel.: (34) 943 81 38 99
Web Site: http://www.domusa.es
Electrical Home Appliance Mfr
N.A.I.C.S.: 335210

Danobatgroup S. Coop. (1)
Arriaga Kalea 1 - Apdo 80, 20870, Elgoibar, Gipuzkoa, Spain
Tel.: (34) 943 74 80 23
Web Site: http://www.sheetmetalprocessing.com
Emp.: 1,000
Metal Sheet Mfr
N.A.I.C.S.: 332322

Subsidiary (Non-US):

Beijing Danobat Machinery Co. Ltd. (2)
Room 2901 Tower B Eagle Run Plaza 26 Xiaoyun Road, Chaoyang, Beijing, China
Tel.: (86) 10 6467 3639
Web Site: http://www.danobatgroup.com
Industrial Machinery Mfr
N.A.I.C.S.: 333310

DANOBAT DO BRASIL LTDA (2)
Alameda Santos 2335 7 andar - Conj 71, 01419-200, Sao Paulo, Brazil
Tel.: (55) 113 082 90 80
Web Site: http://www.danobatgroup.com.br
Industrial Machinery Mfr
N.A.I.C.S.: 333310

DANOBAT Rettificatrici (2)
Via Piave 39, 21026, Gavirate, Varese, Italy
Tel.: (39) 0332 747711
Engineeering Services
N.A.I.C.S.: 237990

Danobat Group Machine Tools India Pvt. Ltd. (2)
Office No 7 2nd Floor Business Avenue Niyoshi Park Road Sanghvi Nagar, Aundh, Pune, 411007, India
Tel.: (91) 20 66 094531
Metal Sheet Mfr
N.A.I.C.S.: 332322
Pravin Mali (Engr-Assembly & Plant Maintenance)

Subsidiary (US):

Danobat Machine Tool Co., Inc. (2)
5515B FM 1960 E, Humble, TX 77346
Tel.: (281) 812-4259
Web Site: http://www.danobatusa.com
Machine Tool Distr
N.A.I.C.S.: 423830

Subsidiary (Non-US):

Goiti Italia Srl (2)
Via Trilussa 26, 27029, Vigevano, Pavia, Italy
Tel.: (39) 0381090679
Metal Sheet Mfr
N.A.I.C.S.: 332322

Newall Uk Ltd (2)
Unit 1 Sturrock Way, Bretton, Peterborough, PE3 HYS, Cambridgeshire, United Kingdom
Tel.: (44) 1733 265566
Web Site: http://www.newall-uk.com
Emp.: 25
Engineeering Services
N.A.I.C.S.: 237990
Malcolm Hunt (Gen Mgr)

Overbeck GmbH (2)
Konrad Adenauer Str 27, 35745, Herborn, Germany
Tel.: (49) 2772 8010
Web Site: http://www.overbeck.de
Grinding & Turning Machinery Mfr
N.A.I.C.S.: 333310
Josu Tornay (Mng Dir)

Dikar S. Coop. (1)
Urarte Kalea 26 - Apdo 193 Pol Industrial San Lorenzo, 20570, Bergara, Gipuzkoa, Spain
Tel.: (34) 943 76 55 48
Web Site: http://www.dikar.es
Rifles & Barrel Mfr
N.A.I.C.S.: 332994

ECENARRO, S.COOP. (1)
Amillaga kalea 15, 20570, Paris, Gipuzkoa, France
Tel.: (33) 943 76 25 43
Web Site: http://www.ecenarro.com
Industrial Machinery Mfr
N.A.I.C.S.: 333310

EMBEGA, S. COOP. (1)
Pol Ind San Miguel s/n, 31132, Villatuerta, Navarra, Spain
Tel.: (34) 948 54 87 00
Web Site: http://www.embega.es
Metal Sheet Mfr
N.A.I.C.S.: 332322

EROSKI S. Coop. (1)
Barrio San Agustin s/n, 48230, Elorrio, Bizkaia, Spain

AND PRIVATE COMPANIES

MONDRAGON CORPORATION

Tel.: (34) 944943444
Web Site: http://www.eroski.es
Supermarket Operating Distr
N.A.I.C.S.: 445110
Beatriz Santos (Dir-Sls)

Eika, S. Coop. (1)
Urresolo 47, Etxebarria, 48277, Etxebarria, Bizkaia, Spain
Tel.: (34) 946 167 732
Web Site: http://www.eika.es
Household Appliances Mfr
N.A.I.C.S.: 335220
Aitor Soria (CEO)

Fagor Automation (Asia) Ltd. (1)
Unit 2307 23/F 113 Argyle Street Mongkok, Kowloon, China (Hong Kong)
Tel.: (852) 23 891 663
Automation System Engineering Services
N.A.I.C.S.: 237990

Fagor Automation (M) SDN.BHD. (1)
No 55 Jalan BP 6/7 - Bandar Bukit Puchong, 47100, Puchong, Selangor, Malaysia
Tel.: (60) 380 622 858
Automation System Engineering Services
N.A.I.C.S.: 237990

Fagor Automation (S) Pte. Ltd. (1)
240 MacPherson Road 06-05 Pines Industrial Building Apartado, 348574, Singapore, Singapore
Tel.: (65) 68417345
Web Site: http://www.agorautomation.com
Automation System Engineering Services
N.A.I.C.S.: 237990
Radhakrishnan Parakkel (Mgr)

Fagor Automation Corp. (1)
2250 Estes Ave, Elk Grove Village, IL 60007
Tel.: (847) 981-1500
Automation System Engineering Services
N.A.I.C.S.: 237990
Harsh Bibra (Gen Mgr)

Fagor Automation France S.a.r.l. (1)
69 rue d Apollon, 63000, Clermont-Ferrand, France
Tel.: (33) 473 277 916
Web Site: http://www.fagorautomation.com
Automotive System Engineering Services
N.A.I.C.S.: 237990

Fagor Automation GMBH (1)
Leonhard-Weiss-Str 34, 73037, Goppingen, Germany
Tel.: (49) 7161 156850
Web Site: http://www.fagorautomation.de
Automotive System Engineering Services
N.A.I.C.S.: 237990

Fagor Automation Korea, Ltd. (1)
Room 305 Star Towers Bldg 76-1 642-831 Sangnam-dong, Sungsan-gu, Changwon, Gyeongnam, Korea (South)
Tel.: (82) 552 392 353
Automation System Engineering Services
N.A.I.C.S.: 237990

Fagor Automation Ltda. (1)
Rua Goncalves - Zarco n 1129-B-2 - Salas 210/212/214, 4450-685, Leca da Palmeira, Portugal
Tel.: (351) 229 968 865
Automation System Engineering Services
N.A.I.C.S.: 237990

Fagor Automation Rus. (1)
Argunovskaya Street 3/1, 129075, Moscow, Russia
Tel.: (7) 4 957 877 445
Web Site: http://www.fagorautomation.ru
Automation System Engineering Services
N.A.I.C.S.: 237990

Fagor Automation Taiwan Co. Ltd. (1)
N 386 Dadun 4th St Nan - Tun 408, Taichung, 40867, Taiwan
Tel.: (886) 423 851 558
Web Site: http://www.fagorautomation.com
Emp.: 22
Automation System Engineering Services
N.A.I.C.S.: 237990
Richard Lee (Mng Dir)

Fagor Automation UK Ltd. (1)
2a Brunel Close Drayton Fields Industrial Estate, Daventry, NN11 8RB, Northamptonshire, United Kingdom
Tel.: (44) 1327 300067
Web Site: http://www.fagorautomation.co.uk
Automation System Engineering Services
N.A.I.C.S.: 237990

Fagor Automation do Brazil Com.Imp.Exp. Ltda. (1)
Sr D Dias de Carvalho Rua Homero Vaz Do Amaral 331, 04774-030, Sao Paulo, Brazil
Tel.: (55) 11 5694 0822
Web Site: http://www.fagorautomation.com.br
Automation System Engineering Services
N.A.I.C.S.: 237990

Fagor Control Systems Pvt. Ltd. (1)
301 Hemkunt Chambers Nehru Place, 110019, New Delhi, India
Tel.: (91) 9717778432
Automation System Engineering Services
N.A.I.C.S.: 237990

Fagor Ederlan, S. Coop. (1)
Carretera Zaragoza s/n, 31300, Tafalla, Navarre, Spain
Tel.: (34) 948 70 02 50
Web Site: http://www.fagorederlan.es
Automobile Parts Mfr
N.A.I.C.S.: 336390

Fagor Electrodomesticos (1)
Bo San Andres S N Apartado 49, Mondragon, 20500, Guipuzcoa, Spain
Tel.: (34) 943719100
Web Site: http://www.fagor.com
Sales Range: $200-249.9 Million
Emp.: 800
Domestic Appliances
N.A.I.C.S.: 335220

Joint Venture (Non-US):

FagorBrandt SAS (2)
89-91 Bd Franklin Roosevelt CS 30002, 92854, Rueil-Malmaison, Cedex, France
Tel.: (33) 1 47 16 65 65
Web Site: http://www.fagorbrandt.com
Sales Range: $100-124.9 Million
Emp.: 300
Mfr of Large Household Appliances; Joint Venture of Elco-Holdings Ltd.(90%) & Fagor Electrodomesticos(10%)
N.A.I.C.S.: 335220

Subsidiary (Domestic):

Grumal Group SL (2)
Gerraundi Kalea, 1-Pol Ind 70, 20730, Guipuzcoa, Azpeitia, Spain
Tel.: (34) 943157008
Web Site: http://www.isaqazpeitia.com
Sales Range: $25-49.9 Million
Emp.: 27
Kitchen Doors Mfr
N.A.I.C.S.: 321911
Juanmari Zudillagahi (Mgr)

Subsidiary (Domestic):

Pemec, S.A. (3)
Pol Industrial 70 - Apdo 100, Azpeitia, 20730, Spain
Tel.: (34) 943157008
Web Site: http://www.grumal.com
Sales Range: $75-99.9 Million
Laminate Mfr
N.A.I.C.S.: 321212

Seitu, S.A. (3)
Pol Industrial 70-Apdo 100, 20730, Azpeltia, Spain
Tel.: (34) 943157008
Web Site: http://www.grumal.com
Lacquered Doors Mfr
N.A.I.C.S.: 321911

Fagor Electronica, S.Coop. (1)
B San Andres s/n - Apdo 33, 20500, Arrasate, Spain
Tel.: (34) 943 71 25 26
Web Site: http://www.fagorelectronica.com
Semiconductor Equipment Mfr
N.A.I.C.S.: 333242

Fagor Italia S.R.L. (1)
Via Jervis 77 Centro Palazzo Uffici PU1, 10015, Ivrea, Italy
Tel.: (39) 0295 301 290
Web Site: http://www.fagorautomation.it

Automation System Engineering Services
N.A.I.C.S.: 237990

GRUPO ULMA (1)
Garagaltza Auzoa 51, 20569, Onati, Gipuzkoa, Spain
Tel.: (34) 943 25 03 00
Web Site: http://www.ulma.es
Industrial Machinery Mfr
N.A.I.C.S.: 333310

Subsidiary (Non-US):

ALPI, S.P.A. (2)
Viale della Repubblica 34, 47015, Modigliana, Forli-Cesena, Italy
Tel.: (39) 0474 947 400
Web Site: http://www.alpiwood.com
Wood Processing Services
N.A.I.C.S.: 321114

Subsidiary (Domestic):

CENTROMAN (2)
Calle Valportillo Primera 4 Poligono Industrial de Alcobendas, 28108, Madrid, Spain
Tel.: (34) 91 661 35 64
Material Handling Equipment Distr
N.A.I.C.S.: 423830

DELEGACION ANDALUCIA (2)
Pg Ind La Negrilla Manzana 1 C/ Interior Nave 6, 41016, Seville, Spain
Tel.: (34) 954 232 349
Web Site: http://www.d-andalucia.csic.es
Packaging Machinery Mfr
N.A.I.C.S.: 333310

DELEGACION CATALUNA (2)
C / Pintor Velazquez 7-9, 08213, Polinya, Barcelona, Spain
Tel.: (34) 93 713 28 45
Packaging Machinery Mfr
N.A.I.C.S.: 333310

DELEGACION LEVANTE S.L. (2)
Edificio Parque de la Albufera Pz Alqueria de la Culla, 4-Planta 9 Ofc 904, 46910, Alfafar, Valencia, Spain
Tel.: (34) 96 122 52 02
Packaging Machinery Mfr
N.A.I.C.S.: 333310

Delegacion Canarias (2)
Pol Ind Valle de Guimar Manzana XIII-Parcelas 21 y 22, 38509, Guimar, Spain
Tel.: (34) 922 505020
Construction Engineering Services
N.A.I.C.S.: 237990

Delegacion Centro S.L. (2)
Av Cerro del Aguila N 3 Edificio 2 Oficina 2B1 Parque Empresarial Sans, SS De Los Reyes, Madrid, 28700, Spain
Tel.: (34) 91 652 37 00
Construction Engineering Services
N.A.I.C.S.: 237990

Delegacion Este S.l. (2)
Pol Ind Sud-Est Pintor Velazquez 7 y 9, 08213, Polinya, Barcelona, Spain
Tel.: (34) 93 7132727
Construction Machinery Mfr
N.A.I.C.S.: 333120

Delegacion Oeste (2)
Pol Ind Espiritu Santo Rua Bell 24-26, 15650, Cambre, A Coruna, Spain
Tel.: (34) 981 649802
Construction Machinery Mfr
N.A.I.C.S.: 333120

Delegacion Sur S.l. (2)
Camino Nuevo s/n, 18210, Peligros, Granada, Spain
Tel.: (34) 958 405028
Construction Machinery Mfr
N.A.I.C.S.: 333120

ESENERGIA (2)
Avda Can Bordoll 159 P Ind Can Roqueta, 8202, Sabadell, Barcelona, Spain
Tel.: (34) 930 014 560
Web Site: http://www.snergia.com
Scientific Research & Devlopment Services
N.A.I.C.S.: 541715

Subsidiary (Non-US):

GH NV (2)
Langlaarsteenweg 168, 2630, Aartselaar, Belgium
Tel.: (32) 3 8706060
Packaging Machinery Mfr
N.A.I.C.S.: 333310
Tom Van Den Zegel (Gen Mgr)

Subsidiary (US):

Harpak-ULMA Packaging, LLC. (2)
175 John Quincy Adams Rd, Taunton, MA 02780
Tel.: (508) 884-2500
Emp.: 30
Packaging Machinery Mfr
N.A.I.C.S.: 333310
Jim Ryan (Sr VP-Mondini Rama)

Subsidiary (Non-US):

Industrias ULMA Venezolana C.A (2)
Edificio El Candil Avda Norte piso 8 Oficina 8-A Urbanizacion La Cande, 1010, Caracas, Venezuela
Tel.: (58) 212 5745703
Steel Piping Material Mfr
N.A.I.C.S.: 331110

Subsidiary (Domestic):

Pol. Ind. Son Noguera (2)
Cas Rossos 12-14, Illes Balears, 07620, Llucmajor, Spain
Tel.: (34) 971 669850
Construction Machinery Mfr
N.A.I.C.S.: 333120

S.L Delegacion Galicia. (2)
Avda de Madrid 73 - 2 Oficina 9, 36214, Vigo, Pontevedra, Spain
Tel.: (34) 986 23 15 30
Packaging Machinery Mfr
N.A.I.C.S.: 333310

ULMA Agricola, S. Coop. (2)
B Garibai 9, 20560, Onati, Gipuzkoa, Spain
Tel.: (34) 943 03 49 00
Web Site: http://www.ulmaagricola.com
Construction Machinery Mfr
N.A.I.C.S.: 333120

Subsidiary (Non-US):

ULMA Andamios y Encofrados Argentina, S.A. (2)
Bernardo de Irigoyen 722 6A, CP1072AAP, Buenos Aires, Argentina
Tel.: (54) 11 4343 1625
Construction Machinery Mfr
N.A.I.C.S.: 333120

ULMA Betonschalungen und Geruste GmbH (2)
Paul-Ehrlich-Strasse 8, 63322, Rodermark, Germany
Tel.: (49) 6074 9294 0
Web Site: http://www.ulmaconstruction.de
Construction Machinery Mfr
N.A.I.C.S.: 333120

ULMA Brasil - Formas e Escoramentos Ltda. (2)
Rua Joao Dias Ribeiro 210 Jd Sagrado Coracao de Jesus, 06693-810, Itapevi, Sao Paulo, Brazil
Tel.: (55) 11 3883 1300
Construction Machinery Mfr
N.A.I.C.S.: 333120

Subsidiary (Domestic):

ULMA C y E, S. Coop. (2)
Ps Otadui 3 - Apdo 13, 20560, Onati, Gipuzkoa, Spain
Tel.: (34) 943 034900
Web Site: http://www.ulmaconstruction.es
Construction Machinery Mfr
N.A.I.C.S.: 333120

Subsidiary (Non-US):

ULMA Chile - Andamios y Moldajes, S.A. (2)
Vizcaya n 325 Pudahuel Ruta 68 Camino Noviciado, Santiago, Chile
Tel.: (56) 2 5990530
Construction Machinery Mfr
N.A.I.C.S.: 333120

ULMA Cimbras y Andamios de Mexico S.A. de C.V. (2)
Via Gustavo Baz Prada 2160 Acceso 5, Col

MONDRAGON CORPORATION — INTERNATIONAL PUBLIC

Mondragon Corporation—(Continued)
La Loma, 54060, Mexico, Mexico
Tel.: (52) 55 5361 6783
Construction Engineering Services
N.A.I.C.S.: 237990

ULMA Cofraje s.r.l. (2)
Sos Chitilei 200 012405 - Sector 1, Bucharest, Romania
Tel.: (40) 31 425 13 22
Construction Machinery Mfr
N.A.I.C.S.: 333120

ULMA Construccion CZ, s.r.o. (2)
Prumyslova 1009, 294 71, Benatky nad Jizerou, Czech Republic
Tel.: (420) 326 910 600
Web Site: http://www.ulma.cz
Construction Machinery Mfr
N.A.I.C.S.: 333120
Miroslav Kapoun (Mng Dir)

ULMA Construccion SK, s.r.o. (2)
Bojnicka 20, 834 04, Bratislava, Slovakia
Tel.: (421) 2 4910 2911
Construction Machinery Mfr
N.A.I.C.S.: 333120

ULMA Construction Systems Canada Inc. (2)
12563 Hwy 50, Bolton, L7E 1M4, ON, Canada
Tel.: (905) 857-8562
Construction Machinery Mfr
N.A.I.C.S.: 333120

Subsidiary (Domestic):

ULMA Conveyor Components S.Coop. (2)
B Zelaieta s/n, 48210, Otxandio, Bizkaia, Spain
Tel.: (34) 945 450075
Web Site: http://www.ulmaconveyor.com
Conveyor Components Mfr
N.A.I.C.S.: 333922

Subsidiary (Non-US):

ULMA Encofrados Peru, S.A. (2)
Av Argentina 2882, Lima, Peru
Tel.: (51) 1 613 6700
Web Site: http://www.ulmaconstruction.com.pe
Construction Engineering Services
N.A.I.C.S.: 237990
Lukasz Siwik (Mgr-Design Team)

ULMA FORMWORK SYSTEMS INDIA PVT. LTD (2)
207 2nd Floor TimeTower Main MG Road Sector 28, 122001, Gurgaon, Haryana, India
Tel.: (91) 124 4205521
Construction Machinery Mfr
N.A.I.C.S.: 333120

Subsidiary (US):

ULMA Form Works, Inc. (2)
58 5th Ave, Hawthorne, NJ 07506
Tel.: (973) 636-2040
Construction Machinery Mfr
N.A.I.C.S.: 333120
Frank Deluccia (Reg Mgr-Sls)

Subsidiary (Non-US):

ULMA Formwork Singapore PTE. LTD. (2)
2 Senoko Way, 758027, Singapore, Singapore
Tel.: (65) 6758 852
Construction Engineering Services
N.A.I.C.S.: 237990
Edward De Marta (Mng Dir)

ULMA Formwork Ukraine Ltd. (2)
3 Derevoobrobna St, 1013, 1013, Kiev, Ukraine
Tel.: (380) 44 255 14 92
Construction Machinery Mfr
N.A.I.C.S.: 333120

ULMA Formworks China R.O. (2)
1009 Fortunegate Mall 1701 West Beijing Road, 200040, Shanghai, China
Tel.: (86) 21 62887070
Construction Engineering Services
N.A.I.C.S.: 237990

ULMA Formworks UAE L.L.C. (2)
Plot No 597-547 Dubai Investments Park, PO Box 282286, Dubai, United Arab Emirates
Tel.: (971) 4 8849444
Construction Engineering Services
N.A.I.C.S.: 237990
Harald Litze (Gen Mgr)

Subsidiary (Domestic):

ULMA Hormigon Polimero, S. Coop. (2)
B Zubillaga 89 Apartado 20, 20560, Madrid, Gipuzkoa, Spain
Tel.: (34) 943 780600
Construction Engineering Services
N.A.I.C.S.: 237990

ULMA INOXTRUCK (2)
Garagaltza auzoa 51 - Apdo 19, 20560, Onati, Gipuzkoa, Spain
Tel.: (34) 902 702 919
Web Site: http://www.ulmainoxtruck.es
Material Handling Equipment Mfr
N.A.I.C.S.: 333310
Fernando Odriozola (Mgr)

Subsidiary (Non-US):

ULMA Kazakhstan (2)
17 Kuishi Dina St Office 501-502, Nur-Sultan, 010010, Kazakhstan
Tel.: (7) 7172 58 05 19
Construction Machinery Mfr
N.A.I.C.S.: 333120

Subsidiary (Domestic):

ULMA Lazkao Forging, S.L. (2)
Cl Zubierreka 52, 20210, Lazkao, Gipuzkoa, Spain
Tel.: (34) 943 805333
Web Site: http://www.ulmalazkao.com
Steel Piping Material Mfr
N.A.I.C.S.: 331110
Mikel Lopetegi (Dir-Sls)

ULMA Manutencion, S. Coop. (2)
B Garagaltza 50 Apartado 67, 20560, Onati, Gipuzkoa, Spain
Tel.: (34) 943 782492
Construction Engineering Services
N.A.I.C.S.: 237990

Subsidiary (Non-US):

ULMA PACKAGING B.V. (2)
Ul Techniekweg 19a, 4143 HW, Leerdam, Netherlands
Tel.: (31) 345 623 800
Web Site: http://www.ulmapackaging.nl
Packaging Machinery Mfr
N.A.I.C.S.: 333310

ULMA PACKAGING GMBH (2)
Einsteinring 11, 89257, Illertissen, Germany
Tel.: (49) 7303 901996 0
Web Site: http://www.ulmapackaging.de
Packaging Machinery Mfr
N.A.I.C.S.: 333310

ULMA PACKAGING LDA (2)
Centro de Negocios Quinta Verde Fraccao B Quinta das Fazendas Novas, 2130-102, Benavente, Portugal
Tel.: (351) 263518030
Web Site: http://www.ulmapackaging.com
Emp.: 10
Packaging Machinery Mfr
N.A.I.C.S.: 333310
Silipe Silva (CEO)

ULMA PACKAGING LIMITED (2)
Unit 4 Woodland Court Coach Crescent Shireoaks, 5818AD, Worksop, United Kingdom
Tel.: (44) 1909506504
Packaging Machinery Mfr
N.A.I.C.S.: 333310
Louise Pearson (Coord-Sls & Mktg)

ULMA PACKAGING LLC (2)
2nd Magistralnaya 8A bldg 10, Olymp Business Centre, 123290, Moscow, Russia
Tel.: (7) 88007074939
Web Site: http://www.ulmapackaging.ru
Packaging Machinery Mfr
N.A.I.C.S.: 333310

ULMA PACKAGING LTDA. (2)
Rua Jose Getulio 579 - Cj 22, 01509-001, Sao Paulo, Brazil
Tel.: (55) 11 4063 1143
Packaging Machinery Mfr
N.A.I.C.S.: 333310

ULMA PACKAGING POLSKA SP.Z.O.O. (2)
Ul Sikorskiego 5, Legionowo, Poland
Tel.: (48) 22 7662250
Web Site: http://www.ulmapackaging.pl
Packaging Machinery Mfr
N.A.I.C.S.: 333310

ULMA PACKAGING PTY LTD (2)
Building 302 Unit 4/6-12 Boronia Road, Brisbane, 4008, QLD, Australia
Tel.: (61) 738606119
Packaging Machinery Mfr
N.A.I.C.S.: 333310
Kayla Beythien (Office Mgr)

ULMA PACKAGING SARL (2)
Le Mas des Entreprises Lot C2 Bis - 5 Avenue Lionel Terray, 69830, Meyzieu, France
Tel.: (33) 4 72 05 68 90
Web Site: http://www.ulmapackaging.fr
Packaging Machinery Mfr
N.A.I.C.S.: 333310

ULMA PACKAGING SRL (2)
Via dell Artigianato n 2, 29010, Gragnano Trebbiense, di Piacenza, Italy
Tel.: (39) 0523 788447
Web Site: http://www.ulmapackaging.it
Packaging Machinery Mfr
N.A.I.C.S.: 333310

ULMA PACKAGING SYSTEMS (SA) (PTY) LTD (2)
Village Crescent - Linbro Village Linbro Business Park, 2146, Sandton, South Africa
Tel.: (27) 11 608 40 05
Emp.: 20
Packaging Machinery Mfr
N.A.I.C.S.: 333310
Eddie Rodman (Gen Mgr)

ULMA PACKAGING UKRAINE (2)
A Akhmatovoy Str 13 Office 380, 02068, Kiev, Ukraine
Tel.: (380) 44 2292877
Packaging Machinery Mfr
N.A.I.C.S.: 333310

Subsidiary (Domestic):

ULMA Piping (2)
B Zubillaga 3, PO Box 14, 20560, Onati, Gipuzkoa, Spain
Tel.: (34) 943 78 05 52
Web Site: http://www.ulmapiping.com
Forged Steel Flanges Mfr
N.A.I.C.S.: 332312

Subsidiary (Non-US):

ULMA Portugal Lda. (2)
Zona Industrial-Rua A s/n Vale de Figueira, Sao Joao da Talha, Lisbon, Portugal
Tel.: (351) 219 947 850
Construction Machinery Mfr
N.A.I.C.S.: 333120

Subsidiary (Domestic):

ULMA Servicios de Manutencion, S. Coop.
Paseo Otadui n 8 Apdo 32, 20560, Onati, Gipuzkoa, Spain
Tel.: (34) 943 71 80 33
Web Site: http://www.ulmacarretillas.com
Construction Machinery Mfr
N.A.I.C.S.: 333120

Subsidiary (Non-US):

ULMA, S.A.R.L. (2)
27 Rue Gustave Eiffel ZI de la Mariniere, 91070, Bondoufle, France
Tel.: (33) 1 69 11 54 50
Web Site: http://www.ulmaconstruction.fr
Emp.: 60
Construction Machinery Mfr
N.A.I.C.S.: 333120
Sanchez Mickel (Pres)

Subsidiary (Domestic):

Ulma Precinox S.coop. (2)
Olaberria 11, PO Box 69, Legazpi, 20230, Gipuzkoa, Spain
Tel.: (34) 943 250 790
Web Site: http://www.ulmaprecinox.com
Packaging Machinery Mfr
N.A.I.C.S.: 333310

IK4-IKERLAN (1)
P J M Arizmendiarrieta 2, 20500, Arrasate, Gipuzkoa, Spain
Tel.: (34) 943 712 400
Web Site: http://www.ikerlan.es
Scientific Research & Devlopment Services
N.A.I.C.S.: 541715
Guillermo Irazoki (Mng Dir)

KIDE S.Coop (1)
Polig Gardotza s/n, 48710, Berriatua, Bizkaia, Spain
Tel.: (34) 946 036 208
Web Site: http://www.kide.com
Air Conditioning Equipment Mfr & Distr
N.A.I.C.S.: 333415

Subsidiary (Non-US):

Kedi Refrigeration Equipment Kunshan Co., Ltd. (2)
No 88 Liyi Road Bordering Industrial Zone, Qiandeng Town, Kunshan, 215343, Jiangsu, China
Tel.: (86) 512 50136878
Industrial Machinery Mfr
N.A.I.C.S.: 333310

LANA, S. COOP. (1)
Santxolopetegi Auzoa Auzoa 24, 20560, Onati, Gipuzkoa, Spain
Tel.: (34) 943 78 07 00
Web Site: http://www.lana.eu
Wood Processing Services
N.A.I.C.S.: 321114

LKS S. COOP. (1)
Polo de Innovacion Garaia Goiru Kalea 7, 20500, Madrid, Gipuzkoa, Spain
Tel.: (34) 902 540 990
Web Site: http://www.lks.es
Emp.: 700
Management Consulting Services
N.A.I.C.S.: 541611

Subsidiary (Non-US):

LKS CA CARIBE S.A. (2)
Paseo Colon Costado oeste de Pizza Hut, San Jose, Costa Rica
Tel.: (506) 2957380
Web Site: http://www.lkscaribe.com
Engineering Services
N.A.I.C.S.: 541330

LKS COLOMBIA (2)
Sucursal Colombia Calle 100 No 17A - 12 Oficina 301, Bogota, Colombia
Tel.: (57) 1 5209775
Web Site: http://www.colombia.lks-global.com
Management Consulting Services
N.A.I.C.S.: 541611
Rodrigo Vargas (Dir-de LKS-Ingeniero Civil)

LKS CORP, S.A. (2)
Av Nueva Tajamar 555 oficina 1402 World Trade Center, Las Condes, Santiago, Chile
Tel.: (56) 2 334 66 88
Web Site: http://www.lks.cl
Management Consulting Services
N.A.I.C.S.: 541611

Subsidiary (Domestic):

LKS IAMM S.L. (2)
Ribera de Axpe 11 Edif A Oficina 205, 48950, Erandio, Bizkaia, Spain
Tel.: (34) 94 605 11 00
Management Consulting Services
N.A.I.C.S.: 541611

Subsidiary (Non-US):

LKS INDIA PVT. LTD. (2)
Rachana Ventura 5th Floor CTS No 1337/1 Survey No 134/1 Opposite Anand, Pune, 411007, Maharastra, India
Tel.: (91) 2066864800
Web Site: http://www.india.lks-global.com
Management Consulting Services
N.A.I.C.S.: 541611
Maria Belen Mendizabal (Dir-Architecture & Design)

AND PRIVATE COMPANIES

Subsidiary (Domestic):

LKS INGENIERIA S. COOP. (2)
Garaia Innovation Centre Goiru Kalea 7, 20500, Arrasate, Spain
Tel.: (34) 943 71 24 88
Management Consulting Services
N.A.I.C.S.: 541611

LKS OUTSOURCING, S.COOP. (2)
Pedro Asua 75 - 77, 01008, Vitoria-Gasteiz, Spain
Tel.: (34) 945 21 80 38
Web Site: http://www.lksoutsourcing.es
Management Consulting Services
N.A.I.C.S.: 541611
Jesus Dorronsoro *(Pres)*

Subsidiary (Non-US):

LKS PERU (2)
Sucursal Peru Calle Monterrey n 341 oficina 802, Santiago de Surco, Lima, 33, Peru
Tel.: (51) 994 657 900
Management Consulting Services
N.A.I.C.S.: 541611
Jorge Portugal *(Country Mgr-Ingeniero Civil)*

Subsidiary (Domestic):

LKS SELECCION Y FORMACION S.L. (2)
Edificio Industrialdea, 20240, Ordizia, Gipuzkoa, Spain
Tel.: (34) 943 160314
Management Consulting Services
N.A.I.C.S.: 541611

LKS TASACIONES S.A. (2)
Goiru Kalea 7, 20500, Arrasate, Gipuzkoa, Spain
Tel.: (34) 902 31 21 00
Web Site: http://www.lkstasaciones.es
Management Consulting Services
N.A.I.C.S.: 541611

Leartiker Elikagaien Teknologia (1)
Xemein Etorbidea 12, 48270, Markina-Xemein, Bizkaia, Spain
Tel.: (34) 946169167
Food Technology Development Services
N.A.I.C.S.: 541715
Naia Andonegi *(Dir-Food Tech)*

Loramendi S.Coop. (1)
Alibarra 26, 01010, Vitoria, Araba, Spain
Tel.: (34) 945 18 43 00
Web Site: http://www.loramendi.com
Laundry Equipment Mfr
N.A.I.C.S.: 333310

Subsidiary (Non-US):

Loramendi China (2)
Room 901-902 Golden Land Building N 32 Liang Ma Bridge Road, Chaoyang, Beijing, 100016, China
Tel.: (86) 10 6462 2139
Industrial Machinery Mfr
N.A.I.C.S.: 333310

Loramendi France SASU (2)
26 rue Rene Cassin, 51350, Cormontreuil, France
Tel.: (33) 3 26 35 10 30
Industrial Machinery Mfr
N.A.I.C.S.: 333310

Subsidiary (US):

Loramendi Inc (2)
250 S Fenway Dr, Fenton, MI 48430
Tel.: (810) 629-0850
Web Site: http://www.loramendi-usa.com
Industrial Machinery Mfr
N.A.I.C.S.: 333310
Urs Geiger *(Mng Dir)*

Subsidiary (Non-US):

Loramendi South Africa (PTI) LTD (2)
Unit 402 Pebble Beach Somerset links office park De Beers Avenue, Somerset West, 7130, South Africa
Tel.: (27) 790373961
Industrial Machinery Mfr
N.A.I.C.S.: 333310

Loramendi Vertriebs GmbH (2)
Am Gierath 8, Lintorf, Germany
Tel.: (49) 2102 8929 0
Industrial Machinery Mfr
N.A.I.C.S.: 333310

MCCTELECOM S. Coop. (1)
Pol Ind Basabe Edif FO 2 Plta, 20550, Aretxabaleta, Gipuzkoa, Spain
Tel.: (34) 943 71 24 51
Web Site: http://www.mcctelecom.es
Engineeering Services
N.A.I.C.S.: 237990

Maier S. Coop. (1)
Poligono Industrial Arabieta Barrio Campanchu s/n, Ajangiz Vizcaya Bizkaia, 48320, Guernica, Biscay, Spain
Tel.: (34) 946259200
Web Site: http://www.maier.es
Thermoplastic Components Mfr
N.A.I.C.S.: 325211

Mapsa S. Coop. (1)
Ctra Echauri 11, 31160, Orkoien, Navarra, Spain
Tel.: (34) 948 32 50 11
Web Site: http://www.mapsa.net
Aluminium Wheel Mfr
N.A.I.C.S.: 336390

Matz-Erreka, S.Coop. (1)
B Ibarreta s/n, Antzuola, Gipuzkoa, Spain
Tel.: (34) 943 78 60 09
Web Site: http://www.matz-erreka.com
Engineeering Services
N.A.I.C.S.: 237990

Mccgraphics S. Coop. (1)
Txirrita-Maleo Biribil, 20100, Errenteria, Gipuzkoa, Spain
Tel.: (34) 902 30 63 16
Web Site: http://www.mccgraphics.com
Emp.: 60
Digital Printing & Marketing Services
N.A.I.C.S.: 323120
Juan Saenz De Argandona *(CEO)*

Mondragon Assembly, S.Coop. (1)
Poligono Industrial Bainetxe Pab. 5-A, 20550, Aretxabaleta, Gipuzkoa, Spain
Tel.: (34) 943 71 20 80
Web Site: http://www.mondragon-assembly.com
Industrial Machinery Mfr
N.A.I.C.S.: 333310

Subsidiary (Non-US):

MCK Automacao Industrial LTDA (2)
R Ladislau Eugenio de Camargo 167 - Ayrosa, Osasco, 06290-170, Sao Paulo, Brazil
Tel.: (55) 11 3653 0240
Web Site: http://www.mckautomacao.com.br
Industrial Machinery Mfr
N.A.I.C.S.: 333310

Oiarso S.Coop (1)
B Zikunaga n 57-F Pol Ibarluze, 20128, Hernani, Gipuzkoa, Spain
Tel.: (34) 943 33 50 20
Web Site: http://www.bexenmedical.com
Disposable Medical Product Mfr
N.A.I.C.S.: 325412

Ondoan S. Coop. (1)
Parque Tecnologico Edif 101 - C, 48170, Zamudio, Bizkaia, Spain
Tel.: (34) 94 452 23 13
Web Site: http://www.ondoan.com
Emp.: 200
Engineeering Services
N.A.I.C.S.: 541330

Orbea S. Coop. (1)
Pol Ind Goitondo S/N, 48269, Mallabia, Spain
Tel.: (34) 943 17 19 50
Web Site: http://www.orbea.com
Bicycle Mfr
N.A.I.C.S.: 336991
Jon Fernandez *(Gen Mgr)*

SORALUCE, S.Coop. (1)
B Osintxu s/n, 20570, Bergara, Gipuzkoa, Spain
Tel.: (34) 943 76 90 76
Web Site: http://www.soraluce.com
Industrial Machinery Mfr
N.A.I.C.S.: 333310

Subsidiary (Non-US):

Bimatec Soraluce Zerspanungstechnologie GmbH (2)
Am Steingraben 6, 65549, Limburg, Germany
Tel.: (49) 6431 97820
Web Site: http://www.bimatec.de
Mill Boring & Turning Machinery Mfr
N.A.I.C.S.: 333310

Chile Soldadura y Corte (2)
Doctor Lira Valencia 1586, Quilicura, Santiago, Chile
Tel.: (56) 2 411 19 00
Web Site: http://www.weldingcutting.com
Industrial Machinery Mfr
N.A.I.C.S.: 333310

Subsidiary (US):

SORALUCE AMERICA, INC. (2)
875 N Michigan Ave Ste 3614, Chicago, IL 60611
Tel.: (815) 315-9258
Web Site: http://www.soraluce-america.com
Industrial Machinery Mfr
N.A.I.C.S.: 333310

Subsidiary (Non-US):

Soraluce France S.A.R.L. (2)
3 Allee Jean Imagem, Torcy, 77200, Marne-la-Vallee, France
Tel.: (33) 1 60 050206
Mill Boring & Turning Machinery Mfr
N.A.I.C.S.: 333517

Soraluce Italia S.R.L. (2)
Via Rovigo 89, 35042, Este, Padova, Italy
Tel.: (39) 0429 603 001
Web Site: http://www.soraluce.it
Mill Boring & Turning Machinery Mfr
N.A.I.C.S.: 333517

Tajo S. Coop. (1)
Pol Industrial Aranguren 9 B Arragua, 20180, Oiartzun, Gipuzkoa, Spain
Tel.: (34) 943 26 00 00
Web Site: http://www.tajo.coop
Home Appliance Mfr
N.A.I.C.S.: 335210

ULMA HANDLING SYSTEMS FRANCE S.A.R.L. (1)
13/17 Rue de la Fontaine, 77700, Serris, France
Tel.: (33) 164 633 173
Web Site: http://www.ulmahandlingsystems.com
Emp.: 20
Industrial Machinery Mfr
N.A.I.C.S.: 333310
Salrgi Gamnaetoni *(Gen Mgr)*

ULMA Handling Systems do Brasil Ltda (1)
Rua Jose Getulio 579 Cj 22 Aclimacao, Sao Paulo, 01509-001, Brazil
Tel.: (55) 11 3711 5940
Industrial Machinery Mfr
N.A.I.C.S.: 333310

URSSA, S. COOP. (1)
Campo de los Palacios 18 - Apdo 284, 1006, Vitoria, Araba, Spain
Tel.: (34) 945 15 85 10
Web Site: http://www.urssa.es
Civil Engineering Construction Services
N.A.I.C.S.: 237990

Subsidiary (Non-US):

URSSA MAROC SARLAU (2)
Residence Lyautey 106 Rue Abderrahmane Sahraoui, 20070, Casablanca, Morocco
Tel.: (212) 6 83 08 89 97
Steel Contruction & Engineering Services
N.A.I.C.S.: 237990

URSSA SARL (2)
Centre d Affaires Erlia ZI de Jalday Lot 115, 64500, Saint-Jean-de-Luz, France
Tel.: (6 83 08 89 97
Steel Contruction & Engineering Services
N.A.I.C.S.: 237990
Frederic Caracciolo *(Branch Dir)*

Plant (Domestic):

URSSA, S. COOP. - PLANT 2 (2)
C/Jundiz n 8 Bajo 3, 1015, Vitoria, Spain
Tel.: (34) 945 118 510
Steel Contruction & Engineering Services
N.A.I.C.S.: 237990

Aogare Cristobal *(Mng Dir)*

Subsidiary (Non-US):

URSSAMEX, SA de CV (2)
glesia N 2 Torre E Piso 6 Despacho 604, Tizapan el alto, 1090, Mexico
Tel.: (52) 55 5616 3936
Steel Contruction & Engineering Services
N.A.I.C.S.: 237990

Unekel, S. Coop. (1)
Barriada de Berrio s/n, 48230, Elorrio, Bizkaia, Spain
Tel.: (34) 94 6820632
Meat Production Services
N.A.I.C.S.: 311613

Urola, S.C. (1)
Urola Kalea s/n - Apdo 3, 20230, Legazpi, Gipuzkoa, Spain
Tel.: (34) 943 73 70 03
Web Site: http://www.urola.com
Packaging Machinery Mfr
N.A.I.C.S.: 333310

Wingroup S.Coop (1)
Urarte 26 Apdo 168, 20570, Bergara, Gipuzkoa, Spain
Tel.: (34) 943 76 90 56
Web Site: http://www.wingroupscoop.com
Fitness & Outdoor Product Distr
N.A.I.C.S.: 423910
Stefanie Wedel *(Dir-Sls & Mktg)*

ategi s.coop (1)
Polo de Innovacion Garaia Edificio B 3a planta, Arrasate, 20500, Mondragon, Gipuzkoa, Spain
Tel.: (34) 943 71 19 30
Web Site: http://www.ategi.com
Purchasing Portal Develolpment Service
N.A.I.C.S.: 519290

MONDURA LIEGENSCHAFTEN AG
Robert Bosch Str 6, D - 67227, Frankenthal, Germany
Tel.: (49) 6233357980
Web Site: http://www.mondura.de
Year Founded: 1998
Rev.: $60,883,085
Emp.: 30
Real Estate Services
N.A.I.C.S.: 531390
Axel Alferi *(CEO)*

Subsidiaries:

Geld & Grund Immobilien Vertriebs GmbH (1)
Neusser Str 538, 50737, Cologne, Germany
Tel.: (49) 2217401316
Real Estate Manangement Services
N.A.I.C.S.: 531390

MONECAM
2 Quai Du Commerce, 69009, Lyon, Rhone, France
Tel.: (33) 472192226
Web Site: http://www.monecam.com
Rev.: $23,200,000
Emp.: 52
Data Processing Services
N.A.I.C.S.: 518210
Frederic Depresle *(DP Mgr)*

MONEDA ASSET MANAGEMENT S.A.
Av Isidora Goyenechea 3621 Piso 8, Las Condes, Santiago, Chile
Tel.: (56) 2 337 7900   CL
Web Site: http://www.moneda.cl
Year Founded: 1993
Investment Fund Management Services
N.A.I.C.S.: 523940
Pablo Echeverria *(Founder, Chm, Partner & Portfolio Mgr-Chilean Equities)*

MONEDA RENTA VARIABLE CHILE FONDO DO INVERSION
Av Isidora Goyenechea 3621 8th

Moneda Renta Variable Chile Fondo do Inversion—(Continued)

Floor, Santiago, Chile
Tel.: (56) 23377900
CFIMRV—(SGO)
Sales Range: Less than $1 Million
Real Estate Services
N.A.I.C.S.: 531390
Pablo Echeverria Benitez *(Mgr-Fund)*

MONETA MONEY BANK A.S.

BB Centrum Vyskocilova 1422/1b, 14028, Prague, Czech Republic
Tel.: (420) 224442549   CZ
Web Site: https://investors.moneta.cz
Year Founded: 1998
MONET—(PRA)
Rev.: $985,811,582
Assets: $20,488,210,726
Liabilities: $19,048,217,514
Net Worth: $1,439,993,212
Earnings: $232,523,824
Emp.: 2,518
Fiscal Year-end: 12/31/23
Bank Holding Company
N.A.I.C.S.: 551111
Tomas Spurny *(Chm-Mgmt Bd & CEO)*

Subsidiaries:

Moneta Auto, s.r.o. (1)
BB Centrum Vyskocilova 1442/1b, Michle, 140 00, Prague, 4, Czech Republic
Tel.: (420) 224446262
Web Site: https://www.monetaauto.cz
Financial Services
N.A.I.C.S.: 523940

Moneta Leasing, s.r.o. (1)
Vyskocilova 1442/1b, Michle, 140 00, Prague, 4, Czech Republic
Tel.: (420) 224444999
Web Site: https://www.monetaleasing.cz
Financial Services
N.A.I.C.S.: 523940

Wuestenrot stavebni sporitelna a.s. (1)
Na Hrebenech II 1718/8, 140 23, Prague, 4, Czech Republic
Tel.: (420) 257092403
Web Site: http://www.wuestenrot.cz
Mortgage Banking
N.A.I.C.S.: 522292
Blanka Hronova *(Mgr)*

MONETARY AUTHORITY OF MACAU

Calcada do Gaio 24-26, Macau, China (Macau)
Tel.: (853) 28568288
Web Site: http://www.amcm.gov.mo
Sales Range: $150-199.9 Million
Emp.: 137
Central Bank
N.A.I.C.S.: 521110
Anselmo L.S. Teng *(Chm)*

MONETARY AUTHORITY OF SINGAPORE

10 Shenton Way MAS Building, Singapore, 079117, Singapore
Tel.: (65) 62255577   SG
Web Site: http://www.mas.gov.sg
Year Founded: 1971
Rev.: $19,813,463,280
Assets: $314,112,724,020
Liabilities: $285,152,391,360
Net Worth: $28,960,332,660
Earnings: $16,901,998,740
Fiscal Year-end: 03/31/19
Central Bank
N.A.I.C.S.: 521110
Hng Kiang Lim *(Deputy Chm)*

MONETTE SPORTS INC.

251 Des Laurentides Blvd, Laval, H7G 2T7, QC, Canada
Tel.: (450) 668-6466

Web Site:
http://www.monettesports.com
Year Founded: 1974
Rev.: $10,000,000
Emp.: 29
Motorcycle Dealers
N.A.I.C.S.: 441227
Alain Trottier *(Owner)*

MONEX GROUP, INC.

ARK Mori Building 25F 1-12-32 Akasaka, Minato-ku, Tokyo, 107-6025, Japan
Tel.: (81) 7024908411   JP
Web Site: https://www.monexgroup.jp
Year Founded: 2004
NNL—(DEU)
Rev.: $441,521,560
Assets: $5,034,453,620
Liabilities: $4,154,510,590
Net Worth: $879,943,030
Earnings: $206,846,730
Emp.: 1,480
Fiscal Year-end: 03/31/24
Holding Company; Financial Services
N.A.I.C.S.: 551112
Takashi Oyagi *(Exec Officer & Chief Strategic Officer-US Segment)*

Subsidiaries:

Docomo Monex Holdings, Inc. (1)
2-11-1 Nagatacho, Chiyoda-ku, Tokyo, Japan **(50.95%)**
Tel.: (81) 362123802
Web Site: https://www.monexgroup.jp
Securities Brokerage Services
N.A.I.C.S.: 523150
Toshihiro Eto *(Pres)*

Subsidiary (Domestic):

Monex, Inc. (2)
Pacific Century Place Marunouchi Building 19th/20th Floor, 1-11-1 Marunouchi Chiyoda-ku, Tokyo, 100-6219, Japan
Tel.: (81) 362123802
Web Site: http://www.monex.co.jp
Securities Broker & Dealer
N.A.I.C.S.: 523150
Nana Otsuki *(Exec Dir)*

Japan Catalyst, Inc. (1)
1-12-32 ARK Mori Building 25F Akasaka, Minato-ku, Tokyo, 107-6025, Japan
Tel.: (81) 35 657 9970
Web Site: https://www.japancatalyst.com
Investment Advisory Services
N.A.I.C.S.: 523999
Taro Hirano *(Pres)*

Monex Boom Securities (H.K.) Limited (1)
Room 2501 25/F AIA Tower 183 Electric Road, North Point, China (Hong Kong)
Tel.: (852) 2 255 8888
Web Site: https://www.boom.com
Stock Trading Services
N.A.I.C.S.: 523999

Monex Business Incubation, Inc. (1)
1-11-1 Marunouchi Pacific Century Place Marunouchi Building, 19th Floor Chiyoda-Ku, Tokyo, 100-6219, Japan
Tel.: (81) 362123750
Web Site: http://www.monexgroup.jp
Financial Support Services
N.A.I.C.S.: 523999

Monex Capital Partners, Inc. (1)
Uchisaiwaicho Dai Bldg 7th Fl 1-3-3 Uchisaiwaicho, Chiyoda-ku, Tokyo, 100-0011, Japan
Tel.: (81) 335957150
Web Site: http://www.monexgroup.jp
Sales Range: $50-74.9 Million
Emp.: 4
Investment Management Service
N.A.I.C.S.: 523999

Monex FX, Inc. (1)
Riverside Yomiuri Bldg 15th Fl 36-2 Nihonbashi Hakozaki-cho, Chuo-ku, Tokyo, 103-0015, Japan **(100%)**
Tel.: (81) 358470461
Web Site: http://www.monexfx.co.jp
Rev.: $19,422,000

Emp.: 30
Financial Products Trading
N.A.I.C.S.: 522299
Toshihiko Katsuya *(Pres)*

Monex Hambrecht (1)
1-11-1, Marunouchi, Chiyoda-ku, Tokyo, 100-6220, Japan **(78.6%)**
Tel.: (81) 362123763
Web Site: http://www.mbinc.jp
Sales Range: $25-49.9 Million
Emp.: 5
Mergers & Acquisitions Advisory Services
N.A.I.C.S.: 519290

Monex Securities Australia Pty Ltd (1)
Suite 1 Level 2 35 Clarence Street, Sydney, 2000, NSW, Australia
Tel.: (61) 29 103 9600
Web Site: https://www.monexsecurities.com.au
Trade Agent Brokerage Services
N.A.I.C.S.: 425120

Monex University, Inc. (1)
1-11-1 Marunouchi Pacific Century Place Marunochi 19F, Chiyoda-Ku, Tokyo, 100-0005, Japan
Tel.: (81) 362123750
Web Site: http://www.monexuniv.co.jp
Educational Support Services
N.A.I.C.S.: 611710

Trade Science Corp. (1)
Waseda Incubation Center Waseda University, 513 Wasede Tsumaki-cho, Shunjuku-ku, Tokyo, 162-0041, Japan **(100%)**
Tel.: (81) 352923851
Rev.: $2,060,890
Investment Advisor
N.A.I.C.S.: 523940

TradeStation Group, Inc. (1)
8050 SW 10th St Ste 4000, Plantation, FL 33324
Tel.: (954) 652-7000
Web Site: http://www.tradestation.com
Sales Range: $125-149.9 Million
Emp.: 392
Online Broker-Dealer
N.A.I.C.S.: 523150
Takashi Oyagi *(Chief Strategic Officer)*

Subsidiary (Non-US):

TradeStation Europe Limited (2)
1 Hay Hill Berkeley Sq, London, W1J 6DH, United Kingdom **(100%)**
Tel.: (44) 8082341993
Web Site: http://www.tradestation-international.com
Sales Range: $75-99.9 Million
Emp.: 20
Brokerage Software & Tutorials; Online Broker-Dealer
N.A.I.C.S.: 523150
Salamon Sredni *(Pres)*

Subsidiary (Domestic):

TradeStation Securities, Inc. (2)
Trade Station Bldg 8050 SW 10th St Ste 2000, Plantation, FL 33324 **(100%)**
Tel.: (954) 652-7000
Web Site: http://www.tradestation.com
Options & Futures Trading
N.A.I.C.S.: 523150
T. Keith Black *(VP-Product Dev)*

MONEX, S.A.P.I. DE C.V.

Av Paseo de la Reforma 284 15th floor Col Juarez, Del Cuauhtemoc, 06600, Mexico, Mexico
Tel.: (52) 52314500
Web Site:
https://www.monex.com.mx
Year Founded: 1985
MONEX—(MEX)
Rev.: $778,223,021
Assets: $11,138,935,649
Liabilities: $10,176,232,292
Net Worth: $962,703,357
Earnings: $188,369,094
Emp.: 3,090
Fiscal Year-end: 12/31/23
Financial Services
N.A.I.C.S.: 551112

Hector Pio Lagos Donde *(Chm)*

Subsidiaries:

Monex Assets Management Inc. (1)
440 Louisiana St Ste 1240, Houston, TX 77002
Tel.: (713) 877-8234
Web Site: https://www.monexwealthus.com
Investment Advisory & Asset Management Services
N.A.I.C.S.: 525110

Monex Canada, Inc. (1)
66 Wellington Street West Suite 3520, PO Box 61, Toronto, M5K 1E7, ON, Canada
Tel.: (647) 943-1680
Web Site: https://www.monexcanada.com
Investment Financing Services
N.A.I.C.S.: 523999

Monex Europe Limited (1)
3rd Floor 1 Bartholomew Lane, London, EC2N 2AX, United Kingdom
Tel.: (44) 2036506300
Web Site: https://www.monexeurope.com
Investment Financing Services
N.A.I.C.S.: 523999
Nick Edgeley *(Mng Dir)*

Monex Securities, Inc. (1)
440 Louisiana St Ste 1240, Houston, TX 77002
Tel.: (713) 877-8234
Web Site: https://monexsec.com
Investment Advisory Services
N.A.I.C.S.: 523940

MONEXA SERVCIES, INC.

Suite 1100 555 West Hastings Street, Vancouver, V6B 4N4, BC, Canada
Tel.: (604) 630-5660   Ca
Web Site: http://www.monexa.com
Year Founded: 2005
Sales Range: $1-9.9 Million
Emp.: 25
Billing Software Services
N.A.I.C.S.: 513210
Jason M. Grant *(CTO)*

MONEY DEBT & CREDIT GROUP LTD.

45 Clarendon Rd, Watford, WD 17 SZ, Hertfordshire, United Kingdom
Tel.: (44) 1923636800
Web Site:
http://www.moneydebtandcredit.com
Sales Range: $1-9.9 Million
Financial Advice
N.A.I.C.S.: 523940
Simon Johnson *(Chm & CEO)*

MONEY FORWARD, INC.

21F Tamachi Station Tower S 3-1-21 Shibaura, Minato-ku, Tokyo, 108-0023, Japan
Tel.: (81) 364539160   JP
Web Site:
https://corp.moneyforward.com
Year Founded: 2012
3994—(TKS)
Rev.: $215,394,200
Assets: $625,919,380
Liabilities: $380,179,980
Net Worth: $245,739,400
Earnings: ($44,773,350)
Fiscal Year-end: 11/30/23
Software Application Development Services
N.A.I.C.S.: 541511
Yosuke Tsuji *(Pres, Pres & CEO)*

Subsidiaries:

Klavis Inc. (1)
18-20 Sanei-cho Park Side Yotsuya 5F, Shinjuku-ku, Tokyo, 160-0008, Japan
Tel.: (81) 364577340
Web Site: https://klavis.recruitment.jp
Online Book Services
N.A.I.C.S.: 513130

Knowledge Labo, Inc. (1)
2-5-8 Imabashi Tradepia Yodoyabashi 9F,

Chuo-ku, Osaka, 541-0042, Japan
Tel.: (81) 66 809 7072
Web Site: https://knowledgelabo.com
Emp.: 55
Financial Services
N.A.I.C.S.: 523999

MONEY MASTERS LEASING & FINANCE LIMITED
Ground Floor 4 Akashdeep Road 1 TPS VI, Santacruz West, Mumbai, 400 054, India
Tel.: (91) 2226613184
Web Site:
https://www.moneymasterscc.in
Year Founded: 1995
535910—(BOM)
Rev.: $308,163
Assets: $3,314,521
Liabilities: $1,501,096
Net Worth: $1,813,425
Earnings: $56,868
Emp.: 10
Fiscal Year-end: 03/31/21
Finance & Leasing Services
N.A.I.C.S.: 525990
Hozef Abdulhussain Darukhanawala *(Mng Dir)*

MONEY PARTNERS GROUP CO., LTD.
33F Sumitomo Fudosan Roppongi Grand Tower 3-2-1 Roppongi, Minato-ku, Tokyo, 106-6233, Japan
Tel.: (81) 345403900
Web Site:
https://www.moneypartners-group.co.jp
Year Founded: 2005
8732—(TKS)
Rev.: $37,187,860
Assets: $438,084,360
Liabilities: $346,813,480
Net Worth: $91,270,880
Earnings: $4,679,880
Fiscal Year-end: 03/31/24
Foreign Exchange Trading
N.A.I.C.S.: 522299
Hideji Fukushima *(Pres)*

Subsidiaries:

Money Partners Solutions Co., Ltd. (1)
3-2-1 Roppongi Sumitomo Real Estate Roppongi Grand Tower 33rd floor, Minato-ku, Tokyo, 106-6233, Japan
Tel.: (81) 345403890
Web Site: https://www.mpsol.co.jp
Emp.: 70
Information Processing Services
N.A.I.C.S.: 518210
Keita Konishi *(Pres & CEO)*

MONEY SQUARE HOLDINGS, INC.
40F Midtown Tower 9-7-1 Akasaka, Minato-ku, Tokyo, 107-0052, Japan
Tel.: (81) 3 3470 5077 JP
Web Site: http://www.m2hd.co.jp
Year Founded: 2002
Sales Range: $10-24.9 Million
Holding Company; Margin Foreign Exchange Trading Services
N.A.I.C.S.: 551112
Hitoshi Aiba *(Pres)*

Subsidiaries:

Money Square Japan, Inc. (1)
40F Midtown Tower 9-7-1 Akasaka, Minato-ku, Tokyo, 107-0052, Japan
Tel.: (81) 3 3470 5050
Web Site: http://www.m2j.co.jp
Margin Foreign Exchange Trading Services
N.A.I.C.S.: 523160

MONEYBOXX FINANCE LIMITED
523-A Somdutt Chambers-II 9, Bhikaji

Cama Place, New Delhi, 110066, Delhi, India
Tel.: (91) 1126171326
Web Site:
https://www.moneyboxxfinance.com
538446—(BOM)
Rev.: $1,502,625
Assets: $9,968,920
Liabilities: $6,672,305
Net Worth: $3,296,615
Earnings: ($405,856)
Emp.: 228
Fiscal Year-end: 03/31/21
Financial Services
N.A.I.C.S.: 525990
Mahesh Kumar Dhanuka *(Mng Dir)*

MONEYMAX FINANCIAL SERVICES LTD.
7 Changi Business Park Vista 01-01 Sookee, Singapore, 486042, Singapore
Tel.: (65) 68122777
Web Site:
https://www.moneymax.com.sg
5WJ—(SES)
Rev.: $216,376,581
Assets: $565,167,765
Liabilities: $444,943,573
Net Worth: $120,224,191
Earnings: $19,068,394
Emp.: 372
Fiscal Year-end: 12/31/23
Pawn Brokers
N.A.I.C.S.: 522310
Yong Guan Lim *(Co-Founder, Chm & CEO)*

Subsidiaries:

MoneyMax Leasing Pte. Ltd. (1)
7 Changi Business Park Vista, Singapore, 486042, Singapore
Tel.: (65) 62800808
Web Site:
https://www.moneymaxleasing.com
Financial Lending Services
N.A.I.C.S.: 523999

Pajak Gadai Pasir Gudang Sdn. Bhd. (1)
No 22 Jalan Tembikai 3 Taman Kota Masai, 81700, Pasir Gudang, Johor, Malaysia
Tel.: (60) 72532822
Web Site: https://pajak-gadai-pasir-gudang-sdn-bhd.business.site
Pawn Brokerage Services
N.A.I.C.S.: 522299

SG e-Auction Pte. Ltd. (1)
SOOKEE HQ 7 Changi Business Park Vista, Singapore, 486042, Singapore
Tel.: (65) 68122800
Web Site: https://www.sgeauction.com
Online Auction Services
N.A.I.C.S.: 445110

MONEYME LIMITED
Level 3 131 Macquarie Street, Sydney, 2000, NSW, Australia
Tel.: (61) 1300669059 AU
Web Site:
https://www.moneyme.com.au
Year Founded: 2013
MME—(ASX)
Rev.: $155,752,103
Assets: $843,205,972
Liabilities: $734,929,908
Net Worth: $108,276,064
Earnings: $8,010,693
Emp.: 90
Fiscal Year-end: 06/30/23
Financial Investment Services
N.A.I.C.S.: 523999
Clayton Howes *(CEO)*

Subsidiaries:

SocietyOne Australia Pty. Limited (1)
G P O Box 5175, Sydney, 2001, NSW, Australia
Tel.: (61) 1300395833

Web Site: https://societyone.com.au
Financial Services
N.A.I.C.S.: 541611

MONEYSUPERMARKET.COM GROUP PLC
MONY House St David's Park, Ewloe, CH5 3UZ, Chester, United Kingdom
Tel.: (44) 1244665700 UK
Web Site:
https://www.moneysupermarket.com
Year Founded: 1993
MONY—(LSE)
Rev.: $489,270,386
Assets: $516,536,228
Liabilities: $245,518,808
Net Worth: $271,017,420
Earnings: $87,477,910
Emp.: 733
Fiscal Year-end: 12/31/22
Online Finance & Travel Price Comparison Services
N.A.I.C.S.: 513199

Subsidiaries:

Decision Technologies Limited (1)
Third Floor High Holborn House 52-54 High Holborn, London, WC1V 6RL, United Kingdom
Tel.: (44) 20 7400 6200
Web Site:
http://www.brodbandchoices.co.uk
Sales Range: $10-24.9 Million
Emp.: 60
Operator of Price Comparison Websites
N.A.I.C.S.: 519290
Michael Phillips *(CEO)*

Icelolly Marketing Limited (1)
1st Floor Park Row House 19-20 Park Row, Leeds, LS1 5JF, United Kingdom
Tel.: (44) 2067884832
Web Site: https://www.icelolly.com
Travel Arrangement Services
N.A.I.C.S.: 561599

Insuresupermarket.com Limited (1)
Moneysupermarket House, St David Park, Ewloe, CH5 3UZ, Flintshire, United Kingdom
Tel.: (44) 1244665700
Financial Activities
N.A.I.C.S.: 523999

Moneysupermarket.com Limited (1)
MoneySuperMarket House, St David's Park, Ewloe, CH5 3UZ, Flintshire, United Kingdom
Tel.: (44) 333 123 1972
Web Site:
https://www.moneysupermarket.com
Online Services
N.A.I.C.S.: 513199

MONEYSWAP PLC
Office 12118 12/F MassMutual Tower, 33 Lockhart Road, Wanchai, China (Hong Kong)
Tel.: (852) 39199888 GI
Web Site:
http://www.moneyswap.com
Online Foreign Exchange Services
N.A.I.C.S.: 522320
Craig Lees Baxter Niven *(Chm & Interim CEO)*

MONEYSWORTH & BEST INC
120 Midair Court, Brampton, L6T 5V1, ON, Canada
Tel.: (905) 790-0650
Web Site: http://www.moneysworth-best.com
Year Founded: 1984
Sales Range: $10-24.9 Million
Emp.: 20
Mfr of Shoe, Leather Care & Repair Products
N.A.I.C.S.: 325612
Nora Nalbandian *(Pres)*

Subsidiaries:

Moneysworth & Best Shoe Care, Inc. (1)
501 Roundtree Dairy Rd Unit 4, Woodbridge, L4L 8H1, ON, Canada (100%)
Tel.: (905) 265-0650
Web Site: http://www.moneysworth-best.com
Provider of Shoe Repair Services & Distributor of Shoe Care Products
N.A.I.C.S.: 458210

MONEYWEB HOLDINGS LIMITED
2nd Floor 20 The Piazza, Melrose Arch, Johannesburg, 2196, South Africa
Tel.: (27) 113448600
Web Site:
http://www.moneyweb.co.za
Internet Publishing & Broadcasting Services
N.A.I.C.S.: 551112

MONGEO JOINT STOCK COMPANY
18th Khoroo, Songinokhairkhan District, Ulaanbaatar, Mongolia
Tel.: (976) 11633449
MOG—(MONG)
Rev.: $35,297
Assets: $238,676
Liabilities: $21,694
Net Worth: $216,982
Earnings: ($2,794)
Fiscal Year-end: 12/31/19
Architectural & Engineering Services
N.A.I.C.S.: 541310

MONGOL MAKH EXPO
Orbit 20th Khoroo, Songinokhairkhan District, Ulaanbaatar, Mongolia
Tel.: (976) 11 331073
Oilseed & Grain Farming Services
N.A.I.C.S.: 111191

MONGOL SECURITIES JOINT STOCK COMPANY
15th Khoroo Gegeenten complex 215, Khan-Uul district, Ulaanbaatar, Mongolia
Tel.: (976) 11462130
MSC—(MONG)
Rev.: $617
Assets: $60,579
Liabilities: $44,147
Net Worth: $16,432
Earnings: ($13,593)
Fiscal Year-end: 12/31/19
Investment Brokerage & Other Financial Investment Services
N.A.I.C.S.: 523999

MONGOL SHILTGEEN JOINT STOCK COMPANY
Gachuurt Village District 20, Bayanzurkh District, Ulaanbaatar, Mongolia
Tel.: (976) 70490041
Year Founded: 2001
MSH—(MONG)
Rev.: $139,312
Assets: $2,048,939
Liabilities: $1,014,558
Net Worth: $1,034,381
Earnings: $13
Fiscal Year-end: 12/31/19
Food Products Mfr
N.A.I.C.S.: 311999
B. Undrah *(Dir)*

MONGOL SHIR JOINT STOCK COMPANY
Chinggis Avenue, Khan-Uul District, Ulaanbaatar, Mongolia
Tel.: (976) 11 342665
Leather & Allied Product Mfr

MONGOL SHIR JOINT STOCK COMPANY

Mongol Shir Joint Stock Company—(Continued)
N.A.I.C.S.: 316990

MONGOLIA ENERGY CORPORATION LIMITED
17th Floor 118 Connaught Road West, Hong Kong, China (Hong Kong)
Tel.: (852) 21388000
Web Site: https://www.mongolia-energy.cn
MOAEF—(OTCIQ)
Rev.: $370,426,898
Assets: $357,105,443
Liabilities: $910,053,308
Net Worth: ($552,947,865)
Earnings: ($204,395,123)
Emp.: 811
Fiscal Year-end: 03/31/23
Energy & Mineral Resources Explorer
N.A.I.C.S.: 213114
Yvette Ong *(Mng Dir)*

MONGOLIA GROWTH GROUP LTD.
First Canadian Place 100 King Street West 56th Floor Suite 5600, Toronto, M5X 1C9, ON, Canada
Tel.: (289) 848-2035   AB
Web Site:
https://www.mongoliagrowth.com
MNGGF—(OTCIQ)
Rev.: $1,389,885
Assets: $43,046,416
Liabilities: $11,616,528
Net Worth: $31,429,888
Earnings: $12,163,911
Emp.: 30
Fiscal Year-end: 12/31/21
Investment Services
N.A.I.C.S.: 523999
Harris Kupperman *(Founder, Chm & CEO)*

MONGOLIAN RESOURCE CORPORATION LIMITED
Suite 14 Level 13 3 Spring Street, Sydney, 2000, NSW, Australia
Tel.: (61) 292514908
Web Site:
http://www.mongolianresource.com
Sales Range: Less than $1 Million
Gold Exploration & Mining Services
N.A.I.C.S.: 212220
Peter Gerard Cook *(Chm & Sec)*

MONGOLIAN STOCK EXCHANGE
Sukhbaatar Square-2, Ulaanbaatar, Mongolia
Tel.: (976) 976310506
Web Site: http://www.mse.mn
Year Founded: 1991
Stock Exchange Services
N.A.I.C.S.: 523210
Rentsen Sodkhuu *(Chm)*

MONGOOSE MINING LTD.
215 Edwards St, Victoria, V9A 3E4, BC, Canada
Tel.: (403) 803-2150   Ca
Year Founded: 2019
Assets: $300,271
Liabilities: $18,644
Net Worth: $281,627
Earnings: ($50,330)
Fiscal Year-end: 12/31/20
Mineral Exploration Services
N.A.I.C.S.: 213115
John van Driesum *(CEO)*

MONICA ELECTRONICS LTD.
21 C/o Ashiyaana Residency Chaudhary Dharambir Market, Badarpur, New Delhi, 110044, India
Tel.: (91) 1130883004
Year Founded: 1975
523544—(BOM)
Rev.: $8,085
Assets: $386,243
Liabilities: $2,655,091
Net Worth: ($2,268,848)
Earnings: ($14,698)
Fiscal Year-end: 03/31/14
Electronic Products Mfr
N.A.I.C.S.: 334419
Anil Jain *(Asst Sec)*

MONIN SAS
16 rue de la Malerie, PO Box 10039, 28402, Nogent-le-Rotrou, France
Tel.: (33) 2 3753 5120   FR
Web Site: http://en.monin.fr
Year Founded: 1797
Sales Range: $25-49.9 Million
Emp.: 100
Door Lock & Hinge Mfr
N.A.I.C.S.: 332510
Julie Leibovici *(CEO)*

Subsidiaries:

Mermier Lemarchand SAS   (1)
Rue de Vire, BP 6, 61800, Tinchebray, France
Tel.: (33) 2 3362 2020
Web Site: http://www.mermier.fr
Sales Range: $50-74.9 Million
Emp.: 18
Garden Tool Mfr
N.A.I.C.S.: 332216

MONINJBAR JOINT STOCK COMPANY
6th Khoroo, Chingeltei District, Ulaanbaatar, Mongolia
Tel.: (976) 11328969
MIB—(MONG)
Rev.: $573,930
Assets: $1,806,051
Liabilities: $1,225,412
Net Worth: $580,639
Earnings: ($73,805)
Fiscal Year-end: 12/31/20
Building Construction Services
N.A.I.C.S.: 236220

MONITIN GROUP
53 Etzel Street, 75706, Rishon le Zion, Israel
Tel.: (972) 39538888
Web Site: http://www.globes.co.il
Year Founded: 1983
Holding Company; Business Information Publisher
N.A.I.C.S.: 551112
Eitan Madmon *(CEO)*

Subsidiaries:

Globes Publisher Itonut (1983) Ltd   (1)
53 Etzel St, 75706, Rishon le Zion, Israel
Tel.: (972) 39538888
Web Site: http://www.globes.co.il
Financial Publisher
N.A.I.C.S.: 513110
Alona Bar-On *(Chm & CEO)*

MONITORAPP CO., LTD.
8F 27 Digital-ro 27ga-gil, Guro-gu, Seoul, 08375, Korea (South)
Tel.: (82) 27490799
Web Site:
https://www.monitorapp.com
Year Founded: 2005
434480—(KRS)
Software Development Services
N.A.I.C.S.: 541511

MONK OFFICE SUPPLY LTD.
800 Viewfield Rd, Victoria, V9A 4V1, BC, Canada
Tel.: (250) 384-0565
Web Site: http://www.monk.ca

Year Founded: 1951
Rev.: $16,383,305
Emp.: 110
Office Stationery Supplier
N.A.I.C.S.: 459410
Adam Taft *(Gen Mgr)*

MONKSMEAD PARTNERSHIP LLP
The Coach House, Upper Woolhampton, Reading, RG7 5TA, Berks, United Kingdom
Tel.: (44) 1285642385
Web Site:
http://www.monksmeadpartners.com
Privater Equity Firm
N.A.I.C.S.: 523999
Nick Theakston *(Partner)*

Subsidiaries:

Beagle Aerospace Limited   (1)
Stony Lane, Christchurch, BH23 1EX, Dorset, United Kingdom
Tel.: (44) 1202482296
Web Site: http://www.beagletg.com
Sales Range: $10-24.9 Million
Emp.: 250
Aircraft Repair, Maintenance & Spare Part Manufacturing Services
N.A.I.C.S.: 336413
John Taylor *(Mng Dir)*

MONMOUTHSHIRE BUILDING SOCIETY
Monmouthshire House John Frost Square, Newport, NP20 1PX, South Wales, United Kingdom
Tel.: (44) 1633 844444
Web Site: http://www.monbs.com
Year Founded: 1869
Rev.: $32,036,410
Assets: $1,407,366,022
Liabilities: $1,324,877,184
Net Worth: $82,488,838
Earnings: $1,167,498
Emp.: 146
Fiscal Year-end: 04/30/19
Mortgage Lending & Other Financial Services
N.A.I.C.S.: 522310
William J. Carroll *(CEO)*

MONNALISA S.P.A.
Via Madame Curie 7 Arezzo, 52100, Arezzo, Italy
Tel.: (39) 055216038
Web Site: https://monnalisa.com
Year Founded: 1968
MNL—(ITA)
Rev.: $55,542,463
Assets: $70,128,457
Liabilities: $33,849,664
Net Worth: $36,278,793
Earnings: ($2,336,380)
Emp.: 267
Fiscal Year-end: 12/31/21
Apparel Product Mfr & Distr
N.A.I.C.S.: 315990
Christian Simoni *(CEO)*

MONNARI TRADE S.A.
Ul Radwanska 6, 90-453, Lodz, Poland
Tel.: (48) 422371334
Web Site: https://emonnari.pl
Year Founded: 2007
MON—(WAR)
Rev.: $78,665,650
Assets: $89,629,319
Liabilities: $17,376,778
Net Worth: $72,252,540
Earnings: $4,667,937
Fiscal Year-end: 12/31/23
Apparel Product Mfr
N.A.I.C.S.: 315250
Miroslaw Bogdan Misztal *(Chm-Mgmt Bd & CEO)*

INTERNATIONAL PUBLIC

MONNO CERAMIC INDUSTRIES LTD.
Islampur Dhamrai, Dhaka, 1350, Bangladesh
Tel.: (880) 27730587
Web Site: https://www.monno.com
Year Founded: 1984
MONNOCERA—(DHA)
Sales Range: Less than $1 Million
Ceramic & Concrete Product Mfr
N.A.I.C.S.: 327110
Rasheed Islam *(Mng Dir)*

Subsidiaries:

Monno Design Ltd.   (1)
20 Iliffe Yard, London, SE17 3QA, United Kingdom
Tel.: (44) 208 908 5353
Glassware & Cleaning Material Whslr
N.A.I.C.S.: 423460
Samiul Islam *(Mng Dir)*

MONNOOS JOINT STOCK COMPANY
Chingiss Avenue, Khan Uul District, Ulaanbaatar, Mongolia
Tel.: (976) 1 134 2038
Textile Products Mfr
N.A.I.C.S.: 314999

MONNOYEUR SAS
117 Rue Charles-michels, 93200, Saint Denis, Cedex 1, France
Tel.: (33) 149226061   FR
Web Site: http://wwwmonnoyeur.com
Year Founded: 1906
Sales Range: $800-899.9 Million
Emp.: 6,000
Earthmoving Machines, Lift Trucks & Engines
N.A.I.C.S.: 333924
Baudouin Monnoyeur *(Pres)*

Subsidiaries:

Aprolis, SAS   (1)
6 rue Claude Nicolas Ledoux, 94046, Creteil, Cedex, France
Tel.: (33) 800 1061 26
Material Handling Equipment Rental & Sales
N.A.I.C.S.: 423830
Benjamin de Castelnau *(CEO)*

Subsidiary (Non-US):

Impact Fork Trucks Limited   (2)
Gainsborough Close, Long Eaton, Nottingham, NG10 1PX, United Kingdom
Tel.: (44) 1159 460777
Web Site: http://www.impact-handling.com
Forklift Trucks Retailer
N.A.I.C.S.: 423830
Marcus Knight *(Gen Mgr-Natl Ops)*

MONO NEXT PUBLIC COMPANY LIMITED
29/9 Moo 4 Chaiyaphruek Road, Bang Phlap Pak Kret, Nonthaburi, 11120, Thailand
Tel.: (66) 21008100
Web Site: https://www.mono.co.th
Year Founded: 2002
MONO—(THA)
Rev.: $55,329,907
Assets: $123,098,173
Liabilities: $87,270,247
Net Worth: $35,827,925
Earnings: ($7,447,978)
Emp.: 742
Fiscal Year-end: 12/31/23
Holding Company
N.A.I.C.S.: 551112
Punnee Worawuthchongsathit *(Chm)*

Subsidiaries:

PT. Mono Technology Indonesia   (1)
50th Floor Menara BCA Grand Indonesia, Jl M H Thamrin No 1, Jakarta, 10310, Indonesia

AND PRIVATE COMPANIES

Tel.: (62) 6623584512
Software Application Store Operator
N.A.I.C.S.: 449210

MONO PHARMACARE LIMITED
GF1A Krinkal Appartment Opp Mahalaxmi Temple, Paldi, Ahmedabad, 380007, Gujarat, India
Tel.: (91) 9978041356
Web Site: https://www.monopharmacare.com
Year Founded: 1994
MONOPHARMA—(NSE)
Emp.: 81
Pharmaceutical Product Mfr & Distr
N.A.I.C.S.: 325412

MONOPOLY, JSC
Dmitrovskoye Highway 100 Bldg 2, Moscow, Russia
Tel.: (7) 881230973
Web Site: https://monopoly.ru
Holding Company
N.A.I.C.S.: 551112
Ilya Dmitriev *(Chm)*

Subsidiaries:

Globaltruck Management PJSC (1)
Gilyarovsky St 39 bld 1, Moscow, 129110, Russia **(75.07%)**
Tel.: (7) 4951378888
Web Site: https://globaltruck.ru
Rev.: $118,100,051
Assets: $145,366,625
Liabilities: $76,610,794
Net Worth: $68,755,831
Earnings: $6,209,874
Fiscal Year-end: 12/31/2018
Transportation Management Services
N.A.I.C.S.: 541614
Alexander Eliseev *(Founder & Chm)*

MONORY ET FILS SA
47 Avenue Maurice Leconte, 80500, Montdidier, Somme, France
Tel.: (33) 322983399
Web Site: http://www.monory.fr
Rev.: $15,700,000
Emp.: 46
Farm Equipment Distr
N.A.I.C.S.: 423820
Dominique Monory *(Pres)*

MONRIF S.P.A.
Via Enrico Mattei 106, 40138, Bologna, Italy
Tel.: (39) 0516006111
Web Site: https://www.monrifgroup.net
MON—(ITA)
Sales Range: $400-449.9 Million
Emp.: 1,788
Publisher of Newspapers
N.A.I.C.S.: 513110

Subsidiaries:

Editrice il Giorno S.p.A. (1)
Via Stradivari 4, 20131, Milan, Italy **(100%)**
Tel.: (39) 02277991
Real Estate Property Lessors
N.A.I.C.S.: 531190

Eucera SpA (1)
Via Giuseppe di Vittorio, Assago, 20090, Milano, Italy
Tel.: (39) 02575771
Advertisement Printing Services
N.A.I.C.S.: 541890

L.M.G. S.r.l. (1)
Via Galileo Galilei 14, Nova Milanese, Italy **(100%)**
Tel.: (39) 036240738
Fabricated Metal Products Mfr
N.A.I.C.S.: 332999

Monrif Net S.r.l. (1)
Via Enrico Mattei 106, 40138, Bologna, Italy
Tel.: (39) 0516006690
Web Site: http://www.quotidiano.net

Sales Range: $25-49.9 Million
Emp.: 10
News Syndicates
N.A.I.C.S.: 516210
Casare Navarotto *(Mgr-Production)*

Poligrafici Editoriale S.p.A. (1)
Via Enrico Mattei N 106, 40138, Bologna, Italy
Tel.: (39) 0516006111
Web Site: http://www.poligraficieditoriale.it
Emp.: 450
Newspaper Publishers
N.A.I.C.S.: 513110

Subsidiary (Domestic):

Poligrafici Printing S.p.A. (2)
Via Enrico Mattei 106, 40138, Bologna, Italy
Tel.: (39) 0516006111
Web Site: https://www.poligraficiprinting.it
Sales Range: $25-49.9 Million
Printing Services
N.A.I.C.S.: 323111
Nicola Natali *(Chm)*

Poligrafici Real Estate Srl (2)
Via Enrico Mattei 106, Bologna, 40138, Italy
Tel.: (39) 0516006111
Real Estate Manangement Services
N.A.I.C.S.: 531390

SPE S.p.A (1)
Viale Milanofiori Strada 3a- Pal B-10, 20090, Assago, Italy
Tel.: (39) 02575771
Newspaper Publishers
N.A.I.C.S.: 513110

MONS BANK A/S
Storegade 29, Stege, 4780, Vordingborg, Denmark
Tel.: (45) 55861500 DK
Web Site: https://www.moensbank.dk
Year Founded: 1877
MNBA—(CSE)
Rev.: $38,325,303
Assets: $665,208,143
Liabilities: $570,030,820
Net Worth: $95,177,323
Earnings: $12,749,056
Emp.: 105
Fiscal Year-end: 12/31/23
Commericial Banking
N.A.I.C.S.: 522110
Flemming Jul Jensen *(CEO)*

MONSET LTD.
3 Burlington Rd, Dublin, Ireland
Tel.: (353) 12948300
Holding Company
N.A.I.C.S.: 551112

MONSOON PLC
Monsoon Bldg, 1 Nicholas Road, London, W11 4AN, United Kingdom
Tel.: (44) 2033723000
Web Site: http://www.monsoon.co.uk
Sales Range: $1-4.9 Billion
Emp.: 4,588
Women's, Men's, Children's Apparel, Home Furnishings & Accessories Mfr & Retailer
N.A.I.C.S.: 458110
Peter Simon *(Founder & Owner)*

Subsidiaries:

Monsoon Accessorize International Limited (1)
1 Nicholas Road, 1 Nicholas Rd, London, W11 4AN, United Kingdom
Tel.: (44) 2033723000
Web Site: http://www.monsoon.co.uk
Sales Range: $100-124.9 Million
Emp.: 500
Womens & Childrens Accessories Mfr
N.A.I.C.S.: 315250
Philip Walker *(Dir-Brand)*

Monsoon Accessorize Ireland Holdings Limited (1)
38 Grafton St, Dublin, 2, Ireland
Tel.: (353) 16717005

Sales Range: $25-49.9 Million
Emp.: 20
Womens Clothing Accessories Mfr
N.A.I.C.S.: 458110
Peter Simon *(Founder)*

Monsoon Accessorize Ireland Limited (1)
38 Grafton St, Dublin, 2, Ireland
Tel.: (353) 16717005
Sales Range: $25-49.9 Million
Emp.: 17
Womens Clothing Accessories Mfr
N.A.I.C.S.: 315250

Monsoon Accessorize Limited (1)
Monsoon Bldg, 1 Nicholas Rd, London, W11 4AN, United Kingdom
Tel.: (44) 2033723000
Web Site: http://www.monsoon.co.uk
Emp.: 600
Womens Clothing Accessories Mfr
N.A.I.C.S.: 424350
Andy Tudor *(Dir-IT)*

MONSTAR LAB, INC.
1-1-39 Hiroo, Shibuya-ku, Tokyo, 150-0012, Japan
Tel.: (81) 3 4455 7251
Web Site: http://www.monstar-lab.com
Year Founded: 2006
Mobile Application Software Development Services
N.A.I.C.S.: 541511
Hiroki Inagawa *(CEO)*

Subsidiaries:

Fuzz Productions LLC (1)
158 Roebling St, Brooklyn, NY 11211
Tel.: (212) 219-7696
Web Site: http://www.fuzzproductions.com
Sales Range: $1-9.9 Million
Emp.: 58
Mobile Application Software Development Services
N.A.I.C.S.: 541511
Nathanial Trienens *(CEO)*

MONSTARLAB HOLDINGS, INC.
Ebisu Prime Square Tower 4F 1-1-39 Hiroo, Shibuya-ku, Tokyo, 150-0012, Japan
Tel.: (81) 344557243
Web Site: https://www.monstar-lab.com
Year Founded: 2006
5255—(TKS)
Rev.: $94,623,140
Assets: $102,528,490
Liabilities: $76,252,950
Net Worth: $26,275,540
Earnings: ($16,696,950)
Fiscal Year-end: 12/31/23
Holding Company
N.A.I.C.S.: 551112
Yoshihiro Nakahara *(Deputy CEO, CFO & Exec VP)*

MONT ROYAL RESOURCES LIMITED
Level 8 2 Bligh Street, Sydney, 2000, NSW, Australia
Tel.: (61) 286517800 AU
Web Site: https://montroyalres.com
Year Founded: 2018
MRZ—(ASX)
Rev.: $17,017
Assets: $6,261,381
Liabilities: $398,966
Net Worth: $5,862,415
Earnings: ($534,871)
Fiscal Year-end: 06/30/23
Exploration & Mining Services
N.A.I.C.S.: 213115
Peter Ruse *(Exec Dir)*

MONT SAINT-SAUVEUR INTERNATIONAL, INC.

MONTAGNE ET NEIGE DEVELOPPEMENT SA

350 Ave Saint Denis, Saint-Sauveur-des-Monts, J0R 1R3, QC, Canada
Tel.: (450) 227-4671
Web Site: http://www.mssi.ca
Sales Range: $50-74.9 Million
Emp.: 1,000
Operators of Hotels & Motels
N.A.I.C.S.: 721110
Louis Dufour *(Pres)*

Subsidiaries:

Jay Peak, Inc. (1)
830 Jay Peak Rd, Jay Peak, VT 05859
Tel.: (802) 988-2611
Web Site: http://www.jaypeakresort.com
Sales Range: $75-99.9 Million
Emp.: 500
All Seasons Resort Operator
N.A.I.C.S.: 721199
Steve Wright *(Pres & Gen Mgr)*

MONTAGNE ET NEIGE DEVELOPPEMENT SA
Parc d'Activites Alpespace 74 Voie Magellan, 73800, Sainte-Helene-du-Lac, France
Tel.: (33) 479650890
Web Site: https://www.mnd.com
Year Founded: 2004
MND—(EUR)
Sales Range: $50-74.9 Million
Emp.: 264
Mountain Infrastructure Construction & Engineering
N.A.I.C.S.: 237310
Xavier Gallot-Lavallee *(Co-Founder & CEO)*

Subsidiaries:

ETS S.A.S (1)
Parc d'activites Alpespace 429 Avenue Leonard de Vinci, 73800, Sainte-Helene-du-Lac, France
Tel.: (33) 4 57 36 00 71
Web Site: http://www.ets.fr
Engineeering Services
N.A.I.C.S.: 237990
Roland Bertholet *(Mng Editor)*

MBS (1)
Z A C Porte de Tarentaise 504 Route des Marais, 73790, Tours-en-Savoie, France
Tel.: (33) 4 79 39 98 98
Web Site: http://www.mbs.fr
Emp.: 30
Event Management Services
N.A.I.C.S.: 711310
David Gromier *(Gen Mgr)*

MND Eastern Europe, s.r.o (1)
Zeleznicna 1095, 05801, Poprad, Slovakia
Tel.: (421) 52 77 21 649
Mountain Infrastructure Construction & Engineering Services
N.A.I.C.S.: 237310
Vladislav Novysedlak *(Mgr)*

MND Iberia, S.A. (1)
Pol Ind Montferrer calle Subinyes B-11 Montferrer, Lleida, 25711, Spain
Tel.: (34) 973351545
Emp.: 3
Mountain Infrastructure Construction & Engineering Services
N.A.I.C.S.: 237310
Dario Frassi *(Gen Mgr)*

MND Sverige AB (1)
Thulegatan 25 SE-852 36, Sundsvall, Vasternorrland, Sweden
Tel.: (46) 60 17 21 50
Mountain Infrastructure Construction & Engineering Services
N.A.I.C.S.: 237310

Techfun (1)
Parc d'Activites Alpespace - 201 Avenue Vasco de Gama, 73800, Sainte-Helene-du-Lac, France
Tel.: (33) 4 79 70 02 33
Web Site: http://www.tech-fun.com
Recreational Services
N.A.I.C.S.: 721214
Pierre Metayer *(Pres)*

MONTAGU PRIVATE EQUITY LLP

Montagu Private Equity LLP—(Continued)

MONTAGU PRIVATE EQUITY LLP
2 More London Riverside, London, SE1 2AP, United Kingdom
Tel.: (44) 2073369955   UK
Web Site: http://www.montagu.com
Year Founded: 1968
Privater Equity Firm
N.A.I.C.S.: 523999
Chris Masterson *(Chm)*

Subsidiaries:

Aqua Lung America, Inc.   (1)
2340 Cousteau Ct, Vista, CA 92081
Tel.: (760) 597-5000
Web Site: http://www.aqualung.com
Sport & Commercial Diving Life Support Products & Protective Breathing Systems Mfr
N.A.I.C.S.: 339920
Jonathan Souder *(Engr-Quality Assurance)*

DEAS Holding A/S   (1)
Dirch Passers Alle 76, 2000, Frederiksberg, Denmark
Tel.: (45) 7030 2020
Web Site: http://www.deas.dk
Holding Company; Property Management Services
N.A.I.C.S.: 551102
Henrik Dahl Jeppesen *(CEO & Member-Exec Bd)*

Subsidiary (Domestic):

DEAS A/S   (2)
Dirch Passers Alle 76, 2000, Frederiksberg, Denmark
Tel.: (45) 7030 2020
Web Site: http://www.deas.dk
Emp.: 450
Property Management Services
N.A.I.C.S.: 531312
Henrik Dahl Jeppesen *(CEO & Member-Exec Bd)*

Evergen   (1)
11621 Research Cir, Alachua, FL 32615
Tel.: (386) 418-8888
Web Site: https://www.rtix.com
Sales Range: $250-299.9 Million
Biological Implant Mfr
N.A.I.C.S.: 325414
Olivier Visa *(Pres & CEO)*

Subsidiary (Non-US):

Collagen Solutions Limited   (2)
3 Robroyston Oval Nova Business Park, Glasgow, G33 1AP, United Kingdom
Tel.: (44) 141 648 9100
Web Site: http://www.collagensolutions.com
Medical Grade Collagen, Tissues & Other Biomaterials Supplier, Developer & Distr
N.A.I.C.S.: 339112
Jamal David Rushdy *(CEO)*

Subsidiary (Domestic):

Cook Biotech Incorporated   (2)
1425 Innovation Pl, West Lafayette, IN 47906-1076
Tel.: (765) 497-3355
Web Site: http://www.cookbiotech.com
Sales Range: $25-49.9 Million
Emp.: 200
Medical Biomaterials Developer & Mfr
N.A.I.C.S.: 325414
Umesh Patel *(Pres)*

Subsidiary (Non-US):

Pioneer Surgical Technology B.V   (2)
Princenhof Park 10, Driebergen, 3972 NG, Netherlands
Tel.: (31) 306934720
Global Surgical Implant Product Distr
N.A.I.C.S.: 423450

Subsidiary (Domestic):

RTI Donor Services, Inc.   (2)
11621 Research Cir, Alachua, FL 32615
Tel.: (386) 418-8888
Web Site: http://www.rtidonorservices.org
Tissue Donation Organization Operator
N.A.I.C.S.: 813212

RTI Services, Inc.   (2)
12240 SW 128th Ct Unit 104, Miami, FL 33186-4781
Tel.: (305) 274-2933
Web Site: https://www.rtiservicesinc.com
Roofing Services
N.A.I.C.S.: 561710
Bob Pierce *(Co-Founder)*

Subsidiary (Non-US):

RTI Surgical-Singapore Pte Ltd   (2)
20 Science Park Road no 03 17A Teletech Park, Singapore Science Park II, Singapore, 117674, Singapore
Tel.: (65) 67169760
Biological Product Mfr
N.A.I.C.S.: 325414

Tutogen Medical GmbH   (2)
Industriestrasse 6, 91077, Neunkirchen, Germany
Tel.: (49) 913499880
Surgical Implants Mfr
N.A.I.C.S.: 339113
Stefan Puskeppelies *(Mng Dir)*

Subsidiary (Domestic):

Zyga Technology, Inc.   (2)
5600 Rowland Rd Ste 200, Minnetonka, MN 55343
Tel.: (855) 455-1061
Web Site: http://www.zyga.com
Surgical Appliance & Supplies Mfr
N.A.I.C.S.: 339113
Jim Bullock *(Pres & CEO)*

Funeral Partners Limited   (1)
Stable Block Hare Hatch Grange Bath Road, Hare Hatch, Reading, RG10 9SA, United Kingdom
Tel.: (44) 118 940 6900
Web Site: http://www.funeralpartners.co.uk
Funeral Services
N.A.I.C.S.: 812210
Phillip Greenfield *(CEO)*

Montagu Private Equity SAS   (1)
41 avenue George V, 75008, Paris, France
Tel.: (33) 1 44 95 11 80
Web Site: http://www.montaguequity.com
Privater Equity Firm
N.A.I.C.S.: 523999
Sylvain Berger-Duquene *(Mng Dir)*

Wireless Logic Group Limited   (1)
Horizon Honey Lane, Hurley, SL6 6RJ, Berks, United Kingdom
Tel.: (44) 330 056 33
Holding Company
N.A.I.C.S.: 551112
Oliver Tucker *(Founder & CEO)*

Subsidiary (Domestic):

Arkessa Limited   (2)
Riverside House Riverside, Bishop's Stortford, CM23 3AJ, United Kingdom
Tel.: (44) 1279 799270
Web Site: http://www.arkessa.com
Wireless Telecommunication Services
N.A.I.C.S.: 517112
Andrew Orrock *(CEO)*

Wireless Logic Ltd.   (2)
Horizon Honey Lane, Hurley, SL6 6RJ, Berks, United Kingdom
Tel.: (44) 330 056 3300
Web Site: http://www.wirelesslogic.com
Wireless Data Solutions
N.A.I.C.S.: 541512
Oliver Tucker *(Co-Founder & CEO)*

MONTAIGNE FASHION GROUP S.A.

3 place des Vosges, 75008, Paris, France
Tel.: (33) 144543232
Web Site: http://www.montaignefashion.com
Sales Range: $1-9.9 Million
Emp.: 20
Women's Apparel Designer & Mfr
N.A.I.C.S.: 315250
Phillipe Gelman *(Pres & CEO)*

MONTANA EXPLORATION CORP.

Suite 2300 144 4th Avenue SW, West Tower Sunlife Plaza, Calgary, T2P 3N4, AB, Canada
Tel.: (403) 265-9091   AB
Web Site:
http://www.montanaexploration.com
Year Founded: 1997
Rev.: $478,000
Assets: $5,175,053
Liabilities: $10,738,044
Net Worth: ($5,562,991)
Earnings: ($2,471,524)
Emp.: 8
Fiscal Year-end: 12/31/16
Oil & Gas Exploration
N.A.I.C.S.: 213112
Charles Vincent Selby *(Chm & CEO)*

MONTANARO EUROPEAN SMALLER COMPANIES TRUST PLC

16 Charlotte Square, Edinburgh, EH2 4DF, United Kingdom
Tel.: (44) 2074488600
Year Founded: 1981
MTE—(LSE)
Assets: $390,214,251
Liabilities: $17,909,073
Net Worth: $372,305,178
Earnings: ($28,768,698)
Fiscal Year-end: 03/31/23
Investment Management Service
N.A.I.C.S.: 523940
Richard M. Curling *(Chm)*

MONTANARO UK SMALLER COMPANIES INVESTMENT TRUST PLC

53 Threadneedle Street, London, EC2R 8AR, United Kingdom
Tel.: (44) 2074488600   UK
Web Site: https://montanaro.co.uk
Year Founded: 1994
MTU—(LSE)
Rev.: $8,011,866
Assets: $277,244,383
Liabilities: $25,941,681
Net Worth: $251,302,702
Earnings: $19,016,662
Fiscal Year-end: 03/31/24
Portfolio Management & Investment Advice
N.A.I.C.S.: 523940
Roger Cuming *(Chm)*

MONTANSTAHL AG

Via Gerrette 2 Industriezone 5 Stabio, 6855, Ticino, Switzerland
Tel.: (41) 916416800
Web Site:
https://www.montanstahl.com
Year Founded: 1983
Steel Products Mfr
N.A.I.C.S.: 331210

Subsidiaries:

Siderval S.p.A.   (1)
Via Chini Battista 60, Talamona, 23018, Sondrio, Italy
Tel.: (39) 0342674111
Web Site: http://www.siderval.it
Steel Products Mfr
N.A.I.C.S.: 331110
Ernesto Riva *(Dir-Sls)*

Subsidiary (Non-US):

Cefival S.A.   (2)
35 Rue du Docteur-Touati, BP 54, 95340, Persan, France
Tel.: (33) 1 39 37 12 27
Web Site: http://www.cefival.fr
Steel Products Mfr
N.A.I.C.S.: 331110

MONTAUK METALS INC.

82 Richmond Street East, Toronto, M5C 1P1, ON, Canada
Tel.: (416) 848-7744   NB
Web Site:
https://montaukmetalsinc.com
Year Founded: 2012
GAYGF—(OTCIQ)
Rev.: $3,539
Assets: $2,182,456
Liabilities: $174,633
Net Worth: $2,007,823
Earnings: ($1,414,309)
Fiscal Year-end: 12/31/21
Gold Mining
N.A.I.C.S.: 212220
Robert D. B. Suttie *(CFO)*

MONTAZA A.D.

Kolubarska 27, 74101, Doboj, Bosnia & Herzegovina
Tel.: (387) 65877888
MONT—(BANJ)
Sales Range: Less than $1 Million
Emp.: 1
Electrical Contracting Services
N.A.I.C.S.: 238210
Velibor Vidakovic *(Pres)*

MONTE CARLO FASHIONS LTD.

B-XXIX-106 GT Road Sherpur, Ludhiana, 141003, India
Tel.: (91) 1615048610
Web Site:
https://www.montecarlocorporate.com
538836—(BOM)
Rev.: $136,507,404
Assets: $179,416,102
Liabilities: $86,328,158
Net Worth: $93,087,944
Earnings: $15,888,736
Emp.: 1,942
Fiscal Year-end: 03/31/23
Men's & Women's Clothing Mfr
N.A.I.C.S.: 315250
Jawahar Lal Oswal *(Chm & Mng Dir)*

MONTEA NV

Industriezone III Zuid Industrielaan 27 bus 6, 9320, Erembodegem, Belgium
Tel.: (32) 53826262   NL
Web Site: https://www.montea.com
MONT—(EUR)
Rev.: $118,098,024
Assets: $2,686,757,921
Liabilities: $1,008,010,818
Net Worth: $1,678,747,103
Earnings: $131,151,341
Emp.: 23
Fiscal Year-end: 12/31/23
Real Estate Investment Holding Company
N.A.I.C.S.: 551112
Jo De Wolf *(CEO & Mng Dir)*

MONTEBALITO S.A.

Calle Maria de Molina 39, 28006, Madrid, 28006, Spain
Tel.: (34) 917816157
Web Site:
https://www.montebalito.com
Year Founded: 1972
MTB—(MAD)
Sales Range: Less than $1 Million
Real Estate Development Services
N.A.I.C.S.: 531390
Pedro Solache Guerras *(Sec)*

MONTEFIORE INVESTMENT SAS

28 rue Bayard, 75008, Paris, France
Tel.: (33) 158186870
Web Site: http://montefiore.fr
Year Founded: 2005
Rev.: $1,317,646,000
Privater Equity Firm

AND PRIVATE COMPANIES

N.A.I.C.S.: 523940
Eric Bismuth *(Founder & CEO)*

MONTEGO BAY ICE COMPANY LIMITED
2 creek street, Montego Bay, Jamaica
Tel.: (876) 952 3067
Year Founded: 1948
Rev.: $195,909
Assets: $1,369,818
Liabilities: $65,372
Net Worth: $1,304,446
Earnings: $103,001
Fiscal Year-end: 12/31/15
Storage Device Rental Services
N.A.I.C.S.: 493120

MONTEGO RESOURCES INC.
800-1199 West Hastings Street, Vancouver, V6C 2C2, BC, Canada
Tel.: (604) 283-1722 BC
Web Site: http://www.montegoresources.ca
Year Founded: 2012
Assets: $1,678,539
Liabilities: $45,310
Net Worth: $1,633,229
Earnings: ($1,412,129)
Fiscal Year-end: 06/30/17
Metal Mining
N.A.I.C.S.: 212290
David Greenway *(CEO)*

MONTEIRO ARANHA S.A.
Av Afranio de Melo Franco 290 pav L2 Sala 101-A, Rio de Janeiro, Brazil
Tel.: (55) 2125550900
Web Site: https://www.monteiroaranha.com.br
MOAR3—(BRAZ)
Rev.: $199,661,424
Assets: $522,711,950
Liabilities: $251,863,028
Net Worth: $270,848,923
Earnings: $157,126,433
Fiscal Year-end: 12/31/23
Investment Management Service
N.A.I.C.S.: 523940
Olavo Egydio Monteiro De Carvalho *(Chm)*

MONTELLO RESOURCES LTD.
836 5th Avenue SW Suite 1206, Calgary, T2P 2L8, AB, Canada
Tel.: (604) 921-1202
Year Founded: 1996
MLORF—(OTCIQ)
Sales Range: Less than $1 Million
Petroleum Product Mfr
N.A.I.C.S.: 324110
William Cawker *(Chm & CEO)*

MONTENEGRIN TELEKOM A.D.
Moskovska 29, 81000, Podgorica, Montenegro
Tel.: (382) 20 433 433
Web Site: http://www.telekom.me
Sales Range: $75-99.9 Million
Emp.: 1,348
Mobile & Communications Services
N.A.I.C.S.: 517111
Ruediger Schulz *(CEO)*

MONTEREY MINERALS, INC.
401 Bay Street Suite 2702, Toronto, M5H 2Y4, ON, Canada
Tel.: (416) 862-7003
Web Site: http://www.montereyminerals.com
Year Founded: 2014
Mineral Exploration Services
N.A.I.C.S.: 212290
James Macintosh *(Pres & CEO)*

MONTERO MINING AND EXPLORATION LTD.
Tel.: (416) 840-9197 BC
Web Site: https://www.monteromining.com
Year Founded: 2006
MXTRF—(OTCIQ)
Assets: $651,449
Liabilities: $1,225,627
Net Worth: ($574,178)
Earnings: ($452,729)
Fiscal Year-end: 12/31/23
Phosphate & Uranium Exploration Services
N.A.I.C.S.: 212390
Sheri Rempel *(CFO)*

MONTERRO INVESTMENT AB
Nybrogatan 17, Stockholm, 114 39, Sweden
Tel.: (46) 8 20 05 56
Web Site: http://www.monterro.com
Privater Equity Firm
N.A.I.C.S.: 523999
Gustav Lagercrantz *(CEO)*

Subsidiaries:

Umbraco A/S (1)
Lindholm havnevej 31, DK-5800, Nyborg, Denmark
Tel.: (45) 39 27 91 11
Web Site: http://www.umbraco.com
Sales Range: $50-74.9 Million
Emp.: 300
Web Content Management Systems
N.A.I.C.S.: 541519
Niels Hartvig *(Founder)*

MONTFORT CAPITAL CORPORATION
181 Bay Street Bay Wellington Tower Suite 2920, Toronto, M5J 2T3, ON, Canada
Tel.: (604) 398-8839
Web Site: https://montfortcapital.com
Year Founded: 1937
MONTF—(OTCIQ)
Rev.: $7,609,748
Assets: $97,847,558
Liabilities: $87,578,364
Net Worth: $10,269,195
Earnings: $1,910,094
Fiscal Year-end: 12/31/21
Financial Investment Services
N.A.I.C.S.: 523999
Michael Walkinshaw *(CEO)*

MONTFORT GROUP
Rue du Mont-Blanc 14, 1201, Geneva, Switzerland
Tel.: (41) 227415900
Web Site: https://mont-fort.com
Asset Management Services
N.A.I.C.S.: 523999

Subsidiaries:

Uniper Energy DMCC (1)
Dubai World Trade Centre Level 22, Dubai, United Arab Emirates
Tel.: (971) 43295467
Web Site: http://www.uniper.energy
Marine Fuel Oil Distr
N.A.I.C.S.: 457210

MONTGERON DIS SAS
72 Avenue Jean Jaures, 91230, Montgeron, Essonne, France
Tel.: (33) 169834800 FR
Sales Range: $25-49.9 Million
Emp.: 108
Supermarkets Owner & Operator
N.A.I.C.S.: 445110
Gilles Marteau *(Mng Dir)*

MONTGOMERY TOMLINSON LTD
Broughton Mills Road, Bretton, Chester, CH4 0BY, United Kingdom
Tel.: (44) 1244661363
Web Site: http://www.montgomery.co.uk
Rev.: $41,451,003
Emp.: 740
Furniture Mfr
N.A.I.C.S.: 326150
Grahame M. Tomlinson *(Mng Dir)*

MONTICIANO PARTICIPACOES S.A.
R Pamplona 818 - Cjto 92, 1405001, Sao Paulo, Brazil
Tel.: (55) 11 3556 5505
Web Site: http://www.monticianopar.com.br
Year Founded: 2007
Dairy Product Mfr & Distr
N.A.I.C.S.: 311511
Rubens Mario Marques de Freitas *(Dir-IR)*

MONTING D.D./PLC
Kestercanekova 1, Zagreb, 1000, Croatia
Tel.: (385) 12356100
Web Site: http://www.monting.hr
Year Founded: 1951
Sales Range: $125-149.9 Million
Emp.: 600
Engineering, Fabrication & Construction
N.A.I.C.S.: 541330
Goran Brletic *(Gen Mgr)*

MONTINVEST A.D.
Cernisevskog 2a, Belgrade, Serbia
Tel.: (381) 11 3081 302 RS
Web Site: http://www.montinvest.rs
Year Founded: 1961
Construction Services
N.A.I.C.S.: 236210
Aleksandar Cvetkovic *(Gen Mgr)*

MONTLUCON VIANDES SAS
21 Rue Benoist D Azy, 03100, Montlucon, Allier, France
Tel.: (33) 470295202
Rev.: $24,200,000
Emp.: 55
Meats Processor
N.A.I.C.S.: 311611
Daniel Cherpozat *(Dir-Sls)*

MONTNETS CLOUD TECHNOLOGY GROUP CO., LTD.
Longtaili Building No 30 Gaoxin Middle 4th Road, Science and Technology Park Nanshan District, Shenzhen, 114051, Liaoning, China
Tel.: (86) 4009002123
Web Site: https://www.montnets.com
Year Founded: 1997
002123—(SSE)
Rev.: $583,704,576
Assets: $882,522,108
Liabilities: $401,664,744
Net Worth: $480,857,364
Earnings: ($101,378,628)
Emp.: 1,500
Fiscal Year-end: 12/31/22
Electric Equipment Mfr
N.A.I.C.S.: 334515
Junji Chun Li *(CFO & VP)*

MONTPELLIER EVENTS
Esplanade Charles De Gaulle, BP 2200, 34000, Montpellier, Herault, France
Tel.: (33) 467616761
Web Site: http://www.montpellier-events.com
Event Management Services
N.A.I.C.S.: 711310
Patricia Martinez *(Fin Dir)*

MONUMENT MINING LIMITED

MONTREAL PORT AUTHORITY
2100 Pierre-Dupuy Ave wing 1, Montreal, H3C 3R5, QC, Canada
Tel.: (514) 283-7011
Web Site: http://www.port-montreal.com
Sales Range: $50-74.9 Million
Emp.: 350
Port Operations
N.A.I.C.S.: 488310
Martin Imbleau *(Pres & CEO)*

MONTRUSCO BOLTON INC.
1501 McGill College Avenue Suite 1200, Montreal, H3A 3M8, QC, Canada
Tel.: (514) 842-6464 Ca
Web Site: http://www.montruscobolton.com
Year Founded: 1984
Sales Range: $75-99.9 Million
Emp.: 45
Holding Company; Investment Management Services
N.A.I.C.S.: 551112
David McAusland *(Chm)*

Subsidiaries:

Montrusco Bolton Investments Inc. (1)
1501 McGill College Avenue Suite 1200, Montreal, H3A 3M8, QC, Canada (100%)
Tel.: (514) 842-6464
Web Site: https://www.montruscobolton.com
Sales Range: $75-99.9 Million
Emp.: 36
Investment Management Service
N.A.I.C.S.: 523940

Joint Venture (Domestic):

Louisbourg Investments Inc. (2)
1000-770 Main Street, Moncton, E1C 1E7, NB, Canada
Tel.: (506) 853-5410
Web Site: https://www.louisbourginvestments.com
Rev.: $876,319,710
Emp.: 12
Pension Fund Endowment & Private Wealth Portfolio Management Services
N.A.I.C.S.: 523940
Luc Gaudet *(CEO)*

Branch (Domestic):

Montrusco Bolton Investments (2)
130 King Street West Suite 1950, Suite 5600, Toronto, M5X 1E3, ON, Canada
Tel.: (416) 860-1257
Web Site: http://www.montruscobolton.com
Investment Management Service
N.A.I.C.S.: 523940

Montrusco Bolton Investments (2)
1501 McGill College Avenue Suite 1200, Montreal, H3A 3M8, QC, Canada
Tel.: (514) 842-6464
Web Site: http://www.montruscobolton.com
Sales Range: $50-74.9 Million
Emp.: 36
Investment Management Service
N.A.I.C.S.: 523940

MONTSERRAT UTILITIES LIMITED
c/o Montserrat Water Authority, PO Box 324, Davy Hill, Montserrat
Tel.: (664) 4912538 Ms
Web Site: https://www.mul.ms
Sales Range: $25-49.9 Million
Emp.: 67
Electricity & Water Supply Services
N.A.I.C.S.: 221122

MONUMENT MINING LIMITED
Suite 1580 - 1100 Melville Street, Vancouver, V6E 4A6, BC, Canada
Tel.: (604) 638-1661
Web Site: https://www.monumentmining.com

MONUMENT MINING LIMITED

Monument Mining Limited—(Continued)
Year Founded: 1997
D7Q1—(DEU)
Rev.: $14,440,000
Assets: $134,025,000
Liabilities: $13,589,000
Net Worth: $120,436,000
Earnings: ($6,497,000)
Emp.: 200
Fiscal Year-end: 06/30/22
Gold Exploration Services
N.A.I.C.S.: 212220
Graham C. Dickson *(Chm)*

MONUMENTAL MINERALS CORPORATION
228 1122 Mainland Street, Vancouver, V6B 5L1, BC, Canada
Tel.: (604) 681-8835 BC
Web Site: https://www.monumental.com
Year Founded: 2020
MNMRF—(OTCQB)
Assets: $4,742,326
Liabilities: $91,748
Net Worth: $4,650,577
Earnings: ($1,820,290)
Fiscal Year-end: 09/30/22
Mineral Mining Services
N.A.I.C.S.: 213115
Jamil Sader *(CEO)*

MONUMENTAL RESIDENCE SICAFI SA
Parque das Technologias Edificio 1, Tagus Park Avenida Professor Doutor Cavaco Silva, PT-2740-256, Porto Salvo, Portugal
Tel.: (351) 21113161
MLMR—(EUR)
Sales Range: Less than $1 Million
Real Estate Investment Services
N.A.I.C.S.: 531210
Tiago Filipe Viana Abrantes da Silva *(Head-Investor Relations & Dir-IR)*

MOO PRINT LIMITED
32-38 Scrutton Street, London, EC2A 4RQ, United Kingdom
Tel.: (44) 207 392 2780
Web Site: http://uk.moo.com
Year Founded: 2004
Sales Range: $25-49.9 Million
Emp.: 107
Card Printing Service
N.A.I.C.S.: 323111
Richard Moross *(Founder & CEO)*

MOODY TECHNOLOGY HOLDINGS LIMITED
20/F Infinitus Plaza 199 Des Voeux Road, Sheung wan, Central, China (Hong Kong)
Tel.: (852) 85225280669
Web Site: http://www.moodytech-holdingltd.com
1400—(HKG)
Rev.: $12,712,378
Assets: $34,139,383
Liabilities: $199,156,417
Net Worth: ($165,017,034)
Earnings: ($19,725,919)
Emp.: 167
Fiscal Year-end: 12/31/22
Holding Company; Fabrics & Yarns Mfr
N.A.I.C.S.: 551112
Lin Qingxiong *(Exec Dir)*

MOODY'S EQUIPMENT
Hwy 16 & 71st Street, PO Box 7, Saskatoon, S7K 3K1, SK, Canada
Tel.: (306) 934-4686

Web Site: http://www.moodysequipment.com
Rev.: $20,866,788
Emp.: 75
Lawn & Garden Equipment
N.A.I.C.S.: 333112
Shaun Kratchmer *(Mgr-Parts-Unity)*

MOOLEC SCIENCE SA
17 Boulevard F W Raiffeisen, 2411, Luxembourg, Luxembourg
Tel.: (352) 26496565 LU
Web Site: https://www.moolecscience.com
Year Founded: 2022
MLEC—(NASDAQ)
Food Products Mfr
N.A.I.C.S.: 311999
Gaston Paladini *(Co-Founder & CEO)*

Subsidiaries:

LightJump Acquisition Corporation (1)
2735 Sand Hill Road Ste 110, Menlo Park, CA 94025
Tel.: (650) 515-3930
Investment Services
N.A.I.C.S.: 523999

MOON ENVIRONMENT TECHNOLOGY CO., LTD.
No 1 Binglun Road, Yantai, 264000, Shandong, China
Tel.: (86) 5356697172
Web Site: https://www.moon-tech.com
Year Founded: 1956
000811—(SSE)
Rev.: $856,674,468
Assets: $1,529,259,264
Liabilities: $787,416,552
Net Worth: $741,842,712
Earnings: $59,785,128
Fiscal Year-end: 12/31/22
Refrigerator Equipment Mfr
N.A.I.C.S.: 333415
Zengqun Li *(Chm)*

Subsidiaries:

Beijing Huayuan Taimeng Energy-Saving Equipment Co., Ltd. (1)
Tel.: (86) 1062701509
Web Site: http://www.powerbeijinghytm.com
Absorption Heat Element Mfr
N.A.I.C.S.: 333415

LSBL Commercial Architectural Design Co., Ltd. (1)
12th Floor Building 1 Longao Jin Building No 8000 Jingshi Road, High-tech Zone, Jinan, China
Tel.: (86) 53188875937
Construction Services
N.A.I.C.S.: 236220

Shandong Lushang Moon Architecture Design Co., Ltd. (1)
12th Floor Building 1 Longaojin Building No 8000 Jingshi Road, High tech Zone, Jinan, China
Tel.: (86) 53188875937
Web Site: http://www.sdlsbl.com
Construction Services
N.A.I.C.S.: 236220

Shandong Shenzhou Refrigeration Equipment Co., Ltd. (1)
Tel.: (86) 53188829276
Web Site: http://www.sz1989.com
Absorption Heat Element Mfr
N.A.I.C.S.: 333415

Yantai Hyundai Heavy Industries Co., Ltd. (1)
No 333 Changjiang Road Yantai etda, Shandong, 264006, China
Tel.: (86) 5352165869
Web Site: http://www.yhhi.com.cn
Industrial Products Mfr
N.A.I.C.S.: 333248

Yantai Moon Heat Exchange Technology Co., Ltd. (1)
331 Changjiang Road Economic and Technological Development Zone, Yantai, Shandong, China
Tel.: (86) 5356960811
Web Site: http://www.blhrjs.com
Air Cooler Mfr
N.A.I.C.S.: 333415

Yantai Moon Heavy Casting Machinery Co., Ltd. (1)
No 50 Shanghai Avenue, Yantai Economic and Technology Development District, Yantai, 264006, China
Tel.: (86) 5356951015
Web Site: https://en.moonheavycasting.com
Machine Tool Casting Product Mfr
N.A.I.C.S.: 333517

MOON RIVER MOLY LTD.
100 King Street West Suite 7010, PO Box 70, Toronto, M5X 1B1, ON, Canada
Tel.: (416) 800-1753
Web Site: https://moonrivermoly.com
MOO—(TSXV)
Rev.: $17,953
Assets: $1,712,133
Liabilities: $208,645
Net Worth: $1,503,489
Earnings: ($3,047,633)
Fiscal Year-end: 12/31/23
Asset Management Services
N.A.I.C.S.: 523940
Jamie Levy *(CFO)*

Subsidiaries:

Sojitz Moly Resources, Inc. (1)
Suite 255 555 Burrard St, Vancouver, v7x 1m7, BC, Canada
Tel.: (604) 684-8351
Sales Range: $50-74.9 Million
Emp.: 2
Financial Investment Services
N.A.I.C.S.: 523999
Mitsuru Ishikawa *(Gen Mgr)*

MOONBAE STEEL CO., LTD.
Hwamin B/D 35 Dongjak-daero, Dongjak-gu, Seoul, 100-161, Korea (South)
Tel.: (82) 27586600
Web Site: https://www.moonbaesteel.co.kr
Year Founded: 1973
008420—(KRS)
Rev.: $147,422,562
Assets: $158,697,560
Liabilities: $29,923,301
Net Worth: $128,774,259
Earnings: $20,108,614
Emp.: 70
Fiscal Year-end: 12/31/22
Steel Product Mfr & Whslr
N.A.I.C.S.: 331221
Chong-Min Bae *(Chm & CEO)*

MOONBAT CO., LTD.
493 Torihokocho Muromachi-dori Shijo Minamiiru, Shimogyo-ku, Kyoto, 600-8491, Japan
Tel.: (81) 753610381
Web Site: https://www.moonbat.co.jp
Year Founded: 1941
8115—(TKS)
Rev.: $70,132,100
Assets: $65,280,360
Liabilities: $31,866,810
Net Worth: $33,413,550
Earnings: $3,602,450
Emp.: 175
Fiscal Year-end: 03/31/24
Plastic Product Mfr & Distr
N.A.I.C.S.: 326199
Takashi Kamata *(Pres & CEO)*

MOONBOUND MINING LTD.

INTERNATIONAL PUBLIC

Suite 600-1090 West Georgia Street, Vancouver, V6E 3V7, BC, Canada
Tel.: (604) 375-5578
Web Site: https://www.mmlmining.ca
Year Founded: 2021
MML—(CNSX)
Assets: $21,818,157
Liabilities: $1,973,012
Net Worth: $19,845,145
Earnings: ($976,080)
Fiscal Year-end: 04/30/24
Mineral Exploration Services
N.A.I.C.S.: 212390
Ann Fehr *(CEO)*

MOONG PATTANA INTERNATIONAL PUBLIC COMPANY LIMITED
No 2/97-104 18-19 Floor Bangna Complex Office Tower Soi Bangna-Trad 25, Bangnanuea Bangna, Bangkok, 10260, Thailand
Tel.: (66) 20208999
Web Site: https://www.moongpattana.com
MOONG—(THA)
Rev.: $23,667,724
Assets: $39,055,240
Liabilities: $7,935,916
Net Worth: $31,119,325
Earnings: $1,181,839
Emp.: 140
Fiscal Year-end: 12/31/23
Consumer Goods Wholesale Distr
N.A.I.C.S.: 425120
Sumeth Lersumitkul *(Chm)*

MOONGIPA CAPITAL FINANCE LIMITED
18/14 W E A Pusa Lane, Karol Bagh, New Delhi, 110 005, India
Tel.: (91) 1141450121
Web Site: https://www.mongipa.com
530167—(BOM)
Rev.: $237,704
Assets: $580,122
Liabilities: $21,256
Net Worth: $558,866
Earnings: ($182,263)
Emp.: 8
Fiscal Year-end: 03/31/23
Financial Services
N.A.I.C.S.: 523999
Pooja Jain *(Exec Dir)*

MOONPIG GROUP PLC
Herbal House 10 Back Hill, London, EC1R 5EN, United Kingdom UK
Web Site: https://www.moonpig.group
Year Founded: 2000
MOON—(LSE)
Rev.: $413,199,001
Assets: $235,617,371
Liabilities: $329,733,164
Net Worth: ($94,115,793)
Earnings: $42,685,359
Emp.: 447
Fiscal Year-end: 04/30/22
Gift, Novelty & Souvenir Retailers
N.A.I.C.S.: 459420
Kate Swann *(Chm)*

Subsidiaries:

Greetz B.V. (1)
Herikerbergweg 1-35, 1101 CN, Amsterdam, Netherlands
Tel.: (31) 205606581
Web Site: https://www.greetz.nl
Greeting Cards Distr
N.A.I.C.S.: 459420

MOOREAST HOLDINGS LTD.
51 Shipyard Road, Singapore, 628139, Singapore
Tel.: (65) 65428001 SG
Web Site: https://www.mooreast.com

Year Founded: 2021
1V3—(CAT)
Rev.: $21,741,804
Assets: $54,409,658
Liabilities: $38,232,240
Net Worth: $16,177,417
Earnings: ($1,399,056)
Emp.: 96
Fiscal Year-end: 12/31/23
Holding Company
N.A.I.C.S.: 551112

Subsidiaries:

Mooreast Asia Pte. Ltd. (1)
51 Shipyard Road, Singapore, 628139, Singapore
Tel.: (65) 65428001
Renewable Energy Consulting Services
N.A.I.C.S.: 541690

Mooreast Europe B.V. (1)
PO Box 81, 2900 AB, Capelle aan den IJssel, Netherlands
Tel.: (31) 626443148
Renewable Energy Consulting Services
N.A.I.C.S.: 541690

MOORIM P&P CO., LTD.
3-36 Ubong-gil, Ulju-gun, Ulsan, Korea (South)
Tel.: (82) 522317000
Web Site:
http://www.moorimpnp.co.kr
Year Founded: 1974
009580—(KRS)
Rev.: $593,737,462
Assets: $1,230,312,335
Liabilities: $722,029,733
Net Worth: $508,282,602
Earnings: $34,467,485
Emp.: 701
Fiscal Year-end: 12/31/22
Paper Pulp Products Mfr & Sales
N.A.I.C.S.: 322299
Do-kyun Lee *(Board of Directors & CEO)*

MOORIM PAPER CO., LTD.
1003 Namgang-ro, Gangnam-Gu, Jinju, Gyeongsangnam-do, Korea (South)
Tel.: (82) 234851651
Web Site: https://www.moorim.co.kr
Year Founded: 1956
009200—(KRS)
Rev.: $1,073,139,818
Assets: $1,863,145,583
Liabilities: $1,334,370,469
Net Worth: $528,775,114
Earnings: $26,660,223
Emp.: 432
Fiscal Year-end: 12/31/22
Printing & Writing Paper Mfr
N.A.I.C.S.: 322220
Dong-Wook Lee *(Chm)*

MOORIM SP CO., LTD.
505 Shinsa-dong, Gangnam-gu, Seoul, 135-887, Korea (South)
Tel.: (82) 234851603
Web Site: http://www.moorim.co.kr
Year Founded: 1956
001810—(KRS)
Rev.: $117,700,063
Assets: $239,912,329
Liabilities: $80,389,977
Net Worth: $159,522,352
Earnings: ($6,652,691)
Emp.: 209
Fiscal Year-end: 12/31/22
Paper Products Mfr
N.A.I.C.S.: 322299
Dong-wook Lee *(Chm)*

Subsidiaries:

Moorim Capital Co., Ltd. (1)
17th floor Building D-1 D Tower Cheongjin-dong 17 Jongno 3-gil, Jongno- gu, Seoul, Korea (South)
Tel.: (82) 237098800
Web Site: https://moorimcapital.co.kr
Financial Loan Services
N.A.I.C.S.: 522291

Moorim Chemtech Co., Ltd. (1)
14 Baekbeom-ro 934 beon-gil, Seo-gu, Incheon, Korea (South)
Tel.: (82) 325718080
Web Site: https://pixelncolor.com
Printing Paper Product Mfr
N.A.I.C.S.: 322230

Moorim Logitech Co., Ltd. (1)
315 Suyang-ri, Gongjiam-eup, Gwangju, Geonggi-do, Korea (South)
Tel.: (82) 317692223
Office Supply Leasing Services
N.A.I.C.S.: 532420

Moorim Powertech Co., Ltd. (1)
41-6 Sangdae-dong 24 Namgang-ro 1317beon-gil, Jinju, Gyeongsangnam-do, Korea (South)
Tel.: (82) 557601100
Web Site:
https://www.moorimpowertech.co.kr
Emp.: 42
Solar Power Installation Services
N.A.I.C.S.: 238210

MOOSEHEAD BREWERIES LIMITED
89 Main Street West, Saint John, E2M 3H2, NB, Canada
Tel.: (506) 635-7000
Web Site: http://www.moosehead.ca
Year Founded: 1867
Sales Range: $150-199.9 Million
Emp.: 310
Beer Mfr & Distr
N.A.I.C.S.: 312120
Andrew Oland *(Pres & CEO)*

Subsidiaries:

The Premium Beer Company (1)
275 Belfield Road, Etobicoke, M9W 7H9, ON, Canada
Tel.: (905) 855-7743
Web Site: http://www.premiumbeer.ca
Emp.: 40
Beverage Whslr
N.A.I.C.S.: 424810
Brendan Jones *(Mgr-District Sls)*

MOOTER MEDIA LIMITED
Office 4 Tennyson St, PO Box 5159, Williamstown, 3016, VIC, Australia
Tel.: (61) 393913220
Web Site:
http://www.mootermedia.com
Sales Range: Less than $1 Million
Computer Technology To Web User
N.A.I.C.S.: 541511
Christopher Geoffrey Jermyn *(Sec)*

MOOVLY MEDIA INC.
1558 West Hastings Street, Vancouver, V6G 3J4, BC, Canada
Tel.: (604) 639-4450   BC
Web Site: https://www.moovly.com
Year Founded: 2006
MVY—(OTCIQ)
Rev.: $1,149,848
Assets: $574,050
Liabilities: $4,709,257
Net Worth: ($4,135,207)
Earnings: ($1,340,258)
Fiscal Year-end: 09/30/20
Computer Services
N.A.I.C.S.: 541519
Kelsey Chin *(CFO)*

MOPOLI - PALMBOOMEN CULTUUR MAATSCHAPPIJ NV
10 Koningin Julianaplein, 2595 AA, Hague, Netherlands
Tel.: (31) 35248800
MOP—(EUR)
Rev.: $1,489,907
Assets: $61,319,194
Liabilities: $337,741
Net Worth: $60,981,453
Earnings: $832,595
Fiscal Year-end: 06/30/23
Holding Company
N.A.I.C.S.: 551112

MORABAHA MARINA FINANCING COMPANY
Al Faisaliah office Tower 14 th Floor King fahad Road, PO Box 2732, Al Rabie District, Riyadh, 11461, Saudi Arabia
Tel.: (966) 8001111810
Web Site: https://www.mrna.sa
Year Founded: 2012
4082—(SAU)
Rev.: $45,471,611
Assets: $326,261,668
Liabilities: $174,435,785
Net Worth: $151,825,883
Earnings: $11,991,835
Emp.: 178
Fiscal Year-end: 12/31/22
Investment Management Service
N.A.I.C.S.: 523999
Abdulrahman Alghimlas *(CEO)*

MORABANC GROUP
Avinguda Meritxell 96, AD 500, Andorra La Vella, Andorra
Tel.: (376) 884205
Web Site: http://www.morabanc.ad
Year Founded: 1952
Emp.: 377
Investment Banking Services
N.A.I.C.S.: 523150
Marc Vilallonga Puy *(Sec)*

Subsidiaries:

Mora Assegurances, SAU (1)
Placa Copriinceps 2, Escaldes-Engordany, Andorra
Tel.: (376) 884874
General Insurance Services
N.A.I.C.S.: 524210

Mora Banc, SAU (1)
Av Sant Antoni 21 Edifici Claperes, La Massana, Andorra
Tel.: (376) 884805
Finance & Banking Services
N.A.I.C.S.: 522110
Jordi Mora Magrina *(Chm)*

Mora Gestio d'Actius, SAU (1)
Carrer de l'Aigueta 3, Andorra La Vella, Andorra
Tel.: (376) 884898
Investment Fund Management Services
N.A.I.C.S.: 523940

Mora Wealth Management AG (1)
Talacker 42, Zurich, 8022, Switzerland
Tel.: (41) 44 256 8050
Web Site: http://www.morawealth.com
Investment Banking & Advisory Services
N.A.I.C.S.: 523150
Ignacio Baigorri *(CEO)*

Subsidiary (US):

Mora Wealth Management LLC (2)
1450 Brickell Ave Ste 2900, Miami, FL 33131
Tel.: (305) 459-5400
Web Site: http://www.morawealth.com
Investment Banking & Advisory Services
N.A.I.C.S.: 523150
Eli Butnaru *(CEO)*

Mora Wealth Management, SA (1)
Luis A de Herrera 1248 Torre 3 oficina 1676, Montevideo, Uruguay
Tel.: (598) 26280693
Wealth Management Services
N.A.I.C.S.: 522180

MORAFCO INDUSTRIES LIMITED
Rakh Canal East Road Behind Govt College of Commerce, Faisalabad, Pakistan
Tel.: (92) 41 8540179
Cooking Oil Mfr
N.A.I.C.S.: 311224

MORARIT PANIFICATIE SA
Str Magurei 3, Neamt, Roman, Romania
Tel.: (40) 233741954
Web Site:
http://www.panificatieroman.ro
Year Founded: 1950
MORA—(BUC)
Rev.: $3,910,959
Assets: $1,779,279
Liabilities: $713,867
Net Worth: $1,065,412
Earnings: $58,328
Emp.: 90
Fiscal Year-end: 12/31/23
Grain Mill Product Mfr
N.A.I.C.S.: 311211

MORARKA FINANCE LIMITED
511 Maker Chambers V 221 Nariman Point, Mumbai, 400021, India
Tel.: (91) 2222832468
Web Site:
https://www.morarkafinance.in
511549—(BOM)
Rev.: $611,861
Assets: $36,834,634
Liabilities: $71,280
Net Worth: $36,763,354
Earnings: $503,999
Emp.: 9
Fiscal Year-end: 03/31/22
Financial Services
N.A.I.C.S.: 523999
Gautam R. Morarka *(Chm)*

MORAVA A.D.
Kneza Milosa 56, 12374, Zabari, Serbia
Tel.: (381) 12250122
Web Site:
http://www.moravazabari.co.rs
Year Founded: 1992
MRZB—(BEL)
Sales Range: Less than $1 Million
Supermarket Operator
N.A.I.C.S.: 445110
Radisa Trailovic *(Exec Dir & Dir)*

MORAVA A.D.
Dure Dakovica, 12000, Pozarevac, Serbia
Tel.: (381) 12523580
Web Site: https://www.fmmorava.com
Year Founded: 1946
Sales Range: Less than $1 Million
Agricultural Machinery Mfr
N.A.I.C.S.: 333111

MORAVAMERMER A.D.
Gospodara Vucica 225, Belgrade, Serbia
Tel.: (381) 11 2412 079
Web Site:
http://www.moravamermer.com
Year Founded: 1947
Sales Range: Less than $1 Million
Emp.: 5
Stone Product Mfr
N.A.I.C.S.: 327991

MORDECHAI AVIV TAASIOT BENIYAH (1973) LTD.
40 Agrippa Street, PO Box 28281, Jerusalem, Israel
Tel.: (972) 26214444
Web Site: https://www.maviv.co.il
Year Founded: 1973

MORDECHAI AVIV TAASIOT BENIYAH (1973) LTD.

Mordechai Aviv Taasiot Beniyah (1973) Ltd.—(Continued)
AVIV—(TAE)
Rev.: $76,992,954
Assets: $269,606,848
Liabilities: $177,364,274
Net Worth: $92,242,574
Earnings: $6,405,304
Emp.: 421
Fiscal Year-end: 12/31/23
New Multifamily Housing Construction (except For-Sale Builders)
N.A.I.C.S.: 236116
Asaf Aviv (CEO)

MORDOVSKAYA ENERGOSBYT COMP
Bolshevistskaya St 117A, Saransk, 430001, Russia
Tel.: (7) 8342234800
Web Site: https://www.mesk.ru
Year Founded: 2005
MRSB—(MOEX)
Sales Range: Less than $1 Million
Electric Power Distribution Services
N.A.I.C.S.: 221122
Lyalkin Vitaly Aleksandrovich (Gen Dir)

MORE ALLIANCE NORDIC AB
Kaserntorget 6, Inom Vallgraven, Gothenburg, 411 18, Sweden
Tel.: (46) 706650649
Web Site: http://morealliance.se
Year Founded: 2006
Marketing & Advertising Services
N.A.I.C.S.: 541613
Johanna Hellmer Wiberg (CEO & Project Mgr)

MORE INVESTMENT HOUSE LTD.
Bsr Tower 1 2 Ben Gurion Rd, Ramat Gan, 5257334, Israel
Tel.: (972) 37554949
Web Site: http://www.moreinvest.co.il
Year Founded: 2006
MRIN—(TAE)
Sales Range: Less than $1 Million
Investment Management Service
N.A.I.C.S.: 523940
Yossi Levi (Founder & Co-CEO)

MORE RETURN PUBLIC COMPANY LIMITED
222/148-150 Baan Suan Chatuchak Condominium Soi Vibhavadi Rangsit 17, Vibhavadi Rangsit Road Chatuchak Sub-district Chatuchak District, Bangkok, 10900, Thailand
Tel.: (66) 21206804
Web Site: http://www.dna2002.com
MORE—(THA)
Rev.: $2,601,064
Assets: $43,374,509
Liabilities: $2,923,267
Net Worth: $40,451,242
Earnings: ($6,665,771)
Emp.: 247
Fiscal Year-end: 12/31/23
DVDs, CDs & Games Retailer
N.A.I.C.S.: 459999

MOREFILED GROUP N.V.
Schouwburgweg 5, 4797, Willemstad, Curacao, Netherlands
Tel.: (31) 235685630
Web Site: https://www.morefieldgroup.nl
Year Founded: 1999
MORE—(EUR)
Assets: $51,514
Liabilities: $44,794
Net Worth: $6,719
Earnings: ($83,989)
Fiscal Year-end: 12/31/19

Holding Company
N.A.I.C.S.: 551112
Frank Lagerveld (Chm-Supervisory Bd)

MORELLA CORPORATION LIMITED
Suite 5 680 Murray Street, West Perth, 6005, WA, Australia
Tel.: (61) 894885100 AU
Web Site: https://www.morellacorp.com
Year Founded: 2001
1MC—(ASX)
Rev.: $351,362
Assets: $8,594,231
Liabilities: $3,095,639
Net Worth: $5,498,592
Earnings: ($2,003,190)
Fiscal Year-end: 06/30/24
Mining Services
N.A.I.C.S.: 213113
James Brown (Mng Dir)

MORELLI GROUP LIMITED
Unit 2 Baird Road, Enfield, EN1 1SJ, Middlesex, United Kingdom
Tel.: (44) 20 8351 5151
Web Site: http://www.morelli.co.uk
Year Founded: 1957
Sales Range: $50-74.9 Million
Emp.: 208
Paint Whslr
N.A.I.C.S.: 424990

Subsidiaries:

Smart Express Ltd. (1)
B4 Mountbatten Business Park Jackson Close, Drayton, Portsmouth, PO6 1US, Hampshire, United Kingdom
Tel.: (44) 2392205160
Web Site: http://www.smartexpress.co.uk
Printing Equipment Distr
N.A.I.C.S.: 423830

MOREPEN LABORATORIES LIMITED
2nd Floor Tower C DLF Cyber Park Udyog Vihar Sector-20, Gurgaon, 122016, India
Tel.: (91) 1244892000
Web Site: https://www.morepen.com
Year Founded: 1956
500288—(BOM)
Rev.: $163,817,103
Assets: $117,136,929
Liabilities: $59,221,276
Net Worth: $57,915,653
Earnings: $13,252,785
Emp.: 1,510
Fiscal Year-end: 03/31/21
Pharmaceuticals Product Mfr
N.A.I.C.S.: 325412
Sushil Suri (Chm & Mng Dir)

MORESCO CORPORATION
5-5-3 Minatojimaminamimachi, Chuo-ku, Kobe, 6500047, Hyogo, Japan
Tel.: (81) 783039010
Web Site: https://www.moresco.co.jp
Year Founded: 1958
5018—(TKS)
Rev.: $226,071,740
Assets: $262,705,770
Liabilities: $98,770,790
Net Worth: $163,934,980
Earnings: $9,096,470
Emp.: 821
Fiscal Year-end: 02/29/24
Oil Research & Development Services
N.A.I.C.S.: 324191
Tamio Akada (Chm & CEO)

Subsidiaries:

Ethylene Chemical Co., Ltd. (1)
12-28 Goiminamikaigan, Ichihara, 290-

0045, Chiba, Japan (60.9%)
Tel.: (81) 436221255
Web Site: https://www.ethy-chemi.co.jp
Emp.: 47
Automotive Chemical Products Mfr & Distr
N.A.I.C.S.: 811191
Shinya Watanabe (Pres)

MATSUKEN Co., Ltd. (1)
MORESCO Hommachi Bldg.6F 3-2-15 Bingo-machi, Chuo-ku, Osaka, 541-0051, Japan (100%)
Tel.: (81) 662624831
Web Site: http://matsuken-moresco.co.jp
Chemicals Mfr
N.A.I.C.S.: 325180

MORESCO (Thailand) Co., Ltd. (1)
700/358 Moo 6 Amata Nakorn Industrial Estate Bangna-Trad Road, Km 57 T Nongmaidaeng A Muangchonburi, Chon Buri, 20000, Thailand
Tel.: (66) 38458606
Web Site: https://www.moresco.co.th
Sales Range: $25-49.9 Million
Industrial Lubricants Mfr & Distr
N.A.I.C.S.: 324191

MORESCO SERVICE Co., Ltd. (1)
5-5-3 Minatojimaminamimachi, Chuo-ku, Kobe, 650-0047, Japan (100%)
Tel.: (81) 783039010
Web Site: https://www.moresco.co.jp
Insurance Services
N.A.I.C.S.: 524113
Koichiro Kaji (Pres)

MORESCO USA Inc. (1)
2755 Carpenter Rd, Ann Arbor, MI 48108-1186
Tel.: (734) 548-0609
Web Site: http://www.moresco.co.jp
Lubricants Mfr & Sales
N.A.I.C.S.: 324191
Hidenori Amaki (Mng Dir)

Moresco Hanano Die-Casting Coating (Shanghai) Co., Ltd. (1)
No 818-A Fulian Road, Boashan District, Shanghai, 201906, China
Tel.: (86) 216 601 0373
Web Site: https://www.moresco-ms.com
Electronic Equipment Mfr & Distr
N.A.I.C.S.: 335312
Liu Yingjin (Chm)

Moresco Hm&Lub India Private Limited (1)
Plot Nos E-465 and E-466 Sanand II Industrial Estate, Ahmedabad, 382110, Gujarat, India
Tel.: (91) 271 768 9010
Chemical Product Mfr & Distr
N.A.I.C.S.: 325199
Nobuhiro Sewaki (Pres)

Moresco Techno Co., Ltd. (1)
5-5-3 Minatojima Minamimachi, Chuo-ku, Kobe, 650-0047, Hyogo, Japan (100%)
Tel.: (81) 783039018
Web Site: http://www.morescotechno.co.jp
Sales Range: Less than $1 Million
Emp.: 14
Automotive Services
N.A.I.C.S.: 811198

PT. Moresco Indonesia (1)
Kawasan Industry Indotaisei Sektor IA Blok K-3B Kalihurip - Cikampek, Karawang, 41373, Indonesia
Tel.: (62) 264 837 1245
Web Site: https://www.moresco.co.id
Chemical Products Mfr
N.A.I.C.S.: 325110
Shinji Usami (Pres)

PT. Moresco Macro Adhesive (1)
APL Office Tower Central Park 23rd Floor Unit 8, Jalan Let Jend S Parman Kav 28, Jakarta, 11470, Indonesia (51%)
Tel.: (62) 2129119026
Hotmelt Adhesive Mfr & Distr
N.A.I.C.S.: 325520
Motohiza Morozumi (Pres & Dir)

Tianjin Moresco Technology Co., Ltd. (1)
No 6 Tongyuan Road, Wangwenzhuang Town Xiqing District, Tianjin, China
Tel.: (86) 228 797 9908

Web Site: https://www.moresco-tj.com
Chemical Products Mfr
N.A.I.C.S.: 325194

WUXI MORESCO TRADING Co., Ltd. (1)
2-18-1210 Longshan Road, Wuxi, 214028, Jiangsu, China
Tel.: (86) 51085222618
Web Site: http://www.moresco-china.com
Sales Management Services
N.A.I.C.S.: 541618
Yingjin Liu (Pres)

INTERNATIONAL PUBLIC

MORET INDUSTRIES GROUP SAS
2 rue Pierre Semard, 02800, Saint-Quentin, France
Tel.: (33) 323372620 FR
Web Site: http://www.moretindustries.com
Year Founded: 1868
Sales Range: $350-399.9 Million
Emp.: 700
Holding Company Services
N.A.I.C.S.: 551112
Olivier Dambricourt (CEO)

Subsidiaries:

De Smet Engineers & Contractors SA (1)
Waterloo Office Park Building O, Box 32, Dreve Richelle 161, 1410, Waterloo, Belgium
Tel.: (32) 2634 2500
Web Site: http://www.dsengineers.com
Emp.: 150
Industrial Plant Design, Construction, Engineering & Contracting Services
N.A.I.C.S.: 541330
Guy Davister (CEO)

MORETON RESOURCES LIMITED
Suite 8 Level 2 113 Wickham Terrace, Spring Hill, 4000, QLD, Australia
Tel.: (61) 7 3831 6088
Web Site: http://www.moretonresources.com.au
Sales Range: Less than $1 Million
Emp.: 11
Underground Coal Gasification Technology Development
N.A.I.C.S.: 211120
Phillip Bryant (CEO & Mng Dir)

MORGAN & BANKS INVESTMENTS PTY. LTD.
Suite 1 Level 1 207 Ben Boyd Road, Neutral Bay, 2089, NSW, Australia
Tel.: (61) 2 8969 7777 AU
Web Site: http://www.morban.com.au
Investment Holding Company
N.A.I.C.S.: 551112
Andrew Banks (Co-Founder & Co-Owner)

Subsidiaries:

Talent2 International Limited (1)
Level 4 77 Pacific Highway, North Sydney, 2060, NSW, Australia (50%)
Tel.: (61) 290876333
Web Site: http://www.talent2.com
Sales Range: $300-349.9 Million
Emp.: 1,700
Human Resources Outsourcing Services & Solutions
N.A.I.C.S.: 541612
Andrew Banks (Chm)

Subsidiary (Domestic):

National Payroll Systems Pty. Ltd. (2)
17-23 Station Street, Malvern, 3144, VIC, Australia
Tel.: (61) 3 9576 0077
Sales Range: $25-49.9 Million
Emp.: 30

AND PRIVATE COMPANIES — MORGAN ADVANCED MATERIALS PLC

Payroll & Human Resource Processing Services
N.A.I.C.S.: 541214

T2 Optimise Pty. Ltd. (2)
Level 35 Central Plaza One 345 Queen St, Brisbane, 4000, QLD, Australia
Tel.: (61) 732957444
Web Site: http://www.talent2.com
Sales Range: $25-49.9 Million
Emp.: 40
Outsourced Learning & Development Services
N.A.I.C.S.: 561499
Andrew Banks *(Chm & Mng Dir)*

Subsidiary (Non-US):

Talent2 K.K. (2)
Kojimachi Central Building 9F 2-2-4 Kojimachi, Chiyoda-ku, Tokyo, 102-0083, Japan
Tel.: (81) 3 6821 4730
Sales Range: $25-49.9 Million
Emp.: 50
Payroll Outsourcing Services
N.A.I.C.S.: 541214

Subsidiary (Domestic):

T2 Tokyo K.K. (3)
Akasaka 2 14 Plaza Building 2nd Floor 2-14-32 Akasaka, Minato-ku, Tokyo, 107-0052, Japan
Tel.: (81) 345887444
Web Site: http://www.talent2.com
Sales Range: $10-24.9 Million
Emp.: 40
Human Resource Consulting & Outsourcing Services
N.A.I.C.S.: 561312
Judina Makumura *(Office Mgr)*

Subsidiary (Non-US):

Talent2 NZ Limited (2)
Ground Floor Montreaux Building 164-168 The Terrace, Wellington, 6011, New Zealand
Tel.: (64) 4 978 1040
Web Site: http://www.talent2.com
Sales Range: $25-49.9 Million
Emp.: 40
Human Resource Consulting & Outsourcing Services
N.A.I.C.S.: 541612

Subsidiary (Domestic):

Talent2 Pty Limited (2)
Level 4 77 Pacific Highway, North Sydney, 2060, NSW, Australia
Tel.: (61) 2 9087 6333
Web Site: http://www.talent2.com
Sales Range: $25-49.9 Million
Emp.: 50
Human Resource Consulting & Outsourcing Services
N.A.I.C.S.: 541612
Nina Idle *(Office Mgr)*

Subsidiary (Non-US):

Talent Partners (Dubai) LLC (3)
148 Emarat Atrium Bldg, Sheikh Zayed Rd, Dubai, United Arab Emirates
Tel.: (971) 43439960
Web Site: http://www.talent2.com
Sales Range: $10-24.9 Million
Emp.: 20
Human Resource Consulting & Outsourcing Services
N.A.I.C.S.: 541612

Subsidiary (Non-US):

Talent2 Singapore Pte. Ltd. (2)
7 Temasek Boulevard, 33-01 Suntec Tower One, Singapore, 038987, Singapore
Tel.: (65) 65118555
Sales Range: $25-49.9 Million
Emp.: 70
Human Resource Consulting & Outsourcing Services
N.A.I.C.S.: 541612
Ellen Lee *(Office Mgr)*

Talent2 UK Executive Limited (2)
Level 7 South 200 Aldersgate Street, London, E1A 4HD, United Kingdom
Tel.: (44) 20 7015 3999
Web Site: http://www.talent2.com
Sales Range: $25-49.9 Million
Emp.: 20
Human Resource Consulting & Outsourcing Services
N.A.I.C.S.: 561312
Paul Dixon *(Mng Dir)*

Subsidiary (Domestic):

Talent2 Works Pty. Ltd. (2)
Suite 3 6 Brodie Hall Drive, Bentley, 6102, WA, Australia
Tel.: (61) 893558300
Web Site: http://www.talent2.com
Emp.: 30
Human Resource Consulting & Outsourcing Services
N.A.I.C.S.: 541612

Subsidiary (Non-US):

Talent2 Works Limited (3)
Level 59 The Center 99 Queens Road, Central, China (Hong Kong)
Tel.: (852) 34733111
Web Site: http://www.talent2.com
Sales Range: $10-24.9 Million
Emp.: 30
Human Resource Consulting & Outsourcing Services
N.A.I.C.S.: 541612
Caleb Baker *(Gen Mgr)*

MORGAN ADVANCED MATERIALS PLC

York House Sheet Street, Windsor, SL4 1DD, Berks, United Kingdom
Tel.: (44) 1753837000   UK
Web Site: https://www.morganadvanced.com
Year Founded: 1856
MGAM—(LSE)
Rev.: $1,280,418,550
Assets: $1,229,228,750
Liabilities: $758,282,590
Net Worth: $470,946,160
Earnings: $101,975,470
Fiscal Year-end: 12/31/21
Carbon & Ceramic Products Mfr
N.A.I.C.S.: 335991
Pete Raby *(CEO)*

Subsidiaries:

Assam Carbon Products Ltd. (1)
Birkuchi Narengi Chandrapur Road, Guwahati, 781 026, India
Tel.: (91) 361 264 0741
Web Site: https://www.assamcarbon.in
Sales Range: $100-124.9 Million
Carbon Products Mfr
N.A.I.C.S.: 335991
Kali Krishna Bhattacharya *(Mng Dir)*

Carbo Chile S.A. (1)
San Eugenio 12462 Parque Ind Estrella del Sur, San Bernardo, 8060550, Santiago, Chile
Tel.: (56) 28541064
Sales Range: $25-49.9 Million
Emp.: 38
Ceramic Component Mfr
N.A.I.C.S.: 327120

Carbo San Luis S.A. (1)
Talcahuano 736 4 piso, C1013AAP, Buenos Aires, Argentina
Tel.: (54) 1143734439
Web Site: http://www.carbosanluis.com.ar
Sales Range: $25-49.9 Million
Emp.: 20
Insulation Ceramic Product Mfr
N.A.I.C.S.: 327993

Certech Inc. (1)
1 Park Pl W, Wood Ridge, NJ 07075
Tel.: (201) 842-6800
Ceramic Products Mfr
N.A.I.C.S.: 327120

Crucible & Cupel Manufacturing (1)
17 Montgomery Way, Malaga, 6090, WA, Australia
Tel.: (61) 892494400
Web Site: http://www.furnaceindustries.com
Sales Range: $50-74.9 Million
Emp.: 20
Ceramic Products Mfr
N.A.I.C.S.: 212323
John Wooton *(Gen Mgr)*

Graficarbo S.r.l. (1)
Via Luigi Maggi 2 Loc Zorlesco, 26841, Casalpusterlengo, Italy (100%)
Tel.: (39) 0377 912 1978
Web Site: https://www.graficarbo.it
Ceramic & Graphite Products Mfr
N.A.I.C.S.: 335991

Graphite Die Mold Inc (1)
18 Airline Rd, Durham, CT 06422-1000
Tel.: (860) 349-4444
Carbon & Graphite Product Mfr
N.A.I.C.S.: 335991

Grupo Industrial Morgan, S.A. de C.V. (1)
Blvd Manuel Avila Camacho No. 460-D Despacho, Naucalpan Edo de Mexico, 53500, Mexico, Mexico (100%)
Tel.: (52) 5555766622
Web Site: http://www.thermalceramics.com
Ceramic Products Mfr
N.A.I.C.S.: 212323

MKGS Morgan Karbon Grafit Sanayi Anonim Sirketi (1)
Osmangazi Mah 2647 Sokak No 27 Kirac, Esenyurt, 34522, Istanbul, Turkiye
Tel.: (90) 2126713287
Web Site: https://www.morgancarbon.com
Electrical Carbon Product Mfr
N.A.I.C.S.: 335991
Husnu Altay *(Gen Mgr)*

MORGANITE ESPANOLA S.A. (1)
Sabino Arana 10, Leioa, 48940, Spain
Tel.: (34) 944642255
Web Site: http://www.morganamt.com
Carbon Products Mfr
N.A.I.C.S.: 339940
Jaume Palacin *(Mng Dir)*

Morgan AM&T (1)
Unit 15 Madeley Rd North Moons Moat, Redditch, B98 9ND, Worcestershire, United Kingdom
Tel.: (44) 152769205
Web Site: http://www.morganamt.com
Emp.: 30
Carbon & Graphite Products Mfr
N.A.I.C.S.: 335991
Don Klas *(CEO)*

Subsidiary (Domestic):

H.J. Tinsley & Co. Limited (2)
Oldmedow Rd Hardwick Industrial Estate, Kings Lynn, Norfolk, PE30 4LF, United Kingdom (100%)
Tel.: (44) 1553765177
Web Site: http://www.hjtinsley.co.uk
Sales Range: $25-49.9 Million
Emp.: 20
Carbon Products Mfr
N.A.I.C.S.: 335991

Subsidiary (Non-US):

Morgan AM&T Italia srl (2)
Via Roma 338, 64014, Martinsicuro, TE, Italy (100%)
Tel.: (39) 08617981
Web Site: http://www.morganamt.com
Sales Range: $25-49.9 Million
Carbon Products Mfr
N.A.I.C.S.: 335991

Morgan AM&T South Africa Pty. Ltd. (2)
149 South Rand Road, Tulisa Park, Johannesburg, 2136, South Africa (100%)
Tel.: (27) 11 296 0000
Web Site: http://www.morganadvancedmaterials.com
Sales Range: $50-74.9 Million
Carbon-Related Products Mfr
N.A.I.C.S.: 325180

Division (Domestic):

Automould (Pty) Limited (3)
25 Hillclimb Rd, Pinetown, 3610, South Africa (100%)
Tel.: (27) 317004675
Web Site: http://www.automould.co.za
Sales Range: $50-74.9 Million
Plastics Product Mfr
N.A.I.C.S.: 326199

Scott Chalmers *(Dir-Mfg)*

Subsidiary (US):

Morgan Advanced Materials and Technology (2)
251 Forrester Dr, Greenville, SC 29607-5328 (100%)
Tel.: (864) 458-7777
Web Site: http://www.morganamt.com
Sales Range: $25-49.9 Million
Mfr of Carbon Components for Electrical Applications
N.A.I.C.S.: 335991

Subsidiary (Non-US):

Morgan Advanced Materials and Technology Canada (3)
5715 Coopers Ave Unit 16, Mississauga, L4Z 2C7, ON, Canada (100%)
Tel.: (905) 501-9500
Web Site: http://www.morganamt.com
Sales Range: $25-49.9 Million
Emp.: 14
Carbon Products Mfr
N.A.I.C.S.: 335991

Subsidiary (Domestic):

National Electrical Carbon Corporation (3)
100 Mill Creek Rd, East Stroudsburg, PA 18301-1222 (100%)
Tel.: (570) 421-9921
Web Site: http://www.nationalelectrical.com
Emp.: 40
Carbon Refractory Products Mfr
N.A.I.C.S.: 335991
Gene Mancini *(Gen Mgr)*

National Electrical Carbon Products Inc (3)
2901 2nd Ave S Ste 140, Birmingham, AL 35233-3904 (100%)
Tel.: (205) 251-4000
Web Site: http://www.morganamt.com
Carbon Products Mfr
N.A.I.C.S.: 335991

National Specialty Products (3)
200 North Town St, Fostoria, OH 44830-1008
Tel.: (419) 436-5989
Sales Range: $50-74.9 Million
Mfr of Special Graphite Products
N.A.I.C.S.: 335991

Pure Carbon Company (3)
441 Hall Ave, Saint Marys, PA 15857-1422 (100%)
Tel.: (814) 781-1573
Web Site: http://www.morganamt.net
Emp.: 300
Carbon Products Mfr
N.A.I.C.S.: 335991
Devin Stauffer *(Mgr)*

Subsidiary (Non-US):

Morgan Holding Netherlands BV (2)
Kernweg 32, PO Box 362, NL 1627 LH, Hoorn, Netherlands (100%)
Tel.: (31) 229255551
Web Site: http://www.national.nl
Sales Range: $1-9.9 Million
Emp.: 35
Holding Company
N.A.I.C.S.: 551112

Morgan Industrial Carbon (2)
21 Amour St, Revesby, 2212, NSW, Australia (100%)
Tel.: (61) 297725600
Web Site: http://www.morgancarbon.com.au
Sales Range: $25-49.9 Million
Carbon Products Mfr
N.A.I.C.S.: 325180

Morgan Karbon Grafit Sanayi A.S. (2)
Ikitelelli Organize Sanayi Bolgesi, B 2 Blok No 156, 34670, Istanbul, Turkiye (100%)
Tel.: (90) 2126713287
Web Site: http://www.morganamt.com
Sales Range: $25-49.9 Million
Carbon Products Mfr
N.A.I.C.S.: 335991

Morgan Materials Hungary Limited (2)

MORGAN ADVANCED MATERIALS PLC

Morgan Advanced Materials plc—(Continued)

Csillagvirag utca 7, 1106, Budapest,
Hungary **(100%)**
Tel.: (36) 1 265 2206
Web Site:
http://www.morganadvancematerials.com
Sales Range: $25-49.9 Million
Carbon Products Mfr
N.A.I.C.S.: 335991
Tibor Fill *(Mng Dir)*

**Morganite Carbon Kabushiki
Kaisha** **(2)**
6 25 Tagawa 3 Chome, Osaka, 532 0027,
Yodogawa Ku, Japan **(100%)**
Tel.: (81) 663097831
Mfr of Electrical Carbon Brushes & Brush
Assemblies, Commutators, Mechanical Carbon Components & Other Carbon-Related
Products
N.A.I.C.S.: 335991

**Morganite Carbon Singapore Pte.
Limited** **(2)**
1093 Lower Delta Rd Unit 0608, Singapore,
169204, Singapore **(100%)**
Tel.: (65) 62960929
Sales Range: $25-49.9 Million
Emp.: 4
Carbon Products Mfr
N.A.I.C.S.: 335991
Derek Nelson *(Gen Mgr)*

Subsidiary (Domestic):

**Morganite Electrical Carbon
Limited** **(2)**
Uppr Forest Way, Morriston, SA6 8PP,
United Kingdom **(100%)**
Tel.: (44) 792763000
Web Site: http://www.morgancarbon.com
Sales Range: $25-49.9 Million
Carbon-Related Products Mfr
N.A.I.C.S.: 335991

Subsidiary (Non-US):

**Morganite Hong Kong Company
Limited** **(2)**
Unit 4-6 11/F Siu Waj Industrial Centre,
29-33 Wing Hong Street, Cheung Sha Wan,
Kowloon, China (Hong Kong) **(100%)**
Tel.: (852) 2 744 3911
Web Site:
http://www.morganadvancedmaterials.com
Sales Range: $25-49.9 Million
Carbon Products Mfr
N.A.I.C.S.: 335991

**Morganite Insulating Products Pty.
Limited** **(2)**
21 Amour St, Revesby, 2212, NSW,
Australia **(100%)**
Tel.: (61) 296934820
Sales Range: $25-49.9 Million
Emp.: 2
Carbon Products Mfr
N.A.I.C.S.: 335991

Morganite Luxembourg S.A.S **(2)**
Usine Windhof, PO Box 15, 8301, Capellen,
Luxembourg **(100%)**
Tel.: (352) 398403
Web Site:
http://www.morganadvancedmaterials.com
Sales Range: $25-49.9 Million
Carbon Products Mfr
N.A.I.C.S.: 335991

Morganite National Carbon AG **(2)**
Steinackerstr 25, CH 8301, Kloten,
Switzerland **(100%)**
Tel.: (41) 44 800 7030
Web Site: http://www.morgancarbon.com
Sales Range: $25-49.9 Million
Emp.: 2
Carbon Products Mfr
N.A.I.C.S.: 325180

Morganite Taiwan Limited **(2)**
25 Hsin Yeh Street, Hsiao Kang, Kaohsiung, 81262, Taiwan **(100%)**
Tel.: (886) 7 871 6131
Web Site:
http://www.morganadvancedmaterials.com
Sales Range: $25-49.9 Million
Carbon Products Mfr
N.A.I.C.S.: 335991

Subsidiary (Domestic):

NP Aerospace Limited **(2)**
473 Foleshill Road, Coventry, CV6 5AQ,
United Kingdom **(70%)**
Tel.: (44) 2476702802
Web Site:
http://www.morgandefencesystems.com
Sales Range: $75-99.9 Million
Emp.: 200
Military & Civilian Composite Product Mfr
N.A.I.C.S.: 315990

Subsidiary (Non-US):

**Shanghai Morgan Carbon Company
Limited** **(2)**
4250 Long Wu Rd, Shanghai, 200241,
China **(70%)**
Tel.: (86) 2164343350
Web Site: http://www.morgan-shanghai.com
Sales Range: $100-124.9 Million
Carbon Products Mfr
N.A.I.C.S.: 325180

**Morgan AM&T (Shanghai) Co.,
Ltd.** **(1)**
No 4250 Long Wu Rd, Minhang, Shanghai,
200241, China
Tel.: (86) 21 6434 3350
Web Site: http://www.morganamt.cn
Emp.: 400
Carbon & Graphite Product Mfr
N.A.I.C.S.: 335991
Boris Jiang *(Gen Mgr)*

Morgan Austria GmbH **(1)**
Iusstrasse 2, Trumau, 2521, Modling,
Austria **(100%)**
Tel.: (43) 22536666
Web Site: http://www.morgan.at
Carbon Products Mfr
N.A.I.C.S.: 335991

Morgan Carbon Czech s.r.o **(1)**
Washingtonova 1599/17, Nove Mesto, 110
00, Prague, Czech Republic
Tel.: (420) 733 172 014
Carbon Products Mfr
N.A.I.C.S.: 335991

Morgan Carbon France S.A. **(1)**
6 Rue du Reservoir, Eguisheim, 68420, Colmar, France
Tel.: (33) 389210960
Carbon Products Mfr
N.A.I.C.S.: 335991

Morgan Carbon Italia S.R.L. **(1)**
Via Roma 338, 64014, Martinsicuro, TE,
Italy
Tel.: (39) 0861 7981
Web Site: https://www.morgancarbon.com
Sales Range: $25-49.9 Million
Emp.: 100
Carbon & Graphite Product Mfr
N.A.I.C.S.: 335991

Morgan Ceramics **(1)**
Morgan Drive, Stourport-on-Severn, DY13
8DW, Worcestershire, United Kingdom
Tel.: (44) 129 982 7000
Web Site:
http://www.morganadvancedmaterials.com
Sales Range: $25-49.9 Million
Emp.: 30
Industrial Ceramic Products Mfr
N.A.I.C.S.: 327120

Subsidiary (Non-US):

**Dalian Morgan Refractories
Limited** **(2)**
931 Xi Nan Road, Sha He Kou District, Dalian, 116033, China **(70%)**
Tel.: (86) 41186651508
Web Site: http://www.thermalceramics.com
Sales Range: $25-49.9 Million
Refractory Mfr
N.A.I.C.S.: 327120

Plant (US):

Morgan Advanced Ceramics **(2)**
225 Theodore Rice Blvd, New Bedford, MA
02745-1269 **(100%)**
Tel.: (508) 995-1725
Web Site: http://www.alberox.com
Sales Range: $50-74.9 Million
Mfr of High Temperature Ceramics, Carbons, Graphites, Refractory & Specialty
Metals
N.A.I.C.S.: 325998

Morgan Advanced Ceramics **(2)**
2425 Whipple Rd, Hayward, CA
94544 **(100%)**
Tel.: (510) 491-1100
Web Site:
http://www.morganadvancedceramics.com
Sales Range: $125-149.9 Million
Mfr of High Temperature Ceramics, Carbons, Graphites, Refractory & Specialty
Metals
N.A.I.C.S.: 325998

Subsidiary (Domestic):

Morgan Advanced Ceramics Ltd. **(2)**
Morgan Drive, Stourport-on-Severn, DY13
8DW, Warwickshire, United
Kingdom **(100%)**
Tel.: (44) 1299827000
Web Site:
http://www.morgantechnicalceramics.com
Mfr of High Temperature Ceramics, Carbons, Graphites, Refractory & Specialty
Metals
N.A.I.C.S.: 212323

Plant (US):

Morgan Advanced Ceramics, Inc. **(2)**
26 Madison Rd, Fairfield, NJ 07004
Tel.: (973) 227-8877
Web Site:
http://www.morganadvancedceramics.com
Sales Range: $25-49.9 Million
Emp.: 30
Ceramic Materials Mfr
N.A.I.C.S.: 327120
Jerry McConvery *(Gen Mgr)*

Morgan Advanced Materials - Technical Ceramics **(2)**
232 Forbes Rd, Bedford, OH
44146 **(100%)**
Tel.: (440) 232-8604
Web Site:
https://www.morganadvancedceramics.com
Sales Range: $50-74.9 Million
Piezoelectric Products Mfr
N.A.I.C.S.: 325998

Plant (Non-US):

**Morgan Technical Ceramics
Certech**
Avenida Fulton No 20, San Juan Del Rio,
Queretaro, Mexico **(100%)**
Tel.: (52) 4272728840
Web Site:
http://www.morgantechnicalceramics.com
Sales Range: $25-49.9 Million
Specialty Steel Products Distr
N.A.I.C.S.: 331513

Division (US):

**Morgan Technical Ceramics
Certech** **(2)**
550 Stewart Rd, Wilkes Barre, PA 18706-1455
Tel.: (570) 823-7400
Web Site: http://www.mtccertech.com
Sales Range: $50-74.9 Million
Emp.: 180
Ceramic Component Mfr
N.A.I.C.S.: 327120
Arthur Kear *(Gen Mgr)*

Plant (Domestic):

**Morgan Technical Ceramics
Certech** **(3)**
1 Park Pl W, Wood Ridge, NJ 07075-2413
Tel.: (201) 939-7400
Web Site: http://www.mtccertech.com
Sales Range: $125-149.9 Million
Ceramic Component Mfr
N.A.I.C.S.: 327120

Plant (Non-US):

**Morgan Technical Ceramics
Certech** **(3)**
92 C&D Brunel Road Earlstrees Industrial
Estate, Corby, NN17 4JW, Northants,
United Kingdom
Tel.: (44) 1536202282
Web Site:
http://www.morgantechnicalceramics.com

INTERNATIONAL PUBLIC

Sales Range: $50-74.9 Million
Ceramic Component Mfr
N.A.I.C.S.: 327120

Subsidiary (Domestic):

**Morgan Technical Ceramics
Limited** **(2)**
Central Park Drive, Central Park, Rugby,
CV23 0WE, Warwickshire, United
Kingdom **(100%)**
Tel.: (44) 1788542166
Web Site:
http://www.morganadvancedceramics.com
Sales Range: $50-74.9 Million
Emp.: 80
Mfr of High Temperature Ceramics, Carbons, Graphites, Refractory & Specialty
Metals
N.A.I.C.S.: 212323

**Morgan Technical Ceramics
Limited** **(2)**
Bewdley Road, Stourport-on-Severn, DY13
8QR, Worcestershire, United Kingdom
Tel.: (44) 1299 872 210
Web Site:
http://www.morgantechnicalceramics.com
Ceramic Product Mfr & Distr
N.A.I.C.S.: 327212

Subsidiary (US):

**Morgan Technical
Ceramics-Auburn** **(2)**
13079 Earhart Ave, Auburn, CA
95602-7419 **(100%)**
Tel.: (530) 823-3401
Web Site: http://www.mtcauburn.com
Sales Range: $25-49.9 Million
Alumina & Zirconia Based Structural Ceramic Parts Mfr & Sales
N.A.I.C.S.: 331313

Subsidiary (Non-US):

MTC ElectroCeramics Limited **(3)**
Bursledon Road, Thornhill, Southampton,
SO19 7TG, United Kingdom
Tel.: (44) 2380 444 811
Web Site:
http://www.morganelectroceramics.com
Electro Ceramic Material Mfr
N.A.I.C.S.: 334419

Plant (Non-US):

**Morgan Technical
Ceramics-Melbourne** **(2)**
4 Redwood Dr Monash Business Pk, Clayton, 3168, VIC, Australia
Tel.: (61) 395509144
Web Site: http://www.mtcmelbourne.com
Sales Range: $50-74.9 Million
Emp.: 60
Ceramic Products Mfr & Sales
N.A.I.C.S.: 212323

Subsidiary (US):

Morgan Thermal Ceramics Inc. **(2)**
2102 Old Savannah Rd, Augusta, GA
30906-2133 **(100%)**
Tel.: (706) 796-4200
Web Site:
http://www.morganthermalceramics.com
Sales Range: $125-149.9 Million
Ceramic Products Mfr
N.A.I.C.S.: 327999

Plant (Domestic):

Thermal Ceramics Inc **(3)**
115 E Mound St, Girard, IL
62640-0138 **(100%)**
Tel.: (217) 627-2101
Web Site: http://www.thermalceramics.com
Sales Range: $25-49.9 Million
Emp.: 10
Refractory Insulating Products Mfr
N.A.I.C.S.: 327992
C. Jones *(Sec)*

**Thermal Ceramics Inc. - Canon City
Plant** **(3)**
515 S 9th St, Canon City, CO 81212
Tel.: (719) 275-7525
Thermal Insulation Product Mfr
N.A.I.C.S.: 327993

AND PRIVATE COMPANIES — MORGAN ADVANCED MATERIALS PLC

Thermal Ceramics Inc. - Elkhart Plant (3)
2730 Industrial Pkwy, Elkhart, IN 46516
Tel.: (706) 796-4200
Web Site: http://www.morganthermalceramics.com
Microporous Insulation Material Mfr
N.A.I.C.S.: 326140

Thermal Ceramics Inc. - Emporia Plant (3)
221 Weaver St, Emporia, KS 66801
Tel.: (620) 343-2308
Ceramic Fiber Mfr
N.A.I.C.S.: 327999

Thermal Ceramics Inc. - Girard Plant (3)
115 E Mound, Girard, IL 62640
Tel.: (217) 627-2101
Emp.: 10
Structural Insulation Material Mfr
N.A.I.C.S.: 327910
Stephen Raines (Gen Mgr)

Subsidiary (Non-US):

Morgan Thermic S.A. (2)
2 Rue Joseph Monier, Montendre, Rueil-Malmaison, Cedex, France (100%)
Tel.: (33) 147162200
Web Site: http://www.thermalceramics.com
Sales Range: $50-74.9 Million
Emp.: 20
Ceramic Products Mfr
N.A.I.C.S.: 212323

Refractarios Nacionales S.A. (2)
Km 34 5 Ruta al Pacifico, Palin Escuintla, Guatemala, Guatemala (100%)
Tel.: (502) 79563400
Web Site: http://www.refractariosnacionales.com
Sales Range: $25-49.9 Million
Emp.: 28
Ceramic Products Mfr
N.A.I.C.S.: 212323

Simonsen & Sons Limited (2)
Mogelvangs Plads 7, 7900, Nykobing, Denmark (100%)
Tel.: (45) 96691300
Web Site: http://www.simonsen.eu
Sales Range: $50-74.9 Million
Ceramic Products Mfr
N.A.I.C.S.: 212323

Thermal Ceramics (2)
1185 Walkers Line, Burlington, L7M 1L1, ON, Canada (100%)
Tel.: (905) 335-3414
Web Site: https://www.morganthermalceramics.com
Sales Range: $1-9.9 Million
Ceramic Products Mfr
N.A.I.C.S.: 212323

Thermal Ceramics Benelux B.V. (2)
Tramweg 27 Tonisseweg, PO Box 45, Oude Tonge, 3255 MB, Netherlands (100%)
Tel.: (31) 187641466
Web Site: http://www.thermalceramics.com
Sales Range: $50-74.9 Million
Emp.: 9
Ceramic Products Mfr
N.A.I.C.S.: 212323

Subsidiary (US):

Thermal Ceramics Caribbean Inc. (2)
Barrio El Tuque Km 257, Ponce, PR 00715 (100%)
Tel.: (787) 843-0195
Web Site: http://www.thermalceramics.com
Sales Range: $25-49.9 Million
High Temperature Ceramics, Carbons, Graphites, Refractory & Specialty Metals Mfr
N.A.I.C.S.: 327999

Subsidiary (Non-US):

Thermal Ceramics Espana, S.L. (2)
Avenida Hermanos Bou 205, Castellon de la Plana, 12100, Spain (100%)
Tel.: (34) 964232552
Web Site: http://www.thermalceramics.com
Sales Range: $50-74.9 Million
Emp.: 10
Ceramic Products Mfr
N.A.I.C.S.: 212323
Migel Campos (Mng Dir)

Thermal Ceramics Italiana S.r.l. (2)
Via Delle Rogge 6, 26841, Casalpusterlengo, LO, Italy (100%)
Tel.: (39) 037 792 2452
Web Site: http://www.thermalceramics.com
Sales Range: $50-74.9 Million
Emp.: 20
Ceramic Products Mfr
N.A.I.C.S.: 212323

Thermal Ceramics NZ Limited (2)
24 Rayner Rd, PO Box 251, Huntly, New Zealand (100%)
Tel.: (64) 78287019
Refractory Mfr
N.A.I.C.S.: 327120

Subsidiary (Domestic):

Thermal Ceramics UK Limited (2)
Tebay Rd, Bromborough, CH62 3PH, Merseyside, United Kingdom (100%)
Tel.: (44) 151 334 4030
Web Site: http://www.thermalceramics.com
Sales Range: $75-99.9 Million
Ceramic Products Mfr
N.A.I.C.S.: 212323

Subsidiary (Non-US):

Thermal Ceramics de France S.A. (2)
Z I Centre de Vie Rue Du Juin 1827, PO Box 75, Cedex, 42160, Andrezieux-Boutheon, France (100%)
Tel.: (33) 477555680
Web Site: http://www.thermalceramics.com
Emp.: 30
Refractory Products Mfr
N.A.I.C.S.: 212323
Laurent Rivollier (Dir-Fin & Admin-France)

Plant (US):

Wesgo Ceramics Div (2)
2425 Whipple Rd, Hayward, CA 94544-7807 (100%)
Tel.: (510) 491-1100
Web Site: http://www.morgantechnicalceramics.com
Sales Range: $50-74.9 Million
Ceramics & Metals Mfr
N.A.I.C.S.: 325998

Subsidiary (Non-US):

Wesgo Ceramics GmbH (2)
Willi Graffer St 11, 91056, Erlangen, Germany (100%)
Tel.: (49) 913179760
Web Site: http://www.morgantechnicalceramics.com
Sales Range: $125-149.9 Million
Ceramic Products Mfr
N.A.I.C.S.: 212323
Serhan Aydin (Mng Dir)

Morgan Ceramics Asia Pte. Ltd. (2)
150 Kg Ampat 05-06A KA Centre, Singapore, 368324, Singapore
Tel.: (65) 65950000
Thermal Ceramic Retailer
N.A.I.C.S.: 444180
Marc Tan (Mng Dir)

Morgan Ceramics Middle East FZE (1)
403/404 B Business Centre 4 RAK Free Trade Zone, PO Box 16124, Ras al Khaimah, Dubai, United Arab Emirates
Tel.: (971) 72041870
Thermal Ceramic Mfr & Retailer
N.A.I.C.S.: 327110

Morgan Electrical Carbon Deutschland GmbH (1)
Zeppelinstrasse 26, 53424, Remagen, Germany
Tel.: (49) 264290400
Electrical Carbon Product Mfr & Retailer
N.A.I.C.S.: 335991

Morgan Kailong (Jingmen) Thermal Ceramics Co. Ltd. (1)
No 20-1 Quankou Road, Dongbao, Jingmen, 448032, Hubei, China
Tel.: (86) 7242309153
Thermal Ceramic Mfr & Retailer
N.A.I.C.S.: 327110

Morgan Korea Company Limited (1)
64-6 Ogye-ri Neungseo-myeon, Yeoju-gun, Yeoju, 469-811, Gyeonggi-do, Korea (South)
Tel.: (82) 31 881 5840
Web Site: http://www.morgankorea.kr
Electronic Components Mfr
N.A.I.C.S.: 334419

Morgan Molten Metal Systems (1)
Quadrant 55-57 High Street, Windsor, SL4 1LP, Berkshire, United Kingdom
Tel.: (44) 1753837000
Web Site: http://www.morganmms.com
Sales Range: $25-49.9 Million
Emp.: 30
Ceramic Crucible & Furnace Mfr
N.A.I.C.S.: 333994

Division (Domestic):

Morgan Molten Metal Products Ltd. (2)
Unit 7 Crucible Business Park, Woodbury Lane, Norton, WR5 2PU, Worcs, United Kingdom (100%)
Tel.: (44) 1905728200
Web Site: http://www.morganitecrucible.com
Sales Range: $75-99.9 Million
Emp.: 9
Ceramic Products Mfr
N.A.I.C.S.: 212323

Subsidiary (Non-US):

Morganite Brazil Ltda (2)
Rua Darcy Pereira 83, Rio de Janeiro, 23565 190, Brazil (100%)
Tel.: (55) 2124181366
Web Site: http://www.thermalceramics.com
Ceramic Products Mfr
N.A.I.C.S.: 212323

Subsidiary (US):

Morganite Crucible Inc. (2)
22 N Plains Industrial Rd Unit 1, Wallingford, CT 06492 (100%)
Tel.: (203) 697-0808
Web Site: http://www.morganitecrucible.com
Sales Range: $25-49.9 Million
Emp.: 14
Mfr of High Temperature Ceramics, Carbons, Graphites, Refractory & Specialty Metals
N.A.I.C.S.: 423840

Morgan Molten Metal Systems (suzhou) Co. Ltd. (1)
No 108 Tongsheng Road Suzhou Industrial Park, Shengpu, 215126, Suzhou, Jiangsu, China
Tel.: (86) 512 6292 3188
Web Site: http://www.morganmms.com
Sales Range: $25-49.9 Million
Emp.: 80
Leather Goods Retailer
N.A.I.C.S.: 458320

Morgan National AB (1)
Maskingatan 11, S 195 60, Marsta, Sweden (100%)
Tel.: (46) 59112020
Web Site: http://www.morgan-national.se
Carbon Products Mfr
N.A.I.C.S.: 335991

Morgan Technical Ceramics (Suzhou) Co. Ltd. (1)
Gongyuanxi Road, Dingshuzhen, Yixing, 214221, Jiangsu, China
Tel.: (86) 51087434988
Ceramic Mfr & Retailer
N.A.I.C.S.: 327110

Morgan Technical Ceramics Australia Pty.Ltd. (1)
4 Redwood Drive Notting Hill, Melbourne, Clayton, 3168, VIC, Australia
Tel.: (61) 395509144
Ceramic Products Mfr
N.A.I.C.S.: 327110

Morgan Technical Ceramics S.a. de C.V. (1)
Av Fulton No 20 Fracc Ind Valle de Oro, San Juan del Rio, 76802, Queretaro, Mexico
Tel.: (52) 427 272 8841
Web Site: http://www.morganplc.com
Sales Range: $75-99.9 Million
Emp.: 250
Brick & Clay Product Distr
N.A.I.C.S.: 423320

Morgan Thermal Ceramics Deutschland GmbH (1)
Borsigstr 4-6, 21465, Reinbek, Germany
Tel.: (49) 4066999350
Thermal Ceramic Retailer
N.A.I.C.S.: 444180
Thomas Schwarz (Gen Mgr)

Morgan Thermal Ceramics International Trading (Shanghai) Co. Ltd. (1)
18 Kang An Road Kangqiao Industrial Zone, Pudong, Shanghai, 201315, China
Tel.: (86) 21 6812 2200
Ceramic Product Distr
N.A.I.C.S.: 423320

Morgan Thermal Ceramics Shanghai Ltd (1)
No 18 Kang'an Road, Kangqiao Industrial Park Pudong New Area, Shanghai, 201315, China
Tel.: (86) 216 812 2200
Web Site: http://www.morganthermalceramics.com
Sales Range: $25-49.9 Million
Emp.: 77
Ceramic Fiber Mfr
N.A.I.C.S.: 327999

Morgan Thermal Ceramics Sukhoy Log LLC (1)
Militseyskaya 2 Sukhoy Log, Sverdlovskaya, 624800, Russia
Tel.: (7) 3437364354
Web Site: http://www.enthermal.slsoz.ru
Silica Mullite Fiber Product Mfr
N.A.I.C.S.: 327910
Sergey Lebedev (Chief Dev Officer)

Morganite Australia Pty Limited (1)
21 Amour St, Revesby, 2212, NSW, Australia
Tel.: (61) 2 9772 5600
Web Site: http://www.morganamt.com.au
Carbon & Graphite Product Mfr
N.A.I.C.S.: 335991

Morganite Canada Corp. (1)
5715 Coopers Ave Unit 16, Mississauga, L4Z 2C7, ON, Canada
Tel.: (905) 501-9500
Insulation Material Mfr
N.A.I.C.S.: 335932

Morganite Crucible India Ltd. (1)
B-11 MIDC Waluj, Aurangabad, 431 136, Maharashtra, India
Tel.: (91) 2406652523
Web Site: https://www.morganmms.com
Rev.: $15,143,733
Assets: $18,997,565
Liabilities: $5,014,819
Net Worth: $13,982,746
Earnings: $127,573
Emp.: 145
Fiscal Year-end: 03/31/2021
Fire Crucible Mfr
N.A.I.C.S.: 327120
Rupesh Khokle (Compliance Officer & Sec)

Morganite Industries Inc (1)
4000 Westchase Blvd Ste 170, Raleigh, NC 27607-3971
Tel.: (919) 821-1253
Web Site: http://www.morganite.com
Emp.: 8
Ceramic Electrical Equipment Mfr
N.A.I.C.S.: 335999
Fred Wollman (Pres)

Murugappa Morgan Thermal Ceramics Ltd. (1)
Dare House Extension V Floor No 02 N S C Bose Road, Chennai, 600 001, India
Tel.: (91) 442 530 6789
Web Site: https://www.murugappamorgan.com
Ceramic Fibre Product Mfr
N.A.I.C.S.: 327120
Raja Mukherjee (CFO)

National Electrical Carbon B.V. (1)

MORGAN ADVANCED MATERIALS PLC

Morgan Advanced Materials plc—(Continued)

Kernweg 32, 1627, Hoorn, Netherlands
Tel.: (31) 229 255555
Web Site: http://www.morganamt.com
Ceramic Tile Mfr
N.A.I.C.S.: 327120

Porextherm Dammstoffe GmbH (1)
Heisinger Strasse 8/10, 87437, Kempten, Germany
Tel.: (49) 831575360
Web Site: http://www.porextherm.com
Innovative Thermal Insulation Mfr & Distr
N.A.I.C.S.: 327993

S.A. Morgan (1)
1110 Ieudzen st 613, B 1930, Grimbergen, Belgium **(100%)**
Tel.: (32) 22522025
Web Site:
https://www.morganadvanced.com
Carbon Products Mfr
N.A.I.C.S.: 335991

Shanghai Morganite Electrical Carbon Co. Limited (1)
4250 Long Wu Road, Shanghai, 200241, China
Tel.: (86) 21 6434 3350
Web Site: http://www.morganite.co
Carbon Products Mfr
N.A.I.C.S.: 339940

Shin-Nippon Thermal Ceramics Corporation (1)
102-01 Chikko-Yawatamachi, Sakai, 590-0901, Osaka, Japan
Tel.: (81) 72 238 5169
Web Site: http://www.thermalceramics.co.jp
Sales Range: $25-49.9 Million
Emp.: 6
High Temperature Insulation Product Mfr
N.A.I.C.S.: 339999
Kenji Komatsu (Gen Mgr)

Thermal Ceramics Asia Pte. Ltd. (1)
150 Kg Ampat 05-06A KA Centre, Singapore, 368324, Singapore
Tel.: (65) 6 595 0000
Web Site:
http://www.morganthermalceramics.com
Sales Range: $25-49.9 Million
Thermal Insulation Product Distr
N.A.I.C.S.: 424610

Thermal Ceramics Polska Sp.zoo (1)
9 Towarowa Str, 44-100, Gliwice, Poland
Tel.: (48) 323053113
Thermal Ceramic Retailer
N.A.I.C.S.: 444180

Thermal Ceramics South Africa Pty. Limited (1)
Corner Marconi & Edison Street, 1560, Springs, Gauteng, South Africa
Tel.: (27) 11 815 6820
Web Site:
http://www.morganthermalceramics.com
Sales Range: $25-49.9 Million
Emp.: 64
Ceramic Fiber Mfr
N.A.I.C.S.: 327999

Thermal Ceramics de Veneuela C.A. (1)
Av 87 No 105-121 Zona Industrial Recreo, Valencia, Venezuela
Tel.: (58) 241 878 3164
Ceramic Products Mfr
N.A.I.C.S.: 327110

W. Haldenwanger Technische Keramik GmbH & Co. KG. (1)
Teplitzer Strasse 27, Waldkraiburg, 84478, Germany
Tel.: (49) 8638 6004 0
Web Site: http://www.haldenwanger.de
Sales Range: $50-74.9 Million
Emp.: 250
Ceramic Products Mfr
N.A.I.C.S.: 327999

Yixing Haldenwanger Fine Ceramic Co. Ltd. (1)
Dingshu Town, 214221, Yixing, Jiangsu, China
Tel.: (86) 510 87182811

Web Site:
http://www.yixinghaldenwanger.com
Ceramic Products Mfr
N.A.I.C.S.: 327110

Yixing Morgan Thermal Ceramics Co. Ltd. (1)
No 2 Beidan Road, Taodu Industrial Park Dingshu Town, Yixing, 214222, Jiangsu, China
Tel.: (86) 5108 743 4988
Web Site: https://www.hl-ifb.com
Insulation Firebrick & Castable Mfr
N.A.I.C.S.: 327120

MORGAN LAW RECRUITMENT CONSULTANCY LTD

4th Floor Clareville House 26-27 Oxendon Street, London, SW1Y 4EL, United Kingdom
Tel.: (44) 207 747 4949
Web Site: http://www.morgan-law.com
Year Founded: 2000
Sales Range: $25-49.9 Million
Emp.: 50
Executive Recruitment
N.A.I.C.S.: 541612
David Morgan (Co-Founder & Partner)

MORGAN MEIGHEN & ASSOCIATES LIMITED

10 Toronto Street, Toronto, M5C 2B7, ON, Canada
Tel.: (416) 366-2931
Web Site:
http://www.mmainvestments.com
Year Founded: 1955
Sales Range: $10-24.9 Million
Emp.: 24
Private Investment Management Firm
N.A.I.C.S.: 523940
Vanessa L. Morgan (Pres & CEO)

Subsidiaries:

Canadian General Investments, Limited (1)
10 Toronto Street, Toronto, M5C 2B7, ON, Canada
Tel.: (416) 366-2931
Web Site: http://www.mmainvestments.com
Rev.: $222,505,465
Assets: $1,146,130,162
Liabilities: $144,893,119
Net Worth: $1,001,237,043
Earnings: $199,317,903
Emp.: 21
Fiscal Year-end: 12/31/2021
Closed-End Equity Fund
N.A.I.C.S.: 523999
Vanessa L. Morgan (Pres & CEO)

Canadian World Fund Limited (1)
10 Toronto Street, Toronto, M5C 2B7, ON, Canada
Tel.: (416) 366-2931
Web Site: http://www.canadianworldfund.ca
Rev.: $12,607,630
Assets: $56,852,628
Liabilities: $2,524,394
Net Worth: $54,328,235
Earnings: $9,901,614
Emp.: 20
Fiscal Year-end: 12/31/2017
Closed-End Equity Fund
N.A.I.C.S.: 525990

Third Canadian General Investment Trust Limited (1)
10 Toronto Street, Toronto, M5C 2B7, ON, Canada
Tel.: (416) 366-2931
Web Site: http://www.mmainvestments.com
Sales Range: $1-9.9 Million
Emp.: 2
Closed-End Investment Fund
N.A.I.C.S.: 523999

MORGAN PHILIPS GROUP

74 avenue de la Faiencerie, L 1510, Luxembourg, Luxembourg
Tel.: (352) 27 1253 3030 LU

Web Site:
http://www.morganphilipsgroup.com
Year Founded: 2013
Holding Company; Recruitment, Talent Management & Outplacement Services
N.A.I.C.S.: 551112
Charles-Henri Dumon (Co-Founder & CEO)

Subsidiaries:

Hudson Global Resources LLC (1)
3a Lva Tolstogo Street, Kiev, 01004, Ukraine
Tel.: (380) 444902916
Web Site: http://www.hudson.ua
Recruitment & Staffing Services
N.A.I.C.S.: 561320
Aleksey Yurchenko (Country Mgr-Ukraine)

Morgan Philips Hudson Espana SLU (1)
Numancia Street 187 7 2, 08034, Barcelona, Spain **(100%)**
Tel.: (34) 934156678
Web Site: http://www.morganphilips.com
Employment Recruiting Services
N.A.I.C.S.: 561311
Miguel Munoz (Head-Fyte Madrid)

Morgan Philips Hudson Sp. z o.o. (1)
Plac Trzech Krzyzy 18, Warsaw, 00499, Poland **(100%)**
Tel.: (48) 223376100
Web Site: http://www.morganphilips.com
Employment Recruiting Services
N.A.I.C.S.: 561311
Jolanta Samul Kowalska (Mng Dir)

Morgan Philips Luxembourg S.A. (1)
74 avenue de la Faiencerie, 1510, Luxembourg, Luxembourg
Tel.: (352) 27 1253 3030
Web Site:
http://www.morganphilipsgroup.com
Recruitment, Talent Management & Outplacement Services
N.A.I.C.S.: 561330
Charles-Henri Dumon (Co-Founder & CEO)

Morgan Philips SA (1)
191 Ave Charles de Gaulle, 92200, Neuilly-sur-Seine, France **(100%)**
Tel.: (33) 158565856
Web Site: http://www.morganphilips.com
Employment Recruiting Services
N.A.I.C.S.: 561311
Raphael Reclus (Mng Dir)

Morgan Philips UK Limited (1)
Chancery House 53-64 Chancery Lane, London, WC2A 1QS, United Kingdom **(100%)**
Tel.: (44) 2071876000
Web Site: http://www.morganphilips.com
Staffing & Recruiting
N.A.I.C.S.: 561311
Alexis de Bretteville (Deputy CEO)

Branch (Domestic):

Morgan Philips UK Limited - Edinburgh (2)
1 Lochrin Square 92 Fountainbridge, Edinburgh, EH3 9QA, United Kingdom
Tel.: (44) 1315554321
Web Site: http://www.morganphilips.com
Employment Solutions Services
N.A.I.C.S.: 561311
Tom Gowing (Reg Dir- England & Fyte)

MORGAN S.A.

94 Rue De Villiers, 92532, Levallois-Perret, Cedex, France
Tel.: (33) 141694500
Web Site: http://www.morgan.fr
Year Founded: 1947
Sales Range: $150-199.9 Million
Emp.: 300
Women's Clothing & Fragrances Designer & Retailer
N.A.I.C.S.: 315250
Dominique Damon (CEO)

INTERNATIONAL PUBLIC

MORGAN SINDALL GROUP PLC

Kent House 14-17 Market Place, London, W1W 8AJ, United Kingdom
Tel.: (44) 2073079200
Web Site:
https://www.morgansindall.com
MGNS—(LSE)
Rev.: $4,559,707,145
Assets: $2,265,084,575
Liabilities: $1,638,727,594
Net Worth: $626,356,981
Earnings: $76,874,527
Emp.: 7,203
Fiscal Year-end: 12/31/22
Construction Services
N.A.I.C.S.: 236210
John Morgan (CEO)

Subsidiaries:

Baker Hicks Limited (1)
One Warwick Technology Park Gallows Hill, Warwick, CV34 6YL, United Kingdom
Tel.: (44) 1926567800
Web Site: https://www.bakerhicks.com
Design & Engineering Services
N.A.I.C.S.: 541330
Alwyn Hanekom (Mng Dir)

BakerHicks AG (1)
Badenstrasse 3, 4057, Basel, Switzerland
Tel.: (41) 613353030
Construction Consulting & Management Services
N.A.I.C.S.: 236220

BakerHicks ApS (1)
Carl Jacobsens Vej 35, 2500, Valby, Denmark
Tel.: (45) 33193200
Architecture Development Services
N.A.I.C.S.: 541310

BakerHicks GmbH (1)
Albert-Nestler-Strasse 26, 76131, Karlsruhe, Germany
Tel.: (49) 72190997595
Construction Consulting & Management Services
N.A.I.C.S.: 236220

BakerHicks S.A. (1)
Avenue Pasteur 6, 1300, Wavre, Belgium
Tel.: (32) 10686301
Construction Consulting & Management Services
N.A.I.C.S.: 236220

Community Solutions Limited (1)
PO Box 811, Cobourg, K9A 4S3, ON, Canada
Tel.: (905) 349-2020
Web Site: https://www.commsolltd.com
Therapist & Rehabilitation Services
N.A.I.C.S.: 621340
Barbara Claiman (Dir)

Community Solutions for Primary Care Ltd. (1)
Chancery Exchange, 10 Furnival St, London, EC4A1AB, United Kingdom **(50%)**
Tel.: (44) 2070923350
Web Site: http://www.community-solutions.co.uk
Sales Range: $25-49.9 Million
Emp.: 44
Real Estate Property Lessors
N.A.I.C.S.: 531190
Lisa Scenna (Mng Dir)

Golden i Limited (1)
Unit 4 Sandridge Park, Saint Albans, AL3 6PH, United Kingdom
Tel.: (44) 3452668523
Web Site: https://goldeni.com
Integrated Property Services
N.A.I.C.S.: 541330

Lovell Later Living LLP (1)
Marston Park, Tamworth, B76 3HN, Staffordshire, United Kingdom
Tel.: (44) 1827305600
Web Site: https://lovelllaterliving.co.uk
Integrated Property Services
N.A.I.C.S.: 531311

Lovell Partnerships Limited (1)

AND PRIVATE COMPANIES

MORIMATSU INTERNATIONAL HOLDINGS COMPANY LIMITED

Lovell House Parkway Court, 271 Springhill Parkway, Glasgow, G69 6GA, United Kingdom
Tel.: (44) 1417735710
Web Site: http://www.lovell.co.uk
Sales Range: $25-49.9 Million
Emp.: 35
Heavy & Civil Engineering Construction
N.A.I.C.S.: 237990
Steve Coleby *(Mng Dir)*

Affiliate (Domestic):

The Compendium Group Limited (2)
2 Estuary Boulevard, Liverpool, L24 8RF, United Kingdom
Tel.: (44) 345 155 9019
Web Site: https://www.compendiumliving.co.uk
Urban Renewal & Regeneration Projects; Joint Venture 50% Owned by Lovell Partnerships Limited & 50% Owned by The Riverside Group
N.A.I.C.S.: 925120
Dave Bullock *(Mng Dir)*

Morgan Est Rail Limited (1)
Harrier House, St Albans Rd E, Hatfield, AL100HE, United Kingdom
Tel.: (44) 1707272516
Web Site: http://www.morganest.com
Sales Range: $25-49.9 Million
Emp.: 50
Heavy & Civil Engineering Construction
N.A.I.C.S.: 237990

Morgan Lovell London Limited (1)
16 Noel Street, London, W1F 8DA, United Kingdom
Tel.: (44) 2077344466
Web Site: https://www.morganlovell.co.uk
Interior & Furniture Design Services
N.A.I.C.S.: 541410

Morgan Lovell Plc (1)
16 Noel Street, London, W1F 8DA, United Kingdom (100%)
Tel.: (44) 2077344466
Web Site: https://www.morganlovell.co.uk
Sales Range: $25-49.9 Million
Interior Design Services
N.A.I.C.S.: 541410

Morgan Sindall Investments Limited (1)
100 St John St Farringdon, London, EC1M 4EH, United Kingdom
Tel.: (44) 2073670100
Web Site: https://www.msinvestments.co.uk
Financial Services
N.A.I.C.S.: 541611
Wes Erlam *(Mng Dir)*

Morgan Sindall Plc - Construction & Infrastructure (1)
Corporation Street, Rugby, CV21 2DW, Warwickshire, United Kingdom
Tel.: (44) 178 853 4500
Web Site: https://www.morgansindall.com
Sales Range: $50-74.9 Million
Emp.: 250
Heavy & Civil Engineering Construction
N.A.I.C.S.: 237990
Pat Boyle *(Mng Dir-Construction)*

Morgan Sindall Professional Services AG (1)
Badenstrasse 3, 4057, Basel, Switzerland
Tel.: (41) 61 335 3030
Web Site: http://www.morgansindall.ch
Health Care Srvices
N.A.I.C.S.: 621999
David Santos *(Mgr-Mktg & Comm)*

Morgan Vinci (1)
Somerton Works, Spytty Rd, Gwent, NP190XU, United Kingdom
Tel.: (44) 1633246566
Heavy & Civil Engineering Construction
N.A.I.C.S.: 237990

Muse Developments Ltd. (1)
Riverside House Irwell Street, Salford, M3 5EN, United Kingdom
Tel.: (44) 161 877 3400
Web Site: https://www.musedevelopments.com
Sales Range: $50-74.9 Million
Emp.: 80
Real Estate Management & Development

N.A.I.C.S.: 531210
Mike Auger *(Head-Residential)*

Muse Places Limited (1)
Riverside House Irwell Street, Manchester, M3 5EN, United Kingdom
Tel.: (44) 1618773400
Web Site: https://museplaces.com
Real Estate Services
N.A.I.C.S.: 531210

Overbury Plc (1)
77 Newman Street, London, W1T 3EW, United Kingdom (100%)
Tel.: (44) 207 307 9000
Web Site: https://www.overbury.com
Sales Range: $50-74.9 Million
New Single-Family Housing Construction
N.A.I.C.S.: 236115

hub West Scotland Limited (1)
2nd Floor The Lighthouse 11 Mitchell Lane, Glasgow, G1 3NU, United Kingdom
Tel.: (44) 1415302150
Web Site: https://www.hubwestscotland.co.uk
Educational Organization Services
N.A.I.C.S.: 611710
Angeline Robertson *(Dir-Partnerships)*

MORGAN VENTURES LIMITED

37 Ring Road Lajpat Nagar-IV, New Delhi, 110 024, India
Tel.: (91) 1126432601
Web Site: https://www.morganventures.in
Year Founded: 1986
526237—(BOM)
Rev.: $1,530,346
Assets: $25,912,483
Liabilities: $19,468,483
Net Worth: $6,444,000
Earnings: $788,438
Emp.: 3
Fiscal Year-end: 03/31/23
Power Generation & Venture Capital Services
N.A.I.C.S.: 221115
Dharam Kumar *(CFO)*

MORGUARD CORPORATION

55 Centre Drive Suite 800, Mississauga, L5B 1M3, ON, Canada
Tel.: (905) 281-3800 Ca
Web Site: https://www.morguard.com
74S—(DEU)
Rev.: $667,043,898
Assets: $8,990,386,538
Liabilities: $5,725,347,735
Net Worth: $3,265,038,803
Earnings: $200,749,476
Emp.: 1,300
Fiscal Year-end: 12/31/21
Provider of Real Estate Services
N.A.I.C.S.: 531390
K. Rai Sahi *(Chm & CEO)*

Subsidiaries:

Morguard Investments Limited (1)
55 City Centre Drive Suite 800, Mississauga, L5B 1M3, ON, Canada
Tel.: (905) 281-3800
Web Site: https://www.morguard.com
Real Estate Brokerage
N.A.I.C.S.: 531210

Morguard North American Residential Real Estate Investment Trust (1)
55 City Centre Drive Suite 800, Mississauga, L5B 1M3, ON, Canada
Tel.: (905) 281-3800
Web Site: https://www.morguard.com
Rev.: $194,539,737
Assets: $2,412,831,576
Liabilities: $1,358,616,185
Net Worth: $1,054,215,391
Earnings: $130,488,215
Fiscal Year-end: 12/31/2020
Real Estate Investment Services
N.A.I.C.S.: 525990
K. Rai Sahi *(Chm & CEO)*

Morguard Real Estate Investment Trust (1)

55 City Center Drive Suite 800, Mississauga, L5B 1M3, ON, Canada (100%)
Tel.: (905) 281-3800
Web Site: https://www.morguard.com
Rev.: $188,873,683
Assets: $1,950,960,948
Liabilities: $1,049,783,775
Net Worth: $901,177,173
Earnings: $3,821,438
Emp.: 8
Fiscal Year-end: 12/31/2021
Real Estate Investment Trust
N.A.I.C.S.: 525990
K. Rai Sahi *(Chm, Pres & CEO)*

Morguard Residential Inc. (1)
77 Bloor Street West Suite 1704, Toronto, M5S 1M2, ON, Canada (100%)
Tel.: (416) 921-3149
Web Site: http://www.morguard.com
Sales Range: $1-9.9 Million
Acquirer, Developer & Manager Multi-Family Rental Properties
N.A.I.C.S.: 531190

Revenue Properties (America) Inc. (1)
2542 Williams Blvd, Kenner, LA 70062-5538
Tel.: (504) 904-8500
Web Site: http://www.morguard.com
Sales Range: $25-49.9 Million
Emp.: 30
Real Estate Manangement Services
N.A.I.C.S.: 531110
John Talano *(Gen Mgr)*

Temple Hotels Inc. (1)
55 City Centre Drive Suite 1000, Mississauga, L5B 1M3, ON, Canada (100%)
Tel.: (905) 281-3800
Web Site: http://www.templehotels.ca
Rev.: $121,533,023
Assets: $329,034,631
Liabilities: $348,599,066
Net Worth: ($19,564,435)
Earnings: ($23,399,334)
Fiscal Year-end: 12/31/2018
Real Estate Investment
N.A.I.C.S.: 525990
Chris J. Cahill *(Chm)*

MORI HAMADA & MATSUMOTO

Marunouchi Kitaguchi Bldg 1-6-5 Marunouchi, Chiyoda-ku, Tokyo, 100-8222, Japan
Tel.: (81) 3621283330
Web Site: http://www.mhmjapan.com
N.A.I.C.S.:
Robyn Nadler *(Attorney)*

Subsidiaries:

Chandler MHM Limited (1)
7th-9th 12th & 16th Floor Bubhajit Building 20 North Sathorn Road, 10500, Bangkok, Thailand
Tel.: (66) 22666485
Web Site: http://www.chandlermhm.com
Law firm
N.A.I.C.S.: 541110
Satoshi Kawai *(Mng Partner)*

MORI HILLS REIT INVESTMENT CORPORATION

1232 Akasaka 1chome, Minato-ku, Tokyo, 107-6006, Japan
Tel.: (81) 362343234
Web Site: https://www.mori-hills-reit.co.jp
Year Founded: 2006
3234—(TKS)
Sales Range: $75-99.9 Million
Real Estate Related Services
N.A.I.C.S.: 531390
Hideyuki Isobe *(Exec Dir)*

MORI TRUST HOTEL REIT, INC.

3-1 Toranomon 4-chome Minato-ku, Tokyo, Japan
Tel.: (81) 364357290
Web Site: http://www.mt-hotelreit.jp
Year Founded: 2016

3478—(TKS)
Sales Range: Less than $1 Million
Real Estate Investment Services
N.A.I.C.S.: 531210
Amane Sakamoto *(Exec Dir)*

MORI TRUST SOGO REIT, INC.

3-1 Toranomon 4-chome, Minato-ku, Tokyo, Japan
Tel.: (81) 364357011
Web Site: https://www.mt-reit.jp
Year Founded: 2001
89610—(TKS)
Sales Range: Less than $1 Million
Real Estate Related Services
N.A.I.C.S.: 531210
Masayuki Yagi *(Exec Dir)*

MORI-GUMI CO., LTD.

4-5-17 Doshomachi, Chuo-ku, Osaka, 541-0045, Japan
Tel.: (81) 662012763
Web Site: https://www.morigumi.co.jp
Year Founded: 1934
1853—(TKS)
Sales Range: Less than $1 Million
Emp.: 360
Construction Engineering Services
N.A.I.C.S.: 541330
Yuji Yoshida *(Pres)*

MORIEN RESOURCES CORP.

1701 Hollis St Suite 800, Halifax, B3J 3M8, NS, Canada
Tel.: (902) 466-7255 Ca
Web Site: https://www.morienres.com
Year Founded: 2012
MOX—(TSXV)
Sales Range: Less than $1 Million
Mineral Exploration & Mining Services
N.A.I.C.S.: 212312
John P.A. Budreski *(Pres & CEO)*

Subsidiaries:

Advanced Primary Minerals USA Corp (1)
651 Madison Rd, Eatonton, GA 31024
Tel.: (706) 485-7677
Mineral Processing Services
N.A.I.C.S.: 212323

MORIMATSU INTERNATIONAL HOLDINGS COMPANY LIMITED

Wing Lok Street Trade Centre 235 Wing Lok Street, Hong Kong, China (Hong Kong)
Tel.: (852) 21570050 HK
Web Site: https://www.morimatsu-online.com
Year Founded: 1990
2155—(HKG)
Rev.: $993,762,499
Assets: $1,219,640,768
Liabilities: $787,183,175
Net Worth: $432,457,594
Earnings: $102,065,744
Emp.: 4,142
Fiscal Year-end: 12/31/22
Holding Company
N.A.I.C.S.: 551112
Koei Nishimatsu *(CEO)*

Subsidiaries:

Pharmadule Morimatsu AB (1)
DanvikCenter 28, 13130, Nacka, Sweden
Tel.: (46) 858742000
Web Site: https://www.pharmadule.com
Pharmaceuticals Mfr
N.A.I.C.S.: 325412

Shanghai Morimatsu Pharmaceutical Equipment Engineering Co., Ltd. (1)
No 29 Jinwen Road, Zhuqiao Airport Industrial Park, Shanghai, China
Tel.: (86) 2138112058
Pharmaceuticals Mfr

// MORIMATSU INTERNATIONAL HOLDINGS COMPANY LIMITED / INTERNATIONAL PUBLIC

Morimatsu International Holdings Company Limited—(Continued)
N.A.I.C.S.: 325412

MORIMOTO CO., LTD.
3-7-4 Ebisu-Minami Shibuya-ku, Tokyo, 150-0022, Japan
Tel.: (81) 357241100
Web Site: http://www.morimoto-real.co.jp
Year Founded: 1983
Sales Range: $1-4.9 Billion
Emp.: 290
Houses, Commercial Facilities, Office Buildings & Hotels Builder & Designer
N.A.I.C.S.: 236115
Hiroyoshi Morimoto *(Pres & CEO)*

MORIMURA BROS., INC.
Bldg Toranomon Towers Office 128Th Toranomon Suite 44 Chome Minato Ku, Tokyo, 105 8451, Japan
Tel.: (81) 335026431
Web Site: http://www.morimura.co.jp
Sales Range: $75-99.9 Million
Emp.: 300
Metal, Chemical & Raw Material Distr
N.A.I.C.S.: 424690
Yusuke Morimura *(Pres & CEO)*

Subsidiaries:

Almatis Limited (1)
1815 2 Nagano, Iwanuki, Iwakuni, 740 0045, Yamaguchi, Japan
Tel.: (81) 827381217
Web Site: http://www.almatis.com
Alumina Based Chemical Mfr & Distr
N.A.I.C.S.: 331313

MORIMURA BROS.(TAIWAN),INC. (1)
15F-2 No 167 Dunhua N Rd, Songshan, Taipei, 105-49, Taiwan
Tel.: (886) 2 2717 7111
Chemical & Raw Material Distr
N.A.I.C.S.: 424690

MORIMURA CHEMICALS Ltd. (1)
4-21-1 Ichinomiya Samukawa, Koza, 253-0111, Kanagawa, Japan
Tel.: (81) 476 75 1604
Web Site: http://www.morimura-chemicals.co.jp
Emp.: 48
Additive Mfr & Distr
N.A.I.C.S.: 325199
Koichi Tsunemi *(Pres & CEO)*

Morimura Bros. (Europe) B.V. (1)
Cannenburgerweg 59C, 1244 RH, Ankeveen, Netherlands
Tel.: (31) 356564564
Web Site: http://morimura.co.jp
Sales Range: $50-74.9 Million
Emp.: 6
Metal, Chemical & Raw Material Importer & Distr
N.A.I.C.S.: 424690
A. Suzuki *(Mng Dir)*

Morimura Bros. (H.K.) Ltd. (1)
Room 707 7th Fl Silvercord Tower 30 Canton Road, Tsim Sha Tsui, Kowloon, China (Hong Kong)
Tel.: (852) 25633227
Sales Range: $25-49.9 Million
Emp.: 20
Metal, Chemical & Raw Material Importer & Distributor
N.A.I.C.S.: 424690

Morimura Bros. (S.Z.) Ltd. (1)
RM 1713 Changping Business Bldg Honghua Road Futian Free Trade Zone, Shenzhen, China
Tel.: (86) 755 8254 2680
Chemical & Raw Material Distr
N.A.I.C.S.: 424690

Morimura Bros. (Shanghai) Co., Ltd. (1)
Room 2908 The Place Tower A, 100 Zunyi Road, Shanghai, 200051, China
Tel.: (86) 2162363906
Web Site: http://www.morimurabros.cn

Metal, Chemical & Raw Material Importer & Distr
N.A.I.C.S.: 325199

Morimura Bros. (USA) Inc. (1)
Parker Plz 10th Fl 400 Kelby St, Fort Lee, NJ 07024
Tel.: (201) 363-9001
Emp.: 5
Metal, Chemical & Raw Material Importer & Distr
N.A.I.C.S.: 424690

Morimura Bros., (Singapore) Pte. Ltd. (1)
101 Thomson Road 09 01A United Square, Singapore, 307591, Singapore
Tel.: (65) 63235055
Web Site: http://www.morimura.co.jp
Sales Range: $50-74.9 Million
Emp.: 5
Metal, Chemical & Raw Material Importer & Distr
N.A.I.C.S.: 424690
Masami Yuemura *(Dir)*

Morimura Bros.,(ASIA) Co., Ltd. (1)
No 50 GMM-Grammy Place 16th Floor RM A2 Sukhumvit Road Asoke, North Klongtoey Wattana, Bangkok, 10110, Thailand
Tel.: (66) 2 665 8900
Emp.: 18
Chemical Raw Material Distr
N.A.I.C.S.: 424690
Muneatsu Hironaka *(Pres)*

Morimura Brothers Trading India Private Ltd. (1)
8C Riaz Garden 29 Kodambakkam High Road, Chennai, 600 034, Tamilnadu, India
Tel.: (91) 44 40424430
Emp.: 9
Chemical & Raw Material Distr
N.A.I.C.S.: 424690
Atsushi Hatano *(Pres)*

MORINAGA & CO., LTD.
1-13-16 Shibaura, Minato-ku, Tokyo, 105-8309, Japan
Tel.: (81) 334560134
Web Site: https://www.morinaga.co.jp
Year Founded: 1899
2201—(TKS)
Rev.: $1,410,362,480
Assets: $1,478,286,840
Liabilities: $601,450,510
Net Worth: $876,836,330
Earnings: $100,167,940
Emp.: 3,093
Fiscal Year-end: 03/31/24
Holding Company; Confectionaries, Foodstuffs, Frozen Desserts & Health Products Mfr & Distr
N.A.I.C.S.: 551112
Machiko Miyai *(Mng Exec Officer)*

Subsidiaries:

Morinaga America Inc. (1)
4 Park Plz Ste 750, Irvine, CA 92614
Tel.: (949) 732-1155
Web Site: https://www.morinaga-america.com
Food Flavor Distr
N.A.I.C.S.: 424690
Terry Kawabe *(CEO)*

Morinaga Angel Dessert Co., Ltd. (1)
6-22-10 Nishitsuruma, Yamato, 242-0005, Kanagawa, Japan
Tel.: (81) 462740783
Web Site: https://www.morinaga-a-dessert.jp
Emp.: 280
Food Whslr
N.A.I.C.S.: 424690

Morinaga Asia Pacific Co., Ltd. (1)
Room 32/33 12th Floor Sino-Thai Tower Sukhumvit 21 Asoke Rd, Klongtoey-Nua Wattana, Bangkok, 10110, Thailand
Tel.: (66) 21171572
Web Site: https://www.morinaga-ap.com
Food Whslr
N.A.I.C.S.: 424690

Morinaga Business Partner Co., Ltd. (1)

2-1-1 Shimosueyoshi, Tsurumi-ku, Yokohama, 230-0012, Kanagawa, Japan
Tel.: (81) 455862510
Web Site: https://www.mbp.morinaga.co.jp
Food Whslr
N.A.I.C.S.: 424490

Morinaga Institute of Biological Science, Inc. (1)
Sachiura 2-1-16, Kanazawa-Ku, Yokohama, 236-0003, Japan
Tel.: (81) 452798215
Web Site: http://www.miobs-e.com
Emp.: 25
Medical Research Development Services
N.A.I.C.S.: 541715
Kazuhiko Kuroda *(Pres)*

Morinaga Market Development Co., Ltd. (1)
5-33-1 Shiba, Minato-ku, Tokyo, Japan
Tel.: (81) 334560163
Web Site: https://www.morinaga-market.co.jp
Emp.: 62
Food Whslr
N.A.I.C.S.: 424490

Morinaga Shoji Co., Ltd. (1)
2-1-1 Shimosueyoshi, Tsurumi-ku, Yokohama, 230-8504, Japan
Tel.: (81) 455842561
Web Site: https://www.morinaga-shoji.co.jp
Food Whslr
N.A.I.C.S.: 424490

Morinaga Takataki Country Co., Ltd. (1)
1919 Furushikiya, Ichihara, 290-0528, Japan
Tel.: (81) 436961266
Web Site: https://www.takatakicc.co.jp
Golf Club Services
N.A.I.C.S.: 713910

Taiwan Morinaga Co., Ltd. (1)
No 22 Section 2 Zhongyang South Road, Beitou, New Taipei City, 112, Taiwan
Tel.: (886) 228914160
Web Site: https://www.morinaga.com.tw
Emp.: 278
Food Whslr
N.A.I.C.S.: 424490

MORINAGA MILK INDUSTRY CO., LTD.
33-1 Shiba 5-Chome, Minato-ku, Tokyo, 108-8384, Japan
Tel.: (81) 337980126   JP
Web Site: https://www.morinagamilk.co.jp
Year Founded: 1917
2264—(TKS)
Rev.: $3,616,059,990
Assets: $3,741,246,780
Liabilities: $1,876,334,430
Net Worth: $1,864,912,350
Earnings: $405,239,270
Emp.: 7,415
Fiscal Year-end: 03/31/24
Holding Company; Milk Production, Dairy Products & Non-Dairy Beverages Mfr & Distr
N.A.I.C.S.: 551112
Michio Miyahara *(Chm)*

Subsidiaries:

Elovi Vietnam Joint Stock Company (1)
Southern PhoYen Industrial Park, Thuan Thanh Pho Yen, Thai Nguyen, Vietnam
Tel.: (84) 2083866562
Web Site: http://www.elovi.com.vn
Dairy Product Whslr
N.A.I.C.S.: 424430

Milei GmbH (1)
Kemptener Str 91, 88299, Leutkirch, Germany (50%)
Tel.: (49) 756 1850
Web Site: https://www.milei.de
Sales Range: $100-124.9 Million
Emp.: 267
Mfr of Whey Powder
N.A.I.C.S.: 311514

Morinaga Milk Industry (Shanghai) Co., Ltd. (1)
Room 205 No 488 Hongxu Road, Minhang District, Shanghai, China
Tel.: (86) 2161151760
Web Site: http://www.morinaga-milk.com.cn
Dairy Product Whslr
N.A.I.C.S.: 424430

Morinaga Nutritional Foods (Asia Pacific) Pte. Ltd. (1)
1 Gateway Drive 17-12/13/14/15 Westgate Tower, Singapore, 608531, Singapore
Tel.: (65) 62543005
Web Site: http://mnf-ap.com
Food Service
N.A.I.C.S.: 424490
Ko Shiino *(Pres)*

Morinaga Nutritional Foods Deutschland GmbH (1)
Zettachring 12, 70567, Stuttgart, Germany (100%)
Tel.: (49) 7118160003
Sales Range: $1-9.9 Million
Emp.: 2
N.A.I.C.S.: 311513

Morinaga Nutritional Foods, Inc. (1)
3838 Del Amo Blvd Ste 201, Torrance, CA 90503 (100%)
Tel.: (310) 787-0200
Web Site: http://www.morinu.com
Sales Range: $1-9.9 Million
Emp.: 15
Soybean Curd Importer & Seller
N.A.I.C.S.: 424510
Hiroyuki Imanishi *(Pres)*

Subsidiary (Domestic):

Turtle Island Foods Inc. (2)
601 Industrial St, Hood River, OR 97031
Tel.: (541) 386-7766
Web Site: http://www.tofurky.com
Sales Range: $10-24.9 Million
Emp.: 77
Food Products Mfr
N.A.I.C.S.: 311999
Sue Tibbott *(CFO)*

Taiwan Morinaga Nutritional Foods Inc. (1)
6th Floor No 153 Sec 2, Ming Sheng East Road, Taipei, 10447, Taiwan (99%)
Tel.: (886) 25011115
Wholesale of Powdered Infant Formula & Baby Foods
N.A.I.C.S.: 424490

MORIO DENKI CO., LTD.
4-34-1 Tateishi, Katsushika-ku, Tokyo, 124-0012, Japan
Tel.: (81) 336913181
Web Site: https://www.morio.co.jp
Year Founded: 1911
6647—(TKS)
Rev.: $49,231,280
Assets: $54,334,200
Liabilities: $23,055,680
Net Worth: $31,278,520
Earnings: $1,394,710
Emp.: 238
Fiscal Year-end: 03/31/24
Electrical Component Mfr & Whslr
N.A.I.C.S.: 335999
Hiroyuki Kikuchi *(Pres)*

Subsidiaries:

Morio Denki Co., Ltd. - Ryugasaki Plant (1)
2 Nadooka, Ryugasaki, 301-0845, Ibaraki, Japan
Tel.: (81) 297621866
Electrical Component Mfr
N.A.I.C.S.: 335999

Morio USA Corporation (1)
3425 N 44th St Ste 400, Lincoln, NE 68504
Tel.: (402) 488-0008
Electrical Component Distr
N.A.I.C.S.: 423610

MORION, INC.

AND PRIVATE COMPANIES

MORIROKU HOLDINGS COMPANY, LTD.

KIMa ave 13a, 199155, Saint Petersburg, 199155, Russia
Tel.: (7) 8123507572   RU
Web Site: https://www.morion.com.ru
Year Founded: 1853
MORI—(MOEX)
Sales Range: Less than $1 Million
Emp.: 490
Quartz Frequency Control Product Mfr
N.A.I.C.S.: 339999
Larisa V. Khadanovich *(Dir-Comml)*

MORIRIN CO., LTD.
4-22-10 Hon-machi, Ichinomiya, 491 8610, Japan
Tel.: (81) 586 25 2281
Web Site: http://www.moririn.co.jp
Emp.: 680
N.A.I.C.S.:
Katsuhiko Mori *(Chm & CEO)*

Subsidiaries:

Toda Kogyo Corp.   (1)
Shiba Mita Mori Building 6F 5-13-15 Shiba, Minato-ku, Tokyo, 108-0014, Japan
Tel.: (81) 354396040
Web Site: https://www.todakogyo.co.jp
Rev.: $173,406,740
Assets: $355,049,540
Liabilities: $259,039,290
Net Worth: $96,010,250
Earnings: ($23,670,410)
Emp.: 1,112
Fiscal Year-end: 03/31/2024
Chemical Products Mfr
N.A.I.C.S.: 325180
Shigeru Takaragi *(Chm & Pres)*

MORIROKU HOLDINGS COMPANY, LTD.
18th Floor Shin-Aoyama Bldg East 1-1 Minami-Aoyama 1-chome Minato-ku, Tokyo, 107-0062, Japan
Tel.: (81) 334036102   JP
Web Site: http://www.moriroku.co.jp
Year Founded: 1663
4249—(TKS)
Rev.: $962,667,180
Assets: $929,075,160
Liabilities: $423,919,130
Net Worth: $505,156,030
Earnings: $19,975,420
Emp.: 4,447
Fiscal Year-end: 03/31/24
Chemical Product Mfr & Distr
N.A.I.C.S.: 325199
Mariko Mori *(Exec Officer-Work-Style, HR & Corp Comm Div & Supvr)*

Subsidiaries:

I.M. Material Corporation   (1)
Ujiden Building 4-8-17 Nishitenma 13th floor reception, Kita-ku, Osaka, 530-0047, Japan
Tel.: (81) 665301011
Crushing Machinery Mfr
N.A.I.C.S.: 333131

Listowel Technology, Inc.   (1)
1700 Mitchell Road South, Listowel, N4W 3H4, ON, Canada
Tel.: (519) 291-9900
Emp.: 450
Automobile Parts Mfr & Distr
N.A.I.C.S.: 336390
Mitsuru Sakuma *(Pres)*

M&C Tech Indiana Corporation   (1)
1928 Technology Dr, Washington, IN 47501
Tel.: (812) 674-2122
Web Site: https://mctechin.com
Automobile Parts Mfr & Distr
N.A.I.C.S.: 336390
Yasuhiro Ito *(Pres)*

Moriroku Chemicals Company, Ltd.   (1)
Shin Aoyama Building East 18th floor 1-1 Minamiaoyama 1-chome, Minato, Tokyo, 107-0062, Japan
Tel.: (81) 33 403 6179
Web Site: https://www.moriroku.co.jp

Emp.: 550
Chemical Product Mfr & Distr
Hidehito Monji *(Pres & CEO)*

Subsidiary (Domestic):

Goko Kasei Industrial Co., Ltd.   (2)
37 Gosei-cho, Omuta, 836-0891, Fukuoka, Japan
Tel.: (81) 944565395
Web Site: https://www.moriroku.co.jp
Emp.: 20
Dye Mfr & Distr
N.A.I.C.S.: 325130
Satoshi Sasaki *(Pres & CEO)*

I.M. Materials Co., Ltd.   (2)
Iwatani Gas Uji Factory 60 Uji Okenoshiri, Uji, 611-0021, Kyoto, Japan
Tel.: (81) 774209111
Chemical Product Grinding Services
N.A.I.C.S.: 212390

Subsidiary (Non-US):

Moriroku (Guangzhou) Trading Co., Ltd.   (2)
Room 2702-03 China Shine Plaza No 9 Lin He Xi Road, Tian He District, Guangzhou, Guangdong, China
Tel.: (86) 2022082133
Resin Product Distr
N.A.I.C.S.: 424690

Moriroku (Shanghai) Co., Ltd.   (2)
Room 6210-6211 Rui Jin Business Center Rui Jin Guest House 118, Rui Jin 2 Road, Shanghai, China
Tel.: (86) 2164660484
Resin Product Distr
N.A.I.C.S.: 424690

Moriroku (Singapore) Pte., Ltd.   (2)
35 Selegie Road 09-21 Parklane Shopping Mall, Singapore, 188307, Singapore
Tel.: (65) 63362280
Web Site: http://www.moriroku.co.jo
Resin Product Distr
N.A.I.C.S.: 424690
Adrian Loh *(Sls Mgr)*

Moriroku (Thailand) Co., Ltd.   (2)
8th Floor Maneeya Center Building 518/5 Ploenchit Road Kwaeng Lumpini, Khet Patumwan, Bangkok, 10330, Thailand
Tel.: (66) 26520607
Resin Product Distr
N.A.I.C.S.: 424690

Moriroku (Tianjin) Co., Ltd.   (2)
RM 3207 32F The Exchange Tower 1 No 189 Nanjjing Road, Heping District, Tianjin, 300051, China
Tel.: (86) 2283192358
Resin Product Distr
N.A.I.C.S.: 424690

Subsidiary (Domestic):

Moriroku Agri Co., Ltd.   (2)
73-1 Hiraishi-Wakamiya Kawachi-cho, Tokushima, 771-0137, Japan
Tel.: (81) 886653339
Web Site: https://www.moriroku-a.com
Agriculture Product Distr
N.A.I.C.S.: 424910

Subsidiary (US):

Moriroku America, Inc.   (2)
15000 Industrial Pkwy, Marysville, OH 43040
Tel.: (937) 553-9235
Resin Product Distr
N.A.I.C.S.: 424690

Subsidiary (Non-US):

Moriroku Austria GmbH   (2)
Heiligenstaedter Strasse 50-52/10, 1190, Vienna, Austria
Tel.: (43) 1369200511
Web Site: http://moriroku.at
Resin Product Distr
N.A.I.C.S.: 424690
Kohei Nomura *(Mng Dir)*

Moriroku Chemicals Korea Co., Ltd.   (2)
Samsung Jeil Bldg 9F 309 Teheran-ro

Yeoksam-dong, Gangnam-gu, Seoul, 06151, Korea (South)
Tel.: (82) 25272700
Resin Product Distr
N.A.I.C.S.: 424690

Moriroku Company (HK) Ltd.   (2)
Room 1704 17/F Tower1 China Hong Kong City 33 Canton Road, Tsim Tsa Tsui, Kowloon, China (Hong Kong)
Tel.: (852) 28650798
Resin Product Distr
N.A.I.C.S.: 424690

Subsidiary (Domestic):

Moriroku Precision Co., Ltd.   (2)
521-5 Shimosouda Hanakawa-cho, Kitaibaraki, 319-1537, Ibaraki, Japan
Tel.: (81) 293432111
Web Site: https://www.moriroku.co.jp
Emp.: 80
Automobile Electrical Component Mfr & Distr
N.A.I.C.S.: 336320
Masakazu Yamada *(Pres & CEO)*

Subsidiary (Non-US):

PT. Moriroku Chemicals Indonesia
M Gold Tower Office 17th Unit 8 Jl K H Noer Alie, Bekasi, 17148, Jawa Barat, Indonesia
Tel.: (62) 2128087120
Emp.: 9
Resin Product Distr
N.A.I.C.S.: 424690
Toru Sakaguti *(Pres)*

Moriroku Chemicals India Pvt. Ltd.   (1)
Office No 1208 Altrade Business Centre 12th Floor DLF Building No-10, Tower-B DLF Cyber City Phase-II, Gurgaon, 122002, Haryana, India
Tel.: (91) 1246434419
Plastic Raw Material Whslr
N.A.I.C.S.: 424610

Moriroku Philippines, Inc.   (1)
115 North Science Avenue, Laguna Technopark, Binan, 4024, Laguna, Philippines
Tel.: (63) 495412892
Automobile Parts Mfr & Distr
N.A.I.C.S.: 336390

Moriroku Technology Company, Ltd.
Shin Aoyama Building East 18th floor 1-1 Minamiaoyama 1-chome, Minato-ku, Tokyo, 107-0062, Japan
Tel.: (81) 334036596
Web Site: https://www.moriroku.co.jp
Emp.: 3,890
Automobile Parts Mfr & Distr
N.A.I.C.S.: 336390
Kazuhiro Hashimoto *(Exec Officer & Supvr-Global Dev)*

Subsidiary (US):

Greenville Technology, Inc.   (2)
5755 State Route 571 E, Greenville, OH 45331
Tel.: (937) 548-1471
Emp.: 611
Automobile Parts Mfr & Distr
N.A.I.C.S.: 336390
Yasushi Nakao *(Pres & CEO)*

Subsidiary (Non-US):

Guangzhou Moriroku Technology Co., Ltd.   (2)
No 13 Tian Yuan Dong Road Yonghe Economic Zone, Guangzhou Economic Zone, Guangzhou, Guangdong, China
Tel.: (86) 2082970096
Automobile Parts Mfr & Distr
N.A.I.C.S.: 336390
Akira Yamazaki *(Pres)*

Subsidiary (Domestic):

Kumamoto Moriroku Kasei Co., Ltd.   (2)
2527 Hirakawa Otsu-cho, Kikuchi-gun, Kumamoto, 869-1231, Japan
Tel.: (81) 962931000

Automobile Parts Mfr & Distr
N.A.I.C.S.: 336390

Subsidiary (Non-US):

Moriroku Technology (Thailand) Co., Ltd.   (2)
Pinthong 1 Industrial Estate 789/170 Moo 1 Tambol Nongkham, Amphur, Si Racha, 20230, Chonburi, Thailand
Tel.: (66) 38348288
Automobile Parts Mfr & Distr
N.A.I.C.S.: 336390
Yusuke Ikuma *(Pres)*

Subsidiary (Domestic):

Moriroku Technology Company, Ltd. - Kanto Plant   (2)
817 Higashishin-machi, Ota, 373-0015, Gunma, Japan
Tel.: (81) 276361000
Emp.: 221
Industrial Machinery Mfr
N.A.I.C.S.: 333248
Kazuyuki Morita *(Mgr)*

Moriroku Technology Company, Ltd. - Suzuka Plant   (2)
2199 Azana-shitanowari Ifuna-cho, Suzuka, 519-0323, Mie, Japan
Tel.: (81) 593716520
Emp.: 177
Industrial Machinery Mfr
N.A.I.C.S.: 333248

Subsidiary (Non-US):

Moriroku Technology De Mexico S.A. De C.V.   (2)
Mineral de Penafiel 137 Santa Fe Ampliacion, Puerto Interior, 36275, Silao, Guanajuato, Mexico
Tel.: (52) 4727237400
Emp.: 103
Automobile Parts Mfr & Distr
N.A.I.C.S.: 336390
Akio Morimoto *(Pres)*

Moriroku Technology India Pvt. Ltd.   (2)
B/6-11 Sector-81 Phase-, Distt Gautam Budh Nagar, Noida, 201 305, Uttar Pradesh, India
Tel.: (91) 1202568573
Automobile Parts Mfr & Distr
N.A.I.C.S.: 336390
Kumar Utsav *(Officer-Technical)*

PT. Moriroku Technology Indonesia   (2)
Surya Cipta City of Industry Jl Surya Lestari Kav I-2IJ Kutamekar, Ciampel, Karawang, Jawa Barat, Indonesia
Tel.: (62) 2678637716
Emp.: 141
Automobile Parts Mfr & Distr
N.A.I.C.S.: 336390

Wuhan Moriroku Technology Co., Ltd.   (2)
N0 216 Sandian Middle Road Jinghe street, Dongxihu District, Wuhan, China
Tel.: (86) 2783898808
Automobile Parts Mfr & Distr
N.A.I.C.S.: 336390

Subsidiary (Domestic):

Yukou Co., Ltd.   (2)
59 Mukouhara Yamakita-machi, Ashigarakami, Yamakita, 258-0111, Kanagawa, Japan
Tel.: (81) 465752815
Automobile Parts Mfr & Distr
N.A.I.C.S.: 336390

Moriroku Technology North America Inc.   (1)
15000 Industrial Pkwy, Marysville, OH 43040
Tel.: (937) 738-7821
Web Site: https://www.mtnaoh.com
Emp.: 67
Automotive Parts Mfr & Whslr
N.A.I.C.S.: 336390

Rainsville Technology, Inc.   (1)
189 RTI Dr, Rainsville, AL 35986
Tel.: (256) 638-9760

MORIROKU HOLDINGS COMPANY, LTD.

Moriroku Holdings Company, Ltd.—(Continued)
Emp.: 440
Automobile Parts Mfr & Distr
N.A.I.C.S.: 336390
Shinichi Sakairi *(Pres)*

Shikoku Kakoh Co., Ltd. (1)
516-1 Nishiyama, Higashikagawa, Shikoku-chuo, 769-2797, Kagawa, Japan
Tel.: (81) 879233111
Web Site: https://www.shikoku-kakoh.com
Emp.: 263
Multilayer Film Mfr
N.A.I.C.S.: 326112

MORISHITA JINTAN CO., LTD.
240 Tamatsukuri 1chome, Chuo-ku, Osaka, 540-8566, Japan
Tel.: (81) 667611131
Web Site: https://www.jintan.co.jp
Year Founded: 1936
4524—(TKS)
Rev.: $82,003,660
Assets: $113,579,630
Liabilities: $33,307,790
Net Worth: $80,271,840
Earnings: $4,607,170
Emp.: 354
Fiscal Year-end: 03/31/24
Health Product Mfr & Distr
N.A.I.C.S.: 325412
Yuji Morishita *(Pres & CEO)*

Subsidiaries:

Morishita Jintan Co., Ltd. - Shiga Plant (1)
960-12 Chidesuwa Ooaza Taga-Sho, Inugami-Gun, Shiga, 522-0314, Japan
Tel.: (81) 749487370
Pharmaceuticals Product Mfr
N.A.I.C.S.: 325412

MORISON INDUSTRIES PLC
28/30 Morison Crescent, Oregun Industrial Area Off Kudirat Abiola Way Oregun, Ikeja, Lagos, Nigeria
Tel.: (234) 8118680526 NG
Web Site: https://morisonplc.ng
Year Founded: 1947
MORISON—(NIGE)
Rev.: $114,626
Assets: $1,160,686
Liabilities: $450,627
Net Worth: $710,059
Earnings: ($79,557)
Emp.: 27
Fiscal Year-end: 12/31/22
Pharmaceuticals Product Mfr
N.A.I.C.S.: 325412
Richard O. Titiloye *(Chm)*

MORITA HOLDINGS CORPORATION
Keihanshin-Midosuji Building 12F 3-6-1 Dosho-machi Osaka-shi, Chuo-ku, Osaka, 541-0045, Japan
Tel.: (81) 662081907
Web Site: http://www.morita119.com
6455—(TKS)
Rev.: $629,305,050
Assets: $923,383,950
Liabilities: $318,020,320
Net Worth: $605,363,630
Earnings: $39,732,710
Emp.: 1,723
Fiscal Year-end: 03/31/24
Firefighting Vehicle & Equipment Mfr
N.A.I.C.S.: 336120
Masahiro Nakajima *(Chm & CEO)*

Subsidiaries:

Aluvo Corporation (1)
1479-1 Kamikanzo, Iwata, Shizuoka, Japan
Tel.: (81) 53 963 5016
Web Site: https://www.aluvo.co.jp
Motor Vehicle Body Parts Mfr
N.A.I.C.S.: 336211

Bronto Skylift Oy AB (1)
Teerivuorenkatu 28, 33300, Tampere, Finland
Tel.: (358) 207927111
Web Site: https://www.brontoskylift.com
Rescue & Fire Fighting Truck Mounted Hydraulic Platforms Mfr & Distr
N.A.I.C.S.: 922160

Hokkaido Morita Corporation (1)
13-2-17 Naebo-cho, Higashi-Ku, Sapporo, 065-0043, Hokkaido, Japan
Tel.: (81) 117214114
Web Site: https://www.h-morita.co.jp
Emp.: 66
Fire Protection Facilities & Equipment Mfr & Repair Services
N.A.I.C.S.: 922160

Kagoshima Morita Pump Corporation (1)
12-32 Matsubara-cho, Kagoshima, 892-0833, Japan
Tel.: (81) 992263383
Web Site: http://www.morita119.com
Fire Prevention Equipment Mfr & Sales
N.A.I.C.S.: 336120

Miyata Industry Co., Ltd. (1)
1-1-1 Shimomachiya, Chigasaki, 253 0087, Kanagawa, Japan (80%)
Tel.: (81) 467851211
Web Site: http://www.gear-m.co.jp
Sales Range: $125-149.9 Million
Emp.: 420
Bicycle & Fire-Extinguisher Mfr
N.A.I.C.S.: 336991

Morita Bohsai Tech Corporation (1)
Shiba 256 Square Building 8F 2-5-6 Shiba, Minato-ku, Tokyo, 105-0014, Japan
Tel.: (81) 337985120
Web Site: http://www.morita119-bt.com
Emp.: 83
Fire Protection Equipments Distr
N.A.I.C.S.: 423990

Morita Corporation - Sanda Factory (1)
1-5 Techno Park, Sanda, 669-1339, Hyogo, Japan
Tel.: (81) 795687800
Fire Trucks Mfr & Sales
N.A.I.C.S.: 333924
Masahiro Nakajima *(CEO)*

Morita Econos Corporation (1)
1-5 Technopark, Sanda, 669-1339, Hyogo, Japan
Tel.: (81) 795687800
Web Site: http://www.morita-econos.com
Sales Range: $50-74.9 Million
Emp.: 242
Environmental Conservation Vehicles Mfr & Distr
N.A.I.C.S.: 336120
Kouki Shirayi *(Pres)*

Morita Engineering Corporation (1)
2-68 Jinmu-cho, Yao, 581-0067, Osaka, Japan
Tel.: (81) 72 995 0621
Web Site: http://www.morita-engineering.com
Specialized Vehicles Trade-in, Fabrication, Repair & Sales
N.A.I.C.S.: 811198

Morita Environmental Tech Corporation (1)
1530 Konoda-cho, Funabashi, 274-0081, Chiba, Japan
Tel.: (81) 47 457 5111
Web Site: http://www.morita119-kt.com
Sales Range: $25-49.9 Million
Emp.: 80
Waste Recycling & Disposal Facilities Construction Services
N.A.I.C.S.: 562998

Morita Miyata Corporation (1)
TOC ARIAKE West Tower 19F 3-5-7 Ariake, Koto-ku, Tokyo, 135-0063, Japan
Tel.: (81) 33 599 3160
Fire Protection Services
N.A.I.C.S.: 922160

Morita Sogo Service Corporation (1)
5-5-20 Shoji-Higashi, Ikuno-ku, Osaka, 544-8585, Japan
Tel.: (81) 667560211

Web Site: http://www.morita119.com
Fire Extinguisher Mfr
N.A.I.C.S.: 339999

Morita Technos Corporation (1)
32 Techno Park, Ikuno-ku, Sanda, 669-1339, Hyogo, Japan
Tel.: (81) 795687171
Web Site: http://www.morita-technos.com
Emp.: 117
Automotive Repair & Maintenance Services
N.A.I.C.S.: 811114

Morita Toyo Corporation (1)
1700-2 Konjinzuka, Sanagu-Cho, Iga, 518-0001, Mie, Japan
Tel.: (81) 595218751
Web Site: http://www.morita119.com
Sales Range: $25-49.9 Million
Emp.: 27
Fire Truck Accessories Mfr
N.A.I.C.S.: 336214
Hiroki Ondo *(Pres)*

Nanjing Chenguang Morita Environment Protection Science & Technology Co., Ltd. (1)
No 188 Tianyuanzhong Road, Jiangning Economic Technical Development Zone, Nanjing, 211100, Jiangsu, China
Tel.: (86) 2552826188
Web Site: http://www.morita119.com
Sales Range: $50-74.9 Million
Emp.: 200
Environmental Conservation Vehicles Mfr & Sales
N.A.I.C.S.: 336120

MORITO CO., LTD.
4-2-4 Minami Hommachi, Chuo-ku, Osaka, 541-0054, Japan
Tel.: (81) 662523551
Web Site: https://www.morito.co.jp
Year Founded: 1908
9837—(TKS)
Rev.: $344,070,610
Assets: $364,631,610
Liabilities: $91,971,480
Net Worth: $272,660,130
Earnings: $15,718,530
Emp.: 60
Fiscal Year-end: 11/30/23
Apparel Accessory Mfr & Whlsr
N.A.I.C.S.: 339993
Nobuyuki Kataoka *(Exec VP)*

Subsidiaries:

Ace Industrial Machinery Co., Ltd. (1)
8F Komagata Plaza Bldg 1-3-16 Komagata, Taito-Ku, Tokyo, 111-0043, Japan
Tel.: (81) 338434854
Web Site: https://www.ace-kouki.co.jp
Kitchen Appliance Distr
N.A.I.C.S.: 423620

GSG Fasteners, LLC (1)
1802 Scovill Dr, Clarksville, GA 30523
Tel.: (706) 754-1000
Web Site: https://www.scovill.com
Cloth Accessory Mfr & Distr
N.A.I.C.S.: 313220

Subsidiary (Non-US):

GSG FATENERS ASIA LIMITED (2)
3/F China Aerospace Centre No 143 Hoi Bun Road Kwun Tong, Kowloon, China (Hong Kong)
Tel.: (852) 36587700
Cloth Accessory Distr
N.A.I.C.S.: 424310

GSG FATENERS INDIA LIMITED (2)
Door No 47 4th Street Swarnapuri Avenue 15 Velampalayam, Tirupur, 641652, India
Tel.: (91) 4216457910
Cloth Accessory Distr
N.A.I.C.S.: 424310

GSG FATENERS UK LIMITED (2)
The Old Courtyard 11 Lower Cookham Road, Maidenhead, SL6 8JN, United Kingdom
Tel.: (44) 1484720187

Cloth Accessory Distr
N.A.I.C.S.: 424310

MATEX INC. (1)
2-1-38 Tsutsui-cho, Chuo-ku, Kobe, 651-0071, Hyogo, Japan
Tel.: (81) 78 261 8484
Web Site: https://www.matex.com
Emp.: 70
Cloth Accessory Mfr
N.A.I.C.S.: 313220

Morito (Europe) B.V. (1)
Kiotoweg 162, 3047 BG, Rotterdam, Netherlands
Tel.: (31) 104378845
Cloth Accessory Distr
N.A.I.C.S.: 424310

Morito Apparel Co., Ltd. (1)
2-4-8 Komagata, Taito-ku, Tokyo, Japan
Tel.: (81) 662523553
Web Site: https://apparel.morito.co.jp
Emp.: 108
Lifestyle Product Mfr & Distr
N.A.I.C.S.: 315990

Morito Industrial Co., (H.K.) Ltd. (1)
RM1715-19A Tower 3 33 Canton Road, Tsim Sha Tsui, Hong Kong, China (Hong Kong)
Tel.: (852) 27366212
Web Site: http://www.moritoproducts.com
Bag Mfr & Distr
N.A.I.C.S.: 316990

Subsidiary (Non-US):

Morito (Shenzhen) Co., Ltd. (2)
Block A Yuhong Industrial Zone Heyi Village Shajing Town, Bao'an District, Shenzhen, 518104, Guang Dong, China
Tel.: (86) 75581499333
Cloth Accessory Mfr
N.A.I.C.S.: 313220

MORIXE HERMANOS S.A.C.I.
Esmeralda 1320 7 A, C1007ABR, Buenos Aires, Argentina
Tel.: (54) 8003336674
Web Site: https://www.morixe.com.ar
Food Products Mfr
N.A.I.C.S.: 311999

MORIYA CORPORATION. CO., LTD.
878 Minami Chitose-cho, Nagano, 380-8533, Japan
Tel.: (81) 262260111
Web Site: http://www.moriya-s.co.jp
Year Founded: 1955
1798—(TKS)
Rev.: $286,382,477
Assets: $202,101,034
Liabilities: $106,646,815
Net Worth: $95,454,218
Earnings: $10,611,163
Fiscal Year-end: 03/31/24
Construction Engineering Services
N.A.I.C.S.: 237990
Yuki Ito *(Pres & CEO)*

MORIYA TRANSPORTATION ENGINEERING & MANUFACTURING CO., LTD.
2-15-1 Fukuura, Kanazawa-ku, Yokohama, 236-0004, Kanagawa, Japan
Tel.: (81) 457853811
Web Site: https://moriya-elevator.co.jp
Year Founded: 1950
6226—(TKS)
Emp.: 334
Industrial Machinery Mfr
N.A.I.C.S.: 333248
Moriya Sadao *(Pres & CEO)*

MORN SUN FEED MILL CO., LTD.
2F No 30 Section 1 Heping West Road, Zhongzheng District, Taipei, 100, Taiwan

Tel.: (886) 223671162
Web Site: https://morn-sun.com.tw
Year Founded: 1958
1240—(TPE)
Rev.: $105,393,365
Assets: $69,232,217
Liabilities: $28,030,579
Net Worth: $41,201,638
Earnings: ($592,659)
Fiscal Year-end: 12/31/22
Animal Feed & Raw Material Mfr
N.A.I.C.S.: 311119
Huang Xun Gao *(Founder)*

MOROZOFF LIMITED
6-11-19 Mikage Honmachi, Higashinada-ku, Kobe, 658-0046, Hyogo, Japan
Tel.: (81) 787978677
Web Site: https://shop.morozoff.co.jp
Year Founded: 1931
2217—(TKS)
Rev.: $247,674,970
Assets: $197,945,710
Liabilities: $58,138,000
Net Worth: $139,807,710
Earnings: $12,159,350
Fiscal Year-end: 01/31/24
Confectionery Product Mfr & Distr
N.A.I.C.S.: 311351
Shinji Yamaguchi *(Pres)*

MORPHO INC.
KANDA SQUARE 11F 2-2-1 Kanda-Nishikicho, Chiyoda-ku, Tokyo, 101-0054, Japan
Tel.: (81) 358053975
Web Site: https://www.morphoinc.com
Year Founded: 2004
3653—(TKS)
Rev.: $16,895,470
Assets: $26,282,630
Liabilities: $3,963,310
Net Worth: $22,319,320
Earnings: ($2,127,000)
Emp.: 143
Fiscal Year-end: 10/31/23
Digital Image Processing Technology
N.A.I.C.S.: 334310
Masaki Hiraga *(Pres)*

MORREY SALES LTD
4451 Lougheed Hwy, Vancouver, V5C 3Z2, BC, Canada
Tel.: (604) 294-1831
Rev.: $14,500,000
Emp.: 28
New & Used Car Dealers
N.A.I.C.S.: 441110
Grant Louie *(Mgr-Sls)*

MORRICE TRANSPORTATION
3049 Devon Drive, Windsor, N8X 4L3, ON, Canada
Tel.: (800) 567-3260
Web Site: http://www.morricetransport.com
Year Founded: 1991
Trucking Transportation Service
N.A.I.C.S.: 484110
Richard Morrice *(Founder)*

MORRIS HOME HOLDINGS LIMITED
Unit 2001 20/F Citicorp Centre 18 Whitfield Road, Causeway Bay, China (Hong Kong)
Tel.: (852) 21063288   Ky
Web Site: http://www.morrisholdings.com.hk
Year Founded: 2002
1575—(HKG)
Rev.: $18,534,625
Assets: $51,513,322
Liabilities: $69,970,165
Net Worth: ($18,456,844)
Earnings: ($28,443,074)
Emp.: 350
Fiscal Year-end: 12/31/22
Sofa Mfr & Distr
N.A.I.C.S.: 337121
Gebing Zou *(Chm & CEO)*
Subsidiaries:
Jennifer Convertibles Inc. (1)
417 Crossways Park Dr, Woodbury, NY 11797
Tel.: (516) 496-1900
Web Site: http://www.jenniferfurniture.com
Sales Range: $75-99.9 Million
Emp.: 417
Sofabed & Leather Specialty Retail Stores
N.A.I.C.S.: 449110

Subsidiary (Domestic):
West Side Convertible Inc. (2)
2424 Broadway, New York, NY 10024
Tel.: (212) 787-8507
Web Site: http://www.jenniferconvertibles.com
Rev.: $660,000
Emp.: 3
Furniture Retailer
N.A.I.C.S.: 449110

MORRISON (WM) SUPERMARKETS PLC
Hilmore House Gain Lane, Bradford, BD3 7DL, United Kingdom
Tel.: (44) 8456115000
Web Site: http://www.morrisons.com
Year Founded: 1899
MZP—(BER)
Rev.: $23,000,217,600
Assets: $14,322,672,000
Liabilities: $8,366,696,400
Net Worth: $5,955,975,600
Earnings: $456,436,800
Emp.: 50,527
Fiscal Year-end: 02/29/20
Grocery Products Retailer
N.A.I.C.S.: 445110
Andrew Higginson *(Chm)*
Subsidiaries:
Chippindale Foods Limited (1)
York Road, Flaxby, Knaresborough, HG5 0RP, North Yorkshire, United Kingdom
Tel.: (44) 1423884042
Web Site: http://www.chippindalefoods.co.uk
Egg Whslr
N.A.I.C.S.: 424440

Stores Group Limited (1)
57 Great Ancoats Street Corner of Blossom Street, Manchester, M4 5AB, United Kingdom
Tel.: (44) 1612367897
Web Site: http://www.store-group.co.uk
Grocery Product Whslr
N.A.I.C.S.: 424490
Mital Morar *(Founder)*

Wm Morrison (HK) Limited (1)
19/F Millennium City 2 No 378 Kwun Tong Road, Kwun Tong, Kowloon, China (Hong Kong)
Tel.: (852) 21643400
Clothing Accessory Distr
N.A.I.C.S.: 458110

MORRISON HERSHFIELD GROUP, INC.
Suite 300 125 Commerce Valley Drive W, Markham, L3T 7W4, ON, Canada
Tel.: (416) 499-3110
Web Site: http://www.morrisonhershfield.com
Year Founded: 1946
Emp.: 1,000
Engineeering Services
N.A.I.C.S.: 541330
Anthony Karakatsanis *(Pres & CEO)*
Subsidiaries:
Morrison Hershfield Corp. (1)
10900 NE 8th St Ste 810, Bellevue, WA 98004
Tel.: (425) 451-1301
Web Site: http://www.morrisonhershfield.com
Sales Range: $1-9.9 Million
Emp.: 22
Engineeering Services
N.A.I.C.S.: 541330
Ron Wilson *(CEO)*

MORRITT PROPERTIES CAYMAN LTD
2289 Colliers Road, PO Box 496, East End, KY1-1106, Cayman Islands
Tel.: (345) 9477449
Web Site: http://www.morritts.com
Sales Range: $10-24.9 Million
Emp.: 140
Resort Owner & Operator
N.A.I.C.S.: 721110
David Morritt *(Founder & Owner)*

MORROW BANK ASA
Lysaker Torg 35, PO Box 448, 1366, Lysaker, Norway
Tel.: (47) 21007450
Web Site: https://morrowbank.no
Year Founded: 2012
MOBA—(OSL)
Rev.: $73,979,309
Assets: $1,064,843,894
Liabilities: $884,417,144
Net Worth: $180,426,750
Earnings: $83,133
Emp.: 83
Fiscal Year-end: 12/31/22
Commercial Banking Services
N.A.I.C.S.: 522110

MORROW PONTIAC BUICK
1411 Yonge St S, PO Box 1029, Walkerton, N0G 2V0, ON, Canada
Tel.: (519) 881-3401
Rev.: $10,520,339
Emp.: 23
Vehicle Repair & Services
N.A.I.C.S.: 811198

MORSES CLUB PLC
Building 1 The Phoenix Centre, 1 Colliers Way, Nottingham, NG8 6AT, United Kingdom
Tel.: (44) 3300450719   UK
Web Site: http://www.morsesclubplc.com
MCL—(AIM)
Rev.: $136,089,706
Assets: $125,982,839
Liabilities: $30,055,848
Net Worth: $95,926,991
Earnings: $294,625
Emp.: 600
Fiscal Year-end: 02/27/21
Housing Loan Services
N.A.I.C.S.: 522390
Paul Smith *(Co-CEO)*

MORSON GROUP LTD.
Adamson House Centenary Way, Salford, M50 1RD, Manchester, United Kingdom
Tel.: (44) 1617071516   UK
Web Site: http://www.morson.com
Year Founded: 1969
Sales Range: $750-799.9 Million
Emp.: 1,327
Technical Staffing & Recruitment Services
N.A.I.C.S.: 541612
Ged Mason *(CEO)*
Subsidiaries:
Morson Human Resources Limited (1)
Adenson House Centenary Way, Salford, M50 1RD, United Kingdom
Tel.: (44) 1617071516
Web Site: http://www.morson.com
Sales Range: $75-99.9 Million
Emp.: 400
Employment Placement Agencies
N.A.I.C.S.: 561311
Ged Mason *(CEO)*

Morson Projects Limited (1)
Adamson House Centenary Way, Salford, M50 1RD, United Kingdom
Tel.: (44) 1617071516
Web Site: http://www.morson.com
Sales Range: $25-49.9 Million
Emp.: 30
Engineering & Project Management Services
N.A.I.C.S.: 541330

MORTERM LIMITED
1601 Lincoln Road, PO Box 24025, Windsor, N8Y 4Y9, ON, Canada
Tel.: (519) 973-8200
Web Site: http://www.morterm.com
Rev.: $11,824,513
Emp.: 70
Cargo Services
N.A.I.C.S.: 488320
Tony De Thomas *(Pres)*

MORTGAGE ADVICE BUREAU (HOLDINGS) LTD
Capital House Pride Place, Derby, DE24 8QR, United Kingdom
Tel.: (44) 1332200020
Web Site: http://www.mortgageadvice.co.uk
Sales Range: $10-24.9 Million
Mortgage Services
N.A.I.C.S.: 522310
Katherine Christina Mary Innes Ker *(Chm)*

MORTGAGE INTELLIGENCE INC.
5770 Hurontario Street Suite 600, Mississauga, L5R 3G5, ON, Canada
Tel.: (905) 283-3300
Web Site: http://www.mortgageintelligence.ca
Year Founded: 1989
Mortgage Banker
N.A.I.C.S.: 522310
Tony Kreutzer *(VP)*

MORTGAGE SERVICE JAPAN LIMITED
Shintora Yasuda Building 4-3-1 Shinbashi, Minato-ku, Tokyo, 105-0004, Japan
Tel.: (81) 354088160
Web Site: https://www.m-s-j.jp
Year Founded: 2005
7192—(TKS)
Rev.: $46,997,100
Assets: $140,403,010
Liabilities: $86,901,670
Net Worth: $53,501,340
Earnings: $5,777,140
Fiscal Year-end: 03/31/24
Mortgage Services
N.A.I.C.S.: 522310
Yasunori Uzawa *(Founder, Chm, Pres & CEO)*

MORTON FRASER MACROBERTS LLP
30-31 Queen St, Edinburgh, EH3 9GL, United Kingdom
Tel.: (44) 1312471000
Web Site: http://www.morton-fraser.com
Emp.: 100
Law firm
N.A.I.C.S.: 541110
Bruce Wood *(Atty)*
Subsidiaries:
MacRoberts LLP (1)

MORTON FRASER MACROBERTS LLP

Morton Fraser MacRoberts LLP—(Continued)
152 Bath St, Glasgow, G2 8JX, United Kingdom
Tel.: (44) 1413329988
Emp.: 80
Law firm
N.A.I.C.S.: 541110
Ian Dickson (Partner)

MORVEST GROUP LIMITED
188 14th Road, Noordwyk, Midrand, 1685, South Africa
Tel.: (27) 87 238 1914
Web Site: http://www.morvest.co.za
Year Founded: 2003
Business Support & Information Technology Services
N.A.I.C.S.: 561499

MORY INDUSTRIES INC.
22nd floor Namba SkyO 5-1-60 Namba, Chuo-ku, Osaka, 542-0076, Japan
Tel.: (81) 647081271
Web Site: https://www.mory.co.jp
Year Founded: 1929
5464—(TKS)
Rev.: $316,605,780
Assets: $464,709,440
Liabilities: $103,770,390
Net Worth: $360,939,050
Earnings: $29,870,590
Emp.: 689
Fiscal Year-end: 03/31/24
Steel Product Mfr & Distr
N.A.I.C.S.: 331110
Hiroaki Mori (Pres)

MOS FOOD SERVICES, INC.
4F ThinkPark Tower 2-1-1 Osaki, Shinagawa-ku, Tokyo, 141-6004, Japan
Tel.: (81) 354877371
Web Site: https://www.mos.co.jp
Year Founded: 1972
8153—(TKS)
Rev.: $759,366,960
Assets: $673,747,360
Liabilities: $203,531,680
Net Worth: $470,215,680
Earnings: $33,095,920
Emp.: 1,370
Fiscal Year-end: 03/31/22
Holding Company; Limited Service Franchise Restaurants Operator & Other Food Service Businesses
N.A.I.C.S.: 551112
Eisuke Nakamura (Pres & Dir-Rep)

Subsidiaries:

MOS Store Company, Inc. (1)
4F ThinkPark Tower 2-1-1 Osaki, Shinagawa-ku, Tokyo, 141-6004, Japan
Tel.: (81) 354877430
Web Site: http://www.mos.jp
Limited Service Franchise Restaurants Operator
N.A.I.C.S.: 722513
Yoshimi Tsuzuki (Chm & Mng Dir-General Strategy Office & Brand Strategy Office)

MOS HOUSE GROUP LIMITED
Room 901 - 903 Siu On Plaza 482 Jaffe Road, Causeway Bay, China (Hong Kong)
Tel.: (852) 28319792
Web Site: https://irasia.com
Year Founded: 1998
1653—(HKG)
Rev.: $19,674,237
Assets: $39,115,877
Liabilities: $22,839,214
Net Worth: $16,276,662
Earnings: $180,454
Emp.: 65
Fiscal Year-end: 03/31/23
Ceramic Tile Mfr
N.A.I.C.S.: 327110

Cheung Chan (Sec)

MOSA INDUSTRIAL CORP.
18 Kehu 3rd Road Central Taiwan Science Park-Huwei park, Yunlin, Huwei, 63247, Taiwan
Tel.: (886) 56361867
Web Site: https://www.twmosa.com
Year Founded: 1988
4564—(TAI)
Rev.: $42,667,123
Assets: $247,943,122
Liabilities: $106,918,241
Net Worth: $141,024,881
Earnings: ($12,134,536)
Fiscal Year-end: 12/31/23
Chemical Product Mfr & Distr
N.A.I.C.S.: 325199
Te-Hsin Wang (Chm & Pres)

MOSCA AG
Gerd-Mosca-Strasse 1, 69429, Waldbrunn, Germany
Tel.: (49) 62749320 De
Web Site: http://www.en-en.mosca.com
Sales Range: $50-74.9 Million
Emp.: 680
Holding Company; Packaging Machinery & Equipment Mfr
N.A.I.C.S.: 551112
Timo Mosca (CEO & Member-Mgmt Bd)

Subsidiaries:

EAM Mosca Canada Ltd (1)
170 William Smith Drive, Whitby, L1N 9N3, ON, Canada
Tel.: (905) 665-8225
Web Site: http://www.eammosca.com
Sales Range: $25-49.9 Million
Emp.: 16
Packaging Machinery & Equipment
N.A.I.C.S.: 333993
Mike Gratz (VP)

EAM Mosca Corporation (1)
675 Jaycee Dr, Hazleton, PA 18202
Tel.: (570) 459-3426
Web Site: http://www.eammosca.com
Rev.: $16,400,000
Emp.: 80
Packaging Machinery & Equipment
N.A.I.C.S.: 423830

EAM-Mosca de Mexico S de RL de CV (1)
Av Las Torres No 800 Col Los Morales, San Nicolas de los Gorza, 66440, San Nicolas, Mexico
Tel.: (52) 818 3337080
Strapping Machine Distr
N.A.I.C.S.: 423830

Maschinenfabriik Gerd Mosca AG (1)
Gerd-Mosca-Strasse 1, 69429, Waldbrunn, Germany **(100%)**
Tel.: (49) 62749320
Web Site: http://www.mosca.com
Packaging Machinery Mfr
N.A.I.C.S.: 333993

Mosca Asia (Thailand) Ltd. (1)
11th Fl Vanit Building II Unit No 11-08 1126/2 New Petchburi Road, 10400, Bangkok, Thailand
Tel.: (66) 265 53188
Strapping Machine Distr
N.A.I.C.S.: 423830

Mosca Asia Pte Ltd. (1)
25 Tagore Ln 04 09, Singapore, 787602, Singapore
Tel.: (65) 65550128
Web Site: http://www.mosca.com.sg
Sales Range: $25-49.9 Million
Emp.: 5
Packaging Machinery & Equipment
N.A.I.C.S.: 333993

Mosca Australia (Pty) Ltd. (1)
Unit 6/58 Frederick Street, Brisbane, 4013, QLD, Australia

Tel.: (61) 732 663005
Web Site: http://www.mosca.com
Strapping Machine Distr
N.A.I.C.S.: 423830
Simone Mosca (Co-CEO)

Mosca Direct Finland OY (1)
Martinkylatie 9 A-C, 01770, Vantaa, Finland
Tel.: (358) 207 498000
Strapping Machine Distr
N.A.I.C.S.: 423830
Vesa Wallden (Mgr-Sls)

Mosca Direct Ltd. (1)
Colliers Way Colliers Business Park, Cotgrave, NG12 3HA, Notts, United Kingdom
Tel.: (44) 1159890209
Web Site: http://www.mosca.com
Sales Range: $25-49.9 Million
Emp.: 28
Packaging Machinery & Equipment
N.A.I.C.S.: 333993
Julie Walton (Dir-Engrg Ops)

Mosca Direct Poland Sp. z o.o. (1)
ul Plowiecka 105/107, 04-501, Warsaw, Poland
Tel.: (48) 228 700033
Web Site: http://www.mosca.com
Strapping Machine Distr
N.A.I.C.S.: 423830

Mosca Direct Shanghai Co., Ltd. (1)
No 5343 Nanting Road, Jinshan District, 201505, Shanghai, China
Tel.: (86) 21 37283550
Corrugated Box Mfr
N.A.I.C.S.: 322211

Mosca Direct Spain S.L. (1)
Pol Ind Les Pedreres Nave 1, E 08390, Mongat, Spain
Tel.: (34) 934690123
Web Site: http://www.moscadirectspain.com
Sales Range: $25-49.9 Million
Emp.: 12
Packaging Machinery & Equipment
N.A.I.C.S.: 333993
Francisco Nicholas (Mng Dir)

Mosca Malaysia SDN. BHD. (1)
No 3 Jalan Canggih 9 Taman Perindustrian Cemerlang, Johor Darul Takzim, 81800, Ulu Tiram, Malaysia
Tel.: (60) 786 13398
Strapping Machine Distr
N.A.I.C.S.: 423830
Vairavan Shanmugam (Gen Mgr)

MOSCHIP TECHNOLOGIES LIMITED
7th Floor My Home Twitza, TSIIC Hyderabad Knowledge City Raidurg Panmaktha Rangareddy, Telangana, 500081, India
Tel.: (91) 4066229292
Web Site: https://www.moschip.com
532407—(BOM)
Rev.: $20,854,183
Assets: $22,117,218
Liabilities: $13,192,275
Net Worth: $8,924,943
Earnings: $880,835
Emp.: 792
Fiscal Year-end: 03/31/22
Semiconductor Product Mfr
N.A.I.C.S.: 334413
Kadiri Ramachandra Reddy (Founder)

Subsidiaries:

Maven Systems Private Limited (1)
2nd Floor Krishna Chambers Sai Chowk Sus road, Pune, 411021, India
Tel.: (91) 2022952851
Web Site: http://www.mavensystems.com
Software Development Services
N.A.I.C.S.: 541511

MosChip Institute of Silicon Systems Private Limited (1)
A-Wing 6th Floor Aurobindo Galaxy, Hyderabad Knowledge City, Hyderabad, 500081, Telangana, India
Tel.: (91) 9573346699
Web Site: https://m-iss.in

INTERNATIONAL PUBLIC

Physical Design Training Centre Services
N.A.I.C.S.: 713940

Softnautics LLP (1)
B block 3rd Floor Westgate SG Highway Makarba, Ahmedabad, 380051, Gujarat, India
Tel.: (91) 7935338580
Semiconductor Component Mfr & Distr
N.A.I.C.S.: 334413

MOSCOVSKIY OBLASTNOI BANK PAO
Bolshaya Semenovskaya St 32 building 1, Moscow, 107023, Russia
Tel.: (7) 4959098191
Web Site: https://www.mosoblbank.ru
Year Founded: 1992
MOBB—(MOEX)
Sales Range: Less than $1 Million
Commercial Banking Services
N.A.I.C.S.: 522110

MOSCOW INTEGRATED POWER COMPANY JSC
Vernadsky Avenue 101 Building 3, Moscow, 119526, Russia
Tel.: (7) 4955877788
Web Site: http://www.oaomoek.ru
Sales Range: Less than $1 Million
Electric Power Distribution Services
N.A.I.C.S.: 237130
Denis N. Bashuk (Mng Dir)

MOSCOW MACHINE BUILDING PLANT VPERED JSC
15 Proezd Entuziastov, 111024, Moscow, Russia
Tel.: (7) 4956734427
Web Site: http://www.eng.mmz-vpered.ru
Helicopter Blade &tail Rotors Mfr
N.A.I.C.S.: 423860
Sergey Ivanovich Shcherbachenko (Gen Dir)

Subsidiaries:

MPO-Rumyantsev JSC (1)
34 Raskovoy str, Moscow, 125015, Russia **(86.47%)**
Tel.: (7) 4956135156
Web Site: http://www.mporum.ru
Automobile Equipment Mfr
N.A.I.C.S.: 334519
Leonid M. Khalfoun (Dir Gen)

MOSEL VITELIC INC.
No 1 Yanxin 1st Road Science Industrial Park, Hsin-chu, Taiwan
Tel.: (886) 35783344
Web Site: https://www.mosel.com.tw
Year Founded: 1991
2342—(TAI)
Rev.: $48,500,996
Assets: $111,742,924
Liabilities: $34,437,848
Net Worth: $77,305,076
Earnings: $5,778,835
Emp.: 1,000
Fiscal Year-end: 12/31/23
Electronic Circuits Mfr
N.A.I.C.S.: 334412
Yixian Tang (Chm, CEO & Gen Mgr)

MOSER BAER INDIA LIMITED
43B Okhla Industrial Estate, New Delhi, 110020, India
Tel.: (91) 1140594444 In
Web Site: http://www.moserbaer.com
Year Founded: 1983
Optical Media & Data Storage Disks Developer & Mfr
N.A.I.C.S.: 334610
Nita Puri (Exec Dir)

Subsidiaries:

Moser Baer Energy Limited (1)
43B Okhla Industrial Estate, 110020, New

AND PRIVATE COMPANIES

Delhi, India
Tel.: (91) 11 26911574
Photovoltaic Systems Mfr
N.A.I.C.S.: 334413

Moser Baer Entertainment
Limited (1)
23 Shah Industrial Estate 2nd Floor, Andheri, 400053, Mumbai, Maharastra, India
Tel.: (91) 22 42174500
Web Site:
   http://www.moserbaerhomevideo.com
Home Videos Distr
N.A.I.C.S.: 423990

Moser Baer India Limited - BOM &
M& ES (1)
66 Udyog Vihar, Noida, Uttar Pradesh, India
Tel.: (91) 1204386000
Optical Storage Devices Mfr
N.A.I.C.S.: 334112

Moser Baer India Limited - Home Entertainment Division (1)
23 Shah Industrial Estate 2nd Floor Office Veera Desai Road, Andheri, 400053, Mumbai, Maharastra, India
Tel.: (91) 22 42174500
Web Site: http://www.moserbaer.com
Optical Storage Devices Mfr
N.A.I.C.S.: 334112

Moser Baer Photo Voltaic Ltd (1)
43 B Okhla Industrial Est Phase III, New
Delhi, 110020, India (100%)
Tel.: (91) 1141635201
Web Site: http://www.moserbaerpv.in
Sales Range: $100-124.9 Million
Emp.: 400
Photographic & Photocopying Equipment Mfr
N.A.I.C.S.: 333310
Rajiv Arya (CEO)

Moser Baer SEZ Developer
Limited (1)
66B SEZ Udyog Vihar, Noida, Uttar
Pradesh, India
Tel.: (91) 1204658000
Optical Storage Devices Mfr
N.A.I.C.S.: 334112
V. C. Agarwal (CEO)

Moser Baer Solar Limited (1)
43B Okhla Industrial Estate, 110020, New
Delhi, India
Tel.: (91) 11 40594444
Web Site: http://www.moserbaersolar.com
Sales Range: $150-199.9 Million
Emp.: 700
Photovoltaic Systems Mfr
N.A.I.C.S.: 334413
Vivek Chaturvedi (Gen Mgr)

Division (Domestic):

Moser Baer Solar Limited (2)
66B SEZ Udyog Vihar, Noida, 201306, Uttar Pradesh, India
Tel.: (91) 120 4658000
Web Site: http://www.moserbaersolar.com
Optical Storage Media Mfr
N.A.I.C.S.: 334112
Rajiv Sahdev (VP-HR)

Moser Baer Technologies Inc. (1)
5450 Campus Dr Ste 200, Canandaigua,
NY 14423-8207
Tel.: (585) 919-2500
Optical Storage Devices Mfr
N.A.I.C.S.: 334112

OM&T B.V. (1)
High Tech Campus 29, 5656 AE, Eindhoven, North Brabant, Netherlands
Tel.: (31) 402171400
Web Site: http://www.om-t.net
Optical Storage Devices Mfr
N.A.I.C.S.: 334112

MOSHI MOSHI RETAIL CORPORATION PUBLIC COMPANY LIMITED
26/18 Village No 10, Bang Khun
Thian Subdistrict Chom Thong District, Bangkok, 10150, Thailand
Tel.: (66) 28913088
Web Site:
   https://www.moshimoshi.co.th
Year Founded: 1973
MOSHI—(THA)
Rev.: $74,242,640
Assets: $106,346,963
Liabilities: $48,490,666
Net Worth: $57,856,296
Earnings: $11,720,789
Emp.: 1,031
Fiscal Year-end: 12/31/23
Recreational Goods Distr
N.A.I.C.S.: 423910
Warapatr Todhanakasem (Chm)

MOSMAN OIL AND GAS LIMITED
Traverse Accountants 24 26 Kent
Street, Sydney, 2000, NSW, Australia
Tel.: (61) 282960000
Web Site:
   https://www.mosmanoilandgas.com
MSMN—(AIM)
Rev.: $1,674,920
Assets: $3,033,601
Liabilities: $569,360
Net Worth: $2,464,241
Earnings: ($4,837,410)
Fiscal Year-end: 06/30/20
Oil & Gas Exploration
N.A.I.C.S.: 211120
John W. Barr (Founder & Chm)

Subsidiaries:

Mosman Operating, LLC (1)
2807 Allen St No 407, Dallas, TX 75204
Tel.: (214) 585-1690
Web Site: https://www.mosman-operating.com
Oil & Gas Field Exploration Services
N.A.I.C.S.: 237120

MOSPEC SEMICONDUCTOR CORP.
No 76 Zhongshan Rd, Xinshi Dist,
T'ainan, 74442, Taiwan
Tel.: (886) 65991621
Web Site:
   https://www.mospec.com.tw
Year Founded: 1987
2434—(TAI)
Rev.: $2,062,821
Assets: $21,261,061
Liabilities: $6,109,062
Net Worth: $15,151,999
Earnings: ($1,187,383)
Fiscal Year-end: 12/31/23
Diodes, Rectifiers & Semiconductor Mfr
N.A.I.C.S.: 334413

Subsidiaries:

Mospec Semiconductor (Shenzhen)
Co., Ltd. (1)
Room902 Bangonglou Xindi Central,
Guangming District, Shenzhen, Guangdong,
China
Tel.: (86) 75529891881
Web Site: http://www.mospec.com.tw
Electronic Components Mfr
N.A.I.C.S.: 334419

MOSS BROS GROUP PLC
8 St John's Hill Clapham Junction,
London, SW11 1SA, United Kingdom
Tel.: (44) 2074477200   UK
Web Site: http://corp.moss.co.uk
Year Founded: 1851
MOSB—(LSE)
Rev.: $163,687,083
Assets: $69,638,742
Liabilities: $33,115,077
Net Worth: $36,523,665
Earnings: ($4,880,651)
Emp.: 945
Fiscal Year-end: 01/26/19
Men's Clothing Retailer
N.A.I.C.S.: 458110

Brian Brick (CEO)

MOSS GENOMICS INC.
Suite 907 1030 West Georgia Street,
Vancouver, V6E 2Y3, BC, Canada
Tel.: (605) 629-5974
Web Site:
   https://www.mossgenomics.com
Year Founded: 2018
MOSS—(CNSX)
Assets: $53,116
Liabilities: $72,674
Net Worth: ($19,558)
Earnings: $97,256
Fiscal Year-end: 06/30/24
Health Care Srvices
N.A.I.C.S.: 621610
Michelle Kira Lee (CFO)

MOSSACK FONSECA & CO.
East 54th Street Marbella Mossfon
Building, Panama, Panama
Tel.: (507) 205 5888
Web Site: http://www.mossfon.com
Year Founded: 1977
Emp.: 500
Law firm
N.A.I.C.S.: 541110
Jurgen Mossack (Co-Founder & Partner)

MOSTOBUD, PJSC
5 Pankivska str, Kiev, 01033, Ukraine
Tel.: (380) 44 494 2995
Year Founded: 1945
MTBD—(UKR)
Bridge Construction & Engineering
Services
N.A.I.C.S.: 237330
Mykhailo Korniev (Deputy Chm & Head-Project Office)

MOSTOSTAL PLOCK S.A.
ul Targowa 12, 09-400, Plock, Poland
Tel.: (48) 243671124
Web Site: https://www.mostostal-plock.pl
Year Founded: 1963
MSP—(WAR)
Rev.: $28,984,502
Assets: $24,941,565
Liabilities: $18,692,581
Net Worth: $6,248,984
Earnings: ($2,973,323)
Emp.: 1,535
Fiscal Year-end: 12/31/23
Engineering & Construction Services
N.A.I.C.S.: 541330
Pawel Rakowski (Member-Mgmt Bd-Production Dept)

MOSTOSTAL WROCLAW S.A.
Ulica Konstruktorska 11A, Warsaw,
02-673, Poland
Tel.: (48) 225485000
Construction Machinery Mfr
N.A.I.C.S.: 333120
Miguel Angel Heras Liorente (Chm)

MOSTOSTAL ZABRZE S.A.
ul Dubois 16, 44-100, Gliwice, Poland
Tel.: (48) 323734444
Web Site: https://mz.pl
Year Founded: 1945
MSZ—(WAR)
Rev.: $343,348,576
Assets: $180,322,408
Liabilities: $106,671,494
Net Worth: $73,650,914
Earnings: $19,301,829
Fiscal Year-end: 12/31/23
Industrial Construction Services
N.A.I.C.S.: 236210
Aleksander Balcer (Vice Chm-Mgmt Bd)

MOTA-ENGIL SGPS, S.A.

MOSTOSTROY-11 AO
Energetikov st 26, Surgut, 628408,
Russia
Tel.: (7) 3452540300
Web Site: https://ms11.ru
Year Founded: 1975
MSTS—(MOEX)
Sales Range: Less than $1 Million
Construction Services
N.A.I.C.S.: 236220
Russu Nikolay Alexandrovich (Gen Mgr)

MOSTOTREST PAO
6 Barclay str building 5, Moscow,
121087, Russia
Tel.: (7) 4956697999
Web Site: https://www.mostro.ru
MSTT—(MOEX)
Rev.: $2,299,476,670
Assets: $2,729,728,290
Liabilities: $2,424,758,380
Net Worth: $304,969,910
Earnings: $8,419,860
Emp.: 29,738
Fiscal Year-end: 12/31/19
Railway, Highway, Bridge, Civil, Industrial & Residential Construction
Services
N.A.I.C.S.: 237310
Vladimir Vlasov (CEO)

Subsidiaries:

OOO Taganka Most (1)
61/2 Zemlyanoi Val Ul, Moscow, 109004,
Russia
Tel.: (7) 4959155483
Construction Engineering Services
N.A.I.C.S.: 541330

MOSTPROJEKT A.D.
Palmira Toljatija 11, 11070, Belgrade,
Serbia
Tel.: (381) 11 3193 801
Web Site: http://www.mostprojekt.rs
Year Founded: 1956
Emp.: 26
Civil Engineering Services
N.A.I.C.S.: 237990

MOSTYLE CORPORATION
3rd Floor No 50 Chou Tze Street,
Nei-Hu, Taipei, 114, Taiwan
Tel.: (886) 287972800   TW
Web Site: http://www.mostyle.com.tw
Year Founded: 1992
Electronic Components Distr
N.A.I.C.S.: 423690
Wilfred Hsiao (Exec VP)

MOSUL BANK FOR DEVELOPMENT & INVESTMENT
Al-Nidhal Street near the White Palace, Baghdad, Iraq
Tel.: (964) 7801882200
Web Site: https://almosulbank.iq
Year Founded: 2001
BMFI—(IRAQ)
Sales Range: Less than $1 Million
Commercial Banking Services
N.A.I.C.S.: 522110

MOTA-ENGIL SGPS, S.A.
Rua do Rego Lameiro 38, 4300-454,
Porto, Portugal
Tel.: (351) 225190300
Web Site: https://www.mota-engil.com
Year Founded: 1946
EGL—(EUR)
Rev.: $6,128,598,080
Assets: $8,495,287,561
Liabilities: $7,672,339,111
Net Worth: $822,948,449
Earnings: $293,497,075
Emp.: 53,340
Fiscal Year-end: 12/31/23

MOTA-ENGIL SGPS, S.A.

Mota-Engil SGPS, S.A.—(Continued)
Construction Engineering Services
N.A.I.C.S.: 541330
Antonio Manuel Queiros Vasconcelos da Mota *(Chm)*

Subsidiaries:

Areagolfe - Gestao, Construcao e Manutencao de Campos de Golfe, S.A. (1)
Quinta da Silva Rua Dr Jose Maria Raposo Lote 153 R/c Esq, Lapas, 2350-085, Torres Novas, Portugal
Tel.: (351) 249819550
Web Site: http://www.areagolfe.com
Golf Course Construction Services
N.A.I.C.S.: 237990

Glan Agua, Ltd (1)
Railway House Station Road Loughrea, Galway, Ireland
Tel.: (353) 909630301
Web Site: http://www.glanagua.ie
Water System Construction Services
N.A.I.C.S.: 237110
Paul Gardner *(Mng Dir)*

Manvia Espana S A (1)
Camino Fontan Porceyo 590 Porceyo, 33211, Asturias, Spain
Tel.: (34) 984204549
Building Construction Services
N.A.I.C.S.: 236220

Mota Internacional - Comercio e Consultadoria Economica, Lda. (1)
Avenida Arriaga 75 - 1 Sala 101 Edificio Monumental Infante, 9000-060, Funchal, Portugal
Tel.: (351) 291233803
Investment Holding Services
N.A.I.C.S.: 551112

Subsidiary (Non-US):

Cosamo (Proprietary) Limited (2)
Diesel Rd Nr 12 - Isando 160, Johannesburg, South Africa
Tel.: (27) 113923664
Logistics Consulting Servies
N.A.I.C.S.: 541614

Mota-Engil Angola, S.A. (2)
Rua Joaquim Cordeiro Da Mata No 61/63 Distrito E Bairro Da Maianga, Luanda, Angola
Tel.: (244) 222350218
Construction Development Services
N.A.I.C.S.: 236220

Subsidiary (Domestic):

Novicer-Ceramicas de Angola, (SU) Limitada. (3)
Municipio De Cacuaco Km 2 4 Da Estrada Kifangondo, Funda, Angola
Tel.: (244) 937081116
Clay Goods Mfr & Distr
N.A.I.C.S.: 327120

Rentaco Angola - Equipamentos e Transportes, (SU) Limitada. (3)
Rua Narciso Do Espirito Santo 52/56 Municipio Da Maianga, Luanda, Angola
Tel.: (244) 923266464
Web Site: http://www.rentaco.co.ao
Construction Equipment Leasing Services
N.A.I.C.S.: 532412

Subsidiary (Non-US):

Mota-Engil S.Tome e Principe, Lda. (2)
Av Marginal 12 De Julho, PO Box 167, Sao Tome, Sao Tome & Principe
Tel.: (239) 2227770
Construction Contracting Services
N.A.I.C.S.: 236116

Sonauta - Sociedade de Navegacao, Lda. (2)
Rua Da Boavista N 182, Luanda, Angola
Tel.: (244) 914249921
Web Site: http://www.sonauta.net
Sea Transportation Services
N.A.I.C.S.: 483111

Mota-Engil Central Europe Ceska Republika, AS (1)
Kavci Hory Office Park Building A Na Hrebenech II 1718/10 Nusle, 140 00, Prague, Czech Republic
Tel.: (420) 261392701
Web Site: http://www.mota-engil.cz
Building Construction Services
N.A.I.C.S.: 236220
Pedro Vasco Rocha Goncalves *(CFO)*

Mota-Engil Central Europe, S.A. (1)
Opolska 110, 31-323, Krakow, Poland
Tel.: (48) 126648000
Web Site: https://www.mota-engil-ce.eu
Civil Construction Services
N.A.I.C.S.: 237990

Mota-Engil Chile S.A. (1)
Av Vitacura 2736 - Of 504, Las Condes, Santiago, Chile
Tel.: (56) 229445500
Web Site: http://www.mota-engil.cl
Civil Construction Services
N.A.I.C.S.: 237990

Mota-Engil Colombia, S.A.S (1)
Carrera 11 87 - 51 Edificio Porvenir Ofi, 301, Bogota, Colombia
Tel.: (57) 14824821
Construction Development Services
N.A.I.C.S.: 236220

Mota-Engil Industria e Inovacao, SGPS, S.A. (1)
Rua Mario Dionisio N 2, 2799-557, Linda-a-Velha, Portugal
Tel.: (351) 214158200
Web Site: http://www.meii.mota-engil.pt
Financial Management Services
N.A.I.C.S.: 551112

Mota-Engil Ireland Construction Limited (1)
Unit 3 4075 Kingswood Road Citywest Business Campus, Dublin, Ireland
Tel.: (353) 15514515
Web Site: http://www.meicltd.com
Emp.: 28,000
Civil Engineering Services
N.A.I.C.S.: 541330
Aine Healy *(Mgr-Quality, Environmental, Health & Safety)*

Mota-Engil Latam Colombia S.A.S. (1)
Carrera 11 87-51 Edificio Porvenir Ofi 301, Bogota, Colombia
Tel.: (57) 14824821
Construction Services
N.A.I.C.S.: 236220

Mota-Engil Minerals & Mining (Malawi) Limited (1)
Nasra Building City Centre, Lilongwe, Malawi
Tel.: (265) 1758910
Mineral Processing Services
N.A.I.C.S.: 213115

Mota-Engil Minerals & Mining (Zimbabwe) (Private) Limited (1)
7 Routledge Street, Harare, Zimbabwe
Tel.: (263) 4795303
Mineral Processing Services
N.A.I.C.S.: 213115

Mota-Engil Peru, S.A. (1)
Av Javier Prado Este N 444 Edificio Torre Prado Pisos 22 y 23, San Isidro, Lima, Peru
Tel.: (51) 14143665
Web Site: https://www.mota-engil.pe
Emp.: 3,000
Road Construction Services
N.A.I.C.S.: 237310
Nuno Figueiredo *(CEO)*

Mota-Engil Railway Engineering, S.A. (1)
Rua do Rego Lameiro N 38, Porto, 4300-454, Portugal
Tel.: (351) 225190300
Construction Services
N.A.I.C.S.: 236220

SGA - Sociedade do Golfe de Amarante, S.A. (1)
Quinta da Deveza - Fregim, 4600-593, Amarante, Portugal
Tel.: (351) 255446060
Web Site: http://www.golfedeamarante.com
Golf Club Operator
N.A.I.C.S.: 713910

Suma - Servicos Urbanos e Meio Ambiente, S.A. (1)
Avenida D Joao II n 30 1, 1990-092, Lisbon, Portugal
Tel.: (351) 217 997 700
Web Site: http://www.suma.pt
Waste Management Services
N.A.I.C.S.: 562998

Subsidiary (Domestic):

Rima - Residuos Industriais e Meio Ambiente, S.A. (2)
Rua da Serra de Campelos N 975, 4620-868, Lousada, Portugal
Tel.: (351) 255881403
Web Site: http://www.rima.pt
Industrial Wastes Treatment Services
N.A.I.C.S.: 562212

Suma (Esposende) - Servicos Urbanos e Meio Ambiente, Lda. (2)
Quinta da Mangalaca Lugar de Goios Marinha, 4740-543, Esposende, Portugal
Tel.: (351) 253966149
Urban Waste Collection Services
N.A.I.C.S.: 562119

Suma (Porto) - Servicos Urbanos e Meio Ambiente, S.A. (2)
Via Adelino Amaro da Costa 315, Maia, 4470-557, Moreira, Portugal
Tel.: (351) 229446328
Waste Management Services
N.A.I.C.S.: 562998

Triaza - Tratamento de Residuos Industriais da Azambuja, S.A. (2)
Quinta da Queijeira EN3 Km 13, 2050-360, Azambuja, Portugal
Tel.: (351) 263099728
Web Site: https://www.triaza.pt
Nonhazardous Waste Management Services
N.A.I.C.S.: 562212

Tracevia do Brazil -Sistemas de Telemtica Rodoviaria Ltda. (1)
Rua Goncalves Dias 2316 Sala 2 - Bairro De Lourdes, Belo Horizonte, 30140-092, Minas Gerais, Brazil
Tel.: (55) 1137289365
Information Technology Management Services
N.A.I.C.S.: 541512

MOTECH INDUSTRIES INC.
6F No 248 Sec 3 Bei-Shen Road, Shen-Keng District, New Taipei City, 22204, Taiwan
Tel.: (886) 226625093
Web Site:
https://www.motechsolar.com
Year Founded: 1981
6244—(TPE)
Rev.: $167,588,344
Assets: $299,197,605
Liabilities: $163,749,398
Net Worth: $135,448,207
Earnings: $8,514,430
Fiscal Year-end: 12/31/22
Solar Product Mfr
N.A.I.C.S.: 334413
Steve Tseng *(Chm)*

MOTHER LTD.
Biscuit Bldg 10 Redchurch St, London, E2 7DD, United Kingdom
Tel.: (44) 20 7012 1999
Web Site:
http://www.motherlondon.com
Emp.: 120
N.A.I.C.S.: 541810
Stef Calcraft *(Founder)*

Subsidiaries:

Madre (1)
Petrona Eyle 450 DTO, CJD, C1107, Buenos Aires, Argentina
Tel.: (54) 11 5787 0500

INTERNATIONAL PUBLIC

N.A.I.C.S.: 541810
Carlos Bayala *(Founding Partner & Creative Dir)*

Mother New York (1)
595 11th Ave, New York, NY 10036
Tel.: (212) 254-2800
Web Site: http://www.mothernewyork.com
Emp.: 70
N.A.I.C.S.: 541810
Paul Malmstrom *(Co-Founder & Chief Creative Officer)*

MOTHERCARE PLC
Westside 1 London Road, Hemel Hempstead, HP3 9TD, Hertfordshire, United Kingdom
Tel.: (44) 1923241000   UK
Web Site:
https://www.mothercareplc.com
MTC—(AIM)
Rev.: $71,546,786
Assets: $28,516,868
Liabilities: $66,836,410
Net Worth: ($38,319,542)
Earnings: $4,201,146
Emp.: 436
Fiscal Year-end: 03/30/24
Holding Company; Maternity Wear, Babies & Pre-School Children's Apparel & Toys Retailer
N.A.I.C.S.: 551112
Matt Stringer *(Officer-Product-Global)*

Subsidiaries:

Mothercare UK Limited (1)
Cherry Tree Road, Watford, WD24 6SH, Herts, United Kingdom
Tel.: (44) 1923241000
Web Site: http://www.mothercare.com
Emp.: 600
Childrens & Infants Clothing Stores
N.A.I.C.S.: 458110

MOTIC (XIAMEN) ELECTRIC GROUP CO., LTD.
No 808 Fangshan South Road Torch Hi-Tech Industrial Development Zone, Xiangan, Xiamen, 361101, Fujian, China
Tel.: (86) 5925628287
Web Site: http://www.motic-electric.com
Year Founded: 2002
300341—(CHIN)
Rev.: $251,873,388
Assets: $313,181,856
Liabilities: $75,655,944
Net Worth: $237,525,912
Earnings: $36,664,056
Emp.: 500
Fiscal Year-end: 12/31/22
Electric Insulation Products Mfr
N.A.I.C.S.: 335932
Yang Wenliang *(Chm)*

MOTIF TECHNOLOGY CO., LTD.
14th Fl Times Square Bldg 246 Sukhumvit Rd, Klongtoey, Bangkok, 10110, Thailand
Tel.: (66) 26533644
Web Site: http://www.motiftech.com
IT Software & Services
N.A.I.C.S.: 513210
Wanchai Riophaibun *(Chm)*

MOTILAL OSWAL FINANCIAL SERVICES LTD.
Motilal Oswal Tower Rahimtullah Sayani Road Opposite Parel ST Depot, Prabhadevi, Mumbai, 400025, Maharashtra, India
Tel.: (91) 2271934263
Web Site:
https://www.motilaloswal.com
MOTILALOFS—(NSE)
Rev.: $503,221,629

AND PRIVATE COMPANIES

Assets: $2,758,820,215
Liabilities: $2,005,486,482
Net Worth: $753,333,733
Earnings: $112,077,214
Emp.: 7,303
Fiscal Year-end: 03/31/23
Financial & Investment Services
N.A.I.C.S.: 523150
Motilal Oswal *(Co-CEO & Mng Dir)*

Subsidiaries:

India Business Excellence Management Company (1)
Apex House Bank Street TwentyEight CyberCity, 72201, Ebene, Mauritius
Tel.: (230) 4673000
Web Site: https://www.ibemc.co
Investment Advisory Services
N.A.I.C.S.: 523940

MO Alternate Investment Private Limited (1)

MO Alternative IFSC Limited (1)

MOPE Investment Advisors Private Limited (1)
Motilal Oswal Towers Junction of Gokhale and Sayani Road, Prabhadevi, Mumbai, 400 025, India
Tel.: (91) 2271934200
Asset Management Services
N.A.I.C.S.: 523940

Motilal Oswal Commodities Broker Pvt. Ltd. (1)
Palm Spring Centre 2nd Floor Palm Court Complex New Link Road, Malad W, Mumbai, 400 064, Maharashtra, India
Tel.: (91) 2230801000
Web Site: http://www.motilaloswal.com
Sales Range: $350-399.9 Million
Emp.: 1,000
Commodity Trading Services
N.A.I.C.S.: 523160

Motilal Oswal Home Finance Limited (1)
Motilal Oswal Tower Rahimtullah Sayani Road Opposite Parel ST Depot, Prabhadevi, Mumbai, 400 025, India
Tel.: (91) 2247189999
Web Site: https://www.motilaloswalhf.com
Financial Management Services
N.A.I.C.S.: 523940
Motilal Oswal *(Chm)*

Motilal Oswal Investment Advisors Pvt. Ltd. (1)
Motilal Oswal Towers 10th Fl Junction Gokhale & Sayani Rd Prabhadevi, Mumbai, 400 025, Maharashtra, India
Tel.: (91) 2271904200
Web Site: http://www.motilaloswalgroup.com
Sales Range: $50-74.9 Million
Emp.: 25
Investment Banking Services
N.A.I.C.S.: 523150
Ashutosh Maheshvari *(CEO)*

Motilal Oswal Private Equity Advisors Pvt. Ltd. (1)
Motilal Oswal tower Gokhale Sayani Junction Parel s t depot, Nariman Point, Mumbai, 400025, Maharashtra, India
Tel.: (91) 2239825500
Web Site: http://www.motilaloswal.com
Sales Range: $50-74.9 Million
Emp.: 20
Private Equity Management Services
N.A.I.C.S.: 522292
Vishal Tulsyan *(CEO & Mng Dir)*

Motilal Oswal Securities Limited (1)
4th Fl Hoechst House Nariman Point, Mumbai, 400 021, Maharashtra, India
Tel.: (91) 2230896680
Web Site: http://www.motilaloswal.com
Financial Services
N.A.I.C.S.: 541611

Motilal Oswal Wealth Management Limited (1)
Motilal Oswal Towers Juction of Gokhale and Sayani Road, Prabhadevi, Mumbai, 400025, India
Tel.: (91) 2271934711

Private Wealth Management Services
N.A.I.C.S.: 523940

MOTIO LIMITED
Level 8 140 Arthur Street, North Sydney, 2060, NSW, Australia
Tel.: (61) 272272277 AU
Web Site: http://xtd.tv
MXO—(ASX)
Rev.: $4,291,525
Assets: $6,539,519
Liabilities: $2,811,063
Net Worth: $3,728,456
Earnings: ($1,163,018)
Fiscal Year-end: 06/30/23
Digital Media System Services
N.A.I.C.S.: 334290
Adam Cadwallader *(Mng Dir)*

MOTION DISPLAY SCANDINAVIA AB
Vaderkvarnsgatan 17c, 753 29, Uppsala, Sweden
Tel.: (46) 184440300
Web Site:
https://www.motiondisplay.com
Year Founded: 2005
Home Appliance Distr
N.A.I.C.S.: 449129
Erik Danielsson *(Founder & Chm)*

MOTION EQUITY PARTNERS S.A.S.
47 Avenue George V, 75008, Paris, France
Tel.: (33) 1 5383 7910 FR
Web Site:
http://www.motionequitypartner.com
Privater Equity Firm
N.A.I.C.S.: 523999
Patrick Eisenchteter *(Mng Partner)*

Subsidiaries:

Motion Equity Partners LLP (1)
2nd Floor 10 Lower Grosvenor Place, London, SW1W 0EN, United Kingdom
Tel.: (44) 7709332652
Web Site:
http://www.motionequitypartners.com
Administrative Office; Private Equity Firm
N.A.I.C.S.: 561110

Tokheim Group S.A.S. (1)
Paris Nord 2 Immeuble Le Cezanne 35 allee des Impressionnistes, PO Box 45027, Villepinte, 95912, Charles de Gaulle, Cedex, France (66%)
Tel.: (33) 1 4990 7700
Web Site: http://www.tokheim.com
Sales Range: $700-749.9 Million
Emp.: 5,400
Fuel Dispensing Equipment Mfr, Whslr & Support Services
N.A.I.C.S.: 333914
Bill Arundel *(Dir-Sls & Mktg)*

Subsidiary (Non-US):

Tokheim GmbH (2)
Lothstrasse 1a, 80335, Munich, Germany
Tel.: (49) 89189530
Web Site: http://www.tokheim.com
Sales Range: $25-49.9 Million
Emp.: 30
Fuel Dispensing Equipment Whslr
N.A.I.C.S.: 423440
Siegfried Kafer *(Gen Mgr)*

Tokheim South Africa (Pty) Ltd. (2)
270 Albert Amon Road, Meadowdale, Germiston, South Africa (100%)
Tel.: (27) 11 657 6000
Web Site: http://www.petro-logic.co.za
Sales Range: $50-74.9 Million
Emp.: 6
Fuel Dispensing Equipment Whslr
N.A.I.C.S.: 423440
Chris Kirstein *(Gen Mgr)*

MOTISONS JEWELLERS LIMITED
SB-110 Motisons Tower Tonk Road

Opp Nagar Nigam Office, Jaipur, 302015, Rajasthan, India
Tel.: (91) 8952020205
Web Site:
https://www.motisonsjewellers.com
Year Founded: 2005
544053—(BOM)
Rev.: $44,456,911
Assets: $40,784,951
Liabilities: $24,131,090
Net Worth: $16,653,862
Earnings: $2,690,143
Emp.: 151
Fiscal Year-end: 03/31/23
Gold Product Mfr & Distr
N.A.I.C.S.: 339910

MOTOCAB SARL
5 Rue Vernet, 75008, Paris, France
Tel.: (33) 153901401
Web Site: http://www.motocab.com
Year Founded: 2005
Emp.: 30
Motorcycle Passenger Transport Services
N.A.I.C.S.: 485999
Jerome Kraffe *(Co-Owner)*

MOTODYNAMICS S.A.
10 Germanikis Scholis Athinon str, 15123, Maroussi, Greece
Tel.: (30) 2106239500
Web Site: https://motodynamics.gr
Year Founded: 1969
MOTO—(ATH)
Sales Range: $25-49.9 Million
Emp.: 120
Scooters, Motorcycles, Inflatable & Fiberglass Boats & Snowmobiles Distr
N.A.I.C.S.: 441227
Ioannis Tavoularis *(Exec VP)*

Subsidiaries:

Motodynamics Ltd. (1)
137 Tsarigradsko Shosse, 1784, Sofia, Bulgaria
Tel.: (359) 29744774
Web Site: http://www.yamaha-motor.bg
Sales Range: $50-74.9 Million
Emp.: 5
Motorcycles Retailer
N.A.I.C.S.: 423110
Theodoros Papadopoulo *(Mgr)*

Motodynamics Srl. (1)
Soseaua Odaii nr 307-309 Sector 1, Otopeni, 075100, Bucharest, Romania
Tel.: (40) 312285534
Web Site: http://www.yamaha-motor.ro
Automobile Assembling & Sales
N.A.I.C.S.: 336110

MOTOGEN CO.
Sanat Blvd West Tabriz Industrial Area, Tabriz, Iran
Tel.: (98) 4134453001
Web Site: https://www.motogen.com
Year Founded: 1973
MOTJ—(THE)
Sales Range: Less than $1 Million
Electric Equipment Mfr
N.A.I.C.S.: 335999

MOTONIC CORPORATION
100 Cheonggyecheon-ro, Jung-gu, Seoul, Korea (South)
Tel.: (82) 27308711
Web Site: https://www.motonic.com
Year Founded: 1974
009680—(KRS)
Rev.: $171,700,783
Assets: $355,960,222
Liabilities: $25,646,010
Net Worth: $330,314,211
Earnings: $16,488,256
Emp.: 270
Fiscal Year-end: 12/31/22
Automobile Parts Mfr

N.A.I.C.S.: 336390
Yoon Yeojeong *(Dir)*

Subsidiaries:

Beijing MOTONIC Corporation (1)
No 13 Kaichuang Street Zhongguancun Science Park East Park, Changping Sector, Beijing, 102200, China
Tel.: (86) 1060736001
Emp.: 60
Automobile Parts Mfr
N.A.I.C.S.: 336390

MOTONIC CORPORATION - Daegu Factory (1)
530 Dalseo-daero, Dalseo-gu, Daegu, Korea (South)
Tel.: (82) 53 583 5111
Automobile Parts Mfr
N.A.I.C.S.: 336390

MOTONIC India Automotive Private Limited (1)
Soorakapuram Road Vayalur Village & Post Thirvallur, Chennai, India
Tel.: (91) 44 2765 8124
Emp.: 95
Automobile Parts Distr
N.A.I.C.S.: 423120

MOTOR OIL (HELLAS) CORINTH REFINERIES S. A.
12A Irodou Attikou Street, 151 24, Maroussi, Greece
Tel.: (30) 2108094000 GR
Web Site: https://www.moh.gr
Year Founded: 1972
MOH—(ATH)
Rev.: $17,948,264,623
Assets: $7,768,118,929
Liabilities: $5,460,788,906
Net Worth: $2,307,330,024
Earnings: $1,043,825,815
Emp.: 2,606
Fiscal Year-end: 12/31/22
Petroleum Refinery & Product Supplier
N.A.I.C.S.: 324110
Vardis J. Vardinoyannis *(Chm & Mng Dir)*

Subsidiaries:

Avin Oil S.A. (1)
12A Irodou Attikou St, PO Box 61095, Marousi, 15124, Athens, Greece
Tel.: (30) 2108093500
Web Site: http://www.avinoil.gr
Lubricant Mfr
N.A.I.C.S.: 324191
Ioannis V. Vardinogiannis *(Chm & CEO)*

Coral Energy Products (Cyprus) Ltd. (1)
178 Athalassas Avenue Irene Tower 3rd Floor, Strovolos, Nicosia, Cyprus
Tel.: (357) 2109476000
Web Site: http://www.coralenergy.com.cy
Petroleum Product Distr
N.A.I.C.S.: 424720
John N. Kosmadakis *(Pres)*

Coral Gas Cyprus Ltd. (1)
178 Athalassas Avenue Irene Tower, Nicosia, Cyprus
Tel.: (357) 70001000
Gas Product Distr
N.A.I.C.S.: 424720

Coral Products & Trading Single Member S.A. (1)
Irodou Attikou 12A, Maroussi, Attiki, Greece
Tel.: (30) 2109476575
Web Site: http://www.coralmarine.gr
Marine Fuel Distr
N.A.I.C.S.: 424720

Coral SRB d.o.o. (1)
Yuri Gagarin 40b, 11070, Novi Beograd, Belgrade, Serbia
Tel.: (381) 116555218
Web Site: https://www.coralenergy.rs
Petroleum Product Distr
N.A.I.C.S.: 424720

Coral Single Member S.A. (1)

MOTOR OIL (HELLAS) CORINTH REFINERIES S. A.

Motor Oil (Hellas) Corinth Refineries S. A.—(Continued)

12 A Irodou Attikou Str, Maroussi, 151 24, Athens, Greece
Tel.: (30) 2109476000
Web Site: http://www.coralenergy.gr
Petroleum Product Distr
N.A.I.C.S.: 424720
John V. Vardinoyannis (Chm)

Cyclon Hellas S.A. (1)
Megaridos Avenue 124, Aspropyrgos, 193 00, Attica, Greece
Tel.: (30) 210 809 3900
Web Site: http://www.cyclon-lpc.com
Plastic Pipe Mfr & Distr
N.A.I.C.S.: 332996

Cytop S.A. (1)
Ave 124 Megaridos, 19300, Aspropyrgos, Greece
Tel.: (30) 2105584500
Web Site: https://www.cytop.gr
Lubricant Product Mfr
N.A.I.C.S.: 324191

L.P.C Single Member S.A. (1)
Megaridos Avenue 124, 193 00, Aspropyrgos, Attica, Greece
Tel.: (30) 2108093900
Web Site: http://www.lpc.gr
Emp.: 200
Lubricant Product Mfr & Distr
N.A.I.C.S.: 324191
John V. Vardinoyannis (Pres)

OFC Aviation Fuel Services S.A. (1)
5th km Spaton-Loutsas Av, 19004, Spata, Greece
Tel.: (30) 2103541100
Web Site: http://www.ofc.gr
Emp.: 28
Fuel Distr
N.A.I.C.S.: 424720
N. Kontaxis (CEO)

MOTOR PRESSE STUTTGART GMBH & CO. KG
Leuschnerstr 1, 70174, Stuttgart, Germany
Tel.: (49) 711 182 01 De
Web Site: http://www.motorpresse.de
Year Founded: 1946
Magazine Publisher
N.A.I.C.S.: 513120
Andrea Rometsch (Mng Dir & CFO)

MOTOR SICH PJSC
15 Motorobudivnykiv Avenue, 69068, Zaporizhzhya, Ukraine
Tel.: (380) 617204236
Web Site: https://www.motorsich.com
Year Founded: 1907
Rev.: $507,618,712
Assets: $922,614,015
Liabilities: $325,828,971
Net Worth: $596,785,044
Earnings: $122,264,748
Emp.: 26,537
Fiscal Year-end: 12/31/16
Aircraft & Helicopter Engine Mfr & Industrial Gas Turbine Installations
N.A.I.C.S.: 336412
Sergei A. Voitenko (Chm)

Subsidiaries:

Motor Sich Middle East SAIF (1)
Executive Ste L1-52, PO Box 120249, SAIF Zone, Sharjah, United Arab Emirates
Tel.: (971) 506896033
Aircraft Spares Production & Maintenance Services
N.A.I.C.S.: 336413

MOTORAIN CO., LTD.
2F 25 Hwangsaeul-ro 258beon-gil, Bundang-gu, Seongnam, 13595, Gyeonggi-do, Korea (South)
Tel.: (82) 7048926058 KR
Web Site: http://www.motrain.co.kr
Automobile Parts Distr
N.A.I.C.S.: 423120

MOTORCADE INDUSTRIES LTD.
90 Kincort Street, Toronto, M6M 5G1, ON, Canada
Tel.: (416) 614-6118
Web Site: http://www.motorcade-ind.com
Year Founded: 1957
Rev.: $22,913,195
Emp.: 150
Automobile Parts Distr
N.A.I.C.S.: 441330

MOTORCYCLE HOLDINGS LIMITED
Tel.: (61) 733802290 AU
Web Site: http://www.mcholdings.com.au
Year Founded: 1989
MTO—(ASX)
Rev.: $388,837,021
Assets: $263,744
Liabilities: $130,084
Net Worth: $133,660
Earnings: $9,435,834
Emp.: 900
Fiscal Year-end: 06/30/24
Holding Company; Motorcycle Dealerships Operator
N.A.I.C.S.: 551112
David Ahmet (Founder, CEO & Mng Dir)

Subsidiaries:

Cassons Pty Ltd (1)
2/25 Wonderland Dr, Eastern Creek, 2766, NSW, Australia
Tel.: (61) 288821900
Web Site: http://www.cassons.com.au
Motor Cycle Distr
N.A.I.C.S.: 423120

Forbes & Davies (NZ) Limited (1)
PO Box 101112, North Shore City, Auckland, New Zealand
Tel.: (64) 94444541
Web Site: https://www.forbesanddavies.co.nz
Motorcycle Tyre Distr
N.A.I.C.S.: 441340

Motorcycle Riding School Pty Ltd (1)
59 Moss Street, Slacks Creek, Logan, 4217, QLD, Australia
Tel.: (61) 734421348
Web Site: http://www.motorcycleridingschools.com
Motorcycle Riding Services
N.A.I.C.S.: 611692

MOTORES & EQUIPOS S.A.
Via Tocumen A Un Costado De Plaza El Conquistador, Panama, Panama
Tel.: (507) 301021112 Pa
Web Site: http://www.motoresyequipos.com
Automotive Heavy Equipment Whslr
N.A.I.C.S.: 423120

MOTORK PLC
5th Floor One New Change, London, EC4M 9AF, United Kingdom
Tel.: (44) 622183909 UK
Web Site: https://www.motork.io
Year Founded: 2010
MTRK—(EUR)
Rev.: $46,341,463
Assets: $104,217,570
Liabilities: $48,498,813
Net Worth: $55,718,757
Earnings: ($14,296,352)
Emp.: 449
Fiscal Year-end: 12/31/23
Software Development Services
N.A.I.C.S.: 541511
Marco Marlia (Founder & CEO)

Subsidiaries:

AutoXY S.p.A. (1)
Via Ludovico Maremonti 41, 73100, Lecco, Italy
Tel.: (39) 0832303995
Web Site: https://www.autoxy.it
Automotive Retailer
N.A.I.C.S.: 423140

Drivek Italia S.r.l. (1)
Via Ludovico Maremonti 41, 73100, Lecco, Italy
Tel.: (39) 0832303995
Web Site: https://www.drivek.it
Automotive Retailer
N.A.I.C.S.: 423140

FranceProNet S.a.S. (1)
61 Rue Pierre Cazeneuve, 31200, Toulouse, France
Tel.: (33) 582952713
Web Site: https://www.francepronet.com
Automotive Retailer
N.A.I.C.S.: 423140

ICO International GmbH (1)
Daimlerstrasse 6, 61449, Steinbach, Germany
Tel.: (49) 695077570
Web Site: https://www.ico-international.de
Automotive Retailer
N.A.I.C.S.: 423140

Motork Italia S.r.l. (1)
Via Ludovico D'Aragona 9, 20123, Milan, Italy
Tel.: (39) 0236758637
Automobile Parts Distr
N.A.I.C.S.: 423110

MOTORPOINT GROUP PLC
Champion House Stephensons Way, Chaddesden, Derby, DE21 6LY, United Kingdom
Tel.: (44) 2037271000 UK
Web Site: https://www.motorpointplc.com
Year Founded: 1998
MOTR—(LSE)
Rev.: $1,371,623,330
Assets: $249,684,423
Liabilities: $210,426,660
Net Worth: $39,257,763
Earnings: ($10,603,383)
Emp.: 710
Fiscal Year-end: 03/31/24
Used Car Dealers
N.A.I.C.S.: 441120
Mark Carpenter (CEO)

MOTORSAZAN COMPANY
Across from shahab khodro KM 9 5 of karaj special road, Tehran, Iran
Tel.: (98) 2144539200
Web Site: https://www.motorsazan.ir
Year Founded: 1987
MSTI—(THE)
Sales Range: Less than $1 Million
Diesel Engine Mfr
N.A.I.C.S.: 333618
Hasan Motallebzadeh (Mng Dir)

MOTORVAC TECHNOLOGIES, INC.
1324 Blundell Rd, Mississauga, L4Y 1M5, ON, Canada
Tel.: (714) 558-4822 DE
Web Site: http://www.motorvac.com
Year Founded: 1993
Sales Range: $10-24.9 Million
Emp.: 80
N.A.I.C.S.: 336390
Paul Baldetti (Pres)

MOTREX CO., LTD.
56 Geumto-ro 80beon-gil, Sujeong-gu, Seongnam, Gyeonggi, Korea (South)
Tel.: (82) 7048926000
Web Site: https://www.motrex.co.kr
Year Founded: 2001
118990—(KRS)
Rev.: $436,040,166
Assets: $389,374,117

Liabilities: $254,325,474
Net Worth: $135,048,643
Earnings: $29,528,875
Emp.: 330
Fiscal Year-end: 12/31/22
Automobile Parts Mfr
N.A.I.C.S.: 336110
Lee Hyung-hwan (CEO)

MOTRUX INC.
731 Belgrave Way, Delta, V3M 5R8, BC, Canada
Tel.: (604) 527-1000
Web Site: http://www.motrux.com
Year Founded: 1974
Rev.: $10,943,938
Emp.: 9
General Freight Trucking Services
N.A.I.C.S.: 484110
Doug Lunde (Pres)

MOTSENG INVESTMENT HOLDINGS (PTY) LTD.
563 Old Pretoria Main Road, Midrand, South Africa
Tel.: (27) 11 267 8000
Web Site: http://www.motseng.co.za
Diversified Investment Holding Company
N.A.I.C.S.: 523999
Ipeleng Mkhari (Founder & CEO)

Subsidiaries:

Motseng Women Investments (Pty) Ltd. (1)
563 Old Pretoria Main Road, Midrand, South Africa
Tel.: (27) 11 267 8000
Investment Services
N.A.I.C.S.: 523999
Ipeleng Mkhari (CEO)

MOTT MACDONALD GROUP LTD.
Mott MacDonald House 8-10 Sydenham Road, Croydon, CR0 2EE, United Kingdom
Tel.: (44) 2087742000
Web Site: http://www.mottmac.com
Year Founded: 1973
Sales Range: $150-199.9 Million
Emp.: 16,000
Holding Company
N.A.I.C.S.: 551112
Keith Howells (Chm-Exec Bd)

Subsidiaries:

BMB Mott MacDonald (1)
Amsterdamseweg 15, Arnhem, 6814 CM, Netherlands
Tel.: (31) 26 357 7111
Web Site: http://www.bmb.mottmac.nl
Sales Range: $25-49.9 Million
Emp.: 70
Engineeering Services
N.A.I.C.S.: 541330
Pieter A. van Stuijvenberg (Mng Dir)

Cambridge Education LLC (1)
400 Blue Hill Dr N Lobby Ste 100, Westwood, MA 02090
Tel.: (781) 915-0040
Web Site: http://www.camb-ed-us.com
Emp.: 50
Education Services
N.A.I.C.S.: 611710
David Jacobson (Dir-Pro Excellence)

Cambridge Education Limited (1)
22 Station Road, Cambridge, CB1 2JD, United Kingdom
Tel.: (44) 1223 578500
Web Site: http://www.camb-ed.com
Education & Consultancy Services
N.A.I.C.S.: 923110

Euroconsult Mott MacDonald (1)
PO Box 441, 6800 AK, Arnhem, Netherlands
Tel.: (31) 263577111

AND PRIVATE COMPANIES — MOTT MACDONALD GROUP LTD.

Web Site:
http://www.euroconsult.mottmac.nl
Sales Range: $25-49.9 Million
Emp.: 75
Engineeering Services
N.A.I.C.S.: 541330
Pieter A. van Stuijvenberg *(Mng Dir)*

Subsidiary (Non-US):

Euroconsult Mott MacDonald (2)
Fifth Floor Block 2 Gamma Business Centre
5 Gamsononsky Pereulok, 115191, Moscow, Russia
Tel.: (7) 0959330550
Web Site:
http://www.euroconsult.mottmac.nl
Sales Range: $25-49.9 Million
Emp.: 20
Engineeering Services
N.A.I.C.S.: 541330

Franklin & Andrews Limited (1)
Canterbury House 35 Newhall Street, Birmingham, B3 3PU, United Kingdom
Tel.: (44) 121 234 1700
Web Site: http://www.franklinandrews.com
Engineering Consulting Services
N.A.I.C.S.: 541330
Alasdair Thompson *(Dir-Dev)*

HLSP Limited (1)
10 Fleet Place, London, EC4M 7RB, United Kingdom
Tel.: (44) 20 7651 0302
Web Site: http://www.hlsp.org
Health Sector Consultancy Services
N.A.I.C.S.: 621999
Ken Grant *(Dir-Technical)*

Habtec Engenharia Sanitaria e Ambiental Ltda (1)
Avenida 13 de maio 13 Grupo 1508, Rio de Janeiro, 20031-901, Brazil
Tel.: (55) 21 2533 0188
Web Site: http://www.mottmac.com.br
Engineering Consulting Services
N.A.I.C.S.: 541330
Aline Martins *(Mgr-Socioeconomic Environment)*

Hatch Mott MacDonald, LLC (1)
111 Wood Ave S, Iselin, NJ 08830-4112
Tel.: (973) 379-3400
Web Site: http://www.hatchmott.com
Sales Range: $200-249.9 Million
Emp.: 600
Engineeering Services
N.A.I.C.S.: 237990
Nicholas DeNichilo *(Pres & CEO)*

MM Pakistan (Private) Limited (1)
17-A/1 Zafar Road Cantt, Lahore, Pakistan
Tel.: (92) 42 36662595
Web Site: http://www.mmpakistan.com
Engineering Consulting Services
N.A.I.C.S.: 541330

Merz & McLellan Botswana (Pty) Limited (1)
Unit 15 Gifp, PO Box 997, Gaborone, Botswana
Tel.: (267) 393 4977
Engineering Consulting Services
N.A.I.C.S.: 541330

Mott MacDonald (Beijing) Limited (1)
B-1205 China International Science & Technology Convention Centre, 12 Yumin Rd, 100029, Beijing, China (100%)
Tel.: (86) 1082250257
Web Site: http://www.mottmac.com
Sales Range: $25-49.9 Million
Emp.: 70
Engineeering Services
N.A.I.C.S.: 541330
Michael Blackburn *(Mng Dir)*

Mott MacDonald (Bulgaria) EOOD (1)
13 Damian Gruev Str, Sofia, 1606, Bulgaria
Tel.: (359) 2 953 1867
Engineering Consulting Services
N.A.I.C.S.: 541330

Mott MacDonald (Malaysia) Sdn. Bhd
Level 6 Ikhlas Point Tower 11 Avenue 5 Bangsar South No 8, Jalan Kerinchi, Kuala Lumpur, 59200, Malaysia
Tel.: (60) 3 2106 5505
Engineering Consulting Services
N.A.I.C.S.: 541330

Mott MacDonald (Philippines) Inc (1)
19th Floor Room 1907 Citiland Herrera Tower VA Rufino Corner Valero St, Salcedo Village, Makati, Manila, Philippines
Tel.: (63) 2 817 77
Engineering Consulting Services
N.A.I.C.S.: 541330

Mott MacDonald (Taiwan) Limited (1)
A3 5F No 6 Sihwei 3rd Road, Kaohsiung, 80250, Taiwan
Tel.: (886) 7 335 3899
Engineering Consulting Services
N.A.I.C.S.: 541330

Mott MacDonald (Thailand) Limited (1)
19th Floor Chamman Phenjati Building 65/159 & 61/162 Rama 9 Road, Huay-Kwang, Bangkok, Thailand
Tel.: (66) 2643 1811
Engineering Consulting Services
N.A.I.C.S.: 541330

Mott MacDonald Africa Limited (1)
Rhapta Road 87, PO Box 44286-001, Kenya-Re Towers Upperhill, Nairobi, Kenya
Tel.: (254) 707 725 106
Engineering Consulting Services
N.A.I.C.S.: 541330

Mott MacDonald Bentley Ltd. (1)
Keighley Road North Yorkshire, Skipton, BD232QR, Yorkshire, United Kingdom (50%)
Tel.: (44) 1756799425
Engineeering Services
N.A.I.C.S.: 541330

Mott MacDonald Canada Ltd (1)
145 Wellington Street West, Toronto, M5J 1H8, ON, Canada
Tel.: (647) 556-3200
Web Site: http://www.mottmac.com
Emp.: 26
Engineering Consulting Services
N.A.I.C.S.: 541330
Kieth Howlles *(Mng Dir)*

Mott MacDonald Environmental Consultants Ltd. (1)
Mott MacDonald House, 8-10 Sydenham Rd, Croydon, CR02EE, Surrey, United Kingdom (100%)
Tel.: (44) 2087742000
Sales Range: $150-199.9 Million
Emp.: 900
Engineeering Services
N.A.I.C.S.: 541330

Mott MacDonald France SAS (1)
33 avenue de la Republique, 75011, Paris, France
Tel.: (33) 1 83 79 00 90
Web Site: http://www.mottmac.fr
Engineering Consulting Services
N.A.I.C.S.: 541330

Mott MacDonald Hong Kong Ltd. (1)
20/f Two Landmark E, 100 Howming, Kwun Tong, China (Hong Kong) (100%)
Tel.: (852) 28285757
Web Site: http://www.mottmac.com.hk
Sales Range: $75-99.9 Million
Emp.: 300
Management Consulting Services
N.A.I.C.S.: 541618
Gary Bacon *(Gen Mgr)*

Mott MacDonald Hungaria Kft (1)
Vaci Street 45 Building F 7th Fl, 1138, Budapest, Hungary (100%)
Tel.: (36) 12882020
Web Site: http://www.mottmac.hu
Sales Range: $25-49.9 Million
Emp.: 30
Engineering Services
N.A.I.C.S.: 541330

Mott MacDonald Inc (1)
1331 Pennsylvannia Ave NW Ste 1410 N, Washington, DC 20004
Tel.: (202) 754-8085
Web Site: http://www.mottmac.com
Engineering Consulting Services

N.A.I.C.S.: 541330
Yvonne Dale *(Dir-Bus Dev)*

Mott MacDonald International Limited (1)
8-10 Sydenham Road, Croydon, CR0 2EE, United Kingdom (100%)
Tel.: (44) 2087742000
Web Site: http://www.mottmac.com
Engineeering Services
N.A.I.C.S.: 541330
Kieth Howells *(Chm)*

Subsidiary (Non-US):

Mott MacDonald Australia Pty Limited (2)
224 Bunda St, Canberra, 2601, ACT, Australia
Tel.: (61) 2 6253 1555
Web Site: http://www.mottmac.com.au
Engineering Consulting Services
N.A.I.C.S.: 541330
Brad Dobson *(Dir-Building Svcs)*

Mott MacDonald Ireland Limited (1)
South Block Rockfield, Dundrum, Dublin, 16, Ireland
Tel.: (353) 1 2916 700
Web Site: http://www.mottmac.ie
Emp.: 150
Engineering Consulting Services
N.A.I.C.S.: 541330
Conor O'Donovan *(Mng Dir)*

Mott MacDonald Japan K.K. (1)
Mott MacDonald Japan KK, Bunkyo-ku, Tokyo, 113-0034, Japan
Tel.: (81) 3 6801 5961
Web Site: http://www.mottmac.jp
Emp.: 10
Engineering Consulting Services
N.A.I.C.S.: 541330
Isao Terasaw *(Gen Mgr)*

Mott MacDonald Kazakhstan LLP (1)
Eurocentre Office 415 4th floor 29 Syganak Street, Nur-Sultan, Kazakhstan
Tel.: (7) 7172 516927
Engineering Consulting Services
N.A.I.C.S.: 541330

Mott MacDonald LLC (1)
Al Gaith Towers Hamdan Street, Abu Dhabi, United Arab Emirates (100%)
Tel.: (971) 2 401 5333
Web Site: http://www.mottmac.com
Sales Range: $25-49.9 Million
Emp.: 200
Engineering Services
N.A.I.C.S.: 541330

Mott MacDonald Limited (1)
8-10 Sydenham Rd, Croydon, CR0 2EE, United Kingdom (100%)
Tel.: (44) 2087742000
Web Site: http://www.mottmac.com
Sales Range: $150-199.9 Million
Emp.: 900
Engineeering Services
N.A.I.C.S.: 541330
Mike Haigh *(Chm)*

Mott MacDonald Limited (1)
100 Howming Street 20/F AIA Kowloon Tower, Landmark East, Kowloon, China (Hong Kong)
Tel.: (852) 28285757
Web Site: http://www.mottmac.com
Sales Range: $75-99.9 Million
Emp.: 300
Management, Engineering & Development Consulting Services
N.A.I.C.S.: 541618

Mott MacDonald Mongolia LLC (1)
Suite 503 City Plaza 6A Seoul Street, Ulaanbaatar, Mongolia
Tel.: (976) 7575 1509
Engineering Consulting Services
N.A.I.C.S.: 541330

Mott MacDonald New Zealand Limited (1)
Level 2 125 The Strand, Parnell, Auckland, 1151, New Zealand
Tel.: (64) 9 375 2400
Engineering Consulting Services
N.A.I.C.S.: 541330

Brad Moyes *(Dir-Bus Dev)*

Mott MacDonald Nominees Ltd. (1)
8-10 Sydenham Road, 20-26 Wellesley Road, Croydon, CR0 2EE, Surrey, United Kingdom (100%)
Tel.: (44) 2087742000
Web Site: http://www.mottmac.com
Sales Range: $150-199.9 Million
Emp.: 5,000
Engineeering Services
N.A.I.C.S.: 541330
Keith Howells *(Gen Mgr)*

Mott MacDonald Norge AS (1)
Vassbotnen 15, Stavanger, 4313, Sandnes, Norway
Tel.: (47) 5187 4318
Engineering Consulting Services
N.A.I.C.S.: 541330
Steve Mckinlay *(Mng Dir)*

Mott MacDonald Pettit Limited (1)
5 Eastgate Ave, Little Island, Cork, Ireland (100%)
Tel.: (353) 214809800
Web Site: http://www.mottmac.ie
Sales Range: $25-49.9 Million
Emp.: 70
Engineeering Services
N.A.I.C.S.: 541330
John Murphy *(Dir-Bus Dev)*

Mott MacDonald Poland Sp z.o.o. (1)
Walicow Street 11, Aurum Building, 00-851, Warsaw, Poland (100%)
Tel.: (48) 225839600
Web Site: http://www.mottmac.pl
Sales Range: $25-49.9 Million
Emp.: 30
Management Consulting Services
N.A.I.C.S.: 541618

Mott MacDonald Private Limited (1)
Unit No 101 First Floor Nomura Building, Hiranandani Gardens, Mumbai, 400 076, Maharashtra, India (100%)
Tel.: (91) 2239810100
Web Site: http://www.mottmacdonald.com
Sales Range: $25-49.9 Million
Emp.: 250
Management Consulting Services
N.A.I.C.S.: 541618
Mike Barker *(Mng Dir)*

Mott MacDonald Romania SRL (1)
Str Traian 246 Et 3 Ap 5 Sector 2, Bucharest, 024046, Romania
Tel.: (40) 376 203 815
Engineering Consulting Services
N.A.I.C.S.: 541330
Andrei Penescu *(Mgr-Comml & Ops)*

Mott MacDonald S D.o.o. (1)
Koce Kapetana 47 4th floor, 11000, Belgrade, Serbia
Tel.: (381) 11 785 66 73
Web Site: http://www.mottmac.rs
Engineering Consulting Services
N.A.I.C.S.: 541330

Mott MacDonald Sa Ltd. (1)
Trafalgar Place Victory Hse, Brighton, BN14FY, United Kingdom (100%)
Tel.: (44) 1273365000
Web Site: http://www.mottmacdonald.com
Sales Range: $75-99.9 Million
Emp.: 300
Engineeering Services
N.A.I.C.S.: 541330
Peter Black *(Mng Dir)*

Mott MacDonald Singapore Pte Ltd. (1)
1 grange Rd 07-01 Orchard Bldg, Singapore, 239693, Singapore (100%)
Tel.: (65) 62931900
Web Site: http://www.mottmac.com
Sales Range: $25-49.9 Million
Emp.: 200
Engineeering Services
N.A.I.C.S.: 541330
Yuou Fook *(Gen Mgr)*

Mott MacDonald South Africa (Pty) Ltd. (1)
Alice Lane Building 1 3rd Floor Corner 5th Street and Fredman Drive, Sandton, Johannesburg, 2196, Waverley, South Africa (100%)

MOTT MACDONALD GROUP LTD.

Mott MacDonald Group Ltd.—(Continued)
Tel.: (27) 110521000
Web Site: http://www.mottmac.com
Sales Range: $75-99.9 Million
Emp.: 300
Engineeering Services
N.A.I.C.S.: 541330
Howard Bate (Dir-Strategic Dev)

Mott MacDonald T Engineering Consultants Limited (1)
Sun Plaza Floor 13 Office 3 Bilim Street, Maslak District, Istanbul, Türkiye
Tel.: (90) 212 366 5819
Engineering Consulting Services
N.A.I.C.S.: 541330

Mott MacDonald Uganda Limited (1)
Plot 3 Moyo Close Off Prince Charles Drive Kololo, Kampala, 22258, Uganda
Tel.: (256) 41 711 7100
Emp.: 21
Engineering Consulting Services
N.A.I.C.S.: 541330
Rose Birungi Namanya (Office Mgr)

Mott MacDonald and Co., LLC (1)
Mbd Business Center Building A 821 Way No 420, Ruwi, 112, Oman **(100%)**
Tel.: (968) 24852000
Web Site: http://www.MottMacdonald.com
Sales Range: $75-99.9 Million
Emp.: 450
Engineeering Services
N.A.I.C.S.: 541330
Ahmed Al Mazroui (Mng Dir)

Mott Macdonald Praha, Spol Sro (1)
Narodni 984-15, Prague, 11000, Czech Republic **(100%)**
Tel.: (420) 221412800
Web Site: http://www.mottmac.cz
Sales Range: $25-49.9 Million
Emp.: 200
Management Consulting Services
N.A.I.C.S.: 541618
Radko Bucek (Mng Dir)

PT Mott MacDonald Indonesia (1)
Graha Cimb Niaga 16th Fl, Jalan Jenderal Sudirman Kav 71, 12190, Jakarta, Indonesia **(100%)**
Tel.: (62) 212526588
Web Site: http://www.mottmac.com
Sales Range: $25-49.9 Million
Emp.: 50
Engineeering Services
N.A.I.C.S.: 541330
Badihi Fitriana (Mgr-Bus Dev)

MOTT MANUFACTURING LTD.
452 Hardy Rd, Brantford, N3T 5L8, ON, Canada
Tel.: (519) 752-7825
Web Site: http://www.mott.ca
Year Founded: 1934
Rev.: $23,684,560
Emp.: 180
Steel Furniture Mfr
N.A.I.C.S.: 337126
Chip Diefendorf (Mgr-Bus Dev)

MOTTA-INTERNACIONAL, S.A.
14 St And Santa Isabel Ave Free Zone, Colon, Panama
Tel.: (507) 4316000
Web Site: http://www.motta-int.com
Year Founded: 1954
Sales Range: $250-299.9 Million
Emp.: 2,000
Consumer Goods Trade Distr
N.A.I.C.S.: 425120

Subsidiaries:

ACI - Agencia Continental de Importaciones, S.A. (1)
Calle 101 70G 83, Bogota, Colombia
Tel.: (57) 1 226 0628
Web Site: http://www.aci.com.co
Consumer Goods Wholesale Trade Distr
N.A.I.C.S.: 425120

MOTUL S.A.
119 Boulevard Felix Faure, Aubervilliers, 93300, France
Tel.: (33) 148117000
Web Site: http://www.motul.com
Year Founded: 1932
Sales Range: $125-149.9 Million
Emp.: 130
Lubricating Oil & Grease Mfr
N.A.I.C.S.: 324191
Ernest Zaugg (Chm)

Subsidiaries:

Chem Arrow Corp. (1)
13643 Live Oak Ln, Irwindale, CA 91706
Tel.: (626) 358-2255
Web Site: http://www.chemarrow.com
Sales Range: $1-9.9 Million
Emp.: 25
Petroleum Lubricating Oil & Grease Mfr
N.A.I.C.S.: 324191
John Brady (VP-Sls)

Motul Deutschland GmbH (1)
Kolner Strasse 263, 51149, Cologne, Germany **(100%)**
Tel.: (49) 220317000
Web Site: http://www.motul.de
Sales Range: $25-49.9 Million
Emp.: 30
Lubricating Oils & Greases Mfr
N.A.I.C.S.: 324191

Motul Iberica SA (1)
Provenza 386 Planta 3a, 08025, Barcelona, Spain **(100%)**
Tel.: (34) 932081130
Web Site: http://www.motul.es
Sales Range: $25-49.9 Million
Emp.: 35
Lubricating Oils & Greases Mfr
N.A.I.C.S.: 324191
Begone Paco (CEO)

Motul Italia Srl (1)
Strada della Cebrosa 86, 10156, Turin, Italy
Tel.: (39) 011 2978911
Motor Oil & Lubricant Distr
N.A.I.C.S.: 423840

Motul U.S.A. Inc. (1)
764b Indigo Ct, Pomona, CA 91767
Tel.: (909) 625-1292
Sales Range: $50-74.9 Million
Emp.: 10
Lubricating Oils & Greases Mfr
N.A.I.C.S.: 424720
David Wolman (Pres)

MOTUS HOLDINGS LIMITED
1 Van Buuren Rd Cnr Van Dort Str Geldenhuis Str, Bedfordview, 2008, South Africa
Tel.: (27) 104934335
Web Site: https://www.motus.co.za
Year Founded: 1948
MTH—(JSE)
Rev.: $5,614,814,267
Assets: $3,520,051,965
Liabilities: $2,582,040,368
Net Worth: $938,011,597
Earnings: $180,082,172
Emp.: 19,817
Fiscal Year-end: 06/30/23
Financial Consulting Services
N.A.I.C.S.: 541611
Graham Dempster (Chm)

Subsidiaries:

ARCO Motor Industry Company Limited (1)
66 Sec 2 Zhongtou West Road, Wufang, Taichung, Taiwan
Tel.: (886) 423319797
Web Site: https://www.arcomotor.com
Automobile Parts Distr
N.A.I.C.S.: 423120

Australian Automotive Group Proprietary Limited (1)
60 O'Riordan Street, Alexandria, NSW, Australia
Tel.: (61) 293315000
Web Site: https://www.aag.com.au
Emp.: 300

Car Dealership Operator
N.A.I.C.S.: 441110

FAI Automotive plc (1)
The Chiltern Trading Estate Groveburry Road, Leighton Buzzard, Bedfordshire, United Kingdom
Tel.: (44) 1525351800
Web Site: https://www.faiauto.com
Automobile Parts Distr
N.A.I.C.S.: 423120

Hyundai Automotive South Africa Proprietary Limited (1)
Cnr Lucas and Norman Road, Bedfordview, Gauteng, South Africa
Tel.: (27) 102488085
Web Site: https://www.hyundai.co.za
Motor Vehicles Mfr
N.A.I.C.S.: 336110

Motus Group (UK) Proprietary Limited (1)
Motus Oakingham House Ground Floor West Wing London Road, Loudwater, High Wycombe, Buckinghamshire, United Kingdom
Tel.: (44) 1494520908
Web Site: https://www.motusuk.com
Emp.: 3,000
Car Dealership Operator
N.A.I.C.S.: 441110

Renault South Africa (Pty) Ltd (1)
12 Ernest Oppenheimer Drive Bruma, 2198, Johannesburg, 2198, South Africa **(60%)**
Tel.: (27) 116077300
Web Site: http://www.renault.co.za
Emp.: 100
Automotive Distr
N.A.I.C.S.: 423110
Niall Lynch (Mng Dir)

MOULAGES INDUSTRIELS DU HAUT BUGEY
Z I Nord D Oyonnax Z I Nord Oyo Lieu Dit Sous Tamas, 01100, Oyonnax, France
Tel.: (33) 474817110
Web Site: http://www.mihb.com
Sales Range: $25-49.9 Million
Emp.: 150
Plastics Products
N.A.I.C.S.: 326199

MOULINVEST SA
Zone Artisanale de Ville, 43220, Dunieres, France
Tel.: (33) 471617000
Web Site: https://www.moulinvest.com
ALMOU—(EUR)
Sales Range: $75-99.9 Million
Wood Products Mfr
N.A.I.C.S.: 321999
Maurice Moulin (Chm & CEO)

MOUNT BURGESS MINING N.L.
8/800 Albany Highway, Perth, 6101, WA, Australia
Tel.: (61) 893550123
Web Site: https://www.mountburgess.com
Year Founded: 1985
MTB—(ASX)
Rev.: $258
Assets: $2,429,420
Liabilities: $3,171,316
Net Worth: ($741,896)
Earnings: ($310,372)
Fiscal Year-end: 06/30/24
Gold & Base Metal Ore Mining & Exploration Services
N.A.I.C.S.: 212220
Nigel Raymond Forrester (Chm & Mng Dir)

MOUNT DAKOTA ENERGY CORP.
363 West 6th Avenue, Vancouver, V5Y 1L1, BC, Canada
Tel.: (604) 689-2454
Web Site: http://www.mountdakota.com
MMO—(TSXV)
Rev.: $1,146
Assets: $69,944
Liabilities: $1,558,435
Net Worth: ($1,488,491)
Earnings: ($75,462)
Fiscal Year-end: 01/31/20
Oil & Gas Exploration & Development Services
N.A.I.C.S.: 211120

MOUNT GIBSON IRON LIMITED
Level 1 2 Kings Park Rd, West Perth, 6005, WA, Australia
Tel.: (61) 894267500
Web Site: https://www.mtgibsoniron.com.au
MTGRF—(OTCIQ)
Rev.: $457,051,280
Assets: $443,575,052
Liabilities: $78,876,202
Net Worth: $364,698,850
Earnings: $4,293,536
Emp.: 389
Fiscal Year-end: 06/30/24
Iron Ore Mining
N.A.I.C.S.: 212210
Seng Hui Lee (Chm)

Subsidiaries:

Koolan Iron Ore Pty Ltd (1)
Level 1 2 Kings Park Road, West Perth, 6005, Western Australia, Australia
Tel.: (61) 894267500
Sales Range: $50-74.9 Million
Emp.: 500
Iron Ore Mining Services
N.A.I.C.S.: 212210
Peter Kerr (CEO)

Mount Gibson Mining Limited (1)
Level 1 2 Kings Park Road, West Perth, 6005, WA, Australia
Tel.: (61) 894267500
Web Site: http://www.mtgibsoniron.com.au
Emp.: 60
Mining Services
N.A.I.C.S.: 212290

MOUNT HOUSING & INFRASTRUCTURE LTD.
122 I Silver Rock Apartment 2Nd Floor Venkatasamy Road West, Rs Puram, Coimbatore, 641002, Tamil Nadu, India
Tel.: (91) 4224973111
Web Site: https://www.mounthousing.com
542864—(BOM)
Rev.: $228,476
Assets: $2,098,172
Liabilities: $1,548,708
Net Worth: $549,463
Earnings: $12,421
Emp.: 4
Fiscal Year-end: 03/31/23
Construction Services
N.A.I.C.S.: 236220
Ramesh Chand Bafna (Chm & Mng Dir)

MOUNT LOGAN CAPITAL INC.
365 Bay Street Suite 800, Toronto, M5H 2V1, ON, Canada
Tel.: (416) 640-4256
Web Site: https://www.mountlogancapital.ca
P31Q—(DEU)
Rev.: $31,060,000
Assets: $1,348,872,000
Liabilities: $1,246,728,000
Net Worth: $102,144,000

Earnings: $18,206,000
Emp.: 9
Fiscal Year-end: 12/31/22
Investment Banking Services
N.A.I.C.S.: 523150
John Robert Anderson *(Chm)*

MOUNT RIDLEY MINES LTD
Ground Floor 186 Stirling Highway, Subiaco, 6009, WA, Australia
Tel.: (61) 861658858
Web Site: https://www.mtridleymines.com.au
MRD—(ASX)
Rev.: $58,410
Assets: $2,647,007
Liabilities: $108,246
Net Worth: $2,538,761
Earnings: ($1,325,689)
Fiscal Year-end: 06/30/24
Metal Mining & Exploration
N.A.I.C.S.: 212290
Johnathon Busing *(Sec)*

MOUNT ROMMEL MINING LIMITED
28 Lawson Crescent Thomastown, Melbourne, 3074, VIC, Australia
Tel.: (61) 39 462 0739
Web Site: http://www.mountrommel.com
Gold Mining Services
N.A.I.C.S.: 212220

MOUNT SHIVALIK INDUSTRIES LIMITED
140th Milestone Delhi - Jaipur Highway Village Gunti, Tehsil Behror Distt, Alwar, 301701, Rajasthan, India
Tel.: (91) 1494 221171
Year Founded: 1993
507522—(BOM)
Sales Range: Less than $1 Million
Emp.: 200
Beer Mfr
N.A.I.C.S.: 312120
B. D. Bali *(Chm & Mng Dir)*

MOUNTAIN ALLIANCE AG
Bavariaring 17, D- 80336, Munich, Germany
Tel.: (49) 892314141
Web Site: https://www.mountain-alliance.de
ECF—(MUN)
Rev.: $165,580
Assets: $36,085,510
Liabilities: $3,223,300
Net Worth: $32,862,210
Earnings: ($1,214,257)
Emp.: 6
Fiscal Year-end: 12/31/23
E-Commerce Business
N.A.I.C.S.: 425120
Daniel Wild *(CEO & Member-Mgmt Bd)*

Subsidiaries:

Aboalarm GmbH (1)
Ridlerstr 57, 80339, Munich, Germany
Tel.: (49) 8925557540
Web Site: https://www.aboalarm.de
Internet Services
N.A.I.C.S.: 517121

Premingo GmbH (1)
Neuhauser Strasse 15a, Munich, 80331, Bavaria, Germany
Tel.: (49) 8918916680
Web Site: http://www.premingo.de
Internet Payment Services
N.A.I.C.S.: 522320

getonTV GmbH (1)
Freibadstrasse 30, 81543, Munich, Germany
Tel.: (49) 8920004640
Web Site: http://www.getontv.de
Advertising Services

N.A.I.C.S.: 541810

MOUNTAIN CAPITAL MANAGEMENT AG
Fuhrstrasse 12, CH-8820, Wadenswil, Switzerland
Tel.: (41) 447838030   CH
Web Site: http://mountain.partners
Holding Company; Venture Capital Firm
N.A.I.C.S.: 551112
Ingo Drexler *(Chief Investment Officer)*

Subsidiaries:

Mountain Partners AG (1)
Poststrasse 17, CH-9001, Saint Gallen, Switzerland
Tel.: (41) 44783 8030
Web Site: http://mountain.partners
Emp.: 50
Venture Capital Firm
N.A.I.C.S.: 523940
Daniel S. Wenzel *(Co-Founder & COO)*

Affiliate (Domestic):

Sandpiper Digital Payments AG (2)
Poststrasse 17, CH-9001, Saint Gallen, Switzerland (49%)
Tel.: (41) 447838030
Web Site: http://www.sandpiper.ch
Transaction & Payment Services
N.A.I.C.S.: 561499
Daniel Sebastian C. Wenzel *(Pres)*

Subsidiary (Domestic):

Ergonomics AG (3)
Nordstrasse 15, 8006, Zurich, Switzerland
Tel.: (41) 58 311 1000
Web Site: http://www.ergonomics.ch
Emp.: 26
Information Technology Solutions
N.A.I.C.S.: 541519

Subsidiary (Non-US):

Multicard Netherlands B.V. (3)
Albert Einsteinstraat 8, 3261 LP, Oud-Beijerland, Netherlands
Tel.: (31) 186 636 530
Web Site: http://www.multicard.nl
Emp.: 25
Identification & Security Services
N.A.I.C.S.: 561621
Peter Kooistra *(Pres)*

Subsidiary (Domestic):

Polyright SA (3)
Rue de la Porte-Neuve 8, CH-1950, Sion, Switzerland
Tel.: (41) 27 303 5000
Web Site: http://www.polyright.com
Digital Payment Solutions
N.A.I.C.S.: 561499

Subsidiary (Non-US):

SECANDA AG (3)
Marienstrasse 10, 78054, Villingen-Schwenningen, Germany (50.3%)
Tel.: (49) 772099450
Web Site: https://secanda.com
Sales Range: $10-24.9 Million
Emp.: 100
Multifunctional Card Services
N.A.I.C.S.: 561499
Ul Meyer-Kessel *(Chm-Supervisory Bd)*

Subsidiary (Domestic):

Multicard GmbH (4)
Marienstrasse 10, D-78054, Villingen-Schwenningen, Germany
Tel.: (49) 7720 838227 0
Web Site: http://www.multicard.de
ID Systems Management, Hardware & Engineering Services
N.A.I.C.S.: 561621
David Haiduk *(Mng Dir)*

Subsidiary (Domestic):

e24 AG (3)
Nordstrasse 15, CH-8006, Zurich, Switzerland

Tel.: (41) 58 311 1031
Web Site: http://www.e-24.ch
Mobile Payment Systems
N.A.I.C.S.: 561499

Subsidiary (Non-US):

payment solution AG (3)
Oskar-Messter-Str 13, 85737, Ismaning, Germany
Tel.: (49) 89 9595 50
Web Site: http://www.paymentsolutions.biz
Payment Transaction Services
N.A.I.C.S.: 561499

MOUNTAIN CHINA RESORTS (HOLDING) LIMITED
Building 6 No 2Nanhugan Lane Chaoyangmennei Avenue, Dongcheng District, Beijing, 100010, China
Tel.: (86) 1066420566
Web Site: http://www.mountainchinaresort.com
Year Founded: 2008
MCG—(TSXV)
Rev.: $599,226
Assets: $42,686,673
Liabilities: $62,010,553
Net Worth: ($19,323,881)
Earnings: ($5,303,858)
Fiscal Year-end: 12/31/21
Home Management Services
N.A.I.C.S.: 721110
Zhenhua Mao *(Chm)*

Subsidiaries:

Heilongjiang Yabuli On Snow Asian Game Village Hotel Co. Ltd. (1)
Windmill Inn Ski Tourism Holiday Zone Yabuli, Shanghai, Heilongjiang, China
Tel.: (86) 45153455066
Hotel & Resort Operating Services
N.A.I.C.S.: 721110

MOUNTAIN CREST BREWING CO.
1314 NE 44th Ave, Calgary, T2E 6L6, AB, Canada
Tel.: (403) 398-9463
Web Site: http://www.damngoodbeer.ca
Sales Range: $50-74.9 Million
Emp.: 3
Brewery
N.A.I.C.S.: 312120
Ravinder Minhas *(Founder, Pres & CEO)*

MOUNTAIN EQUIPMENT CO-OPERATIVE
149 4th Ave W, Vancouver, V5T E10, BC, Canada
Tel.: (604) 707-3300
Web Site: http://www.mec.ca
Year Founded: 1971
Sales Range: $125-149.9 Million
Emp.: 212
Sporting Equipment & Clothing Retailer
N.A.I.C.S.: 459110
Philippe Arrata *(CEO)*

MOUNTAIN PROVINCE DIAMONDS INC.
151 Yonge Street Suite 1100, PO Box 216, Toronto, M5C 2W7, ON, Canada
Tel.: (416) 361-3562   ON
Web Site: https://www.mountainprovince.com
Year Founded: 1986
MPVDF—(OTCIQ)
Rev.: $241,507,829
Assets: $686,448,354
Liabilities: $412,075,378
Net Worth: $274,372,976
Earnings: $216,039,921
Emp.: 13
Fiscal Year-end: 12/31/21

Diamond Mining & Exploration Services
N.A.I.C.S.: 212390
Jonathan Christopher James Comerford *(Chm, Interim Pres & Interim CEO)*

Subsidiaries:

2435386 Ontario Inc. (1)

MOUNTAIN VALLEY MD HOLDINGS, INC.
260 Edgeley Blvd Unit 4, Concord, L4K 3Y4, ON, Canada
Tel.: (647) 725-9755   Ca
Web Site: https://www.mountainvalleymd.com
Year Founded: 2005
MVMD—(CNSX)
Rev.: $44,323
Assets: $6,623,329
Liabilities: $190,589
Net Worth: $6,432,740
Earnings: $5,665,953
Emp.: 10
Fiscal Year-end: 03/31/24
Holding Company
N.A.I.C.S.: 551112
Dennis Hancock *(Pres & CEO)*

Subsidiaries:

Meadow Bay Gold Corp. (1)
Suite 210 - 905 West Pender Street, Vancouver, V6C 1L6, BC, Canada
Tel.: (604) 641-4450
Rev.: $708
Assets: $22,538,629
Liabilities: $98,247
Net Worth: $22,440,382
Earnings: ($766,172)
Fiscal Year-end: 03/31/2018
Gold Mining Services
N.A.I.C.S.: 212220

MOUNTAIN WAREHOUSE LTD.
5 Eccleston Street, London, SW1W 9LX, United Kingdom
Tel.: (44) 20 3828 7700
Web Site: http://www.mountainwarehouse.com
Year Founded: 1997
Clothing Accessory Store Operator
N.A.I.C.S.: 458110
Mark Neale *(Founder)*

MOUNTAINSTAR GOLD INC.
Suite 1500 701 West Georgia Street, Vancouver, V7Y 1C6, BC, Canada
Tel.: (604) 684-6276   BC
Web Site: http://msxgold.com
Sales Range: Less than $1 Million
Gold Mining Services
N.A.I.C.S.: 212220
Brent H. Johnson *(Pres & CEO)*

MOUNTVIEW ESTATES PLC
Mountview House 151 High Street, Southgate, London, N14 6EW, United Kingdom
Tel.: (44) 2089205777   UK
Web Site: https://www.mountviewplc.co.uk
MTVW—(LSE)
Rev.: $89,623,097
Assets: $573,285,051
Liabilities: $39,041,239
Net Worth: $534,243,812
Earnings: $36,498,229
Emp.: 29
Fiscal Year-end: 03/31/22
Property Trading Providers
N.A.I.C.S.: 531312
M. M. Bray *(Sec)*

Subsidiaries:

Louise Goodwin Limited (1)

MOUNTVIEW ESTATES PLC

Mountview Estates PLC—(Continued)
151 High St, Southgate, London, N14 6EW, United Kingdom
Tel.: (44) 2089205777
Web Site: http://www.mountviewplc.co.uk
Sales Range: $50-74.9 Million
Emp.: 25
Property Investment Services
N.A.I.C.S.: 531312

MOURY CONSTRUCT SA
English Street 6A 4430 Ans, 4020, Liege, Belgium
Tel.: (32) 43447211
Web Site: https://www.moury-construct.be
MOUR—(EUR)
Sales Range: $150-199.9 Million
Emp.: 66
Residential & Non-Residential Building Construction Services
N.A.I.C.S.: 541330
Jean-Marie Backes *(Dir-Admin & HR)*

MOUVEMENT DES CAISSES DESJARDINS
1 Complexe Desjardins, PO Box 7, Montreal, H5B 1B2, QC, Canada
Tel.: (514) 281-7000
Web Site: http://www.desjardins.com
Year Founded: 1900
Sales Range: $5-14.9 Billion
Emp.: 45,547
Bank Holding Company
N.A.I.C.S.: 551111
Marie-Huguette Cormier *(Exec VP-HR & Comm)*

Subsidiaries:

Desjardins Financial Corporation Inc. (1)
1 Complexe Desjardins, PO Box 10500, Montreal, H5B 1J1, QC, Canada **(100%)**
Tel.: (514) 281-7301
Web Site: http://www.desjardins.com
Sales Range: $1-4.9 Billion
Emp.: 8,000
Bank Holding Company; Investment Banking & Insurance Services
N.A.I.C.S.: 551111
Monique F. Leroux *(Chm, Pres & CEO)*

Desjardins Financial Security Life Assurance Company (1)
200 rue des Commandeurs, Levis, G6V 6R2, QC, Canada
Tel.: (418) 838-7800
Web Site: https://www.desjardinslifeinsurance.com
Sales Range: $1-4.9 Billion
Emp.: 3,000
Life & Health Insurance Carrier
N.A.I.C.S.: 524113

Subsidiary (Domestic):

Desjardins Financial Security Investments Inc. (2)
1150 rue de Claire-Fontaine St, Quebec, G1R 5G4, QC, Canada
Tel.: (204) 788-4040
Web Site: https://www.dfsi.ca
Emp.: 150
Wealth Management Investment Services
N.A.I.C.S.: 523150

Affiliate (Domestic):

McFarlane Agencies (1967 Ltd) (3)
Suite 100 100 Stockton Ave, Box 882, Okotoks, T1S 1A9, AB, Canada
Tel.: (403) 938-4898
Web Site: https://www.mcfarlaneagencies.com
Sales Range: $50-74.9 Million
Emp.: 20
Insurance Services
N.A.I.C.S.: 524210
Jason McFarlane *(Principal)*

Desjardins General Insurance Group (1)
6300 Blvd de la Rive Sud, CP 3500, Levis,
G6V 6P9, QC, Canada
Tel.: (418) 835-4850
Web Site: http://www.desjardinsinsurance.com
Sales Range: $1-4.9 Billion
Emp.: 4,000
Insurance Services
N.A.I.C.S.: 524128

Subsidiary (Domestic):

State Farm Mutual Automobile Insurance Company (2)
333 First Commerce Drive, Aurora, L4G 8A4, ON, Canada
Tel.: (800) 782-8332
Web Site: http://www.statefarm.ca
Insurance Services
N.A.I.C.S.: 524126

The Personal Insurance Company (2)
3 Robert Speck Pkwy, PO Box 7065, Mississauga, L5A 4K7, ON, Canada
Tel.: (905) 306-4403
Web Site: https://www.thepersonal.com
Sales Range: $300-349.9 Million
Emp.: 900
Automobile & Home Insurance Carrier Service
N.A.I.C.S.: 524126

Desjardins Securities Inc. (1)
1170 rue Peel Bureau 300, Montreal, H3B 0A9, QC, Canada
Tel.: (514) 987-1749
Web Site: https://www.vmdconseil.ca
Sales Range: $200-249.9 Million
Emp.: 350
Securities Brokerage Services
N.A.I.C.S.: 523150

Subsidiary (US):

Nexa Technologies, Inc. (2)
18552 MacArthur Blvd Ste 100, Irvine, CA 92612
Tel.: (972) 590-8669
Web Site: http://www.nexatech.com
Sales Range: $50-74.9 Million
Emp.: 110
Online Brokerage & Trading Services
N.A.I.C.S.: 425120

Regional Power, Inc. (1)
6755 Mississauga Rd Ste 308, Mississauga, L5N7Y2, ON, Canada
Tel.: (416) 593-4717
Web Site: http://www.regionalpower.com
Developer, Manager & Operator of Hydroelectric Facilities
N.A.I.C.S.: 221111
James Carter *(VP-Dev & Ops)*

MOVE ABOUT GROUP AB
Norra Hamngatan 18, 411 06, Gothenburg, Sweden
Tel.: (46) 317992804
Web Site: https://www.moveaboutgroup.com
Year Founded: 2007
MOV—(OMX)
Rev.: $665,118
Assets: $12,251,077
Liabilities: $10,871,206
Net Worth: $1,379,872
Earnings: ($1,739,234)
Emp.: 33
Fiscal Year-end: 12/31/23
Electric Vehicle Mfr
N.A.I.C.S.: 336320
Olof Jonasson *(CEO)*

MOVE LOGISTICS GROUP LIMITED
24-30 Paraite Road, Bell Block, New Plymouth, 4312, New Zealand
Tel.: (64) 67559990
Web Site: https://movelogistics.com
Year Founded: 1869
MOV—(NZX)
Rev.: $207,938,995
Assets: $182,557,416
Liabilities: $137,758,971
Net Worth: $44,798,445

Earnings: ($3,491,029)
Emp.: 1,158
Fiscal Year-end: 06/30/23
Logistic Services
N.A.I.C.S.: 541614
Julia Raue *(Chm)*

Subsidiaries:

Alpha Custom Services Limited (1)
25 Dawson Street, New Plymouth, New Zealand
Tel.: (64) 67598104
Web Site: https://www.alphacustoms.co.nz
Freight Forwarding Services
N.A.I.C.S.: 488510

MOVE WITH US PLC
Grant Hall Saint Ives Business Park, Parsons Green, Saint Ives, PE27 4AA, Cambridgeshire, United Kingdom
Tel.: (44) 1480 409 590
Web Site: http://www.movewithus.co.uk
Year Founded: 1997
Sales Range: $50-74.9 Million
Emp.: 300
Real Estate Broker
N.A.I.C.S.: 531210
Sean King *(CEO)*

MOVEBYBIKE EUROPE AB
Agneslundsvagen 26, 212 15, Malmo, Sweden
Tel.: (46) 406160655
Web Site: https://www.movebybike.se
Year Founded: 2012
6ZR—(DEU)
Emp.: 80
Transportation Services
N.A.I.C.S.: 488510
Behdad Ansari *(Chm)*

MOVENPICK HOLDING AG
Oberneuhofstrasse 12, 6340, Baar, Switzerland
Tel.: (41) 417591717
Web Site: http://www.moevenpick-group.com
Sales Range: $1-4.9 Billion
Emp.: 16,300
Restaurant & Bar Services
N.A.I.C.S.: 721110
Guido Egli *(Pres-Supervisory Bd & CEO)*

Subsidiaries:

MPW Movenpick Wein AG (1)
Oberneuhofstrasse 12, CH-6340, Baar, Switzerland
Tel.: (41) 417668181
Web Site: http://www.movenpickwein.com
Sales Range: $75-99.9 Million
Emp.: 120
Wine Distr
N.A.I.C.S.: 424810

Movenpick Foods Switzerland Ltd. (1)
Luzernerstrasse 9, Postfach 465, CH-6330, Cham, Switzerland
Tel.: (41) 417851919
Web Site: http://www.moevenpick.com
Sales Range: $25-49.9 Million
Emp.: 20
Food Distr
N.A.I.C.S.: 424410
Guido Egli *(CEO)*

Movenpick Gastronomie Schweiz AG (1)
Sloughof Strasse 61, 8152, Glattbrugg, Switzerland
Tel.: (41) 447122222
Web Site: http://www.movenpick.com
Food Distr
N.A.I.C.S.: 424410

MOVIE GAMES SA

INTERNATIONAL PUBLIC

Wernyhory 29a, 02-727, Warsaw, Poland
Tel.: (48) 534206319
Web Site: https://mov.gs
Year Founded: 2016
MVR—(WAR)
Rev.: $1,147,104
Assets: $9,888,211
Liabilities: $3,596,037
Net Worth: $6,292,175
Earnings: ($3,059,197)
Fiscal Year-end: 12/31/23
Software Development Services
N.A.I.C.S.: 541511
Mateusz Andrzej Wczesniak *(CEO)*

MOVINN A/S
Dronningens Tvaergade 9B 1, 1302, Copenhagen, Denmark
Tel.: (45) 88338838
Web Site: https://www.movinn.com
Year Founded: 2014
MOVINN—(CSE)
Rev.: $12,088,235
Assets: $7,703,260
Liabilities: $4,755,538
Net Worth: $2,947,722
Earnings: ($863,538)
Emp.: 30
Fiscal Year-end: 12/31/23
Real Estate Investment Services
N.A.I.C.S.: 531190
Jesper Thaning *(Founder)*

MOWI ASA
Sandviksboder 77AB, 5035, Bergen, Norway
Tel.: (47) 21562300
Web Site: https://www.mowi.com
Year Founded: 1964
MHGVY—(OTCIQ)
Rev.: $5,912,259,875
Assets: $8,891,646,881
Liabilities: $4,839,520,829
Net Worth: $4,052,126,052
Earnings: $474,314,699
Emp.: 14,142
Fiscal Year-end: 12/31/23
Holding Company; Fish Farming & Fish Whslr
N.A.I.C.S.: 551112
Ola Brattvoll *(COO-Sls & Mktg)*

Subsidiaries:

Laschinger Seafood GmbH (1)
Dieter-Gorlitz-Platz 2, 94469, Deggendorf, Germany
Tel.: (49) 9913721040
Web Site: http://www.laschinger.de
Seafood Mfr & Distr
N.A.I.C.S.: 311710
Michael Kellner *(Mng Dir)*

MOWI Singapore Pte Ltd (1)
20 Harbour Drive 05-02 PSA Vista, Singapore, 117612, Singapore
Tel.: (65) 64089070
Web Site: https://www.marineharvest.sg
Sales Range: $125-149.9 Million
Emp.: 10
Fish Farming
N.A.I.C.S.: 112511

Marine Harvest (Fort Williams) Ltd. (1)
Stob Ban House Glen Nevis Business Park, Fort William, PH33 6RX, Scotland, United Kingdom
Tel.: (44) 1397715000
Web Site: http://www.mhsfeedplant.co.uk
Sales Range: $25-49.9 Million
Emp.: 250
Fish Farming Services
N.A.I.C.S.: 112511

Marine Harvest Canada (1)
1046 Cedar Street, Campbell River, V9W 7E2, BC, Canada
Tel.: (250) 850-3276
Web Site: https://mowi.com

AND PRIVATE COMPANIES

Sales Range: $25-49.9 Million
Emp.: 160
Fish Farming
N.A.I.C.S.: 112511

Marine Harvest China (1)
Room 909 Lucky Tower Building B No 3
Dongsanhuan Beilu, Chaoyang District, Beijing, 100027, China
Tel.: (86) 1064620158
Web Site: http://www.marineharvest.com
Sales Range: $25-49.9 Million
Emp.: 10
Seafood Whslr
N.A.I.C.S.: 445250
Xu Wannong (Mng Dir)

Marine Harvest Faroes P/F (1)
Ternubrekkan 3, FO-695, Hellur, Faroe Islands
Tel.: (298) 444733
Emp.: 75
Seafood Processing Services
N.A.I.C.S.: 311710
Hans Jakup Mikkelsen (Gen Mgr)

Marine Harvest Holding AS (1)
Sandviksboder 77AB, 0161, Bergen, Norway
Tel.: (47) 21562000
Web Site: http://www.marineharvest.com
Sales Range: $25-49.9 Million
Emp.: 30
Seafood Processing Services
N.A.I.C.S.: 311710

Marine Harvest Korea Ltd. (1)
Pusan Joong Gu Dong Kwang Dong no 2/4, Dong Yang Bld 205, Busan, 600 022, Korea (South)
Tel.: (82) 512554028
Sales Range: $25-49.9 Million
Emp.: 3
Seafood Whslr
N.A.I.C.S.: 445250

Marine Harvest Norway AS (1)
Sandviksboder 77AB, PO Box 4102, Dreggen, 5835, Bergen, Hordaland, Norway
Tel.: (47) 21562300
Web Site: http://www.marineharvest.com
Seafood Processing Services
N.A.I.C.S.: 311710

Subsidiary (Domestic):

Marine Harvest Terminal AS (2)
Brages Veg 12, Jessheim, 2050, Akershus, Norway
Tel.: (47) 21562300
Web Site: http://www.marineharvest.com
Seafood Products Handling & Freight Forwarding Services
N.A.I.C.S.: 488510

Mowi Labrus AS (2)
Sandviksboder 77AB, 5035, Bergen, Hordaland, Norway
Tel.: (47) 21562300
Web Site: https://mowi.com
Sales Range: $150-199.9 Million
Emp.: 10
Seafood Processing Services
N.A.I.C.S.: 311710

Marine Harvest Spain II. S.L. (1)
Calle Julio Palacios N 26 - 11 puerta 3, 28029, Madrid, Spain
Tel.: (34) 917355208
Sales Range: $25-49.9 Million
Emp.: 3
Seafood Processing Services
N.A.I.C.S.: 311710

Marine Harvest VAP (1)
Kolvestraat 4, Brugge, 8000, Belgium
Tel.: (32) 50458585
Web Site: http://www.marineharvest.com
Sales Range: $75-99.9 Million
Emp.: 350
Fish Farming
N.A.I.C.S.: 112511

Subsidiary (Domestic):

Marine Harvest Pieters N.V. (2)
Kolvestraat 4, 8000, Brugge, West Flanders, Belgium
Tel.: (32) 50458585
Sales Range: $100-124.9 Million
Emp.: 450
Fish Processing & Distr

N.A.I.C.S.: 311710

Subsidiary (Non-US):

Marine Harvest Poland Sp. Z.o.o. (2)
Duninowo 39, Ustka, 76-270, Slupsk, Poland
Tel.: (48) 598100700
Seafood Processing Services
N.A.I.C.S.: 311710

Marine Harvest VAP France S.A.S. (2)
Zone Industrielle Petite Synth Avenue de la Gironde, 59640, Dunkerque, France
Tel.: (33) 328587979
Sales Range: $25-49.9 Million
Emp.: 70
Frozen Seafood Distr
N.A.I.C.S.: 424460

Subsidiary (Domestic):

Marine Harvest Appeti' Marine S.A.S. (3)
ZI Petite Synthe Avenue de la Gironde, 59640, Dunkerque, France
Tel.: (33) 328587979
Sales Range: $25-49.9 Million
Emp.: 70
Seafood Processing & Distr
N.A.I.C.S.: 311710
Fabrice Barreau (Gen Mgr)

Marine Harvest Kritsen S.A.S. (3)
ZA du Vern, BP 50409, 29420, Landivisiau, Finistere, France
Tel.: (33) 298684444
Web Site: http://www.kritsen.fr
Sales Range: $100-124.9 Million
Smoked Salmon & Sea Food Delicatessen Mfr
N.A.I.C.S.: 311710
Christian Pasquier (Mgr)

Marine Harvest Lorient S.A.S. (3)
Zone Halioparc Nord 2 rue Bateliere, 56100, Lorient, Morbihan, France
Tel.: (33) 297373032
Sales Range: $25-49.9 Million
Emp.: 55
Seafood Processing Services
N.A.I.C.S.: 311710
Franck Haberzettel (Plant Mgr)

Marine Harvest Rennes S.A.S. (3)
Beaujardin, BP 40, 35410, Chateaugiron, Ille-et-Vilaine, France
Tel.: (33) 299372424
Sales Range: $25-49.9 Million
Seafood Processing Services
N.A.I.C.S.: 311710

Mowi France SAS (3)
3 rue Leon Calon, 62200, Boulogne-sur-Mer, France
Tel.: (33) 321106766
Sales Range: $25-49.9 Million
Emp.: 130
Seafood Processing Services
N.A.I.C.S.: 311710
Jean Deterre (Gen Mgr)

Subsidiary (Non-US):

Mowi Sterk B.V. (2)
Vuurtorenweg 12, 8531 HJ, Lemmer, Netherlands
Tel.: (31) 514568600
Web Site: http://www.marineharvest.com
Sales Range: $25-49.9 Million
Emp.: 200
Seafood Processing Services
N.A.I.C.S.: 311710

Mowi (1)
Ruta Chinquihue Km 12 S/N, Puerto Montt, Chile
Tel.: (56) 652221910
Web Site: http://www.marineharvest.com
Sales Range: $300-349.9 Million
Emp.: 1,500
Fish Farming
N.A.I.C.S.: 112511

Subsidiary (Domestic):

Cultivadora de Salmones Linao S.A. (2)
Camino Tepual Km 8 Ruta 226, Puerto

Montt, Llanquihue, Chile
Tel.: (56) 65221700
Sales Range: $25-49.9 Million
Emp.: 80
Salmon Fishing Services
N.A.I.C.S.: 114119

Mowi Belgium NV (1)
Kolvestraat 4, 8000, Brugge, Belgium
Tel.: (32) 50458585
Seafood Mfr & Distr
N.A.I.C.S.: 311710

Mowi Bretagne S.A.S. (1)
3 rue Leon Calon, 62 200, Boulogne-sur-Mer, France
Tel.: (33) 321106766
Seafood Product Mfr
N.A.I.C.S.: 486210

Mowi Canada West Inc. (1)
1046 Cedar Street, Campbell River, V9W 8C9, BC, Canada
Tel.: (250) 850-3276
Emp.: 600
Seafood Mfr & Distr
N.A.I.C.S.: 311710

Mowi Chile S.A. (1)
Ruta Chinquihue Km 12 S/N, Puerto Montt, Chile
Tel.: (56) 652221910
Emp.: 800
Seafood Mfr & Distr
N.A.I.C.S.: 311710
Adrian Maldonado (Mgr-Comm & CRS)

Mowi Cuisery SAS (1)
1 allee Michel Joly, 71 290, Cuisery, France
Tel.: (33) 385210400
Seafood Mfr & Distr
N.A.I.C.S.: 311710

Mowi Ducktrap LLC (1)
57 Little River Dr, Belfast, ME 04915
Tel.: (207) 338-6280
Web Site: https://ducktrap.com
Emp.: 100
Fish Farming Services
N.A.I.C.S.: 112511

Mowi Dunkerque SAS (1)
Avenue de la Gironde, 59 640, Dunkerque, France
Tel.: (33) 328647232
Seafood Mfr & Distr
N.A.I.C.S.: 311710

Mowi France SAS (1)
3 rue Leon Calon, 62200, Boulogne-sur-Mer, France
Tel.: (33) 321106766
Seafood Mfr & Distr
N.A.I.C.S.: 311710

Mowi Ireland Ltd. (1)
Ballylar PO, Rinmore Fanad, Letterkenny, F92 T677, Co Donegal, Ireland
Tel.: (353) 749192100
Web Site: http://www.marineharvestireland.com
Sales Range: $50-74.9 Million
Emp.: 240
Fish Farming & Processing Services
N.A.I.C.S.: 112511

Subsidiary (Domestic):

Clare Island Seafarm Ltd. (2)
Cloughmore Achill, Co Mayo, Westport, Connacht, Ireland
Tel.: (353) 9845375
Seafood Processing Services
N.A.I.C.S.: 311710

Fanad Pettigo Teoranta (2)
Ranmore Ballylar Post Office Letter Kenny, Donegal, Ulster, Ireland
Tel.: (353) 749159071
Web Site: http://www.theorganicsalmonco.com
Sales Range: $25-49.9 Million
Emp.: 240
Finfish Farming Services
N.A.I.C.S.: 112511
Jan Feenstra (Mgr)

Mowi Italia S.R.L. (1)
Viale Togliatti 25, 40132, Bologna, Italy
Tel.: (39) 0516752198
Seafood Mfr & Distr

MOWI ASA

N.A.I.C.S.: 311710
Ambrogio Sainaghi (Mng Dir)

Mowi Japan Co., Ltd. (1)
Nichirei Higashi Ginza Building 9F 6-19-20, Tsukiji Higuo-ku, Tokyo, 104-0045, Japan
Tel.: (81) 345337230
Seafood Mfr & Distr
N.A.I.C.S.: 311710

Mowi Japan K.K. (1)
Nichirei Higashi Ginza Building 9F 6-19-20, Tsukiji, Chuo-ku, Tokyo, 104-0033, Japan
Tel.: (81) 345337230
Web Site: https://mowi.com
Seafood Processing Services
N.A.I.C.S.: 311710

Mowi Lemmer BV (1)
Vuurtorenweg 12, 8531 HJ, Lemmer, Netherlands
Tel.: (31) 514568600
Emp.: 149
Seafood Mfr & Distr
N.A.I.C.S.: 311710

Mowi Scotland Limited (1)
Admiralty Park Admiralty Road, Ratho Station Newbridge, Rosyth, KY11 2YW, Fife, United Kingdom
Tel.: (44) 1397701550
Sales Range: $25-49.9 Million
Emp.: 20
Fish Farming
N.A.I.C.S.: 112511

Mowi Scotland Ltd. (1)
Admiralty Park Admiralty Road Fife, Rosyth, KY11 2YW, United Kingdom
Tel.: (44) 1397701550
Seafood Mfr & Distr
N.A.I.C.S.: 311710

Mowi Singapore Pte. Ltd. (1)
20 Harbour Drive 05-02 PSA Vista, Singapore, 117612, Singapore
Tel.: (65) 64089070
Seafood Mfr & Distr
N.A.I.C.S.: 311710

Mowi Turkey Su Urunleri Ticaret A.S. (1)
Cumhuriyet Mahallesi 2257 Sokak No 1/A, Gebze, 41400, Kocaeli, Turkiye
Tel.: (90) 2165105343
Seafood Mfr & Distr
N.A.I.C.S.: 311710

Mowi Turkiye Su Urunleri Ticaret A.S. (1)
Barbaros mah Alzambak sok Varyap Meridyan Sitesi, A Blok Grand Tower Zemin Kat No 10 Atasehir, Istanbul, Turkiye
Tel.: (90) 2165105343
Web Site: https://mowi.com
Fish Farming Services
N.A.I.C.S.: 112511

Mowi USA Holding LLC (1)
8499 NW 80th St, Medley, FL 33166
Tel.: (305) 591-8550
Web Site: http://www.marineharvest.com
Sales Range: $10-24.9 Million
Emp.: 34
Seafood Processing Services
N.A.I.C.S.: 311710

Subsidiary (Domestic):

Mowi USA LLC (2)
8499 NW 80th St, Medley, FL 33166
Tel.: (305) 591-8550
Web Site: http://www.marineharvest.com
Emp.: 100
Fresh & Frozen Seafood Products Retailer
N.A.I.C.S.: 424460
Gianfranco Nattero (Mng Dir)

Subsidiary (Domestic):

Ducktrap River of Maine LLC (3)
57 Little River Dr, Belfast, ME 04915
Tel.: (207) 338-6280
Web Site: http://www.ducktrap.com
Sales Range: $10-24.9 Million
Seafood Smoking Services
N.A.I.C.S.: 311710

Mowi Vietnam Company Ltd. (1)
102/6 Road No 2, Amata Industrial Park

MOWI ASA

Mowi ASA—(Continued)
Long Binh Ward, Bien Hoa, Dong Nai, Vietnam
Tel.: (84) 2513936100
Seafood Mfr & Distr
N.A.I.C.S.: 311710

Mowi USA LLC (1)
8499 NW 80th St, Medley, FL 33166
Tel.: (305) 591-8550
Fish Farming Services
N.A.I.C.S.: 112511

MOYA HOLDINGS ASIA LIMITED
65 Chulia Street OCBC Centre 37-08, Singapore, 049513, Singapore
Tel.: (65) 63650652 SG
Web Site: http://www.moyaasia.com
5WE—(CAT)
Rev.: $191,178,214
Assets: $503,964,431
Liabilities: $222,782,512
Net Worth: $281,181,919
Earnings: $31,122,638
Emp.: 1,518
Fiscal Year-end: 12/31/21
Holding Company
N.A.I.C.S.: 551112
Simon A. Melhem (Exec Dir)

Subsidiaries:

PT Acuatico Air Indonesia (1)
Setiabudi Atrium Building Suite 410 4th Floor Jl H Rasuna Said Kav 62, Jakarta, 12920, Indonesia
Tel.: (62) 215210399
Web Site: http://acuaticogroup.com
Water Treatment Plant Services
N.A.I.C.S.: 221310

PT Aetra Air Jakarta (1)
Jl Raya Kalimalang No 89, Jakarta Timur, 13450, Indonesia
Tel.: (62) 218 690 9999
Web Site: https://www.aetra.co.id
Water Treatment Plant Services
N.A.I.C.S.: 221310

PT Aetra Air Tangerang (1)
Jl Raya Curug No 27 Kadu Jaya, Curug, Tangerang, 15810, Banten, Indonesia
Tel.: (62) 215985477
Web Site: https://aetratangerang.co.id
Water Treatment Plant Services
N.A.I.C.S.: 221310
M. Noer Muis (Co-Pres & Commissioner)

PT Moya Indonesia (1)
Atrium Setiabudi Building 4th Floor Suite 410, Kuningan Setia Budi, Jakarta, 12920, Indonesia
Tel.: (62) 215210399
Water Treatment Plant Services
N.A.I.C.S.: 221310

PT Traya Tirta Cisadane (1)
Jl Raya Serpong No 1-2, Serpong Kec Serpong Kota, Tangerang, 15310, Banten, Indonesia
Tel.: (62) 217565528
Web Site: http://trayatirtacisadane.com
Water Treatment Plant Services
N.A.I.C.S.: 221310

MOYNES FORD SALES LTD.
153 Lindsay Street South, Lindsay, K9V 4S5, ON, Canada
Tel.: (705) 324-9484
Web Site: https://www.moynesford.com
Year Founded: 1971
Sales Range: $10-24.9 Million
New & Used Car Dealers
N.A.I.C.S.: 441110
George Hamilton (Gen Mgr)

MP GROUP INC.
984-4 Bangbae-dong, Seocho-gu, Seoul, Korea (South)
Tel.: (82) 2 596 3300
Web Site: http://www.mrpizza.co.kr
Year Founded: 1990

Sales Range: $100-124.9 Million
Emp.: 425
Pizza Mfr & Distr
N.A.I.C.S.: 311991
Woo-Hyun Jung (Chm)

MP HANKANG CO., LTD.
206 273 Digital-ro Guro-go, Seoul, 08381, Korea (South)
Tel.: (82) 237738373
Year Founded: 2015
219550—(KRS)
Rev.: $15,983,356
Assets: $36,264,173
Liabilities: $1,967,219
Net Worth: $34,296,954
Earnings: $691,541
Emp.: 72
Fiscal Year-end: 12/31/22
Financial Investment Management Services
N.A.I.C.S.: 523940

MPAC GROUP PLC
Station Estate Station Road, Westwood Business Park, Tadcaster, LS24 9SG, North Yorkshire, United Kingdom
Tel.: (44) 2476421100 UK
Web Site: https://www.mpac-group.com
Year Founded: 1874
MPAC—(AIM)
Rev.: $123,327,443
Assets: $163,721,283
Liabilities: $85,205,756
Net Worth: $78,515,526
Earnings: ($504,923)
Emp.: 458
Fiscal Year-end: 12/31/22
Holding Company; Packaging Machinery Mfr, Whslr & Maintenance Services
N.A.I.C.S.: 551112
Tony Steels (CEO)

Subsidiaries:

Arista Laboratories Europe Ltd. (1)
1 Elm Crescent, Kingston upon Thames, KT26HL, Surrey, United Kingdom
Tel.: (44) 2082479100
Web Site: https://www.aristalabs.co.uk
Sales Range: $25-49.9 Million
Emp.: 10
Testing Laboratories
N.A.I.C.S.: 541380

Arista Laboratories Inc. (1)
1470 E Parham Rd, Fairfield, VA 23228 (100%)
Tel.: (804) 271-5572
Web Site: http://www.aristalabs.com
Sales Range: $25-49.9 Million
Emp.: 45
Testing Laboratories
N.A.I.C.S.: 541380

ITCM North America, Inc. (1)
4255 Ruffin Rd Ste 100, San Diego, CA 92123
Tel.: (858) 268-4774
Web Site: https://www.itcm.co
Computer Related Services
N.A.I.C.S.: 541519
Jorge Ruiz de Castilla (CEO)

Subsidiary (Domestic):

Value Logic, Inc. (2)
1351 Distribution Way, Vista, CA 92081
Tel.: (760) 599-9255
Sales Range: $1-9.9 Million
Emp.: 10
Computer System Design Services
N.A.I.C.S.: 541512
Christine Rabiyan (Owner)

Langenpac NV (1)
Edisonstraat 14, PO Box 417, Wijchen, 6604 BV, Netherlands (100%)
Tel.: (31) 246486655
Web Site: http://www.langengroup.com

Sales Range: $25-49.9 Million
Emp.: 130
Unsupported Plastics Packaging Film & Sheet Mfr
N.A.I.C.S.: 326112
Geert van den Heiligenberg (Gen Mgr)

Molmac Engineering Ltd. (1)
Haw Lane, Saunderton, High Wycombe, HP14 4JE, Bucks, United Kingdom (100%)
Tel.: (44) 1844343211
Sales Range: $50-74.9 Million
Emp.: 100
Industrial Supplies Merchant Whslr
N.A.I.C.S.: 423840

Mpac Langen Pte. Ltd. (1)
8 Burn Road 09-01 Trivex, Singapore, 369977, Singapore
Tel.: (65) 63399666
Packaging & Labeling Services
N.A.I.C.S.: 561910

Sasib S.p.A. (1)
Via G Di Vittorio 21/b, Castel Maggiore, 40013, Bologna, Italy
Tel.: (39) 051 632 7711
Web Site: https://www.sasib.com
Sales Range: $500-549.9 Million
Emp.: 150
Machinery for the Food & Beverage Industry
N.A.I.C.S.: 333241

Switchback Group, Inc. (1)
3778 Timberlake Dr, Richfield, OH 44286
Tel.: (330) 523-5200
Web Site: http://www.switchbackgroup.com
Packaging Machinery Equipment Mfr
N.A.I.C.S.: 333993
Dave Shepherd (Partner)

MPACT LIMITED
4th Floor No 3 Melrose Boulevard Melrose Arch, Johannesburg, 2196, South Africa
Tel.: (27) 119945500
Web Site: https://www.mpact.co.za
MPT—(JSE)
Rev.: $677,188,183
Assets: $614,444,597
Liabilities: $325,705,806
Net Worth: $288,738,791
Earnings: $41,059,792
Emp.: 5,156
Fiscal Year-end: 12/31/23
Production of Corrugated Board & High Quality Printed Boxes
N.A.I.C.S.: 322211
Hugh Michael Thompson (Mng Dir-Paper Mfg Bus)

Subsidiaries:

West Coast Paper Traders (Pty) Ltd. (1)
117 Hatfield Street Gardens, Cape Town, 8001, South Africa
Tel.: (27) 21 461 7807
Web Site: https://www.wcpt.co.za
Paper Product Distr
N.A.I.C.S.: 424120
Davin Botha (Gen Mgr)

MPAY SA
ul Jasna 1 lok 421, 00-013, Warsaw, Poland
Tel.: (48) 343905557
Web Site: https://www.mpay.pl
Year Founded: 2003
MPY—(WAR)
Digital Payment Services
N.A.I.C.S.: 522320
Andrzej Basiak (Pres)

MPB TECHNOLOGIES INC.
147 Hymus Blvd, Pointe-Claire, H9R 1ER, QC, Canada
Tel.: (514) 694-8751
Web Site: http://www.mpb-technologies.ca
Year Founded: 1977
Rev.: $12,412,500
Emp.: 150

INTERNATIONAL PUBLIC

Communication Service
N.A.I.C.S.: 517810
Morrel Bachynski (Founder)

MPC CONTAINER SHIPS ASA
Munkedamsveien 45, 0250, Oslo, Norway
Tel.: (47) 21563162 NO
Web Site: https://www.mpc-container.com
Year Founded: 2017
MPCC—(OSL)
Rev.: $711,282,000
Assets: $954,744,000
Liabilities: $201,263,000
Net Worth: $753,481,000
Earnings: $325,116,000
Emp.: 33
Fiscal Year-end: 12/31/23
Container Shipping ervices
N.A.I.C.S.: 488330
Constantin Baack (CEO)

MPC ENERGY SOLUTIONS N.V.
Apollolaan 151 Unit 121, 1077, Amsterdam, Netherlands NL
Web Site: https://www.mpc-energysolutions.com
Year Founded: 2020
MPCES—(OSL)
Rev.: $9,092,000
Assets: $123,098,000
Liabilities: $53,664,000
Net Worth: $69,434,000
Earnings: ($8,502,000)
Emp.: 13
Fiscal Year-end: 12/31/23
Renewable Energy Services
N.A.I.C.S.: 221210
Martin Vogt (CEO)

MPC MUNCHMEYER PETERSEN & CO. GMBH
Palmaille 67, 22767, Hamburg, Germany
Tel.: (49) 403802201 De
Web Site: http://www.mpc-group.com
Year Founded: 1846
Sales Range: $200-249.9 Million
Emp.: 1,000
Investment Holding Company
N.A.I.C.S.: 551112
John Benjamin Schroeder (Member-Mgmt Bd)

Subsidiaries:

Ferrostaal GmbH (1)
Hohenzollernstrasse 24, Essen, 45128, Germany
Tel.: (49) 201 818 01
Web Site: http://www.ferrostaal.com
Sales Range: $1-4.9 Billion
Emp.:
Holding Company; Industrial Plant Construction & Support Services
N.A.I.C.S.: 551112
Joachim Ludwig (Member-Exec Bd)

Subsidiary (Domestic):

Coutinho & Ferrostaal GmbH & Co. KG (2)
Valentinskamp 70, Hamburg, 20355, Germany
Tel.: (49) 40 38022 7500
Web Site: http://www.cnfinternational.com
Steel Trading Services
N.A.I.C.S.: 423510
Michael Doelle (Exec Dir)

Subsidiary (US):

Coutinho & Ferrostaal Inc. (3)
16510 Northchase Dr, Houston, TX 77060
Tel.: (281) 999-9995
Web Site: http://www.cnfinternational.com
Sales Range: $25-49.9 Million
Emp.: 70
Steel Trading Services
N.A.I.C.S.: 423510
Dave Whitney (Mgr-Sls)

AND PRIVATE COMPANIES

Subsidiary (Non-US):

Ferrostaal Australia Pty Ltd (2)
Unit 10/2 Eden Park Drive, Macquarie, 2113, NSW, Australia
Tel.: (61) 2 9338 3900
Web Site: http://www.ferrostaal.com.au
Emp.: 25
Industrial Services in Plant Construction & Engineering (Petrochemicals, Power, Solar, Oil & Gas), OEM Equipment Supplier, Financing & Services for Printing, Plastics, Packaging & Recycling
N.A.I.C.S.: 541330
Carsten Wendler (Mng Dir)

Joint Venture (Non-US):

Ferrostaal Christof Romania SRL (2)
Strada Trandafirilor 49 A, 107084, Brazii, Romania
Tel.: (40) 344 401027
Plant Design & Construction Services
N.A.I.C.S.: 541420

Subsidiary (US):

Ferrostaal Incorporated (2)
363 N Sam Houston Pkwy E Ste 1710, Houston, TX 77060-2409
Tel.: (281) 741-6700
Web Site: http://www.ferrostaal.us
Holding Company
N.A.I.C.S.: 551112

Subsidiary (Domestic):

Ferrostaal Equipment Solutions North America, Inc. (3)
363 N Sam Houston Pkwy E Ste 1710, Houston, TX 77060
Tel.: (281) 741-6700
Printing, Plastics, Packaging & Recycling Equipment Solutions, Including Financing, Spare Parts & Maintenance & Technical Support
N.A.I.C.S.: 522220

Subsidiary (Non-US):

Ferrostaal Mexico, S.A. de C.V. (2)
Rio Nilo No 47, Col Cuauhtemoc, CP 06500, Mexico, DF, Mexico
Tel.: (52) 55 52 42 3500
Web Site: http://www.ferrostaal.com.mx
Industrial Services in Plant Construction & Engineering (Petrochemicals, Power, Solar, Oil & Gas), OEM Equipment Supplier, Financing & Services for Printing, Plastics, Packaging & Recycling
N.A.I.C.S.: 541330
Mariano Chiappe (Mng Dir)

Ferrostaal Philippines Inc. (2)
Unit 2706 One Corporate Center Julia Vargas corner Meralco Avenue, Ortigas Center, Pasig City, Manila, 1605, Philippines
Tel.: (63) 2 655 7700
Industrial Plant Construction & Support Services
N.A.I.C.S.: 236210

Subsidiary (Domestic):

Ferrostaal Piping Supply GmbH (2)
Hohenzollernstrasse 24, 45128, Essen, Germany
Tel.: (49) 201 818 1798
Pipes & Pipeline Equipment Supplier
N.A.I.C.S.: 423830

Subsidiary (Non-US):

Ferrostaal Procurement Services NV (2)
Brouwersvliet 25, Antwerp, 2000, Belgium
Tel.: (32) 3 240 1612
Industrial Plant Construction & Support Services
N.A.I.C.S.: 236210

Ferrostaal Singapore Pte. Ltd. (2)
33 Ubi Avenue 3 #06-15, Singapore, 408868, Singapore
Tel.: (65) 6756 2188
Integrated Printing Systems Distr
N.A.I.C.S.: 333248

Ferrostaal do Brasil Comercio e Industria Ltda. (2)
Av das Nacoes Unidas 22 351, Sao Paulo, 04795-904, Brazil
Tel.: (55) 11 55 419877
Web Site: http://www.ferrostaal.com.br
Industrial Services in Plant Construction & Engineering for Petrochemicals, Power, Solar, Oil & Gas Industries
N.A.I.C.S.: 541330
Fabio Lobo (CEO)

Subsidiary (Domestic):

Intergrafica Print & Pack GmbH Druckmaschinenvertrieb (2)
Hohenzollernstrasse 24, 24 45128, Essen, Germany
Tel.: (49) 20181808
Web Site: http://www.ipp-group.net
Graphic Systems
N.A.I.C.S.: 541430
Manuella Schuett (Sec)

MPC Munchmeyer Petersen Capital AG (1)
Palmaille 67, 22767, Hamburg, Germany (49%)
Tel.: (49) 40380224200
Web Site: https://www.mpc-capital.com
Rev.: $41,891,866
Assets: $167,876,550
Liabilities: $32,332,352
Net Worth: $135,544,197
Earnings: $14,482,774
Emp.: 169
Fiscal Year-end: 12/31/2023
Asset & Investment Management Services
N.A.I.C.S.: 523940
Axel Schroeder Jr. (Chm-Supervisory Bd)

Subsidiary (Non-US):

CPM Anlagen Vertrieb GmbH (2)
Annagasse 5 Stiege 2 Top 16, 1010, Vienna, Austria
Tel.: (43) 1 5855670 0
Financial Investment Services
N.A.I.C.S.: 523999

Subsidiary (Domestic):

Deutsche SachCapital GmbH (2)
Palmaille 71, 22767, Hamburg, Germany
Tel.: (49) 40 808075 5655
Web Site: http://www.deutsche-sachcapital.com
Financial Investment Services
N.A.I.C.S.: 523999
Christian Sternberg (Mng Dir-Portfolio Mgmt & IR)

Subsidiary (Non-US):

MPC Munchmeyer Petersen Real Estate Services B.V. (2)
Strawinskylaan 835, 1077 XX, Amsterdam, Netherlands
Tel.: (31) 20 714 71 30
Real Estate Manangement Services
N.A.I.C.S.: 531390

Subsidiary (Domestic):

MPC Real Value Fund Verwaltungsgesellschaft mbH (2)
Gerberstr 6, 25451, Quickborn, Schleswig-Holstein, Germany
Tel.: (49) 40 380224242
Financial Investment Services
N.A.I.C.S.: 523999

MPC Rendite-Fonds Leben plus Management GmbH (2)
Pinneberger Strasse 9, 25451, Quickborn, Germany
Tel.: (49) 40 38022242
Financial Investment Services
N.A.I.C.S.: 523999

Talleur GmbH (2)
Grosser Burstah 45, 20457, Hamburg, Germany
Tel.: (49) 40 320 866 0
Web Site: http://www.talleur.com
Financial Investment Services
N.A.I.C.S.: 523999

Affiliate (Domestic):

Wilhelmsen Ahrenkiel Ship Management GmbH & Co. KG (2)
Palmaille 75, 22767, Hamburg, Germany (50%)
Tel.: (49) 40380223800
Web Site: https://www.wilhelmsen-ahrenkiel.com
Cargo Ship Management & Support Services
N.A.I.C.S.: 488390
Jan-Eric Panitzki (COO & Member-Mgmt Bd)

Affiliate (Non-US):

Wilhelmsen Ship Management Singapore Pte. Ltd. (2)
1 Kim Seng Promenade #15-07, Great World City West Tower, 237994, Singapore, Singapore
Tel.: (65) 65134670
Ship Management Services
N.A.I.C.S.: 336611

MPC PLUS INC
9F Rosedale building 280 Gwangpyeonno, Seoul, 135-744, Korea (South)
Tel.: (82) 234014114
Web Site: http://www.mpc.co.kr
Year Founded: 1991
050540—(KRS)
Rev.: $43,317,828
Assets: $22,165,349
Liabilities: $15,535,654
Net Worth: $6,629,695
Earnings: ($254,064)
Emp.: 1,369
Fiscal Year-end: 12/31/22
Customer Relationship Management Services
N.A.I.C.S.: 541613
Sung Sang Yun (CEO)

MPDV MIKROLAB GMBH
Romerring 1, 74821, Mosbach, Germany
Tel.: (49) 626192090
Web Site: http://www.mpdv.com
Year Founded: 1977
Rev.: $22,760,100
Emp.: 155
Engineeering Services
N.A.I.C.S.: 541330
Jurgen Kletti (Mng Dir)

Subsidiaries:

MPDV Asia Pte. Ltd. (1)
46 Kim Yam Road, 01-11 The Herencia, 239351, Singapore, Singapore
Tel.: (65) 68367790
Web Site: http://www.mpdv.com
Software Development Services
N.A.I.C.S.: 541511

MPDV S.A.R.L. (1)
11 Bis Rue de la Fourmilliere, 37530, Charge, France
Tel.: (33) 247575745
Web Site: http://www.mpdv.fr
Software Development Services
N.A.I.C.S.: 541511

MPDV Schweiz AG (1)
Zurcherstrasse 83, 8500, Frauenfeld, Switzerland
Tel.: (41) 527283900
Software Development Services
N.A.I.C.S.: 541511
Philipp Hunziker (Acct Mgr-IT)

MPDV Software and Technology Services (Shanghai) Co., Ltd. (1)
425 Yishan Road, Pole Tower Unit 903 XuHui District, Shanghai, 200235, China
Tel.: (86) 2156321032
Web Site: http://www.mpdv.com
Software Development Services
N.A.I.C.S.: 541511

MPDV USA Inc. (1)
10730 W 143rd St Ste 32, Orland Park, IL 60462
Tel.: (708) 966-4290
Web Site: http://www.mpdv.com
Software Development Services

MPHB CAPITAL BERHAD

N.A.I.C.S.: 541511
Frank Fischer (COO & Gen Mgr)

MPH CONSULTING SERVICES DMCC
Office 703 Indigo Icon Tower Jumeirah Lakes Towers Cluster F, PO Box 34246, Dubai, United Arab Emirates
Tel.: (971) 44474677 AE
Web Site: http://www.mphexperts.com
Emp.: 100
Engineering & Consulting Services
N.A.I.C.S.: 541330

MPH HEALTH CARE AG
Grunauer Strabe 5, 12557, Berlin, Germany
Tel.: (49) 30863214560
Web Site: https://www.mph-ag.de
Year Founded: 2008
93M1—(DEU)
Rev.: $33,094,827
Assets: $255,765,278
Liabilities: $16,803,863
Net Worth: $238,961,416
Earnings: $31,421,216
Emp.: 1
Fiscal Year-end: 12/31/22
Pharmaceuticals Mfr
N.A.I.C.S.: 325412
Patrick Brenske (Member-Mgmt Bd)

Subsidiaries:

CR Capital AG (1)
Heinrich-Hertz-Str 1b, 14532, Kleinmachnow, Germany
Tel.: (49) 3320332070
Web Site: https://cr-energy.de
Financial Services
N.A.I.C.S.: 523999

MPHB CAPITAL BERHAD
39th Floor Menara Multi Purpose Capital Square, No 8 Jalan Munshi Abdullah, 50100, Kuala Lumpur, Malaysia
Tel.: (60) 326948333
Web Site: https://www.mphbcap.com.my
MPHBCAP—(KLS)
Rev.: $14,019,048
Assets: $373,350,688
Liabilities: $7,461,799
Net Worth: $365,888,889
Earnings: $43,004,444
Emp.: 2
Fiscal Year-end: 12/31/22
Investment Holding Company
N.A.I.C.S.: 551112
And Yeng Kheoh (CEO)

Subsidiaries:

ENE (East Coast) Sdn. Bhd. (1)
97 Jalan Tun Ismail, 25000, Kuantan, Pahang, Malaysia
Tel.: (60) 9 514 2970
Web Site: http://www.magnum4d.com.my
Sales Range: $50-74.9 Million
Emp.: 10
Betting Services
N.A.I.C.S.: 713290

ENE (East Malaysia) Sdn. Bhd. (1)
Lot 12227 Block 16 KCLD P1B-6-1 Jalan Datuk Tawi Sli Trinity Hub, 93250, Kuching, Sarawak, Malaysia
Tel.: (60) 8 255 5989
Web Site: http://www.magnum4dem.com.my
Sales Range: $25-49.9 Million
Emp.: 45
Betting Services
N.A.I.C.S.: 713290
Liew Kee Chuan (Reg Mgr)

ENE (Melaka) Sdn. Bhd. (1)
332 and 333 Taman Melaka Raya Off Jalan Taman, 75000, Melaka, Malaysia
Tel.: (60) 6 284 5993
Web Site: http://www.magnum4dmk.com.my

MPHB CAPITAL BERHAD

MPHB Capital Berhad—(Continued)
Sales Range: $50-74.9 Million
Emp.: 20
Betting Services
N.A.I.C.S.: 713290

ENE (Negeri Sembilan) Sdn. Bhd. (1)
14 Jalan Era Square 2 Era Square, 70200, Seremban, Negeri Sembilan, Malaysia
Tel.: (60) 67621218
Sales Range: $50-74.9 Million
Emp.: 10
Betting Services
N.A.I.C.S.: 713290
H. S. Gangn (Mgr)

ENE (Penang) Sdn. Bhd. (1)
294 and 296 Vantage Point Jalan Jelutong, 11600, Penang, Malaysia
Tel.: (60) 4 281 5923
Web Site: http://www.magnum4dpg.com.my
Sales Range: $50-74.9 Million
Emp.: 19
Betting & Entertainment Services
N.A.I.C.S.: 713290
Perambalam S. (Mgr)

ENE (Perak) Sdn. Bhd. (1)
No 1 1A Hala Datuk 5 Jalan Datoh, 30000, Ipoh, Perak, Malaysia
Tel.: (60) 52416793
Betting Services
N.A.I.C.S.: 713290

ENE (Selangor) Sdn. Bhd. (1)
19 Jalan Maharajalela, 50150, Kuala Lumpur, Malaysia
Tel.: (60) 32 148 8366
Web Site: http://www.magnum4d.com.my
Sales Range: $25-49.9 Million
Emp.: 30
Betting Services
N.A.I.C.S.: 713290

M4D (Johor) Sdn. Bhd. (1)
84 Jalan Sutera Tanjung 8/3 Taman Sutera Utama, Skudai, 81300, Johor Bahru, Malaysia
Tel.: (60) 7 558 8317
Web Site: http://www.magnum4d.com.my
Emp.: 26
Sports Betting Services
N.A.I.C.S.: 713290

Magnum 4D Berhad (1)
Wisma Magnum 111 Jalan Pudu, 55100, Kuala Lumpur, Malaysia
Tel.: (60) 32 078 6233
Web Site: http://www.magnum4d.my
Sales Range: $75-99.9 Million
Emp.: 241
Amusement & Gaming Services
N.A.I.C.S.: 713990

Magnum Information Technology Sdn. Bhd. (1)
Wisma Magnum 111 Jalan Pudu, 55100, Kuala Lumpur, Malaysia
Tel.: (60) 327328100
Web Site: http://www.magnumit.com
Sales Range: $25-49.9 Million
Emp.: 20
Information Technology Consulting Services
N.A.I.C.S.: 541690

Multi-Purpose Insurans Bhd. (1)
11st Fl Blk 8 Lbh Farquhar, 10200, George Town, Penang, Malaysia
Tel.: (60) 42613487
Web Site: http://www.mpib.com.my
General Insurance Services
N.A.I.C.S.: 524128
Liew Yaw Lian (COO)

Secure Tangent Sdn. Bhd. (1)
Wisma Magnum 111 Jalan Pudu, 55100, Kuala Lumpur, Wilayah Persekutuan, Malaysia
Tel.: (60) 327328100
Sales Range: $25-49.9 Million
Emp.: 20
Information Technology Consulting Services
N.A.I.C.S.: 541690

Syarikat Perniagaan Selangor Sdn. Bhd. (1)
Lot 18 1st Floor No 2 Tasik Ampang, Jalan Hulu Kelang, 68000, Ampang, Selangor, Malaysia
Tel.: (60) 342566536
Property Management Services
N.A.I.C.S.: 531311

Subsidiary (Domestic):

Flamingo Management Sdn. Bhd. (2)
5 Tasik Ampang Jalan Hulu Kelang, 68000, Ampang, Selangor Darul Ehsan, Malaysia
Tel.: (60) 342563288
Web Site: http://flamingo.com.my
Home Management Services
N.A.I.C.S.: 721110

MPI CORPORATION
No 155 Chungho St, Zhubei, 30267, Hsinchu, Taiwan
Tel.: (886) 35551771
Web Site: http://www.mpi-corporation.com
Year Founded: 1995
Semiconductor Mfr
N.A.I.C.S.: 334413
Brian Green (Chm)

Subsidiaries:

MPI America, Inc. (1)
2360 Qume Dr Ste C, San Jose, CA 95131
Tel.: (408) 770-3650
Semiconductors & Related Solid-state Devices Mfr
N.A.I.C.S.: 334413
Rob Carter (Pres)

Subsidiary (Domestic):

Celadon Systems, Inc. (2)
13795 Frontier Ct, Burnsville, MN 55337
Tel.: (952) 232-1700
Web Site: http://www.celadonsystems.com
Instrument Mfr for Measuring & Testing Electricity & Electrical Signals
N.A.I.C.S.: 334515
Bryan J. Root (Co-Founder)

MPI HOLDINGS LTD
Bookers Vineyard, Bolney, Haywards Heath, RH17 5NB, United Kingdom
Tel.: (44) 1444 881091
Web Site: http://www.mpi.uk.net
Year Founded: 1998
Rev.: $34,589,280
Frozen Fish & Rubber Distr
N.A.I.C.S.: 424420
Mark Pratt (Mng Dir)

MPI MLIN D.D.
Ustikolina bb, Sarajevo, 73250, Bosnia & Herzegovina
Tel.: (387) 3 822 1053
Web Site: http://www.mlinustikolina.ba
MLUSRK3—(SARE)
Rev.: $1,008,094
Assets: $4,610,630
Liabilities: $3,195,144
Net Worth: $1,415,486
Earnings: $926
Emp.: 25
Fiscal Year-end: 12/31/20
Grain Mill Operator
N.A.I.C.S.: 311211

MPIL CORPORATION LIMITED
Udyog Bhavan 2nd Floor, 29 Walchand Hirachand Marg Ballard Estate, Mumbai, 400 001, India
Tel.: (91) 2267476080
Web Site: https://www.mpilcorporation.com
Year Founded: 1959
500450—(BOM)
Rev.: $219,047
Assets: $2,891,723
Liabilities: $823,422
Net Worth: $2,068,300
Earnings: $20,823
Emp.: 2
Fiscal Year-end: 03/31/21
Financial Investment Services
N.A.I.C.S.: 523999
Milan Dalal (Chm)

MPL PLASTICS LTD.
2 Ashish Warehouse Corporation Punjab Foundry Industrial Estate, Near Classic Studio Mira Bhayander Road Kashimira Mira Road East, Thane, 401104, India
Tel.: (91) 2228455450
Web Site: https://www.mplindia.in
Year Founded: 1972
526143—(BOM)
Rev.: $133,634
Assets: $591,495
Liabilities: $2,811,054
Net Worth: ($2,219,558)
Earnings: $22,298,708
Emp.: 2
Fiscal Year-end: 03/31/22
Plastics Product Mfr
N.A.I.C.S.: 326199
Madhup B. Vaghani (Exec Dir)

MPLUS CORP.
27 Oksan Industrial Complex Road Oksanmyeon, Heungdeok-Gu, Cheongju, 28101, Chungcheongbuk-do, Korea (South)
Tel.: (82) 432727079
Web Site: https://www.mplusi.co.kr
Year Founded: 2003
259630—(KRS)
Rev.: $70,363,260
Assets: $164,007,826
Liabilities: $116,291,164
Net Worth: $47,716,662
Earnings: ($7,426,389)
Emp.: 265
Fiscal Year-end: 12/31/21
Polymer Battery Mfr
N.A.I.C.S.: 335910
Jongsung Kim (CEO)

MPO GROUP
Aachener Strasse 60-62, 50674, Cologne, Germany
Tel.: (49) 2219216700 FR
Web Site: http://www.mpo.de
Year Founded: 1957
Sales Range: $250-299.9 Million
Emp.: 1,500
Mfr & Replication of Pre-recorded Media
N.A.I.C.S.: 334610
Marco Bauer (Acct Mgr-Video)

MPORIUM GROUP PLC
105-106 New Bond Street, London, W1S 1DN, United Kingdom
Tel.: (44) 203 841 8411
Web Site: http://www.mporium.com
Mobile Commerce Software
N.A.I.C.S.: 513210
Aleksander Ohrn (CTO)

MPOWER GROUP LIMITED
Level 4 15 Bourke Road, Australia Square, Sydney, 2020, NSW, Australia
Tel.: (61) 287884600 AU
Web Site: https://www.mpower.com.au
MPR—(ASX)
Rev.: $3,010,817
Assets: $17,407,185
Liabilities: $17,819,845
Net Worth: ($412,660)
Earnings: ($490,785)
Emp.: 140
Fiscal Year-end: 06/30/24
Investment Holding Company
N.A.I.C.S.: 551112
Nathan Wise (CEO & Mng Dir)

INTERNATIONAL PUBLIC

Subsidiaries:

MPower Group Pty. Limited (1)
10 Williamson Road, Ingleburn, 2565, NSW, Australia
Tel.: (61) 2 8788 4600
Web Site: http://www.mpower.com.au
Holding Company; Integrated Power Technologies Design & Engineering
N.A.I.C.S.: 551112
Anthony Csillag (Mng Dir-Projects)

Subsidiary (Non-US):

M+H Power Pacific Limited (2)
Unit B 237 Bush Rd, Albany, 0632, Auckland, New Zealand
Tel.: (64) 98692339
Web Site: https://www.mhpower.co.nz
Solar Products, Emergency Lighting & Industrial Battery Whslr
N.A.I.C.S.: 423830

Subsidiary (Domestic):

MPower Products Pty. Ltd. (2)
9 Mosrael Place, Rowville, 3178, VIC, Australia
Tel.: (61) 397630555
Web Site: http://www.mpower.com.au
Solar Products, Emergency Lighting & Industrial Battery Designer, Mfr & Whslr
N.A.I.C.S.: 335999

MPower Projects Pty. Ltd. (2)
10 Williamson Road, Ingleburn, 2565, NSW, Australia
Tel.: (61) 2 8788 4600
Web Site: http://www.mpower.com.au
Integrated Power Installation Contractor
N.A.I.C.S.: 238990
Anthony Csillag (Mng Dir)

MPS BUILDERS & MERCHANTS LTD.
Lock Lane, Warwick, CV34 5AG, United Kingdom
Tel.: (44) 1926411181 UK
Web Site: http://www.mpsmerchants.com
Year Founded: 1995
Sales Range: $10-24.9 Million
Emp.: 61
Building Supply Distr
N.A.I.C.S.: 444180
Craig Barnwell (Gen Mgr)

MPS INFOTECNICS LIMITED
703 Arunachal Building 19 Barakhamba, Connaught Place, New Delhi, 110001, India
Tel.: (91) 1143571042 In
Web Site: https://www.mpsinfotec.com
Year Founded: 1989
Rev.: $2,456,273
Assets: $72,270,104
Liabilities: $7,659,792
Net Worth: $64,610,313
Earnings: ($1,266,428)
Fiscal Year-end: 03/31/19
Software Development Services
N.A.I.C.S.: 541511
Peeyush Kumar Aggarwal (Chm & Mng Dir)

MPS LIMITED
HMG Ambassador 5th Floor 137 Residency Road, Bengaluru, 560025, India
Tel.: (91) 8669781008
Web Site: https://www.mpslimited.com
MPSLTD—(NSE)
Rev.: $61,365,602
Assets: $66,144,020
Liabilities: $15,344,140
Net Worth: $50,799,880
Earnings: $13,091,937
Emp.: 2,210
Fiscal Year-end: 03/31/23

AND PRIVATE COMPANIES

Educational Books Publishing Services
N.A.I.C.S.: 513130
Sunit Malhotra *(CFO & Sec)*
Subsidiaries:
App-eLearn Pty. Ltd. (1)
Level 3 478 George Street, Sydney, 2000, NSW, Australia
Tel.: (61) 290526839
Web Site: https://www.app-elearn.com
E-Learning Development Services
N.A.I.C.S.: 611430

Liberate Learning Pty. Ltd. (1)
Level 5 171 Collins St, Melbourne, 3000, VIC, Australia
Tel.: (61) 1300448060
Web Site: https://liberatelearning.com.au
E-Learning Development Services
N.A.I.C.S.: 611430

MPS Europa AG (1)
Baarermatte 1, 6340, Baar, Switzerland
Tel.: (41) 417491616
Web Site: https://www.mpseuropa.ch
Learning Services
N.A.I.C.S.: 611710

MPS Interactive Systems Limited (1)
91 Springboard Lotus Plot No D-5 Road No 20, Marol MIDC Andheri East, Mumbai, 400 069, Maharashtra, India
Tel.: (91) 2266438100
Web Site: http://www.mpsinteractive.com
Learning Services
N.A.I.C.S.: 611710

Research Square AJE LLC (1)
601 W Main St Ste 102, Durham, NC 27701
Tel.: (919) 886-4846
Web Site: https://www.researchsquare.com
Emp.: 300
Software Development Services
N.A.I.C.S.: 541511

Topsim GmbH (1)
Neckarhalde 55, 72070, Tubingen, Germany
Tel.: (49) 707179420
Web Site: https://www.topsim.com
Computer Software Development Services
N.A.I.C.S.: 541511

MPT SOLUTION CO., LTD.
75/25 Moo 11 Phaholyothin Rd T Klong-Nueng A Klong-Luang, Pathumthani, 12120, Thailand
Tel.: (66) 29081939
Automobile Spare Parts Mfr
N.A.I.C.S.: 336390

MPX INTERNATIONAL CORPORATION
5255 Yonge Street Suite 701, Toronto, M2N 6P4, ON, Canada
Tel.: (416) 840-3725
Web Site: https://www.mpxinternational.com
Year Founded: 2015
MPXI—(CNSX)
Rev.: $6,223,272
Assets: $40,054,476
Liabilities: $21,995,402
Net Worth: $18,059,074
Earnings: ($21,054,814)
Fiscal Year-end: 09/30/21
Cannabis Product Mfr & Distr
N.A.I.C.S.: 325412
Jeremy S. Budd *(Gen Counsel, Sec & Exec VP)*
Subsidiaries:
Canveda Inc. (1)
760 Technology Drive, Peterborough, K9J 6X7, ON, Canada
Tel.: (705) 243-1910
Web Site: https://www.canveda.ca
Cannabis Product Distr
N.A.I.C.S.: 424590
David Swales *(Gen Mgr)*

Holyworld SA (1)
52 Rue de Divonne, 1260, Nyon, Switzerland
Tel.: (41) 58 748 4880
Web Site: https://holyworld.ch
Cannabis Derived Forming Services
N.A.I.C.S.: 111998

Spartan Wellness Corporation (1)
1000 Innovation Dr Suite 500, Kanata, K2K 3E7, ON, Canada
Tel.: (416) 282-6110
Web Site: https://www.spartanwellness.ca
Healtcare Services
N.A.I.C.S.: 621999
J. C. Migneault *(COO)*

MQ HOLDING AB
Nellickevagen 24, 412 63, Gothenburg, Sweden
Tel.: (46) 31 388 80 99   SE
Web Site: http://www.mq.se
Sales Range: $200-249.9 Million
Holding Company; Men & Women Clothes Mfr
N.A.I.C.S.: 551112

MQ RETAIL AB
Sankt Eriksgatan 5, 411 05, Gothenburg, Sweden
Tel.: (46) 313888000
Web Site: http://www.mq.se
Sales Range: $200-249.9 Million
Emp.: 530
Clothing Stores
N.A.I.C.S.: 458110
Tony Siberg *(VP)*

MQ TECHNOLOGY BERHAD
Plot 86B Lintang Bayan Lepas 9 Bayan Lepas Industrial Park 4, Bayan Lepas, 11900, Penang, Malaysia
Tel.: (60) 46465888   MY
Web Site: https://www.mqtech.com.my
Year Founded: 2003
MQTECH—(KLS)
Rev.: $1,428,475
Assets: $14,210,232
Liabilities: $737,088
Net Worth: $13,473,144
Earnings: ($3,188,261)
Emp.: 80
Fiscal Year-end: 09/30/23
Investment Holding Services
N.A.I.C.S.: 551112
Gerald Nicholas Eng Hoe Tan *(Exec Dir)*
Subsidiaries:
Microlead Precision Technology Sdn. Bhd. (1)
Plot 86B Lintang Bayan Lepas 9 Bayan Lepas Industrial Park 4, 11900, Bayan Lepas, Penang, Malaysia
Tel.: (60) 46465888
Web Site: https://www.microlead.com.my
High Precision Tool Mfr
N.A.I.C.S.: 333514

MR BRICOLAGE SA
1 rue Montaigne, 45380, La Chapelle-Saint-Mesmin, France
Tel.: (33) 238435000   FR
Web Site: https://mr-bricolage.com
Year Founded: 1965
ALMRB—(EUR)
Sales Range: $250-299.9 Million
Decoration Product Distr
N.A.I.C.S.: 459420
Christophe Mistou *(CEO)*

MR D.I.Y. GROUP (M) BERHAD
Lot 1851-A & 1851-B Jalan KPB 6 Kawasan Perindustrian Balakong, 43300, Seri Kembangan, Selangor, Malaysia
Tel.: (60) 389611338   MY
Web Site: https://www.mrdiy.com
Year Founded: 2005
MRDIY—(KLS)
Rev.: $843,564,444
Assets: $703,406,984
Liabilities: $400,156,825
Net Worth: $303,250,159
Earnings: $100,095,026
Emp.: 16,500
Fiscal Year-end: 12/31/22
Departmental Store Operator
N.A.I.C.S.: 455110
Lim Chen Hwee *(Sr VP-Fin)*
Subsidiaries:
MRD (Central) Sdn. Bhd. (1)
Lot 1851-A & 1851-B Jalan KPB 6 Kawasan Perindustrian Balakong, 43300, Seri Kembangan, Selangor Darul Ehsan, Malaysia
Tel.: (60) 389611338
Web Site: https://www.mrdollar.co
Drink & Grocery Product Retailer
N.A.I.C.S.: 424410

Mr. Dollar Sdn. Bhd. (1)
Lot 1851-A and 1851-B Jalan KPB 6, Kawasan Perindustrian Balakong, 43300, Seri Kembangan, Selangor, Malaysia
Tel.: (60) 389611338
Web Site: http://www.mrdollar.co
Home Products Retailer
N.A.I.C.S.: 455219

MR MAX HOLDINGS LTD.
1-5-7 Matsuda, Higashi-ku, Fukuoka, 812-0064, Japan
Tel.: (81) 926231111   JP
Web Site: https://www.mrmax.co.jp
Year Founded: 1925
8203—(FKA)
Rev.: $1,181,995,760
Assets: $793,101,760
Liabilities: $478,966,400
Net Worth: $314,135,360
Earnings: $33,173,360
Emp.: 727
Fiscal Year-end: 02/28/23
Discount Department Store Owner & Operator
N.A.I.C.S.: 455110

MR PRICE GROUP LIMITED
65 Masabalala Yengwa Ave, Stamford Hill, Durban, 4001, South Africa
Tel.: (27) 313108000
Web Site: https://mrpcareers.com
MRPLY—(OTCIQ)
Rev.: $2,003,823,399
Assets: $1,574,583,556
Liabilities: $759,936,188
Net Worth: $814,647,369
Earnings: $180,821,508
Emp.: 27,775
Fiscal Year-end: 03/31/24
Cosmetics Retailer
N.A.I.C.S.: 456120
Mark McNeil Blair *(CEO)*

MR SUNSTROM GMBH
Moritzburger Weg 67, 01109, Dresden, Germany
Tel.: (49) 3518838130
Web Site: http://www.sunstrom.de
Year Founded: 2000
Rev.: $18,306,028
Emp.: 65
Photovoltaic Systems Design & Installation Services
N.A.I.C.S.: 237130

MR. BLUE
18th floor 570 Yangcheon-ro, Gangseo-gu, Seoul, 07551, Korea (South)
Tel.: (82) 23370610
Web Site: https://www.mrblue.com
Year Founded: 2014
207760—(KRS)
Rev.: $59,179,727
Assets: $104,626,647
Liabilities: $52,278,727
Net Worth: $52,347,920
Earnings: $2,392,700
Emp.: 105
Fiscal Year-end: 12/31/22
Online Comic Publishing Services
N.A.I.C.S.: 513199
Seung-Jeen Joe *(CEO)*

MR. ONION CORP.
F28 No97 hsin tai5 Rd, Sijhih, Taipei, Taiwan
Tel.: (886) 226975167
Web Site: http://www.mr-onion.com
2740—(TPE)
Rev.: $3,902,989
Assets: $3,513,782
Liabilities: $2,706,806
Net Worth: $806,977
Earnings: ($1,242,531)
Fiscal Year-end: 12/31/21
Restaurant Operators
N.A.I.C.S.: 722511
Chun-Hsien Lu *(Chm & Pres)*

MRC AGROTECH LIMITED
Unit no 1208 The Summit Business Bay, Andheri Kurla Road Prakashwadi Chakala Andheri, Mumbai, 400069, Maharashtra, India
Tel.: (91) 2240156765
Web Site: https://www.mrcagro.com
Year Founded: 2015
540809—(BOM)
Rev.: $862,012
Assets: $2,162,319
Liabilities: $632,592
Net Worth: $1,529,727
Earnings: $40,929
Fiscal Year-end: 03/31/23
Industrial Equipment Mfr & Distr
N.A.I.C.S.: 333914
Chandu K. Jain *(Chm)*

MRC ALLIED INC.
4th Floor Spirit of Communication Centre 106 Carlos Palanca St, Legazpi Village, Makati, 1229, Philippines
Tel.: (63) 288467910
Web Site: https://www.mrcallied.com
Year Founded: 1990
MRC—(PHI)
Rev.: $33,332
Assets: $22,956,321
Liabilities: $19,927,708
Net Worth: $3,028,613
Earnings: ($1,198,324)
Emp.: 15
Fiscal Year-end: 12/31/20
Real Estate Services
N.A.I.C.S.: 531390
Jimmy Tiu Yaokasin *(Chm)*

MRE-III-PROYECTO CINCO, SOCIMI, S.A.
Avenida Diagonal 640, 08017, Barcelona, Spain
Tel.: (34) 934841500
Web Site: http://www.mreiiiproyectocinco.com
Year Founded: 2016
MLMRE—(EUR)
Sales Range: Less than $1 Million
Real Estate Investment Trust Services
N.A.I.C.S.: 525990
Javier Faus *(Chm & CEO)*

MREIT INC.
18/F Alliance Global Tower 36th St cor 11th Avenue, Uptown Bonifacio, Taguig, 1634, Philippines
Tel.: (63) 88946331
Web Site: https://www.mreit.com.ph
Year Founded: 2020

MREIT INC.

MREIT Inc.—(Continued)
MREIT—(PHI)
Rev.: $75,047,475
Assets: $1,109,526,396
Liabilities: $168,142,295
Net Worth: $941,384,101
Earnings: $3,039,521
Emp.: 1
Fiscal Year-end: 12/31/23
Real Estate Investment Trust Services
N.A.I.C.S.: 531190
Francisco C. Canuto (Chm)

MRF LIMITED
114 Greams Road, Chennai, 600 006, India
Tel.: (91) 4428292777
Web Site: https://www.mrftyres.com
Year Founded: 1946
MRF—(NSE)
Rev.: $2,234,932,245
Assets: $3,082,423,890
Liabilities: $1,251,438,825
Net Worth: $1,830,985,065
Earnings: $174,320,055
Emp.: 18,180
Fiscal Year-end: 03/31/21
Tiles Mfr
N.A.I.C.S.: 336390
K. M. Mammen (Chm & Mng Dir)

Subsidiaries:

MRF Corp Ltd. (1)
Tarapore Towers V Floor 826 Anna Salai, Chennai, 600 002, India
Tel.: (91) 4428251033
Web Site: http://www.mrfpaints.com
Sales Range: $200-249.9 Million
Emp.: 1,000
Tiles Mfr
N.A.I.C.S.: 326211

MRF Lanka (P) Ltd. (1)
Tel.: (94) 315674745
Web Site: https://www.mrflanka.com
Precured Tread Rubber Mfr
N.A.I.C.S.: 326299

MRG METALS LIMITED
12 Anderson St West, Ballarat, 3350, VIC, Australia
Tel.: (61) 353305800
Web Site:
https://www.mrgmetals.com.au
MRQ—(ASX)
Rev.: $5,443
Assets: $4,812,820
Liabilities: $149,263
Net Worth: $4,663,557
Earnings: ($565,608)
Fiscal Year-end: 06/30/24
Gold, Copper & Other Metal Mining Services
N.A.I.C.S.: 212220
Shane Turner (Sec)

MRI BOTSWANA LIMITED
Plot 20623 Block 3, Private Bag BR 256, Gaborone, Botswana
Tel.: (267) 3903066
Web Site: http://www.mri.co.bw
Sales Range: $1-9.9 Million
Emp.: 66
Emergency Transportation Services
N.A.I.C.S.: 621910
Dennis Alexander (Chm)

MRK HOLDINGS INC.
2-2-9 Kawara-Machi, Chuo-ku, Osaka, Japan
Tel.: (81) 662335000
Web Site:
http://www.mrkholdings.co.jp
Year Founded: 1978
9980—(TKS)
Rev.: $129,450,240
Assets: $145,558,810
Liabilities: $49,330,430
Net Worth: $96,228,380
Earnings: $1,487,250
Emp.: 1,788
Fiscal Year-end: 03/31/24
Apparel Store Operator
N.A.I.C.S.: 458110
Toru Shiota (Pres & CEO)

MRM
5 avenue Kleber, 75016, Paris, France
Tel.: (33) 158447000
Web Site:
https://www.mrminvest.com
MRM—(EUR)
Rev.: $11,013,382
Assets: $286,993,309
Liabilities: $137,030,002
Net Worth: $149,963,307
Earnings: ($3,865,746)
Emp.: 4
Fiscal Year-end: 12/31/22
Real Estate Investment Services
N.A.I.C.S.: 525990
Marine Pattin (CFO)

MRO-TEK REALTY LIMITED
No 6 New BEL Road Chikkamaranahalli, Bengaluru, 560 054, India
Tel.: (91) 8042499000
Web Site: https://www.mro-tek.com
Year Founded: 1984
532376—(BOM)
Rev.: $4,449,692
Assets: $8,956,305
Liabilities: $10,191,291
Net Worth: ($1,234,986)
Earnings: ($1,018,821)
Emp.: 88
Fiscal Year-end: 03/31/21
Communication Product Mfr & Sales
N.A.I.C.S.: 339999
Srivatsa Ganesh (CFO)

Subsidiaries:

MRO-TEK Technologies Private Limited (1)

MRP AGRO LIMITED
House No 100 First Floor Ward No 23 Infront Of Thane Ajak, Civil Line Road Tikamgarh, Tehsils, 472001, Madhya Pradesh, India
Tel.: (91) 7683240342
Web Site: https://www.mrpagro.com
Year Founded: 2018
543262—(BOM)
Rev.: $3,438,735
Assets: $1,033,303
Liabilities: $61,024
Net Worth: $972,279
Earnings: $37,002
Emp.: 4
Fiscal Year-end: 03/31/23
Food Grain Distr
N.A.I.C.S.: 424510
Manish Kumar Jain (Chm & Mng Dir)

MRP CONSULT GMBH
Getreidemarkt 14, 1010, Vienna, Austria
Tel.: (43) 1 890 666 1
Web Site: http://www.mrp-hotels.com
Hotel Development & Strategic Consulting Services
N.A.I.C.S.: 541618
Martin Schaffer (Partner)

Subsidiaries:

hcb hospitality competence berlin GmbH (1)
Savignyplatz 9/10, 10623, Berlin, Germany
Tel.: (49) 303434740
Web Site:
http://www.hospitalitycompetence.com
Hospitality Management Services

N.A.I.C.S.: 541618
Olaf Steinhage (Founder & Mng Partner)

MRP INVESTMENTS LTD.
21 HaArbah Street Platinum House, Tel Aviv, 64793, Israel
Tel.: (972) 36935643
Year Founded: 1963
MRP—(TAE)
Rev.: $4,862,940
Assets: $79,296,352
Liabilities: $53,348,802
Net Worth: $25,947,550
Earnings: $3,366,070
Fiscal Year-end: 12/31/22
Equity Investment Firm
N.A.I.C.S.: 523999

MRS LOGISTICA S.A.
Praia de Botafogo 228 sala 1201E ala B Botafogo, 22250-906, Rio de Janeiro, 22250-906, RJ, Brazil
Tel.: (55) 8009793636
Web Site: https://www.mrs.com.br
Year Founded: 1996
MRSA5B—(BRAZ)
Rev.: $1,152,844,037
Assets: $3,229,307,935
Liabilities: $2,087,783,502
Net Worth: $1,141,524,433
Earnings: $214,538,347
Fiscal Year-end: 12/31/23
Rail Freight Transportation Services
N.A.I.C.S.: 488210
Felix Lopez Cid (Dir-HR & Mgmt)

MRS MAC'S PTY. LTD.
5-9 Marchant Way, Morley, 6062, WA, Australia
Tel.: (61) 894425222
Web Site:
http://www.mrsmacs.com.au
Year Founded: 1954
Emp.: 330
Food Product Mfr & Distr
N.A.I.C.S.: 311412
Paul Slaughter (CEO)

MRS OIL NIGERIA PLC
2 TinCan Island Port Road Apapa, Lagos, Nigeria
Tel.: (234) 8090300000
Web Site:
https://www.mrsoilnigplc.net
Year Founded: 1913
MRS—(NIGE)
Rev.: $74,597,058
Assets: $29,997,346
Liabilities: $16,304,094
Net Worth: $13,693,252
Earnings: $974,176
Emp.: 88
Fiscal Year-end: 12/31/22
Petroleum Product Whslr
N.A.I.C.S.: 424720
Patrice Alberti (Chm)

MRS. BECTOR'S FOOD SPECIALITIES LTD.
Emaar Digital Greens Tower A First Floor Unit No 22-27 Sector 61, Gurgaon, 122102, Haryana, India
Tel.: (91) 1244096300
Web Site:
https://www.bectorfoods.com
Year Founded: 1978
543253—(BOM)
Rev.: $164,757,748
Assets: $99,676,638
Liabilities: $34,414,603
Net Worth: $65,262,035
Earnings: $10,799,592
Emp.: 2,377
Fiscal Year-end: 03/31/23
Cookie & Cracker Mfr
N.A.I.C.S.: 311821
Rajni Bector (Founder & Chm)

INTERNATIONAL PUBLIC

MRT INC.
3rd floor Frame Jinnanzaka 1-18-2 Jinnan, Shibuya-ku, Tokyo, 150-0041, Japan
Tel.: (81) 366961110
Web Site: https://medrt.co.jp
Year Founded: 2000
6034—(TKS)
Rev.: $38,335,630
Assets: $45,879,390
Liabilities: $12,450,040
Net Worth: $33,429,350
Earnings: $3,665,530
Emp.: 175
Fiscal Year-end: 12/31/23
Medical Recruitment Services
N.A.I.C.S.: 561311
Hyoe Tomita (Chm)

MRUGESH TRADING LIMITED
252 Swantraveer Savarkar Rashtriya Smarak Veer Savarkarmarg, Next to Mayer Banglow Shivaji Park, Mumbai, 400 008, India
Tel.: (91) 7043653947
Web Site:
https://www.mrugeshtrading.in
Year Founded: 1984
512065—(BOM)
Rev.: $267
Assets: $37,659
Liabilities: $29,581
Net Worth: $8,078
Earnings: ($19,187)
Fiscal Year-end: 03/31/21
Investment Management Service
N.A.I.C.S.: 523999
Rajesh Agarwal (CFO)

MRV ENGENHARIA E PARTICIPACOES S.A.
Avenida Professor Mario Werneck 621 Estoril, Belo Horizonte, 30455-610, Minas Gerais, Brazil
Tel.: (55) 3136158153
Web Site: https://www.mrv.com.br
Year Founded: 1979
MRVE3—(BRAZ)
Rev.: $1,499,275,653
Assets: $3,636,039,848
Liabilities: $2,371,205,868
Net Worth: $1,264,833,981
Earnings: $185,159,140
Fiscal Year-end: 12/31/19
Real Estate Developer & Builder
N.A.I.C.S.: 236117
Rubens Menin Teixeira de Souza (Chm)

Subsidiaries:

Prime Incorporacoes e Construcoes S.A. (1)
Av Comendador Gustavo Paiva 2789 Sala 214, Mangabeiras, Maceio, 57031-530, Alagoas, Brazil
Tel.: (55) 8232356620
Web Site:
http://www.primeincorporacoes.com.br
Building Construction Services
N.A.I.C.S.: 236220

MS & CONSULTING CO., LTD.
Kodenmachoshinnihonbashi Bld 49 Nihonbashikodenma, Chuo-Ku, Tokyo, Japan
Tel.: (81) 356491185
Web Site: https://req.msandc.co.jp
Year Founded: 2008
6555—(TKS)
Rev.: $16,952,190
Assets: $25,169,500
Liabilities: $5,133,160
Net Worth: $20,036,340
Earnings: $808,260
Emp.: 131
Fiscal Year-end: 02/29/24
Marketing Services

AND PRIVATE COMPANIES

N.A.I.C.S.: 541613
Akinori Namiki (Pres)

Subsidiaries:

MS&Consulting (Thailand) Co., Ltd. (1)
388 Exchange Tower 29th Floor Room 2901-2904, Sukhumvit Road Khlong Toei Road Khlong Toei District, Bangkok, 10110, Thailand
Tel.: (66) 21049236
Web Site: https://www.msandc.co.th
Business Consulting Services
N.A.I.C.S.: 541611

MS AUTOTECH COMPANY LIMITED

1023 Nogok-li Naenam-Myeon, Gyeongju, Gyeongbuk, Korea (South)
Tel.: (82) 547701810
Web Site: https://www.ms-global.com
Year Founded: 1982
123040—(KRS)
Rev.: $1,553,280,006
Assets: $1,182,868,425
Liabilities: $828,585,736
Net Worth: $354,282,689
Earnings: $86,691,658
Emp.: 344
Fiscal Year-end: 12/31/22
Automobile Parts Mfr
N.A.I.C.S.: 336390
An Byeongho (Gen Mgr)

Subsidiaries:

MyungShin Industrial Co. (1)
Automobile Parts Mfr
N.A.I.C.S.: 336390

MS CONCEPT LIMITED

Room 2313 23/F Hong Kong Plaza 186-191 Connaught Road West, Hong Kong, China (Hong Kong)
Tel.: (852) 2 972 4111 Ky
Web Site: http://www.mrsteak.com.hk
Year Founded: 2000
8447—(HKG)
Rev.: $22,259,755
Assets: $16,744,184
Liabilities: $10,599,834
Net Worth: $6,144,349
Earnings: $491,672
Emp.: 212
Fiscal Year-end: 03/31/21
Restaurant Operators
N.A.I.C.S.: 722511
Tai Wah Kwong (Chm & CEO)

MS GROUP HOLDINGS LTD.

Room 907 Tower 1 Enterprise Square 9 Sheung Yuet Road, Kowloon Bay, Kowloon, China (Hong Kong)
Tel.: (852) 27958361 Ky
Web Site: http://www.msgh.com.hk
Year Founded: 2007
1451—(HKG)
Rev.: $37,887,359
Assets: $32,989,344
Liabilities: $6,796,085
Net Worth: $26,193,258
Earnings: $1,987,840
Emp.: 740
Fiscal Year-end: 12/31/21
Plastic Bottle Mfr & Distr
N.A.I.C.S.: 326160
Peter Kwok Keung Chung (CEO)

MS HOLDINGS LIMITED

22 Pandan Road, Singapore, 609274, Singapore
Tel.: (65) 62663455
Web Site: http://www.mohsengcranes.com
40U—(SES)
Rev.: $12,356,356
Assets: $36,905,938
Liabilities: $18,844,481
Net Worth: $18,061,457
Earnings: ($2,119,949)
Emp.: 84
Fiscal Year-end: 04/30/22
Crane Rental Services
N.A.I.C.S.: 532412
Chui Hwa Ng (Chm)

MS INDUSTRIE AG

Brienner Strasse 7, D-80333, Munich, Germany
Tel.: (49) 8920500900 De
Web Site: https://ms-industrie.de
Year Founded: 1991
MSAG—(MUN)
Rev.: $272,324,729
Assets: $223,445,365
Liabilities: $140,765,502
Net Worth: $82,679,863
Earnings: $4,912,222
Emp.: 826
Fiscal Year-end: 12/31/23
Financial Investment
N.A.I.C.S.: 523999
Andreas Aufschnaiter (Member-Mgmt Bd)

Subsidiaries:

Elektromotorenwerk Grunhain GmbH (1)
Bahnhofstr 12, Grunhain-Beierfeld, 08344, Schwarzenberg, Germany
Tel.: (49) 377452200
Web Site: https://www.emgr.de
Motor Component Mfr
N.A.I.C.S.: 336390
Peter C. Weilguni (Mng Dir)

MS Industrie Verwaltungs GmbH (1)
Karlstrasse 8-20, 78549, Spaichingen, Germany
Tel.: (49) 74247010
Staffing Services
N.A.I.C.S.: 561311

MS Land & Buildings LLC (1)
7031 Grand National Dr Ste 101, Orlando, FL 32819
Tel.: (407) 512-1213
Web Site: http://www.connectionflorida.net
Real Estate Rental Services
N.A.I.C.S.: 531110

MS Plastic Welders LLC (1)
Highview Dr, Webberville, MI 48892
Tel.: (517) 223-1059
Emp.: 35
Industrial Engineering Component Mfr
N.A.I.C.S.: 336412

MS Powertrain Technologie GmbH (1)
Neuenbuhlstrasse 6, Schura, 78647, Trossingen, Germany
Tel.: (49) 74247010
Industrial Engineering Component Mfr
N.A.I.C.S.: 336412
Bernhard Lehr (Co-CEO)

MS INTERNATIONAL PLC

Balby Carr Bank, Doncaster, DN4 8DH, United Kingdom
Tel.: (44) 1302322133 UK
Web Site: https://www.msiplc.com
MSI—(AIM)
Rev.: $101,182,725
Assets: $109,420,013
Liabilities: $57,045,964
Net Worth: $52,374,049
Earnings: $6,696,275
Emp.: 447
Fiscal Year-end: 04/30/22
Industrial Equipment Mfr
N.A.I.C.S.: 333248
David Kirkup (Sec)

Subsidiaries:

Global-MSI Sp. z o.o. (1)
Ul Dzialowskiego 13, 30-399, Krakow, Poland
Tel.: (48) 126416702
Web Site: http://www.global-msi.pl
Gasoline Station Services
N.A.I.C.S.: 457110

Global-MSI plc (1)
Balby Carr Bank, Doncaster, DN4 8DH, United Kingdom
Tel.: (44) 1302361558
Web Site: http://www.global-msi.com
Gasoline Station Services
N.A.I.C.S.: 457110

MSI-Defence Systems Inc. (1)
1298 Galleria Blvd, Rock Hill, SC 29730
Tel.: (803) 328-2636
Defense Equipment Mfr
N.A.I.C.S.: 332994

MSI-Defence Systems Ltd. (1)
Salhouse Road, Norwich, NR7 9AY, Norfolk, United Kingdom
Tel.: (44) 1603484065
Web Site: http://www.msi-dsl.com
Defense Equipment Mfr
N.A.I.C.S.: 332994

MSI-Forks Garfos Industriais Ltda. (1)
Professor Campos de Oliveira 310, Sao Paulo, SP, Brazil
Tel.: (55) 1156941000
Web Site: http://www.msiforks.com.br
Forklift Fork Mfr & Distr
N.A.I.C.S.: 333924

MSI-Forks Inc. (1)
Mount Gallant Rd 280, Rock Hill, SC 29730
Tel.: (803) 980-6800
Forklift Fork Mfr & Distr
N.A.I.C.S.: 333924

MSI-Forks Ltd. (1)
Balby Carr Bank, Doncaster, DN4 8DH, United Kingdom
Tel.: (44) 1302366961
Forklift Fork Mfr & Distr
N.A.I.C.S.: 333924

MSI-Quality Forgings Ltd. (1)
Balby Carr Bank, Doncaster, DN4 8DH, United Kingdom
Tel.: (44) 1302325906
Web Site: http://www.msi-forge.com
Emp.: 375
Machinery Equipment Mfr & Distr
N.A.I.C.S.: 333248

MSI-Sign Group BV (1)
De Hoef 8, Gameren, 5311 GH, Zaltbommel, Netherlands
Tel.: (31) 418639631
Marketing & Advertising Services
N.A.I.C.S.: 541810

Petrol Sign GmbH (1)
Owiedenfeldstr 1, 30559, Hannover, Germany
Tel.: (49) 51187989347
Marketing & Advertising Services
N.A.I.C.S.: 541810

Petrol Sign Ltd. (1)
Balby Carr Bank, Doncaster, DN4 8DH, United Kingdom
Tel.: (44) 1302346960
Marketing & Advertising Services
N.A.I.C.S.: 541810

MS&AD INSURANCE GROUP HOLDINGS, INC.

Tokyo Sumitomo Twin Building West Tower 27-2 Shinkawa 2-chome, Chuo-ku, Tokyo, Japan
Tel.: (81) 351170306
Web Site: https://www.ms-ad-hd.com
Year Founded: 2008
8725—(NGO)
Rev.: $49,678,166,560
Assets: $242,327,629,280
Liabilities: $210,357,018,960
Net Worth: $31,970,610,320
Earnings: $2,543,894,320
Emp.: 401
Fiscal Year-end: 03/31/22
Holding Company; Insurance Services
N.A.I.C.S.: 551112
Yasuzo Kanasugi (Exec Officer)

Subsidiaries:

AIOI Nissay Dowa Europe Limited (1)
7th Floor 52-56 Leadenhall Street, London, EC3A 2BJ, United Kingdom
Tel.: (44) 3450704471
Web Site: https://www.aioinissaydowa.eu
General Insurance Services
N.A.I.C.S.: 524210

AIOI Nissay Dowa Life Insurance of Europe AG (1)
Carl-Zeiss-Ring 25, 85737, Ismaning, Germany
Tel.: (49) 1803324243
General Insurance Services
N.A.I.C.S.: 524210
Diana Strasser (Gen Mgr-HR)

Aioi Nissay Dowa Insurance Company Ltd. (1)
15-10 Nishi-Tenma 4-chome, Kita-ku, Osaka, 530 8555, Japan
Tel.: (81) 663631121
Web Site: http://www.aioinissaydowa.co.jp
Sales Range: $1-4.9 Billion
Fire, Marine, Casualty & Automobile Insurance
N.A.I.C.S.: 524128
Masanori Yoneda (Exec VP)

Subsidiary (Domestic):

Aioi Life Insurance Co., Ltd. (2)
3-1-6 Nihombashi, Chuo-ku, Tokyo, 103-0027, Japan
Tel.: (81) 332730101
General Insurance Services
N.A.I.C.S.: 524210

Subsidiary (US):

Royal State Financial Corp. (2)
1600 Kapiolani Blvd, Honolulu, HI 96814
Tel.: (808) 951-1712
Sales Range: $1-9.9 Million
Emp.: 110
Direct Property & Casualty Insurance Carriers
N.A.I.C.S.: 524126

Aioi Nissay Dowa Insurance Services USA Corporation (1)
21061 S Western Ave Ste 200, Torrance, CA 90501
Tel.: (424) 558-3311
Web Site: https://aioiusa.com
Automobile Insurance Services
N.A.I.C.S.: 524298

Aioi Nissay Dowa Services Asia Pte. Ltd. (1)
71 Robinson Road 14-01, Singapore, 68895, Singapore
Tel.: (65) 85505719
Web Site: https://www.msad-aisasia.com
Financial Services
N.A.I.C.S.: 524210

Bangkok Chayolife Company, Limited (1)
25 Bangkok Insurance/ Y W C A Building 10th Floor South Sathorn Road, Tungmahamek Sathorn, Bangkok, 10120, Thailand
Tel.: (66) 22857575
Life Insurance Consultant Services
N.A.I.C.S.: 524210

Cholamandalam MS Risk Services Limited (1)
GEE GEE Universal 6th Floor No 2 MC Nicholas Road, Chetpet, Chennai, 600031, India
Tel.: (91) 4440445600
Web Site: https://cholarisk.com
Engineering Services
N.A.I.C.S.: 541330

DTRIC Insurance Company, Limited (1)
1600 Kapiolani Blvd Ste 1100, Honolulu, HI 96814-3878
Tel.: (808) 951-1700
Web Site: https://www.dtric.com
General Insurance Services
N.A.I.C.S.: 524210
Takuya Mitsueda (Pres & CEO)

MS&AD INSURANCE GROUP HOLDINGS, INC.

MS&AD Insurance Group Holdings, Inc.—(Continued)

Hong Leong MSIG Takaful Berhad (1)
Level 5 Tower B PJ City Development No 15A Jalan 219 Seksyen 51A, 46100, Petaling Jaya, Selangor Darul Ehsan, Malaysia
Tel.: (60) 376501800
Web Site: https://www.hlmtakaful.com.my
Financial Services
N.A.I.C.S.: 524210

Insure The Box Limited (1)
PO Box 1308, Newcastle, NE12 2BF, United Kingdom
Tel.: (44) 3331030030
Web Site: https://www.insurethebox.com
Emp.: 15
Telematics Car Insurance Services
N.A.I.C.S.: 524298

InterRisk Asia (Thailand) Co., Ltd. (1)
175 Sathorn City Tower 9/1 Floor South Sathorn Road, Thungmahamek Sathorn, Bangkok, 10120, Thailand
Tel.: (66) 26795998
Web Site: https://www.interriskthai.co.th
Financial Services
N.A.I.C.S.: 524210

InterRisk Consulting (Shanghai) Co., Ltd. (1)
Room T10-2 34th Floor Shanghai World Financial Center, No 100 Century Avenue Pudong New District, Shanghai, China
Tel.: (86) 2168410611
Web Site: https://www.inter-shanghai.com.cn
Life Insurance Consultant Services
N.A.I.C.S.: 524210

Little Family SS Insurance Co., Ltd. (1)
5-22-33 Higashigotanda Tk Ikedayama Building Wework, Shinagawa-ku, Tokyo, 141-0022, Japan
Tel.: (81) 120850076
Web Site: https://www.littlefamily-ssi.com
Fire Insurance Services
N.A.I.C.S.: 524113

MBTS Broking Services Company Limited (1)
Sathorn City Tower Building Floor 12/1 175 South Sathorn Road, Sathorn, Bangkok, 10120, Thailand
Tel.: (66) 267962058
Web Site: https://www.mbtsbroking.com
Life Insurance Consultant Services
N.A.I.C.S.: 524210

MOTER Technologies, Inc. (1)
21061 S Western Ave Ste 200, Torrance, CA 90501
Tel.: (424) 558-3317
Web Site: https://moter.ai
Software Development Services
N.A.I.C.S.: 541511

MS Amlin AG (1)
Kirchenweg 5, 8008, Zurich, Switzerland
Tel.: (41) 443894000
Reinsurance Investment Services
N.A.I.C.S.: 524130
Chris Beazley (CEO)

MS Amlin Insurance SE (1)
Koning Albert II laan 37, 1030, Brussels, Belgium
Tel.: (32) 28947000
Reinsurance Services
N.A.I.C.S.: 524130
Veronique Perottino (Country Mgr)

MS&AD InterRisk Research Institute & Consulting, Inc. (1)
Waterras Annex 10F and 11F 2-105 Kanda Awajicho, Chiyoda-ku, Tokyo, 101-0063, Japan
Tel.: (81) 352968911
Web Site: http://www.irric.co.jp
Research & Consulting Services
N.A.I.C.S.: 541690
Terumi Nakamura (Pres)

MSI GuaranteedWeather, LLC (1)
7400 W 132nd St Ste 260, Overland Park, KS 66213
Web Site: https://www.guaranteedweather.com
Construction & Transportation Services
N.A.I.C.S.: 532412

MSIG Holdings (U.S.A.), Inc. (1)
1251 Ave of the Americas 8th Fl, New York, NY 10020
Tel.: (212) 446-3600
Web Site: https://www.msigusa.com
Financial Services
N.A.I.C.S.: 524210

MSIG Insurance (Hong Kong) Limited (1)
9/F 1111 King's Road, Taikoo Shing, China (Hong Kong)
Tel.: (852) 28940555
Web Site: https://www.msig.com.hk
General Insurance Services
N.A.I.C.S.: 524210
Philip Kent (CEO)

MSIG Insurance (Malaysia) Bhd. (1)
evel 18 Menara Hap Seng 2 Plaza Hap Seng No 1 Jalan P Ramlee, 50250, Kuala Lumpur, Malaysia
Tel.: (60) 320508228
Web Site: https://www.msig.com.my
Financial Services
N.A.I.C.S.: 524210

MSIG Insurance (Singapore) Pte. Ltd. (1)
4 Shenton Way 21-01 SGX Centre 2, Singapore, 068807, Singapore
Tel.: (65) 68277602
Web Site: https://www.msig.com.sg
General Insurance Services
N.A.I.C.S.: 524210
Takahiro Sawada (Mng Dir)

MSIG Insurance (Thailand) Public Company Limited (1)
1908 MSIG Building New Petchburi Road, Bangkapi Huaykwang, Bangkok, 10310, Thailand
Tel.: (66) 28258888
Web Site: http://www.msig-thai.com
General Insurance Services
N.A.I.C.S.: 524210
Rattapol Gitisakchaiyakul (CEO)

MSIG Insurance Europe AG (1)
An den Dominikanern 11-27, 50668, Cologne, Germany
Tel.: (49) 221379910
Web Site: http://www.msig-europe.com
General Insurance Services
N.A.I.C.S.: 524210
Klaus M. Przybyla (Chm)

MSIG Insurance Services, Inc. (1)
15 Independence Blvd, Warren, NJ 07059-0602
Financial Services
N.A.I.C.S.: 524210

MSIG Mingtai Insurance Co., Ltd. (1)
No 22 Section 2 Renai Road, Zhongzheng District, Taipei, 106443, Taiwan
Tel.: (886) 227725678
Web Site: https://www.msig-mingtai.com.tw
General Insurance Services
N.A.I.C.S.: 524210

MSIG Service and Adjusting (Thailand) Company Limited (1)
175 Sathorn City Tower 12th Floor South Sathorn Road, Thungmahamek Sathorn, Bangkok, 10120, Thailand
Tel.: (66) 26796165
Financial Services
N.A.I.C.S.: 524298

Mitsui Sumitomo Insurance (China) Company Limited (1)
34-T70 Shanghai World Financial Center 100 Century Avenue, Pilot Free Trade Zone, Shanghai, 200120, China
Tel.: (86) 2168777800
Web Site: http://www.ms-ins.com.cn
Property & Casualty Insurance Services
N.A.I.C.S.: 524126

Mitsui Sumitomo Insurance (London Management) Ltd (1)
71 Fenchurch Street, London, EC3M 4BS, United Kingdom
Tel.: (44) 207 977 8321
Web Site: https://www.msi-europe.com
Sales Range: $200-249.9 Million
General Insurance Services
N.A.I.C.S.: 524210
Andrew McKee (CEO)

Mitsui Sumitomo Insurance Claims Adjusting Company Limited (1)
2-27-2 Shinkawa Tokyosumitomo Twin Bldg 5f, Chuo-ku, Tokyo, 104-0033, Japan
Tel.: (81) 332975400
General Insurance Services
N.A.I.C.S.: 524210

Mitsui Sumitomo Insurance Co., Ltd. (1)
9 Kanda-Surugadai 3-chome, Chiyoda-ku, Tokyo, 104-8252, Japan
Tel.: (81) 120258365
Web Site: https://www.ms-ins.com
Emp.: 21,249
Non-Life Insurance Services
N.A.I.C.S.: 524298
Yasuyoshi Karasawa (Chm)

Joint Venture (Non-US):

BPI/MS Insurance Corporation (2)
18TH Floor BPI Philam Life Building Ayala Avenue, 6811 Ayala Avenue, Makati, 1209, Philippines
Tel.: (63) 288409700
Web Site: https://www.bpims.com
Sales Range: $300-349.9 Million
Non-Life Insurance Products & Services; Owned by Bank of the Philippine Islands & by Mitsui Sumitomo Insurance Co., Ltd.
N.A.I.C.S.: 524126
Cezar P. Consing (Chm)

Subsidiary (Non-US):

MS Amlin Plc (2)
The Leadenhall Building 122 Leadenhall Street, London, EC3V 4AG, United Kingdom
Tel.: (44) 2077461052
Web Site: https://www.msamlin.com
Rev.: $3,574,680,669
Assets: $13,114,267,263
Liabilities: $9,087,469,920
Net Worth: $4,026,797,343
Earnings: ($626,895)
Emp.: 2,400
Fiscal Year-end: 12/31/2016
Commercial Insurance & Reinsurance Services
N.A.I.C.S.: 524128
Tom Clementi (CEO-MS Amlin Underwriting Ltd)

Subsidiary (Domestic):

Allied Cedar Insurance Group Limited (3)
The Leadenhall Building 122 Leadenhall Street, London, EC3V 4AG, United Kingdom
Tel.: (44) 1603 628034
General Insurance Services
N.A.I.C.S.: 524210

Subsidiary (Non-US):

MS Amlin Corporate Services Limited (3)
Tel.: (44) 2077461000
Web Site: http://www.amlin.com
Holding Company; Strategic Planning Services
N.A.I.C.S.: 551112

Subsidiary (Non-US):

MS First Capital Insurance Limited (2)
6 Raffles Quay 21-00, Singapore, 048580, Singapore
Tel.: (65) 62222311
Web Site: https://www.msfirstcapital.com.sg
Personal & Commercial Insurance Services
N.A.I.C.S.: 524298
Ramaswamy Athappan (CEO)

MSIG Insurance (Vietnam) Company Limited (2)
10th Floor CornerStone Building 16 Phan Chu Trinh Street, Phan Chu Trinh Ward Hoan Kiem District, Hanoi, Vietnam
Tel.: (84) 2439369188
Web Site: https://www.msig.com.vn
Sales Range: $50-74.9 Million
Emp.: 51
General Insurance Services
N.A.I.C.S.: 524210
Pham Thi Kim Anh (Deputy Gen Dir)

Subsidiary (Domestic):

Mitsui Direct General Insurance Co., Ltd. (2)
2-5-1 Koraku, Bunkyo-ku, Tokyo, 112-0004, Japan
Tel.: (81) 120258312
Web Site: https://www.mitsui-direct.co.jp
Sales Range: $200-249.9 Million
Insurance Services
N.A.I.C.S.: 524126

Mitsui Sumitomo Aioi Life Insurance Co., Ltd. (2)
2-27-2 Shinkawa, Chuo-ku, Tokyo, 104-8258, Japan
Tel.: (81) 120321875
Web Site: https://www.msa-life.co.jp
Sales Range: $300-349.9 Million
Emp.: 2,431
Life Insurance
N.A.I.C.S.: 524113

Subsidiary (Non-US):

Mitsui Sumitomo Insurance (Malaysia) Bhd. (2)
Level 15 Menara Hap Seng 2 Plaza Hap Seng No 1 Jalan P Ramlee, Kuala Lumpur, 50250, Malaysia
Tel.: (60) 320508228
Web Site: http://www.msig.com.my
Sales Range: $300-349.9 Million
Emp.: 700
Insurance Services
N.A.I.C.S.: 524298
Mohd Sallehuddin Othman (Chm)

Subsidiary (US):

Mitsui Sumitomo Marine Management (USA), Inc. (2)
560 Lexington Ave 20th Fl, New York, NY 10022
Tel.: (212) 446-3600
Web Site: http://www.msigusa.com
Sales Range: $25-49.9 Million
Emp.: 135
Business Management Services
N.A.I.C.S.: 561110

Subsidiary (Domestic):

Mitsui Sumitomo MetLife Insurance Co., Ltd. (2)
1-3-7 Yaesu, Chuo-ku, Tokyo, 103-0028, Japan
Tel.: (81) 120 125 104
Web Site: http://www.ms-primary.com
Emp.: 400
Life Insurance
N.A.I.C.S.: 524113

Subsidiary (US):

Transverse Insurance Group LLC (2)
155 Village Blvd 2nd Fl, Princeton, NJ 08540
Tel.: (609) 250-7841
Web Site: http://www.transverseinsurance.com
Insurance Services
N.A.I.C.S.: 524298
Erik Matson (Chm & CEO)

Subsidiary (Domestic):

Arrowood Surplus Lines Insurance Company (3)
3600 Arco Corporate Dr, Charlotte, NC 28273
Tel.: (704) 522-3208
Property & Casualty Insurance Services
N.A.I.C.S.: 524126

Mitsui Sumitomo Insurance Company (Europe) Limited (1)
The Leadenhall Building 122 Leadenhall Street, London, EC3V 4AG, United Kingdom
Tel.: (44) 2079778321

INTERNATIONAL PUBLIC

Web Site: https://www.msi-europe.com
Financial Services
N.A.I.C.S.: 524210

Mitsui Sumitomo Primary Life Insurance Co., Ltd. (1)
Yaesu First Financial Building 1-3-7 Yaesu, Chuo-ku, Tokyo, 103-0028, Japan
Tel.: (81) 120125104
Web Site: https://www.ms-primary.com
Emp.: 410
Fire Insurance Services
N.A.I.C.S.: 524113

PT. Asuransi MSIG Indonesia (1)
Summitmas II Building 15th Floor Jl Jenderal Sudirman Kav 61-62, Jakarta, 12190, Indonesia
Tel.: (62) 212523110
Web Site: https://www.msig.co.id
General Insurance Services
N.A.I.C.S.: 524210
Tsutomu Aoki *(Pres)*

Vortex Insurance Agency, LLC (1)
7400 W 132nd St Ste 260, Overland Park, KS 66213
Tel.: (913) 253-1215
Web Site: https://vortexinsurance.com
Weather Insurance Services
N.A.I.C.S.: 524298

MSC CO., LTD.
45-73 Sojuhoeya-ro, Yangsan, 50518, Gyeongnam, Korea (South)
Tel.: (82) 553891001
Web Site: https://www.msckorea.com
Year Founded: 1974
009780—(KRS)
Rev.: $156,697,332
Assets: $162,761,817
Liabilities: $60,637,940
Net Worth: $102,123,878
Earnings: $13,901,603
Fiscal Year-end: 12/31/22
Food Additives Mfr
N.A.I.C.S.: 311942
Kil Jae Kim *(Pres)*

Subsidiaries:

Genfood Co., Ltd. (1)
45-73 Sojuhoeya-ro, Yangsan, Gyeongsangnam-do, Korea (South)
Tel.: (82) 553891864
Sauce & Flavor Mfr
N.A.I.C.S.: 311942

Miryang Agar-Agar Co., Ltd. (1)
58-31 Bongui-ro, Sannae-myeon, Miryang, Gyeongsangnam-do, Korea (South)
Tel.: (82) 553520544
Natural Agar Mfr
N.A.I.C.S.: 325411

Myeongshin Fertilizer Co., Ltd. (1)
335-6 Eunhyeonjakdong-ro Samdong-Myeon, Ulju-gun, Ulsan, Korea (South)
Tel.: (82) 522648951
Fertilizer Mfr
N.A.I.C.S.: 325311

MSEM, A.S.
Collo Louky 126, 738 01, Frydek-Mistek, Czech Republic
Tel.: (420) 724008031 CZ
Web Site: http://www.msem.cz
Sales Range: $25-49.9 Million
Emp.: 230
Power Distr; Installation & Construction Services
N.A.I.C.S.: 221122
George Neumann *(CFO)*

MSG GROUP GMBH
Robert-Buerkle-Strasse 1, 85737, Ismaning, Germany
Tel.: (49) 89961010
Web Site: http://www.msg-systems.com
Year Founded: 1980
Emp.: 9,000
Holding Company
N.A.I.C.S.: 551112

Johann Ranft *(Dir-Mktg & Comm)*

Subsidiaries:

BELTIOS GmbH (1)
Kattrepelsbrucke 1, 20095, Hamburg, Germany
Tel.: (49) 40570159800
Web Site: http://www.beltios.com
Financial Services
N.A.I.C.S.: 523999

BSM Bankingsysteme und Managementberatung GmbH (1)
Windmuhlstr 1, 60329, Frankfurt am Main, Germany
Tel.: (49) 692429460
Web Site: http://www.bsmgmbh.de
Financial Services
N.A.I.C.S.: 523999

Beihilfe-Service Gesellschaft mbH (1)
Englschalkinger Strasse 14, 81925, Munich, Germany
Tel.: (49) 89262029280
Web Site: http://www.beihilfe-service.com
Information Technology Services
N.A.I.C.S.: 513210

Conplan GmbH (1)
Robert-Burkle-Strasse 1, Ismaning, 85737, Munich, Germany
Tel.: (49) 893061080
Web Site: http://www.conplan.de
Information Technology Services
N.A.I.C.S.: 513210
Stephanie Theil *(Mng Dir)*

FJA-US, Inc. (1)
633 Seventeenth St Ste 1400, Denver, CO 80202
Tel.: (303) 534-2700
Information Technology Services
N.A.I.C.S.: 513210
Mark Johnson *(Mgr-Software Engrg)*

Finnova AG (1)
Merkurstrasse 6, 5600, Lenzburg, Switzerland
Tel.: (41) 628864747
Web Site: http://www.finnova.com
Emp.: 400
Banking Services
N.A.I.C.S.: 522110
Hendrik Lang *(CEO)*

Global Side GmbH (1)
Englschalkinger Str 14, 81925, Munich, Germany
Tel.: (49) 89262029100
Web Site: http://www.globalside.com
Information Technology Services
N.A.I.C.S.: 513210

Impavidi GmbH (1)
An der Wuhlheide 232, 12459, Berlin, Germany
Tel.: (49) 30347475000
Web Site: http://www.impavidi.de
Management Consulting Services
N.A.I.C.S.: 541618
Kerstin Fullner-Kronemann *(Office Mgr)*

Innovas GmbH (1)
Theodor-Heuss-Ring 19-21, 50668, Cologne, Germany
Tel.: (49) 2213975670
Web Site: http://www.innovas.de
Information Technology Services
N.A.I.C.S.: 513210

M3 Management Consulting GmbH (1)
Robert-Burkle-Strasse 1, Ismaning, 85737, Munich, Germany
Tel.: (49) 8913928500
Web Site: http://www.m3maco.com
Emp.: 70
Management Consulting Services
N.A.I.C.S.: 541618
Karsten Redenius *(Chm & Mng Dir)*

Nexontis Consulting GmbH (1)
Altrottstrasse 31, 69190, Walldorf, Germany
Tel.: (49) 6227899140
Web Site: http://www.nexontis.com
Information Technology Services
N.A.I.C.S.: 513210

Gunther Farber *(Founder, Co-CEO & Mng Dir)*

PiAL Consult GmbH (1)
Dammtorwall 7a, 20354, Hamburg, Germany
Tel.: (49) 4035018840
Web Site: http://www.pial-consult.com
Management Consulting Services
N.A.I.C.S.: 541618
Daniela Kern *(Sr Project Mgr)*

Plaut (Schweiz) Consulting AG (1)
Eichwatt 3, 8105, Regensdorf, Switzerland
Tel.: (41) 448712828
Management Consulting Services
N.A.I.C.S.: 513210

Plaut Consulting CZ, s.r.o. (1)
Regus Business Centre Klimentska 1216/46, Nove Mesto, 110 00, Prague, Czech Republic
Tel.: (420) 222191043
Information Technology Services
N.A.I.C.S.: 513210
Vera Korbelova *(Mng Dir)*

Plaut Consulting LLC (1)
Skakovaya 32 Bldg 2, 125040, Moscow, Russia
Tel.: (7) 4959461549
Web Site: http://www.msg-plaut.com
Management Consulting Services
N.A.I.C.S.: 541618
Maria Rozhnikovskaya *(Mktg Dir)*

Plaut Consulting Polska Sp.z.o.o. (1)
ul Bojkowska 37, 44-101, Gliwice, Poland
Tel.: (48) 324612700
Management Consulting Services
N.A.I.C.S.: 541618
Rafal Wysocki *(Mgr-SAP Bus Unit)*

Plaut Consulting Romania, S.R.L. (1)
Strada Dr Carol Davila nr 37 Sector 5, Bucharest, Romania
Tel.: (40) 311047351
Web Site: http://www.plaut.com
Management Consulting Services
N.A.I.C.S.: 541618

Plaut Management & IT Consulting AG (1)
Schochenmuhlestrasse 4, 6340, Baar, Switzerland
Tel.: (41) 417609923
Information Technology Services
N.A.I.C.S.: 513210

Prevo System AG (1)
Elisabethenanlage 7, 4051, Basel, Switzerland
Tel.: (41) 612054040
Web Site: http://www.prevo.ch
Information Technology Services
N.A.I.C.S.: 513210
Thomas Burri *(CTO)*

Softproviding AG (1)
Dornacherstrasse 210, 4053, Basel, Switzerland
Tel.: (41) 615082121
Web Site: http://www.softproviding.com
Information Technology Services
N.A.I.C.S.: 513210
Philip Meyer *(Head-Support)*

Spheos GmbH & Co. KG (1)
Birkenleiten 41, 81543, Munich, Germany
Tel.: (49) 896283390
Web Site: http://www.spheos.com
Information Technology Services
N.A.I.C.S.: 513210

msg David GmbH (1)
Mittelweg 7, 38106, Braunschweig, Germany
Tel.: (49) 531243790
Web Site: http://www.msg-david.de
Information Technology Services
N.A.I.C.S.: 513210
Dirk Schafer *(Mng Dir)*

msg Global Solutions AG (1)
Eichwatt 3, 8105, Regensdorf, Switzerland
Tel.: (41) 433886223
Information Technology Services
N.A.I.C.S.: 513210
Christoph Knapp *(Exec VP)*

msg Global Solutions Asia Private Limited (1)
138 Cecil Street 05-01 Cecil Court, Singapore, 069538, Singapore
Tel.: (65) 65598800
Management Consulting Services
N.A.I.C.S.: 541618
Aditya Kumar *(Exec VP)*

msg Global Solutions Benelux B.V. (1)
Nieuwegracht 23, 3512 LC, Utrecht, Netherlands
Tel.: (31) 308500090
Management Consulting Services
N.A.I.C.S.: 541618
Peter de Bruijne *(Mng Dir)*

msg Global Solutions Bulgaria Ltd. (1)
Boulevard Tsar Osvoboditel 21 5th Floor Office No 10, 1000, Sofia, Bulgaria
Tel.: (359) 24518400
Management Consulting Services
N.A.I.C.S.: 541618
Nikola Djokic *(Exec VP)*

msg Global Solutions Canada Inc. (1)
1 King Street West Suite 4800 - 77, Toronto, M5H 1A1, ON, Canada
Tel.: (416) 479-4475
Management Consulting Services
N.A.I.C.S.: 541618
Sven Roehl *(Exec VP & Head-Insurance Innovation)*

msg Global Solutions Iberia S.L.U. (1)
Hecop Centro de Negocios Calle de Josefa Valcarcel 8, 28027, Madrid, Spain
Tel.: (34) 913208070
Management Consulting Services
N.A.I.C.S.: 541618
Aykut Tellibayraktar *(Mng Dir)*

msg Global Solutions India Private Limited (1)
Block 11 2nd Floor Wing-B Primal Projects Pvt Ltd SEZ Outer Ring Road, Varthur Hobli Bellandur Village, Bengaluru, 560103, India
Tel.: (91) 8049215400
Management Consulting Services
N.A.I.C.S.: 541618
Sriram Krishnan *(Exec VP)*

msg Global Solutions Italia S.r.l. (1)
Viale Lunigiana 46, 20125, Milan, Italy
Tel.: (39) 0284500670
Management Consulting Services
N.A.I.C.S.: 541618
Agostino Assi *(Exec VP)*

msg Global Solutions Korea Ltd. (1)
LS Yongsan Tower 191 Hangangno 2-ga, Yongsan-gu, Seoul, 140-702, Korea (South)
Tel.: (82) 237813003
Management Consulting Services
N.A.I.C.S.: 541618
Chirag Shah *(Exec VP)*

msg Global Solutions Philippines Inc. (1)
28th Floor Pacific Star Bldg Sen Gil Puyat Avenue cor Makati Avenue, Makati, 1200, Philippines
Tel.: (63) 29678900
Management Consulting Services
N.A.I.C.S.: 541618
Teresita Dy *(Exec VP)*

msg Global Solutions South East Europe d.o.o. (1)
Omladinskih Brigada 90g Building 2100 Floor 7, 11070, Novi Beograd, Serbia
Tel.: (381) 113533510
Management Consulting Services
N.A.I.C.S.: 541618
Nikola Djokic *(Exec VP)*

msg Global Solutions do Brasil Ltda. (1)
Rua Tijuco Preto 393 - Sala 172, Sao Paulo, 03316-000, Brazil
Tel.: (55) 11995491896
Management Consulting Services
N.A.I.C.S.: 541618
Ismael Nieto *(Exec VP)*

msg Global digital South East Europe d.o.o. (1)

MSG GROUP GMBH

msg group GmbH—(Continued)
Omladinskih Brigada 90g, 11000, Belgrade, Serbia
Tel.: (381) 113533510
Management Consulting Services
N.A.I.C.S.: 541618

msg Industry Advisors AG (1)
Robert-Burkle-Strasse 1, Ismaning, 85737, Munich, Germany
Tel.: (49) 89961011300
Web Site: http://www.msg-advisors.com
Management Consulting Services
N.A.I.C.S.: 541618
Thomas Praska *(CEO)*

msg Life Central Europe GmbH (1)
Elsenheimerstr 65, 80687, Munich, Germany
Tel.: (49) 711949587000
Information Technology Services
N.A.I.C.S.: 513210

msg Life Iberia, Unipessoal Lda. (1)
Paseo de la Castellana 95 15 - Edificio Torre Europa, 28046, Madrid, Spain
Tel.: (34) 914185044
Information Technology Services
N.A.I.C.S.: 513210

msg Netconomy Inc. (1)
506 Carnegie Ctr Ste 401, Princeton, NJ 08540
Tel.: (609) 524-0400
Information Technology Services
N.A.I.C.S.: 513210

msg Nexinsure AG (1)
Robert-Burkle-Strasse 1, Ismaning, 85737, Munich, Germany
Tel.: (49) 89961017100
Web Site: http://www.nexinsure.com
Insurance Platform Services
N.A.I.C.S.: 524298

msg Services AG (1)
Robert-Burkle-Strasse 1, Ismaning, 85737, Munich, Germany
Tel.: (49) 89961010
Web Site: http://www.msg-services.de
Information Technology Services
N.A.I.C.S.: 513210
Marcus Woelm *(Sr Mgr-Sls)*

msg Systems (Shanghai) Co., Ltd. (1)
Room 1603 Pinzun Executive Mansion 597 Langao Road, Putuo District, Shanghai, 200333, China
Tel.: (86) 2152991586
Management Consulting Services
N.A.I.C.S.: 541618

msg Systems AG (1)
Eichwatt 3, 8105, Regensdorf, Switzerland
Tel.: (41) 433886220
Information Technology Services
N.A.I.C.S.: 513210

msg Systems Romania S.R.L. (1)
Str Brassai Samuel nr 9, 400104, Cluj-Napoca, Romania
Tel.: (40) 733900533
Management Consulting Services
N.A.I.C.S.: 541618
Radu Jinga *(Gen Mgr)*

msg systems AG (1)
Robert-Buerkle-Strasse 1, 85737, Ismaning, Germany
Tel.: (49) 89 96101 0
Web Site: http://www.msg-systems.com
Emp.: 7,500
IT Consulting & Systems Integration Services
N.A.I.C.S.: 541690
Hans Zehetmaier *(Founder & Chm-Exec Bd)*

Subsidiary (Non-US):

Plaut AG (2)
Modecenterstrasse 17 Unit 4/6, A-1110, Vienna, Austria **(50.9%)**
Tel.: (43) 1 23 000 12
Web Site: http://www.plaut.com
Sales Range: $25-49.9 Million
Emp.: 280
Information Technology Consulting Services
N.A.I.C.S.: 541690

Johann Grafl *(CEO & Member-Mgmt Bd)*

Subsidiary (Non-US):

Plaut (Switzerland) Consulting AG (3)
Adlikerstr 246, CH-8105, Regensdorf, Switzerland
Tel.: (41) 18712828
Web Site: http://www.plaut.ch
Management Consulting Services
N.A.I.C.S.: 541618

Plaut Business Consulting GmbH (3)
Dammtorwall 7, D-85737, Hamburg, Germany
Tel.: (49) 89962800
Web Site: http://www.plaut.com
Sales Range: $25-49.9 Million
Emp.: 50
Business Consulting Services
N.A.I.C.S.: 541611
Leoplod Stehr *(Mng Dir)*

Plaut Consulting Ltd. (3)
Phase One Heathrow Blvd 286 Bath Road, West Drayton, London, UB7 0DQ, Middlesex, United Kingdom
Tel.: (44) 2087547574
Web Site: http://www.plaut.co.uk
Sales Range: $25-49.9 Million
Emp.: 42
Management Consulting Services
N.A.I.C.S.: 541618

Plaut Deutschland GmbH (3)
Dammtorwall 7a, DE-20354, Hamburg, Germany **(100%)**
Tel.: (49) 40 32509638 0
Web Site: http://www.plaut.com
Sales Range: $25-49.9 Million
Emp.: 200
Business Consulting & Solution-Oriented IT Implementation
N.A.I.C.S.: 541618
Johann Grafl *(CEO)*

msg Plaut Deutschland GmbH (3)
Dammtorwall 7a, 20354, Hamburg, Germany
Tel.: (49) 40 32509638 0
Web Site: http://www.msg-plaut.com
Computer Consulting Services
N.A.I.C.S.: 541690
Stefan Dehn *(Mng Dir)*

Subsidiary (Domestic):

msg global solutions Deutschland GmbH (2)
Robert-Buerkle-Strasse 1, 85737, Ismaning, Germany
Tel.: (49) 899400337 0
Computer Systems Design
N.A.I.C.S.: 541512
Bernhard Lang *(CEO)*

Subsidiary (US):

msg global solutions Inc. (3)
1 Independence Way, Princeton, NJ 08540
Tel.: (609) 524-0400
Web Site: http://www.msg-global.com
Computer System Design Services
N.A.I.C.S.: 541512
Bernhard Lang *(CEO)*

Affiliate (Domestic):

msg life ag (2)
Humboldtstrasse 35, 70771, Leinfelden-Echterdingen, Germany **(49.09%)**
Tel.: (49) 711 94958 0
Web Site: http://www.msg-life.com
Rev.: $175,402,065
Assets: $83,547,617
Liabilities: $41,897,599
Net Worth: $41,650,018
Earnings: ($1,569,084)
Emp.: 1,117
Fiscal Year-end: 12/31/2019
Software & Consulting Services
N.A.I.C.S.: 513210
Rolf Zielke *(Chm-Mgmt Bd)*

Subsidiary (US):

FJA-US, Inc. (3)
1040 Ave of the Americas 4th Fl, New York, NY 10018

Tel.: (212) 840-2618
Web Site: http://www.fja-us.com
Information Technology Consulting Services
N.A.I.C.S.: 541512
Marc Dutton *(CEO)*

Subsidiary (Non-US):

msg life Austria Ges.m.b.H. (3)
Wiedner Hauptstrasse 76/1/4, 1040, Vienna, Austria
Tel.: (43) 1 58070 0
Web Site: http://www.msg-life.com
Information Technology Consulting Services
N.A.I.C.S.: 541512

msg life Benelux B.V (3)
De Witbogt 26, 5652 AG, Eindhoven, Netherlands
Tel.: (31) 40 2026337
Information Technology Consulting Services
N.A.I.C.S.: 541512
Erwin van der Wal *(Mng Dir)*

msg life Czechia spol. s.r.o. (3)
Na Strzi 1702/65, 140 00, Prague, Czech Republic
Tel.: (420) 222 191 507
Information Technology Consulting Services
N.A.I.C.S.: 541512

Subsidiary (Domestic):

msg life Deutschland gmbh (3)
Prinzenallee 11, 40549, Dusseldorf, Germany
Tel.: (49) 211 520659 00
Information Technology Consulting Services
N.A.I.C.S.: 541512

Subsidiary (Non-US):

msg life Iberia Unipessoal Lda (3)
Avenida dos Aliados n 54 5 Andar, 4000-064, Porto, Portugal
Tel.: (351) 2 23203110
Information Technology Consulting Services
N.A.I.C.S.: 541512

msg life Poland Sp. z o.o. (3)
Al Jerozolimskie 96, 00-807, Warsaw, Poland
Tel.: (48) 22 275 56 71
Information Technology Consulting Services
N.A.I.C.S.: 541512
Tomasz Dybowski *(Head-Insurance Market Dev)*

msg life Slovakia s.r.o. (3)
Hranicna 18, 82105, Bratislava, Slovakia
Tel.: (421) 2 32221 270
Information Technology Consulting Services
N.A.I.C.S.: 541512

msg life Switzerland AG (3)
Kaiserstrasse 8, 4310, Rheinfelden, Switzerland
Tel.: (41) 61 90691 20
Information Technology Consulting Services
N.A.I.C.S.: 541512

Subsidiary (Domestic):

msg life consulting gmbh (3)
Pascalstrasse 12, 52076, Aachen, Germany
Tel.: (49) 2408 93801 0
Emp.: 9
Information Technology Consulting Services
N.A.I.C.S.: 541512

msg life metris gmbh (3)
Leopoldstrasse 1, 78112, Saint Georgen, Germany
Tel.: (49) 7724 88070 0
Information Technology Consulting Services
N.A.I.C.S.: 541512

Subsidiary (Non-US):

msg life odateam d.o.o. (3)
Titova Cesta 8, 2000, Maribor, Slovenia
Tel.: (386) 22356200
Web Site: http://www.msg-life.com
Emp.: 30
Information Technology Consulting Services
N.A.I.C.S.: 541512
Andrej Kline *(Mng Dir)*

msg treorbis GmbH (1)
Bei dem Neuen Krahn 2, 20457, Hamburg, Germany
Tel.: (49) 4033441500

INTERNATIONAL PUBLIC

Web Site: http://www.msg-treorbis.de
Financial Services
N.A.I.C.S.: 523999
Michael Neuhaus *(Mng Dir)*

msgGillardon AG (1)
Edisonstrasse 2, 75015, Bretten, Germany
Tel.: (49) 725293500
Web Site: http://www.msg-gillardon.de
Information Technology Services
N.A.I.C.S.: 541512
Thomas Bieth *(Principal & Sls Mgr)*

MSK MARITIME SPEDITION-KONTOR GMBH

5th Floor Alter Fischmarkt 1, 20457, Hamburg, Germany
Tel.: (49) 40376880
Web Site: http://www.msk-spedition.de
Year Founded: 1987
Rev.: $11,035,200
Emp.: 15
Cargo Transportation Services
N.A.I.C.S.: 488320
Andreas Hagenah *(Mng Dir)*

MSM CONTRACTS LTD.

Unit 45a Seagoe Industrial Estate, Portadown, BT63 5QE, Armagh, United Kingdom
Tel.: (44) 2838335047
Web Site: http://www.msmcontracts.co.uk
Year Founded: 1985
Sales Range: $10-24.9 Million
Emp.: 81
Construction Services
N.A.I.C.S.: 236210
Robert Mackey *(Mng Dir)*

MSM CORPORATION INTERNATIONAL LTD.

Level 8 90 Collins Street, Melbourne, 3000, VIC, Australia
Tel.: (61) 390154036
Web Site: http://www.msmci.com
MSM—(ASX)
Rev.: $47,610
Assets: $2,308,616
Liabilities: $477,376
Net Worth: $1,831,240
Earnings: ($293,883)
Fiscal Year-end: 06/30/20
Investment Services
N.A.I.C.S.: 523999
Mark Clements *(Sec)*

MSM INTERNATIONAL LIMITED

8 Robinson Road 03-00 ASO Building, Singapore, 048544, Singapore
Tel.: (65) 65380779 SG
Web Site: https://www.msmmgroup.com
Year Founded: 1973
5QR—(CAT)
Rev.: $19,136,085
Assets: $22,804,444
Liabilities: $15,797,037
Net Worth: $7,007,407
Earnings: $84,868
Emp.: 305
Fiscal Year-end: 03/31/24
Investment Holding Services
N.A.I.C.S.: 551112
Kee Sieng Chan *(Co-Founder & Chm)*

Subsidiaries:

FIC Kitchen Technology Sdn. Bhd. (1)
Lot 3210 Jalan KPB 5 Kawasan Perindustrian Kampung Baru Balakong, 43300, Seri Kembangan, Selangor, Malaysia
Tel.: (60) 16 328 9091
Web Site: https://www.fickitchen.com
Food & Beverage Equipment Mfr & Distr

Flexacon Automation System Sdn. Bhd. (1)
No 11 Jalan Mega 2/1 Kawasan Perindustrian Mega 2, Semenyeh, 43500, Hulu Langat, Selangor, Malaysia
Tel.: (60) 387276029
Web Site: http://www.flexaconauto.com
Conveyor Equipment Mfr
N.A.I.C.S.: 333922

MSM Equipment Manufacturer Sdn. Bhd. (1)
Lot 1801 Jalan KPB 1 Kaw Perindustrian Kampung Baru, Balakong, 43300, Seri Kembangan, Selangor, Malaysia
Tel.: (60) 389612181
Stainless-Steel Kitchen Equipment & Furniture Mfr
N.A.I.C.S.: 337126

MSM Kitchen Sdn. Bhd. (1)
Lot 1801 Jalan KPB 1 Kawasan Perindustrian Kampung Baru Balakong, 43300, Seri Kembangan, Selangor, Malaysia
Tel.: (60) 389612181
Web Site: https://www.msmkitchen.com
Refrigerator & Cooking Appliance Mfr & Distr
N.A.I.C.S.: 335220

MSM Metal Industries Sdn. Bhd. (1)
Lot 1909 Jalan KPB 5 Kawasan Perindustrian Kampung Baru Balakong, 43300, Seri Kembangan, Selangor, Malaysia
Tel.: (60) 38 962 6618
Web Site: https://www.msmmgroup.com
Emp.: 230
Sheet Metal Mfr
N.A.I.C.S.: 332322

Marc16 Equipment Manufacturing Sdn. Bhd. (1)
Lot 21579 Jalan industrial Park 3 Persiaran Cassia Selatan 5, Batu Kawan Simpang Ampat, 14110, Penang, Malaysia
Tel.: (60) 45899988
Web Site: http://www.marc16.com
Automation Machinery & Equipment Mfr
N.A.I.C.S.: 334512

OMS Technology Sdn. Bhd. (1)
Lot 1909 Jln KPB5 Kws Perindustrian Kampung Baru, Balakong, 43300, Seri Kembangan, Selangor, Malaysia
Tel.: (60) 389626618
Web Site: http://www.oms-technology.com
Stainless-Steel Kitchen Equipment Mfr
N.A.I.C.S.: 337126

Toyomi Engineering Sdn. Bhd. (1)
Lot 1909 Jalan KPB 5 Kawasan Perindustrian Kg Baru, Balakong, 43300, Seri Kembangan, Selangor, Malaysia
Tel.: (60) 389615352
Web Site: http://www.toyomi.com.my
Fabricated Metal Products Mfr
N.A.I.C.S.: 332312

MSOFT THAILAND CO., LTD.
43 Thai CC Tower 17th Floor Room No 174 South Sathorn Road, Yannawa Sathon, Bangkok, 10120, Thailand
Tel.: (66) 26739980 TH
Web Site: http://www.msoft.co.th
Software Development Services
N.A.I.C.S.: 541511

MSP STEEL & POWER LIMITED
16/S Block A New Alipore, Kolkata, 700 053, India
Tel.: (91) 3340057777
Web Site: https://www.mspsteel.com
Year Founded: 1968
MSPL—(NSE)
Rev.: $235,334,886
Assets: $206,258,120
Liabilities: $125,399,970
Net Worth: $80,858,150
Earnings: $666,038
Emp.: 1,073
Fiscal Year-end: 03/31/21
Iron & Steel Mfr

N.A.I.C.S.: 331110
Suresh Kumar Agrawal *(Chm)*

MSR INDIA LIMITED
Plot No D 16 Road No 73 Phase 4 Extension, Jeedimetla, Hyderabad, 500055, Telangana, India
Tel.: (91) 4065577456
Web Site: https://www.msrindia.in
508922—(BOM)
Rev.: $3,172,952
Assets: $4,549,853
Liabilities: $2,904,349
Net Worth: $1,645,504
Earnings: $2,485,505
Fiscal Year-end: 03/31/23
Renewable Power Generation Services
N.A.I.C.S.: 221118
Durgaadideva Varaprasad Challa *(Mng Dir & CFO)*

MST GOLF GROUP BERHAD
8 Jalan SS 13/5, 47500, Subang Jaya, Selangor, Malaysia
Tel.: (60) 355668666
Web Site: https://www.mstgolfgroup.com
Year Founded: 1989
MSTGOLF—(KLS)
Rev.: $68,874,286
Assets: $87,347,513
Liabilities: $33,256,296
Net Worth: $54,091,217
Earnings: $3,677,037
Emp.: 602
Fiscal Year-end: 12/31/23
Golf Product Distr
N.A.I.C.S.: 423860
Heng Kok Wee *(CFO)*

MSTC LTD.
Plot no CF 18/2 Street No 175 Action Area 1C New Town, Kolkata, 700156, India
Tel.: (91) 03323400000
Web Site: https://www.mstcindia.co.in
Year Founded: 1956
MSTCLTD—(NSE)
Rev.: $1,356,917,835
Assets: $3,068,193,765
Liabilities: $2,306,587,920
Net Worth: $761,605,845
Earnings: $154,189,035
Emp.: 335
Fiscal Year-end: 03/31/21
Online Shopping Services
N.A.I.C.S.: 541511
Surinder Kumar Gupta *(Chm & Mng Dir)*

Subsidiaries:

Ferro Scrap Nigam Limited (1)
F S N L Bhawan Equipment Chowk Central Avenue, Post Box No 37, Dist Durg, Bhilai, 490001, Chattisgarh, India
Tel.: (91) 7882222474
Web Site: https://fsnl.nic.in
Steel Mfrs
N.A.I.C.S.: 331110
Manobendra Ghoshal *(Mng Dir)*

MSW (UK) LTD.
Acton Grove Long Eaton, Nottingham, NG10 1FY, United Kingdom
Tel.: (44) 1159462316 UK
Web Site: http://www.mswukltd.com
Year Founded: 1969
Rev.: $46,876,924
Emp.: 25
Steel Decking Service
N.A.I.C.S.: 238120
Derek Johnston *(Owner & Mng Dir)*

MSX RESOURCES SA
ul. Lucka 2/4/6, 00-845, Warsaw, Poland

Tel.: (48) 22 487 53 40
Web Site: http://msxresources.com
Sales Range: $1-9.9 Million
Construction & Development Services
N.A.I.C.S.: 541330
Wielkoslaw Prezemko Staniszewski *(Member-Mgmt Bd)*

Subsidiaries:

MOST-BUD Sp. z o.o. (1)
ul Mokra 2, 26 600, Radom, Masovian, Poland
Tel.: (48) 483317133
Web Site: http://www.mostbud.com.pl
Industrial Construction Services
N.A.I.C.S.: 236210
Marian Franaszczuk *(Pres)*

MOSTOSTAL-EXPORT Development S.A (1)
ul Obrzezna 5 Lok 1113, 02 691, Warsaw, Masovian, Poland
Tel.: (48) 223291373
Web Site: http://www.mexdev.com.pl
Building Construction Services
N.A.I.C.S.: 236116

MT EDUCARE LIMITED
Office No 220 2nd Floor Neptunes Flying Colors, Pandit Dindayal Upadhyay Marg LBS Cross Road Mulund W, Mumbai, 400 080, India
Tel.: (91) 222937700
Web Site: https://www.mteducare.com
Year Founded: 1988
534312—(BOM)
Rev.: $15,435,106
Assets: $51,501,327
Liabilities: $31,987,410
Net Worth: $19,513,917
Earnings: ($4,126,190)
Emp.: 410
Fiscal Year-end: 03/31/21
Exam Preparation Services
N.A.I.C.S.: 611691
Mahesh R. Shetty *(Founder)*

Subsidiaries:

Lakshya Forum for Competitions Pvt. Ltd. (1)
SCF 99-102, Chotti Baradari, Patiala, 147001, India
Tel.: (91) 9988850474
Educational Support Services
N.A.I.C.S.: 611710
Saahil Harjai *(Founder)*

MT EVELYN & DISTRICTS FINANCIAL SERVICES LIMITED
Shop 2 35-39 Wray Crescent, Mount Evelyn, Canberra, 3796, Victoria, Australia
Tel.: (61) 3 9737 1833
Web Site: http://www.medfsl.com.au
Rev.: $1,496,547
Assets: $1,995,024
Liabilities: $337,627
Net Worth: $1,657,398
Earnings: $205,920
Fiscal Year-end: 06/30/17
Banking Services
N.A.I.C.S.: 522110

MT GAS JOINT STOCK COMPANY
Unit 707-708 7th floor-1-5 Le Duan Street, Distric 1, Ho Chi Minh City, Vietnam
Tel.: (84) 8 39105987
Web Site: http://www.mtgas.com.vn
Sales Range: $1-9.9 Million
Gas Distribution Services
N.A.I.C.S.: 221210
Nguyen Thi Lan Phuong *(Exec Dir)*

MT GENEX CORPORATION
4F Toranomon 40MT Building 5131 Toranomon, Minato-Ku, Tokyo, 106-0041, Japan
Tel.: (81) 354054011
Web Site: https://www.mt-genex.co.jp
Year Founded: 1961
9820—(TKS)
Rev.: $25,051,900
Assets: $33,056,610
Liabilities: $7,218,120
Net Worth: $25,838,490
Earnings: $1,830,970
Fiscal Year-end: 03/31/24
Renewal Construction Services
N.A.I.C.S.: 236118
Hitoshi Suzuki *(Pres)*

MT MALCOLM MINES NL
8 Sarich Court, Osborne Park, 6019, WA, Australia
Tel.: (61) 862446617 AU
Web Site: https://www.mtmalcolm.com.au
Year Founded: 2020
M2M—(ASX)
Rev.: $30,107
Assets: $5,140,059
Liabilities: $302,149
Net Worth: $4,837,910
Earnings: ($867,424)
Fiscal Year-end: 06/30/23
Gold Exploration Services
N.A.I.C.S.: 212220
Robert Downey *(Chm)*

MT-IDEAS S.A.
Mendez de Andes 1442, C1406FUB, Buenos Aires, Argentina
Tel.: (54) 1144311801
Web Site: http://www.mt-ar.com
Emp.: 12
Industrial Machinery Distr
N.A.I.C.S.: 423830

MTAG GROUP BERHAD
PLO 226 Jalan Kencana Mas Kawasan Perindustrian Tebrau III, 81100, Johor Bahru, Johor, Malaysia
Tel.: (60) 73513333 MY
Web Site: https://www.mtaggroup.com
Year Founded: 1995
MTAG—(KLS)
Rev.: $32,574,025
Assets: $48,459,446
Liabilities: $3,270,030
Net Worth: $45,189,415
Earnings: $6,364,229
Emp.: 189
Fiscal Year-end: 06/30/23
Industrial Product Distr
N.A.I.C.S.: 423830
Chaw Kam Shiang *(Mng Dir)*

MTAR TECHNOLOGIES LIMITED
18 Technocrats Industrial Estate, Balanagar, Hyderabad, 500037, Telangana, India
Tel.: (91) 4044553333
Web Site: https://www.mtar.in
Year Founded: 1970
543270—(BOM)
Precision Component Mfr
N.A.I.C.S.: 332721
Sudipto Bhattacharya *(CFO)*

Subsidiaries:

Gee Pee Aerospace & Defence Private Limited (1)

MTB METALS CORP.
Suite 410 - 325 Howe Street, Vancouver, V6C 1Z7, BC, Canada
Tel.: (604) 687-3520
Web Site: https://www.mtb-metals.com

MTB METALS CORP.

MTB Metals Corp.—(Continued)
Year Founded: 1999
MBYMF—(OTCQB)
Mineral Exploration Services
N.A.I.C.S.: 213114
Lawrence McKeen Roulston (Pres & CEO)

MTD CAPITAL BHD.
1 Jalan Batu Caves, 68100, Batu Caves, Selangor Darul Ehsan, Malaysia
Tel.: (60) 361951111
Web Site: http://www.mtdgroup.com
Sales Range: $350-399.9 Million
Express Highway Road Construction Services
N.A.I.C.S.: 237310
Hussain Abdul Rahman (Chm)

Subsidiaries:

MTD ACPI Engineering Berhad (1)
1 Jalan Batu Caves, 68100, Batu Caves, Selangor Darul Ehsan, Malaysia
Tel.: (60) 361951111
Web Site: http://www.mtdacpi.com
Rev.: $60,115,963
Assets: $90,733,553
Liabilities: $68,651,223
Net Worth: $22,082,330
Earnings: ($1,641,165)
Emp.: 437
Fiscal Year-end: 03/31/2019
Construction & Property Management Services
N.A.I.C.S.: 236220
Bee Kuan Chan (Co-Sec)

Subsidiary (Domestic):

MTD Construction Sdn. Bhd. (2)
Lot 8359 Mukim Of Batu 8 1 Jalan Batu Caves, Batu Caves, 68100, Selangor, Malaysia
Tel.: (60) 3 6189 9022
Construction Engineering Services
N.A.I.C.S.: 541330

Metacorp Berhad (1)
1 Jalan Batu Caves, Batu Caves, 68100, Selangor, Malaysia
Tel.: (60) 361951111
Web Site: http://www.metacorp.com.my
Sales Range: $100-124.9 Million
Emp.: 300
Property Development Services
N.A.I.C.S.: 236210
Dato Azmil (Mng Dir)

Subsidiary (Domestic):

Dimensi Timal Sdn. Bhd. (2)
1 Jalan Batu Caves, 68100, Batu Caves, Selangor, Malaysia
Tel.: (60) 3 6195 1111
Granite Quarrying Services
N.A.I.C.S.: 212321
Nik Faizul (Gen Mgr)

Metacorp Properties Sdn. Bhd. (2)
42A Jalan TU 2 Taman Tasik Utama, Ayer Keroh, Malacca, Malaysia
Tel.: (60) 62321128
Web Site: http://www.alloymtd.com
Sales Range: $25-49.9 Million
Emp.: 10
Property Development Services
N.A.I.C.S.: 236220
Calvin Choe (Sr VP)

Modal Ehsan Sdn. Bhd (2)
Lot 507 Taman Sutera Sales Office, Kajang, 43000, Selangor, Malaysia
Tel.: (60) 387393636
Property Management Services
N.A.I.C.S.: 531312

South Luzon Tollway Corporation (1)
6 F 104 Rada Street Legaspi Village, Makati, Philippines
Tel.: (63) 27510371
Web Site: http://www.mtdsltc.com
Tollway Construction & Maintenance Services
N.A.I.C.S.: 237310

MTECH COMMUNICATIONS PLC
36B Olawale Onitiri-Cole, Road 42 Lekki Phase 1, Lagos, Nigeria
Tel.: (234) 1 2711537
Web Site: http://www.mtechcomm.com
Year Founded: 2001
Radio & Television Programming Provider
N.A.I.C.S.: 541840
Sheri Williams (Co-Founder & Chm)

MTEKVISION CO., LTD
C S Tower 6F 601 58 Pangyo-ro 255beon-gil, Bundang-gu, Seongnam, 13486, Gyeonggi-do, Korea (South)
Tel.: (82) 31 627 0100
Web Site: http://www.mtekvision.com
Year Founded: 1999
Sales Range: $125-149.9 Million
Emp.: 246
Semiconductor Product Mfr
N.A.I.C.S.: 334413
Michael Sungmin Lee (CEO)

Subsidiaries:

MtekVision America, Inc. (1)
3003 N 1st St Ste 105, San Jose, CA 95134-2004
Tel.: (408) 519-5800
Semiconductor Product Distr
N.A.I.C.S.: 423690

MTG CO., LTD.
4-13 Honjindori, Nakamura-ku, Nagoya, 453-0041, Aichi, Japan
Tel.: (81) 524815001
Web Site: https://www.mtg.gr.jp
Year Founded: 1996
7806—(TKS)
Rev.: $426,491,860
Assets: $386,043,410
Liabilities: $83,215,330
Net Worth: $302,828,080
Earnings: $14,066,560
Emp.: 1,506
Fiscal Year-end: 09/30/23
Cosmetic Product Mfr & Distr
N.A.I.C.S.: 325620
Tsuyoshi Matsushita (Pres)

Subsidiaries:

Blaze Corporation (1)
2-30 Honjin-dori, Nakamura-ku, Nagoya, 453-0041, Japan
Tel.: (81) 524145527
Web Site: https://www.blaze-inc.co.jp
Electric Motorcycle Mfr & Retailer
N.A.I.C.S.: 336991

Goto No Tsubaki Inc. (1)
1-17 Chuo-cho, Goto, 853-0002, Nagasaki, Japan
Tel.: (81) 959763330
Web Site: https://www.gotonotsubaki.co.jp
Cosmetic Product Mfr & Retailer
N.A.I.C.S.: 325620

M's Agency Co., Ltd. (1)
2-32 Honjintori Mtg Hikari Building, Nakamura-ku, Nagoya, 453-0041, Aichi, Japan
Marketing Services
N.A.I.C.S.: 541613

MTG (Shanghai) Trading Co., Ltd. (1)
801-2 Want Want Plaza 211 ShiMenYiRd, Jingan District, Shanghai, 200041, China
Tel.: (86) 2162720220
Fitness Product Mfr
N.A.I.C.S.: 339920

MTG (Shenzhen) Trading Co., Ltd. (1)
712 710 Tower 4 Hongfalingyu estate N5, Centre Ward Baoan District, Shenzhen, 518101, China
Tel.: (86) 75529430345
Fitness Product Retailer
N.A.I.C.S.: 459110

MTG Formavita Co., Ltd. (1)
6-5 Nihonbashi Kabutocho 8th Floor Kabutocho 6th Heiwa Building, Chuo-ku, Tokyo, 103-0026, Japan
Tel.: (81) 356430860
Web Site: http://www.mtg-fv.co.jp
Home Appliance Product Retailer
N.A.I.C.S.: 449210

MTG Medical Co., Ltd. (1)
4-13 Honjintori MTG 2nd Hikari Building, Nakamura-ku, Nagoya, 453-0041, Aichi, Japan
Tel.: (81) 120315332
Medical Device Mfr & Distr
N.A.I.C.S.: 339112

MTG Pacific Pte. Ltd. (1)
25 Harrison Road 08-00 Chin Lim Building, Singapore, 369646, Singapore
Web Site: http://www.mtg.sg
Fitness Product Mfr
N.A.I.C.S.: 339920
Tsuyoshi Matsushita (Pres)

MTG Professional Co., Ltd. (1)
2-32 Honjin-dori Mtghikari Building 7F, Nakamura-ku, Nagoya, 453-0041, Japan
Tel.: (81) 524812836
Web Site: http://www.mtg-pro.co.jp
Pharmaceutical Product Retailer
N.A.I.C.S.: 456110

MTG Taiwan Co., Ltd. (1)
3F-1 No 79 Huayin St, Datong Dist, Taipei, 10351, Taiwan
Tel.: (886) 225587100
Fitness Product Retailer
N.A.I.C.S.: 459110

MTG METRO GRATIS KST
Madarasz Viktor u 47-49 V emelet, 1138, Budapest, Hungary
Tel.: (36) 14316400
Web Site: http://www.metropol.hu
Sales Range: $25-49.9 Million
Emp.: 60
Newspaper Publishing
N.A.I.C.S.: 513110
Peter Hivatal (Mng Dir)

MTI LTD.
35th Floor Tokyo Opera City Tower 3-20-2 Nishi-Shinjuku, Shinjuku-ku, Tokyo, 163-1435, Japan
Tel.: (81) 353336789
Web Site: https://www.mti.co.jp
Year Founded: 1996
9438—(TKS)
Rev.: $189,997,820
Assets: $206,708,950
Liabilities: $82,045,480
Net Worth: $124,663,470
Earnings: $5,338,770
Emp.: 1,184
Fiscal Year-end: 09/30/23
Plastics Molded Products Mfr
N.A.I.C.S.: 326199
Minoru Takei (Exec VP)

Subsidiaries:

MShift, Inc. (1)
530 Lytton Ave 2nd Fl, Palo Alto, CA 94301
Tel.: (510) 933-5901
Web Site: http://anywheremobile.io
Mobile Banking Services
N.A.I.C.S.: 522110
Scott Moeller (Founder, Chm & CEO)

Mediano Ltd. (1)
3-20-2 Nishi-Shinjuku Tokyo Opera City Tower 35th Floor, Shinjuku-ku, Tokyo, Japan
Tel.: (81) 35 333 6021
Web Site: https://www.mediano-ltd.co.jp
Emp.: 34
Web Advertising Services
N.A.I.C.S.: 541890

Mytrax Inc. (1)
28th Floor Opera City Tower 3-20-2 Nishi-Shinjuku, Shinjuku-Ku, Tokyo, 163-1428, Japan
Tel.: (81) 3 5333 6076
Web Site: http://www.mytrax.co.jp

INTERNATIONAL PUBLIC

Software Development Services
N.A.I.C.S.: 541511

Pharumo, Inc. (1)
Tokyo Opera City Tower 52F 3-20-2 Nishi-Shinjuku, Shinjuku-ku, Tokyo, 163-1452, Japan
Tel.: (81) 35 333 0553
Web Site: https://pharumo.jp
Administrative Management Services
N.A.I.C.S.: 541611

MTI WIRELESS EDGE LTD.
11 Hamelacha St Afek Industrial Park, Rosh Ha'Ayin, 4809121, Israel
Tel.: (972) 39008900
Web Site: https://www.mtiwe.com
Year Founded: 1998
MWE—(AIM)
Rev.: $45,630,000
Assets: $44,700,000
Liabilities: $16,670,000
Net Worth: $28,030,000
Earnings: $4,080,000
Emp.: 240
Fiscal Year-end: 12/31/23
Antennas & Antenna Systems Mfr
N.A.I.C.S.: 334419
Zvi Borovitz (Founder)

Subsidiaries:

Global Wave Technologies Pvt Limited (1)
17/SDF 4thFloor Special Economic Zone Kakkanad, Cochin, 682 037, India
Tel.: (91) 4842413344
Web Site: https://www.globalwavetechnologies.com
Construction Services
N.A.I.C.S.: 236220
Ariel Melamed (CEO)

M.T.I Summit SPB Ltd. (1)
Kondratyevsky pr 15 building 3 lit And of 331-c, 195197, Saint Petersburg, Russia
Tel.: (7) 8126271480
Web Site: http://summitspb.ru
Electronic Component Mfr & Distr
N.A.I.C.S.: 334419
Yoni Cohen (Gen Dir)

Mottech Water Solutions Ltd. (1)
11 Hamelacha St, Rosh Ha'Ayin, 4809121, Israel
Tel.: (972) 99616000
Web Site: http://www.mottech.com
Canal & Irrigation Services
N.A.I.C.S.: 221310
David Shani (CEO)

MTM CRITICAL METALS LIMITED
2/38 Colin Street, West Perth, 6005, WA, Australia
Tel.: (61) 863910112
Web Site: https://mtmcriticalmetals.com.au
Year Founded: 2020
MTM—(ASX)
Rev.: $10,578
Assets: $5,816,926
Liabilities: $261,573
Net Worth: $5,555,354
Earnings: $1,140,563
Fiscal Year-end: 06/30/23
Exploration & Mining Services
N.A.I.C.S.: 213115
Simon Adams (CFO & Sec)

MTN GROUP LIMITED
Innovation Centre 216 14th Avenue, Fairland, Roodepoort, 2195, Gauteng, South Africa
Tel.: (27) 119123000   ZA
Web Site: https://www.mtn.com
Year Founded: 1994
MTN—(JSE)
Rev.: $11,673,972,053
Assets: $22,957,255,569
Liabilities: $15,026,088,150
Net Worth: $7,931,167,418

AND PRIVATE COMPANIES

Earnings: $212,137,855
Emp.: 17,462
Fiscal Year-end: 12/31/23
Telecommunication Servicesb
N.A.I.C.S.: 517112
Paul D. Norman *(Chief HR Officer)*

Subsidiaries:

Global Sourcing Company LLC (1)
3rd Floor 304 Muhaisnah 4, PO Box 5293,
Al Mezan Buiding LLC Al quisais, Dubai,
United Arab Emirates
Tel.: (971) 42204413
Web Site: http://www.globalsourcingco.com
Interior Design & Construction Services
N.A.I.C.S.: 541410

MTN (Zambia) Limited (1)
Tel.: (260) 966750750
Mobile Communications Services
N.A.I.C.S.: 517112
Komba Malukutila *(Gen Mgr)*

MTN Afghanistan Limited (1)
MTN Park Plaza Opposite Share-Naw Park,
Kabul, Afghanistan
Web Site: http://www.mtn.com.af
Communication Product Services
N.A.I.C.S.: 517810
Mohammad Nabi *(Project Mgr)*

MTN Business Solutions Botswana Proprietary Limited (1)
Plot 50361/C Block C Denis Todd Office Park Fairgrounds, Gaborone, Botswana
Tel.: (267) 31889670
Communication Product Services
N.A.I.C.S.: 517810

MTN Business Solutions Namibia Proprietary Limited (1)
1st Floor Millennium Crown Building, Corner Robert Mugabe and Dr AB May Streets, Windhoek, Namibia
Tel.: (264) 612098000
Mobile Communications Services
N.A.I.C.S.: 517112

MTN Business Solutions Proprietary Limited (1)
216 14th Avenue Fairland, Roodepoort, 2195, Gauteng, South Africa
Tel.: (27) 831231800
Web Site: http://www.mtnbusiness.co.za
Communication Product Services
N.A.I.C.S.: 517810

MTN Network Solutions (1)
3 Alice Lane, Sandton, Johannesburg, 2146, South Africa
Tel.: (27) 11 301 6000
Virtual Private Network Services
N.A.I.C.S.: 541513

MTN Nigeria Communications Ltd. (1)
Tel.: (234) 80310180
Sales Range: $550-599.9 Million
Emp.: 1,500
Telecommunications
N.A.I.C.S.: 517810
Ferdi Moolman *(CEO)*

MTN Rwandacell Limited (1)
MTN Centre, PO Box 264, NyarutaramaKigali, Kigali, Rwanda
Web Site: http://www.mtn.co.rw
Communication Product Services
N.A.I.C.S.: 517810
Mitwa Kaemba Ngambi *(CEO)*

MTN South Africa (Pty) Ltd. (1)
216-14Th Avenue, Fairland, Roodepoort, 2195, South Africa
Tel.: (27) 119123216
Web Site: http://www.mtn.co.za
Sales Range: $800-899.9 Million
Cellular Network Services
N.A.I.C.S.: 517112
Godfrey Motsa *(CEO)*

MTN Uganda Ltd. (1)
Web Site: http://www.mtn.co.ug
Telecommunication Servicesb
N.A.I.C.S.: 517112
Dorcas Muhwezi *(Gen Mgr-Customer Experience)*

Mascom Wireless Botswana (Pty) Limited (1)

Tsholetsa House Plot 4705, Gaborone, Botswana
Web Site: http://www.mascom.bw
Telecommunication Servicesb
N.A.I.C.S.: 517112

Orbicom (Pty) Limited (1)
75 Republic Road, Randburg, Johannesburg, 2125, South Africa
Tel.: (27) 11 289 3600
Sales Range: $25-49.9 Million
Emp.: 85
Satellite & Wireless Communications Services
N.A.I.C.S.: 517112
Gerdus Van Eeden *(CTO)*

Simfy Africa Proprietary Limited (1)
Ground Floor Darter Studios 4 Darters Road, Gardens, Cape Town, 8001, Western Cape, South Africa
Tel.: (27) 861174639
Web Site: https://simfy.africa
Emp.: 60
Internet Entertainment Site Publishing Services
N.A.I.C.S.: 513199

Swazi MTN Ltd. (1)
Mahlalekhukhwini House, Portion 14 of Farm 50 Cnr MR103 and Nshakabili Road Ezulwini, Mbabane, H100, Eswatini
Tel.: (268) 24060000
Web Site: http://www.mtn.co.sz
Sales Range: $25-49.9 Million
Telecommunication Servicesb
N.A.I.C.S.: 517112
Wandile Mthsali *(CEO)*

MTORRES DISENOS INDUSTRIALES SAU

Ctra Pamplona-Huesca Km 9, 31119, Torres de Elorz, Navarra, Spain
Tel.: (34) 948317811
Web Site: http://www.mtorres.es
Year Founded: 1975
Sales Range: $125-149.9 Million
Emp.: 490
Machine Tool & Machinery Mfr & Distr
N.A.I.C.S.: 333517
Manuel Torres Martinez *(Founder)*

Subsidiaries:

Pacifica Engineering, Inc. (1)
21520 30th Dr SE Ste 210, Bothell, WA 98021
Tel.: (425) 984-2700
Web Site: http://www.pacifica-engineering.com
Sales Range: $1-9.9 Million
Emp.: 85
Design Engineering, Tool Design, Program Management & Other Engineering Services
N.A.I.C.S.: 541330
Eric Weber *(Engr-Design)*

MTOUCHE TECHNOLOGY BERHAD

Lot 11 3 11th Floor Menara Lien Hoe No 8 Persiaran Tropicana, Tropicana Golf and Country Resort, 47410, Petaling Jaya, Selangor, Malaysia
Tel.: (60) 378860100   MY
Web Site: https://www.mtouche.com
Year Founded: 2002
0092—(KLS)
Rev.: $3,145,633
Assets: $21,382,510
Liabilities: $4,098,782
Net Worth: $17,283,728
Earnings: ($14,107,749)
Emp.: 40
Fiscal Year-end: 09/30/23
Telecommunication Servicesb
N.A.I.C.S.: 517810
Boon Koon Tang *(Exec Dir)*

Subsidiaries:

Mobile Fusion Pte. Ltd. (1)
10 Ubi Crescent Ubi Techpark Lobby B 01-16, Singapore, 408564, Singapore
Tel.: (65) 62949901

Web Site: http://mfusion.com.sg
Mobile Application Development Services
N.A.I.C.S.: 541511

mTouche (Cambodia) Co., Ltd. (1)
VTrust Office Center Parkway Square Room 2FH2 No 113, Mao Tse Toung Blvd 245 Khan Chamkamorn, Phnom Penh, Cambodia
Tel.: (855) 23 666 6315
Mobile Value-Added Services
N.A.I.C.S.: 517810

mTouche (HK) Limited (1)
Room 6 19/F Nan Fung Centre 264-298 Castle Peak Road, Tsuen Wan, New Territories, China (Hong Kong)
Tel.: (852) 27831620
Mobile Message Services
N.A.I.C.S.: 561421

mTouche (Thailand) Company Limited (1)
219/12 Asoke Towers Building 5th Floor Soi Asoke, Sukhumvit 21 Rd North Klongtoey Wattana, Bangkok, 10110, Thailand
Tel.: (66) 26644499
Mobile Application Development Services
N.A.I.C.S.: 541511

mTouche (Vietnam) Co. Ltd. (1)
Room 509/1 5th Floor Ford Thang Long Building 109 Lang Ha Street, Lang Ha ward Dong Da district, Hanoi, Vietnam
Tel.: (84) 437724828
Mobile Application Development Services
N.A.I.C.S.: 541511

mTouche Pte. Ltd. (1)
57 Ubi Ave 1 UBI Center 06-12 S, Singapore, 408936, Singapore
Tel.: (65) 62386130
Software Development Services
N.A.I.C.S.: 541511
Diana Saad *(Country Mgr)*

MTQ CORPORATION LIMITED

100 Tuas South Avenue 8, Singapore, 128373, Singapore
Tel.: (65) 67777651
Web Site: https://www.mtq.com.sg
M05—(SES)
Rev.: $62,122,268
Assets: $92,470,545
Liabilities: $45,765,839
Net Worth: $46,704,705
Earnings: $2,858,096
Emp.: 414
Fiscal Year-end: 03/31/23
Oil & Gas Industry Services
N.A.I.C.S.: 333132
Boon Wee Kuah *(CEO-Grp)*

Subsidiaries:

Binder Asia Pte. Ltd. (1)
182 Pandan Loop, Singapore, 128373, Singapore
Tel.: (65) 62511523
Software Development Services
N.A.I.C.S.: 541519

Binder Group Pty. Ltd. (1)
404 Orrong Road, Welshpool, 6106, WA, Australia
Tel.: (61) 862422400
Pipe Clamp Mfr
N.A.I.C.S.: 332996

In-Line Valve Company Limited (1)
6 The Galloway Centre Express Way Hambridge Lane, Newbury, RG14 5TL, United Kingdom
Tel.: (44) 163545025
Web Site: https://www.inlinevalve.co.uk
Industrial Valve Mfr
N.A.I.C.S.: 332911

MTQ Engineering Pte Ltd (1)
100 Tuas South Avenue 8, Singapore, 128373, Singapore
Tel.: (65) 67777651
Emp.: 200
Oil Filed Equipment Repairing & Rental Services
N.A.I.C.S.: 532412
Vincent Tan Hai York *(Mng Dir)*

MTQ Equipment Rental Pte. Ltd. (1)
182 Pandan Loop, Singapore, 128373, Singapore
Tel.: (65) 67777651
Web Site: http://www.mtq.com.sg
Emp.: 120
Oil Filed Equipment Rental Services
N.A.I.C.S.: 532412

MTQ Fabrication Pte. Ltd. (1)
182 Pandan Loop, Singapore, 128373, Singapore
Tel.: (65) 67777651
Emp.: 100
Oil Filed Steel Structures Fabrication Services
N.A.I.C.S.: 332999
Vincent Tan *(Mng Dir)*

MTQ Holdings Pty Ltd (1)
80 Achievement Crescent, Acacia Ridge, 4110, QLD, Australia
Tel.: (61) 732462000
Investment Management Service
N.A.I.C.S.: 523999

MTQ Oilfield Services W.L.L. (1)
Building 498 Road 1508 HIDD 115, Manama, Bahrain
Tel.: (973) 17166800
Oil & Gas Field Equipment Mfr
N.A.I.C.S.: 333132
Asif Salim Vorajee *(Gen Mgr)*

Neptune Marine Services Limited (1)
404 Orrong Road Welshpool, Perth, 6106, WA, Australia
Tel.: (61) 862422222
Web Site: http://www.neptunems.com
Rev.: $52,856,344
Assets: $32,139,017
Liabilities: $9,849,784
Net Worth: $22,289,233
Earnings: ($23,406,115)
Emp.: 221
Fiscal Year-end: 03/31/2018
Oil, Gas & Marine Engineering Services
N.A.I.C.S.: 237990
Robin King *(CEO)*

Subsidiary (Non-US):

Neptune Marine Pacific Pte Ltd (2)
54 Loyang Way, Singapore, 508747, Singapore
Tel.: (65) 6543 4058
Sales Range: $25-49.9 Million
Emp.: 30
Oil & Gas Field Services
N.A.I.C.S.: 213112

Subsidiary (Domestic):

Neptune Marine Services International Pty Ltd (2)
404 Orrong Rd, Welshpool, 6106, WA, Australia
Tel.: (61) 862422222
Web Site: http://www.neptunems.com
Emp.: 100
Oil & Gas Field Services
N.A.I.C.S.: 213112
Robin King *(CEO)*

Subsidiary (Non-US):

Neptune Offshore Services Ltd (2)
Spurryhillock Stonehaven, Aberdeen, AB39 2NH, United Kingdom
Tel.: (44) 1569 767 888
Web Site: http://www.neptunems.com
Sales Range: $25-49.9 Million
Emp.: 50
Oil & Gas Offshore Services
N.A.I.C.S.: 213112

Sea-Struct International Pte Ltd (2)
54 Loyang Way, Singapore, 508747, Singapore
Tel.: (65) 65434058
Web Site: http://www.sea-struct.com.au
Sales Range: $50-74.9 Million
Emp.: 15
Oil & Gas Field Services
N.A.I.C.S.: 213112
Kevin May *(Gen Mgr)*

Subsidiary (Domestic):

Sea-Struct Pty Ltd (2)
10 Sultan Way, Perth, 6159, Western Aus-

MTQ CORPORATION LIMITED

MTQ Corporation Limited—(Continued)
tralia, Australia
Tel.: (61) 894304753
Web Site: http://www.sea-struct.com.au
Sales Range: $50-74.9 Million
Emp.: 10
Oil & Gas Field Services
N.A.I.C.S.: 213112

Subsidiary (Non-US):

Subsea Stabilisation Indonesia (2)
Jl RE Martadinata, Sekupang, Batam, 29428, Indonesia
Tel.: (62) 778322655
Web Site: http://www.neptunems.com
Oil & Gas Field Services
N.A.I.C.S.: 213112

Pemac Pte. Ltd. (1)
No 54 Loyang Way, Singapore, 508747, Singapore
Tel.: (65) 65425611
Web Site: https://www.mtqpemac.com.sg
Oil & Gas Field Equipment Mfr
N.A.I.C.S.: 333132

Premier Sea & Land Pte. Ltd. (1)
54 Loyang Way, Singapore, 508747, Singapore
Tel.: (65) 6 543 1433
Web Site: https://www.mtqpremier.com.sg
Oilfield Equipment Whslr & Rental Services
N.A.I.C.S.: 423830
Zakaria Ishak (Mgr)

MTR CORPORATION LIMITED

MTR Headquarters Building Telford Plaza 33 Wai Yip Street, Kowloon Bay, China (Hong Kong)
Tel.: (852) 28610020 HK
Web Site: https://www.mtr.com.hk
Year Founded: 1975
0066—(HKG)
Rev.: $7,282,323,923
Assets: $44,273,390,673
Liabilities: $21,415,517,528
Net Worth: $22,857,873,145
Earnings: $1,033,649,852
Emp.: 33,405
Fiscal Year-end: 12/31/23
Railways Transportation Services
N.A.I.C.S.: 488210
Margaret Wai-ching Cheng (Dir-HR)

Subsidiaries:

MTR Academy (HK) Company Limited (1)
1/F MTR Hung Hom Building 8 Cheong Wan Road Hung Hom, Kowloon Bay, Kowloon, China (Hong Kong)
Tel.: (852) 25203535
Web Site: https://www.mtracademy.com
Academy School Services
N.A.I.C.S.: 611519

MTR Corporation (Crossrail) Limited (1)
Providence House Providence Place, Islington, London, N1 0NT, United Kingdom
Tel.: (44) 2074440213
Web Site: http://www.mtrcrossrail.co.uk
Emp.: 1,000
Rail Transportation Services
N.A.I.C.S.: 488210
Andy Boyle (Dir-Ops)

MTR Express (Sweden) AB (1)
Klarabergsviadukten 90, 111 64, Stockholm, Sweden
Tel.: (46) 858097166
Web Site: https://mtrx.travel
Commuter Railway System Operator
N.A.I.C.S.: 485999

Metro Trains Melbourne Pty. Ltd. (1)
Collins Street West, PO Box 538, Melbourne, 8007, VIC, Australia
Tel.: (61) 800406865
Web Site: https://www.metrotrains.com.au
Public Transport Services
N.A.I.C.S.: 485999

Ngong Ping 360 Limited (1)
11 Tat Tung Road Tung Chung, Lantau, Hong Kong, China (Hong Kong)
Tel.: (852) 36660606
Web Site: https://www.np360.com.hk
Resort Operator
N.A.I.C.S.: 713990

Octopus Holdings Limited (1)
46/F Manhattan Place 23 Wang Tai Road, Kowloon Bay, Kowloon, China (Hong Kong) (57.4%)
Tel.: (852) 22662222
Web Site: http://www.octopus.com.hk
Holding Company
N.A.I.C.S.: 551112

Subsidiary (Domestic):

Octopus Cards Limited (2)
46th Floor Manhattan Place 23 Wang Tai Road, Kowloon Bay, Kowloon, China (Hong Kong)
Tel.: (852) 22662222
Web Site: http://www.octopus.com.hk
Smart Card Services
N.A.I.C.S.: 522210

Octopus Connect Limited (2)
46 F Manhattan Place 23 Wang Tai Rd, Kowloon, China (Hong Kong)
Tel.: (852) 22662200
Customer Relationship Management & Consumer Research Services
N.A.I.C.S.: 541910

Octopus International Projects Limited (2)
36th Fl Wanchai Rd, Kowloon, China (Hong Kong)
Tel.: (852) 22662200
Automatic Fare Collection Consultancy Services
N.A.I.C.S.: 541690
Brian Chambers (Mng Dir)

Octopus Investments Limited (2)
23 Wang Tai Road Manhattan Place Level 464, Kowloon, China (Hong Kong)
Tel.: (852) 22662200
Web Site: http://www.octopus.com.hk
Holding Company; Investment Services
N.A.I.C.S.: 551112

Octopus Rewards Limited (2)
46F Manhattan Place 23 Wang Tai Road Kowloon Bay, Kowloon, China (Hong Kong)
Tel.: (852) 22662200
Consumer Reward Program Operator
N.A.I.C.S.: 522390

TraxComm Limited (1)
Fo Tan Railway House No 9 Lok King Street, Wai Yip Street, Fotan, New Territories, China (Hong Kong) (100%)
Tel.: (852) 29938333
Web Site: http://www.traxcomm.hk
Sales Range: $25-49.9 Million
Emp.: 12
Wholesale Bandwidth Services for Telecommunications
N.A.I.C.S.: 517810
Kenneth K. H. Lau (Mng Dir)

MTT GROUP HOLDINGS LIMITED

No 107 How Ming Street The entire 8th floor of Guoji Group Center, Kwun Tong, Kowloon, China (Hong Kong)
Tel.: (852) 37558400 Ky
Web Site:
https://www.mttgholdings.com
Year Founded: 2020
2350—(HKG)
Holding Company
N.A.I.C.S.: 551112
Charlie Ka Wai Ip (Founder)

Subsidiaries:

Multisoft Limited (1)
6/F Kwok Kee Group Centre 107 How Ming Street, Kwun Tong, Kowloon, China (Hong Kong)
Tel.: (852) 37558400
Web Site: https://www.multisoft.com.hk
Information Technology Consulting Services
N.A.I.C.S.: 541512

TriTech Distribution Limited (1)
8/F Kwok Kee Group Centre 107 How Ming Street, Kwun Tong, Kowloon, China (Hong Kong)
Tel.: (852) 39583000
Web Site: https://www.ttdist.com
Communication System Installation Services
N.A.I.C.S.: 238210

MTU AERO ENGINES AG

Dachauer Strasse 665, 80995, Munich, Germany
Tel.: (49) 8914890
Web Site: https://www.mtu.de
MTX—(MUN)
Rev.: $5,920,054,810
Assets: $11,263,889,480
Liabilities: $8,103,509,670
Net Worth: $3,160,379,810
Earnings: ($112,594,740)
Emp.: 12,170
Fiscal Year-end: 12/31/23
Holding Company; Aircraft Engine Mfr
N.A.I.C.S.: 551112
Klaus Eberhardt (Chm-Supervisory Bd)

Subsidiaries:

International Aero Engines AG (1)
400 Main St, East Hartford, CT 06118
Tel.: (860) 565-0140
Web Site: http://www.i-a-e.com
Sales Range: $75-99.9 Million
Emp.: 400
Aircraft Engine Mfr
N.A.I.C.S.: 336412
Earl E. Exum (Executives)

MTU Aero Engines Finance B.V. (1)
Herengracht 450-454, Amsterdam, 1017 CA, North Holland, Netherlands
Tel.: (31) 206233490
Investment Services
N.A.I.C.S.: 523999

MTU Aero Engines GmbH (1)
Dachauer Str 665, Munich, 80995, Germany
Tel.: (49) 8914890
Web Site: http://www.mtu.de
Aircraft Engine Mfr
N.A.I.C.S.: 336412

Subsidiary (Non-US):

MTU Aero Engines Polska Sp. z.o.o. (2)
Tajecina 108, 36-002, Jasionka, Subcarpathian, Poland
Tel.: (48) 177710482
Emp.: 500
Turbine Airfoils & Engine Components Mfr
N.A.I.C.S.: 333611
Krzysztof Zuzak (Mng Dir)

MTU Maintenance Berlin-Brandenburg GmbH (2)
Tel.: (49) 337882400
Emp.: 500
Engines & Industrial Gas Turbines Maintenance Services
N.A.I.C.S.: 811198

MTU Maintenance Canada Ltd. (2)
6020 Russ Baker Way, Richmond, V7B 1B4, BC, Canada
Tel.: (604) 233-5700
Web Site: http://www.mtucanada.com
Sales Range: $50-74.9 Million
Emp.: 409
Aircraft Engine Maintenance Services
N.A.I.C.S.: 488190
Ralph Schmidt (Pres)

Subsidiary (Domestic):

MTU Maintenance Hannover GmbH (2)
Munchner Strasse 31, 30855, Langenhagen, Germany
Tel.: (49) 51178060
Aircraft Engine Repair & Maintenance Services
N.A.I.C.S.: 811198
Stefan Weingartner (Chm)

MTU Aero Engines North America Inc.-Design & Engineering (1)
795 Brook St Bldg 5, Rocky Hill, CT 06067
Tel.: (860) 258-9700
Web Site: http://www.mtuusa.com
Sales Range: $25-49.9 Million
Emp.: 60
Aircraft Engine Engineering Services
N.A.I.C.S.: 541330
Jonathan Leach (Pres & CEO)

MTU Aero Engines Shanghai Ltd. (1)
No 88 Keyuan Rd German Center Building, Shanghai, 201203, China
Tel.: (86) 2150273522
Aircraft Engine Maintenance Services
N.A.I.C.S.: 532411

MTU Maintenance Dallas Inc. (1)
615 Westport Pkwy Ste 600, Grapevine, TX 76051
Tel.: (830) 326-9400
Aircraft Engine Maintenance Services
N.A.I.C.S.: 532411

MTU Maintenance IGTService do Brasil Ltd. (1)
Avenida Cruzada Bandeirantes 205, 06705-140, Cotia, Sao Paulo, Brazil
Tel.: (55) 1141482777
Aircraft Engine Maintenance Services
N.A.I.C.S.: 532411

MTU Maintenance Lease Services B.V. (1)
Strawinskylaan 1573, 1077 XX, Amsterdam, Netherlands
Tel.: (31) 207052590
Aircraft Engine Maintenance Services
N.A.I.C.S.: 532411
Klaas Nijhof (Mgr-Asset)

MTU Maintenance Serbia d.o.o. (1)
Cetvrta Centralna Radna 1, 22330, Nova Pazova, Serbia
Tel.: (381) 8914898302
Aircraft Engine Mfr
N.A.I.C.S.: 336413

MTU Maintenance Service Center Ayutthaya Ltd. (1)
91/9 Moo 9 Rojana Industrial Park 2 T Kanham A, Uthai, Phra Nakhon Si Ayutthaya, 13210, Thailand
Tel.: (66) 35719209
Aircraft Engine Maintenance Services
N.A.I.C.S.: 532411

MTU Maintenance Service Centre Australia Pty. Ltd. (1)
2 Tarlton Crescent, Perth, 6105, WA, Australia
Tel.: (61) 402523656
Aircraft Engine Maintenance Services
N.A.I.C.S.: 532411

MTU Maintenance Service Centre Ayutthaya Ltd. (1)
91/9 Moo 9, Rojana Industrial Park 2 T-Kanham A-Uthai, Phra Nakhon Si Ayutthaya, 13210, Thailand
Tel.: (66) 17610078845
Aircraft Maintenance Services
N.A.I.C.S.: 488119

MTU Maintenance do Brasil Ltda. (1)
Avenida Cruzada Bandeirantes 205, Cotia, 06705-140, SP, Brazil
Tel.: (55) 1141482777
Gas Turbine Mfr
N.A.I.C.S.: 333611

MTU Turbomeca Rolls-Royce GmbH (1)
Am Soldnermoos 17, 85399, Hallbergmoos, Germany
Tel.: (49) 81 160 0900
Web Site: https://www.mtr390.com
Sales Range: $25-49.9 Million
Emp.: 15
Mfr of Turboshaft Engines; Owned 33% by MTU Engines Holding AG, 33% by Rolls-Royce Group plc & 33% by Turbomeca
N.A.I.C.S.: 333618
Ralf Breiling (Mng Dir)

MTY FOOD GROUP INC.

8210 Transcanada Road, Saint Laurent, H4S 1M5, QC, Canada

AND PRIVATE COMPANIES

Tel.: (514) 336-8885   BC
Web Site: https://www.mtygroup.com
Year Founded: 1979
9MF—(DEU)
Rev.: $560,520,830
Assets: $1,819,038,031
Liabilities: $1,252,177,604
Net Worth: $566,860,427
Earnings: $58,811,028
Emp.: 7,062
Fiscal Year-end: 11/30/22
Fast Food Restaurant Franchisor & Operator
N.A.I.C.S.: 722513
Stanley Ma (Chm)

Subsidiaries:

BBQ Holdings, Inc.   (1)
12701 Whitewater Dr Ste 100, Minnetonka, MN 55343
Tel.: (952) 294-1300
Web Site: https://www.bbq-holdings.com
Rev.: $206,442,000
Assets: $204,423,000
Liabilities: $140,076,000
Net Worth: $64,347,000
Earnings: $24,021,000
Emp.: 397
Fiscal Year-end: 01/02/2022
Restaurant Operators
N.A.I.C.S.: 722511
Albert Hank (COO)

Subsidiary (Domestic):

Famous Dave's Ribs-U, Inc.   (2)
12701 Whitewater Dr Ste 200, Minnetonka, MN 55343-4164
Tel.: (952) 294-1300
Web Site: http://www.famousdaves.com
Restaurant Operating Services
N.A.I.C.S.: 722511

Granite City Food & Brewery Ltd   (2)
12701 Whitewater Dr Ste 290, Minnetonka, MN 55343
Tel.: (952) 215-0660
Sales Range: $125-149.9 Million
Emp.: 2,816
Restaurant & Brewery Owner & Operator
N.A.I.C.S.: 722511
R. J. Nab (VP-Brewmaster)

Subsidiary (Domestic):

Granite City - Creve Coeur, Inc.   (3)
W Oaks Shopping Ctr 11411 Olive Blvd, Creve Coeur, MO 63141
Tel.: (314) 432-3535
Restaurant Operating Services
N.A.I.C.S.: 722511

Granite City - Orland Park, Inc.   (3)
14035 S La Grange Rd, Orland Park, IL 60462
Tel.: (708) 364-1212
Restaurant Operating Services
N.A.I.C.S.: 722511

Granite City Restaurant Operations, Inc.   (3)
701 Xenia Ave S Ste 120, Minneapolis, MN 55416
Tel.: (952) 215-0660
Restaurant Operating Services
N.A.I.C.S.: 722511

Granite City of Kansas Ltd.   (3)
1701 Vlg W Pkwy, Kansas City, KS 66111
Tel.: (913) 334-2255
Restaurant Operating Services
N.A.I.C.S.: 722511
Angie Compton (Mgr)

Granite City of Ohio, Inc.   (3)
2300 Vlg Dr W Ste 130, Maumee, OH 43537
Tel.: (419) 878-9050
Sales Range: $25-49.9 Million
Emp.: 89
Restaurant Operating Services
N.A.I.C.S.: 722511

Subsidiary (Domestic):

Granite City, Inc.   (2)
31715 W 8 Mile Rd, Livonia, MI 48152
Tel.: (248) 478-0033

Web Site: http://www.granitecitymi.com
Kitchen & Bathroom Installation Services
N.A.I.C.S.: 238350

Papa Murphy's Holdings, Inc.   (1)
8000 NE Pkwy Dr Ste 350, Vancouver, WA 98662
Tel.: (360) 260-7272
Web Site: http://www.papamurphys.com
Rev.: $126,429,000
Assets: $246,724,000
Liabilities: $147,701,000
Net Worth: $99,023,000
Earnings: $4,324,000
Emp.: 1,288
Fiscal Year-end: 12/31/2018
Restaurant Holding Company
N.A.I.C.S.: 551112
Laura Szeliga (CMO)

Subsidiary (Domestic):

Papa Murphy's International, Inc.   (2)
8000 NE Pkwy Dr 350, Vancouver, WA 98662
Tel.: (360) 260-7272
Web Site: http://www.papamurphys.com
Sales Range: $25-49.9 Million
Pizza Restaurants Operator
N.A.I.C.S.: 722511

Wetzel's Pretzels LLC   (1)
35 Hugus Alley Ste 300, Pasadena, CA 91103
Tel.: (626) 432-6900
Web Site: http://www.wetzels.com
Pretzel Retail Franchisor
N.A.I.C.S.: 533110
Bill Phelps (Founder & CEO)

sweetFrog Enterprises, LLC   (1)
10800 Midlothian Turnpike Ste 300, Richmond, VA 23235
Tel.: (804) 893-3151
Web Site: http://sweetfrog.com
Owns, Operates & Franchises Self-Serve Yogurt Restaurants
N.A.I.C.S.: 722513
Adam Silverman (Dir-Ops)

MTZ POLYFILMS LIMITED

New India Centre 4th Floor 17 Co-Operage Road, Mumbai, 400039, Maharashtra, India
Tel.: (91) 22 22049090
Year Founded: 1985
Sales Range: $10-24.9 Million
Emp.: 140
Polyester Film Product Mfr
N.A.I.C.S.: 326113
Sanjay B. Shah (Chm)

MU SIGMA, INC.

Aviator Building 7th Floor to 14th Fl Ascendas ITPL SEZ EPIP Zone, Whitefield Road, Bengaluru, 560066, India
Tel.: (91) 80 7154 8000   DE
Web Site: http://www.mu-sigma.com
Year Founded: 2004
Outsourced Quantitative Analytics for Marketing, Supply Chain & Risk Modeling for Corporate Clients
N.A.I.C.S.: 561499
Dhiraj C. Rajaram (Founder)

Subsidiaries:

Mu Sigma Business Solutions Pvt Ltd.   (1)
Level 4 & 5 Kalyani Platina Opp Tata Motors, Brookefield, Bengaluru, 560066, Whitefield, India   (100%)
Tel.: (91) 8040549100
Web Site: http://www.mu-sigma.com
Sales Range: $25-49.9 Million
Emp.: 300
Outsourced Marketing & Supply Chain Analytics
N.A.I.C.S.: 561499
Sayandeb Banerjee (Head-Consumer Fin & Insurance Bus)

Mu Sigma Limited   (1)
2 Churchill Ct 58 Station Rd, North, Harrow,
HA2 7SA, Middlesex, United Kingdom   (100%)
Tel.: (44) 8455575630
Web Site: http://www.mu-sigma.com
Emp.: 25
Outsourced Marketing & Supply Chain Analytics
N.A.I.C.S.: 561499

MU YAN TECHNOLOGY GROUP CO., LIMITED

Room 1703B Zhongzhou Building No 3088, Jintian Road Futian District, Shenzhen, 518000, Guandong, China
Tel.: (86) 75583257679   NV
Year Founded: 2013
MYTG—(OTCIQ)
Rev.: $160,631
Assets: $7,119,425
Liabilities: $3,583,457
Net Worth: $3,535,968
Earnings: $160,631
Emp.: 37
Fiscal Year-end: 07/31/21
Cosmetic Product Distr
N.A.I.C.S.: 424210
Zhao Lixin (Pres & CEO)

MUA LTD.

4 Leoville L Homme street, Port Louis, Mauritius
Tel.: (230) 2075500
Web Site: https://www.mua.mu
Year Founded: 1948
MUAL—(MAU)
Rev.: $171,732,582
Assets: $526,040,538
Liabilities: $405,530,756
Net Worth: $120,509,783
Earnings: $7,663,089
Emp.: 772
Fiscal Year-end: 12/31/22
Financial Related Services
N.A.I.C.S.: 541611
Dominique Galea (Chm)

Subsidiaries:

MUA Insurance (Kenya) Limited   (1)
Lynwood Court 2nd Floor Waiyaki Way, PO Box 30129-00100, Westlands, Nairobi, Kenya
Tel.: (254) 732178000
Web Site: http://www.mua.co.ke
General Insurance Services
N.A.I.C.S.: 524210
Bertrand Casteres (Chm)

Subsidiary (Non-US):

MUA Insurance (Rwanda) Limited   (2)
KN 4th Avenue plot 10610 Grand pension Plaza Ground 8th floor, PO Box 82, Nyarugenge City center, Kigali, Rwanda
Tel.: (250) 788125024
Insurance Services
N.A.I.C.S.: 524210
Erneste Gerald Lemaire (Chm)

MUA Insurance (Uganda) Limited   (2)
9th Floor Northern Wing Workers House Pilkington Road, Kampala, Uganda
Tel.: (256) 41434965960
Web Site: http://www.mua.co.ug
Insurance Services
N.A.I.C.S.: 524210
Bertrand Casteres (Chm)

Phoenix of Tanzania Company Limited   (2)
Phoenix House Mezzanine Floor Plot No 719/11 Azikiwe/Jamuhuri Street, Dar es Salaam, Tanzania
Tel.: (255) 222122777
Web Site: http://www.mua.co.tz
Insurance Services
N.A.I.C.S.: 524210
Lakshmana Lutchmenairraidoo (Chm)

MUANG MAI GUTHRIE PUBLIC COMPANY LIMITED

9/17 Thepkrasattri Road, Rasada Muang, Phuket, 83000, Thailand
Tel.: (66) 76211332
Web Site: http://www.mmguthrie.com
Year Founded: 1996
Rubber & Latex Mfr
N.A.I.C.S.: 326299
P. Tantiphiriyakit (Chm)

Subsidiaries:

Muang Mai Guthrie Public Company Limited - Phuket Plant   (1)
27 Moo 1 Maikhao, Thalang, Phuket, 83000, Thailand
Tel.: (66) 76 327222 3
Rubber & Latex Mfr
N.A.I.C.S.: 326299

Muang Mai Guthrie Public Company Limited - Suratthani Plant   (1)
7 Moo 8 Klong Cha-Eun, Phanom, Surat Thani, 84250, Thailand
Tel.: (66) 77 398067 8
Rubber & Latex Mfr
N.A.I.C.S.: 326299

Muang Mai Guthrie Public Company Limited - Thungsong Plant   (1)
329 Moo 2 Thumyai, Thungsong, 80110, Nakhon Si Thammarat, Thailand
Tel.: (66) 75 773123 4
Rubber & Latex Mfr
N.A.I.C.S.: 326299

MUANG THAI INSURANCE PUBLIC COMPANY LIMITED

252 Rachadaphisek Road, Huaykwang, Bangkok, 10310, Thailand
Tel.: (66) 22903333
Web Site: https://www.muangthaiinsurance.com
Year Founded: 1932
MTI—(THA)
Rev.: $518,378,362
Assets: $916,054,608
Liabilities: $738,491,106
Net Worth: $177,563,502
Earnings: $19,134,059
Emp.: 1,339
Fiscal Year-end: 12/31/23
Insurance Agencies & Brokerage Services
N.A.I.C.S.: 524210
Photipong Lamsam (Chm)

MUANGTHAI CAPITAL PUBLIC COMPANY LIMITED

332/ 1Jaransanitwong Road, Bangplad, Bangkok, 10700, Thailand
Tel.: (66) 24838888   TH
Web Site: https://www.muangthaicap.com
Year Founded: 1992
MTC—(THA)
Rev.: $715,967,404
Assets: $4,383,347,871
Liabilities: $3,451,633,622
Net Worth: $931,714,249
Earnings: $143,229,467
Emp.: 14,873
Fiscal Year-end: 12/31/23
Vehicle Title Loans & Personal Loans
N.A.I.C.S.: 522310
Apichart Pengsritong (Co-Chm)

MUAR BAN LEE GROUP BERHAD

JR52 Lot 1818 Jalan Raja Kawasan Perindustrian Bukit Pasir, 84300, Muar, Johor Darul Takzim, Malaysia
Tel.: (60) 69859998   MY
Web Site: https://www.mbl.com
MBL—(KLS)
Rev.: $53,508,433
Assets: $59,662,800
Liabilities: $19,162,543
Net Worth: $40,500,257
Earnings: $2,656,048
Emp.: 92

MUAR BAN LEE GROUP BERHAD

Muar Ban Lee Group Berhad—(Continued)

Fiscal Year-end: 12/31/20
Oilseed Crushing & Extracting Services
N.A.I.C.S.: 333241
King Tai Tan (Dir-Fin)

MUBADALA INVESTMENT COMPANY PJSC

Al Mamoura A Building, Abu Dhabi, 45005, United Arab Emirates
Tel.: (971) 24130000 AE
Web Site: https://www.mubadala.com
Year Founded: 2017
Investment Holding Company
N.A.I.C.S.: 551112
Khaldoon Khalifa Al Mubarak (CEO & Mng Dir)

Subsidiaries:

Compania Espanola de Petroleos, S.A.U. **(1)**
Cepsa Tower Paseo de la Castellana 259 A, 28046, Madrid, Spain **(63%)**
Tel.: (34) 913376000
Web Site: http://www.cepsa.com
Emp.: 10,146
Oil & Petrochemical Refining Services
N.A.I.C.S.: 324110
Philippe Boisseau (CEO)

Subsidiary (Domestic):

ASFALTOS ESPANOLES, S.A. **(2)**
Salou Road S/N, 43006, Tarragona, Spain
Tel.: (34) 977 55 30 73
Web Site: http://www.asesa.es
Petroleum Refining Services
N.A.I.C.S.: 324110
Montserrat Vallverdu (CEO)

ATLAS, S.A. **(2)**
Calle de Loma Larga, 51004, Ceuta, Spain
Tel.: (34) 956 52 20 55
Petroleum Product Distr
N.A.I.C.S.: 424720

Subsidiary (Non-US):

CEPSA (RHOURDE EL ROUNI) LIMITED **(2)**
2nd Floor Midtown Plaza, PO Box 448, 1106, Georgetown, Cayman Islands
Tel.: (34) 91 337 72 10
Petrochemical Products Mfr
N.A.I.C.S.: 324110

Subsidiary (Domestic):

CEPSA AVIACION, S.A. **(2)**
Av del Partenon 12, 28042, Madrid, Spain
Tel.: (34) 902 32 21 10
Airline Chartering Services
N.A.I.C.S.: 481212

Subsidiary (Non-US):

CEPSA CHEMICAL (SHANGHAI), CO., LTD **(2)**
159 Pugong Road Chemical Industrial District, Shanghai, 201507, China
Tel.: (86) 215 703 7000
Chemical Products Mfr
N.A.I.C.S.: 325998

Subsidiary (Domestic):

CEPSA COMERCIAL GALICIA SA **(2)**
Travesia Coruna 2, 36208, Vigo, Spain
Tel.: (34) 986214666
Petroleum Product Distr
N.A.I.C.S.: 424720

CEPSA COMERCIAL NOROESTE, S.L. **(2)**
Av de los Reyes Leoneses 14, 24008, Leon, Spain
Tel.: (34) 987 87 64 11
Petrochemical Products Mfr
N.A.I.C.S.: 324110

CEPSA COMERCIAL NORTE, S.L. **(2)**
Pol Ind Mutilva Baja Calle E 7, Mutilva, 31092, Navarra, Spain

Tel.: (34) 948291771
Petroleum Product Distr
N.A.I.C.S.: 424720

CEPSA Card, S.A. **(2)**
Av del Partenon 12, 28042, Madrid, Spain
Tel.: (34) 902 32 21 10
Business Support Services
N.A.I.C.S.: 561499

CEPSA EP ESPANA S.L.U. **(2)**
Cepsa Tower Paseo de la Castellana 259 A, 28046, Madrid, Spain
Tel.: (34) 91 337 60 00
Petrochemical Products Mfr
N.A.I.C.S.: 324110

CEPSA EP S.A.U. **(2)**
Cepsa Tower Paseo de la Castellana 259 A, 28046, Madrid, Spain
Tel.: (34) 91 337 60 00
Oil & Gas Exploration Services
N.A.I.C.S.: 211120

Subsidiary (Non-US):

CEPSA Italia, S.p.A. **(2)**
Palazzo A/6 Viale Milano Fiori, Assago, 20090, Milan, Italy
Tel.: (39) 02 824 2186
Petrochemicals & Fine Chemicals Mfr
N.A.I.C.S.: 325110

CEPSA Maghreb, S.A. **(2)**
Avenue des FAR 46, 20000, Casablanca, Morocco
Tel.: (212) 672 865 239
Petroleum & Petrochemical Products Mfr
N.A.I.C.S.: 324199

CEPSA OLEO E GAS DO BRASIL, LTDA. **(2)**
Rua Do Carmo N 43 9 Andar, Rio de Janeiro, Brazil
Tel.: (55) 713 634 3000
Natural Gas Distr
N.A.I.C.S.: 221210

Subsidiary (Domestic):

CEPSA PETRONUBA S.A.U. **(2)**
Poligono Nuevo Puerto S/N, 21810, Palos de la Frontera, Spain
Tel.: (34) 959369111
Freight Transportation Services
N.A.I.C.S.: 483211

Subsidiary (Non-US):

CEPSA Quimica Netherlands, B.V. **(2)**
Beursplein 37, 3011, Rotterdam, Netherlands
Tel.: (31) 78 652 62 04
Petroleum Production Services
N.A.I.C.S.: 324110

Subsidiary (Domestic):

CEPSA Quimica, S.A. **(2)**
Cepsa Tower Paseo de la Castellana 259 A, 28046, Madrid, Spain
Tel.: (34) 91 337 60 00
Petroleum & Petrochemistry Mfr
N.A.I.C.S.: 324199

Subsidiary (Non-US):

CEPSA CHIMIE BECANCOUR, INC. **(3)**
5250 Becancour Boulevard, Becancour, G9H 3X3, QC, Canada **(100%)**
Tel.: (819) 294-1414
Web Site: http://www.cepsa.ca
Chemical Products Mfr
N.A.I.C.S.: 325998

Deten Quimica, S.A. **(3)**
Rua Hidrogenio 1744, Complexo Industrial de Camacari, 42810-010, Camacari, Bahia, Brazil **(97.82%)**
Tel.: (55) 7136343000
Web Site: http://www.deten.com.br
Petroleum & Petrochemical Products Mfr
N.A.I.C.S.: 324199
Jose Luis Goncalves de Almeida (Dir Gen)

Subsidiary (Domestic):

CEPSA S.A. **(2)**
Torre Cepsa Paseo de la Castellana 259 A, 28046, Madrid, Spain

Tel.: (34) 91 3376000
Petrochemical Product Distr
N.A.I.C.S.: 424690

Subsidiary (Non-US):

CEPSA UK, Ltd. **(2)**
Audrey House 16-20 Ely Pl, London, EC1N 6SN, United Kingdom
Tel.: (44) 2078312788
Petrochemicals & Fine Chemicals Mfr
N.A.I.C.S.: 325110
Juan Iturralde (Gen Mgr)

Subsidiary (Domestic):

CMD AEROPUERTOS CANARIOS SL **(2)**
Poligono Industrial Valle de Guimar, Guimar, 38500, Santa Cruz de Tenerife, Spain
Tel.: (34) 922 50 53 44
Petrochemical Product Distr
N.A.I.C.S.: 424720

COMPANIA ESPANOLA DE PETROLEOS ATLANTICO, S.A. **(2)**
Paseo Torrelarragoiti Poligono, Zamudio, 48170, Bilbao, Biscay, Spain
Tel.: (34) 944 04 14 79
Petroleum Product Distr
N.A.I.C.S.: 424720

EXPRESOIL, DISTRIBUIDORA DE GASOLEOS SL **(2)**
Crta de Tarrega 19, Agramunt, 25310, Lleida, Spain
Tel.: (34) 973 39 22 32
Natural Gas Distr
N.A.I.C.S.: 221210

GENERACION ELECTRICA PENINSULAR S.A. **(2)**
Cepsa Tower Paseo de la Castellana 259 A, 28046, Madrid, Spain
Tel.: (34) 91 337 60 00
Eletric Power Generation Services
N.A.I.C.S.: 221118

PETROLEOS DE CANARIAS, S.A. **(2)**
C/ Sagasta 41, Las Palmas de Gran Canaria, 35008, Las Palmas, Spain
Tel.: (34) 928 45 35 15
Petrochemical Product Distr
N.A.I.C.S.: 324110

PETROPESCA SL **(2)**
Lugar Muelle Comercial Calle Guadalete, El Puerto de Sta Maria, 11500, Cadiz, Spain
Tel.: (34) 956 56 99 03
Petroleum Product Distr
N.A.I.C.S.: 424720

Subsidiary (Non-US):

PROPEL-PRODUTOS DE PETROLEO, L.D.A. **(2)**
R Gen Mario Firmino Miguel 3, Parede, Lisbon, Portugal
Tel.: (351) 217 217 600
Petrochemical Products Mfr
N.A.I.C.S.: 324110

Subsidiary (Domestic):

RED ESPANOLA DE SERVICIOS S.A.U **(2)**
Cepsa Tower Paseo de la Castellana 259 A, 28046, Madrid, Spain
Tel.: (34) 91 337 60 00
Logistics Consulting Servies
N.A.I.C.S.: 541614

SERVICAR CAMPO DE LAS NACIONES SA **(2)**
Cepsa Tower Paseo de la Castellana 259 A, 28046, Madrid, Spain
Tel.: (34) 91 337 60 00
Petroleum Product Distr
N.A.I.C.S.: 424720

SOCOPAR SL **(2)**
Calle de Zurdo y Giraldez 40, Navas de Oro, 40470, Segovia, Spain
Tel.: (34) 921 59 12 32
Natural Gas Distr
N.A.I.C.S.: 221210

Dental Care Alliance, LLC **(1)**
6240 Lake Osprey Dr, Sarasota, FL 34240-8421

INTERNATIONAL PUBLIC

Tel.: (941) 955-3150
Web Site: http://www.dentalcarealliance.com
Dental Practices Management Consulting Services
N.A.I.C.S.: 541611
Mitchell B. Olan (Chm)

Emirates Defence Industries Company **(1)**
Al Raha Beach HQ Building, Abu Dhabi, United Arab Emirates
Tel.: (971) 220 56666
Web Site: http://www.edic.ae
Defence Products & Arms Mfr
N.A.I.C.S.: 332994
Khaled Al Qubaisi (Chm)

Subsidiary (Non-US):

MNR Group SA **(2)**
rue de Quemper, 68200, Mulhouse, France
Tel.: (33) 389623000
Web Site: http://www.manurhin-group.com
Cartridge Making & Munitions Production Machinery Mfr
N.A.I.C.S.: 332992

International Petroleum Investment Company PJSC **(1)**
IPIC Square Muroor 4th Road, PO Box 7528, Abu Dhabi, United Arab Emirates
Tel.: (971) 26336555
Sales Range: $5-14.9 Billion
Holding Company; Hydrocarbon & Petrochemical Investment & Development Operations
N.A.I.C.S.: 551112

Subsidiary (Domestic):

Aabar Investment PJSC **(2)**
23rd Floor IPIC Building Muroor 4th Street, PO Box 107888, Abu Dhabi, United Arab Emirates
Tel.: (971) 26264466
Investment Management Service
N.A.I.C.S.: 523999

Subsidiary (Domestic):

Aabar Properties LLC **(3)**
IPIC Square 21st Floor 4th Street Muroor Road, Abu Dhabi, United Arab Emirates
Tel.: (971) 2 222 2233
Real Estate Manangement Services
N.A.I.C.S.: 531210

Subsidiary (Non-US):

Falcon Private Bank Ltd. **(3)**
Pelikanstrasse 37, PO Box 1376, 8021, Zurich, Switzerland
Tel.: (41) 442275555
Web Site: http://www.falconprivatebank.com
Financial Services
N.A.I.C.S.: 522320
Alastair Fiddes (COO)

Subsidiary (Domestic):

IFS Independent Financial Services AG **(4)**
Habsburgerstrasse 12, 6003, Lucerne, Switzerland
Tel.: (41) 581782800
Web Site: http://www.ifsag.ch
Wealth Management Services
N.A.I.C.S.: 523999
Markus Beck (Chm)

PWS Private Wealth Services AG **(4)**
Stockerstrasse 55, 8002, Zurich, Switzerland
Tel.: (41) 44 218 90 90
Wealth Management Services
N.A.I.C.S.: 523999

Subsidiary (Non-US):

NOVA Chemicals Corporation **(2)**
2100 250 5 Street SW West Tower, PO Box 2518, Calgary, T2P 0R4, AB, Canada **(100%)**
Tel.: (403) 750-3600
Web Site: https://www.novachem.com
Sales Range: $1-4.9 Billion
Plastics & Chemicals Mfr & Marketer
N.A.I.C.S.: 325110
John Thayer (Sr VP-Sls & Mktg)

AND PRIVATE COMPANIES

MUBADALA INVESTMENT COMPANY PJSC

Plant (Domestic):

NOVA Chemicals Corporation - Moore Plant (3)
510 Moore Line, Mooretown, N0N 1M0, ON, Canada
Tel.: (519) 862-2961
Plastics Product Mfr
N.A.I.C.S.: 325211

NOVA Chemicals Corporation - Sarnia Plant
Manufacturing East Corporate Center, PO Box 3060, Sarnia, N7T 8C1, ON, Canada
Tel.: (519) 862-2911
Emp.: 1,000
Plastics Product Mfr
N.A.I.C.S.: 325211
Rob Thompson (VP-Mfg East)

NOVA Chemicals Corporation - St. Clair River Plant (3)
285 Albert Street, Corunna, N0N 1G0, ON, Canada
Tel.: (519) 862-1445
Plastics Product Mfr
N.A.I.C.S.: 325211

Subsidiary (US):

NOVA Chemicals, Inc.
1555 Coraopolis Heights Rd, Moon Township, PA 15108 (100%)
Tel.: (412) 490-4000
Polyethylene & Plastics Chemical Mfr
N.A.I.C.S.: 325211

Unit (Domestic):

NOVA Chemicals, Inc. - Performance Styrenics (4)
400 Frankfort Rd, Monaca, PA 15061
Tel.: (724) 770-5555
Styrene Mfr
N.A.I.C.S.: 325180

Subsidiary (US):

Nova Chemicals Olefins LLC (3)
10902 Fitzgerald Rd, Mont Belvieu, TX 77580
Tel.: (281) 385-3660
Petrochemical Producer
N.A.I.C.S.: 325110

Mamoura Diversified Global Holding PJSC (1)
Mamoura A Building, PO Box 45005, Abu Dhabi, United Arab Emirates
Tel.: (971) 2 413 0000
Web Site: http://www.mubadala.com
Rev.: $22,602,412,930
Assets: $103,002,630,740
Liabilities: $43,479,558,880
Net Worth: $59,523,071,860
Earnings: $3,630,736,980
Fiscal Year-end: 12/31/2019
Investment Management Service
N.A.I.C.S.: 523999
Mohammed Zayed Al Nahyan (Chm)

Subsidiary (Domestic):

Abu Dhabi Aircraft Technologies LLC (2)
PO Box 46450, Abu Dhabi, United Arab Emirates
Tel.: (971) 2 575 7555
Web Site: http://www.adat.ae
Aircraft Machinery Maintenance Services
N.A.I.C.S.: 811121
John Ball (CFO)

Abu Dhabi Finance PJSC (2)
7th Floor behind Al Raha Mall, Abu Dhabi, United Arab Emirates
Tel.: (971) 2 401 8555
Web Site: http://www.adf.ae
Financial Services
N.A.I.C.S.: 523999
Christopher Taylor (CEO)

Abu Dhabi Future Energy Company PJSC (2)
PJSC Building Airport Road Masdar City, Khalifa City A, Abu Dhabi, 54115, United Arab Emirates
Tel.: (971) 2 653 3333
Investment Management Service
N.A.I.C.S.: 523940

Holding (Domestic):

Al Taif Technical Services PJSC (2)
PO Box 43337, Abu Dhabi, United Arab Emirates
Tel.: (971) 2 4185 500
Web Site: http://www.altaif.ae
Emp.: 1,000
Defense Machinery Mfr
N.A.I.C.S.: 333248
Cyril Arar (CEO)

Joint Venture (US):

EMI Music Publishing (2)
75 9th Ave, New York, NY 10011
Tel.: (212) 492-1200
Music Publisher & Distr
N.A.I.C.S.: 512230

Subsidiary (Non-US):

EMI Music Publishing (Belgium) SA NV (3)
E Plaskylaan 179, 1030, Brussels, Belgium
Tel.: (32) 22450320
Sales Range: $10-24.9 Million
Emp.: 4
Music Publisher & Distr
N.A.I.C.S.: 512250

EMI Music Publishing (Greece) LLC (3)
259 Messoghion Avenue, N Psychiko, 154 51, Athens, Greece
Tel.: (30) 2106714626
Sales Range: $10-24.9 Million
Emp.: 2
Music Publisher & Distr
N.A.I.C.S.: 512230

EMI Music Publishing (Holland) B.V. (3)
Groest 91 93, 1211 EB, Hilversum, Netherlands
Tel.: (31) 356462000
Sales Range: $25-49.9 Million
Emp.: 15
Music Publisher & Distr
N.A.I.C.S.: 512250

EMI Music Publishing Canada (3)
109 Atlantic Ave Ste 301, Toronto, M6K 1X4, ON, Canada
Tel.: (416) 583-5481
Web Site: http://www.emimusicpub.com
Music Publisher & Distr
N.A.I.C.S.: 512230

EMI Music Publishing Ceska Republika, a.s. (3)
Kovarova 39, Stodulky, 155 00, Prague, Czech Republic
Tel.: (420) 296397115
Web Site: http://www.emi.com
Sales Range: $10-24.9 Million
Emp.: 2
Music Publisher & Distr
N.A.I.C.S.: 512230

EMI Music Publishing Chile (3)
Alfredo Barros Errazuriz, Providencia, 1954, Santiago, Chile
Tel.: (56) 22091009
Sales Range: $10-24.9 Million
Emp.: 5
Music Publisher & Distr
N.A.I.C.S.: 512250

EMI Music Publishing Denmark A/S (3)
Bjorns Tradgardsgrand 1, SE 116-21, Stockholm, Sweden
Tel.: (46) 8 441 19 60
Web Site: http://www.sonyatv.com
Emp.: 19
Music Publisher & Distr
N.A.I.C.S.: 512250
Patrik Sventelius (Mng Dir)

EMI Music Publishing Hong Kong (3)
Unit 207 Prosterhui Millenni Plz, 6-8 Harbour Road, North Point, China (Hong Kong)
Tel.: (852) 29565400
Web Site: http://www.sonyatv.com
Sales Range: $25-49.9 Million
Emp.: 13
Music Publisher & Distr
N.A.I.C.S.: 512250

EMI Music Publishing Italia SRL (3)
Via Moremendo 2 27, 20149, Milan, Italy
Tel.: (39) 0248010216
Sales Range: $25-49.9 Million
Emp.: 23
Music Publisher & Distr
N.A.I.C.S.: 512250

EMI Music Publishing Ltd. (3)
30 Golden Sq, London, W1F 9LD, United Kingdom
Tel.: (44) 2030593059
Music Publisher & Distr
N.A.I.C.S.: 512230

EMI Music Publishing Malaysia SDN BHD (3)
Suite 21 7 The Boulevard Lingakaran Syed Putra, Mid Valley City, 59200, Kuala Lumpur, Malaysia
Tel.: (60) 22016888
Music Publishing & Distr
N.A.I.C.S.: 512250

EMI Music Publishing Mexico (3)
Blvd Manuel Avila Camacho 76 Piso 5, Col Lomas de Chapultepec Miguel Hidalgo, Mexico, 11000, Mexico
Tel.: (52) 5555407930
Sales Range: $10-24.9 Million
Emp.: 25
Music Publishing & Distr
N.A.I.C.S.: 512230

EMI Music Publishing Portugal (3)
Praca Nuno Rodriguez dos Santos, Urban Das Laranjeiras 7, 1600 171, Lisbon, Portugal
Tel.: (351) 217217400
Sales Range: $10-24.9 Million
Emp.: 5
Music Publisher & Distributor
N.A.I.C.S.: 512250

EMI Music Publishing Scandinavia AB (3)
Sveavagen 24 26, 103 63, Stockholm, Sweden
Tel.: (46) 858795500
Sales Range: $10-24.9 Million
Emp.: 14
Music Publisher & Distr
N.A.I.C.S.: 512250
Johnny Tennander (Mng Dir)

EMI Music Publishing Spain (3)
Calle Gran Via 39 7a Planta, Madrid, 28013, Spain
Tel.: (34) 915239940
Sales Range: $10-24.9 Million
Emp.: 20
Music Publisher & Distr
N.A.I.C.S.: 512250
Juan Ignacio (Mng Dir)

Holding (US):

GlobalFoundries Inc. (2)
400 Stonebreak Rd Ext, Malta, NY 12020 (88.28%)
Tel.: (518) 305-9013
Web Site: https://www.gf.com
Rev.: $7,392,000,000
Assets: $18,044,000,000
Liabilities: $6,940,000,000
Net Worth: $11,104,000,000
Earnings: $1,018,000,000
Emp.: 13,000
Fiscal Year-end: 12/31/2023
Holding Company; Semiconductor Mfr & Distr; Owned 65.8% by Mubadala Development Company PJSC & 34.2% by Advanced Micro Devices, Inc.
N.A.I.C.S.: 551112
Gregg Bartlett (CTO)

Subsidiary (Non-US):

GlobalFoundries Engineering Private Limited (3)
9th Floor Block N1 Balsa Manyata Embassy Business Park, Nagawara Outer Ring Road, Bengaluru, 560045, India
Tel.: (91) 8067182300
Semiconductor Mfr
N.A.I.C.S.: 334413

GlobalFoundries Europe Sales & Support GmbH (3)
Sankt Martin Str 64, 81541, Munich, Germany
Tel.: (49) 899607910
Semiconductor Mfr
N.A.I.C.S.: 334413

GlobalFoundries Management Services LLC & Co. KG (3)
Wilschdorfer Landstrasse 101, 01109, Dresden, Germany
Tel.: (49) 3512770
Semiconductor Mfr
N.A.I.C.S.: 334413

GlobalFoundries Singapore Pte. Ltd. (3)
60 Woodlands Industrial Park D Street 2, Singapore, 738406, Singapore
Tel.: (65) 63622838
Web Site: https://gf.com
Sales Range: $1-4.9 Billion
Emp.: 6,004
Semiconductor Mfr & Distr
N.A.I.C.S.: 334413

Subsidiary (Non-US):

GlobalFoundries Europe Ltd. (4)
Surrey Technology Centre 40 Occam Road, Surrey Research Park, Guildford, GU2 7YG, Surrey, United Kingdom
Tel.: (44) 1483888494
Web Site: http://www.globalfoundries.com
Sales Range: $50-74.9 Million
Emp.: 2
Semiconductor Distr
N.A.I.C.S.: 423690

GlobalFoundries Japan K.K. (4)
Yokohama Landmark Tower 38F 2-2-1 Minatomirai, Nishi-ku, Yokohama, 220-8138, Kanagawa, Japan
Tel.: (81) 452100701
Web Site: http://www.globalfoundries.com
Sales Range: $25-49.9 Million
Emp.: 100
Semiconductor Distr
N.A.I.C.S.: 423690
Shigeru Shimauchi (Country Mgr)

GlobalFoundries Taiwan Ltd. (4)
15F-1 No 289 Kuang Fu Road Section 2, Hsin-chu, 30071, ROC, Taiwan
Tel.: (886) 35163366
Web Site: http://www.globalfoundries.com
Sales Range: $25-49.9 Million
Emp.: 14
Semiconductor Distr
N.A.I.C.S.: 423690

Subsidiary (Non-US):

GlobalFoundries Technologies LLC (3)
HQ Building 13th Floor Highway E10 Channel St, PO Box 62755, Abu Dhabi, United Arab Emirates
Tel.: (971) 24963900
Semiconductor Equipment Distr
N.A.I.C.S.: 423690

Subsidiary (Domestic):

GlobalFoundries U.S. Inc. (3)
400 Stonebreak Rd Ext, Malta, NY 12020
Tel.: (518) 305-9013
Semiconductor Mfr & Distr
N.A.I.C.S.: 334413

Subsidiary (Domestic):

GlobalFoundries U.S. 2 LLC (4)
1000 River St, Essex Junction, VT 05452
Tel.: (802) 769-0111
Semiconductor Mfr
N.A.I.C.S.: 334413

Subsidiary (Domestic):

Injazat Data Systems (2)
Mohammed Bin Zayed City, PO Box 8230, Abu Dhabi, United Arab Emirates (100%)
Tel.: (971) 26992700
Web Site: http://www.injazat.com
Sales Range: $125-149.9 Million
Emp.: 500
IT & Business Process Server; Owned by Mubadala Development Company & Electronic Data Systems
N.A.I.C.S.: 561499
Khaled Al Melhi (CEO)

MUBADALA INVESTMENT COMPANY PJSC

Mubadala Investment Company PJSC—(Continued)

Liwa Energy Limited LLC (2)
Al Mubadala Building New Airport Road,
Abu Dhabi, United Arab Emirates
Tel.: (971) 24132222
Investment Management Service
N.A.I.C.S.: 523940

Subsidiary (Non-US):

Mubadala Petroleum (SE Asia) Limited (2)
1 Raffles Place 11-61 One Raffles Place
Tower 2, 048616, Singapore, Singapore
Tel.: (65) 6 236 2940
Oil & Gas Exploration Services
N.A.I.C.S.: 213112

Subsidiary (Domestic):

Mubadala Petroleum LLC (2)
Sowwah Square Al Maryah Island Al
Maqam Tower 27 28 & 29 Floor, PO Box
4887, Abu Dhabi, United Arab Emirates
Tel.: (971) 2 818 6000
Web Site:
http://www.mubadalapetroleum.com
Oil & Gas Exploration Services
N.A.I.C.S.: 213112
Maurizio La Noce (CEO)

Subsidiary (Non-US):

Sanad Aero Solutions GmbH (2)
Zurich Aiport, 8058, Zurich, Switzerland
Tel.: (41) 58 688 57 65
Web Site: http://www.sanad.ae
Aviation Equipment & Machinery Mfr
N.A.I.C.S.: 336412
Troy Lamberth (CEO)

Holding (Domestic):

Strata Manufacturing PJSC (2)
PO Box 86519, Al Ain, United Arab Emirates
Tel.: (971) 3 7071300
Web Site: http://www.strata.ae
Aircraft Machinery Mfr
N.A.I.C.S.: 336411
Ismail Abdulla (CEO)

Tawam Molecular Imaging Centre LLC (2)
PO Box 220323, Al Ain, Abu Dhabi, United Arab Emirates
Tel.: (971) 3 704 1777
Web Site: http://www.tmic.ae
Health Care Srvices
N.A.I.C.S.: 621999
Muhammad Ali Chaudhry (Mng Dir)

Nireus S.A. (1)
1st Klm Koropiou, Koropi, 19400, Greece
Tel.: (30) 2106624280
Web Site: http://www.nireus.gr
Sales Range: $100-124.9 Million
Emp.: 1,000
Fish Farming Services
N.A.I.C.S.: 112511
Aristeidis Belles (Co-Founder & Chm)

Subsidiary (Non-US):

ILKNAK SU URUNLERI SAN Ve TIC A.S. (2)
Cahar Dudayev Bul 6518 Sok Urganclar
Site No 44 A Block K 2 D 5, Karsiyaka,
35590, Izmir, Turkiye
Tel.: (90) 2323304086
Web Site: http://www.ilknak.com
Fish Farming Services
N.A.I.C.S.: 112511
Orhan Uncel (Chm)

Subsidiary (Domestic):

KEGO AGRI S.A (2)
10 klm Nea Artaki-Psahna Road, Evia, Nea
Artaki, Greece
Tel.: (30) 2221042032
Web Site: http://www.kegoagri.gr
Fish Farming Services
N.A.I.C.S.: 112511
Aristeides Belles (Chm & CEO)

Truist Insurance Holdings, Inc. (1)
301 College St Ste 208, Asheville, NC 28801
Tel.: (828) 225-2044
Web Site: http://www.truistinsurance.com
Holding Company
N.A.I.C.S.: 551112
Wes Dasher (Pres)

Subsidiary (Domestic):

8121 Insurance Management, Inc. (2)
2201 Cantu Ct Ste 102, Sarasota, FL 34232
Tel.: (941) 377-4842
Sales Range: $1-9.9 Million
Emp.: 10
Direct Property & Casualty Insurance Carriers
N.A.I.C.S.: 524126
Alex Hahn (CEO)

BB&T Insurance Services, Inc. (2)
4309 Emperor Blvd Ste 300, Durham, NC 27703
Tel.: (919) 281-4500
Sales Range: $75-99.9 Million
Insurance Services
N.A.I.C.S.: 524210
Wes Dasher (Pres-Insurance-Mid,Atlantic Reg)

Subsidiary (Domestic):

AmRisc, LP (3)
20405 State Hwy Ste 430, Houston, TX 77070
Tel.: (281) 257-6700
Web Site: http://www.amrisc.com
Underwriting Services
N.A.I.C.S.: 561499

Unit (Domestic):

BB&T - J. Rolfe Davis Insurance (3)
850 Concourse Pkwy S Ste 200, Maitland, FL 32751-6145
Tel.: (407) 691-9600
Web Site: http://insurance.bbt.com
Sales Range: $1-9.9 Million
Emp.: 45
Insurance Agents
N.A.I.C.S.: 524210

BB&T - J.V. Arthur (3)
112 N Loudoun St, Winchester, VA 22601-3310
Tel.: (540) 662-3865
Web Site: http://www.insurance.bbt.com
Sales Range: $1-9.9 Million
Emp.: 40
Insurance Agents
N.A.I.C.S.: 524210

BB&T - John Burnham Insurance Services (3)
750 B St Ste 2400, San Diego, CA 92101-2476
Tel.: (619) 525-2807
Web Site: http://www.insurance.bbt.com
Sales Range: $10-24.9 Million
Emp.: 75
Insurance Agents
N.A.I.C.S.: 524210

BB&T Insurance Services, Inc. - Burkey Risk Services (3)
1661 Sandspur Rd, Maitland, FL 32751
Tel.: (407) 682-1122
Web Site: http://insurance.bbt.com
Sales Range: $1-9.9 Million
Emp.: 9
Insurance Agents
N.A.I.C.S.: 524210

BB&T Insurance Services, Inc. - Frederick Underwriters (3)
5280 Corporate Dr Ste 250A, Frederick, MD 21703-2852
Tel.: (301) 662-1147
Sales Range: $1-9.9 Million
Emp.: 60
Insurance Underwriting Services
N.A.I.C.S.: 524298

BB&T Insurance Services, Inc. - TCFC (3)
47 Airpark Ct, Greenville, SC 29607
Tel.: (864) 297-4444
Sales Range: $1-9.9 Million
Emp.: 105
Insurance Agencies & Brokerages
N.A.I.C.S.: 524210

Thomas Parrish (VP)

Subsidiary (Domestic):

Liberty Benefit Insurance Services, Inc. (3)
5446 Thornwood Dr Ste 200, San Jose, CA 95123
Tel.: (408) 360-0300
Sales Range: $25-49.9 Million
Emp.: 48
Insurance Services
N.A.I.C.S.: 524210

Subsidiary (Domestic):

Constellation Affiliated Partners LLC (2)
667 Madison Ave 16th Fl, New York, NY 10065
Tel.: (212) 235-1000
Insurance Services
N.A.I.C.S.: 524298
Bill Goldstein (CEO)

Holding (Domestic):

Coastal Insurance Underwriters, Inc. (3)
816 Hwy A1A Ste 206, Ponte Vedra Beach, FL 32082
Tel.: (904) 285-7683
Web Site: http://www.ciuins.com
Insurance Services
N.A.I.C.S.: 524298
Charles Bushong (Pres & CEO)

Subsidiary (Domestic):

Cybercom International Corp. (4)
232 Canal Blvd, Ponte Vedra Beach, FL 32082-3744
Tel.: (904) 517-5610
Web Site: http://www.cybercom-intl.com
Business to Business Electronic Markets
N.A.I.C.S.: 425120
Erez Wolf (Owner)

Subsidiary (Domestic):

Kensington Vanguard National Land Services, LLC (2)
39 W 37th St 3rd Fl, New York, NY 10018
Tel.: (212) 532-8686
Web Site: http://www.kvnational.com
Insurance Agencies
N.A.I.C.S.: 524210
Brian M. Cooper (Co-CEO)

Subsidiary (Domestic):

GRS Title Services, LLC (3)
901 E Byrd St Suite 1100, Richmond, VA 23219
Tel.: (804) 486-9465
Web Site: http://www.grs-global.com
Insurance Services
N.A.I.C.S.: 524127
Stephen W. Francis (Dir)

Subsidiary (Domestic):

Wellington Insurance Group, Inc. (2)
6801 Calmont Ave, Fort Worth, TX 76116
Tel.: (817) 732-2111
Web Site:
http://www.wellingtoninsgroup.com
Holding Company
N.A.I.C.S.: 551112
Paul R. Poston (Pres & CEO)

MUBARAK TEXTILE MILLS LIMITED
20-KM Off Ferozepur Road, Lahore, Pakistan
Tel.: (92) 4235950674
Web Site: https://www.mtmpk.com
Year Founded: 1991
MUBT—(PSX)
Rev.: $30,885
Assets: $985,238
Liabilities: $190,281
Net Worth: $794,957
Earnings: $(5,447)
Emp.: 8
Fiscal Year-end: 06/30/23
Textile Mill Operator
N.A.I.C.S.: 313110

INTERNATIONAL PUBLIC

Zulfiqar Ali (CEO)

MUDA HOLDINGS BERHAD
Lot 7 Jalan 51A/241, 46100, Petaling Jaya, Selangor Darul Ehsan, Malaysia
Tel.: (60) 378759549   MY
Web Site: https://www.muda.com.my
MUDA—(KLS)
Rev.: $352,884,758
Assets: $480,338,348
Liabilities: $191,639,745
Net Worth: $288,698,603
Earnings: $24,106,005
Fiscal Year-end: 12/31/20
Paper Mills
N.A.I.C.S.: 322120
Chiun Cheong Lim (Mng Dir)

Subsidiaries:

Federal Packages Sdn. Bhd. (1)
391 Jalan Tasek Simpang Ampat, Seberang Perai Selatan, 14120, Penang, Malaysia
Tel.: (60) 45886240
Web Site: https://www.federalpack.com.my
Sales Range: $150-199.9 Million
Emp.: 400
Corrugated Boards & Paper Bags Mfr
N.A.I.C.S.: 322211

Intrapac (Australia) Pty. Ltd. (1)
Unit 12 5 Meridian Place, Baulkham Hills, 2153, NSW, Australia
Tel.: (61) 288829120
Web Site: https://www.intrapac.com
Paper Products Mfr
N.A.I.C.S.: 322110

Intrapac (Singapore) Pte. Ltd. (1)
14 Arumugam Road 08-01 LTC Building C,
Singapore, 409959, Singapore   (70%)
Tel.: (65) 63831132
Web Site: http://www.muda.com.my
Sales Range: $25-49.9 Million
Emp.: 25
Paper Products Trade Whslr
N.A.I.C.S.: 425120

Affiliate (Domestic):

Ee Sin Paper Products Pte. Ltd. (2)
14 Arumugam Road 08-01 LTC Building C,
Singapore, 409959, Singapore   (42%)
Tel.: (65) 62887787
Web Site: https://www.espp.com.sg
Stationery & Textbooks Whslr
N.A.I.C.S.: 424120
Sih Eng Chu (Sec)

Intrapac Trading (M) Sdn. Bhd. (1)
1 1/2 Miles Off Jalan Sungai Chua, 43000, Kajang, Selangor, Malaysia
Tel.: (60) 387322626
Web Site: http://www.muda.com.my
Sales Range: $25-49.9 Million
Emp.: 35
Cartons & Paper Bags Distr
N.A.I.C.S.: 424130

MC Pack (Malaysia) Sdn. Bhd. (1)
No 9 Jalan Persiaran Teknologi Taman Teknologi Johor, 81400, Senai, Johor Darul Takzim, Malaysia
Tel.: (60) 75993688
Web Site: http://www.muda.com
Emp.: 99
Carton Boxes Mfr
N.A.I.C.S.: 322211

Muda Packaging Industries (Qingyuan) Ltd. (1)
Longtang, Qingyuan, 511540, Guangdong, China
Tel.: (86) 7636816193
Web Site: http://www.muda.com.my
Paper Product Distr
N.A.I.C.S.: 424110

Muda Packaging Industries Sdn. Bhd. (1)
1 1/2 Miles Off Jalan Sungai Chua, 43000, Kajang, Selangor Darul Ehsan, Malaysia
Tel.: (60) 387693000
Packaging Materials Mfr
N.A.I.C.S.: 326140
Phai Cheng Chew (Gen Mgr)

AND PRIVATE COMPANIES

Muda Paper Converting Sdn. Bhd. (1)
789 Jalan Tasek Simpang Ampat, Seberang Prai Selatan, 14120, Penang, Malaysia
Tel.: (60) 45682719
Web Site: https://www.mpmsb.com
Packaging Materials Mfr
N.A.I.C.S.: 322220

Muda Paper Mills Sdn. Bhd. (1)
391 Jalan Tasek Simpang Ampat, Seberang Perai Selatan, 14120, Penang, Malaysia
Tel.: (60) 45887335
Web Site: https://www.mpmsb.com
Paper Products Mfr
N.A.I.C.S.: 322120

Muda Pasifik Sdn. Bhd. (1)
No 9 Persiaran Teknologi Taman Teknologi Johor, 81400, Senai, Johor Darul Takzim, Malaysia
Tel.: (60) 75990233
Emp.: 200
Corrugated Carton & Paper Bags Mfr
N.A.I.C.S.: 322211
Chew Keng Soo *(Gen Mgr)*

Quantum Total Packages Sdn. Bhd. (1)
Lot 10115 PT759 Jalan Perusahaan 1, Kawasan Perusahaan Parit Buntar, 34200, Parit Buntar, Perak, Malaysia
Tel.: (60) 57164896
Web Site: https://qtpsb.com
Printing Material Mfr
N.A.I.C.S.: 323120

MUDAJAYA GROUP BERHAD
PH1 Menara Mudajaya No 12A Jalan PJU 73, Mutiara Damansara, 47810, Petaling Jaya, Selangor Darul Ehsan, Malaysia
Tel.: (60) 378067899
Web Site: https://www.mudajaya.com
MUDAJYA—(KLS)
Rev.: $64,590,899
Assets: $407,590,053
Liabilities: $263,888,889
Net Worth: $143,701,164
Earnings: $5,177,778
Emp.: 500
Fiscal Year-end: 12/31/22
Property Development Services
N.A.I.C.S.: 531311
James Tet Foh Wong *(CEO & Mng Dir)*

Subsidiaries:

Mudajaya Corporation Berhad (1)
No 134 Site Office Mudajaya Jalan Ampang, 50450, Kuala Lumpur, Malaysia
Tel.: (60) 321612903
Sales Range: $25-49.9 Million
Emp.: 50
Civil Engineering Services
N.A.I.C.S.: 541330
Wee Teck Nam *(Exec Dir)*

Subsidiary (Domestic):

MJC City Development Sdn. Bhd. (2)
Bd 108 Batu Kawah New Township Jalan Batu Kawa, 93250, Kuching, Sarawak, Malaysia
Tel.: (60) 82452633
Sales Range: $25-49.9 Million
Emp.: 37
Residential Property Development Services
N.A.I.C.S.: 236116

Mudajaya Land Sdn Bhd (2)
No 2 Jalan Bukit Kota Bukit Damansara, 50480, Kuala Lumpur, Wilayah Persekutuan, Malaysia
Tel.: (60) 362529881
Property Development Services
N.A.I.C.S.: 236116

MUDANJIANG HENGFENG PAPER CO., LTD.
No 11 Hengfeng Road, Yangming District, Mudanjiang, 157013, Heilongjiang, China
Tel.: (86) 4536886668
Web Site: https://www.hengfengpaper.com
Year Founded: 1952
600356—(SHG)
Rev.: $344,815,127
Assets: $429,575,730
Liabilities: $82,664,319
Net Worth: $346,911,412
Earnings: $18,100,410
Emp.: 2,000
Fiscal Year-end: 12/31/22
Cigarette Paper Products Mfr
N.A.I.C.S.: 339999
Xiang Xu *(Chm-Grp)*

MUDIT FINLEASE LIMITED
17 New Rohatak Road Karol Bagh, New Delhi, 110 005, India
Tel.: (91) 11 23527704
Web Site: http://www.muditfinlease.com
Year Founded: 1989
Rev.: $438,782
Assets: $1,956,956
Liabilities: $653,883
Net Worth: $1,303,073
Earnings: $156,426
Emp.: 8
Fiscal Year-end: 03/31/18
Non Banking Financial Services
N.A.I.C.S.: 523999
Pavel Garg *(Exec Dir)*

MUDIX JOINT STOCK COMPANY
6th Khoroo, Bayangol District, Ulaanbaatar, Mongolia
Tel.: (976) 11 369115
MUDX—(MONG)
Sales Range: Less than $1 Million
Building Construction Services
N.A.I.C.S.: 236220

MUDRA FINANCIAL SERVICES LIMITED
3rd Floor Vaastu Darshan B Wing Azad Road Above Central Bank of India, Andheri East, Mumbai, 400 069, India
Tel.: (91) 61919293
Web Site: https://www.mudrafinancial.in
Year Founded: 1994
539819—(BOM)
Rev.: $72,359
Assets: $1,215,168
Liabilities: $14,501
Net Worth: $1,200,667
Earnings: $12,071
Emp.: 4
Fiscal Year-end: 03/31/23
Financial Lending Services
N.A.I.C.S.: 532411
Dipen Maheshwari *(Mng Dir)*

MUDUNURU LIMITED
3rd Floor The Glitz Shriram Panorama Hills NVP College Road, Pandurangapuram, Visakhapatnam, 530 003, Andhra Pradesh, India
Tel.: (91) 9907247247
Web Site: https://www.mudunuru.com
538743—(BOM)
Rev.: $558,672
Assets: $660,337
Liabilities: $407,329
Net Worth: $253,008
Earnings: $10,211
Emp.: 15
Fiscal Year-end: 03/31/21
Software Development Services
N.A.I.C.S.: 541511
P. Uday Bhaskar *(Exec Dir)*

MUEHL PRODUCT & SERVICE AG
Bahnhofstr 15, Weimar, 99448, Germany
Tel.: (49) 36450 33215
Web Site: http://www.muehl.de
MPS—(DEU)
Sales Range: Less than $1 Million
Construction Materials Distr
N.A.I.C.S.: 423320

MUEHLBAUER HOLDING AG
Tel.: (49) 94619520
MUB—(MUN)
Rev.: $512,648,267
Assets: $685,514,309
Liabilities: $403,828,762
Net Worth: $281,685,547
Earnings: $53,438,347
Emp.: 4,194
Fiscal Year-end: 12/31/23
Industrial Machinery Mfr
N.A.I.C.S.: 333248
Josef Muehlbauer *(Founder, Chm-Mgmt Bd & Co-CEO)*

MUEHLHAN AG
Schlinckstrasse 3, 21107, Hamburg, Germany
Tel.: (49) 40752710
Web Site: https://www.muehlhan.com
Year Founded: 1881
M4N—(DEU)
Rev.: $328,688,078
Assets: $198,478,671
Liabilities: $113,528,680
Net Worth: $84,949,991
Earnings: $374,613
Emp.: 2,790
Fiscal Year-end: 12/31/20
Ship Building & Repairing Services
N.A.I.C.S.: 336611
Stefan Muller-Arends *(Chm & CEO)*

Subsidiaries:

Certified Coatings Company (1)
2320 Cordelia Rd, Fairfield, CA 94534
Tel.: (707) 639-4414
Ship Building & Repairing Services
N.A.I.C.S.: 336611
David Brockman *(Mng Dir)*

Muehlhan A/S (1)
Vejlevej 270, 7323, Give, Denmark
Tel.: (45) 6 447 1313
Web Site: http://www.muehlhan.dk
Ship Building & Repairing Services
N.A.I.C.S.: 336611
Jens Moerk *(CEO)*

Subsidiary (Domestic):

Muehlhan Wind Service A/S (2)
Navervej 10, 7000, Fredericia, Denmark
Tel.: (45) 73706323
Ship Building & Repairing Services
N.A.I.C.S.: 336611

Muehlhan B.V. (1)
James Wattweg 26, 3133 KK, Vlaardingen, Netherlands
Tel.: (31) 104264960
Ship Building & Repairing Services
N.A.I.C.S.: 336611
Philippe Pfeiffer *(Mng Dir)*

Muehlhan Bulgaria Ltd. (1)
Petko Staynov 5, Varna, 9009, Bulgaria
Tel.: (359) 52600373
Ship Building & Repairing Services
N.A.I.C.S.: 336611
Krasimir Kolev *(Mng Dir)*

Muehlhan Canada Inc. (1)
1969 Upper Water Street Suite 1300 Purdys Wharf Tower II, Halifax, B3J 3R7, NS, Canada
Tel.: (403) 589-7838
Ship Building & Repairing Services
N.A.I.C.S.: 336611
Vandad Pachai *(Mgr-Sls)*

Muehlhan Cyprus Limited (1)
Christou Kelly str John Kennedy 51 Residence 51 Ap A501 Neapolis, 3106, Limassol, Cyprus
Tel.: (357) 25222826
Ship Building & Repairing Services
N.A.I.C.S.: 336611

Muehlhan Dehan Qatar W.L.L. (1)
Office 704B 7th Floor Zone 14 St 214 Building 18 Fereej Abdul Aziz, Doha, Qatar
Tel.: (974) 44373412
Ship Building & Repairing Services
N.A.I.C.S.: 336611
Gautam Arya *(Mng Dir)*

Muehlhan Deutschland GmbH (1)
Zur Westpier 40, 28755, Bremen, Germany
Tel.: (49) 421 693 2683
Web Site: http://www.muehlhan-deutschland.de
Ship Building & Repairing Services
N.A.I.C.S.: 336611
Rene Pourrier *(Mng Dir)*

Subsidiary (Domestic):

Beschichtungswerk Wyhlen GmbH (2)
Degussaweg 1, 79639, Grenzach-Wyhlen, Germany
Tel.: (49) 76244017
Ship Building & Repairing Services
N.A.I.C.S.: 336611
Dieter Niehues *(Mng Dir)*

Muehlhan Ellas S.A. (1)
Istanbul Turkiye Subesi Buyukdere Cad Spring Giz Plaza Kat 13 aslak, 34398, Istanbul, Turkiye
Tel.: (90) 2123665706
Ship Building & Repairing Services
N.A.I.C.S.: 336611

Muehlhan Hellas S.A. (1)
12 Palaska Street Skaramanga, Haidari, 12462, Athens, Greece
Tel.: (30) 2105576994
Ship Building & Repairing Services
N.A.I.C.S.: 336611
Theodosius Nalbantudis *(Mng Dir)*

Muehlhan Industrial Services Ltd. (1)
Muehlhan Services Center Souter Head Road Altens Industrial Estate, Aberdeen, AB12 3LF, United Kingdom
Tel.: (44) 1224875952
Ship Building & Repairing Services
N.A.I.C.S.: 336611
Jim West *(Mng Dir)*

Muehlhan Morflot OOO (1)
st Gapsalskaya 5 lit Ah pom 10-N, 198035, Saint Petersburg, Russia
Tel.: (7) 8123357533
Web Site: https://www.muehlhan.ru
Ship Building & Repairing Services
N.A.I.C.S.: 336611

Muehlhan Polska Sp. z o.o. (1)
ul Bronowicka 27, 71-012, Szczecin, Poland
Tel.: (48) 918140900
Ship Building & Repairing Services
N.A.I.C.S.: 336611
Zbigniew Skrzydlowski *(Chm)*

Muehlhan S.A.R.L. (1)
71 Rue Henri Gautier, Montoir de Bretagne, 44550, Saint-Nazaire, France
Tel.: (33) 240226553
Ship Building & Repairing Services
N.A.I.C.S.: 336611
Christian Guienne *(Mng Dir)*

Ruwad Al Athaiba International LLC (1)
Unit 82 Super Plaza Building No 340 Way 4805 Azaiba North, Muscat, Oman
Tel.: (968) 24138303
Ship Building & Repairing Services
N.A.I.C.S.: 336611

MUELLES DE PENCO S.A.
Av Santa Maria 5888, Vitacura, Santiago, Chile
Tel.: (56) 2320804
Web Site: http://www.muellesdepenco.cl
MUELLES—(SGO)

MUELLES DE PENCO S.A.

MUELLES DE PENCO S.A.—(Continued)
Sales Range: Less than $1 Million
Ferry Service Providers
N.A.I.C.S.: 484122

MUENCHENER TIERPARK HELLABRUNN AG
Tierparkstr 30, 81543, Munich, Germany
Tel.: (49) 89625080
Web Site: https://www.hellabrunn.de
Year Founded: 1911
Recreational Facility & Services
N.A.I.C.S.: 713990
Rasem Baban *(Member-Mgmt Bd)*

MUFIN GREEN FINANCE LIMITED
202 2nd Floor Best Sky Tower Netaji Subhash Place, Pitampura, New Delhi, 110034, India
Tel.: (91) 1143094300
Web Site:
https://www.apmfinvest.com
Year Founded: 2016
542774—(BOM)
Rev.: $2,085,474
Assets: $14,045,181
Liabilities: $175,689
Net Worth: $13,869,492
Earnings: $1,485,379
Emp.: 3
Fiscal Year-end: 03/31/22
Banking Financial Services
N.A.I.C.S.: 522299
Tribhuwan Nath Chaturvedi *(Chm)*

MUGEN ESTATE CO., LTD.
1-9-7 Otemachi Chiyoda-ku, Tokyo, 100-0004, Japan
Tel.: (81) 366650581
Web Site: http://www.mugen-estate.co.jp
3299—(TKS)
Rev.: $366,127,600
Assets: $569,766,580
Liabilities: $372,352,620
Net Worth: $197,413,960
Earnings: $25,899,770
Emp.: 363
Fiscal Year-end: 12/31/23
Real Estate Services
N.A.I.C.S.: 531390
Shinichi Fujita *(Pres)*

Subsidiaries:

FUJI HOME Co., Ltd. (1)
1-9-7 Otemachi Financial City South Tower 16th Floor, Otemachi Chiyoda-ku, Tokyo, 100-0004, Japan
Tel.: (81) 366650940
Web Site: http://www.fuji-home.co.jp
Real Estate Manangement Services
N.A.I.C.S.: 531210
Keiji Shoda *(Pres)*

Mugen Funding Co., Ltd. (1)
Otemachi Financial City South Tower 16th Floor 1-9-7 Otemachi, Chiyoda-ku, Tokyo, 100-0004, Japan
Tel.: (81) 366650621
Brokerage Business Services
N.A.I.C.S.: 523150
Hiroaki Sato *(Pres)*

Mugen Investment Advisors Co., Ltd. (1)
3-19-3 Nihonbashi-Hamacho, Chuo-ku, Tokyo, 103-0007, Japan
Tel.: (81) 356237466
Brokerage Business Services
N.A.I.C.S.: 523150
Shinichi Fujita *(Pres)*

MUGHAL IRON & STEEL INDUSTRIES LTD.
31-A Shadman 1, Lahore, Pakistan
Tel.: (92) 4235960841
Web Site:
https://www.mughalsteel.com
Year Founded: 1950
MUGHAL—(PSX)
Rev.: $242,436,412
Assets: $215,245,817
Liabilities: $123,968,376
Net Worth: $91,277,441
Earnings: $12,521,058
Emp.: 2,250
Fiscal Year-end: 06/30/23
Metal Products Mfr
N.A.I.C.S.: 332999
Khurram Javaid *(CEO)*

MUHAK CO., LTD.
6 Bongam Industrial Complex 2-gil, Masanhoewon-gu, Changwon, 51341, Gyeongnam, Korea (South)
Tel.: (82) 15882226
Web Site: https://www.muhak.co.kr
Year Founded: 1929
033920—(KRS)
Rev.: $117,222,485
Assets: $464,602,423
Liabilities: $96,012,216
Net Worth: $368,590,207
Earnings: ($10,126,159)
Emp.: 391
Fiscal Year-end: 12/31/22
Wine & Liquor Producer
N.A.I.C.S.: 312130
Choi Jae-Ho *(Chm)*

MUHAN INVESTMENT CO., LTD.
3F Daehyun Blue Tower 1338-11, Seocho-gu, Seoul, 137-860, Korea (South)
Tel.: (82) 25594500
Web Site: http://www.muhanic.com
Year Founded: 1996
Sales Range: $1-9.9 Million
Investment Services
N.A.I.C.S.: 523999
Dong Myung Park *(CEO)*

MUHIBBAH ENGINEERING (M) BHD.
Lot 586 & 579 2nd Mile Jalan Batu Tiga Lama, 41300, Klang, Selangor Darul Ehsan, Malaysia
Tel.: (60) 333424323
Web Site: https://www.muhibbah.com
Year Founded: 1972
5703—(KLS)
Rev.: $248,408,325
Assets: $835,120,688
Liabilities: $423,526,950
Net Worth: $411,593,738
Earnings: $618,503
Emp.: 1,243
Fiscal Year-end: 12/31/21
Investment Holdings; Civil, Marine & Structural Engineering Contract Works
N.A.I.C.S.: 551112
Ngan Boon Mac *(Mng Dir)*

Subsidiaries:

Ann Bee (M) Sdn. Bhd. (1)
Lot 7 Solok Sultan Hishamuddin Lima Kawasan Perusahaan, Selat Klang Utara, 42000, Port Klang, Selangor, Malaysia
Tel.: (60) 331761795
Sales Range: $25-49.9 Million
Emp.: 100
Aluminum Foils & Carbonless Papers Mfr
N.A.I.C.S.: 332999
Ngan Boon Mac *(Mng Dir)*

Citech Energy Recovery System Malaysia Sdn. Bhd. (1)
Lot 586 579 2nd Mile Jalan Batu Tiga Lama, 41300, Klang, Selangor Darul Ehsan, Malaysia
Tel.: (60) 33 342 4323
Web Site: https://www.citech.co.uk
Oil & Gas Equipment Mfr
N.A.I.C.S.: 333132
Pang Sheh Haur *(Gen Mgr)*

Subsidiary (Non-US):

Citech Energy Recovery Solutions UK Ltd. (2)
Salisbury House Saxon Way Priory Park West, Hessle, HU13 9PB, East Yorkshire, United Kingdom
Tel.: (44) 1482719746
Oil & Gas Equipment Mfr
N.A.I.C.S.: 333132
Ashleigh Ogden *(Gen Mgr)*

Exact Analytical Sdn. Bhd. (1)
29B Jalan Kenari 17E Bandar Puchong Jaya, Bandar Puchong Jaya, 47100, Puchong, Selangor, Malaysia
Tel.: (60) 380765531
Web Site:
https://www.exactanalytical.com.my
Engineering & Construction Services
N.A.I.C.S.: 541330

Exact Automation Sdn. Bhd. (1)
No 173 Jalan Kenari 23A, Bandar Puchong Jaya, 47100, Puchong, Selangor, Malaysia
Tel.: (60) 380765693
Web Site:
https://www.exactautomation.com.my
Industrial Machinery & Equipment Whslr
N.A.I.C.S.: 423830
Ahmad Aiman Zorkepli *(Project Mgr)*

Exact Oil & Gas Sdn. Bhd. (1)
29-A Jalan Kenari 17E, Bandar Puchong Jaya, 47100, Puchong, Selangor, Malaysia
Tel.: (60) 38 076 5778
Web Site: https://www.exactoilgas.com
Oil & Gas Equipment Mfr
N.A.I.C.S.: 333132
Nurul Hilaliah Yussof *(Mgr-Sls)*

FES Equipment Services Sdn. Bhd. (1)
Lot 9895 Jalan Kampung Jawa Section 35 Bandar Shah Alam, 40460, Shah Alam, Selangor, Malaysia
Tel.: (60) 333737835
Industrial Crane Equipment Mfr
N.A.I.C.S.: 333132

Favelle Favco Berhad (1)
Lot 586 Jalan Batu Tiga Lama, 41300, Klang, Selangor, Malaysia (100%)
Tel.: (60) 333495465
Web Site: https://www.favellefavco.com
Rev.: $125,877,884
Assets: $289,709,630
Liabilities: $134,605,503
Net Worth: $155,104,127
Earnings: $9,009,101
Emp.: 439
Fiscal Year-end: 12/31/2022
Holding Company; Crane Designer & Mfr
N.A.I.C.S.: 551112
Ngan Boon Mac *(Exec Dir)*

Subsidiary (US):

Favelle Favco Cranes (USA) Inc. (2)
26360 FM 106 Port of Harlingen, Harlingen, TX 78550
Tel.: (956) 428-7488
Web Site: https://www.favellefavco.com
Sales Range: $25-49.9 Million
Cranes Distr
N.A.I.C.S.: 423810

Subsidiary (Non-US):

Favelle Favco Cranes Pte. Ltd. (2)
50 Tagore Lane 03-10E, Mandai Industrial Building, Singapore, 787494, Singapore
Tel.: (65) 63663508
Sales Range: $50-74.9 Million
Offshore Crane Rental Services
N.A.I.C.S.: 532412

Favelle Favco Cranes Pty. Ltd. (2)
No 28 Yarrunga Street, Prestons, Sydney, 2170, NSW, Australia
Tel.: (61) 296082000
Sales Range: $25-49.9 Million
Cranes Distr
N.A.I.C.S.: 423810

Subsidiary (Domestic):

Favelle Favco Equipment Services Sdn. Bhd. (2)

INTERNATIONAL PUBLIC

Lot 9895 Jalan Kampung Jawa Section 35 Bandar Shah Alam, 40460, Shah Alam, Selangor, Malaysia
Tel.: (60) 333737835
Web Site: http://www.favellefavco.com
Crane Rental Services
N.A.I.C.S.: 238990

Subsidiary (Non-US):

Favelle Favco Machinery & Equipment L.L.C. (2)
Level 01 Yateem Optician Building Khalifa Street, PO Box 47973, Abu Dhabi, United Arab Emirates
Tel.: (971) 2 627 7948
Web Site: https://www.favellefavco.com
Emp.: 8
Cranes Distr
N.A.I.C.S.: 423810

Kroll Cranes A/S (2)
Nordkranvej 2, 3540, Lynge, Denmark
Tel.: (45) 48187400
Web Site: https://www.krollcranes.dk
Sales Range: $25-49.9 Million
Emp.: 55
Crane Mfr
N.A.I.C.S.: 333120
Henrik Nielsen *(Mng Dir)*

Favelle Favco Cranes (M) Sdn. Bhd. (1)
42 Persiaran Bunga Tanjung 2 Senawang Industrial Park, 70400, Seremban, Negeri Sembilan, Malaysia
Tel.: (60) 6 676 8866
Web Site: https://www.favellefavco.com
Sales Range: $200-249.9 Million
Emp.: 800
Cranes Distr
N.A.I.C.S.: 423810

ITS Konsortium Sdn. Bhd. (1)
Suite F07 Block 2320 Century Square, Jalan Usahawan, 63000, Cyberjaya, Selangor, Malaysia
Tel.: (60) 383192773
Sales Range: $25-49.9 Million
Emp.: 20
Investment Holding Services
N.A.I.C.S.: 551112

MEB Construction Sdn. Bhd. (1)
Lot 586 2nd Mile Jalan Batu Tiga Lama, 41300, Klang, Selangor, Malaysia
Tel.: (60) 333424323
Engineering & Construction Services
N.A.I.C.S.: 541330

MEB Fleet Sdn Bhd (1)
Lot Telok Gedong 10426 Jalan Pelabuhan Barat, 42000, Port Klang, Selangor, Malaysia
Tel.: (60) 331652122
Engineeering Services
N.A.I.C.S.: 541330

MEB Marketing Sdn. Bhd. (1)
Lot 586 2nd Mile Jalan Batu Tiga Lama, 41300, Port Klang, Selangor, Malaysia
Tel.: (60) 333424323
Web Site: http://www.muhibbah.com
Engineeering Services
N.A.I.C.S.: 541330

Muhibbah Airline Support Industries Sdn. Bhd. (1)
Lot 586 2nd Mile Jalan Batu Tiga Lama, 41300, Klang, Selangor, Malaysia
Tel.: (60) 333424323
Web Site: https://www.masi.com.my
Aeronautical Equipment Mfr
N.A.I.C.S.: 334511

Muhibbah Construction Pty. Ltd. (1)
Level 5 19 Lang Parade, Milton, 4064, QLD, Australia
Tel.: (61) 733686700
Engineering & Construction Services
N.A.I.C.S.: 541330

Muhibbah Engineering (Cambodia) Co. Ltd. (1)
No 175 Street 339 Sangkat Boeng Kark 1, Khan Toul Kork, Phnom Penh, Cambodia
Tel.: (855) 23367988
Engineering & Construction Services
N.A.I.C.S.: 541330
Khieng Hann *(Mng Dir)*

AND PRIVATE COMPANIES

Muhibbah Engineering (Philippines) Corporation (1)
Engineering & Construction Services
N.A.I.C.S.: 541330
Iris Cuabo *(Officer-HR)*

Muhibbah Engineering (Singapore) Pte. Ltd. (1)
30 Mandai Estate 02-05 Mandai Industrial Building, Singapore, 729918, Singapore
Tel.: (65) 63669508
Engineering & Construction Services
N.A.I.C.S.: 541330

Muhibbah Engineering Co (Qatar) (1)
Room 3A 2nd Floor Financial Square Building 2 C-Ring Road, PO Box 37834, Doha, Qatar
Tel.: (974) 4 410 6777
Web Site: http://www.muhibbahengineering.com
Sales Range: $200-249.9 Million
Emp.: 600
Marine Construction Services
N.A.I.C.S.: 237990
Amina Paib *(Mgr-Bus Dev)*

Muhibbah Engineering Middle East LLC
Room 3A 2nd Floor Financial Square Building 2 C-Ring Road, Doha, Qatar
Tel.: (974) 444106777
Engineering & Construction Services
N.A.I.C.S.: 541330

Muhibbah Marine Engineering (Deutschland) GmbH (1)
Uhlengrund 15b, 21244, Buchholz, Germany
Tel.: (49) 41 812 8680
Web Site: https://www.muhibbah.de
Marine Support Services
N.A.I.C.S.: 541330

Muhibbah Marine Engineering Sdn. Bhd. (1)
Lot 923 Teluk Gong Mukim Kelang Selat Lumut, Pelabuhan, 42000, Klang, Selangor, Malaysia
Tel.: (60) 331656666
Web Site: https://www.mmesb.com.my
Sales Range: $50-74.9 Million
Ship Building & Repair Services
N.A.I.C.S.: 336611
K. C. Ooi *(Mng Dir)*

Muhibbah Offshore Services Ltd. (1)
CIMB Trust Limited Level 14A Main Office Tower Financial Park Labuan, Jalan Merdeka, 87000, Labuan, Malaysia
Tel.: (60) 87414252
Marine Engineering Services
N.A.I.C.S.: 541330

Muhibbah Petrochemical Engineering Sdn. Bhd.. (1)
Lot 579 2nd Mile Jalan Batu Tiga Lama, Kelang, 41300, Selangor, Malaysia
Tel.: (60) 333424323
Web Site: http://www.muhibbah.com.my
Sales Range: $25-49.9 Million
Emp.: 20
Construction Services
N.A.I.C.S.: 236116

Muhibbah Reefers Sdn. Bhd. (1)
Lot 579 2nd Mile Jalan Batu Tiga Lama, 41300, Port Klang, Selangor, Malaysia
Tel.: (60) 333424323
Containers Mfr & Distr
N.A.I.C.S.: 332439

Muhibbah Steel Industries Sdn. Bhd. (1)
Lot 923 29256 Telok Gong Mukim Kelang, Selat Lumut, 42000, Port Klang, Selangor, Malaysia
Tel.: (60) 331656266
Web Site: https://muhibbahsi.com.my
Emp.: 400
Steel Structures Fabrication Services
N.A.I.C.S.: 332111
Ngan Boon Mac *(Mng Dir)*

Sedia Teguh Sdn. Bhd. (1)
No 5 Jalan Seri Rejang 1 Taman Sri Rampai, 53300, Kuala Lumpur, Malaysia
Tel.: (60) 341444096

Web Site: https://www.sediateguh.com
Oil & Gas Equipment Mfr
N.A.I.C.S.: 333132
Ruzaini Kamaruz-Zaman *(COO)*

Shanghai Favco Engineering Machinery Manufacturing Co. Ltd. (1)
1 Lijiang Road, Minhang District, Shanghai, 200245, China
Tel.: (86) 2134707221
Engineering & Construction Services
N.A.I.C.S.: 541330

Strata Niaga Sdn. Bhd. (1)
612 Block A Kelana Square No 17 Jalan SS7/26, 47301, Petaling Jaya, Malaysia
Tel.: (60) 378043087
Web Site: https://www.strataniaga.com
Engineeering Services
N.A.I.C.S.: 541330

MUKESH BABU FINANCIAL SERVICES LTD
111 Maker Chambers III 223 Nariman Point, Mumbai, 400021, India
Tel.: (91) 2226232051
Web Site: https://mbfsl.com
Year Founded: 1984
530341—(BOM)
Rev.: $1,379,534
Assets: $34,195,816
Liabilities: $7,604,196
Net Worth: $26,591,619
Earnings: $584,078
Emp.: 6
Fiscal Year-end: 03/31/23
Financial Services
N.A.I.C.S.: 522291
Mukesh C. Babu *(Chm & Mng Dir)*

Subsidiaries:

Mukesh Babu Securities Limited (1)
301/302 Sagar Ave SV Rd Opp Shoppers Stop Andheri W, Mumbai, 400058, India
Tel.: (91) 2222834462
Web Site: http://www.mukeshbabu.com
Emp.: 50
Investment Advisory Services
N.A.I.C.S.: 523940

MUKESH STEELS LIMITED
Gill Road Miller Ganj, Ludhiana, 141003, Punjab, India
Tel.: (91) 161 2510921
Rev.: $321,041
Assets: $3,609,345
Liabilities: $3,764,445
Net Worth: ($155,100)
Earnings: ($1,189,856)
Fiscal Year-end: 03/31/16
Iron & Steel Distr
N.A.I.C.S.: 423510
Krishan Chand Gupta *(Chm & Mng Dir)*

MUKHTAR TEXTILE MILLS LIMITED
P-48 St No 1 Dougluspura, Faisalabad, Pakistan
Tel.: (92) 41 2610018
Web Site: http://www.mukhtartextile.com
Rev.: $34,056
Assets: $421,157
Liabilities: $153,639
Net Worth: $267,518
Earnings: ($1,410)
Emp.: 2
Fiscal Year-end: 06/30/17
Textile Spinning Mill
N.A.I.C.S.: 313110

MUKTA ARTS LTD
3rd Floor Mukta House Behind Whistling Woods Institute, Filmcity Goregaon E, Mumbai, 400065, India
Tel.: (91) 2233649400
Web Site: https://www.muktaarts.com
532357—(NSE)
Rev.: $4,068,764

Assets: $34,293,850
Liabilities: $14,105,911
Net Worth: $20,187,938
Earnings: $961,391
Emp.: 56
Fiscal Year-end: 03/31/21
Movie Production & Distribution
N.A.I.C.S.: 512110
Subhash Ghai *(Chm)*

Subsidiaries:

Whistling Woods International Limited (1)
Filmcity Complex Goregaon East, Mumbai, 400065, Maharashtra, India
Tel.: (91) 8451803852
Web Site: https://www.whistlingwoods.net
Education Services
N.A.I.C.S.: 611710
Subhash Ghai *(Chm)*

MUKTINATH BIKAS BANK LIMITED
Kamaladi Hattisar Sadak Kathamandu Metropolitian City-28, Kathmandu, Nepal
Tel.: (977) 14529837
Web Site: https://www.muktinathbank.com.np
Year Founded: 2007
MNBBL—(NEP)
Rev.: $63,792,834
Assets: $851,894,844
Liabilities: $793,372,505
Net Worth: $58,522,339
Earnings: $10,076,080
Emp.: 1,547
Fiscal Year-end: 07/15/21
Banking Services
N.A.I.C.S.: 522110
Bharat Raj Dhakal *(Chm)*

Subsidiaries:

Muktinath Capital Limited (1)
Narayanchaur, Naxal, Kathmandu, 44600, Nepal
Tel.: (977) 14546108
Web Site: https://www.muktinathcapital.com
Investment Banking Services
N.A.I.C.S.: 523999
Kabindra Dhoj Joshi *(CEO)*

MULANN SA
9 rue Blaise Pascal, 22300, Lannion, France
Tel.: (33) 296141659
Web Site: http://www.mulann.com
MLMUL—(EUR)
Sales Range: $1-9.9 Million
Test Laboratory Product Mfr & Distr
N.A.I.C.S.: 541380
Jean-Luc Renou *(Chm & CEO)*

MULBERRY GROUP PLC
The Rookery Chilcompton, Bath, BA3 4EH, Somerset, United Kingdom
Tel.: (44) 1761234500 UK
Web Site: https://www.mulberry.com
Year Founded: 1971
MUL—(AIM)
Rev.: $194,576,019
Assets: $149,865,800
Liabilities: $136,014,799
Net Worth: $13,851,002
Earnings: ($44,531,989)
Fiscal Year-end: 03/30/24
Clothing & Luxury Fashion Bags For Men & Women Providers
N.A.I.C.S.: 315210
Godfrey Pawle Davis *(Chm)*

Subsidiaries:

Mulberry Company (Sales) Limited (1)
The Rookery, Chilcompton, BA3 4EH, Somerset, United Kingdom
Tel.: (44) 1761234230
Men & Women Clothing Retailer

N.A.I.C.S.: 458110

Mulberry Company (Switzerland) GmbH (1)
Storchengasse 4, 8001, Zurich, Switzerland
Tel.: (41) 434973610
Men & Women Clothing Retailer
N.A.I.C.S.: 458110

MULIANG VIAGOO TECHNOLOGY, INC.
2498 Wanfeng Highway Lane 181, Fengjing Town Jinshan District, Shanghai, 201501, China
Tel.: (86) 2167355092 NV
Year Founded: 2014
MULG—(OTCIQ)
Rev.: $8,656,862
Assets: $22,145,203
Liabilities: $4,865,706
Net Worth: $17,279,497
Earnings: $1,838,281
Emp.: 110
Fiscal Year-end: 12/31/23
Fertilizer Mfr & Distr
N.A.I.C.S.: 325312
Lirong Wang *(Chm, Pres & CEO)*

MULLEN GROUP LTD.
121A-31 Southridge Drive, Okotoks, T1S 2N3, AB, Canada
Tel.: (403) 995-5200 AB
Web Site: https://www.mullen-group.com
MTL—(TSX)
Rev.: $1,155,767,070
Assets: $1,503,539,031
Liabilities: $808,354,957
Net Worth: $695,184,074
Earnings: $56,665,234
Emp.: 7,202
Fiscal Year-end: 12/31/21
Specialized Transportation & Related Services to the Oil & Natural Gas Industry
N.A.I.C.S.: 488510
Murray K. Mullen *(Chm, Pres & CEO)*

Subsidiaries:

APPS Transport Group Inc. (1)
6495 Tomken Road, Mississauga, L5T 2X7, ON, Canada
Tel.: (800) 465-2513
Web Site: https://www.appsexpress.com
Asset-based Full-service Transportation Company
N.A.I.C.S.: 488999
Rob McDonald *(Pres)*

Subsidiary (Domestic):

APPS Cartage Inc. (2)
6495 Tomken Road, Mississauga, L5T 2X7, ON, Canada
Tel.: (905) 451-2720
Web Site: https://www.appsexpress.com
Sales Range: $75-99.9 Million
Emp.: 400
Freight Transportation Services
N.A.I.C.S.: 484110
Brent T. Byers *(VP)*

Argus Carriers Ltd. (1)
3839 Myrtle Street, Burnaby, V5C 4G1, BC, Canada
Tel.: (604) 433-1556
Web Site: http://www.arguscarriers.com
Freight Transportation Services
N.A.I.C.S.: 484110

B & R Eckel's Transport Ltd. (1)
5514B-50 Ave, Bonnyville, T9N 2G8, AB, Canada
Tel.: (780) 826-3889
Web Site: https://www.breckels.com
Sales Range: $50-74.9 Million
Emp.: 310
Oil & Gas Transportation Services
N.A.I.C.S.: 213112
Victor Ringuette *(Pres)*

Canadian Dewatering L.P. (1)
8350 1st Street NW, Edmonton, T6P 1X2,

MULLEN GROUP LTD.

Mullen Group Ltd.—(Continued)
AB, Canada
Tel.: (780) 400-2260
Web Site:
  https://www.canadiandewatering.com
Emp.: 45
Dewatering Contractors
N.A.I.C.S.: 238910

Canadian Hydrovac Ltd. (1)
8000 Buckingham Dr, Sherwood Park, T8H 0X5, AB, Canada
Tel.: (780) 449-0505
Web Site:
  http://www.canadianhydrovac.com
Freight Transportation Services
N.A.I.C.S.: 484110

Cascade Carriers L.P. (1)
6111 Ogdendale Rd SE, Calgary, T2C 2A4, AB, Canada
Tel.: (403) 236-7110
Web Site: http://www.cascadecarriers.com
Sales Range: $25-49.9 Million
Dry Bulk Transportation Services
N.A.I.C.S.: 484230
Kevin James (Sr VP)

Cascade Energy Services L.P. (1)
108 Elbow Drive NE Bay 2, Redcliff, V1J 7C4, AB, Canada
Tel.: (403) 504-1155
Web Site: http://www.cascade-energy.ca
Emp.: 250
Freight Trucking Services
N.A.I.C.S.: 484110
Geoff Derouin (VP & Gen Mgr)

Courtesy Freight Systems Ltd. (1)
230 Main St, Thunder Bay, P7B 6S4, ON, Canada
Tel.: (807) 623-0101
Web Site: http://www.courtesyfreight.com
Freight Transportation Services
N.A.I.C.S.: 488510

E-Can Oilfield Services L.P. (1)
5113 46 St, Box 510, Elk Point, T0A 1A0, AB, Canada
Tel.: (780) 724-4018
Web Site: https://www.e-can-oilfield.com
Sales Range: $75-99.9 Million
Emp.: 200
Oilfield Hauling Services
N.A.I.C.S.: 562998

Formula Powell L.P. (1)
PO Box 1328, Grande Prairie, T8V 4Z1, AB, Canada
Tel.: (780) 814-6045
Web Site: https://formulapowell.com
Sales Range: $50-74.9 Million
Drilling Mud Storage & Distr
N.A.I.C.S.: 424690

Gardewine Group Limited Partnership (1)
60 Eagle Drive, Winnipeg, R2R 1V5, MB, Canada
Tel.: (204) 633-5795
Web Site: https://www.gardewine.com
Emp.: 1,700
Freight Trucking Services
N.A.I.C.S.: 484110

Grimshaw Trucking L.P. (1)
11510 - 151 Street, Edmonton, T5M 3N6, AB, Canada
Tel.: (780) 414-2850
Web Site: https://www.grimshaw-trucking.com
Transportation Services
N.A.I.C.S.: 484110
Tom Hanna (Dir-Equipment-HSE)

Heavy Crude Hauling L.P. (1)
6601-62nd Street, Lloydminster, T9V 3T6, AB, Canada
Tel.: (780) 875-5358
Web Site:
  https://www.heavycrudehauling.com
Sales Range: $25-49.9 Million
Emp.: 100
Fluid Hauling Services
N.A.I.C.S.: 484220
Vicki Steele (VP & Controller)

Hi-Way 9 Express Ltd. (1)
711 Elgin Close, Drumheller, T0J 0Y0, AB, Canada
Tel.: (403) 823-4242
Web Site: http://www.hi-way9.com
Emp.: 450
Freight Transportation Services
N.A.I.C.S.: 484110
Reg Trentham (VP & Gen Mgr)

Inter-Urban Delivery Service, Ltd. (1)
#1-31543 King Road, Abbotsford, V2T 5Z2, BC, Canada
Tel.: (604) 852-8998
Web Site: http://www.inter-urban.com
Trucks & Trailers Operator
N.A.I.C.S.: 484110
Walter McDonald (Pres)

International Warehousing & Distribution Inc. (1)
7347 Kimbel St, Mississauga, L4T 3M6, ON, Canada
Tel.: (905) 673-0020
Web Site: http://www.iwdgroup.com
Container Delivery Services
N.A.I.C.S.: 484110
Steve Cox (Pres)

Jay's Transportation Group Ltd. (1)
100 McDonald Street, PO Box 4560, Regina, S4P 3Y3, SK, Canada
Tel.: (306) 569-9369
Web Site: https://www.jays.ca
Emp.: 400
Freight Trucking Services
N.A.I.C.S.: 484110

Kleysen Group L.P. (1)
2800 Mcgillivray Blvd, PO Box 210, Winnipeg, R3Y 1N3, MB, Canada
Tel.: (204) 488-5360
Web Site: http://www.kleysen.com
Sales Range: $125-149.9 Million
Emp.: 350
Oil Transportation Services
N.A.I.C.S.: 484110
Christiane Devlin (Mgr-HR)

MTL US Corp.
10850 Nesbitt Ave S, Minneapolis, MN 55437
Tel.: (952) 888-0762
Web Site: https://mtlcorp.com
Measuring Equipment Mfr & Distr
N.A.I.C.S.: 334513

Mill Creek Motor Freight L.P. (1)
101 Earl Thompson Road, Ayr, N0B 1E0, ON, Canada
Tel.: (519) 623-6632
Web Site: http://millcreek.on.ca
General Freight Trucking Services
N.A.I.C.S.: 484121
Renate Hargreaves (Gen Mgr)

Monarch Messenger Services Ltd. (1)
4710 78 Avenue SE, Calgary, T2C 2W9, AB, Canada
Tel.: (403) 279-2455
Transportation Services
N.A.I.C.S.: 488999

Mullen Oilfield Services L.P. (1)
600 333 - 11 Avenue S W, Calgary, T2R 1L9, AB, Canada
Tel.: (403) 213-4711
Web Site: https://www.mullenoilfield.com
Sales Range: $25-49.9 Million
Emp.: 150
Drilling Equipments Moving Services
N.A.I.C.S.: 561990
Rick Henning (VP)

Mullen Trucking L.P. (1)
100 80079 Maple Leaf Rd East, PO Box 87, Aldersyde, T0L 0A0, AB, Canada
Tel.: (403) 652-8888
Web Site: http://www.mullentrucking.com
Emp.: 55
Freight Trucking Services
N.A.I.C.S.: 484121
Ed Scherbinski (Pres)

Number 8 Freight Ltd. (1)
43871 Progress Way, Chilliwack, V2R 0E6, BC, Canada
Tel.: (604) 823-6966
Web Site: http://www.number8freight.com
Freight Transportation Services
N.A.I.C.S.: 484110

OK Drilling Services L.P. (1)
5436 Blindman Crescent, Red Deer, T4S 2M4, AB, Canada
Tel.: (403) 343-8860
Web Site: https://www.okdrilling.com
Sales Range: $50-74.9 Million
Emp.: 15
Hole Drilling Services
N.A.I.C.S.: 213112
Joel Blacquiere (VP-Operations)

PE Ben Oilfield Services LP (1)
607-17 Ave, Nisku, T9E 7T2, AB, Canada
Tel.: (780) 955-5000
Web Site: http://www.peben.com
Sales Range: $50-74.9 Million
Emp.: 15
Oil & Gas Transportation, Material Handling & Storage Services
N.A.I.C.S.: 486990

Subsidiary (Domestic):

Pe Ben Industries Company Ltd. (2)
605 17 Avenue, Nisku, T9 EAST 72, AB, Canada
Tel.: (780) 440-4425
Web Site: http://www.peben.com
Sales Range: $50-74.9 Million
Oil Storage & Transport Services
N.A.I.C.S.: 486110

Pacific Coast Express Limited (1)
10299 Grace Rd, Surrey, V3V3V7, BC, Canada (100%)
Tel.: (604) 582-3230
Web Site: http://www.pcx.ca
Motor Freight Services
N.A.I.C.S.: 484122

Payne Transportation L.P. (1)
435 Lucas Ave Group 200 RR 2, PO Box 67, Winnipeg, R3C 2E6, MB, Canada
Tel.: (204) 953-1400
Web Site:
  http://www.paynetransportation.com
Sales Range: $25-49.9 Million
Emp.: 20
Food Transportation Services
N.A.I.C.S.: 488490
Tom Payne (Pres & CEO)

Premay Equipment L.P. (1)
607 - 17th Avenue, Nisku, T9E 7T2, AB, Canada
Tel.: (780) 447-5555
Web Site: https://www.premay.com
Emp.: 150
Warehousing & Freight Trucking Services
N.A.I.C.S.: 484121

Premay Pipeline Hauling L.P. (1)
22703 - 112 Avenue, Edmonton, T5S 2M4, AB, Canada
Tel.: (780) 447-3014
Web Site: https://www.premaypipeline.com
Sales Range: $25-49.9 Million
Freight Trucking Services
N.A.I.C.S.: 484121
Paul Schultz (Sr VP)

RDK Transportation Co. Inc. (1)
2 Cory Lane, Saskatoon, S7K 3J7, SK, Canada
Tel.: (306) 651-6955
Web Site: http://www.rdktransportation.com
Freight Transportation Services
N.A.I.C.S.: 488510

Recon Utility Search L.P. (1)
4724-42 Avenue Highway 13, Box 88, Hardisty, T0B 1V0, AB, Canada
Tel.: (780) 888-2283
Web Site: http://www.reconlp.ca
Hydrovac Excavation Services
N.A.I.C.S.: 238910

Smook Contractors Ltd. (1)
101 Hayes Road, Thompson, R8N 1M3, MB, Canada
Tel.: (204) 677-1560
Web Site: http://www.smook.ca
Heavy Construction Services
N.A.I.C.S.: 237990

Spearing Service L.P. (1)
23 Marion Ave, Box 83, Oxbow, S0C 2B0, SK, Canada
Tel.: (306) 483-2848
Web Site: https://www.spearingservice.com

Sales Range: $25-49.9 Million
Oilfield Trucking Services
N.A.I.C.S.: 484230

TREO Drilling Services L.P. (1)
RR 2, Ponoka, T4J 1R2, AB, Canada
Tel.: (403) 723-8600
Web Site: https://www.treodrilling.com
Sales Range: $200-249.9 Million
Emp.: 400
Geothermal Drilling Services
N.A.I.C.S.: 213111
Rod Schmidt (Pres)

Tenold Transportation Limited Partnership (1)
19470 94th Ave, Surrey, V4N 4E5, BC, Canada
Tel.: (604) 888-7822
Web Site: http://tenold.com
Sales Range: $25-49.9 Million
Truckload Transportation Services
N.A.I.C.S.: 484122
Perry Simpson (VP-Fin & Admin)

Withers L.P. (1)
3602-93 Street County of GP No 1, Grande Prairie, T8W 5A8, AB, Canada
Tel.: (780) 539-5347
Web Site: http://witherslp.com
Sales Range: $25-49.9 Million
Emp.: 50
Oilfield Trucking Services
N.A.I.C.S.: 484121

MULLENLOWE GROUP

C-Space 37-45 City Road, London, EC1Y 1AT, United Kingdom
Tel.: (44) 2075845033
Web Site:
  http://www.mullenlowegroup.com
Marketing/Communications
N.A.I.C.S.: 541613
Kristen Cavallo (CEO-Global)

MULLER & PHIPPS (INDIA) LIMITED

204 Madhava Bldg Bandra Kurla Complex, Bandra East, Mumbai, 400 051, India
Tel.: (91) 2226591191 In.
Web Site: https://www.mulphico.co.in
Year Founded: 1917
501477—(BOM)
Rev.: $500,426
Assets: $580,025
Liabilities: $822,457
Net Worth: ($242,432)
Earnings: $25,454
Fiscal Year-end: 03/31/23
Toilet Preparation Distr
N.A.I.C.S.: 424210
Saloni A. Shah (Sec)

MULLER DIE LILA LOGISTIK AG

Ferdinand-Porsche-Strasse 4, 74354, Besigheim, Germany
Tel.: (49) 71438100
Web Site: https://www.lila-logistik.com
MLL—(DEU)
Rev.: $287,028,277
Assets: $229,240,683
Liabilities: $188,342,299
Net Worth: $40,898,384
Earnings: $1,975,927
Emp.: 2,307
Fiscal Year-end: 12/31/23
General Freight Trucking Long-Distance Less Than Truckload
N.A.I.C.S.: 484121
Peter Klaus (Chm-Supervisory Bd)

Subsidiaries:

Muller - Die lila Logistik Boblingen GmbH (1)
Eugen-Zeyher-Strasse 1, Althengstett, 75382, Calw, Germany
Tel.: (49) 714381046101
Logistics Consulting Servies

AND PRIVATE COMPANIES

Muller - Die lila Logistik Ceska k.s. (1)
Prumyslova 290, 346 01, Horsovsky Tyn, Czech Republic
Tel.: (420) 373738112
Logistics Consulting Servies
N.A.I.C.S.: 541614

Muller - Die lila Logistik Fulfillment Solutions GmbH & Co. KG (1)
Am Buchberg 8, 74572, Blaubeuren, Germany
Tel.: (49) 79538830
Logistic Services
N.A.I.C.S.: 541614

Muller - Die lila Logistik Marbach GmbH & Co. KG (1)
Daimlerstrasse 1, 71563, Affalterbach, Germany
Tel.: (49) 71438100
Logistics Consulting Servies
N.A.I.C.S.: 541614

Muller - Die lila Logistik Mittlerer Neckar GmbH (1)
Murrer Str 1, 71691, Freiberg am Neckar, Germany
Tel.: (49) 71438100
Logistics Consulting Servies
N.A.I.C.S.: 541614

Muller - Die lila Logistik Nord GmbH & Co. KG (1)
Junkersstrasse 47 - 59, Ennigloh, 32257, Bunde, Germany
Tel.: (49) 714381046090
Logistics Consulting Servies
N.A.I.C.S.: 541614

Muller - Die lila Logistik Ost GmbH & Co. KG (1)
Sachtlebenstrasse 1, 41541, Dormagen, Germany
Tel.: (49) 714381046416
Logistics Consulting Servies
N.A.I.C.S.: 541614

Muller - Die lila Logistik Polska Sp. z o.o. (1)
Ul Zygmuntowska 90, 44-113, Gliwice, Poland
Tel.: (48) 323319800
Web Site: https://www.lila-logistik.com
Logistics Consulting Servies
N.A.I.C.S.: 541614

Muller - Die lila Logistik Route GmbH (1)
Ferdinand-Porsche-Str 4, Ottmarsheim, 74354, Besigheim, Germany
Tel.: (49) 71438100
Logistics Consulting Servies
N.A.I.C.S.: 541614

Muller - Die lila Logistik Sud GmbH & Co. KG (1)
Carl-Benz-Strasse 9, 64653, Lorsch, Germany
Tel.: (49) 61513566958
Logistics Consulting Servies
N.A.I.C.S.: 541614

Muller - Die lila Logistik Sudost GmbH & Co. KG (1)
Kehlacker 5, 86650, Wemding, Germany
Tel.: (49) 714381046603
Logistics Consulting Servies
N.A.I.C.S.: 541614

Muller - Die lila Logistik Sudwest GmbH & Co. KG (1)
Alte B40 Nr 1, 67292, Kirchheimbolanden, Germany
Tel.: (49) 63524034955
Logistics Consulting Servies
N.A.I.C.S.: 541614

Muller - Die lila Logistik Zwenkau GmbH (1)
Zeschwitzerstrasse 2, 04442, Zwenkau, Germany
Tel.: (49) 342035690
Logistics Consulting Servies
N.A.I.C.S.: 541614

Value Added Logistics Sp. z o.o. (1)
Ul Staszica 7, 55-011, Siechnice, Poland
Tel.: (48) 667663778
Logistics Consulting Servies
N.A.I.C.S.: 541614

MULLER-STEINAG GROUP
Bohler 5, 6221, Rickenbach, Switzerland
Tel.: (41) 848200610
Web Site: http://www.mueller-steinag.ch
Prefabricated Concrete Products Mfr
N.A.I.C.S.: 327331
Sebastian Muller-Kleeb *(Co-Owner)*

Subsidiaries:

MULLER-STEINAG ELEMENT AG (1)
Bohler 5, 6221, Rickenbach, Switzerland
Tel.: (41) 848200210
Web Site: http://www.ms-element.ch
Prefabricated Concrete Elements Mfr
N.A.I.C.S.: 327331
Renato Tettamanti *(CFO)*

MULLION CO., LTD.
9-11 Tomihisacho, Shinjuku-Ku, Tokyo, 162-0067, Japan
Tel.: (81) 332267841
Web Site: https://www.mullion.co.jp
Year Founded: 1986
3494—(TKS)
Real Estate Development Services
N.A.I.C.S.: 531311
Keiji Fukuda *(Founder, Chm & Pres)*

MULLVERWERTUNG BORSIGSTRASSE GMBH
Borsigstrasse 6, 22113, Hamburg, Germany
Tel.: (49) 40 73189 0   De
Web Site: http://www.mvb-hh.de
Emp.: 100
Waste Incineration Plant Services
N.A.I.C.S.: 562213
Jorg Mischer *(Dir-Comml)*

MULPHA INTERNATIONAL BHD.
Suite 111 The Office Club Level 11 Menara Mudajaya No 12A, Jalan PJU 7/3 Mutiara Damansara, 47810, Petaling Jaya, Selangor Darul Ehsan, Malaysia
Tel.: (60) 377186288
Web Site: https://www.mulpha.com.au
MULPHA—(KLS)
Rev.: $205,485,291
Assets: $1,252,419,471
Liabilities: $500,371,429
Net Worth: $752,048,042
Earnings: $18,307,725
Emp.: 1,056
Fiscal Year-end: 12/31/22
Property Development Services
N.A.I.C.S.: 531311
Seng Huang Lee *(Chm)*

Subsidiaries:

Golden Cignet Sdn Bhd (1)
73 Jalan Perai Jaya 3 Bandar Perai Jaya, 13600, Penang, Malaysia
Tel.: (60) 43901116
Sales Range: $25-49.9 Million
Emp.: 13
Residential Property Development Services
N.A.I.C.S.: 236116

HDFI Pty Limited (1)
Level 5 99 Macquarie Street, Sydney, NSW, Australia
Tel.: (61) 292685000
Real Estate Property Investment Services
N.A.I.C.S.: 525990

Leisure Farm Corporation Sdn Bhd (1)
No 8 Jalan Peranginan Leisure Farm, Johor Bahru, 81560, Gelang Patah, Johor, Malaysia
Tel.: (60) 78691037
Web Site: https://www.leisurefarm.com.my
Emp.: 100
Property Management Services
N.A.I.C.S.: 531312

Mulpha Australia Limited (1)
L9 117 Macquarie Street, Sydney, 2000, NSW, Australia
Tel.: (61) 292395500
Web Site: https://www.mulpha.com.au
Sales Range: $25-49.9 Million
Emp.: 120
Property Management Services
N.A.I.C.S.: 531312

Subsidiary (Domestic):

Bimbadgen Estate Pty Limited (2)
790 McDonalds Rd, Pokolbin, 2320, NSW, Australia
Tel.: (61) 249984600
Web Site: https://www.bimbadgen.com.au
Vineyard Cultivation Services
N.A.I.C.S.: 115112

Enacon Parking Pty Limited (2)
2 Cathedral St Cook Philip Park, Sydney, 2000, NSW, Australia
Tel.: (61) 293808850
Web Site: https://www.enacon.com.au
Sales Range: $25-49.9 Million
Emp.: 6
Parking Lot Operator
N.A.I.C.S.: 812930

Mulpha Hotel Investments (Australia) Pty Limited (2)
L 5 99 Macquarie St, Sydney, 2000, NSW, Australia
Tel.: (61) 292395500
Web Site: http://www.mulpha.com.au
Emp.: 40
Investment Management Service
N.A.I.C.S.: 523999

Mulpha Investments Pty Limited (2)
Level 5 99 Macquarie Street, Sydney, 2000, NSW, Australia
Tel.: (61) 292685000
Real Estate Property Investment Services
N.A.I.C.S.: 525990

Mulpha Transport House Pty Limited (2)
Level 5 99 Macquarie Street, Sydney, 2000, NSW, Australia
Tel.: (61) 292685000
Property Management Services
N.A.I.C.S.: 531312

Mulpha Capital Partners Sdn Bhd (1)
Lot 17 Jalan Semangat Sek 13, Petaling Jaya, 46200, Selangor, Malaysia
Tel.: (60) 379572233
Residential Property Development Services
N.A.I.C.S.: 236115

Mulpha Hotels Australia Pty Ltd (1)
Level 5 99 Macquarie St, Sydney, 2000, NSW, Australia
Tel.: (61) 292395500
Home Management Services
N.A.I.C.S.: 721110

Mulpha Private Wealth Pty. Limited (1)
Level 9 117 Macquarie Street, Sydney, 2000, NSW, Australia
Tel.: (61) 299589008
Web Site: https://pindariprivatewealth.com.au
Wealth Management Services
N.A.I.C.S.: 524128

Mulpha Sanctuary Cove Harbour One Pty. Limited (1)
Jabiru House 1 Masthead Way, The Marine Village, Sanctuary Cove, 4212, QLD, Australia
Tel.: (61) 1300553217
Web Site: https://harbourone.com.au
Property Development Services
N.A.I.C.S.: 531311

Soak City Pty. Limited (1)
Level 9 117 Macquarie Street, Sydney, 2000, NSW, Australia
Tel.: (61) 292706186
Web Site: https://www.soakcity.com.au
Car Wash Services
N.A.I.C.S.: 811192

Swing City Pty. Limited (1)
2-6 Norbrik Dr, Bella Vista, 2153, NSW, Australia
Tel.: (61) 1300320604
Web Site: https://www.swingcitygolf.com.au
Golf Course Services
N.A.I.C.S.: 713910

MULSANNE GROUP HOLDING LIMITED
111 Shanshan Road, Haishu, Ningbo, Zhejiang, China
Tel.: (86) 4008701978   Ky
Web Site: http://www.gxggroup.cn
Year Founded: 2007
1817—(HKG)
Rev.: $326,609,852
Assets: $494,230,464
Liabilities: $397,568,153
Net Worth: $96,662,311
Earnings: $1,312,880
Emp.: 603
Fiscal Year-end: 12/31/22
Holding Company
N.A.I.C.S.: 551112
Yong Yu *(CEO)*

MULTANOVA AG
Aathalstrasse 84, 8610, Uster, Switzerland
Tel.: (41) 432882820   CH
Web Site: http://www.multanova.ch
Year Founded: 1952
Sales Range: $1-9.9 Million
Emp.: 10
Traffic Monitoring System Mfr
N.A.I.C.S.: 334513
Ralf Schumacher *(Mgr-Fin)*

MULTI COMMODITY EXCHANGE OF INDIA LTD.
Exchange Square Suren Road Chakala Andheri East, Mumbai, 400093, Maharashtra, India
Tel.: (91) 2267318888
Web Site: https://www.mcxindia.com
Year Founded: 2003
MCX—(NSE)
Rev.: $67,477,410
Assets: $341,592,615
Liabilities: $148,004,220
Net Worth: $193,588,395
Earnings: $30,742,530
Emp.: 338
Fiscal Year-end: 03/31/21
Commodity Exchange
N.A.I.C.S.: 523210
Sanjay Wadhwa *(CFO)*

Subsidiaries:

Multi Commodity Exchange Clearing Corporation Limited (1)
255 Exchange Square Suren Road, Andheri East, Mumbai, 400093, India
Tel.: (91) 2268646000
Web Site: https://www.mcxccl.com
Fund Settlement Services
N.A.I.C.S.: 525920
Rajesh Agrawal *(CFO)*

MULTI INDOCITRA TBK
Green Central City Commercial Area Lt 6F Jl Gajah Mada No 188, Jakarta, 11120, Indonesia
Tel.: (62) 2129368888
Web Site: https://www.mic.co.id
MICE—(INDO)
Rev.: $70,563,426
Assets: $86,304,180
Liabilities: $28,463,765
Net Worth: $57,840,415
Earnings: $2,231,949
Emp.: 396
Fiscal Year-end: 12/31/23

MULTI INDOCITRA TBK

Multi Indocitra Tbk—(Continued)
Cosmetic & Personal Care Product Distr
N.A.I.C.S.: 456120
Anthony Honoris *(Chm)*

Subsidiaries:

P.T. Multitrans Nusantara Logistik
Sudirman Plaza Plaza Marein 17th floor Jl Jend Sudirman Kav 76-78, South Jakarta, 12910, Indonesia
Tel.: (62) 2157935980
Logistics & Transportation Services
N.A.I.C.S.: 541614

PT Citra Makmur Ritailindo (1)
Green Central City Commercial Area 6th Floor Jl Gajah Mada, No 188 RT003 RW005, Jakarta Barat, 11120, Indonesia
Tel.: (62) 2129368888
Cosmetics Products Mfr
N.A.I.C.S.: 325620

PT Digital Niaga Indonesia (1)
Green Central City Commercial Area Lt 6 Jl Gajah Mada no 188, Glodok Taman Sari, Tangerang, 11120, Banten, Indonesia
Tel.: (62) 2122526508
Web Site: https://dnicommercio.com
Cosmetics Products Mfr
N.A.I.C.S.: 325620

PT Multielok Cosmetic (1)
Kawasan Industri Modern Cikande Jl Modern Industri I Kav 2-6, Kawasan Industri Modern Cikande Kibin Kab, Serang, 42186, Cikande, Indonesia
Tel.: (62) 21254401765
Web Site: https://multielokcosmetic.com
Cosmetics Products Mfr
N.A.I.C.S.: 325620

PT Nusapangan Sukses Makmur (1)
Jl Halim Perdana Kusuma No 53 RT 001 RW 001 Komplek Pergudangan 10, Kel Jurumudi Baru Kec-Benda, Tangerang, Banten, Indonesia
Tel.: (62) 215516228
Cosmetics Products Mfr
N.A.I.C.S.: 325620

MULTI PLUS DM INC.

10389 Cote de Liesse, Dorval, H9P 2Z3, QC, Canada
Tel.: (514) 422-8881
Web Site:
  http://www.multiplusdm.com
Year Founded: 1987
Packaged Frozen Food Distr
N.A.I.C.S.: 424420
Danny Matteo *(Founder, Pres & CEO)*

MULTI SPORTS HOLDINGS LTD.

Level 18 The Gardens North Tower Mid Valley City, Lingkaran Syed Putra, 59200, Kuala Lumpur, Malaysia
Tel.: (60) 322648888
Web Site: http://www.mzcan.com
5150—(KLS)
Sales Range: $150-199.9 Million
Holding Company; Sport Shoe Soles Mfr
N.A.I.C.S.: 551112
Huozhi Lin *(Chm)*

MULTI SURFACE SOLUTIONS ASA

Frydenbergveien 48, 0575, Oslo, Norway
Tel.: (47) 92895885
Web Site: http://www.mss-asa.com
Architectural Services
N.A.I.C.S.: 541310
Thomas Holst *(CEO)*

MULTI WAYS HOLDINGS LIMITED

3E Gul Circle, Singapore, 629633, Singapore
Tel.: (65) 62875252 Ky
Web Site:
  https://www.multiways.com.sg
Year Founded: 1988
MWG—(NYSEAMEX)
Rev.: $36,016,000
Assets: $58,001,000
Liabilities: $36,174,000
Net Worth: $21,827,000
Earnings: $1,739,000
Emp.: 92
Fiscal Year-end: 12/31/23
Holding Company
N.A.I.C.S.: 551112
Eng Hock Lim *(Chm)*

MULTI-CHEM LIMITED

18 Boon Lay Way 05-113 Tradehub 21, Singapore, 609966, Singapore
Tel.: (65) 68631318
Web Site:
  https://www.multichem.com.sg
AWZ—(SES)
Rev.: $498,690,449
Assets: $289,031,281
Liabilities: $179,810,649
Net Worth: $109,220,632
Earnings: $20,543,058
Emp.: 594
Fiscal Year-end: 12/31/23
Printed Circuit Board Mfr
N.A.I.C.S.: 334412
Eugene Boon Tiong Pui *(Reg Dir)*

Subsidiaries:

E-Secure Asia Pte. Ltd. (1)
18 Boon Lay Way 04-108 TradeHub 21, Singapore, 609966, Singapore
Tel.: (65) 65160088
Internet & Network Product Distr
N.A.I.C.S.: 423430

Subsidiary (Non-US):

E Fortify Asia Sdn. Bhd. (2)
25-3A Menara 1MK Kompleks Mont Kiara No 1, Jalan Kiara, 50480, Kuala Lumpur, Malaysia
Tel.: (60) 327886868
Internet & Network Product Distr
N.A.I.C.S.: 423430

M-Security Technology Indochina Pte. Ltd. (1)
14th Floor Ladeco Building 266 Doi Can Street, Lieu Giai Ward Ba Dinh District, Hanoi, Vietnam
Tel.: (84) 2439350970
Cyber Security Services
N.A.I.C.S.: 541519
Trung Luong *(Acct Mgr)*

M-Security Technology Sdn. Bhd. (1)
13-1 Menara 1 MK Kompleks 1 Mont Kiara No 1 Jalan Kiara, Mont Kiara, 50480, Kuala Lumpur, Malaysia
Tel.: (60) 327886868
Sales Range: $25-49.9 Million
Emp.: 50
Security Software Development Services
N.A.I.C.S.: 541511

M-Solutions Technology (Thailand) Co., Ltd. (1)
25 Bangkok Insurance Building 21st Floor South Sathorn Road, Thungmahamek Sathorn, Bangkok, 10120, Thailand
Tel.: (66) 20596500
Web Site: http://www.mtechpro.com
Sales Range: $25-49.9 Million
Emp.: 40
Security & Multimedia Software Development Services
N.A.I.C.S.: 327910

M.SaaS Lanka (Private) Limited (1)
106 Bernards Business Park Dutugemunu Street, Kohuwala, 10250, Dehiwala-Mount Lavinia, Sri Lanka
Tel.: (94) 117112111
Internet & Network Product Distr

N.A.I.C.S.: 423430
Siva Sankar *(Country Mgr)*

M.Tech (Shanghai) Co., Ltd. (1)
Room 902 Honi International Plaza No 199 North Chengdu Road, Jing'an District, Shanghai, 200041, China
Tel.: (86) 2162171989
Cyber Security Services
N.A.I.C.S.: 541519

M.Tech Products (HK) Pte Limited (1)
Tel.: (852) 23692678
Web Site: http://www.mtechpro.com
Sales Range: $25-49.9 Million
Security Software Development Services
N.A.I.C.S.: 541511

M.Tech Products Aust Pty Limited (1)
Suite 309/50 Holt Street, Surry Hills, 2010, NSW, Australia
Tel.: (61) 289870400
Web Site: http://www.multichem.com.sg
Emp.: 10
Circuit Boards Mfr & Chemicals Distr
N.A.I.C.S.: 334412

M.Tech Products Japan Kabushiki Kaisha (1)
10th Floor ACN Kyobashi Yaesu Building 2-8-3 Kyobashi, Chuo-ku, Tokyo, 104-0031, Japan
Tel.: (81) 6565160088
Cyber Security Services
N.A.I.C.S.: 541519

M.Tech Products Korea Limited Liability Company (1)
93 Gyesansae-ro, Gyeyang-gu, Incheon, 20165, Korea (South)
Tel.: (82) 6565160051
Cyber Security Services
N.A.I.C.S.: 541519

M.Tech Products New Zealand Limited (1)
C/- Mcveagh Fleming 5-7 Corinthian Drive, Albany, North Shore, 0632, New Zealand
Tel.: (64) 94154477
Internet & Network Product Distr
N.A.I.C.S.: 423430

M.Tech Products Philippines, Inc. (1)
Unit 2904 88 Corporate Center Valero Corner Sedeno St, Salcedo Village, Makati, 1227, Philippines
Tel.: (63) 277298839
Web Site: http://www.mtechpro.com
Sales Range: $25-49.9 Million
Emp.: 20
Security Software Development Services
N.A.I.C.S.: 541511

M.Tech Products Pte Ltd (1)
18 Boon Lay Way 06-111 Tradehub 21, Singapore, 609966, Singapore
Tel.: (65) 65160088
Web Site: http://www.mtechpro.com
Emp.: 100
Security & Multimedia Software Development Services
N.A.I.C.S.: 541511

M.Tech Products TW Pte. Ltd. (1)
Tel.: (886) 226599128
Web Site: http://www.multichem.com.sg
Sales Range: $25-49.9 Million
Emp.: 15
Circuit Board Mfr & Chemicals Distr
N.A.I.C.S.: 334412

M.Tech Solutions (India) Private Limited (1)
N1 Block 2nd Floor Manyata Embassy Business Park Outer Ring Rd, Nagavara, Bengaluru, 560045, Karnataka, India
Tel.: (91) 8043022146
Web Site: https://www.mtechpro.in
Emp.: 500
Cyber Security Services
N.A.I.C.S.: 541519
Anupama Kumari *(Product Mgr)*

Multi-Chem (Huaian) Co., Ltd. (1)
No 168 Foxconn Road Economic Development Area, Huai'an, 223005, Jiangsu, China
Tel.: (86) 510 8866 8188

Web Site: http://www.multichem.com.sg
Printed Circuit Board Mfr
N.A.I.C.S.: 334412

Multi-Chem Electronics (Kunshan) Co., Ltd. (1)
No 22 Zangji Road Kunshan ETD Zone, Kunshan, 215300, Jiangsu, China
Tel.: (86) 51286176689
Precision Drilling Services
N.A.I.C.S.: 213112

Multi-Chem PCB (Kunshan) Co., Ltd. (1)
No 255 Nan Zi Road Free Trade Zone, Kunshan, Jiangsu, China
Tel.: (86) 51286176689
Precision Drilling Services
N.A.I.C.S.: 213112

PT. M.Tech Products (1)
Ariobimo Central Building 7th Floor Jl HR Rasuna Said X-2 Kav 5, Jakarta, 12950, Indonesia
Tel.: (62) 215226210
Sales Range: $25-49.9 Million
Emp.: 30
Security & Multimedia Software Development Services
N.A.I.C.S.: 541511

SecureOneAsia Pte. Ltd. (1)
16H Enterprise Road, Singapore, 627657, Singapore
Tel.: (65) 68631318
Internet & Network Product Distr
N.A.I.C.S.: 423430
Steven Loh *(Dir-Professional Svcs)*

Subsidiary (Non-US):

M-Security Tech Philippines Inc. (2)
Unit 2904 88 Corporate Center Valero Corner Sedeno Streets, Salcedo Village, Makati, 1227, Philippines
Tel.: (63) 277298837
Cyber Security Services
N.A.I.C.S.: 541519

MULTI-METAL DEVELOPMENT LTD.

638 Millbank Road, Vancouver, V5Z 4B7, BC, Canada
Tel.: (604) 689-7902 BC
Web Site: https://multimetdev.com
MLYCF—(OTCIQ)
Assets: $21,357,851
Liabilities: $10,339,011
Net Worth: $11,018,839
Earnings: ($1,252,049)
Fiscal Year-end: 06/30/22
Metal Mining Services
N.A.I.C.S.: 212290
Brett A. Kagetsu *(Sec)*

MULTI-USAGE HOLDINGS BERHAD

12A-03 Menara Boustead Penang, 39 Jalan Sultan Ahmad Shah, 10050, Penang, Malaysia
Tel.: (60) 42272858
Web Site: https://www.muh.com.my
MUH—(KLS)
Rev.: $3,009,564
Assets: $18,129,481
Liabilities: $876,132
Net Worth: $17,253,348
Earnings: $909,694
Emp.: 26
Fiscal Year-end: 06/30/23
Property Development Services
N.A.I.C.S.: 531311
Kim Cheng Ang *(Chm)*

Subsidiaries:

Multi-Usage Cement Products Sdn. Bhd. (1)
Lot 1678 Jalan Gajah Mati, Machang Bubok, 14020, Bukit Mertajam, Penang, Malaysia
Tel.: (60) 44872366

Sales Range: $25-49.9 Million
Emp.: 12
Building Materials Mfr
N.A.I.C.S.: 339999

Multi-Usage Trading Sdn. Bhd. (1)
12A-03 Menara Boustead Penang 39 Jalan Sultan Ahmad Shah, 10500, Penang, Malaysia
Tel.: (60) 42272858
Sales Range: $25-49.9 Million
Emp.: 10
Building Materials Whslr
N.A.I.C.S.: 444180

TF Land Sdn. Bhd. (1)
267 Jalan Machang Bubok Taman Machang Bubok, 14020, Bukit Mertajam, Penang, Malaysia
Tel.: (60) 45512635
Web Site: https://www.tfland.com.my
Emp.: 20
Property Development Services
N.A.I.C.S.: 531390
Ang Teng Kok (CEO)

MULTI24 SA
Parque das Tecnologias Edificio 1 Tagus Park Avenida, 2740-256, Porto Salvo, Portugal
Tel.: (351) 211131378
MLM24—(EUR)
Sales Range: $1-9.9 Million
Real Estate Investment Services
N.A.I.C.S.: 531210
Samuel Morrow (Exec Dir)

MULTIBANK, INC.
Via Espana No 127 Prosperidad Building, PO Box 0823-05627, Panama, Panama
Tel.: (507) 2943500
Web Site:
  https://www.multibank.com.pa
Year Founded: 1990
MULT—(PAN)
Rev.: $284,980,908
Assets: $4,924,243,318
Liabilities: $4,540,217,243
Net Worth: $384,026,075
Earnings: $8,685,281
Emp.: 1,041
Fiscal Year-end: 12/31/23
Banking Services
N.A.I.C.S.: 522110
Rodolfo Tabash Espinach (Pres)

MULTIBAX PCL
211 Moo 3 Tung Sukhala Sriracha, Chon Buri, 20230, Thailand
Tel.: (66) 38491725
Web Site: https://www.multibax.com
Year Founded: 1995
MBAX—(THA)
Rev.: $33,088,514
Assets: $40,559,615
Liabilities: $26,008,002
Net Worth: $14,551,613
Earnings: ($1,113,966)
Fiscal Year-end: 12/31/23
Polyethylene Bags Mfr
N.A.I.C.S.: 325211
Prakit Seksarn (Bd of Dirs & Chm)

MULTICAMPUS CORPORATION
14F 508 Eonju-ro, Gangnam-gu, Seoul, Korea (South)
Tel.: (82) 262629118
Web Site: http://www.credu.com
Year Founded: 2000
067280—(KRS)
Rev.: $274,192,412
Assets: $223,771,994
Liabilities: $91,564,217
Net Worth: $132,207,778
Earnings: $23,208,802
Emp.: 880
Fiscal Year-end: 12/31/22
Online Education Services
N.A.I.C.S.: 611710
Yeong Hwi Yim (CEO)

MULTICHOICE GROUP LIMITED
144 Bram Fischer Drive, Ferndale, Randburg, 2194, South Africa
Tel.: (27) 112893000   ZA
Web Site:
  https://www.multichoice.co.za
Year Founded: 1993
MCG—(JSE)
Rev.: $2,904,498,290
Assets: $2,315,877,807
Liabilities: $2,372,278,908
Net Worth: ($56,401,101)
Earnings: ($219,055,963)
Emp.: 7,100
Fiscal Year-end: 03/31/24
Subscriber Management Solutions & Digital Satellite Television Platforms Broadcasting Services
N.A.I.C.S.: 516120
Calvo Mawela (CEO)

Subsidiaries:

DStv Media Sales Proprietary Limited (1)
MultiChoice City 144 Bram Fischer, Randburg, Johannesburg, South Africa
Tel.: (27) 112893000
Web Site: http://www.dstvmediasales.com
Media Buying Services
N.A.I.C.S.: 541830
Shaun Chettiar (Head-Sls, Digital & VOD)

Irdeto B.V. (1)
Taurus Ave 105, Hoofddorp, 2132 LS, Netherlands
Tel.: (31) 23 556 2000
Web Site: http://www.irdeto.com
Sales Range: $150-199.9 Million
Emp.: 1,000
Design, Develop & Market End-to-End Solutions to Manage & Protect Content from Unauthorized Access
N.A.I.C.S.: 561621
Ben Bennett (Sr VP-Bus Dev)

Subsidiary (US):

Cloakware, Inc. (2)
8320 Old Courthouse Rd, Vienna, VA 22182
Tel.: (703) 752-4830
Web Site: http://www.cloakware.com
Sales Range: $50-74.9 Million
Emp.: 105
Software Publisher
N.A.I.C.S.: 513210
Graham Kill (CEO)

Unit (Non-US):

Irdeto - Australia (2)
St 2 Level 16 275 Alfred Street, Sydney, 2060, NSW, Australia
Tel.: (61) 299573388
Web Site: http://www.irdeto.com
Sales Range: $25-49.9 Million
Emp.: 5
Content Security Solutions
N.A.I.C.S.: 561621

Irdeto - Brazil (2)
Rua Manoel da Nobrega 211, Conj 72, 04001 081, Sao Paulo, Brazil
Tel.: (55) 11 3266 5313
Content Security Solutions
N.A.I.C.S.: 561621
Giovani Henrique (Country Mgr-Latin America & Caribbean)

Irdeto - China (2)
Suite 300 Beijing Sunflower Tower Chaoyang Dist 37 Maizidian Street, Beijing, 100026, China
Tel.: (86) 1085276460
Web Site: http://www.irdeto.com
Sales Range: $25-49.9 Million
Emp.: 250
Content Security Solutions
N.A.I.C.S.: 561621

Irdeto - South Korea (2)
10F Dongwha Bldg Annex 120-20 Seosomun-dong, Jung-gu, Seoul, 100-814, Korea (South)
Tel.: (82) 10 4406 8265
Web Site: http://www.irdeto.com
Content Security Solutions
N.A.I.C.S.: 561621

Subsidiary (Domestic):

Irdeto Access B.V. (2)
Taurus Avenue 105, 2132 LS, Hoofddorp, Netherlands
Tel.: (31) 235562222
Web Site: http://www.irdeto.com
Sales Range: $25-49.9 Million
Emp.: 250
Multimedia Security Software Development Services
N.A.I.C.S.: 541511
Andrew Wajs (CTO)

MultiChoice Angola Limitada (1)
Edificio Potche Rua CS5B Via A1, Talatona, Luanda, Angola
Tel.: (244) 923120000
Emp.: 333
Television Broadcasting Services
N.A.I.C.S.: 516120
Glauco Ferreira (Mng Dir)

MultiChoice Kenya Limited (1)
Jamhuri Road off Ngong Road, PO Box 60406, 00200, Nairobi, Kenya
Tel.: (254) 711066000
Emp.: 300
Television Broadcasting Services
N.A.I.C.S.: 516120
Nancy Matimu (Mng Dir)

MultiChoice Nigeria Limited (1)
Plot 1381 Tiamiyu Savage Street, Victoria Island, Lagos, Nigeria
Tel.: (234) 12703232
Emp.: 1,000
Television Broadcasting Services
N.A.I.C.S.: 516120
John Ugbe (CEO)

MultiChoice South Africa Holdings (Proprietary) Limited (1)
251 Oak Avenue, Ferndale, 2125, Randburg, South Africa
Tel.: (27) 112893000
Web Site: http://www.multichoice.co.za
Emp.: 1,500
Television Broadcasting Services
N.A.I.C.S.: 516120
Natasha Abed (Gen Mgr)

MultiChoice Zambia Limited (1)
Plot no 34772/34773 Alick Nkhata Road, Lusaka, Zambia
Tel.: (260) 211368300
Emp.: 350
Television Broadcasting Services
N.A.I.C.S.: 516120
Juliana Mwila (Chm)

MULTICONSULT ASA
Nedre Skoyen vei 2, 0276, Oslo, Norway
Tel.: (47) 21585000
Web Site:
  https://www.multiconsultgroup.com
0R8N—(LSE)
Rev.: $449,673,009
Assets: $278,039,350
Liabilities: $186,366,710
Net Worth: $91,672,640
Earnings: $27,989,562
Emp.: 2,954
Fiscal Year-end: 12/31/22
Consulting & Designing Engineering
N.A.I.C.S.: 541330
Grethe Bergly (CEO)

Subsidiaries:

Bomek Consulting AS (1)
Tollbugata 9, 8006, Bodo, Norway
Tel.: (47) 75548630
Web Site: http://www.bomek-consulting.no
Engineering Company
N.A.I.C.S.: 541330

Iterio AB (1)
Ringvagen 100C, Sodermalm, Stockholm, Sweden
Tel.: (46) 841036300
Web Site: https://www.iterio.se
Emp.: 80
Building Management Consulting Services
N.A.I.C.S.: 541611

LINK Arkitektur AS (1)
Kirkegata 4, 0153, Oslo, Norway
Tel.: (47) 21522200
Web Site: https://linkarkitektur.com
Emp.: 470
Architectural Design Services
N.A.I.C.S.: 541310
Grethe Haugland (Mng Dir)

Multiconsult Asia Pte. Ltd. (1)
237 Pandan Loop 07-11A Westech Building, Singapore, 128424, Singapore
Tel.: (65) 67473728
Engineering Consulting Services
N.A.I.C.S.: 541330
Thor Orjan Holt (VP-Oil & Gas)

Multiconsult Polska Sp. z o.o. (1)
Bonifraterska 17, 00-203, Warsaw, Poland
Tel.: (48) 222460700
Web Site: https://www.multiconsult-polska.com
Emp.: 280
Engineering Consulting Services
N.A.I.C.S.: 541330

Multiconsult UK Ltd. (1)
4th Floor International House Dover Place, Ashford, TN23 1HU, Kent, United Kingdom
Tel.: (44) 1233754485
Engineering Consulting Services
N.A.I.C.S.: 541330
Anders Gustav Pettersen (Mng Dir)

MULTIEXPORT FOODS S.A.
Av Cardonal 2501, Puerto Montt, Chile
Year Founded: 1983
MULTIFOODS—(SGO)
Rev.: $568,402,000
Assets: $666,616,000
Liabilities: $303,905,000
Net Worth: $362,711,000
Earnings: $43,425,000
Fiscal Year-end: 12/31/19
Aquaculture & Fishing Services
N.A.I.C.S.: 112511

MULTIFAG AS
Frednesoya 21, Porsgrunn, 3933, Norway
Tel.: (47) 80035500
Web Site: http://www.multifag.no
Electrical Engineering, Plumbing & Ventilation Services
N.A.I.C.S.: 238210
Frode Heimark (CEO)

MULTIFIELD INTERNATIONAL HOLDINGS LTD
Units 22-28 25/F Tower A Southmark No 11 Yip Hing Street, Wong Chuk Hang, Hong Kong, China (Hong Kong)
Tel.: (852) 28022668
Web Site:
  http://www.multifield.com.hk
0898—(HKG)
Sales Range: $25-49.9 Million
Emp.: 220
Commercial & Residential Building Investment Services
N.A.I.C.S.: 531311
Kenneth Chi Yung Lau (Chm)

MULTIMETAVERSE HOLDINGS LIMITED
Building D3 No 718 Lingshi Road Jingan District, Shanghai, 200072, China   VG
Year Founded: 2021
MMV—(NASDAQ)
Rev.: $558,448
Assets: $25,946,935
Liabilities: $32,393,919
Net Worth: ($6,446,984)

MULTIMETAVERSE HOLDINGS LIMITED

MULTIMETAVERSE HOLDINGS LIMITED—(Continued)
Earnings: ($2,253,774)
Emp.: 204
Fiscal Year-end: 12/31/22
Holding Company
N.A.I.C.S.: 551112
Yiran Xu (CEO)

MULTIMICRO CLOUD SA
14 Avenue Henri Becquerel, 33 700, Merignac, France
Tel.: (33) 556477899 FR
Web Site: http://www.multimicro.fr
MLMMC—(EUR)
Sales Range: Less than $1 Million
Software Development Services
N.A.I.C.S.: 513210
Jean Pierre Peyrucq (CEO)

MULTINA, INC.
1375 rue Janelle, Drummondville, J2C 3E4, QC, Canada
Tel.: (819) 478-5292
Year Founded: 1963
Rev.: $60,189,091
Emp.: 575
Transportation Mfr
N.A.I.C.S.: 423860
Gerard Nadeau (Founder)

MULTIPANEL UK LTD.
Unit 6 Site 2 Oak Business Units Thorverton Road Matford, Exeter, EX2 8FS, Devon, United Kingdom
Tel.: (44) 1392 823015
Web Site: http://www.multipaneluk.co.uk
Year Founded: 2004
Sales Range: $25-49.9 Million
Emp.: 22
Aluminium Composite Mfr
N.A.I.C.S.: 331315
Andrew Cock (Mng Dir)

MULTIPLAN EMPREENDIMENTOS IMOBILIARIOS S.A.
Av das Americas 4200/Bloco 2 5 andar - Barra da Tijuca, Rio de Janeiro, 22640-102, Brazil
Tel.: (55) 2130315200 BR
Web Site: https://www.multiplan.com.br
Year Founded: 1974
MULT3—(BRAZ)
Rev.: $404,740,054
Assets: $2,300,712,733
Liabilities: $917,923,223
Net Worth: $1,382,789,510
Earnings: $203,520,590
Emp.: 416
Fiscal Year-end: 12/31/23
Real Estate, Mall Management & Construction Services
N.A.I.C.S.: 236220
Jose Isaac Peres (Founder)

Subsidiaries:

County Estates Limited (1)
Kingfisher House 17 Albury Close, Reading, RG30 1BD, United Kingdom
Tel.: (44) 1189508366
Web Site: http://www.countryestates.co.uk
Real Estate Development Services
N.A.I.C.S.: 531390

Jundiai Shopping Center Ltda. (1)
Avenida Nove de Julho 3333 Anhangabau, Jundiai, 13208-056, Brazil
Tel.: (55) 1145884591
Web Site: http://www.jundiaishopping.com.br
Shopping Center Services
N.A.I.C.S.: 445131

ParkShopping Campo Grande Ltda. (1)
Estrada do Monteiro 1200, Campo Grande, Rio de Janeiro, 23045-830, RJ, Brazil
Tel.: (55) 2130034175
Web Site: http://www.parkshoppingcampo.com.br
Shopping Center Services
N.A.I.C.S.: 445131

Patio Savassi Administracao de Shopping Center Ltda. (1)
Av Do Contorno 6061 Sao Pedro, 30110-929, Belo Horizonte, MG, Brazil
Tel.: (55) 32638521
Web Site: http://www.patiosavassi.com
Shopping Center Services
N.A.I.C.S.: 445131

Teatro VillageMall Ltda. (1)
Avenida das Americas 3 900, Barra da Tijuca, Rio de Janeiro, RJ, Brazil
Tel.: (55) 2130034177
Web Site: http://www.shoppingvillagemall.com.br
Shopping Center Services
N.A.I.C.S.: 445131

MULTIPLEX SITES TRUST
Level 22 135 King Street, Sydney, 2000, NSW, Australia
Tel.: (61) 293222000 AU
Investment Management Service
N.A.I.C.S.: 523940

MULTIPLICA INSIDE S.L.
Passeig de Sant Joan 2 Entl 1a, Barcelona, 08010, Spain
Tel.: (34) 932492070 ES
Web Site: https://multiplica.com
Year Founded: 2000
Digital Consulting Services
N.A.I.C.S.: 541690
David Boronat (Founder & Pres)

MULTIPLUS HOLDINGS LTD
101 B Wing Bhaveshwar Plaza LBS Marg Ghatkopar-West, Mumbai, 400086, India
Tel.: (91) 2225005046
Web Site: https://www.multiplusholdings.com
Year Founded: 1982
505594—(BOM)
Rev.: $770,841
Assets: $2,789,869
Liabilities: $108,627
Net Worth: $2,681,242
Earnings: $647,119
Emp.: 3
Fiscal Year-end: 03/31/23
Investment Services
N.A.I.C.S.: 523999
Jignesh R. Sheth (Chm & Mng Dir)

MULTIPROJEKT AUTOMATYKA SP. Z O.O.
ul Cysterow 20a, 31-553, Krakow, Poland
Tel.: (48) 124139058 PL
Web Site: http://www.multiprojekt.pl
Automation Component Distr
N.A.I.C.S.: 423690

MULTIPURPOSE TRADING & AGENCIES LTD.
B-1 Kalindi Colony, New Delhi, 110065, India
Tel.: (91) 1142908812
Web Site: https://www.multipurposetrading.in
Year Founded: 1979
504356—(BOM)
Rev.: $40,526
Assets: $584,450
Liabilities: $13,939
Net Worth: $570,511
Earnings: $23,450
Fiscal Year-end: 03/31/23
Real Estate Related Services
N.A.I.C.S.: 531390
Ashish Singh (Chm & Mng Dir)

MULTIQ INTERNATIONAL AB
Ideon Scheelevagen 17, SE-223 70, Lund, Sweden
Tel.: (46) 10 2116600
Web Site: http://www.multiq.com
MULQ—(OMX)
Rev.: $16,883,664
Assets: $17,080,213
Liabilities: $5,326,350
Net Worth: $11,753,862
Earnings: ($124,522)
Emp.: 66
Fiscal Year-end: 12/31/20
Electronic Monitor Display Mfr
N.A.I.C.S.: 335999
Lars-Goran Mejvik (CEO-Acting)

MULTISISTEMA PJSC
1st Magistralny Tupik 11c1 Business Center YARD, Moscow, 123290, Russia
Tel.: (7) 4959276168
Web Site: https://www.multisistema.ru
Year Founded: 2002
MSST—(MOEX)
Sales Range: Less than $1 Million
Utility Management Services
N.A.I.C.S.: 237110
Dmitry Vladimirovich Chalyi (CEO & Gen Dir)

MULTISTACK INTERNATIONAL LIMITED
17 Friars Road, Moorabbin, 3189, VIC, Australia
Tel.: (61) 385868204 AU
Web Site: https://www.multistack.com.au
MSI—(ASX)
Rev.: $422,455
Assets: $3,369,336
Liabilities: $4,228,067
Net Worth: ($858,731)
Earnings: ($1,223,290)
Emp.: 3
Fiscal Year-end: 12/31/22
Air Conditioning Equipment Whslr
N.A.I.C.S.: 423730

MULTITEC
195 Ave Parc d'Activites de l'Aerd, 34470, Perols, Herault, France
Tel.: (33) 467138030
Web Site: http://www.multitec.fr
Rev.: $44,400,000
Emp.: 171
N.A.I.C.S.: 238210
Eric Genot (Mng Dir)

MULTITUDE SE
Ratamestarinkatu 11 A, 00520, Helsinki, Finland
Tel.: (358) 942452356
Web Site: https://www.ferratumgroup.com
FRU—(DEU)
Rev.: $229,188,431
Assets: $815,052,882
Liabilities: $618,679,042
Net Worth: $196,373,840
Earnings: $12,945,176
Emp.: 670
Fiscal Year-end: 12/31/22
Mobile Lending & Banking Services
N.A.I.C.S.: 513210
Juhani Vanhala (Chm)

Subsidiaries:

Bhawana Capital Private Limited (1)
The Executive Centre Level 18 One Horizon Centre DLF5, Gurgaon, 122002, India
Tel.: (91) 1246687879
Web Site: https://bhawanafinance.com
Financial Services
N.A.I.C.S.: 522320

CapitalBox AB (1)

INTERNATIONAL PUBLIC

Linnegatan 22, 114 47, Stockholm, Sweden
Tel.: (46) 200180020
Web Site: https://www.capitalbox.com
Financial Services
N.A.I.C.S.: 522320

Ferratum Australia Pty Ltd (1)
44 St Georges Terrace, Perth, 6000, WA, Australia
Tel.: (61) 1300433772
Web Site: http://www.ferratum.com.au
Financial Management Services
N.A.I.C.S.: 541611

Ferratum Bank plc (1)
ST Business Centre 120 The Strand, Gzira, GZR 1027, Malta
Tel.: (356) 3031198504
Web Site: http://www.ferratum.de
Financial Management Services
N.A.I.C.S.: 541611

Ferratum Canada Inc. (1)
Suite 304 500 Danforth Avenue, Toronto, M4K 1P6, ON, Canada
Web Site: https://flexmoney.ca
Financial Management Services
N.A.I.C.S.: 541611

Ferratum Sweden AB (1)
Wennerbergsgatan 10 2tr, 112 58, Stockholm, Sweden
Tel.: (46) 70899933
Web Site: http://www.ferratumbusiness.dk
Financial Management Services
N.A.I.C.S.: 541611

Ferratum UK Ltd. (1)
Suite 318 25 Goodlass Road, Liverpool, L24 9HJ, Merseyside, United Kingdom
Tel.: (44) 1516018611
Web Site: http://www.ferratum.co.uk
Financial Management Services
N.A.I.C.S.: 541611

Suomen Joustava Oy (1)
Ratamestarinkatu 11 A, 00520, Helsinki, Finland
Tel.: (358) 800552136
Web Site: https://www.joustava.fi
Banking & Financial Services
N.A.I.C.S.: 541611

Swespar AB (1)
Wennerbergsgatan 10, 112 58, Stockholm, Sweden
Tel.: (46) 771119119
Web Site: http://www.swespar.se
Financial Management Services
N.A.I.C.S.: 541611

UAB Ferratum Finance (1)
Zalgirio str 135, LT-08217, Vilnius, Lithuania
Tel.: (370) 52333330
Web Site: http://www.ferratum.lt
Financial Management Services
N.A.I.C.S.: 541611

Vector Procurement Solutions Inc. (1)
4711 Yonge Street 10th Floor, Toronto, M2N 6K8, ON, Canada
Tel.: (416) 814-7770
Web Site: https://www.vectorprocurement.com
Banking & Financial Services
N.A.I.C.S.: 541611

MULTIVERSE MINING & EXPLORATION PLC
262A Corporation Drive Dolphin Estate, Ikoyi, Lagos, Nigeria
Tel.: (234) 8033086465
Web Site: http://www.multiverseplc.com
Year Founded: 2002
MULTIVERSE—(NIGE)
Rev.: $111,452
Assets: $11,954,256
Liabilities: $10,444,784
Net Worth: $1,509,471
Earnings: ($805,850)
Emp.: 7
Fiscal Year-end: 12/31/19
Granite Quarrying Services
N.A.I.C.S.: 212313
Ayedun Fasina (CEO & Mng Dir)

AND PRIVATE COMPANIES

MULVIHILL CAPITAL MANAGEMENT INC.
121 King Street West Suite 2600
Standard Life Centre, Toronto, M5H 3T9, ON, Canada
Tel.: (416) 681-3966
Web Site: http://www.mulvihill.com
Year Founded: 1995
Provider of Investment Services
N.A.I.C.S.: 523940
John P. Mulvihill *(Chm & CEO)*

Subsidiaries:

Mulvihill Premium Canadian (1)
121 King St W Ste 2600, Toronto, M5H 3T9, ON, Canada (100%)
Tel.: (416) 681-3966
Web Site: http://www.mulvihill.com
Sales Range: $50-74.9 Million
Emp.: 20
Provider of Investment Services
N.A.I.C.S.: 523940

Mulvihill Premium Canadian Bank (1)
121 King St W Ste 2600, Toronto, M5H 3T9, ON, Canada (100%)
Tel.: (416) 681-3900
Web Site: http://www.mulvihill.com
Sales Range: $1-9.9 Million
Emp.: 52
Mutual Fund
N.A.I.C.S.: 525910
John P. Mulvihill *(VP & Portfolio Mgr)*

Mulvihill Premium Yield Fund (1)
121 King Street West Suite 2600 Standard Life Centre, PO Box 113, Toronto, M5H 3T9, ON, Canada
Tel.: (416) 681-3966
Web Site: https://mulvihill.com
Tax-efficient Distributions
N.A.I.C.S.: 541213

MUMIAS SUGAR COMPANY LIMITED
Kakamega-Bungoma Road Kakamega Countybr, PO Box Private Bag, Mumias, Kenya
Tel.: (254) 711094000
Web Site: http://www.mumias-sugar.com
MSC—(NAI)
Sales Range: $10-24.9 Million
Emp.: 1,689
Sugar Mfr
N.A.I.C.S.: 111930
Wesley Koech *(Dir-Info & Comm Tech)*

MUN SIONG ENGINEERING LIMITED
No 35 Tuas Road, Jurong, 638496, Singapore
Tel.: (65) 64116570 SG
Web Site: https://www.mun-siong.com
Year Founded: 1969
MF6—(SES)
Rev.: $53,932,440
Assets: $57,052,185
Liabilities: $17,647,504
Net Worth: $39,404,681
Earnings: ($2,124,517)
Emp.: 1,200
Fiscal Year-end: 12/31/23
Mechanical & Electrical Engineering Services
N.A.I.C.S.: 541330
Woei Fen Cheng *(Chm & CEO)*

Subsidiaries:

Pegasus Advance Engineering (US) Inc. (1)
4527 So Columbia Ave Ste B2-A, Hammond, IN 46320
Tel.: (219) 203-1595
Engineeering Services
N.A.I.C.S.: 541330

Pegasus Advance Industrial Company Ltd. (1)
No 32 Zhongheng Street, Xiaogang District, Kaohsiung, Taiwan
Tel.: (886) 73754678
Oil & Gas Mfr
N.A.I.C.S.: 333132

Pegasus Industrial Midwest Limited Liability Company (1)
5485 N 5000E Rd, Bourbonnais, IL 60914
Tel.: (815) 386-5838
Web Site: https://www.pegasus-ind.com
Oil & Gas Equipment Distr
N.A.I.C.S.: 423830

MUNAWLA CARGO CO. LTD.
King Khalid Street Near Passport office, Dammam, 31491, Saudi Arabia
Tel.: (966) 138341655
Web Site: https://www.munawlacargo.com.sa
Year Founded: 1997
9571—(SAU)
Rev.: $37,032,606
Assets: $13,716,303
Liabilities: $4,932,100
Net Worth: $8,784,203
Earnings: $2,574,823
Emp.: 218
Fiscal Year-end: 12/31/22
Logistic Services
N.A.I.C.S.: 541614

MUNCHENER HYPOTHEKEN-BANK EG
Karl-Scharnagl-Ring 10, 80539, Munich, Germany
Tel.: (49) 8953870 De
Web Site: https://www.muenchenerhyp.de
Year Founded: 1896
Real Estate & Banking Services
N.A.I.C.S.: 531390
Louis Hagen *(CEO)*

MUNCHENER RUCKVERSICHERUNGS AG
Koniginstrasse 107, 80802, Munich, Germany
Tel.: (49) 8938910 De
Web Site: http://www.munichre.com
Year Founded: 1880
MUV2—(DUS)
Rev.: $86,545,475,120
Assets: $383,708,317,200
Liabilities: $34,584,290,620
Net Worth: $349,124,026,580
Earnings: $3,601,199,680
Emp.: 39,281
Fiscal Year-end: 12/31/21
Reinsurance & Financial Services
N.A.I.C.S.: 524130
Thomas Blunck *(Member-Mgmt Bd)*

Subsidiaries:

ALLYSCA Assistance GmbH (1)
Rosenheimer Strasse 116a, 81669, Munich, Germany
Tel.: (49) 89418640
Web Site: https://www.allysca.de
Insurance Services
N.A.I.C.S.: 524210
Markus Kunze *(Mng Dir)*

ARTES Assekuranzservice GmbH (1)
Uerdinger Str 58, 40474, Dusseldorf, Germany
Tel.: (49) 2 11 4 77 88 00
Web Site: http://www.artes-makler.de
General Insurance Services
N.A.I.C.S.: 524210

American Digital Title Insurance Company (1)
4949 S Syracuse St Ste 540, Denver, CO 80237
Tel.: (720) 630-7751
Web Site: https://www.americandigitaltitle.com
Insurance Services
N.A.I.C.S.: 524210

American Modern Surplus Lines Insurance Company (1)
7000 Midland Blvd, Amelia, OH 45102
Tel.: (800) 543-2644
General Insurance Services
N.A.I.C.S.: 524210

Amicus Legal Ltd. (1)
1 London Road, Arundel, BN18 9BH, West Sussex, United Kingdom
Tel.: (44) 1903 883811
Web Site: http://www.amicuslegal.co.uk
Emp.: 7
General Insurance Services
N.A.I.C.S.: 524210

ArztPartner almeda AG (1)
Balanstrasse 49, Munich, 81541, Germany
Tel.: (49) 89 480 590
Health Care Assistance Services
N.A.I.C.S.: 923130

Associated Asset Management Corporation B.V. (1)
Julianaplein 10, 's-Hertogenbosch, 5211 BC, North Brabant, Netherlands
Tel.: (31) 736449722
Asset Management Services
N.A.I.C.S.: 523940

Astoria Energy LLC (1)
1710 Steinway St, Astoria, NY 11105
Tel.: (718) 274-7700
Web Site: http://www.astoriaenergy.com
Fossil Fuel Power Generation
N.A.I.C.S.: 221112
Chuck McCall *(CEO)*

Autobahn Tank & Rast GmbH (1)
Andreas Hermes Strasse 729, 53175, Bonn, Germany
Tel.: (49) 2289220
Web Site: http://www.tank.rast.de
Gas Station Operator
N.A.I.C.S.: 457110
Karl-H. Rolfes *(CEO)*

Subsidiary (Domestic):

AXXE Reisegastronomie GmbH (2)
Clevischer Ring 127, 51063, Cologne, Germany
Tel.: (49) 2219647670
Web Site: http://www.axxe.de
Motorway Restaurant & Hotel Services
N.A.I.C.S.: 722511
Wolfgang Fritze *(Mng Dir)*

B&D Business Solutions B.V. (1)
Euclideslaan 71, Utrecht, 3508 AE, Netherlands
Tel.: (31) 30 236 4364
Debt Collection Services
N.A.I.C.S.: 561440

Bank Austria Creditanstalt Versicherungsdienst GmbH (1)
Berggasse 31/5 Stock, Vienna, 1090, Austria
Tel.: (43) 5050542330
Sales Range: $50-74.9 Million
Emp.: 6
Commercial Banking Services
N.A.I.C.S.: 522110
Thorsten Mueller *(Mng Dir)*

Bell & Clements (London) Ltd (1)
55 King William Street, London, EC4R 9AD, United Kingdom
Tel.: (44) 2072836222
Web Site: http://www.bellandclements.com
Sales Range: $50-74.9 Million
Emp.: 90
Insurance Brokerage Services
N.A.I.C.S.: 524210

Bell & Clements Inc (1)
11921 Freedom Dr Ste 1150, Reston, VA 20190
Tel.: (571) 283-0400
Web Site: http://www.bellandclements.com
Insurance Brokerage Services
N.A.I.C.S.: 524210
Dave Toombs *(VP-Underwriting)*

Bell & Clements Underwriting Managers Ltd (1)

MUNCHENER RUCKVERSICHERUNGS AG

55 King William Street, London, EC4R 9AD, United Kingdom
Tel.: (44) 2072836222
Sales Range: $50-74.9 Million
Emp.: 90
Insurance Underwriting Services
N.A.I.C.S.: 524127
Mark Balcombe *(Gen Mgr)*

BioEnergie Elbe-Elster GmbH & Co. KG (1)
Lauchhammerstrasse 45, 04910, Elsterwerda, Germany
Tel.: (49) 3533 48670
Eletric Power Generation Services
N.A.I.C.S.: 221118

BioEnergie Verwaltungs-GmbH (1)
Lauchhammerstrasse 45, 4910, Elsterwerda, Germany
Tel.: (49) 3533 48670
Eletric Power Generation Services
N.A.I.C.S.: 221118

Blewett & Associates Inc. (1)
630 Wharncliffe Rd S Suite 4, London, N6J 4V7, ON, Canada
Tel.: (519) 685-5353
Web Site: https://www.blewett-ins.com
Insurance Services
N.A.I.C.S.: 524210

Bos Incasso B.V. (1)
Verl Lodewijkstraat 16, Groningen, 9723 ZL, Netherlands
Tel.: (31) 88 267 00 00
Web Site: http://www.bosincasso.nl
Debt Collection Services
N.A.I.C.S.: 561440

CAPITAL PLAZA Holding GmbH & Co. Singapur KG (1)
Victoriaplatz 2, 40477, Dusseldorf, Germany
Tel.: (49) 211 49370
Investment Management Service
N.A.I.C.S.: 523940

CBIG - Canadian Benefits Investment & Insurance Group Inc. (1)
492 Victoria Street, Prince George, V2L 2J7, BC, Canada
Tel.: (250) 564-7484
Web Site: https://www.cbiggroup.ca
Insurance Services
N.A.I.C.S.: 523999

CJSIC "European Travel Insurance" (1)
4 Dobryninskiy Pereulok Bldg 8 Office C 14-01, 119049, Moscow, Russia
Tel.: (7) 495 626 5800
Web Site: http://www.erv.ru
Sales Range: $50-74.9 Million
Emp.: 25
Travel Insurance Services
N.A.I.C.S.: 524298

Compagnie Europeenne d'Assurances S.A. (1)
40 Rue du Trois Fontanot, 92024, Nanterre, France
Tel.: (33) 1 46 43 64 64
Travel Insurance Services
N.A.I.C.S.: 524298

Corion Pty Limited (1)
L 3 143 Macquarie St, Sydney, 2000, NSW, Australia
Tel.: (61) 292722045
Fire Insurance Services
N.A.I.C.S.: 524113

D.A.S. Oigusabikulude Kindlustuse AS (1)
Toompuiestee 5/Luise 2, 10142, Tallinn, Estonia
Tel.: (372) 679 9450
Web Site: http://www.das.ee
General Insurance Services
N.A.I.C.S.: 524210

D.A.S. Towarzystwo Ubezpieczen Ochrony Prawnej S.A. (1)
Ul Wspolna 25, 00-519, Warsaw, Poland
Tel.: (48) 224530000
Web Site: http://www.das.pl
Insurance Services
N.A.I.C.S.: 524210

DAS Consultancy & Detachering Rotterdam B.V. (1)

MUNCHENER RUCKVERSICHERUNGS AG — INTERNATIONAL PUBLIC

Munchener Ruckversicherungs AG—(Continued)

Beursplein 37, 3011 AA, Rotterdam, Netherlands
Tel.: (31) 10 205 1833
Web Site: http://www.das.nl
Business Management Consulting Services
N.A.I.C.S.: 541618

DAS Holding N.V. (1)
Karspeldreef 15, Amsterdam, 1102 BB, Netherlands
Tel.: (31) 206517517
Investment Management Service
N.A.I.C.S.: 523999

DAS Incasso Arnhem B.V. (1)
Industrieweg Oost 13, 6662 NE, Elst, Netherlands
Tel.: (31) 88 773 3000
Web Site: http://www.dasincasso.nl
Debt Collection Services
N.A.I.C.S.: 561440

DAS Incasso Rotterdam B.V. (1)
Beursplein 37, 3011 AA, Rotterdam, Netherlands
Tel.: (31) 10 2 051 740
Debt Collection Services
N.A.I.C.S.: 561440

DAS LEGAL SERVICES LIMITED (1)
D A S House Quay Side Quay Side Temple Back, Avon, Bristol, BS1 6NH, United Kingdom
Tel.: (44) 117 934 2000
Sales Range: $75-99.9 Million
Emp.: 400
Legal Protection Services
N.A.I.C.S.: 541199

DAS Legal Expenses Insurance Co., Ltd. (1)
7/F Shinsa Building 630-2 Shinsa-dong, Gangnam-gu, Seoul, 135 895, Korea (South)
Tel.: (82) 25177133
Web Site: http://www.das.co.kr
Emp.: 40
General Insurance Services
N.A.I.C.S.: 524210

DAS Legal Finance B.V. (1)
Karspeldreef 15, Postbus 23000, 1102 BB, Amsterdam, Netherlands
Tel.: (31) 20 6 517 517
Web Site: http://www.das.nl
Legal Protection & General Insurance Services
N.A.I.C.S.: 541199

DAS Legal Protection Ireland Limited (1)
Europa House Harcourt street, Dublin, 2, Ireland
Tel.: (353) 1 670 7470
Web Site: http://www.das.ie
Sales Range: $50-74.9 Million
Emp.: 20
Insurance Services
N.A.I.C.S.: 524298
Adrienne O'Sullivan *(CEO)*

DAS Services Limited (1)
D A S House Quay Side Quay Side Temple Back, Bristol, BS1 6NH, Avon, United Kingdom
Tel.: (44) 1179342000
Legal Protection Services
N.A.I.C.S.: 541199

DKV - Alpha Vermogensverwaltungs GmbH (1)
Aachener Str 300, 50933, Cologne, Germany
Tel.: (49) 221 5780
Financial Management Services
N.A.I.C.S.: 523940

DKV - Beta Vermogensverwaltungs GmbH (1)
Aachener Str 300, 50933, Cologne, Germany
Tel.: (49) 172 2999350
Financial Management Services
N.A.I.C.S.: 523940

DKV Deutsche Krankenversicherung Aktiengesellschaft (1)
Aachener Strasse 300, 50933, Cologne, Germany
Tel.: (49) 22157894018
Web Site: https://www.dkv.com
Health Insurance Services
N.A.I.C.S.: 524114

DKV Residenz am Tibusplatz gGmbH (1)
Tibusplatz 1-7, Munster, 48143, Germany
Tel.: (49) 25148350
Web Site: http://www.dkv-residenz-am-tibusplatz.de
Senior Citizen Housing Services
N.A.I.C.S.: 623312

DKV Servicios, S.A. (1)
Avenida Cesar Augusto 33, Zaragoza, 50004, Spain
Tel.: (34) 976289100
Health Care Srvices
N.A.I.C.S.: 621999

DKV-Residenz in der Contrescarpe GmbH (1)
Am Wandrahm 40-43, Bremen, 28195, Germany
Tel.: (49) 42132290
Web Site: http://www.dkv-rc.de
Residential Care Services
N.A.I.C.S.: 623312
Andreas Lammers *(Mng Dir)*

DRA Debt Recovery Agency B.V. (1)
Loire 188-190, Hague, 2491 AM, Netherlands
Tel.: (31) 704525355
Debt Collection Services
N.A.I.C.S.: 561440

ERGO Asia Management Pte. Ltd. (1)
70 Anson Road 13-01 Hub Synergy Point, Singapore, 79905, Singapore
Tel.: (65) 63251738
Web Site: http://www.ergo.com
Business Management Consulting Services
N.A.I.C.S.: 541611

ERGO Austria International AG (1)
ERGO Center Businesspark Marximum Objekt 3 Modecenterstrasse 17, 1110, Vienna, Austria
Tel.: (43) 1 274444 0
Web Site: http://www.ergo-austria.com
Sales Range: $200-249.9 Million
Emp.: 415
Insurance Services
N.A.I.C.S.: 524298
Josef Adelmann *(Member-Mgmt Bd)*

ERGO Direkt Lebensversicherung AG (1)
Am Concordepark 1/D2, Schwechat, 2320, Austria
Tel.: (43) 1 707 80 80
Web Site: http://www.ergodirekt.at
Life Insurance & Pension Fund Management Services
N.A.I.C.S.: 524113

ERGO Eletbiztosito Zrt. (1)
Futo Utca 47-53 III Emelet Corvin Irodahaz, 1082, Budapest, Hungary
Tel.: (36) 1 877 1111
Web Site: http://www.ergo.hu
Fire Insurance Services
N.A.I.C.S.: 524113
Laszlo Freund *(CEO)*

ERGO Funds AS (1)
A H Tammsaare Tee 47, 11316, Tallinn, Estonia
Tel.: (372) 610 6500
Web Site: http://www.ergo.ee
Pension Fund Management Services
N.A.I.C.S.: 525110
Annika Loigu *(Head-Comm)*

ERGO General Insurance Company S.A. (1)
97 Vas Sofias Ave, 11521, Athens, Greece
Tel.: (30) 210 3705300
Web Site: http://www.ergohellas.gr
Property & Casualty Insurance Services
N.A.I.C.S.: 524126

ERGO Grubu Holding A.S. (1)
Saray Mah Dr Adnah Buyukdeniz Caddesi No 4 Akkom Ofis Park 2, Blok Kat 10-14 Umraniye, 34768, Istanbul, Turkiye
Tel.: (90) 216 666 76 66
Web Site: http://www.ergoturkiye.com
General Insurance Services
N.A.I.C.S.: 524210

ERGO Immobilien-GmbH 14.Victoria & Co. KG (1)
Lindenstr 59, Kreien, 19386, Germany
Tel.: (49) 3873322565
Real Estate Management Services
N.A.I.C.S.: 531390

ERGO Immobilien-GmbH 4. DKV & Co. KG (1)
Lindenstr 59, Kreien, 19386, Germany
Tel.: (49) 3873322565
Real Estate Management Services
N.A.I.C.S.: 531390

ERGO Immobilien-GmbH 5. Hamburg-Mannheimer & Co. KG (1)
Lindenstr 59, Kreien, 19386, Germany
Tel.: (49) 3873322565
Real Estate Management Services
N.A.I.C.S.: 531390

ERGO Immobilien-GmbH 6. Hamburg-Mannheimer & Co. KG (1)
Lindenstr 59, 19386, Kreien, Germany
Tel.: (49) 38733 22565
Real Estate Management Services
N.A.I.C.S.: 531390

ERGO Immobilien-GmbH 7. Hamburg-Mannheimer & Co. KG (1)
Lindenstr 59, 19386, Kreien, Germany
Tel.: (49) 38733 22565
Real Estate Management Services
N.A.I.C.S.: 531390

ERGO Immobilien-Verwaltungs-GmbH (1)
Lindenstr 59, 19386, Kreien, Germany
Tel.: (49) 38733 22565
Real Estate Management Services
N.A.I.C.S.: 531390

ERGO International Services GmbH (1)
Victoriaplatz 2, Dusseldorf, 40477, Germany
Tel.: (49) 21149371910
General Insurance Services
N.A.I.C.S.: 524210

ERGO Latvija Versicherung AG (1)
Skanstes St 50, Riga, 10130, Latvia
Tel.: (371) 6708 1700
Web Site: http://www.ergo.lv
Sales Range: $100-124.9 Million
Emp.: 150
Property & Casualty Insurance Services
N.A.I.C.S.: 524126
Kestutis Bagdonavicius *(Chm)*

ERGO Lebensversicherung Aktiengesellschaft (1)
Uberseering 45, Hamburg, 22297, Germany
Tel.: (49) 40 6 37 60
Fire Insurance Services
N.A.I.C.S.: 524113

ERGO Pensionsfonds Aktiengesellschaft (1)
Victoriaplatz 1, Dusseldorf, 40198, Germany
Tel.: (49) 211 4770
Web Site: http://www.ergo.de
Emp.: 3,500
Pension Fund Services
N.A.I.C.S.: 525110

ERGO Pensionskasse AG (1)
Victoriaplatz 1, Dusseldorf, 40477, Germany
Tel.: (49) 2114770
Pension Fund Management Services
N.A.I.C.S.: 525110

ERGO Poistovna, a.s. (1)
Apollo Business Center II Prievozska 4C, 821 08, Bratislava, Slovakia
Tel.: (421) 2 32112 020
Web Site: http://www.victoria-volksbanken.sk
Fire Insurance Services
N.A.I.C.S.: 524113
Miriam Cizmazia *(Chm & CEO)*

ERGO Private Capital Gesundheit GmbH & Co. KG (1)
Victoriaplatz 2, Dusseldorf, 40477, Germany

ERGO Private Capital GmbH (1)
Victoriaplatz 2, Dusseldorf, 40477, Germany
Tel.: (49) 21149370
Web Site: http://www.ergo.de
Investment Advisory Services
N.A.I.C.S.: 523940
Torsten Oletzky *(Mng Dir)*

ERGO Private Capital GmbH (1)
Victoriaplatz 2, Dusseldorf, 40477, Germany
Tel.: (49) 211 49370
Investment Management Service
N.A.I.C.S.: 523940

ERGO Private Capital Leben GmbH & Co. KG (1)
Victoriaplatz 2, Dusseldorf, 40477, Germany
Tel.: (49) 21149370
Real Estate Development Services
N.A.I.C.S.: 531390

ERGO Private Equity Leben GmbH (1)
Victoriaplatz 2, 40477, Dusseldorf, Germany
Tel.: (49) 211 4770
Web Site: http://www.ergo.de
Investment Management Service
N.A.I.C.S.: 523940

ERGO RUSS Versicherung AG (1)
Butyurskaya Street 46 Bld 1, 127015, Moscow, Russia
Tel.: (7) 495 725 78 90
Web Site: http://www.ergorussia.ru
Sales Range: $50-74.9 Million
Emp.: 100
Property & Casualty Insurance Services
N.A.I.C.S.: 524126

ERGO Sigorta ve Emeklilik Satis Aracilik Hizmetleri Limited Sirketi (1)
Cevat Yurdakul Bulvari Cetin Apt No 4 Seyhan/Adana, Seyhan, Adana, Turkiye
Tel.: (90) 322 458 93 91
General Insurance Services
N.A.I.C.S.: 524298

ERGO Specialty GmbH (1)
Uberseering 45, 22297, Hamburg, Germany
Tel.: (49) 40 63763578
General Insurance Services
N.A.I.C.S.: 524210

ERGO Versicherungsgruppe AG (1)
Victoriaplatz 2, Dusseldorf, 40477, Germany **(100%)**
Tel.: (49) 21149370
Web Site: http://www.ergo.com
Sales Range: $1-4.9 Billion
Insurance Services
N.A.I.C.S.: 524298
Nikolaus von Bomhard *(Chm-Supervisory Bd)*

Subsidiary (Non-US):

Bank Austria Creditanstalt Versicherung AG (2)
ERGO Center Businesspark Marximum/Objekt 3, Modecenterstrasse 17, A 1110, Vienna, Austria
Tel.: (43) 1313830
Web Site: http://www.ba-versicherung.at
Sales Range: $150-199.9 Million
Emp.: 300
Insurance Services
N.A.I.C.S.: 524298
Josef Adelmann *(Mng Dir)*

D.A.S. Defensa del Automovilista y de Siniestros Internacional S.A. de Seguros (2)
Pleuropa 41 6th Fl, 08908, Hospitalet, Spain
Tel.: (34) 934547705
Web Site: http://www.das.es
Sales Range: $50-74.9 Million
Emp.: 81
Insurance Services
N.A.I.C.S.: 524298

Subsidiary (Domestic):

D.A.S. Deutscher Automobil Schutz Allgemeine Rechtsschutz-Versicherungs-AG (2)
Thomas Dehler Strasse 2, 81728, Munich, Germany **(99.9%)**
Tel.: (49) 8962757101
Web Site: http://www.wenn-das-dann-das.de
Sales Range: $300-349.9 Million
Emp.: 800
Insurance Services

AND PRIVATE COMPANIES — MUNCHENER RUCKVERSICHERUNGS AG

N.A.I.C.S.: 524298

Subsidiary (Non-US):

D.A.S. Difesa Automobilistica Sinistri, S.p.A. di Assicurazione (2)
Via Enrico Fermi 9/B, 37135, Verona, Italy
Tel.: (39) 0458372611
Web Site: https://www.das.it
Sales Range: $25-49.9 Million
Emp.: 40
Insurance Services
N.A.I.C.S.: 524298

D.A.S. Hellas Allgemeine Rechtsschutz-Versicherungs-AG (2)
Leoforos Sygrou 44, 117 42, Athens, Greece
Tel.: (30) 2109001300
Web Site: http://www.das.gr
Sales Range: $50-74.9 Million
Emp.: 25
Insurance Services
N.A.I.C.S.: 524298

D.A.S. Luxemburg Allgemeine Rechtsschutz-Versicherung Societe Anonyme (2)
3 Rue Thomas Edison, 1445, Strassen, Luxembourg (100%)
Tel.: (352) 455758
Web Site: http://www.das.lu
Sales Range: $50-74.9 Million
Emp.: 12
Insurance Services
N.A.I.C.S.: 524298
Oliver Wienand *(Mng Dir)*

D.A.S. S.A. belge d'assurances de Protection Juridique (2)
6 Ave Lloyd George, 1000, Brussels, Belgium
Tel.: (32) 26455111
Web Site: http://www.das.be
Sales Range: $25-49.9 Million
Emp.: 200
Insurance Services
N.A.I.C.S.: 524298
Daemen Gustav *(Gen Mgr)*

D.A.S. pojist'ovna pravni ochrany a.s. (2)
BB Centrum Beta Vyskocilova 1481/4, 10100, Prague, Czech Republic
Tel.: (420) 267990711
Web Site: http://www.das.cz
Sales Range: $1-9.9 Million
Emp.: 50
Insurance Services
N.A.I.C.S.: 524298
Jitta Chizzola *(CEO)*

DAS Legal Expenses Co. (2)
Av De Provence 82, Mallenk, 1000, Lausanne, Switzerland
Tel.: (41) 216239223
Sales Range: $25-49.9 Million
Emp.: 50
Insurance Services
N.A.I.C.S.: 524298

DAS Legal Expenses Insurance Company Limited (2)
Trinity Quay 2 Avon Street, Bristol, BS2 0PT, Avon, United Kingdom (100%)
Tel.: (44) 3448939013
Web Site: https://www.das.co.uk
Sales Range: $150-199.9 Million
Emp.: 300
Insurance Services
N.A.I.C.S.: 524298

DAS Osterreichische Allgemeine Rechtsschutz Versicherungs AG (2)
Hernalser Guertel 17, 1170, Vienna, Austria (100%)
Tel.: (43) 1404640
Web Site: http://www.das.at
Sales Range: $150-199.9 Million
Emp.: 500
Insurance Services
N.A.I.C.S.: 524298
Loenger Johannes *(Gen Mgr)*

DAS Rechtsbijstand (2)
Karspeldreef 15, 1102 BB, Amsterdam, Netherlands (80%)
Tel.: (31) 206517517
Web Site: http://www.das.nl

Sales Range: $300-349.9 Million
Emp.: 650
Insurance Services
N.A.I.C.S.: 524298
Errick Pouv *(Mng Dir)*

DKV Belgium S.A./N.V. (2)
(100%)
Tel.: (32) 22876411
Web Site: http://www.dkv.be
Sales Range: $150-199.9 Million
Emp.: 350
Health Insurance
N.A.I.C.S.: 524114

DKV Luxembourg SA (2)
43 Ave J F Kennedy, 1855, Luxembourg, Luxembourg (100%)
Tel.: (352) 4264641
Web Site: http://www.dkv.lu
Sales Range: $25-49.9 Million
Emp.: 50
Insurance Services
N.A.I.C.S.: 524298

Subsidiary (Domestic):

Deutsche Krankenversicherung AG (2)
Aachener Strasse 300, 50933, Cologne, 50933, Germany (99.9%)
Tel.: (49) 2215780
Web Site: http://www.dkv.com
Sales Range: $1-4.9 Billion
Emp.: 2,700
Life & Health Insurance
N.A.I.C.S.: 524298

Subsidiary (Non-US):

ERGO ASIGURARI DE VIATA SA (2)
1 Bucuresti Sectorul, Bucharest, 014459, Romania
Tel.: (40) 312248600
Web Site: http://www.ergo.ro
Sales Range: $50-74.9 Million
Emp.: 20
General Insurance Services
N.A.I.C.S.: 524210
Josef Adelmann *(Chm-Mgmt Bd)*

Subsidiary (Domestic):

ERGO Gourmet GmbH (2)
Victoriaplatz 2, 40198, Dusseldorf, Germany
Tel.: (49) 2 11 477 8002
Web Site: http://www.ergo-gourmet.eu
Catering Services
N.A.I.C.S.: 722320

Subsidiary (Non-US):

ERGO Insurance NV/SA (2)
Boulevard Bischoffsheim 1-8, 1000, Brussels, Belgium (100%)
Tel.: (32) 25355711
Web Site: http://www.ergo.be
Sales Range: $150-199.9 Million
Emp.: 400
Insurance Services
N.A.I.C.S.: 524298
Nathalie Daheemm *(Dir-Mktg)*

Subsidiary (Non-US):

ERGO Insurance Service GmbH (3)
ERGO Center Businesspark Marximum Objekt 3 Modecenterstrasse 17, Vienna, 1110, Austria
Tel.: (43) 1 27444 0
Web Site: http://www.ergo-austria.at
Sales Range: $150-199.9 Million
General Insurance Services
N.A.I.C.S.: 524210
Peter Bonyhadi *(Project Mgr)*

ERGO Zivljenjska zavarovalnica d.d. (3)
Slandrova Cesta 4, Ljubljana, 1000, Slovenia
Tel.: (386) 1 600 50 30
Web Site: http://www.ergo.si
Fire Insurance Services
N.A.I.C.S.: 524113
Andrej Kocic *(Chm-Mgmt Bd)*

Subsidiary (Non-US):

ERGO Insurance Pte. Ltd. (2)
5 Temasek Boulevard #04-01 Suntec Tower Five, Singapore, 038985, Singapore
Tel.: (65) 6829 9199
Web Site: http://www.ergo.com.sg
Sales Range: $50-74.9 Million
General Insurance Services
N.A.I.C.S.: 524298
Karl-Heinz Jung *(CEO)*

ERGO Life Insurance SE (2)
Gelezinio Vilko G-ve 6 a, 03507, Vilnius, Lithuania
Tel.: (370) 526830 21
Web Site: http://www.ergo.lt
Sales Range: $350-399.9 Million
Emp.: 900
Insurance Services
N.A.I.C.S.: 524113
Kestutis Bagdonavicius *(CEO)*

Subsidiary (Domestic):

ERGO Versicherung Aktiengesellschaft (2)
ERGO-Platz 1, 40198, Dusseldorf, Germany
Tel.: (49) 211 477 7100
Web Site: http://www.ergo.de
Property & Casualty Insurance Products & Services
N.A.I.C.S.: 524126

ERGO Versicherungs- und Finanzierungs-Vermittlung GmbH (2)
Uberseering 45, 22297, Hamburg, Germany
Tel.: (49) 40 63764376
General Insurance Services
N.A.I.C.S.: 524210

Subsidiary (Non-US):

ERGO pojistovna, a.s. (2)
BB Centrum Building BETA Vyskocilova 1481/4, 140 00, Prague, 4, Michle, Czech Republic
Tel.: (420) 221 585 111
Web Site: http://www.ergo.cz
Sales Range: $25-49.9 Million
Emp.: 30
Insurance Services
N.A.I.C.S.: 524298

ERGO zivotna poistovna, a.s. (2)
Prievozska 4C, Bratislava, 821 08, Slovakia
Tel.: (421) 2 3211 2020
Web Site: http://www.ergo.sk
Fire Insurance Services
N.A.I.C.S.: 524113

Ergolsvicre A.S. (2)
Kisikli Caddesi No:30, Altunizade, 34662, Istanbul, Turkiye
Tel.: (90) 216 474 2000
Web Site: http://www.ergoisvicre.com.tr
Insurance Services
N.A.I.C.S.: 524210

Hamburg-Mannheimer Filial af Hamburg-Mannheimer Versicherungs-AG tysk forsikringsselskab (2)
PO Box 151, 0900, Copenhagen, Denmark
Tel.: (45) 70206501
Web Site: http://www.hamburg-mannheimer.dk
Sales Range: $50-74.9 Million
Emp.: 3
Insurance Services
N.A.I.C.S.: 524298

Subsidiary (Domestic):

Hamburg-Mannheimer Rechtsschutzversicherungs-AG (2)
Uberseering 45, 22297, Hamburg, Germany
Tel.: (49) 4063760
Web Site: http://www.ergo.de
Sales Range: $25-49.9 Million
Emp.: 50
Insurance Services
N.A.I.C.S.: 524298
Thorften Oletzki *(Mng Dir)*

Hamburg-Mannheimer Sachversicherungs-AG (2)
Uberseering 45, 22297, Hamburg, Germany
Tel.: (49) 4063760
Web Site: http://www.hamburg-mannheimer.de

Sales Range: $600-649.9 Million
Emp.: 2,400
Insurance Services
N.A.I.C.S.: 524298

Subsidiary (Non-US):

Hamburg-Mannheimer Skade Filial af Hamburg-Mannheimer Sachversicherungs-AG tysk forsikringsselskab (2)
PO Box 151, DK 0900, Copenhagen, Denmark
Tel.: (45) 70206501
Web Site: http://www.hamburg-mannheimer.dk
Insurance Services
N.A.I.C.S.: 524298

Subsidiary (Domestic):

Hamburg-Mannheimer Versicherungs-AG (2)
Uberseering 45, Hamburg, 22297, Germany
Tel.: (49) 4063760
Web Site: http://www.ergo.de
Sales Range: $600-649.9 Million
Emp.: 2,500
Insurance Services
N.A.I.C.S.: 524298
Thorsten Oletzky *(CEO)*

Subsidiary (Non-US):

LAVG Zuid B.V. (2)
St Ignatiusstraat 267, Breda, 4817 KK, Netherlands
Tel.: (31) 765224266
Debt Collection Services
N.A.I.C.S.: 561440

Subsidiary (Domestic):

Longial GmbH (2)
Fischerstrasse 10, 40477, Dusseldorf, Germany
Tel.: (49) 21149377600
Web Site: https://www.longial.de
Pension Fund Management Services
N.A.I.C.S.: 525110

Subsidiary (Non-US):

Menzis (2)
Lawickse Allee 130, 6709 DZ, Wageningen, Netherlands (100%)
Tel.: (31) 745 53 60
Sales Range: $75-99.9 Million
Emp.: 240
Insurance Services
N.A.I.C.S.: 524298

Nieuwe Hollandse Lloyd Verzekeringsgroep NV (2)
Polanerbaan 11, 3447, Woerden, Netherlands (100%)
Tel.: (31) 348571911
Web Site: http://www.nhl-verzekeringen.nl
Sales Range: $75-99.9 Million
Emp.: 230
Insurance Services
N.A.I.C.S.: 524298

Sopockie Towarzystwo Ubezpieczen na Zycie Ergo Hestia Spolka Akcyjna (2)
ul Hestii 1, 81-731, Sopot, Poland
Tel.: (48) 585556000
Fire Insurance Services
N.A.I.C.S.: 524113
Schollkopf Thomas *(Mgr)*

Joint Venture (Non-US):

Storebrand Helseforsikring AS (2)
Havedkontr Filitstad Brygge 1, PO Box 1382, N 0114, Oslo, Vica, Norway (50%)
Tel.: (47) 22311330
Web Site: http://www.storebrandhelse.no
Sales Range: $50-74.9 Million
Emp.: 60
Insurance Services
N.A.I.C.S.: 524298

Subsidiary (Non-US):

Union Medica la Fuencisla, SA Compania de Seguros (2)
Diego de Leon 45, Madrid, 28006, Spain
Tel.: (34) 913790400

MUNCHENER RUCKVERSICHERUNGS AG   INTERNATIONAL PUBLIC

Munchener Ruckversicherungs AG—(Continued)
Insurance
N.A.I.C.S.: 524113

VICTORIA General Insurance Company S.A. (2)
21 Tsimiski St, Thessaloniki, 54624, Greece
Tel.: (30) 2310371100
Web Site: http://www.ergohellas.gr
Sales Range: $75-99.9 Million
Emp.: 150
Reinsurance Agents
N.A.I.C.S.: 524130
Theodore Kokkalas (Pres)

VICTORIA-VOLKSBANKEN Versicherungsaktiengesellschaft (2)
Schottengasse 10, 1013, Vienna, Austria
Tel.: (43) 1313410
Web Site: http://www.victoria.at
Sales Range: $75-99.9 Million
Emp.: 180
Insurance Services
N.A.I.C.S.: 524298
Ingo Lorenzoni (Mng Dir & Chm-Mgmt Bd)

Van Arkel Gerechtsdeurwaarders B.V. (2)
Pompoenweg 15, Leiden, 2321 DK, Netherlands
Tel.: (31) 715352700
Web Site: http://www.vanarkelincasso.nl
Sales Range: $25-49.9 Million
Emp.: 120
Debt Collection Services
N.A.I.C.S.: 561440
P. A. J. van Diest (Principal)

Subsidiary (Domestic):

Victoria Krankenversicherung AG (2)
Victoriaplatz 2, D 40198, Dusseldorf, Germany   (100%)
Tel.: (49) 2114770
Web Site: http://www.ergo.de
Sales Range: $1-4.9 Billion
Emp.: 6,000
Health Insurance
N.A.I.C.S.: 524113

Victoria Lebensversicherung AG (2)
Victoriaplatz 1, 40198, Dusseldorf, Germany   (92%)
Tel.: (49) 2114770
Web Site: http://www.victoria.de
Sales Range: $1-4.9 Billion
Emp.: 5,897
Fire Insurance Services
N.A.I.C.S.: 524113
Torsten Olesky (Pres)

Subsidiary (Non-US):

Victoria-Seguros de Vida, S.A. (2)
Avenida Liberdade 200, 1250 147, Lisbon, Codex, Portugal
Tel.: (351) 213134100
Web Site: http://www.victoria-seguros.pt
Sales Range: $150-199.9 Million
Emp.: 300
Insurance Services
N.A.I.C.S.: 524298

Subsidiary (Domestic):

Vorsorge Lebensversicherung AG (2)
Rather Strasse 110a, 40476, Dusseldorf, Germany   (100%)
Tel.: (49) 211 21022 9500
Web Site: http://www.vorsorge-leben.de
Sales Range: $50-74.9 Million
Emp.: 80
Insurance Services
N.A.I.C.S.: 524298

Subsidiary (Non-US):

Vorsorge Luxemburg Lebensversicherung S.A. (2)
6 Parc D Activitie, Syrdall, L 5365, Munsbach, Luxembourg
Tel.: (352) 2648551
Sales Range: $25-49.9 Million
Emp.: 48
Insurance Services
N.A.I.C.S.: 524298

ERGO Vida Seguros y Reaseguros, Sociedad Anonima (1)
Avenida Cesar Augusto 33, Zaragoza, 50004, Spain
Tel.: (34) 976289100
Fire Insurance Services
N.A.I.C.S.: 524113

ERGO zivotno osiguranje d.d. (1)
Radnicka 80, 10000, Zagreb, Croatia
Tel.: (385) 16397640
Web Site: http://www.ergo-osiguranje.hr
Sales Range: $50-74.9 Million
Emp.: 15
General Insurance Services
N.A.I.C.S.: 524210

EUROALARM Assistance Prague, s.r.o. (1)
Krizikova 36a, 186 00, Prague, Czech Republic
Tel.: (420) 221 860 619
Web Site: http://www.euro-alarm.cz
General Insurance Services
N.A.I.C.S.: 524210

Economic Data Research B.V. (1)
Loire 192-198, Hague, 2491 AM, Netherlands
Tel.: (31) 704 52 52 52
Credit & Recovery Information Services
N.A.I.C.S.: 812199

Economic Data Resources B.V. (1)
Loire 192-198, Hague, 2491 AM, Netherlands
Tel.: (31) 704525252
Credit Protection Services
N.A.I.C.S.: 812199

Euro-Center (Thailand) Co. Ltd. (1)
Evergreen Pl 10th Fl Close to Asia Hotel, 318 Phyathai Road, Ratchathewi, Bangkok, 10400, Thailand
Tel.: (66) 26963626
Web Site: http://www.euro-center.com
Travel & Health Insurance Services
N.A.I.C.S.: 524114

Euro-Center Cape Town (Pty.) Ltd. (1)
18th Floor Metropolitan Center 7 Coen Steytler Ave, Foreshore, Cape Town, 8001, South Africa
Tel.: (27) 21 440 9999
Travel Assistance Services
N.A.I.C.S.: 541599
Tanja Roug (Gen Mgr)

Euro-Center China (HK) Co., Ltd. (1)
8/F Bld C E Lake Villas 35 Dongzhimenwai Dajie, Dongcheng District, Beijing, 100027, China
Tel.: (86) 10 8455 9500
Emp.: 20
Insurance Services
N.A.I.C.S.: 524298
Vladimir Alidis (Gen Mgr)

Euro-Center USA, Inc. (1)
65 W 36th St Ste 602, New York, NY 10018
Tel.: (212) 265-8522
Web Site: http://www.euro-center.com
Health Care Assistance Services
N.A.I.C.S.: 923130

Euro-Center Yerel Yardim Hizmetleri Ltd. Sti (1)
Ilk Belediye Cad Vural Arikan Apt No 5 Daire 3, Macka, 34367, Istanbul, Beyoglu, Turkiye
Tel.: (90) 2123154000
Web Site: http://www.euro-center.com
Travel & Healthcare Insurance Services
N.A.I.C.S.: 524114

Euro-Center, S.A. (1)
Avda Antonio Maura 22, 07012, Palma de Mallorca, Spain
Tel.: (34) 971726003
Web Site: https://www.euro-center.com
Health Insurance Services
N.A.I.C.S.: 524114
Hanne Stender (Office Mgr)

Europaeiske Rejseforsikring A/S (1)
Frederiksberg Alle 3, 1790, Copenhagen, Denmark
Tel.: (45) 33252525
Web Site: http://www.europaeiske.dk
Sales Range: $100-124.9 Million
Emp.: 140
Travel Insurance Services
N.A.I.C.S.: 524298
Richard Bader (Chm-Supervisory Bd)

Europaische Reiseversicherung AG (1)
Thomas-Dehler-Str 2, 81737, Munich, Germany   (100%)
Tel.: (49) 8941661102
Web Site: https://www.ergo-reiseversicherung.de
Sales Range: $200-249.9 Million
Emp.: 300
Travel Insurance
N.A.I.C.S.: 524298
Richard Bader (Chm-Mgmt Bd)

Europeiska Forsokringsaktiebolaget (1)
Lofstroms Alle 6A, Box 1, 172 13, Sundbyberg, Sweden
Tel.: (46) 770 456 900
Web Site: http://www.erv.se
General Insurance Services
N.A.I.C.S.: 524210

Evropska Cestovni Pojistovna A.S. (1)
Krizikova 237/36a, Prague, 186 00, Czech Republic
Tel.: (420) 2 2186 0860
Web Site: http://www.ervpojistovna.cz
Sales Range: $50-74.9 Million
Emp.: 50
General Insurance Services
N.A.I.C.S.: 524298

Exolvo GmbH (1)
Uberseering 34, Hamburg, 22297, Germany
Tel.: (49) 4063689383
Web Site: http://www.exolvo.de
Sales Range: $50-74.9 Million
Emp.: 10
Real Estate Management Services
N.A.I.C.S.: 531390

FAIRANCE GmbH (1)
Victoriaplatz 1, 40477, Dusseldorf, Germany
Tel.: (49) 21 14 93 70
Investment Management Service
N.A.I.C.S.: 523940

Flexitel Telefonservice GmbH (1)
Lutzowstrasse 105/106, Berlin, 10785, Germany
Tel.: (49) 30 26 04 26
Web Site: http://www.flexitel.de
Telephone Answering Services
N.A.I.C.S.: 561421
Reinhard Wolf (Mng Dir)

GBG Vogelsanger Strasse GmbH (1)
Aachener Str 300, 50933, Cologne, Germany
Tel.: (49) 2215783359
Real Estate Management Services
N.A.I.C.S.: 531390

Gebaude Service Gesellschaft Uberseering 35 mbH (1)
Uberseering 35, 22297, Hamburg, Germany
Tel.: (49) 40 63766789
Building Maintenance Services
N.A.I.C.S.: 561720

Global Standards LLC (1)
1 State St, Hartford, CT 06103
Tel.: (800) 417-3437
Engineeering Services
N.A.I.C.S.: 541330

Great Lakes Insurance UK Limited (1)
10 Fenchurch Avenue, London, EC3M 5BN, United Kingdom
Tel.: (44) 2030037000
Commercial Insurance Services
N.A.I.C.S.: 524210

Great Lakes Reinsurance (UK) Plc. (1)
Plantation Place 30 Fenchurch Street, London, EC3M 3AJ, United Kingdom
Tel.: (44) 20 3003 7000
Web Site: http://www.munichre.com
Reinsurance Services
N.A.I.C.S.: 524130
Achim Stegner (CEO)

Great Lakes Services Ltd. (1)
Plantation Place, London, EC3M 3AJ, United Kingdom
Tel.: (44) 20 3003 7000
Web Site: http://www.muicre.com
Emp.: 500
General Insurance Services
N.A.I.C.S.: 524210

GroupHEALTH Global Benefit Systems Inc. (1)
400-15315 31 Avenue, Surrey, V3Z 6X2, BC, Canada
Web Site: https://www.grouphealth.ca
Emp.: 1,000
Insurance Brokerage Services
N.A.I.C.S.: 524210

Groves, John & Westrup Limited (1)
Silkhouse Court Tithebarn Street, Liverpool, L2 2QW, United Kingdom
Tel.: (44) 1514738000
Web Site: http://www.gjwltd.co.uk
Emp.: 35
Boat Insurance Services
N.A.I.C.S.: 524298

HMI Sp. z o.o. (1)
Armii Ludowej 26, Warsaw, 00-609, Poland
Tel.: (48) 225793300
Sales Range: $50-74.9 Million
Emp.: 10
General Insurance Services
N.A.I.C.S.: 524210

HSB Associates, Inc (1)
245 5th Ave At 28 St Ste 1101, New York, NY 10016
Tel.: (860) 722-5539
Insurance Services
N.A.I.C.S.: 524298

HSB Engineering Insurance Services Limited (1)
Chancery Place 50 Brown Street, Manchester, M2 2JT, United Kingdom
Tel.: (44) 8453455510
Web Site: http://www.hsbeil.com
Emp.: 200
General Insurance Services
N.A.I.C.S.: 524210
Stephennie Watkins (CEO)

HSB Japan KK (1)
7F Yokohama Plaza Building 2-6 Kinko-cho, Kanagawa-ku, Yokohama, 221-0056, Kanagawa, Japan
Tel.: (81) 454503540
Web Site: http://www.hsb-japan.com
Sales Range: $25-49.9 Million
Emp.: 30
Laboratory Testing Services
N.A.I.C.S.: 541380
Satoru Watanabe (Pres)

HSB Solomon Associates LLC (1)
5400 LBJ Freeway Ste 1400, Dallas, TX 75240
Tel.: (972) 945-9901
Web Site: https://www.solomoninsight.com
Data Management Services
N.A.I.C.S.: 518210

HSB Technical Consulting & Services (Shanghai) Company, Ltd. (1)
Far East Intern Plaza 319 Xianxia Rd Room 909 Building A, Shanghai, 200051, China
Tel.: (86) 2162351717
Web Site: http://www.hsbct.com
Business Management Consulting Services
N.A.I.C.S.: 541611

Hamburg-Mannheimer Rechtsschutz Schaden-Service GmbH (1)
Uberseering 45, 22297, Hamburg, Germany
Tel.: (49) 4063760
General Insurance Services
N.A.I.C.S.: 524210

Hartford Steam Boiler (M) Sdn. Bhd (1)
27B-6 6th Floor Jln Pju 1/42 Dataran Prima, 47301, Petaling Jaya, Malaysia
Tel.: (60) 3 7804 5708
Steam Boiler Mfr & Distr
N.A.I.C.S.: 332410

AND PRIVATE COMPANIES

MUNCHENER RUCKVERSICHERUNGS AG

Hartford Steam Boiler (Singapore), PTE Ltd. (1)
Vision Exchange 2 Venture Drive 24-01, Singapore, 575624, Singapore
Tel.: (65) 64562293
Web Site: http://www.hsbglobalstandards.com
Sales Range: $25-49.9 Million
Emp.: 17
Steam Boiler Mfr
N.A.I.C.S.: 332410

Hartford Steam Boiler Colombia Ltda. (1)
Cl 68 6 82 Piso 2, Bogota, Colombia
Tel.: (57) 12172641
Steam Boiler Mfr
N.A.I.C.S.: 332410

Hartford Steam Boiler International-GmbH (1)
Landersumer Weg 40a, 48431, Rheine, Germany
Tel.: (49) 5971914360
Steam Boiler Mfr
N.A.I.C.S.: 332410

Hartford Steam Boiler UK Limited (1)
Unit 7 Brewery Yard Deva City Office Park Trinity Way, Salford, M3 7BB, United Kingdom
Tel.: (44) 1618329502
Industrial Inspection Services
N.A.I.C.S.: 926150
Gareth Davey *(Mgr-Quality)*

Hestia Kontakt Sp. z o.o. (1)
Hestii 1, Sopot, Poland
Tel.: (48) 59 810 80 86
General Insurance Services
N.A.I.C.S.: 524210

Hestia Loss Control Sp. z o.o. (1)
Hestii 1, Sopot, 81-731, Poland
Tel.: (48) 58 555 60 00
General Insurance Services
N.A.I.C.S.: 524210

IDEENKAPITAL Anlagebetreuungs GmbH (1)
Berliner Allee 27-29, Dusseldorf, 40212, Germany
Tel.: (49) 211 13608 0
Business Management Consulting Services
N.A.I.C.S.: 541618
Christian Schmucker *(Mng Dir)*

IDEENKAPITAL Financial Engineering GmbH (1)
Tel.: (49) 211136080
Financial Services
N.A.I.C.S.: 523999

IDEENKAPITAL Financial Service GmbH (1)
Berliner Allee 27-29, Dusseldorf, 40212, Germany
Tel.: (49) 211 1 36 08 0
Emp.: 20
Financial Services
N.A.I.C.S.: 523999
Christian Schmucker *(Mgr)*

IDEENKAPITAL GmbH (1)
Berliner Allee 27-29, 40212, Dusseldorf, Germany
Tel.: (49) 211136080
Web Site: http://www.ideenkapital.de
Investment Management Service
N.A.I.C.S.: 523940

IDEENKAPITAL Media Finance GmbH (1)
Berliner Allee 27-29, 40212, Dusseldorf, Germany
Tel.: (49) 21113608770
Investment Management Service
N.A.I.C.S.: 523940

IDEENKAPITAL Metropolen Europa GmbH & Co. KG (1)
Berliner Allee 27-29, 40212, Dusseldorf, Germany
Tel.: (49) 211136080
Business Support Services
N.A.I.C.S.: 561499

IDEENKAPITAL Schiffsfonds Treuhand GmbH (1)
Berliner Allee 27-29, Dusseldorf, 40212, Germany
Tel.: (49) 211136080
Investment Management Service
N.A.I.C.S.: 523940

IK Einkaufsmarkte Deutschland Verwaltungsgesellschaft mbH (1)
Berliner Allee 27-29, 40212, Dusseldorf, Germany
Tel.: (49) 211862840
Investment Management Service
N.A.I.C.S.: 523940

IK FE Fonds Management GmbH (1)
Berliner Allee 27-29, Dusseldorf, 40212, Germany
Tel.: (49) 21113608
Investment Management Service
N.A.I.C.S.: 523940

IK US Portfolio Invest DREI Verwaltungs-GmbH (1)
Berliner Allee 27-29, Dusseldorf, 40212, Germany
Tel.: (49) 211 136080
Investment Advisory Services
N.A.I.C.S.: 523940

IKFE Properties I AG (1)
Drahtzugstrasse 18, 8008, Zurich, Switzerland
Tel.: (41) 443898989
Real Estate Development Services
N.A.I.C.S.: 531390

IRIS Capital Fund II German Investors GmbH & Co. KG (1)
Kreuzstr 34, 40210, Dusseldorf, Germany
Tel.: (49) 211 136080
Investment Management Service
N.A.I.C.S.: 523940

ITERGO Informationstechnologie GmbH (1)
ERGO-Platz 1, 40198, Dusseldorf, Germany
Tel.: (49) 2114770
Software Development Services
N.A.I.C.S.: 541511

Ideenkapital Client Service GmbH (1)
Berliner Allee 27 - 29, 40212, Dusseldorf, Germany
Tel.: (49) 211 13 608 0
Web Site: http://www.ideenkapital.de
Investment Fund Management Services

Ideenkapital Fonds Treuhand GmbH (1)
Berliner Allee 27-29, Dusseldorf, 40212, Germany
Tel.: (49) 211136080
Web Site: http://www.ideenkapital.de
Emp.: 20
General Insurance Services
N.A.I.C.S.: 524210
Thomas Bister-Fuesser *(CEO)*

Ideenkapital erste Investoren Service GmbH (1)
Berliner Allee 27-29, Dusseldorf, 40212, Germany
Tel.: (49) 211136080
Web Site: http://www.ideenkapital.de
Emp.: 15
Financial Services
N.A.I.C.S.: 523999

Itus Verwaltungs AG (1)
Bavariafilmplatz 7, 82031, Grunwald, Bayern, Germany
Tel.: (49) 89 38 91 0
Investment Management Service
N.A.I.C.S.: 523940

Jordan Health Cost Management Services W.L.L. (1)
Al-Said Commercial Complex- BLDG No 48 Ahmad Zaki St, PO Box 20661, Shmeisani Area, Amman, 11118, Jordan
Tel.: (962) 65699071
Web Site: http://www.mednetjordan.com
Administrative Management Services
N.A.I.C.S.: 561110

KA Koln Assekuranz.Agentur GmbH (1)
Scheidtweilerstr 4, 50933, Cologne, Germany
Tel.: (49) 22139761200
Web Site: https://www.koeln-assekuranz.com
General Insurance Services
N.A.I.C.S.: 524210
Martin R. Albus *(Head-Marine Claims Mgmt & Legal Affairs)*

Kapdom-Invest GmbH (1)
Pr-t VERNADSKOGO d 103 korp 2, 117526, Moscow, Russia
Tel.: (7) 495 797 87 70
Management Consulting Services
N.A.I.C.S.: 541611

Kuik & Partners Gerechtsdeurwaarders & Incassobureau B.V. (1)
Ukkelstraat 10, Eindhoven, 5628 TE, Netherlands
Tel.: (31) 402940222
Debt Collection Services
N.A.I.C.S.: 561440

LEGIAL AG (1)
Web Site: http://www.legial.de
Commercial Banking Services
N.A.I.C.S.: 522110

Landelijke Associatie van Gerechtsdeurwaarders B.V. (1)
Van Elmptstraat 16-1 T/M 16-4, Groningen, 9723 ZL, Netherlands
Tel.: (31) 503693300
Web Site: http://www.munichre.com
Debt Collection Services
N.A.I.C.S.: 561440

MAYFAIR Holding GmbH & Co. Singapur KG (1)
Victoriaplatz 2, 40477, Dusseldorf, Germany
Tel.: (49) 211 49370
Investment Management Service
N.A.I.C.S.: 523940

MEAG MUNICH ERGO Asset Management GmbH (1)
Oskar Von Miller Ring 18, Munich, 80333, Germany **(60%)**
Tel.: (49) 8924890
Web Site: http://www.meag.com
Sales Range: $400-449.9 Million
Emp.: 600
Private & Institutional Investment & Portfolio Management Services
N.A.I.C.S.: 523940
Thomas Kabisch *(CEO & CIO)*

Affiliate (Domestic):

MEAG Cash Management GmbH (2)
Oskar-Von-Miller-Ring 18, Munich, 80333, Germany
Tel.: (49) 8924890
Web Site: http://www.meag.com
Investment Management Service
N.A.I.C.S.: 523940

Subsidiary (Non-US):

MEAG Hong Kong Limited (2)
Units 3702-4 Gloucester Tower 15 Queen's Road, Central, China (Hong Kong)
Tel.: (852) 21022800
Investment Management Service
N.A.I.C.S.: 523940

MEAG Luxembourg S.a.r.l. (2)
15 Rue Notre Dame, 2240, Luxembourg, Luxembourg
Tel.: (352) 26 20 20 60
Asset Management Services
N.A.I.C.S.: 523940

Subsidiary (Domestic):

MEAG MUNICH ERGO Kapitalanlagegesellschaft mbH (2)
Am Munchner Tor 1, 80805, Munich, Germany
Tel.: (49) 8924890
Web Site: http://www.meag.com
Asset Management Services
N.A.I.C.S.: 523940

Affiliate (Domestic):

MEAG Property Management GmbH (2)
Oberanger 44, 80331, Munich, Germany
Tel.: (49) 89 38 84 16 20
Web Site: http://www.meag.com
Property Management Services
N.A.I.C.S.: 531312

MR Beteiligungen 14. GmbH (1)
Koniginstr 107, 80802, Munich, Germany
Tel.: (49) 89 38910
Investment Management Service
N.A.I.C.S.: 523940

MR Beteiligungen USD AG & Co. KG (1)
Bavariafilmplatz 7, 82031, Grunwald, Germany
Tel.: (49) 8938910
Investment Management Service
N.A.I.C.S.: 523940

MR Parkview Holding Corporation (1)
1679 S Dupont Hwy Ste 100, Dover, DE 19901
Tel.: (302) 674-8670
Investment Management Service
N.A.I.C.S.: 523940

MR RENT-Investment GmbH (1)
Koniginstr 107, Munich, 80802, Germany
Tel.: (49) 421 1686610
Investment Management Service
N.A.I.C.S.: 523940

MR Solar GmbH & Co. KG (1)
Karl-Martell-Str 60, Nuremberg, 90431, Bayern, Germany
Tel.: (49) 911 148 1396
Sales Range: $25-49.9 Million
Emp.: 20
Photovoltaic Panel Installation Services
N.A.I.C.S.: 238210
Michal Dallos *(Gen Mgr)*

MTU Moje Towarzystwo Ubezpieczeniowe S. A. (1)
Ul Hestii 1, 81-731, Sopot, Poland
Tel.: (48) 58 555 63 04
Web Site: http://www.mtu.pl
General Insurance Services
N.A.I.C.S.: 524210

Manion Wilkins & Associates Ltd. (1)
500 - 21 Four Seasons Place, Toronto, M9B 0A5, ON, Canada
Tel.: (416) 234-5044
Web Site: https://www.manionwilkins.com
Administration & Consulting Services
N.A.I.C.S.: 541611

Marina Salud S.A. (1)
Partida Beniadla S/N, 03700, Denia, Spain
Tel.: (34) 966 429 002
Web Site: http://www.marinasalud.es
Hospital Management Services
N.A.I.C.S.: 541611

Marina Sp.z.o.o. (1)
Rzemieslnicza 38, Sopot, 81-855, Poland
Tel.: (48) 585556672
Accounting Services
N.A.I.C.S.: 541219

MedNet Bahrain W.L.L. Manama (1)
The Adress Tower Bldg 655 Road 3614 Block 436 Office No 61-64 6th Fl, PO Box 21643, Seef District, Manama, Bahrain
Tel.: (973) 175 66 175
Web Site: http://www.mednet.com
Emp.: 34
Managed Health Care Services
N.A.I.C.S.: 621999

MedNet Greece S.A. (1)
3 Pergamou Str, Nea Smirni, Athens, 17121, Greece
Tel.: (30) 210 9307900
Web Site: http://www.mednet.com.gr
Emp.: 100
Health Insurance Services
N.A.I.C.S.: 524114

MedNet Holding GmbH (1)
Koniginstrasse 107, 80802, Munich, Germany
Tel.: (49) 8938910
Investment Management Service
N.A.I.C.S.: 523940

MedNet UAE FZ L.L.C. (1)
Dubai Internet City Building No 13 2nd

MUNCHENER RUCKVERSICHERUNGS AG

Munchener Ruckversicherungs AG—(Continued)

Floor Office No 210-216, Dubai, United Arab Emirates
Tel.: (971) 4 3900749
Web Site: http://www.mednet-uae.com
Health Care Srvices
N.A.I.C.S.: 621610

Mediastream Vierte Medien GmbH (1)
Tolzer Str 5, 82031, Grunwald, Germany
Tel.: (49) 89 69379898
Investment Management Service
N.A.I.C.S.: 523940

Merkur Grundstucks- und Beteiligungs-Gesellschaft mit beschrankter Haftung (1)
Karl-Rudolf-Str 176, Friedrichstadt, 40215, Dusseldorf, Germany
Tel.: (49) 211370482
Real Estate Manangement Services
N.A.I.C.S.: 531390

Midwest Enterprises, Inc. (1)
810 Main St, Cincinnati, OH 45202
Tel.: (513) 621-1616
Emp.: 15
Real Estate Management Services
N.A.I.C.S.: 531390
Bobby Cox (Pres)

Munchener de Argentina Servicios Tecnicos S.R.L (1)
Calle 25 de Mayo 555 piso 21, C1002ABK, Buenos Aires, Argentina
Tel.: (54) 11 45 15 41 00
Web Site: http://www.munichre.com
Emp.: 20
Business Management Consulting Services
N.A.I.C.S.: 541618
Daniel Alves (Mgr)

Munchener de Venezuela C.A. (1)
Torre Las Mercedes Piso 2 Chuao Ciudad Comercial Tamanaco, Apartado 61485, Caracas, 1060, Venezuela
Tel.: (58) 212 918 52 00
Web Site: http://www.munichre.com
Sales Range: $50-74.9 Million
Emp.: 12
Reinsurance Services
N.A.I.C.S.: 524130

Munich Health Holding AG (1)
Konigintr 107, Munich, 80802, Germany
Tel.: (49) 8938910
Investment Management Service
N.A.I.C.S.: 523999

Munich Health North America, Inc. (1)
555 College Rd E, Princeton, NJ 08543
Tel.: (609) 243-8805
Web Site: http://www.munichhealthna.com
Reinsurance Services
N.A.I.C.S.: 524130
Gary M. Stropoli (Reg Mgr-Fin & Controlling)

Division (Domestic):

Munich Health North America, Inc. - Reinsurance Division (2)
555 College Rd E, Princeton, NJ 08543
Tel.: (609) 577-2610
Web Site: http://www.munichhealthnare.com
General Reinsurance Services
N.A.I.C.S.: 524130

Munich Life Management Corporation Ltd. (1)
390 Bay St 26 Fl, Toronto, M5H 2Y2, ON, Canada
Tel.: (416) 359-2200
Web Site: http://www.munichre.ca
Emp.: 25
Reinsurance Services
N.A.I.C.S.: 524130

Munich Management Pte. Ltd. (1)
13-01 20 Collyer Quay, Singapore, 49319, Singapore
Tel.: (65) 62201768
Insurance Management Services
N.A.I.C.S.: 524298

Munich Re America Corporation (1)
555 College Rd E, Princeton, NJ 08543-5241
Tel.: (609) 243-4200
Web Site: https://www.munichre.com
Sales Range: $75-99.9 Million
Emp.: 120
Holding Company
N.A.I.C.S.: 551112
Peter Roeder (Chm)

Holding (Domestic):

Munich Reinsurance America, Inc (2)
555 College Rd E, Princeton, NJ 08540-6616
Tel.: (609) 243-4200
Web Site: http://www.munichreamerica.com
Reinsurance Services
N.A.I.C.S.: 524130
Anthony J. Kuczinski (Pres & CEO)

Subsidiary (Domestic):

HSB Group, Inc. (3)
1 State St, Hartford, CT 06103-3199
Tel.: (860) 722-1866
Web Site: http://www.munichre.com
Specialty Insurance Products, Engineering Services & Management Consulting
N.A.I.C.S.: 524126
William M. Heckles (Sr VP & Chief Reinsurance Officer)

Subsidiary (Domestic):

The Hartford Steam Boiler Inspection and Insurance Company (4)
1 State St, Hartford, CT 06103
Tel.: (860) 722-1866
Web Site: http://www.hsb.com
Sales Range: $150-199.9 Million
Emp.: 310
Engineering Insurance
N.A.I.C.S.: 524126
Stephanie A. Watkins (Sr VP-Bus-Intl)

Subsidiary (Non-US):

HSB Engineering Insurance Limited (5)
New London House, 6 London Street, London, EC3R 7LP, United Kingdom
Tel.: (44) 2072647000
Web Site: http://www.hsbeil.com
Sales Range: $100-124.9 Million
Emp.: 30
Property & Machinery Insurance Services
N.A.I.C.S.: 524128

Subsidiary (Non-US):

The Boiler Inspection and Insurance Company of Canada (6)
390 Bay Street Suite 400, Toronto, M5H 2Y2, ON, Canada
Tel.: (647) 524-8169
Web Site: http://www.biico.com
Sales Range: $10-24.9 Million
Insurance Services
N.A.I.C.S.: 524268
John R. Mulvihill (Pres & CEO)

Subsidiary (Domestic):

HSB Professional Loss Control (5)
1 Locomotive Dr, Lenoir City, TN 37771
Tel.: (865) 376-1131
Web Site: http://www.hsbplc.com
Sales Range: $50-74.9 Million
Emp.: 6
Risk Management Consulting Services Specializing in Property Loss Control
N.A.I.C.S.: 541618

HSB Solomon L.L.C. (5)
5400 lb jfreeway ste1400, Dallas, TX 75240
Tel.: (972) 739-1700
Web Site: http://www.solomononline.com
Sales Range: $150-199.9 Million
Emp.: 78
Management Consulting Services
N.A.I.C.S.: 524126
Charles Reith (Pres & CEO)

Structural Integrity Associates, Inc. (5)
5215 Hellyer Ave Ste 210, San Jose, CA 95138
Tel.: (408) 978-8200
Web Site: http://www.structint.com
Structural Analysis & Solutions
N.A.I.C.S.: 541330
Jenny McGrew (Mgr-Contracts)

Subsidiary (Domestic):

Anatech Corp. (6)
5435 Oberlin Dr, San Diego, CA 92121
Tel.: (858) 455-6350
Web Site: http://www.anatech.com
Sales Range: $10-24.9 Million
Emp.: 22
Engineering Services
N.A.I.C.S.: 541330
Randy J. James (Pres)

Subsidiary (Non-US):

Munich American Reassurance Co. (3)
Tel.: (770) 350-3200
Web Site: http://www.marclife.com
Reinsurance Services
N.A.I.C.S.: 524130
Paige S. Freeman (Gen Counsel, Sec & VP)

Division (Domestic):

Munich Re America Broker Market (3)
555 College Rd E, Princeton, NJ 08543
Tel.: (609) 243-4200
Web Site: http://www.munichreamerica.com
Property & Casualty Reinsurance Services
N.A.I.C.S.: 524130

Subsidiary (Domestic):

Munich Re America Brokers, Inc. (3)
555 College Rd E, Princeton, NJ 08543
Tel.: (609) 243-4900
Web Site: http://www.munichreamerica.com
Sales Range: $25-49.9 Million
Emp.: 100
Reinsurance Services
N.A.I.C.S.: 524130

Division (Domestic):

Munich Re America Direct Facultative (3)
555 College Rd E, Princeton, NJ 08543
Tel.: (609) 243-4200
Web Site: http://www.munichreamerica.com
Individual Risk Reinsurance Services
N.A.I.C.S.: 524130

Munich Re America Direct Treaty (3)
555 College Rd E, Princeton, NJ 08543-5241
Tel.: (609) 243-4200
Web Site: http://www.munichreamerica.com
Reinsurance Marketing & Underwriting Services
N.A.I.C.S.: 524130

Munich Re America HealthCare (3)
555 College Rd E, Princeton, NJ 08543-5242
Tel.: (609) 243-4200
Web Site: http://www.munichreamerica.com
Healthcare Reinsurance Services
N.A.I.C.S.: 524130

Subsidiary (Domestic):

Munich Re Stop Loss, Inc. (4)
8333 NW 53rd St Ste 501, Doral, FL 33136
Tel.: (305) 265-1422
Web Site: http://www.munichrestoploss.com
Rev: $60,000,000
Emp.: 18
Stop Loss Reinsurance Services
N.A.I.C.S.: 524130
Marjorie Dixey (VP)

Division (Domestic):

Munich Re America Specialty Markets (3)
555 College Rd E, Princeton, NJ 08543
Tel.: (609) 243-4200
Web Site: http://www.munichreamerica.com
Reinsurance Services
N.A.I.C.S.: 524130
John Vasturia (Pres)

INTERNATIONAL PUBLIC

Subsidiary (Domestic):

Olympic Health Management Systems, Inc. (3)
2219 Rimland Dr, Bellingham, WA 98226-8660
Tel.: (360) 647-9080
Web Site: http://www.ohmsystems.com
Sales Range: $10-24.9 Million
Emp.: 400
Health & Life Insurance Administration Services
N.A.I.C.S.: 524298

The Midland Company (3)
7000 Midland Blvd, Amelia, OH 45102-2607
Tel.: (513) 943-7100
Holding Company; Title, Life, Property & Casualty Insurance Products & Services
N.A.I.C.S.: 551112
Kate Reed (Sr VP & Head-HR)

Subsidiary (Domestic):

Midland-Guardian Co. (4)
7000 Midland Blvd, Amelia, OH 45102-2608
Tel.: (513) 943-7100
Holding Company; Insurance Services
N.A.I.C.S.: 551112

Subsidiary (Domestic):

American Modern Insurance Group, Inc. (5)
7000 Midland Blvd, Amelia, OH 45102-2607
Tel.: (513) 943-7200
Web Site: http://www.amig.com
Sales Range: $1-4.9 Billion
Emp.: 1,200
Specialty Property & Casualty Insurance Services
N.A.I.C.S.: 524126
Tammy Nelson (Chief Mktg Officer & Sr VP)

Subsidiary (Domestic):

American Family Home Insurance Company (6)
7000 Midland Blvd, Amelia, OH 45102-2608
Tel.: (513) 943-7100
Web Site: http://www.amig.com
Sales Range: $10-24.9 Million
Emp.: 1,200
Property & Casualty Insurance Services
N.A.I.C.S.: 524126

American Modern Home Insurance Company (6)
7000 Midland Blvd, Amelia, OH 45102-2646
Tel.: (513) 943-7100
Web Site: https://amig.testingitnow.com
Home Owner's Insurance Services
N.A.I.C.S.: 524126
John W. Hayden (Pres)

American Modern Life Insurance Company (6)
7000 Midland Blvd, Amelia, OH 45102-2608
Tel.: (513) 943-7100
Web Site: http://www.amig.com
Sales Range: $75-99.9 Million
Emp.: 800
Fire Insurance Services
N.A.I.C.S.: 524113

Specialty Insurance Services Corp. (6)
7000 Midland Blvd, Amelia, OH 45102
Tel.: (513) 947-5828
Web Site: http://www.siservices.com
Sales Range: $10-24.9 Million
Emp.: 100
Insurance Services
N.A.I.C.S.: 524298
Kevin Morreale (Sr VP)

Munich Re Capital Limited (1)
St Helens 1 Undershaft, London, EC3A 8EE, United Kingdom
Tel.: (44) 2078863900
Sales Range: $50-74.9 Million
Emp.: 100
Reinsurance Services
N.A.I.C.S.: 524130

Munich Re Capital Markets New York, Inc. (1)
1177 Avenue of the Americas 15th Fl, New York, NY 10036
Tel.: (212) 887-6310

AND PRIVATE COMPANIES MUNCHENER RUCKVERSICHERUNGS AG

Web Site: http://www.munichre.com
Reinsurance Services
N.A.I.C.S.: 524130

Munich Re Holding Company (UK) Ltd. (1)
St Helens 1 Undershaft, London, EC3A 8EE, United Kingdom
Tel.: (44) 2030037000
Web Site: http://www.munichre.com
Emp.: 400
Reinsurance Services
N.A.I.C.S.: 524130

Munich Re India Services Private Limited (1)
302 Peninsula Towers Peninsula Corporate Park Ganpatrao Kadam Marg, Lower Parel, Mumbai, 400 013, India
Tel.: (91) 22 24 97 90 10
Web Site: http://www.munichre.com
Reinsurance Services
N.A.I.C.S.: 524130

Munich Re Japan Services K.K. (1)
Sanno Park Tower, PO Box 4, Tokyo, 100-6114, Japan
Tel.: (81) 3 52 51 68 71
Web Site: http://www.munichre.co.jp
General Reinsurance Services
N.A.I.C.S.: 524130
Christain Kraut (Pres)

Munich Re Oficina de Representacion en Colombia (1)
Carrera 7 No 71-21 Torre B Oficina 902, Bogota, Colombia
Tel.: (57) 1 326 96 00
Web Site: http://www.munichre.com
Reinsurance Services
N.A.I.C.S.: 524130
Rolf-Dieter Krahmer (Gen Mgr)

Munich Re UK Services Limited (1)
10 Fenchurch Avenue, London, EC3M 5BN, United Kingdom
Tel.: (44) 2030037000
General Insurance Services
N.A.I.C.S.: 524298

Munich Re Underwriting Agents (DIFC) Limited (1)
Level 4 Unit 4 Dubai International Financial Centre, PO Box 506512, Al Fatan, Dubai, United Arab Emirates
Tel.: (971) 4 37 11 032
Life Insurance & Health Reinsurance Services
N.A.I.C.S.: 524113

Munich Re Underwriting Limited (1)
Saint Helens 1 Undershaft, London, EC3A 8EE, United Kingdom
Tel.: (44) 20 7886 3900
Web Site: http://www.watkins-syndicate.co.uk
Sales Range: $50-74.9 Million
Emp.: 100
Insurance Brokerage Services
N.A.I.C.S.: 524210
Tim Coskun (Dir-Risk & Compliance)

Subsidiary (Domestic):

Northern Marine Underwriters Limited (2)
Goodbard House 9 Infirmary Street, Leeds, LS1 2JP, United Kingdom
Tel.: (44) 113 243 0666
Web Site: http://www.nmu.co.uk
Marine Insurance Services
N.A.I.C.S.: 524126

Munich Re do Brasil Resseguradora S.A. (1)
Tel.: (55) 1151021500
Web Site: http://www.munichre.com.br
Sales Range: $50-74.9 Million
Emp.: 60
Reinsurance Services
N.A.I.C.S.: 524130
Adriana Seemann (Chief Innovation & Bus Dev Officer)

Munich Re of Malta Holding Limited (1)
Development House St Anne Street, Floriana, Malta
Tel.: (356) 22480821
Investment Management Service
N.A.I.C.S.: 523940

Munich Re of Malta p.l.c. (1)
Level 4 Whitehall Mansions Ta' Xbiex Seafront, Ta' Xbiex, XBX 1026, Malta
Tel.: (356) 224 808 21
Reinsurance Services
N.A.I.C.S.: 524130
Konstantin von Jagow (CEO)

Munich Reinsurance Company of Africa Ltd (1)
Tel.: (27) 112422000
Web Site: http://www.munichre.com
Reinsurance Services
N.A.I.C.S.: 524130
N. N. N. Radebe (Chm)

Subsidiary (Non-US):

Munich Mauritius Reinsurance Co. Ltd. (2)
Ebene Business Park, Reduit, Mauritius
Tel.: (230) 454 97 00
Web Site: http://www.munichre.com
Emp.: 30
Reinsurance Services
N.A.I.C.S.: 524130

Munich Reinsurance Company of Canada (1)
390 Bay Street Suite 2200, Toronto, M5H 2Y2, ON, Canada
Tel.: (416) 366-9206
Web Site: https://www.munichre.com
Sales Range: $350-399.9 Million
Emp.: 135
Reinsurance Services
N.A.I.C.S.: 524130
Claudette Cantin (Chief Actuarial Officer, Chief Risk Officer & Sr VP)

Munich-American Global Services (Munich) GmbH (1)
Koniginstr 107, 80802, Munich, Germany
Tel.: (49) 89 342577
General Insurance Services
N.A.I.C.S.: 524210

Munich-Canada Management Corp. Ltd. (1)
390 Bay St Suite 2200, Toronto, M5H 2Y2, ON, Canada
Tel.: (416) 359-2147
Sales Range: $200-249.9 Million
Emp.: 300
Reinsurance Services
N.A.I.C.S.: 524130

Munichre New Zealand Service Limited (1)
Level 15 PWC Tower 188 Quay St, Auckland, 1010, New Zealand
Tel.: (64) 9 303 4628
Sales Range: $50-74.9 Million
Emp.: 8
General Insurance Services
N.A.I.C.S.: 524210
Martin Victor Kreft (Mng Dir)

N.M.U. (Holdings) Limited (1)
Goodbard Houses Infirmary Street, Leeds, LS1 2JS, West Yorkshire, United Kingdom
Tel.: (44) 113 243 0666
Investment Management Service
N.A.I.C.S.: 523940

NMU Group Limited (1)
148 Leadenhall Street, London, EC3V 4QT, United Kingdom
Tel.: (44) 20 3008 7843
Web Site: http://www.nmu.co.uk
General Insurance Services
N.A.I.C.S.: 524210

Nassau Incasso Services Den Haag B.V. (1)
Reeuwijkse Poort 301 A, 2811 NV, Reeuwijk, Netherlands
Tel.: (31) 182 397344
Web Site: http://www.nassauincasso.nl
Debt Collection Services
N.A.I.C.S.: 561440

New Reinsurance Company Ltd. (1)
Zollikerstrasse 226, 8008, Zurich, Switzerland
Tel.: (41) 58 226 65 00
Web Site: http://www.newre.com

Sales Range: $100-124.9 Million
Emp.: 126
Property & Casualty Reinsurance Services
N.A.I.C.S.: 524130
Jean-Luc Bourgault (Chief Underwriting Officer-Property & Casualty)

Nightingale Legal Services ltd. (1)
3 Fersfield Perrymead, BA2 5AR, Bath, United Kingdom - England
Tel.: (44) 1225 830034
Legal Support Services
N.A.I.C.S.: 541199

Olympic Health Management Services Inc. (1)
2219 Rimland Dr, Bellingham, WA 98227
Tel.: (360) 647-9080
Health Insurance Services
N.A.I.C.S.: 524114

PLATINIA Verwaltungs-GmbH (1)
Tolzer Str 5, 82031, Grunwald, Germany
Tel.: (49) 211 13608770
Investment Management Service
N.A.I.C.S.: 523940

PRORENDITA EINS Verwaltungsgesellschaft mbH (1)
Gansemarkt 45, 20354, Hamburg, Germany
Tel.: (49) 40 448585
Investment Management Service
N.A.I.C.S.: 523940

PRORENDITA VIER Verwaltungsgesellschaft mbH (1)
Gansemarkt 45, 20354, Hamburg, Germany
Tel.: (49) 89 6110110
Investment Management Service
N.A.I.C.S.: 523940

ProVictor Immobilien GmbH (1)
Provinzialplatz 1, 40591, Dusseldorf, Germany (50%)
Tel.: (49) 211 9780
Real Estate Manangement Services
N.A.I.C.S.: 531390

Reden Solar SAS (1)
ZAC Des Champs de Lescaze, 47310, Roquefort, France
Tel.: (33) 553772131
Web Site: http://www.reden.solar
Emp.: 100
Solar Energy Services
N.A.I.C.S.: 221118

Roanoke Insurance Group Canada Inc. (1)
390 Bay Street Munich Re Centre 22nd Floor, Toronto, M5H 2Y2, ON, Canada
Insurance Brokerage Services
N.A.I.C.S.: 524210

Roanoke Insurance Group Inc. (1)
1501 E Woodfield Rd Ste 400W, Schaumburg, IL 60173
Web Site: https://www.roanokegroup.com
Insurance Services
N.A.I.C.S.: 523999

Roanoke International Brokers Limited (1)
St Helens 1 Undershaft, London, EC3A 8EE, United Kingdom
Tel.: (44) 2078863800
Web Site: https://www.roanokebrokers.com
Sales Range: $50-74.9 Million
Emp.: 12
Insurance Brokerage Services
N.A.I.C.S.: 524210
Rick King (Mgr-Technical)

Roanoke International Insurance Agency Inc. (1)
1930 Thoreau Dr N Ste 101, Schaumburg, IL 60173
Tel.: (800) 762-6653
General Insurance Services
N.A.I.C.S.: 524210

Schloss Hohenkammer GmbH (1)
Schlossstrasse 20, Hohenkammer, 85411, Germany
Tel.: (49) 8137 93 40
Web Site: http://www.schlosshohenkammer.de
Hotel Management & Forestry Services
N.A.I.C.S.: 721110

Gabriela Brucher (Head-Meeting & Event Sls)

Schrombgens & Stephan GmbH, Versicherungsmakler (1)
Uerdinger Str 58, Dusseldorf, 40474, Germany
Tel.: (49) 211478870
Web Site: http://www.s-s-vm.de
Sales Range: $25-49.9 Million
Emp.: 20
Risk Managemeng Srvices
N.A.I.C.S.: 541618
Helmut Gratz (Mng Dir)

Seldac 1. Kommunaler-Rendite-Fonds GmbH & Co. KG (1)
Berliner Allee 27-29, 40212, Dusseldorf, Germany
Tel.: (49) 21113608650
Investment Fund Management Services
N.A.I.C.S.: 523940

Seminaris Hotel- und Kongressstatten-Betriebsgesellschaft mbH (1)
Soltauer Str 3, 21335, Luneburg, Germany
Tel.: (49) 4131 713 700
Web Site: http://www.seminaris.de
Sales Range: $10-24.9 Million
Emp.: 90
Home Management Services
N.A.I.C.S.: 721110

Sopocki Instytut Ubezpieczen S.A. (1)
Ul Hestii 1, Sopot, 81-731, Poland
Tel.: (48) 58 555 6000
Web Site: http://www.siu.pl
General Insurance Services
N.A.I.C.S.: 524210

Sopockie Towarzystwo Doradcze Sp. z o.o. (1)
Hestii 1, Sopot, 81-731, Poland
Tel.: (48) 58 555 65 94
Management Consulting Services
N.A.I.C.S.: 541618

Sopockie Towarzystwo Ubezpieczen Ergo Hestia Spolka Akcyjna (1)
ul Hestii 1, 81-731, Sopot, Poland
Tel.: (48) 801107107
Web Site: https://www.ergohestia.pl
General Insurance Services
N.A.I.C.S.: 524210

Sterling Life Insurance Company (1)
2219 Rimland Dr, Bellingham, WA 98227
Tel.: (360) 647-9080
Web Site: http://www.sterlingplans.com
Sales Range: $250-299.9 Million
Emp.: 320
Life & Health Insurance Services
N.A.I.C.S.: 524114
Michael A. Muchnicki (CEO)

Sydney Euro-Center Pty. Ltd. (1)
Ste 2 level 8 S Tower 1-5 Railway St, Chatswood, 2067, NSW, Australia
Tel.: (61) 28274 5700
Sales Range: $50-74.9 Million
Emp.: 7
Insurance Services
N.A.I.C.S.: 524298
Bodil Fricke (Gen Mgr)

TAS Assekuranz Service GmbH (1)
Emil von Behring Strasse 2, Frankfurt am Main, 60439, Germany
Tel.: (49) 69605080
Sales Range: $50-74.9 Million
Emp.: 16
Insurance Brokerage Services
N.A.I.C.S.: 524210

TAS Touristik Assekuranz Service International GmbH (1)
Emil-von-Behring-Strasse 2, Frankfurt, 60439, Germany
Tel.: (49) 69605080
Web Site: http://www.tas-makler.de
Emp.: 20
General Insurance Services
N.A.I.C.S.: 524210
Claudia Bekaert (Gen Mgr)

TAS Touristik Assekuranzmakler und Service GmbH (1)
Emil-von-Behring-Strasse 2, 60439, Frank-

MUNCHENER RUCKVERSICHERUNGS AG

Munchener Ruckversicherungs AG—(Continued)
furt am Main, Germany
Tel.: (49) 69 60508 0
Web Site: http://www.tas-makler.de
Travel & Health Assistance Services
N.A.I.C.S.: 923130

TIS Holdings Inc. (1)
6500 Poe Ave Ste 110, Dayton, OH 45414
Tel.: (937) 890-3101
Web Site: http://www.tisholdings.com
Investment Management Service
N.A.I.C.S.: 523940
Greg Merrick (Pres)

The Atlas Insurance Agency, Inc. (1)
7000 Midland Blvd, Amelia, OH 45102
Tel.: (800) 643-7770
Web Site: http://www.atlasagency.net
Insurance Services
N.A.I.C.S.: 524210
Robert K. W. H. Nobriga (Chm)

The Polytechnic Club, Inc. (1)
1 State St Fl 20 Bldg 400 Columbus Blvd,
Hartford, CT 06103
Tel.: (860) 722-5161
Web Site: https://www.ontwenty.com
Sales Range: $10-24.9 Million
Emp.: 24
Restaurant Management Services
N.A.I.C.S.: 722511

The Princeton Excess and Surplus Lines Insurance Company Ltd. (1)
555 College Rd E, Princeton, NJ 08543
Web Site: https://www.peslic.com
Commercial Insurance Services
N.A.I.C.S.: 524210

The Roanoke Companies Inc. (1)
1475 E Woodfield Rd Ste 500, Schaumburg, IL 60173
Tel.: (847) 969-1420
Web Site: http://www.roanoketrade.com
Insurance Services
N.A.I.C.S.: 524298
Jim Valatkas (CFO & Sr VP)

Trade Insurance Services Inc (1)
61 Broadway, New York, NY 10006
Tel.: (888) 571-1675
Emp.: 20
Insurance Brokerage Services
N.A.I.C.S.: 524210
William Sterrett (Gen Mgr)

VB VICTORIA Zastupanje u Osiguranju d.o.o. (1)
9 Varsavska, Zagreb, 10000, Croatia
Tel.: (385) 13369809
General Insurance Services
N.A.I.C.S.: 524210

VHDK Beteiligungsgesellschaft mbH (1)
Victoriaplatz 1, 40477, Dusseldorf, Germany
Tel.: (49) 2114770
Investment Management Service
N.A.I.C.S.: 523940

VICTORIA Erste Beteiligungsgesellschaft mbH (1)
Victoriaplatz 1, 40477, Dusseldorf, Germany
Tel.: (49) 211 4770
Investment Management Service
N.A.I.C.S.: 523940

VICTORIA Immobilien-Fonds GmbH (1)
Victoriaplatz 1, Dusseldorf, 40477, Germany
Tel.: (49) 2114770
Real Estate Development Services
N.A.I.C.S.: 531390

VICTORIA Vierte Beteiligungsgesellschaft mbH (1)
Victoriaplatz 1, 40477, Dusseldorf, Germany
Tel.: (49) 2114982417
Investment Management Service
N.A.I.C.S.: 523940

VICTORIA-VOLKSBANKEN Biztosito Zrt. (1)
Futo Utca 47-53 III Emelet, Budapest, 1082, Hungary
Tel.: (36) 1 877 1100
Web Site: http://www.victoria-volksbanken.hu
Health Insurance Services
N.A.I.C.S.: 524114

VV-Consulting Gesellschaft fur Risikoanalyse, Vorsorgeberatung und Versicherungsvermittlung GmbH
Business Park Marximum ERGO Center Modec, 1110, Vienna, Austria
Tel.: (43) 1 98181
Financial Consulting Services
N.A.I.C.S.: 541611

Victoria Vierter Bauabschnitt Management GmbH (1)
Victoriaplatz 1, 40477, Dusseldorf, Germany
Tel.: (49) 211 4770
Investment Management Service
N.A.I.C.S.: 523940

Viwis GmbH (1)
Thomas-Dehler-Strasse 2, 81737, Munich, Germany
Tel.: (49) 89 62 75 77 00
Web Site: http://www.viwis.de
Sales Range: $25-49.9 Million
Emp.: 20
Software Development Services
N.A.I.C.S.: 541511
Werner Kohn (Mng Dir)

Vorsorge Service GmbH (1)
Rather Str 110a, 40476, Dusseldorf, Germany
Tel.: (49) 211210229500
General Insurance Services
N.A.I.C.S.: 524210

WISMA ATRIA Holding GmbH & Co. Singapur KG (1)
40477, 40477, Dusseldorf, Germany
Tel.: (49) 211 9780
Investment Management Service
N.A.I.C.S.: 523940

WNE Solarfonds Suddeutschland 2 GmbH & Co. KG (1)
Karl-Martell-Str 60, Nuremberg, 90431, Germany
Tel.: (49) 9111481136
Sales Range: $25-49.9 Million
Emp.: 23
Electric Signal Testing Equipment Mfr
N.A.I.C.S.: 334515
Salvatore Telami (Gen Mgr)

Watkins Syndicate Hong Kong Limited (1)
Unit 2201 22/F AIA Plz 18 Hysan Avenue, Causeway Bay, China (Hong Kong)
Tel.: (852) 2808 0632
Web Site: http://www.watkins-syndicate.co.uk
Sales Range: $50-74.9 Million
Emp.: 9
General Insurance Services
N.A.I.C.S.: 524210

Watkins Syndicate Middle East Limited (1)
Dubai International Financial Centre Gate Precinct Building 5, PO Box 506518, 5th Floor Tenancy 9, Dubai, United Arab Emirates
Tel.: (971) 4 446 9200
Web Site: http://www.watkins-syndicate.co.uk
Emp.: 7
Insurance Underwriting Services
N.A.I.C.S.: 524113

Watkins Syndicate Singapore Pte. Limited (1)
8 Marina View Asia Square Tower 1 14-01, Singapore, 018960, Singapore
Tel.: (65) 6395 0188
Web Site: http://www.watkins-syndicate.co.uk
General Insurance Services
N.A.I.C.S.: 524210

Windpark Grossberendten 2 GmbH & Co KG (1)
Kurfurstenallee 23 a, 28211, Bremen, Germany
Tel.: (49) 421 1686640
Eletric Power Generation Services
N.A.I.C.S.: 221118

Windpark Hilmersdorf GmbH & Co KG (1)
Stephanitors Bollwerk 3, Bremen, 28217, Germany
Tel.: (49) 421 1686610
Eletric Power Generation Services
N.A.I.C.S.: 221118

Windpark Kruge GmbH & Co KG (1)
Stephanitorsbollwerk 3, 28211, Bremen, Germany
Tel.: (49) 4211686610
Web Site: http://www.wpd.de
Emp.: 300
Eletric Power Generation Services
N.A.I.C.S.: 221118

Windpark Marwitz GmbH & Co KG (1)
Stephanitors Bollwerk 3, Bremen, 28217, Germany
Tel.: (49) 421 1686610
Web Site: http://www.wpd.de
Emp.: 1,000
Eletric Power Generation Services
N.A.I.C.S.: 221118

Windpark Mittelhausen GmbH & Co KG (1)
Kurfurstenallee 23a, Bremen, 28211, Germany
Tel.: (49) 4211686610
Eletric Power Generation Services
N.A.I.C.S.: 221118

Windpark Sassenberg GmbH & Co KG (1)
Kurfurstenallee 23a, Bremen, 28211, Germany
Tel.: (49) 421 460344400
Eletric Power Generation Services
N.A.I.C.S.: 221118

Windsor Health Plan, Inc. (1)
7100 Commerce Way Ste 285, Brentwood, TN 37027
Tel.: (615) 782-7800
Web Site: http://www.windsorhealthplan.com
Emp.: 100
Health Care Insurance Services
N.A.I.C.S.: 524114
Tim Mullen (COO)

Windsor HomeCare Network, LLC (1)
7100 Commerce Way, Brentwood, TN 37027
Tel.: (800) 793-3684
Health Care Insurance Services
N.A.I.C.S.: 524114

Wohnungsgesellschaft Brela mbH (1)
Uberseering 45, 22297, Hamburg, Germany
Tel.: (49) 40 63760
Real Estate Manangement Services
N.A.I.C.S.: 531390

almeda GmbH (1)
Rosenheimer Strasse 116 a, 81669, Munich, Germany
Tel.: (49) 89 480 59 0
Web Site: http://www.almeda.com
Emp.: 113
Health Care Srvices
N.A.I.C.S.: 621999
Markus Kunze (Head-Sls & Mktg)

almeda Versicherungs-Aktiengesellschaft (1)
Rosenheimer Strasse 116 a, 81669, Munich, Germany
Tel.: (49) 89 480 59 0
Web Site: http://www.almeda.com
Sales Range: $100-124.9 Million
Emp.: 300
Travel & Healthcare Assistance Services
N.A.I.C.S.: 561599
Martin Bartetzko (Member-Mgmt Bd)

goMedus GmbH & Co. KG (1)
Scheidtweilerstrasse 4, 50933, Cologne, Germany
Tel.: (49) 221 578 29 91
Web Site: http://www.gomedus.de
Health Care Srvices
N.A.I.C.S.: 621999

goMedus Partnerkliniken GmbH (1)
Aachener Str 300, Cologne, 50933, Germany
Tel.: (49) 2215780

INTERNATIONAL PUBLIC

Sales Range: $1-4.9 Billion
Emp.: 3,000
Health Insurance Services
N.A.I.C.S.: 524114

m:editerran POWER GmbH & Co. KG (1)
Karl-Martell-Str 60, Nuremberg, 90431, Germany
Tel.: (49) 911 1481396
Emp.: 2,000
Electronic Components Mfr
N.A.I.C.S.: 334419
Vonbo Ries (Gen Mgr)

miCura Pflegedienste Berlin GmbH (1)
Mollendorffstrasse 104-105, 10367, Berlin, Germany
Tel.: (49) 30 64 09 02 31
Web Site: http://www.micura.de
Nursing Care Services
N.A.I.C.S.: 623110

miCura Pflegedienste Bremen GmbH (1)
Am Wandrahm 40-43, 28195, Bremen, Germany
Tel.: (49) 4 21 4 67 55 62
Web Site: http://www.micura.de
Nursing Care Services
N.A.I.C.S.: 623110

miCura Pflegedienste Dusseldorf GmbH (1)
Munsterstr 332, 40470, Dusseldorf, Germany
Tel.: (49) 2 11 40 88 00
Nursing Care Services
N.A.I.C.S.: 623110

miCura Pflegedienste GmbH Niederlassung Koln (1)
Aachener Strasse 300, Cologne, 50933, Germany
Tel.: (49) 2 21 51 09 05 91
Web Site: http://www.micura.de
Health Care Services
N.A.I.C.S.: 621999
Melanie Monecke (Branch Mgr)

miCura Pflegedienste Hamburg GmbH (1)
Neubergerweg 233, Hamburg, 22419, Germany
Tel.: (49) 40 53 20 30 90
Web Site: http://www.micura.de
Sales Range: $10-24.9 Million
Emp.: 22
Nursing Care Services
N.A.I.C.S.: 623110
Uwe Peters (Mng Dir)

miCura Pflegedienste Krefeld GmbH (1)
Platz der Wiedervereinigung 4, Krefeld, 47805, Germany
Tel.: (49) 21 51 65 89 49
Web Site: http://www.micura.de
Sales Range: $10-24.9 Million
Emp.: 35
Nursing Care Services
N.A.I.C.S.: 623110
Uwe Peters (Mng Dir)

miCura Pflegedienste Munchen GmbH (1)
Pippinger Str 49, 81245, Munich, Germany
Tel.: (49) 89 20 20 44 70
Nursing Care Services
N.A.I.C.S.: 623110

miCura Pflegedienste Munchen Ost GmbH (1)
Ottobrunner Strasse 34, Munich, 81737, Germany
Tel.: (49) 89 62 14 60 05
Web Site: http://www.micura.de
Nursing Care Services
N.A.I.C.S.: 623110

miCura Pflegedienste Munster GmbH (1)
Tibusplatz 6, Munster, 48143, Germany
Tel.: (49) 2 513 99 55 80
Web Site: http://www.micura.de
Nursing Care Services
N.A.I.C.S.: 623110

miCura Pflegedienste Nurnberg GmbH (1)

Michael-Ende-Str 1, 90439, Nuremberg, Germany
Tel.: (49) 9 112744860
Web Site: http://www.micura.de
Sales Range: $10-24.9 Million
Emp.: 30
Nursing Care Services
N.A.I.C.S.: 623110

welivit New Energy GmbH (1)
Karl-Martell-Str 60, 90431, Nuremberg, Germany
Tel.: (49) 911 148 1396
Eletric Power Generation Services
N.A.I.C.S.: 221118

wpd Windpark Wergzahna GmbH & Co KG (1)
Stephanitorbollwerk 3, Bremen, 28217, Germany
Tel.: (49) 4211686610
Web Site: http://www.wpd.de
Financial Services
N.A.I.C.S.: 523999

MUNDIAL S.A.
Av Dr Nilo Pecanha 2825 Sala 703, Bairro Chacara das Pedras, Porto Alegre, 91330-001, Brazil
Tel.: (55) 5133585000
Web Site: http://www.mundial-sa.com.br
Year Founded: 1931
MNDL3—(BRAZ)
Emp.: 3,800
Kitchen Knives Scissor & Beauty Implement Electric Motor Mfr
N.A.I.C.S.: 332215
Julio Cesar Camara (Chief Plng & Control Officer)

Subsidiaries:

Hercules S.A. - Fabrica de Talheres (1)
R Do Paraiso 148 - 14 Floor/conj 141, 4103000, Sao Paulo, Brazil
Tel.: (55) 51 3524 1500
Web Site: http://www.hercules.ind.br
Sales Range: $1-9.9 Million
Cutlery Mfr & Whslr
N.A.I.C.S.: 332215
Michael Lenn Ceitlin (Dir-IR)

MUNDIAL S.A. - PRODUTOS DE CONSUMO
Rua do Paraiso 148 14 andar, Bairro Paraiso, Sao Paulo, 04103-000, SP, Brazil
Tel.: (55) 1135241500 BR
Web Site: https://www.mundial.com
Year Founded: 1896
MNDL3—(BRAZ)
Sales Range: Less than $1 Million
Apparel Store Operator
N.A.I.C.S.: 315990
Michael Lenn Ceitlin (Chm, CEO, Officer-IR & Member-Exec Bd)

MUNDORO CAPITAL INC.
1040 West Georgia Street 14th Floor, Vancouver, V6E 4H1, BC, Canada
Tel.: (604) 669-8055 BC
Web Site: https://www.mundoro.com
MUN—(TSXV)
Rev.: $2,333,013
Assets: $6,340,652
Liabilities: $3,119,941
Net Worth: $3,220,711
Earnings: $913,509
Fiscal Year-end: 12/31/23
Investment Services; Gold Mining
N.A.I.C.S.: 523999
Teo Dechev (Pres & CEO)

Subsidiaries:

Mundoro Exploratie Cooperatie U.A. (1)
Zuidplein 126 Wtc Toren H, 1077 XV, Amsterdam, Netherlands
Tel.: (31) 202403080

Gold Ore Mining Services
N.A.I.C.S.: 212220

MUNIC S.A.
39 avenue de Paris, 94800, Villejuif, France
Tel.: (33) 142119325
Web Site: https://www.munic.io
Year Founded: 2002
ALMUN—(EUR)
Sales Range: $1-9.9 Million
Vehicle Electronic Product Mfr
N.A.I.C.S.: 336320
Aaron Solomon (Chm & CEO)

MUNICIPAL BANK PLC
6 Vrabcha Street, 1000, Sofia, Bulgaria
Tel.: (359) 29300111
Web Site: http://www.municipalbank.bg
Year Founded: 1996
Rev.: $14,689,540
Assets: $1,173,538,783
Liabilities: $1,108,435,291
Net Worth: $65,103,491
Earnings: $922,999
Fiscal Year-end: 12/31/19
Banking Services
N.A.I.C.S.: 522110
Stefan Nenov (Chm-Supervisory Bd)

MUNICIPAL ENTERPRISES LIMITED
927 Rocky Lake Dr, PO Box 48100, Bedford, B4A 3Z2, NS, Canada
Tel.: (902) 835-3381
Web Site: http://www.municipalgroup.ca
Sales Range: $200-249.9 Million
Emp.: 2,000
Holding Company
N.A.I.C.S.: 551112
Carl B. Potter (Pres & CEO)

Subsidiaries:

Dexter Construction Company Limited (1)
Rocky Lake Drive, Box 48100, Bedford, B4A 3Z2, NS, Canada
Tel.: (902) 835-3381
Web Site: https://www.dexter.ca
Emp.: 1,000
Civil Construction Services
N.A.I.C.S.: 237990
Brian Reimer (Mgr-Estimating & Engrg)

Envirosoil Limited (1)
927 Rocky Lake Dr, PO Box 48100, Bedford, B4A 3Z2, NS, Canada
Tel.: (902) 835-3381
Web Site: https://r3environmentalsystems.com
Soil Remediation
N.A.I.C.S.: 562910

Fero Waste & Recycling Inc. (1)
203 Desbrisay Avenue, Moncton, E1E 0G7, NB, Canada
Tel.: (506) 855-3376
Web Site: http://www.fero.ca
Waste Collection, Management & Recycling Services
N.A.I.C.S.: 562111

General Liquids Canada (1)
1233 Rocky Lake Drive, Waverley, Halifax, B4A 3X5, NS, Canada
Tel.: (902) 835-3311
Web Site: https://www.general-liquids.ca
Asphalt & Asphalt-Related Products Research & Mfr
N.A.I.C.S.: 324121

Royal Environmental Inc. (1)
69 Colonel Joseph Scott Drive, Lower Sackville, B4C 4B1, NS, Canada
Tel.: (902) 445-4500
Web Site: https://www.municipalenvironmental.com
Waste Management & Recycling Services
N.A.I.C.S.: 562111

MUNOTH CAPITAL MARKET LTD.
Shanti Nivas - Office Building Opposite Shapath V Near Karnavati Club, S G Road, Ahmedabad, 380058, India
Tel.: (91) 7926937954
Web Site: https://www.munoth.com
Year Founded: 1982
Rev.: $48,229
Assets: $668,179
Liabilities: $10,518
Net Worth: $657,661
Earnings: ($26,498)
Fiscal Year-end: 03/31/19
Financial Investment Services
N.A.I.C.S.: 523999
Shantilal Misrimal Jain (CFO)

MUNOTH COMMUNICATION LIMITED
Munoth Communication Limited Munoth Centre 343 Triplicane High Road, Chennai, 600 005, India
Tel.: (91) 4428591190
Web Site: https://www.munothcomm.com
Year Founded: 1984
Rev.: $11,630
Assets: $1,268,674
Liabilities: $156,708
Net Worth: $1,111,967
Earnings: ($81,437)
Emp.: 6
Fiscal Year-end: 03/31/19
Mobile Phone Mfr
N.A.I.C.S.: 334220
Lalchand Munoth (Chm)

MUNOTH FINANCIAL SERVICES LIMITED
Munoth Centre 343 Triplicane High Road, Chennai, 600 005, India
Tel.: (91) 4428591185
Web Site: https://www.munothfinancial.com
Year Founded: 1990
531821—(BOM)
Rev.: $6,081,314
Assets: $141,743,708
Liabilities: $16,724,165
Net Worth: $125,019,543
Earnings: ($2,772,352)
Emp.: 11
Fiscal Year-end: 03/31/23
Financial Management Services
N.A.I.C.S.: 523999
Lalchand Munoth (Chm)

MUNSHAAT REAL ESTATE PROJECTS COMPANY KSCC
Sharq Block 6 Mubarak Al-Kabeer Street ITS Tower Mezzanine Floor, PO Box 1393, Dasman, Kuwait, 15464, Kuwait
Tel.: (965) 22467188
Web Site: https://www.munshaat.com
Year Founded: 2003
MUNSHAAT—(KUW)
Rev.: $39,430,622
Assets: $293,813,146
Liabilities: $299,272,274
Net Worth: ($5,459,128)
Earnings: $4,499,964
Emp.: 21
Fiscal Year-end: 12/31/22
Real Estate Services
N.A.I.C.S.: 531390
Abdulla Fuad Althaqeb (Chm)

MUNTENIA MEDICAL COMPETENCES S.A.
2 Pictor Nicolae Grigorescu Street, Pitesti, Romania
Tel.: (40) 348457736 RO
Health Care Srvices

N.A.I.C.S.: 621610
Eugenia Dinca (Dir-Medical)

MUNTERS AB
Farogatan 33, SE-164 51, Kista, Sweden
Tel.: (46) 8 626 6300
Web Site: http://www.munters.com
Year Founded: 1955
Air Treatment Solutions; Humidity & Climate Control Technologies Mfr
N.A.I.C.S.: 333414
Per-Arne Hakansson (Grp VP-HR)

Subsidiaries:

Hawa Munters Co. Ltd. (1)
44 Al Amir Mosaid Ibn Abdulaziz Street, PO Box 3790, Al Sulaimania Dist, 11481, Riyadh, Saudi Arabia (100%)
Tel.: (966) 14771514
Web Site: http://www.munters.co.uk
Sales Range: $1-9.9 Million
Emp.: 4
N.A.I.C.S.: 337126

M-Tech Systems USA, LLC (1)
115 Perimeter Ctr Pl NE Ste 845, Atlanta, GA 30346
Tel.: (678) 990-2345
Web Site: https://mtechsystems.io
Custom Computer Programming & Software Services
N.A.I.C.S.: 541511
Chris Blosfeld (Dir-Sls)

Minex Romania SRL (1)
85 Metalurgiei Bvd sector 4, District 4, 041832, Bucharest, Romania
Tel.: (40) 213060281
Web Site: http://www.minexgroup.eu
Humidity Controller Distr
N.A.I.C.S.: 423830

Munters (HK) Pte. Ltd. (1)
Rm 9B-08 9F Dragon Industrial Building 93 King Lam Street, Cheung Sha Wan, Kowloon, China (Hong Kong) (100%)
Tel.: (852) 25781466
Web Site: http://www.munters.com.cn
Sales Range: $25-49.9 Million
Emp.: 2
Dehumidification Mfr
N.A.I.C.S.: 333413

Munters (Pty) Ltd. (1)
22 Angus Crescent Edenvale, Long Meadow East, Modderfontein, 1610, South Africa
Tel.: (27) 119719700
Web Site: http://www.munters.co.za
Sales Range: $25-49.9 Million
Emp.: 30
N.A.I.C.S.: 337126
Philip Dickirson (Gen Mgr)

Munters (Thailand) Co. Ltd. (1)
121/107 RS Tower Building 40th Floor Zone B Ratchadapisek Road, Dindaeng, Bangkok, 10400, Thailand
Tel.: (66) 26422670
Heating Equipment Distr
N.A.I.C.S.: 423730

Munters Air Treatment Equipment Co. Ltd. (1)
No 12 Yu Hua Road Tianzhu Airport, Industrial Zone Area B, Beijing, 101300, China
Tel.: (86) 80481121
Web Site: https://www.munters.cn
N.A.I.C.S.: 337126

Munters Brazil Industria Comerico Ltda (1)
Anselmo De Lima Filho 343 C, CIC, CEP 81290 250, Curitiba, Parana, Brazil (100%)
Tel.: (55) 4133175050
Web Site: http://www.munters.com.br
Sales Range: $1-9.9 Million
Emp.: 90
N.A.I.C.S.: 337126

Munters Corporation (1)
79 Monroe St, Amesbury, MA 01913
Tel.: (978) 241-1100
Web Site: http://www.muntersamerica.com
Sales Range: $75-99.9 Million
Emp.: 600

MUNTERS AB

Munters AB—(Continued)
Mfr of Dehumidifiers & Moisture Control Devices
N.A.I.C.S.: 333415

Munters Des Champs (1)
225 S Magnolia Ave, Buena Vista, VA 24416
Tel.: (540) 291-1111
Sales Range: $25-49.9 Million
Emp.: 200
Heat Exchanger & Air Conditioning Equipment Mfr
N.A.I.C.S.: 332410

Munters Europe AB (1)
Borgarfjordsgatan 16, PO Box 1150, 164 40, Kista, Sweden (100%)
Tel.: (46) 86266300
Web Site: http://www.munters.se
Sales Range: $50-74.9 Million
Emp.: 100
Holding Company; Regional Managing Office
N.A.I.C.S.: 551112
Per Segerstrom (Gen Mgr)

Subsidiary (Non-US):

Munters A/S (2)
(50%)
Tel.: (45) 44953355
Web Site: http://www.munters.dk
Sales Range: $25-49.9 Million
Emp.: 8
Energy & Heating Technology
N.A.I.C.S.: 333415

Munters AG (2)
Hardturmstrasse 175, CH 8005, Zurich, Switzerland
Tel.: (41) 44 2720865
Web Site: http://www.munters.ch
Sales Range: $25-49.9 Million
Emp.: 3
Moisture Control & Restoration Services
N.A.I.C.S.: 333413

Munters BV (2)
Japrlarwag 4, PO Box 655, NL 2400, Alphen aan den Rijn, Netherlands (100%)
Tel.: (31) 172421600
Web Site: http://www.polygongroup.com
Sales Range: $25-49.9 Million
N.A.I.C.S.: 337126

Subsidiary (Domestic):

Munters Nederland B.V. (3)
Energieweg 69, PO Box 229, NL 2400 AE, Alphen aan den Rijn, Netherlands (100%)
Tel.: (31) 00172433231
Web Site: http://www.munters.nl
Sales Range: $25-49.9 Million
Emp.: 15
Energy & Heating Technology
N.A.I.C.S.: 333415
Hans Heutman (Mgr-Comml)

Subsidiary (Non-US):

Munters France S.A.S. (2)
106 Boulevard Heloise, Argenteuil, F 95815, France
Tel.: (33) 134115757
Web Site: http://www.munters.fr
Sales Range: $25-49.9 Million
Emp.: 30
Energy & Heating Technology
N.A.I.C.S.: 333415

Subsidiary (Domestic):

Munters Services SA (3)
106 Boulevard Heloise, 95815, Argenteuil, Cedex, France (100%)
Tel.: (33) 134115757
Web Site: http://www.munters.com
Sales Range: $25-49.9 Million
Emp.: 30
Air Treatment Solutions; Humidity & Climate Control Technologies
N.A.I.C.S.: 334512
Prius Bascal (Mng Dir)

Subsidiary (Non-US):

Munters GmbH (2)
(100%)
Web Site: http://www.munters.de

Sales Range: $25-49.9 Million
Emp.: 40
Energy & Heating Technology
N.A.I.C.S.: 333415

Munters Italy S.p.A. (2)
Via Strada Piani, Chiusavecchia, 12084, Imperia, Italy (100%)
Web Site: http://www.munters.it
Sales Range: $25-49.9 Million
Emp.: 100
HumiCool HVAC Mfr
N.A.I.C.S.: 333415

Munters Ltd. (2)
10 Ramsey Rd, Hitching Brook Bus Park, Huntingdon, PE29 6FY, Cambshire, United Kingdom (100%)
Tel.: (44) 1480432243
Web Site: http://www.munters.co.uk
Sales Range: $25-49.9 Million
Emp.: 35
Energy & Heating Technology
N.A.I.C.S.: 333415

Subsidiary (Domestic):

Munters Moisture Control Services (3)
Blackstone Road, Huntingdon, PE29 6EE, United Kingdom (100%)
Tel.: (44) 1480432243
Web Site: http://www.munters.co.uk
Sales Range: $25-49.9 Million
Emp.: 20
N.A.I.C.S.: 337126
Simon Hurst (Dir-Major & Complex Loss-UK)

Subsidiary (Non-US):

Munters NV (2)
Ingberthoeveweg 3 E, 2630, Aartselaar, Belgium (100%)
Tel.: (32) 34582434
Sales Range: $1-9.9 Million
Emp.: 13
N.A.I.C.S.: 337126

Munters Oy (2)
Lyhtytie22, PO Box 36, Helsinki, 740, Finland (100%)
Tel.: (358) 98386030
Web Site: http://www.munters.fi
Sales Range: $1-9.9 Million
Emp.: 30
N.A.I.C.S.: 337126
Hanno Ojaonn (Gen Mgr)

Munters Spain SA (2)
Europa Empresarial Edificio Londres C Playa de Liencres 2, 28290, Madrid, Spain
Tel.: (34) 916400902
Sales Range: $25-49.9 Million
Emp.: 14
N.A.I.C.S.: 337126
Anna Perez (Dir-Mktg)

Munters Trocknungsservice Ges m.b.H (2)
Brunner Str 59 59, Vienna, 1230, Austria (100%)
Tel.: (43) 616429892
Web Site: http://www.munters.at
Sales Range: $25-49.9 Million
Emp.: 26
N.A.I.C.S.: 337126

Munters Finland Oy (1)
Hakamaenkuja 3, 01510, Vantaa, Finland
Tel.: (358) 207768230
Heating Equipment Distr
N.A.I.C.S.: 423730
Markku Stenfors (Mgr-Sls)

Munters GmbH (1)
Glattalstr 501, 8153, Rumlang, Switzerland
Tel.: (41) 523438886
Heating Equipment Distr
N.A.I.C.S.: 423730

Munters GmbH (1)
Zweigniederlassung Wien Eduard-Kittenberger-Gasse 56 Obj 6, 1235, Vienna, Austria
Tel.: (43) 16164298
Heating Equipment Distr
N.A.I.C.S.: 423730

Munters India Humidity Control Pvt Ltd (1)

Office No 08 2nd Floor Madhuban Building Koregaon Park Lane No 5, Above Canara Bank, Pune, 411001, India
Tel.: (91) 2066818900
Heating Equipment Distr
N.A.I.C.S.: 423730
Kishunk Rajput (Mgr-Sls)

Munters KK (1)
27-2 Funado 3 Chome, Itabashi Ku, Tokyo, 174-0041, Japan (100%)
Tel.: (81) 359700021
Web Site: http://www.munters.jp
Sales Range: $900-999.9 Million
N.A.I.C.S.: 337126

Subsidiary (Domestic)

Berner International Co. Ltd. (2)
Nihon Jitensha Kaikan 9-15 Akasaka 1-chome, Minato-ku, Tokyo, 107, Japan
Tel.: (81) 335856421
Marketing & Sales of Dehumidification & Heat Recovery Systems & Products
N.A.I.C.S.: 332811

Munters Kerulai Air Treatment Equipment (Guangdong) Co Ltd (1)
No 81 Fenxi Yi Road, Wanjiang District, 523055, Dongguan, Guangdong, China
Tel.: (86) 76922188788
Heating Equipment Distr
N.A.I.C.S.: 423730
Iris Woo (Reg Mgr)

Munters Pte. Ltd. (1)
16 Tai Seng Street 02-01, 04-00 Jubilee Industrial Bldg, Singapore, 534138, Singapore (100%)
Tel.: (65) 67446828
Web Site: http://www.munters.com.sg
Sales Range: $25-49.9 Million
Emp.: 14
Air Treatment Solutions & Climate Control Technologies
N.A.I.C.S.: 333413
S. K. Pang (Mng Dir)

Munters Pty Ltd. (1)
21 Union Rd, Albury, 2640, NSW, Australia
Tel.: (61) 260256422
Web Site: http://www.munters.com.au
Sales Range: $25-49.9 Million
Emp.: 12
N.A.I.C.S.: 337126
Wonhee Lee (Mng Dir)

Munters Sp. z o.o. (1)
Oddzial w Polsce ul Swietojanska 55/11, 81-391, Gdynia, Poland
Tel.: (48) 583053517
Heating Equipment Distr
N.A.I.C.S.: 423730

Munters de Mexico S.A. de C.V. (1)
Callos Rosseau 500, Parque Ind Milimex, 66600, Monterrey, Apodaca, Mexico (100%)
Tel.: (52) 8183693519
Web Site: http://www.munters.com
Sales Range: $50-74.9 Million
Emp.: 200
N.A.I.C.S.: 337126

Munters, Inc. (1)
7025 Tomken Road Unit 247, Mississauga, L5S 1R6, ON, Canada (100%)
Tel.: (905) 564-6466
Web Site: http://www.munters.com
Sales Range: $50-74.9 Million
Emp.: 4
Sale of Energy & Heating Technology
N.A.I.C.S.: 423730
Manjit Chahal (Controller)

Rotor Source, Inc (1)
17444 Opportunity Ave, Baton Rouge, LA 70817
Tel.: (225) 753-1700
Web Site: http://www.rotorsource.com
Rev.: $3,778,000
Emp.: 10
Warm Air Heating & Air-Conditioning Equipment & Supplies Merchant Whslr
N.A.I.C.S.: 423730
Spencer Goland (Pres)

MUNTERS GROUP AB
Borgarfjordsgatan 16, 16440, Kista, Sweden

INTERNATIONAL PUBLIC

Tel.: (46) 86266300
Web Site: https://www.munters.com
Year Founded: 1955
MTRS—(OMX)
Rev.: $1,304,710,257
Assets: $1,567,057,237
Liabilities: $1,074,582,970
Net Worth: $492,474,266
Earnings: $73,430,929
Emp.: 4,981
Fiscal Year-end: 12/31/23
Information Technology Services
N.A.I.C.S.: 541512
Grete Solvang Stoltz (VP)

Subsidiaries:

Automated Environments LLC (1)
PO Box 278, Renville, MN 56284 (80%)
Tel.: (320) 329-4340
Web Site: http://www.automatedenvironments.com
Rev.: $1,500,000
Emp.: 5
Provider of Computer Services
N.A.I.C.S.: 423430
Art Briggs (VP)

EDPAC International Ltd. (1)
Carrigaline Industrial Park, Carrigaline, Cork, Ireland
Tel.: (353) 214372850
Web Site: https://www.edpac.com
Air Cooling System Mfr & Distr
N.A.I.C.S.: 333415

MTech Systems America Latina Ltda. (1)
Rua Bahia 850 Sala 3 Bairro do Salto, Blumenau, 89031-000, SC, Brazil
Tel.: (55) 4733346109
Poultry & Swine Farm Operator
N.A.I.C.S.: 112390

Munters (Vietnam) Co., Ltd. (1)
Villa 1161 Street No 57, Thao Dien Ward Thu Duc City, Ho Chi Minh City, Vietnam
Tel.: (84) 2838256838
Industrial Dehumidification System Mfr & Distr
N.A.I.C.S.: 333415

Munters Belgium S.A. (1)
Oude Baan 3, 2800, Mechelen, Belgium
Tel.: (32) 15285611
Ventilating Equipment Mfr & Distr
N.A.I.C.S.: 333414

Munters Canada Inc. (1)
7025 Tomken Road Unit 247, Mississauga, L5S 1R6, ON, Canada
Tel.: (905) 564-6466
Air Treatment Services
N.A.I.C.S.: 238220

Munters Czech s.r.o. (1)
Slevacska 2368/ 68, 615 00, Brno, Czech Republic
Tel.: (420) 775569657
Air Conditioning System Distr
N.A.I.C.S.: 423730

Munters Israel Ltd. (1)
18 Hasivim Street, Petah Tikva, 49517, Israel
Tel.: (972) 39206200
Climate Control Services
N.A.I.C.S.: 541350

Munters Korea Co., Ltd. (1)
8 Nonhyeon-ro 105-gil, Gangnam-gu, Seoul, Korea (South)
Tel.: (82) 27618701
Climate Control Services
N.A.I.C.S.: 541350

Munters Netherlands B.V. (1)
Munters Nederland Westbaan 140, 2841 MC, Moordrecht, Netherlands
Tel.: (31) 884049000
Industrial Dehumidification System Mfr & Distr
N.A.I.C.S.: 333415

Munters Reventa GmbH (1)
Im Gewerbegebiet 3, Horstmar, 48612, Steinfurt, Germany
Tel.: (49) 255893920
Web Site: https://www.reventa.de

AND PRIVATE COMPANIES

Emp.: 130
Poultry & Swine Farm Operator
N.A.I.C.S.: 112390

Munters-Form Endustri Sistemleri Sanayive Ticaret AS (1)
Camlik Mahallesi Ikbal Caddesi Dinc Sokak, Niyazi Bey Is Merkezi No 31 Serifali Umraniye, 34770, Istanbul, Turkiye
Tel.: (90) 2165941865
Climate Control Services
N.A.I.C.S.: 238220

Proflute AB (1)
Borgarfjordsgatan 16, SE-164 26, Kista, Sweden
Tel.: (46) 739121600
Web Site: https://proflute.se
Desiccant Rotor Mfr & Distr
N.A.I.C.S.: 335312

MUNZING CHEMIE GMBH
Salzstrasse 174, 74076, Heilbronn, Germany
Tel.: (49) 7131987100
Web Site: http://www.munzing.com
Year Founded: 1830
Sales Range: $25-49.9 Million
Emp.: 3,400
Chemical Additive Mfr
N.A.I.C.S.: 325998
Michael Munzing *(Mng Dir)*

Subsidiaries:

MUNZING Australia Pty. Ltd. (1)
3 Warringah Close, Somersby, 2250, NSW, Australia
Tel.: (61) 243407800
Chemical Products Mfr
N.A.I.C.S.: 325998
Malcolm Rae *(Comml Dir)*

MUNZING CHEMIE Iberia S.A. (1)
C/ Francesc Layret 2, Montornes del Valles, 08170, Barcelona, Spain
Tel.: (34) 93 5722075
Chemical Additive Distr
N.A.I.C.S.: 424690

MUNZING Corporation (1)
1455 Broad St Ste 3, Bloomfield, NJ 07003
Tel.: (973) 279-1306
Web Site: http://www.munzing.com
Rev.: $11,500,000
Emp.: 30
Paints & Paint Additives Mfr
N.A.I.C.S.: 325510
Terri Dober *(Mgr-Sls-West Coast)*

MUNZING Emulsions Chemie GmbH (1)
Dr-Bergius-Strasse 16-24, 06729, Elsteraue, Germany
Tel.: (49) 34418291022
Chemical Products Mfr
N.A.I.C.S.: 325998

MUNZING International S.a.r.L. (1)
23 rue Aldringen, 1118, Luxembourg, Luxembourg
Tel.: (352) 2627 1520
Chemical Additive Distr
N.A.I.C.S.: 424690
Stephane Guiot *(Pres)*

MUNZING Malaysia Sdn. Bhd. (1)
C22 Susur Lencongan Timur Kanan Kawasan Perindustrian Cendana, 08000, Sungai Petani, Kedah, Malaysia
Tel.: (60) 44233388
Chemical Products Mfr
N.A.I.C.S.: 325998
William Lee *(Sls Mgr)*

MUNZING Micro Technologies GmbH (1)
Dr -Bergius-Strasse 16-24, 06729, Elsteraue, Germany
Tel.: (49) 3441 829 10 22
Web Site: http://www.munzing.com
Emp.: 60
Chemical Additive Mfr
N.A.I.C.S.: 325998
Dr Munzing *(Gen Mgr)*

MUNZING Mumbai Pvt. Ltd. (1)
502 Arcadia Building NCPA Marg, Nariman Point, Mumbai, 400021, India
Tel.: (91) 2268562301
Chemical Products Mfr
N.A.I.C.S.: 325998

MUNZING Shanghai Co. Ltd. (1)
Room 404-408 Building 12 No 128 Xiangyin Rd USST National Science Park, Shanghai, 200433, China
Tel.: (86) 21 6149 1561
Chemical Additive Distr
N.A.I.C.S.: 424690

Magrabar, LLC (1)
6100 Madison Ct, Morton Grove, IL 60053
Tel.: (847) 965-7550
Web Site: http://www.magrabar.com
Chemical Additive Mfr
N.A.I.C.S.: 325998
Colin J. Hoather *(VP-Fin)*

Suddeutsche Emulsions-Chemie GmbH (1)
Rhenaniastrasse 46, 68199, Mannheim, Germany
Tel.: (49) 621844870
Web Site: http://www.secemulsion.de
Chemical Products Mfr
N.A.I.C.S.: 325998
Malte Koffka *(Mng Dir)*

MURA EUROPEAN FASHION DESIGN, PROIZVODNJA OBLACIL D.D.
Plese 2, 9000, Murska Sobota, Slovenia
Tel.: (386) 2 513 2100
Web Site: http://www.murafashion.com
Year Founded: 1925
Sales Range: $75-99.9 Million
Emp.: 4,600
Clothing Mfr
N.A.I.C.S.: 315250
Simona Sarotar Zizek *(Sec)*

MURAKAMI CORPORATION
11-5 Tenma-cho, Aoi-Ku, Shizuoka, 420-8550, Shizuoka, Japan
Tel.: (81) 542531890
Web Site: https://www.murakami-kaimeido.co.jp
7292—(TKS)
Rev.: $691,412,610
Assets: $706,040,540
Liabilities: $137,150,890
Net Worth: $568,889,650
Earnings: $38,913,070
Emp.: 3,760
Fiscal Year-end: 03/31/24
Glass Mfr
N.A.I.C.S.: 327211
Taro Murakami *(Pres & CEO)*

Subsidiaries:

Eiji Corporation (1)
748 Hyodayu, Fujieda-shi, Shizuoka, 426-8601, Japan
Tel.: (81) 546352330
Automobile Parts Mfr & Distr
N.A.I.C.S.: 336390

Jiaxing Murakami Corporation (1)
No 1432 Changsheng East Road Economic Development Zone, Jiaxing, Zhejiang, China
Tel.: (86) 573 83912001
Rear View Mirror Mfr & Distr
N.A.I.C.S.: 336390

Murakami Ampas (Thailand) Co., Ltd. (1)
531 Moo4 Bangpoo Industrial Estate Sukhumvit Road Tambol Praeksa, Amphur Muang, Samut Prakan, 10280, Thailand
Tel.: (66) 27092856
Rear View Mirror Mfr & Distr
N.A.I.C.S.: 336390

Murakami Business Service Corporation (1)
11-5 Tenma-cho, Aoi-ku Shizuoka-shi, Shizuoka, 420-8550, Japan
Tel.: (81) 542531870
Temporary Staffing Services

N.A.I.C.S.: 561320

Murakami Corporation (Thailand) Ltd. (1)
No 191/46 CTI Tower 20th Floor Ratchadapisek Road, Klongtoey Sub-District Klongtoey District, Bangkok, 10110, Thailand
Tel.: (66) 22584660
Rear View Mirror Mfr & Distr
N.A.I.C.S.: 336390

Murakami Corporation - Oigawa Plant (1)
1700 Zenzaemon Fujieda, Shizuoka, 426-0053, Japan
Tel.: (81) 54 635 2410
Web Site: http://www.murakami-kaimeido.co.jp
Rear View Mirror Mfr
N.A.I.C.S.: 336390

Murakami Corporation - Tsuiji Plant (1)
550-1 Tsuijikami, Fujieda, 426-0032, Shizuoka, Japan
Tel.: (81) 54 635 1402
Web Site: http://www.murakami-kaimeido.jp
Rear View Mirror Mfr
N.A.I.C.S.: 336390
Enao Tsuji *(Mgr)*

Murakami East Japan Corporation (1)
135-10 Nishishinmachi, Ota, 373-0847, Gunma, Japan
Tel.: (81) 276313951
Web Site: http://www.oew.co.jp
Emp.: 267
Door Mirrors & Lamps Mfr
N.A.I.C.S.: 423120
Tao Murakami *(Pres)*

Murakami Express Corporation (1)
109 Oyaizu, Yaizu, 425-0073, Japan
Tel.: (81) 546215072
Truck Transportation Services
N.A.I.C.S.: 532120

Murakami Germany GmbH (1)
Obergstrasse 3D, 38102, Braunschweig, Germany
Tel.: (49) 53121965278
Marketing Research Service
N.A.I.C.S.: 541910

Murakami Kasei Corporation (1)
Yurakucho Denki Building 3rd Floor 7-1-1 Yuraku-cho, Chiyoda-ku, Tokyo, 100-0006, Japan
Tel.: (81) 362734120
Web Site: https://murakami-kasei.co.jp
Plastic Material Mfr & Distr
N.A.I.C.S.: 325211

Murakami Kyushu Corporation (1)
660-1 Usunoin, Asakura-shi, Fukuoka, 838-1301, Japan
Tel.: (81) 946265151
Automobile Parts Mfr & Distr
N.A.I.C.S.: 336390

Murakami Manufacturing (Thailand) Co., Ltd. (1)
1 Moo5 Rojana Industrial Park Amphur U-Thai, Pranakorn, Ayutthaya, 13210, Thailand
Tel.: (66) 35227202
Rear View Mirror Mfr
N.A.I.C.S.: 336390

Murakami Manufacturing India Private Limited (1)
Plot No - 19 Japanese Industrial Park Mandal GIDC, Vithalapur Ta- Mandal, Ahmedabad, 382120, Gujarat, India
Tel.: (91) 2715671303
Injection Mold Mfr & Distr
N.A.I.C.S.: 333511

Murakami Manufacturing Mexico, S.A. de C.V. (1)
Boulevard Paseo de la Plata 1123 Parque Industrial SUMAR I, Morelos, Zacatecas, Mexico
Tel.: (52) 4924782700
Web Site: https://www.murakami-mx.com
Emp.: 365
Auto Parts Mfr
N.A.I.C.S.: 336390

MURAMOTO ELECTRON (THAILAND) PCL

Michael A. Rodenberg *(Chm & CEO)*

Murakami Manufacturing USA Inc. (1)
575 Water Tower Byp, Campbellsville, KY 42718
Tel.: (270) 469-3939
Rear View Mirror Mfr
N.A.I.C.S.: 336390

Murakami Mold Engineering (Thailand) Co., Ltd. (1)
826/5 Moo4 Bangpoo Industrial Estate, Tambol Praeksa Amphur Muang, Samut Prakan, 10280, Thailand
Tel.: (66) 106623247013
Injection Mold Mfr & Distr
N.A.I.C.S.: 333511

Murakami Saikyu (Thailand) Co., Ltd. (1)
826/5 Moo4 Bangpoo Industrial Estate Tambol Praeksa, Amphur Muang, Samut Prakan, 10280, Thailand
Tel.: (66) 2324 7013
Rear View Mirror Mfr & Distr
N.A.I.C.S.: 336390

PT Murakami Delloyd Indonesia (1)
Greenland International Industrial Center Blok CF Lot 5C Deltamas, Cikarang Pusat, Bekasi, 17530, Lippo Cikarangt, Indonesia (51%)
Tel.: (62) 2122157002
Automobile Parts Mfr
N.A.I.C.S.: 336390

MURAKI CORPORATION
2-24-27 Sekido, Tama-Shi, Tokyo, 206-0011, Japan
Tel.: (81) 423575600
Web Site: https://www.muraki.co.jp
Year Founded: 1957
7477—(TKS)
Rev.: $69,821,840
Assets: $37,093,760
Liabilities: $14,403,840
Net Worth: $22,689,920
Earnings: $987,360
Emp.: 257
Fiscal Year-end: 03/31/22
Automobile Parts Distr
N.A.I.C.S.: 441330
Kiyomi Nagai *(Pres)*

MURAL ONCOLOGY PLC
10 Earlsfort Terrace, Dublin, D02 T380, Ireland
Tel.: (353) 19058020   IE
Web Site: https://www.muraloncology.com
Year Founded: 2017
MURA—(NASDAQ)
Assets: $301,745,000
Liabilities: $37,928,000
Net Worth: $263,817,000
Earnings: ($207,447,000)
Emp.: 117
Fiscal Year-end: 12/31/23
Biotechnology Research & Development Services
N.A.I.C.S.: 541714

MURAMOTO ELECTRON (THAILAND) PCL
No 886 Ram Intra Road, Khan Na Yao, Bangkok, 10230, Thailand
Tel.: (66) 251812806
Web Site: https://www.metco.co.th
Year Founded: 1987
METCO—(THA)
Rev.: $495,992,210
Assets: $253,033,368
Liabilities: $80,475,338
Net Worth: $172,558,029
Earnings: $6,673,948
Emp.: 2,338
Fiscal Year-end: 09/30/23
Electronic Components Mfr
N.A.I.C.S.: 334419
Yoichi Muramoto *(Chm & Pres)*

MURAMOTO ELECTRON (THAILAND) PCL

Muramoto Electron (Thailand) PCL—(Continued)

Subsidiaries:

Muramota Asia Pte., Ltd. (1)
5 Tampines Central 6 03-38 Telepark, Singapore, 529482, Singapore
Tel.: (65) 62212500
Plastic Part Whslr
N.A.I.C.S.: 424610

Muramota Audio-Visual Philippines, Inc. (1)
First Street Block-A1 Mactan Economic Zone 1, Cebu, Lapu-Lapu, 6015, Philippines
Tel.: (63) 323400296
Web Site: https://www.muramoto.com
Emp.: 410
Automotive Product Mfr & Distr
N.A.I.C.S.: 327215

Muramota Industry Company Limited (1)
3-1-56 Takatsukadai, Nishi-ku, Kobe, 651-2271, Japan
Tel.: (81) 789911600
Plastics Product Mfr
N.A.I.C.S.: 333248

Muramota Manufacturing De Mexico, S. De R.L. (1)
Tres Sur No 9071 Ciudad Industrial, 22444, Tijuana, BC, Mexico
Tel.: (52) 6646074838
Electrical Part Mfr & Distr
N.A.I.C.S.: 335999

Muramoto Manufacturing Europe s.r.o. (1)
Skandinavska 991, Zebrak, Czech Republic
Tel.: (420) 774536805
Emp.: 170
Metal Component Mfr
N.A.I.C.S.: 336370

Muramoto USA Inc. (1)
3760 Convoy St Ste 219, San Diego, CA 92111
Tel.: (619) 661-2574
Metal Part Mfr & Distr
N.A.I.C.S.: 332812

P.T. Muramoto Electronika Indonesia (1)
Industrial Park Plot 9J Cikarang Selatan, East Jakarta, Bekasi, 17550, Indonesia
Tel.: (62) 218970380
Automobile Parts Mfr
N.A.I.C.S.: 333248

Sima Technology Co., Ltd. (1)
99 Mu 1 Tambol Thongchainue Amphur, Pakthongchai, Nakhon Ratchasima, 30150, Thailand
Tel.: (66) 44081131
Emp.: 1,219
Pressed Metal Parts Mfr
N.A.I.C.S.: 332322
Kazunobu Kawabe (Pres)

MURATA MACHINERY, LTD.

136 Takeda-Mukaishiro-cho, Fushimi-ku, Kyoto, 612-8418, Japan
Tel.: (81) 756728138 JP
Web Site: http://www.muratec.net
Year Founded: 1935
Rev.: $3,792,875,680
Assets: $5,281,814,560
Liabilities: $1,557,105,440
Net Worth: $3,724,709,120
Earnings: $487,484,800
Emp.: 8,100
Fiscal Year-end: 03/31/22
Textile Machinery, Automated Systems, Communications Equipment & Machine Tools Mfr
N.A.I.C.S.: 333248
Daisuke Murata (Pres & CEO)

Subsidiaries:

Cimcorp Oy (1)
Satakunnantie 5, 28400, Ulvila, Finland
Tel.: (358) 10 2772 000
Web Site: http://www.cimcorp.com

Sales Range: $25-49.9 Million
Emp.: 300
Robotic Distribution Systems Developer
N.A.I.C.S.: 541330
Ilpo Nummelin (VP-Customer Support)

Subsidiary (Non-US):

Cimcorp Automation Ltd. (2)
635 South Service Road, Grimsby, L3M 4E8, ON, Canada
Tel.: (905) 643-9700
Web Site: http://cimcorp.com
Sales Range: $25-49.9 Million
Emp.: 60
Automated Material Handling System Mfr & Whslr
N.A.I.C.S.: 333998
Rick Trigatti (Pres)

KDS MANUFACTURING (M) SDN BHD (1)
Lot7963 Batu22 Jalan Air Hitam Kulai, 81000, Johor, Malaysia
Tel.: (60) 766 38616
Construction Hand Tool Mfr
N.A.I.C.S.: 333991

MURATA DO BRASIL COMERCIO E REPRESENTACAO DE MAQUINAS LTDA.
Estr de Santa Isabel n 3383 KM 385 Bloco A Bairro do Una, 08599-000, Itaquaquecetuba, SP, Brazil
Tel.: (55) 114 6486222
Web Site: http://www.muratec.com.br
Textile Machinery Distr
N.A.I.C.S.: 423830

MURATA MACHINERY INDIA PRIVATE LTD. (1)
1010 Hemkunt Tower 98 Nehru Place, 110 019, New Delhi, India
Tel.: (91) 112 6280046
Web Site: http://www.murata.net
Textile Machinery Distr
N.A.I.C.S.: 423830
Anindya Chaudhuri (CFO)

MURATA MACHINERY MEXICO S.DE R.L DE C.V. (1)
Londres 226 Piso 6 Delegacion Cuauhtemoc, Juarez, Mexico, 06600, Mexico
Tel.: (52) 555 2073064
Textile Machinery Distr
N.A.I.C.S.: 423830

MURATA TOOLS, LTD. (1)
881-1 Ichihashi Kamono-cho, Minokamo, 505-0056, Gifu, Japan
Tel.: (81) 574 273000
Industrial Machinery Mfr & Distr
N.A.I.C.S.: 333310
Yosuke Murata (Mgr)

MURATEC INFORMATION SYSTEMS, LTD. (1)
136 Takeda-Mukaishiro-cho, Fushimi-ku, Kyoto, 612-8686, Japan
Tel.: (81) 756 728257
Software Development Services
N.A.I.C.S.: 541511

MURATEC MECHATRONICS CO., LTD. (1)
37 Yuge Ryuo-cho, Gamou-gun, Shiga, 520-2501, Japan
Tel.: (81) 748 572000
Software Development Services
N.A.I.C.S.: 541511

Murata (Thailand) Co., Ltd. (1)
898/43-44 SV City Tower 2 25th Floor Rama 3 Road, Bangpongpang Yannawa, Bangkok, 10120, Thailand (100%)
Tel.: (66) 2294773440
Sales Range: $25-49.9 Million
Emp.: 24
Textile Machinery Mfr
N.A.I.C.S.: 333248
Yoshikatsu Nakayama (Mng Dir)

Murata Machinery (H.K.), Ltd. (1)
Unit A 31/F Legend Tower 7 Shing Yip Street Kwun Tong, Wang Hoi Rd Kowloon Bay, Kowloon, China (Hong Kong) (100%)
Tel.: (852) 23320009
Sales Range: $25-49.9 Million
Emp.: 10
Industrial Machinery & Equipment Whslr

Murata Machinery (Shanghai) Co., Ltd. (1)
150 Xin Gao Rd Qingpu Industrial Zone, Shanghai, 201700, China (100%)
Tel.: (86) 2169212300
Web Site: http://www.muratec.net
Industrial Machinery & Equipment Whslr
N.A.I.C.S.: 423830

Murata Machinery Europe GmbH (1)
Hanns-Martin-Schleyer-Strasse 3, 47877, Willich, Germany (100%)
Tel.: (49) 21549140
Web Site: http://www.muratec.com
Sales Range: $25-49.9 Million
Emp.: 30
Industrial Machinery & Equipment Whslr
N.A.I.C.S.: 423830

Murata Machinery Singapore Pte. Ltd. (1)
69 Ubi Crescent 06-01, Singapore, 408561, Singapore (100%)
Tel.: (65) 65451228
Web Site: http://www.muratec.net
Sales Range: $25-49.9 Million
Emp.: 40
Industrial Machinery & Equipment Whslr
N.A.I.C.S.: 423830

Murata Machinery Taiwan, Ltd. (1)
18F No 17 Sec 1 Chengde Rd, Taipei, 10351, Taiwan (100%)
Tel.: (886) 225585505
Web Site: http://www.muratec.net
Sales Range: $50-74.9 Million
Emp.: 125
Industrial Machinery Mfr
N.A.I.C.S.: 333248

Murata Machinery USA, Inc. (1)
2120 Queen City Dr, Charlotte, NC 28266-7609 (100%)
Tel.: (704) 394-8331
Web Site: http://www.muratec-usa.com
Sales Range: $50-74.9 Million
Emp.: 190
Wholesale Distribution & Servicing of Textile Machinery
N.A.I.C.S.: 333517
Lloyd Keller (Mgr-Sls-Eastern Reg)

Subsidiary (Domestic):

Muratec America, Inc. (2)
3301 E Plano Pkwy Ste 100, Plano, TX 75074 (100%)
Tel.: (469) 429-3300
Web Site: http://www.muratec.com
Sales Range: $25-49.9 Million
Emp.: 60
Facsimile Equipment & Cellular Telephones Mfr
N.A.I.C.S.: 423690
James C. D'Emidio (Pres)

Murata Machinery, Ltd. - Inuyama Plant (1)
2 Nakajima Hashizume, Inuyama, 484-8502, Aichi, Japan
Tel.: (81) 568 65 3101
Textile Machinery Mfr
N.A.I.C.S.: 333248

Murata Machinery, Ltd. - Ise Factory (1)
100 Takegahana-cho Ise-shi, Mie, 516-0005, Japan
Tel.: (81) 596 361260
Textile Machinery Mfr
N.A.I.C.S.: 333248

Murata Machinery, Ltd. - KAGA FACTORY (1)
So 1-1 Nango-machi, Kaga, 922-0821, Ishikawa, Japan
Tel.: (81) 761 732121
Textile Machinery Mfr
N.A.I.C.S.: 333248

Murata Parts Sales, Ltd. (1)
136 Takeda-Mukaishiro-cho, Fushimi-ku, Kyoto, 612-8686, Japan (100%)
Tel.: (81) 756728371
Sales Range: $25-49.9 Million
Emp.: 60
Industrial Machinery Mfr
N.A.I.C.S.: 333248

INTERNATIONAL PUBLIC

Muratec (Beijing) Co.,Ltd. (1)
Unit 2101 Blk-A ZhuBang 2000 Business Ctr, No 100 Balizhuang Xili Chaoyan, 100025, Beijing, China (100%)
Tel.: (86) 1085865004
Web Site: http://www.muratec.net
Industrial Machinery & Equipment Whslr
N.A.I.C.S.: 423830

Muratec Automation Co., Ltd. (1)
2 Nakajima Hashizume, Inuyama, 484-8502, Aichi, Japan (100%)
Tel.: (81) 568653101
Web Site: http://www.muratec.net
Sales Range: $125-149.9 Million
Emp.: 500
Development, Design, Manufacturing, Assembly, Sales, Installation, Training, Repair & Maintenance of Automated Material Handling Systems for Semiconductor Industry
N.A.I.C.S.: 333248

Muratec Automation Europe Sarl (1)
Parc des Fontaines, 38190, Bernin, France (100%)
Tel.: (33) 476751383
Web Site: http://www.muratec.net
Industrial Machinery & Equipment Whslr
N.A.I.C.S.: 423830

Muratec-KDS Corporation (1)
39 Matsuda-cho Higashi-Kujo Minami-ku, 601-8036, Kyoto, Japan (100%)
Tel.: (81) 756627318
Web Site: http://www.murata-kds.jp
Sales Range: $100-124.9 Million
Emp.: 500
Machine Tools Mfr
N.A.I.C.S.: 333517
Motoyoshi Yatsuzuka (Pres & CEO)

PT.MURATA MACHINERY INDONESIA (1)
Ruko Gyan Plaza D-4 Jln Terusan Pasirkoja Blok 8, 40222, Bandung, Indonesia
Tel.: (62) 226 046633
Textile Machinery Distr
N.A.I.C.S.: 423830

MURATA MANUFACTURING CO., LTD.

10-1 Higashikotari 1-chome, Nagaokakyo-shi, Kyoto, 617-8555, Japan
Tel.: (81) 759519111 JP
Web Site: https://www.murata.com
Year Founded: 1944
PJX—(SES)
Rev.: $15,780,268,240
Assets: $23,834,686,480
Liabilities: $5,233,162,880
Net Worth: $18,601,523,600
Earnings: $2,294,711,760
Emp.: 75,184
Fiscal Year-end: 03/31/21
Electric Equipment Mfr
N.A.I.C.S.: 334419
Tsuneo Murata (Chm)

Subsidiaries:

Anamizu Electronics Industries, Ltd. (1)
Chi-53 Ohmachi Anamizu-Machi, Housu, Ishikawa, 927-0026, Japan
Tel.: (81) 768 52 1050
Coil Products Mfr
N.A.I.C.S.: 334416

Anamizu Murata Manufacturing Co., Ltd. (1)
53 Chino Omachi Anamizu-cho, Hoshu-gun, Ishikawa, 927-0026, Japan
Tel.: (81) 768521050
Web Site: https://corporate.murata.com
Emp.: 340
Electronic Capacitor Mfr
N.A.I.C.S.: 334416

Asuwa Electronics Industries, Ltd. (1)
1321 Emorinaka 2-chome, Fukui, 918-8025, Japan
Tel.: (81) 776353988
Web Site: http://www.murata.com
Electronic Components Mfr

AND PRIVATE COMPANIES

MURATA MANUFACTURING CO., LTD.

N.A.I.C.S.: 334419

Asuwa Murata Manufacturing Co., Ltd. (1)
2-1321 Emorinaka, Fukui, 918-8025, Japan
Tel.: (81) 776353988
Web Site: https://corporate.murata.com
Emp.: 88
Electronic Capacitor Mfr
N.A.I.C.S.: 334416

Azumi Murata Manufacturing Co., Ltd. (1)
1020 Toyoshina Takaya, Azumino, 399-8204, Nagano, Japan
Tel.: (81) 263722811
Web Site: https://corporate.murata.com
Emp.: 402
Electronic Capacitor Mfr
N.A.I.C.S.: 334416

Dongguan Murata Electronics Co., Ltd. (1)
Wan Ji Industrial Park, Shajiao Village Shipai Town, Dongguan, 523300, Guangdong, China
Tel.: (86) 76986922888
Electronic Capacitor Mfr
N.A.I.C.S.: 334416

Fukui Murata Manufacturing Co., Ltd. (1)
13-1 Okamotocho, Echizen, 915-8601, Fukui, Japan
Tel.: (81) 77 821 8301
Web Site: https://corporate.murata.com
Emp.: 4,800
Capacitors, Microwave Devices & EMI Suppression Filters Mfr
N.A.I.C.S.: 334416
Takashi Yasushi Murata *(Chm & CEO)*

Hakui Murata Manufacturing Co., Ltd. (1)
52 Yanagibashi Yanagibashimachi, Hakui, 925-8555, Ishikawa, Japan
Tel.: (81) 76 722 3111
Web Site: http://www.murata.com
Sales Range: $25-49.9 Million
Piezoelectric Ceramic Components Mfr
N.A.I.C.S.: 334419
Fumiya Kayahara *(Pres)*

Himi Murata Manufacturing Co., Ltd. (1)
12-5 Oura, Himi, 935-0103, Toyama, Japan
Tel.: (81) 766915511
Web Site: https://corporate.murata.com
Emp.: 220
Electronic Capacitor Mfr
N.A.I.C.S.: 334416

Ise Murata Manufacturing Co., Ltd. (1)
2-1-4 Atsudai, Tsu, 514-0131, Mie, Japan
Tel.: (81) 592364300
Web Site: https://corporate.murata.com
Emp.: 164
Electronic Capacitor Mfr
N.A.I.C.S.: 334416

Iwami Murata Manufacturing Co., Ltd. (1)
Ohda Yi 795-1 Ohda-cho, Oda, 694-0064, Shimane, Japan
Tel.: (81) 854820300
Electronic Components Mfr
N.A.I.C.S.: 334419

Iwate Murata Manufacturing Co., Ltd. (1)
1-15-10 Kamiioka, Morioka, 020-0854, Iwate, Japan
Tel.: (81) 196373431
Web Site: https://corporate.murata.com
Emp.: 328
Electronic Capacitor Mfr
N.A.I.C.S.: 334416

Izumo Murata Manufacturing Co., Ltd. (1)
2308 Kaminae Hikawa-cho, Hikawa-gun, Izumo, 699-0696, Shimane, Japan
Tel.: (81) 853723330
Web Site: https://corporate.murata.com
Sales Range: $800-899.9 Million
Emp.: 5,383
Capacitor Mfr
N.A.I.C.S.: 334419

Kanazawa Murata Manufacturing Co., Ltd. (1)
18 Chi Soya-cho, Hakusan, 920-2101, Ishikawa, Japan
Tel.: (81) 762731151
Web Site: https://corporate.murata.com
Sales Range: $400-449.9 Million
Emp.: 2,730
Microwave Devices Mfr
N.A.I.C.S.: 334419

Plant (Domestic):

Kanazawa Murata Manufacturing Co., Ltd. - Sendai Plant (2)
2-6 Akedori 3-chome, Izumi-ku, Sendai, 981-3206, Miyagi, Japan
Tel.: (81) 22 342 7111
Piezoelectric Products & Microwave Device Mfr
N.A.I.C.S.: 334419

Kanazu Murata Manufacturing Co., Ltd. (1)
2-10-28 Hananomori, Awara, 919-0633, Fukui, Japan
Tel.: (81) 77 673 1155
Web Site: http://www.murata.com
Emp.: 305
Electronic Components Mfr
N.A.I.C.S.: 334419

Komatsu Murata Manufacturing Co., Ltd. (1)
93 Hikarimachi, Komatsu, 923-0804, Ishikawa, Japan
Tel.: (81) 76 121 9111
Web Site: https://corporate.murata.com
Sales Range: $200-249.9 Million
Emp.: 800
Module Pruducts Mfr
N.A.I.C.S.: 334419

Komoro Murata Manufacturing Co., Ltd. (1)
190 Kashiwagi, Komoro, 384-8511, Nagano, Japan
Tel.: (81) 267224111
Web Site: https://corporate.murata.com
Emp.: 421
Electronic Capacitor Mfr
N.A.I.C.S.: 334416

Korea Murata Electronics Company, Limited (1)
21st Fl-22nd Fl GT Tower East Seocho Daero 411, Seocho-gu, Seoul, 06615, Korea (South)
Tel.: (82) 2 561 2347
Web Site: http://www.murata.com
Electronic Components Distr
N.A.I.C.S.: 423690

Murata Active Partner Co., Ltd. (1)
Nihonseimei Kyoto Santetsu Building Shiokojitori Shinmachinishi Hairu, Shimogyoku, Kyoto, 600-8216, Japan
Tel.: (81) 75 342 5401
Web Site: http://www.map-partner.co.jp
Human Resource Consulting Services
N.A.I.C.S.: 541612

Murata Company Limited (1)
Unit 1801-08 Level 18 Tower 1 Grand Century Place, 193 Prince Edward Road West Mongkok, Kowloon, China (Hong Kong)
Tel.: (852) 23763898
Electronic Components Distr
N.A.I.C.S.: 423690
Masahiko Kondo *(Gen Mgr)*

Murata Eiko Co., Ltd. (1)
26-10 Tenjin 2-chome, Nagaokakyo, 617-8566, Kyoto, Japan
Tel.: (81) 759542060
Electronic Components Mfr
N.A.I.C.S.: 334419

Murata Electronics (India) Private Limited (1)
Prestige Palladium Bayan Building 10th Floor Old No 12, New No 43/1 Greams Road Thousand Lights, Chennai, 600 006, India
Tel.: (91) 4466930300
Electronic Capacitor Mfr
N.A.I.C.S.: 334416

Murata Electronics (Malaysia) Sdn. Bhd. (1)
Plot 15 Jalan Bemban, Bemban Industrial Park, 31000, Batu Gajah, Perak, Malaysia
Tel.: (60) 53629388
Web Site: https://corporate.murata.com
Sales Range: $200-249.9 Million
Emp.: 1,252
Electronic Component Mfr & Distr
N.A.I.C.S.: 334419
Kaoru Kumekawa *(Mng Dir)*

Murata Electronics (Netherlands) B.V. (1)
Wegalaan 2, 2131HC, Hoofddorp, Netherlands
Tel.: (31) 235698410
Sales Range: $50-74.9 Million
Emp.: 85
Electronic Components Distr
N.A.I.C.S.: 423690
G. Atkins *(Gen Mgr)*

Murata Electronics (Thailand), Ltd. (1)
Northern Region Industrial Estate 63 Moo 4, Tambol Ban Klang Amphur Muang, Lamphun, 51000, Thailand
Tel.: (66) 53581166
Web Site: https://corporate.murata.com
Emp.: 6,194
Electronic Components Mfr
N.A.I.C.S.: 334419

Murata Electronics (UK) Limited (1)
One Fleet Ancells Business Park Ancells Road, Fleet, GU51 2UN, Hampshire, United Kingdom
Tel.: (44) 125 281 1666
Web Site: https://www.murata.com
Emp.: 20
Electronic Components Distr
N.A.I.C.S.: 423690

Murata Electronics (Vietnam) Co., Ltd. (1)
Room 501 5th Floor V Building 125-127 Ba Trieu Street, Nguyen Du Ward Hai Ba Trung District, Hanoi, Vietnam
Tel.: (84) 2436374666
Web Site: http://www.murata.com.sg
Emp.: 10
Electronic Components Distr
N.A.I.C.S.: 423690
Hoo Chee Seng *(Gen Dir)*

Murata Electronics Co., Ltd. (1)
Yokohama Landmark Tower 19F 2-2-1 Minatomirai, Nishi-ku, Yokohama, 220-8119, Japan
Tel.: (81) 45 225 6350
Web Site: http://www.murata.co.jp
Sales Range: $75-99.9 Million
Emp.: 110
Electronic Components Distr
N.A.I.C.S.: 423690
Satoshio Sonoda *(Pres)*

Murata Electronics Europe B.V. (1)
Wegalaan 2, 2132 JC, Hoofddorp, Netherlands
Tel.: (31) 235698410
Electronic Capacitor Mfr
N.A.I.C.S.: 334416

Murata Electronics Europe B.V. (1)
Office 8B Calle Electronica 19, Badalona, 08915, Barcelona, Spain
Tel.: (34) 935820259
Electronic Capacitor Mfr
N.A.I.C.S.: 334416

Murata Electronics Europe B.V. (1)
Holbeinstrasse 23, 90441, Nuremberg, Germany
Tel.: (49) 91166870
Electronic Capacitor Mfr
N.A.I.C.S.: 334416

Murata Electronics Europe B.V. (1)
Office Nr 3 3B Building I Infopark Setany 1, 1117, Budapest, Hungary
Tel.: (36) 9116687139
Electronic Capacitor Mfr
N.A.I.C.S.: 334416

Murata Electronics Europe B.V. (1)
Via Mazzini 3/A, 20063, Cernusco sul Naviglio, Milan, Italy
Tel.: (39) 02959681
Electronic Capacitor Mfr
N.A.I.C.S.: 334416

Murata Electronics Europe B.V. (1)
Centre d'Affaires La Boursidiere - Rue de la Boursidiere, BP 199, Le Plessis Robinson, 92357, Paris, Cedex, France
Tel.: (33) 140948300
Electronic Capacitor Mfr
N.A.I.C.S.: 334416

Murata Electronics Europe B.V. (1)
One Fleet Ancells Business Park Ancells Road, Fleet, GU51 2UN, Hampshire, United Kingdom
Tel.: (44) 1252811666
Electronic Capacitor Mfr
N.A.I.C.S.: 334416

Murata Electronics North America, Inc. (1)
2200 Lake Park Dr SE, Smyrna, GA 30080-7604 (100%)
Tel.: (770) 436-1300
Web Site: http://www.murataamericas.com
Sales Range: $75-99.9 Million
Emp.: 150
Fixed & Variable Ceramic Capacitors & Related Products Distr
N.A.I.C.S.: 423690

Subsidiary (Domestic):

Peregrine Semiconductor Corporation (2)
9380 Carroll Park Dr, San Diego, CA 92121 (100%)
Tel.: (858) 731-9400
Web Site: http://www.psemi.com
Mixed Signal & Radio Frequency Semiconductor Products Mfr
N.A.I.C.S.: 334413
Takaki Murata *(Interim CEO)*

Resonant Inc. (2)
10900 Stonelake Blvd Ste 100 Office 02 130, Austin, TX 78759
Tel.: (805) 308-9803
Web Site: http://www.resonant.com
Rev.: $2,178,000
Assets: $28,361,000
Liabilities: $13,105,000
Net Worth: $15,256,000
Earnings: ($35,970,000)
Emp.: 73
Fiscal Year-end: 12/31/2021
Radio Frequency Filter Design Developer
N.A.I.C.S.: 334413
Dylan J. Kelly *(COO)*

Subsidiary (Domestic):

Resonant LLC (3)
110 Castilian Dr Ste 100, Santa Barbara, CA 93117
Tel.: (805) 308-9803
Web Site: http://www.resonant.com
Radio Frequency Filter Design Developer
N.A.I.C.S.: 334413

Murata Electronics Oy (1)
Myllynkivenkuja 6, 01621, Vantaa, Finland (100%)
Tel.: (358) 9879181
Sales Range: $100-124.9 Million
Emp.: 1,000
Electronic Measurement Device Mfr
N.A.I.C.S.: 334519

Murata Electronics Philippines Inc. (1)
Unit 3A 3B Third Floor LTI Admin Building 1 Annex 2 North Main Avenue, Laguna Technopark, Binan, 4024, Laguna, Philippines
Tel.: (63) 495407308
Electronic Components Distr
N.A.I.C.S.: 423690

Murata Electronics Singapore (Pte.) Ltd. (1)
200 Yishun Avenue 7, Singapore, 768927, Singapore
Tel.: (65) 6 758 4233
Web Site: http://www.murata.com.sg
Sales Range: $450-499.9 Million
Emp.: 1,260
Electronic Component Mfr & Distr
N.A.I.C.S.: 334419
Toshikazu Sasaki *(Mng Dir)*

Murata Electronics Trading (Shanghai) Co., Ltd. (1)
11/Floor 5 Corporate Avenue 150 Hubin

MURATA MANUFACTURING CO., LTD.

Murata Manufacturing Co., Ltd.—(Continued)
Road, Huangpu District, Shanghai, 200021, China
Tel.: (86) 2132054626
Electronic Components Distr
N.A.I.C.S.: 423690

Murata Electronics Trading (Shenzhen) Co., Ltd. (1)
25/Floor Tower A Kingkey 100 5016 Shennan East Road, Luohu District, Shenzhen, 518001, Guangdong, China
Tel.: (86) 75582022080
Web Site: http://www.sz1.murata.com.cn
Electronic Components Distr
N.A.I.C.S.: 423690

Murata Electronics Trading (Tianjin) Co., Ltd. (1)
Unit 4605-4606 46/F Metropolitan Tower 183 Nanjing Road, Heping District, Tianjin, 300051, China
Tel.: (86) 2223310138
Web Site: https://corporate.murata.com
Electronic Components Distr
N.A.I.C.S.: 423690

Murata Electronics Trading Mexico, S. A. de C.V. (1)
12 de Diciembre No 1370 Esq Con Guadalupe Piso 1 Int, B Fraccionamiento Chapalita, 45040, Zapopan, Jalisco, Mexico
Tel.: (52) 333 125 3425
Web Site: http://www.murata.com
Sales Range: $25-49.9 Million
Emp.: 11
Electronic Components Distr
N.A.I.C.S.: 423690

Murata Electronique SAS (1)
18-22 Avenue Edouard Herriot, 92356, Le Plessis-Robinson, Cedex, France
Tel.: (33) 140948300
Web Site: http://www.murata.com
Sales Range: $25-49.9 Million
Emp.: 27
Electronic Components Distr
N.A.I.C.S.: 423690

Murata Elettronica S.p.A. (1)
Via San Carlo 1, 20867, Caponago, Monza Brianza, Italy
Tel.: (39) 02 95968.1
Web Site: http://www.murata.it
Sales Range: $25-49.9 Million
Emp.: 30
Electronic Components Distr
N.A.I.C.S.: 423690

Murata Energy Device Wuxi Co., Ltd. (1)
No 41 Zhujiang Road, Xinwu District, Wuxi, Jiangsu, China
Tel.: (86) 51085238707
Web Site: https://corporate.murata.com
Emp.: 5,000
Electronic Capacitor Mfr
N.A.I.C.S.: 334416

Murata Integrated Passive Solutions SAS (1)
2 rue de la Girafe, 14000, Caen, France
Tel.: (33) 231535400
Electronic Capacitor Mfr
N.A.I.C.S.: 334416

Murata Land & Building Co., Ltd. (1)
10-1 Higashikotari 1-chome, Nagaokakyo, 617-8555, Kyoto, Japan
Tel.: (81) 759556897
Web Site: https://www.murata-mlb.co.jp
Real Estate Manangement Services
N.A.I.C.S.: 531390

Murata Manufacturing Company, Ltd. - Oyama Plant (1)
1-480 inuzuka, Oyama, 323-8678, Tochigi, Japan
Tel.: (81) 285 30 1510
Web Site: http://www.murata.com
Electronic Capacitor Mfr
N.A.I.C.S.: 334416

Murata Manufacturing Company, Ltd. - Yasu Division (1)
2288 Oshinohara, Yasu, 520-2393, Shiga, Japan
Tel.: (81) 775875111
Semiconductor Equipment Mfr
N.A.I.C.S.: 334413

Murata Manufacturing Company, Ltd. - Yokaichi Plant (1)
4-1 Higashiokino 4-chome, Higashi-omi, 527-8558, Shiga, Japan
Tel.: (81) 748225500
Ceramic Products Mfr
N.A.I.C.S.: 327120

Murata Power Solutions Inc. (1)
129 Flanders Rd, Westborough, MA 01581
Tel.: (508) 339-3000
Web Site: https://www.murata-ps.com
Sales Range: $125-149.9 Million
Emp.: 300
Designer, Mfr & Distr of Electronic Components for Conversion & Storage of Electrical Power
N.A.I.C.S.: 334419

Subsidiary (Non-US):

Murata Power Solutions (Celab) Limited (2)
25a Woolmer Way, Bordon, GU35 9QE, Hampshire, United Kingdom
Tel.: (44) 1420477011
Sales Range: $25-49.9 Million
Emp.: 65
Electronic Components Mfr
N.A.I.C.S.: 334419
Julian Wood (Mng Dir)

Murata Power Solutions (Guangzhou) Limited (2)
Guangzhou Economic & Tech Development Zone 5th Floor Bldg A1, Bei Wei No 1 District, Guangzhou, 510730, Guangdong, China
Tel.: (86) 2082218066
Sales Range: $75-99.9 Million
Electronic Components Mfr
N.A.I.C.S.: 334419

Murata Power Solutions (Milton Keynes) Limited (2)
Tanners Drive Blakelands North, Milton Keynes, MK14 5BU, United Kingdom
Tel.: (44) 1908615232
Web Site: http://www.murata-ps.com
Electronic Components Mfr
N.A.I.C.S.: 335999

Murata Power Solutions (Shanghai) Co., Limited (2)
16-17 Lane 912 Bibo Road, Zhangjiang High-Technology Park, Shanghai, China
Tel.: (86) 215 027 3678
Web Site: http://www.murata.com
Sales Range: $25-49.9 Million
Emp.: 45
Electronic Components Mfr
N.A.I.C.S.: 335999

Murata Power Solutions Co., Ltd. (2)
Meiji Seimei Gotanda Building, 2-27-4 Nishigotanda, Shinagawa-Ku, Tokyo, 141-0031, Japan
Tel.: (81) 3 3779 1031
Web Site: http://www.murata-ps.jp
Electronic Components Mfr
N.A.I.C.S.: 335999

Murata Shizuki FC Solutions Co., Ltd. (1)
285 Nishimanai, Ugo-machi Ogatsu-gun, Akita, 012-1131, Japan
Tel.: (81) 183558881
Web Site: https:/corporate.murata.com
Emp.: 63
Electronic Capacitor Mfr
N.A.I.C.S.: 334416

Murata Software Co., Ltd. (1)
4-3-8 Minato Mirai, Nishi-ku, Yokohama, 220-0012, Kanagawa, Japan
Tel.: (81) 452273036
Software Development Services
N.A.I.C.S.: 541511

Murata Vios, Inc. (1)
700 Commerce Dr Ste 190, Woodbury, MN 55125-9232
Tel.: (651) 888-8001
Web Site: https://www.viosmedical.com
Electronic Capacitor Mfr
N.A.I.C.S.: 334416

Murata World Comercial Ltda. (1)
Rua Tijuçо Preto 393-Sala 151/152/153, Tatuape, Sao Paulo, 03316-000, SP, Brazil
Tel.: (55) 112 090 0330
Web Site: http://www.murata.com
Electronic Components Distr
N.A.I.C.S.: 423690

Ogaki Murata Manufacturing Co., Ltd. (1)
Ogaki Factory 1122 Arao-cho, Ogaki, 503-0034, Gifu, Japan (66.6%)
Tel.: (81) 58 493 0240
Web Site: https://corporate.murata.com
Emp.: 130
Electronics Circuit Substrates
N.A.I.C.S.: 334419

Okayama Murata Manufacturing Co., Ltd. (1)
77 Fukumoto Oku-cho, Setouchi, 701-4241, Okayama, Japan
Tel.: (81) 86 924 0911
Web Site: https://corporate.murata.com
Sales Range: $400-449.9 Million
Emp.: 2,087
Capacitors & Microwave Devices Mfr
N.A.I.C.S.: 334419

Philippine Manufacturing Co. of Murata, Inc. (1)
Lot 2-A Phase 1B Barangay Pantay Bata, First Philippine Industrial Park, Tanauan, Batangas, Philippines
Tel.: (63) 434552092
Electronic Capacitor Mfr
N.A.I.C.S.: 334416

Pieclex Co., Ltd. (1)
2288 Oshinohara, Yasu, 520-2393, Shiga, Japan
Tel.: (81) 775868135
Web Site: https://www.pieclex.com
Textile Products Distr
N.A.I.C.S.: 424310

Sabae Murata Manufacturing Co., Ltd. (1)
2-82 1-chome Miyukicho, Sabae, 916-0015, Fukui, Japan
Tel.: (81) 77 852 3440
Web Site: http://www.murata.com
Emp.: 523
Capacitors & Metal Component Mfr
N.A.I.C.S.: 334416

Saitama Murata Manufacturing Co., Ltd. (1)
18 Gomigaya, Tsurugashima, 350-2281, Saitama, Japan
Tel.: (81) 492852511
Electronic Capacitor Mfr
N.A.I.C.S.: 334416

Shenzhen Murata Technology Co., Ltd. (1)
15 Cuijing Road Longtian Street, Shenzhen Grand Industrial Zone PingShan District, Shenzhen, 518118, Guangdong, China
Tel.: (86) 75589336668
Web Site: https://corporate.murata.com
Emp.: 1,800
Electronic Capacitor Mfr
N.A.I.C.S.: 334416

SyChip Electronic Technology (Shanghai) Ltd. (1)
11/Floor 5 Corporate Avenue 150 Hubin Road, Huangpu District, Shanghai, 200021, China
Tel.: (86) 2136355700
Web Site: http://www.murata.com
Mobile Software Development Services
N.A.I.C.S.: 541511

Sychip Inc. (1)
2805 N Dallas Parkway Ste 400, Plano, TX 75093
Tel.: (972) 202-8888
Sales Range: $25-49.9 Million
Emp.: 4
Computer Logic Modules
N.A.I.C.S.: 334413

Taiwan Murata Electronics Co., Ltd. (1)
No 451 Sec 3 Zhongqing Road, Xitun District, Taichung, 40761, Taiwan
Tel.: (886) 42 425 4151
Web Site: http://www.murata.com

INTERNATIONAL PUBLIC

Electronic Capacitor Mfr & Distr
N.A.I.C.S.: 334416

Thai Murata Electronics Trading, Ltd. (1)
Thaniya Plaza Building 10th Floor 52 Silom Road Suriyawongse, Bangrak, Bangkok, 10500, Thailand
Tel.: (66) 2 036 0000
Web Site: http://www.murata.com
Sales Range: $25-49.9 Million
Emp.: 30
Electronic Components Distr
N.A.I.C.S.: 423690

Tohoku Murata Manufacturing Company, Ltd. (1)
1-1 Shimosugishita Takakura Hiwadamachi, Koriyama, 963-0531, Fukushima, Japan
Tel.: (81) 24 958 3811
Web Site: http://corporate.murata.com
Primary & Rechargeable Cell Battery Designer & Mfr
N.A.I.C.S.: 335910
Tetsuro Arito (Pres)

Plant (Domestic):

Tohoku Murata Manufacturing Company, Ltd. - Kanuma Plant (2)
18 Satsuki-cho, Kanuma, 322-8501, Tochigi, Japan
Tel.: (81) 50 3807 3960
Web Site: http://corporate.murata.com
Primary & Rechargeable Cell Battery Mfr
N.A.I.C.S.: 335910

Tohoku Murata Manufacturing Company, Ltd. - Motomiya Plant (2)
2 Toinokuchi Motomiya, Motomiya, 969-1180, Fukushima, Japan
Tel.: (81) 24 333 4330
Web Site: http://corporate.murata.com
Primary & Rechargeable Cell Battery Mfr
N.A.I.C.S.: 335910

Toko, Inc. (1)
18 Gomigaya, Tsurugashima, 350-2281, Saitama, Japan (63.83%)
Tel.: (81) 492852511
Web Site: http://www.toko.co.jp
Rev: $325,958,000
Assets: $456,127,000
Liabilities: $223,210,000
Net Worth: $232,917,000
Earnings: $35,895,500
Emp.: 452
Fiscal Year-end: 12/31/2015
Coil-Applied Products & Semiconductors Mfr & Sales
N.A.I.C.S.: 334416
Etsuo Hayakawa (Exec Operating Officer)

Subsidiary (Non-US):

Huacheng TOKO Electronics Co., Ltd. (2)
20F No 99 Xinpu 6th St, Taoyuan Dist, Taoyuan, 330007, Taiwan
Tel.: (886) 33583180
Web Site: http://www.tokohc.com.tw
Semiconductor Mfr
N.A.I.C.S.: 334413

Seoul TOKO Co., Ltd. (2)
KEUMKANG PENTERIUM IT TOWER A-205 215, Galmachi-ro, Seoul, Korea (South)
Tel.: (82) 31 730 0707
Semiconductor Mfr
N.A.I.C.S.: 334413

Shantou S. E. Z. Huajian Electronics Co., Ltd (2)
NO 3 Longxin 5th Street Longxin Proccessing Distrct, Longhu District, Shantou, China
Tel.: (86) 754 88832671
Semiconductor Mfr
N.A.I.C.S.: 334413

TOKO (Shanghai Waigaoqiao F. T. Z.) Inc. (2)
Block B 4F No 180 Rijing Road Waigaoqiao F.T.Z., Shanghai, China
Tel.: (86) 21 58660550
Semiconductor Mfr
N.A.I.C.S.: 334413

Branch (Domestic):

TOKO (Shanghai Waigaoqiao F. T. Z.) Inc. - Beijing Office (3)

Room 2904 No 7 Building, Liyuanli Changyang District, Beijing, China
Tel.: (86) 10 8526 1198
Semiconductor Mfr
N.A.I.C.S.: 334413

Subsidiary (Non-US):

TOKO Electronics (Thailand) Co., Ltd (2)
Bangkok Business Building Room No 1309, 54 Sukhumvit 21(Asoke) Road Kwaeng Klong Toey Nua, 10110, Bangkok, Thailand
Tel.: (66) 2 261 9200
Semiconductor Mfr
N.A.I.C.S.: 334413

Tokyo Denpa Co., Ltd. (1)
1-15-10 Kamiioka, Ota-ku, Morioka, 020-0854, Iwate, Japan (100%)
Tel.: (81) 196373431
Web Site: https://corporate.murata.com
Sales Range: $75-99.9 Million
Emp.: 326
Electric Equipment Mfr
N.A.I.C.S.: 334419
Fumiya Kayahara (Pres)

Tome Murata Manufacturing Co., Ltd. (1)
4-11-1 Nakae Sanuma Sakomachi, Hasama-cho, Tome, 987-0511, Miyagi, Japan
Tel.: (81) 220223621
Web Site: https://corporate.murata.com
Emp.: 577
Electronic Coil Products Mfr
N.A.I.C.S.: 334416

Toyama Murata Manufacturing Co., Ltd. (1)
345 Uwano, Toyama, 939-8195, Japan
Tel.: (81) 76 429 5469
Web Site: https://corporate.murata.com
Sales Range: $400-449.9 Million
Emp.: 1,970
Piezoelectric Components Mfr
N.A.I.C.S.: 334419

Wakura Murata Manufacturing Co., Ltd. (1)
1 Ube Ishizakimachi, Nanao, 926-0173, Ishikawa, Japan
Tel.: (81) 76 762 4488
Web Site: http://www.murata.com
Electronic Module Products Mfr
N.A.I.C.S.: 334419

Wuxi Murata Electronics Co., Ltd. (1)
Plant No 1 No 6 Xingchuang 1st Road, Wuxi Export Processing Zone B Zone, Wuxi, 214028, Jiangsu, China
Tel.: (86) 5108 528 2111
Web Site: http://www.murata.com
Electronic Components Mfr & Distr
N.A.I.C.S.: 334416

MURCHISON HOLDINGS LIMITED

7 Dallas Street, Mount Waverley, 31497, VIC, Australia
Tel.: (61) 3 9807 5639
Web Site:
http://www.murchisongroup.com
Sales Range: $1-9.9 Million
Investment Services
N.A.I.C.S.: 523999
Wendy Cheung (Mgr-Admin)

Subsidiaries:

Quest Stockbrokers (HK) Limited (1)
13/F Unit 1305 General Commercial Building 164 Des Voeux Road, Central, China (Hong Kong)
Tel.: (852) 28776828
Web Site: http://www.qsbhk.com
Custodian & Nominee Services
N.A.I.C.S.: 523991

MURCHISON MINERALS LTD.

Suite 2500 120 Adelaide Street West, Toronto, M5H 1T1, ON, Canada
Tel.: (416) 350-3776 Ca

Web Site:
http://www.murchisonminerals.com
Year Founded: 2001
Rev.: $18,376
Assets: $981,788
Liabilities: $131,836
Net Worth: $849,952
Earnings: ($1,898,829)
Fiscal Year-end: 12/31/18
Metal Exploration & Mining Services
N.A.I.C.S.: 212290
Jean-Charles Potvin (Founder, Chm, Pres & CEO)

MURDOCH GROUP INC.

22 Government Road East, Kirkland Lake, P2N 3P4, ON, Canada
Tel.: (705) 567-3277
Web Site:
http://www.murdochgroupinc.com
Rev.: $18,617,812
Emp.: 125
Vehicle Rental Services
N.A.I.C.S.: 532111
Rob Murdoch (Pres)

MUREX S.A.S

8 rue Bellini, 75782, Paris, Cedex 16, France
Tel.: (33) 144053200
Web Site: http://www.murex.com
Year Founded: 1986
Sales Range: $300-349.9 Million
Emp.: 255
Software Developer
N.A.I.C.S.: 513210
Maroun Edde (CEO)

Subsidiaries:

MUREX Advanced Technologies Ltd. (1)
The Oval Block 1 Level 4 Shelbourne Road, Ballsbridge, Dublin, Ireland
Tel.: (353) 1 43 98 500
Software Publisher
N.A.I.C.S.: 513210

MUREX America Latina (1)
Av Brigadeiro Faria Lima 3015 13th floor Cj 131, 01452-000, Sao Paulo, Brazil
Tel.: (55) 11 3076 3960
Software Publisher
N.A.I.C.S.: 513210

MUREX Andino Pacifico (1)
Av Cerro el plomo 5630 piso9 Las Condes, 7560742, Santiago, Chile
Tel.: (56) 2 2666 4211
Software Publisher
N.A.I.C.S.: 513210

MUREX Australia Pty Ltd (1)
1 Castlereagh Street Suite 1401 Level 14, Sydney, 2000, NSW, Australia
Tel.: (61) 2 9232 9700
Web Site: http://www.murex.com
Software Publisher
N.A.I.C.S.: 513210

MUREX Canada Software Limited (1)
100 Adelaide Street West suite 710, Toronto, M5H 1S3, ON, Canada
Tel.: (416) 640-4999
Software Publisher
N.A.I.C.S.: 513210

MUREX Financial Software (1)
1701 Level 17 Tower E1 Oriental Plaza 1 East Chang An Avenue, Dong Cheng District, Beijing, 100738, China
Tel.: (86) 10 5651 2600
Software Publisher
N.A.I.C.S.: 513210

MUREX Gulf LLC (1)
Tower I Al Fattan Currency House Mezzanine floor Unit no M07, Dubai, United Arab Emirates
Tel.: (971) 44057400
Software Publisher
N.A.I.C.S.: 513210

MUREX Hong Kong Limited (1)

99 Queen's Road Level 4607-11 The Center, Central, China (Hong Kong)
Tel.: (852) 3796 7224
Software Publisher
N.A.I.C.S.: 513210

MUREX International Luxembourg SA (1)
68-70 Boulevard de la Petrusse, 2320, Luxembourg, Luxembourg
Tel.: (352) 26123511
Software Publisher
N.A.I.C.S.: 513210

MUREX Korea Ltd. (1)
Seoul Finance Center Level 21 136, Sejong-daero Jung-gu, Seoul, 100-768, Korea (South)
Tel.: (82) 2 3782 4840
Software Publisher
N.A.I.C.S.: 513210

MUREX Software (1)
Bld 1 ProHub Business Center 13th floor - office N 16, Presnenskaya Naberezhnaya 8, 123317, Moscow, Russia
Tel.: (7) 4956461702
Software Publisher
N.A.I.C.S.: 513210

MUREX Systems Sal (1)
Kantari Corner Center 14th floor Fakhereddine Street, Mina El Hosn, Beirut, Lebanon
Tel.: (961) 1 356 000
Software Publisher
N.A.I.C.S.: 513210
Salim Edde (Gen Mgr)

MUREX Tokyo (1)
NBF Hibiya building 6F 1-1-7 Uchisaiwaicho, Chiyoda-ku, Tokyo, 100-0011, Japan
Tel.: (81) 3 3519 8510
Software Publisher
N.A.I.C.S.: 513210

Murex (UK) Limited (1)
68 King William Street, London, EC4N 7DZ, United Kingdom
Tel.: (44) 2079592232
Software Publisher
N.A.I.C.S.: 513210

Murex North America, Inc. (1)
810 7th Ave, New York, NY 10019
Tel.: (212) 381-4300
Software Publisher
N.A.I.C.S.: 513210

Murex Southeast Asia Pte Ltd (1)
Marina Bay Financial Centre Tower 2 10 Marina Boulevard 19-01, Singapore, 18983, Singapore
Tel.: (65) 6216 02 88
Software Publisher
N.A.I.C.S.: 513210

MURGITROYD GROUP LIMITED

Scotland House 165-169 Scotland Street, Glasgow, G5 8PL, United Kingdom
Tel.: (44) 1413078400
Web Site: http://murgitroydgroup.com
Holding Company; Intellectual Property Advisory Services
N.A.I.C.S.: 551112

Subsidiaries:

Murgitroyd & Company Limited (1)
Scotland House 165-169 Scotland Street, Glasgow, G5 8PL, Scotland, United Kingdom
Tel.: (44) 1413078400
Web Site: http://www.murgitroyd.com
Sales Range: $25-49.9 Million
Emp.: 200
Patent & Trade Mark Attorney Services
N.A.I.C.S.: 541110

MURMANSKAYA TEC AO

Ul Shmidta 14, 183038, Murmansk, Russia
Tel.: (7) 8152688359
Web Site: http://www.murmantec.com
Electric Power Distribution Services
N.A.I.C.S.: 221122

MURO CORPORATION

7-1 Kiyohara Industrial Park, Tochigi, Utsunomiya, 321-3231, Japan
Tel.: (81) 286677121
Web Site: https://www.muro.co.jp
Year Founded: 1958
7264—(TKS)
Rev.: $156,359,550
Assets: $214,368,910
Liabilities: $71,070,720
Net Worth: $143,298,190
Earnings: $8,705,370
Emp.: 1,145
Fiscal Year-end: 03/31/24
Autoparts Mfr
N.A.I.C.S.: 441330
Masafumi Muro (Pres)

Subsidiaries:

3MT (THAILAND) CO., LTD. (1)
22/51 Sukhapiban 2 Road Prawet, Prawet, Bangkok, 10250, Thailand
Tel.: (66) 20091770
Emp.: 4
Auto Parts Mfr & Distr
N.A.I.C.S.: 336390

MURO Tech Vietnam Corporation (1)
Plot 207 Amata Industrial Zone, Long Binh Ward, Bien Hoa, Dong Nai, Vietnam
Tel.: (84) 2513936301
Fastener Mfr & Distr
N.A.I.C.S.: 339993

Muro North America Inc. (1)
7 Tilbury Court, Brampton, L6T 3T4, ON, Canada
Tel.: (905) 451-7667
Web Site: https://muro.com
Fastener Mfr & Distr
N.A.I.C.S.: 339993

Muro Tech Xiaogan Hubei Co., Ltd. (1)
No 110 Wenchang Avenue, Xiaogan Hi-tech Development Zone, Hubei, China
Tel.: (86) 712 211 1966
Motor Vehicle Parts Mfr
N.A.I.C.S.: 336390

Murotech Ohio Corporation (1)
550 McKinley Rd, Saint Marys, OH 45885
Tel.: (419) 394-6529
Web Site: https://murotech.com
Sales Range: $1-9.9 Million
Emp.: 130
Metal Stamping Services
N.A.I.C.S.: 336370

PT. Murotech Indonesia (1)
Suryacipta City of Industry JL Surya Lestari Kav I-2H, Kutamekar Ciampel, Karawang, 41363, Jawa Barat, Indonesia
Tel.: (62) 2678637784
Fastener Mfr & Distr
N.A.I.C.S.: 339993

MUROMACHI CHEMICALS, INC.

1-38-5 Shinkatsudachi-Machi, Omuta, Fukuoka, 836-0895, Japan
Tel.: (81) 927538145
Web Site: https://www.muro-chem.co.jp
Year Founded: 1947
4885—(TKS)
Emp.: 270
Pharmaceutical Product Mfr & Distr
N.A.I.C.S.: 325412
Junichi Aoki (Pres)

MURPHY FORD SALES LTD.

1341 Pembroke Street West, Pembroke, K8A 5R3, ON, Canada
Tel.: (613) 735-6861
Web Site:
http://www.murphyford.com
Year Founded: 1966
Sales Range: $10-24.9 Million
Emp.: 28
New & Used Car Dealers
N.A.I.C.S.: 441110

MURPHY FORD SALES LTD.

Murphy Ford Sales Ltd.—(Continued)
Tracey Coulas (Bus Mgr)

MURRAY & ROBERTS (BOTSWANA) LIMITED
Plot 1214 Nkuruma Road Old Industrial Site, PO Box 657, Gaborone, Botswana
Tel.: (267) 395 1871
Web Site:
 http://www.botswana.murrob.com
Civil Engineering Construction Services
N.A.I.C.S.: 237990

MURRAY & ROBERTS (NAMIBIA) LIMITED
7 Joule Street Southern Industria, PO Box 33, Windhoek, 33, Namibia
Tel.: (264) 61 23 8500
Web Site:
 http://www.namibia.murrob.com
Construction Engineering Services
N.A.I.C.S.: 541330

MURRAY & ROBERTS HOLDINGS LTD.
6th Floor Douglas Roberts Centre 22 Skeen Boulevard, Bedfordview, 2007, South Africa
Tel.: (27) 114566200   ZA
Web Site: https://www.murrob.com
MUR—(JSE)
Rev.: $658,023,427
Assets: $442,933,491
Liabilities: $345,710,242
Net Worth: $97,223,249
Earnings: ($14,908,269)
Emp.: 5,443
Fiscal Year-end: 06/30/23
Construction & Engineering Services; Building Material Supplier
N.A.I.C.S.: 236220
Henry Johannes Laas (CEO)

Subsidiaries:

Cementation Canada Inc.   (1)
590 Graham Drive, North Bay, P1B 7S1, ON, Canada
Tel.: (705) 472-3381
Web Site: https://en.cementation.com
Sales Range: $100-124.9 Million
Emp.: 120
Mine Infrastructure Engineering Services
N.A.I.C.S.: 213113
Roy Slack (Pres)

Subsidiary (Domestic):

Merit Consultants International Inc.   (2)
Suite 301 700 West Pender Street, Vancouver, V6C 1G8, BC, Canada
Tel.: (604) 669-8444
Web Site: https://www.meritconsultants.net
Project & Construction Management Services
N.A.I.C.S.: 541990
Jay Collins (Pres)

Cementation SudAmerica SA   (1)
Avenida del Valle 787 Oficina 403 Ciudad Empresarial, Huechuraba, Huechuraba, 850702, Santiago, Chile
Tel.: (56) 2 7133100
Web Site: http://www.cementation.com
Sales Range: $25-49.9 Million
Emp.: 13
Mining Engineering Services
N.A.I.C.S.: 541330
Raul Chaparro (Mgr-Bus Dev)

Cementation USA Inc   (1)
10150 S Centennial Pkwy Ste 400, Sandy, UT 84070
Tel.: (801) 937-4120
Web Site: https://en.cementation.com
Metal Mining Services
N.A.I.C.S.: 213114

Concor Holdings (Pty) Limited   (1)
Concor House 13 Church St Ext, Johannesburg, 2092, South Africa   (100%)
Tel.: (27) 114952222
Web Site: http://www.concor.co.za
Sales Range: $250-299.9 Million
Emp.: 1,000
Engineering & Contracting Services
N.A.I.C.S.: 237310

Concor Technicrete (Proprietary) Limited   (1)
Mainreese Khoutkatter, Haudiport, Johannesburg, 1725, South Africa   (100%)
Tel.: (27) 116746900
Web Site: http://www.technicrete.co.za
Sales Range: $25-49.9 Million
Emp.: 30
Concrete Supplier
N.A.I.C.S.: 327310
Christo van Zyl (Dir-Sls & Mktg)

GCR Mongolia LLC   (1)
New Millennium Building Level 5 15th khoroo, Khan Uul District, Ulaanbaatar, 17011, Mongolia
Tel.: (976) 77119797
Web Site: https://www.gcrmongolia.mn
Underground Mine Contracting Services
N.A.I.C.S.: 213114

Murray & Roberts Building Products (Proprietary) Limited   (1)
35 Emerald St, Futura, Polokwane, 0699, South Africa
Tel.: (27) 152932631
Web Site: http://www.technicrete.co.za
Emp.: 30
Concrete Products Mfr
N.A.I.C.S.: 327331
Tienie Swart (Gen Mgr)

Murray & Roberts Cementation (Proprietary) Limited   (1)
The Interchange 22 Skeen Boulevard, Bedfordview, 2007, South Africa
Tel.: (27) 112015000
Web Site:
 https://www.cementation.murrob.com
Mineral Mining Services
N.A.I.C.S.: 212390
Allan Widlake (Dir-Bus Dev)

Subsidiary (US):

Terra Nova Technologies, Inc.   (2)
10770 Rockville St, Santee, CA 92071   (100%)
Tel.: (619) 596-7400
Web Site: https://www.tntinc.com
Mining Machinery & Services
N.A.I.C.S.: 333922
Ron Kelly (Pres)

Murray & Roberts Concessions (Proprietary) Limited   (1)
6th Floor Douglas Roberts Centre 22 Skeen Boulevard, Bedfordview, 2007, South Africa
Tel.: (27) 114566200
Web Site:
N.A.I.C.S.: 541330
Ron Parker (Mgr-Comml Projects)

Murray & Roberts Construction (Proprietary) Limited   (1)
20 Skeen Boulevard, Bedfordview, 2007, South Africa
Tel.: (27) 11 456 1000
Web Site:
 http://www.construction.murrob.com
Construction Engineering Services
N.A.I.C.S.: 541330

Murray & Roberts Limited   (1)
Douglas Roberts Centre 22 Skeen Boulevard, Bedfordview, 2007, South Africa
Tel.: (27) 114566200
Web Site: https://www.murrob.com
Emp.: 156
Construction Engineering Services
N.A.I.C.S.: 541330

Murray & Roberts Limited   (1)
Douglas Roberts Centre 22 Skeen Boulevard, Bedfordview, 2007, South Africa
Tel.: (27) 114566200
Web Site: https://www.murrob.com
Emp.: 156
Construction Engineering Services
N.A.I.C.S.: 541330

Murray & Roberts Limited   (1)
Douglas Roberts Centre 22 Skeen Boulevard, Bedfordview, 2007, South Africa
Tel.: (27) 114566200
Web Site: https://www.murrob.com
Emp.: 156
Construction Engineering Services
N.A.I.C.S.: 541330

Murray & Roberts Limited   (1)
Douglas Roberts Centre 22 Skeen Boulevard, Bedfordview, 2007, South Africa
Tel.: (27) 114566200
Web Site: https://www.murrob.com
Emp.: 156
Construction Engineering Services
N.A.I.C.S.: 541330

Murray & Roberts Marine (Proprietary) Limited   (1)
6th Floor 73 Hertzog Boulevard Soreshore, Cape Town, 8001, South Africa
Tel.: (27) 21 431 3400
Web Site: http://www.marine.murrob.com
Emp.: 25
Marine Engineering Services
N.A.I.C.S.: 541330
Andrew Fanton (Mng Dir-Johannesburg)

Murray & Roberts Projects (Proprietary) Limited   (1)
22 Skeen Boulevard, Bedfordview, 2007, South Africa
Tel.: (27) 114561000
Web Site:
 https://www.powerenergy.murrob.com
Civil Engineering Construction Services
N.A.I.C.S.: 237990

Murray & Roberts Properties Services (Proprietary) Limited   (1)
Long St Thibault Sq, Cape Town, 8001, South Africa
Tel.: (27) 21 4190340
Property Management Services
N.A.I.C.S.: 531311

RUC Cementation Mining Contractors (Proprietary) Limited   (1)
181 Western Road, Kalgoorlie, 6430, WA, Australia
Tel.: (61) 89 021 7777
Web Site: https://www.ruc.com.au
Sales Range: $125-149.9 Million
Emp.: 35
Raise Boring Equipment Distr
N.A.I.C.S.: 423810
Barry Upton (Mng Dir)

Rocla (Proprietary) Limited   (1)
Cnr Main Reef Road and Houtkapper Street, PO Box 92, Roodepoort, 1725, South Africa
Tel.: (27) 116707600
Emp.: 40
Concrete Products Mfr
N.A.I.C.S.: 327331

Tolcon-Lehumo (Proprietary) Limited   (1)
1st Floor Acacia Block Pellmeadow Office Park 60 Civin Drive, Bedfordview, 2008, South Africa
Tel.: (27) 11 4539422
Web Site: http://www.tolcon.co.za
Sales Range: $25-49.9 Million
Emp.: 25
Toll Highway Operating Services
N.A.I.C.S.: 488490

Toll Road Concessionaires (Proprietary) Limited   (1)
60 Civin Drive, Johannesburg, 2007, South Africa
Tel.: (27) 11 453 9422
Web Site: http://www.tolcon.tolco.co.za
Sales Range: $200-249.9 Million
Emp.: 950
Toll Highway Operating Services
N.A.I.C.S.: 488490
Judy van Es (Mng Dir)

Wade Walker (Proprietary) Limited   (1)
Douglas Roberts Centre 22 Skeen Boulevard, Bedfordview, 2007, South Africa
Tel.: (27) 114561000
Web Site: https://www.wadewalker.co.za

Sales Range: $25-49.9 Million
Emp.: 78
Electrical Control & Instrumentation Construction Services
N.A.I.C.S.: 541330

MURRAY COD AUSTRALIA LTD
2 - 4 Lasscock Road, Griffith, 2680, NSW, Australia
Tel.: (61) 269625470   AU
Web Site:
 https://www.murraycodaustralia.com
Year Founded: 2010
MCA—(ASX)
Rev.: $7,059,774
Assets: $91,256,584
Liabilities: $30,436,068
Net Worth: $60,820,517
Earnings: ($4,152,748)
Emp.: 42
Fiscal Year-end: 06/30/24
Aquaculture Services
N.A.I.C.S.: 112519
Ross Anderson (Chm)

Subsidiaries:

Murray Darling Fisheries Pty Ltd   (1)
1795 Old Narrandera Road, Euberta, Wagga Wagga, 2650, NSW, Australia
Tel.: (61) 26 922 9447
Web Site:
 https://www.murraydarlingfisheries.com.au
Fish Distr
N.A.I.C.S.: 424460

MURRAY GM FORT ST JOHN
11204 Alaska Road, Fort Saint John, V1J 5T5, BC, Canada
Tel.: (250) 785-8005
Web Site:
 http://www.murraygmbc.com
New & Used Car Dealers
N.A.I.C.S.: 441110
Faron Young (Mgr-Svc)

MURRAY RIVER ORGANICS GROUP LIMITED
32 Crompton Way, Dandenong South, 3175, VIC, Australia
Tel.: (61) 387928500
Web Site:
 http://www.murrayriverorganics.com
Rev.: $42,110,971
Assets: $80,147,996
Liabilities: $55,364,412
Net Worth: $24,783,584
Earnings: ($8,417,858)
Fiscal Year-end: 06/30/19
Dried Fruit Mfr & Distr
N.A.I.C.S.: 311423
Albert Zago (CFO)

MURREE BREWERY COMPANY LIMITED
3-National Park Road, Rawalpindi, Pakistan
Tel.: (92) 515567041
Web Site:
 https://www.murreebrewery.com
Year Founded: 1860
MUREB—(KAR)
Rev.: $71,680,037
Assets: $84,379,855
Liabilities: $12,393,470
Net Worth: $71,986,386
Earnings: $8,780,695
Emp.: 1,808
Fiscal Year-end: 06/30/19
Beer, Liquor & Alcoholic Products Mfr
N.A.I.C.S.: 312120
Isphanyar M. Bhandara (CEO)

Subsidiaries:

Murree Glass Ltd.   (1)
Plot No 10/2 Phase-III, Industrial Estate, Hattar, Pakistan

AND PRIVATE COMPANIES

Tel.: (92) 995617233
Web Site: http://www.murreebrewery.com
Glass Container Mfr
N.A.I.C.S.: 327213

Tops Food & Beverages (1)
National Park Road, Rawalpindi, Pakistan
Tel.: (92) 515567047
Web Site: http://www.murreebrewery.com.pk
Sales Range: $25-49.9 Million
Emp.: 150
Mfr of Beverages & Condiments
N.A.I.C.S.: 722515
Isphanyar Bhandara *(CEO)*

MURUDESHWAR CERAMICS LIMITED
Naveen Complex 8th Floor 14 M G Road, Bengaluru, 560 001, India
Tel.: (91) 8025584181
Web Site:
https://www.naveentile.com
Year Founded: 1983
MURUDCERA—(NSE)
Rev.: $11,159,134
Assets: $64,429,297
Liabilities: $18,956,260
Net Worth: $45,473,037
Earnings: ($1,620,883)
Emp.: 285
Fiscal Year-end: 03/31/21
Tiles Mfr
N.A.I.C.S.: 327120
Satish Rama Shetty *(CEO & Mng Dir)*

MUSASHI CO., LTD.
82036 Ginza, Chuo-ku, Tokyo, 104-0061, Japan
Tel.: (81) 335467711
Web Site:
https://www.musashinet.co.jp
Year Founded: 1946
7521—(TKS)
Rev.: $219,055,400
Assets: $297,654,910
Liabilities: $98,046,130
Net Worth: $199,608,780
Earnings: $5,069,870
Emp.: 193
Fiscal Year-end: 03/31/24
Printing & Industrial Equipment Whslr
N.A.I.C.S.: 423830
Masataka Hatori *(Pres)*

Subsidiaries:

FBM Co., Ltd. (1)
Sanki Building 2-13-7 Iidabashi, Chiyoda-ku, Tokyo, 102-0072, Japan
Tel.: (81) 362723453
Web Site: https://www.f-b-m.co.jp
Emp.: 41
Printing System Equipment Mfr
N.A.I.C.S.: 333248

Musashi ABC Co., Ltd. (1)
191 Shintomi 1-9-1 Shintomi, Chuo-ku, Tokyo, 104-0041, Japan
Tel.: (81) 362284810
Web Site: https://www.musashi-abc.co.jp
Emp.: 300
Data Entry Services
N.A.I.C.S.: 518210

Musashi Engineering CO., LTD. (1)
3-11-7 Nishishimbash, Minato-ku, Tokyo, 105-0003, Yubinbango, Japan
Tel.: (81) 334372911
Web Site: http://www.tellac.co.jp
Cash Handling Equipment Mfr
N.A.I.C.S.: 333310

Musashi I Techno Co., Ltd. (1)
3-6-1 Nagatanaka, Higashi-osaka, 577-0013, Osaka, Japan
Tel.: (81) 667446311
Web Site: https://www.musashi-i-techno.co.jp
Emp.: 70
Data Entry Services
N.A.I.C.S.: 518210

Musashi Image Joho Co., Ltd. (1)
1-7-12 Shinonome, Koto-ku, Tokyo, 135-0062, Japan
Tel.: (81) 362284056
Web Site: https://www.musashi-ij.co.jp
Emp.: 120
Data Entry Services
N.A.I.C.S.: 518210

Musashi Kousan Co., Ltd. (1)
Maison Musashi 3rd Building 4-13-13 Shimoigusa, Suginami-ku, Tokyo, 167-0022, Japan
Tel.: (81) 333956041
Web Site: https://www.musashikousan.co.jp
Real Estate Rental Services
N.A.I.C.S.: 531210

MUSASHI KOGYO CO., LTD.
20-18 Inari-cho, Hanno, 357-0037, Japan
Tel.: (81) 42 973 7731
Year Founded: 1950
Sales Range: $25-49.9 Million
Emp.: 140
Solenoid Products Mfr
N.A.I.C.S.: 332999
Yasuaki Maruyama *(Pres)*

Subsidiaries:

Shindengen Mechatronics Co., Ltd. (1)
11-8 Inari-cho, Hanno, 357-0037, Saitama, Japan (52.5%)
Tel.: (81) 429716211
Web Site: http://www.smt.shindengen.co.jp
Sales Range: $50-74.9 Million
Emp.: 60
Solenoid Sales & Manufacturing
N.A.I.C.S.: 423610

MUSASHI SEIMITSU INDUSTRY CO., LTD.
39-5 Daizen Ueta-cho, Toyohashi, Aichi, Japan
Tel.: (81) 532258111
Web Site: https://www.musashi.co.jp
Year Founded: 1938
7220—(TKS)
Rev.: $2,312,951,370
Assets: $1,919,140,790
Liabilities: $1,090,306,280
Net Worth: $828,834,510
Earnings: $52,357,810
Emp.: 16,763
Fiscal Year-end: 03/31/24
Motor Vehicle Parts Mfr
N.A.I.C.S.: 336350
Hiroshi Otsuka *(Pres & CEO-Grp)*

Subsidiaries:

Johann Hay GmbH & Co. KG (1)
Haystrasse 7-13, 55566, Bad Sobernheim, Germany
Tel.: (49) 6751830
Automotive Components Mfr
N.A.I.C.S.: 336390
Ralph Onken *(CEO)*

Kyushu Musashi Seimitsu Co., Ltd. (1)
2605-7 Ichitake Nishiki-cho, Kuma-gun, Kumamoto, 868-0302, Japan
Tel.: (81) 966382121
Web Site: https://kmusashi.co.jp
Emp.: 684
Vehicle Parts Mfr
N.A.I.C.S.: 333612
Tatsuya Nakashima *(Gen Mgr-It Div)*

Musashi Asia Co.,Ltd. (1)
Sathorn City Tower 19th Floor 175 South Sathorn Road, Thungmahamek Sathorn, Bangkok, 10120, Thailand
Tel.: (66) 26796691
Vehicle Parts Distr
N.A.I.C.S.: 423840
Susira Treesupapchaikul *(Mgr)*

Musashi Auto Parts (Nantong) Co., Ltd. (1)
No332 Eastern Partway, Economic-Technological Development Area, Nantong, 226000, Jiangsu, China
Tel.: (86) 51351085688
Transportation Equipment Mfr
N.A.I.C.S.: 336999

Musashi Auto Parts (Tianjin) Co., Ltd. (1)
No21 South Caiyuan Road, Wuqing Developmetn Area, Tianjin, 301700, China
Tel.: (86) 2258981711
Transportation Equipment Mfr
N.A.I.C.S.: 336999

Musashi Auto Parts (Zhongshan)Co., Ltd. (1)
No 40 42 Yanjiang East No 4 Road, Torch Development Zone, Zhongshan, 528437, Guang Dong, China
Tel.: (86) 76085336689
Vehicle Parts Distr
N.A.I.C.S.: 423840

Musashi Auto Parts Canada Inc. (1)
333 Domville Street, Arthur, N0G 1A0, ON, Canada
Tel.: (519) 848-2800
Rev.: $101,088,000
Emp.: 41
Steering Systems Mfr
N.A.I.C.S.: 336330

Musashi Auto Parts Co., Ltd. (1)
60/27 Moo 19 Navanakorn Industrial Estate, Tumbol Klong Neung Amphur Klong Luang, Pathumthani, 12120, Thailand
Tel.: (66) 25291753
Vehicle Parts Distr
N.A.I.C.S.: 423840

Musashi Auto Parts India Pvt. Ltd. (1)
Plot No 33-35 46-60 Sector-7 Industrial Growth Center, Bawal Distt, Rewari, 123501, HR, India
Tel.: (91) 1284308200
Vehicle Parts Distr
N.A.I.C.S.: 423840
Umasankar Padavala *(Sr Mgr)*

Musashi Auto Parts Mexico, S.A. de C.V. (1)
Circuito Exportacion 262, Parque Industrial Tres Naciones 2da Etapa, 78395, San Luis Potosi, Mexico
Tel.: (52) 4442548940
Vehicle Parts Distr
N.A.I.C.S.: 423840
Victor Galvan Rivera *(Fin Mgr)*

Musashi Auto Parts Michigan Inc. (1)
195 Brydges Dr, Battle Creek, MI 49037
Tel.: (269) 965-0057
Vehicle Parts Distr
N.A.I.C.S.: 423840
Ted Zhu *(Sr Mgr)*

Musashi Auto Parts UK Ltd. (1)
6 Hawtin Park Gellihaf Pontllanfraith, Blackwood, NP12 2EU, United Kingdom
Tel.: (44) 1443866100
Vehicle Parts Distr
N.A.I.C.S.: 423840

Musashi Auto Parts Vietnam Co.,Ltd. (1)
Plot G-1 Thang Long Industrial Park II, Yen My, Hung Yen, Vietnam
Tel.: (84) 2213974670
Vehicle Parts Distr
N.A.I.C.S.: 423840

Musashi Bad Sobernheim GmbH & Co. KG (1)
Haystrasse 7-13, 55566, Bad Sobernheim, Germany
Tel.: (49) 6751830
Web Site: https://www.eu.musashi-group.com
Software Services
N.A.I.C.S.: 541511

Musashi Casting Co., Ltd. (1)
1-29 Nagatanocho, Fukuchiyama, 620-0853, Kyoto, Japan
Tel.: (81) 773272058
Web Site: https://www.musashi-casting.co.jp
Emp.: 112
Automotive Products Whslr
N.A.I.C.S.: 423120

Musashi Energy Solutions Co., Ltd. (1)

MUSASHI SEIMITSU INDUSTRY CO., LTD.

Tel.: (81) 551388008
Capacitor Mfr & Whslr
N.A.I.C.S.: 334416
Kouji Takahashi *(CEO)*

Musashi Europe GmbH (1)
Haystrase 7-13, 55566, Bad Sobernheim, Germany
Tel.: (49) 6751830
Vehicle Parts Distr
N.A.I.C.S.: 423840
Yusuke Fukuda *(Mng Dir)*

Musashi Hann. Muenden Holding GmbH (1)
Am Rodland 14, 34346, Hann. Munden, Germany
Tel.: (49) 55417005100
Web Site: http://www.hmh.de.musashi-group.com
Hardware Mfr
N.A.I.C.S.: 332510

Musashi Hungary Fuzesabony Kft. (1)
Patak ut 2, 3390, Fuzesabony, Hungary
Tel.: (36) 36542275
Web Site: https://fue.musashi.hu
Transportation Equipment Mfr
N.A.I.C.S.: 336999

Musashi Hungary Manufacturing, Ltd. (1)
Tel.: (36) 25551800
Web Site: http://www.musashi.hu
Motor Vehicle Parts Mfr
N.A.I.C.S.: 336390

Musashi India Pvt. Ltd. (1)
Unit No 611 612 614 6th Floor Emaar Palms Spring Plaza, Golf Course Road Sector 54, Gurgaon, 122002, HR, India
Tel.: (91) 1244912700
Vehicle Parts Distr
N.A.I.C.S.: 423840

Musashi Leinefelde Machining GmbH & Co. KG (1)
Zeisstrase 9, Worbis, 37327, Leinefelde, Germany
Tel.: (49) 36055464500
Transportation Equipment Mfr
N.A.I.C.S.: 336999

Musashi North America Inc. (1)
2000 Town Ctr Ste 1320, Southfield, MI 48075
Tel.: (248) 386-1600
Vehicle Parts Distr
N.A.I.C.S.: 423840
Fred Krause *(Mgr-Sls)*

Musashi Seimitsu Industry Co., Ltd. - Akemi Plant 1 (1)
2-18 Akemi-cho, Aichi, Toyohashi, Japan
Tel.: (81) 532258111
Vehicle Parts Mfr
N.A.I.C.S.: 333612

Musashi Seimitsu Industry Co., Ltd. - Akemi Plant 2 (1)
3-29 Akemi-cho, Aichi, Toyohashi, Japan
Tel.: (81) 532292088
Vehicle Parts Mfr
N.A.I.C.S.: 333612

Musashi Seimitsu Industry Co., Ltd. - Horai Plant (1)
10 Yamamotomae Nagashino, Aichi, Toyohashi, Japan
Tel.: (81) 536 32 0555
Cut & Grind Mfr
N.A.I.C.S.: 333517

Musashi Seimitsu Industry Co., Ltd. - Suzuka Plant (1)
3-12-16 Oike, Mie, Suzuka, Japan
Tel.: (81) 593780621
Vehicle Parts Mfr
N.A.I.C.S.: 333612

Musashi Seimitsu Investment (Zhongshan) Co., Ltd. (1)
No 40 42 Yanjiang East No4 Road, Torch Development Zone, Zhongshan, 528437, Guangdong, China
Tel.: (86) 76085336689
Transportation Equipment Mfr
N.A.I.C.S.: 336999

MUSASHI SEIMITSU INDUSTRY CO., LTD.

Musashi Seimitsu Industry Co., Ltd.—(Continued)

Musashi Spain Villalba S.L. (1)
Camino del Molino n 5, Poligono Industrial Pabellon 29, 28400, Madrid, Spain
Tel.: (34) 918561400
Transportation Equipment Mfr
N.A.I.C.S.: 336999

Musashi da Amazonia Ltda. (1)
Av Flamboyant 931 Dist Industrial II, Manaus, 69075-000, AM, Brazil
Tel.: (55) 9221217100
Vehicle Parts Distr
N.A.I.C.S.: 423840

Musashi do Brasil Ltda. (1)
Av Antonio Vicente Novelino, 111 Panco, Brasilia, 53630-000, Igarassu, Brazil
Tel.: (55) 8135436000
Vehicle Parts Distr
N.A.I.C.S.: 423840
Yuri Monteiro (Sls Mgr)

P.T. Musashi Auto Parts Indonesia (1)
EJIP Industrial Park Plot 3J-2, Cikarang Selatan, Bekasi, 17550, Indonesia
Tel.: (62) 218970866
Vehicle Parts Distr
N.A.I.C.S.: 423840

MUSASHINO KOGYO CO., LTD.
3366 Shinjuku, Shinjuku-ku, Tokyo, 160-0022, Japan
Tel.: (81) 333520052
Web Site: https://www.musashino-k.co.jp
Year Founded: 1920
9635—(TKS)
Rev.: $8,474,020
Assets: $39,514,580
Liabilities: $15,837,560
Net Worth: $23,677,020
Earnings: $26,440
Emp.: 25
Fiscal Year-end: 03/31/24
Movie Theater & Real Estate Services
N.A.I.C.S.: 512131
Yoshikatsu Kohno (Pres)

MUSATINII SA
str Tipografiei nr 1, Suceava, Romania
Tel.: (40) 230 523640
Web Site: http://www.musatinii.ro
Sales Range: Less than $1 Million
Emp.: 39
Commercial Printing Services
N.A.I.C.S.: 323111
Grigoras Ilie (Pres)

MUSCAT CITY DESALINATION CO SAOG
PO Box 1935, 114, Muscat, Oman
Tel.: (968) 24130826
Web Site: https://www.mcdcoman.com
MCDE—(MUS)
Rev.: $46,816,537
Assets: $238,402,098
Liabilities: $194,453,942
Net Worth: $43,948,156
Earnings: $6,091,747
Emp.: 47
Fiscal Year-end: 12/31/21
Investment Management Service
N.A.I.C.S.: 523940
Ahmad Fuaad Mohd Kenali (Chm)

MUSCAT ELECTRONICS COMPANY L.L.C.
Muscat Electronics Building Beside Ruwi Hotel, Ruwi, 114, Oman
Tel.: (968) 24796202
Web Site: http://www.muscatelectronics.com
Year Founded: 1979
Sales Range: $25-49.9 Million
Emp.: 170
Home Appliances & Electronics Distr
N.A.I.C.S.: 423620
Mohamed Musa Al-Yousef (Chm-Mgmt Bd)

Subsidiaries:

Muscat Electronics Company L.L.C. - AC Division (1)
Ground floor beside Haffa House Hotel, Ruwi-Mumtaz area, Muscat, Oman
Tel.: (968) 24702982
Electronic Equipment Whslr
N.A.I.C.S.: 423620

Muscat Electronics Company L.L.C. - Office Automation Division (1)
Mezzanine Floor Gulf House, Central Business District Ruwi, Muscat, Oman
Tel.: (968) 24796591
Electronic Equipment Whslr
N.A.I.C.S.: 423620

MUSCAT GASES COMPANY S.A.O.G
Azaiba North Way 48 Sultanate, PO Box 11, 124, Rusayl, Oman
Tel.: (968) 24446138
Web Site: https://www.muscatgas.com
Year Founded: 1983
MGMC—(MUS)
Rev.: $46,331,967
Assets: $29,187,364
Liabilities: $12,744,626
Net Worth: $16,442,738
Earnings: $344,872
Emp.: 373
Fiscal Year-end: 12/31/21
Natural & Industrial Gas Mfr
N.A.I.C.S.: 211130
Omar Ahmed Salim Qatan (Chm)

MUSCAT INSURANCE COMPANY SAOG
Building No 233 Street 281 Way 3501 Al Alam Street Al Khuwair, PO Box 72, Bousher Muscat, 112, Ruwi, Oman
Tel.: (968) 22364400
Web Site: https://www.micsaog.com
Year Founded: 1995
MCTI—(MUS)
Rev.: $37,800,915
Assets: $111,146,625
Liabilities: $65,851,944
Net Worth: $45,294,681
Earnings: $1,996,302
Emp.: 147
Fiscal Year-end: 12/31/21
Holding Company
N.A.I.C.S.: 551112
Bipin Dharamsey Nensey (Vice Chm)

MUSCAT OVERSEAS CO., L.L.C.
Hormuz Building Near Ruwi Roundabout, PO Box 488, 112, Muscat, Oman
Tel.: (968) 24703844 OM
Web Site: http://www.muscatoverseas.com
Year Founded: 1974
Sales Range: $200-249.9 Million
Emp.: 1,500
Diverse Holding Company; Trading, Contracting; Industrial; Marine Oil & Gas Drilling; Onfield Supplies; Travel; Tours; Cargo; Agriculture; Irrigation; Landscaping; Farm Development; Real Estate
N.A.I.C.S.: 551112
Mustahail Ahmed Al Mashani (Chm)

Subsidiaries:

Agriculture Modern Engineering Co. LLC (1)
Bounsher Ghala Bldg 155 157, PO Box 1285, Muscat, 114, Oman (100%)
Tel.: (968) 24592358
Provider of Engineering Services
N.A.I.C.S.: 541330

Kemach Equipment (Pty) Ltd. (1)
Portion 6 Aero Star Park Jet Park Road, Witfield, 1469, South Africa
Tel.: (27) 11 826 6710
Web Site: http://www.kemachjcb.co.za
Mining Construction Quarrying & Building Equipment Distr
N.A.I.C.S.: 423810

Majan Shipping & Transport Co. LLC (1)
PO Box 488, Ruwi, 112, Oman (100%)
Tel.: (968) 703844
Web Site: http://www.muscatoverseas.com
Provider of Shipping Services
N.A.I.C.S.: 488330

Muscat Overseas Agriculture Co. LLC (1)
115 Madinat Qaboos, PO Box 352, 115, Muscat, Oman (100%)
Tel.: (968) 247987556
Web Site: http://www.muscatoverseas.com
Sales Range: $25-49.9 Million
Emp.: 56
Mfr of Agricultural Chemicals
N.A.I.C.S.: 325998

Muscat Overseas Engineering Co. LLC (1)
Bounsher Ghala Bldg 155-157, PO Box 1288, Muscat, 114, Oman (100%)
Tel.: (968) 24597950
Sales Range: $25-49.9 Million
Emp.: 250
Provider of Engineering Services
N.A.I.C.S.: 541330
Bala Chandra (Gen Mgr)

Muscat Overseas Industrial & Marine Equipment Trading Co. LLC (1)
Bounsher Ghala Bldg 155 157, PO Box 1288, Muttrah, 114, Oman (100%)
Tel.: (968) 24597950
Web Site: http://www.muscatoverseas.com
Sales Range: $25-49.9 Million
Emp.: 97
Provider of Industrial & Marine Equipment
N.A.I.C.S.: 334290

Muscat Overseas Oilfield Supplies Co. LLC (1)
PO Box 3310, Muscat, 111, Oman (100%)
Tel.: (968) 24593325
Sales Range: $25-49.9 Million
Emp.: 21
Provider of Oilfield Supplies
N.A.I.C.S.: 333132

Qais Omani Establishment LLC (1)
PO Box 656, 100, Muscat, Oman (100%)
Tel.: (968) 24 703 844
Web Site: http://www.muscatoverseas.com
Provider of Property Management Services
N.A.I.C.S.: 531210

United Media Services LLC (1)
PO Box 3305, 112, Ruwi, Oman
Tel.: (968) 24 700 896
Web Site: http://www.umsoman.com
Strategic Media & Communication Services
N.A.I.C.S.: 519290
Alpana Roy (VP)

MUSCAT THREAD MILLS SAOG
PO Box 122, Rusayl, 124, Muscat, Oman
Tel.: (968) 24446806
Web Site: https://www.muscatthreads.com
Year Founded: 1996
MTMI—(MUS)
Rev.: $9,419,856
Assets: $7,432,640
Liabilities: $2,399,403
Net Worth: $5,033,237
Earnings: $293,591
Emp.: 75
Fiscal Year-end: 12/31/19
Thread Mfr

INTERNATIONAL PUBLIC

N.A.I.C.S.: 313110
Nihal S. Kodagoda (Gen Mgr)

MUSGRAVE GROUP PLC
Musgrave House Ballycurreen Airport Road, Cork, Ireland
Tel.: (353) 21 4522100
Web Site: http://www.musgravegroup.com
Year Founded: 1876
Sales Range: $5-14.9 Billion
Holding Company; Food & Grocery Products Whslr & Distr
N.A.I.C.S.: 551112
Noel Keeley (CEO)

Subsidiaries:

Musgrave Budgens Londis (1)
Musgrave House Widewater Place, Moorhall Road, Harefield, UB9 6NF, Middlesex, United Kingdom (100%)
Tel.: (44) 8700500158
Sales Range: $500-549.9 Million
Emp.: 300
Grocery Store Chain Operator
N.A.I.C.S.: 445110

Musgrave Espana, S.A.U. (1)
Ctra Casa del Leon km2, 03293, Elche, Spain
Tel.: (34) 966 657300
Web Site: http://www.musgrave.es
Grocery Product Distr
N.A.I.C.S.: 424490

Musgrave Operating Partners Ireland Limited (1)
Newcastle Road, Lucan, Dublin, Ireland
Tel.: (353) 163 02000
Web Site: http://www.musgravegroup.ie
Grocery Product Distr
N.A.I.C.S.: 424490
Eoin McCormack (Mng Dir)

Ritter Courivaud Limited (1)
Unit 4 Westlinks, Alperton Lane, Wembley, HA0 1ER, Middlesex, United Kingdom
Tel.: (44) 2089914350
Web Site: https://www.rittercourivaud.co.uk
Fine Foods Importer & Distr
N.A.I.C.S.: 424410

Superquinn Ltd. (1)
Sutton Cross, Dublin, 13, Ireland
Tel.: (353) 18322744
Web Site: http://www.superquinn.ie
Sales Range: $800-899.9 Million
Emp.: 2,500
Online & Storefront Grocery Stores
N.A.I.C.S.: 445110
Richard Collins (Sec & Dir-Fin)

MUSGRAVE MINERALS LIMITED
Ground Floor 5 Ord Street, West Perth, 6005, WA, Australia
Tel.: (61) 893241061
Web Site: http://www.musgraveminerals.com
MGV—(ASX)
Rev.: $291,803
Assets: $37,472,149
Liabilities: $1,716,957
Net Worth: $35,755,193
Earnings: ($1,212,670)
Emp.: 5
Fiscal Year-end: 06/30/22
Nickel & Copper Mining Services
N.A.I.C.S.: 212230
Graham Ascough (Chm)

MUSICMAGPIE PLC
First Floor One Stockport Exchange Railway Road, Stockport, SK1 3SW, United Kingdom
Tel.: (44) 8704792705 UK
Web Site: https://www.musicmagpieplc.com
Year Founded: 2007
MMAG—(AIM)
Rev.: $183,386,771
Assets: $60,146,428

Liabilities: $35,477,152
Net Worth: $24,669,275
Earnings: ($5,977,026)
Emp.: 683
Fiscal Year-end: 11/30/22
Software Development Services
N.A.I.C.S.: 541511
Martin Hellawell *(Chm)*

MUSIKHAUS THOMANN E.K.
Treppendorf 30, Burgebrach, Burgebrach, 96138, Germany
Tel.: (49) 9546 9223 55
Web Site: http://www.thomann.de
Year Founded: 1954
Sales Range: $200-249.9 Million
Emp.: 860
Musical Instruments & Audio Equipment Mail Order & Electronic Shopping
N.A.I.C.S.: 459140
Hans Thomann *(Mng Dir)*

MUSK METALS CORP.
Suite 2905 - 700 West Georgia Street, PO Box 10112, Vancouver, V7Y 1C6, BC, Canada
Tel.: (604) 717-6605
Web Site: https://www.muskmetals.ca
1I3—(DEU)
Assets: $1,391,303
Liabilities: $389,759
Net Worth: $1,001,545
Earnings: ($558,242)
Fiscal Year-end: 03/31/23
Mineral Exploration Services
N.A.I.C.S.: 213115

MUSKOKA DELIVERY SERVICES INC.
581 Ecclestone Drive, Bracebridge, ON, Canada
Tel.: (705) 645-1258
Web Site:
http://www.muskokadelivery.com
Year Founded: 1987
Transportation Services
N.A.I.C.S.: 484110
Patty Craymer *(Mgr-Customer Svc & Admin)*

MUST CAPITAL INC.
121 King Street West Suite 2150, Toronto, M5H 3T9, ON, Canada
Tel.: (604) 722-5225   ON
Web Site: http://www.intrinsic-mi.com
Year Founded: 2010
MUST.H—(TSXV)
Assets: $709
Liabilities: $86,301
Net Worth: ($85,592)
Earnings: ($322,817)
Fiscal Year-end: 12/31/23
Holding Company; Medical Imaging Software Developer & Publisher
N.A.I.C.S.: 551112
Mike Marrandino *(CEO)*

Subsidiaries:

Intrinsic4D LLC   (1)
40701 Woodward Ave Ste 250, Bloomfield Hills, MI 48304
Tel.: (248) 469-8811
Web Site: http://www.intrinsic-mi.com
Medical Imaging Software Developer & Publisher
N.A.I.C.S.: 513210
Sonny Lacey *(VP-Product Design & Customer Engagement)*

MUSTAFA SULTAN ENTERPRISES LLC
Mustafa Sultan House 1st Floor Al-Khuwair Street Way No 3503, Muscat, 112, Oman
Tel.: (968) 24636162

Web Site:
http://www.mustafasultan.com
Sales Range: $150-199.9 Million
Emp.: 700
Holding Company
N.A.I.C.S.: 551112
Akber Sultan *(Co-Founder & Vice Chm)*

Subsidiaries:

City Exchange L.L.C.   (1)
Bur Dubai Behind Astoria Hotel, PO Box 29395, Dubai, United Arab Emirates
Tel.: (971) 3937868
Trading Services
N.A.I.C.S.: 561499

Mustafa Sultan Electronics Co. LLC   (1)
Mustafa Sultan House 1st Fl, Al-khuwair Way No 3503, Muscat, 112, Oman
Tel.: (968) 24636162
Web Site: http://www.mustafasultan.com
Emp.: 300
Electronics Products
N.A.I.C.S.: 423690
Mohan Chengat *(Gen Mgr)*

Unit (Domestic):

Mustafa Sultan Electronics Co. LLC-Lighting Business Unit   (2)
Mustafa Sultan House 1st Floor, Al-Khuwair Street Way No 3503, Muscat, 112, Oman
Tel.: (968) 24636071
Lighting Products
N.A.I.C.S.: 335139
N. Vasan *(Gen Mgr)*

Mustafa Sultan Enterprises Military Division   (1)
Mustafa Sultan House 1st Floor, Al-Khuwair Street Way No 3503, Muscat, 112, Oman
Tel.: (968) 24636092
Web Site: http://www.omantel.net.om
Sales Range: $25-49.9 Million
Emp.: 3
Military Services
N.A.I.C.S.: 336992
Surendra Mehta *(Gen Mgr)*

Mustafa Sultan Exchange Co. LLC   (1)
Al Habib Building Ground Fl Opposite OC Center, Ruwi Street PO Box 2131, Ruwi, 112, Oman
Tel.: (968) 24707025
Web Site: http://www.mustafasultan.com
Emp.: 200
Trading Services
N.A.I.C.S.: 561499
P. K. Subudhi *(Gen Mgr)*

Mustafa Sultan Office Technology Co. LLC   (1)
Mustafa Sultan Office Technology Building, PO Box 3340, Al Noor Street, Ruwi, 112, Oman
Tel.: (968) 24636822
Web Site: http://www.mustafasultan.com
Emp.: 70
Computer & Office Equipment
N.A.I.C.S.: 423430
Ashwin Choudhury *(Office Mgr)*

Mustafa Sultan Refrigeration & Air Conditioning Services Co. LLC.   (1)
3rd Floor - Office No 312 Al-Khuwair Street Way No 3503, Mustafa Sultan House, Muscat, Oman
Tel.: (968) 24636848
Refrigeration & Air Conditioning Mfr
N.A.I.C.S.: 333415

Mustafa Sultan Science & Industry Co. LLC   (1)
Mustafa Sultan House Mezzanine Floor, Al-Khwwair Street Way No 3503, Muscat, Oman
Tel.: (968) 24636190
Web Site: http://www.mustafasultan.com
Sales Range: $25-49.9 Million
Emp.: 60
Research Services
N.A.I.C.S.: 541715
S. Mansukhani *(Gen Mgr)*

Mustafa Sultan Security & Communication Systems Co. LLC   (1)

Mustafa Sultan House 1st Floor Al-Khuwair Street Way No 3503, Muscat, Oman
Tel.: (968) 24636121
Web Site: http://www.mustafasultan.com
Sales Range: $25-49.9 Million
Emp.: 100
Security & Communications Systems
N.A.I.C.S.: 561621
J. Raman *(Gen Mgr)*

Mustafa Sultan Telecommunications Co. LLC   (1)
Mustafa Sultan House Ground Floor, Al-Khuwair Street Way No 3503, Muscat, 3340, Oman
Tel.: (968) 24636051
Web Site: http://www.mustafasultan.com
Sales Range: $25-49.9 Million
Emp.: 30
Telecommunication Servicesb
N.A.I.C.S.: 517810
Sushil Jani *(Gen Mgr)*

MUSTANG ENERGY PLC
48 Chancery Lane c/o Keystone Law, London, WC2A 1JF, United Kingdom
Tel.: (44) 61416220007   UK
Web Site:
https://www.mustangplc.com
CYK—(LSE)
Assets: $502,971
Liabilities: $58,200
Net Worth: $444,771
Earnings: ($314,857)
Emp.: 5
Fiscal Year-end: 12/31/20
Natural Gas Distribution
N.A.I.C.S.: 221210
Dean L. Gallegos *(Mng Dir)*

MUSTEK LIMITED
322 15th Road Randjespark, Midrand, Johannesburg, 1685, South Africa
Tel.: (27) 112371000
Web Site: http://www.mustek.co.za
MST—(JSE)
Rev.: $534,764,679
Assets: $302,251,872
Liabilities: $219,467,041
Net Worth: $82,784,831
Earnings: $11,597,714
Emp.: 1,253
Fiscal Year-end: 06/30/23
Computer Products Assembler & Distr
N.A.I.C.S.: 423430
Hein Engelbrecht *(CEO)*

Subsidiaries:

Mecer Inter-Ed Proprietary Limited   (1)
322 Fifteenth Road, Randjespark, Midrand, 1685, South Africa
Tel.: (27) 107300860
Web Site: https://mecerintered.co.za
Computer System Design Services
N.A.I.C.S.: 541512

Rectron Holdings Limited   (1)
152 15th Road, Randjespark Midrand, Johannesburg, 1685, South Africa
Tel.: (27) 112031000
Web Site: http://www.rectron.co.za
Sales Range: $75-99.9 Million
Emp.: 230
Computer Component Distr
N.A.I.C.S.: 423430
Spencer Chen *(Mng Dir)*

MUSTEK SYSTEMS, INC.
No 25 R&D Road II Hsinchu Science Park, Hsinchu, 300, Taiwan
Tel.: (886) 35779373
Web Site: http://www.mustek.com.tw
Year Founded: 1988
Sales Range: $1-9.9 Million
Digital Photo Frames Mfr
N.A.I.C.S.: 337122
Eric Chen *(Chm & Gen Mgr)*

Subsidiaries:

Mustek Pacific, Inc.   (1)
2F No 25 R&D Road II Science-Based Industrial Park, Hsin-chu, 30075, Taiwan
Tel.: (886) 35779373
Web Site: http://www.mustek.com.tw
Sales Range: $50-74.9 Million
Emp.: 100
Digital Imaging Equipments Distr
N.A.I.C.S.: 423410
Duke Tu *(Mgr-Sls)*

Mustek, Inc.   (1)
14751 Franklin Unit B, Tustin, CA 92780
Tel.: (949) 788-3600
Web Site: http://www.mustek.com
Imaging Devices Mfr & Distr
N.A.I.C.S.: 621512

MUSTERA PROPERTY GROUP LIMITED
15 McCabe Street, North Fremantle, 6159, WA, Australia
Tel.: (61) 893867069
Web Site:
https://www.mustera.com.au
MPX—(ASX)
Rev.: $45,913,547
Assets: $39,128,921
Liabilities: $25,268,242
Net Worth: $13,860,679
Earnings: $5,548,240
Fiscal Year-end: 06/30/24
Commercial, Industrial & Residential Property Investment & Development
N.A.I.C.S.: 531390
Nicholas Zborowski *(Exec Dir)*

MUSTGROW BIOLOGICS CORP.
1005 201 1st Ave S, Saskatoon, S7K 1J5, SK, Canada
Tel.: (306) 668-2652   Ca
Web Site: https://www.mustgrow.ca
Year Founded: 2014
MGRO—(TSXV)
Rev.: $4,786
Assets: $5,270,283
Liabilities: $1,400,115
Net Worth: $3,870,168
Earnings: ($4,111,576)
Fiscal Year-end: 12/31/22
Biotechnology Research & Development Services
N.A.I.C.S.: 541714
Brad Munro *(Chm)*

MUSTIKA RATU TBK
Graha Mustika Ratu Jl Gatot Subroto No 74-75, Jakarta, 12870, Indonesia
Tel.: (62) 218306754
Web Site: https://mustika-ratu.co.id
Year Founded: 1978
MRAT—(INDO)
Rev.: $19,520,706
Assets: $41,185,424
Liabilities: $15,086,615
Net Worth: $26,098,810
Earnings: ($916,502)
Emp.: 380
Fiscal Year-end: 12/31/23
Cosmetics Distr
N.A.I.C.S.: 456120
S. S. Mooryati Soedibyo *(Founder)*

MUT-TSCHAMBER MISCH- UND TRENNTECHNIK GMBH
Industriestrasse 12, Wehr, 79662, Germany
Tel.: (49) 776252060
Web Site: http://www.mut-tschamber.de
Rev.: $12,502,330
Emp.: 35
Industrial Equipment Mfr
N.A.I.C.S.: 333248
Hanspeter Tschamber *(Mng Dir)*

MUTANDIS SCA

MUT-TSCHAMBER Misch- und Trenntechnik GmbH—(Continued)

MUTANDIS SCA
22 Boulevard Abdelkrim Khattabi,
20100, Casablanca, Morocco
Tel.: (212) 666627370
Web Site: https://www.mutandis.com
Year Founded: 2008
MUT—(CAS)
Sales Range: Less than $1 Million
Food Products Mfr
N.A.I.C.S.: 311999

MUTARES SE & CO. KGAA
Arnulfstrasse 19, 80335, Munich,
Germany
Tel.: (49) 8992927760 De
Web Site: https://mutares.com
Year Founded: 2008
MUX—(MUN)
Rev.: $5,176,178,387
Assets: $4,800,419,473
Liabilities: $3,564,521,471
Net Worth: $1,235,898,002
Earnings: $405,232,366
Emp.: 27,345
Fiscal Year-end: 12/31/23
Investment Holding Company
N.A.I.C.S.: 551112
Kristian Schleede (*Chief Restructuring Officer & Member-Exec Bd*)

Subsidiaries:

Alan Dick Communications Ltd (1)
11 Billet Lane, Scunthorpe, DN15 9YH,
United Kingdom
Tel.: (44) 1724292860
Web Site: https://adcomms.ltd
Emp.: 100
Mobile Telecommunications Services
N.A.I.C.S.: 517112
Carl Pocknell (*Mng Dir*)

Aperam Stainless Services & Solutions Tubes Europe SAS (1)
1 Rue Prele, F 55170, Ancerville, France
Tel.: (33) 329797474
Stainless Steel Tube Mfr
N.A.I.C.S.: 331210
Lakshmi N. Mittal (*Chm*)

Arriva Danmark A/S (1)
Skojtevej 26, 2770, Kastrup, Denmark
Tel.: (45) 72302500
Web Site: http://www.arriva.dk
Sales Range: $1-4.9 Billion
Emp.: 100
Bus, Train & Water Transportation Service Provider
N.A.I.C.S.: 485113

Arriva LITAS d.o.o. (1)
Mose Pijade 9, 12000, Pozarevac, Serbia
Tel.: (381) 12538400
Web Site: https://mobilitas.rs
Railway Freight Transportation Services
N.A.I.C.S.: 482111
Predrag Basta (*Mgr-Technical & Maintenance*)

BEXity GmbH (1)
Warneckestrasse 7, 1110, Vienna, Austria
Tel.: (43) 504300
Web Site: https://www.bexity.com
Logistic & Warehousing Services
N.A.I.C.S.: 493110
Gerald Gregori (*Head-Sls*)

Balcke-Durr Engineering Private Ltd. (1)
Vijaya Tower 3 rd Floor 4 Kodambakkam
High Road, Chennai, India
Tel.: (91) 9344931139
Heat Exchanger & Component Distr
N.A.I.C.S.: 423830
S. Janarthanan (*Mng Dir*)

Balcke-Durr GmbH (1)
Theodorstrasse 180, 40472, Dusseldorf,
Germany
Tel.: (49) 211586710
Web Site: https://www.balcke-duerr.com
Emp.: 500
Heat Exchangers & Boilers Mfr
N.A.I.C.S.: 332410
Subsidiary (Domestic):

Balcke-Durr Rothemuhle GmbH (2)
Raiffeisenstr 12, 57462, Olpe, Germany
Tel.: (49) 276194100
Heat Exchanger & Component Distr
N.A.I.C.S.: 423830

Subsidiary (Non-US):

LOTERIOS s.r.l. (2)
Via Monte Grappa 44, 21040, Gerenzano,
VA, Italy
Tel.: (39) 02 9648281
Web Site: http://www.loterios.com
Metal Pressure Equipment Mfr & Whslr
N.A.I.C.S.: 423510

Balcke-Durr Technologies India Private Ltd. (1)
Vijaya Tower 3 rd Floor 4 Kodambakkam
High Road, Chennai, India
Tel.: (91) 9344931138
Heat Exchanger & Component Distr
N.A.I.C.S.: 423830
Shridhar Ranganathan (*Mng Dir*)

Balcke-Durr Torino Srl (1)
Str Robecco 19, 20013, Magenta, MI, Italy
Tel.: (39) 0297266211
Heat Exchanger & Component Distr
N.A.I.C.S.: 423830

Castelli S.p.A. (1)
via Einstein 63, 40017, San Giovanni in
Persiceto, Bologna, Italy (100%)
Tel.: (39) 051 820 111
Web Site: http://www.haworth.it
Sales Range: $25-49.9 Million
Emp.: 250
Office Furniture Mfr
N.A.I.C.S.: 337214

Castelli S.r.l. i.L. (1)
Contra delle Fontanelle 35, 36100, Vicenza,
Italy
Tel.: (39) 0444300645
Web Site: http://www.castellisrl.net
Castrol Industrial Oil Distr
N.A.I.C.S.: 424720

Donges SteelTec GmbH (1)
Tel.: (49) 61518890
Web Site: https://www.donges-steeltec.de
Emp.: 200
Steel Construction & Engineering Services
N.A.I.C.S.: 541330
Stephan Langer (*Bus Area Mgr-Bridge Construction*)

Subsidiary (Non-US):

Kalzip GmbH (2)
Tel.: (49) 26198340
Sales Range: $50-74.9 Million
Emp.: 160
Aluminum Rolling & Extruding Mill
N.A.I.C.S.: 331318
Joachim Wolke (*Dir-Adv*)

Subsidiary (Non-US):

Kalzip Asia Pte Limited (3)
Level 2 9 Tuas Avenue 2, Singapore,
639449, Singapore
Tel.: (65) 97586675
Roofing Sheet Mfr
N.A.I.C.S.: 332322

Kalzip FZE (3)
Jafza One Tower A Office A602, Jebel Ali
Free Zone, Dubai, United Arab Emirates
Tel.: (971) 48820925
Roofing Sheet Mfr
N.A.I.C.S.: 332322
Duncan Clark (*Head-Ops*)

Kalzip GmbH (3)
Mozartstrasse 25 Sales Area D/A/CH, 2320,
Schwechat, Austria
Tel.: (43) 1 749 29 66
Roofing Sheet Mfr
N.A.I.C.S.: 332322

Kalzip Guangzhou Limited (3)
Suite 2310 North Tower The Hub 1068 Xin
Gang East Road, 510335, Guangzhou,
China
Tel.: (86) 20 89 04 74 08
Web Site: http://www.kalzip.com

Roofing Sheet Mfr
N.A.I.C.S.: 332322
Lami Cen (*Mgr-Fin*)

Subsidiary (US):

Kalzip Inc (3)
161 W Lincolnway Ste E 20 -22, Valparaiso,
IN 46383
Tel.: (219) 286-3481
Web Site: https://www.kalzip.com
Roofing Sheet Mfr
N.A.I.C.S.: 332322

Subsidiary (Non-US):

Kalzip India Private Limited (3)
Unit 310 3rd Floor Vipul Agora Next to Sahara Mall M G Road, Gurgaon, 122002,
Haryana, India
Tel.: (91) 1244848800
Roofing Sheet Mfr
N.A.I.C.S.: 332322

Kalzip Italy SRL (3)
Via Serbelloni 47, 20064, Gorgonzola, Italy
Tel.: (39) 02 36542081
Roofing Sheet Mfr
N.A.I.C.S.: 332322
Francesco Corona (*Mgr-Technical*)

Kalzip Limited (3)
Haydock Lane Haydock, Saint Helens,
WA11 9TY, United Kingdom
Tel.: (44) 1942 295 500
Roofing Sheet Mfr
N.A.I.C.S.: 332322

Kalzip Spain S.L.U. (3)
Calle de Embajadores 187 planta 4, Torre
Rioja, 28045, Madrid, Spain
Tel.: (34) 913430343
Roofing Sheet Mfr
N.A.I.C.S.: 332322

Subsidiary (Non-US):

Normek Oy (2)
Pakkalankuja 7, FI 01510, Vantaa, Finland
Tel.: (358) 204207000
Web Site: http://www.normek.fi
Steel Structure & Glass Facade Supplier
N.A.I.C.S.: 332311
Klaus Saarikallio (*Mng Dir*)

EUPEC Pipecoatings France S.A. (1)
21 route du Guindal, 59820, Gravelines,
France
Tel.: (33) 3 2858 0220
Web Site: http://www.eupec-pipecoatings.com
Sales Range: $250-299.9 Million
Emp.: 120
Pipeline Coating Services
N.A.I.C.S.: 332812
Guissol Bernard (*Mng Dir*)

Elastomer Solutions GmbH (1)
Higis-Ring 15, Wiesbaum, 54578, Wiesbaden, Germany
Tel.: (49) 6593980700
Web Site: https://www.elastomer-solutions.com
Elastomeric & Plastic Component Mfr & Distr
N.A.I.C.S.: 325211

Subsidiary (Non-US):

DF Elastomer Solutions Lda. (2)
E N 13 Km 16 Recto do Mindelo, 4485-473,
Porto, Portugal
Tel.: (351) 252669010
Elastomeric & Plastic Component Mfr & Distr
N.A.I.C.S.: 325211
Sandra Ferreira (*CFO*)

Elastomer Solutions Maroc S.a.r.l. (2)
Zone Franche d'Exportation Tanger Ilot 64
Lot 3, 90100, Tangiers, Morocco
Tel.: (212) 539395893
Elastomeric & Plastic Component Mfr & Distr
N.A.I.C.S.: 325211
Aiman Ekdiha (*Engr-Logistics & Production Plng*)

Elastomer Solutions Mexico S. de R.L. de C.V. (2)
Circuito Fresnillo Poniente No 21, Parque
Industrial Fresnillo, 99059, Fresnillo, Zacatecas, Mexico
Tel.: (52) 4939357831
Elastomeric & Plastic Component Mfr & Distr
N.A.I.C.S.: 325211

Elastomer Solutions s.r.o. (2)
Tovarenska 422, 01861, Belusa, Slovakia
Tel.: (421) 424651811
Elastomeric & Plastic Component Mfr & Distr
N.A.I.C.S.: 325211
Maria Zabojnikova (*CFO & Fin Mgr*)

Eltel Networks Energetyka S.A. (1)
Gutkowo 81 g, 11-041, Olsztyn, Poland
Tel.: (48) 895222500
Power & Communication Network Services
N.A.I.C.S.: 237130
Stanislaw Szymanski (*Project Dir*)

Eltel Networks Engineering S.A. (1)
ul Kolowa 8, 30-134, Krakow, Poland
Tel.: (48) 601820457
Electrical Structure Design Services
N.A.I.C.S.: 541330

FDT Flachdach Technologie S.A./N.V. (1)
Rue du Bosquet 4, 1400, Nivelles, Belgium
Tel.: (32) 67411818
Web Site: http://www.fdt.be
Synthetic Membrane Distr
N.A.I.C.S.: 424690

FDT France S. A.S. (1)
Le Cesar building 12 chaussee Jules Cesar,
BP 80209, Cergy-Pontoise, 95523, Osny,
France
Tel.: (33) 130320800
Web Site: https://www.fdt-france.fr
Waterproofing Terrace Roof Mfr & Distr
N.A.I.C.S.: 325510

Falkenroth Umformtechnik GmbH (1)
Asenbach 1, 58579, Schalksmuhle, Germany
Tel.: (49) 23559060
Web Site: https://alkenroth-umformtechnik.de
Sales Range: $25-49.9 Million
Emp.: 100
Die Forging Parts Mfr
N.A.I.C.S.: 331110
Rolf Wenzler (*Mng Dir*)

Frigoscandia Akeri AB (1)
Landskronavagen 11, 252 32, Helsingborg,
Sweden
Tel.: (46) 42178041
Chilled & Frozen Food Distr
N.A.I.C.S.: 424490

Frigoscandia B. V (1)
Handelsweg 35, 2988 DB, Ridderkerk,
Netherlands
Tel.: (31) 783031328
Food & Home Goods Delivery Services
N.A.I.C.S.: 722513

Frigoscandia Denmark A / S (1)
Bogildsmindevej 3, 9400, Norresundby,
Denmark
Tel.: (45) 96356700
Food & Home Goods Delivery Services
N.A.I.C.S.: 722513

Frigoscandia Transport AS (1)
Verkseier Furulunds vei 1, NO-0668, Oslo,
Norway
Tel.: (47) 22171515
Food & Home Goods Delivery Services
N.A.I.C.S.: 722513

GEA Farm Technologies Japy SAS (1)
Cours De Gray, 21850, Saint Apollinaire,
Cote-d'Or, France
Tel.: (33) 380718211
Emp.: 15
Agricultural Machinery Mfr
N.A.I.C.S.: 333111
Yves Speidel (*Mng Dir*)

Ganter Interior GmbH (1)

AND PRIVATE COMPANIES

Am Kraftwerk 4, 79183, Waldkirch, Germany
Tel.: (49) 768140180
Web Site: https://ganter-group.com
Emp.: 150
Interior Design & Furnishing Services
N.A.I.C.S.: 541410

Ganter Italia S. r. l. (1)
Via Luis-Zuegg 40, 39012, Merano, Italy
Tel.: (39) 0473015000
Interior Design & Furnishing Services
N.A.I.C.S.: 541410

Gesenkschmiede Schneider GmbH (1)
Ulmer Strasse 112, 73431, Aalen, Germany
Tel.: (49) 73615970
Web Site: https://gsa-aalen.de
Emp.: 340
Steel Forging Mfr
N.A.I.C.S.: 331110

Glaserne Molkerei GmbH (1)
Meiereiweg 1, Dechow, 19217, Rehna, Germany
Tel.: (49) 3376020770
Web Site: https://glaeserne-molkerei.de
Emp.: 120
Dairy Products Mfr
N.A.I.C.S.: 311514

Gotene Kyltransporter AB (1)
Jarnvagsgatan 24, 533 30, Gotene, Sweden
Tel.: (46) 51126600
Web Site: https://www.gotenekyl.se
Transportation Services
N.A.I.C.S.: 485991

Japy Tech S. A. S. (1)
Route de Gray, F-21850, Saint Apollinaire, France
Tel.: (33) 380718204
Web Site: https://www.japy-tech.com
Milk Tank Mfr & Distr
N.A.I.C.S.: 311514

KLANN Packaging GmbH (1)
Waldkirchener Str 11, 84030, Landshut, Germany
Tel.: (49) 87170030
Web Site: http://www.klann.de
Emp.: 100
Tin Packaging Product Mfr
N.A.I.C.S.: 332431

Kalzip France S.A.S. (1)
11 rue de Courtalin Batiment B-2eme etage, Magny-le-Hongre, 77700, Seine-et-Marne, France
Tel.: (33) 160435710
Roofing & Facade System Distr
N.A.I.C.S.: 423330

Kalzip Ltd. (1)
Haydock Lane, Haydock Industrial Estate Haydock, Saint Helens, WA11 9TY, Merseyside, United Kingdom
Tel.: (44) 1942295500
Roofing & Facade System Distr
N.A.I.C.S.: 423330
Gill Webster *(Office Mgr-Sls)*

Kirchhoff GmbH & Co. KG (1)
Oststrasse 1, 58553, Halver, Germany
Tel.: (49) 235391810
Web Site: http://www.kico.de
Emp.: 800
Locking & Mechatronic System Mfr
N.A.I.C.S.: 332510
Dirk Aldermann *(Mng Dir)*

Subsidiary (Domestic):

KICO Kunststofftechnik GmbH (2)
Oststrasse 7, 58553, Halver, Germany
Tel.: (49) 235391810
Locking & Mechatronic System Mfr
N.A.I.C.S.: 332510

Subsidiary (Non-US):

KICO-Polska Sp. z.o.o. (2)
ul Luzycka 50, 66-200, Swiebodzin, Poland
Tel.: (48) 684784570
Locking & Mechatronic System Mfr
N.A.I.C.S.: 332510
Ewa Sitek *(Plant Mgr)*

Subsidiary (Domestic):

Kirchhoff Immobilien GmbH & Co. KG (2)

Florianstrasse 8, 59597, Erwitte, Germany
Tel.: (49) 294397969
Web Site: http://www.wohnen-am-markt.de
Residential Apartment Services
N.A.I.C.S.: 531110

Knorr-Bremse RailServices (UK) Limited (1)
Wolverton Works Stratford Road, Wolverton, Milton Keynes, MK12 5NT, United Kingdom (100%)
Tel.: (44) 1908574400
Web Site: http://www.knorr-bremse.co.uk
Sales Range: $800-899.9 Million
Emp.: 3,000
Railway Rolling Stock Refurbishment
N.A.I.C.S.: 336510

Lapeyre SAS (1)
2-3 rue Andre Karman, PO Box 149, 93300, Aubervilliers, France (100%)
Tel.: (33) 148117400
Web Site: https://www.lapeyre.fr
Sales Range: $100-124.9 Million
Emp.: 400
Hardware Retailer
N.A.I.C.S.: 444140
Marc Tenart *(CEO)*

Light Mobility Solutions GmbH (1)
Feldstrasse 18, D-63179, Obertshausen, Germany
Tel.: (49) 61047060
Web Site: https://lms-automotive.com
Automotive Interior Parts Distr
N.A.I.C.S.: 423120

Mann+Hummel France S.A.S. (1)
ZA Autoroutiere Boulevard de la Communication, Louverne, Laval, 53061, France
Tel.: (33) 243498000
Sales Range: $200-249.9 Million
Emp.: 520
Industrial Filters & Filtration Systems
N.A.I.C.S.: 333998
Langer Bruno *(Mgr)*

Mann+Hummel GmbH - Sonneberg (1)
Friedrich-Engels-Str 157, 96515, Sonneberg, Germany
Tel.: (49) 36758770
Web Site: http://www.sonneberg.de
Sales Range: $100-124.9 Million
Emp.: 400
Industrial Filter & Filtration System Mfr
N.A.I.C.S.: 333248

MoldTecs GmbH (1)
Friedrich-Engels-Str 157, D-96515, Sonneberg, Germany
Tel.: (49) 36758770
Automotive Plastic Parts Distr
N.A.I.C.S.: 423120

MoldTecs S. A. S. (1)
ZA Autoroutiere Boulevard de la Communication, 53061, Laval, France
Tel.: (33) 243498000
Web Site: https://moldtecs.com
Emp.: 400
Plastic Parts & Complex Moulded System Mfr
N.A.I.C.S.: 326199

Mutares Austria GmbH (1)
Oppolzergasse 6/2b, 1010, Vienna, Austria
Tel.: (43) 8992927760
Automotive & Mobility Services
N.A.I.C.S.: 811198

Mutares Benelux B. V. (1)
Herengracht 500, 1017 CB, Amsterdam, Netherlands
Tel.: (31) 203995487
Automotive & Mobility Services
N.A.I.C.S.: 811198

Mutares France S.A.S. (1)
73 Boulevard Haussmann, 75008, Paris, France
Tel.:(33) 140980250
Holding Company Services
N.A.I.C.S.: 551112

Mutares Iberia S. L. U. (1)
Calle Claudio Coello 78, 28001, Madrid, Spain
Tel.: (34) 917455933
Company Reorganization & Optimization Services

N.A.I.C.S.: 541611

Mutares Italy S.r.l. (1)
Via Manin 13, 20121, Milan, Italy
Tel.: (39) 027268781
Holding Company Services
N.A.I.C.S.: 551112

Mutares Nordics Oy (1)
Etelainen Makasiinikatu 4, 00130, Helsinki, Finland
Tel.: (358) 505575112
Holding Company Services
N.A.I.C.S.: 551112
Jesse Petaja *(Mgr)*

MuxTec GmbH (1)
Arnulfstrasse 19, 80335, Munich, Germany
Tel.: (49) 8954198617
Web Site: https://muxtec.com
Emp.: 15
Information Technology Services
N.A.I.C.S.: 541519

Nordec Envelope Oy (1)
Itamerenkatu 5, Helsinki, Finland
Tel.: (358) 204207000
Construction Engineering Services
N.A.I.C.S.: 541330

Nordec Oy (1)
Itamerenkatu 5, Helsinki, Finland
Tel.: (358) 204207000
Construction Engineering Services
N.A.I.C.S.: 541330

Nordec Sp.z. o.o. (1)
Ul Lukowska 7/9, 64-600, Oborniki, Poland
Tel.: (48) 612968320
Construction Engineering Services
N.A.I.C.S.: 541330

Nordec s. r. o. (1)
Pekarska 695/10a, 155 00, Prague, Czech Republic
Tel.: (420) 737204586
Residential Building Construction Services
N.A.I.C.S.: 236220

Norsilk SAS (1)
La Cour Martin 45 rue de la Bruyere, Boulleville, 27210, Bernay, France
Tel.: (33) 227363000
Web Site: http://www.norsilk.com
Emp.: 150
Wood Product Distr
N.A.I.C.S.: 423310
Jean-Arnaud Pichon *(Comml Dir)*

Platinum GmbH i.l. (1)
Am Ockenheimer Graben 23, 55411, Bingen, Germany
Tel.: (49) 6721305930
Web Site: http://www.platinum.com
Animal Feed Mfr
N.A.I.C.S.: 311119

Prenatal Moeder En Kind BV (1)
Vlotbrugweg 10, NL 1332 AH, Almere, Netherlands
Tel.: (31) 365322000
Web Site: http://www.prenatal.nl
Sales Range: $50-74.9 Million
Emp.: 120
Chain of Retail Shops for Child & Infant Wear; Maternity Ready-to-Wear
N.A.I.C.S.: 458110
P. Brussen *(Mng Dir)*

PrimoTECS S. P. A. (1)
Via Martin Luther King 6, 10051, Avigliana, Italy
Tel.: (39) 0119317111
Web Site: https://www.primotecs.com
Automotive Metal Parts Services
N.A.I.C.S.: 811111

Rasche Holding GmbH (1)
Petershager Weg 169-173, 32425, Minden, Germany
Tel.: (49) 571946460
Web Site: https://www.rasche.eu
Emp.: 140
Complex Construction Services
N.A.I.C.S.: 532412

Rasche Umformtechnik GmbH&Co.KG (1)
Unterm Grunen Berg 2-4, D-58840, Plettenberg, Germany
Tel.: (49) 23916040

MUTARES SE & CO. KGAA

Web Site: https://www.rasche.de
Emp.: 180
Steel & Titanium Processing Services
N.A.I.C.S.: 423510

Repartim S. A. S. (1)
61 rue du Colombier, 37700, Saint-Pierre-des-Corps, France
Tel.: (33) 970834321
Web Site: https://www.repartim.fr
Emp.: 250
Lock & Plumbing Repair Services
N.A.I.C.S.: 561622

Rubbens NV (1)
Zwaluwbeekstraat 12, B-9150, Kruibeke, Belgium
Tel.: (32) 3253 0191
Web Site: http://www.rubbens.com
Sales Range: $25-49.9 Million
Emp.: 73
Custom Commercial Kitchen Appliances & Equipment Mfr
N.A.I.C.S.: 333310

Subsidiary (Domestic):

EGC SA (2)
Rue des Iles 5, 4970, Stavelot, Belgium
Tel.: (32) 8086 2541
Web Site: http://www.rubbens.com
Custom Commercial Kitchen Appliances & Equipment Mfr
N.A.I.C.S.: 333310

SELZER Fertigungstechnik GmbH & Co. KG (1)
Bahnhofstrasse 1, 35759, Driedorf, Germany
Tel.: (49) 2775810
Web Site: https://www.selzer-automotive.de
Sales Range: $100-124.9 Million
Emp.: 400
Automotive Subassemblies Mfr
N.A.I.C.S.: 336310

SFC Solutions Automotive S. r. l. (1)
Sos Campulungului nr 1, Sat Piscani Dirmanesti, 117360, Arges, Romania
Tel.: (40) 348457070
Injection Molding Machine Mfr
N.A.I.C.S.: 333511

SFC Solutions Czestochowa Sp.z.o.o. (1)
Legionow 244, 42-202, Czestochowa, Poland
Tel.: (48) 607047700
Emp.: 800
Fluid Transfer System Product Mfr
N.A.I.C.S.: 332912

SFC Solutions Italy S. R. L. (1)
Via Torino 140, 10073, Cirie, TO, Italy
Tel.: (39) 0119216212
Emp.: 390
Automotive & Industrial Sealing Mfr
N.A.I.C.S.: 339991

SFC Solutions Spain Borja S.L. (1)
Poligono Industrial Barbalanca 0, Borja, 50540, Zaragoza, Spain
Tel.: (34) 976866003
Emp.: 140
Degas & Cooling System Hose Mfr
N.A.I.C.S.: 326220

STADA Production Ireland Limited (1)
Waterford Rd, Clonmel, Ireland
Tel.: (353) 526177777
Sales Range: $50-74.9 Million
Emp.: 200
Pharmaceutical & Health Care Products Mfr
N.A.I.C.S.: 325412

Societe Nouvelle CGVL S.A.S.U. (1)
1 bis Villa Charles, F-93806, Epinay-sur-Seine, France
Tel.: (33) 1 4971 2929
Web Site: http://www.cgvl.fr
Sales Range: $50-74.9 Million
Emp.: 535
Industrial Vehicle & Driver Rental Services
N.A.I.C.S.: 532120

Special Melted Products Ltd. (1)
President Way, Sheffield, United Kingdom
Tel.: (44) 1142720081
Web Site: https://specialmeltedproducts.com
Nickel Alloy Mfr

MUTARES SE & CO. KGAA

Mutares SE & Co. KGaA—(Continued)
N.A.I.C.S.: 331523

Steyr Motors Betriebs GmbH (1)
Im Stadtgut B1, A-4407, Steyr, Austria
Tel.: (43) 72522220
Web Site: https://www.steyr-motors.com
Diesel Engine Mfr & Distr
N.A.I.C.S.: 333618

Terranor A / S (1)
Harup Bygade 20-22, 8600, Silkeborg, Denmark
Tel.: (45) 31908070
Web Site: https://terranor.dk
Emp.: 250
Road Maintenance & Construction Services
N.A.I.C.S.: 561599

Terranor Oy (1)
Teollisuuskatu 21, 00510, Helsinki, Finland
Tel.: (358) 3007636
Web Site: https://terranor.fi
Emp.: 20
Road Maintenance & Construction Services
N.A.I.C.S.: 561599

VALTI (1)
Courtangis Road, BP 20, 21500, Montbard, Cedex, France
Tel.: (33) 380895456
Web Site: https://valtitubes.com
Stainless Steel Tube Mfr & Whslr
N.A.I.C.S.: 331210

keeeper GmbH (1)
Postdamm 43, 32351, Stemwede, Germany
Tel.: (49) 57738010
Web Site: http://www.keeeper.com
Emp.: 450
Plastic Household Appliance Product Mfr
N.A.I.C.S.: 335220

Subsidiary (Domestic):

FASANA GmbH (2)
Adolf-Halstrick-Strasse 6, 53881, Euskirchen, Germany
Tel.: (49) 22518120
Web Site: https://fasana.de
Emp.: 200
Tissue & Toilet Paper Mfr
N.A.I.C.S.: 322291
Markus Classen *(Mng Dir)*

Subsidiary (Non-US):

Keeeper S.A. (2)
Rue du progres 1, 6220, Fleurus, Belgium
Tel.: (32) 81611693
Plastic Household Appliance Product Mfr
N.A.I.C.S.: 335220

Keeeper Sp.z o.o (2)
ul Mokra 3, 85-810, Bydgoszcz, Poland
Tel.: (48) 523604500
Plastic Household Appliance Product Mfr
N.A.I.C.S.: 335220
Przemyslaw Rajmann *(Mgr-Pur)*

MUTHOOT CAPITAL SERVICES LTD.

Muthoot Towers 3rd Floor M G Road, Cochin, 682035, Kerala, India
Tel.: (91) 4846619600
Web Site:
https://www.muthootcap.com
511766—(BOM)
Rev.: $68,937,960
Assets: $349,416,795
Liabilities: $273,035,490
Net Worth: $76,381,305
Earnings: $7,024,290
Emp.: 1,649
Fiscal Year-end: 03/31/21
Financial Management Services
N.A.I.C.S.: 523999
Thomas John Muthoot *(Chm)*

MUTHOOT FINANCE LIMITED

2nd floor Muthoot Chambers Opp Saritha Theatre Complex Banerji Road, Kochi, 682 018, India
Tel.: (91) 4842394712
Web Site:
https://www.muthootfinance.com
Year Founded: 1997
MUTHOOTFIN—(NSE)
Rev.: $1,670,413,563
Assets: $10,417,198,701
Liabilities: $7,804,875,897
Net Worth: $2,612,322,804
Earnings: $550,275,590
Emp.: 26,716
Fiscal Year-end: 03/31/22
Financial Lending Services
N.A.I.C.S.: 522310
Alexander George Muthoot *(Deputy Mng Dir)*

MUTHOOT MICROFIN LIMITED

5th Floor Muthoot Towers M G Road, Ernakulam, 682035, Kerala, India
Tel.: (91) 4844277500
Web Site:
https://www.muthootmicrofin.com
Year Founded: 2010
544055—(BOM)
Rev.: $175,296,893
Assets: $1,033,738,919
Liabilities: $836,686,020
Net Worth: $197,052,899
Earnings: $19,863,347
Emp.: 10,227
Fiscal Year-end: 03/31/23
Financial Investment Services
N.A.I.C.S.: 523910

MUTO SEIKO CO.

1-60-1 Unumakawasakicho, Kakamigahara, 509-0147, Gifu, Japan
Tel.: (81) 583711100
Web Site: https://www.muto.co.jp
Year Founded: 1970
7927—(TKS)
Rev.: $173,942,150
Assets: $194,849,580
Liabilities: $69,834,650
Net Worth: $125,014,930
Earnings: $11,719,530
Emp.: 263
Fiscal Year-end: 03/31/24
Plastic Molding Mfr & Distr
N.A.I.C.S.: 326199

MUTOH HOLDINGS CO., LTD.

3-1-3 Ikejiri, Setagaya-ku, Tokyo, 154-8560, Japan
Tel.: (81) 367587100
Web Site: https://www.mutoh-hd.co.jp
Year Founded: 1952
7999—(TKS)
Rev.: $153,408,640
Assets: $258,204,320
Liabilities: $52,572,080
Net Worth: $205,632,240
Earnings: $7,482,640
Fiscal Year-end: 03/31/22
CAD Systems & Plotters, Drafters Mfr
N.A.I.C.S.: 334118
Toshihiro Sakamoto *(Chm)*

Subsidiaries:

Mutoh America Inc. (1)
4405 E Baseline Rd Ste 120, Phoenix, AZ 85042 (85%)
Tel.: (480) 968-7772
Web Site: https://www.mutoh.com
Sales Range: $25-49.9 Million
Emp.: 25
Large Format Graphic Printers Distr
N.A.I.C.S.: 423430
Brian Phipps *(Pres)*

Mutoh Belgium nv (1)
Archimedesstraat 13, 8400, Oostende, Belgium (100%)
Tel.: (32) 59561400
Web Site: https://mutoh.eu
Inkjet Printers & Sign Cutting Plotters Whslr
N.A.I.C.S.: 423430
Nick Decock *(Mgr-Intl Mktg)*

Mutoh Deutschland GmbH (1)
Schiess-Strasse 52, 40549, Dusseldorf, Germany (100%)
Tel.: (49) 2113854740
Sales Range: $25-49.9 Million
Emp.: 4
Retailer of Drafting Equipment, Plotters & Printers
N.A.I.C.S.: 333310

Mutoh Itex Co., Ltd. (1)
3-1-3 Ikejiri MUTOH Ikejiri Building, Setagaya-ku, Tokyo, 154-8560, Japan
Tel.: (81) 36 758 7088
Web Site: https://www.mutoh-itex.jp
Emp.: 247
Computer Programming Services
N.A.I.C.S.: 541511

Mutoh North Europe S.A. (1)
6 Place de Nancy, 2212, Luxembourg, Luxembourg
Tel.: (352) 2 702 3045
Web Site: https://mutohnorth.eu
Emp.: 700
Photographic Equipment Whslr
N.A.I.C.S.: 423410

MUTSCHLER HOLDING AG

Rigistrasse 60, 8006, Zurich, Switzerland
Tel.: (41) 44 268 18 60
Holding Company
N.A.I.C.S.: 551112
Klaus Mutschler *(Chm)*

Subsidiaries:

Skandia Leben AG (1)
Birmensdorferstrasse 108, Postfach 8418, Zurich, 8036, Switzerland
Tel.: (41) 848 33 66 99
Web Site: http://www.skandia.ch
Life Insurance Products & Services
N.A.I.C.S.: 524113
Armin Holzmuller *(Chm & Pres-Admin Council)*

MUTTER VENTURES, S.A.

C/ Zamora 48 4to 4ta, 08005, Barcelona, Spain
Tel.: (34) 932209595
Web Site: https://www.mutter.me
Year Founded: 2018
MLMUT—(EUR)
Rev.: $22
Assets: $6,529,435
Liabilities: $5,467,091
Net Worth: $1,062,344
Earnings: ($2,611,697)
Emp.: 43
Fiscal Year-end: 12/31/23
Investment Management Service
N.A.I.C.S.: 523999
Christian Rodriguez Fornos *(Chm)*

Subsidiaries:

Saldados, S.L. (1)
Calle Casanova Num 180 Planta LC, 08036, Barcelona, Spain
Tel.: (34) 932717879
Web Site: https://saldados.es
Online Legal Services
N.A.I.C.S.: 541199

MUTTO OPTRONICS CORPORATION

12th Floor No 408 Ruiguang Road, Neihu District, Taipei, 114, Taiwan
Tel.: (886) 227006958
4950—(TPE)
Rev.: $3,611,813
Assets: $13,761,179
Liabilities: $2,527,889
Net Worth: $11,233,291
Earnings: ($6,808,774)
Fiscal Year-end: 12/31/20
Stainless Steel Product Mfr & Distr
N.A.I.C.S.: 331110

MUTUA MADRILENA AUTOMOVILISTA, SOCIEDAD DE SEGUROS A PRIMA FIJA

Paseo de la Castellana 33, 28046, Madrid, Spain

INTERNATIONAL PUBLIC

Tel.: (34) 902 555 555
Web Site: http://www.mutua.es
Insurance Products & Services
N.A.I.C.S.: 524298
Ignacio Garralda Ruiz de Velasco *(Chm)*

MUTUAL BENEFITS ASSURANCE PLC

Aret Adams House 233 Ikorodu Road, Lagos, Nigeria
Tel.: (234) 9054644444
Web Site: https://www.mutualng.com
Year Founded: 1995
MBENEFIT—(NIGE)
Rev.: $24,782,786
Assets: $68,803,540
Liabilities: $52,980,984
Net Worth: $15,822,555
Earnings: $2,325,219
Emp.: 157
Fiscal Year-end: 12/31/22
Life & Property Insurance Services
N.A.I.C.S.: 524298
Akin A. Ogunbiyi *(Chm)*

Subsidiaries:

Mutual Benefits Microfinance Bank Limited (1)
10 Apapa Road Oyingbo West Africa, Lagos, Nigeria
Tel.: (234) 907 029 3251
Web Site:
https://www.mutualbenefitsmfb.ng
Financial Banking Services
N.A.I.C.S.: 522110
Oriola Kazeem *(CEO & Mng Dir)*

MUTUAL CONSTRUCTION

3985 Graveley Street, Burnaby, V5C 3T4, BC, Canada
Tel.: (604) 294-5991
Web Site:
http://www.mutualconst.com
Year Founded: 1950
Rev.: $14,452,183
Emp.: 50
Construction Services
N.A.I.C.S.: 423320
R. M. Dickson *(VP & Gen Mgr)*

MUTUAL CORPORATION

9th Floor Osaka JA Building 1-2-5 Nishitenma, Kita-ku, Osaka, 530-0047, Japan
Tel.: (81) 66 315 8610
Web Site: http://www.mutual.co.jp
Year Founded: 1949
2773—(JAS)
Rev.: $91,166,240
Assets: $162,091,600
Liabilities: $54,082,160
Net Worth: $108,009,440
Earnings: $5,198,160
Emp.: 163
Fiscal Year-end: 03/31/22
Packaging Products Equipment Mfr
N.A.I.C.S.: 333993
Hiroshi Enomoto *(Pres & COO)*

Subsidiaries:

Mutual (Thailand) Co., Ltd. (1)
888/201 Moo 19 Soi Yingcharoen Project 2 Bangplee-Tamru Rd, Bang Phli, 10540, Samutprakarn, Thailand
Tel.: (66) 21747277
Web Site: http://www.mutual-thailand.com
Packaging Machinery Mfr
N.A.I.C.S.: 333993

Mutual Corporation - Kanto Factory (1)
Ro-55-125, Yachimata, 289-1144, Chiba, Japan
Tel.: (81) 43 440 0530
Web Site: http://www.mutual.co.jp
Packaging Machinery Mfr
N.A.I.C.S.: 333993

Wist Co., Ltd. (1)

2-26 3-chome Hikaridai, Seikacho Soraku-gun, Kyoto, 619-0237, Japan
Tel.: (81) 77 498 6767
Web Site: https://www.wist.co.jp
Emp.: 30
Automation Machinery Mfr.
N.A.I.C.S.: 333248

MUTUAL TRANSPORTATION SERVICES INC.
627 Lyons Lane Suite 403, Oakville, L6J 5Z7, ON, Canada
Tel.: (905) 339-3889
Web Site:
    https://www.mutualtransport.com
Year Founded: 1995
Sales Range: $10-24.9 Million
Emp.: 30
Transportation & Logistics Service Provider
N.A.I.C.S.: 484110
Christopher Chapin *(VP)*

MUTUAL TRUST BANK PLC
MTB Centre 26 Gulshan Avenue Plot 5 Block SE D Gulshan 1, Dhaka, 1212, Bangladesh
Tel.: (880) 29846966
Web Site:
    https://www.mutualtrustbank.com
Year Founded: 1999
MTB—(CHT)
Rev.: $45,120,770
Assets: $3,123,523,411
Liabilities: $2,926,193,947
Net Worth: $197,329,464
Earnings: $11,256,496
Emp.: 2,340
Fiscal Year-end: 12/31/20
Banking Services
N.A.I.C.S.: 523150
Md. Wakiluddin *(Co-Chm)*

Subsidiaries:

MTB Capital Limited (1)
Chandrashila Suvastu Tower 69/1 Panthapath, Bangla Motor, Dhaka, 1205, Bangladesh
Tel.: (880) 29641158
Web Site: https://www.mtbcap.com
Portfolio Management Services
N.A.I.C.S.: 523150
Ashadul Islam *(Compliance - Officer & Sec)*

MTB Exchange (UK) Limited (1)
25 Whitechapel, London, E1 1DU, United Kingdom
Tel.: (44) 2086162214
Web Site: https://www.mtbexchangebd.com
Financial Services
N.A.I.C.S.: 523150
Anisur Rahman *(CEO)*

MTB Securities Limited (1)
WW Tower Level 4 68, Motijheel C/A, Dhaka, 1000, Bangladesh
Tel.: (880) 223388163
Web Site: https://www.mtbsecurities.com
Brokerage Services
N.A.I.C.S.: 523150

MUTUAL TRUST PTY LTD.
Level 32 360 Collins Street, Melbourne, 3000, VIC, Australia
Tel.: (61) 3 9605 9500   AU
Web Site:
    http://www.mutualtrust.com.au
Wealth Management & Advisory Services
N.A.I.C.S.: 523999
Gordon Dickinson *(Chm)*

MUTUAL-TEK INDUSTRIES CO., LTD.
No 25 Ln 195 Huacheng Rd, Xinzhuang Dist, New Taipei City, 242, Taiwan
Tel.: (886) 222763210
6407—(TPE)
Rev.: $65,658,260

Assets: $85,910,981
Liabilities: $43,287,614
Net Worth: $42,623,367
Earnings: $933,876
Fiscal Year-end: 12/31/23
Circuit Board Mfr & Distr
N.A.I.C.S.: 334412
Hsu-Tung Chen *(Chm)*

MUTUELLE DES FONCTIONNAIRES DU QUEBEC, CORPORATION DE GESTION
625 rue Saint Amable, Quebec, G1R 2G5, QC, Canada
Tel.: (418) 644-4229
Year Founded: 1941
Rev.: $690,535,000
Emp.: 10
General Insurance Services
N.A.I.C.S.: 524114
Constance Lemieux *(Pres)*

MUVONI TECHNOLOGY GROUP LIMITED
267 West Street, Centurion, 0157, South Africa
Tel.: (27) 126634920   ZA
Web Site: http://www.muvoni.com
Year Founded: 2001
Sales Range: $10-24.9 Million
Automated Fingerprint Identification Services
N.A.I.C.S.: 561611
Vhonani Mufamadi *(Chm)*

MUYUAN FOOD CO., LTD.
Longsheng Industrial Park Wolong District, Neixiang County, Nanyang, 473000, China
Tel.: (86) 4000658989   CN
Web Site:
    https://www.muyuanfoods.com
Year Founded: 1992
002714—(SSE)
Rev.: $17,525,599,884
Assets: $27,089,844,444
Liabilities: $14,724,763,092
Net Worth: $12,365,081,352
Earnings: $1,862,568,864
Emp.: 3,200
Fiscal Year-end: 12/31/22
Pig Breeding, Production & Distr
N.A.I.C.S.: 112210

MUZA S.A.
Ul Sienna 73, 00-833, Warsaw, Poland
Tel.: (48) 226211775
Web Site: https://www.muza.com.pl
MZA—(WAR)
Rev.: $17,383,384
Assets: $16,832,825
Liabilities: $6,562,500
Net Worth: $10,270,325
Earnings: $3,311,484
Fiscal Year-end: 12/31/23
Books Publishing Services
N.A.I.C.S.: 513130
Marcin Garlinski *(Chm-Mgmt Bd)*

MUZALI ARTS LIMITED
3 B-44 Near Manav Mandir Kantol Road Yerla, Nagpur, 441501, Maharashtra, India
Tel.: (91) 8446581165   In
Web Site:
    https://www.muzaliarts.com
Year Founded: 1995
539410—(BOM)
Rev.: $172,604
Assets: $1,713,116
Liabilities: $160,210
Net Worth: $1,552,906
Earnings: ($382,602)
Fiscal Year-end: 03/31/23
Financial Investment Services

N.A.I.C.S.: 523999
Mahesh Jagdevrao Raut *(Mng Dir)*

MUZHU MINING LTD.
Suite 1400 1125 Howe Street, Vancouver, V6Z 2K8, BC, Canada
Tel.: (778) 709-3398   BC
Web Site:
    https://www.muzhumining.ca
Year Founded: 2018
MUZU—(CNSX)
Rev.: $1,200
Assets: $799,937
Liabilities: $152,020
Net Worth: $647,918
Earnings: ($298,956)
Fiscal Year-end: 03/31/24
Mineral Mining Services
N.A.I.C.S.: 213115
Connor Pantaleo *(VP)*

MV AGUSTA S.P.A.
Via Giovanni Macchi 144, 21100, Varese, VA, Italy
Tel.: (39) 0332254443   IT
Web Site: http://www.mvagusta.com
Year Founded: 1907
Sales Range: $300-349.9 Million
Motorcycle Mfr
N.A.I.C.S.: 336991
Claudio Castiglioni *(Pres)*

MV COTSPIN LTD.
Om Tower 32 8th Floor Chowringhee Road, Kolkata, 700071, West Bengal, India
Tel.: (91) 332466780
Web Site: https://mvcotspinltd.com
Year Founded: 1993
Textile Products Distr
N.A.I.C.S.: 424310
Vijaya Kumari *(CFO)*

MVC MOBILE VIDEOCOMMUNICATION GMBH
Campus Kronberg 7, 61476, Kronberg, Germany
Tel.: (49) 6963399100   De
Web Site: https://www.mvc.de
Emp.: 100
Telecommunications contractor
N.A.I.C.S.: 517121

MVISE AG
City Gate 1, 40291, Dusseldorf, Germany
Tel.: (49) 2117817800
Web Site: https://www.mvise.de
C1V—(MUN)
Rev.: $15,454,180
Assets: $9,658,862
Liabilities: $9,647,824
Net Worth: $11,039
Earnings: ($3,775,235)
Emp.: 71
Fiscal Year-end: 12/31/23
Communication Software Publishing Services
N.A.I.C.S.: 513210
Manfred Goetz *(Chm-Mgmt Bd)*

MVL LIMITED
1201-BHemkunt Chamber 89 Nehru Place, Sector-15 II, New Delhi, 110019, Delhi, India
Tel.: (91) 41613145
Web Site: http://www.mvl.in
Year Founded: 1986
Rev.: $21,504
Assets: $80,408,650
Liabilities: $55,093,977
Net Worth: $25,314,673
Earnings: ($3,669,095)
Emp.: 129
Fiscal Year-end: 03/31/18
Real Estate Manangement Services
N.A.I.C.S.: 531390

Prem Adip Rishi *(Chm)*

MVM MAGYAR VILLAMOS MUVEK ZRT.
Szentendrei ut 207-209, 1031, Budapest, Hungary
Tel.: (36) 1 304 2000
Web Site: http://www.mvm.hu
Sales Range: $1-4.9 Billion
Emp.: 1,600
Electricity & Natural Gas Distr
N.A.I.C.S.: 221112
Peter Csiba *(Chm & CEO)*

Subsidiaries:

CEEGEX Ltd. (1)
Devai u 26-28, Devai Center, 1134, Budapest, Hungary
Tel.: (36) 13041090
Web Site: http://www.ceegex.hu
Natural Gas Production & Storage Services
N.A.I.C.S.: 213112
Roland Lajtai *(CEO)*

Energo-Merkur Ltd. (1)
Kesmark utca 14, 1158, Budapest, Hungary
Tel.: (36) 614143152
Web Site: http://www.energo-merkur.hu
Natural Gas Production & Storage Services
N.A.I.C.S.: 213112

MAVIR Hungarian Independent Transmission Operator Company Ltd. (1)
Aniko u 4, 1031, Budapest, Hungary
Tel.: (36) 13041000
Web Site: http://www.mavir.hu
Electric Power Transmission Services
N.A.I.C.S.: 221121
Csomai Kamilla *(CEO)*

MVM BSZK Ltd. (1)
Szentendrei ut 207-209, 1031, Budapest, Hungary
Tel.: (36) 13043105
Natural Gas Production & Storage Services
N.A.I.C.S.: 213112

MVM Erbe Zrt. (1)
Budafoki ut 95, 1117, Budapest, Hungary
Tel.: (36) 1 382 4700
Web Site: http://www.erbe.hu
Engineeering Services
N.A.I.C.S.: 541330

MVM Eszak-Budai Futoeromu Kft. (1)
Kunigunda utja 49, 1037, Budapest, Hungary
Tel.: (36) 1 439 0755
Power Plant
N.A.I.C.S.: 221118

MVM GTER Zrt. (1)
Kinizsi u 26, 2040, Budaors, Hungary
Tel.: (36) 1 304 2424
Web Site: http://www.gter.hu
Power Plant; Electric Power Generation Sevices
N.A.I.C.S.: 221118

MVM Hungarowind Kft. (1)
Szentendrei ut 207-209, 1031, Budapest, Hungary
Tel.: (36) 1 304 23 95
Web Site: http://www.hungarowind.hu
Wind Electric Power Generation
N.A.I.C.S.: 221115

MVM KONTO Zrt. (1)
Pf 152, 7031, Paks, Gagarin u, Hungary
Tel.: (36) 75501701
Financial, Accounting & Payroll Services
N.A.I.C.S.: 541219

MVM MIFU Kft. (1)
Tatar u 29/b, 3531, Miskolc, Hungary
Tel.: (36) 46 501 280
Web Site: http://www.mvm.hu
Power Plant
N.A.I.C.S.: 221118

MVM NET Tavkozlesi Szolgaltato Zrt. (1)
Robert Karoly krt 59, 1134, Budapest, Hungary
Tel.: (36) 1 304 20 00
Web Site: http://www.mvm.hu

MVM MAGYAR VILLAMOS MUVEK ZRT.

MVM Magyar Villamos Muvek Zrt.—(Continued)
Telecommunication Servicesb
N.A.I.C.S.: 517810

MVM OVIT Zrt. (1)
Korvasut sor 105, 1158, Budapest, Hungary
Tel.: (36) 1 414 3200
Web Site: http://www.ovit.hu
Construction, Maintenance & Development of High-Voltage Power Lines & Transformer Stations
N.A.I.C.S.: 237130

MVM Paks II. Zrt. (1)
Gagarin utca 1, 7030, Paks, Hungary
Tel.: (36) 75 501 647
Web Site: http://www.mvm.hu
Power Plant Development
N.A.I.C.S.: 561499

MVM Paksi Atomeromu Zrt. (1)
Pf 71, 7031, Paks, Hungary
Tel.: (36) 75 505 000
Web Site: http://www.atomeromu.hu
Nuclear Power Plant
N.A.I.C.S.: 221113

MVM Partner Zrt. (1)
Szentendrei ut 207-209, 1031, Budapest, Hungary **(100%)**
Tel.: (36) 1 304 2169
Web Site: http://www.mvmp.hu
Electricity & Natural Gas Sales
N.A.I.C.S.: 221122
Gyorgy Major *(CEO)*

MVM VILLKESZ Kft. (1)
Kinizsi u 26, 2400, Budaors, Hungary
Tel.: (36) 23 427 400
Web Site: http://www.villkesz.hu
Maintenance of Property & Property Planning Activities
N.A.I.C.S.: 561499

MVMI Informatika Zrt. (1)
Dozsa Gyorgy u 30-32, 7030, Budapest, Hungary
Tel.: (36) 75 501 941
Web Site: http://www.mvmi-informatika.hu
Information Technology Services
N.A.I.C.S.: 541519

MVMI Information Technologies Service Centre Ltd. (1)
PF 110, 7031, Paks, Hungary
Tel.: (36) 75501941
Web Site: http://www.mvmi-informatika.hu
Information Technology Consulting Services
N.A.I.C.S.: 541512

Magyar Foldgazkereskedo Zrt. (1)
Szechenyi Istvan Ter 7-8, 1051, Budapest, Hungary
Tel.: (36) 1 354 7000
Web Site: http://www.magyarfoldgazkereskedo.hu
Rev.: $3,564,449
Emp.: 50
Natural Gas Wholesale & Open Market Trade
N.A.I.C.S.: 221210
Gyorgy Harmati *(Chm-Supervisory Bd)*

Magyar Foldgaztarolo Zrt (1)
Vaci ut 144-150, 1138, Budapest, Hungary
Tel.: (36) 13547050
Web Site: http://www.magyarfoldgaztarolo.hu
Rev.: $194,592
Emp.: 20
Natural Gas Production & Storage Services
N.A.I.C.S.: 213112
Laszlo Zoltan Fritsch *(Member-Mgmt Bd)*

PANRUSGAS Gas Trading Plc. (1)
Alkotas u 50, 1123, Budapest, Hungary
Tel.: (36) 14894500
Web Site: http://www.panrusgaz.hu
Natural Gas Production & Storage Services
N.A.I.C.S.: 213112
Ilona Tabori *(Dir-Fin)*

Vertesi Eromu Zrt. (1)
PO Box 23, 2841, Oroszlany, Hungary
Tel.: (36) 34 360 255
Web Site: http://www.vert.hu
Emp.: 1,000
Power Plant
N.A.I.C.S.: 221118

MVP CAPITAL CO. LTD.

3rd Fl Aahn Lap Blldg 220 Pangyoyeok-Ro, Bundang-Gu, Seongnam, 463-400, Korea (South)
Tel.: (82) 3180179620
Web Site: http://www.mvpc.co.kr
Year Founded: 2000
Sales Range: $50-74.9 Million
Emp.: 15
Venture Capital Services
N.A.I.C.S.: 523910
Nam Ki-Mun *(CEO)*

MVV ENERGIE AG

Luisenring 49, 68159, Mannheim, Germany
Tel.: (49) 6212900 De
Web Site: https://www.mvv.de
MVV1—(MUN)
Rev.: $7,488,411,229
Assets: $10,545,799,968
Liabilities: $8,166,639,995
Net Worth: $2,379,159,972
Earnings: $1,153,665,576
Emp.: 6,260
Fiscal Year-end: 09/30/23
Energy District Heating & Water Supplier
N.A.I.C.S.: 221330
Peter Kurz *(Chm-Supervisory Bd)*

Subsidiaries:

BEEGY GmbH (1)
Katharina-Paulus-Strasse 6 B, 65824, Schwalbach am Taunus, Germany
Tel.: (49) 62140188188
Web Site: https://www.beegy.com
Renewable Energy Services
N.A.I.C.S.: 221114
Carsten Bruns *(Mng Dir)*

BFE Institut fur Energie und Umwelt GmbH. (1)
Rotwiesen 20, 69242, Muhlhausen, Germany
Tel.: (49) 62229550
Web Site: http://www.bfe-institut.com
Sales Range: $25-49.9 Million
Emp.: 100
Energy Consulting & Waste Disposal Services
N.A.I.C.S.: 541690
Matthias Dreja *(Mng Dir)*

Biokraft Naturbrennstoffe GmbH. (1)
Andrestrasse 71, 63067, Offenbach, Germany
Tel.: (49) 6980600
Web Site: http://www.biokraftgmbh.de
Wood Chips & Pellets Processing Services
N.A.I.C.S.: 113310

Biomassen-Heizkraftwerk Altenstadt GmbH. (1)
Triebstr 90, 86972, Altenstadt, Bavaria, Germany
Tel.: (49) 8861 23540
Electric Power Distribution Services
N.A.I.C.S.: 221122

Blue Village Franklin Mobil GmbH (1)
Luisenring 49, 68159, Mannheim, Germany
Tel.: (49) 6212901559
Web Site: https://www.franklin-mobil.de
Car Sharing Services
N.A.I.C.S.: 532111
Oliver Lennertz *(Mng Dir)*

CTZ s.r.o. (1)
Sokolovska 572, 686 01, Uherske Hradiste, Czech Republic
Tel.: (420) 572552917
Electricity Production & Distribution Services
N.A.I.C.S.: 221122

Ceskolipska teplarenska a.s. (1)
Liberecka 132, 470 01, Ceska Lipa, Czech Republic
Tel.: (420) 487805901
Emp.: 28
Hot Water Production & Distribution Services
N.A.I.C.S.: 221310

EnDaNet GmbH (1)
Magdeburger Allee 34, 99086, Erfurt, Germany
Web Site: http://www.endanet.com
Network Operator Services
N.A.I.C.S.: 517121

Energienetze Offenbach GmbH (1)
Andrestrasse 71, 63067, Offenbach, Germany
Tel.: (49) 698060111
Web Site: http://www.energienetze-offenbach.de
Energy Distribution Services
N.A.I.C.S.: 221122

G-Ronn S.R.O. (1)
Kacirkova 982/4, 158 00, Prague, Czech Republic
Electricity Production & Distribution Services
N.A.I.C.S.: 221122

IGS Netze GmbH (1)
Ludwig-Hermann-Str 100, 86368, Gersthofen, Germany
Tel.: (49) 8214792568
Web Site: http://www.igs-netze.de
Power Distribution Services
N.A.I.C.S.: 221122

Industriepark Gersthofen Servicegesellschaft mbH. (1)
Ludwig-Hermann-Str 100, 86368, Gersthofen, Germany
Tel.: (49) 8214790
Sales Range: $150-199.9 Million
Emp.: 145
Power Supply & Waste Management Services
N.A.I.C.S.: 221122
Holger Amberg *(Mng Dir)*

Kothen Energie GmbH. (1)
Lelitzer Strasse 27 b, 06366, Kothen, Germany
Tel.: (49) 349650550
Web Site: http://www.koethenergie.de
Sales Range: $75-99.9 Million
Emp.: 24
Gas Supply & Transportation Services
N.A.I.C.S.: 221210

Subsidiary (Domestic):

Kothen Energie Netz GmbH. (2)
Lelitzer Strasse 27 b, 06366, Kothen, Germany
Tel.: (49) 3496505515
Web Site: http://www.netzgesellschaft-koethen.de
Sales Range: $25-49.9 Million
Emp.: 10
Natural Gas Transportation Services
N.A.I.C.S.: 486210
Patrick Wrobel *(Mng Dir)*

MDW Muldendienst West GmbH (1)
Intzestrasse 24, 60314, Frankfurt am Main, Germany
Tel.: (49) 692443620
Web Site: https://www.muldendienst-west.de
Waste Management Services
N.A.I.C.S.: 562998

MVV BioPower GmbH. (1)
Am Nordhafen 12, 15711, Konigs Wusterhausen, Brandenburg, Germany
Tel.: (49) 3375219910
Sales Range: $50-74.9 Million
Emp.: 27
Eletric Power Generation Services
N.A.I.C.S.: 221111

MVV Enamic GmbH. (1)
Luisenring 49, 68159, Mannheim, Germany
Tel.: (49) 6212903388
Web Site: https://www.mvv.de
Eletric Power Generation Services
N.A.I.C.S.: 221118
Dirk Ebert *(Mng Dir)*

Subsidiary (Domestic):

DC-Datacenter-Group GmbH (2)
In der Aue 2, Wallmenroth, 57584, Altenkirchen, Germany
Tel.: (49) 274193210
Web Site: https://datacenter-group.com
Emp.: 200
IT Planning & Consulting Services

INTERNATIONAL PUBLIC

N.A.I.C.S.: 541611
Frank Ernst *(Mng Dir)*

MVV Enamic Regioplan GmbH (1)
Besselstrasse 14/16, 68219, Mannheim, Germany
Tel.: (49) 621876750
Sales Range: $25-49.9 Million
Emp.: 25
Construction Management Services
N.A.I.C.S.: 237310
Markus Prien *(Mng Dir)*

MVV Energiedienstleistungen GmbH (1)
Luisenring 49, 68159, Mannheim, Germany
Tel.: (49) 6212903388
Sales Range: $200-249.9 Million
Emp.: 870
Infrastrcuture Management Services
N.A.I.C.S.: 237990

MVV Energiedienstleistungen GmbH IK Korbach (1)
Limmerstrasse 2, 34497, Korbach, Germany
Tel.: (49) 56315069710
Eletric Power Generation Services
N.A.I.C.S.: 221118

MVV Environment Devonport Limited (1)
Creek Road, Plymouth, PL5 1FL, United Kingdom
Tel.: (44) 752393150
Waste Energy Generation Services
N.A.I.C.S.: 221117
Colin James *(Ops Mgr)*

MVV Environment Ridham Limited (1)
Ridham Dock Biomass Facility Lord Nelson Road, Iwade, Sittingbourne, ME9 8FQ, United Kingdom
Tel.: (44) 1795342212
Electric Power Distribution Services
N.A.I.C.S.: 221122
Paul Carey *(Mng Dir)*

MVV ImmoSolutions GmbH (1)
Salzufer 8, 10587, Berlin, Germany **(100%)**
Tel.: (49) 3025597 100
Web Site: http://www.mvv-ed.de
Energy Consulting Services
N.A.I.C.S.: 541690

MVV Industriepark Gersthofen GmbH (1)
Ludwig-Hermann-Str 100, 86368, Gersthofen, Germany
Tel.: (49) 8214790
Web Site: https://www.mvv.de
Energy Distribution Services
N.A.I.C.S.: 221122

MVV Insurance Services GmbH (1)
Luisenring 49, 68159, Mannheim, Germany
Tel.: (49) 6212900
Web Site: https://www.mvv.de
Insurance Agency Services
N.A.I.C.S.: 524210
Martin Auer *(Mng Dir)*

MVV Netze GmbH (1)
Luisenring 49, 68159, Mannheim, Germany
Tel.: (49) 6212902121
Web Site: https://www.mvv-netze.de
Emp.: 500
Energy Supply Services
N.A.I.C.S.: 221122
Volker Glatzer *(Mng Dir)*

MVV Trading GmbH (1)
Luisenring 49, 68159, Mannheim, Germany **(92.5%)**
Tel.: (49) 6212900
Electric Power Distribution Services
N.A.I.C.S.: 221122
Thies Langmaack *(Mng Dir)*

MVV Umwelt GmbH (1)
Otto-Hahn-Strasse 1, 68169, Mannheim, Germany **(100%)**
Tel.: (49) 6212904601
Sales Range: $125-149.9 Million
Emp.: 200
Eletric Power Generation Services
N.A.I.C.S.: 221118
Martin Becker-Rethmann *(Mng Dir)*

AND PRIVATE COMPANIES

Subsidiary (Domestic):

MVV Umwelt Ressourcen GmbH (2)
Otto-Hahn-Strasse 1, 68169, Mannheim, Germany
Tel.: (49) 6212904601
Web Site: https://www.mvv.de
Sales Range: $75-99.9 Million
Emp.: 45
Environmental Consulting Services
N.A.I.C.S.: 541620
Christian Hower-Knobloch *(Mng Dir)*

MVV Windenergie GmbH (1)
Luisenring 49, 68159, Mannheim, 68159, Germany
Tel.: (49) 6212900
Wind Electric Power Generation
N.A.I.C.S.: 221115
Bjorn Wenzlaff *(Mng Dir)*

Subsidiary (Domestic):

Iberdrola Renovables Deutschland GmbH (2)
Charlottenstrasse 63, Berlin, 10117, Germany
Tel.: (49) 30 76767320
Web Site: http://www.iberdrola.es
Emp.: 14
Eletric Power Generation Services
N.A.I.C.S.: 221118
Juergen Blume *(Gen Mgr)*

MVV decon GmbH. (1)
Augustaanlage 62-64, 68165, Mannheim, Germany
Tel.: (49) 6214329870
Web Site: http://www.mvv-decon.com
Energy Consulting Services
N.A.I.C.S.: 541690

Monarch Solar LLC (1)
4336 Waccamaw Blvd, Myrtle Beach, SC 29579
Tel.: (843) 817-6527
Web Site: http://www.monarchsolarenergy.com
Solar Panels Installation Services
N.A.I.C.S.: 238210
Fahyre Panhuis *(Dir-Ops)*

Netrion GmbH (1)
Luisenring 49, 68159, Mannheim, Germany
Tel.: (49) 6212902121
Web Site: http://www.netrion.de
Emp.: 120
Electric Power Distribution Services
N.A.I.C.S.: 221122
Volker Glatzer *(Mng Dir)*

Netzgesellschaft Kothen mbH (1)
Lelitzer Strasse 27b, 06366, Kothen, Germany
Tel.: (49) 3496505577
Web Site: https://www.netzgesellschaft-koethen.de
Natural Gas Distr
N.A.I.C.S.: 221210

RZ-Products GmbH (1)
In der Aue 2, Wallmenroth, 57584, Altenkirchen, Germany
Tel.: (49) 274193210
Web Site: https://datacenter-products.com
IT Security Product Mfr
N.A.I.C.S.: 334290
Ralf Siefen *(Mng Dir)*

Regioplan Ingenieure Salzburg GmbH. (1)
Siezenheimer Strasse 39A, 5020, Salzburg, Austria
Tel.: (43) 6624516220
Web Site: http://www.regioplan.org
Sales Range: $25-49.9 Million
Emp.: 7
Landscape Designing Services
N.A.I.C.S.: 541320

SWKiel Speicher GmbH (1)
Uhlenkrog 32, 24113, Kiel, Germany
Tel.: (49) 4315942160
Web Site: https://www.swkiel-speicher.de
Gas Storage Services
N.A.I.C.S.: 237120

Soluvia Billing GmbH (1)
Andrestr 71, 63067, Offenbach, Hesse, Germany
Tel.: (49) 69 86605 0
Web Site: http://www.soluvia-billing.de
Sales Range: $25-49.9 Million
Emp.: 20
Utility Billing & Customer Care Services
N.A.I.C.S.: 541219
Dietmar Sperfeld *(Mng Dir)*

Soluvia Energy Services GmbH (1)
Andrestr 71, 63067, Offenbach, Germany
Tel.: (49) 6980602701
Web Site: http://www.soluvia-energy-services.de
Energy Metering Services
N.A.I.C.S.: 221122

Soluvia IT-Services GmbH (1)
Uhlenkrog 32, 24113, Kiel, Germany
Tel.: (49) 4315942233
Web Site: https://www.soluvia-it-services.de
Emp.: 190
IT Consulting Services
N.A.I.C.S.: 541618

Soluvia Metering GmbH (1)
Andrestrasse 71, 63067, Offenbach, Germany
Tel.: (49) 6980602101
Web Site: http://www.soluvia-metering.de
Sales Range: $25-49.9 Million
Emp.: 65
Utility Metering Services
N.A.I.C.S.: 561990
Gerald Hornfeck *(Mng Dir)*

Stadtwerke Kiel Aktiengesellschaft (1)
Uhlenkrog 32, 24113, Kiel, Germany (51%)
Tel.: (49) 43198793000
Web Site: https://www.stadtwerke-kiel.de
Sales Range: $550-599.9 Million
Emp.: 950
Electricity, Gas & Water Utility Administration Services
N.A.I.C.S.: 926130
Wolfgang Podolske *(Dir-Comm)*

Subsidiary (Domestic):

SWKiel Netz GmbH (2)
Uhlenkrog 32, 24113, Kiel, Germany
Tel.: (49) 431 5943410
Web Site: https://www.swkiel-netz.de
Electricity & Gas & Water Distribution Systems Operation & Maintenance Services
N.A.I.C.S.: 221122

SWKiel Service GmbH (2)
Knooper Weg 75, 24116, Kiel, Germany
Tel.: (49) 431594010
Web Site: http://www.stadtwerke-kiel.de
Sales Range: $150-199.9 Million
Emp.: 1,000
Electrical Engineering Services
N.A.I.C.S.: 541330

Termizo A.S. (1)
Dr M Horakove 571/56, 460 07, Liberec, 7, Czech Republic
Tel.: (420) 482428671
Web Site: https://tmz.enetiqa.cz
Environmental Consulting Services
N.A.I.C.S.: 541620
Pavel Bernat *(Co-Chm)*

Termo Decin A.S. (1)
Obloukova 958/25, 405 02, Decin, Czech Republic
Tel.: (420) 412552440
Web Site: https://ted.enetiqa.cz
Thermal Energy Distribution Services
N.A.I.C.S.: 221122

Windpark Kirchberg GmbH & Co. KG (1)
Fichtenstrasse 1, 74592, Kirchberg, Germany
Tel.: (49) 79549269022
Web Site: http://www.windpark-kirchberg.de
Renewable Energy Services
N.A.I.C.S.: 221114

Windwarts Energie GmbH (1)
Hanomaghof 1, 30449, Hannover, Germany
Tel.: (49) 5111235730
Web Site: http://www.windwaerts.de
Power Generation Services
N.A.I.C.S.: 221118

econ solutions GmbH (1)
Franz-Josef-Delonge-Str 12, 81249, Munich, Germany
Tel.: (49) 6212905200
Web Site: https://www.econ-solutions.de
Software Development Services
N.A.I.C.S.: 541511

juwi AG (1)
Energie-Allee 1, 55286, Worrstadt, Germany (63%)
Tel.: (49) 673296570
Web Site: https://www.juwi.de
Renewable Power Supply Facilities Mfr
N.A.I.C.S.: 335311
Fred Jung *(Co-Founder)*

Subsidiary (Non-US):

juwi Energia Odnawialna Sp. z o.o. (2)
ul Opolska 100, 31 223, Krakow, Poland
Tel.: (48) 12 29 988 00
Renewable Power Supply Facilities Mfr
N.A.I.C.S.: 335311

juwi Energias Renovables - Centro America y el Caribe, Ltda. (2)
Edificio Torres del Parque Piso N 3, Sabana Norte, San Jose, Costa Rica
Tel.: (506) 2290 9310
Renewable Power Supply Facilities Mfr
N.A.I.C.S.: 335311

juwi Energias Renovables de Chile Ltda. (2)
Avenida Vitacura No 2808 Ofic 801, Santiago, Chile
Tel.: (56) 22 912 3700
Renewable Power Supply Facilities Mfr
N.A.I.C.S.: 335311

juwi Energias Renovables, S.L.U (2)
Moro Zeit no 11 3 5, 46001, Valencia, Spain
Tel.: (34) 96 338 29 67
Renewable Power Supply Facilities Mfr
N.A.I.C.S.: 335311

juwi Energie Rinnovabili Srl (2)
Via Sommacampagna 59/D, 37137, Verona, Italy
Tel.: (39) 0458626355
Web Site: https://www.juwi.com
Renewable Power Supply Facilities Mfr
N.A.I.C.S.: 335311

juwi Hellas A.E. (2)
24 Vouliagmenis Avenue, 167 77, Elliniko, Greece
Tel.: (30) 2109638570
Emp.: 12
Renewable Power Supply Facilities Mfr
N.A.I.C.S.: 335311
Harris Panagiotis *(Mng Dir)*

juwi India Renewable Energies Pvt Ltd (2)
No 2 Yashika 3rd Floor 100 Feet Road, MCHS Jakkur Layout Ward No 7 Jakkur, Bengaluru, 560064, India
Tel.: (91) 8029535093
Web Site: https://www.juwi.in
Renewable Power Supply Facilities Mfr
N.A.I.C.S.: 335311

juwi O&M GmbH (2)
84 quai de la Fosse, 44100, Nantes, France
Tel.: (33) 228449204
Web Site: http://www.juwi.fr
Plant Instrument & Equipment Installation Services
N.A.I.C.S.: 237130

juwi Philippines, Inc. (2)
Regus One E-Com 4/F Unit 2C Ocean Drive Mall of Asia Complex, Pasay City, Manila, 1300, Philippines
Tel.: (63) 287379508
Web Site: https://www.juwi.com
Renewable Power Supply Facilities Mfr
N.A.I.C.S.: 335311

juwi Renewable Energies (Pty) Ltd (2)
20th Floor The Halyard 4 Christiaan Barnard Street, Foreshore, Cape Town, 8001, South Africa
Tel.: (27) 218316100
Web Site: https://www.juwi.co.za
Renewable Power Supply Facilities Mfr

N.A.I.C.S.: 335311

juwi Renewable Energies Limited (2)
Nelson House Blythe Valley Park, Solihull, B90 8BG, United Kingdom
Tel.: (44) 1217331119
Renewable Power Supply Facilities Mfr
N.A.I.C.S.: 335311

juwi Renewable Energies Private Limited (2)
320 Serangoon Road Centrium Square 12-04, 152 Beach Road, Singapore, 218108, Singapore
Tel.: (65) 65169820
Web Site: https://www.juwi.com
Renewable Power Supply Facilities Mfr
N.A.I.C.S.: 335311

juwi Renewable Energies Thai Co., Ltd (2)
399 Interchange21 Tower 32 33 Floor Room TT03 Sukhumvit Road, Khlong Toei Nuea Watthana, Bangkok, 10110, Thailand
Tel.: (66) 26603806
Web Site: https://www.juwi.com
Renewable Power Supply Facilities Mfr
N.A.I.C.S.: 335311

juwi Renewable Energy Pty (2)
Level 3 199 George Street, Brisbane, 4000, QLD, Australia
Tel.: (61) 731070908
Web Site: https://www.juwi.com.au
Renewable Power Supply Facilities Mfr
N.A.I.C.S.: 335311

juwi Shizen Energy Inc. (2)
Ichigo Hongo Bldg 3F 5-33-10, Hongo Bunkyo Ward, Tokyo, 113-0033, Japan
Tel.: (81) 356845404
Web Site: https://www.juwi.com
Renewable Power Supply Facilities Mfr
N.A.I.C.S.: 335311

Subsidiary (US):

juwi Wind, LLC (2)
1710 29th St Unit 1068, Boulder, CO 80301
Tel.: (303) 953-5180
Renewable Power Supply Facilities Mfr
N.A.I.C.S.: 335311

Subsidiary (Non-US):

juwi Yenilenebilir Enerji A.S (2)
Ilkbahar Mahallesi Galip Erdem Caddesi 621, No: 17 Oran, Cankaya, Turkiye
Tel.: (90) 3922235279.
Renewable Power Supply Facilities Mfr
N.A.I.C.S.: 335311

Subsidiary (Domestic):

juwi renewable IPP Beteiligungs GmbH (2)
Energie-Allee 1, 55286, Worrstadt, Germany
Tel.: (49) 673296571705
Solar Equipment Mfr
N.A.I.C.S.: 333414

Subsidiary (Non-US):

juwi s.r.o. (2)
Mydlarska 105/10, 460 10, Prague, Czech Republic
Tel.: (420) 482 427 016
Renewable Power Supply Facilities Mfr
N.A.I.C.S.: 335311

Subsidiary (US):

juwi solar Inc. (2)
1710 29th St Ste 1068, Boulder, CO 80301
Tel.: (303) 440-7430
Web Site: http://www.juwiamericas.com
Solar Power Plant Contract Services
N.A.I.C.S.: 221114
John Tembrock *(VP)*

mobiheat Osterreich GmbH (1)
Irrsberg 97, Sankt Lorenz, 5310, Mondsee, Austria
Tel.: (43) 6641547781
Web Site: http://www.mobiheat.at
Heating Services
N.A.I.C.S.: 238220

mobiheat Schweiz GmbH (1)

MVV ENERGIE AG

MVV Energie AG—(Continued)
Brandbachstrasse 10, 8305, Dietlikon, Switzerland
Tel.: (41) 448001616
Web Site: http://www.mobiheat-schweiz.ch
Radiator Repair Services
N.A.I.C.S.: 811114

reginova GmbH. (1)
Ringlerstrasse 28, 85057, Ingolstadt, Germany
Tel.: (49) 841804411
Web Site: http://www.reginova.de
Sales Range: $75-99.9 Million
Emp.: 4
Heating Systems Building & Installation Services
N.A.I.C.S.: 221330

MWALIMU COOPERATIVE SAVINGS & CREDIT SOCIETY LIMITED

Mwalimu Co-operative Hse, Tom Mboya Street, 00200, Nairobi, Kenya
Tel.: (254) 733 333 454
Web Site:
  http://www.mwalimusacco.coop
Banking Services
N.A.I.C.S.: 522180
Robert Shibutse (CEO)

Subsidiaries:

Equatorial Commercial Bank Limited (1)
Equatorial Fidelity Centre Waiyaki Way Opposite New Safaricom Hse, PO Box 52467, 200, Nairobi, Kenya
Tel.: (254) 20 4981000
Web Site: http://www.equatorialbank.co.ke
Commercial Banking Services
N.A.I.C.S.: 522110
Dan Ameyo (Chm)

MWB FAIRTRADE WERTPAPIERHANDELSBANK AG

Rottenbucher Strabe 28, 82166, Grafelfing, Germany
Tel.: (49) 89858520   De
Web Site:
  https://www.mwbfairtrade.com
Year Founded: 1993
MWB0—(BER)
Assets: $57,489,789
Liabilities: $36,902,528
Net Worth: $20,587,261
Earnings: ($518,821)
Emp.: 69
Fiscal Year-end: 12/31/23
Security Banking Services
N.A.I.C.S.: 523999
Michael Wilhelm (Chm-Supervisory Bd)

Subsidiaries:

MWB Wertpapierhandelsbank AG (1)
Rottenbucher Strasse 28, 82166, Grafelfing, Germany
Tel.: (49) 89858520
Web Site: http://www.mwbfairtrade.com
Sales Range: $50-74.9 Million
Emp.: 28
Banking Services
N.A.I.C.S.: 522110

MWE HOLDINGS BERHAD

30 02 30th Floor Menara Multi-Purpose Capital Square, No 8 Jalan Munshi Abdullah, 50100, Kuala Lumpur, Malaysia
Tel.: (60) 32 698 3232
Web Site: http://www.mweh.com.my
Rev.: $81,474,155
Assets: $202,133,272
Liabilities: $53,455,748
Net Worth: $148,677,525
Earnings: ($20,887,292)
Fiscal Year-end: 03/31/18
Investment Holding Company

N.A.I.C.S.: 551112
King Hua Tang (Mng Dir)

Subsidiaries:

Davex Holdings Berhad (1)
Plot 32 Lorong Perusahaan Maju 8 Bukit Tengah Industrial Park, 136000, Prai, Penang, Malaysia
Tel.: (60) 40 5070 517
Web Site: http://www.davislighting.com
Holding Company; Lighting Mfr & Distr
N.A.I.C.S.: 551112

Subsidiary (Non-US):

Daviscomms (S) Pte. Ltd. (2)
Block 70 Ubi Crescent 01-07 Ubi Techpark, Singapore, 408570, Singapore (68%)
Tel.: (65) 65471127
Web Site: http://www.daviscomms.com.sg
Wireless Communication Product Mfr
N.A.I.C.S.: 334220
T. K. Liew (Sr Mgr-Pur)

Subsidiary (Non-US):

Daviscomms (Malaysia) Sdn. Bhd. (3)
Plot 18 Lorong Perusahaan Maju 1 Kawasan Perusahaan Perai 4, 13600, Perai, Penang, Malaysia (100%)
Tel.: (60) 265471127
Web Site: http://www.daviscomms.com.sg
Sales Range: $25-49.9 Million
Wireless Communication Products Design & Mfr
N.A.I.C.S.: 334220

Dongfeng Commercial Vehicle (Malaysia) Sdn Bhd (1)
Lot 11, Jalan Perusahaan 2 Kawasan Perusahaan PkNS, Batu Caves, 68000, Selangor Darul Ehsan, Malaysia (53%)
Tel.: (60) 361878000
Web Site: http://www.dongfeng.my
Truck Assembling & Distribution
N.A.I.C.S.: 336120
Lim Khoon Yee (Mng Dir)

MWE Golf & Country Club Berhad (1)
No 1 Valan Merah Kesumba U9/18 Seksyen U9, 40000, Shah Alam, Malaysia
Tel.: (60) 3 7846 5989
Web Site: http://www.monterez-golf.com
Golf & Country Club Resort
N.A.I.C.S.: 713910
Chow Chee Keong (Gen Mgr)

MWE Properties Sdn Bhd (1)
1st Floor ClubHouse City Gardens Condominium, Letter Box 12M, Persiaran Raja Chulan, Kuala Lumpur, 50200, Malaysia
Tel.: (60) 320266037
Web Site: http://www.mwep.com
Property Development Services
N.A.I.C.S.: 531390

Subsidiary (Domestic):

MWE Advanced Structure Sdn Bhd (2)
No 1 Jalan Merah Kesumba U9/18 Seksyen U9, Shah Alam, 40000, Selangor, Malaysia
Tel.: (60) 378466766
Building Construction Services
N.A.I.C.S.: 236210

United Sweethearts Garment Sdn Bhd (1)
846 Jalan ray 14298 Sungei Bakap Seberang Perai Selatan, Penang, Malaysia (100%)
Tel.: (60) 4 585 8188
Web Site: http://www.mweusg.com
Textile Mfr & Distr
N.A.I.C.S.: 313210
Suat Bee Goh (Gen Mgr)

MWO

29 Foral St, The Carriage Hall, London, WC2E 9TD, United Kingdom
Tel.: (44) 20 7379 8844
Rev.: $18,607,260
Emp.: 25
Advertising, Broadcast, Communications, Digital/Interactive, Outdoor, Print

N.A.I.C.S.: 541810
Adrian Kemsley (Creative Dir)

MWS INDUSTRIEHOLDING GMBH

Egerbach 48, Kufstein, 6334, Schwoich, Austria
Tel.: (43) 5372 5300 0   AT
Web Site: http://www.mws.eu
Year Founded: 2004
Sales Range: $150-199.9 Million
Emp.: 300
Holding Company; Aluminum Casting & CNC Machining
N.A.I.C.S.: 551112
Detlef Buchmann (Mng Partner-Tech Austria & Slovakia)

Subsidiaries:

MWS Alugauss GmbH (1)
Ebentaler Strasse 137, 9020, Klagenfurt, Austria
Tel.: (43) 463333230
Web Site: http://www.mws-aluguss.eu
Emp.: 40
Aluminum Casting Mfr
N.A.I.C.S.: 331523
Detlef Buchmann (Mng Dir)

Plant (Domestic):

MWS Aluguss GmbH - Klagenfurt Plant (2)
Ebentaler Strasse 137, Klagenfurt, 9020, Austria
Tel.: (43) 463 33323 0
Web Site: http://www.mws-aluguss.at
Sales Range: $25-49.9 Million
Aluminum Casting Mfr
N.A.I.C.S.: 331523
Franz Matschnigg (Gen Mgr)

MWS Casting s.r.o. (1)
Priemyselna 908, SK-966 01, Hlinik nad Hronom, Slovakia (100%)
Tel.: (421) 45 678 9020
Web Site: http://www.mws-casting.sk
Aluminum Casting Mfr
N.A.I.C.S.: 331523
Uran Skopec (Gen Mgr)

MWS Friedrichshafen GmbH (1)
Colsmanstrasse 25, Friedrichshafen, 88045, Germany
Tel.: (49) 7541 7002 0
Web Site: http://www.mws.eu
Sales Range: $50-74.9 Million
Emp.: 250
Aluminum Casting Mfr
N.A.I.C.S.: 331523
Christoph Senft (Mng Dir)

MWS Garching GmbH (1)
Zeppelinstrasse 22, Garching, 85748, Germany
Tel.: (49) 89 329 094 0
Sales Range: $50-74.9 Million
Emp.: 250
Aluminum Casting Mfr
N.A.I.C.S.: 331523
Christoph Senft (Co-Mng Dir)

MWS Hightec GmbH (1)
Merkurstrasse 8, 4452, Ternberg, Austria
Tel.: (43) 7256 6054 0
Web Site: http://www.mws.eu
Emp.: 60
Aluminum Casting & Machining
N.A.I.C.S.: 331523
Detlef Buchmann (Gen Mgr)

MWUK HOLDING COMPANY LIMITED

3 Long Acre, Willow Farm Business Park, Castle Donington, DE74 2UG, Derbyshire, United Kingdom
Tel.: (44) 1332856800
Web Site:
  http://www.dimensions.co.uk
Emp.: 200
Investment Management Service
N.A.I.C.S.: 551112

INTERNATIONAL PUBLIC

Subsidiaries:

MWUK Limited (1)
3 Long Acre Willow Farm Business Park, Derby, Castle Donington, DE74 2UG, United Kingdom
Tel.: (44) 1332856800
Web Site: http://www.dimensions.co.uk
Work Wear & Personal Protective Equipment Mfr & Distr
N.A.I.C.S.: 315250
Stuart Graham (Chm)

Subsidiary (Domestic):

Work Uniforms Direct Limited (2)
12A Balloo Avenue, County Down, Bangor, BT19 7QT, United Kingdom
Tel.: (44) 8454631018
Web Site:
  http://www.workuniformsdirect.com
Women Work Wear Mfr & Distr
N.A.I.C.S.: 315250

MX GOLD CORP.

900-570 Granville Street, Vancouver, V6C 3P1, BC, Canada
Tel.: (604) 808-1706   BC
Year Founded: 1999
MXL—(OTCIQ)
Assets: $77,373
Liabilities: $1,099,227
Net Worth: ($1,021,854)
Earnings: ($819,236)
Fiscal Year-end: 12/31/19
Gold & Other Metal Mining Services
N.A.I.C.S.: 212290
Dan Omeniuk (CEO & CFO)

MXC CAPITAL LIMITED

25 Victoria Street, London, SW1H 0EX, United Kingdom
Tel.: (44) 207 965 8149   UK
Web Site: http://www.mxccapital.com
Year Founded: 2009
Rev.: $1,394,990
Assets: $89,501,970
Liabilities: $3,233,841
Net Worth: $86,268,129
Earnings: ($10,196,649)
Emp.: 10
Fiscal Year-end: 08/31/18
Investment & Advisory Services
N.A.I.C.S.: 551112
Ian Smith (Co-Founder & CEO)

MXP PARTNERS LLP

80 Victoria Street, London, SW1E 5JL, United Kingdom
Tel.: (44) 2031956527   UK
Web Site: http://www.maxcap-partners.com
Year Founded: 2006
Private Equity Services
N.A.I.C.S.: 523999
Michael George (Founder)

Subsidiaries:

Amber Taverns Limited (1)
The Victory Offices 112 Victory Road, Blackpool, FY1 3NW, United Kingdom
Tel.: (44) 1253 757158
Web Site: http://www.ambertaverns.co.uk
Sales Range: $25-49.9 Million
Emp.: 25
Pub Operator
N.A.I.C.S.: 722410
Clive Preston (Founder)

MY AGENCY

131-151 Great Titchfield St, London, W1W 5BB, United Kingdom
Tel.: (44) 02073366691
Web Site:
  http://www.myagencyuk.com
Sales Range: $10-24.9 Million
Emp.: 12
N.A.I.C.S.: 541810
Nick Wright (Mng Partner)

AND PRIVATE COMPANIES

MY CHAU PRINTING & PACKAGING HOLDINGS COMPANY
18 Luy Ban Bich St Tan Thoi Hoa Ward, Tan Phu, Ho Chi Minh City, Vietnam
Tel.: (84) 2839611587
Web Site: https://mychau.com.vn
Year Founded: 1957
MCP—(HOSE)
Rev.: $20,304,761
Assets: $13,146,302
Liabilities: $2,914,570
Net Worth: $10,231,732
Earnings: $718,610
Emp.: 1,000
Fiscal Year-end: 12/31/23
Holding Company
N.A.I.C.S.: 551112

MY E.G. SERVICES BERHAD
Level 43A MYEG Tower No 8 Jalan Damansara, Empire City PJU 8, 47820, Petaling Jaya, Selangor, Malaysia
Tel.: (60) 376648000
Web Site: https://www.myeg.com.my
MYEG—(KLS)
Rev.: $131,289,593
Assets: $350,641,913
Liabilities: $67,793,220
Net Worth: $282,848,693
Earnings: $66,130,515
Emp.: 2,482
Fiscal Year-end: 12/31/20
Software Solutions & Maintenance Services
N.A.I.C.S.: 541511
Thean Soon Wong *(Mng Dir)*

Subsidiaries:

Beli Mart Sdn. Bhd. (1)
Level 6 Myeg Tower Empire City, Jalan Damansara PJU 8, 47820, Petaling Jaya, Selangor, Malaysia
Tel.: (60) 172200810
Web Site: https://www.beli.com.my
Grocery Product Distr
N.A.I.C.S.: 445110

Buy Now Asia Sdn. Bhd. (1)
Unit A-5-3 Block A Jaya One No 72A Jalan Universiti, 46200, Petaling Jaya, Selangor, Malaysia
Tel.: (60) 379548166
Web Site: https://www.buynowasia.com
Online Shopping Services
N.A.I.C.S.: 513210

MY E.G. Capital Sdn. Bhd. (1)
Level 43A MYEG Tower No 8 Jalan Damansara Empire City PJU 8, 47820, Petaling Jaya, Selangor, Malaysia
Tel.: (60) 376648000
Web Site: https://www.myeg.com.my
Investment Services
N.A.I.C.S.: 523999

Subsidiary (Domestic):

CardBiz Solutions Sdn. Bhd. (2)
Level 30 MYEG Tower No 8 Jalan Damansara Empire City PJU 8, 47820, Petaling Jaya, Selangor, Malaysia
Tel.: (60) 378903000
Web Site: https://www.cardbiz.com.my
Software Services
N.A.I.C.S.: 541511
Wesley Tan *(Exec Dir-Bus Dev)*

Hurr Tv Sdn. Bhd. (2)
MYEG Tower Block N Level 39 Empire City Damansara Jalan Damansara, Damansara Perdana PJU 8, 47820, Petaling Jaya, Selangor, Malaysia
Tel.: (60) 376648000
Web Site: https://www.hurr.tv
Television Services
N.A.I.C.S.: 516120
Nisa Hamdan *(Mgr-Channel)*

Muca Wellness Sdn. Bhd. (1)
No 8 Jalan Damansara Empire City PJU 8, 47820, Petaling Jaya, Selangor, Malaysia
Tel.: (60) 1139904055

Wellness Services
N.A.I.C.S.: 812112

MY FOOD BAG GROUP LIMITED
Level 3 56 Parnell Road, Auckland, 1052, New Zealand
Tel.: (64) 98869840   NZ
Web Site: https://www.myfoodbag.co.nz
Year Founded: 2012
MFB—(NZX)
Rev.: $105,080,144
Assets: $64,922,847
Liabilities: $30,247,010
Net Worth: $34,675,837
Earnings: $4,694,976
Emp.: 224
Fiscal Year-end: 03/31/23
Catering Operator
N.A.I.C.S.: 722320
Mark Winter *(CEO)*

MY FOODIE BOX LIMITED
9 Foundry Street, Maylands, Adelaide, 6051, WA, Australia
Tel.: (61) 863639222   AU
Web Site: https://www.myfoodiebox.com.au
Year Founded: 2017
MBX—(ASX)
Rev.: $3,857,436
Assets: $80,377
Liabilities: $1,430,797
Net Worth: ($1,350,421)
Earnings: ($2,726,722)
Fiscal Year-end: 06/30/23
Food Products Distr
N.A.I.C.S.: 445298
Kyla Garic *(Sec)*

MY HUMBLE HOUSE HOSPITALITY MANAGEMENT CONSULTING CO., LTD.
No 12 Sec 1 Zhongxiao E Rd Zhongzheng Dist, Taipei, Taiwan
Web Site: http://www.mhh-group.com
Year Founded: 2000
2739—(TAI)
Rev.: $157,988,646
Assets: $445,513,113
Liabilities: $406,729,963
Net Worth: $38,783,150
Earnings: $13,539,324
Emp.: 1,492
Fiscal Year-end: 12/31/23
Hotel & Resort Management Services
N.A.I.C.S.: 721110
Tsai Po-Han *(Chm & CEO-Interim)*

MY MONEY SECURITIES LIMITED
10A Under Hill Lane Civil Lines, Delhi, 110 054, India
Tel.: (91) 1123987870
Web Site: https://www.mymoneyviews.com
538862—(BOM)
Rev.: $121,704
Assets: $2,435,993
Liabilities: $376,671
Net Worth: $2,059,322
Earnings: $31,583
Emp.: 10
Fiscal Year-end: 03/31/23
Stock Brokerage Services
N.A.I.C.S.: 523150
Vikas Seth *(Mng Dir)*

MY SIZE, INC.
4 Hayarden st, PO Box 1026, Airport City, 7010000, Israel
Tel.: (972) 7236009030   DE
Web Site: https://www.mysizeid.com
Year Founded: 1999

MYSZ—(NASDAQ)
Rev.: $6,996,000
Assets: $8,991,000
Liabilities: $4,256,000
Net Worth: $4,735,000
Earnings: ($6,380,000)
Emp.: 22
Fiscal Year-end: 12/31/23
Mobile Application Developer
N.A.I.C.S.: 541512
Ronen Luzon *(CEO & Founder)*

MY XUAN BRICK TILE POTTERY & CONSTRUCTION
Hamlet Suoi Nhum Hac Dich, Tan Thanh dist, Vung Tau, Ba Ria, Vietnam
Tel.: (84) 2543876770
Web Site: https://www.myxuan-vt.com.vn
Year Founded: 1988
GMX—(HNX)
Rev.: $28,679,200
Assets: $18,835,500
Liabilities: $7,341,200
Net Worth: $11,494,300
Earnings: $4,358,200
Fiscal Year-end: 12/31/22
Bricks Mfr
N.A.I.C.S.: 327120
Luu Ngoc Thanh *(Chm-Mgmt Bd)*

MYANMAR AIRWAYS INTERNATIONAL
08-02 Sakura Tower 339 Bagyoke Aung San Rd, Yangon, Myanmar
Tel.: (95) 1255260
Web Site: http://www.maiair.com
Sales Range: $75-99.9 Million
Emp.: 500
Oil Transportation Services
N.A.I.C.S.: 481111

MYANMAR INVESTMENTS INTERNATIONAL LIMITED
37th Floor Singapore Land Tower, 50 Raffles Place, Singapore, 048623, Singapore
Tel.: (65) 6 829 7251   VG
Web Site: http://www.myanmarinvest.com
MIL—(AIM)
Rev.: $476
Assets: $36,825,623
Liabilities: $315,226
Net Worth: $36,510,397
Earnings: ($10,853,101)
Fiscal Year-end: 09/30/21
Investment Services
N.A.I.C.S.: 523999
Anthony Michael Dean *(Dir-Fin)*

MYBEST GROUP SPA
Viale Casiraghi 359, 20099, Sesto San Giovanni, Italy
Tel.: (39) 03282318851
Web Site: http://www.mybestgroup.it
ALMBG—(EUR)
Sales Range: Less than $1 Million
General Marketing Services
N.A.I.C.S.: 541910
Fabio Regolo *(Pres)*

MYBET HOLDING SE
Karl-Liebknecht-Strasse 32, 10178, Berlin, Germany
Tel.: (49) 302290830
Web Site: http://www.mybet-se.com
XMY—(DEU)
Sales Range: $25-49.9 Million
Emp.: 135
Adult Gaming Services; Lottery, Casino & Sports Betting
N.A.I.C.S.: 713290
Volker Heeg *(Chm)*

MYCONIC CAPITAL CORP.

Subsidiaries:

ANYBET GmbH (1)
Steckelhoern 9, 22765, Hamburg, Germany
Tel.: (49) 408537880
Web Site: http://www.anybet.de
Sales Range: $50-74.9 Million
Emp.: 25
Gambling Machines & Gaming Software Development & Sales
N.A.I.C.S.: 423990

DSM Lottoservice GmbH (1)
Morgenstrasse 18, Dornbirn Dist, 6890, Lustenau, Vorarlberg, Austria
Tel.: (43) 5577 63070
Web Site: http://www.mybet-se.com
Gambling Device Sales
N.A.I.C.S.: 713290

DigiDis S. L. (1)
C Gran Via 1 5th Left, 28014, Madrid, Spain
Tel.: (34) 91 523 50 11
Web Site: http://www.digidis.net
Gambling Software Distr
N.A.I.C.S.: 423430

JAXX GmbH (1)
Behringstr 16 a, Hamburg, 22756, Germany
Tel.: (49) 408537880
Web Site: http://www.mybet.com
Sales Range: $25-49.9 Million
Emp.: 35
Casino Operation Services
N.A.I.C.S.: 713210
Christoph Tonn *(Mng Dir)*

JAXX UK Ltd. (1)
80 Great Portland St 4th Fl, London, W1W 7NW, United Kingdom
Tel.: (44) 2071835222
Web Site: http://www.jaxx.com
Sales Range: $50-74.9 Million
Emp.: 6
Casino & Sports Betting Services
N.A.I.C.S.: 713210

pferdewetten-service.de GmbH (1)
Schutzenstr 11, 76530, Baden-Baden, Germany
Tel.: (49) 7221 3989422
Horse Race Betting Services
N.A.I.C.S.: 711219

MYBUCKS S.A.
9 rue du Laboratoire, L-1911, Luxembourg, Luxembourg
Tel.: (352) 28813401   LU
Web Site: http://www.mybucks.com
Year Founded: 2011
MBC—(DEU)
Rev.: $51,185,530
Assets: $237,987,674
Liabilities: $285,805,685
Net Worth: ($47,818,011)
Earnings: ($41,298,981)
Emp.: 1,148
Fiscal Year-end: 06/30/19
Financial Service Provider
N.A.I.C.S.: 541611
Dave Van Niekerk *(Founder)*

Subsidiaries:

MyBucks Bank Mozambique S.A. (1)
Av 25 de Setembro n 1821 3rd Floor, Maputo, Mozambique
Tel.: (258) 21422247
Financial Banking Services
N.A.I.C.S.: 522110

MyBucks Banking Corporation Ltd. (1)
Ekistics House Convention Drive City Centre, PO Box 31567, Lilongwe, Malawi
Tel.: (265) 1722500
Web Site: http://www.mybucksbanking.mw
Financial Banking Services
N.A.I.C.S.: 522110
Zandile Shaba *(Mng Dir)*

MYCONIC CAPITAL CORP.
1917 West 4th Avenue Suite 340, Vancouver, V6J 1M7, BC, Canada

MYCONIC CAPITAL CORP.

Myconic Capital Corp.—(Continued)
Tel.: (604) 351-6647
Web Site:
http://www.auraliteinvestments.com
Assets: $2,855,761
Liabilities: $13,055
Net Worth: $2,842,706
Earnings: ($5,034,460)
Asset Management Services
N.A.I.C.S.: 523940
Adam Deffett *(Interim CEO)*

MYCROFT BUSINESS COMPUTERS INC.
1038 Portage Avenue, Winnipeg, R3G 0S2, MB, Canada
Tel.: (204) 779-1700 MB
Web Site: http://www.microage.ca
Year Founded: 1980
Sales Range: $10-24.9 Million
Information Technology Integration, Consulting & Technical Support Services
N.A.I.C.S.: 541519
Stan Wiebe *(Pres & Gen Mgr)*

MYCRONIC AB
Nytorpsvagen 9, PO Box 3141, 183 03, Taby, Sweden
Tel.: (46) 86385200
Web Site: https://www.mycronic.com
MYCR—(OMX)
Rev.: $479,455,262
Assets: $687,478,341
Liabilities: $246,986,428
Net Worth: $440,491,912
Earnings: $69,403,467
Emp.: 1,991
Fiscal Year-end: 12/31/22
Development, Manufacture & Marketing of Laser Pattern Generators
N.A.I.C.S.: 333242
Charlott Samuelsson *(Sr VP-Pattern Generators)*

Subsidiaries:

MRSI Automation (Shenzhen) Co., Ltd. (1)
101 Block A Huahan Innovation Park Langshan Road, Shenzhen, 518057, Guangdong, China
Tel.: (86) 75526414155
Electronic Product Mfr & Distr
N.A.I.C.S.: 332999

MRSI Systems, LLC (1)
554 Clark Rd, Tewksbury, MA 01876
Tel.: (978) 667-9449
Web Site: https://www.mrsisystems.com
Die Bonding Mfr
N.A.I.C.S.: 333514
Michael Chalsen *(Pres)*

MYDATA automation AB (1)
Nytorpsvagen 9, 183 03, Taby, Sweden
Tel.: (46) 86385200
Web Site: http://www.mydata.com
Sales Range: $50-74.9 Million
Emp.: 300
Electronics Production Equipment Mfr
N.A.I.C.S.: 333242

Subsidiary (US):

MYDATA automation, Inc. (2)
320 Newburyport Tpke, Rowley, MA 01969
Tel.: (978) 948-6919
Web Site: http://www.micronic.com
Sales Range: $25-49.9 Million
Emp.: 20
Electronics Production Equipment Mfr
N.A.I.C.S.: 333242

Micronic Japan K.K. (1)
Mitsugi Kotobukicho Building, 1-1-3 Kotobuki-cho Fuchu-shi, Tokyo, 1830056, Japan
Tel.: (81) 423541220
Web Site: http://www.micronic.se
Sales Range: $25-49.9 Million
Emp.: 60

Consumer Electronics Repair & Maintenance
N.A.I.C.S.: 811210

Micronic Laser Systems, Inc (1)
1922 Zanker Rd, San Jose, CA 95112
Tel.: (408) 392-2260
Web Site: http://www.micronic.com
Semiconductor & Related Device Mfr
N.A.I.C.S.: 334413

Molecular Diagnostics Korea Inc. (MDxK) (1)
5F 80 Nonhyeon-Ro, Gangnam-gu, 137-897, Seoul, Korea (South)
Tel.: (82) 2578 8848
Web Site: http://www.mdxk.co.kr
Sales Range: $10-24.9 Million
Emp.: 25
Molecular Imaging Mfr
N.A.I.C.S.: 621512

Mycronic (Shanghai) Co., Ltd. (1)
Unit 106 E Block Lane 168 Da Duhe Road, Putuo District, Shanghai, 200062, China
Tel.: (86) 2132523785
Laser Writer Equipment Mfr & Distr
N.A.I.C.S.: 333242

Mycronic BV (1)
High Tech Campus 10, 5656 AE, Eindhoven, Netherlands
Tel.: (31) 402620667
Laser Writer Equipment Mfr & Distr
N.A.I.C.S.: 333242

Mycronic Co., Ltd. (1)
3rd Floor Jung-San Bldg 1026-8, Sanbon-Dong, Gunpo, 15808, Gyeonggi, Korea (South)
Tel.: (82) 313875111
Laser Writer Equipment Mfr & Distr
N.A.I.C.S.: 333242

Mycronic Fukuoka Co., Ltd. (1)
1-9-25 Enokida, Hakata-ku, Fukuoka, 812-0004, Japan
Tel.: (81) 922607009
Laser Writer Equipment Mfr & Distr
N.A.I.C.S.: 333242

Mycronic GmbH (1)
Biberger Strasse 93, Unterhaching, 82008, Munich, Germany
Tel.: (49) 8945242480
Laser Writer Equipment Mfr & Distr
N.A.I.C.S.: 333242

Mycronic Inc. (1)
554 Clark Rd, Tewksbury, MA 01876
Tel.: (978) 948-6919
Laser Writer Equipment Mfr & Distr
N.A.I.C.S.: 333242

Mycronic Ltd. (1)
Unit 2 Concept Park Innovation Close, Poole, BH12 4QT, Dorset, United Kingdom
Tel.: (44) 1202723585
Laser Writer Equipment Mfr & Distr
N.A.I.C.S.: 333242

Mycronic Pte. Ltd. (1)
9 Tagore Lane 02-08/09 9 Tagore, Singapore, 787472, Singapore
Tel.: (65) 62817997
Laser Writer Equipment Mfr & Distr
N.A.I.C.S.: 333242

Mycronic S.A.S. (1)
1 rue de Traversiere, 94513, Rungis, Cedex, France
Tel.: (33) 141801580
Laser Writer Equipment Mfr & Distr
N.A.I.C.S.: 333242

Mycronic Technologies Corp. (1)
KDX Chofu Bldg 1-18-1 Chofugaoka, Chofu, 182-0021, Tokyo, Japan
Tel.: (81) 424339400
Laser Writer Equipment Mfr & Distr
N.A.I.C.S.: 333242

Shenzhen Axxon Automation Co. Ltd. (1)
Building A14 Silicon Valley Power Automotive Electronics Pioneer Park, No 334 Guiyue Road Guanlan Longhua District, Shenzhen, China
Tel.: (86) 75583586066
Web Site: https://www.axxonauto.com
Fluid Control Equipment Mfr

N.A.I.C.S.: 334519

MYDAS REAL ESTATE INVESTMENTS LTD.
Raoul Wallenberg Street 2, Tel Aviv, 69719, Israel
Tel.: (972) 37684150
MYDS—(TAE)
Rev.: $1,473,960
Assets: $56,228,484
Liabilities: $37,930,100
Net Worth: $18,298,383
Earnings: $398,674
Fiscal Year-end: 12/31/23
Miscellaneous Financial Investment Activities
N.A.I.C.S.: 523999
Meir Jacobson *(Chm)*

MYDECINE INNOVATIONS GROUP INC.
Suite 1890 - 1075 West Georgia Street, Vancouver, V6E 3C9, BC, Canada
Tel.: (604) 559-8880 BC
Web Site: https://mydecine.com
Year Founded: 2013
MYCOF—(OTCIQ)
Rev.: $136,267
Assets: $7,456,013
Liabilities: $4,670,550
Net Worth: $2,785,464
Earnings: ($21,081,621)
Fiscal Year-end: 12/31/20
Plant Grower
N.A.I.C.S.: 115112

MYER PTY LTD
800 Collins Street, Docklands, 3008, VIC, Australia
Tel.: (61) 136937
Web Site: https://www.myer.com.au
MYR—(ASX)
Rev.: $2,036,762,877
Assets: $1,891,033,539
Liabilities: $1,717,185,028
Net Worth: $173,848,511
Earnings: $35,551,216
Emp.: 12,500
Fiscal Year-end: 07/31/21
Department Store Owner & Operator
N.A.I.C.S.: 455110
Davina Gunn *(Gen Mgr-Investor Relations)*

Subsidiaries:

Marcs David Lawrence Pty. Ltd. (1)
13 Doody Street, Alexandria, 2017, NSW, Australia
Tel.: (61) 280809000
Web Site: http://www.marcs.com.au
Men & Women Cloth Retailer
N.A.I.C.S.: 458110

Myer Pty Ltd (1)
314-336 Bourke St, Melbourne, 3000, VIC, Australia
Tel.: (61) 396611111
Departmental Store Operator
N.A.I.C.S.: 455110

The Myer Emporium Pty Ltd (1)
619 Doncaster Road, Doncaster, 3108, VIC, Australia
Tel.: (61) 388483100
Apparel Retailer
N.A.I.C.S.: 458110

sass & bide Pty Ltd (1)
13 Doody Street, Alexandria, 2015, NSW, Australia
Tel.: (61) 261901352
Web Site: https://www.sassandbide.com
Apparel Retailer
N.A.I.C.S.: 458110

sass & bide Retail Pty Ltd (1)
Stu 104 30 40 Harcourt Pde, Rosebery, 2018, NSW, Australia
Tel.: (61) 296671667
Women's Clothing Retailer

N.A.I.C.S.: 458110

INTERNATIONAL PUBLIC

MYFC HOLDING AB
Saltmatargatan 8A, 113 59, Stockholm, Sweden
Tel.: (46) 706562007
Web Site: http://www.myfc.se
MYFC—(OMX)
Rev.: $91,560
Assets: $7,407,692
Liabilities: $1,725,479
Net Worth: $5,682,214
Earnings: ($5,913,189)
Emp.: 11
Fiscal Year-end: 12/31/20
Fuel Cell Technology Mfr
N.A.I.C.S.: 334413
Michael Glantz *(CEO)*

MYHAMMER HOLDING AG
Franklinstrasse 28/29, 10587, Berlin, Germany
Tel.: (49) 30 23322 815
Web Site: http://www.myhammer-holding.de
Year Founded: 1999
MYRK—(DEU)
Rev.: $24,687,624
Assets: $18,546,424
Liabilities: $4,912,960
Net Worth: $13,633,464
Earnings: $4,421,664
Emp.: 121
Fiscal Year-end: 12/31/20
Online Portal Services
N.A.I.C.S.: 551112
Claudia Frese *(Chm-Mgmt Bd)*

MYHEALTHCHECKED PLC
The Maltings East Tyndall Street, Cardiff, CF24 5EA, Wales, United Kingdom
Tel.: (44) 2079338780 UK
Web Site:
http://investors.myhealthchecked.com
Year Founded: 2008
MHC—(AIM)
Rev.: $28,167,130
Assets: $14,425,650
Liabilities: $3,254,229
Net Worth: $11,171,421
Earnings: $1,914,920
Emp.: 21
Fiscal Year-end: 12/31/22
Oil & Gas Exploration Services
N.A.I.C.S.: 213112
Penny McCormick *(CEO)*

MYHERITAGE LTD
3 Ariel Sharon Blvd, Or Yehuda, Israel
Tel.: (972) 36280000
Web Site: http://www.myheritage.com
Online Genealogy Platform; Software Products & Services
N.A.I.C.S.: 541512
Gilad Japhet *(Founder & CEO)*

Subsidiaries:

Filae SA (1)
Tour Gamma B 193/197 Rue de Bercy, 75582, Paris, France (95.88%)
Tel.: (33) 144849510
Web Site: http://www.filae.com
Sales Range: Less than $1 Million
Internet Network Services
N.A.I.C.S.: 517121
Toussaint Roze *(Chm, CEO & Dir-IR)*

MYHOME REAL ESTATE DEVELOPMENT GROUP CO., LTD.
5F Shuiguohu Plaza No 10 Donghu Road, Wuchang District, Wuhan, 430071, Hubei, China
Tel.: (86) 2787833669
Web Site: http://www.000667.com

AND PRIVATE COMPANIES

000667—(SSE)
Rev.: $644,510,039
Assets: $4,338,018,582
Liabilities: $3,289,685,285
Net Worth: $1,048,333,297
Earnings: $14,508,987
Fiscal Year-end: 12/31/20
Real Estate Development Services
N.A.I.C.S.: 531311
Daoming Liu *(Chm)*

MYKLEBUST VERFT AS
Gnr 18 Bnr 37, 6082, Gursken, Norway
Tel.: (47) 7002 6200
Web Site: http://www.kleven.no
Emp.: 150
Ship Building Services
N.A.I.C.S.: 336611
Age Magne Sandvik *(Mgr-Sls-After Sls)*

MYLIFE LEBENSVERSICHERUNG AG
Herzberger Landstrasse 25, 37085, Gottingen, Germany
Tel.: (49) 55199760   De
Web Site: http://www.mylife-leben.de
Life Insurance Product & Services
N.A.I.C.S.: 524113
Michael Dreibrodt *(Chm-Mgmt Bd & CEO)*

MYMBN BERHAD
No 17 19 21 23 & 25 Jalan Melaka Raya 26, Taman Melaka Raya, 75000, Melaka, Malaysia
Tel.: (60) 62922628
Web Site:
  https://www.mymbn.com.my
Year Founded: 2012
MBN—(KLS)
Rev.: $14,746,355
Assets: $9,885,006
Liabilities: $2,078,225
Net Worth: $7,806,782
Earnings: $207,309
Fiscal Year-end: 12/31/23
Investment Management Service
N.A.I.C.S.: 523999
Chin Chee Cheah *(COO)*

MYMETICS CORPORATION
c/o Mymetics SA Route de la Corniche 4, CH-1066, Epalinges, Switzerland
Tel.: (41) 216534535   DE
Web Site: http://www.mymetics.com
MYMX—(OTCEM)
Rev.: $1,262,631
Assets: $8,991,945
Liabilities: $88,699,808
Net Worth: ($79,707,863)
Earnings: ($5,901,693)
Emp.: 14
Fiscal Year-end: 12/31/22
Biotechnology Research & Development Services
N.A.I.C.S.: 325414
Sylvain Fleury *(Chief Scientific Officer)*

Subsidiaries:

Mymetics B.V.   (1)
J H Oortweg 21, 2333 CH, Leiden, Netherlands
Tel.: (31) 652341420
Biotechnology Research & Development Services
N.A.I.C.S.: 541714

MYNARIC AG
Bertha Kipfmuller Strase 2 8, 81249, Munich, Germany
Tel.: (49) 810579990
Web Site: https://www.mynaric.com
Year Founded: 2009

M0YN—(DEU)
Rev.: $5,816,965
Assets: $128,519,318
Liabilities: $181,710,555
Net Worth: ($53,191,237)
Earnings: ($100,936,758)
Emp.: 314
Fiscal Year-end: 12/31/23
Communication Equipment Mfr
N.A.I.C.S.: 334220
Manfred Krischke *(Chm-Supervisory Bd)*

MYNDTEC INC.
1900 Minnesota Court Suite 122, Mississauga, L5N 3C9, ON, Canada
Tel.: (416) 569-0430   ON
Web Site: https://myndtec.com
Year Founded: 2008
MYTC—(CNSX)
Rev.: $473,723
Assets: $2,991,546
Liabilities: $5,761,792
Net Worth: ($2,770,246)
Earnings: ($2,385,238)
Fiscal Year-end: 12/31/21
Medical Device Mfr
N.A.I.C.S.: 339112
Craig Leon *(CEO)*

MYNET INC.
A-Place Aoyama 3F 2-11-3 Kita Aoyama, Minato-ku, Tokyo, 107-0061, Japan
Tel.: (81) 368644221
Web Site: https://mynet.co.jp
Year Founded: 2006
3928—(TKS)
Rev.: $61,803,530
Assets: $26,537,870
Liabilities: $17,647,010
Net Worth: $8,890,860
Earnings: $1,013,870
Emp.: 272
Fiscal Year-end: 12/31/23
Smartphone Services
N.A.I.C.S.: 517810
Minoru Iwaki *(Pres & CEO)*

MYNEWS HOLDINGS BERHAD
Lot No 3 Jalan Teknologi 3/1 Taman Sains Selangor 1 Seksyen 3 PJU 5, Kota Damansara, 47810, Petaling Jaya, Selangor Darul Ehsan, Malaysia
Tel.: (60) 361586000   MY
Web Site: https://mynews.com.my
Year Founded: 1996
MYNEWS—(KLS)
Rev.: $158,955,160
Assets: $137,985,417
Liabilities: $86,479,539
Net Worth: $51,505,878
Earnings: ($3,352,416)
Emp.: 2,729
Fiscal Year-end: 10/31/23
Investment Holding Services
N.A.I.C.S.: 551112
Tai Hock Dang *(CEO-Food)*

Subsidiaries:

DKE Technology Sdn. Bhd.   (1)
Lot 3 01 Level 3 1 First Avenue Bandar Utama, 47800, Petaling Jaya, Selangor, Malaysia
Tel.: (60) 377262566
Software Development Services
N.A.I.C.S.: 541511

MYNK1906 INDUSTRIES INDIA LIMITED
Vile Parle East Vile Parle, Mumbai, 400057, Maharashtra, India
Tel.: (91) 22 24967999
Year Founded: 1985
Sales Range: $100-124.9 Million
Textile Product Whslr

N.A.I.C.S.: 424310
Navmeet Arora *(CEO)*

MYOUNG SHIN INDUSTRY CO., LTD.
91 Cheonbuksandan-ro Cheonbuk-myeon, Gyeongju, Gyeongsangbuk-do, Korea (South)
Tel.: (82) 547402665
Web Site:
  https://myoungshinindustry.com
Year Founded: 1982
009900—(KRS)
Rev.: $1,162,190,683
Assets: $712,747,984
Liabilities: $418,373,726
Net Worth: $294,374,258
Earnings: $65,740,939
Emp.: 163
Fiscal Year-end: 12/31/22
Automotive Parts Mfr & Distr
N.A.I.C.S.: 336390
Lim Dong Shin *(CFO)*

Subsidiaries:

Simwon Development Co., Ltd.   (1)
131 Sandan 1-gil, Sapgyo-eup, Yesan, Chungcheongnam-do, Korea (South)
Tel.: (82) 7049015152
Automobile Parts Mfr & Distr
N.A.I.C.S.: 336390

Simwon Tech Inc.   (1)
22f B 282 Hagui-ro, Dongan-gu, Anyang, Gyeonggi-do, Korea (South)
Tel.: (82) 7044885100
Automobile Parts Mfr & Distr
N.A.I.C.S.: 336390

MYP LTD.
9 Battery Road 09-03 MYP Centre, Singapore, 049910, Singapore
Tel.: (65) 62246838   SG
Web Site: https://www.myp.com.sg
Year Founded: 2005
F86—(SES)
Rev.: $13,198,222
Assets: $493,635,420
Liabilities: $286,537,977
Net Worth: $207,097,443
Earnings: ($6,343,831)
Emp.: 12
Fiscal Year-end: 03/31/24
Investment Services
N.A.I.C.S.: 523999
Jonathan Tahir *(Exec Chm, Chm & CEO)*

Subsidiaries:

Island Line Pte Ltd.   (1)
200 Cantonment Road 09-01, Southpoint, Singapore, 89763, Singapore
Tel.: (65) 6236 6288
Shipping Services
N.A.I.C.S.: 488510

SSC Shipping Agencies Pte Ltd   (1)
200 Cantonment Road 09-01 Southpoint, Singapore, 089763, Singapore
Tel.: (65) 62204906
Web Site:
  http://www.singaporeshipping.com.sg
Marine Terminal Operation Services
N.A.I.C.S.: 488320

MYRIAD GROUP AG
Care of GHR Rechtsanwalte AG Bahnhofstrasse 64, PO Box 3268, 8001, Zurich, Switzerland
Tel.: (41) 44 823 8900   CH
Web Site:
  http://www.myriadgroup.com
Year Founded: 1999
MYRN—(SWX)
Sales Range: $10-24.9 Million
Holding Company; Mobile Telecommunications Software Solutions & Services
N.A.I.C.S.: 551112
Bruce Jackson *(CTO)*

MYS GROUP CO., LTD.

Subsidiaries:

Myriad France SAS   (1)
Batiment Athena 11 Avenue du Lac de Constance, BP 350, 73375, Le Bourget du Lac, France   (100%)
Tel.: (33) 4 7926 4860
Web Site: http://www.myriadgroup.com
Mobile Telecommunications Software Developer & Services
N.A.I.C.S.: 513210

Myriad Group Korea Co., Ltd.   (1)
Samsung-Dong 158, Tongsung 15 Kangnam-Ku, Seoul, 135 092, Korea (South)   (100%)
Tel.: (82) 25623985
Web Site: http://www.myriadgroup.com
Mobile Software Development Services
N.A.I.C.S.: 513210

Myriad Technology AG   (1)
Selnaustrasse 28, 8001, Zurich, Switzerland   (100%)
Tel.: (41) 448238900
Web Site: http://www.myriadgroup.com
Sales Range: $25-49.9 Million
Emp.: 12
Mobile Software Development Services
N.A.I.C.S.: 513210

MYRIAD INTERACTIVE MEDIA, INC.
7 Ingram Drive Suite 128, Toronto, M6M 2L7, ON, Canada   DE
Web Site: http://www.myriadim.com
Year Founded: 1999
MYRY—(OTCBB)
Rev.: $89,793
Assets: $186,210
Liabilities: $127,667
Net Worth: $58,543
Earnings: ($773,170)
Emp.: 5
Fiscal Year-end: 06/30/14
Web Development & Internet Marketing Services
N.A.I.C.S.: 541810
Derek Ivany *(Pres, CEO & CFO)*

MYRIAD URANIUM CORP.
600-1090 W Georgia St, Vancouver, V6E 3V7, BC, Canada
Tel.: (604) 418-2877   Ca
Web Site: https://myriaduranium.com
Year Founded: 2018
MMC—(CNSX)
Rev.: $2,521
Assets: $1,309,246
Liabilities: $7,244
Net Worth: $1,302,003
Earnings: ($213,712)
Fiscal Year-end: 04/30/21
Mineral Exploration Services
N.A.I.C.S.: 213115
Peter Smith *(CEO)*

MYS GROUP CO., LTD.
MYS Industry Park Xinbeitou, Guangming District, Shenzhen, 518107, Guangdong, China
Tel.: (86) 75529751666
Web Site: https://www.szmys.com
Year Founded: 2000
002303—(SSE)
Rev.: $579,802,860
Assets: $1,039,382,604
Liabilities: $341,194,464
Net Worth: $698,188,140
Earnings: $18,902,052
Emp.: 3,674
Fiscal Year-end: 12/31/22
Packaging Products Mfr
N.A.I.C.S.: 561910
Wang Zhijun *(Chm, Pres & Gen Mgr)*

Subsidiaries:

Chongqing Mys Environmental Protection & Technology Company Ltd.   (1)

5113

MYS GROUP CO., LTD.

MYS Group Co., Ltd.—(Continued)
No 199 Tuzhu Middle Road, Tuzhu Town
Shapingba District, Chongqing, China
Tel.: (86) 2361768888
Cardboard & Plastic Packaging Mfr
N.A.I.C.S.: 322220

Dongguan Maxron Internet Of Things Technology Co., Ltd. (1)
Dongguan Maxron Building 2 No 628 Dadong Road, Dazhou Village Qiaotou, Dongguan, China
Tel.: (86) 76986939999
Cardboard & Plastic Packaging Mfr
N.A.I.C.S.: 322220

Dongguan Mys Environmental Protection & Technology Company Ltd. (1)
Mys Industry Park, The First Industrial Zone Qiaotou, Dongguan, China
Tel.: (86) 76986938888
Cardboard & Plastic Packaging Mfr
N.A.I.C.S.: 322220

Hejiang Jincai Printing & Packaging Co., Ltd. (1)
Three Mile Intersection, Yanba Hutou Town, Chongqing, China
Tel.: (86) 8305100708
Cardboard & Plastic Packaging Mfr
N.A.I.C.S.: 322220

Jiangsu Yangjinxin Printing & Packaging Co., Ltd. (1)
South Street and the 1 Road, YangHe New City, Suqian, China
Tel.: (86) 52784922608
Cardboard & Plastic Packaging Mfr
N.A.I.C.S.: 322220

Jincai Printing & Packaging Co., Ltd. (1)
Guanguang Rd Guanlan Street, Tianluohu Industrial Park Guihua Industrial Area Baoan District, Shenzhen, Guangdong, China
Tel.: (86) 75581475048
Cardboard & Plastic Packaging Mfr
N.A.I.C.S.: 322220

Luzhou Jincai Printing & Packaging Co., Ltd. (1)
Wine Industrial Park, Huang Yi Town Jiangyang District, Luzhou, Sichuan, China
Tel.: (86) 8303652398
Cardboard & Plastic Packaging Mfr
N.A.I.C.S.: 322220

Mianzhu Jincai Printing & Packaging Co., Ltd. (1)
5 Groups, Corning Village, Mianzhu, Sichuan, China
Tel.: (86) 8303652398
Cardboard & Plastic Packaging Mfr
N.A.I.C.S.: 322220

Mys Taiwan Co., Limited (1)
Cardboard & Plastic Packaging Mfr
N.A.I.C.S.: 322220

Shenzhen Golden Ocean Culture & Creative Co., Ltd. (1)
No 12/15 Y1-4 Floor, BanTian Creative Industrial Park Longgang District, Shenzhen, China
Cardboard & Plastic Packaging Mfr
N.A.I.C.S.: 322220

Shichuan Jincai Printing & Packaging Co., Ltd. (1)
Ship Dam Three Fork in the Road, Hutou Town Hejiang County, Luzhou, Sichuan, China
Tel.: (86) 52784922608
Cardboard & Plastic Packaging Mfr
N.A.I.C.S.: 322220

Sichuan Lu-Mei Supply Chain Management Co., Ltd. (1)
4th Gate, Wine Industry Park Huang Yi Town Jiangyang Aera, Luzhou, Sichuan, China
Tel.: (86) 75581475048
Cardboard & Plastic Packaging Mfr
N.A.I.C.S.: 322220

Sichuan Yi-Mei Supply Chain Management Co., Ltd. (1)

No 5 Guang Yuan Road West Liangang Economic and Techmological, Development Zone, Yibin, Sichuan, China
Tel.: (86) 8315488666
Cardboard & Plastic Packaging Mfr
N.A.I.C.S.: 322220

Suzhou Mys Environmental Protection & Technology Company Ltd. (1)
No 699 Naxiang Road Wujiang Economic Development Zone, Wujiang, Jiangsu, China
Tel.: (86) 51288810999
Cardboard & Plastic Packaging Mfr
N.A.I.C.S.: 322220

Xiaomeiji Technology Co., Ltd. (1)
Mys Industry Park, Xinbeitou Guangming District, Shenzhen, China
Tel.: (86) 75521381818
Cardboard & Plastic Packaging Mfr
N.A.I.C.S.: 322220

Zhongda Green Valley Industry Co., Ltd. (1)
6th Floor Xinqiang Investment Building Southern District No 2, Xinbeitou Gunagming District, Shenzhen, China
Tel.: (86) 75521021225
Cardboard & Plastic Packaging Mfr
N.A.I.C.S.: 322220

Zhongshan Mys Environmental Protection & Technology Company Ltd. (1)
No 43 4th Floor 2 Building Technology West Road Torch Development, Zone Science, Zhongshan, China
Tel.: (86) 76089933980
Cardboard & Plastic Packaging Mfr
N.A.I.C.S.: 322220

MYSAFETY GROUP AB
Radmansgatan 40, 113 57, Stockholm, Sweden
Tel.: (46) 84465500
Web Site: https://investor.mysafety.se
Year Founded: 1999
SAFETY.B—(OMX)
Rev.: $83,359
Assets: $2,346,231
Liabilities: $418,669
Net Worth: $1,927,562
Earnings: ($2,110,203)
Emp.: 94
Fiscal Year-end: 12/31/22
Information Technology Consulting Services
N.A.I.C.S.: 541512

MYSON CENTURY, INC.
8 F-6 No 248 Sec 2 Yonghua Rd, Anping Dist, Tainan City, 708008, Taiwan
Tel.: (886) 35784866
Web Site: https://www.myson.com.tw
Year Founded: 1990
5314—(TPE)
Rev.: $576,306
Assets: $5,760,091
Liabilities: $1,931,151
Net Worth: $3,828,940
Earnings: ($83,513)
Fiscal Year-end: 12/31/22
Semiconductor Devices Mfr
N.A.I.C.S.: 334413
Chien I-Sen (Chm & Pres)

MYSORE PAPER MILLS LIMITED
No 32 1st Floor, D Devaraj Urs Road, Bengaluru, 560001, India
Tel.: (91) 22266979
Web Site: https://www.mpm.co.in
Year Founded: 1937
Sales Range: $50-74.9 Million
News Printing Mill Operator
N.A.I.C.S.: 322120
Viswanath S. Malghan (CFO)

MYSORE PETRO CHEMICALS LIMITED

D - 4 Jyothi Complex 134 / 1 Infantry Road, Bengaluru, 560 001, Karnataka, India
Tel.: (91) 8022868372
Web Site:
https://www.mysorepetro.com
Year Founded: 1969
506734—(BOM)
Rev.: $3,237,684
Assets: $30,972,256
Liabilities: $5,352,881
Net Worth: $25,619,375
Earnings: $2,484,479
Emp.: 4
Fiscal Year-end: 03/31/23
Chemical Product Whslr
N.A.I.C.S.: 424690
M. M. Dhanuka (Chm, CEO & Mng Dir)

MYSTAR ENGINEERING CORPORATION
7-19-1 Nishi-Gotanda, Shinagawa-ku, Tokyo, 141-0031, Japan
Tel.: (81) 3 6756 0311
Web Site: http://www.mystar.co.jp
Year Founded: 1974
Rev.: $176,923,680
Assets: $122,201,280
Liabilities: $48,199,200
Net Worth: $74,002,080
Earnings: $5,019,240
Emp.: 1,859
Fiscal Year-end: 03/31/19
Semiconductor Equipment Manufacturing, Testing & Engineering Services
N.A.I.C.S.: 334413
Daisuke Hirano (Pres)

Subsidiaries:

Sigma Communications Inc. (1)
Mita NN Building 3F 4-1-23 Shiba, Minato-ku, Tokyo, 108-0014, Japan
Tel.: (81) 345316571
Web Site: http://www.sigma-com.co.jp
Emp.: 527
Facility Management Services
N.A.I.C.S.: 541613

MYSTATE LIMITED
Level 2 137 Harrington Street, Hobart, 7000, TAS, Australia
Tel.: (61) 138001
Web Site:
https://www.mystatelimited.com.au
MYS—(ASX)
Rev.: $319,793,001
Assets: $6,122,047,918
Liabilities: $5,811,593,192
Net Worth: $310,454,726
Earnings: $23,563,702
Emp.: 62
Fiscal Year-end: 06/30/24
Banking Services
N.A.I.C.S.: 522110
Scott A. Lukianenko (Sec)

Subsidiaries:

MyState Bank Limited (1)
Level 2 137 Harrington Street, Hobart, TAS, Australia
Tel.: (61) 138001
Trustee & Wealth Management Services
N.A.I.C.S.: 522180

MyState Financial (1)
144 Collins Street, MyState Financial, Hobart, 7000, TAS, Australia
Tel.: (61) 362330679
Web Site: http://www.mystate.com.au
Sales Range: $75-99.9 Million
Financial Services
N.A.I.C.S.: 541611
John Gilbert (CEO)

TPT Wealth Limited (1)
1/65 St John Street, Launceston, 7250, TAS, Australia
Tel.: (61) 1300138044

INTERNATIONAL PUBLIC

Web Site:
http://www.tasmanianperpetual.com.au
Emp.: 20
Financial Services
N.A.I.C.S.: 541611
Tim Ruthersord (COO)

MYSTIQUE MECHANICAL LTD.
300 3605 29 Street NE, Calgary, T1Y 5W4, AB, Canada
Tel.: (403) 250-3543
Web Site:
http://www.mystiquemech.ca
Year Founded: 1982
Rev.: $10,013,618
Emp.: 90
Plumbing & Sewer Cleaners Service Provider
N.A.I.C.S.: 238220
Ted Rohling (Pres)

MYT NETHERLANDS PARENT B.V.
Einsteinring 9, Aschheim, 85609, Munich, Germany
Tel.: (49) 89127695614 NL
Web Site:
https://investors.mytheresa.com
Year Founded: 2019
MYTE—(NYSE)
Rev.: $902,589,094
Assets: $747,650,279
Liabilities: $280,021,469
Net Worth: $467,628,811
Earnings: ($26,740,017)
Emp.: 1,817
Fiscal Year-end: 06/30/24
Holding Company
N.A.I.C.S.: 551112
Michael Kliger (CEO & Member-Mgmt Bd)

MYTECH GROUP BHD
Level 9 Block K No 2 Jalan Solaris, Solaris Mont' Kiara, 50480, Kuala Lumpur, Malaysia
Tel.: (60) 362099000
Web Site:
https://www.widetechbhd.com.my
Year Founded: 1984
MYTECH—(KLS)
Rev.: $2,647,596
Assets: $10,030,467
Liabilities: $1,026,370
Net Worth: $9,004,097
Earnings: $304,656
Fiscal Year-end: 03/31/22
Spring Mfr
N.A.I.C.S.: 332613
Suan Phang Loh (Exec Dir)

Subsidiaries:

Wire Master Spring Sdn. Bhd. (1)
722 Lorong Perindustrian Bukit Minyak 9 Taman Perindustrian, Bukit Minyak, 14100, Seberang Perai Tengah, Penang, Malaysia
Tel.: (60) 45081500
Web Site: http://www.wiremaster.com.my
Sales Range: $25-49.9 Million
Emp.: 30
Precision Springs Mfr
N.A.I.C.S.: 332613

MYUNGJIN HOLDINGS CORP.
16 Maeheon-ro, Seocho-gu, Hanam, Korea (South)
Tel.: (82) 221550416
Seafood Distr
N.A.I.C.S.: 424460
Jin-Rang Jung (CEO)

MYUNGMOON PHARMACEUTICAL CO., LTD.
7 Gangnam-daero 54-Gil, Gangnam-gu, Seoul, Korea (South)
Tel.: (82) 267112000
Web Site: http://www.mmpharm.co.kr
Year Founded: 1983

AND PRIVATE COMPANIES

017180—(KRS)
Rev.: $112,921,738
Assets: $171,050,742
Liabilities: $100,338,731
Net Worth: $70,712,011
Earnings: $5,839,992
Emp.: 297
Fiscal Year-end: 12/31/22
Pharmaceuticals Product Mfr
N.A.I.C.S.: 325412
Seok Min Woo *(Vice Chm)*

Subsidiaries:

Myungmoon pharmaceutical Co., Ltd. - HWASUNG FACTORY (1)
901-1 Sangsin-Ri Hyangnam-Myun, Hwaseong, Gyeonggi-do, Korea (South)
Tel.: (82) 31 353 3519
Pharmaceuticals Product Mfr
N.A.I.C.S.: 325412

MYUNMOON PHARM CO., LTD.

7 Gangnam-daero 54-Gil, Gangnam-gu, Seoul, Korea (South)
Tel.: (82) 267112000
Web Site:
https://www.mmpharm.co.kr
Year Founded: 1983
017180—(KRS)
Rev.: $112,921,738
Assets: $171,050,742
Liabilities: $100,338,731
Net Worth: $70,712,011
Earnings: $5,839,992
Emp.: 297
Fiscal Year-end: 12/31/22
Pharmaceuticals Product Mfr
N.A.I.C.S.: 325412
Woo Seok-Min *(Vice Chm)*

Subsidiaries:

IshimotoBio-Chemical Laboratory Co., Ltd. (1)
784-14 Tawaraguchicho, Nara, Ikoma, 630-0243, Japan
Tel.: (81) 743756862
Web Site: https://www.mical-ishimoto.com
Nutritional Food Mfr
N.A.I.C.S.: 311999

Trb Chemedica S.a. (1)
Rue Michel-Servet 12, 1206, Les Geneveys-sur-Coffrane, Switzerland
Tel.: (41) 227034900
Web Site: https://www.trbchemedica.com
Emp.: 900
Pharmaceutical Preparation Mfr
N.A.I.C.S.: 325412

MZI RESOURCES LTD.

Level 2 100 Royal Street, Perth, 6004, WA, Australia
Tel.: (61) 8 9328 9800   AU
Web Site: http://www.mzi.com.au
Year Founded: 1997
Rev.: $33,202,825
Assets: $129,151,583
Liabilities: $157,449,809
Net Worth: ($28,298,226)
Earnings: ($27,647,297)
Emp.: 26
Fiscal Year-end: 06/30/18
Mineral Exploration Services
N.A.I.C.S.: 212390
John Westdorp *(CEO-Interim & CFO)*

MZT PUMPI A.D.

Str Pero Nakov bb, 1000, Skopje, North Macedonia
Tel.: (389) 22549817
Web Site: https://www.pumpi.mk
Year Founded: 1945
MZPU—(MAC)
Rev.: $3,624,749
Assets: $7,988,485
Liabilities: $2,786,437
Net Worth: $5,202,049
Earnings: $95,386

Emp.: 110
Fiscal Year-end: 12/31/23
Pumps Mfr
N.A.I.C.S.: 333914
Vesna Mitreska *(Mgr-Sector Pumps)*

N BROWN GROUP PLC

Griffin House 40 Lever Road, Manchester, M60 6ES, United Kingdom
Tel.: (44) 1612368256
Web Site: https://www.nbrown.co.uk
BWNG—(LSE)
Rev.: $764,990,455
Assets: $972,628,903
Liabilities: $490,006,367
Net Worth: $482,622,535
Earnings: $1,018,460
Emp.: 1,697
Fiscal Year-end: 03/02/24
Mail-Order Shopping Services
N.A.I.C.S.: 458110
Craig Lovelace *(CFO)*

Subsidiaries:

Figleaves Global Trading Limited (1)
2nd Floor Solar House 915 High Road, North Finchley, London, N12 8QJ, United Kingdom
Tel.: (44) 2031700169
Web Site: https://www.figleaves.com
Intimate Apparels Online Retailer
N.A.I.C.S.: 424350
Julia Reynolds *(CEO)*

High and Mighty Limited (1)
Griffin House 40 Lever St, Manchester, M60 6ES, United Kingdom
Tel.: (44) 3450682572
Web Site: https://www.jacamo.co.uk
Huge Size Clothing Retailer
N.A.I.C.S.: 458110
Jay Pesticcio *(Mgr-Store-Cardiff)*

House of Bath (1)
1 Bartlett St, Bath, BA1 2QZ, United Kingdom
Tel.: (44) 8712300867
Web Site: http://www.houseofbath.co.uk
Mail Order Sales of Home Furnishings & Accessories
N.A.I.C.S.: 449129

J D W Finance Limited (1)
Griffin House 40 Lever Street, Manchester, M60 6ES, United Kingdom
Tel.: (44) 8712312000
Sales Range: $150-199.9 Million
Emp.: 3,500
Financial Support Services
N.A.I.C.S.: 541611

J D Williams & Co. Limited (1)
Griffin Ho 40 Lever St, Manchester, M606ES, United Kingdom (100%)
Tel.: (44) 1612368256
Web Site: http://www.jdwilliams.co.uk
Sales Range: $250-299.9 Million
Emp.: 950
Electronic Shopping & Mail-Order Houses
N.A.I.C.S.: 425120
Alan White *(CEO)*

Subsidiary (Domestic):

Gray & Osbourn Limited (2)
Griffin House 40 Lever Street, Manchester, M60 6ES, Lancashire, United Kingdom
Tel.: (44) 1612368256
Web Site: http://www.grayandosbourn.co.uk
Sales Range: $200-249.9 Million
Electronic Shopping & Mail-Order Houses
N.A.I.C.S.: 458110

JD Williams & Company Ltd. (1)
Griffin House 40 Lever Street, Manchester, M60 6ES, United Kingdom (100%)
Tel.: (44) 8712312000
Sales Range: $200-249.9 Million
Emp.: 800
Electronic Shopping & Mail-Order Houses
N.A.I.C.S.: 425120

Oxendale & Co. Limited (1)
Griffin House 40 Lever Street, Manchester, M60 6ES, United Kingdom (100%)
Tel.: (44) 1612368256
Electronic Shopping & Mail-Order Houses

N.A.I.C.S.: 425120

N CITRON, INC.

4F 19 Eonju-ro 148-gil, Gangnam-gu, Seoul, 486-255, Gyeonggi-do, Korea (South)
Tel.: (82) 263401000
Web Site: http://www.n-citron.com
Year Founded: 2000
101400—(KRS)
Sales Range: $25-49.9 Million
Digital Audio Amplifier Mfr
N.A.I.C.S.: 334310
Han Sang Woo *(Deputy Gen Mgr)*

N G INDUSTRIES LTD.

37A Dr Meghnad Saha Sarani, Kolkata, 700029, India
Tel.: (91) 3324197542
Web Site: https://www.ngind.com
Year Founded: 1994
530897—(BOM)
Rev.: $1,641,437
Assets: $2,298,494
Liabilities: $250,160
Net Worth: $2,048,334
Earnings: $83,799
Emp.: 68
Fiscal Year-end: 03/31/21
Health Care & Medical Services
N.A.I.C.S.: 621999
Ashok Kumar Goenka *(Co-Founder)*

N MAS UNO IBG SA

Calle Padilla 17, Madrid, 28006, Spain
Tel.: (34) 91 745 84 84
Web Site: http://www.nplusone.com
Rev.: $2,240,000,000
Emp.: 100
Fiscal Year-end: 12/31/14
Wealth Management Services
N.A.I.C.S.: 523999
Santiago Eguidazu *(Chm)*

Subsidiaries:

N+1 Mercapital SL (1)
Padilla 17, 28006, Madrid, Spain
Tel.: (34) 91 557 80 00
Web Site: http://www.mercapital.com
Privater Equity Firm
N.A.I.C.S.: 523999
Federico Pastor *(Chm)*

Holding (Domestic):

Secuoya Grupo de Comunicacion, S.A. (2)
Avenida de Espana 1, 28760, Tres Cantos, Madrid, Spain
Tel.: (34) 913717569
Web Site: https://secuoyacontentgroup.com
Rev.: $107,015,995
Assets: $118,288,937
Liabilities: $108,917,219
Net Worth: $9,371,718
Earnings: $3,104,361
Emp.: 1,357
Fiscal Year-end: 12/31/2023
Broadcasting Services
N.A.I.C.S.: 516120
Raul Berdones *(Chm)*

N R SPUNTECH INDUSTRIES LTD.

HaHaroshet 1, PO Box 3328, Tiberias, 14133, Israel
Tel.: (972) 46732360
Web Site: https://www.spuntech.com
Year Founded: 1996
SPNTC—(TAE)
Rev.: $202,766,677
Assets: $176,587,371
Liabilities: $93,850,254
Net Worth: $82,737,117
Earnings: $9,155,961
Fiscal Year-end: 12/31/23
Nonwoven Fabric Mills
N.A.I.C.S.: 313230
Hezi Nissan *(CEO)*

N S E INTEGRATIONS

Les Seignes, 03250, Nizerolles, Allier, France
Tel.: (33) 473671400
Web Site: http://www.nse-groupe.com
Rev.: $23,600,000
Emp.: 163
Assembly & Integration Services for the Military, Industrial & Aerospace Segments
N.A.I.C.S.: 334412
Francois Lacoste *(Pres & CEO)*

N. LEVENTERIS S.A.

74 Dragatsaniou Str, 18545, Piraeus, Greece
Tel.: (30) 2104220581
Web Site: https://www.leventeris.gr
Year Founded: 1948
LEBEK—(ATH)
Sales Range: Less than $1 Million
Emp.: 16
Wire Rope Mfr & Distr
N.A.I.C.S.: 332618
Leventeri Areti *(Pres)*

Subsidiaries:

N. LEVENTERIS S.A. - HIGH CARBON STEEL WIRE UNIT (1)
Industrial area of Volos, Volos, 38500, Greece
Tel.: (30) 24210 95309
Wire Ropes Mfr
N.A.I.C.S.: 332618

N. R. INTERNATIONAL LIMITED

3rd Floor Draupadi Mansion 11, Brabourne Road, Kolkata, 700001, West Bengal, India
Tel.: (91) 3322318932
Web Site:
https://www.nrinternationalltd.in
Year Founded: 1991
Sales Range: Less than $1 Million
Emp.: 17
Coal Whslr
N.A.I.C.S.: 423520
Nirmal Modi *(Chm)*

N. STENNING & CO. PTY LTD.

174 Parramatta Road, Camperdown, 2050, NSW, Australia
Tel.: (61) 285949100
Web Site:
http://www.nstenning.com.au
Year Founded: 1953
Sales Range: $10-24.9 Million
Emp.: 30
Medical Supplies Distr
N.A.I.C.S.: 423450
Gordon Stenning *(Mng Dir)*

N. TEPPERMAN LTD.

2595 Ouellette Ave, Windsor, N8X 4V8, ON, Canada
Tel.: (519) 969-9700   ON
Web Site:
http://www.teppermans.com
Year Founded: 1925
Furniture Retailer
N.A.I.C.S.: 449110
Andrew Tepperman *(Pres)*

N.B.I. INDUSTRIAL FINANCE COMPANY LIMITED

21 Strand Road Ground Floor, Kolkata, 700 001, India
Tel.: (91) 22437725
Web Site: https://www.nbi-india.co.in
Year Founded: 1936
NBIFIN—(NSE)
Rev.: $1,217,589
Assets: $294,722,127
Liabilities: $12,040,861
Net Worth: $282,681,266

N.B.I. Industrial Finance Company Limited—(Continued)
Earnings: $632,228
Emp.: 5
Fiscal Year-end: 03/31/23
Financial Services
N.A.I.C.S.: 523150
S. P. Kumar (CFO & Mgr)

N.C. HOUSING PCL
1/765 Moo 17 Soi Amporn Phaholyothin Rd Km 26 Tambol Kookhot, Lumlookka District, Pathumthani, 12130, Thailand
Tel.: (66) 299350807
Web Site: https://ncgroup.co.th
NCH-F—(THA)
Rev.: $69,079,911
Assets: $163,306,279
Liabilities: $71,638,624
Net Worth: $91,667,655
Earnings: $4,441,303
Emp.: 265
Fiscal Year-end: 12/31/23
Real Estate Management Services
N.A.I.C.S.: 531390

N.D. METAL INDUSTRIES LTD.
417 Maker Chambers V Nariman Point, Mumbai, 400021, Maharashtra, India
Tel.: (91) 2222822383
Web Site: https://ndmil.com
Year Founded: 1992
512024—(BOM)
Rev.: $127,007
Assets: $1,675,007
Liabilities: $1,228,571
Net Worth: $446,436
Earnings: $22,121
Emp.: 20
Fiscal Year-end: 03/31/23
Metal Fabricator Mfr
N.A.I.C.S.: 332119

N.D. RUBBER PUBLIC COMPANY LIMITED
129 Moo 3 Nongchak-Phanasnikom Road, Nongeiroon Sub-district Banbueng District, Chon Buri, 20220, Thailand
Tel.: (66) 38160707
Web Site: https://www.ndrubber.co.th
NDR—(THA)
Rev.: $24,412,760
Assets: $30,337,201
Liabilities: $8,361,190
Net Worth: $21,976,011
Earnings: ($1,898,866)
Emp.: 251
Fiscal Year-end: 12/31/23
Tires & Tubes Mfr & Distr
N.A.I.C.S.: 326299
Boonlai Jamparat (Gen Mgr-Production Dept)

N.G. BAILEY & CO. LTD.
Denton Hall, Ilkley, LS29 OHH, West Yorkshire, United Kingdom
Tel.: (44) 1943601933
Web Site: http://www.ngbailey.co.uk
Year Founded: 1921
Sales Range: $550-599.9 Million
Emp.: 3,500
Electrical, Mechanical & Instrumentation Engineers & Contractors; Passive Fire Control Engineers; Installation of Voice & Data; Switchgear & Motor Controls Manufacturing
N.A.I.C.S.: 238210
Cal Bailey (Dir-Sustainability)

Subsidiaries:

Bailey Maintenance Services-Newcastle (1)
321 Ordsall Lane, Manchester, M5 3HP, Salford, United Kingdom (100%)
Tel.: (44) 161 872 0171
Web Site: http://www.ngbailey.co.uk
Sales Range: $10-24.9 Million
Emp.: 50
Planned & Preventative Building Maintenance Services
N.A.I.C.S.: 561790
Jon Lucas (Dir-Strategic Accts)

Bailey Teswaine Ltd. (1)
8 Lanark Square, Glengall Bridge, London, E14 9RE, United Kingdom (100%)
Tel.: (44) 2070930800
Web Site: http://www.baileyteswaine.co.uk
Sales Range: $100-124.9 Million
Emp.: 350
Telecommunication Servicesb
N.A.I.C.S.: 517112

Kedington (NI) Limited (1)
Unit 12c Harbour Court, Belfast, BT3 9HB, United Kingdom
Tel.: (44) 28 90 450090
Web Site: http://www.kedington.com
Emp.: 30
Cable Product Whslr
N.A.I.C.S.: 335929
Lawrence Flavelle (Gen Mgr)

N.G. Bailey Manufacturing Ltd. (1)
Denton Hall, Ilkley, LS29 0HH, W Yorkshire, United Kingdom (100%)
Tel.: (44) 1943 816117
Sales Range: $50-74.9 Million
Mfr Facilities
N.A.I.C.S.: 339999

NG Bailey (1)
Phoenix Crescent Strathclyde Business Park, Bellshill, ML4 3NJ, United Kingdom (100%)
Tel.: (44) 1698 743400
Web Site: http://www.baileymaintenance.co.uk
Sales Range: $25-49.9 Million
Emp.: 20
Engineering, IT & Facilities Business Services
N.A.I.C.S.: 541330
Mike Darlington (Mng Dir-Engrg North & Scotland)

NG Bailey (1)
7 Brown Lane West, Leeds, LS12 6EH, United Kingdom (100%)
Tel.: (44) 113 234 3443
Web Site: http://www.ngbailey.com
Sales Range: $25-49.9 Million
Emp.: 400
Engineering, IT Services & Offsite Manufacture
N.A.I.C.S.: 237990
Mike Darlington (Mng Dir-Engrg)

NG Bailey Limited (1)
Cutler Heights Lane, Bradford, BD4 9JF, United Kingdom
Tel.: (44) 1274682856
Construction Engineering Services
N.A.I.C.S.: 237990

N.I STEEL CO., LTD.
Hwamin B/D 35 Dongjak-daero, Dongjak-gu, Seoul, Korea (South)
Tel.: (82) 27586789
Web Site: https://ni.hcrst.com
Year Founded: 1972
008260—(KRS)
Rev.: $272,584,285
Assets: $304,840,041
Liabilities: $160,494,231
Net Worth: $144,345,811
Earnings: $37,421,633
Emp.: 221
Fiscal Year-end: 12/31/22
Steel Products Mfr
N.A.I.C.S.: 331110
Jong-Min Bae (CEO)

Subsidiaries:

N.I STEEL Co., Ltd.- Bu-san Division (1)
Tel.: (82) 513238601
Steel Products Mfr
N.A.I.C.S.: 331110

N.I STEEL Co., Ltd. - Dae-gu Division (1)
1-6 Bungi Taepyeongno2-ga, Jung-gu, Daegu, Korea (South)
Tel.: (82) 53 254 0110
Steel Products Mfr
N.A.I.C.S.: 331110

N.I STEEL Co., Ltd. - Dang-jin Division (1)
753 Sunseong-ro Sunseong-myeon, Songak-myeon, Dangjin, Chungcheongnam-do, Korea (South)
Tel.: (82) 413578701
Steel Products Mfr
N.A.I.C.S.: 331110

N.I STEEL Co., Ltd. - Kwang-yang Division (1)
600 Baekun-ro Gwangyang-eup, Gwangyang, Jeollanam-do, Korea (South)
Tel.: (82) 617955662
Steel Products Mfr
N.A.I.C.S.: 331110

N.I STEEL Co., Ltd. - Po-hang Division (1)
Tel.: (82) 542787771
Steel Products Mfr
N.A.I.C.S.: 331110

N.K. INDUSTRIES LTD.
7th Floor Popular House Ashram Road, Ahmedabad, 380009, Gujarat, India
Tel.: (91) 7966309999
Web Site: http://www.nkindustriesltd.com
Year Founded: 1987
Castor Oil Mfr & Whslr
N.A.I.C.S.: 324191
Nimish K. Patel (Chm & Mng Dir)

N.K. SHACOLAS (HOLDINGS) LTD.
Shacolas House 200 Lemesos Avenue, Athalassa, 2025, Strovolos, Cyprus
Tel.: (357) 22740300
Web Site: http://www.ctcgroup.com
Holding Services
N.A.I.C.S.: 551112

Subsidiaries:

Cyprus Trading Corporation Plc (1)
Shacolas House Athalassa 200 Lemesos Avenue, Strovolos, 2025, Nicosia, Cyprus (87%)
Tel.: (357) 22740300
Web Site: http://www.ctcgroup.com
Sales Range: Less than $1 Million
Holding Company; Consumer Goods, Vehicles, Tobacco, Home Furnishings & Electric Appliances Distr
N.A.I.C.S.: 551112
Demetris Demetriou (Chm)

Subsidiary (Domestic):

ARGOSY TRADING CO. LTD (2)
Industrial Area nisou, Nissou, Nicosia, 1507, Cyprus
Tel.: (357) 22741000
Web Site: http://www.ctcgroup.com
Sales Range: $50-74.9 Million
Emp.: 300
Tobacco Products Whslr
N.A.I.C.S.: 424940
George Demetriades (Gen Mgr)

ARTVIEW CO. LTD (2)
Industrial Area Pera Chorio, Nissou, Nicosia, 1507, Cyprus
Tel.: (357) 22741000
Sales Range: $25-49.9 Million
Emp.: 25
Luxury Cosmetics & Fragrances Services
N.A.I.C.S.: 456120
Victoria Guezukutchukian (Gen Mgr)

CASSANDRA TRADING LTD (2)
Industrial Area Pera Chorio, PO Box 21355, Nissou, 1507, Nicosia, Cyprus
Tel.: (357) 22741000
Web Site: http://www.ctcgroup.com
Emp.: 20
Tobacco Product Distr
N.A.I.C.S.: 424940
Antonis Hatzilazarou (Mng Dir)

Christis Dairies Limited (2)
PO Box 17102, 2261, Nicosia, Cyprus
Tel.: (357) 22443044
Web Site: http://www.christis.com.cy
Milk, Cheese & Dairy Products Mfr & Distr
N.A.I.C.S.: 311513

Affiliate (Domestic):

Ermes Department Stores Ltd. (2)
Yannis Kranidiotis 154, PO Box 22273, Latsia, Nicosia, 2235, Cyprus
Tel.: (357) 22365000
Web Site: http://www.ermes.com.cy
Sales Range: $450-499.9 Million
Emp.: 1,100
Departmental Store Operator
N.A.I.C.S.: 455110
George Aniliades (Mng Dir)

Subsidiary (Domestic):

HOB House of Beauty Ltd. (2)
11 Dighenis Akritas Avenue, 1055, Nicosia, Cyprus
Tel.: (357) 22 746 722
Cosmetics Distr
N.A.I.C.S.: 456120
Dina Christophi (Brand Mgr-Lancome)

SCANDIA COMPANY LTD (2)
Shacolas House Athalassa, PO Box 21744, Nicosia, 21744 1589, Cyprus
Tel.: (357) 22740400
Web Site: http://www.scandia.com.cy
Sales Range: $25-49.9 Million
Emp.: 115
Home Appliances Retail Services
N.A.I.C.S.: 449210
Stelios Athanasiou (Mgr)

SUPERHOME CENTER (DIY) LTD (2)
Kampou st, PO Box 12658, Strovolos, 2030, Cyprus
Tel.: (357) 22205409
Web Site: http://www.superhome.com.cy
Emp.: 250
Hose Hold Products Mfr
N.A.I.C.S.: 449129
Giovanni George (Gen Mgr)

N.K.INDUSTRIES LTD.
7th Floor Popular House, Ashram Road, Ahmedabad, 380009, Gujarat, India
Tel.: (91) 7966309999
Web Site: https://www.nkindustriesltd.com
Year Founded: 1987
519494—(BOM)
Rev.: $2,179,522
Assets: $227,502,716
Liabilities: $268,614,615
Net Worth: ($41,111,900)
Earnings: $223,140
Emp.: 201
Fiscal Year-end: 03/31/23
Oilseed Processing Services
N.A.I.C.S.: 311224
Nimish K. Patel (Chm & Mng Dir)

N.P. SPINNING MILLS LIMITED
702 Uni Tower I I Chundrigar Rd, Karachi, Pakistan
Tel.: (92) 212410663
Web Site: http://www.npgroup.org
Year Founded: 1993
Sales Range: $10-24.9 Million
Spinning Mills
N.A.I.C.S.: 313110

N.PRIOR ENERGY GMBH
Gustav Elster Str 1, Leer, 26789, Germany
Tel.: (49) 1 9799 0110
Web Site: http://www.n-prior.com
Sales Range: $125-149.9 Million
Emp.: 200

AND PRIVATE COMPANIES

Wind Energy & Biomass Energy System Development Services
N.A.I.C.S.: 221118
Ingo de Buhr *(Mng Dir)*

N.R. AGARWAL INDUSTRIES LTD.
502-A/501-B Fortune Terraces 5th Floor Opp City Mall, New Link Road Andheri West, Mumbai, 400 053, India
Tel.: (91) 2267317500
Web Site: https://www.nrail.com
NRAIL—(NSE)
Rev.: $213,236,305
Assets: $124,799,269
Liabilities: $48,588,898
Net Worth: $76,210,371
Earnings: $11,906,181
Emp.: 1,364
Fiscal Year-end: 03/31/23
Coated Duplex Board & Newsprint
N.A.I.C.S.: 322130
Rajendra Nagindas Agarwal *(Chm & Mng Dir)*

Subsidiaries:

N.R. Agarwal Industries Ltd. - Unit I (1)
Plot No 169 Phase II GIDC, Valsad, 396 195, Gujarat, India
Tel.: (91) 2602401634
Web Site: http://www.nrail.com
Coated Board Mfr
N.A.I.C.S.: 322220

N.R. Agarwal Industries Ltd. - Unit II (1)
Plot No 1 Phase I GIDC, Vapi, Valsad, 396 195, Gujarat, India
Tel.: (91) 2602400979
Web Site: http://www.nrail.com
Newsprint Mfr
N.A.I.C.S.: 322120

N.R. Agarwal Industries Ltd. - Unit III (1)
Plot No 901 Phase III GIDC, Valsad, 396 195, Gujarat, India
Tel.: (91) 2602400052
Web Site: http://www.nrail.com
Coated Board Mfr
N.A.I.C.S.: 322220

N.R. Agarwal Industries Ltd. - Unit IV (1)
Plot No 901 Phase III GIDO Vapi, Valsad, 396 195, Gujarat, India
Tel.: (91) 2602400052
Web Site: http://www.nrail.com
Sales Range: $25-49.9 Million
Emp.: 80
Coated Board Mfr
N.A.I.C.S.: 322220

N.RUNS AG
Nassauer Strasse 60, 61440, Oberursel, Germany
Tel.: (49) 61716990
Web Site: http://www.nruns.com
Year Founded: 2001
Sales Range: $1-9.9 Million
Emp.: 30
IT Consulting, Security & Infrastructure Services
N.A.I.C.S.: 541690
Donald Lee *(CEO & Mng Dir)*

N.V. NEDERLANDSE GASUNIE
Concourslaan 17, 9727 KC, Groningen, Netherlands
Tel.: (31) 505219111
Web Site: http://www.gasunie.nl
Year Founded: 1963
Rev.: $1,431,405,052
Assets: $11,339,814,346
Liabilities: $4,692,997,302
Net Worth: $6,646,817,044
Earnings: $461,382,320
Emp.: 1,482
Fiscal Year-end: 12/31/19

Gas Transportation Services
N.A.I.C.S.: 486210
Han Fennema *(Chm-Exec Bd & CEO)*

Subsidiaries:

BBL Company V.O.F. (1)
Concourslaan 17, 9727 KC, Groningen, Netherlands (60%)
Tel.: (31) 505212150
Web Site: http://www.bblcompany.com
Sales Range: $25-49.9 Million
Water Sewer & Pipeline Construction
N.A.I.C.S.: 237120

C.V. Gasexpansie Ijmond (1)
PO Box 19, 9700MA, Groningen, Netherlands (50%)
Tel.: (31) 505219111
Web Site: http://www.gasunie.com.nl
Sales Range: $500-549.9 Million
Emp.: 1,000
Hydroelectric Power Generation
N.A.I.C.S.: 221111

Gas Transport Services B.V. (1)
Concourslaan 17, 9727 KC, Groningen, Netherlands
Tel.: (31) 505212250
Web Site: http://www.gasunietransportservices.nl
Sales Range: $50-74.9 Million
Emp.: 1,000
Gas Transmission Systems Operator
N.A.I.C.S.: 486210

Gasunie BBL B.V. (1)
PO Box 19, 9700MA, Groningen, Netherlands (100%)
Tel.: (31) 505219111
Web Site: http://www.gasunie.nl
Sales Range: $25-49.9 Million
Emp.: 100
Gas Lines Construction
N.A.I.C.S.: 237120

Gasunie Deutschland GmbH & Co. KG (1)
Pelikanplatz 5, 30177, Hannover, Germany
Tel.: (49) 511 6406070
Pipeline Gas Transport Services
N.A.I.C.S.: 486210

Gasunie Engineering B.V. (1)
Concourslaan 17, 9727 KC, Groningen, Netherlands (100%)
Tel.: (31) 505212525
Web Site: http://www.engineering.gasunie.nl
Sales Range: $350-399.9 Million
Emp.: 1,500
Engineeering Services
N.A.I.C.S.: 541330

Gasunie Infrastruktur AG (1)
Dammstrasse 19, 6301, Zug, Switzerland
Tel.: (41) 417 232210
Web Site: http://www.gasunieinfrastructure.com
Pipeline Gas Transport Services
N.A.I.C.S.: 486210
Ulco Vermeulen *(Chm)*

Gasunie LNG Holding B.V. (1)
Concourslaan 17, 9727 KC, Groningen, Netherlands (100%)
Tel.: (31) 505212255
Web Site: http://www.gasunie.nl
Sales Range: $250-299.9 Million
Emp.: 1,000
Holding Company
N.A.I.C.S.: 551112

Gasunie Zuidwending B.V. (1)
PO Box 19, 9700MA, Groningen, Netherlands (100%)
Tel.: (31) 505219111
Web Site: http://www.gasunie.nl
Sales Range: $200-249.9 Million
Emp.: 1,000
Water Sewer & Pipeline Construction
N.A.I.C.S.: 237120

Gate Terminal B.V. (1)
Maasvlakteweg 991, 3199 LZ, Rotterdam, Netherlands (50%)
Tel.: (31) 181799000
Web Site: http://www.gateterminal.com
Engineeering Services
N.A.I.C.S.: 541330

Gate Terminal Management B.V. (1)
Oslo 20, 2993 LD, Barendrecht, Netherlands (50%)
Tel.: (31) 180646880
Web Site: http://www.gateterminal.com
Sales Range: $25-49.9 Million
Emp.: 50
Management Consulting Services
N.A.I.C.S.: 541618

Vertogas B.V. (1)
Concourslaan 17, 9727 KC, Groningen, Netherlands
Tel.: (31) 505 219222
Web Site: http://www.vertogas.nl
Pipeline Gas Transport Services
N.A.I.C.S.: 486210

Zuidwending V.O.F. (1)
PO Box 19, Groningen, 9700 MA, Netherlands (50%)
Tel.: (31) 505219111
Web Site: http://www.gasunie.nl
Sales Range: $25-49.9 Million
Emp.: 50
Water Sewer & Pipeline Construction
N.A.I.C.S.: 237120

N.V. ROTTERDAM-RIJN PIJPLEIDING MAATSCHAPPIJ
Butaanweg 215, 3196 KC, Rotterdam, Netherlands
Tel.: (31) 102958444
Web Site: http://www.rrpweb.nl
Year Founded: 1958
Sales Range: $25-49.9 Million
Emp.: 55
Crude Oil & Oil Product Transportation Services
N.A.I.C.S.: 486110
Bas Chandelier *(Mng Dir)*

N1 HOLDINGS LIMITED
Suite 502 Level 5 77 King Street, Sydney, 2000, NSW, Australia
Tel.: (61) 292626262
Web Site: https://www.n1holdings.com.au
Year Founded: 2011
N1H—(ASX)
Rev.: $8,440,512
Assets: $61,223,970
Liabilities: $60,745,299
Net Worth: $478,671
Earnings: $844,624
Emp.: 587
Fiscal Year-end: 06/30/22
Holding Company
N.A.I.C.S.: 551112
Ren Hor Wong *(Chm & CEO)*

N1 TECHNOLOGIES, INC.
35 New Road, PO Box 198, Belize, Belize
Tel.: (501) 4037759908
Nanotechnology Research & Development Services
N.A.I.C.S.: 541713
Thomas Easton *(Sec)*

N2N CONNECT BERHAD
Wisma N2N Level 9 Tower 2 Avenue 3 Bangsar South No 8, Jalan Kerinchi, 59200, Kuala Lumpur, Malaysia
Tel.: (60) 322411818 MY
Web Site: https://www.n2nconnect.com
Year Founded: 2000
N2N—(KLS)
Rev.: $21,801,020
Assets: $65,129,948
Liabilities: $5,089,109
Net Worth: $60,040,839
Earnings: $3,964,513
Emp.: 200
Fiscal Year-end: 12/31/22
Electronic Securities Trading Platform Developer & Services
N.A.I.C.S.: 541511

Boon Hwa Tiang *(Co-Founder & Mng Dir)*

Subsidiaries:

N2N Advanced Learning Sdn. Bhd. (1)
Wisma N2N Level 9 Tower 2 Avenue 3 Bangsar South No 8 Jalan Kerinchi, 59200, Kuala Lumpur, Malaysia
Tel.: (60) 322411818
Web Site: http://www.learning.asiaebroker.com
Financial Management Services
N.A.I.C.S.: 541611

N2N Connect Pte. Ltd. (1)
22 Sin Ming Lane 06-76, Midview City, Singapore, 068808, Singapore
Tel.: (65) 65364832
Securities Trading Platform Marketing, Sales & Consultancy Services
N.A.I.C.S.: 541690

N2N-AFE (Hong Kong) Limited (1)
Unit 1907B-1910A 19/F 18 Tak Fung Street, One Harbourfront Hunghom, Kowloon, China (Hong Kong) (100%)
Tel.: (852) 23292188
Web Site: https://afe.hk
Financial Investment Information, Securities Trading & Settlement Services
N.A.I.C.S.: 518210

X8NET Sdn. Bhd. (1)
Wisma N2N Level 9 Tower 2 Avenue 3, Bangsar South No 8 Jalan Kerinch, 59200, Kuala Lumpur, Malaysia
Tel.: (60) 322411818
Web Site: https://www.xeightnet.com
Software Development Services
N.A.I.C.S.: 541511

N2N TECHNOLOGIES LIMITED
Sun Lounge Ground Floor One Earth, Opp Magarpatta City Hadapsar, Pune, 411 028, India
Tel.: (91) 2030525201
Web Site: https://www.n2ntechno.com
512279—(BOM)
Rev.: $73,533
Assets: $776,105
Liabilities: $109,370
Net Worth: $666,735
Earnings: $3,885
Fiscal Year-end: 03/31/23
Information Technology Consulting Services
N.A.I.C.S.: 541512
Rahul Shah *(Founder & CEO)*

N2OFF INC.
Kibbutz Alonim, Kiryat Tivon, 3657700, Israel
Tel.: (972) 722116144 DE
Web Site: https://www.n2off.com
Year Founded: 2004
NITO—(NASDAQ)
Rev.: $394,004
Assets: $6,492,213
Liabilities: $754,872
Net Worth: $5,737,341
Earnings: ($5,739,600)
Emp.: 6
Fiscal Year-end: 12/31/22
Fruits & Vegetables Pre & Post Harvest Treatment Products Developer
N.A.I.C.S.: 325320
David Palach *(CEO)*

NAAMAN GROUP NV LTD.
Address 2 Afek Park, Rosh Ha'Ayin, 4809202, Israel
Tel.: (972) 32111710
Web Site: http://www.naamanp.co.il
Porcelain Product Mfr
N.A.I.C.S.: 327110
Raz Schwartz *(CEO)*

NAAPBOOKS LIMITED

NAAPBOOKS LIMITED

Naapbooks Limited—(Continued)
3Rd Floor Bbc Law Garden, Ahmedabad, 380006, Gujarat, India
Tel.: (91) 7948940505
Web Site:
  https://www.naapbooks.com
Year Founded: 2015
543351—(BOM)
Emp.: 50
Software Development Services
N.A.I.C.S.: 541511
Ashish Jain *(Co-Founder & CEO)*

NAAS TECHNOLOGY INC.
Room 101 Jia He Guo Xin Mansion No 15 Baiqiao Street, Guangqumennei Dongcheng District, Beijing, 100062, China
Tel.: (86) 1085599000
Web Site: http://www.risecenter.com
Year Founded: 2007
NAAS—(NASDAQ)
Rev.: $14,220,033
Assets: $169,440,301
Liabilities: $102,200,416
Net Worth: $67,239,886
Earnings: ($863,700,692)
Emp.: 311
Fiscal Year-end: 12/31/22
Education Training Services
N.A.I.C.S.: 611710
Lihong Wang *(Chm)*

Subsidiaries:

Edge Franchising Co., Limited (1)
22/F The Zoroastrian Building 101 Leighton Road, Causeway Bay, China (Hong Kong)
Tel.: (852) 29722555
Web Site:
  https//www.theedgefranchising.com
Educational Consulting Services
N.A.I.C.S.: 611710

NABA ALSAHA MEDICAL SERVICES CO.
PO Box 887, Al Khobar, 31911, Saudi Arabia
Tel.: (966) 138555000
Web Site: https://www.nams.sa
Year Founded: 1984
9546—(SAU)
Rev.: $48,626,035
Assets: $73,789,505
Liabilities: $25,765,641
Net Worth: $48,023,863
Earnings: $13,968,227
Emp.: 760
Fiscal Year-end: 12/31/23
Health Care Srvices
N.A.I.C.S.: 621610
Abd Al-Wahhab Muhammad Saad Al-Ajroush *(Chm)*

NABALTEC AG
Alustrasse 50 - 52, 92421, Schwandorf, Germany
Tel.: (49) 9431530
Web Site: https://www.nabaltec.de
Year Founded: 1994
NTG—(DEU)
Rev.: $220,917,503
Assets: $310,055,006
Liabilities: $153,515,201
Net Worth: $156,539,805
Earnings: $12,606,195
Emp.: 516
Fiscal Year-end: 12/31/23
Chemical Product Mfr & Whslr
N.A.I.C.S.: 325510
Johannes Heckmann *(CEO & Member-Mgmt Bd)*

NABATI FOODS GLOBAL INC.
1570 505 Burrard Street, Vancouver, V7X 1M5, BC, Canada
Tel.: (604) 416-4099

Year Founded: 2020
MEALF—(OTCIQ)
Rev.: $210,850
Assets: $97,597
Liabilities: $3,802,701
Net Worth: ($3,705,104)
Earnings: ($2,198,728)
Fiscal Year-end: 12/31/22
Food Product Mfr & Distr
N.A.I.C.S.: 311412
Ahmad Yehya *(Pres, CEO & COO)*

NABCO HOUSING INC.
686 Rang Riviere Est, Sainte-Brigide-d'Iberville, J0J 1X0, QC, Canada
Tel.: (450) 293-3125
Web Site:
  http://www.nabcohousing.com
Sales Range: $10-24.9 Million
Emp.: 30
Building Construction Services
N.A.I.C.S.: 236220
M. Florian Bessette *(VP & Mgr-Sls)*

NABERTHERM GMBH
Bahnhofstr 20, 28865, Lilienthal, Germany
Tel.: (49) 42989220
Web Site:
  http://www.nabertherm.com
Year Founded: 1947
Rev.: $28,829,460
Emp.: 500
Furnace Mfr
N.A.I.C.S.: 333994

Subsidiaries:

Nabertherm (Shanghai) Industrial Furnaces Ltd. (1)
150 Lane No 158 Pingbei Road, Minhang District, Shanghai, 201109, China
Tel.: (86) 2164902960
Web Site: http://www.nabertherm-cn.com
Industrial Furnace Distr
N.A.I.C.S.: 423830

Nabertherm Iberica, SL (1)
c/Marti i Julia 8 Bajos 7a, 8940, Cornella de Llobregat, Spain
Tel.: (34) 934744716
Web Site: http://www.nabertherm.es
Industrial Furnace Distr
N.A.I.C.S.: 423830

Nabertherm Inc. (1)
54 Read's Way, New Castle, DE 19720
Tel.: (302) 322-3665
Web Site: http://www.nabertherm.com
Emp.: 5
Industrial Furnace Mfr
N.A.I.C.S.: 333994
John Crowther *(Mgr-Technical Sls)*

Nabertherm Italia (1)
via Trento N 17, 50139, Florence, Italy
Tel.: (39) 03483820278
Web Site: http://www.nabertherm.it
Industrial Furnace Distr
N.A.I.C.S.: 423830

Nabertherm SARL (1)
35 Allee des Impressionnistes, BP 44011, 95911, Roissy-en-France, Cedex, France
Tel.: (33) 153561800
Web Site: http://www.nabertherm.fr
Industrial Furnace Distr
N.A.I.C.S.: 423830

Nabertherm Switzerland AG (1)
Batterieweg 6, 4614, Hagendorf, Switzerland
Tel.: (41) 622096070
Web Site: http://www.nabertherm.ch
Industrial Furnace Distr
N.A.I.C.S.: 423830

NABI GYARTO ES KERESKEDELMI KFT.
Ujszasz U 45, 1165, Budapest, Hungary
Tel.: (36) 14017399
Web Site: http://www.nabi.hu
Year Founded: 1993

Sales Range: $350-399.9 Million
Emp.: 1,855
Mfr & Sales of Buses
N.A.I.C.S.: 485410

NABIL BANK LTD.
Nabil Center Beena Marga Durbar Marg, Kathmandu, Nepal
Tel.: (977) 14221718
Web Site: https://www.nabilbank.com
Year Founded: 2010
NABIL—(NEP)
Rev.: $145,104,371
Assets: $2,460,480,472
Liabilities: $2,172,392,765
Net Worth: $288,087,707
Earnings: $39,261,884
Emp.: 1,271
Fiscal Year-end: 07/15/21
Banking Services
N.A.I.C.S.: 522110
Roshan Koirala *(Head-HR)*

Subsidiaries:

Nabil Investment Banking Ltd. (1)
3rd Floor Central Plaza Narayanchaur, Kathmandu, Nepal
Tel.: (977) 14511604
Web Site: https://www.nabilinvest.com.np
Sales Range: $50-74.9 Million
Emp.: 10
Investment Banking Services
N.A.I.C.S.: 523150
Pravin Raman Parajuli *(CEO)*

NABLE COMMUNICATIONS, INC.
Sampyeong-dong Uspace1 A-dong 701-ho 660 Daewangpangyo-ro, Bundang-gu, Seongnam, 13494, Gyeonggi-do, Korea (South)
Tel.: (82) 316281250
Web Site:
  https://www.nablecomm.com
Year Founded: 2003
153460—(KRS)
Rev.: $14,035,187
Assets: $28,092,935
Liabilities: $3,067,124
Net Worth: $25,025,811
Earnings: $4,047,963
Emp.: 111
Fiscal Year-end: 12/31/22
IP Telephony, IMS Enabler (Application Server) & IMS Client Solutions
N.A.I.C.S.: 541519
Jong-Hwa Cho *(VP)*

NABLUS SURGICAL CENTER
An Najah St, Nablus, Palestine
Tel.: (970) 92341501
Web Site: http://www.nsh-pal.ps
Year Founded: 1995
NSC—(PAL)
Rev.: $8,440,748
Assets: $29,339,725
Liabilities: $18,260,933
Net Worth: $11,078,792
Earnings: $1,130,745
Fiscal Year-end: 12/31/23
Healthcare Services
N.A.I.C.S.: 621491
Amjad Mohammad Osamah Mohammad Saleh Bishtawi *(Chm)*

NABORS INDUSTRIES LTD.
Crown House 2nd Floor 4 Par la Ville Road, Hamilton, HM08, Bermuda
Tel.: (441) 2921510
Web Site: https://www.nabors.com
Year Founded: 1952
NBR—(NYSE)
Rev.: $3,049,801,000
Assets: $5,277,965,000
Liabilities: $4,735,955,000
Net Worth: $542,010,000
Earnings: ($11,784,000)

INTERNATIONAL PUBLIC

Emp.: 12,000
Fiscal Year-end: 12/31/23
Contract Drilling & Oilfield Transportation & Support Services
N.A.I.C.S.: 213111
Anthony G. Petrello *(Chm, Pres & CEO)*

Subsidiaries:

Canrig Drilling Technology, Ltd. (1)
8223 Willow Pl Dr S, Houston, TX 77070
Tel.: (281) 774-5600
Web Site: http://www.canrig.com
Sales Range: $150-199.9 Million
Emp.: 350
Drilling Equipment Mfr & Distr
N.A.I.C.S.: 423810

Nabors Alaska Drilling, Inc. (1)
2525 C St Ste 200, Anchorage, AK 99503-2632 (100%)
Tel.: (907) 263-6000
Web Site: http://www.nabors.com
Drilling Services
N.A.I.C.S.: 551112
Dave Hebert *(Gen Mgr)*

Nabors Drilling International Limited (1)
515 W Greens Rd Ste 1200, Houston, TX 77067-4536
Tel.: (281) 874-0035
Web Site: http://www.nabors.com
Sales Range: $200-249.9 Million
Emp.: 500
Oil Well Drilling Services
N.A.I.C.S.: 213111

Nabors Drilling Technologies USA, Inc. (1)
515 W Greens Rd Ste 1200, Houston, TX 77067
Tel.: (281) 874-0035
Web Site: http://www.nabors.com
Sales Range: $350-399.9 Million
Emp.: 600
Drilling Services
N.A.I.C.S.: 213111

Nabors Global Holdings Ltd. (1)
Mintflower Place 8 Par-la-Ville Rd, Hamilton, HM 08, Bermuda
Tel.: (441) 12921510
Investment Management Service
N.A.I.C.S.: 523999

Nabors Industries Inc. (1)
515 W Greens Rd Ste 1200, Houston, TX 77067
Tel.: (281) 874-0035
Web Site: http://www.nabors.com
Oilfield Transportation & Support Services
N.A.I.C.S.: 213111

Nabors International Finance Inc. (1)
515 W Greens Rd Ste 900, Houston, TX 77067
Tel.: (281) 874-0036
Oil & Gas Wells Drilling Services
N.A.I.C.S.: 213111

Nabors Offshore (1)
515 W Greens Rd Ste 1200, Houston, TX 77067
Tel.: (281) 874-0035
Web Site: http://www.e-rig.com
Sales Range: $400-449.9 Million
Emp.: 669
Offshore Well Servicing, Workovers & Completion Services; Domestic & International
N.A.I.C.S.: 213112

Branch (Domestic):

Nabors Offshore (2)
610 Palm Ave, Houma, LA 70363 (100%)
Tel.: (985) 868-1874
Web Site: http://www.nabor.com
Sales Range: $50-74.9 Million
Emp.: 3
Offshore Oil Operations
N.A.I.C.S.: 213111

Nabors Well Services (1)
515 W Greens Rd Ste 1200, Houston, TX 77067-4536
Tel.: (281) 874-0035
Web Site: http://www.nabors.com

AND PRIVATE COMPANIES / NABTESCO CORPORATION

Sales Range: $1-4.9 Billion
Emp.: 4,000
Oil & Gas Support Services
N.A.I.C.S.: 213112

Holding (Non-US):

International Sea Drilling Ltd. (2)
332 Raglan St, PO Box 161, Sale, 3850, VIC, Australia **(100%)**
Tel.: (61) 351432011
Web Site: http://www.nabors.com
Sales Range: $25-49.9 Million
Emp.: 50
Offshore Drilling & Workover Contractor
N.A.I.C.S.: 333132

Nabors International Argentina S.R.L. (2)
Rodriguez Pena 680, Luzuriaga Maipu, 5513, Mendoza, Argentina **(100%)**
Tel.: (54) 2614051100
Web Site: http://www.nabors.com
Sales Range: $150-199.9 Million
Emp.: 350
Land Drilling & Workover Contractor
N.A.I.C.S.: 213112

Subsidiary (Domestic):

Nabors Well Services Co (2)
7515 Rosedale Hwy, Bakersfield, CA 93308
Tel.: (661) 589-3970
Sales Range: $25-49.9 Million
Emp.: 10
Well-Servicing & Workover Contractor
N.A.I.C.S.: 237120
Dave Werner *(VP & Gen Mgr)*

Holding (Non-US):

Pool Arabia Company Ltd. (2)
PO Box 2862, 31952, Al Khobar, Saudi Arabia **(51%)**
Tel.: (966) 38914982
Web Site: http://www.alturkigroup.com
Oil & Gas Field Services
N.A.I.C.S.: 213112

Pool International (2)
Portugal E 100 47 Republica Del Salvador, Quito, Ecuador **(100%)**
Tel.: (593) 22446338
Sales Range: $25-49.9 Million
Emp.: 45
Land Drilling & Workover Contractor
N.A.I.C.S.: 213112

Peak Oilfield Services Company (1)
5015 Business Park Blvd Ste 4000, Anchorage, AK 99503
Tel.: (907) 263-7000
Web Site: http://www.peakalaska.com
Sales Range: $75-99.9 Million
Drilling Oil & Gas Wells
N.A.I.C.S.: 811310
Tom Pellegrom *(Pres & CEO)*

Peak USA Energy Services Ltd. (1)
515 W Greens Rd Ste 600, Houston, TX 77067
Tel.: (281) 872-7325
Rev.: $34,065,707
Emp.: 400
Heavy Machinery Transport
N.A.I.C.S.: 484230
Tony Petreolo *(COO)*

Ryan Directional Services, Inc. (1)
2719 61st Ave SE, Calgary, T2C 4X3, AB, Canada
Tel.: (403) 236-2157
Oil & Gas Well Drilling Services
N.A.I.C.S.: 213111

Ryan Energy Technologies USA, Inc. (1)
19510 Oil Center Blvd, Houston, TX 77073
Tel.: (281) 443-1414
Web Site: http://www.nabors.com
Sales Range: $50-74.9 Million
Emp.: 60
Drilling Services
N.A.I.C.S.: 213111

NABRIVA THERAPEUTICS PLC

25-28 North Wall Quay IFSC, Dublin, 1, Ireland

Tel.: (353) 16492000 AT
Web Site: http://www.nabriva.com
Year Founded: 2005
NBRV—(NASDAQ)
Rev.: $36,935,000
Assets: $31,765,000
Liabilities: $28,472,000
Net Worth: $3,293,000
Earnings: ($57,185,000)
Emp.: 24
Fiscal Year-end: 12/31/22
Biopharmaceutical Mfr
N.A.I.C.S.: 325412
Theodore R. Schroeder *(CEO)*

Subsidiaries:

Nabriva Therapeutics GmbH. (1)
Leberstrasse 20, 1110, Vienna, Austria
Tel.: (43) 1740930
Web Site: https://www.nabriva.com
Pharmaceuticals Product Mfr
N.A.I.C.S.: 325412
Ted Schroeder *(CEO)*

Nabriva Therapeutics Ireland Designated Activity Company (1)
Alexandra House Office 225/227 The Sweepstakes, Ballsbridge, Dublin, D04 C7H2, Ireland
Tel.: (353) 16641700
Pharmaceuticals Product Mfr
N.A.I.C.S.: 325412

Zavante Therapeutics, Inc. (1)
8988 Gainsborough Ave, San Diego, CA 92129-3100
Tel.: (678) 664-9841
Research & Development in Biotechnology
N.A.I.C.S.: 541714
Cam L. Garner *(Co-Founder & Chm)*

NABTESCO CORPORATION

JA Kyosai Building 2-7-9 Hirakawacho, Chiyoda-ku, Tokyo, 102-0093, Japan
Tel.: (81) 352131133 JP
Web Site: https://www.nabtesco.com
Year Founded: 2003
6268—(TKS)
Rev.: $2,365,443,790
Assets: $2,992,440,850
Liabilities: $1,036,352,390
Net Worth: $1,956,088,460
Earnings: $103,187,860
Emp.: 8,158
Fiscal Year-end: 12/31/23
Holding Company
N.A.I.C.S.: 551112
Katsuhiro Teramoto *(Pres & CEO)*

Subsidiaries:

Adcos GmbH (1)
Zollstockgurtel 67, 50969, Cologne, Germany
Tel.: (49) 2211680590
Web Site: https://www.adcos.de
Software Development Services
N.A.I.C.S.: 541511

Changzhou Nabtesco Precision Machinery Co., Ltd. (1)
No 116 West Wujin Avenue, Wujin High Tech Industrial Zone, Changzhou, 213166, Jiangsu, China
Tel.: (86) 51986220221
Gear Wheel Mfr & Distr
N.A.I.C.S.: 336350

Cmet Inc. (1)
Sumitomo Fudosan Shin-yokohama Bld 2-5-5 Shin-yokohama, Kohoku-ku, Yokohama, 222-0033, Kanagawa, Japan **(92.5%)**
Tel.: (81) 454785561
Web Site: https://www.cmet.co.jp
Sales Range: $25-49.9 Million
Industrial Machinery & Equipment Whslr
N.A.I.C.S.: 423830

Diavac Limited (1)
495 Owadashinden, Yachiyo, Chiba, 276-0046, Japan **(100%)**
Tel.: (81) 474595311
Web Site: http://www.diavac.co.jp

Emp.: 69
Industrial Furnace & Oven Mfr
N.A.I.C.S.: 333994

Gilgen Door Systems (Suzhou) Co., Ltd. (1)
Block No 28 Unit A Suzhou Industrial Square 428 Xinglong Street, Suzhou, 215126, Jiangsu, China
Tel.: (86) 512 6283 6732
Web Site: http://www.nabtesco.com
Building Materials Distr
N.A.I.C.S.: 423320

Gilgen Door Systems AG (1)
Freiburgstrasse 34, 3150, Schwarzenburg, Switzerland **(100%)**
Tel.: (41) 317344111
Web Site: https://www.gilgendoorsystems.com
Sales Range: $150-199.9 Million
Emp.: 1,100
Automatic Door Mfr
N.A.I.C.S.: 332321

Gilgen Door Systems Austria GmbH (1)
Concorde Business Park 1/E/1/4, 2320, Schwechat, Austria
Tel.: (43) 17065866
Web Site: http://www.gilgendoorsystems.at
Emp.: 9
Automatic Door Distr
N.A.I.C.S.: 423310

Gilgen Door Systems France S.A.S. (1)
Immeuble Ampere 21 rue Alexis de Tocqueville, Antony, 92182, Cedex, France
Tel.: (33) 146 666 680
Emp.: 5
Automatic Door Mfr
N.A.I.C.S.: 332321
Jacques Mongiraud *(Office Mgr)*

Gilgen Door Systems Germany GmbH (1)
Am Froschbachle 10, 77815, Buhl, Germany
Tel.: (49) 722380887610
Web Site: http://www.gilgendoorsystems.de
Sales Range: $50-74.9 Million
Emp.: 10
Automatic Door Distr
N.A.I.C.S.: 423310

Gilgen Door Systems Italy Srl. (1)
Via della Fisica 4, 40068, San Lazzaro di Savena, BO, Italy
Tel.: (39) 051704945
Web Site: http://www.gilgendoorsystems.it
Sales Range: $50-74.9 Million
Emp.: 9
Automatic Door Distr
N.A.I.C.S.: 423310

Gilgen Door Systems UK Limited (1)
Halesfield 4, Telford, Shropshire, United Kingdom
Tel.: (44) 870 000 5252
Web Site: http://www.gilgendoorsystems.co.uk
Automatic Door Mfr
N.A.I.C.S.: 332321

Gilgen Door Systems UK Ltd. (1)
Crow House Crow Arch Lane, Ringwood, BH24 1PD, Hampshire, United Kingdom **(100%)**
Tel.: (44) 1425462000
Web Site: http://www.gilgendoorsystems.co.uk
Sales Range: $10-24.9 Million
Emp.: 50
Security Systems
N.A.I.C.S.: 561621

Gilgen Nabtesco (Hong Kong) Limited (1)
Unit 513 Global Gateway Tower 63 Wing Hong Street, Cheung Sha Wan, Kowloon, China (Hong Kong)
Tel.: (852) 35807708
Platform Door Inspection Services
N.A.I.C.S.: 541350

Jiangsu Nabtesco KTK Railroad Products Co., Ltd. (1)
No 19 Fengxi Road, Wujin High-Tech Industrial Zone, Changzhou, 213164, Jiangsu, China
Tel.: (86) 51969693333
Brake System Mfr & Distr
N.A.I.C.S.: 336340

NABCO Entrances, Inc. (1)
S82 W18717 Gemini Dr, Muskego, WI 53150-0906
Web Site: http://www.nabcoentrances.com
Sales Range: $25-49.9 Million
Emp.: 100
Developer & Mfr of Automatic & Device Activated Entrance Systems & Doors
N.A.I.C.S.: 332321

NABTEC Co., Ltd. (1)
7-3-3 Takatsukadai, Nishi-ku, Kobe, 651-2271, Hyogo, Japan
Tel.: (81) 789963705
Web Site: http://www.nabtec.co.jp
Sales Range: $50-74.9 Million
Machinery Design Services
N.A.I.C.S.: 333248

Nabco Auto Door (Beijing) Co., Ltd. (1)
2F Liandong U Valley No 15 Jingsheng South Fourth Street, Majuqiao Tongzhou District, Beijing, 101102, China **(98%)**
Tel.: (86) 1060503958
Web Site: https://www.nabco.cn
Automatic Door Parts Mfr
N.A.I.C.S.: 332321

Nabco Canada Inc. (1)
110 W Beaver Creek Rd Unit 12, Richmond Hill, L4B 1J9, ON, Canada
Tel.: (905) 771-5043
Automation Equipment Mfr
N.A.I.C.S.: 334512

Subsidiary (Domestic):

Royal Doors Limited (2)
105 Henri Dunant St, Moncton, E1E 1E4, NB, Canada
Tel.: (506) 857-4075
Web Site: https://www.royaldoorltd.com
Automatic Door Mfr
N.A.I.C.S.: 321911
Daniel Everson *(Pres)*

Nabco Door Ltd. (1)
Dojima Avanza 20F 1-6-20 Dojima, Kita-ku, Osaka, 530-0003, Japan **(63.4%)**
Tel.: (81) 661367284
Web Site: https://www.nabco-door.co.jp
Emp.: 416
Metal Fittings & Construction Hardware Mfr, Sales & Installation
N.A.I.C.S.: 423610

Nabco Engineering Ltd. (1)
1121-1123 Hollywood Plaza 610 Mathan Road, Kowloon, China (Hong Kong) **(100%)**
Tel.: (852) 22434477
Web Site: http://www.gilgen.systems.com
Sales Range: $25-49.9 Million
Emp.: 12
Trade Contractor
N.A.I.C.S.: 238990

Nabco System Co., Ltd. (1)
32nd floor Kasumigaseki Building 3-2-5 Kasumigaseki, Chiyoda-ku, Tokyo, 100-6032, Japan
Tel.: (81) 335916411
Web Site: https://www.nabcosystem.co.jp
Emp.: 845
Automation Equipment Mfr
N.A.I.C.S.: 334512

Nabco Systems Co., Ltd. (1)
32nd Floor Kasumigaseki Building 3-2-5, Kasumigaseki Chiyoda-ku, Tokyo, Japan
Tel.: (81) 120072586
Web Site: https://www.nabcosystem.co.jp
Emp.: 845
Landscaping Services
N.A.I.C.S.: 561730

Nabco Toto Ltd. (1)
253-2 Kaizoe Misaki-cyo Kume-gun, 708-1543, Okayama, Japan **(75%)**
Tel.: (81) 868640881
Metal Window & Door Mfr
N.A.I.C.S.: 332321

Nabmic B.V. (1)

NABTESCO CORPORATION

Nabtesco Corporation—(Continued)
Brouwerstraat 34, 2984AR, Ridderkerk, Netherlands **(90%)**
Tel.: (31) 180530590
Web Site: http://www.nabmic.com
Emp.: 10
Chemical & Products Merchant Whslr
N.A.I.C.S.: 424690
Valentino Bald *(Mgr-Tech)*

Nabtesco (China) Precision Equipment Co., Ltd. (1)
No 116 West Wujin Avenue, Wujin High-Tech Industrial Zone, Changzhou, 213166, Jiangsu, China
Tel.: (86) 51988020020
Precision Reduction Gear Mfr & Distr
N.A.I.C.S.: 333612

Nabtesco Aerospace Europe GmbH (1)
Tiefenbroicher Weg 15, 40472, Dusseldorf, Germany
Tel.: (49) 21117932800
Aircraft Part Mfr
N.A.I.C.S.: 336413

Nabtesco Aerospace Singapore Pte. Ltd. (1)
401 Commonwealth Drive 05-04 Haw Par Technocentre, Singapore, 149598, Singapore
Tel.: (65) 91690731
Aircraft Part Mfr
N.A.I.C.S.: 336413

Nabtesco Aerospace, Inc. (1)
12413 Willows Rd NE, Kirkland, WA 98034 **(100%)**
Tel.: (425) 602-8400
Web Site: https://www.nabtescoaero.com
Sales Range: $25-49.9 Million
Emp.: 40
Aircraft Parts & Auxiliary Equipment Mfr
N.A.I.C.S.: 336413

Nabtesco Automotive Corporation (1)
2-7-9 Hirakawacho, Chiyoda-ku, Tokyo, 102-0093, Japan
Tel.: (81) 3 5213 1190
Web Site: http://www.nabtesco-automotive.com
Sales Range: $50-74.9 Million
Automotive Parts Mfr & Distr
N.A.I.C.S.: 336390
Ataru Inoue *(Pres)*

Joint Venture (Non-US):

Minda Nabtesco Automotive Pvt. Ltd. (2)
B-64/1 Wazirpur Industrial Area North East, Delhi, 110052, India **(49%)**
Tel.: (91) 7838885888
Commercial Vehicles Air Brake Systems Mfr
N.A.I.C.S.: 336340

Plant (Domestic):

Nabtesco Automotive Corporation - Yamagata Plant (2)
5-1 Kanaya Murayama, Yamagata, 995-0004, Japan
Tel.: (81) 237 53 3151
Automotive Parts Mfr & Distr
N.A.I.C.S.: 336390

Nabtesco Automotive Products (Thailand) Co., Ltd. (1)
41-37 Blk D6 Moo 6 Soi Plucharoen Bangna-Trad Rd, 16 5 km Bang-Chaloang Bang-ple, 10540, Bangkok, Samut Prakarn, Thailand **(80%)**
Tel.: (66) 23370139
Motor Vehicle Supplies & New Parts Whslr
N.A.I.C.S.: 423120

Nabtesco Corporation - Gifu Plant (1)
1110-1 Miyashiro Tarui-cho, Fuwa-gun, Gifu, 503-2192, Japan
Tel.: (81) 584 22 3121
Precision Machinery Mfr
N.A.I.C.S.: 332721

Nabtesco Corporation - Iwakuni Plant (1)
Nagano 1808, Iwakuni, 740-0045, Yamaguchi, Japan
Tel.: (81) 82 739 1500
Web Site: http://www.nabtesco.com
Precision Tool Mfr
N.A.I.C.S.: 332216

Nabtesco Corporation - Kobe Plant (1)
3-3 Takatsukadai 7-chome, Nishi-ku, Kobe, 651-2271, Hyogo, Japan
Tel.: (81) 78 993 0300
Web Site: http://www.nabtesco.com
Precision Machinery Mfr
N.A.I.C.S.: 332721

Nabtesco Corporation - Konan Plant (1)
35 Uozakihama-machi, Higashinada-ku, Kobe, 658-0024, Hyogo, Japan
Tel.: (81) 78 413 2531
Web Site: http://www.nabtesco.com
Precision Tool Mfr
N.A.I.C.S.: 332216

Nabtesco Corporation - Seishin Plant (1)
1617-1 Fukuyoshidai 1-chome, Nishi-ku, Kobe, 651-2413, Japan
Tel.: (81) 78 967 1551
Web Site: http://www.nabtesco.com
Precision Tool Mfr
N.A.I.C.S.: 332216

Nabtesco Corporation - Tarui Plant (1)
1414 Tarui-cho, Fuwa-gun, Gifu, 503-2121, Japan
Tel.: (81) 584 22 2111
Precision Machinery Mfr
N.A.I.C.S.: 332721

Nabtesco Corporation - Tsu Plant (1)
594 Icchoda Katada-cho, Tsu, 514-8553, Mie, Japan
Tel.: (81) 59 237 4600
Precision Machinery Mfr
N.A.I.C.S.: 332721

Nabtesco Europe GmbH (1)
Anna-Ohl-Strasse 2, 65555, Limburg, Germany
Tel.: (49) 643128550
Web Site: https://nabtesco.eu
Automation Equipment Mfr
N.A.I.C.S.: 334512

Nabtesco Gilgen Hong Kong Limited. (1)
Unit 605-606 6/F Trendy Centre 682 Castle Peak Road, Kowloon, China (Hong Kong)
Tel.: (852) 2243 4477
Transportation Equipment Maintenance Services
N.A.I.C.S.: 811114

Nabtesco ITG GmbH (1)
Thalheimer Strasse 7, 09125, Chemnitz, Germany
Tel.: (49) 371530180
Web Site: http://www.nabtesco-itg.de
Auto Parts Mfr
N.A.I.C.S.: 336390

Nabtesco India Private Limited (1)
Industrial plot No 485/9B 14th Cross 4th Phase, Peenya Industrial Area, Bengaluru, 560.058, Karnataka, India
Tel.: (91) 8041234901
Web Site: https://www.nabtesco.co.in
Hydraulic Equipment Mfr
N.A.I.C.S.: 333996

Nabtesco Link Corporation (1)
300-1 Fuchu Tarui-cho, Fuwa-gun, Gifu, 503-2114, Japan
Tel.: (81) 584241123
Automation Equipment Mfr
N.A.I.C.S.: 334512

Nabtesco Marine Control Systems (Shanghai) Co., Ltd. (1)
Building No 5 Lane 777 YuanDong Road, Fengxian, Shanghai, 201401, China **(100%)**
Tel.: (86) 2167101551
Web Site: http://www.nabtesco.com
Sales Range: $25-49.9 Million
Emp.: 15
Engine Equipment Mfr
N.A.I.C.S.: 333618

Nabtesco Marine Europe B.V. (1)
Touwslagerstraat 17, 2984 AW, Ridderkerk, Netherlands
Tel.: (31) 180530590
Web Site: https://www.nabtesco.nl
Marine Vessel Equipment Mfr
N.A.I.C.S.: 336611

Nabtesco Marine Machinery (Shanghai) Co., Ltd. (1)
Building No 5 Lane 777 YuanDong Road, Fengxian County, Shanghai, 201401, China
Tel.: (86) 2167101551
Engine Remote Control Equipment Mfr & Distr
N.A.I.C.S.: 334290

Nabtesco Marine Service Co., Ltd. (1)
1617-1 Fukuyoshidai 1-chome, Nishi-ku Kobe, Kobe, 651-2413, Japan **(100%)**
Tel.: (81) 789671404
Web Site: http://www.nabtesco.com
Emp.: 200
Management Consulting Services
N.A.I.C.S.: 541618

Nabtesco Marine Service Singapore Pte Ltd. (1)
401 Commonwealth Drive 05-04, Haw Par Technocentre, Singapore, 149598, Singapore **(100%)**
Tel.: (65) 62256559
Web Site: http://www.nabtesco-marine.com.sg
Sales Range: $25-49.9 Million
Emp.: 10
Management Consulting Services
N.A.I.C.S.: 541618

Nabtesco Marine Shikoku Co., Ltd. (1)
2nd Fl Kawashita Bldg 3-43 Kitatoryucho 1-chome, Imabari, 794-0803, Ehime, Japan
Tel.: (81) 898240089
Automation Equipment Mfr
N.A.I.C.S.: 334512

Nabtesco Marinetec Co., Ltd. (1)
29-1 Gupyoung-Ro, Saha-Gu, Busan, 49454, Korea (South) **(85%)**
Tel.: (82) 512649380
Web Site: http://www.nabtesco.com
Sales Range: $25-49.9 Million
Emp.: 23
Engine Equipment Mfr
N.A.I.C.S.: 333618

Nabtesco Motion Control, Inc. (1)
23976 Fwy Park Dr, Farmington Hills, MI 48335-2816 **(100%)**
Tel.: (248) 553-3020
Sales Range: $25-49.9 Million
Emp.: 100
Industrial Machinery Mfr
N.A.I.C.S.: 333248

Nabtesco Oclap S.r.l. (1)
Via Della Rimembranza 13, Piscina, 10060, Turin, Italy
Tel.: (39) 0121571811
Automation Equipment Mfr
N.A.I.C.S.: 334512

Nabtesco Power Control (Thailand) Co., Ltd. (1)
700/905 Moo 5 Amatanakorn Industrial Estate Tambol Nongkakha, Amphur Panthong, Chon Buri, 20160, Thailand
Tel.: (66) 3 818 5229
Web Site: https://www.nabtesco.com
Hydraulic Motor Mfr & Distr
N.A.I.C.S.: 336211

Nabtesco Power Control Europe B.V. (1)
Brouwerstraat 34, Ridderkerk, 2984AR, Netherlands
Tel.: (31) 180530595
Web Site: http://www.nabtesco.com
Sales Range: $25-49.9 Million
Emp.: 11
Electrical Equipment & Component Mfr
N.A.I.C.S.: 335999

Nabtesco Precision Europe GmbH (1)
Tiefenbroicher Weg 15, 40472, Dusseldorf, Germany **(100%)**
Tel.: (49) 211173790
Web Site: https://www.nabtesco.de
Sales Range: $25-49.9 Million
Electrical Equipment & Component Mfr
N.A.I.C.S.: 335999

Nabtesco Railroad Products (Beijing) Co., Ltd. (1)
A-2 Bodaxing Industrial Zone 24-Hao Kechuang 3 jie Eastern Section, Beijing Economic and Technological Development Zone, Beijing, 100023, Yizhuang, China **(100%)**
Tel.: (86) 106 789 2877
Web Site: https://www.nabtesco.com
Sales & Manufacturing of Brake Products for Railroad Vehicles
N.A.I.C.S.: 488210

Nabtesco Service Co., Ltd. (1)
2-10-2 Higashigotanda Higashigotanda Square 16th floor, Shinagawa-ku, Tokyo, 141-0022, Japan **(100%)**
Tel.: (81) 334476911
Web Site: https://www.nabtesco-service.co.jp
Emp.: 158
Transportation Equipment & Supplies Whslr
N.A.I.C.S.: 423860

Nabtesco Service Southeast Asia Co., Ltd. (1)
50 GMM Grammy Place 18th Fl Room 1808 Sukhumvit 21 Asok Rd, Klongtoey-Nua Wattana, Bangkok, 10110, Thailand
Tel.: (66) 22580733
Automation Equipment Mfr
N.A.I.C.S.: 334512

Nabtesco Technology Ventures AG (1)
Seefeldstrasse 215, 8008, Zurich, Switzerland
Tel.: (41) 44 269 6144
Web Site: https://www.nabtesco-ventures.com
Asset Management Services
N.A.I.C.S.: 523940
Hiroshi Nerima *(Pres, CEO & Mng Partner)*

OVALO GmbH (1)
Anna-Ohl-Strasse 2, 65555, Limburg, Germany
Tel.: (49) 643128550
Web Site: https://www.ovalo.de
Motion Control Component Mfr
N.A.I.C.S.: 333612
Daisuke Numata *(Co-CEO)*

Pacraft Co., Ltd. (1)
8th Floor 4-17-5 Shiba, Minato-ku, Tokyo, 108-0014, Japan
Tel.: (81) 362751343
Web Site: https://pacraft-global.com
Emp.: 293
Packaging Equipment Mfr & Distr
N.A.I.C.S.: 333993

Shanghai Nabtesco Business Management Co., Ltd. (1)
Room 1705 17th Floor Yuexiu Building No 388 Fushan Road, Pudong New District, Shanghai, 200122, China
Tel.: (86) 2150320980
Web Site: https://www.nabtesco.cn
Emp.: 12
Automation Equipment Mfr
N.A.I.C.S.: 334512

Shanghai Nabtesco Hydraulic Co., Ltd. (1)
No 905 Rongle East Road, Songjiang District, Shanghai, 201613, China **(55%)**
Tel.: (86) 2157741831
Web Site: https://www.snhc.com.cn
Fluid Power Pump & Motor Mfr
N.A.I.C.S.: 333996

Shanghai Nabtesco Hydraulic Equipment Trading Co., Ltd. (1)
Room 1704 No 388 Fushan Road, Pudong New Area, Shanghai, 200122, China
Tel.: (86) 2120773080
Web Site: https://www.nabtesco-snht.cn
Hydraulic Equipment Distr
N.A.I.C.S.: 423830

Shanghai Nabtesco Motion-equipment Trading Co., Ltd. (1)

AND PRIVATE COMPANIES

Room No 1706 No 388 Fushan Rd Pudong New Area, Shanghai, 200122, China
Tel.: (86) 21 3363 2200
Machine Tool Distr
N.A.I.C.S.: 423830

Shikoku Marine Customer Service Co., Ltd. (1)
1-3-43 Kitatoryucho 1-chome, Imabari, 794-0803, Ehime, Japan (75%)
Tel.: (81) 898240089
Web Site: http://www.nabtesco.com
Sales Range: $25-49.9 Million
Emp.: 19
Marine Cargo Handling
N.A.I.C.S.: 488320

T.S.Mechatech Co., Ltd. (1)
1110-1 Miyashiro, Tarui-cho, Gifu, 503-2124, Fuwa-gun, Japan
Tel.: (81) 584232004
Web Site: https://www.tsmechatech.jp
Emp.: 260
Fluid Power Pump & Motor Mfr
N.A.I.C.S.: 333996

TS Heatronics Co., Ltd. (1)
307-8 Nakayama-cho, Midori-ku, Yokohama, 226-0011, Kanagawa, Japan (95%)
Tel.: (81) 459376215
Web Site: http://www.tsheatronics.co.jp
Electronic Components Mfr
N.A.I.C.S.: 334419

TS Precision Co., Ltd. (1)
2-36 Hinode-machi, Iwakuni, 740-0014, Yamaguchi, Japan (100%)
Tel.: (81) 82 724 6010
Web Site: https://www.tsprecision.co.jp
Sales Range: $25-49.9 Million
Machine Tools Mfr
N.A.I.C.S.: 333517
Yasuhiro Tsukuda (Pres)

Taiwan Nabtesco Service Co., Ltd. (1)
No 122-12 Chung-Hua Rd Hsin Chu Industrial Area, Hu Kou, Hsin-chu, Taiwan
Tel.: (886) 36960234
Sales Range: $25-49.9 Million
Emp.: 6
Navigational Services to Shipping
N.A.I.C.S.: 488330
Kobayashi Akio (Mgr)

Toyo Jidoki America Corporation - CA Branch (1)
18195 E McDurmott Ste F, Irvine, CA 92614
Tel.: (949) 387-2911
Weighing Machinery Mfr
N.A.I.C.S.: 333993

Toyo Jidoki Co., Ltd. (1)
8th Floor 4-17-5 Shiba, Minato-ku, Tokyo, 108-0014, Japan (100%)
Tel.: (81) 362751343
Web Site: http://toyojidoki.com
Sales Range: $50-74.9 Million
Emp.: 200
Packaging Machinery Mfr
N.A.I.C.S.: 333993

Subsidiary (Non-US):

Dalian Toyo Jidoki Co., Ltd. (2)
Bldg No 11 No 99 Huaihe Zhong Road, Jingang Industry Park Dalian Development Zone, Dalian, 116620, China
Tel.: (86) 4118 754 9177
Web Site: http://www.tyj.co.jp
Industrial Machinery Mfr
N.A.I.C.S.: 333248

Toyo Jidoki Co., Ltd. - Iwakuni Plant (1)
Nagano 1808, Iwakuni, 740-0045, Yamaguchi, Japan
Tel.: (81) 827391500
Automation Equipment Mfr
N.A.I.C.S.: 334512

Toyo Jidoki Europe GmbH (1)
Tiefenbroicher Weg 15, 40472, Dusseldorf, Germany
Tel.: (49) 21117379115
Packaging Machine Services
N.A.I.C.S.: 561910

Tstm Co., Ltd. (1)
2798-51 Minamiyosida-cho Ehime, 791-8042, Matsuyama, Japan (100%)
Tel.: (81) 899712124
Web Site: http://www.tstm.co.jp
Sales Range: $25-49.9 Million
Emp.: 38
Textile Machinery Mfr
N.A.I.C.S.: 333248
Takaki Shineha (Gen Mgr)

NAC CO., LTD.
42F Shinjuku Center Bldg 1-25-1 Nishishinjuku, Shinjuku-ku, Tokyo, Japan
Tel.: (81) 333462111 JP
Web Site: https://www.nacoo.com
Year Founded: 1971
9788—(TKS)
Rev.: $359,802,130
Assets: $248,635,150
Liabilities: $98,489,000
Net Worth: $150,146,150
Earnings: $9,491,960
Emp.: 1,687
Fiscal Year-end: 03/31/24
Holding Company
N.A.I.C.S.: 551112
Yuya Kawakami (Mng Exec Officer)

Subsidiaries:

Kunimoku House Co., Ltd. (1)
1-24 11 Chome, Toyohira, Sapporo, 062-0902, Hokkaido, Japan
Tel.: (81) 118122141
Web Site: http://www.kunimoku-house.co.jp
Emp.: 23
Interior Design Services
N.A.I.C.S.: 541410
Hideki Masaki (Pres & CEO)

TOMOE Wines & Spirits Co., Ltd. (1)
Osaki Bright Core 18th floor 5-5-15 Kitashinagawa, Shinagawa-ku, Tokyo, 141-0001, Japan
Tel.: (81) 334425190
Web Site: https://www.tomoe-wines.com
Emp.: 14
Wine & Distilled Beverages Distr
N.A.I.C.S.: 424820

NAC CONSTRUCTORS LTD.
21 Queen Street, Morriston, N0B 2C0, ON, Canada
Tel.: (519) 821-8000
Web Site: https://www.nacsworld.com
Year Founded: 1996
Sales Range: $250-299.9 Million
Emp.: 900
Holding Company; Water Treatment Facility & Other Plant Construction Services
N.A.I.C.S.: 551112
Denis Gagnon (Chm)

Subsidiaries:

North America Construction (1993) Ltd. (1)
21 Queen Street, Morriston, N0B 2C0, ON, Canada
Tel.: (519) 821-8000
Web Site: https://www.nacsworld.com
Sales Range: $75-99.9 Million
Emp.: 310
Building Contractors
N.A.I.C.S.: 238220
Scott McPherson (Pres-Construction-North America)

NACALAI TESQUE, INC.
498 Higashitamaya-cho Nijo Karasuma, Kyoto, 604-0855, Japan
Tel.: (81) 752511723
Web Site: http://www.nacalai.co.jp
Year Founded: 1846
Sales Range: $125-149.9 Million
Emp.: 300
Research Chemical Mfr & Distr
N.A.I.C.S.: 325411
Dai Nakadai (Pres)

Subsidiaries:

Nacalai Tesque, Inc. - Kyoto Factory (1)
17 Ishibashi Kaide-cho, Muko, 617-0004, Japan
Tel.: (81) 75 932 1755
Sales Range: $125-149.9 Million
Emp.: 289
Industrial Chemicals Mfr
N.A.I.C.S.: 325998

Nacalai USA, Inc. (1)
10225 Barnes Canyon Rd Ste A103, San Diego, CA 92121
Tel.: (858) 404-0403
Web Site: http://www.nacalaiusa.com
Emp.: 4
Industrial Chemical Import & Distr
N.A.I.C.S.: 424690
Toshi Ono (VP)

NACHI-FUJIKOSHI CORP.

NACHI-FUJIKOSHI CORP.
1-1-1 Fujikoshi-Honmachi, Toyama, 930-8511, Japan
Tel.: (81) 764235111
Web Site: https://www.nachi-fujikoshi.co.jp
Year Founded: 1928
6474—(TKS)
Rev.: $2,498,378,960
Assets: $3,460,183,760
Liabilities: $1,946,551,200
Net Worth: $1,513,632,560
Earnings: $118,454,160
Emp.: 7,259
Fiscal Year-end: 11/30/22
Fluid Power Pump & Motor Mfr
N.A.I.C.S.: 333996
Hiroo Honma (Chm)

Subsidiaries:

Baojia Nachi Robot Application Development Qingdao Inc. (1)
No 67 Xinyue Road, High tech Industrial Development Zone, Qingdao, Shandong, China
Tel.: (86) 53258759267
Roller Bearing Mfr
N.A.I.C.S.: 332991

Daesung Nachi Hydraulics Co., Ltd. (1)
8 Yusangongdan 8-gil, Yangsan, 50592, Gyeongsangnam-do, Korea (South)
Tel.: (82) 553719710
Industrial Robots Mfr
N.A.I.C.S.: 336411
Kairos Dalsik Jang (CEO)

FUJIKOSHI Accounting Co., Ltd (1)
1-1-1 Fujikoshi-Honmachi, Toyama, 930-8511, Japan
Tel.: (81) 76 423 5095
Web Site: http://www.nachi-fujikoshi.co.jp
Accounting Services
N.A.I.C.S.: 541219

FUJIKOSHI Com Service Co., Ltd. (1)
1-1-1 Fujikoshi-Honmachi, Toyama, 930-8511, Japan
Tel.: (81) 764235042
Web Site: http://www.nachi-fujikoshi.co.jp
Facility Management Services
N.A.I.C.S.: 561210

FUJIKOSHI Information Systems Co., Ltd. (1)
1-1-1 Fujikoshi-Honmachi, Toyama, 930-8511, Japan
Tel.: (81) 76 493 0980
Web Site: http://www.nachi.co.jp
Software Development Services
N.A.I.C.S.: 541511

Fujikoshi-Nachi (Malaysia) Sdn. Bhd. (1)
No 17 Jalan USJ 21/3, 47630, Subang Jaya, Selangor, Malaysia
Tel.: (60) 380247900
Web Site: http://www.nachi.com.au
Sales Range: $25-49.9 Million
Emp.: 10
Metal Cutting Machine Tool Mfr
N.A.I.C.S.: 333517

Hokuriku Kinzoku Co., Ltd. (1)
2-2-15 Shinjo-honmachi, Toyama-shi, Toyama, 930-0996, Japan
Tel.: (81) 764515217
Web Site: http://www.nachi-fujikoshi.co.jp
Ball Bearing Mfr
N.A.I.C.S.: 332991

NACHI (SHANGHAI) PRECISION TOOLS CO., LTD. (1)
Yitong Industry Zone 258 Fengmao Rd Malu Town, Jiading, Shanghai, 201801, China
Tel.: (86) 21 6915 7200
Precision Tool Engineering Services
N.A.I.C.S.: 541330

NACHI BRASIL LTDA (1)
Av Joao XXIII 2 330, Jardim Sao Pedro, Mogi das Cruzes, 08830-000, Sao Paulo, Brazil
Tel.: (55) 1147938800
Web Site: https://www.nachi.com.br
Emp.: 230
Ball Bearing Mfr
N.A.I.C.S.: 332991

NACHI Bearing Manufacturing Co., Ltd. (1)
193 Mizuhashi-iseya, Toyama-shi, Toyama, 939-3524, Japan
Tel.: (81) 764782098
Ball Bearing Mfr
N.A.I.C.S.: 332991

NACHI CZECH s.r.o. (1)
Prumyslova 2732, 440 01, Louny, Czech Republic
Tel.: (420) 415930930
Sales Range: $25-49.9 Million
Emp.: 60
Car Air Conditioner Bearing Mfr & Distr
N.A.I.C.S.: 332991

NACHI Hokuriku Co., Ltd. (1)
Nachi Hokuriku Bldg 2-3-60 Ishigane, Toyama-shi, Toyama, 930-0966, Japan
Tel.: (81) 764243991
Web Site: http://www.nachi-fujikoshi.co.jp
Seal Products Distr
N.A.I.C.S.: 423510

NACHI Hydraulics Co., Ltd. (1)
353 Fuchumachi-chisato, Toyama-shi, Toyama, 939-2622, Japan
Tel.: (81) 764693829
Hydraulic Equipment Mfr
N.A.I.C.S.: 332912

NACHI INDUSTRIES PTE. LTD. (1)
No 2 Joo Koon Way, Jurong, 628943, Singapore
Tel.: (65) 68613944
Web Site: http://www.nachinip.com.sg
Sales Range: $50-74.9 Million
Emp.: 150
Heat Treatment Services
N.A.I.C.S.: 332811
Makoto Sano (Mng Dir)

NACHI Kouzai Co., Ltd. (1)
3-3-26 Yoneda-machi, Toyama, 931-8304, Japan
Tel.: (81) 76 438 4343
Web Site: http://www.nachi-fujikoshi.co.jp
Ball Bearing Mfr
N.A.I.C.S.: 332991

NACHI Kyushu Co., Ltd. (1)
1-10-30 Sanno, Hakata-ku, Fukuoka, 812-0015, Japan
Tel.: (81) 92 441 2505
Industrial Machinery Whslr
N.A.I.C.S.: 423830

NACHI Logistics Co., Ltd. (1)
1-1 Kumonmyo, Toyama, 939-8002, Japan
Tel.: (81) 76 425 0262
Web Site: http://www.nachi-logistics.jp
Logistics Consulting Servies
N.A.I.C.S.: 541614

NACHI Machinery Engineering Co., Ltd. (1)
1-1-1 Fujikoshi-Honmachi, Toyama-shi, Toyama, 930-8511, Japan
Tel.: (81) 764920708
Industrial Machinery Mfr
N.A.I.C.S.: 333248

NACHI Nihonkai Bearing Co., Ltd. (1)

NACHI-FUJIKOSHI CORP.

Nachi-Fujikoshi Corp.—(Continued)
285 Mizuhashi-iseya, Toyama-shi, Toyama, 939-3524, Japan
Tel.: (81) 764782171
Web Site: http://www.nachi-fujikoshi.co.jp
Ball Bearing Mfr
N.A.I.C.S.: 332991

NACHI Robot Engineering Co., Ltd. (1)
Shiodome Sumitomo Bldg 17F 1-9-2 Higashi-Shinbashi, Minato-ku, Tokyo, 105-0021, Japan
Tel.: (81) 3 5568 5180
Machine Tools Mfr
N.A.I.C.S.: 333517
Tamei Yuji *(Gen Mgr)*

NACHI Sanyo Co., Ltd. (1)
Nihonseimei Hiroshima Hikarimachi Bldg 8F 1-10-19 Hikarimachi, Higashi-ku, Hiroshima, 732-0052, Japan
Tel.: (81) 82 568 7461
Machine Tool Distr
N.A.I.C.S.: 423830

NACHI Seiko Co., Ltd. (1)
160 Nagaresugi, Toyama-shi, Toyama, 939-8032, Japan
Tel.: (81) 764252695
Machine Tools Mfr
N.A.I.C.S.: 333517

NACHI TECHNOLOGY (THAILAND) CO., LTD. (1)
5/5 M 2 Rojana Industrial Nongbua, Ban Khai, Rayong, 21120, Thailand
Tel.: (66) 38961682
Ball Bearing Mfr
N.A.I.C.S.: 332991

NACHI TECHNOLOGY INC. (1)
713 Pushville Rd, Greenwood, IN 46143
Tel.: (317) 535-5000
Web Site: http://www.nachitech.com
Emp.: 125
Automotive Bearing Mfr
N.A.I.C.S.: 332991

NACHI TOOL AMERICA INC. (1)
717 Pushville Rd, Greenwood, IN 46143
Tel.: (317) 535-0320
Web Site: http://www.nachi-fujikoshi.co.jp
Emp.: 10
Industrial Machinery & Equipment Mfr
N.A.I.C.S.: 333248

NACHI Tateyama Bearing Co., Ltd. (1)
161 Nagaresugi, Toyama, 939-8032, Japan
Tel.: (81) 764248848
Ball Bearing Mfr
N.A.I.C.S.: 332991

NACHI Thermotech Co., Ltd. (1)
176-12 Ogake, Namerikawa, 936-0802, Toyama, Japan
Tel.: (81) 764712981
Sales Range: $25-49.9 Million
Emp.: 6
Environmental Engineering Services
N.A.I.C.S.: 541330
Kawai Yuken *(Mgr-Quality Control)*

NACHI Tohoku Seiko Co., Ltd. (1)
3-1174-3 Tachiyagawa, Yamagata-shi, Yamagata, 990-2251, Japan
Tel.: (81) 236862116
Hydraulic Equipment Mfr
N.A.I.C.S.: 333248

NACHI Tool Engineering Co., Ltd. (1)
1-1-1 Fujikoshi-Honmachi, Toyama-shi, Toyama, 930-8511, Japan **(100%)**
Tel.: (81) 764235337
Web Site: http://www.nachi-fujikoshi.co.jp
Emp.: 30
Machine Tools Mfr
N.A.I.C.S.: 333515

NACHI Tool Genesis Co., Ltd. (1)
106-1 Nagaresugi, Toyama-shi, Toyama, 939-8032, Japan
Tel.: (81) 764252281
Emp.: 80
Machine Tools Mfr
N.A.I.C.S.: 333517
Nogawa Yafusagi *(Pres)*

NACHI Toyama Bearing Co., Ltd. (1)
171 Takauchi, Toyama-shi, Toyama, 939-2254, Japan
Tel.: (81) 764672201
Web Site: http://www.nachi-fujikoshi.co.jp
Ball & Roller Bearings Mfr
N.A.I.C.S.: 332991

NACHI Yatsuo Bearing Co., Ltd. (1)
47 Urano Fukujima Yatsuomachi, Toyama, 939-2376, Japan
Tel.: (81) 764542627
Web Site: http://www.nachi-fujikoshi.co.jp
Ball & Roller Bearings Mfr
N.A.I.C.S.: 332991

NACHI-TOKIWA CORP. (1)
Shiodome Sumitomo Bldg 17F, 1-9-2 Higashi-Shinbashi Minato-ku, Tokyo, 105-0021, Japan
Tel.: (81) 3 6252 3677
Web Site: http://www.nachi-tokiwa.co.jp
Sales Range: $50-74.9 Million
Emp.: 7
Machine Tool Distr
N.A.I.C.S.: 423830
Iwao Kodera *(Pres)*

Nachi (Australia) Pty. Ltd. (1)
Unit 3 23-29 South Street, Rydalmere, 2116, NSW, Australia
Tel.: (61) 298981511
Web Site: http://www.nachi.de
Sales Range: $25-49.9 Million
Emp.: 11
Industrial Supplies Whslr
N.A.I.C.S.: 423840

Nachi (Jiangsu) Industries Co., Ltd. (1)
39 Nanyuan Road, Economic and Technological Development Zone South, Zhangjiagang, 215618, Jiangsu, China
Tel.: (86) 51235007616
Industrial Robots Mfr
N.A.I.C.S.: 336411

Nachi (Shanghai) Co., Ltd. (1)
Yitong Industrial Est Zone 258, Fengmao Rd Malu Town, 201801, Shanghai, China
Tel.: (86) 2169152200
Web Site: http://www.nachi-fujikoshi.co.jp
Industrial Supplies Whslr
N.A.I.C.S.: 423840

Nachi America Inc. (1)
715 Pushville Rd, Greenwood, IN 46143-9782
Tel.: (317) 530-1001
Web Site: http://www.nachiamerica.com
Industrial Machinery & Equipment Whslr
N.A.I.C.S.: 423830

Division (Domestic):

NACHI AMERICA INC. - MIAMI BRANCH-LATIN AMERICA DIVISION (2)
2315 N W 107th Ave, Doral, FL 33172
Tel.: (305) 591-0054
Web Site: http://www.nachi-fujikoshi.co.jp
Machine Tools Mfr
N.A.I.C.S.: 333517

Nachi C.H. Dongguan Corp. (1)
East Jiangnan Road Guancheng High Tech Park, Eastern Industrial Zone, Dongguan, Guangdong, China
Tel.: (86) 76987011028
Industrial Robots Mfr
N.A.I.C.S.: 336411

Nachi C.Y. Corp. (1)
No 109 Kao Young North Rd, Longtan, Taoyuan, 32543, Taiwan
Tel.: (886) 34717651
Industrial Robots Mfr
N.A.I.C.S.: 336411

Nachi Canada Inc. (1)
89 Courtland Ave Unit No 2, Concord, L4K 3T4, ON, Canada
Tel.: (905) 660-0088
Web Site: https://www.nachiamerica.com
Sales Range: $25-49.9 Million
Emp.: 13
Business Service Centers
N.A.I.C.S.: 561439

Nachi Europe GmbH (1)
Bischofstr 99, 47809, Krefeld, Germany
Tel.: (49) 2151650460
Web Site: http://www.nachi.de
Sales Range: $25-49.9 Million
Emp.: 25
Industrial Machinery & Equipment Whslr
N.A.I.C.S.: 423830

Nachi Forging Technology (Thailand) Co., Ltd. (1)
5/8 M 2 Rojana Industrial Park Nongbua, Ban Khai, Rayong, 21120, Thailand
Tel.: (66) 38017891
Industrial Robots Mfr
N.A.I.C.S.: 336411

Nachi Kansai Co., Ltd. (1)
Sumitomo Nakanoshima Bldg 5F 3-2-18, Nakanoshima Kita-ku, Osaka, 530-0005, Japan
Tel.: (81) 671782200
Web Site: http://www.nachi-fujikoshi.co.jp
Industrial Machinery & Equipment Whslr
N.A.I.C.S.: 423830

Nachi Kanto Co., Ltd. (1)
Shiodome Sumitomo Bldg 17F 1-9-2 Higashi-Shinbashi Minato-ku, Tokyo, 105-0021, Japan
Tel.: (81) 355685190
Web Site: http://www.nachi-fujikoshi.co.jp
Sales Range: $25-49.9 Million
Emp.: 40
Industrial Machinery & Equipment Whslr
N.A.I.C.S.: 423830

Nachi Mexicana, S.A. de C.V. (1)
Aerotech Industrial Park Tequisquiapan No 2, Galeras Town Colon Municipality, 76295, Queretaro, Mexico
Tel.: (52) 4421532424
Web Site: http://nachimx.com
Sales Range: $50-74.9 Million
Emp.: 10
Professional Equipment & Supplies Whslr
N.A.I.C.S.: 423490

Nachi Pilipinas Industries, Inc. (1)
1st Avenue Manalac Compound Sta Maria Industrial Estate, Bagumbayan Taguig Metro, Manila, 1634, Philippines
Tel.: (63) 288383620
Web Site: http://www.nachipilipinas.com
Sales Range: $25-49.9 Million
Emp.: 50
Industrial Machinery & Equipment Whslr
N.A.I.C.S.: 423830

Nachi Precision Tool India Private Ltd. (1)
179 Sector4, IMT Manesar District, Gurgaon, 122 050, Haryana, India
Tel.: (91) 1244936000
Industrial Robots Mfr
N.A.I.C.S.: 336411
M. G. Shankar *(Pres)*

Nachi Robotic Systems Inc. (1)
46200 W 12 Mile Rd, Novi, MI 48377
Tel.: (248) 305-6545
Web Site: https://www.nachirobotics.com
Sales Range: $25-49.9 Million
Emp.: 50
Industrial Machinery & Equipment Whslr
N.A.I.C.S.: 423830
Curt Rusu *(Pres & CEO)*

Nachi Singapore Pte. Ltd. (1)
2 Joo Koon Way, Jurong Town, Singapore, 628943, Singapore
Tel.: (65) 65587393
Web Site: http://www.nachinit.com.sg
Sales Range: $25-49.9 Million
Emp.: 20
Metal Service Centers & Metal Whslr
N.A.I.C.S.: 423510
Takano Akihiro *(Mng Dir)*

Nachi Taiwan Co., Ltd. (1)
2F No 23 Lane 15 Sec 6 Minquan E Rd, Neihu Dist, Taipei, Taiwan
Tel.: (886) 227921895
Industrial Robots Mfr
N.A.I.C.S.: 336411

Nachi Technology India Private Limited (1)
Unit No 108 1st Floor Sewa Corporate Park MG Road, Gurgaon, 122002, Haryana, India

INTERNATIONAL PUBLIC

Tel.: (91) 1244502900
Web Site: https://nachi-india.com
Emp.: 120
Roller Bearing Mfr
N.A.I.C.S.: 332991
Tarun Girdhar *(Deputy Mgr)*

Nachi Technology Mexico S.A. de C.V. (1)
Tequisquiapan No 2, Aerotech Industrial Park Localidad Galeras Municipio de Colon, 76295, Queretaro, Mexico
Tel.: (52) 4421532410
Industrial Robots Mfr
N.A.I.C.S.: 336411

Nachi Tokai Co., Ltd. (1)
Nachi Nagoya Bldg 2-120-3 Takayashiro, Meitou-ku, Nagoya, 465-0095, Japan
Tel.: (81) 527696911
Industrial Machinery & Equipment Whslr
N.A.I.C.S.: 423830

Nachi Tool Technology Co., Ltd. (1)
176 Ogake, Namerikawa, 936-0802, Toyama, Japan
Tel.: (81) 764562556
Industrial Robots Mfr
N.A.I.C.S.: 336411

Nachi Vietnam Co., Ltd. (1)
1502B 15 Floor Lot A1 Indochina Plaza Hanoi 241 Xuan Thuy street, Dich Vong Hau ward Cau Giay Dist, Hanoi, Vietnam
Tel.: (84) 2437678605
Industrial Robots Mfr
N.A.I.C.S.: 336411

Nachi-Fujikoshi (China) Co., Ltd. (1)
5th Floor Building A National Convention and Exhibition Center, 1988 Zhuguang Road Qingpu District, Shanghai, 201702, China
Tel.: (86) 2169152200
Web Site: http://www.nachi.com.cn
Industrial Robots Mfr
N.A.I.C.S.: 336411

Nachi-Fujikoshi Corp. - Higashi-Toyama Plant (1)
3-1-1 Yoneda-machi, Toyama, 931-8511, Japan
Tel.: (81) 764384411
Emp.: 300
Machine Tools Mfr
N.A.I.C.S.: 333517

Nachi-Fujikoshi Corp. - Mizuhashi Plant (1)
201-1 Iseya Mizuhashi, Toyama, 939-3524, Japan
Tel.: (81) 764791780
Machine Tools Mfr
N.A.I.C.S.: 333517

Nachi-Fujikoshi Corp. - Nagaresugi Plant (1)
160 Nagaresugi, Toyama, 939-8032, Japan
Tel.: (81) 76 425 26
Machine Tools Mfr
N.A.I.C.S.: 333517

Nachi-Fujikoshi Corp. - Namerikawa Plant (1)
176 Ogake, Namerikawa, 936-0802, Toyama, Japan
Tel.: (81) 764712320
Web Site: http://www.nachi-fujikoshi.co.jp
Machine Tools Mfr
N.A.I.C.S.: 333517

P.T. Nachi Indonesia (1)
Tempo Scan Tower 31st Floor JI HR Rasuna Said Kav 3-4, Kuningan, Jakarta, 12950, Indonesia
Tel.: (62) 215272841
Web Site: http://www.nachi.co.id
Sales Range: $50-74.9 Million
Emp.: 33
Industrial Machinery & Equipment Whslr
N.A.I.C.S.: 423830

SHANGHAI NACHI SAW CO., LTD. (1)
1F 5 Building 33 Forward Road, Malu Town Jiading, Shanghai, 201801, China
Tel.: (86) 2169155899
Machine Tools Mfr
N.A.I.C.S.: 333517

AND PRIVATE COMPANIES

Shanghai Nachi Bearings Co., Ltd. (1)
258 Fengmao Road, Yitong Industry Zone Malu Town Jiading, Shanghai, 201801, China
Tel.: (86) 2169156200
Industrial Robots Mfr
N.A.I.C.S.: 336411

Specialty Tooling Systems, Inc. (1)
4315 3 Mile Rd NW, Grand Rapids, MI 49534
Tel.: (616) 784-2353
Web Site: https://www.specialtytoolingsystems.com
Emp.: 68
Industrial Automation Services
N.A.I.C.S.: 541330

Toyama Atsuen Co., Ltd. (1)
45 Nakata, Toyama, 931-8453, Japan
Tel.: (81) 764375806
Web Site: http://www.nachi-fujikoshi.co.jp
Specialty Steel Products Mfr
N.A.I.C.S.: 331110

NACHMO KNITEX LTD.
Texcellence Complex Khokhara, Mehmedabad, Ahmedabad, 380021, Gujarat, India
Tel.: (91) 7922773513
Textile Products Mfr
N.A.I.C.S.: 314999
Chintan N. Parikh *(Chm)*

NACIONAL A.D.
Auto put br 5, Novi Beograd, 11070, Belgrade, Serbia
Tel.: (381) 11 2601 156
Web Site: http://www.nacional-bgd.com
Year Founded: 1996
Sales Range: Less than $1 Million
Emp.: 34
Home Management Services
N.A.I.C.S.: 721110

NACIONAL FINANCIERA F.N.C.
Colonia Guadelupe Inn Insurgentes Sur 1971, 01020, Mexico, DF, Mexico
Tel.: (52) 5553256000
Web Site: http://www.nafin.com.mx
Year Founded: 1934
Sales Range: $200-249.9 Million
Emp.: 1,000
Industrial Development Banking
N.A.I.C.S.: 522299
Pedro Arguelles Rodriguez *(VP-Credit)*

Subsidiaries:

Nasinsa Securities (1)
330 Madison Ave Ste 665, New York, NY 10017
Tel.: (646) 495-5172
Sales Range: $25-49.9 Million
Emp.: 3
Brokers & Traders
N.A.I.C.S.: 541840

NACITY PROPERTY SERVICE GROUP CO., LTD.
10F Unit 1 Block A Lianhe Mans 2 Zijinghua Road, Xihu District, Hangzhou, 310012, China
Tel.: (86) 57188255580
Web Site: https://www.nacityres.com
603506—(SHG)
Rev.: $259,280,850
Assets: $322,057,382
Liabilities: $174,430,335
Net Worth: $147,627,048
Earnings: $20,407,631
Fiscal Year-end: 12/31/22
Property Management Services
N.A.I.C.S.: 531311

NACO TULSH
Khoroo 4, Nalaikh District, Ulaanbaatar, Mongolia

Tel.: (976) 5 023 0227
Coal Mining Services
N.A.I.C.S.: 213113

NACTIS SAS
ZI La Mariniere 34-36 Rue Gutenberg, 91070, Bondoufle, France
Tel.: (33) 1 60 86 85 32
Web Site: http://www.nactis.fr
Food Processing Services
N.A.I.C.S.: 311999
Daniel Faguer *(CEO)*

Subsidiaries:

Nactis Benelux (1)
Liebiglaan 11, 2900, Schoten, Belgium
Tel.: (32) 3 641 95 00
Web Site: http://www.nactis.fr
Savoury Flavors Mfr
N.A.I.C.S.: 311942

NADATHUR ESTATES PVT LTD.
3rd Floor Nadathur Place Plot No 23 8th Main Road 3rd Block, Jayanagar, Bengaluru, 560 011, India
Tel.: (91) 80 66709900
Web Site: http://www.nadathur.com
Emp.: 35
Private Investment Firm
N.A.I.C.S.: 523999
Nadathur Sarangapani Raghavan *(Founder)*

Subsidiaries:

Nadathur Fareast Pte Ltd. (1)
23 Amoy Street, Singapore, 069858, Singapore
Tel.: (65) 65959350
Financial Investment Services
N.A.I.C.S.: 523999

NADAYU PROPERTIES BERHAD
No 8 10 Jalan Jurutera U1/23 Seksyen U1, Kawasan Perindustrian Hicom Glenmarie, 40150, Shah Alam, Selangor Darul Ehsan, Malaysia
Tel.: (60) 55697363
Year Founded: 1976
Sales Range: $125-149.9 Million
Property Development Services
N.A.I.C.S.: 531390

Subsidiaries:

Dynastic Lion Sdn Bhd (1)
Level 5 Menara Standard Charteres PS 38 No 30 Jalan Sultan Ismail, Kuala Lumpur, 50250, Malaysia (100%)
Tel.: (60) 3 2141 5775
Web Site: http://www.nadayu.com.my
Emp.: 104
Investment Holdings
N.A.I.C.S.: 523999
Davina Chew *(Sr Acct Exec)*

Subsidiary (Domestic):

Puncak Kencana Sdn Bhd (2)
11th Floor Menara Tun Razak Jalan Raja Laut, Kuala Lumpur, 50350, Malaysia
Tel.: (60) 3 26935622
Sales Range: $25-49.9 Million
Emp.: 70
Housing Project Development Services
N.A.I.C.S.: 236117

Pembangunan Bandar Mutiara Sdn. Bhd. (1)
72 Jalan Tasek SS1 Bandar Tasek Mutiara, Seberang Perai Selatan, 14120, Pulau Penang, Penang, Malaysia
Tel.: (60) 45087888
Web Site: http://www.btm.com.my
Residential Building Construction Services
N.A.I.C.S.: 236116

NADEEM TEXTILE MILLS LTD.
801-804 Lakson Square Building No 3-A Sarwar Shaheed Road, Karachi, Pakistan

Tel.: (92) 2135220481
Web Site: https://www.nadeem.com.pk
Year Founded: 1984
NATM—(PSX)
Rev.: $38,373,327
Assets: $29,780,501
Liabilities: $17,088,080
Net Worth: $12,692,421
Earnings: ($2,118,849)
Emp.: 1,145
Fiscal Year-end: 06/30/23
Textile Mfr
N.A.I.C.S.: 314999
Nadeem Ahmed *(Chm)*

NADEP LAGHUBITTA BITTIYA SANSTHA LTD.
Gajuri 1, PO Box 3785, Dhading, Kathmandu, Nepal
Tel.: (977) 10402111
Web Site: https://www.nadeplaghubitta.com
NADEPP—(NEP)
Rev.: $5,836,741
Assets: $39,710,901
Liabilities: $33,382,141
Net Worth: $6,328,760
Earnings: ($83,791)
Emp.: 286
Fiscal Year-end: 07/16/23
Financial Educational Training Services
N.A.I.C.S.: 611710
Upendra Karki *(CEO)*

NADER HOLDING GMBH & CO. KG
Hindenburgring 39 37115, Duderstadt, Germany
Tel.: (49) 5527947371
Web Site: https://www.naeder-holding.com
Year Founded: 1919
Emp.: 8,000
Investment Holding Company
N.A.I.C.S.: 551112

Subsidiaries:

Ottobock SE & Co. KgaA (1)
Max-Nader-Strasse 15, Duderstadt, Germany (80%)
Tel.: (49) 55278480
Medical Equipment Mfr
N.A.I.C.S.: 339112
Frolich Klaus *(Dir-Mfr)*

Subsidiary (US):

Otto Bock HealthCare LP (2)
1501 Alterra Pkwy Ste 600, Austin, TX 78758
Web Site: http://www.ottobockus.com
Medical Equipment Mfr
N.A.I.C.S.: 339112
Brad Ruhl *(Mng Dir)*

Subsidiary (Non-US):

Otto Bock Middle East FZ-LLC (2)
Dubai Science Park Laboratory Complex 207, Dubai, United Arab Emirates
Tel.: (971) 42418777
Medical Equipment Mfr
N.A.I.C.S.: 339112
Saman Nakhdjavani *(Area Mgr)*

Otto Bock Philippines Corp. (2)
1601-1602 16/F Taipan Place F Ortigas Jr Road Ortigas Center, Pasig, Philippines
Tel.: (63) 27181083
Medical Equipment Mfr
N.A.I.C.S.: 339112

Otto Bock Romania srl (2)
Chitila-Mogosoaia Ring Road No 3 Ground Floor, Ilfov County, Chitila, Romania
Tel.: (40) 214363110
Web Site: http://www.ottobock.ro
Medical Equipment Mfr
N.A.I.C.S.: 339112

Otto Bock South East Asia Co., Ltd. (2)
Singapore Representative Office 57 Mohamed Sultan Road, 01-05 Sultan Link, Singapore, Singapore
Tel.: (65) 69068248
Medical Equipment Mfr
N.A.I.C.S.: 339112

Otto Bock Vietnam Co., Ltd. (2)
Lot D 01 Tan Thuan Street Tan Thuan Export Processing Zone, Tan Thuan Dong Ward District 7, Ho Chi Minh City, Vietnam
Tel.: (84) 931799138
Web Site: http://www.ottobock.vn
Medical Equipment Mfr
N.A.I.C.S.: 339112
Matthias Kittler *(Country Mgr)*

Ottobock (Mauritius) Ltd. (2)
Socota Phoenicia Business Park Sayed Hossen Road, Solferino, Phoenix, Mauritius
Tel.: (230) 5834990
Medical Equipment Mfr
N.A.I.C.S.: 339112

Ottobock Kenya Limited (2)
Nairobi Business Park Block A Ground Floor Ngong Road 4 Ngong Road 4, PO Box 1029, Nairobi, Kenya
Tel.: (254) 745333647
Medical Equipment Mfr
N.A.I.C.S.: 339112
Catherine Kamau *(Office Mgr)*

Ottobock Lanka (Private) Limited (2)
No 63 Gothami Raod, Colombo, Sri Lanka
Tel.: (94) 112697208
Web Site: http://www.ottobock.lk
Medical Equipment Mfr
N.A.I.C.S.: 339112
Bernard O'Keeffe *(Pres)*

PT. Ottobock Healthcare Indonesia (2)
Taman Tekno Blok F1/FG BSD Selatan, Tangerang, Banten, Indonesia
Tel.: (62) 2129666597
Web Site: http://www.ottobock.id
Medical Equipment Mfr
N.A.I.C.S.: 339112

NADEX CO., LTD.
9-27 Furuwatari-cho, Naka-ku, Nagoya, 460-8338, Aichi, Japan
Tel.: (81) 5232322
Web Site: https://www.nadex.co.jp
Year Founded: 1950
7435—(TKS)
Rev.: $227,621,960
Assets: $207,435,020
Liabilities: $77,905,460
Net Worth: $129,529,560
Earnings: $5,777,140
Emp.: 835
Fiscal Year-end: 04/30/24
Welding Equipment & Electronic Control Equipment Mfr
N.A.I.C.S.: 333992
Toshiyuki Takada *(Pres & CEO)*

Subsidiaries:

Ishikotec Co., Ltd. (1)
1-11-1 Kukuchinishimachi, Amagasaki, 661-0978, Hyogo Pref, Japan
Tel.: (81) 664218980
Web Site: https://www.ishikotec.co.jp
Stainless Steel Mfr
N.A.I.C.S.: 331110

NADEX (THAILAND) CO., LTD. (1)
104/11 B5 Bldg Moo17 Theparak RD Tambol Bangsaotong, District Bangsaotong, Samut Prakan, 10540, Thailand
Tel.: (66) 2 315 2911
Welding Equipment Distr
N.A.I.C.S.: 423830

NADEX MEXICANA, S.A. de C.V (1)
Avenida Nezahualcoyotl No44 Colonia Cumbress de Conin El Marques, 76246, Mexico, Queretaro, Mexico
Tel.: (52) 442 403 9348
Web Site: https://www.nadex.co.jp
Welding Equipment Mfr & Distr

NADEX CO., LTD.

NADEX CO., LTD.—(Continued)
N.A.I.C.S.: 333992
NADEX Machinery (Shanghai) CO., LTD. (1)
815 Shengfu Road, Xinzhuang Industrial Zone, Shanghai, China
Tel.: (86) 215 442 7877
Web Site: https://www.nadex.com.cn
Welding Equipment Mfr & Distr
N.A.I.C.S.: 333992

NADEX PRODUCTS CO., LTD. (1)
1-21 Himegaoka, Kani, 509-0249, Gifu, Japan
Tel.: (81) 57 462 1101
Web Site: https://www.nadex-p.jp
Emp.: 160
Welding Equipment Mfr
N.A.I.C.S.: 333992

NADEX USA CO., LTD. (1)
24775 Crestview Ct, Farmington Hills, MI 48335
Tel.: (248) 957-6380
Welding Equipment Mfr & Distr
N.A.I.C.S.: 333992

Nadex Engineering Co., Ltd. (1)
160/160 ITF Silom Palace 12 nd Fl Sirom Rd Suriwong, Bangrak, Bangkok, 10500, Thailand
Tel.: (66) 231529112
Web Site: https://www.nadex.co.th
Industrial Equipment Distr
N.A.I.C.S.: 423830

Nadex of America Corporation (1)
24775 Crestview Ct, Farmington Hills, MI 48335
Tel.: (248) 477-3900
Welding Equipment Mfr
N.A.I.C.S.: 333992

P.T. Nadesco Engineering Indonesia (1)
Jl Jababeka IX-A Kawasan Industri Jababeka 1 Blok P2H1 Kel Wangunharja, Kec Cikarang Utara, Bekasi, 17530, Jawa Barat, Indonesia
Tel.: (62) 2129093132
Industrial Equipment Distr
N.A.I.C.S.: 423830

PT. NADESCO INDONESIA (1)
Ruko Easton Blok D-2 Jl Gn Panderman Kav 005 Lippo Cikarang, Bekasi, 17550, Jawa Barat, Indonesia
Tel.: (62) 21 2909 3132
Welding Equipment Mfr & Distr
N.A.I.C.S.: 333992

Tamari Industry Co., Ltd. (1)
1-1 Gorota Yonezu-cho, Nishio, 445-0802, Aichi, Japan
Tel.: (81) 563571171
Web Site: https://www.tamari.co.jp
Industrial Machinery Mfr
N.A.I.C.S.: 333248

NADIA SIGNALISATION
1 rue Denis Papin, BP 30736, 49307, Cholet, Cedex, France
Tel.: (33) 2 41 65 06 17
Web Site: http://www.nadia-europ.com
Sales Range: $10-24.9 Million
Emp.: 116
Holding Company; Road Signs Mfr & Designer
N.A.I.C.S.: 551112
Thomas Mallet (VP)

NADLER LARIMER E MARTINELLI S.R.L.
Via Boccaccio 39, 20123, Milan, Italy
Tel.: (39) 02 48 19 48 57
Web Site: http://www.nadler.it
Year Founded: 1981
Rev.: $46,000,000
Emp.: 15
N.A.I.C.S.: 541810
Mario Martinelli (Pres)

NADRO S.A. DE C.V.
Vasco de Quiroga 3100 Col Centro Santa Fe, 01210, Mexico, DF, Mexico
Tel.: (52) 5552924343   MX
Web Site: www.nadro.com.mx
Year Founded: 1943
Sales Range: $1-4.9 Billion
Emp.: 5,300
Pharmaceuticals & Hygiene & Beauty Products Distr
N.A.I.C.S.: 424210
Pablo Escandon Cusi (Pres)

NAEEM HOLDING
Km 28 Cairo Alex Road Building B16 Phase 1 Smart Village, 6th of October City, Giza, Egypt
Tel.: (20) 235355000
Web Site: https://www.naeemholding.com
Year Founded: 2006
NAHO.CA—(EGX)
Sales Range: $10-24.9 Million
Holding Company
N.A.I.C.S.: 551112
Iman A. Sadek (Head-IR)

Subsidiaries:

Etihad Capital PJSC (1)
Office 1003 Level 10 Boulevard Plaza Tower 2, PO Box 119244, Burj Khalifa Area Downtown, 119244, Dubai, United Arab Emirates
Tel.: (971) 43824724
Web Site: http://etihadcapital.com
Financial Investment Services
N.A.I.C.S.: 523999
Jassem Elzahry (Chm)

Naeem Financial Investments S.A.E. (1)
Smart Village- Building B16- Phase 1 Km 28 Cairo - Alex Road, Box 61, Giza, 12577, 6th of October City, Egypt
Tel.: (20) 235318400
Financial Investment Services
N.A.I.C.S.: 523999

NAFAIS HOLDING COMPANY K.S.C.
Sharq Ahmad Aljaber St Securities Group Building mezzanine, Kuwait, Kuwait
Tel.: (965) 22287634
Web Site: http://www.nafais.com.kw
Sales Range: $25-49.9 Million
Holding Company
N.A.I.C.S.: 551112
Qutaiba Adnan Mohamed Al-Wazzan (CEO)

NAFCO CO., LTD.
7F 2-6-10 Uomachi, Kokurakita-ku, Kitakyushu, Fukuoka, Japan
Tel.: (81) 935215155
Web Site: https://www.nafco.tv
Year Founded: 1970
2790—(TKS)
Sales Range: Less than $1 Million
Emp.: 1,472
Furniture Product Mfr
N.A.I.C.S.: 449110
Takumi Ishida (Pres & CEO)

NAFOODS GROUP JOINT STOCK COMPANY
47 Nguyen Canh Hoan Street, Ninh Binh, Nghe An, Vietnam
Tel.: (84) 2837447666
Web Site: https://www.nafoods.com
Year Founded: 1995
NAF—(HNX)
Food Products Mfr
N.A.I.C.S.: 311999
Nguyen Manh Hung (Chm)

NAFPAKTOS TEXTILE INDUSTRY S.A.
40-44 Ag Georgiou Str, 151 21, Pefki, Attika, Greece
Tel.: (30) 2106140430
Web Site: https://www.nafpaktos-yarns.gr
Year Founded: 1989
NAYP—(ATH)
Sales Range: $10-24.9 Million
Emp.: 108
Cotton Yarn & Fabric Mfr
N.A.I.C.S.: 313110
Anastasios Polychronos (Bd of Dirs & VP)

Subsidiaries:

Energiaki Pinias 2 S.A. (1)
Kolokotroni 95, Athens, Greece
Tel.: (30) 2106140430
Web Site: http://www.energiakipineias2-sa.gr
Clothing Mfr
N.A.I.C.S.: 313310

Sofades Ginning Mills S.A. (1)
2nd km E O Sofades, 43300, Athens, Greece
Tel.: (30) 2443022272
Web Site: http://www.ekkokkistiria-sofadon-sa.gr
Clothing Mfr
N.A.I.C.S.: 313310

NAFTA AD
Francuska 12, Belgrade, Serbia
Tel.: (381) 113346502
Web Site: http://www.nafta.co.rs
Year Founded: 2001
NFTA—(BEL)
Sales Range: $50-74.9 Million
Petroleum Product Whslr
N.A.I.C.S.: 424720
Dragana Dordevic (Mng Dir)

NAGA DHUNSERI GROUP LIMITED
Dhunseri House 4A Woodburn Park, Kolkata, 700020, India
Tel.: (91) 3322801950
Web Site: https://www.nagadhunserigroup.com
Year Founded: 1918
NDGL—(NSE)
Rev.: $4,027,848
Assets: $43,074,937
Liabilities: $488,750
Net Worth: $42,586,186
Earnings: $295,332
Emp.: 9
Fiscal Year-end: 03/31/19
Investment Management Service
N.A.I.C.S.: 523150
Mrigank Dhanuka (Mng Dir)

NAGACORP LTD.
Suite 2806 Central Plaza 18 Harbour Road, Wanchai, China (Hong Kong)
Tel.: (852) 28773918
Web Site: http://www.nagacorp.com
Year Founded: 1995
3918—(HKG)
Rev.: $460,693,000
Assets: $2,589,656,000
Liabilities: $740,329,000
Net Worth: $1,849,327,000
Earnings: $107,254,000
Emp.: 6,398
Fiscal Year-end: 12/31/22
Hotel & Casino Owner & Operator
N.A.I.C.S.: 721120
Lip Keong Chen (Founder & CEO)

Subsidiaries:

Karambunai Corp Bhd. (1)
No 9020 Nexus Drive West Karambunai, Menggatal, 88450, Kota Kinabalu, Sabah, Malaysia
Tel.: (60) 88411111
Web Site: http://www.karambunaicorp.com
Property Development Services

N.A.I.C.S.: 236118
Yiy Fon Chen (CEO)

Subsidiary (Domestic):

Bukit Unggul Country Club Bhd. (2)
Sepang, PO Box 20, Kampung Dengkil, 43807, Selangor, Malaysia
Tel.: (60) 389201129
Web Site: http://www.bukitunggul.com
Sales Range: $50-74.9 Million
Emp.: 100
Golf Club Management Services
N.A.I.C.S.: 713910
May Wong (Gen Mgr)

Karambunai Resorts Sdn. Bhd. (2)
1 Nexus Drive East Karambunai, Menggatal, 88450, Kota Kinabalu, Sabah, Malaysia
Tel.: (60) 88411111
Web Site: http://www.nexus-resort-karambunai.com
Sales Range: $50-74.9 Million
Emp.: 300
Resort Management Services
N.A.I.C.S.: 721120

Subsidiary (Domestic):

Dapan Holdings Sdn. Bhd. (3)
Lot 10 Ground & 1st Floor Block B Iramanis Centre Off Ring Road, 88300, Kota Kinabalu, Sabah, Malaysia
Tel.: (60) 88383333
Web Site: http://www.bandarsiera.com
Emp.: 20
Property Development Services
N.A.I.C.S.: 531390

Karambunai Golf Management Bhd. (3)
101 88993, Locked Bag 101, 88993, Kota Kinabalu, Sabah, Malaysia
Tel.: (60) 88411215
Web Site: http://www.karambunaigolf.com
Sales Range: $25-49.9 Million
Emp.: 100
Golf Club Management Services
N.A.I.C.S.: 713910

Nexus Bay Resort Karambunai Sdn. Bhd. (3)
Locked Bag 100, Kota Kinabalu, 88993, Sabah, Malaysia
Tel.: (60) 88480888
Web Site: http://www.nexusresort.com
Sales Range: $10-24.9 Million
Emp.: 3
Resort Management Services
N.A.I.C.S.: 721110
Peter Strenger (Mgr-Hotel)

Nexus Resort Karambunai Sdn. Bhd. (3)
Off Jalan Sepangar Bay Locked Bag 100, 88993, Kota Kinabalu, Sabah, Malaysia
Tel.: (60) 88480888
Web Site: http://www.nexusresort.com
Sales Range: $100-124.9 Million
Resort Hotel Operation Services
N.A.I.C.S.: 721110

NagaWorld Limited (1)
Rm 2806 28 F Central Plz 18 Harbour Rd, Wanchai, China (Hong Kong)
Tel.: (852) 25246123
Web Site: http://www.nagaworld.com
Gaming Hotels & Entertainment Services
N.A.I.C.S.: 721110

NAGAHORI CORPORATION
15-3 1-chome Ueno, Taito-ku, Tokyo, 110-8546, Japan
Tel.: (81) 338328266
Web Site: https://www.nagahori.co.jp
Year Founded: 1962
8139—(TKS)
Rev.: $144,230,200
Assets: $168,383,140
Liabilities: $84,277,500
Net Worth: $84,105,640
Earnings: $3,430,590
Emp.: 484
Fiscal Year-end: 03/31/24
Jewelry Product Mfr & Whslr
N.A.I.C.S.: 339910
Morihiro Nagahori (Chm)

AND PRIVATE COMPANIES

Subsidiaries:

NAGAHORI CORPORATION - Mobara Plant (1)
3210-17 Honno, Mobara, 299-4114, Chiba, Japan
Tel.: (81) 475345251
Jewelry Product Mfr
N.A.I.C.S.: 339910

NAGAILEBEN CO., LTD.
2-1-10 kajicho, Chiyoda-ku, Tokyo, 101-0044, Japan
Tel.: (81) 352898200
Web Site:
  https://www.nagaileben.co.jp
Year Founded: 1950
7447—(TKS)
Rev.: $102,082,640
Assets: $290,641,940
Liabilities: $25,066,600
Net Worth: $265,575,340
Earnings: $17,552,840
Emp.: 500
Fiscal Year-end: 08/31/24
Medical Wear Mfr & Whslr
N.A.I.C.S.: 315990
Ichiro Sawanobori *(Pres)*

NAGAKAWA GROUP JOINT STOCK COMPANY
Area 9, Phuc Yen, Vinh Phuc, Vietnam
Tel.: (84) 2113873568
Web Site:
  https://www.nagakawa.com.vn
Year Founded: 2002
NAG—(HNX)
Rev.: $56,176,964
Assets: $48,040,384
Liabilities: $38,884,057
Net Worth: $9,156,327
Earnings: $617,625
Fiscal Year-end: 12/31/21
Home Appliances Mfr & Distr
N.A.I.C.S.: 449210

NAGAMBIE RESOURCES LIMITED
533 Zanelli Road, PO Box 339, Nagambie, 3608, VIC, Australia
Tel.: (61) 357941750   AU
Web Site:
  https://www.nagambieresources.au
Year Founded: 2004
NAG—(ASX)
Rev.: $183,210
Assets: $15,601,828
Liabilities: $5,347,000
Net Worth: $10,254,828
Earnings: ($1,862,687)
Emp.: 3
Fiscal Year-end: 06/30/24
Mineral Mining & Exploration
N.A.I.C.S.: 327999
Michael Ward Trumbull *(Chm)*

NAGANO KEIKI CO., LTD.
1-30-4 Higashimagome, Ohta-ku, Tokyo, 143-8544, Japan
Tel.: (81) 337765311
Web Site:
  https://www.naganokeiki.co.jp
Year Founded: 1896
7715—(TKS)
Rev.: $449,050,350
Assets: $478,352,480
Liabilities: $210,105,460
Net Worth: $268,247,020
Earnings: $35,753,490
Emp.: 2,467
Fiscal Year-end: 03/31/24
Pressure Measurement Instrument Mfr
N.A.I.C.S.: 334513
Shigeo Yoda *(Chm)*

Subsidiaries:

Ashcroft-Nagano Keiki Holdings, Inc. (1)
250 E Main St, Stratford, CT 06614-5145
Tel.: (203) 378-8281
Web Site: http://www.ashcroft.com
Pressure Measurement Instrument Mfr
N.A.I.C.S.: 334513

Subsidiary (Non-US):

Ashcroft Instruments (Suzhou) CO., LTD. (2)
1508 Lin-Hu Ave, Wujiang Fen-Hu Economic Development Zone, Wujiang, 215211, China
Tel.: (86) 5126 326 9101
Web Site: http://www.ashcroft.com.cn
Pressure Measurement Instrument Mfr
N.A.I.C.S.: 334513

Ashcroft Instruments GmbH (2)
Max-Planck-Str 1, 52499, Baesweiler, Germany
Tel.: (49) 2 401 8080
Web Site: https://www.ashcroft.eu
Emp.: 2,000
Pressure Measurement Instrument Mfr
N.A.I.C.S.: 334513
Steve Culmone *(Pres & CEO)*

Ashcroft Instruments Mexico, S.A. de C.V.C (2)
General Mariano Arista No 54 Nave 8 Col Argentina Poniente, Deleg Miguel Hildalgo, 11230, Mexico, Mexico
Tel.: (52) 5550823030
Web Site: https://ashcroft.com.mx
Pressure Measurement Instrument Mfr
N.A.I.C.S.: 334513

Ashcroft Instruments Singapore Pte Ltd (2)
Block 1004 Toa Payoh North 07-15/17, Singapore, 318995, Singapore
Tel.: (65) 62526602
Web Site: https://www.ashcroft.com
Pressure Measurement Instrument Mfr
N.A.I.C.S.: 334513

Willy Instrumentos de Medicao e Controle Ltda (2)
Tel.: (55) 1142247424
Pressure Measurement Instrument Distr
N.A.I.C.S.: 423830

Castec Co.,Ltd. (1)
2-717-6 Toyonodai Inside Toyonodai Techno Town, Kazo, 349-1148, Saitama, Japan
Tel.: (81) 480722035
Web Site: https://www.castec-inc.com
Emp.: 190
Casting Mold Parts Mfr & Distr
N.A.I.C.S.: 333511

Epoch Nagano, Co., Ltd. (1)
119-3 Kabatake, Ueda, 386-1108, Nagano Prefecture, Japan
Tel.: (81) 268224080
Web Site: http://www.epoch.nagano.jp
Dormitory Maintenance Services
N.A.I.C.S.: 721310

FUKUDA CO., LTD. (1)
3-16-5 Nukui, Nerima-ku, Tokyo, 176-0021, Japan
Tel.: (81) 335771111
Emp.: 129
Pressure Measurement Instrument Mfr
N.A.I.C.S.: 334513
Masakazu Uchibori *(Pres)*

Subsidiary (Domestic):

FUKUDA CO., LTD. - Shizuoka factory (2)
2543-1 Shizutani, Makinohara, 421-0404, Shizuoka, Japan
Tel.: (81) 548273111
Industrial Measuring Equipment Mfr
N.A.I.C.S.: 334513

FUKUDA CO., LTD. - Tohoku Factory (2)
39-1 Ohdairamoriai-Azashimizuda, Shiroishi, 989-0217, Miyagi, Japan
Tel.: (81) 224242672
Industrial Measuring Equipment Mfr
N.A.I.C.S.: 334513

Subsidiary (Non-US):

Fukuda (Thailand) Co., Ltd. (2)
33 Soi Wachiratham Satit 51 Sukhumvit101/1 Rd, Phrakhanong, Bangkok, 10260, Thailand
Tel.: (66) 23971295
Pressure Measurement Instrument Repair & Distr
N.A.I.C.S.: 423830

Subsidiary (US):

Fukuda USA, Inc. (2)
2721 Pioneer Dr, Bowling Green, KY 42101
Tel.: (270) 745-7300
Pressure Measurement Instrument Mfr
N.A.I.C.S.: 334513

Subsidiary (Non-US):

Nagano Fukuda (Tianjin) Instruments Co., Ltd. (2)
7th Factory Fenghua Industrial Park No 80 9th Avenue TEDA, Tianjin, 300457, China
Tel.: (86) 1087582461
Web Site: https://www.fukuda-tj.com.cn
Pressure Measurement Instrument Mfr
N.A.I.C.S.: 334513

PT. FUKUDA TECHNOLOGY (2)
Kompleks Cikarang Square B-22, Cikarang, Bekasi, 17730, Indonesia
Tel.: (62) 2129094511
Industrial Measuring Equipment Distr
N.A.I.C.S.: 423830
Sammy Jonathan *(Mng Dir)*

Futaba Sokki Co., Ltd. (1)
8-21-14 Higashiogu, Arakawa-ku, Tokyo, 116-0012, Japan
Tel.: (81) 338946848
Web Site: http://www.futabass.co.jp
Manometer Mfr
N.A.I.C.S.: 334513
Kazumasa Tsukada *(CEO)*

Nagano Co., Ltd. (1)
3-15-16 Central, Ota-ku, Tokyo, 143-0024, Japan
Web Site: http://www.kk-nagano.co.jp
Heater Mfr
N.A.I.C.S.: 333414

Nagano Keiki Co., Ltd. - The Electronic Instrument Plant (1)
2480 Mitakedo, Ueda-shi, Nagano, 386-0412, Japan
Tel.: (81) 268427530
Industrial Measuring Equipment Mfr
N.A.I.C.S.: 334513

Nagano Keiki Co., Ltd. - The measurement Instrument Plant (1)
1150 Akiwa, Ueda-shi, Nagano, 386-8501, Japan
Tel.: (81) 268227530
Industrial Measuring Equipment Mfr
N.A.I.C.S.: 334513

Nagano Keiso Co., Ltd. (1)
1-30-4 Higashi-Magome, Ota-ku, Tokyo, 143-0022, Japan
Tel.: (81) 357183281
Web Site: https://www.nagano-keiso.co.jp
Industrial Measuring Equipment Mfr
N.A.I.C.S.: 334513

New-Era Co., Ltd. (1)
1-7-21 Nakagawahigashi, Ikuno-ku, Osaka, 544-0000, Japan
Tel.: (81) 667548585
Automobile Parts Mfr
N.A.I.C.S.: 336390
Hiroshi Miyashita *(Pres)*

Subsidiary (Non-US):

New-Era International Co., Ltd. (2)
Bangphlee Industrial Estate Tambol Bangsaothong, Amphur, Bang Sao Thong, 10540, Samutprakarn, Thailand
Tel.: (66) 231520268
Automobile Parts Mfr
N.A.I.C.S.: 336390

S3C, Inc. (1)
1296 Lawrence Sta Rd Ste 200, Sunnyvale, CA 94089
Tel.: (408) 746-3081
Web Site: http://www.s3cinc.com

NAGARJUNA AGRITECH LIMITED

Emp.: 20
Pressure Measurement Instrument Mfr
N.A.I.C.S.: 334513
M. Yunus *(CTO)*

Sun Cast Co., Ltd. (1)
1086 Hanya, Shimotsuma, 304-0005, Ibaraki, Japan
Tel.: (81) 296444175
Web Site: https://www.suncast.co.jp
Emp.: 123
Auto Parts Distr
N.A.I.C.S.: 423120

Yoshitomi-Mahshin, Co., Ltd. (1)
6585-2 Oaza Konami, Suwa, 392-0131, Nagano Prefecture, Japan
Tel.: (81) 266587781
Emp.: 41
Measuring Instruments Mfr
N.A.I.C.S.: 334515
Toshiaki Miyazaki *(Pres & CEO)*

NAGAOKA INTERNATIONAL CORPORATION
Nomura Real Estate Osaka Building 7F 1-8-15 Azuchi-cho, Chuo-ku, Osaka, 541-0052, Japan
Tel.: (81) 662616600
Web Site:
  https://www.nagaokajapan.co.jp
6239—(TKS)
Rev.: $59,121,100
Assets: $63,773,660
Liabilities: $20,233,660
Net Worth: $43,540,000
Earnings: $7,153,000
Emp.: 184
Fiscal Year-end: 06/30/24
Industrial Machinery Mfr
N.A.I.C.S.: 333248
Yasuhisa Umezu *(Pres & CEO)*

Subsidiaries:

NAGAOKA International Corporation - Kaizuka Factory (1)
2-12 Nishiki minami-cho, Kaizuka, 597-0094, Osaka, Japan
Tel.: (81) 724318100
Web Site: https://www.nagaokajapan.co.jp
Industrial Machinery Mfr
N.A.I.C.S.: 333248

Nagaoka (Beijing) Trading Co., Ltd. (1)
East Tower 10F Beijing World Financial Center No 1 Dong San, Huan Zhong Road Chaoyang District, Beijing, 100020, China
Tel.: (86) 1059680098
Water Treatment Equipment Distr
N.A.I.C.S.: 423830

Nagaoka Equipment (Dalian) Co., Ltd. (1)
No 17 Songjia Road, Xijin Village Desheng Town DDA, Dalian, 116635, Liaoning, China
Tel.: (86) 41162782000
Industrial Machinery Mfr
N.A.I.C.S.: 333248

Nagaoka Equipment (Dalian) Co., Ltd. (1)
No 17 Songjia Road DDA, Xijin Village Desheng Town, Dalian, 116635, Liaoning, China
Tel.: (86) 41162782000
Petrochemical Mfr & Distr
N.A.I.C.S.: 325110

Nagaoka Vietnam Co., Ltd. (1)
Standard Factory No 1B Plot No D-10, Thang Long Industrial Park II Di Su Ward, My Hao, Hung Yen, Vietnam
Tel.: (84) 2212238666
Petrochemical Mfr & Distr
N.A.I.C.S.: 325110

NAGARJUNA AGRITECH LIMITED
56 Nagarjuna Hills, Punjagutta, Hyderabad, 500 082, Telangana, India
Tel.: (91) 4023357248

NAGARJUNA AGRITECH LIMITED

Nagarjuna Agritech Limited—(Continued)
Web Site:
http://www.nagarjunaagritechltd.com
Year Founded: 1987
531832—(BOM)
Rev.: $317,127
Assets: $467,948
Liabilities: $122,272
Net Worth: $345,676
Earnings: ($20,241)
Fiscal Year-end: 03/31/23
Herbal Medicine Mfr & Distr
N.A.I.C.S.: 325411
Kvln Raju (CEO & Mng Dir)

NAGARJUNA FERTILIZERS & CHEMICALS LTD.
Nagarjuna Hills, Hyderabad, 500082, Andhra Pradesh, India
Tel.: (91) 4023357200
Web Site:
http://www.nagarjunafertilizers.com
Sales Range: $650-699.9 Million
Fertilizers & Agricultural Chemicals Mfr
N.A.I.C.S.: 325311
K. S. Raju (Chm)

Subsidiaries:

NACL Industries Ltd (1)
Plot No 12A C Block Lakshmi Towers Nagarjuna Hills, Punjagutta, Hyderabad, 500082, Telangana, India
Tel.: (91) 4033605123
Web Site: https://www.naclind.com
Rev.: $164,623,095
Assets: $133,168,035
Liabilities: $76,029,135
Net Worth: $57,138,900
Earnings: $6,960,135
Emp.: 1,204
Fiscal Year-end: 03/31/2021
Agrochemical Mfr
N.A.I.C.S.: 325320
R. K. S. Prasad (CFO & Exec VP-Fin)

Nagarjuna Fertilizers & Chemicals Ltd. - Kakinada Plant (1)
Nagarjuna Road, Kakinada, 533 003, Andhra Pradesh, India
Tel.: (91) 884 2360390
Fertilizer Mfr
N.A.I.C.S.: 327910
Rahul Raju (Mng Dir)

Nagarjuna Oil Corporation Limited (1)
MD Chambers Old No 31 New No 53 Dr Radha Krishnan Salai, Mylapore, Chennai, 600 004, Tamil Nadu, India
Tel.: (91) 44 28431000
Web Site: http://www.nocl.co.in
Petroleum Product Mfr
N.A.I.C.S.: 327910
K. S. Raju (Chm)

NAGARRO SE
Baierbrunner Strasse 15, 81379, Munich, Germany
Tel.: (49) 897850000   De
Web Site: https://www.nagarro.com
NA9—(DEU)
Rev.: $924,167,926
Assets: $667,108,785
Liabilities: $489,379,452
Net Worth: $177,729,333
Earnings: $83,447,011
Emp.: 18,250
Fiscal Year-end: 12/31/22
Software Development Services
N.A.I.C.S.: 541511
Manas Fuloria (Co-Founder)

Subsidiaries:

Advanced Technology Consulting Service Inc. (1)
155 Chestnut Ridge Rd Ste 108, Montvale, NJ 07645
Tel.: (201) 663-9159
Web Site: https://www.atcs.com
Information Technology Consulting Services
N.A.I.C.S.: 541512

Nagarro Allgeier ES Denmark A/S (1)
Sondre Ringvej 55, 2605, Brondby, Denmark
Tel.: (45) 42206488
Information Technology Services
N.A.I.C.S.: 541511

Nagarro Allgeier ES France SAS (1)
8a Rue Icare, 67960, Entzheim, France
Tel.: (33) 787117979
Information Technology Services
N.A.I.C.S.: 541511

Nagarro Allgeier ES GmbH (1)
Westerbachstrasse 32, 61476, Kronberg, Germany
Tel.: (49) 61733363000
Information Technology Services
N.A.I.C.S.: 541511

Nagarro ES Denmark A/S (1)
Marielundvej 41, 2730, Herlev, Denmark
Tel.: (45) 42206488
Information Technology Services
N.A.I.C.S.: 541519

Nagarro ES GmbH (1)
Westerbachstrasse 32, 61476, Kronberg, Germany
Tel.: (49) 61733363000
Information Technology Consulting Services
N.A.I.C.S.: 541512

Nagarro GmbH (1)
Baierbrunner Strasse 15, 81379, Munich, Germany
Tel.: (49) 897850000
Information Technology Services
N.A.I.C.S.: 541511

Nagarro Software S.A. de C.V. (1)
Ricardo Margain 575 Parque Col Santa Engracia, San Pedro Garza Garcia, Monterrey, Nuevo Leon, Mexico
Tel.: (52) 8112537200
Information Technology Consulting Services
N.A.I.C.S.: 541512

Nagarro iQuest Technologies SRL (1)
14 Somesului Street, 400145, Cluj-Napoca, Romania
Tel.: (40) 372343400
Information Technology Services
N.A.I.C.S.: 541519

NAGASE & CO., LTD.
5-1 Nihonbashi-Kobunacho, Chuo-ku, Tokyo, 103-8355, Japan
Tel.: (81) 336610819   JP
Web Site: https://www.nagase.co.jp
Year Founded: 1832
8012—(TKS)
Rev.: $5,949,984,890
Assets: $5,237,340,960
Liabilities: $2,584,648,810
Net Worth: $2,652,692,150
Earnings: $148,077,220
Emp.: 7,528
Fiscal Year-end: 03/31/24
Development, Production, Sale & Import of Dyestuffs, Chemicals, Plastics & Biochemical Products & Attendant Machinery
N.A.I.C.S.: 325211
Hiroshi Nagase (Chm)

Subsidiaries:

3D Glass Solutions, Inc. (1)
5601-B Balloon Fiesta Pkwy NE, Albuquerque, NM 87113
Tel.: (505) 916-5590
Web Site: https://www.3dgsinc.com
Glass Ceramic Mfr & Distr
N.A.I.C.S.: 327212
Jeb H. Flemming (Founder & CTO)

Aience Inc. (1)
Kowa Edobori Bldg 3F 1 Chome-21-7 Edobori, Nishi-ku, Osaka, 550-0002, Japan
Tel.: (81) 662252323
Web Site: https://www.aience.co.jp
Waste Water Treatment Services
N.A.I.C.S.: 221320

Norifumi Yoshida (Pres & CEO)

Aikawa Kogyo Co., Ltd. (1)
Toyo Bldg 3f, Setagaya-Ku, Tokyo, 154-0011, Japan
Tel.: (81) 354861711
Chemical Product Whslr
N.A.I.C.S.: 424690

Armada Nutrition LLC (1)
4637 Port Royal Rd, Spring Hill, TN 37174
Tel.: (931) 451-7808
Web Site: http://www.armadanutrition.com
Nutritional Food Products Mfr
N.A.I.C.S.: 311999
Brent Laffey (Pres)

Automotive Mold Technology Co., Ltd. (1)
Amata City Industrial Estate Rayong 7/117 Moo 4 Mabyangporn Pluakdaeng, Rayong, 21140, Thailand
Tel.: (66) 38025860
Web Site: https://www.amt.co.th
Automobile Parts Mfr
N.A.I.C.S.: 336390
Fumio Iwatsuki (Pres)

CAPTEX Co., Ltd. (1)
1-91 Shlinokl, Maigi-cho, Okazaki, 444-3511, Aichi, Japan
Tel.: (81) 564663031
Web Site: http://www.captex.co.jp
Battery Power Source Controller Mfr
N.A.I.C.S.: 335999

Canada Mold Technology, Inc. (1)
1075 Ridgeway Road, Woodstock, N4V 1E3, ON, Canada   (100%)
Tel.: (519) 421-0711
Web Site: http://www.canada-mold.com
Sales Range: $25-49.9 Million
Emp.: 50
Automobiles Molds Mfr
N.A.I.C.S.: 326199

Choko Co., Ltd. (1)
1-1-17 Shinmachi, Nishi-ku, Osaka, 550-0013, Japan
Tel.: (81) 665352222
Web Site: https://nagase-ins.jp
Insurance Services
N.A.I.C.S.: 524210
Satoshi Doi (Pres)

Cytech Products Inc. (1)
906 Peterson Dr, Elizabethtown, KY 42701
Tel.: (270) 769-1046
Web Site: http://www.cytechproducts.com
Rev.: $4,891,898
Chemical Product Mfr & Distr
N.A.I.C.S.: 325998
Ronald Johnson (Mgr-Mktg)

Datai (Shanghai) Chemical Trading Co., Ltd. (1)
1018 Hua Lian Development Building 728 Xln Hua Road, Shanghai, China
Tel.: (86) 2131757478
Paint Distr
N.A.I.C.S.: 424950

Fukui Yamada Chemical Co., Ltd. (1)
Aza 111-1 49 Yonozu Mikuni-cho, Sakai, 913-0036, Fukui, Japan
Tel.: (81) 776826000
Web Site: https://www.fukuiyamadachem.co.jp
Emp.: 81
Chemical Products Mfr
N.A.I.C.S.: 325199
Daisuke Sasaki (Pres)

Guangzhou Nagase Trading Ltd. (1)
Room 1201 1202 1208 R F Center No 10 Huaxia Road, Pearl River New Town Tianhe District, Guangzhou, 510613, China
Tel.: (86) 2038139300
Sales Range: $50-74.9 Million
Emp.: 10
Chemical & Plastic Products Distr
N.A.I.C.S.: 424690

Hayashiba Co., Ltd. (1)
Nihon-Seimei Okayama Bldg II Shinkan 1-1-3 Shimoishii, Kita-ku, Okayama, 700-0907, Japan
Tel.: (81) 862244311
Emp.: 681
Food Mfr & Distr

INTERNATIONAL PUBLIC

N.A.I.C.S.: 311999

Honshu Rheem Co., Ltd. (1)
4-8-11 minami-hashimoto, Chuo-ku, Sagamihara, 252-0253, Kanagawa-ken, Japan
Tel.: (81) 427733111
Web Site: http://www.honshu-r.co.jp
Fiber Drum Mfr & Distr
N.A.I.C.S.: 322219
Kouji Nakano (Pres)

Huizhou Sanli Three Synergy Precision Co., Ltd. (1)
Long Hai 2nd Rd 308, Hui Yang Qu, Huizhou, Guangdong, China
Tel.: (86) 336653826
Metal Molding Parts Mfr
N.A.I.C.S.: 333511

Infinite Material Solutions, LLC (1)
1091 Sutherland Ave, River Falls, WI 54022
Tel.: (347) 487-8880
Web Site: http://infinitematerialsolutions.com
Automobile Parts Mfr
N.A.I.C.S.: 336390
Lawrence Doerr (COO)

Inkron Oy (1)
Kutojantie 2a, 02630, Espoo, Finland
Tel.: (358) 105812650
Web Site: https://inkron.com
Semiconductor Equipment Mfr
N.A.I.C.S.: 333242

Interfacial Consultants LLC (1)
The Cervenka Ctr N4660 1165th St, Prescott, WI 54021
Tel.: (715) 629-5188
Web Site: https://ifllc.com
Business Consulting Services
N.A.I.C.S.: 541611

KN Platech America Corporation (1)
1755 McCall Dr, Shelbyville, IN 46176
Tel.: (317) 392-7707
Web Site: https://www.knplatech.com
Plastic Blow Molded Component Mfr & Distr
N.A.I.C.S.: 333511
Mark Haler (Mgr-Ops)

Kawai Hiryo Corporation (1)
2251 Maeno, Iwata, 438-0068, Shizuoka, Japan
Tel.: (81) 538356450
Web Site: https://kawai-hiryo.com
Organic Fertilizer & Agricultural Chemical Mfr & Whslr
N.A.I.C.S.: 325199

Kotobuki Kasei Corp. (1)
7-9 Satsukicho, Kanuma Industrial Park, Kanuma, 322-0014, Tochigi, Japan
Tel.: (81) 289720112
Web Site: https://www.kotobukikasei.com
Emp.: 89
Plastic Products Mfr & Distr
N.A.I.C.S.: 326199

Mianyang Chenghong Electronic Chemicals Co., Ltd. (1)
No 327 Sanjiang Avenue, Mianyang, Sichuan, China
Tel.: (86) 51080622313
Electronic Product Mfr & Distr
N.A.I.C.S.: 334419

NAGASE-OG COLORS & CHEMICALS CO., LTD. (1)
1-17 Shinmachi 1-chome, Nishi-ku, Osaka, 550-8668, Japan
Tel.: (81) 665352200
Web Site: http://www.ognagase.co.jp
Sales Range: $75-99.9 Million
Emp.: 110
Purchasing & Sale of Dyestuffs, Industrial Chemicals & Related Products
N.A.I.C.S.: 424690
Katsuhiko Ichino (Pres & CEO)

NW Consultant Service (Shenzhen) Ltd. (1)
Room329 3B NO 109 Lijia Road, Henggang Longgang District, Shenzhen, China
Tel.: (86) 75528654082
Business Management Consulting Services
N.A.I.C.S.: 541618

NWP International Trading (Shenzhen) Co., Ltd. (1)
Rm2411 Gold Central Tower No 3037 Jin-

tian Rd, Futian District, Shenzhen, China
Tel.: (86) 75583599373
Plastic Product Distr
N.A.I.C.S.: 424610

Nafuko Co., Ltd. (1)
54 Floor 4 Room 4 A Harintron Tower North Sathorn Rd Silom, Bangrak, Bangkok, 10500, Thailand
Tel.: (66) 817613702
Web Site: http://www.nafuko.com
Packaging Material Mfr & Distr
N.A.I.C.S.: 326112
Takamitsu Nagase (Pres)

Nagase (China) Co., Ltd. (1)
5th Floor Building B One ITC China World Plaza 1901 Huashan Road, Xuhui District, Shanghai, 200030, China
Tel.: (86) 2122210222
Web Site: http://www.nagase.cn
Logistic Services
N.A.I.C.S.: 541614

Nagase (Europa) GmbH (1)
Werdener Strasse 4, 40227, Dusseldorf, Germany (100%)
Tel.: (49) 211866200
Web Site: https://www.nagase.eu
Emp.: 22
Distribution of Dyestuffs, Chemicals & Electronic Materials
N.A.I.C.S.: 424690

Nagase (Hong Kong) Ltd. (1)
Suits 607-9 6/F South Tower World Finance Centre 17 Canton Road, Tsim Sha Tsui, Kowloon, China (Hong Kong) (100%)
Tel.: (852) 23750000
Web Site: http://www.nagase.com.hk
Sales Range: $25-49.9 Million
Emp.: 50
Distribution of Chemicals, Synthetic Resins & Machines
N.A.I.C.S.: 424690
Mizumori Mory (Mng Dir)

Nagase (Malaysia) Sdn Bhd (1)
Suite 16 01 Level 16 Menara IGB Mid Valley City Lingkaran Syed Putra, 59200, Kuala Lumpur, Malaysia (100%)
Tel.: (60) 322832366
Web Site: http://www.e-nagase.com
Sales Range: $25-49.9 Million
Emp.: 50
Distribution of Chemicals, Synthetic Resins & Electronic Materials
N.A.I.C.S.: 424690
Tamotsu Isobe (Mng Dir)

Nagase (Taiwan) Co., Ltd. (1)
16th Floor No 248 Section 3 Nanjing East Road, Songshan District, Taipei, 105, Taiwan
Tel.: (886) 227733668
Web Site: https://www.nagase.com.tw
Emp.: 60
Electric Component Whslr
N.A.I.C.S.: 423690
Takahashi Atsushi (COO)

Nagase (Thailand) Co., Ltd. (1)
No 952 Ramaland Building 14th Floor Rama IV Rd Kwaeng Suriyawongse, Khet Bangrak, Bangkok, 10500, Thailand (100%)
Tel.: (66) 28257000
Web Site: https://www.nagase.co.th
Sales Range: $75-99.9 Million
Emp.: 120
Distribution of Chemicals, Synthetic Resins & Electronic Materials
N.A.I.C.S.: 424690

Nagase Abrasive Materials Co., Ltd. (1)
1-1-17 Shinmachi, Nishi-ku, Osaka, 550-8668, Japan
Tel.: (81) 665352527
Web Site: https://www.nagase-kenma.co.jp
Abrasive Equipment Whslr
N.A.I.C.S.: 423440

Nagase America Corporation (1)
546 5th Ave 16th Fl, New York, NY 10036-5000 (100%)
Tel.: (212) 703-1340
Web Site: http://www.nagaseamerica.com
Sales Range: $50-74.9 Million
Emp.: 50

Dyestuffs, Chemicals & Synthetic Resins Mfr & Whlsr
N.A.I.C.S.: 424690
Keiichiro Yamashita (Treas)

Subsidiary (Domestic):

Fitz Chem LLC (2)
450 E Devon Ave, Itasca, IL 60143
Tel.: (630) 467-8383
Web Site: http://www.fitzchem.com
Sales Range: $1-9.9 Million
Emp.: 40
Specialty Chemicals Distr
N.A.I.C.S.: 424690
Robert Becker (Pres)

Nagase Beauty Care Co., Ltd. (1)
3F Nagase Sangyo Honmachi Building 1-2-8 Nihonbashi Honmachi, Chuo-ku, Tokyo, 103-0023, Japan (100%)
Tel.: (81) 336653617
Web Site: https://nbc.jp
Emp.: 113
Cosmetic & Health Food Whslr
N.A.I.C.S.: 424210

Nagase Business Expert Co., Ltd. (1)
5-1 Nihonbashi-Kobunacho, Chuo-ku, Tokyo, Japan
Tel.: (81) 336653125
Administrative Services
N.A.I.C.S.: 541611

Nagase Business Management and Planning (Shanghai) Co., Ltd. (1)
03 7F Eco City 1788 Nanjing Road W, Shanghai, 200040, China (100%)
Tel.: (86) 21 3360 7851
Web Site: http://www.nagase.co.jp
Business Management Consulting Services
N.A.I.C.S.: 541611

Nagase C&G Technology (Shanghai) Co., Ltd. (1)
Room 825 8F Best Western Shanghai Ruite Building No 1888 Yi Shan Road, Shanghai, 201103, China
Tel.: (86) 2133607171
Chemical Products Distr
N.A.I.C.S.: 424690

Nagase CMS Technology (Shanghai) Co., Ltd. (1)
Room 825 8F Best Western Shanghai Ruite Building No 1888 Yi Shan Road, Jingan District, Shanghai, 201103, China
Tel.: (86) 2133607171
Web Site: http://www.nagase.co.jp
Industrial Equipment Maintenance Services & Distr
N.A.I.C.S.: 811310

Nagase California Corporation (1)
303 Almaden Blvd Ste 550, San Jose, CA 95110
Tel.: (408) 567-9728
Web Site: http://www.nagaseamerica.com
Sales Range: $25-49.9 Million
Emp.: 30
Electronic-Related Materials, Machinery & Equipment Sales
N.A.I.C.S.: 423690

Nagase Chemical Co., Ltd (1)
12-15 Nihonbashi-Kobunacho, Chuo-ku, Tokyo, 103-0024, Japan
Tel.: (81) 356407431
Web Site: https://www.nagase-chemical.co.jp
Emp.: 90
Specialty Chemicals Distr
N.A.I.C.S.: 424690

Nagase Chemspec Co., Ltd. (1)
5-1 Nihonbashi-Kobunacho, Chuo-ku, Tokyo, 103-8355, Japan
Tel.: (81) 3 3665 3726
Web Site: http://www.nagase.co.jp
Emp.: 7
Specialty Chemicals Distr
N.A.I.C.S.: 424690
Masatoshi Hachisuka (Pres)

Nagase ChemteX (Wuxi) Corporation (1)
B-B Machinery and Electronic Industry Park, Wuxi National Hi-tech Industrial Development Zone, Jiangsu, 214028, China

Tel.: (86) 51085200052
Plastic Product Mfr & Distr
N.A.I.C.S.: 326199

Nagase ChemteX America Corp. (1)
100 Innovation Ct, Delaware, OH 43015
Tel.: (740) 362-4444
Web Site: http://www.nagasechemtex.com
Sales Range: $1-9.9 Million
Adhesive Mfr & Distr
N.A.I.C.S.: 325520
Chuck Feeny (Pres)

Nagase ChemteX Corporation (1)
1-1-17 Shinmachi, Nishi-ku, Osaka, 550-8668, Japan
Tel.: (81) 665352582
Web Site: https://www.nagasechemtex.co.jp
Emp.: 560
Resin Mfr & Distr
N.A.I.C.S.: 325211
Satoru Fujii (Pres & CEO)

Nagase Electronics Technology (Xiamen) Co., Ltd. (1)
No 15 Hongxi Road, Torch High-tech Zone Xiang'an Industrial Zone, Xiamen, China
Tel.: (86) 5923167258
Crystal Glass Mfr
N.A.I.C.S.: 327215

Nagase Elex Co., Ltd. (1)
(100%)
Tel.: (81) 336610819
Plastics Product Mfr
N.A.I.C.S.: 326199

Nagase Engineering Service Korea Co.,Ltd (1)
Anyang Trade Center Bisan-dong 925 161 Simin-daero, Dongan-gu, Anyang, 431-050, Gyeonggi-do, Korea (South)
Tel.: (82) 313890881
Web Site: https://nagase-eng.co.kr
Sales Range: $25-49.9 Million
Emp.: 8
Industrial Equipment Maintenance & Engineering Services
N.A.I.C.S.: 811310
S. M. Yang (Gen Mgr)

Nagase Enterprise Mexico S.A.de C.V. (1)
Av Cerro Gordo No 130 Int 4002, Col Cerro Gordo, 37129, Leon, Guanajuato, Mexico
Tel.: (52) 4777811961
Web Site: http://www.nagase.co.jp
Sales Range: $25-49.9 Million
Emp.: 4
Intermediate Trading & Market Development Services
N.A.I.C.S.: 238990

Nagase Filter Co., Ltd (1)
2-16-18 Hishie, Higashiosaka, Osaka, Japan (100%)
Tel.: (81) 72 968 1400
Web Site: http://www.nagasefilter.co.jp
Planning, Production, Processing, Quality Testing & Sale of Metal Filters
N.A.I.C.S.: 332999

Nagase General Service Co., Ltd (1)
5-1 Nihonbashi-Kobunacho, Chuo-ku, Tokyo, 103-8355, Japan
Tel.: (81) 3 3665 3313
Web Site: http://www.nagase.co.jp
Sales Range: $25-49.9 Million
Emp.: 40
Real Estate Manangement Services
N.A.I.C.S.: 531390
Kotaro Tsuji (VP)

Nagase Holdings America Corporation (1)
546 5th Ave 19th Fl, New York, NY 10036-5000
Tel.: (212) 703-1340
Web Site: https://nagaseamerica.com
Investment Services
N.A.I.C.S.: 523999

Nagase India Private Ltd. (1)
7th Floor Godrej BKC Plot No C-68 G Block Bandra Kurla Complex, Bandra East, Mumbai, 400051, Maharashtra, India
Tel.: (91) 9833658773
Web Site: http://www.nagase.co.in
Sales Range: $25-49.9 Million
Emp.: 2
Chemical Products Distr

N.A.I.C.S.: 424690

Nagase Information Development, Ltd (1)
Nagase Sangyo Honcho Building 1-2-8 Nihonbashi Honcho, Chuo-ku, Tokyo, 103-0023, Japan
Tel.: (81) 332313581
Web Site: https://www.nid.nagase.co.jp
Emp.: 78
Software Development Services
N.A.I.C.S.: 541511
Mitsuaki Ido (Pres)

Nagase Korea Corporation (1)
Danam Bldg 23F 10 Sowol-Ro, Jung Gu, Seoul, 04527, Korea (South) (100%)
Tel.: (82) 27348745
Web Site: https://www.nagase.co.kr
Sales Range: Less than $1 Million
Emp.: 16
Plastic & Other Chemicals Mfr & Distr
N.A.I.C.S.: 325211

Nagase Logistics Co., Ltd. (1)
4-45 Higashi Tsukaguchicho 2-chome, Amagasaki, 661-0011, Hyogo, Japan (100%)
Tel.: (81) 664278651
Web Site: http://www.nagase.co.jp
Logistics & Warehousing Services
N.A.I.C.S.: 541614

Nagase Logistics Support Co., Ltd. (1)
2-4-45 Higashitsukaguchioyo, Amagasaki, 661-0011, Hyogo, Japan
Tel.: (81) 664273571
Logistic Services
N.A.I.C.S.: 541614

Nagase Medicals Co., Ltd. (1)
4-323 Senzo, Itami, 664-0898, Hyogo, Japan
Tel.: (81) 727787501
Web Site: http://www.nagase-medicals.co.jp
Emp.: 180
Pharmaceuticals Product Mfr
N.A.I.C.S.: 325412
Mitsuru Akasawa (Pres)

Nagase Philippines Corporation (1)
12th floor Salcedo Towers 169 H V Dela Costa Street, Salcedo Village, Makati, 1227, Philippines (100%)
Tel.: (63) 277502933
Web Site: https://www.nagase.com.ph
Emp.: 25
N.A.I.C.S.: 325211

Nagase Philippines International Services Corp. (1)
12th Floor Salcedo Towers 169 H V Dela Costa Street, Salcedo Village, Makati, 1227, Philippines
Tel.: (63) 27502935
Emp.: 35
Electrical Equipment Distr
N.A.I.C.S.: 423610

Nagase Plastics Co., Ltd. (1)
1-1-17 Shinmachi, Nishi-ku, Osaka, 550-0013, Japan
Tel.: (81) 665331134
Web Site: https://www.nagaseplastics.co.jp
Sales Range: $50-74.9 Million
Emp.: 102
Plastic Product Distr
N.A.I.C.S.: 424610

Nagase Sanbio Co., Ltd. (1)
1-17 Shinmachi 1-chome, Nishi-ku, Osaka, 550-8668, Japan
Tel.: (81) 665352318
Sales Range: $25-49.9 Million
Emp.: 2
Feed Enzymes & Additives Distr
N.A.I.C.S.: 424690

Nagase Singapore (Pte) Ltd. (1)
600 North Bridge Road 11-01 Parkview Square, Singapore, 188778, Singapore (100%)
Tel.: (65) 63980088
Web Site: http://www.nagase.co.jp
Sales Range: $75-99.9 Million
Emp.: 110
Sales & Marketing of Chemicals, Synthetic Resins, Dyestuffs, Electronic Materials, Machines & Devices
N.A.I.C.S.: 424690

NAGASE & CO., LTD.

Nagase & Co., Ltd.—(Continued)

Nagase Specialty Materials NA LLC (1)
450 E Devon Ave Ste 300, Itasca, IL 60143
Tel.: (630) 467-8383
Web Site: https://www.nsm-na.com
Emp.: 4,000
Chemical Product Mfr & Distr
N.A.I.C.S.: 325199

Nagase Techno Service Co., Ltd. (1)
529 Komagi, Nagareyama, 270-0132, Chiba, Japan
Tel.: (81) 471551210
Emp.: 108
Logistic Services
N.A.I.C.S.: 541614
Tsutomu Kanda (Pres)

Nagase Techno-Engineering Co., Ltd (1)
887 Nippa-cho, Kouhoku-ku, Yokohama, 223-0057, Kanagawa, Japan
Tel.: (81) 455410222
Web Site: https://www.nagase-nte.co.jp
Sales Range: $25-49.9 Million
Emp.: 80
Semiconductor Equipment Mfr
N.A.I.C.S.: 334413

Nagase Trade Management Co., Ltd. (1)
2-6-4 Otemachi Tokiwabashi Tower, Chiyoda-ku, Tokyo, 100-8142, Japan
Tel.: (81) 336653125
Web Site: https://www.nagase.co.jp
Emp.: 256
Business Management Consulting Services
N.A.I.C.S.: 541611

Nagase Vietnam Co., Ltd. (1)
Unit 1203 Corner Stone building 16 Phan Chu Trinh Street, Hoan Kiem District, Hanoi, Vietnam
Tel.: (84) 2439264126
Marketing Services
N.A.I.C.S.: 541613

Nagase Wahlee Plastics Corporation (1)
9F No 37 Sec 3 Minchuan E Rd, Zhongshan Dist, Taipei, Taiwan
Tel.: (886) 225062400
Web Site: https://www.nwp.com.tw
Resin Distr
N.A.I.C.S.: 424690

Nagase do Brasil Comercio de Produtos Quimicos Ltda. (1)
Rua Cubatao 86 304 e 306, Vila Mariana, Sao Paulo, 04013-000, Brazil
Tel.: (55) 1132513111
International Trade Financing Services
N.A.I.C.S.: 522299

Nagase-Landauer, Ltd. (1)
Block C22-1 Suwa, Tsukuba, 300-2686, Ibaraki, Japan (50%)
Tel.: (81) 298393322
Web Site: https://www.nagase-landauer.co.jp
Radiation Testing Services
N.A.I.C.S.: 541380

Nishinihon Nagase Co., Ltd. (1)
4-1-37 Tenjin, Chuo-ku, Fukuoka, 810-0001, Japan
Tel.: (81) 924062772
Web Site: https://www.nishinihon-nagase.co.jp
Sales Range: $25-49.9 Million
Emp.: 43
Industrial Chemical Distr
N.A.I.C.S.: 424690

Nissei Technology Corporation (1)
3-2-8 Minatojima-minamimachi, Chuo-ku, Kobe, 650-0047, Hyogo, Japan
Tel.: (81) 783065963
Web Site: http://www.nisseig.com
Plastic Lens Mfr
N.A.I.C.S.: 333310
Ryugo Tsujihana (Pres & CEO)

ON Colors & Chemicals (Shanghai) Co., Ltd. (1)
6F Building 75 No 1066 North Qinzhou Road Caohejing Hi-Tech Park, Shanghai, 200233, China
Tel.: (86) 2154261812
Textile Product Whslr
N.A.I.C.S.: 424310

ON Textile Chemicals (Shanghai) Co., Ltd. (1)
Rm1012 10F Hongcao Bldg 67 No 421 Hongcao Road, Caohejing Hi-Tech Park, Shanghai, China
Tel.: (86) 2164855976
Textile Product Mfr & Whslr
N.A.I.C.S.: 314999

P.T. Nagase Impor-Ekspor Indonesia (1)
Wisma Keiai 12th floor Jl Jend Sudirman Kav 3, Jakarta, 10220, Indonesia (90%)
Tel.: (62) 2157900391
Web Site: http://www.nagase.com
Sales Range: $50-74.9 Million
Emp.: 25
Chemicals, Plastics, Electronics & Healthcare Products Importer, Exporter & Sales
N.A.I.C.S.: 424690

PT. Toyo Quality One Indonesia (1)
JL Raya Cimerame No 275, Padalarang, Bandung, 40553, Indonesia
Tel.: (62) 226860620
Flame Lamination Product Mfr
N.A.I.C.S.: 326130

Pac Tech Asia Sdn. Bhd. (1)
No 14 Medan Bayan Lepas Technoplex Phase 4 Bayan Lepas Industrial Zone, 11900, Bayan Lepas, Penang, Malaysia
Tel.: (60) 46440986
Web Site: http://www.pactech.de
Emp.: 150
Electronic Components Mfr
N.A.I.C.S.: 334419

Pac Tech USA-Packaging Technologies Inc. (1)
328 Martin Ave, Santa Clara, CA 95050
Tel.: (408) 588-1925
Semiconductor Equipment Mfr & Distr
N.A.I.C.S.: 333242

Pac Tech-Packaging Technologies GmbH (1)
Am Schlangenhorst 7 - 9, 14641, Nauen, Germany
Tel.: (49) 3321 44 95 100
Web Site: http://www.pactech.com
Sales Range: $50-74.9 Million
Emp.: 15
Wafer Level Packaging Equipment Mfr
N.A.I.C.S.: 333993
Thomas Oppert (VP-Global Sls-Marketing)

Prinova Gida ve Kimya Ticareti Limited (1)
Sti Yesilkoy Mah Ataturk Cad EGS Business Park No 12 B3 Blok No 267, Bakirkoy, Istanbul, Turkiye
Tel.: (90) 2125731395
Food Products Distr
N.A.I.C.S.: 424490

Prinova Group LLC (1)
6525 Muirfield Dr, Hanover Park, IL 60133
Tel.: (630) 868-0300
Web Site: http://www.prinovaglobal.com
High Quality Ingredients, Flavors & Nutrient Premixes Mfr
N.A.I.C.S.: 311999

SN Tech Corporation (1)
6-27 Mizuhai 5-chome, Higashi, Osaka, Japan
Tel.: (81) 662680145
Recycling Services
N.A.I.C.S.: 562111

Screen DecoraPrint Co., Ltd. (1)
Screen Yasu Plant Mikami 2426-1, Yasu, 520-2323, Shiga, Japan
Tel.: (81) 775865045
Decorative Printing Mfr
N.A.I.C.S.: 323111

Setsunan Kasei Co., Ltd. (1)
2-Chome 2-1 Techno-Stage, Izumi, Osaka, Japan
Tel.: (81) 725 51 0055
Plastic Product Whslr
N.A.I.C.S.: 424610

Shanghai Hua Chang Trading Co., Ltd. (1)
Room 2708 27F T1 Raffles City No 1133 Changning Road, Changning District, Shanghai, 200051, China
Tel.: (86) 2162481133
Resin Product Distr
N.A.I.C.S.: 424610

Shanghai Nagase Trading Co., Ltd. (1)
Floor 5 Building B OneITC Guomaohui Plaza No 1901 Huashan Road, Xuhui District, Shanghai, 200030, China (100%)
Tel.: (86) 2122210222
Web Site: https://www.nagase.cn
Sales Range: $25-49.9 Million
Emp.: 100
Plastics
N.A.I.C.S.: 325211

Sofix Corp. (1)
2800 Riverport Rd, Chattanooga, TN 37406-1702
Tel.: (423) 624-3500
Web Site: http://www.sofix.net
Sales Range: $25-49.9 Million
Emp.: 32
Mfr & Sale of Colorformers
N.A.I.C.S.: 325998
Paul Cahill (Pres)

TQ-1 de Mexico S.A. de C.V. (1)
HR San Francisco del Rincon • Leon KM 5 8 Purisima de Bustos Center, Purisima del Rincon, 36400, Guanajuato, Mexico
Tel.: (52) 4767575568
Web Site: http://www.t1mle.com.mx
Automotive Seat Pad Mfr & Distr
N.A.I.C.S.: 336360

Tianjin Nagase International Trading Co., Ltd. (1)
No 2803 2805 28th Floor Tianjin International Finance Center Building, 36 Chifeng Road Heping District, Tianjin, 300051, China
Tel.: (86) 2283191231
Chemical Products Distr
N.A.I.C.S.: 424690

Tokai Spring Mfg. (Foshan) Co., Ltd. (1)
Xinyuan Road Nanba1 Of Jili Park Of Foshan, High-Tech Industries Development Zone In Chancheng District, Foshan, Guangdong, China
Tel.: (86) 75785399705
Web Site: http://www.tokai-riki.co.jp
Spring Product Mfr & Distr
N.A.I.C.S.: 332613

Totaku Industries Suzhou Co., Ltd (1)
9 Datong Road Export Processing Zone, Suzhou New & Hi-tech District, Suzhou, 215151, China
Tel.: (86) 512 6269 6006
Emp.: 100
Plastic Products Mfr & Distr
N.A.I.C.S.: 326199
Nakamata Keiji (Gen Mgr)

Totaku Industries, Inc. (1)
1-33 Mitsuya Minami 1-chome, Yodogawa-ku, Osaka, 532-0035, Japan
Tel.: (81) 6 6308 6410
Web Site: http://www.totaku.co.jp
Sales Range: $150-199.9 Million
Emp.: 270
Plastic Products Mfr & Distr
N.A.I.C.S.: 326199
Kozo Toyoda (Pres)

Toyo Quality One (Guangzhou) Co., Ltd. (1)
NNorth Rd Guangzhou Huadu Auto City, Xinhua Town Huadu, Guangzhou, 510800, China
Tel.: (86) 2086733138
Automotive Parts Mfr & Distr
N.A.I.C.S.: 336390

Toyo Quality One Ningbo Co., Ltd. (1)
No 302 Chengnan East Road, Cicheng Town Jiangbei District, Ningbo, 315031, China
Tel.: (86) 57487570057
Web Site: https://www.tq1nb.com
Chemical Product Mfr & Distr

INTERNATIONAL PUBLIC

N.A.I.C.S.: 325199

Wuxi Chenghong Electronic Chemicals Co., Ltd. (1)
Room 102 1 Building No 27 Xiejing Rd, Cheng Jiang JiangYin, Wuxi, Jiangsu, China
Tel.: (86) 51080622313
Electronic Product Mfr & Distr
N.A.I.C.S.: 334419

Xenomax-Japan Co., Ltd. (1)
10-24 Toyocho, Tsuruga, 914-8550, Fukui, Japan
Tel.: (81) 770214785
Web Site: https://www.xenomax.jp
Polyimide Film Mfr & Distr
N.A.I.C.S.: 326113
Ono Koichi (Pres)

Xiamen Nagase Trading Co., Ltd. (1)
Room 809 Commercial building Paragon Center No 1 Lianyue Road, Xiamen, 361000, Fujian, China
Tel.: (86) 5922200213
Web Site: http://www.nagase.co.jp
Sales Range: $25-49.9 Million
Emp.: 20
Chemical Products Distr
N.A.I.C.S.: 424690

eX. Grade Co., Ltd. (1)
5F Daido-Showacho Dai 2 Bldg 1-30 Showacho 5-chome, Abeno-ku, Osaka, Japan
Tel.: (81) 666237633
Electronic Equipment Mfr & Distr
N.A.I.C.S.: 336320

NAGASE BROTHERS INC.
Kichijojiko Honkan 1-29-2 Kichijoji Minami-cho, Musashino-Shi, Tokyo, 180-0003, Japan
Tel.: (81) 422457015
Web Site: http://www.toshin.com
Year Founded: 1976
9733—(TKS)
Rev.: $350,237,460
Assets: $583,570,460
Liabilities: $393,427,200
Net Worth: $190,143,260
Earnings: $17,199,220
Emp.: 1,185
Fiscal Year-end: 03/31/24
Educational Support Services
N.A.I.C.S.: 611710

NAGAWA CO., LTD.
1-4-1 marunouchieiraku Bld 22F Marunouchi, Chiyoda-ku, Tokyo, 100-0005, Japan
Tel.: (81) 352888666
Web Site: https://group.nagawa.co.jp
Year Founded: 1966
9663—(TKS)
Rev.: $296,082,160
Assets: $541,131,360
Liabilities: $47,364,240
Net Worth: $493,767,120
Earnings: $29,204,560
Emp.: 514
Fiscal Year-end: 03/31/22
Construction Machinery Leasing & Distr
N.A.I.C.S.: 532490
Osamu Takahashi (Pres)

NAGINA GROUP
91-B/1 MM Alam Road Gulberg-III, Lahore, Pakistan
Tel.: (92) 42 3575 6270
Web Site: http://www.nagina.com
Year Founded: 1967
Emp.: 3,500
Holding Company
N.A.I.C.S.: 551112
Enam Ellahi Shaikh (Chm)

Subsidiaries:

Ellahi International (Pvt) Ltd. (1)

AND PRIVATE COMPANIES — NAHEE GROUP

91-B/1 MM Alam Road Gulberg-III, Lahore, Pakistan
Tel.: (92) 42 3575 6270
Import, Export & Trading Services
N.A.I.C.S.: 561499

Ellcot Spinning Mills Limited (1)
Nagina House 91-B/1 MM Alam Rd Gulberg-III, Lahore, 54660, Pakistan
Tel.: (92) 4235756270
Web Site: https://www.nagina.com
Rev.: $43,976,672
Assets: $38,136,230
Liabilities: $23,672,150
Net Worth: $14,464,080
Earnings: $1,509,999
Emp.: 957
Fiscal Year-end: 06/30/2023
Yarn Mfr & Electricity Generating Services
N.A.I.C.S.: 237990
Shafqat Ellahi Shaikh (CEO & Mng Dir)

Nagina Cotton Mills Limited (1)
Nagina House 91-B/1 MM Alam Road Gulberg-III, Lahore, Pakistan
Tel.: (92) 4235756270
Rev.: $46,115,533
Assets: $45,288,090
Liabilities: $28,498,397
Net Worth: $16,789,693
Earnings: $2,122,337
Emp.: 1,069
Fiscal Year-end: 06/30/2023
Cotton Production Services
N.A.I.C.S.: 115111
Shaukat Ellahi (CEO & Mng Dir)

Prosperity Weaving Mills Limited (1)
Nagina House 91-B/1 M M Alam Road Gulberg-III, Lahore, 54660, Pakistan
Tel.: (92) 4235756270
Rev.: $52,720,371
Assets: $25,074,929
Liabilities: $17,759,277
Net Worth: $7,315,653
Earnings: $550,882
Emp.: 1,306
Fiscal Year-end: 06/30/2023
Apparel & Home Furnishing Fabrics Mfr
N.A.I.C.S.: 313220
Mohsin Gilani (Sec)

NAGOYA ELECTRIC WORKS CO., LTD.
29-1 Mentoku Shinoda, Amami-shi, Nagoya, 490-1294, Aichi, Japan
Tel.: (81) 524431111   JP
Web Site: https://www.nagoya-denki.co.jp
Year Founded: 1958
67970—(NGO)
Rev.: $116,167,823
Assets: $179,986,786
Liabilities: $42,814,668
Net Worth: $137,172,118
Earnings: $11,100,099
Emp.: 430
Fiscal Year-end: 03/31/24
Information Equipment & systems Provider & Mfr
N.A.I.C.S.: 541519
Koichi Isono (Mng Dir)

Subsidiaries:

Conlux Matsumoto Co. Ltd. (1)
2 Hotaka, Azumino, 399 8303, Nagano, Japan (100%)
Tel.: (81) 263810155
Web Site: http://www.conluxmatsumoto.com
Electronic Equipment Distr
N.A.I.C.S.: 423690
Shuzo Nagaku (Pres)

Informex Matsumoto Co., Ltd. (1)
2571-1 Toyoshina, Azumino, 399-8205, Nagano, Japan
Tel.: (81) 263882110
Web Site: https://www.inform-ex.co.jp
Solar Traffic Light & Led Indicator Mfr & Distr
N.A.I.C.S.: 334290

NAGOYA LUMBER CO., LTD.
2-6-41 Sannoh, Nakagawa, Nagoya, 4540011, Aichi, Japan
Tel.: (81) 523211526
Web Site: http://www.meimoku.co
Year Founded: 1945
Building Materials Mfr
N.A.I.C.S.: 327120
Kohtaro Niwa (Pres)

NAGOYA RAILROAD CO., LTD.
1-2-4 Meieki, Nakamura-ku, Nagoya, 450 8501, Japan
Tel.: (81) 5712111   JP
Web Site: https://www.meitetsu.co.jp
Year Founded: 1921
9048—(TKS)
Rev.: $3,973,409,810
Assets: $8,614,185,050
Liabilities: $5,546,788,110
Net Worth: $3,067,396,940
Earnings: $161,284,000
Fiscal Year-end: 03/31/24
Transportation Services
N.A.I.C.S.: 485112
Takashi Ando (Chm)

Subsidiaries:

Gifu Bus Co., Ltd. (1)
4-20 Kokonoecho, Gifu, 500-8722, Japan
Tel.: (81) 582408800
Web Site: http://www.gifubus.co.jp
Emp.: 682
Cargo Transportation Services
N.A.I.C.S.: 488490

Meitetsu Department Store Co., Ltd. (1)
1-2-1 Meieki, Nakamura-ku, Nagoya, 450-8505, Japan
Tel.: (81) 525851111
Web Site: https://www.e-meitetsu.com
Emp.: 559
Clothing Whslr
N.A.I.C.S.: 424350
Hiroshi Shibata (Pres)

Meitetsu Kyosho Co Ltd (1)
2-14-19 Meiekiminami Sumitomo Life Nagoya Building 10th floor, Nakamura-ku, Nagoya, 450-8618, Japan
Tel.: (81) 525821011
Web Site: https://www.mkyosho.co.jp
Emp.: 337
Car Dealer
N.A.I.C.S.: 441110

Meitetsu Transport Co., Ltd. (1)
2-12-8 Aoi, Higashi-Ku, Nagoya, 461-0004, Japan (51.09%)
Tel.: (81) 529355721
Rev.: $1,073,376,010
Assets: $909,361,390
Liabilities: $560,736,330
Net Worth: $348,625,060
Earnings: $27,950,160
Fiscal Year-end: 03/31/2020
Transport Services
N.A.I.C.S.: 485999
Wataru Uchida (Pres)

NAGOYA STOCK EXCHANGE, INC.
3-8-20 Sakae Naka-ku, Nagoya, 460-0008, Japan
Tel.: (81) 522623171
Web Site: http://www.nse.or.jp
Year Founded: 1949
Sales Range: $25-49.9 Million
Emp.: 45
Stock Exchange Services
N.A.I.C.S.: 523210
Masaki Takeda (Pres)

NAGPUR POWER & INDUSTRIES LIMITED
20th Floor Nirmal Building, Nariman Point, Mumbai, 400021, India
Tel.: (91) 2222023055
Web Site: https://www.nagpurpowerind.com
Year Founded: 1946
532362—(BOM)
Rev.: $5,388,306
Assets: $12,458,019
Liabilities: $2,516,981
Net Worth: $9,941,038
Earnings: ($446,889)
Emp.: 9
Fiscal Year-end: 03/31/23
Manganese Mfr
N.A.I.C.S.: 331110
Gautam P. Khandelwal (Chm)

Subsidiaries:

The Motwane Manufacturing Company Pvt. Ltd (1)
Gyan Baug Nashik Road, Nashik, 422 101, Maharashtra, India
Tel.: (91) 18002337766
Web Site: https://www.motwane.com
Emp.: 250
Electronic Testing Equipment Mfr
N.A.I.C.S.: 334515
Gautam Khandelwal (Chm)

NAGREEKA CAPITAL & INFRASTRUCTURE LTD.
18 R N Mukherjee Road, Kolkata, 700001, India
Tel.: (91) 3322108828
Web Site: https://www.nagreeka.com
532895—(BOM)
Rev.: $1,500,634
Assets: $16,346,295
Liabilities: $13,335,190
Net Worth: $3,011,105
Earnings: $23,933
Emp.: 5
Fiscal Year-end: 03/31/21
Financial Services
N.A.I.C.S.: 523999
Sunil Patwari (Mng Dir)

NAGREEKA EXPORTS LIMITED
7 Kala Bhavan 3 Mathew Road Opera House, Mumbai, 400 004, India
Tel.: (91) 2261447500
Web Site: https://nagreeka.com
Year Founded: 1989
NAGREEKAEXP—(NSE)
Rev.: $52,595,841
Assets: $48,032,566
Liabilities: $34,273,588
Net Worth: $13,758,978
Earnings: ($1,136,355)
Emp.: 770
Fiscal Year-end: 03/31/21
Yarn Mfr
N.A.I.C.S.: 339999
Mahendra Patwari (Exec Dir)

NAHANNI CONSTRUCTION LTD.
100 Nahanni Drive, PO Box 2076, Yellowknife, X1A 2P6, NT, Canada
Tel.: (867) 873-2975
Web Site: https://www.nahannincl.com
Year Founded: 2006
Sales Range: $10-24.9 Million
Emp.: 85
Construction Services
N.A.I.C.S.: 236220
Dwight Peart (Treas & Sec)

NAHAR CAPITAL AND FINANCIAL SERVICES LIMITED
Nahar Tower 375 Industrial Area-A, Ludhiana, 141003, Punjab, India
Tel.: (91) 1612600701
Web Site: https://www.owmnahar.com
Year Founded: 2006
NAHARCAP—(NSE)
Rev.: $2,572,164
Assets: $121,674,798
Liabilities: $10,933,132
Net Worth: $110,741,666
Earnings: $517,342
Emp.: 20
Fiscal Year-end: 03/31/20
Investment Services
N.A.I.C.S.: 523999
Jawahar Lal Oswal (Chm)

NAHAR INDUSTRIAL ENTERPRISES LIMITED
Focal Point, Ludhiana, 141010, India
Tel.: (91) 1612600701
Web Site: https://www.owmnahar.com
Year Founded: 1983
519136—(BOM)
Rev.: $217,866,435
Assets: $163,143,505
Liabilities: $48,077,262
Net Worth: $115,066,243
Earnings: $9,462,502
Emp.: 7,304
Fiscal Year-end: 03/31/23
Textile Mfr
N.A.I.C.S.: 314999
Kamal Oswal (Mng Dir)

NAHAR POLY FILMS LIMITED
Nahar Tower 376 Industrial Area-A, Ludhiana, 141003, India
Tel.: (91) 1612600701
Web Site: https://www.owmnahar.com
Year Founded: 1949
523391—(BOM)
Rev.: $67,342,289
Assets: $156,165,541
Liabilities: $31,564,806
Net Worth: $124,600,735
Earnings: $11,697,750
Emp.: 310
Fiscal Year-end: 03/31/22
Polypropylene Film Mfr
N.A.I.C.S.: 326112
Satish Kumar Sharma (Exec Dir)

NAHAR SPINNING MILLS LIMITED
Nahar Tower Industrial Area-A, Ludhiana, 141 003, India
Tel.: (91) 1144747101
Web Site: https://www.owmnahar.com
Year Founded: 1980
500296—(BOM)
Rev.: $289,220,623
Assets: $300,582,541
Liabilities: $178,017,990
Net Worth: $122,564,551
Earnings: $5,653,134
Emp.: 10,981
Fiscal Year-end: 03/31/21
Textile Products Mfr
N.A.I.C.S.: 314999
Dinesh Oswal (Mng Dir)

NAHDI MEDICAL COMPANY
PO Box 17129, Abruq Ar Rughamah District, Jeddah, 21484, Saudi Arabia
Tel.: (966) 126535353
Web Site: https://nahdi.sa
Year Founded: 1986
4164—(SAU)
Rev.: $2,297,343,772
Assets: $1,318,465,029
Liabilities: $720,309,002
Net Worth: $598,156,026
Earnings: $236,718,255
Emp.: 5,000
Fiscal Year-end: 12/31/22
Health Care Srvices
N.A.I.C.S.: 621610
Karim Dimitri (Chief Comml Officer)

NAHEE GROUP
House 26 Road 03 Block I, Banani, Dhaka, 1213, Bangladesh
Tel.: (880) 29871137
Web Site: https://www.nahee.com.bd

NAHEE GROUP

Nahee Group—(Continued)

NAHEEACP—(DHA)
Sales Range: Less than $1 Million
Aluminum Mfr
N.A.I.C.S.: 331315
Subsidiaries:

Nahee Aluminum Composite Panel
Ltd.
House-26 Road-03 Block-I, Banani, Dhaka,
1213, Bangladesh
Tel.: (880) 29871137
Aluminum Composite Panel Mfr
N.A.I.C.S.: 331315

Nahee Geo-Textile Industries
Limited (1)
House-26 Road-03 Block-I, Banani, Dhaka,
1213, Bangladesh
Tel.: (880) 29871137
Nonwoven Fabric Mill Mfr
N.A.I.C.S.: 313230
Abu Noman Howlader (Mng Dir)

Nahee SS Pipes Industries Ltd. (1)
House-26 Road-03 Block-I, Banani, Dhaka,
1213, Bangladesh
Tel.: (880) 29871137
Steel Pipe & Tube Mfr
N.A.I.C.S.: 331210
Abu Noman Howlader (Mng Dir)

NAHL GROUP PLC
Bevan House Kettering Parkway, Kettering Venture Park, Kettering, NN15
6XR, Northamptonshire, United Kingdom
Tel.: (44) 1536527500
Web Site:
https://www.nahlgroupplc.co.uk
Year Founded: 1993
NAH—(AIM)
Rev.: $52,286,039
Assets: $121,449,129
Liabilities: $49,093,663
Net Worth: $72,355,466
Earnings: $485,988
Emp.: 283
Fiscal Year-end: 12/31/22
Insurance Claims Assistance Services
N.A.I.C.S.: 524298
Russell Atkinson (CEO)
Subsidiaries:

Bush & Company Rehabilitation
Limited (1)
Unit C Daventry Interchange Sopwith Way,
Drayton Fields, Daventry, NN11 8PB,
United Kingdom
Tel.: (44) 1327876210
Web Site: https://www.bushco.co.uk
Law firm
N.A.I.C.S.: 541110
Helen Jackson (Mng Dir)

Homeward Legal Limited (1)
Bevan House Kettering Parkway, Kettering
Venture Park, Kettering, NN15 6XR,
Northamptonshire, United Kingdom
Tel.: (44) 2074065840
Web Site: http://www.fitzalanpartners.co.uk
Marketing & Advertising Services
N.A.I.C.S.: 541810

Searches UK Limited (1)
Basepoint Business Centre Little High St,
Shoreham-by-Sea, BN43 5EG, West Sussex, United Kingdom
Tel.: (44) 8000431815
Web Site: https://www.searchesuk.co.uk
Law firm
N.A.I.C.S.: 541110
Hannah Banks (Gen Mgr)

NAHRIN AG
Industriestrasse 27, 6060, Sarnen,
Switzerland
Tel.: (41) 416600044
Web Site: http://www.nahrin.ch
Year Founded: 1954
Sales Range: $25-49.9 Million

Emp.: 280
Food Products Mfr
N.A.I.C.S.: 311941
Michel Justrich (CEO)
Subsidiaries:

Similasan AG
Haus Similasan, Jonen, 8916, Aargau, Switzerland
Tel.: (41) 566499050
Web Site: http://www.similasan.com
Sales Range: $25-49.9 Million
Emp.: 90
Over-the-Counter Homeopathic Medication
Mfr
N.A.I.C.S.: 325412
Urs Lehmann (CEO)

Division (US):

Similasan Corporation (2)
1805 Shea Ctr Dr Ste 270, Highlands
Ranch, CO 80129-1537
Tel.: (303) 539-4060
Web Site: http://www.similasanusa.com
Sales Range: $25-49.9 Million
Emp.: 10
Over-the-Counter Homeopathic Medications
Importer & Distr
N.A.I.C.S.: 325412
Jury Batur (Mgr-Ops)

NAIGAI CO., LTD.
7-8-5 Akasaka, Minato-ku, Tokyo,
107-0052, Japan
Tel.: (81) 362301650
Web Site: https://www.naigai.co.jp
Year Founded: 1920
8013—(TKS)
Rev.: $92,318,890
Assets: $79,365,460
Liabilities: $38,278,910
Net Worth: $41,086,550
Earnings: $794,080
Emp.: 154
Fiscal Year-end: 01/31/24
Textile Product Mfr & Whslr
N.A.I.C.S.: 315120
Kenji Imaizumi (Pres)
Subsidiaries:

INTEXT Co., Ltd. (1)
6-3 Yurinokidai, Sanda, Hyogo, Japan
Tel.: (81) 795656661
Logistics Consulting Servies
N.A.I.C.S.: 541614

NAP Co., Ltd. (1)
2-11-19 Sakae, Naka-ku, Nagoya, Aichi,
Japan
Tel.: (81) 522657522
Textile Products Distr
N.A.I.C.S.: 424310

Naigai Co., Ltd. - Rondex
Division (1)
Yanagibashi First Bldg 2F 2-19-6 Taitou-ku,
Tokyo, Japan
Tel.: (81) 358223824
Socks Distr
N.A.I.C.S.: 424340

Rondex (Thailand) Co., Ltd (1)
Eastern Seaboard Industrial Estate 64/64
Moo 4 T Pluakdaeng, Pluak Daeng, 21140,
Rayong, Thailand
Tel.: (66) 38955300
Web Site: https://www.rondex.co.th
Emp.: 45
Rubber Thread Mfr
N.A.I.C.S.: 313220

Sentire-One Co., Ltd. (1)
Dojima Axis Building 4F 2-2-28 Dojimahama, Kita-ku, Osaka, 530-0004, Japan
Tel.: (81) 664423873
Web Site: https://www.sentire-one.co.jp
Other Miscellaneous Goods Mfr & Distr
N.A.I.C.S.: 316990

Shanghai Naigai Trading Co.,
Ltd. (1)
Suite 2681 Tower B City Center of Shanghai No 100 Zunyi Lu, Shanghai, China
Tel.: (86) 2162372350

Socks Distr
N.A.I.C.S.: 424340

NAIGAI TEC CORPORATION
7th floor Sun Towers Center Building
21122 Sangenjaya, Setagaya-ku, Tokyo, 154-0024, Japan
Tel.: (81) 354331123
Web Site: https://www.naigaitec.co.jp
Year Founded: 1961
3374—(TKS)
Rev.: $257,875,930
Assets: $179,441,670
Liabilities: $103,836,490
Net Worth: $75,605,180
Earnings: $5,605,280
Emp.: 195
Fiscal Year-end: 03/31/24
Pneumatic Device Whslr
N.A.I.C.S.: 334419
Hirokazu Gonda (Chm)
Subsidiaries:

NAIGAIKIZAI TRADING SHANGHAI
CO., LTD. (1)
Room 1207 12F No 567 Maotai Rd, Changning District, Shanghai, China
Tel.: (86) 2160250968
Measuring Equipment Mfr & Distr
N.A.I.C.S.: 334515

NAIGAI TRANS LINE LTD.
Sunrise Building 5F 2-6-8 Bingo-cho,
Chuo-ku, Osaka, 541-0051, Japan
Tel.: (81) 662604701
Web Site: https://www.ntl-naigai.co.jp
Year Founded: 1980
9384—(TKS)
Rev.: $228,865,200
Assets: $165,636,580
Liabilities: $21,135,290
Net Worth: $144,501,290
Earnings: $21,560,690
Emp.: 320
Fiscal Year-end: 12/31/23
Freight Forwarding Services
N.A.I.C.S.: 488510
Subsidiaries:

Flying Fish Inc. (1)
3F Shin-Nihonbashi Bldg 3-8-2 Nihonbashi,
Chuo-ku, Tokyo, 103-0027, Japan
Tel.: (81) 335107791
Web Site: https://www.flyingfish.co.jp
Multimodal Transportation Services
N.A.I.C.S.: 532411

NTL Naigai Trans Line (Korea) Co.,
Ltd. (1)
12F The Exchange Seoul Building 21
Mugyo-ro, Jung, Seoul, 04520, Korea
(South)
Tel.: (82) 23194050
Web Site: http://www.ntl-naigai.com
Sales Range: $25-49.9 Million
Cargo Services
N.A.I.C.S.: 488320

NTL Naigai Trans Line (S) Pte.
Ltd. (1)
80 Robinson Road 17-01/01A, Singapore,
068899, Singapore
Tel.: (65) 63245878
Web Site: https://www.ntl-sin.com.sg
Sales Range: $25-49.9 Million
Warehousing & Storage Services
N.A.I.C.S.: 493110

NTL Naigai Trans Line (Thailand)
Co., Ltd. (1)
Liberty Square Building 14th Fl Rm 1402
287 Silom Rd, Silom Bangrak, Bangkok,
10500, Thailand
Tel.: (66) 20667700
Web Site: https://www.ntl-naigai.co.th
Cargo Management Services
N.A.I.C.S.: 488320

NTL Naigai Trans Line (USA)
Inc. (1)
970 W 190th St Ste 580, Torrance, CA
90502

INTERNATIONAL PUBLIC

Tel.: (310) 436-8700
Web Site: http://www.ntl-naigaiusa.com
Sales Range: $25-49.9 Million
Emp.: 10
Cargo Services
N.A.I.C.S.: 488320
Linda Carter (Mgr-Ops)

NTL-LOGISTICS (HK) LIMITED (1)
RM611-612 6 FLOOR TOWER II Cheung
Sha Wan Plaza, 833 Cheung Sha Wan
Road, Kowloon, China (Hong Kong)
Tel.: (852) 36695000
Web Site: https://www.ntl-naigai.com.hk
Cargo Services
N.A.I.C.S.: 488320

NTL-LOGISTICS (INDIA) PRIVATE
LIMITED (1)
153 1st Floor Okhla Industrial Estate Phase
III, New Delhi, 110 020, India
Tel.: (91) 11 4665 6500
Web Site: http://www.ntllogistics.com
Emp.: 30
Freight Forwarding Services
N.A.I.C.S.: 488510

Naigai Busan Logistics Center Co.,
Ltd. (1)
434 Shinhang-ro, Jinhae-gu, Changwon,
51619, Gyeongsangnam-do, Korea (South)
Tel.: (82) 555407302
International Freight Forwarding Services
N.A.I.C.S.: 488510

Naigai-Eunsan Logistics Co.,
Ltd. (1)
343 Shinhang 8-ro, Jinhae-gu, Changwon,
51619, Gyeongsangnam-do, Korea (South)
Tel.: (82) 556068100
International Freight Forwarding Services
N.A.I.C.S.: 488510

Ntl Naigai Trans Line (Myanmar) Co.,
Ltd. (1)
International Freight Forwarding Services
N.A.I.C.S.: 488510
Moh Moh (Gen Mgr)

Ntl-Logistics (Shenzhen) Limited (1)
Tel.: (86) 75522966976
International Freight Forwarding Services
N.A.I.C.S.: 488510

PT. NTL Naigai Trans Line
Indonesia (1)
Menara Cakrawala 16th Floor Jl M H Thamrin No 9, Jakarta, 10340, Indonesia
Tel.: (62) 2139833152
Web Site: https://www.ntl-naigai.co.id
Sales Range: $25-49.9 Million
Emp.: 10
Cargo Services
N.A.I.C.S.: 488320

Shanghai NTL-Logistics Limited (1)
Room 801 Ocean Tower No 550 Yan an E
Road, Shanghai, 200001, China
Tel.: (86) 2153855100
Web Site: https://www.ntl-china.com.cn
Emp.: 28
Marine Shipping Services
N.A.I.C.S.: 483111

UCI Airfreight Japan, Inc. (1)
CAMCO Nishi Honmachi Bldg 11F 1-1
Awaza 2-chome, Nishi-ku, Osaka, 550-
0011, Japan
Tel.: (81) 665431270
Web Site: https://www.ucijapan.co.jp
Air Freight Transportation Services
N.A.I.C.S.: 532411

NAIKAI ZOSEN CORPORATION
226-6 Sawa Setoda-cho, Onomichi,
722-2413, Hiroshima, Japan
Tel.: (81) 845272111
Web Site:
https://www.naikaizosen.co.jp
Year Founded: 1944
7018—(TKS)
Rev.: $306,591,630
Assets: $289,643,590
Liabilities: $225,235,750
Net Worth: $64,407,840
Earnings: $14,945,210

AND PRIVATE COMPANIES   **NAKAKITA YAKUHIN CO., LTD.**

Emp.: 585
Fiscal Year-end: 03/31/24
Ship Building & Repair Services
N.A.I.C.S.: 336611

NAIM HOLDINGS BERHAD
9th Floor Wisma Naim 2 1/2 Mile Rock Road, 93200, Kuching, Sarawak, Malaysia
Tel.: (60) 82411667
Web Site: https://www.naim.com.my
NAIM—(KLS)
Rev.: $78,003,386
Assets: $381,756,614
Liabilities: $109,453,757
Net Worth: $272,302,857
Earnings: $5,306,243
Emp.: 911
Fiscal Year-end: 12/31/22
Construction & Property Development Services
N.A.I.C.S.: 531312
Abdul Hamed Sepawi *(Chm)*

Subsidiaries:

Desa Ilmu Sdn. Bhd. (1)
Ground Floor Wisma Naim Lot 2679 Jalan Rock, 93200, Kuching, Sarawak, Malaysia
Tel.: (60) 82422001
Property Development Services
N.A.I.C.S.: 531390

Khidmat Mantap Sdn. Bhd. (1)
Gd Floor Wisma Naim 2 1/2 Miles Rock Road, 93300, Kuching, Sarawak, Malaysia
Tel.: (60) 82422001
Property Development Services
N.A.I.C.S.: 531390

NCSB Engineering Sdn. Bhd. (1)
No 7 Ground Floor Wisma Naim Jln Rock, 93200, Kuching, Sarawak, Malaysia
Tel.: (60) 82422001
Sales Range: $25-49.9 Million
Emp.: 30
Property Development Services
N.A.I.C.S.: 531390

TR Bricks Sdn. Bhd. (1)
No.430 Jln Tudan Technology Park Permylaya, 98100, Lutong, Sarawak, Malaysia
Tel.: (60) 85663499
Sales Range: $25-49.9 Million
Emp.: 6
Bricks Mfr
N.A.I.C.S.: 327120
Peter Kai Chin Chieng *(Mng Dir)*

NAIN TECH CO., LTD.
6 Masan 6-Ro Jinwi-Myeon, Pyeongtaek, Gyeonggi-do, Korea (South)
Tel.: (82) 314760305
Web Site: http://www.naintec.co.kr
Year Founded: 2006
267320—(KRS)
Rev.: $68,123,722
Assets: $110,124,904
Liabilities: $87,927,071
Net Worth: $22,197,832
Earnings: $320,776
Emp.: 116
Fiscal Year-end: 12/31/22
Secondary Battery Laminator Mfr
N.A.I.C.S.: 335910
Park Geun Noh *(CEO)*

NAIPU MINING MACHINERY CO., LTD.
No 18 Jili Avenue, Shangrao Economic & Technological Development Zone, Shangrao, 334100, Jiangxi, China
Tel.: (86) 7938457210
Web Site: http://www.naipu.com
Year Founded: 2005
300818—(SSE)
Rev.: $161,334,726
Assets: $293,988,541
Liabilities: $123,349,371
Net Worth: $170,639,170
Earnings: $28,215,154

Emp.: 600
Fiscal Year-end: 12/31/21
Mining Equipment Mfr & Distr
N.A.I.C.S.: 333131
Hao Zheng *(Chm)*

Subsidiaries:

Beijing Naipu International Trade Co., Ltd. (1)
Room 315 3rd Floor Jinhui Building Building 6 Wangjing East Park, Chaoyang District, Beijing, China
Tel.: (86) 1064466538
Mining Machinery & Equipment Mfr & Distr
N.A.I.C.S.: 333131

Naipu Mining Machine Mexico Co., Ltd. (1)
Rio Tiber 97 Desp 204, Cuauhtemoc, Mexico, Mexico
Tel.: (52) 84148399
Mining Machinery & Equipment Mfr & Distr
N.A.I.C.S.: 333131

Naipu Mining Machinery Chile Co., Ltd. (1)
Los Militares 5620 of 601, Las Condes, Santiago, Chile
Tel.: (56) 229939760
Mining Machinery & Equipment Mfr & Distr
N.A.I.C.S.: 333131

Naipu Mining Machinery Mongolia Co., Ltd. (1)
Suite 1203 Fides Tower Zaisan Street, Ulaanbaatar, Mongolia
Tel.: (976) 70136888
Mining Machinery & Equipment Mfr & Distr
N.A.I.C.S.: 333131

Naipu Mining Peru Limited Liability Company (1)
Av Juan Antonio Pezet 105 Dpto 801, San Isidro, Lima, Peru
Tel.: (51) 966742717
Mining Machinery & Equipment Mfr & Distr
N.A.I.C.S.: 333131

Shanghai Naipu International Trade Co., Ltd. (1)
Room 14F D1 Jiangsu Building No 526 Laoshan Road, Pudong New District, Shanghai, China
Tel.: (86) 2162544688
Mining Machinery & Equipment Mfr & Distr
N.A.I.C.S.: 333131

NAIROBI STOCK EXCHANGE LIMITED
55 Westlands Road, PO Box 43633, Nairobi, Kenya
Tel.: (254) 202831000
Web Site: https://www.nse.co.ke
Year Founded: 1954
Sales Range: $25-49.9 Million
Emp.: 35
Stock Exchange Services
N.A.I.C.S.: 523210
Bob Karina *(Vice Chm)*

NAJRAN CEMENT COMPANY
9204 King Saud Road, PO Box 1006, Najran, 66256-3579, Saudi Arabia
Tel.: (966) 175299990
Web Site: https://www.najrancement.com
Year Founded: 2005
3002—(SAU)
Rev.: $142,830,556
Assets: $646,226,370
Liabilities: $114,748,967
Net Worth: $531,477,403
Earnings: $30,329,023
Emp.: 686
Fiscal Year-end: 12/31/22
Cement Mfr
N.A.I.C.S.: 327310
Mohammed Mane Sultan Aballala *(Chm)*

NAK SEALING TECHNOLOGIES CORPORATION

No 336 Industrial Road Nankang Industrial Zone, Nant'ou, 54065, Taiwan
Tel.: (886) 492255011
Web Site: https://www.nak.com.tw
9942—(TAI)
Rev.: $156,529,835
Assets: $173,068,243
Liabilities: $43,412,275
Net Worth: $129,655,968
Earnings: $32,064,847
Fiscal Year-end: 12/31/23
Oil Seals & Automotive Seals Mfr
N.A.I.C.S.: 339991
Zhengfu Shi *(Chm)*

Subsidiaries:

Kish Nak Oil Seal Mfg. Co., Ltd. (1)
Unit 502 Floor 5 No 308 Kolahdooz Ave, Tehran, Iran
Tel.: (98) 2122567451
Sealing Product Mfr & Distr
N.A.I.C.S.: 339991

Kunshan Maoshun Sealing Products Industrial Co., Ltd. (1)
No 510 Hengchangjing Road, Zhoushi Town, Kunshan, 215337, Jiangsu, China
Tel.: (86) 51257661139
Web Site: https://en.ksnak.com
Sales Range: $100-124.9 Million
Emp.: 300
Seal Products Mfr
N.A.I.C.S.: 339991

NAK Do Brasil Industria E Comercio De Componentes De Vedacao Ltda. (1)
Rua Soldado Benedito Eliseo Dos Santos Nro 10, Sao Paulo, 02177-020, Brazil
Tel.: (55) 1138073001
Web Site: http://www.nakbrasil.com.br
Sealing Products Mfr
N.A.I.C.S.: 339991

NAK International Ltd. (1)
House 8 Factory Street, Reutov, 143960, Moscow, Russia
Tel.: (7) 4955459400
Web Site: http://www.naksealing.ru
Sealants Distr
N.A.I.C.S.: 424690

NAK Sealing Products (Thailand) Co., Ltd. (1)
120/36 Moo 12 Soi 21/2 Kingkaew-Bangplee Road Tumbul Rachatewa, Ampur Bangplee, Samut Prakan, 10540, Thailand
Tel.: (66) 27501988
Seal Products Distr
N.A.I.C.S.: 423840

NAK Sealing Technologies (India) Pvt. Ltd. (1)
P-1 Phase II Dr Vikram Sarabhai Industrial Estate, Thiruvanmiyur, Chennai, 600 041, Tamilnadu, India
Tel.: (91) 4466475857
Web Site: http://www.nak.com.tw
Sales Range: $25-49.9 Million
Emp.: 30
Seal Products Distr
N.A.I.C.S.: 423840

NAKABAYASHI CO., LTD.
5-1 Higashi-Sakashita 2-Chome, Itabashi-ku, Tokyo, 174-8602, Japan
Tel.: (81) 358607565   JP
Web Site: https://www.nakabayashi.co.jp
Year Founded: 1951
7987—(TKS)
Rev.: $403,494,230
Assets: $383,148,650
Liabilities: $197,282,060
Net Worth: $185,866,590
Earnings: $5,790,360
Emp.: 2,228
Fiscal Year-end: 03/31/24
Paper Product & Office Equipment Mfr & Whslr
N.A.I.C.S.: 322230
Hideaki Yumoto *(Pres)*

Subsidiaries:

Kagukuro Co., Ltd. (1)

Kyoyu Building 1F / 2F 2-11 Kandasudacho, Chiyoda-ku, Tokyo, 101-0041, Japan
Tel.: (81) 120999939
Web Site: https://www.kagukuro.com
Emp.: 108
Office Furniture Mfr & Distr
N.A.I.C.S.: 337214

Kokusai Chart Corporation (1)
1-30 Akabori, Okegawa, 363-0002, Saitama, Japan   (99.99%)
Tel.: (81) 48 728 8269
Web Site: http://www.kokusai-chart.com
Sales Range: Less than $1 Million
Recording Product Mfr
N.A.I.C.S.: 334513
Minoru Sosizaki *(Gen Mgr-Sls Div)*

Leaman Co., Ltd. (1)
68-1 Minamikawara Seiho-cho, Aisai, 496-0911, Aichi Prefecture, Japan
Tel.: (81) 567270165
Web Site: https://leaman.co.jp
Emp.: 67
Child Seat Mfr
N.A.I.C.S.: 336360

Nippon Tsushinshi Co., Ltd. (1)
Mukaioka 1-13-1, Bunkyo-ku, Tokyo, 113-0023, Japan
Tel.: (81) 366290230
Web Site: https://www.e-ntk.co.jp
Emp.: 388
Business Process Outsourcing Services
N.A.I.C.S.: 561422

Womanstaff Co., Ltd. (1)
2-6-8 Ginza 5th Floor Nippon Life Ginza Building, Chuo-ku, Tokyo, 104-0061, Japan
Tel.: (81) 352501555
Web Site: https://www.womanstaff.co.jp
Staffing Services
N.A.I.C.S.: 561320

NAKABOHTEC CORROSION PROTECTING CO., LTD.
1-17-21 Shinkawa, Chuo-ku, Tokyo, 104-0033, Japan
Tel.: (81) 355415813
Web Site: https://www.nakabohtec.co.jp
Year Founded: 1951
1787—(TKS)
Sales Range: Less than $1 Million
Emp.: 250
Anticorrosion Material Services
N.A.I.C.S.: 561499
Hajime Myoi *(Pres & COO)*

NAKAKITA SEISAKUSHO CO., LTD.
1-1 Fukonominami-cho, Daito, 574-8691, Osaka, Japan
Tel.: (81) 728711331
Web Site: https://www.nakakita-s.co.jp
Year Founded: 1937
6496—(TKS)
Sales Range: $150-199.9 Million
Industrial Valve Mfr
N.A.I.C.S.: 332911
Kenichi Nakakita *(Chm)*

NAKAKITA YAKUHIN CO., LTD.
3-5-15 Marunouchi, Naka-ku, Nagoya-city, Aichi, 460-8515, Japan
Tel.: (81) 529713681
Web Site: https://www.nakakita.co.jp
Year Founded: 1914
Pharmaceuticals Mfr
N.A.I.C.S.: 325412

Subsidiaries:

Yakuhan Pharmaceutical Co., Ltd. (1)
27 Kitanosato, Kitahiroshima, 061-1111, Hokkaido, Japan
Tel.: (81) 113731033
Pharmaceutical Product Mfr & Distr
N.A.I.C.S.: 325412

NAKAMICHI LEASING CO., LTD.

Nakakita Yakuhin Co., Ltd.—(Continued)

NAKAMICHI LEASING CO., LTD.
3-3 Kita1-Johigashi, Chuo-Ku, Sapporo, 060-8539, Japan
Tel.: (81) 112802266
Web Site: https://www.nakamichi-leasing.co.jp
8594—(SAP)
Sales Range: Less than $1 Million
Equipment Rental & Leasing Services
N.A.I.C.S.: 532490
Hiroshi Seki *(Pres)*

NAKAMOTO PACKS CO., LTD.
2-8 Karahori-Cho Tennoji, Osaka, 543-0012, Japan
Tel.: (81) 667620431
Web Site: https://www.npacks.co.jp
Year Founded: 1941
7811—
Rev.: $314,526,580
Assets: $272,844,470
Liabilities: $141,707,830
Net Worth: $131,136,640
Earnings: $7,494,130
Emp.: 937
Fiscal Year-end: 02/29/24
Commercial Printing Services
N.A.I.C.S.: 323111
Jun Kawata *(Pres)*

Subsidiaries:

Nakamoto Packs USA,Inc (1)
Ste 1615 404 James Robertson Pkwy,
Nashville, TN 37219
Tel.: (615) 647-7526
Commercial Printing Equipment Mfr
N.A.I.C.S.: 323111

Santac Co., Ltd. (1)
13-3 Minooki-Cho, Fukuyama, Hiroshima, Japan
Tel.: (81) 849549578
Melding Product Mfr & Distr
N.A.I.C.S.: 326199

NAKAMURA CHOUKOU CO., LTD.
2727 Tsurutamachi, Nishi-ku Sakai City, Osaka, 593-8323, Japan
Tel.: (81) 722740007
Web Site: https://www.nakamura-gp.co.jp
Year Founded: 1970
6166—(TKS)
Rev.: $15,949,930
Assets: $39,679,830
Liabilities: $34,034,890
Net Worth: $5,644,940
Earnings: $951,840
Emp.: 355
Fiscal Year-end: 03/31/24
High-Precision Parts, Cutting Tools & Diamon Saw Wire Mfr
N.A.I.C.S.: 333515
Makoto Inoue *(Pres)*

Subsidiaries:

Nakamura Choukou Co., Ltd. - Izumi Factory (1)
2-1-3 Ayumino, Izumi, 594-1157, Osaka, Japan
Tel.: (81) 725532525
Cutting Tool Mfr
N.A.I.C.S.: 333515

Nippon Nozzle Co., Ltd. (1)
2-1-1 Murotani, Nishi-ku, Kobe, 651-2241, Japan
Tel.: (81) 789916821
Web Site: http://www.nippon-nz.com
Emp.: 80
Industrial Equipment Mfr & Distr
N.A.I.C.S.: 333248
Makoto Inoue *(Chm)*

SHANGHAI NAKAMURA CHOUKOU TRADING CO., LTD. (1)
Room 1506 No 2067 West Yanan Road, Changning District, Shanghai, 200336, China
Tel.: (86) 2162130389
Cutting Tool Mfr & Distr
N.A.I.C.S.: 333515
Hiroyuki Taue *(Chm)*

NAKAMURAYA CO., LTD.
Shinjuku 3-chome 26-13, Shinjuku-ku, Tokyo, 160-0022, Japan
Tel.: (81) 120370293
Web Site: https://www.nakamuraya.co.jp
Year Founded: 1923
2204—(TKS)
Sales Range: $350-399.9 Million
Confectionery Product Mfr & Distr
N.A.I.C.S.: 311351
Tatsuya Suzuki *(Chm & Pres)*

NAKANIHON KOGYO CO., LTD.
8 Kiori, Ama, Aichi, Japan
Tel.: (81) 524445141
Web Site: https://www.nakanihon-ro.co.jp
96430—(NGO)
Sales Range: Less than $1 Million
Advertising Services
N.A.I.C.S.: 541810
Toru Hattori *(Chm & Pres)*

NAKANISHI INC.
700 Shimohinata, Kanuma, 322-8666, Tochigi, Japan
Tel.: (81) 289643380
Web Site: https://www.nsk-nakanishi.co.jp
Year Founded: 1930
7716—(TKS)
Rev.: $423,216,280
Assets: $998,045,120
Liabilities: $195,712,360
Net Worth: $802,332,760
Earnings: $161,900,150
Emp.: 2,049
Fiscal Year-end: 12/31/23
Surgical & Medical Instruments Mfr
N.A.I.C.S.: 339112

Subsidiaries:

Dental X S.p.a (1)
Via Marzotto 11 Dueville, 36031, Vicenza, Italy
Tel.: (39) 0444 367400
Medical Equipment Distr
N.A.I.C.S.: 423450

NSK America Corp. (1)
1800 Global Pkwy, Hoffman Estates, IL 60192
Tel.: (847) 843-7664
Web Site: https://www.nskamericacorp.com
Machine Tool Distr
N.A.I.C.S.: 423120

Subsidiary (Domestic):

DCI International, LLC (2)
305 N Springbrook Rd, Newberg, OR 97132
Tel.: (503) 538-8343
Web Site: https://www.dcionline.com
Sales Range: $10-24.9 Million
Emp.: 70
Mfr; & Distributor of Dental Equipment, Components & Replacement Parts
N.A.I.C.S.: 339114
John Spencer *(CEO)*

Subsidiary (Domestic):

Pelton & Crane Group (3)
11727 Fruehauf Dr, Charlotte, NC 28273
Tel.: (704) 588-2126
Web Site: http://www.pelton.net
Dental Equipment, Components & Replacement Parts Mfr & Distr
N.A.I.C.S.: 339114
Starla Smith *(Sec)*

NSK America Latina Ltda (1)
Rua Doutor Joao Colin 1995 America, Joinville, 89204-003, SC, Brazil
Tel.: (55) 4738046569
Web Site: https://www.brasil.nsk-dental.com
Medical Equipment Distr
N.A.I.C.S.: 423450

NSK Asia Pte Ltd. (1)
51 Changi Business Park Central 2 07-10 The Signature, Singapore, 486066, Singapore
Tel.: (65) 63765018
Medical Equipment Distr
N.A.I.C.S.: 423450

NSK Dental Spain SA (1)
C/ Rozabella 8 Europa Empresarial Edificio Roma baja Oficina A, Las Rozas, 28290, Madrid, Spain
Tel.: (34) 916266128
Web Site: https://www.spain.nsk-dental.com
Medical Equipment Distr
N.A.I.C.S.: 423450

NSK Dental korea Co., Ltd (1)
501-504 19 Yangpyeong-ro 21ga-gil, Yeongdeungpo-gu, Seoul, 07207, Korea (South)
Tel.: (82) 226338990
Web Site: https://www.korea.nsk-dental.com
Medical Equipment Distr
N.A.I.C.S.: 423450

NSK Europe GmbH (1)
Elly-Beinhorn-Str 8, 65760, Eschborn, Germany
Tel.: (49) 6196776060
Web Site: https://www.germany.nsk-dental.com
Medical Equipment Distr
N.A.I.C.S.: 423450

NSK Middle East (1)
Room 6EA-701 7th Floor East Wing No 6 Dubai Airport Free Zone, PO Box 54318, Dubai, United Arab Emirates
Tel.: (971) 42045507
Medical Equipment Distr
N.A.I.C.S.: 423450
Sharath Shetty *(Sls Mgr-Technical)*

NSK Oceania Ltd (1)
Ground Floor Suite D 272 Parnell Road, PO Box 28100, Parnell, Auckland, 1052, New Zealand
Tel.: (64) 95292383
Web Site: https://www.new-zealand.nsk-dental.com
Medical Equipment Distr
N.A.I.C.S.: 423450

NSK Oceania Pty Ltd (1)
Unit 12 809-821 Botany Road, Rosebery, 2018, NSW, Australia
Tel.: (61) 28 306 3000
Web Site: https://www.australia.nsk-dental.com
Medical Equipment Distr
N.A.I.C.S.: 423450

NSK Rus & CIS (1)
2 Entuziastov bulvar 11th floor, 109544, Moscow, Russia
Tel.: (7) 4959679607
Web Site: https://www.russia.nsk-dental.com
Medical Equipment Distr
N.A.I.C.S.: 423450

NSK Shanghai Co., Ltd (1)
Room 702 Tower 1 SOHO Tianshan Plaza No 421 ZiYun Road, Changning District, Shanghai, 200051, China
Tel.: (86) 2162527272
Medical Equipment Distr
N.A.I.C.S.: 423450

NAKANISHI MFG. CO., LTD.
5-4-14 Tatsumi-Minami, Ikuno-ku, Osaka, 544-0015, Japan
Tel.: (81) 667911111
Web Site: https://www.nakanishi.co.jp
Year Founded: 1958
5941—(TKS)
Sales Range: $150-199.9 Million
Kitchen Equipment Mfr & Distr
N.A.I.C.S.: 332215
Ichiro Nakanishi *(Sr Mng Dir & Dir-Admin)*

NAKANO CORPORATION
4-2-28 Kudan-Kita, Chiyoda-ku, Tokyo, 102-0073, Japan
Tel.: (81) 332654661
Web Site: https://www.wave-nakano.co.jp
Year Founded: 1933
1827—(TKS)
Rev.: $710,013,150
Assets: $532,871,760
Liabilities: $254,200,770
Net Worth: $278,670,990
Earnings: $17,483,450
Emp.: 1,331
Fiscal Year-end: 03/31/24
Construction Engineering & Real Estate Development Services
N.A.I.C.S.: 237990
Akira Asai *(Vice Chm)*

Subsidiaries:

NAKANO INTERNATIONAL CORPORATION (1)
111 W Saint John St Ste 514, San Jose, CA 95113
Tel.: (408) 286-9702
Construction Engineering Services
N.A.I.C.S.: 541330

Nakano Construction Sdn. Bhd. (1)
Block B 15-4-2 Magan Salak Park, Jalan 1/125E Taman Desa Petaling, Kuala Lumpur, 57100, Malaysia
Tel.: (60) 3 9059 6977
Web Site: http://www.nakaho-const.com
Emp.: 150
Construction Engineering & Real Estate Development Services
N.A.I.C.S.: 237990
San Tsan Soh *(Mng Dir)*

Nakano Consulting Shanghai Co., Ltd. (1)
Room 711 Union Development Building, 728 Xinhua Road, Shanghai, China
Tel.: (86) 21 5258 3923
Construction Engineering & Real Estate Development Services
N.A.I.C.S.: 237990

Nakano Development Co., Ltd. (1)
2-15 Chiyoda-ku Gobancho, Tokyo, 102-0076, Japan
Tel.: (81) 3 3265 4770
Construction Engineering & Real Estate Development Services
N.A.I.C.S.: 237990

Nakano Singapore (Pte.) Ltd. (1)
1 Coleman Street Ste 06-02, The Adelphi, Singapore, 179803, Singapore
Tel.: (65) 6333 4933
Web Site: http://www.nakano.com.sg
Emp.: 40
Construction Engineering & Real Estate Development Services
N.A.I.C.S.: 237990

Nakano Vietnam Co., Ltd. (1)
Unit 1411-1412 14th Floor Daeha Business Center 360 Kim Ma Street, Ngoc Khanh Ward Ba Dinh District, Hanoi, Vietnam
Tel.: (84) 2437247552
Emp.: 20
Construction Engineering & Real Estate Development Services
N.A.I.C.S.: 237990
Takanori Iwata *(Gen Dir)*

Nf Agency Co., Ltd. (1)
Gobancho NAKANO Building 1F 4-7 Gobancho, Chiyoda-ku, Tokyo, 102-0076, Japan
Tel.: (81) 332654770
Civil Engineering & Construction Services
N.A.I.C.S.: 541330

Nf Realty Co., Ltd. (1)
Gobancho NAKANO Building 1F 4-7 Gobancho, Chiyoda-ku, Tokyo, 102-0076, Japan
Tel.: (81) 332629446
Civil Engineering & Construction Services
N.A.I.C.S.: 541330

Oshima Kogyo Co., Ltd. (1)
1-11-24 Fukuura, Kanazawa-Ku, Yokohama, 102-0073, Knagawa, Japan
Tel.: (81) 457916321

Web Site: https://www.ohshima.co.jp
Emp.: 46
Construction Engineering & Real Estate Development Services
N.A.I.C.S.: 541330

PT Indonakano (1)
Tel.: (62) 215203674
Web Site: http://www.indonakano.co.id
Construction Engineering & Real Estate Development Services
N.A.I.C.S.: 237990

PT Nakano S Batam (1)
Jalan Laksamana Bintan Komp Tanah Mas Blok G3A, Sei Panas, Batam, Indonesia
Tel.: (62) 0788 463004
Construction Engineering & Real Estate Development Services
N.A.I.C.S.: 237990

TRYNET Holdinngs CO.,Ltd. (1)
Prefecture Trynet Building 3F Matsuo Shiroda 573-1, Nagano, Iida, 395-0812, Japan
Tel.: (81) 265249320
Civil Engineering & Construction Services
N.A.I.C.S.: 541330

Thai Nakano Co., Ltd. (1)
Tel.: (66) 23080500
Construction Engineering & Real Estate Development Services
N.A.I.C.S.: 237990

NAKANO REFRIGERATORS CO., LTD.
2-15-4 Shibaura, Minato-Ku, Tokyo, 108-8543, Japan
Tel.: (81) 334551311
Web Site: https://www.nakano-reiki.com
Year Founded: 1946
6411—(TKS)
Rev.: $233,899,100
Assets: $250,695,310
Liabilities: $60,846,380
Net Worth: $189,848,930
Earnings: $13,499,360
Emp.: 119
Fiscal Year-end: 12/31/23
Refrigerator Mfr & Distr
N.A.I.C.S.: 335220

NAKATAKE CO., LTD.
2-10-7 Kinshi Nakatake Building, Sumida-ku, Tokyo, 130-0013, Japan
Tel.: (81) 3 5637 2888   JP
Web Site: https://www.nakatake.jp
Year Founded: 1997
Emp.: 100
Furniture Mfr & Importer
N.A.I.C.S.: 337126

Subsidiaries:

FPK Nakatake Co., Ltd. (1)
16-1 Muchiushi, Yaizu, 425-0007, Shizuoka, Japan
Tel.: (81) 54 621 3161
Web Site: https://www.f-p-k.co.jp
Custom-Made Furniture Mfr
N.A.I.C.S.: 337214

NAKAYAMA STEEL WORKS LTD.
1-1-66 Funamachi, Taisho-ku, Osaka, 551-8551, Japan
Tel.: (81) 665553111
Web Site: https://www.nakayama-steel.co.jp
Year Founded: 1923
5408—(TKS)
Rev.: $1,219,181,450
Assets: $1,005,295,070
Liabilities: $314,199,740
Net Worth: $691,095,330
Earnings: $58,855,440
Emp.: 2,057
Fiscal Year-end: 03/31/24
Steel Product Mfr & Distr
N.A.I.C.S.: 331110
Sachihiro Nakamura *(Mng Dir)*

NAKAYAMAFUKU CO., LTD.
1-22-9 Shimanouchi, Chuo-ku, Osaka, 542-0082, Japan
Tel.: (81) 662513051
Web Site:
    https://www.nakayamafuku.co.jp
Year Founded: 1947
7442—(TKS)
Rev.: $413,529,600
Assets: $300,457,520
Liabilities: $94,622,000
Net Worth: $205,835,520
Earnings: $5,498,240
Emp.: 365
Fiscal Year-end: 03/31/22
Household Appliance Whslr
N.A.I.C.S.: 423620
Nobuhiro Ishikawa *(Chm & Pres)*

Subsidiaries:

Interform Inc. (1)
5-1 Shinkocho, Chuo-ku, Kobe, 650-0041, Hyogo, Japan
Tel.: (81) 783928423
Web Site: http://www.interform-inc.com
Interior Goods Mfr
N.A.I.C.S.: 334519
Ishikawa Norihiro *(CEO)*

NAKAYO, INC.
1-3-2 Sojacho, Maebashi, 371-0853, Gunma, Japan
Tel.: (81) 272531111
Web Site: https://www.nyc.co.jp
Year Founded: 1944
6715—(TKS)
Rev.: $113,824,200
Assets: $140,707,070
Liabilities: $36,374,830
Net Worth: $104,332,240
Earnings: ($8,381,480)
Emp.: 745
Fiscal Year-end: 03/31/24
Telecommunication Equipment Mfr & Distr
N.A.I.C.S.: 334290
Yoshiji Tanimoto *(Pres & CEO)*

NAKED WINES PLC
4th Floor The Union Building 51-59 Rose Lane, Norwich, NR1 1BY, United Kingdom
Tel.: (44) 1603281800   UK
Web Site:
    https://www.nakedwinesplc.co.uk
NWINF—(OTCQX)
Rev.: $439,653,081
Assets: $312,794,518
Liabilities: $190,256,178
Net Worth: $122,538,340
Earnings: ($21,623,463)
Emp.: 383
Fiscal Year-end: 03/31/23
Wine Retailer
N.A.I.C.S.: 312130
James Crawford *(Interim CFO & Mng Dir-UK)*

Subsidiaries:

Naked Wines International Limited (1)
Norvic House, Chapel Field Road, Norwich, NR2 1RP, United Kingdom
Tel.: (44) 1603 281869
Web Site: http://www.nakedwines.com
Online Wine Retailer
N.A.I.C.S.: 445320

Subsidiary (Non-US):

Naked Wines Australia Pty Limited (2)
18 Sydney Rd, Manly, Newport, 2095, NSW, Australia
Tel.: (61) 300898677
Web Site: https://www.nakedwines.com.au
Online Wine Retailer
N.A.I.C.S.: 445320
Mark Pollard *(Dir-Wine)*

Subsidiary (US):

NakedWines.com, Inc. (2)
135 Gasser Dr, Napa, CA 94559
Web Site: http://us.nakedwines.com
Online Wine Retailer
N.A.I.C.S.: 445320

NAKODA GROUP OF INDUSTRIES LTD.
Plot No 239 South Old Bagadganj Small Factory Area, Nagpur, 440008, Maharashtra, India
Tel.: (91) 7122778824
Web Site: https://www.nakodas.com
Year Founded: 1989
NGIL—(NSE)
Rev.: $6,554,499
Assets: $4,968,407
Liabilities: $3,084,779
Net Worth: $1,883,628
Earnings: $109,298
Emp.: 33
Fiscal Year-end: 03/31/23
Food Products Mfr
N.A.I.C.S.: 311999
Pratul Wate *(Compliance Officer & Sec)*

NAKODA LIMITED
Atlanta Room No 64 6th Floor Nariman Point, Mumbai, 400 021, India
Tel.: (91) 2222824740
Web Site: http://www.nakodaltd.com
Sales Range: $1-9.9 Million
Emp.: 825
Polyester Yarn Mfr & Distr
N.A.I.C.S.: 313110
Babulal G. Jain *(Co-Founder, Chm & Co-Mng Dir)*

NAKSH PRECIOUS METALS LTD.
105 1st Floor Barodia Tower Plot No 12 D Block Central Market, Prashant Vihar, New Delhi, 110085, India
Tel.: (91) 8530217555
Web Site: https://nakshmetals.com
539402—(BOM)
Rev.: $22,405
Assets: $1,306,841
Liabilities: $707,713
Net Worth: $599,128
Earnings: ($10,582)
Emp.: 4
Fiscal Year-end: 03/31/23
Automobile Parts Distr
N.A.I.C.S.: 423120
Atul Kumar Jain *(Chm & Mng Dir)*

NALIN LEASE FINANCE LIMITED
Gandhi Nursing Home Buld Dr Nalinkant Gandhi Road Sabarkantha, Himatnagar, 383001, Gujarat, India
Tel.: (91) 2772242264
Web Site: https://www.nalinfin.co.in
531212—(BOM)
Rev.: $712,963
Assets: $3,635,569
Liabilities: $316,390
Net Worth: $3,319,179
Earnings: $358,799
Emp.: 18
Fiscal Year-end: 03/31/23
Finance Services
N.A.I.C.S.: 523999
Harsh Dilipkumar Gandhi *(Exec Dir)*

NALWA SONS INVESTMENTS LIMITED
Jindal Centre 12 Bhikaiji Cama Place, New Delhi, 110066, India
Tel.: (91) 1141462000   In
Web Site:
    https://www.nalwasons.com
Year Founded: 1970

532256—(BOM)
Rev.: $11,672,885
Assets: $1,129,013,345
Liabilities: $173,385,588
Net Worth: $955,627,756
Earnings: $7,896,853
Emp.: 4
Fiscal Year-end: 03/31/23
Investment Holding Company
N.A.I.C.S.: 551112
Mahender Kumar Goel *(CEO)*

NAM CHEONG LIMITED
BO3-B-17-1 Menara 3A No 3, Jalan Bangsar KL Eco City, 59200, Kuala Lumpur, Malaysia
Tel.: (60) 322806777   BM
Web Site:
    http://www.namcheong.com.my
Year Founded: 1968
1MZ—(SES)
Rev.: $103,455,160
Assets: $198,375,056
Liabilities: $307,688,509
Net Worth: ($109,313,453)
Earnings: $35,464,301
Emp.: 264
Fiscal Year-end: 12/31/23
Ship Building Services
N.A.I.C.S.: 336611
Su Kouk Tiong *(Chm)*

Subsidiaries:

SKOM Sdn Bhd (1)
BO3-B-17-1 Menara 3A KL Eco City No 3 Jalan Bangsar, 59200, Kuala Lumpur, Malaysia
Tel.: (60) 322806777
Web Site: https://www.skom.com.my
Logistic Services
N.A.I.C.S.: 484110

NAM DINH EXPORT FOODSTUFF AND AGRICULTURAL PRODUCTS PROCESSING JSC
Tran Nhan Tong Street Tran Quang Khai Ward, Nam Dinh, Vietnam
Tel.: (84) 2283867999
Web Site: https://namdinhfoods.com
Meat, Seafood & Poultry Production & Distribution
N.A.I.C.S.: 311612

NAM FATT CORPORATION BERHAD
40B Persiaran Sultan Ibrahim, 41300, Kelang, Selangor Darul Ehsan, Malaysia
Tel.: (60) 333420766
Sales Range: $25-49.9 Million
Construction & Property Development Services
N.A.I.C.S.: 531312
Seng Chong Yeoh *(Co-Sec)*

Subsidiaries:

Nam Fatt Fabricators Sdn. Bhd. (1)
Lot 2 Section 15 Jalan Utas 15/7 Shah Alam Industrial Estate, Shah Alam, 40000, Selangor, Malaysia
Tel.: (60) 350329677
Sales Range: $25-49.9 Million
Emp.: 30
Seal Products Distr
N.A.I.C.S.: 332999

S.S.A.S. Golf Resort Management Services Sdn. Bhd. (1)
1 Club House Jalan Kelab Golf 13/6, 40100, Shah Alam, Selangor Darul Ehsan, Malaysia
Tel.: (60) 355105872
Golf Club Management Services
N.A.I.C.S.: 339920

Swissma Building Technologies Sdn. Bhd. (1)
Jalan Utas 15/7 Shah Alam Industrial Es-

NAM FATT CORPORATION BERHAD

Nam Fatt Corporation Berhad—(Continued)
tate, PO Box 7053, 40700, Shah Alam, Selangor Darul Ehsan, Malaysia
Tel.: (60) 355191360
Web Site: https://www.swissma.com
Sales Range: $25-49.9 Million
Emp.: 50
Roofing & Building Construction Services
N.A.I.C.S.: 238160
Low Ping Hing *(Gen Mgr)*

NAM HENG OIL MILL CO. SDN. BHD.
141 Jalan Rahmat, Batu Pahat, 83000, Johor, Malaysia
Tel.: (60) 7 434 0443   MY
Emp.: 6
Mining & Milling Machinery Mfr & Distr
N.A.I.C.S.: 333131
Meng Kuan Guan *(Principal)*

Subsidiaries:

Phratra Sdn. Bhd   (1)
523 Jalan Kluang Batu 2 1/2, Batu Pahat, 83000, Johor, Malaysia
Tel.: (60) 7 434 3754
Industrial Real Estate Investment & Development
N.A.I.C.S.: 531390

NAM HWA CONSTRUCTION CO., LTD.
40 Buckra1st Hwasun-eup, Hwasun, Korea (South)
Web Site:
http://www.namhwaconst.co.kr
091590—(KRS)
Rev.: $69,637,090
Assets: $157,440,009
Liabilities: $24,026,957
Net Worth: $133,413,052
Earnings: $15,915,292
Emp.: 91
Fiscal Year-end: 12/31/22
Civil Engineering Construction Services
N.A.I.C.S.: 541330
Jae-Hun Choi *(Board of Directors & CEO)*

NAM KIM STEEL JOINT STOCK COMPANY
Lot A1 D2 Street Dong An 2 Industrial Park, Hoa Phu Ward, Thu Dau Mot, Binh Duong, Vietnam
Tel.: (84) 2743748848
Web Site: https://tonnamkim.com
Year Founded: 2002
NKG—(HOSE)
Rev.: $766,154,129
Assets: $504,098,521
Liabilities: $280,667,872
Net Worth: $223,430,649
Earnings: $4,837,251
Emp.: 1,336
Fiscal Year-end: 12/31/23
Aluminum Sheet Mfr
N.A.I.C.S.: 331315
Ho Minh Quang *(Chm)*

NAM LEE PRESSED METAL INDUSTRIES LIMITED
21 Sungei Kadut Street 4, Singapore, 729048, Singapore
Tel.: (65) 62575388
Web Site:
https://www.namlee.com.sg
Year Founded: 1975
G0I—(SES)
Rev.: $117,751,760
Assets: $158,340,867
Liabilities: $45,276,769
Net Worth: $113,064,098
Earnings: ($743,979)
Emp.: 1,165
Fiscal Year-end: 09/30/23

Steel & Aluminum Products Mfr
N.A.I.C.S.: 331513
Poon Miew Yong *(Exec Dir)*

Subsidiaries:

Creative Holdings (HK) Limited   (1)
Room 1401 14/F Hong Kong and Macau Building, 156-157 Connaught Road Central, Sheung Wan, China (Hong Kong)
Tel.: (852) 23300111
Investment Holding Services
N.A.I.C.S.: 551112

NL Metals Sdn Bhd   (1)
No 2 Jalan Tampoi 7 Kawasan Perusahaan Tampoi, Johor Bahru, 81200, Johor, Malaysia
Tel.: (60) 73341187
Aluminium Window Mfr
N.A.I.C.S.: 332321

NAM LIONG GLOBAL CORPORATION
No 10 Lane 41 Chou-Wei Street Yen-Chou Li, Yong-Kang Dist, T'ainan, 710004, Taiwan
Tel.: (886) 62534161
Web Site:
https://www.namliong.com.tw
Year Founded: 1972
5450—(TPE)
Rev.: $96,370,791
Assets: $106,402,057
Liabilities: $55,151,268
Net Worth: $51,250,789
Earnings: $5,553,544
Fiscal Year-end: 12/31/22
Fabrics Mfr
N.A.I.C.S.: 313310
Shun-Ching Chang *(CEO)*

NAM LONG INVESTMENT CORPORATION
6 Nguyen Khac Vien, Tan Phu Ward District 7, Ho Chi Minh City, Vietnam
Tel.: (84) 2854161718
Web Site:
https://www.namlongvn.com
Year Founded: 1992
NLG—(HOSE)
Rev.: $131,074,578
Assets: $1,178,782,404
Liabilities: $621,232,884
Net Worth: $557,549,519
Earnings: $32,979,670
Emp.: 834
Fiscal Year-end: 12/31/23
Real Estate Development Services
N.A.I.C.S.: 531390

NAM SENG INSURANCE PUBLIC COMPANY LIMITED
767 Krungthep-Nonthaburi Rd, Bangsue, 10800, Bangkok, Thailand
Tel.: (66) 20163333
Web Site:
http://www.namsengins.co.th
Year Founded: 1948
NSI—(THA)
Rev.: $73,287,366
Assets: $134,275,408
Liabilities: $87,722,996
Net Worth: $46,552,412
Earnings: $5,352,360
Emp.: 566
Fiscal Year-end: 12/31/20
General Insurance Services
N.A.I.C.S.: 524210
Somboon Fusriboon *(Vice Chm)*

NAM TAI PROPERTY INC.
Nam Tai Estate No 2 Namtai Road Gushu Community, Xixiang Township Baoan District, Shenzhen, Guangdong, China
Tel.: (86) 75527490666   VG
Web Site: http://www.namtai.com
Year Founded: 1975

NTP—(NYSE)
Rev.: $71,206,000
Assets: $701,210,000
Liabilities: $452,382,000
Net Worth: $248,828,000
Earnings: $15,693,000
Emp.: 111
Fiscal Year-end: 12/31/20
Investment Services
N.A.I.C.S.: 334220
Jiabiao Wang *(CEO)*

Subsidiaries:

Nam Tai Electronic & Electrical Products Limited   (1)
Unit 1201 12th Floor Tower 1 Lippo Center 89 Queensway, Admiralty, Hong Kong, China (Hong Kong)   (100%)
Tel.: (852) 23410273
Web Site: http://www.namtai.com
Emp.: 10
Electronic Manufacturing & Design
N.A.I.C.S.: 334419

Nam Tai Electronic (Shenzhen) Co., Ltd.   (1)
Gushu Industrial Zone, Shenzhen, Guangdong, China
Tel.: (86) 75527490666
Web Site: http://www.namtai.com.cn
Electronic Components Mfr
N.A.I.C.S.: 334419

Nam Tai Investment Limited   (1)
Rm 1201 12/F Lippo Ctr Twr 1 89 Queensway Admiralty, Hong Kong, China (Hong Kong)
Tel.: (852) 23410273
Investment Management Service
N.A.I.C.S.: 523999

Nam Tai Investments Consultant (Macao Commercial Offshore) Company Limited   (1)
Unit A & C 17th Floor Edificio Comercial Rodrigues, Macau, China (Macau)   (100%)
Tel.: (853) 28356333
Sales Range: $50-74.9 Million
Data Processing Services
N.A.I.C.S.: 518210

NAM THEUN 2 POWER COMPANY LIMITED
Unit 09 23 Singha Rd, PO Box 5862, Nongbone Village, Vientiane, Lao People's Democratic Republic
Tel.: (856) 21263900
Web Site: http://www.namtheun2.com
Sales Range: $150-199.9 Million
Emp.: 500
Hydroelectric Power Generation
N.A.I.C.S.: 221111
Michel Robino *(CEO)*

NAM VIET CORPORATION
19D Tran Hung Dao Sreet My Qui Ward, Long Xuyen, An Giang, Vietnam
Tel.: (84) 2963834060
Web Site:
https://www.navicorp.com.vn
Year Founded: 1993
ANV—(HOSE)
Rev.: $182,891,868
Assets: $210,642,004
Liabilities: $93,309,884
Net Worth: $117,332,120
Earnings: $1,614,710
Emp.: 6,300
Fiscal Year-end: 12/31/23
Seafood Whslr
N.A.I.C.S.: 424460
Doan Toi *(Founder, Vice Chm & CEO)*

NAM VIET JOINT STOCK COMPANY
18F Tang Nhon Phu, Phuoc Long B Ward District 9, Ho Chi Minh City, Vietnam

INTERNATIONAL PUBLIC

Tel.: (84) 2837282102
Web Site: https://navifico.vn
Year Founded: 1963
NAV—(HOSE)
Rev.: $5,328,190
Assets: $4,971,686
Liabilities: $221,656
Net Worth: $4,750,030
Earnings: $869,608
Emp.: 513
Fiscal Year-end: 12/31/23
Construction Material Mfr & Whslr
N.A.I.C.S.: 327390

NAM.R SA
4 Rue Foucault, 75116, Paris, France
Tel.: (33) 185800801
Web Site: https://www.namr.com
Year Founded: 2017
ALNMR—(EUR)
Emp.: 250
Software Development Services
N.A.I.C.S.: 541511
Lila Tretikov *(Co-Founder)*

NAMA A.D.
Janka Veselinovica 1, Sabac, Serbia
Tel.: (381) 15 342 111
Web Site: http://www.tpnamaad.rs
Year Founded: 1958
NAMA—(BEL)
Sales Range: Less than $1 Million
Real Estate Manangement Services
N.A.I.C.S.: 531390
Slavica Donlic *(Exec Dir)*

NAMA CHEMICALS COMPANY
Jubail Industrial City Road 263, PO Box 10661, Jubail, 31961, Saudi Arabia
Tel.: (966) 133585002
Web Site: https://nama.com.sa
Year Founded: 1992
2210—(SAU)
Rev.: $118,729,102
Assets: $268,635,774
Liabilities: $206,258,236
Net Worth: $62,377,538
Earnings: ($40,649,317)
Fiscal Year-end: 12/31/23
Chemical Products Mfr
N.A.I.C.S.: 325180
Hazem Mansour Al-Fardan *(Chm)*

Subsidiaries:

Arabian Alkali Company   (1)
PO Box 12010, Jubail Industrial City, 31961, Jubail, Saudi Arabia
Tel.: (966) 133583400
Web Site: https://www.causticprills.com
Chemical Products Mfr
N.A.I.C.S.: 325199
Sanjay Narvekar *(Accountant)*

Jubail Chemical Industries LLC   (1)
Road 263, PO Box 10661, Jubail Industrial City, 31961, Jubail, Saudi Arabia
Tel.: (966) 13 358 5002
Web Site: https://www.nama.com.sa
Chemical Products Mfr
N.A.I.C.S.: 325199

NAMA Europe LLC   (1)
Oberlanderweg 44, Merligen, 3658, Bern, Switzerland
Tel.: (41) 61 841 1156
Web Site: https://www.namaeurope.com
Chemical Products Distr
N.A.I.C.S.: 424690
Alexander Denzler *(Gen Mgr)*

NAMA Germany GmbH   (1)
Rontgenstrasse 12, 79539, Lorrach, Germany
Tel.: (49) 76219405410
Web Site: https://www.namagermany.com
Chemical Products Mfr
N.A.I.C.S.: 325199
Alexander Denzler *(Gen Mgr)*

NAMA D.D.

Tomsiceva ulica 2, 1000, Ljubljana, Slovenia
Tel.: (386) 14258300
Web Site: https://www.nama.si
NALN—(LJU)
Sales Range: $25-49.9 Million
Emp.: 200
Department Store Owner & Operator
N.A.I.C.S.: 455110
Branka Jerala *(Dir-Sls & Mktg)*

NAMAKWA DIAMONDS LIMITED
Longpoint Office Park 4th Floor West Wing, Cnr Monte Casino Blvd & Witkoppen Road Fourways, Johannesburg, Gauteng, South Africa
Tel.: (27) 11 465 4505
Sales Range: $50-74.9 Million
Emp.: 324
Diamond Mining Services
N.A.I.C.S.: 212390
Mitford Mundell *(CEO)*

Subsidiaries:

Namakwa Diamond Holdings (Pty) Ltd. (1)
209 SA Diamond Ctr 225 Main St, Johannesburg, 2001, Gauteng, South Africa
Tel.: (27) 113348886
Web Site: http://www.namakwadiamonds.com
Sales Range: $50-74.9 Million
Emp.: 20
Diamond Mining Services
N.A.I.C.S.: 212390

NAMASTE BITTIYA SANSTHA LIMITED
Umesh Marg, Ghorahi, Nepal
Tel.: (977) 82 561659
Sales Range: Less than $1 Million
Financial Services
N.A.I.C.S.: 523999

NAMBA PRESS WORKS CO., LTD.
8 3 8 Kojima Ogawa 8 Chome, Kurashiki, 711-8688, Okayama, Japan
Tel.: (81) 864733111
Web Site: http://www.namba-press.co.jp
Year Founded: 1942
Sales Range: $250-299.9 Million
Emp.: 800
Mfr of Seating & Furniture for Public Buildings
N.A.I.C.S.: 337127
Tamae Namba *(CEO)*

Subsidiaries:

Bloomington-Normal Seating Company (1)
2031 Warehouse Rd, Normal, IL 61761-1038
Tel.: (309) 452-7878
Web Site: http://www.bnseating.com
Sales Range: $25-49.9 Million
Emp.: 55
Mfr of Automotive Seating; Joint Venture of Namba Press Works Co., Ltd. & Magna Interior Systems (50%)
N.A.I.C.S.: 336360
Hank Inoue *(Pres)*

NAMCHOW FOOD GROUP SHANGHAI CO., LTD.
12th Floor Building A No 1397 Yishan Road, Xuhui, Shanghai, 200233, China
Tel.: (86) 2161955678
Web Site: http://www.ncbakery.com
Year Founded: 2010
605339—(SHG)
Rev.: $401,739,886
Assets: $584,265,825
Liabilities: $127,604,857
Net Worth: $456,660,968
Earnings: $22,544,800
Fiscal Year-end: 12/31/22
Bakery Products Mfr
N.A.I.C.S.: 311812
Liao Meihui *(CFO)*

NAMCHOW HOLDINGS CO., LTD.
No 100 Sec 4 Yenping Road, Taipei, Taiwan
Tel.: (886) 225351251
Web Site: https://www.namchow.com.tw
Year Founded: 1952
1702—(TAI)
Rev.: $741,685,639
Assets: $990,253,797
Liabilities: $580,137,949
Net Worth: $410,115,848
Earnings: $40,588,899
Emp.: 4,733
Fiscal Year-end: 12/31/23
Soap Detergent Mfr & Distr
N.A.I.C.S.: 325611
Kevin Lee *(Exec VP)*

Subsidiaries:

Namchow (Thailand) Ltd. (1)
75/27-29 18th-19th Floor Ocean Tower 2 Soi Sukhumvit 19 Sukhumvit Road, North Klongtoey Wattana, Bangkok, 10110, Thailand
Tel.: (66) 20337800
Web Site: http://www.namchow.co.th
Rice Cracker & Rice Snacks Mfr
N.A.I.C.S.: 311999

Nankyo Japan Co., Ltd. (1)
5-14-40 Futago, Takatsu-ku, Kawasaki, 213-0002, Kanagawa, Japan
Tel.: (81) 448115661
Web Site: http://www.nanyo.org
Cosmetic Industry Machinery Mfr & Distr
N.A.I.C.S.: 333310

NAMESILO TECHNOLOGIES CORP.
1100 1199 West Hastings Street, Vancouver, V6E 3T5, BC, Canada
Tel.: (604) 644-0072
Web Site: https://www.brisio.com
Year Founded: 1993
URLOF—(OTCIQ)
Rev.: $33,244,995
Assets: $32,018,835
Liabilities: $28,520,036
Net Worth: $3,498,799
Earnings: ($1,561,727)
Fiscal Year-end: 12/31/22
Software Applications
N.A.I.C.S.: 513210

NAMESON HOLDINGS LIMITED
Unit A-C 21/F Block 1 Tai Ping Industrial Centre 57 Ting Kok Road, Tai Po, New Territories, China (Hong Kong)
Tel.: (852) 2 111 8468   Ky
Web Site: http://www.namesonholdings.com
Year Founded: 1990
1982—(HKG)
Rev.: $521,140,079
Assets: $620,942,868
Liabilities: $285,221,600
Net Worth: $335,721,268
Earnings: $35,547,404
Emp.: 14,100
Fiscal Year-end: 03/31/22
Knitwear Product Mfr & Distr
N.A.I.C.S.: 315120
Ting Chung Wong *(Founder, Co-Chm & Co-CEO)*

Subsidiaries:

Huizhou Nanxuan Knitting Factory Limited (1)
No 4 East Road Yunshan, Huizhou, 516000, Guangdong, China
Tel.: (86) 7523316993
Knitwear Product Mfr
N.A.I.C.S.: 315120

NAMHAE CHEMICAL CORP.
1384 Yeosusandan-ro, Yeosu, 59618, Jeollanam-do, Korea (South)
Tel.: (82) 616885500
Web Site: https://www.nhchem.co.kr
Year Founded: 1974
025860—(KRS)
Rev.: $1,664,057,023
Assets: $692,521,554
Liabilities: $292,154,980
Net Worth: $400,366,574
Earnings: $36,248,355
Emp.: 512
Fiscal Year-end: 12/31/22
Agricultural Chemical Mfr
N.A.I.C.S.: 325311
Kim Jeong-Ho *(Mng Dir-Planning)*

NAMHWA INDUSTRIAL CO., LTD.
162 Seoho-ro, Cheonggye-myeon, Muan-gun, Jeollanam-do, Korea (South)
Tel.: (82) 614509025
Web Site: https://www.muangc.co.kr
Year Founded: 1990
111710—(KRS)
Rev.: $23,344,261
Assets: $140,115,580
Liabilities: $10,862,985
Net Worth: $129,252,595
Earnings: $15,833,546
Emp.: 86
Fiscal Year-end: 12/31/22
Golf Club Operator
N.A.I.C.S.: 713910
You ByeongMong *(Dir-Mgmt)*

NAMI CORP.
Unit M2-3 Level M2 The Vertical Podium Avenue 3 No 8 Jalan Kerinchi, Bangsar South City, 59200, Kuala Lumpur, 59200, Malaysia
Tel.: (60) 322424913   NV
Web Site: https://www.nink-cs.com
Year Founded: 2012
NINK—(OTCIQ)
Rev.: $3,916
Assets: $78,985
Liabilities: $4,815,648
Net Worth: ($4,736,663)
Earnings: ($690,350)
Fiscal Year-end: 06/30/21
Mineral Exploration & Mining Services
N.A.I.C.S.: 213115
Calvin Chin *(CEO)*

NAMIBIA ASSET MANAGEMENT LIMITED
1st Floor Millenium House CO Dr AB May Street and Robert Mugabe Ave, PO Box 23329, Windhoek, Namibia
Tel.: (264) 61275700
Web Site: https://www.namasset.com.na
Year Founded: 1996
NAM—(NAM)
Rev.: $4,144,378
Assets: $2,846,148
Liabilities: $1,139,271
Net Worth: $1,706,877
Earnings: $683,169
Fiscal Year-end: 09/30/23
Asset Management Services
N.A.I.C.S.: 523940
Anton Pillay *(Chm)*

NAMIBIA BREWERIES LIMITED
Iscor Street Northern Industrial, Windhoek, Namibia
Tel.: (264) 613204999
Web Site: https://www.nambrew.com
NBS—(NAM)
Rev.: $225,271,525
Assets: $194,712,102
Liabilities: $83,408,296
Net Worth: $111,303,806
Earnings: $268,835,733
Emp.: 852
Fiscal Year-end: 06/30/23
Breweries
N.A.I.C.S.: 312120
Abrie du Plooy *(Mgr-Supply)*

NAMIBIA CRITICAL METALS INC.
Suite 802 Sun Tower 1550 Bedford Highway, Halifax, B4A 1E6, NS, Canada
Tel.: (902) 835-8760   Ca
Web Site: https://www.namibiacriticalmetal.com
Year Founded: 2005
NMREF—(OTCQB)
Rev.: $56,848
Assets: $19,409,052
Liabilities: $1,142,574
Net Worth: $18,266,477
Earnings: ($1,788,618)
Fiscal Year-end: 11/30/23
Metal Mining Services
N.A.I.C.S.: 212290
Donald M. Burton *(Pres & Sec)*

Subsidiaries:

Namibia Rare Earths (Pty) Ltd. (1)
8 Brandberg Street, Windhoek, Namibia (95%)
Tel.: (264) 61225826
Metal Exploration Services
N.A.I.C.S.: 213114

NAMIBIAN STOCK EXCHANGE ASSOCIATION
Robert Moran Ave 4 Interim Burg St, PO Box 2401, Windhoek, Namibia
Tel.: (264) 61227647
Web Site: http://www.nsx.com.na
Sales Range: Less than $1 Million
Emp.: 9
Stock Exchange Services
N.A.I.C.S.: 523210
Manda Steynberg *(Mgr-Ops)*

NAMJESTAJ D.D.
25 Novembar bb, Gradacac, Bosnia & Herzegovina
Tel.: (387) 35817344
Sales Range: Less than $1 Million
Emp.: 187
Furniture Mfr
N.A.I.C.S.: 321999

NAMKWANG ENGINEERING & CONSTRUCTION
5th floor 29 Chungjeong-ro, Seodaemun-gu, Seoul, 134-814, Korea (South)
Tel.: (82) 230110114
Web Site: https://www.namkwang.co.kr
Year Founded: 1947
001260—(KRS)
Rev.: $345,441,040
Assets: $265,322,852
Liabilities: $183,252,258
Net Worth: $82,070,594
Earnings: $14,828,086
Emp.: 544
Fiscal Year-end: 12/31/22
Construction Services
N.A.I.C.S.: 236210
Kyu Min Lim *(CEO)*

NAMLIONG SKYCOSMOS, INC.

Namkwang Engineering & Construction—(Continued)

NAMLIONG SKYCOSMOS, INC.
Unit 1010-15 10/F Tower B New Mandarin Plaza 14 Science Museum Road, Tsim Tsa Tsui, KLN, China (Hong Kong)
Tel.: (852) 98626962 NV
Year Founded: 2005
NLSC—(OTCIQ)
Liabilities: $69,821
Net Worth: ($69,821)
Earnings: ($69,066)
Emp.: 9,600
Fiscal Year-end: 12/31/22
Bio-fuel Mfr
N.A.I.C.S.: 325199
Kwok Wai Davy Chan *(Pres, CEO, CFO, Principal Acctg Officer, Treas & Sec)*

NAMPAK LTD.
Nampak House Hampton Office Park 20 Georgian Crescent East, Bryanston, Sandton, 2191, South Africa
Tel.: (27) 117196300 ZA
Web Site: https://www.nampak.com
NPK—(JSE)
Rev.: $952,381,632
Assets: $1,089,319,242
Liabilities: $776,416,462
Net Worth: $312,902,780
Earnings: $25,750,002
Emp.: 5,766
Fiscal Year-end: 09/30/21
Packaging Products
N.A.I.C.S.: 326199
Peter M. Surgey *(Chm)*

Subsidiaries:

Bullpak Ltd. (1)
Tel.: (254) 202365101
Paper Sack Mfr & Distr
N.A.I.C.S.: 322220

Burcap Plastics (Pty) Ltd. (1)
26 Cypress Dve Glen Anil, 4051, Durban, South Africa
Tel.: (27) 315692783
Plastics Product Mfr
N.A.I.C.S.: 326199

CarnaudMetalbox Zimbabwe Ltd. (1)
35-36 Auckland Road, PO Box ST 128, Southerton, Harare, Zimbabwe (100%)
Tel.: (263) 242620091
Web Site: https://cmb.co.zw
Glass Container Mfr
N.A.I.C.S.: 327213

Crown Cork Company (Mozambique) Lda (1)
Av das Industrias Km 3, 1450, Matola, Mozambique (50%)
Tel.: (258) 21475306
Plastics Product Mfr
N.A.I.C.S.: 326199

Malbak Ltd (1)
4 Pybus Road Wierda Valley, Sandton, 2196, South Africa
Tel.: (27) 113204400
Sales Range: $50-74.9 Million
Emp.: 250
Packaging Products Mfr
N.A.I.C.S.: 322220

Nampak Bevcan Nigeria Ltd. (1)
Area 5, OPIC Industrial Estate, Agbara, Ogun, Nigeria
Tel.: (234) 9038868468
Beverage Can Mfr & Distr
N.A.I.C.S.: 332431
Andrew Loggie *(Mng Dir)*

Nampak Corrugated (Swaziland) Ltd (1)
Matsapha Industrial Site, PO Box 618, Manzini, M200, Eswatini
Tel.: (268) 517 2000
Corrugated Containers Mfr
N.A.I.C.S.: 322211

Paul Backhouse *(Gen Mgr)*

Nampak DivFood Botswana (Pty) Ltd (1)
Pitikwe Area Ponatshego Mokane St 6394, PO Box 1290, Lobatse, Botswana (74%)
Tel.: (267) 5300338
Web Site: http://www.nampak.com
Can Mfr
N.A.I.C.S.: 332431

Nampak Healthcare Darmstadt GmbH (1)
Wittichstr 6, Darmstadt, 64295, Germany
Tel.: (49) 615198080
Sales Range: $25-49.9 Million
Emp.: 40
Packaging Materials Mfr
N.A.I.C.S.: 322220

Nampak International Ltd (1)
7th Floor Victory House Prospect Hill, Douglas, IM1 1EQ, Isle of Man
Tel.: (44) 1624695280
Sales Range: $25-49.9 Million
Emp.: 11
Packaging Products Mfr
N.A.I.C.S.: 322220
David Tocher *(Gen Mgr)*

Nampak Kenya Ltd. (1)
Tel.: (254) 202365101
Metal Packaging Product Mfr & Distr
N.A.I.C.S.: 332999
Ian Randall *(Mng Dir)*

Nampak Liquid Botswana (Pty) Ltd. (1)
Plot 25001 Maakgadigau Street West, Gaborone, Botswana
Tel.: (267) 3187209
Plastic Bottle Distr
N.A.I.C.S.: 424610

Nampak Metal Packaging Ltd. (1)
Nampak House Hampton Office Park 20 Georgian Crescent East, Bryanston, Johannesburg, 2191, South Africa (100%)
Tel.: (27) 117196300
Web Site: http://www.nampak.com
Sales Range: $25-49.9 Million
Emp.: 100
Metal Tank Mfr
N.A.I.C.S.: 332431

Nampak Nigeria Ltd. (1)
PMB 21588 3-7 Metal Box Road, Ogba Industrial Estate, Ikeja, Lagos, Nigeria
Tel.: (234) 8034021878
Packaging Product Mfr & Distr
N.A.I.C.S.: 332431
Terry Wilson *(Mng Dir)*

Nampak Products Ltd. (1)
(100%)
Tel.: (27) 117196300
Web Site: http://www.nampak.com
Sales Range: $1-4.9 Billion
Emp.: 10,000
Plastics Product Mfr
N.A.I.C.S.: 326199

Nampak Tanzania Ltd. (1)
PO Box 618, Dar es Salaam, Tanzania (100%)
Tel.: (255) 222864251
Web Site: https://www.nampak.com
Sales Range: $25-49.9 Million
Emp.: 97
Plastics Product Mfr
N.A.I.C.S.: 326199
Ian Randall *(Mng Dir)*

Nampak Wiegand Glass (Pty) Ltd. (1)
Corner Of Smith And Emmanuel Roads, Private Bag 1, Germiston, 1401, South Africa (100%)
Tel.: (27) 11 865 0000
Web Site: http://www.npwg.co.za
Glass Container Mfr
N.A.I.C.S.: 327213
David Ungerer *(Sr Mgr-Quality Control)*

Nampak Zambia Ltd. (1)
Plot 8214 Mungwi Road, Heavy Industrial Area, Lusaka, Zambia
Tel.: (260) 1242753
Plastic Bottle Mfr & Distr
N.A.I.C.S.: 326160

Stewart Lamb *(Mng Dir)*

NAMSUN ALUMINUM CO., LTD.
288 Nongongjungang-ro Nongongeup, Dalseong-gun, Daegu, 42983, Korea (South)
Tel.: (82) 536105200
Web Site: https://www.namsun.co.kr
Year Founded: 1947
008350—(KRS)
Rev.: $196,152,810
Assets: $307,716,675
Liabilities: $72,526,249
Net Worth: $235,190,427
Earnings: $21,421,665
Emp.: 608
Fiscal Year-end: 12/31/22
Aluminium Products Mfr
N.A.I.C.S.: 332321
Ki-jae Park *(CEO)*

NAMSUNG CORP.
15F 130 Digital-ro, Geumcheon-gu, Seoul, 152-050, Korea (South)
Tel.: (82) 221091550
Web Site: http://www.namsung.com
Year Founded: 1965
004270—(KRS)
Rev.: $75,271,211
Assets: $207,973,683
Liabilities: $116,317,591
Net Worth: $91,656,092
Earnings: $2,448,442
Emp.: 63
Fiscal Year-end: 12/31/22
Electronic Product Distr & Exportation Services
N.A.I.C.S.: 423620
Bong-Soo Yoon *(Chm & CEO)*

NAMSYS INC.
150 King Street West, Toronto, M5H 1J9, ON, Canada
Tel.: (905) 857-9500 ON
Web Site: https://www.namsys.com
NMYSF—(OTCIQ)
Rev.: $4,220,229
Assets: $5,246,015
Liabilities: $515,843
Net Worth: $4,730,172
Earnings: $1,090,843
Emp.: 12
Fiscal Year-end: 10/31/22
Financial Technology Services
N.A.I.C.S.: 541511
K. Barry Sparks *(CEO)*

NAMUGA CO.,LTD
7F U Space 2-B 670 Daewang Pangyo-Ro, Jungwon-gu, Seongnam, Gyeonggi-do, Korea (South)
Tel.: (82) 7070128400
Web Site: https://www.namuga.co.kr
Year Founded: 2004
190510—(KRS)
Rev.: $398,336,067
Assets: $168,047,691
Liabilities: $72,552,078
Net Worth: $95,495,612
Earnings: $24,036,317
Emp.: 123
Fiscal Year-end: 12/31/22
Camera Module Mfr
N.A.I.C.S.: 334220

NAMURA SHIPBUILDING CO., LTD.
1-9 Itachibori 2-chome Nikken Bldg. 8F, Nishi-ku, Osaka, 550-0012, Japan
Tel.: (81) 665433561 JP
Web Site: https://www.namura.co.jp
Year Founded: 1911
7014—(TKS)
Rev.: $892,389,660
Assets: $1,155,368,510

INTERNATIONAL PUBLIC

Liabilities: $627,236,120
Net Worth: $528,132,390
Earnings: $131,895,940
Emp.: 1,055
Fiscal Year-end: 03/31/24
Ship Building Services
N.A.I.C.S.: 336611
Shuu Mukou *(Exec Officer)*

Subsidiaries:

Genkai Technical Engineering Co., Ltd. (1)
5-1 Shioya Kurogawa-cho, Imari, 848-0121, Saga, Japan
Tel.: (81) 955270360
Web Site: https://www.genkaitec.co.jp
Emp.: 84
Shipyard Equipment Mfr
N.A.I.C.S.: 336611

Imari Steel Center Co., Ltd. (1)
5-1 Shioya Kurogawa-cho, Imari, 848-0121, Saga, Japan
Tel.: (81) 955271221
Web Site: http://www.iscsp.co.jp
Ship Building Services
N.A.I.C.S.: 336611

Meiwa Sangyo Co., Ltd. (1)
5-1 Shioya Kurogawa-cho, Imari, Saga, Japan
Tel.: (81) 955272107
Ship Material Distr
N.A.I.C.S.: 423860

N-Wave Vietnam Company Limited (1)
7th Floor Profomilk Plaza 51-51B-53 Vo Van Tan Street, Ward 6 District 3, Ho Chi Minh City, Vietnam
Tel.: (84) 2835200071
Ship Building Services
N.A.I.C.S.: 336611

Namura Engineering Co., Ltd. (1)
5-1 Shioya Kurogawa-cho, Imari, Saga, Japan
Tel.: (81) 955271154
Ship Building Services
N.A.I.C.S.: 336611

Namura Information Systems Co., Ltd. (1)
3448-8 Banre Building 2F Tachibana-cho, Imari, 848-0027, Saga, Japan
Tel.: (81) 955259207
Web Site: https://www.namurainfo.com
Emp.: 159
Software Development Services
N.A.I.C.S.: 541511

Namura Marine Co., Ltd. (1)
5-1 Shioya Kurogawa-cho, Imari, Saga, Japan
Tel.: (81) 955271618
Ship Building Services
N.A.I.C.S.: 336611

Sasebo Heavy Industries Co., Ltd. (1)
1 Tategami-cho, Sasebo, Nagasaki, 857-8501, Japan
Tel.: (81) 956 25 9111
Web Site: http://www.ssk-sasebo.co.jp
Sales Range: $300-349.9 Million
Emp.: 787
Steel Products Mfr & Sales
N.A.I.C.S.: 331110
Mitsushi Mori *(Mng Exec Officer)*

The Hakodate Dock Co., Ltd. (1)
20-3 Benten-cho, Hakodate, 040-8605, Japan
Tel.: (81) 138223170
Web Site: https://www.hakodate-dock.co.jp
Emp.: 427
Ship Building Services
N.A.I.C.S.: 336611
Yoshinori Sekikawa *(Pres)*

NAMUTECH CO., LTD.
Tel.: (82) 232887900
Web Site:
https://www.namutech.co.kr
242040—(KRS)
Rev.: $81,469,600
Assets: $78,408,135

Liabilities: $44,797,098
Net Worth: $33,611,037
Earnings: $479,944
Emp.: 130
Fiscal Year-end: 12/31/22
Information Technology Consulting Services
N.A.I.C.S.: 541512
Chul Jung (CEO)

Subsidiaries:

Acornsoft Co., Ltd. (1)
3Fl NSB 41 Teheran-ro 8-gil, Gangnam-gu, Seoul, Korea (South)
Tel.: (82) 25540301
Web Site: https://www.cocktailcloud.io
Software Development Services
N.A.I.C.S.: 541511

Aspens Co., Ltd. (1)
IT Valley B-dong Indeokwon 40 lmi-ro, Uiwang, Gyeonggi, Korea (South)
Tel.: (82) 16884908
Web Site: https://www.aspens.co.kr
Software Development Services
N.A.I.C.S.: 541511

Cyram Inc. (1)
904 U-Space 2B 670 Daewangpangyo-ro, Bundang-gu, Seongnam, 13494, Gyeanggi, Korea (South)
Tel.: (82) 317398352
Web Site: https://www.cyram.com
Software Development Services
N.A.I.C.S.: 541511

Namu Intelligence Co., Ltd. (1)
150 Donggyecheon-ro I-PLEX Room 207, Dong-gu, Gwangju, 61436, Korea (South)
Tel.: (82) 624172200
Web Site: https://www.namuintelligence.com
Medical Device Mfr
N.A.I.C.S.: 339112

NAMYANG DAIRY PRODUCTS CO., LTD.
240 Dosan-daero, Gangnam-gu, Seoul, Korea (South)
Tel.: (82) 27341305
Web Site:
 htttps://company.namyangi.com
Year Founded: 1964
003920—(KRS)
Rev.: $739,894,225
Assets: $692,032,707
Liabilities: $126,024,090
Net Worth: $566,008,617
Earnings: ($60,165,281)
Emp.: 2,109
Fiscal Year-end: 12/31/22
Dairy Products Mfr
N.A.I.C.S.: 311514
Won-Sik Hong (Chm)

Subsidiaries:

Namyang Dairy Products Co., Ltd. - Cheonan Factory (1)
216 Cheongsu-dong, Cheonan, Chungcheongnam-do, Korea (South)
Tel.: (82) 41 565 0121
Milk Production Services
N.A.I.C.S.: 112120

Namyang Dairy Products Co., Ltd. - Cheonan New Factory (1)
San 45-2 Jisan-ri Mokcheon-eup, Cheonan, Chungcheongnam-do, Korea (South)
Tel.: (82) 41 621 5700
Milk Production Services
N.A.I.C.S.: 112120

Namyang Dairy Products Co., Ltd. - Cheonan Plant 1 (1)
331-55 Gyocheonjisan-gil Mokcheon-eup, Dongnam-gu, Cheonan, Chungcheongnam-do, Korea (South)
Tel.: (82) 416215700
Healthy Dairy Product Mfr
N.A.I.C.S.: 311514

Namyang Dairy Products Co., Ltd. - Cheonan Plant 2 (1)
978 Pungse-ro, Dongnam-gu, Cheonan, Chungcheongnam-do, Korea (South)

Tel.: (82) 415650121
Healthy Dairy Product Mfr
N.A.I.C.S.: 311514

Namyang Dairy Products Co., Ltd. - Gongju Factory (1)
160 Bongan-ri Janggi-myeon, Gongju, Chungcheongnam-do, Korea (South)
Tel.: (82) 41 857 1551
Milk Production Services
N.A.I.C.S.: 112120

Namyang Dairy Products Co., Ltd. - Gyeongju Factory (1)
820 Yonggang-dong, Gyeongju, Gyeongsangbuk-do, Korea (South)
Tel.: (82) 54 776 5011
Milk Production Services
N.A.I.C.S.: 112120

Namyang Dairy Products Co., Ltd. - Gyeongju Plant (1)
4443-7 Saneop-ro, Gyeongju, Gyeongsangbuk-do, Korea (South)
Tel.: (82) 547765011
Healthy Dairy Product Mfr
N.A.I.C.S.: 311514

Namyang Dairy Products Co., Ltd. - Honam Factory (1)
278 Chongok-ri Geumcheon-myeon, Naju, Jeollanam-do, Korea (South)
Tel.: (82) 61 339 7500
Milk Production Services
N.A.I.C.S.: 112120

Namyang Dairy Products Co., Ltd. - Naju Plant (1)
5785 Yeongsan-ro, Geumcheon-myeon, Naju, Jeollanam-do, Korea (South)
Tel.: (82) 613397500
Healthy Dairy Product Mfr
N.A.I.C.S.: 311514

Namyang Dairy Products Co., Ltd. - Sejong Plant (1)
836-11 Janggi-ro, Janggun-myeon, Sejong, Korea (South)
Tel.: (82) 4485715515
Healthy Dairy Product Mfr
N.A.I.C.S.: 311514

NAMYONG TERMINAL PUBLIC COMPANY LIMITED
1168/52 Lumpini Tower 19th Fl Rama IV Road, Thungmahamek Sathorn, Bangkok, 10120, Thailand
Tel.: (66) 26797357
Web Site:
 https://www.namyongterminal.com
NYT—(THA)
Rev.: $51,450,272
Assets: $202,972,628
Liabilities: $102,400,354
Net Worth: $100,572,274
Earnings: $12,756,942
Emp.: 85
Fiscal Year-end: 12/31/23
Wharf Operations
N.A.I.C.S.: 488310
Borwornsak Uwanno (Chm)

Subsidiaries:

The Seahorse Ferries Co., Ltd. (1)
1168/76 Lumpini Tower 26th Floor Rama IV Road, Thungmahamek Sathorn, Bangkok, 10120, Thailand
Tel.: (66) 938458278
Web Site: https://www.theseahorseferry.com
Marine Transportation Services
N.A.I.C.S.: 926120

The Seahorse Ferry Co., Ltd. (1)
1168/76 26th Floor Lumpini Tower Rama 4 Road, Thungmahamek Sathorn, Bangkok, 10120, Thailand
Tel.: (66) 858426018
Web Site: https://www.seahorse-ferries.com
Marine Transportation Services
N.A.I.C.S.: 926120

NAN HAI CORPORATION LIMITED
12/F The Octagon No 6 Sha Tsui Road, Tsuen Wan, New Territories, China (Hong Kong)
Tel.: (852) 25268802
Web Site: http://en.nanhaicorp.com
Year Founded: 1990
0680—(HKG)
Rev.: $1,291,188,212
Assets: $5,613,195,154
Liabilities: $5,184,378,444
Net Worth: $428,816,710
Earnings: ($326,284,704)
Emp.: 15,899
Fiscal Year-end: 12/31/20
Property Development
N.A.I.C.S.: 531312
Rong Liu (CEO)

Subsidiaries:

CE Holdings Limited (1)
c/o Belmont-Trust Limited - Belmont Chambers, Road Town, Virgin Islands (British) (70%)
Tel.: (284) 4945800
Holding Company
N.A.I.C.S.: 551112

Subsidiary (Non-US):

C&E Canada, Inc (2)
50 Bloor St W Unit C06, M4W 3L8, Toronto, ON, Canada (100%)
Tel.: (416) 309-1921
Web Site: http://www.crabtree-evelyn.ca
Cosmetic & Skin Care Mfr
N.A.I.C.S.: 456120

Crabtree & Evelyn (HK) LTD. (2)
Shop M-16 Vcity MTR Floor 83 Rural Committee Road, Tuen Mun, China (Hong Kong) (100%)
Tel.: (852) 24993330
Web Site: http://www.crabtree-evelyn.com.hk
Store Retailers
N.A.I.C.S.: 459999

Crabtree & Evelyn (Malaysia) Sdn Bhd (2)
G080 Mid Valley Megamall Lingkaran Shed Putra, Kuala Lumpur City Centre, Kuala Lumpur, 50200, Malaysia (100%)
Tel.: (60) 2284 9482
Web Site: http://www.crabtree-evelyn.com
Skin Care & Home Fragrances Products Mfr
N.A.I.C.S.: 423990

Crabtree & Evelyn (Overseas) Ltd (2)
15 Bonhill St, Shoreditch, London, EC2P 2EA, United Kingdom
Tel.: (44) 800 046 7914
Web Site: http://www.crabtree-evelyn.co.uk
Personal Care Product Distr
N.A.I.C.S.: 424210

Crabtree & Evelyn (Singapore) Pte Ltd (2)
10 Anson Road 06-17 International Plaza, Singapore, 079903, Singapore (100%)
Tel.: (65) 67351611
Web Site: http://www.crabtree-evelyn.com.sg
Cosmetics & SKin care Products Mfr
N.A.I.C.S.: 456120

Crabtree & Evelyn Australia Pty Ltd (2)
42 Fairchild St, Heatherton, Melbourne, 3202, VIC, Australia (100%)
Tel.: (61) 385511000
Web Site: http://www.crabtree-evelyn.com.au
Online Skincare Products Mfr
N.A.I.C.S.: 423990

Crabtree & Evelyn Austria GmbH (2)
Karntnerring 11-13, 1010, Vienna, Austria (100%)
Tel.: (43) 15130380
Web Site: http://www.crabtree-evelyn.eu
Skin Care Product Mfr
N.A.I.C.S.: 424990

Crabtree & Evelyn Deutschland GmbH (2)
Robert Bosch Strasse 1, Landsberg, 86899, Landsberg am Lech, Germany (100%)
Tel.: (49) 819192340
Web Site: http://www.crabtree-evelyn.eu
Skin Care & Home Fragrances Products Mfr
N.A.I.C.S.: 423990

Subsidiary (US):

Crabtree & Evelyn, Ltd. (2)
102 Peake Brook Rd, Woodstock, CT 06281
Tel.: (860) 928-2761
Web Site: http://www.crabtree-evelyn.com
Online Cosmetics, Beauty Supplies & Perfume Retailer
N.A.I.C.S.: 456120
Mark Baker (Controller)

Chinese Media Net, Inc. (1)
9 Park Pl 2nd Fl, Great Neck, NY 11021-5030
Tel.: (516) 466-8626
Web Site: http://www.dwnews.com
Online Newspaper Publishing Services
N.A.I.C.S.: 513110

Dadi Entertainment Limited (1)
39th Fl New World Tower 1 16-18 Queens Rd, Central, China (Hong Kong)
Tel.: (852) 9257 3619
Movie Production & Distribution Services
N.A.I.C.S.: 512110

HK01 Company Limited (1)
11/F The Octagon 6 Sha Tsui Road New Territories, Tsuen Wan, China (Hong Kong)
Tel.: (852) 21170101
Culture & Media Services
N.A.I.C.S.: 541890

NAN JUEN INTERNATIONAL CO., LTD.
6th Floor No 202 Xingfu Road, Taoyuan District, Taoyuan, 330063, Taiwan
Tel.: (886) 33642777
Year Founded: 1977
6584—(TPE)
Rev.: $62,493,293
Assets: $109,850,639
Liabilities: $60,722,196
Net Worth: $49,128,443
Earnings: $4,085,202
Fiscal Year-end: 12/31/22
Building Component Mfr
N.A.I.C.S.: 332311

NAN LIU ENTERPRISES CO., LTD.
No 699 Silin Road, Yanchao District, Kaohsiung, Taiwan
Tel.: (886) 76116616
Web Site:
 .https://www.nanliugroup.com
Year Founded: 1978
6504—(TAI)
Rev.: $202,068,078
Assets: $339,587,809
Liabilities: $225,064,055
Net Worth: $114,523,754
Earnings: $3,920,043
Emp.: 922
Fiscal Year-end: 12/31/23
Sanitary Textile Materials & Other Personal Care Products Mfr
N.A.I.C.S.: 322291
Chin-San Huang (Founder & Chm)

NAN NAN RESOURCES ENTERPRISE LIMITED
8/F Tower 2 Admiralty Centre 18 Harcourt Road, Admiralty, Hong Kong, China (Hong Kong)
Tel.: (852) 3 845 5790   BM
Web Site:
 http://www.nannanlisted.com
1229—(HKG)
Rev.: $38,725,084
Assets: $79,486,505
Liabilities: $50,570,607
Net Worth: $28,915,897

NAN NAN RESOURCES ENTERPRISE LIMITED

Nan Nan Resources Enterprise Limited—(Continued)
Earnings: $8,512,680
Emp.: 140
Fiscal Year-end: 03/31/22
Coal Investment Services
N.A.I.C.S.: 523999
Man Fai Kwan (Chm & Mng Dir)

NAN PAO RESINS CHEMICAL CO., LTD.
No12 Nanhaipu Nanhai Vil, Xigang Dist, T'ainan, 723, Taiwan
Tel.: (886) 679528018   TW
Web Site:
  http://www.adhesivegluemaker.com
Year Founded: 1961
Sales Range: $250-299.9 Million
Emp.: 450
Synthetic Resin Mfr
N.A.I.C.S.: 325211
Cheng-Hsien Wu (Chm)

Subsidiaries:

Dairen Chemical Corporation (1)
9th Fl 301 Song Kiang Rd, Taipei, 104, Taiwan
Tel.: (886) 225020238
Web Site: http://www.dcc.com.tw
Sales Range: $25-49.9 Million
Emp.: 90
Chemical Products
N.A.I.C.S.: 325998
Suhon Lin (Chm)

Subsidiary (Non-US):

Dairen Chemical (Jiangsu) Co., Ltd. (2)
1 Dalian Rd, Chemical Industry Park, Yangzhou, 211900, Jiangsu, China **(100%)**
Tel.: (86) 51483268888
Web Site: http://www.dcc.com.tw
Sales Range: $50-74.9 Million
Chemicals Mfr
N.A.I.C.S.: 325998

Dairen Chemical (M) Sdn. Bhd. (2)
Plo 18 Tanjung Langsat Industrial Est, Mukim Sungai Tiram Pasir Gudan, Johor, 81700, Malaysia **(100%)**
Tel.: (60) 72565800
Web Site: http://www.dcc.com.tw
Sales Range: $25-49.9 Million
Emp.: 70
Chemicals Mfr
N.A.I.C.S.: 325998
Jong Yuh Lih (Mng Dir)

Fuqing Nan Pao Resins Co., Ltd (1)
Hong Kuan Industry Village, Xi To, Fuqing, Fu Jian, China
Tel.: (86) 591 8529 1391
Synthetic Resin & Adhesive Mfr
N.A.I.C.S.: 325520

Nan Pao Electronic Material Company (1)
No 510 Zhongshan Rd, Xigang Dist, T'ainan, 723, Taiwan
Tel.: (886) 6 7956032
Synthetic Resin & Adhesive Mfr
N.A.I.C.S.: 325520

Nan Pao Resins (China) Co., Ltd (1)
No 600 Kunhia Road Kunshan Economic & Technological Zone, Kunshan, Jiangsu, China
Tel.: (86) 512 57708888
Web Site: http://www.nanpao.net
Adhesive Mfr
N.A.I.C.S.: 325520

Nan Pao Resins (Dong-Guan) Co., Ltd (1)
Yue Yuen Industrial Estate, HuangJiang, Dongguan, GuangDong, China
Tel.: (86) 769 8366 4815
Web Site: http://www.nanpao.com.cn
Synthetic Resin & Adhesive Mfr
N.A.I.C.S.: 325520

Nan Pao Resins (Fo Shan) Co., Ltd (1)
No 12 Kohler Avenue, Leping Sanshui, Foshan, GuangDong, China
Tel.: (86) 757 87393000
Synthetic Resin & Adhesive Mfr
N.A.I.C.S.: 325520

Nan Pao Resins (Vietnam) Co., Ltd (1)
No 10 Thong Nhat Road Song Than 2 Industrial Park, Di An, Binh Duong, Vietnam
Tel.: (84) 65 03790378
Synthetic Resin & Adhesive Mfr
N.A.I.C.S.: 325520

Nan Pao Resins Chemical Phils., Inc (1)
6/F Unit 606 Pagel Bldg 1215 Acaia St Madrigal Business Park, Ayala Alabang, Muntinlupa, 1780, Philippines
Tel.: (63) 2 8224098
Synthetic Resin & Adhesive Mfr
N.A.I.C.S.: 325520

Nan Pao Resins India Pvt Ltd. (1)
204 Abhishek off New Link Road, Andheri W, Mumbai, 400053, India
Tel.: (91) 22 67418500
Synthetic Resin & Adhesive Mfr
N.A.I.C.S.: 325520
Mukesh Nautiyal (Head-Bus Mktg & Sls)

PT Indo Nan Pao Resins Chemical Co., Ltd. (1)
JL Pajajaran Raya No 44, Jatiuwung, Tangerang, Indonesia
Tel.: (62) 21 5918810
Synthetic Resin & Adhesive Mfr
N.A.I.C.S.: 325520

Thai Nan Pao Resins Chemical., Ltd (1)
412 Kor Soi 1c Bangpoo Industrial Tumbon Preaksa, Amphur Muang, Samut Prakan, 10280, Thailand
Tel.: (66) 2 323 2761
Synthetic Resin & Adhesive Mfr
N.A.I.C.S.: 325520
Pari Lai (Deputy Mgr-Mktg)

NAN TSAN CO., LTD.
23rd Floor No 1086 Zhongzheng Road, Taoyuan District, Taoyuan, 330, Taiwan
Tel.: (886) 33253568
Year Founded: 1974
4712—(TPE)
Rev.: $74,921
Assets: $2,461,199
Liabilities: $411,884
Net Worth: $2,049,315
Earnings: ($393,015)
Fiscal Year-end: 12/31/23
Seafood Distr
N.A.I.C.S.: 445250

NAN YANG DYEING & FINISHING CO., LTD.
No 233 Section 3 Nanshan Road, Shanjiao Village Luzhu District, Taoyuan, 338, Taiwan
Tel.: (886) 225940361
Web Site: https://www.nydf.com.tw
Year Founded: 1964
1410—(TAI)
Rev.: $7,266,850
Assets: $43,578,925
Liabilities: $7,156,153
Net Worth: $36,422,772
Earnings: $429,020
Fiscal Year-end: 12/31/23
Fabrication Dyeing & Pigment Mfr
N.A.I.C.S.: 325130
Ho Chun (Chm & Pres)

NANAIMO CHRYSLER LTD.
4170 Wellington Road, Nanaimo, V9T 2H3, BC, Canada
Tel.: (250) 758-1191
Web Site:
  http://www.nanaimochrysler.com
Year Founded: 1975
Rev.: $18,200,000
Emp.: 50
New & Used Car Dealers
N.A.I.C.S.: 441110

Graeme McWhinnie (Mgr-Parts)

NANALYSIS SCIENTIFIC CORP.
Bay 1 4600 5 Street NE, Calgary, T2E 7C3, AB, Canada
Tel.: (403) 769-9499
Web Site: https://www.nanalysis.com
Year Founded: 2019
NSCIF—(OTCQX)
Rev.: $6,159,673
Assets: $18,766,115
Liabilities: $7,545,091
Net Worth: $11,221,024
Earnings: ($2,877,226)
Fiscal Year-end: 12/31/20
Scientific Instrument Mfr
N.A.I.C.S.: 334517
Sean Krakiwsky (Founder, Pres & CEO)

Subsidiaries:

K'(Prime) Technologies Inc. (1)
Unit 105 90 Freeport Blvd NE, Calgary, T3J 5J9, AB, Canada
Tel.: (403) 226-5897
Web Site: http://www.kprime.net
Laboratory Equipment Supplier & Services
N.A.I.C.S.: 423450
Kham Lin (Pres)

Nanalysis Corp. (1)
Bay 1 4600 5th Street NE, Calgary, T2E 7C3, AB, Canada
Tel.: (403) 769-9499
Electronic Medical Device Mfr & Distr
N.A.I.C.S.: 334510

Nanalysis GmbH (1)
HaydnPlatz 3, 76133, Karlsruhe, Germany
Tel.: (49) 15901921291
Electrical & Electronic Equipment Mfr
N.A.I.C.S.: 336320

RS2D S.A.S. (1)
13 rue Vauban, 67450, Mundolsheim, France
Tel.: (33) 390405400
Web Site: https://rs2d.com
Emp.: 200
Software Development Services
N.A.I.C.S.: 541511

NANAVATI VENTURES LIMITED
S 414 OM Plaza Adarsh App CPHS, Vijalpor Jalalpore, Navsari, 396445, India
Tel.: (91) 9316691337
Web Site:
  https://www.nventures.co.in
Year Founded: 2010
543522—(BOM)
Rev.: $1,923,830
Assets: $1,029,435
Liabilities: $15,107
Net Worth: $1,014,328
Earnings: $10,263
Emp.: 8
Fiscal Year-end: 03/31/23
Investment Management Service
N.A.I.C.S.: 523999

NANCAL TECHNOLOGY CO., LTD.
Zhongguancun Internet Innovation Center, Building 5 No 10 Xibeiwang East Road Haidian District, Beijing, 100193, Haidian, China
Tel.: (86) 1058741908
Web Site: https://www.nancal.com
Year Founded: 2006
603859—(SHG)
Rev.: $173,458,851
Assets: $439,030,926
Liabilities: $80,875,862
Net Worth: $358,155,065
Earnings: $27,830,706
Emp.: 600
Fiscal Year-end: 12/31/22

INTERNATIONAL PUBLIC

Energy Management System Services
N.A.I.C.S.: 926110
Jun Zu (Chm)

NANCY K. BROWN (NKB) AESTHETICS, INC.
46 Gariepy Crescent NW, Edmonton, T6M 1A1, AB, Canada
Tel.: (780) 484-4197
Web Site:
  http://www.nancykbrown.com
Year Founded: 1991
Rev.: $17,002,568
Emp.: 100
Beauty Equipment & Cosmetics Supplier
N.A.I.C.S.: 456120

NANCY SERVICES AUTOMOBILES NASA
28 Av Du 69e Rgt D Infanterie, 54270, Nancy, Meurthe Et Moselle, France
Tel.: (33) 383214343
Web Site: http://wwww.groupe-ph.com
Rev.: $21,100,000
Emp.: 27
Automobile Dealership
N.A.I.C.S.: 441110
Alexandre Berron (Gen Mgr)

NANDANI CREATION LTD.
G-13 Kartarpura Ind Area Bais Godam, Jaipur, 302006, Rajasthan, India
Tel.: (91) 1414037596
Web Site:
  https://www.nandanicreation.com
Year Founded: 2012
NANDANI—(NSE)
Rev.: $5,939,356
Assets: $5,772,604
Liabilities: $2,296,025
Net Worth: $3,476,578
Earnings: $13,165
Emp.: 91
Fiscal Year-end: 03/31/23
Clothing Mfr
N.A.I.C.S.: 315990
Anuj Mundhra (CEO)

NANDO'S GROUP HOLDINGS, LTD.
64 3rd Avenue, Inanda, Sandton, 2196, South Africa
Tel.: (27) 11 442 4349
Web Site: http://www.nandos.co.za
Year Founded: 1987
Sales Range: $75-99.9 Million
Emp.: 600
Fast Food Restaurants Operator & Franchiser
N.A.I.C.S.: 722513
David P. Niven (CEO)

NANEXA AB
Virdings Alle 2, 75450, Uppsala, Sweden
Tel.: (46) 18100300
Web Site: https://www.nanexa.com
Year Founded: 2007
NANEXA—(DEU)
Pharmaceuticals Product Mfr
N.A.I.C.S.: 325412
David Westberg (CEO)

NANFANG BLACK SESAME GROUP CO., LTD.
Nanfang Food Building No 36 Shuangyong Rd Qingxiu Area, Nanning, 530000, Guangxi, China
Tel.: (86) 7715672331
Web Site:
  https://www.nanfangfood.com

AND PRIVATE COMPANIES — NANJING CENTRAL EMPORIUM (GROUP) STOCKS CO., LTD.

Year Founded: 1984
000716—(SSE)
Rev.: $423,423,936
Assets: $657,331,740
Liabilities: $302,692,572
Net Worth: $354,639,168
Earnings: ($19,710,756)
Fiscal Year-end: 12/31/22
Food Products Mfr
N.A.I.C.S.: 311999
Qingwen Wei *(Chm)*

NANFANG COMMUNICATION HOLDINGS LIMITED
1 Cencun Road Luoyang Town Wujin District, Changzhou, Jiangsu, China
Tel.: (86) 51988798288 Ky
Web Site: http://www.jsnfgroup.com
1617—(HKG)
Rev.: $88,972,182
Assets: $208,391,929
Liabilities: $99,883,789
Net Worth: $108,508,140
Earnings: ($1,137,661)
Emp.: 320
Fiscal Year-end: 12/31/22
Fiber Optic Cable Mfr & Distr
N.A.I.C.S.: 335921
Ming Shi *(CEO)*

NANFANG ZHONGJIN ENVIRONMENT CO., LTD.
No 46 Renhe Avenue Renhe Street, Yuhang District, Hangzhou, 310015, Zhejiang, China
Tel.: (86) 57186397850
Web Site: http://www.nfzje.com
Year Founded: 1991
300145—(CHIN)
Rev.: $765,298,545
Assets: $1,137,895,797
Liabilities: $778,306,338
Net Worth: $359,589,458
Earnings: $28,251,862
Fiscal Year-end: 12/31/23
Pumps & Pumping Equipment Mfr
N.A.I.C.S.: 333914
Hang Jun *(Chm)*

Subsidiaries:

CNP Pumps India Pvt. Ltd. (1)
B-5 502 TJSB House Sambhav IT Park Behind Aplab Company, Wagle Indl Esate MIDC, Thane, India
Tel.: (91) 2225818400
Web Site: http://www.cnpindia.com
Pump Mfr & Distr
N.A.I.C.S.: 333996
Shardul Patel *(Engr-Project & Sls)*

PT. Southern Indonesia (1)
Jl Kartini Raya 64-A3 Lantai 6 Kel Kartini Kec Sawah Besar, Jakarta Pusat, 10750, Indonesia
Tel.: (62) 2162200955
Web Site:
 https://www.southernindonesia.com
Pump Distr
N.A.I.C.S.: 423830
Asmawardy H. C. Siagian *(Coord-Sls & Mktg)*

NANFENG VENTILATOR CO., LTD.-A
Shishan Road Nanhai District, Foshan, 528225, Guangdong, China
Tel.: (86) 75786693188
Web Site: http://www.ntfan.com
Year Founded: 1988
300004—(CHIN)
Rev.: $64,603,529
Assets: $279,387,229
Liabilities: $43,182,892
Net Worth: $236,204,337
Earnings: ($2,963,794)
Fiscal Year-end: 12/31/23
Air Treatment System Mfr
N.A.I.C.S.: 334512

Subsidiaries:

Foshan Nanfang-RITCO Energy Clean Technology Co., Ltd. (1)
Nanfang Ventilator Co Ltd Shi Southern Section Third Ring West Rd, Xiaotang Shishan Town Nanhai District, Foshan, Guangdong, China
Tel.: (86) 75781006598
Web Site: https://www.nanfang-ritco.com
Electrostatic Precipitator Mfr
N.A.I.C.S.: 333413

NANG KUANG PHARMACEUTICAL CO., LTD.
No 1001 Zhongshan Rd, Xinhua Dist, Tainan City, 71243, Taiwan
Tel.: (886) 65984121
Web Site:
 http://www.nangkuang.com.tw
Year Founded: 1963
1752—(TAI)
Rev.: $60,672,451
Assets: $112,076,572
Liabilities: $36,691,868
Net Worth: $75,384,704
Earnings: $11,005,816
Emp.: 600
Fiscal Year-end: 12/31/22
Pharmaceuticals Product Mfr
N.A.I.C.S.: 325412
Yu-Bei Wang *(Gen Mgr)*

NANHUA BIO-MEDICINE CO., LTD.
3F Building B1 Lugu Science Innovation and Pioneering Park No 1698, Yuelu West Avenue High-tech Zone, Changsha, 410205, Hunan, China
Tel.: (86) 73185810285
Web Site: http://www.ccidmedia.com
Year Founded: 1991
000504—(SSE)
Rev.: $28,129,140
Assets: $77,649,624
Liabilities: $66,434,472
Net Worth: $11,215,152
Earnings: ($1,781,676)
Fiscal Year-end: 12/31/22
Biotechnology Research & Development Services
N.A.I.C.S.: 541714
Yang Yun *(Chm)*

NANHUA FUTURES CO., LTD.
Rooms 301 401 501 701 901 1001 1101 and 1201 Hengdian Building, Shangcheng District, Hangzhou, 310000, Zhejiang, China
Tel.: (86) 57187833551
Web Site: http://www.nanhua.net
Year Founded: 1996
603093—(SHG)
Rev.: $957,910,997
Assets: $4,800,161,616
Liabilities: $4,333,325,551
Net Worth: $466,836,065
Earnings: $34,546,782
Emp.: 1,000
Fiscal Year-end: 12/31/22
Investment Brokerage Services
N.A.I.C.S.: 524210
Xufeng Luo *(Chm)*

Subsidiaries:

HGNH International Financial (Singapore) Pte. Ltd. (1)
4 Shenton Way 18-04 SGX Centre 2, Singapore, 068807, Singapore
Tel.: (65) 69329800
Web Site: http://www.henghua.sg
Financial Banking Services
N.A.I.C.S.: 523150

Nanhua Financial UK Co. Limited (1)
3rd Floor 2 Royal Exchange Buildings, London, EC3V 3LF, United Kingdom
Tel.: (44) 2037466466

Web Site: http://www.nanhuafinancial.co.uk
Financial Services
N.A.I.C.S.: 523999

NANHUA INSTRUMENTS CO., LTD.
1 Kehong Rd, Guicheng Nanhai District, Foshan, 528251, Guangdong, China
Tel.: (86) 75786718778
Web Site:
 https://www.nanhua.com.cn
Year Founded: 1996
300417—(CHIN)
Rev.: $17,988,048
Assets: $69,402,528
Liabilities: $4,471,740
Net Worth: $64,930,788
Earnings: ($4,651,452)
Fiscal Year-end: 12/31/22
Analytical Instrument Mfr
N.A.I.C.S.: 334519
Yaoguang Yang *(Chm)*

NANJI E-COMMERCE CO., LTD.
No 22 Wulong Road Shengze town, Wujiang, Jiangsu, China
Tel.: (86) 512 63551037
Year Founded: 1958
Sales Range: $250-299.9 Million
Computer Services
N.A.I.C.S.: 541519
Yiming Gu *(Gen Mgr)*

NANJING AOLIAN AE & EA CO., LTD.
No 16 Debang Road Dongshanqiao Industrial Zone Moling Street, Jiangning District, Nanjing, 211153, China
Tel.: (86) 2552745422
Web Site: https://www.njaolian.com
Year Founded: 2001
300585—(CHIN)
Rev.: $68,767,787
Assets: $134,416,042
Liabilities: $31,680,813
Net Worth: $102,735,229
Earnings: $735,829
Fiscal Year-end: 12/31/23
Automotive Electronic Parts Mfr & Distr
N.A.I.C.S.: 336320
Guangshui Chen *(Chm)*

NANJING BAOSE CO., LTD.
No 15 Jingming Street Jiangning Binjiang Economic Development Zone, Nanjing, 211178, Jiangsu, China
Tel.: (86) 2552104438
Web Site: https://www.baose.com
Year Founded: 1994
300402—(CHIN)
Rev.: $197,850,276
Assets: $299,894,400
Liabilities: $205,284,456
Net Worth: $94,609,944
Earnings: $8,475,948
Emp.: 940
Fiscal Year-end: 12/31/22
Pressure Vessels & Pipe fittings Mfr
N.A.I.C.S.: 332919
Jianguo Liu *(Deputy Gen Mgr)*

NANJING BESTWAY INTELLIGENT CONTROL TECHNOLOGY CO., LTD.
No 50 Baoxiang Road, Jiangning Binjiang Economic Development Zone, Nanjing, 211161, Jiangsu, China
Tel.: (86) 2586127716
Web Site: https://www.njbestway.com
Year Founded: 2007
301195—(SSE)
Rev.: $88,581,426
Assets: $127,997,762

Liabilities: $51,985,685
Net Worth: $76,012,077
Earnings: $22,586,218
Fiscal Year-end: 12/31/21
Software Development Services
N.A.I.C.S.: 541511

NANJING BUSINESS AND TOURISM CORP., LTD.
No 77 Yunnan North Road, Nanjing, 210006, China
Tel.: (86) 2583306789 CN
Web Site: https://www.nantex.com.cn
Year Founded: 1978
600250—(SHG)
Rev.: $115,411,440
Assets: $238,870,102
Liabilities: $136,143,002
Net Worth: $102,727,100
Earnings: $5,926,860
Emp.: 320
Fiscal Year-end: 12/31/22
Textile, Garments & Silk Mfr; Multi-Industry Business Developer
N.A.I.C.S.: 313210
Shen Ying *(Chm, Sec-Party & Gen Mgr)*

Subsidiaries:

Jiangyin Nantai Home Textiles Corp. Ltd. (1)
No 3886 ZhenCheng Road, Huangtu town, Jiangyin, Jiangsu, China
Tel.: (86) 51086659119
Web Site: http://www.jynantai.com
Emp.: 1,600
Curtain Mfr
N.A.I.C.S.: 314120

Nanjing Real Pharmaceutical Co Ltd. (1)
17th Fl Tower Skandia Nanjing Hexi St, Nanjing, 210009, Jiangsu, China
Tel.: (86) 25 8328 2573
Web Site: http://www.realph.com
Pharmaceutical Research, Production, Distr, Import/Export Business & Technology Services
N.A.I.C.S.: 325412

NANJING CANATAL DATACENTRE ENVIRONMENTAL TECH CO., LTD.
No 88 Suyuan Avenue, Jiangning Economic and Technological Development Zone, Nanjing, 211111, Jiangsu, China
Tel.: (86) 2584916666
Web Site:
 https://www.canatal.com.cn
Year Founded: 2003
603912—(SHG)
Rev.: $87,715,532
Assets: $283,626,224
Liabilities: $143,020,061
Net Worth: $140,606,163
Earnings: $5,124,909
Fiscal Year-end: 12/31/22
Refrigeration Equipment Mfr & Distr
N.A.I.C.S.: 333415
He Genlin *(Chm)*

NANJING CENTRAL EMPORIUM (GROUP) STOCKS CO., LTD.
No 10 Yurun Road, Jianye District, Nanjing, 210041, Jiangsu, China
Tel.: (86) 2566008022 CN
Web Site: http://www.600280.com
Year Founded: 1991
600280—(SHG)
Rev.: $350,574,967
Assets: $1,717,919,265
Liabilities: $1,584,265,569
Net Worth: $133,653,696
Earnings: ($7,504,380)
Fiscal Year-end: 12/31/22

NANJING CENTRAL EMPORIUM (GROUP) STOCKS CO., LTD.

Nanjing Central Emporium (Group) Stocks Co., Ltd.—(Continued)
Commodity Contracts Dealing Services
N.A.I.C.S.: 523160
Zhu Jun *(Chm, Pres & Gen Mgr)*

NANJING CHEMICAL FIBRE CO., LTD.
Building 9 Jinjihuizhiyuan No 66 Yapeng Road Jiangxinzhou Street, Jianye District, Nanjing, 210019, Jiangsu, China
Tel.: (86) 2584208005
Web Site: http://www.ncfc.cn
Year Founded: 1992
600889—(SHG)
Rev.: $72,992,640
Assets: $270,076,543
Liabilities: $111,059,868
Net Worth: $159,016,675
Earnings: ($24,811,446)
Fiscal Year-end: 12/31/22
Chemical Fiber Mfr & Distr
N.A.I.C.S.: 313110
Chen Jianjun *(Chm)*

NANJING CHERVON AUTO PRECISION TECHNOLOGY CO., LTD.
No 159 Jiangjun Avenue Moling Street, Jiangning District Jiangning Development Zone, Nanjing, 210006, China
Tel.: (86) 2584998888
Web Site:
https://www.chervonauto.com
Year Founded: 2012
603982—(SHG)
Rev.: $244,933,514
Assets: $883,263,055
Liabilities: $482,775,621
Net Worth: $400,487,434
Earnings: ($21,670,066)
Fiscal Year-end: 12/31/22
Automobile Parts Mfr
N.A.I.C.S.: 336390
Longquan Pan *(Chm)*

NANJING CHIXIA DEVELOPMENT CO., LTD.
No 251 Heyan Road, Qixia District, Nanjing, 210046, Jiangsu, China
Tel.: (86) 2585600533
Web Site: http://www.chixia.com
Year Founded: 1999
600533—(SHG)
Rev.: $489,715,848
Assets: $3,547,485,624
Liabilities: $2,855,722,557
Net Worth: $691,763,067
Earnings: $56,646,333
Fiscal Year-end: 12/31/21
Real Estate Management Services
N.A.I.C.S.: 531390
Jinsong Jiang *(Chm & Pres)*

NANJING DEVELOP ADVANCED MANUFACTURING CO., LTD.
No 8 Dixi Road, Jiangbei New District, Nanjing, 210046, Jiangsu, China
Tel.: (86) 2568553220
Web Site: https://www.nj-develop.com
Year Founded: 2009
688377—(SHG)
Rev.: $137,987,717
Assets: $323,111,155
Liabilities: $95,344,306
Net Worth: $227,766,848
Earnings: $17,053,349
Fiscal Year-end: 12/31/22
Oil & Gas Equipment Mfr
N.A.I.C.S.: 333132
Li Zhang *(Chm & Gen Mgr)*

NANJING ESTUN AUTOMATION CO., LTD.
1888 Jiyin Avenue, Jiangning District, Nanjing, 211106, Jiangsu, China
Tel.: (86) 2552785597
Web Site: https://www.estun.com
Year Founded: 1993
002747—(SSE)
Rev.: $544,861,301
Assets: $1,158,390,446
Liabilities: $727,375,601
Net Worth: $431,014,845
Earnings: $23,348,997
Emp.: 920
Fiscal Year-end: 12/31/22
Metal Forming & Electro-Hydraulic Robotic Machines Mfr
N.A.I.C.S.: 333515
Wu Bo *(Chm)*

Subsidiaries:

ESTUN Industrial Technology Europe S.r.l.   (1)
Via Alessandro Volta 39, 21010, Cardano al Campo, VA, Italy
Tel.: (39) 0331716000
Web Site: http://www.estuneurope.eu
Automation Product Mfr
N.A.I.C.S.: 334512

Estun Automation Co., Ltd.   (1)
16 shuige Road Jiangning Development Zone, Nanjing, China
Tel.: (86) 2558328505
Motion Controller Mfr
N.A.I.C.S.: 335314

M.A.i. GmbH & Co. KG   (1)
Hummendorfer Strasse 74, 96317, Kronach, Germany
Tel.: (49) 9261910000
Web Site: http://www.m-a-i.de
Industrial Automation Equipments Mfr
N.A.I.C.S.: 333511

Pamoco SpA   (1)
Via R Lombardi 19/6, 20153, Milan, Italy
Tel.: (39) 023456091
Web Site: http://www.pamoco.it
Automation Product Mfr
N.A.I.C.S.: 334512

Trio Motion Technology LLC   (1)
187 Northpointe Blvd Ste 105, Freeport, PA 16229
Tel.: (412) 612-8333
Motion Controller Mfr
N.A.I.C.S.: 335314

NANJING GAOKE COMPANY LIMITED
Building A Gaoke Center No 8 Xuejin Road, Qixia District, Nanjing, 210023, China
Tel.: (86) 2585800700
Web Site: https://www.600064.com
Year Founded: 1992
600064—(SHG)
Rev.: $630,404,508
Assets: $5,251,477,781
Liabilities: $2,772,557,508
Net Worth: $2,478,920,273
Earnings: $337,293,282
Fiscal Year-end: 12/31/22
Land Development & Other Property Related Services
N.A.I.C.S.: 237210
Yimin Xu *(Chm & Sec-Party Committee)*

NANJING HANRUI COBALT CO LTD
No 527 Jiangjun Avenue, Jiangning District, Nanjing, 211100, Jiangsu, China
Tel.: (86) 2552108170
Web Site: http://www.hrcobalt.com
Year Founded: 1997
300618—(CHIN)
Rev.: $674,495,761
Assets: $1,094,846,558
Liabilities: $349,909,373
Net Worth: $744,937,185
Earnings: $19,471,062
Fiscal Year-end: 12/31/23
Cobalt Powder Mfr & Distr
N.A.I.C.S.: 331410
Liang Jie *(Chm)*

NANJING HICIN PHARMACEUTICAL CO.,LTD
No 1 Hengfa road Economic and Technological Development Zone, Nanjing, 210046, Jiangsu, China
Tel.: (86) 2583222911
Web Site: https://www.hicin.cn
Year Founded: 2003
300584—(CHIN)
Rev.: $72,936,665
Assets: $198,438,551
Liabilities: $59,349,725
Net Worth: $139,088,826
Earnings: $5,115,052
Emp.: 300
Fiscal Year-end: 12/31/23
Pharmaceutical Preparation Mfr & Distr
N.A.I.C.S.: 325412
Cao Yuping *(Chm & Gen Mgr)*

NANJING HUAMAI TECHNOLOGY CO., LTD.
No 11 Runfa Road Dongshan Gaoqiao Industry Gathering Zone, Jiangning District, Nanjing, 211103, Jiangsu, China
Tel.: (86) 2552707128
Web Site: https://www.huamai.cn
Year Founded: 1998
603042—(SHG)
Rev.: $153,623,406
Assets: $249,007,543
Liabilities: $102,071,867
Net Worth: $146,935,676
Earnings: ($13,404,199)
Emp.: 1,500
Fiscal Year-end: 12/31/22
Telecommunication Product Mfr & Distr
N.A.I.C.S.: 334220
Xu Aimin *(Chm)*

NANJING INFORM STORAGE EQUIPMENT (GROUO) CO., LTD.
No 470 Yinhua Street, Jiangning District, Nanjing, 211102, Jiangsu, China
Tel.: (86) 2552726370
Web Site:
https://www.informrack.com
Year Founded: 1997
603066—(SHG)
Rev.: $216,392,581
Assets: $426,776,576
Liabilities: $248,982,089
Net Worth: $177,794,487
Earnings: $18,616,296
Fiscal Year-end: 12/31/22
Storage Shelve Mfr & Distr
N.A.I.C.S.: 337215
Jin Yueyue *(Gen Mgr)*

NANJING JULONG SCIENCE & TECHNOLOGY CO., LTD.
No 8 Julong Road, Jiangbei New District, Nanjing, 210032, Jiangsu, China
Tel.: (86) 2558647479
Web Site: http://www.njjulong.cn
Year Founded: 1999
300644—(CHIN)
Rev.: $257,605,875
Assets: $290,282,131
Liabilities: $166,393,570
Net Worth: $123,888,561
Earnings: $10,218,400
Fiscal Year-end: 12/31/23
Plastic Product Mfr & Distr

INTERNATIONAL PUBLIC

N.A.I.C.S.: 325211
Liu Shuyang *(Chm)*

NANJING KANGNI MECHANICAL & ELECTRICAL CO., LTD.
No 19 Hengda Road Nanjing Economic and Technological Development Zone, Nanjing, 210039, China
Tel.: (86) 2583497082
Web Site: https://www.kn-nanjing.com
Year Founded: 2000
603111—(SHG)
Rev.: $462,607,638
Assets: $841,268,671
Liabilities: $317,520,033
Net Worth: $523,748,637
Earnings: $37,697,863
Fiscal Year-end: 12/31/22
Vehicle Door Mfr
N.A.I.C.S.: 336320

Subsidiaries:

KANGNI RAIL TRANSIT EQUIPMENT, CORP.   (1)
32 Power Dam Way Ste 208, Plattsburgh, NY 12901
Tel.: (571) 599-9815
Vehicle Door Distr
N.A.I.C.S.: 423310

KANGNI TECHNOLOGY SERVICE S.A.R.L   (1)
71 Rue Albert Dhalenne Saint Ouen, 93400, Paris, France
Tel.: (33) 628636433
Vehicle Door Distr
N.A.I.C.S.: 423310

Kangni Rail Transit Equipment (Thailand) Co., Ltd.   (1)
3081 Bhiraj Tower at Emquartier 689 Sukhumvit Road Soi 35, Klongtan Nuea Vadhana, Bangkok, 10110, Thailand
Tel.: (66) 20172770
Automotive Mechanical & Electrical Mfr
N.A.I.C.S.: 336320

NANJING KING-FRIEND BIOCHEMICAL PHARMACEUTICAL CO., LTD.
No 16 Xuefu Road, High&New Tech Development Zone, Nanjing, 210061, China
Tel.: (86) 2586990701
Web Site: https://www.nkf-pharma.com
Year Founded: 2000
603707—(SHG)
Rev.: $564,837,775
Assets: $1,258,909,717
Liabilities: $431,152,857
Net Worth: $827,756,860
Earnings: $162,293,821
Fiscal Year-end: 12/31/21
Pharmaceutical Product Mfr & Distr
N.A.I.C.S.: 325412

NANJING NANGANG IRON & STEEL UNITED CO., LTD.
No 8 Xingjiadian Xingfu Road, Jiangbei New District, Nanjing, 210035, China
Tel.: (86) 4008861729
Web Site: https://www.njsteel.com.cn
Year Founded: 2000
Emp.: 100
Steel Product Mfr & Distr
N.A.I.C.S.: 332313
Zhu Ruirong *(Pres)*

NANJING OLO HOME FURNISHING CO., LTD.
No 218 Qingshuiting West Road, Jiangning Economic and Technological Development Zone, Nanjing, 211100, Jiangsu, China
Tel.: (86) 2552718000

AND PRIVATE COMPANIES

Web Site: http://www.olo-home.com
Year Founded: 2005
603326—(SHG)
Rev.: $233,946,288
Assets: $309,147,939
Liabilities: $165,187,115
Net Worth: $143,960,825
Earnings: $19,728,404
Fiscal Year-end: 12/31/22
Household Furniture Mfr & Distr
N.A.I.C.S.: 337122
Nina Yanti Miao *(Chm)*

NANJING PANDA ELECTRONICS CO., LTD.
Room 1701 No 301 Zhongshan East Raod, Xuanwu District, Nanjing, 210002, Jiangsu, China
Tel.: (86) 2584801144   CN
Web Site:
http://www.chinapanda.com.cn
Year Founded: 1936
600775—(SHG)
Rev.: $583,263,018
Assets: $823,170,072
Liabilities: $288,201,972
Net Worth: $534,968,100
Earnings: $5,684,206
Emp.: 3,143
Fiscal Year-end: 12/31/22
Electronic Components Mfr
N.A.I.C.S.: 334419
Guixiang Zhou *(Chm)*

NANJING PHARMACEUTICAL COMPANY LIMITED
9th Floor Building A Yunmicheng No 19 Ningshuang Road, Yuhuatai District, Nanjing, 210012, Jiangsu, China
Tel.: (86) 2584552601
Web Site: http://www.njyy.com
Year Founded: 1994
600713—(SHG)
Rev.: $6,913,325,472
Assets: $3,965,949,629
Liabilities: $3,164,085,260
Net Worth: $801,864,370
Earnings: $77,398,628
Fiscal Year-end: 12/31/21
Pharmaceutic Product Mfr & Distr
N.A.I.C.S.: 325412
Zhou Jianjun *(Chm)*

NANJING PORT CO., LTD.
Room 1001 Building A Nanjing Port Building No 19 Gonggong Road, Gulou District, Nanjing, 210011, Jiangsu, China
Tel.: (86) 2558815738
Web Site: http://www.nj-port.com
Year Founded: 2001
002040—(SSE)
Rev.: $115,629,119
Assets: $705,813,956
Liabilities: $182,451,661
Net Worth: $523,362,296
Earnings: $19,738,044
Fiscal Year-end: 12/31/20
Cargo Handling Services
N.A.I.C.S.: 488310
Zhao Jianhua *(Chm)*

NANJING PUBLIC UTILITIES DEVELOPMENT CO., LTD.
18F Building A4 No 8 Bailongjiang East Street, Innovation Complex Xincheng Science Park Jianye District, Nanjing, 210019, Jiangsu, China
Tel.: (86) 2586383611
Web Site: http://www.zhong-bei.com
Year Founded: 1992
000421—(SSE)
Rev.: $998,604,828
Assets: $2,170,881,648
Liabilities: $1,607,318,856
Net Worth: $563,562,792

Earnings: $8,498,412
Fiscal Year-end: 12/31/22
Electric Power Generation & Vehicle Transportation Services
N.A.I.C.S.: 221111
Wang Wei *(Chm & Sec-Party Committee)*

NANJING PUTIAN TELECOMMUNICATIONS CO., LTD.
No 1 Putian Road Qinhuai District, Nanjing, 210012, Jiangsu, China
Tel.: (86) 25 5230 2518
Sales Range: $250-299.9 Million
Communication Equipment Mfr
N.A.I.C.S.: 334210
Qian Xu *(Chm)*

NANJING QUANXIN CABLE TECHNOLOGY CO., LTD.
Block E Gulou Innovation Plaza No 18 Qingjiang South Road, Gulou District, Nanjing, 210036, Jiangsu, China
Tel.: (86) 2583245761
Web Site: https://www.qx-kj.com
300447—(CHIN)
Rev.: $153,269,064
Assets: $381,796,740
Liabilities: $118,410,552
Net Worth: $263,386,188
Earnings: $26,567,892
Emp.: 300
Fiscal Year-end: 12/31/22
Transmission Cables Mfr
N.A.I.C.S.: 335929
Xianglou Chen *(Chm & Gen Mgr)*

NANJING RAILWAY NEW TECHNOLOGY CO., LTD.
No 19 Longtai Road, Jiangbei New District, Nanjing, 210061, Jiangsu, China
Tel.: (86) 2558744466
Web Site: https://www.njlew.com.cn
Year Founded: 1994
301016—(CHIN)
Rev.: $48,959,676
Assets: $173,912,450
Liabilities: $31,541,746
Net Worth: $142,370,704
Earnings: $7,637,859
Fiscal Year-end: 12/31/23
Railroad Rolling Stock Mfr
N.A.I.C.S.: 336510
Wang Chong *(Chm & Gen Mgr)*

NANJING RED SUN CO., LTD.
No 18 Gutan Avenue Gaochun Economic Development Zone, Nanjing, 211300, Jiangsu, China
Tel.: (86) 2557883588
Web Site:
http://www.chinaredsun.com
Year Founded: 1991
000525—(SSE)
Rev.: $904,163,364
Assets: $1,443,424,320
Liabilities: $1,247,103,000
Net Worth: $196,321,320
Earnings: $102,814,920
Fiscal Year-end: 12/31/22
Chemical Fertiliser Mfr
N.A.I.C.S.: 325311
Yang Xiu *(Chm)*

NANJING RESEARCH INSTITUTE OF SURVEYING MAPPING & GEOTECHNICAL INVESTIGATION CO., LTD.
No 88 Chuangyi Road, Jianye District, Nanjing, 210019, Jiangsu, China
Tel.: (86) 2584780620
Web Site: https://www.njcky.com
Year Founded: 1991
300826—(SSE)
Rev.: $116,995,752

Assets: $346,839,862
Liabilities: $182,073,232
Net Worth: $164,766,630
Earnings: $12,550,963
Fiscal Year-end: 12/31/21
Surveying Services
N.A.I.C.S.: 541370
Chu Zhengwei *(Chm)*

NANJING SAMPLE TECHNOLOGY COMPANY LIMITED
Sample Technology Park No 10 Maqun Avenue, Qixia District, Nanjing, China
Tel.: (86) 2584356666
Web Site:
https://www.samples.com.cn
Year Founded: 2000
1708—(HKG)
Rev.: $71,978,193
Assets: $420,960,619
Liabilities: $202,134,259
Net Worth: $218,826,360
Earnings: ($42,241,057)
Emp.: 261
Fiscal Year-end: 12/31/22
Video Security Systems Mfr
N.A.I.C.S.: 334310
Min Sha *(Chm)*

Subsidiaries:

Nanjing City Intelligent Transportation Co., Ltd.   (1)
No 10 Maqun Avenue, Qixia District, Nanjing, 210049, Jiangsu, China
Tel.: (86) 255 886 6405
Web Site: https://www.njits.com.cn
Intelligent Transportation Services
N.A.I.C.S.: 485999

Sample Technology (H.K.) Co., Limited   (1)
Room 3112a 31 F Shun Tak Center West Tower 168-200 Connaught Road, Central, China (Hong Kong)
Tel.: (852) 25419100
Sales Range: $25-49.9 Million
Emp.: 6
Video Security System Mfr
N.A.I.C.S.: 334290
Man Li *(Gen Mgr)*

NANJING SANCHAO ADVANCED MATERIALS CO., LTD.
Zecheng Road 77 Chunhua street Jiangning District, Nanjing, 211124, China
Tel.: (86) 2584154668
Web Site: http://www.diasc.com.cn
Year Founded: 1999
300554—(CHIN)
Rev.: $67,755,583
Assets: $166,852,868
Liabilities: $52,481,090
Net Worth: $114,371,778
Earnings: $3,790,978
Fiscal Year-end: 12/31/23
Cutting Tool Mfr & Distr
N.A.I.C.S.: 333515
Zou Yuyao *(Chm)*

Subsidiaries:

SCD Co., Ltd.   (1)
10-15 1-Chome Shimokitakata, Mihara, 729-0414, Hiroshima, Japan
Tel.: (81) 848864880
Web Site: https://scd-jp.com
Semiconductor & Related Device Mfr
N.A.I.C.S.: 334413

NANJING SCIYON WISDOM TECHNOLOGY GROUP CO., LTD.
No 1266 Qingshuiting East Road, Jiangning District, Nanjing, 211102, China
Tel.: (86) 2568598968

Web Site: https://www.sciyon.com
Year Founded: 1993
002380—(SSE)
Rev.: $162,069,336
Assets: $416,366,028
Liabilities: $182,021,580
Net Worth: $234,344,448
Earnings: ($60,890,076)
Emp.: 1,000
Fiscal Year-end: 12/31/22
Thermal Process Automation Products Mfr & Sales
N.A.I.C.S.: 334513
Guo Yao Liu *(Founder & Chm)*

NANJING SECURITIES CO., LTD.
No 389 Jiangdong Middle Road, Nanjing, 210019, China
Tel.: (86) 2583367888
Web Site: https://www.njzq.com.cn
Year Founded: 1990
601990—(SHG)
Rev.: $281,940,989
Assets: $7,253,215,927
Liabilities: $4,887,406,527
Net Worth: $2,365,809,400
Earnings: $90,652,293
Fiscal Year-end: 12/31/22
Securities Brokerage Services
N.A.I.C.S.: 523150
Jianfeng Li *(Chm)*

NANJING SHENGHANG SHIPPING CO., LTD.
Building 7 No 12 Xinglong Road Nanjing Area Pilot Free Trade Zone, Qixia, Nanjing, 210031, Jiangsu, China
Tel.: (86) 2585668080
Web Site: https://www.njshsh.com
Year Founded: 1994
001205—(SSE)
Rev.: $121,893,876
Assets: $392,783,040
Liabilities: $182,545,272
Net Worth: $210,237,768
Earnings: $23,738,832
Fiscal Year-end: 12/31/22
Transportation Services
N.A.I.C.S.: 541614
Taoyuan Li *(Chm & Gen Mgr)*

NANJING SINOLIFE UNITED COMPANY LIMITED
Maqun Science Park 3 Qingma Road, Qixia District, Nanjing, Jiangsu, China
Tel.: (86) 2586819188   CN
Web Site: https://www.zs-united.com
Year Founded: 1999
3332—(HKG)
Rev.: $38,589,080
Assets: $61,352,975
Liabilities: $15,891,455
Net Worth: $45,461,520
Earnings: ($2,000,138)
Emp.: 298
Fiscal Year-end: 12/31/22
Nutritional Supplements Retailer
N.A.I.C.S.: 456191
Pinghu Gui *(Founder, Founder, Chm, Chm & Exec Dir)*

NANJING SUNLORD ELECTRONICS CORPORATION LTD.
3-9F Lvdi Zhichaung C No 4 Yupan West Street, Yuhua District, Nanjing, 210012, Jiangsu, China
Tel.: (86) 2583677628
Web Site: http://www.jssunlord.com
Year Founded: 1999
300975—(SSE)
Rev.: $791,947,260
Assets: $595,502,388
Liabilities: $354,188,484

NANJING SUNLORD ELECTRONICS CORPORATION LTD.

Nanjing Sunlord Electronics Corporation Ltd.—(Continued)
Net Worth: $241,313,904
Earnings: $18,579,132
Emp.: 900
Fiscal Year-end: 12/31/22
Electronic Product Mfr & Distr
N.A.I.C.S.: 334419
Hongzhi Sha (Chm & Gen Mgr)

NANJING TANKER CORPORATION
No 324 North Zhongshan Road, Nanjing, 210003, China
Tel.: (86) 2558586145
Web Site: http://www.njtc.com.cn
Year Founded: 1993
Sales Range: $650-699.9 Million
Emp.: 3,057
Marine Freight Services
N.A.I.C.S.: 483111
Dong Jianjun (VP)

NANJING TOUA HARDWARE & TOOLS CO., LTD.
6 Zhidao Road, Dongshan Subdistrict Jiangning District, Nanjing, 211103, Jiangsu, China
Tel.: (86) 2552174008
Web Site: https://www.touatools.com
Year Founded: 2000
301125—(CHIN)
Rev.: $64,046,757
Assets: $148,054,220
Liabilities: $56,375,623
Net Worth: $91,678,597
Earnings: $659,864
Fiscal Year-end: 12/31/23
Hardware Tools Mfr
N.A.I.C.S.: 333515
Shufang Ma (Chm)

NANJING VISHEE MEDICAL TECHNOLOGY CO., LTD.
Building 9 Yunmi Information Industry Square No 19 Ningshuang Road, Yuhuatai District, Nanjing, 210012, Jiangsu, China
Tel.: (86) 2569670036
Web Site: https://www.vishee.com
Year Founded: 2001
688580—(SSE)
Rev.: $45,155,645
Assets: $236,463,983
Liabilities: $21,855,956
Net Worth: $214,608,027
Earnings: $13,173,156
Fiscal Year-end: 12/31/22
Medical Product Mfr & Distr
N.A.I.C.S.: 339112
Zhiyu Wang (Chm & Gen Mgr)

NANJING WELL PHARMACEUTICAL GROUP CO., LTD.
Building 5 R&D Zone 5 Xuzhuang Software Park No 64 Suning Avenue, Xuanwu District, Nanjing, 210042, Jiangsu, China
Tel.: (86) 2585732322
Web Site: http://www.well-js.com
Year Founded: 2000
603351—(SHG)
Rev.: $155,985,902
Assets: $300,197,678
Liabilities: $92,068,170
Net Worth: $208,129,508
Earnings: $13,342,029
Fiscal Year-end: 12/31/22
Pharmaceutical Product Mfr & Distr
N.A.I.C.S.: 325412

NANJING WONDUX ENVIRONMENTAL PROTECTION TECHNOLOGY CORP., LTD.
No 57 Qiande Road Jiangning High-tech Zone, Jiangning, Nanjing, 211100, Jiangsu, China
Tel.: (86) 2584913518
Web Site: https://www.njwds.com
Year Founded: 2007
688178—(SSE)
Rev.: $120,724,723
Assets: $302,070,853
Liabilities: $127,875,056
Net Worth: $174,195,796
Earnings: $3,139,204
Fiscal Year-end: 12/31/22
Waste Management Services
N.A.I.C.S.: 562998
Jun Liu (Chm & Gen Mgr)

NANJING XINLIAN ELECTRONICS CO., LTD.
No 28 Jiayuan Middle Road Jiangning Development Zone, Nanjing, 211100, Jiangsu, China
Tel.: (86) 2568105959
Web Site: https://www.xldz.com
Year Founded: 2007
002546—(SSE)
Rev.: $87,144,876
Assets: $508,855,932
Liabilities: $54,006,264
Net Worth: $454,849,668
Earnings: $1,566,864
Fiscal Year-end: 12/31/22
Software & Hardware Provider
N.A.I.C.S.: 513210
Mih Hu (Chm)

NANJING YUEBOO POWER SYSTEM CO., LTD.
4F Block 4 No 18 Jialingjiang East Street, Jianye District, Nanjing, 210019, China
Tel.: (86) 2589635189
Web Site: http://www.yuebooemt.com
300742—(SSE)
Rev.: $19,978,920
Assets: $171,633,384
Liabilities: $184,256,748
Net Worth: ($12,623,364)
Earnings: ($29,912,220)
Fiscal Year-end: 12/31/22
Automotive Parts Mfr & Distr
N.A.I.C.S.: 336320

NANKAI CHEMICAL CO., LTD.
Yotsubashi Star Building 1-chome-12-19 Minamihorie, Nishi-ku, Osaka, 550-0015, Japan
Tel.: (81) 665325590
Web Site: https://www.nankai-chem.co.jp
Year Founded: 1951
4040—(TKS)
Rev.: $132,114,070
Assets: $133,905,380
Liabilities: $84,323,770
Net Worth: $49,581,610
Earnings: $7,654,380
Fiscal Year-end: 03/31/24
Chemical Product Mfr & Distr
N.A.I.C.S.: 325998
Hideo Kanno (Pres)

NANKAI ELECTRIC RAILWAY CO., LTD.
2-1-41 Shikitsu Higashi, Naniwa-ku, Osaka, 556-8503, Japan
Tel.: (81) 666447121
Web Site: https://www.howto-osaka.com
Year Founded: 1885
9044—(TKS)
Rev.: $1,596,936,340
Assets: $6,283,796,500
Liabilities: $4,253,852,280
Net Worth: $2,029,944,220
Earnings: $158,150,860
Fiscal Year-end: 03/31/24
Railroads, Buses, Ferries Operator; Real Estate Rental & Leasing Services; Shopping Mall Management Services; Apartment Building Construction Services
N.A.I.C.S.: 482111

Subsidiaries:

Nankai Tatsumura Construction Co., Ltd. (1)
3519 Nambanaka, Naniwa-ku, Osaka, 556-0011, Japan
Tel.: (81) 666447802
Web Site: https://www.nantatsu.co.jp
Rev.: $288,367,860
Assets: $200,514,350
Liabilities: $96,254,820
Net Worth: $104,259,530
Earnings: $7,271,000
Emp.: 441
Fiscal Year-end: 03/31/2024
Construction Engineering Services
N.A.I.C.S.: 541330

NANKAI PLYWOOD CO., LTD.
1-15-10 Matsufukucho, Takamatsu, 760-0067, Kagawa, Japan
Tel.: (81) 878253615
Web Site: https://www.nankaiplywood.co.jp
Year Founded: 1955
7887—(TKS)
Rev.: $157,146,140
Assets: $213,198,940
Liabilities: $54,373,860
Net Worth: $158,825,080
Earnings: $6,266,280
Emp.: 1,810
Fiscal Year-end: 03/31/24
Plywood Material Mfr & Distr
N.A.I.C.S.: 321211
Toru Maruyama (Pres & CEO)

NANKANG RUBBER TIRE CORPORATION LTD.
6F Rm 608 No 136 Sec 3 Ren-ai Rd, Da-an District, Taipei, Taiwan
Tel.: (886) 227071000
Web Site: https://www.nankang-tyre.com
2101—(TAI)
Rev.: $256,776,667
Assets: $1,361,013,749
Liabilities: $1,022,268,642
Net Worth: $338,745,106
Earnings: $4,382,452
Emp.: 1,814
Fiscal Year-end: 12/31/23
Rubber Tire Mfr
N.A.I.C.S.: 326211
Cai-Yun Zhan (Gen Mgr)

NANNI INDUSTRIES
11 Avenue de l Abbe Edme Mariotte, 33260, La Teste, France
Tel.: (33) 556223060
Web Site: http://www.nannidiesel.com
Rev.: $29,700,000
Emp.: 65
Marine Engine Mfr & Distr
N.A.I.C.S.: 333618
Amalia Festa (CEO)

Subsidiaries:

Nanni Trading SRL (1)
Via Degli Olmetti 5/B, 00060, Formello, Italy
Tel.: (39) 063 0884251
Web Site: http://www.nannitrading.it
Marine Diesel Engine Distr
N.A.I.C.S.: 423830

NANNING BALING TECHNOLOGY CO., LTD.
No 21 Hi-tech Avenue East Section Hi-tech Zone, Nanning, 530007, Guangxi, China
Tel.: (86) 7713216598

INTERNATIONAL PUBLIC

Web Site: http://www.baling.com.cn
Year Founded: 2001
002592—(SSE)
Rev.: $77,562,576
Assets: $166,786,776
Liabilities: $67,126,644
Net Worth: $99,660,132
Earnings: $1,898,208
Fiscal Year-end: 12/31/22
Automobile Parts Mfr
N.A.I.C.S.: 336390
Yu Gu (Chm & Gen Mgr)

NANNING DEPARTMENT STORE CO., LTD.
No 39 Chaoyang Road, Nanning, 530012, Guangxi, China
Tel.: (86) 7712098888
Web Site: https://www.nnbh.com.cn
Year Founded: 1956
600712—(SHG)
Rev.: $123,775,295
Assets: $262,928,277
Liabilities: $127,248,566
Net Worth: $135,679,712
Earnings: $404,474
Fiscal Year-end: 12/31/21
Departmental Store Operator
N.A.I.C.S.: 455110
Qin Yaobei (Chm)

NANO CO., LTD.
60 Magong gongdan-ro Cheongni, Sangju, 37257, Gyeongbuk, Korea (South)
Tel.: (82) 10545335887
Web Site: https://www.nanoin.com
Year Founded: 1999
187790—(KRS)
Rev.: $51,239,404
Assets: $53,632,274
Liabilities: $34,680,711
Net Worth: $18,951,563
Earnings: ($7,289,798)
Emp.: 72
Fiscal Year-end: 12/31/22
Chemical Products Mfr
N.A.I.C.S.: 325199
Shin Dong-Woo (CEO)

Subsidiaries:

Nano Automotive SL (1)
Tel.: (34) 948848255
Automobile Parts Mfr
N.A.I.C.S.: 336390
Rahee Hong (Mgr-Logistic & Pur)

Nano Yufeida Co., Ltd. (1)
Shangjiucheng Huaguoqing Shishan Town, Chuxiong, 651600, Yunnan, China
Tel.: (86) 8788715558
Titanium Dioxide Powder Mfr
N.A.I.C.S.: 325180

NANO DIMENSION LTD
2 Ilan Ramon, Nes Ziyyona, 7403635, Israel
Tel.: (972) 737509142
Web Site: https://www.nano-di.com
NNDM—(NASDAQ)
Rev.: $56,314,000
Assets: $1,064,338,000
Liabilities: $48,552,000
Net Worth: $1,015,786,000
Earnings: ($55,660,000)
Emp.: 510
Fiscal Year-end: 12/31/23
3D Print Multilayer Circuit Boards Mfr
N.A.I.C.S.: 333248
Amit Dror (Co-Founder & Officer-Customer Success)

Subsidiaries:

Essmtec AG (1)
Mosenstrasse 20, 6287, Aesch, Switzerland
Tel.: (41) 9196060
Web Site: https://essemtec.com
Electric Equipment Mfr

AND PRIVATE COMPANIES

Global Inkjet Systems Company (1)
Edinburgh House Cowley Road, St John's Innovation Park, Cambridge, United Kingdom
Tel.: (44) 1223733733
Web Site: https://www.globalinkjetsystems.com
Electric Equipment Mfr
N.A.I.C.S.: 334419

NANO LABS LTD.
30th Floor Dikaiyinzuo No 29 East Jiefang Road, Hangzhou, China
Tel.: (86) 57186656957 Ky
Web Site: https://www.nano.cn
Year Founded: 2021
Rev.: $10,846,170
Assets: $48,501,915
Liabilities: $50,753,431
Net Worth: ($2,251,516)
Earnings: ($35,217,110)
Emp.: 157
Fiscal Year-end: 12/31/23
Memory Chip Product Mfr & Distr
N.A.I.C.S.: 334413
Jianping Kong *(CEO & Chm)*

NANO MEDIA INC.
4F 3-2-1 Nishi-Shimbashi, Shinagawa-ku, Tokyo, 105-0003, Japan
Tel.: (81) 3 6409 6300 JP
Web Site: http://www.nanomedia.jp
Aerospace, Electronics & Multimedia Company
N.A.I.C.S.: 335999
Kazuhiro Shiraishi *(Chm)*

NANO ONE MATERIALS CORP.
101B8575 Government St, Burnaby, V3N 4V1, BC, Canada
Tel.: (604) 420-2041 BC
Web Site: https://www.nanoone.ca
LBMB—(TSXV)
Sales Range: Less than $1 Million
Mineral Exploration Services
N.A.I.C.S.: 213114
Paul Frank Matysek *(Chm)*

NANO-X IMAGING LTD.
Communications Center, Neve Ilan, 9085000, Israel
Tel.: (972) 29950506 Il
Web Site: https://www.nanox.vision
Year Founded: 2011
NNOX—(NASDAQ)
Rev.: $1,304,000
Assets: $363,170,000
Liabilities: $71,022,000
Net Worth: $292,148,000
Earnings: ($61,798,000)
Emp.: 186
Fiscal Year-end: 12/31/21
Biotechnology Research & Development Services
N.A.I.C.S.: 541714
Ran Poliakine *(Co-Founder, Chm & CEO)*

NANOBIOSYS INC.
HanShin IT Tower II 9th Floor 47 Digital-ro 9-gil Geumcheon-gu, Seoul, 153-712, Korea (South)
Tel.: (82) 2 20253019
Web Site: http://www.nanobiosys.co.kr
Bio-Diagnostic Labchip Technology, Efficient Bio-Reagents & Portable Mini High-Speed Diagnostic Equipment
N.A.I.C.S.: 339112

NANOBIOTIX
60 rue de Wattignies, 75012, Paris, France
Tel.: (33) 140260470
Web Site: https://www.nanobiotix.com
NBTX—(NASDAQ)
Rev.: $5,866,074
Assets: $73,410,677
Liabilities: $106,628,427
Net Worth: ($33,217,751)
Earnings: ($70,060,038)
Emp.: 102
Fiscal Year-end: 12/31/22
Medical Device Mfr
N.A.I.C.S.: 339112
Laurent Levy *(CEO & Member-Exec Bd)*

Subsidiaries:

Curadigm S.A.S. (1)
60 Rue de Wattignies, 75012, Paris, France
Tel.: (33) 140260652
Web Site: https://www.curadigm.com
Medical Clinic Operator
N.A.I.C.S.: 621310

Nanobiotix Corp. (1)
245 Main st 3rd Fl, Cambridge, MA 02142
Tel.: (617) 712-1568
Biopharmaceutical Product Development Services
N.A.I.C.S.: 541714

NANOBRICK CO., LTD.
Sandan-Ro 52 Beon-Gil 68, Pyeongtaek, 17746, Gyeonggi-do, Korea (South)
Tel.: (82) 316639420
Web Site: http://www.nanobrick.co.kr
Year Founded: 2007
286750—(KRS)
Rev.: $5,475,842
Assets: $21,580,061
Liabilities: $13,799,540
Net Worth: $7,780,521
Earnings: ($1,839,895)
Emp.: 51
Fiscal Year-end: 12/31/22
Chemicals Mfr
N.A.I.C.S.: 325998
James Joo *(CEO)*

NANOCARRIER CO., LTD.
Ohnoya-Kyobashi Bldg 1-4-10 Kyobashi, Chuo-ku, Tokyo, 104-0031, Japan
Tel.: (81) 332410550
Web Site: http://www.nanocarrier.co.jp
Year Founded: 1996
4571—(TKS)
Rev.: $892,350
Assets: $33,519,310
Liabilities: $10,906,500
Net Worth: $22,612,810
Earnings: ($5,155,800)
Fiscal Year-end: 03/31/24
Cancer Pharmaceutical Researcher & Mfr
N.A.I.C.S.: 325412
Ichiro Nakatomi *(Pres & CEO)*

NANOCHEMTECH INC.
42-34 wanjangchun-ro, Namsamyun Chuingu, Yongin, gyunggido, Korea (South)
Tel.: (82) 316719466
Web Site: http://www.nanosbiz.com
Year Founded: 2000
091970—(KRS)
Rev.: $38,475,492
Assets: $36,063,450
Liabilities: $14,545,840
Net Worth: $21,517,610
Earnings: ($13,155,418)
Emp.: 58
Fiscal Year-end: 12/31/22
Polymers Mfr
N.A.I.C.S.: 326113
Won Seo Choi *(CEO)*

Subsidiaries:

NanoChemTech Inc. - Ansung 2 Factory (1)
38 Mountain Donghang-ri Yangsung-myun, Anseong, Gyoenggi-do, Korea (South)
Tel.: (82) 313234516
Organic Polymer Mfr
N.A.I.C.S.: 325998

NANOCMS CO., LTD.
48 4Sandan 4-Ro Jiksan-Eup, Seobuk-Gu, 31040, Cheonan, 31040, Chungcheongnam-do, Korea (South)
Tel.: (82) 415873901
Web Site: https://www.en.nanocms.co.kr
Year Founded: 2003
247660—(KRS)
Rev.: $5,683,289
Assets: $40,191,560
Liabilities: $16,405,053
Net Worth: $23,786,507
Earnings: $158,301
Emp.: 32
Fiscal Year-end: 12/31/22
Electronic Components Mfr
N.A.I.C.S.: 334419
Dong-Geun An *(Mng Dir)*

NANOCO GROUP PLC
Science Centre, The Heath Business & Technical Park, Runcorn, WA7 4QX, United Kingdom
Tel.: (44) 1928761422
Web Site: https://www.nanocotechnology.com
NANO—(AIM)
Rev.: $2,838,993
Assets: $12,535,829
Liabilities: $8,392,067
Net Worth: $4,143,761
Earnings: ($5,967,179)
Emp.: 37
Fiscal Year-end: 07/31/21
Solid State Lighting, Solar Energy, Life Sciences & Next Generation Displays
N.A.I.C.S.: 335110
Nigel Leroy Pickett *(CTO)*

NANOENTEK INC.
12F 5 Digital-ro 26-gil, Guro-gu, Seoul, 8389, Korea (South)
Tel.: (82) 62207728
Web Site: https://www.nanoentek.com
039860—(KRS)
Rev.: $26,998,912
Assets: $48,533,298
Liabilities: $4,316,674
Net Worth: $44,216,624
Earnings: $3,577,985
Emp.: 141
Fiscal Year-end: 12/31/22
Medical Device Mfr
N.A.I.C.S.: 334510

Subsidiaries:

NanoEnTek USA Inc. (1)
5627 Stoneridge Dr Ste 304, Pleasanton, CA 94588
Tel.: (925) 225-0108
Medical Device Distr
N.A.I.C.S.: 423450

NanoEntek Bio-Technology(Beijing) Ltd. (1)
Room 302 3F Building 19 No 88 Liuxiang Road, Fengtai District, Beijing, China
Tel.: (86) 1059207980
Microfluidic Chip Mfr & Distr
N.A.I.C.S.: 334413

NANOFILM TECHNOLOGIES INTERNATIONAL LIMITED
11 Tai Seng Drive Level 6, Ayer Rajah Ind Estate, Singapore, 139959, Singapore

Tel.: (65) 62811888 SG
Web Site: https://www.nti-nanofilm.com
Year Founded: 1999
MZH—(SES)
Rev.: $134,074,074
Assets: $470,725,592
Liabilities: $149,583,428
Net Worth: $321,142,164
Earnings: $2,040,445
Emp.: 2,215
Fiscal Year-end: 12/31/23
Information Technology Services
N.A.I.C.S.: 541512
Shi Xu *(Founder & Chm)*

Subsidiaries:

Nanofilm Technologies Japan Limited (1)
3rd Floor of Nova International Building 3-28-7 Okusawa, Setagaya-ku, Tokyo, Japan
Tel.: (81) 337295020
Web Site: http://www.nanofilm.co.jp
Coating Metal Product Mfr & Distr
N.A.I.C.S.: 332812

NANOFORM FINLAND OYJ
Cultivator II Viikinkaari 4, 00790, Helsinki, Finland
Tel.: (358) 293700150
Web Site: https://www.nanoform.com
Year Founded: 2008
NANOFH—(HEL)
Rev.: $2,769,787
Assets: $84,324,074
Liabilities: $12,074,351
Net Worth: $72,249,723
Earnings: ($22,400,037)
Emp.: 165
Fiscal Year-end: 12/31/23
Pharmaceutical Product Mfr & Distr
N.A.I.C.S.: 325412
Albert Haeggstrom *(CFO)*

NANOGATE SE
Zum Schacht 3, 66287, Quierschied, Germany
Tel.: (49) 682595910 De
Web Site: http://www.nanogate.de
Year Founded: 1999
N7G—(DEU)
Sales Range: $250-299.9 Million
Emp.: 1,800
Nanotechnology Research & Development Services
N.A.I.C.S.: 541713
Klaus-Gunter Vennemann *(Chm-Supervisory Bd)*

Subsidiaries:

HTP High Tech Plastics GmbH (1)
Eumigstrasse 6, 8753, Fohnsdorf, Austria
Tel.: (43) 3573 3106 0
Web Site: http://www.htp.at
Plastic Products Mfr & Whslr
N.A.I.C.S.: 326199
Ronald Prettner *(Co-CEO)*

Nanogate Electronic Systems GmbH (1)
Fabriksgelande 1, 7201, Neudorfl, Austria
Tel.: (43) 2622606
Chemical Component Mfr
N.A.I.C.S.: 325998

Nanogate Het Engineering GmbH (1)
Herrenberger Str 56, 71034, Boblingen, Germany
Tel.: (49) 70314916140
Chemical Component Mfr
N.A.I.C.S.: 325998

Nanogate Het Engineering India Pvt Ltd. (1)
Banashankari Stage 2, Bengaluru, 560070, India
Tel.: (91) 8026719155

NANOGATE SE

Nanogate SE—(Continued)
Chemical Component Mfr
N.A.I.C.S.: 325998
Vishwas R. *(Sr Engr-Design)*

Nanogate Kierspe GmbH (1)
Am Funkenhof 2, 58566, Kierspe, Germany
Tel.: (49) 2359914050
Chemical Component Mfr
N.A.I.C.S.: 325998

Nanogate Management Services GmbH (1)
Zum Schacht 3, Gottelborn, 66287, Quierschied, Germany
Tel.: (49) 682595910
Chemical Component Mfr
N.A.I.C.S.: 325998
Wolfgang Schmidt *(Mgr-HR)*

Nanogate Medical Systems GmbH (1)
Osemundstrasse 27-29, 58566, Kierspe, Germany
Tel.: (49) 23595080960
Chemical Component Mfr
N.A.I.C.S.: 325998

Nanogate Netherlands Bv (1)
Spaarpot 102a, 5667 KZ, Geldrop, Netherlands
Tel.: (31) 402894894
Chemical Component Mfr
N.A.I.C.S.: 325998
Jaap Dekker *(Mng Dir)*

Nanogate Neunkirchen GmbH (1)
Beim alten Hof 10, 66538, Neunkirchen, Germany
Tel.: (49) 682595910
Chemical Component Mfr
N.A.I.C.S.: 325998

Nanogate Nrw GmbH (1)
Golsberger Strasse 1, 58513, Ludenscheid, Germany
Tel.: (49) 23515676700
Chemical Component Mfr
N.A.I.C.S.: 325998

Nanogate Pd Systems GmbH (1)
Altenhagener Strasse 13, 32107, Bad Salzuflen, Germany
Tel.: (49) 520891160
Chemical Component Mfr
N.A.I.C.S.: 325998

Nanogate Schwabisch Gmund GmbH (1)
Guglingstrasse 74, 73529, Schwabisch Gmund, Germany
Tel.: (49) 717191070
Chemical Component Mfr
N.A.I.C.S.: 325998

Nanogate Slovakia s.r.o. (1)
Stanicna 502, 95201, Vrable, Slovakia
Tel.: (421) 37 776 8514
Web Site: http://www.nanogate.com
Motor Vehicle Parts & Electronic Components Mfr & Distr
N.A.I.C.S.: 336390

Nanogate Textile & Care Systems GmbH (1)
Zum Schacht 3, Gottelborn, 66287, Quierschied, Germany
Tel.: (49) 682595910
Chemical Component Mfr
N.A.I.C.S.: 325998

NANOGROUP SA

Tel.: (48) 604741303
Web Site: https://www.nanogroup.eu
NNG—(WAR)
Rev.: $513,211
Assets: $2,192,983,988
Liabilities: $882,206,553
Net Worth: $1,310,777,436
Earnings: ($2,008,684,954)
Fiscal Year-end: 12/31/23
Biotechnology Research & Development Services
N.A.I.C.S.: 541714
Marek Borzestowski *(Chm)*

NANOHELIX CO. LTD.

43-15, Techno 5-ro, Yuseong-gu, Daejeon, 34014, Korea (South)
Tel.: (82) 428679055
Web Site: https://www.nanohelix.net
Year Founded: 2008
Biotechnology Research & Development Services
N.A.I.C.S.: 541714

NANOLLOSE LIMITED

Suite 5 CPC 145 Stirling Highway, Nedlands, 6009, WA, Australia
Tel.: (61) 893893120   AU
Web Site: https://www.nanollose.com
Year Founded: 2014
NC6—(ASX)
Rev.: $205,985
Assets: $161,559
Liabilities: $310,926
Net Worth: ($149,367)
Earnings: ($772,271)
Fiscal Year-end: 06/30/24
Support Activities for Metal Mining
N.A.I.C.S.: 213114
Wayne Best *(Chm)*

NANOLOGICA AB

Forskargatan 20G, 151 36, Sodertalje, Sweden
Tel.: (46) 841074949
Web Site: https://www.nanologica.com
Year Founded: 2004
NICA—(OMX)
Emp.: 15
Biotechnology Research & Development Services
N.A.I.C.S.: 541714
Gisela Sitbon *(Chm)*

NANOMETRICS INC.

250 Herzberg Road, Kanata, K2K 2A1, ON, Canada
Tel.: (613) 592-6776
Web Site: http://www.nanometrics.ca
Year Founded: 1986
Monitoring Solutions & Controlling Equipment Mfr & Distr
N.A.I.C.S.: 334519
Tim Hayman *(VP-R&D)*

Subsidiaries:

Nanometrics Inc. - Oil & Gas Division (1)
344 - 12th Avenue SW Suite 150, Calgary, T2R 0H2, AB, Canada
Tel.: (403) 648-7250
Measuring & Controlling Device Mfr
N.A.I.C.S.: 334513
David Shorey *(VP)*

NANOOMTECH CO., LTD.

57 Cheomdan Venture So-ro, Buk-gu, Gwangju, 61003, Korea (South)
Tel.: (82) 629558588
Web Site: https://www.nanoomtech.co.kr
Year Founded: 2005
Medical & Electronic Device Mfr
N.A.I.C.S.: 334510
Choi Mu Jin *(CEO)*

NANOPAC (M) SDN BHD

27 Jalan Raja Wali 2 Bandar Puchong Jaya, Puchong, 47100, Selangor, Malaysia
Tel.: (60) 3 8070 7428
Web Site: http://www.nanopac.com.my
Year Founded: 2003
Nanotechnology Products Researcher, Developer & Mfr
N.A.I.C.S.: 541713
Cheng Kok Leong *(Chm)*

NANOREPRO AG

Untergasse 8, 35037, Marburg, Germany
Tel.: (49) 6421951449
Web Site: https://www.nanorepro.com
NN6—(MUN)
Rev.: $3,510,307
Assets: $45,766,450
Liabilities: $1,192,180
Net Worth: $44,574,271
Earnings: ($5,177,150)
Emp.: 18
Fiscal Year-end: 12/31/23
Stem Cell Research
N.A.I.C.S.: 621511
Olaf Stiller *(Chm-Supervisory Bd)*

NANOSONICS LIMITED

7-11 Talavera Road Macquarie Park, Sydney, 2113, NSW, Australia
Tel.: (61) 280631600   AU
Web Site: https://www.nanosonics.com.au
NAN—(ASX)
Rev.: $113,522,970
Assets: $158,479,567
Liabilities: $36,816,907
Net Worth: $121,662,660
Earnings: $8,661,859
Emp.: 466
Fiscal Year-end: 06/30/24
Decontamination Products Developer & Researcher Focused on Reducing the Spread of Infection
N.A.I.C.S.: 541715
McGregor Grant *(CFO & Sec)*

Subsidiaries:

Nanosonics Europe GmbH (1)
Poppenbutteler Bogen 66, House E, 22399, Hamburg, Germany
Tel.: (49) 404 685 6885
Web Site: https://www.nanosonics.eu
Infection Control Devices Mfr
N.A.I.C.S.: 334510

Nanosonics Europe Limited (1)
Unit 2 Linfit Court Colliers Way Clayton West, Huddersfield, HD8 9WL, West Yorkshire, United Kingdom
Tel.: (44) 1484860581
Ultrasound Probe Mfr & Distr
N.A.I.C.S.: 334510
Gareth Daly *(Acct Mgr)*

Nanosonics Japan KK (1)
5-27-3 Sendagaya Yamato Building 8F, Shibuya-ku, Tokyo, 151-0051, Japan
Tel.: (81) 367728080
Web Site: https://www.nanosonics.jp
Ultrasound Probe Mfr & Distr
N.A.I.C.S.: 334510
Katsumi Maruyama *(Country Mgr & Pres)*

Nanosonics UK Limited (1)
Unit 2 Linfit Court Colliers Way Clayton West, Huddersfield, HD8 9WL, West Yorkshire, United Kingdom
Tel.: (44) 1484860581
Web Site: https://www.nanosonics.co.uk
Ultrasound Probe Mfr & Distr
N.A.I.C.S.: 334510

NANOSPHERE HEALTH SCIENCES INC.

1090 West Georgia Street Suite 488, Vancouver, V6E 3V7, BC, Canada
Tel.: (604) 351-3351   BC
Web Site: https://www.nanospherehealth.com
Year Founded: 2005
NSHSF—(OTCIQ)
Assets: $60,049
Liabilities: $1,371,924
Net Worth: ($1,311,875)
Earnings: ($281,752)
Fiscal Year-end: 12/31/22
Gold Mining Services
N.A.I.C.S.: 212220
Victor Goncalves *(Exec VP)*

INTERNATIONAL PUBLIC

NANOSYNTH GROUP PLC

27-28 Eastcastle Street, London, W1W 8DH, United Kingdom
Tel.: (44) 1621770472   UK
Web Site: http://www.remotemonitored.com
NNN—(LSE)
Rev.: $141,622
Assets: $10,212,891
Liabilities: $848,961
Net Worth: $9,363,930
Earnings: ($1,966,959)
Emp.: 24
Fiscal Year-end: 12/31/20
Aviation Management & Consultancy Services
N.A.I.C.S.: 488119
Trevor Brown *(Exec Dir)*

Subsidiaries:

Cloudveil Limited (1)
52 West Street, Farnham, GU9 7DX, United Kingdom
Tel.: (44) 1252717419
Web Site: http://www.cloudveil.co.uk
Software Services
N.A.I.C.S.: 541511

Geocurve Limited (1)
Tintagel House London Road, Colchester, CO5 9BP, United Kingdom
Tel.: (44) 1621770472
Web Site: http://www.geocurve.co.uk
Software Services
N.A.I.C.S.: 541511

GyroMetric Systems Limited (1)
Unit 23 The Heathcoat Building Nottingham Science and Technology Park, University Boulevard, Nottingham, NG7 2QJ, United Kingdom
Tel.: (44) 1159226995
Rotating Shaft Services
N.A.I.C.S.: 238290
John Richardson *(CEO)*

NANOTECH SYSTEMS INC.

1518-1030 West Georgia Street, Vancouver, V6E 2Y3, BC, Canada
Tel.: (604) 689-8383
Web Site: http://www.nano-techgroup.com
Year Founded: 2002
Pharmaceuticals Product Mfr
N.A.I.C.S.: 325412
Terrance G. Owen *(CEO)*

NANOTRONIX CO., LTD.

5th Sehwa Bldg Fl 66-9 NonHyeondong, Gangnam-gu, Seoul, 135-010, Korea (South)
Tel.: (82) 2 3444 7755
Web Site: http://www.nano-tronix.com
Year Founded: 2000
Measuring & Testing Device Mfr
N.A.I.C.S.: 334515
Jin Ho Han *(CEO)*

NANOVATION MICROTECH, INC.

Osterbrogade 226 St Tv, 2100, Copenhagen, Denmark   NV
Year Founded: 2016
Rev.: $794
Liabilities: $105,599
Net Worth: ($105,599)
Earnings: ($133,121)
Fiscal Year-end: 08/31/20
Tea Kalabas & Bombilla Mfr
N.A.I.C.S.: 327110
Qi Kang Xie *(Pres, CEO, Treas & Sec)*

NANOVEU LTD.

Tel.: (61) 862449095
Web Site: https://www.nanoveu.com
NVU—(ASX)
Rev.: $69,843
Assets: $349,427

AND PRIVATE COMPANIES — NANTONG JIANGSHAN AGROCHEMICAL & CHEMICAL CO., LTD.

Liabilities: $423,951
Net Worth: ($74,525)
Earnings: ($1,471,221)
Fiscal Year-end: 12/31/23
Mobile Accessory Mfr
N.A.I.C.S.: 334220
Alfred Chong (Founder, Chm & CEO)
Subsidiaries:

Nanoveu Pte Ltd (1)
20 Ayer Rajah Crescent 08-09, Singapore, 139964, Singapore
Tel.: (65) 65570155
Web Site: https://www.nanoveu.com
Cutting-Edge Nanotechnology Services
N.A.I.C.S.: 541713

NANOXPLORE INC.
4500 Thimens Blvd, Montreal, H4R 2P2, QC, Canada
Tel.: (514) 935-1377
Web Site: https://www.nanoxplore.ca
Year Founded: 2011
N13—(DEU)
Rev.: $95,030,921
Assets: $116,743,566
Liabilities: $38,046,127
Net Worth: $78,697,439
Earnings: ($8,527,703)
Emp.: 438
Fiscal Year-end: 06/30/24
Graphene Company; High Volume Graphene Powder Supplier & Mfr
N.A.I.C.S.: 212290
Soroush Nazarpour (Founder, Pres & CEO)
Subsidiaries:

Canuck Compounders Inc. (1)
180 Sheldon Drive, Cambridge, ON, Canada
Tel.: (519) 621-6521
Web Site: https://www.canuckcompounders.com
Polymer Compound Mfr & Distr
N.A.I.C.S.: 325991

RMC Advanced Technologies Inc. (1)
1400 Burris Rd, Newton, NC 28658
Tel.: (418) 484-5282
Carbon & Graphite Product Mfr
N.A.I.C.S.: 335991

NANSIN CO., LTD.
JPR Ningyo-cho Building 1-17-4 Nihombashi Ningyo-cho, Chuo-Ku, Tokyo, 103-0013, Japan
Tel.: (81) 368923016
Web Site: https://www.nansin.co.jp
Year Founded: 1947
7399—(TKS)
Rev.: $89,085,040
Assets: $152,992,400
Liabilities: $45,486,320
Net Worth: $107,506,080
Earnings: $1,723,040
Emp.: 178
Fiscal Year-end: 03/31/22
Caster Mfr & Distr
N.A.I.C.S.: 332510
Takahiro Yamamoto (Sr Mng Dir)
Subsidiaries:

NANSIN CO., LTD. - Chiba New Town Plant (1)
1-2-1 Midoridai, Inzai, 270-2331, Chiba, Japan
Tel.: (81) 476808111
Hardware Mfr
N.A.I.C.S.: 332510

NANSO TRANSPORTATION CO., LTD.
582 Togane, Togane, 283-0802, Chiba, Japan
Tel.: (81) 475543581
Web Site: https://www.nanso.co.jp
Year Founded: 1942

9034—(TKS)
Rev.: $102,279,456
Assets: $232,421,474
Liabilities: $89,289,701
Net Worth: $143,131,774
Earnings: $10,459,198
Fiscal Year-end: 03/31/24
Freight Truck Transportation Services
N.A.I.C.S.: 484122

NANTEX INDUSTRY CO., LTD.
No 9 Industrial 1st Road, Lin-yuan, 832, Kaohsiung, Taiwan
Tel.: (886) 76413621
Web Site: https://www.nantex.com.tw
2108—(TAI)
Rev.: $292,424,267
Assets: $559,428,704
Liabilities: $61,125,639
Net Worth: $498,303,065
Earnings: $30,966,577
Emp.: 739
Fiscal Year-end: 12/31/23
Rubber & Latex Products Mfr
N.A.I.C.S.: 325212
Tony Tung-Yuan Yang (Chm)
Subsidiaries:

ZhenJiang Nantex Chemical Industry Co., Ltd. (1)
No 99 Linjiang West Road, Zhenjiang New Area, Zhenjiang, Jiangsu, China
Tel.: (86) 51183366688
Web Site: http://www.nantex.com.tw
Sales Range: $50-74.9 Million
Emp.: 226
Nitrile Rubber Mfr
N.A.I.C.S.: 325212

NANTON NICKEL CORP.
Suite 800 1199 West Hastings Street, Vancouver, V6E 3T5, BC, Canada
Tel.: (604) 304-0068   BC
Year Founded: 2011
Nickel Mining
N.A.I.C.S.: 212230
Adam Cegielski (Chief Product Officer)

NANTONG ACETIC ACID CHEMICAL CO., LTD.
No 968 Jiangshan Road, Nantong Economic & Technological Development Zone, Jiangsu, 226009, China
Tel.: (86) 51385559168
Web Site: https://www.ntacf.com
Year Founded: 1959
603968—(SHG)
Rev.: $504,102,887
Assets: $445,343,802
Liabilities: $151,588,701
Net Worth: $293,755,101
Earnings: $56,369,393
Fiscal Year-end: 12/31/22
Chemical Product Mfr & Distr
N.A.I.C.S.: 325998
Gord Chu (Sls Mgr)

NANTONG CHAODA EQUIPMENT CO., LTD.
High-tech Zone, Rugao, Jiangsu, China
Tel.: (86) 51387735878
Web Site: https://www.chaodamould.com
Year Founded: 2005
301186—(CHIN)
Rev.: $88,334,155
Assets: $288,804,534
Liabilities: $110,508,648
Net Worth: $178,295,887
Earnings: $13,439,056
Emp.: 900
Fiscal Year-end: 12/31/23
Automobile Parts Mfr & Distr
N.A.I.C.S.: 336211
Jianjun Feng (Chm)

NANTONG GUOSHENG INTELLIGENCE TECHNOLOGY GROUP CO., LTD.
No 2 Yongtong Road, Gangzha Economic & Technological Development zone chongchuan district, Nantong, 226003, Jiangsu, China
Tel.: (86) 4006847900
Web Site: https://www.ntgszk.com
Year Founded: 1999
688558—(SSE)
Rev.: $163,307,776
Assets: $283,103,585
Liabilities: $68,482,725
Net Worth: $214,620,859
Earnings: $26,043,358
Fiscal Year-end: 12/31/22
Metalworking Machinery Product Mfr
N.A.I.C.S.: 333519
Weiguo Pan (Chm & Gen Mgr)
Subsidiaries:

Chelsearobot Automatic (Nantong) Co., Ltd. (1)
No 2 Yongtong road, Economic Development Zone Gangzha, Nantong, 226003, Jiangsu, China
Tel.: (86) 51385602596
Web Site: https://www.chelsearobot.cn
Industrial Machinery Mfr & Distr
N.A.I.C.S.: 333248

Jiangsu Dawei Precision Technology Co., Ltd. (1)
No 188 zhonghuang road, Chongchuang, Nantong, Jiangsu, China
Tel.: (86) 51385602596
Industrial Machinery Mfr & Distr
N.A.I.C.S.: 333248

Nantong Guosheng Machine Components Co., Ltd. (1)
No 398 Rongsheng Road, Chongchuang District, Nantong, Jiangsu, China
Tel.: (86) 51385690618
Machine Tool Mfr & Distr
N.A.I.C.S.: 333517

Nantong Guosheng Precision Machinery Co., Ltd. (1)
No 9 qingdao road, Tongzhou district, Nantong, Jiangsu, China
Tel.: (86) 51386559908
Cutting Machine Tool Mfr
N.A.I.C.S.: 333515

Nantong S.leading Intelligence Technology Co., Ltd. (1)
No 458 Tingping Road, Chongchuang, Nantong, Jiangsu, China
Tel.: (86) 51389066069
Industrial Machinery Mfr & Distr
N.A.I.C.S.: 333248

Nantong SLD New Energy Technology Co., Ltd. (1)
No 888 Bihua Road, Tongzhou, Nantong, Jiangsu, China
Tel.: (86) 51386559908
Industrial Machinery Mfr & Distr
N.A.I.C.S.: 333248

Nantong SLW.MT Equipment Technology Co., Ltd. (1)
No 188 Zhonghuang Road, Chongchuang District, Nantong, Jiangsu, China
Tel.: (86) 51386600510
Machine Tool Mfr & Distr
N.A.I.C.S.: 333517

NANTONG HAIXING ELECTRONICS CO., LTD.
No 519 Tongyang South Road, Pingchao Town Tongzhou District, Nantong, 226000, Jiangsu, China
Tel.: (86) 51386718818
Web Site: https://www.haistar.com.cn
Year Founded: 1998
603115—(SHG)
Rev.: $247,838,362
Assets: $339,733,181
Liabilities: $54,704,291
Net Worth: $285,028,890

Earnings: $31,971,074
Fiscal Year-end: 12/31/22
Electronic Product Mfr & Distr
N.A.I.C.S.: 334416
Xiaobing Zhou (Chm)

NANTONG JIANGHAI CAPACITOR CO., LTD.
No 79 Tongyang South Road, Pingchao Town Tongzhou District, Nantong, 226361, Jiangsu, China
Tel.: (86) 51386726012
Web Site: https://www.jianghai.com
Year Founded: 1958
002484—(SSE)
Rev.: $634,843,872
Assets: $986,468,652
Liabilities: $260,502,372
Net Worth: $725,966,280
Earnings: $92,838,096
Emp.: 1,400
Fiscal Year-end: 12/31/22
Electronic Capacitor Mfr
N.A.I.C.S.: 334416
Chen Weidong (Chm)
Subsidiaries:

Europtronic (Suzhou) Co., Ltd. (1)
No 1618 Yundongdadao Wujiang Economic Development Zone, Suzhou, 215200, Jiangsu, China
Tel.: (86) 51263401650
Web Site: http://www.europtronic.com
Emp.: 300
Electronic Components Mfr
N.A.I.C.S.: 334416

Jauch Quartz America, Inc. (1)
14601 NW Arabian Way, Seabeck, WA 98380
Tel.: (360) 633-7200
Web Site: http://www.jauchusa.com
Frequency Control Products Mfr
N.A.I.C.S.: 334419
Christian Schwenk (Pres)

Jauch Quartz France (1)
Tel.: (33) 146999540
Sales Range: $25-49.9 Million
Emp.: 8
Frequency Control Devices Mfr
N.A.I.C.S.: 334419

Jauch Quartz UK Ltd. (1)
7 Priory Court Tuscam Way, Camberley, GU15 3YX, Surrey, United Kingdom
Tel.: (44) 1276605900
Web Site: http://www.jauch.co.uk
Sales Range: $25-49.9 Million
Emp.: 10
Frequency Control Products Mfr & Distr
N.A.I.C.S.: 334515
Nicholas Ribton (Mng Dir)

Jianghai America Inc. (1)
3104 Sunrise Rdg Ln, Hacienda Heights, CA 91745
Tel.: (626) 274-1692
Web Site: http://www.jianghai-america.com
Electrolytic Capacitor Mfr
N.A.I.C.S.: 334416

Jianghai Europe Electronic Components GmbH (1)
Uerdinger Strasse 125, 47799, Krefeld, Germany
Tel.: (49) 21516520880
Web Site: http://www.jianghai-europe.com
Sales Range: $25-49.9 Million
Emp.: 6
Aluminum Electrolytic Capacitors Mfr
N.A.I.C.S.: 334416
Ole Bjorn (Gen Mgr)

NANTONG JIANGSHAN AGROCHEMICAL & CHEMICAL CO., LTD.
No 998 Jiangshan Road, Economic And Technological Development Zone, Nantong, 226017, Jiangsu, China
Tel.: (86) 51383502727
Web Site: https://www.jsac.com.cn

5145

NANTONG JIANGSHAN AGROCHEMICAL & CHEMICAL CO., LTD.

Nantong Jiangshan Agrochemical & Chemical Co., Ltd.—(Continued)
Year Founded: 1990
600389—(SHG)
Rev.: $1,172,167,701
Assets: $914,438,973
Liabilities: $449,382,352
Net Worth: $465,056,622
Earnings: $258,957,200
Fiscal Year-end: 12/31/22
Agricultural Chemical Product Mfr
N.A.I.C.S.: 325320
Jian Xue (Chm, Pres & Gen Mgr)

NANTONG JIANGTIAN CHEMICAL CO., LTD.
No 16 Central Road, Economic & Technological Development Zone, Nantong, 226009, Jiangsu, China
Tel.: (86) 51383599150
Web Site: https://www.ntjtc.com
Year Founded: 1999
300927—(SSE)
Rev.: $103,515,516
Assets: $111,516,912
Liabilities: $22,080,708
Net Worth: $89,436,204
Earnings: $8,956,116
Fiscal Year-end: 12/31/22
Chemical Product Mfr & Distr
N.A.I.C.S.: 325520
Hui Zhu (Chm & Gen Mgr)

NANTONG XINGQIU GRAPHITE CO., LTD.
Huaxing Road No 8, Jiuhua Industrial Park Jiuhua Town, Rugao, Jiangsu, China
Tel.: (86) 4001000129
Web Site: http://www.ntxingqiu.com
Year Founded: 2001
688633—(SHG)
Rev.: $91,433,324
Assets: $292,327,177
Liabilities: $101,825,563
Net Worth: $190,501,614
Earnings: $19,893,023
Emp.: 500
Fiscal Year-end: 12/31/23
Graphite Equipment Mfr
N.A.I.C.S.: 335991
Shujuan Qian (Chm)

NANXING MACHINERY CO., LTD.
Nanxing Road Science and Technology Industrial Park, Houjie Town, Dongguan, Guangdong, China
Tel.: (86) 76988803333
Web Site: https://www.nanxingmac.com
Year Founded: 1996
002757—(SSE)
Rev.: $415,630,332
Assets: $550,571,580
Liabilities: $208,123,344
Net Worth: $342,448,236
Earnings: $40,763,736
Emp.: 980
Fiscal Year-end: 12/31/22
Panel Furniture Equipment Mfr
N.A.I.C.S.: 333243

NANYA NEW MATERIAL TECHNOLOGY CO., LTD.
No 158 Changxiang Road, Nanxiang Town Jiading District, Shanghai, 201802, China
Tel.: (86) 2169178431
Web Site: http://www.ccl-china.com
Year Founded: 2000
688519—(SSE)
Rev.: $530,460,867
Assets: $686,410,869
Liabilities: $310,582,743
Net Worth: $375,828,125

Earnings: $6,301,882
Fiscal Year-end: 12/31/22
Electronic Product Mfr & Distr
N.A.I.C.S.: 334419
Xiuyin Bao (Chm)

NANYA TECHNOLOGY CORPORATION
No 98 Nanlin Rd, Taishan Dist, Taipei, 243, Taiwan
Tel.: (886) 229045858
Web Site: https://www.nanya.com
Year Founded: 1995
2408—(TAI)
Rev.: $977,543,571
Assets: $6,290,286,332
Liabilities: $831,502,568
Net Worth: $5,458,783,763
Earnings: ($243,292,250)
Emp.: 1,639
Fiscal Year-end: 12/31/23
Electronic Parts Research & Development, Design, Manufacture & Sales
N.A.I.C.S.: 334419
Pei-Ing Lee (Pres)

Subsidiaries:

Nanya Technology (HK) Co., Ltd. (1)
Room 509 Tower A Tian' an Tech-Venture Park, Chegong Temple Area, Futian District, Shenzhen, 518040, Guangdong, China (100%)
Tel.: (86) 76683344381
Web Site: http://www.nanya.com
PC Mfr & Distr
N.A.I.C.S.: 334118

Nanya Technology (SH) Co., Ltd. (1)
Rm 1003 1005 Cloud Nine Plz No 1118 YanAn W Rd, Shanghai, 200052, China (100%)
Tel.: (86) 2152586005
Web Site: http://www.nanya.com
Sales Range: $25-49.9 Million
Emp.: 13
PC Mfr & Distr
N.A.I.C.S.: 541512

Nanya Technology Corporation, U.S.A. (1)
5104 Old Ironsides Dr Ste 113, Santa Clara, CA 95054
Tel.: (408) 961-4000
Sales Range: $25-49.9 Million
Emp.: 50
Computer Peripheral Equipment Distr
N.A.I.C.S.: 423430
Ken Hurley (Pres)

Nanya Technology Europe GmbH (1)
Pemperforter str 50, 40211, Dusseldorf, Germany (100%)
Tel.: (49) 2115285050
Web Site: http://www.nanya.com
Sales Range: $25-49.9 Million
PC Mfr & Distr Including Technical Support
N.A.I.C.S.: 541512

Nanya Technology Japan (1)
3-24-18 Takanawa Minato-ku, 108 0074, Tokyo, Japan (100%)
Tel.: (81) 354752390
Web Site: http://www.nanya.com
Sales Range: $25-49.9 Million
Emp.: 10
PC & Electronics Distr
N.A.I.C.S.: 334111

NANYANG HOLDINGS LIMITED
Room 1808 St George's Building 2 Ice House Street, Central, China (Hong Kong)
Tel.: (852) 25224147 BM
Web Site: http://www.nanyangholdingsltd.com
Year Founded: 1947
0212—(HKG)
Rev.: $20,985,225
Assets: $657,687,840
Liabilities: $11,867,445
Net Worth: $645,820,395

Earnings: $1,564,170
Emp.: 12
Fiscal Year-end: 12/31/22
Investment Management Service
N.A.I.C.S.: 523940
Ching Yung Hung (Mng Dir)

NANYANG TOPSEC TECHNOLOGIES GROUP INC.
Room 109 Building 1 Hechen Huizhao Industrial Park Northeast Corner, Jinping District, Shantou, 515041, Guangdong, China
Tel.: (86) 75487278712
Web Site: http://www.nanyangcable.com
Year Founded: 1985
002212—(SSE)
Rev.: $497,437,748
Assets: $1,682,812,189
Liabilities: $309,586,760
Net Worth: $1,373,225,429
Earnings: $28,794,819
Fiscal Year-end: 12/31/22
Holding Company; Cable Product Mfr
N.A.I.C.S.: 551112
Li Xueying (Chm & Gen Mgr)

NANYO CORPORATION
3198 Hakataekimae, Hakata-ku, Fukuoka, 812-8556, Japan
Tel.: (81) 924727331 JP
Web Site: https://www.nanyo.co.jp
Year Founded: 1950
7417—(TKS)
Rev.: $251,120,510
Assets: $283,476,460
Liabilities: $120,262,340
Net Worth: $163,214,120
Earnings: $13,160,510
Emp.: 508
Fiscal Year-end: 03/31/24
Construction Machinery Distr
N.A.I.C.S.: 423810
Eiichiro Takeuchi (Pres)

Subsidiaries:

Hamamura Yuatsu Co., Ltd. (1)
199 Yoshiwara Wakamatsu, Onga Town Onga District, Fukuoka, 811-4304, Japan
Tel.: (81) 932936781
Web Site: https://hamamura-onga.com
Emp.: 15
Semiconductor Product Distr
N.A.I.C.S.: 423690

Kyoei Communication Industry Co., Ltd. (1)
3-1-9 Higashi, Shibuya-ku, Tokyo, 150-0011, Japan
Tel.: (81) 334009171
Web Site: https://www.kyoei-tsushin.co.jp
Emp.: 19
Motor & Material Distr
N.A.I.C.S.: 423910

Kyoritsu Saisekisho Co., Ltd. (1)
1496 Tojinmachi Miyata, Miyawaka, 823-0011, Fukuoka, Japan
Tel.: (81) 949322211
Web Site: https://kyoritsu-sss.com
Emp.: 22
Quarrying Machinery Mfr & Distr
N.A.I.C.S.: 333131

NANYO Heavy Vehicles Co., Ltd. (1)
58-2 Shishimizu Tomiai-cho, Minami-ku, Kumamoto, 861-4163, Japan
Tel.: (81) 963572341
Web Site: https://nanyo-j.jp
Emp.: 20
Construction Machinery Rental Services
N.A.I.C.S.: 532412

NANYO International Trading (Shanghai) Co., Ltd. (1)
Room 2105 Longhu Center Building 13 No 79 Jinshan East Road, High-tech Zone, Suzhou, 215011, Jiangsu, China
Tel.: (86) 51268086052
Web Site: https://www.nanyo.cn

Emp.: 22
Machine Tool Distr
N.A.I.C.S.: 423830

NANYO Rentec Co., Ltd. (1)
3-19-8 Hakataekimae, Hakata-ku, Fukuoka, 812-0011, Japan
Tel.: (81) 924310666
Web Site: https://www.nanyo-rentec.biz
Emp.: 152
Construction Machinery Rental Services
N.A.I.C.S.: 532412

TODAKA Corporation (1)
1-3-21 Aozaki, Oita, 870-0278, Japan
Tel.: (81) 975211379
Web Site: https://www.todaka-oita.jp
Emp.: 53
Precision Parts Mfr & Distr
N.A.I.C.S.: 332216

United C & N Co., Ltd. (1)
No 276 3rd FL Chung Ching N Road, Datong District, Taipei, Taiwan
Tel.: (886) 225980460
Semiconductor Product Distr
N.A.I.C.S.: 423690

NAOS EMERGING OPPORTUNITIES COMPANY LIMITED
Level 34 25 Martin Place, 19 Martin Place, Sydney, 2000, NSW, Australia
Tel.: (61) 290021576
Web Site: http://www.naos.com.au
NCC—(ASX)
Rev.: $703,101
Assets: $55,542,060
Liabilities: $15,054,241
Net Worth: $40,487,820
Earnings: ($298,029)
Emp.: 9
Fiscal Year-end: 06/30/23
Investment Services
N.A.I.C.S.: 523999
David Rickards (Chm)

NAOS EX-50 OPPORTUNITIES COMPANY LIMITED
Level 34 25 Martin Place, Sydney, 2000, NSW, Australia
Tel.: (61) 290021576 AU
Web Site: https://www.naos.com.au
NAC—(ASX)
Assets: $31,208,393
Liabilities: $11,992,442
Net Worth: $19,215,951
Earnings: ($8,889,525)
Emp.: 8
Fiscal Year-end: 06/30/24
Investment Management Service
N.A.I.C.S.: 523940
Rajiv Sharma (Head-Legal & Compliance)

NAPATECH A/S
Tobaksvejen 23 A, DK-2860, Soborg, Denmark
Tel.: (45) 45961500
Web Site: https://www.napatech.com
0QJ4—(LSE)
Rev.: $22,952,641
Assets: $28,066,154
Liabilities: $15,296,118
Net Worth: $12,770,037
Earnings: ($6,982,825)
Emp.: 81
Fiscal Year-end: 12/31/22
Ethernet Network Acceleration Adapter Hardware Mfr
N.A.I.C.S.: 334118
Henrik Brill Jensen (COO)

Subsidiaries:

Napatech Inc. (1)
1 New Hampshire Ave Ste 125, Portsmouth, NH 03801
Communication Equipment Mfr
N.A.I.C.S.: 334290

AND PRIVATE COMPANIES

NAPER HOLDING A/S
Brobekkveien 80, PO Box 1156, Sentrum, 107, Oslo, Norway
Tel.: (47) 22 63 6400
Web Site: http://www.naper.no
Year Founded: 1982
Sales Range: $50-74.9 Million
Emp.: 270
Commercial Printing
N.A.I.C.S.: 541430

NAPIER VENTURES INC.
615 - 800 West Pender Street, Vancouver, V6C 2V6, BC, Canada
Tel.: (403) 922-1685   BC
Web Site:
    http://www.napierventuresinc.com
Year Founded: 2007
NAP—(TSXV)
Sales Range: Less than $1 Million
Investment Services
N.A.I.C.S.: 523999
Rob Cohoe (Pres)

NAPLOY CORP.
95 Lias Estate, Kafe District FCT, Abuja, 900108, Nigeria
Tel.: (234) 13072133163   WY
Year Founded: 2023
Assets: $67,970
Liabilities: $59,759
Net Worth: $8,211
Earnings: ($20,301)
Fiscal Year-end: 07/31/24
Health Care Srvices
N.A.I.C.S.: 621610

NAPREDAK A.D.
Industrijska Zona bb, Kotor, 85330, Montenegro
Tel.: (382) 32311100   Me
Web Site: http://www.napredak.com
Furniture & Home Product Distr
N.A.I.C.S.: 423220
Brankica Markovic (Mgr)

NAPREDAK A.D.
Pelagicevo Bb, 76256, Pelagicevo, Bosnia & Herzegovina
Tel.: (387) 54 810 144
NAPR—(BANJ)
Sales Range: $1-9.9 Million
Emp.: 35
Crop Farming Services
N.A.I.C.S.: 111998
Jovan Erletic (Chm-Mgmt Bd)

NAPREDAK A.D.
Djure Djakovica 55, Svilajnac, 35210, Serbia
Tel.: (381) 35314395
Year Founded: 1948
NAPS—(BEL)
Sales Range: Less than $1 Million
Emp.: 38
Apparel Product Mfr
N.A.I.C.S.: 315990

NAPREDAK A.D.
Alekse Santica 4, Velika Plana, Serbia
Tel.: (381) 26 514 467
Year Founded: 1947
Sales Range: $1-9.9 Million
Grain Mill Product Mfr
N.A.I.C.S.: 311211
Dragan Filipovic (Exec Dir)

NAPREDAK A.D.
Dunavska obala bb, Apatin, Serbia
Tel.: (381) 25 772 155
Year Founded: 1989
NPRA—(BEL)
Sales Range: $1-9.9 Million
Emp.: 50

Hydraulic Structure Construction Services
N.A.I.C.S.: 237990
Zoran Banjac (Mng Dir)

NAPREDAK A.D.
Paje Jovanovica 1, Pirot, Serbia
Tel.: (381) 10 321 812
Year Founded: 2002
Sales Range: Less than $1 Million
Emp.: 18
Building Construction Services
N.A.I.C.S.: 236220
Jovica Krstic (Exec Dir)

NAPREDAK A.D.
Golubinacki put bb, Stara Pazova, Serbia
Tel.: (381) 22 310 432
Web Site: http://www.napredak.rs
Year Founded: 1998
Sales Range: $1-9.9 Million
Emp.: 141
Cereal Crop Farming Services
N.A.I.C.S.: 111998
Milan Sveljo (Dir)

NAPREDAK A.D.
Knjaza Milosa 70, Pozega, Serbia
Tel.: (381) 31 3816 277
Year Founded: 1991
Sales Range: $1-9.9 Million
Emp.: 85
Wood Products Mfr
N.A.I.C.S.: 321999
Vojimir Stankovic (Exec Dir)

NAPSTER GROUP PLC
55 Poland Street, London, W1F 7NL, United Kingdom
Tel.: (44) 116 2424012   UK
Web Site: http://www.napster.group
NAPS—(AIM)
Sales Range: Less than $1 Million
Emp.: 54
Investment Management Service
N.A.I.C.S.: 523940
Anthony Matchett (Founder)
Subsidiaries:

Rhapsody International, Inc.   (1)
701 5th Ave Ste 3100, Seattle, WA 98104
Tel.: (415) 934-2000
Web Site: http://www.rhapsody.com
Digital Music Services
N.A.I.C.S.: 516210
Matt Eccles (Gen Counsel & Sr VP)

NARA CELLAR CO., LTD.
A-7F H Business Park 25 Beobwon-ro 11-gil, Songpa-gu, Seoul, Korea (South)
Tel.: (82) 24054300
Web Site: https://www.naracellar.com
Year Founded: 1990
405920—(KRS)
Alcoholic Beverage Distr
N.A.I.C.S.: 424820
SungJae Lee (CEO)

NARA MOLD & DIE CO., LTD.
675 Gongdna-ro, Seongsan-gu, Changwon, Gyeongsangnam-do, Korea (South)
Tel.: (82) 552393600
Web Site: https://www.naramnd.com
Year Founded: 1999
051490—(KRS)
Rev.: $167,376,615
Assets: $180,943,991
Liabilities: $106,885,440
Net Worth: $74,058,551
Earnings: $7,457,471
Emp.: 261
Fiscal Year-end: 12/31/22
Mold Mfr
N.A.I.C.S.: 333511

Young-Jo Kim (Pres & Co-CEO)
Subsidiaries:

Nara Kunshan Stamping Die Co., Ltd.   (1)
3289 Beimen road, Kunshan, Jiangsu, China
Tel.: (86) 18112638185
Industrial Mold Mfr
N.A.I.C.S.: 333511

Nara M Tech Co., Ltd   (1)
24 Janggye-gil, Cheongbuk-eup, Pyeongtaek, Gyeonggi-do, Korea (South)
Tel.: (82) 316158813
Industrial Mold Mfr
N.A.I.C.S.: 333511

Nara M Tech Co., Ltd - Oksan Factory   (1)
180-7 Hojuk-ri, Oksan-myeon, Cheongwon, Chungcheongbuk-do, Korea (South)
Tel.: (82) 43 716 0332
Industrial Mold Mfr
N.A.I.C.S.: 333511

Nara M&D Co., Ltd   (1)
675 Gongdna-ro, Seongsan-gu, Changwon, Gyeongsangnam-do, Korea (South)
Tel.: (82) 552393600
Web Site: https://www.naramnd.com
Emp.: 300
Mold Die Mfr
N.A.I.C.S.: 333511

Nara M&D Co., Ltd - Sungsan Factory   (1)
74-2 Sungsan-dong, Changwon, Gyeongsangnam-do, Korea (South)
Tel.: (82) 55 239 4000
Industrial Mold Mfr
N.A.I.C.S.: 333511

Nara Pla Tech Co., Ltd   (1)
683 Gongdan-ro, Sungsan-gu, Changwon, Gyeongsangnam-do, Korea (South)
Tel.: (82) 552393760
Web Site: https://www.narapt.com
Industrial Mold Mfr
N.A.I.C.S.: 333511

PT.NARA Summit Industry   (1)
JL Meranti III Blok L No 10-2, Delta Silicon Industrial park Lemahabang, Bekasi, Indonesia
Tel.: (62) 2189903027
Web Site: https://www.narasummit.com
Mold Die Mfr
N.A.I.C.S.: 333511

NARAE NANOTECH CORPORATION
250 Baegok-daero Idong-eup, Cheoin-gu, Yongin, 17134, Gyeonggi-do, Korea (South)
Tel.: (82) 313372600
Web Site:
    https://www.naraenano.co.kr
Year Founded: 1990
137080—(KRS)
Rev.: $67,527,034
Assets: $142,236,256
Liabilities: $59,424,264
Net Worth: $82,811,992
Earnings: $1,934,326
Emp.: 279
Fiscal Year-end: 12/31/22
Electronic Component Mfr & Distr
N.A.I.C.S.: 334419
Dongwon Jang (CEO)
Subsidiaries:

Naraenanotech (Guangzhou) Co., Ltd.   (1)
12F RM 1202 1206 Macau YouthInnovation Tribe, No 85 Xiangxue Ave Middle Rd Huangpu District, Guangzhou, China
Tel.: (86) 2031704270
Industrial Equipment Mfr & Distr
N.A.I.C.S.: 333413

NARAINGARH SUGAR MILLS LTD.
Village Banondi PO Shahzadpur Teh-

NARBADA GEMS & JEWELLERY LTD.

sil Naraingarh, Ambala, 134202, Haryana, India
Tel.: (91) 1734 277388
Sales Range: $25-49.9 Million
Sugar Mfr
N.A.I.C.S.: 311314
Rangoli Aggarwal (Sec)

NARASAKI SANGYO CO., LTD.
Presto 1 7 Bldg 7-1 Kita1jho-nishi, Chuo-ku, Sapporo, 060-0001, Hokkaido, Japan
Tel.: (81) 112715271
Web Site: https://www.narasaki.co.jp
Year Founded: 1943
8085—(TKS)
Rev.: $710,277,550
Assets: $400,889,890
Liabilities: $238,548,290
Net Worth: $162,341,600
Earnings: $15,209,610
Emp.: 413
Fiscal Year-end: 03/31/24
Electronic Equipment & Machinery Whslr
N.A.I.C.S.: 423620
Katsuhisa Nakamura (Pres)
Subsidiaries:

Narasaki Stax Co., Ltd.   (1)
2-13-24 Motonakano, Tomakomai, 053-8522, Hokkaido, Japan
Tel.: (81) 144352222
Cargo Transportation Services
N.A.I.C.S.: 488490
Shigeki Akimoto (Chm)

Narasaki Trade (Shanghai) Co., Ltd.   (1)
Room 503-505 Block B Far East International Plaza No 317 Xianxia Road, Shanghai, 200051, China
Tel.: (86) 216 235 1212
Web Site: https://www.narasaki.com.cn
Industrial Machinery Distr
N.A.I.C.S.: 423830

NARASOFT CO., LTD.
3F Ranix Bldg 131 Nonhyeon-ro, Seocho-gu, Seoul, Korea (South)
Tel.: (82) 234877988   KR
Web Site: http://www.narasoft.com
Year Founded: 2002
288490—(KRS)
Information Technology Services
N.A.I.C.S.: 541519
Phil Bartos (Pres & CEO)

NARAYANA HRUDAYALAYA LTD.
No 258/A Bommasandra Industrial Area Anekal Taluk, Bengaluru, 562158, India
Tel.: (91) 8071222636
Web Site:
    https://www.narayanahealth.org
NH—(NSE)
Rev.: $610,703,216
Assets: $674,387,262
Liabilities: $328,465,331
Net Worth: $345,921,931
Earnings: $94,675,918
Emp.: 11,726
Fiscal Year-end: 03/31/24
Health Care Srvices
N.A.I.C.S.: 621610
Viren Shetty (Grp COO)

NARBADA GEMS & JEWELLERY LTD.
3-6-291/4/B 2nd Floor, Hyderguda, Hyderabad, 500029, Telangana, India
Tel.: (91) 4048506411
Web Site:
    https://www.narbadajewellery.com
Year Founded: 1993
519455—(BOM)
Rev.: $11,218,056

NARBADA GEMS & JEWELLERY LTD.

Narbada Gems & Jewellery Ltd.—(Continued)
Assets: $9,853,822
Liabilities: $4,512,032
Net Worth: $5,341,790
Earnings: $425,838
Emp.: 110
Fiscal Year-end: 03/31/23
Jewelry Mfr
N.A.I.C.S.: 339910
Sanjay Kumar Sanghi *(Chm & Mng Dir)*

NARENDRA PROPERTIES LIMITED
Makanji House 2nd Floor Old No 25 New No 49, Barnaby Road Kilpauk, Chennai, 600010, Tamil Nadu, India
Tel.: (91) 4442696600
Web Site: https://www.narendraproperties.com
531416—(BOM)
Rev.: $930,739
Assets: $4,437,803
Liabilities: $137,414
Net Worth: $4,300,390
Earnings: $515,319
Emp.: 12
Fiscal Year-end: 03/31/23
Commercial Building Construction Services
N.A.I.C.S.: 236220
S. Ramalingam *(Chm)*

NARF INDUSTRIES PLC
5 Fleet Place, London, EC4M 7RD, United Kingdom UK
Web Site: https://www.narfgroup.com
Year Founded: 2018
NFINF—(OTCIQ)
Rev.: $2,547,125
Assets: $3,912,298
Liabilities: $2,109,689
Net Worth: $1,802,609
Earnings: ($18,425,707)
Emp.: 17
Fiscal Year-end: 12/31/22
Information Technology Services
N.A.I.C.S.: 541512

NARI HAMICO MINERALS JOINT STOCK COMPANY
To 14 Phuong Quang Trung, Phu Ly, Ha Nam, Vietnam
Tel.: (84) 351 851 035
Web Site: http://www.hamico.vn
Year Founded: 1967
Sales Range: $1-9.9 Million
Mining Services
N.A.I.C.S.: 212311

NARMADA AGROBASE LTD.
401 Silicon Tower Above Freezland Restaurant, Nr National Handloom Law Garden, Ahmedabad, 390009, Gujarat, India
Tel.: (91) 7940370886
Web Site: https://www.narmadaagrobase.com
Year Founded: 1988
543643—(BOM)
Rev.: $6,003,993
Assets: $3,275,571
Liabilities: $1,371,357
Net Worth: $1,904,214
Earnings: $78,197
Emp.: 10
Fiscal Year-end: 03/31/23
Cotton Seed Product Mfr
N.A.I.C.S.: 311119
Neerajkumar Sureshchandra Agrawal *(Chm & Mng Dir)*

NARMADA GELATINES LIMITED
Caravas Room no 28 1st floor 15 civil lines, Jabalpur, 482001, Madhya Pradesh, India
Tel.: (91) 7612648627
Web Site: https://www.narmadagelatines.com
526739—(BOM)
Rev.: $19,159,263
Assets: $22,503,090
Liabilities: $3,557,327
Net Worth: $18,945,763
Earnings: $1,154,490
Emp.: 196
Fiscal Year-end: 03/31/21
Pharmaceuticals Product Mfr
N.A.I.C.S.: 325412
Ashok Kumar Kapur *(Exec Dir)*

NARMADA MACPLAST DRIP IRRIGATION SYSTEMS LTD.
16/A Parulnagar Society 1st Floor Bhuyangdev Char Rasta, Opp Mahakali Temple Sola Road Ghatlodia, Ahmedabad, 380 061, India
Tel.: (91) 7927498670
Web Site: https://www.narmadadrip.com
Year Founded: 2007
517431—(BOM)
Rev.: $505,706
Assets: $787,279
Liabilities: $472,490
Net Worth: $314,789
Earnings: $95
Fiscal Year-end: 03/31/21
Plastic Product & Raw Material Distr
N.A.I.C.S.: 424610
Vrajlal Vaghasia *(Chm & Mng Dir)*

NARNIA (HONG KONG) GROUP COMPANY LIMITED
Jiapu Economic Development Area, Changxing County, Huzhou, Zhejiang, China
Tel.: (86) 5726296728 Ky
Web Site: http://www.narnia.hk
Year Founded: 2002
8607—(HKG)
Rev.: $48,955,093
Assets: $35,516,146
Liabilities: $17,769,024
Net Worth: $17,747,122
Earnings: ($442,822)
Emp.: 296
Fiscal Year-end: 12/31/22
Fabric Product Mfr & Distr
N.A.I.C.S.: 313230
Shunhua Dai *(Founder & Chm)*

NARODNA BANKA SLOVENSKA
Imricha Karvasa 1, 813 25, Bratislava, Slovakia
Tel.: (421) 257871111
Web Site: http://www.nbs.sk
Year Founded: 1993
Rev.: $367,041,067
Assets: $57,371,155,584
Liabilities: $56,764,794,760
Net Worth: $606,360,824
Earnings: $197,116,193
Emp.: 1,110
Fiscal Year-end: 12/31/18
Banking Services
N.A.I.C.S.: 521110
Karol Mrva *(Exec Dir-Risk Mgmt)*

NARODOWY BANK POLSKI
ul Swietokrzyska 11-21, Warsaw, 919, Poland
Tel.: (48) 226531000
Web Site: http://www.nbp.pl
Sales Range: $1-4.9 Billion
Emp.: 3,000
Banking Services
N.A.I.C.S.: 521110
Marek Belka *(Pres)*

NARRYER METALS LIMITED
Level 5 191 St Georges Terrace, Perth, 6005, WA, Australia
Tel.: (61) 292999690
Web Site: https://www.narryer.com.au
Year Founded: 2021
NYM—(ASX)
Rev.: $7,327
Assets: $1,005,094
Liabilities: $155,824
Net Worth: $849,270
Earnings: ($1,931,675)
Fiscal Year-end: 06/30/23
Metal Exploration Services
N.A.I.C.S.: 213114

NAS AIRPORT SERVICES LIMITED
PO Box 19010, PO Box 19010, Nairobi, 00501, Kenya
Tel.: (254) 20 6972000
Web Site: http://www.nascat.com
Year Founded: 1949
Sales Range: $75-99.9 Million
Emp.: 800
Food Manufacturing, Production & In-Flight Airport Catering & Support Services
N.A.I.C.S.: 722320
Faith Githaiga *(Grp Mgr-HR)*

NAS STAN A.D.
Pozeska 65b, PO Box 2040, Belgrade, Serbia
Tel.: (381) 11 3050 751
Web Site: http://www.a-nasstan.com
Year Founded: 1971
Sales Range: Less than $1 Million
Emp.: 14
Architectural Designing Services
N.A.I.C.S.: 541310

NASA BANKA AD BIJELJINA
Patrijarha Pavla 3, 76300, Bijeljina, Bosnia & Herzegovina
Tel.: (387) 55 232 317
Web Site: http://www.nasa-banka.com
Year Founded: 1999
PIBB—(BANJ)
Sales Range: Less than $1 Million
Banking Services
N.A.I.C.S.: 523150
Petar Lazic *(Member-Mgmt Bd)*

NASA SLOGA A.D.
Svetozara Markovica 135, Kovin, Serbia
Tel.: (381) 13 742 428
Web Site: http://www.nasa-sloga.rs
Year Founded: 2014
Sales Range: Less than $1 Million
Emp.: 8
Construction Materials Mfr
N.A.I.C.S.: 327331

NASCON ALLIED INDUSTRIES PLC
15B Ikosi Rd, Oregun, Ikeja, Lagos, Nigeria
Tel.: (234) 7008880888
Web Site: https://nascon.dangote.com
Year Founded: 1973
NASCON—(NIGE)
Rev.: $43,513,461
Assets: $41,103,762
Liabilities: $27,008,642
Net Worth: $14,095,120
Earnings: $4,048,326
Emp.: 590
Fiscal Year-end: 12/31/22
Salt Distr
N.A.I.C.S.: 424490
Paul Farrer *(Mng Dir)*

INTERNATIONAL PUBLIC

NASH DOM BULGARIA HOLDING AD SOFIA
ul Aleksandar Kusev 20, 1142, Lovech, Bulgaria
Tel.: (359) 879400061
HDOM—(BUL)
Sales Range: Less than $1 Million
Food Mfr
N.A.I.C.S.: 311999

NASIRMACHINE ENGINEERING CO.
9th-3rd Floor-NO 315-Kalantari Square-Seyyed Jamaloddin Asad Abadi Ave, Yousef Abad, Tehran, Iran
Tel.: (98) 2188618493
Web Site: https://www.nasirmachine.com
Year Founded: 1994
Automobile Parts Mfr
N.A.I.C.S.: 336110
Mahmoud Aliabadi Farahani *(Chm)*

NASPERS LIMITED
40 Heerengracht, Cape Town, 8001, South Africa
Tel.: (27) 214062121 ZA
Web Site: https://www.naspers.com
Year Founded: 1915
NPSNY—(OTCIQ)
Rev.: $6,778,000,000
Assets: $65,498,000,000
Liabilities: $20,893,000,000
Net Worth: $44,605,000,000
Earnings: $9,954,000,000
Emp.: 27,573
Fiscal Year-end: 03/31/23
Media Holding Company
N.A.I.C.S.: 551112
Basil Sgourdos *(Fin Dir)*

Subsidiaries:

Compera nTime Internet Movel S.A. (1)
Lauro Muller 116 Salas 3 003 e 3 004, Rio de Janeiro, 22290-906, Brazil
Tel.: (55) 2121586050
Online Publishing Services
N.A.I.C.S.: 513199

Kalahari.net (1)
11 Adderley St, 8001, Cape Town, Western Cape, South Africa
Tel.: (27) 21 468 9200
Web Site: http://www.kalahari.com
Online Shopping Services
N.A.I.C.S.: 425120

Media24 Proprietary Limited (1)
40 Heerengracht, Cape Town, 8001, South Africa
Tel.: (27) 214062021
Web Site: https://www.media24.com
Digital Media Services
N.A.I.C.S.: 541840

OLX Global B.V. (1)
Taurusavenue 105, 2132 LS, Hoofddorp, Netherlands (100%)
Tel.: (31) 235562636
Web Site: http://www.olx.com
Holding Company; Mobile & Online Classifieds Platform Publishing & Data Services
N.A.I.C.S.: 551112
Leonardo Rubinstein *(CEO-Asia, Latin America, Middle East & Africa)*

OOO KEH eKommerz (1)
Lesnaya ul 7, Moscow, 125047, Russia (100%)
Tel.: (7) 495 228 36 30
Web Site: http://www.avito.ru
Online Classified Advertising Services
N.A.I.C.S.: 541810
Jonas Nordlander *(Co-Founder, CEO & Exec Dir)*

Sanook Online Limited (1)
2/4 9th Floor Vibhavadee-Rangsit Road, Thungsonghong Laksi, Bangkok, 10210, Thailand
Tel.: (66) 29550099
Web Site: http://www.sanook.com

AND PRIVATE COMPANIES

Sales Range: $25-49.9 Million
Emp.: 10
Internet Service Provider
N.A.I.C.S.: 517810

SuperSport International (Pty) Limited (1)
137 Bram Fischer Drive, Ferndale, 2123, Randburg, South Africa
Tel.: (27) 116866000
Web Site: http://www.supersport.com
Sales Range: $25-49.9 Million
Emp.: 16
Sports Programme Broadcasting Services
N.A.I.C.S.: 516120
Graham Abrahams *(Member-Mgmt Bd & Dir-Enterprises & Regulatory)*

Via Afrika Limited (1)
11th Floor 40 Heerengracht, Cape Town, 8001, South Africa
Tel.: (27) 214063314
Web Site: http://www.viaafrika.com
Emp.: 28
Educational Textbook Publishers
N.A.I.C.S.: 513130
Christina Watson *(CEO)*

NASS VALLEY GATEWAY LTD.
422 Richards Street Suite 170, Vancouver, V6B 2Z4, BC, Canada
Tel.: (609) 651-0032   BC
Web Site:
  https://www.nassvalleygateway.com
Year Founded: 2005
NSVGF—(OTCIQ)
Rev.: $14,005
Assets: $14,566
Liabilities: $11,662,142
Net Worth: ($11,647,576)
Earnings: ($2,186,860)
Fiscal Year-end: 12/31/22
Metal Ore Mining & Exploration Services
N.A.I.C.S.: 212290
Gavin Collier *(CEO)*

NASSAUISCHE SPARKASSE
Rheinstrasse 42 46, 65185, Wiesbaden, Germany
Tel.: (49) 36401010
Web Site: http://www.naspa.de
Sales Range: $200-249.9 Million
Emp.: 2,428
Commercial Savings Bank
N.A.I.C.S.: 522110
Gunter Hogner *(Member-Mgmt Bd)*

NASU DENKI-TEKKO CO., LTD.
v8th & 9th Floors Pmo Shinjuku Gyoenmae 1-12 Shinjuku 2-chome, Shinjuku-ku, Tokyo, 160-0022, Japan
Tel.: (81) 333516131
Web Site:
  https://www.nasudenki.co.jp
Year Founded: 1939
5922—(TKS)
Rev.: $154,237,740
Assets: $292,386,740
Liabilities: $112,059,330
Net Worth: $180,327,410
Earnings: $12,228,500
Emp.: 366
Fiscal Year-end: 03/31/24
Steel Product Mfr & Distr
N.A.I.C.S.: 332312
Mikio Nasu *(Chm)*

NATASA MINING LTD
Suite 107 109 Pitt Street, Sydney, 2000, NSW, Australia
Tel.: (61) 292338011   Ky
Web Site:
  http://www.natasamining.com
Sales Range: Less than $1 Million
Mining & Exploration
N.A.I.C.S.: 213112
John B. Maguire *(Sec)*

NATCO ECONOMICALS LTD.
304 Abhijit - 1 Nr Mithakhali Six Road Navarangpura, Daryaganj, Ahmedabad, 380 006, Gujarat, India
Tel.: (91) 2652333455
Web Site: http://www.natecoltd.com
Rev.: $112,359
Assets: $499,858
Liabilities: $14,599
Net Worth: $485,259
Earnings: $30,829
Fiscal Year-end: 03/31/18
Financial Investment Services
N.A.I.C.S.: 523999
Ashish Pandya *(Chm)*

NATCO PHARMA LTD
Natco House Road No 2 Banjara Hills, Hyderabad, 500 034, India
Tel.: (91) 4023547532
Web Site:
  https://www.natcopharma.co.in
NATCOPHARM—(NSE)
Rev.: $337,114,082
Assets: $678,304,658
Liabilities: $93,951,202
Net Worth: $584,353,456
Earnings: $85,762,244
Emp.: 4,491
Fiscal Year-end: 03/31/23
Pharmaceuticals Pharmaceuticals Indian Bulk Drugs Formulations
N.A.I.C.S.: 424210
Venkaiah Chowdary Nannapaneni *(Chm & Mng Dir)*

Subsidiaries:

NATCO Pharma Inc. (1)
297 Mine Bank Rd, Wellsville, PA 17365
Tel.: (717) 432-7779
Web Site: http://www.pasavemart.com
Pharmacies & Drug Stores
N.A.I.C.S.: 456110

Natco Pharma (Canada) Inc. (1)
2000 Argentia Road Plaza 1 Suite 200, Mississauga, L5N 1P7, ON, Canada
Tel.: (905) 997-3353
Web Site: https://www.natcopharma.ca
Pharmaceuticals Product Mfr
N.A.I.C.S.: 325412

Natco Pharma Asia Pte. Ltd. (1)
62 Ubi Road 1 03-21 Oxley Bizhub 2, Singapore, 408734, Singapore
Tel.: (65) 83221702
Web Site: https://natcopharmaasia.com
Pharmaceuticals Product Mfr
N.A.I.C.S.: 325412
Girish Virkar *(CEO)*

Natco Pharma Limited - Chemical-R & D Division (1)
B-11 Industrial Estate, Sanathnagar, Hyderabad, 500 018, Telangana, India
Tel.: (91) 4023710575
Web Site: http://www.natcopharma.co.in
Sales Range: $25-49.9 Million
Emp.: 350
Chemicals Mfr
N.A.I.C.S.: 325199
Durga Prasad K. *(VP-R&D)*

Natco Pharma Limited - Pharma Division (1)
Kothur Post Kothur Mandal, Mahbubnagar, 509228, Andhra Pradesh, India
Tel.: (91) 8548257289
Pharmaceutical Preparation Mfr
N.A.I.C.S.: 325412

Natco Pharma Limited - Pharma Division-Parenterals (1)
Vijayapuri North Nagarjuna Sagar Peddavura mandal, Nalgonda, 508 202, Telangana, India
Tel.: (91) 8680276661
Web Site: http://www.natcopharma.co.in
Sales Range: $50-74.9 Million
Emp.: 5,000
Pharmaceutical Preparation Mfr
N.A.I.C.S.: 325412

Natcofarma Do Brasil Ltda. (1)
Av das Nacoes Unidas 14171 4th Floor, Rochavera Marble Tower, Sao Paulo, 04794-000, SP, Brazil
Tel.: (55) 1135682213
Web Site: https://natcofarma.com
Pharmaceuticals Product Mfr
N.A.I.C.S.: 325412

NATH BIO-GENES (INDIA) LIMITED
Nath House Nath Road, Aurangabad, 431005, India
Tel.: (91) 2402376314
Web Site:
  http://www.nathbiogenes.com
537291—(BOM)
Rev.: $36,198,921
Assets: $95,053,882
Liabilities: $26,332,186
Net Worth: $68,721,695
Earnings: $4,197,758
Emp.: 482
Fiscal Year-end: 03/31/23
Feed
N.A.I.C.S.: 111120
Satish Kagliwal *(Mng Dir)*

Subsidiaries:

JV- Nath Bio-Genes CA LLC (1)

NATH INDUSTRIES LIMITED
1 Chateau Windsor 86 Veer Nariman Road Churchgate, Mumbai, 400020, Maharashtra, India
Tel.: (91) 2222875653
Web Site: https://www.ramapulp.com
502587—(BOM)
Rev.: $49,652,239
Assets: $51,854,062
Liabilities: $22,696,049
Net Worth: $29,158,012
Earnings: $320,640
Fiscal Year-end: 03/31/23
Paper Mfr
N.A.I.C.S.: 322120
Sanjay Dadhich *(Mgr-Mktg)*

Subsidiaries:

Nath Pulp & Paper Mills Limited (1)
Nath House Nath Road, Aurangabad, 431005, Maharashtra, India
Tel.: (91) 240 237 6314
Web Site: https://www.nathpaper.com
Rev.: $20,858,291
Assets: $17,770,850
Liabilities: $13,168,182
Net Worth: $4,602,668
Earnings: $856,841
Fiscal Year-end: 03/31/2019
Paper Products Mfr
N.A.I.C.S.: 322130
Akash Kagliwal *(CEO)*

NATION GOLD CORP.
750-1095 West Pender Street, Vancouver, V6E 2M6, BC, Canada
Tel.: (604) 659-6556   BC
Web Site: https://www.nationgold.ca
Year Founded: 1996
NATN—(CNSX)
Gold Exploration Services
N.A.I.C.S.: 212220
Mark Bailey *(CEO)*

NATION GROUP (THAILAND) PUBLIC COMPANY LIMITED
1854 9th 10th 11th Floors Debaratana Rd, BangnaTai Bangna, Bangkok, 10260, Thailand
Tel.: (66) 23383333
Web Site:
  https://www.nationgroup.com
Year Founded: 1971
NATION—(THA)
Sales Range: $25-49.9 Million
Newspaper Publishing Services
N.A.I.C.S.: 513110

NATION MEDIA GROUP LIMITED

Marut Arthakaivalvatee *(Chm & Member-Exec Bd)*

NATION LANKA FINANCE PLC
No 28 Dickmans Road, 05, Colombo, Sri Lanka
Tel.: (94) 114760800
Web Site: https://nationlanka.com
Year Founded: 1987
CSF—(COL)
Rev.: $12,592,964
Assets: $38,637,206
Liabilities: $33,536,333
Net Worth: $5,100,872
Earnings: ($661,777)
Emp.: 391
Fiscal Year-end: 03/31/21
Financial Banking Services
N.A.I.C.S.: 523150
Shubhani Jayawardana *(Officer-Compliance & Risk & Sec)*

Subsidiaries:

Asian Finance Ltd. (1)
No 20 RA de Mel Mawatha, Colombo, 00300, Sri Lanka
Tel.: (94) 112438141
Web Site: http://www.asianfinance.lk
Sales Range: $50-74.9 Million
Emp.: 100
Financial Management Services
N.A.I.C.S.: 522291
Nalin Kumara *(Mgr-Real Estate)*

Ceylinco Investment Corporation Ltd (1)
22 1/2 Mihindu Mawatha, Kurunegala, 6000, Wayamba Palata, Sri Lanka
Tel.: (94) 372233696
Emp.: 11
Real Estate Manangement Services
N.A.I.C.S.: 531312
Nalin Jayetileke *(Mng Dir)*

NATION MEDIA GROUP LIMITED
Nation Centre Kimathi Street, PO Box 49010, 00100, Nairobi, Kenya
Tel.: (254) 203288000   KE
Web Site:
  https://www.nationmedia.com
Year Founded: 1959
NMGK—(NAI)
Rev.: $61,996,480
Assets: $107,567,460
Liabilities: $35,377,160
Net Worth: $72,190,300
Earnings: $435,890
Emp.: 930
Fiscal Year-end: 12/31/20
Broadcasting Services; Newspaper & Magazine Publisher
N.A.I.C.S.: 516120
Wilfred D. Kiboro *(Chm)*

Subsidiaries:

Africa Broadcasting Uganda Limited (1)
Kampala Serena Conference Centre, PO Box 35933, Kampala, 35933, Uganda
Tel.: (256) 414563400
Web Site: https://www.ntvuganda.co.ug
Sales Range: $25-49.9 Million
Emp.: 50
Television Broadcasting Services
N.A.I.C.S.: 516120

Monitor Publications Limited (1)
29/35 8th Street, PO Box 12141, Kampala, Uganda
Tel.: (256) 312301250
Web Site: https://www.monitor.co.ug
Sales Range: $50-74.9 Million
Emp.: 240
Newspaper Publishers
N.A.I.C.S.: 513110

Nation Marketing & Publishing Limited (1)
Nation Centre Kimathi Street, PO Box 49010, 00100, Nairobi, Kenya

NATION MEDIA GROUP LIMITED

Nation Media Group Limited—(Continued)
Tel.: (254) 203288000
Web Site:
http://www.theweeklyadvertiser.com
Sales Range: $450-499.9 Million
Emp.: 1,600
Publishing & Marketing Services
N.A.I.C.S.: 513199

Nation Media Group Limited - Broadcasting Division (1)
Nation Centre Kimathi Street, PO Box 49010, 00100, Nairobi, Kenya
Tel.: (254) 203288000
Sales Range: $200-249.9 Million
Emp.: 800
Broadcasting Services
N.A.I.C.S.: 516120
Emmanuel Juma *(Head-News)*

Nation Media Group Limited - Nation Carriers Division (1)
Nation Centre Kimathi Street, PO Box 49101-00100, Nairobi, Kenya
Tel.: (254) 203288000
Sales Range: $300-349.9 Million
Emp.: 1,100
Courier Service
N.A.I.C.S.: 492110
Linus Gitahi *(CEO)*

Nation Media Group Limited - Newspaper Division (1)
Nation Centre Kimathi Street, PO Box 49010, 00100, Nairobi, Kenya
Tel.: (254) 203288000
Web Site: http://www.nationmedia.com
Sales Range: $200-249.9 Million
Emp.: 566
Newspaper Publishers
N.A.I.C.S.: 513110
Joseph Odindo *(Dir-Editorial)*

NATIONAL ACCESS CANNABIS CORP.
56 Aberfoyle Crescent Unit 200, Etobicoke, M8X 2W4, ON, Canada
Tel.: (647) 689-6382
META—(TSXV)
Rev.: $41,400,754
Assets: $47,068,728
Liabilities: $25,897,792
Net Worth: $21,170,935
Earnings: ($24,546,299)
Fiscal Year-end: 08/31/19
Pharmaceutical Products Distr
N.A.I.C.S.: 424210
Mark Goliger *(CEO)*

NATIONAL ACCIDENT HELPLINE LIMITED
1430 Montagu Court Kettering Parkway, Kettering, NN15 6XR, Northants, United Kingdom
Tel.: (44) 1536 527 500
Web Site: http://www.national-accident-helpline.co.uk
Year Founded: 1993
Sales Range: $10-24.9 Million
Emp.: 71
Insurance Claims Services
N.A.I.C.S.: 524292
Geri Payne *(Compliance Officer)*

NATIONAL AEROSPACE FASTENERS CORPORATION
No 1 Taiping East Road, Pingzhen District, Taoyuan, 32466, Taiwan
Tel.: (886) 34508868
Web Site: https://www.nafco.com.tw
Year Founded: 1997
3004—(TAI)
Rev.: $100,416,099
Assets: $166,065,038
Liabilities: $89,859,443
Net Worth: $76,205,596
Earnings: $10,059,289
Emp.: 724
Fiscal Year-end: 12/31/23
Aerospace Equipment Mfr
N.A.I.C.S.: 336413

Chris Lee *(CFO & Mgr-Mgmt Dept)*
Subsidiaries:

Nafco Suzhou Precision Limited Corporation (1)
No 269 2nd Road, Kunshan Comprehensive Bonded Area, Suzhou, 215300, Jiangsu, China
Tel.: (86) 512573677779192
Web Site: https://www.nafcosuzhou.cn
Commercial Aircraft Engine Part Mfr
N.A.I.C.S.: 336412

NATIONAL AGRICULTURAL DEVELOPMENT COMPANY
PO Box 2557, Riyadh, 11461, Saudi Arabia
Tel.: (966) 112027777
Web Site: http://www.nadec.com
Year Founded: 1981
6010—(SAU)
Rev.: $852,501,690
Assets: $1,362,566,333
Liabilities: $404,500,104
Net Worth: $958,066,228
Earnings: $80,548,459
Fiscal Year-end: 12/31/23
Cattle Farming, Agricultural Development, Food Processing & Distribution Services
N.A.I.C.S.: 112111
Mazen Ahmed Al Jubeir *(Chm)*

NATIONAL AGRICULTURAL HOLDINGS LIMITED
Room 1604-05 Block 3 Prudential Tower No 21 Canton Road, Tsimshatsui, Kowloon, China (Hong Kong)
Tel.: (852) 2886 7188   Ky
Web Site: http://www.natagri.com.hk
Sales Range: $10-24.9 Million
Emp.: 394
Holding Company; Agricultural Services
N.A.I.C.S.: 551112
Li-Jun Chen *(Chm)*

Subsidiaries:

Shanghai Qianlong Network Technology Co., Limited (1)
World Plaza 26th Floor 855 South Pudong Road, Shanghai, China
Tel.: (86) 21 58369889
Computer Network System Integration Services
N.A.I.C.S.: 541512

Shanghai Xin Long Information Technology Co., Limited (1)
1036 Long Yu Building Room 902 South Pudong Road, Pudong New Area, Shanghai, 200120, China **(100%)**
Tel.: (86) 21 51095778
Software Consulting Services
N.A.I.C.S.: 541512

NATIONAL AGRICULTURE MARKETING CO.
Abdulaziz Road, Yasmeed King, Riyadh, Saudi Arabia
Tel.: (966) 0591616638   SA
Year Founded: 1987
4160—(SAU)
Assets: $27,453,762
Liabilities: $19,150,157
Net Worth: $8,303,605
Earnings: ($1,741,345)
Emp.: 14
Fiscal Year-end: 12/31/23
Agricultural Product Whslr
N.A.I.C.S.: 424480

NATIONAL ALUMINIUM COMPANY LIMITED
Nalco Bhawan P/1 Nayapalli, Bhubaneswar, 751 013, India
Tel.: (91) 6742301988
Web Site: https://www.nalcoindia.com

Year Founded: 1981
NATIONALUM—(NSE)
Rev.: $1,737,364,666
Assets: $2,113,375,697
Liabilities: $539,564,774
Net Worth: $1,573,810,923
Earnings: $172,011,270
Emp.: 5,190
Fiscal Year-end: 03/31/23
Aluminum Production Services
N.A.I.C.S.: 331313
Braja Kishore Dash *(Gen Mgr-Fin)*

Subsidiaries:

CAPTIVE POWER PLANT (1)
Nalco Nagar, Angul, Bhubaneswar, 759 145, Orissa, India
Tel.: (91) 6764220158
Web Site: http://nalcoindia.com
Aluminium Raw Materials Distr
N.A.I.C.S.: 331313

PORT FACILITIES (1)
Port Area, Visakhapatnam, 530 035, Andhra Pradesh, India
Tel.: (91) 8912561433
Web Site: http://nalcoindia.com
Aluminium Raw Materials Distr
N.A.I.C.S.: 331313

SMELTER PLANT (1)
Nalco Nagar-759 145, Angul, Bhubaneswar, Orissa, India
Tel.: (91) 6764220169
Aluminium Raw Materials Distr
N.A.I.C.S.: 331313

NATIONAL ALUMINIUM PRODUCTS COMPANY SAOG
PO Box 15, Rusyal, 124, Muscat, Oman
Tel.: (968) 24446450   OM
Web Site: https://www.napcooman.com
Year Founded: 1984
NAPI—(MUS)
Rev.: $91,923,786
Assets: $94,301,914
Liabilities: $73,126,824
Net Worth: $21,175,090
Earnings: ($2,805,678)
Emp.: 378
Fiscal Year-end: 12/31/20
Aluminium Products Mfr
N.A.I.C.S.: 339999
Abdul Rasheed Al Balushi *(Plant Mgr)*

NATIONAL ALUMINUM & PROFILE CO.
Beit Iba Qusin Junction, Nablus, Palestine
Tel.: (970) 92347222
Web Site: https://www.napco.ps
Year Founded: 1991
NAPCO—(PAL)
Rev.: $19,989,849
Assets: $67,849,706
Liabilities: $48,367,099
Net Worth: $19,482,607
Earnings: ($2,370,644)
Emp.: 200
Fiscal Year-end: 12/31/23
Aluminium Products Mfr
N.A.I.C.S.: 331318
Khaled Muhtaseb *(Vice Chm)*

NATIONAL ALUMINUM INDUSTRIAL COMPANY
Abu Nassar commercial complex building No 41 Dahiyat Al Yasmeen, PO Box 941203, Al Shoura Str, Amman, 11194, Jordan
Tel.: (962) 64370565
Web Site: http://www.nalco.com.jo
Year Founded: 1994
NATA—(AMM)
Rev.: $7,961,567
Assets: $17,969,841
Liabilities: $3,236,913

Net Worth: $14,732,927
Earnings: $11,090
Emp.: 265
Fiscal Year-end: 12/31/20
Aluminum Sheet Mfr
N.A.I.C.S.: 331315
Hasan Al-Haj Hasan *(Gen Mgr)*

NATIONAL ARTS CENTRE CORPORATION
53 Elgin Street at Conference Square, Ottawa, K1P 5W1, ON, Canada
Tel.: (613) 947-7000
Web Site: http://www.nac-cna.ca
Sales Range: $25-49.9 Million
Emp.: 925
Performing Arts
N.A.I.C.S.: 711310
Brigitte Haentjens *(Artistic Dir-French Theatre)*

NATIONAL ARTS COUNCIL
Goodman Arts Centre 90 Goodman Road Blk A 01-01, Singapore, 439053, Singapore
Tel.: (65) 63469400
Web Site: https://www.nac.gov.sg
Year Founded: 1991
Arts Event Operator
N.A.I.C.S.: 711320

NATIONAL ARTS ENTERTAINMENT & CULTURE GROUP LIMITED
Room M 21/F Kings Wing Plaza 1 No 3 On Kwan Street, Shek Mun Shatin, Hong Kong, China (Hong Kong)
Tel.: (852) 2851 2118   Ky
Web Site: http://www.nationalarts.hk
Year Founded: 2001
Rev.: $19,643,447
Assets: $301,148,054
Liabilities: $282,610,659
Net Worth: $18,537,396
Earnings: ($53,062,601)
Emp.: 511
Fiscal Year-end: 12/31/18
Film Production & Distribution Services
N.A.I.C.S.: 512110
Kai Weng Chow *(CEO)*

Subsidiaries:

Convoy Global Holdings Limited (1)
39/F Convoy 169 Electric Road, North Point, China (Hong Kong)
Tel.: (852) 3601 3601
Web Site: http://www.convoy.com.hk
Insurance & Financial Services
N.A.I.C.S.: 524298
Wing Fai Ng *(Pres)*

National Arts Travel Limited (1)
Unit 2A-4 2/F Jone Mult Factory Building 169 Wai Yip Street Kwun Tong, Kowloon, China (Hong Kong)
Tel.: (852) 37026377
Web Site: http://www.natravel.com.hk
Travel Tour Operator
N.A.I.C.S.: 561520

NATIONAL ASSET RECONSTRUCTION COMPANY LIMITED
Birla Centurion Unit No 01 8th Floor Century Mill, Pandurang Budhkar Marg Worli, Mumbai, 400030, India
Tel.: (91) 0226960111
Web Site: https://www.narcl.co.in
Emp.: 100
Financial Services
N.A.I.C.S.: 523999

Subsidiaries:

SREI Infrastructure Finance Ltd (1)
Vishwakarma 86C Topsia Road South, Kolkata, 700 046, West Bengal, India

Tel.: (91) 3361607734
Web Site: http://www.srei.com
Rev.: $187,385,648
Assets: $1,876,640,489
Liabilities: $3,917,298,723
Net Worth: ($2,040,658,234)
Earnings: ($1,331,933,337)
Emp.: 28
Fiscal Year-end: 03/31/2023
Equipment Financing
N.A.I.C.S.: 522220
Hemant Kanoria (Chm & Mng Dir)

Subsidiary (Domestic):

Srei Mutual Fund Asset Management Pvt. Ltd. (2)
Paradise 51K / 51L Bhulabhai Desai Road
Breach Candy, Mumbai, 400026, India
Tel.: (91) 2266284201
Web Site: http://www.sreimf.com
Asset Management Services
N.A.I.C.S.: 523940
Rupesh Poddar (CFO)

NATIONAL AUSTRALIA BANK LIMITED

Level 28 395 Bourke Street, Docklands, Melbourne, 3000, VIC, Australia
Tel.: (61) 800152015   AU
Web Site: https://www.nab.com.au
Year Founded: 1858
NAB—(ASX)
Rev.: $13,225,205,590
Assets: $663,953,437,350
Liabilities: $616,991,353,680
Net Worth: $46,962,083,670
Earnings: $1,960,680,210
Emp.: 34,841
Fiscal Year-end: 09/30/20
Financial Investment Services
N.A.I.C.S.: 523999
A. David Gall (Chief Customer Officer)

Subsidiaries:

Aviva Investors Australia Limited (1)
Level 28 Freshwater Place 2 Southbank Boulevard, Southbank, 3006, VIC, Australia
Tel.: (61) 392200300
Emp.: 5
Investment Management Service
N.A.I.C.S.: 523999
Peter Poulopoulos (Mgr-Bus Dev-VIC,SA & TAS)

Bank of New Zealand (1)
(100%)
Tel.: (64) 49150400
Web Site: http://www.bnz.co.nz
Sales Range: $50-74.9 Million
Emp.: 12
Banking
N.A.I.C.S.: 522110
Darcy Tim (Dir-Structured Fin-Corporate and Institutional Property Fin)

Subsidiary (Domestic):

BNZ International Funding Limited (2)
Level 14 BNZ Tower 125 Queen Street, Auckland, 1010, New Zealand
Tel.: (64) 93751300
Financial Management Services
N.A.I.C.S.: 523999

Custom Fleet (NZ) Limited (2)
Level 1 GE Building, PO Box 3630, 8 Tangihua Street, Auckland, 1140, New Zealand
Tel.: (64) 95734800
Web Site: http://www.customfleet.co.nz
Car Rental Services
N.A.I.C.S.: 532111

Custom Service Leasing Limited (1)
Level 11 83 Clarence Street, Sydney, 2000, NSW, Australia
Tel.: (61) 800812681
Web Site: https://www.customfleet.com.au
Sales Range: $75-99.9 Million
Emp.: 165
Car Rental Services
N.A.I.C.S.: 532111

Godfrey Pembroke Limited (1)
Level 1 105-153 Miller Street, PO Box 1969, North Sydney, 2060, NSW, Australia (100%)
Tel.: (61) 1300783684
Web Site: https://www.godfreypembroke.com.au
Sales Range: $25-49.9 Million
Emp.: 20
Investment Advisory & Asset Management Services
N.A.I.C.S.: 523940

JB Were (NZ) Pty Limited (1)
Level 38 Vero Centre 48 Shortland Street, Auckland, 1010, New Zealand
Tel.: (64) 99271200
Web Site: http://www.jbwere.co.nz
Portfolio Management Services
N.A.I.C.S.: 523940
Justin Greiner (CEO)

NAB Investments Limited (1)
6-8 Tokenhouse Yard, London, EC2R 7AJ, United Kingdom
Tel.: (44) 1412235918
Financial Investment Services
N.A.I.C.S.: 523999

NBA Properties Limited (1)
L 4 800 Bourke St, Docklands, Melbourne, 3008, Australia
Tel.: (61) 386419083
Property Management Services
N.A.I.C.S.: 531311

National Australia Bank-London (1)
88 Wood Street, London, EC2V 7QQ, United Kingdom (100%)
Tel.: (44) 2077102100
Web Site: http://www.nab.com.au
Sales Range: $200-249.9 Million
Emp.: 400
International Banking & Financial Services
N.A.I.C.S.: 523150

National Australia Finance (Asia) Limited (1)
Level 27 One Pacific Place 88 Queensway, Hong Kong, China (Hong Kong)
Tel.: (852) 2826 8163
Financial Management Services
N.A.I.C.S.: 523999

National Australia Financial Management Ltd. (1)
330 Collins St 1st Fl, Melbourne, 3000, VIC, Australia (100%)
Tel.: (61) 386419083
Web Site: http://www.nab.com.au
Information & Technology Services
N.A.I.C.S.: 525990

Subsidiary (Domestic):

MLC Investments Limited (2)
105-153 Miller St, North Sydney, 2060, NSW, Australia
Tel.: (61) 132652
Investment Management Service
N.A.I.C.S.: 523999

National Australia Trustees Ltd. (1)
Level 5 800 Bourke St Docklands, Melbourne, 3008, VIC, Australia (100%)
Tel.: (61) 3 8634 2910
Web Site: http://www.national.com.au
Sales Range: $75-99.9 Million
Emp.: 60
Estate Planning, Corporate Trust Services, Personal Asset Management
N.A.I.C.S.: 522299

National Equities Limited (1)
800 Bourke St, Docklands, Melbourne, 3008, VIC, Australia
Tel.: (61) 386419083
Investment Management Service
N.A.I.C.S.: 523999

National Wealth Management Holdings Limited (1)
Level 6 Mlc Bldg, 105 153 Miller St, Sydney, 2060, NSW, Australia (100%)
Tel.: (61) 299578000
Web Site: http://www.mlc.com.au
Sales Range: $700-749.9 Million
Emp.: 1,200
Provider of International Banking & Financial Services

N.A.I.C.S.: 523940

Subsidiary (Domestic):

WM Life Australia Limited (2)
L 6 509 St Kilda Rd, Melbourne, 3004, Australia
Tel.: (61) 398298989
Life Insurance Management Services
N.A.I.C.S.: 524298

Navigator Australia Limited (1)
509 Saint Kilda Rd, Melbourne, 3004, VIC, Australia
Tel.: (61) 1300428482
Commercial Banking Services
N.A.I.C.S.: 522110

WM Group Pty Limited (1)
509 Saint Kilda St, Melbourne, 3001, VIC, Australia
Tel.: (61) 386344721
Financial Management Services
N.A.I.C.S.: 523999

NATIONAL BANK AG

Theaterplatz 8, 45127, Essen, Germany
Tel.: (49) 20181150
Web Site: http://www.national-bank.de
Sales Range: $150-199.9 Million
Emp.: 800
Banking Services
N.A.I.C.S.: 522299
Reinhold Schulte (Chm-Supervisory Bd)

Subsidiaries:

NB-Immobilien GmbH (1)
Bredeneyer Strasse 116, Essen, 45133, Germany
Tel.: (49) 201878950
Web Site: http://www.nb-i.de
Real Estate Property Lessors
N.A.I.C.S.: 531190
Frank Saelzer (Gen Mgr)

NB-Versicherungs-Service GmbH (1)
Bredeneyer Kreuz 1-3, Essen, 45133, Germany
Tel.: (49) 2018275941
Insurance Agencies & Brokerages
N.A.I.C.S.: 524210

NATIONAL BANK FOR FOREIGN ECONOMIC ACTIVITY OF THE REPUBLIC OF UZBEKISTAN

101 Amir Temur Avenue, 100084, Tashkent, Uzbekistan
Year Founded: 1991
Banking Services
N.A.I.C.S.: 522110
Mirsoatov Alisher Kudratullaevich (Chm)

Subsidiaries:

Asia Invest Bank CJSC (1)
2nd Kazachiy lane 3 building 1, 119180, Moscow, Russia
Tel.: (7) 4953633702
Web Site: http://www.ai-bank.ru
Commercial Banking Services
N.A.I.C.S.: 522110
Goulamov Rasuljan Takhirovich (Chm-Mgmt Bd)

Chinoz Textile LLC (1)
100 Samarkandskaya Street, Tashkent, Uzbekistan
Tel.: (998) 70 5933192
Web Site: http://www.chinoztextile.uz
Sales Range: $150-199.9 Million
Emp.: 505
Cotton Yarn Mfr
N.A.I.C.S.: 313110

Fresco LLC (1)
Tashovul Village, Kuychirchik District, Tashkent, Uzbekistan
Tel.: (998) 71 2330079
Web Site: http://www.fresco-llc.uz

Sales Range: $25-49.9 Million
Emp.: 34
Fruit & Vegetable Juice Mfr
N.A.I.C.S.: 311421

Gazalkent Stone LLC (1)
St Mramornaya House 1, Gazalkent, Tashkent, Uzbekistan
Tel.: (998) 71 2338456
Investment Management Service
N.A.I.C.S.: 523940

Tashkent Palace New LLC (1)
Mirabad Area Street Buyuk Turon 56, Tashkent, Uzbekistan
Tel.: (998) 98 1255800
Investment Management Service
N.A.I.C.S.: 523940

Uzinvestproject LLC (1)
88 Mustaqillik str, Tashkent, 100000, Uzbekistan
Tel.: (998) 71 237 33 63
Web Site: http://www.uzinvestproject.uz
Emp.: 10
Software Development Services
N.A.I.C.S.: 541511
Abbasova Shafoat Akbarovna (Gen Dir)

NATIONAL BANK LIMITED

116/1 Kazi Nazrul Islam Avenue Banglamotor, Dhaka, 1000, Bangladesh
Tel.: (880) 24103293140
Web Site: https://www.nblbd.com
NBL—(CHT)
Rev.: $167,946,421
Assets: $4,762,156,001
Liabilities: $4,380,243,685
Net Worth: $381,912,316
Earnings: $297,442,315
Emp.: 4,902
Fiscal Year-end: 12/31/22
Commercial Banking Services
N.A.I.C.S.: 522110
Zainul Haque Sikder (Chm)

Subsidiaries:

Gulf Overseas Exchange Company LLC (1)
P O Box No 3931, Ruwi, 112, Muscat, Oman
Tel.: (968) 94039911
Web Site: https://www.gulfexchangeoman.com
Money Exchange Services
N.A.I.C.S.: 522320

NBL Capital & Equity Management Ltd. (1)
Printers Building 8th Floor 5 Rajuk Avenue, Dhaka, 1000, Bangladesh
Tel.: (880) 247118816
Web Site: https://www.nblceml.com
Commercial Bank Services
N.A.I.C.S.: 522110
Parveen Haque Sikder (Chm)

NBL Money Transfer (Maldives) Pvt. Ltd. (1)
Gadhamoo Building Gr Floor Boduthakurufaanu Magu, Henveiru, Male, Maldives
Tel.: (960) 3335512
Money Exchange Services
N.A.I.C.S.: 522320

NBL Money Transfer Payment Foundation S.A. (1)
5 Diplari Street Ground Floor, Athens, Greece
Tel.: (30) 21032328445
Banking Services
N.A.I.C.S.: 522110

NBL Money Transfer Pte Ltd. (1)
10 A Roberts Lane, Singapore, 218289, Singapore
Tel.: (65) 62964440
Web Site: https://www.nblmt.com.sg
Sales Range: $50-74.9 Million
Emp.: 7
Money Transmission Services
N.A.I.C.S.: 522390
Parveen Haque Sikder (Chm)

NBL Money Transfer Sdn Bhd (1)
No 50G 50-2, Jalan Tun Tan Siew Sin,

NATIONAL BANK LIMITED

National Bank Limited—(Continued)
50050, Kuala Lumpur, Federal Territory, Malaysia
Tel.: (60) 320311100
Web Site: https://nblmt.com.my
Money Transmission Services
N.A.I.C.S.: 522390
Akhtar Uddin Ahmed (CEO)

NATIONAL BANK OF ANGUILLA LTD
PO Box 44, The Valley, Anguilla
Tel.: (264) 4972101
Web Site: http://www.nba.ai
Year Founded: 1984
Sales Range: $10-24.9 Million
Emp.: 80
Banking Services
N.A.I.C.S.: 522110
Ernest Valentine Banks (CEO)

Subsidiaries:

NBA (Private Banking and Trust) Limited (1)
Conrad W Fleming Corporate Building St Mary's Road, The Valley, Anguilla
Tel.: (264) 4977096
Web Site: http://www.nbaoffshore.ai
Commercial Banking Services
N.A.I.C.S.: 522110
Marisa Gumbs (Mgr-Ops)

NATIONAL BANK OF AZERBAIJAN
Rashid Behbudov Str 32, Baku, Azerbaijan
Tel.: (994) 124931122
Web Site: http://www.cbar.az
Sales Range: $25-49.9 Million
Emp.: 600
Banking Services
N.A.I.C.S.: 521110
Elman Siraj Rustamov (Member-Mgmt Bd & Governor)

NATIONAL BANK OF BAHRAIN
NBB Tower Government Avenue, PO Box 106, Manama, Bahrain
Tel.: (973) 17228800 BH
Web Site: https://www.nbbonline.com
Year Founded: 1957
NBB—(BAH)
Rev.: $500,251,983
Assets: $12,692,766,770
Liabilities: $11,165,221,082
Net Worth: $1,527,545,688
Earnings: $187,528,182
Emp.: 837
Fiscal Year-end: 12/31/22
Banking Services
N.A.I.C.S.: 522110
Hussain Al Hussaini (CEO-Treasury, Capital Markets & Wealth Mgmt)

NATIONAL BANK OF CAMBODIA
22-24 Preah Norodom Blvd, PO Box 67, Phnom Penh, Cambodia
Tel.: (855) 23722563
Web Site: http://www.nbc.org.kh
Year Founded: 1954
Sales Range: $200-249.9 Million
Emp.: 1,000
Banking Services
N.A.I.C.S.: 521110
Neav Chanthana (Deputy Governor)

Subsidiaries:

May Bank (Cambodia) Plc. (1)
No 4B Street 114 Kramoun Sar, Phnom Penh, Cambodia
Tel.: (855) 23210123
Commercial Banking Services
N.A.I.C.S.: 522110

Sacom Bank (Cambodia) Plc. (1)
60 Preah Norodom Blvd Sangkat Cheychumneas, Phnom Penh, Cambodia
Tel.: (855) 23223422
Web Site: http://www.sacombank.com.kh
Commercial Banking Services
N.A.I.C.S.: 522110
Nguyen Nhi Than (Gen Dir)

NATIONAL BANK OF CANADA
600 De la Gauchetiere Street West 4th floor, Montreal, H3B 4L2, QC, Canada
Tel.: (514) 394-8497
Web Site: https://www.nbc.ca
Year Founded: 1859
Rev.: $6,201,133,560
Assets: $259,423,605,000
Liabilities: $246,607,511,760
Net Worth: $12,816,093,240
Earnings: $1,629,489,240
Emp.: 26,517
Fiscal Year-end: 10/31/20
Commercial Banking Services
N.A.I.C.S.: 522110
Brigitte Hebert (Exec VP-Employee Experience)

Subsidiaries:

ATA IT Ltd. (1)
25 Bangkok Insurance Building 25th/29th Floor South Sathorn Road, Thungmahamek Sathorn, Bangkok, 10120, Thailand
Tel.: (66) 21054574
Web Site: http://www.ata-it-th.com
Banking Services
N.A.I.C.S.: 522110

Advanced Bank of Asia Limited (1)
148 Preah Sihanouk Blvd, Sangkat Boeung Keng Kang I Khan Boeung Keng Kang, Phnom Penh, Cambodia
Tel.: (855) 23255333
Web Site: http://www.ababank.com
Financial Investment Services
N.A.I.C.S.: 523999

Credigy Ltd. (1)
3715 Davinci Ct Ste 200, Norcross, GA 30092
Tel.: (678) 728-7310
Web Site: http://www.credigy.net
Banking Services
N.A.I.C.S.: 522110
Wallace Greene (Mng Dir-Credit & Investments)

Innocap Investment Management Inc. (1)
1555 Peel Street 6th Floor, Montreal, H3A 3L8, QC, Canada
Tel.: (514) 390-4773
Web Site: http://www.innocap.com
Investment Management Service
N.A.I.C.S.: 523999

Natbank, N.A. (1)
4031 Oakwood Blvd, Hollywood, FL 33020 (100%)
Tel.: (954) 922-9992
Web Site: http://www.natbank.ca
Sales Range: $75-99.9 Million
Emp.: 25
Savings, Loans & Commercial Banking Services
N.A.I.C.S.: 522110
Kathleen Zicat (Chm)

Natcan Trust Company (1)
4 Place Laval Suite 600, Laval, H7N 5Y3, QC, Canada (100%)
Tel.: (514) 871-7639
Sales Range: $50-74.9 Million
Emp.: 75
N.A.I.C.S.: 522110
Eric Le Slamme (Pres & CEO)

Division (Domestic):

NatExport (2)
600 Gauchetiere 5th Fl, Montreal, H3B 4L3, QC, Canada (100%)
Tel.: (514) 394-6321
Web Site: http://www.bnc.ca
Sales Range: $50-74.9 Million
Emp.: 20
N.A.I.C.S.: 522210

National Bank Acquisition Holding Inc (1)
600 Rue De La Gauchetiere O, Montreal, H3B 4L2, QC, Canada
Tel.: (514) 394-4385
Web Site: http://www.nbc.ca
Commercial Banking Services
N.A.I.C.S.: 522110

Subsidiary (Domestic):

National Bank Investments Inc. (2)
1155 Metcalfe Street 5th Floor, Montreal, H3B 4S9, QC, Canada
Web Site: http://www.nbinvestments.ca
Banking Services
N.A.I.C.S.: 522110
Annamaria Testani (Sr VP-Sls-Natl)

National Bank Financial & Co. Inc. (1)
1155 Metcalfe Street 5th floor, Montreal, H3B 4S9, QC, Canada (100%)
Tel.: (514) 879-2222
Web Site: https://nbfwm.ca
Sales Range: $1-4.9 Billion
Emp.: 2,700
N.A.I.C.S.: 523910

Branch (Domestic):

National Bank Financial & Co. Inc. - Toronto Office (2)
130 King Street West Suite 3200, PO Box 21, Toronto, M5X 1J9, ON, Canada
Tel.: (416) 869-3707
Web Site: http://www.nbfinancial.com
Sales Range: $300-349.9 Million
Emp.: 650
Securities Brokerage
N.A.I.C.S.: 523150

National Bank Life Insurance Company (1)
1100 Robert-Bourassa blvd 5th floor, Montreal, H3B 2G7, QC, Canada (100%)
Tel.: (514) 871-7500
Web Site: http://www.nbc.ca
N.A.I.C.S.: 522210

Subsidiary (Domestic):

National Bank Insurance Firm Inc. (2)
1100 University 11th Fl, Montreal, H3B 2G7, QC, Canada
Tel.: (514) 871-7500
Insurance Management Services
N.A.I.C.S.: 524298

National Bank Realty Inc. (1)
600 Rue De La Gauchetiere O Bureau 200, Montreal, H3B 4L2, QC, Canada
Tel.: (514) 394-4385
Commercial Banking Services
N.A.I.C.S.: 522110

National Bank Trust (1)
600 rue De La Gauchetiere Ouest 28th floor, Montreal, H3B 4L2, QC, Canada
Tel.: (514) 871-7100
Web Site: http://www.bnc.ca
Sales Range: $1-4.9 Billion
Emp.: 17,000
N.A.I.C.S.: 522210

National Bank of Canada Financial Inc. (1)
65 E 55th St 8th Fl, New York, NY 10022
Tel.: (212) 632-8500
Financial Investment Services
N.A.I.C.S.: 523999

NATIONAL BANK OF EGYPT
National Bank of Egypt Tower, PO Box 11611, 1187 Corniche El Nil, Cairo Plaza, Cairo, Egypt
Tel.: (20) 25760777
Web Site: http://www.nbe.com.eg
Year Founded: 1898
Sales Range: $1-4.9 Billion
Emp.: 11,903
Banking Services
N.A.I.C.S.: 522110
Hesham Ahmed Mahmoud Okasha (Chm)

INTERNATIONAL PUBLIC

Subsidiaries:

Al Ahly Mortgage Finance Co. (1)
56 Gameat Al Dowal Al Arabia St Mohandessin, Giza, Egypt
Tel.: (20) 33322900
Web Site: http://www.amf.eg
Mortgage Banking Services
N.A.I.C.S.: 522292
Ismail Saleh Abdoun (Chm & Mng Dir)

Al-Ahli Leasing Company (1)
El Gezira Plaza Administration Building 5th floor, Sheikh Zayed City, Egypt
Tel.: (20) 238541400
Financial Services
N.A.I.C.S.: 522320

Dubai International Financial Centre. (1)
Sheikh Zayed Road, PO Box 74777, Dubai, United Arab Emirates
Tel.: (971) 43622255
Web Site: http://www.difc.ae
Financial Services
N.A.I.C.S.: 522320
Maktoum Mohammed Rashid Al Maktoum (CEO)

National Bank of Egypt (UK) Limited, (1)
11 Waterloo Place, London, SW1Y 4AU, United Kingdom
Tel.: (44) 2073891200
Web Site: http://www.nbeuk.com
Commercial Banking Services
N.A.I.C.S.: 522110
Farouk Abdel Baki El-Okdah (Chm)

NATIONAL BANK OF ETHIOPIA
PO Box 5558, Addis Ababa, Ethiopia
Tel.: (251) 115517438
Web Site: http://www.nbe.gov.et
Year Founded: 1963
Banking Services
N.A.I.C.S.: 521110
Teklewold Atnafu (Governor)

NATIONAL BANK OF FUJAIRAH
Hamad Bin Abdullah Street, PO Box 887, Fujairah, United Arab Emirates
Tel.: (971) 48157555
Web Site: https://www.nbf.ae
Year Founded: 1982
NBF—(EMI)
Rev.: $798,818,191
Assets: $14,083,305,897
Liabilities: $12,295,219,083
Net Worth: $1,788,086,814
Earnings: $197,435,744
Emp.: 802
Fiscal Year-end: 12/31/22
Commercial Banking Services
N.A.I.C.S.: 522110
Saleh Mohamed Hamad Al Sharqi (Chm)

NATIONAL BANK OF GEORGIA
2 Sanapiro St, 0114, Tbilisi, Georgia
Tel.: (995) 322406544
Web Site: http://www.nbg.gov.ge
Year Founded: 1991
Central Bank
N.A.I.C.S.: 521110
Koba Gvenetadze (Chm)

NATIONAL BANK OF GREECE S.A.
93 Aiolou st, 105 51, Athens, Greece
Tel.: (30) 2104848484 GR
Web Site: https://www.nbg.gr
Year Founded: 1841
ETE—(ATH)
Rev.: $2,541,549,752
Assets: $84,300,669,113
Liabilities: $77,312,756,313
Net Worth: $6,987,912,799
Earnings: $1,210,878,480

AND PRIVATE COMPANIES

Emp.: 8,763
Fiscal Year-end: 12/31/22
Commercial & Investment Banking Services
N.A.I.C.S.: 522110
Ioannis Kyriakopoulos *(Gen Mgr-Grp Real Estate)*

Subsidiaries:

Astir Palace Vouliagmenis S.A. (1)
40 Apollonos Street Vouliagmeni, 16671, Athens, Greece **(85.35%)**
Tel.: (30) 2108902000
Web Site: http://investor.astir-palace.com
Sales Range: $25-49.9 Million
Emp.: 306
Hotels & Resort Operator
N.A.I.C.S.: 721110

Ethniki Factors S.A. (1)
Athinon Avenue 128-132 Ifigeneias Str, 10442, Athens, Greece
Tel.: (30) 2105181251
Web Site: https://www.nbgfactors.gr
Emp.: 33
Factoring Services
N.A.I.C.S.: 522299
Eleni A. Tzakou *(Chm)*

Ethniki General Insurance (Cyprus) Ltd (1)
Ifiginias St No 7, PO Box 16272, 2087, Strovolos, Cyprus
Tel.: (357) 22841000
Sales Range: $50-74.9 Million
Emp.: 60
General Insurance Services
N.A.I.C.S.: 524210
George Photiou *(Gen Mgr)*

Ethniki Insurance (Cyprus) Ltd (1)
Ifigenias 7 Ifigenias St, PO Box 21254, 1505, Strovolos, Cyprus
Tel.: (357) 22841000
Insurance Management Services
N.A.I.C.S.: 524298

Ethnodata S.A. (1)
86 Gargittou & Porou St, Gerakas, 15344, Pallini, Attiki, Greece
Tel.: (30) 210 3578700
Web Site: http://www.ethnodata.gr
Sales Range: $75-99.9 Million
Emp.: 488
Information Technology Consulting Services
N.A.I.C.S.: 541512
Dimitris Vrailas *(Pres)*

Finans Leasing A.S. (1)
Nispetiye Caddesi Akmerkez B Kulesi Kat 10, Etiler, 34620, Istanbul, Turkiye
Tel.: (90) 212 349 11 11
Web Site: http://www.finansleasing.com.tr
Financial Lending Services
N.A.I.C.S.: 522220
A. Murat Alacakaptan *(Gen Mgr)*

IB Tech A.S. (1)
Tubitak MAM Teknoloji Serbest Bolgesi IBTech Binasi, Tubitak Gebze Yerleskesi, 41470, Gebze, Kocaeli, Turkiye
Tel.: (90) 262 679 1500
Information Technology Consulting Services
N.A.I.C.S.: 541512

Kadmos S.A. (1)
3rd km PEO Thebes, Athens, Greece
Tel.: (30) 2262025500
Web Site: http://www.kadmosaete.com
Banking Services
N.A.I.C.S.: 522110

NBG (Malta) Holdings Ltd (1)
302/304 Townsquare Qui-Si-Sana Place, Sliema, SLM 3112, Malta
Tel.: (356) 21318969
Web Site: http://www.nbg.com.mt
Emp.: 25
Investment Management Service
N.A.I.C.S.: 523999
Cenk Kahraman *(CEO)*

NBG Asset Management Luxemburg S.A. (1)
21st Century Building 21 rue de Bitbourg, L-1273, Luxembourg, Luxembourg
Tel.: (352) 27848249
Web Site: https://www.nbgam.lu
Banking Services

N.A.I.C.S.: 522110
Efstratio Sarantinos *(Chm)*

NBG Asset Management Mutual Funds S.A. (1)
103-105 Syngrou Ave, 11745, Athens, Greece
Tel.: (30) 2109007400
Web Site: https://www.nbgam.gr
Sales Range: $50-74.9 Million
Emp.: 50
Asset Management Services
N.A.I.C.S.: 523940
Efstratios Sarantinos *(Gen Mgr)*

NBG Bank Malta Ltd (1)
302/304 Townsquare Qui-Si-Sana Place, Sliema, SLM 3112, Malta
Tel.: (356) 21318969
Web Site: http://www.nbg.com.mt
Sales Range: $50-74.9 Million
Emp.: 23
Financial Banking Services
N.A.I.C.S.: 523150
Cenk Kahraman *(Mng Dir)*

NBG Finance Plc (1)
Old Change House 128 Queen Victoria Street, London, EC4V 4BJ, United Kingdom
Tel.: (44) 2076615656
Web Site: http://www.nbgibe.co.uk
Sales Range: $50-74.9 Million
Emp.: 45
Financial Management Services
N.A.I.C.S.: 523999
Pavlos Stellakis *(CEO)*

NBG Insurance Brokers S.A. (1)
24 Poliklitou and Evripidou Str, 105 51, Athens, Greece
Tel.: (30) 2103259573
Banking Services
N.A.I.C.S.: 522110

NBG International Limited (1)
Old Change House 128 Queen Victoria Street, London, EC4V 4BJ, United Kingdom
Tel.: (44) 2076615656
Holding Company
N.A.I.C.S.: 551112

Subsidiary (Domestic):

NBGI Private Equity Limited (2)
128 Queen Victoria St Old Change House, London, EC4V 4BJ, United Kingdom **(100%)**
Tel.: (44) 2076615678
Web Site: http://www.nbgipe.co.uk
Sales Range: $25-49.9 Million
Emp.: 50
Privater Equity Firm
N.A.I.C.S.: 523999
Pavlos Stellakis *(Chm & CEO)*

Holding (Domestic):

ATR Group Ltd. (3)
16 Denmore Road Bridge of Don, Aberdeen, AB23 8JW, United Kingdom
Tel.: (44) 1224 222 777
Web Site: http://www.atrgroup.co.uk
Emp.: 50
Holding Company; Commercial & Industrial Equipment Rental Services
N.A.I.C.S.: 551112
Keith Moorhouse *(CEO)*

Subsidiary (Domestic):

ATR Equipment Solutions Ltd. (4)
16 Denmore Road Bridge of Don, Aberdeen, AB23 8JW, United Kingdom
Tel.: (44) 1224 222 777
Web Site: http://www.atrgroup.co.uk
Emp.: 100
Commercial & Industrial Equipment Rental Services
N.A.I.C.S.: 532490
Keith Moorhouse *(CEO)*

Underwater Engineering Services Limited (4)
West Pitmillan Foveran, Ellon, AB41 6AL, Aberdeenshire, United Kingdom
Tel.: (44) 1358 789 808
Web Site: http://www.uesltd.net
Emp.: 2
Underwater Engineering Equipment Rental & Maintenance Services

N.A.I.C.S.: 532490
Keith Moorhouse *(Mng Dir)*

Branch (Non-US):

NBGI Private Equity Limited - Turkey (3)
Adbi Ipekci Caddesi Altin Sokak No 2, Ahmet Kara Is Hani K 6 No 24, Nisantasi, Istanbul, 34367, Turkiye
Tel.: (90) 212 224 5902
Privater Equity Firm
N.A.I.C.S.: 523999

Subsidiary (Non-US):

NBGI Private Equity S.A.S (3)
37 Rue la Perouse, Paris, 75116, France
Tel.: (33) 1 58 56 18 95
Web Site: http://www.nbgipe.com
Sales Range: $50-74.9 Million
Emp.: 5
Investment Management Service
N.A.I.C.S.: 523999
Laurent Allegot *(Dir-Investment)*

Holding (Domestic):

Peter's Food Service Ltd. (3)
Bedwas House Industrial Estate, Caerphilly, CF83 8XP, United Kingdom
Tel.: (44) 2920853200
Web Site: http://www.petersfood.com
Sales Range: $100-124.9 Million
Meat & Pastry Products for the Catering & Retail Markets; Meat Pies, Sausage Rolls, Sausages, Beefburgers, Cooked Meats, Bacon & Pork Products Mfr
N.A.I.C.S.: 424420
David Peek *(Dir-Fin)*

NBG Leasing IFN S.A. (1)
George Constantinescu 3, 14012, Bucharest, Romania
Tel.: (40) 214091000
Web Site: http://www.nbgleasing.ro
Sales Range: $50-74.9 Million
Emp.: 7
Vehicle Leasing Services
N.A.I.C.S.: 532112
Aries Gogos *(Gen Mgr)*

NBG Property Services S.A. (1)
6 Kar Servias, Athens, 10562, Greece
Tel.: (30) 2103340011
Emp.: 17
Property Management Services
N.A.I.C.S.: 531312
Aristotelis Karytinos *(CEO)*

NBG Securities S.A. (1)
Kifissias 66, 15125, Athens, Greece
Tel.: (30) 2107720000
Web Site: http://www.nbgsecurities.com
Sales Range: $50-74.9 Million
Emp.: 100
Financial Brokerage Services
N.A.I.C.S.: 523150

National P&A Securities (1)
91 Michalakopoulou Street, Athens, 11528, Greece
Tel.: (30) 2107720000
Web Site: http://www.nationalpkonline.gr
Sales Range: $5-14.9 Billion
Emp.: 100
Investment & Management Services
N.A.I.C.S.: 523999
Panos Goutakis *(CEO)*

S.C. Garanta Asigurari S.A. (1)
19-21 Ion Mihalache Boulevard, 11171, Bucharest, Romania
Tel.: (40) 21 307 9971
Web Site: https://www.garanta.ro
Sales Range: $50-74.9 Million
Emp.: 80
Insurance Management Services
N.A.I.C.S.: 524298
Marian Baches *(Deputy Gen Mgr)*

Stopanska Banka AD-Skopje (1)
11 Oktomvri 7, 1000, Skopje, North Macedonia **(70.8%)**
Tel.: (389) 23295295
Web Site: http://www.stb.com.mk
Sales Range: $700-749.9 Million
Emp.: 1,508
Provider of Banking Services
N.A.I.C.S.: 522110

NATIONAL BANK OF KUWAIT S.A.K.

NATIONAL BANK OF KUWAIT S.A.K.
Al Shuhadaa Street Sharq, PO Box 95, Safat, 13001, Kuwait, Kuwait
Tel.: (965) 22291111 KW
Web Site: http://www.nbk.com
Year Founded: 1952
NBK—(KUW)
Rev.: $5,303,328,779
Assets: $122,339,657,267
Liabilities: $106,402,611,010
Net Worth: $15,937,046,258
Earnings: $1,911,094,341
Emp.: 8,049
Fiscal Year-end: 12/31/23
Banking Services
N.A.I.C.S.: 522110
Isam Jassem Al-Sager *(Grp CEO)*

Subsidiaries:

Boubyan Bank K.S.C. (1)
Al-Qibla - Abo Bakr Al-Seddiq - Al-Hamad Towers - 3rd Bilding - Beside, PO Box 25507, Al-Khrafi Tower, Kuwait, 13116, Kuwait **(58.34%)**
Tel.: (965) 22282000
Web Site: https://www.bankboubyan.com
Rev.: $922,070,916
Assets: $25,612,652,345
Liabilities: $22,428,606,715
Net Worth: $3,184,045,630
Earnings: $176,388,573
Emp.: 1,715
Fiscal Year-end: 12/31/2022
Banking Services
N.A.I.C.S.: 522110
Abdulaziz Abdullah Dakheel Al-Shaya *(Chm)*

Credit Bank of Iraq S.A. (1)
Elwiya 102/Saadoun St No 187, Baghdad, Iraq **(75%)**
Web Site: http://www.creditbankofiraq.com
Sales Range: Less than $1 Million
Banking Services
N.A.I.C.S.: 522110

NBK (International) Plc (1)
13 George Street, London, W1U 3QJ, United Kingdom
Tel.: (44) 2072242277
Web Site: http://www.nbk.com
Sales Range: $50-74.9 Million
Commericial Banking
N.A.I.C.S.: 522110

NBK (Lebanon) S.A.L. (1)
B A C Bldg Justinian Street Sanayeh, PO Box 11-5727, Riad El-Solh, 1107 2200, Beirut, Lebanon
Tel.: (961) 1743333
Web Site: http://www.nbk.com
Sales Range: $50-74.9 Million
Commericial Banking
N.A.I.C.S.: 522110

NBK Banque Privee (Suisse) S.A. (1)
Quai du Mont Blanc 21, PO Box 1923, 1211, Geneva, Switzerland
Tel.: (41) 22 906 4343
Web Site: https://www.nbkswiss.com
Commericial Banking
N.A.I.C.S.: 522110

NBK Investment Management Limited (1)
13 George Street, W1U3QJ, London, United Kingdom
Tel.: (44) 2072242288
Web Site: http://www.nbk.com
Insurance Agencies & Brokerages
N.A.I.C.S.: 524210

National Bank of Kuwait (1)
299 Park Ave 17, New York, NY 10171
Tel.: (212) 303-9800
Sales Range: $50-74.9 Million
Emp.: 30
Banking Services
N.A.I.C.S.: 522110

National Bank of Kuwait (Lebanon) S.A.L. (1)
PO Box 11-5727, Riad El-Solh, 1107 2200, Beirut, Lebanon

NATIONAL BANK OF KUWAIT S.A.K.

National Bank of Kuwait S.A.K.—(Continued)
Tel.: (961) 1759700
Commercial Banking Services
N.A.I.C.S.: 522110
Habib Karabet (Gen Mgr)

National Bank of Kuwait France SA (1)
90 Avenue Des Champs-Elysees, 75008, Paris, France
Tel.: (33) 156598600
Commercial Banking Services
N.A.I.C.S.: 522110

Watani Financial Brokerage Company K.S.C. (1)
Abdullah Al-Ahmed Street Al-Naqi Building Office 17, PO Box 21350, Safat, 13074, Kuwait, Kuwait
Tel.: (965) 22595102
Commercial Banking Services
N.A.I.C.S.: 522110
Joseph Awad (Mgr-Compliance)

Watani Investment Company (1)
Floor 34 NBK Tower Jaber Al-Mubarak and AlShuhada street, PO Box 4950, Block 7 Plot 6 Sharq, Kuwait, 13050, Safat, Kuwait
Tel.: (965) 2 224 6900
Web Site: https://www.nbkcapital.com
Financial Investment Activities
N.A.I.C.S.: 523999

Watani Wealth Management Company (1)
Al Mukmal Tower 8th Floor Prince Saud Al Faisal Street, PO Box 15385, AL Khaldiah District, Jeddah, 21444, Saudi Arabia
Tel.: (966) 11 277 7650
Web Site: https://www.nbkwm.com.sa
Wealth Management Services
N.A.I.C.S.: 523940
Musaad Al-Sudairy (CEO)

NATIONAL BANK OF KUWAIT-EGYPT
Al Shuhada Street Sharq, PO Box 95, 13001, Kuwait, Kuwait
Tel.: (965) 2242 2011
Web Site: http://www.nbk.com
Year Founded: 1980
NBKE.CA—(EGX)
Rev.: $3,163,175,506
Assets: $97,306,030,743
Liabilities: $83,746,643,072
Net Worth: $13,559,387,671
Earnings: $846,957,680
Emp.: 7,179
Fiscal Year-end: 12/31/20
Banking Services
N.A.I.C.S.: 522110
Isam Jassem Al-Sager (Vice Chm & Grp CEO)

NATIONAL BANK OF KYRGYZ REPUBLIC
Umetalieva Street 101, 720040, Bishkek, Kyrgyzstan
Tel.: (996) 669011
Web Site: http://www.nbkr.kg
Banking Services
N.A.I.C.S.: 521110
Abdybaly Tegin Suerkul (Deputy Chm)

NATIONAL BANK OF MALAWI
7 Henderson St, Blantyre, 265, Malawi
Tel.: (265) 1820622 MW
Web Site: http://www.natbank.co.mw
Year Founded: 1971
Sales Range: $25-49.9 Million
Emp.: 850
Commercial Banking Services
N.A.I.C.S.: 522110
George B. Partridge (Chm)

Subsidiaries:

Asset Finance Division (1)
Henderson st, PO Box 945, Blantyre, Malawi (100%)
Tel.: (265) 1823670
Web Site: http://www.natbank.co.mw
Sales Range: $75-99.9 Million
Emp.: 8
Financial Lending Services
N.A.I.C.S.: 525990
Oswin Kasunda (Head-Personal & Banking)

Stockbrokers Malawi Limited (1)
Able House, PO Box 2598, Hanover St, Blantyre, Malawi (75%)
Tel.: (265) 622803
Web Site: http://www.stockbrokersmalawi.com
Financial Investment Activities
N.A.I.C.S.: 523999

NATIONAL BANK OF OMAN SAOG
PO Box 751, 112, Ruwi, 112, Oman
Tel.: (968) 24770000
Web Site: https://www.nbo.com
Year Founded: 1973
NBOB—(MUS)
Rev.: $587,945
Assets: $12,525,016
Liabilities: $10,772,911
Net Worth: $1,752,105
Earnings: $150,729
Fiscal Year-end: 12/31/23
Banking Services
N.A.I.C.S.: 522110
Abdullah Ali Jabor Al Thani (Deputy Chm)

NATIONAL BANK OF ROMANIA
25 Lipscani Street Sector 3, Bucharest, 30031, Romania
Tel.: (40) 213130410
Web Site: http://www.bnro.ro
Year Founded: 1880
Sales Range: $1-4.9 Billion
Emp.: 2,000
Banking Services
N.A.I.C.S.: 522110
Mugur Constantin Isarescu (Chm & Governor)

NATIONAL BANK OF SERBIA
12 Kralja Petra St, 11 000, Belgrade, Serbia
Tel.: (381) 113027100
Web Site: http://www.nbs.rs
Sales Range: $150-199.9 Million
Emp.: 2,700
Banking Services
N.A.I.C.S.: 521110
Bojan Markovic (CFO)

NATIONAL BANK OF TAJIKISTAN
Avenue Rudaki 38/1, 734025, Dushanbe, Tajikistan
Tel.: (992) 446003227
Web Site: http://www.nbt.tj
Sales Range: Less than $1 Million
Commercial Banking Services
N.A.I.C.S.: 522110
Kholiqzoda Hokim Hikmatullo (Chm)

NATIONAL BANK OF THE REPUBLIC OF BELARUS
20, Nezavisimosty Ave, 220008, Minsk, Belarus
Tel.: (375) 172192303
Web Site: http://www.nbrb.by
Sales Range: $25-49.9 Million
Banking Services
N.A.I.C.S.: 521110
Petr A. Mamanovich (Deputy Chm)

NATIONAL BANK OF THE REPUBLIC OF MACEDONIA
Blvd Kuzman Josifovski Pitu 1, PO Box 401, 1000, Skopje, North Macedonia
Tel.: (389) 3108260
Web Site: http://www.nbrm.gov.mk
Sales Range: $10-24.9 Million
Emp.: 412
Banking Services
N.A.I.C.S.: 521110
Petar Goshev (Pres)

NATIONAL BANK OF UKRAINE
9 Instytutska St, 01601, Kiev, Ukraine
Tel.: (380) 442536921
Web Site: http://www.bank.gov.ua
Sales Range: $500-549.9 Million
Banking Services
N.A.I.C.S.: 521110
Mykola P. Lavruk (Exec Dir-Admin Issues)

NATIONAL BANK OF UMM AL QAIWAIN
PO Box 800, Umm al-Quwain, United Arab Emirates
Tel.: (971) 67066666
Web Site: https://www.nbq.ae
Year Founded: 1982
NBQ—(ABU)
Rev.: $211,386,877
Assets: $4,023,185,126
Liabilities: $2,487,399,395
Net Worth: $1,535,785,730
Earnings: $136,838,007
Emp.: 347
Fiscal Year-end: 12/31/23
Banking Services
N.A.I.C.S.: 522110
Rashid Saud Ahmed Al Mualla (Chm)

Subsidiaries:

Twin Towns Marketing Management L.L.C. (1)
PO Box 800, Umm Al-Quwain, Sharjah, United Arab Emirates
Tel.: (971) 67457000
Marketing Management Services
N.A.I.C.S.: 541613

NATIONAL BANK TRUST PJSC
3 Izvestkovy per, Moscow, 109004, Russia
Tel.: (7) 4956479021
Web Site: http://www.trust.ru
Sales Range: Less than $1 Million
Investment Banking Services
N.A.I.C.S.: 523150
Alexander Sokolov (Chm-Mgmt Bd & CEO)

NATIONAL BISCUIT INDUSTRIES LTD SAOG
PO Box 29, PO Box 29, Rusayl, 124, Muscat, Oman
Tel.: (968) 24446034
Web Site: https://nationalbiscuits.com.om
Year Founded: 1982
NBII—(MUS)
Rev.: $30,734,090
Assets: $34,976,612
Liabilities: $15,301,314
Net Worth: $19,675,297
Earnings: $607,894
Emp.: 400
Fiscal Year-end: 06/30/22
Biscuit Mfr
N.A.I.C.S.: 311919
Aiman Hamed Khalfan Al Hadhrami (Mgr-HR)

NATIONAL BUSINESS INITIATIVE
5th Floor 61 Katherine Street Dennehof, PO Box 294, Sunnyside Office Park Parktown, Sandton, 2196, South Africa
Tel.: (27) 115446000

INTERNATIONAL PUBLIC

Web Site: http://www.nbi.org.za
Year Founded: 1995
Sales Range: $25-49.9 Million
Emp.: 20
Financial Investment Services
N.A.I.C.S.: 523999
Joanne Yawitch (CEO)

NATIONAL CABLE & WIRE MFG. CO.
Al-Rabiah - Khalil Al-Dabbas St, PO Box 927104, Amman, 11190, Jordan
Tel.: (962) 65511484
Web Site: http://www.cableco.com.jo
Year Founded: 1985
WIRE—(AMM)
Rev.: $9,344,165
Assets: $28,612,004
Liabilities: $12,150,881
Net Worth: $16,461,123
Earnings: ($3,652,133)
Emp.: 153
Fiscal Year-end: 12/31/20
Cable & Wire Mfr
N.A.I.C.S.: 332618
Khaled Said (Mng Dir)

NATIONAL CAN INDUSTRIES LIMITED
90-92 Chifley Drive, Preston, 3072, VIC, Australia
Tel.: (61) 392769629 AU
Web Site: http://www.ncipackaging.com
Year Founded: 1954
Sales Range: $150-199.9 Million
Holding Company; Metal & Plastic Packaging Products Mfr
N.A.I.C.S.: 551112
Frauke Tyrrell (Owner & Vice Chm)

Subsidiaries:

NCI Holdings Pty. Ltd. (1)
90-92 Chifley Drive, Preston, 3072, VIC, Australia
Tel.: (61) 392769600
Holding Company
N.A.I.C.S.: 551112

Subsidiary (Domestic):

National Can Australia Pty. Ltd. (2)
90-92 Chifley Drive, Preston, 3072, VIC, Australia
Tel.: (61) 392769600
Web Site: http://www.ncipackaging.com
Metal & Plastic Packaging Products Mfr
N.A.I.C.S.: 332431
Anthony Hengel (CEO)

NATIONAL CEMENT COMPANY P.S.C
PO Box 4041, Dubai, United Arab Emirates
Tel.: (971) 43388885
Web Site: https://www.nationalcement.ae
Year Founded: 1968
NCC—(DFM)
Rev.: $51,165,869
Assets: $569,233,290
Liabilities: $20,683,675
Net Worth: $548,549,616
Earnings: $16,944,566
Emp.: 437
Fiscal Year-end: 12/31/23
Cement Mfr
N.A.I.C.S.: 327310

NATIONAL CENTRAL COOLING COMPANY PJSC
13 Floor West Tower Abu Dhabi Mall, PO Box 29478, Abu Dhabi, United Arab Emirates
Tel.: (971) 22020400
Web Site: https://www.tabreed.ae
Year Founded: 1998

78SU—(LSE)
Rev.: $657,665,823
Assets: $4,033,350,633
Liabilities: $2,142,901,359
Net Worth: $1,890,449,275
Earnings: $116,140,004
Emp.: 957
Fiscal Year-end: 12/31/23
Cooling & Conditioning Systems
N.A.I.C.S.: 333415
Khaled Abdulla Al Qubaisi *(Chm)*

Subsidiaries:

Bahrain District Cooling Company (1)
Flat 3501-1 B 35th Floor West Tower BWTC Building Road 365 Block 316, PO Box 20120, Manama, Bahrain
Tel.: (973) 17822001
Web Site: https://www.tabreedbahrain.com
Chilled Water Distribution Services
N.A.I.C.S.: 221310

CoolTech Energy Water Treatment LLC (1)
PO Box 49965, Dubai, United Arab Emirates
Tel.: (971) 43404190
Web Site: http://www.cooltechgulf.com
Sales Range: $25-49.9 Million
Emp.: 20
Water Quality Services
N.A.I.C.S.: 924110

Emirates Pre-insulated Pipes Industries LLC (1)
Icad-1 Musaffah, PO Box 73830, Abu Dhabi, United Arab Emirates
Tel.: (971) 25501991
Web Site: https://www.eppi.ae
Piping System Mfr
N.A.I.C.S.: 238220

Ian Banham & Associates- Consulting Engineers (1)
PO Box 2853, Abu Dhabi, United Arab Emirates
Tel.: (971) 26411606
Web Site: https://www.ianbanham.com
Engineering Consulting Services
N.A.I.C.S.: 541330

Tabreed Oman SAOC (1)
PO Box 3391, 111, Seeb, 111, Oman
Tel.: (968) 24170033
Web Site: https://www.tabreedoman.com
Chilled Water Distribution Services
N.A.I.C.S.: 221310
Abdullah Said Al-Hinai *(CEO)*

NATIONAL CHEMICAL & PLASTIC INDUSTRIES COMPANY
Al-Zaafrania Industrial Strip, Baghdad, Iraq
Tel.: (964) 7733770
Year Founded: 1962
INCP—(IRAQ)
Sales Range: Less than $1 Million
Plastic Materials Mfr
N.A.I.C.S.: 325211

NATIONAL CHEMICAL COMPANY
NCC House 42 Lowr Leeson St, Dublin, 2, Ireland
Tel.: (353) 161314000   IE
Web Site: http://www.ncc.ie
Year Founded: 1969
Sales Range: $25-49.9 Million
Emp.: 23
Chemicals & Plastics Distr
N.A.I.C.S.: 325998
Alan Looney *(Mng Dir)*

NATIONAL CHLORINE INDUSTRIES CO. LTD.
Al-Mowaqqer, PO Box 37, 16310, Amman, Jordan
Tel.: (962) 64050291
Web Site: http://www.chlorine.com.jo

Year Founded: 1991
NATC—(AMM)
Rev.: $14,252,330
Assets: $34,600,796
Liabilities: $2,317,057
Net Worth: $32,283,739
Earnings: $2,395,628
Emp.: 173
Fiscal Year-end: 12/31/20
Chemical Products Mfr
N.A.I.C.S.: 325998
Mohammad S. Alasad *(Gen Mgr)*

NATIONAL CITIZEN COMMERCIAL JOINT STOCK BANK
28C-28D Ba Trieu Phuong Hang Bai Ward, Hoan Kiem District, Hanoi, Vietnam
Tel.: (84) 462693355
Web Site: https://www.ncb-bank.vn
Year Founded: 1995
NVB—(HNX)
Rev.: $93,177,700
Assets: $8,984,724,200
Liabilities: $8,408,301,400
Net Worth: $576,422,800
Earnings: $800
Emp.: 1,275
Fiscal Year-end: 12/31/22
Banking Services
N.A.I.C.S.: 522110
Dung Tien Nguyen *(Chm-Mgmt Bd)*

NATIONAL CLEANING COMPANY K.S.C.C.
PO Box 25702, Safat, 13118, Kuwait, 13118, Kuwait
Tel.: (965) 1849849
Web Site: https://www.ncc-kw.com
Year Founded: 1979
CLEANING—(KUW)
Rev.: $113,856,666
Assets: $346,225,613
Liabilities: $239,906,246
Net Worth: $106,319,367
Earnings: ($7,088,938)
Emp.: 10,000
Fiscal Year-end: 12/31/21
Waste Management & Pest Control Services
N.A.I.C.S.: 562998
Muayad Alshawwa *(Chief Budgeting & Bus Dev Officer)*

NATIONAL COMPANY FOOD CONTRACT CORPORATION
Moscow str 29/3, Nur-Sultan, 010000, Kazakhstan
Tel.: (7) 7172 59 12 21
Web Site: http://www.fcc.kz
Year Founded: 1920
Grain Product Mfr
N.A.I.C.S.: 111199
Tobylbek Ye. Omarov *(Mng Dir)*

NATIONAL COMPANY FOR GLASS INDUSTRIES
PO Box 41619, Riyadh, 11531, Saudi Arabia
Tel.: (966) 112652323
Web Site: https://www.zoujaj-glass.com
Year Founded: 1990
2150—(SAU)
Rev.: $29,947,213
Assets: $218,679,179
Liabilities: $34,251,945
Net Worth: $184,427,234
Earnings: $27,817,889
Emp.: 300
Fiscal Year-end: 12/31/22
Glass Container Mfr
N.A.I.C.S.: 327213

Subsidiaries:

Damman Factory for Glass Bottles (1)

PO Box 580, PO Box 580, Dammam, 31421, Saudi Arabia **(100%)**
Tel.: (966) 38421090
Web Site: http://www.glassonline.com
Sales Range: $25-49.9 Million
Emp.: 55
Glass Bottle Mfr
N.A.I.C.S.: 327213
Yousef Al Salman *(Gen Mgr)*

National Factory for Glass Bottles (1)
PO Box 41619, Riyadh, 11531, Saudi Arabia **(100%)**
Tel.: (966) 12652323
Sales Range: $125-149.9 Million
Glass Bottle Mfr
N.A.I.C.S.: 327213

NATIONAL COMPANY FOR TOURISIM INVESTMENT
Abo Nawas Street-sec102-St 10-buld 8, Baghdad, Iraq
Tel.: (964) 7171054
Year Founded: 1978
HNTI—(IRAQ)
Sales Range: Less than $1 Million
Financial Investment Services
N.A.I.C.S.: 523999

NATIONAL COMPANY KAZAKHSTAN ENGINEERING JSC
10 Kunaeva St, Yesil district, Nur-Sultan, 010000, Kazakhstan
Tel.: (7) 7172 61 19 01
Web Site: http://www.ke.kz
Year Founded: 2003
KZEN—(KAZ)
Sales Range: $200-249.9 Million
Military Equipment Mfr
N.A.I.C.S.: 336992
Bizhanov Dimash Nurahmetovich *(Deputy Chm)*

Subsidiaries:

Uralsk Plant Zenit JSC (1)
Sarayshyk St 28, West Kazakhstan Region, 090000, Oral, Kazakhstan
Tel.: (7) 87112514006
Web Site: https://www.zenit.kz
Industrial Equipment Mfr & Distr
N.A.I.C.S.: 333415

NATIONAL CONSUMER HOLDING COMPANY
East - Khalid Bin Al Waleed Street-City Tower - 9th Fl - Office No 1, PO Box 3767, Safat, Kuwait, 13038, Kuwait
Tel.: (965) 22493267
Web Site: https://www.ncciikw.com
NCCI—(KUW)
Rev.: $3,551,961
Assets: $90,805,073
Liabilities: $1,671,208
Net Worth: $89,133,865
Earnings: $640,859
Emp.: 6
Fiscal Year-end: 12/31/22
Consumer Product Mfr, Importer & Sales
N.A.I.C.S.: 339999
Ahmed Mohammed Body *(Vice Chm)*

NATIONAL CORPORATION FOR TOURISM AND HOTELS
PO Box 6942, Abu Dhabi, United Arab Emirates
Tel.: (971) 24099999
Web Site: https://www.ncth.com
Year Founded: 1996
NCTH—(ABU)
Rev.: $182,205,534
Assets: $775,396,045
Liabilities: $162,009,978
Net Worth: $613,386,066
Earnings: $18,536,698

Fiscal Year-end: 12/31/23
Tourism & Hotel Management Services
N.A.I.C.S.: 561520
Hamdan Mubarak Al Nahyan *(Chm)*

NATIONAL CREDIT AND COMMERCE BANK PLC
13/1 - 13/2 Toyenbee Circular Road, Motijheel C/A, Dhaka, 1000, Bangladesh
Tel.: (880) 9666700008
Web Site: https://www.nccbank.com.bd
NCCBANK—(CHT)
Rev.: $116,970,600
Assets: $2,755,855,154
Liabilities: $2,544,584,679
Net Worth: $211,270,475
Earnings: $24,111,902
Emp.: 2,477
Fiscal Year-end: 12/31/22
Commercial Banking Services
N.A.I.C.S.: 522110
S. M. Abu Mohsin *(Chm)*

Subsidiaries:

NCCB Securities & Financial Services Limited (1)
NCC Bank Bhaban 3rd Floor 13/1 and 13/2 Toyenbee Circular Road, Motijheel C/A, Dhaka, Bangladesh
Tel.: (880) 27114097
Security & Financial Services
N.A.I.C.S.: 523999
Monzurul Alam *(COO)*

NATIONAL DEVELOPMENT BANK PLC
No 40 Nawam Mawatha, 2, Colombo, 2, Sri Lanka
Tel.: (94) 112448888
Web Site: https://www.ndbbank.com
Year Founded: 1979
NDB.N0000—(COL)
Rev.: $408,741,791
Assets: $2,409,030,515
Liabilities: $2,192,350,738
Net Worth: $216,679,777
Earnings: $733,596,671
Emp.: 2,786
Fiscal Year-end: 12/31/23
Investment Management Service
N.A.I.C.S.: 523940
Manique Kiriella Bandara *(Compliance Officer & Asst VP)*

Subsidiaries:

NDB Capital Holdings Limited (1)
Level 1 NDB Capital Building No 135 Bauddhaloka Mawatha, 4, Colombo, Sri Lanka
Tel.: (94) 112300385
Web Site: https://www.ndbch.com
Rev.: $2,593
Investment Banking Services
N.A.I.C.S.: 523150
Vajira Kulatilaka *(CEO)*

Subsidiary (Domestic):

NDB Securities (Pvt) Limited (2)
Level 2 NDB Capital Building No 135 Bauddhaloka Mawatha, 4, Colombo, Sri Lanka
Tel.: (94) 112131000
Web Site: https://www.ndbs.lk
Banking Services
N.A.I.C.S.: 522110
Arjun Fernando *(Chm)*

NDB Wealth Management Limited (2)
Level G NDB Capital Building No 135 Bauddhaloka Mawath, 04, Colombo, Sri Lanka
Tel.: (94) 112303232
Web Site: https://ndbwealth.com
Banking Services
N.A.I.C.S.: 522110

NDB Capital Limited (1)
Uday Tower 6th Floor 57 & 57/A Gulshan

NATIONAL DEVELOPMENT BANK PLC

National Development Bank PLC—(Continued)
Avenue Circle-1, Dhaka, 1212, Bangladesh
Tel.: (880) 2222288626
Web Site: https://www.ndbcapital.com
Banking Services
N.A.I.C.S.: 522110
Sarath Wikramanayake *(Chm)*

NDB Zephyr Partners Lanka (Pvt) Limited (1)
No 48/5/1 West Wing Parkway Building Park Street, 02, Colombo, Sri Lanka
Tel.: (94) 112303810
Web Site: http://www.zmlp.com
Banking Services
N.A.I.C.S.: 522110
Senaka Kakirawaragodage *(Mng Dir)*

NATIONAL DRILLING CO.
P.O. Box: 70 Dokki, Cairo, Egypt
Tel.: (20) 225177388
Web Site: https://www.ndcdrill.com
Year Founded: 1981
NDRL.CA—(EGX)
Sales Range: Less than $1 Million
Oil & Gas Extraction Services
N.A.I.C.S.: 211120
Adel Mohammed Ahmad Al Khayat *(Vice Chm)*

NATIONAL ELECTRIC VEHICLE SWEDEN AB
Saabvagen 5, SE-461 38, Trollhattan, Sweden
Tel.: (46) 520 850 00   SE
Web Site: http://www.nevs.com
Year Founded: 2012
Rev.: $10,917,837
Assets: $4,390,953,486
Liabilities: $2,444,144,955
Net Worth: $1,946,808,531
Earnings: ($367,282,521)
Emp.: 3,925
Fiscal Year-end: 12/31/19
Investment Holding Company
N.A.I.C.S.: 551112
Morgan Fransson *(COO & Sr Dir-Value Stream Mgmt)*

NATIONAL ELECTRONICS HOLDINGS LIMITED
Suite 3201 Gloucester Tower The Landmark, 11 Pedder Street, Central, China (Hong Kong)
Tel.: (852) 2 529 2021   HK
Web Site: http://www.national.com.hk
Year Founded: 1985
0213—(HKG)
Rev.: $89,584,853
Assets: $1,075,535,863
Liabilities: $738,046,097
Net Worth: $337,489,766
Earnings: $11,773,035
Emp.: 200
Fiscal Year-end: 03/31/22
Holding Company; Watch Mfr
N.A.I.C.S.: 551112
Jimmy Yuen Ching Lee *(Chm)*

Subsidiaries:

Duprey Limited (1)
11Fl Shing Dao Indus Building 232 Aberdeen Main Rd, Aberdeen, China (Hong Kong)
Tel.: (852) 25279082
Sales Range: $25-49.9 Million
Emp.: 20
Glass Mfr
N.A.I.C.S.: 327211
Bonnie Wong *(Mgr)*

Eastbond (Hong Kong) Limited (1)
15F Shing Dao Industrial Building 232 Aberdeen Main Road, Aberdeen, China (Hong Kong)
Tel.: (852) 25541151
Sales Range: $25-49.9 Million
Emp.: 20
Watch Distr
N.A.I.C.S.: 423490

National Electronics & Watch Company Ltd. (1)
15/F Shing Dao Industrial Building 232 Aberdeen Main Road, Aberdeen, China (Hong Kong)
Tel.: (852) 25541151
Web Site: http://www.national.com.hk
Sales Range: $25-49.9 Million
Emp.: 20
Watch Mfr
N.A.I.C.S.: 334519

National Electronics (Consolidated) Limited (1)
Suite 3201 Gloucester Tower The Landmark 11 Pedder Street, Central, China (Hong Kong)
Tel.: (852) 25292021
Watch Distr
N.A.I.C.S.: 423940
Loewe Bon Chi Lee *(Mng Dir)*

National Properties Holdings Limited (1)
Rm 3201 32F The Landmark Gloucester Tower 11 Pedder St, Central, China (Hong Kong)
Tel.: (852) 25292626
Sales Range: $50-74.9 Million
Emp.: 20
Property Management Services
N.A.I.C.S.: 531312

St. Thomas Developments Incorporated (1)
3 Sultan St, Toronto, M5S 1L6, ON, Canada
Tel.: (416) 922-5363
Web Site: http://www.onestthomas.com
Sales Range: $50-74.9 Million
Emp.: 10
Real Estate Property Development Services
N.A.I.C.S.: 531210
Yuen Kuilee *(Pres)*

NATIONAL ENERGY EQUIPMENT, INC.
1850 Derry Road East, Mississauga, L5S 1Y6, ON, Canada
Tel.: (905) 564-2422
Web Site: https://www.nee.ca
Sales Range: $50-74.9 Million
Emp.: 285
Industrial Equipment Mfr
N.A.I.C.S.: 423830
Tom Ferries *(Pres & CEO)*

NATIONAL ENGINEERING PTY LTD
288 Boorowa St, Young, 2594, New South Wales, Australia
Tel.: (61) 263829360
Year Founded: 1890
Structural Engineering Services
N.A.I.C.S.: 238120
Norman Chapmin *(Gen Mgr)*

NATIONAL ENTERPRISES LIMITED
Level 15 Tower D International Waterfront Center Wrightson Road, Port of Spain, Trinidad & Tobago
Tel.: (868) 6250015   TT
Web Site: https://nel.co.tt
Year Founded: 1999
NEL—(TRI)
Rev.: $58,635,096
Assets: $485,555,424
Liabilities: $603,817
Net Worth: $484,951,607
Earnings: ($67,270,338)
Fiscal Year-end: 09/30/23
Portfolio Management & Investment Advice
N.A.I.C.S.: 523940
Ingrid L. A. Lashley *(Chm)*

Subsidiaries:

NGC Trinidad & Tobago LNG Limited (1)
Orinoco Drive, Point Lisas Industrial Estate, Couva, Trinidad & Tobago
Tel.: (868) 6361098
Web Site: http://ngl.co.tt
Emp.: 800
Natural Gas Distribution Services
N.A.I.C.S.: 221210

NATIONAL FEDERATION OF AGRICULTURAL CO-OPERATIVE ASSOCIATIONS
8 3 Otemachi 1 chome, Chiyoda ku, Tokyo, 100 0004, Japan
Tel.: (81) 332457111
Web Site: http://www.zennoh.or.jp
Year Founded: 1972
Sales Range: $1-4.9 Billion
Emp.: 10,822
Farm Supplies
N.A.I.C.S.: 424910
Genichi Jinde *(Pres & CEO)*

Subsidiaries:

Zen-Noh Grain Corporation (1)
1127 E Service Rd Hwy 190, Covington, LA 70433
Tel.: (985) 867-3500
Web Site: http://www.cgb.com
Sales Range: $75-99.9 Million
Emp.: 200
Provider of Buying, Outshipping, Storage & Export of Feedgrains & Feed Ingredients
N.A.I.C.S.: 424510
Richard Pemberton *(CFO)*

Joint Venture (Domestic):

CGB Enterprises Inc. (2)
1127 Hwy 190 E Service Rd, Covington, LA 70433
Tel.: (985) 867-3500
Web Site: https://www.cgb.com
Sales Range: $50-74.9 Million
Emp.: 150
Grain Handling, Storage & Export Services
N.A.I.C.S.: 424510
Kevin D. Adams *(Pres & CEO)*

Subsidiary (Domestic):

CGB Diversified Services, Inc. (3)
1608 B W Lafayette Ave, Jacksonville, IL 62650
Tel.: (217) 479-6000
Web Site: http://www.diversifiedservices.com
Insurance Agencies & Brokerages
N.A.I.C.S.: 524210

Consolidated Grain & Barge Co. (3)
1127 Highway 190 East Service Rd, Covington, LA 70433
Tel.: (985) 867-3500
Web Site: https://www.cgbgrain.com
Agricultural Products Distr & Transporation & Financial Services
N.A.I.C.S.: 488310
Kevin Adams *(Pres & CEO)*

Subsidiary (Domestic):

Colusa Elevator Company (4)
2531 N County Rd 1750, Colusa, IL 62329-0026
Tel.: (217) 755-4221
Web Site: http://www.colusaelevator.com
Sales Range: $10-24.9 Million
Emp.: 12
Grain Storage & Drying Services
N.A.I.C.S.: 493130
Dale Griffiths *(Gen Mgr)*

Plant (Domestic):

Colusa Elevator Company (5)
13 Broadway St, Nauvoo, IL 62354
Tel.: (217) 453-2216
Web Site: http://www.colusaelevator.com
Grain Storage & Drying
N.A.I.C.S.: 493130
Gene McEntee *(Office Mgr)*

Subsidiary (Domestic):

River Bend Transport Company Inc. (3)
300 3 Rivers Pkwy, North Bend, OH 45052-9638
Tel.: (513) 941-1200

Web Site: http://www.riverbendtransport.com
Sales Range: $50-74.9 Million
Emp.: 10
Local & Long Distance Trucking; Freight Forwarding Services
N.A.I.C.S.: 484121
Gregory Beck *(VP)*

NATIONAL FERTILIZERS LTD
A-11 Sector-24, Noida, 201 301, Uttar Pradesh, India
Tel.: (91) 1202412294
Web Site: https://www.nationalfertilizers.com
Year Founded: 1974
NFL—(NSE)
Rev.: $1,629,673,500
Assets: $1,148,263,935
Liabilities: $856,128,000
Net Worth: $292,135,935
Earnings: $32,361,420
Emp.: 3,213
Fiscal Year-end: 03/31/21
Nitrogenous Fertilizer Mfr
N.A.I.C.S.: 325311
Dharam Pal *(Co-Sec)*

NATIONAL FIBRES LIMITED
Plot No 16-20 Sector 22 Korangi Industrial Area, Karachi, Pakistan
Tel.: (92) 21 5068931
Synthetic Fiber Mfr
N.A.I.C.S.: 325220

NATIONAL FILM BOARD OF CANADA
Station Centre-ville, PO Box 6100, Montreal, H3C 3H5, QC, Canada
Tel.: (514) 283-9000
Web Site: http://www.help.nfb.ca
Year Founded: 1939
Sales Range: $50-74.9 Million
Emp.: 500
Film Promoter & Production Services
N.A.I.C.S.: 512110
Andre Picard *(Dir Gen-Creation & Innovation)*

Subsidiaries:

National Film Board of Canada (1)
927 Stanford St, Santa Monica, CA 90403-2223
Tel.: (212) 629-8890
Film Promoter
N.A.I.C.S.: 512199

NATIONAL FINANCE CO. S.A.O.G
PO Box 1706, 112, Ruwi, Oman
Tel.: (968) 24470000
Web Site: https://www.nationalfinance.co.om
Year Founded: 1987
NFCI—(MUS)
Rev.: $127,034,468
Assets: $1,331,167,041
Liabilities: $1,055,214,419
Net Worth: $275,952,622
Earnings: $28,847,502
Emp.: 356
Fiscal Year-end: 12/31/23
Financial Services
N.A.I.C.S.: 523999
Taya Jandal Ali *(Chm)*

NATIONAL FITTINGS LIMITED
SF No 112 Mathapur Road Kaniyur, Sulur Taluk Karumathampatti, Coimbatore, 641659, Tamil Nadu, India
Tel.: (91) 9943293000
Web Site: https://www.nationalfitting.com
531289—(BOM)
Rev.: $10,489,563
Assets: $10,698,423
Liabilities: $4,110,425
Net Worth: $6,587,998

AND PRIVATE COMPANIES

Earnings: $526,383
Emp.: 166
Fiscal Year-end: 03/31/23
Steel Pipe Fitting Mfr
N.A.I.C.S.: 331210
A. V. Palaniswamy *(Mng Dir)*

NATIONAL FLOUR MILLS LIMITED
27-29 Wrightson Road, PO Box 1154, Port of Spain, Trinidad & Tobago
Tel.: (868) 6252416   TT
Web Site: https://www.nfm.co.tt
Year Founded: 1972
NFM—(TRI)
Rev.: $60,567,117
Assets: $63,491,224
Liabilities: $24,541,577
Net Worth: $38,949,648
Earnings: $3,399,478
Emp.: 355
Fiscal Year-end: 12/31/20
Flour & Animal Feeds Mfr
N.A.I.C.S.: 311211
Sati Jagmohan *(Sec)*

NATIONAL FOODS HOLDINGS LTD.
10 Stirling Road, PO Box 269, Harare, Zimbabwe
Tel.: (263) 4781182
Web Site: http://www.nationalfoods.co.zw
NTFD—(ZIM)
Rev.: $343,577,747
Assets: $185,306,714
Liabilities: $78,659,231
Net Worth: $106,647,483
Earnings: $7,529,867
Emp.: 1,762
Fiscal Year-end: 06/30/23
Food & Beverage Products Mfr & Distr;
N.A.I.C.S.: 311999
Michael Lashbrook *(CEO)*

NATIONAL FOODS LIMITED
12/CL-6 Claremont Road Civil Lines, PO Box 15509, Karachi, 75530, Pakistan
Tel.: (92) 2135662687
Web Site: https://www.nfoods.com
Year Founded: 1970
NATF—(KAR)
Rev.: $174,142,262
Assets: $95,375,149
Liabilities: $59,260,022
Net Worth: $36,115,127
Earnings: $9,840,298
Emp.: 753
Fiscal Year-end: 06/30/19
Food Products Mfr
N.A.I.C.S.: 236210
Abdul Majeed *(Founder)*

Subsidiaries:

National Foods DMCC   (1)
Office No 24-19 24th Floor Reef Tower JLT, Cluster O, Dubai, United Arab Emirates
Tel.: (971) 44487111
Food Products Mfr
N.A.I.C.S.: 311999

NATIONAL GAS & INDUSTRIALIZATION CO.
331 Prince Abdulaziz Ibn Musaid Ibn Jalawi St, PO Box 564, North Of King Fahad Medical City Building 331 Olaya, Riyadh, 12221, Al Olaya, Saudi Arabia
Tel.: (966) 114664999
Web Site: https://www.gasco.com.sa
Year Founded: 1963
2080—(SAU)
Rev.: $554,648,340
Assets: $639,515,961
Liabilities: $176,920,702

Net Worth: $462,595,259
Earnings: $57,075,996
Emp.: 1,863
Fiscal Year-end: 12/31/22
Liquefied Petroleum Gas Distribution Services
N.A.I.C.S.: 221210
Ali Mohammed Al-Sflan *(Deputy Chm)*

NATIONAL GAS COMPANY OF TRINIDAD & TOBAGO LIMITED
Orinoco Drive Industrial Estate, Couva, Point Lisas, Trinidad & Tobago
Tel.: (868) 6364662
Web Site: http://www.ngc.co.tt
Sales Range: $150-199.9 Million
Emp.: 500
Purchase, Compress, Transport, Sell & Distribute Natural Gas to Industrial Users
N.A.I.C.S.: 221210
Olave Maria Thorne *(VP-Corp Compliance & Governance)*

Subsidiaries:

Eastern Caribbean Gas Pipeline Co Ltd   (1)
2nd Floor Tail Building 11 Maraval Road, Port of Spain, Trinidad & Tobago
Tel.: (868) 6288814
Gas Pipeline Construction & Management Services
N.A.I.C.S.: 237120

National Energy Corporation of Trinidad and Tobago Limited   (1)
Rivulet & Factory Roads Brechin Castle, Point Lisas, Couva, Trinidad & Tobago
Tel.: (868) 636 8471
Web Site: http://www.nec.co.tt
Sales Range: $50-74.9 Million
Emp.: 115
Energy Project Planning, Development & Construction Services
N.A.I.C.S.: 237130

NATIONAL GAS COMPANY SOAG
Al Khuwair Office ONEIC Building, Al Khuwair, Muscat, Oman
Tel.: (968) 22084900
Web Site: https://www.nationalgasco.net
Year Founded: 1981
NGCI—(MUS)
Rev.: $239,542,804
Assets: $175,964,206
Liabilities: $98,439,980
Net Worth: $77,524,226
Earnings: ($4,075,772)
Emp.: 177
Fiscal Year-end: 12/31/21
Oil & Gas Exploration Services
N.A.I.C.S.: 457210
Abdullah Suleiman Al Harthy *(Chm)*

Subsidiaries:

NGC Consolidated Holding Sdn. Bhd.   (1)

NGC Energy FZE   (1)
PO Box 5403, Fujairah, United Arab Emirates
Tel.: (971) 92249132
Sales Range: $75-99.9 Million
Emp.: 16
Liquefied Petroleum Gas Distr
N.A.I.C.S.: 221210

NGC Energy India Private Limited   (1)
Room 407 Trade and Transport Terminal Krishnapatnam Port, Krishnapatnam, Nellore, 524 344, Andhra Pradesh, India
Tel.: (91) 984 095 0234
Web Site: https://www.ngcenergy.in
Liquefied Petroleum Gas Distr
N.A.I.C.S.: 424710

NGC Energy Saudi LLC   (1)
King Fahd Road Al Rakah Al Janubiyah, Al Khobar, 34226, Saudi Arabia
Tel.: (966) 13 832 3313
Web Site: https://www.ngcenergy.com.sa
Natural Gas Distribution Services
N.A.I.C.S.: 221210

NGC Energy Sdn. Bhd.   (1)
Lot 3A-01 Level 3A Tower Block Menara Millennium 8 Jalan Damanlela, Bukit Damansara, 50490, Kuala Lumpur, Malaysia
Tel.: (60) 1300885808
Web Site: https://www.ngcenergy.com.my
Gas & Oil Exploration Services
N.A.I.C.S.: 213112

NATIONAL GENERAL INDUSTRIES LIMITED
3rd Floor Surya Plaza K-185/1 Sarai Julena New Friends Colony, New Delhi, 110 025, India
Tel.: (91) 1149872442
Web Site: https://www.modisteel.com
531651—(BOM)
Rev.: $1,744,883
Assets: $4,019,471
Liabilities: $434,686
Net Worth: $3,584,785
Earnings: $26,701
Emp.: 52
Fiscal Year-end: 03/31/23
Steel Mfrs
N.A.I.C.S.: 332312
Ashok Kumar Modi *(Chm & Co-Mng Dir)*

NATIONAL GENERAL INSURANCE CO. (P.S.C.)
Levels Ground 3 5 6 NGI House Port Saeed Street, PO Box 154, Deira, Dubai, United Arab Emirates
Tel.: (971) 42115800   AE
Web Site: https://www.ngi.ae
Year Founded: 1980
NGI—(DFM)
Rev.: $203,056,555
Assets: $370,049,120
Liabilities: $213,911,865
Net Worth: $156,137,255
Earnings: $20,387,441
Emp.: 418
Fiscal Year-end: 12/31/23
General Insurance Services
N.A.I.C.S.: 524298
Adel Mohammed Saleh Al Zarouni *(Vice Chm)*

NATIONAL GRID PLC
1-3 Strand, London, WC2N 5EH, United Kingdom
Tel.: (44) 2070043000   UK
Web Site: https://www.nationalgrid.com
Year Founded: 1990
NG—(LSE)
Rev.: $25,056,803,837
Assets: $124,116,384,751
Liabilities: $86,383,489,018
Net Worth: $37,732,895,733
Earnings: $2,798,535,723
Emp.: 31,425
Fiscal Year-end: 03/31/24
Holding Company; Electricity Transmission
N.A.I.C.S.: 551112
Andrew Agg *(CFO)*

Subsidiaries:

DTV Services Limited   (1)
Broadcast Centre BC3 D5, 201 Wood Lane, London, W12 7TP, United Kingdom
Tel.: (44) 8708809980
Web Site: http://www.freeview.co.uk
Holding Company; Digital Television Services
N.A.I.C.S.: 551112

Intelig 23   (1)

NATIONAL GRID PLC

Praia de Botafogo 370/1o andar, Rio de Janeiro, 22250-909, Brazil
Tel.: (55) 21 25 36 08 00
Web Site: http://www.intelig.net.br
Telecommunications; Joint Venture of National Grid (50%), France Telecom (25%) & Sprint (25%)
N.A.I.C.S.: 517111

NGG Finance plc   (1)
1-3 Strand, London, WC2N 5EH, United Kingdom
Tel.: (44) 2070043226
Financial Management Services
N.A.I.C.S.: 523999

National Grid Electricity System Operator Limited   (1)
Faraday House Warwick Technology Park Gallows Hill, Warwick, CV34 6DA, United Kingdom
Tel.: (44) 926653400
Web Site: https://www.nationalgrideso.com
Emp.: 670
Electric Power Distribution Services
N.A.I.C.S.: 221122
Fintan Slye *(Chm & Exec Dir)*

National Grid Electricity Transmission Plc   (1)
1-3 Strand, London, WC2N 5EH, United Kingdom
Tel.: (44) 2070043000
Emp.: 200
Electric Power Transmission Services
N.A.I.C.S.: 221121
Sir Teter Gershon *(Chm)*

National Grid Gas plc   (1)
National grid House Warwick Technology Park Gallows Hill, Warwick, CV34 6DA, United Kingdom
Tel.: (44) 1926653000
Web Site: https://www.nationalgas.com
Sales Range: $1-4.9 Billion
Emp.: 2,500
Gas Transmission & Distribution Services
N.A.I.C.S.: 221210

National Grid Grain LNG Limited   (1)
Isle of Grain, Rochester, ME3 0AB, Kent, United Kingdom
Tel.: (44) 1634270000
Emp.: 250
Natural Gas Extraction Services
N.A.I.C.S.: 211130
Simon Culkin *(Gen Mgr)*

National Grid Holdings Limited   (1)
Grand Buildings 1-3 Strand, London, WC2N 5EH, United Kingdom
Tel.: (44) 2070043201
Investment Management Service
N.A.I.C.S.: 523999

National Grid Metering Limited   (1)
1-3 Strand, London, WC2N 5EH, West Midlands, United Kingdom
Tel.: (44) 1214248000
Sales Range: $100-124.9 Million
Emp.: 50
Gas Metering Equipment Installation Services
N.A.I.C.S.: 238210
Jon Butterworth *(Mng Dir)*

National Grid Property Limited   (1)
7 Hertford Street, London, W1J 7RH, United Kingdom
Tel.: (44) 1256308803
Web Site: http://www.nationalgrid.com
Sales Range: $75-99.9 Million
Emp.: 102
Land Reclamation & Management Services
N.A.I.C.S.: 531312

National Grid Renewables, LLC   (1)
8400 Normandale Lake Blvd Ste 1200, Bloomington, MN 55437
Tel.: (952) 988-9000
Web Site: https://www.nationalgridrenewables.com
Renewable Solar Energy Services
N.A.I.C.S.: 221114
Cordi O'Hara *(Chm)*

National Grid USA   (1)
40 Sylvin Rd, Waltham, MA 02451 **(100%)**
Tel.: (781) 907-1520
Sales Range: $1-4.9 Billion
Emp.: 2,000
Holding Company; Owner of Public Utilities

NATIONAL GRID PLC

National Grid plc—(Continued)
N.A.I.C.S.: 221118
Dianne Kenney (Risk Mngmt Dir)

Subsidiary (Domestic):

Nantucket Electric Company (2)
Fairgrounds Rd, Nantucket, MA
02254 **(100%)**
Tel.: (508) 389-2000
Transmission & Distribution of Electricity
N.A.I.C.S.: 221118

New England Power Company (2)
1 Metrotech Ctr, Brooklyn, NY 11201-3850
Tel.: (508) 389-2000
Sales Range: $450-499.9 Million
Emp.: 2,000
Electric Power Transmission Services
N.A.I.C.S.: 221122

Subsidiary (Non-US):

Opinac North America, Inc. (2)
Toronto Dominion Bank Tower Toronto-Dominion Ctr., Ste. 4800, Toronto, M5K
1E6, ON, Canada **(100%)**
Generates Electricity
N.A.I.C.S.: 221122

Subsidiary (Domestic):

Transgas Inc. (2)
87 Industrial Ave E, Lowell, MA 01852-5109
Tel.: (978) 856-2900
Web Site: https://www.transgasinc.com
Sales Range: $25-49.9 Million
Emp.: 80
Transportation of Cryogenic Liquids
N.A.I.C.S.: 484230
Timothy Mehan (VP-Ops)

Sunbeam Solar, LLC (1)
1570 Northern Ave, Kingman, AZ 86409
Tel.: (928) 530-6089
Web Site: http://www.sunbeamsolar-llc.com
Solar Panels Installation Services
N.A.I.C.S.: 238210

Vibrant Solar, LLC (1)
591 Benjamin's Way, Lewisville, TX 75057
Tel.: (972) 600-2808
Web Site: https://www.vibrantsolar.com
Solar Panels Installation Services
N.A.I.C.S.: 238210

Virtue Solar, LLC (1)
1740 Broadway St Ste 6, Charlottesville, VA
22902
Tel.: (540) 407-8353
Web Site: https://www.virtuesolar.com
Solar Panels Installation Services
N.A.I.C.S.: 238210

NATIONAL GROUP OF COMPANIES LLC

16-C Peoples Colony, Faisalabad,
38090, Pakistan
Tel.: (92) 41111252627
Web Site: http://www.national-group.com
Year Founded: 1978
Sales Range: $150-199.9 Million
Emp.: 620
Holding Company
N.A.I.C.S.: 551112
Imraan Zahid (Mng Dir)

Subsidiaries:

Asim Textile Mills Ltd. (1)
J K House 32-W Main Boulevard, Madina
Town, Faisalabad, 38090, Pakistan
Tel.: (92) 4187219536
Web Site: https://www.asimtextile.com
Sales Range: $150-199.9 Million
Emp.: 541
Polyester & Cotton Yarn Mfr
N.A.I.C.S.: 313110
Khalid Jabbar (Sec)

J.A. Textile Mills Ltd. (1)
JK House 32-W Main Road, Madian Town,
Faisalabad, 38090, Pakistan
Tel.: (92) 418721953
Web Site: https://www.jatml.com
Rev.: $121,184
Assets: $2,959,759
Liabilities: $1,232,959
Net Worth: $1,726,800
Earnings: ($120,773)
Emp.: 50
Fiscal Year-end: 06/30/2023
Textile Mfr
N.A.I.C.S.: 314999
Imran Zahid (CEO)

Zeeshan Energy Limited (1)
318-319 Clifton Centre, Khayaban-e-Roomi,
Karachi, 75600, Pakistan
Tel.: (92) 2111125
Web Site: http://www.national-group.com
Electric Power
N.A.I.C.S.: 221122

NATIONAL GYPSUM COMPANY

Riyadh Royal Commission Yanbu Industrial Area Second, Tahlia Street,
Dammam, Saudi Arabia
Tel.: (966) 114641963
Web Site: http://www.gypsco.com.sa
Year Founded: 1959
2090—(SAU)
Rev.: $13,837,555
Assets: $108,330,169
Liabilities: $11,761,108
Net Worth: $96,569,061
Earnings: $1,367,306
Emp.: 280
Fiscal Year-end: 12/31/23
Gypsum Product Mfr & Whslr
N.A.I.C.S.: 327420
Thomas C. Nelson (Chm, Pres & CEO)

NATIONAL HIGHWAYS AUTHORITY OF INDIA

G 5&6 Sector 10, Dwarka, New
Delhi, 110 075, India
Tel.: (91) 11 25074100
Web Site: http://www.nhai.org
NHAI—(NSE)
Sales Range: Less than $1 Million
Highway Authority
N.A.I.C.S.: 921190
Santosh Kumar Yadav (Chm)

Subsidiaries:

National Highways Logistic Management Limited (1)
2nd Floor D21 Corporate Park Sector 21,
Dwarka, New Delhi, 110077, India
Tel.: (91) 1125308800
Web Site: https://nhlml.org
Logistics Consulting Services
N.A.I.C.S.: 541614

NATIONAL HOLDING KAZAGRO JSC

36 Kenessary Street, Nur-Sultan,
010000, Kazakhstan
Tel.: (7) 7172390024
Web Site: http://www.nhkazagro.kz
Holding Company
N.A.I.C.S.: 551112
Rakhmet Gazizovich Baynakov (Mng Dir)

Subsidiaries:

Agricultural Credit Corporation
JSC (1)
28a Zheltoksan Street, Nur-Sultan, 010000,
Kazakhstan **(100%)**
Tel.: (7) 7172591591
Web Site: http://www.agrocredit.kz
Rev.: $474,217,572
Assets: $3,096,173,345
Liabilities: $2,107,642,832
Net Worth: $988,530,513
Earnings: $64,802,604
Emp.: 758
Fiscal Year-end: 12/31/2023
Agricultural Credit Services
N.A.I.C.S.: 525990

KazAgroFinance JSC (1)
51 Kenesary St VP-4, Nur-Sultan, 010000,
Kazakhstan **(100%)**
Tel.: (7) 7172 580437
Web Site: http://www.kaf.kz
Sales Range: $25-49.9 Million
Emp.: 400
Agricultural Financial Services
N.A.I.C.S.: 525990
Asylkhan Bolatovich Dzhuvashev (Deputy Chm)

NATIONAL HOTELS COMPANY B.S.C.

1st Floor Diplomat Radisson Blu Hotel Building 59 Road 1701, PO Box
5243, 317, Manama, 317, Bahrain
Tel.: (973) 17530838
Web Site:
https://www.nhcbahrain.com
NHOTEL—(BAH)
Rev.: $18,190,340
Assets: $219,014,777
Liabilities: $4,870,701
Net Worth: $214,144,076
Earnings: $7,609,305
Emp.: 325
Fiscal Year-end: 12/31/22
Home Management Services
N.A.I.C.S.: 721110
Faisal Ahmed Al Zayani (Chm)

NATIONAL HOUSEHOLD FURNITURE INDUSTRY CO.

Bessan Enterace of Duhok Road,
Mosul, Iraq
Tel.: (964) 60 850009
Year Founded: 1986
Household Furniture Mfr
N.A.I.C.S.: 337121

NATIONAL HOUSING FINANCE PLC

National Plaza 8th floor 109 Bir Uttam CR Dutta Road, Dhaka, 1205,
Bangladesh
Tel.: (880) 29670612
Web Site:
https://www.nationalhousingbd.com
NHFIL—(DHA)
Rev.: $18,792,237
Assets: $221,086,956
Liabilities: $195,773,042
Net Worth: $25,313,914
Earnings: $3,030,951
Emp.: 193
Fiscal Year-end: 12/31/21
Home Loans & Financial Services
N.A.I.C.S.: 522310
Mohammad Sarwar Kamal (Sec & VP)

NATIONAL INDUSTRIALIZATION COMPANY

The Business Gate Building No C3
Eastern Ring Road, PO Box 26707,
Riyadh, 11496, Saudi Arabia
Tel.: (966) 112222205
Web Site: https://www.tasnee.com
Year Founded: 1985
2060—(SAU)
Rev.: $1,035,291,828
Assets: $6,574,563,925
Liabilities: $3,269,556,326
Net Worth: $3,305,007,599
Earnings: $289,485,135
Emp.: 3,200
Fiscal Year-end: 12/31/22
Industrial Joint-Stock Holding Company
N.A.I.C.S.: 551112
Mutlaq Hamad Al-Morished (CEO)

Subsidiaries:

Al-Rowad National Plastic Co.Ltd (1)
PO Box 29452, 11457, Riyadh, Saudi
Arabia **(99.91%)**
Tel.: (966) 12651966
Web Site: http://www.rowadplastic.com

INTERNATIONAL PUBLIC

Plastics Materials & Basic Forms & Shapes
Whslr
N.A.I.C.S.: 424610

Al-Salam Aircraft Company Ltd (1)
PO Box 8012, 11482, Riyadh, Saudi Arabia
Tel.: (966) 12203966
Web Site: http://www.alsalamaircraft.com.sa
Automotive Repair & Maintenance
N.A.I.C.S.: 811198

Arabian Axles and Foundries and
Spare Parts Company Ltd. (1)
PO Box 8491, 31482, Dammam, Saudi
Arabia
Tel.: (966) 38121267
Web Site: http://www.masabik.com
Civil Engineering Construction
N.A.I.C.S.: 237990

National Batteries Company Ltd (1)
PO Box 177, 11383, Riyadh, Saudi
Arabia **(80%)**
Tel.: (966) 12650019
Web Site: http://www.battariat.com
Sales Range: $150-199.9 Million
Emp.: 300
Electrical Apparatus & Equipment Wiring
Supplies & Construction Material Whslr
N.A.I.C.S.: 423610

National Industrialization & Energy
Services Company Co. Ltd. (1)
PO Box 28589, 11447, Riyadh, Saudi Arabia
Tel.: (966) 12911111
Web Site: http://www.taqa.com.sa
Emp.: 25
Energy Wire Mfr
N.A.I.C.S.: 335929

National Industrialization Petrochemical Marketing Company (1)
Business Gate Building C3 Qurtuba Area,
PO Box 26707, King Khalid International
Airport Road, 11496, Riyadh, Saudi
Arabia **(99.91%)**
Tel.: (966) 11 222 2205
Web Site: https://www.tasneemarketing.com
Sales Range: $10-24.9 Million
Emp.: 50
Petrochemicals & Chemicals Marketer
N.A.I.C.S.: 424690

National Inspection and Technical
Testing Co. Ltd. (1)
PO Box 3998, Dammam, 31481, Saudi
Arabia
Tel.: (966) 38281835
Web Site: https://fahssituv.com
Sales Range: $25-49.9 Million
Emp.: 25
Testing Laboratories
N.A.I.C.S.: 541380

National Lead Smelting Co. Ltd (1)
2nd Industrial Zone 3rd Stage, PO Box
43169, Riyadh, 11561, Saudi
Arabia **(71.74%)**
Tel.: (966) 112652424
Web Site: https://www.rasass.com.sa
Plastics Material & Resin Mfr
N.A.I.C.S.: 325211

National Metal Manufacturing & Casting Company Ltd (1)
PO Box 10882, 31961, Al Jubayl, Saudi
Arabia **(29.2%)**
Tel.: (966) 133588000
Web Site: http://www.maadaniyah.com
Sales Range: $75-99.9 Million
Engineering Services
N.A.I.C.S.: 541330
Mutlaq Hamad Al-Morished (Chm)

National Operation and Industrial Services Co.Ltd (1)
Al Akaria Building Tower 1 Sitteen Street,
PO Box 86868, 11632, Riyadh, Saudi
Arabia **(61.66%)**
Tel.: (966) 14762800
Web Site: http://www.khadamat.com.sa
Industrial Supplies Whslr
N.A.I.C.S.: 423840

National Petrochemical Industrialization Company Ltd. (1)
PO Box 26707, 11496, Riyadh, Saudi Arabia
Tel.: (966) 14767166

AND PRIVATE COMPANIES

Web Site: http://www.tasnee.com
Sales Range: $50-74.9 Million
Emp.: 120
Petrochemical Mfr
N.A.I.C.S.: 325110

National Worldwide Industrial Advancement Company Ltd (1)
PO Box 26707, 11496, Riyadh, Saudi Arabia (99.85%)
Tel.: (966) 14767166
Web Site: http://www.tasnee.com
Electric Power Distribution
N.A.I.C.S.: 221122

Saudi Polyolefins Co.Ltd (1)
PO Box 35579, 31961, Al Jubayl, Saudi Arabia (75%)
Tel.: (966) 3416449
Plastics Material & Resin Mfr
N.A.I.C.S.: 325211

TUV-Middle East Ltd (1)
Office No 41 GEMS Building No 737 Road No 1510 Block No 115, Bahrain International Investment Park, Hidd, Bahrain (57.94%)
Tel.: (973) 17877391
Web Site: http://www.tuv-nord.com
Sales Range: $50-74.9 Million
Emp.: 50
Direct Health & Medical Insurance Carriers
N.A.I.C.S.: 524114

NATIONAL INDUSTRIES GROUP HOLDING S.A.K.
PO Box 417, Safat, 13005, Kuwait, 13005, Kuwait
Tel.: (965) 24849466
Web Site: https://www.nig.com.kw
Year Founded: 1960
NIND—(KUW)
Rev.: $362,621,213
Assets: $4,190,914,980
Liabilities: $2,366,417,347
Net Worth: $1,824,497,634
Earnings: $323,777,243
Emp.: 1,800
Fiscal Year-end: 12/31/21
Holding Company
N.A.I.C.S.: 551112
Saad Mohammed Abdullah Al Saad (Chm)

Subsidiaries:

Al-Ahleia Insurance Company S.A.K.
East Block 2 Ahmed Al Jaber Street Building No21, PO Box 1602, Al Ahleia Insurance Tower Sharq Safat, Kuwait, 13017, Kuwait
Tel.: (965) 1888444
Web Site: https://www.alahleia.com
Rev.: $367,241,412
Assets: $1,325,316,013
Liabilities: $852,480,172
Net Worth: $472,835,841
Earnings: $58,429,829
Emp.: 180
Fiscal Year-end: 12/31/2022
Insurance & Reinsurance Services
N.A.I.C.S.: 524126
Ayman Abdullatif Ali Al-Shayea (Chm)

BI Group plc (1)
Unit 1 1st Ave Maybrook Indus Estate, Minworth, B76 1BA, Sutton Coldfield, West Midlands, United Kingdom - England
Tel.: (44) 1213512129
Web Site: http://www.bi-group.com
Sales Range: $25-49.9 Million
Emp.: 6
Engineeering Services
N.A.I.C.S.: 541330

Subsidiary (Non-US):

GMT GmbH (2)
Odenwaldstrasse 19, 64521, Gross-Gerau, Germany
Tel.: (49) 615217870
Web Site: http://www.gmt.de
Gas Meters & Regulators Mfr
N.A.I.C.S.: 333132

Prestige Medical Limited (2)
East House Duttons Way Shadsworth Business Park, Blackburn, BB1 2QR, United Kingdom
Tel.: (44) 1254682622
Web Site: http://www.prestigemedical.co.uk
Sales Range: $25-49.9 Million
Emp.: 60
Medical Equipment Mfr
N.A.I.C.S.: 339112

UCB Comercial Cast-Profil S.A. (2)
Pol San Miguel C Albert Einstein n 64, Villanueva de Gallego, 50830, Zaragoza, Barcelona, Spain
Tel.: (34) 976185767
Web Site: http://www.unitedcastbar.com
Emp.: 50
Cast Iron Foundry Services
N.A.I.C.S.: 331511

UCB Ferrocast Limited (2)
Spital Lane, Chesterfield, S41 0EX, Derbyshire, United Kingdom
Tel.: (44) 1246 269293
Web Site: http://www.unitedcastbar.com
Emp.: 3
Iron Bar Mfr
N.A.I.C.S.: 331110

UCB Germany GmbH (2)
Schillerstrasse 38, 68623, Lampertheim, Germany
Tel.: (49) 6241 9724 0
Web Site: http://www.unitedcastbar.de
Sales Range: $25-49.9 Million
Emp.: 25
Iron Product Mfr
N.A.I.C.S.: 331110

Cinpres Gas Injection Inc (1)
11850 Whitmore Lk Rd Ste B, Whitmore Lake, MI 48189
Tel.: (734) 449-8301
Web Site: http://www.bi-group.com
Emp.: 2
Injection Molded Plastic Products Mfr
N.A.I.C.S.: 326199
Kevin Brady (Mgr-Sls)

Eagle Proprietary Investments Limited (1)
Emirates Financial Towers Dubai International Financial Centre, PO Box 506725, Office S2205 Level 22 South Tower, Dubai, United Arab Emirates
Tel.: (971) 43129000
Web Site: https://www.eagle-investments.com
Investment Banking Services
N.A.I.C.S.: 523150

Ikarus Petroleum Industries Company K.S.C.C. (1)
First Floor Touristic Enterprises Company Building, Jahra Street Shouweikh, Kuwait, Kuwait
Tel.: (965) 24965885
Web Site: http://ikarus.com.kw
Rev.: $2,778,284
Assets: $383,449,333
Liabilities: $54,745,634
Net Worth: $328,703,699
Earnings: $2,364,135
Fiscal Year-end: 12/31/2016
Petrochemical Mfr
N.A.I.C.S.: 325110
Reyadh S. Ali Al-Edrissi (Chm & CEO)

Kuwait Financial Centre S.A.K. (1)
AlSharq Block 1 Ahmad AlJaber Street Universal Tower Floor 3, PO Box 23444, Al Qiblah Safat, 13095, Kuwait, 13095, Kuwait
Tel.: (965) 22248000
Web Site: https://www.markaz.com
Rev.: $61,110,208
Assets: $687,269,655
Liabilities: $254,129,156
Net Worth: $433,140,499
Earnings: $15,197,114
Emp.: 166
Fiscal Year-end: 12/31/2022
Financial Investment Services
N.A.I.C.S.: 523999
Diraar Yusuf Alghanim (Chm)

NIC Holdings (UK) Plc (1)
1 First Avenue Minworth, Sutton Coldfield, B76 1BA, United Kingdom
Tel.: (44) 1213512129
Building Materials Mfr

N.A.I.C.S.: 327331

National Industries Company K.S.C. (1)
Industrial Shuwaikh 2 -Block 1 Area 92 - Al-Zaben Complex, Kuwait, Kuwait (51%)
Tel.: (965) 24642100
Web Site: https://www.nicbm.com
Rev.: $162,428,568
Assets: $383,053,586
Liabilities: $100,204,053
Net Worth: $282,849,534
Earnings: $12,409,516
Emp.: 1,800
Fiscal Year-end: 12/31/2023
Building Materials Mfr
N.A.I.C.S.: 321999
Abdulaziz Ibrahim Al-Rabiah (Chm)

Noor Financial Investment Co. K.S.C.C (1)
Noor Building Intersection of Jahra Street and Airport Road, PO Box 3311, Shuwaikh Safat, 13034, Kuwait, 13034, Kuwait
Tel.: (965) 1818080
Web Site: https://www.noorinvestment.com
Rev.: $47,505,850
Assets: $371,901,508
Liabilities: $86,113,429
Net Worth: $285,788,079
Earnings: $64,577,182
Emp.: 1,000
Fiscal Year-end: 12/31/2022
Investment Services
N.A.I.C.S.: 523999
Abdulghani Mohammed S. Behbehani (Vice Chm)

Sulaibiyha Factories Group (1)
PO Box 3356, Safat, Kuwait, 13034, Kuwait
Tel.: (965) 44674055
Industrial Services
N.A.I.C.S.: 321999

UCB Austria (1)
Gradner Strasse 66, 8055, Graz, Austria
Tel.: (43) 3167 11028
Web Site: http://www.bi-group.com
Sales Range: $25-49.9 Million
Emp.: 6
Iron Product Mfr
N.A.I.C.S.: 332999

United Cast Bar (UK) Limited (1)
Spital Lane, Chesterfield, S41 0EX, Derbyshire, United Kingdom
Tel.: (44) 1246201194
Web Site: http://www.unitedcastbar.com
Emp.: 400
Iron Casting Bar Mfr
N.A.I.C.S.: 331110

NATIONAL INSTITUTE FOR HEALTH & CLINICAL EXCELLENCE
71 High Holborn Midcity Pl, London, WC1V 6NA, United Kingdom
Tel.: (44) 2070675800
Web Site: http://www.nice.org.uk
Year Founded: 2000
Sales Range: $50-74.9 Million
Emp.: 120
Public Health Programs
N.A.I.C.S.: 923120
Andrew Dillon (CEO)

NATIONAL INSURANCE COMPANY
National Towers Complex, PO Box 1819, Al-Bireh, Palestine
Tel.: (970) 22983800
Web Site: https://www.nic-pal.com
Year Founded: 1992
NIC—(PAL)
Rev.: $53,963,897
Assets: $110,594,851
Liabilities: $66,956,613
Net Worth: $43,638,238
Earnings: ($590,820)
Fiscal Year-end: 12/31/23
General Insurance Services
N.A.I.C.S.: 524298
Bashar Hussein (CEO & Deputy Gen Mgr-Strategic, Plng, Mktg, Dev, and Risk Mgmt)

NATIONAL INVESTMENTS COMPANY K.S.C.C.

NATIONAL INSURANCE COMPANY (P.S.C)
Shameisani Sayed Qutob Street Beside Bahrain Embassy - Building 29, PO Box 6156, Amman, 11118, Jordan
Tel.: (962) 65681979
Web Site: http://www.natinsurance.com.jo
Year Founded: 1965
NAAI—(AMM)
Rev.: $25,091,320
Assets: $37,867,744
Liabilities: $24,631,428
Net Worth: $13,236,316
Earnings: $1,252,699
Emp.: 62
Fiscal Year-end: 12/31/20
General Insurance Services
N.A.I.C.S.: 524126

NATIONAL INSURANCE COMPANY BERHAD
Unit 12 & 13 Block A Regent Square 150, Simpang, Kampong Kiajong, BS 8672, Brunei Darussalam
Tel.: (673) 2426888
Web Site: http://www.national.com.bn
Year Founded: 1969
Sales Range: $200-249.9 Million
Emp.: 38
Insurance Services
N.A.I.C.S.: 524298
Kolja Klun (Gen Mgr)

NATIONAL INTERNATIONAL HOLDING COMPANY K.S.C.P.
Abdulazai Al Sager street Al Raya Tower 2 45th floor, PO Box 25825, Sharq, Kuwait, 13119, Kuwait
Tel.: (965) 22255925 KW
Web Site: https://www.nih-kw.com
Year Founded: 1979
NIH—(KUW)
Rev.: $22,183,669
Assets: $176,663,008
Liabilities: $28,576,213
Net Worth: $148,086,795
Earnings: $5,509,568
Emp.: 10
Fiscal Year-end: 12/31/22
Holding Company
N.A.I.C.S.: 551112
Ahmed Attia Al Salamouny (Fin Mgr)

NATIONAL INVESTMENT TRUST LIMITED
NBP Building 6th Floor, I I Chundrigar Road, Karachi, Pakistan
Tel.: (92) 111648648
Web Site: http://www.nit.com.pk
Sales Range: $300-349.9 Million
Investment Trust Services
N.A.I.C.S.: 523999
Manzoor Ahmed (Mng Dir & COO)

NATIONAL INVESTMENTS COMPANY K.S.C.C.
Al Aiban Al Osaimi & Partners 18 -20th Floor Baitak Tower, PO Box 74, Ahmed Al Jaber Street Safat Square, Kuwait, 13001, Kuwait
Tel.: (965) 22266666
Web Site: https://www.nic.com.kw
Year Founded: 1987
NINV—(KUW)
Rev.: $64,776,236
Assets: $880,597,354
Liabilities: $175,377,815
Net Worth: $705,219,539
Earnings: $29,799,473
Emp.: 63
Fiscal Year-end: 12/31/22
Investment Services
N.A.I.C.S.: 523999
Hamad Ahmed Al-Ameeri (Chm)

NATIONAL INVESTMENTS FUND LIMITED

National Investments Company K.S.C.C.—(Continued)

NATIONAL INVESTMENTS FUND LIMITED
Unit 3705 37/F 118 Connaught Road West, Hong Kong, China (Hong Kong)
Tel.: (852) 2267 8664
Web Site: http://www.nif-hk.com
Rev.: $287,895
Assets: $12,033,686
Liabilities: $18,709,722
Net Worth: ($6,676,036)
Earnings: ($3,215,772)
Emp.: 10
Fiscal Year-end: 12/31/19
Investment Management Service
N.A.I.C.S.: 523940
Cheong Yee Chan *(Exec Dir)*

Subsidiaries:

Old Peak Limited (1)
28 Hennessy Road Suite 901 9th Floor, Wanchai, China (Hong Kong)
Tel.: (852) 36677700
Investment Holding Services
N.A.I.C.S.: 551112

NATIONAL IRANIAN COPPER INDUSTRIES COMPANY
No 22 11th Street Khaled Eslamboli St, PO Box 15115-416, Tehran, Iran
Tel.: (98) 21 82138000
Web Site: http://www.nicico.com
Year Founded: 1976
Copper & Nickel Ore Mining Services
N.A.I.C.S.: 212230
Ardeshir Saad Mohammadi *(CEO)*

NATIONAL IRANIAN LEAD & ZINC COMPANY
corner of Zarir Alley-Building No 15, Ground Floor-Unit 1, Motahari St-Turkmenistan St, Tehran, Iran
Tel.: (98) 2188449449
Web Site: https://www.nilzco.com
Year Founded: 1981
SORB1—(THE)
Lead & Zinc Mining Services
N.A.I.C.S.: 212230

Subsidiaries:

Alvand Rouinkaran Chemical Products Company Ltd. (1)
26 km of Zanjan-Tehran Old Road, 4551168745, Zanjan, Iran
Tel.: (98) 858820878
Chemical Products Mfr
N.A.I.C.S.: 325998
Abolfazl Amiri *(CEO)*

Angooran Miners Company Limited (1)
No 16 and 18 Third Alley Moallem Street Etemadiyeh, Zanjan, Iran
Tel.: (98) 2433420632
Chemical Products Mfr
N.A.I.C.S.: 325998
Ali Fazlavi *(CEO)*

Bandar Abbas Zinc Production Company Limited (1)
Unit 2 Ground Floor No 15 Development Building Zarrir St Motahhari Ave, Tehran, Iran
Tel.: (98) 2188421537
Web Site: http://www.bzpc.ir
Chemical Products Mfr
N.A.I.C.S.: 325998
Hossein Ebadifar *(Comml Dir)*

Iran Zinc Production Company Ltd. (1)
No 45 Fourth Alley Shahrdari Street Etemadiyeh, Zanjan, Iran
Tel.: (98) 2133423000
Chemical Products Mfr
N.A.I.C.S.: 325998
Mehdi Gharibu *(CEO)*

Parsian Catalyst Chemical Company Ltd. (1)
Sixth Bahrevari Street Zinc Special Town 5 km of Bijar Road, 453515357, Zanjan, Iran
Tel.: (98) 2432383440
Chemical Products Mfr
N.A.I.C.S.: 325998
Yaser Dehghan *(CEO)*

Qeshm Zinc Melting & Reduction Company (1)
20 km Dargahan-to-Lotf Road, Qeshm, Hormozgan, Iran
Tel.: (98) 76353754009
Chemical Products Mfr
N.A.I.C.S.: 325998
Mehdi Movahednia *(CEO)*

Shomalshargh Shahrood Industrial & Mining Company (1)
Opposite Fatemiyeh Mosque Behind Police Station 13 Tehran Street, Shahrood, Tehran, Semnan, Iran
Tel.: (98) 323643115
Chemical Products Mfr
N.A.I.C.S.: 325998
Ali Nasiri *(CEO)*

Zangan Zinc Industry LLP (1)
Special Road of Zangan Zinc Industry 10 km of Dandi Road, 5 km of Bijar Road, 4537155664, Zanjan, Iran
Tel.: (98) 2433420912
Chemical Products Mfr
N.A.I.C.S.: 325998
Hasan Ahmadian *(CEO)*

Zanjan Acid Makers Company (1)
10th Bahrevari st 5th Zanjan-Bijar road, Industrial Zinc zone, Zanjan, Iran
Tel.: (98) 24323830724
Web Site: http://www.acidsazan.ir
Chemical Products Mfr
N.A.I.C.S.: 325998
Gholam Ali Gheiratmand *(CEO)*

Zinc Industry Development Commercial Company (1)
No 15 Turkmenistan Street Motahhari Avenue, Tehran, Iran
Tel.: (98) 2188473762
Chemical Products Mfr
N.A.I.C.S.: 325998
Abolfazl Banan *(CEO)*

NATIONAL IRANIAN OIL COMPANY
Room 504 5th Floor NIOC First Central Building Hafez Crossing, PO Box 15875-1863, Taleghani Ave, Tehran, Iran
Tel.: (98) 2161622597
Web Site: http://www.en.nioc.ir
Sales Range: $5-14.9 Billion
Emp.: 45,000
Oil Production Services
N.A.I.C.S.: 211120
Rokneddin Javadi Ali Kardor *(Mng Dir-Investment & Fin Affairs)*

Subsidiaries:

Arvandan Oil & Gas Company (1)
Khamenei Ave, Khorramshahr, Iran
Tel.: (98) 632 4214021
Storage Tank Mfr
N.A.I.C.S.: 493190
Hesham Shahbazi *(Supvr-HSE)*

Iranian Central Oil Fields Company (1)
No 22 Esfandiar Ave Niayesh Crossroad Vali-asr Ave, Tehran, Iran
Tel.: (98) 21 22018403
Web Site: http://www.icofc.ir
Oil & Gas Production Services
N.A.I.C.S.: 211130
Salb Ali Karimi *(Mng Dir)*

Subsidiary (Domestic):

East Oil & Gas Production Company (2)
No 18 Payam 6 St Payam Ave Sheshsad Dastgah, Mashhad, Iran
Tel.: (98) 511 7633011
Web Site: http://www.eogpc.ir

Natural Gas Distr
N.A.I.C.S.: 221210

South Zagros Oil & Gas Production Company (2)
Parvaneh St Karimkhan Zand Blvd, Shiraz, Iran
Tel.: (98) 711 2138204
Web Site: http://www.szogpc.com
Natural Gas Distr
N.A.I.C.S.: 221210
Morteza Roudaki *(Head-Corrosion Eng Dept)*

West Oil & Gas Production Company (2)
No 42 Zan Blvd Naft Sq, Kermanshah, Iran
Tel.: (98) 831 8370072
Web Site: http://www.wogpc.ir
Oil & Gas Production Services
N.A.I.C.S.: 211130
Pedram Simani *(Supvr-HSE)*

Iranian Fuel Conservation Organization (1)
No 23 East Daneshvar St North Shiraz St Molasadra St Vanak Sq, Tehran, Iran
Tel.: (98) 21 88604760
Web Site: http://www.ifco.ir
Fuel Conservation Services
N.A.I.C.S.: 213112

Iranian Off-shore Oil Company (1)
No 12 Khakzad St Turaj St Modares Cross Valiasr St, Tehran, Iran
Tel.: (98) 21 22664470
Web Site: http://www.iooc.co.ir
Oil & Gas Exploration Services
N.A.I.C.S.: 213112
Mohammad B. Soleimani *(Mgr-Production Affairs)*

Iranian Oil Terminals Company (1)
No 17 Beyhaghi St Argentine Sq, Tehran, Iran
Tel.: (98) 21 88732221
Web Site: http://www.nioc-iotc.com
Crude Oil & Petroleum Product Mfr & Distr
N.A.I.C.S.: 211120

Karoon Oil & Gas Production Company (1)
Karoon Industrial Zone, Ahvaz, Khouzestan, Iran
Tel.: (98) 611 4446464
Web Site: http://www.kogpc.nisoc.ir
Crude Oil Mfr
N.A.I.C.S.: 211120

Khazar Exploration & Production Company (1)
No 19 11th St Khaled Eslamboli St, Tehran, Iran
Tel.: (98) 21 88722430
Web Site: http://www.kepco.ir
Oil & Gas Exploration & Production Services
N.A.I.C.S.: 211130

MSP Kala Naft co. (1)
Shahid Mousa Kalantari St Sepahbod Qarani Avenue, PO Box 15815 1775, Tehran, 15988 44816, Iran
Tel.: (98) 21 82019
Web Site: http://www.kalanaft.com
Oil & Gas Exploration Services
N.A.I.C.S.: 213112
Ezatollah Akbari *(Chm)*

Maroun Oil & Gas Company (1)
Ahwaz Mahshahr Rd Km 12, Ahvaz, Khouzestan, Iran
Tel.: (98) 611 4434073
Web Site: http://mogpc.nisoc.ir
Oil & Gas Production Services
N.A.I.C.S.: 211130

Naftiran Intertrade Company Sarl (1)
Av de la Tour-Haldimand 6, 1009, Pully, Switzerland
Tel.: (41) 21 31065 65
Web Site: http://www.naftiran.com
Trading & Financial Services
N.A.I.C.S.: 522320

National Iranian Drilling Company (1)
Airport Square Pasdaran Blvd, PO Box 901 61635, Ahvaz, Khouzestan, Iran
Tel.: (98) 611 4440151

Web Site: http://www.nidc.ir
Emp.: 16,000
Oil & Gas Well Drilling Services
N.A.I.C.S.: 213111
Muhammad Alami *(Vice Chm)*

National Iranian South Oil Company (1)
NISOC Building Fadaeyane Islam St, Ahvaz, Iran
Tel.: (98) 611 4447094
Web Site: http://www.nisoc.ir
Oil & Gas Production & Exploration Services
N.A.I.C.S.: 213112
Hamid Bovard *(Chm)*

Petroleum Engineering & Development Company (1)
No 61 Shahid Kalantari St Sapehbod Qarani Avenue, PO Box 15998846511, Tehran, Iran
Tel.: (98) 21 88898650
Web Site: http://www.pedec.ir
Emp.: 500
Oil & Gas Field Management Services
N.A.I.C.S.: 213112
Roknoddin Javadi *(Chm)*

NATIONAL JOINT-STOCK COMPANY NAFTOGAZ OF UKRAINE
Khmelnytsky St 6, Kiev, 01001, Ukraine
Tel.: (380) 445863537
Web Site: http://www.naftogaz.com
Oil & Gas Development, Drilling, Refining, Transportation & Storage
N.A.I.C.S.: 213111
Evgen Bakulin *(Chm)*

Subsidiaries:

PJSC Ukrtransgas (1)
Klovsky descent 9 / 1, Kiev, 01021, Ukraine
Tel.: (380) 442 543438
Web Site: http://www.utg.ua
Oil & Gas Exploration Services
N.A.I.C.S.: 213112
Myroslav Khymko *(Deputy Chm)*

SE Naukanaftogaz (1)
Kyivska str 8, Kyevo-Sviatishynskyi Dist, 08132, Vyshneve, Ukraine
Tel.: (380) 443 917401
Web Site: http://www.naukanaftogaz.com
Oil & Gas Exploration Services
N.A.I.C.S.: 213112
Berezuk Lubov *(Deputy Dir-Fin Affairs)*

Ukrgasvydobuvannia AC (1)
26/28 Kudriavska Str, 04053, Kiev, Ukraine
Tel.: (380) 444 612990
Oil & Gas Exploration Services
N.A.I.C.S.: 213112

Ukrtransnafta Joint Stock Company (1)
18/7 Kutuzova Str, 01133, Kiev, Ukraine
Tel.: (380) 442 015701
Web Site: http://www.ukrtransnafta.com
Oil & Gas Transportation Services
N.A.I.C.S.: 486210
Volodymyr Vorotyuk *(Deputy Head-Procurement & Supply Dept)*

NATIONAL LAGHUBITTA BITTIYA SANSTHA LIMITED
Banepa-10,, Kavrepalanchowk, Nepal
Tel.: (977) 011665573
Web Site: https://nationalmicrofinance.com.np
NMFBS—(NEP)
Commercial Bank
N.A.I.C.S.: 522110

Subsidiaries:

Mahila Sahayatra Microfinance Bittiya Sanstha Ltd. (1)
Majhgaun Chitlang 5, Makwanpur, Hetauda, Nepal
Tel.: (977) 57693941
Web Site: http://www.mahilasahayatra.com.np

AND PRIVATE COMPANIES

Sales Range: Less than $1 Million
Commercial Banking Services
N.A.I.C.S.: 522110
Amrit Charan Shrestha *(Chm)*

Summit Laghubitta Bittiya Sanstha Ltd. (1)
Anarmani, Bhadrapur, Nepal
Tel.: (977) 65540633
Web Site: http://www.summitbank.com.np
Sales Range: Less than $1 Million
Financial Services
N.A.I.C.S.: 523999
Debendra Bahadur Basnet *(CEO)*

NATIONAL LIFE INSURANCE COMPANY LIMITED
NLI Tower 54 Kazi Nazrul Islam Avenue Karwan Bazar, Dhaka, 1215, Bangladesh
Tel.: (880) 58151271
Web Site: https://www.nlibd.com
Year Founded: 1985
NATLIFEINS—(CSE)
Rev.: $1,363,007
Assets: $14,277,885
Liabilities: $7,654,185
Net Worth: $6,623,701
Earnings: $497,543
Fiscal Year-end: 12/31/23
Insurance Services
N.A.I.C.S.: 524298
Khasru Chowdhury *(Deputy Mng Dir)*

Subsidiaries:

NLI Securities Ltd. (1)
79 Motijheel Rd, Dhaka, Bangladesh
Tel.: (880) 29587956
Web Site: http://nlisecurities.com
Home Loan Services
N.A.I.C.S.: 522310
Shafiqur Rahman Tito *(Chm)*

NATIONAL MANAGING HOLDING BAITEREK JSC
55A Mangilik El Avenue, Yesil District, Nur-Sultan, 010000, Kazakhstan
Tel.: (7) 172907800 KZ
Web Site: http://baiterek.gov.kz
BTRK—(KAZ)
Rev.: $1,948,842,482
Assets: $27,351,486,242
Liabilities: $22,660,135,815
Net Worth: $4,691,350,427
Earnings: $851,092,458
Emp.: 5,125
Fiscal Year-end: 12/31/22
Investment Holding Company
N.A.I.C.S.: 551112
Askar Mamin *(Chm)*

Subsidiaries:

Damu Fund JSC (1)
Gogol St 111, Almaty, A05C9Y3, Kazakhstan
Tel.: (7) 7272448271
Web Site: http://www.damu.kz
Fund Management Services
N.A.I.C.S.: 523940
Buribaeva Gaukhar Asylbekovna *(Co-Chm)*

Development Bank of Kazakhstan JSC (1)
Mangilik Yel avenue 55a, Yesil district, Z05T3E2, Nur-Sultan, Kazakhstan (100%)
Tel.: (7) 7172792600
Web Site: https://www.kdb.kz
Rev.: $376,096,923
Assets: $6,762,028,572
Liabilities: $5,643,962,389
Net Worth: $1,118,066,183
Earnings: $28,601,622
Emp.: 217
Fiscal Year-end: 12/31/2019
Banking Services
N.A.I.C.S.: 522110
Sharipov Asset *(Mng Dir & Member-Mgmt Bd)*

Subsidiary (Domestic):

DBK-Leasing JSC (2)
20 Dostyk str, Nur-Sultan, 010000, Kazakhstan
Tel.: (7) 172 79 05 45
Web Site: http://www.kdbl.kz
Financial Lending Services
N.A.I.C.S.: 533110
Aubakirov Duman Baurzhanuly *(Chm)*

Investment Fund of Kazakhstan Joint Stock Company (1)
Mangilik el Avenue 55a BC Baiterek 2-3rd Floor, 010000, Nur-Sultan, Kazakhstan
Tel.: (7) 7172559596
Web Site: http://www.ifk.kz
Investment Management Service
N.A.I.C.S.: 523940
Sakishev Yermek Rakhatovych *(Chm)*

KazakhExport EIC JSC (1)
Mangilik Yel Building 55 A Business Centre Baiterek 11 Floor, Nur-Sultan, Kazakhstan
Tel.: (7) 7172955656
Web Site: http://www.en.kazakhexport.kz
Insurance Services
N.A.I.C.S.: 524210

KazakhExport Export Insurance company JSC (1)
Abay Ave 109b 3rd Floor Office 333, Globus Business Center, Almaty, Kazakhstan
Tel.: (7) 273395656
Insurance Services
N.A.I.C.S.: 524210

Kazakhstan Project Preparation Fund Limited Liability Partnership (1)
55a Mangilik Yel Ave Baiterek Business Center Block B 7th Floor, Z05T3E2, Nur-Sultan, Kazakhstan
Tel.: (7) 7172790450
Web Site: http://www.kppf.kz
Investment Management Service
N.A.I.C.S.: 523999
Aizada Zhunisbekova *(Mng Dir)*

QazTech Ventures Joint Stock Company (1)
Mangilik El Avenue 55A, Nur-Sultan, Kazakhstan
Tel.: (7) 7172571014
Web Site: http://www.qaztech.vc
Private Equity Services
N.A.I.C.S.: 523940
Nurgozhin Adil Ergaliuly *(Chm)*

Qazaqstan Investment Corporation Joint Stock Company (1)
55A Mangilik El Ave, Esil District, Z05T3E2, Astana, Kazakhstan
Tel.: (7) 7172554222
Web Site: https://qic.kz
Investment Services
N.A.I.C.S.: 523999

Subsidiary (Domestic):

ArcelorMittal Temirtau (2)
1 Republic Avenue, 101407, Temirtau, Kazakhstan
Tel.: (7) 7212493249
Web Site: https://www.arcelormittal.kz
Iron & Steel Mills
N.A.I.C.S.: 331110

NATIONAL MARINE DREDGING COMPANY PJSC
Mussafah Street 16, PO Box 3649, Abu Dhabi, United Arab Emirates
Tel.: (971) 25130000 AE
Web Site: https://nmdcgroup.azureweb.net
Year Founded: 1976
NMDC—(EMI)
Rev.: $765,109,630
Assets: $1,569,754,768
Liabilities: $605,341,687
Net Worth: $964,413,081
Earnings: $49,227,545
Emp.: 1,823
Fiscal Year-end: 12/31/19
Dredging Services
N.A.I.C.S.: 237990
Mohamed Thani Murshid Al Rumaithi *(Chm)*

Subsidiaries:

Abu Dhabi Marine Dredging Company S.P.C. (1)
Flat 302 Building 105 Road 59 Block 257 Amwaj, PO Box 54082, Manama, Bahrain
Tel.: (973) 77176671
Marine Dredging Services
N.A.I.C.S.: 237990

Emarat Europe Fast Building Technology System Factory L.L.C (1)
Abu Dhabi Industrial City, PO Box 106660, Mussafah, Abu Dhabi, United Arab Emirates
Tel.: (971) 25500700
Web Site: https://www.nmdc-construction.com
Precast Concrete Mfr
N.A.I.C.S.: 327390

National Marine & Infrastructure India Private Limited (1)
404 4th Floor Centre Point Andheri-Kurla Road JB Nagar, Andheri-East, Mumbai, 400059, Maharashtra, India
Tel.: (91) 2240232807
Marine Dredging Services
N.A.I.C.S.: 237990

NATIONAL MEDIA GROUP
13 str 1 Prechistenskaya, Naberezhnaya, 119034, Moscow, Russia
Tel.: (7) 4959881112
Web Site: http://nmg.ru
Year Founded: 2008
Media Holding Company
N.A.I.C.S.: 551112
Alina Kabaeva *(Chm)*

NATIONAL MEDICAL CARE COMPANY
Al Imam Ahmad Ibn Hanbal St Ar Rayan Area, PO Box 29393, Riyadh, 11457, Saudi Arabia
Tel.: (966) 114931881
Web Site: http://www.care.med.sa
4005—(SAU)
Rev.: $244,750,007
Assets: $456,664,576
Liabilities: $119,752,532
Net Worth: $336,912,043
Earnings: $45,347,246
Emp.: 1,500
Fiscal Year-end: 12/31/22
Hospital Management; Medical Equipment & Pharmaceutical Distr
N.A.I.C.S.: 622110
Mohammed Abdulrahman Algesayer *(Chief HR Officer)*

NATIONAL METALLIC INDUSTRIES & BICYCLES CO.
Al-Mahmoudia, Baghdad, Iraq
Tel.: (964) 5462910
Year Founded: 1964
IMIB—(IRAQ)
Sales Range: Less than $1 Million
Bicycle Mfr
N.A.I.C.S.: 336991

NATIONAL MINERAL WATER COMPANY SAOG
PO BOX 2740, Ruwi, 112, Oman
Tel.: (968) 24628900
Web Site: http://www.nmwcoman.com
Year Founded: 1979
NMWI—(MUS)
Rev.: $15,622,772
Assets: $15,005,886
Liabilities: $9,958,305
Net Worth: $5,047,580
Earnings: ($743,627)
Emp.: 196
Fiscal Year-end: 12/31/23
Mineral Water Mfr
N.A.I.C.S.: 312112

NATIONAL MINING COMPANY TAU-KEN SAMRUK JSC
17/10 E-10 Street, Yessil District, Nur-Sultan, 010000, Kazakhstan
Tel.: (7) 7172 55 9090 KZ

NATIONAL PAINTS FACTORIES CO. LTD.

Web Site: http://www.tks.kz
Year Founded: 2009
Rev.: $709,960,376
Assets: $1,744,768,748
Liabilities: $79,024,105
Net Worth: $1,665,744,643
Earnings: $116,827,916
Emp.: 1,342
Fiscal Year-end: 12/31/18
Copper Zinc & Lead Ore Exploration & Mining Services
N.A.I.C.S.: 551112
Tutkushev Yerzhan Beksultanovich *(Chm)*

Subsidiaries:

ShalkiyaZinc Ltd JSC (1)
Mustafa Shokai Street building 32, Zhanakorgan District Shalkiya, 120302, Almaty, Kyzylorda, Kazakhstan (100%)
Tel.: (7) 7272 311 06 24
Web Site: http://www.zinc.kz
Zinc Ore Mining Services
N.A.I.C.S.: 212230
Ramazanov Bulat Mnaidarovich *(Chm-Mgmt Bd)*

NATIONAL OIL SHALE COMPANY PLC
PO Box 962497, Amman, 11196, Jordan
Tel.: (962) 65833615
Web Site: http://www.shaleenergy.jo
Year Founded: 2007
SHLE—(AMM)
Sales Range: Less than $1 Million
Emp.: 3
Eletric Power Generation Services
N.A.I.C.S.: 221112
Abdullah Shawabkeh *(Chm)*

NATIONAL OXYGEN LTD
1B First Floor Arihant Jashn 38 121 Rukmani Lakshmipathy Salai, Egmore, Chennai, 600 008, India
Tel.: (91) 4428520096
Web Site: https://www.nolgroup.com
507813—(BOM)
Rev.: $5,482,318
Assets: $4,911,529
Liabilities: $4,311,871
Net Worth: $599,658
Earnings: ($149,495)
Emp.: 100
Fiscal Year-end: 03/31/21
Industrial Gas Mfr
N.A.I.C.S.: 325120

NATIONAL PAINTS FACTORIES CO. LTD.
PO Box 5822, Sharjah, United Arab Emirates
Tel.: (971) 65130000
Web Site: http://www.national-paints.com
Year Founded: 1969
Sales Range: $700-749.9 Million
Emp.: 2,200
Paint Mfr & Distr
N.A.I.C.S.: 325510

Subsidiaries:

National Paints - Jordan (1)
PO Box 533, Amman, 11592, Abu Alanda, Jordan
Tel.: (962) 64790790
Web Site: http://www.national-paints.com
Paint Distr
N.A.I.C.S.: 424950
Micfaem Fayezf *(CEO)*

National Paints - Kazakhstan (1)
PO Box 42689, Almaty, Kazakhstan
Tel.: (7) 3272573850
Web Site: http://www.national-paints.com
Paint Distr
N.A.I.C.S.: 424950

National Paints - Kyrgyzstan (1)
PO Box 47786, Bishkek, Kyrgyzstan

NATIONAL PAINTS FACTORIES CO. LTD.

National Paints Factories Co. Ltd.—(Continued)
Tel.: (996) 6312670540
Web Site: http://www.national-paints.com
Paint Distr
N.A.I.C.S.: 424950

National Paints - Qatar (1)
PO Box 40544, Doha, Qatar
Tel.: (974) 44601602
Web Site: http://www.national-paints.com
Paint Distr
N.A.I.C.S.: 424950

National Paints - Russia (1)
PO Box 4369, Moscow, Russia
Tel.: (7) 4954653196
Web Site: http://www.national-paints.com
Paint Distr
N.A.I.C.S.: 424950

National Paints - Sudan (1)
PO Box 10885, Khartoum, Sudan
Tel.: (249) 185 310490
Web Site: http://www.national-paints.com
Paint Distr
N.A.I.C.S.: 424950

NATIONAL PENSION SERVICE OF KOREA
Kukmin-Yeonkum Bldg 13 Shincheon-dong, Songpa-gu, Seoul, Korea (South)
Web Site: http://english.nps.or.kr
Year Founded: 1987
Pension Benefit Administration & Financing Services
N.A.I.C.S.: 524292
Sung Joo Kim *(Chm & CEO)*

Subsidiaries:

Brisa Auto-Estradas de Portugal, S.A. (1)
Quinta da Torre da Aguilha - Edificio Brisa, 2785-599, Sao Domingos de Rana, Portugal
Tel.: (351) 214448500
Web Site: http://www.brisa.pt
Rev.: $853,839,235
Earnings: $180,718,820
Emp.: 2,344
Fiscal Year-end: 12/31/2018
Highway & Street Construction Services
N.A.I.C.S.: 237310
Vasco De Mello *(Chm)*

Subsidiary (US):

BRISA NORTH AMERICA, INC (2)
1420 Peachtree St N E 220, Atlanta, GA 30309-3049
Tel.: (404) 835-8400
Road & Building Construction Services
N.A.I.G.S.: 237310

Subsidiary (Domestic):

BRISA O&M, S.A. (2)
Quinta Da Torre Da Agulha Edificio Brisa, Sao Domingos de Rana, 2785-599, Portugal
Tel.: (351) 214448500
Civil Engineering Construction Services
N.A.I.C.S.: 237310

Subsidiary (US):

BRISA UNITED STATES, LLC (2)
2755 Nothwoods Pkwy, Norcross, GA 30071
Tel.: (404) 835-8400
Sales Range: $25-49.9 Million
Emp.: 7
Highway & Street Construction Services
N.A.I.C.S.: 237310

Subsidiary (Domestic):

Brisa - Servicos Viarios, SGPS, S.A. (2)
Quinta da Torre Da Aguilha, Edificio Brisa Domingos De Ran, Cascais, 2785-599, Portugal
Tel.: (351) 214448500
Web Site: http://www.brisa.pt
Other Holding Companies Offices
N.A.I.C.S.: 551112

Brisa Assistencia Rodoviaria, S.A. (2)
Quinta Da Aguilha, Quinta Da Torre Da Aguilha, Cascais, 2785599S AO, Portugal
Tel.: (351) 214448500
Web Site: http://www.brisa.pt
All Other Support Activities for Transportation
N.A.I.C.S.: 488999
Vasco Mello *(Pres)*

Brisa Internacional, SGPS, S.A. (2)
Edificio Brisa, Quinta Da Torre Da Aguilha, Cascais, Portugal
Tel.: (351) 214449100
Other Holding Companies Offices
N.A.I.C.S.: 551112

CONTROLAUTO - CONTROLO TECNICO AUTOMOVEL, S.A. (2)
Rua Alfredo Lopes Vilaverde 15-B Room 7, 2770-009, Paco d'Arcos, Portugal
Tel.: (351) 21 441 8376
Web Site: https://www.controlauto.pt
Emp.: 40
Automotive Control & Maintenance Services
N.A.I.C.S.: 811121
Zosa Enjra *(Gen Mgr)*

M. CALL, S.A. (2)
Taguspark Edificio Mcall Tecnologia III Corpo 5, 2740-257, Porto Salvo, Portugal
Tel.: (351) 707 50 30 40
Web Site: http://www.mcall.pt
Emp.: 80
Business Process Outsourcing Services
N.A.I.C.S.: 561499
Joel Pereira *(Mng Dir)*

NATIONAL PETROLEUM CORPORATION
4F No 140 Sec 6 Roosevelt Road, Taipei, Taiwan
Tel.: (886) 229356500
Web Site: http://www.npcgas.com.tw
9937—(TAI)
Rev.: $802,355,083
Assets: $405,907,110
Liabilities: $224,568,028
Net Worth: $181,339,082
Earnings: $25,604,205
Fiscal Year-end: 12/31/23
Gas Station Operating Services
N.A.I.C.S.: 457120

NATIONAL PHARMACEUTICAL ASSOCIATION LIMITED
Mallinson House, Saint Albans, AL1 3NP, Herts, United Kingdom
Tel.: (44) 1727832161
Web Site: http://www.npa.co.uk
Year Founded: 1921
Sales Range: $10-24.9 Million
Emp.: 120
Pharmaceutical Industry Promoter
N.A.I.C.S.: 813920
Michael Holden *(Pres)*

NATIONAL PLASTIC INDUSTRIES LIMITED
4th Floor Vilco Center Subhash Rd opp Garware Lane Victory Society, Navpada Vile Parle East Vile Parle, Mumbai, 400057, India
Tel.: (91) 2267669920
Web Site: https://www.nationalplastic.com
Year Founded: 1952
526616—(BOM)
Rev.: $10,620,942
Assets: $12,837,367
Liabilities: $8,765,942
Net Worth: $4,071,425
Earnings: $324,348
Emp.: 267
Fiscal Year-end: 03/31/21
Household Plastic Furniture Mfr
N.A.I.C.S.: 337126
Paresh V. Parekh *(Co-Mng Dir)*

Subsidiaries:

NATIONAL PLASTIC INDUSTRIES LIMITED - PATNA UNIT (1)
Plot No B-1 to B-7 Industrial Area, Fatuha, Patna, India
Tel.: (91) 612 2440910
Plastic Furniture Mfr
N.A.I.C.S.: 337126

NATIONAL PLASTIC INDUSTRIES LIMITED - SILVASSA UNIT (1)
Plot No 263 Near Dadra 66 KVA Substation, Village Dadra, Silvassa, Dadra Nagarhaveli, India
Tel.: (91) 260 668368
Plastic Furniture Mfr
N.A.I.C.S.: 337126

NATIONAL PLASTIC TECHNOLOGIES LTD.
Thiru Complex II Floor, 44 Pantheon Road Egmore, Chennai, 600 008, India
Tel.: (91) 4443404340
Web Site: https://nationalgroup.in
Year Founded: 1989
531287—(BOM)
Rev.: $25,191,188
Assets: $16,346,502
Liabilities: $12,106,109
Net Worth: $4,240,393
Earnings: $737,833
Emp.: 365
Fiscal Year-end: 03/31/23
Plastics Product Mfr
N.A.I.C.S.: 326199
Sudershan Parakh *(Co-Mng Dir)*

NATIONAL PLYWOOD INDUSTRIES LIMITED
5 Fancy Lane 7th Floor, Kolkata, 700001, India
Tel.: (91) 3322480116
Web Site: https://www.natply.com
Year Founded: 1951
516062—(BOM)
Plywood Mfr
N.A.I.C.S.: 321211
Piyush Periwal *(Chm & Mng Dir)*

NATIONAL POLYMER INDUSTRIES LTD.
Squibb Road Tongi Industrial Area, Cherag Ali, Gazipur, Bangladesh
Tel.: (880) 29802304
Web Site: https://www.nationalpolymer.net
Year Founded: 1987
NPOLYMER—(DHA)
Rev.: $59,962,940
Assets: $68,331,228
Liabilities: $48,254,423
Net Worth: $20,076,805
Earnings: $1,412,690
Emp.: 1,334
Fiscal Year-end: 06/30/23
Pipes Mfr
N.A.I.C.S.: 332996
Riad Mahmud *(CEO & Mng Dir)*

NATIONAL PORTFOLIO SECURITIES PLC.
Mahfaza Building 33 Issam Ajlouni Street, PO Box 926721, Shemisani, Amman, 11190, Jordan
Tel.: (962) 65609000
Web Site: https://www.npsc.com.jo
Year Founded: 1982
MHFZ—(AMM)
Rev.: $233,232
Assets: $10,953,484
Liabilities: $1,836,425
Net Worth: $9,117,059
Earnings: ($310,099)
Emp.: 11
Fiscal Year-end: 12/31/20

INTERNATIONAL PUBLIC

Asset Management & Brokerage Services
N.A.I.C.S.: 523150
Mohammed Bahjat Amin Al Belbeisi *(Chm)*

NATIONAL POULTRY P.L.C.
Bayader Wadi El-seer, PO Box 140785, Amman, 11814, Jordan
Tel.: (962) 65865081
Web Site: http://www.npc-jordan.com
Year Founded: 1994
NATP—(AMM)
Rev.: $78,198,598
Assets: $83,187,437
Liabilities: $14,279,402
Net Worth: $68,908,035
Earnings: ($7,828,376)
Emp.: 1,519
Fiscal Year-end: 12/31/20
Poultry Management Services
N.A.I.C.S.: 311615
Husni Badran *(Mgr-Fin & Admin)*

NATIONAL PROPERTY FUND OF THE SLOVAK REPUBLIC
Trnavska cesta 100, 821 01, Bratislava, Slovakia
Tel.: (421) 2 322 82 700
Web Site: http://www.natfund.gov.sk
Year Founded: 1991
Sales Range: $550-599.9 Million
Emp.: 40
Privatization Projects Implementation
N.A.I.C.S.: 925120
Jozef Kojda *(Pres)*

Subsidiaries:

Zapadoslovenska energetika, a.s. (1)
Culenova 6, 816 47, Bratislava, Slovakia
Tel.: (421) 377763880
Web Site: http://www.zse.sk
Electric Power Distr; Owned 51% by National Property Fund of the Slovak Republic & 49% by E.ON Energie AG
N.A.I.C.S.: 221122
Eva Milucka *(Chm-Supervisory Bd)*

NATIONAL REAL ESTATE COMPANY K.S.C.
Kuwait City Sharq Al-Shuhada Street Al-Hamra Tower 58th floor, PO Box 22644, Safat, 13087, Kuwait, 13087, Kuwait
Tel.: (965) 1804404
Web Site: https://www.nrec.com.kw
NRE—(KUW)
Rev.: $40,297,162
Assets: $1,734,964,945
Liabilities: $594,494,306
Net Worth: $1,140,470,639
Earnings: ($112,665,322)
Emp.: 145
Fiscal Year-end: 12/31/23
Real Estate Services
N.A.I.C.S.: 531390
Faisal Jamil Sultan Al-Essa *(Chm)*

Subsidiaries:

Aqaba National Real Estate Projects Company (1)
Aqaba Special Economic Zone ASEA -Aqaba Back Road, PO Box 1559, ADC Warehousing and Industries Park, 77110, Al Aqabah, Jordan
Tel.: (962) 32060671
Web Site: http://nrecjordan.com
Sales Range: $50-74.9 Million
Real Estate Manangement Services
N.A.I.C.S.: 531312

Locrete Industries Co. (1)
Warehouse 18 Kuwait Free Trade Zone Shuwaikh, Kuwait, Kuwait
Tel.: (965) 24610082
Sales Range: $50-74.9 Million
Emp.: 25
Real Estate Manangement Services

NATIONAL REAL ESTATE DEVELOPMENT AND INVESTMENTS COMPANY SAOG
PO Box 84, 100, Muscat, Oman
Tel.: (968) 24482607
Year Founded: 1974
NRED—(MUS)
Rev.: $6,437
Assets: $16,167,477
Liabilities: $2,400,808
Net Worth: $13,766,669
Earnings: ($5,254,807)
Fiscal Year-end: 12/31/23
Real Estate Development Services
N.A.I.C.S.: 531390
Ahmed Mohsin Ali *(Deputy Chm & Deputy Chm)*

NATIONAL REINSURANCE CORPORATION OF THE PHILIPPINES
31st Floor BPI-Philam Life Makati
6811 Ayala Avenue, Makati, 1227, Philippines
Tel.: (63) 289887400
Web Site: https://www.nat-re.com
NRCP—(PHI)
Reinsurance Services
N.A.I.C.S.: 524130
Yvonne S. Yuchengco *(Vice Chm)*

NATIONAL RESERVE BANK JSC
10A Prospekt 60-letiya Oktyabrya, Moscow, 117036, Russia
Tel.: (7) 4952 13 32 00
Web Site: http://www.nrb.ru
Commercial Banking Services
N.A.I.C.S.: 522110
Efremov Sergey Vladimirovich *(Chm-Mgmt Bd)*

NATIONAL RESERVE BANK OF TONGA
Queen Salote Rd, PO Box 25, Nuku'alofa, Tonga
Tel.: (676) 24057
Web Site: http://www.reservebank.to
Sales Range: $1-9.9 Million
Emp.: 63
Banking Services
N.A.I.C.S.: 522110
Siosi Cocker Mafi *(CEO)*

NATIONAL SAVINGS BANK
Savings House 255 Galle Road, Colombo, 3, Sri Lanka
Tel.: (94) 112573008   LK
Web Site: http://www.nsb.lk
Year Founded: 1972
Rev.: $686,923,534
Assets: $6,418,638,108
Liabilities: $6,157,463,256
Net Worth: $261,174,852
Earnings: $49,303,647
Emp.: 4,715
Fiscal Year-end: 12/31/19
Retail & Commercial Banking
N.A.I.C.S.: 522180
Christine S. Jesudian *(Deputy Gen Mgr-Credit-Intl)*

Subsidiaries:

NSB Fund Management Co. Ltd.   (1)
Savings House 1st Floor No 255 Galle Road, Colombo, 03, Sri Lanka
Tel.: (94) 11 2564601
Stock Broker
N.A.I.C.S.: 523150
B. P. J. Gunasekara *(CEO)*

NATIONAL SHIPPING COMPANY OF SAUDI ARABIA
Olaya Towers B Floors 12-15, PO Box 8931, Olaya District Olaya Street, Riyadh, 11492, Saudi Arabia
Tel.: (966) 114785454   SA
Web Site: https://www.bahri.sa
Year Founded: 1979
4030—(SAU)
Rev.: $2,288,382,882
Assets: $6,105,345,154
Liabilities: $3,141,646,980
Net Worth: $2,963,698,174
Earnings: $309,984,535
Emp.: 583
Fiscal Year-end: 12/31/22
Shipping & Transportation Services
N.A.I.C.S.: 488390
Mohammed Abdulaziz Al-Sarhan *(Chm)*

Subsidiaries:

Mideast Ship Management Ltd.   (1)
One JLT Level 10 Jumeirah, PO Box 32890, Lakes Towers, Dubai, United Arab Emirates   **(100%)**
Tel.: (971) 43840400
Sales Range: $25-49.9 Million
Emp.: 100
Marine Services
N.A.I.C.S.: 488320

NSCSA (America) Inc.   (1)
400 E Pratt St Ste 400, Baltimore, MD 21202   **(100%)**
Tel.: (410) 625-7000
Web Site: http://www.nscsaamerica.com
Sales Range: $25-49.9 Million
Emp.: 40
Transportation Services
N.A.I.C.S.: 488510
Charles Atkinson *(Mgr-Natl Sls)*

National Chemical Carriers Ltd. Co.
Sitteen St Malaz Area, PO Box 8931, Riyadh, Saudi Arabia
Tel.: (966) 014773934
Web Site: http://www.nscsa.com
Sales Range: $25-49.9 Million
Emp.: 20
Petrochemical Transportation Services; Owned 80% by National Shipping Company of Saudi Arabia & 20% by Saudi Basic Industries Corporation
N.A.I.C.S.: 488330

National Shipping Company of Saudi Arabia (America) Inc   (1)
400 E Pratt St Ste 400, Baltimore, MD 21202
Tel.: (410) 625-7000
Web Site: http://www.nscsa.com
Sales Range: $25-49.9 Million
Emp.: 40
Cargo Transportation Services
N.A.I.C.S.: 488320

Vela International Marine Limited   (1)
28th Floor Armada Tower 2 Cluster P Jumeirah Lake Towers Sheikh Zayed, Dubai, United Arab Emirates
Tel.: (971) 43840777
Web Site: http://www.vela.ae
Sales Range: $350-399.9 Million
Emp.: 950
Marine Transportation of Crude Oil & Refined Products, Vessel Operations, Fleet Personnel Management, Freight Forwarding & Dry-Docking
N.A.I.C.S.: 483111
Mohammed S. Gusaier *(Pres & CEO)*

NATIONAL SHOOTING COMPANY K.S.C.C.
6th Ring Road Subhan Behind Hunting and Equestrian Club, PO Box 21770, In Front of Military Hospital Safat, Kuwait, 13078, Kuwait
Tel.: (965) 24759999
Web Site: http://www.mayadeen.com
MAYADEEN—(KUW)
Sales Range: $1-9.9 Million
Firearms Training, Equipment & Services
N.A.I.C.S.: 332994

Mohammed Saud Sulaiman Al-Abdullah *(CEO)*

NATIONAL SILICON INDUSTRY GROUP CO., LTD.
4th Floor Building 5 865 Changning Road, Shanghai, 201306, China
Tel.: (86) 2152589038
Web Site: https://www.nsig.com
Year Founded: 2015
688126—(SHG)
Rev.: $505,490,684
Assets: $3,574,949,939
Liabilities: $830,645,572
Net Worth: $2,744,304,367
Earnings: $45,634,451
Fiscal Year-end: 12/31/22
Silicone Products Mfr
N.A.I.C.S.: 334413
Tzu-Yin Chiu *(Pres)*

Subsidiaries:

Shanghai Simgui Technology Co., Ltd.   (1)
No 200 Xinlai Road, Jiading District, Shanghai, 201815, China
Tel.: (86) 2169522599
Web Site: http://www.simgui.com.cn
Silicon Wafer Mfr & Distr
N.A.I.C.S.: 334413

Zing Semiconductor Corporation   (1)
No 1000 Yunshui Road, Lingang New Area Pilot Free Trade Zone, Shanghai, 201306, China
Tel.: (86) 2151855700
Web Site: https://www.zingsemi.com
Emp.: 1,200
Semiconductor Product Mfr
N.A.I.C.S.: 334413

NATIONAL STANDARD (INDIA) LIMITED
Lodha Excelus 10th Floor Apollo Mill Compound, N M Joshi Marg Mahalaxmi East, Mumbai, 400 011, Maharashtra, India
Tel.: (91) 2261334400
Web Site: https://www.nsil.net.in
Year Founded: 1962
504882—(BOM)
Rev.: $3,347,629
Assets: $30,387,531
Liabilities: $1,084,887
Net Worth: $29,302,644
Earnings: $988,874
Fiscal Year-end: 03/31/23
Real Estate Development Services
N.A.I.C.S.: 531210
Rameshchandra Chechani *(CFO)*

NATIONAL STANDARD BANK JSC
The Party Lane 1 Building 57 P 2 3, 115093, Moscow, Russia
Tel.: (7) 4956647344
Web Site: http://www.ns-bank.ru
Year Founded: 2002
Sales Range: Less than $1 Million
Secured Financial Transaction Services
N.A.I.C.S.: 522320

NATIONAL STEEL AND AGRO INDUSTRIES LIMITED
621 Tulsiani Chambers, Nariman Point, Mumbai, 400 021, Maharastra, India
Tel.: (91) 2222025098
Web Site: http://www.nsail.com
Year Founded: 1987
NATNLSTEEL—(NSE)
Rev.: $216,591,457
Assets: $83,312,761
Liabilities: $254,699,704
Net Worth: ($171,386,943)
Earnings: ($31,040,223)
Emp.: 714

Fiscal Year-end: 03/31/21
Steel Products Mfr
N.A.I.C.S.: 339999
Santosh Shahra *(Chm)*

NATIONAL STEEL INDUSTRY COMPANY P.L.C.
Zarqa - Wadi Al-Ash - Riad Saeed Al-Mufleh Street Industrial, PO Box 2059, Zarqaa, Amman, 13110, Jordan
Tel.: (962) 53652802
Web Site: https://national-steel.com
Year Founded: 1979
NAST—(AMM)
Rev.: $17,469,486
Assets: $8,627,907
Liabilities: $2,095,384
Net Worth: $6,532,523
Earnings: ($204,548)
Emp.: 73
Fiscal Year-end: 12/31/20
Steel Products Mfr
N.A.I.C.S.: 331110

NATIONAL STOCK EXCHANGE OF INDIA LIMITED
Exchange Plaza C-1 Block G Bandra Kurla Complex Bandra E, Mumbai, 400 051, India
Tel.: (91) 2226598100   In
Web Site: https://www.nseindia.com
Year Founded: 1992
Rev.: $1,296,700,860
Assets: $4,860,355,500
Liabilities: $2,174,936,400
Net Worth: $2,685,419,100
Earnings: $709,566,585
Emp.: 1,197
Fiscal Year-end: 03/31/22
Stock Exchange
N.A.I.C.S.: 523210
J. Ravichandran *(Pres-Grp)*

Subsidiaries:

India Index Services and Products Limited   (1)
Exchange Plaza C-1 Block G Bandra Kurla Complex Bandra East, Mumbai, 400051, India
Tel.: (91) 2226598386
Web Site: http://www.nseindia.com
Index-Related Services & Products; Owned 50% by National Stock Exchange of India Limited & 50% by CRISIL Ltd.
N.A.I.C.S.: 561499

NSE Data & Analytics Limited   (1)
Exchange Plz Plot C/1 G Block, Bandra-Kurla Complex, Mumbai, 400051, Maharashtra, India   **(100%)**
Tel.: (91) 2226598385
Web Site: http://www.nseindia.com
Internet Trading Platforms
N.A.I.C.S.: 523999

NSE. IT (US) Inc.   (1)
103 Carnegie Ctr Ste 212, Princeton, NJ 08540
Tel.: (609) 275-7282
Software Development Services
N.A.I.C.S.: 541511

NSE.IT   (1)
Exchange Plz Plot C/1 G Block, Bandra-Kurla Complex, Mumbai, 400051, Maharashtra, India   **(100%)**
Tel.: (91) 2226598100
Web Site: http://www.nseit.biz
Information Technology Services
N.A.I.C.S.: 541511
Padmanaban Ramesh *(CEO)*

National Securities Depository Ltd.   (1)
Trade World A wing 4th Floor Kamala Mills Compound Lower Parel, Mumbai, 400 013, Maharashtra, India   **(100%)**
Tel.: (91) 2224994200
Web Site: http://www.nsdl.co.in
Depository Services
N.A.I.C.S.: 522180
B. A. Prabhakar *(Chm & Dir-Pub Interest)*

NATIONAL STORAGE REIT

National Stock Exchange of India Limited—(Continued)

NATIONAL STORAGE REIT
Level 16 1 Eagle Street, Brisbane, 4000, QLD, Australia
Tel.: (61) 732188100
Web Site: https://www.nationalstorage.com.au
Year Founded: 2000
NSR—(ASX)
Sales Range: $100-124.9 Million
Storage Centers Investment Services
N.A.I.C.S.: 523999
Claire Fidler *(Sec)*

Subsidiaries:

Wine Ark Pty. Ltd. (1)
PO Box 7148, South Sydney BC, Alexandria, 2014, NSW, Australia
Tel.: (61) 1300946327
Web Site: http://www.wine-ark.com.au
Wine Retailer
N.A.I.C.S.: 445320

NATIONAL TAX AGENCY
3-1-1 Kasumigaseki, Chiyoda-ku, Tokyo, 100-8978, Japan
Tel.: (81) 335814161
Web Site: https://www.nta.go.jp
Year Founded: 1949
Collection Agency Services
N.A.I.C.S.: 561440

NATIONAL TEA COMPANY LIMITED
BGIC Tower 7th Floor 34 Topkhana Road, Dhaka, 1000, Bangladesh
Tel.: (880) 29575256
Web Site: https://www.ntclbd.org
Year Founded: 1978
NTC—(CHT)
Rev.: $11,849,454
Assets: $38,234,805
Liabilities: $31,783,353
Net Worth: $6,451,452
Earnings: ($2,425,621)
Emp.: 393
Fiscal Year-end: 06/30/21
Tea Farming Services
N.A.I.C.S.: 621999
Kabir Hossain *(Chm)*

NATIONAL TECHNOLOGY GROUP
King Abdulaziz Street Rashid Al-Ballaa Building, PO Box 220625, Riyadh, 11461, Saudi Arabia
Tel.: (966) 14768813
Web Site: http://www.ntg.com.sa
Sales Range: $150-199.9 Million
Emp.: 500
IT Services
N.A.I.C.S.: 541512
Sulaiman AlBallaa *(Vice Chm)*

Subsidiaries:

Arabic Computer Systems Ltd. (1)
King Abdulaziz Street Rashid Al-Ballaa Building, PO Box 220625, Riyadh, 11311, Saudi Arabia
Tel.: (966) 112920707
Web Site: http://www.acs.com.sa
Sales Range: $75-99.9 Million
Emp.: 400
IT Solution & Services
N.A.I.C.S.: 541512
Ghiyath F. Al-Darsouni *(Gen Mgr-Sys Integration)*

Direct FN Ltd. (1)
Jumaria Lake Tower Cluster V Jumaria Buss Ctr 2 25th Fl Unit 205-206, PO Box 26730, Dubai, United Arab Emirates
Tel.: (971) 432 59996
Web Site: http://www.directfn.com
Emp.: 15
Software Development Services
N.A.I.C.S.: 541511
Waleed-Rashid Alballaa *(Gen Mgr)*

Ebttikar Technology Company (1)
Haif Commercial Center Makkah Road, PO Box 52908, Riyadh, 11573, Saudi Arabia
Tel.: (966) 141 62222
Web Site: http://www.ebttikar.com
Information Technology Services
N.A.I.C.S.: 541512
Mohammed Al-Saafein *(Project Mgr)*

Future Communications Guidance Int. (1)
PO Box 8431, 11482, Riyadh, Saudi Arabia
Tel.: (966) 121 95577
Web Site: http://www.fcgi.com.sa
Telecommunication Servicesb
N.A.I.C.S.: 517410
Bilal Idris *(Gen Mgr)*

Getronics Middle East (1)
4th Fl Ste 33, Rahid Al-Ballaa Building, 11461, Riyadh, Saudi Arabia
Tel.: (966) 14740555
Sales Range: $25-49.9 Million
Emp.: 50
IT & Communication Technology Services; Owned by Getronics N.V. & National Technology Group
N.A.I.C.S.: 541512

Mubasher Financial Services BSC (1)
Seef Area Platinum Tower Bldg 190 Road 2803 Office 181 13 Fl, Manama, Bahrain
Tel.: (973) 175 56139
Web Site: http://www.mubashertrade.com
Emp.: 120
Brokerage Services
N.A.I.C.S.: 523150
Wael Darwish *(Gen Mgr)*

National Net Ventures (1)
3508 Prince Sultan Bin Abdulaziz Street, PO Box 366784, 11393, Riyadh, Saudi Arabia
Tel.: (966) 114 774245
Web Site: http://www.n2v.com
Emp.: 200
Software Development Services
N.A.I.C.S.: 541511
Muhammad Arrabi *(CTO & Head-Mktg)*

Subsidiary (Non-US):

GamesXP (2)
Building 33 Nakeeb Umran Al Maayta St, Amman, Jordan
Tel.: (962) 658 18826
Web Site: http://www.gamesxp.com
Online Game Publisher
N.A.I.C.S.: 541511
Fadi Sarsak *(Mgr-Bus Dev)*

Net Advantage (2)
Office 2501 JBC 2 Jumeirah Lake Towers Al Wasl Road, PO Box 213189, Jumeirah, Dubai, 213189, United Arab Emirates
Tel.: (971) 442 30300
Web Site: http://www.netad-vantage.net
Emp.: 8
Media & Advertising Services
N.A.I.C.S.: 541810
Rosy Ajaka *(Mgr-Sls)*

NATIONAL TUBES LIMITED
131-142 Tongi Industrial Area, Gazipur, Dhaka, 1710, Bangladesh
Tel.: (880) 2224412785
Web Site: https://www.ntl.gov.bd
Year Founded: 1964
NTLTUBES—(DHA)
Rev.: $3,159,770
Assets: $69,652,043
Liabilities: $8,829,555
Net Worth: $60,822,488
Earnings: ($960,177)
Emp.: 161
Fiscal Year-end: 06/30/22
Pipes Mfr
N.A.I.C.S.: 327332
Shahidul Haque Bhuiyan *(Chm)*

NATIONAL TYRE & WHEEL LIMITED
Level 2 385 Macarthur Avenue, Moorooka, Hamilton, 4007, QLD, Australia

Tel.: (61) 1800681298 AU
Web Site: https://www.ntaw.com.au
Year Founded: 1989
NTD—(ASX)
Rev.: $356,190,570
Assets: $275,839,342
Liabilities: $197,516,693
Net Worth: $78,322,649
Earnings: $829,327
Emp.: 850
Fiscal Year-end: 06/30/24
Automobile Parts Distr
N.A.I.C.S.: 336390
John Peter Ludemann *(CEO & Mng Dir)*

Subsidiaries:

Black Rubber Pty. Ltd. (1)
14 Miles Road, Kewdale, 6105, WA, Australia
Tel.: (61) 894796762
Web Site: https://www.black-rubber.net.au
Tyre & Wheel Whslr
N.A.I.C.S.: 423130

Carters Tyre Service Limited (1)
52 Highbrook Drive, East Tamaki, Auckland, 2013, New Zealand
Tel.: (64) 99549000
Web Site: https://www.carterstyres.co.nz
Motor Vehicles Mfr
N.A.I.C.S.: 336211

Dynamic Wheel Co Pty Limited (1)
82 Vision Street, Dandenong South, 3175, VIC, Australia
Tel.: (61) 1300655870
Web Site: https://www.dynamicwheelco.com.au
Automotive Repair Services
N.A.I.C.S.: 811111

Exclusive Tyre Distributors Pty Ltd (1)
385 Macarthur Avenue, PO Box 283, Moorooka, Hamilton, 4007, QLD, Australia
Tel.: (61) 1800681298
Web Site: https://www.exclusivetyres.com.au
Tire Distr
N.A.I.C.S.: 441340

Exclusive Tyres Distributors Pty. Ltd. (1)
385 Macarthur Avenue, PO Box 283, Hamilton, 4007, QLD, Australia
Tel.: (61) 1800681298
Web Site: https://www.exclusivetyres.com.au
Emp.: 8,500
Tyre & Wheel Whslr
N.A.I.C.S.: 423130

Integrated OE Pty. Ltd. (1)
16 Scammel Street, Campbellfield, 3061, VIC, Australia
Tel.: (61) 393088008
Web Site: https://www.integratedoe.com.au
Tyre & Wheel Whslr
N.A.I.C.S.: 423130

Statewide Tyre Distribution Pty Ltd (1)
265 Hanson Rd, Wingfield, Adelaide, 5013, SA, Australia
Tel.: (61) 883472999
Web Site: https://www.statewidetyres.com.au
Tire Distr
N.A.I.C.S.: 441340

NATIONAL UNITED RESOURCES HOLDINGS LTD
Suite 5208 52/F Central Plaza 18 Harbour Road, Wanchai, China (Hong Kong)
Tel.: (852) 3918 9300
Web Site: http://www.nur.com.hk
Sales Range: $25-49.9 Million
Emp.: 73
Outdoor Advertising Services; Coal Trading
N.A.I.C.S.: 541850
Songlin Tian *(Exec Dir)*

INTERNATIONAL PUBLIC

NATIONAL VETERINARY CARE LTD
Unit 1 28 Burnside Road, Ormeau, 4208, QLD, Australia
Tel.: (61) 730630900 AU
Web Site: http://www.nvcltd.com.au
Year Founded: 2013
Rev.: $65,733,648
Assets: $97,206,908
Liabilities: $40,018,844
Net Worth: $57,188,063
Earnings: $5,370,552
Fiscal Year-end: 06/30/18
Veterinary Services
N.A.I.C.S.: 541940
Alex Whan *(Gen Mgr-Veterinary Svcs)*

Subsidiaries:

Albion Vet Surgery Pty Ltd (1)
97 Albion Road, Albion, 4010, QLD, Australia
Tel.: (61) 733577849
Web Site: http://albionvetsurgery.com.au
Veterinary Care Services
N.A.I.C.S.: 541940
Amanda Darblshire *(Head-Veterinarian)*

Fitzroy Operations Pty Ltd (1)
113-115 Scotchmer St, Fitzroy, 3068, VIC, Australia (100%)
Tel.: (61) 394892195
Veterinary Care Services
N.A.I.C.S.: 541940

Lower Hutt Veterinary Services Ltd (1)
53 Rutherford St, Lower Hutt, 5010, New Zealand
Tel.: (64) 45698830
Veterinary Care Services
N.A.I.C.S.: 541940

NATIONAL WORLD PLC
1 Farringdon Street Gate House, London, EC4M 7LG, United Kingdom
Tel.: (44) 2075838304 UK
Web Site: https://www.nationalworld.com
News Publishing Services
N.A.I.C.S.: 513110
David Montgomery *(Chm)*

NATIONALE-NEDERLANDEN OTWARTY FUNDUSZ EMERYTALNY
Ludna 2, 00-406, Warsaw, Poland
Tel.: (48) 225220304
Investment Management Service
N.A.I.C.S.: 523999

NATIONGATE HOLDINGS BERHAD
2005 Tingkat Perusahaan Satu Kawasan Perindustrian Prai, Pulau, Perai, Pinang, Malaysia
Tel.: (60) 43989001
Web Site: https://www.nationgate.com.my
NATGATE—(KLS)
Rev.: $138,941,334
Assets: $159,959,478
Liabilities: $68,088,139
Net Worth: $91,871,339
Earnings: $13,261,841
Emp.: 858
Fiscal Year-end: 12/31/23
Holding Company
N.A.I.C.S.: 551112

NATIONS TRUST BANK PLC
No 242 Union Place, 2, Colombo, 2, Sri Lanka
Tel.: (94) 114313131
Web Site: https://www.nationstrust.com
Year Founded: 1999
NTB.X0000—(COL)
Rev.: $272,536,989

Assets: $1,718,099,877
Liabilities: $1,514,624,170
Net Worth: $203,475,707
Earnings: $38,184,085
Emp.: 2,238
Fiscal Year-end: 12/31/23
Personal & Corporate Banking Services
N.A.I.C.S.: 522110
Ramanika Unamboowe *(Exec VP-HR)*

Subsidiaries:

Nations Insurance Brokers
Limited (1)
Level 9 Millennium House 46/58 Navam Mawatha, Colombo, 00200, Western Province, Sri Lanka
Tel.: (94) 114218271
Web Site: http://www.nationstrustbank.com
Sales Range: $50-74.9 Million
Emp.: 34
Insurance Brokerage Services
N.A.I.C.S.: 524210
Ursula Wijeyasuriya *(Mgr)*

NATIONWIDE BUILDING SOCIETY
Nationwide House Pipers Way, Swindon, SN38 1NW, United Kingdom
Tel.: (44) 3452660350   UK
Web Site:
 https://www.nationwide.co.uk
Year Founded: 1848
NBS—(LSE)
Rev.: $11,483,898,300
Assets: $337,446,402,300
Liabilities: $316,464,365,700
Net Worth: $20,982,036,600
Earnings: $2,065,190,400
Fiscal Year-end: 04/04/23
Banking Services
N.A.I.C.S.: 522110
Chris Rhodes *(CFO)*

Subsidiaries:

Derbyshire Building Society (1)
Duffield Hall, Duffield, DE56 1AG, Derbyshire, United Kingdom
Tel.: (44) 8456004005
Web Site: http://www.thederbyshire.co.uk
Sales Range: $75-99.9 Million
Emp.: 520
Banking Services
N.A.I.C.S.: 522110

Nationwide Life (1)
21 The Parade, Swindon, SN1 1BB, Wilts, United Kingdom   (100%)
Tel.: (44) 793583100
Sales Range: $100-124.9 Million
Emp.: 150
Provider of Insurance
N.A.I.C.S.: 524128

Nationwide Trust Ltd. (1)
Nationwide House, 20 Lower Dagnall St, Saint Albans, AL3 4RR, Herdford, United Kingdom   (100%)
Tel.: (44) 1727832241
Web Site: http://www.nationwide.co.uk
Sales Range: $125-149.9 Million
Emp.: 150
Brokerage
N.A.I.C.S.: 523910

Silverstone Master Issuer plc (1)
1 Kings Arms Yard, London, EC2R 7AF, United Kingdom
Tel.: (44) 2073973600
Commercial Banking Services
N.A.I.C.S.: 522110

UCB Home Loans Corporation
Limited (1)
Portman House Richmond Hill, Bournemouth, BH2 6EP, Dorset, United Kingdom
Tel.: (44) 8004643014
Web Site: http://www.ucbhomeloans.co.uk
Mortgage Lending Services
N.A.I.C.S.: 522310

NATIONWIDE EXPRESS COURIER SERVICES BERHAD
Lot 11 A Persiaran Selangor Section 15, 40200, Shah Alam, Selangor, Malaysia
Tel.: (60) 351633333   MY
Web Site:
 http://www.nationwide2u.com
Year Founded: 1985
NATWIDE—(KLS)
Rev.: $19,701,232
Assets: $12,916,669
Liabilities: $5,479,650
Net Worth: $7,437,019
Earnings: ($2,393,900)
Fiscal Year-end: 03/31/18
Courier Service
N.A.I.C.S.: 492110
Harani Khalid *(Sr Mgr-Legal & Compliance)*

NATIONWIDE EXPRESS HOLDINGS BHD
Lot 6 and 7 Jalan Utas 15/7 Section 15, 40000, Shah Alam, Selangor, Malaysia
Tel.: (60) 380733333
Web Site:
 http://www.nationwide.com.my
Year Founded: 1985
9806—(KLS)
Rev.: $11,844,608
Assets: $18,188,528
Liabilities: $22,553,685
Net Worth: ($4,365,157)
Earnings: ($2,661,367)
Emp.: 1,092
Fiscal Year-end: 03/31/21
Courier Service
N.A.I.C.S.: 492110
Puan Nor Waziah Haji Wari *(Sr Mgr-Natl Sls)*

NATIONWIDE FLEET INSTALLATIONS LTD.
Nasmyth Business Park James Nasmyth Way Unit F2A, Patricroft Manchester, Manchester, M30 0SN, United Kingdom
Tel.: (44) 1617866600
Web Site:
 https://nationwidefleetinstall.com
Year Founded: 1995
Electrical Contractor
N.A.I.C.S.: 238210
Graham Appleyard *(Mng Dir)*

Subsidiaries:

Avian Mobile Ltd. (1)
11-13 Falcon Court, London, United Kingdom
Tel.: (44) 2086052700
Web Site: https://www.avianfleet.com
Telecommunication Servicesb
N.A.I.C.S.: 517810
Graham Price *(Mng Dir)*

NATIONZ TECHNOLOGIES INC.
Nations Tower No 109 Baoshen Road, Nanshan District, Shenzhen, 518057, China
Tel.: (86) 75586309900
Web Site:
 https://www.nationstech.com
Year Founded: 2000
300077—(CHIN)
Rev.: $167,835,564
Assets: $520,358,904
Liabilities: $275,527,980
Net Worth: $244,830,924
Earnings: ($4,560,192)
Emp.: 1,500
Fiscal Year-end: 12/31/22
Integrated Circuits & Chips Mfr
N.A.I.C.S.: 334412
Sun Yingtong *(Chm & Gen Mgr)*

NATIVE MINERAL RESOURCES HOLDINGS LIMITED
Suite 10 6-14 Clarence Street, Port Macquarie, 2444, NSW, Australia
Tel.: (61) 265837833   AU
Web Site:
 https://www.nmresources.com.au
Year Founded: 2020
NMR—(ASX)
Rev.: $344
Assets: $369,023
Liabilities: $242,073
Net Worth: $126,950
Earnings: ($2,430,236)
Fiscal Year-end: 06/30/23
Holding Company
N.A.I.C.S.: 551112
Chris Jacobs *(CFO)*

NATIXIS BANK JSC
Tsvetnoi Boulevard 2, 127051, Moscow, Russia
Tel.: (7) 4957871717
Web Site: http://www.natixis.ru
Rev.: $9,973,915
Assets: $394,651,671
Liabilities: $364,993,425
Net Worth: $29,658,246
Earnings: ($470,952)
Emp.: 16,000
Fiscal Year-end: 12/31/20
Investment Banking & Financial Services
N.A.I.C.S.: 523150
Edith Aviles *(Vice Chm)*

NATOCO CO., LTD.
18 Shogayama Uchikoshi cho, Miyoshi, 470-0213, Aichi, Japan
Tel.: (81) 561322285
Web Site: https://www.natoco.co.jp
Year Founded: 1948
4627—(TKS)
Rev.: $142,962,760
Assets: $204,475,600
Liabilities: $43,156,830
Net Worth: $161,318,770
Earnings: $6,742,590
Emp.: 209
Fiscal Year-end: 10/31/23
Paint Product Mfr
N.A.I.C.S.: 325510
Tadaharu Kasuya *(Chm)*

Subsidiaries:

Natoco Paint Chemical Industry
(Qingdao) Co., Ltd (1)
Daguhe Industrial Park Ligezhuangzhen, Jiaozhou, Qingdao, 266316, Shandong, China
Tel.: (86) 53288284186
Web Site: http://www.natoco.cn
Paint Product Mfr & Distr
N.A.I.C.S.: 325510

Tomoe Corporation (1)
35-5 Cassin, Uchikoshi-cho, Miyoshi, 470-0213, Aichi, Japan
Tel.: (81) 561 34 3171
Web Site: http://www.tomoe-k.co.jp
Emp.: 44
Paint Product Mfr & Distr
N.A.I.C.S.: 325510

NATOM A.D.
Ivana Milutinovica bb, Nis, Serbia
Tel.: (381) 18 4248789
Year Founded: 2003
Sales Range: Less than $1 Million
Broom & Brush Mfr
N.A.I.C.S.: 339994

NATORI CO., LTD.
5-5-1 Oji, Kita-ku, Tokyo, 114-8611, Japan
Tel.: (81) 353908111   JP
Web Site: https://www.natori.co.jp

Year Founded: 1948
2922—(TKS)
Rev.: $314,490,580
Assets: $287,125,180
Liabilities: $121,386,040
Net Worth: $165,739,140
Earnings: $9,254,000
Emp.: 770
Fiscal Year-end: 03/31/24
Miscellaneous Food Products Mfr; Seafood, Meat, Dairy, Snack Foods & Processed Agricultural Products Mfr
N.A.I.C.S.: 311710
Koichirou Natori *(Mng Exec Officer)*

NATRAJ PROTEINS LIMITED
Nagpur Kalan Ordinance Factory Road, Nagpur Kalan, Itarsi, 461 111, MP, India
Tel.: (91) 7572262636
Web Site:
 https://www.natrajproteins.com
Year Founded: 1990
530119—(BOM)
Rev.: $17,228,320
Assets: $10,683,916
Liabilities: $5,140,987
Net Worth: $5,542,929
Earnings: $84,863
Emp.: 43
Fiscal Year-end: 03/31/23
Edible Oil Mfr & Distr
N.A.I.C.S.: 311224
Kailash Chand Sharma *(Chm & Mng Dir)*

NATRONIX SEMICONDUCTOR TECHNOLOGY LTD.
Vel Vilas 3/21 Kottur Garden 3rd Main Road, Kotturpuram, Chennai, 600 085, India
Tel.: (91) 8939431392
Web Site: http://www.natronix.net
Electronics Mfr
N.A.I.C.S.: 334419
Vellayan Selvaraj *(Mng Dir)*

Subsidiaries:

SPEL Semiconductor Ltd (1)
5 CMDA Industrial Estate, MM Nagar, Chennai, 603 209, Tamil Nadu, India   (55.9%)
Tel.: (91) 4447405300
Web Site: https://www.natronix.net
Rev.: $2,917,469
Assets: $22,718,105
Liabilities: $12,884,508
Net Worth: $9,833,597
Earnings: $1,178,678
Emp.: 161
Fiscal Year-end: 03/31/2021
Semiconductor Assembly & Test Services
N.A.I.C.S.: 333242
Dorairaj Balakrishnan *(CEO)*

NATS HOLDINGS LIMITED
4000 Parkway Whiteley, Fareham, PO15 7FL, Hants, United Kingdom
Tel.: (44) 1489616001
Web Site: http://www.nats.aero
Rev.: $1,231,881,472
Assets: $2,565,216,768
Liabilities: $1,376,776,960
Net Worth: $1,188,439,808
Earnings: $152,045,824
Emp.: 4,310
Fiscal Year-end: 03/31/18
Air Traffic Control Services
N.A.I.C.S.: 488111
Nigel Fotherby *(Dir-Fin)*

Subsidiaries:

NATS (USA) Inc (1)
601 Pennsylvania Ave NW Ste 900, Washington, DC 20004
Tel.: (202) 220-3070
Air Traffic Control Services

NATS HOLDINGS LIMITED

NATS Holdings Limited—(Continued)
N.A.I.C.S.: 488111

NATS En-Route Limited (1)
Corporate & Technical Centre 4000 Parkway, Whiteley, Fareham, PO15 7FL, United Kingdom
Tel.: (44) 1489616001
Web Site: http://www.nats.co.uk
Sales Range: $1-4.9 Billion
Emp.: 3,500
Air Traffic Control Services
N.A.I.C.S.: 488111

NATS Services (Asia Pacific) Pte. Limited (1)
51 Changi Business Park Central 2 04-06 The Signature, Singapore, 486066, Singapore
Tel.: (65) 6 850 7210
Automated Teller Machine Consultancy Services
N.A.I.C.S.: 541611

NATS Services (Hong Kong) Limited (1)
2/F Cathay Dragon House 11 Tung Fai Road, Hong Kong International Airport, Hong Kong, China (Hong Kong)
Tel.: (852) 2 167 8650
Automated Teller Machine Consultancy Services
N.A.I.C.S.: 541611

NATS Services LLC (1)
P C 118 Al Nadha Towers 2 Floor 4, PO Box 303, Muscat, Oman
Tel.: (968) 9 462 6024
Automated Teller Machine Consultancy Services
N.A.I.C.S.: 541611

NATS Services Limited (1)
Corporate & Technical Centre 4000 Parkway, Whiteley, Fareham, PO15 7FL, United Kingdom
Tel.: (44) 1489616001
Airport Services
N.A.I.C.S.: 488119

NATTYSWANKY HOLDINGS CO., LTD.
1-19-8 Nishishinjuku, Shinjuku, 160-0023, Japan
Tel.: (81) 359093013
Web Site: http://www.nattyswanky.com
7674—(TKS)
Rev.: $50,062,490
Assets: $32,443,840
Liabilities: $14,243,810
Net Worth: $18,200,030
Earnings: $1,751,230
Fiscal Year-end: 01/31/24
Hotel & Resort Operator
N.A.I.C.S.: 721110
Yuji Iseki (Pres)

NATUNOLA AGRITECH INC.
661 St Lawrence Street, Winchester, K0C 2K0, ON, Canada
Tel.: (613) 774-9998
Web Site: http://www.natunola.com
Sales Range: $1-9.9 Million
Proprietary Natural Ingredients Developer, Mfr & Sales
N.A.I.C.S.: 541715
Fong Han Nam (Pres, CEO & COO)

NATUR INTERNATIONAL CORP.
Jachthavenweg 124 Suite 770, 1081 KJ, Amsterdam, Netherlands
Tel.: (31) 0205787700
Web Site: http://www.int.natur.eu
NTRU—(OTCIQ)
Sales Range: $1-9.9 Million
Holding Company; Home Care & Medical Staffing
N.A.I.C.S.: 551112
Michael Jones (Chief Strategy Officer)

Subsidiaries:

Interim Healthcare of Wyoming, Inc. (1)
1010 E 1st St Ste A, Casper, WY 82601
Tel.: (307) 266-1152
Web Site: http://www.interimhealthcare.com
Sales Range: $10-24.9 Million
Emp.: 31
Women Healthcare Services
N.A.I.C.S.: 621610
John L. Busshaus (CFO)

NATURA & CO HOLDING S.A.
Avenida Alexandre Colares No 1188 Sala A17-Bloco A, Parque Anhanguera, Sao Paulo, 05106-000, SP, Brazil
Tel.: (55) 1143897881
Web Site: http://www.naturaeco.com
Year Founded: 1969
NTCO3—(BRAZ)
Rev.: $5,331,992,621
Assets: $8,524,681,424
Liabilities: $3,913,959,517
Net Worth: $4,610,721,906
Earnings: $593,181,773
Emp.: 19,955
Fiscal Year-end: 12/31/23
Cosmetic Product Distr
N.A.I.C.S.: 456120
Roberto De Oliveira Marques (Co-Chm & CEO)

Subsidiaries:

Natura Cosmeticos SA (1)
Av Alexandre Colares 1188, 05106-000, Sao Paulo, SP, Brazil
Tel.: (55) 1143897317
Web Site: http://www.natura.com.br
Cosmetics Personal Hygiene & Perfumery Products Mfr
N.A.I.C.S.: 325620
Pedro Luiz Barreiros Passos (Co-Founder)

Subsidiary (Non-US):

Avon Products, Inc. (2)
Building 6 Chiswick Park, London, W4 5HR, United Kingdom
Tel.: (44) 1604232425
Web Site: http://www.avoninvestor.com
Rev.: $2,769,200,000
Assets: $2,161,700,000
Liabilities: $3,402,900,000
Net Worth: ($1,241,200,000)
Earnings: ($428,100,000)
Emp.: 13,000
Fiscal Year-end: 12/31/2022
Holding Company; Cosmetics Mfr & Distr
N.A.I.C.S.: 551112
Angela Cretu (CEO)

Subsidiary (Non-US):

Avon Beauty Products India Pvt. Ltd. (3)
401 Paras Trade Centre Sector 2 Gwal Pahari, Faridabad Expressway, Gurgaon, 122003, Haryana, India
Tel.: (91) 12441508000
Emp.: 10
Beauty Product Whslr
N.A.I.C.S.: 456120

Avon Beauty Products, SARL (3)
Lot 2 Lotissement ATAWFIK Quartier industriel, Oukacha Rue el Koutia Ain Sebaa, Casablanca, 20250, Morocco
Tel.: (212) 522679696
Cosmetics Mfr
N.A.I.C.S.: 456120

Avon Colombia Ltda. (3)
Calle 14 52a - 272, Medellin, 050001, Colombia
Tel.: (57) 43657600
Web Site: http://www.avon.com.co
Cosmetics Mfr & Whslr
N.A.I.C.S.: 456120

Avon Cosmeticas, Ltd. (3)
Av Paul Harris no 1 Ed D, Mem Martins, 2710-724, Sintra, Portugal (100%)
Tel.: (351) 219226100
Web Site: https://www.avon.com.pt

Sales Range: $75-99.9 Million
Emp.: 100
Sale of Cosmetics & Fragrances
N.A.I.C.S.: 456120

Avon Cosmeticos, Ltda. (3)
Avenida Interlagos 4300, Sao Paulo, 04660-907, Jurubatuba, Brazil (100%)
Tel.: (55) 1130270200
Web Site: https://www.avon.com.br
Sales Range: $1-4.9 Billion
Emp.: 3,600
Cosmetics & Fragrances Mfr & Retailer
N.A.I.C.S.: 325620

Avon Cosmetics (Greece) Sole Partner Ltd. (3)
135 Marathonos Avenue, Athens, 15344, Gerakas, Greece
Tel.: (30) 2106605500
Web Site: http://www.avoncosmetics.gr
Sales Range: $75-99.9 Million
Emp.: 125
Cosmetics Mfr & Distr
N.A.I.C.S.: 456120

Avon Cosmetics (Malaysia) Sdn. Bhd. (3)
Lot 13A Jalan 219 Seksyen 51A, 46100, Petaling Jaya, Selangor, Malaysia (70%)
Tel.: (60) 379657100
Web Site: http://www.shop.avon.my
Sales Range: $125-149.9 Million
Emp.: 170
Sales of Cosmetics & Fragrances
N.A.I.C.S.: 456191
Romulus Sirbu (Mng Dir)

Avon Cosmetics (Moldova) S.R.L. (3)
Bd Stefan cel Mare 65 blr 500, Chisinau, Moldova
Tel.: (373) 22267651
Cosmetic Product Distr
N.A.I.C.S.: 456120

Avon Cosmetics (Romania) S.R.L. (3)
Web Site: http://www.avon.ro
Cosmetic Product Whslr
N.A.I.C.S.: 456120

Avon Cosmetics (Taiwan) Ltd. (3)
14th Floor No 88 Dunhua North Road, Songshan, Taipei, 10084, Taiwan
Tel.: (886) 229019000
Web Site: http://shop.avon.com.tw
Cosmetics Products Mfr
N.A.I.C.S.: 456120

Avon Cosmetics (Thailand) Ltd. (3)
1765 Ramkhamhaeng Rd, Hua Mark Bangkapi, Bangkok, 10240, Thailand (100%)
Tel.: (66) 27273300
Web Site: http://www.avon.co.th
Sales Range: $50-74.9 Million
Emp.: 300
Cosmetics & Fragrance Sales
N.A.I.C.S.: 456120

Avon Cosmetics (Ukraine) (3)
Kharkivske shosse 5, Boryspil district village Shchaslyve, 08325, Kiev, Ukraine
Tel.: (380) 800505080
Web Site: https://my.avon.ua
Sales Range: $100-124.9 Million
Emp.: 400
Cosmetic Mfr & Whslr
N.A.I.C.S.: 456120

Avon Cosmetics (Vietnam) Limited (3)
E Town Building364 Cong Hoa St Ward 13, Tan Binh District, Ho Chi Minh City, Vietnam
Tel.: (84) 8 812 4004
Sales Range: $150-199.9 Million
Cosmetics, Fragrances & Toiletries Mfr & Distr
N.A.I.C.S.: 325620

Avon Cosmetics Bulgaria EOOD (3)
Tel.: (359) 29765800
Web Site: http://www.avon.bg
Emp.: 75
Beauty Care Products Mfr
N.A.I.C.S.: 456120

Avon Cosmetics Egypt, S.A.E (3)

INTERNATIONAL PUBLIC

7 Mohamed Metwally El Sharaawy St Sheraton Heliopolis, Cairo, Egypt
Tel.: (20) 222668883
Web Site: http://www.avon.com.eg
Cosmetic Mfr & Whslr
N.A.I.C.S.: 456120

Avon Cosmetics Finland Oy (3)
Itamerenkatu 1, 00180, Helsinki, Finland
Tel.: (358) 968509494
Sales Range: $25-49.9 Million
Emp.: 15
Cosmetics Mfr & Distr
N.A.I.C.S.: 456191

Avon Cosmetics GmbH (3)
Zeppelinstrasse 3, 85399, Hallbergmoos, Germany (100%)
Tel.: (49) 81129999020
Web Site: https://www.avon.de
Sales Range: $250-299.9 Million
Emp.: 600
Mfr & Sale of Cosmetics & Fragrances
N.A.I.C.S.: 325620

Avon Cosmetics Hungary Kozmetikai Cikk Kereskedelmi Kft. (3)
Haraszti ut 3, 2100, Godollo, Hungary
Tel.: (36) 28511111
Web Site: http://avononline.avon.hu
Sales Range: $150-199.9 Million
Cosmetics Distr
N.A.I.C.S.: 456120

Subsidiary (Domestic):

Avon Cosmetics Limited (3)
Nunn Mills Road, Northampton, NN1 5PA, United Kingdom (100%)
Tel.: (44) 1604232425
Sales Range: $900-999.9 Million
Emp.: 711
Mfr & Sell Cosmetics & Perfumes
N.A.I.C.S.: 325620

Subsidiary (Non-US):

Avon Cosmetics Ltd. (3)
Victoria St West, PO Box 92155, Auckland, 1142, New Zealand (100%)
Tel.: (64) 508777007
Web Site: http://www.avon.co.nz
Sales Range: $50-74.9 Million
Emp.: 400
Sales of Cosmetics & Fragrances
N.A.I.C.S.: 456120

Avon Cosmetics Polska Sp zoo (3)
Slowicza 32, Warsaw, 02-170, Poland
Tel.: (48) 228782700
Web Site: http://www.pl.avon.com
Sales Range: $300-349.9 Million
Emp.: 600
Cosmetics Mfr & Distr
N.A.I.C.S.: 456191

Avon Cosmetics SIA (3)
Duntes 3, Riga, 1012, Latvia
Tel.: (371) 67389788
Cosmetics Products Mfr
N.A.I.C.S.: 456120

Avon Cosmetics de Venezuela, C.A. (3)
Centro Comercial Propatria Nivel 1 Local 34, Caracas, Venezuela (100%)
Tel.: (58) 2128703474
Web Site: http://www.ve.avon.com
Sales Range: $800-899.9 Million
Emp.: 1,200
Cosmetics & Fragrances Mfr & Whslr
N.A.I.C.S.: 325620

Avon Cosmetics s.r.l. a Socio Unico (3)
Via Salvo d Acquisto n 8/14, 22078, Turate, Italy
Tel.: (39) 0296485111
Web Site: https://www.avon.it
Cosmetic Product Mfr & Whslr
N.A.I.C.S.: 456120

Avon Cosmetics sro (3)
Amazon Court Karolinska 661/4, 186 00, Prague, Czech Republic
Sales Range: $75-99.9 Million
Emp.: 100
Cosmetics Mfr & Distr
N.A.I.C.S.: 456191

Avon Cosmetics, Inc. (3)

Gercon Plaza 7901 Makati Ave Salcedo Village, Makati, 1227, Philippines **(100%)**
Tel.: (63) 8642688
Sales Range: $400-449.9 Million
Emp.: 590
Sales of Cosmetics & Fragrances
N.A.I.C.S.: 456120

Avon Cosmetics, S.A. (3)
Carretera Madrid-Barcelona, Km 34 200, 28805, Alcala de Henares, Spain **(75%)**
Tel.: (34) 918879000
Web Site: https://www.avon.es
Sales Range: $200-249.9 Million
Emp.: 400
Mfr & Sale of Cosmetics & Fragrances
N.A.I.C.S.: 325620

Avon Cosmetics, S.A. de C.V. (3)
Ave Universidad 1778, Col Oxtopulco Universidad, Mexico, 4318, DF, Mexico **(100%)**
Tel.: (52) 5554202099
Sales Range: $1-4.9 Billion
Emp.: 3,000
Mfr & Sale of Cosmetics & Fragrances
N.A.I.C.S.: 325620

Avon Cosmetics, S.p.A. (3)
Via 25 Aprile 15, Olgiate Comasco, 22077, Como, Italy **(100%)**
Tel.: (39) 031998111
Web Site: http://www.avon.it
Sales Range: $200-249.9 Million
Emp.: 500
Mfr & Sale of Cosmetics & Fragrances
N.A.I.C.S.: 325620

Avon EMEA Finance Service Centre Spolka z o.o. (3)
Ul Fabryczna 5, 00-446, Warsaw, Poland
Tel.: (48) 223350500
Web Site: http://www.avonpolska.pl
Emp.: 50
Financial Services
N.A.I.C.S.: 921130

Avon Eesti OU (3)
Tel.: (372) 6612614
Cosmetics Products Mfr
N.A.I.C.S.: 456120

Subsidiary (US):

Avon Foundation (3)
1345 Ave of the Americas, New York, NY 10105-0196
Tel.: (212) 282-5000
Web Site: http://www.avonfoundation.org
Sales Range: $250-299.9 Million
Foundation Focusing on Breast Cancer Research & Domestic Violence
N.A.I.C.S.: 813211

Subsidiary (Non-US):

Avon Industrial Ltda. (3)
Av Interlagos 4300, Sao Paulo, 04660-907, SP, Brazil
Tel.: (55) 8007082866
Web Site: http://www.avon.com.br
Cosmetic Product Mfr & Whslr
N.A.I.C.S.: 456120

Avon Kozmetik Urunleri Sanayi ve Ticaret Anonim Sirketi (3)
Tekfen Kagithane Ofispark A Blok Floor 4/11 Merkez Mah, Baglar Cad No 14 Kagithane, Istanbul, Turkiye
Tel.: (90) 2124731100
Web Site: https://kozmetik.avon.com.tr
Sales Range: $50-74.9 Million
Emp.: 250
Cosmetic Products Mfr & Whslr
N.A.I.C.S.: 456120

Avon Kozmetika doo (3)
Bani 110, 10010, Zagreb, Croatia
Tel.: (385) 16650010
Web Site: https://www.avon.hr
Sales Range: $10-24.9 Million
Emp.: 40
Cosmetics Marketer & Distr
N.A.I.C.S.: 325620

Avon Operations Polska Sp. z o.o. (3)
Ul Stacyjna 77, Garwolin, 08-400, Poland
Tel.: (48) 256828000
Web Site: http://www.pl.avon.com

Sales Range: $700-749.9 Million
Emp.: 2,000
Cosmetics Mfr
N.A.I.C.S.: 325620

Avon Products (China) Co., Ltd. (3)
Unit 03-04 7th Floor Jianye Square 18 Huacheng Avenue, Zhujiang New City Tianhe, Guangzhou, 510620, China **(100%)**
Tel.: (86) 4008202869
Web Site: http://www.avon.com.cn
Sales Range: $150-199.9 Million
Cosmetics Manufacturing & Distribution
N.A.I.C.S.: 456120

Avon Products (FEBO) Ltd. (3)
Rm 2201 2 22/F Oxford House Tai Koo 979 King s Rd, Quarry Bay, China (Hong Kong) **(100%)**
Tel.: (852) 25922900
Web Site: http://www.avoncompany.com
Sales Range: $150-199.9 Million
Cosmetics Sales & Distribution
N.A.I.C.S.: 456120

Avon Products Manufacturing, Inc. (3)
CPIP Batino Calambe, Laguna, 4027, Philippines **(100%)**
Tel.: (63) 495456011
Sales Range: $100-124.9 Million
Emp.: 300
Mfr & Sale of Cosmetics & Fragrances
N.A.I.C.S.: 325620

Avon Products Pty. Ltd. (3)
120 Old Pittwater Rd, Sydney, 2100, NSW, Australia **(100%)**
Tel.: (61) 299367555
Web Site: http://www.avon.com.au
Sales Range: $200-249.9 Million
Emp.: 500
Mfr & Sales of Cosmetics & Fragrances
N.A.I.C.S.: 325620

Avon SAS (3)
Paris Nord 2 85 Avenue Des Nations-BP 68013 Roissy CDG, 95970, Paris, France **(100%)**
Tel.: (33) 147036810
Web Site: http://www.avon.fr
Sales Range: $100-124.9 Million
Emp.: 200
Cosmetics & Fragrances Sales
N.A.I.C.S.: 456120

Cosmeticos Avon S.A. (3)
Apoquindo No 5950 floor 7, commune of Las Condes, Santiago, Chile **(100%)**
Tel.: (56) 227128678
Web Site: https://www.avon.cl
Sales Range: $300-349.9 Million
Emp.: 600
Cosmetics & Fragrances Retailer & Mfr
N.A.I.C.S.: 325620

Cosmeticos Avon, S.A.C.I. (3)
Martin Rodriguez 4013 Victoria, Partido San Fernando, 1644, Buenos Aires, Argentina
Tel.: (54) 1147468000
Web Site: http://www.ar.avon.com
Sales Range: $750-799.9 Million
Emp.: 700
Cosmetics & Fragrances Retailer & Mfr
N.A.I.C.S.: 456191

Productos Avon de Guatemala S.A. (3)
Calzada Roosevelt 11-08, z2 de Mixco, Guatemala, 1057, Guatemala **(100%)**
Tel.: (502) 24106841
Sales Range: $150-199.9 Million
Mfr & Sale of Cosmetics & Fragrances
N.A.I.C.S.: 325620

Productos Avon, S.A. (3)
Car Central Km 4 7, 15001, Lima, Peru **(100%)**
Tel.: (51) 13172866
Web Site: http://www.avon.com.pe
Sales Range: $150-199.9 Million
Emp.: 300
Sales of Cosmetics & Fragrances
N.A.I.C.S.: 456120

Productos Avon, S.A. (3)
Av Ch de Gaulle 264, Edificio Avon, Santo Domingo, 9999, Dominican Republic **(100%)**

Tel.: (809) 8092459453
Web Site: http://www.do.avon.com
Sales Range: $100-124.9 Million
Emp.: 300
Sales of Cosmetics & Fragrances
N.A.I.C.S.: 456120

Productos Avon, S.A. de C.V. (3)
(100%)
Sales Range: $50-74.9 Million
Emp.: 15
Sales of Cosmetics & Toiletries
N.A.I.C.S.: 456120

UAB Avon Cosmetics (3)
Tel.: (370) 852109757
Web Site: http://www.avon.lt
Cosmetic Product Distr
N.A.I.C.S.: 456120

Subsidiary (Non-US):

Natura Cosmeticos S.A. (2)
Thomas Edison 2659 2nd Floor Oficina No 1, B1638BEL, Buenos Aires, Argentina
Tel.: (54) 1148376100
Sales Range: $50-74.9 Million
Emp.: 100
Cosmetics Whslr
N.A.I.C.S.: 424210

Natura Distribuidora de Mexico, S.A. de C.V. (2)
Tel.: (52) 15522826000
Cosmetics Distr
N.A.I.C.S.: 456120

Natura Europa S.A.S. (2)
10 Rue Chevreul, 92150, Suresnes, France
Tel.: (33) 184170736
Web Site: https://www.naturabrasil.fr
Sales Range: $25-49.9 Million
Emp.: 30
Cosmetics Whslr
N.A.I.C.S.: 424210

NATURAL BEAUTY BIO TECHNOLOGY LTD

Level 54 Hopewell Centre 183 Queen s Road East, Hong Kong, China (Hong Kong)
Tel.: (852) 29801888
Web Site: http://www.nblife.com
0157—(HKG)
Rev.: $47,184,647
Assets: $86,697,169
Liabilities: $16,230,804
Net Worth: $70,466,365
Earnings: $3,353,012
Emp.: 511
Fiscal Year-end: 12/31/18
Skin Care Services
N.A.I.C.S.: 812112
Ah Tsang Sun *(Sec)*

Subsidiaries:

Shanghai Natural Beauty Cosmetics Company Limited (1)
No 94 Erlu Road Minhang District, Shanghai, 201107, China
Tel.: (86) 13860935529
Beauty Product Mfr & Distr
N.A.I.C.S.: 325620

NATURAL BIOCON INDIA LIMITED

G-4 New York Corner Devmoti Owners Associations Near Kiran Motors, Bodakdev S G Road, Ahmedabad, 380054, Gujarat, India
Tel.: (91) 9904070141
Web Site:
http://www.naturalbiocon.com
Year Founded: 1992
24151—(KOL)
Rev.: $150,387
Assets: $1,620,706
Liabilities: $154,331
Net Worth: $1,466,375
Earnings: $21,474
Emp.: 3
Fiscal Year-end: 03/31/23
Agriculture Produce Mfr

N.A.I.C.S.: 111998
Prakhar Dubey *(Compliance Officer & Sec)*

NATURAL CAPSULES LIMITED

Trident Towers 4th FL No 23 100 Feet Road, Jaynagar II Block, Bengaluru, 560 011, India
Tel.: (91) 8026561562 In
Web Site:
https://www.naturalcapsules.com
Year Founded: 1993
524654—(BOM)
Rev.: $20,734,920
Assets: $34,621,569
Liabilities: $16,847,311
Net Worth: $17,774,258
Earnings: $2,211,642
Emp.: 250
Fiscal Year-end: 03/31/23
Capsule Shells Mfr & Whslr
N.A.I.C.S.: 325412
Sunil Laxminarayan Mundra *(Mng Dir)*

NATURAL COOL HOLDINGS LIMITED

29 Tai Seng Avenue 07-01 Natural Cool Lifestyle Hub, Singapore, 534119, Singapore
Tel.: (65) 64545775
Web Site: https://www.natcool.com
5IF—(CAT)
Rev.: $109,188,821
Assets: $67,103,689
Liabilities: $54,995,077
Net Worth: $12,108,612
Earnings: $305,234
Emp.: 571
Fiscal Year-end: 12/31/23
Air Conditioning Systems Installation Services
N.A.I.C.S.: 333415
Joo Peng Tsng *(CEO)*

Subsidiaries:

JAD Solutions Pte. Ltd. (1)
87 Defu Lane 10 05-02, Singapore, 539219, Singapore
Tel.: (65) 93669050
Web Site: https://www.jad-venture.com
Air Valve Mfr & Distr
N.A.I.C.S.: 332911

Lifestyle Guru Pte. Ltd. (1)
87 Defu Lane 10 06-01, Singapore, 539219, Singapore
Tel.: (65) 64545225
Web Site: https://www.lifestyleguru.com.sg
Emp.: 300
Air Conditioner Mfr & Distr
N.A.I.C.S.: 333415

Loh & Sons Paint Co (S) Pte. Ltd. (1)
123 Pioneer Road, Singapore, 639596, Singapore
Tel.: (65) 62641248
Web Site: http://www.cougarpaint.com
Painting Chemical Mfr & Distr
N.A.I.C.S.: 325510

Natural Cool Airconditioning & Engineering Pte Ltd (1)
29 Tai Seng Avenue 07-01 Natural Cool Lifestyle Hub, Singapore, 534119, Singapore
Tel.: (65) 6 454 7667
Web Site: https://www.naturalcool.com.sg
Sales Range: $100-124.9 Million
Emp.: 300
Airconditioning Systems Installation & Maintenance Services
N.A.I.C.S.: 238220

Subsidiary (Domestic):

NC (Singapore) Pte. Ltd. (2)
29 Tai Seng Ave 07-01, Singapore, 534119, Singapore
Tel.: (65) 65521711

NATURAL COOL HOLDINGS LIMITED

Natural Cool Holdings Limited—(Continued)
Airconditioning Systems Installation & Maintenance Services
N.A.I.C.S.: 238220

Natural Cool Investments Pte. Ltd. (1)
29 Tai Seng Avenue 07-01, Singapore, 534119, Singapore
Tel.: (65) 64545225
Web Site: http://www.naturalcool.com.sg
Investment Management Service
N.A.I.C.S.: 523999

Yummy (S) Pte. Ltd. (1)
87 Defu Lane 10 02-01, Singapore, 539219, Singapore
Tel.: (65) 67415588
Web Site: https://yummyfood.com.sg
Chinese Food Mfr & Distr
N.A.I.C.S.: 311999

iFocus Pte. Ltd. (1)
18 Boon Lay Way 02-138 Trade Hub 21, Singapore, 609966, Singapore
Tel.: (65) 65602009
Web Site: http://www.ifocus.com.sg
Software Development Services
N.A.I.C.S.: 541519

NATURAL DESTINY INC.
Room 902 Unit 1 Pearl Business Building, Jiande, 311600, Zhejiang, China
Tel.: (86) 571 64197788   NV
Year Founded: 2015
Food & Beverage Distr
N.A.I.C.S.: 424490
Jianrong Xia (CEO)

NATURAL F&P CORP.
Natural B/D #99-5 Munjeong-Dong Songpa-Gu, Seoul, 138-200, Korea (South)
Tel.: (82) 2 400 4418
Web Site: http://www.naturalfnp.com
Emp.: 200
Food, Pharmaceuticals & Cosmetics Mfr
N.A.I.C.S.: 311999
Hyun Jick Lee (Pres)

NATURAL FOOD INTERNATIONAL HOLDING LIMITED
7/F West Tower Baidu International Building No 1 Haitian Road, Nanshan District, Shenzhen, China
Tel.: (86) 4006836080   Ky
Web Site: https://www.szwgmf.com
Year Founded: 2007
1837—(HKG)
Rev.: $255,493,326
Assets: $232,797,408
Liabilities: $39,542,119
Net Worth: $193,255,289
Earnings: $21,097,558
Emp.: 682
Fiscal Year-end: 12/31/23
Holding Company
N.A.I.C.S.: 551112
Changqing Gui (Chm)

NATURAL HEALTH TRENDS CORP.
Units 1205-07 12F Mira Place Tower A 132 Nathan Road, Tsimshatsui, Kowloon, China (Hong Kong)
Tel.: (852) 31070800   DE
Web Site:
    https://www.naturalhealthtrend.com
Year Founded: 1988
NHTC—(NASDAQ)
Rev.: $49,134,000
Assets: $82,817,000
Liabilities: $32,666,000
Net Worth: $50,151,000
Earnings: $313,000
Emp.: 140
Fiscal Year-end: 12/31/22
Natural Health Products Distr
N.A.I.C.S.: 424210
Chris T. Sharng (Pres)

Subsidiaries:

NHT Global Hong Kong Limited (1)
Units 1205-07 12/F Mira Place Tower A 132 Nathan Rd, Tsim Sha Tsui, Kowloon, China (Hong Kong)
Tel.: (852) 31073300
Web Site: https://www.en.nhtglobal.com.hk
Cosmetic Product Whslr
N.A.I.C.S.: 424210
Chris Sharng (Pres)

NHT Global Inc. (1)
609 Deep Valley Dr Ste 395, Rolling Hills Estates, CA 90274   (100%)
Tel.: (310) 541-0888
Web Site: https://unitedstates.nhtglobal.com
Sales Range: $25-49.9 Million
Emp.: 6
Distr of Natural Health Products
N.A.I.C.S.: 456191
Karyn Simmons (VP-Strategic Initiatives)

NHTC Global Singapore Pte. Ltd. (1)
229 Mountbatten Road 03-28 Mountbatten Square, Singapore, 398007, Singapore
Tel.: (65) 67180738
Web Site:
    http://www.singapore.nhtglobal.com
Cosmetic Product Whslr
N.A.I.C.S.: 424210

NHTK Ltd. (1)
135-839 6F Sun Tower 890-30, Kangnam-Ku, Seoul, 135-090, Korea (South)
Tel.: (82) 25580155
Cosmetic Product Whslr
N.A.I.C.S.: 424210

NATURAL ORGANIC FOOD GROUP PEI INC.
6 MacAleer Drive, Charlottetown, C1A 7L3, PE, Canada
Tel.: (902) 566-5211
Rev.: $19,997,339
Emp.: 120
Natural & Organic Food Mfr & Distr
N.A.I.C.S.: 424470
Scott Dingwell (Owner)

NATURAL RESOURCE HOLDINGS, INC.
Wattova 10, Ostrava, 70200, Czech Republic
Tel.: (420) 228881919   NV
Web Site: http://www.boxxyinc.com
Year Founded: 2016
NRHI—(OTCIQ)
Rev.: $13,711
Liabilities: $388,324
Net Worth: ($388,324)
Earnings: ($40,744)
Fiscal Year-end: 04/30/23
Online Health & Beauty Products Retailer
N.A.I.C.S.: 456199
Yao Bin Lian (Pres, CEO, CFO, COO, Treas & Sec)

NATURAL RESOURCE HOLDINGS, LTD.
7 Menachem Begin St, 52521, Tel Aviv, Israel
Tel.: (972) 36088982   Il
Web Site: http://www.nrh.co.il
Year Founded: 2008
Holding Company; Metal Mining
N.A.I.C.S.: 551112

NATURAL RESOURCES CORPORATION
76 Playfair Road #03-06 LHK2 Building, Singapore, 367996, Singapore
Tel.: (65) 62875955   DE
Year Founded: 2013
Emp.: 15
Dairy Based Ingredients & Milk Powder Products Mfr
N.A.I.C.S.: 311514
Elsa Holzgraf Esculier (Pres, CEO, Treas & Sec)

NATURALENDO TECH CO., LTD.
58 301ho 255beongil Pangyo-ro, Bundang-gu, Seongnam, Gyeonggi-do, Korea (South)
Tel.: (82) 7046013139
Web Site:
    https://www.naturalendo.co.kr
Year Founded: 2001
168330—(KRS)
Rev.: $10,700,284
Assets: $30,533,662
Liabilities: $2,476,806
Net Worth: $28,056,856
Earnings: ($7,734,473)
Emp.: 67
Fiscal Year-end: 12/31/22
Medicine, Health Food & Cosmetics Mfr
N.A.I.C.S.: 325411
Jong-Sun Lee (Head-Dept)

Subsidiaries:

Naturalendo Tech Co., Ltd. - Icheon Factory (1)
481-17 Seoicheon-ro Majang-myeon, Icheon, Gyeonggi-do, Korea (South)
Tel.: (82) 7046013104
Hormone Biotechnology Product Mfr
N.A.I.C.S.: 325413

NATURALLY SPLENDID ENTERPRISES LTD.
108-19100 Airport Way, Pitt Meadows, V3Y 0E2, BC, Canada
Tel.: (604) 465-0548   BC
Web Site:
    https://www.otcmarkets.com
Year Founded: 2010
NSP—(OTCIQ)
Rev.: $2,324,426
Assets: $4,286,069
Liabilities: $3,736,554
Net Worth: $549,514
Earnings: ($5,379,691)
Emp.: 38
Fiscal Year-end: 12/31/19
Healthy Food Mfr
N.A.I.C.S.: 311999
J. Craig Goodwin (Co-Founder, Pres & CEO)

Subsidiaries:

Chi Hemp Industries Inc. (1)
109-19100 Airport Way, Pitt Meadows, V3Y 0E2, BC, Canada
Tel.: (877) 251-7333
Web Site: http://www.chii.ca
Food Mfr
N.A.I.C.S.: 311999

Prosnack Natural Foods Inc. (1)
108 - 375 Lynn Ave, North Vancouver, V7J 2C4, BC, Canada
Tel.: (604) 980-6160
Web Site: http://www.prosnack.com
Food Mfr
N.A.I.C.S.: 311999

NATURE & ENVIRONMENT CO., LTD.
12F Nurikum Bld 396 World Cup buk-ro, Mapo-gu, Seoul, Korea (South)
Tel.: (82) 25579830
Web Site: https://www.e-nne.kr
Year Founded: 1999
043910—(KRS)
Rev.: $56,655,080
Assets: $92,434,947
Liabilities: $35,571,384
Net Worth: $56,863,563
Earnings: $79,202

INTERNATIONAL PUBLIC

Emp.: 74
Fiscal Year-end: 12/31/22
Steel Product Mfr & Environmental Engineering Services
N.A.I.C.S.: 331210
Byung-Yong Lee (CEO)

NATURE & LOGIS SA
Rue de Touraine, Saint-Pavace, 72190, Nantes, France
Tel.: (33) 243811503
Web Site: http://www.natureetlogis.fr
Year Founded: 2009
MLNAT—(EUR)
Sales Range: Less than $1 Million
Civil Engineering Services
N.A.I.C.S.: 237990
Thadde Girandier (Chm, CEO & Dir-IR)

NATURE ENERGY TECHNOLOGY HOLDINGS LIMITED
95 Yueshan Road, Yuecheng Town, Jiangyin, Jiangsu, China
Tel.: (86) 51086683831   Ky
Web Site: http://www.jyhyne.com
Year Founded: 2011
1597—(HKG)
Holding Company
N.A.I.C.S.: 551112
Cheng Liquan Richard (Chm)

NATURE GROUP PLC
Ordnance House 31 Pier Road, Saint Helier, JE4 8PW, Jersey
Tel.: (44) 1841 533611
Web Site: http://www.ngrp.com
Rev.: $15,033,605
Assets: $27,939,935
Liabilities: $21,348,235
Net Worth: $6,591,701
Earnings: ($4,143,505)
Emp.: 67
Fiscal Year-end: 12/31/16
Waste Water Treatment Services
N.A.I.C.S.: 562211

NATURE HOME HOLDING LIMITED
Suite 2601 26/F Tower 2 The Gateway Harbour City, Tsim Sha Tsui, Kowloon, China (Hong Kong)
Tel.: (852) 28586665   Ky
Web Site: http://www.nature-home.com.hk
Rev.: $490,373,077
Assets: $762,170,920
Liabilities: $420,648,174
Net Worth: $341,522,746
Earnings: $22,029,243
Emp.: 4,964
Fiscal Year-end: 12/31/19
Wood Flooring
N.A.I.C.S.: 321918
Alex Kwok Keung Lai (CFO & Sec)

Subsidiaries:

Nature Flooring Industries Inc. (1)
40 Lloyd Ave Ste 306, Malvern, PA 19355
Tel.: (610) 280-9800
Web Site: http://www.nature-flooring.com
Flooring Product Mfr & Distr
N.A.I.C.S.: 321918

Nature Home (China) Co., Ltd. (1)
No 8 Longpan West Rd New District Shunde, Foshan, Guangdong, China
Tel.: (86) 75722824288
Web Site: http://www.natureflooring.org
Wood Flooring Product Distr
N.A.I.C.S.: 423310

NATURE WOOD GROUP LIMITED
Avenida da Amizade no 1287 Chong Fok Centro Comercial 13 E, Macau, China (Macau)
Tel.: (853) 28553594   VG

Web Site: https://www.nature-wood.com
Year Founded: 2011
NWGL—(NASDAQ)
Rev.: $55,339,277
Assets: $68,046,687
Liabilities: $80,538,363
Net Worth: ($12,491,676)
Earnings: $4,778,895
Emp.: 318
Fiscal Year-end: 12/31/22
Wood Product Mfr & Distr
N.A.I.C.S.: 321999
Jianjun Zeng *(CEO)*

NATURE'S DISCOUNT, INC.
Bridge Street Mall, Bridgetown, BB11103, Barbados
Tel.: (246) 6259500
Web Site:
https://www.naturesdiscount.com
Emp.: 100
Food & Health Supplement Retailer
N.A.I.C.S.: 456191

NATURE'S PATH FOODS INC.
9100 Van Horne Way, Richmond, V6X 1W3, BC, Canada
Tel.: (604) 248-8777
Web Site:
http://www.naturespath.com
Year Founded: 1985
Sales Range: $75-99.9 Million
Emp.: 375
Organic & Natural Breakfast Food Mfr
N.A.I.C.S.: 311230
Arran Stephens *(Co-Founder)*

NATURECELL CO., LTD
5F 10 Gukhoe-daero 76-gil, Yeongdeungpo, Seoul, 150-870, Korea (South)
Tel.: (82) 25454137
Web Site:
https://www.naturecell.co.kr
Year Founded: 1960
007390—(KRS)
Rev.: $16,532,293
Assets: $72,114,110
Liabilities: $28,273,793
Net Worth: $43,840,318
Earnings: ($5,226,020)
Emp.: 116
Fiscal Year-end: 12/31/22
Fruit Juices & Organic Foods Mfr
N.A.I.C.S.: 311411
Jeong-Chan Ra *(CEO)*

Subsidiaries:

Naturecell Co., Ltd - Yeongyang Factory (1)
64 Jusil 1-gil, Yeongyang, Gyeongsangbukdo, Korea (South)
Tel.: (82) 7070196876
Beverages Mfr
N.A.I.C.S.: 311421

NATUREL YENILENEBILIR ENERJI TICARET AS
Kizilirmak Mahallesi 1450 Sokak ATM Plaza No 1 / 68 B Blok Kat 14, Cukurambar, 6510, Ankara, Turkiye
Tel.: (90) 3124671833
Web Site:
https://www.naturelenerji.com.tr
Year Founded: 2009
NATEN—(IST)
Rev.: $62,437,473
Assets: $473,745,718
Liabilities: $167,701,271
Net Worth: $306,044,447
Earnings: $7,783,338
Fiscal Year-end: 12/31/23
Eletric Power Generation Services
N.A.I.C.S.: 221111
Yusuf Senel *(Chm)*

NATURES ORGANICS PTY. LTD.
31 Cornhill St, Ferntree Gully, 3156, VIC, Australia
Tel.: (61) 397590300
Web Site:
http://www.naturesorganics.com.au
Year Founded: 1981
Personal Care Product Mfr
N.A.I.C.S.: 424210
Justin Dowel *(Mng Dir)*

NATUREWISE BIOTECH & MEDICALS CORP.
6F No 36 Sec 3 Bade Rd, Songshan Dist, Taipei, 105, Taiwan
Tel.: (886) 225706300
Web Site:
https://www.naturewise.com.tw
Year Founded: 2000
4732—(TAI)
Biotechnology Research & Development Services
N.A.I.C.S.: 541714
Chung-Yang Huang *(Chm & Pres)*

NATURGY ENERGY GROUP, S.A.
Avenida de America 38, 28028, Barcelona, VA, Spain
Tel.: (34) 900100339   ES
Web Site: https://www.naturgy.com
Year Founded: 1843
NTGY—(VAL)
Rev.: $36,655,514,785
Assets: $43,589,466,868
Liabilities: $32,819,987,049
Net Worth: $10,769,479,819
Earnings: $1,970,645,370
Emp.: 6,753
Fiscal Year-end: 12/31/22
Holding Company; Natural Gas & Electric Power Supplier, Marketer & Distr
N.A.I.C.S.: 551112
Francisco Reynes Massanet *(Chm & CEO)*

Subsidiaries:

Comercializadora Regulada Gas & Power, S.A. (1)
Avenida de America 38, 28028, Madrid, Spain
Tel.: (34) 900100502
Web Site:
https://www.comercializadoraregulada.es
Gas Distribution Services
N.A.I.C.S.: 221210

Companhia Distribuidora de Gas do Rio de Janeiro, S.A. (1)
Avenida Pedro Segundo, 68 Sao Cristovao, 20941 070, Rio de Janeiro, Brazil (54.2%)
Tel.: (55) 21 311 56565
Emp.: 500
Natural Gas Distr
N.A.I.C.S.: 221210
Bruno Armbrust *(CEO)*

Empresa de Distribucion Electrica Metro Oeste, S.A. (1)
Av Diogenes de la Rosa Edif 812, Albrook, Panama, Panama
Tel.: (507) 3157222
Web Site: https://www.naturgy.com.pa
Electricity Distribution Services
N.A.I.C.S.: 221122

Gas Galicia Sociedad para el Desarrollo del Gas, S.A. (1)
Rua Lisboa S N Edificio Area C, Local 31 H I J, 15703, Santiago de Compostela, Spain (68.45%)
Tel.: (34) 981569100
Web Site: http://www.gasnaturalfenosa.com
Sales Range: $75-99.9 Million
Emp.: 100
Natural Gas Distr
N.A.I.C.S.: 221210

Subsidiary (Domestic):

Gas Natural La Coruna, S.A. (2)
Rafael Alberti 8, 15008, La Coruna, Spain (56.4%)
Tel.: (34) 981173214
Natural Gas Distr
N.A.I.C.S.: 221210

Gas Natural Andalucia S.A. (1)
Rivero 8, 41004, Seville, Spain (100%)
Tel.: (34) 954 48 01 00
Natural Gas Distr
N.A.I.C.S.: 221210

Gas Natural Castilla La-Mancha, S.A. (1)
Reino Unido 6, 45005, Toledo, Spain (95%)
Tel.: (34) 0902199199
Natural Gas Distr
N.A.I.C.S.: 221210

Gas Natural Castilla y Leon, S.A. (1)
Recondo s/n Junto a la Estacion al Norte, 47007, Valladolid, Spain (90.1%)
Tel.: (34) 902 199 199
Web Site: http://www.gasnatural.com
Natural Gas Distr
N.A.I.C.S.: 221210
Juan Antonio Pazos *(Gen Mgr-North)*

Gas Natural Cegas, S.A. (1)
Grabador Esteve 14, 46004, Valencia, Spain (99.7%)
Tel.: (34) 963537700
Natural Gas Distr
N.A.I.C.S.: 221210

Gas Natural Comercializadora, S.A. (1)
Avda San Luis 77, 28033, Madrid, Spain
Tel.: (34) 900402020
Gas Distribution Services
N.A.I.C.S.: 221210

Gas Natural Europe, S.A.S. (1)
20 Avenue Andre Prothin, La Defense, 92927, Paris, Cedex, France
Tel.: (33) 181932800
Web Site: http://www.naturgy.fr
Gas Distribution Services
N.A.I.C.S.: 221210

Gas Natural Mexico, S.A. de C.V. (1)
Jaime Balmes 8 Piso 7, Mexico, 11510, Mexico (71.8%)
Tel.: (52) 5552792400
Web Site:
http://www.gasnaturalmexico.com.mx
Sales Range: $125-149.9 Million
Emp.: 200
Natural Gas Distr
N.A.I.C.S.: 221210

Gas Natural Murcia SDG, S.A. (1)
Fuensanta 6, 30012, Murcia, Spain (99.9%)
Tel.: (34) 968347560
Natural Gas Distr
N.A.I.C.S.: 221210

Gas Natural Redes GLP, S.A. (1)
Avenida de San Luis 77, 28033, Madrid, Spain
Tel.: (34) 900510511
Web Site: https://www.gnredesglp.es
Gas Distribution Services
N.A.I.C.S.: 221210

Gas Natural Rioja, S.A. (1)
Jorge Vigon 51 Bjs, 26003, Logrono, Spain (87.5%)
Tel.: (34) 900760760
Natural Gas Distr
N.A.I.C.S.: 221210

Gas Navarra, S.A. (1)
Ave Sancho El Fuerte 26, 31008, Pamplona, Spain (90%)
Tel.: (34) 948176611
Natural Gas Distr
N.A.I.C.S.: 221210

Gas Sur S.A. (1)
Anibal Pinto 215, Concepcion, Chile
Tel.: (56) 6004011200
Web Site: https://www.gassur.cl
Natural Gas Distribution Services
N.A.I.C.S.: 221210

Gasnor S.A. (1)
Necochea 122, San Miguel de Tucuman, Tucuman, Argentina
Tel.: (54) 8104441444
Web Site: http://www.gasnor.com
Natural Gas Distribution Services
N.A.I.C.S.: 221210

Gasoducto del Pacifico S.A. (1)
Avda B O Higgins 940 10th Floor, Concepcion, Chile
Tel.: (56) 412262900
Web Site: http://www.gaspacifico.com
Natural Gas Transportation Services
N.A.I.C.S.: 486210

Natural Energy, S.A. (1)
Av Corrientes 800 29th floor, Odeon Tower, Buenos Aires, Argentina
Tel.: (54) 8101226372
Web Site: https://www.naturalenergy.com.ar
Natural Gas Distribution Services
N.A.I.C.S.: 221210

Naturgy Ban, S.A. (1)
Av Corrientes 800 Torre Odeon Piso 29, C1043AAU, Buenos Aires, Argentina (50.4%)
Tel.: (54) 1143092786
Web Site: https://www.naturgy.com.ar
Emp.: 670
Natural Gas Distr
N.A.I.C.S.: 221210
Antonio Gallart Gabas *(Chm)*

Naturgy Ltd. (1)
24-28 Tara Street, Dublin, Ireland
Tel.: (353) 18849400
Web Site: http://www.naturgy.ie
Natural Gas Distribution Services
N.A.I.C.S.: 221210
Liam Faulkner *(CEO)*

Nedgia, S.A. (1)
Avenida de Americano no 38, 28028, Madrid, Spain
Tel.: (34) 900100252
Web Site: https://www.nedgia.es
Gas Distribution Services
N.A.I.C.S.: 221210

Operacion y Mantenimiento Energy, S.A. (1)
Paseo del Club Deportivo 1 Edificio 5, Parque Empresarial La Finca, ES-28223, Pozuelo de Alarcon, Madrid, Spain (100%)
Tel.: (34) 912103900
Contract Power Plant Operation & Maintenance Services
N.A.I.C.S.: 238990

UFD Distribucion Electricidad, S.A. (1)
Avenida de America 38, 28028, Madrid, Spain
Tel.: (34) 900111999
Web Site: https://www.ufd.es
Electricity Distribution Services
N.A.I.C.S.: 221122

NATURHOUSE HEALTH, S.A.
Calle Claudio Coello 91 4 Planta, 28006, Madrid, Spain
Tel.: (34) 914323853   ES
Web Site:
https://www.naturhouse.com
Year Founded: 1991
NTH—(MAD)
Rev.: $55,643,007
Assets: $53,919,859
Liabilities: $20,104,868
Net Worth: $33,814,991
Earnings: $12,415,278
Emp.: 207
Fiscal Year-end: 12/31/23
Food Products Mfr
N.A.I.C.S.: 311999
Felix Revuelta Fernandez *(Chm & CEO)*

NATURITE AGRO PRODUCTS LTD.
Sy No 711-713 Lalgadi Malakpet, R R Dist, Shamirpet, 500 078, Telangana, India

NATURITE AGRO PRODUCTS LTD.

Naturite Agro Products Ltd.—(Continued)
Tel.: (91) 4027564884
Web Site:
https://www.naturiteagroprod.com
Year Founded: 1990
538926—(BOM)
Rev.: $936,383
Assets: $2,861,519
Liabilities: $1,325,316
Net Worth: $1,536,203
Earnings: ($70,643)
Emp.: 21
Fiscal Year-end: 03/31/23
Spice Oil & Oleoresin Mfr & Distr
N.A.I.C.S.: 311942
Srinivasa Rao Sriramshetty (Chm)

NATURO INDIABULL LIMITED

1st Floor 51 Lohiya Colony 200 Feet Bye-Pass Vaishali Nagar, Jaipur, 302021, Rajasthan, India
Tel.: (91) 9928234076
Web Site:
https://www.naturoindiabull.com
Year Founded: 2016
543579—(BOM)
Rev.: $1,950,327
Assets: $3,472,202
Liabilities: $550,854
Net Worth: $2,921,348
Earnings: $124,573
Emp.: 12
Fiscal Year-end: 03/31/23
E-Commerce Site Operator
N.A.I.C.S.: 459999

NATUZZI S.P.A.

Via Iazzitiello 47, Santeramo In Colle, 70029, Bari, Italy
Tel.: (39) 0808820111   IT
Web Site: https://www.natuzzi.com
Year Founded: 1959
NTZ—(NYSE)
Rev.: $575,414,473
Assets: $452,737,862
Liabilities: $339,056,880
Net Worth: $113,680,981
Earnings: $1,581,973
Emp.: 4,053
Fiscal Year-end: 12/31/22
Leather-Upholstered Furniture Mfr, Marketer & Retailer
N.A.I.C.S.: 337121
Pasquale Natuzzi (Founder, Chm & CEO)

Subsidiaries:

I.M.P.E.-Industria Meridionale Poliuretani Espansi S.p.A. (1)
Via S Francesco a Patria 134 Localita Ponte Riccio, Qualiano, Naples, 80019, Italy
Tel.: (39) 0818198811
Web Site: http://www.impespa.it
Polyurethane Foam Mfr & Whslr
N.A.I.C.S.: 326150

Italholding S.r.l. (1)
Via Giovanni Paisiello 27, Rome, 198, Italy (100%)
Tel.: (39) 068557451
Holding Company
N.A.I.C.S.: 551112

Italsofa Bahia Ltda. (1)
Urbana 838, Simoes Filho, Salvador, 43700 000, Bahia, Brazil (97.99%)
Tel.: (55) 7135943100
Furniture Mfr & Distr
N.A.I.C.S.: 337121

Italsofa Nordeste S/A (1)
Via Urbana S/N Cia Sul, Simoes Filho, 43700-000, Bahia, Brazil
Tel.: (55) 7135943100
Web Site: http://www.natuzzi.com
Sales Range: $50-74.9 Million
Emp.: 180
Household Furniture Mfr
N.A.I.C.S.: 337121

Italsofa Romania S.R.L. (1)
B-dul Unirii Nr 40, 430232, Baia Mare, Maramures, Romania (100%)
Tel.: (40) 262207001
Web Site: http://www.natuzzi.com
Sales Range: $550-599.9 Million
Emp.: 1,400
Furniture Whslr
N.A.I.C.S.: 423210

Italsofa Shanghai Ltd. (1)
No 1433 Qixin Road, Shanghai, China (100%)
Tel.: (86) 2154544510
Web Site: http://www.italsofa.com
Sales Range: $400-449.9 Million
Emp.: 1,500
Upholstered Household Furniture Mfr
N.A.I.C.S.: 337121

Minuano Nordeste S.A. (1)
Av Sao Jose Do Caboclo S No, Pojuca, Camacari, Brazil (100%)
Tel.: (55) 7136458500
Furniture Mfr & Distr
N.A.I.C.S.: 337121

Nacon S.p.A. (1)
Via Iazzitiello 47, Santeramo In Colle, Bari, Italy (100%)
Tel.: (39) 0808820111
Furniture Whslr
N.A.I.C.S.: 423210
Pasquale Natuzzi (Chm)

Natuzzi Americas, Inc. (1)
130 W Commerce Ave, High Point, NC 27260-4906 (100%)
Tel.: (336) 887-8300
Web Site: http://www.natuzzi.com
Sales Range: $50-74.9 Million
Emp.: 70
Furniture Distr
N.A.I.C.S.: 423210
Jason W. Camp (Pres)

Natuzzi Benelux S.A. (1)
Herenthoutseweg 136, Brussels, 2200, Belgium (100%)
Tel.: (32) 14282232
Web Site: http://www.natuzzi.be
Sales Range: $25-49.9 Million
Emp.: 20
Upholstered Household Furniture Mfr
N.A.I.C.S.: 337121

Natuzzi Germany GmbH (1)
Hohenzollernring 79-83, Koln, 50672, Cologne, Germany (100%)
Tel.: (49) 221168860
Web Site: http://www.natuzzi.de
Sales Range: $25-49.9 Million
Emp.: 15
Furniture Whslr
N.A.I.C.S.: 423210

Natuzzi Iberica S.A. (1)
Monte Esquinza 30-5 Dcha, Madrid, 28010, Spain (100%)
Tel.: (34) 917460158
Web Site: http://www.natuzzifranquicia.es
Sales Range: $25-49.9 Million
Emp.: 100
Furniture Retailer
N.A.I.C.S.: 449110

Natuzzi Japan K.K. (1)
New Horizon Ebisu Building 2nd Floor 3-14-20, Higashi Shibuya-Ku, Tokyo, 150-0011, Japan (100%)
Tel.: (81) 357746013
Sales Range: $50-74.9 Million
Emp.: 4
Furniture Distr
N.A.I.C.S.: 423210

Natuzzi Russia OOO (1)
Bolshoy Zlatoustinsky Pereulok 1 Bld 1 Office 102, 101000, Moscow, Russia
Tel.: (7) 4959802438
Household Furniture Distr
N.A.I.C.S.: 423210
Olga Pavlova (Mgr-Mktg)

Natuzzi Services Limited (1)
Riverbridge House 3065 Admirals Park Anchor Boulevard, Crossways Business Park, Dartford, DA2 6SL, Kent, United Kingdom
Tel.: (44) 1322312550
Web Site: http://www.natuzzi.co.uk
Sales Range: $50-74.9 Million
Emp.: 60
Furniture Whslr
N.A.I.C.S.: 423210

Natuzzi Switzerland AG (1)
Riegistrasse 9, Zurich, 8006, Switzerland
Tel.: (41) 432683268
Web Site: http://www.natuzzi.ch
Sales Range: $50-74.9 Million
Emp.: 5
Furniture Whslr
N.A.I.C.S.: 423210

Natuzzi Trade Service S.r.l. (1)
Via Iazzitiello 47, Santeramo In Colle, Bari, 70029, Italy (100%)
Tel.: (39) 0808820111
Real Estate Agents & Brokers
N.A.I.C.S.: 531210
Cesare Laberinti (Chm)

Natuzzi Trading Shanghai Ltd (1)
Rm 803 Jiaqi Building No 666 Gubei Rd, Changning Dist, Shanghai, 200021, China
Tel.: (86) 2162080101
Sales Range: $25-49.9 Million
Emp.: 22
Household Furniture Distr
N.A.I.C.S.: 423210
Simon Hughes (Mgr-Sls & Mktg)

NATWEST GROUP PLC

Gogarburn, PO Box 1000, Edinburgh, EH12 1HQ, United Kingdom
Tel.: (44) 3707020135   UK
Web Site:
https://www.natwestgroup.com
Year Founded: 1727
NWG—(NYSE)
Rev.: $14,272,352,640
Assets: $1,061,726,178,240
Liabilities: $1,004,969,409,080
Net Worth: $56,756,769,160
Earnings: $4,496,768,640
Fiscal Year-end: 12/31/21
Financial Investment Services
N.A.I.C.S.: 551111
Alison Murray (CFO)

Subsidiaries:

Adam & Company Group plc (1)
40 Princes Street, Edinburgh, EH2 2BY, United Kingdom (100%)
Tel.: (44) 1313809500
Web Site:
https://www.adamandcompany.co.uk
Sales Range: $100-124.9 Million
Emp.: 250
Private Bank
N.A.I.C.S.: 522180

Subsidiary (Non-US):

Adam & Company International Limited (2)
Royal Bank Place 1 Glategny Esplanade, PO Box 402, Saint Peter Port, GY1 3GB, Guernsey
Tel.: (44) 1481 715055
Web Site: http://www.adambank.com
Offshore Banking & Investment Services
N.A.I.C.S.: 523150

Subsidiary (Domestic):

Adam & Company Investment Management Limited (2)
40 Princes Street, Edinburgh, EH2 2BY, United Kingdom
Tel.: (44) 1313809500
Web Site: https://adamandcompany.co.uk
Emp.: 100
Investment Management Service
N.A.I.C.S.: 523999

Capital House Investment Management Limited (1)
BNY Mellon Centre 160 Queen Victoria Street, London, EC4V 4LA, United Kingdom (100%)
Tel.: (44) 2071634300
Investment Management
N.A.I.C.S.: 523940

Coutts & Company (1)
440 Strand, London, WC2R 0QS, United Kingdom (100%)
Tel.: (44) 2077531365
Web Site: https://www.coutts.com

INTERNATIONAL PUBLIC

Sales Range: $700-749.9 Million
Emp.: 2,000
Private Bank
N.A.I.C.S.: 522180
Peter Flavel (CEO)

Subsidiary (Non-US):

Coutts & Co Channel Islands (2)
23/25 Broad Street, PO Box 6, Saint Helier, JE4 8ND, Jersey
Tel.: (44) 1534 282345
Web Site: http://www.coutts.com
Commercial Banking Services
N.A.I.C.S.: 522110

Coutts & Co Isle of Man (2)
Royal Bank House 2 Victoria Street, PO Box 59, Douglas, IM99 1DU, Isle of Man
Tel.: (44) 1624 632222
Web Site: http://www.coutts.com
Sales Range: $50-74.9 Million
Emp.: 15
Commercial Banking Services
N.A.I.C.S.: 522110

National Westminster Bank Plc (1)
 (100%)
Tel.: (44) 2070855000
Web Site: http://www.natwest.com
Rev.: $10,991,280,640
Assets: $459,838,108,160
Liabilities: $437,757,061,120
Net Worth: $22,081,047,040
Earnings: $2,791,329,280
Emp.: 13,200
Fiscal Year-end: 12/31/2017
International Banking & Financial Services
N.A.I.C.S.: 522110

Subsidiary (Domestic):

Lombard North Central PLC (2)
3 Princess Way, Redhill, RH1 1NP, Surrey, United Kingdom (100%)
Tel.: (44) 1737774111
Web Site: http://www.lombard.co.uk
Sales Range: $150-199.9 Million
Emp.: 500
International Banking & Financial Services
N.A.I.C.S.: 522110

Unit (Domestic):

NatWest Insurance Services (2)
37 Broad St, PO Box 106, Bristol, BS99 7NQ, United Kingdom (100%)
Tel.: (44) 1179263000
Web Site: http://www.natwest.com
Sales Range: $50-74.9 Million
Emp.: 100
Insurance Services
N.A.I.C.S.: 524128

NatWest Mortgage Services (2)
Priory House 38 Colmore Circus, PO Box 156, Birmingham, B4 6AL, United Kingdom (100%)
Tel.: (44) 1212343000
Web Site: http://www.natwest.com
Sales Range: $150-199.9 Million
Emp.: 500
Mortgage Company
N.A.I.C.S.: 522310

Subsidiary (US):

NatWest New York (2)
101 Park Ave 10th Fl, New York, NY 10178
Tel.: (212) 792-4099
Investment Management Service
N.A.I.C.S.: 523940

Unit (Non-US):

NatWest Personal Banking (2)
16 Library Pl, Saint Helier, JE4 8NH, Jersey
Tel.: (44) 1534282828
Commercial Banking Services
N.A.I.C.S.: 522110
Steve Camm (Mng Dir-Retail & Inlt Personal Banking)

NatWest Private Banking (2)
Tel.: (44) 8453050600
Web Site: http://www.natwest.com
Commercial Banking Services
N.A.I.C.S.: 522110

Subsidiary (Domestic):

National Westminster Home Loans Limited (2)

AND PRIVATE COMPANIES — NATWEST GROUP PLC

15 Bishopsgate, PO Box 34, London, EC2M 3UR, United Kingdom **(100%)**
Tel.: (44) 1274394611
Web Site: http://www.natwest.com
Sales Range: $600-649.9 Million
Emp.: 2,500
Home Mortgage Finance
N.A.I.C.S.: 522310

National Westminster Life Assurance Limited (2)
Trinity Quay Avon Street, Bristol, BS2 0YY, United Kingdom
Tel.: (44) 1179404040
Investment Management Service
N.A.I.C.S.: 523940

Subsidiary (US):

RBS Holdings USA Inc. (2)
600 Washington Blvd, Stamford, CT 06901 **(100%)**
Tel.: (203) 897-2700
Holding Company; Investment Banking & Securities Brokerage Services
N.A.I.C.S.: 551111
Edwin L. Netzger *(Pres)*

Subsidiary (Domestic):

RBS Securities Inc. (3)
600 Washington Blvd, Stamford, CT 06901 **(100%)**
Tel.: (203) 897-2700
Web Site: http://mib.rbs.com
Sales Range: $450-499.9 Million
Emp.: 525
Investment Banking & Securities Dealing Services
N.A.I.C.S.: 523150

Nordisk Renting AB (1)
Jakobsbergsgatan 13 8th floor, 111 44, Stockholm, Sweden
Tel.: (46) 729815002
Web Site: https://www.nordiskrenting.se
Real Estate Rental Services
N.A.I.C.S.: 531190

Subsidiary (Non-US):

Nordisk Renting Oy (2)
Etelaesplanadi 12 4th Fl, Helsinki, 00130, Finland
Web Site: http://www.nordiskrenting.fi
Sales Range: $50-74.9 Million
Emp.: 5
Property Rental & Leasing Services
N.A.I.C.S.: 531110

Privilege Insurance Company Limited (1)
The Wharf Neville Street, Leeds, LS1 4AZ, United Kingdom
Tel.: (44) 800 051 6990
Web Site: http://www.privilege.com
Automobile & Home Insurance Services
N.A.I.C.S.: 524126

RBS Holdings N.V. (1)
Gustav Mahlerlaan 350, 1082 ME, Amsterdam, Netherlands
Tel.: (31) 206289393
Web Site: http://www.rbs.nl
Rev.: $66,276,450
Assets: $3,362,131,350
Liabilities: $3,159,595,950
Net Worth: $202,535,400
Earnings: $17,670,000
Emp.: 20
Fiscal Year-end: 12/31/2019
Bank Holding Company
N.A.I.C.S.: 551111

Subsidiary (Non-US):

JSC SB RBS (Kazakhstan) Limited (2)
45 Kazhymukan Street, Almaty, 050059, Kazakhstan
Tel.: (7) 7272 58 15 05
Web Site: http://www.rbs.com
Commercial Banking Services
N.A.I.C.S.: 522110

RBS (New Zealand) Limited (2)
254 Church Street, PO Box 13, Onehunga, Auckland, 1061, New Zealand
Tel.: (64) 96360696
Web Site: https://www.rbs.co.nz
Electronic Equipment Mfr & Distr
N.A.I.C.S.: 334419

RBS Asia Corporate Finance Limited. (2)
29/F AIA Central 1 Connaught Rd, Central, China (Hong Kong)
Tel.: (852) 27003000
Investment Management Service
N.A.I.C.S.: 523940

RBS Asia Limited (2)
7 Fl Linken House Taikoo Place 979 Kings Rd, Quarry Bay, China (Hong Kong)
Tel.: (852) 2966 2800
Securities Brokerage Services
N.A.I.C.S.: 523150
Donald Workman *(Chm-Asia Pacific)*

RBS Business Services Private Limited (2)
4th Floor Trade World A Wing Kamala Mills Compound, Senapati Bapat Marg Lower Parel, Mumbai, 400013, India
Tel.: (91) 2240021534
Financial Management Services
N.A.I.C.S.: 523999

RBS Corporate Finance (Australia) Limited (2)
L 29 88 Phillip St Abn Amro Twr, Sydney, 2000, NSW, Australia
Tel.: (61) 282595000
Web Site: http://www.rbs.com.au
General Insurance Services
N.A.I.C.S.: 524210

RBS Equity Capital Markets (Australia) Limited (2)
RBS Tower 88 Phillip Street, Sydney, 2000, NSW, Australia
Tel.: (61) 282595000
Financial Management Services
N.A.I.C.S.: 523999

Subsidiary (US):

RBS Finance NV (North America), Inc. (2)
101 Park Ave 10th Fl, New York, NY 10178
Tel.: (212) 269-1700
Financial Management Services
N.A.I.C.S.: 523999

Subsidiary (Non-US):

RBS Global Banking (Luxembourg) S.A. (2)
Espace Kirchberg The Square Building A-40 Avenue J F Kennedy, 1855, Luxembourg, Luxembourg
Tel.: (352) 270330355
Commercial Banking Services
N.A.I.C.S.: 522110

RBS Holdings (Australia) Pty Limited (2)
88 Phillip St, Sydney, 2000, NSW, Australia
Tel.: (61) 2 8259 5000
Sales Range: $150-199.9 Million
Emp.: 330
Investment Banking Services
N.A.I.C.S.: 523150

The Royal Bank of Scotland (China) Co. Limited (2)
25th Fl Azia Ctr 1233 Lu Jia Zui Ring Road, Pudong New Area, Shanghai, China
Tel.: (86) 21 2893 9600
Web Site: http://www.rbsbank.com.cn
Commercial Banking Services
N.A.I.C.S.: 522110

The Royal Bank of Scotland N.V. (2)
Tel.: (31) 206288900
Web Site: http://www.abnamro.com
Sales Range: $1-4.9 Billion
Emp.: 20,000
Commercial & Investment Banking
N.A.I.C.S.: 522110

Subsidiary (Non-US):

RBS Bank (Romania) SA (3)
Cladirea Lakeview Str Barbu Vacarescu nr 301-311 Etaj 3 Sector 2, Bucharest, 20276, Romania
Tel.: (40) 21 20 20 800
Web Site: http://www.rbs.ro
Commercial Banking Services
N.A.I.C.S.: 522110

RBS Capital Markets (Canada) Limited (3)
Royal Bank Plaza 200 Bay Street, PO Box 114, T-D Ctr, Toronto, M5J 2W7, ON, Canada **(100%)**
Tel.: (416) 842-7575
Sales Range: $50-74.9 Million
Emp.: 50
Investment Banking & Securities Brokerage Services
N.A.I.C.S.: 523150

Branch (Domestic):

RBS Capital Markets (Canada) Ltd. - Montreal (4)
1 Place Ville Marie Suite 300, Montreal, H3B 4R8, QC, Canada **(100%)**
Tel.: (514) 878-7000
Web Site: http://gbm.rbs.com
Sales Range: $50-74.9 Million
Emp.: 8
Investment Banking & Securities Brokerage Services
N.A.I.C.S.: 523150

Subsidiary (Non-US):

RBS Financial Services (India) Private Limited (2)
A-6 1st Floor Ring Road South Extension Part 1, New Delhi, 110049, India
Tel.: (91) 11 4614 2493
Web Site: http://www.rbs.in
Financial Management Services
N.A.I.C.S.: 523999

RBS Group (Australia) Pty. Limited (3)
88 Phillip Street, Sydney, 2000, NSW, Australia
Tel.: (61) 282595000
Web Site: http://www.rbs.com
Sales Range: $500-549.9 Million
Emp.: 100
Holding Company; Investment Banking, Brokerage & Equity Investment Services
N.A.I.C.S.: 551112

Subsidiary (Domestic):

RBS Hollandsche N.V. (3)
Gustav Mahlerlaan 350, Postbus 12925, 1082 ME, Amsterdam, Netherlands
Tel.: (31) 204649999
Commercial Banking Services
N.A.I.C.S.: 522110

Subsidiary (Non-US):

RBS Securities Japan Limited (3)
Atago Green Hills MORI Tower 2-5-1 Atago, Minato-ku, Tokyo, 105-6232, Japan **(100%)**
Tel.: (81) 362663500
Sales Range: $50-74.9 Million
Emp.: 100
Securities Brokerage & Dealing Services
N.A.I.C.S.: 523150

The Royal Bank of Scotland - France (3)
94 Boulevard Haussmann, 75008, Paris, France **(100%)**
Tel.: (33) 155062212
Web Site: http://www.mib.rbs.com
Private Equity Banking Services
N.A.I.C.S.: 522180

The Royal Bank of Scotland Asia Limited (3)
7/F Seoul Finance Center 136 Sejongdaero, Jung-gu, Seoul, 100-768, Korea (South)
Tel.: (82) 2 2131 6400
Web Site: http://www.rbs.com
Commercial Banking Services
N.A.I.C.S.: 522110

Representative Office (Non-US):

The Royal Bank of Scotland N.V. - Athens (3)
45 Akti Miaouli, Piraeus, 18536, Greece
Tel.: (30) 210 459 6500
Sales Range: $50-74.9 Million
Emp.: 100
Commercial Banking & Financial Services
N.A.I.C.S.: 522110

The Royal Bank of Scotland N.V. - Bangkok (3)
3-4 Fl Bangkok City Tower 179/3 S Sathorn Rd, Sathorn, 10120, Thailand
Tel.: (66) 2 679 5900
Web Site: http://mib.rbs.com
Commercial Banking Services
N.A.I.C.S.: 522110

The Royal Bank of Scotland N.V. - Brussels (3)
Rue de la Chancellerie 17 A, 1000, Brussels, Belgium
Tel.: (32) 2 546 0546
Web Site: http://www.rbs.be
Commercial Banking Services
N.A.I.C.S.: 522110

The Royal Bank of Scotland N.V. - Doha (3)
Qatar Financial Centre Tower Level 12 West Bay, Doha, Qatar
Tel.: (974) 4 4967 498
Web Site: http://mib.rbs.com
Commercial Banking Services
N.A.I.C.S.: 522110

The Royal Bank of Scotland N.V. - Istanbul (3)
Tanbury Ali Efendi Sokak 13, Etiler, Istanbul, 34337, Turkiye
Tel.: (90) 2123594040
Web Site: http://www.rbs.com.tr
Sales Range: $100-124.9 Million
Emp.: 200
Commercial Banking & Financial Services
N.A.I.C.S.: 522110

The Royal Bank of Scotland N.V. - Madrid (3)
Jose Ortega y Gasset 29, Madrid, 28006, Spain
Tel.: (34) 91 438 5100
Sales Range: $150-199.9 Million
Emp.: 200
Loans, Bonds, Financial Transaction & Equity Investment Services
N.A.I.C.S.: 523150

The Royal Bank of Scotland N.V. - Mumbai (3)
7th Floor 4 North Avenue Maker Maxity Bandra Kurla Complex, Bandra East, Mumbai, 400 051, India
Tel.: (91) 22 6623 2400
Web Site: http://www.rbs.in
Sales Range: $100-124.9 Million
Emp.: 250
International Banking
N.A.I.C.S.: 522299

The Royal Bank of Scotland N.V. - Prague (3)
Jungmannova 24, 110 00, Prague, Czech Republic
Tel.: (420) 244 051 111
Web Site: http://www.rbs.cz
Commercial Banking Services
N.A.I.C.S.: 522110

The Royal Bank of Scotland N.V. - Rome (3)
Via Po 25a, 00198, Rome, Italy
Tel.: (39) 068537851
Web Site: http://mib.rbs.com
Sales Range: $75-99.9 Million
Emp.: 10
Commercial Banking & Financial Services
N.A.I.C.S.: 522110

The Royal Bank of Scotland N.V. - Singapore (3)
Level 26 One Raffles Quay South Tower, Singapore, 048583, Singapore
Tel.: (65) 65188888
Sales Range: $100-124.9 Million
Emp.: 200
Commercial Banking & Financial Services
N.A.I.C.S.: 522110
Madan Menon *(Head-Intl Banking-Asia Pacific)*

The Royal Bank of Scotland N.V. - Sydney (3)
Level 23 88 Phillip Street, Sydney, Australia
Tel.: (61) 2 8259 5000
Web Site: http://www.rbs.com.au
Commercial Banking Services
N.A.I.C.S.: 522110

NATWEST GROUP PLC

NatWest Group plc—(Continued)

The Royal Bank of Scotland N.V. - Tokyo (3)
Shin-Marunouchi Center Building 1-6-2
Marunouchi, Chiyoda-ku, Tokyo, 100-0005, Japan
Tel.: (81) 3 6266 3000
Sales Range: $150-199.9 Million
Emp.: 400
Commercial Banking Services
N.A.I.C.S.: 522110
Kazuhiko Shibata (Branch Mgr)

The Royal Bank of Scotland N.V. - Vienna (3)
Karntner Ring 5-7/7, Vienna, 1010, Austria
Tel.: (43) 1 205 1160 1213
Web Site: http://mib.rbs.com
Sales Range: $50-74.9 Million
Emp.: 15
Commercial Banking & Financial Services
N.A.I.C.S.: 522110

The Royal Bank of Scotland N.V. - Zurich (3)
Lerchenstrasse 24, PO Box 2921, CH-8022, Zurich, Switzerland
Tel.: (41) 44 286 1200
Web Site: http://mib.rbs.com
Sales Range: $200-249.9 Million
Emp.: 360
Commercial Banking & Financial Services
N.A.I.C.S.: 522110

RBS Invoice Finance Limited (1)
50 Smith House Elmwood Avenue, Feltham, TW13 7QD, Mddx, United Kingdom (100%)
Tel.: (44) 8706000520
Web Site: http://www.rbsif.co.uk
Sales Range: $350-399.9 Million
Emp.: 600
International Banking & Financial Services
N.A.I.C.S.: 522110

RoyScot Trust plc (1)
3 Princess Way, Redhill, RH1 1NP, Surrey, United Kingdom (100%)
Tel.: (44) 1242224455
Banking Services
N.A.I.C.S.: 522320

Royal Bank Equity Finance (1)
12-13 Saint Andrew Square, Edinburgh, EH2 2AF, United Kingdom (100%)
Tel.: (44) 1315233333
Web Site: http://gbm.rbs.com
Sales Range: $50-74.9 Million
Emp.: 50
Private Equity Bank
N.A.I.C.S.: 522180

Subsidiary (Domestic):

Whiteaway Laidlaw Bank Limited (2)
Queens Court 24 Queen Street, Manchester, M2 5HX, United Kingdom
Tel.: (44) 1618335444
Web Site: http://www.wlbank.co.uk
Sales Range: $25-49.9 Million
Emp.: 50
Banking Services
N.A.I.C.S.: 522110

Royal Scottish Assurance plc (1)
31 St Andrew Square, Edinburgh, EH2 2AG, United Kingdom (100%)
Tel.: (44) 1315233333
Web Site: http://www.rbs.co.uk
Sales Range: $50-74.9 Million
Emp.: 50
Banking Services
N.A.I.C.S.: 522320

Tesco Personal Finance Limited (1)
George House 4th Floor, 36 North Hanover Street, Glasgow, G1 2YG, United Kingdom
Tel.: (44) 8457104010
Financial & Insurance Services; Owned 50% by The Royal Bank of Scotland Group plc & 50% by Tesco plc
N.A.I.C.S.: 522210
Andrew Thomas Higginson (Chm)

The One Account Ltd. (1)
Amsterdam Place Amsterdam Way, Norwich, NR6 6JA, United Kingdom
Tel.: (44) 345 301 0101
Web Site: https://www.oneaccount.com

Online Transaction Services
N.A.I.C.S.: 522320

The Royal Bank of Scotland (Gibraltar) Limited (1)
(100%)
Tel.: (350) 73200
Web Site: http://www.rbs.co.uk
Offshore Banking Services
N.A.I.C.S.: 522320

The Royal Bank of Scotland (Guernsey) Limited (1)
Royal Bank Place 1 Glategny Esplanade, Saint Peter Port, GY1 4BQ, Guernsey (100%)
Tel.: (44) 1481710051
Sales Range: $350-399.9 Million
Emp.: 1,000
Offshore Banking Services
N.A.I.C.S.: 522320

Subsidiary (Domestic):

The Royal Bank of Scotland Trust Company (Guernsey) Limited (2)
Royal Bank Pl, PO Box 62, 1 Glategny Esplanade, GY1 4BQ, Saint Peter Port, Guernsey (100%)
Tel.: (44) 1481710051
Web Site: http://www.rbsint.com
Offshore Banking Services
N.A.I.C.S.: 522320

The Royal Bank of Scotland (I.O.M.) Limited (1)
2 Athol Street, 2 Victoria St, Douglas, IM99 1AN, Isle of Man (100%)
Tel.: (44) 1624646464
Offshore Banking Services
N.A.I.C.S.: 522320

Subsidiary (Domestic):

Isle of Man Bank Limited (2)
2 Athol St, Douglas, IM99 1AN, Isle of Man
Tel.: (44) 1624637000
Investment Banking Services
N.A.I.C.S.: 523150

The Royal Bank of Scotland (Jersey) Ltd. (1)
PO Box 678, Saint Helier, JE4 8YN, Jersey (100%)
Tel.: (44) 153459215
Web Site: http://www.rbs.co.uk
Offshore Banking Services
N.A.I.C.S.: 522320

Subsidiary (Domestic):

The Royal Bank of Scotland Trust Company (Jersey) Limited (2)
71 Bath St, PO Box 64, Saint Helier, JE4 8PJ, Jersey (100%)
Tel.: (44) 1534285500
Web Site: http://www.rbs.co.uk
Sales Range: $600-649.9 Million
Emp.: 2,000
Offshore Banking
N.A.I.C.S.: 522320

The Royal Bank of Scotland Group - Investor Relations (1)
280 Bishopsgate, London, EC2M 4RB, United Kingdom
Tel.: (44) 2076721758
Web Site: http://www.investors.rbs.com
Investor Relations Services
N.A.I.C.S.: 541820

The Royal Bank of Scotland International (Holdings) Limited (1)
71 Bath St, Saint Helier, JE2 4SU, Jersey
Tel.: (44) 1534285200
Investment Management Service
N.A.I.C.S.: 523940
Wendy Phillis (Chief Risk Officer-RBS Intl)

The Royal Bank of Scotland plc (1)
Web Site: http://www.rbs.co.uk
Personal, Commercial & Investment Banking Services
N.A.I.C.S.: 522110

Subsidiary (Domestic):

Williams & Glyn Limited (2)
135 Bishopsgate, London, EC2M 3UR, United Kingdom

Tel.: (44) 20 7085 5000
Web Site: http://rbsbranchinformation.co.uk
Personal, Commercial & Investment Banking
N.A.I.C.S.: 522110

Ulster Bank Ireland Limited (1)
Tel.: (353) 16084000
Sales Range: $5-14.9 Billion
Emp.: 2,000
Commercial & Private Banking Services
N.A.I.C.S.: 522110
Bobbie Bergin (Dir-Comm & Corp Svcs)

Subsidiary (Non-US):

Ulster Bank Limited (2)
11-16 Donegall Square East, Belfast, BT1 5UB, N Ireland, United Kingdom (100%)
Tel.: (44) 2890276000
Web Site: http://www.ulsterbank.co.uk
Commercial & Private Banking
N.A.I.C.S.: 522110

NAUKA-SVYAZ OAO

2-ya Khutorskaya st House 38A
Building 15, Moscow, 127287, Russia
Tel.: (7) 4955029092
Web Site: https://oaonsv.ru
Year Founded: 1999
NSVZ—(MOEX)
Sales Range: Less than $1 Million
Telecommunication Services
N.A.I.C.S.: 517810
Yashchenko Alexander Vyacheslavovich (Chm)

NAURA TECHNOLOGY GROUP CO., LTD.

No 8 Wenchang Avenue Beijing Economic-Technological, No 1 Jiuxianqiao East Road Chao Yang District, Beijing, 100015, China
Tel.: (86) 1057846789
Web Site: https://www.naura.com
Year Founded: 2001
002371—(SSE)
Rev.: $3,109,891,673
Assets: $7,553,018,191
Liabilities: $4,056,447,858
Net Worth: $3,496,570,333
Earnings: $549,184,010
Fiscal Year-end: 12/31/23
Electronic Equipment & Component Mfr
N.A.I.C.S.: 334419
Jinrong Zhao (Chm)

Subsidiaries:

Beijing NAURA Microelectronics Equipment Co., Ltd. (1)
No 8 Wenchang Avenue, Economic and Tech Dev Zone, Beijing, 100176, China
Web Site: http://www.naura.com
Electronic Production Equipment Mfr
N.A.I.C.S.: 811210

Subsidiary (US):

Akrion Systems, LLC (2)
6330 Hedgewood Dr Ste 150, Allentown, PA 18106
Tel.: (610) 391-9200
Web Site: http://www.akrionsystems.com
Batch-Immersion & Single-Wafer Wet Cleaning Systems for the Semiconductor Industry Mfr
N.A.I.C.S.: 334413
Ismail Kashkoush (CTO & Gen Mgr- New Product & New Market Dev)

Subsidiary (Domestic):

Goldfinger Technologies LLC (3)
6330 Hedgewood Dr Ste 150, Allentown, PA 18106-9268
Tel: (714) 445-2000
Semiconductor Machinery
N.A.I.C.S.: 333242

Beijing NAURA New Energy Technology Co., Ltd. (1)
No 1 Jiuxianqiao East Road, Chaoyang Dist, Beijing, 100015, China

INTERNATIONAL PUBLIC

Tel.: (86) 1064363680
Semiconductor Equipment Mfr
N.A.I.C.S.: 334413

Beijing NAURA Vacuum Technology Co., Ltd. (1)
Bldg M4 No 1 Jiuxianqiao East Road, Chaoyang Dist, Beijing, 100015, China
Tel.: (86) 1084572692
Semiconductor Equipment Mfr
N.A.I.C.S.: 334413

Beijing Sevenstar Electronics Technology Co., Ltd. (1)
Bldg M2 No1 Jiuxianqiao East Road, Chaoyang Dist, Beijing, 100015, China
Tel.: (86) 1064362934
Semiconductor Equipment Mfr
N.A.I.C.S.: 334413

Beijing Sevenstar Flow Co., Ltd. (1)
No 8 Wenchang Avenue, Economic and Technological Development Zone, Beijing, 100176, China
Tel.: (86) 1056178013
Web Site: http://www.en.mfcsevenstar.com
Gas Flow Measurement & Control Product Mfr
N.A.I.C.S.: 334513

NAURA Akrion Inc. (1)
6330 Hedgewood Dr Ste 150, Allentown, PA 18106
Tel.: (610) 391-9200
Web Site: http://www.naura-akrion.com
Water Treatment Equipment Distr
N.A.I.C.S.: 423850
Jun Wu (Pres & CEO)

Sevenstar Semiconductor Technologies Co., Ltd. (1)
No 6 Zhuyuan 3rd Street, Beijing Tianzhi Export Proecssing Zone Shunyi Dist, Beijing, 101312, China
Tel.: (86) 1061468620
Semiconductor Equipment Mfr
N.A.I.C.S.: 334413

NAUTICAWT LIMITED

12 Tai Seng Link 05-01A, Singapore, 534233, Singapore
Tel.: (65) 62982671   SG
Web Site: http://www.nauticawt.com
Year Founded: 2011
42D—(CAT)
Assets: $1,632,733
Liabilities: $1,319,652
Net Worth: $313,081
Earnings: ($669,822)
Fiscal Year-end: 12/31/22
Offshore Engineering Services
N.A.I.C.S.: 541330
John Gronbech (Founder & CEO)

Subsidiaries:

AWT International (Asia) Sdn. Bhd. (1)
Lot A Level 16 Tower 2 Etiqa Towers, Kuala Lumpur, 50450, Malaysia
Tel.: (60) 321623127
Emp.: 6
Engineering Consulting Services
N.A.I.C.S.: 541330

NAUTILUS PLUS INC

3550 1ere Rue, St. Hubert, Longueuil, J3Y 8Y5, QC, Canada
Tel.: (514) 666-5814
Web Site:
http://www.nautilusplus.com
Sales Range: $75-99.9 Million
Emp.: 850
Fitness Center
N.A.I.C.S.: 713940
Richard Blais (Pres & Gen Mgr)

NAUVATA ENGINEERING PVT. LTD

No 42 A Block 6th Floor Brigade Software Park 27th Cross BSK-II Stage, Bengaluru, 560 070, India
Tel.: (91) 80 67209100
Web Site: http://www.nauvata.com

Year Founded: 2005
Engineering & Project Management Services
N.A.I.C.S.: 541330
Ashwin Raikar *(Founder, CEO & Mng Dir)*

Subsidiaries:

Litwin PEL LLC (1)
PO Box 44715, Mussaffah, Abu Dhabi, United Arab Emirates
Tel.: (971) 25070100
Web Site: http://www.litwinme.ae
Oil & Gas Field Engineering Services
N.A.I.C.S.: 213112
Ashwin Raikar *(CEO)*

NAV CANADA

77 Metcalfe Street, PO Box 3411, Station T, Ottawa, K1P 5L6, ON, Canada
Tel.: (613) 563-5588 Ca
Web Site: http://www.navcanada.ca
Year Founded: 1996
Rev.: $1,099,649,880
Assets: $3,370,882,200
Liabilities: $3,349,455,480
Net Worth: $21,426,720
Earnings: $76,524,000
Emp.: 5,000
Fiscal Year-end: 08/31/19
Air Traffic Control, Flight Information Services Including Weather Briefings & Airport Advisory Services & Air Navigation & Approach Aids
N.A.I.C.S.: 488111
Marc Courtois *(Chm)*

NAVA BANKA D.D.

Tratinska 27, 10000, Zagreb, Croatia
Tel.: (385) 13096202
Web Site: http://www.navabanka.hr
NVBA-R-A—(ZAG)
Sales Range: $1-9.9 Million
Banking & Financial Services
N.A.I.C.S.: 523150
Visnjica Malisa *(Vice Chm-Supervisory Bd)*

NAVA LIMITED

Nava Bharat Chambers 6-3-1109/1 Raj Bhavan Road, Hyderabad, 500 082, Telangana, India
Tel.: (91) 4023403501
Web Site: https://www.nbventures.com
Year Founded: 1972
513023—(BOM)
Rev.: $497,599,557
Assets: $1,466,805,631
Liabilities: $691,998,639
Net Worth: $774,806,992
Earnings: $78,253,184
Emp.: 1,016
Fiscal Year-end: 03/31/22
Power Generation Services
N.A.I.C.S.: 221118
Ashok Devineni *(Chm)*

Subsidiaries:

Nava Bharat (Singapore) Pte Limited (1)
120 Lower Delta Road 05-14 Cendex Centre, Singapore, 169208, Singapore
Tel.: (65) 62788996
Sales Range: $75-99.9 Million
Emp.: 3
Eletric Power Generation Services
N.A.I.C.S.: 221118
Ashwin Devineni *(Gen Mgr)*

Nava Bharat Energy India Limited (1)
6-3-1109/1 Nava Bharat Chambers Raj Bhavan Road, Hyderabad, 500 082, Andhra Pradesh, India
Tel.: (91) 4023403501
Web Site: http://www.nbv.in

Sales Range: $75-99.9 Million
Emp.: 52
Electric Power Generation Services
N.A.I.C.S.: 221118

PT Nava Bharat Indonesia (1)
Menara Karya 28th Floor M 16 JI H R Rasuna Said Block X-5 Kav 1-2, Jakarta, 12950, Indonesia
Tel.: (62) 21 5789 5999
Web Site: http://www.nbventures.com
Eletric Power Generation Services
N.A.I.C.S.: 221118

NAVA NAKORN PUBLIC COMPANY LIMITED

999 Moo 13 Phaholyothin Rd Klong Nueng, KlongLuang, Pathumthani, 12120, Thailand
Tel.: (66) 25290031 TH
Web Site: http://www.navanakorn.co.th
Year Founded: 1971
NNCL—(THA)
Rev.: $30,352,658
Assets: $131,851,245
Liabilities: $26,470,130
Net Worth: $105,381,115
Earnings: $11,649,492
Fiscal Year-end: 12/31/23
Industrial Estate Services
N.A.I.C.S.: 531390
Perayaluk Tangsunawan *(Deputy Mng Dir-Mgmt)*

NAVAL GROUP SA

40/42 rue du Docteur Finlay, 75732, Paris, Cedex 15, France
Tel.: (33) 1 4059 5000 FR
Web Site: http://www.naval-group.com
Sales Range: $1-4.9 Billion
Emp.: 13,429
Military Ship Building & Repair Services
N.A.I.C.S.: 336611
Herve Guillou *(Chm & CEO)*

Subsidiaries:

Kership SAS (1)
ZI du Moros, BP 521, 29185, Concarneau, Cedex, France (45%)
Tel.: (33) 2 9860 6313
Web Site: http://www.kership.com
Military & Law Enforcement Ship Building & Repair Services
N.A.I.C.S.: 336611

Subsidiary (Domestic):

Kership Lorient SAS (2)
ZI de Rohu, 56000, Lorient, France
Tel.: (33) 297768910
Military & Law Enforcement Ship Building & Repair Services
N.A.I.C.S.: 336611

Naval Energies SAS (1)
40-42 rue du Docteur Finlay, 75015, Paris, Cedex, France
Tel.: (33) 140595000
Web Site: http://www.naval-energies.com
Marine Renewable Energy Services
N.A.I.C.S.: 221118
Laurent Schneider-Maunoury *(Pres)*

Naval Group Australia Pty Ltd (1)
Level 2 1 Richmond Road, PO Box 3065, Keswick, 5035, SA, Australia
Tel.: (61) 870992100
Web Site: http://www.naval-group.com.au
Maritime Environment Services
N.A.I.C.S.: 444230

Naval Group India Pte Ltd (1)
Unit No-302 3rd Floor Piramal Tower Peninsula Corporate Park, Ganpatrao Kadam Marg Lower Parel, Mumbai, 400013, India
Tel.: (91) 2268257000
Web Site: http://www.india.naval-group.com
Marine Renewable Energy Services
N.A.I.C.S.: 221118

Sirehna SA (1)

5 rue de l Halbrane, 44340, Bouguenais, France
Tel.: (33) 244765757
Web Site: http://www.sirehna.com
Emp.: 80
Maritime Environment Services
N.A.I.C.S.: 444230

NAVALO FINANCIAL SERVICES GROUP LIMITED

Level 2 Suite 4 789 Toorak Road, Hawthorn East, 3123, VIC, Australia
Tel.: (61) 1300338496 AU
Web Site: https://www.navalo.com.au
Year Founded: 2015
PYR—(ASX)
Rev.: $12,373,376
Assets: $81,794,031
Liabilities: $74,743,555
Net Worth: $7,050,477
Earnings: ($6,602,394)
Fiscal Year-end: 06/30/23
Financial Investment Services
N.A.I.C.S.: 523999
Piers Redward *(Mng Dir)*

NAVAMEDIC ASA

Henrik Ibsens gate 100, 255, Oslo, Norway
Tel.: (47) 67112540
Web Site: https://www.navamedic.com
Year Founded: 2002
NAVA—(OSL)
Rev.: $35,297,894
Assets: $35,356,734
Liabilities: $15,984,851
Net Worth: $19,371,883
Earnings: $2,718,548
Emp.: 29
Fiscal Year-end: 12/31/22
Pharmaceuticals Product Mfr
N.A.I.C.S.: 325412
Kathrine Gamborg Andreassen *(CEO)*

Subsidiaries:

Impolin AB (1)
Kanalvagen 15, 183 38, Taby, Sweden
Tel.: (46) 854499900
Web Site: https://www.impolin.se
Pharmaceutical Product Mfr & Distr
N.A.I.C.S.: 325412

Navamedic AB (1)
Goteborgsvagen 74, 433 63, Savedalen, Sweden
Tel.: (46) 313351190
Health Supplement Product Distr
N.A.I.C.S.: 456191

NAVANA GROUP OF COMPANIES

Navana Toyota 3S Center 205-207 Tejgaon I/A, Post Box 3301, Dhaka, 1208, Bangladesh
Tel.: (880) 29892911
Web Site: http://www.navana.com
Year Founded: 1953
Holding Company
N.A.I.C.S.: 551112
Shafiul Islam Kamal *(Chm)*

Subsidiaries:

Aftab Automobiles Limited (1)
125/A Motijheel Commercial Area, Dhaka, 1000, Bangladesh
Tel.: (880) 29552212
Web Site: https://www.aftabautomobiles.com
Rev.: $10,808,276
Assets: $227,193,455
Liabilities: $177,362,377
Net Worth: $49,831,079
Earnings: $37,552
Emp.: 277
Fiscal Year-end: 06/30/2023
Automobile Parts Mfr
N.A.I.C.S.: 336110
Shafiul Islam *(Chm)*

Biponen Limited (1)

Islam Chamber 13th Floor 125/A Motijheel Commercial Area, Dhaka, Bangladesh
Tel.: (880) 2 9552212
Bio-Medical & Electro-Medical Equipment Mfr
N.A.I.C.S.: 334510
Md. Anwar Hossain *(Deputy Gen Mgr)*

Navana Battery Ltd. (1)
Islam Chamber 4th Floor 125/A Motijheel Commercial Area, Dhaka, 1000, Bangladesh
Tel.: (880) 2 9552212
Sales Range: $25-49.9 Million
Emp.: 82
Automotive Battery Mfr
N.A.I.C.S.: 335910

Navana CNG Limited (1)
205-207 Tejgaon I/A Dhaka, Dhaka, 1208, Bangladesh
Tel.: (880) 29892585
Web Site: https://www.navanacng.com
Rev.: $49,286,723
Assets: $153,934,724
Liabilities: $125,984,915
Net Worth: $27,949,809
Earnings: $129,824
Emp.: 551
Fiscal Year-end: 06/30/2022
Gas Conversion Kit Mfr
N.A.I.C.S.: 339999
Shafiul Islam Kamal *(Chm)*

Navana Construction Ltd. (1)
House #35 Road #9/A, Dhanmondi, Dhaka, Bangladesh
Tel.: (880) 2 9121602
Construction Services
N.A.I.C.S.: 237990

Navana Electronics Ltd. (1)
Islam Chamber 125/A Motijheel Commercial Area, Post Box 3301, Dhaka, 1000, Bangladesh
Tel.: (880) 2 9552212
Electronic Products Mfr
N.A.I.C.S.: 334419

Navana Furniture Ltd. (1)
Islam Chamber 125/A Motijheel Commercial Area, Dhaka, 1000, Bangladesh
Tel.: (880) 2 9552212
Furniture Mfr
N.A.I.C.S.: 337214

Navana Interlinks Ltd. (1)
Islam Chamber 13th Floor, 125/A Motijheel Commercial Area, Dhaka, 1000, Bangladesh
Tel.: (880) 2 9552212
Sales Range: $50-74.9 Million
Emp.: 8
Electrical, Construction & Security Equipment Distr
N.A.I.C.S.: 423610
Kazi Mominul Hoque *(Gen Mgr)*

Navana Limited (1)
Islam Chamber 125/A Motijheel Commercial Area, Post Box 3301, Dhaka, 1000, Bangladesh
Tel.: (880) 2 9552212
Automotive Distr
N.A.I.C.S.: 441227

Navana Logistics Limited (1)
Tower Hamlet 3rd Floor, 16 Kamal Ataturk Avenue, Banani C/A, Dhaka, 1213, Bangladesh
Tel.: (880) 2 8810836
Web Site: http://www.navana-logistics.com
Shipping Services
N.A.I.C.S.: 488510

Navana Paints Ltd. (1)
388/A Tejgaon I/A, Dhaka, 1208, Bangladesh
Tel.: (880) 2 9137978
Sales Range: $25-49.9 Million
Emp.: 54
Paint Mfr & Sales
N.A.I.C.S.: 325510

Navana Real Estate Ltd. (1)
House 3/A Road 90, Gulshan-02, 1212, Dhaka, Bangladesh
Tel.: (880) 1730150390
Web Site: http://www.navana-realestate.com
Emp.: 35
Real Estate Development Services

NAVANA GROUP OF COMPANIES

Navana Group of Companies—(Continued)
N.A.I.C.S.: 485999
Shafiul Islam Kamal (Chm)

Navana Taxi Cab Co. Ltd. (1)
Plots 24 & 25 Road 6 Sector 9, Uttara, Dhaka, 1230, Bangladesh
Tel.: (880) 2 8963035
Taxi & Car Rental Services
N.A.I.C.S.: 485310

NAVARRE MINERALS LIMITED
and Principal Place of Business Level 4 100 Albert Road, PO Box 385, South Melbourne, 3205, VIC, Australia
Tel.: (61) 396927222
Web Site:
https://www.navarre.com.au
NML—(ASX)
Rev.: $3,553,967
Assets: $22,410,464
Liabilities: $1,604,776
Net Worth: $20,805,688
Earnings: $1,791,587
Fiscal Year-end: 06/30/24
Gold & Other Metal Mining Services
N.A.I.C.S.: 212220
Geoff McDermott (Mng Dir)

NAVCOM INDUSTRIES LIMITED
Nav Maharashtra House 5th Floor Opp Shaniwar Wada, Shaniwar Peth, Pune, 411 030, India
Tel.: (91) 32944144
Web Site:
http://www.navcomindustries.com
Year Founded: 1991
Sales Range: Less than $1 Million
Edible Oil Mfr
N.A.I.C.S.: 311224

NAVER CORPORATION
NAVER 1784 95 Jeongjail-ro, Bundang-gu, Seongnam, Gyeonggi-do, Korea (South)
Tel.: (82) 15883830 KR
Web Site: https://www.navercorp.com
Year Founded: 1999
NHNCF—(OTCIQ)
Rev.: $7,178,008,385
Assets: $26,526,302,989
Liabilities: $8,535,715,563
Net Worth: $17,990,587,426
Emp.: 4,381
Fiscal Year-end: 12/31/23
Software Development Services
N.A.I.C.S.: 541511
Dae-gyu Byun (Chm)

Subsidiaries:

Dongman Entertainment Corp. (1)
Room 323506 Building 5 No 1 Futong East Street, Chaoyang District, Beijing, China
Tel.: (86) 1057076671
Web Site: http://www.dongmancorp.cn
Entertainment Services
N.A.I.C.S.: 711190

Drama Inc. (1)
650 Hamilton Ave SE, Atlanta, GA 30312-3778
Tel.: (404) 600-6070
Web Site: http://www.dramainc.net
Electronic Shopping
N.A.I.C.S.: 512110
Scott Poythress (Partner)

Greenweb Service Corp. (1)
15th Floor J-platz 186 Gasan digital 1-ro, Geumcheon-gu, Seoul, Korea (South)
Tel.: (82) 262961100
Web Site: http://www.gwebscorp.com
Advertising Services
N.A.I.C.S.: 541810

LINE Corporation (1)
JR Shinjuku Miraina Tower 23rd Floor 4-1-6 Shinjuku, Shinjuku-ku, Tokyo, 160-0022, Japan
Tel.: (81) 343162050
Web Site: http://www.linecorp.com
Rev.: $2,115,482,320
Assets: $4,964,197,840
Liabilities: $3,362,538,130
Net Worth: $1,601,659,710
Earnings: ($471,484,720)
Emp.: 6,998
Fiscal Year-end: 12/31/2019
Internet Search Portal & Gaming Services
N.A.I.C.S.: 516210
In-Joon Hwang (CFO)

Line Technology Vietnam Co., Ltd. (1)
Floor 20-21 Tower 1 Capital Place Building 29 Lieu Giai Street, Ba Dinh District, Hanoi, Vietnam
Tel.: (84) 2462956360
Web Site: http://www.linetechnology.com.vn
Software Development Services
N.A.I.C.S.: 541511
Ikebe Tomohiro (Chm)

NAVER Business Platform Corp. (1)
Green Factory 6 Buljeong-ro, Bundang-gu, Seongnam, 463-824, Korea (South)
Tel.: (82) 15663880
Web Site: http://www.nbp-corp.com
Online Advertising Services
N.A.I.C.S.: 541810
Weongi Park (CEO)

NAVER China Corp. (1)
Room 1001 10th Floor Block B Fuma Building Building 1, Guangshun North Street Chaoyang District, Beijing, China
Tel.: (86) 1059646299
Web Site: http://www.navercorp.cn
Internet Search Portal Services
N.A.I.C.S.: 519290

NAVER I&S Corporation (1)
3rd 4th Fl Bundang M Tower 8 Gumi-ro, Bundang-gu, Seongnam, 463-050, Gyeonggi-do, Korea (South)
Tel.: (82) 15663950
Web Site: http://www.naverins.com
Integrated Management Support Services
N.A.I.C.S.: 541611

NAVER Labs Corp. (1)
3F Bundang M Tower 8 Gumi-ro, Bundang-gu, Seongnam, 13638, Gyeonggi-do, Korea (South)
Tel.: (82) 15226590
Web Site: http://www.naverlabs.com
Technology Research & Development Services
N.A.I.C.S.: 541715
Sangok Seok (CEO)

NHN China Corporation (1)
9th Floor Suite B Building 1 No 33 Guangshun Avenue, Wangjing, Beijing, 100102, China
Tel.: (86) 1059646000
Web Site: http://www.nhncorp.cn
Internet Service Provider
N.A.I.C.S.: 517810

NIT Service Corp. (1)
9th Floor DTC Tower 49 Daewangpangyo-ro 644beon-gil, Bundang-gu, Seongnam, Gyeonggi-do, Korea (South)
Tel.: (82) 15446573
Web Site: http://www.nits-corp.com
Network Security Services
N.A.I.C.S.: 561621

Poshmark, Inc. (1)
203 Redwood Shores Pkwy 8th Fl, Redwood City, CA 94065
Tel.: (650) 262-4771
Web Site: http://www.poshmark.com
Rev.: $326,009,000
Assets: $608,673,000
Liabilities: $191,054,000
Net Worth: $417,619,000
Earnings: ($98,329,000)
Emp.: 750
Fiscal Year-end: 12/31/2021
Online Shopping Services
N.A.I.C.S.: 423940

Studio Lico Corp. (1)
11th floor Pangyo Techone Tower 131 Bundangnaegok-ro, Bundang-gu, Seongnam, Gyeonggi-do, Korea (South)
Tel.: (82) 18337138
Web Site: https://www.studiolico.com
Animation Services
N.A.I.C.S.: 541921

NAVEXIM SA
Strada Domneasca Nr 105, 800201, Galati, Romania
Tel.: (40) 236412751
Web Site: https://www.navexim.ro
Year Founded: 1991
NAXY—(BUC)
Rev.: $162,450
Assets: $545,355
Liabilities: $241,516
Net Worth: $303,839
Earnings: $13,120
Emp.: 1
Fiscal Year-end: 12/31/23
Industrial Machinery & Equipment Whslr
N.A.I.C.S.: 423860

NAVIG8 LIMITED
First Island House Peter Street, Saint Helier, JE4 8SG, Jersey
Tel.: (44) 20 7436 8996
Web Site:
http://www.navig8group.com
Year Founded: 2007
Emp.: 350
Ship Management Services
N.A.I.C.S.: 561499
Geir Magne Karlsen (CFO)

Subsidiaries:

Navig8 Europe Ltd. (1)
2nd Floor Kinnaird House 1 Pall Mall East, London, SW1Y 5AU, United Kingdom
Tel.: (44) 20 7467 5888
Cargo Brokerage & Commercial Management Services
N.A.I.C.S.: 488320

NAVIGANT CORPORATE ADVISORS LIMITED
804 Meadows Sahar Plaza Complex J B Nagar, Andheri-Kurla Road Andheri East, Mumbai, 400 059, India
Tel.: (91) 2241204837
Web Site:
https://www.navigantcorp.com
539521—(BOM)
Rev.: $762,173
Assets: $1,283,880
Liabilities: $164,678
Net Worth: $1,119,201
Earnings: $102,884
Emp.: 5
Fiscal Year-end: 03/31/23
Financial Services
N.A.I.C.S.: 522320
Sarthak Vijlani (Founder, Chm, Mng Dir & CFO)

NAVIGATOR EQUITY SOLUTIONS SE
Laan van Diepenvoorde 3, 5582 LA, Waalre, Netherlands
Tel.: (31) 402135930
Web Site: https://navstone.eu
NUQA—(STU)
Financial Investment Services
N.A.I.C.S.: 523999
Jens Bodenkamp (Chm)

NAVIGATOR GLOBAL INVESTMENTS LIMITED
Level 21 10 Eagle Street, Brisbane, 4000, QLD, Australia
Tel.: (61) 732186200 AU
Web Site:
https://www.navigatorglobal.com.au
NGI—(ASX)
Rev.: $276,284,000

INTERNATIONAL PUBLIC

Assets: $787,854,000
Liabilities: $124,640,000
Net Worth: $663,214,000
Earnings: $66,305,000
Emp.: 306
Fiscal Year-end: 06/30/24
Wealth Management & Investing Services
N.A.I.C.S.: 523999
Amber Stoney (CFO & Sec)

Subsidiaries:

Lighthouse Investment Partners, LLC (1)
3801 PGA Blvd Ste 500, Palm Beach Gardens, FL 33410
Tel.: (561) 741-0820
Web Site:
https://www.lighthousepartners.com
Investment Management Service
N.A.I.C.S.: 541618
Jacks Swan (Exec Mng Dir)

Holding (Domestic):

Mesirow Advanced Strategies, Inc. (2)
353 N Clark St, Chicago, IL 60654
Tel.: (312) 595-6000
Investment Management Service
N.A.I.C.S.: 523940

Lighthouse Partners Limited (HK) (1)
20/F Central Tower 28 Queen's Road, Central, China (Hong Kong)
Tel.: (852) 2 159 9612
Web Site:
http://www.lighthousepartners.com
Emp.: 2
Investment Management Service
N.A.I.C.S.: 541618
Barry Timmins (Mgr)

Lighthouse Partners NY LLC (1)
680 5th Ave 17th Fl, New York, NY 10019
Tel.: (212) 588-0342
Web Site:
http://www.lighthousepartners.com
Sales Range: $25-49.9 Million
Emp.: 80
Investment Management Service
N.A.I.C.S.: 541618
Robert P. Swan (COO)

Lighthouse Partners UK LLC (1)
83 Baker St Ste 503, London, W1U 6AG, United Kingdom
Tel.: (44) 2070347031
Web Site:
http://www.lighthousepartners.com
Investment Management Service
N.A.I.C.S.: 541618
Peter Coates (Mng Dir)

NAVIGATOR HOLDINGS LTD.
The Verde 10 Bressenden Place, London, SW1E5DH, United Kingdom
Tel.: (44) 2073404850 MH
Web Site:
https://www.navigatorgas.com
NVGS—(NYSE)
Rev.: $473,792,000
Assets: $2,096,738,000
Liabilities: $923,326,000
Net Worth: $1,173,412,000
Earnings: $53,473,000
Emp.: 155
Fiscal Year-end: 12/31/22
Natural Gas Transportation
N.A.I.C.S.: 486210
David J. Butters (Chm)

NAVIGAZIONE MONTANARI S.P.A.
Via Ceccarini 36, 61032, Fano, Pesaro, Italy
Tel.: (39) 07218801 IT
Web Site: http://www.navmont.com
Year Founded: 1889
Sales Range: $150-199.9 Million
Emp.: 336
Maritime Transportation Services

N.A.I.C.S.: 483211
Corrado A. Montanari *(Chm & Mng Dir)*

NAVIGO INVEST AB
Stora Nygatan 31, 411 08, Gothenburg, Sweden
Tel.: (46) 702034080
Web Site: https://navigoinvest.com
PEGRO.PREF—(OMX)
Rev.: $191,390,920
Assets: $243,431,182
Liabilities: $193,090,274
Net Worth: $50,340,909
Earnings: $8,366,142
Emp.: 609
Fiscal Year-end: 12/31/20
Investment Services
N.A.I.C.S.: 523999
Peter Sandberg *(Chm & Partner)*

NAVIMO INTERNATIONAL
15 rue Ingenieur Verriere, BP 435, 56325, Lorient, Cedex, France
Tel.: (33) 2 9787 3659
Web Site: http://www.plastimo.com
Year Founded: 2003
Sales Range: $125-149.9 Million
Emp.: 750
Recreational Boat Equipment Mfr & Supplier
N.A.I.C.S.: 336612

Subsidiaries:

Navimo Espana (1)
Poligono Industrial Les Hortes, Resseguidor, 08302, Mataro, Spain
Tel.: (34) 937507504
Web Site: http://www.navimo.es
Sales Range: $25-49.9 Million
Emp.: 30
Marine Products Distr
N.A.I.C.S.: 423910

Navimo Holland BV (1)
Industrieweg 4, 2871 JE, Schoonhoven, Netherlands
Tel.: (31) 182320522
Web Site: http://www.navimo.nl
Sales Range: $25-49.9 Million
Emp.: 15
Marine Products Distr
N.A.I.C.S.: 423910

Navimo Nordic AB (1)
Lundenvagen 2, 473 31, Henan, Sweden
Tel.: (46) 30436060
Web Site: http://www.navinordic.com
Sales Range: $50-74.9 Million
Emp.: 15
Marine Products Distr
N.A.I.C.S.: 423910
Michael Anderson *(Gen Mgr)*

Navimo UK Ltd. (1)
Hamilton Business Park Botley Road, Hedge End, Southampton, SO30 2HE, United Kingdom
Tel.: (44) 1489778850
Web Site: http://www.plastimo.com
Rev.: $41,000,000
Emp.: 248
Marine Products Mfr
N.A.I.C.S.: 339920

PLASTIMO AMS (1)
Rua Teofilo Otoni n 48, 20090-070, Rio de Janeiro, Brazil
Tel.: (55) 21 821 45119
Recreational Boat Distr
N.A.I.C.S.: 423910

Plastimo Marine Roumanie Srl (1)
Str Negoiu 153, Municipiului Fagaras, Brasov, Romania
Tel.: (40) 26821006
Recreational Boat Distr
N.A.I.C.S.: 423910

Plastimo USA, Inc. (1)
7455 16th St E Ste 107, Sarasota, FL 34243
Tel.: (941) 360-1888
Web Site: http://www.lalizas.com
Emp.: 4

Marine Products Distr
N.A.I.C.S.: 423910
Spyros Spinoulas *(CEO)*

NAVIN FLUORINE INTERNATIONAL LTD
Office No 602 Natraj by Rustomjee Near Western Express Highway, Sir Mathuradas Vasanji Road Andheri East, Mumbai, 400069, Maharashtra, India
Tel.: (91) 2266509999
Web Site: https://www.nfil.in
Year Founded: 1967
NAVINFLUOR—(NSE)
Rev.: $203,737,170
Assets: $325,618,020
Liabilities: $73,881,990
Net Worth: $251,736,030
Earnings: $35,910,420
Emp.: 182
Fiscal Year-end: 03/31/22
fluorine chemicals
N.A.I.C.S.: 325120
Vishad P. Mafatlal *(Chm)*

Subsidiaries:

Manchester Organics Limited (1)
The Heath Business and Technical Park, Runcorn, WA7 4QX, Cheshire, United Kingdom
Tel.: (44) 1928710200
Web Site: https://www.manchesterorganics.com
Chemical Products Mfr
N.A.I.C.S.: 325180

NAVINFO CO., LTD.
NavInfo Building No 1 Yongxu South Road, Haidian District, Beijing, 100094, China
Tel.: (86) 1082306399
Web Site: https://www.navinfo.com
002405—(SSE)
Rev.: $329,042,989
Assets: $1,410,437,471
Liabilities: $201,921,587
Net Worth: $1,208,515,884
Earnings: ($47,418,495)
Emp.: 1,000
Fiscal Year-end: 12/31/20
Electronic Navigation Systems Mfr
N.A.I.C.S.: 334511
Patrick Cheng *(Vice Chm & CEO)*

Subsidiaries:

Guangzhou Bozhan Hengteng Information Technology Co., Ltd. (1)
Room 1907 Tower B Poly Fengxing Plaza 242, Tianhe District, Guangzhou, Guangdong, China
Tel.: (86) 2038109018
Emp.: 5
Geographic Information Services
N.A.I.C.S.: 541370
Wane Anchao *(CEO)*

NAVION CAPITAL, INC.
639 5 Ave SW Suite 1250, Calgary, T2P 0M9, AB, Canada
Tel.: (604) 802-7372
NAVN.P—(TSXV)
Assets: $65,127
Liabilities: $6,902
Net Worth: $58,225
Earnings: ($37,169)
Fiscal Year-end: 11/30/20
Business Consulting Services
N.A.I.C.S.: 541611

NAVIOS MARITIME CONTAINERS L.P.
7 Avenue de Grande Bretagne Office 11B2, Monte Carlo, 98000, Monaco
Tel.: (377) 9798 2140 MH
Web Site: http://www.navios-containers.com
Year Founded: 2017

NMCI—(NASDAQ)
Rev.: $141,532,000
Assets: $460,302,000
Liabilities: $270,322,000
Net Worth: $189,980,000
Earnings: $7,507,000
Fiscal Year-end: 12/31/19
Marine Transportation Services
N.A.I.C.S.: 811310
Angeliki Frangou *(Chm & CEO)*

NAVIOS MARITIME HOLDINGS INC.
7 Avenue de Grande Bretagne Office 11B2, Monte Carlo, MC 98000, Monaco
Tel.: (377) 97982140 MH
Web Site: http://www.navios.com
NM—(NYSE)
Rev.: $255,397,000
Assets: $924,311,000
Liabilities: $782,220,000
Net Worth: $142,091,000
Earnings: $87,306,000
Emp.: 989
Fiscal Year-end: 12/31/22
Dry Bulk Cargo Handling
N.A.I.C.S.: 488320
Vasiliki Papaefthymiou *(Exec VP-Legal)*

Subsidiaries:

Navios South American Logistics Inc. (1)
Aguada Park Free Zone, Paraguay 2141 Of 1603, Montevideo, Uruguay
Tel.: (598) 2104595000
Web Site: http://www.navioslogistics.com
Rev.: $254,154,000
Assets: $793,575,000
Liabilities: $645,909,000
Net Worth: $147,666,000
Earnings: ($4,442,000)
Emp.: 989
Fiscal Year-end: 12/31/2022
Logistics & Distribution Services
N.A.I.C.S.: 541614
Angeliki Frangou *(Chm)*

NAVIOS MARITIME PARTNERS L.P.
7 Avenue de Grande Bretagne Office 11B2, 98000, Monte Carlo, 98000, Monaco
Tel.: (377) 2129083946 GR
Web Site: https://www.navios-mlp.com
Year Founded: 2007
NMM—(NYSE)
Rev.: $1,306,889,000
Assets: $5,147,566,000
Liabilities: $2,377,114,000
Net Worth: $2,770,452,000
Earnings: $433,645,000
Fiscal Year-end: 12/31/23
Drybulk Carriers Owner & Operator
N.A.I.C.S.: 483111

Subsidiaries:

Navios Maritime Acquisition Corporation (1)
Strathvale House 90 N Church Street, PO Box 309, Grand Cayman, Georgetown, KY1-1104, Cayman Islands (43.1%)
Tel.: (345) 2323066
Web Site: http://www.navios-acquisition.com
Rev.: $361,438,000
Assets: $1,568,997,000
Liabilities: $1,239,140,000
Net Worth: $329,857,000
Earnings: $27,609,000
Fiscal Year-end: 12/31/2020
Investment Services
N.A.I.C.S.: 523999
Anna Kalathakis *(Sr VP-Legal Risk Mgmt)*

Affiliate (Non-US):

Navios Maritime Midstream Partners LP (2)

7 Avenue de Grande Bretagne Office 11B2, Monte Carlo, MC 98000, Monaco
Tel.: (377) 97982140
Web Site: http://www.navios-midstream.com
Rev.: $83,052,000
Assets: $456,547,000
Liabilities: $200,816,000
Net Worth: $255,731,000
Earnings: $14,631,000
Fiscal Year-end: 12/31/2017
Marine Transportation Services
N.A.I.C.S.: 483111
Vasiliki Papaefthymiou *(Sec)*

Navios Tankers Management Inc. (1)
85 Akti Miaouli Street, 185 38, Piraeus, Greece
Tel.: (30) 2104595000
Web Site: http://www.naviostankers-management.com
Marine Tanker Services
N.A.I.C.S.: 488390

NAVIS CAPITAL PARTNERS LIMITED
Level 17 Quill 7 Tower 9 Jalan Stesen Sentral 5, Kuala Lumpur Sentral, Kuala Lumpur, 50470, Malaysia
Tel.: (60) 3 2302 3888
Web Site: http://www.naviscapital.com
Year Founded: 1998
Holding Company; Private & Public Equity Investment Services
N.A.I.C.S.: 551112
Nicholas Rupert Heylett Bloy *(Co-Founder & Co-Mng Partner)*

Subsidiaries:

Adampak Limited (1)
6 Loyang Way 4, Singapore, 507605, Singapore
Tel.: (65) 67479922
Web Site: http://www.adampak.com
Sales Range: $25-49.9 Million
Label Converting Services
N.A.I.C.S.: 561910

Subsidiary (Non-US):

Adampak (Suzhou) Co., Ltd. (2)
Suzhuo Industrial Park EPZB No 288 Shengpu Road B1, Suzhou, Jiangsu, China
Tel.: (86) 51262819922
Industrial Labels Mfr
N.A.I.C.S.: 322299

Adampak (Thailand) Ltd (2)
36 M001 Hi-Tech Industrial Estate G12 T Baalane A Bangpan-In, Ayutthaya, Thailand
Tel.: (66) 3535 1992
Die Cut & Label Mfr
N.A.I.C.S.: 322230

Aident Corporation (Tianjin) Ltd. (2)
No 16-2 Xiang An Road TEDA, Tianjin, 300457, China
Tel.: (86) 2266298100
Labels & Nameplates Mfr
N.A.I.C.S.: 322299

Aident Corporation Sdn. Bhd (2)
790 Jalan Perindustrian Bkt Minyak 4 Kawasan Perindustrian, Bkt Minyak Bkt Mertajam, 14000, Pulau Penang, Malaysia
Tel.: (60) 45096000
Web Site: http://www.aident.com.my
Printing Silk Screen Self Adhesive & Barcode Label Mfr
N.A.I.C.S.: 323111
Kok Kuang Tan *(CEO)*

Subsidiary (Domestic):

Aident Corporation (KL) Sdn. Bhd (3)
Lot 8 Jalan Satu Kawasan Perusahaan Balakong Cheras Jaya, 43200, Cheras, Selangor, Malaysia
Tel.: (60) 3 90752918
Web Site: http://www.adampak.com
Emp.: 70
Die Cutting Component Mfr
N.A.I.C.S.: 322230
Tamkok Kuang *(CEO)*

NAVIS CAPITAL PARTNERS LIMITED

Navis Capital Partners Limited—(Continued)

Blueprint Group Pty Ltd (1)
Building C 192 Burwood Rd, Hawthorn, 3122, VIC, Australia
Tel.: (61) 3 9006 7401
Web Site: http://www.blueprintgroup.com.au
Emp.: 2,500
Holding Company; Field Marketing Services
N.A.I.C.S.: 551112
Victor Davies (CEO)

Holding (Domestic):

Ausrep Pty Ltd (2)
Building C 192 Burwood Rd, Hawthorn, 3122, VIC, Australia
Tel.: (61) 383734094
Web Site: http://www.ausrep.com.au
Sales Range: $25-49.9 Million
Emp.: 100
Sales & Merchandising Services for Suppliers to Hardware Retail Industry
N.A.I.C.S.: 541613
Chloe Watson (Office Mgr)

Club Sales & Merchandising Pty Limited (2)
Building 1 64 Talavera Rd, Macquarie Park, Sydney, 2113, NSW, Australia
Tel.: (61) 298895527
Business Support Services
N.A.I.C.S.: 561499

Powerforce Total Merchandising Pty Limited (2)
25 Ellingworth Parade, Box Hill, Melbourne, 3128, Australia
Tel.: (61) 398996622
Advertising Services
N.A.I.C.S.: 541810

Holding (Non-US):

Resource Experience Limited (2)
Blueprint House Old Bracknell Lane West, Bracknell, RG12 7FS, Berkshire, United Kingdom
Tel.: (44) 1344 418383
Web Site: http://www.relfm.com
Sales Range: $75-99.9 Million
Emp.: 100
Marketing Consulting Services
N.A.I.C.S.: 541613
Rebecca Ahern (Mng Dir)

Retail Insight Limited (2)
18-20 George Street, Richmond, TW9 1HY, Surrey, United Kingdom
Tel.: (44) 20 3021 1890
Web Site: http://www.retailinsight.co.uk
Emp.: 50
Marketing Consulting Services
N.A.I.C.S.: 541613
Paul Boyle (CEO)

Holding (Domestic):

The Artel Group Pty Limited (2)
23 Cleg Street, Artarmon, 2064, NSW, Australia
Tel.: (61) 2 9966 5252
Web Site: http://www.theartelgroup.com.au
General Management Consulting Services
N.A.I.C.S.: 541810

Navis Capital (India) Private Limited (1)
Quadrant C 1st Floor The IL&FS Financial Centre, Bandra Kurla Complex, Mumbai, 400051, India
Tel.: (91) 22 2653 3591
Web Site: http://www.naviscapital.com
Emp.: 100
Private Equity Investment Advisory & Portfolio Management Services
N.A.I.C.S.: 523999
Michael Octoman (Partner)

Navis Capital Australia Pty. Ltd. (1)
Level 8 56 Pitt Street, Sydney, 2000, NSW, Australia
Tel.: (61) 2 8024 7800
Web Site: http://www.naviscapital.com
Emp.: 7
Private Equity Investment Advisory & Portfolio Management Services
N.A.I.C.S.: 523999
Kelvin Mak (Mgr-Investment-Private Equity)

Navis Capital Holding Ltd. (1)
12th Floor Two Pacific Place 142 Sukhumvit Road, Klongtoey, Bangkok, 10110, Thailand
Tel.: (66) 2 653 2155
Web Site: http://www.naviscapital.net
Private Equity Investment Advisory & Portfolio Management Services
N.A.I.C.S.: 523999

Navis Capital Partners (Hong Kong) Limited (1)
12st Floor 8 Wyndham Street, Central, China (Hong Kong)
Tel.: (852) 2526 0238
Web Site: http://www.naviscapital.net
Private Equity Investment Advisory & Portfolio Management Services
N.A.I.C.S.: 523999

Navis Capital Partners (Singapore) Pte. Ltd. (1)
20 Collyer Quay 10-01 Tung Centre, Singapore, 049319, Singapore
Tel.: (65) 6438 0711
Web Site: http://www.naviscapital.net
Private Equity Investment Advisory & Portfolio Management Services
N.A.I.C.S.: 523999
Jean-Christophe Marti (Partner)

Navis Management Sdn. Bhd. (1)
Level 17 Quill 7 Tower 9 Jalan Stesen Sentral 5, Kuala Lumpur Sentral, Kuala Lumpur, 50470, Malaysia
Tel.: (60) 3 2302 3888
Web Site: http://www.naviscapital.com
Emp.: 43
Private Equity Investment Advisory & Portfolio Management Services
N.A.I.C.S.: 523999
Nicholas Rupert Heylett Bloy (Co-Mng Partner)

SEG International Bhd. (1)
No 9 Jalan Teknologi Taman Sains Selangor Kota Damansara PJU 5, 47810, Petaling Jaya, Selangor, Malaysia **(66.58%)**
Tel.: (60) 362873777
Web Site: https://segi.investor.net.my
Rev.: $45,278,095
Assets: $79,430,476
Liabilities: $52,578,201
Net Worth: $26,852,275
Earnings: $8,504,127
Emp.: 1,392
Fiscal Year-end: 12/31/2022
University Owner & Operator
N.A.I.C.S.: 611310
Cheryl Poh Yee Chong (Grp CFO & Co-Sec)

Texon International (Asia) Ltd (1)
Unit 2209 22nd Floor Wu Chung House 213 Queens Road East, Wanchai, China (Hong Kong)
Tel.: (852) 3973 7330
Web Site: http://www.texon.com
Footwear Materials Design, Mfr & Distr
N.A.I.C.S.: 424340
Stan Lamb (CEO)

Subsidiary (Non-US):

Texon Components GmbH (2)
Moselstrasse 7, 66954, Pirmasens, Germany
Tel.: (49) 6331 55140
Web Site: http://www.texon.com
Footwear Material Design Distr
N.A.I.C.S.: 424340
Heinz-Peter Schutz (Sls Dir)

Texon France SA (2)
ZI La Bergerie 10 Rue Eiffel, Maine-et-Loire, 49280, La Seguiniere, France
Tel.: (33) 241 49 40 30
Web Site: http://www.texon.com
Footwear Material Design Distr
N.A.I.C.S.: 424340

Texon India Pvt. Ltd (2)
273 Tambaram Velacherry Main Road Narayanapuram, Pallikkaranai, Chennai, 100, Tamil Nadu, India
Tel.: (91) 44 224 61801
Web Site: http://www.texon.com
Footwear Materials Design, Mfr & Distr
N.A.I.C.S.: 424340
Vikash Bajargyan (Gen Mgr)

Texon Italia S.p.A. (2)
Via Cimitero Vecchio 8, Cassolnovo Pavia, 27023, Milan, Italy
Tel.: (39) 0381 920011
Web Site: http://www.texon.it
Footwear Materials Design, Mfr & Distr
N.A.I.C.S.: 316210

Texon Materiales, S.L. (2)
Poligono Industrial Pla d En Coll Carrer Del, Fresser 21-23, Montcada i Reixac, 08110, Barcelona, Spain
Tel.: (34) 93 300 2424
Web Site: http://www.texon.com
Footwear Materials Design, Mfr & Distr
N.A.I.C.S.: 424340
Alberto Gonzales Ravelo (Comml Dir)

Texon Mockmuhl GmbH (2)
Roigheimer Strasse 69-72, D 74219, Mockmuhl, Germany
Tel.: (49) 6298 209 162
Web Site: http://www.texon.com
Footwear Materials Design, Mfr & Distr
N.A.I.C.S.: 424340
Jurgen Rotsche (Sls Mgr)

Texon OZ Pty Ltd (2)
Unit 22 391 Settlement Road, Thomastown, 3074, VIC, Australia
Tel.: (61) 3 9464 0744
Web Site: http://www.texon.com
Footwear Materials Design, Mfr & Distr
N.A.I.C.S.: 424340

Texon Oesterreich G.m.b.H (2)
Industriestrasse 7, A-2100, Korneuburg, Austria
Tel.: (43) 2262 61910 0
Web Site: http://www.texon.com
Footwear Materials Design, Mfr & Distr
N.A.I.C.S.: 424340
Josef Putschoegl (Mng Dir)

NAVITAS LIMITED

Level 8 Brookfield Place 125 St Georges Terrace, Perth, 6000, WA, Australia
Tel.: (61) 893149600
Web Site: http://www.navitas.com
Rev.: $726,620,580
Assets: $648,047,871
Liabilities: $625,564,296
Net Worth: $22,483,575
Earnings: $(43,164,219)
Emp.: 8,000
Fiscal Year-end: 06/30/18
Education Services
N.A.I.C.S.: 611710
Rod Jones (Founder)

Subsidiaries:

ACL Pty Ltd. (1)
Level 4 11 York St, Sydney, 2000, NSW, Australia
Tel.: (61) 2 9252 3788
Language Training Services
N.A.I.C.S.: 611630

Australian College of Applied Psychology Pty Ltd. (1)
Locked Bag 11, Strawberry Hills, Sydney, 2012, NSW, Australia
Tel.: (61) 299646170
Web Site: http://www.acap.edu.au
Sales Range: $10-24.9 Million
Emp.: 90
Education Training Services
N.A.I.C.S.: 611710
Andrew Little (Gen Mgr)

Cambridge Ruskin International College Limited (1)
Eastings Building East Road, Cambridge, CB1 1PT, United Kingdom
Tel.: (44) 1223695703
Web Site: http://www.cric.navitas.com
Sales Range: $10-24.9 Million
Emp.: 15
Education Training Services
N.A.I.C.S.: 611710
Paul Lockhart-Thomas (Principal & Dir-College)

Cytech Intersearch Pty Ltd. (1)
65 Justin St, Lilyfield, Sydney, 2040, NSW, Australia

INTERNATIONAL PUBLIC

Tel.: (61) 299646270
Web Site: http://www.cytechintersearch.com
Recruitment & Consulting Services
N.A.I.C.S.: 561311

EduGlobal Australia Pty Ltd. (1)
Level One Wynyard Green 11 York St, Sydney, 2000, NSW, Australia
Tel.: (61) 299646200
Web Site: http://www.eduglobal.com.au
Sales Range: $10-24.9 Million
Emp.: 2
Educational Consulting Services
N.A.I.C.S.: 611710
Anna Xu (Mgr)

Educational Enterprises Australia Pty Ltd. (1)
16-20 Coglin St, Adelaide, 5000, SA, Australia
Tel.: (61) 882169000
Web Site: http://www.eynesburyinternational.edu.au
Sales Range: $10-24.9 Million
Emp.: 100
Education Training Services
N.A.I.C.S.: 611710
Margo Styles (Mgr-Intl Admissions & Student Svcs)

Fraser International College Ltd. (1)
Fraser International College 8999 Nelson Way, Burnaby, V5A 4B5, BC, Canada
Tel.: (778) 782-5011
Web Site: http://www.fraseric.ca
Sales Range: $10-24.9 Million
Emp.: 65
Educational Support Services
N.A.I.C.S.: 611710
Bev Hudson (Mng Dir)

Hawthorn Learning Pty Ltd. (1)
442 Auburn Rd, Locked Bag 12, Hawthorn, 3122, VIC, Australia
Tel.: (61) 398154001
Web Site: http://www.hawthornenglish.com
Language Training Services
N.A.I.C.S.: 611630
Ann Simons (Mgr-Admissions)

International College Wales Ltd. (1)
2nd Fl Margam Bldg Swansea University Singleton Park, Swansea, SA2 8PP, Wales, United Kingdom
Tel.: (44) 1792602888
Web Site: http://www.icws-uk.co.uk
Sales Range: $10-24.9 Million
Emp.: 20
Education Training Services
N.A.I.C.S.: 611710
Sharon Davies-Smith (COO, Principal & Dir-College)

London IBT Ltd. (1)
Brunel University Russell Building Kingston Lane, Uxbridge, UB8 3PH, Greater London, United Kingdom
Tel.: (44) 1895 265 540
Web Site: http://www.lbic.navitas.com
Sales Range: $10-24.9 Million
Emp.: 14
Education Training Services
N.A.I.C.S.: 611710
Peter Hedley (Dir-Academic & Support Svcs)

Melbourne Institute of Business and Technology Pty Ltd. (1)
Deakin College at Deakin University Burwood Campus 221 Burwood Hwy, Burwood, Melbourne, 3125, VIC, Australia
Tel.: (61) 392445197
Web Site: http://www.mibt.vic.edu.au
Education Training Services
N.A.I.C.S.: 611710
John Duncan (Dir-College)

Navitas College of Public Safety Pty Ltd. (1)
Level 10 123 Lonsdale St, Melbourne, 3000, VIC, Australia
Tel.: (61) 1800061199
Web Site: http://www.ncps.edu.au
Sales Range: $10-24.9 Million
Emp.: 25
Education Training Services
N.A.I.C.S.: 611710

Navitas Education Centre Pte Ltd. (1)

AND PRIVATE COMPANIES

90 and 92 Jalan Rajah, Singapore, 329162, Singapore
Tel.: (65) 65938000
Web Site: http://www.curtin.edu.sg
Sales Range: $10-24.9 Million
Emp.: 30
Education Training Services
N.A.I.C.S.: 611710

Navitas UK Holdings Limited (1)
HIBT Bldg College Ln Campus, Hatfield, A10 9AB, Hertfordshire, United Kingdom
Tel.: (44) 1895265540
Education Training Services
N.A.I.C.S.: 611710

Navitas Workforce Solutions Pty Ltd. (1)
Level 3 206 Bourke St, Melbourne, 3000, VIC, Australia
Tel.: (61) 396330100
Web Site:
http://www.navitasworkforcesolutions.com
Sales Range: $10-24.9 Million
Emp.: 70
Education Training Services
N.A.I.C.S.: 611710
Rod Jones *(CEO)*

Queensland Institute of Business and Technology Pty Ltd. (1)
Level 5 International Building M14176 Messines Ridge Rd, Mt Gravatt, Brisbane, 4122, QLD, Australia
Tel.: (61) 737356900
Web Site: http://www.griffith.edu.au
Sales Range: $10-24.9 Million
Emp.: 40
Education Training Services
N.A.I.C.S.: 611710
Leigh Pointon *(Dir-Academic)*

South Australian Institute of Business & Technology Pty Ltd. (1)
City E Campus N Terrace, Adelaide, 5000, SA, Australia
Tel.: (61) 883021555
Web Site: http://www.saibt.sa.edu.au
Sales Range: $10-24.9 Million
Emp.: 30
Education Training Services
N.A.I.C.S.: 611710
Matt Stanton *(Principal & Dir-College)*

Study Overseas Global Pvt Ltd. (1)
S-2 Level Block E Intl Trade Tower Nehru Pl, New Delhi, 110019, India
Tel.: (91) 1141653071
Web Site:
http://www.studyoverseasglobal.com
Sales Range: $25-49.9 Million
Emp.: 210
Educational Consultancy Services
N.A.I.C.S.: 611710
Sangeeta Mubai *(Mgr)*

Study Overseas India Pvt Ltd. (1)
S-2 Level Block E Intl Trade Tower Nehru Pl, New Delhi, 110 019, India
Tel.: (91) 1141653071
Web Site:
http://www.studyoverseasglobal.com
Sales Range: $10-24.9 Million
Emp.: 75
Educational Consultancy Services
N.A.I.C.S.: 611710
Anil Kumar *(Dir-Fin)*

Sydney Institute of Business and Technology Pty Ltd. (1)
Level 2 Bldg E3A Macquarie Dr Macquarie University, North Ryde, 2109, NSW, Australia
Tel.: (61) 298506222
Web Site: http://www.sibt.nsw.edu.au
Emp.: 40
Educational Consultancy Services
N.A.I.C.S.: 611710
Morwenna Shahani *(Principal & Dir-College)*

NAVITUS ENERGY PLC
7B 1 Awudu Ekpekha Boulevard Lekki Phase 1, Lagos, Nigeria
Tel.: (234) 1 842 9441
Year Founded: 1976
Petroleum Product Mfr
N.A.I.C.S.: 324199
Olurotimi Arigbede *(CEO & Mng Dir)*

NAVKAR URBANSTRUCTURE LIMITED
304 S G Road Circle P Near Prahaladnagar, Ahmedabad, 380015, India
Tel.: (91) 7948484095
Web Site:
https://navkarurbanstructure.com
Year Founded: 1992
531494—(BOM)
Rev.: $1,151,181
Assets: $16,877,708
Liabilities: $6,163,744
Net Worth: $10,713,964
Earnings: $69,653
Emp.: 2
Fiscal Year-end: 03/31/21
Readymix Concrete Mfr
N.A.I.C.S.: 327320
Harsh Shah *(Chm & Mng Dir)*

NAVKETAN MERCHANTS LIMITED
12 Waterloo Street, Kolkata, 700 069, West Bengal, India
Tel.: (91) 3322485923
Web Site:
http://www.navketanmerchants.com
539525—(BOM)
Rev.: $6,628
Assets: $5,913,889
Liabilities: $177
Net Worth: $5,913,711
Earnings: ($6,685)
Emp.: 2
Fiscal Year-end: 03/31/21
Yarn & Fabric Trading Services
N.A.I.C.S.: 424990
Kamal Dani *(Mng Dir)*

NAVNEET EDUCATION LTD
Navneet Bhavan Bhavani Shankar Road, Dadar West, Mumbai, 400028, India
Tel.: (91) 2266626565
Web Site: https://www.navneet.com
NAVNETEDUL—(NSE)
Rev.: $115,782,030
Assets: $161,140,980
Liabilities: $34,078,590
Net Worth: $127,062,390
Earnings: $7,631,715
Emp.: 3,000
Fiscal Year-end: 03/31/21
Educational, Children's & Other Books Publisher; Scholastic Paper & Non-Paper Stationery Products
N.A.I.C.S.: 513130
Amit D. Buch *(Compliance Officer & Sec)*

Subsidiaries:

ESense Learning Private Limited (1)
Benefice Business House 1041 Mathuradas Mill Estate 126 N M Joshi Marg, Lower Parel West, Mumbai, 400 013, India
Tel.: (91) 2262809000
Web Site: http://www.esense.in
Education Management Services
N.A.I.C.S.: 611710
Harshil Gala *(CEO)*

Genext Students Private Limited (1)
Grafalco Ediciones S.L. (1)
Camino de las Bodegas 9, Fuente El Saz, Madrid, 28 140, Spain
Tel.: (34) 916200203
Web Site: http://www.grafalco.es
Sales Range: $25-49.9 Million
Emp.: 11
Books Publishing Services
N.A.I.C.S.: 513120

NAVODAY ENTERPRISES LTD.
B-713 Crystal Plaza New Link Road Opposite Infinity Shopping Mall, Andheri West, Mumbai, 400053, India
Tel.: (91) 8317208293
Web Site:
https://www.navodayenterprise.in
Year Founded: 2007
543305—(BOM)
Rev.: $3,609,701
Assets: $1,594,783
Liabilities: $1,153,112
Net Worth: $441,671
Earnings: $49,585
Fiscal Year-end: 03/31/21
Business Consulting Services
N.A.I.C.S.: 541611
Anand V. Mode *(Mng Dir)*

NAVYA SA
1 Rue du Dr Fleury-Pierre Papillon, 69100, Villeurbanne, France
Tel.: (33) 469731710
Web Site: https://www.navya.tech
Year Founded: 2014
2JZ—(BER)
Sales Range: Less than $1 Million
Robotic Machinery Services
N.A.I.C.S.: 333998
Pierre Lahutte *(Chief Strategy & Dev Officer)*

NAWALOKA HOSPITALS PLC
No 23 Deshamanya HK Dharmadasa Mawatha, 2, Colombo, 2, Sri Lanka
Tel.: (94) 115577111
Web Site: https://www.nawaloka.com
Year Founded: 1985
NHL—(COL)
Rev.: $52,502,082
Assets: $68,963,261
Liabilities: $46,036,068
Net Worth: $22,927,192
Earnings: ($331,395)
Emp.: 2,305
Fiscal Year-end: 03/31/22
Health Care Srvices
N.A.I.C.S.: 622110
Indika Prasath Balasuriya *(Head-IT)*

NAWARAT PATANAKARN PUBLIC COMPANY LIMITED
18th-19th Floor Bangna Towers A 2/3 Moo 14 Bangna-Trad Road Km 6 5, Bangkaew Bangplee, Samut Prakan, 10540, Thailand
Tel.: (66) 7302100
Web Site: https://www.nawarat.co.th
Year Founded: 1976
NWR—(THA)
Rev.: $327,062,297
Assets: $544,211,276
Liabilities: $486,667,198
Net Worth: $57,544,077
Earnings: ($28,615,630)
Emp.: 2,122
Fiscal Year-end: 12/31/23
Concrete Products Mfr
N.A.I.C.S.: 327331
Prasertphand Pipatanakul *(Chm)*

Subsidiaries:

Advance Prefab Company Limited (1)
2/3 Moo 14 Bangna Towers A 18th Floor Bangna-Trad Road Km 6 5, Bangkaew, Bang Phli 10540, Samut Prakan, Thailand
Tel.: (66) 27302117
Web Site: http://www.advanceprefab.co.th
Precast Concrete Product Mfr & Distr
N.A.I.C.S.: 327390
Anuchit Chotibut *(Mgr-Sls & Mktg)*

Taste Maker Company Limited (1)
2/3 BangnaTowers A Building 19th Floor Moo 14 Bangna-Trad Road, Bangkaew, Bang Phli, 10540, Samut Prakan, Thailand
Tel.: (66) 20667460
Web Site: http://tastemaker.co.th
Hotel Services
N.A.I.C.S.: 721110

Utility Business Alliance Company Limited (1)
21st Floor Suntowers Building A 123 Viphavadee-Rangsit Road, Jompol Jatujak, Bangkok, 10900, Thailand
Tel.: (66) 27893232
Web Site: http://www.uba.co.th
Waste Water Treatment Services
N.A.I.C.S.: 221320

Plant (Domestic):

Utility Business Alliance Company Limited - Dindaeng Wastewater Treatment Plant (2)
Mitmaitree Road, Din Daeng, Bangkok, 10400, Thailand
Tel.: (66) 22485057
Waste Water Treatment Services
N.A.I.C.S.: 221320

Utility Business Alliance Company Limited - Nong Khaem Wastewater Treatment Plant (2)
Soi Petchkasem 104 Petchkasem Road Nongkangplu, Nong Khaem, Bangkok, 10160, Thailand
Tel.: (66) 2444287173
Waste Water Treatment Services
N.A.I.C.S.: 221320

Utility Business Alliance Company Limited - Thungkhru Wastewater Treatment Plant (2)
Soi Pracha Uthit 90 Pracha Uthit Road, Thung Khru, Bangkok, 10140, Thailand
Tel.: (66) 246279668
Waste Water Treatment Services
N.A.I.C.S.: 221320

NAWI BROTHERS GROUP LTD.
Yigal Alon St Migdal Alon 2, Tel Aviv, Israel
Tel.: (972) 35102585
Web Site: https://nawigroup.com
Year Founded: 1983
NAWI—(TAE)
Rev.: $102,877,744
Assets: $940,278,753
Liabilities: $716,294,781
Net Worth: $223,983,972
Earnings: $39,425,334
Emp.: 3
Fiscal Year-end: 12/31/23
Miscellaneous Financial Investment Activities
N.A.I.C.S.: 523999
Shaul Nawi *(CEO)*

NAXS AB
Nybrogatan 8, SE-114 34, Stockholm, Sweden
Tel.: (46) 766400040
Web Site: https://www.naxs.se
Year Founded: 2007
NAXS—(OMX)
Rev.: $953,998
Assets: $91,702,902
Liabilities: $167,769
Net Worth: $91,535,134
Earnings: $431,830
Emp.: 1
Fiscal Year-end: 12/31/23
Investment Fund Services
N.A.I.C.S.: 525910
Gosta Lundgren *(CFO)*

NAYAX LTD.
3 Arik Einstein St Bldg B 1st Floor, Herzliya, 4659071, Israel
Tel.: (972) 37694380
Web Site: https://www.nayax.com
Year Founded: 2005
NYAX—(NASDAQ)
Rev.: $173,514,000
Assets: $230,488,000
Liabilities: $125,853,000
Net Worth: $104,635,000
Earnings: ($37,509,000)
Emp.: 800
Fiscal Year-end: 12/31/22
Cashless Payment Device Mfr

NAYAX LTD.

Nayax Ltd.—(Continued)
N.A.I.C.S.: 334118
Yair Nechmad *(Chm & CEO)*

Subsidiaries:

Adskylabs S.A. (1)
De Mac Donalds Plaza del Sol 100 meters south & 50 meters west, Curridabat, San Jose, Costa Rica
Tel.: (506) 86962929
Software Development & Design Services
N.A.I.C.S.: 541512

Alpokami OU (1)
Seminari 19, 44316, Rakvere, Estonia
Tel.: (372) 6668777
Web Site: https://alpokami.com
Vending Machine Operators
N.A.I.C.S.: 561520

Bischof Handels-GmbH (1)
Radetzkystrasse 154, 6845, Hohenems, Austria
Tel.: (43) 557676700
Web Site: https://www.bischof-automaten.com
Industrial Machinery Distr
N.A.I.C.S.: 423690

Combis d.o.o. (1)
Radnicka cesta 21, 10 000, Zagreb, Croatia
Tel.: (385) 13651222
Web Site: https://www.combis.hr
Emp.: 400
Information Technology Services
N.A.I.C.S.: 541512

Danbit A/S (1)
Vaerkstedsvej 39, 4600, Koge, Denmark
Tel.: (45) 56662020
Web Site: https://www.danbit.dk
Vending Machine Operators
N.A.I.C.S.: 561520

Ege Group Ltd. (1)
Residential Complex Mladost 4 bl 460A, City of Fountains Complex, Sofia, Bulgaria
Tel.: (359) 24164121
Web Site: https://www.egegroup.eu
Information Technology Services
N.A.I.C.S.: 541519

Gack Spiel- Und Freizeit GmbH (1)
Brusseler Str 28, Gildehaus, 48455, Bad Bentheim, Germany
Tel.: (49) 592478970
Web Site: https://gack.de
Amusement Machines Mfr
N.A.I.C.S.: 325194

Handav Kft. (1)
Veka u 32, 1029, Budapest, Hungary
Tel.: (36) 304159514
Welding Machine Distr
N.A.I.C.S.: 423440

Hansab UAB (1)
Savanoriu PR 180A, 03154, Vilnius, Lithuania
Tel.: (370) 52058800
Web Site: https://www.hansab.lt
Emp.: 305
Welding Machine Distr
N.A.I.C.S.: 423440

InOne Technology, LLC (1)
190 Lakefront Dr, Hunt Valley, MD 21030
Tel.: (410) 666-3800
Web Site: http://www.inonetechnology.com
Vending Machine Mfr
N.A.I.C.S.: 333310
Greg Hasslinger *(VP-Sls)*

Inepro B.V. (1)
Pondweg 7, 2153PK, Nieuw-Vennep, Netherlands
Tel.: (31) 252744044
Web Site: https://www.nayax.com
Welding Machine Distr
N.A.I.C.S.: 423440

Jimark s.r.o. (1)
Na Jarov 2425/4, 130 00, Prague, Czech Republic
Tel.: (420) 284861065
Web Site: https://www.jimark.cz
Vending Machine Operators
N.A.I.C.S.: 561520

Kenmart Vending Services Limited (1)
Rose Avenue Park Room No 4 Block C
Rose Avenue, PO Box 1044, 00502, Nairobi, Kenya
Tel.: (254) 755898135
Web Site: https://www.kenmartvending.com
Cashless Payment Processing Services
N.A.I.C.S.: 522320

Langley Wholesale Ltd. (1)
15515 24 Ave Unit 70, Surrey, BC, Canada
Tel.: (604) 881-2223
Web Site: https://www.langleywholesale.ca
Welding Machine Distr
N.A.I.C.S.: 423440

Multivend Services Ltd. (1)
Naggar Street, Mosta, Malta
Tel.: (356) 21470153
Web Site: https://www.multivendservices.com
Vending Machine Operators
N.A.I.C.S.: 561520

Nayax Australia Pty. Ltd. (1)
Suite 1 Level 4 100 William Street, Woolloomooloo, NSW, Australia
Tel.: (61) 1300343484
Financial Services
N.A.I.C.S.: 523999

Nayax China Ltd. (1)
No 567 Tianyaoqiao Road Room 210 2 /F, Xuhui District, Shanghai, China
Tel.: (86) 2122876701
Welding Machine Distr
N.A.I.C.S.: 486210

Nayax GmbH (1)
Engelblecker Strasse 142a, 41066, Mönchengladbach, Germany
Tel.: (49) 21619162019
Financial Services
N.A.I.C.S.: 523999

Nayax KK (1)
Jinbocho Center Building 3F 2-5 Kanda Jinbocho, Chiyoda-ku, Tokyo, Japan
Tel.: (81) 357878302
Cashless Payment & Telemetry System Mfr
N.A.I.C.S.: 334118

Nayax NZ Ltd. (1)
Suite 3326 Level 33 ANZ Centre 23-29 Albert Street, Auckland, New Zealand
Tel.: (64) 98844154
Vending Machine Services
N.A.I.C.S.: 532490

Nayax UK Ltd. (1)
The Maylands Building Maylands Avenue, Hemel Hempstead, United Kingdom
Tel.: (44) 2034554800
Cashless Payment & Internet Things Services
N.A.I.C.S.: 522320

Pobad International Ltd. (1)
Plot No 150 Manet-Lekma Junction Spintex Rd, Accra, Ghana
Tel.: (233) 302918075
Web Site: https://pobadint.com
Energy & Automobile Services
N.A.I.C.S.: 541420

Retail Pro International, LLC (1)
400 Plaza Dr Ste 200, Folsom, CA 95630
Tel.: (916) 605-7200
Web Site: http://www.retailpro.com
Point of Sale & Retail Management Software Solutions
N.A.I.C.S.: 513210
Kerry Lemos *(Chm & CEO)*

Uko Technik GmbH (1)
Teichweg 4, 5400, Hallein, Austria
Tel.: (43) 59088400
Web Site: https://www.uko-microshops.com
Vending Machine Operators
N.A.I.C.S.: 561520

Vending Automater ApS (1)
Erhvervsparken 23, 4621, Gadstrup, Denmark
Tel.: (45) 70203433
Web Site: https://vendingautomater.dk
Vending Machine Operators
N.A.I.C.S.: 561520

Vertex Vending Services Ltd. (1)
11 Triq il-Mastrudaxxa, Qormi, Malta
Tel.: (356) 21667059
Web Site: https://www.vertexvending.com
Vending Machine Operators
N.A.I.C.S.: 561520

Vp Salestech AB (1)
Flygfaltsgatan 28, 423 37, Torslanda, Sweden
Tel.: (46) 87475250
Web Site: https://www.vpsalestech.se
Cashless Payment Processing Services
N.A.I.C.S.: 522320

NAYLOR INDUSTRIES PLC.

Naylor House Valley Road, Wombwell, S73 0BS, South Yorkshire, United Kingdom
Tel.: (44) 1226 790591
Web Site: http://www.naylor.co.uk
Year Founded: 1890
Sales Range: $50-74.9 Million
Emp.: 230
Construction Product Mfr
N.A.I.C.S.: 327390
Edward Naylor *(CEO)*

Subsidiaries:

Naylor Concrete Products Ltd (1)
Whaley Road, Barugh Green, Barnsley, S75 1HT, South Yorkshire, United Kingdom
Tel.: (44) 1924267286
Construction Materials Mfr
N.A.I.C.S.: 327390
Paul Cartwright *(Mng Dir)*

Naylor Drainage Ltd (1)
49 Cowley St, Methil, Leven, KY8 3QQ, Fife, United Kingdom
Tel.: (44) 1592717900
Construction Materials Mfr
N.A.I.C.S.: 327390

Naylor Specialist Plastics Ltd (1)
Unit 47 Coneygre Industrial Estate Coneygre Road, Tipton, Tipton, Tipton, United Kingdom
Tel.: (44) 121 522 0290
Plastic Tank Mfr
N.A.I.C.S.: 326121

NAYSAA SECURITIES LIMITED

102104 Shivam Chamber SV Road, Goregaon West, Mumbai, 400062, India
Tel.: (91) 2226760404
Web Site: https://www.naysaasecurities.com
538668—(BOM)
Rev.: $244,248
Assets: $1,636,263
Liabilities: $1,217,369
Net Worth: $418,894
Earnings: $56,094
Emp.: 1
Fiscal Year-end: 03/31/21
Investment Advisory Services
N.A.I.C.S.: 523940
Vikram Jayantilal Lodha *(Exec Dir)*

NAYTEMPORIKI PUBLISHING S.A.

Lenorman Str 205, 10442, Athens, Greece
Tel.: (30) 210 5198000
Web Site: http://www.naftemporiki.gr
Year Founded: 1974
Newspaper Publishing Services
N.A.I.C.S.: 513110
Athanasiadou G. Irini *(Chm & CEO)*

NAZA CORPORATION HOLDINGS SDN BHD

Platinum Park Persiaran KLCC, 50088, Kuala Lumpur, Malaysia
Tel.: (60) 323868000
Web Site: https://www.naza.com.my
Emp.: 100
Property Development, Engineering & Construction & Motor Vehicle Mfr
N.A.I.C.S.: 336211

Subsidiaries:

Berjaya Energies Sdn Bhd (1)
09-03 and 09-05 Level 9 East Berjaya Times Square No 1 Jalan Imbi, 55100, Kuala Lumpur, Malaysia
Tel.: (60) 326886333
Electric Power Distribution Services
N.A.I.C.S.: 221121

NAZARA TECHNOLOGIES LIMITED

51-54 Maker Chambers Iii, Nariman Point, Mumbai, 400021, India
Tel.: (91) 2240330800
Web Site: https://www.nazara.com
Year Founded: 1999
543280—(BOM)
Rev.: $136,742,402
Assets: $204,040,525
Liabilities: $46,184,282
Net Worth: $157,856,244
Earnings: $7,361,669
Emp.: 74
Fiscal Year-end: 03/31/23
Video Game Design & Development Services
N.A.I.C.S.: 513210
Vikash Mittersain *(Chm & Co-Mng Dir)*

Subsidiaries:

Next Wave Multimedia Private Limited (1)
1st Floor Old No 98 New No 165 Avvai Shanmugam Salai Royapettah, Chennai, 600 014, India (71.88%)
Tel.: (91) 4445530452
Web Site: https://www.nextwavemultimedia.com
Mobile Game Developer
N.A.I.C.S.: 513210

Nodwin Gaming Private Limited (1)
119 Sector 31 Near Raheja Atlantis, Gurgaon, 122001, Haryana, India
Tel.: (91) 124 422 7198
Web Site: https://nodwingaming.com
Online Gambling Services
N.A.I.C.S.: 513210
Sidharth Kedia *(CEO)*

Openplay Technologies Private Limited (1)
Suite No 451 4th Floor 77 Elliot Road, Kolkata, 700016, West Bengal, India
Tel.: (91) 4045190099
Web Site: https://www.openplaytech.com
Information Technology Services
N.A.I.C.S.: 541519

Paper Boat Apps Private Limited (1)
505 Wellington Business Park 1 Andheri Kurla Road, Andheri East, Mumbai, 400059, Maharashtra, India (99.33%)
Tel.: (91) 226 694 0030
Web Site: https://www.kiddopia.com
Application Development Services
N.A.I.C.S.: 513210

NAZIR COTTON MILLS LIMITED

61-K Gulberg-III, Lahore, Pakistan
Tel.: (92) 4235763768
Web Site: https://www.nazircotton.com
NCML—(PSX)
Rev.: $14,970
Assets: $1,424,866
Liabilities: $793,862
Net Worth: $631,004
Earnings: $(85,327)
Emp.: 16
Fiscal Year-end: 06/30/23
Yarn Mfr
N.A.I.C.S.: 313110
Maqbool Hussain Bhutta *(CFO)*

NB DISTRESSED DEBT INVESTMENT FUND LIMITED

1st & 2nd Floors Elizabeth House

AND PRIVATE COMPANIES

Les Ruettes Brayes, Saint Peter Port, GY1 1EW, Guernsey
Tel.: (44) 1481700300
Web Site: http://www.nbddif.com
Year Founded: 1939
NBDG—(LSE)
Rev.: $8,496,913
Assets: $96,720,247
Liabilities: $1,573,508
Net Worth: $95,146,739
Earnings: $7,220,521
Fiscal Year-end: 12/31/22
Business Support Services
N.A.I.C.S.: 561499
John Hallam *(Chm)*

NB FOOTWEAR LIMITED
Venkatachalapathy illam Old No 42 New No 62 53 rd Street Ashok nagar, Chennai, 600 083, India
Tel.: (91) 4428170596
Web Site: https://www.nbfootwear.in
Year Founded: 1987
523242—(BOM)
Assets: $408
Liabilities: $140,627
Net Worth: ($140,219)
Earnings: ($27,768)
Fiscal Year-end: 03/31/23
Clothing Product Mfr & Distr
N.A.I.C.S.: 316210

NB GLOBAL CORPORATE INCOME TRUST
Level 1 575 Bourke Street, Melbourne, 3000, VIC, Australia
Tel.: (61) 1300032754   AU
Web Site: http://www.nb.com
NBI—(ASX)
Rev.: $37,681,224
Assets: $598,645,700
Liabilities: $50,124,150
Net Worth: $548,521,551
Earnings: ($106,783,900)
Fiscal Year-end: 06/30/22
Investment Management Service
N.A.I.C.S.: 525910

NB GLOBAL MONTHLY INCOME FUND LIMITED
BNP Paribas House St Julians Avenue, Saint Peter Port, GY1 1WA, Guernsey
Tel.: (44) 2032149035
Web Site: http://www.nbgfrif.com
NBMI—(LSE)
Rev.: $21,725,148
Assets: $336,130,657
Liabilities: $18,721,485
Net Worth: $317,409,172
Earnings: $17,124,895
Fiscal Year-end: 12/31/20
Investment Management Service
N.A.I.C.S.: 525990
Rupert Dorey *(Chm)*

NB PRIVATE EQUITY PARTNERS LIMITED
Floor 2 Trafalgar Court Les Banques, PO Box 286, Saint Peter Port, GY1 4LY, Guernsey
Tel.: (44) 1481742742
Web Site: https://www.nbprivateequity.com
NBPE—(LSE)
Rev.: $7,054,768
Assets: $1,489,813,804
Liabilities: $182,323,968
Net Worth: $1,307,489,836
Earnings: ($31,261,551)
Fiscal Year-end: 12/31/23
Investment Services
N.A.I.C.S.: 523999
John P. Buser *(Mng Dir-Neuberger Berman & Head-Private Investment Portfolios)*

NBA QUANTUM PLC
3000 Cathedral Hill, Guildford, GU2 7YB, Surrey, United Kingdom
Tel.: (44) 20 7318 9780
Web Site: http://www.nbagroup.com
Sales Range: $1-9.9 Million
Emp.: 19
Management Consulting Services
N.A.I.C.S.: 561499
Peter D. Elliott-Hughes *(CEO)*

Subsidiaries:

Bionic Productions Limited (1)
Pinewood Road, Buckinghamshire, Iver, SL0 0NH, United Kingdom
Tel.: (44) 1753655886
Computer Aided Design Engineering Services
N.A.I.C.S.: 541512

DMS International Incorporated (1)
10613 Concord St, Kensington, MD 20895
Tel.: (301) 949-8110
Web Site: http://www.dmsintl.com
Business Consulting Services
N.A.I.C.S.: 561499

Lucid Edge Pty. Ltd. (1)
Level 2 Suite 28 Building 61 38 Driver Ave, Moore Park, Sydney, 2021, NSW, Australia
Tel.: (61) 293317845
Web Site: http://www.lucidedge.com.au
Information Technology Consulting Services
N.A.I.C.S.: 541512
Malcolm Beddows *(Gen Mgr)*

Quantum Asia Pvt Ltd (1)
34/A Hitech City Station Road Khanmet, Madhapur, Hyderabad, 500 081, India
Tel.: (91) 4044662300
Web Site: http://www.quantumasia.in
Information Technology Consulting Services
N.A.I.C.S.: 541512

Quantum Consulting Australia PTY Ltd. (1)
Level 11 251 Adelaide Terrace, PO Box 3499, Perth, 6000, WA, Australia
Tel.: (61) 893253233
Web Site: http://www.quantumconsulting.net.au
Management Consulting Services
N.A.I.C.S.: 541611

Rock Hunter Limited (1)
5a Priory Grove, Stone, SW8 2PD, United Kingdom
Tel.: (44) 2076270416
Web Site: http://www.rockhunter.co.uk
Information Technology Consulting Services
N.A.I.C.S.: 541512

NBCC (INDIA) LIMITED
NBCC Bhawan Lodhi Road, New Delhi, 110 003, India
Tel.: (91) 1143591555
Web Site: https://nbccindia.in
Year Founded: 1960
NBCC—(NSE)
Rev.: $1,074,452,695
Assets: $1,544,143,049
Liabilities: $1,289,432,264
Net Worth: $254,710,785
Earnings: $33,332,330
Emp.: 1,362
Fiscal Year-end: 03/31/23
Industrial Building Construction
N.A.I.C.S.: 236210
Deepti Gambhir *(Officer-Compliance & Sec)*

NBD-BANK JSC
6 Gorkogo Street, Nizhniy Novgorod, 603600, Russia
Tel.: (7) 8312 20 00 22
Web Site: http://www.nbdbank.ru
Financial Transaction Services
N.A.I.C.S.: 522320
Aleksander Georgievich Sharonov *(Chm-Mgmt Bd)*

NBH CAPITAL CO., LTD.
22nd Floor D Tower Donuimun 134 Tongil-ro, Jongno-gu, Seoul, Korea (South)
Tel.: (82) 264710675
Web Site: https://nbhcapital.co.kr
Year Founded: 2007
Investment Services
N.A.I.C.S.: 523999

NBN CO. LIMITED
Level 11 100 Arthur Street, North Sydney, 2060, NSW, Australia
Tel.: (61) 2 9926 1900
Web Site: http://www.nbnco.com.au
Year Founded: 2009
Rev.: $1,986,596,500
Assets: $23,035,377,540
Liabilities: $17,875,852,400
Net Worth: $5,159,525,140
Earnings: ($3,430,307,160)
Emp.: 6,243
Fiscal Year-end: 06/30/19
Broadband Services
N.A.I.C.S.: 517112
Ziggy Switkowski *(Chm)*

NBS CAPITAL, INC.
11-300 Earl Grey Drive, Ottawa, K2T1C1, ON, Canada
Tel.: (613) 232-1567
NBS.P—(TSXV)
Rev.: $1,374
Assets: $327,709
Liabilities: $1
Net Worth: $327,708
Earnings: ($79,688)
Fiscal Year-end: 06/30/19
Asset Management Services
N.A.I.C.S.: 523940
Paul Barbeau *(Chm & CEO)*

NBT INC.
14F Tower1 Majestar-city 12 Seochodaero 38-gil, Seocho-Gu, Seoul, 06728, Korea (South)
Tel.: (82) 7088959156
Web Site: http://www.nbt.com
Year Founded: 2012
236810—(KRS)
Rev.: $75,813,772
Assets: $74,103,374
Liabilities: $36,244,728
Net Worth: $37,858,647
Earnings: $1,562,212
Emp.: 61
Fiscal Year-end: 12/31/21
Advertising Services
N.A.I.C.S.: 541810
Seunghyeok Kim *(CFO)*

NBTM NEW MATERIALS GROUP CO., LTD.
No 1508 Jingjiang Road Yinzhou Industrial Zone, Ningbo, China
Tel.: (86) 57487399810
Web Site: https://www.pm-china.com
600114—(SHG)
Rev.: $523,178,403
Assets: $910,133,874
Liabilities: $506,914,607
Net Worth: $403,219,267
Earnings: $21,865,587
Fiscal Year-end: 12/31/22
Powder Metallurgy Tool Mfr
N.A.I.C.S.: 332117

Subsidiaries:

Changchun Tongmuo Fawer New Materials Co., Ltd. (1)
High-Tech Zone Yue Da Road Industrial Park on the 9th Factory, Jilin, China
Tel.: (86) 43185811906
Powder Metallurgy Car Shock Absorber Parts Mfr
N.A.I.C.S.: 332117

GuangDong NBTM New Materials Co., Ltd. (1)
Du Ruan Town of Mian Three Road on the 8th, Pengjiang, Jiangmen, Guangdong, China
Tel.: (86) 43185811906
Powder Metallurgy Car Shock Absorber Parts Mfr
N.A.I.C.S.: 332117

Guangdong Dongmu New Materials Co., Ltd. (1)
No 8 Jingmian 3rd Road, Duruan Town Pengjiang District, Jiangmen, Guangdong, China
Tel.: (86) 7503285415
Metallurgy Powder Mfr & Distr
N.A.I.C.S.: 332117

Lianyung Dongmujianghe New Material Co., Ltd. (1)
36 Huanghai Avenue Economic & Technological Development Zone, Lianyungang, Jiangsu, China
Tel.: (86) 51882342157
Metallurgy Powder Mfr & Distr
N.A.I.C.S.: 332117

Lianyungang NBTM New Materials Co., Ltd. (1)
No 36 Huanghai Road Economic and Technological Development Zone, Lianyungang, Jiangsu, China
Tel.: (86) 43185811906
Powder Metallurgy Car Shock Absorber Parts Mfr
N.A.I.C.S.: 332117

NBTM (Tianjin) Powder Metallurgy Co., Ltd. (1)
Xixing Economic Development Zone on the 16th Avenue, Tianjin, China
Tel.: (86) 43185811906
Powder Metallurgy Car Shock Absorber Parts Mfr
N.A.I.C.S.: 332117

Nanjing Dongmu Powder Metallurgy Co., Ltd. (1)
No 7 Gaoke 7th Road High-tech Zone, Nanjing, China
Tel.: (86) 2558843438
Metallurgy Powder Mfr & Distr
N.A.I.C.S.: 332117

Nanjing NBTM Powder Metallurgy Co., Ltd. (1)
No 8 High - Tech Road High - Tech Zone, Nanjing, China
Tel.: (86) 43185811906
Powder Metallurgy Car Shock Absorber Parts Mfr
N.A.I.C.S.: 332117

Nearmap Australia Pty Ltd (1)
Level 4 Tower One International Towers 100 Barangaroo Avenue, Barangaroo, 2000, NSW, Australia
Tel.: (61) 280760700
Web Site: http://www.nearmap.com
Aerial Geophysical Surveying Services
N.A.I.C.S.: 541360
Rob Newman *(CEO)*

Ningbo Dongmu New Materials Group Co., Ltd. (1)
No 1508 Jingjiang Road Yinzhou Industrial Park, Ningbo, 315191, Zhejiang, China
Tel.: (86) 57487399810
Metallurgy Powder Mfr & Distr
N.A.I.C.S.: 332117

Shanghai Fuchi High- Tech Co., Ltd. (1)
4318 Yixian Road, Baoshan District, Shanghai, 200940, China
Tel.: (86) 2156445177
Web Site: https://www.future-sh.com.cn
Soft Magnetic Material Mfr
N.A.I.C.S.: 334610

Shanxi Dongmu Huasheng Powder Metallurgy Co., Ltd. (1)
168 Huajin Avenue, Linyi, Shanxi, China
Tel.: (86) 3594065715
Metallurgy Powder Mfr & Distr
N.A.I.C.S.: 332117

Shanxi NBTM HuaSheng Powder Metallurgy Co., Ltd. (1)
168 Road Jin Hua, Linyi, Shanxi, China
Tel.: (86) 43185811906

NBTM NEW MATERIALS GROUP CO., LTD.

NBTM New Materials Group Co., Ltd.—(Continued)
Powder Metallurgy Car Shock Absorber Parts Mfr
N.A.I.C.S.: 332117

ZheJiang NBTM Keda Magnetoelectricity Co., Ltd. (1)
No 882 North Huancheng Road, Wukang Town Deqing County, Huzhou, 313200, Zhejiang, China
Tel.: (86) 5728088064
Web Site: http://www.kdm-mag.com
Emp.: 477
Magnetic Powder Core Mfr
N.A.I.C.S.: 332999
Ke Xin (Gen Mgr)

Zhejiang Dongmu Keda Magnetoelectric Co., Ltd. (1)
No 882 North Huancheng Road, Fuxi Subdistrict Deqing County, Huzhou, 313200, Zhejiang, China
Tel.: (86) 5728088064
Web Site: https://www.kdm-mag.com
Magnetic Powder Mfr & Distr
N.A.I.C.S.: 332117

NC HOLDINGS CO., LTD.
5F Kanda Mitsubishi Building 3-6-3 Kanda Kajicho, Chiyoda-ku, Tokyo, 101-0045, Japan
Tel.: (81) 366250001   JP
Web Site: https://www.nc-hd.jp
Year Founded: 2016
6236—(TKS)
Rev.: $138,220,720
Assets: $143,322,080
Liabilities: $69,221,680
Net Worth: $74,100,400
Earnings: $3,252,480
Fiscal Year-end: 03/31/23
Holding Company; Conveyor Equipment Mfr
N.A.I.C.S.: 551112

Subsidiaries:

Nippon Conveyor Co., Ltd. (1)
5F Kanda Mitsubishi Building 3-6-3 Kandakaji-cho, Chiyodaku, Tokyo, 101-0045, Japan
Tel.: (81) 368593511
Web Site: https://www.conveyor.co.jp
Emp.: 282
Conveyor Mfr & Whslr
N.A.I.C.S.: 333922
Hironori Kajiwara (Pres)

Subsidiary (Domestic):

Nippon Conveyor Co., Ltd. - Himeji Plant (2)
745-1 Nakamura Kodera-cho, Kanzaki-gun, Hyogo, 679-2166, Japan
Tel.: (81) 792326747
Belt Conveyor System Mfr
N.A.I.C.S.: 333922

NC KAZAKHSTAN TEMIR ZHOLY JSC
6 Konaeva Street, Nur-Sultan, 010000, Kazakhstan
Tel.: (7) 7172930113   KZ
Web Site: http://www.railways.kz
Year Founded: 1997
TMJL—(KAZ)
Rev.: $4,240,696,697
Assets: $10,831,895,676
Liabilities: $6,974,989,490
Net Worth: $3,856,906,186
Earnings: $299,912,598
Emp.: 116,465
Fiscal Year-end: 12/31/23
Cargo & Passenger Transportation Services
N.A.I.C.S.: 488210
Kanat Kalievich Alpysbayev (Chm-Mgmt Bd)

Subsidiaries:

JSC Kaztemirtrans (1)
Administrative building Izumrudny kvartal 10 D Kunayev str, Nur-Sultan, 010000, Kazakhstan
Tel.: (7) 8 7172 930 201
Web Site: http://www.kazcargo.kz
Car Repair Services
N.A.I.C.S.: 811111
Elyubaev Sanzhar Bakhytovich (Co-Chm & Pres)

KTZ-Freight Transportation LLP (1)
Tel.: (7) 172603030
Web Site: https://www.ktzh-gp.kz
Freight Transportation Services
N.A.I.C.S.: 488510

NC& CO., LTD.
5th Floor, Uspace1 A Building, 660, Bundang-gu, Seongnam, Gyeonggi-do, Korea (South)
Tel.: (82) 234604780
Web Site: https://www.nextchip.com
Year Founded: 1997
092600—(KRS)
Rev.: $71,019,254
Assets: $88,057,341
Liabilities: $31,216,177
Net Worth: $56,841,164
Earnings: ($27,856,236)
Emp.: 120
Fiscal Year-end: 12/31/22
Semiconductor Mfr
N.A.I.C.S.: 334413

NCAB GROUP AB
Lofstroms alle 5, 172 66, Sundbyberg, Sweden
Tel.: (46) 840300050   SE
Web Site: https://www.ncabgroup.com
Year Founded: 1993
NCAB—(OMX)
Rev.: $419,470,904
Assets: $284,835,483
Liabilities: $172,832,710
Net Worth: $112,002,772
Earnings: $39,070,499
Emp.: 587
Fiscal Year-end: 12/31/22
Holding Company; Printed Circuit Board Mfr & Distr
N.A.I.C.S.: 551112
Michael Larsson (VP-Sls)

Subsidiaries:

NCAB Group Benelux B.V. (1)
Lingewei 101, 4004 LH, Tiel, Netherlands
Tel.: (31) 344622556
Electrical & Electronic Mfr
N.A.I.C.S.: 334419

NCAB Group Denmark A/S (1)
Bag Haverne 30, Koge, Denmark
Tel.: (45) 56161680
Electrical & Electronic Product Mfr
N.A.I.C.S.: 335999

NCAB Group France S.A.S. (1)
10 Bis rue Nicephore Niepce, 45700, Villemaur-sur-Vanne, France
Tel.: (33) 218200140
Web Site: https://www.ncabgroup.com
Electrical & Electronic Mfr
N.A.I.C.S.: 334419

NCAB Group Germany GmbH (1)
Elsenheimer Strasse 7, 80687, Munich, Germany
Tel.: (49) 89150016640
Electrical & Electronic Product Mfr
N.A.I.C.S.: 335999

NCAB Group Iberia S.A.U. (1)
Jose Antonio Zapata 3 2 Planta, 28045, Madrid, Spain
Tel.: (34) 915398877
Web Site: https://www.ncabgroup.com
Electrical & Electronic Mfr
N.A.I.C.S.: 334419

NCAB Group Italy S.r.l. (1)
Via Stazione 123, 21020, Mornago, VA, Italy
Tel.: (39) 0331946748

Electrical & Electronic Product Mfr
N.A.I.C.S.: 335999

NCAB Group Norway AS (1)
Storgata 10, Gjovik, Norway
Tel.: (47) 61114100
Electrical & Electronic Product Mfr
N.A.I.C.S.: 335999

NCAB Group Polska Sp. z.o.o (1)
Diamond Business Park Ul J Pawla II 66, 05-500, Piaseczno, Poland
Tel.: (48) 224627990
Electrical & Electronic Product Mfr
N.A.I.C.S.: 335999

NCAB Group ShenZhen Electronics Co Ltd. (1)
11th Floor Chiwan Tower No 8 Chiwan 6th Rd, Qianhai & Shekou FTA, Shenzhen, 518067, China
Tel.: (86) 75521622069
Electrical & Electronic Product Mfr
N.A.I.C.S.: 335999

NCAB Group South East Asia Sdn Bhd (1)
138-03-03 Unit No 3 3rd Floor Anson Cube Jalan Anson, Georgetown, 10400, Penang, Malaysia
Tel.: (60) 42170785
Electrical & Electronic Product Mfr
N.A.I.C.S.: 335999

NCAB Group Sweden AB (1)
Lofstroms alle 5, 172 66, Sundbyberg, Sweden
Tel.: (46) 840300000
Web Site: https://www.ncabgroup.com
Printed Circuit Board Mfr & Whslr
N.A.I.C.S.: 334418
Rikard Wallin (Mng Dir & Grp VP-Nordic)

NCAB Group UK Ltd. (1)
Units 1-3 Hopton Industrial Estate London Road, Devizes, SN10 2EU, Wiltshire, United Kingdom
Tel.: (44) 1380736140
Electrical & Electronic Product Mfr
N.A.I.C.S.: 335999

NCAB Group USA, Inc. (1)
10 Starwood Dr, Hampstead, NH 03841
Tel.: (603) 329-4551
Web Site: https://www.ncabgroup.com
Printed Circuit Board Mfr & Whslr
N.A.I.C.S.: 334418
Martin Magnusson (Pres)

Subsidiary (Domestic):

Bare Board Group, Inc. (2)
8565 B Somerset Dr, Largo, FL 33773
Tel.: (727) 549-2200
Web Site: http://www.bareboard.com
Sales Range: $25-49.9 Million
Electronic Parts & Equipment Merchant Whslr
N.A.I.C.S.: 423690

NCAB Macedonia A.D. (1)
Ul Vojvodinska 69/6, Prilep, North Macedonia
Tel.: (389) 23090010
Circuit Board Mfr
N.A.I.C.S.: 334412

Phase 3 Technologies Inc. (1)
780 Montague Expy Ste 401, San Jose, CA 95131-1318
Web Site: http://www.p3ti.com
Emp.: 17
Bare Printed Circuit Board Mfr
N.A.I.C.S.: 334412
Christopher Doyle (Mgr-Sls)

NCC BLUEWATER PRODUCTS LIMITED
NCC House Madhapur, Hyderabad, 500 081, Telangana, India
Tel.: (91) 4023268888   In
Web Site: https://www.nccbpl.com
Year Founded: 1992
519506—(BOM)
Rev.: $76,051
Assets: $949,667
Liabilities: $11,942
Net Worth: $937,726

INTERNATIONAL PUBLIC

Earnings: $40,513
Fiscal Year-end: 03/31/23
Aquaculture Farming Services
N.A.I.C.S.: 112512
J. S. N. Raju (Exec Dir)

NCC GROUP PLC
XYZ Building 2 Hardman Boulevard Spinningfields, Manchester, M3 3AQ, United Kingdom
Tel.: (44) 1612095200   UK
Web Site: https://www.nccgroup.com
Year Founded: 1999
NCC—(LSE)
Rev.: $367,263,260
Assets: $586,942,356
Liabilities: $225,517,292
Net Worth: $361,425,064
Earnings: $13,577,200
Emp.: 1,897
Fiscal Year-end: 05/31/21
IInformation Security Services
N.A.I.C.S.: 541519
Chris Stone (Chm)

Subsidiaries:

Accumuli Limited (1)
XYZ Building 2 Hardman Boulevard Spinningfields, Manchester, M3 3AQ, United Kingdom
Tel.: (44) 1612095200
Web Site: http://www.nccgroup.trust
Information Security Solutions
N.A.I.C.S.: 561621

Escrow Associates LLC (1)
8302 Dunwoody Pl Ste 150, Atlanta, GA 30350
Tel.: (770) 518-2451
Web Site: http://www.escrowassociates.com
Sales Range: $25-49.9 Million
Emp.: 14
Data Processing, Hosting & Related Services
N.A.I.C.S.: 518210

Escrow Europe AG (1)
Ibelweg 18A, CH 6300, Zug, Switzerland
Tel.: (41) 417632800
Web Site: http://www.escroweurope.ch
Sales Range: $25-49.9 Million
Emp.: 5
Software Escrow, Assurance & Secure Access Services
N.A.I.C.S.: 541519

Escrow Europe BV (1)
Veemkade 396, 1019 HE, Amsterdam, Netherlands
Tel.: (31) 20 620 1733
Web Site: http://www.escroweurope.nl
Sales Range: $25-49.9 Million
Emp.: 12
Software Escrow, Assurance & Secure Access Services
N.A.I.C.S.: 541519

Fox-IT B.V. (1)
Olof Palmestraat 6, 2616 LM, Delft, Netherlands
Tel.: (31) 152847999
Web Site: https://www.fox-it.com
Cyber Security Services
N.A.I.C.S.: 922190
Inge Bryan (Mng Dir)

NCC Group Escrow Europe (Switzerland) AG (1)
Ibelweg 18A, 6300, Zug, Switzerland
Tel.: (41) 417632800
Escrow Agency Services
N.A.I.C.S.: 523997

NCC Group GmbH (1)
Leibnizstrasse 1, 85521, Ottobrunn, Germany
Tel.: (49) 895997620
Web Site: http://www.nccgroupescrow.de
Sales Range: $25-49.9 Million
Emp.: 10
Software Escrow, Assurance & Secure Access Services
N.A.I.C.S.: 541519

NCC Group Inc. (1)

AND PRIVATE COMPANIES

1731 Technology Dr Ste 880, San Jose, CA 95110-1370
Tel.: (408) 441-4660
Web Site: http://www.nccgroup.us
Software Escrow, Assurance & Secure Access Services
N.A.I.C.S.: 541519
Adam Rudderman *(Dir-Bug Bounty Svcs Practice)*

NCC Group Japan KK (1)
4-20-3 Ebisu Yebisu Garden Place Tower 18F, Shibuya-ku, Tokyo, 150-6018, Japan
Tel.: (81) 357895392
Web Site: https://www.nccgroup.com
Cyber Security Services
N.A.I.C.S.: 922190

NCC Group Security Services Espana SLU (1)
Plaza Manuel Gomez-Moreno Num 2 Piso 19 Puerta B, Edificio Alfredo Mahou, 28020, Madrid, Spain
Tel.: (34) 663967328
Web Site: https://www.nccgroup.com
Cyber Security Services
N.A.I.C.S.: 922190

NCC Group Software Resilience (Europe) BV (1)
Van Heuven Goedhartlaan 13A, Amstelveen, 1181 LE, Amsterdam, Netherlands
Tel.: (31) 206207151
Escrow Agency Services
N.A.I.C.S.: 523991

NGS Secure (1)
Manchester Technology Centre, Oxford Road, Manchester, M1 7EF, United Kingdom
Tel.: (44) 161 209 5111
Web Site: http://www.nccgroup.com
Security Software Development & Security Testing Services
N.A.I.C.S.: 541519

Branch (Domestic):

NGS Secure (2)
Suite 311 Eagle Tower, Montpellier Drive, Cheltenham, GL50 1TA, United Kingdom
Tel.: (44) 208 401 0070
Web Site: http://www.ngssecure.com
Sales Range: $25-49.9 Million
Emp.: 50
Security Software Development & Security Testing Services
N.A.I.C.S.: 541511

Payment Software Company Limited (1)
268 Bath Road, Slough, London, SL1 4DX, Berkshire, United Kingdom
Tel.: (44) 1753727066
Financial Transaction Processing Services
N.A.I.C.S.: 522320

Site Confidence Limited (1)
Kings Court, Kingston Road, Leatherhead, KT22 7SL, United Kingdom
Tel.: (44) 1372 383 800
Web Site: http://www.nccgroup.com
Sales Range: $25-49.9 Million
Emp.: 45
Website Performance Monitoring Services
N.A.I.C.S.: 541519
Simon Austin *(Dir-Technical)*

iSEC Partners, Inc. (1)
444 Spear St Ste 105, San Francisco, CA 94105
Tel.: (415) 217-0052
Sales Range: $25-49.9 Million
Emp.: 30
Security Consulting Services
N.A.I.C.S.: 541690
Scott Stender *(Co-Founder & Partner)*

NCC LIMITED

NCC House, Madhapur, Hyderabad, 500 081, India
Tel.: (91) 4023268888
Web Site: https://www.ncclimited.com
Year Founded: 1978
NCC—(NSE)
Rev.: $1,100,917,545
Assets: $1,848,193,620
Liabilities: $1,101,619,155
Net Worth: $746,574,465
Earnings: $38,634,960
Emp.: 4,881
Fiscal Year-end: 03/31/21
Construction Engineering Services
N.A.I.C.S.: 541330
A. A. V. Ranga Raju *(Mng Dir)*

Subsidiaries:

NCC Infrastructure Holdings Limited (1)
NCC House, Madhapur, Hyderabad, 500 081, Telangana, India
Tel.: (91) 4023268888
Web Site: https://www.nccinfra.com
Real Estate Services
N.A.I.C.S.: 531390

NCC Urban Infrastructure Limited (1)
NCC House Survey No 64 7th Floor Opp Durgam Cheruvu, Madhapur, Hyderabad, 500 081, India
Tel.: (91) 4023268789
Web Site: https://www.nccurban.com
Real Estate Services
N.A.I.C.S.: 531390

NCDH GROUP AG

Bellerivestrasse 201, 8008, Zurich, Switzerland
Tel.: (41) 444422000
Web Site: https://www.ncdh.ch
Year Founded: 1987
Holding Company
N.A.I.C.S.: 551112

NCL INDUSTRIES LIMITED

103162 NCL PEARL 7th Floor Opp Hyderabad Bhawan, Sarojini Devi Road East Maredpally, Secunderabad, 500026, India
Tel.: (91) 4030120000
Web Site: https://www.nclind.com
502168—(BOM)
Rev.: $189,952,076
Assets: $177,309,255
Liabilities: $86,577,773
Net Worth: $90,731,482
Earnings: $19,853,666
Emp.: 922
Fiscal Year-end: 03/31/21
Cement Mfr
N.A.I.C.S.: 327310
K. Gautam *(Exec Dir)*

Subsidiaries:

NCL Alltek and Seccolor Ltd. (1)
Opp Byrraju Foundation Petbasheerabad Kompally Road, Hyderabad, 500 055, India
Tel.: (91) 40 49693333
Web Site: http://www.nclseccolor.com
Textured Spray Plaster & Paint Mfr
N.A.I.C.S.: 325510

NCL HOMES LTD (1)
5th Floor NCL Ganga Plaza Above IDBI Bank, Pet Basheerabad Quthbullapur, Hyderabad, 500067, India
Tel.: (91) 799 799 9001
Web Site: https://nclhomes.in
Residential Building Construction Services
N.A.I.C.S.: 236116

NCL Industries Limited - Boards Division (1)
10th Floor Unity Buildings JC Road, Bengaluru, 560052, India
Tel.: (91) 80 22122984
Web Site: http://www.nclind.com
Sales Range: $25-49.9 Million
Emp.: 3
Particleboard Mfr
N.A.I.C.S.: 321219

NCL Industries Limited - Cement Division (1)
Door No 50-48-13 P&T colony Sitammadhara, Visakhapatnam, 530 013, India
Tel.: (91) 9390809944
Sales Range: $25-49.9 Million
Emp.: 8
Cement Mfr

N.A.I.C.S.: 327310
K. V. Dilip Kumar *(Deputy Gen Mgr)*

NCL INTERNATIONAL LOGISTICS PUBLIC COMPANY LIMITED

56 SOI Somdet Phra chao tak Sin 12/1 Somdejprachaotaksin Road, Bukkhalo Thonburi, Bangkok, 10600, Thailand
Tel.: (66) 24594945   TH
Web Site: https://www.nclthailand.com
Year Founded: 1994
NCL—(THA)
Rev.: $21,091,124
Assets: $28,193,890
Liabilities: $18,450,851
Net Worth: $9,743,038
Earnings: ($9,581,477)
Emp.: 133
Fiscal Year-end: 12/31/23
Logistic Services
N.A.I.C.S.: 541614
Admiral Surapong Amnucksoradeja *(Chm)*

Subsidiaries:

NCL Inter Logistics (S) Pte. Ltd. (1)
8 Burn Road 10-08 Trivex, Singapore, 369977, Singapore
Tel.: (65) 67021081
Logistic Services
N.A.I.C.S.: 488510
Mar Cheng *(Reg CEO)*

Subsidiary (US):

NCL International Logistics USA Inc. (2)
7372 Walnut Ave Ste W, Buena Park, CA 90620
Tel.: (714) 735-8004
Logistic Services
N.A.I.C.S.: 488510

Subsidiary (Non-US):

Qingdao National Container Line Co., Ltd. (2)
Room 2118 New World Building No 9 Fuzhou South Road, Shinan District, Qingdao, China
Tel.: (86) 53286677776
Logistic Services
N.A.I.C.S.: 488510

NCL RESEARCH & FINANCIAL SERVICES LIMITED

79 Nagindas Master Road Bhagyoday Building 3rd Floor Fort, Mumbai, 400023, India
Tel.: (91) 2222703249
Web Site: https://www.nclfin.com
Year Founded: 1985
530557—(BOM)
Rev.: $451,196
Assets: $15,471,986
Liabilities: $590,768
Net Worth: $14,881,218
Earnings: $72,022
Emp.: 10
Fiscal Year-end: 03/31/23
Security Brokerage Services
N.A.I.C.S.: 523150
Goutam Bose *(Chm & Mng Dir)*

NCONDEZI ENERGY LIMITED

Coastal Building Wickhams Cay II Road Town, PO Box 2221, Tortola, Virgin Islands (British)
Tel.: (284) 20 7183 5402   VG
Web Site:
  http://www.ncondezienergy.com
NCCL—(AIM)
Sales Range: Less than $1 Million
Emp.: 4
Coal Exploration & Power Generation Services
N.A.I.C.S.: 212115

NCSOFT CORPORATION

Hanno Pengilly *(CEO)*

Subsidiaries:

Ncondezi Services UK Ltd (1)
3 Grafton Street, Mayfair, London, W1S 4EE, United Kingdom
Tel.: (44) 2071835402
Sales Range: $50-74.9 Million
Emp.: 8
Coal Mining Support Services
N.A.I.C.S.: 213113

NCS&A CO., LTD.

3-3-23 Nakanoshima, Kita-ku, Osaka, 530-6112, Japan
Tel.: (81) 664431991
Web Site: https://ncsa.jp
Year Founded: 1966
9709—(TKS)
Rev.: $124,975,270
Assets: $126,984,710
Liabilities: $45,992,380
Net Worth: $80,992,330
Earnings: $10,152,960
Emp.: 1,335
Fiscal Year-end: 03/31/24
Computer System & Software Development Services
N.A.I.C.S.: 513210
Takahiro Tsuji *(Pres)*

Subsidiaries:

Every Co., Ltd. (1)
2-10-14 Atago, Chuo-ku, Niigata, 950-0944, Japan
Tel.: (81) 252113260
Web Site: https://www.everycar.jp
Used Car Distr
N.A.I.C.S.: 441120
Yuichiro Watabe *(Pres & CEO)*

NCS&A Shanghai Co. Ltd. (1)
Room 1003 Bldg 7 No 3088 Gonghexin Road, Jingan District, Shanghai, 200072, China
Tel.: (86) 2156430003
Web Site: http://www.ncsash.cn
Software Development Services
N.A.I.C.S.: 541511
Lv Xingping *(Chm & Gen Mgr)*

NCSOFT CORPORATION

12 Daewangpangyo-ro 644beon-gil, Bundang-gu, Seongnam, 13494, Gyeonggi-do, Korea (South)
Tel.: (82) 221863300   KR
Web Site: https://kr.ncsoft.com
Year Founded: 1997
036570—(KRS)
Rev.: $1,321,076,094
Assets: $3,261,286,184
Liabilities: $846,734,768
Net Worth: $2,414,551,416
Earnings: $157,459,616
Emp.: 5,023
Fiscal Year-end: 12/31/23
Software Development Services
N.A.I.C.S.: 513210
Park Byung-moo *(Co-CEO)*

Subsidiaries:

NC Interactive, Inc. (1)
6801 N Capital of Texas Hwy Bldg 1 Ste 102, Austin, TX 78731-1780   (100%)
Tel.: (512) 498-4000
Web Site: http://us.ncsoft.com
Sales Range: $25-49.9 Million
Emp.: 300
Online Game Development & Publishing
N.A.I.C.S.: 513210

Subsidiary (Domestic):

ArenaNet, Inc. (2)
3180 139th Ave SE 5th Fl, Bellevue, WA 98005   (100%)
Tel.: (425) 247-2500
Web Site: https://www.arena.net
Sales Range: $100-124.9 Million
Emp.: 260
Online Games Developer & Publisher
N.A.I.C.S.: 513210

NCSOFT CORPORATION

NCsoft Corporation—(Continued)
Jason VandenBerghe (Dir-Design)

NC Japan K.K. (1)
TRI SEVEN ROPPONGI 11th floor 7-7-7 Roppongi, Minato-ku, Tokyo, 106-0032, Japan (60%)
Tel.: (81) 354102515
Web Site: https://www.ncjapan.co.jp
Sales Range: $50-74.9 Million
Emp.: 185
Online Game Development & Publishing
N.A.I.C.S.: 513210

NC Taiwan Co., Ltd. (1)
6F No 738 Zhongzheng Road Zhonge District, Zhonghe Dist, Taipei, 23511, Taiwan (85%)
Tel.: (886) 2 8024 3300
Web Site: http://www.nctaiwan.com
Sales Range: $50-74.9 Million
Emp.: 180
Online Games Publishing Services
N.A.I.C.S.: 513210
Joshua Lu (Pres)

NCsoft China Co., Ltd. (1)
19/F A Building No 18 Guobin Road, Yangpu District, Shanghai, 200433, China (100%)
Tel.: (86) 21 5175 7100
Web Site: http://www.ncsoft.net
Online Game Development & Publishing
N.A.I.C.S.: 513210

NCsoft Europe Ltd. (1)
5th Floor Mocatta House Trafalgar Place, Brighton, BN1 4DU, United Kingdom (100%)
Tel.: (44) 1273872000
Web Site: http://eu.ncsoft.com
Emp.: 32
Online Game Development & Publishing
N.A.I.C.S.: 513210
Dong-il Kim (Gen Mgr)

NCT ALLIANCE BERHAD

Menara NCT No 2 Jalan BP 4/9 Bandar Bukit Puchong, Selangor Darul Ehsan, 47100, Puchong, Selangor, Malaysia
Tel.: (60) 80643333 **MY**
Web Site: https://www.nctalliance.com
Year Founded: 1996
NCT—(KLS)
Rev.: $60,835,635
Assets: $178,166,622
Liabilities: $45,301,398
Net Worth: $132,865,225
Earnings: $8,245,807
Fiscal Year-end: 12/31/23
Data Management Services
N.A.I.C.S.: 518210
Tea Sor Hua (Sec)

Subsidiaries:

CL Solutions Limited (1)
Unit 4 G/F Po Lung Centre 11 Wang Chiu Road, Kowloon Bay, Kowloon, China (Hong Kong)
Tel.: (852) 29890300
Web Site: http://www.clsghk.com
Electronic Components Mfr
N.A.I.C.S.: 334419

Grand-Flo Electronic System Sdn. Bhd (1)
No G-9-2 & 3 Lorong Bayan Indah 1 Bay Avenue Queensbay, Sungai Nibong, 11900, Penang, Malaysia
Tel.: (60) 46456991
Data Management Services
N.A.I.C.S.: 518210

Guangzhou CL Solutions Limited (1)
Room 3811 Jiangwan Business Center 298 Yanjiang Zhong Road, Guangzhou, China
Tel.: (86) 2083863338
Software Development Services
N.A.I.C.S.: 513210

Innoceria Sdn. Bhd. (1)
22A Jalan Perniagaan Vorteks 3 Pusat Perniagaan Vorteks, Simpang Empat, 14100, Penang, Malaysia

Tel.: (60) 45899887
Data Management Services
N.A.I.C.S.: 518210

NCT INTERNATIONAL B.V.

Minervum 7208A, PO Box 5669, 4817 ZJ, Breda, Netherlands
Tel.: (31) 765315780 **NI**
Web Site: http://www.nctww.com
Year Founded: 1983
Holding Company; Plastic Raw Materials Distr
N.A.I.C.S.: 551112
Eric Korstanje (Mgr-Comml)

Subsidiaries:

NCT Finland (1)
Palatsinraitti 1A20, 33210, Tampere, Finland
Tel.: (358) 106669933
Plastic Material Distr
N.A.I.C.S.: 424610

NCT Germany (1)
Schulenburgring 106, 21031, Hamburg, Germany
Tel.: (49) 4073098431
Plastic Material Distr
N.A.I.C.S.: 424610

NCT Holland B.V. (1)
Minervum 7208 A, Breda, 4817 ZJ, Netherlands
Tel.: (31) 765315780
Sales Range: $25-49.9 Million
Emp.: 16
Plastic Material Distr
N.A.I.C.S.: 424610
Bart Vrijens (Dir-Fin)

NCT India (1)
190A First Floor Pettukola Towers Poonthamallee High Road, Kilpauk, 600010, Chennai, Tamil Nadu, India
Tel.: (91) 4426651041
Sales Range: $50-74.9 Million
Emp.: 5
Plastic Material Distr
N.A.I.C.S.: 424610

NCT Italy (1)
Riviera Marco Polo 11, 30174, Mestre, Italy
Tel.: (39) 0415352201
Plastic Material Distr
N.A.I.C.S.: 424610

NCT Poland (1)
Ul Druzyn Strzeleckich 3, 80-180, Gdansk, Poland
Tel.: (48) 583201647
Plastic Material Distr
N.A.I.C.S.: 424610

NCT Spain (1)
Carrer Balmes 281 Atico, 08006, Barcelona, Spain
Tel.: (34) 691909735
Plastic Material Distr
N.A.I.C.S.: 424610
Roel de groot (Area Mgr)

NCT Turkey (1)
Esenkent Cad Enverpasa Cad 34510 No 8 - 8N Daire 28, Esenyurt, 34510, Istanbul, Türkiye
Tel.: (90) 212 236 3115
Web Site: http://www.nctww.com
Emp.: 1
Plastic Material Distr
N.A.I.C.S.: 424610
Demet Kaya (Office Mgr)

ND GRAPHIC PRODUCT LIMITED

55 Interchange Way Unit 1, Concord, L4K 5W3, ON, Canada
Tel.: (416) 663-6416
Web Site: http://www.ndgraphics.com
Year Founded: 1981
Rev.: $26,113,000
Emp.: 86
Graphic Products Whslr
N.A.I.C.S.: 323111
Mark West (Pres)

ND SOFTWARE CO., LTD.

3369 Wada, Nanyo-shi, Yamagata, 992-0479, Japan
Tel.: (81) 238 473477
Web Site: http://www.ndsoft.jp
Rev.: $137,000,640
Assets: $172,662,720
Liabilities: $83,853,840
Net Worth: $88,808,880
Earnings: $11,117,760
Emp.: 959
Fiscal Year-end: 03/31/18
Software Developer
N.A.I.C.S.: 513210
Hiroshi Sato (Pres)

NDA SECURITIES LIMITED

E-157 2nd Floor Kalkaji, New Delhi, 110019, India
Tel.: (91) 1146204000
Web Site: https://www.ndaindia.com
Year Founded: 1992
511535—(BOM)
Rev.: $688,220
Assets: $1,966,980
Liabilities: $925,652
Net Worth: $1,041,328
Earnings: $94,707
Emp.: 35
Fiscal Year-end: 03/31/23
Securities Brokerage Services
N.A.I.C.S.: 523150
Sanjay Agarwal (Mng Dir)

Subsidiaries:

NDA Commodity Brokers Pvt. Ltd. (1)
Prospect Chamber Annexe Shop 21 2nd Floor Dr D N Road Fort, Mumbai, 400 001, India
Tel.: (91) 2222834099
Sales Range: $50-74.9 Million
Emp.: 4
Commodity Brokerage Services
N.A.I.C.S.: 523160
Pramod Gupta (Gen Mgr)

NDATALYZE CORP.

5614A Burbank Road SE, Calgary, T2H 1Z4, AB, Canada
Tel.: (780) 996-0049
Web Site: http://www.medxtractor.com
Year Founded: 2018
NDAT—(CNSX)
Rev.: $72,749
Assets: $662,921
Liabilities: $28,891
Net Worth: $634,030
Earnings: ($117,497)
Emp.: 5
Fiscal Year-end: 02/29/24
Cannabis Oil Mfr
N.A.I.C.S.: 325412
James Durward (Pres)

Subsidiaries:

Mindbalanced Inc. (1)

NDC AUSTRALIA PTY LTD

6 Holt Street, McMahons Point, 2060, NSW, Australia
Tel.: (61) 90080300
Web Site: https://www.nationaldentalcare.com
Emp.: 100
Dental Services
N.A.I.C.S.: 339116

NDF ENTERPRISES LTD.

PO Box 1187, Coquitlam, V3J 6Z9, BC, Canada
Tel.: (604) 888-7949
Web Site: http://www.ndf-fab.com
Year Founded: 1980
Mechanical Contracting, Management Consulting Services & Fabricated Metals Mfr

INTERNATIONAL PUBLIC

N.A.I.C.S.: 237130
Neil Fredrikson (Pres)

NDFOS CO.,LTD.

224-7 Hansam-ro Daeso-myeon, Eumseong, Chungbuk, Korea (South)
Tel.: (82) 438813325
Web Site: https://www.ndfos.com
Year Founded: 2010
238090—(KRS)
Rev.: $68,729,089
Assets: $132,695,871
Liabilities: $25,168,655
Net Worth: $107,527,216
Earnings: ($15,150,933)
Emp.: 128
Fiscal Year-end: 12/31/22
Adhesive Tape Mfr
N.A.I.C.S.: 322220
Jung In-Hee (CFO)

NDL CONSTRUCTION LTD.

83 Symington Lane S, PO Box 53 Grp 612 SS6, Winnipeg, R5T 0E3, MB, Canada
Tel.: (204) 255-7300
Web Site: https://www.ndlconstruction.com
Year Founded: 1974
Building Construction Services
N.A.I.C.S.: 236220
Harold Barg (Owner)

NDX UAB

Ozo St 25, 07150, Vilnius, Lithuania
Tel.: (370) 52042112
Web Site: http://www.ndx.lt
Investment Holding Company
N.A.I.C.S.: 551112
Petras Jasinskas (CEO)

Subsidiaries:

Doggy AB (1)
Doggyvagen 1, 447 84, Vargarda, Sweden
Tel.: (46) 771 64 64 00
Web Site: http://www.doggy.se
Sales Range: $50-74.9 Million
Emp.: 160
Cat & Dog Food Mfr & Sales
N.A.I.C.S.: 311111
Kristina Hard Forser (Dir-Mktg & Innovation)

NDX Energija UAB (1)
Ozo g 25, 07150, Vilnius, Lithuania
Tel.: (370) 5 204 2112
Web Site: http://www.ndxenergija.lt
Emp.: 3
Investment Firm
N.A.I.C.S.: 523999
Ignas Staskevicius (Chm-Mgmt Bd)

NE NEUNGYULE, INC.

Business Tower 10th Floor 396 World Cup buk-ro, Mapo-gu, Seoul, 03925, Korea (South)
Tel.: (82) 220147114
Web Site: https://www.neungyule.com
Year Founded: 1980
053290—(KRS)
Rev.: $61,536,357
Assets: $86,230,712
Liabilities: $20,696,990
Net Worth: $65,533,722
Earnings: $3,483,899
Emp.: 380
Fiscal Year-end: 12/31/22
Books Publishing Services
N.A.I.C.S.: 513130
Min Hong Joo (CEO)

NEARCTIC NICKEL MINES, INC.

160 Matheson Blvd East Suite 5, Mississauga, L4V 1V4, ON, Canada
Tel.: (416) 277-4528
NNMIF—(OTCIQ)
Sales Range: Less than $1 Million

AND PRIVATE COMPANIES

Mineral Resource Services
N.A.I.C.S.: 212290
Glen Erikson (Pres)

NEATE ROLLER LIMITED
6820 Rexwood Road, Mississauga,
L4V 1L8, ON, Canada
Tel.: (416) 213-7411
Year Founded: 1975
Rev.: $153,023,112
Emp.: 150
Food Service
N.A.I.C.S.: 722310
Paul Paul (Pres & CEO)

NEBAG AG
Tel.: (41) 432430790
Web Site: https://www.nebag.ch
NBEN—(SWX)
Sales Range: Less than $1 Million
Investment Management Service
N.A.I.C.S.: 523940
Martin Wipfli (Chm)

NEBU RESOURCES INC.
80 Richmond St West Suite 1400
Suite 520, Toronto, M5H 2A4, ON,
Canada
Tel.: (416) 363-1210
Web Site:
 http://www.neburesources.com
Year Founded: 2006
NBU—(TSXV)
Assets: $7,097
Liabilities: $836,819
Net Worth: ($829,722)
Earnings: ($66,146)
Fiscal Year-end: 11/30/22
Mineral Exploration Services
N.A.I.C.S.: 213114
Mark Mungo (CFO)

NEC CAPITAL SOLUTIONS LIMITED
Shinagawa Intercity C building 15-3
Konan 2-chome, Minato-ku, Tokyo,
108-6219, Japan
Tel.: (81) 367208400
Web Site: https://www.necap.co.jp
Year Founded: 1978
8793—(TKS)
Rev.: $1,691,214,770
Assets: $7,385,769,430
Liabilities: $6,481,587,530
Net Worth: $904,181,900
Earnings: $46,494,740
Emp.: 880
Fiscal Year-end: 03/31/24
Financial Services
N.A.I.C.S.: 523940
Tomoshige Shimura (Exec Officer-Credit & Collection Dept)

Subsidiaries:

NEC Capital Solutions Hong Kong
Limited (1)
25th Floor The Metropolis Tower 10 Metropolis Drive, Hunghom, Kowloon, China
(Hong Kong)
Tel.: (852) 27335341
Leasing Services
N.A.I.C.S.: 532490

NEC Capital Solutions Malaysia Sdn.
Bhd. (1)
Suite 18 01 Level 18 The Gardens South
Tower Mid Valley City, Lingkaran Syed Putra, 59200, Kuala Lumpur, Malaysia
Tel.: (60) 322849881
Web Site: https://www.necap.co.jp
Leasing Services
N.A.I.C.S.: 532490
Tony Wong (Sr Mgr)

NEC Capital Solutions Singapore Pte.
Limited (1)
80 Bendemeer Road 08-01, Singapore,
339949, Singapore
Tel.: (65) 63792507

Web Site: https://www.necap.co.jp
Leasing Services
N.A.I.C.S.: 532490

RISA Funds & Assets Solutions,
Inc. (1)
19F Shinagawa Intercity Tower C 2-15-3
Konan, Minato, Tokyo, 108-6219, Japan
Tel.: (81) 357968670
Web Site: https://www.risa-p.com
Financial Services
N.A.I.C.S.: 523210
Jun Kiriyama (Pres)

RISA Loan Services Inc. (1)
19F Shinagawa Intercity Tower C 2-15-3
Konan, Minato-ku, Tokyo, 108-6219, Japan
Tel.: (81) 357968650
Web Site: https://www.risa-p.com
Real Estate Rental Services
N.A.I.C.S.: 531311

RISA Loan Servicing Inc. (1)
19F Shinagawa Intercity Tower C 2-15-3
Konan, Minato, Tokyo, 108-6219, Japan
Tel.: (81) 357968650
Web Site: https://www.risa-p.com
Financial Services
N.A.I.C.S.: 523210
Masahiro Taguchi (Pres)

RISA Partners Asia Pte. Ltd. (1)
9 Raffles Place 52-01 Republic Plaza, Singapore, 048619, Singapore
Tel.: (65) 65325425
Web Site: https://www.risa-p.com
Investment Management Service
N.A.I.C.S.: 523210
Chua Taik Him (Chm)

Reboot Technology Services and
Capitech Limited (1)
Shinagawa Intercity C building 15-3 Konan
2-chome, Minato-ku, Tokyo, 108-6219, Japan
Tel.: (81) 367208395
Web Site: https://www.rebootts.com
Information & Communications Technology
Equipment Distr
N.A.I.C.S.: 423690

NEC CORPORATION
7-1 Shiba 5-chome, Minato-ku, Tokyo, 108-8001, Japan
Tel.: (81) 334541111   JP
Web Site: https://www.nec.com
Year Founded: 1899
6701—(TKS)
Rev.: $22,984,701,820
Assets: $27,943,867,540
Liabilities: $14,132,120,510
Net Worth: $13,811,747,030
Earnings: $988,333,810
Emp.: 105,276
Fiscal Year-end: 03/31/24
Communications Systems & Equipment, Computers & Industrial Electronic Systems & Electron Devices
Mfr & Sales
N.A.I.C.S.: 334111
Nobuhiro Endo (Chm)

Subsidiaries:

Avaloq Group AG (1)
Schwerzistrasse 6, 8807, Freienbach, Switzerland
Tel.: (41) 58 316 3117
Web Site: http://www.avaloq.com
Holding Company; Banking & Financial Industry Business Process Outsourcing Software Publisher & Support Services
N.A.I.C.S.: 551112
Ronald Strassler (Member-Exec Bd)

Subsidiary (Non-US):

Avaloq Asia Pacific Pte. Ltd. (2)
One Phillip Street 06 Suite 01, Singapore,
48692, Singapore
Tel.: (65) 64381017
Software Development Services
N.A.I.C.S.: 541511

Avaloq Australia Pty. Ltd. (2)
L14 175 Pitt St, Sydney, 2000, NSW, Australia

Tel.: (61) 280745600
Software Development Services
N.A.I.C.S.: 541511
Daniel Egli (Project Mgr)

Subsidiary (Domestic):

Avaloq Evolution AG (2)
Allmendstrasse 140, 8027, Zurich, Switzerland
Tel.: (41) 583161010
Web Site: http://www.avaloq.com
Banking & Financial Industry Business Process Outsourcing Software Publisher & Support Services
N.A.I.C.S.: 513210

Subsidiary (Non-US):

Avaloq France SAS (2)
19 rue Marbeuf, 75008, Paris, France
Tel.: (33) 1 84 76 01 50
Web Site: http://www.avaloq.com
Emp.: 10
Software Development Services
N.A.I.C.S.: 541511
Philippe Shintowski (Gen Mgr)

Avaloq Hong Kong Limited (2)
50 Level 20 Infinitus Plaza 199 Des Voeux
Rd, Sheung Wan, Central, China (Hong
Kong)
Tel.: (852) 21599632
Software Development Services
N.A.I.C.S.: 541511

Subsidiary (Domestic):

Avaloq Licence AG (2)
Schwerzistrasse 6, 8807, Freienbach, Switzerland
Tel.: (41) 58 316 31 17
Software Licensing Services
N.A.I.C.S.: 533110

Subsidiary (Non-US):

Avaloq Luxembourg Sarl (2)
19 rue Eugene Ruppert, 2453, Luxembourg, Luxembourg
Tel.: (352) 27495410
Software Development Services
N.A.I.C.S.: 541511
Frederic Kemp (Mng Dir)

Avaloq Sourcing (Deutschland)
AG (2)
Kurfurstendamm 119, 10711, Berlin, Germany
Tel.: (49) 306521040
Software Development Services
N.A.I.C.S.: 541511
Hamid Shefaat (Head-IT Ops)

Avaloq UK Ltd. (2)
8 Angel Court 1st Floor, London, EC2R
7HP, United Kingdom
Tel.: (44) 207 796 3587
Web Site: http://www.avaloq.com
Software Development Services
N.A.I.C.S.: 541511
Jonathan Davis (Mng Dir)

KMD A/S (2)
Lautrupparken 40-42, 2750, Ballerup, Denmark
Tel.: (45) 4 460 1000
Web Site: https://www.kmd.dk
Sales Range: $700-749.9 Million
Information Technology & Consulting Services & Software Development
N.A.I.C.S.: 541519
Eva Beineke (CEO)

NEC (China) Co., Ltd. (1)
7th Floor Tower D2 Diplomatic Office Building, No 19 Dongfang East Road Chaoyang
District, Beijing, 100600, China
Tel.: (86) 1059181111
Web Site: https://cn.nec.com
Emp.: 1,308
Information Technology Services
N.A.I.C.S.: 541511

NEC (UK) Ltd. (1)
Odyssey Bus Pk West End Rd, Ruislip,
HA4 6QE, Middlesex, United
Kingdom (100%)
Tel.: (44) 2088362000
Web Site: http://www.nec.co.uk

NEC CORPORATION

Sales Range: $75-99.9 Million
Emp.: 250
Sale of Communications Equipment,
Plasma Screens Pojectors, Fax Machines &
Mobile Phones
N.A.I.C.S.: 423690

NEC Access Technica, Ltd. (1)
800 Shimomata, Kakegawa, 436-0025, Shizuoka, Japan
Tel.: (81) 537231111
Web Site: http://www.necat.co.jp
Networking Component Mfr
N.A.I.C.S.: 334118

NEC Advanced Software Technology
(Beijing) Co., Ltd. (1)
7th Floor D2 Building Diplomatic Office
Building, Dongfang East Road Chaoyang
District, Beijing, 100600, China
Tel.: (86) 1059181111
Web Site: https://cn.nec.com
Emp.: 169
Software Development Services
N.A.I.C.S.: 541511
Kai Xing (Program Mgr)

NEC Africa (Pty) Ltd. (1)
International House 7th Fl Mama Ngina
Street, PO Box 45137-00100, Nairobi, Kenya
Tel.: (254) 203310301
Information Technology Services
N.A.I.C.S.: 519290

NEC Africa (Pty) Ltd. (1)
2nd Floor Aquarius House Office 5C Katima
Mulilo Road, PO Box 32682-10101, Lusaka,
Zambia
Tel.: (260) 211293052
Telecommunication Maintenance Services
N.A.I.C.S.: 541511

NEC Argentina S.A. (1)
Elvira Rawson De Dellepiane 150 Catatalsederia, 1602, Buenos Aires,
Argentina (100%)
Tel.: (54) 01140106000
Web Site: http://www.nec.com.ar
Sales Range: $25-49.9 Million
Emp.: 100
Mfr Sales & Service of Communications
Equipment & Computer Products
N.A.I.C.S.: 449210

NEC Asia Pacific Pte. Ltd. (1)
80 Bendemeer Road 05-01/02, Singapore,
339949, Singapore
Tel.: (65) 62738333
Web Site: https://sg.nec.com
Telecommunication Equipment Whslr
N.A.I.C.S.: 423690

NEC Asia Pte Ltd. (1)
 (100%)
Sales Range: $75-99.9 Million
Emp.: 300
Information Technology Services Including
Outsourcing, Hosting, Web Design, Software Development & Educational Services
N.A.I.C.S.: 541512
Tan Boon Chin (Mng Dir-Safety Div-Global)

NEC Australia Pty. Ltd. (1)
649-655 Springvale Road, Mulgrave, 3170,
VIC, Australia (100%)
Tel.: (61) 3 9262 1111
Web Site: http://www.nec.com.au
Sales Range: $500-549.9 Million
Emp.: 1,500
Mfr & Sale of Communications Equipment,
Computers & Consumer Electronic Equipment
N.A.I.C.S.: 334118
Michael Barber (Mng Dir)

Subsidiary (Domestic):

NEC IT Services Australia Pty.
Ltd. (2)
649-655 Springvale Road, Mulgrave, 3170,
VIC, Australia
Tel.: (61) 392621111
Information & Communication Technology
Management Services
N.A.I.C.S.: 541519

NEC IT Solutions Australia Pty
Ltd (2)
649-655 Springvale Road, Mulgrave, 3170,

NEC CORPORATION

NEC Corporation—(Continued)
VIC, Australia
Tel.: (61) 3 9262 1111
Web Site: http://www.nec.com.au
Emp.: 800
Information Technology Services & Consulting
N.A.I.C.S.: 541519

NEC Canada, Inc. (1)
5995 Avebury Rd, Mississauga, L5R 3P9, ON, Canada
Tel.: (905) 712-5600
Sales Range: $25-49.9 Million
Emp.: 12
Information Technology Consulting Services
N.A.I.C.S.: 541512

NEC Capital (UK) Plc (1)
1 Victoria Road, London, LW3 6BL, United Kingdom **(100%)**
Tel.: (44) 2087523833
Web Site: http://www.nec.com
Sales Range: $50-74.9 Million
Emp.: 4
Provider of Group Financial Services & Treasury Operations in Europe
N.A.I.C.S.: 522320

NEC Chile S.A. (1)
Enrique Foster Sur N 20, Piso, Las Condes, Chile
Tel.: (56) 26408200
Web Site: http://www.nec.cl
Sales Range: $50-74.9 Million
Emp.: 150
Telecommunication Servicesb
N.A.I.C.S.: 517810

NEC Computers Netherland B.V. (1)
Takenfosplein 3, NL 6538 SZ, Nijmegen, Netherlands **(100%)**
Tel.: (31) 246489280
Sales Range: $200-249.9 Million
Emp.: 350
Financial Services
N.A.I.C.S.: 523999

NEC Computertechno, Ltd. (1)
1088-3 Otsumachi, Kofu, 400-0055, Yamanashi, Japan
Tel.: (81) 552434111
Web Site: http://www.nec-computertechno.co.jp
Computer Peripheral Equipment Distr
N.A.I.C.S.: 423430

NEC Corporation (2)
1810 Changgang Building 86 Mapo daero, Mapo-gu, Seoul, 04168, Korea (South)
Tel.: (82) 7086768500
Web Site: http://kr.nec.com
Enterprise System Development Services
N.A.I.C.S.: 513210

NEC Corporation (Thailand) Ltd. (1)
2nd 24th Floor Serm-mit Tower 159 Sukhumvit 21 Road Klongtoey Nua, Wattana, Bangkok, Thailand
Tel.: (66) 22591192
Web Site: http://www.nec.co.th
Sales Range: $75-99.9 Million
Emp.: 350
Technical Consulting Services
N.A.I.C.S.: 541690

NEC Corporation Abiko Plant (1)
1131 Hinode, Abiko, 270 1198, Chiba, Japan **(100%)**
Tel.: (81) 471821111
Web Site: http://www.nec.co.jp
Sales Range: $400-449.9 Million
Emp.: 2,500
Mfr of Digital Switching Systems, EPBXS, Facsimile Machines & Electro-Mechanical Devices
N.A.I.C.S.: 334514

NEC Corporation Fuchu Plant (1)
10 Nisshin Cho 1 Chome, Fuchu, 183 8501, Tokyo, Japan **(100%)**
Tel.: (81) 423641111
Web Site: http://www.nec.co.jp
Sales Range: $800-899.9 Million
Emp.: 3,000
Mfr of Computers & Associated Equipment, Broadcasting Equipment, Radar Equipment & Industrial Control Systems
N.A.I.C.S.: 334220

NEC Corporation India Private Limited (1)
18th Floor Tower C Advant Navis Business Park Sector 142, Noida, 201305, Uttar Pradesh, India
Tel.: (91) 1206615714
Web Site: http://in.nec.com
Telecommunication Equipment Whslr
N.A.I.C.S.: 423690

NEC Corporation Mita Plant (1)
33-7 Shiba 5-chome, Minato-ku, Tokyo, 108-8422, Japan **(100%)**
Tel.: (81) 334521111
Sales Range: $1-4.9 Billion
Emp.: 6,845
Mfr of Computer Software
N.A.I.C.S.: 541511

NEC Corporation Sagamihara Plant (1)
1120 Shimokuzawa, Sagamihara, 252-5298, Kanagawa, Japan **(100%)**
Tel.: (81) 427731111
Web Site: http://www.nec.co.jp
Sales Range: $800-899.9 Million
Emp.: 4,740
Mfr of Electronic Devices
N.A.I.C.S.: 334514

NEC Corporation Yokohama Plant (1)
1753 Shimonumabe, Nakahara-ku, Kawasaki, 211-8666, Kanagawa, Japan **(100%)**
Tel.: (81) 444331111
Web Site: http://www.nec.co.jp
Sales Range: $400-449.9 Million
Emp.: 2,260
Mfr of Communications Equipment
N.A.I.C.S.: 334290

NEC Corporation of America, Inc. (1)
6535 N State Hwy 161, Irving, TX 75039-2402 **(100%)**
Tel.: (214) 262-2000
Web Site: http://www.necam.com
Sales Range: $200-249.9 Million
Emp.: 800
Mfr & Sale of Communications Equipment
N.A.I.C.S.: 334210
Paul DiPietra (Sr Acct Mgr-Dept of Justice & Federal Law Enforcement Advanced Re)

Subsidiary (Domestic):

NEC America (2)
4100 Holiday St NW Ste 200, Canton, OH 44718-2589 **(100%)**
Tel.: (330) 492-4499
Sales Range: $25-49.9 Million
Emp.: 30
Developer of Software & Computer Products Distr
N.A.I.C.S.: 449210

Branch (Domestic):

NEC Corporation of America (2)
10850 Gold Ctr Dr Ste 200, Rancho Cordova, CA 95670 **(88.32%)**
Tel.: (916) 463-7000
Web Site: http://www.necam.com
Sales Range: $25-49.9 Million
Emp.: 50
Producer & Marketer of a Broad Range of Desktop & Mobile Computers & Servers
N.A.I.C.S.: 423430

Subsidiary (Domestic):

NEC Financial Services, LLC (2)
250 Pehle Ave Ste 309, Saddle Brook, NJ 07663-5888
Tel.: (800) 451-5361
Web Site: http://www.neclease.com
Emp.: 30
Financial Lending Services
N.A.I.C.S.: 522220
Herschel Salan (Pres)

NEC Laboratories America, Inc. (2)
4 Independence Way Sutie 200, Princeton, NJ 08540-6634 **(100%)**
Tel.: (609) 520-1555
Web Site: https://www.nec-labs.com
Sales Range: $25-49.9 Million
Emp.: 80
Fundamental Research Activities
N.A.I.C.S.: 541715

Carla Saams (Sr Mgr-Admin)

NEC Solutions Inc. (2)
500 Park Blvd Ste 1100, Itasca, IL 60143-1286 **(100%)**
Tel.: (630) 467-3000
Web Site: http://www.necsolutions.com
Sales Range: $10-24.9 Million
Emp.: 50
Mfr & Sale of Computers & Peripheral Equipment
N.A.I.C.S.: 493110

NEC Sphere Communications Inc. (2)
300 Tri-State International Ste 150, Lincolnshire, IL 60069
Tel.: (847) 793-9600
Web Site: http://www.necsphere.com
Software Development Services
N.A.I.C.S.: 541511

NEC Tokin America, Inc. (2)
2560 N 1st St Ste 100, San Jose, CA 95131
Tel.: (408) 324-1790
Web Site: https://www.tokin.com
Emp.: 20
Electronic Components Mfr
N.A.I.C.S.: 334419
Yoshio Ito (Pres)

NMI Corporation (2)
6535 State Hwy 161, Irving, TX 75039-2402 **(100%)**
Tel.: (214) 262-4068
Sale of Communications Equipment
N.A.I.C.S.: 423690

NetCracker Technology Corporation (2)
University Ofc Park III 95 Sawyer Rd, Waltham, MA 02453
Tel.: (781) 419-3300
Web Site: https://www.netcracker.com
Integrated Communication Services
N.A.I.C.S.: 519290

Subsidiary (Domestic):

NetCracker Technology Solutions Inc. (3)
95 Sawyer Rd, Waltham, MA 02453 **(100%)**
Tel.: (513) 723-7000
Web Site: http://www.netcracker.com
Sales Range: $1-4.9 Billion
Business & Operational Support System Services
N.A.I.C.S.: 541519

Subsidiary (Non-US):

NetCracker Technology EMEA Limited (4)
2010 Cambourne Business Park, Cambourne, Cambridge, CB23 6DW, Cambs, United Kingdom **(100%)**
Tel.: (44) 1223705000
Web Site: http://www.netcracker.com
Sales Range: $75-99.9 Million
Emp.: 50
Holding Company
N.A.I.C.S.: 551112

NetCracker Technology Solutions Singapore Pte. Ltd. (4)
30 Cecil Street 11-08 Prudential Tower, Singapore, 049712, Singapore **(100%)**
Tel.: (65) 65572277
Web Site: http://www.netcracker.com
Sales Range: $250-299.9 Million
Holding Company
N.A.I.C.S.: 551112

NetCracker Technology do Brasil Ltda (4)
Praca General Gentil Falcao 108 4th Floor, Sao Paulo, 04571-150, Brazil
Tel.: (55) 1155046700
Web Site: http://www.netcracker.com
Sales Range: $25-49.9 Million
Emp.: 90
Data Processing Services
N.A.I.C.S.: 518210

NEC Deutschland GmbH (1)
Tel.: (49) 21153690 **(100%)**

INTERNATIONAL PUBLIC

Sales Range: $25-49.9 Million
Emp.: 25
Sale & Marketing of Communications Equipment & Computer Products
N.A.I.C.S.: 449210
Yuichi Kojima (Mng Dir)

NEC Deutschland GmbH (1)
Thurgauerstrasse 101, Glattpark, 8152, Zurich, Switzerland
Tel.: (41) 444884911
Telecommunication Equipment Whslr
N.A.I.C.S.: 423690

NEC Display Solutions Poland (1)
ul Bociana 22A, 31-231, Krakow, Poland
Tel.: (48) 12 614 53 53
Web Site: http://www.nec-display-solutions.com
Emp.: 3
Desktop & Large Screen Display Distr
N.A.I.C.S.: 423690
Mariusz Orzechowski (Mgr-Sls & Mktg)

NEC Eastern Europe Kft. (1)
ul Wspolna 47 49, 00-684, Warsaw, Poland
Tel.: (48) 222443845
Telecommunication Equipment Whslr
N.A.I.C.S.: 423690

NEC Eastern Europe Ltd. (1)
NEC Eastern Europe Kft Ungvar Street 64-66, Budapest, Hungary
Tel.: (36) 18146424
Web Site: https://hu.nec.com
Digital Transmission System Mfr
N.A.I.C.S.: 333613

NEC Energy Devices (Wujiang) Co., Ltd. (1)
No 368 Shanhu West Road Wujiang Economic Development Zone, Wujiang, 215200, Jiangsu, China
Tel.: (86) 512 6343 8111
Rechargeable Battery Mfr & Distr
N.A.I.C.S.: 335910

NEC Engineering, Ltd. (1)
4-10-27 Higashishinagawa Sumitomofudosanshinagawa Bldg, Shinagawa-Ku, Tokyo, 140-0002, Japan
Tel.: (81) 367131111
Web Site: http://www.nec-eng.co.jp
Information Technology Consulting Services
N.A.I.C.S.: 541512

NEC Enterprise Communication Technologies, Inc. (1)
300 Tri State International Ste 150, Lincolnshire, IL 60069
Tel.: (847) 793-9600
Software Services
N.A.I.C.S.: 541511
Vadivel Subramaniam (Mgr-Software Dev)

NEC Europe & UK Ltd. (1)
Athene Odyssey Business Park West End Road, South Ruislip, London, HA4 6QE, Middlesex, United Kingdom **(100%)**
Tel.: (44) 2088362000
Web Site: http://uk.nec.com
Sales Range: $1-4.9 Billion
Emp.: 300
Sales, Marketing & Distribution of Communications Equipment & Electronic Devices
N.A.I.C.S.: 449210
Chris Jackson (Pres & CEO)

Division (Non-US):

NEC Europe Ltd. - NEC Laboratories Europe Division (2)
Kurfursten-Anlage 36, 69115, Heidelberg, Germany
Tel.: (49) 6221 4342 0
Web Site: http://uk.nec.com
Emp.: 110
Network & Software Research Laboratory Services
N.A.I.C.S.: 541380

NEC Fielding Information Technology Services (Beijing) Co., Ltd. (1)
603A 6th Floor Building LD02 Liangmaqiao Diplomatic Office Building, No 19 Dongfang East Road Chaoyang District, Beijing, 100600, China
Tel.: (86) 1082319620
Web Site: http://www.nefits.com.cn
Information Technology Consulting Services

AND PRIVATE COMPANIES

N.A.I.C.S.: 541512

NEC Fielding, Ltd.
4-28 Mita 1-chome, Minato-ku, Tokyo, 108 0073, Japan
Tel.: (81) 334527093
Web Site: http://www.fielding.co.jp
Emp.: 6,170
Computer & IT Services
N.A.I.C.S.: 541512
Osamu Mikami *(Mng Exec Officer-Corp Plng Dept & Mgmt Sys Dept)*

NEC France S.A.S. (1)
29 rue des Hautes Patures, 92737, Nanterre, France
Tel.: (33) 146494649
Web Site: https://www.nec.fr
Telecommunication & Electronic Products Distr
N.A.I.C.S.: 423690

Subsidiary (Domestic):

NEC Display Solutions (2)
29 rue des Hautes Patures, Nanterre, 92737, France
Tel.: (33) 1 46 49 46 49
Web Site: http://www.nec-display-solutions.fr
Emp.: 60
Desktop & Large Screen Display Distr
N.A.I.C.S.: 423690

NEC Hong Kong Ltd. (1)
25th Floor The Metropolis Tower 10 Metropolis Drive, Hunghom, Kowloon, China (Hong Kong) (100%)
Tel.: (852) 2 369 0335
Web Site: https://hk.nec.com
Sales Range: $25-49.9 Million
Emp.: 90
Sales & Marketing of Communications Equipment & Computer Products
N.A.I.C.S.: 449210
Elsa Wong *(Mng Dir)*

NEC Iberica S.L. (1)
Anabel Segura 7, 28108, Alcobendas, Madrid, Spain
Tel.: (34) 91 203 2900
Web Site: https://es.nec.com
Telecommunication Equipment Whslr
N.A.I.C.S.: 423690
Takaaki Goto *(Product Mgr)*

NEC Information Systems (Shanghai), Ltd. (1)
8F T2 Raffles City Changning 1189 Changning Road, Changning District, Shanghai, China
Tel.: (86) 2150480286
IT Product Whslr
N.A.I.C.S.: 423690

NEC International Logistics (Shanghai) Ltd. (1)
16E/F East Tower Shanghai New Hualian Mansion, No 755 Middle HuaiHai Road, Shanghai, 200020, China
Tel.: (86) 21 6445 1720
Web Site: http://www.necl.nec.com.hk
Logistics & Freight Transportation Services
N.A.I.C.S.: 541614

NEC Italia s.p.a. (1)
Viale Enrico Forlanini 23, 20134, Milan, Italy
Tel.: (39) 02484151
Web Site: http://www.nec.it
Telecommunication Network Services
N.A.I.C.S.: 517111
Stefano Asperti *(Pres)*

NEC Laboratories Europe GmbH (1)
Kurfursten-Anlage 36, 69115, Heidelberg, Germany
Tel.: (49) 62 214 3420
Web Site: https://www.neclab.eu
Information Technology Research Services
N.A.I.C.S.: 519290
Jurgen Quittek *(Mng Dir)*

NEC Latin America S.A. (1)
Av Paulista 2300 16 Andar, 01310-300, Sao Paulo, Brazil
Tel.: (55) 1131517000
Broadband Internet Services
N.A.I.C.S.: 517810

NEC Logistics, Ltd. (1)
1-403 Kosugi-cho Nakahara-ku, Kawasaki, 211-0063, Kanagawa, Japan (49%)
Tel.: (81) 44 733 4629
Web Site: http://www.necl.co.jp
Emp.: 2,120
Logistic Services
N.A.I.C.S.: 541614
Naoki Yoshimura *(Pres)*

Subsidiary (Non-US):

NEC Logistics (Shenzhen) Ltd. (2)
Room 806 Building B, Shenzhen, 518038, China
Tel.: (86) 755 8348 0034
Logistics & Freight Transportation Services
N.A.I.C.S.: 541614

NEC Logistics Hong Kong Limited (2)
Suite 2002 Exchange Tower 33 Wang Chiu Road Kowloon Bay, Kowloon, China (Hong Kong)
Tel.: (852) 2723 1569
Web Site: http://www.nipponexpress-necl.com.hk
Sales Range: $25-49.9 Million
Emp.: 215
Logistics & Warehousing Services
N.A.I.C.S.: 493110

Subsidiary (Non-US):

NEC Logistics (Thailand) Co., Ltd (3)
12th Floor Thaniya Plaza Building 52 Silom Road Kwaeng Suriyawongse, Bangrak, Bangkok, 10500, Thailand
Tel.: (66) 2238 1370
Web Site: http://www.necl.co.th
Emp.: 70
Logistics Consulting Servies
N.A.I.C.S.: 541614

NEC Logistics Singapore Pte. Ltd. (3)
49 Jalan Pemimpin 02-01 APS Industrial Building, Singapore, 577203, Singapore
Tel.: (65) 66039600
Freight Transportation Services
N.A.I.C.S.: 488510

Subsidiary (Non-US):

NEC Logistics Taiwan Ltd. (2)
15th Floor No 181 Fu Hsing North Road, Songshan District, Taipei, 10596, Taiwan
Tel.: (886) 227122465
Freight Shipping Operation Management Services
N.A.I.C.S.: 483111

Nippon Express NEC Logistics (Shanghai) Ltd. (2)
702 7th Floor No 1189 Changning Road, Shanghai, 200051, China
Tel.: (86) 2164451720
Web Site: http://www.nittsu-necl.co.jp
Logistics & Freight Transportation Services
N.A.I.C.S.: 541614

NEC Malaysia Sdn. Bhd. (1)
Suite 19 01 Level 19 The Gardens South Tower, Mid Valley City Lingkaran Syed Putra, 59200, Kuala Lumpur, Malaysia (100%)
Tel.: (60) 3 2299 6322
Web Site: http://my.nec.com
Sales Range: $25-49.9 Million
Emp.: 100
Sales & Marketing of Communication & Computer Products
N.A.I.C.S.: 449210

NEC Nederland B.V. (1)
Olympia 4, 1213 NT, Hilversum, Netherlands
Tel.: (31) 356899111
Web Site: http://nl.nec.com
Information Technology Services
N.A.I.C.S.: 519290

NEC Network and Sensor Systems, Ltd. (1)
1120 Shimokuzawa, Chuo-ku, Sagamihara, 252-5298, Kanagawa, Japan (100%)
Tel.: (81) 427710625
Web Site: http://www.necnets.co.jp
Emp.: 130
Defense Communications Products Mfr
N.A.I.C.S.: 334419

NEC Networks & System Integration Corporation (1)
3-9-14 Shibaura, Minato-ku, Tokyo, 108-8515, Japan (51.43%)
Tel.: (81) 342121000
Web Site: https://www.nesic.co.jp
Rev.: $2,376,328,050
Assets: $1,883,169,170
Liabilities: $842,219,760
Net Worth: $1,040,949,410
Earnings: $101,324,690
Emp.: 53
Fiscal Year-end: 03/31/2024
System Integration Services
N.A.I.C.S.: 238210
Yushi Ushijima *(Pres)*

Subsidiary (Domestic):

NEC Networks & System Integration Services Ltd. (2)
3-9-14 Shibaura, Minato-ku, Tokyo, 108-8515, Japan
Tel.: (81) 332191611
Web Site: https://www.nesic.co.jp
Electrical Communications Installation & Maintenance Services
N.A.I.C.S.: 238210

Subsidiary (Non-US):

NESIC Philippines Inc. (2)
2nd Floor Eurovilla II 118 Vicente A, Rufino St, Makati, 1229, Philippines
Tel.: (63) 28924831
Web Site: http://www.nesic.com.ph
Telecommunications Systems Integration Services
N.A.I.C.S.: 517810

Subsidiary (Domestic):

Nichiwa Co., Ltd. (2)
1765 Kamigata, Nichinan, 889-3151, Miyazaki, Japan
Tel.: (81) 98 727 1311
Web Site: https://www.nichiwa-corp.co.jp
Emp.: 156
Communication Networking Services
N.A.I.C.S.: 541512
Hashimoto Jialong *(Pres & Dir)*

Subsidiary (Non-US):

PT. NESIC BUKAKA (2)
Jl Raya Pasar Minggu 17 A Graha Anugerah Lt 5, Kebagusan Pasar Minggu, 12780, Jakarta, Indonesia
Tel.: (62) 217944333
Telecommunication Servicesb
N.A.I.C.S.: 541618

Subsidiary (Domestic):

Q&A Corporation (2)
Totate Nagai Bldg 2-12-24 Shibuya, Shibuya-ku, Tokyo, 150-0002, Japan (56%)
Tel.: (81) 3 5466 1960
Web Site: http://www.qac.jp
Sales Range: $100-124.9 Million
Emp.: 331
Technical & Marketing Support Services
N.A.I.C.S.: 541990
Tetsuo Kawada *(Pres & CEO)*

Subsidiary (Non-US):

TNSi Europe GmbH (2)
Amsterdamer Str 230, Cologne, 50735, Germany
Tel.: (49) 22197753611
Web Site: http://www.t-ns.co.jp
Emp.: 2
Intergrated Network Design Services
N.A.I.C.S.: 541512
Yasuhiro Kosaka *(Gen Mgr)*

Subsidiary (Domestic):

Toyo Networks & System Integration Co., Ltd (2)
18 Nihon-odori Naka-ku, Yokohama, 231 0021, Kanagawa, Japan
Tel.: (81) 452265908
Web Site: http://www.t-ns.co.jp
Sales Range: $75-99.9 Million
Emp.: 288
Network Systems Integration Services
N.A.I.C.S.: 541512

NEC CORPORATION

Shunji Suyama *(Sr VP)*

NEC Neva Communications Systems JSC (1)
M Bogdanovicha St 155B Office 503, Minsk, 220040, Belarus
Tel.: (375) 172625408
Telecommunication Servicesb
N.A.I.C.S.: 541511
Lioudmila Petrovskaia *(Head-Rep Office)*

NEC Neva Communications Systems JSC (1)
Kazakhstan st Tole bi 69, Almaty, Kazakhstan
Tel.: (7) 4997540570
Telecommunication Servicesb
N.A.I.C.S.: 541511

NEC New Zealand Limited (1)
Level 6 NEC House 40 Taranaki Street, PO Box 1936, Wellington, 6011, New Zealand
Tel.: (64) 43811111
Web Site: http://www.nec.co.nz
Sales Range: $25-49.9 Million
Emp.: 70
Telecommunications Equipment Mfr
N.A.I.C.S.: 334419
Takashi Tada *(Mng Dir)*

NEC Nexsolutions, Ltd. (1)
1-4-28 Mita International Building, Mita Minato-Ku, Tokyo, 108-8338, Japan
Tel.: (81) 357305000
Web Site: http://www.nec-nexs.com
Emp.: 1,940
Network Systems Integration Services
N.A.I.C.S.: 541512

NEC OncoImmunity AS (1)
Oslo Cancer Cluster Innovation Park Ullernchausseen 64, 0379, Oslo, Norway
Tel.: (47) 9 001 5242
Web Site: https://www.oncoimmunity.com
Neoantigen Prediction Software Development Services
N.A.I.C.S.: 541511
Richard Stratford *(Co-Founder & CEO)*

NEC Philippines, Inc. (1)
4th Fl Rufino Bldg 6784 Ayala Ave, Makati, 1226, Philippines
Tel.: (63) 28486400
Web Site: http://www.nec.com.ph
Sales Range: $25-49.9 Million
Emp.: 92
Information Technology Consulting Services
N.A.I.C.S.: 541512
Elizabeth Tirona Pangan *(Pres)*

NEC Platform Technologies (Suzhou) Co., Ltd. (1)
No 499 Jiangxing East Road, Wujiang Economic and Technological Development Zone, Suzhou, 215217, Jiangsu, China
Tel.: (86) 51263315198
Access Network Equipment Mfr
N.A.I.C.S.: 334210

NEC Platform Technologies Hong Kong Limited (1)
Suites 901-04 AIA Kowloon Tower Landmark East 100 How Ming Street, Kwun Tong, China (Hong Kong)
Tel.: (852) 26923802
Web Site: https://www.nept.nec.com.hk
Computer Peripheral Equipment Mfr
N.A.I.C.S.: 334118

NEC Platforms, Ltd. (1)
2-3 Kanda-Tsukasamachi, Chiyoda-ku, Tokyo, 101-8532, Japan
Tel.: (81) 33 259 1311
Web Site: https://www.necplatforms.co.jp
Emp.: 7,010
Telecommunications Equipment Mfr
N.A.I.C.S.: 334290
Kimihiko Fukuda *(Pres)*

NEC Portugal Telecommunicacoes e Sistemas, S.A. (1)
Dificio Espace Alameda dos Oceanos n 59 Piso 0 Bloco 2 Letra B, Parque das Nacoes, 1990-207, Lisbon, Portugal
Tel.: (351) 212948400
Web Site: https://pt.nec.com
Telecommunication Equipment Whslr
N.A.I.C.S.: 423690

NEC Portugal-Telecomunicacoes e Sistemas SA (1)

NEC CORPORATION

INTERNATIONAL PUBLIC

NEC Corporation—(Continued)
Alameda dos Oceanos n59 Piso 0 Bloco 2 Letra B Parque das Nacoes, Apartado 309, Lisbon, 1990-207, Caparica, Portugal
Tel.: (351) 212948400
Web Site: http://www.necportugal.pt
Telecommunication Equipment Distr
N.A.I.C.S.: 423690

NEC Saudi Arabia Ltd. (1)
Main Oleya Street, PO Box 15534, Riyadh, 11454, Saudi Arabia
Tel.: (966) 114653381
Information Technology Consulting Services
N.A.I.C.S.: 541512

NEC Scandinavia AB (1)
Kronborgsgrand 1, 164 46, Kista, Sweden
Tel.: (46) 10 214 8600
Web Site: https://se.nec.com
Sales Range: $25-49.9 Million
Emp.: 41
Telecommunication Equipment Distr
N.A.I.C.S.: 423440
Benny Ekman (Mng Dir)

NEC Scandinavia AB (1)
Olaf Helsets vei 6, 0694, Oslo, Norway
Tel.: (47) 22628995
Web Site: https://se.nec.com
Telecommunication Equipment Whslr
N.A.I.C.S.: 423690

NEC Soft, Ltd. (1)
NEC Soft Head Office Building 1-18-7 Shinkiba, Koto-ku, Tokyo, 136-8627, Japan
Tel.: (81) 3 5534 2222
Web Site: http://www.necsoft.co.jp
Rev.: $1,294,992,000
Emp.: 4,853
Information Technology Consulting Services
N.A.I.C.S.: 541512

Subsidiary (Non-US):

NEC Soft (Jinan) Co., Ltd. (2)
5/F Suite C Qilu Software Park Chuangye Plaza, No 1 Shunhua Road, Jinan, 250101, Shandong, China
Tel.: (86) 53186517777
Web Site: http://www.necsoft.com.cn
Software Development Services
N.A.I.C.S.: 541511

NEC Solution Innovators, Ltd. (1)
1-18-7 Shinkiba, Koto-ku, Tokyo, 136-8627, Japan
Tel.: (81) 355342687
Web Site: https://www.nec-solutioninnovators.co.jp
Emp.: 12,565
Business Consulting Services
N.A.I.C.S.: 541611

NEC Solutions (China) Co., Ltd. (1)
20 Floor Ciros Plaza 388 Nanjing Road West, Shanghai, 200003, China
Tel.: (86) 2123293333
Web Site: http://www.necsl.com.cn
Emp.: 500
Information Technology & Networking Services
N.A.I.C.S.: 541512

NEC Space Technologies, Ltd. (1)
1-10 Nissin-cho, Fuchu, 183-8551, Tokyo, Japan
Tel.: (81) 423544000
Web Site: http://www.ntspace.co.jp
Sales Range: Less than $1 Million
Emp.: 515
Testing Space Communication Equipment Mfr
N.A.I.C.S.: 334290
Kunio Kondo (Pres)

NEC System Technologies (Hangzhou), Ltd (1)
6F-7F Dongzhong Software Park No 590 Changhe Road, Binjiang District, Hangzhou, China
Tel.: (86) 571 87859333
Web Site: http://www.necsthz.com.cn
Information Technology Software Distr
N.A.I.C.S.: 423430

NEC TOKIN Electronics (Thailand) Co., Ltd (1)
60/76 Moo 19 Nava Nakorn Industrial Estate Phase II Klongnung, Klongluang, Pathumthani, 12120, Thailand
Tel.: (66) 2529 2470
Web Site: http://www.nec-tokin.co.th
Electronic Chip & Capacitor Mfr
N.A.I.C.S.: 334416

NEC TOKIN Electronics (Xiamen) Corporation (1)
No 9 Ri-xin Road Xinglin Ji-mei Zone, Xiamen, Fujian, China
Tel.: (86) 592 6214371
Electronic Components Mfr
N.A.I.C.S.: 334419

NEC TOKIN Europe GmbH (1)
Hellersbergstrasse 14, 41460, Neuss, Germany
Tel.: (49) 2131595350
Web Site: http://www.nec-tokin-europe.com
Network Device Materials Distr
N.A.I.C.S.: 423690

NEC TOKIN Korea, Co., Ltd. (1)
518 Korea City Airr-Terminal B/D 159-6 Samsung-Dong, Kangnam, 135-728, Seoul, Korea (South)
Tel.: (82) 2 551 3651
Web Site: http://www.nec-tokin.co.kr
Electronic Device Distr
N.A.I.C.S.: 423690

NEC TOKIN Singapore Pte. Ltd. (1)
101 Thomson Road 09-05 United Square, Singapore, 307591, Singapore
Tel.: (65) 63453181
Sales Range: $25-49.9 Million
Emp.: 14
Electronic Equipment Distr
N.A.I.C.S.: 423610

NEC TOKIN Taiwan Co.,Ltd. (1)
Room 411 No 9 Lane 3 Minsheng W Road, Taipei, 104, Taiwan
Tel.: (886) 2 2521 3998
Web Site: http://www.nec-tokin.com
Electronic Components Distr
N.A.I.C.S.: 423690

NEC Taiwan Ltd. (1)
7 F No 167 Sec 2, Nan King East Rd, Taipei, 104, Taiwan **(100%)**
Tel.: (886) 225150000
Web Site: http://www.nec.com.tw
Sales Range: $100-124.9 Million
Emp.: 500
Sale of Communications Equipment & Computers
N.A.I.C.S.: 449210
Henry Lee (Pres)

NEC Technologies (Thailand) Co., Ltd. (1)
60 76 Nava Nakorn Industrial Est, Paholyothin Rd Klong Luang, Pathumthani, 12120, Thailand **(100%)**
Tel.: (66) 25292470
Web Site: http://www.nec-tokin.co.th
Sales Range: $800-899.9 Million
Emp.: 3,000
Mfr & Sale of Communications Equipment & Electronic Components
N.A.I.C.S.: 334220

NEC Technologies (UK) Ltd. (1)
Level 3 Imperium Imperial Way, Reading, RG2 0TD, Berkshire, United Kingdom **(100%)**
Tel.: (44) 1189257190
Web Site: http://www.nectech.co.uk
Sales Range: $25-49.9 Million
Emp.: 60
Mfr & Sale of Communications Equipment & Computers
N.A.I.C.S.: 449210
Lionel Poisson (Mng Dir)

NEC Telecom Software Philippines, Inc. (1)
7F E Block 2 Bldg Cebu IT Park, Apas, Cebu, 6000, Philippines
Tel.: (63) 32 233 9142
Web Site: http://www.ntsp.com.ph
Sales Range: $75-99.9 Million
Emp.: 300
Software Development Services
N.A.I.C.S.: 541511
Yoshifumi Sakaguchi (Pres)

NEC Telecommunications & Information Technology Ltd. (1)
thumthani, 12120, Thailand
Tel.: (66) 2529 2470
Web Site: http://www.nec-tokin.co.th
Electronic Chip & Capacitor Mfr
N.A.I.C.S.: 334416

Dikilitas Emirhan Cad No 113 Barbaros Plaza is Merkezi C Blok Kat 10, Besiktas, 34349, Istanbul, Turkiye
Tel.: (90) 212 347 7968
Web Site: https://tr.nec.com
Information Technology Services
N.A.I.C.S.: 541511
Tomoki Naka (Pres)

NEC Telecommunications & Information Technology Ltd. (1)
3 Abu-El Feda Street Abu-El Feda Build 9th Floor, Zamalek, Cairo, Egypt
Tel.: (20) 227356778
Telecommunication Servicesb
N.A.I.C.S.: 541511
Hassan Abou Khatwa (Gen Mgr)

NEC Telecommunications & Information Technology Ltd. (1)
Lot N 12 3 rue Doudou Mokhtar, 16028, Ben Aknoun, Alger, Algeria
Tel.: (213) 23381639
Information Technology Services
N.A.I.C.S.: 519290

NEC Telecommunications and Information Technology Ltd. (1)
Dikilitas Emirhan Cad No 113 Barbaros Plaza is Merkezi C Blok Kat 10, Besiktas, 80700, Istanbul, Turkiye
Tel.: (90) 212 347 7968
Web Site: http://www.nec
Emp.: 40
Information Technology Consulting Services
N.A.I.C.S.: 541512

NEC Ukraine, LLC (1)
B Khmelnitskogo st 17 52A office 245, 01034, Kiev, Ukraine
Tel.: (380) 442308634
Business Support Services
N.A.I.C.S.: 561499

NEC Unified Solutions Hellas S.A. (1)
52 Aigialeias Str, 151 25, Maroussi, Athens, Greece
Tel.: (30) 2106300888
Telecommunication Servicesb
N.A.I.C.S.: 541511
George Tsiourakis (Chm & Mng Dir)

NEC Vietnam Co., Ltd. (1)
12th Floor Gelex Tower 52 Le Dai Hanh Str, Hai Ba Trung Dist, Hanoi, Vietnam
Tel.: (84) 243 933 3585
Web Site: https://vn.nec.com
Telecommunication Equipment Whslr
N.A.I.C.S.: 423690
Tran Thanh Van (Mgr-HR)

NEC Viewtechnology Trading (Shenzhen), Ltd. (1)
5F Changping Business Tower Honghua Road, Futian Free Trade Zone, Shenzhen, 518038, China
Tel.: (86) 755 3330 1288
Consumer Electronics Mfr & Distr
N.A.I.C.S.: 334220

NEC West Africa Limited (1)
7th Floor CBC Building Plot 11 Olubunmi Owa Street Off Admiralty Way, Lekki Phase 1, Lagos, Nigeria
Tel.: (234) 19035632
Telecommunication Equipment Whslr
N.A.I.C.S.: 423690
Sandeep Kulkarni (CTO)

NEC XON Holdings (Proprietary) Limited (1)
1 Mints Street Old Mint Office Park, Louwlardia, Centurion, 1683, South Africa
Tel.: (27) 112374500
Web Site: https://www.nec.xon.co.za
Telecommunication Equipment Maintenance Services
N.A.I.C.S.: 541511

NEC XON Systems Namibia (Proprietary) Limited (1)
Mandume Ndemufayo Ave, Windhoek, Namibia
Tel.: (264) 61400707
Telecommunication Servicesb
N.A.I.C.S.: 541511
Jannie Engelbrecht (Mng Dir)

NEC Yamanashi Ltd. (1)
747 Otsukimachimagi, Otsuki, 401-0016, Yamanashi, Japan
Tel.: (81) 554232111
Web Site: http://www.nec-yamanashi.co.jp
Optical Communication Devices Mfr
N.A.I.C.S.: 334290

NEC de Colombia S.A. (1)
Cra 9 No 80-32, Bogota, Colombia
Tel.: (57) 16445600
Web Site: http://www.nec.com.co
Sales Range: $25-49.9 Million
Emp.: 100
Telecommunication Servicesb
N.A.I.C.S.: 517810

NEC de Mexico, S.A, de C.V. (1)
Jaime Balmes No 8 Piso 3, Col Los Morales Polanco, CP 11510, Mexico, Mexico **(100%)**
Tel.: (52) 5521226500
Web Site: http://www.necmex.com
Sales Range: $50-74.9 Million
Emp.: 150
Mfr & Sale of Communications Equipment
N.A.I.C.S.: 334290

NEC de Venezuela, C.A. (1)
Avenida Ernesto Blohm Torre Diamen Piso 8 Of 81 Apartado 1060 A, Chuao, 64790, Caracas, Venezuela
Tel.: (58) 29598020
Web Site: https://www.nec.com.ve
Telecommunication Servicesb
N.A.I.C.S.: 541511

NICDC Logistics Data Services Limited (1)
Unit No B 602 6th Floor Tower B Plot No 7 Sector 142, Greater Noida Express Way Advant Navis Business Park, Noida, 201305, India
Tel.: (91) 1202459753
Web Site: http://nldsl.in
Logistics Consulting Servies
N.A.I.C.S.: 541614
Sanjay K. Murthy (Chm)

Northgate Public Services Limited (1)
Peoplebuilding 2 Peoplebuilding Estate Maylands Avenue, Hemel Hempstead, HP2 4NW, Hert, United Kingdom
Tel.: (44) 1344401111
Web Site: http://www.northgateps.com
Software Publisher
N.A.I.C.S.: 513210
Stephen Callaghan (CEO)

Subsidiary (Domestic):

APD Communications Ltd (2)
Newlands Centre Inglemire Lane, Hull, HU6 7TQ, United Kingdom
Tel.: (44) 1482808300
Web Site: http://www.apdcomms.com
Sales Range: $10-24.9 Million
Mobile IT Solutions
N.A.I.C.S.: 541511
Ian Abel (Mgr-People & Qualtiy)

P.T. NEC Indonesia (1)
Summitmas I 4th Floor Jl Jend Sudirman Kav 61-62, Jakarta, 12190, Indonesia
Tel.: (62) 21 520 1215
Web Site: http://id.nec.com
Software Development & Telecommunication Services
N.A.I.C.S.: 541511
Ichiro Kurihara (Pres)

PERNEC Corporation Bhd. (1)
No 21 Jalan Setiawangsa 8, Taman Setiawangsa, 54200, Kuala Lumpur, Malaysia
Tel.: (60) 34 259 6000
Web Site: https://www.pernec.com.my
Communication Equipment Mfr & Whslr
N.A.I.C.S.: 334290
Azizul Abdul Aziz (CEO)

Sharp NEC Display Solutions, Ltd. (1)
MS Shibaura Bldg 10 F 4 13 23 Shibaura, Minato-ku, Tokyo, 108 0023, Japan **(34%)**
Tel.: (81) 354465311
Web Site: https://www.nec-display.com
Sales Range: $100-124.9 Million
Emp.: 700

AND PRIVATE COMPANIES

NEDBANK GROUP LIMITED

Mfr of Computers; Joint Venture of NEC Corporation (50%) & Mitsubish Electric Corporation (50%)
N.A.I.C.S.: 334118
Helen Sheldrake *(Sls Mgr-Channel)*

Subsidiary (US):

Sharp NEC Display Solutions of America, Inc. (2)
500 Park Blvd Ste 1100, Itasca, IL 60143
Tel.: (858) 831-9327
Web Site: http://www.necdisplay.com
Electronic Display Equipment & Projectors Distr
N.A.I.C.S.: 423690
Betsy Larson *(VP-Sls-Channel)*

ZAO NEC Neva Communications Systems (1)
Revolutsii shosse 102 build 2, 195279, Saint Petersburg, Russia
Tel.: (7) 8124383999
Web Site: http://www.nec.com
Sales Range: $25-49.9 Million
Emp.: 100
Public Switching Systems Mfr
N.A.I.C.S.: 334290
Hiroshi Kiwada *(CEO)*

NEC TOKIN ELECTRONICS (PHILIPPINES), INC.
1 Ring Road Light Industry Science Park II Barangay La Mesa, Calamba, 4027, Laguna, Philippines
Tel.: (63) 49 545 6122
Electronic Components Distr
N.A.I.C.S.: 423690

NECHAKO REAL ESTATE LTD
421 Pacific Street, Vancouver, V6Z 2P5, BC, Canada
Tel.: (604) 685-5951
Year Founded: 1990
Rev.: $191,000,000
Emp.: 50
Real Estate Brokerage & Services
N.A.I.C.S.: 531210

NECO INSURANCE LIMITED
Beema Bhawan Gyaneshwor, PO Box No 12271, Anmnagar, Kathmandu, Nepal
Tel.: (977) 14542263
Web Site: https://www.neco.com.np
Year Founded: 1994
NIL—(NEP)
Rev.: $19,717,075
Assets: $62,359,976
Liabilities: $29,313,535
Net Worth: $33,046,441
Earnings: $5,283,252
Fiscal Year-end: 07/16/23
Insurance Services
N.A.I.C.S.: 524298
Rohit Kumar Bhattarai *(Chm)*

NECTAR LIFESCIENCES LIMITED
SCO 38-39 Sector 9d, Chandigarh, 160009, India
Tel.: (91) 5047915
Web Site: https://www.neclife.com
Year Founded: 1995
NECLIFE—(NSE)
Rev.: $240,750,783
Assets: $337,307,744
Liabilities: $192,340,649
Net Worth: $144,967,095
Earnings: ($10,000,536)
Emp.: 1,693
Fiscal Year-end: 03/31/21
Pharmaceuticals Product Mfr
N.A.I.C.S.: 325412
Sanjiv Goyal *(Founder, Chm & Mng Dir)*

NEDAP N.V.
Parallelweg 2, 7141 DC, Groenlo, Netherlands
Tel.: (31) 544471111
Web Site: https://www.nedap.com
NEDAP—(EUR)
Rev.: $248,822,577
Assets: $145,345,349
Liabilities: $57,719,620
Net Worth: $87,625,728
Earnings: $20,185,625
Emp.: 872
Fiscal Year-end: 12/31/22
Sensor-Based Tracking & Security Systems
N.A.I.C.S.: 334512
Ruben M. Wegman *(CEO & Member-Mgmt Bd)*

Subsidiaries:

Inventi B.V (1)
Industrieweg 20, Neede, 7161 BX, Netherlands
Tel.: (31) 545280960
Web Site: http://www.nedap-inventi.nl
Electronic Components Mfr
N.A.I.C.S.: 334419
Miranda Hoetenk *(Gen Mgr)*

Nedap Asia Ltd (1)
Austin Plaza 15F Units 3-5 No 83 Austin Road, Kowloon, China (Hong Kong)
Tel.: (852) 31049930
Web Site: https://www.nedapasia.com
Industrial Automation Solutions
N.A.I.C.S.: 238210

Nedap Belgie N.V. (1)
Maria-Theresialaan 2, 1800, Vilvoorde, Belgium
Tel.: (32) 22572540
Software Development Services
N.A.I.C.S.: 541511

Nedap Belgium NV (1)
Maria-Theresialaan 2, 1800, Vilvoorde, Belgium
Tel.: (32) 544471666
Web Site: http://www.nedapsecurity.com
Sales Range: $25-49.9 Million
Emp.: 5
Security Consulting Services
N.A.I.C.S.: 561612

Nedap Beveiligingstechniek B.V. (1)
Groenekanseweg 24a, 3737 AG, Groenekan, Netherlands
Tel.: (31) 346570104
Web Site: http://www.nedap-retail.nl
Sales Range: $25-49.9 Million
Emp.: 15
Security & Tracking Systems
N.A.I.C.S.: 561621

Nedap China Ltd (1)
Room 2306 Raffles City Office Tower 2 No 1189, Changning Road, Shanghai, 200051, China
Tel.: (86) 2161561620
Security Management Services
N.A.I.C.S.: 561621

Nedap Deutschland GmbH (1)
Mies van der Rohe Business Park Girmesgath 5 Gebaude B1 3 OG, 47803, Krefeld, Germany
Tel.: (49) 21519639100
Web Site: https://www.nedap-retail.com
Sales Range: $10-24.9 Million
Emp.: 30
Security & Tracking Systems
N.A.I.C.S.: 561621

Nedap FZE (1)
Dubai Digital Park Office 402 Building A4, PO Box 341213, Silicon Oasis, Dubai, United Arab Emirates
Tel.: (971) 43712512
Software Development Services
N.A.I.C.S.: 541511

Nedap France S.A. (1)
Nedap France 8-10 chemin d Andresy, 95610, Eragny-sur-Oise, France
Tel.: (33) 161030304
Web Site: http://www.nedapfrance.fr
Security & Tracking Systems
N.A.I.C.S.: 561621

Nedap GmbH (1)
Rheinstrasse 10-C, D-14513, Teltow, Germany
Tel.: (49) 332844660
Web Site: http://www.nedap-aeos.com
Security & Tracking Systems
N.A.I.C.S.: 561621

Nedap Great Britain Ltd. (1)
1230 Arlington Business Park, Theale, RG7 4SA, Reading, United Kingdom
Tel.: (44) 1189166820
Web Site: https://nedap.com
Sales Range: $25-49.9 Million
Emp.: 18
Security & Tracking Systems
N.A.I.C.S.: 561621

Nedap Iberia S.A. (1)
Paseo de la Castellana 43, 28046, Madrid, Spain
Tel.: (34) 918406767
Web Site: https://www.nedap.es
Sales Range: $25-49.9 Million
Emp.: 100
Security & Tracking Systems
N.A.I.C.S.: 561621

Subsidiary (Domestic):

Sappers Iberia S.L (2)
Avda de Los LLanos N 18 Nivel 1, Alpedrete, 28430, Madrid, Spain
Tel.: (34) 918498955
Web Site: http://www.sappers-iberia.es
Emp.: 3
Security Management Services
N.A.I.C.S.: 561621
Antonio Carmona *(Mgr)*

Nedap Inc. (1)
25 Corporate Dr Ste 101, Burlington, MA 01803
Tel.: (781) 349-6200
Information Technology Consulting Services
N.A.I.C.S.: 541690

Nedap Polska Sp. z o.o. (1)
Aleja Niepodleglosci 18, 02-653, Warsaw, Poland
Tel.: (48) 544471111
Software Development Services
N.A.I.C.S.: 541511

NEDBANK GROUP LIMITED
135 Rivonia Road, Sandown, Sandton, 2196, South Africa
Tel.: (27) 112944444 ZA
Web Site:
   https://personal.nedbank.co.za
NED—(JSE)
Rev.: $4,335,913,983
Assets: $66,169,425,110
Liabilities: $60,048,954,890
Net Worth: $6,120,470,220
Earnings: $814,224,907
Emp.: 25,924
Fiscal Year-end: 12/31/22
Bank Holding Company
N.A.I.C.S.: 551111
Fred Swanepoel *(CIO)*

Subsidiaries:

NedBank Mocambique S.A. (1)
Av Julius Nyerere n 590, PO Box 3698, Maputo, Mozambique
Tel.: (258) 21488400
Web Site: http://www.nedbank.co.mz
Commercial Banking Services
N.A.I.C.S.: 522110
Belisario Tinga *(Mgr)*

Nedbank (Lesotho) Limited (1)
115-117 Griffith Hill Kingsway Street, Maseru, Lesotho
Tel.: (266) 22282100
Web Site: http://www.nedbank.co.ls
Commercial Banking Services
N.A.I.C.S.: 522110
Ashley Sutton-Pryce *(Chm-Acting)*

Nedbank Limited (1)
135 Rivonia Road, Sandton, 2196, South Africa
Tel.: (27) 11 294 4444
Web Site: http://www.nedbank.co.za
Sales Range: $1-4.9 Billion
Investment Management Firm
N.A.I.C.S.: 523940

Subsidiary (Domestic):

BoE (Pty) Limited (2)
BoE Clock Tower Clock Tower Precinct V&A Waterfront, Cape Town, 8000, Eastern Cape, South Africa
Tel.: (27) 214166375
Securities Brokerage Services
N.A.I.C.S.: 523150

Subsidiary (Non-US):

Fairbairn Private Bank (Jersey) Limited (2)
28 New St, JE2 3TE, Saint Helier, Channel Islands, Jersey (67%)
Tel.: (44) 534887889
Web Site: http://www.fairbairnpb.com
Sales Range: $50-74.9 Million
Emp.: 30
Private Bank
N.A.I.C.S.: 522180

Fairbairn Trust Company Limited (2)
Fairbairn House, PO Box 192, Rohais, Saint Peter Port, Guernsey
Tel.: (44) 1481710895
Trust Management Services
N.A.I.C.S.: 523991

Nedbank (Malawi) Limited (2)
PO Box 750, Blantyre, Malawi
Tel.: (265) 620477
Sales Range: $50-74.9 Million
Emp.: 78
Banking & Investment Services
N.A.I.C.S.: 523150
Masi Masi *(Mgr-Relationship)*

Nedbank (Swaziland) Limited (2)
3rd Floor Ned Centre Building Corner Sozisa and Dr Sishayi Road, Swazi Plaza, Mbabane, Eswatini
Tel.: (268) 24081000
Web Site: https://www.nedbank.co.sz
Rev.: $31,451,474
Assets: $440,554,940
Liabilities: $385,487,202
Net Worth: $55,067,738
Earnings: $5,337,602
Fiscal Year-end: 12/31/2020
Banking Services
N.A.I.C.S.: 522110
Lindiwe Mlambo *(Head-Internal Audit)*

Subsidiary (Domestic):

Nedbank Group Insurance Company Ltd. (2)
Newton Crescent 1, Lenasia South Ext 1, 1829, Johannesburg, Gauteng, South Africa
Tel.: (27) 11 294 4444
Security Brokerage Services
N.A.I.C.S.: 523150

Subsidiary (Non-US):

Nedbank Namibia Limited (2)
12-20 Dr Frans Indongo Street, Windhoek, 9000, Namibia
Tel.: (264) 612952052
Web Site: http://www.nedbank.com.na
Sales Range: $75-99.9 Million
Commercial Banking Services
N.A.I.C.S.: 522110
Lionel J. Matthews *(Mng Dir)*

Nedbank Private Wealth Limited (2)
St Marys Court 20 Hill Street, Douglas, Isle of Man
Tel.: (44) 1624645000
Web Site:
   http://www.nedbankprivatewealth.com
Sales Range: $75-99.9 Million
Emp.: 150
Private Banking Services
N.A.I.C.S.: 522110
Craig Blenkinsop *(Dir-Ops & Fin)*

Subsidiary (Domestic):

Nedcor Investments Limited (2)
135 Rivonia Rd, Johannesburg, 2196, Gauteng, South Africa
Tel.: (27) 114801213
Web Site:
   http://www.nedgroupinvestments.co.za

NEDBANK GROUP LIMITED

Nedbank Group Limited—(Continued)
Sales Range: $50-74.9 Million
Emp.: 9
Investment Management Service
N.A.I.C.S.: 523999

Subsidiary (Non-US):

Nedcor Trade Services Limited (2)
5th Fl Barkly Wharf Le Caudan Waterfront
Old Pavilion St, Port Louis, Mauritius
Tel.: (230) 2100249
Web Site: http://www.nedcormauritius.co.mu
Sales Range: $50-74.9 Million
Emp.: 6
Commercial Banking Services
N.A.I.C.S.: 522110
Christo Roets (Mng Dir)

Subsidiary (Domestic):

Nedgroup Collective Investments Limited (2)
160 Lynnwood Rd, Menlo Park, Pretoria, 0081, Gauteng, South Africa
Tel.: (27) 214166011
Web Site: http://www.nedgroupinvestments.co.za
Investment Management Service
N.A.I.C.S.: 523940
Nic Andrew (Mng Dir)

Nedgroup Insurance Company Limited (2)
276 Rustenburg Rd, Johannesburg, 2001, Gauteng, South Africa
Tel.: (27) 114801637
Insurance Services
N.A.I.C.S.: 524210

Nedgroup Life Assurance Company Ltd (2)
Ground Floor 19 Hurst Grove Musgrave, 19 Hurst Grove, Durban, 4018, South Africa
Tel.: (27) 0860263543
Security Brokerage Services
N.A.I.C.S.: 523150
Angela Vernes (Head-Ops)

Nedgroup Wealth Management Limited (2)
135 Revonia Road, Sandown, 2196, Kwazulu-Natal, South Africa
Tel.: (27) 112944444
Web Site: http://www.nedbank.co.za
Sales Range: $1-4.9 Billion
Emp.: 5,000
Wealth Management Services
N.A.I.C.S.: 523940
Mike Brown (CEO)

Syfrets Securities Limited (2)
Nedcor Sandton 135 Rivonia Rd, Johannesburg, 2196, Gauteng, South Africa
Tel.: (27) 114801000
Securities Brokerage Services
N.A.I.C.S.: 523150

Nedgroup Trust Limited (1)
Fairbairn House Rohais, PO Box 192, Saint Peter Port, GY1 3LT, Guernsey
Tel.: (44) 1481710895
Fiduciary Services
N.A.I.C.S.: 523991

NEDELJNE NOVINE A.D.
Kralja Petra I 21, Backa Palanka, Serbia
Tel.: (381) 216041576
Year Founded: 2002
NEDN—(BEL)
Rev.: $86,100
Assets: $14,168
Liabilities: $4,769
Net Worth: $9,400
Earnings: ($6,315)
Fiscal Year-end: 12/31/23
Newspaper Publishing Services
N.A.I.C.S.: 513110
Nada Dedijer (Exec Dir)

NEDERLANDSE FINANCIERINGS-MAATSCHAPPIJ VOOR ONTWIKKELINGSLANDEN N.V.
Anna van Saksenlaan 71, 2593 HW, Hague, Netherlands
Tel.: (31) 703149696 NI
Web Site: http://www.fmo.nl
Year Founded: 1970
Rev.: $320,346,032
Assets: $9,507,739,064
Liabilities: $6,166,291,837
Net Worth: $3,341,447,227
Earnings: $169,247,801
Emp.: 533
Fiscal Year-end: 12/31/18
Corporate Financing & Development Services
N.A.I.C.S.: 525990
Linda Broekhuizen (Co-Chief Investment Officer & Member-Mgmt Bd)

Subsidiaries:

FMO Antillen N.V. (1)
Schottegatweg Oost 44, Willemstad, Curacao
Tel.: (599) 94615555
Investment Management Service
N.A.I.C.S.: 523940

NEDERLANDSE WATERSCHAPSBANK N.V.
Rooseveltplantsoen 3, 2517 KR, Hague, Netherlands
Tel.: (31) 704166266 NI
Web Site: http://www.nwbbank.com
Year Founded: 1954
Rev.: $1,867,926,480
Assets: $107,736,131,300
Liabilities: $105,724,862,740
Net Worth: $2,011,268,560
Earnings: $106,386,700
Emp.: 66
Fiscal Year-end: 12/31/19
Financial Services
N.A.I.C.S.: 523999
Lidwin M. T. van Velden (CEO)

NEDERMAN HOLDING AB
Sydhamnsgatan 2, 252 28, Helsingborg, Sweden
Tel.: (46) 42188700
Web Site: https://www.nederman.com
NMAN—(OMX)
Rev.: $448,619,584
Assets: $518,778,960
Liabilities: $359,977,296
Net Worth: $158,801,664
Earnings: $13,477,632
Emp.: 2,124
Fiscal Year-end: 12/31/20
Holding Company; Industrial Cleaning, Environmental Control & Filtration Equipment Mfr & Distr
N.A.I.C.S.: 551112
Sven Kristensson (Pres & CEO)

Subsidiaries:

AB Norclean (1)
Vare 44, 43291, Varberg, Sweden
Tel.: (46) 340 465 00
Web Site: http://www.norclean.se
Industrial Air Filtration Equipment Distr
N.A.I.C.S.: 423830

AB Ph. Nederman & Co. (1)
Sydhamnsgatan 2, 252 28, Helsingborg, Sweden (100%)
Tel.: (46) 42188700
Sales Range: $75-99.9 Million
Emp.: 270
Industrial Cleaning, Environmental Control & Filtration Equipment Mfr
N.A.I.C.S.: 333248
Sven Kristensson (CEO)

Subsidiary (Non-US):

Nederman & Co S.R.L. (2)
31-33 Constantin Sandu Aldea St Ap 2, Bucharest, Romania
Tel.: (40) 31 405 4318
Web Site: http://www.nederman.ro

Sales Range: $25-49.9 Million
Emp.: 4
Industrial Machinery Distr
N.A.I.C.S.: 423830

Nederman International Trading Shanghai Co. Ltd (2)
Factory No 4 No 98 Tianying Road, Qingpu Industrial Park, Shanghai, 201712, China
Tel.: (86) 2169225502
Web Site: http://www.nederman.cn
Industrial Machinery Distr
N.A.I.C.S.: 423830

Nederman Polska Sp zo.o. (2)
ul Okolna 45A, 05-270, Marki, Poland
Tel.: (48) 22 761 6000
Web Site: https://www.nederman.com
Pump & Pumping Equipment Mfr
N.A.I.C.S.: 333914
Sven Kristensson (Pres & CEO)

Nederman S.A.S. (2)
14 rue de la Perdrix, BP 45036, Tremblay en France, 95912, Roissy-en-France, Cedex, France
Tel.: (33) 14 938 1890
Web Site: https://www.nederman.com
Emp.: 12
Industrial Machinery Distr
N.A.I.C.S.: 423830
Alain David (Gen Mgr)

Subsidiary (Domestic):

Toredal Verkstad AB (2)
Jung Smedstorpet 1, Kvanum, 535 92, Sweden
Tel.: (46) 51 22 11 00
Web Site: http://www.nederman.com
Emp.: 20
Metal Sheet Processing Services
N.A.I.C.S.: 423510
Dorinel Lapadat (Gen Mgr)

Arboga-Darenth Ltd (1)
Unit 91 Seedlee Road Walton Summit Centre, Bamber Bridge, Preston, PR5 8AE, Lancashire, United Kingdom
Tel.: (44) 1322 341451
Web Site: http://www.arbogadarenth.com
Industrial & Commercial Machinery Distr
N.A.I.C.S.: 423830

Auburn FilterSense LLC (1)
800 Cummings Ctr 355W, Beverly, MA 01915
Tel.: (978) 927-4304
Web Site: http://www.filtersense.com
Measuring Instrument & Controlling Device Mfr
N.A.I.C.S.: 334519

Dantherm Filtration OOO (1)
Rjasanskij Prospekt 75 Tower 4 Floor 11, 109456, Moscow, Russia
Tel.: (7) 495 6424130
Web Site: http://www.danthermfiltration.ru
Industrial Air Filtration Equipment Repair Service & Distr
N.A.I.C.S.: 811310

Energy Save System Ltd. (1)
Unit 12 Pipewell Road, Kettering, NN14 2SW, United Kingdom
Tel.: (44) 1536680994
Web Site: https://www.energy-savesystem.com
Dust Extraction Services
N.A.I.C.S.: 562910

Environmental Filtration Technologies LLC (1)
4404-A Chesapeake Dr, Charlotte, NC 28216-3413
Tel.: (704) 399-7441
Web Site: http://www.environmentalfiltration.com
Sales Range: $125-149.9 Million
Emp.: 385
Industrial Filtration & Pollution Control Equipment Mfr
N.A.I.C.S.: 333248

Subsidiary (Domestic):

LCI Corporation International (2)
4433 Chesapeake Dr, Charlotte, NC 28216-3412 (100%)
Tel.: (704) 394-8341
Web Site: http://www.lcicorp.com

INTERNATIONAL PUBLIC

Sales Range: $25-49.9 Million
Emp.: 50
Special Industry Machinery
N.A.I.C.S.: 333248
Jamie Horton (Mgr-Process Separations)

MikroPul LLC (2)
4433 Chesapeake Dr, Charlotte, NC 28216
Tel.: (704) 859-2723
Web Site: http://www.mikropul.com
Sales Range: $25-49.9 Million
General Industrial Machinery Mfr
N.A.I.C.S.: 334416

Division (Non-US):

MikroPul (Pty) Limited (3)
Corner Beyers Naude Dr And Judges Ave Evapark Block B, 2194, Johannesburg, South Africa (100%)
Tel.: (27) 0114780456
Web Site: http://www.mikropul.co.za
General Industrial Machinery
N.A.I.C.S.: 423830

MikroPul Australia Pty Ltd. (3)
Unit 3 453 2-455 Victoria Street, Wetherill Park, 2164, NSW, Australia (100%)
Tel.: (61) 297562933
Web Site: http://www.mikropul.com
Sales Range: $25-49.9 Million
Emp.: 6
General Industrial Machinery Mfr
N.A.I.C.S.: 423830
Chris Dixon (Mgr-Engrg)

MikroPul Canada, Inc. (3)
245 Matheson Blvd E Unit 10, Mississauga, L4Z 3C9, ON, Canada (100%)
Tel.: (905) 712-0722
Web Site: http://www.mikropul.com
Sales Range: $1-9.9 Million
Emp.: 10
Air Pollution Control Equipment Mfr
N.A.I.C.S.: 423730

Division (Domestic):

MikroPul Chatham (3)
17 Watchung Ave, Chatham, NJ 07928 (100%)
Tel.: (973) 635-1115
Web Site: http://www.mikropul.com
Sales Range: $25-49.9 Million
Emp.: 2
Process, Particle Size Reduction & Dust Control Equipment Mfr
N.A.I.C.S.: 541990

Division (Non-US):

MikroPul GmbH (3)
Edmund-Rumpler-St r 2, 51149, Cologne, Germany
Tel.: (49) 220393910
Web Site: http://www.nederman-mikropul.com
Sales Range: $25-49.9 Million
Emp.: 200
General Industrial Machinery Mfr
N.A.I.C.S.: 423830
Markus Schilli (Mgr-Sls)

Division (Domestic):

MikroPul Pittsburgh (3)
2591 Wexford Bayne Rd Ste 302, Sewickley, PA 15143
Tel.: (724) 934-3910
Web Site: http://www.mikropul.com
Sales Range: $25-49.9 Million
Emp.: 8
General Industrial Machinery Mfr
N.A.I.C.S.: 541330
Scott Gongaware (Mgr)

Division (Non-US):

MikroPul S de RL de CV (3)
Av Lomas Verdes 480-302B Col Lomas Verdes, CP 53120, Naucalpan, Mexico (100%)
Tel.: (52) 55 5343 8224
Web Site: http://www.mikropul.com
General Industrial Machinery Mfr
N.A.I.C.S.: 423830

Subsidiary (Domestic):

Pneumafil Corporation (2)

AND PRIVATE COMPANIES

4404 A Chesapeake Dr, Charlotte, NC 28297
Tel.: (704) 399-7441
Web Site: http://www.pneumafil.com
Sales Range: $100-124.9 Million
Emp.: 400
Industrial Air Ventilation & Filtration Systems Mfr
N.A.I.C.S.: 333413
Jay Todd *(Mgr-Applications)*

Fa Ph. Nederman GmbH (1)
Otto Probst Strasse 36 I 1, Vienna, 1120, Austria (100%)
Tel.: (43) 018896734
Sales Range: $50-74.9 Million
Emp.: 3
Industrial Cleaning, Environmental Control & Filtration Equipment Mfr
N.A.I.C.S.: 333248

Gasmet Technologies (Asia) Ltd. (1)
Room 811 8th Floor Po Lung Centre 11 Wang Chiu Road, Kowloon Bay, China (Hong Kong)
Tel.: (852) 35687586
Precision Instrument Mfr & Distr
N.A.I.C.S.: 334519
Leung Shu Key Keith *(Mng Dir)*

Gasmet Technologies (UK) Ltd. (1)
Woolleys Farm Welford Road, Naseby, Northampton, NN6 6DP, United Kingdom
Tel.: (44) 1908227722
Precision Instrument Mfr & Distr
N.A.I.C.S.: 334519
Ken Roberts *(Mng Dir)*

Gasmet Technologies GmbH (1)
Ostring 4, 76131, Karlsruhe, Germany
Tel.: (49) 721626560
Precision Instrument Mfr & Distr
N.A.I.C.S.: 334519
Marco Signori *(Mng Dir)*

Gasmet Technologies Inc. (1)
5865 McLaughlin Rd Unit 1, Mississauga, L5R 1B8, ON, Canada
Precision Instrument Mfr & Distr
N.A.I.C.S.: 334519

Gasmet Technologies Oy (1)
Mestarintie 6, 01730, Vantaa, Finland
Tel.: (358) 975900400
Web Site: http://www.gasmet.com
Emp.: 120
Precision Instrument Mfr & Distr
N.A.I.C.S.: 334519
Mari Fromholdt *(Dir-Admin)*

Luwa Air Engineering (Pte.) Ltd. (1)
1 Scotts Road 26-09 Shaw Centre, Singapore, 228208, Singapore
Tel.: (65) 67375033
Textile Machinery Equipment Mfr & Distr
N.A.I.C.S.: 333248

Luwa America, Inc. (1)
4433 Chesapeake Dr, Charlotte, NC 28216
Tel.: (704) 504-7879
Textile Machinery Equipment Mfr & Distr
N.A.I.C.S.: 333248

Menardi Filters Europe A/S (1)
Industrivej 13, Assens, 9550, Mariager, Denmark
Tel.: (45) 99680998
Air Filtration Product Distr
N.A.I.C.S.: 423620

NEO Monitors AS (1)
Prost Stabels vei 22, 2019, Skedsmokorset, Norway
Tel.: (47) 40001613
Web Site: http://www.neomonitors.com
Gas Analyzer Mfr & Distr
N.A.I.C.S.: 334513

National Conveyors Company, Inc. (1)
33 Nicholson Rd, East Granby, CT 06026 (100%)
Tel.: (860) 325-4001
Web Site: http://www.nationalconveyors.com
Metal Chip Processing & Conveying Services
N.A.I.C.S.: 333922
Donald B. Brant Jr. *(CEO)*

Nederman A/S (1)
Industriveien 7A, PO Box 26, Haugenstua, 2020, Skedsmokorset, Norway (100%)
Tel.: (47) 22790210
Web Site: https://www.nederman.com
Sales Range: $25-49.9 Million
Emp.: 26
Industrial Cleaning, Environmental Control & Filtration Equipment Mfr
N.A.I.C.S.: 333248
Biorninge Inga *(Mgr-Mktg & Sls)*

Subsidiary (Domestic):

Dantherm Filtration A/S (2)
Kjell Haver Regnskapsservice As Welhavens Vei 5, Sandnes, 4319, Rogaland, Norway
Tel.: (47) 516 86060
Industrial Air Filtration Equipment Distr
N.A.I.C.S.: 423830

Nederman CR s.r.o. (1)
Krajankova 3176/2, 141 00, Prague, Czech Republic
Tel.: (420) 2810123312
Web Site: https://www.nederman.com
Sales Range: $25-49.9 Million
Emp.: 20
Industrial Machinery Distr
N.A.I.C.S.: 423830
Miroslav Bartko *(Gen Mgr)*

Nederman Canada Ltd. (1)
5865 McLaughlin Road Unit 1, Mississauga, L5R 1B8, ON, Canada
Tel.: (905) 366-2200
Web Site: http://www.nederman.com
Sales Range: $25-49.9 Million
Industrial Cleaning, Environmental Control & Filtration Equipment Mfr
N.A.I.C.S.: 333248

Nederman Danmark (1)
Industrivej 13, Assens, 9550, Mariager, Denmark
Tel.: (45) 99680900
Web Site: http://www.nederman.com
Sales Range: $200-249.9 Million
Emp.: 1,100
Industrial Air Filtration Equipment Design, Manufacturing & Installation Services
N.A.I.C.S.: 333413
Carsten Christensen *(CFO)*

Subsidiary (Non-US):

Dantherm Filtration (Suzhou) Co Ltd (2)
No 855 Unit 10 Zhujiang Rd SndShiShan Industrial Belt, Suzhou, 215129, China
Tel.: (86) 512 6690 7500
Web Site: http://www.danthermfiltration.com
Sales Range: $25-49.9 Million
Emp.: 80
Industrial Air Filtration Products Mfr & Distr
N.A.I.C.S.: 333248
Irposarikka Sarikka *(Gen Mgr)*

Dantherm Filtration AB (2)
Sadelgatan 10, 213 77, Malmo, Sweden
Tel.: (46) 40 671 95 00
Web Site: http://www.danthermfiltration.se
Industrial Air Filtration Equipment Mfr & Distr
N.A.I.C.S.: 333248

Dantherm Filtration Co Ltd (2)
66/1 Moo 11 Bangkruay-Sainoi Road T, Bangbuatong, A Bangbuatong, Nonthaburi, 11110, Thailand
Tel.: (66) 27151300
Web Site: http://www.danthermfiltration.co.th
Industrial Air Filtration Equipment Mfr & Distr
N.A.I.C.S.: 333248

Dantherm Filtration Holding GmbH (2)
Industriestr 9, Friesenheim, 77948, Germany
Tel.: (49) 78219660
Web Site: http://www.nederman.de
Sales Range: $25-49.9 Million
Emp.: 13
Industrial Air Filtration Equipment Mfr & Distr
N.A.I.C.S.: 333998
Detles Stark *(Gen Mgr)*

Subsidiary (US):

Dantherm Filtration, Inc. (2)
150 Transit Ave, Thomasville, NC 27360-8927
Tel.: (336) 821-0800
Industrial Air Filtration Equipment Design, Manufacturing & Installation Services
N.A.I.C.S.: 333413

Subsidiary (Non-US):

Nederman Filtration GmbH (2)
Industriestrasse 9, D 77948, Friesenheim, Germany
Tel.: (49) 78219660
Web Site: http://www.nederman.com
Sales Range: $25-49.9 Million
Emp.: 113
Industrial Air Filtration Equipment Design, Manufacturing & Installation Services
N.A.I.C.S.: 333413
Ralf Klopfer *(Mng Dir)*

Nederman Danmark A/S (1)
Industrivej 13, Assens, 9550, Mariager, Denmark
Tel.: (45) 9 968 0900
Web Site: http://www.nederman.com
Industrial Air Filtration Products Mfr & Distr
N.A.I.C.S.: 333413

Division (Domestic):

Nederman Danmark AS (2)
Ryttermarken 3, 3520, Farum, Denmark
Tel.: (45) 70200302
Web Site: https://www.nederman.com
Emp.: 10
Industrial Equipment Whsr
N.A.I.C.S.: 423830
Leif Jorgensen *(Gen Mgr)*

Nederman GmbH (1)
Nurtinger Strasse 50, 73257, Kongen, Germany (100%)
Tel.: (49) 7024868990
Web Site: https://www.nederman.com
Sales Range: $25-49.9 Million
Emp.: 40
Industrial Cleaning, Environmental Control & Filtration Equipment Mfr
N.A.I.C.S.: 333248

Nederman GmbH (1)
Grawatschgasse 4/Top15 3 OG, 1230, Vienna, Austria
Emp.: 5
Industrial Machinery Distr
N.A.I.C.S.: 423830
Peter Stadlbauer *(Mgr)*

Nederman Iberica S.A. (1)
Avda Camino de lo Cortao 34 Nave 5, San Sebastian de los Reyes, 28703, Madrid, Spain (100%)
Tel.: (34) 916592430
Web Site: https://www.nederman.com
Sales Range: $25-49.9 Million
Emp.: 20
Industrial Cleaning, Environmental Control & Filtration Equipment Mfr
N.A.I.C.S.: 333248
Havier Krohn *(Mng Dir)*

Nederman Inc. (1)
6330 Commerce Dr, Westland, MI 48185
Tel.: (734) 729-3344
Web Site: http://www.nedermanusa.com
Sales Range: $25-49.9 Million
Emp.: 25
Industrial Cleaning, Environmental Control & Filtration Equipment Mfr
N.A.I.C.S.: 333248
Travis Baker *(Dir-Mktg)*

Nederman India Private Limited (1)
No 203 2nd Floor A Wing Shoppers Orbit Alandi Road Vishrantwadi, Pune, 411 015, Maharashtra, India
Tel.: (91) 20 40760009
Web Site: http://www.nedermanindia.com
Rev.: $100,000,000
Emp.: 25
Industrial Vacuum Cleaner Mfr & Distr
N.A.I.C.S.: 333310

Nederman Ltd. (1)
Unit 91 Seedlee Road Walton Summit Bamber Bridge, Preston, PR5 8AE, Lancashire, United Kingdom
Tel.: (44) 1772334721
Web Site: https://www.nederman.com

NEDERMAN HOLDING AB

Sales Range: $50-74.9 Million
Emp.: 55
Industrial Cleaning, Environmental Control & Filtration Equipment Mfr
N.A.I.C.S.: 333248

Nederman Magyarorszag Kft (1)
Csanyi Laszlo u 34, 1043, Budapest, Hungary
Tel.: (36) 12720277
Web Site: http://www.nederman.com
Industrial Machinery Distr
N.A.I.C.S.: 423830

Nederman Makine Sanayi Ve Ticaret Limited (1)
Istanbul Ticaret Sarayi K 9 No 565-569, Esenler, 34235, Istanbul, Turkiye
Tel.: (90) 8070143
Web Site: https://www.nederman.com
Industrial Machinery & Parts Mfr
N.A.I.C.S.: 333248

Nederman Makine Sanayi Ve Ticaret Limited Sirketi (1)
Istanbul Trade Palace K 9 No 565-569, Esenler, Istanbul, 34235, Turkiye
Tel.: (90) 5353460888
Industrial Air Filtration Product Mfr & Distr
N.A.I.C.S.: 333413

Nederman MikroPul GmbH (1)
Welserstrasse 5-7, 51149, Cologne, Germany
Tel.: (49) 220393910
Industrial Air Filtration Product Mfr & Distr
N.A.I.C.S.: 333413

Nederman MikroPul Poland Sp. z o.o. (1)
Ul Okolna 45A, 05-270, Marki, Poland
Tel.: (48) 227616000
Industrial Air Filtration Product Mfr & Distr
N.A.I.C.S.: 333413

Nederman MikroPul Pty Ltd (1)
1/848 Mountain Highway, Bayswater, 3153, VIC, Australia
Tel.: (61) 387203700
Web Site: https://www.nedermanmikropul.com
Industrial Air Filtration Product Mfr & Distr
N.A.I.C.S.: 333413

Nederman N.V. (1)
Bergensesteenweg 181, 1600, Saint Pieters-Leeuw, Belgium
Tel.: (32) 23342250
Web Site: https://www.nederman.com
Sales Range: $25-49.9 Million
Emp.: 15
Industrial Machinery Distr
N.A.I.C.S.: 423830
Geerd Ceule *(Gen Mgr)*

Subsidiary (Domestic):

LEDA bvba (2)
Rosselstraat 1, Lede, 9340, Belgium
Tel.: (32) 53804378
Automotive Installation Services
N.A.I.C.S.: 561990

Nederman Nederland B.V. (1)
Wiekenweg 33, 3815 KL, Amersfoort, Netherlands
Tel.: (31) 332988122
Industrial Air Filtration Product Mfr & Distr
N.A.I.C.S.: 333413

Nederman Norclean B.V. (1)
Wiekenweg 133, 3815 KL, Amersfoort, Netherlands
Tel.: (31) 104357644
Web Site: http://www.nederman-norclean.nl
Industrial Vacuum Systems Distr
N.A.I.C.S.: 423830

Nederman Nordic AB (1)
Rannabanan 6, 252 31, Helsingborg, Sweden
Tel.: (46) 42188787
Web Site: https://www.nederman.com
Industrial Air Filtration Product Mfr & Distr
N.A.I.C.S.: 333413
Mikael Brandsten *(Partner & Dir-Dev)*

Nederman OOO (1)
St Leninskaya Sloboda 19, 115280, Moscow, Russia
Tel.: (7) 4952690445

NEDERMAN HOLDING AB

Nederman Holding AB—(Continued)
Web Site: http://www.nederman.com
Industrial Air Filtration Product Mfr & Distr
N.A.I.C.S.: 333413

Nederman S. de R.L. de C.V. (1)
C No 869 Int 5 and 6, Conj Industrial Palma Excelsa Parque Industrial Jurica, 76127, Santiago de Queretaro, Mexico
Tel.: (52) 4422511116
Industrial Air Filtration Product Mfr & Distr
N.A.I.C.S.: 333413

Nederman SEA Co., Ltd. (1)
700/694 Moo 7 T Donhuaroh, Amata Nakorn IE A Muang, Chon Buri, 20000, Thailand
Tel.: (66) 33674600
Industrial Air Filtration Product Mfr & Distr
N.A.I.C.S.: 333413

Nederman Svenska Forsaljnings AB (1)
Helsingborg, Box 602, 251 06, Helsingborg, Sweden
Tel.: (46) 42 188700
Web Site: http://www.nederman.com
Emp.: 270
Industrial Machinery Distr
N.A.I.C.S.: 423830
Ola Olsson *(Gen Mgr)*

Nederman do Brasil (1)
Av Jose Alves de Oliveira 710 Galpao B-1, Jundiai, Sao Paulo, 13213-105, Brazil
Tel.: (55) 1145256765
Web Site: https://www.nederman.com
Sales Range: $25-49.9 Million
Emp.: 10
Automotive Parts Mfr & Distr
N.A.I.C.S.: 336390
Mauricio Sampaio *(Country Mgr)*

Nederman do Brasil Comercio de Produtos de Exaustao Ltda. (1)
Av Jose Alves de Oliveira 710 Galpao B-1, Jundiai, Sao Paulo, 13213-105, Brazil
Tel.: (55) 1145256565
Web Site: https://www.nederman.com
Industrial Air Filtration Product Mfr & Distr
N.A.I.C.S.: 333413

Nordfab Europe AS (1)
Industrivej 13, Assens, 9550, Mariager, Denmark
Tel.: (45) 86471100
Web Site: http://www.nordfab.com
Dust Collection Equipment Mfr & Distr
N.A.I.C.S.: 333413

Nordfab LLC (1)
150 Transit Ave, Thomasville, NC 27360
Tel.: (336) 821-0801
Emp.: 150
Dust Collection Equipment Mfr & Distr
N.A.I.C.S.: 333413

Nordfab Pty. Ltd. (1)
1/848 Mountain Hwy, Bayswater, 3153, VIC, Australia
Tel.: (61) 387203700
Web Site: https://www.nederman.com
Air Filtration Equipment Mfr
N.A.I.C.S.: 333413

NEDERMAN HOLDING AB
Sydhamnsgatan 2, SE-251 06, Helsingborg, Sweden
Tel.: (46) 42 18 87 00
Web Site:
http://www.nedermangroup.com
Year Founded: 1944
Holding Company
N.A.I.C.S.: 551112
Matthew Cusick *(CFO & Sr VP)*

Subsidiaries:

Luwa Air Engineering AG (1)
Weiherallee 11a, CH 8610, Uster, Switzerland
Tel.: (41) 449431100
Web Site: http://www.luwa.com
Air Conditioning & Controls, Heat Recovery Systems, Filtration & Waste Handling Systems & Air Cleaning Systems Mfr
N.A.I.C.S.: 333415

Subsidiary (Non-US):

Ingenieurburo Otto Kuehnen (2)
Liechtensteinstrasse 63, 1090, Vienna, Austria
Tel.: (43) 1313560
Web Site: http://www.kuehnen.com
Sales Range: $125-149.9 Million
Emp.: 5
Heating Products
N.A.I.C.S.: 333414
Stefan Kuehnen *(Mng Dir)*

Luwa (India) Private Ltd. (2)
95 Industrial Suburb 2nd Stage Tumkur Road Yeswanthapura, Bengaluru, 560 022, India
Tel.: (91) 8023370277
Web Site: http://www.luwa.com
Sales Range: $25-49.9 Million
Sales of Air Conditioning & Controls, Heat Recovery Systems, Filtration & Waste Handling Systems & Air Cleaning Systems
N.A.I.C.S.: 334512
Juerg Staub *(Pres)*

Luwa (UK) Ltd. (2)
Wrigley St, Oldham, OL4 1HN, Lancs, United Kingdom
Tel.: (44) 1616248185
Web Site: http://www.luwa.co.uk
Sales Range: $25-49.9 Million
Emp.: 10
N.A.I.C.S.: 333310

Luwa Air Engineering (Shanghai) Co., Ltd. (2)
310 Sunshine Road, Jiading District, Shanghai, 201818, China
Tel.: (86) 2159900187
Web Site: http://www.luwa.com
Sales Range: $25-49.9 Million
Sales of Air Conditioning & Controls, Heat Recovery Systems, Filtration & Waste Handling Systems & Air Cleaning Systems
N.A.I.C.S.: 423830
Peter Schnickmann *(Gen Mgr)*

Luwa Anlagentechnik GmbH (2)
Rosemarinstrasse 25, D 09117, Chemnitz, Germany
Tel.: (49) 3718380
Web Site: http://www.luwa.com
Sales Range: $25-49.9 Million
Mfr of Electronic Communication Equipment
N.A.I.C.S.: 334220

Luwa Engineering (Pte.) Ltd. (2)
Shaw Center 1 Scotts Road Apartment 16-04, Singapore, 228 208, Singapore
Tel.: (65) 67375033
Web Site: http://www.luwa.com.sg
Sales Range: $25-49.9 Million
Sales of Air Conditioning & Controls, Heat Recovery Systems, Filtration & Waste Handling Systems & Air Cleaning Systems
N.A.I.C.S.: 423830
Hans Luethard *(Gen Mgr)*

Affiliate (Non-US):

Luwa Japan Ltd. (2)
Pacific square 25 12 NISHIKI nakaku 2nd flr, Naka Ku, Nagoya, 460 0003, Japan
Tel.: (81) 522188511
Web Site: http://www.puretec.co.jp
Sales Range: $25-49.9 Million
Dust Collection & Air Conditioning Design & Mfr
N.A.I.C.S.: 333414
Makoto Hata *(Mgr-Sls)*

NEDIC AGRAR A.D.
Marsala Tita 17, 23274, Bocar, Serbia
Tel.: (381) 23 789 602
Web Site: http://www.nedicagrar.rs
Year Founded: 2001
Sales Range: Less than $1 Million
Emp.: 22
Cereal Crop Farming Services
N.A.I.C.S.: 111998

NEEDS WELL, INC.
13th Floor of New Otani Garden Court 4-1 Kioicho, Chiyoda-ku, Tokyo, 102-0094, Japan
Tel.: (81) 362656763
Web Site: https://www.needswell.com
3992—(TKS)
Rev.: $57,885,695
Assets: $39,293,029
Liabilities: $14,760,489
Net Worth: $24,532,540
Earnings: $5,530,228
Emp.: 565
Fiscal Year-end: 09/30/23
Software Application Development Services
N.A.I.C.S.: 541511
Kozo Funatsu *(Pres & CEO)*

NEELAMALAI AGRO INDUSTRIES LTD.
Katary Estate Katary PO, The Nilgiris, Coonoor, 643213, Tamil Nadu, India
Tel.: (91) 4232284235
Web Site:
https://www.neelamalaiagro.com
508670—(BOM)
Rev.: $3,235,765
Assets: $30,403,621
Liabilities: $944,332
Net Worth: $29,459,289
Earnings: $3,371,860
Emp.: 562
Fiscal Year-end: 03/31/23
Tea Farming Services
N.A.I.C.S.: 111998
Ajit Thomas *(Chm)*

NEELKANTH ROCKMINERALS LIMITED
Flat No 606 Scheme, Jodhpur, Rajasthan, India
Tel.: (91) 9352121839
Web Site: https://www.neelrock.com
531049—(BOM)
Rev.: $76,299
Assets: $941,392
Liabilities: $28,513
Net Worth: $912,879
Earnings: $26,753
Fiscal Year-end: 03/31/23
Granite Mfr
N.A.I.C.S.: 327991

NEERAJ PAPER MARKETING LIMITED
218-222 Aggarwal Prestige Mall Plot No 02 Near M2K Cinema Pitampura, Delhi, 110 034, India
Tel.: (91) 1147527700
Web Site:
https://www.neerajpaper.com
Year Founded: 1995
539409—(BOM)
Rev.: $26,371,297
Assets: $8,104,766
Liabilities: $4,854,529
Net Worth: $3,250,237
Earnings: $61,759
Emp.: 20
Fiscal Year-end: 03/31/23
Paper Product Mfr & Distr
N.A.I.C.S.: 322120
Deepak Goel *(Chm)*

NEFAB AB
Lantmatargrand 5, PO Box 2184, 553 20, Jonkoping, Sweden
Tel.: (46) 771590000   SE
Web Site: http://www.nefab.com
Year Founded: 1949
Sales Range: $500-549.9 Million
Packaging Solution Services
N.A.I.C.S.: 561910
Anna Stalenbring *(Exec VP-Legal & IR)*

Subsidiaries:

NEFAB TURKEY AMBALAJ SAN. VE TIC. LTD. STI (1)
Mecidiyekoy Ortaklar Cd no 26/3, Sisli, 34394, Istanbul, Turkiye
Tel.: (90) 2122759043
Packaging Services
N.A.I.C.S.: 561910
Sedat Kantur *(Mng Dir)*

Nefab (Malaysia) Sdn Bhd (1)
Lot 1282-B Batu 8, Seksyen 32 Jalan Bukit Kemunin, 40470, Shah Alam, Selangor, Malaysia
Tel.: (60) 351247199
Web Site: http://www.nefab.com
Sales Range: $25-49.9 Million
Emp.: 5
Non-Durable Goods Whslr
N.A.I.C.S.: 424990

Nefab Bijl B.V. (1)
Hermesweg 28, Barneveld, 3771 ND, Netherlands (100%)
Tel.: (31) 342490147
Web Site: http://www.nefab.nl
Sales Range: $25-49.9 Million
Emp.: 18
Wood Products Mfr
N.A.I.C.S.: 321999
Koen Adams *(Mng Dir)*

Nefab China Marketing Department (1)
Floor 6 No 1068 Mao Tai Rd, 200336, Shanghai, PRC, China (100%)
Tel.: (86) 2132516900
Web Site: http://www.nefab.com.cn
Sales Range: $25-49.9 Million
Emp.: 50
Packaging Machinery Marketer
N.A.I.C.S.: 333993

Nefab Danmark A/S (1)
Kobenhavnsvej 69, 4000, Roskilde, Denmark (100%)
Tel.: (45) 43543013
Web Site: http://www.nefab.dk
Sales Range: $25-49.9 Million
Emp.: 3
Non-Durable Goods Whslr
N.A.I.C.S.: 424990
Martin Gradman *(Pres)*

Nefab Embalagens Ltda (1)
Estrada Sao Judas 35 - Jd Das Oliveiras, Embu das Artes, Sao Paulo, Brazil
Tel.: (55) 1147855050
Packaging Services
N.A.I.C.S.: 561910

Nefab Inc. (1)
211 Jameson Drive, Peterborough, K9J 6X6, ON, Canada (100%)
Tel.: (705) 748-4888
Web Site: http://www.nefab.ca
Sales Range: $25-49.9 Million
Emp.: 50
Wood Products Mfr
N.A.I.C.S.: 321999
Mark Robinson *(Pres)*

Nefab India Private Ltd. (1)
401 4th Fl A Wing Galleria Building, Hiranandani Gardens, Powai, 400 076, Mumbai, India (100%)
Tel.: (91) 2267108862
Web Site: http://www.nefab.in
Sales Range: $25-49.9 Million
Emp.: 3
Packaging Solutions Sales
N.A.I.C.S.: 488991

Nefab Logistics AB (1)
Slottsgatan 14, Box 2184, 550 02, Jonkoping, Sweden (100%)
Tel.: (46) 771590000
Web Site: http://www.nefab.com
Sales Range: $50-74.9 Million
Emp.: 23
Office Machinery & Equipment Rental & Leasing
N.A.I.C.S.: 532420
Anna Stalenbring *(CFO)*

Nefab Mexico SA de CV (1)
Francisco Villa 3 San Agustin De Las Flores, Tlajomulco de Zuniga, Jalisco, 45645, Mexico
Tel.: (52) 44 221 70138
Web Site: http://www.nefab.com.mx
Packaging Solutions, Including Corrugated & Foam, Wood Crates, Export Packaging, Logistics, Design & Engineering Services

AND PRIVATE COMPANIES / NEFINSA S.A.

N.A.I.C.S.: 321920

Nefab Packaging Belgium N.V. (1)
Skaldenstraat 121, F1 Haven 3230, 9042,
Gent, Belgium (99%)
Tel.: (32) 92318282
Web Site: http://www.nefab.be
Sales Range: $25-49.9 Million
Emp.: 30
Paperboard Box Mfr
N.A.I.C.S.: 322219
Koen Adams *(Mng Dir)*

**Nefab Packaging Czech Republic
s.r.o.** (1)
Pisecna 509/5 Brnenske Ivanovice, Brno,
620 00, Czech Republic
Tel.: (420) 543214743
Packaging Services
N.A.I.C.S.: 561910
Juraj Horvath *(Mng Dir)*

**Nefab Packaging Engineering (Dong-
guan) Co., Ltd.** (1)
Sanheng Road-turn in by Shuilang Road
Datang, Dalingshan, Dongguan, 523837,
Guangdong, China
Tel.: (86) 76982784111
Packaging Services
N.A.I.C.S.: 561910
Lijun Wei *(Mng Dir)*

**Nefab Packaging Engineering (Shen-
zhen) Co. Ltd.** (1)
Silicon Valley Power Longhua Town, Bao
An, 518109, Shenzhen, China (100%)
Tel.: (86) 75528123971
Web Site: http://www.nefab.com
Packaging Machinery Mfr
N.A.I.C.S.: 333993

**Nefab Packaging Engineering (Wuxi)
Co. Ltd** (1)
No 16 Xing Chuang Road 4, Wuxi-
Singapore Industrial Park, 214028, Wuxi,
Jiangsu, China (100%)
Tel.: (86) 51085200310
Web Site: http://www.nefab.com.cn
Engineering Services
N.A.I.C.S.: 541330

Nefab Packaging France S.A.S. (1)
RN 20 Nord, Salbris, 41300,
France (100%)
Tel.: (33) 254968255
Web Site: http://www.nefab.fr
Emp.: 80
Industrial & Personal Service Paper Whslr
N.A.I.C.S.: 424130
Dethare Benoit *(Gen Mgr)*

**Nefab Packaging Germany
GmbH** (1)
Industriestrasse 25, Unterriexingen,
D-71706, Markgroningen, Germany
Tel.: (49) 7147 22 06 0
Web Site: http://www.nefab.de
Sales Range: $25-49.9 Million
Wood Container; Plastic Pallets Mfr & Pack-
aging Services
N.A.I.C.S.: 321920
Stefan Muller *(CEO)*

Nefab Packaging Hungary Kft. (1)
East Gate Business Park B1 Epulet Fot,
Fot, 2151, Hungary (100%)
Tel.: (36) 27 395 960
Web Site: http://www.nefab.hu
Emp.: 55
Packaging & Crating Mfr
N.A.I.C.S.: 488991
Laszlo Nith *(Mng Dir)*

Nefab Packaging Inc. (1)
204 Airline Dr Ste 100, Coppell, TX 75019
Tel.: (469) 444-5320
Web Site: http://www.nefab.us
Packaging Solutions
N.A.I.C.S.: 561910
Brian Bulatao *(CEO)*

Branch (Domestic):

Nefab Packaging (2)
850 Mark St, Elk Grove Village, IL 60007
Tel.: (630) 451-5300
Web Site: http://www.nefab.us
Sales Range: $10-24.9 Million
Emp.: 150
Boxes, Wood Containers Mfr

N.A.I.C.S.: 321920
Mike Tecorelli *(Gen Mgr)*

Nefab Packaging (2)
115 Broadway, Dover, NH 03820
Tel.: (603) 367-8857
Web Site: http://www.nefab.us
Sales Range: $150-199.9 Million
Emp.: 600
Industrial Packaging Services
N.A.I.C.S.: 561910
Ken Wilson *(Dir-Global Bus Dev/Energy)*

Nefab Packaging Inc. (2)
2988 E Ana St, Rancho Dominguez, CA
90221-5603
Tel.: (310) 603-2501
Web Site: http://www.nefab.us
Emp.: 75
Wood Containers
N.A.I.C.S.: 321920
Mark Banish *(Gen Mgr)*

Nefab Packaging, Inc.-Collierville (2)
300 Commerce Rd, Collierville, TN 38017
Tel.: (901) 853-2500
Web Site: http://www.nefab.us
Sales Range: $25-49.9 Million
Emp.: 55
Wood Containers
N.A.I.C.S.: 321920
Terry Williams *(Gen Mgr)*

Subsidiary (Domestic):

Plastiform, Inc. (2)
3418 International Pl, Irving, TX 75062
Tel.: (972) 241-2593
Web Site: http://www.plastiform-dallas.com
Sales Range: $1-9.9 Million
Emp.: 40
Mfg Thermofromed Packaging
N.A.I.C.S.: 326113
Donna Lee *(Mgr-Ops)*

Subsidiary (Domestic):

Precision Formed Plastics, Inc. (3)
3245 Royalty Row, Irving, TX 75062
Tel.: (972) 579-8803
Web Site: http://www.precision-dallas.com
Sales Range: $1-9.9 Million
Emp.: 27
Plastics Foam Products
N.A.I.C.S.: 326150
Elwyn Jones *(VP)*

**Nefab Packaging Netherlands
B.V.** (1)
Hermesweg 28, 3771 ND, Barneveld, Neth-
erlands
Tel.: (31) 342490147
Packaging Services
N.A.I.C.S.: 561910
Marco Waarma *(Acct Mgr)*

Nefab Packaging Norway A/S (1)
Lersbrygga 16, Sande in Vestfold, 3070,
Oslo, Norway
Tel.: (47) 33785850
Web Site: http://www.nefab.no
Sales Range: $25-49.9 Million
Emp.: 15
Industrial & Personal Service Paper Whslr
N.A.I.C.S.: 424130
Eric Allum *(CEO & Mng Dir)*

Nefab Packaging OU (1)
Killustiku 6 Lagedi Rae Vald, 75303, Harju-
maa, Estonia (100%)
Tel.: (372) 6349800
Web Site: http://www.nefab.ee
Sales Range: $25-49.9 Million
Emp.: 100
Wood Container & Pallet Mfr
N.A.I.C.S.: 321920
Erikki Susi *(Mgr-Sls)*

**Nefab Packaging Poland Sp. z
o.o.** (1)
30 Stycznii 43, 83-110, Elblag,
Poland (100%)
Tel.: (48) 587217410
Web Site: http://www.nefab.pl
Sales Range: $25-49.9 Million
Emp.: 10
Non-Durable Goods Whslr
N.A.I.C.S.: 424990
Tomasz Budzynowski *(Mgr-Site)*

**Nefab Packaging Romania
S.R.L.** (1)
Str Andrei Saguna No 3 Bldg U5, Timi-
soara, 300119, Romania (100%)
Tel.: (40) 256283423
Web Site: http://www.nefab.ro
Sales Range: $25-49.9 Million
Emp.: 9
Coated & Laminated Packaging Paper &
Plastics Film Mfr
N.A.I.C.S.: 322220
Valentin Cica *(Mng Dir)*

Nefab Packaging Slovakia S.r.o (1)
Industrial Park Gena Ul Zeppelina 2, 934
01, Levice, Slovakia (100%)
Tel.: (421) 366356500
Web Site: http://www.nefab.com
Wood Container & Pallet Mfr
N.A.I.C.S.: 321920

Nefab Packaging Sweden AB (1)
Nordgrens vag 5, 822 81, Alfta, Sweden
Tel.: (46) 771590000
Web Site: http://www.nefab.se
Packaging Services
N.A.I.C.S.: 561910

Nefab Packaging UK Limited (1)
151 Silbury Boulevard, Milton Keynes, MK9
1LH, United Kingdom
Tel.: (44) 2476717811
Web Site: http://www.nefab.co.uk
Sales Range: $25-49.9 Million
Emp.: 4
Wood Container & Pallet Mfr
N.A.I.C.S.: 321920

Nefab Plywood Pontevedra, S.L. (1)
Ctra de Barbudo s/n, Ponte Caldelas,
36828, Pontevedra, Spain
Tel.: (34) 986750150
Packaging Services
N.A.I.C.S.: 561910

**Nefab RA-Produtos de Embalagem
Lda** (1)
Rua Jorge Ferreirinha 1096, 4470-314,
Maia, Portugal (100%)
Tel.: (351) 229439220
Web Site: http://www.nefab.com
Sales Range: $25-49.9 Million
Emp.: 80
Durable Goods Whslr
N.A.I.C.S.: 423990
Luzia Pereira *(Gen Mgr)*

Nefab S.A. (1)
Calle Gutenberg 23, Pol Ind El Lomo
Getafe, 28906, Madrid, Spain (89%)
Tel.: (34) 916966911
Web Site: http://www.nefab.es
Sales Range: $25-49.9 Million
Emp.: 78
Packaging Solutions
N.A.I.C.S.: 561910
Martin Ignacao *(Mng Dir)*

Nefab Singapore Pte Ltd (1)
7 Kian Teck Drive, Singapore, 628824,
Singapore (60%)
Tel.: (65) 68620178
Sales Range: $25-49.9 Million
Emp.: 10
Freight Transportation Arrangement
N.A.I.C.S.: 488510

Nefab Specialemballage AB (1)
Nordgrensvagen 5, Balsta, 74634,
Sweden (100%)
Tel.: (46) 771590000
Web Site: http://www.nefab.se
Emp.: 250
Plastics Product Mfr
N.A.I.C.S.: 326199
Frank Hall *(Mgr)*

Nefab Srl (1)
Via Magretti 22, Paderno Dugnano, Milan,
20037, Italy
Tel.: (39) 0299048520
Packaging Services
N.A.I.C.S.: 561910
Fabio Gerna *(Mng Dir)*

Nefab Teknik AB (1)
Nordgrens Vag 5, Alfta, Gavle, 822 92,
Sweden (100%)
Tel.: (46) 771590000
Web Site: http://www.nefab.se

Machine Tool (Metal Cutting Types) Mfr
N.A.I.C.S.: 333517
Marco Kase *(Mng Dir)*

**Nefab Verpackungstechnik
GmbH** (1)
Bahnhofstrasse 16, 4063, Horsching, Aus-
tria
Tel.: (43) 720303660
Packaging Services
N.A.I.C.S.: 561910
Jurgen Leppelt *(Mgr-Sls)*

Nefab, S.A.U. (1)
c/ Florida 17 Oficina 2 1 dcha, Vitoria-
Gasteiz, 01005, Alava, Spain
Tel.: (34) 945131542
Packaging Services
N.A.I.C.S.: 561910
Pepi Marin *(Acct Mgr)*

Oy Nefab Ab (1)
Lars Sonckin kaari 16, 02600, Espoo, Fin-
land
Tel.: (358) 108301100
Packaging Services
N.A.I.C.S.: 561910

PolyFlex Products, Inc. (1)
34481 Industrial Rd, Livonia, MI 48150
Tel.: (734) 458-4194
Web Site: http://www.polyflexpro.com
Sales Range: $10-24.9 Million
Emp.: 24
Mfr & Designer of Custom Packaging
N.A.I.C.S.: 326199

Reflex Packaging, Inc. (1)
2210 S Huron Dr, Santa Ana, CA 92704
Tel.: (714) 619-8520
Web Site: http://www.reflexpackaging.com
Paperboard Mills, Nsk
N.A.I.C.S.: 322130
Forrest Smith *(Founder)*

NEFF KITCHENS, INC.
151 East Drive, Brampton, L6T 1B5,
ON, Canada
Tel.: (905) 791-7770
Web Site: http://neffkitchens.com
Rev.: $15,215,366
Emp.: 175
Kitchen Furniture Design & Mfr
N.A.I.C.S.: 332215
Miro Nowak *(Pres & CEO)*

NEFINSA S.A.
Plaza Canovas del Castillo 1 4-7,
46005, Valencia, Spain
Tel.: (34) 963333301
Web Site: http://www.nefinsa.es
Sales Range: $450-499.9 Million
Emp.: 1,777
Investor Services
N.A.I.C.S.: 523160
Emilio Serratosa Ridaura *(Pres)*

Subsidiaries:

**Air Nostrum Lineas Aereas Del Medi-
terraneo SA** (1)
Ave Comarques Der Bais Vallencia 2, Quart
De Doblet, 46930, Valencia, Spain (100%)
Tel.: (34) 961960200
Web Site: http://www.airnostrum.es
Sales Range: $450-499.9 Million
Emp.: 1,500
Provider of Scheduled Air Transportation
N.A.I.C.S.: 481111
Carlos Bertomeu *(CEO)*

Subsidiary (Non-US):

CityJet DAC (2)
Swords Business Campus Balheary Road,
Swords, Dublin, Ireland
Tel.: (353) 1 8 700 100
Web Site: http://www.cityjet.com
Passenger Air Transportation Services
N.A.I.C.S.: 481111
Cathal O'Connell *(Chief Comml Officer)*

**Corporacion Empresarial de Materi-
ales de Construccion** (1)
Paseo De Recolepos 3 Planta 5, 28004,
Madrid, Spain
Tel.: (34) 91 594 90 00

NEFINSA S.A.

Nefinsa S.A.—(Continued)
Web Site: http://www.coemac.com
Sales Range: $100-124.9 Million
Emp.: 554
Building Construction Materials Mfr & Whslr
N.A.I.C.S.: 423330
Gonzalo Serratosa Lujan (Deputy Chm)

Subsidiary (Non-US):

Lusoceram-Empreendimentos Ceramicos, S.A. (2)
Rua Castilho 39 8 A D, 1269, Lisbon, Portugal (53%)
Tel.: (351) 213815540
Web Site: http://www.lusoceram.com
Mfr of Clay Roof Tiles & Clay Blocks
N.A.I.C.S.: 327120

Subsidiary (Domestic):

Uralita Tejados, S.A. (2)
Pataseo De Recoletoas 3, 28004, Madrid, Spain (53%)
Tel.: (34) 915949000
Web Site: http://www.uralita.com
Concrete Roof Tile Mfr
N.A.I.C.S.: 327390

Subsidiary (Non-US):

Ursa France, S.A.S. (2)
35 Grande Allee du 12 Fevrier 1934, Paris, Noisiel, France
Tel.: (33) 160177760
Web Site: http://www.ursa.fr
Sales Range: $25-49.9 Million
Emp.: 40
Roofing Siding & Insulation Material Merchant Whslr
N.A.I.C.S.: 423330

Subsidiary (Domestic):

Ursa Iberica Aislantes, S.A. (2)
Casp 17-6 Planta, 08010, Barcelona, Spain
Tel.: (34) 933441100
Web Site: http://www.ursa.es
Plastics Product Mfr
N.A.I.C.S.: 326199

Subsidiary (Non-US):

Ursa Italia S.R.L. (2)
Via Paracelso 16, Palazzo Andromeda, 20864, Agrate Brianza, Monza and Brianza, Italy
Tel.: (39) 0396898576
Web Site: http://www.ursa.it
Emp.: 10
Structural Clay Product Mfr
N.A.I.C.S.: 327120
Antonio Tenice (Mgr-Commi)

Ursa U.K. Ltd (2)
Grupo Aralita Crest House, 102-104 Church Rd, Teddington, TW118PY, Middlesex, United Kingdom
Tel.: (44) 2089779697
Web Site: http://www.ursa-uk.co.uk
Roofing Siding & Insulation Material Merchant Whslr
N.A.I.C.S.: 423330

Davmes,S.A. (1)
Plaza America 2, 46004, Valencia, Spain
Tel.: (34) 963333301
Web Site: http://www.nefinsa.es
Sales Range: $25-49.9 Million
Emp.: 20
Land Subdivision
N.A.I.C.S.: 237210

La Canada Tochosa, S.A. (1)
Plaza America 2-3, Valencia, 46004, Spain
Tel.: (34) 963333301
Web Site: http://www.nefinsa.es
Grain Farming
N.A.I.C.S.: 111199

Mejana, S.A. (1)
Plaza America 2, Valencia, 46004, Spain
Tel.: (34) 963333301
Mortgage & Nonmortgage Loan Brokers
N.A.I.C.S.: 522310

Sansemisa, S.A. (1)
Plz America 2 3rd Fl, Valencia, 46004, Spain
Tel.: (34) 963333301

Web Site: http://www.nefinsa.es
Sales Range: $50-74.9 Million
Emp.: 5
Mortgage & Nonmortgage Loan Brokers
N.A.I.C.S.: 522310
Imereo Serrapora (Gen Mgr)

Uralita Sistemas de Tuberias, S.A. (1)
Paseo Recoletos 3, Madrid, 28004, Spain
Tel.: (34) 915949000
Web Site: http://www.uralita.com
Sales Range: $50-74.9 Million
Emp.: 200
Plastics Product Mfr
N.A.I.C.S.: 326199
Jabier Serraposa (Pres)

Ursa Benelux BVBA (1)
Pitantiestraat 127, 8870, Waregem, Belgium
Tel.: (32) 56738484
Web Site: http://www.ursa-online.com
Sales Range: $50-74.9 Million
Emp.: 150
Specialty Trade Contractors
N.A.I.C.S.: 238990
Jean-Eddy Sannier (Plant Mgr)

Ursa Beograd d.o.o. (1)
III Bulevar 25, Novi Beograd, 11070, Belgrade, Serbia
Tel.: (381) 11137548
Roofing Siding & Insulation Material Merchant Whslr
N.A.I.C.S.: 423330

Ursa Polska Sp. z.o.o. (1)
UL Armii Krajowej 12, 42-520, Dabrowa Gornicza, Poland
Tel.: (48) 322680101
Web Site: http://www.ursa.pl
Sales Range: $50-74.9 Million
Emp.: 150
Mineral Wool Mfr
N.A.I.C.S.: 327993

Ursa SK S.r.o (1)
Kapitulska 15, 81101, Bratislava, Slovakia
Tel.: (421) 244461628
Web Site: http://www.ursa.sk
Roofing Siding & Insulation Material Merchant Whslr
N.A.I.C.S.: 423330

Ursa Zagreb d.o.o. (1)
Puskariceva 15, Lucko, Zagreb, 10250, Croatia
Tel.: (385) 16526386
Web Site: http://www.ursa.hr
Business Services
N.A.I.C.S.: 561499

NEFTEPROMBANK CJSC
31 Bld 3 Obraztsova St, Moscow, 127018, Russia
Tel.: (7) 4952342200
Web Site: http://www.nefteprom.com
Year Founded: 1992
Sales Range: Less than $1 Million
Commercial & Investment Banking Services
N.A.I.C.S.: 523150

NEGIN TABAS COAL COMPANY
Mosala Street East Saadat Abad Palace Street No 182, Hakim Nezami Alley, 816479413, Isfahan, Iran
Tel.: (98) 3131307091
Web Site: https://www.negintabas.ir
Year Founded: 1999
Coal Mining Services
N.A.I.C.S.: 212114
Ali Roomi (Chm)

NEGOTIUM INTERNATIONAL TRADE LIMITED
G/12 Ground Floor Asaf Ali Road, New Delhi, 110002, India
Tel.: (91) 8376885252 In
Web Site: https://www.mahadushinational.com
Year Founded: 1994
Rev: $127,452

Assets: $2,337,159
Liabilities: $1,822,263
Net Worth: $514,896
Earnings: $280
Emp.: 2
Fiscal Year-end: 03/31/18
Jewelry Whslr
N.A.I.C.S.: 423940
Raju Yadav (CFO & Compliance Officer)

NEGRI SEMBILAN OIL PALMS BERHAD
Suite 2B-3A-2 Block 2B Level 3A Plaza Sentral Jalan Stesen Sentral 5, Kuala Lumpur Sentral, 50470, Kuala Lumpur, Malaysia
Tel.: (60) 322614633
Web Site: https://www.nsop.com.my
NSOP—(KLS)
Rev: $23,652,366
Assets: $166,890,002
Liabilities: $19,259,267
Net Worth: $147,630,735
Earnings: $6,632,673
Fiscal Year-end: 12/31/22
Palm Oil Mfr
N.A.I.C.S.: 311225
Wei Lei Goh (Chm)

NEHA INTERNATIONAL LIMITED
501 Manbhum Jade Towers Rajbhavan Road, Hyderabad, 500082, Telangana, India
Tel.: (91) 40 66134759
Web Site: http://www.nehainternational.com
Rev: $1,292,505,786
Assets: $402,627,048
Liabilities: $1,049,828,532
Net Worth: ($647,201,484)
Earnings: ($126,625,068)
Fiscal Year-end: 03/31/19
Rose Growing & Export Services
N.A.I.C.S.: 111422
Gaddam Vinod Reddy (Chm & Mng Dir)

NEIL INDUSTRIES LIMITED
14/113 Civil Lines 402-403 Kan Chambers, Kanpur, 208 001, Uttar Pradesh, India
Tel.: (91) 5122303325
Web Site: https://www.neil.co.in
Year Founded: 1983
539016—(BOM)
Rev: $359,175
Assets: $6,652,587
Liabilities: $671,351
Net Worth: $5,981,236
Earnings: $222,025
Emp.: 9
Fiscal Year-end: 03/31/23
Financial Support Services
N.A.I.C.S.: 523999
Arvind Kumar Mittal (Mng Dir)

NEIMETH INTERNATIONAL PHARMACEUTICALS PLC
Plot 16 Akanni Doherty Layout, Oregun Industrial Estate Oregun, Ikeja, 21111, Lagos, Nigeria
Tel.: (234) 8054431508
Web Site: https://www.neimethplc.com.ng
NEIMETH—(NIGE)
Rev: $2,500,108
Assets: $10,109,882
Liabilities: $8,447,354
Net Worth: $1,662,529
Earnings: ($3,242,070)
Emp.: 202
Fiscal Year-end: 12/31/23
Pharmaceuticals Product Mfr
N.A.I.C.S.: 325412

INTERNATIONAL PUBLIC

Ambrosie Bryant Chueloka Orjiako (Chm)

NEINOR HOMES SA
20 Henao Street, 48009, Bilbao, Spain
Tel.: (34) 900110022
Web Site: https://www.neinorhomes.com
HOME—(VAL)
Rev: $633,995,277
Assets: $1,766,394,376
Liabilities: $716,627,308
Net Worth: $1,049,767,068
Earnings: $98,072,134
Emp.: 291
Fiscal Year-end: 12/31/23
Home Construction Services
N.A.I.C.S.: 236115
Jorge Pepa (Chief Dev Officer & Exec VP)

Subsidiaries:

Quabit Inmobiliaria S.A. (1)
C/ Roger de Lauria 19 5 planta, 46002, Valencia, Spain
Tel.: (34) 963812570
Sales Range: $600-649.9 Million
Emp.: 217
Real Estate Development & Management Services
N.A.I.C.S.: 531390
Felix Abanades Lopez (Chm)

NEKHEESGUI EDLEL JOINT STOCK COMPANY
3rd Khoroo, Khan Uul District, Ulaanbaatar, Mongolia
Tel.: (976) 11342232
NXE—(MONG)
Rev: $303,211
Assets: $818,780
Liabilities: $202,888
Net Worth: $615,892
Earnings: $51,411
Fiscal Year-end: 12/31/20
Textile Products Mfr
N.A.I.C.S.: 314999

NEKISON ENGINEERING & CONTRACTORS LTD.
17 St Lawrence Avenue, Toronto, M8Z 5T8, ON, Canada
Tel.: (416) 259-4631
Web Site: http://www.nekison.com
Plumbing & Construction Services
N.A.I.C.S.: 238220
Ramesh Jain (Pres)

NEKKAR ASA
Andoyfaret 15, 4623, Kristiansand, Norway
Tel.: (47) 90676544 NO
Web Site: https://nekkar.com
Year Founded: 1966
NKR—(OSL)
Rev: $35,793,737
Assets: $46,844,910
Liabilities: $14,425,919
Net Worth: $32,418,991
Earnings: $2,940,975
Emp.: 64
Fiscal Year-end: 12/31/22
Holding Company; Marine Cargo Handling Equipment Developer & Mfr
N.A.I.C.S.: 551112
Trym Skeie (Chm)

Subsidiaries:

Intellilift AS (1)
Andoyfaret 31, 4623, Kristiansand, Norway
Tel.: (47) 90635223
Web Site: https://nekkar.com
Drilling Oil & Gas Well Services
N.A.I.C.S.: 213111

Syncrolift AS (1)
Kleverveien 3, 1543, Vestby, Norway
Tel.: (47) 64907910

Web Site: https://syncrolift.com
Ship Lifting Equipment Distr
N.A.I.C.S.: 488390

TTS Group - Port & Logistics (1)
Laksevagneset 12, NO-5847, Bergen, Norway (100%)
Tel.: (47) 55947400
Web Site: http://www.tts-marine.com
Sales Range: $25-49.9 Million
Emp.: 350
Marine Cargo Handling Equipment Designer & Mfr
N.A.I.C.S.: 333924

Subsidiary (Domestic):

TTS Cranes Norway AS (2)
Folke Bernadottes Vei 38, Fyllingsdalen, Bergen, 5147, Norway
Tel.: (47) 55348400
Web Site: http://www.ttsgroup.com
Emp.: 70
Crane & Winch Whslr
N.A.I.C.S.: 423830

TTS Handling Systems AS (2)
Holterkollveien 6, PO Box 49, NO-1441, Drobak, Norway (100%)
Tel.: (47) 64907910
Sales Range: $25-49.9 Million
Emp.: 17
Heavy-Load Marine Cargo Handling Systems Mfr
N.A.I.C.S.: 333310

Subsidiary (Non-US):

TTS Port Equipment AB (2)
Kampegatan 3, Gothenburg, 411 04, Sweden (100%)
Tel.: (46) 317257900
Web Site: http://www.ttsgroup.com
Sales Range: $25-49.9 Million
Emp.: 20
Linkspans, Lashing Kerbs, Trailer Tressles & Auto-Mooring Equipment Mfr
N.A.I.C.S.: 333310

Subsidiary (Domestic):

TTS Ships Equipment AS (2)
Folke Bernadottesvei 38, PO Box 3517, Fyllingsdalen, Bergen, 5147, Norway (100%)
Tel.: (47) 55113050
Web Site: http://www.tts-se.com
Sales Range: $25-49.9 Million
Marine Vessel Equipment Mfr
N.A.I.C.S.: 336999

NEKTAN PLC
Suite 971 Europort Europort Road, Gibraltar, GX11 1AA, Gibraltar
Tel.: (350) 442034782648 GI
Web Site: http://www.nektan.com
Year Founded: 2011
NKTN—(LSE)
Rev.: $28,650,665
Assets: $5,554,501
Liabilities: $20,275,133
Net Worth: ($14,720,632)
Earnings: ($11,694,019)
Emp.: 91
Fiscal Year-end: 06/30/19
Software Development Services
N.A.I.C.S.: 513210
Gary Shaw (Founder & CEO-Interim)

NEL ASA
Karenslyst Alle 49, 0279, Oslo, Norway
Tel.: (47) 23248950
Web Site:
 https://www.nelhydrogen.com
Year Founded: 1927
D7G—(DEU)
Rev.: $91,777,295
Assets: $642,020,321
Liabilities: $138,638,832
Net Worth: $503,381,489
Earnings: ($108,181,138)
Emp.: 514
Fiscal Year-end: 12/31/22
Electric Power Distribution Services

N.A.I.C.S.: 221122
Jon Andre Lokke (CEO)

Subsidiaries:

Nel Hydrogen A/S (1)
Vejlevej 5, 7400, Herning, Denmark
Tel.: (45) 96275600
Renewable Energy Services
N.A.I.C.S.: 221111

Nel Hydrogen Electrolyser AS (1)
Heddalsvegen 11, PO Box 24, 3671, Notodden, Norway
Tel.: (47) 35093838
Renewable Energy Services
N.A.I.C.S.: 221111

NELCAST LIMITED
159 TTK Road Alwarpet, Chennai, 600 018, India
Tel.: (91) 4424983111
Web Site: https://www.nelcast.com
Year Founded: 1982
532864—(BOM)
Rev.: $127,865,488
Assets: $131,453,486
Liabilities: $70,794,428
Net Worth: $60,659,058
Earnings: $1,941,672
Emp.: 1,121
Fiscal Year-end: 03/31/22
Iron Casting Mfr
N.A.I.C.S.: 339999
P. Vijaya Bhaskar Reddy (Deputy Mng Dir)

Subsidiaries:

Nelcast USA Inc (1)
1802 Johns Dr, Glenview, IL 60025
Tel.: (847) 657-1308
Sales Range: $50-74.9 Million
Emp.: 1
Ductile Iron & Grey Iron Casting Distr
N.A.I.C.S.: 423510

NELCO LIMITED
EL-6 Electronics Zone MIDC Mahape, Navi Mumbai, 400 710, India
Tel.: (91) 2267918728
Web Site: https://www.nelco.in
Year Founded: 1940
504112—(BOM)
Rev.: $37,875,427
Assets: $31,440,561
Liabilities: $18,905,341
Net Worth: $12,535,220
Earnings: $2,379,953
Emp.: 93
Fiscal Year-end: 03/31/23
Software Development Services
N.A.I.C.S.: 541511
Girish V. Kirkinde (Officer-Compliance, Sec & Head-Legal)

NELLY GROUP AB
Lundbygatan 1, 506 30, Boras, Sweden
Tel.: (46) 107032000
Web Site:
 https://www.nellygroup.com
Year Founded: 1936
NELLY—(OMX)
Rev.: $121,666,807
Assets: $78,413,742
Liabilities: $65,900,512
Net Worth: $12,513,230
Earnings: ($6,715,558)
Emp.: 221
Fiscal Year-end: 12/31/22
Ecommerce Services
N.A.I.C.S.: 449210
Marcus Lindqvist (Pres & CEO)

NELSON BROS. OILFIELD SERVICES (1997) LTD.
5399 Jubilee Avenue, PO Box 6487, Drayton Valley, T7A 1R9, AB, Canada

Tel.: (780) 542-5777
Web Site:
 http://www.nelsonbros.ab.ca
Year Founded: 1987
Rev.: $14,112,131
Emp.: 80
Oil & Gas Field Services
N.A.I.C.S.: 324191
Garry Nelson (Owner)

NELSON LUMBER COMPANY LTD
12727 St Albert Trail, Edmonton, T5J 3M6, AB, Canada
Tel.: (780) 452-9151
Web Site: http://www.nelson-homes.com
Sales Range: $50-74.9 Million
Emp.: 400
Timber & Home Building
N.A.I.C.S.: 321999
Lorne Schreiner (Gen Mgr-Edmonton)

NELSON RIVER CONSTRUCTION INC.
101 Dawson Rd N, Winnipeg, R2J 0S6, MB, Canada
Tel.: (204) 949-8700
Web Site:
 https://www.nelsonriver.com
Year Founded: 1923
Rev.: $17,649,825
Emp.: 300
Highway Construction & Underground Services
N.A.I.C.S.: 237310
Gord Lee (Pres & CEO)

Subsidiaries:

Nelson Environmental Inc. (1)
5 Burks Way, Winnipeg, R2J 3R8, MB, Canada
Tel.: (204) 949-7500
Web Site:
 http://www.nelsonenvironmental.com
Waste Water Treatment Services
N.A.I.C.S.: 221320
Martin Hildebrand (Pres)

NEM INSURANCE PLC
199 Ikorodu Road Obanikoro, PO Box 654, Lagos, Nigeria
Tel.: (234) 144895607
Web Site: https://www.nem-insurance.com
Year Founded: 1948
NEM—(NIGE)
Rev.: $24,699,702
Assets: $33,966,399
Liabilities: $13,833,053
Net Worth: $20,133,347
Earnings: $4,026,397
Emp.: 219
Fiscal Year-end: 12/31/22
General & Non Insurance Services
N.A.I.C.S.: 524298
Adewale Teluwo (Chm)

Subsidiaries:

NEM Asset Management Ltd. (1)
NEM House 199 Ikorodu Road Obanikoro, Lagos, Nigeria
Tel.: (234) 14489560
Web Site: http://www.nemasset.com
Financial Investment Services
N.A.I.C.S.: 523940
Tope Smart (Chm)

NEM Health Limited (1)
Nem House 199 Ikorodu Road, Obanikoro, Lagos, Nigeria
Tel.: (234) 2013300150
Web Site: https://nem-health.com
Health Care Srvices
N.A.I.C.S.: 621610

NEMASKA LITHIUM INC.
600 boul de Maisonneuve Ouest

Suite 750, Montreal, H3A 3J2, QC, Canada
Tel.: (418) 704-6038 QC
Web Site:
 https://nemaskalithium.com
Year Founded: 2007
NMX—(OTCIQ)
Rev.: $5,801,458
Assets: $896,997,691
Liabilities: $473,837,985
Net Worth: $423,159,706
Earnings: ($20,337,719)
Emp.: 131
Fiscal Year-end: 06/30/19
Lithium Exploration & Development Services
N.A.I.C.S.: 212290
Jacques Mallette (Chm)

NEMETALI A.D.
Jovana Raskovica 1, 79000, Prijedor, Bosnia & Herzegovina
Tel.: (387) 52242282
NMTL—(BANJ)
Sales Range: Less than $1 Million
Emp.: 8
Clay & Kaolin Mining Services
N.A.I.C.S.: 212323
Sasa Grbic (Pres)

NEMETALI OGRAZDEN AD
239 Marshall Tito Street, Strumica, North Macedonia
Tel.: (389) 34326888
Web Site:
 https://www.ograzden.com.mk
Year Founded: 1955
NEME—(MAC)
Rev.: $4,593,101
Assets: $8,994,693
Liabilities: $5,552,354
Net Worth: $3,442,340
Earnings: $231,972
Fiscal Year-end: 12/31/23
Mining Services
N.A.I.C.S.: 212290

NEMETSCHEK SE
Konrad-Zuse-Platz 1, 81829, Munich, Germany
Tel.: (49) 895404590 De
Web Site:
 https://www.nemetschek.com
Year Founded: 1963
NEMKY—(OTCIQ)
Rev.: $940,011,537
Assets: $1,406,694,657
Liabilities: $582,567,392
Net Worth: $824,127,265
Earnings: $178,010,076
Emp.: 3,415
Fiscal Year-end: 12/31/23
Information Technology Products & Services for Designing, Constructing & Managing Buildings & Real Estate
N.A.I.C.S.: 541511
Kurt Dobitsch (Chm-Supervisory Bd)

Subsidiaries:

123erfasst.de GmbH (1)
Korkenstrasse 8, 49393, Lohne, Germany
Tel.: (49) 4442888690
Web Site: https://www.123erfasst.de
Software Development Services
N.A.I.C.S.: 541511

AUER - Die Bausoftware GmbH (1)
Oberst-lepperdinger-strasse 19, Wals-Siezenheim, 5071, Austria
Tel.: (43) 6622232400
Web Site: http://www.bausoftware.at
Sales Range: $25-49.9 Million
Emp.: 17
Software Development Services
N.A.I.C.S.: 541511
Helmuth Houtek (Mng Dir)

Abvent S.A. (1)
58 rue Saint Lazare, 75009, Paris, France

NEMETSCHEK SE

Nemetschek SE—(Continued)
Tel.: (33) 153010505
Web Site: https://abvent.com
Software Development Services
N.A.I.C.S.: 541511

Allplan Cesko s.r.o. (1)
Zerotinova 1133/32, 130 00, Prague, Czech Republic
Tel.: (420) 225384880
Web Site: https://www.allplan.com
Architectural Design Services
N.A.I.C.S.: 541310
Igor Seifert *(Dir-Technical)*

Allplan Deutschland GmbH (1)
Konrad-Zuse-Platz 1, 81829, Munich, Germany
Tel.: (49) 89927932600
Web Site: https://www.allplan.com
Architectural Design Services
N.A.I.C.S.: 541310

Allplan France S.A.R.L. (1)
8 Place Des Vins De France, 75012, Paris, France
Tel.: (33) 180493200
Architectural Design Services
N.A.I.C.S.: 541310

Allplan Inc. (1)
10 N High St Ste 110, West Chester, PA 19380
Tel.: (610) 429-9800
Architectural Design Services
N.A.I.C.S.: 541310

Allplan Infrastructure GmbH (1)
Andreas-Hofer-Platz 17/4, 8010, Graz, Austria
Tel.: (43) 316269786
Web Site: http://www.allplan.com
Architectural Design Services
N.A.I.C.S.: 541310
Vanja Samec *(Mng Dir)*

Allplan Italy Srl (1)
Via GB Trener 8, 38121, Trento, Italy
Tel.: (39) 0461430430
Web Site: https://www.allplan.com
Building Design & Management Software Development Services
N.A.I.C.S.: 561790

Allplan Osterreich Ges.m.b.H. (1)
Donau-City-Strasse 1 Vienna Tech Gate Tower 1 Stock, 1220, Vienna, Austria
Tel.: (43) 6622232390
Architectural Design Services
N.A.I.C.S.: 541310

Allplan Schweiz AG (1)
Hertistrasse 2c, 8304, Wallisellen, Switzerland
Tel.: (41) 448397676
Web Site: https://www.allplan.com
Architectural Design Services
N.A.I.C.S.: 541310

Allplan Slovensko s.r.o. (1)
Bajkalska 19B, 821 01, Bratislava, Slovakia
Tel.: (421) 249251444
Architectural Design Services
N.A.I.C.S.: 541310
Martin Hudec *(CFO)*

Allplan Systems Espaha S.A. (1)
Calle Raimundo Fernandez Villaverde N 30 Esc 3 1 Office 314, 28003, Madrid, Spain
Tel.: (34) 915714877
Architectural Design Services
N.A.I.C.S.: 541310

Allplan UK Ltd. (1)
5 Charter Point Way Ashby Park, Ashby de la Zouch, LE65 1NF, United Kingdom
Tel.: (44) 1530560126
Architectural Design Services
N.A.I.C.S.: 541310

Bluebeam AB (1)
Kistagangen 12, 164 40, Kista, Sweden
Tel.: (46) 848002320
Architectural Design Services
N.A.I.C.S.: 541310

Bluebeam GmbH (1)
Konrad-Zuse-Platz 1, 81829, Munich, Germany
Tel.: (49) 89540459490
Web Site: https://www.bluebeam.com

Architectural Design Services
N.A.I.C.S.: 541310
Georg Reindl *(Mng Dir)*

Bluebeam Limited UK, Ltd. (1)
20 Eastbourne Terrace Ste 5 07, Paddington, London, W2 6LG, United Kingdom
Tel.: (44) 2038689061
Architectural Design Services
N.A.I.C.S.: 541310

Canvas Solutions Inc. (1)
11911 Freedom Dr Ste 850, Reston, VA 20190
Tel.: (866) 242-9334
Web Site: http://www.canvassolutions.com
Advertising Agencies
N.A.I.C.S.: 541810
James Quigley *(CEO)*

DACODA GmbH (1)
Felix-Wankel-Str 32, 72108, Rottenburg am Neckar, Germany
Tel.: (49) 7472 937910
Web Site: http://www.dacoda.net
Sales Range: $25-49.9 Million
Emp.: 5
Building Design Software Development Services
N.A.I.C.S.: 541511

DC-Software Doster & Christmann GmbH (1)
Konrad-Zuse-Platz 1, 81829, Munich, Germany
Tel.: (49) 711810020
Web Site: https://www.dc-software.de
Software Development Services
N.A.I.C.S.: 541511

DDS Building Innovation AS (1)
Oksnevad Industrial Park Engelsvollvegen 264, Klepp Stasjon, 4353, Klepp, Norway
Tel.: (47) 51788900
Web Site: http://www.dds-bi.no
Building Information Modeling Services
N.A.I.C.S.: 541310

Data Design System AS (1)
Oksnevad Naeringspark Engelsvollvegen 264, Klepp Stasjon, 4353, Klepp, Norway
Tel.: (47) 51788900
Building Information Modeling Services
N.A.I.C.S.: 541310

Data Design System GmbH (1)
Ludinghauser Strasse 3, 59387, Ascheberg, Germany
Tel.: (49) 259382490
Building Information Modeling Services
N.A.I.C.S.: 541310

Design Data Corp. (1)
1501 Old Cheney Rd, Lincoln, NE 68512
Tel.: (402) 441-4000
Web Site: http://www.sds2.com
Sales Range: $1-9.9 Million
Emp.: 65
Prepackaged Software Publishers
N.A.I.C.S.: 513210
David Sweigart *(Pres)*

Friedrich + Lochner GmbH (1)
Stuttgarter Strasse 36, 70469, Stuttgart, Germany
Tel.: (49) 711810020
Web Site: http://www.frilo.eu
Software Development Services
N.A.I.C.S.: 541511

Graphisoft Asia Ltd. (1)
Admiralty Centre Tower 2/ Level 11 18 Harcourt Road, Admiralty, Hong Kong, China (Hong Kong)
Tel.: (852) 39753260
Architect Construction Design Services
N.A.I.C.S.: 541310

Graphisoft Brasil Servigos de Tecnologia da Informacao Ltda. (1)
Rua do Rocio 288 Cj 92, Vila Olimpia, 04552-000, Sao Paulo, Brazil
Tel.: (55) 1130454350
Architect Construction Design Services
N.A.I.C.S.: 541310

Graphisoft Mexico S.A. de C.V. (1)
Insurgentes Sur 662 Col Del Valle Norte, 03100, Mexico, Mexico
Tel.: (52) 5550468800
Web Site: https://graphisoft.com

Architect Construction Design Services
N.A.I.C.S.: 541310

Graphisoft SE (1)
Graphisoft Park, 1031, Budapest, Hungary
Tel.: (36) 14373000
Web Site: https://graphisoft.com
Sales Range: $25-49.9 Million
Emp.: 245
Construction & Architecture Software Products & Services
N.A.I.C.S.: 513210
Huw Roberts *(CEO)*

Subsidiary (Domestic):

Graphisoft CAD Studio Kft (2)
Graphisoft Park 1 Zahony utca 7, 1031, Budapest, Hungary
Tel.: (36) 14373366
Web Site: http://www.cadstudio.hu
Graphic Software Development Services
N.A.I.C.S.: 541511

Subsidiary (Non-US):

Graphisoft Deutschland GmbH (2)
Landaubogen 10, 81373, Munich, Germany (100%)
Tel.: (49) 89746430
Web Site: https://graphisoft.com
Sales Range: $25-49.9 Million
Emp.: 25
Construction & Architecture Software Products & Services
N.A.I.C.S.: 513210

Graphisoft Japan, K.K. (2)
Akasaka Noah Building 4F 3-2-12 Akasaka, Minato-ku, Tokyo, 107-0052, Japan (100%)
Tel.: (81) 355453800
Web Site: http://www.graphisoft.co.jp
Emp.: 37
Construction & Architecture Software Products & Services
N.A.I.C.S.: 513210

Subsidiary (US):

Graphisoft North America, Inc. (2)
1601 Trapelo Rd Ste 162, Waltham, MA 02451
Tel.: (617) 485-4200
Web Site: https://graphisoft.com
Emp.: 50
Software Development Services
N.A.I.C.S.: 541511
Steve Benford *(Mng Dir)*

Subsidiary (Domestic):

Graphisoft R&D Szamitastechnikai Fejleszto zrt. (2)
Graphisoft Park 1 Zahony u, 1031, Budapest, Hungary (85.8%)
Tel.: (36) 14373000
Web Site: http://www.graphisoft.hu
Sales Range: $50-74.9 Million
Construction & Architecture Software Products & Services
N.A.I.C.S.: 513210

Subsidiary (Non-US):

Graphisoft Spain, S.L. (2)
Avda Filipinas 1bis Pl 4, 28003, Madrid, Spain (100%)
Tel.: (34) 915358750
Web Site: http://www.archicad.es
Sales Range: $25-49.9 Million
Emp.: 7
Construction & Architecture Software Products & Services
N.A.I.C.S.: 513210

Subsidiary (US):

Graphisoft U.S., Inc. (2)
1601 Trapelo Rd Ste 162, Waltham, MA 02451-2802 (100%)
Tel.: (617) 485-4202
Web Site: http://graphisoft.com
Sales Range: $25-49.9 Million
Emp.: 12
Software for Architectural Design & Construction
N.A.I.C.S.: 513210
Steve Benford *(Mng Dir)*

INTERNATIONAL PUBLIC

Subsidiary (Non-US):

Graphisoft UK Ltd. (2)
Harman House 1 George Street, Uxbridge, London, UB8 1QQ, United Kingdom (100%)
Tel.: (44) 1895527590
Web Site: https://graphisoft.com
Sales Range: $25-49.9 Million
Emp.: 3
Construction & Architecture Software Products & Services
N.A.I.C.S.: 513210

MAXON COMPUTER Inc (1)
2640 Lavery Ct Ste A, Newbury Park, CA 91320
Tel.: (805) 376-3333
Web Site: http://www.maxon.net
Software Development Services
N.A.I.C.S.: 541511

MAXON Competence Center (1)
207 Rue Gallieni, 92100, Boulogne-Billancourt, France
Tel.: (33) 146218222
Emp.: 4
Software Development Services
N.A.I.C.S.: 541511
Eric Goode *(Mgr)*

MAXON Computer GmbH (1)
Max-planck-str 20, 61381, Friedrichsdorf, Germany (100%)
Tel.: (49) 617259060
Web Site: http://www.maxon.net
Sales Range: $25-49.9 Million
Emp.: 45
Software Development Services
N.A.I.C.S.: 541511

Subsidiary (Non-US):

MAXON Computer Japan (2)
Sankyo Meguro Bldg 301 Kamiosaki 4-5-37, Shinagawa-Ku, Tokyo, 141-0021, Japan
Tel.: (81) 357590530
Web Site: http://www.maxon.net
Sales Range: $25-49.9 Million
Emp.: 5
Hardware Mfr & Software Development Services
N.A.I.C.S.: 332510

MAXON Computer Ltd (2)
Doolittle Mill Froghall Road, Ampthill, MK45 2ND, Bedfordshire, United Kingdom
Tel.: (44) 1525406799
Web Site: http://www.maxon.net
Sales Range: $25-49.9 Million
Emp.: 6
Hardware Mfr & Software Development Services
N.A.I.C.S.: 332510

NEMETSCHEK ESPANA S.A (1)
C Del Pinar 5 28006 Madrid C/ Vallespir 19, 08173, Sant Cugat del Valles, Barcelona, Spain
Tel.: (34) 915714877
Web Site: http://www.nemetschek.es
Sales Range: $25-49.9 Million
Emp.: 15
Building Design & Management Software Development Services
N.A.I.C.S.: 541511

NEMETSCHEK FRANCE SARL (1)
Ctr Objectif 2 Rue Louis Armand, 92661, Asnieres, France
Tel.: (33) 146134700
Web Site: http://www.nemetschek.fr
Sales Range: $25-49.9 Million
Emp.: 42
Software Development Services
N.A.I.C.S.: 541511

NEMETSCHEK Slovensko s.r.o (1)
Za Kasarnou 1, Bratislava, 83103, Slovakia
Tel.: (421) 249251178
Web Site: http://www.nemetschek.sk
Sales Range: $25-49.9 Million
Emp.: 100
Building Design & Management Software Development Services
N.A.I.C.S.: 561790

NEMETSCHEK Vectorworks Inc (1)
7150 Riverwood Dr, Columbia, MD 21046
Tel.: (410) 290-5114

AND PRIVATE COMPANIES

Web Site: http://www.nemetschek.net
Sales Range: $25-49.9 Million
Emp.: 110
Software Development Services
N.A.I.C.S.: 541511
Richard Diehl *(Chm)*

NEMETSCHEK s.r.o (1)
Zerotinova 1133/32, 130 00, Prague, Czech Republic
Tel.: (420) 225384880
Web Site: http://www.nemetschek.cz
Software Development Services
N.A.I.C.S.: 541511

NEVARIS Bausoftware GmbH (1)
Hanna-Kunath-Strasse 3, 28199, Bremen, Germany
Tel.: (49) 421596600
Web Site: https://www.nevaris.com
Emp.: 250
Architectural Design Services
N.A.I.C.S.: 541310

NEVARIS Bausoftware GmbH (1)
Aubergstrasse 15, 5161, Elixhausen, Austria
Tel.: (43) 6628908000
Architectural Design Services
N.A.I.C.S.: 541310

Nemetschek Bausoftware GmbH (1)
Im Finigen 3, 28832, Achim, Germany
Tel.: (49) 42029890
Web Site: http://www.bausoftware.de
Sales Range: $25-49.9 Million
Emp.: 100
Software Development Services
N.A.I.C.S.: 541511
Micheal Homscheid *(Gen Mgr)*

Nemetschek CREM Solutions GmbH & Co. KG (1)
Hauptsitz Ratingen Kokkolastrasse 2, 40882, Ratingen, Germany
Tel.: (49) 2102 5546 0
Web Site: http://www.crem-solutions.de
Software Development Services
N.A.I.C.S.: 541511

Nemetschek CREM Verwaltungs GmbH (1)
Konrad-zuse-platz 1, Munich, 81829, Germany
Tel.: (49) 21 02554 60
Web Site: http://www.nemetschek.com
Software Development Services
N.A.I.C.S.: 541511

Nemetschek Deutschland GmbH (1)
Konrad-Zuse-Platz 1, 81829, Munich, Germany
Tel.: (49) 89 927930
Web Site: http://www.nemetschek.com
Real Estate Software Development Services
N.A.I.C.S.: 541511

Nemetschek Engineering GmbH (1)
Stadionstrasse 6, 5071, Wals-Siezenheim, Austria
Tel.: (43) 6628541110
Web Site: http://www.nemetschek-engineering.at
Sales Range: $25-49.9 Million
Emp.: 25
Software Development Services
N.A.I.C.S.: 541511

Nemetschek Fides & Partner AG (1)
Hertistrasse 2 C, 8304, Wallisellen, Switzerland
Tel.: (41) 448397676
Web Site: http://www.nfp.ch
Sales Range: $25-49.9 Million
Emp.: 1
Building Design & Management Software Development Services
N.A.I.C.S.: 541511

Nemetschek Scia B.V. (1)
Wassenaarweg 40, 6843 NW, Arnhem, Netherlands
Tel.: (31) 263201230
Web Site: http://www.scia.net
Sales Range: $25-49.9 Million
Emp.: 11
Structural Engineering, Design & Management Software Development Services
N.A.I.C.S.: 541511

Nevaris BIM Software GmbH (1)
Herbert-Bayer-Strasse 4, 13086, Berlin, Germany
Tel.: (49) 30755699975
Architectural Design Services
N.A.I.C.S.: 541310

Precast Software Engineering GmbH (1)
Urstein Sud 19/1/6, Puch bei Hallein, 5412, Hallein, Austria
Tel.: (43) 6245210010
Web Site: http://www.allplan-precast.com
Software Engineering Services
N.A.I.C.S.: 541511
Werner Maresch *(Mng Dir)*

RISA Tech, Inc. (1)
26632 Towne Centre Dr Ste 210, Foothill Ranch, CA 92610
Tel.: (949) 951-5815
Web Site: http://www.risa.com
Software Development Services
N.A.I.C.S.: 541511
Debbie Penko *(COO)*

Subsidiary (Domestic):

Adapt Corporation (2)
1733 Woodside Rd Ste 220, Redwood City, CA 94061
Tel.: (650) 306-2400
Web Site: http://www.adaptsoft.com
Structural Engineering Software Development Services
N.A.I.C.S.: 541511
Florian B. Aalami *(Pres & CEO)*

SCIA Cz s.r.o (1)
Slavickova 827/1a, 638 00, Brno, Czech Republic
Tel.: (420) 530501570
Computer Peripheral Equipment Distr
N.A.I.C.S.: 423430

SCIA International NV (1)
Industrieweg 1007, 3540, Herk-de-Stad, Belgium
Tel.: (32) 13551775
Web Site: http://www.nemetschek-scia.com
Sales Range: $25-49.9 Million
Emp.: 25
Building Design & Management Software Development Services
N.A.I.C.S.: 541511

Subsidiary (Domestic):

SCIA nv (2)
Industrieweg 1007, 3540, Herk-de-Stad, Belgium
Tel.: (32) 13 551775
Web Site: http://www.scia.net
Building Design & Management Software Development Services
N.A.I.C.S.: 561790

SCIA Sarl (1)
10 R Chateau, 59100, Roubaix, France
Tel.: (33) 328332867
Software Development Services
N.A.I.C.S.: 541511

SCIA Sk s.r.o (1)
Murgasova 1298/16, 010 01, Zilina, Slovakia
Tel.: (421) 415003070
Sales Range: $25-49.9 Million
Emp.: 2
Building Design & Management Software Development Services
N.A.I.C.S.: 541511
Milan Hrae *(Gen Mgr)*

Scia France S.A.R.L. (1)
67 Place Rihour, 59000, Lille, France
Tel.: (33) 184020090
Web Site: https://www.scia.net
Architectural Design Services
N.A.I.C.S.: 541310

Scia Nederland B.V. (1)
Wassenaarweg 40, 6843 NW, Arnhem, Netherlands
Tel.: (31) 263201230
Architectural Design Services
N.A.I.C.S.: 541310

Solibri DACH GmbH (1)
Uberseeallee 10, 20457, Hamburg, Germany

Tel.: (49) 40808074638
Architect Design Services
N.A.I.C.S.: 541310

Solibri LLC (1)
17470 N Pacesetter Way, Scottsdale, AZ 85255
Tel.: (480) 305-2120
Architect Design Services
N.A.I.C.S.: 541310
J. D. Sherrill *(VP-Sls)*

Solibri Oy (1)
Tammasaarenkatu 5 HTC Santa Maria, 00180, Helsinki, Finland
Tel.: (358) 509191354
Web Site: https://www.solibri.com
Architect Design Services
N.A.I.C.S.: 541310

Solibri UK Ltd. (1)
4 Carrwood Park Selby Road, Leeds, LS15 4LG, United Kingdom
Tel.: (44) 1133372031
Architect Design Services
N.A.I.C.S.: 541310
Andrew Bellerby *(Mng Dir)*

Spacewell Netherlands B.V. (1)
Groningensingel 1 1st floor wing B, 6835 EA, Arnhem, Netherlands
Tel.: (31) 850449309
Software Development Services
N.A.I.C.S.: 541511

Vectorworks Canada, Inc. (1)
Suite 611 207 West Hastings Street, Vancouver, V6B 1H7, BC, Canada
Tel.: (604) 800-1811
Architectural Design Services
N.A.I.C.S.: 541310

Vectorworks UK, Ltd. (1)
St Peter's House Oxford Square Oxford Street, Newbury, RG14 1JQ, Berkshire, United Kingdom
Tel.: (44) 1635580318
Architectural Design Services
N.A.I.C.S.: 541310

dRofus AB (1)
Mailbox 2325, 111 75, Stockholm, Sweden
Tel.: (46) 18136060
Software Development Services
N.A.I.C.S.: 541511

dRofus AS (1)
Badstugata 2, 0183, Oslo, Norway
Tel.: (47) 22331570
Web Site: https://www.drofus.com
Software Development Services
N.A.I.C.S.: 541511
Hakon Clausen *(CTO)*

dRofus Pty. Ltd. (1)
1502/275 Alfred Street, North Sydney, 2060, NSW, Australia
Tel.: (61) 1300376387
Software Development Services
N.A.I.C.S.: 541511
Chris Razzell *(Mng Dir)*

NEMIROFF HOLDING
31 Gorky St, Nemirov, 28000, Vinnytsya Oblast, Ukraine
Tel.: (380) 445855662
Web Site: http://www.nemiroff.ua
Year Founded: 1992
Sales Range: $450-499.9 Million
Emp.: 500
Vodka Producer & Distr
N.A.I.C.S.: 312140
Yelena Neselovskaya *(Dir-Quality Assurance)*

NEMO S.R.L.
Viale Brianza 30, 20823, Lentate sul Seveso, MB, Italy
Tel.: (39) 03621660500   IT
Web Site:
    http://www.nemolighting.com
Year Founded: 1993
Light Designer & Mfr
N.A.I.C.S.: 335132
Federico Palazzari *(Owner)*

NEO GROUP LIMITED

Subsidiaries:

Ilti Luce S.r.l. (1)
Lungo Dora P Colletta 113/9, Turin, 10153, Italy
Tel.: (39) 011 248 2291
Web Site: http://www.iltiluce.com
Sales Range: $25-49.9 Million
Emp.: 35
Light Emitting Diode Mfr
N.A.I.C.S.: 334419

NEO CREMAR CO., LTD.
7 Dosan-daero 89-gil, Gangnam-gu, Seoul, 05836, Korea (South)
Tel.: (82) 24014088
Web Site: https://www.cremar.co.kr
Year Founded: 2007
311390---(KRS)
Rev.: $20,481,119
Assets: $60,114,705
Liabilities: $22,726,707
Net Worth: $37,387,998
Earnings: ($598,001)
Emp.: 66
Fiscal Year-end: 12/31/22
Food Additive Product Mfr
N.A.I.C.S.: 311999
Jae-Hwan Kim *(CEO)*

NEO ENERGY METALS PLC
27-28 Eastcastle Street, London, W1W 8DH, United Kingdom   UK
Web Site:
    https://www.neoenergymetals.com
Year Founded: 2015
NEO---(LSE)
Rev.: $17,650
Assets: $680,218
Liabilities: $4,123,396
Net Worth: ($3,443,178)
Earnings: ($817,347)
Emp.: 2
Fiscal Year-end: 03/31/22
Holding Company
N.A.I.C.S.: 551112
James Longley *(Board of Directors & Chm)*

NEO FINANCE AB
A Vivulskio St 7, 3162, Vilnius, Lithuania
Tel.: (370) 68700300
Web Site:
    https://www.neofinance.com
Year Founded: 2014
NEOFI---(RSE)
Rev.: $4,228,931
Assets: $17,349,945
Liabilities: $14,829,792
Net Worth: $2,520,153
Earnings: $144,612
Emp.: 35
Fiscal Year-end: 12/31/21
Financial Investment Services
N.A.I.C.S.: 523999
Evaldas Remeikis *(Chm)*

Subsidiaries:

Paskolu Klubas UAB (1)
A Vivulskio str 7, 03162, Vilnius, Lithuania
Tel.: (370) 870080075
Web Site: https://www.paskoluklubas.lt
Home Loan Services
N.A.I.C.S.: 522310

UAB Finomark (1)
A Vivulskio str 7, 03162, Vilnius, Lithuania
Tel.: (370) 52078897
Web Site: https://www.finomark.lt
Business Loan Services
N.A.I.C.S.: 522310
Grazvydas Balcas *(CEO)*

NEO GROUP LIMITED
1 Enterprise Road, Singapore, 629813, Singapore
Tel.: (65) 6896 7757

NEO GROUP LIMITED

Neo Group Limited—(Continued)

Web Site:
http://www.neogroup.com.sg
Year Founded: 1992
Rev.: $132,387,167
Assets: $119,314,464
Liabilities: $88,749,572
Net Worth: $30,564,893
Earnings: $3,778,102
Emp.: 1,211
Fiscal Year-end: 03/31/19
Caterer & Food Retailer
N.A.I.C.S.: 722320
Kah Kiat Neo *(Founder, Chm & CEO)*

Subsidiaries:

Best Catering Pte. Ltd. (1)
1 Enterprise Road, Singapore, 629813, Singapore
Tel.: (65) 62611011
Web Site: http://www.bestcatering.com.sg
Catering Services
N.A.I.C.S.: 722310

CT Vegetables & Fruits Pte Ltd (1)
14 Joo Koon Circle, Singapore, 629045, Singapore
Tel.: (65) 67792694
Web Site: http://www.ctfresh.com.sg
Fresh Fruit & Vegetable Whslr
N.A.I.C.S.: 424480

Chilli Manis Catering Pte. Ltd. (1)
1 Enterprise Road, Singapore, 629813, Singapore
Tel.: (65) 62501112
Web Site: http://www.chillimanis.com.sg
Food Catering Services
N.A.I.C.S.: 722310

Choz Catering Pte. Ltd. (1)
1 Enterprise Road, Singapore, 629813, Singapore
Tel.: (65) 62352281
Web Site: http://www.choz.com.sg
Food Catering Services
N.A.I.C.S.: 722310

Deli Hub Catering Pte. Ltd. (1)
1 Enterprise Road, Singapore, 629813, Singapore
Tel.: (65) 65150020
Web Site: http://www.delihub.com.sg
Food Catering Services
N.A.I.C.S.: 722310

Hi-Q Global Sdn. Bhd. (1)
No 3343 Jalan Pekeliling Tanjung 27, Kawasan Perindustrian Indahpura, 81000, Kulai, Malaysia
Tel.: (60) 76606388
Web Site: http://www.hiqglobal.com
Plastics Product Mfr
N.A.I.C.S.: 326199

I DO Flowers & Gifts Pte. Ltd. (1)
No 1 Enterprise Road, Singapore, 629813, Singapore
Tel.: (65) 62674200
Web Site: http://idoflower.com
Flower & Gift Retailer
N.A.I.C.S.: 459420

Kim Paradise Pte. Ltd. (1)
1 Enterprise Road, Singapore, 629813, Singapore
Tel.: (65) 62551000
Web Site: http://www.kimparadise.com.sg
Food Catering Services
N.A.I.C.S.: 722320

Lavish Dine Catering Pte Ltd (1)
20 Bukit Batok Crescent 11-13 Enterprise Centre, Singapore, 658080, Singapore
Tel.: (65) 63922688
Web Site: http://www.lavish.com.sg
Food Catering Services
N.A.I.C.S.: 722310
Richie Ling Boon Yew *(Dir-Bus Dev)*

Liang Yuan Pte. Ltd. (1)
7 Enterprise Road, Singapore, 629813, Singapore
Tel.: (65) 62647757
Web Site: http://www.liangyuan.com.sg
Food Catering Services
N.A.I.C.S.: 722310

NKK Import & Export Trading Pte. Ltd. (1)
1 Enterprise Road Unit 9, Singapore, 629813, Singapore
Tel.: (65) 6264 2089
Web Site: http://www.nkktrading.com
Food Products Distr
N.A.I.C.S.: 445298

Niwa Sushi Pte. Ltd. (1)
1 Enterprise Road, Singapore, 629813, Singapore
Tel.: (65) 68337955
Web Site: http://www.umisushi.com.sg
Emp.: 200
Food Retailer
N.A.I.C.S.: 445298

Orange Clove Catering Pte. Ltd. (1)
1 Kaki Bukit Road Enterprise One 05-03/04, Singapore, 415934, Singapore
Tel.: (65) 65150991
Web Site: http://www.orangeclove.com.sg
Catering Services
N.A.I.C.S.: 722320

Savoury Catering Pte. Ltd. (1)
1 Enterprise Road, Singapore, 629813, Singapore
Tel.: (65) 63150820
Web Site: http://www.savorykitchen.com.sg
Food Catering Services
N.A.I.C.S.: 722310

U-Market Place Enterprise Pte. Ltd. (1)
1 Enterprise Road, Singapore, 629813, Singapore
Tel.: (65) 62655949
Web Site: http://www.umarket.com.sg
Food Mfr
N.A.I.C.S.: 311999

Ye Liang How Catering Service Pte. Ltd. (1)
8A Admiralty Street 03-20/21 Food Xchange Admiralty, Singapore, 757437, Singapore
Tel.: (65) 68522852
Web Site: http://howscatering.com.sg
Food Catering Services
N.A.I.C.S.: 722310

NEO INFRACON LTD.

52/52-A Nanubhai Desai Road 9 Mulji Thakarsi Building, Sindhi Lane, Mumbai, 400 004, Maharashtra, India
Tel.: (91) 2223856390
Web Site:
https://www.neoinfraconltd.com
Year Founded: 1981
514332—(BOM)
Rev.: $953,564
Assets: $3,649,973
Liabilities: $2,921,480
Net Worth: $728,493
Earnings: ($19,843)
Emp.: 4
Fiscal Year-end: 03/31/23
Real Estate Development Services
N.A.I.C.S.: 531390
Dilip K. Mehta *(CFO)*

Subsidiaries:

New-Tech Infrastructure Pvt. Ltd. (1)
No 2 Pillappa Industrial Estate Neelagiri Thop, Sunkadakatte, Bengaluru, 560091, India
Tel.: (91) 9900003589
Web Site: https://www.newtechinfra.co.in
Information Technology Services
N.A.I.C.S.: 518210

NEO MARKETING CO., LTD.

11F Yomeishu Building 16-25, Nanpeidai-cho Shibuya, Tokyo, 150-0036, Japan
Tel.: (81) 363282880
Web Site: https://corp.neo-m.jp
Year Founded: 2000
4196—(TKS)
Rev.: $16,129,750
Assets: $9,755,840
Liabilities: $5,133,160
Net Worth: $4,622,680
Earnings: $1,403,820
Emp.: 170
Fiscal Year-end: 09/30/23
Marketing Support Business
N.A.I.C.S.: 561990
Mitsunobu Hashimoto *(CEO)*

NEO TECHNICAL SYSTEM CO., LTD.

Dookyo Local Industrial Complex 38-9 Yongdae-Gil Jooksan-Myun, Anseong, Gyeonggi-do, Korea (South)
Tel.: (82) 316710170
Web Site: https://www.neotis.co.kr
Year Founded: 2000
085910—(KRS)
Rev.: $61,645,423
Assets: $111,036,369
Liabilities: $51,260,829
Net Worth: $59,775,541
Earnings: $3,959,561
Emp.: 214
Fiscal Year-end: 12/31/22
Micro Bit Product Mfr
N.A.I.C.S.: 333515
Sang-Hoon Kwon *(CEO)*

NEO TELEMEDIA LIMITED

Room 901B 9th Floor Empire Centre 68 Mody Road, Tsim Sha Tsui, Kowloon, China (Hong Kong)
Tel.: (852) 31517988 Ky
Web Site: http://www.neo-telemedia.com
Year Founded: 2002
8167—(HKG)
Rev.: $67,875,645
Assets: $489,908,805
Liabilities: $361,361,265
Net Worth: $128,547,540
Earnings: ($710,558)
Emp.: 246
Fiscal Year-end: 12/31/22
Investment Management Service
N.A.I.C.S.: 523940
Wei Tao *(Exec Dir)*

NEO-CONCEPT INTERNATIONAL GROUP HOLDINGS LIMITED

10/F Seaview Centre No 139-141 Hoi Bun Road, Kwun Tong, Kowloon, China (Hong Kong)
Tel.: (852) 27988639 Ky
Web Site: https://www.neo-ig.com
Year Founded: 2021
NCI—(NASDAQ)
Rev.: $22,300,791
Assets: $11,600,439
Liabilities: $11,905,990
Net Worth: ($305,551)
Earnings: $565,158
Emp.: 24
Fiscal Year-end: 12/31/23
Holding Company
N.A.I.C.S.: 551112

NEOCHIM AD

Iztochna industrialna zona ul Himkombinatska 3, Dimitrovgrad, 6403, Bulgaria
Tel.: (359) 39165205
Web Site: https://www.neochim.bg
Year Founded: 1951
NEOH—(BUL)
Rev.: $191,960,452
Assets: $97,250,767
Liabilities: $20,033,961
Net Worth: $77,216,806
Earnings: $26,138,256
Emp.: 1,250
Fiscal Year-end: 12/31/21
Chemical Products Mfr
N.A.I.C.S.: 325180
Aleksandar Dochev Ganev *(Dir-IR)*

NEOCITY GROUP

1 Korazin St Moldavsky House, Givatayim, 53583, Israel
Tel.: (972) 35712525
Web Site: https://neocitygroup.com
Rev.: $9,971,295
Assets: $49,203,963
Liabilities: $34,970,482
Net Worth: $14,233,481
Earnings: ($766,779)
Emp.: 30
Fiscal Year-end: 12/31/17
Real Estate Investment & Development Services
N.A.I.C.S.: 531390
Ehud Benshach *(Chm)*

NEOCOM MULTIMEDIA SA

190 Boulevard Haussmann, 75008, Paris, France
Tel.: (33) 1 72 71 20 20
Web Site: http://www.neocom.fr
Year Founded: 1986
MLNEO—(EUR)
Sales Range: $25-49.9 Million
Telecommunication Servicesb
N.A.I.C.S.: 517112
Didier Derderian *(Chm & CEO)*

NEOCORE TECHNOLOGY CO., LTD

No 31 Ke Jung Road Science-Based Park, Chu-Nan, Miao-li, 350, Taiwan
Tel.: (886) 37585585
Web Site: https://neocore.com.tw
Year Founded: 1998
4131—(TPE)
Rev.: $2,781,728
Assets: $8,341,463
Liabilities: $5,809,743
Net Worth: $2,531,720
Earnings: ($1,203,108)
Fiscal Year-end: 12/31/22
Medical Material Mfr
N.A.I.C.S.: 339112

NEODECORTECH S.P.A.

Via Provinciale 2, 24040, Filago, Bergamo, Italy
Tel.: (39) 035996111
Web Site: https://www.iubenda.com
NDT—(ITA)
Rev.: $212,037,557
Assets: $182,120,656
Liabilities: $98,725,448
Net Worth: $83,395,208
Earnings: $9,105,331
Emp.: 228
Fiscal Year-end: 12/31/22
Paper Product Mfr & Distr
N.A.I.C.S.: 322299
Luigi Cologni *(CEO)*

Subsidiaries:

Cartiere di Guarcino S.p.A. (1)
2 Via Madonna Di Loreto, Guarcino, 03016, Frosinone, Italy
Tel.: (39) 07754891
Web Site: https://www.cdgspa.com
Emp.: 170
Decor Paper Mfr
N.A.I.C.S.: 322299

Subsidiary (Domestic):

Bio Energia Guarcino S.r.l. (2)
Via Madonna di Loreto 2, Guarcino, 03016, Frosinone, Italy
Tel.: (39) 07754891
Web Site: https://www.begsrl.eu
Electric Power Distribution Services
N.A.I.C.S.: 221122

NEOEN SA

22 rue Bayard, 75008, Paris, France
Tel.: (33) 170916262
Web Site: https://www.neoen.com
Year Founded: 2008

NEOEN—(EUR)
Rev.: $543,060,652
Assets: $6,770,451,112
Liabilities: $4,704,511,116
Net Worth: $2,065,939,996
Earnings: $49,320,095
Emp.: 361
Fiscal Year-end: 12/31/22
Renewable Energy Consulting Services
N.A.I.C.S.: 541690
Xavier Barbaro *(Chm & CEO)*

Subsidiaries:

Npinvestment SA (1)
32 Wigmore Street, London, W1U 2RP, United Kingdom
Tel.: (44) 79526296
Web Site: https://www.npim.co.uk
Real Estate Network Services
N.A.I.C.S.: 531210

NEOFECT CO., LTD.
801 8th floor Gyeonggi Enterprise Growth Center, Pangyo 2nd Techno Valley 42 Changup-ro Sujeong-gu, Seongnam, Gyeonggi-do, Korea (South)
Tel.: (82) 318898521   KR
Web Site: https://www.neofect.com
Year Founded: 2010
290660—(KRS)
Rev.: $20,096,629
Assets: $38,634,228
Liabilities: $31,291,103
Net Worth: $7,343,125
Earnings: ($7,380,032)
Emp.: 60
Fiscal Year-end: 12/31/22
Health Care Products Mfr
N.A.I.C.S.: 325412
Scott Kim *(CEO)*

NEOGAMES S.A.
10 Habarzel St Building C 16th Floor, Tel Aviv, 6971014, Israel
Tel.: (972) 733723107   LU
Web Site: https://www.neogames.com
Year Founded: 2014
NGMS—(NASDAQ)
Rev.: $165,698,000
Assets: $460,944,000
Liabilities: $315,605,000
Net Worth: $145,339,000
Earnings: ($18,965,000)
Emp.: 216
Fiscal Year-end: 12/31/22
Software Development Services
N.A.I.C.S.: 541511
Oded Gottfried *(CTO)*

NEOGEM INDIA LIMITED
G-32 Gems & Jewellery Complex 3 SEEPZ - SEZ, Andheri E, Mumbai, 400 096, India
Tel.: (91) 2228291123
Web Site: https://www.neogemindia.com
Year Founded: 1991
526195—(BOM)
Rev.: $10,319
Assets: $5,702,954
Liabilities: $4,796,434
Net Worth: $906,520
Earnings: ($82,285)
Emp.: 29
Fiscal Year-end: 03/31/21
Jewelry Mfr
N.A.I.C.S.: 339910
Gaurav Mahindra Doshi *(Chm & Mng Dir)*

NEOGEN CHEMICALS LTD.
1002 Dev Corpora Cadbury Junction Eastern Express Highway, Thane W, Thane, 400601, Maharashtra, India
Tel.: (91) 2225497300
Web Site: https://neogenchem.com
Year Founded: 1989
542665—(BOM)
Rev.: $82,804,388
Assets: $126,347,341
Liabilities: $68,494,695
Net Worth: $57,852,647
Earnings: $5,991,248
Emp.: 581
Fiscal Year-end: 03/31/23
Chemicals Mfr
N.A.I.C.S.: 325998
Haridas Kanani *(Founder, Chm & Mng Dir)*

NEOGLORY PROSPERITY INC.
Chaoshanxi road, Economic and Technological Development Zone, Ma'anshan, Anhui, China
Tel.: (86) 57985615358
Web Site: http://www.xgycgroup.com
002147—(SSE)
Rev.: $255,781,031
Assets: $1,693,290,709
Liabilities: $1,725,867,751
Net Worth: ($32,577,042)
Earnings: ($499,027,952)
Emp.: 899
Fiscal Year-end: 12/31/20
Industrial Equipment Mfr
N.A.I.C.S.: 333248
Hualong Hu *(Fin Dir)*

NEOIMMUNETECH, INC.
Innovalley C-1003 253 Pangyo-Ro, Bundang-Gu, Seongnam, 13486, Gyeonggi-do, Korea (South)
Tel.: (82) 2408019065
Web Site: https://www.neoimmunetech.com
Year Founded: 2014
950220—(KRS)
Rev.: $1,090,308
Assets: $110,364,873
Liabilities: $15,920,573
Net Worth: $94,444,300
Earnings: ($46,755,389)
Emp.: 92
Fiscal Year-end: 12/31/22
Research & Experimental Development Services
N.A.I.C.S.: 541715
Se Hwan Yang *(Founder, Pres & CEO)*

NEOJAPAN INC.
Yokohama Land Mark Tower 10F 2-2-1 Minatomirai, Nishi-ku, Yokohama, 220-8110, Japan
Tel.: (81) 456405900
Web Site: https://www.neo.co.jp
Year Founded: 1992
3921—(TKS)
Rev.: $46,900,350
Assets: $61,129,980
Liabilities: $16,186,470
Net Worth: $44,943,510
Earnings: $6,778,040
Emp.: 285
Fiscal Year-end: 01/31/24
Software Development & Marketing
N.A.I.C.S.: 334610
Akinori Saito *(Pres)*

NEOLARA CORP.
Contiguo a la Guardia de Asistencia Rural, San Vito Coto Brus, 60801, Puntarenas, Costa Rica
Tel.: (506) 3072690177   WY
Web Site: https://neolara-construction.com
Year Founded: 2022
Rev.: $21,300
Assets: $78,845
Liabilities: $78,500
Net Worth: $345

Earnings: ($14,377)
Fiscal Year-end: 06/30/24
Construction Services
N.A.I.C.S.: 236210

NEOLIFE SA
304 Route Nationale 6 Celtic Parc Batiment Avalon II, 69760, Limonest, France
Tel.: (33) 478256308
Web Site: http://www.neolife-solutions.com
Year Founded: 2012
ALNLF—(EUR)
Sales Range: $1-9.9 Million
Building Products & Solutions
N.A.I.C.S.: 321211
Patrick Marche *(Chm)*

NEOMETALS LTD
Level 1 1292 Hay St, West Perth, 6005, WA, Australia
Tel.: (61) 893221182
Web Site: https://www.neometals.com.au
NMT—(LSE)
Rev.: $363,327
Assets: $28,134,658
Liabilities: $3,778,938
Net Worth: $24,355,720
Earnings: ($25,485,465)
Emp.: 25,000
Fiscal Year-end: 06/30/24
Support Activities for Metal Mining
N.A.I.C.S.: 213114
Christopher J. Reed *(CEO & Mng Dir)*

NEON EQUITY AG
Morfelder Landstrasse 277, 60598, Frankfurt am Main, Germany
Tel.: (49) 69408027270
Web Site: https://www.neon-equity.com
D77—(DUS)
Rev.: $107,921
Assets: $312,799,482
Liabilities: $26,991,150
Net Worth: $285,808,332
Earnings: $20,893,589
Emp.: 2
Fiscal Year-end: 12/31/23
Investment Management Service
N.A.I.C.S.: 523999
Thomas Olek *(CEO)*

NEONODE, INC.
Karlavagen 100, 115 26, Stockholm, Sweden
Tel.: (46) 86671717   DE
Web Site: https://www.neonode.com
Year Founded: 2001
NEON—(NASDAQ)
Rev.: $5,670,000
Assets: $21,198,000
Liabilities: $1,780,000
Net Worth: $19,418,000
Earnings: ($4,883,000)
Emp.: 45
Fiscal Year-end: 12/31/22
Electronic Components Mfr
N.A.I.C.S.: 334419
Ulf Rosberg *(Chm)*

Subsidiaries:

NEON Technology Inc. (1)
1965 Avenida Plz Real, Oceanside, CA 92056
Tel.: (760) 630-8668
Web Site: https://www.neontech.com
Emp.: 25
Electronic Parts & Equipment Merchant Whslr
N.A.I.C.S.: 423690

Neonode Americas Inc. (1)
2880 Zanker Rd, San Jose, CA 95134
Tel.: (408) 496-6722

Electronic Parts & Equipment Merchant Whslr
N.A.I.C.S.: 423690

Neonode Japan Inc. (1)
1-10-3-901 Roppongi, Minato-ku, Tokyo, 106-0032, Japan
Tel.: (81) 362748073
Electronic Parts & Equipment Merchant Whslr
N.A.I.C.S.: 423690
Daisuke Moro *(Gen Mgr)*

Neonode Korea Ltd. (1)
414-303 Geumgang Apt 126 Gyenam-ro, 606 Seobusaetgil, Bucheon, 14537, Gyeonggi-do, Korea (South)
Tel.: (82) 1056122270
Electronic Parts & Equipment Merchant Whslr
N.A.I.C.S.: 423690
Richard Kim *(Gen Mgr)*

Neonode Taiwan Ltd. (1)
Rm 2406 International Trade Building Keelung Rd Sec 1, Keelung Rd Sec 1, Taipei, 11012, Taiwan
Tel.: (886) 6227576001
Electronic Parts & Equipment Merchant Whslr
N.A.I.C.S.: 423690
Ian Lin *(Gen Mgr)*

Neonode Technologies AB (1)
Storgatan 23C, PO Box 5082, 114 55, Stockholm, Sweden
Tel.: (46) 86671717
Electronic Parts & Equipment Merchant Whslr
N.A.I.C.S.: 423690
Ulf Martensson *(Exec VP-Ops)*

Neonode, Inc. (1)
651 Byrdee Way Contra Costa, Lafayette, CA 94549
Tel.: (925) 768-0620
Web Site: http://www.neonode.com
Sales Range: $25-49.9 Million
Emp.: 40
Network Access & Communications Devices Mfr
N.A.I.C.S.: 334111

NEONTECH CO., LTD.
1745-3 Gwangyang-Dong, Dongan-Gu, Anyang, Gyeonggi-do, Korea (South)
Tel.: (82) 313528740
Web Site: https://www.neontech.co.kr
Year Founded: 2018
306620—(KRS)
Rev.: $45,890,043
Assets: $67,892,691
Liabilities: $35,612,418
Net Worth: $32,280,272
Earnings: ($4,104,369)
Emp.: 152
Fiscal Year-end: 12/31/21
General Machinery Mfr
N.A.I.C.S.: 333998
Seongil Hwang *(CEO)*

NEOOTO CO.,LTD.
19 Saemunan-ro 5-gil, Jongno-gu, Seoul, Korea (South)
Tel.: (82) 260212217
Web Site: https://www.neooto.kr
Year Founded: 2010
212560—(KRS)
Rev.: $125,814,146
Assets: $118,682,175
Liabilities: $44,386,081
Net Worth: $74,296,094
Earnings: $6,021,861
Emp.: 126
Fiscal Year-end: 12/31/22
Automobile Parts Mfr
N.A.I.C.S.: 336110
Sun Hyun Kim *(Chm)*

NEOPAN 22 BAHMAN COMPANY
Heaven Street-St Miremad-H 13-No

Neopan 22 Bahman Company—(Continued)
40-Second Floor Of Unit 9, Tehran, Iran
Tel.: (98) 88733897
Year Founded: 1976
Emp.: 180
Wood Products Mfr
N.A.I.C.S.: 321999
Seyed Hamid Adibifar *(CEO)*

NEOPHARM CO., LTD.
309-8 Techno 2-ro, Yuseong-Gu, Daejeon, 305-510, Korea (South)
Tel.: (82) 428640038
Web Site: http://www.neopharm.co.kr
Year Founded: 2000
092730—(KRS)
Rev.: $65,220,417
Assets: $119,151,476
Liabilities: $10,075,789
Net Worth: $109,075,687
Earnings: $13,059,739
Emp.: 147
Fiscal Year-end: 12/31/22
Pharmaceuticals Product Mfr
N.A.I.C.S.: 325412
Lim Woo Jae *(Mng Dir)*

NEOPHARM LABS INC.
865 Michele-Bohec Blvd, Blainville, J7C 5J6, QC, Canada
Tel.: (450) 435-8864
Web Site: https://www.neopharm.ca
Year Founded: 1990
Sales Range: $25-49.9 Million
Emp.: 130
Pharmaceutical Testing & Analysis Services
N.A.I.C.S.: 541380
Nancy Shore *(Sr Dir-Quality Assurance)*

NEOPLANTA A.D.
Primorska 90, 21000, Novi Sad, Serbia
Tel.: (381) 21 4873 882
Web Site: http://www.neoplanta.rs
Year Founded: 1885
Sales Range: $75-99.9 Million
Emp.: 754
Meat Processing Services
N.A.I.C.S.: 311612

NEOPROJEKT A.D.
Yuri Gagarin 229/I lokal 285, Novi Beograd, Serbia
Tel.: (381) 11 3186 515
Year Founded: 2000
Sales Range: Less than $1 Million
Emp.: 2
Architectural Designing Services
N.A.I.C.S.: 541310

NEORION HOLDINGS S.A.
67 Akti Miaouli Street, 18537, Athens, Greece
Tel.: (30) 210 452 0778
Web Site: http://www.neorion-holdings.gr
Holding Company
N.A.I.C.S.: 551112
Nikolaos Tavoularis *(Chm & CEO)*

NEOS CORPORATION
10F No 2 Annex Sumitomo Fudosan Kanda Building 1-23-1 Kandasuda-cho, Chiyoda-ku, Tokyo, 101-0041, Japan
Tel.: (81) 352091590
Web Site: https://www.neoscorp.jp
Year Founded: 2004
3627—(TKS)
Rev.: $61,938,240
Assets: $71,679,900
Liabilities: $26,708,030
Net Worth: $44,971,870
Earnings: $517,570
Emp.: 192
Fiscal Year-end: 02/29/24
Communications & Computer-Related Services
N.A.I.C.S.: 517810
Masashi Ikeda *(Pres & CEO)*

Subsidiaries:
Neos Vietnam International Co., Ltd. (1)
Tang 7 toa nha Ocean Park so 1 Dao Duy Anh, Phuong Phuong Mai quan Dong Da, Hanoi, Vietnam
Tel.: (84) 2436400592
Web Site: https://neoscorp.vn
Emp.: 250
Software Development Services
N.A.I.C.S.: 541511

NEOS RESOURCES PLC
55 Gower Street, London, WC1E 6HQ, United Kingdom
Tel.: (44) 223108934
Web Site: http://www.neosplc.com
Emp.: 112
Biodiesel Crop Development Services
N.A.I.C.S.: 111998
Marie Edwards *(Sec)*

Subsidiaries:
D1 Oils India Private Limited (1)
M-Blk 38 1 Middle Cir Connaught Pl, New Delhi, 110001, India
Tel.: (91) 1143450800
Web Site: http://www.d1plc.com
Sales Range: $10-24.9 Million
Emp.: 39
Jatropha Plantation Services
N.A.I.C.S.: 115112

D1 Oils Plant Science Belgium N.V. (1)
Derbystraat 71, Zwijnaarde, Gent, 9051, East Flanders, Belgium
Tel.: (32) 92415614
Web Site: http://www.quinvita.com
Sales Range: $25-49.9 Million
Emp.: 5
Petroleum Refining Services
N.A.I.C.S.: 324110
Henk Joos *(CEO)*

NEOSEM INC.
12-26 Simin-daero 327beon-gil, Anyang, 14055, Gyeonggi-do, Korea (South)
Tel.: (82) 3180918800
Web Site: https://www.neosem.com
Year Founded: 2016
253590—(KRS)
Rev.: $55,425,982
Assets: $97,095,921
Liabilities: $50,868,583
Net Worth: $46,227,338
Earnings: $7,421,536
Emp.: 99
Fiscal Year-end: 12/31/22
Semiconductor Test Equipment Developer & Mfr
N.A.I.C.S.: 334413

Subsidiaries:
Neosem Inc. (1)
12-26 Simindaero327beongil, Dongan-gu, Anyang, 16521, Gyeonggi-do, Korea (South)
Tel.: (82) 31 8091 8800
Web Site: http://www.neosem.com
Semiconductor Test Equipment Developer & Mfr
N.A.I.C.S.: 333242

Subsidiary (US):
Flexstar Technology Inc. (2)
1965 Concourse Dr, San Jose, CA 95131
Tel.: (408) 643-7000
Web Site: http://www.flexstar.com
Sales Range: $10-24.9 Million
Emp.: 45
Test Equipment for Electronic & Electrical Circuits
N.A.I.C.S.: 334515
Andrew Warner *(CEO)*

Neosem Technology, Inc. (2)
Pond Springs Rd Ste 105, Austin, TX 78729
Tel.: (925) 301-8905
Web Site: http://www.neosemtech.com
Semiconductor Test Equipment Design, Mfr & Support Services
N.A.I.C.S.: 334413

NEOSPERIENCE SPA
Via Orzinuovi 20 Torre Athena, 25125, Brescia, Italy
Tel.: (39) 0303537300
Web Site: https://www.neosperience.com
Year Founded: 2006
NSP—(ITA)
Sales Range: $10-24.9 Million
Digital Marketing Services
N.A.I.C.S.: 541613
Dario Patrizio Melpignano *(Co-Founder, Pres & CEO)*

NEOSS LIMITED
Windsor House Cornwall Road, Harrogate, HG1 2PW, United Kingdom
Tel.: (44) 1423817733
Web Site: http://www.neoss.com
Year Founded: 2000
Sales Range: $10-24.9 Million
Emp.: 100
Dental Implant Mfr
N.A.I.C.S.: 339114
Fredrik Engman *(Co-Founder & CTO)*

Subsidiaries:
Neoss AB (1)
Molnlycke Fabriker 3, 43535, Molnlycke, Sweden
Tel.: (46) 31 88 12 80
Medical Equipment Distr
N.A.I.C.S.: 423450

Neoss Australia Pty. Ltd (1)
PO Box 404, New Farm, Brisbane, 4005, QLD, Australia
Tel.: (61) 7 3216 0165
Web Site: http://www.neoss.com
Medical Equipment Distr
N.A.I.C.S.: 423450

Neoss GmbH (1)
Im MediaPark 8, 50670, Cologne, Germany
Tel.: (49) 221 55405 322
Web Site: http://www.neoss.de
Medical Equipment Mfr & Distr
N.A.I.C.S.: 339114
Rainer Woyna *(Dir-Mktg)*

Neoss Inc. (1)
21860 Burbank Blvd Ste 190 N Entrance, Woodland Hills, CA 91367
Tel.: (818) 432-2600
Web Site: http://www.neoss.com
Medical Equipment Distr
N.A.I.C.S.: 423450

Neoss Italia S.r.l. (1)
Via Marco Antonio Colonna 42, 20149, Milan, Italy
Tel.: (39) 02 92952 1
Web Site: http://www.neossitalia.it
Medical Equipment Mfr & Distr
N.A.I.C.S.: 339114
Alessandra Negroni *(Mgr-Mktg & Activities)*

NEOSTAR AD
Trg Mladenaca 5, 21000, Novi Sad, Serbia
Tel.: (381) 21526088
Web Site: https://www.neostar.rs
Year Founded: 1974
ZVNS—(BEL)
Rev.: $393,696
Assets: $2,818,684
Liabilities: $61,085
Net Worth: $2,757,599
Earnings: ($24,401)
Emp.: 7
Fiscal Year-end: 12/31/23
Office Space Rental Services
N.A.I.C.S.: 531120

Petar Skokandic *(Mng Dir)*

NEOVACS S.A.
3-5 Impasse Reille, 75014, Paris, France
Tel.: (33) 153109300
Web Site: https://neovacs.fr
ALNEV—(EUR)
Sales Range: Less than $1 Million
Biopharmaceutical Mfr, Developer & Researcher
N.A.I.C.S.: 325412
Bernard Fanget *(VP-Pharmaceutical Dev)*

NEOWIZ HOLDINGS CORPORATION
NEOWIZ Pangyo Tower 14 Daewangpangyoro, 645beon-Gil Bundang-Gu, Seongnam, 13487, Gyeonggi-do, Korea (South)
Tel.: (82) 260012000 KR
Web Site: https://www.neowiz.com
Year Founded: 1997
042420—(KRS)
Rev.: $228,548,577
Assets: $616,990,920
Liabilities: $112,451,667
Net Worth: $504,539,253
Earnings: ($53,991,982)
Emp.: 8
Fiscal Year-end: 12/31/22
Holding Company; Online Games Developer & Publisher
N.A.I.C.S.: 551112
Sangwook Kim *(CEO)*

Subsidiaries:
NEOWIZ (1)
14 Daewangpangyo-ro 645beon-gil, Bundang-gu, Seongnam, 13487, Gyeonggi-do, Korea (South)
Tel.: (82) 3180236600
Web Site: https://www.neowiz.com
Rev.: $225,932,947
Assets: $429,587,032
Liabilities: $77,720,943
Net Worth: $351,866,089
Earnings: $10,022,554
Emp.: 1,036
Fiscal Year-end: 12/31/2022
Videogame Developer, Mfr & Whslr
N.A.I.C.S.: 513210
Shim Jung Mi *(Dir)*

Subsidiary (Non-US):
GameOn Co., Ltd. (2)
7th floor PMO Akihabara II 2-3-10 Higashi-kanda, Chiyoda-ku, Tokyo, 101-0031, Japan
Tel.: (81) 354476320
Web Site: https://www.gameon.co.jp
Sales Range: $75-99.9 Million
Emp.: 190
Videogames Developer & Distr
N.A.I.C.S.: 513210

NHN Bugs Corporation (1)
586 Gangnam-daero, Gangnam-gu, Seoul, 463400, Korea (South)
Tel.: (82) 3180382947
Web Site: www.bugscorp.co.kr
Rev.: $50,503,516
Assets: $71,865,133
Liabilities: $15,233,157
Net Worth: $56,631,976
Earnings: $1,938,277
Emp.: 133
Fiscal Year-end: 12/31/2022
Online Music Services
N.A.I.C.S.: 518210
Sangmin Lee *(Mgr-Team)*

NEP NORWAY SAS
Okern Torgvei 13, Oslo, Norway
Tel.: (47) 23688000
Web Site: http://www.nepnorway.com
OB Production Services
N.A.I.C.S.: 512110
Lise Heidal *(Mng Dir)*

NEP REALTY & INDUSTRY PUBLIC COMPANY LIMITED
No 41 Soi Phahonyothin 5 Phahonyothin Road, Phaya Thai, Bangkok, 10400, Thailand
Tel.: (66) 22714213   TH
Web Site: https://www.nep.co.th
Year Founded: 1953
NEP—(THA)
Rev.: $3,771,894
Assets: $17,611,224
Liabilities: $1,055,874
Net Worth: $16,555,350
Earnings: ($1,103,748)
Fiscal Year-end: 12/31/23
Plastic Packaging Product Mfr & Distr
N.A.I.C.S.: 326199
Somchai Vanichsenee *(Chm)*

NEPAL BANGLADESH BANK LTD.
Beena Marg, PO Box No 9062, 44600, Kathmandu, Kamladi, Nepal
Tel.: (977) 15970015   NP
Web Site: https://www.nabilbank.com
Year Founded: 1994
NBB—(NEP)
Rev.: $32,498,434
Assets: $660,363,918
Liabilities: $552,833,174
Net Worth: $107,530,744
Earnings: $13,751,734
Emp.: 879
Fiscal Year-end: 07/16/19
Banking, Mortgage & Financial Services
N.A.I.C.S.: 522110
Gyanendra Prasad Dhungana *(CEO)*

NEPAL BANK LIMITED
Dharmapath, Kathmandu, Nepal
Tel.: (977) 14247999
Web Site:
  https://www.nepalbank.com.np
Year Founded: 1937
NBL—(NEP)
Rev.: $99,971,067
Assets: $1,872,448,465
Liabilities: $1,593,109,087
Net Worth: $279,339,378
Earnings: $24,903,947
Emp.: 2,504
Fiscal Year-end: 07/15/21
Commercial Banking Services
N.A.I.C.S.: 522110
Krishna Bahadur Adhikari *(CEO)*

NEPAL COMMUNITY DEVELOPMENT BANK LIMITED
Puspalal Prak, Rupandehi, Butwal, Nepal
Tel.: (977) 71 541817
Web Site: http://www.ncdbank.com
Commercial Banking Services
N.A.I.C.S.: 522110
Pashupati Ghimire *(Chm)*

NEPAL CREDIT & COMMERCE BANK LTD.
Bagbazar, PO Box 12559, Kathmandu, Nepal
Tel.: (977) 14246991   NP
Web Site:
  http://www.nccbank.com.np
Year Founded: 1996
NCCB—(NEP)
Rev.: $68,410,934
Assets: $768,305,189
Liabilities: $664,315,433
Net Worth: $103,989,756
Earnings: $8,843,869
Fiscal Year-end: 07/16/19
Commercial Banking & Credit Card Services
N.A.I.C.S.: 522110

Ramesh Sapkota *(COO-Treasury Back & Middle Office)*

NEPAL DOORSANCHAR CO., LTD.
Doorsanchar Bhawan Bhadrakali Plaza, Kathmandu, Nepal
Tel.: (977) 14210106
Web Site: https://www.ntc.net.np
Year Founded: 1973
NTC—(NEP)
Sales Range: Less than $1 Million
Telecommunication Servicesb
N.A.I.C.S.: 517112
Dilliram Adhikari *(Mng Dir)*

NEPAL FILM DEVELOPMENT COMPANY LIMITED
NFDC Complex Balaju Industrial District, PO Box 549, Kathmandu, Nepal
Tel.: (977) 1 4350947
Web Site: http://www.nfdc.com.np
NFD—(NEP)
Sales Range: Less than $1 Million
Motion Picture Equipment Leasing Services
N.A.I.C.S.: 532490

NEPAL FINANCE LIMITED
Kamaladi-28 IT Plaza, PO Box 6867, Kathmandu, Nepal
Tel.: (977) 14545885
Web Site:
  https://www.nepalfinancelimited.np
NFS—(NEP)
Rev.: $2,042,958
Assets: $23,933,017
Liabilities: $16,408,066
Net Worth: $7,524,950
Earnings: $152,621
Fiscal Year-end: 07/16/23
Financial Services
N.A.I.C.S.: 523999
Hirendra Man Pradhan *(Chm)*

NEPAL INSURANCE COMPANY LIMITED
Ameer Bhawan 1st 7th Floor Ganeshthan Kamaladi, PO Box 3623, Kathmandu, Nepal
Tel.: (977) 5321353
Web Site:
  https://en.nepalinsurance.com
Year Founded: 1947
NICL—(NEP)
Rev.: $11,872,647
Assets: $40,550,651
Liabilities: $18,564,483
Net Worth: $21,986,168
Earnings: $2,828,063
Emp.: 275
Fiscal Year-end: 07/16/23
Insurance Services
N.A.I.C.S.: 524298
Arjun Paudel Sharma *(Chm)*

NEPAL INVESTMENT MEGA BANK LIMITED
Durbar Marg, PO Box 3412, Kathmandu, Nepal
Tel.: (977) 5342530
Web Site: https://www.nimb.com.np
NIMB—(NEP)
Rev.: $116,034,850
Assets: $1,939,928,247
Liabilities: $1,665,377,490
Net Worth: $274,550,756
Earnings: $31,135,458
Emp.: 1,408
Fiscal Year-end: 07/15/21
Corporate Banking & Investment Services
N.A.I.C.S.: 522110
Jyoti Prakash Pandey *(CEO)*

Subsidiaries:

City Express Finance Company Limited   (1)
Shree Kingsway Tower, Ghantaghar, Kathmandu, Nepal
Tel.: (977) 1 4244 009
Web Site:
  http://www.cityexpressfinance.com.np
Financial Services
N.A.I.C.S.: 523999
Chandra Tandan *(Chm)*

NIBL Ace Capital Ltd.   (1)
PO Box 23224, Lazimpat, Kathmandu, Nepal
Tel.: (977) 14005157
Web Site: https://www.niblcapital.com
Asset Management Services
N.A.I.C.S.: 531390

Nepal Investment Bank Limited   (1)
Narayan Chour Naxal, PO Box 13383, Kathmandu, Nepal
Tel.: (977) 14441110
Emp.: 70
Corporate Banking & Financial Services
N.A.I.C.S.: 521110
Pradeep Nepal *(Head-IT)*

Subsidiary (Domestic):

Ace Capital Ltd.   (2)
Lal Colony Marg Lal Darbur, PO Box 13383, Kathmandu, 977, Nepal
Tel.: (977) 14426161
Web Site: http://www.acecapital.com.np
Sales Range: $50-74.9 Million
Emp.: 30
Merchant Banking Services
N.A.I.C.S.: 522110

NEPAL LIFE INSURANCE COMPANY LIMITED
Kamaladi Kathmandu, GPO Box 11030, Kathmandu, Nepal
Tel.: (977) 14169082
Web Site:
  https://www.nepallife.com.np
Year Founded: 2001
NLIC—(NEP)
Sales Range: $25-49.9 Million
Insurance Services
N.A.I.C.S.: 524298
Ramesh Gupta *(Chm)*

NEPAL RASTRA BANK
Central Office Baluwatar, Kathmandu, Nepal
Tel.: (977) 14410386
Web Site: http://www.nrb.org.np
Year Founded: 1956
Sales Range: $150-199.9 Million
Central Bank
N.A.I.C.S.: 521110

NEPAL SBI BANK LIMITED
Kamaladi, Kathmandu, Nepal
Tel.: (977) 15970333
Web Site: https://nsbl.statebank
Year Founded: 1993
SBI—(NEP)
Rev.: $174,280
Assets: $1,987,530
Liabilities: $31,455
Net Worth: $1,956,075
Earnings: $86,422
Emp.: 1,004
Fiscal Year-end: 07/15/20
Banking Services
N.A.I.C.S.: 522110
Anukool Bhatnagar *(CEO & Mng Dir)*

NEPAL SEVA LAGHUBITTA BITTIYA SANSTHA LTD.
kavrepalanchok, Sanga, Banepa, Nepal
Tel.: (977) 16204707
Web Site: http://www.nslbsl.com.np
Sales Range: Less than $1 Million
Financial Consulting Services
N.A.I.C.S.: 541611

Madan Gopal Shrestha *(Chm)*

NEPAL SHARE MARKETS & FINANCE LIMITED
Putalisadak Share Markets Commercial Complex Ramshahpath, PO Box No 9909, Kathmandu, Nepal
Tel.: (977) 14252332
Web Site: http://www.nsm.com.np
NSM—(NEP)
Rev.: $504,362
Assets: $8,573,636
Liabilities: $5,707,145
Net Worth: $2,866,491
Earnings: $66,375
Emp.: 15
Fiscal Year-end: 03/31/23
Banking Services
N.A.I.C.S.: 522110

NEPAL STOCK EXCHANGE LTD.
Singhadur Plaza, Kathmandu, Nepal
Tel.: (977) 1 4250758
Sales Range: $50-74.9 Million
Stock Exchange Services
N.A.I.C.S.: 523210
Laxman Neupane *(Chm)*

NEPC INDIA LTD.
36 Wallajah Road, Chennai, 600002, India
Tel.: (91) 4428586812
Web Site: http://www.nepcindia.com
Sales Range: $1-9.9 Million
Wind Turbine Generator Mfr
N.A.I.C.S.: 333611
Tirupathi Kumar Khemka *(Mng Dir)*

NEPES ARK CORPORATION
587-32 Gwahaksaneop 2-ro Ochangeup, Cheongwon-gu, Cheongju, Chungcheongbuk-do, Korea (South)
Tel.: (82) 432400500
Web Site: https://www.nepes.co.kr
Year Founded: 2019
330860—(KRS)
Rev.: $114,203,053
Assets: $339,925,677
Liabilities: $149,584,924
Net Worth: $190,340,752
Earnings: $19,072,164
Emp.: 465
Fiscal Year-end: 12/31/22
Semiconductor Device Mfr & Distr
N.A.I.C.S.: 334413

NEPES CORPORATION LIMITED
Hayyim Building 2415 Nambusunhwan-ro, Seocho-gu, Seoul, Korea (South)
Tel.: (82) 234702700
Web Site: https://www.nepes.co.kr
Year Founded: 1990
033640—(KRS)
Rev.: $451,026,074
Assets: $868,192,887
Liabilities: $567,281,753
Net Worth: $300,911,133
Earnings: $59,502,842
Emp.: 582
Fiscal Year-end: 12/31/22
Semiconductors & Electronic Components Mfr
N.A.I.C.S.: 334413
Byung-Koo Lee *(CEO)*

Subsidiaries:

NEPES Advanced Materials Corporation.   (1)
99 Seokam-ro, Palbong-Dong, 54587, Iksan, Jeollabuk-do, Korea (South)
Tel.: (82) 638332020
Web Site: http://www.nepesamc.com

NEPES CORPORATION LIMITED

Nepes Corporation Limited—(Continued)
Sales Range: $25-49.9 Million
Emp.: 70
Semiconductor Devices Mfr
N.A.I.C.S.: 334413
Joung-Kook Lee (CEO)

NEPES ENC (1)
2415 Nambusunhwan-ro, Seocho-gu,
Seoul, Korea (South)
Tel.: (82) 234702858
Web Site: https://www.nepesenc.co.kr
Sales Range: $25-49.9 Million
Emp.: 25
Room Cleaning Services
N.A.I.C.S.: 562910

NEPES JAPAN (1)
18 Sankyo Bldg 6F 2-16-3 Nihonbashi,
Chuo-ku, Tokyo, 103-0027, Japan
Tel.: (81) 352053515
Web Site: http://www.nepes.co.kr
Sales Range: $25-49.9 Million
Emp.: 3
Energy Saving Equipments Mfr
N.A.I.C.S.: 334515

NEPES LED (1)
587-32 Kwahak saneop 2ro, Ochang-eup,
Cheongwon, 363-886, Chungbuk, Korea
(South)
Tel.: (82) 7048776433
Web Site: http://www.nepesled.com
Sales Range: $25-49.9 Million
Emp.: 30
Light Emitting Diode Mfr
N.A.I.C.S.: 335139
B. K. Lee (CEO)

Photizo Co., Ltd. (1)
644-7 Gak-ri Ochang-myeon, Cheongwon,
363-883, Chungcheongbuk-do, Korea
(South)
Tel.: (82) 432165611
Web Site: http://www.photizo.co.kr
Semiconductor Mfr
N.A.I.C.S.: 333242

NEPI ROCKCASTLE N.V.

2nd Floor 30 Athol Street, IM1 1JB,
Douglas, Isle of Man
Tel.: (44) 1624654704   IM
Web Site:
  http://www.nepirockcastle.com
NRP—(EUR)
Rev.: $563,089,745
Assets: $8,404,226,737
Liabilities: $3,652,310,410
Net Worth: $4,751,916,327
Earnings: $526,328,513
Emp.: 587
Fiscal Year-end: 12/31/23
Real Estate Investment
N.A.I.C.S.: 531390
Alexandru Morar (CEO)

Subsidiaries:

Bonarka City Center Sp. z o.o. (1)
ul Kamienskiego 11, 30-644, Krakow, Poland
Tel.: (48) 122986001
Web Site: https://www.bonarka.com.pl
Shopping Mall Operator
N.A.I.C.S.: 531120

E-Power Supply s.r.o. (1)
Velka Okruzna 59A, 010 01, Zilina, Slovakia
Tel.: (421) 907873093
Web Site: https://www.e-powersupply.eu
Electric Power Supply Services
N.A.I.C.S.: 221122

Energit Sp. z o.o. (1)
ul Kamienskiego 11, 30-644, Krakow, Poland
Tel.: (48) 122986027
Web Site: https://www.energit.pl
Telecommunication Services
N.A.I.C.S.: 517111

Floreasca Business Park SRL (1)
Calea Floreasca 169, Bucharest, 077190,
Romania   **(100%)**
Tel.: (40) 755116681
Web Site:
  http://www.floreascabusinesspark.ro

Real Estate Manangement Services
N.A.I.C.S.: 531390
Alexandru Godri (Property Mgr)

Forum Gdansk Property Sp. Z o.o. (1)

Forum Gdansk Sp. Z o.o. (1)
Forum Gdansk Targ Sienny 7, 80-806,
Gdansk, Poland
Tel.: (48) 587326120
Web Site: https://www.forumgdansk.pl
Shopping Mall Operator
N.A.I.C.S.: 531120

General Investment S.R.L. (1)

Mlyny a.s. (1)
Stefanikova trieda 61, 949 01, Nitra, Slovakia
Tel.: (421) 373221111
Web Site: https://mlyny-nitra.sk
Real Estate Development Services
N.A.I.C.S.: 531390

NEPI Croatia Management d.o.o. (1)
Ulica Vice Vukova 6, 10000, Zagreb, Croatia
Tel.: (385) 16661449
Shopping Center Operator
N.A.I.C.S.: 531120

NEPI Czech Management s.r.o. (1)
Rybna 682/14, 110 00, Prague, Czech Republic
Tel.: (420) 475317000
Shopping Center Operator
N.A.I.C.S.: 531120

NEPI Investment Management SRL (1)
Floreasca Business Park Building A 5th
Floor, 169A Calea Floreasca, Bucharest,
014459, Romania   **(100%)**
Tel.: (40) 21 232 1398
Web Site: http://nepirockcastle.com
Investment Management Service
N.A.I.C.S.: 523940

NEPI Real Estate Development d.o.o. (1)
Bulevar Milutina Milankovica 9d PC GTC 41
5th Floor, 11070, Belgrade, Serbia
Tel.: (381) 114414644
Shopping Center Operator
N.A.I.C.S.: 531120

NEPI Rockcastle Hungary Kft. (1)
Arena Mall Kerepesi ut 9, 1087, Budapest,
Hungary
Tel.: (36) 18807004
Shopping Center Operator
N.A.I.C.S.: 561499

NEPI Rockcastle Lithuania UAB (1)
Ozo str 18, LT-08243, Vilnius, Lithuania
Tel.: (370) 52100156
Shopping Center Operator
N.A.I.C.S.: 561499

NEPI Slovakia Management s.r.o. (1)
Velka Okruzna 59A, 01001, Zilina, Slovakia
Tel.: (421) 413213420
Shopping Center Operator
N.A.I.C.S.: 531120

NEPIOM Ltd. (1)
Central Business Centre 135 Michelangelo
Borg Street, The Penthouse Level 6 Spinola
Bay St, Saint Julian's, Malta
Tel.: (356) 21377444
Shopping Center Operator
N.A.I.C.S.: 561499

Ploiesti Shopping City SRL (1)
Str Republicii 76, Village Blejoi Commune
Blejoi Jud Prahova, 107070, Ploiesti, Romania
Tel.: (40) 751077835
Web Site:
  https://www.ploiestishoppingcity.ro
Shopping Mall Operator
N.A.I.C.S.: 531120

Rockcastle Global Real Estate Company Limited (1)
Level 3 Alexander House 35 Cybercity,
Ebene, Mauritius
Tel.: (230) 211 1398
Web Site: http://www.rockcastleglobalre.mu

Sales Range: $50-74.9 Million
Real Estate Investment Services
N.A.I.C.S.: 531390
Paul Pretorius (COO)

Rockcastle Poland Sp. z o.o. (1)
1st Floor Cosmopolitan Building 4 Twarda
Street, 00-105, Warsaw, Poland
Tel.: (48) 224199000
Shopping Mall Operator
N.A.I.C.S.: 531120

Severin Shopping Center SRL (1)
Bvd Mihai Viteazu Nr 78, Drobeta-Turnu
Severin, Romania
Tel.: (40) 352401212
Web Site:
  https://www.severinshoppingcenter.ro
Shopping Mall Services
N.A.I.C.S.: 812990

Shopping City Piatra Neamt SRL (1)
Bulevardul Decebal 79, 610046, Piatra
Neamt, Romania
Tel.: (40) 333401197
Web Site:
  https://www.shoppingcitypiatraneamt.ro
Shopping Mall Operator
N.A.I.C.S.: 531120

Uzdaroji akcine bendrove Ozantis (1)

Vulcan Residential Park SRL (1)
Calea Floreasca nr 169A Floreasca 169
Cladirea A Etajul 5, Sectiunea A5 1 Biroul
nr 46 Sector 1, Bucharest, Romania
Tel.: (40) 741885226
Web Site: https://vulcan-residence.ro
Residential Building Construction Services
N.A.I.C.S.: 531110

NEPON INC.

1-4-2 Shibuya, Shibuya-ku, Tokyo,
150-0002, Japan
Tel.: (81) 334093131
Web Site: https://www.nepon.co.jp
Year Founded: 1948
7985—(TKS)
Rev.: $51,386,140
Assets: $45,635,440
Liabilities: $28,270,970
Net Worth: $17,364,470
Earnings: $423,040
Emp.: 296
Fiscal Year-end: 03/31/24
Thermal & Sanitary Equipment Mfr & Distr
N.A.I.C.S.: 333415
Takeshi Kawamoto (COO & Exec VP)

NEPTUN-OLIMP SA

No1 Plopilor Street, 905500, Mangalia, Constanta, Romania
Tel.: (40) 723601826
Web Site:
  https://www.neptunolimp.com
NEOL—(BUC)
Rev.: $222,056
Assets: $5,544,929
Liabilities: $1,253,335
Net Worth: $4,291,595
Earnings: $125,311
Emp.: 7
Fiscal Year-end: 12/31/22
Hotel Services
N.A.I.C.S.: 721110

NEPTUNE COMPANY

16 Gukjegeumyung-ro 8-gil,
Yeongdeungpo-gu, Seoul, Korea
(South)
Tel.: (82) 27692162
Web Site: https://neptunecompany.kr
Year Founded: 2015
217270—(KRS)
Rev.: $22,601,264
Assets: $326,954,367
Liabilities: $35,766,091
Net Worth: $291,188,276
Earnings: ($130,765,301)
Emp.: 65

Fiscal Year-end: 12/31/22
Financial Investment Management
Services
N.A.I.C.S.: 523940

NEPTUNE DEVELOPERS LIMITED

Neptune House Karma Stambh LBS
Road, Vikhroli, Mumbai, 4000 083,
India
Tel.: (91) 2267770600
Web Site:
  http://www.neptunegroup.in
Sales Range: $50-74.9 Million
Emp.: 170
Real Estate Developers
N.A.I.C.S.: 236117
Nayan Bheda (Co-Founder)

NEPTUNE DIGITAL ASSETS CORP.

Suite 2700 The Stack 1133 Melville
Street, Vancouver, V6E 4E5, BC,
Canada
Tel.: (604) 319-6955
Web Site:
  https://neptunedigitalassets.com
NPPTF—(OTCQB)
Rev.: $1,616,068
Assets: $42,771,692
Liabilities: $601,638
Net Worth: $42,170,053
Earnings: ($1,592,221)
Fiscal Year-end: 08/31/21
Information Technology Services
N.A.I.C.S.: 541512
Dustin Zinger (Mgr-IR)

NEPTUNE EXPORTS LTD.

84/1A Topsia Road South Trinity
Plaza 3rd Floor, Kolkata, 700046,
India
Tel.: (91) 3340556800
Web Site:
  http://www.neptuneexports.co.in
Year Founded: 1982
512522—(BOM)
Rev.: $107,382
Assets: $2,628,133
Liabilities: $22,579
Net Worth: $2,605,554
Earnings: $36,093
Fiscal Year-end: 03/31/20
Galvanized Steel Coil Distr
N.A.I.C.S.: 423510

NEPTUNE WELLNESS SOLUTIONS, INC.

545 Promenade du Centropolis Suite
100, Laval, H7T 0A3, QC, Canada
Tel.: (450) 687-2262   QC
Web Site:
  http://www.neptunecorp.com
NEPT—(NASDAQ)
Rev.: $52,615,338
Assets: $30,928,258
Liabilities: $58,488,927
Net Worth: ($27,560,669)
Earnings: ($88,802,558)
Emp.: 50
Fiscal Year-end: 03/31/23
Natural Product Extraction Services
N.A.I.C.S.: 325998
Toni Rinow (COO)

Subsidiaries:

Acasti Pharma Inc. (1)
3009 boul de la Concorde East Suite 102,
Laval, H7E 2B5, QC, Canada
Tel.: (450) 687-2262
Web Site: https://www.acasti.com
Rev.: $184,000
Assets: $79,123,000
Liabilities: $11,168,000
Net Worth: $67,955,000
Earnings: ($42,429,000)
Fiscal Year-end: 03/31/2023

AND PRIVATE COMPANIES — NESTE OYJ

Pharmaceuticals Mfr
N.A.I.C.S.: 325412
Pierre Lemieux *(Founder)*

Sprout Foods, Inc. (1)
50 Chestnut Ridge Rd, Montvale, NJ
07645 **(50.1%)**
Tel.: (212) 244-0250
Web Site:
http://www.sproutorganicfoods.com
Sales Range: $1-9.9 Million
Emp.: 15
Organic Foods Production, Marketing & Distr
N.A.I.C.S.: 445298

NERDS ON SITE, INC.
4026 Meadowbrook Dr Unit 120, London, N6L 1C9, ON, Canada
Web Site:
https://www.nerdsonsite.com
Year Founded: 1996
NERD—(CNSX)
Rev.: $7,917,831
Assets: $1,827,791
Liabilities: $1,245,716
Net Worth: $582,075
Earnings: ($1,085,623)
Fiscal Year-end: 05/31/21
Information Technology Management Services
N.A.I.C.S.: 541512
Charles Regan *(CEO)*

NERETVA A.D.
Socijalistickog saveza bb, Belgrade, Serbia
Tel.: (381) 11 8257 006
Year Founded: 1990
Sales Range: Less than $1 Million
Emp.: 2
Food Products Mfr
N.A.I.C.S.: 311212

NERO AG
Ruppurrer Strasse 1a, 76137, Karlsruhe, Germany
Tel.: (49) 721627260
Web Site: http://www.nero.com
Software Developer
N.A.I.C.S.: 513210
Jenny Menhart *(Dir-Mktg-EMEA)*

Subsidiaries:

Nero Development & Services GmbH (1)
Ruppurrer Strasse 1a, 76137, Karlsruhe, Germany
Tel.: (49) 721 62726499
Software Development Services
N.A.I.C.S.: 541511

Nero K.K. (1)
Rover Center-kita 8F-B 1-2-2 Nakagawa-chuou, Tsuzuki-ku, Yokohama, 224-0003, Kanagawa, Japan
Tel.: (81) 45 910 0240
Web Site: http://www.nero-anz.com
Software Development Services
N.A.I.C.S.: 541511

NERUDE LAGHUBITTA BITTIYA SANSTHA
Bhupi Balaram Marg, Biratnagar, Nepal
Tel.: (977) 21463032 NP
Web Site: http://www.nerude.org.np
Year Founded: 2007
NLBBL—(NEP)
Sales Range: Less than $1 Million
Financial Services
N.A.I.C.S.: 523999
Rishi Prasad Neupane *(Sec & Head-HR)*

NERVGEN PHARMA CORP.
Suite 1703 Three Bentall Centre 595 Burrard Street, Vancouver, V7X 1J1, BC, Canada
Tel.: (604) 488-5421
Web Site: http://www.nervgen.com
NGENF—(OTCQX)
Assets: $5,221,944
Liabilities: $590,678
Net Worth: $4,631,267
Earnings: ($8,750,694)
Fiscal Year-end: 12/31/20
Pharmaceutical Product Mfr & Distr
N.A.I.C.S.: 325412
Paul Brennan *(Pres & CEO)*

NES PETROL D.O.O
Cara Lazara 31, Banja Luka, 78000, Bosnia & Herzegovina
Tel.: (387) 65 888 688
Web Site: http://www.nespetrol.com
Petroleum & Petroleum Products Wholesaler
N.A.I.C.S.: 424720

NESCO LIMITED
Nesco Center Western Express Highway, Goregaon East, Mumbai, 400063, India
Tel.: (91) 2266450123
Web Site: https://www.nesco.in
Year Founded: 1939
505355—(BOM)
Rev.: $93,897,131
Assets: $317,772,876
Liabilities: $42,421,915
Net Worth: $275,350,961
Earnings: $43,497,754
Emp.: 220
Fiscal Year-end: 03/31/24
Tool Mfr
N.A.I.C.S.: 333514
Sumant J. Patel *(Chm)*

Subsidiaries:

Nesco Limited - Karamsad Plant (1)
Anand-Sojitra Road, Dist Anand, Karamsad, 388325, Gujarat, India
Tel.: (91) 2692 660400
Emp.: 22
Forging Tool Mfr
N.A.I.C.S.: 332216
Bongani Rantho *(Gen Mgr)*

Nesco Limited - Vishnoli Plant (1)
Nadiad-Khambat Road, Vishnoli PO Dist Anand, Petlad, 388327, Gujarat, India
Tel.: (91) 2697 235347
Web Site: http://www.nesco.in
Forging Tool Mfr
N.A.I.C.S.: 332216

NESMA HOLDING CO. LTD.
PO Box 7195, Jeddah, 21462, Saudi Arabia
Tel.: (966) 126693322 SA
Web Site: http://www.nesma.com
Year Founded: 1981
Sales Range: $10-24.9 Million
Emp.: 10,000
Administrative, Staffing, Technical & Logistical Support Services
N.A.I.C.S.: 561110
Saleh Ali Al Turki *(Founder)*

Subsidiaries:

NESMA & Partners Contracting Ltd. (1)
PO Box 1498, Al Khobar, 31952, Saudi Arabia
Tel.: (966) 138519000
Web Site: http://www.nesma-partners.com
Provider of Process Engineering, Procurement, Construction & Project Management Services
N.A.I.C.S.: 541330

Nesma Airlines (1)
5 El Madina Street Nesma Airlines Building El Nozha El Gedida, Cairo, Egypt
Tel.: (20) 2 2621 7591
Web Site: http://www.nesmaairlines.com
Commercial Airline Services
N.A.I.C.S.: 481111
Amr Mokhlis *(Mgr-Ground Handling)*

Nesma Batterjee (1)
PO Box 1498, Al Khobar, Saudi Arabia
Tel.: (966) 3 8971050
Construction & Offshore Drilling Services
N.A.I.C.S.: 213111

Nesma Electric (1)
PO Box 7195, 21462, Jeddah, Saudi Arabia
Tel.: (966) 2727 635
Web Site: http://www.nesmaelectric.com
Electric Power Distribution Services
N.A.I.C.S.: 221122
Mladen Predovan *(Dir-Tech)*

Nesma Embroidery (1)
Al Rawdah District Darweesh Kayyal St, Jeddah, Saudi Arabia
Tel.: (966) 2 6837897
Web Site: http://www.nesma-emb.com
Tailoring & Embroidery Services
N.A.I.C.S.: 313110

Nesma Medical Supplies Co. (1)
Al Quds Al Hammra, 23212, Jeddah, Saudi Arabia
Tel.: (966) 12 669 3322
Medical Product Distr
N.A.I.C.S.: 423450

NESSTRA SERVICES (UK) LTD
22/23 Progress Business Centre, Whittle Parkway, Slough, SL1 6DQ, Berkshire, United Kingdom
Tel.: (44) 1628668018 UK
Web Site: http://www.nesstra.com
Year Founded: 1960
Sales Range: $125-149.9 Million
Emp.: 15
Chemical Plastic Electronic Communication & Industrial Product Distr
N.A.I.C.S.: 425120
Gerry Oliver *(Controller-Fin)*

Subsidiaries:

Nesstra Commercial Ltda (1)
Avenida Iberapuera No 2907 10 Andar Conjunto 1008, Moema, 04229-200, Sao Paulo, Brazil
Tel.: (55) 1135421003
Industrial Supplies Whslr
N.A.I.C.S.: 423840

Nesstra Ghana Ltd (1)
9 - 11 Dadedan Road North Industrial Area, PO Box 7136, Accra, Ghana
Tel.: (233) 302220651
Industrial Supplies Whslr
N.A.I.C.S.: 423840
Bob Hitti *(Gen Mgr)*

Nesstra Services South Africa (Pty) Limited (1)
38 Main Road, Albertinia, 6695, South Africa
Tel.: (27) 287351041
Industrial Supplies Whslr
N.A.I.C.S.: 423840

NESSUS HOTELES PERU SA
Av La Paz N 463, Miraflores, Lima, Peru
Tel.: (51) 2414050
Year Founded: 2002
NESSUSC1—(LIM)
Rev.: $41,391,275
Assets: $112,079,642
Liabilities: $100,727,061
Net Worth: $11,352,580
Earnings: ($7,299,382)
Fiscal Year-end: 12/31/22
Hotel & Restaurant Operator
N.A.I.C.S.: 721110

NESTE OYJ
Keilaranta 21, PO Box 95, 00095, Espoo, Finland
Tel.: (358) 1045811 FI
Web Site: https://www.neste.com
Year Founded: 1948
NTOIF—(OTCIQ)
Rev.: $14,433,048,240
Assets: $12,055,175,600
Liabilities: $4,772,940,640
Net Worth: $7,282,234,960
Earnings: $876,963,360
Emp.: 4,833
Fiscal Year-end: 12/31/20
Oil, Gas, Petroleum & Plastic Production; Oil & Chemicals Trading, Shipping; Natural Gas Importing & Marketing
N.A.I.C.S.: 211120
Matti Lehmus *(Pres & CEO)*

Subsidiaries:

AS Reola Gaas (1)
Vana-kuuste Kambja Vald, Tartu, 62033, Estonia
Tel.: (372) 7301750
Web Site: http://www.reolagaas.ee
Sales Range: $25-49.9 Million
Emp.: 25
Petroleum Product Whslr
N.A.I.C.S.: 424720
Jaanus Mumm *(Gen Mgr)*

Agri Trading Fats & Oils, LLC (1)
340 Michigan St SE, Hutchinson, MN 55350
Web Site: https://www.agritradingcorp.com
Agriculture Product Distr
N.A.I.C.S.: 424510

LLC Neste Saint-Petersburg (1)
Pulkovskoe Shosse 32 A, 196158, Saint Petersburg, Russia
Tel.: (7) 812 703 0616
Web Site: http://www.nesteoil.ru
Emp.: 1,000
Petroleum Product Whslr
N.A.I.C.S.: 424720

Mahoney Environmental Solutions, LLC (1)
712 Essington Rd, Joliet, IL 60435
Web Site: https://www.mahoneyes.com
Environmental Services
N.A.I.C.S.: 541620

Mahoney Environmental, Inc. (1)
712 Essington Rd, Joliet, IL 60435
Web Site: https://www.mahoneyes.com
Oil Collection & Recycling Services
N.A.I.C.S.: 562119
John Mahoney *(CEO)*

Subsidiary (Domestic):

Waste Oil Recyclers, Inc. (2)
6 Union St, Modena, PA 19358
Tel.: (484) 436-2190
Web Site: https://wasteoilrecyclers.com
Coal, Mineral & Ore Merchant Whslr
N.A.I.C.S.: 423520
Jim Bricker *(Pres)*

Neste (Shanghai) Trading Company Limited (1)
Room 604 - 605 Tower 1 Jing'an Kerry Center, Jing'an District, Shanghai, 200040, China
Tel.: (86) 2161230608
Aviation Fuel Mfr & Distr
N.A.I.C.S.: 325110

Neste (Suisse) S.A. (1)
Chemin des Coquelicots 16, 1214, Vernier, Switzerland
Tel.: (41) 225618000
Renewable Energy Consulting Services
N.A.I.C.S.: 541690

Neste Air (1)
Helsinki-Vantaa Lentokenttä, PO Box 16, 01531, Vantaa, Finland
Tel.: (358) 9822201
N.A.I.C.S.: 211120

Neste Asia Pacific Pte. Ltd. (1)
7 Temasek Boulevard 33-01 Suntec Tower 1, Singapore, 038987, Singapore
Tel.: (65) 62231222
Web Site: https://www.neste.sg
Aviation Fuel Mfr & Distr
N.A.I.C.S.: 325110

Neste Canada Inc. (1)
Water Park Place 10 Bay Street Suite 320, Toronto, M5J 2R8, ON, Canada
Tel.: (416) 368-1600
Web Site: https://www.nesteoil.com

NESTE OYJ

Neste Oyj—(Continued)

Sales Range: $25-49.9 Million
Emp.: 3
Adhesive Resins Mfr
N.A.I.C.S.: 325211

Neste Crude Oil, Inc. (1)
1800 W Loop S Ste 1700, Houston, TX 77027-3409
Tel.: (713) 407-4400
Web Site: http://www.neste.com
Sales Range: $50-74.9 Million
Emp.: 25
Crude Petroleum & Natural Gas
N.A.I.C.S.: 211120
Carrol Gafford *(Office Mgr)*

Subsidiary (Domestic):

Neste Petroleum (Products), Inc. (2)
1800 W Loop S, Houston, TX 77027
Tel.: (713) 407-4400
Web Site: http://www.neste.com
Sales Range: $50-74.9 Million
International Trading & Supply
N.A.I.C.S.: 213112

Neste Petroleum, Inc. (2)
1800 W Loop S Ste 1700, Houston, TX 77027-3219
Tel.: (713) 407-4400
Web Site: http://www.nesteoil.com
Sales Range: $50-74.9 Million
International Trading & Supply
N.A.I.C.S.: 213112

Neste Eesti AS (1)
Sopruse pst 155, 13417, Tallinn, Estonia
Tel.: (372) 6285500
Web Site: https://www.neste.ee
Sales Range: $25-49.9 Million
Emp.: 25
Petroleum Product Whslr
N.A.I.C.S.: 424720

Neste Jacobs Oy (1)
Teknologiantie 36, Kilpilahti, Porvoo, Finland (100%)
Tel.: (358) 1045811
Web Site: http://www.nestejacobs.com
Sales Range: $150-199.9 Million
Emp.: 750
Engineering & Construction Management Services
N.A.I.C.S.: 541330
Jarmo Suominen *(CEO & Mng Dir)*

Subsidiary (Domestic):

Rintekno Oy (2)
Swing Life Science Center, Keilaranta 14, 2150, Espoo, Finland
Tel.: (358) 946981
Web Site: http://www.rintekno.com
Sales Range: $125-149.9 Million
Emp.: 230
Industrial & Service Facility Design & Construction
N.A.I.C.S.: 236210

Neste LPG AB (1)
Box 803, 851 23, Sundsvall, Sweden
Tel.: (46) 60 67 89 20
Web Site: http://www.nesteoil.se
Petroleum Product Mfr
N.A.I.C.S.: 324199

Neste Markkinointi Oy (1)
Keilaranta 21, PO Box 95, FI-02150, Espoo, Finland (100%)
Tel.: (358) 1045811
Web Site: https://www.nesteoil.com
Sales Range: $250-299.9 Million
Emp.: 700
Domestic Oil Marketing
N.A.I.C.S.: 424720

Neste Oil (Suisse) S.A. (1)
Chemin des Coquelicots 16, 1214, Vernier, Geneva, Switzerland
Tel.: (41) 22 561 8000
Web Site: http://www.nesteoil.com
Emp.: 50
Petroleum Products Sales
N.A.I.C.S.: 424720

Neste Oil N.V. (1)
Industrieweg 154, 3583, Beringen, Belgium
Tel.: (32) 11459511
Web Site: http://www.nesteoil.com

Sales Range: $25-49.9 Million
Polyalphaolefins Products Mfr
N.A.I.C.S.: 325211

Neste Oil Netherlands B.V. (1)
Antarcticaweg 185, Maasvlakte, Rotterdam, 3199 KA, Netherlands
Tel.: (31) 181 354 111
Web Site: http://www.neste.com
Emp.: 200
Diesel Refining Services
N.A.I.C.S.: 324110

Neste Oil Singapore Pte. Ltd (1)
250 N Bridge Rd 17-01 Raffles City Tower, Singapore, 179101, Singapore
Tel.: (65) 62231222
Web Site: http://www.neste.com
Sales Range: $75-99.9 Million
Emp.: 200
Gasoline Components Whslr
N.A.I.C.S.: 423440

Neste Oil US Inc (1)
1800 W Loop S Ste 1700, Houston, TX 77027-3219
Tel.: (713) 407-4560
Web Site: http://www.neste.com
Sales Range: $25-49.9 Million
Emp.: 17
Petroleum Refineries Services
N.A.I.C.S.: 324110

Neste Renewable Fuels Oy (1)
Keilaranta 8, 00095, Espoo, Finland
Tel.: (358) 1045811
Petroleum Refining Services
N.A.I.C.S.: 324110
Matti Lievonen *(Gen Mgr)*

Neste St. Petersburg OOO (1)
32A Pulkovo Highway, 196158, Saint Petersburg, Russia
Tel.: (7) 812 703 0616
Web Site: http://www.neste.ru
Petroleum Product Mfr & Distr
N.A.I.C.S.: 211120

Neste US, Inc. (1)
3040 Post Oak Blvd Ste 1700, Houston, TX 77056 (100%)
Tel.: (713) 407-4400
Web Site: https://www.neste.com
Crude Oil Products Trader & Supplier
N.A.I.C.S.: 213112

SIA Neste Latvija (1)
Bauskas Street 58a, Riga, 1004, Latvia
Tel.: (371) 66013379
Web Site: https://www.neste.lv
Petroleum Products Sales
N.A.I.C.S.: 424720

Sterling Logistics, LLC (1)
340 Michigan St SE, Hutchinson, MN 55350
Tel.: (320) 234-4367
Web Site: https://www.sterlinglogmn.com
Logistic Services
N.A.I.C.S.: 488510

UAB Neste Lietuva (1)
P Luksio str 32 Domus Gallery Business Center 6th floor, 08222, Vilnius, Lithuania
Tel.: (370) 85 212 3389
Web Site: https://www.neste.lt
Petroleum Products Sales
N.A.I.C.S.: 424720

NESTLE S.A.
Avenue Nestle 55, 1800, Vevey, Switzerland
Tel.: (41) 219241111 CH
Web Site: https://www.nestle.com
Year Founded: 1866
NESN—(SWX)
Rev: $98,624,547,360
Assets: $157,574,140,740
Liabilities: $96,729,925,050
Net Worth: $60,844,215,690
Earnings: $19,144,405,350
Emp.: 276,000
Fiscal Year-end: 12/31/21
Dairy Products Mfr
N.A.I.C.S.: 551112
Paul Bulcke *(Chm)*

Subsidiaries:

A/S Nestle Norge (1)

Hoffsveien 1A, 0275, Oslo, Norway (100%)
Tel.: (47) 6 781 7400
Web Site: http://www.nestle.no
Sales Range: $25-49.9 Million
Emp.: 50
Mfr of Beverages
N.A.I.C.S.: 311423

ASB-Bebidas e Alimentos Ltda (1)
Estancia Potreiro s/n Sala 01, Aguas de Santa Barbara, 18770-000, Brazil
Tel.: (55) 1437652900
Web Site: http://www.nestle.com.br
Emp.: 100
Packed Food & Soft Drink Distr
N.A.I.C.S.: 424420

Balaban Gida Sanayi ve Ticaret Anonim Sirketi (1)
1 Organize Sanayi Bolgesi 7 No'lu Yol No 24, Hanli, 54060, Arifiye, Sakarya, Turkiye
Tel.: (90) 264 276 91 22
Web Site: http://www.balabangida.com.tr
Chocolate Mfr & Distr
N.A.I.C.S.: 311351

Blue Bottle Coffee, Inc. (1)
476 9th St, Oakland, CA 94607
Tel.: (510) 653-3394
Web Site: https://bluebottlecoffee.com
Coffee Roaster Whslr
N.A.I.C.S.: 423990

Bubchen-Werk Ewald Hermes Pharmazeutische Fabrik GmbH (1)
Coesterweg 37, 59494, Soest, Germany
Tel.: (49) 29217060
Food Mfr
N.A.I.C.S.: 311999

Centres de Recherche et Developpement Nestle S.A.S. (1)
2 rue Charles Tellier, 6000, Beauvais, France
Tel.: (33) 3 44 12 12 12
Dairy Products Mfr
N.A.I.C.S.: 311514

Centroproizvod a.d. (1)
Dobanovacki put bb, Surcin, 11271, Belgrade, Serbia
Tel.: (381) 11 3773 600
Web Site: http://www.centroproizvod.rs
Sales Range: $100-124.9 Million
Emp.: 730
Food Mfr
N.A.I.C.S.: 311999

Cereal Partners Worldwide S.A. (1)
Chemin Viaduc 1, PO Box 1000, Lausanne, 1016, Switzerland
Tel.: (41) 216225511
Web Site: http://www.cerealpartners.com
Sales Range: $50-74.9 Million
Emp.: 150
Cereal Mfr; Owned 50% by General Mills, Inc. & 50% by Nestle S.A.
N.A.I.C.S.: 311230
David V. Clark II *(Pres & CEO)*

Chocolates Garoto S.A (1)
Praca Meyerfreund 1 Gloria, Vila Velha, 29122-900, Brazil
Tel.: (55) 27 3320 1531
Web Site: http://www.garoto.com.br
Chocolate Mfr
N.A.I.C.S.: 311352

Compania Centroamericana de Productos Lacteos, S.A. (1)
Res Prolacsa contiguo a Colegio Ruben Dario, Matagalpa, 61, Nicaragua
Tel.: (505) 2773 9011
Emp.: 270
Dairy Products Mfr
N.A.I.C.S.: 311514
Evelyn Bruggletta *(Gen Mgr)*

Davigel Belgilux S.A. (1)
Rijksweg 19, 2880, Bornem, Belgium
Tel.: (32) 3 393 9470
Web Site: https://www.davigel.be
Food Product Mfr & Distr
N.A.I.C.S.: 311999

Subsidiary (Non-US):

Dongguan Hsu Fu Chi Foods Company Limited (2)

INTERNATIONAL PUBLIC

Zhouwu Industrial Zone, Dongcheng District, Dongguan, 523118, Guangdong, China
Tel.: (86) 76922259888
Cakes & Cookies Mfr
N.A.I.C.S.: 311821

Davigel Espana S.A. (1)
Reial - B 4 2 122, 08960, Sant Just Desvern, Spain
Tel.: (34) 934 70 61 61
Food Product Whslr
N.A.I.C.S.: 424420

East Springs International N.V (1)
Teleportboulevard 140, Amsterdam, 1043 EJ, Netherlands
Tel.: (31) 205405800
Food Product Whslr
N.A.I.C.S.: 424420

Eco de Los Andes S.A. (1)
Av 12 de octubre y Gran Canaria, Quilmes, C1878AAB, Argentina
Tel.: (54) 11 4349 1700
Web Site: http://www.ecodelosandes.com.ar
Mineral Water Mfr
N.A.I.C.S.: 312112

Erikli Su ve Mesrubat Sanayi ve Ticaret A.S. (1)
Erikli Plaza Orhaneli Yolu 2 Km Nilufer, Bursa, Turkiye
Tel.: (90) 224 280 60 00
Web Site: http://www.erikli.com.tr
Mineral Water Mfr
N.A.I.C.S.: 312112

Erlenbacher Backwaren GmbH (1)
Wasserweg 39, Gross-Gerau, 64521, Germany
Tel.: (49) 6152 8030
Web Site: http://www.erlenbacher.de
Bakery Product Mfr & Distr
N.A.I.C.S.: 311813
Wolfgang Thul *(Mng Dir)*

Fagal Srl (1)
Industrial Park Block 21B, Santa Cruz de la Sierra, Santa Cruz, Bolivia
Tel.: (591) 346 3237
Web Site: http://www.fagalbolivia.com
Bakery Product Mfr & Distr
N.A.I.C.S.: 311821

Froneri Ltd. (1)
Richmond House Leeming Bar Northallerton, North Yorkshire, London, United Kingdom
Tel.: (44) 1677 423 397
Web Site: http://www.froneri.com
Ice Cream Whslr
N.A.I.C.S.: 424430
Philip Graham *(Sec)*

Subsidiary (Non-US):

Fonterra Brands (Tip Top) Limited (2)
113 Carbine Rd, Mount Wellington, Auckland, New Zealand
Tel.: (64) 95737200
Web Site: http://www.tiptop.co.nz
Sales Range: $100-124.9 Million
Emp.: 420
Mfr of Ice Cream, Frozen Novelties, Frozen Desserts & Frozen Snack Products
N.A.I.C.S.: 311520

Galderma (Thailand) Ltd. (1)
98 Sathorn Square Office Tower 30th Floor Room No 3001-3003, North Sathorn Road Silom Bangrak, Bangkok, 10500, Thailand
Tel.: (66) 20231800
Pharmaceuticals Product Mfr
N.A.I.C.S.: 325412

Galderma (UK) Ltd. (1)
Meridien House 69-71 Clarendon Road, Watford, WD17 1DS, Hertfordshire, United Kingdom
Tel.: (44) 1923208950
Pharmaceuticals Product Mfr
N.A.I.C.S.: 325412
Alexandra Tretiakova *(Gen Mgr)*

Galderma Argentina S.A. (1)
Av Libertador 1855 Vicente Lopez, Buenos Aires, Argentina
Tel.: (54) 1143298220
Pharmaceuticals Product Mfr
N.A.I.C.S.: 325412

AND PRIVATE COMPANIES

NESTLE S.A.

Galderma Austria GmbH (1)
Gertrude-Frohlich-Sandner-Strasse 3 A, Vienna, 1100, Austria
Tel.: (43) 73271599310
Pharmaceuticals Product Mfr
N.A.I.C.S.: 325412

Galderma BeNeLux B.V. (1)
Gravinnen van Nassauboulevard 91, 4811 BN, Breda, Netherlands
Tel.: (31) 183691919
Food Mfr
N.A.I.C.S.: 311999

Galderma Chile Laboratorios Ltda. (1)
Av Las Condes 11283 Office 1001B, Las Condes, Chile
Tel.: (56) 224807500
Pharmaceuticals Product Mfr
N.A.I.C.S.: 325412

Galderma Hong Kong Limited (1)
22/F Cambridge House Taikoo Place 979 Kings Road, Quarry Bay, China (Hong Kong)
Tel.: (852) 28240333
Pharmaceuticals Product Mfr
N.A.I.C.S.: 325412

Galderma Italia S.p.A. (1)
Centro Direzionale Colleoni Palazzo Taurus-Ingresso 1, 20864, Milan, Italy
Tel.: (39) 039634691
Pharmaceuticals Product Mfr
N.A.I.C.S.: 325412

Galderma Laboratories South Africa (Pty) Ltd. (1)
Wedgefield Office Park No 17 Muswell Road South Block D Phase 2, Bryanston, 2021, South Africa
Tel.: (27) 117062339
Pharmaceuticals Product Mfr
N.A.I.C.S.: 325412

Galderma Mexico, S.A. de C.V. (1)
Calzada Mariano Escobedo 476-Floor 10 Colonia Nueva Anzures, 11590, Mexico, Mexico
Tel.: (52) 91262000
Pharmaceuticals Product Mfr
N.A.I.C.S.: 325412

Galderma Nordic AB (1)
Seminariegatan 21, 752 28, Uppsala, Sweden
Tel.: (46) 184440330
Pharmaceuticals Product Mfr
N.A.I.C.S.: 325412

Galderma Singapore Private Ltd. (1)
1 Kim Seng Promenade Great World City West Tower 14-10, Singapore, Singapore
Tel.: (65) 68389360
Pharmaceuticals Product Mfr
N.A.I.C.S.: 325412

Galderma Trading (Shanghai) Co., Limited (1)
Room 3710 Lippo Plaza No 222 Huai-HaiZhong Road, Shanghai, China
Tel.: (86) 2123159666
Pharmaceuticals Product Mfr
N.A.I.C.S.: 325412

Galderma de Colombia S.A. (1)
Carrera 14 N93 B-32, Bogota, Colombia
Tel.: (57) 16227560
Pharmaceuticals Product Mfr
N.A.I.C.S.: 325412

Gerber Chile S.A. (1)
Roger de Flor 2800, Santiago, Chile
Tel.: (56) 2 3384000
Food Product Whslr
N.A.I.C.S.: 424420

Ghadeer Mineral Water Co. WLL (1)
Dahyit Al Yasmine Area, Amman, 142393, Jordan
Tel.: (962) 6 550 5510
Mineral Water Mfr
N.A.I.C.S.: 312112

Helados y Postres S.A. (1)
Cl Capelamendi N 3, Vitoria, 1013, Alava, Spain
Tel.: (34) 945 010 800
Web Site: http://www.helados.nestle.es
Ice Cream Mfr & Distr

N.A.I.C.S.: 424490

Hsu Fu Chi International Limited (1)
Zhouwu Industrial District, Dongcheng, Dongguan, 523118, Guangdong, China (60%)
Tel.: (86) 76922259888
Web Site: http://www.hsufuchifoods.com
Sales Range: $1-4.9 Billion
Emp.: 1,430
Candy, Cake & Cookie Products Mfr
N.A.I.C.S.: 311340

Industrial Surindu S.A. (1)
Av Gonzalo Suarez, 31135, Quito, Ecuador
Tel.: (593) 22232400
Food Product Whslr
N.A.I.C.S.: 424420

Industrias Alimenticias Fagal S.R.L. (1)
Parque Industrial Manzana 21B, Santa Cruz, Bolivia
Tel.: (591) 346 3237
Web Site: https://www.industriasfagal.blogspot.com
Biscuit Mfr
N.A.I.C.S.: 311821

Kaffeknappen Norge AS (1)
Okernveien 121, 0579, Oslo, Norway
Tel.: (47) 22511010
Web Site: http://www.kaffeknappen.no
Sales Range: $25-49.9 Million
Emp.: 35
Coffee Beans & Coffee Machine Distr
N.A.I.C.S.: 424490

Kaffeknappen Sverige AB (1)
Gavlegatan 12 A, Stockholm, 113 30, Sweden
Tel.: (46) 8 34 55 55
Coffee Bean & Coffee Machine Whslr
N.A.I.C.S.: 424490

Koine S.p.A. (1)
Via Roma 8, Madone, 24040, Bergamo, Italy
Tel.: (39) 035 9009710
Web Site: http://www.koinespa.it
Nutritional Food Products Mfr
N.A.I.C.S.: 311999

LLC Nestle Ukraine (1)
72-B Verkhniy Val str, Kiev, 04655, Ukraine
Tel.: (380) 44 490 8000
Sales Range: $150-199.9 Million
Emp.: 350
Dairy Products Distr
N.A.I.C.S.: 424430

LLC Technocom (1)
Pr-t Moskovskiy 6 BC Petrivka-Center office 607, Kiev, 4073, Ukraine
Tel.: (380) 44 425 93 06
Web Site: http://www.technocom.com.ua
Emp.: 50
Dehydrated Food Mfr
N.A.I.C.S.: 311423

Laboratorios Galderma, S.A. (1)
Parque Norte Business Center, C/Serrano Galvache 56 Birch Building 5th Floor, 28033, Madrid, Spain
Tel.: (34) 902027595
Pharmaceuticals Product Mfr
N.A.I.C.S.: 325412

Life Ventures S.A. (1)
Entre Deux Villes 10, 1814, La Tour de Peilz, Switzerland
Tel.: (41) 219242111
Financial Management Services
N.A.I.C.S.: 523999

Malher S.A (1)
48 Calle 15-74 Zona 12, Guatemala, Guatemala
Tel.: (502) 2423 2323
Web Site: http://www.malher.com
Nutritional Food Product Mfr & Distr
N.A.I.C.S.: 311999

Marcas Nestle, S.A. de C.V. (1)
Av Ejercito Nacional 453 col Granada, Seccion Miguel Hidalgo, 11520, Mexico, Mexico
Tel.: (52) 55 5262 5000
Dairy Product Whslr
N.A.I.C.S.: 424430

Merrick Pet Care, Inc. (1)

101 SE 11th Ave Ste 200, Amarillo, TX 79101
Tel.: (806) 364-0002
Web Site: https://www.merrickpetcare.com
Pet Food Retailer
N.A.I.C.S.: 459910
Peter P. Shepherd *(Grp VP)*

Mucos Pharma CZ, s.r.o. (1)
Uhrineveska 448, 252 43, Pruhonice, Czech Republic
Tel.: (420) 26 718 8510
Web Site: https://www.mucos.cz
Emp.: 40
Pharmaceuticals Product Mfr
N.A.I.C.S.: 325412

Mucos Pharma GmbH & Co. KG (1)
Miraustrasse 17, 13509, Berlin, Germany
Tel.: (49) 89 638 3720
Web Site: https://www.wobenzym.de
Pharmaceuticals Product Mfr
N.A.I.C.S.: 325412

NDB Gida Sanayi ve Ticaret Anonim Sirketi (1)
Buyukdere D N 255 Nurol PLZ K 6 Maslak, Istanbul, Turkiye
Tel.: (90) 212 329 59 55
Food Product Mfr & Whslr
N.A.I.C.S.: 311999

Nescalin, S.A. de C.V. (1)
Av Ejercito Nacional 453 Granada, Seccion Miguel Hidalgo, Mexico, 11520, Mexico
Tel.: (52) 5552509944
Dairy Product Whslr
N.A.I.C.S.: 424430

Nespresso Belgique S.A. (1)
Rue de Birminghamstraat 221, 1070, Brussels, Belgium
Tel.: (32) 27880960
Coffee Machine & Accessory Retailer
N.A.I.C.S.: 459999

Nespresso Hellas S.A. (1)
4 Patroklou street, 15125, Maroussi, Greece
Tel.: (30) 2106884111
Web Site: http://www.nespresso.com
Coffee Bean & Coffee Machine Whslr
N.A.I.C.S.: 424490

Nespresso Israel Ltd (1)
36 Shaham, 49517, Petah Tiqwa, Israel
Tel.: (972) 3 924 1334
Web Site: https://www.nespresso.com
Coffee Bean & Coffee Machine Whslr
N.A.I.C.S.: 424490

Nespresso Italiana S.p.A. (1)
4/B Galleria S Babila, 20122, Milan, Italy
Tel.: (39) 027 771 191
Web Site: http://www.nespresso.com
Coffee Roasting Machinery Mfr
N.A.I.C.S.: 333241

Nespresso Nederland B.V. (1)
Stroomweg 14, 1181 VX, Amstelveen, Netherlands
Tel.: (31) 205699323
Web Site: http://www.nespresso.com
Coffee Bean & Coffee Machine Whslr
N.A.I.C.S.: 424490

Nespresso UK Ltd (1)
1 Butterwick, London, W6 8DL, United Kingdom
Tel.: (44) 8081008844
Web Site: http://www.nespresso.com
Coffee Machine Mfr
N.A.I.C.S.: 333241

Nestec York Ltd (1)
St George's House, PO Box 204, Croydon, CR9 1NR, United Kingdom
Tel.: (44) 190460 36 82
Food Product Whslr
N.A.I.C.S.: 424420

Nestle (Fiji) Ltd. (1)
Lot 1 Wailekutu Industrial SubDivision Veisari, PO Box 3042, Lami, 3042, Fiji
Tel.: (679) 362113
Web Site: https://www.nestle.com
Sales Range: $25-49.9 Million
Emp.: 14
N.A.I.C.S.: 311920

Nestle (Malaysia) Bhd. (1)

22nd Floor Menara Surian 22-1 1 Jalan PJU 7/3, Mutiara Damansara, 47810, Petaling Jaya, Selangor, Malaysia (72.6%)
Tel.: (60) 379656000
Web Site: http://www.nestle.com.my
Sales Range: $25-49.9 Million
Emp.: 100
Milk, Sauces
N.A.I.C.S.: 311511
Juan Jose Aranols Campillo *(CEO)*

Subsidiary (Domestic):

Nestle Cold Storage (Malaysia) Sdn. Bhd. (2)
1 Jalan Pju 7/3 Mutiara Damansara, Petaling Jaya, 47810, Selangor, Malaysia (51%)
Tel.: (60) 379656000
Web Site: http://www.nestle.com.my
Mfr of Coffee & Other Beverages
N.A.I.C.S.: 311920

Nestle Foods (Malaysia) Sdn. Bhd. (2)
22-1 22nd Fl Menara Surian No 1 Jalan PJU 7/3, Mutiara Damansara, 47810, Petaling Jaya, Malaysia (55.7%)
Tel.: (60) 379656000
Web Site: http://www.nestle.com.my
Sales Range: $25-49.9 Million
Emp.: 1,000
Mfr of Coffee & Other Beverages
N.A.I.C.S.: 311920
Peter Vogt *(Mng Dir)*

Nestle Products Sdn. Bhd. (2)
Lot 7316 Persiaran Sijangkang Utama, Taman Industri Sijangkan Utama Telok Panglima Garang, 42500, Kuala Langat, Selangor, Malaysia
Tel.: (60) 33 123 3000
Web Site: https://www.nestle.com.my
Emp.: 1,000
Mfr of Coffee & Other Beverages
N.A.I.C.S.: 311920

Nestle (PNG) Ltd. (1)
PO Box 420, Lae, Papua New Guinea (100%)
Tel.: (675) 4726261
Sales Range: $100-124.9 Million
Emp.: 500
Mfr of Roasted Coffee & Other Beverages
N.A.I.C.S.: 311920

Nestle (South Africa) (Pty.) Ltd. (1)
Anslow Office Park 8 Anslow Crescent, Bryanston, 2021, South Africa (100%)
Tel.: (27) 11 514 6000
Web Site: http://www.nestle.co.za
Sales Range: $150-199.9 Million
Emp.: 600
Food Products
N.A.I.C.S.: 311423

Plant (Domestic):

Nestle (South Africa) (Pty) Ltd - Estcourt Factory (2)
155 Victoria St, Estcourt, 3310, South Africa
Tel.: (27) 36 342 2200
Web Site: http://www.nestle.com
Emp.: 420
Dairy Products Mfr
N.A.I.C.S.: 311514

Nestle (South Africa) (Pty) Ltd - Mossel Bay Factory (2)
2 Depot Street Voorbaai, 6506, Mossel Bay, South Africa
Tel.: (27) 44 606 4015
Dairy Products Mfr
N.A.I.C.S.: 311514

Nestle (South Africa) (Pty) Ltd - Ndabeni Factory (2)
10 Bayete Road, Ndabeni, Cape Town, 7405, South Africa
Tel.: (27) 21 530 7500
Food Product Whslr
N.A.I.C.S.: 424420

Nestle (Thailand) Ltd. (1)
The Offices at Central World 38th - 43rd floor 999/9 Rama I Road, Patumwan, Bangkok, 10330, Thailand
Tel.: (66) 26578000
Web Site: https://www.nestle.co.th

NESTLE S.A.

Nestle S.A.—(Continued)
Sales Range: $150-199.9 Million
Emp.: 800
Mfr of Evaporated Milk
N.A.I.C.S.: 311514

Subsidiary (Domestic):

Carnation Manufacturing Co. (Thailand) Ltd. (2)
500 Ploenchit Rd, 10330, Bangkok, Thailand
Tel.: (66) 26578000
Fluid Milk & Other Dairy Products Mfr
N.A.I.C.S.: 311511

Nestle Foods (Thailand) Ltd. (2)
999/9 43th floor The offices at Central World Building Rama I road, Pathumwan, Bangkok, 10330, Thailand **(100%)**
Tel.: (66) 26578000
Web Site: http://www.nestle.co.th
Sales Range: $25-49.9 Million
Emp.: 100
Mfr of Roasted Coffee
N.A.I.C.S.: 311920

Affiliate (Domestic):

Quality Coffee Products Ltd. (2)
500 Ploenchit Lumpini, Pathumwan, 10330, Bangkok, Thailand **(50%)**
Tel.: (66) 2 2569119
Coffee
N.A.I.C.S.: 311920

Nestle (Ireland) Ltd. (1)
3030 Lakedrive Citywest Business Campus, Dublin, Ireland
Tel.: (353) 14497777
Food Mfr
N.A.I.C.S.: 311999

Nestle Adriatic B&H d.o.o. (1)
Fra Andjela Zvizdovica 1/14 B, P P 599, 71 000, Sarajevo, Bosnia & Herzegovina
Tel.: (387) 112019493
Web Site: http://www.nestle.ba
Sales Range: $25-49.9 Million
Emp.: 17
Dairy Products Distr
N.A.I.C.S.: 424430

Nestle Adriatic Foods d.o.o. (1)
Milutina Milankovica 11 a, 11070, Belgrade, Serbia
Tel.: (381) 11 201 93 00
Dairy Product Mfr & Distr
N.A.I.C.S.: 311514

Nestle Adriatik Makedonija d.o.o.e.l. (1)
8 Mi Septemvri 16, Skopje, 1000, North Macedonia
Tel.: (389) 2 3089 501
Web Site: http://www.nestle.mk
Sales Range: $25-49.9 Million
Emp.: 18
Dairy Product Mfr & Distr
N.A.I.C.S.: 311514
Dejan Miljkovic (Gen Mgr)

Nestle Algerie SpA (1)
Quartier d'affaires d'Alger Bab Ezzouar Ilot 2 Lots no 15 et 16, 16311, Algiers, Algeria
Tel.: (213) 21 988200
Dairy Product Mfr & Distr
N.A.I.C.S.: 311514

Nestle Angola Lda (1)
Tensai Business Centre Zona CS8 Gleba GV22 Talatona Luanda Sul, 1138, Luanda, Angola
Tel.: (244) 934 764604
Dairy Product Whslr
N.A.I.C.S.: 424430

Nestle Argentina S.A. (1)
Avenida del Libertador 1855, PO Box 1638, BGE Vicente Lopez, Buenos Aires, Argentina
Tel.: (54) 1143298100
Web Site: http://www.nestle.com.ar
Sales Range: $350-399.9 Million
Emp.: 1,900
Food & Beverage Products Mfr & Distr
N.A.I.C.S.: 311423

Nestle Asean (Malaysia) Sdn. Bhd. (1)
22-1 Tingkat 22 Menara Surian No 1 Jalan Pju 7/3 Mutiara Damansara, Petaling Jaya, 47810, Malaysia
Tel.: (60) 6 686 3900
Dairy Product Whslr
N.A.I.C.S.: 424430

Nestle Australia Ltd. (1)
Building D 1 Homebush Bay Drive, Rhodes, 2138, NSW, Australia **(100%)**
Tel.: (61) 28 756 2000
Web Site: https://www.nestle.com.au
Sales Range: $150-199.9 Million
Emp.: 800
Mfr of Food & Beverages
N.A.I.C.S.: 311423

Subsidiary (Domestic):

Nestle Confectionery Ltd. (2)
1 Homebush Bay Drive, Rhodes, 2138, NSW, Australia
N.A.I.C.S.: 311920

Petersville Australia Ltd. (2)
201 Sussex Street, Sydney, 2001, Australia **(100%)**
N.A.I.C.S.: 311920

Nestle Baltics, UAB (1)
J Jasinskio Str 16A, 03163, Vilnius, Lithuania
Tel.: (370) 5 252 6600
Web Site: https://www.nestle.lt
Food Mfr
N.A.I.C.S.: 311999

Nestle Bangladesh Ltd. (1)
Ninakabbo Level 4 227/A Tejgaon-Gulshan Link Road, Tejgaon Industrial Area, Dhaka, 1208, Bangladesh
Tel.: (880) 29882759
Mfr of Roasted Coffee
N.A.I.C.S.: 311920

Nestle Belgilux S.A. (1)
Rue de Birmingham 221, 1070, Brussels, Belgium **(100%)**
Tel.: (32) 2 529 5252
Web Site: https://www.nestle.be
Sales Range: $25-49.9 Million
Emp.: 200
Mfr of Food & Beverages
N.A.I.C.S.: 311423

Nestle Bolivia S.R.L. (1)
Parque Industrial UV 31, Santa Cruz, Bolivia **(100%)**
Tel.: (591) 33480015
Confectionery & Milk Products Mfr
N.A.I.C.S.: 311920

Nestle Brasil Ltda. (1)
Avenida Doutour Chucri Zaidan 246, Sao Paulo, 04583 110, Brazil **(100%)**
Tel.: (55) 1155084400
Web Site: http://www.nestle.com.br
Sales Range: $350-399.9 Million
Emp.: 1,200
Mfr of Coffee & Other Beverages
N.A.I.C.S.: 311920

Nestle Bulgaria A.D. (1)
128 Europa Blvd, 1360, Sofia, Bulgaria **(100%)**
Tel.: (359) 29390333
Web Site: http://www.nestle.bg
Mfr of Coffee & Other Beverages
N.A.I.C.S.: 311920

Nestle Business Services AOA, Inc. (1)
Malhacan Road, Malhacan, Meycauayan, 3020, Philippines
Tel.: (63) 24792600
Dairy Products Distr
N.A.I.C.S.: 424430

Nestle Cameroun (1)
Immeuble Activa Rue Prince de Galles AKWA, BP 2622, Douala, Cameroon **(100%)**
Tel.: (237) 67 711 6504
Web Site: http://www.nestle.com
Mfr of Roasted Coffee & Other Beverages
N.A.I.C.S.: 311920

Nestle Canada Inc. (1)
25 Sheppard Ave W, Toronto, M2N 6S6, ON, Canada **(100%)**
Tel.: (416) 218-3030
Web Site: https://www.madewithnestle.ca
Sales Range: $750-799.9 Million
Emp.: 3,400
Mfr of Chocolate Drinks, Coffee, Tea, Canned Foods, Pet Foods & Other Food Products
N.A.I.C.S.: 311352

Plant (Domestic):

Nestle Canada Inc. - Brampton (2)
9050 Airport Rd Ste 101, Brampton, L6S 6G9, ON, Canada
Tel.: (905) 458-3600
Web Site: http://www.nestle.ca
Sales Range: $75-99.9 Million
Emp.: 300
Dried & Dehydrated Fruits Vegetables & Soup Mixes
N.A.I.C.S.: 311423

Nestle Canada Inc. - Calgary (2)
5970 Ctr St SE Ste 100, Calgary, T2H 0C1, AB, Canada
Tel.: (403) 252-2285
Web Site: http://www.nestle.ca
Sales Range: $25-49.9 Million
Emp.: 25
Mfr of Food Products
N.A.I.C.S.: 333241

Nestle Canada Inc. - Dorval (2)
20 Ave Guthrie, Dorval, H9P 2Y1, QC, Canada
Tel.: (514) 420-0875
Web Site: http://www.nestlecanada.com
Sales Range: $25-49.9 Million
Emp.: 135
Frozen Specialties
N.A.I.C.S.: 311412

Nestle Canada Inc. - Edmonton (2)
9002 20 St Nw, Edmonton, T6P 1K8, AB, Canada
Tel.: (780) 442-1460
Web Site: http://www.nestle.ca
Sales Range: $25-49.9 Million
Emp.: 25
Dried & Dehydrated Fruits Vegetables & Soup Mixes
N.A.I.C.S.: 311423

Nestle Canada Inc. - London (2)
980 Wilton Grove Rd, London, N6N 1C7, ON, Canada
Tel.: (519) 686-0182
Web Site: http://www.nestle.ca
Sales Range: $75-99.9 Million
Emp.: 300
Mfr of Ice Cream
N.A.I.C.S.: 311520

Nestle Canada Inc. - Montreal (2)
20 Guthrie Ave, Montreal, H9P 2Y1, QC, Canada
Tel.: (514) 420-0875
Web Site: http://www.nestle.ca
Sales Range: $25-49.9 Million
Emp.: 150
Ice Cream & Other Dairy Products Mfr
N.A.I.C.S.: 311520

Nestle Canada Inc. - Toronto (2)
25 Sheppard Ave W, Toronto, M2N 6S6, ON, Canada
Tel.: (416) 535-2181
Web Site: https://www.madewithnestle.ca
Sales Range: $75-99.9 Million
Emp.: 500
Mfr of Candy & Other Confections
N.A.I.C.S.: 311352

Nestle Canada Inc. - Trenton (2)
1 Douglas Rd, PO Box 1800, Trenton, K8V 5S7, ON, Canada
Tel.: (613) 394-4712
Web Site: http://www.nestle.ca
Sales Range: $25-49.9 Million
Emp.: 200
Frozen Fruits & Vegetables
N.A.I.C.S.: 311411

Unit (Domestic):

Nestle Foodservices Canada (2)
25 Sheppard Ave W, North York, M2N 6S8, ON, Canada
Tel.: (416) 218-3030
Web Site: http://www.nestle.ca
Sales Range: $75-99.9 Million
Emp.: 560
Mfr, Marketer & Distributor of Food & Beverage Products for the Food Service Industry
N.A.I.C.S.: 333241

Nestle Capital Canada Ltd (1)
25 Sheppard Ave W, North York, M2N 6S8, ON, Canada
Tel.: (416) 218-3030
Web Site: http://www.corporate.nestle.ca
Emp.: 500
Food Products Mfr
N.A.I.C.S.: 311999

Nestle Caribbean, Inc. (1)
Churchill Roosevelt Hwy & Uriah Butler Hwy, Valsayn, Trinidad & Tobago
Tel.: (868) 6636832
Dairy Product Whslr
N.A.I.C.S.: 424430

Nestle Catering Services N.V. (1)
Birminghamstraat 221, Brussels, 1070, Belgium
Tel.: (32) 2 529 55 30
Web Site: http://www.nestleprofessional.be
Sales Range: $10-24.9 Million
Emp.: 30
Catering Services
N.A.I.C.S.: 722320

Nestle Ceski S.R.O. (1)
Mezi Vodami 2035/31, Prague, 14320, Czech Republic
Tel.: (420) 261 32 1111
Web Site: http://www.nestle.cz
Cookies, Biscuits & Chocolates Mfr
N.A.I.C.S.: 311821

Nestle Chile S.A. (1)
Av Las Condes N 11287, Las Condes, Santiago, Chile **(100%)**
Tel.: (56) 22 338 4000
Web Site: https://www.nestle.cl
Sales Range: $100-124.9 Million
Emp.: 400
Food & Food Products Mfr
N.A.I.C.S.: 311423

Nestle China Ltd (1)
9th Floor Tower B Lei Shing Hong Plaza No 8 Wangjing Street, Chaoyang District, Beijing, 100102, China **(100%)**
Tel.: (86) 108 434 7888
Web Site: https://www.nestle.com.cn
Sales Range: $100-124.9 Million
Emp.: 400
Mfr of Roasted Coffee & Other Beverages
N.A.I.C.S.: 311920

Subsidiary (Domestic):

Nestle Dairy Farm Qingdao Ltd. (2)
Level 9 Tower B LSH Plaza Wangjing Avenue 8, Chaoyang District, Beijing, 100102, China **(100%)**
Tel.: (86) 1084347888
Web Site: http://www.nestle.com
Mfr of Roasted Coffee
N.A.I.C.S.: 311920

Nestle Dairy Farm Tianjin Ltd. (2)
7-8 Avenue Nanhailu 149, PO Box 8, Tianjin, 300457, China **(75%)**
Tel.: (86) 2225326313
Ice Cream Mfr
N.A.I.C.S.: 311520

Nestle Qingdao Ltd. (2)
Unit EFG 10th Floor Block A Sunshine Building No 61, Hong Kong Road Middle Road, Qingdao, 266071, Shandong, China **(100%)**
Tel.: (86) 5328575038
Web Site: https://www.nestle.com.cn
Milk-Based Foods Production
N.A.I.C.S.: 311511

Nestle Tianjin Ltd. (2)
Room 1620-1625 16th Floor Innovation Building No 11 Nanma Road, Heping District, Tianjin, 300022, China **(100%)**
Tel.: (86) 222 755 2588
Web Site: http://www.nestle.com.ca
Mfr of Coffee & Other Beverages
N.A.I.C.S.: 311920

Nestle Cote d'Ivoire (1)
Rue Du Lycee Technique, PO Box 1840, Abidjan, Cote d'Ivoire **(86.5%)**
Tel.: (225) 22404545

AND PRIVATE COMPANIES

NESTLE S.A.

Sales Range: $200-249.9 Million
Emp.: 850
Plant Science & Nutrition Research
N.A.I.C.S.: 311423

Nestle Danmark A/S (1)
Arne Jacobsens Alle 7, 2300, Copenhagen,
Denmark (100%)
Tel.: (45) 8 030 0100
Web Site: https://www.nestle.dk
Sales Range: $25-49.9 Million
Emp.: 170
Dairy Products & Chocolate Mfr
N.A.I.C.S.: 311352
Anette Smed *(Mgr-HR)*

Nestle Del Uruguay S.A. (1)
Calle Carlos Crocker 2883 Esq Gral Julio A
Roletti, 12000, Montevideo,
Uruguay (100%)
Tel.: (598) 25080621
Web Site: http://www.nestle.com.uy
Sales Range: $25-49.9 Million
Emp.: 100
Mfr of Chocolate Products
N.A.I.C.S.: 311352
Samuel Ruiz *(Gen Mgr)*

Nestle Deutschland AG (1)
Lyoner Strasse 23, 60528, Frankfurt am
Main, Germany
Tel.: (49) 6966710
Web Site: https://www.nestle.de
Sales Range: $150-199.9 Million
Emp.: 1,000
Mfr of Food Products
N.A.I.C.S.: 311423

Subsidiary (Domestic):

Heimbs Kafee GmbH & Co KG (2)
Rebenring 30, 38106, Braunschweig,
Germany (100%)
Tel.: (49) 5313 800 2400
Web Site: https://www.heimbs.com
Sales Range: $25-49.9 Million
Emp.: 105
Coffee for Caterers
N.A.I.C.S.: 311920
Klaus Rodel *(Mng Dir)*

Herta GmbH (2)
Westerholter Strasse 750-770, 45701,
Herten, Germany (100%)
Tel.: (49) 23663010
Web Site: https://www.herta.de
Sales Range: $150-199.9 Million
Emp.: 400
Marketing of Delicatessen Products
N.A.I.C.S.: 445110
Michael Muench *(Chm)*

Maggi GmbH (2)
Lyoner Strasse 23, 60528, Frankfurt am
Main, Germany (100%)
Tel.: (49) 6966712841
Web Site: https://www.maggi.de
Sales Range: $25-49.9 Million
Emp.: 100
Mfr of Sauces
N.A.I.C.S.: 311423
Andreas Peters *(Mgr-Mktg)*

Nestle Nutrition GmbH (2)
Lyoner Strasse 23, 60528, Frankfurt,
Germany (100%)
Tel.: (49) 6966711
Web Site: http://www.nestle.de
Sales Range: $150-199.9 Million
Emp.: 1,000
Condensed & Evaporated Milk
N.A.I.C.S.: 311514

Nestle Scholler GmbH & Co. KG (2)
Northwest Ring 201, 90419, Nuremberg,
Germany
Tel.: (49) 9119380
Web Site: http://www.schoeller.de
Sales Range: $25-49.9 Million
Emp.: 225
Ice Cream Mfr
N.A.I.C.S.: 311520

Nestle Dominicana, S.A. (1)
Apartado 900, Santo Domingo, Dominican
Republic (97.6%)
Tel.: (809) 5085000
Plant Science & Nutrition Research
N.A.I.C.S.: 311423

Nestle Dongguan Limited (1)
No 123 Guantai Road, Nancheng District,
Dongguan, 523000, Guangdong, China
Tel.: (86) 76922407872
Food Products Mfr
N.A.I.C.S.: 311999

Subsidiary (Domestic):

Nestle Hulunbeir Limited (2)
No 899 Haisan Road, Labu Dalin Town, Ergun, 022250, China
Tel.: (86) 47 0683 0100
Milk Powder Mfr
N.A.I.C.S.: 311999

Nestle Ecuador S.A. (1)
Ave Gonzalez Suarez 31 - 135 Apartado
4574-A, Quito, 170345, Ecuador (100%)
Tel.: (593) 22232400
Web Site: http://www.nestle.com.ec
Research & Development
N.A.I.C.S.: 541715
Rodrigo Camacho *(Pres)*

Nestle Egypt S.A.E. (1)
Summit 44 90 El Shamaly Street, PO Box
No 400 & 401, Al Tagamoaa El Khames,
New Cairo, 118350, Egypt (100%)
Tel.: (20) 22 614 6400
Web Site: http://www.nestle.com.eg
Sales Range: $25-49.9 Million
Emp.: 250
Mfr of Coffee & Other Beverages
N.A.I.C.S.: 311920

Subsidiary (Domestic):

Societe des Eaux Minerales Vittor S.A.E. (2)
8 Dar el Shefa St-Garden City, Cairo,
Egypt (90.2%)
Mfr of Roasted Coffee & Other Beverages
N.A.I.C.S.: 311920

Nestle El Salvador S.A. (1)
Centro Corporativo Madreselva, Apartado
06 497, Avenido El Espino y Calzada El
Almendro, 06497, Antiguo Cuscatlan, El
Salvador (100%)
Tel.: (503) 2 288 8400
Web Site: https://www.nestle-centroamerica.com
Sales Range: $25-49.9 Million
Emp.: 49
Mfr of Coffee & Other Beverages
N.A.I.C.S.: 311920

Subsidiary (Non-US):

Cereal Partners Espana AEIE (2)
Paisos Catalans 49, Barcelona, Esplugues
De Llobreg, Spain
Mfr of Breakfast Foods
N.A.I.C.S.: 311230

La Cocinera (2)
Avenida Becastia 2, Edificio Hapung 2,
28030, Madrid, Spain (65.5%)
Tel.: (34) 916604900
Frozen Ready-to-Serve Dishes
N.A.I.C.S.: 311412

Nestle Portugal S.A. (2)
Rua Alexandre Herculano 8, 2799-554,
Linda-a-Velha, Portugal (100%)
Tel.: (351) 214148930
Web Site: https://empresa.nestle.pt
Sales Range: $75-99.9 Million
Mfr of Milk Products
N.A.I.C.S.: 311514

Productos del Cafe S.A. (2)
Avenida Tarragona No 50, 43206, Reus,
Spain (100%)
Tel.: (34) 977300200
Web Site: http://www.productosdelcafe.com
Sales Range: $25-49.9 Million
Emp.: 14
N.A.I.C.S.: 311920

Nestle Espana S.A. (1)
Avenida Paisos Catalans 25-51, 08950, Esplugues de Llobregat, Barcelona,
Spain (100%)
Tel.: (34) 934805100
Web Site: http://www.nestle.es
Sales Range: $200-249.9 Million
Emp.: 1,000
Mfr of Food Products, Pharmaceuticals,
Dermatologicals & Cosmetics
N.A.I.C.S.: 325412

Nestle Finance International Ltd (1)
7 Rue Nicolas Bove, Luxembourg, 1253,
Luxembourg
Tel.: (352) 26 44 05 21
Financial Management Services
N.A.I.C.S.: 523999

Nestle Finance S.A. (1)
Avenue Nestle 55, Vevey, 1800, Switzerland
Tel.: (41) 21 924 11 11
Financial Management Services
N.A.I.C.S.: 523999

Nestle Food LLC (1)
House 2 Bldg 1 Paveletskaya Sq, Moscow,
115054, Russia (100%)
Tel.: (7) 4957257000
Web Site: http://www.nestle.com.ru
Sales Range: $100-124.9 Million
Emp.: 500
Mfr of Coffee & Ice Cream Products
N.A.I.C.S.: 311920

Subsidiary (Domestic):

Nestle Zhukovsky Ice Cream LLC (2)
Paveletskaya sq 2 Bldg 1, 115054, Moscow, Russia (88.54%)
Tel.: (7) 4957257000
Web Site: http://www.nestle.ru
Mfr of Ice Creams, Coffee & Other Beverages
N.A.I.C.S.: 311920

Nestle Food S.r.o. (1)
Mezi Vodami 2035/31, 143 20, Prague,
Czech Republic (100%)
Tel.: (420) 26 132 1111
Web Site: https://www.nestle.cz
Sales Range: $100-124.9 Million
Emp.: 300
Mfr of Roasted Coffee
N.A.I.C.S.: 311920

Nestle Foods Kenya Ltd. (1)
Pate Road Industrial Area, PO Box 30265,
00100, Nairobi, Kenya (100%)
Tel.: (254) 20 399 0000
Web Site: http://www.nestle.ke.com
Sales Range: $25-49.9 Million
Emp.: 100
Mfr of Food & Beverages
N.A.I.C.S.: 311423

Nestle France SAS (1)
7 Blvd Pierre Carle, PO Box 900, F 77446,
Noisiel, France (100%)
Tel.: (33) 160532100
Web Site: http://www.nestle.fr
Sales Range: $150-199.9 Million
Emp.: 800
Mfr of Coffee
N.A.I.C.S.: 311920

Subsidiary (Domestic):

Chambourcy Roche aux Fees (2)
361 Avenue de General de Gaulle,
F-92140, Clamart, France
Tel.: (33) 1 630 22 18
Yogurt Mfr
N.A.I.C.S.: 311511

Herta S.A. (2)
2 Route Jean Pierre Clause, Clause 2 illkics, 67400, Illkirch-Graffenstaden,
France (100%)
Tel.: (33) 388676111
Web Site: http://www.croquonslavie.fr
Emp.: 100
Mfr of Delicatessen Products
N.A.I.C.S.: 333998

Houdebine S.A. (2)
P A De Kerguilloten, 56920, Noyal-Pontivy,
France (50%)
Tel.: (33) 297383111
Web Site: http://www.houdebine.fr
Sales Range: $75-99.9 Million
Emp.: 300
N.A.I.C.S.: 311920
Andae Gac *(Mng Dir)*

Nestle Clinical Nutrition S.A. (2)
7 Blvd Pierre Carle Noisiel, PO Box 900,
77446, Marne-la-Vallee, France (100%)
Tel.: (33) 160532100
Web Site: http://www.nestleclinicalnutrition.com

Sales Range: $25-49.9 Million
Emp.: 75
Mfr of Nutritional Food Products
N.A.I.C.S.: 456191

Nestle Coffee Specialties France S.A. (2)
Blvd Pierre Carle 7, PO Box 900, 77186,
Noisiel, France (100%)
Tel.: (33) 160532100
Web Site: http://www.nestle.fr
Sales Range: $300-349.9 Million
Emp.: 2,000
Mfr of Roasted Coffee & Other Beverages
N.A.I.C.S.: 311920

Nestle Enterprises S.A. (2)
7 Blvd Pierre Carle, BP 900, Noisiel, 77446,
Marne-la-Vallee, France (100%)
Tel.: (33) 160532100
Mfr of Coffee & Other Beverages
N.A.I.C.S.: 311920

Nestle Finance France S.A. (2)
7 Blvd Pierre Carle, PO Box 900, Noisiel,
77446, Marne-la-Vallee, France (100%)
Tel.: (33) 160534354
Web Site: http://www.nestle.com
Mfr of Coffee & Other Beverages
N.A.I.C.S.: 311920

S.B.E.C.M. Societe de Bouchages Emballages Conditionnement Moderne S.a.r.l. (2)
Rue de la Plaine, 47230, Lavardac,
France (50%)
N.A.I.C.S.: 311920

Wallon Imprimeur S.A.S. (2)
7 Rue De Bois Des Jarraux, 3270, Saint
Yorre, France (100%)
Tel.: (33) 470593737
Web Site: http://www.wallon.fr
Sales Range: $25-49.9 Million
Emp.: 60
N.A.I.C.S.: 311920
Matthew Giromini *(Pres)*

Nestle Gabon (1)
Rte d'Owendo, Libreville, Gabon (100%)
Tel.: (241) 512 2020
Sales Range: $25-49.9 Million
Emp.: 58
Mfr of Pharmaceuticals
N.A.I.C.S.: 325412

Nestle Ghana Ltd. (1)
No 33 South Legon Commercial Area Motorway Extension, Dzorwulu, Accra,
Ghana (100%)
Tel.: (233) 80 012 0001
Sales Range: $25-49.9 Million
Emp.: 70
Mfr of Roasted Coffee & Other Beverages
N.A.I.C.S.: 311920

Nestle Globe Inc. (1)
25 Sheppard Ave W, Toronto, M2N 6S6,
ON, Canada
Tel.: (416) 218-3030
Web Site: http://www.nestle.ca
Dairy Product Whslr
N.A.I.C.S.: 424430

Nestle Guatemala S.A. (1)
Km 14 5 Hwy Roosevelt, 2 61 Zone 3
Mixco, Guatemala, 1057,
Guatemala (100%)
Tel.: (502) 25976860
N.A.I.C.S.: 311920

Nestle Guinee (1)
Boite postale 4109, Corniche Sud/Coleah,
Conakry, Papua New Guinea (99%)
Tel.: (675) 1 41 40 40
Mfr of Coffee & Other Beverages
N.A.I.C.S.: 311920

Nestle Health Science S.A. (1)
Rue des Remparts 2, 1095, Lutry, Switzerland
Tel.: (41) 21 924 22 00
Web Site: http://www.nestlehealthscience.com
Sales Range: $25-49.9 Million
Emp.: 100
Nutritional Product Mfr
N.A.I.C.S.: 311999
Eric Bouchard *(CFO)*

Unit (US):

Aimmune Therapeutics, Inc. (2)

NESTLE S.A.

Nestle S.A.—(Continued)
8000 Marina Blvd Ste 300, Brisbane, CA 94005
Tel.: (650) 614-5220
Web Site: http://www.aimmune.com
Rev: $5,851,000
Assets: $204,369,000
Liabilities: $100,345,000
Net Worth: $104,024,000
Earnings: $(248,497,000)
Emp.: 275
Fiscal Year-end: 12/31/2019
Pharmaceuticals Mfr
N.A.I.C.S.: 325412
Becki Filice *(Sr VP-Product & Portfolio Mgmt)*

Subsidiary (Non-US):

Aimmune Therapeutics UK Limited (3)
10 Eastbourne Terrace, London, W2 6LG, United Kingdom
Tel.: (44) 2086290240
Pharmaceutical Products Distr
N.A.I.C.S.: 424210
Christie Coutin *(Assoc Dir-HR)*

Subsidiary (Non-US):

Atrium Innovations Inc. (2)
Place Alexis-Nihon Tower 2 24-E Floor, 3500 Boulevard de Maisonneuve Ouest Bureau 2405, Quebec, H3Z 3C1, QC, Canada **(75%)**
Tel.: (514) 205-6240
Web Site: http://www.atrium-innovations.com
Health & Nutrition Industry Dietary Supplement Products Developer, Mfr & Marketer
N.A.I.C.S.: 325412
James Masterson *(Gen Mgr)*

Subsidiary (Non-US):

MCO Health B.V (3)
Wormerweg 1, 1311 XA, Almere, Netherlands
Tel.: (31) 36 546 0900
Web Site: https://www.atrium-innovations.nl
Nutritional Supplement Distr
N.A.I.C.S.: 456191

Subsidiary (Non-US):

Minami Nutrition Health BVBA (4)
Haverstraat 1 bus 2, Antwerp, 2000, Belgium
Tel.: (32) 34587954
Web Site: https://www.minami-nutrition.com
Nutrition Products Mfr & Distr
N.A.I.C.S.: 325412

Subsidiary (Non-US):

Minami Nutrition NV-SA (3)
R & D Production University Business Centre, Leugstraat 61, 2630, Aartselaar, Antwerp, Belgium
Tel.: (32) 34587954
Web Site: http://www.minami-nutrition.com
Nutritional Supplement Distr
N.A.I.C.S.: 456191

Mucos Emulsionsgesellschaft mbH (3)
Miraustr 17, Berlin, 13509, Germany
Tel.: (49) 3041402510
Web Site: http://www.mucos.berlin
Nutritional Supplement Distr
N.A.I.C.S.: 456191

Subsidiary (Non-US):

AAZ-Pharma B.V (4)
Wormerweg 1, 1311 XA, Almere, Netherlands
Tel.: (31) 543 475883
Pharmaceuticals Product Mfr
N.A.I.C.S.: 325412

Subsidiary (Domestic):

Mucos Pharma Verwaltungs GmbH (4)
Miraustrasse 17, 13509, Berlin, Germany
Tel.: (49) 30 4140250
Sales Range: $25-49.9 Million
Emp.: 75
Enzyme Products Mfr

N.A.I.C.S.: 325411
Karin Ruettgers *(Gen Mgr)*

Subsidiary (US):

Pure Encapsulations, LLC (3)
490 Boston Post Rd, Sudbury, MA 01776
Tel.: (978) 443-1999
Web Site: https://www.pureencapsulations.com
Pharmaceutical Products Mfr & Sales
N.A.I.C.S.: 325412

Subsidiary (Domestic):

Trophic Canada Ltd. (3)
1-150 Via Renzo Drive, Richmond Hill, L4S 0J7, ON, Canada
Tel.: (250) 492-8820
Web Site: https://gardenoflifecanada.com
Medicinal & Botanical Mfr
N.A.I.C.S.: 325411

Unit (Domestic):

Nestle Healthcare Nutrition (2)
Route des Avouillons 30, CH 1196, Gland, Switzerland
Tel.: (41) 22 363 51 92
Nutritional Product Mfr
N.A.I.C.S.: 311999

Subsidiary (US):

Nestle HealthCare Nutrition, Inc. (3)
1007 US Hwy 202/206 Bldg JR2, Bridgewater, NJ 08807 **(100%)**
Tel.: (952) 848-6000
Web Site: https://www.nestlehealthscience.us
Sales Range: $150-199.9 Million
Emp.: 950
Nutritional Product Mfr
N.A.I.C.S.: 311999

Nestle Healthcare Nutrition, S.A. (1)
Avenida Paisos Catalans 25-51 Esplugues De Llobregat, Esplugues de Llobregat, Barcelona, 8950, Spain
Tel.: (34) 934805100
Food Product Whslr
N.A.I.C.S.: 424420

Nestle Hellas S.A. (1)
Patroklou 4, 15125, Maroussi, Athens, Greece **(100%)**
Tel.: (30) 2106884111
Web Site: https://www.nestle.gr
Sales Range: $550-599.9 Million
Emp.: 400
Mfr of Food & Food Products
N.A.I.C.S.: 311423

Branch (Domestic):

Nestle Hellas S.A. (2)
Patroklou 4, Maroussi, 151 25, Athens, Greece **(100%)**
Tel.: (30) 210 688 4111
Web Site: https://www.nestle.gr
Retailer of Coffee
N.A.I.C.S.: 311920

Nestle Holdings (U.K.) PLC (1)
1 City Place, Gatwick, RH6 0PA, Surrey, United Kingdom **(100%)**
Tel.: (44) 2086863333
Web Site: http://www.nestle.co.uk
Sales Range: $150-199.9 Million
Emp.: 500
Holding Company
N.A.I.C.S.: 551112

Subsidiary (Non-US):

Nestle (Ireland) Ltd. (2)
3030 Lakedrive Citywest Business Campus, Dublin, 24, Ireland **(100%)**
Tel.: (353) 1 449 7777
Web Site: https://www.nestle.co.uk
Sales Range: $25-49.9 Million
Emp.: 100
Food Manufacturing
N.A.I.C.S.: 311423
Stefano Agostini *(CEO)*

Subsidiary (Domestic):

Nestle UK Ltd. (2)
1 City Place, Gatwick, RH6 0PA, United Kingdom **(100%)**
Tel.: (44) 208 686 3333

Web Site: https://www.nestle.co.uk
Sales Range: $150-199.9 Million
Confections & Snack Foods Mfr
N.A.I.C.S.: 311352
Stefano Agostini *(CEO-Ireland)*

Plant (Domestic):

Nestle UK Ltd - Dalston Factory (3)
Dalston, Carlisle, CA5 7NH, Cumbria, United Kingdom
Tel.: (44) 122 871 3100
Web Site: https://www.nestle.co.uk
Emp.: 300
Dairy Products Mfr
N.A.I.C.S.: 311514

Nestle UK Ltd - Fawdon Factory (3)
Rowan Drive, Fawdon, Newcastle upon Tyne, NE3 3TR, United Kingdom
Tel.: (44) 191 202 4200
Web Site: https://www.nestle.co.uk
Dairy Products Mfr
N.A.I.C.S.: 311514

Nestle UK Ltd - Girvan Factory (3)
Grangestone Industrial Estate, Girvan, KA26 9PL, United Kingdom
Tel.: (44) 146 571 4440
Web Site: https://www.nestle.co.uk
Dairy Products Mfr
N.A.I.C.S.: 311514

Nestle UK Ltd - Halifax Factory (3)
Albion Mills, Halifax, HX3 9XT, West Yorkshire, United Kingdom
Tel.: (44) 142 286 2286
Web Site: https://www.nestle.co.uk
Dairy Products Mfr
N.A.I.C.S.: 311514

Nestle UK Ltd - Hayes Factory (3)
North Hyde Garden, Hayes, UB3 4RF, Middlesex, United Kingdom
Tel.: (44) 208 282 4282
Web Site: http://www.nestle.co.uk
Dairy Products Mfr
N.A.I.C.S.: 311514

Nestle UK Ltd - York Factory (3)
Haxby Road, York, YO30 6HQ, United Kingdom
Tel.: (44) 190 460 4604
Web Site: https://www.nestle.co.uk
Dairy Products Mfr
N.A.I.C.S.: 311514

Nestle HomeCare S.A.S. (1)
7 boulevard Pierre Carle, BP 940, Noisiel, 77446, Marne-la-Vallee, France
Tel.: (33) 970 809 806
Web Site: http://www.nhc.info
Women Healthcare Services
N.A.I.C.S.: 621610

Nestle Hondurena S.A. (1)
Colonia Santa Barbara Carretera Al Batallon, Tegucigalpa, DC, Honduras **(100%)**
Tel.: (504) 2399448
Sales Range: $25-49.9 Million
Emp.: 50
Mfr of Food & Food Products
N.A.I.C.S.: 311423

Nestle Hong Kong Limited (1)
18 Wang Lok Street, Yuen Long Industrial Estate, Yuen Long, New Territories, China (Hong Kong)
Tel.: (852) 2 797 9811
Web Site: https://www.nestle.com.hk
Mfr of Roasted Coffee
N.A.I.C.S.: 311920

Nestle Hong Kong Ltd. (1)
7/F Manhattan Place 23 Wang Tai Road, PO Box 68868, Kowloon Bay, Kowloon, China (Hong Kong) **(100%)**
Tel.: (852) 2 859 6333
Web Site: https://www.nestle.com.hk
Sales Range: $25-49.9 Million
Emp.: 100
N.A.I.C.S.: 311920

Nestle Hungaria Kft (1)
Lechner Odon Fasor 7, 1095, Budapest, Hungary **(100%)**
Tel.: (36) 12241200
Web Site: https://www.nestle.hu
Emp.: 1,300
Mfr of Roasted Coffee & Other Beverages
N.A.I.C.S.: 311920

INTERNATIONAL PUBLIC

Nestle India Ltd. (1)
Nestle House Jacaranda Marg M Block DLF City Phase II, National Highway 8, Gurgaon, 122 002, India
Tel.: (91) 124 238 9300
Web Site: https://www.nestle.in
Sales Range: $100-124.9 Million
Emp.: 450
N.A.I.C.S.: 311920
Suresh Narayanan *(Chm & Mng Dir)*

Nestle International Travel Retail S.A. (1)
12 rue Entre-deux-villes, 1800, Vevey, Switzerland
Tel.: (41) 219245733
Web Site: http://www.nestletravelretail.com
Food Mfr
N.A.I.C.S.: 311999

Nestle Iran (Private Joint Stock Company) (1)
16th Km Old Qazvin road, Mahmoodie City, 1994834573, Tehran, Iran
Tel.: (98) 2188623780
Web Site: http://www.nestle.ir
Dairy Products Distr
N.A.I.C.S.: 424430

Nestle Italiana S.p.A. (1)
Via del Mulino 6, Assago, 20057, Milan, Italy **(100%)**
Tel.: (39) 0281811
Web Site: https://www.nestle.it
Cheese & Other Dairy Products Mfr
N.A.I.C.S.: 311513
Lucio Scaratti *(Gen Mgr)*

Subsidiary (Domestic):

San Bernardo S.p.A. (2)
Via Ottavio Rovere 41, 12075, Garessio, CN, Italy
Tel.: (39) 0174 805211
Bottled Water Mfr
N.A.I.C.S.: 312112

Nestle Japan Ltd. (1)
7-1-15 Gokodori, Chuo-ku, Kobe, 651-0087, Hyogo, Japan **(100%)**
Tel.: (81) 12 088 8523
Web Site: https://www.nestle.co.jp
Sales Range: $125-149.9 Million
Emp.: 300
Food & Beverage Mfr & Whslr
N.A.I.C.S.: 311351
Chris Johnson *(CEO & Chm)*

Subsidiary (Domestic):

Nestle Confectionaries Ltd (2)
Sannomiya Bldg S Nestle House, 7 1 15 Gokodori, Kobe, 651 0087, Japan **(100%)**
Tel.: (81) 782307120
Web Site: http://www.nestle.co.jp
Sales Range: $1-4.9 Billion
Emp.: 115
Mfr of Coffee & Other Beverages
N.A.I.C.S.: 311920

Nestle Jordan Trading Co., Ltd. (1)
4 Cir, PO Box 5719, 9 Bahgap Alhimsi St, 11183, Amman, Jordan **(49%)**
Tel.: (962) 65931655
Sales Range: $25-49.9 Million
Emp.: 100
Mfr of Coffee & Other Beverages
N.A.I.C.S.: 311920

Nestle Kenya Ltd. (1)
Pate Road Industrial Area, PO Box 30265, 00100, Nairobi, Kenya
Tel.: (254) 7291107134
Food Mfr
N.A.I.C.S.: 311999

Nestle Korea Ltd. (1)
10 15-16 fl 10 15-16 Westgate Tower 70 Chungjeong-ro, Seodaemun-gu, Seoul, Korea (South) **(100%)**
Tel.: (82) 2 361 0000
Web Site: https://www.nestle.co.kr
Sales Range: $150-199.9 Million
Emp.: 700
Mfr of Coffee & Other Beverages
N.A.I.C.S.: 311920

Nestle Kuban LLC (1)
Timashevsk st Hybrid 2a, 352700, Krasnodar, Russia

AND PRIVATE COMPANIES

Tel.: (7) 861 302 4393
Web Site: https://www.nestle.ru
Emp.: 1,200
Food Products Distr
N.A.I.C.S.: 424430

Nestle Kuwait General Trading Co., W.L.L. (1)
Building Street 6 Sulaibiyah Area Near Egility Company, PO Box 29096, Kuwait, 29096, Kuwait (49%)
Tel.: (965) 24678377
Sales Range: $25-49.9 Million
Emp.: 166
Mfr of Coffee & Other Beverages
N.A.I.C.S.: 311920
Giusette Pasqualine *(Gen Mgr)*

Nestle Lanka Ltd. (1)
T B Jayah Mawatha Darley Road 440, PO Box 189, 10, Colombo, 10, Sri Lanka (100%)
Tel.: (94) 112697821
Web Site: https://www.nestle.com
Sales Range: $25-49.9 Million
Emp.: 240
Mfr of Breakfast Food & Beverages
N.A.I.C.S.: 311423

Nestle Maghreb S.A. (1)
Casa Nearshore Park 10 Nr 401-402-502 Bd Al Quods 1100, Sidi Maarouf, 20270, Casablanca, Morocco
Tel.: (212) 52 015 8800
Web Site: http://www.nestlemaghreb.com
Emp.: 140
Dairy Products Distr
N.A.I.C.S.: 424430
David Saudan *(Gen Mgr)*

Nestle Mali S.A.U. (1)
BP 940, Bamako, Mali
Tel.: (223) 20 21 01 53
Dairy Product Whslr
N.A.I.C.S.: 424430

Nestle Malta Ltd (1)
Pantar Road, Lija, 2023, Malta
Tel.: (356) 23389000
Web Site: http://www.nestle.com.mt
Sales Range: $50-74.9 Million
Emp.: 80
Dairy Products Distr
N.A.I.C.S.: 424430

Nestle Marcas Peru, S.A.C. (1)
Av Camino Real Nro 1268 Urb, Lima, Peru
Tel.: (51) 1 436 40 40
Dairy Product Whslr
N.A.I.C.S.: 424430

Nestle Maroc S.A. (1)
12 Ave Ali Abderrazak, Casablanca, 20000, Morocco (100%)
Tel.: (212) 22250320
Mfr of Roasted Coffee & Other Beverages
N.A.I.C.S.: 311920

Nestle Mexico S.A. de C.V. (1)
Blvd Miguel de Cervantes Saavedra 301 Torre Sur PB, Alcaldia Miguel Hidalgo Col Granada, 11520, Mexico, DF, Mexico (100%)
Tel.: (52) 555 262 5000
Web Site: http://www.nestle.com.mx
Mfr of Coffee & Various Food Beverages
N.A.I.C.S.: 311920

Nestle Middle East FZE (1)
PO Box 17327, Jebel Ali Free Zone, Dubai, United Arab Emirates (100%)
Tel.: (971) 48838000
Sales Range: $100-124.9 Million
Emp.: 300
N.A.I.C.S.: 311920

Nestle Milkpak Ltd (1)
308 Uppr Mall G, PO Box 874, Lahore, 54000, Pakistan (100%)
Tel.: (92) 425757082
N.A.I.C.S.: 311920

Nestle Mocambique Lda (1)
Rua Desportistas North 333 3 Andar Bloco 1 Jat V, Maputo, Mozambique
Tel.: (258) 21 360 379
Dairy Products Distr
N.A.I.C.S.: 424430

Nestle Nederland B.V. (1)
Stroombaan 14, 1181 VX, Amstelveen, Netherlands (100%)
Tel.: (31) 205699323
Web Site: https://www.nestle.nl
Sales Range: $25-49.9 Million
Emp.: 250
Soups, Instant Coffee, Powdered Milk Products
N.A.I.C.S.: 311514
Marc Boersch *(Dir)*

Nestle Nespresso Beijing Limited (1)
Unit 901 Level 9 One Indigo 20 Jiuxianqiao Road, Chaoyang District, Beijing, 100016, China
Tel.: (86) 108002652590
Food Mfr
N.A.I.C.S.: 311999

Nestle Nespresso S.A. (1)
Chaussee de la Guinguette 10, 1800, Vevey, Switzerland (100%)
Tel.: (41) 276172270
Web Site: https://www.nespresso.com
Sales Range: $100-124.9 Million
Emp.: 800
Mfr of Coffee & other Beverages
N.A.I.C.S.: 311920
Jean-Marc Duvoisin *(CEO)*

Subsidiary (Non-US):

Nespresso Osterreich GmbH & Co. OHG (2)
Wiedner Gurtel 9, 1100, Vienna, Austria
Tel.: (43) 1 512 63 80
Web Site: http://www.nespresso.com
Coffee Brewing Equipment Distr
N.A.I.C.S.: 423830

Subsidiary (US):

Nespresso USA Inc. (2)
111 W 33rd St 5th Fl, New York, NY 10120-1220 (100%)
Tel.: (212) 755-0585
Web Site: https://www.nespresso.com
Sales Range: $50-74.9 Million
Emp.: 100
Coffee Products
N.A.I.C.S.: 424490

Nestle New Zealand Ltd. (1)
Level 3 12-16 Nicholls Lane, Parnell, Auckland, 1010, New Zealand (100%)
Tel.: (64) 9 367 2800
Web Site: https://www.nestle.co.nz
Sales Range: $25-49.9 Million
Emp.: 100
Mfr of Roasted Coffee & Other Beverages
N.A.I.C.S.: 311920
Gary W. Tickle *(Executives)*

Plant (Domestic):

Nestle New Zealand Limited - Manukau Factory (2)
244 Cavendish Drive, Wiri, 2025, Auckland, New Zealand
Tel.: (64) 92786099
Web Site: http://www.nestle.co.nz
Dairy Products Mfr
N.A.I.C.S.: 311514

Nestle Nigeria PLC (1)
20 24 Industrial Avenue, Ikeja, Nigeria (100%)
Tel.: (234) 19478720
Mfr of Roasted Coffee & Other Beverages
N.A.I.C.S.: 311920
Martin Woolnough *(CEO)*

Nestle Nordeste Alimentos e Bebidas Ltda (1)
Rod Br-324 Km 529 - S/n Cis, Feira de Santana, Brazil
Tel.: (55) 75 3604 0700
Sales Range: $250-299.9 Million
Emp.: 756
Dairy Products Distr
N.A.I.C.S.: 424430

Nestle Nouvelle-Caledonia S.A.S. (1)
Lot No 81, Morault Pentecost P K 6, Noumea, New Caledonia (100%)
Tel.: (687) 415151
Web Site: http://www.nestle.au
Sales Range: $25-49.9 Million
Emp.: 100
N.A.I.C.S.: 311920

Nestle Osterreich GmbH (1)
Wiedner Gurtel 9, 1100, Vienna, Austria (100%)
Tel.: (43) 154 6710
Web Site: https://www.nestle.at
Sales Range: $25-49.9 Million
Emp.: 700
Baby Formula, Tea & Coffee
N.A.I.C.S.: 311514
Angela Teml *(Head-Corporate Communications)*

Nestle Pakistan Limited (1)
308 Upper Mall, PO Box 874, Lahore, Pakistan
Tel.: (92) 42111637853
Web Site: https://www.nestle.com
Rev: $746,798,326
Assets: $420,360,748
Liabilities: $399,392,326
Net Worth: $20,968,421
Earnings: $47,362,767
Emp.: 4,063
Fiscal Year-end: 12/31/2019
Food Products Mfr
N.A.I.C.S.: 311999
Yawar Ali *(Chm)*

Nestle Panama S.A. (1)
Urbanizacion La Loma Calle 69 Oeste 74D Apartado 0834-00368, Urbanzacian La Loma, Panama, 9A, Panama (100%)
Tel.: (507) 2291333
Web Site: http://www.nestle.com.pa
Sales Range: $100-124.9 Million
Emp.: 400
Mfr of Food & Beverages
N.A.I.C.S.: 311421

Nestle Paraguay S.A. (1)
Republica Dominicana 282, Asuncion, Paraguay (100%)
Tel.: (595) 21 28 82.000
Web Site: https://www.nestle.com.py
Emp.: 80
Marketing, Logistics, Distribution, Sales & Finance of Various Packaged Foods
N.A.I.C.S.: 541613

Nestle Peru S.A. (1)
Ave Los Castillos Cuadra s/n, Urb Industrial Sanra Rosa Ate Vitarte, Lima, Peru (100%)
Tel.: (51) 1 436 4040
Web Site: https://www.nestle.com
Mfr of Roasted Coffee & Other Beverages
N.A.I.C.S.: 311920

Nestle Philippines, Inc. (1)
No 31 Plaza Drive Rockwell Center, Makati, 1200, Philippines (100%)
Tel.: (63) 28 898 0061
Web Site: https://www.nestle.com.ph
Sales Range: $150-199.9 Million
Emp.: 3,700
Mfr of Roasted Coffee
N.A.I.C.S.: 311920
Kais Marzouki *(CEO)*

Nestle Polska S.A. (1)
Domaniewska 32, 02-672, Warsaw, Poland (100%)
Tel.: (48) 22 325 2525
Web Site: https://www.nestle.pl
Emp.: 5,000
Mfr of Coffee & Other Beverages
N.A.I.C.S.: 311920

Subsidiary (Domestic):

Winiary S.A. (2)
Lodzka 153, 62-800, Kalisz, Poland
Tel.: (48) 627650201
Web Site: http://www.winiary.pl
Sales Range: $75-99.9 Million
Emp.: 700
N.A.I.C.S.: 311920
Thomas Lazarowicz *(Mgr-Factory)*

Nestle Polynesie S.A.S. (1)
Cours de l'Union Sacree 103 Fariipiti, 98716, Papeete, French Polynesia
Tel.: (689) 0054 94 00
Dairy Products Distr
N.A.I.C.S.: 424430

Nestle Product Technology Centre Lebensmittelforschung GmbH (1)
Lange Str 21, 78224, Singen, Germany
Tel.: (49) 7731 140

NESTLE S.A.

Web Site: http://www.ptc-singen.de
Dairy Products Distr
N.A.I.C.S.: 424430

Nestle Products (Mauritius) Ltd. (1)
6th floor Tower 1 Nexteracom Building, Ebene, Mauritius (100%)
Tel.: (230) 405 3700
Sales Range: $25-49.9 Million
Emp.: 45
Plant Science & Nutrition Research
N.A.I.C.S.: 311423

Nestle Professional Food A/S (1)
Industrivej 36, 4683, Ronnede, Denmark
Tel.: (45) 5 679 2222
Web Site: https://www.nestleprofessionalfood.dk
Food Mfr
N.A.I.C.S.: 311999
Henrik Rump *(Mgr-Sls)*

Nestle Purina PetCare Deutschland GmbH (1)
Albert-Latz-Strasse 6, 53879, Euskirchen, Germany
Tel.: (49) 2251 8110
Web Site: http://www.purina.de
Emp.: 400
Pet Food Mfr & Distr
N.A.I.C.S.: 424990
Hubert Wieser *(Mng Dir)*

Nestle Purina PetCare Espana S.A. (1)
Avda Can Campanya s/n Pol Ind Comte de Sert, 08755, Castellbisbal, Barcelona, Spain
Tel.: (34) 900802522
Web Site: http://www.purina.es
Emp.: 150
Pet Food Mfr & Distr
N.A.I.C.S.: 311119

Nestle Purina PetCare France S.A.S. (1)
BP 900, 77446, Marne-la-Vallee, France
Tel.: (33) 806800361
Web Site: http://www.purina.fr
Pet Care Services
N.A.I.C.S.: 812910

Nestle Purina PetCare de Colombia S.A. (1)
Transversal 18 no 96 41 piso 12, Bogota, Colombia
Tel.: (57) 1800 051 0842
Web Site: http://www.purina.com.co
Pet Food Mfr
N.A.I.C.S.: 311119

Nestle R&D Center (Pte) Ltd (1)
29 Quality Road, Singapore, 618802, Singapore
Tel.: (65) 6890 0100
Web Site: http://www.nestle.com
Dairy Products Mfr
N.A.I.C.S.: 311514

Nestle Romania S.R.L. (1)
George Constantinescu Street no 3 staircase A floor 7 Sector 2, Bucharest, 020339, Romania
Tel.: (40) 21 204 4000
Web Site: https://www.nestle.ro
Food Mfr
N.A.I.C.S.: 311999

Nestle Rossiya LLC (1)
Paveletskaya sq 2 building 1, 115054, Moscow, Russia
Tel.: (7) 4957257000
Web Site: https://www.nestle.ru
Dairy Product Mfr & Distr
N.A.I.C.S.: 311514

Nestle Scholler Produktions GmbH (1)
Hamburger Strasse 4, Uelzen, 29525, Germany
Tel.: (49) 5 81 87 0
Emp.: 450
Dairy Product Whslr
N.A.I.C.S.: 424430
Holger Sitzler *(Mgr)*

Nestle Senegal (1)
KM 14 Rte de Rufisque, CP 796, Dakar, Senegal (100%)
Tel.: (221) 77 672 0168
Web Site: https://www.nestle.com

NESTLE S.A.

Nestle S.A.—(Continued)
Breakfast Foods & Confection Mfr
N.A.I.C.S.: 311230

Nestle Servicios Corporativos, S.A. de C.V (1)
Epigmenio Gonzalez 59 Colonia Industrial, Queretaro, 76159, Mexico
Tel.: (52) 442 211 8300
Food Products Mfr
N.A.I.C.S.: 311999

Nestle Servicios Industriales, S.A. de C.V. (1)
Av Ejercito Naciona No 453 Granada, Seccion Miguel Hidalgo, Mexico, 11520, Mexico
Tel.: (52) 55 5262 5000
Food Products Mfr
N.A.I.C.S.: 311999

Nestle Shanghai Limited (1)
No 318 Yutang Road Songjiang Industrial Zone, Songjiang District, Shanghai, 201613, China
Tel.: (86) 2157741718
Soft Drinks Mfr
N.A.I.C.S.: 312111

Nestle Singapore Pte. Ltd. (1)
15A Changi Business Park Central 1 05-02/03 Eightrium, Changi Business Park, Singapore, 486035, Singapore **(100%)**
Tel.: (65) 68367000
Web Site: https://www.nestle.com.sg
Sales Range: $100-124.9 Million
Emp.: 300
Mfr of Instant Noodles
N.A.I.C.S.: 311423

Nestle Skin Health India Private Ltd. (1)
Lotus Corporate Park D Wing, Unit 801 and 802 Off Western Express Highway Goregaon East, Mumbai, 400 063, India
Tel.: (91) 2240331818
Pharmaceuticals Product Mfr
N.A.I.C.S.: 325412
Stuart Raetzman *(CEO)*

Nestle Slovakia Ltd. (1)
Plynarenska 1, 821 09, Bratislava, Slovakia **(100%)**
Tel.: (421) 24 920 1311
Web Site: http://www.nestle.sk
Sales Range: $100-124.9 Million
Emp.: 500
Mfr of Roasted Coffee & Other Beverages
N.A.I.C.S.: 311920

Nestle Suisse S.A. (1)
Rue Entre-deux-Villes 10, La Tour-de-Peilz, 1814, Vevey, Switzerland **(100%)**
Tel.: (41) 21 924 5111
Web Site: https://www.nestle.ch
Sales Range: $25-49.9 Million
Emp.: 700
Food & Beverage Product Mfr & Distr
N.A.I.C.S.: 311999

Nestle Sul Alimentos e Bebidas Ltda (1)
Av Dr Chucri Zaidan 246 - 20 andar - Vila cordiero, Sao Paulo, 04583-110, Brazil
Tel.: (55) 11 5908 4400
Packed Food & Soft Drink Distr
N.A.I.C.S.: 424420

Nestle Sverige AB (1)
(100%)
Tel.: (46) 4 219 9100
Web Site: https://www.nestle.se
Sales Range: $25-49.9 Million
Emp.: 150
N.A.I.C.S.: 311920

Subsidiary (Domestic):

Zoegas Kaffe AB (2)
Angel Holmes V 25, PO Box 7173, 250 07, Helsingborg, Sweden **(100%)**
Tel.: (46) 42193300
Web Site: http://www.nestle.se
Sales Range: $75-99.9 Million
Emp.: 80
Coffee Production & Exportation
N.A.I.C.S.: 311920
Magnus Nordin *(Mng Dir)*

Nestle Syria S.A. (1)
Al-Kousour Street Khan-Al Sheih, PO Box 9444, Damascus, Syria
Tel.: (963) 11 683 15 01
Dairy Products Distr
N.A.I.C.S.: 424430

Nestle TC Asia Pacific Pte Ltd (1)
15A Changi Business Park Central 1 05-02/03 Tampines, Singapore, 486035, Singapore
Tel.: (65) 68367000
Dairy Product Whslr
N.A.I.C.S.: 424430

Nestle Taiwan Limited (1)
8 F & 8 F-1 No 399 Rui Kwang Rd, Neihu District, Taipei, 11492, Taiwan **(100%)**
Tel.: (886) 2 773 9910
Web Site: http://www.nestle.com.tw
Sales Range: $100-124.9 Million
Emp.: 350
Nutrition, Health & Wellness Products & Services
N.A.I.C.S.: 311999

Nestle Togo S.A.U (1)
Cite OUA Lot N 8 a Cote de la Primature 09, BP 9173, Lome, Togo
Tel.: (228) 22 26 30 50
Dairy Products Distr
N.A.I.C.S.: 424430

Nestle Trading Private Limited Company (1)
Istiqlal St Industrial Zone, Beit Jala, Palestine
Tel.: (970) 2 2777666
Sales Range: $25-49.9 Million
Emp.: 35
Dairy Products Distr
N.A.I.C.S.: 424430
Anton Hazboun *(Gen Mgr)*

Nestle Treasury Centre-Middle East & Africa Ltd (1)
Office No 21-208 Level 21 South Tower Emirates Financial Towers DIFC, PO Box 17327, Dubai, United Arab Emirates
Tel.: (971) 4 807 9247
Investment Management Service
N.A.I.C.S.: 523940

Nestle Trinidad and Tobago Ltd. (1)
Churchill-Roosevelt Highway, PO Box 172, Valsayn, Trinidad & Tobago
Tel.: (868) 663 6832
Web Site: http://www.nestle.com
Sales Range: $100-124.9 Million
Emp.: 500
Mfr of Roasted Coffee & Other Beverages
N.A.I.C.S.: 311920

Nestle Tunisia S.A. (1)
13 rue Ibn Nadim, BP 217, TN 1082, Tunis, Tunisia
Tel.: (216) 71849544
Mfr of Roasted Coffee & Other Beverages
N.A.I.C.S.: 311920

Nestle Turkiye A.S. (1)
Nurol Plaza A Blok Kat 6 Buyukdere Caddesi No 255, Maslak Sariyer, 34398, Istanbul, Turkiye
Tel.: (90) 212 329 6000
Web Site: https://www.nestle.com.tr
Sales Range: $25-49.9 Million
Emp.: 200
Mfr of Roasted Coffee
N.A.I.C.S.: 311920

Nestle Turkiye Gida Sanayi A.S. (1)
Nurol Plaza A Blok Kat 6 Buyukdere Caddesi No 255 Maslak Sisli, 34398, Istanbul, Turkiye
Tel.: (90) 212 329 60 00
Web Site: http://www.nestle.com.tr
Baby Food Product Mfr & Whslr
N.A.I.C.S.: 311999

Nestle USA, Inc. (1)
800 N Brand Blvd, Glendale, CA 91203-1245 **(100%)**
Tel.: (818) 549-6000
Web Site: http://www.nestleusa.com
Sales Range: $5-14.9 Billion
Emp.: 17,000
Beverages, Food Services, Foreign Trade, Nutrition, Pet Care & Sales
N.A.I.C.S.: 311514
Karen Crawford *(Dir)*

Subsidiary (Domestic):

Buitoni North America (2)

INTERNATIONAL PUBLIC

30003 Bainbridge Rd, Solon, OH 44139
Tel.: (440) 349-5757
Web Site: http://www.buitoni.com
Sales Range: $350-399.9 Million
Emp.: 1,773
Refrigerated Fresh Potatoes, Pasta & Pasta Sauces Distribution
N.A.I.C.S.: 311412
Roz O'Hearn *(Mgr-PR)*

Dreyer's Grand Ice Cream Holdings, Inc. (2)
5929 College Ave, Oakland, CA 94618
Tel.: (510) 601-4300
Web Site: https://www.icecream.com
Sales Range: $1-4.9 Billion
Emp.: 5,979
Ice Cream & Frozen Dairy Dessert Products
N.A.I.C.S.: 311520
Diane McIntyre *(Mgr-PR)*

Subsidiary (Domestic):

Dreyer's Grand Ice Cream (3)
5929 College Ave, Oakland, CA 94618
Tel.: (510) 652-8187
Web Site: http://www.dreyer.com
Sales Range: $50-74.9 Million
Emp.: 200
Mfr of Ice Cream
N.A.I.C.S.: 311520
Tom Chole *(Plant Mgr)*

Nestle Dreyer's Ice Cream Company (3)
5929 College Ave, Oakland, CA 94618
Tel.: (510) 652-8187
Ice Cream Mfr & Distr
N.A.I.C.S.: 311520

The Haagen-Dazs Shoppe Company, Inc. (3)
500 Washington Ave S 2040, Minneapolis, MN 55415
Tel.: (612) 337-3303
Web Site: http://www.haagen-dazs.com
Ice Cream Store Operator
N.A.I.C.S.: 722515

Subsidiary (Domestic):

Edy's Grand Ice Cream Company (2)
100 Enterprise Dr Ste 700, Rockaway, NJ 07866 **(100%)**
Tel.: (973) 659-6100
Web Site: http://www.edys.com
Sales Range: $25-49.9 Million
Emp.: 45
Ice Cream & Ices
N.A.I.C.S.: 424430

Unit (Domestic):

Edy's Grand Ice Cream Midwest Region (3)
601 Wall St, Glendale Heights, IL 60139-1906
Tel.: (630) 924-7755
Web Site: http://www.edys.com
Sales Range: $75-99.9 Million
Mfr of Ice Cream Products
N.A.I.C.S.: 424430

Subsidiary (Domestic):

Gerber Products Company (2)
12 Vreeland Rd, Florham Park, NJ 07932-1521
Tel.: (973) 593-7500
Web Site: http://www.gerber.com
Sales Range: $50-74.9 Million
Emp.: 200
Baby Products Mfr
N.A.I.C.S.: 424490

Subsidiary (Non-US):

Alima-Gerber SA (3)
Ul Gen Stanislawa Maczka 1, 35 959, Rzeszow, Poland
Tel.: (48) 178753300
Web Site: http://www.gerber.pl
Sales Range: $25-49.9 Million
Emp.: 30
Mfr of Canned Specialties
N.A.I.C.S.: 311422

Subsidiary (Domestic):

Gerber Products Company (3)

4301 Harriet Ave, Fort Smith, AR 72904-1607
Tel.: (479) 784-5206
Web Site: http://www.gerber.com
Baby Foods Including Meats Packaged In Cans & Jars
N.A.I.C.S.: 311422

Gerber Products Company (3)
445 State St, Fremont, MI 49413-0001
Tel.: (231) 928-2000
Web Site: http://www.gerber.com
Infant & Baby Product Mfr & Services
N.A.I.C.S.: 311999

Gerber Products Company of Puerto Rico, Inc. (3)
San Juan Indus Park Carr 1 Km 25-30 Barrio Quelerada Arenas, San Juan, PR 00926
Tel.: (787) 769-7745
Web Site: http://www.gerber.com
Sales Range: $25-49.9 Million
Emp.: 74
Baby Foods & Baby Needs Distr
N.A.I.C.S.: 311999

Gerber Products Division-Baby Care (3)
PO Box 120, Reedsburg, WI 53959-0901
Tel.: (608) 524-4343
Web Site: http://www.gerberrealtors.com
Sales Range: $125-149.9 Million
Mfr of Foods, Toys & Accessories for Babies-Nipples, Bottles, Sterilizers, Dishes & Plates, Bedding, Breast Pumps, Safety Products
N.A.I.C.S.: 326299

Subsidiary (Domestic):

LJ Minor (2)
2621 W 25th St, Cleveland, OH 44113-4708 **(100%)**
Tel.: (216) 861-8350
Sales Range: $25-49.9 Million
Emp.: 247
Mfr of Food Base
N.A.I.C.S.: 311422
John Auld *(Mgr-Factory)*

Nestle Capital Corporation (2)
800 N Brand Blvd, Glendale, CA 91203-1245 **(100%)**
Tel.: (818) 549-6000
Web Site: http://www.nestlesa.com
Sales Range: $600-649.9 Million
Emp.: 1,500
Short-Term Business Credit Institutions, Except Agricultural
N.A.I.C.S.: 522299

Division (Domestic):

Nestle Clinical Nutrition (2)
2150 E Lake Cook Rd Ste 800, Buffalo Grove, IL 60089-8227
Tel.: (847) 317-2800
Web Site: http://www.nestle-nutrition.com
Sales Range: $75-99.9 Million
Emp.: 200
Clinical Nutrition
N.A.I.C.S.: 424490

Nestle FoodServices (2)
800 N Brand Blvd, Glendale, CA 91203-1245
Tel.: (818) 549-6000
Web Site: http://www.nestleusa.com
Sales Range: $25-49.9 Million
Emp.: 40
Food & Beverage Products for the Food Services Industry
N.A.I.C.S.: 311514

Nestle Foreign Trade (2)
800 N Brand Blvd, Glendale, CA 91203-1245
Tel.: (818) 549-6000
Web Site: http://www.nestleusa.com
Sales Range: $450-499.9 Million
Emp.: 2,000
Wholesale Trade Agency
N.A.I.C.S.: 425120

Subsidiary (Domestic):

Nestle Holdings, Inc. (2)
1209 Orange St, Wilmington, DE 19801
Tel.: (818) 549-6000
Investment Management Service

AND PRIVATE COMPANIES   NESTLE S.A.

N.A.I.C.S.: 523940

Division (Domestic):

Nestle Nutrition (2)
4590 MacArthur Blvd, Newport Beach, CA 92660-2030
Tel.: (949) 252-0838
Sales Range: $25-49.9 Million
Emp.: 1
Pharmaceuticals Preparations
N.A.I.C.S.: 424490
Gary W. Tickle (Executives)

Nestle Pizza Division (2)
885 Sunset Rdg, Northbrook, IL 60062
Tel.: (847) 400-1100
Web Site: http://www.nestleusa.com
Sales Range: $250-299.9 Million
Emp.: 200
Frozen Pizza Mfr
N.A.I.C.S.: 311412

Branch (Domestic):

Nestle Pizza Division-Medford (3)
940 S Whelen Ave, Medford, WI 54451-1745
Tel.: (715) 748-5550
Sales Range: $150-199.9 Million
Emp.: 500
Frozen Pizza Mfr
N.A.I.C.S.: 311412

Nestle Pizza Division-Tombstone Pizza (3)
W 227 N 6088 Sussex Rd, Sussex, WI 53089-3968
Tel.: (262) 246-8013
Sales Range: $150-199.9 Million
Frozen Pizza Mfr
N.A.I.C.S.: 311412

Division (Domestic):

Nestle Prepared Foods Company (2)
30003 Bainbridge Rd, Solon, OH 44139-2290
Tel.: (440) 349-5757
Web Site: http://www.nestleusa.com
Frozen Foods & Entrees Mfr
N.A.I.C.S.: 311520
Kevin Pulte (Mgr-Mktg)

Group (Domestic):

Nestle Prepared Foods Co. - Handheld Foods Group (3)
345 Inverness Dr S B 200, Englewood, CO 80112-5622
Tel.: (303) 790-0303
Web Site: http://www.nestleusa.com
Sales Range: $300-349.9 Million
Emp.: 1,400
Specialty Frozen Foods Mfr
N.A.I.C.S.: 311412

Division (Domestic):

Nestle Purina PetCare Company (2)
Checkerboard Sq, Saint Louis, MO 63164-0001
Tel.: (314) 982-1000
Web Site: http://www.purina.com
Sales Range: $1-4.9 Billion
Emp.: 6,749
Mfr of Pet Food
N.A.I.C.S.: 311111

Subsidiary (Domestic):

Golden Products Corporation (3)
Checkerboard Sq 6 T, Saint Louis, MO 63164-0001   (100%)
Tel.: (314) 982-2400
Web Site: http://www.purina.nestle.com
Sales Range: $200-249.9 Million
Emp.: 1,000
Mfr of Cat Box Filler & Processors of Absorbent Clays
N.A.I.C.S.: 459910

Division (Domestic):

Nestles Purina Petcare (4)
300 Airport Rd, Cape Girardeau, MO 63702   (100%)
Tel.: (573) 334-6618

Sales Range: $25-49.9 Million
Emp.: 45
Mfr of Clay Products
N.A.I.C.S.: 339999

Subsidiary (Non-US):

Nestle Belgilux S.A. (3)
Rue de Birmingham 221, 1070, Brussels, Belgium   (100%)
Tel.: (32) 2 529 5252
Web Site: https://www.nestle.be
Emp.: 43
Mfr of Dietary Soy Protein, Baby Formulas & Pet Products
N.A.I.C.S.: 311111

Nestle Purina PetCare Canada (3)
2500 Royal Windsor Drive, Mississauga, L5J 1K8, ON, Canada   (100%)
Tel.: (905) 822-1611
Web Site: https://www.purina.ca
Emp.: 300
Animal Feeds & Pet Foods Mfr; Grocery Products
N.A.I.C.S.: 311119

Plant (Domestic):

Nestle Purina PetCare Co. - Nebraska (3)
E Hwy 33, Crete, NE 68333
Tel.: (402) 826-8700
Sales Range: $75-99.9 Million
Emp.: 300
Mfr of Dog & Cat Food
N.A.I.C.S.: 311111

Nestle Purina PetCare Co. - Ohio (3)
5 N 2nd St, Zanesville, OH 43701-3401   (100%)
Tel.: (740) 454-8575
Web Site: http://www.nestlepurina.com
Sales Range: $25-49.9 Million
Emp.: 130
Mfr of Soft, Moist Pet Foods
N.A.I.C.S.: 311111
Roger Brecht (Plant Mgr)

Nestle Purina PetCare Co. - Wisconsin (3)
150 W Riverview Dr, Jefferson, WI 53549-1842
Tel.: (920) 674-1500
Sales Range: $75-99.9 Million
Emp.: 267
Dog & Cat Food
N.A.I.C.S.: 311111

Subsidiary (Domestic):

Nestle Purina PetCare Global Resources, Inc. (3)
Checkerboard Sq, Saint Louis, MO 63164-0001
Tel.: (314) 982-1000
Pet Food Mfr
N.A.I.C.S.: 311119

Subsidiary (Non-US):

Nestle Purina PetCare Hungary Kft. (3)
Lechner Odon Fasor 7, 1095, Budapest, Hungary   (100%)
Tel.: (36) 680442881
Web Site: http://www.nestle.hu
Sales Range: $25-49.9 Million
Emp.: 250
Producer of Feed & Livestock
N.A.I.C.S.: 311611

Nestle Purina PetCare Italiana S.p.A. (3)
Viale Giulio Richard 5, Milan, 20143, Italy   (100%)
Tel.: (39) 0281811
Web Site: http://www.nestle.it
Sales Range: $25-49.9 Million
Emp.: 100
Mfr of Animal Feed Products
N.A.I.C.S.: 311514

Nestle Purina PetCare Korea (3)
International Insurance Building 5 Ka Namdaemun Road Choong Ku, Seoul, 135953, Korea (South)
Tel.: (82) 25613210

Sales Range: Less than $1 Million
Emp.: 100
Mfr & Marketer of Animal Feed Products
N.A.I.C.S.: 311514

Nestle Purina Petfoods (3)
Stationsweg 43, 3331LR, Zwijndrecht, Netherlands   (100%)
Tel.: (31) 786254848
Web Site: http://www.purina.nl
Sales Range: $125-149.9 Million
Emp.: 80
Mfr & Distributor of Pet Foods
N.A.I.C.S.: 311111

Unit (Domestic):

Nestle Purina Product Technology Center (3)
3916 Pettis Rd, Saint Joseph, MO 64503-1542
Tel.: (816) 232-0300
Sales Range: $50-74.9 Million
Emp.: 120
Food Research
N.A.I.C.S.: 541720
Micheal Quinn (Dir-HR)

Subsidiary (Non-US):

Purina Alimentos Ltda. (3)
Av Prof Benedito Montenegro s/n, Paulinia, 13140 000, Paulinia, SP, Brazil   (100%)
Tel.: (55) 19 3884 9800
Sales Range: $300-349.9 Million
Emp.: 1,200
Animal Feeds & Pet Foods
N.A.I.C.S.: 311119

Subsidiary (Domestic):

Purina Mills, LLC (3)
PO Box 66812, Saint Louis, MO 63166
Tel.: (314) 982-1000
Web Site: http://www.purina.com
Sales Range: $300-349.9 Million
Emp.: 1,500
Pet Food Products
N.A.I.C.S.: 311119

Subsidiary (Non-US):

Ralston Purina Overseas Finance N.V. (3)
De Ruyterkade 62, Willemstad, Curacao
Web Site: http://www.ralstonpurina.nl
Provider of Financial Services
N.A.I.C.S.: 522299

Unit (Domestic):

Nestle R&D Center (2)
809 Collins Ave, Marysville, OH 43040-1308
Tel.: (937) 642-7015
Web Site: http://www.nestle.com
Sales Range: $25-49.9 Million
Emp.: 220
Research Facility
N.A.I.C.S.: 311514

Subsidiary (Domestic):

Nestle Transportation Co. (2)
5448 Oakview Dr, Allentown, PA 18104-9311   (100%)
Tel.: (610) 391-7946
Sales Range: Less than $1 Million
Emp.: 3
Heavy Duty Truck Repair Services
N.A.I.C.S.: 484121

Nestle Transportation Co. (2)
800 Nestle Ct, Dekalb, IL 60115-8676   (100%)
Tel.: (815) 754-2588
Web Site: http://www.nestle.com
Sales Range: $25-49.9 Million
Emp.: 50
Transportation Services
N.A.I.C.S.: 484121

Plant (Domestic):

Nestle USA, Inc. - Bloomington (2)
2501 Beich Rd, Bloomington, IL 61704-6558
Tel.: (309) 829-1031
Web Site: http://www.nestleusa.com
Chocolate & Other Confectionery Products Mfr
N.A.I.C.S.: 311340

Nestle USA, Inc. - Charlotte (2)
9115 Harris Corners Pkwy Ste 125, Charlotte, NC 28269-7521
Tel.: (704) 921-8350
Web Site: http://www.nestleusa.com
Sales Range: $25-49.9 Million
Emp.: 20
Dry Condensed & Evaporated Dairy Products
N.A.I.C.S.: 311514

Nestle USA, Inc. - Dekalb (2)
800 Nestle Ct, Dekalb, IL 60115-8676
Tel.: (815) 754-2500
Web Site: http://www.nestleusa.com
Sales Range: $25-49.9 Million
Emp.: 250
Distr of Food Products
N.A.I.C.S.: 493110

Nestle USA, Inc. - Denver (2)
2083 Truda Dr, Denver, CO 80233-1360
Tel.: (303) 452-7180
Web Site: http://www.nestleusa.com
Sales Range: $25-49.9 Million
Emp.: 1
Evaporated Milk
N.A.I.C.S.: 311514

Nestle USA, Inc. - Dublin (2)
6625 Eiterman Rd, Dublin, OH 43016
Tel.: (614) 526-5200
Web Site: http://www.nestle.com
Sales Range: $25-49.9 Million
Emp.: 120
Food Testing Services
N.A.I.C.S.: 541380

Nestle USA, Inc. - Eau Claire (2)
1200 Nestle Ave, Eau Claire, WI 54703
Tel.: (715) 839-9440
Web Site: http://www.nestleusa.com
Sales Range: $100-124.9 Million
Emp.: 454
Mfr of Infants Food Cereal
N.A.I.C.S.: 311230

Nestle USA, Inc. - Eden Prairie (2)
7500 Flying Cloud Dr Ste 740, Eden Prairie, MN 55344-3748
Tel.: (952) 914-7840
Web Site: http://www.nestleusa.com
Sales Range: $10-24.9 Million
Emp.: 40
Retail of Evaporated Milk
N.A.I.C.S.: 311514

Nestle USA, Inc. - Edison (2)
2035 State Route 27 Ste 3004, Edison, NJ 08817-3351
Tel.: (732) 650-2100
Web Site: http://www.nestleusa.com
Sales Range: $25-49.9 Million
Emp.: 15
Food Mfr
N.A.I.C.S.: 311999

Nestle USA, Inc. - Honolulu (2)
3375 Koapaka Ste F 22045, Honolulu, HI 96819-4445
Tel.: (818) 549-6000
Web Site: http://www.nestleusa.com
Sales Range: $25-49.9 Million
Emp.: 7
General Groceries
N.A.I.C.S.: 311340

Subsidiary (Domestic):

Nestle USA, Inc. - Itasca (2)
1445 Norwood Ave, Itasca, IL 60143-1128
Tel.: (630) 773-2090
Web Site: http://www.nestleusa.com
Sales Range: $100-124.9 Million
Emp.: 400
Candy & Other Confectionery Products Mfr
N.A.I.C.S.: 311340

Plant (Domestic):

Nestle USA, Inc. - Jacksonville (2)
1111 Carnation Way, Jacksonville, IL 62650
Tel.: (217) 243-9175
Web Site: http://www.nestleusa.com
Sales Range: $25-49.9 Million
Emp.: 203
Cream Substitutes
N.A.I.C.S.: 311514

Nestle USA, Inc. - McDonough (2)
1 Nestle Ct, McDonough, GA 30253

NESTLE S.A.

Nestle S.A.—(Continued)
Tel.: (770) 914-5298
Web Site: http://www.nestleusa.com
Sales Range: $25-49.9 Million
Emp.: 120
Mfr of Evaporated Milk
N.A.I.C.S.: 311514

Nestle USA, Inc. - Mira Loma (2)
3450 Dulles Dr, Mira Loma, CA 91752-3242
Tel.: (909) 360-7200
Web Site: http://www.nestleusa.com
Sales Range: $25-49.9 Million
Emp.: 250
Distribution Centre for Nestle
N.A.I.C.S.: 311412

Nestle USA, Inc. - New Milford (2)
201 Housatonic Ave, New Milford, CT 06776-5540
Tel.: (860) 355-0911
Sales Range: $25-49.9 Million
Emp.: 150
Dried & Dehydrated Fruits Vegetables & Soup Mixes
N.A.I.C.S.: 541720
Dennis Gasparini (Fin)

Nestle USA, Inc. - Phoenix (2)
3701 E La Salle St, Phoenix, AZ 85040-3977
Tel.: (602) 458-2001
Sales Range: $25-49.9 Million
Emp.: 30
Data Center for Nestle
N.A.I.C.S.: 518210

Nestle USA, Inc. - Quincy (2)
2 Adams Pl, Quincy, MA 02169-7456
Tel.: (781) 356-4000
Web Site: http://www.nestleusa.com
Sales Range: $25-49.9 Million
Emp.: 8
Chocolate & Cocoa Products
N.A.I.C.S.: 311351

Nestle USA, Inc. - San Ramon (2)
12667 Alcosta Blvd Ste 120, San Ramon, CA 94583
Tel.: (925) 327-2200
Web Site: http://www.nestleusa.com
Sales Range: $25-49.9 Million
Emp.: 20
Mfr of Dry Condensed & Evaporated Dairy Products
N.A.I.C.S.: 311514

Nestle USA, Inc. - Solon (2)
30003 Bainbridge Rd, Solon, OH 44139-2205
Tel.: (440) 349-5757
Web Site: http://www.nestleusa.com
Sales Range: $500-549.9 Million
Emp.: 1,883
Food & Beverage Mfr
N.A.I.C.S.: 311520

Subsidiary (Domestic):

PTC (2)
201 Housatonic Ave, New Milford, CT 06776-5540 (100%)
Tel.: (860) 355-0911
Web Site: http://www.nestleusa.com
Sales Range: $25-49.9 Million
Emp.: 130
Food Research
N.A.I.C.S.: 541511

Vitality Foodservice Holding Corporation (2)
400 N Tampa St Ste 1500, Tampa, FL 33602-4716
Tel.: (813) 301-4600
Investment Management Service
N.A.I.C.S.: 523999

Nestle Unternehmungen Deutschland GmbH (1)
Lyoner Str 23, Frankfurt am Main, 60528, Germany
Tel.: (49) 6966711
Web Site: http://www.nestle.de
Investment Management Service
N.A.I.C.S.: 523999

Nestle Venezuela S.A. (1)
Calle Altagracia Edificio P G Piso 3 Urbanizacion Sorokaima, Sector La Trinidad, Caracas, 1080, Venezuela (100%)
Tel.: (58) 2128208000
Web Site: https://www.nestle.com.ve
Sales Range: $100-124.9 Million
Emp.: 300
Food & Beverage Products Mfr & Distr
N.A.I.C.S.: 311920

Nestle Versorgungskasse GmbH (1)
Lyoner Str 23, 60528, Frankfurt am Main, Germany
Tel.: (49) 69 667 10
Financial Management Services
N.A.I.C.S.: 523999

Nestle Vietnam Ltd. (1)
5th Floor Empress Tower 138-142, Hai Ba Trung Da Kao Ward District 1, Ho Chi Minh City, Vietnam (100%)
Tel.: (84) 283 911 3737
Web Site: https://www.nestle.com.vn
Sales Range: $25-49.9 Million
Emp.: 300
Mfr of Coffee & Other Beverages
N.A.I.C.S.: 311920

Nestle WCO GmbH Conow (1)
Am Kalischacht 3, Malliss, 19294, Germany
Tel.: (49) 38750 3010
Baby Food Product Mfr
N.A.I.C.S.: 311999

Nestle Wagner GmbH (1)
In den Schemeln 4, Braunshausen, 66620, Nonnweiler, Germany
Tel.: (49) 68736650
Web Site: https://www.original-wagner.de
Frozen Food Product Mfr
N.A.I.C.S.: 311412

Nestle Watercoolers Service LLC (1)
Kashirskoye shosse 19, Domodedovo, 142000, Moscow, Russia
Tel.: (7) 495 980 5 980
Web Site: http://www.nestle-purelife.ru
Mineral Water Mfr
N.A.I.C.S.: 312112

Nestle Waters (Suisse) S.A. (1)
Route de la Gare 1, Henniez, 1525, Switzerland
Tel.: (41) 266686868
Web Site: https://www.henniez.ch
Sales Range: $100-124.9 Million
Emp.: 300
Mineral Water Mfr
N.A.I.C.S.: 312112
Bene Venti (Gen Mgr)

Nestle Waters S.A.S. (1)
12 Boulevard Garibaldi, 92130, Issy-les-Moulineaux, France (100%)
Tel.: (33) 160532118
Web Site: http://www.nestle-waters.com
Sales Range: $75-99.9 Million
Emp.: 200
Holding Company; Bottled Water Mfr & Distr
N.A.I.C.S.: 551112

Subsidiary (US):

Great Spring Waters of America (2)
5482 Route Nine W, Newburgh, NY 12550
Tel.: (845) 569-4292
Sales Range: $50-74.9 Million
Emp.: 9
Groceries & Related Products
N.A.I.C.S.: 424490

Great Spring Waters of America (2)
4250 Baldwin Ave, El Monte, CA 91731-1102
Tel.: (626) 442-5612
Sales Range: $25-49.9 Million
Emp.: 65
Mineral & Spring Water
N.A.I.C.S.: 424490
Kevin Horton (Gen Mgr)

Affiliate (Non-US):

La Vie (2)
National Highway 1A, Khanh Hau Ward, Tan An, Long An, Vietnam (65%)
Tel.: (84) 72 351 1801
Web Site: https://www.laviewater.com
Bottled Water Mfr; Joint Venture of Nestle Waters France (65%) & Long An General Trading Company (35%)
N.A.I.C.S.: 312112

Subsidiary (Non-US):

Nestle Waters (UK) Holdings Ltd (2)
St Georges House, Croydon, CR9 1NR, Surrey, United Kingdom
Tel.: (44) 2086863333
Mineral Water Mfr & Distr
N.A.I.C.S.: 312112

Nestle Waters Benelux S.A. (2)
Rue Birmingham 221, 1070, Brussels, Belgium
Tel.: (32) 25 58 12 11
Bottled Water Mfr
N.A.I.C.S.: 312112

Nestle Waters Brasil - Bebidas e Alimentos Ltda (2)
Avenida Presidente Wilson 1628 - Mooca, Sao Paulo, Brazil
Tel.: (55) 11 96160 1110
Packed Food & Soft Drink Distr
N.A.I.C.S.: 424420

Nestle Waters Direct Deutschland GmbH (2)
Sperberweg 49, 41468, Neuss, Germany
Tel.: (49) 18 05 99 59 90
Web Site: http://www.nestle-waters-direct.de
Mineral Water Mfr
N.A.I.C.S.: 312112

Nestle Waters Egypt S.A.E. (2)
6 Rue Dar El Chefa, Cairo, 11451, Egypt
Tel.: (20) 227919030
Mineral Water Mfr
N.A.I.C.S.: 312112

Nestle Waters Espana, S.A. (2)
Calle Arago 210 Atico 1 A, 8011, Barcelona, Spain (100%)
Tel.: (34) 934526010
Sales Range: $25-49.9 Million
Emp.: 65
Bottler & Retailer of Water
N.A.I.C.S.: 424490

Nestle Waters GB Ltd. (1)
Trinity Court Church Street, Rickmansworth, WD3 1LD, Herts, United Kingdom (100%)
Tel.: (44) 192 389 7700
Web Site: https://www.nestle.co.uk
Sales Range: $25-49.9 Million
Emp.: 60
Mineral Water
N.A.I.C.S.: 312112

Nestle Waters Gida ve Mesrubat Sanayi Ticaret A.S. (2)
Uludao Cad No 216, Kestel, 30415, Bursa, Turkiye
Tel.: (90) 224 280 55 00
Web Site: http://www.nestlewaters.com.tr
Mineral Water Mfr
N.A.I.C.S.: 312112

Nestle Waters Middle East Investments FZCO (2)
3rd Floor-Dubai World Central HQ Building Nr, PO Box 17327, New Al Maktoum International Airport Jebel Ali, Dubai, 32243, United Arab Emirates
Tel.: (971) 48100000
Web Site: http://www.nestle.com
Investment Management Service
N.A.I.C.S.: 523940

Nestle Waters Polska S.A. (2)
Lopuszanska Street 38 B, 02-232, Warsaw, Poland
Tel.: (48) 22 668 8575
Web Site: http://www.darnatury.pl
Mineral Water Mfr
N.A.I.C.S.: 312112

Nestle Waters direct Portugal, comercio e distribuicao de produtos alimentares, S.A. (2)
Rua Jose Pereira Lote AE, Sao Joao Da Talha, Famoes, 1685-635, Portugal
Tel.: (351) 707 215 215
Web Site: http://www.edensprings.pt
Mineral Water Mfr & Distr
N.A.I.C.S.: 312112

Subsidiary (US):

Perrier Group of America Inc. (2)
5 Warehouse Ln, Elmsford, NY 10523-1542
Tel.: (914) 345-2045

INTERNATIONAL PUBLIC

Web Site: http://www.perrier.com
Sales Range: $50-74.9 Million
Emp.: 100
Bottled Water Mfr
N.A.I.C.S.: 312112

Perrier Group of America Inc. (2)
170 W Commercial Ave, Moonachie, NJ 07074-1706
Tel.: (201) 531-2060
Sales Range: $25-49.9 Million
Emp.: 70
Mineral or Spring Water Bottling
N.A.I.C.S.: 424490

Subsidiary (Non-US):

Sanpellegrino S.p.A. (2)
Viale Giulio Richard 5, Assago, 20090, Italy (99.6%)
Tel.: (39) 0231971
Web Site: http://www.sanpellegrino.it
Emp.: 2,000
Mineral Water Bottler & Distr
N.A.I.C.S.: 312112

Subsidiary (US):

Sweet Leaf Tea Co. (2)
515 S Congress Ave, Austin, TX 78704
Tel.: (512) 328-7775
Sales Range: $25-49.9 Million
Emp.: 10
Soft Drinks Mfr
N.A.I.C.S.: 312111

Nestle Zambia Trading Limited (1)
Plot 7403 Mungwi Road Krimanvi Park Bloc C, Lusaka, Zambia
Tel.: (260) 965030800
Web Site: http://www.nestle-ea.com
Sales Range: $25-49.9 Million
Emp.: 40
Dairy Products Distr
N.A.I.C.S.: 424430

Nestle Zimbabwe (Pvt) Ltd. (1)
38 Samora Machel Avenue, PO Box 1668, Harare, Zimbabwe (100%)
Tel.: (263) 242 702 3937
Web Site: http://www.nestle.co.za
Sales Range: $25-49.9 Million
Emp.: 150
Mfr of Roasted Coffee & Other Beverages
N.A.I.C.S.: 311920

Nestle de Colombia S.A. (1)
Transversal 18 96-41, Apartado Aereo 5959, Santafe de, Bogota, Colombia (100%)
Tel.: (57) 1 219 0800
Web Site: https://www.nestle.com
Sales Range: $25-49.9 Million
Emp.: 200
Mfr of Coffee & Other Beverages
N.A.I.C.S.: 311920

Subsidiary (Domestic):

Comestibles La Rosa S.A. (2)
Transversal 1896 41 Apartado Aero 5959, Bogota, Colombia
Tel.: (57) 15219000
Web Site: http://www.nestle.com.co
Mfrs. Biscuits
N.A.I.C.S.: 311812

Nestle-Findus Oy (1)
Keilasatama 5, PO Box 50, Espoo, 2150, Finland (100%)
Tel.: (358) 1039511
Web Site: http://www.nestle.fi
Sales Range: $50-74.9 Million
Emp.: 160
Frozen Food & Beverage Mfr & Distr
N.A.I.C.S.: 311710
Johanna Sewon-Kievari (Mng Dir)

Nestle-JMP Jamaica Ltd. (1)
Pan Jamaican Building 60 Knutsford Blvd, PO Box 281, 60 Knutsford Boulevard, Kingston, Jamaica
Tel.: (876) 926 1300
Web Site: http://www.nestlecaribbean.com
Sales Range: $25-49.9 Million
Emp.: 70
Mfr of Roasted Coffee
N.A.I.C.S.: 311920

Nestrade SA (1)
Rue d'Entre-deux-Villes 12, PO Box 380,

1814, Geneva, Switzerland **(100%)**
Tel.: (41) 219245111
Web Site: http://www.nestrade.com
Sales Range: $700-749.9 Million
Emp.: 1,600
Export/Import of Nestle Products, Specialty Ingredients, Machines & Technical Equipment for Food Manufacturing
N.A.I.C.S.: 425120

Novartis Nutrition GmbH **(1)**
Postfach 82, 1205, Vienna, Austria
Tel.: (43) 133235070
Web Site: http://www.novartis.at
Sales Range: $25-49.9 Million
Emp.: 15
Mfr & Sales of Pharmaceuticals & Nutritional Products
N.A.I.C.S.: 325412

Oscar A/S **(1)**
Industrivej 36, Ronnede, 4683, Denmark
Tel.: (45) 56 79 22 22
Web Site: http://www.oscar.dk
Sales Range: $25-49.9 Million
Emp.: 55
Food Products Mfr
N.A.I.C.S.: 311999
Jens Erik Nissen *(Dir-Exports)*

Subsidiary (Non-US):

Puljonki Oy **(2)**
Vepsanjoentie 10, Juuka, 83900, Finland
Tel.: (358) 207 66 11 66
Web Site: http://www.puljonki.fi
Sales Range: $25-49.9 Million
Emp.: 40
Food Product Mfr & Distr
N.A.I.C.S.: 311999
Kai Iiskola *(Pres)*

Osem Group **(1)**
61 Jabotinsky St, PO Box 1578, 49517, Petah Tiqwa, Israel **(100%)**
Tel.: (972) 39265265
Web Site: http://www.osem.co.il
Sales Range: $1-4.9 Billion
Emp.: 4,800
Food & Beverage Products Mfr & Distr
N.A.I.C.S.: 311999
Dan Propper *(Chm)*

P.T. Nestle Indonesia **(1)**
Arkadia Green Park Tower G 11th Floor Jalan Letjen, T B Simatupang Kav 88 Kebagusan Pasar Minggu, Jakarta Selatan, 12520, Indonesia **(100%)**
Tel.: (62) 215 086 6000
Web Site: https://www.nestle.co.id
Emp.: 3,700
Holding Company; Coffee & Tea Mfr
N.A.I.C.S.: 551112

Subsidiary (Domestic):

P.T. Nestle Beverages Indonesia **(2)**
J1 Let Jend TB Simatupang Kav 88, Bandar Lampung, Jakarta, 12520, Indonesia **(70%)**
Tel.: (62) 2178836000
Web Site: http://www.nestle.indonesia.com
Coffee & Tea Mfr
N.A.I.C.S.: 311920

P.T. Nestle Confectionery Indonesia **(2)**
7 F Wisma Nestle Arkadia Office Park, TB Simatupang Kav 88, Letjen, Jakarta, 12520, Indonesia **(100%)**
Tel.: (62) 2178836000
Rev.: $43,000,000
Emp.: 1,232
Provider of Confectionary Services
N.A.I.C.S.: 311423

Payco Foods Corporation **(1)**
1-1 Calle 3 Lotes 10, Bayamon, PR 00961-4554
Tel.: (787) 269-6615
Web Site: http://www.nestle.com
Dairy Products Distr
N.A.I.C.S.: 424430
Santiao Casas *(Exec Mgr)*

Subsidiary (Domestic):

SWIRL Corporation **(2)**
Los Frailes Ind Park Calle E Lote 5, Guaynabo, PR 00969
Tel.: (787) 731-4551

Sales Range: $25-49.9 Million
Emp.: 14
Coffee Brewing Equipment Distr
N.A.I.C.S.: 423440
Nelson Pena *(Pres)*

Productos Nestle (Nicaragua) S.A.
Costado Oeste Hospital Bertha Calderon, Managua, Nicaragua **(100%)**
Tel.: (505) 22809040
Sales Range: $25-49.9 Million
Emp.: 60
Dehydrated Food Mfr
N.A.I.C.S.: 311423
Chris Johnson *(Reg Dir & Exec VP)*

Purina PetCare (Malaysia) Sdn. Bhd. **(1)**
22-1 22nd Floor Manara Surian 1 Jalan PJU 7-3, Mutiara-Damasara, Petaling Jaya, 47810, Selangor, Malaysia
Tel.: (60) 379656000
Web Site: http://www.purina.com.my
Pet Food Mfr
N.A.I.C.S.: 311111

Saudi Food Industries Ltd. **(1)**
Makkah Road Km 21, PO Box 8261, Jeddah, 21482, Saudi Arabia
Tel.: (966) 25910034
Sales Range: $50-74.9 Million
Emp.: 200
Food Preparations
N.A.I.C.S.: 311423

Scholler Ice-Cream Ltd **(1)**
Postford Mill, Guildford, GU4 8RT, United Kingdom
Tel.: (44) 1483205500
Ice Cream Mfr
N.A.I.C.S.: 311520

Seroyal USA, LLC **(1)**
112 Technology Dr, Pittsburgh, PA 15275
Web Site: https://www.seroyal.com
Pharmaceuticals Product Mfr
N.A.I.C.S.: 325412

Shanghai Totole Food Limited **(1)**
969 Xing Hua Rd 13 Bridge S Cao An Rd, Shanghai, China
Tel.: (86) 21 59139518
Food Product Whslr
N.A.I.C.S.: 424420

Societe Francaise des Eaux Regionales S.A.S. **(1)**
20 Rue Rouget de l Isle, 92130, Issy-les-Moulineaux, France
Tel.: (33) 899963192
Food Product Whslr
N.A.I.C.S.: 424420

Societe Immobiliere de Noisiel S.A. **(1)**
7 Boulevard Pierre Carle, 77186, Noisiel, France
Tel.: (33) 1 60 53 21 00
Dairy Product Whslr
N.A.I.C.S.: 424430

Societe Industrielle de Transformation de Produits Agricoles S.A.S. **(1)**
3 Blvd Eiffel, 21600, Longvic, France
Tel.: (33) 3 29 32 72 04
Emp.: 240
Food Products Mfr
N.A.I.C.S.: 311423
Nathalie Danet *(Mgr)*

Societe des Produits Alimentaires de Caudry S.A.S. **(1)**
Rue de l'Europe, 59540, Caudry, France
Tel.: (33) 3 27 76 54 54
Food Products Distr
N.A.I.C.S.: 424420

Societe pour l'Exportation des Produits Nestle S.A. **(1)**
Agence de Beirut pour le Liban Nestle Building Dbayeh - main Road, Beirut, Lebanon
Tel.: (961) 454 8595
Web Site: https://www.nestle.com
Plant Science & Nutrition Research
N.A.I.C.S.: 445110

Sofinol S.A. **(1)**
Via Cantonale 8, 6928, Manno, Switzerland

Tel.: (41) 916119100
Sales Range: $25-49.9 Million
Emp.: 32
Refined Oil Mfr
N.A.I.C.S.: 311225
Pierre Giannoni *(Mgr-Factory)*

Springs Water Factory Co. Ltd **(1)**
PO Box 35022, 31488, Dammam, Saudi Arabia
Tel.: (966) 3 8121320
Mineral Water Mfr
N.A.I.C.S.: 312112

Suomen Nestle Oy **(1)**
Keilasatama 5, 02151, Espoo, Finland **(100%)**
Tel.: (358) 103 9511
Web Site: https://www.nestle.fi
Emp.: 16
Coffee, Tea & Cocoa Manufacturing
N.A.I.C.S.: 311920

Swaziland Fruit Canners (Pty.) Ltd. **(1)**
PO Box 77, Malkerns, Eswatini
Tel.: (268) 5283001
Plant Science & Nutrition Research
N.A.I.C.S.: 445298

Terra Canis GmbH **(1)**
Friedrichstrasse 1A, 80801, Munich, Germany
Tel.: (49) 8969 334 1500
Web Site: http://www.terracanis.co.uk
Food Mfr
N.A.I.C.S.: 311999

Unilac, Inc. **(1)**
Calle 69 O No 74 Urbanizacion La Loma, Panama, Panama
Tel.: (507) 229 13 33
Food Product Whslr
N.A.I.C.S.: 424420

Xiamen Yinlu Food Group Co., Ltd. **(1)**
3 F Jixiang Garden No 3 Jianye Road, Xiamen, Fujian, China **(60%)**
Tel.: (86) 592 5375555
Web Site: http://www.yinlu.cn
Sales Range: $800-899.9 Million
Food Products Mfr
N.A.I.C.S.: 311422

NESTRO PETROL A.D. BANJA LUKA

Kralja Petra I Karadordevica 83A, 78000, Banja Luka, RS, Bosnia & Herzegovina
Tel.: (387) 51490345
Web Site:
https://www.nestropetrol.com
Year Founded: 1945
PTRL-R-A—(BANJ)
Sales Range: $150-199.9 Million
Emp.: 631
Petrol & Oil Distr
N.A.I.C.S.: 424720
Tkachou Kiryl *(CEO)*

NESTRONICS LTD.

18 Boon Lay Way Ste 07-105 Trade Hub 21, Singapore, 609966, Singapore
Tel.: (65) 63089570
Web Site:
http://www.nestronics.com.sg
Year Founded: 1979
Sales Range: $25-49.9 Million
Emp.: 200
Electronics Manufacturing Services
N.A.I.C.S.: 334419
Joseph Sze Meng Tan *(Mng Dir)*

NET AVENUE TECHNOLOGIES LIMITED

New No 16 Old No 13 1st Floor Prithvi Avenue, Alwarpet Teynampe, Chennai, 600018, India
Tel.: (91) 4442789289
Web Site: https://www.natl.in
Year Founded: 1998

CBAZAAR—(NSE)
Rev.: $4,399,354
Assets: $2,748,792
Liabilities: $2,507,434
Net Worth: $241,358
Earnings: $227,020
Emp.: 85
Fiscal Year-end: 03/31/23
Online Shopping Services
N.A.I.C.S.: 425120

NET HOLDING A.S.

Bade Sokak No 9 Etiler, Besiktas, 34337, Istanbul, Turkiye
Tel.: (90) 2123580444
Web Site:
https://www.netholding.com
Year Founded: 1981
NTHOL—(IST)
Rev.: $104,263,903
Assets: $848,381,214
Liabilities: $313,382,342
Net Worth: $534,998,873
Earnings: $90,756,436
Emp.: 5,360
Fiscal Year-end: 12/31/22
Holding Company
N.A.I.C.S.: 551112
Besim Tibuk *(Chm)*

Subsidiaries:

Ekspres Yatirim Menkul Degerler A.S. **(1)**
19 Mayis Mahallesi 19 Mayis Caddesi No 13 Kat 3, Sisli, 34363, Istanbul, Turkiye
Tel.: (90) 2124127777
Web Site: http://www.ekspresyatirim.com
Financial Services
N.A.I.C.S.: 541611

Inter Turizm ve Seyahat A.S. **(1)**
19 Mayis Caddesi Net Plaza No 13 Kat 2, Sisli, 34360, Istanbul, Turkiye
Tel.: (90) 2129850909
Hotel Management & Real Estate Development Services
N.A.I.C.S.: 531320

Merit International Turistik Isletmeler ve Hizmetler A.S. **(1)**
19 Mayis Caddesi Net Plaza No 13 Kat 2-3, Sisli, 34360, Istanbul, Turkiye
Tel.: (90) 2122897777
Hotel Management & Real Estate Development Services
N.A.I.C.S.: 531320

Merit Turizm Yatirim ve Isletme A.S. **(1)**
Bade Sok No 9, Etiler, 34337, Istanbul, Turkiye
Tel.: (90) 2123580444
Hotel Management & Real Estate Development Services
N.A.I.C.S.: 531320

Net Montenegro D.O.O. **(1)**
Bulevar Dzordza Vasingtona 51, 81000, Podgorica, Montenegro
Tel.: (382) 33421020
Hotel Management & Real Estate Development Services
N.A.I.C.S.: 531320

Net Turistik Yayinlar Sanayi ve Tic. A.S. **(1)**
19 Mayis Cad No 13 Kat 7 Net Plaza, Sisli, Istanbul, Turkiye
Tel.: (90) 2129850999
Web Site: https://www.netyayin.com.tr
Educational Books Publishing Services
N.A.I.C.S.: 513130
Cem Toker *(Chm)*

NET INSIGHT AB

Smidesvagen 7, Box 1200, 171 23, Solna, Sweden
Tel.: (46) 86850400
Web Site: https://www.netinsight.net
Year Founded: 1997
NETI.B—(OMX)
Rev.: $55,529,217
Assets: $83,228,901

NET INSIGHT AB

Net Insight AB—(Continued)
Liabilities: $21,466,337
Net Worth: $61,762,564
Earnings: $5,966,407
Emp.: 146
Fiscal Year-end: 12/31/23
Video, Data & Voice Networking Services
N.A.I.C.S.: 334220
Gunilla Fransson *(Chm)*

Subsidiaries:

Net Insight Pte. Ltd. (1)
81 Ubi Avenue 4 10-15 UB One, Singapore, 408830, Singapore
Tel.: (65) 66362350
Media Production Services
N.A.I.C.S.: 512110

Net Insight, Inc. (1)
770 Paseo Camarillo Ste 320, Camarillo, CA 93010
Tel.: (805) 484-7819
Web Site: https://www.netinsight.net
Video, Data & Voice Networking Services
N.A.I.C.S.: 334220
Don Donnelly *(Head-Sls-Americas)*

NET INSURANCE S.P.A.

Via Giuseppe Antonio Guattani 4, 00161, Rome, Italy
Tel.: (39) 06893261
Web Site: http://www.netinsurance.it
Year Founded: 2000
NET—(ITA)
Rev.: $87,203,792
Assets: $644,466,610
Liabilities: $549,963,597
Net Worth: $94,503,013
Earnings: $8,928,406
Emp.: 123
Fiscal Year-end: 12/31/22
Life Insurance
N.A.I.C.S.: 524113
Andrea Battista *(CEO)*

NET NEW ENERGY TECHNOLOGIES AG

AuhofstraSSe 8 C04, A-1130, Vienna, Austria
Tel.: (43) 676 7735402
Web Site: http://www.newenergytechnology.at
WTE—(VIE)
Sales Range: Less than $1 Million
Industrial Boiler Mfr
N.A.I.C.S.: 332410
Oleksii Parkhomenko *(Member-Mgmt Bd)*

NET ONE ASIA PTE. LTD.

1 Irving Place 07 11 12 The Commerze Irving, Singapore, 369546, Singapore
Tel.: (65) 63925773
Web Site: https://netoneasia.com
Information Technology & Services
N.A.I.C.S.: 561210
Koh Ching Lan *(Mgr-Bus Solution)*

NET PACIFIC FINANCIAL HOLDINGS LIMITED

35 Selegie Road 10-25, Singapore, 188307, Singapore
Tel.: (65) 65423488
Web Site: https://www.netpac.com.sg
5QY—(CAT)
Rev.: $510,017
Assets: $12,985,086
Liabilities: $1,197,721
Net Worth: $11,787,365
Earnings: ($706,266)
Fiscal Year-end: 12/31/23
Investment Services
N.A.I.C.S.: 523999
Chor Wei Ong *(CEO)*

NET PIX SHORTS DIGITAL MEDIA LIMITED

1402 Z A Tower Yari Road, Versova Andheri West, Mumbai, India
Tel.: (91) 8828231678
Web Site: https://www.netpixshorts.com
Year Founded: 2019
543247—(BOM)
Rev.: $69,504
Assets: $837,132
Liabilities: $134,392
Net Worth: $702,740
Earnings: ($4,232)
Fiscal Year-end: 03/31/23
Digital Media Services
N.A.I.C.S.: 541840
Danish Zakaria Aghadi *(Mng Dir)*

NET PROTECTIONS HOLDINGS, INC.

Sumitomo Fudosan Kojimachi First Building 5th Floor 4-2-6 Kojimachi, Chiyoda-ku, Tokyo, 102-0083, Japan
Tel.: (81) 351597881
Web Site: https://corp.netprotections.com
Year Founded: 2018
7383—(TKS)
Rev.: $137,778,840
Assets: $398,444,190
Liabilities: $280,918,390
Net Worth: $117,525,800
Earnings: ($5,473,080)
Emp.: 412
Fiscal Year-end: 03/31/24
Holding Company
N.A.I.C.S.: 551112
Shin Shibata *(Pres)*

NET ZERO INFRASTRUCTURE PLC

1-2 Charterhouse Mews, London, EC1M 6BB, United Kingdom
Tel.: (44) 2081243630 UK
Web Site: https://www.nziplc.com
Year Founded: 2021
NZI—(LSE)
Assets: $692,317
Liabilities: $56,853
Net Worth: $635,464
Earnings: ($811,586)
Emp.: 4
Fiscal Year-end: 03/31/23
Miscellaneous Financial Investment Activities
N.A.I.C.S.: 523999

NET ZERO RENEWABLE ENERGY INC.

6040 Progress Street, Niagara Falls, L2G-0C4, ON, Canada
Tel.: (289) 488-1699 ON
Web Site: http://www.ehthybrid.com
Year Founded: 2010
EHT—(TSXV)
Rev.: $171,530
Assets: $1,750,192
Liabilities: $27,090,808
Net Worth: ($25,340,616)
Earnings: ($4,302,615)
Emp.: 16
Fiscal Year-end: 11/30/20
Energy Solutions
N.A.I.C.S.: 335311
John Gamble *(CEO)*

NET-A-GO TECHNOLOGY COMPANY LIMITED

Suite 1307 Cityplaza Four 12 Taikoo Wan Road, Taikoo Shing, China (Hong Kong)
Tel.: (852) 28112768
Web Site: http://www.u-banquetgroup.com

1483—(HKG)
Rev.: $33,439,553
Assets: $86,949,518
Liabilities: $26,675,423
Net Worth: $60,274,095
Earnings: ($20,393,880)
Emp.: 2,192
Fiscal Year-end: 12/31/22
Wedding Banquet Services
N.A.I.C.S.: 722320
Kangqiao Sang *(Chm)*

Subsidiaries:

Choi Fook Seafood Restaurant Limited (1)
3/F Olympia Plaza 255 Kings Road, North Point, China (Hong Kong)
Tel.: (852) 25668289
Restaurant Operators
N.A.I.C.S.: 722511

NET-LINX AG

Kathe-Kollwitz-Ufer 76, Dresden, 01309, Germany
Tel.: (49) 351318750 De
Web Site: http://www.net-linx.com
Year Founded: 1973
Sales Range: $50-74.9 Million
Emp.: 500
Provider of Advertising Management & Directory Publishing Software Solutions
N.A.I.C.S.: 541511
Holm Hallbauer *(Chm & CEO)*

NET263 LTD.

No 13 Chaoqian Road, Changping, Beijing, 100013, China
Tel.: (86) 1069726414
Web Site: https://www.net263.com
002467—(SSE)
Rev.: $125,709,948
Assets: $371,828,340
Liabilities: $58,748,976
Net Worth: $313,079,364
Earnings: $4,497,012
Emp.: 500
Fiscal Year-end: 12/31/22
Communication Service
N.A.I.C.S.: 517810
Jing Liang *(VP)*

NET4 INDIA LIMITED

139-A-1 S F Mohammadpur, New Delhi, 1100666, India
Tel.: (91) 1126711150 In
Web Site: http://www.net4.com
Year Founded: 1985
IP Communication Solutions & Services
N.A.I.C.S.: 517810

NETAC TECHNOLOGY CO., LTD.

Floor 16 18 19 Langke Building No 10 Gaoxin South 6th Road, South District Gaoxin District Nanshan District, Shenzhen, 518057, Guangdong, China
Tel.: (86) 75526727642
Web Site: https://www.netac.com
Year Founded: 1999
300042—(CHIN)
Rev.: $248,808,456
Assets: $190,227,960
Liabilities: $24,393,096
Net Worth: $165,834,864
Earnings: $8,723,052
Fiscal Year-end: 12/31/22
Computer Storage Device Mfr.
N.A.I.C.S.: 334112
Lu Zhirong *(Chm & Gen Mgr)*

NETANEL GROUP LTD.

50 Anilwitz St Tel Aviv, Holon, 58322, Israel
Tel.: (972) 35059998

INTERNATIONAL PUBLIC

Web Site: https://www.netanel.co.il
NTGR—(TAE)
Rev.: $100,232,075
Assets: $379,144,627
Liabilities: $296,439,283
Net Worth: $82,705,345
Earnings: $35,563,751
Fiscal Year-end: 12/31/23
Other Community Housing Services
N.A.I.C.S.: 624229
Dan Netanel *(CEO)*

NETAS TELEKOMUNIKASYON ANONIM SIRKETI

Yenisehir Mahallesi Osmanli Bulvari No11, Kurtkoy-Pendik, 34912, Istanbul, Turkiye
Tel.: (90) 2165222000
Web Site: https://www.netas.com.tr
Year Founded: 1967
NETAS—(IST)
Rev.: $235,650,482
Assets: $194,117,422
Liabilities: $186,573,291
Net Worth: $7,544,131
Earnings: $3,401,876
Emp.: 1,682
Fiscal Year-end: 12/31/23
Telecommunication Equipment Rental Services
N.A.I.C.S.: 532490
Xiao Ming *(Chm)*

Subsidiaries:

BDH Bilisim Destek Hizmetleri Sanayi ve Ticaret A.S. (1)
Mahallesi Cemal Bey Caddesi No 110, Baglarbasi Maltepe, 34844, Istanbul, Turkiye
Tel.: (90) 2165001700
Web Site: https://www.bdh.com.tr
Emp.: 1,100
Information Technology Services
N.A.I.C.S.: 541511

NETRD Bilgi Teknolojileri ve Telekomunikasyon A.S. (1)
Yenisehir Mah Osmanli Bulvari A Blok No 11A/30, Pendik, Istanbul, Turkiye
Tel.: (90) 216 522 2100
Web Site: https://www.netrd.com.tr
Telecommunication Services
N.A.I.C.S.: 517810

Netas Bilisim Teknolojileri A.S. (1)
Orhanli Mah Irfan Cad No 28, Orhanli-Tuzla, 34956, Istanbul, Turkiye
Tel.: (90) 2163945323
Web Site: https://www.netasbilisim.com.tr
Information Technology Services
N.A.I.C.S.: 541511

NETBAY PUBLIC COMPANY LIMITED

No 719/5 8-9 Rama 6 Road, Wangmai Pathumwan, Bangkok, 10330, Thailand
Tel.: (66) 26201800
Web Site: http://www.netbaythailand.com
Year Founded: 2004
NETBAY—(THA)
Rev.: $14,227,655
Assets: $21,175,721
Liabilities: $6,027,041
Net Worth: $15,148,680
Earnings: $5,263,207
Emp.: 111
Fiscal Year-end: 12/31/23
Software Development Services
N.A.I.C.S.: 541511
Pichit Viwatrujirapong *(Vice Chm)*

NETBISCUITS GMBH

Europaallee 10, 67657, Kaiserslautern, Germany
Tel.: (49) 631 68036 100
Web Site: http://www.netbiscuits.com
Year Founded: 2000

Sales Range: $10-24.9 Million
Emp.: 80
Web Applications
N.A.I.C.S.: 513210

Subsidiaries:

Netbiscuits Pte Ltd (1)
#03-25 The Aquarius 21 Science Park Road, Singapore, 117628, Singapore
Tel.: (65) 6777 8337
Web Applications
N.A.I.C.S.: 513210

Netbiscuits, Inc. (1)
44 W 28th St 8th Fl, New York, NY 10001
Tel.: (646) 794-4375
Web Applications
N.A.I.C.S.: 513210

NETCALL PLC

Bedford Heights Brickhill Drive Suite 203, Bedford, MK41 7PH, Hertfordshire, United Kingdom
Tel.: (44) 3303336100
Web Site: https://www.netcall.com
NET—(AIM)
Rev.: $41,353,436
Assets: $77,361,528
Liabilities: $40,135,561
Net Worth: $37,225,967
Earnings: $3,258,528
Emp.: 252
Fiscal Year-end: 06/30/22
Telephone Call Handling Solutions
N.A.I.C.S.: 513210
Michael Jackson (Chm)

Subsidiaries:

Netcall Technology Limited (1)
Suite 203 Bedford Heights Brickhill Drive, Bedford, MK41 7PH, Cambridgeshire, United Kingdom
Tel.: (44) 1480495300
Telecommunication Servicesb
N.A.I.C.S.: 517810

Q-Max Systems Limited (1)
Netcall House 10 Harding Way, Saint Ives, PE27 3WR, Cambridgeshire, United Kingdom
Tel.: (44) 1480 484110
Web Site: http://www.q-max.co.uk
Workforce Management Software Development Services
N.A.I.C.S.: 541511

NETCARE LIMITED

76 Maude Street Corner West Street, Sandton, 2196, South Africa
Tel.: (27) 113010000
Web Site: http://www.netcare.co.za
Year Founded: 1996
NTC—(JSE)
Rev.: $1,251,544,693
Assets: $1,468,277,020
Liabilities: $885,201,576
Net Worth: $583,075,444
Earnings: $70,554,188
Emp.: 18,568
Fiscal Year-end: 09/30/23
Healtcare Services
N.A.I.C.S.: 622110
Richard H. Friedland (CEO)

Subsidiaries:

Medicross Healthcare Group Pty Ltd (1)
Sunninghill Crescent Office Park Building 2 First floor 3 Eglin Road, Johannesburg, 2191, South Africa (80%)
Tel.: (27) 102056600
Web Site: http://www.medicross.co.za
Healtcare Services
N.A.I.C.S.: 621111

Netcare 911 Pty Ltd (1)
Tel.: (27) 10 209 8911
Web Site: https://www.netcare911.co.za
Pre-Hospital Emergency Services
N.A.I.C.S.: 624230
Brian Armstrong (COO)

Netcare Hospitals Proprietary Limited (1)
No 2 Bunting Road, Auckland Park, Johannesburg, 2193, Gauteng, South Africa
Tel.: (27) 114824321
Web Site: http://www.netcare.co.za
Health Care Srvices
N.A.I.C.S.: 621999

Netcare International UK Limited (1)
2nd Floor Tenterden House 3 Tenterden Street, Hanover Square, London, W1S 1TD, United Kingdom
Tel.: (44) 2071547800
Web Site: http://www.netcareuk.com
Healtcare Services
N.A.I.C.S.: 622110

NETCENTS TECHNOLOGY, INC.

1000-1021 West Hastings Street, Vancouver, V6E0C3, BC, Canada
Tel.: (604) 633-9967
Web Site: http://www.net-cents.com
Rev.: $6,817
Assets: $3,120,427
Liabilities: $4,864,494
Net Worth: ($1,744,067)
Earnings: ($5,100,862)
Fiscal Year-end: 10/31/19
Information Technology Management Services
N.A.I.C.S.: 541512
Mehdi Mehrtash (VP-Product)

NETCOMPANY GROUP AS

Strandgade 3, DK-1401, Copenhagen, Denmark
Tel.: (45) 70131440
Web Site:
https://www.netcompany.com
60N—(NASDAQ)
Rev.: $367,857,103
Assets: $558,801,068
Liabilities: $248,232,821
Net Worth: $310,568,247
Earnings: $58,235,538
Emp.: 2,500
Fiscal Year-end: 12/31/19
Information Technology Consulting Services
N.A.I.C.S.: 541511
Andre Rogaczewski (Founder & CEO)

Subsidiaries:

Intrasoft International SA (1)
2B Rue Nicolas Bove, L-1253, Luxembourg, Luxembourg (100%)
Tel.: (352) 4410122000
Web Site: http://www.intrasoft-intl.com
Sales Range: $75-99.9 Million
Emp.: 140
Computer Equipment & Software Whslr
N.A.I.C.S.: 423430

Subsidiary (Non-US):

Intracom Cyprus Ltd (2)
Limassol Ave 58, Engomi, Nicosia, 2015, Cyprus
Tel.: (357) 22477400
Web Site: http://www.intracom.gr
Telecommunication Servicesb
N.A.I.C.S.: 517810

Intracom IT Services (2)
Jabal Amman 3rd Circle, PO Box 2323 Tla'a El-Ali, 19 Queen Musbah str, Amman, 11953, Jordan (80%)
Tel.: (962) 64622016
Web Site: http://www.intracom.gr
Computer System Design Services
N.A.I.C.S.: 541512

Intracom IT Services Denmark A/S (2)
Bregnerodvej 127, 3460, Birkerod, Denmark
Tel.: (45) 70227712
Web Site: http://www.intracom-it.dk
Sales Range: $350-399.9 Million
Emp.: 25
Information Technology Consulting Services

N.A.I.C.S.: 541512
Albert Menashe (CEO)

Intrasoft International Belgium SA (2)
Tour Bastion Place du Champ de Mars 5/10, 1050, Brussels, Belgium (100%)
Tel.: (32) 22381711
Web Site: http://www.intrasoft-intl.com
Sales Range: $25-49.9 Million
Emp.: 60
Computer System Design Services
N.A.I.C.S.: 541512
Athanassios Kotsis (Chm)

Intrasoft International Bulgaria Ltd. (2)
Ami Bue str 84-86, 1612, Sofia, Bulgaria
Tel.: (359) 29757707
IT Services
N.A.I.C.S.: 541519

Intrasoft International East Africa Ltd. (2)
West End Towers 6th Floor Waiyaki Way, PO Box 1896, 00606, Nairobi, Kenya
Tel.: (254) 20421400
IT Services
N.A.I.C.S.: 541519

Intrasoft International ME FZC (2)
Business Center 4 Office 511B, PO Box 16929, Ras al Khaimah, United Arab Emirates
Tel.: (971) 72075902
IT Services
N.A.I.C.S.: 541519

Intrasoft International Scandinavia A/S (2)
Bregnroedvej 127, 3460, Birkerod, Denmark
Tel.: (45) 70227712
Web Site: http://www.intrasoft-intl.dk
IT Services
N.A.I.C.S.: 541519
Albert Menashe (CEO)

Intrasoft International South Africa (Pty). Ltd. (2)
Building 9 Fairways Office Park 5 Niblick Way PostNet Suite 51, Private Bag X15, Somerset West, Cape Town, 7129, South Africa
Tel.: (27) 210010779
IT Services
N.A.I.C.S.: 541519

Subsidiary (US):

Intrasoft International USA Inc. (2)
800 Boylston St Fl 16, Boston, MA 02199
Tel.: (857) 453-6614
IT Services
N.A.I.C.S.: 541519

Subsidiary (Non-US):

Intrasoft Jordan Ltd. (2)
Yathreb Street Golden Rose Building, PO Box 2323, Dabuq Amman Tla'a El-Ali, 11953, Amman, Jordan
Tel.: (962) 64603333
IT Services
N.A.I.C.S.: 541519

NETDRAGON WEBSOFT HOLDINGS LIMITED

Building 851 58 Hot Spring Branch Road, Fuzhou, 350001, Fujian, China
Tel.: (86) 59187085777 Ky
Web Site: http://www.netdragon.com
Year Founded: 1999
0777—(HKG)
Rev.: $1,104,386,400
Assets: $1,548,752,400
Liabilities: $622,252,800
Net Worth: $926,499,600
Earnings: $107,265,600
Emp.: 5,135
Fiscal Year-end: 12/31/22
Online Game Publisher
N.A.I.C.S.: 513210
Dejian Liu (Chm)

Subsidiaries:

Cherrypicks Limited (1)

17/F - 19/F 10 Knutsford Terrace, Tsimshatsui, Kowloon, China (Hong Kong)
Tel.: (852) 2 127 7788
Web Site: https://www.cherrypicks.com
Software Development Services
N.A.I.C.S.: 513210
Yuki Kwan (Sr Project Mgr)

Edmodo, Inc. (1)
777 Mariners Island Blvd, San Mateo, CA 94401
Tel.: (650) 513-2735
Web Site: http://www.edmodo.com
Professional, Scientific & Technical Services
N.A.I.C.S.: 541990

JumpStart Games, Inc. (1)
500 W 190th St Ste 300, Gardena, CA 90248
Tel.: (310) 533-3400
Web Site: http://www.jumpstart.com
Educational Computer Software Mfr
N.A.I.C.S.: 513210
Jim Czulewicz (Chief Revenue Officer)

Mynd.ai, Inc. (1)
4/F No 29 Building Fangguyuan Section 1 Fangzhuang, Fengtai District, Beijing, 100078, China (74.39%)
Tel.: (86) 1087675611
Web Site: http://www.rybbaby.com
Rev.: $413,564,000
Assets: $404,390,000
Liabilities: $278,832,000
Net Worth: $125,558,000
Earnings: ($37,831,000)
Emp.: 1,365
Fiscal Year-end: 12/31/2023
Educational Support Services
N.A.I.C.S.: 611710
Chimin Cao (Chm)

Subsidiary (Non-US):

Alphabet Playhouse Childcare & Learning Centre Pte Ltd (2)
16 Dublin Road, Singapore, 239805, Singapore
Tel.: (65) 66535618
Web Site:
http://www.alphabetplayhouse.com.sg
Kindergarten Services
N.A.I.C.S.: 624410

Alphabet Playhouse at East Coast Pte Ltd (2)
440A Upper East Coast Road, Singapore, 466497, Singapore
Tel.: (65) 66535618
Kindergarten Services
N.A.I.C.S.: 624410

Global Eduhub Pte. Ltd. (2)
32 Sam Leong Road, Singapore, 207922, Singapore
Tel.: (65) 65505060
Education Services
N.A.I.C.S.: 611710

Mulberry Learning Centre at Tanjong Pagar Pte Ltd (2)
5 Tanjong Pagar Plaza 02-01, Singapore, 081005, Singapore
Tel.: (65) 66538082
Web Site: https://mulberrylearning.com
Kindergarten Services
N.A.I.C.S.: 624410

NASCANS Pte. Ltd. (2)
32 Sam Leong Road, Singapore, 207922, Singapore
Tel.: (65) 66538008
Web Site: http://www.nascans.com
Education Services
N.A.I.C.S.: 611710

NetDragon Websoft (Hong Kong) Limited (1)
Units 2001-05 11 20th Floor Harbour Centre 25 Harbour Road, Wanchai, China (Hong Kong)
Tel.: (852) 28507066
Software Development Services
N.A.I.C.S.: 513210

Promethean World Limited (1)
Promethean House Lower Philips Rd, Whitebirk Industrial Estate, Blackburn, BB1 5TH, Lancashire, United Kingdom
Tel.: (44) 125 429 8598

NETDRAGON WEBSOFT HOLDINGS LIMITED

NetDragon Websoft Holdings Limited—(Continued)

Web Site: http://www.prometheanworld.com
Educational Software & Online Services
N.A.I.C.S.: 513210
Allyson Krause (Head-Legal)

Subsidiary (US):

Promethean Inc. (2)
4550 N Point Pkwy Ste 370, Alpharetta, GA 30022
Web Site: http://www.prometheanworld.com
Educational Support Services
N.A.I.C.S.: 611710

Subsidiary (Domestic):

Promethean Limited (2)
Promethean House Lower Philips Rd, Whitebirk Industrial Estate, Blackburn, BB1 5TH, Lancashire, United Kingdom
Tel.: (44) 1254298598
Web Site: https://www.prometheanworld.com
Educational Guidance Services
N.A.I.C.S.: 611710
Ian Curtis (Exec VP-EMEA & Asia Pacific Markets)

NETEASE, INC.
NetEase Building No 599 Wangshang Road, Binjiang District, Hangzhou, 310052, China
Tel.: (86) 57189853378 Ky
Web Site: https://ir.netease.com
Year Founded: 1997
NTES—(NASDAQ)
Rev.: $14,326,007,837
Assets: $25,742,824,823
Liabilities: $8,024,570,226
Net Worth: $17,718,254,597
Earnings: $4,064,746,206
Emp.: 29,128
Fiscal Year-end: 12/31/23
Online Game Services
N.A.I.C.S.: 541519
Charles Zhaoxuan Yang (CFO)

Subsidiaries:

Beijing NetEase Youdao Computer System Co., Ltd. (1)
No 16 Ke Yun Rd, Tianhe District, Guangzhou, 510665, China
Tel.: (86) 2085106370
Web Site: http://www.163.com
Emp.: 1,000
Internet Service Provider
N.A.I.C.S.: 517810
Sandy Leung (CEO)

Guangzhou Boguan Telecommunication Technology Limited (1)
2/F No 25 Jian Hua Road, Tian He Industry Park, Guangzhou, 510665, China (100%)
Tel.: (86) 2085105163
Internet Technology
N.A.I.C.S.: 513199

Guangzhou NetEase Interactive Entertainment Co., Ltd. (1)
Netease Mansion Building E Guangzhou Information Port No 16, Guangzhou, 510665, China
Tel.: (86) 2085105163
Computer Software Development Services
N.A.I.C.S.: 541511

NetEase Information Technology (Beijing) Co., Ltd. (1)
26/F SP Tower D Tsinghua Science Park Building 8, Haidian District, Beijing, 100084, China (100%)
Tel.: (86) 1082558163
Internet Technology
N.A.I.C.S.: 541511

StormNet Information Technology (Shanghai) Co., Ltd. (1)
Floor 5 ShuYu Buliding No 1028 PanYu Road, Shanghai, 200030, China
Tel.: (86) 2164475675
Computer Software Development Services
N.A.I.C.S.: 541511

Ujia E-commerce Co., Ltd. (1)
No 599 Commercial Rd, Binjiang Dist, Hangzhou, 310052, Zhejiang, China
Tel.: (86) 57189852364
Online Game Software Development Services
N.A.I.C.S.: 541511

Zhejiang Weiyang Technology Co., Ltd. (1)
Rm 402 No 3 Lane 51 Dengyun Rd, Gongshu, Hangzhou, Zhejiang, China
Tel.: (86) 57188182938
Information Technology Consulting Services
N.A.I.C.S.: 541512

NETEL TECHNOLOGY (HOLDINGS) LIMITED
Flat C 9/F Max Share Centre 373 King's Road, North Point, China (Hong Kong)
Tel.: (852) 2907 3777 Ky
Web Site: http://www.neteltech.com.hk
Rev.: $3,717,203
Assets: $3,820,971
Liabilities: $3,517,857
Net Worth: $303,114
Earnings: ($396,261)
Emp.: 35
Fiscal Year-end: 05/31/18
Holding Company
N.A.I.C.S.: 551112
James Ang (Founder & Chm)

Subsidiaries:

Gbjobs.com Ltd. (1)
Flat C/D 9/F Max Share Centre 373 Kings Road, North Point, China (Hong Kong)
Tel.: (852) 36102666
Web Site: http://www.hk.gbjobs.com
Recruitment Services
N.A.I.C.S.: 561311

NETENT AB
Vasagatan 16, SE-111 20, Stockholm, Sweden
Tel.: (46) 8 578 54 500
Web Site: http://www.netent.com
Year Founded: 1996
Rev.: $192,146,701
Assets: $445,548,772
Liabilities: $343,021,591
Net Worth: $102,527,181
Earnings: $45,961,998
Emp.: 862
Fiscal Year-end: 12/31/19
Online Gaming Software Development Services
N.A.I.C.S.: 541511
Therese Hillman (CEO)

Subsidiaries:

Net Entertainment Malta Ltd. (1)
The Marina Business Centre Abate Rigord Street, Ta' Xbiex, XBX 1120, Malta
Tel.: (356) 21 31 16 21
Online Gaming Software Development Services
N.A.I.C.S.: 541511
Bjorn Krantz (Mng Dir)

NETEX KNOWLEDGE FACTORY SA
Icaro 44 Oleiros, 15172, A Coruna, Spain
Tel.: (34) 981634067
Web Site: https://www.netexlearning.com
NTX—(MAD)
Sales Range: Less than $1 Million
Information Technology Services
N.A.I.C.S.: 541511
Carlos Ezquerro (CEO)

NETFONDS AG
Tel.: (49) 408222670
Web Site: https://www.netfonds.de
Year Founded: 2000
NF4—(DEU)
Emp.: 453
Banking Financial Services
N.A.I.C.S.: 523150
Ingo Middelmenne (Head-IR)

NETGEM SA
103 Rue de Grenelle CS 10841, FR-75345, Paris, Cedex 07, France
Tel.: (33) 155625562
Web Site: https://www.netgem.com
Year Founded: 1996
NTG—(EUR)
Sales Range: $25-49.9 Million
Communication Software, Hardware & Equipment Mfr
N.A.I.C.S.: 334290
Joseph Haddad (Founder, Chm & CEO)

Subsidiaries:

Netgem Tv Ltd. (1)
Kingsway House 103 Kingsway, London, WC2B 6QX, United Kingdom
Tel.: (44) 207 242 0163
Web Site: https://www.netgem.co.uk
Digital TV Music & Video Streaming Services
N.A.I.C.S.: 512110
Balaji Dhumal (Head-Ops)

Video Futur Entertainment Group SA (1)
27 rue d'Orleans, 92200, Neuilly-sur-Seine, France
Tel.: (33) 155625562
Web Site: http://www.videofutur.fr
Sales Range: $10-24.9 Million
Emp.: 125
Internet-Based DVD Rental & Video on Demand Services
N.A.I.C.S.: 512120

NETINFO, INC.
23 Aglantzias Ave, 2108, Nicosia, Cyprus
Tel.: (357) 22753636
Web Site: https://www.netinfo.eu
Year Founded: 2000
Mobile Financial Services
N.A.I.C.S.: 522320
Vassos Aristodemou (Pres & CEO)

NETJOY HOLDINGS LIMITED
5/F Building 3 396 Guilin Road, Xuhui, Shanghai, 200233, China
Tel.: (86) 2154722297 Ky
Web Site: http://www.netjoy.com
Year Founded: 2012
2131—(HKG)
Holding Company
N.A.I.C.S.: 551112
Jiaqing Xu (Pres)

NETLINK COMPUTER INC.
13720 Mayfield Place, Richmond, V6V 2E4, BC, Canada
Tel.: (604) 288-8080
Web Site: http://www.ncix.com
Year Founded: 1996
Rev.: $10,201,541
Emp.: 250
Computer Dealers
N.A.I.C.S.: 449210
Steve Wu (Pres)

NETLINK NBN TRUST
750E Chai Chee Road 07-03 ESR BizPark Chai Chee, Singapore, 469005, Singapore
Tel.: (65) 67182828 SG
Web Site: https://www.netlinknbn.com
Year Founded: 2017
CJLU—(SES)
Rev.: $299,165,590
Assets: $2,975,476,370
Liabilities: $1,023,973,684
Net Worth: $1,951,502,687
Earnings: $81,011,100

INTERNATIONAL PUBLIC

Emp.: 338
Fiscal Year-end: 03/31/23
Internet Service Provider
N.A.I.C.S.: 517810
Yew Heng Tong (CEO)

NETLINK SOLUTIONS (INDIA) LIMITED
507 Laxmi Plaza Laxmi Industrial Estate New Link Road, Andheri - West, Mumbai, 400 053, Maharashtra, India
Tel.: (91) 2226335583
Web Site: https://www.nsil.co.in
Year Founded: 1984
509040—(BOM)
Rev.: $861,975
Assets: $2,092,692
Liabilities: $198,202
Net Worth: $1,894,491
Earnings: $572,472
Emp.: 4
Fiscal Year-end: 03/31/23
Software Development Services
N.A.I.C.S.: 541511
Rupa M. Modi (CFO)

Subsidiaries:

Aditya Infotech (1)
507 Laxmi Plaza Laxmi Industrial Estate New Link Road, Andheri West, Mumbai, 400 053, India
Tel.: (91) 222 633 5583
Web Site: https://www.adityainfotech.com
Information Technology Services
N.A.I.C.S.: 541519

NETLINKZ LIMITED
65 Stanley Street, Darlinghurst, 2010, NSW, Australia
Tel.: (61) 293299700 AU
Web Site: https://www.netlinkz.com
NET—(ASX)
Rev.: $12,257,569
Assets: $14,007,577
Liabilities: $1,893,586
Net Worth: $12,113,991
Earnings: ($6,440,464)
Emp.: 180
Fiscal Year-end: 06/30/22
Software Development Services
N.A.I.C.S.: 541511
James Tsiolis (CEO & Mng Dir)

NETMARBLE CORP.
Netmarble Building 38 Digital-ro26-gil, Guro-gu, Seoul, 08393, Korea (South)
Tel.: (82) 222717114
Web Site: https://netmarble.com
Year Founded: 2000
251270—(KRS)
Rev.: $2,050,504,148
Assets: $6,853,585,040
Liabilities: $2,541,657,955
Net Worth: $4,311,927,085
Earnings: ($679,836,249)
Emp.: 856
Fiscal Year-end: 12/31/22
Mobile Game Design & Development Services
N.A.I.C.S.: 541512
Young-Sik Kwon (CEO)

Subsidiaries:

Jam City, Inc. (1)
3525 Eastham Dr, Culver City, CA 90232
Tel.: (310) 205-4800
Web Site: https://www.jamcity.com
Online Game Development & Support
N.A.I.C.S.: 541519
Chris DeWolfe (CEO)

Subsidiary (Non-US):

Ludia Inc. (2)
410 St-Nicolas St Ste 400, Montreal, H2Y 2P5, QC, Canada
Tel.: (514) 313-3370
Web Site: http://www.ludia.com

Online Game Development Services
N.A.I.C.S.: 541511
Alexa Thabet *(Co-Founder & CEO)*

Subsidiary (Domestic):

TinyCo, Inc.   (2)
225 Bush St Ste 1900, San Francisco, CA 94104
Tel.: (251) 332-2536
Web Site: http://www.tinyco.com
Computer Related Services
N.A.I.C.S.: 541519
Brian DeGraf *(Mgr-Content)*

Netmarble (Thailand) Co., Ltd.   (1)
G Tower Grand Rama 9 15th Floor Rama 9 Rd, Huai Khwang Subdistrict Huai Khwang District, Bangkok, 10310, Thailand
Tel.: (66) 21698205
Web Site: https://www.netmarble.in.th
Mobile Software Development Services
N.A.I.C.S.: 541511

NETMEDIA S.A.
15 Woronicza Str, 02-625, Warsaw, Poland
Tel.: (48) 22 492 08 01
Web Site: http://www.netmedia.com.pl
Tourism & Information Technology Services
N.A.I.C.S.: 519290
Andrzej Wierzba *(Pres)*

NETMORE GROUP AB
Halsingegatan 49, 113 31, Stockholm, Sweden
Tel.: (46) 731721000
Web Site: http://www.netmoregroup.com
NETM.B—(OMX)
Rev.: $3,917,547
Assets: $11,795,370
Liabilities: $8,327,077
Net Worth: $3,468,293
Earnings: ($7,327,242)
Emp.: 32
Fiscal Year-end: 12/31/20
Wireless Telecommunication Services
N.A.I.C.S.: 517112
Erik Hallberg *(CEO)*

NETO M.E HOLDINGS LTD.
5 Meir Ezra St, PO Box 655, Kiryat Malachi, 75864, Israel
Tel.: (972) 88608585
Web Site: https://www.neto.org.il
Year Founded: 1940
NTO—(TAE)
Rev.: $1,208,891,541
Assets: $531,994,190
Liabilities: $271,656,302
Net Worth: $260,337,888
Earnings: $25,004,835
Fiscal Year-end: 12/31/23
Food Products Mfr & Distr
N.A.I.C.S.: 311999

NETO MALINDA TRADING LTD.
5 Meir Ezra Street, PO Box 655, Kiryat Malachi, 75864, Israel
Tel.: (972) 88608585
Web Site: http://www.neto.org.il
NTML—(TAE)
Rev.: $1,204,979,674
Assets: $529,758,522
Liabilities: $174,235,665
Net Worth: $355,522,857
Earnings: $25,033,844
Fiscal Year-end: 12/31/23
Fish & Seafood Merchant Wholesalers
N.A.I.C.S.: 424160
Oren Avni *(CEO)*

NETOP SOLUTIONS A/S
Bregnerodvej 127, 3460, Birkerod, Denmark
Tel.: (45) 45902525
Web Site: http://www.netop.com
Year Founded: 1981
Sales Range: $10-24.9 Million
Emp.: 151
Software Development & Sales
N.A.I.C.S.: 513210
Kent F. Madsen *(CEO)*

NETPAY INTERNATIONAL, INC.
2 Hamanofim St, Herzliya, 4672562, Pituach, Israel
Tel.: (972) 36126966
Web Site: https://www.netpay-intl.com
Year Founded: 2016
NTPY—(OTCEM)
Rev.: $3,608
Assets: $649,545
Liabilities: $903,536
Net Worth: ($253,991)
Earnings: ($225,367)
Emp.: 1
Fiscal Year-end: 03/31/20
Cosmetic Product Mfr & Distr
N.A.I.C.S.: 325620
Alon Elbaz *(Chm, Pres, CEO, CFO & Chief Acctg Officer)*

NETPOSA TECHNOLOGIES LIMITED
26F BLK C Wangjing SOHO Tower 2 1 Futong AVE, Chaoyang District, 100102, Beijing, China
Tel.: (86) 1082325566
Web Site: http://www.netposa.com
300367—(SSE)
Rev.: $42,347,244
Assets: $464,180,337
Liabilities: $433,032,744
Net Worth: $31,147,593
Earnings: ($82,143,542)
Emp.: 1,000
Fiscal Year-end: 12/31/20
Video Surveillance Management Platforms
N.A.I.C.S.: 334310

NETPROFILE FINLAND OY
Kasarmikatu 44, 00130, Helsinki, Finland
Tel.: (358) 9 6812 080
Web Site: http://www.netprofile.fi
Sales Range: $10-24.9 Million
Emp.: 12
N.A.I.C.S.: 541820
Christina Forsgard *(Partner & Sr Consultant)*

NETRAMARK HOLDINGS INC.
Suite 101 1655 Dupont Street, Toronto, M6P 3S9, ON, Canada
Tel.: (647) 223-7165
Web Site: https://www.netramark.com
Year Founded: 2016
AINMF—(OTCQB)
Rev.: $84,321
Assets: $6,861,528
Liabilities: $811,036
Net Worth: $6,050,493
Earnings: ($10,031,969)
Emp.: 8
Fiscal Year-end: 09/30/22
Holding Company
N.A.I.C.S.: 551112
George Achilleos *(CEO)*

NETRICOM INC.
575 boulevard Morgan Baie d'Urfe, Montreal, H9X 3T6, QC, Canada
Tel.: (514) 457-4488
Web Site: http://www.netricom.com
Telecommunication Servicesb
N.A.I.C.S.: 517810
Steve Rouleau *(Sr VP-Sls & Mktg)*

NETRIPPLES SOFTWARE LIMITED
Goodlife Retreat 1-2-36/2 Street No 4Kakatiya Nagar, Hyderabad, 500007, Telangana, India
Tel.: (91) 9666999800
Web Site: https://www.netripples.com
Year Founded: 1993
542117—(BOM)
Software Development Services
N.A.I.C.S.: 541511
Mazhar Pasha *(Founder, Pres & Mng Dir)*

NETSCIENTIFIC PLC
Anglo House Bell Lane Office Village Bell Lane, Buckinghamshire, Amersham, HP6 6FA, United Kingdom
Tel.: (44) 2035141800
Web Site: http://www.netscientific.net
NSCI—(AIM)
Rev.: $1,267,357
Assets: $36,547,589
Liabilities: $4,684,423
Net Worth: $31,863,166
Earnings: $4,637,718)
Emp.: 26
Fiscal Year-end: 12/31/22
Investment Holding Company; Healthcare Medical Technology & Pharmaceutical Mfr
N.A.I.C.S.: 523999
Ilian Iliev *(CEO)*

Subsidiaries:

Advanced Biosensors, Inc.   (1)
6849 Bellflower Ct, Mentor, OH 44060
Tel.: (888) 794-1468
Healtcare Services
N.A.I.C.S.: 621999

EMV Capital Limited   (1)
20 St Andrew Street, London, EC4A 3AG, United Kingdom
Tel.: (44) 2037616138
Web Site: https://emvcapital.com
Venture Capital Investment Services
N.A.I.C.S.: 523910

Glycotest, Inc.   (1)
613 Schiller Ave, Merion Station, PA 19066
Tel.: (484) 431-3483
Web Site: https://www.glycotest.com
Food Testing Services
N.A.I.C.S.: 541380
Lawrence Cohen *(CEO)*

ProAxsis Ltd.   (1)
Unit 1B Concourse Building 3 Catalyst Inc Queens Road Titanic Quarter, Belfast, BT3 9DT, United Kingdom
Tel.: (44) 289 073 0444
Web Site: https://proaxsis.com
Medical Center Services
N.A.I.C.S.: 622110
David Ribeiro *(CEO)*

NETSTARS CO., LTD.
3F Sumitomo Fudosan Hatchobori Building 3-3-5 Hatchobori, Chuo-ku, Tokyo, 104-0032, Japan
Tel.: (81) 362603788
Web Site: https://netstars.co.jp
Year Founded: 2009
5590—(TKS)
Rev.: $26,374,800
Assets: $201,036,950
Liabilities: $150,931,920
Net Worth: $50,105,030
Earnings: ($2,460,230)
Fiscal Year-end: 12/31/23
Internet Provider Services
N.A.I.C.S.: 517410
Chuck Chen *(CTO)*

NETSURIT (PTY) LTD
No 21 Fourteenth Street Marlboro North, Sandton, South Africa
Tel.: (27) 11 555 7000
Web Site: http://www.netsurit.com
Year Founded: 1995
Information Technology & Services
N.A.I.C.S.: 541511
Orrin Klopper *(CEO)*

Subsidiaries:

Cyber City, Inc.   (1)
224 W 30th St, New York, NY 10001
Tel.: (212) 633-0649
Web Site: http://www.cybercity.nyc
Computer Related Services
N.A.I.C.S.: 541519
Dean Lentz *(CEO & Partner)*

Netsurit Inc.   (1)
224 W 30th St Ste 1008, New York, NY 10001
Tel.: (844) 638-3683
Web Site: https://netsurit.com
IT Consulting Services
N.A.I.C.S.: 541690

Subsidiary (Domestic):

Iteam Consulting, LLC   (2)
6100 Indian School Rd NE Ste 100, Albuquerque, NM 87110
Tel.: (505) 796-5656
Web Site: http://www.iteamnm.com
Computer Related Services
N.A.I.C.S.: 541519
Peggy Benson *(Partner)*

Real Time Consultants, Inc.   (1)
777 Corporate Dr, Mahwah, NJ 07430
Tel.: (201) 512-1777
Web Site: http://www.rtcnj.com
Sales Range: $1-9.9 Million
Emp.: 30
Information Technology & Services
N.A.I.C.S.: 541511
James Bohlin *(Principal)*

Vital I/O, Inc.   (1)
4 Industrial Pkwy, Brunswick, ME 04011
Tel.: (207) 319-1100
Web Site: http://www.vital-io.com
Computer Software Development & Applications
N.A.I.C.S.: 541511
Tara Carpenter *(Principal)*

NETSURVEY BOLINDER AB
Humlegardsgatan 14 3rd Floor, 11446, Stockholm, Sweden
Tel.: (46) 86929100
Web Site: http://www.netsurvey.se
Sales Range: $1-9.9 Million
Emp.: 26
Internet Survey Services
N.A.I.C.S.: 561499
Peter Bolinder *(Founder & Mng Dir)*

NETSWEEPER INC.
Suite 4 156 Columbia Street W, Waterloo, N2L 3L3, ON, Canada
Tel.: (519) 772-0889
Web Site: http://www.netsweeper.com
Year Founded: 1999
Internet Content Filtering & Web Threat Management Services
N.A.I.C.S.: 513210
Perry Roach *(Founder)*

Subsidiaries:

Deep Nines Inc.   (1)
14643 Dallas Pkwy, Dallas, TX 75254
Tel.: (214) 273-6996
Web Site: http://www.deepnines.com
Rev.: $17,000,000
Emp.: 39
Computer Software Development
N.A.I.C.S.: 541511

Netsweeper India   (1)
5-12-2 Arihant Majestic Towers J N Road, Koyambedu, Chennai, 600 107, India
Tel.: (91) 44 420 421 76
Information Technology Consulting Services
N.A.I.C.S.: 541512

Netsweeper Limited   (1)
4A Canberra House, London House, Saint

NETSWEEPER INC.

Netsweeper Inc.—(Continued)
Albans, AL1 1LE, Hertfordshire, United Kingdom
Tel.: (44) 1442 800 172
Information Technology Consulting Services
N.A.I.C.S.: 541512

Netsweeper MEA (1)
F110-02 HQ Building, PO Box 341102, Dubai Silicon Oasis, Dubai, United Arab Emirates
Tel.: (971) 5 55368 565
Information Technology Consulting Services
N.A.I.C.S.: 541512

NETTER GMBH
Fritz-Ullmann-Strasse 9, 55252, Mainz-Kastel, Germany
Tel.: (49) 613429010
Web Site: http://www.nettervibration.com
Year Founded: 1953
Rev.: $16,692,213
Emp.: 70
Industrial Vibrator Supply Services
N.A.I.C.S.: 423840
Achim Werkmann *(Mng Dir)*

Subsidiaries:

NetterVibration Espana S.L. (1)
Errota Kalea 8, Villabona, 20150, Guipuzcoa, Spain
Tel.: (34) 943694994
Web Site: http://www.NetterVibration.es
Industrial Supplies Whslr
N.A.I.C.S.: 423840
Javier Vazquez *(Area Mgr-Sls)*

NetterVibration Polska Sp. z o.o. (1)
AL W Korfantego 195/17, 40-153, Katowice, Poland
Tel.: (48) 322050947
Web Site: http://www.nv-polska.pl
Industrial Supplies Whslr
N.A.I.C.S.: 423840
Grzegorz Bozek *(Area Mgr-Sls)*

NETTLINX LIMITED
5922 My Home Sarovar Plaza 3rd Floor Secretariat Road, Saifabad, Hyderabad, 500 063, Telangana, India
Tel.: (91) 4023232200
Web Site: https://www.nettlinx.com
511658—(BOM)
Rev.: $4,739,602
Assets: $8,919,735
Liabilities: $2,833,470
Net Worth: $6,086,265
Earnings: $350,096
Emp.: 41
Fiscal Year-end: 03/31/22
Web Hosting Services
N.A.I.C.S.: 518210
Manohar Loka Reddy *(Chm)*

Subsidiaries:

Nettlinx Reality Pvt Limited (1)
5-9-22 3rd Floor My Home Sarovar Plaza Secretariat Road, Saifabad, Hyderabad, 500 063, Andhra Pradesh, India
Tel.: (91) 4023232200
Web Site: https://www.nettlinx.com
Sales Range: $25-49.9 Million
Emp.: 50
Web Hosting Services
N.A.I.C.S.: 518210
Jagdish Shamkumar *(Mgr-IT)*

Nettlinx, Inc. (1)
1400 Kennedy Blvd, Union City, NJ 07087
Tel.: (201) 330-9394
Web Site: https://www.nettlinxinc.com
Sales Range: $25-49.9 Million
Software Development & Business Process Outsourcing Services
N.A.I.C.S.: 561499

NETUM GROUP PLC
Yliopistonkatu 58 B, 33100, Tampere, Finland
Tel.: (358) 415295555
Web Site: https://www.netum.fi
Year Founded: 2000
NETUM—(HEL)
Rev.: $40,005,474
Assets: $35,490,686
Liabilities: $21,680,804
Net Worth: $13,809,882
Earnings: ($1,160,037)
Emp.: 393
Fiscal Year-end: 12/31/23
Information Technology Services
N.A.I.C.S.: 541512
Mari Ala-Sorvari *(CFO)*

Subsidiaries:

Buutti Oy (1)
Teknologiantie 2B6, 90590, Oulu, Finland
Tel.: (358) 4578730664
Web Site: https://buutticonsulting.com
Emp.: 110
Information Technology & Software Development Services
N.A.I.C.S.: 541511

NETUREN CO., LTD.
Oval Court Ohsaki Mark West 2-17-1 Higashi-Gotanda, Shinagawa-ku, Tokyo, 141-8639, Japan
Tel.: (81) 334435441
Web Site: https://www.k-neturen.co.jp
Year Founded: 1946
5976—(TKS)
Rev.: $378,125,050
Assets: $532,851,930
Liabilities: $93,478,620
Net Worth: $439,373,310
Earnings: $10,192,620
Emp.: 1,627
Fiscal Year-end: 03/31/24
Heating System Mfr
N.A.I.C.S.: 333414
Shigeru Mizoguchi *(Pres)*

Subsidiaries:

ASAHI-DENPA CO., LTD. (1)
1-3-5 Maesawa, Higashikurume, 203-0032, Tokyo, Japan
Tel.: (81) 424713675
Web Site: https://www.asahidenpa.co.jp
Sales Range: $25-49.9 Million
Emp.: 20
Induction Heating Equipment Mfr
N.A.I.C.S.: 333414
Hirotaka Ono *(Pres)*

KYUSHU KOUSHUHA NETUREN CO.LTD. (1)
12-25 Kitaminato-cho, Wakamatsu-ku, Kitakyushu, 808-0027, Fukuoka, Japan
Tel.: (81) 937613531
Web Site: https://www.kyu-neturen.co.jp
Sales Range: $25-49.9 Million
Emp.: 30
Heating Equipment Mfr
N.A.I.C.S.: 333414

Komatsu Undercarriage China Corporation (1)
No 9 Qunying Rd Jining High Newly Area, Jining, 272073, Shandong, China
Tel.: (86) 5372717116
Sales Range: $25-49.9 Million
Emp.: 51
Construction Equipments Crawler Components Mfr
N.A.I.C.S.: 333120

Korea Heat Treatment Co., Ltd. (1)
26 Hodong-ro 58beon-gil, Nam-gu, Pohang, Gyeongsangbuk-do, Korea (South)
Tel.: (82) 542789111
Heating Equipment Mfr
N.A.I.C.S.: 333414

Korea Neturen Co., Ltd. (1)
Tel.: (82) 543339991
Web Site: http://www.korneturen.co.kr
Induction Heating Equipment Mfr
N.A.I.C.S.: 333994

NETUREN HEAT TREAT CO. LTD. (1)
Oval Ct Ohsaki Mark W 2-17-1 Higashi-gotanda, Shinagawa-ku, Tokyo, 141-8639, Japan
Tel.: (81) 334435441
Sales Range: $25-49.9 Million
Emp.: 50
Heating Equipment Mfr
N.A.I.C.S.: 333414

NETUREN HIRAKATA CO., LTD. (1)
2-26-35 Kasuga Nishimachi, Hirakata, 573-0136, Osaka, Japan
Tel.: (81) 728584701
Web Site: https://www.netuhira.co.jp
Emp.: 28
Heating Equipment Mfr
N.A.I.C.S.: 333414
Takatsugu Kawakami *(Pres)*

NETUREN HYMEC CO., LTD. (1)
3060-3 Okami, Hiratsuka, 254-0012, Kanagawa, Japan
Tel.: (81) 463544204
Web Site: http://www.n-hymec.co.jp
Sales Range: $25-49.9 Million
Test Equipment Mfr
N.A.I.C.S.: 334515

NETUREN KAKOGAWA CO., LTD. (1)
745 Nakakawakami, Kakogawa, 675-1216, Hyogo, Japan
Tel.: (81) 794380496
Web Site: https://www.n-kakogawa.co.jp
Emp.: 18
Heating Equipment Mfr
N.A.I.C.S.: 333414

NETUREN KOMATSU CO., LTD (1)
1-37-3 Kogyodanchi, Komatsu, 923-0994, Ishikawa, Japan
Tel.: (81) 761232466
Heating Equipment Mfr
N.A.I.C.S.: 333414

NETUREN MEINAN CO., LTD. (1)
2-17-1 Higashi-Gotanda Oval Court Ohsaki Mark West, Shinagawa-ku, Tokyo, 141-0022, Japan
Tel.: (81) 334435443
Sales Range: $25-49.9 Million
Emp.: 80
Heating Equipment Mfr
N.A.I.C.S.: 333414
Shigeru Mizoguchi *(Pres)*

NETUREN RYUGASAKI CO., LTD. (1)
120-1 Sumizaki, Inashiki, 300-1416, Ibaraki, Japan
Tel.: (81) 297872225
Web Site: http://www.k-neturen.co.jp
Heating Equipment Mfr
N.A.I.C.S.: 333414

NETUREN TAKUTO CO., LTD. (1)
883 Iida-cho, Minami-ku, Hamamatsu, 435-0028, Shizuoka, Japan
Tel.: (81) 534622045
Web Site: http://www.n-takuto.co.jp
Sales Range: $25-49.9 Million
Emp.: 14
Induction Heating Equipment Mfr
N.A.I.C.S.: 333414

Neturen America Corporation (1)
2995 Moser Ct, Hamilton, OH 45011
Tel.: (513) 863-1900
Induction Heating Equipment Mfr
N.A.I.C.S.: 333994

Neturen Co. Ltd. - Induction Heating Division (1)
7-4-10 Tamura, Hiratsuka, 254-0013, Kanagawa, Japan
Tel.: (81) 463551552
Web Site: http://www.k-neturen.co.jp
Sales Range: $200-249.9 Million
Emp.: 700
Induction Heating Equipment Mfr
N.A.I.C.S.: 333414

Plant (Domestic):

Neturen Co. Ltd. - Amagasaki Plant (2)
2-28-8 Ohama-cho, Amagasaki, 660-0095, Hyogo, Japan
Tel.: (81) 664122211
Sales Range: $25-49.9 Million
Emp.: 50
Induction Heating Equipment Mfr
N.A.I.C.S.: 333414

Neturen Co. Ltd. - Hiratsuka Plant (2)
7-4-10 Tamura, Hiratsuka, 254-0013, Kanagawa, Japan
Tel.: (81) 463551553
Web Site: http://www.k-neturen.co.jp
Sales Range: $25-49.9 Million
Emp.: 120
Induction Heating Equipment Mfr
N.A.I.C.S.: 333414

Neturen Co. Ltd. - Kani Plant (2)
3-2 Himegaoka, Kani, 509-0249, Gifu, Japan
Tel.: (81) 574606822
Web Site: http://www.k-neturen.co.jp
Induction Heating Equipment Mfr
N.A.I.C.S.: 333414

Neturen Co. Ltd. - Kariya Plant (2)
84-10 Jiuda Nishizakai-cho, Kariya, 448-0006, Aichi, Japan
Tel.: (81) 566364621
Web Site: http://www.k-neturen.co.jp
Sales Range: $150-199.9 Million
Induction Heating Equipment Mfr
N.A.I.C.S.: 333414
Shigeru Mizoguchi *(Pres)*

Neturen Co. Ltd. - Kobe Plant (2)
2-4-2 Akamatsudai, Kita-ku, Kobe, 651-1516, Hyogo, Japan
Tel.: (81) 789833374
Web Site: http://www.k-neturen.co.jp
Induction Heating Equipment Mfr
N.A.I.C.S.: 333414

Neturen Co. Ltd. - Nagoya Plant (2)
97-2 Hiromi Nishizakai-cho, Kariya, 448-0006, Aichi, Japan
Tel.: (81) 566 26 1415
Web Site: http://www.k-neturen.co.jp
Sales Range: $150-199.9 Million
Emp.: 170
Induction Heating Equipment Mfr
N.A.I.C.S.: 333414

Neturen Co. Ltd. - Samukawa Plant (2)
7-8-41 Ichinomiya Samukawa-cho, Koza, 253-0111, Kanagawa, Japan
Tel.: (81) 467742525
Web Site: http://www.k-neturen.co.jp
Sales Range: $25-49.9 Million
Emp.: 27
Induction Heating Equipment Mfr
N.A.I.C.S.: 333414

Neturen Co. Ltd. - Specialty Steel & Wire Products Division (1)
Oval Court Ohsaki Mark West 2-17-1 Higashi-Gotanda, Shinagawa-ku, Tokyo, 141-8639, Japan
Tel.: (81) 3 3443 5444
Web Site: http://www.k-neturen.co.jp
Sales Range: $125-149.9 Million
Emp.: 300
Spring Steel Wire Mfr
N.A.I.C.S.: 332613

Plant (Domestic):

Neturen Co. Ltd. - Ako Plant (2)
1586-1 Shimogawara Higashiune, Ako, 678-1185, Hyogo, Japan
Tel.: (81) 791493221
Web Site: http://www.k-neturen.co.jp
Emp.: 130
Steel Pole Mfr
N.A.I.C.S.: 331222

Neturen Co. Ltd. - Hiratsuka Plant (2)
7-4-10 Tamura, Hiratsuka, 254-0013, Kanagawa, Japan
Tel.: (81) 463551238
Web Site: http://www.k-neturen.co.jp
Sales Range: $25-49.9 Million
Emp.: 30
Spring Steel Wire Mfr
N.A.I.C.S.: 331110

Neturen Co. Ltd. - Iwaki Plant (2)
24-1 Yoshimakogyodanchi, Iwaki, 970-1144, Fukushima, Japan
Tel.: (81) 246367770
Spring Steel Wire Mfr
N.A.I.C.S.: 331110

AND PRIVATE COMPANIES

Neturen USA, Inc. (1)
15335 Endeavor Dr Ste 105, Noblesville, IN 46060
Tel.: (317) 674-8371
Web Site: http://www.k-neturen.co.jp
Sales Range: $25-49.9 Million
Emp.: 2
Heating Equipments Mfr
N.A.I.C.S.: 333994

R F ENERGY CO., LTD. (1)
2-19-8 Tsumadanishi, Atsugi, 243-0815, Kanagawa, Japan
Tel.: (81) 462234401
Heating Equipment Mfr
N.A.I.C.S.: 333414

Yancheng Neturen Co., Ltd. (1)
158 Zhangjian Road, Economic Development Zone, Dafeng, 224100, Jiangsu, China
Tel.: (86) 51583857905
Web Site: http://www.neturen.com.cn
Metal Hardening Services & Maintenance
N.A.I.C.S.: 332811

NETVISTA VENTURES LTD.
26 Diamond Plaza Ground Floor Poddar Road, Malad East, Mumbai, 400 097, Maharashtra, India
Tel.: (91) 22 25800009
Sales Range: Less than $1 Million
Information Technology Services
N.A.I.C.S.: 541512

NETWEALTH GROUP LIMITED
Tel.: (61) 396551300 AU
Web Site:
  http://www.netwealth.com.au
Year Founded: 1999
NWL—(ASX)
Rev.: $132,784,558
Assets: $104,358,143
Liabilities: $24,488,199
Net Worth: $79,869,944
Earnings: $42,563,387
Emp.: 500
Fiscal Year-end: 06/30/22
Financial Services
N.A.I.C.S.: 541611
Jodie Henson (Chief Legal Officer, Chief Risk Officer & Sec)

Subsidiaries:

Netwealth Investment Limited (1)
Level 6/180 Flinders Street, Melbourne, 3000, VIC, Australia
Tel.: (61) 396551300
Web Site: https://www.netwealth.com.au
Financial Services
N.A.I.C.S.: 523999
Grant Boyle (CFO)

NETWEB TECHNOLOGIES INDIA LIMITED
Plot No-H1 Pocket- 9 Faridabad Industrial Town FIT Sector- 57, Faridabad, Ballabgarh, 121004, Haryana, India
Tel.: (91) 1292310400
Web Site:
  https://www.netwebindia.com
Year Founded: 1999
NETWEB—(NSE)
Rev.: $54,012,780
Assets: $32,233,140
Liabilities: $20,880,821
Net Worth: $11,352,319
Earnings: $5,688,643
Emp.: 250
Fiscal Year-end: 03/31/23
Information Technology Services
N.A.I.C.S.: 541512
Hemant Agarwal (COO)

NETWEEK S.P.A.
Via Campi 29/L Merate LC, 20122, Merate, Italy
Tel.: (39) 03999891
NTW—(ITA)
Sales Range: $75-99.9 Million
Emp.: 272
Media Commerce Services
N.A.I.C.S.: 518210
Mauro Albani (Exec Mgr-Corp Acctg Documents)

Subsidiaries:

DMedia Commerce Spa (1)
Via Aretina 25, 50069, Pontassieve, Florence, Italy
Tel.: (39) 0558363040
Web Site: http://www.dmail.it
Online Business & Trading Services
N.A.I.C.S.: 425120

Subsidiary (Non-US):

D-Mail Direct S.r.l. (2)
Bd Natiunile Unite Nr 4 Bl 106 Parter Sector 5, Bucharest, 050122, Romania
Tel.: (40) 213360444
Web Site: http://www.dmail.ro
Online Business & Trading Services
N.A.I.C.S.: 425120
Corbu Dragos (Mgr)

D-Mail Venda Directa s.a. (2)
Av Dr Luis SA Parque Monserrate Pavilhao C Zona Industrial da, Abrunheira, 2710-022, Sintra, Portugal
Tel.: (351) 21 915 6560
Web Site: http://www.dmail.pt
Household Products Online Sales
N.A.I.C.S.: 449210

D-Mail s.r.o. (2)
Piaristicka 22/8, 370 01, Ceske Budejovice, Czech Republic
Tel.: (420) 389139139
Web Site: http://www.dmail.cz
Household Products Online Sales
N.A.I.C.S.: 449210

DMedia Group S.p.A. (1)
Via Campi 29/L, 23807, Merate, Lecco, Italy
Tel.: (39) 0399989206
Web Site: http://www.dmediagroup.it
Sales Range: $25-49.9 Million
Emp.: 30
Magazine Publishing Services
N.A.I.C.S.: 513199
Mauro Toselli (Dir-IT)

Subsidiary (Domestic):

Editoriale La Cronaca S.r.l (2)
Corso Vittorio Emanuele II 52, 46100, Mantua, Italy
Tel.: (39) 0376321989
Web Site: http://www.dmediagroup.et
Online Publishing Services
N.A.I.C.S.: 513110
Francesca Porcelli (Co-CEO)

Editrice Vimercatese S.r.l. (2)
Via Camillo Benso Conte Di Cavour 59, Vimercate, 2871, Milan, Italy
Tel.: (39) 039625151
Scientific Book Publishing Services
N.A.I.C.S.: 513199

Giornale di Merate S.r.l (2)
Via Baslini 10, 23807, Merate, Lecco, Italy
Tel.: (39) 09989300
Web Site: http://www.giornaledimerate.it
Online Newspaper Publishing Services
N.A.I.C.S.: 513110
Gianluigi Vigano (Mgr-Admin)

Publisette s.r.l. (2)
Via Catania 14, 90141, Palermo, Italy
Tel.: (39) 0917302750
Web Site: http://www.publisette.it
Advertising Agencies
N.A.I.C.S.: 541810

Promotion Lecco S.r.l. (1)
Via Aspromonte 52, 23900, Lecco, Italy
Tel.: (39) 0341285875
Web Site: http://www.giornaledilecco.it
Advertising Agencies
N.A.I.C.S.: 541810
Gianluigi Vigano (CEO)

NETWORK CN INC.
Unit 705B 7th FL New East Ocean Centre 9 Science Museum Road TST, Kowloon, China (Hong Kong)
Tel.: (852) 90290586 DE
Web Site: https://www.ncnmedia.com
Year Founded: 1993
NWCN—(OTCIQ)
Rev.: $106,498
Assets: $484,019
Liabilities: $6,821,773
Net Worth: ($6,337,754)
Earnings: ($925,278)
Emp.: 8
Fiscal Year-end: 12/31/22
Outdoor Advertising
N.A.I.C.S.: 541890
Earnest Chi Wah Leung (Chm & CEO)

NETWORK CO. A.D.
Bogdana Zerajica 6, 11000, Belgrade, Serbia
Tel.: (381) 64 3 171 808
Web Site: http://www.network.rs
Sales Range: $1-9.9 Million
Emp.: 40
Telecommunication Servicesb
N.A.I.C.S.: 541618

NETWORK FOR ELECTRONIC TRANSFERS (SINGAPORE) PTE LTD.
298 Tiong Bahru Road #06-01 Central Plaza, Singapore, Singapore
Tel.: (65) 6274 1212
Web Site: http://www.nets.com.sg
Year Founded: 1985
Financial Transactions & Payment Processing Services
N.A.I.C.S.: 522320
Jeffrey Goh (CEO)

Subsidiaries:

Banking Computer Services Private Limited (1)
11 Tampines Concourse #02-05, Singapore, 528729, Singapore
Tel.: (65) 6416 9000
Payment Services
N.A.I.C.S.: 522320

NETWORK INNOVATION AB
Smedjegatan 8 4tr, 131 54, Nacka, Sweden
Tel.: (46) 855576260
Web Site: http://www.ni.se
Year Founded: 1994
Sales Range: $10-24.9 Million
Emp.: 30
Printing Supplies Distr
N.A.I.C.S.: 423420
Erik Nasman (Mng Dir)

NETWORK INNOVATIONS INC.
4424 Manilla Road SE, Calgary, T2G 4B7, AB, Canada
Tel.: (403) 287-5000
Web Site: http://www.networkinv.com
Telecommunication Servicesb
N.A.I.C.S.: 517810
Derek Dawson (Pres)

Subsidiaries:

Field Intelligence Inc. (1)
10035 Carroll Canyon Rd Ste F, San Diego, CA 92131-1113
Tel.: (858) 208-6334
Web Site: http://www.fieldintell.com
Cloud Based Software Solution Services
N.A.I.C.S.: 513210
Arturo Gomez (Pres)

NETWORK LTD.
W-39 Okhla Industrial Area Phase - II, New Delhi, 110020, India
Tel.: (91) 11 40564881
Web Site:
  http://www.networklimited.net
Rev.: $722,932
Assets: $834,167
Liabilities: $3,985
Net Worth: $830,182
Earnings: ($59,874)
Fiscal Year-end: 03/31/19
Computer Software Development Services
N.A.I.C.S.: 541511
Vikas Jain (Sec)

NETWORK MEDIA GROUP INC.
2071525 W 8th Ave, Vancouver, V6J 1T5, BC, Canada
Tel.: (778) 870-5028 BC
Web Site:
  https://www.networkmediagroup.ca
Year Founded: 2010
NETWF—(OTCQB)
Rev.: $5,381,782
Assets: $14,972,480
Liabilities: $6,996,289
Net Worth: $7,976,191
Earnings: ($242,346)
Emp.: 30
Fiscal Year-end: 11/30/23
Investment Services
N.A.I.C.S.: 523999
Derik Murray (CEO)

Subsidiaries:

Network Entertainment Inc. (1)
1488 Frances Street, Vancouver, V5L 1Y9, BC, Canada
Tel.: (604) 739-8825
Web Site:
  http://www.networkentertainment.ca
Sport & Entertainment Program Services
N.A.I.C.S.: 711310
Derik Murray (Founder & CEO)

NETWORK PEOPLE SERVICES TECHNOLOGIES LIMITED
427/428/429 Lodha Supremus 2 A wing road no 22, near new passport office Wagle Industrial Estate, Thane, 400604, India
Tel.: (91) 2261482100
Web Site: https://www.npstx.com
Year Founded: 2013
NPST—(NSE)
Rev.: $4,937,498
Assets: $4,684,036
Liabilities: $1,250,968
Net Worth: $3,433,068
Earnings: $782,243
Emp.: 229
Fiscal Year-end: 03/31/23
Information Technology Services
N.A.I.C.S.: 541512

NETWORK RAIL LIMITED
1 Eversholt Street, London, NW1 2DN, United Kingdom
Tel.: (44) 3457114141
Web Site:
  http://www.networkrail.co.uk
Rev.: $12,970,299,160
Assets: $107,307,400,200
Liabilities: $93,248,209,600
Net Worth: $14,059,190,600
Earnings: ($815,989,720)
Emp.: 42,181
Fiscal Year-end: 03/31/22
Holding Company
N.A.I.C.S.: 551112
Jeremy Westlake (CFO)

Subsidiaries:

Network Rail (High Speed) Limited (1)
Singlewell IMD Henhurst Road, Cobham, Gravesend, DA12 3AN, Kent, United Kingdom
Tel.: (44) 1233739450
Railway Freight Transportation Services

NETWORK RAIL LIMITED

Network Rail Limited—(Continued)
N.A.I.C.S.: 482111
Lewis Atherton *(Mgr-Programme)*

Network Rail Certification Body Limited (1)
The QuadrantElder gate, Milton Keynes, MK9 1EN, United Kingdom
Tel.: (44) 1908784002
Web Site: http://www.net-cert.co.uk
Railway Freight Transportation Services
N.A.I.C.S.: 482111

Network Rail Consulting Limited (1)
42 Upper Berkeley Street, London, W1H 5PW, United Kingdom
Tel.: (44) 2033560454
Web Site: http://www.networkrailconsulting.com
Railway Freight Transportation Services
N.A.I.C.S.: 482111
Nigel Ash *(Mng Dir)*

Network Rail Infrastructure Finance PLC (1)
Kings Place 90 York Way, London, N1 9AG, United Kingdom
Tel.: (44) 2075578000
Railway Freight Transportation Services
N.A.I.C.S.: 482111

Network Rail Infrastructure Ltd (1)
40 Melton St, Birmingham, B1 1RT, United Kingdom (100%)
Tel.: (44) 2075578000
Web Site: http://www.networkrail.co.uk
Sales Range: $250-299.9 Million
Emp.: 1,000
Public Transport System
N.A.I.C.S.: 926120

Victoria Place Shopping Centre Ltd. (1)
115 Buckingham Palace Road, London, SW1W 9SJ, United Kingdom
Tel.: (44) 2079318811
Web Site: https://victoriaplace.co.uk
Beauty Product Retailer
N.A.I.C.S.: 456120

NETWORK TECHNOLOGY PLC

26 Victoria Way, Burgess Hill, RH15 9NF, West Sussex, United Kingdom
Tel.: (44) 1444870408
Web Site: http://www.network-technology.com
Year Founded: 1985
Rev.: $6,261,266
Assets: $6,125,005
Liabilities: $6,098,022
Net Worth: $26,982
Earnings: $98,486
Emp.: 37
Fiscal Year-end: 03/31/18
Mfr of Computer Hardware & Software for Local Area Networks
N.A.I.C.S.: 513210
Klaus Bollmann *(Co-Founder, Chm & CEO)*

Subsidiaries:

Ringdale (UK) Ltd. (1)
26 Victoria Way, Burgess Hill, RH15 9NF, West Sussex, United Kingdom (100%)
Tel.: (44) 1444871349
Web Site: http://www.ringdale.com
Sales Range: $25-49.9 Million
Emp.: 30
Developer & Mfr of Network Connectivity Products
N.A.I.C.S.: 513210
Clive Sadler *(Mgr-Data Storage Sys)*

Ringdale GmbH (1)
Cochemer Strasse 12 14, D 68309, Mannheim, Germany (100%)
Tel.: (49) 62171860
Web Site: http://www.ringdale.com
Sales Range: $25-49.9 Million
Emp.: 4
Mfr of Computer Connectivity Products & Developer of Local Area Network Software
N.A.I.C.S.: 334118

Ringdale KK (1)
3-34-3 Minamisenzoku, Ota-ku, Tokyo, 145-0063, Japan
Tel.: (81) 352885310
Web Site: http://www.ringdale.jp
Computer Peripheral Distr
N.A.I.C.S.: 423430

Ringdale, Inc. (1)
101 Halmar Cove, Georgetown, TX 78628 (100%)
Tel.: (512) 288-9080
Web Site: http://www.ringdale.com
Sales Range: $25-49.9 Million
Emp.: 30
Developer & Mfr of Network Connectivity Products
N.A.I.C.S.: 513210

NETX HOLDINGS BERHAD

Lot 13 2 13th Floor Menara Lien Hoe No 8 Persiaran Tropicana, Tropicana Golf and Country Resort, 47410, Petaling Jaya, Malaysia
Tel.: (60) 378878818 MY
Web Site: https://www.netx.com.my
Year Founded: 2000
NETX—(KLS)
Rev.: $3,663,829
Assets: $32,924,577
Liabilities: $8,863,098
Net Worth: $24,061,479
Earnings: ($3,107,323)
Fiscal Year-end: 11/30/23
Software Development Services
N.A.I.C.S.: 541511
Sik Eek Tan *(Exec Dir)*

NETYEAR GROUP CORPORATION

2-15-2 KR Ginza II, Chuo-ku, Tokyo, 104-0061, Japan
Tel.: (81) 363690500
Web Site: https://www.netyear.net
Year Founded: 1999
3622—(TKS)
Rev.: $54,314,480
Assets: $30,482,320
Liabilities: $10,764,160
Net Worth: $19,718,160
Earnings: $1,936,000
Emp.: 349
Fiscal Year-end: 03/31/21
Internet Marketing Tools & Consulting Services
N.A.I.C.S.: 425120
Fujiguro Ishiguro *(Pres & CEO)*

NETZ GROUP LTD.

Derech Abba Hillel Silver 12 Ayalon Insurance Tower 14th Fl, Ramat Gan, 5250606, Israel
Tel.: (972) 3 7362511
Web Site: http://www.netzgroup.com
Year Founded: 1988
NETZ—(TAE)
Rev.: $15,759,951
Assets: $143,930,172
Liabilities: $91,454,218
Net Worth: $52,475,954
Earnings: $6,862,651
Emp.: 52
Fiscal Year-end: 12/31/19
Real Estate Manangement Services
N.A.I.C.S.: 531390
Tzvi Ytzik *(CEO)*

Subsidiaries:

Netz United States (H.Y) Ltd. (1)
Dereh Menahem Begin 125, Tel Aviv, 6701201, Israel
Tel.: (972) 37362511
Sales Range: $1-9.9 Million
Real Estate Development Services
N.A.I.C.S.: 531390
Jacques Albert Amouyal *(Chm)*

NEUCA S.A.

Fortezna 35-37, 87-100, Torun, Poland
Tel.: (48) 566694000 PL
Web Site: https://www.neuca.pl
Year Founded: 1994
NEU—(WAR)
Rev.: $2,821,820,831
Assets: $1,215,801,638
Liabilities: $982,032,357
Net Worth: $233,769,281
Earnings: $37,077,827
Emp.: 3,981
Fiscal Year-end: 12/31/22
Pharmaceutical Whslr & Logistics Services
N.A.I.C.S.: 424210
Piotr Sucharski *(Chm-Mgmt Bd & Gen Dir)*

Subsidiaries:

ACP Pharma S.A. (1)
ul Domaniewska 50, 02 672, Warsaw, Poland
Tel.: (48) 22 611 4750
Web Site: http://www.acppharma.pl
Pharmaceuticals Distr
N.A.I.C.S.: 424210

Diabdis Sp. z o.o. (1)
Ligocka 103, 40-569, Katowice, Poland
Tel.: (48) 22 307 3787
Web Site: https://diabdis.com
Scientific Research Development Services
N.A.I.C.S.: 541715

Eskulap Sp. z o.o. (1)
ul On Broniewskiego 26A, 58-400, Kamienna Gora, Poland
Tel.: (48) 75 645 5800
Web Site: https://www.eskulap.net.pl
General Medical Practice Services
N.A.I.C.S.: 621111

Experior S.L. (1)
Avenida Menendez y Pelayo 3-5, 46010, Valencia, Spain
Tel.: (34) 961452190
Clinical Research Services
N.A.I.C.S.: 541715

Neuca Med Sp. z o.o. (1)
ul Fortezna 35-37, 87-100, Torun, Poland
Tel.: (48) 800880027
Web Site: https://neucamed.pl
General Medical Practice Services
N.A.I.C.S.: 621111

Ortopedio.pl Sp. z o.o. (1)
Street Fortezna 35-37, 87-100, Torun, Poland
Tel.: (48) 800888717
Web Site: https://www.ortopedio.pl
Orthopedic Equipment Distr
N.A.I.C.S.: 423450

Pratia S.A. (1)
103 Ligocka Street, 40-568, Katowice, Poland
Tel.: (48) 327898444
Web Site: https://pratia.com
Diagnostic Medical Care Services
N.A.I.C.S.: 621512
Karolina Borkowska *(Mgr-Up)*

Swiat Zdrowia S.A. (1)
ul Fortezna 35-37, 87-100, Torun, Poland
Tel.: (48) 800880027
Web Site: https://www.swiat-zdrowia.pl
Marketing Services
N.A.I.C.S.: 541613

NEUE PRESSEGESELLSCHAFT MBH & CO. KG

Frauenstrasse 77, 89073, Ulm, Germany
Tel.: (49) 731 156 0 De
Web Site: http://www.neue-pressegesellschaft.de
Newspaper Publishers
N.A.I.C.S.: 513110
Andreas Simmet *(Chm & Mng Dir)*

Subsidiaries:

Markisches Medienhaus GmbH & Co. KG (1)
Kellenspring 6, 15230, Frankfurt, Germany

INTERNATIONAL PUBLIC

Newspaper Publishing & Services
N.A.I.C.S.: 513110
Andreas Simmet *(Mng Dir)*

Subsidiary (Domestic):

Lausitzer VerlagsService GmbH (2)
Strasse der Jugend 54, 03002, Cottbus, Germany (100%)
Tel.: (49) 355481555
Web Site: http://www.lr-medienhaus.de
Newspaper Publishers
N.A.I.C.S.: 513110
Clemens Braun *(Mng Dir)*

NEULAND LABORATORIES LTD

11th Floor 5th Level Phoenix IVY Building Plot No 573AIII Road No 82, Jubilee Hills, Hyderabad, 500034, Telangana, India
Tel.: (91) 4067611600
Web Site: https://www.neulandlabs.com
NEULANDLAB—(NSE)
Rev.: $130,085,619
Assets: $180,833,507
Liabilities: $73,482,031
Net Worth: $107,351,476
Earnings: $11,006,091
Emp.: 1,427
Fiscal Year-end: 03/31/21
Research based Chemistry & Mfr
N.A.I.C.S.: 424210
Davuluri Rama Mohan Rao *(Chm & Co-Mng Dir)*

Subsidiaries:

Neuland Laboratories K.K. (1)
2F Maruishi Building Bekkan Annex 1-10-1 Kajicho, Chiyoda-Ku, Tokyo, Japan
Tel.: (81) 335265171
Pharmaceutical Ingredient Mfr
N.A.I.C.S.: 325412

NEUMARKTER LAMMSBRAEU GEBR. EHRNSPERGER E.K.

Amberger Str 1, Neumarkt, 92318, Germany
Tel.: (49) 91814040
Web Site: http://www.lammsbraeu.de
Rev.: $25,067,147
Emp.: 85
Brewery Services
N.A.I.C.S.: 312120
Franz Ehrnsperger *(Owner)*

NEUPATH HEALTH, INC.

9-6400 Millcreek Drive, Mississauga, L5N 3E7, ON, Canada
Tel.: (905) 858-1368
Web Site: https://www.neupath.com
NPTH—(TSXV)
Rev.: $49,914,672
Assets: $31,549,498
Liabilities: $15,058,521
Net Worth: $16,490,976
Earnings: ($144,227)
Emp.: 156
Fiscal Year-end: 12/31/23
Health Care Srvices
N.A.I.C.S.: 621610
Dianne Carmichael *(Chm)*

Subsidiaries:

CompreMed Canada Inc. (1)
665 Davis Drive Suite 201, Newmarket, L3Y 2R2, ON, Canada
Tel.: (905) 953-5445
Web Site: http://www.compremed.com
Health Assessment Services
N.A.I.C.S.: 621999

NEURAL GROUP INC.

Tokyo Midtown Hibiya Hibiya Mitsui Tower 32F 1-1-2 Yurakucho, Chiyoda-ku, Tokyo, 100-0006, Japan
Tel.: (81) 332494103

Web Site: https://www.neural-group.com
Year Founded: 2018
4056—(TKS)
Rev.: $22,532,020
Assets: $23,333,190
Liabilities: $20,015,070
Net Worth: $3,318,120
Earnings: ($4,608,500)
Fiscal Year-end: 12/31/23
Building Construction Services
N.A.I.C.S.: 236220
Yuichi Sasaki (CTO)

Subsidiaries:

Neural Group (Thailand) Co., Ltd. (1)
87/2 36th Floor Office number 11 CRC Tower All Seasons Place, Wireless Road Lumpini Phatumwan, Bangkok, 10330, Thailand
Tel.: (66) 26253028
Web Site: https://th.neural-group.com
Person Safety Monitoring Services
N.A.I.C.S.: 561621

Neural Marketing Inc. (1)
21st Floor Shinagawa Seaside Canal Tower 4-12-6, Higashi-Shinagawa Shinagawa-ku, Tokyo, 140-0002, Japan
Tel.: (81) 120668625
Web Site: https://www.neuralmarketing.co.jp
Software Development Services
N.A.I.C.S.: 541519

NEUREN PHARMACEUTICALS LIMITED
At the offices of Lowndes Jordan Level 15 HSBC Tower 188 Quay Street, Auckland, 1141, New Zealand
Tel.: (64) 390920480
Web Site: https://www.neurenpharma.com
Year Founded: 2001
NURPF—(OTCIQ)
Rev.: $163,519,515
Assets: $168,905,388
Liabilities: $29,128,125
Net Worth: $139,777,263
Earnings: $106,996,117
Emp.: 24
Fiscal Year-end: 12/31/23
Pharmaceutical Researcher, Developer & Mfr
N.A.I.C.S.: 325412
Larry Glass (Chief Science Officer)

Subsidiaries:

Neuren Pharmaceuticals (Australia) Pty Ltd. (1)
Suite 201 697 Burke Road, Camberwell, 3124, VIC, Australia
Tel.: (61) 390920480
Web Site: https://www.neurenpharma.com
Pharmaceuticals Product Mfr
N.A.I.C.S.: 325412
Patrick Davies (Chm)

Neuren Pharmaceuticals Inc. (1)
3 Bethesda Metro Ctr Ste 700, Bethesda, MD 20814
Tel.: (301) 941-1830
Web Site: http://www.neurenpharma.com
Sales Range: $25-49.9 Million
Emp.: 1
Pharmaceutical Drug Mfr
N.A.I.C.S.: 325412

NEURIZER LTD
Level 5 19 Grenfell Street, PO Box 12, Adelaide, 5000, SA, Australia
Tel.: (61) 881329100
Web Site: https://neurizer.com.au
NRZ—(ASX)
Rev.: $126,368
Assets: $86,350,734
Liabilities: $37,593,716
Net Worth: $48,757,018
Earnings: ($3,741,858)
Emp.: 40
Fiscal Year-end: 06/30/24
Crude Petroleum Extraction Services
N.A.I.C.S.: 211120
Daniel Justyn Peters (Chm)

NEUROMAMA, LTD.
Blvd Benito Juarez Km 25.500, Quinta del Mar Int Suite 28, Rosarito, 22710, BC, Mexico
Tel.: (52) 664 290 5048   NV
Year Founded: 2011
Search Engine Operator
N.A.I.C.S.: 541519

NEUROMEKA CO., LTD.
4F Econet Center 78 Achasanro, Seongdong-gu, Seoul, 4782, Korea (South)
Tel.: (82) 7047913103
Web Site: https://en.neuromeka.com
Year Founded: 2013
348340—(KRS)
Industrial Machinery Mfr
N.A.I.C.S.: 333310

NEURON BIOPHARMA SA
Avda de la Innovacion 1 Edificio BIC, 18016, Granada, Spain
Tel.: (34) 958 750 598
Web Site: http://www.neuronbio.com
NEU—(MAD)
Sales Range: Less than $1 Million
Biopharmaceutical Mfr
N.A.I.C.S.: 325412
Fernando Valdivieso Amate (Chm)

Subsidiaries:

Neol Biosolutions SA (1)
Avenida de la Vega 15, Alcobendas, 28108, Madrid, Spain
Tel.: (34) 958750598
Biotechnology Research & Development Services
N.A.I.C.S.: 541714
Javier Velasco Alvarez (CEO)

NEURONES S.A.
Immeuble Le Clemenceau 1 205 avenue Georges Clemenceau, 92024, Nanterre, Cedex, France
Tel.: (33) 141374137
Web Site: https://www.neurones.net
NRO—(EUR)
Rev.: $718,086,553
Assets: $666,135,333
Liabilities: $260,268,724
Net Worth: $405,866,609
Earnings: $47,747,680
Emp.: 6,406
Fiscal Year-end: 12/31/22
IT Services
N.A.I.C.S.: 541512

Subsidiaries:

AS International Group (1)
120 - 122 rue Reaumur, 75002, Paris, France
Tel.: (33) 144510551
Web Site: https://www.asinter-group.com
Information Technology Consulting Services
N.A.I.C.S.: 541512
Jean-Pierre Lafont (CEO)

AS Synergie (1)
120/122 Rue Reaumur, Paris, 75002, France
Tel.: (33) 144510551
Emp.: 45
Information Technology Services
N.A.I.C.S.: 519290

AS Technologie (1)
26 Rue Des Victoires, Paris, 75002, France
Tel.: (33) 1 44 51 05 51
Information Technology Services
N.A.I.C.S.: 519290

AS Telecom & Reseaux (1)
26 Rue Notre Dame Des Victoires, Paris, 75002, France
Tel.: (33) 144510551
Information Technology Services
N.A.I.C.S.: 519290

Cloud Temple SAS (1)
215 Avenue Georges Clemenceau, 92024, Nanterre, Cedex, France
Tel.: (33) 141917777
Web Site: http://www.cloud-temple.com
Emp.: 300
Software Development Services
N.A.I.C.S.: 541511
Frank Dubray (Pres)

Codilog SA (1)
Building Le Clemenceau 1 205 avenue Georges Clemenceau, 92024, Nanterre, Cedex, France
Tel.: (33) 141375230
Web Site: https://www.codilog.fr
Consulting Firm Services
N.A.I.C.S.: 541618
Jean Velut (Founder & CEO)

Codilog-Knowledge Sas (1)
205 avenue Georges-Clemenceau, Immeuble Le Clemenceau 1, 92024, Nanterre, Cedex, France   (72%)
Tel.: (33) 141375222
Web Site: http://www.codilog.fr
Sales Range: $25-49.9 Million
Emp.: 50
Computer System Design Services
N.A.I.C.S.: 541512
Jean Velut (Pres, Partner & Dir-Publication)

Colombus Consulting (1)
138 av des Champs-Elysees, 75008, Paris, France
Tel.: (33) 142818150
Web Site: https://colombus-consulting.com
Sales Range: $25-49.9 Million
Management Consulting Services
N.A.I.C.S.: 541618

Deodis SA (1)
Cnit 2 Level 2 2 Place de la Defense, La Defense, 92053, Paris, Cedex, France
Tel.: (33) 171156868
Web Site: https://www.deodis.com
IT Management & Consulting Services
N.A.I.C.S.: 541618
Alister Seglond (Acct Mgr)

Edugroupe (1)
152 Avenue de Malakoff, 75016, Paris, France
Tel.: (33) 171197030
Web Site: http://edugroupe.com
Information Technology Services
N.A.I.C.S.: 519290

Everience GmbH (1)
Berliner Allee 58, 64295, Darmstadt, Germany
Tel.: (49) 61517809915
Web Site: http://www.everience.com
Management Consultancy Services
N.A.I.C.S.: 541611
Bernard Lewis (Mng Dir)

Finaxys (1)
1 Terrasse Bellini, la Defense, 92919, Paris, Cedex, France
Tel.: (33) 171113580
Web Site: https://www.finaxys.com
Sales Range: $25-49.9 Million
Information Technology Consulting Services
N.A.I.C.S.: 541512
Guillaume Blanchetiere (Founder & Chm)

Help-Line Sas (1)
148 Avenue Jean Jaures, 69007, Lyon, France   (93%)
Tel.: (33) 141377000
Web Site: http://www.helpline.fr
Computer System Design Services
N.A.I.C.S.: 541512

INTRINsec Sarl (1)
Tour CBX 1 Passerelle des Reflets, 92400, Courbevoie, France   (85%)
Tel.: (33) 141917777
Web Site: http://www.intrinsec.com
Sales Range: $25-49.9 Million
Emp.: 100
Computer System Design Services
N.A.I.C.S.: 541512

Mobiapps SAS (1)
14 Rue Jules, Verne, 44700, Orvault, France
Tel.: (33) 981998766
Web Site: https://www.mobiapps.fr
Mobile Application Development Services
N.A.I.C.S.: 541511

Neurones IT Asia Pte. Ltd. (1)
5 Tampines Central 1 02-05 Tampines Plaza, Singapore, 529541, Singapore
Tel.: (65) 66786890
Information Technology Services
N.A.I.C.S.: 541511
Daniel Ta (Gen Mgr)

Neurones IT SAS (1)
Le Clemenceau 1 Building 205 avenue Georges-Clemenceau, 92024, Nanterre, Cedex, France
Tel.: (33) 141374137
Web Site: http://www.neurones-it.com
Emp.: 800
Information Technology Services
N.A.I.C.S.: 541511
Franck Emsellem (Acct Mgr-Delivery)

RS2i (1)
44 Avenue Georges Pompidou, 92300, Levallois-Perret, France
Tel.: (33) 141066130
Web Site: https://www.rs2i.fr
Sales Range: $25-49.9 Million
Television Broadcasting Services
N.A.I.C.S.: 516120

Viaaduc (1)
152 avenue de Malakoff, 75016, Paris, France
Tel.: (33) 171197030
Web Site: http://www.viaaduc.com
Sales Range: $25-49.9 Million
Information Technology Services
N.A.I.C.S.: 519290

NEUROS CO., LTD.
274 Techno 2-ro, Yuseong-gu, Daejeon, 305-510, Korea (South)
Tel.: (82) 428657300
Web Site: http://www.neuros.com
Year Founded: 2000
126870—(KRS)
Rev.: $31,624,316
Assets: $72,176,065
Liabilities: $38,214,547
Net Worth: $33,961,517
Earnings: ($7,027,150)
Emp.: 132
Fiscal Year-end: 12/31/22
Turbo Machinery & Turbo Engine Mfr
N.A.I.C.S.: 333611

Subsidiaries:

Neuros Turbo Machinery Corporation Inc. (1)
Rm 2F-A Bldg 3 No 159 Zhujiabang Road, Xiaokunshan Town Songjiang District, Shanghai, 201103, China
Tel.: (86) 2154323757
Gas Turbo Engine Distr
N.A.I.C.S.: 423860

NEUROSCIENTIFIC BIOPHARMACEUTICALS LIMITED
Suite 5 85 Forrest St, Cottesloe, 6011, WA, Australia
Tel.: (61) 863821800   AU
Web Site: https://www.neuroscientific.com
NSB—(ASX)
Rev.: $1,596,398
Assets: $3,629,723
Liabilities: $57,214
Net Worth: $3,572,509
Earnings: $216,486
Fiscal Year-end: 06/30/24
Biotechnology Research & Development Services
N.A.I.C.S.: 541714
Matthew Liddelow (CEO & Mng Dir)

NEUROSENSE THERAPEUTICS LTD.
Ha-Menofim 11, Herzliya, Israel
Tel.: (972) 587531153   IL

NEUROSENSE THERAPEUTICS LTD.

NeuroSense Therapeutics Ltd.—(Continued)
Web Site: https://www.neurosense-tx.com
Year Founded: 2017
NRSN—(NASDAQ)
Rev.: $4,231,000
Assets: $3,176,000
Liabilities: $5,050,000
Net Worth: ($1,874,000)
Earnings: ($11,280,000)
Emp.: 16
Fiscal Year-end: 12/31/23
Biotechnology Research & Development Services
N.A.I.C.S.: 541714
Alon Ben-Noon *(CEO & Founder)*

NEUROSOFT S.A.
466 Irakliou Ave & Kiprou, Iraklio Attikis, 141 22, Athens, Greece
Tel.: (30) 2106855061   GR
Web Site: https://www.neurosoft.gr
Year Founded: 1994
NRST—(ITA)
Rev.: $18,102,062
Assets: $11,745,880
Liabilities: $8,046,238
Net Worth: $3,699,642
Earnings: ($3,216,652)
Emp.: 201
Fiscal Year-end: 12/31/20
Integrated Software Solutions
N.A.I.C.S.: 513210
Nikolaos Vasilonikolidakis *(Chm)*

Subsidiaries:

Neurosoft Romania Software and Services SRL   (1)
Global City Bus Park Bucuresti Nord Ave No 10 O21 Bldg 5th Fl, 077190, Voluntari, Ilfov, Romania
Tel.: (40) 21 2720000
Web Site: http://www.neurosoft.gr
Sales Range: $25-49.9 Million
Emp.: 1
Information Technology Services
N.A.I.C.S.: 541512

NEUROTECH INTERNATIONAL LIMITED
Suite 5 CPC 145 Stirling Highway, Nedlands, 6009, WA, Australia
Tel.: (61) 893893130   AU
Web Site: https://www.neurotechnational.com
Year Founded: 2016
NTI—(ASX)
Rev.: $2,227,220
Assets: $8,155,306
Liabilities: $210,136
Net Worth: $7,945,170
Earnings: ($3,632,546)
Fiscal Year-end: 06/30/24
Medical Device Mfr & Distr
N.A.I.C.S.: 334510
Peter J. L. Griffiths *(CEO)*

Subsidiaries:

AAT Medical Limited   (1)
Block LS3 Life Sciences Park San Gwann Industrial Estate, San Gwann, SGN3000, Malta
Tel.: (356) 19143521678
Web Site: http://www.mentetech.com
Medical Device Distr
N.A.I.C.S.: 423450
Wolfgang Storf *(CEO)*

NEUSOFT CORPORATION
Neusoft Park No 2 Xinxiu Street, Hunnan New District, Shenyang, 110179, China
Tel.: (86) 2483667788   CN
Web Site: https://www.neusoft.com
Year Founded: 1991
600718—(SHG)
Rev.: $1,328,998,404
Assets: $2,649,647,263
Liabilities: $1,342,236,229
Net Worth: $1,307,411,034
Earnings: ($48,141,012)
Emp.: 20,000
Fiscal Year-end: 12/31/22
Software Research, Design, Development, Production, Sales, Training & Service Business Solutions
N.A.I.C.S.: 541512
Yongfeng Wang *(Vice Chm & Pres)*

Subsidiaries:

Chengdu Neusoft Institute of Information   (1)
No 1 Dongruan Road Qingchengshan, Qing Cheng Shan, Dujiangyan, 611844, Sichuan, China
Tel.: (86) 2882878136
Web Site: http://en.ccnlit.com
Educational Support Services
N.A.I.C.S.: 611710

Dalian Neusoft Institute of Information   (1)
No 8 Software Park Road, 116023, Dalian, Liaoning, China
Tel.: (86) 41184760003
Web Site: http://www.neusoft.com
IT Solutions & Services
N.A.I.C.S.: 519290

Nanhai Neusoft Institute of Information   (1)
Nanhai Software Science & Telechnology Park, Foshan, China
Tel.: (86) 13510909928
Colleges Universities & Professional Schools
N.A.I.C.S.: 611310

Neusoft America Inc.   (1)
3000 RDU Center Dr Ste 119, Morrisville, NC 27560
Tel.: (919) 600-6701
Software Services
N.A.I.C.S.: 541511

Neusoft Cloud Technology Co., Ltd.   (1)
No.2 Xinxiu Street, Hunnan New District, Shenyang, 110179, China
Tel.: (86) 2483667788
Web Site: https://www.neusoft.com
Cloud & IT Services
N.A.I.C.S.: 518210

Subsidiary (Domestic):

Moshi Moshi Hotline Dalian, Inc.   (2)
502 Building No 23 Dalian Software Park No 40 Software Park East Road, Shahekou District, Dalian, China   (85.1%)
Tel.: (86) 41139990622
Telemarketing Services
N.A.I.C.S.: 561422

Neusoft Japan Co., Ltd.   (1)
Tokyo Fashion Town Bldg East 7F 3-6-11, Ariake Koutou-Ku, Tokyo, 135-8071, Japan
Tel.: (81) 335709270
Software Services
N.A.I.C.S.: 541511

Neusoft Medical Systems Co., Ltd   (1)
Neusoft Park Hun Nan Hi Tech Industrial Park, 110179, Shenyang, Liao Ning, China
Tel.: (86) 2483665681
Web Site: http://www.medical.neusoft.com
Sales Range: $200-249.9 Million
Emp.: 1,500
HMO Medical Centers
N.A.I.C.S.: 621491

Neusoft Technology Solutions GmbH   (1)
Hugh-Greene-Weg 2-4, 22529, Hamburg, Germany
Tel.: (49) 4030067700
Web Site: https://www.neusoft.de
Software Services
N.A.I.C.S.: 541511
Zhuowei Sun *(Mng Dir)*

SC Neusoft EDC SRL   (1)
9 Pavel Rosca Street, 400148, Cluj-Napoca, Romania
Tel.: (40) 364410111
Web Site: https://neusoft.ro
Information Technology Services
N.A.I.C.S.: 541519

NEUSOFT EDUCATION TECHNOLOGY COMPANY LIMITED
No 6 Software Park Road, Dalian, 116023, China
Tel.: (86) 41184835288   Ky
Web Site: http://www.neuedu.com
Year Founded: 2000
9616—(HKG)
Educational Support Services
N.A.I.C.S.: 611710
Liu Jiren *(Chm)*

NEUTRIK AG
Im alten Riet 143, 9494, Schaan, Liechtenstein
Tel.: (423) 2372424
Web Site: http://www.neutrik.com
Sales Range: $75-99.9 Million
Emp.: 500
Entertainment Connector Systems Mfr
N.A.I.C.S.: 334310
Oliver Dobler *(Mgr-Design Grp)*

Subsidiaries:

Contrik AG   (1)
Steinackerstrasse 35, 8902, Urdorf, Switzerland
Tel.: (41) 447365010
Web Site: http://www.contrik.ch
Sales Range: $25-49.9 Million
Emp.: 20
Entertainment Connector Systems Mfr
N.A.I.C.S.: 334310
Markus Sawade *(Mng Dir)*

Neutrik France Sarl   (1)
13 rue du Parchamp, 92100, Boulogne-Billancourt, France
Tel.: (33) 141316750
Web Site: http://www.neutrik-france.com
Entertainment Connector Systems Mfr
N.A.I.C.S.: 334310
Francois Glaser *(Gen Mgr)*

Neutrik Hong Kong Ltd.   (1)
Suite 18 7th Floor Shatin Galleria 18-24 Shan Mei Street Fotan, Shatin, Hong Kong, China (Hong Kong)
Tel.: (852) 2687 6055
Electronic Components Distr
N.A.I.C.S.: 423690
Brahms Lee *(Mgr-Application Engrg)*

Neutrik India Pvt. Ltd.   (1)
Level 3 Neo Vikram, New Link Road Above Audi Show Room, Andheri West, Mumbai, 400058, India
Tel.: (91) 982 05 43 424
Web Site: http://www.neutrik.in
Emp.: 5
Electronic Components Distr
N.A.I.C.S.: 423690
Ketan Anklesaria *(Country Mgr)*

Neutrik Limited   (1)
Yusen-Higashinihonbashi-Ekimae Bldg Higashinihonbashi 3-7-19, Chuo-ku, Tokyo, 103-0004, Japan
Tel.: (81) 3 3663 4733
Web Site: http://www.neutrik.co.jp
Electronic Components Distr
N.A.I.C.S.: 423690

Neutrik UK Ltd.   (1)
Westridge Business Park, Cothey Way, Ryde, PO33 1QT, Isle of Wight, United Kingdom
Tel.: (44) 1983811441
Web Site: http://www.neutrik.co.uk
Sales Range: $50-74.9 Million
Emp.: 120
Entertainment Connector Systems Mfr
N.A.I.C.S.: 334310
Chris Arnold *(Mgr-Production)*

Neutrik USA Inc.   (1)
195 Lehigh Ave, Lakewood, NJ 08701
Tel.: (732) 901-9488
Web Site: http://www.neutrikusa.com
Sales Range: $25-49.9 Million
Emp.: 20
Entertainment Connector Systems Mfr
N.A.I.C.S.: 334310
Peter Milbery *(Pres)*

Neutrik Vertrieb GmbH   (1)
Felix-Wankel-strasse 1, Dachau, 85221, Germany
Tel.: (49) 8131280890
Web Site: http://www.neutrik.de
Emp.: 50
Entertainment Connector Systems Mfr
N.A.I.C.S.: 334310

Ningbo Neutrik Trading Co., Ltd.   (1)
Shiqi Street Yingian Road West Fengjian Village, Yin Zhou Area, Ningbo, 315153, Zhejiang, China
Tel.: (86) 574 882504 88
Web Site: http://www.neutrik.com.cn
Electronic Components Distr
N.A.I.C.S.: 423690
Max Young *(Mgr-Quality)*

NEUTRISCI INTERNATIONAL INC.
630 Granville St, Vancouver, V7Y 1H4, BC, Canada
Tel.: (403) 264-6320   Ca
Web Site: https://www.neutrisci.com
Year Founded: 2009
1N9—(DEU)
Rev.: $337,179
Assets: $244,129
Liabilities: $698,591
Net Worth: ($454,462)
Earnings: ($567,693)
Fiscal Year-end: 12/31/22
Pharmaceutical Preparation Mfr
N.A.I.C.S.: 325412
Glen Rehman *(CEO)*

NEVADA COPPER CORP.
250 - 200 Burrard Street, Vancouver, V6C 3L6, BC, Canada
Tel.: (604) 683-8992   BC
Web Site: https://www.nevadacopper.com
Year Founded: 1999
NEVDQ—(OTCEM)
Rev.: $9,000
Assets: $767,849,000
Liabilities: $397,056,000
Net Worth: $370,793,000
Earnings: ($20,344,000)
Emp.: 89
Fiscal Year-end: 12/31/20
Copper Mining Services
N.A.I.C.S.: 212230
Greg French *(VP & Head-Exploration)*

Subsidiaries:

Nevada Copper, Inc.   (1)
61 E Pursel Ln, Yerington, NV 89447
Tel.: (775) 463-3510
Web Site: https://www.nevadacopper.com
Copper Exploration Services
N.A.I.C.S.: 212230

NEVADA EXPLORATION INC.
Suite 1400 - 885 West Georgia Street, Vancouver, V6C 3E8, BC, Canada
Tel.: (604) 601-2006
Web Site: https://www.urz3.com
Year Founded: 2006
NVDEF—(OTCQB)
Rev.: $23,411
Assets: $1,290,789
Liabilities: $393,155
Net Worth: $897,633
Earnings: ($2,618,760)
Fiscal Year-end: 04/30/21
Gold Exploration Services
N.A.I.C.S.: 212220
Wade A. Hodges *(Chief Discovery Officer)*

AND PRIVATE COMPANIES

Subsidiaries:

Pediment Gold LLC (1)
10 Greg St 100, Sparks, NV 89431-6265
Tel.: (775) 359-7740
Sales Range: $50-74.9 Million
Emp.: 2
Gold Exploration Services
N.A.I.C.S.: 213114
Wade Hodges *(Mgr)*

NEVADA LITHIUM RESOURCES INC.
Suite 1570-505 Burrard Street One Bentall Centre, Vancouver, V7X 1M5, BC, Canada
Tel.: (604) 900-3341 BC
Web Site: https://www.nvlithium.com
Year Founded: 2020
NVLHF—(OTCQB)
Assets: $6,571,285
Liabilities: $212,612
Net Worth: $6,358,673
Earnings: ($1,713,432)
Fiscal Year-end: 04/30/22
Mineral Mining Services
N.A.I.C.S.: 213115

NEVADA SUNRISE METALS CORPORATION
Suite 408 - 1199 West Pender Street, Vancouver, V6E 2R1, BC, Canada
Tel.: (604) 428-8028
Web Site: https://www.nevadasunrise.ca
Year Founded: 2007
NVSGF—(OTCIQ)
Rev.: $3,613
Assets: $875,699
Liabilities: $589,242
Net Worth: $286,456
Earnings: ($1,381,329)
Fiscal Year-end: 09/30/19
Mineral Exploration Services
N.A.I.C.S.: 213114
Michael D. Sweatman *(Chm & CFO-Interim)*

NEVADA ZINC CORPORATION
82 Richmond Street East, Toronto, M5C 1P1, ON, Canada
Tel.: (416) 409-8441 ON
Web Site: https://www.nevadazinc.com
Year Founded: 2010
6GX—(DEU)
Assets: $76,344
Liabilities: $323,849
Net Worth: ($247,505)
Earnings: ($544,968)
Fiscal Year-end: 12/31/22
Gold Exploration Services
N.A.I.C.S.: 212220
R. Bruce Durham *(Pres & CEO)*

NEVADO RESOURCES CORPORATION
23 floor 1177 West Hastings Street, Vancouver, V6K 2K3, BC, Canada
Tel.: (604) 377-0403 Ca
Web Site: http://www.nevadoresources.com
Year Founded: 2006
VDO.H—(TSXV)
Assets: $504,722
Liabilities: $135,946
Net Worth: $368,777
Earnings: ($144,958)
Fiscal Year-end: 12/31/23
Investment Services
N.A.I.C.S.: 523999

NEVENA A.D.
Dorda Stamenkovica bb, 16000, Leskovac, Serbia
Tel.: (381) 16 213 665
Web Site: http://www.nevena.co.rs
Year Founded: 1953
Sales Range: Less than $1 Million
Emp.: 77
Cosmetics Products Mfr
N.A.I.C.S.: 325620

NEW AGE EXPLORATION LIMITED
Level 2 480 Collins Street, Melbourne, 3000, VIC, Australia
Tel.: (61) 396140600
Web Site: https://www.nae.net.au
NAE—(ASX)
Rev.: $59,376
Assets: $3,287,130
Liabilities: $211,599
Net Worth: $3,075,532
Earnings: ($2,302,469)
Fiscal Year-end: 06/30/24
Uranium, Gold & Other Mineral Exploration Services
N.A.I.C.S.: 212290
Adrien Michelle Wing *(Co-Sec)*

NEW AGE METALS INC.
18-8511 General Currie Rd, Richmond, V6Y 1M3, BC, Canada
Tel.: (604) 685-1870 BC
Web Site: https://www.newagemetals.com
Year Founded: 1996
NAM—(OTCIQ)
Rev.: $13,466
Assets: $10,061,722
Liabilities: $263,979
Net Worth: $9,797,743
Earnings: ($562,773)
Fiscal Year-end: 04/30/21
Platinum Exploration Services
N.A.I.C.S.: 212290
Harry Barr *(Chm & CEO)*

Subsidiaries:

Mystery Creek Resources, Inc. (1)
1600 A St Ste 310, Anchorage, AK 99501
Tel.: (907) 277-0607
Coal Whslr
N.A.I.C.S.: 423520

NEW AMSTERDAM INVEST N.V.
Herengracht 280, 1016 BX, Amsterdam, Netherlands
Tel.: (31) 208546168 NI
Web Site: https://www.newamsterdaminvest.nl
Year Founded: 2021
NAI—(EUR)
Rev.: $5,062,369
Assets: $93,222,210
Liabilities: $44,353,681
Net Worth: $48,868,529
Earnings: ($5,294,183)
Fiscal Year-end: 12/31/23
Investment Management Service
N.A.I.C.S.: 523999
Aren Van Dam *(CEO)*

NEW ART HOLDINGS CO., LTD.
1-15-2 Ginza, Chuo-ku, Tokyo, 104 0061, Japan
Tel.: (81) 335678091
Web Site: https://www.newart-ir.jp
Year Founded: 1994
7638—(TKS)
Rev.: $139,464,390
Assets: $145,360,510
Liabilities: $86,749,640
Net Worth: $58,610,870
Earnings: $7,171,850
Emp.: 851
Fiscal Year-end: 03/31/24
Bridal Jewelry Designer & Mfr
N.A.I.C.S.: 339910
Tetsuya Shiraishi *(Exec VP)*

NEW ASIA CONSTRUCTION & DEVELOPMENT CORP.
15-16Fl No 760 Sec 4 Bade Rd, Sungshan Chiu, Taipei, 105, Taiwan
Tel.: (886) 225288008
Web Site: http://www.newasia.com.tw
2516—(TAI)
Rev.: $282,113,891
Assets: $219,945,641
Liabilities: $169,796,521
Net Worth: $50,149,120
Earnings: $5,704,012
Emp.: 339
Fiscal Year-end: 12/31/23
Construction Engineering Services
N.A.I.C.S.: 237990

NEW ASIA HOLDINGS, INC.
60 Paya Lebar Road 1208 Paya Lebar Square Lobby 1, Singapore, 079019, Singapore
Tel.: (65) 68208885 NV
Web Site: https://www.newasiainc.com
Year Founded: 2001
NAHD—(OTCIQ)
Rev.: $7,500
Assets: $15,828
Liabilities: $1,358,530
Net Worth: ($1,342,702)
Earnings: ($187,539)
Fiscal Year-end: 12/31/23
Investment Services
N.A.I.C.S.: 523999
Kok Peng Lin *(Chm, CEO & CFO)*

NEW BEST WIRE INDUSTRIAL CO., LTD.
NO 12-19 laiganliao, Chiali District, Tainan City, Taiwan
Tel.: (886) 67263311
Web Site: https://www.newbest.com.tw
5013—(TPE)
Rev.: $282,453,460
Assets: $261,263,077
Liabilities: $114,727,730
Net Worth: $146,535,347
Earnings: $21,813,401
Emp.: 500
Fiscal Year-end: 12/31/22
Steel Pole Mfr
N.A.I.C.S.: 331222
Yu-Tang Wu *(Chm)*

Subsidiaries:

Chuzhou New Best Extra Clean Materials Tech Co., Ltd. (1)
965 Shuangcheng Road Suchu Modern Industrial Park, Chuzhou, Anhui, China
Tel.: (86) 5503877700
Carbon Steel Wire Mfr & Distr
N.A.I.C.S.: 331513

New Best Wire Vietnam Industrial Company Limited (1)
Lo so CN1-1 Khu Cong Nghiep Minh Quang, Phuong Bach Sam, My Hao, Hung Yen, Vietnam
Tel.: (84) 2216513666
Carbon Steel Wire Mfr & Distr
N.A.I.C.S.: 331513

NEW BRUNSWICK POWER CORPORATION
515 King Street STN A, PO Box 2000, Fredericton, E3B 4X1, NB, Canada
Tel.: (506) 458-4444
Web Site: http://www.nbpower.com
Year Founded: 1920
Sales Range: $1-4.9 Billion
Emp.: 2,500
Electric Utility Services
N.A.I.C.S.: 221122
Edward Barrett *(Chm)*

NEW BUBBLEROOM SWEDEN AB
Prognosgatan 11, 504 64, Boras, Sweden
Tel.: (46) 84111717
Web Site: https://www.bubbleroom.se
Year Founded: 2005
BBROOM—(OMX)
Rev.: $43,472,910
Assets: $24,511,089
Liabilities: $12,693,828
Net Worth: $11,817,262
Earnings: ($2,911,629)
Emp.: 66
Fiscal Year-end: 12/31/23
Online Shopping Services
N.A.I.C.S.: 425120
Freddy Sobin *(Chm)*

NEW CENTRUY RESOURCES
Suite 23 513 Hay Street, Subiaco, 6008, WA, Australia
Tel.: (61) 8 6142 0989
Web Site: http://www.newcenturyresources.com
Assets: $18,464,822
Liabilities: $16,422,772
Net Worth: $2,042,051
Earnings: ($3,406,903)
Coal & Gold Exploration Services
N.A.I.C.S.: 212115
Evan Cranston *(Chm)*

NEW CENTURY GROUP HONG KONG LIMITED
Unit 3808 38/F West Tower Shun Tak Centre Nos 168-200 Connaught Road, Central, China (Hong Kong)
Tel.: (852) 2 530 1668 BM
Web Site: http://www.ncgrp.com.hk
0234—(HKG)
Rev.: $10,413,974
Assets: $267,122,223
Liabilities: $19,770,312
Net Worth: $247,351,911
Earnings: ($881,578)
Emp.: 31
Fiscal Year-end: 03/31/22
Hotel Operations & Cruise Ship Charter Services
N.A.I.C.S.: 721120
Ion Kuan Sio *(Deputy Chm)*

Subsidiaries:

ETC Finance Limited (1)
Room 3807 38/F West Wing Shun Tak Centre 168-200 Connaught Road, Sheung Wan, Central, China (Hong Kong)
Tel.: (852) 29168328
Web Site: https://etcfinance.com.hk
Mortgage Services
N.A.I.C.S.: 522310

NEW CENTURY HEALTHCARE HOLDING CO. LIMITED
21/F West Tower Genesis Beijing No 8 Xinyuan South Road, Chaoyang District, Beijing, China
Tel.: (86) 1051783369 Ky
Web Site: http://www.ncich.com.cn
Year Founded: 2002
1518—(HKG)
Rev.: $89,358,844
Assets: $126,554,314
Liabilities: $75,820,633
Net Worth: $50,733,680
Earnings: $40,936,849
Emp.: 1,246
Fiscal Year-end: 12/31/22
Health Care Srvices
N.A.I.C.S.: 622210
Lan Teng *(Dir-HR)*

NEW CENTURY SHIPBUILDING CORPORATION

NEW CENTURY SHIPBUILDING CORPORATION

New Century Shipbuilding Corporation—(Continued)
Xingang Port, Jingjiang, 214514, Jiangsu, China
Tel.: (86) 52384216239
Web Site: http://www.ncship.com.ch
Sales Range: $1-4.9 Billion
Emp.: 4,717
Ship Building & Repairing Services
N.A.I.C.S.: 336611
Haijin Liu *(CEO)*

Subsidiaries:

New Times Shipbuilding Co., Ltd. (1)
Xingang Port, Jingjiang, Jiangsu, China
Tel.: (86) 52384216239
Emp.: 3,200
Water Transportation Services
N.A.I.C.S.: 488390

NEW CHINA LIFE INSURANCE CO., LTD.
Xinhua Insurance Building No 12 Jianguomenwai Street, Chaoyang District, Beijing, China
Tel.: (86) 1085213233
Web Site: https://www.newchinalife.com
Year Founded: 1996
601336—(SHG)
Rev.: $31,233,084,180
Assets: $153,880,446,960
Liabilities: $138,302,054,160
Net Worth: $15,578,392,800
Earnings: $2,190,443,370
Emp.: 36,309
Fiscal Year-end: 12/31/20
Investment Management Service
N.A.I.C.S.: 523999
Xingfeng Gong *(VP)*

NEW CITY DEVELOPMENT GROUP LIMITED
Unit D 17/F MG Tower 133 Hoi Bun Road Kwun Tong, Kowloon, China (Hong Kong)
Tel.: (852) 28621600
Web Site: http://www.newcitygroup.com.hk
Year Founded: 1998
0456—(HKG)
Rev.: $25,514,437
Assets: $294,803,137
Liabilities: $200,186,891
Net Worth: $94,616,246
Earnings: ($8,952,631)
Emp.: 69
Fiscal Year-end: 12/31/21
Investment Management Service
N.A.I.C.S.: 523940
Junran Han *(Chm)*

NEW COMMERCE SPLIT CORP.
200 Front Street West Suite 2510, PO Box 51, Toronto, M5V 3K2, ON, Canada
Tel.: (416) 304-4440
Web Site: https://www.quadravest.com
YCM.PR.B—(TSX)
Sales Range: Less than $1 Million
Commercial Bank Services
N.A.I.C.S.: 522110
Laura L. Johnson *(Portfolio Mgr)*

NEW CONCEPTS HOLDINGS LIMITED
Office B 3/F Kingston International Centre 19 Wang Chiu Road, Kowloon Bay, China (Hong Kong)
Tel.: (852) 35889600
Web Site: https://www.primeworld-china.com
2221—(HKG)
Rev.: $84,462,682
Assets: $104,809,664
Liabilities: $73,926,048
Net Worth: $30,883,616
Earnings: $2,203,623
Emp.: 318
Fiscal Year-end: 03/31/22
Holding Company; Construction & Engineering Services
N.A.I.C.S.: 236220
Yongjun Zhu *(Chm)*

Subsidiaries:

New Concepts Foundation Limited (1)
Room 801-806 Tower A New Mandarin Plaza 14 Science Museum Rd, Tsim Sha Tsui East, Kowloon, China (Hong Kong)
Tel.: (852) 27507008
Web Site: http://www.ncfl.com.hk
Building Construction Services
N.A.I.C.S.: 236220
Chu Shu Cheong *(Founder & Mng Dir)*

NEW CONSTRUCTOR'S NETWORK CO., LTD.
Akasaka Eight One Building 2-13-5 Nagatacho, Chiyoda-ku, Tokyo, 100-0014, Japan
Tel.: (81) 368976311
Web Site: https://ncn-se.co.jp
Year Founded: 1996
7057—(TKS)
Rev.: $52,866,780
Assets: $37,822,420
Liabilities: $23,650,580
Net Worth: $14,171,840
Emp.: 138
Fiscal Year-end: 03/31/24
Construction Services
N.A.I.C.S.: 236220
Tsuneo Sugiyama *(Founder & Chm)*

NEW COSMOS ELECTRIC CO., LTD.
2-5-4 Mitsuyanaka, Yodogawa-ku, Osaka, 532-0036, Japan
Tel.: (81) 663083112 JP
Web Site: https://www.new-cosmos.co.jp
Year Founded: 1934
6824—(TKS)
Rev.: $254,681,131
Assets: $441,605,426
Liabilities: $126,772,346
Net Worth: $314,833,080
Earnings: $19,550,705
Fiscal Year-end: 03/31/24
Gas Sensor Mfr
N.A.I.C.S.: 334519
Tesshi Shigemori *(Chm)*

Subsidiaries:

Figaro Engineering Inc. (1)
1-5-11 Senbanishi, Mino, 562-8505, Osaka, Japan
Tel.: (81) 727282560
Web Site: https://www.figaro.co.jp
Sales Range: $25-49.9 Million
Emp.: 220
Gas Sensor & Detection Equipment Developer, Mfr & Marketer
N.A.I.C.S.: 334511

Subsidiary (US):

Figaro USA, Inc. (2)
121 S Wilke Rd Ste 300, Arlington Heights, IL 60005
Tel.: (847) 832-1701
Web Site: http://www.figarosensor.com
Gas Sensor & Detection Equipment Whslr
N.A.I.C.S.: 423830
Kazuaki Watanabe *(Pres & CEO)*

Affiliate (Non-US):

Tianjin Figaro Electronic Co., Ltd. (2)
Tianjin Economic-Technological Development Zone, No 19 Weishan Road, Tianjin, 300457, China
Tel.: (86) 2225325913
Web Site: https://www.tjfigaro.com
Emp.: 170
Gas Sensor & Detection Equipmen Mfr
N.A.I.C.S.: 334511

New Cosmos BIE B.V. (1)
Maxwellstraat 7, 1704 SG, Heerhugowaard, Netherlands
Tel.: (31) 725765630
Gas Detector Mfr & Distr
N.A.I.C.S.: 334519

New Cosmos Electric (Shanghai) Co., Ltd. (1)
4th Plant No 385 Dongxing Road Songjiang Industrial Zone, Shanghai, 201613, China
Tel.: (86) 2167743138
Gas Detector Distr
N.A.I.C.S.: 423690

New Cosmos Electric Korea Co., Ltd. (1)
3rd & 4th Floor BMY Yeoksam Tower 16 Teheran-ro 27-gil, Gangnam-gu, Seoul, Korea (South)
Tel.: (82) 25553102
Web Site: https://www.new-cosmos.co.kr
Household Gas Alarm Mfr & Distr
N.A.I.C.S.: 334519

New Cosmos USA, Inc. (1)
650 Warrenville Rd Ste 101, Lisle, IL 60532
Tel.: (847) 749-3064
Web Site: https://www.denovadetect.com
Gas Alarm Mfr & Distr
N.A.I.C.S.: 334519

NEW COUNTRY MEDICAL SUPPLIES COMPANY LLC
PO Box 23412, Dubai, United Arab Emirates
Tel.: (971) 43537733 AE
Pharmaceuticals Product Mfr
N.A.I.C.S.: 325412

NEW DAWN ENERGY LIMITED
PO Box 36797, Merivale, Christchurch, 8146, New Zealand
Tel.: (64) 3 377 0045 NZ
Year Founded: 2012
Sales Range: $1-9.9 Million
Oil & Natural Gas Exploration, Development & Extraction
N.A.I.C.S.: 213112
Archibald Geoffrey Loudon *(Founder)*

NEW DAWN MINING CORP.
1st Floor KPMG House 133 Josiah tongogara Street, Bulawayo, Zimbabwe
Tel.: (263) 9 75810 Ky
Web Site: http://www.newdawnmining.com
Sales Range: $50-74.9 Million
Emp.: 2,820
Gold Ore Exploration & Mining Services
N.A.I.C.S.: 212220
Ian R. Saunders *(Pres & CEO)*

Subsidiaries:

Casmyn Mining Zimbabwe (Private) Ltd (1)
Habib Hs 121 R Mugabe Way Btn, 12th & 13th Aves, Bulawayo, Zimbabwe
Tel.: (263) 975810
Web Site: http://www.falgold.co.cw
Mining Services
N.A.I.C.S.: 212390

NDM Casmyn Ltd (1)
Metallum House Unit 3 89 Manor Farm Rd, Alperton, Wembley, HA0 1BA, Middlesex, United Kingdom
Tel.: (44) 20 8991 7310
Web Site: http://www.ndmltd.com
Gold Mining Services
N.A.I.C.S.: 212220

NEW DELHI TELEVISION LIMITED
B 50-A 2nd Floor 2nd Floor Archana

INTERNATIONAL PUBLIC

Complex, Greater Kailash - I, New Delhi, 110048, India
Tel.: (91) 1141577777
Web Site: https://www.ndtv.com
Year Founded: 1984
NDTV—(NSE)
Rev.: $55,678,350
Assets: $61,964,175
Liabilities: $38,692,700
Net Worth: $23,271,476
Earnings: $10,218,390
Emp.: 464
Fiscal Year-end: 03/31/21
News & Television Stations
N.A.I.C.S.: 516120
Prannoy Roy *(Co-Chm)*

Subsidiaries:

Aidem Ventures (1)
HDIL Kaledonia 3rd Floor 3/B Andheri Sahar Road, Andheri E, Mumbai, 400069, Maharashtra, India
Tel.: (91) 2266665000
Web Site: http://www.aidem.in
Sales Range: $25-49.9 Million
Emp.: 100
Advertising Services
N.A.I.C.S.: 541810
Ashok Kumar Gupta *(Chm)*

NDTV Convergence Limited (1)
W-17 2nd Floor Greater Kailash-I, New Delhi, 110048, India
Tel.: (91) 1166176452
Web Site: http://www.ndtv.com
Sales Range: $25-49.9 Million
Emp.: 85
Television Broadcasting Services
N.A.I.C.S.: 516120

NDTV Lifestyle Limited (1)
207 Okhla Indust Estate Phase 3, New Delhi, 110020, India
Tel.: (91) 1141577800
Web Site: http://www.ndtvgoodtimes.com
Sales Range: $25-49.9 Million
Emp.: 200
Television Broadcasting Services
N.A.I.C.S.: 516120
Shibani Sharma Khanna *(Head-Channel)*

NDTV Networks BV (1)
Martinus Nijhofflaan 2, 2624 ES, Delft, South Holland, Netherlands
Tel.: (31) 157890100
Sales Range: $25-49.9 Million
Emp.: 30
Television Broadcasting Services
N.A.I.C.S.: 516120

NEW DESTINY MINING CORP.
888 Dunsmuir St Suite 888, Vancouver, V6C 3K4, BC, Canada
Tel.: (604) 488-3900 BC
Web Site: https://www.newdestinymining.com
Year Founded: 2009
6ND1—(DEU)
Assets: $23,512
Liabilities: $1,055,970
Net Worth: ($1,032,458)
Earnings: ($552,517)
Fiscal Year-end: 06/30/23
Metal Mining Services
N.A.I.C.S.: 212290
Barry Brown *(CFO)*

NEW EAST NEW MATERIALS CO., LTD.
101 Huangjiao Road, Taizhou, 314500, China
Tel.: (86) 57388366244
603110—(SHG)
Rev.: $56,750,972
Assets: $116,316,360
Liabilities: $22,656,306
Net Worth: $93,660,054
Earnings: $2,768,014
Fiscal Year-end: 12/31/22
Chemical Product Mfr & Distr
N.A.I.C.S.: 325998

NEW EMPIRE CONTRACTORS LTD
3000 Langstaff Road Unit 7, Concord, L4K 4R7, ON, Canada
Tel.: (905) 660-4341
Web Site:
http://newempiredesignbuild.com
Year Founded: 1988
Rev.: $19,352,500
Emp.: 10
Construction Services
N.A.I.C.S.: 236210
Domenic Tersigni (VP)

NEW ENERGY EXCHANGE LTD.
Unit 10-11 10/F West Tower Shun Tak Centre, 168-200 Connaught Road, Central, China (Hong Kong)
Tel.: (852) 31128461 VG
EBODF—(OTCEM)
Sales Range: $1-9.9 Million
Emp.: 223
Holding Company; Network Security Software & Renewable Energy Products
N.A.I.C.S.: 551112
Xiangyi Zeng (CEO)

Subsidiaries:
China Green Holdings Limited (1)
19/F China Hong Kong Tower 8 Hennessy Road, 25 Harbour Rd, Wanchai, China (Hong Kong)
Tel.: (852) 25989838
Emp.: 4
Holding Company; Agricultural Services
N.A.I.C.S.: 551112
Shao Fang Sun (Mng Dir)

NEW ENERGY METALS CORP.
2300-1177 West Hastings Street, Vancouver, V6E 2K3, BC, Canada
Tel.: (604) 484-1232
Web Site:
http://www.newenergymetals.ca
NEMCF—(OTCIQ)
Assets: $1,237,194
Liabilities: $114,745
Net Worth: $1,122,449
Earnings: ($3,431,606)
Fiscal Year-end: 06/30/19
Mineral Exploration Services
N.A.I.C.S.: 213115

NEW ENERGY MINERALS LTD
Level 3 9 Bowman Street, South Perth, 6151, WA, Australia
Tel.: (61) 892172400 AU
Web Site:
http://www.newenergyminerals.com
Year Founded: 1999
NXE—(ASX)
Sales Range: Less than $1 Million
Ruby Stone Mining Services
N.A.I.C.S.: 212390
Ian Daymond (Chm)

NEW ENERGY ONE ACQUISITION CORPORATION PLC
201 Temple Chambers 3-7 Temple Avenue, London, EC4Y 0DT, United Kingdom
Tel.: (44) 2075838304 UK
Web Site: https://www.neoa.london
Year Founded: 2021
NEOA—(LSE)
Investment Management Service
N.A.I.C.S.: 523999
Volker Beckers (Chm)

NEW EQUITY VENTURE INT. AB
Birger Jarlsgatan 18 A 5tr, Stockholm, 10243, Sweden
Tel.: (46) 8 410 59 140

Web Site:
http://www.newequityventure.com
N.A.I.C.S.:
Thomas Jansson (CEO)

Subsidiaries:
Ayima Limited (1)
1st Floor 1 Lindsey Street, London, EC1M 5QG, United Kingdom
Tel.: (44) 207 148 5970
Web Site: http://www.ayima.com
Webpage Development Services
N.A.I.C.S.: 541511

NEW ERA ELECTRONICS CO., LTD.
No 45 15th 10th Wangjianli, Xinwu District, Taoyuan, 327, Taiwan
Tel.: (886) 34722191
Web Site: http://www.nee.com.tw
Year Founded: 1984
4909—(TPE)
Rev.: $15,466,341
Assets: $79,314,605
Liabilities: $6,213,551
Net Worth: $73,101,054
Earnings: ($1,712,316)
Fiscal Year-end: 12/31/22
Computer Component Mfr & Distr
N.A.I.C.S.: 334118
Yung-Hui Chang (Chm & CEO)

Subsidiaries:
NEE International, LLC (1)
4022 E Broadway Rd Ste 119, Phoenix, AZ 85040
Tel.: (602) 910-4650
Web Site: https://www.neeinternational.com
Printed Circuit Board Mfr
N.A.I.C.S.: 334412

NEW FOCUS AUTO TECH HOLDINGS LIMITED
5 F 180 Hennessy Road, Wanchai, China (Hong Kong)
Tel.: (852) 36783083
Web Site: https://www.nfa360.com
0360—(HKG)
Rev.: $83,070,608
Assets: $237,758,976
Liabilities: $139,060,022
Net Worth: $98,698,954
Earnings: ($6,710,699)
Emp.: 785
Fiscal Year-end: 12/31/22
Automobile Parts Mfr
N.A.I.C.S.: 441330

Subsidiaries:
New Focus Lighting & Power Technology (Shanghai) Co., Ltd. (1)
No 4589 Waiqinsong Road Qingpu, Shanghai, 201712, China
Tel.: (86) 2159224688
Web Site: http://www.newfocusauto.com
Emp.: 1,000
Automobile Accessory Product Mfr & Whslr
N.A.I.C.S.: 336390
Hanfei Wen (Gen Mgr)

New Focus Richahaus Co. Ltd. (1)
2F 86 Chiu Tsung Rd Sec 1, Taipei, 11494, Taiwan
Tel.: (886) 227936556
Automotive Parts Sales
N.A.I.C.S.: 423120

NEW FOOD CLASSICS
4211 13A St SE, Calgary, T2G 3J6, AB, Canada
Tel.: (403) 299-0844
Web Site:
http://www.newfoodclassics.com
Sales Range: $125-149.9 Million
Emp.: 300
Mfr of Food Products
N.A.I.C.S.: 311999
Nashir Vasanji (Partner)

NEW FORESTS PTY. LIMITED
Level 23 141 Walker Street, North Sydney, 2060, NSW, Australia
Tel.: (61) 2 9406 4100 AU
Web Site:
http://www.newforests.com.au
Year Founded: 2005
Emp.: 49
Natural Resource Investment Funds Portfolio Management Services
N.A.I.C.S.: 523940
David Brand (CEO)

Subsidiaries:
New Forests Inc. (1)
275 Battery St Ste 510, San Francisco, CA 94111
Tel.: (415) 321-3300
Web Site: http://www.newforests-us.com
Real Estate Manangement Services
N.A.I.C.S.: 531390
Timothy Robards (Mgr-Investment & Ops-Forestry & Carbon Science)

Timberlink Australia Pty. Ltd. (1)
Lot 3b 1490 Ferntree Gully Road, Knoxfield, 3180, VIC, Australia
Tel.: (61) 8 9360 3113
Web Site:
http://www.timberlinkaustralia.com.au
Sales Range: $150-199.9 Million
Emp.: 380
Sawmills & Wood Products Whslr
N.A.I.C.S.: 321113

NEW FOUND GOLD CORP.
555 Burrard Street, P.O. Box 272, Vancouver, V7X 1M8, BC, Canada
Tel.: (604) 562-9664
Web Site:
https://www.newfoundgold.ca
NFGC—(NYSEAMEX)
Rev.: $954,600
Assets: $86,588,627
Liabilities: $21,288,664
Net Worth: $65,299,962
Earnings: ($70,397,110)
Emp.: 100
Fiscal Year-end: 12/31/22
Gold Mining Services
N.A.I.C.S.: 212220
Collin Kettell (Co-Founder & Chm)

NEW FRONTIER HEALTH CORPORATION
10 Jiuxianqiao Road Hengtong Business Park B7 Building 1/F, Chaoyang District, Beijing, 100015, China
Tel.: (86) 10 59277000 Ky
Web Site: http://www.new-frontier.com
Year Founded: 2018
Rev.: $346,331,971
Assets: $2,055,395,037
Liabilities: $880,061,681
Net Worth: $1,175,333,355
Earnings: ($81,485,351)
Emp.: 3,309
Fiscal Year-end: 12/31/20
Investment Services
N.A.I.C.S.: 523999
Antony Leung (Co-Founder & Co-Chm)

NEW FRONTIER PROPERTIES LIMITED
2nd Floor 86 Brook Street, London, W1K 5AY, United Kingdom
Tel.: (44) 2070163960
Web Site:
http://www.newfrontierprop.com
NFPE—(JSE)
Rev.: $18,701,548
Assets: $155,069,168
Liabilities: $211,158,583
Net Worth: ($56,089,415)
Earnings: ($85,728,646)
Fiscal Year-end: 08/31/19

Real Estate Services
N.A.I.C.S.: 531390
Michael E. Riley (CEO)

NEW FRONTIER VENTURES INC.
Suite 1700 333 Bay Street Bay-Adelaide Centre, Toronto, M5H 2R2, ON, Canada
Tel.: (647) 252-1674 Ca
Web Site:
http://www.gravitasfinancial.com
VFI.X—(CNSX)
Assets: $1,827
Liabilities: $319,431
Net Worth: ($317,604)
Earnings: ($126,800)
Fiscal Year-end: 12/31/23
Investment Research & Analysis Services
N.A.I.C.S.: 541990
David Carbonaro (Co-Founder)

NEW GLOBAL ACREAGE RESOURCES LTD.
1200 Waterfront Centre 200 Burrard Street, Vancouver, V7X 1T2, BC, Canada
Tel.: (713) 626-4700 BC
Year Founded: 2014
Holding Company
N.A.I.C.S.: 551112
Tony Henshaw (CEO & CFO)

NEW GLOBAL MINING LTD
Level 6 533 Hay Street, Perth, 6000, WA, Australia
Tel.: (61) 893251155
Web Site:
http://www.newglobalmining.com.au
Sales Range: $50-74.9 Million
Emp.: 10
Gold & Base Metal Mining Services
N.A.I.C.S.: 212220
Mark Nevill (Chm)

NEW GOLD INC.
Brookfield Place181 Bay Street Suite 3320, Toronto, M5J 2T3, ON, Canada
Tel.: (416) 324-6000 BC
Web Site: https://www.newgold.com
Year Founded: 1980
NGD—(NYSEAMEX)
Rev.: $786,500,000
Assets: $2,286,000,000
Liabilities: $1,496,800,000
Net Worth: $789,200,000
Earnings: ($64,500,000)
Emp.: 1,542
Fiscal Year-end: 12/31/23
Gold, Silver & Copper Exploration & Mining
N.A.I.C.S.: 212220
Ian Pearce (Chm)

Subsidiaries:
Cerro San Pedro Project Minera San Xavier, S.A. de C.V. (1)
Camino Cerro San Pedro 200, Fraccionamiento Tangamanga, 78280, San Luis Potosi, Cerro San Pedro, Mexico
Tel.: (52) 4448146151
Web Site: http://www.msx.com.mx
Sales Range: $1-9.9 Million
Emp.: 20
Gold & Silver Mining Services
N.A.I.C.S.: 212220

NEW GUINEA GOLD CORPORATION
900 595 Howe Street, Vancouver, V6C 1V5, BC, Canada
Tel.: (604) 689-1515
Web Site:
http://www.newguineagold.ca
NGUGF—(TSXV)
Sales Range: Less than $1 Million

NEW GUINEA GOLD CORPORATION

New Guinea Gold Corporation—(Continued)
Gold Mining
N.A.I.C.S.: 212220
Ces E. Iewago (Chm)

NEW GUOMAI DIGITAL CULTURE CO., LTD.
No 1207 Jiangning Road, Shanghai, 200060, China
Tel.: (86) 2162762171
Web Site: http://www.besttoneh.com
Year Founded: 1992
600640—(SHG)
Rev.: $492,941,746
Assets: $769,636,254
Liabilities: $147,021,559
Net Worth: $622,614,695
Earnings: ($28,032,994)
Fiscal Year-end: 12/31/22
Holding Company
N.A.I.C.S.: 551112
Zhang Wei (Chm)

Subsidiaries:

Oriental Pearl Group Co., Ltd. (1)
No 757 Yishan Road, Xuhui District, Shanghai, China
Tel.: (86) 2133396666
Internet Entertainment Services
N.A.I.C.S.: 516210

NEW HEIGHTS LTD.
49 Hoghton Road, Leyland, PR25 1XX, United Kingdom
Tel.: (44) 7850327101
Web Site: http://www.new-heights.co.uk
Furniture Sales
N.A.I.C.S.: 449110
Richard Hepworth (Co-Founder)

Subsidiaries:

Sofa Workshop Ltd (1)
Lordsworth Barn Lodsworth, Petworth, GU28 9BS, W Sussex, United Kingdom
Tel.: (44) 798343400
Web Site: http://www.sofaworkshop.com
Sales Range: $50-74.9 Million
Emp.: 125
Sofa Mfr
N.A.I.C.S.: 337126

NEW HOLLAND WINE COMPANY PTY. LTD.
Ground Level 26 Greenhill Road, Wayville, 5034, Australia
Tel.: (61) 883736330
Web Site: http://www.newhollandwine.com.au
Producer & Packager of Wines
N.A.I.C.S.: 312130
Lance Bradfield (Owner)

NEW HOONG FATT HOLDINGS BERHAD
Lot 5043 Jalan Teratai Meru, 41050, Kelang, Selangor, Malaysia
Tel.: (60) 333778288
Web Site: https://www.newhoongfatt.com.my
Year Founded: 1977
NHFATT—(KLS)
Rev.: $61,452,698
Assets: $126,063,915
Liabilities: $18,237,037
Net Worth: $107,826,878
Earnings: $5,650,582
Emp.: 939
Fiscal Year-end: 12/31/22
Tools & Dies Mfr
N.A.I.C.S.: 333514
Foong Keng Kam (Chm)

Subsidiaries:

Ampire Auto Parts (Shanghai) Co. Ltd. (1)
Changjiang Software Park Room 339 of Building C, 180 South Changjiang Road Baoshan District, Shanghai, 200493, China
Tel.: (86) 2166780259
Web Site: https://ampire-auto.com
Automotive Part & Accessory Mfr
N.A.I.C.S.: 336390
Frieda Chen (Mgr-Fin)

Auto Global Parts Industries Sdn. Bhd. (1)
Automotive Part & Accessory Mfr
N.A.I.C.S.: 336390

Jhi Soon Manufacturing Industries Sdn. Bhd. (1)
Lot 5046 5 1/2 Miles Jalan Meru, 41050, Kelang, Selangor, Malaysia
Tel.: (60) 333923599
Web Site: http://www.newhoongfatt.com.my
Sales Range: $50-74.9 Million
Emp.: 250
Automotive Metal Parts Mfr
N.A.I.C.S.: 332510

NJ Manufacturing Industries Sdn. Bhd. (1)
Lot 5026 5 1/2 Miles Jalan Meru, Kelang, 41050, Selangor, Malaysia
Tel.: (60) 3 3377 5188
Web Site: http://www.nj.com.my
Sales Range: $150-199.9 Million
Emp.: 300
Automotive Parts Mfr & Distr
N.A.I.C.S.: 423120

New Hoong Fatt Auto Supplies Sdn. Bhd. (1)
Lot 5043 Jalan Teratai, Meru, 41050, Kelang, Selangor Darul Ehsan, Malaysia
Tel.: (60) 333778308
Web Site: http://www.newhoongfatt.com.my
Sales Range: $150-199.9 Million
Emp.: 280
Automotive Parts & Accessories Distr
N.A.I.C.S.: 423120

Subsidiary (Domestic):

New Kean Tat Auto Parts Sdn. Bhd. (2)
No 6 Jalan Setia Rawang 1 Taman Setia, Rawang, 48000, Selangor, Malaysia
Tel.: (60) 360913087
Motor Vehicle Parts & Accessories Distr
N.A.I.C.S.: 423120

PT NHF Auto Supplies Indonesia (1)
Jl Kapuk Kamal Raya No 39 RT 007/RW01 Kec Penjaringan Kel Kamal Muara, Jakarta Utara, 14470, Indonesia
Tel.: (62) 2129511475
Automotive Part & Accessory Mfr
N.A.I.C.S.: 336390

NEW HOPE CORPORATION LIMITED
Level 18 175 Eagle Street, Brisbane, 4000, QLD, Australia
Tel.: (61) 734180500
Web Site: https://www.newhopegroup.com.au
NHPEF—(OTCIQ)
Rev.: $1,960,249,611
Assets: $2,625,759,947
Liabilities: $851,623,250
Net Worth: $1,774,136,697
Earnings: $753,171,666
Emp.: 743
Fiscal Year-end: 07/31/22
Support Activities for Coal Mining
N.A.I.C.S.: 213113
Robert Dobson Millner (Chm)

Subsidiaries:

Northern Energy Corporation Limited (100%)
Level 5 60 Edward Street, Brisbane, 4000, QLD, Australia
Tel.: (61) 733030695
Web Site: http://www.northernenergy.com.au
Sales Range: $50-74.9 Million
Emp.: 8
Coal Exploration & Development
N.A.I.C.S.: 212114

NEW HOPE DAIRY CO., LTD.
No 366 Jinshi Road, Jinjiang District, Chengdu, 610023, Sichuan, China
Tel.: (86) 2886748930
Web Site: https://www.newhopedairy.cn
Year Founded: 2006
002946—(SSE)
Rev.: $1,404,912,600
Assets: $1,332,459,180
Liabilities: $958,128,912
Net Worth: $374,330,268
Earnings: $50,756,004
Fiscal Year-end: 12/31/22
Dairy Product Mfr & Distr
N.A.I.C.S.: 333241
Xi Gang (Chm)

NEW HOPE GROUP CO., LTD.
Floor 24 Block 2 New Hope Zhongding International 366 Jinshi Road, Jinjiang District, Chengdu, 610041, Sichuan, China
Tel.: (86) 2865721666
Web Site: http://www.newhopegroup.com
Year Founded: 1982
Sales Range: $5-14.9 Billion
Emp.: 70,000
Investment Management Service
N.A.I.C.S.: 523940
Yonghao Liu (Chm)

Subsidiaries:

MYANMAR NEW HOPE FARMS CO., LTD (1)
Plot No 33 Industrial Area Taikgyi-Bago High Way Road, Nyaung Inn Village, Pyinmana, Myanmar
Tel.: (95) 973229369
Animal Food Distr
N.A.I.C.S.: 424910

NEW HOPE AGROTECH BANGLADESH LTD (1)
Char Bausia Bausia, Gazaria, Munshiganj, Bangladesh
Tel.: (880) 1857222701
Animal Food Distr
N.A.I.C.S.: 424910

NEW HOPE BULACAN AGRICULTURE INC. (1)
Tibag Brgy, Pulilan, 0645, Bulacan, Philippines
Tel.: (63) 448153628
Animal Food Distr
N.A.I.C.S.: 424910

NEW HOPE CENTRAL LUZON AGRICULTURE INC. (1)
Sto Nino San Simon, Pampanga, Philippines
Tel.: (63) 9176995288
Animal Food Distr
N.A.I.C.S.: 424910

NEW HOPE EGYPT CO. LTD (1)
Plot No 7197-The seventh Industrial Zone, Sadat City, Egypt
Tel.: (20) 482630130
Animal Food Distr
N.A.I.C.S.: 424910

NEW HOPE FARMS BANGLADESH CO., LTD (1)
Mamarishpur Mollikbari, Bhaluka, Mymensingh, Bangladesh
Tel.: (880) 1784397016
Animal Food Distr
N.A.I.C.S.: 424910

NEW HOPE LANKA LTD (1)
No 225A Kurunduwatte Road, Ekala, Ja-Ela, Sri Lanka
Tel.: (94) 112229696
Animal Food Distr
N.A.I.C.S.: 424910

NEW HOPE SOUTH AFRICA (PTY) LTD (1)
Groud floor 2 Skeen Boulevard, Bedfordview, South Africa
Tel.: (27) 114503965

INTERNATIONAL PUBLIC

Animal Food Distr
N.A.I.C.S.: 424910
Hugo Cilliers (Mgr-Sls)

NEW HOPE TARLAC AGRICULTURE INC. (1)
Mac Arthur Hiway Brgy Parsolingan, Gerona, Tarlac, Philippines
Tel.: (63) 459313435
Animal Food Distr
N.A.I.C.S.: 424910

NEW HOPE TURKEY YEM HAYVANCILIK GIDA ITHALAT IHRACAT SANAYI VE TICARET LIMITED SIRKETI (1)
Cinarli Mah Ziyapasa Bulv Basar Apt No 55 Kat 4/16, Seyhan, Adana, Turkiye
Tel.: (90) 5395077286
Animal Food Distr
N.A.I.C.S.: 424910

New Hope Dong Thap Aquafeed Produuction co., Ltd. (1)
Section I-3 and I-5 Area C widening Sadec Industrial Park, Dong Thap, Vietnam
Tel.: (84) 673764978
Animal Feed Mfr
N.A.I.C.S.: 311119

New Hope Feed Mill Bangladesh Ltd. (1)
Bhangnahati Sreepur, Gazipur, Bangladesh
Tel.: (880) 682551015
Animal Feed Mfr
N.A.I.C.S.: 311119

New Hope Hochiminh City Co., Ltd. (1)
Vinh Loc Indutrial Zone, Binh Tan District, Ho Chi Minh City, Vietnam
Tel.: (84) 837650622
Animal Food Distr
N.A.I.C.S.: 424910

New Hope Liuhe Co., Ltd. (1)
National Hi-Tech Industrial Development Zone, Mianyang, Sichuan, China
Tel.: (86) 2882000876
Web Site: http://www.newhopeagri.com
Rev.: $19,592,895,464
Assets: $18,924,289,571
Liabilities: $12,871,566,418
Net Worth: $6,052,723,153
Earnings: ($202,233,330)
Emp.: 62,000
Fiscal Year-end: 12/31/2022
Animal Feed Mfr & Distr
N.A.I.C.S.: 311119
Chang Liu (Chm)

New Hope Pampanga Agriculture Inc. (1)
Baliti Mac Arthur Highway, San Fernando, Pampanga, Philippines
Tel.: (63) 45887352
Animal Food Distr
N.A.I.C.S.: 424910

New hope Hanoi Co., Ltd. (1)
Sai Dong Industrial Zone B Sai Dong Ward, Long Bien District, Hanoi, Vietnam
Tel.: (84) 438752430
Animal Food Distr
N.A.I.C.S.: 424910

PT. Hope of Indonesia (1)
Jalan Kapasa Raya No 2, Makassar, 90241, Indonesia
Tel.: (62) 411511218
Web Site: http://www.hope-indonesia.com
Liquor Mfr
N.A.I.C.S.: 312120

PT. NEW HOPE FARM INDONISIA (1)
JL Ahmad Yani NO 1 kel pegambiran kec lemahwungkuk cirebon, Cirebon, Jawa Barat, Indonesia
Tel.: (62) 231830519
Animal Food Distr
N.A.I.C.S.: 424910

PT. NEW HOPE MEDAN (1)
Komplek Cemara Asri Jl Boulevard Blok C6 No 12 Sampali-Percut Sei, uan-Deli Serdang 2371, Medan, Indonesia
Tel.: (62) 616636081
Animal Food Distr
N.A.I.C.S.: 424910

PT. New Hope Jawa Timur (1)
Raya Sawunggaling 162 RT01 RW01 Desa Jemundo Kec Taman Sidoarjo, Surabaya, Indonesia
Tel.: (62) 317883809
Animal Feed Mfr
N.A.I.C.S.: 311119

SICHUAN NEW HOPE AGRIBUSINESS (CAMBODIA) CO., LTD (1)
special economy zone national road 4, Phnom Penh, Cambodia
Tel.: (855) 979405010
Animal Food Distr
N.A.I.C.S.: 424910

NEW HORIZON AIRCRAFT LTD.

3187 Highway 35, Lindsay, K9V 4R1, ON, Canada
Tel.: (613) 866-1935   BC
Web Site: https://www.horizonaircraft.com
Year Founded: 2022
HOVR—(NASDAQ)
Assets: $3,652,212
Liabilities: $16,899,608
Net Worth: ($13,247,396)
Earnings: ($6,027,923)
Emp.: 16
Fiscal Year-end: 05/31/24
Aircraft Equipment Mfr
N.A.I.C.S.: 336412

NEW HORIZON CAPITAL

Suites 1702-03 17/F One Exchange Square 8 Connaught Place, Central, China (Hong Kong)
Tel.: (852) 2801 6988
Web Site: http://www.nhfund.com
Year Founded: 2005
Privater Equity Firm
N.A.I.C.S.: 523999
Zhang Jie *(Mng Dir)*

NEW HORIZON CAPITAL CO. LTD.

2-8-6 Nishishinbashi 4th Floor Sumitomo Fudosan Hibiya Bldg, Minato-ku, Tokyo, 105-0003, Japan
Tel.: (81) 3 3519 1260   JP
Web Site: http://newhorizon.jp
Year Founded: 2006
Investment Holding Company
N.A.I.C.S.: 551112
Yaushi Ando *(CEO)*

NEW HORIZON GROUP LTD.

7 Menachem Betin Street, Ramat Gan, 52521, Israel
Tel.: (972) 37549599
Year Founded: 1979
Assets: $1,174,748
Liabilities: $7,353,851
Net Worth: ($6,179,102)
Earnings: ($1,007,344)
Emp.: 4
Fiscal Year-end: 12/31/18
Real Estate Development Services
N.A.I.C.S.: 531390

NEW HORIZON HEALTH LIMITED

13/F building T1 No 400 jianger Road Changhe street, Herui international science & Technology Plaza Binjiang District, Hangzhou, 310052, Zhejiang, China
Tel.: (86) 57186430935   Ky
Web Site: https://www.newhorizonbio.com
Year Founded: 2015
6606—(HKG)
Rev.: $117,199,522
Assets: $394,489,091
Liabilities: $69,431,095
Net Worth: $325,057,997
Earnings: ($12,304,755)
Emp.: 878
Fiscal Year-end: 12/31/22
Health Care Srvices
N.A.I.C.S.: 621610
Xiaotian Yu *(Chief Medical Officer)*

Subsidiaries:

Hangzhou Neohalo Biotechnology Limited (1)
Room 205 2nd Floor Building 1 No 400 Jianger Road Changhe Street, Binjiang District, Hangzhou, Zhejiang, China
Tel.: (86) 57186700733
Web Site: https://www.neohalobio.com
Laboratory Equipment Mfr & Distr
N.A.I.C.S.: 334516

NEW HUADU SUPERCENTER CO., LTD.

4F No 28 Fuxin Road Sunshine City Phase 3, Gulou District, Fuzhou, 350003, Fujian, China
Tel.: (86) 59187987972
Web Site: http://www.nhd-mart.com
002264—(SSE)
Rev.: $424,274,760
Assets: $375,452,064
Liabilities: $169,295,724
Net Worth: $206,156,340
Earnings: $28,753,920
Fiscal Year-end: 12/31/22
Departmental Store Operator
N.A.I.C.S.: 455110
Guotao Ni *(Chm)*

NEW IMAGE GROUP LIMITED

19 Mahunga Drive Mangere Bridge, Auckland, 2022, New Zealand
Tel.: (64) 96222388
Web Site: http://www.newimage.asia
Sales Range: $50-74.9 Million
Emp.: 200
Health Products Mfr & Distr
N.A.I.C.S.: 325412
Graeme Lindsay Clegg *(Founder & Chm)*

Subsidiaries:

BioActive Technologies International Limited (1)
19 Mahunga Drive Mangere Bridge, Auckland, 2022, New Zealand
Tel.: (64) 96229650
Web Site: http://www.newimagegroup.co.nz
Emp.: 100
Nutraceutical Products Mfr & Distr
N.A.I.C.S.: 311514
Graeme Clegg *(Chm)*

New Image Health Sciences (Pty) Limited (1)
Edward Building Edward Street, Bellville, 7530, Western Cape, South Africa
Tel.: (27) 219104910
Sales Range: $50-74.9 Million
Emp.: 3
Nutrition Product Distr
N.A.I.C.S.: 424490
Dante Gous *(Gen Mgr)*

New Image International Limited (1)
19 Mahunga Drive Mangere Bridge, Auckland, 2022, New Zealand
Tel.: (64) 96222388
Web Site: http://www.newimage.asia
Sales Range: $25-49.9 Million
Emp.: 40
Nutrition Product Distr
N.A.I.C.S.: 456191
Graeme Clegg *(Founder & Chm)*

Subsidiary (Non-US):

NZ New Image SDN BHD (2)
A-20-1 to A-20-2 Tower A Northpoint Offices Mid Valley City, No 1 Medan Syed Putra Utara, 59200, Kuala Lumpur, Malaysia
Tel.: (60) 320359999
Web Site: http://www.newimageasia.com.my
Sales Range: $25-49.9 Million
Emp.: 20
Nutritional Drinks Mfr & Distr
N.A.I.C.S.: 311514

New Zealand International Far East Philippines Limited (2)
Unit 1806 Centerpoint Bldg Garnet Rd Corner Julia Vergas Ave, Ortigas Ctr, Pasig, 1605, Philippines
Tel.: (63) 26873161
Web Site: http://www.newimageasia.com
Sales Range: $25-49.9 Million
Emp.: 5
Nutritional Beverages Mfr & Distr
N.A.I.C.S.: 311514
Namhoat Chua *(VP)*

New Image International Singapore (Pte) Limited (1)
Bldg Ubi 55 04-12/13 Ubi Ave 1, Singapore, 408935, Singapore
Tel.: (65) 68386766
Sales Range: $25-49.9 Million
Emp.: 4
Nutritional Beverages Mfr & Distr
N.A.I.C.S.: 311514
Graeme Lindsay Clegg *(Chm)*

New Zealand New Image Limited (1)
Unit 1802 18/F CFC Tower 28 Mody Road, TsimShaTsui, Kowloon, China (Hong Kong)
Tel.: (852) 23011142
Web Site: http://www.newimageasia.com
Sales Range: $25-49.9 Million
Emp.: 4
Nutritional Beverages Mfr & Distr
N.A.I.C.S.: 311514

NEW INFINITY HOLDINGS LTD.

2197 Riverside Drive Unit 405, Ottawa, K1H 7X3, ON, Canada
Tel.: (613) 523-0005
NIHL—(OTCIQ)
Assets: $1,000
Liabilities: $41,000
Net Worth: ($40,000)
Earnings: ($18,000)
Fiscal Year-end: 12/31/19
Software Development Services
N.A.I.C.S.: 541511
Chris Lancey *(Pres & CEO)*

NEW JAPAN CHEMICAL CO., LTD.

218 Bingocho, Chuo-ku, Osaka, 541-0051, Japan
Tel.: (81) 662020624
Web Site: https://www.nj-chem.co.jp
Year Founded: 1919
4406—(TKS)
Rev.: $217,224,430
Assets: $265,153,540
Liabilities: $143,027,180
Net Worth: $122,126,360
Earnings: $1,454,200
Emp.: 298
Fiscal Year-end: 03/31/24
Chemical Products Mfr
N.A.I.C.S.: 325199
Mantaro Fujimoto *(Chm)*

Subsidiaries:

Albess Co., Ltd. (1)
2-1-8 Bingomachi Bingomachi-Nomura Building, Chuo-ku, Osaka, 541-0051, Japan
Tel.: (81) 662036925
Detergent Distr
N.A.I.C.S.: 424690

Emery Oleochemicals Rika Sdn. Bhd. (1)
Lot 4 Jalan Perak Kawasan Perusahaan, Teluk Panglima Garang, 42500, Selangor, Malaysia
Tel.: (60) 333268686
Alcohol Mfr & Distr
N.A.I.C.S.: 312130

Grandee Biotechnologies Sdn. Bhd. (1)
Lot 206A Jalan2/5 Gebeng Industrial Estate Phase II, 26080, Kuantan, Pahang Darul Makmur, Malaysia
Tel.: (60) 95838068
Detergent Mfr & Distr
N.A.I.C.S.: 325611

Iwatani Rika Co., Ltd. (1)
49-111-12 Yonetsu Mikuni-cho, Sakai, 913-0036, Fukui, Japan
Tel.: (81) 776826248
Emp.: 6
Detergent Mfr & Distr
N.A.I.C.S.: 325611

NJC Europe Co., Ltd. (1)
3 Howarth Court Gateway Crescent Broadway Business Park, Chadderton, Oldham, OL9 9XB, United Kingdom
Tel.: (44) 1612191926
Chemical Products Distr
N.A.I.C.S.: 424690

NJC Korea Co., Ltd. (1)
402 12 Teheran-ro 104-gil, Gangnam-gu, Seoul, 135-502, Korea (South)
Tel.: (82) 25531545
Chemical Products Distr
N.A.I.C.S.: 424690

New Japan Chemical Co., Ltd. - Kawasaki Plant (1)
7-2 Ukishima-cho, Kawasaki-ku, Kawasaki, 210-0862, Kanagawa, Japan
Tel.: (81) 442883275
Plasticizer Mfr
N.A.I.C.S.: 325199

New Japan Chemical Co., Ltd. - Kyoto Plant (1)
13 Yoshijima Yagura-cho, Fushimi-ku, Kyoto, 612-8224, Japan
Tel.: (81) 756112201
Organic Chemical Mfr
N.A.I.C.S.: 325199

New Japan Chemical Co., Ltd. - Sakai Plant (1)
3-5-1 Shinmachi Chikko, Nishi-ku, Sakai, 592-8331, Japan
Tel.: (81) 722803480
Plasticizer Mfr
N.A.I.C.S.: 325199

New Japan Chemical Co., Ltd. - Tokushima Plant (1)
1 Enokise Kawauchi-cho, Tokushima, 771-0144, Japan
Tel.: (81) 886650321
Organic Chemical Mfr
N.A.I.C.S.: 325199

Nice Rika Biotechnologies Sdn. Bhd. (1)
Lot 206A Jalan2/5, Gebeng Industrial Estate Phase II, 26080, Kuantan, Pahang, Malaysia
Tel.: (60) 95838068
Surfactant Distr
N.A.I.C.S.: 424690

Nissin Chemical Co., Ltd. (1)
12-18 Goi Minami Kaigan, Ichihara, 290-0045, Chiba, Japan
Tel.: (81) 436223611
Plasticizer Mfr
N.A.I.C.S.: 325199

Nitto Kasei Kogyo K.K. (1)
2-17-2 Nakayama, Midori-Ku, Yokohama, 226-0019, Japan
Tel.: (81) 459314665
Metallic Soap Mfr & Distr
N.A.I.C.S.: 325199

Taiwan NJC Corporation (1)
No 45 Zhongzheng Road, Minxiong Industrial Zone Minxiong Township, Chiayi, 62146, Taiwan
Tel.: (886) 52219900
Detergent Mfr & Distr
N.A.I.C.S.: 325611

NEW JCM GROUP CO., LTD

Building 4 No 3 Fengxiu Middle Road, Haidian District, Beijing, 100094, China
Tel.: (86) 1056931000
Web Site: https://en.ldocean.com.cn
Year Founded: 2005
300157—(CHIN)
Rev.: $65,117,520
Assets: $314,043,912
Liabilities: $266,159,088

NEW JCM GROUP CO., LTD

New Jcm Group CO., Ltd—(Continued)
Net Worth: $47,884,824
Earnings: ($15,167,412)
Emp.: 400
Fiscal Year-end: 12/31/22
Seismic Data Processing, 3D Data Interpretation, Reservoir Characterization & Engineering Software Products
N.A.I.C.S.: 513210
Subsidiaries:

AE&E Geomicrobial Technologies, Inc. (1)
7th Floor Building 16 Yard 37 Chaoqian Road, Changping District, Beijing, 102200, China
Tel.: (86) 106 441 1688
Web Site: https://www.aee-t.com
Emp.: 50
Software Development Services
N.A.I.C.S.: 541715

Beijing GDF Oil & Gas Tech., Inc. (1)
Room 1316 No 1 Incubator 3B Buliding Zhongguancun Software Park, West Dongbeiwang Road Haidian District, Beijing, 100193, China
Tel.: (86) 108 282 6002
Web Site: https://www.gdfoil.com
Sales Range: $25-49.9 Million
Emp.: 80
Software Development Services
N.A.I.C.S.: 541511

Dynamic Geosolutions 2008 Ltd. (1)
No 610 633-6 Ave SW, Calgary, T2P 3G3, AB, Canada
Tel.: (403) 265-8559
Web Site: http://www.dgs2008.com
Geophysical Software Development Services
N.A.I.C.S.: 541511

Energy Prospecting Technology USA, Inc. (1)
6100 Corporate Dr Ste 180, Houston, TX 77036
Tel.: (713) 376-8878
Web Site: http://www.ldocean.com.cn
Software Development Services
N.A.I.C.S.: 541511

GoldenMiles PetroTech, Inc. (1)
Room 505 Building 2A Silicon Valley Bright City No 1 Nongda S Road, Haidian District, Beijing, China
Tel.: (86) 1082828395
Web Site: http://www.ldocean.com.cn
Software Development Services
N.A.I.C.S.: 541511

NEW JOURNEY HEALTH TECHNOLOGY GROUP CO., LTD.

28th Floor Fortune Financial Center No 5 East Third Ring Road, Chaoyang District, Beijing, 100020, Sichuan, China
Tel.: (86) 1085235985
Web Site: http://www.hkmg.com
Year Founded: 2001
002219—(SSE)
Rev.: $442,643,292
Assets: $792,153,648
Liabilities: $544,292,892
Net Worth: $247,860,756
Earnings: $21,849,048
Fiscal Year-end: 12/31/22
Pharmaceuticals Product Mfr
N.A.I.C.S.: 325412
Lin Yanglin *(Chm)*
Subsidiaries:

Sichuan Qili Pharmaceutical Co., Ltd. (1)
No 6 Tianhong Road Chengdu High-tech Industrial Development Zone, West District, Chengdu, 611731, China
Tel.: (86) 2887828188
Web Site: http://www.qili.com

Pharmaceutical Mfr & Distr
N.A.I.C.S.: 325412

NEW KINPO GROUP

10th Fl 99 Nan-Jing E Rd Sec 5, Taipei, 105, Taiwan
Tel.: (886) 2 2764 4560
Web Site: http://www.kinpo.com.tw
Year Founded: 1973
Electronic Machinery Equipment Mfr & Distr
N.A.I.C.S.: 334419
Sheng-Hsiung Hsu *(Chm)*
Subsidiaries:

XYZprinting, Inc. (1)
9877 Waples Str, San Diego, CA 92121
Tel.: (855) 999-3348
Web Site: http://www.us.xyzprinting.com
Printing Services
N.A.I.C.S.: 323111

NEW LEAF VENTURES, INC.

1910-1030 West Georgia Street, Vancouver, V6E 2Y3, BC, Canada
Tel.: (604) 330-9220
Web Site: http://www.newleafventuresinc.com
Year Founded: 2018
0IC0—(DEU)
Rev.: $1,462,860
Assets: $1,691,545
Liabilities: $2,691,982
Net Worth: $(1,000,437)
Earnings: ($2,599,085)
Fiscal Year-end: 12/31/22
Pharmaceutical Product Mfr & Distr
N.A.I.C.S.: 325412
Robert Colwell *(Co-Founder)*
Subsidiaries:

New Leaf Real Estate, LLC (1)
3100 Richmond Ave Ste 500, Houston, TX 77098
Tel.: (713) 820-4017
Web Site: https://www.newleafre.com
Real Estate Brokerage Services
N.A.I.C.S.: 531210
David Houston *(Founder)*

New Leaf Services LLC (1)
1321 W Randol Mill Rd Ste 114, Arlington, TX 76012
Web Site: https://www.newleafservicesllc.com
Therapy & Credentialing Services
N.A.I.C.S.: 621340

NEW LESHI INFORMATION & TECHNOLOGY CORP.

No 6819 Building 6184 Room No 6 College Road, Haidian District, Beijing, 100025, China
Tel.: (86) 105 166 5282
Web Site: http://www.letv.com
Year Founded: 2004
300104—(SSE)
Rev.: $69,481,947
Assets: $845,371,507
Liabilities: $2,969,748,805
Net Worth: $(2,124,377,298)
Earnings: ($1,622,363,866)
Emp.: 4,885
Fiscal Year-end: 12/31/19
Internet Service Provider
N.A.I.C.S.: 517121
Yanfeng Liu *(Chm, CFO & Gen Mgr)*

NEW LIGHT APPARELS LIMITED

GC-29 Shivaji Enclave Raja Garden, New Delhi, 110 027, Delhi, India
Tel.: (91) 1145613885
Web Site: https://www.newlightapparels.com
Year Founded: 1959
540243—(BOM)
Rev.: $73,230,622
Assets: $135,720,880

Liabilities: $115,049,457
Net Worth: $20,671,423
Earnings: ($6,245,429)
Emp.: 15
Fiscal Year-end: 03/31/23
Textile Product Mfr & Distr
N.A.I.C.S.: 315120
Sandeep Makkad *(Mng Dir)*

NEW MARKETS ADVISORY LIMITED

Plot No 51 2nd Floor J P Road Azad Nagar Metro Station, Next to Sony Mony, Mumbai, 400058, Maharashtra, India
Tel.: (91) 2222661541
Web Site: https://www.newmarketadvisory.com
508867—(BOM)
Rev.: $10,079
Assets: $270,273
Liabilities: $61,527
Net Worth: $208,746
Earnings: ($12,981)
Emp.: 3
Fiscal Year-end: 03/31/21
Information Technology Consulting Services
N.A.I.C.S.: 541512
Kishore Kanhiyalal Jain *(CEO)*

NEW MAURITIUS HOTELS LIMITED

Beachcomber House Botanical Garden street, 74213, Curepipe, 74213, Mauritius
Tel.: (230) 6019000
Web Site: https://www.beachcomber-hotels.com
Year Founded: 1952
NMHL—(MAU)
Rev.: $304,204,032
Assets: $911,501,770
Liabilities: $673,669,375
Net Worth: $237,832,394
Earnings: $49,294,224
Fiscal Year-end: 06/30/23
Home Management Services
N.A.I.C.S.: 721110
Gilbert Espitalier-Noel *(CEO)*
Subsidiaries:

Mautourco Ltd. (1)
84 Gustave Colin Street, Forest Side, Curepipe, Mauritius (51%)
Tel.: (230) 6043000
Web Site: http://mautourco.com
Sales Range: $100-124.9 Million
Emp.: 250
Tour & Cruise Operator
N.A.I.C.S.: 561520

NEW MOMENTUM CORP.

Room 1303 13/F Technology Plaza 651 Kings Road, North Point, China (Hong Kong)
Tel.: (852) 29110119
Year Founded: 1999
NNAX—(OTCQB)
Rev.: $931,936
Assets: $115,109
Liabilities: $599,557
Net Worth: $(484,448)
Earnings: ($188,853)
Emp.: 1
Fiscal Year-end: 12/31/22
Investment Services
N.A.I.C.S.: 523999

NEW NORDIC HEALTHBRANDS AB

New Nordic AB The Point Hyllie Boulevard 34 Postfack 37, 211 43, Malmo, Sweden
Tel.: (46) 40239520
Web Site: https://www.newnordic.se

NNH—(OMX)
Rev.: $45,660,270
Assets: $23,572,171
Liabilities: $13,028,464
Net Worth: $10,543,707
Earnings: ($264,408)
Emp.: 71
Fiscal Year-end: 12/31/22
Food & Health Supplement Distr
N.A.I.C.S.: 456191
Karl Kristian Bergman Jensen *(CEO)*

NEW ORIENTAL EDUCATION & TECHNOLOGY GROUP INC.

No 6 Haidian Zhongjie, Haidian District, Beijing, 100080, China
Tel.: (86) 1060908000
Web Site: https://investor.neworiental.org
Year Founded: 1993
EDU—(NYSE)
Rev.: $4,313,586,000
Assets: $7,531,673,000
Liabilities: $3,482,659,000
Net Worth: $4,049,014,000
Earnings: $235,363,000
Emp.: 67,935
Fiscal Year-end: 05/31/24
Educational Programs, Services & Products
N.A.I.C.S.: 923110
Michael Minhong Yu *(Founder & Chm)*

NEW ORIENTAL ENERGY & CHEMICAL CORP

Xicheng Industrial Zone, Luoshan, Henan, 464200, China
Tel.: (86) 3762169990
Web Site: http://www.neworientalenergy.com
Sales Range: $25-49.9 Million
Emp.: 1,200
Fertilizer Mfr & Distr
N.A.I.C.S.: 325314
Donglai Li *(CFO)*

NEW PACIFIC METALS CORP.

Suite 1750-1066 West Hastings Street, Vancouver, V6E 3X1, BC, Canada
Tel.: (604) 633-1368
Web Site: https://www.newpacificmetals.com
Year Founded: 1972
NEWP—(NYSEAMEX)
Rev.: $155,943
Assets: $118,307,541
Liabilities: $2,336,655
Net Worth: $115,970,886
Earnings: ($8,100,132)
Emp.: 64
Fiscal Year-end: 06/30/23
Investment Services
N.A.I.C.S.: 523999
Rui Feng *(Founder & CEO)*
Subsidiaries:

Whitehorse Gold Corp. (1)
Suite 1750-1066 West Hastings Street, Vancouver, V6E 3X1, BC, Canada
Tel.: (604) 336-5919
Web Site: https://tincorp.com
Gold Exploration Services
N.A.I.C.S.: 213114
Jean Zhang *(CFO)*

NEW PALACE INTERNATIONAL CO., LTD.

B1 1F-1 1F-2 2F 3F No 456 Han Shi Dong Rd, Taichung, Taiwan
Tel.: (886) 422475222
Web Site: http://www.newpalace.com.tw
8940—(TAI)
Rev.: $50,390,331
Assets: $69,404,916

Liabilities: $43,214,917
Net Worth: $26,189,999
Earnings: $3,842,310
Emp.: 350
Fiscal Year-end: 12/31/23
Restaurant Operating Services
N.A.I.C.S.: 722511
Yu-Yun Wang *(Chm)*

NEW PETCETERA RETAIL LIMITED
4611 Viking Way Ste 285, Richmond, V6V 2K9, BC, Canada
Tel.: (604) 244-7387
Web Site: http://www.petcetera.ca
Year Founded: 1997
Sales Range: $50-74.9 Million
Emp.: 250
Retail Pet Store Operator; Obedience Training, Pet Photography & Daycare Services
N.A.I.C.S.: 459910
Daniel Urbani *(Founder, Pres & CEO)*

NEW PLUS KNITTING PUBLIC COMPANY LIMITED
34 Moo 20 Suvintawong Road Saladang Bangnumpeaw, Chachoengsao, 24000, Thailand
Tel.: (66) 38593129
Web Site: https://www.newplus.co.th
Year Founded: 1972
NPK—(THA)
Rev.: $7,046,358
Assets: $14,585,476
Liabilities: $1,955,570
Net Worth: $12,629,906
Earnings: ($248,424)
Fiscal Year-end: 12/31/23
Apparel Product Mfr & Distr
N.A.I.C.S.: 315120
Chamnean Chokvathana *(Chm & Mng Dir)*

NEW POWER PLASMA CO LTD
214 Saneop-ro 155beon-gil, Gwonseon-gu, Suwon, Gyeonggi-do, Korea (South)
Tel.: (82) 316127600
Web Site: https://www.newpower.co.kr
Year Founded: 1999
144960—(KRS)
Rev.: $270,658,012
Assets: $485,725,534
Liabilities: $281,774,992
Net Worth: $203,950,542
Earnings: $19,600,684
Emp.: 303
Fiscal Year-end: 12/31/22
Remote Plasma Generator Mfr
N.A.I.C.S.: 334419
Soon-im Wi *(CEO)*

Subsidiaries:

New Power Plasma Co Ltd - Jeon-Ju Factory (1)
49 Yusang-ro Deokjin-gu, Jeonju, Jeollabuk-do, Korea (South)
Tel.: (82) 316127600
Generator Mfr
N.A.I.C.S.: 335312

NEW PROVENANCE EVERLASTING HOLDINGS LIMITED
Unit 1102 11/F Shui On Centre No 6-8 Harbour Road, Wanchai, China (Hong Kong)
Tel.: (852) 3 919 9988 BM
Web Site:
   http://www.npegroup.com.hk
2326—(HKG)
Rev.: $33,822,296
Assets: $80,614,951
Liabilities: $13,284,295
Net Worth: $67,330,656
Earnings: ($701,264)
Emp.: 134
Fiscal Year-end: 03/31/22
Investment Holding Company
N.A.I.C.S.: 551112
Lik Man Sin *(Chm & CEO)*

NEW RAY MEDICINE INTERNATIONAL HOLDINGS LIMITED
Room 911B 9/F Tower 1 Silvercord 30 Canton Road Tsim Sha Tsui, Kowloon, China (Hong Kong)
Tel.: (852) 2152 2030 Ky
Web Site:
   http://www.newraymedicine.com
Rev.: $15,233,535
Assets: $87,178,448
Liabilities: $3,136,286
Net Worth: $84,042,162
Earnings: ($5,664,037)
Emp.: 35
Fiscal Year-end: 12/31/19
Pharmaceuticals Distr
N.A.I.C.S.: 424210
Yang Liu *(Chm)*

NEW RETAIL CO., LTD.
5F No 66 Nanjing W Rd, Datong Dist, Taipei, 11071, Taiwan
Tel.: (886) 225596189
3085—(TPE)
Rev.: $5,522,684
Assets: $8,101,460
Liabilities: $2,753,025
Net Worth: $5,348,435
Earnings: ($677,110)
Fiscal Year-end: 12/31/22
Online Marketing Services
N.A.I.C.S.: 541870
Xu Han Lin *(Chm)*

NEW SEA UNION TECHNOLOGY GROUP CO., LTD.
168 Jingmao Road Suzhou Industrial Park, Suzhou, 215021, Jiangsu, China
Tel.: (86) 5127606666
Web Site: http://www.nsu.com.cn
Year Founded: 1997
002089—(SSE)
Rev.: $24,678,108
Assets: $254,080,476
Liabilities: $116,998,128
Net Worth: $137,082,348
Earnings: ($41,717,052)
Fiscal Year-end: 12/31/22
Communication Network Equipment Mfr
N.A.I.C.S.: 334290

NEW SECURITIES EXCHANGE
Miljana Vukova bb, Podgorica, 81000, Montenegro
Tel.: (382) 81230670
Web Site: http://www.mnse.me
Year Founded: 2001
Stock Exchange
N.A.I.C.S.: 523210
Sasa Popovic *(Chm)*

NEW SILK ROUTE ADVISORS PVT. LTD.
407 Ceejay House Shivsagar Estate Dr Annie Besant Road, Worli, Mumbai, 400 018, India
Tel.: (91) 2266180900 In
Web Site:
   http://www.nsrpartners.com
Year Founded: 2006
Private Equity Investments
N.A.I.C.S.: 523999
Vivek Sett *(Partner)*

Subsidiaries:

New Silk Route Advisors (Dubai) Limited (1)
Shangri-la Hotel Office Tower 7th Floor, PO Box 75322, Sheikh Zayed Road, Dubai, United Arab Emirates
Tel.: (971) 43211772
Web Site: http://www.nsrpartners.com
Sales Range: $50-74.9 Million
Emp.: 5
Private Equity Investments
N.A.I.C.S.: 523999
Jens Yahya Zimmermann *(Partner)*

New Silk Route Advisors Pvt. Ltd. - Bengaluru (1)
125 Suite Regus Business Center, RMZ Millenia Tower B Level 1, No 1&2 Murphy Rd, 560 008, Bengaluru, India
Tel.: (91) 8040224103
Web Site: http://www.nsrpartners.com
Private Equity Investments
N.A.I.C.S.: 523999

New Silk Route Partners LLC (1)
540 Madison Ave 38th Fl, New York, NY 10022
Tel.: (646) 744-0380
Web Site: http://www.nsrpartners.com
Sales Range: $50-74.9 Million
Emp.: 20
Private Equity Investments
N.A.I.C.S.: 523999
Ajay Kaul *(Head-IR)*

NEW SILKROUTES GROUP LIMITED
456 Alexandra Road 19-02 Fragrance Empire Building, Singapore, 119962, Singapore
Tel.: (65) 63770100 SG
Web Site:
   http://www.newsilkroutes.org
BMT—(SES)
Rev.: $29,413,000
Assets: $31,173,000
Liabilities: $52,305,000
Net Worth: ($21,132,000)
Earnings: ($35,131,000)
Emp.: 160
Fiscal Year-end: 06/30/22
Holding Company; IT & Petroleum Products Distr
N.A.I.C.S.: 551112
Beng Hong Ong *(Sec)*

Subsidiaries:

Digiland Pte. Ltd. (1)
05-07/08 1093 Lower Delta Road, Ban Teck Han Building #05-02, Singapore, 169204, Singapore
Tel.: (65) 67389416
Web Site: https://www.digiland.com.sg
Information Technology Products & Services
N.A.I.C.S.: 541519

Dr Chua's Family Clinic Pte. Ltd. (1)
Blk 638 Jurong West Street 61 02-04 Pioneer Mall, Singapore, 640638, Singapore
Tel.: (65) 6 792 8505
Web Site: https://www.drchuafc.com.sg
Family Healthcare & Wellness Services
N.A.I.C.S.: 621999

Greedygums Pte. Ltd. (1)
165 Bukit Merah Central 04-3685, Singapore, 150165, Singapore
Tel.: (65) 62702918
Web Site: http://greedygums.com
Dental Equipment Whslr
N.A.I.C.S.: 423450
Y. F. William *(Gen Mgr)*

HK Family Clinic & Surgery Pte. Ltd. (1)
410 Ang Mo Kio Ave 10 01-817, Singapore, 560410, Singapore
Tel.: (65) 65528757
Clinical Healthcare Services
N.A.I.C.S.: 621999

HL Clinic Pte. Ltd. (1)
9 Telok Blangah Crescent 01-135, Singapore, 090009, Singapore
Tel.: (65) 62721986

Clinical Healthcare Services
N.A.I.C.S.: 621999

HL Dermahealth Aesthetic Clinic Pte. Ltd. (1)
12 Telok Blangah Crescent 01-111, Singapore, 090012, Singapore
Tel.: (65) 62769007
Clinical Healthcare Services
N.A.I.C.S.: 621999

HL Family Clinic & Surgery (Bedok) Pte. Ltd. (1)
89 Bedok North Street 4 01-83, Singapore, 460089, Singapore
Tel.: (65) 64420494
General Medical Services
N.A.I.C.S.: 622110

Healthsciences International Pte. Ltd. (1)
456 Alexandra Road 19-02 Fragrance Empire Building, Singapore, 119962, Singapore
Tel.: (65) 63770100
Web Site: http://www.healthsciences.sg
Clinical Healthcare Services
N.A.I.C.S.: 621999
Goh Jin Hian *(Exec Dir)*

International Energy Group Pte. Ltd. (1)
456 Alexandra Road 19-02 Fragrance Empire Building, Singapore, 119962, Singapore
Tel.: (65) 6 377 0100
Web Site: https://www.iegroup.sg
Energy Products & Services
N.A.I.C.S.: 211120

Subsidiary (Non-US):

New Silkroutes Group (Europe) Limited (2)
Canter Business Centre Patri Felicjan, Bilocca Street, Marsa, MRS 152, Malta (100%)
Tel.: (356) 2569 2801
Computer & Energy Products Distr
N.A.I.C.S.: 541519

Subsidiary (Domestic):

IEG Malta Limited (3)
Canter Business Centre Patri Felicjan, Bilocca Street, Marsa, MRS 1524, Malta (90%)
Tel.: (356) 2569 2801
Energy Products & Services
N.A.I.C.S.: 211120

Lily Aw Medical Services Pte. Ltd. (1)
446 Pasir Ris Drive 6 01-116, Singapore, 510446, Singapore
Tel.: (65) 65822122
Clinical Healthcare Services
N.A.I.C.S.: 621999

Orange Orthodontics & Dentofacial Orthopaedics Pte. Ltd. (1)
304 Orchard Road Lucky Plaza Suite 05-42/44, Singapore, 238863, Singapore
Tel.: (65) 6 737 0544
Web Site:
   https://www.orangeorthodontics.com.sg
Dental Services
N.A.I.C.S.: 621210
Joyce Goh *(Mgr-Practice)*

The Dental Hub@SG Pte. Ltd. (1)
460 Alexandra Road 02-16 PSA Building Alexandra Retail Center, Singapore, 119963, Singapore
Tel.: (65) 6 274 9682
Web Site: https://www.thedentalhub.co
Dental Services
N.A.I.C.S.: 621210

NEW SOURCES ENERGY N.V.
Apollolaan151,1077 AR, Amsterdam, Netherlands
Tel.: (31) 202390299 Nl
Web Site:
   https://www.newsourcesenergy.com
Year Founded: 2002
NSE—(EUR)
Sales Range: Less than $1 Million
Holding Company; Renewable Energy Electricity Generation Services

NEW SOURCES ENERGY N.V.

N.A.I.C.S.: 551112
Frans Wieringa (CEO)

NEW SOUTH WALES RUGBY LEAGUE LTD
Rugby League Central Driver Ave,
Moore Park, Sydney, 2021, NSW,
Australia
Tel.: (61) 292327566
Web Site: http://www.nswrl.com.au
Sales Range: $50-74.9 Million
Emp.: 15
Sports Club
N.A.I.C.S.: 711211
John Chalk (Pres)

NEW SOUTH WALES SUGAR MILLING CO-OPERATIVE LIMITED
Suite 1 Level 1 Cnr River and Martin
St, Ballina, 2478, NSW, Australia
Tel.: (61) 266812700
Web Site:
  http://sunshinesugar.com.au
Year Founded: 1978
Sugar Products Mfr
N.A.I.C.S.: 311314
Chris Connors (CEO)

Subsidiaries:

New South Wales Sugar Milling Co-Operative Limited - Broadwater Mill (1)
117 Pacific Highway, Broadwater, 2472, NSW, Australia
Tel.: (61) 2 6620 8200
Cane Sugar Mfr
N.A.I.C.S.: 311314

New South Wales Sugar Milling Co-Operative Limited - Condong Mill (1)
McLeod Street, Condong, 2484, NSW, Australia
Tel.: (61) 2 6670 1700
Web Site:
  http://www.sunshinesugars.com.au
Cane Sugar Mfr
N.A.I.C.S.: 311314
Greg Peterson (Mng Dir)

NEW SOUTH WALES TREASURY CORPORATION
Level 7 Deutsche Bank Place 126
Phillip Street, Sydney, 2000, NSW,
Australia
Tel.: (61) 293259325 AU
Web Site:
  http://www.tcorp.nsw.gov.au
Year Founded: 1983
Sales Range: $25-49.9 Million
Emp.: 130
Central Financing Services
N.A.I.C.S.: 523940
Stephen W. Knight (CEO)

Subsidiaries:

TCorp Nominees Pty Limited (1)
Level 22 Governor Phillip Tower, 1 Farrer Pl, Sydney, 2000, NSW, Australia
Tel.: (61) 293259325
Web Site: http://www.tcorp.com.au
Sales Range: $50-74.9 Million
Emp.: 100
Government Loan Service
N.A.I.C.S.: 523999
Amelia McArdle (Mgr-HR)

NEW SPARKLE ROLL INTERNATIONAL GROUP LIMITED
Rooms 2028-36 20/F Sun Hung Kai
Center 30 Harbour Road, Wanchai,
China (Hong Kong)
Tel.: (852) 22999966 BM
Web Site: http://www.hk970.com
0970—(HKG)
Rev.: $557,772,333
Assets: $609,776,682
Liabilities: $258,264,522
Net Worth: $351,512,161
Earnings: $4,064,676
Emp.: 161
Fiscal Year-end: 03/31/22
Distributions of Comic Books
N.A.I.C.S.: 513120
Hao Jiang Zheng (Co-Chm & CEO)

NEW STANDARD ENERGY LIMITED
6 Outram Street, West Perth, 6005,
WA, Australia
Tel.: (61) 8 9481 7477
Web Site:
  http://www.newstandard.com.au
Rev.: $2,765
Assets: $443,316
Liabilities: $167,684
Net Worth: $275,632
Earnings: ($750,291)
Emp.: 2
Fiscal Year-end: 06/30/18
Oil & Gas Exploration Company
N.A.I.C.S.: 211120
Xiaofeng Liu (Mng Dir)

NEW STAR INVESTMENT TRUST PLC
201 Bishopsgate, London, EC2M
3AE, Essex, United Kingdom
Tel.: (44) 2078181818
Web Site: https://www.nsitplc.com
Year Founded: 2000
NSI—(LSE)
Rev.: $3,047,377
Assets: $156,330,202
Liabilities: $370,056
Net Worth: $155,960,146
Earnings: $4,032,125
Fiscal Year-end: 06/30/23
Investment Trust Management Services
N.A.I.C.S.: 523940
Geoffrey Howard-Spink (Chm)

NEW STRATUS ENERGY, INC.
372 Bay Street Suite 301, Toronto,
M5H 2W9, ON, Canada
Tel.: (647) 498-9109 AB
Web Site:
  https://newstratusenergy.com
Year Founded: 2005
NSE—(TSXV)
Rev.: $20,114,067
Assets: $81,496,259
Liabilities: $59,366,258
Net Worth: $22,130,000
Earnings: $11,608,066
Fiscal Year-end: 03/31/22
Oil & Gas Exploration Services
N.A.I.C.S.: 211120
Jose Francisco Arata (CEO)

NEW TALISMAN GOLD MINES LIMITED
541 Parnell Road, Parnell, Auckland,
New Zealand
Tel.: (64) 93031893
Web Site:
  https://www.newtalismangold.com
Year Founded: 1986
NTL—(ASX)
Rev.: $3,792
Assets: $6,283,989
Liabilities: $731,202
Net Worth: $5,552,788
Earnings: ($1,626,504)
Emp.: 100
Fiscal Year-end: 03/31/23
Gold & Silver Mining
N.A.I.C.S.: 212220
S. Jane Bell (Sec)

Subsidiaries:

Cobalt Blue Holdings Limited (1)
Suite 1703 100 Miller Street, North Sydney, 2060, NSW, Australia
Tel.: (61) 282870660
Web Site:
  https://www.cobaltblueholdings.com
Rev.: $935,497
Assets: $27,351,763
Liabilities: $4,511,886
Net Worth: $22,839,877
Earnings: ($25,103,499)
Fiscal Year-end: 06/30/2024
Cobalt Exploration Services
N.A.I.C.S.: 212290
Andrew Tong (Mgr)

NEW TIMES ENERGY CORPORATION LIMITED
Room 1402 14/F New World Tower 1
16-18 Queens Road, Central, China
(Hong Kong)
Tel.: (852) 31062061 BM
Web Site: http://www.nt-energy.com
0166—(HKG)
Rev.: $2,666,435,040
Assets: $276,092,070
Liabilities: $107,583,353
Net Worth: $168,508,718
Earnings: $36,452,505
Emp.: 132
Fiscal Year-end: 12/31/22
Oil & Gas Exploration Services
N.A.I.C.S.: 213112
Stewart Kam Chiu Cheng (Chm)

Subsidiaries:

High Luck Group Limited (1)
Avenida General Manuel Belgrano 1584, Salta, Argentina
Tel.: (54) 3874227697
Web Site: https://highluckgroup.com
Investment Holding Services
N.A.I.C.S.: 551112

NEW TOYO INTERNATIONAL HOLDINGS LTD.
10 Anson Road 18 25 International
Plaza, Singapore, 628079, Singapore
Tel.: (65) 62382188
Web Site: https://www.newtoyo.com
N08—(SES)
Rev.: $232,066,197
Assets: $192,078,315
Liabilities: $52,491,100
Net Worth: $139,587,215
Earnings: $10,643,793
Fiscal Year-end: 12/31/23
Printed Cartoon Labels & Paper Mfr
N.A.I.C.S.: 333993
Steven Wen Hwa Yen (Founder & Chm)

Subsidiaries:

New Toyo (Vietnam) Aluminium Paper Packaging Co., Ltd. (1)
Lot 15 17 19 and 21 Industrial Zone of Linh Trung II EPZ, Binh Chieu Ward Thu Duc City, Ho Chi Minh City, Vietnam
Tel.: (84) 2837291768
Web Site: https://newtoyovn.com
Sales Range: $400-449.9 Million
Emp.: 185
Aluminium Products Mfr
N.A.I.C.S.: 331313

New Toyo Aluminium Paper Product Co (Pte) Ltd (1)
16 Soon Lee Road, Singapore, 628079, Singapore
Tel.: (65) 62656882
Emp.: 80
Laminated Paper Products Mfr
N.A.I.C.S.: 322120
Chris Leong (Gen Mgr)

New Toyo International Co (Pte) Ltd (1)
47 Scotts Road 05-03 Goldbell Towers, Singapore, 228233, Singapore
Tel.: (65) 62382188
Web Site: http://www.newtoyo.com
Emp.: 20
Paper Products Mfr

N.A.I.C.S.: 322120

NEW TREND INTERNATIONAL LOGIS-TECH COLTD
No 26 Cuibao Road Baolong Street,
Longgang District, Shenzhen,
518116, Guangdong, China
Tel.: (86) 75582684590
Web Site: http://www.nti56.com
Year Founded: 2000
300532—(CHIN)
Rev.: $430,324,173
Assets: $722,560,035
Liabilities: $490,787,712
Net Worth: $231,772,323
Earnings: $54,682,731
Fiscal Year-end: 12/31/23
Logistic Services
N.A.I.C.S.: 541614
Shao Jianfeng (Chm)

NEW TROIS ELECTRONICS (SHENZHEN) LTD.
Ta Yong Development Zone 4
Fuyung, Shenzhen, Guandong, China
Tel.: (86) 75527311870
Year Founded: 2001
Emp.: 100
Electronic Equipment Distr
N.A.I.C.S.: 423690

NEW UNIVERSE ENVIRONMENTAL GROUP LIMITED
Rm 2110-2112 Telford House 16
Wang Hoi Road, Kowloon, China
(Hong Kong)
Tel.: (852) 24356811 Ky
Web Site: http://www.nuigl.com
Year Founded: 1996
0436—(HKG)
Rev.: $75,091,253
Assets: $193,040,865
Liabilities: $55,913,723
Net Worth: $137,127,143
Earnings: $581,910
Emp.: 655
Fiscal Year-end: 12/31/22
Waste Water Treatment Services
N.A.I.C.S.: 221320
Yu Xi (Chm & CEO)

Subsidiaries:

Fair Time International Limited (1)
Suites 501-3 5/F Chinachem Leighton Plaza 29 Leighton Road, Causeway Bay, China (Hong Kong)
Tel.: (852) 31762020
Web Site: http://www.fairtime.com.hk
Watch Mfr
N.A.I.C.S.: 334519

Jiangsu New Universe Environmental Engineering Management Limited (1)
No 466 Dingmao Zhihui Road, Zhenjiang New District, Zhenjiang, 212009, Jiangsu, China
Tel.: (86) 51185958166
Web Site: http://www.nui-yxhb.com
Environmental Consulting Services
N.A.I.C.S.: 541620
Ling Yun He (Gen Mgr)

Jiangsu Xin Yu Environmental Technologies Limited (1)
No 466 Dingmao zhihui Road, Zhenjiang New District, Zhenjiang, 212006, Jiangsu, China
Tel.: (86) 51180870691
Plastic Injection Mfr
N.A.I.C.S.: 326112

Taixing Xin Xin Resources Recycling Company Limited (1)
No 9 Shugang Road Taixing Economic Development Zone, Taixing, 225400, Jiangsu, China
Tel.: (86) 15366022433
Plastic Injection Mfr
N.A.I.C.S.: 326112

AND PRIVATE COMPANIES

Taizhou New Universe Solid Waste Disposal Company Limited (1)
No 9 Shugang Road Taixing Economic Development Zone, Taixing, 225300, Jiangsu, China
Tel.: (86) 52386116680
Hazardous Waste Treatment Services
N.A.I.C.S.: 562211

Yancheng NUHF Environmental Technology Limited (1)
Huafeng Industrial Park Dafeng, Yancheng, 224100, Jiangsu, China
Tel.: (86) 51583552881
Hazardous Waste Treatment Services
N.A.I.C.S.: 562211
Qi Li *(Deputy Gen Mgr)*

Yancheng New Universe Solid Waste Disposal Company Limited (1)
No 338 Tongyu Road South, Area 3 Xindun Village Yancheng Economic Development Zone, Yancheng, 224007, Jiangsu, China
Tel.: (86) 51588821565
Hazardous Waste Treatment Services
N.A.I.C.S.: 562211

Zhenjiang New Universe Solid Waste Disposal Company Limited (1)
No 208 Yuehe Street, New Materials Industrial Park Zhenjiang New District, Zhenjiang, 212006, Jiangsu, China
Tel.: (86) 51183352275
Emp.: 20
Hazardous Waste Treatment Services
N.A.I.C.S.: 562211
Yuan Liu *(Gen Mgr)*

Zhenjiang Sinotech Eco-Electroplating Development Limited (1)
No 198 Zhencheng Road, Chemical Industrial Park of Zhenjiang New Area, Zhenjiang, 212006, Jiangsu, China
Tel.: (86) 51185959999
Electroplating Waste Treatment Services
N.A.I.C.S.: 562211

NEW VENTURETEC LTD.
C/O FRIEDLI CORPORATE FINANCE AG FREIGUTSTRASS, 8002, ZURICK, Switzerland
Tel.: (41) 4112832900
Web Site:
http://www.newventuretec.com
NEV—(SWX)
Rev.: $28,681,026
Assets: $53,869,780
Liabilities: $20,965,314
Net Worth: $32,904,466
Earnings: $26,055,742
Emp.: 150
Fiscal Year-end: 09/30/18
Investment Services
N.A.I.C.S.: 523999
Peter Friedli *(Chm)*

NEW VISION PRINTING & PUBLISHING COMPANY LIMITED
Plot 19/21 First Street Industrial Area, PO Box 9815, Kampala, Uganda
Tel.: (256) 414337000 UG
Web Site: http://www.newvision.co.ug
Year Founded: 1986
NVL—(UGAN)
Rev.: $21,109,175
Assets: $23,083,593
Liabilities: $6,325,267
Net Worth: $16,758,326
Earnings: ($253,922)
Emp.: 500
Fiscal Year-end: 06/30/21
Newspaper Publishing Services
N.A.I.C.S.: 513110
Robert Kabushenga *(CEO & Mng Dir)*

NEW WAVE ESPORTS CORP.
401 217 Queen St West, Toronto, M5V 0R2, ON, Canada
Tel.: (416) 917-5847 Ca

Web Site:
http://www.newwavecorp.com
Year Founded: 2006
NWAI—(CNSX)
Rev.: $3,634
Assets: $1,858,398
Liabilities: $885,793
Net Worth: $972,605
Earnings: ($1,531,577)
Fiscal Year-end: 03/31/24
Mushroom Farming Services
N.A.I.C.S.: 111411

NEW WAVE GROUP AB
Kungsportsavenyen 10, SE 411 36, Gothenburg, Sweden
Tel.: (46) 317128900
Web Site: https://www.nwg.se
NEWA-B—(OMX)
Rev.: $828,308,372
Assets: $1,024,998,361
Liabilities: $473,282,943
Net Worth: $551,715,418
Earnings: $109,472,028
Emp.: 2,313
Fiscal Year-end: 12/31/22
Leisure Wear, Promo Wear, Shoes & Accessories Designer
N.A.I.C.S.: 458110
Ernest R. Johnson *(Mgr-North America)*

Subsidiaries:

Ahead Inc. (1)
270 Samuel Barnet Blvd, New Bedford, MA 02745
Tel.: (508) 985-9898
Web Site: https://aheadweb.com
Sporting Goods & Accessories Mfr & Distr
N.A.I.C.S.: 339920

B.T.C. Activewear Ltd. (1)
Point 1 Opus 9 Axletree Way, Great Bridge, Wednesbury, WS10 9QY, United Kingdom
Tel.: (44) 1215057770
Home Furnishing Distr
N.A.I.C.S.: 423220

CJSC New Wave Group (1)
4th Syromyatnichesky Side St 1-2, 105120, Moscow, Russia (51%)
Tel.: (7) 04959163976
Sales Range: $25-49.9 Million
Emp.: 40
Mens & Boys Clothing & Furnishings Whslr
N.A.I.C.S.: 424350

Craft of Scandinavia AB (1)
Evedalsgatan 5, 504 35, Boras, Sweden (100%)
Tel.: (46) 337223210
Web Site: http://www.craftsportswear.com
Sales Range: $25-49.9 Million
Sporting & Recreational Goods & Supplies Whslr
N.A.I.C.S.: 423910

Cutter & Buck, Inc. (1)
701 N 34th St Ste 400, Seattle, WA 98103-3415
Tel.: (206) 830-6812
Web Site: http://www.cutterbuck.com
Sales Range: $125-149.9 Million
Emp.: 359
Men's & Women's Apparel Designer, Mfr & Distr
N.A.I.C.S.: 315210
Joel Freet *(CEO)*

DJ Frantextil AB (1)
Akarevagen 18, 455 83, Dingle, Sweden
Tel.: (46) 524 283 70
Emp.: 100
Textile Products Mfr
N.A.I.C.S.: 314999
Asa Liberg *(Gen Mgr)*

Dahetra A/S (1)
Niels Bohrs Vej 21, 8660, Skanderborg, Denmark (100%)
Tel.: (45) 86572800
Web Site: http://www.dahetra.dk
Sales Range: $25-49.9 Million
Family Clothing Stores
N.A.I.C.S.: 458110

Division (Domestic):

Hurricane Purchase A/S (2)
Niels Bohrs Vej 21, 8660, Skanderborg, Denmark
Tel.: (45) 86572800
Web Site: http://www.dahetra.dk
Sales Range: $25-49.9 Million
Emp.: 42
Family Clothing Stores
N.A.I.C.S.: 458110

Dahlin Johansson Frantextil AB (1)
Akarevagen 18, 455 83, Dingle, Sweden (100%)
Tel.: (46) 5 242 8370
Web Site: https://www.dochj.se
Sales Range: $50-74.9 Million
Emp.: 4
Mens & Boys Clothing & Furnishings Whslr
N.A.I.C.S.: 424350

Desk Top Ideas Ltd (1)
1 Wennman Road Thame Park Business Centre, Thame, OX9 3XA, Oxfordshire, United Kingdom
Tel.: (44) 8448757624
Web Site: http://www.desktopideas.com
Promotional Durable Goods Distr
N.A.I.C.S.: 423990

Destination Kosta AB (1)
Glasbruksstigen 17, Kosta, 365 43, Lessebo, Sweden
Tel.: (46) 761400866
Web Site: https://destinationkosta.se
Glass Products Mfr
N.A.I.C.S.: 327215

Dressmart GmbH (1)
Robert Bosch Str 1, 59199, Bonen, Germany (100%)
Tel.: (49) 238392180
Web Site: http://www.hefa.se
Mens & Boys Clothing & Furnishings Whslr
N.A.I.C.S.: 424350

GC Sportswear OY (1)
Vihiojantie 1, 33800, Tampere, Finland
Tel.: (358) 444022440
Web Site: http://www.gcsuomi.fi
Sports Wear Mfr & Distr
N.A.I.C.S.: 315250

Glasma AB (1)
Langgatan 22, 361 31, Emmaboda, Sweden (100%)
Tel.: (46) 47148150
Web Site: https://glasma.com
Sales Range: $25-49.9 Million
Emp.: 12
Purchased Glass Product Mfr
N.A.I.C.S.: 327215

Hefa AB (1)
Orrekulla Industrigata 61, Hisings Karra, Gothenburg, 425 36, Sweden (100%)
Tel.: (46) 317125600
Web Site: http://www.hefa.com
Sales Range: $25-49.9 Million
Emp.: 20
Mens & Boys Clothing & Furnishings Whslr
N.A.I.C.S.: 424350

Subsidiary (Non-US):

Texet GmbH (2)
Geigelsteinstrasse 10, Oberaudorf, 83080, Visselhovede, Germany
Tel.: (49) 8033979250
Web Site: http://www.texeteurope.com
Promotional Clothing Wear Distr
N.A.I.C.S.: 424350

Intraco Holding B.V. (1)
Noorddijk 88, 1521 PD, Wormerveer, Netherlands
Tel.: (31) 756475420
Web Site: http://www.intraco.nl
Sales Range: $25-49.9 Million
Emp.: 47
Gift Novelty & Souvenir Stores
N.A.I.C.S.: 459420

Intraco Hong Kong Ltd. (1)
26th Floor China Century Tower 178 Gloucester Road, Wanchai, China (Hong Kong)
Tel.: (852) 28029932
Web Site: http://www.intraco.nl
Mens & Boys Clothing & Furnishings Whslr
N.A.I.C.S.: 424350

Intraco Shenzhen Ltd (1)
Room 1206 Baoan Tower 800 Dongfang Road, Futian District, Shenzhen, China
Tel.: (86) 755 83898388
Sales Range: $25-49.9 Million
Emp.: 2
Communication Equipment Distr
N.A.I.C.S.: 423690
Micheal Zeng *(Gen Mgr)*

Intraco Trading B.V. (1)
Noorddijk 88, 1521 PD, Wormerveer, Netherlands (100%)
Tel.: (31) 756475420
Web Site: http://www.intraco.nl
Sales Range: $25-49.9 Million
Gift Novelty & Souvenir Stores
N.A.I.C.S.: 459420

Jobman Workwear AB (1)
Jupitervagen 2A, PO Box 2044, 194 43, Upplands Vasby, Sweden (100%)
Tel.: (46) 86302900
Web Site: https://www.jobman.se
Sales Range: $25-49.9 Million
Emp.: 21
Gents Clothing Whslr
N.A.I.C.S.: 424350

Kosta Forlag AB (1)
Stora Vagen 77, Kosta, 360 25, Halmstad, Sweden (80%)
Tel.: (46) 47834934
Web Site: https://www.kostaforlag.se
Sales Range: $25-49.9 Million
Emp.: 5
Publisher
N.A.I.C.S.: 513199

Make Your Own Design in Scandinavia AB (1)
Hollandsgatan 5, Ytterby, Orebro, Sweden (100%)
Tel.: (46) 303246550
Women's Clothing Store
N.A.I.C.S.: 458110

New Wave Austria GmbH (1)
Muhlgraben 43 D, Erl, 6343, Tirol, Austria (100%)
Tel.: (43) 5373200600
Web Site: http://www.newwave-austria.at
Sales Range: $25-49.9 Million
Emp.: 10
Family Clothing Stores
N.A.I.C.S.: 458110

New Wave Danmark A/S (1)
Lyskaer 13A, 2730, Herlev, Denmark (100%)
Tel.: (45) 43437100
Web Site: https://www.newwave.dk
Sales Range: $25-49.9 Million
Family Clothing Stores
N.A.I.C.S.: 458110
Kjell Kaspersen *(Mgr)*

New Wave Footwear AB (1)
Skomaskinsgatan 6, PO Box 343, 70146, Orebro, Sweden (100%)
Tel.: (46) 19209200
Sales Range: $25-49.9 Million
Emp.: 15
Footwear Wholesalers
N.A.I.C.S.: 424340
Goran Titus *(Gen Mgr)*

New Wave France SAS (1)
7 Rue Jean Perrin, 69680, Chassieu, France (100%)
Tel.: (33) 472523927
Women's Clothing Store
N.A.I.C.S.: 458110

New Wave GmbH (1)
Geigelsteinstrasse 10, Oberaudorf, 83080, Rosenheim, Germany (100%)
Tel.: (49) 80339790
Web Site: https://www.newwave-germany.de
Sales Range: $25-49.9 Million
Emp.: 25
Sporting & Recreational Goods & Supplies Whslr
N.A.I.C.S.: 423910

New Wave Group Bangladesh (1)
House 60 Park Road, Baridhara, Dhaka, 1212, Bangladesh
Tel.: (880) 2 883 11 29
Sales Range: $25-49.9 Million
Emp.: 46
Sporting Goods Distr

NEW WAVE GROUP AB

New Wave Group AB—(Continued)
N.A.I.C.S.: 423910

New Wave Group China (1)
4th Floor Building E Nr 1978 Lianhua Road,
Shanghai, 201103, China
Tel.: (86) 216 145 8828
Web Site: http://www.newwave.cn
Clothing Apparel Mfr & Distr
N.A.I.C.S.: 315250

New Wave Group Factory Shop AB (1)
Alberts Vag 9, 52010, Gallstad,
Sweden **(100%)**
Tel.: (46) 32126040
Web Site: http://www.nwg.se
Sales Range: $25-49.9 Million
Emp.: 5
Family Clothing Stores
N.A.I.C.S.: 458110

New Wave Group Incentives AB (1)
Orrekulla Industrigata 61, Gothenburg, 425 36, Sweden
Tel.: (46) 317128900
Web Site: http://www.nwg.se
Sales Range: $25-49.9 Million
Emp.: 35
Textile Products Distr
N.A.I.C.S.: 424310
Torsten Jansson *(CEO & Mng Dir)*

New Wave Group India Pvt Ltd. (1)
1/32 Ulsoor Rd Cross, Bengaluru, 560 042, India
Tel.: (91) 8025585838
Web Site: http://www.nwg.se
Sales Range: $25-49.9 Million
Sporting Goods Distr
N.A.I.C.S.: 423910

New Wave Group International Trading Ltd. (1)
4th Floor Building E 1978 Lian Huan Road Ming Road, 1978 Lian Huan Road, Shanghai, 201103, China
Tel.: (86) 2161458828
Web Site: http://www.newwave.cn
Sales Range: $25-49.9 Million
Emp.: 35
Mens & Boys Clothing & Furnishings Whslr
N.A.I.C.S.: 424350

New Wave Group SA (1)
Chemin des Polonais 3, 2016, Cortaillod,
Switzerland **(100%)**
Tel.: (41) 328433232
Web Site: https://www.nwgroup.ch
Mens & Boys Clothing & Furnishings Whslr
N.A.I.C.S.: 424350

New Wave Group Vietnam (1)
L3 Dien Bien Phu Street Ward 25, Dist Binh Thanh, Ho Chi Minh City, Vietnam
Tel.: (84) 835121088
Sales Range: $25-49.9 Million
Emp.: 27
Sporting Goods Distr
N.A.I.C.S.: 423910
Cuong Nguyen *(Country Mgr)*

New Wave Iceland ehf. (1)
Hofoabakka 9, 110, Reykjavik, Iceland
Tel.: (354) 5206020
Web Site: https://www.newwave.is
Pamphlet Distr
N.A.I.C.S.: 424920

New Wave Italia S.r.l (1)
Via P Togliatti 28, Codogno, 26845, Lodi,
Italy **(100%)**
Tel.: (39) 0377316011
Web Site: https://www.newwave.it
Mens & Boys Clothing & Furnishings Whslr
N.A.I.C.S.: 424350

New Wave Mode AB (1)
Akarevagen 18, 455 83, Dingle,
Sweden **(100%)**
Tel.: (46) 52428200
Web Site: https://www.newwave.se
Sales Range: $50-74.9 Million
Emp.: 85
Mens & Boys Clothing & Furnishings Whslr
N.A.I.C.S.: 424350

New Wave Norway A/S (1)
Bjornstadmyra 4-6, 1712, Sarpsborg, Norway

Tel.: (47) 69143700
Sales Range: $50-74.9 Million
Emp.: 75
Sporting Goods & Accessories Distr
N.A.I.C.S.: 423910
Morten Halvorsen *(Mng Dir)*

New Wave Profile Professionals AB (1)
Ga Oxelosundsvagen 1, Nykoping, 611 38, Sweden
Tel.: (46) 15537590
Web Site: http://www.newwaveprofile.com
Sales Range: $50-74.9 Million
Emp.: 9
Sporting Cloth & Accessories Distr
N.A.I.C.S.: 423910

New Wave Sports AB (1)
Evedalsgatan 5, Box 1774, 501 17, Boras, Sweden
Tel.: (46) 33 722 3200
Web Site: http://www.newwavesports.se
Sporting Goods Distr
N.A.I.C.S.: 423910

New Wave Sportswear AS (1)
Bjornstadmyra 4-6, Gralum, 1712, Sarpsborg, Norway **(100%)**
Tel.: (47) 69143700
Web Site: http://www.newwave.no
Sales Range: $50-74.9 Million
Emp.: 65
Sporting & Recreational Goods & Supplies Whslr
N.A.I.C.S.: 423910
Morten Halvorsen *(Gen Dir)*

Division (Domestic):

Sagaform A/S (2)
Karenslyst Alle 5, 0278, Oslo, Norway
Tel.: (47) 24110830
Sales Range: $25-49.9 Million
Emp.: 20
General Merchandise Stores
N.A.I.C.S.: 455219

Texet Norge A/S (2)
Karenslyst Alle 5, 0278, Oslo,
Norway **(100%)**
Tel.: (47) 24110820
Web Site: http://www.texet.no
Sales Range: $25-49.9 Million
Emp.: 20
Mens & Boys Clothing & Furnishings Whslr
N.A.I.C.S.: 424350

New Wave Sportswear B.V. (1)
Reactorweg 201, 3542 AD, Utrecht,
Netherlands **(100%)**
Tel.: (31) 302083030
Web Site: https://www.newwavetextiles.nl
Sales Range: $25-49.9 Million
Sporting & Recreational Goods & Supplies Whslr
N.A.I.C.S.: 423910

New Wave Sportswear Ltd. (1)
Lapponia Ho Bury St, Ruislip, HA47TL, Middlesex, United Kingdom **(100%)**
Tel.: (44) 1895613933
Web Site: http://www.newwavesportswear.co.uk
Sporting & Recreational Goods & Supplies Whslr
N.A.I.C.S.: 423910

New Wave Sportswear S.A. (1)
Carrer Mallorca 1, Sant Quirze del Valles, 08192, Barcelona, Spain **(100%)**
Tel.: (34) 937219505
Web Site: https://www.newwave.es
Sales Range: $25-49.9 Million
Emp.: 25
Sporting & Recreational Goods & Supplies Whslr
N.A.I.C.S.: 423910
Francesc Tuscet *(Gen Mgr)*

New Wave Trading Shanghai Ltd (1)
4th Floor Building E Nr 1978 Lianhua Road, Minhang District, Shanghai, 201103, China
Tel.: (86) 2161458828
Web Site: http://www.newwave.cn
Stationery & Sport Apparel Distr
N.A.I.C.S.: 424120

Newpoint SP. z.o.o. (1)
Lubuska 47, Ploty, Poland
Tel.: (48) 684519929

Clothing Accessories Retailer
N.A.I.C.S.: 458110

OKB Restaurang AB (1)
Stora Vagen 75, 360 52, Kalmar, Kosta,
Sweden **(100%)**
Tel.: (46) 478 348 30
Web Site: http://www.kostabodaarthotel.com
Sales Range: $250-299.9 Million
Emp.: 600
Restaurant
N.A.I.C.S.: 722511

OY Trexet Finland AB (1)
Juvan Teollisuuskatu 12, 02920, Espoo,
Finland **(100%)**
Tel.: (358) 95259580
Web Site: https://www.newwave.fi
Sales Range: $25-49.9 Million
Emp.: 30
Mens & Boys Clothing & Furnishings Whslr
N.A.I.C.S.: 424350

Orrefors Kosta Boda Holding AB (1)
Stora Vagen 96 Kosta, 360 52, Kalmar,
Sweden **(100%)**
Tel.: (46) 47834500
Web Site: http://www.kostaboda.se
Sales Range: $250-299.9 Million
Emp.: 600
Holding Company
N.A.I.C.S.: 551112

Subsidiary (Domestic):

Orrefors Kosta Boda AB (2)
Bruksomradet, Orrefors, Nybro, 380 40, Sweden
Tel.: (46) 481 34 000
Web Site: http://www.orrefors.se
Rev.: $57,770,700
Emp.: 330
Glassware & Glass Article Mfr
N.A.I.C.S.: 327215
Magnus Andersson *(CEO)*

SEA Glasbruk AB (2)
Hulterstad, Kosta, 36052, Halmstad,
Sweden **(100%)**
Tel.: (46) 47850310
Web Site: http://www.seaglasbruk.se
Sales Range: $25-49.9 Million
Emp.: 1
Pressed & Blown Glass & Glassware Mfr
N.A.I.C.S.: 327212

Orrefors Kosta Boda LLC (1)
1317 Route 73 Ste 106, Mount Laurel, NJ 08054
Tel.: (856) 768-5400
Home Furnishing Distr
N.A.I.C.S.: 423220

Paris Glove of Canada Inc. (1)
2315 Cohen, Montreal, H4R 2N7, QC, Canada
Tel.: (514) 345-0135
Web Site: https://auclair.com
Sales Range: $25-49.9 Million
Sporting Gloves Mfr & Distr
N.A.I.C.S.: 339920

Pax Scandinavia AB (1)
Stubbengatan 2, PO Box 343, 703 44, Orebro, Sweden **(100%)**
Tel.: (46) 19209210
Web Site: https://www.paxskor.se
Sales Range: $25-49.9 Million
Emp.: 15
Footwear Whslr
N.A.I.C.S.: 424340

ProJob Workwear AB (1)
Akarevagen 18, 455 83, Dingle,
Sweden **(100%)**
Tel.: (46) 5 241 7690
Web Site: https://www.projob.se
Sales Range: $25-49.9 Million
Emp.: 10
Men's Clothing Stores
N.A.I.C.S.: 458110

Sagaform AB (1)
Segloravagen 19, 504 64, Boras,
Sweden **(100%)**
Tel.: (46) 33233800
Web Site: http://www.sagaform.com
Sales Range: $25-49.9 Million
Gift Novelty & Souvenir Stores
N.A.I.C.S.: 459420

INTERNATIONAL PUBLIC

Sagaform APS (1)
Banemarksvej 50 E, Brondby, 2605, Denmark
Tel.: (45) 43437100
Family Clothing Stores
N.A.I.C.S.: 458110

Sagaform Forsaljnings AB (1)
Trandaredsgatan 200, 50752, Boras, 50752, Sweden **(100%)**
Tel.: (46) 33233800
Web Site: http://www.sagaform.se
Sales Range: $25-49.9 Million
Emp.: 35
Gift Novelty & Souvenir Stores
N.A.I.C.S.: 459420

Sagaform GmbH (1)
Celler Strasse 1, D-27374, Visselhovede, Germany
Tel.: (49) 4262959840
Web Site: http://www.sagaform.com
Household & Fine China Retail
N.A.I.C.S.: 327110

Sagaform Inc. (1)
1317 Route 73 N Ste 201, Mount Laurel, NJ 08054
Tel.: (856) 626-1340
Web Site: http://www.sagaform.com
Sales Range: $50-74.9 Million
Home Furnishing Whslr
N.A.I.C.S.: 423220

Seger Europe AB (1)
Jordgubbsvagen 24, 523 61, Gallstad,
Sweden **(100%)**
Tel.: (46) 32126050
Web Site: https://www.seger.se
Sales Range: $75-99.9 Million
Sporting & Recreational Goods & Supplies Whslr
N.A.I.C.S.: 423910

Svensk Form i Kosta AB (1)
Storgatan 85, 36051, Hovmantorp,
Sweden **(100%)**
Tel.: (46) 708998095
Mens & Boys Clothing & Furnishings Whslr
N.A.I.C.S.: 424350

Texet AB (1)
Jupitervagen 2, PO Box 5004, 194 43, Upplands Vasby, Sweden **(100%)**
Tel.: (46) 86302900
Web Site: https://www.jobmantexet.se
Sales Range: $25-49.9 Million
Mens & Boys Clothing & Furnishings Whslr
N.A.I.C.S.: 424350

Texet Benelux N.V. (1)
Nieuwlandlaan 24D I Z Aarschot B 224, 3200, Aarschot, Belgium **(75%)**
Tel.: (32) 16571157
Web Site: http://www.texet.be
Sales Range: $25-49.9 Million
Advertising Services
N.A.I.C.S.: 541810

Texet Denmark A/S (1)
Kometvej 8C, 8700, Horsens, Denmark
Tel.: (45) 86572800
Web Site: https://www.texet.dk
Clothing Retailer
N.A.I.C.S.: 458110

Texet Deutchland GmbH (1)
Cellerstrasse 1, Visselhovede, 27374, Bremen, Germany **(100%)**
Tel.: (49) 426230355
Web Site: http://www.texeteurope.com
Sporting & Recreational Goods & Supplies Whslr
N.A.I.C.S.: 423910

Texet France SAS (1)
103 Quai du President Roosevelt, 92130, Issy-les-Moulineaux, France
Tel.: (33) 141330314
Web Site: https://www.texet.fr
Sales Range: $25-49.9 Million
Emp.: 6
Advertising Services
N.A.I.C.S.: 541810

Texet Poland Ltd (1)
ul Krzemowa 1, Zlotniki, 62-002, Suchy Las, Poland
Tel.: (48) 61 868 5671
Web Site: https://www.texet.pl
Emp.: 20

AND PRIVATE COMPANIES

Textile Products Advertising Agency Services
N.A.I.C.S.: 541810

Texet Poland Sp. z o.o. (1)
ul Krzemowa 1, Zlotniki, 62-002, Suchy Las, Poland
Tel.: (48) 618685671
Web Site: https://www.texet.pl
Cloth & Fabric Distr
N.A.I.C.S.: 424310

Topline Keramiek B.V. (1)
Lindberghstr 45, NL 7903 BM, Hoogeveen, Netherlands **(100%)**
Tel.: (31) 523 238 238
Web Site: http://www.toppoint.com
Sales Range: $25-49.9 Million
Emp.: 25
Stationery & Office Supplies Mfr & Distr
N.A.I.C.S.: 339940

Toppoint BV (1)
F Hazemeijerstraat 400 B04, 7555 RJ, Hengelo, Netherlands
Tel.: (31) 742077900
Web Site: https://www.toppoint.com
Paper Packaging Product Distr
N.A.I.C.S.: 424130

Toppoint Nederland B.V. (1)
Stationsweg 14 A, Bergentheim, 7691AR, Zwolle, Netherlands **(100%)**
Tel.: (31) 523238238
Web Site: http://www.toppoint.com
Sales Range: $75-99.9 Million
Emp.: 120
Stationery & Office Supplies Whslr
N.A.I.C.S.: 424120

Totemco B.V. (1)
Stationsweg 14 A, Bergentheim, 7690AA, Zwolle, Netherlands
Tel.: (31) 206373937
Stationery & Office Supplies Whslr
N.A.I.C.S.: 424120

Tournament Solutions LLC (1)
6 School St, Manchester, MA 01944
Web Site:
https://www.tournamentsolutions.com
Golf Tournament Services
N.A.I.C.S.: 713910

United Brands of Scandinavia Ire Ltd. (1)
Unit A 6 KCR Ind Est, Kimmage, Dublin, Ireland **(100%)**
Tel.: (353) 14924836
Web Site: http://www.united-brands.ie
Sales Range: $50-74.9 Million
Emp.: 3
Mens & Boys Clothing & Furnishings Whslr
N.A.I.C.S.: 424350

United Brands of Scandinavia Ltd. (1)
Unit 1 Hirwaun Industrial Estate, Hirwaun, Aberdare, CF44 9UP, United Kingdom **(100%)**
Tel.: (44) 1685812111
Web Site: https://www.united-brands.co.uk
Sales Range: $25-49.9 Million
Clothing Stores
N.A.I.C.S.: 458110

X-Tend B.V. (1)
Nipkowstraat 1A, PO Box 40041, 8013 RJ, Zwolle, Netherlands **(100%)**
Tel.: (31) 388509100
Web Site: http://www.craft.se
Sales Range: $25-49.9 Million
Emp.: 15
Sporting & Recreational Goods & Supplies Whslr
N.A.I.C.S.: 423910

NEW WAVE HOLDINGS LTD.
101 Kitchener Road 02-17 Jalan Besar Plaza, Singapore, 208511, Singapore
Tel.: (65) 62683377   SG
Web Site:
https://www.newwave.com.sg
Year Founded: 1999
5FX—(CAT)
Rev.: $17,364,484
Assets: $21,429,381
Liabilities: $8,948,907
Net Worth: $12,480,474
Earnings: ($374,459)
Fiscal Year-end: 03/31/23
Holding Company
N.A.I.C.S.: 551112
Kian Soon Ong (CEO)

Subsidiaries:

Eplus Technologies Sdn. Bhd. (1)
No 12 Jalan Makmur 2 Taman Perindustrian Cemerlang, Ulu Tiram, 81800, Johor Bahru, Malaysia
Tel.: (60) 78624090
Electrical Cable & Electronic Component Distr
N.A.I.C.S.: 423610

General Electronics & Instrumentation Corporation Private Limited (1)
101 Kitchener Road 02-17 Jalan Besar Plaza, Singapore, 208511, Singapore
Tel.: (65) 62987633
Electronic Parts & Equipment Distr
N.A.I.C.S.: 423690

MNPL Aluminium Centre Sdn. Bhd. (1)
No 12 Jalan Makmur 2 Taman Perindustrian Cemerlang, 81800, Johor Bahru, Malaysia
Tel.: (60) 72893007
Aluminum Alloy Plate & Stainless Steel Product Distr
N.A.I.C.S.: 423510

MNPL Metals Co., Ltd. (1)
323 North QingYang Road, Kunshan, 215300, Jiang Su, China
Tel.: (86) 51250136322
Aluminium Product Distr
N.A.I.C.S.: 423510

Manufacturing Network Pte. Ltd. (1)
8 First Lok Yang Road, Jurong, Singapore, 629731, Singapore
Tel.: (65) 68622311
Aluminium Product Distr
N.A.I.C.S.: 423510

NEW WEST ENERGY SERVICES INC.
500 435 4th Avenue SW, Calgary, T2P 3A8, AB, Canada
Tel.: (403) 984-9798
Web Site:
http://www.newwestenergy.com
Year Founded: 1986
Rev.: $14,876,367
Assets: $9,291,892
Liabilities: $9,967,889
Net Worth: ($675,997)
Earnings: ($1,812,591)
Fiscal Year-end: 12/31/18
Oil & Gas Exploration Services
N.A.I.C.S.: 213112
Gerry E. Kerkhoff (Pres & CEO)

Subsidiaries:

Porterco Oilfield Services Inc. (1)
5B Parkdale Way, Slave Lake, T0G2A0, AB, Canada
Tel.: (780) 805-4000
Oil & Gas Drilling Services
N.A.I.C.S.: 213112

NEW WESTERN GROUP LIMITED
Suite 2101 21/F Chinachem Century Tower 178 Gloucester Road, Wanchai, China (Hong Kong)
Tel.: (852) 2 539 0678
Web Site:
http://www.megalogic.com.hk
Rev.: $8,004,437
Assets: $40,799,581
Liabilities: $1,524,997
Net Worth: $39,274,584
Earnings: ($2,578,986)
Emp.: 31
Fiscal Year-end: 12/31/19
Fabless Semiconductor Mfr
N.A.I.C.S.: 334413
Leo Tak Wing Sung (CEO & Sec)

Subsidiaries:

MiniLogic Device Corporation Limited (1)
Unit 508-9 IC Development Ctr 6 Science Park West Ave, Hong Kong Science Park, Sha Tin, China (Hong Kong)
Tel.: (852) 2319 1080
Web Site: http://www.minilogic.com.hk
Emp.: 15
Electronic Components Mfr
N.A.I.C.S.: 334419

NEW WORLD RESOURCE CORP.
620 650 West Georgia St, PO Box 11604, Vancouver, V6B 4N9, BC, Canada
Tel.: (604) 669-2701
Web Site:
http://www.newworldresource.com
Year Founded: 1983
NW—(DEU)
Sales Range: Less than $1 Million
Mineral Exploration Services
N.A.I.C.S.: 213114
John E. Lando (Pres, CEO & Sec)

Subsidiaries:

New World Resource Bolivia S.A. (1)
Calacoto c 20 N, 7780, La Paz, Bolivia
Tel.: (591) 2 2793192
Mineral Exploration Services
N.A.I.C.S.: 212390

NEW WORLD RESOURCES LIMITED
Unit 24-26 Level 3 22 Railway Road, Subiaco, 6008, WA, Australia
Tel.: (61) 892261356
Web Site: https://newworldres.com
NWC—(ASX)
Rev.: $927
Assets: $29,717,399
Liabilities: $1,919,099
Net Worth: $27,798,300
Earnings: ($11,270,940)
Fiscal Year-end: 06/30/22
Mining Industry
N.A.I.C.S.: 212290
Richard Hill (Chm)

NEW WORLD SOLUTIONS INC.
4711 Yonge Street 10th Floor, Toronto, M2N 6K8, ON, Canada
Tel.: (416) 453-4708   BC
Web Site:
https://www.newworldsolutions.com
Year Founded: 1982
NEWS—(CNSX)
Rev.: $338,895
Assets: $9,193,230
Liabilities: $612,059
Net Worth: $8,581,171
Earnings: ($11,992,097)
Emp.: 5
Fiscal Year-end: 04/30/21
Engine Mfr
N.A.I.C.S.: 336310
Andrew Ryu (Chm)

Subsidiaries:

REGI U.S., Inc. (1)
7520 N Market St Ste 10, Spokane, WA 99217
Tel.: (509) 474-1040
Rev.: $60,000
Assets: $63,370
Liabilities: $2,698,623
Net Worth: ($2,635,253)
Earnings: ($2,259,996)
Emp.: 7
Fiscal Year-end: 04/30/2019
Lightweight & High Efficiency Engine Mfr
N.A.I.C.S.: 336310
Paul Willard Chute (Chm, CEO & CFO)

NEW YORK FRIES
199 Four Valley Drive, Vaughan, L4K 0B8, ON, Canada
Tel.: (905) 760-2244
Web Site:
http://www.newyorkfries.com
Year Founded: 1984
Emp.: 150
Fast Food Restaurants
N.A.I.C.S.: 722513
Jay Gould (Founder)

Subsidiaries:

South St. Burger Co (1)
1220 Yonge St Ste 400, Toronto, M4T 1W1, ON, Canada
Tel.: (416) 963-5005
Web Site: http://www.southstburger.com
Fast Food Restaurants
N.A.I.C.S.: 722513
Thomas McNaughtan (VP-Ops)

NEW ZEALAND ENERGY CORP.
11 Young Street, PO Box 24 147, New Plymouth, 4312, New Zealand
Tel.: (64) 67574470   BC
Web Site:
https://newzealandenergy.com
Year Founded: 2010
NZERF—(OTCIQ)
Rev.: $1,429,987
Assets: $11,279,807
Liabilities: $8,624,121
Net Worth: $2,655,687
Earnings: ($1,432,159)
Fiscal Year-end: 12/31/23
Oil & Gas Exploration Services
N.A.I.C.S.: 211120
James Willis (Chm)

NEW ZEALAND KING SALMON
93 Beatty Street Tahunanui, Nelson, 7011, New Zealand
Tel.: (64) 35485714   NZ
Web Site:
http://www.kingsalmon.co.nz
Year Founded: 2009
NZK—(ASX)
Rev.: $111,905,502
Assets: $142,909,689
Liabilities: $29,096,890
Net Worth: $113,812,799
Earnings: $17,016,746
Emp.: 400
Fiscal Year-end: 01/31/24
Fish Distr
N.A.I.C.S.: 424460
John Ryder (Chm)

NEW ZEALAND OIL & GAS LIMITED
Level 1 36 Tennyson St, Te Aro, Wellington, 6011, New Zealand
Tel.: (64) 44952424
Web Site: http://www.nzog.com
Sales Range: $25-49.9 Million
Emp.: 10
Oil, Gas Exploration & Production
N.A.I.C.S.: 325120
Catherine McKelvey (CFO)

Subsidiaries:

Cue Energy Resources Limited (1)
Level 3 10 Queen Street, Melbourne, 3000, VIC, Australia
Tel.: (61) 386104000
Web Site: https://www.cuenrg.com.au
Rev.: $33,159,054
Assets: $75,643,029
Liabilities: $32,297,676
Net Worth: $43,345,352
Earnings: $9,474,492
Fiscal Year-end: 06/30/2024
Oil & Gas Exploration

NEW ZEALAND OIL & GAS LIMITED

New Zealand Oil & Gas Limited—(Continued)
N.A.I.C.S.: 213112
Matthew Boyall (CEO)

Subsidiary (Domestic):

Cue Exploration Pty. Ltd. (2)
Level 3 10 Queen Street, Melbourne, 3000, VIC, Australia
Tel.: (61) 386104000
Web Site: http://www.cuenrg.com.au
Exploration Services
N.A.I.C.S.: 213114

NEW ZEALAND POST LIMITED
Ground Floor 7 Waterloo Quay, Wellington, New Zealand
Tel.: (64) 9 367 9710
Web Site: http://www.nzpost.co.nz
Rev.: $612,946,080
Assets: $1,096,178,790
Liabilities: $315,210,210
Net Worth: $780,968,580
Earnings: ($81,322,890)
Emp.: 7,000
Fiscal Year-end: 06/30/19
Postal Service
N.A.I.C.S.: 517111
Malcolm Shaw (Chief Governance & Sustainability Officer)

Subsidiaries:

Datam Limited (1)
1 Victoria Street, Petone, Lower Hutt, 5012, New Zealand
Tel.: (64) 4 568 8200
Business Process Outsourcing Services
N.A.I.C.S.: 541511

Express Couriers Ltd (1)
Level 12 New Zealand Post House 7 Waterloo Quay, Wellington, New Zealand
Tel.: (64) 800 501 501
Web Site: http://www.expresscouriers.co.nz
Sales Range: $300-349.9 Million
Emp.: 2,000
Express Courier Services
N.A.I.C.S.: 492110

Subsidiary (Domestic):

Contract Logistics (2)
25 Pukekiwiriki Place, Highbrook East Tamaki, Auckland, 2161, New Zealand
Tel.: (64) 800 456447
Web Site: http://www.contractlogistics.co.nz
Logistics & Warehousing Services
N.A.I.C.S.: 541614
Allifa Connelly (Mgr)

CourierPost (2)
151 Victoria St West Level 2 CourierPost House, PO Box 90 949, Auckland, New Zealand
Tel.: (64) 800 268 743
Web Site: http://www.courierpost.co.nz
Express Courier Services
N.A.I.C.S.: 492110

Pace (2)
Level One 25 Pukekiwiriki Place, PO Box 8561, Highbrook East Tamaki, Auckland, 2013, New Zealand
Tel.: (64) 9 574 0290
Web Site: http://www.pace.co.nz
Emp.: 20
Express Courier Services
N.A.I.C.S.: 492110
Steven Craig (Mgr)

Localist Limited (1)
Level 2 104 Quay Street, Auckland, 1011, New Zealand
Tel.: (64) 800 030 030
Web Site: http://www.localist.co.nz
Sales Range: $25-49.9 Million
Emp.: 60
Online Shopping Services
N.A.I.C.S.: 541511
Andrew Robertson (CFO)

New Zealand Post Holdings Limited (1)
Lvl 12 NZ Post Corporate Office 7-27 Waterloo Qu, Wellington, 39990, New Zealand
Tel.: (64) 44964999

Investment Management Service
N.A.I.C.S.: 523940

Parcel DirectGroup Pty Limited (1)
15 Bridge St, Pymble, 2073, NSW, Australia
Tel.: (61) 2 8823 5400
Parcel Delivery Services
N.A.I.C.S.: 492210

The New Zealand Home Loan Company Limited (1)
Level 1 903 Victoria Street, Hamilton, 3024, New Zealand
Tel.: (64) 78390998
Web Site: http://www.nzhl.co.nz
Emp.: 20
Home Loan Providers
N.A.I.C.S.: 522291
Julian Travaglia (CEO)

NEW ZEALAND RURAL LAND COMPANY LIMITED
Level 1 85 Fort Street Auckland CBD, Auckland, 1010, New Zealand
Tel.: (64) 92182177   NZ
Web Site: https://www.nzrlc.co.nz
Year Founded: 2020
NZL—(NZX)
Rev.: $9,699,842
Assets: $233,700,473
Liabilities: $92,726,066
Net Worth: $140,974,407
Earnings: $6,858,768
Fiscal Year-end: 12/31/23
Lessors of Other Real Estate Property
N.A.I.C.S.: 531190
Richard Milsom (Mng Dir)

NEW-YORK HAMBURGER GUMMI-WAAREN COMPAGNIE AG
Otto-Brenner-Str 17, 21337, Luneburg, Germany
Tel.: (49) 4131 22 44 0
Web Site: http://www.nyh.de
Sales Range: $10-24.9 Million
Elastomer & Thermoplastic Mfr
N.A.I.C.S.: 325211
Bernd Menzel (Chm-Exec Bd)

Subsidiaries:

Hercules Sagemann GmbH (1)
Otto-Brenner-Str 17, D-21337, Luneburg, Germany
Tel.: (49) 4131 2244 300
Web Site: http://www.hercules-saegemann.de
Comb & Brush Mfr
N.A.I.C.S.: 325620

NEWAG SA
Ul Wyspianskiego 3, 33-300, Nowy Sacz, Poland
Tel.: (48) 184496360
Web Site: https://www.newag.pl
Year Founded: 1876
NWG—(WAR)
Rev.: $312,778,454
Assets: $439,791,920
Liabilities: $235,951,473
Net Worth: $203,840,447
Earnings: $24,156,758
Emp.: 1,300
Fiscal Year-end: 12/31/23
Rail Vehicles Mfr
N.A.I.C.S.: 336510
Urszula Makosz (Mgr-PR)

NEWATER TECHNOLOGY, INC.
1 Ruida Road, Laishan District, Yantai, 264003, Shandong, China
Tel.: (86) 535 8012930   VG
Web Site: http://www.dtnewa.com
Year Founded: 2012
Rev.: $51,158,766
Assets: $93,235,861
Liabilities: $54,384,369
Net Worth: $38,851,492

Earnings: $5,562,761
Emp.: 216
Fiscal Year-end: 12/31/20
Wastewater Treatment Equipment Mfr & Distr
N.A.I.C.S.: 333310
Yuebiao Li (Chm & CEO)

NEWAY GROUP HOLDINGS LIMITED
Chung Tai Printing Group Building 11 Yip Cheong Street On Lok Tsuen, Fanling, NT, China (Hong Kong)
Tel.: (852) 26696111
Web Site: http://www.chungtai.com.hk
0055—(HKG)
Rev.: $57,298,926
Assets: $145,829,478
Liabilities: $45,341,526
Net Worth: $100,487,952
Earnings: ($306,155)
Emp.: 1,190
Fiscal Year-end: 12/31/22
Labels & Plastic Cards Printing
N.A.I.C.S.: 513191
Larry Chai Hong Suek (CEO)

Subsidiaries:

Delight Source Limited (1)
5/F Chung Tai Printing Group Building 11 Yip Cheong Street, Fanling, New Territories, China (Hong Kong)
Tel.: (852) 26696126
Emp.: 6
Printing Product Distr
N.A.I.C.S.: 424120
Kam Cheong Lau (Mgr)

Kam Hon Printing (Shenzhen) Co., Ltd. (1)
No 77 Hengping Road Heng Gang Town Long Gang District, Shenzhen, 518115, China
Tel.: (86) 75528626111
Printing Product Distr
N.A.I.C.S.: 424120

Neway Group Holdings Limited - Shenzhen Factory (1)
Long Gang Avenue Heng Gang Section Bao An Community Yuan Shan Street, Long Gang District, Shenzhen, Guangdong, China
Tel.: (86) 75528687560
Printing Products Mfr
N.A.I.C.S.: 323113

Star Entertainment (Universe) Limited (1)
Unit 801 & 802 8/F East Ocean Centre 98 Granville Road, TST East, Kowloon, China (Hong Kong)
Tel.: (852) 27211190
Web Site: http://www.starentertainment.com.hk
Concert Promotion Services
N.A.I.C.S.: 711130

NEWAY VALVE (SUZHOU) CO., LTD.
No 666 Taishan Road Suzhou High-tech Zone, New District, Suzhou, 215129, Jiangsu, China
Tel.: (86) 51266628154
Web Site: https://www.newayvalve.com
Year Founded: 1997
603699—(SHG)
Rev.: $569,914,067
Assets: $978,636,649
Liabilities: $512,242,310
Net Worth: $466,394,339
Earnings: $65,442,729
Fiscal Year-end: 12/31/22
Industrial Valve Mfr & Distr
N.A.I.C.S.: 332911
Lu Liangfeng (Chm)

Subsidiaries:

NEWAY Valvulas DO Brasil LTDA. (1)

INTERNATIONAL PUBLIC

Est Amadeu Rocha Rodrigues 100 Iporanga, Sorocaba, Sao Paulo, Brazil
Tel.: (55) 1533256700
Pressure Valve Distr
N.A.I.C.S.: 423830

Neway Flow Control DMCC (1)
Office 3606 JBC1 Cluster G Jumeirah Lake Towers, PO Box 214954, Dubai, United Arab Emirates
Tel.: (971) 44562947
Pressure Valve Distr
N.A.I.C.S.: 423830
Devi Kumaran (Project Mgr)

Neway Valve (Europe) S.r.l. (1)
Via Forcella 3, 20144, Milan, Italy
Tel.: (39) 0287264010
Pressure Valve Distr
N.A.I.C.S.: 423830
Graziano Pittaluga (Mgr-Bus Dev)

Neway Valve (Singapore) Pte Ltd (1)
100G Pasir Panjang Rd 08-21, Interlocal Centre, Singapore, 118523, Singapore
Tel.: (65) 66847968
Web Site: http://www.newayvalve.com
Emp.: 10
Pressure Valve Distr
N.A.I.C.S.: 423830
Sunny Lie (Dir-Mktg & Bus Dev)

Neway Valve Europe B.V. (1)
Curieweg 19 4th Floor, 3208 KJ, Spijkenisse, Netherlands
Tel.: (31) 181457070
Pressure Valve Distr
N.A.I.C.S.: 423830
Fang Wang (Mgr-Fin)

Neway Valve International INC (1)
9757 Stafford Centre Dr, Stafford, TX 77477
Tel.: (281) 969-5500
Pressure Valve Distr
N.A.I.C.S.: 423830

Neway Valve West Africa FZE (1)
Lekki Coastal Road, Tiye Town Akodo Ibeju-Lekki LGA, Lagos, Nigeria
Tel.: (234) 7061725358
Chemical Product Mfr & Distr
N.A.I.C.S.: 325998

NEWAYS ELECTRONICS INTERNATIONAL NV
Science Park Eindhoven 5010, 5692 EA, Son, Netherlands
Tel.: (31) 402679200
Web Site: http://www.newayselectronics.com
NEWAYS—(EUR)
Rev.: $587,800,045
Assets: $287,673,460
Liabilities: $162,389,295
Net Worth: $125,284,165
Earnings: ($4,808,560)
Emp.: 2,705
Fiscal Year-end: 12/31/20
Electronics Manufacturing Services
N.A.I.C.S.: 334412
Adrie van Bragt (COO)

Subsidiaries:

Neways Advanced Applications B.V. (1)
Science Park Eindhoven 5004, PO Box 57, 5692 EA, Son, Netherlands
Tel.: (31) 40 267 3500
Web Site: http://www.neways-advanced-applications.nl
Sales Range: $75-99.9 Million
Emp.: 250
Electronic Engineering Products Mfr
N.A.I.C.S.: 541330

Neways Cable & Wire Solutions B.V. (1)
Tel.: (31) 47 541 8200
Web Site: http://www.neways.nl
Sales Range: $25-49.9 Million
Emp.: 90
Engineering & Logistic Managment Services
N.A.I.C.S.: 541330

Neways Electronics Echt B.V. (1)

AND PRIVATE COMPANIES

Voltaweg 10, PO Box 84, 6101 XK, Echt, Netherlands
Tel.: (31) 47 541 8200
Web Site: https://www.newayselectronics.com
Sales Range: $50-74.9 Million
Emp.: 120
Electrical Assembling & Logistic Managment Services
N.A.I.C.S.: 333519

Neways Electronics Production GmbH (1)
Wilhelmine-Reichard-Str 4, D-34123, Kassel, Germany
Tel.: (49) 56158591700
Web Site: http://www.neways-kassel.de
Sales Range: $50-74.9 Million
Emp.: 140
Electronic Components Mfr
N.A.I.C.S.: 334419

Neways Electronics US Inc. (1)
1880 Milmont Dr, Milpitas, CA 95035
Tel.: (408) 618-4789
Electronic Components Mfr
N.A.I.C.S.: 334419

Neways Industrial Systems B.V. (1)
Science Park Eindhoven 5010, Son, 5692 EA, Son, Netherlands
Tel.: (31) 402673000
Web Site: http://www.neways-industrial-systems.nl
Sales Range: $50-74.9 Million
Emp.: 200
Electronic Equipment Assembling Services
N.A.I.C.S.: 336110

Neways Leeuwarden B.V. (1)
Simon Vestdijkwei 2, 8914 AX, Leeuwarden, Netherlands
Tel.: (31) 58 215 4700
Web Site: http://www.neways-leeuwarden.nl
Sales Range: $25-49.9 Million
Emp.: 100
Electronic Product Mfr & Distr
N.A.I.C.S.: 335999

Neways Micro Electronics B.V. (1)
Tel.: (31) 47 541 9500
Web Site: http://www.neways-micro-electronics.nl
Sales Range: $25-49.9 Million
Emp.: 70
Hybrid Electronic Products Mfr
N.A.I.C.S.: 334419

Neways Micro Electronics China Co. Ltd. (1)
1st Floor Building 9 Originality Industry Park No 100 Dicui Road, Liyuan Development Zone Binhu, Wuxi, 214072, Jiangsu, China
Tel.: (86) 51085160825
Sales Range: $25-49.9 Million
Emp.: 100
Electronic Components Mfr
N.A.I.C.S.: 334416

Neways Neunkirchen GmbH (1)
Am Gneisenaufloz 6, 66538, Neunkirchen, Germany
Tel.: (49) 68 219 8080
Web Site: http://www.neways.nl
Sales Range: $50-74.9 Million
Emp.: 150
Electronic Components Mfr
N.A.I.C.S.: 334416

Neways Slovakia a.s. (1)
Trencianska 864/68, Nova Dubnica, 018 51, Trencin, Slovakia
Tel.: (421) 42 444 1911
Web Site: http://www.abc.com
Sales Range: $75-99.9 Million
Emp.: 400
Financial Management Services
N.A.I.C.S.: 541611
Peter Wesse (Mgr)

Neways Technologies B.V. (1)
Science Park Eindhoven 5709, Son, 5692 EP, Son, Netherlands
Tel.: (31) 402679333
Web Site: http://www.neways.nl
Sales Range: $25-49.9 Million
Emp.: 70
Electrical Engineering Services
N.A.I.C.S.: 541330

Neways Technologies GmbH (1)
Fichtenweg 8, 99098, Erfurt, Germany
Tel.: (49) 3 620 3960
Web Site: https://www.newayselectronics.com
Electronic Components Mfr
N.A.I.C.S.: 334419

Neways Vertriebs-GmbH (1)
Wilhelmine-Reichard-Str 4, 34058, Kassel, Germany
Tel.: (49) 56158591700
Web Site: http://www.neways-kassel.de
Sales Range: $50-74.9 Million
Emp.: 100
Financial Management Services
N.A.I.C.S.: 523999

NEWBORN TOWN, INC.
12/F Tower A CEC Development Building Sanyuanqiao, Chaoyang, Beijing, China
Tel.: (86) 1053687809 Ky
Web Site: http://www.newborntown.com
Year Founded: 2009
9911—(HKG)
Rev.: $393,077,599
Assets: $241,518,467
Liabilities: $67,701,863
Net Worth: $173,816,604
Earnings: $40,341,834
Emp.: 846
Fiscal Year-end: 12/31/22
Internet Publishing Services
N.A.I.C.S.: 513199
Chunhe Liu (Chm & CEO)
Subsidiaries:

BlueCity Holdings Limited (1)
Block 2 Tower B Room 028 No 22 Pingguo Shequ, Bai Zi Wan Road Chaoyang District, Beijing, 100022, China
Tel.: (86) 1058769855
Rev.: $164,944,573
Assets: $93,483,011
Liabilities: $25,159,543
Net Worth: $68,323,468
Earnings: ($47,437,485)
Emp.: 801
Fiscal Year-end: 12/31/2021
Holding Company
N.A.I.C.S.: 551112
Baoli Ma (Founder, Chm & CEO)

NEWBURY BUILDING SOCIETY
17 Bartholomew Street, Newbury, RG14 5LY, Berks, United Kingdom
Tel.: (44) 1635 555700
Web Site: http://www.newbury.co.uk
Year Founded: 1856
Rev.: $39,172,246
Assets: $1,558,044,394
Liabilities: $1,453,845,643
Net Worth: $104,198,750
Earnings: $5,784,156
Emp.: 123
Fiscal Year-end: 10/31/19
Mortgage Lending & Other Financial Services
N.A.I.C.S.: 522310
Roland Gardner (CEO)

NEWBURY PHARMACEUTICALS AB
Scheeletorget 1, Medicon Village, 223 81, Lund, Sweden
Tel.: (46) 46121120
Web Site: https://www.newburypharma.com
Year Founded: 2020
NEWBRY—(OMX)
Rev.: $1,019,517
Assets: $7,238,867
Liabilities: $2,336,848
Net Worth: $4,902,019
Earnings: ($1,928,842)
Emp.: 5
Fiscal Year-end: 12/31/23
Pharmaceutical Product Mfr & Distr

NEWCASTLE ENERGY CORP.

N.A.I.C.S.: 325412
Christoffer Tell (CFO)

NEWBURY RACECOURSE PLC
The Racecourse, Newbury, RG14 7NZ, Berkshire, United Kingdom
Tel.: (44) 1635019079 UK
Web Site: https://www.newburyracecourse.uk
Rev.: $24,485,741
Assets: $72,538,452
Liabilities: $8,233,402
Net Worth: $64,305,050
Earnings: $2,274,084
Emp.: 80
Fiscal Year-end: 12/31/18
Holding Company; Racetrack, Golf Course & Other Recreational Facilities Owner & Operator
N.A.I.C.S.: 551112
Dominic J. Burke (Chm)

NEWCAP HOLDING A/S
NewCap Holding A/S Oslo Plads 2, 2100, Copenhagen, Denmark
Tel.: (45) 23705885
Web Site: https://www.newcap.dk
NEWCAP—(CSE)
Rev.: $20,257
Assets: $5,742,935
Liabilities: $548,393
Net Worth: $5,194,542
Earnings: ($1,077,976)
Emp.: 3
Fiscal Year-end: 12/31/22
Holding Company
N.A.I.C.S.: 551112
Peter Steen Christensen (CEO)

NEWCAPEC ELECTRONICS CO., LTD.
No 18 Yingchun Street, Zhengzhou High & New Technology Industrial Development Zone, Zhengzhou, China
Tel.: (86) 37156599683
Web Site: https://www.newcapec.net
Year Founded: 2000
300248—(CHIN)
Rev.: $149,497,979
Assets: $388,250,081
Liabilities: $69,796,668
Net Worth: $318,453,413
Earnings: $15,143,192
Emp.: 900
Fiscal Year-end: 12/31/23
Smart Card Mfr & Distr
N.A.I.C.S.: 326199
Weiguo Yang (Chm)
Subsidiaries:

Newcapec Malaysia Sdn. Bhd. (1)
A-33A-6 Level 33A Tower A Menara UOA Bangsar No 5 Jalan Bangsar, Utama 1, 59000, Kuala Lumpur, Malaysia
Tel.: (60) 322019426
Electronic Products Mfr
N.A.I.C.S.: 334413

NEWCASTLE BUILDING SOCIETY
Portland House New Bridge Street, Newcastle upon Tyne, NE1 8AL, United Kingdom
Tel.: (44) 0191 244 2000
Web Site: http://www.newcastle.co.uk
Year Founded: 1863
Rev.: $139,160,760
Assets: $5,786,910,360
Liabilities: $5,490,751,080
Net Worth: $296,159,280
Earnings: $14,952,240
Emp.: 1,039
Fiscal Year-end: 12/31/19
Insurance & Financial Services
N.A.I.C.S.: 522180

Phil Moorhouse (Chm)
Subsidiaries:

MANCHESTER BUILDING SOCIETY (1)
125 Portland Street, Manchester, M1 4QD, United Kingdom
Tel.: (44) 1619238000
Web Site: http://www.themanchester.co.uk
Rev.: $9,533,910
Assets: $300,778,427
Liabilities: $278,731,770
Net Worth: $22,046,657
Earnings: ($467,056)
Emp.: 31
Fiscal Year-end: 12/31/2020
Sound Financial Products Providers
N.A.I.C.S.: 541611
Paul A. Lynch (CEO)

New Castle Mortgage, LLC (1)
2323 21st Ave Ste 200, Nashville, TN 37212
Tel.: (615) 279-3476
Mortgage Services
N.A.I.C.S.: 522310

Newcastle Financial Services Limited (1)
New Bridge St, Portland House, Newcastle upon Tyne, NE1 8AL, United Kingdom
Tel.: (44) 1912442000
Web Site: http://www.newcastle.co.uk
Sales Range: $75-99.9 Million
Emp.: 500
Business Services
N.A.I.C.S.: 561499
Jim Willen (CEO)

Newcastle Mortgage Corporation Limited (1)
New Bridge Street, Portland House, Newcastle upon Tyne, NE1 8AL, United Kingdom
Tel.: (44) 1912442000
Sales Range: $350-399.9 Million
Credit Intermediation Services
N.A.I.C.S.: 522390

Newcastle Strategic Solutions Limited (1)
New Bridge St, Portland House, Newcastle upon Tyne, NE1 8AL, United Kingdom
Tel.: (44) 1912442000
Web Site: http://www.nssl.info
Sales Range: $150-199.9 Million
Emp.: 600
Management Consulting Services
N.A.I.C.S.: 541618
Phil Grand (Mng Dir)

Newton Facilities Computer Leasing Limited (1)
New Bridge St Portland House, Newcastle upon Tyne, NE1 8AL, United Kingdom
Tel.: (44) 1912442000
Web Site: http://www.newcastle.co.uk
Sales Range: $150-199.9 Million
Emp.: 600
Computer Related Services
N.A.I.C.S.: 541519

Newton Facilities Computer Purchasing Ltd (1)
New Bridge Street, Portland House, Newcastle upon Tyne, NE1 8AL, United Kingdom
Tel.: (44) 1912442000
Sales Range: $200-249.9 Million
Emp.: 600
Software Reproducing
N.A.I.C.S.: 334610
Chris Hilton (Chm)

NEWCASTLE ENERGY CORP.
Kanata, Ottawa, Canada BC
Year Founded: 1981
MTLO—(TSXV)
Rev.: $13,721,037
Assets: $32,805,053
Liabilities: $17,412,922
Net Worth: $15,392,131
Earnings: ($6,429,801)
Emp.: 104
Fiscal Year-end: 03/31/22
Petroleum & Natural Gas Exploration, Development & Extraction

5233

NEWCASTLE ENERGY CORP.

Newcastle Energy Corp.—(Continued)
N.A.I.C.S.: 211120
Robin Peterson (CFO)

Subsidiaries:

Derek Resources (USA) Inc. (1)
32 Tubb Town Rd, Newcastle, WY 82701
Tel.: (604) 331-1757
Sales Range: $50-74.9 Million
Emp.: 2
Oil Well Drilling Services
N.A.I.C.S.: 213111
Robin Peterson (Gen Mgr)

NEWCITY (BANGKOK) PUBLIC COMPANY LIMITED
666 Rama 3 Road Bangpongpang, Yan Nawa, Bangkok, 10120, Thailand
Tel.: (66) 22946999   **TH**
Web Site: https://www.newcity.co.th
Year Founded: 1964
NC—(THA)
Rev.: $15,525,452
Assets: $23,253,675
Liabilities: $9,450,505
Net Worth: $13,803,170
Earnings: $605,848
Fiscal Year-end: 12/31/23
Apparel Product Distr
N.A.I.C.S.: 424350
Boonpakorn Chokwathana (Chm & Pres)

NEWCORE GOLD LTD.
Suite 1560 - 200 Burrard Street, Vancouver, V6C 3L6, BC, Canada
Tel.: (604) 484-4399   **BC**
Web Site: https://newcoregold.com
Year Founded: 2010
NCAUF—(OTCQX)
Assets: $34,151,291
Liabilities: $125,763
Net Worth: $34,025,529
Earnings: ($1,790,479)
Emp.: 18
Fiscal Year-end: 12/31/23
Investment Services
N.A.I.C.S.: 523999
Douglas B. Forster (Chm)

NEWEGG COMMERCE, INC.
Room 1003B 10th Floor BeiKong Technology Building No 10 Baifuquan, Changping District, Beijing, 102200, China
Tel.: (86) 1089788107   **VG**
Web Site: http://www.lianluosmart.com
NEGG—(NASDAQ)
Rev.: $1,720,273,000
Assets: $542,095,000
Liabilities: $386,873,000
Net Worth: $155,222,000
Earnings: ($57,429,000)
Emp.: 1,355
Fiscal Year-end: 12/31/22
Home Respiratory, Oxygen Homecare Products & Other Medical Devices Developer & Marketer
N.A.I.C.S.: 339112
Zhitao He (Chm)

Subsidiaries:

Newegg Inc. (1)
16839 E Gale Ave, City of Industry, CA 91745
Tel.: (626) 271-9700
Web Site: http://www.newegg.com
Sales Range: $1-4.9 Billion
Emp.: 1,000
On-Line Only Computer Electronics & Computing Products Distr
N.A.I.C.S.: 449210
Fred Chang (Founder)

Subsidiary (Domestic):

ABS Computer Technologies Inc. (2)
18045 Rowland St, City of Industry, CA 91748-1205
Tel.: (626) 271-1580
Sales Range: $10-24.9 Million
Emp.: 120
Designs & Builds Made-to-Order Personal Computers
N.A.I.C.S.: 334118
Sam Liu (Mgr-PDS)

NuTrend Automotive Inc. (2)
17560 Rowland St, City of Industry, CA 91748
Web Site: http://www.nutrend.com
Online Specialized Automotive Products Retailer & Whslr
N.A.I.C.S.: 441330

NEWEVER TRADE WINGS LIMITED
238B AJC Bose Road Unit 4B 4th Floor, Kolkata, 700 020, West Bengal, India
Tel.: (91) 3365016503
Web Site: http://www.newever.in
Rev.: $8,844,394
Assets: $13,223,005
Liabilities: $9,674,675
Net Worth: $3,548,330
Earnings: $7,695
Fiscal Year-end: 03/31/16
Iron, Steel & Other Commodities Trading
N.A.I.C.S.: 523160
Kousik Brahma (CFO)

NEWFIELD RESOURCES LIMITED
Unit 16A 81 Briggs Street, Perth, 6101, WA, Australia
Tel.: (61) 865580810   **AU**
Web Site: https://www.newfieldresources.com
NWF—(ASX)
Rev.: $347,611
Assets: $93,767,879
Liabilities: $27,380,006
Net Worth: $66,387,872
Earnings: ($7,065,612)
Emp.: 243
Fiscal Year-end: 06/30/23
Diversified Exploration Company
N.A.I.C.S.: 212290
Anthony Ho (Exec Dir)

Subsidiaries:

Stellar Diamonds Limited (1)
7 Bell Yard, London, WC2A 2JR, United Kingdom
Tel.: (44) 2070107686
Diamond Mining Services
N.A.I.C.S.: 212311

NEWFLEX TECHNOLOGY CO., LTD.
181 Manhae-ro, Danwon-gu, Ansan, 425-839, Gyeonggi-do, Korea (South)
Tel.: (82) 314949325
Web Site: https://www.newflex.co.kr
Year Founded: 1992
085670—(KRS)
Rev.: $199,647,575
Assets: $134,303,980
Liabilities: $83,097,167
Net Worth: $51,206,813
Earnings: $11,054,179
Emp.: 372
Fiscal Year-end: 12/31/22
Printed Circuit Board Mfr
N.A.I.C.S.: 334412
Lim Woo-Hyeon (Co-CEO)

NEWFOUNDLAND DISCOVERY CORP.
700-838 West Hastings Street, Vancouver, V6E 4A6, BC, Canada
Tel.: (604) 537-4174
Web Site: https://newfoundlanddiscovery.ca
NEWD—(CNSX)
Rev.: $3,506
Assets: $7,592,618
Liabilities: $700,655
Net Worth: $6,891,963
Earnings: ($1,652,281)
Fiscal Year-end: 04/30/21
Mineral Exploration Services
N.A.I.C.S.: 213114
Glen Wallace (CFO)

NEWGATE PRIVATE EQUITY LLP
38 Jermyn Street Suite 3B, London, SW1Y 6DN, United Kingdom
Tel.: (44) 7767 823825
Web Site: http://www.newgatepe.com
Year Founded: 2003
Privater Equity Firm
N.A.I.C.S.: 523999
Grant Roberts (Partner)

Subsidiaries:

Newgate Private Equity Limited (1)
128 Gregories Road, Beaconsfield, HP9 1HT, Bucks, United Kingdom
Tel.: (44) 2079790000
Web Site: http://www.newgatepe.com
Private Equity & Investment Management Firm
N.A.I.C.S.: 523999
Grant Roberts (Partner)

Holding (Domestic):

Expro International Group Ltd. (2)
2nd Floor Davidson House, Forbury Square, Reading, RG1 3EU, Berks, United Kingdom
Tel.: (44) 11895913411
Web Site: http://www.exprogroup.com
Gas & Oil Well Management Services
N.A.I.C.S.: 213112
John McAlister (Gen Counsel)

Subsidiary (Non-US):

Expro Group Malaysia Sdn. Bhd. (3)
13th Floor West Block Wisma Selangor Dredging 142C, Bangsar, Kuala Lumpur, 50450, Malaysia
Tel.: (60) 320847000
Web Site: http://www.exprogroup.com
Oil & Gas Well Management Services
N.A.I.C.S.: 213112

Expro International B.V. (3)
Nijverheidsweg 4, 1785 AA, Den Helder, Netherlands
Tel.: (31) 223677900
Web Site: http://www.exprogroup.com
Oil & Gas Well Management Services
N.A.I.C.S.: 213112

Subsidiary (Non-US):

Expro Group Australia Pty Ltd (3)
53- 55 Bannister Road, Canning Vale, 6155, WA, Australia
Tel.: (61) 892135555
Web Site: http://www.expro.com
Gas & Oil Well Management Services
N.A.I.C.S.: 213112

Expro Norway A/S (3)
Energivegen 12A, Tananger, 4056, Norway
Tel.: (47) 51695400
Web Site: http://www.exprogroup.com
Oil & Gas Well Management Services
N.A.I.C.S.: 213112

Holding (Domestic):

Innovia Films Limited (2)
Lowther R&D Centre West Road, Wigton, CA7 9XX, Cumbria, United Kingdom
Tel.: (44) 16973 42281
Web Site: http://www.innoviafilms.com
Industrial Film Mfr
N.A.I.C.S.: 326112

Subsidiary (Non-US):

Innovia Films (Asia Pacific) Pty. Ltd. (3)

INTERNATIONAL PUBLIC

19 Potter St, PO Box 341, Craigieburn, 3064, VIC, Australia   **(100%)**
Tel.: (61) 393030600
Web Site: http://www.innoviafilms.com
Industrial Film Mfr
N.A.I.C.S.: 326112

Innovia Films (Commercial) Ltd. (3)
Rodovia Miguel Melhado Campos, km79 Santa Candida Vinhedo, Sao Paulo, 13288-003, Brazil
Tel.: (55) 1931124747
Web Site: http://www.innoviafilms.com
Industrial Film Mfr
N.A.I.C.S.: 326112

Innovia Films BVBA (3)
Sluisweg 8, 9820, Merelbeke, Belgium
Tel.: (32) 9 241 1211
Web Site: http://www.innoviafilms.com
Industrial Film Mfr
N.A.I.C.S.: 326112
Vorst Frans (Gen Mgr)

Subsidiary (US):

Innovia Films, Inc. (3)
360 Interstate N Pkwy Ste 460, Atlanta, GA 30339-2401
Tel.: (770) 818-3000
Web Site: http://www.innoviafilms.com
Industrial Film Mfr
N.A.I.C.S.: 326112

Holding (Non-US):

Parques Reunidos Servicios Centrales SA (2)
Paseo de la Castellana 216 16th floor, 28046, Madrid, Spain
Tel.: (34) 91 526 97 00
Web Site: http://www.parquesreunidos.com
Amusement, Water, Theme, Nature & Animal Parks Operator
N.A.I.C.S.: 713110
Pascal Ferracci (CEO)

Subsidiary (US):

Kennywood Entertainment, Inc. (3)
4800 Kennywood Blvd, West Mifflin, PA 15122
Tel.: (412) 461-0500
Web Site: http://www.kennywood.com
Amusement Park Owner & Operator
N.A.I.C.S.: 713110
Jerome Gibas (Gen Mgr)

Palace Entertainment Holdings, Inc. (3)
4590 MacArthur Blvd Ste 400, Newport Beach, CA 92660
Tel.: (949) 261-0404
Web Site: http://www.palaceentertainment.com
Amusement Park Owner & Operator
N.A.I.C.S.: 713110

Subsidiary (Domestic):

Raging Waters (4)
2333 S White Rd, San Jose, CA 95148-1518
Tel.: (408) 238-9900
Web Site: http://www.rwsplash.com
Amusement Park
N.A.I.C.S.: 713110

Raging Waters (4)
111 Raging Waters Dr, San Dimas, CA 91773-3928
Tel.: (909) 802-2200
Web Site: http://www.ragingwaters.com
Amusement Park
N.A.I.C.S.: 713110

Silver Springs, Inc. (4)
5656 E Silver Springs Blvd, Silver Springs, FL 34488
Tel.: (352) 261-5840
Web Site: http://www.silversprings.com
Family Entertainment Parks
N.A.I.C.S.: 713110

Water Country Corp. (4)
2300 Lafayette Rd, Portsmouth, NH 03801
Tel.: (603) 427-1112
Web Site: http://www.watercountry.com
Amusement Park Operator
N.A.I.C.S.: 713110

Subsidiary (US):

Sea Life Park Hawaii (3)
41-202 Kalanianaole Hwy 7, Waimanalo, HI 96795
Tel.: (808) 259-2500
Web Site: http://www.sealifeparkhawaii.com
Marine Mammal Park & Research Center
N.A.I.C.S.: 712190

Subsidiary (Non-US):

Tropical Island Management GmbH (3)
Tropical Islands Allee 1, Krausnick, D 15910, Brandenburg, Germany
Tel.: (49) 35477605228
Web Site: http://www.tropical-islands.de
Tourist Accommodation Establishments
N.A.I.C.S.: 721110

NEWGEN SOFTWARE TECHNOLOGIES LIMITED

A-6 Satsang Vihar Marg Qutab Institutional Area, New Delhi, 110 067, India
Tel.: (91) 01126964733   In
Web Site: http://www.newgensoft.com
Year Founded: 1992
Sales Range: $75-99.9 Million
Emp.: 2,300
Software Developer
N.A.I.C.S.: 513210
Virender Jeet (Sr VP-Tech)

Subsidiaries:

Newgen Software Inc. (1)
1364 Beverly Rd Ste 300, McLean, VA 22101
Tel.: (703) 749-2855
Web Site: http://www.newgensoft.com
Software Development Services
N.A.I.C.S.: 541511
Diwakar Nigam (Chm & CEO)

Newgen Software Technologies Canada Limited (1)
2425 Matheson Blvd East Suite 765, Mississauga, L4W 5K4, ON, Canada
Tel.: (905) 361-2824
Software Development Services
N.A.I.C.S.: 541511

Newgen Software Technologies Pte Ltd. (1)
30 Raffles Place 17-38 Chevron house, Singapore, 048622, Singapore
Tel.: (65) 6221 8432
Software Development Services
N.A.I.C.S.: 541511

NEWGLAB PHARMA CO.,LTD

92 1412 Joma-ru 385beon-gil Wonmi-dong Bucheon Techno Valley U1 center, Sinheung-ro, Bucheon, 14491, Gyeonggi-do, Korea (South)
Tel.: (82) 326837903
Web Site: https://www.newglab.com
Year Founded: 2004
214870—(KRS)
Rev.: $16,652,147
Assets: $22,968,533
Liabilities: $39,628,854
Net Worth: $(16,660,321)
Earnings: $(55,190,925)
Emp.: 34
Fiscal Year-end: 12/31/22
CCTV Camera Mfr
N.A.I.C.S.: 334220
Son Jin Bok (VP)

NEWJAISA TECHNOLOGIES PVT LTD.

3839 2nd Main Rd next to Esteem Enclave Esteem Enclave, Sarvobhogam Nagar Arekere, Bengaluru, 560078, Karnataka, India
Tel.: (91) 8088403455
Web Site: https://www.newjaisa.com
Year Founded: 2020
NEWJAISA—(NSE)
Rev.: $54,151,277
Assets: $26,796,992
Liabilities: $15,486,733
Net Worth: $11,310,259
Earnings: $8,190,611
Emp.: 250
Fiscal Year-end: 03/31/23
Electronic Parts Distr
N.A.I.C.S.: 423690
Sharad Kumar Somani (CMO)

NEWLAND DIGITAL TECHNOLOGY CO., LTD.

Newland Technology Park No 1 Rujiang West Road, Mawei, Fuzhou, 350015, Fujian, China
Tel.: (86) 59183979333
Web Site: https://dt.newland.com.cn
Year Founded: 1994
000997—(SSE)
Rev.: $1,034,733,960
Assets: $1,731,064,608
Liabilities: $841,953,528
Net Worth: $889,111,080
Earnings: $(53,593,488)
Emp.: 5,000
Fiscal Year-end: 12/31/22
Application Software Developing Services
N.A.I.C.S.: 513210
Jing Wang (Chm, Pres & Gen Mgr)

Subsidiaries:

Fujian Newl & Auto-ID Tech. Co., Ltd. (1)
No 1 Rujiang West Rd, Mawei, Fuzhou, 350001, Fujian, China
Tel.: (86) 59183979500
Web Site: http://www.newlandaidc.com
Software Development Services
N.A.I.C.S.: 513210

Newl & Europe BV (1)
Rolweg 25, 4104 AV, Culemborg, Netherlands
Tel.: (31) 345870033
Web Site: https://www.newland-id.com
Software Development Services
N.A.I.C.S.: 513210

Newl & Payment Technology Limited (1)
Newland Science & Technology Park No 1 Rujiang Xi Rd, Mawei Dist, Fuzhou, 350015, Fujian, China
Tel.: (86) 59183979622
Web Site: http://www.newlandpayment.com
Electronic Payment Services
N.A.I.C.S.: 522320

NEWLAT FOOD S.P.A.

Via J F Kennedy 16, 42124, Reggio Emilia, RE, Italy
Tel.: (39) 05227901   IT
Web Site: https://www.newlat.it
Year Founded: 2004
NWL—(ITA)
Rev.: $875,746,771
Assets: $902,532,288
Liabilities: $709,731,759
Net Worth: $192,800,530
Earnings: $17,124,407
Emp.: 2,303
Fiscal Year-end: 12/31/23
Food Products Mfr
N.A.I.C.S.: 311813
Angelo Mastrolia (Chm)

Subsidiaries:

Centrale del Latte d'Italia S.p.A. (1)
Via Filadelfia 220, 10137, Turin, Italy
Tel.: (39) 0113240200
Web Site: https://centralelatteitalia.com
Emp.: 620
Dairy Product Mfr & Distr
N.A.I.C.S.: 311511

Newlat GmbH (1)
Franzosenstrasse 9, 68169, Mannheim, Germany
Tel.: (49) 62132350
Web Site: https://www.newlat.de
Emp.: 130
Food Product Mfr & Distr
N.A.I.C.S.: 311919

Symington's Ltd. (1)
Thornes Farm Business Park Pontefract Lane, Leeds, LS9 0DN, United Kingdom
Tel.: (44) 1132706061
Web Site: https://symingtons.com
Food Product Mfr & Distr
N.A.I.C.S.: 311991

NEWLEAD HOLDINGS LTD.

83 Akti Miaouli & Flessa Str, Piraeus, 185 38, Greece
Tel.: (30) 2130148000   BM
Web Site: http://www.newleadholdings.com
NEWLF—(OTCIQ)
Sales Range: $25-49.9 Million
Emp.: 39
Gasoline, Jet Fuel, Heating Oil & Edible Oil Transport Services
N.A.I.C.S.: 483111
Spyros Gianniotis (Deputy Chm)

NEWLINK TECHNOLOGY, INC.

5/F Tower A Xueqing Jiachuang Building Xueqing Road, Haidian, Beijing, 100083, China
Tel.: (86) 1082665899   Ky
Web Site: http://www.xnewtech.com
Year Founded: 2011
9600—(HKG)
Information Technology Services
N.A.I.C.S.: 541512
Shuchun Zhai (Chm)

NEWLOOK CAPITAL INC.

1550 Appleby Line Suite 100Burlington, Burlington, L7L6V1, ON, Canada
Tel.: (905) 331-3697
Web Site: http://www.newlookcapital.com
Privater Equity Firm
N.A.I.C.S.: 523999
Gavin Treanor (Partner & Head-Global Sls)

Subsidiaries:

Mack Fire Protection, LLC (1)
15 Industrial Park Pl, Middletown, CT 06457
Tel.: (860) 632-8053
Web Site: http://www.mackfire.com
Specialty Trade Contractors
N.A.I.C.S.: 238990
William J. Wells (Mgr)

NEWLOX GOLD VENTURES CORP.

355 Burrard Street 10th Floor, Vancouver, V6C 2G8, BC, Canada
Tel.: (778) 738-0546   BC
Web Site: https://www.newloxgold.com
Year Founded: 2011
LUX—(CNSX)
Rev.: $2,590,191
Assets: $5,403,840
Liabilities: $2,568,755
Net Worth: $2,835,085
Earnings: $(1,694,343)
Fiscal Year-end: 03/31/23
Gold Mining
N.A.I.C.S.: 212220
Ryan Jackson (Pres & CEO)

NEWMAN S.A.

51 Ave Du Marechal LeClerc, 49309, Cholet, France
Tel.: (33) 241715151
Web Site: http://www.newman.fr
Year Founded: 1984
Sales Range: $50-74.9 Million
Emp.: 260
Jean Apparel Mfr
N.A.I.C.S.: 315210

Leon Cligman (Owner)

NEWMARK REIT MANAGEMENT LIMITED

Como Centre Level 17 644 Chapel Street, South Yarra, 3141, VIC, Australia
Tel.: (61) 398203344   AU
Year Founded: 2021
NPR—(ASX)
Rev.: $19,736,697
Assets: $362,484,916
Liabilities: $147,422,894
Net Worth: $215,062,022
Earnings: ($5,785,883)
Fiscal Year-end: 06/30/23
Property Management Services
N.A.I.C.S.: 531311
Matthew Sweeney (CFO)

NEWMARK SECURITY PLC

91 Wimpole Street, London, W1G 0EF, United Kingdom
Tel.: (44) 2073550070   UK
Web Site: https://www.newmarksecurity.com
Year Founded: 1997
NWT—(LSE)
Rev.: $23,974,620
Assets: $20,156,711
Liabilities: $8,901,212
Net Worth: $11,255,499
Earnings: $232,170
Emp.: 112
Fiscal Year-end: 04/30/21
Electronic & Physical Security System Mfr
N.A.I.C.S.: 334419
Maurice Dwek (Chm)

Subsidiaries:

Grosvenor Technology Limited (1)
1st Floor Endeavour House Coopers End Road, London Stansted Airport, Stansted, CM24 1SJ, Essex, United Kingdom
Tel.: (44) 127 983 8000
Web Site: https://www.grosvenortechnology.com
Electronic Security System Mfr
N.A.I.C.S.: 423690
Colin Leatherbarrow (Dir-Technical)

Subsidiary (US):

Grosvenor Technology LLC (2)
3009 Greene St, Hollywood, FL 33020
Tel.: (754) 300-2999
Electronic Security System Distr
N.A.I.C.S.: 423690
Andy Rainforth (Mng Dir)

Subsidiary (Domestic):

Newmark Technology Limited (2)
Millars Three Southmill Road, Bishop's Stortford, CM23 3DH, Herts, United Kingdom
Tel.: (44) 1279 658000
Web Site: http://www.newmarktechnology.com
Electronic Security System Mfr
N.A.I.C.S.: 334419

Safetell Limited (1)
46 Fawkes Ave, Dartford, DA1 1JQ, Kent, United Kingdom
Tel.: (44) 132 222 3233
Web Site: https://www.safetell.co.uk
Security Equipment Mfr
N.A.I.C.S.: 334419
Anton Pieterse (Mng Dir)

Vema B.V. (1)
Nijverheidstraat 14, 1135 GE, Edam, Netherlands
Tel.: (31) 299 364 735
Electronic Security System Distr
N.A.I.C.S.: 423610

NEWMAX TECHNOLOGY CO., LTD.

No 269 HouKe Road Section 1, ouke

NEWMAX TECHNOLOGY CO., LTD.

Newmax Technology Co., Ltd.—(Continued)
Road Houli District, Taichung, 421, Taiwan
Tel.: (886) 423696889
Web Site: https://www.newmax.com.tw
Year Founded: 1999
3630—(TPE)
Rev.: $49,984,898
Assets: $215,038,333
Liabilities: $111,352,281
Net Worth: $103,686,052
Earnings: ($14,284,901)
Emp.: 1,300
Fiscal Year-end: 12/31/22
Glass & Plastic Len Mfr
N.A.I.C.S.: 339115
Liang Qitai *(Chm)*

NEWNORTH PRINT LTD
Newnorth House College Street
Kempston, Bedford, MK42 8NA, United Kingdom
Tel.: (44) 1234341111
Web Site: http://www.newnorth.co.uk
Year Founded: 1980
Rev.: $12,448,838
Emp.: 60
Printing Services
N.A.I.C.S.: 323111
Garry Hardy *(Mng Dir)*

NEWNOTE FINANCIAL CORP.
Suite 709 700 West Pender Street, Vancouver, V6C 1G8, BC, Canada
Tel.: (604) 229-0480 BC
Web Site: http://www.newnotefinancial.com
Year Founded: 2010
NWWTF—(OTCIQ)
Sales Range: Less than $1 Million
Crypto-Currency Related Software Products
N.A.I.C.S.: 513210
Paul Dickson *(Pres & CEO)*

NEWOCEAN ENERGY HOLDINGS LIMITED
23rd Floor of The Sun's Group Centre 200 Gloucester Road, Wanchai, China (Hong Kong)
Tel.: (852) 28918961
Web Site: https://www.newoceanlpg.com
0342—(HKG)
Rev.: $2,473,816,150
Assets: $1,524,913,515
Liabilities: $950,049,268
Net Worth: $574,864,247
Earnings: $479,276,266
Emp.: 957
Fiscal Year-end: 12/31/20
Liquefied Petroleum Gas Sales & Distr
N.A.I.C.S.: 424720
Brian Ka Fai Siu *(Exec Dir)*

NEWONDER SPECIAL ELECTRIC CO., LTD.
Office A801 8F Building No 2 Yard No 1 Lize Middle 1st Road, Chaoyang District, Beijing, 065201, China
Tel.: (86) 1085577061
Web Site: https://www.xinhuadu.com.cn
Year Founded: 1985
301120—(SSE)
Transformer Product Mfr & Distr
N.A.I.C.S.: 335311
Yong Tan *(Chm & Gen Mgr)*

NEWPATH RESOURCES INC
220 333 Terminal Avenue, Vancouver, V6A 4C1, BC, Canada
Tel.: (604) 484-0942 BC
Web Site: https://newpathresources.com
Year Founded: 2006
OMNI—(TSXV)
Assets: $1,191,916
Liabilities: $2,422,307
Net Worth: ($1,230,391)
Earnings: ($1,692,653)
Fiscal Year-end: 04/30/24
Cannabidiol Products Marketer & Distr
N.A.I.C.S.: 111419
Alex McAulay *(CEO)*

NEWPEAK METALS LIMITED
Level 27 111 Eagle Street, Brisbane, 4000, QLD, Australia
Tel.: (61) 733030650 AU
Web Site: https://newpeak.com.au
Year Founded: 1995
NPM—(DEU)
Rev.: $27,326
Assets: $7,251,554
Liabilities: $436,236
Net Worth: $6,815,318
Earnings: $47,411
Fiscal Year-end: 06/30/22
Crude Petroleum Extraction
N.A.I.C.S.: 211120
Priy Jayasuriya *(CFO)*

NEWPORT CAPITAL GROUP PTY LTD.
Level 5 153 Walker St, Sydney, 2060, NSW, Australia
Tel.: (61) 289236333
Web Site: http://www.newportcapital.com.au
Year Founded: 1989
Venture Capital Funds
N.A.I.C.S.: 523999
Lou Richard *(Founder & Mng Dir)*

NEWPORT EXPLORATION LIMITED
Suite 2022168 Marine Drive, West Vancouver, Vancouver, V7V 1K3, BC, Canada
Tel.: (604) 685-6851
Web Site: https://www.newport-exploration.com
Year Founded: 1979
NWX—(TSXV)
Sales Range: Less than $1 Million
Mineral Exploration Services
N.A.I.C.S.: 212290
Ian Rozier *(Pres & CEO)*

NEWPORT GOLD, INC.
168 Queen Street South, Mississauga, L5M1K8, ON, Canada
Tel.: (905) 542-4990
Web Site: http://www.newportgold.com
Year Founded: 2003
NWPG—(OTCIQ)
Mineral Exploration Services
N.A.I.C.S.: 213114
Derek Bartlett *(Pres, CEO & Sec)*

NEWQUEST CAPITAL ADVISORS (HK) LTD.
Room 2902 29/F Prosperity Tower 39 Queens Road, Central, China (Hong Kong)
Tel.: (852) 3905 3600 HK
Web Site: http://www.nqcap.com
Year Founded: 2011
Investment Management Service
N.A.I.C.S.: 523940
Lung-Chi Lee *(Partner & Gen Counsel)*

Subsidiaries:

Integreon Managed Solutions, Inc. (1)
1450 Broadway Ste 1100, New York, NY 10018
Tel.: (866) 312-7023
Web Site: http://www.integreon.com
Corporate Legal, Accounting, Research & Document Preparation Services
N.A.I.C.S.: 561499
Al J McNee *(Chief Revenue Officer)*

NEWRACE LTD.
No 1608 North Circle Road State Highway, Zhangzhou, 363000, Fujian, China
Tel.: (86) 596 260 0308 VG
Investment Holding Company
N.A.I.C.S.: 551112
Jianhui Lai *(Owner)*

Subsidiaries:

China Zenix Auto International Limited (1)
No 1608 North Circle Road State Highway, Zhangzhou, 363000, Fujian, China (100%)
Tel.: (86) 5962600308
Web Site: http://www.zenixauto.com
Rev.: $271,101,724
Assets: $483,764,405
Liabilities: $172,024,341
Net Worth: $311,740,064
Earnings: ($61,187,838)
Emp.: 3,284
Fiscal Year-end: 12/31/2020
Steel Wheel Mfr
N.A.I.C.S.: 336390
Martin Cheung *(CFO)*

Subsidiary (Domestic):

Zhengxing Wheel Group Co., Ltd. (2)
319 Line North Circle City State Highway, Zhangzhou, 363000, Fujian, China
Tel.: (86) 596 2600918
Emp.: 1,000
Automobile Component Mfr & Distr
N.A.I.C.S.: 336110
Henter Shi *(Mgr-Sls)*

NEWRANGE GOLD CORPORATION
250 - 750 West Pender St, Vancouver, V6C 2T7, BC, Canada
Tel.: (604) 669-0868
Web Site: https://www.newrangegold.com
Year Founded: 2006
NRG—(OTCIQ)
Assets: $4,326,024
Liabilities: $394,823
Net Worth: $3,931,201
Earnings: ($1,666,475)
Fiscal Year-end: 04/30/21
Metal Exploration Services
N.A.I.C.S.: 213114
Robert G. Carrington *(Pres, Founder & Chm)*

NEWREST ASL NIGERIA PLC
1 Service Road Murtala Muhammed International Airport, PO Box 4953, Ikeja, Lagos, Nigeria
Tel.: (234) 8159393540
Web Site: http://www.aslafrica.com
Year Founded: 1996
Rev.: $10,155,852
Assets: $13,717,377
Liabilities: $9,907,516
Net Worth: $3,809,861
Earnings: $993,231
Emp.: 337
Fiscal Year-end: 12/31/17
Catering & Hospitality Services
N.A.I.C.S.: 722320
Jonathan Stent-Torriani *(Co-CEO & Member-Exec Bd)*

NEWREST GROUP INTERNATIONAL S.A.S.
61 Boulevard Lazare Carnot, 31000, Toulouse, France
Tel.: (33) 562893988 FR
Web Site: http://www.newrest.eu
Year Founded: 2005
Emp.: 5,000
Holding Company; Air & Rail Transportation Industry Catering, Logistics Consulting & Support Services Contractor
N.A.I.C.S.: 551112
Pierre Brugere *(VP-Sls & Mktg)*

Subsidiaries:

CGA Newrest Catering SA (1)
BP 55, Conakry, Guinea
Tel.: (224) 622 79 09 12
Emp.: 60
Catering Services
N.A.I.C.S.: 722320
Sebastien Joly *(Mng Dir)*

Catering Aerien Developpement S.A. (1)
8 allee Henri Potez, F-31700, Blagnac, France
Tel.: (33) 561711313
In-Flight Airline Catering Services
N.A.I.C.S.: 722320

EIS Portugal Servicios de Catering Lda. (1)
Rua D Edificio 78 Aeroporto de Lisboa, 1749-079, Lisbon, Portugal
Tel.: (351) 218 558 228
Web Site: http://www.newrest.eu
Sales Range: $10-24.9 Million
Emp.: 44
Airline Catering Services
N.A.I.C.S.: 722310
Emmanuelle Boccardo Puig *(VP)*

Newrest ALL LTD (1)
437 North Woolwich Road, London, E16 2BS, United Kingdom
Tel.: (44) 2 074 744 553
Emp.: 95
Catering Services
N.A.I.C.S.: 722320

Newrest Algerie Holding SPA (1)
Tour ABC 3eme Etage - Pins - Maritimes Mohamadia, Algiers, Algeria
Tel.: (213) 21 89 13 61
Emp.: 685
Holding Company
N.A.I.C.S.: 551112
Jean Boher *(Mng Dir)*

Newrest Angola SA (1)
69A Rua Francisco Sotto Mayor - Bairro Azul, Municipio Ingombota, Luanda, Angola
Tel.: (244) 222 353 938
Emp.: 920
Catering Services
N.A.I.C.S.: 722320
Sountou Bousso *(Mng Dir)*

Newrest Antilles SAS (1)
Bat 2 Lot Palmiers Multipliants - ZA Bois Quarre, Lamentin, Martinique, France
Tel.: (33) 5 96 70 19 38
Emp.: 80
Catering Services
N.A.I.C.S.: 722320
Thomas Ginouves *(Mng Dir)*

Newrest Bolivia Soporte SRL (1)
Km 11 carretera al Norte Parque Empresarial Coronado, Santa Cruz, Bolivia
Tel.: (591) 3 388 82 24
Emp.: 640
Catering Services
N.A.I.C.S.: 722320
Yvon Martinez *(Gen Mgr)*

Newrest Cameroun SA (1)
BP 32 28, Douala, Cameroon
Tel.: (237) 99 41 62 16
Emp.: 215
Catering Services
N.A.I.C.S.: 722320
Louis Malikite *(Mng Dir)*

Newrest Canonica Catering SA (1)
5 Route de Laeroport, CP 567, 1215, Geneva, Switzerland
Tel.: (41) 22 717 78 81
Emp.: 135
Catering Services

AND PRIVATE COMPANIES

N.A.I.C.S.: 722320
Philippe Tetu (Mng Dir)

Newrest Catering Ltd. (1)
Pindarou 26 Aradippou, Larnaca, 7100, Cyprus
Tel.: (357) 24 816 804
Emp.: 120
Catering Services
N.A.I.C.S.: 722320
Michael Reich (Unit Mgr)

Newrest Catering Polynesie SA (1)
Allee Pierre Loti - Titioro, BP 50352, 98 716, Papeete, Tahiti, French Polynesia
Tel.: (689) 40 471 147
Web Site: http://www.newrest.eu
Emp.: 200
Catering Services
N.A.I.C.S.: 722320
Arnaud Pradel (Mng Dir)

Newrest Catering SA (1)
Immeuble Henda 3eme etage - 10 Rue de l'Ile de Rhodes, Les Jardins Du Lac, 1053, Tunis, Tunisia
Tel.: (216) 71 19 80 74
Emp.: 2,400
Catering Services
N.A.I.C.S.: 722320
Alain Masson (Mng Dir)

Newrest Chile Soporte LDA (1)
Avenida el Retiro 1235 - Parque los Maitenes, Parque Industrial ENEA - Pudahuel, Santiago, Chile
Tel.: (56) 2 23 07 24 00
Emp.: 360
Catering Services
N.A.I.C.S.: 722320
Jean-Paul Llanusa (Mng Dir)

Newrest Congo (1)
Quartier Mpita - KM4 - Proche de la Residence Pemba, BP 1220, Pointe Noire, Congo, Republic of
Tel.: (242) 68 909 860
Emp.: 180
Catering Services
N.A.I.C.S.: 722320
Thomas Neveu (Mng Dir)

Newrest Dubrovnik, d.o.o. (1)
Dubrovnik Airport Dobrota 24, Cilipi, 20213, Dubrovnik, Croatia
Tel.: (385) 20773302
Web Site: http://www.newrest.eu
Emp.: 50
Catering Services
N.A.I.C.S.: 722320

Newrest Gabon SAURL (1)
Galerie Corail Zone Cora Wood, BP 2963, Port-Gentil, Gabon
Tel.: (241) 1 56 86 52
Emp.: 435
Catering Services
N.A.I.C.S.: 722320
Erik Delfour (Mng Dir)

Newrest Ghana (1)
Plot No 28 - Off Spintex Road, Tema Motorway Industrial Area, Accra, Ghana
Tel.: (233) 540 106 684
Emp.: 470
Catering Services
N.A.I.C.S.: 722320
Rita Soeze (Mgr-Sls)

Newrest Group Holding, S.L. (1)
Avenida Central 42 - Parque Logistico Prologis, Nave M - Centro de Carga Aereo, 28042, Madrid, Spain (100%)
Tel.: (34) 917462660
Web Site: http://www.newrest.eu
Emp.: 422
Air & Rail Transportation Industry Catering & Food Service Contractor Services
N.A.I.C.S.: 551112
Frederic Gatteau (Gen Mgr-Spain)

Subsidiary (Domestic):

Newrest Servair, S.L. (2)
Avenida central 42 - Parque Logistico Prologis, Nave M - Centro de Carga Aereo, 28042, Madrid, Spain
Tel.: (34) 917462660
Web Site: http://www.newrest.eu
Airline Catering & Food Service Contractor
N.A.I.C.S.: 722320

Frederic Gatteau (Gen Mgr-Spain)

Newrest Gulf LLC (1)
Al Dafna - Palm Tower B - 35th Floor - Office 3506, PO Box 23710, Doha, Qatar
Tel.: (974) 441 12 245
Emp.: 45
Catering Services
N.A.I.C.S.: 722320
Ashok Bhattacharya (Head-Fin & Admin)

Newrest Hellas SA (1)
Athens International Airport - Eleftherios Venizelos Building 14A, Spata, 19019, Athens, Greece
Tel.: (30) 210 35 41 150
Emp.: 720
Catering Services
N.A.I.C.S.: 722320
Manuella Hajjar Kapagiannidi (Mng Dir)

Newrest Holding Canada Inc. (1)
2620 Avenue Andre, Dorval, H9P 1K6, QC, Canada
Tel.: (514) 685-8262
Emp.: 160
Holding Company
N.A.I.C.S.: 551112
Frederic Hillion (Mng Dir)

Newrest Inflight Services BV (1)
Pelikaanweg 2-12, Schiphol Airport, 1118 DX, Amsterdam, Netherlands
Tel.: (31) 20 540 01 90
Emp.: 220
Catering Services
N.A.I.C.S.: 722320
Jurgen Van de Port (Mng Dir)

Newrest Liberia Limited (1)
BMC compound - Tubman Boulevard, Congo Town, Monrovia, Liberia
Tel.: (231) 555 541 000
Emp.: 10
Catering Services
N.A.I.C.S.: 722320
Jean-Luc Sadran (Mng Dir)

Newrest Madagascar SARL (1)
Lot M A III 8 - Route d'Ivato Maibahoaka Ivato 101, Antananarivo, Madagascar
Tel.: (261) 333 165 700
Emp.: 815
Catering Services
N.A.I.C.S.: 722320
Pierre Martens (Mng Dir)

Newrest Maroc Services SA (1)
280 Boulevard Yacoub El Mansour, Casablanca, 20100, Morocco
Tel.: (212) 522 95 66 43
Emp.: 3,100
Catering Services
N.A.I.C.S.: 722320
Olivier Suarez (COO-North Africa Div)

Newrest Mozambique (1)
Rua dos Governadores 61 - 1, Bairro Sommerschield, Maputo, Mozambique
Tel.: (258) 847 221 551
Emp.: 10
Catering Services
N.A.I.C.S.: 722320

Newrest Peru SAC (1)
Calle A esq Calle 1 Lote 4 Mz B - Zona 6 Urb Lotizacion Industrial, Bocanegra Alto Provincia Constitucional del, Callao, Peru
Tel.: (51) 748 2111
Emp.: 1,950
Catering Services
N.A.I.C.S.: 722320
Olivier Billerey (Mng Dir)

Newrest Servair Belgium BVBA (1)
Nieuwbrugstraat 83, 1830, Machelen, Belgium
Tel.: (32) 2 720 78 60
Web Site: http://www.newrest.com
Emp.: 30
Catering Services
N.A.I.C.S.: 722320
Bernard Martinez (Gen Mgr)

Newrest Supply Oilfields Services Inc. (1)
20/f Pearlbank Center 146 Valero St, Salcedo Village, Makati, 1227, Philippines
Tel.: (63) 2 817 8919
Web Site: http://www.newrest-sos.com.ph
Emp.: 240

Logistics Consulting Servies
N.A.I.C.S.: 541614
Louis Paul Heussaff (Chm & CEO)

Newrest Uganda Inflight Services Ltd. (1)
Plot No M92 Sebugwawo Drive - Airside Road, PO Box 728, Entebbe, Uganda
Tel.: (256) 414 32 16 70
Emp.: 190
Catering Services
N.A.I.C.S.: 722320
Zied Manoubi (Deputy Gen Mgr)

Newrest Wagons-Lits Austria GmbH (1)
Newrest Wagons-Lits Ausitra GmbH, 1100, Vienna, Austria
Tel.: (43) 1 893 98 06 0
Emp.: 440
Catering Services
N.A.I.C.S.: 722320
Pierre Magnard (Mng Dir)

Newrest Wagons-Lits S.A.S. (1)
87 rue du Charolais, 75012, Paris, France (60%)
Tel.: (33) 153441801
Web Site: http://www.newrest.eu
Sales Range: $300-349.9 Million
Emp.: 1,500
Train Catering & Support Services Contractor; Owned 60% by Newrest Group International S.A.S. & 40% by Accor S.A.
N.A.I.C.S.: 722320

Newrest Zambia Limited (1)
AP 22 Terminal Building Kenneth Kaunda International Airport, Lusaka, 10101, Zambia
Tel.: (260) 97 613 49 37
Emp.: 130
Catering Services
N.A.I.C.S.: 722320
Tinashe Gandize (Head-Fin & Acctg)

dnata Newrest South Africa (1)
18 Kelly Road, Jet Park, Johannesburg, 1462, South Africa
Tel.: (27) 11 397 6767
Web Site: http://www.newrest.eu
Emp.: 645
Catering Services
N.A.I.C.S.: 722320
Marc Starke (COO)

NEWRIVER REIT PLC
89 Whitfield Street, London, W1T 4DE, United Kingdom
Tel.: (44) 2033285800
Web Site: https://www.nrr.co.uk
Year Founded: 2009
Rev.: $164,474,640
Assets: $1,753,215,720
Liabilities: $709,050,960
Net Worth: $1,044,164,760
Earnings: ($48,398,040)
Emp.: 149
Fiscal Year-end: 03/31/19
Real Estate Investment Services
N.A.I.C.S.: 531210
Mark Davies (CFO)

NEWRIVER RETAIL LTD
16 New Burlington Place, London, W1S 2HX, United Kingdom
Tel.: (44) 2033285800
Web Site: http://www.nrr.co.uk
Year Founded: 2009
NRR—(AIM)
Rev.: $100,063,964
Assets: $1,112,108,452
Liabilities: $549,876,600
Net Worth: $562,231,852
Earnings: ($36,115,352)
Emp.: 56
Fiscal Year-end: 03/31/22
Real Estate Investment Services
N.A.I.C.S.: 525990
Mark Davies (Co-CFO)

Subsidiaries:

Bravo Inns Limited (1)

NEWS GROUP INTERNATIONAL HOLDING

44 Knutsford Road, Warrington, WA4 1AG, United Kingdom
Tel.: (44) 192 557 3420
Web Site: https://www.bravoinns.com
Pub Services
N.A.I.C.S.: 722410

NewRiver Retail (UK) Limited (1)
37 Maddox Street, London, W1S 2PP, United Kingdom
Tel.: (44) 20 3328 5800
Web Site: http://www.nrr.co.uk
Emp.: 40
Real Estate Manangement Services
N.A.I.C.S.: 531390
Lucy Mitchell (Mgr-Mktg)

NEWROADS CHRYSLER DODGE JEEP RAM
17615 Yonge Street, Newmarket, L3Y 5H6, ON, Canada
Tel.: (905) 898-1900
Web Site: https://www.newroads.ca
New & Used Car Dealers
N.A.I.C.S.: 441110
Michael Croxon (Pres)

NEWRON PHARMACEUTICALS SPA
via Antonio Meucci 3, 20091, Bresso, Milan, Italy
Tel.: (39) 026103461
Web Site: https://www.newron.com
NWRN—(DUS)
Rev.: $6,576,732
Assets: $40,141,377
Liabilities: $55,282,754
Net Worth: ($15,141,377)
Earnings: ($18,878,696)
Emp.: 23
Fiscal Year-end: 12/31/22
Therapeutic Applications Mfr
N.A.I.C.S.: 334510
Marco Caremi (Exec VP-Bus Dev)

Subsidiaries:

Newron Pharmaceuticals U.S. Inc. (1)
89 Headquarters Plz N Ste 347, Morristown, NJ 07960
Tel.: (973) 993-1873
Therapeutic Applications Mfr
N.A.I.C.S.: 334510

Newron Sweden AB (1)
Sodra Fiskartorpsvagen 15 C, 114 33, Stockholm, Sweden
Tel.: (46) 87860911
Therapeutic Applications Mfr
N.A.I.C.S.: 334510

NEWS GROUP INTERNATIONAL HOLDING
Dubai Silicon Oasis, PO Box 341138, Dubai, United Arab Emirates
Tel.: (971) 4 356 4100
Web Site:
http://www.newsgroupholding.com
Year Founded: 2002
Emp.: 400
Holding Company; News Sourcing, Monitoring, Distribution & Analysis Services
N.A.I.C.S.: 551112
Mazen Nahawi (Founder & Pres)

Subsidiaries:

Interactive Limited (1)
Silicon Oasis Le Solarium Building Office 317, Dubai, United Arab Emirates
Tel.: (971) 3564100
Web Site: http://www.interactive-ltd.com
Software Development Services
N.A.I.C.S.: 541511
Hussein Ahmad (Dir-Govt Projects)

Media Watch Middle East (1)
Offices 317-321 Le Solarium Bldg, PO Box 341138, Dubai Silicon Oasis, Dubai, United Arab Emirates
Tel.: (971) 4 356 4100

NEWS GROUP INTERNATIONAL HOLDING

News Group International Holding—(Continued)
Web Site: http://www.mediawatchme.com
Emp.: 250
News Monitoring Services
N.A.I.C.S.: 519290
Mazen Nahawi (CEO)

MediaSource FZC (1)
PO Box 341138, Dubai, United Arab Emirates
Tel.: (971) 4 356 4200
Web Site: http://www.mediasource.me
Media Streaming Services
N.A.I.C.S.: 518210
Ben Smalley (Mng Dir)

NGI Context (1)
Dabouq King Abdullah II St Bldg 183 4th Floor, PO Box 815505, Amman, Jordan
Tel.: (962) 6 5353610
Web Site: http://www.ngicontext.com
Content Development Services
N.A.I.C.S.: 518210
Siba Sami Ammari (Sr Editor)

Salience Insight Limited (1)
3 Lloyd's Avenue, London, EC3N 3DS, United Kingdom
Tel.: (44) 20 3036 0618
Web Site: http://www.salienceinsight.com
Media Measurement Services
N.A.I.C.S.: 519290
Giselle Bodie (CEO)

Subsidiary (US):

CARMA International, Inc. (2)
1615 M St NW, Washington, DC 20036
Tel.: (202) 223-2111
Web Site: http://www.carma.com
Media Content Analysis Services
N.A.I.C.S.: 519290
Alison Tedor (VP)

NEWS INVEST SA
90 Avenue de Wagram, 75017, Paris, France
Tel.: (33) 153670751
Web Site:
https://www.newsinvest.com
MLNEI—(EUR)
Sales Range: Less than $1 Million
Online & Off-Line Marketing Services
N.A.I.C.S.: 541613
Stephane Moity (Mng Dir & Dir-IR)

NEWS NETWORK CORPORATION PUBLIC COMPANY LIMITED
944 Samyan Mitrtown Project 28th Floor Room No 2807-2810, Rama IV Road Wang Mai Subdistrict Pathum Wan District, Bangkok, 10330, Thailand
Tel.: (66) 22738351
Web Site:
https://www.newsnetwork.co.th
Year Founded: 1998
NEWS—(THA)
Rev.: $1,383,116
Assets: $37,041,691
Liabilities: $13,806,634
Net Worth: $23,235,057
Earnings: ($15,587,344)
Fiscal Year-end: 12/31/23
Software Development Services
N.A.I.C.S.: 541511
Arak Ratboriharn (Pres & CEO)

NEWS2U HOLDINGS, INC.
14F Kioicho Bldg 3-12 Kioi-cho, Chiyoda-ku, Tokyo, 102-0094, Japan
Tel.: (81) 50 3646 1717
Web Site: http://www.news2u-group.com
Year Founded: 2001
Holding Company
N.A.I.C.S.: 551112
Minako Suematsu (CEO)

Subsidiaries:

The Japan Times Ltd. (1)
14F Kioicho Bldg 3-12 Kioicho, Chiyoda-ku, Tokyo, 102-0094, Japan
Tel.: (81) 50 3646 0123
Web Site: http://www.japantimes.co.jp
Newspaper & Magazine Publisher
N.A.I.C.S.: 513110
Minako Suematsu (Chm)

NEWSCOPE CAPITAL CORPORATION
82 Richmond Street East, Toronto, M5C 1P1, ON, Canada
Web Site:
https://www.pharmather.com
PHRM—(CNSX)
Sales Range: Less than $1 Million
Pharmaceutical Product Mfr & Distr
N.A.I.C.S.: 325412
Fabio Chianelli (Chm & CEO)

NEWSHIP LTD
Fernside Place 179 Queens Road, Weybridge, KT13 0AH, United Kingdom
Tel.: (44) 1932858044 UK
Web Site: http://www.newship.co.uk
Sales Range: $200-249.9 Million
Emp.: 750
Holding Company
N.A.I.C.S.: 551112
Stephen Compsoh (CEO)

Subsidiaries:

Beatson Clark plc (1)
The Glass Works, Greasbrough Road, Rotherham, CF40 1NY, United Kingdom (100%)
Tel.: (44) 709828141
Web Site: http://www.beatsonclark.co.uk
Sales Range: $75-99.9 Million
Emp.: 500
Glass Container Mfr
N.A.I.C.S.: 327213
Lynn Sidebottom (Dir-Sls & Mktg)

Gowrings Mobility Ltd. (1)
Daytona Dr, Thatcham, RG19 4ZD, Berkshire, United Kingdom
Tel.: (44) 8456088020
Web Site: http://www.gowringsmobility.co.uk
Sales Range: $25-49.9 Million
Emp.: 100
Wheelchair Accessible Vehicle Mfr
N.A.I.C.S.: 336110
Nigel Brice (Mng Dir)

James Gibbons Format Ltd. (1)
Vulcan Rd, Bilston, WV14 7JG, W Midlands, United Kingdom (100%)
Tel.: (44) 902405500
Web Site: http://www.jgf.co.uk
Sales Range: $50-74.9 Million
Emp.: 250
Architectural Ironmonger
N.A.I.C.S.: 332323

Jenks & Cattell Engineering Ltd. (1)
Neachells Lane, Wednesfield, Wolverhampton, WV11 3PU, United Kingdom
Tel.: (44) 1902305530
Web Site: http://www.jcel.co.uk
Emp.: 70
Mfr Services
N.A.I.C.S.: 332999
Barry Downs (Dir-Ops)

Newship Property (1)
Fernside Place 179 Queens Road, Weybridge, KT13 0AH, Surrey, United Kingdom
Tel.: (44) 1932 856647
Web Site: http://www.newship.co.uk
Sales Range: $50-74.9 Million
Emp.: 12
Property Management Services
N.A.I.C.S.: 531190
Stephen Compson (CEO)

Pont Packaging B.V. (1)
Bolderweg 22, 1329 BB, Almere, Netherlands (100%)
Tel.: (31) 365323220
Web Site: http://www.ponteurope.com

Sales Range: $10-24.9 Million
Emp.: 20
Glass & Plastic Containers & Closures Mfr
N.A.I.C.S.: 327213

Subsidiary (Non-US):

Pont Emballage SAS (2)
Sogaris B4 - Cellules 15-16-17, 94150, Rungis, France
Tel.: (33) 149849770
Glass Packaging Mfr
N.A.I.C.S.: 327213
Laurent Faya (Dir-Fin)

Pont Packaging GmbH (2)
Tomphecke 61, 41169, Monchengladbach, Germany
Tel.: (49) 2161566260
Web Site: http://www.ponteurope.com
Emp.: 14
Glass Packaging Mfr
N.A.I.C.S.: 327213
Frank Salmann (Mng Dir)

QDOS Event Hire Limited (1)
179 Queens Road, Weybridge, KT13 0AH, Surrey, United Kingdom
Tel.: (44) 8458620952
Web Site: http://www.qdoseventhire.co.uk
Temporary Accomodation Facilities
N.A.I.C.S.: 531190

Rollalong Ltd. (1)
Woolsbridge Industrial Park, Three Legged Cross, Wimborne Minster, BH21 6SF, United Kingdom (100%)
Tel.: (44) 824541
Web Site: http://www.rollalong.co.uk
Sales Range: $100-124.9 Million
Emp.: 320
Portable, Temporary, Semi-Permanent or Permanent Buildings Mfr
N.A.I.C.S.: 236220
Martin Sayers (Mng Dir)

NEWSPHONE HELLAS S.A.
280 Thisseos Avenue, Kallithea, 176 75, Athens, Greece
Tel.: (30) 2109472222
Web Site: http://www.newsphone.gr
Year Founded: 1995
NEWS—(ATH)
Sales Range: $75-99.9 Million
Emp.: 2,000
Mobile Marketing Services
N.A.I.C.S.: 561422
George Theodossis (Chm)

Subsidiaries:

Call Center Hellas S.A. (1)
280 Thisseos Av, 17675, Athens, Greece
Tel.: (30) 210 9499000
Web Site: http://www.callcenter.gr
Telecommunication Services
N.A.I.C.S.: 517810

NOETRON SA (1)
L Thiseos 280, 17675, Kallithea, Greece
Tel.: (30) 2109472350
Web Site: http://www.noetron.gr
Information Technology Consulting Services
N.A.I.C.S.: 541512
Vasilis Patras (Dir-Digital Svcs)

NEWSTAR CAPITAL
Suite 125 625 Parsons Road SW, Edmonton, T6X 0N9, AB, Canada
Tel.: (780) 489-9866
Web Site:
https://www.newstarcapital.com
N.A.I.C.S.:
John Mather (Chm)

Subsidiaries:

2267166 Alberta Ltd. (1)
Suite 125 625 Parsons Road SW, Edmonton, T6X 0N9, AB, Canada
Tel.: (780) 489-9866
Web Site: https://newstarcapital.com
Holding Company
N.A.I.C.S.: 551112

NEWSWEST CORP.

INTERNATIONAL PUBLIC

5716 Burbank Rd SE, Calgary, T2H 1Z4, AB, Canada
Tel.: (403) 253-8856
Web Site: http://www.newswest.ca
Sales Range: $50-74.9 Million
Emp.: 275
Magazines Books & Comics Distribution Services
N.A.I.C.S.: 513130
John Carmichael (Sr VP-Sls)

NEWTEC UMWELTTECHNIK GMBH
Am Borsigturm 62, 13507, Berlin, Germany
Tel.: (49) 306953780
Web Site: http://www.newtec-umwelttechnik.de
Year Founded: 1997
Sales Range: $50-74.9 Million
Emp.: 100
Electrolytic Water Disinfection Services
N.A.I.C.S.: 221310
Yuan Gao (CEO)

Subsidiaries:

Newtec Water Systems NV (1)
Industrial Park Mechelen-Noord Zandvoortstraat 5, 2800, Mechelen, Belgium
Tel.: (32) 15 28 84 10
N.A.I.C.S.: 221310

NEWTEL PARTICIPACOES S.A.
Av Rio Branco 311 - Sala 523/parte, 20040903, Rio de Janeiro, Brazil
Tel.: (55) 2121967200
Financial Management Services
N.A.I.C.S.: 523999
Fernando Jose Do Amaral Friedheim (CTO & Dir-IR)

NEWTERRA LTD.
155 Wellington Street West, Toronto, M5V 3J7, ON, Canada
Tel.: (416) 490-7848
Web Site: http://www.newterra.com
Year Founded: 1863
Emp.: 200
Modular Water Treatment Systems Designer & Mfr
N.A.I.C.S.: 562998
Doug Conley (VP-Sls)

Subsidiaries:

H2o Engineering, Inc. (1)
189 Granada Dr, San Luis Obispo, CA 93401
Tel.: (805) 547-0303
Web Site: http://www.h2oengineering.com
Rev.: $1,800,000
Emp.: 15
Other Commercial & Service Industry Machinery Mfr
N.A.I.C.S.: 333310
Robert Moncrief (Pres)

MARG Inc. (1)
1555 Coraopolis Hts Rd, Ste 4100, Coraopolis, PA 15108
Tel.: (724) 703-3020
Web Site: http://www.tigg.com
High-quality Carbon & Media Adsorption Equipment
N.A.I.C.S.: 325998

Newterra Group Ltd. - Air Instruments Division (1)
4961 King Street E Unit T1, PO Box 463, Beamsville, L0R 1B0, ON, Canada
Tel.: (866) 840-0014
Web Site: http://www.air.newterra.com
Analytical Instrument Mfr
N.A.I.C.S.: 334516

newterra GmbH (1)
Steinbruchstrasse 8, 35428, Langgons, Germany
Tel.: (49) 6447886050
Filter Mfr

N.A.I.C.S.: 333998

newterra S.p.A. (1)
Isidora Goyenechea 2925 of 305, Las Condes, Santiago, Chile
Tel.: (56) 223032771
Waste Water Management Services
N.A.I.C.S.: 562998

NEWTON 21 EUROPE SA
Avenue Gustave Demey 57 3rd Floor, 1160, Brussels, Belgium
Tel.: (32) 27339760
Web Site: http://www.newton21.com
Year Founded: 1998
Sales Range: $25-49.9 Million
Emp.: 250
Digital Marketing, Communications, Public Relations & Advertising Services
N.A.I.C.S.: 541613
Alain Mahaux *(CEO)*

Subsidiaries:

Newton 21 Roma (1)
Via Marianna Dionigi 29, 00153, Rome, Italy
Tel.: (39) 065717201
Web Site: http://www.newton21.it
Sales Range: $25-49.9 Million
Emp.: 19
Consumer Marketing
N.A.I.C.S.: 541810

Vivactis Benelux (1)
Avenue Gustave Demey 57, PO Box 1160, Brussels, Belgium
Tel.: (32) 27339760
Web Site: http://www.spin-vivactis.be
Sales Range: $25-49.9 Million
Emp.: 35
Advertising Agency Services
N.A.I.C.S.: 541810
Stephanie Schor *(Mng Dir)*

Vivactis Conseil (1)
114 Avenue Charles de Gaulle, 9220, Neuilly-sur-Seine, France
Tel.: (33) 146676200
Web Site: http://www.vivactis-groupe.com
Advertising Agency Services
N.A.I.C.S.: 541810

vivactis ALINA + (1)
17 Rue Jean Daudin, PO Box 75015, Paris, France
Tel.: (33) 1 46 67 62 00
Advertising Agency Services
N.A.I.C.S.: 541810

NEWTON EUROPE LTD
2 Kingston Business Park Kingston Bagpuize, Oxfordshire, OX13 5FE, United Kingdom
Tel.: (44) 1865601300
Web Site: https://www.newtoneurope.com
Year Founded: 2001
Management Consulting Services
N.A.I.C.S.: 541618

Subsidiaries:

Fluxx Limited (1)
9 Marshalsea Road, London, SE1 1EP, United Kingdom
Tel.: (44) 2072427797
Web Site: http://fluxx.uk.com
Management Consulting Services
N.A.I.C.S.: 541618

Subsidiary (Domestic):

Albion Brand Communications, Ltd. (2)
103 The Tea Bldg 56 Shoreditch High St, London, E1 6JJ, United Kingdom
Tel.: (44) 2070338900
Web Site: https://www.albion.co
Advertising, Communications, Digital/Interactive, Print, T.V.
N.A.I.C.S.: 541810

NEWTON NORDIC AB
Lokstallsgatan 8, SE 582 73, Linkoping, Sweden
Tel.: (46) 102221600 SE
Web Site: http://www.newtonnordic.com
Year Founded: 2009
Rev.: $1,397,497
Assets: $1,469,301
Liabilities: $534,778
Net Worth: $934,522
Earnings: ($308,650)
Emp.: 11
Fiscal Year-end: 12/31/19
Aerial Cinema Systems Mfr
N.A.I.C.S.: 334310
Robin Kahlbom *(VP-Product & Bus Dev)*

NEWTON RESOURCES LTD
Suite 4117 41/F Jardine House 1 Connaught Place, Central, China (Hong Kong)
Tel.: (852) 25218168
Web Site: http://www.newton-resources.com
1231—(HKG)
Rev.: $201,487,000
Assets: $60,871,000
Liabilities: $32,893,000
Net Worth: $27,978,000
Earnings: ($2,222,000)
Emp.: 23
Fiscal Year-end: 12/31/22
Iron Ore Mining Services
N.A.I.C.S.: 212210
Yue Kan Luk *(CFO & Sec)*

NEWTOPIA, INC.
33 Bloor Street East 5th Floor, Toronto, M4W 3H1, ON, Canada
Web Site: https://www.newtopia.com
Year Founded: 2008
NEWU—(TSXV)
Rev.: $7,387,711
Assets: $1,761,605
Liabilities: $8,873,785
Net Worth: ($7,112,180)
Earnings: ($4,984,027)
Fiscal Year-end: 12/31/23
Health Care Srvices
N.A.I.C.S.: 621610
Jeff Ruby *(Founder & CEO)*

NEWTREE CO., LTD.
6-14 Baekjegobun-ro 27-gil, Songpa-gu, Seoul, Korea (South)
Tel.: (82) 25653494
Web Site: https://inewtree.com
Year Founded: 2001
270870—(KRS)
Rev.: $152,362,438
Assets: $112,506,862
Liabilities: $36,735,436
Net Worth: $75,771,426
Earnings: $3,644,325
Emp.: 90
Fiscal Year-end: 12/31/22
Health Food Product Mfr
N.A.I.C.S.: 333241
Seungho Han *(Dir)*

NEWTREE SA
Boulevard du Souverain 24 Watermael-Boitsfort, 1170, Brussels, Belgium
Tel.: (32) 27705620
Web Site: https://www.newtree.com
NEWT—(EUR)
Sales Range: $1-9.9 Million
Emp.: 15
Chocolate Product Mfr
N.A.I.C.S.: 311352
Benoit De Bruyn *(Mng Dir)*

Subsidiaries:

NEWTREE America, Inc. (1)
PO Box 800, San Anselmo, CA 94979
Tel.: (616) 935-9933
Web Site: http://www.newtree.com
Chocolate Products Mfr & Distr
N.A.I.C.S.: 311351

NEWTREE sarl (1)
31 Rue de la Convention, Parc d'Activites Garigliano, 38200, Vienne, France
Tel.: (33) 474574610
Web Site: http://www.newtree.fr
Emp.: 5
Chocolate Product Mfr
N.A.I.C.S.: 311351

NEX METALS EXPLORATIONS LTD
45 Guthrie Street, Osborne Park, 6017, WA, Australia
Tel.: (61) 892216813
Web Site: https://www.nexmetals.com
NME—(ASX)
Rev.: $431,659
Assets: $1,312,271
Liabilities: $4,034,591
Net Worth: ($2,722,320)
Earnings: ($1,369,334)
Fiscal Year-end: 06/30/22
Mining & Exploration
N.A.I.C.S.: 213114
Kenneth Malcolme Allen *(Mng Dir & Sec)*

NEX POINT PUBLIC COMPANY LIMITED
999/999 Moo 4, Bangchalong Bang Phli, Samut Prakan, 10540, Thailand
Tel.: (66) 20263599
Web Site: https://www.nexpoint.co.th
Year Founded: 1997
NEX—(THA)
Rev.: $274,743,145
Assets: $321,914,741
Liabilities: $201,097,351
Net Worth: $120,817,390
Earnings: $21,171,768
Fiscal Year-end: 12/31/23
Small Metal Pieces Mfr
N.A.I.C.S.: 332322
Aek Angsananont *(Chm)*

Subsidiaries:

Single Point Energy and Environment Co., Ltd. (1)
224/31 Victoria Building Muang Thong Thani Bond Street, Bangpood Pakkred, Nonthaburi, 11120, Thailand
Tel.: (66) 2 960 2055
Web Site: http://www.polymerenergythailand.com
Waste Treatment Services
N.A.I.C.S.: 562211

Single Point Parts (Thailand) Public Company Limited - Factory No.2 (1)
53 Moo 3 Intra Industrial Park Estate Tumbon Namtal, Amphur Inburi, Sing Buri, 16110, Thailand
Tel.: (66) 36 533 380
Plastics Product Mfr
N.A.I.C.S.: 326199

Skyfrog Co., Ltd. (1)
230 CS TOWER Building 9th Flr Ratchadapisek Rd, Huaykhwang, Bangkok, 10310, Thailand
Tel.: (66) 269287314
Web Site: https://www.skyfrog.net
Information Technology Services
N.A.I.C.S.: 541511

Terabyte Net Solution Public Company Limited (1)
230 CS Tower 12 Floor Ratchadapisek Rd, Huai Khwang Sub-district Huai Khwang District, Bangkok, 10310, Thailand
Tel.: (66) 269287314
Web Site: https://www.terabytenet.com
Networking Infrastructure Equipment
N.A.I.C.S.: 334220

Terabyte Plus Public Co., Ltd. (1)
230 Cs Tower 12Th Flr Ratchadapisek Rd, Huaykwang, Bangkok, Thailand
Tel.: (66) 269287314
Web Site: https://www.terabyteplus.com
Information Technology Services
N.A.I.C.S.: 518210

NEXA RESOURCES S.A.
37A Avenue J F Kennedy, L-1855, Luxembourg, Luxembourg
Tel.: (352) 28263727 LU
Web Site: https://www.nexaresources.com
Year Founded: 2014
NEXA—(NYSE)
Rev.: $3,033,990,000
Assets: $4,891,782,000
Liabilities: $3,181,528,000
Net Worth: $1,710,254,000
Earnings: $76,394,000
Emp.: 5,625
Fiscal Year-end: 12/31/22
Zinc Mining Services
N.A.I.C.S.: 212230
Jaime Ardila *(Chm)*

Subsidiaries:

Karmin Exploration Inc. (1)
First Canadian Place 100 King Street West Suite 5700, Toronto, M5X 1C7, ON, Canada
Tel.: (416) 367-0369
Web Site: http://www.karmin.com
Assets: $12,254,475
Liabilities: $1,777,250
Net Worth: $10,477,226
Earnings: ($1,117,525)
Fiscal Year-end: 04/30/2018
Mineral Exploration Services
N.A.I.C.S.: 213114
John A. Iannozzi *(CFO)*

NEXAM CHEMICAL HOLDING AB
Industrigatan 27, Box 165, 234 23, Lomma, Sweden
Tel.: (46) 40413620
Web Site: https://www.nexamchemical.com
NEXAM—(OMX)
Rev.: $20,770,463
Assets: $26,047,374
Liabilities: $5,851,995
Net Worth: $20,195,379
Earnings: ($1,189,506)
Emp.: 53
Fiscal Year-end: 12/31/22
Chemical Products Mfr
N.A.I.C.S.: 325998
Johan Arvidsson *(CEO)*

Subsidiaries:

Nexam St Andrews Ltd. (1)
Prestonhall Industrial Estate, Cupar, KY15 4RD, Fife, United Kingdom
Tel.: (44) 1334657655
Chemical Products Mfr
N.A.I.C.S.: 325998

Plasticolor Hungary Kft (1)
Fo ut 272, 2330, Dunaharaszti, Hungary
Tel.: (36) 2 453 6215
Web Site: https://www.plasticolor.hu
Master Batch Mfr
N.A.I.C.S.: 326199

Plasticolor Polska Sp. z o.o. (1)
Ul Poznanska 47, 62-023, Gadki, Poland
Tel.: (48) 618171727
Web Site: http://www.plasticolor.4b.pl
Master Batch Mfr
N.A.I.C.S.: 326199

NEXANS S.A.
4 allee de l Arche, 92400, Courbevoie, France
Tel.: (33) 178150000 FR
Web Site: https://www.nexans.com
NEX—(EUR)
Rev.: $9,057,041,760
Assets: $6,862,176,880
Liabilities: $5,062,805,280
Net Worth: $1,799,371,600

NEXANS S.A.

Nexans S.A.—(Continued)
Earnings: $201,431,360
Emp.: 24,962
Fiscal Year-end: 12/31/22
Power & Communication Cables Mfr
N.A.I.C.S.: 335929
Vincent Dessale *(COO & Sr Exec VP-Building & Territories Northern Bus Grp)*

Subsidiaries:

Nexans (Suzhou) Cables Solutions Co. Ltd. (1)
No 1588 Songwei Road, Wuzhong Economic and Technological Development Zone, Suzhou, 215124, Jingsu, China
Tel.: (86) 51288171200
Fiber Optic Cable Mfr
N.A.I.C.S.: 335921

Nexans (Yanggu) New Rihui Cables Co. Ltd. (1)
N 14 Xihum, Yanggu, Shandong, 252311, China
Tel.: (86) 6356318999
Fiber Optic Cable Mfr
N.A.I.C.S.: 335921
Rain Zhang *(Dir-Quality)*

Nexans Chile S.A. (1)
San Francisco 4761, San Miguel, 8930029, Santiago, Chile
Tel.: (56) 223520100
Web Site: https://www.nexans.cl
Emp.: 200
Fiber Optic Cable Mfr
N.A.I.C.S.: 335921
Gwenael Gilbert *(Plant Mgr)*

Nexans High Voltage USA Inc. (1)
1716 Bushy Park Rd, Goose Creek, SC 29445
Tel.: (919) 818-1700
Fiber Optic Cable Mfr
N.A.I.C.S.: 335921
Emmanuel Martin-Lauzer *(Dir-Bus Dev)*

Nexans Industry Solutions A/S (1)
Livovej 47 - 49, 8800, Viborg, Denmark
Tel.: (45) 86620015
Web Site: http://www.be-cablecon.dk
Fiber Optic Cable Mfr
N.A.I.C.S.: 335921
Klaus Moller *(CEO)*

Nexans Kabelmetal Ghana Ltd. (1)
Steel Works Road, Heavy Industrial Area, Tema, Ghana
Tel.: (233) 303304102
Web Site: http://www.nexans.com.gh
Fiber Optic Cable Mfr
N.A.I.C.S.: 335921
Francis Husinu *(Mgr-Technical)*

Nexans Participations (1)
16 Rue de Monceau, 75008, Paris, France
Tel.: (33) 156698400
Web Site: http://www.nexans.gr
Holding Company
N.A.I.C.S.: 551112

Subsidiary (Domestic):

Alsafil SAS (2)
21 Vieux Chemin de Bergheim, 67600, Selestat, France
Tel.: (33) 3 88 92 09 22
Fabricated Wire Product Mfr
N.A.I.C.S.: 332618

Subsidiary (Non-US):

Elektrokontakt SRL de CV (2)
Blvd Republica Lote 3 Parque Industrial Aeropuerto, Piedras Negras, 26090, Coahuila, Mexico
Tel.: (52) 8787861070
Electronic Cable Mfr
N.A.I.C.S.: 335921

Subsidiary (Domestic):

Eurocable (2)
10 Noiregoutte, PO Box 4, 88230, Plainfaing, France
Tel.: (33) 329523030
Web Site: http://www.nexans.fr
Cable Mfr

N.A.I.C.S.: 331318

Subsidiary (Non-US):

GPH Vilnius (2)
Naugarduko 96, 3011, Vilnius, Lithuania
Tel.: (370) 5 2395209
Web Site: http://www.gph.net
Sales Range: $25-49.9 Million
Emp.: 14
Electronic Components Mfr
N.A.I.C.S.: 334419
Vidmantas Melnikas *(Gen Mgr)*

Indeco S.A. (2)
Av Industrial 794, Lima, 1, Peru
Tel.: (51) 12054810
Web Site: http://www.nexans.pe
Sales Range: $100-124.9 Million
Emp.: 418
Cable Mfr
N.A.I.C.S.: 335929
Jose Ortiz Ugarte *(Mgr-Comml)*

Intercond Services SpA (2)
Via Piemonte 20, 20096, Pioltello, Milan, Italy
Tel.: (39) 02 929 10 1
Web Site: http://www.intercond.com
Sales Range: $50-74.9 Million
Emp.: 149
Fabricated Wire Products Mfr & Distr
N.A.I.C.S.: 332618
Darioea Pasquali *(Gen Mgr)*

Liban Cables SAL (2)
Justienen Street Chamber of commerce and industry bldg, PO BOX 11-6008, Beirut, Lebanon
Tel.: (961) 1350040
Web Site: https://www.libancables.com
Emp.: 500
Fiber Optic Cable Mfr
N.A.I.C.S.: 335921
Bassam Al-Hibri *(Gen Mgr)*

Plant (Domestic):

Liban Cables SAL - Jbeil Factory (3)
Nahr Ibrahim, Jbeil, Lebanon
Tel.: (961) 9 448550
Web Site: http://www.nexans.com
Fiber Optic Cable Mfr
N.A.I.C.S.: 335921

Subsidiary (Non-US):

MAKRIS-GPH Ltd. (2)
5 General Konstantin Konstantinov St., 1336, Sofia, Bulgaria
Tel.: (359) 29250868
Web Site: http://www.nexans-power-accessories.com
Sales Range: $50-74.9 Million
Emp.: 7
Wiring Supplies Distr
N.A.I.C.S.: 423610

NV Nexans Benelux SA (2)
Heideveld 12, Beersel, 1654, Huizingen, Belgium (100%)
Tel.: (32) 23632602
Web Site: http://www.nexans.be
Sales Range: $25-49.9 Million
Power & Communications Cables Mfr
N.A.I.C.S.: 331318

Subsidiary (Domestic):

Euromold NV (3)
Zuid III - Industrielaan 12, 9320, Erembodegem, Belgium (100%)
Tel.: (32) 53850211
Web Site: http://www.nexans.be
Sales Range: $50-74.9 Million
Prefabricated Cable Accessories Mfr & Distr
N.A.I.C.S.: 331318

NV Nexans Harnessess SA (3)
Heideveld 1, 1654, Huizingen, Belgium (100%)
Tel.: (32) 23631711
Web Site: http://www.nexans.be
Sales Range: $25-49.9 Million
Emp.: 25
Mfr of Wiring Harnesses for Aircraft, Satellites & Industrial Vehicles
N.A.I.C.S.: 334220

Nexans Benelux S.A. (3)
Heideveld 12, 1654, Huizingen, Belgium

Tel.: (32) 23632602
Sales Range: $100-124.9 Million
Emp.: 30
Cable Wire Mfr & Distr
N.A.I.C.S.: 335921

Nexans Harnesses SA (3)
Heideveld 1, 1654, Huizingen, Belgium
Tel.: (32) 2 363 17 11
Web Site: http://www.nexans.fr
Wire Product Mfr
N.A.I.C.S.: 332618

Subsidiary (Non-US):

Nexans Nederland BV (3)
Overschieseweg 314, 3112 NC, Schiedam, Netherlands
Tel.: (31) 102483444
Web Site: https://www.nexans.nl
Fiber Optic Cable Mfr
N.A.I.C.S.: 335921

Subsidiary (Domestic):

Nexans Network Solutions NV (3)
Alsembergsesteenweg 2 Bus 3, 1501, Buizingen, Belgium
Tel.: (32) 23633800
Emp.: 5
Fiber Optic Cable Mfr
N.A.I.C.S.: 335921
Prashant Kshirsagar *(Gen Mgr)*

Division (Domestic):

Nexans Network Solutions NV - Euromold Division (4)
Zuid Iii - Industrielaan 12, 9320, Erembodegem, Belgium
Tel.: (32) 53 85 02 11
Web Site: http://www.nexans.be
Electronic Cable Mfr
N.A.I.C.S.: 335931

Subsidiary (Non-US):

Nexans Re SA (3)
534 Rue de Neudorf, 2220, Luxembourg, Luxembourg
Tel.: (352) 2704471
Fiber Optic Cable Mfr
N.A.I.C.S.: 335921
Ellen Stack Pettit *(Gen Mgr)*

Subsidiary (Domestic):

Opticable NV (3)
Parc Industriel - Zone B, Avenue de l'Europe, 7080, Frameries, Belgium (100%)
Tel.: (32) 65610422
Web Site: http://www.nexans.be
Sales Range: $50-74.9 Million
Emp.: 150
Optical Fibre Mfr
N.A.I.C.S.: 331318

S.A. Nexans Cabling Solutions N.V. (3)
Alsembergsesteenweg 2 B 3, Buizingen, B 1501, Belgium (100%)
Tel.: (32) 23633800
Sales Range: $25-49.9 Million
Emp.: 50
LAN Cabling Solutions Provider
N.A.I.C.S.: 331318
Mark Rogers *(Gen Mgr)*

Subsidiary (Non-US):

Nexans (China) Wires & Cables Co., Ltd. (2)
Room 1102-1104 Greentech Tower No 436 Hengfeng Road, Shanghai, 200070, China (100%)
Tel.: (86) 2133359400
Web Site: http://www.nexans.cn
Wire & Cable Mfr & Distr
N.A.I.C.S.: 335921

Plant (Domestic):

Nexans China Wire & Cables Co. Ltd - Waigaoqiao Plant (3)
No 1 Middle Fute Road Waigaoqiao Free Trade Zone, Shanghai, 200131, China
Tel.: (86) 21 5046 2990
Sales Range: $50-74.9 Million
Emp.: 20
Fiber Optic Cable Mfr

INTERNATIONAL PUBLIC

N.A.I.C.S.: 335921
Kevin Yuu *(Mgr-Sls)*

Subsidiary (Non-US):

Nexans (Nanning) Communications Co., Ltd. (2)
No 7 Jin Kai Road, Guang Xi, 530031, Nanning, China (100%)
Tel.: (86) 7714516068
Web Site: http://www.nexans.com
Telecommunications Cable Mfr
N.A.I.C.S.: 331318

Nexans (Shanghai) Electrical Materials Co., Ltd. (2)
1 Fl No 138 Hedan Road, Waigaoqiao Free Trade Zone, 200131, Shanghai, China (100%)
Tel.: (86) 2158681588
Web Site: http://www.nexans.com.cn
Power & Communication Cable Mfr
N.A.I.C.S.: 331318

Nexans Angola, Lda (2)
Casa Dos Desportistas Sala 305 Ilha Do Cabo, Luanda, Angola
Tel.: (244) 923 923 123
Web Site: http://uglex.com
Sales Range: $25-49.9 Million
Electronic Cable Mfr
N.A.I.C.S.: 335921

Nexans Australia Holding Pty Limited (2)
207 Sunshine Rd, Tottenham, Tottenham, 3012, VIC, Australia
Tel.: (61) 392814444
Web Site: http://www.olex.com.au
Sales Range: $100-124.9 Million
Emp.: 20
Investment Management Service
N.A.I.C.S.: 523999
Graeme Moncrieff *(Mng Dir)*

Subsidiary (Domestic):

Olex Holdings Pty. Ltd. (3)
207 Sunshine Rd, Tottenham, 3012, VIC, Australia
Tel.: (61) 3 9281 4444
Web Site: http://www.olex.com.au
Holding Company; Electric Power Cable Mfr
N.A.I.C.S.: 551112

Subsidiary (Domestic):

Olex Australia Pty. Ltd. (4)
207 Sunshine Rd, Tottenham, 3012, VIC, Australia
Tel.: (61) 392814444
Web Site: http://www.olex.com.au
Sales Range: $150-199.9 Million
Emp.: 700
Electric Power Cable Mfr
N.A.I.C.S.: 335929
Stephen Thunder *(CFO)*

Subsidiary (Non-US):

Olex New Zealand Ltd. (4)
69 Paraite Road Bell Block, New Plymouth, 4312, New Zealand
Tel.: (64) 67559800
Web Site: http://www.olex.co.nz
Sales Range: $25-49.9 Million
Emp.: 150
Electric Power Cable Mfr
N.A.I.C.S.: 335929

Subsidiary (Non-US):

Nexans Brasil SA (2)
Avenida Ibirapuera 2332 Torre Ibirapuera I Cj 81/82, Sao Paulo, 04028-900, Brazil
Tel.: (55) 1130841600
Sales Range: $75-99.9 Million
Power & Communication Cable Mfr
N.A.I.C.S.: 331318

Nexans Canada Inc. (2)
700-55 Commerce Valley West, Thornhill, L3T 7V9, ON, Canada (100%)
Tel.: (905) 944-4300
Web Site: https://www.nexans.ca
Sales Range: $25-49.9 Million
Mfr of Electrical Wire & Cable
N.A.I.C.S.: 335999

Nexans Colombia S.A. (2)
Parque Industrial Manzana B Via Cafe Ma-

AND PRIVATE COMPANIES — NEXANS S.A.

drid km 3, Bucaramanga, Colombia **(80%)**
Tel.: (57) 76762929
Web Site: http://www.nexans.com.co
Sales Range: $25-49.9 Million
Emp.: 181
Cable Mfr
N.A.I.C.S.: 335929
Luis Ernesto Silva *(CEO)*

Nexans Communications (Shanghai) Cable Co. Ltd **(2)**
No 135 82 Lane Nanchen Road, Shanghai, 200436, China
Tel.: (86) 21 5613 0606
Web Site: http://www.nexans.cn
Fiber Optic Cable Mfr
N.A.I.C.S.: 335921

Subsidiary (Domestic):

Nexans Copper France SAS **(2)**
4 Rue Mozart, 92110, Clichy, France
Tel.: (33) 3 21 79 47 25
Electrical Wire Mfr
N.A.I.C.S.: 332618

Subsidiary (Non-US):

Nexans Deutschland Industries GmbH & Co. KG **(2)**
Kabelkamp 20, 30179, Hannover, Germany **(100%)**
Tel.: (49) 5116760
Web Site: http://www.nexans.de
Sales Range: $75-99.9 Million
Emp.: 400
Power & Communication Cables Mfr
N.A.I.C.S.: 331318

Subsidiary (Domestic):

Confecta GmbH **(3)**
Eduard-Maurer-Strasse 13, 16761, Hennigsdorf Berlin, Germany
Tel.: (49) 3302 200 435
Web Site: http://www.confecta.de
Emp.: 5,200
Electronic Cable Mfr & Distr
N.A.I.C.S.: 335921
Manfred Schloegel *(Gen Mgr)*

Elektrokontakt Gmbh **(3)**
Vohenstrausser Str 20, Floss, 92685, Germany
Tel.: (49) 9603200
Electronic Components Mfr
N.A.I.C.S.: 334419

Euromold GmbH **(3)**
Aplerbecker Strasse 456, 44287, Dortmund, Germany **(100%)**
Tel.: (49) 231945130
Sales Range: $25-49.9 Million
Emp.: 40
Power Cable Mfr
N.A.I.C.S.: 331318

Kabeltrommel GmbH & Co. KG **(3)**
Camp-Spich-Str 55/59, 53842, Troisdorf, Germany
Tel.: (49) 224125240
Web Site: https://www.kabeltrommel.de
Wire & Cable Products Mfr
N.A.I.C.S.: 332618

Metrofunkkabel Union GmbH **(3)**
Lepsiusstrasse 89, Postfach 41 01 09, 12111, Berlin, Germany
Tel.: (49) 307901860
Web Site: http://www.metrofunk.de
Emp.: 10
Electrical Cables Mfr
N.A.I.C.S.: 335921
R. Raszynski *(CEO)*

Mobil Electric Gmbh **(3)**
Vohenstrausser Str 20, Floss, 92685, Germany
Tel.: (49) 9603200
Web Site: http://www.autoelectric.de
Sales Range: $100-124.9 Million
Emp.: 450
Cable & Wire Mfr
N.A.I.C.S.: 332618

Nexans Deutschland GmbH & Co. KG **(3)**
Kabelkamp 20, 30179, Hannover, Germany
Tel.: (49) 5116760
Web Site: http://www.nexans.de

Power & Communication Cables Mfr
N.A.I.C.S.: 331318

Nexans Power Accessories Germany GmbH **(3)**
Ferdinand-Porsche-Str 12, 95028, Hof, Germany **(100%)**
Tel.: (49) 928183060
Web Site: http://www.nexans-power-accessories.com
Sales Range: $50-74.9 Million
Emp.: 160
Cable Armatures Mfg
N.A.I.C.S.: 335312

Nexans Powers Accessories Germany GMBH **(3)**
Ferdinand-Porsche-Str 12, Hof, 95028, Germany
Tel.: (49) 9281 8306 0
Web Site: http://www.nexans-power-accessories.com
Emp.: 200
Low & Medium Voltage Accessories Mfr
N.A.I.C.S.: 335999
Peter Ahlers *(Mng Dir)*

Nexans Superconductors GmbH **(3)**
Chemiepark Knapsack, Hurth, 50354, Germany
Tel.: (49) 2233486597
Web Site: http://www.nexans.de
Emp.: 18
Electronic Cable Mfr
N.A.I.C.S.: 335921
Frank Schmidt *(Mng Dir)*

Nexans autoelectric GmbH **(3)**
Vohenstrausser Str 20, 92685, Floss, Germany
Tel.: (49) 9603 200
Web Site: http://www.autoelectric.com
Sales Range: $400-449.9 Million
Electronic Components Mfr
N.A.I.C.S.: 334419

Division (Domestic):

Nexans autoelectric GmbH **(4)**
Vohenstrausser Strasse 20, 92685, Floss, Germany
Tel.: (49) 9603200
Web Site: http://www.autoelectric.com
Sales Range: $25-49.9 Million
Cable Mfr
N.A.I.C.S.: 331318

Subsidiary (Domestic):

Nexans France **(2)**
4 allee de l'Arche, CS 70088, La Defense, 92070, Paris, Cedex, France **(100%)**
Tel.: (33) 178150000
Web Site: https://www.nexans.fr
Sales Range: $50-74.9 Million
Emp.: 28,500
Power & Communications Cables Mfr
N.A.I.C.S.: 331318

Subsidiary (Non-US):

Nexans Hellas Industrial SA **(2)**
15 Messoghion Str, 115 26, Athens, Rentis, Greece
Tel.: (30) 2111207700
Web Site: http://www.nexans.gr
Emp.: 30
Power & Communications Cable Mfr
N.A.I.C.S.: 335921

Nexans IKO Sweden AB **(3)**
Kabelgatan 1 A, Grimsas, 514 81, Tranemo, Sweden **(100%)**
Tel.: (46) 32580000
Web Site: http://www.nexans.se
Sales Range: $75-99.9 Million
Emp.: 500
Power & Communications Cable Mfr
N.A.I.C.S.: 331318

Subsidiary (Domestic):

Axjo Kabel AG **(3)**
Balderasvagen 31, 332 35, Gislaved, Sweden **(100%)**
Tel.: (46) 37180365
Web Site: http://www.axjokabel.se
Sales Range: $125-149.9 Million
Emp.: 2
Cable Mfr
N.A.I.C.S.: 331318

Subsidiary (Non-US):

Nexans Iberia, S.L. **(2)**
Avda Sant Julia 98-102 Pol Ind Congost, Granollers, 08403, Barcelona, Spain **(100%)**
Tel.: (34) 937131133
Web Site: https://www.nexans.es
Sales Range: $25-49.9 Million
Emp.: 50
Power & Communication Cable Mfr
N.A.I.C.S.: 331318

Nexans Iletisim Endustri ve Ticaret AS **(3)**
Mecidiyekoy Mahallesi Oguz sokak No 4 BIZ Plaza Kat A/1, Mecidiyetoy sisli, 34387, Istanbul, Turkiye
Tel.: (90) 2122660160
Web Site: http://www.nexans.com.tr
Sales Range: $25-49.9 Million
Emp.: 500
Power & Communications Cable Mfr
N.A.I.C.S.: 331318

Plant (Domestic):

Nexans Turkiye Iletisim Endustri ve Ticaret AS - Denizli Factory **(3)**
Izmir Karayolu 6 Km, 20200, Denizli, Turkiye
Tel.: (90) 258 371 21 80
Sales Range: $50-74.9 Million
Emp.: 215
Fabricated Wire Product Mfr
N.A.I.C.S.: 332618

Nexans Turkiye Iletisim Endustri ve Ticaret AS - Tuzla Factory **(3)**
Mecidiyekoy Mah Oguz Sokak No 4 Ronesans Biz Plaza Kat A/1, Mecidiyekoy Sisli, 34387, Istanbul, Turkiye
Tel.: (90) 2122660160
Web Site: http://www.nexans.com.tr
Fabricated Wire Product Mfr
N.A.I.C.S.: 332618

Subsidiary (Non-US):

Nexans Indelqui S.A. **(2)**
Av 1 2 de Octubre 2130 Quilmes, 1832 Llavallol, Buenos Aires, B1879AAF, Argentina
Tel.: (54) 1140030000
Sales Range: $50-74.9 Million
Emp.: 215
Copper Pipe Mfr
N.A.I.C.S.: 331410

Subsidiary (Domestic):

Nexans Interface SA **(2)**
25 Avenue Jean Jaures, BP 11, 8330, Vrigne-aux-Bois, France
Tel.: (33) 324526161
Electrical Wire Mfr
N.A.I.C.S.: 331420

Subsidiary (Non-US):

Nexans Ireland Ltd **(2)**
Cornamaddy, Athlone, West Meath, Ireland **(100%)**
Tel.: (353) 906475001
Web Site: http://www.nexans.com
Sales Range: $25-49.9 Million
Emp.: 110
Power & Communications Cable Distr
N.A.I.C.S.: 331318

Nexans Italia Spa **(2)**
Via Piemonte 20, Borgo Piave, 20096, Pioltello, MI, Italy **(100%)**
Tel.: (39) 02929101
Web Site: http://www.nexans.it
Emp.: 200
Power & Communication Cables Mfr
N.A.I.C.S.: 331318

Subsidiary (Domestic):

Cabloswiss S.p.a **(3)**
Via Ancona 22, 20060, Trezzano Rosa, Milan, Italy
Tel.: (39) 02 90968358
Web Site: http://www.cabloswiss.it
Sales Range: $25-49.9 Million
Emp.: 2
Fiber Optic Cable Mfr
N.A.I.C.S.: 335921
Massimo Fumagalli *(Gen Mgr)*

Nexans Wires Italia SpA **(3)**
Via Piemonte 20, Vimercate, 20096, Pioltello, Italy
Tel.: (39) 02929101
Web Site: http://www.nexans.it
Sales Range: $25-49.9 Million
Covered Specialty Wire Conductors Mfr
N.A.I.C.S.: 335931

Subsidiary (Non-US):

Nexans Jydsk Denmark A/S **(2)**
Savvaerksvej 18 Klarking, Juelsminde, 7130, Denmark **(100%)**
Tel.: (45) 75693399
Web Site: http://www.nexans.dk
Sales Range: $25-49.9 Million
Emp.: 30
Power & Communications Cable Mfr
N.A.I.C.S.: 331318
Yvon Raak *(Sr Exec VP-Logistics & Indus Policies)*

Nexans Kazakhstan **(2)**
Office 8 Floor 4 Blg 22/37 Markova Street, Almaty, 050040, Kazakhstan
Tel.: (7) 727 390 0389
Web Site: http://kz.nexans.com
Fiber Optic Cable Mfr
N.A.I.C.S.: 335921

Nexans Korea Ltd **(2)**
50 Sadong-gil Nami-myeon, Seowon-gu, Cheongju, 28183, Chungcheongbuk-do, Korea (South) **(100%)**
Tel.: (82) 432700200
Web Site: http://www.nexans.co.kr
Sales Range: $75-99.9 Million
Emp.: 226
Power & Communications Cable Mfr
N.A.I.C.S.: 331318

Affiliate (Non-US):

Daesung Vietnam Power Cable Company **(3)**
116 Ha Huy Tap Rd, Yen Vien Town Gialam, Hanoi, Vietnam
Tel.: (84) 4 878 0960
Cable Mfr
N.A.I.C.S.: 331318

Subsidiary (Domestic):

Daeyoung Cable Co., Ltd **(3)**
842 Deokgeum-ro Geumwang-eup, Eumseong, 27681, Choongcheongbuk-do, Korea (South) **(100%)**
Tel.: (82) 438805300
Web Site: http://www.nexans.co.kr
Sales Range: $25-49.9 Million
Mfr of Low Voltage Cables & Automotive Wire Conductors
N.A.I.C.S.: 331318

Kudong Electric Wire Co., Ltd **(3)**
600-14 Tokso-ri, Wabu-up Namyangju-si, Kyung Gi-Do, Seoul, Korea (South)
Tel.: (82) 222369892
Winding Wire Mfr
N.A.I.C.S.: 334220

Kukdong Electric Wire Co. Ltd **(3)**
29-23 Yongjeong-ri Chopyung-myeon, Jincheon, 365-853, Chungcheongbuk-do, Korea (South)
Tel.: (82) 435302000
Web Site: http://www.cablekukdong.co.kr
Sales Range: $250-299.9 Million
Offshore Electric Cable Mfr & Distr
N.A.I.C.S.: 335921

Affiliate (Non-US):

VINA Daesung Cable Company **(3)**
135 Bui Thi Xuan, Hanoi, Vietnam
Tel.: (84) 48272314
Telecommunications Cable Mfr
N.A.I.C.S.: 331318

Subsidiary (Non-US):

Nexans Maroc SA **(2)**
Bd Ahl Loghlam, Sidi Moumen, 20400, Casablanca, Morocco **(100%)**
Tel.: (212) 522762920
Web Site: https://www.nexans.be
Sales Range: $150-199.9 Million
Emp.: 675
Power & Communications Cable Mfr
N.A.I.C.S.: 331318

NEXANS S.A.

Nexans S.A.—(Continued)

Nexans Norway A/S (2)
Innspurten 9, 0663, Etterstad, Oslo,
Norway **(100%)**
Tel.: (47) 22886100
Web Site: https://www.nexans.no
Sales Range: $25-49.9 Million
Emp.: 100
Power & Communications Cable Mfr
N.A.I.C.S.: 331318
Anne Lise Aukner *(CEO)*

Subsidiary (Domestic):

Nexans Power Accessories France SAS (2)
10 Chemin du Loup, Donchery, France
Tel.: (33) 324277850
Wiring Supplies Distr
N.A.I.C.S.: 423610

Subsidiary (Non-US):

Nexans Power Accessories Poland sp. z.o.o. (2)
Ul Wiejska 18, 47-400, Raciborz, Poland
Tel.: (48) 32 418 23 49
Sales Range: $25-49.9 Million
Emp.: 11
Electronic Cable Mfr
N.A.I.C.S.: 335921

Nexans Power Networks Nigeria Ltd (2)
Km 12 Lagos-ibadan Expressway Mabgoro Bus Stop, Near MFM Prayer City, Magboro, Ogun, Nigeria
Tel.: (234) 80 727 333 75
Web Site: http://www.nexans.de
Power Cable Mfr
N.A.I.C.S.: 335929

Nexans Romania SRL (2)
13 - 17 Sevastopol St 1st floor apart 204, 1st district, 010990, Bucharest, Romania
Tel.: (40) 21 206 60 20
Web Site: http://www.nexans.ro
Cable Products Mfr
N.A.I.C.S.: 332618

Nexans Schweiz AG (2)
Av Francois-Borel 17, 2016, Cortaillod, Switzerland
Tel.: (41) 328435555
Web Site: http://www.nexans.ch
Sales Range: $75-99.9 Million
Power & Communications Cable Mfr
N.A.I.C.S.: 331318
Marco Spinelli *(CEO & Sls Mgr)*

Branch (Domestic):

Nexans Schweiz AG (Breitenbach) (3)
Passwangstrasse 20, 4226, Breitenbach, Switzerland
Tel.: (41) 617854210
Web Site: http://www.nexans.ch
Indoor & Industrial Cable Mfr
N.A.I.C.S.: 331318

Subsidiary (Non-US):

Nexans Suisse S.A. (2)
Avenue Francois-Borel 17, 2016, Cortaillod, Switzerland
Tel.: (41) 328435555
Web Site: https://www.nexans.ch
Electronic Cable Mfr
N.A.I.C.S.: 332618
Marco Spinelli *(CEO & Mgr-Sls)*

Nexans UK Ltd (2)
Chesney Wold Bleak Hall, Abbey Rd, Milton Keynes, MK6 1LA, United Kingdom **(100%)**
Tel.: (44) 1908250850
Web Site: http://www.nexans.co.uk
Sales Range: $25-49.9 Million
Power & Communications Cable Mfr
N.A.I.C.S.: 331318

Subsidiary (Domestic):

Hi-Wire Ltd (Glasgow) (3)
111 Barie Road, Hillington Industrial Estate, Glasgow, G52 4PX, United Kingdom **(100%)**
Tel.: (44) 1418809645
Web Site: http://www.hi-wire.co.uk

Winding Wire Mfr
N.A.I.C.S.: 334220

Nexans Logistics Ltd. (3)
Nexans House-Chesney Wold-Bleak Hall, Milton Keynes, MK6 1LA, Buckinghamsire, United Kingdom **(100%)**
Tel.: (44) 1908250850
Web Site: http://www.nexans.co.uk
Sales Range: $25-49.9 Million
Electrical Cable Distr
N.A.I.C.S.: 238210

Nexans Power Accessories UK Ltd (3)
Unit 1 Aire & Calder Industrial Park Lock Lane, Castleford, WF10 2JA, United Kingdom
Tel.: (44) 1977669966
Sales Range: $50-74.9 Million
Emp.: 14
Wiring Supplies Distr
N.A.I.C.S.: 423610

Subsidiary (US):

Nexans USA Inc (2)
600 Parker St, Elm City, NC 27822
Web Site: http://www.nexans.com
Sales Range: $50-74.9 Million
Electrical Wiring Supplies Mfr
N.A.I.C.S.: 335931

Subsidiary (Domestic):

Autoelectric of America Inc (3)
12500 San Pedro Ave Ste 300, San Antonio, TX 78216
Tel.: (210) 402-6003
Web Site: http://www.autoelectric.de
Automotive Electronic Parts Mfr
N.A.I.C.S.: 336320

Nexans Energy USA Inc. (3)
25 Oakland Ave, Chester, NY 10918
Tel.: (845) 469-2141
Web Site: http://www.nexans.gr
Sales Range: $25-49.9 Million
Diversified Wire & Cable Mfr
N.A.I.C.S.: 332618

Subsidiary (Domestic):

Nexans Wires (2)
128 avenue Jean Jaures, BP 30, 02300, Chauny, France **(100%)**
Tel.: (33) 323386900
Web Site: http://www.nexans.com
Sales Range: $75-99.9 Million
Emp.: 300
Cable & Wiring Mfr
N.A.I.C.S.: 335921

Subsidiary (Domestic):

Societe Lensoise de Cuivre (3)
Blvd Du Marais, PO Box 302, 62334, Lens, Cedex, France **(100%)**
Tel.: (33) 321794725
Web Site: http://www.nexans.fr
Cable Mfr
N.A.I.C.S.: 331318

Societe de Coulee Continue du Cuivre (3)
42 Rue Ferdinand Buisson, PO Box 105, 2300, Chauny, Sanbrin, France **(100%)**
Tel.: (33) 323384100
Web Site: http://www.sccc.com
Sales Range: $25-49.9 Million
Emp.: 95
Cable Mfr
N.A.I.C.S.: 331318

Subsidiary (Non-US):

PT. Nexans Indonesia (2)
Jl Manunggal 27 A Cibubur, Ciracas, Jakarta, 13720, Indonesia
Tel.: (62) 218703467
Web Site: http://www.nexans.com.sg
Electric Cable Wire Mfr
N.A.I.C.S.: 335921

Nexans Power Accessoires France SAS (1)
Zone Industrielle D24, 08350, Donchery, France
Tel.: (33) 324277850
Web Site: http://www.nexanspoweraccessories.fr

Fiber Optic Cable Mfr
N.A.I.C.S.: 335921

Nexans Singapore Pte. Ltd. (1)
460 Alexandra Road 28-01 PSA Building, Singapore, 119963, Singapore
Tel.: (65) 63170101
Web Site: https://www.nexans.com.sg
Fiber Optic Cable Mfr
N.A.I.C.S.: 335921
Candy Teo *(Reg Dir-Sls)*

Nippon High Voltage Cable Corporation (1)
42-1 Shintomi, Futtsu, 293-0011, Chiba, Japan
Tel.: (81) 439801400
Web Site: http://www.nexans.jp
Fiber Optic Cable Mfr
N.A.I.C.S.: 335921
Akira Sogabe *(Engr-Process)*

Reka Kaapeli Oy (1)
Kaapelikatu 2, 05800, Hyvinkaa, Finland
Tel.: (358) 207200222
Web Site: http://www.reka.fi
Nordic Cable Mfr
N.A.I.C.S.: 335929
Jukka Poutanen *(CEO)*

NEXBIS LIMITED
Level 40 100 Miller Street, North Sydney, 2060, NSW, Australia
Tel.: (61) 296571311 AU
Web Site: http://www.nexbis.com.au
Sales Range: $1-9.9 Million
Internet Application-Developer
N.A.I.C.S.: 517111
Yu Ye Chua *(Exec VP-Strategy & Plng)*

Subsidiaries:

Sapio AB (1)
Munkbron 11, 111 28, Stockholm, Sweden
Tel.: (46) 8227905
Web Site: http://www.sapio.se
Information Technology Consulting & Development Services
N.A.I.C.S.: 541511

NEXCO RESOURCES, INC.
1095 West Pender Street Suite 750, Vancouver, V6E 2M6, BC, Canada
Tel.: (778) 908-2730 Ca
Year Founded: 2012
Assets: $257,671
Liabilities: $29,363
Net Worth: $228,308
Earnings: ($87,879)
Fiscal Year-end: 08/31/20
Mineral Exploration Services
N.A.I.C.S.: 213115
Zayn Kalyan *(CEO & CFO)*

NEXCOM INTERNATIONAL CO., LTD.
9F No 920 Zhongzheng Rd, Zhonghe Dist, New Taipei City, 23586, Taiwan
Tel.: (886) 282267786
Web Site: https://www.nexcom.com
Year Founded: 1992
8234—(TPE)
Rev: $247,528,281
Assets: $276,509,271
Liabilities: $165,936,560
Net Worth: $110,572,711
Earnings: $29,092,799
Fiscal Year-end: 12/31/22
Computer Peripheral Equipment Distr
N.A.I.C.S.: 423430
Mao-Chang Lin *(Chm)*

Subsidiaries:

Beijing NexGemo Technology Co., Ltd. (1)
1 Fazhan Road Beijing International Information Industry Base, Huilongguan Changping District, Beijing, China
Tel.: (86) 108 072 2025
Web Site: https://www.nexgemo.com
Computer Product Mfr

INTERNATIONAL PUBLIC

N.A.I.C.S.: 334111

EMBUX Technology Co., Ltd. (1)
FL13 No 916 Zhongzheng Rd, Zhonghe Dist, New Taipei City, 235, Taiwan
Tel.: (886) 282267786
Web Site: https://www.embux.com
Data Processing Services
N.A.I.C.S.: 518210

GreenBase Technology Corp. (1)
13F No 922 Zhongzheng Rd, Zhonghe Dist, New Taipei City, 23586, Taiwan
Tel.: (886) 282267786
Video Surveillance Services
N.A.I.C.S.: 561621

NexAIoT Co., Ltd. (1)
12F No 922 Zhongzheng Rd, Zhonghe Dist, New Taipei City, 23586, Taiwan
Tel.: (886) 282267796
Web Site: https://www.nexaiot.com
Emp.: 90
Automation Solution Services
N.A.I.C.S.: 518210
Joe Lin *(Pres)*

NexCOBOT Co., Ltd. (1)
13F No 916 Zhongzheng Rd, Zhonghe Dist, New Taipei City, 23586, Taiwan
Tel.: (886) 282267786
Web Site: https://www.nexcobot.com.tw
Robot & Motion Services
N.A.I.C.S.: 541690

Nexcom China Co., Ltd. (1)
201 Floor 2 Unit 2 Building 15 Yard 3 Gaolizhang Road, Haidian District, Beijing, 100094, China
Tel.: (86) 105 704 2680
Mobile Computing Solution Services
N.A.I.C.S.: 541512

Nexcom Europe Ltd. (1)
10 Vincent Avenue Crownhill Business Centre, Milton Keynes, MK8 0AB, Buckinghamshire, United Kingdom
Tel.: (44) 190 826 7121
Mobile Computing Solution Services
N.A.I.C.S.: 541512

Nexcom Shanghai Co., Ltd. (1)
Room 406-407 Building C No 154 Lane 953 Jianchuan Road, Minhang District, Shanghai, 201108, China
Tel.: (86) 2152785868
Mobile Computing Solution Services
N.A.I.C.S.: 541512

Nexcom Surveillance Technology Corp. (1)
Floor 8 Building B3 Xiufeng Industrial Zone GanKeng Community, Buji Street LongGang District, Shenzhen, 518112, China
Tel.: (86) 75583647768
Mobile Computing Solution Services
N.A.I.C.S.: 541512

TMR Technologies Co., Ltd. (1)
13F No 916 Chung-Cheng Rd, Zhonghe District, New Taipei City, 23586, Taiwan
Tel.: (886) 282267786
Mobile Computing Solution Services
N.A.I.C.S.: 541512

NEXCYCLE PLASTICS INC.
235 Wilkinson Road, Brampton, L6T 4M2, ON, Canada
Tel.: (905) 454-2666
Web Site: http://nexcycle.com
Year Founded: 1985
Rev: $51,966,656
Emp.: 175
Plastic Recycling Materials Supplier
N.A.I.C.S.: 562212
Keith Harradence *(Pres)*

NEXE GRUPA D.D.
Vinogradska 6, 31500, Nasice, Croatia
Tel.: (385) 31616250
Web Site: http://www.nexe.hr
Roof Tile, Brick, Concrete & Cement Mfr
N.A.I.C.S.: 327310

Subsidiaries:

Cement market d.o.o. (1)
Brace Radica 200, 31500, Nasice, Osijek-Baranja, Croatia
Tel.: (385) 31 227 390
Building Materials Distr
N.A.I.C.S.: 444180

Dilj d.o.o. (1)
Ciglarska 33, 32100, Vinkovci, Croatia
Tel.: (385) 32337166
Bricks & Roofing Tiles Mfr
N.A.I.C.S.: 327120

Ekonex d.o.o. (1)
Brace Radica 200, Nasice, 31500, Osijek-Baranja, Croatia
Tel.: (385) 31227372
Web Site: http://www.nexe.hr
Sales Range: $25-49.9 Million
Emp.: 8
Hazardous Waste Collection Services
N.A.I.C.S.: 562112
Zoran Bareolovac *(Mgr)*

Feravino d.o.o. (1)
Fericeva 16, 31 512, Fericanci, Osijek-Baranja, Croatia
Tel.: (385) 31603213
Web Site: http://www.feravino.hr
Sales Range: $25-49.9 Million
Emp.: 173
Wine Mfr
N.A.I.C.S.: 312130
Drazen Babic *(Mng Dir)*

IGM Strazilovo d.o.o. (1)
Karlovacki Vinogradi BB, Sremski Karlovci, 212, Vojvodina, Serbia
Tel.: (381) 21 881 641
Web Site: http://www.nexe.rs
Bricks Mfr
N.A.I.C.S.: 327331

Igma d.o.o. (1)
Ciglana 10, 48000, Koprivnica, Croatia
Tel.: (385) 48628300
Sales Range: $100-124.9 Million
Emp.: 150
Pebbles & Sand Excavation Services
N.A.I.C.S.: 212321
Vladimir Sinjeri *(Head-Svc-Concrete Elements)*

Luka Tranzit Osijek d.o.o. (1)
Vukovarska 229 b, 31000, Osijek, Croatia
Tel.: (385) 31515100
Sales Range: $25-49.9 Million
Emp.: 83
General Warehousing Services
N.A.I.C.S.: 493110

Nasicecement d.d. (1)
Tajnovac 1, 31500, Nasice, Croatia
Tel.: (385) 31616100
Web Site: http://www.nexe.hr
Sales Range: $125-149.9 Million
Emp.: 300
Cement Mfr
N.A.I.C.S.: 327310
Zoran Bartolovic *(Mgr-Production)*

Nasicki autocentar d.o.o. (1)
Vinogradska 6, 31500, Nasice, Croatia
Tel.: (385) 31617317
Web Site: http://www.nac.hr
Emp.: 7
Automobile Dealers
N.A.I.C.S.: 441110
Natasa Ibriks *(Mng Dir)*

Nexe beton d.o.o. Nasice (1)
Brace Radica 200, 31500, Nasice, Croatia
Tel.: (385) 31616100
Sales Range: $50-74.9 Million
Emp.: 119
Concrete Mfr
N.A.I.C.S.: 327320

Nexe d.o.o. Sarajevo (1)
Alipasina 22A, 71000, Sarajevo, Bosnia & Herzegovina
Tel.: (387) 33565240
Web Site: http://www.nexe.hr
Sales Range: $25-49.9 Million
Emp.: 10
Concrete Mfr
N.A.I.C.S.: 327320

Nexe kamen d.o.o. (1)
Kolubarska bb, 74000, Doboj, Bosnia & Herzegovina
Tel.: (387) 51315064
Web Site: http://www.nexe.hr
Minerals & Stone Excavation Services
N.A.I.C.S.: 213115

Osilovac d.o.o. (1)
Osilovacka 34, 31512, Fericanci, Croatia
Tel.: (385) 31603019
Sales Range: $25-49.9 Million
Emp.: 70
Cattle Breeding & Fish Farming Services
N.A.I.C.S.: 112511
Drazen Baic *(Gen Mgr)*

Polet a.d. (1)
Zeleznicka 13, 23272, Novi Becej, Serbia
Tel.: (381) 23 771 200
Web Site: http://www.polet.rs
Tiles Mfr
N.A.I.C.S.: 327120

Polet keramika d.o.o. (1)
Zeleznicka 13, Novi Becej, 23272, Serbia
Tel.: (381) 23 773 231
Web Site: http://www.nexe.com
Sales Range: $50-74.9 Million
Emp.: 150
Tiles Mfr
N.A.I.C.S.: 327120
Sladjana Budimlic *(Gen Mgr)*

Slavonija IGM d.o.o. (1)
Brace Radica 200, 31500, Nasice, Croatia
Tel.: (385) 31227300
Sales Range: $50-74.9 Million
Emp.: 127
Bricks Mfr
N.A.I.C.S.: 327120

Tvornica opeke Sarajevo d.o.o. (1)
Rakovicka cesta 194, 71000, Sarajevo, Bosnia & Herzegovina
Tel.: (387) 33772680
Bricks Mfr
N.A.I.C.S.: 327120

NEXE INNOVATIONS INC.

6845 Hawthrone Dr, Windsor, N8T 3B8, ON, Canada
Tel.: (604) 359-4725
Web Site:
https://nexeinnovations.com
NEXE—(TSXV)
Rev.: $110,264
Assets: $26,953,523
Liabilities: $2,136,175
Net Worth: $24,817,348
Earnings: ($4,824,283)
Emp.: 16
Fiscal Year-end: 05/31/24
Asset Management Services
N.A.I.C.S.: 523940
Kam Mangat *(VP)*

NEXEC HOLDING GMBH

Speditionstrasse 21, 40221, Dusseldorf, Germany
Tel.: (49) 211 542 086 418 De
Web Site: http://www.nexec.de
Year Founded: 1979
Ecommerce Services
N.A.I.C.S.: 551112
Valentin Schutt *(CEO)*

NEXEN CORPORATION

2595 Kimhae-daero, 50932, Gimhae, 50932, Gyeongsangnam-do, Korea (South)
Tel.: (82) 553330771
Web Site:
https://www.nexencorp.co.kr
Year Founded: 1968
005720—(KRS)
Rev.: $2,304,029,655
Assets: $3,625,529,396
Liabilities: $1,990,911,598
Net Worth: $1,634,617,798
Earnings: $1,362,877
Emp.: 880
Fiscal Year-end: 12/31/22
Rubber Products Mfr
N.A.I.C.S.: 326299
Kang Ho Chan *(CEO)*

Subsidiaries:

Nexen Corporation - Gimhae Plant (1)
262-14 Andong Gimhae, 621-914, Kimhae, Gyeongsangnam-do, Korea (South)
Tel.: (82) 553330771
Web Site: http://www.nexencorp.co.kr
Sales Range: $200-249.9 Million
Emp.: 600
Automotive Tire Mfr
N.A.I.C.S.: 326211

Nexen Corporation - Sihwa Plant (1)
200 Hyeomnyeok-ro, Siheung, 15088, Gyeonggi-do, Korea (South)
Tel.: (82) 31 499 2751
Web Site: http://www.nexencorp.com
Sales Range: $25-49.9 Million
Emp.: 90
Tires & Tire Products Mfr
N.A.I.C.S.: 326211

Nexen Tire Corp. (1)
355 Chungnyeol-ro, Yangsan, Gyeongsangnam-do, Korea (South)
Tel.: (82) 553705114
Web Site: http://www.nexentire.com
Rev.: $1,992,224,581
Assets: $3,025,306,279
Liabilities: $1,800,996,467
Net Worth: $1,224,309,812
Earnings: ($21,096,868)
Emp.: 4,131
Fiscal Year-end: 12/31/2022
Automotive Tire Mfr
N.A.I.C.S.: 326211
Travis Kang *(CEO)*

NEXERA ENERGY, INC.

11411- 54th Street SE, Calgary, T2C 5R9, AB, Canada
Tel.: (403) 262-6000 AB
Web Site: https://nexeraenergy.com
Year Founded: 1997
NGY—(TSXV)
Rev.: $1,454,590
Assets: $2,823,754
Liabilities: $18,806,689
Net Worth: ($15,982,935)
Earnings: ($1,712,204)
Fiscal Year-end: 12/31/22
Oil & Natural Gas Exploration & Development Services
N.A.I.C.S.: 211120
Shelby D. Beattie *(CEO)*

NEXGEN ENERGY LTD.

Suite 3150 - 1021 West Hastings Street, Vancouver, V6E 0C3, BC, Canada
Tel.: (604) 428-4112 BC
Web Site:
https://www.nexgenenergy.ca
Year Founded: 2011
NXE—(NYSE)
Rev.: $2,180,214
Assets: $433,821,197
Liabilities: $77,557,586
Net Worth: $356,263,611
Earnings: $47,146,451
Emp.: 56
Fiscal Year-end: 12/31/22
Uranium Exploration & Mining
N.A.I.C.S.: 212390
Christopher W. McFadden *(Chm)*

NEXGENRX INC.

191 The West Mall Suite 905, Toronto, M9C 5L6, ON, Canada
Tel.: (416) 695-3393
Web Site: https://www.nexgenrx.com
Year Founded: 2003
NEGXF—(OTCIQ)
Rev.: $8,170,460
Assets: $22,802,068
Liabilities: $16,976,446
Net Worth: $5,825,623
Earnings: ($250,676)
Fiscal Year-end: 12/31/23
Health Care Insurance Services
N.A.I.C.S.: 524114
Ronald C. Loucks *(Founder, Pres & CEO)*

Subsidiaries:

Canadian Benefit Administrators Ltd. (1)
124 Main Street South, Georgetown, L7G 3E6, ON, Canada
Tel.: (905) 873-4103
Web Site: https://www.canadianbenefits.com
Administrative Services
N.A.I.C.S.: 561110

My Benetech Inc. (1)
124 Main Street South, Georgetown, L7G 3E6, ON, Canada
Tel.: (416) 642-1355
Web Site: https://www.mybenetech.com
Administrative Services
N.A.I.C.S.: 561110

NEXGOLD MINING CORP.

The Exchange Tower 130 King Street West Suite 3680, PO Box 99, Toronto, M5X 1B1, ON, Canada
Tel.: (416) 214-4654 ON
Web Site: https://nexgold.com
Year Founded: 1997
NEXG—(TSX)
Assets: $86,934,536
Liabilities: $13,461,121
Net Worth: $73,473,416
Earnings: ($9,888,610)
Emp.: 22
Fiscal Year-end: 12/31/23
Gold Ore Exploration & Mine Development Services.
N.A.I.C.S.: 213114
Bill Fisher *(Chm)*

Subsidiaries:

Blackwolf Copper & Gold Ltd. (1)
Suite 3123 - 595 Burrard Street, Box 49139, Vancouver, V7X 1J1, BC, Canada
Tel.: (604) 343-2997
Web Site:
https://blackwolfcopperandgold.com
Rev.: $18,377
Assets: $2,232,690
Liabilities: $2,517,569
Net Worth: ($284,879)
Earnings: ($4,695,301)
Emp.: 35
Fiscal Year-end: 10/31/2022
Mineral Exploration Services
N.A.I.C.S.: 213114
Robert McLeod *(Chm)*

Subsidiary (Domestic):

Optimum Ventures Ltd. (2)
611-8th Street, Stewart, V0T 1W0, BC, Canada
Tel.: (604) 229-7565
Web Site: http://www.optimumventures.ca
Rev.: $62,387
Assets: $4,182,459
Liabilities: $474,879
Net Worth: $3,707,580
Earnings: ($1,884,734)
Fiscal Year-end: 06/30/2022
Mineral Exploration Services
N.A.I.C.S.: 213115

NEXGRAM HOLDINGS BERHAD

1-01 Level 11 Menara MBMR, 1 Jalan Syed Putra, 58000, Kuala Lumpur, Malaysia
Tel.: (60) 374934036 MY
Web Site: https://www.nexgram.co
NEXGRAM—(KLS)
Rev.: $6,565,176
Assets: $32,072,416
Liabilities: $11,933,030
Net Worth: $20,139,386
Earnings: ($4,012,503)
Fiscal Year-end: 07/31/22
Holding Company

NEXGRAM HOLDINGS BERHAD

Nexgram Holdings Berhad—(Continued)
N.A.I.C.S.: 551112
Yek Siew Lee (Mng Dir)

Subsidiaries:

Associate Partners Laboratories Sdn Bhd (1)
B02-A-16 Menara 3 KL Eco City No 3 Jalan Bangsar, 59200, Kuala Lumpur, Malaysia
Tel.: (60) 16 261 2683
Web Site: https://aplabworld.com
Testing Lab Operator Services
N.A.I.C.S.: 541380

Centrix Security Sdn. Bhd. (1)
No 11G Jalan Kuchai Maju 5 Off Jalan Kuchai Lama, 58200, Kuala Lumpur, Malaysia
Tel.: (60) 379829809
Web Site: https://www.centrixsecurity.com
Security System Product Distr
N.A.I.C.S.: 423610

Glove Alliances Sdn. Bhd. (1)
SO-28-01 Menara 1 KL Eco City No 3 Jalan Bangsar, 59200, Kuala Lumpur, Malaysia
Tel.: (60) 374934036
Web Site: https://www.glovealliance.com
Medical Glove Product Mfr & Distr
N.A.I.C.S.: 339113

Nexgram Biomedic Sdn. Bhd. (1)
SO-28-01 Menara 1 KL Eco City No 3 Jalan Bangsar, 59200, Kuala Lumpur, Malaysia
Tel.: (60) 374934036
Web Site: https://www.nexgrambiomedic.com
Pharmaceutical Product Mfr & Retailer
N.A.I.C.S.: 325412

PT NDS Global Teknologi (1)
Jl Dewi Sartika No 12B RT 4/RW 7 Cililitan, Kec Kramat Jati Jakarta, Jakarta Timur, 13640, Indonesia
Tel.: (62) 218092859
Medical Device Distr
N.A.I.C.S.: 423450
Devi Erna Rachmawati (Chm)

Sensorlink Sdn. Bhd. (1)
No 51 Jalan Kuchai Maju 1 Off Jalan Kuchai Lama, 58200, Kuala Lumpur, Malaysia
Tel.: (60) 379837270
Web Site: https://www.sensorlink.com.my
Security System Product Distr
N.A.I.C.S.: 423610

Tri-G Technologies Sdn. Bhd. (1)
6-2 Tingkat 2 Jalan PJS 8/12A Dataran Mentari, 46160, Petaling Jaya, Selangor, Malaysia
Tel.: (60) 356135722
Web Site: http://www.trigtechnologies.com
Medical Equipment Distr
N.A.I.C.S.: 423450

Vaccines Lab Sdn. Bhd. (1)
SO-28-01 Menara 1 KL Eco City No 3 Jalan Bangsar, 59200, Kuala Lumpur, Malaysia
Tel.: (60) 374934036
Web Site: https://www.vaccineslab.com
Vaccine Research & Development Services
N.A.I.C.S.: 541714

NEXI SPA
Corso Sempione 55, 20149, Milan, Italy
Tel.: (39) 0234881   IT
Web Site: https://www.next.it
Year Founded: 1939
NEXI—(ITA)
Rev.: $6,274,077,272
Assets: $28,437,068,854
Liabilities: $28,309,023,311
Net Worth: $128,045,543
Earnings: ($1,082,194,043)
Emp.: 10,580
Fiscal Year-end: 12/31/22
Holding Company; Payment, Interbank Clearing & Securities Services
N.A.I.C.S.: 551112
Giuseppe Capponcelli (Vice Chm)

Subsidiaries:

Bassilichi S.p.A. (1)
24 Via Petrocchi Policarpo, 50127, Florence, Italy
Tel.: (39) 0577 578121
Web Site: http://www.bassilichi.it
Sales Range: $350-399.9 Million
Emp.: 1,107
Business Process Outsourcing Services
N.A.I.C.S.: 561499
Marco Bassilichi (Chm)

Subsidiary (Non-US):

TAS Eastern Europe d.o.o (2)
Bulevar Mihajla Pupina 115 Z, 11070, Belgrade, Serbia
Tel.: (381) 112697393
Web Site: https://www.tasgroup.rs
Emp.: 50
Payroll Services
N.A.I.C.S.: 541214

Help Line S.p.A. (1)
Via Sen Guglielmo Pelizzo 8-8/1, Cividale del Friuli, 33043, Udine, Italy
Tel.: (39) 0432744311
Web Site: https://www.helpline.it
Customer Care Services
N.A.I.C.S.: 541613
Andrea Stedile (Chm)

Nexi Payments S.p.A. (1)
Corso Sempione 55, 20145, Milan, Italy
Tel.: (39) 0234881
Web Site: http://www.cartasi.it
Electronic Payment Services
N.A.I.C.S.: 522320
Antonio Patuelli (Vice Chm)

Outsourcing Applicativo e Servizi Innovativi S.p.A. (1)
Via Elio Chianesi 110/d, 00128, Rome, Italy
Tel.: (39) 06507551
Web Site: https://www.cedacri.it
Application & Administrative Outsourcing Services
N.A.I.C.S.: 522320
Alfredo Pallini (Mng Dir)

NEXIA HEALTH TECHNOLOGIES INC.
15 Allstate Parkway 6th floor, Markham, L3R5B4, ON, Canada
Tel.: (905) 415-3063
NGH.H—(TSXV)
Sales Range: Less than $1 Million
Health Care Software Applications
N.A.I.C.S.: 513210
Azmin Daya (Pres & CEO)

NEXION GROUP LTD.
Ground Floor 12 Newcastle Street, Perth, 6000, WA, Australia
Tel.: (61) 1300436110   AU
Web Site: https://www.nexiongroup.io
Year Founded: 2018
NNG—(ASX)
Rev.: $5,174,274
Assets: $2,288,278
Liabilities: $3,242,154
Net Worth: ($953,876)
Earnings: $2,270,745)
Fiscal Year-end: 06/30/23
Information Technology Services
N.A.I.C.S.: 541512
Paul Glass (CEO)

Subsidiaries:

Nexion Networks Pty. Ltd. (1)
Ground Floor 12 Newcastle Street, Perth, 6000, WA, Australia
Tel.: (61) 1300436110
Web Site: https://www.nexionnetworks.com
Telecommunication Engineering Services
N.A.I.C.S.: 541330

NEXION TECHNOLOGIES LIMITED
Unit 10-03 Novelty BizCentre 18 Howard Road, Singapore, 369585, Singapore
Web Site: https://www.nexion.com.hk
Year Founded: 2002
8420—(HKG)
Rev.: $5,434,000
Assets: $7,165,000
Liabilities: $1,718,000
Net Worth: $5,447,000
Earnings: ($1,160,000)
Emp.: 22
Fiscal Year-end: 12/31/22
Information Technology Services
N.A.I.C.S.: 541512
Edgardo Osillada Gonzales II (CTO)

NEXIS FIBERS A.S.
Chemlonska 1, 066 12, Humenne, Slovakia
Tel.: (421) 57 771 3130   Sk
Web Site: http://www.nexis-fibers.com
Year Founded: 2007
Emp.: 576
Fiber Mfr
N.A.I.C.S.: 313110
Jan Kuceravy (CEO)

NEXIS FIBERS SIA
Vishku Str 21, LV-5410, Daugavpils, Latvia
Tel.: (371) 654 02112   LV
Web Site: http://www.nexisfiber.com
Emp.: 100
Fiber Mfr
N.A.I.C.S.: 313110
Androey Veselov (Gen Mgr)

NEXITY SA
19 rue de Vienne - TSA 50029, 75801, Paris, Cedex, France
Tel.: (33) 185551000
Web Site: https://www.nexity.fr
Year Founded: 1995
NXI—(EUR)
Rev.: $4,376,102,219
Assets: $9,379,152,226
Liabilities: $7,236,701,624
Net Worth: $2,142,450,602
Earnings: $40,546,418
Emp.: 7,431
Fiscal Year-end: 12/31/23
Residential & Commercial Real Estate Developer
N.A.I.C.S.: 236116
Alain Dinin (Chm & CEO)

Subsidiaries:

Accessite SAS (1)
35 quai du Lazare, CS 90601, 13002, Marseille, Cedex, France
Tel.: (33) 491003300
Web Site: http://accessite.siteo.com
Asset Management Services
N.A.I.C.S.: 523940

Bureaux A Partacer SAS (1)
21 Place de la Republique, 75003, Paris, France
Tel.: (33) 972365822
Web Site: http://www.bureauxapartager.com
Trust Management Services
N.A.I.C.S.: 525920

Domitys SAS (1)
42 Avenue Raymond Poincare, 75116, Paris, France
Tel.: (33) 153656060
Web Site: http://www.domitys.fr
Real Estate Development Services
N.A.I.C.S.: 531390

Iselection SAS (1)
400 Promenade des Anglais, CS 23150, 06203, Nice, Cedex, France
Tel.: (33) 800003020
Web Site: https://www.iselection.com
Real Estate Rental Services
N.A.I.C.S.: 531390

L Espace SAS (1)
23 Boulevard Jules Ferry Ile-de-France, 75011, Paris, France
Tel.: (33) 149296232
Web Site: http://www.lespace-paris.fr
Implementation & Logistical Services
N.A.I.C.S.: 541614

INTERNATIONAL PUBLIC

Nexity Belgium SA (1)
Rue Basse 21-23, 1180, Brussels, Belgium
Tel.: (32) 23733835
Web Site: http://www.nexity-belgium.be
Property Rental Services
N.A.I.C.S.: 531390
Stefan Heyndrickx (Mgr-Data)

Nexity Holdinc Italia SARL (1)
C so G Ferraris 110, 10129, Turin, Italy
Tel.: (39) 0258299302
Web Site: http://www.nexity.it
Real Estate Development Services
N.A.I.C.S.: 531390

Nexity Polska SP.Z.O.O (1)
Aleje Jerozolimskie 98, 00-807, Warsaw, Poland
Tel.: (48) 222929045
Web Site: http://www.nexity.pl
Real Estate Development Services
N.A.I.C.S.: 531390

Nexity Portugal SARL (1)
Rua Carlos Alberto Mota Pinto n 9 Amoreiras Plaza Building, Piso 4 Esc 4B2, 1070-374, Lisbon, Portugal
Tel.: (351) 215893700
Web Site: http://www.nexity.pt
Property Development Services
N.A.I.C.S.: 531390
Fernando Vasco Costa (CEO & Gen Mgr)

Nexity Studea SA (1)
19 rue de Vienne-TSA 10034, 75801, Paris, Cedex, France
Tel.: (33) 185551312
Web Site: https://www.nexity-studea.com
Apartment Rental Services
N.A.I.C.S.: 531110
Gilles Karp (Deputy Mng Dir)

Primosud SAS (1)
30 rue Louis Rege, 13008, Marseille, France
Tel.: (33) 491321616
Web Site: https://www.primosud.fr
Real Estate Development Services
N.A.I.C.S.: 531390

Tereneo SAS (1)
Parc de la Haute Borne-10 rue Horus, 59650, Villeneuve d'Ascq, France
Tel.: (33) 320645467
Web Site: http://www.tereneo.com
Construction Services
N.A.I.C.S.: 236220

NEXJ SYSTEMS, INC.
10 York Mills Road Suite 700, Toronto, M2P 2G4, ON, Canada
Tel.: (416) 222-5611   Ca
Web Site: https://www.nexj.com
NXJ—(TSX)
Rev.: $11,994,699
Assets: $12,269,280
Liabilities: $8,010,547
Net Worth: $4,258,732
Earnings: ($366,107)
Emp.: 143
Fiscal Year-end: 12/31/21
Software Publisher
N.A.I.C.S.: 513210
William M. Tatham (Founder)

Subsidiaries:

NexJ Health Inc. (1)
10 York Mills Road Suite 700, Toronto, M2P 2G4, ON, Canada
Tel.: (416) 227-3700
Web Site: http://www.nexjhealth.com
Health Software Development Services
N.A.I.C.S.: 541511
Gary Baksi (Exec VP & Gen Mgr)

NEXLIVING COMMUNITIES INC.
45 Alderney Drive, Dartmouth, B2Y 2N6, NS, Canada
Tel.: (416) 876-6617   Ca
Web Site: https://nexliving.ca
Year Founded: 2011
NXLV—(TSXV)
Rev.: $13,951,269
Assets: $186,685,171

Liabilities: $130,328,271
Net Worth: $56,356,899
Earnings: ($1,664,127)
Fiscal Year-end: 12/31/23
Silver Mining
N.A.I.C.S.: 212220
T. Turner *(Chm)*

NEXOLON CO., LTD.
740-59 Sinheung Dong, Jollabukdo, Iksan, Korea (South)
Tel.: (82) 220467000
Web Site: http://www.nexolon.com
Sales Range: $125-149.9 Million
Emp.: 565
Semiconductor Devices Mfr
N.A.I.C.S.: 334413
Woo-Jeong Lee *(CEO)*

NEXON CO., LTD.
1-4-5 Roppongi, Minato-ku, Tokyo, 106-0032, Japan
Tel.: (81) 335237911
Web Site:
 https://www.company.nexon.co.jp
Year Founded: 2002
3659—(TKS)
Rev.: $2,797,198,546
Assets: $7,255,388,173
Liabilities: $1,265,464,156
Net Worth: $5,989,924,017
Earnings: $469,666,336
Emp.: 8,231
Fiscal Year-end: 12/31/23
Software Development Services
N.A.I.C.S.: 541511
Shiro Uemura *(CFO)*

Subsidiaries:

Copersons Corporation (1)
3/F 694-10 Yeoksam-Dong Gangnam-Gu, Seoul, 135-917, Korea (South)
Tel.: (82) 2 3465 9600
Web Site: http://www.copersons.com
Online Gambling Services
N.A.I.C.S.: 513210

Fantage.com Inc. (1)
400 Kelby St 15th Fl, Fort Lee, NJ 07024-2945
Tel.: (201) 944-6622
Web Site: http://www.fantage.com
Online Gambling Services
N.A.I.C.S.: 513210

Moria Japan Company Ltd. (1)
Inami Bldg 6F 3-24-2 Hongo, Bunkyo-ku, Tokyo, 112-0033, Japan
Tel.: (81) 3 5842 6761
Web Site: http://www.moriajapan.com
Medical Equipment Distr
N.A.I.C.S.: 423450

N Media Platform Co., Ltd. (1)
GBII/C - 5F 25 Pangyo-ro 256 beon-gil, Bundang-gu, Seongnam, Gyeonggi-do, Korea (South)
Tel.: (82) 16445910
Web Site: http://www.nmp-corp.com
Software Development Services
N.A.I.C.S.: 513210

NEXON Europe S.a.r.l. (1)
7 rue Guillaume Kroll, 1930, Luxembourg, Luxembourg
Tel.: (352) 26 64 96 19
Web Site: http://www.en.nexoneu.com
Sales Range: $25-49.9 Million
Emp.: 38
Online Gambling Services
N.A.I.C.S.: 513210

NXC Corporation (1)
17 Eunsu gil, Jeju, Jeju-do, Korea (South)
Tel.: (82) 647456000
Web Site: http://www.nxc.com
Game Development Services
N.A.I.C.S.: 611699
Jungju Kim *(Founder)*

Neople Inc. (1)
3198-8 1100-ro, Jeju, 690-802, Jeju-do, Korea (South)
Tel.: (82) 649031551
Web Site: https://www.neople.co.kr
Software Development Services
N.A.I.C.S.: 513210
Jeff Nam *(Dir-Mgmt Plng Dept)*

Nexon America Inc. (1)
2130 E Mariposa Ave, El Segundo, CA 90245
Tel.: (213) 858-5930
Web Site: https://www.nexon.net
Emp.: 140
Online Gambling Services
N.A.I.C.S.: 513210
Jung Soo *(Gen Mgr)*

Nexon Korea Corporation (1)
7 Pangyo-ro 256 beon-gil, Bundang-gu, Seongnam, 13487, Gyeonggi-do, Korea (South)
Tel.: (82) 15887701
Software Development Services
N.A.I.C.S.: 513210

Subsidiary (Domestic):

Nat Games Co., Ltd. (2)
5F 2621 Nanbusunhwan-ro, Gangnam-gu, Seoul, 06267, Korea (South)
Tel.: (82) 264217755
Web Site: http://www.natgames.co.kr
Software Development Services
N.A.I.C.S.: 513210
Yong Hyun Park *(CEO)*

Subsidiary (US):

Nexon M Inc. (2)
6121 Hollis St Ste 6, Emeryville, CA 94608
Tel.: (510) 969-2303
Web Site: http://www.nexonm.com
Software Development Services
N.A.I.C.S.: 513210
Alex Hart *(Office Mgr)*

Nexon Networks Corporation (1)
Building B 25 Pangyo-Ro 256 Beon-Gil, Bundang-gu, Seongnam, Gyeonggi-do, Korea (South)
Tel.: (82) 317792500
Web Site: https://www.nexon-networks.com
Software Development Services
N.A.I.C.S.: 513210

NEXON GAMES CO., LTD.
2621 Nambusunhwan-ro, Gangnam-gu, Seoul, 06267, Korea (South)
Tel.: (82) 264217777
Web Site:
 https://www.nexongames.co.kr
Year Founded: 2015
225570—(KRS)
Rev.: $101,531,568
Assets: $249,696,394
Liabilities: $67,879,973
Net Worth: $181,816,421
Earnings: $4,638,848
Emp.: 1,034
Fiscal Year-end: 12/31/22
Financial Investment Management Services
N.A.I.C.S.: 523940
Kang In Soo *(CFO)*

NEXON GT CO., LTD.
25 256-beongil Pangyo-ro, Bundang-gu, Seongnam, Gyeonggi, Korea (South)
Tel.: (82) 25256603
Web Site: http://www.nexon-gt.com
Year Founded: 1993
041140—(KRS)
Rev.: $43,014,322
Assets: $120,661,290
Liabilities: $13,409,426
Net Worth: $107,251,864
Earnings: $20,777,997
Emp.: 186
Fiscal Year-end: 12/31/22
Online Game Software Development Services
N.A.I.C.S.: 513210
Jeung Jun Kim *(CEO)*

NEXONIA, INC.
2 St Clair Avenue East Suite 750, Toronto, M4T 2T5, ON, Canada
Tel.: (416) 480-0688
Web Site: http://www.nexonia.com
Expense Report & Mobile Software Services
N.A.I.C.S.: 513210
Christine Song *(VP-HR)*

Subsidiaries:

ExpenseWatch, Inc. (1)
620 W Germantown Pike Ste 220, Plymouth Meeting, PA 19462
Web Site: http://www.expensewatch.com
Software Publisher
N.A.I.C.S.: 513210
Alan Davis *(VP-Tech Svcs)*

NEXOPTIC TECHNOLOGY CORP.
409 Granville Street Suite 1500, Vancouver, V6C 1T2, BC, Canada
Tel.: (604) 669-7330 BC
Web Site: https://www.nexoptic.com
Year Founded: 2007
NXO—(OTCIQ)
Rev.: $71
Assets: $1,914,824
Liabilities: $723,002
Net Worth: $1,191,822
Earnings: ($4,541,780)
Fiscal Year-end: 12/31/20
Investment Services
N.A.I.C.S.: 523999
Paul Tavis McKenzie *(CEO)*

Subsidiaries:

NexOptic Asia Ltd. (1)

NEXPONOR SICAFI SA
rua Tomas Ribeiro 111, 1250-228, Lisbon, Portugal
Tel.: (351) 213103620
ALNOR—(EUR)
Sales Range: $1-9.9 Million
Real Estate Support Services
N.A.I.C.S.: 531390
Joaquim Meirelles *(CEO)*

NEXSTIM PLC
Elimaenkatu 9 B, 00510, Helsinki, Finland
Tel.: (358) 92727170
Web Site: https://www.nexstim.com
NXTMH—(HEL)
Rev.: $10,281,347
Assets: $11,023,857
Liabilities: $6,632,683
Net Worth: $4,391,174
Earnings: $1,410,344
Emp.: 39
Fiscal Year-end: 12/31/22
Medical Device Mfr
N.A.I.C.S.: 339112
Henri Hannula *(VP-Intl-Sls)*

Subsidiaries:

Nexstim Germany GmbH (1)
Lyoner Str 15, 60528, Frankfurt, Germany
Tel.: (49) 6966554149
Electro Medical Mfr
N.A.I.C.S.: 334510

Nexstim, Inc. (1)
1360 Union Hill Rd Ste 5B, Alpharetta, GA 30004-8491
Tel.: (770) 664-1000
Web Site: http://www.nexstim.com
Medical Device Mfr
N.A.I.C.S.: 339112

NEXT 15 GROUP PLC
60 Great Portland Street, London, W1W 7RT, United Kingdom
Tel.: (44) 2031288000 UK
Web Site: https://www.next15.com
Year Founded: 1981
NFG—(AIM)
Rev.: $638,203,075
Assets: $603,856,832
Liabilities: $520,412,718
Net Worth: $83,444,113
Earnings: ($89,153,326)
Emp.: 2,983
Fiscal Year-end: 01/31/22
Offices of Other Holding Companies
N.A.I.C.S.: 551112
Tim Dyson *(CEO)*

Subsidiaries:

463 Communications, LLC (1)
77 Maiden Ln Fl 3, San Francisco, CA 94104
Tel.: (415) 609-7155
Web Site: http://www.463.com
Emp.: 20
Public Relations Consulting Services
N.A.I.C.S.: 541820
Tom Galvin *(Co-Partner)*

Activate Marketing Services, LLC (1)
100 Montgomery St Ste 1101, San Francisco, CA 94104
Tel.: (888) 500-9689
Web Site: https://www.activatems.com
Advertising Services
N.A.I.C.S.: 541810
Ed Grossman *(Co-Founder & CEO)*

Subsidiary (Domestic):

Green Leads, LLC (2)
59 Colby Corner #122, East Hampstead, NH 03826
Tel.: (978) 633-3233
Web Site: http://www.green-leads.com
Professional, Scientific & Technical Services
N.A.I.C.S.: 541990
Linda J. Flanagan *(Mgr)*

Agent3 Limited (1)
75 Bermondsey Street, London, SE1 3XF, United Kingdom
Tel.: (44) 207 127 0706
Web Site: https://www.agent3.com
Marketing Services
N.A.I.C.S.: 541613
Paul Mackender *(Chief Revenue Officer)*

Archetype Agency AB (1)
Ferkens Grand 1, 111 30, Stockholm, Sweden
Tel.: (46) 70 716 3599
Marketing Services
N.A.I.C.S.: 541613

Archetype Agency Beijing Limited (1)
Room 1703-1705 Tower2 Guanghualu Soho No 22 Guanghua Road, Chaoyang District, Beijing, 10020, China
Tel.: (86) 105 900 6010
Marketing Services
N.A.I.C.S.: 541613

Archetype Agency GmbH (1)
Nymphenburger Strasse 168, 80634, Munich, Germany
Tel.: (49) 89 998 3700
Marketing Services
N.A.I.C.S.: 541613

Archetype Agency Limited (1)
Unit 1102-1103 11th Floor 299 QRC 287 - 299 Queens Road, Central, China (Hong Kong)
Tel.: (852) 2 534 8700
Marketing Services
N.A.I.C.S.: 541613

Archetype Agency Limited (1)
100 Union Street, London, SE1 0NL, United Kingdom
Tel.: (44) 208 846 0700
Marketing Services
N.A.I.C.S.: 541613

Archetype Agency Private Limited (1)
2nd Floor TDI Centre Plot No 7, Jasola, New Delhi, 110025, India
Tel.: (91) 114 061 2000
Marketing Services
N.A.I.C.S.: 541613

Archetype Agency Pte Limited (1)

NEXT 15 GROUP PLC

Next 15 Group plc—(Continued)

36 Prinsep Street 05-01/02, Singapore, 188648, Singapore
Tel.: (65) 6 603 9000
Marketing Services
N.A.I.C.S.: 541613

Archetype Agency Pty Limited (1)
Level 3 10-14 Waterloo Street, Surry Hills, Sydney, 2010, NSW, Australia
Tel.: (61) 29 956 5733
Marketing Services
N.A.I.C.S.: 541613

Archetype Agency S.L.
Gran Via 27 8 Derecha, 28013, Madrid, Spain
Tel.: (34) 65 045 2276
Marketing Services
N.A.I.C.S.: 541613

Archetype Agency SARL (1)
4-6 Boulevard Montmartre, 75009, Paris, France
Tel.: (33) 15 699 7130
Marketing Services
N.A.I.C.S.: 541613

Archetype Agency SRL (1)
8 Piazzale Principessa Clotilde, 20121, Milan, Italy
Tel.: (39) 0220 2021
Marketing Services
N.A.I.C.S.: 541613

Archetype Agency Sdn. Bhd. (1)
BO3-B-12-1 Menara 3A No 3 Jalan Bangsar KL Eco City, 59200, Kuala Lumpur, Malaysia
Tel.: (60) 39 212 3950
Marketing Services
N.A.I.C.S.: 541613

Beyond Corporation Limited (1)
75 Bermondsey Street, London, SE1 3XF, United Kingdom
Tel.: (44) 20 7908 6555
Web Site: http://bynd.com
Sales Range: $25-49.9 Million
Emp.: 25
Mobile Software Development Services
N.A.I.C.S.: 541511
Charlie Lyons (Gen Mgr)

Bite Communications Group Limited (1)
60 Great Portland Street, London, W1W 7RT, United Kingdom
Tel.: (44) 2087411123
Sales Range: $25-49.9 Million
Emp.: 5
Holding Company; Public Relations Agencies
N.A.I.C.S.: 551112
Andy Cunningham (Gen Mgr)

Subsidiary (Domestic):

Bite Communications Ltd. (2)
60 Great Portland Street, London, W1W 7RT, United Kingdom
Tel.: (44) 2087411123
Sales Range: $10-24.9 Million
Public Relations Agency
N.A.I.C.S.: 541820
Louise Waller (Assoc Dir-PR)

Branch (Non-US):

Bite Communications Ltd., UK filial (3)
Kungsatan 17, 111 43, Stockholm, Sweden
Tel.: (46) 8402 0100
Web Site: http://www.bitecommunications.com
Rev.: $20,000,000
Emp.: 8
N.A.I.C.S.: 541820

Subsidiary (Non-US):

Bite Marketing Consulting Pty Limited (3)
Level 3 10-14 Waterloo Street Surry Hills, Sydney, 2010, NSW, Australia
Tel.: (61) 299565733
Marketing Consulting Services
N.A.I.C.S.: 541613

bite communications (3)
Level 3 10-14 Waterloo Street Surry Hills, Sydney, 2010, NSW, Australia
Tel.: (61) 299565733
N.A.I.C.S.: 541820

bite communications (3)
Room 1602 Bldg No15 China Central Pl 89 Jianguo Rd, Chaoyang District, Beijing, 100025, China
Tel.: (86) 10 6530 7200
Web Site: http://www.bitecommunications.com
N.A.I.C.S.: 541820

bite communications (3)
Bldg 1 Rm 304 No 508 Jiashan Road Xuhui District, Shanghai, 200040, China
Tel.: (86) 21 6289 8585
Web Site: http://www.bitecommunications.com
Sales Range: $10-24.9 Million
N.A.I.C.S.: 541820

Subsidiary (Domestic):

bullet (2)
SouthBank House Black Prince Rd, London, SE1 7SJ, United Kingdom
Tel.: (44) 2071931386
Web Site: http://www.bulletonline.com
Sales Range: $25-49.9 Million
Public Relations Agency
N.A.I.C.S.: 541820

Brandwidth Group Limited (1)
75 Bermondsey Street, London, SE1 3XF, United Kingdom
Tel.: (44) 207 509 0808
Web Site: https://brandwidth.com
Digital Marketing Consulting Services
N.A.I.C.S.: 541613

Conversion Rate Experts Limited (1)
207 Regent Street, London, W1B 3HH, United Kingdom
Tel.: (44) 203 368 6212
Web Site: https://conversion-rate-experts.com
Digital Marketing Consulting Services
N.A.I.C.S.: 541613

Elvis Communications Limited (1)
172 Drury Lane, London, WC2B 5QR, United Kingdom
Tel.: (44) 20 3150 2100
Web Site: http://www.eliscommunications.com
Advertising Services, Brand Strategy & Content
N.A.I.C.S.: 541810
Tanya Brookefield (CEO)

Encore Digital Media Limited (1)
75 Bermondsey Street, London, SE1 3XF, United Kingdom
Tel.: (44) 207 908 6444
Web Site: https://www.encoredigitalmedia.net
Digital Marketing Consulting Services
N.A.I.C.S.: 541613
Russell Kearney (Chief Revenue Officer)

M. Booth & Associates (1)
666 3 Ave 7th Fl, New York, NY 10017
Tel.: (212) 481-7000
Web Site: https://www.mbooth.com
N.A.I.C.S.: 541810
Margaret Booth (Chm)

Mach49 LLC (1)
900 Veterans Blvd 6th Fl, Redwood City, CA 94063
Tel.: (650) 549-4903
Web Site: https://www.mach49.com
Management Consulting Services
N.A.I.C.S.: 541611
Linda Yates (CEO)

Mach49 Singapore Pte Ltd (1)
Mova Building 22 Jln Kilang, Singapore, 159419, Singapore
Tel.: (65) 6 692 9029
Management Consulting Services
N.A.I.C.S.: 541611

Next Fifteen Communications Hong Kong Limited (1)
Flat 12A 46 Lyndhurst Terrace, Central, China (Hong Kong)
Tel.: (852) 28218600

Sales Range: $25-49.9 Million
Emp.: 10
Investor & Media Relations Consulting Services
N.A.I.C.S.: 561499

ODD London Limited (1)
75 Bermondsey Street, London, SE1 3XF, United Kingdom
Tel.: (44) 207 490 7900
Web Site: https://www.oddlondon.com
Marketing Services
N.A.I.C.S.: 541613

Palladium Group Limited (1)
75 Bermondsey Street, London, SE1 3XF, United Kingdom
Tel.: (44) 203 882 8567
Web Site: https://palladiumdigital.co.uk
Digital Marketing Consulting Services
N.A.I.C.S.: 541613
James Prebble (Co-Founder)

Planning-inc Limited (1)
90 Union Street, London, SE1 0NW, United Kingdom
Tel.: (44) 203 998 7310
Web Site: https://www.planning-inc.co.uk
Marketing Services
N.A.I.C.S.: 541613

Publitek Limited (1)
75 Bermondsey Street, London, SE1 3XF, United Kingdom
Tel.: (44) 158 239 0980
Web Site: https://www.publitek.com
Marketing & Advertising Services
N.A.I.C.S.: 541613
Simon Krelle (Mng Dir)

Savanta Group Limited (1)
54 Bermondsey Street, London, SE1 3UD, United Kingdom
Tel.: (44) 2076323434
Web Site: http://savanta.com
Business Support Services
N.A.I.C.S.: 561499
Roger Perowne (CEO)

Subsidiary (US):

M.S.I. International East, Inc. (2)
650 Park Ave, King of Prussia, PA 19406
Tel.: (610) 265-2000
Web Site: http://www.msimsi.com
Rev.: $5,500,000
Emp.: 60
Marketing Research & Public Opinion Polling
N.A.I.C.S.: 541910
Dianne M. Vickery (VP & Grp Mgr)

Story Worldwide, LLC (1)
48 W 25th St, New York, NY 10010
Tel.: (212) 481-3452
Web Site: http://www.storyworldwide.com
Advetising Agency
N.A.I.C.S.: 541810
Simon Kelly (CEO)

Branch (Non-US):

Story Worldwide, LLC - London (2)
75 Bermondsey Street, London, SE1 3XF, United Kingdom
Tel.: (44) 207 908 6425
Web Site: http://www.storyworldwide.co.uk
Advetising Agency
N.A.I.C.S.: 541810
Stephen Woodford (Chm)

Text 100 Limited (1)
6th Floor 110 High Holborn, London, WC1V 6JS, United Kingdom
Tel.: (44) 20 8846 0700
Emp.: 80
Public Relations Consulting Services
N.A.I.C.S.: 541820
Lewis Webb (Dir-Digital)

Subsidiary (Non-US):

Beijing Text 100 Consulting Services Limited (2)
Room 1702 Tower C Grand Pacific Building 8A Guangua Road, Beijing, 100026, China
Tel.: (86) 10 6583 2131
Public Relations Services
N.A.I.C.S.: 541820

Text 100 (Pty) Limited (2)

INTERNATIONAL PUBLIC

2nd Fl Block A Sandton Close 2 Cnr St 5 and Norwich Close, Sandton, 2196, Gauteng, South Africa
Tel.: (27) 11 775 5700
Sales Range: $25-49.9 Million
Emp.: 1
Public Relations Consulting Services
N.A.I.C.S.: 541820

Text 100 AB (2)
Vastmannagatan 4, Stockholm, 111 24, Sweden
Tel.: (46) 8 54 55 14 50
Public Relations Consulting Services
N.A.I.C.S.: 541820

Text 100 Hong Kong (2)
26th Floor 46 Lyndhurst Terrace, Central, China (Hong Kong)
Tel.: (852) 2973 0222
Web Site: http://www.text100.com
Public Relations & Marketing Agency
N.A.I.C.S.: 541820

Text 100 Italy Srl (2)
Via Scarlatti 12, Milan, 20124, Italy
Tel.: (39) 02 202 0211
Web Site: http://www.text100.com
Emp.: 50
Public Relations Consulting Services
N.A.I.C.S.: 541820

Text 100 Pty Limited (2)
Level 6 77 Berry Street, North Sydney, 2060, NSW, Australia
Tel.: (61) 2 9956 5733
Emp.: 2
Public Relations Consulting Services
N.A.I.C.S.: 541820
Katie Perich (Gen Mgr)

Text 100 Public Relations (2)
100 Montgomery St Ste 1101, San Francisco, CA 94103
Tel.: (415) 593-8400
Web Site: http://www.text100.com
Rev.: $50,000,000
Emp.: 55
High Technology, Public Relations
N.A.I.C.S.: 541820

Branch (Non-US):

Text 100 Amsterdam BV (3)
Herengracht 478, 1017 BR, Amsterdam, Netherlands
Tel.: (31) 20 530 43 33
Web Site: http://www.text100.nl
Emp.: 10
N.A.I.C.S.: 541820

Text 100 Beijing (3)
Unit 1023 Tower B Hanwei Plz, No 7 Guanghua Rd, Beijing, 100004, China
Tel.: (86) 10 6583 2131
Web Site: http://www.text100.com
Emp.: 15
N.A.I.C.S.: 541810
Laure Garboua (Gen Mgr)

Branch (Domestic):

Text 100 Boston Corp. (3)
31 Milk St Ste 201, Boston, MA 02109
Tel.: (617) 723-1044
Web Site: http://www.text100.com
Sales Range: $10-24.9 Million
Emp.: 15
N.A.I.C.S.: 541820

Branch (Non-US):

Text 100 Copenhagen (3)
Havnegade 39, DK-1058, Copenhagen, Denmark
Tel.: (45) 333 65 333
N.A.I.C.S.: 541820

Text 100 France (3)
17, rue de la Banque, 75002, Paris, France
Tel.: (33) 1 56 99 71 30
Web Site: http://www.text100.com
Emp.: 18
N.A.I.C.S.: 541820
Cecile Missildine (Dir-EMEA)

Text 100 Helsinki (3)
Toolonkatu 3 A 4th floor, 00100, Helsinki, Finland
Tel.: (358) 9 856 196 00

AND PRIVATE COMPANIES

N.A.I.C.S.: 541810
Markku Vansa *(Mng Dir)*

Text 100 Hong Kong (3)
Ste 3805 Level 38 Hopewell Center, 183 Queens Rd E, Wanchai, China (Hong Kong)
Tel.: (852) 2821 8694
Web Site: http://www.text100.com
Sales Range: $10-24.9 Million
Emp.: 7
N.A.I.C.S.: 541820
Jeremy Woolf *(Sr VP)*

Text 100 India Pvt. Ltd. (3)
2nd Fl TDI Centre Plot No.7, near Appolo Hospital, Jasola, New Delhi, 110 025, India
Tel.: (91) 11 406 12000
Web Site: http://www.text100.com
N.A.I.C.S.: 541820
Nibha Bhandari *(Gen Mgr)*

Text 100 India-Bangalore (3)
2nd Floor Lakeview Manor (near RBI Qtrs) 20 Annaswamy Mudaliar Street, Ulsoor, Bengaluru, 560042, India
Tel.: (91) 80 255 48808 11
Web Site: http://www.text100.com
Emp.: 15
N.A.I.C.S.: 541820

Text 100 Japan K.K. (3)
Soteira Building 10 Ichiban-cho Chiyoda-ku, Tokyo, 100-0082, Japan
Tel.: (81) 3 5210 1981
Web Site: http://www.text100.com
Emp.: 7
N.A.I.C.S.: 541820
Tomoko Akizawa *(Mng Dir)*

Text 100 Johannesburg Pty. Ltd. (3)
Block 8 1st Floor Bentley Office Park, PO Box 2370, Corner Bevan and Wessels Rd, Rivonia, 2196, South Africa
Tel.: (27) 11 803 2800
Web Site: http://www.text100.com
Emp.: 12
N.A.I.C.S.: 541820
Dominick Pienaar *(Gen Mgr)*

Text 100 London Ltd. (3)
Level 5 The Triangle, 5-17 Hammersmith Grove, London, W6 0LG, United Kingdom
Tel.: (44) 20 8846 0700
Web Site: http://www.text100.com
Emp.: 44
N.A.I.C.S.: 541820

Text 100 Madrid S.L. (3)
Plaza de Colon n2 Torre 1, Planta 17, 28046, Madrid, Spain
Tel.: (34) 91 561 94 15
Web Site: http://www.text100.com
Emp.: 20
N.A.I.C.S.: 541820
Virginia Huerta *(Gen Mgr)*

Text 100 Milan S.R.L. (3)
Via Scarlatti 12, 20124, Milan, Italy
Tel.: (39) 02 2020 211
Web Site: http://www.text100.com
Sales Range: $10-24.9 Million
Emp.: 12
N.A.I.C.S.: 541820
Barbara Ghirimoldi *(Mng Dir)*

Text 100 Mumbai (3)
113 Mittal Chambers 11th Fl, 228, Nariman Point, Mumbai, 400 021, India
Tel.: (91) 22 6659 5519
Web Site: http://www.text100.com
Emp.: 30
N.A.I.C.S.: 541820

Text 100 Munich GmbH (3)
Nymphenburgerstrasse 168, 80634, Munich, Germany
Tel.: (49) 89 99 83 700
Web Site: http://www.text100.com
Emp.: 24
N.A.I.C.S.: 541820
Christina Pantele *(Office Mgr)*

Branch (Domestic):

Text 100 New York Corp. (3)
352 Park Ave S 7th Fl, New York, NY 10010
Tel.: (212) 529-4600
Web Site: http://www.text100.com
Sales Range: $25-49.9 Million
Emp.: 50
N.A.I.C.S.: 541820
Scott Friedman *(Dir-North America)*

Branch (Non-US):

Text 100 New Zealand (3)
70 Shortland Street, Auckland, New Zealand
Tel.: (64) 9 913 7520
Web Site: http://www.text100.com
Emp.: 4
Full-Service Public Relations
N.A.I.C.S.: 541820

Text 100 Oslo (3)
Munkedamsveien 61, 0270, Oslo, Norway
Tel.: (47) 41 600 100
Emp.: 4
N.A.I.C.S.: 541820

Branch (Domestic):

Text 100 Rochester Corp. (3)
4 Commercial St Ste 500, Rochester, NY 14614
Tel.: (585) 697-7723
Sales Range: $10-24.9 Million
Emp.: 29
N.A.I.C.S.: 541820
Erin Humphrey *(VP)*

Branch (Non-US):

Text 100 Shanghai (3)
Unit 2005 Ascenda Plz, 333 Tian Yao Qiao Rd, Shanghai, 200030, China
Tel.: (86) 21 6426 3989
Web Site: http://www.text100.com
Emp.: 10
Public Relations
N.A.I.C.S.: 541820
Michelle Yang *(Mng Dir)*

Text 100 Singapore Pvt. Ltd. (3)
20 Cross Street #03-07/08, China Square Central, Singapore, 048422, Singapore
Tel.: (65) 6603 9000
Web Site: http://www.text100.com
Sales Range: $10-24.9 Million
Emp.: 25
N.A.I.C.S.: 541820
Marc Ha *(Acct Dir)*

Text 100 Stockholm (3)
Saltmatargatan 9, 113 59, Stockholm, Sweden
Tel.: (46) 8 545 51 450
Emp.: 15
N.A.I.C.S.: 541820

Text 100 Sunny Relations (3)
5F Centra Bldg 1550-11 Seocho-Dong Seocho-Gu, Seoul, 137-070, Korea (South)
Tel.: (82) 2 587 3308
Web Site: http://www.text100.com
Emp.: 20
N.A.I.C.S.: 541820
Jay Park *(Pres)*

Text 100 Sydney (3)
Level 28 100 Miller St., NSW 2060, Sydney, Australia
Tel.: (61) 2 9956 5733
Web Site: http://www.text100.com
N.A.I.C.S.: 541820
Anne Costello *(Reg Dir)*

Subsidiary (Non-US):

Text 100 SL (2)
Brim 19 5th Floor, 28004, Madrid, Spain
Tel.: (34) 91 561 94 15
Web Site: http://www.text100.es
Sales Range: $25-49.9 Million
Emp.: 20
Public Relations Consulting Services
N.A.I.C.S.: 541820
Virginia Huerta *(Mng Dir)*

Text 100 Taipei (2)
7/F No 51 Tung-Hsin Rd, Taipei, 110, Taiwan
Tel.: (886) 2 7718 7777
Web Site: http://www.apexpr.com.tw
Public Relations Consulting Services
N.A.I.C.S.: 541820
Jimmy Chang *(Gen Mgr)*

Vox Public Relations India Private Limited (2)
III Floor Lakeview Manor 20 Annaswamy Mudaliar Street Ulsoor, Bengaluru, 560042, India
Tel.: (91) 80 42898282
Web Site: http://www.voxpr.co.in
Public Relations Consulting Services
N.A.I.C.S.: 541820
Joshy Mathews *(Mng Dir)*

Text Hundred India Private Limited (1)
2nd Floor Lakeview Manor 20 Annaswamy Mudaliar Street Ulsoor, Bengaluru, 560 042, India
Tel.: (91) 80 4089 7272
Web Site: http://www.text100.com
Emp.: 35
Public Relations Consulting Services
N.A.I.C.S.: 541820
Sayantani Roy *(Mgr)*

The Blueshirt Group LLC (1)
100 Montgomery St Ste 1600, San Francisco, CA 94104 (85%)
Tel.: (415) 217-7722
Web Site: http://www.blueshirtgroup.com
Crisis Communications, Investor Relations, Media Relations, Public Relations
N.A.I.C.S.: 541810
Chris Danne *(Co-Founder & Mng Partner)*

Branch (Domestic):

The Blueshirt Group LLC - New York (2)
250 Park Ave S 6th Fl, New York, NY 10003
Tel.: (212) 871-3927
Web Site: http://www.blueshirtgroup.com
N.A.I.C.S.: 541820
Brinlea Johnson *(Mng Dir)*

The Craft Consulting Limited (1)
Fairview Court Fairview Rd, Cheltenham, GL52 2EX, United Kingdom
Tel.: (44) 755 509 3903
Management Consulting Services
N.A.I.C.S.: 541611
Mark Wiseman-Smith *(Dir)*

The OutCast Agency (1)
100 Montgomery St, San Francisco, CA 94107
Tel.: (415) 392-8282
Web Site: http://www.theoutcastagency.com
Sales Range: $25-49.9 Million
Emp.: 70
Public Relations Consulting Services
N.A.I.C.S.: 541820
Amy Swanson *(Partner-New York)*

The OutCast Agency LLC (1)
100 Montgomery St Ste 1201, San Francisco, CA 94104
Tel.: (415) 392-8282
Web Site: http://www.thisisoutcast.com
Sales Range: $10-24.9 Million
Emp.: 70
Public Relations Agency
N.A.I.C.S.: 541820
Caryn Marooney *(CEO & Partner)*

Branch (Domestic):

The OutCast Agency LLC - New York (2)
666 3rd Ave 7th Fl, New York, NY 10172
Tel.: (646) 737-9921
Web Site: http://www.outcastpr.com
Sales Range: $10-24.9 Million
Public Relations Agency; Communications & Marketing Agency
N.A.I.C.S.: 541820
Angela D'Arcy *(VP)*

Upstream Asia (China) Consulting Ltd (1)
Room 801 11th Floor Beijing Inn Building 5 East Shuijing Hutong, Dong Cheng District, Beijing, 100010, China
Tel.: (86) 10 6530 7200
Public Relations Services
N.A.I.C.S.: 541820

Velocity Partners Limited (1)
The Poppy Factory 20 Petersham Road, Richmond, TW10 6UR, Surrey, United Kingdom

NEXT CAPITAL PTY LIMITED

Tel.: (44) 208 940 4099
Web Site: https://velocitypartners.com
Marketing Services
N.A.I.C.S.: 541613
Stan Woods *(Mng Dir)*

Velocity Partners US Inc. (1)
666 3rd Ave, New York, NY 10017
Tel.: (347) 708-1720
Marketing & Advertising Services
N.A.I.C.S.: 541613

NEXT BIOMETRICS GROUP ASA

Apotekergata 10B, 0180, Oslo, Norway
Tel.: (47) 22700095
Web Site:
    https://www.nextbiometrics.com
Year Founded: 2000
0QWK—(LSE)
Rev.: $4,295,954
Assets: $11,255,311
Liabilities: $2,387,770
Net Worth: $8,867,541
Earnings: ($4,279,789)
Emp.: 27
Fiscal Year-end: 12/31/22
Biometric Sensor Devices Specializing in Fingerprint Authentication
N.A.I.C.S.: 541519
Petter Fjellstad *(Chm)*

Subsidiaries:

NEXT Biometrics China Ltd. (1)
Room 231 No 635 Bibo Road, Zhangjiang Hi-Tech Park, Shanghai, 201203, China
Tel.: (86) 2158370310
Fingerprint Sensor Services
N.A.I.C.S.: 561611

NEXT Biometrics Inc. (1)
12011 Bel-Red Rd Ste 201, Bellevue, WA 98005
Tel.: (425) 406-7055
Fingerprint Sensor Services
N.A.I.C.S.: 561611
Tian Xiao *(Dir-Sensor & Thin Film Tech)*

NEXT Biometrics Taiwan Ltd. (1)
10F No 87 Zhengzhou Rd, Datong Dist, Taipei, 103607, Taiwan
Tel.: (886) 225580698
Fingerprint Sensor Services
N.A.I.C.S.: 561611

NEXT Biometrics s.r.o. (1)
Na Porici 1047/26, 110 00, Prague, Czech Republic
Tel.: (420) 4067055
Fingerprint Sensor Services
N.A.I.C.S.: 561611

NEXT CAPITAL LIMITED

2nd Floor Imperial Court Building Dr Ziauddin Ahmed Road, Karachi, 75530, Pakistan
Tel.: (92) 21111639825   PK
Web Site:
    https://www.nextcapital.com.pk
Year Founded: 2009
NEXT—(PSX)
Rev.: $428,834
Assets: $2,938,506
Liabilities: $1,398,606
Net Worth: $1,539,899
Earnings: ($349,727)
Emp.: 67
Fiscal Year-end: 06/30/23
Finance Advisory Services
N.A.I.C.S.: 523940
Muhammad Najam Ali *(CEO)*

NEXT CAPITAL PTY LIMITED

Level 30/31 25 Bligh Street, GPO Box 4076, Sydney, 2000, NSW, Australia
Tel.: (61) 28222555
Web Site:
    http://www.nextcapital.com.au
Year Founded: 2005

NEXT CAPITAL PTY LIMITED

Next Capital Pty Limited—(Continued)
Investment Services
N.A.I.C.S.: 523940
Sandy Lockhart *(Founding Partner)*
Subsidiaries:

Alloggio Group Limited (1)
Level 40 2-26 Park Street, Sydney, 2000, NSW, Australia
Tel.: (61) 240479987
Web Site: http://www.alloggio.com.au
Rev.: $21,326,747
Assets: $71,001,201
Liabilities: $54,715,713
Net Worth: $16,285,489
Earnings: $1,540,563
Fiscal Year-end: 06/30/2022
Hotel Operator
N.A.I.C.S.: 721110
Michael Potts *(CFO)*

New Zealand Bus Limited (1)
2-12 Allen Street, Wellington, 6011, New Zealand
Tel.: (64) 4 802 4100
Web Site: http://www.nzbus.co.nz
Sales Range: $450-499.9 Million
Emp.: 25
Bus Charter Services
N.A.I.C.S.: 485510
Zane Fulljames *(CEO)*

NEXT DIGITAL LIMITED

1/F 8 Chun Ying Street Tseung Kwan O Industrial Estate, Tseung Kwan O, Hong Kong, New Territories, China (Hong Kong)
Tel.: (852) 2744 2733
Web Site: http://www.nextdigital.com.hk
Rev.: $166,542,875
Assets: $269,732,867
Liabilities: $142,712,601
Net Worth: $127,020,266
Earnings: ($43,438,223)
Emp.: 2,539
Fiscal Year-end: 03/31/19
Newspaper Publishing Services
N.A.I.C.S.: 513110
Subsidiaries:

Eat & Travel Weekly Company Limited (1)
1/F 8 Chun Ying Street Tseung Kwan O Industrial Estate, Tseung Kwan O, New Territories, China (Hong Kong)
Tel.: (852) 29907748
Web Site: http://www.etw.nextdigital.com.hk
Periodical Publishing Services
N.A.I.C.S.: 513120

Paramount Printing Company Limited (1)
3 Chun Kwong Street T K O Industrial Estate West, Tseung Kwan O, New Territories, China (Hong Kong)
Tel.: (852) 28968688
Web Site: http://www.paramount.com.hk
Newspaper Publishing Services
N.A.I.C.S.: 513110

NEXT EDGE CAPITAL CORP.

1 Toronto Street Suite 200, Toronto, M5C 2V6, ON, Canada
Tel.: (416) 775-3600
Web Site: http://www.nextedgecapital.com
Year Founded: 2006
Investment Management Service
N.A.I.C.S.: 523940
Richard Goode *(Exec VP)*

NEXT ENTERTAINMENT WORLD CO., LTD.

5 Hakdong-Ro 9-Gil, Gangnam-gu, Seoul, Korea (South)
Tel.: (82) 234909300
Web Site: https://www.its-new.co.kr
160550—(KRS)
Rev.: $119,358,323
Assets: $255,348,738
Liabilities: $130,519,331
Net Worth: $124,829,407
Earnings: ($16,197,490)
Emp.: 43
Fiscal Year-end: 12/31/22
Film & Music Distr; Other Related Media Services
N.A.I.C.S.: 512120

NEXT GAMES

Aleksanterinkatu 9A, 00100, Helsinki, Finland
Tel.: (358) 447585754
Web Site: http://www.nextgames.com
6NG—(BER)
Rev.: $38,860,262
Assets: $38,793,070
Liabilities: $13,218,827
Net Worth: $25,574,243
Earnings: ($9,288,119)
Emp.: 107
Fiscal Year-end: 12/31/19
Software Development Services
N.A.I.C.S.: 513210
Teemu Huuhtanen *(CEO)*

NEXT GEN WATER CORP. LTD.

FT B 33/F Blk 1 Victoria Ctr, 15 Watson Road, North Point, China (Hong Kong)
Tel.: (852) 25702177 NV
Web Site: http://www.nextgenwater.net
Year Founded: 2014
Water Harvester Machinery Mfr & Distr
N.A.I.C.S.: 333310
Tom Moore *(Pres & CEO)*

NEXT MEDIAWORKS LTD.

Unit 701 A Tower - 2 Indiabulls Finance Centre Senapti Bapat Marg, Elphinstone Road, Mumbai, 400 018, India
Tel.: (91) 2244104104
Web Site: https://www.nextmediaworks.com
Year Founded: 1981
NEXTMEDIA—(NSE)
Rev.: $4,125,030
Assets: $13,753,740
Liabilities: $24,830,715
Net Worth: ($11,076,975)
Earnings: ($4,197,375)
Emp.: 2
Fiscal Year-end: 03/31/22
Newspaper Publishing Services
N.A.I.C.S.: 513110
Diksha Singh *(Compliance Officer & Sec)*

NEXT PLC

Desford Road Enderby, Leicester, LE19 4AT, United Kingdom
Tel.: (44) 3337774577
Web Site: http://www.nextplc.co.uk
NXT—(LSE)
Rev.: $6,931,330,472
Assets: $5,963,519,313
Liabilities: $3,894,849,785
Net Worth: $2,068,669,528
Earnings: $1,010,477,152
Emp.: 31,947
Fiscal Year-end: 01/27/24
Clothing, Furniture & Housewares Retailer, Catalog Sales & E-Commerce
N.A.I.C.S.: 458110
Seonna Anderson *(Sec)*
Subsidiaries:

Lipsy Limited (1)
43-44 Berners Street, London, W1T 3ND, United Kingdom
Tel.: (44) 2074 362010
Web Site: http://www.lipsy.co.uk
Apparel Retailer
N.A.I.C.S.: 458110
Nicole Baron *(Mgr-Sls-Wholesale)*

Next Retail Limited (1)
Desford Road, Enderby, Leicester, LE19 4AT, United Kingdom
Tel.: (44) 333 777 4577
Web Site: https://www.next.co.uk
Home Product Distr
N.A.I.C.S.: 449129

Next Sourcing Services Limited (1)
House 217 Road 2 New/10 Old Mirpur DOHS, Mirpur, Dhaka, 1216, Bangladesh
Tel.: (880) 2 808 0973
Web Site: https://nextsourcingbd.com
Fashion Brand Distr
N.A.I.C.S.: 458110

Ventura Group Limited (1)
Room 277 CEME Marsh Way, Rainham, RM13 8EU, Essex, United Kingdom
Tel.: (44) 208 596 5125
Web Site: https://venturagroup.co.uk
Human Resouce Services
N.A.I.C.S.: 541612

NEXT TECHNOLOGY HOLDING INC.

No 1 Gaobei South Coast Yi An Men 111 Block 37, Chao Yang District, Beijing, China
Tel.: (86) 18350283270 WY
Web Site: http://www.wetradegroup.net
Year Founded: 2019
NXTT—(NASDAQ)
Rev.: $11,671,335
Assets: $46,229,241
Liabilities: $4,509,731
Net Worth: $41,719,510
Earnings: ($9,147,415)
Emp.: 35
Fiscal Year-end: 12/31/22
Online Information Services
N.A.I.C.S.: 519290
Zheng Dai *(Founder & Chm)*

NEXTAGE CO., LTD.

Shinyoung-cho, 1-1 Meiji Yasuda Life Insurance Nagoya Building 14F, Naka-ku, Nagoya, 460-0004, Aichi, Japan
Tel.: (81) 522288541
Web Site: http://www.nextage.jp
3186—(TKS)
Rev.: $3,285,959,760
Assets: $1,258,453,730
Liabilities: $786,940,370
Net Worth: $471,513,360
Earnings: $81,932,040
Emp.: 6,920
Fiscal Year-end: 11/30/23
Used Car Dealers
N.A.I.C.S.: 441120
Seiji Hirota *(Pres & CEO)*

NEXTAGE THERAPEUTICS LTD.

13B Einstein St Weizmann Science Par, Ness Ziona, 6158101, Israel
Tel.: (972) 732244440
Web Site: https://www.nextar.co.il
Year Founded: 1982
NXTG—(TAE)
Rev.: $242,022
Assets: $302,528
Liabilities: $1,058,710
Net Worth: ($756,182)
Earnings: ($1,161,210)
Fiscal Year-end: 12/31/23
Pharmaceutical Preparation Manufacturing
N.A.I.C.S.: 325412
Itai Bar-Natan *(CFO)*

NEXTALARM AG

Promenadeplatz 12, 90333, Munich, Germany
Tel.: (49) 89244118416
Web Site: http://www.nextalarm.com
Year Founded: 2000
Alarm Monitoring Systems
N.A.I.C.S.: 561621
H. Alexander Elliot *(Pres & CEO)*

NEXTBILLION TECHNOLOGY PRIVATE LIMITED

Vaishnavi Tech Park 3rd & 4th Floor, Sarjapur Main Road, Bellandur, 560103, Bengaluru, India
Tel.: (91) 9108800604 In
Web Site: https://groww.in
Financial Services
N.A.I.C.S.: 523999
Subsidiaries:

Indiabulls Asset Management Company Limited (1)
Indiabulls Finance Centre Tower - 1, 11th Floor, Senapati Bapat Marg Elphinstone West, Mumbai, 400 013, India
Tel.: (91) 2261891300
Web Site: http://www.indiabullsamc.com
Financial Services
N.A.I.C.S.: 523150
Abdul Hamid Shabdi *(Head-Ops & IR)*

NEXTCOM GROUP

1 Horesh Halonim St Ramat Ishay Industrial Park, Kefar Yehoshua, 36582, Israel
Tel.: (972) 732320200
Web Site: https://nextcomgroup.com
Year Founded: 1992
NXTM—(TAE)
Rev.: $119,411,366
Assets: $91,488,802
Liabilities: $60,817,201
Net Worth: $30,671,601
Earnings: $1,968,982
Emp.: 386
Fiscal Year-end: 12/31/22
Communications Infrastructure Construction Services
N.A.I.C.S.: 237130
Moshe Gur *(VP-Technical Svcs)*

NEXTDC LIMITED

20 Wharf Street, Brisbane, 4000, QLD, Australia
Tel.: (61) 731774777
Web Site: https://www.nextdc.com
NXT—(ASX)
Rev.: $292,525,373
Assets: $3,483,371,380
Liabilities: $1,101,493,719
Net Worth: $2,381,877,661
Earnings: ($29,477,831)
Emp.: 180
Fiscal Year-end: 06/30/24
Data Center Facilities Owner & Operator
N.A.I.C.S.: 541513
Craig Scroggie *(CEO, CEO, Mng Dir & Mng Dir)*
Subsidiaries:

Asia Pacific Data Centre (1)
Level 13 135 King St, Sydney, 2000, NSW, Australia (98.6%)
Tel.: (61) 289737684
Web Site: http://www.asiapacificdc.com
Rev.: $48,424,722
Assets: $208,496,977
Liabilities: $26,969,832
Net Worth: $181,527,145
Earnings: $41,642,263
Fiscal Year-end: 06/30/2018
Data Center Real Estate Investment Services
N.A.I.C.S.: 523999
Vishant Narayan *(CEO)*

NEXTECH3D.AI CORPORATION

Suite 501 121 Richmond St W, The

Studio District, Toronto, M5H 2K1, ON, Canada
Web Site: https://www.nextechar.com
NEXCF—(OTCQX)
Rev.: $2,382,205
Assets: $12,658,422
Liabilities: $2,960,040
Net Worth: $9,698,382
Earnings: ($19,234,110)
Fiscal Year-end: 12/31/22
Software Development Services
N.A.I.C.S.: 541511

Subsidiaries:

Jolokia Corporation (1)
Ste 125 877 Cedar St, Santa Cruz, CA 95060
Tel.: (408) 689-0290
Web Site: https://www.jolokia.com
Information Technology Services
N.A.I.C.S.: 541511
Pete Mastin *(CEO)*

NEXTEDIA SA
6 rue Jadin, 75017, Paris, France
Tel.: (33) 174313636 FR
Web Site: https://www.nextedia.com
Year Founded: 2000
ALNXT—(EUR)
Sales Range: $25-49.9 Million
Emp.: 20
Mobile Based Marketing Services
N.A.I.C.S.: 541613
Marc Negroni *(Chm & CEO)*

NEXTEL ITALIA SRL
Via San Massimo 13, 35030, Selvazzano Dentro, PD, Italy
Tel.: (39) 0662202455 IT
Web Site: http://www.nextel.it
Telecommunication Servicesb
N.A.I.C.S.: 517810

NEXTEL TELECOMUNICACIONES S.A.
Alcala 91, 28009, Madrid, Spain
Tel.: (34) 915773841 ES
Web Site: http://www.nextel-es.com
Telecommunication Servicesb
N.A.I.C.S.: 517810

NEXTENERGY SOLAR FUND LIMITED
Floor 2 Trafalgar Court Les Banques, Saint Peter Port, GY1 4LY, Guernsey
Tel.: (44) 2037460700
Web Site:
  https://www.nextenergysolar.com
NESF—(LSE)
Rev.: $83,343,853
Assets: $1,104,809,392
Liabilities: $253,483,969
Net Worth: $851,325,423
Earnings: $60,989,649
Emp.: 4,000
Fiscal Year-end: 03/31/23
Investment Management Service
N.A.I.C.S.: 525990

NEXTEYE CO., LTD.
65 NEXTEYE Building 13Fan Road, Dongbian District, Anyang, 430-070, Gyeonggi, Korea (South)
Tel.: (82) 313892204
Web Site: https://www.nexteye.com
Year Founded: 1998
137940—(KRS)
Rev.: $24,694,569
Assets: $99,041,324
Liabilities: $21,773,166
Net Worth: $77,268,158
Earnings: ($3,133,125)
Emp.: 117
Fiscal Year-end: 12/31/22
Machine Vision Systems Mfr
N.A.I.C.S.: 334413
Jenny Kim *(CFO)*

NEXTFERM TECHNOLOGIES
2 Haytzira Street, Yokneam, 2066728, Israel
Tel.: (972) 779988100
Web Site: https://www.nextferm.com
NXFR—(TAE)
Rev.: $283,000
Assets: $8,742,000
Liabilities: $3,739,000
Net Worth: $5,003,000
Earnings: ($4,254,000)
Fiscal Year-end: 09/30/23
Food & Beverage Services
N.A.I.C.S.: 722310
Tzafra Cohen *(Sr VP-R&D)*

Subsidiaries:

NextFerm Technologies USA Inc. (1)
830 Morris Tpke Ste 401, Short Hills, NJ 07078
Tel.: (908) 209-2338
Research Development & Technologies Services
N.A.I.C.S.: 541714

NEXTGEN BIOMED LTD.
Oppenheimer St 7, Rehovot, 7670107, Israel
Tel.: (972) 33742282
Web Site: https://www.nextgen-biomed.com
Year Founded: 1990
NXGN—(TAE)
Assets: $72,109
Liabilities: $342,589
Net Worth: ($270,479)
Earnings: ($3,923,194)
Emp.: 187
Fiscal Year-end: 12/31/23
Surgical & Medical Instrument Manufacturing
N.A.I.C.S.: 339112
Uri Zenko *(CEO)*

NEXTGEN FOOD ROBOTICS CORP.
855 Terminal Avenue, Vancouver, V6A 2M9, BC, Canada BC
Web Site: https://www.nextgenai.ca
Year Founded: 2016
NGRBF—(OTCIQ)
Food Product Machinery Mfr
N.A.I.C.S.: 333241

NEXTGEN, INC.
Shirokane-takanawa Station bldg 6F 1-27-6 Shirokane, Minatoku, Tokyo, 108-0072, Japan
Tel.: (81) 332346855
Web Site: https://www.nextgen.co.jp
Year Founded: 2001
3842—(TKS)
Rev.: $23,280,420
Assets: $21,660,970
Liabilities: $8,711,980
Net Worth: $12,948,990
Earnings: $1,097,260
Emp.: 144
Fiscal Year-end: 03/31/24
Telecommunication Network Integration Services
N.A.I.C.S.: 541519
Shinji Onishi *(Pres & CEO)*

Subsidiaries:

LignApps, Inc. (1)
1-27-6 Shirokane, Minato-ku, Tokyo, 108-0072, Japan
Tel.: (81) 357933322
Web Site: https://www.lignapps.co.jp
Network Consulting & Integration Services
N.A.I.C.S.: 541512
Shinji Onishi *(Pres)*

NextGen Business Solutions, Inc. (1)
12 Upjohn Rd Suite 6B, North York, M3B 2V9, ON, Canada
Tel.: (416) 250-0148
Web Site:
   https://www.nextgenbizsolution.com
Bookkeeping Services
N.A.I.C.S.: 541219

NEXTGENESIS HOLDINGS CORP.
3/F Asiatrust Bank Bldg 1424 Quezon Ave, Quezon City, Metro Manila, Philippines
Tel.: (63) 2924 5787 PH
Year Founded: 1960
Sales Range: $10-24.9 Million
Holding Company
N.A.I.C.S.: 551112
Elizabeth T. Miranda *(Head-Retail Banking Sector & First VP)*

NEXTGREEN GLOBAL BERHAD
Level 6-02 Menara LGB No 1 Jalan Wan Kadir, Taman Tun Dr Ismail, 6000, Kuala Lumpur, Malaysia
Tel.: (60) 377252088 MY
Web Site:
   https://nextgreenglobal.listed.com
Year Founded: 1982
NGGB—(KLS)
Rev.: $6,969,844
Assets: $83,911,568
Liabilities: $25,828,010
Net Worth: $58,083,558
Earnings: $2,653,404
Fiscal Year-end: 12/31/22
Magazines & Books Printing & Publishing Services
N.A.I.C.S.: 323113
Lim Thiam Huat *(Mng Dir)*

Subsidiaries:

BHS Book Printing Sdn Bhd (1)
Lot 4 Lorong CJ 1/1 B, Kawasan Perindustrian Cheras Jaya, 43200, Cheras, Selangor, Malaysia
Tel.: (60) 390763399
Web Site: http://www.bhsprint.com
Magazine & Book Printing Services
N.A.I.C.S.: 513120

NEXTIN INC.
23-12 Dongtansandan 9-gil, Dongtanmyeon, Hwaseong, 18487, Gyeonggi-do, Korea (South)
Tel.: (82) 316292300
Web Site: https://www.nextinsol.com
Year Founded: 2010
348210—(KRS)
Rev.: $88,161,184
Assets: $92,953,985
Liabilities: $16,531,898
Net Worth: $76,422,087
Earnings: $33,295,279
Emp.: 52
Fiscal Year-end: 12/31/22
Semiconductor Device Mfr & Distr
N.A.I.C.S.: 334413
Chang Jae-Ki *(Exec Dir)*

NEXTLEAF SOLUTIONS
3 - 68 Schooner St, Vancouver, V6B 1A4, BC, Canada
Tel.: (604) 283-2301
Web Site:
   https://www.nextleafsolutions.com
Year Founded: 2017
OILS—(CNSX)
Rev.: $7,523,159
Assets: $6,446,451
Liabilities: $3,325,043
Net Worth: $3,121,408
Earnings: $168,643
Fiscal Year-end: 09/30/23
Healthcare Services
N.A.I.C.S.: 423450
Ryan Ko *(VP)*

NEXTMUNE AB
Strandvagen 7A, 114 56, Stockholm, Sweden
Tel.: (46) 768837884
Web Site: http://www.nextmune.com
Veterinary Services
N.A.I.C.S.: 541940
Magnus Kjellberg *(CEO)*

Subsidiaries:

Spectrum Labs, Inc. (1)
2801 S 35th St, Phoenix, AZ 85281
Tel.: (480) 898-0611
Web Site: http://www.vetallergy.com
Veterinary Services
N.A.I.C.S.: 541940
Jon Levin *(CEO)*

NEXTONE, INC.
10F Yebisu Garden Place 4-20-3 Ebisu, Shibuya-ku, Tokyo, 150-6010, Japan
Tel.: (81) 354755029
Web Site: https://www.nex-tone.co.jp
Year Founded: 2000
7094—(TKS)
Rev.: $88,792,130
Assets: $87,000,820
Liabilities: $52,926,270
Net Worth: $34,074,550
Earnings: $3,509,910
Fiscal Year-end: 03/31/24
Digital Marketing Services
N.A.I.C.S.: 541870
Masahiro Anan *(Co-Pres & CEO)*

Subsidiaries:

MCJP Inc. (1)
Ebisu Prime Square Tower 20F 1-1-39, Hiroo Shibuya-ku, Tokyo, 150-0012, Japan
Tel.: (81) 357668084
Web Site: http://www.mcjp.co.jp
Music Publishers
N.A.I.C.S.: 512230

NexTone Systems Inc. (1)
8th floor Ebisu Prime Square Tower 1-1-39, Hiroo Shibuya-ku, Tokyo, 150-0012, Japan
Tel.: (81) 357668085
Web Site: https://www.nxt-sys.jp
Software Development Services
N.A.I.C.S.: 541511

NEXTRACTION ENERGY CORP.
104 2nd Street SW, Calgary, T2P 0C7, AB, Canada
Tel.: (403) 514-8005 Ca
Web Site: http://www.nextraction.com
Year Founded: 1984
Sales Range: $1-9.9 Million
Oil & Natural Gas Exploration Services
N.A.I.C.S.: 213114
Patrick Hyland *(Co-Founder & Pres)*

Subsidiaries:

Cowboy Exploration Ltd. (1)
PO Box 20373, Calgary, T2P 4J4, AB, Canada
Tel.: (403) 932-7477
Oil & Natural Gas Exploration Services
N.A.I.C.S.: 211120

NEXTRADIOTV
12 rue d'Oradour sur Glane, 75015, Paris, France
Tel.: (33) 1 71 19 11 91 FR
Web Site: http://www.nextradiotv.com
Year Founded: 2000
Sales Range: $200-249.9 Million
Emp.: 787
Radio Broadcasting Services
N.A.I.C.S.: 516110
Alain Weill *(Chm & CEO)*

NEXTRONICS ENGINEERING CORP.
2F No 31 Lane 169 Kang Ning

NEXTRONICS ENGINEERING CORP.

Nextronics Engineering Corp.—(Continued)
Street, Hsi-chih District, New Taipei City, Taiwan
Tel.: (886) 266162000
Web Site:
https://www.nextrongroup.com
8147—(TPE)
Rev.: $36,398,806
Assets: $48,810,087
Liabilities: $21,503,486
Net Worth: $27,306,600
Earnings: $3,805,053
Emp.: 480
Fiscal Year-end: 12/31/22
Electrical & Electronic Product Mfr
N.A.I.C.S.: 336320
Chi-Lin Hsu *(Chm)*

NEXTSOURCE MATERIALS INC.
Exchange Tower 130 King Street West Suite 1940, Toronto, M5X 2A2, ON, Canada
Tel.: (416) 364-4911
Web Site:
https://www.nextsourcematerial.com
Year Founded: 2004
1JWA—(DEU)
Rev.: $1,156,840
Assets: $92,848,702
Liabilities: $40,545,698
Net Worth: $52,303,004
Earnings: ($9,000,028)
Emp.: 265
Fiscal Year-end: 06/30/24
Mine Development Company
N.A.I.C.S.: 212390
Brent Nykoliation *(Exec VP)*

NEXTSTAGE AM
19 Avenue George V, 75008, Paris, France
Tel.: (33) 153934940
Web Site: http://www.nextstage.com
Privater Equity Firm
N.A.I.C.S.: 523999
Gregoire Sentilhes *(Pres)*

NEXTURE CORPORATION
Seokcheon Building 7th Floor Samsungro 570, Gangnam-gu, Seoul, Korea (South)
Tel.: (82) 216614390
Web Site: http://www.patigames.com
Year Founded: 2011
194510—(KRS)
Rev.: $57,440,514
Assets: $121,546,974
Liabilities: $70,394,093
Net Worth: $51,152,881
Earnings: $6,924,173
Emp.: 36
Fiscal Year-end: 12/31/22
Computer Games
N.A.I.C.S.: 513210

NEXTURNBIOSCIENCE CO., LTD.
121 Beon-Gil 35 Giheundanji-Ro, Giheung-Gu, Yongin, Gyeonggi-Do, Korea (South)
Tel.: (82) 312882088
Web Site: https://www.nexturn.co.kr
Year Founded: 2007
089140—(KRS)
Rev.: $22,235,667
Assets: $153,596,750
Liabilities: $70,550,602
Net Worth: $83,046,148
Earnings: ($3,595,896)
Emp.: 59
Fiscal Year-end: 12/31/22
Automatic Lathe Mfr
N.A.I.C.S.: 333517
Jungchan Lee *(Co-CEO)*

NEXTWARE LTD.
4311 Kitakubojicho, Chuo-ku, Osaka, 541-0057, Japan
Tel.: (81) 662810304
Web Site: https://www.nextware.co.jp
Year Founded: 1990
4814—(TKS)
Rev.: $18,640,200
Assets: $11,151,070
Liabilities: $2,372,990
Net Worth: $8,778,080
Earnings: ($1,064,210)
Fiscal Year-end: 03/31/24
System Development Services
N.A.I.C.S.: 541512
Takayoshi Toyoda *(Pres & CEO)*

NEXUS AG
Irmastrasse 1, 78166, Donaueschingen, Germany
Tel.: (49) 771229600
Web Site: https://careers.nexus-ag.de
NXU—(MUN)
Rev.: $266,540,450
Assets: $454,485,356
Liabilities: $172,899,158
Net Worth: $281,586,198
Earnings: $26,525,996
Emp.: 1,690
Fiscal Year-end: 12/31/23
Health Care System Software
N.A.I.C.S.: 541511
Edgar Kuner *(Member-Exec Bd)*

Subsidiaries:

ANT-Informatik AG (1)
Hertistrasse 2c, CH-8304, Wallisellen, Switzerland
Tel.: (41) 445522929
Web Site: https://www.ant-informatik.ch
Information Technology Services
N.A.I.C.S.: 541511

ANT-Informatik GmbH (1)
Wilhelmstrasse 56, D-53721, Siegburg, Germany
Tel.: (49) 22418987030
Information Technology Services
N.A.I.C.S.: 541512

Astraia Software GmbH (1)
Occamstr 20, 80802, Munich, Germany
Tel.: (49) 8912711470
Web Site: http://www.astraia.com
Health Care Srvices
N.A.I.C.S.: 621999
Uwe Hannemann *(Mng Dir)*

Creativ Software AG (1)
Unterdorfstrasse 83, Widnau, 9443, Saint Gallen, Switzerland
Tel.: (41) 717272170
Web Site: https://www.creativ.ch
Information Technology Services
N.A.I.C.S.: 541511

E&L Medical Systems GmbH (1)
Wetterkreuz 19, 91058, Erlangen, Germany
Tel.: (49) 913 181 0330
Web Site: https://de-de.eundl.de
Information Technology Services
N.A.I.C.S.: 541511
Esther Denis *(Project Mgr)*

GePaDo - Softwarelosungen fur Genetik - GmbH (1)
Wartburgstrasse 46, 01309, Dresden, Germany
Tel.: (49) 35165698550
Web Site: https://www.gepado.de
Genetic Software Services
N.A.I.C.S.: 541715

HeimSoft Solutions AG (1)
Industriestrasse 65, 3052, Zollikofen, Switzerland
Tel.: (41) 319705151
Web Site: https://www.heimsoft.ch
Emp.: 6
Software Development Services
N.A.I.C.S.: 541511

Highsystem AG (1)
Vulkanstrasse 120, 8048, Zurich, Switzerland
Tel.: (41) 438432000
Web Site: https://www.highsystem.ch
Emp.: 21
Information Technology Services
N.A.I.C.S.: 541511
Marco Denti *(Acct Mgr)*

NEXUS / CLOUD IT GmbH (1)
Irmastrasse 1, 78166, Donaueschingen, Germany
Tel.: (49) 772184820
Web Site: http://www.nexus-it.de
Information Technology Services
N.A.I.C.S.: 541512

NEXUS / E&L GmbH (1)
Hugo-Junkers-Strasse 13, 90411, Nuremberg, Germany
Tel.: (49) 9131810330
Web Site: https://de-de.eundl.de
Emp.: 110
Software Medical Documentation Services
N.A.I.C.S.: 621512

NEXUS / PASCHMANN GmbH (1)
Virchowstrasse 41, 46047, Oberhausen, Nordrhein-Westfalen, Germany
Tel.: (49) 208820770
Web Site: http://www.nexus-paschmann.de
Sales Range: $25-49.9 Million
Emp.: 30
Healthcare System Software Development Services
N.A.I.C.S.: 541511

NEXUS Digitale Dokumentationssysteme Projektentwicklungsges.mbH (1)
Gupferlingstr 29, 1170, Vienna, Austria
Tel.: (43) 13200567
Information Technology Software Solutions
N.A.I.C.S.: 541511

NEXUS France S.A.S (1)
1 place Jean-Baptiste Burlot, 03700, Bellerive-sur-Allier, France
Tel.: (33) 476957900
Web Site: https://www.nexus-france.fr
Emp.: 1,000
Information Technology Services
N.A.I.C.S.: 541511
Becard Jean-Philippe *(Mgr-Fin & Admin)*

NEXUS Nederland B.V. (1)
Lage Biezenweg 3, 4131 LV, Vianen, Netherlands
Tel.: (31) 880287100
Web Site: https://www.nexus-nederland.nl
Health Care Srvices
N.A.I.C.S.: 621999
Bernard Bresser *(Product Mgr)*

NEXUS Polska Sp. z o.o. (1)
Ul Szyperska 14, 61-754, Poznan, Poland
Tel.: (48) 616460981
Web Site: https://www.nexuspolska.pl
Emp.: 150
Information Technology Services
N.A.I.C.S.: 541511
Tomasz Walczak *(Project Mgr)*

NEXUS SISINF SL (1)
Ronda Jean Monnet 248 1 2, Sabadell, 08205, Barcelona, Spain
Tel.: (34) 937205969
Web Site: https://www.nexus-spain.es
Emp.: 1,500
Information Technology Services
N.A.I.C.S.: 541511
David Pujol Gili *(Sls Mgr)*

NEXUS Schweiz GmbH (1)
Grenzstrasse 5a, Schenkon, 6214, Lucerne, Zurich, Switzerland
Tel.: (41) 415211111
Web Site: https://www.nexus-schweiz.ch
Emp.: 250
Customized Software Development Services
N.A.I.C.S.: 541511

NEXUS Swisslab GmbH (1)
Sachsendamm 2-7, 10829, Berlin, Germany
Tel.: (49) 30626010
Web Site: https://www.nexus-swisslab.de
Information Technology Services
N.A.I.C.S.: 541511
Guido Hetmainczyk-Treetzen *(Head-Sls)*

INTERNATIONAL PUBLIC

NEXUS/ASTRAIA GmbH (1)
Adalperostrasse 80, 85737, Ismaning, Germany
Tel.: (49) 89540204700
Web Site: https://www.astraia.com
Emp.: 50
Women Healthcare Software Services
N.A.I.C.S.: 621111

NEXUS/Chili GmbH (1)
Friedrich-Ebert-Str 2, Dossenheim, 69221, Heidelberg, Germany
Tel.: (49) 62211807910
Web Site: https://www.nexus-chili.com
Information Technology Services
N.A.I.C.S.: 541511
Uwe Engelmann *(CEO & Partner)*

NEXUS/IPS GmbH (1)
Bertha-von-Suttner-Str 1, 34131, Kassel, Germany
Tel.: (49) 561942880
Digital Pathology Services
N.A.I.C.S.: 621512

NEXUS/Marabu GmbH (1)
Sachsendamm 2-7, 10829, Berlin, Germany
Tel.: (49) 30585842200
Web Site: https://www.nexus-marabu.de
Emp.: 1,500
Information Technology Services
N.A.I.C.S.: 541511
Sandra Hanke *(Mktg Mgr)*

NEXUS/Switspot GmbH (1)
Heiner Fleischmann Strasse 9, 74172, Neckarsulm, Germany
Tel.: (49) 7132488020
Web Site: http://www.switspot.com
Information Technology Services
N.A.I.C.S.: 541511

NEXUS/dis GmbH (1)
Hanauer Landstrasse 293, 60314, Frankfurt am Main, Germany
Tel.: (49) 69583004200
Web Site: https://www.nexus-frauenklinik.de
Health Care Srvices
N.A.I.C.S.: 621999

Nexus/Digital Pathology Gmbh (1)
Irmastrasse 1, 78166, Donaueschingen, Germany
Tel.: (49) 771229600
Web Site: https://www.nexus-ag.de
Emp.: 1,700
Digital Pathology Services
N.A.I.C.S.: 621512

RVC Medical IT B.V. (1)
De Brand 10-19, 3823 LH, Amersfoort, Netherlands
Tel.: (31) 332056565
Web Site: https://rvc-medical-it.com
Emp.: 65
Healthcare Software Services
N.A.I.C.S.: 621111

Sophrona Solutions Inc. (1)
7701 S Western Ave Ste 205, Oklahoma City, OK 73139
Web Site: https://sophrona.com
Eye Care Service
N.A.I.C.S.: 622310

Zwicky Electronic AG (1)
Hohgasse 25, 8598, Bottighofen, Switzerland
Tel.: (41) 716728010
Web Site: https://www.zwicky-ag.ch
Emp.: 1,000
Information Technology Services
N.A.I.C.S.: 541512

ifa systems AG (1)
Augustinusstrasse 11 b, 50226, Frechen, Germany (52.6%)
Tel.: (49) 2234933670
Web Site: https://ifasystems.de
Sales Range: $10-24.9 Million
IT Solutions For Eye Care Specialists
N.A.I.C.S.: 541512
Jorg Polis *(CEO)*

Subsidiary (US):

Inoveon Corp. (2)
800 Research Pkwy Ste 370, Oklahoma City, OK 73104
Tel.: (405) 271-9025
Web Site: https://www.inoveon.com

Emp.: 16
Eye Care System
N.A.I.C.S.: 339112
Carsten Becker *(CFO)*

ifa united i-tech, Inc. (2)
6750 N Andrews Ave Ste 200, Fort Lauderdale, FL 33309
Web Site: https://ifasystems.info
Health IT for Eye Care
N.A.I.C.S.: 541519

oneICT AG (1)
Hertistrasse 2C, CH-8304, Wallisellen, Switzerland
Tel.: (41) 442005555
Web Site: https://www.oneict.ch
Information Technology Consulting Services
N.A.I.C.S.: 541511

NEXUS BONDS LIMITED

Level 16 Deutsche Bank Place Cnr Hunter & Phillip Streets, Sydney, 2000, NSW, Australia
Tel.: (61) 2 8258 2978   AU
Web Site:
   http://www.nexusbonds.com.au
Financial Services
N.A.I.C.S.: 523999
Ian S. Thompson *(Sec)*

NEXUS GOLD CORP.

Suite 802-750 West Pender St, Vancouver, V8C 2T8, BC, Canada
Tel.: (604) 558-1919
Web Site: https://www.nxs.gold
GH00—(DEU)
Rev.: $5,389
Assets: $1,178,054
Liabilities: $1,657,744
Net Worth: ($479,689)
Earnings: ($845,867)
Fiscal Year-end: 01/31/24
Gold Exploration Services
N.A.I.C.S.: 212220
Alex Klenman *(Pres & CEO)*

NEXUS INDUSTRIAL REIT

211-1540 Cornwall Road, Oakville, L6J 7W5, ON, Canada
Tel.: (416) 613-1262   ON
Web Site: https://www.nexusreit.com
Year Founded: 2012
J6D—(DEU)
Rev.: $119,046,178
Assets: $1,859,911,153
Liabilities: $1,104,542,719
Net Worth: $755,368,434
Earnings: $120,841,854
Emp.: 18
Fiscal Year-end: 12/31/23
Real Estate Investment Trust
N.A.I.C.S.: 525990
Kelly C. Hanczyk *(CEO)*

NEXUS INDUSTRIES LTD.

Audrey House 16-20 Ely Place, London, EC1N 6SN, United Kingdom
Tel.: (44) 1952 238 100
Web Site: http://www.nexusinds.com
Year Founded: 1969
Sales Range: $100-124.9 Million
Emp.: 987
Electrical & Electronic Component Mfr
N.A.I.C.S.: 335999
Mike Laycock *(Dir-Sls)*

Subsidiaries:

Nexus Electrical (Jiaxing) Ltd (1)
No 1438 Jiachuang Road Xiuzhou Industrial Park, Jiaxing, Zhejiang, China
Tel.: (86) 57383570200
Electrical & Electronic Component Distr
N.A.I.C.S.: 423610
Yolanda Ho *(Supvr-Supply Chain)*

Nexus Industries GmbH (1)
Holstenplatz 20b, 22765, Hamburg, Germany
Tel.: (49) 40890668780

Electrical & Electronic Component Distr
N.A.I.C.S.: 423610

Nexus Mid East Electrical LLC (1)
Office 806 Makateb Building Behind Honda Showroom, PO Box 118704, Port Saeed Deira, Dubai, United Arab Emirates
Tel.: (971) 42500636
Electrical & Electronic Component Distr
N.A.I.C.S.: 423610
Prakash Babu *(Mgr-Supply Chain)*

NEXUS INFRASTRUCTURE PLC

Nexus Park Avenue East Skyline 120, Great Notley, Braintree, CM77 7AL, Essex, United Kingdom
Tel.: (44) 1376559550   UK
Web Site: https://www.nexus-infrastructure.com
Year Founded: 1976
NEXS—(AIM)
Rev.: $111,397,158
Assets: $137,030,166
Liabilities: $98,376,858
Net Worth: $38,653,308
Earnings: ($1,154,844)
Fiscal Year-end: 09/30/22
Engineeering Services
N.A.I.C.S.: 541330
Mike Morris *(CEO)*

Subsidiaries:

Tamdown Group Limited (1)
Nexus Park Avenue East - Skyline 120, Great Notley, Braintree, CM77 7AL, Essex, United Kingdom
Tel.: (44) 1376320856
Web Site: https://www.tamdown.com
Engineeering Services
N.A.I.C.S.: 541330
Rob Kendal *(Mng Dir)*

TriConnex Limited (1)
Nexus Park Avenue East Skyline 120, Braintree, CM77 7AL, Essex, United Kingdom
Tel.: (44) 1376332680
Web Site: https://www.triconnex.co.uk
Engineeering Services
N.A.I.C.S.: 541330
David Topping *(Mng Dir)*

eSmart Networks Limited (1)
Nexus Park Avenue East Skyline 120, Great Notley, Braintree, CM77 7AL, Essex, United Kingdom
Tel.: (44) 1376332689
Web Site: https://www.esmartnetworks.co.uk
Engineeering Services
N.A.I.C.S.: 541330
Simon Gallagher *(Mng Dir)*

NEXUS MINERALS LIMITED

Level 2 41-47 Colin Street, West Perth, 6005, WA, Australia
Tel.: (61) 894811749
Web Site: https://www.nexus-minerals.com
NXM—(ASX)
Rev.: $200,731
Assets: $7,574,597
Liabilities: $600,460
Net Worth: $6,974,137
Earnings: ($16,168,925)
Emp.: 6
Fiscal Year-end: 06/30/22
Gold Ore & Silver Ore Mining
N.A.I.C.S.: 212220
Paul Boyatzis *(Chm)*

NEXUS SURGICAL AND MEDI-CARE LIMITED

Gala No 4 Saarthak Building No 1 Square Industrial Park, Tungarphata Vasai East Palghar, Thane, 401208, India
Tel.: (91) 8433598185
Web Site:
   https://www.nexusmed.co.in
Year Founded: 1992

538874—(BOM)
Rev.: $187,867
Assets: $109,770
Liabilities: $67,454
Net Worth: $42,317
Earnings: $20,467
Fiscal Year-end: 03/31/23
Software Publishing Services
N.A.I.C.S.: 513210

NEXUS URANIUM CORP.

Suite 503 - 905 West Pender Street, Vancouver, V6C 1L6, BC, Canada
Tel.: (604) 722-9842   BC
Year Founded: 2017
GIDMF—(OTCQB)
Assets: $8,197,995
Liabilities: $227,058
Net Worth: $7,970,937
Earnings: ($732,754)
Fiscal Year-end: 11/30/22
Mineral Exploration Services
N.A.I.C.S.: 213115
Jeremy Poirier *(CEO)*

NEXWISE INTELLIGENCE CHINA LIMITED

No 88 Ruixiang Road, Huangpu District, Guangzhou, 510535, Guangdong, China
Tel.: (86) 2083982000
Web Site:
   https://www.nexwise.com.cn
Year Founded: 2008
301248—(SSE)
Rev.: $105,378,624
Assets: $315,721,692
Liabilities: $89,537,292
Net Worth: $226,184,400
Earnings: $7,896,096
Fiscal Year-end: 12/31/22
Building Construction Services
N.A.I.C.S.: 236210
Chao Sun *(Chm)*

NEXXCHANGE AG

Landstrasser Hauptstrasse 1/12, Vienna, 1030, Austria
Tel.: (43) 1 606 20 70 71
Web Site:
   http://www.nexxchange.com
Information Support Services
N.A.I.C.S.: 519290
Harald Rodler *(Mgr)*

NEXXEN INTERNATIONAL LTD.

82 Yigal Alon St 13th Floor, Tel Aviv, 6789124, Israel
Tel.: (972) 35453900
Web Site: https://nexxen.com
Year Founded: 2007
NEXN—(NASDAQ)
Rev.: $104,101,830
Assets: $296,907,114
Liabilities: $125,619,624
Net Worth: $171,287,490
Earnings: $7,060,293
Emp.: 1,087
Fiscal Year-end: 12/31/22
Mobile Marketing Ad-Technology Services
N.A.I.C.S.: 513210
Amy Rothstein *(Chief Legal Officer & Head-Corp Dev)*

Subsidiaries:

Amobee, Inc. (1)
100 Marine Pkwy Ste 575, Redwood City, CA 94065-5172
Tel.: (650) 802-8871
Web Site: http://www.amobee.com
Sales Range: $25-49.9 Million
Emp.: 50
Mobile Advertising Solutions
N.A.I.C.S.: 513210
Gabi Schindler *(CMO)*

Subsidiary (Domestic):

Turn, Inc. (2)
901 Marshall St Ste 200, Redwood City, CA 94063
Tel.: (650) 353-4399
Web Site: http://www.amobee.com
Advertising Services
N.A.I.C.S.: 541890

Videology, Inc. (2)
1500 Whetstone Way Ste 500, Baltimore, MD 21230
Tel.: (410) 276-8700
Web Site: http://www.videologygroup.com
Video Advertising Software & Services
N.A.I.C.S.: 512199
Scott Ferber *(Chm & CEO)*

RhythmOne, LLC (1)
3600 136th Pl SE #400, Bellevue, WA 98006
Tel.: (415) 655-1450
Web Site: http://www.rhythmone.com
Online Marketing Services
N.A.I.C.S.: 517810
Karim Rayes *(Chief Product Officer)*

Subsidiary (Domestic):

Burst Media Corporation (2)
8 New England Executive Park, Burlington, MA 01803
Tel.: (781) 272-5544
Web Site: http://www.burstmedia.com
Sales Range: $25-49.9 Million
Emp.: 60
Advertising Services
N.A.I.C.S.: 541810
Harry Klein *(COO)*

Subsidiary (Non-US):

Burst Media Corporation Ltd. (3)
Third Floor 47 50 Margaret Street, London, W1W 8SB, United Kingdom
Tel.: (44) 2035514710
Emp.: 18
Advertising Services
N.A.I.C.S.: 541810
Donald Hamilton *(Mng Dir)*

Subsidiary (Domestic):

Perk Inc. (2)
720 Brazos Ste 110, Austin, TX 78701
Tel.: (519) 827-1999
Web Site: http://www.perk.com
Digital Rewards Platform Developer & Operator
N.A.I.C.S.: 551112
Shaun Worley *(VP-Product Mgmt & Mktg)*

blinkx, Inc. (2)
1 Market Plz Spear Tower Ste 1810, San Francisco, CA 94105
Tel.: (415) 655-1450
Web Site: http://www.blinkx.com
Sales Range: $25-49.9 Million
Emp.: 30
Video Search Engine
N.A.I.C.S.: 519290

NEXYZ.GROUP CORPORATION

NEXYZ Square Bldg 20-4, Sakuragaoka-cho Shibuya-ku, Tokyo, 150-0031, Japan
Tel.: (81) 354597444
Web Site: https://www.nexyzgroup.jp
Year Founded: 1987
4346—(TKS)
Rev.: $155,646,770
Assets: $109,505,050
Liabilities: $83,264,960
Net Worth: $26,240,090
Earnings: $5,303,320
Fiscal Year-end: 09/30/23
Telemarketing, Advertising Related & Broadband Services
N.A.I.C.S.: 561422
Yasuhiro Matsui *(Exec Dir)*

Subsidiaries:

Brangista, Inc. (1)
20-4 Sakuragaokacho, Shibuya-Ku, Tokyo, 150-0031, Japan

NEXYZ.GROUP CORPORATION

Nexyz.Group Corporation—(Continued)
Tel.: (81) 364151183
Web Site: https://www.brangista.com
Rev.: $32,316,220
Assets: $27,537,560
Liabilities: $11,592,150
Net Worth: $15,945,410
Earnings: $4,105,110
Emp.: 317
Fiscal Year-end: 09/30/2023
Internet Entertainment Services
N.A.I.C.S.: 516210
Keiryo Iwamoto *(Pres)*

Idea Cube Corporation (1)
Nekushiizsukueabiru 20-4 Sakuragaoka-cho, Shibuya-ku, Tokyo, 150-0031, Japan
Tel.: (81) 354596531
Web Site: http://www.idea-cube.co.jp
Marketing & Promotional Website Services
N.A.I.C.S.: 541810

Nexyz.BB Corporation (1)
Nexies Square Building 20-4, Sakuragaoka-cho Shibuya-ku, Tokyo, 150-0031, Japan
Tel.: (81) 364151210
Web Site: http://www.nexyz.jp
Internet Service Providers & Support Services
N.A.I.C.S.: 517810

Nexyz.Trade, Inc. (1)
20-4 Sakuragaoka-cho, Shibuya-ku, Tokyo, 150-0031, Japan   (86%)
Tel.: (81) 364151512
Web Site: http://www.nexyztrade.co.jp
Financial Acquisition Services
N.A.I.C.S.: 523999
Yoshitaka Kitao *(Chm)*

Nexyz.VP, Inc. (1)
Nekushiizsukueabiru 20-4, Shibuya-ku, Tokyo, 150-0031, Japan
Tel.: (81) 354597444
Web Site: http://www.nexyz.co.jp
Sales Range: $50-74.9 Million
Emp.: 24
Investment Venture Services
N.A.I.C.S.: 523999

NEYCER INDIA LTD.
145 St Mary s Road Alwarpet, Chennai, 600018, India
Tel.: (91) 4445088111
Web Site: https://www.neycer.in
Year Founded: 1960
Sanitary Products Mfr
N.A.I.C.S.: 325620

NF CORPORATION
6-3-20 Tsunashima Higashi, Kohoku-ku, Yokohama, 223-8508, Japan
Tel.: (81) 45 545 8128
Web Site: http://www.nfcorp.co.jp
Year Founded: 1959
Measurement & Control Equipment Mfr
N.A.I.C.S.: 334515
Tsuneo Takahashi *(Pres)*

Subsidiaries:

Chiyoda Electronics Co., Ltd. (1)
1-3-11 Nishiki-cho, Warabi, 355-0005, Saitama, Japan   (100%)
Tel.: (81) 484325580
Web Site: http://www.kk-chiyoda.co.jp
Sales Range: $10-24.9 Million
Emp.: 100
Power Supplies Mfr
N.A.I.C.S.: 335999
Hiroshi Kurihara *(Pres)*

NF Techno Commerce Co., Ltd. (1)
Meiko Building 3-1-13 Nishi-Ikebukuro, Toshima-ku, Tokyo, 171-0021, Japan
Tel.: (81) 359571809
Measurement Instrument Distr
N.A.I.C.S.: 423830

NFC CORPORATION
15-8 Gaetbeol-Ro 145 Beon-Gil, Yeonsu-Gu, Incheon, Korea (South)
Tel.: (82) 328311091

Web Site:
https://www.nfcneweng.co.kr
Year Founded: 2012
265740—(KRS)
Rev.: $24,143,728
Assets: $56,308,580
Liabilities: $12,381,455
Net Worth: $43,927,125
Earnings: $1,435,921
Emp.: 98
Fiscal Year-end: 12/31/22
Perfumes & Cosmetic Product Mfr
N.A.I.C.S.: 325620
Woo-Young Ryu *(CEO)*

NFD HOLDING D.D.
Trdinova 4, 1000, Ljubljana, Slovenia
Tel.: (386) 12300600
Web Site: http://www.nfdholding.si
Sales Range: $500-549.9 Million
Emp.: 1,170
Financial Investment Services
N.A.I.C.S.: 523999
Franci Strajnar *(Chm-Mgmt Bd)*

Subsidiaries:

HOTELI PIRAN D.D. (1)
Stjenkova 1, 6330, Piran, Slovenia
Tel.: (386) 5 66 67 100
Web Site: http://www.hotel-piran.si
Emp.: 30
Hotel Operating Services
N.A.I.C.S.: 721110
Alex Pinter *(Mgr)*

Metropol group d.d. (1)
Obala 77, Portoroz, 6320, Slovenia
Tel.: (386) 56901000
Web Site: http://www.metropol-resort.com
Sales Range: $10-24.9 Million
Emp.: 77
Hotel Services
N.A.I.C.S.: 721110
Valentina Kojek Putar *(Mgr-Sls)*

Terme Maribor d.d. (1)
Ulica Heroja Slandra 10, SI 2000, Maribor, Slovenia
Tel.: (386) 22344320
Web Site: http://www.termemb.si
Sales Range: $50-74.9 Million
Emp.: 300
Hotel Services
N.A.I.C.S.: 721120

NFI GROUP INC.
711 Kernaghan Avenue, Winnipeg, R2C 3T4, MB, Canada
Tel.: (204) 224-1251
Web Site: https://www.nfigroup.com
Year Founded: 1930
9NF—(DEU)
Rev.: $2,685,231,000
Assets: $2,699,960,000
Liabilities: $1,997,047,000
Net Worth: $702,913,000
Earnings: ($136,164,000)
Emp.: 8,500
Fiscal Year-end: 12/31/23
Heavy Duty Transit Buses Mfr
N.A.I.C.S.: 336510
Colin Pewarchuk *(Gen Counsel, Sec & Exec VP)*

Subsidiaries:

Alexander Dennis Limited (1)
91 Glasgow Road, Falkirk, FK1 4JB, Scotland, United Kingdom
Tel.: (44) 1324 621 672
Web Site: http://www.alexander-dennis.com
Sales Range: $550-599.9 Million
Emp.: 2,000
Commercial Bus Mfr, Distr & Whslr
N.A.I.C.S.: 336211
Colin Robertson *(CEO)*

Subsidiary (Non-US):

Alexander Dennis (Asia Pacific) Limited (2)
Units A-B 9 Floor YHC Tower 1 Sheung Yuet Road, Kowloon Bay, Kowloon, China (Hong Kong)
Tel.: (852) 27578057
Web Site: http://www.alexander-dennis.com
Commercial Bus Assembly & Whslr
N.A.I.C.S.: 423110

Alexander Dennis (Malaysia) SdnBhd (2)
A-3-13A Empire Office Empire Subang Jln SS 16/1 SS 16, 47500, Subang Jaya, Selangor, Malaysia
Tel.: (60) 356335788
Automobile Parts Distr
N.A.I.C.S.: 423120
Ahmad Taufeeq *(Mgr-Technical Sls)*

Alexander Dennis (Singapore) Services Pte Limited (2)
421 Tagore Industrial Avenue 01-14, Singapore, 787805, Singapore
Tel.: (65) 6257 0217
Automobile Parts Distr
N.A.I.C.S.: 423120
Nicholas Burton *(Mgr-After Sls-South East Asia)*

Subsidiary (US):

Alexander Dennis Incorporated (2)
31566 Railroad Canyon Rd Ste 342, Canyon Lake, CA 92587-9446
Tel.: (951) 244-9429
Web Site: http://www.alexander-dennis.com
Commercial Bus & Bus Parts Whslr
N.A.I.C.S.: 423110

Subsidiary (Domestic):

Plaxton Limited (2)
Plaxton Park Cayton Low Road, Eastfield, Scarborough, YO11 3BY, North Yorks, United Kingdom
Tel.: (44) 1723581500
Web Site: http://www.plaxtonlimited.co.uk
Emp.: 700
Automobile Parts Distr
N.A.I.C.S.: 423120
Martin Brailey *(Reg Dir-Sls)*

Carfair Composites Inc. (1)
692 Mission Street, Winnipeg, R2J 0A3, MB, Canada
Tel.: (204) 258-4010
Web Site:
https://www.carfaircomposites.com
Emp.: 700
Fiberglass Plastic Mfr
N.A.I.C.S.: 326199

New Flyer Industries Canada ULC (1)
711 Kernaghan Avenue, Winnipeg, R2C 3T4, MB, Canada
Tel.: (204) 224-1251
Web Site: http://www.newflyer.com
Sales Range: $25-49.9 Million
Emp.: 150
Bus Bodies Assembling Services
N.A.I.C.S.: 336211

New Flyer of America Inc. (1)
6200 Glenn Carlson Dr, Saint Cloud, MN 56301
Tel.: (320) 203-0576
Web Site: http://www.newflyer.com
Sales Range: $50-74.9 Million
Emp.: 200
Heavy Duty Buses Mfr
N.A.I.C.S.: 336120

Subsidiary (Domestic):

ARBOC Specialty Vehicles, LLC (2)
51166 Greenfield Prkwy, Middlebury, IN 46540-8220
Tel.: (574) 825-4880
Web Site: https://www.arbocsv.com
Motor Vehicle Body Mfr
N.A.I.C.S.: 336211
Kim Yoder *(VP-Sls & Mktg)*

Motor Coach Industries International, Inc. (2)
200 E Oakton St, Des Plaines, IL 60018
Web Site: http://www.mcicoach.com
Holding Company; Commercial Bus & Bus Parts Mfr, Whslr & Leasing Services
N.A.I.C.S.: 551112
Ian Smart *(Pres-Bus)*

INTERNATIONAL PUBLIC

Plant (Domestic):

New Flyer of America Inc. - Crookston Facility (2)
214 5th Ave SW, Crookston, MN 56716-2118
Tel.: (218) 277-7100
Web Site: http://www.newflyer.com
Sales Range: $100-124.9 Million
Emp.: 300
Heavy Duty Buses Mfr
N.A.I.C.S.: 336120

Subsidiary (Domestic):

TCB Enterprises, LLC. (2)
4600 Wyland Dr, Elkhart, IN 46516
Tel.: (574) 522-3971
Sales Range: $25-49.9 Million
Emp.: 85
Light Emitting Diode Mfr
N.A.I.C.S.: 334413
Robert Lober *(Pres)*

New MCI Holdings, Inc. (1)

NFK HOLDINGS CO., LTD.
7-8-4 Minami Aoyama, Minato-ku, Tokyo, 107-0062, Kanagawa, Japan
Tel.: (81) 455758000
Web Site: https://www.nfk-hd.co.jp
Year Founded: 1950
6494—(TKS)
Rev.: $14,059,470
Assets: $37,300,230
Liabilities: $3,972,610
Net Worth: $33,327,620
Earnings: $5,221,900
Emp.: 85
Fiscal Year-end: 03/31/24
Burners & Combustion Equipment Mfr
N.A.I.C.S.: 333914
Yosuke Sekiguchi *(Pres & CEO)*

NFL BIOSCIENCES SA
199 rue Helene Boucher, 34170, Castelnau-le-Lez, France
Tel.: (33) 411937667
Web Site:
https://www.nflbiosciences.com
Year Founded: 2006
ALNFL—(EUR)
Biotechnology Research & Development Services
N.A.I.C.S.: 541714
Ignacio Faus *(Chm)*

NFL HOLDINGS LTD.
94 Water Street, Charlottetown, C1A 1A6, PE, Canada
Tel.: (902) 566-3838
Year Founded: 1939
Rev.: $30,409,819
Emp.: 580
Water Transportation Services
N.A.I.C.S.: 532411
Mark MacDonald *(Pres)*

NFO DRIVES AB
Tubba Torg 5, 37432, Karlshamn, Sweden
Tel.: (46) 45437029
Web Site: https://www.nfodrives.se
Year Founded: 1996
Electrical Motor Machine Mfr
N.A.I.C.S.: 335312
Johan Braun *(Mng Dir)*

NFON AG
Zielstattstr 36, 81379, Munich, Germany
Tel.: (49) 89453000
Web Site: https://blog.nfon.com
Year Founded: 2007
NFN—(DEU)
Rev.: $90,892,656
Assets: $81,587,032
Liabilities: $29,528,522
Net Worth: $52,058,509

AND PRIVATE COMPANIES

Earnings: ($883,096)
Emp.: 453
Fiscal Year-end: 12/31/23
Telecommunication Servicesb
N.A.I.C.S.: 517810
Rainer-Christian Koppitz *(Chm-Supervisory Bd)*

Subsidiaries:

Deutsche Telefon Standard
GmbH (1)
Wilhelm-Theodor-Romheld-Strasse 26,
55130, Mainz, Germany
Tel.: (49) 6131327970
Web Site: https://www.deutsche-telefon.de
Emp.: 80
Telecommunication Servicesb
N.A.I.C.S.: 517810

NFON Polska Sp.z.o.o. (1)
Ul Przeskok 2, 00-032, Warsaw, Poland
Tel.: (48) 222464996
Telecommunication & Information Services
N.A.I.C.S.: 517810

Nfon France S.A.S (1)
81 Rue Reaumur, 75002, Paris, France
Tel.: (33) 188453800
Web Site: https://www.nfon.com
Telecommunication Servicesb
N.A.I.C.S.: 517810

Nfon GmbH (1)
Linzer Strasse 55, 3100, Saint Polten, Austria
Tel.: (43) 274275566
Web Site: https://www.nfon.com
Telecommunication Servicesb
N.A.I.C.S.: 517810

Nfon Iberia SL (1)
Paseo de la Castellana 135 7 Planta,
28046, Madrid, Spain
Tel.: (34) 910616600
Web Site: https://www.nfon.com
Telecommunication Servicesb
N.A.I.C.S.: 517810

Nfon UK Ltd. (1)
The Atrium 1 Harefield Road, Uxbridge,
UB8 1PH, Middlesex, United Kingdom
Tel.: (44) 2037406740
Web Site: https://www.nfon.com
Telecommunication Servicesb
N.A.I.C.S.: 517810

Onwerk GmbH (1)
Krugerstr 7-11, 68219, Mannheim, Germany
Tel.: (49) 6218755510
Web Site: http://www.onwerk.de
Software Development Services
N.A.I.C.S.: 541511

NFQ ADVERTISING GROUP
Ul Dmitriya Ulyanova 19, Moscow,
117036, Russia
Tel.: (7) 495 745 5108
Year Founded: 1992
Emp.: 150
N.A.I.C.S.: 541810
Dmitry Kazansky *(Gen Dir)*

NG ENERGY INTERNATIONAL CORP.
Suite 321 5940 MacLeod Trail SW,
Calgary, T2H 2G4, AB, Canada
Tel.: (604) 609-6110   AB
Web Site: https://ngenergyintl.com
Year Founded: 1998
GASXF—(OTCQX)
Sales Range: Less than $1 Million
Oil & Gas Exploration Services
N.A.I.C.S.: 213112
Serafino Iacono *(CEO)*

Subsidiaries:

Bolivar Energy Colombia Inc. (1)
Calle 92 No 13-68 Edificio Palko 92 Apto
201, Bogota, Colombia
Tel.: (57) 4165439732
Web Site: https://www.bolivarenergy.co
Oil & Gas Exploration Services
N.A.I.C.S.: 213111

NGAGE SPECIALIST RECRUITMENT LIMITED
222 Bishopsgate, London, EC2M
4QD, United Kingdom
Tel.: (44) 20 7422 7300
Web Site:
  http://www.ngagerecruitment.com
Year Founded: 2007
Staffing & Recruiting
N.A.I.C.S.: 561311
Tim Cook *(CEO)*

Subsidiaries:

GCS Recruitment Specialists
Limited (1)
1st Floor Cannongate House 62-64 Cannon
Street, London, EC4N 6AE, United Kingdom
Tel.: (44) 207 710 4141
Web Site: http://www.uk.gcsrecruitment.com
Employee Recruitment Services
N.A.I.C.S.: 561311
Amanda Cleary *(Mgr-HR)*

Subsidiary (US):

GCS Recruitment Specialists
Inc. (2)
90 Broad St 10th Fl, Brooklyn, NY 10004
Tel.: (646) 751-7892
Web Site: http://www.gcsrecruitment.com
Employee Placement Services
N.A.I.C.S.: 561311

NGAI HING HONG CO LTD
Unit 3 6 F Hopeful Factory Centre 10
Wo Shing Street Fo Tan, Sha Tin,
China (Hong Kong)
Tel.: (852) 26931663
Web Site: http://www.nhh.com.hk
1047—(HKG)
Rev.: $254,229,125
Assets: $142,156,081
Liabilities: $62,169,908
Net Worth: $79,986,173
Earnings: $12,436,123
Emp.: 626
Fiscal Year-end: 06/30/21
Plastic Resin Mfr
N.A.I.C.S.: 325211
Sai Chung Hui *(Co-Founder & Chm)*

Subsidiaries:

NHH Coltec Ltd. (1)
Tel.: (852) 26931772
Web Site: http://www.nhh.com.hk
Sales Range: $75-99.9 Million
Emp.: 200
Pigments, Color Masterbatches, Functional
Masterbatches & Compounded Plastic Resins Mfr
N.A.I.C.S.: 325130
Galen Ng *(Gen Mgr)*

NHH International Trading
Limited (1)
Unit 3 6th Floor Hopeful Factory Center, 10
Wo Shing Street Fo Tan, Sha Tin, China
(Hong Kong)
Tel.: (852) 26931663
Web Site: http://www.nhh.com.hk
Sales Range: $25-49.9 Million
Emp.: 50
Plastics Material & Resin Mfr
N.A.I.C.S.: 325211

Ngai Hing Engineering Plastic (Hong
Kong) Limited (1)
No 9 Dai Shun Street Tai Po Industrial Estate, Tai Po, NT, China (Hong Kong)
Tel.: (852) 26600208
Web Site: http://www.nhh.com.hk
Sales Range: $25-49.9 Million
Emp.: 40
Plastics Material & Resin Mfr
N.A.I.C.S.: 325211
Ben Tat Ching Ng *(Pres)*

Ngai Hing Engineering Plastic (Hong
Kong) Ltd. (1)
No 9 Dai Shun Street, Tai Po Industrial Estate, Tai Po, New Territories, China (Hong Kong)

Tel.: (852) 26600208
Web Site: https://www.nhh.com.hk
Plastics Material & Resin Mfr
N.A.I.C.S.: 325211

Ngai Hing Hong Plastic Materials
(Hong Kong) Ltd. (1)
Unit 36th Fl Hopeful Factory Ctr, 10 Wo
Shing St Fo Tan, Sha Tin, China (Hong Kong)
Tel.: (852) 26931663
Web Site: http://www.nhh.com.hk
Sales Range: $25-49.9 Million
Emp.: 50
Plastics Materials & Basic Forms & Shapes Whslr
N.A.I.C.S.: 424610

Ngai Hing PlastChem Co., Ltd. (1)
Room 6 6th Fl Hopeful Fty Ctr, Sha Tin,
China (Hong Kong)
Tel.: (852) 26931663
Web Site: http://www.nhh.com.hk
Sales Range: $25-49.9 Million
Emp.: 50
Plastics Material & Resin Mfr
N.A.I.C.S.: 325211

Shanghai Ngai Hing Plastic Materials
Co., Ltd. (1)
No 8100 Songze Ave, Qingpu Industrial
Zone, Shanghai, 201707, China
Tel.: (86) 2169213333
Web Site: http://www.nhh.com.hk
Plastics Material & Resin Mfr
N.A.I.C.S.: 325211
Sam Hui *(Gen Mgr)*

NGAI STAR XANH TRANSPORTATION COMPANY LIMITED
No 5 Vo Thi Sau, May To Ward Ngo
Quyen District, Haiphong, Vietnam
Tel.: (84) 2253836024   VN
Container Shipping ervices
N.A.I.C.S.: 488510

NGE CAPITAL LIMITED
Level 4 North Building 333 Collins
Street, Melbourne, 3000, VIC, Australia
Tel.: (61) 396482290
Web Site: http://ngecapital.com.au
NGE—(OTCIQ)
Rev.: $338,656
Assets: $23,953,398
Liabilities: $136,382
Net Worth: $23,817,016
Earnings: ($1,982,134)
Fiscal Year-end: 12/31/20
Investment Services
N.A.I.C.S.: 523999
David Lamm *(Chm & Chief Investment Officer)*

NGEE ANN KONGSI
Unit 563 A Balestier Rd, Singapore,
329879, Singapore
Tel.: (65) 6737 9555
Web Site:
  http://www.ngeeann.com.sg
Emp.: 30
Non-Profit Holding Company
N.A.I.C.S.: 551112
Chiang Long Teo *(Pres)*

Subsidiaries:

Ngee Ann Development Pte. Ltd. (1)
391A Orchard Road 26-01, Ngee Ann City
Tower A, Singapore, 238873, Singapore
Tel.: (65) 62339988
Emp.: 10
Commercial Real Estate Leasing Services
N.A.I.C.S.: 531190
Sandy Loh *(Acct Mgr)*

Ngee Ann Traditional Chinese Medicine Centre Ltd (1)
Blk 33 Bedok South Avenue 2 01-319, Singapore, 460033, Singapore
Tel.: (65) 62433960
Hospital Management Services
N.A.I.C.S.: 622110

NGIU KEE CORPORATION (M) BERHAD

NGENEBIO CO., LTD.
3F 307 288 Digital-ro, Guro-Gu,
Seoul, 08390, Korea (South)
Tel.: (82) 28679798
Web Site: https://www.ngenebio.com
Year Founded: 2015
354200—(KRS)
Rev.: $8,450,466
Assets: $43,078,051
Liabilities: $23,652,292
Net Worth: $19,425,760
Earnings: ($7,505,431)
Emp.: 119
Fiscal Year-end: 12/31/22
Professional Training Services
N.A.I.C.S.: 541990
Jong-Jin Yoon *(Ops Mgr)*

NGENIC AB
Kungsgatan 41, 753 21, Uppsala,
Sweden
Tel.: (46) 184721818
Web Site: https://www.ngenic.se
Year Founded: 2010
NGENIC—(OMX)
Rev.: $6,933,111
Assets: $7,752,100
Liabilities: $5,962,237
Net Worth: $1,789,862
Earnings: ($1,995,354)
Emp.: 60
Fiscal Year-end: 12/31/23
Renewable Energy Services
N.A.I.C.S.: 221210
Bjorn Berg *(CEO)*

NGERN TID LOR PUBLIC COMPANY LIMITED
428 Ari Hills 9th-15th Floor Phahonyothin Road, Samsennai Phayathai,
Bangkok, 10400, Thailand
Tel.: (66) 27921394
Web Site: https://www.tidlor.com
Year Founded: 2006
TIDLOR—(THA)
Rev.: $521,742,678
Assets: $2,754,116,410
Liabilities: $1,972,456,013
Net Worth: $781,660,397
Earnings: $104,238,512
Fiscal Year-end: 12/31/23
Insurance Brokerage Services
N.A.I.C.S.: 524210
Athitaya Phoonwathu *(Chief Insurance Officer)*

NGIU KEE CORPORATION (M) BERHAD
Lot LG03 G04B2-1 03 Wisma Saberkas Jalan Tun Abang Haji Openg,
93000, Kuching, Sarawak, Malaysia
Tel.: (60) 82252636
Sales Range: $25-49.9 Million
Supermarket Operations
N.A.I.C.S.: 445110
Siew Kat Yong *(CEO)*

Subsidiaries:

Ngiu Kee (Bintulu) Sdn. Bhd. (1)
Sublot 53-58 BDA-Shahida Shop Houses
Lot 2343-2348 & Lot 259, 97008, Bintulu,
Sarawak, Malaysia
Tel.: (60) 86335997
Supermarket Management Services
N.A.I.C.S.: 445110

Ngiu Kee (Lawas) Sdn. Bhd. (1)
No 425-431 Jalan Sloating Trusan Road,
98850, Lawas, Sarawak, Malaysia
Tel.: (60) 85284220
Sales Range: $25-49.9 Million
Emp.: 50
Supermarket Management Services
N.A.I.C.S.: 445110

Ngiu Kee (Sibu) Sdn. Bhd. (1)
No 3-19 Jalan Bako Wisma Lee Hua
Brooke Drive, 96007, Sibu, Sarawak, Malaysia

NGIU KEE CORPORATION (M) BERHAD

Ngiu Kee Corporation (M) Berhad—(Continued)
Tel.: (60) 84327163
Web Site: http://www.nksporeonline.com
Sales Range: $25-49.9 Million
Emp.: 70
Supermarket Management Services
N.A.I.C.S.: 445110

Ngiu Kee (Wisma Saberkas) Sdn. Bhd. (1)
Lot LG03 G04B2 & 1 03 Wisma Saberkas Jalan Tun Abang Haji Openg, 93000, Kuching, Sarawak, Malaysia
Tel.: (60) 82252636
Supermarket Management Services
N.A.I.C.S.: 445110

Pacific-Ngiu Kee Sdn. Bhd. (1)
Basement Fl Ctr Point Sabah No 1 Jalan Ctr Point, 88000, Kota Kinabalu, Sabah, Malaysia
Tel.: (60) 88250596
Web Site: http://www.ngiukee.com
Sales Range: $50-74.9 Million
Emp.: 150
Supermarket Management Services
N.A.I.C.S.: 445110

NGK INSULATORS, LTD.

2-56 Suda-cho Mizuho, Nagoya, 467-8530, Japan
Tel.: (81) 528727862 JP
Web Site: https://www.ngk.co.jp
Year Founded: 1919
5333—(TKS)
Rev.: $3,826,614,930
Assets: $7,453,277,360
Liabilities: $2,804,960,110
Net Worth: $4,648,317,250
Earnings: $268,114,820
Emp.: 19,540
Fiscal Year-end: 03/31/24
Engineering Services, Electrical Insulators, Industrial Ceramic Products & Beryllium-Copper Products Mfr
N.A.I.C.S.: 444180
Ryohei Iwasaki (Sr VP)

Subsidiaries:

Akechi Insulators Co Ltd (1)
200 1001-Akechicho, Ena, 509-7712, Gifu, Japan
Tel.: (81) 573542121
Web Site: https://www.akechi-gaishi.co.jp
Emp.: 239
Industrial & Electrical Equipments Mfr & Distr
N.A.I.C.S.: 423610
Toru Nagura (Pres)

Chubu Energys Co., Ltd. (1)
1 Kamikobari, Inuyama, 484-0000, Aichi, Japan
Tel.: (81) 568672996
Electronic Components Mfr
N.A.I.C.S.: 334419

Energy Support Corporation (1)
1 Kamikobari, Inuyama, 484-8505, Aichi, Japan
Tel.: (81) 56 867 0851
Power Distribution Equipment Mfr & Distr
N.A.I.C.S.: 335311

Energys Sangyo Co., Ltd. (1)
1 Kamikobari, Inuyama, 484-0000, Aichi, Japan
Tel.: (81) 568680001
Energy Consulting Services
N.A.I.C.S.: 541690

FM Industries, Inc. (1)
221 Warren Ave, Fremont, CA 94539
Tel.: (510) 668-1900
Web Site: https://www.fmindustries.com
Sales Range: $100-124.9 Million
Emp.: 400
Machine Shops
N.A.I.C.S.: 332710

Subsidiary (Domestic):

LJ Engineering & Manufacturing Inc. (2)
440 Aldo Ave, Santa Clara, CA 95054
Tel.: (408) 988-0151

Web Site: http://www.lj-eng.com
Sales Range: $25-49.9 Million
Emp.: 100
Machine Shops
N.A.I.C.S.: 332710

Heisei Ceramics Co Ltd (1)
3108 Kashiki, Oyamada mura Ayama-gun, Mie, 518-1403, Japan
Tel.: (81) 595470341
Web Site: http://www.ngk.co.jp
Refractories Mfr & Distr
N.A.I.C.S.: 327120

Hokuriku Energys Co., Ltd. (1)
11-1 Wakabadai Shika-machi, Hakui-gun, Ishikawa, 925-0375, Japan
Tel.: (81) 767381246
Switchgear & Switchboard Apparatus Mfr
N.A.I.C.S.: 335313

Ikebukuro Horo Kogyo Co., Ltd. (1)
735 shimotomi, Tokorozawa, 359-0001, Saitama, Japan
Tel.: (81) 429421181
Glass Lined Apparatus Mfr
N.A.I.C.S.: 331221

Kansai Energys Corporation (1)
1 of 2617 Okura Wakai-cho, Kasai, 675-2456, Hyogo, Japan
Tel.: (81) 79 044 2548
Web Site: https://www.kansai-energys.co.jp
Emp.: 520
Painted Parts Mfr & Distr
N.A.I.C.S.: 325510

Locke Insulators, Inc. (1)
2525 Insulator Dr, Baltimore, MD 21230
Tel.: (410) 752-8020
Web Site: http://www.ngk.co.jp
Electrical Insulating Material Mfr
N.A.I.C.S.: 334419

NGK Adrec Co Ltd (1)
3040 Misano, Mitake-cho Kani-gun, Gifu, 505-0112, Japan
Tel.: (81) 574671151
Web Site: https://www.ngk-adrec.co.jp
Sales Range: $125-149.9 Million
Emp.: 240
Refractories Mfr
N.A.I.C.S.: 327120

NGK Automotive Ceramics Korea Co Ltd (1)
A Asset Tower 369 Gangnam-Daero, Seocho-Gu, Seoul, 06621, Korea (South)
Tel.: (82) 25387788
Web Site: http://www.ngk.co.jp
Sales Range: $25-49.9 Million
Emp.: 6
Ceramic Products Mfr & Distr
N.A.I.C.S.: 332999

NGK Automotive Ceramics Mexico, S de R.L. de C.V. (1)
Ave Tecnologico 1320 Monterrey Technology Park, 65550, Cienega de Flores, Nuevo Leon, Mexico
Tel.: (52) 818 288 1000
Automotive Ceramic Products Mfr
N.A.I.C.S.: 336390

NGK Automotive Ceramics USA Inc (1)
39625 Lewis Dr Ste 500, Novi, MI 48377
Tel.: (248) 489-7190
Web Site: http://www.ngk-detroit.com
Automotive Ceramics Distr
N.A.I.C.S.: 423120

NGK Berylco France (1)
103 Quai Jean Pierre Fougerat, 44220, Coueron, France
Tel.: (33) 240386750
Web Site: http://www.ngkbf.com
Sales Range: $50-74.9 Million
Emp.: 53
Beryllium Products Mfr & Distr
N.A.I.C.S.: 424690
Philippe Payan (Mgr-Production & QHSE)

NGK Berylco U.K. Ltd. (1)
Houston Park Montford Street, Salford, M50 2RP, United Kingdom
Tel.: (44) 1617457162
Web Site: http://www.ngkberylco.co.uk
Emp.: 10
Beryllium Copper Products Mfr & Distr

N.A.I.C.S.: 331523
Justin Dodds (Gen Mgr)

NGK Building Service, Ltd. (1)
2-56 Suda-cho, Mizuho-ku, Nagoya, 467-8530, Japan
Tel.: (81) 528727681
Building Maintenance Services
N.A.I.C.S.: 561730

NGK Ceramic Device Co., Ltd. (1)
434-3 Gotanda Shimozue, Komaki, 485-8557, Aichi, Japan
Tel.: (81) 568741801
Web Site: http://www.ncdk.jp
Emp.: 1,180
Electric Device Mfr
N.A.I.C.S.: 334419

NGK Ceramics (Thailand) Co., Ltd. (1)
88/20 Moo 4, Klongsuan Sub-district Bangbor District, Samut Prakan, 10560, Thailand
Tel.: (66) 2 300 9696
Automotive Ceramics Mfr & Distr
N.A.I.C.S.: 336390

NGK Ceramics Europe S.A (1)
Rue des Azalees 1, 7331, Baudour, Belgium
Tel.: (32) 65760210
Web Site: https://www.ngkceramicseurope.be
Sales Range: $150-199.9 Million
Emp.: 300
Automotive Ceramics Mfr
N.A.I.C.S.: 423120

NGK Ceramics Mexico, S.de R.L.de C.V. (1)
Ave Tecnologico 1320, Monterrey Technology Park, 65550, Cienega de Flores, Nuevo Leon, Mexico
Tel.: (52) 81 8288 1000
Web Site: http://www.ngk.co.jp
Ceramic Tile Mfr
N.A.I.C.S.: 327120

NGK Ceramics Polska Sp z o.o (1)
ul J Gutenberga 6, 44-109, Gliwice, Poland
Tel.: (48) 327807000
Web Site: https://www.ngk.com.pl
Emp.: 3,500
Automotive Parts Mfr & Distr
N.A.I.C.S.: 423120
Yasukazu Hijikata (Pres)

NGK Ceramics South Africa (Pty) Ltd (1)
Corner of Munich Mobile Roads, Airport Industria, Cape Town, 7525, South Africa
Tel.: (27) 213808100
Web Site: https://www.ngkceramics.co.za
Sales Range: $75-99.9 Million
Emp.: 150
Automotive Ceramics Mfr & Distr
N.A.I.C.S.: 423120
Achim Wende (Mgr-Fin)

NGK Ceramics Suzhou Co., Ltd. (1)
58 Lushan Road, Suzhou New District, Suzhou, 215129, Jiangsu, China
Tel.: (86) 51266612000
Electronic Components Mfr
N.A.I.C.S.: 334419
Minoru O'Hara (CEO)

NGK Ceramics USA Inc (1)
119 Mazeppa Rd, Mooresville, NC 28115
Tel.: (704) 664-7000
Web Site: https://www.ngkceramics.com
Sales Range: $25-49.9 Million
Emp.: 100
Automotive Ceramics Distr
N.A.I.C.S.: 423120
Steve Dailey (Pres)

NGK Chem-Tech, Ltd. (1)
2-56 Suda-cho, Mizuho-ku, Nagoya, 467-8530, Japan
Chemical Products Mfr & Distr
N.A.I.C.S.: 325998

NGK Deutsche Berylco GmbH (1)
Westerbachstrasse 32, 61476, Kronberg, Germany
Tel.: (49) 6173993400
Web Site: http://www.ngkdbg.de
Sales Range: $25-49.9 Million
Emp.: 13
Beryllium Products Mfr & Distr

N.A.I.C.S.: 325998

NGK Electronics Devices (M) Sdn. Bhd. (1)
Plot 10 Phase 4, Bayan Lepas Free Industrial Zone, 11900, Penang, Malaysia
Tel.: (60) 4 643 4318
Ceramic Electronic Component Mfr & Distr
N.A.I.C.S.: 327110

NGK Electronics Devices, Inc. (1)
2701-1 Higashi-bun Omine-cho, Mine, 759-2212, Yamaguchi, Japan
Tel.: (81) 83 754 0100
Web Site: https://www.ngked.co.jp
Ceramic Electronic Component Mfr & Distr
N.A.I.C.S.: 327110
Hideki Shimizu (Pres)

NGK Electronics USA, Inc. (1)
2520 Mission College Blvd Ste 104, Santa Clara, CA 95054
Tel.: (408) 330-6900
Web Site: http://www.ngk.co.jp
Emp.: 20
Semiconductor Devices Mfr
N.A.I.C.S.: 334413
Joe Aihara (Pres)

NGK Europe GmbH (1)
Westerbachstrasse 32, 61476, Kronberg, Germany
Tel.: (49) 61739930
Web Site: https://www.ngk-e.de
Sales Range: $50-74.9 Million
Emp.: 65
Automotive Parts Mfr & Distr
N.A.I.C.S.: 423120
Atsushi Matsuda (Mng Dir)

NGK Filtec Ltd (1)
2791 Hagien, Chigasaki, 253-0071, Kanagawa, Japan
Tel.: (81) 467858555
Web Site: https://www.ngk-nft.co.jp
Sales Range: $50-74.9 Million
Emp.: 122
Ceramic Membrane Filter Systems Mfr & Distr
N.A.I.C.S.: 212323

NGK Fine Molds Ltd (1)
4-5-6 Minato-machi, Handa, 475-0823, Aichi, Japan
Tel.: (81) 569235885
Web Site: https://www.ngk-fine-molds.co.jp
Emp.: 18
Industrial Molds Mfr & Distr
N.A.I.C.S.: 333511

NGK Globetronics Technology Sdn. Bhd. (1)
Plot 10 Phase 4, Bayan Lepas Free Industrial Zone, 11900, Penang, Malaysia
Tel.: (60) 4 644 4906
Ceramic Electronic Component Mfr & Distr
N.A.I.C.S.: 327110

NGK INSULATORS (CHINA) INVESTMENT CO., LTD. (1)
Room 1903A Dawning Centre Tower A No 500 Hongbaoshi Road, Changning District, Shanghai, 201103, China
Tel.: (86) 21 6208 4488
Web Site: http://www.ngk.co.jp
Investment Management Service
N.A.I.C.S.: 523999

NGK Insulators Shanghai Co Ltd (1)
Room 1903 Tower A DongYin Ctr 500 Hongbaoshi Rd, Shanghai, 201103, Chang Ning, China
Tel.: (86) 2162084488
Web Site: http://www.ngk.co.jp
Sales Range: $25-49.9 Million
Emp.: 11
Electrical Insulators Mfr & Distr
N.A.I.C.S.: 423610
Horiu Kosuke (Gen Mgr)

NGK Insulators Suzhou Co., Ltd. (1)
401 Jianlin Road, Suzhou New District, Suzhou, 215151, Jiangsu, China
Tel.: (86) 512 6616 4888
Electronic Insulating Material Mfr
N.A.I.C.S.: 334419

NGK Insulators of Canada Ltd (1)
1501 avenue McGill College Bureau 515, Ste 700 E Tower, Montreal, H3A 3M8, QC, Canada

Tel.: (514) 281-8488
Sales Range: $50-74.9 Million
Emp.: 6
Electrical Polymer Insulator Whslr
N.A.I.C.S.: 423610
Steven Toyama *(Gen Mgr)*

NGK Insulators, Ltd - High Performance Ceramics Division (1)
1 Maegata-cho, Handa, 475-0825, Aichi, Japan
Tel.: (81) 569235461
Electronic Ceramic Component Mfr
N.A.I.C.S.: 334419

NGK Insulators, Ltd. - Ishikawa Plant (1)
1-1 Nomi, Nomi, 929-0108, Ishikawa, Japan
Tel.: (81) 761 55 6100
Web Site: http://www.ngk.co.jp
Electronic Components Mfr
N.A.I.C.S.: 334419

NGK Kilntech Corporation (1)
2-56 Suda-cho, Mizuho-ku, Nagoya, 467-8530, Japan
Tel.: (81) 528727874
Web Site: http://www.ngkkiln-tech.com
Sales Range: $25-49.9 Million
Emp.: 30
Furnaces & Infrared ceramic Heaters Mfr & Distr
N.A.I.C.S.: 333414

NGK Life Co Ltd (1)
2-56 Suda-cho, Mizuho-ku, Nagoya, 467-8530, Japan
Tel.: (81) 528727190
Web Site: http://www.ngk-detroit.com
Finance & Insurance Services
N.A.I.C.S.: 524210

NGK Locke Inc (1)
2525 Insulator Dr, Baltimore, MD 21230
Tel.: (410) 347-1700
Web Site: http://www.ngk-locke.com
Electrical Equipment Mfr & Distr
N.A.I.C.S.: 423610

NGK Locke Polymer Insulators Inc (1)
1609 Diamond Springs Rd, Virginia Beach, VA 23455
Tel.: (757) 460-3649
Web Site: http://www.ngk-polymer.com
Electrical Polymer Insulator Mfr & Distr
N.A.I.C.S.: 423610

NGK Logistics Ltd (1)
2-56 Suda cho, Mizuho-ku, Nagoya, 467-8530, Aichi, Japan
Tel.: (81) 8727436
Web Site: http://www.ngk.com
Emp.: 40
Logistic Services
N.A.I.C.S.: 541614

NGK Metals Corporation (1)
917 US Hwy 11 S, Sweetwater, TN 37874
Tel.: (423) 337-5521
Web Site: http://www.ngkmetals.com
Beryllium Containing Metal Mfr
N.A.I.C.S.: 332312

NGK Metex Corporation (1)
1-9-3 Shintone, Kazo, 349-1158, Saitama, Japan
Tel.: (81) 48 072 6401
Beryllium Copper Wrought Product Mfr
N.A.I.C.S.: 331529

NGK Mettex Corporation (1)
1-9-3 Shintone Otonemachi, Kitasaitamagun, Saitama, 349-1158, Japan
Tel.: (81) 480726401
Web Site: http://www.ngk.co.jp
Beryllium Copper Wrought Products Mfr
N.A.I.C.S.: 331420

NGK North America, Inc. (1)
1105 N Market St Ste 1300, Wilmington, DE 19801-1241
Tel.: (302) 654-1344
Electronic Components Mfr
N.A.I.C.S.: 334419

NGK Okhotsk Ltd (1)
534-2 Yobito, Abashiri, Hokkaido, 099-2421, Japan
Tel.: (81) 152483111
Ceramic Electronic Component Mfr
N.A.I.C.S.: 423690

NGK Optoceramics Co Ltd (1)
434-3 Gotanda, Shimozue, Komaki, 485-8557, Aichi, Japan
Tel.: (81) 568741801
Web Site: http://www.ngk-detroit.com
Ceramic Electronic Component Mfr
N.A.I.C.S.: 423690

NGK Printer Ceramics Co Ltd (1)
434-3 Gotanda, Shimozue, Komaki, 485-8557, Aichi, Japan
Tel.: (81) 568741801
Web Site: http://www.ngk-detroit.com
Ceramic Electronic Component Mfr
N.A.I.C.S.: 423690

NGK Sports Development Co., Ltd / Moronoki Tennis Club (1)
2-446 Moronoki, Midori-ku, Nagoya, 458-0817, Japan
Tel.: (81) 528772171
Web Site: https://www.moronoki.com
Tennis Club Operations
N.A.I.C.S.: 713940
Hideo Mizuno *(Mng Dir)*

NGK Stanger Pty. Ltd. (1)
14 Childs Road, Epping, 3076, VIC, Australia
Tel.: (61) 39 401 6200
Web Site: https://www.ngkstanger.com.au
Power Distribution Equipment Mfr & Distr
N.A.I.C.S.: 335311

NGK Technica, Ltd. (1)
2-56 Suda-cho, Mizuho-Ku, Nagoya, 467-8530, Japan
Tel.: (81) 52 872 7310
Web Site: http://www.ngk-detroit.com
Technical Consulting Services
N.A.I.C.S.: 541690

NGK Techniocera Suzhou Co., Ltd. (1)
2-24 Taishan Road, Suzhou New District, Jiangsu, 215129, China
Tel.: (86) 5126 661 8000
Heating Device Mfr & Distr
N.A.I.C.S.: 333414

NGK Technocera Suzhou Co., Ltd. (1)
89-2 Taishan Road, Suzhou New District, Jiangsu, 215129, China
Tel.: (86) 51266618000
Web Site: http://www.ngk.co.jp
Electronic Components Mfr
N.A.I.C.S.: 334419

NGK Technologies India Pvt. Ltd. (1)
803 8th Floor Vatika City Point, Gurgaon, 122002, Haryana, India
Tel.: (91) 124 448 8891
Web Site: https://ngkindia.co.in
Beryllium Copper Product Distr
N.A.I.C.S.: 423510

NGK Yu-Service Co Ltd (1)
2-56 Suda-cho, Mizuho ku, Nagoya, 467-8530, Japan
Tel.: (81) 528727604
Web Site: http://www.ngk-detroit.com
Group Welfare Services
N.A.I.C.S.: 525120

P.T NGK Ceramics Indonesia (1)
East Jakarta Industrial Park Plot No 1J, Cikarang Selatan, Bekasi, 17550, Jawa Barat, Indonesia
Tel.: (62) 218971160
Web Site: http://www.ngkceramics.co.za
Sales Range: $250-299.9 Million
Emp.: 1,000
Automotive Ceramics Mfr & Distr
N.A.I.C.S.: 423120
Katsuhiko Kmoroi *(Dir-Fin)*

Risshin Electronics Co., Ltd. (1)
871-8 Ichi, Komoro, 384-0083, Japan
Tel.: (81) 2 6722 8881
Electronic Components Mfr
N.A.I.C.S.: 334419

SIAM NGK Technocera Co., Ltd. (1)
11 Moo 1 WHA Saraburi Industrial Land Bua-Luay, Nongkhae, 18140, Saraburi, Thailand
Tel.: (66) 36 373 641
Web Site: http://www.ngk.co.jp

Sales Range: $50-74.9 Million
Emp.: 150
Electronic Component Mfr & Distr
N.A.I.C.S.: 334419

Soshin Device Co., Ltd. (1)
13-4 Oyamada, Takaoka Town, Miyazaki, 880-2214, Japan
Tel.: (81) 985824261
Web Site: https://www.soshin-device.co.jp
Emp.: 174
Electronic Components Mfr
N.A.I.C.S.: 334419

Soshin Electronics (HK) Ltd. (1)
Unit 1303 13/F Austin Tower 22-26 Austin Avenue, Tsimshatsui, Kowloon, China (Hong Kong)
Tel.: (852) 75532900333
Web Site: http://www.soshin-ele.com
Electronic Components Distr
N.A.I.C.S.: 423690

Soshin Electronics Europe GmbH (1)
Westerbachstrasse 32, 61476, Kronberg, Germany
Tel.: (49) 6173993108
Electronic Component Mfr & Distr
N.A.I.C.S.: 334419

Soshin Electronics of America Inc. (1)
3001 Winchester Blvd Ste 14, Campbell, CA 95008
Tel.: (408) 748-6928
Web Site: http://www.soshin-ele.com
Emp.: 2
Electronic Equipment Distr
N.A.I.C.S.: 423690

Soshina Electonics (M) Sdn. Bhd. (1)
1408 Level 14 Taiping Financial Tower No 6001 Yitian Road, Futian District, Shenzhen, 518048, China
Tel.: (86) 7553 290 0333
Electronic Equipment Mfr & Distr
N.A.I.C.S.: 334419

Soshina Electronics (SZ) Limited (1)
Lot 14 Batu Berendam FTZ Phase 3, Batu Berendam, 75350, Malacca, Malaysia
Tel.: (60) 6 284 8501
Electronic Equipment Mfr & Distr
N.A.I.C.S.: 334419

Soshina Electronics of America Inc. (1)
3001 Winchester Blvd Ste 14, Campbell, CA 95008
Tel.: (408) 748-6928
Electronic Equipment Mfr & Distr
N.A.I.C.S.: 334419

Taiwan Soshin Electric Co., Ltd. (1)
No 97 Section 2 Dunhua S Rd, Da'an District, Taipei, 10682, Taiwan
Tel.: (886) 277111030
Electronic Components Mfr
N.A.I.C.S.: 334419

NGL FINE-CHEM LTD.
301 E Square Subhash Road, Vile Parle East, Mumbai, 400057, India
Tel.: (91) 2240842222   In
Web Site:
https://www.nglfinechem.com
524774—(NSE)
Rev.: $44,797,321
Assets: $37,800,590
Liabilities: $10,061,347
Net Worth: $27,739,243
Earnings: $6,810,981
Emp.: 329
Fiscal Year-end: 03/31/22
Pharmaceuticals Product Mfr
N.A.I.C.S.: 325412
Rahul Jayant Nachane *(Mng Dir)*

NGL SUPPLY CO. LTD.
435 4th Avenue SW Suite 550, Calgary, T2P 3A8, AB, Canada
Tel.: (403) 265-1977
Web Site: http://www.nglsupply.com
Natural Gas Distr
N.A.I.C.S.: 221210
Mark Mundy *(VP-Logistics)*
Subsidiaries:

NGL Supply Terminals Company (1)
720 S Colorado Blvd Ste, Denver, CO 80246
Tel.: (303) 839-1806
Natural Gas Distr
N.A.I.C.S.: 221210

NGO HAN JOINT STOCK COMPANY
Phuoc Thai Village Long Thanh District, Dong Nai, Ho Chi Minh City, Vietnam
Tel.: (84) 613 841 578   VN
Web Site:
http://www.ngohanwire.com
Year Founded: 1987
Sales Range: $50-74.9 Million
Emp.: 227
Magnet Wire Mfr
N.A.I.C.S.: 332618
Ngo Thi Thong *(Founder, Chrm & CEO)*

NGO QUYEN PROCESSING EXPORT JOINT STOCK COMPANY
326-328 Ngo Quyen Street, Racha Gia, Kien Giang, Vietnam
Tel.: (84) 773866228
Web Site:
http://www.ngoprexco.com.vn
Year Founded: 2005
NGC—(HNX)
Rev.: $8,412,200
Assets: $12,702,200
Liabilities: $13,334,300
Net Worth: ($632,100)
Earnings: ($641,200)
Emp.: 500
Fiscal Year-end: 12/31/22
Frozen Seafood Product Mfr & Distr
N.A.I.C.S.: 311710

NGP MELBOURNE PTY. LTD.
972 Nepean Highway, Moorabbin, 3189, VIC, Australia
Tel.: (61) 385066700
Web Site:
http://www.ngpmelbourne.com.au
Automotive Retailer
N.A.I.C.S.: 441110
Philip Goldman *(CFO)*

NGS GROUP AB
Kungsgatan 12, 111 35, Stockholm, Sweden
Tel.: (46) 850580830
Web Site: https://www.ngsgroup.se
Year Founded: 2007
NGS—(OMX)
Rev.: $53,495,930
Assets: $34,391,713
Liabilities: $11,619,695
Net Worth: $22,772,018
Earnings: $343,739
Emp.: 384
Fiscal Year-end: 12/31/22
Management Consulting Services
N.A.I.C.S.: 541611
Ingrid Nordlund *(CEO)*
Subsidiaries:

Human Capital Group HCG AB (1)
Kungsgatan 12 7tr, 111 35, Stockholm, Sweden
Tel.: (46) 854699260
Web Site: https://humancapital.se
Staffing & Recruiting Services
N.A.I.C.S.: 561311

Nurse & Doc Partner AB (1)
Skeppsbrokajen 8, 371 33, Karlskrona, Sweden
Tel.: (46) 455302800

NGS GROUP AB

NGS Group AB—(Continued)
Web Site: https://nursedocpartner.se
Staffing & Recruiting Services
N.A.I.C.S.: 561311

Qsearch AB (1)
Kungsgatan 12 7tr, 111 35, Stockholm, Sweden
Tel.: (46) 850580890
Web Site: https://www.qsearch.se
Staffing & Recruiting Services
N.A.I.C.S.: 561311

Socionomuthyrning AB (1)
Kungsgatan 12 7 tr, 111 35, Stockholm, Sweden
Tel.: (46) 84460400
Web Site: https://www.socionomuthyrning.se
Recruitment Consulting Services
N.A.I.C.S.: 541612

Source Executive Recruitment Sweden AB (1)
Kungsgatan 12 7tr, 111 35, Stockholm, Sweden
Tel.: (46) 841044100
Web Site: https://source-executive.se
Staffing & Recruiting Services
N.A.I.C.S.: 561311

Vikariepoolen AB (1)
Kungsgatan 12 7tr, 111 35, Stockholm, Sweden
Tel.: (46) 850580800
Web Site: https://www.vikariepoolen.se
Staffing & Recruiting Services
N.A.I.C.S.: 561311

NGSC LIMITED
96 Road #12-04 SIF Building, Singapore, 149544, Singapore
Tel.: (65) 4793866
Web Site: http://www.ngscinvestment.com
Year Founded: 1953
B07—(SES)
Assets: $29,092,014
Liabilities: $1,011,660
Net Worth: $28,080,354
Earnings: $14,884,234
Fiscal Year-end: 03/31/20
Investment Holding Company; Satellite-Based Services
N.A.I.C.S.: 551112
Ven Jee Koit *(Controller-Fin)*

NGX LIMITED
Level 9 28 The Esplanade, Perth, 6000, WA, Australia
Tel.: (61) 893226322
Web Site: https://www.ngxlimited.com
Year Founded: 2021
NGX—(ASX)
Rev.: $9,401
Assets: $10,012,832
Liabilities: $228,345
Net Worth: $9,784,488
Earnings: ($2,277,921)
Fiscal Year-end: 06/30/23
Mineral Exploration Services
N.A.I.C.S.: 213115
Ian Middlemas *(Chm)*

NH FOODS LTD.
Breeze Tower 2-4-9 Umeda, Kita-ku, Osaka, 530-0001, Japan
Tel.: (81) 675253026 JP
Web Site: https://www.nipponham.co.jp
Year Founded: 1949
2282—(TKS)
Rev.: $8,615,685,520
Assets: $6,333,946,570
Liabilities: $2,769,821,350
Net Worth: $3,564,125,220
Earnings: $185,595,580
Emp.: 55,580
Fiscal Year-end: 03/31/24
Ham & Sausage Products, Fresh Meat, Processed Food & Delicatessen Products Mfr

N.A.I.C.S.: 311612
Yoshihide Hata *(Pres & CEO)*
Subsidiaries:

Beef Producers Australia Pty. Ltd. (1)
1-21 Madeline Street, Strathfield, 2136, NSW, Australia **(100%)**
Tel.: (61) 296420355
N.A.I.C.S.: 311612

Day-Lee Foods Inc. (1)
10350 Heritage Park Dr Ste 111, Santa Fe Springs, CA 90670 **(100%)**
Tel.: (562) 903-3020
Web Site: https://www.day-lee.com
Sales Range: $50-74.9 Million
Emp.: 30
Retailer of Meat & Poultry Products
N.A.I.C.S.: 424470
Hironobu Yamane *(Pres)*

Ege-Tav Ege Tarim Hayvancilik Yatirim Ticaret ve Sanayi Anonim Sirketi (1)
Uluyol Bagyurdu Area Ankara Asfalti No 30, Kemalpasa, Izmir, Türkiye
Tel.: (90) 232 463 4083
Web Site: https://www.bolez.com.tr
Chicken Feed Mfr
N.A.I.C.S.: 311119

FOOD SAFETY EVALUATION & RESEARCH INSTITUTE CO., LTD. (1)
No 619 Ziri Road, Minhang, Shanghai, 200041, China
Tel.: (86) 21 6145 0555
Web Site: http://www.foodsafety-eri.com.cn
Sales Range: $25-49.9 Million
Emp.: 26
Food Researching & Mfr
N.A.I.C.S.: 311999

HOKO Co., Ltd. (1)
2-1-1 Osaki, 3-19-15 Takanawa, Shinagawa-ku, Tokyo, 141-6011, Japan
Tel.: (81) 354752420
Sales Range: $150-199.9 Million
Emp.: 776
Seafood Processing Services
N.A.I.C.S.: 311710
Juichi Suezawa *(Pres)*

Hakodate Carl Raymon Co., Ltd. (1)
3-92 Suzuranokacho, Hakodate, 042-0958, Japan
Tel.: (81) 138554596
Sausages & Prepared Meats Mfr
N.A.I.C.S.: 311999

Hokkaido Nippon Ham Fighters Baseball Club (1)
1 F Village, Toyohira-ku, Kitahiroshima, 061-1116, Hokkaido, Japan
Tel.: (81) 570005586
Web Site: https://www.fighters.co.jp
Sales Range: $75-99.9 Million
Emp.: 150
Professional Basketball Team
N.A.I.C.S.: 711211

Japan Food Corporation (1)
Think Park Tower 1-1 Osaki 2-chome, Shinagawa-ku, Tokyo, 141-6010, Japan
Tel.: (81) 345558660
Web Site: https://www.japanfoodcorp.co.jp
Emp.: 164
Processed Livestock & Marine Products Mfr & Distr
N.A.I.C.S.: 424460

Kanto Nippon Food, Inc. (1)
2-1-1 Osaki Suinkupakutawa13f, Shinagawa-Ku, Tokyo, 141-0032, Japan
Tel.: (81) 354362929
Fresh Meat Product Distr
N.A.I.C.S.: 424470

Kyodo Food Products Co., Ltd. (1)
New Plaza Building 403 2-21 Taiyuji-cho, Kita-ku, Osaka, Japan
Tel.: (81) 663156366
Web Site: https://www.kyodo-food.co.jp
Food Products Mfr & Distr
N.A.I.C.S.: 311999
Kazuko Yamada *(Pres)*

NH Foods Australia Pty. Ltd. (1)
Level 8 2 Elizabeth Plaza, North Sydney, 2060, NSW, Australia **(100%)**
Tel.: (61) 289180000
Web Site: http://www.nh-foods.com.au
Sales Range: $500-549.9 Million
Emp.: 50
Fresh Meat, Ham, Sausage & Processed Foods
N.A.I.C.S.: 311612
Andrew McDonald *(Sls Mgr)*

Subsidiary (Domestic):

Oakey Beef Exports Pty. Ltd. (2)
Oakey Connection Road, PO Box 156, Oakey, 4401, QLD, Australia **(100%)**
Tel.: (61) 746920000
Web Site: http://www.nh-foods.com.au
Emp.: 750
Processing, Manufacture & Sale of Beef
N.A.I.C.S.: 311612
Kurt Wockner *(Mgr-Livestock)*

Whyalla Beef Pty. Ltd. (2)
Suttons Road, PO Box 101, Beebo, Texas, 2410, QLD, Australia **(100%)**
Tel.: (61) 746509177
Web Site: http://www.whyallabeef.com.au
Sales Range: $25-49.9 Million
Cattle Fattening & Production
N.A.I.C.S.: 112112
Shigeru Sawada *(Pres)*

NH Foods Chile y Compania Limitada (1)
Av Andres Bello 2687 of 1002, Las Condes, 7591538, Santiago, Chile **(100%)**
Tel.: (56) 2 2438 6800
Web Site: http://www.nhfoodschile.cl
Sales Range: $25-49.9 Million
Emp.: 50
Procurement & Sale of Pork for Japanese Market & Production/Export of Marine Products
N.A.I.C.S.: 112210
Christian Galdames *(COO)*

NH Foods Taiwan Ltd. (1)
2nd Floor 4th Floor No 1 Guangfu South Road, Taipei, Taiwan **(100%)**
Tel.: (886) 227425000
Web Site: https://www.nhfoods.com.tw
Sales Range: $25-49.9 Million
Emp.: 20
Sales & Distribution of Meat Products, Livestock, Fisheries, Vegetables, Fruits & Flowers
N.A.I.C.S.: 311612
Shinichiro Kunishima *(Pres)*

NH Foods U.K. Ltd. (1)
1 St Katharines Way, London, E1W 1UN, United Kingdom **(100%)**
Tel.: (44) 2074807146
Web Site: http://nhfoods-europe.com
Sales Range: $25-49.9 Million
Emp.: 5
Export & Sales of Marine Products, Fresh Meats & Processed Meats
N.A.I.C.S.: 311612
Kevin Mimura *(Gen Mgr)*

Nagasaki-Nippon Ham Co., Ltd. (1)
39 Momozugo Kawatana-cho, Higashisonogi-gun, Nagasaki, Japan
Tel.: (81) 956832486
Web Site: http://www.nipponham.co.jp
Sales Range: $25-49.9 Million
Emp.: 160
Meat Processing Services
N.A.I.C.S.: 311612

New Wave Leathers Pty Ltd (1)
4 Raymond Road, Laverton, 3026, VIC, Australia
Tel.: (61) 383688888
Sales Range: $25-49.9 Million
Emp.: 125
Leather Tanning & Finishing
N.A.I.C.S.: 316110

Nippon Chilled Logistics, Inc. (1)
Tel.: (81) 442702741
Sales Range: $25-49.9 Million
Emp.: 5
Logistics Consulting Servies
N.A.I.C.S.: 541614

Nippon Dry Foods Co., Ltd. (1)
2-1-1 Osaki, Shinagawa-Ku, Tokyo, 141-6011, Japan

INTERNATIONAL PUBLIC

Tel.: (81) 345558302
Emp.: 776
Dry Food Products Mfr
N.A.I.C.S.: 311999

Nippon Food Packer, Inc. (1)
838-1 Takagawara Ishiicho, Myozai-gun, Tokushima, 779-3223, Japan
Tel.: (81) 886744191
Meat Processing Services
N.A.I.C.S.: 311613

Nippon Ham Business Expert Corporation (1)
2-7-5 Shimmachi Keihanshinfudosanshimmachi Bldg, Nishi-Ku, Osaka, 550-0013, Japan
Tel.: (81) 6 6534 3506
Information Technology Consulting Services
N.A.I.C.S.: 541512

Nippon Ham Customer Communication Co., Ltd. (1)
2-4-9 Umeda Osaka Breeze Tower 19th Floor, Kita-ku, Osaka, 530-0001, Japan
Tel.: (81) 675253300
Web Site: https://www.nhcc.co.jp
Processed Ham Mfr
N.A.I.C.S.: 311612

Nippon Ham Hokkaido Factory Co., Ltd. (1)
Hokkaido Asahikawa Industrial Park 1-3-1-37, Asahikawa, 078-8271, Japan
Tel.: (81) 166761186
Web Site: https://www.nipponham-hokkaidofa.co.jp
Processed Ham Mfr
N.A.I.C.S.: 311612

Nippon Ham Life Service Co., Ltd. (1)
3-6-14 Minamihommachi Ito Bldg 3f, Chuo-Ku, Osaka, 541-0054, Japan
Tel.: (81) 662823082
Insurance Agencies & Brokerage Services
N.A.I.C.S.: 524210

Nippon Logistics Center, Inc (1)
12-3 Ukishima-cho, Kawasaki-ku, Kawasaki, 210-0862, Kanagawa, Japan
Tel.: (81) 445781001
Web Site: https://www.nbcweb.co.jp
Emp.: 238
Logistics Consulting Servies
N.A.I.C.S.: 541614

Nippon Luna, Inc. (1)
106 Nishikubo Kamizuya, Yawata, 614-8183, Kyoto, Japan
Tel.: (81) 120014367
Sales Range: $25-49.9 Million
Emp.: 282
Soft Drinks Mfr
N.A.I.C.S.: 312111

Nippon Pure Food, Inc. (1)
14F Think Park Tower 2-1-1 Osaki, Shinagawa-ku, Tokyo, 141-6014, Japan
Tel.: (81) 367488024
Sales Range: $100-124.9 Million
Emp.: 300
Meat Packing Services
N.A.I.C.S.: 311612

Nippon Shokuhin Mexicana S.A. de C.V. (1)
Av patria 1501 Jardines Universidad, 451110, Zapopan, Mexico
Tel.: (52) 3336820552
Processed Meat Mfr
N.A.I.C.S.: 311612

Nippon White Farm Co., Ltd. (1)
102-100 Mayasguhuru, Yokohama, 039-4101, Kamikita, Japan
Tel.: (81) 175783934
Sales Range: $150-199.9 Million
Emp.: 512
Meat Processing Services
N.A.I.C.S.: 311612

Osaka Football Club Co., Ltd (1)
1-1 Nagai-koen, Higashisumiyoshi-ku, Osaka, 546-0034, Japan
Tel.: (81) 666093750
Web Site: https://www.cerezo.jp
Football Team
N.A.I.C.S.: 711211

AND PRIVATE COMPANIES

Redondo's Inc. (1)
94-140 Leokane st, Waipahu, HI 96797-2209
Tel.: (808) 671-5444
Web Site: https://www.redondos.com
Sales Range: $25-49.9 Million
Emp.: 40
Mfr of Meat Products
N.A.I.C.S.: 311612

Shandong Rilong Foodstuffs Co., Ltd. (1)
Food Industrial Zone, Laiyang, 265231, Shandong, China
Tel.: (86) 5357708323
Sales Range: $100-124.9 Million
Emp.: 35
Processed Food Mfr
N.A.I.C.S.: 311999

Thai Nippon Foods Co., Ltd. (1)
1/21 Rojana Industrial Park Moo 5, Kanham Village U-Thai District, Ayutthaya, 13210, Thailand (100%)
Tel.: (66) 3533004652
Web Site: https://thainipponfoods.com
Sales Range: $200-249.9 Million
Emp.: 800
Meat Packaging & Foods Processor
N.A.I.C.S.: 311612

Thai Nippon Meat Packers Co., Ltd. (1)
14 Fl legion House, Bangkok, 10330, Thailand (100%)
Tel.: (66) 22553505
Web Site: http://www.nipponmnh.co.jp
Sales Range: $25-49.9 Million
Emp.: 15
N.A.I.C.S.: 311612

The Marine Foods Corporation (1)
11th Floor ThinkPark Tower 2-1-1 Osaki, Shinagawa-ku, Tokyo, 141-6011, Japan
Tel.: (81) 364201155
Web Site: https://www.marinefoods.co.jp
Emp.: 1,451
Processed Marine Food Products Mfr & Whslr
N.A.I.C.S.: 424460
Katsunori Fujiwara *(Pres)*

Thomas Borthwick & Sons (Australia) Pty. Ltd. (1)
113 Main Street, Bakers Creek, MacKay, 4740, QLD, Australia (100%)
Tel.: (61) 749528888
Web Site: http://www.mcs.net.au
Sales Range: $200-249.9 Million
Emp.: 600
Veal Product Mfr
N.A.I.C.S.: 311612
Malcolm Kinman *(Mgr-Livestock)*

Weihai Nippon Shokuhin Co., Ltd. (1)
Export Processing Zone Weihai Economic Development Zone, Weihai, 264200, China
Tel.: (86) 6315903998
Processed Meat Mfr
N.A.I.C.S.: 311612

Wingham Beef Export Pty Ltd (1)
1295 Gloucester Rd, PO Box 13, Wingham, 2429, NSW, Australia (100%)
Tel.: (61) 265911000
Web Site: https://www.nh-foods.com.au
Sales Range: $100-124.9 Million
Emp.: 400
N.A.I.C.S.: 311612

NH PRIME REIT CO., LTD.
5F NH Foundation Building 2 Gukjejong-ro 8-gil, Yeongdeungpo-Gu, Seoul, 07330, Korea (South)
Tel.: (82) 262642843
Web Site: https://www.nhreits.com
Year Founded: 2018
338100—(KRS)
Real Estate Services
N.A.I.C.S.: 531210
Cheol-Su Seo *(CEO)*

NH SL SPECIAL PURPOSE ACQUISITION CO., LTD.
9F 60 Yeoui-daero, Yeongdeungpo-gu, Seoul, Korea (South)
Tel.: (82) 27505744
Year Founded: 2014
Assets: $4,079,731
Liabilities: $359,315
Net Worth: $3,720,416
Earnings: ($3,246)
Financial Investment Management Services
N.A.I.C.S.: 523940
Jong Wook Kim *(CEO)*

NH SPECIAL PURPOSE ACQUISITION 7 CO., LTD.
60 Yeoui-daero, Yeongdeungpo-gu, Seoul, Korea (South)
Tel.: (82) 27505639
Year Founded: 2015
Financial Investment Management Services
N.A.I.C.S.: 523940
Jun-Hyo Lee *(CEO)*

NHA BE WATER SUPPLY JOINT STOCK COMPANY
No 1179 Nguyen Van Linh, Tan Phong Ward District 7, Ho Chi Minh City, Vietnam
Tel.: (84) 19001210
NBW—(HNX)
Rev.: $29,973,305
Assets: $10,959,025
Liabilities: $4,266,374
Net Worth: $6,692,651
Earnings: $653,608
Fiscal Year-end: 12/31/20
Water Supply Services
N.A.I.C.S.: 221310
Nguyen Ngoc Trang *(Deputy Mgr)*

NHC COMMUNICATIONS, INC.
5450 Cote De Liesse, Mont Royal, H4P 1A5, QC, Canada
Tel.: (514) 735-2741
Web Site: http://www.nhc.com
Year Founded: 1986
Sales Range: $1-9.9 Million
Emp.: 48
Physical-Layer High-Speed Switched Accessed Solutions for Voice & Data Networks Designer & Mfr
N.A.I.C.S.: 517112
Marvin Garellek *(Dir-Mktg & Domestic Sls)*

Subsidiaries:

NHC Communications USA, Inc. (1)
PO Box 3578, Manassas, VA 20108
Tel.: (514) 735-2741
Network Switching & Test Equipment Mfr
N.A.I.C.S.: 517810

NHC Europe S.A. (1)
18 rue Kleber, Courbevoie, 92400, Paris, France
Tel.: (33) 141999920
Network Switching & Test Equipment Mfr
N.A.I.C.S.: 517810

NHC FOODS LIMITED
D-22/8 TTC Industrial Area MIDC Industrial Area Turbhe, Mumbai, 400 705, India
Tel.: (91) 2269875000
Web Site: https://www.nhcgroup.com
Year Founded: 1960
517554—(BOM)
Rev.: $19,676,686
Assets: $8,332,882
Liabilities: $5,276,758
Net Worth: $3,056,124
Earnings: $210,587
Emp.: 30
Fiscal Year-end: 03/31/23
Food Products Mfr & Distr
N.A.I.C.S.: 311999
Alpa A. Shah *(Exec Dir)*

Subsidiaries:

Intra Metal Trading LLC (1)
Business Center 1 M Floor The Meydan Hotel Meydan Free Zone, PO Box 241677, Meydan, United Arab Emirates
Tel.: (971) 551820216
Web Site: https://www.intrametal.ae
Metal Trading & Recycling Services
N.A.I.C.S.: 541420

NHI HIEP BRICK - TILE JOINT STOCK COMPANY
1/8 Quyet Thang Quarter Binh Thang Ward, Di An, Binh Duong, Vietnam
Tel.: (84) 2743749080
Web Site: https://gachngoinhihiep.com
Year Founded: 1952
NHC—(HNX)
Rev.: $1,362,500
Assets: $6,492,400
Liabilities: $1,052,100
Net Worth: $5,440,300
Earnings: ($102,100)
Fiscal Year-end: 12/31/23
Tiles & Bricks Mfr
N.A.I.C.S.: 327331
Nguyen Hong Chau *(Chm-Mgmt Bd)*

NHI OMAN
Building No 900 Way No 63 Al Fursan Street, Wadi Kabir, Muscat, Oman
Tel.: (968) 24816313
Web Site: http://www.nhioman.com
Educational Consulting Services
N.A.I.C.S.: 611710
Robert MacLean *(Principal)*

NHK SPRING CO., LTD.

NHK SPRING CO., LTD.
3-10 Fukuura, Kanazawa-ku, Yokohama, 236-0004, Japan
Tel.: (81) 457867511 JP
Web Site: https://www.nhkspg.co.jp
Year Founded: 1939
5991—(TKS)
Rev.: $5,069,433,740
Assets: $4,562,810,290
Liabilities: $1,782,816,150
Net Worth: $2,779,994,140
Earnings: $259,032,680
Emp.: 20,524
Fiscal Year-end: 03/31/24
Suspensions & Springs Mfr
N.A.I.C.S.: 332613
Takashi Kayamoto *(Pres & CEO)*

Subsidiaries:

Ayase Seimitsu Co., Ltd (1)
1-13-6 Yoshiokahigashi, Ayase, 252-1125, Kanagawa, Japan
Tel.: (81) 467767631
Web Site: https://www.ayase-seimitsu.co.jp
Automobile Parts Mfr
N.A.I.C.S.: 336390
Shibata Liu *(Pres)*

Eguzkia-NHK, S.A. (1)
Poligono induatrial Jondarrea, Alsasua, 31000, Navarra, Spain
Tel.: (34) 948562013
Sales Range: $50-74.9 Million
Emp.: 100
Suspension & Spring Mfr
N.A.I.C.S.: 334519
Bernardo Gomez *(Branch Mgr)*

Faurecia-NHK Kyushu Co., Ltd. (1)
9-9 Shinhama-cho Kanda-manchi, Miyako-gun, Fukuoka, 800-0321, Japan
Tel.: (81) 934353300
Automotive Seat Mfr & Distr
N.A.I.C.S.: 336360

G.L.G. Corporation (1)
2 1 12 Kita Kase, Saiwai Ku, Kawasaki, 212 0057, Kanagawa, Japan (100%)
Tel.: (81) 445992471
Web Site: http://www.linx-shinkawasaki.com
Sales Range: $10-24.9 Million
Emp.: 60
Operation of Golf Driving Range
N.A.I.C.S.: 611620
Kido Koro Hideaki *(Mgr)*

Horikiri, Inc (1)
1827-4 Kamikoya, Yachiyo, 276-0022, Chiba, Japan
Tel.: (81) 474841111
Web Site: https://horikiri.co.jp
Sales Range: $50-74.9 Million
Emp.: 174
Industrial Spring Mfr
N.A.I.C.S.: 332613
Yukihiro Seki *(Pres)*

Iberica de Suspensiones, S.A. (1)
Poligono Industrial La Mina S/N, 12520, Nules, Castellon, Spain
Tel.: (34) 964674212
Web Site: http://www.sogefi.it
Sales Range: $50-74.9 Million
Emp.: 200
Suspension & Spring Mfr
N.A.I.C.S.: 334519

Ites Co., Ltd (1)
1-60 Kuribayashi-cho, Totsuka-ku, Otsu, 520-2151, Shiga, Japan
Tel.: (81) 775995015
Web Site: https://www.ites.co.jp
Emp.: 92
Motor Vehicle Parts Mfr
N.A.I.C.S.: 336390

Japan Power Fastening Co., Ltd. (1)
1-8-3 Senba Nishi, Minoh, Osaka, 562-0036, Japan
Tel.: (81) 668732251
Web Site: https://www.jpf-net.co.jp
Emp.: 160
Mfr of Industrial Metal Fasteners & Tools for Construction
N.A.I.C.S.: 333519

Muelles y Ballestas Hispani-Alemanas S.A. (1)
Camino Viejo de Castellon a Onda s/n, Villarreal, 12540, Spain
Tel.: (34) 964 521 050
Sales Range: $25-49.9 Million
Motor Vehicle Component Mfr
N.A.I.C.S.: 336390
Miguel Ruiz *(Gen Mgr)*

NHK FLEX Co., Ltd. (1)
2445-5 Nishiminowa, Ina, 399-4501, Nagano, Japan
Tel.: (81) 26 576 3280
Web Site: https://www.nhkflex-co-ltd.co.jp
General Industrial Equipment Mfr & Distr
N.A.I.C.S.: 333415

NHK Fastener do Brasil Industria e Comercio Ltda. (1)
Av Francisco Monteiro 4140, Sta Luzia Ribeirao Pires, 09441-000, Sao Paulo, Brazil
Tel.: (55) 1148283488
Web Site: http://www.nhkfastener.com.br
Sales Range: $50-74.9 Million
Emp.: 180
Fastener Mfr
N.A.I.C.S.: 339993

NHK International Corp. (1)
46855 Magellan Dr, Novi, MI 48377
Tel.: (248) 926-0111
Web Site: http://www.nhkinternational.com
Sales Range: $25-49.9 Million
Emp.: 62
Distribution of Automotive Springs
N.A.I.C.S.: 541330
Hideto Enomoto *(Pres & CEO)*

NHK MEC CORPORATION (1)
3-21-10 Shin-yokohama, Kohoku-ku, Yokohama, 222-0033, Japan
Tel.: (81) 454758905
Web Site: https://www.nhkmec.com
Electronic Components Distr
N.A.I.C.S.: 423690

NHK Manufacturing (Malaysia) SDN. BHD (1)
Lot 44 Persiaran Bunga Tanjung 1 Senawang Industrial Park, 70400, Seremban, Negeri Sembilan, Malaysia
Tel.: (60) 66787495
Web Site: https://www.nhkmfg.com.my

NHK SPRING CO., LTD.

NHK Spring Co., Ltd.—(Continued)
Emp.: 300
Printed Circuit Board Mfr
N.A.I.C.S.: 334412
H. Sugiura (Chm)

NHK Morse Co., Ltd. (1)
3 21 10 Shinyokohama, Kohoku-ku, Yokohama, 222 0033, Japan
Tel.: (81) 454758710
Web Site: http://www.nhkmec.com
Mfr & Sales of Push-Pull Cable, Mechanical Control Devices for Marine & Other Applications
N.A.I.C.S.: 335929

NHK Parking Systems Co., Ltd (1)
2-8-19 Kitakyuki Yokohama West Exit, Nishi-ku, Yokohama, 220-0004, Japan
Tel.: (81) 453262890
Web Site: https://www.nhk-ps.co.jp
Parking Garage Systems & Equipments Mfr & Distr
N.A.I.C.S.: 334419

NHK Precision (Thailand) Co., Ltd. (1)
878 MQO 2 Bangpoo Industrial Estate Preakasamai, Muangsamutprakarn, Samut Prakan, 10280, Thailand
Tel.: (66) 211711007
Automotive Break Mfr
N.A.I.C.S.: 336390

NHK Precision Co., Ltd. (1)
2-1-49 Numame, Isehara, 259-1126, Kanagawa, Japan (100%)
Tel.: (81) 463945235
Web Site: https://www.nisseiko.co.jp
Sales Range: $25-49.9 Million
Emp.: 227
Mfr & Sales of Precision Products Including Cross-Recessed-Head Screw Punches & Disk Springs
N.A.I.C.S.: 332613

NHK Sales Co., Ltd. (1)
8F NBF Comodio Shiodome Bldg 2-14-1 Higashi-Shinbashi, Minato-ku, Tokyo, 105-0021, Japan
Tel.: (81) 368541600
Web Site: https://www.nippan-inc.co.jp
Sales Range: $100-124.9 Million
Emp.: 343
Sale, Export & Import of Springs, Automotive Parts, Industrial Fasteners & Machinery
N.A.I.C.S.: 334519

NHK Seating of America Inc. (1)
2298 W State Rd 28, Frankfort, IN 46041
Tel.: (765) 659-4781
Web Site: https://www.nhkseating.com
Emp.: 700
Automotive Seat Mfr
N.A.I.C.S.: 336360
Yushiyuki Shindo (Pres)

NHK Seating of America, Inc. (1)
2298 W State Rd 28, Frankfort, IN 46041-9185
Tel.: (765) 659-4781
Web Site: http://www.nhkseating.com
Automobile Seats Mfr
N.A.I.C.S.: 336360
Rich Reck (Gen Mgr)

NHK Spring (Thailand) Co., Ltd. (1)
Bangna Tower A 6th-7th floor 2/3 Moo 14 Bangna-Trad Rd km 6 5, PO Box 2558, Bangkaew Bangplee, Samut Prakan, 10540, Thailand
Tel.: (66) 27302200
Web Site: https://www.nhkspg.co.th
Mfr of Furniture
N.A.I.C.S.: 337211

NHK Spring India Ltd. (1)
Plot No 31 Sector 3 Industrial Model Township, Manesar, Gurgaon, 122 050, Haryana, India
Tel.: (91) 1244590700
Web Site: https://www.nhkspringindia.com
Sales Range: $125-149.9 Million
Emp.: 135
Automotive Suspension Component & Utility Vehicle Mfr
N.A.I.C.S.: 336330
Toru Kadowaki (Mng Dir)

NHK Spring Philippines, Inc. (1)
Phase 3-109 East Main Ave SEPZ Laguna Technopark Brgy Malamig, Laguna, Binan, 4024, Philippines
Tel.: (63) 49 541 1103
Web Site: https://www.nhkspringph.com
Foam Parts Mfr
N.A.I.C.S.: 326150
Daisuke Sakatani (Pres)

NHK Spring Precision (Guangzhou) Co., Ltd. (1)
No 189 Lianguang Road, East District Economic and Technological Development Zone, Guangzhou, 510760, Guangdong, China
Tel.: (86) 208 226 6456
Web Site: https://www.nspgz.com
Valve Spring Mfr
N.A.I.C.S.: 332911

NHK Spring Precision of America Inc. (1)
10600 Freeport Dr, Louisville, KY 40258-1883
Tel.: (502) 935-5556
Web Site: https://nhkprecision.com
Automotive Sell Valve Spring Mfr & Distr
N.A.I.C.S.: 336390
Duane Smothers (Supvr-Production)

NHK Spring Production Company (1)
56 Suzukawa, Isehara, 259-1146, Japan
Tel.: (81) 46 394 8425
Web Site: https://www.nkiko-nhkspg.co.jp
Automobile Parts Mfr
N.A.I.C.S.: 336310

NHK Spring R&D Center, Inc. (1)
3 10 Fukuura, Kanazawa Ku, Yokohama, 236 0004, Japan
Tel.: (81) 457867511
Sales Range: $800-899.9 Million
Emp.: 4,000
Suspension Mfr
N.A.I.C.S.: 334519

NHK Transport Co., Ltd. (1)
3-10 Fukuura, Kanazawa-Ku, Yokohama, 236-0004, Kanagawa, Japan
Tel.: (81) 457880811
Web Site: https://www.nhktrs.com
Emp.: 494
Transport, Storage, Importing & Exporting Services
N.A.I.C.S.: 488510

NHK of America Suspension Components Inc. (1)
3251 Nashville Rd, Bowling Green, KY 42101
Tel.: (270) 842-4006
Web Site: https://www.nhknasco.com
Sales Range: $50-74.9 Million
Emp.: 210
Coil Spring Mfr
N.A.I.C.S.: 332613

NHK-Associated Spring Suspension Components Inc. (1)
3251 Nashville Rd, Bowling Green, KY 42101
Tel.: (270) 842-4006
Web Site: http://www.nascospg.com
Sales Range: $25-49.9 Million
Emp.: 350
Suspension Spring Components Mfr
N.A.I.C.S.: 332613

NHK-Uni Spring (Guangzhou) Co., Ltd. (1)
No 28 Kaiyuan Road Economic Technology Development East Zone, Guangzhou, 510530, Guangdong, China
Tel.: (86) 2082266136
Web Site: http://www.nus.com.cn
Emp.: 520
Coil Spring & Stabilizer Mfr
N.A.I.C.S.: 332613

New Mather Metals Inc. (1)
326 Page Dr, Franklin, KY 42134-6242
Tel.: (270) 598-5900
Web Site: http://nhknewmathermetals.com
Sales Range: $25-49.9 Million
Emp.: 100
Automotive Spring & Suspension Mfr
N.A.I.C.S.: 334519

Nippatsu Service Co., Ltd. (1)
NHK Spring West Exit Building 3-32-1 Tsuruya-cho, Kanagawa-ku, Yokohama, 221-0835, Kanagawa, Japan (100%)
Tel.: (81) 453167700
Web Site: https://www.nhkspg-nsv.com
Sales Range: $1-4.9 Billion
Emp.: 4,000
Insurance, Real Estate, Travel Agent Services; Sales of Fuel Oil, Petroleum Products & Auto Parts
N.A.I.C.S.: 524298

Nippon Shaft Co., Ltd. (1)
1-15 2-Chome Sachiura, Kanazawa-ku, Yokohama, 236-0003, Japan
Tel.: (81) 45 782 2561
Web Site: http://www.nipponshaft.co.jp
Emp.: 153
Sports Equipment Mfr
N.A.I.C.S.: 339920

Sindai Co., Ltd. (1)
3-3-6 Shindencho, Aichi, Takahama, 444-1301, Japan
Tel.: (81) 566521221
Web Site: http://www.sindai.co.jp
Emp.: 385
Automotive Parts Distr & Mfr
N.A.I.C.S.: 336390

Sumihatsu Co., Ltd. (1)
4F Akihabara center place Bldg 1 Kandaaioi-cho, Chiyoda, Tokyo, 101-0029, Japan (100%)
Tel.: (81) 368541481
Mfr & Sales of Leaf Springs, Coil Springs, Railway Points, Rail Clips, Control Cable
N.A.I.C.S.: 332613

Tohoku Nippatsu Co., Ltd. (1)
18-25-2 Fujine, Waga-cho, Kitakami, 024-0334, Iwate, Japan (100%)
Tel.: (81) 197735221
Web Site: https://www.tnkspg.co.jp
Sales Range: $50-74.9 Million
Emp.: 214
Automotive Springs Mfr
N.A.I.C.S.: 334519

Tokuhatsu Co., Ltd (1)
1-1-1 Kitagawara, Itami, 664-0837, Hyogo, Japan
Tel.: (81) 727826966
Web Site: https://www.tokuhatsu.co.jp
Sales Range: $50-74.9 Million
Emp.: 214
Industrial Spring Mfr & Distr
N.A.I.C.S.: 332722
Hitoshi Kotagiri (Pres)

Topura Co., Ltd. (1)
201 Soya, Hadano, 257-0031, Kanagawa, Japan
Tel.: (81) 463822711
Web Site: https://www.topura.co.jp
Emp.: 579
Machine Screws & Bolts Mfr
N.A.I.C.S.: 332722

Uni Auto Parts Manufacture Co., Ltd. (1)
No 40-10 Bogongkeng, Xihu Village Sanyi Township Miaoli, Hsinchu, Taiwan (100%)
Tel.: (886) 37873801
Web Site: http://www.uni-auto.com.tw
Sales Range: $200-249.9 Million
Emp.: 550
Mfr of Leaf Springs, Coil Springs & Automobile Seats
N.A.I.C.S.: 332613

Uni Flex Co Ltd (1)
2445 5 Kitahara, Nishi Minowa, Ina, 399-4501, Nagano, Japan
Tel.: (81) 265763287
Web Site: http://www.uniflex-co-ltd.co.jp
Mfr of Control Cables, Shifter Systems & Adjustable Pedals
N.A.I.C.S.: 331420

Yokohama Kiko Co., Ltd. (1)
2-11-1 Fukuura, Kanazawa-Ku, Yokohama, 236-0004, Japan
Tel.: (81) 457877301
Web Site: https://www.yokohamakiko.com
Sales Range: $10-24.9 Million
Emp.: 80
Mfr of Stabilizer Bars & Lighting Devices
N.A.I.C.S.: 335931

NHN CORP.

NHN Play Museum 16 Daewangpangyo-ro 645beon-gil, Bundang-gu, Seongnam, 13487, Gyeonggi-do, Korea (South)
Tel.: (82) 15446859
Web Site: https://www.nhnent.com
Year Founded: 2013
181710—(KRS)
Rev.: $1,622,105,149
Assets: $2,320,314,610
Liabilities: $792,129,115
Net Worth: $1,528,185,495
Earnings: ($24,626,208)
Emp.: 874
Fiscal Year-end: 12/31/22
Game Software Development Services
N.A.I.C.S.: 513210
Joon Ho Lee (Chm)

Subsidiaries:

Accommate Co., Ltd. (1)
72 Digital-ro 26-gil, Guro-gu, Seoul, Korea (South)
Tel.: (82) 25156885
Web Site: https://www.accommate.com
Information Technology Services
N.A.I.C.S.: 541511

NHN BigFoot Corp. (1)
NHN Play Museum 16 Daewangpangyo-ro 645beon-gil, Bundang-gu, Seongnam, 13487, Gyeonggi, Korea (South)
Tel.: (82) 15446859
Web Site: http://www.nhnbigfoot.com
Game Development Services
N.A.I.C.S.: 541511

NHN Ticketlink Corporation (1)
NHN Play Museum 16 Daewangpangyo-ro 645beon-gil, Bundang-gu, Seongnam, 13487, Gyeonggi, Korea (South)
Tel.: (82) 16443850
Web Site: http://www.ticketlink.co.kr
Entertainment & Game Software Services
N.A.I.C.S.: 513210

NHN KCP CORP.

72 Digital-ro 26-gil, Guro-gu, Seoul, 08393, Korea (South)
Tel.: (82) 15448667
Web Site: https://www.kcp.co.kr
Year Founded: 1994
060250—(KRS)
Rev.: $631,059,308
Assets: $359,097,476
Liabilities: $206,806,208
Net Worth: $152,291,268
Earnings: $26,785,619
Emp.: 398
Fiscal Year-end: 12/31/22
Electronic Payment Services
N.A.I.C.S.: 522320
Park Jun-Seok (CEO)

NHP PRODUCTION IMPORT - EXPORT JSC

8th floor 52 Nguyen Chi Thanh, Dong Da Dist, Hanoi, Vietnam
Tel.: (84) 432669067
Web Site: http://www.nhpvietnam.com
Polypropylene Woven Bag Mfr
N.A.I.C.S.: 314910

NHPC LTD.

NHPC Office Complex Sector-33, Faridabad, 121003, Haryana, India
Tel.: (91) 1292588500
Web Site: https://www.nhpcindia.com
Year Founded: 1975
533098—(BOM)
Rev.: $1,353,024,399
Assets: $10,321,618,608
Liabilities: $5,897,502,548
Net Worth: $4,424,116,060
Earnings: $507,732,150
Emp.: 4,776
Fiscal Year-end: 03/31/23
Hydroelectric Power Distr

AND PRIVATE COMPANIES

N.A.I.C.S.: 221111
Avinash Kumar *(Exec Dir)*

Subsidiaries:

Bundelkhand Saur Urja Limited (1)
TC-43/V Vibhuti Khand Gomti Nagar, Lucknow, 226010, Uttar Pradesh, India
Tel.: (91) 5222720952
Web Site: https://www.bsulindia.com
Solar Power Services
N.A.I.C.S.: 221114
Shri Ratish Kumar *(Chm)*

Chenab Valley Power Projects Private Limited (1)
Chenab Jal Shakti Bhawan Opposite Saraswati Dham Rail Head Complex, Jammu, 180012, Uttar Pradesh, India
Tel.: (91) 1912475516
Web Site: https://www.cvppindia.com
Solar Power Services
N.A.I.C.S.: 221114
Sudhir Anand *(Sec)*

NHDC Limited (1)
NHDCPeriser Shyamala Hills, Bhopal, 462013, India
Tel.: (91) 7554030014
Web Site: https://www.nhdcindia.com
Power Supply Services
N.A.I.C.S.: 221122

National High Power Test Laboratory Private Limited (1)
Core 8 1st Floor Scope Complex Lodhi Road, New Delhi, 110 003, India
Tel.: (91) 1124369550
Web Site: http://www.nhptl.com
Power Supply Services
N.A.I.C.S.: 221122
R. N. Singh *(Chm)*

NI HSIN GROUP BERHAD
No 45 Jalan Taming Dua Taman Taming Jaya, 43300, Seri Kembangan, Selangor, Malaysia
Tel.: (60) 389616815
Web Site: https://www.ni-hsin.com
NIHSIN—(KLS)
Rev: $7,577,708
Assets: $28,965,173
Liabilities: $3,947,378
Net Worth: $25,017,795
Earnings: ($1,595,633)
Emp.: 250
Fiscal Year-end: 12/31/21
Stainless Steel Mfr
N.A.I.C.S.: 331513
Yit Chan Tai *(Co-Sec)*

Subsidiaries:

BlackBixon Sdn. Bhd. (1)
47 Jalan Taming Dua Tmn Taming Jaya, 43300, Seri Kembangan, Selangor, Malaysia
Tel.: (60) 389612268
Web Site: https://www.blackbixon.com
Home Appliance Distr
N.A.I.C.S.: 423620

Ever-Grow Advanced Materials Sdn. Bhd. (1)
47 Jalan Taming Dua Taman Taming Jaya, 43300, Seri Kembangan, Selangor, Malaysia
Tel.: (60) 389619463
Web Site: https://www.ever-grow.com.my
Sales Range: $25-49.9 Million
Emp.: 50
Clad Metal & Stainless Steel Convex Mirror Mfr
N.A.I.C.S.: 331110

Ni Hsin Corporation Sdn. Bhd. (1)
No 45 Jln Taming Dua Taman Tanming Jaya, 43300, Seri Kembangan, Selangor, Malaysia
Tel.: (60) 389616815
Web Site: http://www.insage.com
Sales Range: $50-74.9 Million
Emp.: 200
Cookware Mfr
N.A.I.C.S.: 332215

Ni Hsin Ecologistics Sdn. Bhd. (1)
No 47 Jalan Taming 2 Taman Taming Jaya, 43300, Seri Kembangan, Selangor, Malaysia
Tel.: (60) 389611500
Web Site: https://www.nh-ecolog.com
Logistics & Warehousing Services
N.A.I.C.S.: 541614

Steel Crafts Europa S.R.L. (1)
Zona Industriale Via Stretta Nr 63, Sabbio Chiese, 25070, Brescia, Italy
Tel.: (39) 0307640079
Web Site: https://www.steelcrafts.it
Stainless Steel Mfr & Services
N.A.I.C.S.: 331210

NIAGARA MOTORS LTD
1537 Niagara Stone Rd, Virgil, L0S 1T0, ON, Canada
Tel.: (905) 468-2145
Web Site: http://www.niagaramotors.com
Year Founded: 1947
Rev.: $25,758,891
Emp.: 55
New & Used Car Dealers
N.A.I.C.S.: 441110
Troy Milinkovich *(Mgr-New Car Sls)*

NIAGARA THERAPY
Colomendy Industrial Estate, Rhyl Road, Denbigh, LL16 5TS, United Kingdom
Tel.: (44) 1745811229 UK
Web Site: http://www.niagaratherapy.co.uk
Adjustable Beds & Massage Products Mfr
N.A.I.C.S.: 337910
Allen Aikman *(Chm)*

NIAGARA VENTURES CORPORATION
7 St Thomas Street Unit 406, Toronto, M5S 2B7, ON, Canada
Tel.: (416) 669-1016 ON
Year Founded: 2012
NIA—(TSXV)
Investment Holding Company
N.A.I.C.S.: 551112
Ron McEachern *(Chm & CEO)*

NIBE INDUSTRIER AB
Hannabadsvagen 5, Box 14, 285 21, Markaryd, Sweden
Tel.: (46) 433273000 SE
Web Site: http://www.nibe.com
Year Founded: 1989
NIBE.B—(OMX)
Rev.: $4,369,233,939
Assets: $6,378,749,988
Liabilities: $3,549,504,997
Net Worth: $2,829,244,991
Earnings: $592,973,484
Emp.: 20,900
Fiscal Year-end: 12/31/23
Electric Heating Applications, Components & Systems Mfr
N.A.I.C.S.: 333415
Hans Linnarson *(Chm)*

Subsidiaries:

ABK AS (1)
Brobekkveien 80, 0582, Oslo, Norway
Tel.: (47) 23170520
Air Conditioning & Warm Air Heating Equipment Mfr
N.A.I.C.S.: 333415

ABK-Qviller AS (1)
Postboks 64, Vollebekk, Oslo, Norway
Tel.: (47) 23170520
Web Site: https://www.abkqviller.no
Heating & Air-conditioning Equipment Distr
N.A.I.C.S.: 423730

ATE-Electronics S.r.l. (1)
Via Ugo Scaletta 13, Giaveno, 10094, Turin, Italy
Tel.: (39) 011 937 8575
Web Site: https://www.ate-electronics.com
Capacitor & Power Resistor Mfr
N.A.I.C.S.: 334416

Ait-Varmeteknik-Sverige AB (1)
Franska Vagen 24, 393 56, Kalmar, Sweden
Tel.: (46) 4 220 3880
Web Site: https://www.ait.se
Heat Pump Mfr
N.A.I.C.S.: 333415

Akvaterm Oy (1)
Janismaantie 12, 67800, Kokkola, Finland (70%)
Tel.: (358) 6 824 4200
Web Site: http://www.akvaterm.fi
Sales Range: $1-9.9 Million
Emp.: 40
Water Heater Mfr & Distr
N.A.I.C.S.: 333414

Alpha-InnoTec France EURL (1)
16 Rue des Couturieres, 67240, Bischwiller, France
Tel.: (33) 3 88 06 24 10
Web Site: http://www.schulthess-group.com
Water Heater Mfr & Whslr
N.A.I.C.S.: 333310

Alpha-InnoTec Sun GmbH (1)
Gewerbepark BAB1 Nr 19, 66636, Tholey, Germany
Tel.: (49) 6853 300536
Web Site: http://www.alpha-innotec.nl
Water Heater Mfr & Whslr
N.A.I.C.S.: 333310

Askoma AG (1)
Industriestrasse 1, 4922, Butzberg, Switzerland
Tel.: (41) 62 958 7080
Web Site: https://www.en.askoma.com
Screw In Heater & Flange Heater Mfr
N.A.I.C.S.: 333414

Askoma Sdn. Bhd. (1)
3-B Jalan Dewani 1/1 Taman Perindustrian Dewani, 81100, Johor Bahru, Malaysia
Tel.: (60) 7 276 1717
Web Site: https://www.askoma.com.my
Injection Moulding & Plastic Parts Mfr
N.A.I.C.S.: 326199

Backer AB (1)
Fabriksgatan 11, Box 84, 282 71, Sosdala, Sweden
Tel.: (46) 4 516 6100
Web Site: https://www.backergroup.com
Emp.: 350
Heating Element & System Mfr
N.A.I.C.S.: 333415
Cecilia Fors *(Sls Mgr-Area)*

Backer Alpe S. de R.L. de C.V. (1)
Venado Street No 45 Col Los Olivos, Tlahuac, 13210, Mexico, Mexico
Tel.: (52) 55 845 0505
Web Site: https://www.backeralpe.com
Heating Equipment Mfr
N.A.I.C.S.: 333414

Backer BHV AB (1)
Fabriksgatan 11, 28010, Sosdala, Skane, Sweden
Tel.: (46) 45166100
Web Site: http://www.backer.se
Sales Range: $100-124.9 Million
Emp.: 350
Electrical Equipment & Component Mfr
N.A.I.C.S.: 335999

Division (Domestic):

Backer BHV AB - Calesco Division (2)
Vastra Avagen 11, 734 51, Kolback, Sweden
Tel.: (46) 220 453 00
Web Site: http://www.backercalesco.com
Heating Equipment Mfr
N.A.I.C.S.: 333414

Backer BHV-Calesco Div. (1)
Vastra Avagen 11, Kolback, S 734 51, Vasteras, Sweden
Tel.: (46) 22045300
Web Site: http://www.calescofoil.se
Sales Range: $25-49.9 Million
Emp.: 80
Electrical Equipment & Component Mfr
N.A.I.C.S.: 335999

Backer BHV/Calesco France Sarl (1)
20 rue de la Villette, 69328, Lyon, Cedex 03, France
Tel.: (33) 42 668 5037
Web Site: http://www.backercalesco.se
Electric Heating Applications Mfr
N.A.I.C.S.: 333994

Backer Cellnergy Engineering Pte. Ltd. (1)
Blk 51 Batok Crescent 06-26, Singapore, 658077, Singapore
Tel.: (65) 66650568
Web Site: http://www.backercellnergy.com
Heating Jacket & Silicon Rubber Heater Mfr
N.A.I.C.S.: 333414

Backer EHP Inc (1)
4700 John Bragg Hwy, Murfreesboro, TN 37127
Tel.: (615) 907-6900
Web Site: http://www.backerehp.com
Emp.: 40
Water Heater Mfr & Whslr
N.A.I.C.S.: 333310
Ryan Taylor *(Dir-Engrg-Products-HVAC)*

Backer ELC AG (1)
Wynental Strasse 1, 5001, Aarau, Switzerland
Tel.: (41) 628376285
Sales Range: $25-49.9 Million
Emp.: 4
Heating Equipment Mfr
N.A.I.C.S.: 333414
Christoph Frey *(Mng Dir)*

Backer Elektro CZ A.S. (1)
Policska 444, Hlinsko, Olomouc, Czech Republic
Tel.: (420) 46 303 0612
Web Site: https://www.backer-elektro.cz
Household Appliances Mfr
N.A.I.C.S.: 335220

Backer Eltop S.r.o. (1)
Miretice 32, Miretice, 539 55, Pardubice, Czech Republic
Tel.: (420) 46 934 4176
Web Site: https://www.backer-eltop.cz
Heating Element & Ceramic Heater Mfr
N.A.I.C.S.: 333414
Michal Tichy *(Mgr-Export Sls)*

Backer Facsa S.L. (1)
Ctra De Ribes Km 50, 8591, Aiguafreda, Barcelona, Spain
Tel.: (34) 93 844 2600
Web Site: http://www.backerfacsa.es
Heating Equipment Mfr
N.A.I.C.S.: 333414

Backer Fer s.r.l. (1)
Via Statale 255 N 293, Terre Del Reno, 44047, Ferrara, Italy
Tel.: (39) 0532 350000
Web Site: http://www.backerfer.com
Heating Equipment Mfr & Distr
N.A.I.C.S.: 333414

Backer Grand Heater Co., Ltd. (1)
119 Moo 6 T Khok-kham A Muang Samutsakorn, Samut Sakhon, 74000, Thailand
Tel.: (66) 3 481 2034
Web Site: https://www.backergrandheater.com
Heating Element Mfr
N.A.I.C.S.: 333414

Backer Heating Technologies Co., Ltd. (1)
Hong Hua Ling Ind Estate, Longxi Village Long Gang District, Shenzhen, China
Tel.: (86) 75528930369
Heat Pump Mfr
N.A.I.C.S.: 333415

Backer Heating Technologies France SARL (1)
20 rue de la Villette, 69328, Lyon, France
Tel.: (33) 426685037
Heating Element Mfr
N.A.I.C.S.: 333414

Backer Heating Technologies, Inc. (1)
1390 Gateway Dr, Elgin, IL 60124-7842
Tel.: (847) 931-1304
Web Site: https://www.backerhti.com

NIBE INDUSTRIER AB

INTERNATIONAL PUBLIC

NIBE Industrier AB—(Continued)
Sales Range: $25-49.9 Million
Emp.: 5
Resistance Heating Flexible Circuits Developer, Mfr & Marketer
N.A.I.C.S.: 334418
J. Paul Turner *(Pres)*

Backer Hotwatt, Inc. (1)
16A Electronics Ave, Danvers, MA 01923-1011
Tel.: (978) 777-0070
Web Site: https://www.hotwatt.com
Resistance Heating Elements Designer & Mfr
N.A.I.C.S.: 333415
Dennis Rubino *(Dir-Ops)*

Subsidiary (Domestic):

Sun Electric Heater Company (2)
45 Mason St, Salem, MA 01970
Tel.: (978) 744-2240
Web Site: http://www.sunelectricheater.com
Electrical Apparatus & Related Equipment Merchant Whslr
N.A.I.C.S.: 423610
Jerry Carroll *(Office Mgr)*

Backer Marathon, Inc. (1)
808 Hackberry Ln, Del Rio, TX 78840
Tel.: (830) 775-1417
Web Site: https://www.backermarathon.com
Emp.: 2,200
Temperature Sensors & Heating Elements Designer & Mfr
N.A.I.C.S.: 332410
Mike Wrob *(Pres)*

Backer OBR Sp. z.o.o. (1)
ul Glowackiego 39, 74-200, Pyrzyce, Poland
Tel.: (48) 91 481 9900
Web Site: https://www.backerobr.pl
Heating Equipment Mfr
N.A.I.C.S.: 333414
Ewa Bogacka *(Chm-Mgmt Bd & Dir-Economic)*

Backer Wolff GmbH (1)
Zum Lonnenhohl 11, 44319, Dortmund, Germany
Tel.: (49) 2315 655 7840
Web Site: https://www.weichenheizung.de
Heating Element Mfr
N.A.I.C.S.: 333414
Christopher Frey *(Mng Dir)*

Backer-Springfield Dongguan Co., Ltd. (1)
Beimian Xiubian Industrial Park, Humen Town, Dongguan, 523900, Guangdong, China
Tel.: (86) 76988629188
Web Site: http://www.backer-springfield.com.cn
Heating Element Mfr
N.A.I.C.S.: 333414

Backer-Wilson Elements Pty. Ltd. (1)
Unit 2/22 Loyalty Road, North Rocks, 2151, NSW, Australia
Tel.: (61) 28 677 8976
Web Site: https://www.backer-wilson.com.au
Heating Element Mfr
N.A.I.C.S.: 333414
Dianne Hunter *(Mgr-Admin)*

Bentone AB (1)
Nasvagen 8, 341 34, Ljungby, Sweden
Tel.: (46) 3 728 6700
Web Site: https://www.bentone.com
Gas Burner Mfr
N.A.I.C.S.: 333414
Niclas Persson *(Sls Mgr-Export)*

Biawar Produkcja Sp z.o.o (1)
Nibe Biawar al Jana Pawla II 57, 15-703, Bialystok, Poland
Tel.: (48) 856628490
Web Site: http://www.biawar.com.pl
Electric Water Heater Mfr
N.A.I.C.S.: 333414
Bartosz Skwierczynski *(Plant Mgr)*

Brewer & Bunney Ltd. (1)
Unit 9 Barncoose Ind Estate, Redruth, TR15 3XX, United Kingdom
Tel.: (44) 1209214121
Web Site: https://www.brewerandbunney.co.uk
Laundry Equipment Distr
N.A.I.C.S.: 423850

BriskHeat Corporation (1)
4800 Hilton Corporate Dr, Columbus, OH 43232 **(60%)**
Web Site: https://www.briskheat.com
Miscellaneous Product Mfr
N.A.I.C.S.: 339999

Briskheat Corporation HK Limited (1)
15 Queen s Road, Central, China (Hong Kong)
Tel.: (852) 28428428
Heating Element Mfr
N.A.I.C.S.: 333414

Briskheat Shenzhen Trading Company Limited (1)
Room 401 4F Hong Hua Center No 52 Heping Road, Longhua District, Shenzhen, 518109, Guangdong, China
Tel.: (86) 75525192767
Heating Element Mfr
N.A.I.C.S.: 333414

Briskheat Technology Company Co. Ltd. (1)
4800 Hilton Corp Dr, Columbus, OH 43232
Web Site: https://www.briskheat.com
Heating Equipment Mfr
N.A.I.C.S.: 333414

CK Fires Ltd. (1)
1 Evonic House Clifford Park Clifford Lane, Stratford-upon-Avon, CV37 8HW, Warwickshire, United Kingdom
Tel.: (44) 178 926 3868
Web Site: https://www.evonicfires.co.uk
Electric Fire & Stove Mfr
N.A.I.C.S.: 333414

CTC AB (1)
Nasvagen 8, 341 34, Ljungby, Sweden
Tel.: (46) 37288000
Web Site: http://www.ctc.se
Heat Pump & Pellet Boiler Mfr
N.A.I.C.S.: 333414
Bjorn Alm *(Product Mgr)*

CTC Ferrofil AS (1)
Runnibakken 7, Arnes, 2150, Nes, Norway
Tel.: (47) 6 390 4000
Web Site: https://www.ctc.no
Emp.: 13
Water Heater & Electric Boiler Mfr
N.A.I.C.S.: 333414

CTC Giersch AG (1)
Furtbachstrasse 16/18, Buchs, 8107, Zurich, Switzerland
Tel.: (41) 848838838
Web Site: http://www.ctc-giersch.ch
Heat Pump Mfr
N.A.I.C.S.: 333414

Calesco Foil AB (1)
Vastra Avagen 11, Kolback, Vasteras, 73040, Kolback, Sweden
Tel.: (46) 22045300
Web Site: http://www.calescofoil.se
Electric Housewares & Household Fan Mfr
N.A.I.C.S.: 335210

Cetetherm AB (1)
Fridhemsvagen 15, 372 38, Ronneby, Sweden
Tel.: (46) 4 577 5592
Web Site: https://www.cetetherm.com
Heating & Cooling System Mfr
N.A.I.C.S.: 333414
Roger Dahlstrand *(Mgr-Sls-Nordic)*

Cetetherm LLC (1)
18-ya Line of Vasylievsky Ostrov 29 Liter B Office, B314/1 Business Centre, Saint Petersburg, 199178, Russia
Tel.: (7) 8123329152
Heating & Cooling System Mfr
N.A.I.C.S.: 333414
Yury Galkin *(Gen Mgr)*

Cetetherm SAS (1)
Route du Stade ZI du Moulin Sur Turdine, 69490, Pontcharra, France
Tel.: (33) 474055350
Heating & Cooling System Mfr
N.A.I.C.S.: 333414

Contura Stoves Ltd. (1)
Skulptorvagen 10, Box 134, 285 23, Markaryd, Sweden
Tel.: (46) 433275100
Web Site: https://www.contura.eu
Stove Mfr & Distr
N.A.I.C.S.: 335220

DZD Slovensko Spol s.r.o. (1)
Boynicka 3, 831 04, Bratislava, Slovakia
Tel.: (421) 2 446 37911
Heating Equipment Mfr
N.A.I.C.S.: 333414
Robert Kabina *(Gen Mgr)*

DZD Strojirna s.r.o. (1)
Drazice 69, 294 71, Benatky nad Jizerou, Czech Republic
Tel.: (420) 326370911
Web Site: http://www.dzd.cz
Emp.: 350
Water Heater Mfr
N.A.I.C.S.: 335220

Danotherm Electric A/S (1)
Naesbyvej 20, 2610, Rodovre, Denmark
Tel.: (45) 36732222
Web Site: http://www.danotherm.dk
Sales Range: $25-49.9 Million
Emp.: 65
Electronic Resistor Mfr
N.A.I.C.S.: 334416
Michael H. Laursen *(Mng Dir)*

E. Braude (London) Ltd. (1)
Liberta House, Sandhurst, GU47 8JR, Berkshire, United Kingdom
Tel.: (44) 1252876123
Web Site: http://www.braude.co.uk
Electric Tank Heater & Heat Exchanger Mfr
N.A.I.C.S.: 332410
David Snoxhill *(Gen Mgr)*

Electro Therm s.a.s (1)
26 rue du 35eme Regiment d'Aviation Parc du Chene, 69673, Bron, Cedex, France
Tel.: (33) 472158590
Web Site: https://www.electrotherm.fr
Heating Equipment Distr
N.A.I.C.S.: 423720

Electron Etto s.r.o. (1)
Skolni 185, Hustopece nad Becvou, 753 66, Olomouc, Czech Republic
Tel.: (420) 58 162 6366
Web Site: https://www.etto.cz
Heating Element Mfr
N.A.I.C.S.: 333414

Elektrotermija Ltd. (1)
Bela Zemlja bb, Uzice, Serbia
Tel.: (381) 31572114
Web Site: https://www.elektrotermija.rs
Heating Equipment Distr
N.A.I.C.S.: 423720

Eltop Praha S.r.o. (1)
Miretice 32, Miretice u Hlinska, Chrudim, 53955, Czech Republic
Tel.: (420) 469344176
Web Site: http://www.eltoppraha.cz
Sales Range: $25-49.9 Million
Emp.: 85
Major Household Appliance Mfr
N.A.I.C.S.: 335220
Jan Lesny *(Mng Dir)*

Eltwin A/S (1)
Torsovej 1b, 8240, Risskov, Denmark
Tel.: (45) 86216100
Web Site: http://www.eltwin.dk
Emp.: 150
Industrial Electronic Mfr
N.A.I.C.S.: 334419
Jorn Kristensen *(CEO)*

Eltwin Sp. z.o.o. (1)
Przemyslowa 2, 73-110, Stargard Szczecinski, Poland
Tel.: (48) 918315939
Industrial Electronic Mfr
N.A.I.C.S.: 334419

Emin Teknik Hortum Ve Makine AS (1)
Aydinli Mh Aydinli Cd No 117, Tuzla, 34953, Istanbul, Turkiye
Tel.: (90) 2163931020
Web Site: http://www.eminteknik.com.tr
Metal Flex Hose & Compensator Mfr
N.A.I.C.S.: 332913

Enertech AB (1)
PO Box 309, 341 26, Ljungby, Sweden
Tel.: (46) 37288000
Heating Element Mfr
N.A.I.C.S.: 333414

Enertech Global LLC (1)
2506 S Elm St, Greenville, IL 62246
Tel.: (618) 664-9010
Web Site: https://www.enertechusa.com
Geothermal Heat Pump Distr
N.A.I.C.S.: 423730
Brad Lanter *(CFO)*

Enertech GmbH (1)
Adjutantenkamp 18, 58675, Hemer, Germany
Tel.: (49) 2 372 9650
Web Site: https://www.giersch.de
Gas & Fuel Burner Mfr
N.A.I.C.S.: 333414
Josef Wrobel *(Mng Dir)*

Erdwarme plus GmbH (1)
Waldhuttenstrasse 48, Heinersreuth, 95500, Bayreuth, Germany
Tel.: (49) 9203686551
Web Site: http://www.erdwaermeplus.de
Sales Range: $125-149.9 Million
Emp.: 300
Water Heater Mfr & Whslr
N.A.I.C.S.: 333310

FPI Fireplace Products International Ltd. (1)
6988 Venture Street, Delta, V4G1H4, BC, Canada **(65%)**
Tel.: (604) 946-5155
Web Site: https://www.regency-fire.com
Emp.: 300
Woodstove Products Mfr
N.A.I.C.S.: 321999

Subsidiary (US):

Fireplace Products U.S., Inc. (2)
860 Embarcadero Dr, West Sacramento, CA 95605
Tel.: (916) 371-1101
Wood Product Distr
N.A.I.C.S.: 423990

Fireplace Products Australia Pty. Ltd. (1)
1-3 Conquest Way, Hallam, 3803, VIC, Australia
Tel.: (61) 39 799 7277
Web Site: https://www.regency-fire.com.au
Gas Fireplace & Wood Stove Mfr
N.A.I.C.S.: 333414

Flex Academy D.O.O. (1)
Free Zone BB, Priboj, Serbia
Tel.: (381) 33448265
Web Site: http://www.flexacademydoo.com
Metal Flex Hose & Compensator Mfr
N.A.I.C.S.: 332913

Gaumer Company, Inc. (1)
13616 Hempstead Rd, Houston, TX 77040 **(60%)**
Tel.: (713) 460-5200
Web Site: http://www.gaumer.com
Sales Range: $25-49.9 Million
Emp.: 115
Industrial Heating Equipment & Supplies Mfr & Whslr
N.A.I.C.S.: 333994
Gaurav Dhingra *(Pres)*

Gazco Ltd. (1)
Osprey Road Sowton Industrial Estate, Exeter, EX2 7JG, Devon, United Kingdom
Tel.: (44) 1392261990
Gas Fireplace & Stove Mfr
N.A.I.C.S.: 333414

Genvex A/S (1)
Sverigesvej 6, 6100, Haderslev, Denmark
Tel.: (45) 73 53 27 00
Web Site: http://www.genvex.dk
Emp.: 70
Ventilation System Mfr & Distr
N.A.I.C.S.: 333415

HT Heizeelemente Deutschland GmbH (1)
Brinkeweg 18, 33758, Schloss Holte-Stukenbrock, Germany
Tel.: (49) 52079912290

AND PRIVATE COMPANIES — NIBE INDUSTRIER AB

Web Site: http://www.ht-heizelemente.de
Heating Element Mfr
N.A.I.C.S.: 333414

HT S.p.A. (1)
Via Conegliano 73/B, Susegana, 31058, Treviso, Italy
Tel.: (39) 0438454111
Web Site: http://www.htspa.it
Cartridge Heater Mfr
N.A.I.C.S.: 333414

Heating Group International B.V. (1)
Bijsterhuizen 5118, 6604 LX, Wijchen, Netherlands
Tel.: (31) 243434222
Web Site: https://www.heatinggroup.com
Heating Equipment Mfr & Distr
N.A.I.C.S.: 333414

Heatpoint B.V. (1)
Botter 7, 2411 NM, Bodegraven, Netherlands
Tel.: (31) 172651006
Web Site: http://www.heatpoint.nl
Heating System Mfr
N.A.I.C.S.: 333414
Frans De Wildt (Mng Dir)

Heatrod Elements Ltd. (1)
Wardley Industrial Estate, North Holloway Drive, Manchester, M28 2DP, United Kingdom
Tel.: (44) 1617946122
Web Site: http://www.heatrod.com
Sales Range: $25-49.9 Million
Emp.: 50
Basic Inorganic Chemical Mfr
N.A.I.C.S.: 325180

Heatron, Inc. (1)
3000 Wilson Ave, Leavenworth, KS 66048-4637
Tel.: (913) 946-1394
Web Site: http://www.heatron.com
Sales Range: $25-49.9 Million
Emp.: 120
Custom Design & Manufacture of Heating Components for OEMs in Multiple Industries
N.A.I.C.S.: 333414
Robert H. Martter (Pres & CEO)

Hemi Heating AB (1)
Hansavagen 5F, PO Box 2077, 151 02, Sodertalje, Sweden
Tel.: (46) 855423250
Web Site: http://www.hemiheating.se
Heating System Mfr
N.A.I.C.S.: 333414

Hoiax AS (1)
Trippeveine 5, 1618, Fredrikstad, Norway
Tel.: (47) 69355500
Web Site: http://www.hoiax.no
Sales Range: $25-49.9 Million
Emp.: 65
Activities for Water Transportation
N.A.I.C.S.: 488390

HydraulikService i Markaryd AB (1)
Jarnvagsgatan 7, 28532, Markaryd, Sweden
Tel.: (46) 43316750
Web Site: https://www.hydraulikservice.se
Industrial Hose Distr
N.A.I.C.S.: 423840

Hyper Engineering Pty. Ltd. (1)
4/14 Ralph Black Drive, Wollongong, 2500, NSW, Australia
Tel.: (61) 242292069
Web Site: http://www.hypereng.com
Electronic Software Driven Soft Starter Mfr
N.A.I.C.S.: 335999
Rudra Prasad Ghosal (Mng Dir)

JSC Evan (1)
St Julius Fuchik 8, 603016, Nizhniy Novgorod, Russia
Tel.: (7) 8312888555
Web Site: https://www.evan.ru
Heating Equipment Mfr
N.A.I.C.S.: 333414
Igor Dmitriev (Dir-Sls)

Jac. De Vries Gesta B.V. (1)
Aambeeld 19, 1671 NT, Medemblik, Netherlands
Tel.: (31) 299684226
Web Site: https://jacdevriesgesta.nl
Electric Heating Element Mfr & Distr

N.A.I.C.S.: 333414

Jevi A/S (1)
Godthabsvej 7, DK-7100, Vejle, Denmark
Tel.: (45) 75830211
Web Site: http://www.jevi.dk
Sales Range: $25-49.9 Million
Emp.: 85
Electric Heating Solutions Supplier
N.A.I.C.S.: 334519

KKT Chillers Inc. (1)
765 Dillon Dr, Wood Dale, IL 60191
Tel.: (847) 734-1600
Web Site: http://www.kkt-chillersusa.com
Heat Pump Mfr
N.A.I.C.S.: 333414
John Carmody (Pres)

KNUT d.o.o. (1)
Na postajo 40, Velike Lasce, 1315, Turjak, Slovenia
Tel.: (386) 1 788 99 16
Web Site: http://www.knut.si
Sales Range: $25-49.9 Million
Emp.: 8
Water Heater Mfr & Whslr
N.A.I.C.S.: 333414

KNV Energietechnik GmbH (1)
Gahberggasse 11, 4861, Schorfling am Attersee, Austria
Tel.: (43) 7662 8963 0
Emp.: 30
Electrical Heating Equipment Mfr
N.A.I.C.S.: 333414
Josef Kottl (Gen Mgr)

KVM-Conheat A/S (1)
Industrivej 6, 5492, Vissenbjerg, Denmark
Tel.: (45) 6447 3100
Web Site: http://www.kvm-conheat.dk
Sales Range: $25-49.9 Million
Emp.: 36
Heating Equipment Mfr
N.A.I.C.S.: 333414

KVM-Genvex A/S (1)
Sverigesvej 6, DK-6100, Haderslev, Denmark
Tel.: (45) 73532700
Web Site: http://www.kvm-conheat.com
Emp.: 50
Heating Element Mfr
N.A.I.C.S.: 333414
Michael Kanstrup Jensen (CEO)

Kaukora Oy (1)
Tuotekatu 11, 21200, Raisio, Finland
Tel.: (358) 24374600
Web Site: http://jaspi.fi
Sales Range: $50-74.9 Million
Emp.: 150
Electrical Equipment & Component Mfr
N.A.I.C.S.: 335999
Jorma Hummelin (Mng Dir)

Kiloval Oy (1)
Linnunrata 5, Lovisa, 7900, Finland
Tel.: (358) 1951731
Sales Range: $50-74.9 Million
Emp.: 20
Electrical Heating Equipment Mfr
N.A.I.C.S.: 333414
Jorma Kallapera (Mng Dir)

Lodur Amager A/S (1)
Kongevej 246, Gram, Arhus, Denmark
Tel.: (45) 73821312
Store Retailers
N.A.I.C.S.: 459999

Lodur City Vest A/S (1)
Kongevej 246, Gram, Arhus, Denmark
Tel.: (45) 73821313
Store Retailers
N.A.I.C.S.: 459999

Lotus Heating Systems A/S (1)
Agertoften 6, 5550, Langeskov, Denmark
Tel.: (45) 6323 7070
Web Site: http://www.lotusstoves.com
Sales Range: $25-49.9 Million
Emp.: 25
Wood Stove Mfr
N.A.I.C.S.: 333414

Loval Oy (1)
Loviisa Linnurata 4, Loviisa, Lovisa, 7900, Finland
Tel.: (358) 1951731

Web Site: http://www.loval.fi
Sales Range: $50-74.9 Million
Emp.: 200
Electrical Equipment & Component Mfr
N.A.I.C.S.: 335999

Lund & Sorensen A/S (1)
Maserativej 4, 7100, Vejle, Denmark
Tel.: (45) 75 85 78 22
Web Site: http://www.ls-windpower.com
Emp.: 25
Heating Equipment Mfr
N.A.I.C.S.: 333414
Carsten Nygaard Lund (Mng Dir)

Lund & Sorensen Electric Heating Equipment Accessory Co Ltd (1)
Beijing Representative Office Room 1704 Di Yang Tower No H2, DongSanHuan Bei Lu Chaoyang, Beijing, 100027, China
Tel.: (86) 10 6433 3092
Web Site: http://www.ls-windpower.com
Sales Range: $25-49.9 Million
Emp.: 5
Electric Equipment Mfr
N.A.I.C.S.: 335999
Ole Beakby (Gen Mgr)

Lund & Sorensen Electric Heating Inc (1)
Fuyuan Road Bei Tianjin Hi-tech Industrial Park Development Area, Wuqing, Tianjin, 301700, China
Tel.: (86) 1064333092
Heating Equipment Mfr
N.A.I.C.S.: 333414
Peter Yu (Mgr-Sls)

Metro Therm A/S (1)
Rundinsvej 55, 3200, Helsinge, Denmark
Tel.: (45) 48770000
Web Site: http://www.metrotherm.dk
Sales Range: $25-49.9 Million
Emp.: 100
Fluid Power Pump & Motor Mfr
N.A.I.C.S.: 333996
Mikael Schroder (Mng Dir)

Metro Therm AB (1)
Franskavagen 24, 39356, Kalmar, Sweden
Tel.: (46) 480420730
Web Site: http://www.metrotherm.se
Sales Range: $25-49.9 Million
Emp.: 15
Heating Equipment Mfr
N.A.I.C.S.: 333414

Meyer Vastus AB, Oy (1)
Sepantie 2, 07230, Askola, Finland
Tel.: (358) 195740200
Web Site: https://www.meyervastus.fi
Sales Range: $25-49.9 Million
Emp.: 25
Electrical Equipment & Component Mfr
N.A.I.C.S.: 335999

Motron A/S (1)
Torsovej 3, 8240, Risskov, Denmark
Tel.: (45) 87368600
Industrial Electronic Mfr
N.A.I.C.S.: 334419

NIBE AirSite AB (1)
Elementvagen 1, 437 36, Lindome, Sweden
Tel.: (46) 313113200
Web Site: https://www.nibeairsite.com
Heat Pump Mfr
N.A.I.C.S.: 333415

NIBE Element (1)
Fabriksgatan 11, Sosdala, 28010, Sweden
Tel.: (46) 45166100
Web Site: http://www.nibe.se
Emp.: 300
Water Heater Mfr & Whslr
N.A.I.C.S.: 333310

Subsidiary (Domestic):

Backer EHP AB (2)
Fabriksgatan 11, Sosdala, 28010, Sweden
Tel.: (46) 451 66 100
Web Site: http://www.backer.se
Sales Range: $100-124.9 Million
Emp.: 220
Water Heater Mfr & Whslr
N.A.I.C.S.: 333310
Christer Fredriksson (Mng Dir)

NIBE Energietechniek B.V. (1)

Steenpad 11, 4797 SG, Willemstad, Netherlands
Tel.: (31) 168 477722
Sales Range: $25-49.9 Million
Emp.: 2
Power Boiler & Heat Exchanger Mfr
N.A.I.C.S.: 332410
Christian Blanc (Gen Mgr)

NIBE Energy Systems Oy (1)
Juurakkotie 3, 1510, Vantaa, Finland
Tel.: (358) 9 274 6970
Electrical Heating Equipment Mfr
N.A.I.C.S.: 333414
Andres Johensson (Gen Mgr)

NIBE Industrier AB - NIBE Wind Components Division (1)
Maserativej 4, 7100, Vejle, Denmark
Tel.: (45) 6 155 1411
Web Site: https://www.nibewind.com
Electrical Heating Equipment Mfr
N.A.I.C.S.: 333414

NIBE Stoves (1)
Box 134, SE-285 23, Markaryd, Sweden
Tel.: (46) 433 75 100
Web Site: http://www.contura.se
Sales Range: $50-74.9 Million
Emp.: 50
Water Heater Mfr & Whslr
N.A.I.C.S.: 333414

NIBE Systemtechnik GmbH (1)
Am Reiherpfahl 3, 29223, Celle, Germany
Tel.: (49) 5141 75460
Web Site: http://www.nibe.de
Sales Range: $25-49.9 Million
Emp.: 50
Heat Pump Mfr
N.A.I.C.S.: 333914

NIBE Warmetechnik AG (1)
Winterthurestrasse 710, 8247, Flurlingen, Switzerland
Tel.: (41) 52 6470030
Heat Pump Mfr
N.A.I.C.S.: 333914

Nathan Projects BVBA (1)
Lozenberg 4, 1932, Zaventem, Belgium
Tel.: (32) 832529125
Web Site: https://bizzy.org
Information Technology Services
N.A.I.C.S.: 541511

Nathan Systems B.V. (1)
Mega 2, 6902 KL, Zevenaar, Netherlands
Tel.: (31) 264459845
Heating & Cooling Equipment Mfr & Distr
N.A.I.C.S.: 333415

Nibe AB (1)
Hannabadsvagen 5, 285 32, Markaryd, Sweden
Tel.: (46) 433273000
Web Site: http://www.nibe.eu
Sales Range: $200-249.9 Million
Emp.: 1,000
Heating Equipment Mfr
N.A.I.C.S.: 333414
Gerteric Lindquist (CEO & Mng Dir)

Nibe Energy Systems France SAS (1)
Industrial Zone RD 28 Rue du Pou du Ciel, 01600, Reyrieux, France
Tel.: (33) 474009292
Web Site: http://www.nibe.fr
Heat Pump Mfr
N.A.I.C.S.: 333414
Nicolas Jaubert (Product Mgr)

Nibe Energy Systems Limited (1)
Unit 3C Broom Business Park Bridge Way, Chesterfield, S41 9QG, United Kingdom
Tel.: (44) 8450951200
Web Site: http://www.nibe.co.uk
Sales Range: $25-49.9 Million
Emp.: 25
Pump & Pumping Equipment Mfr
N.A.I.C.S.: 333914
Phil Hurley (Mng Dir)

Nibe Foyers France S.A.S. (1)
Z D activite Du Chapotin, Chaponnay, Lyon, France
Tel.: (33) 437235750
Sales Range: $50-74.9 Million
Emp.: 5

NIBE INDUSTRIER AB

NIBE Industrier AB—(Continued)
Plumbing & Heating Equipment & Supplies Whslr
N.A.I.C.S.: 423720

Nibe-Biawar Sp. z.o.o. (1)
al Jana Pawla II 57, 15-703, Bialystok, Poland
Tel.: (48) 856628490
Web Site: http://www.biawar.com.pl
Sales Range: $100-124.9 Million
Emp.: 300
Heating Equipment Mfr
N.A.I.C.S.: 333414
Mariusz Ptak *(Mng Dir)*

Nordpeis AS (1)
Gjellebekkstubben 9-11, 3420, Lierskogen, Norway
Tel.: (47) 32244700
Web Site: http://www.nordpeis.no
Sales Range: $25-49.9 Million
Emp.: 15
Store Retailers
N.A.I.C.S.: 459999
Stian F. Varre *(Mng Dir)*

Norske Backer AS (1)
Jostein Svendheims Veg 8210, Kongsvinger, 2212, Norway
Tel.: (47) 62828828
Web Site: http://www.norskebacker.no
Sales Range: $25-49.9 Million
Emp.: 50
Electrical Apparatus & Equipment Wiring Supplies & Related Equipment Merchant Whslr
N.A.I.C.S.: 423610

Northstar Poland Sp. z.o.o. (1)
27 Stycznia 47-47, Trzcianka, 64-980, Poland
Tel.: (48) 672162136
Web Site: http://www.northstar.pl
Sales Range: $50-74.9 Million
Emp.: 200
Concrete Block & Brick Mfr
N.A.I.C.S.: 327331

OU Kliimaseade (1)
Laki 14A, 10621, Tallinn, Estonia
Tel.: (372) 639 1430
Web Site: https://www.kliimaseade.ee
Air Conditioning & Heating Equipment Distr
N.A.I.C.S.: 423730

Omni Control Technology Inc (1)
1 Main St Ste 4, Whitinsville, MA 01588
Tel.: (508) 234-9121
Web Site: https://www.omnicontroltech.com
Control Panel & Wiring Component Mfr
N.A.I.C.S.: 335999
Peter J. Bedigian *(CEO)*

Osby Parca AB (1)
Radiatorvagen 4, 283 43, Osby, Sweden
Tel.: (46) 47917700
Web Site: http://www.osbyparca.se
Heating Boiler Mfr
N.A.I.C.S.: 333414
Ola Svensson *(Acct Mgr)*

Pellux GmbH (1)
Gahberggasse 11, 4861, Schorfling am Attersee, Austria
Tel.: (43) 76628963
Web Site: http://www.pellux.de
Boiler Mfr
N.A.I.C.S.: 333414

Rhoss Deutschland GmbH (1)
Holzlestrase 23 D, 72336, Balingen, Germany
Tel.: (49) 7433260270
Heating & Cooling Equipment Mfr
N.A.I.C.S.: 333414

Rotterdamse Elementen Fabriek B.V. (1)
Gouderakstraat 7, 3079, Rotterdam, Netherlands
Tel.: (31) 104793500
Web Site: https://ref.nl
Electric Heating Element Mfr & Distr
N.A.I.C.S.: 333414

S.C. TRUST EURO THERM S.R.L. (1)
D N Piatra Neamt Roman Km 2 Garcina, Piatra Neamt, 610330, Neamt, Romania
Tel.: (40) 233 206206
Web Site: http://www.trust-expert.ro
Sales Range: $25-49.9 Million
Emp.: 100
Thermal Power Plant Construction Services
N.A.I.C.S.: 237130

SAN Electro Heat A/S (1)
Gillelejevej 30b, 3230, Graested, Denmark
Tel.: (45) 4839 8888
Web Site: http://www.san-as.com
Sales Range: $25-49.9 Million
Emp.: 6
Heating Equipment Mfr & Distr
N.A.I.C.S.: 333414
Michael H. Laursen *(Mng Dir)*

Schulthess Group AG (1)
Landstrasse 37 Wolfhausen, 8633, Zurich, Switzerland
Tel.: (41) 552535111
Web Site: http://www.schulthess.ch
Sales Range: $300-349.9 Million
Emp.: 1,055
Heating, Cooling & Laundry Equipment Mfr
N.A.I.C.S.: 333415
Martin Keller *(CFO)*

Subsidiary (Domestic):

Alpha-InnoTec GmbH (2)
Logistikcenter Gauerhof, Altishofen, 6246, Lucerne, Switzerland (70%)
Tel.: (41) 627482000
Web Site: http://www.alpha-innotec.ch
Pump & Pumping Equipment Mfr
N.A.I.C.S.: 333914

Subsidiary (Non-US):

Alpha-InnoTec Norge AS (3)
Gamle Forusvei 51b, 4033, Stavanger, Norway
Tel.: (47) 51 66 05 95
Web Site: http://www.alpha-innotec.no
Heat Pump Mfr
N.A.I.C.S.: 333914

Subsidiary (Non-US):

Alpha-Innotec GmbH (2)
Industriestrasse 3, Kasendorf, 95359, Wurzburg, Germany (100%)
Tel.: (49) 922899060
Web Site: http://www.alpha-innotec.de
Sales Range: $125-149.9 Million
Emp.: 350
Refrigeration Equipment & Supplies Whslr
N.A.I.C.S.: 423740
Werner Karlen *(Mng Dir)*

KKT Chillers (2)
Industriestrasse 3, 95359, Kasendorf, Germany (100%)
Tel.: (49) 9228 9977 0
Web Site: http://www.kkt-chillers.com
Sales Range: $25-49.9 Million
Emp.: 100
Air-Conditioning & Warm Air Heating Equipment & Commercial & Industrial Refrigeration Equipment Mfr
N.A.I.C.S.: 333415

Subsidiary (US):

KKT KRAUS USA Corp (3)
Erica Alvi 1351 Brummel Ave, Elk Grove Village, IL 60007
Tel.: (847) 734-1600
Web Site: http://www.kkt-kraus.de
Medical Cooling Equipment Mfr
N.A.I.C.S.: 339112

Subsidiary (Domestic):

Merker AG (2)
Landstrasse 37, Wolfhausen, Zurich, 8633, Switzerland (100%)
Tel.: (41) 448472100
Web Site: http://www.schulthess.ch
Sales Range: $25-49.9 Million
Emp.: 400
Electrical Appliance Television & Radio Set Whslr
N.A.I.C.S.: 423620
Thomas Marder *(Gen Mgr)*

Subsidiary (Non-US):

Novelan GmbH (2)
Industriestrasse 3, 95359, Kasendorf, Germany (100%)
Tel.: (49) 9228996070
Web Site: http://www.novelan.com
Refrigeration Equipment & Supplies Whslr
N.A.I.C.S.: 423740
Wettel Heinz *(Mng Dir)*

Subsidiary (Domestic):

Schulthess Maschinen AG (2)
Landstrasse 37, Wolfhausen, 8633, Zurich, Switzerland (100%)
Tel.: (41) 552535111
Web Site: http://www.schulthess.ch
Sales Range: $25-49.9 Million
Emp.: 200
Household Laundry Equipment Mfr
N.A.I.C.S.: 335220

Subsidiary (Non-US):

Schulthess Maschinen GmbH (2)
Hetzendorferstrasse 191, A-1130, Vienna, Austria (100%)
Tel.: (43) 18039800
Web Site: http://www.schulthess.at
Emp.: 20
Service Establishment Equipment & Supplies Whslr
N.A.I.C.S.: 423850
Christian Zlabinger *(Country Mgr)*

Subsidiary (Domestic):

Wamatec SA (2)
Via Industria, 6814, Lamone, Switzerland (100%)
Tel.: (41) 916046042
Durable Goods Whslr
N.A.I.C.S.: 423990

Shel NIBE Manufacturing Co Ltd (1)
Building No 5 Hong Hua Ling Industrial Estate LongXi Village, Long Gang District, Shenzhen, China
Tel.: (86) 755 289 303 69
Web Site: http://www.nibe.com
Electrical Heating Equipment Mfr
N.A.I.C.S.: 333414

Sinus-Jevi Electric Heating B.V. (1)
Nijverheidsweg 2, Medemblik, Leiden, Noord-Holland, Netherlands
Tel.: (31) 227549100
Web Site: http://www.sinusjevi.com
Sales Range: $25-49.9 Million
Emp.: 20
Commercial & Industry Machinery Mfr
N.A.I.C.S.: 333310

Slovak Republic DZ Drazice-Slovensko spol.s.r.o. (1)
Bojnicka 3, 831 04, Bratislava, Slovakia
Tel.: (421) 2 44637911
Web Site: http://www.dzd.cz
Sales Range: $25-49.9 Million
Emp.: 7
Water Heater Mfr & Distr
N.A.I.C.S.: 333414

Sol & Energiteknik SE AB (1)
Esbjornarp 10, 561 92, Huskvarna, Sweden
Tel.: (46) 365 1345
Web Site: https://www.solenergi.org
Water Heater Equipment Mfr
N.A.I.C.S.: 333414

Stovax Group Ltd. (1)
Falcon Road Sowton Industrial Estate, Exeter, EX2 7LF, United Kingdom
Tel.: (44) 1392474000
Heating Element Mfr
N.A.I.C.S.: 333414

Stovax Ltd. (1)
Falcon Road Sowton Industrial Estate, Exeter, EX2 7LF, United Kingdom
Tel.: (44) 1392474000
Web Site: http://www.stovax.com
Emp.: 337
Gas Fireplace & Wood Stove Mfr
N.A.I.C.S.: 333414
Michelle Bowler *(Mgr-Pur)*

Structurgruppen AB (1)
Magasinsgatan 8C, Box 102 40, Kungsbacka, 43423, Sweden
Tel.: (46) 300 566 400
Web Site: http://www.structurgruppen.se

INTERNATIONAL PUBLIC

Sales Range: $25-49.9 Million
Emp.: 6
Heating Equipment Mfr
N.A.I.C.S.: 333415

TH Qviller AS (1)
Brobekkveien 80A building 13, 0582, Oslo, Norway
Tel.: (47) 63870800
Web Site: http://www.qviller.no
Heat Pump Mfr
N.A.I.C.S.: 333414

Tellus Ignis S.L. (1)
Vallveric 85, 08304, Mataro, Barcelona, Spain
Tel.: (34) 93 001 31 92
Web Site: http://www.tellusignis.com
Sales Range: $25-49.9 Million
Emp.: 5
Heating Equipment Distr
N.A.I.C.S.: 333415

Tempeff North America Ltd. (1)
675 Washington Ave, Winnipeg, R2K 1M4, MB, Canada
Tel.: (204) 783-1902
Web Site: http://www.tempeffnorthamerica.com
Energy Recovery Equipment Mfr
N.A.I.C.S.: 333414
Ken Smith *(Gen Mgr)*

Teplovi Nasosy Ltd (1)
Predslavynska Street 35 Bldg 21 201, 03150, Kiev, Ukraine
Tel.: (380) 44 229 55 69
Web Site: http://www.teplonasos.ua
Sales Range: $25-49.9 Million
Emp.: 5
Water Heater Mfr & Whslr
N.A.I.C.S.: 333415
Ostap Kucheruk *(Dir)*

TermaTech A/S (1)
Gunnar Clausens Vej 36, 8260, Viby, Denmark
Tel.: (45) 87 42 00 35
Sales Range: $50-74.9 Million
Emp.: 15
Wood Burning Stove Distr
N.A.I.C.S.: 423720
Soren Toft *(Gen Mgr)*

Termopompeni Sistemi Ltd. (1)
10 Rilyanik Str Fl 2 Ap 4, Pancharevo, 1137, Sofia, Bulgaria
Tel.: (359) 893 314848
Web Site: http://www.nibe.bg
Sales Range: $25-49.9 Million
Emp.: 10
Heating Equipment Mfr
N.A.I.C.S.: 333415

Termorad Spolka Z.o.o. (1)
ul Topiel 42, 26-600, Radom, Poland
Tel.: (48) 369 9470
Web Site: https://www.termorad.pl
Heating Element Mfr
N.A.I.C.S.: 333414

The Climate Control Group, Inc. (1)
7300 SW 44th St, Oklahoma City, OK 73179 (100%)
Tel.: (405) 745-6000
Web Site: http://www.climatemaster.com
Holding Company; Climate Control Products Mfr
N.A.I.C.S.: 551112
Laurie Rogers *(CFO & VP-Fin)*

Subsidiary (Domestic):

ClimaCool Corp. (2)
15 S Virginia, Oklahoma City, OK 73106
Tel.: (405) 815-3000
Web Site: http://www.climacoolcorp.com
Emp.: 40
Air Conditioning & Warm Air Heating Equipment Mfr
N.A.I.C.S.: 333415
Tiffany Bates Abruzzo *(Reg Mgr-Sls)*

ClimateCraft, Inc. (2)
518 N Indiana Ave, Oklahoma City, OK 73106
Tel.: (405) 415-9230
Web Site: http://www.climatecraft.com
Emp.: 20
Custom Air Handling Equipment Mfr
N.A.I.C.S.: 333415

AND PRIVATE COMPANIES

ClimateMaster, Inc. (2)
7300 SW 44th St, Oklahoma City, OK 73179-4307
Tel.: (405) 745-6000
Web Site: http://www.climatemaster.com
Emp.: 600
Geothermal & Water Source Heat Pumps Mfr
N.A.I.C.S.: 333415
Richard Aldridge (CEO)

International Environmental Corporation (2)
5000 I 40 W, Oklahoma City, OK 73128
Tel.: (405) 605-5000
Web Site: http://www.iec-okc.com
Emp.: 250
Fan Coil & Air Handling Units Mfr
N.A.I.C.S.: 333415

Koax Corp. (2)
510 N Indiana Ave, Oklahoma City, OK 73106-2607
Tel.: (405) 235-0455
Web Site: http://www.koax.com
Air Conditioning & Warm Air Heating Equipment Mfr
N.A.I.C.S.: 333415

Thermogas S.A. (1)
Anthousis Avenue 12, Pallini, 15351, Greece
Tel.: (30) 210 6665552
Web Site: http://www.thermogea.gr
Sales Range: $25-49.9 Million
Emp.: 11
Gas Appliance Installation Services
N.A.I.C.S.: 238290

Thermtec Ltd (1)
Unit 5 6 Hall Farm Industrial Units Cess Road Martham Great Yarmouth, Norfolk, NR29 5DR, United Kingdom
Tel.: (44) 1493 748666
Water Heating Equipment Mfr & Distr
N.A.I.C.S.: 333414

Turboflame AB (1)
Nasvagen 8, 341 34, Ljungby, Sweden
Tel.: (46) 37286725
Web Site: http://www.turboflame.se
Gas & Oil Burner Mfr
N.A.I.C.S.: 333414

Unipipe Ltd. (1)
40 Southern Cross Business Park Boghall Road, County Wicklow, Bray, Co Wicklow, Ireland
Tel.: (353) 1 286 4888
Web Site: https://www.unipipe.ie
Heating Equipment Distr
N.A.I.C.S.: 333415

Varde Ovne A/S (1)
Soldalen 12, Vejle, 7100, Denmark
Tel.: (45) 74 82 00 03
Web Site: http://www.vardeovne.dk
Emp.: 8
Wood Stove Mfr
N.A.I.C.S.: 333414
Jan Meldgaard (CEO)

Viggo Wahl Pedersen AS (1)
Trippeveien 5, Fredrikstad, Norway
Tel.: (47) 69355500
Web Site: https://viggowahl.no
Waste Treatment Services
N.A.I.C.S.: 221310

Volund Varmeteknik A/S (1)
Brogardsvej 7, 6920, Videbaek, Denmark
Tel.: (45) 97 17 20 33
Power Boiler & Heat Exchanger Mfr
N.A.I.C.S.: 332410

WaterFurnace International Inc. (1)
9000 Conservation Way, Fort Wayne, IN 46809
Web Site: http://www.waterfurnace.com
Water Source Heat Pump Mfr & Distr
N.A.I.C.S.: 333414
Robert Brown (VP-Engrg)

WaterFurnace Renewable Energy, Inc. (1)
9000 Conservation Way, Fort Wayne, IN 46809 (100%)
Tel.: (260) 478-5667
Web Site: http://www.waterfurnace.com
Sales Range: $75-99.9 Million
Emp.: 267
Geothermal Heating & Cooling System Mfr

N.A.I.C.S.: 333415

Waterkotte Austria GmbH (1)
Carolinenstrasse 10, Viktring, 9073, Klagenfurt, Austria
Tel.: (43) 4632940300
Web Site: https://www.waermepumpeaustria.at
Heating Equipment Distr
N.A.I.C.S.: 423720

Waterkotte GmbH (1)
Gewerkenst 15, 44628, Herne, Germany
Tel.: (49) 232393760
Web Site: https://www.waterkotte.eu
Heating Equipment Mfr & Distr
N.A.I.C.S.: 333414

ait Schweiz AG (1)
Industrial Park, 6246, Altishofen, Switzerland
Tel.: (41) 582522000
Web Site: http://www.ait-schweiz.ch
Heating Pump Mfr
N.A.I.C.S.: 333415
Pascal Morach (Head-IT)

ait-austria GmbH (1)
Industriezentrum No-Sud Street 15, Object 77 Stairs 4 2nd Floor Top 7 Wiener, 2355, Neudorfl, Austria
Tel.: (43) 22366604960
Web Site: http://www.ait-austria.at
Ventilation & Heating Pump Mfr
N.A.I.C.S.: 333415

NIBEC CO., LTD.
116 Bamdi-gil Iwol-Myeon, Iwol-Myeon Iwol electricity-electronic Agro-industrial Complex, Jincheon, 27816, Chungcheongbuk-do, Korea (South)
Tel.: (82) 435327458
Web Site: https://www.nibec.co.kr
Year Founded: 2000
138610—(KRS)
Rev.: $16,621,227
Assets: $57,681,759
Liabilities: $29,456,102
Net Worth: $28,225,657
Earnings: ($2,904,610)
Emp.: 72
Fiscal Year-end: 12/31/22
Bone Regenerative Medicines & Dental Supplies Mfr
N.A.I.C.S.: 325411
Chong-Pyoung Chung (CEO)

NIBLOCK (BUILDERS) LTD.
Anerley Works 135 Anerley Road, London, SE20 8AJ, United Kingdom
Tel.: (44) 2087783449
Web Site: http://www.niblock.co.uk
Year Founded: 1959
Rev.: $10,173,400
Emp.: 34
Building Contracting Services
N.A.I.C.S.: 238190
Martin Waters (Mng Dir)

NIBSA SA
Juan Griego 4429, Saint Joaquin, Santiago, Chile
Tel.: (56) 4898000
NIBSA—(SGO)
Sales Range: Less than $1 Million
Mineral Exploration Services
N.A.I.C.S.: 213114
Felix Rafael Concha Undurraga (Chm)

NIC ASIA BANK LIMITED
Trade Tower, PO Box 11022, Thapathali, Kathmandu, Nepal
Tel.: (977) 15970101
Web Site:
https://www.nicasiabank.com
Year Founded: 1998
NICA—(NEP)
Rev.: $171,641,876
Assets: $1,906,330,199
Liabilities: $1,775,884,328
Net Worth: $130,445,531

Earnings: $27,322,131
Emp.: 3,472
Fiscal Year-end: 07/16/19
Banking Services
N.A.I.C.S.: 522110
Tulsi Ram Agrawal (Chm)

NIC AUTOTEC, INC.
Ariake Frontier Building Tower-B 11F 3-7-26 Ariake, Koto-ku, Tokyo, 135-0063, Japan
Tel.: (81) 355308066
Web Site: https://www.nic-inc.co.jp
Year Founded: 1971
5742—(TKS)
Rev.: $50,297,211
Assets: $59,954,940
Liabilities: $27,704,619
Net Worth: $32,250,321
Earnings: ($1,004,283)
Emp.: 220
Fiscal Year-end: 03/31/23
Industrial Machinery Mfr
N.A.I.C.S.: 333248
Hiroshi Nishikawa (Chm & CEO)

Subsidiaries:

NIC Autotec (Thailand) Co., Ltd. (1)
111/09-10 Moo 4 Tambol Klongsuan, Tambol Klongsuan Amphur Bangbor, Samut Prakan, 10560, Thailand
Tel.: (66) 213658412
Electronic Components Mfr
N.A.I.C.S.: 334419

NIC GROUP PLC
NIC House Masaba Road Upperhill, PO Box 44599, 00100, Nairobi, Kenya
Tel.: (254) 202888217   KE
Web Site: http://nicgroup.com
Year Founded: 1959
Rev.: $176,788,051
Assets: $1,979,255,616
Liabilities: $1,645,979,741
Net Worth: $333,275,875
Earnings: $39,786,413
Fiscal Year-end: 12/31/17
Retail, Corporate Banking, Brokerage, Property & Investment Banking Services
N.A.I.C.S.: 523150
Livingstone Murage (Sec)

Subsidiaries:

NC Bank Uganda Limited (1)
Rwenzori Towers Plot 4 6 Nakasero Road, PO Box 28707, Kampala, Uganda
Tel.: (256) 312188400
Web Site: http://ug.ncbagroup.com
Financial Investment Services
N.A.I.C.S.: 523999
Grace Jethro Kavuma (Chm)

NIC NADEJDA AD
Tel.: (359) 24606448
NAD—(BUL)
Sales Range: Less than $1 Million
Financial Investment Services
N.A.I.C.S.: 523999

NICARAGUA SUGAR ESTATES LIMITED
Km 4 Carretera a Masaya, Managua, Nicaragua
Tel.: (505) 22744150
Web Site:
http://www.nicaraguasugar.com
Year Founded: 1890
Sales Range: $550-599.9 Million
Emp.: 5,000
Sugar, Ethanol & Electric Energy Producer & Exporter
N.A.I.C.S.: 311314
Carlos Pellas Chamorro (Pres)

NICCA CHEMICAL CO., LTD.

4-23-1 Bunkyo Fukui Prefecture, Fukui, 910-8670, Japan
Tel.: (81) 776240213
Web Site: https://www.nicca.co.jp
Year Founded: 1941
44630—(TKS)
Rev.: $331,476,710
Assets: $376,068,715
Liabilities: $159,207,136
Net Worth: $216,861,579
Earnings: $12,395,111
Emp.: 1,500
Fiscal Year-end: 12/31/23
Textile Chemical Surfactants, Dry Cleaning & Professional Cleaning Agents, Cosmetic Products & Agricultural Products Mfr & Sales
N.A.I.C.S.: 325611
Yasumasa Emori (Pres)

Subsidiaries:

Demi Beijing International Trading Co., Ltd. (1)
508 Wanfu Building No 72 Tiantan East Road, Dong cheng District, Beijing, 100061, China
Tel.: (86) 1067167978
Basic Chemicals Mfr
N.A.I.C.S.: 325180

Demi Korea Co., Ltd. (1)
1501 15th floor 186 Gasan Digital 1-ro, Geumcheon-gu, Seoul, Korea (South)
Tel.: (82) 25468338
Web Site: https://www.demikorea.com
Cosmetics Products Mfr
N.A.I.C.S.: 325620

Dongguan Nicca New Material Co., Ltd. (1)
Unit 101 and 201 Bldg 8 No 5, Sima Environmental Protection Industrial Road, Dongguan, 523570, Guangdong, China
Tel.: (86) 76989363389
Surfactant Mfr & Distr
N.A.I.C.S.: 325613

Emori Engineering Co., Ltd. (1)
Hanadonohigashi 1-chome Emori Minami Fukui Building, Fukui, 918-8013, Japan (25%)
Tel.: (81) 776366100
Web Site: https://www.emori.co.jp
Emp.: 15
Industrial Equipment Design & Engineering Services
N.A.I.C.S.: 541420
Yasumasa Emori (Pres)

EraL Co., Ltd. (1)
5-11-14 Minami Aoyama H & M Minami Aoyama EAST-B1F, Minato-ku, Tokyo, 107-0062, Japan
Tel.: (81) 354649552
Web Site: https://www.eral.co.jp
Cosmetic Product Distr
N.A.I.C.S.: 456102
Yasumasa Emori (Chm)

Guangzhou Nicca Chemical Co., Ltd. (1)
Unit 621 & 622 Bldg A 257 Junye Road, Huangpu District, Guangzhou, 510530, Guangdong, China
Tel.: (86) 2082211314
Sales Range: $25-49.9 Million
Emp.: 70
Organic Chemical Mfr
N.A.I.C.S.: 325199

Hong Kong Nicca Chemical Ltd. (1)
Unit 1608 & 1610 Profit Industrial Building, No 1-15 Kwai Fung Crescent, Kwai Chung, China (Hong Kong)
Tel.: (852) 24626232
Sales Range: $25-49.9 Million
Emp.: 25
Industrial Supplies Whslr
N.A.I.C.S.: 423840
Shinichi Morinaga (Gen Mgr-Japan)

Nicca Chemical (China) Co., Ltd. (1)
Tel.: (86) 57182697550
Web Site: http://www.nicca.cn
Sales Range: $25-49.9 Million
Organic Chemical Mfr
N.A.I.C.S.: 325199

NICCA CHEMICAL CO., LTD.

Nicca Chemical Co., Ltd.—(Continued)

Nicca Chemical Co., Ltd - Sabae Factory (1)
1-1 1-chome Miyukicho, Sabae, 916-0015, Fukui, Japan
Tel.: (81) 77 851 8100
Web Site: https://www.nicca.co.jp
Organic Chemical Mfr
N.A.I.C.S.: 325199

Nicca Chemical Co., Ltd. - Kanto Factory (1)
2345 Ushirogusa, 289-2613, Asahi, Japan
Tel.: (81) 479552511
Sales Range: $25-49.9 Million
Emp.: 50
Bactericide & Disinfectants Mfr
N.A.I.C.S.: 325612
Kushima Hiroshi (Gen Mgr)

Nicca Chemical Co., Ltd. - Kashima Factory (1)
16-25 Higashifukashiba, Kamisu, 314-0103, Ibaraki, Japan
Tel.: (81) 29 990 0780
Web Site: https://www.nicca.co.jp
Organic Chemical Mfr
N.A.I.C.S.: 325199

Nicca Chemical Research & Development Center (Shanghai) Co., Ltd. (1)
3F/No 12 Bldg 201 Minyi Road, Songjiang District, Shanghai, 201612, China
Tel.: (86) 2154277300
Basic Chemicals Mfr
N.A.I.C.S.: 325180

Nicca Korea Co., Ltd. (1)
502-ho Jeiplatz 186 Gasan digital 1-ro, Geumcheon-gu, Seoul, 08502, Korea (South)
Tel.: (82) 27797727
Web Site: http://www.niccakorea.com
Sales Range: $25-49.9 Million
Emp.: 100
Organic Chemical Mfr
N.A.I.C.S.: 325199

Nicca Korea Co., Ltd. - Daegu Factory (1)
18-6 Seongseo-ro, Dalso-gu, Daegu, 42725, Korea (South)
Tel.: (82) 537202204
Basic Chemicals Mfr
N.A.I.C.S.: 325180

Nicca U.S.A., Inc. (1)
1044 S Nelson Dr, Fountain Inn, SC 29644
Tel.: (864) 862-1426
Web Site: https://www.niccausa.com
Sales Range: $25-49.9 Million
Emp.: 25
Organic Chemical Mfr
N.A.I.C.S.: 325199
Shin Masuda (CEO)

Nicca Vietnam Co., Ltd. (1)
Plot 224/6 Road 2 Amata Industrial Park, Long Binh Ward, Bien Hoa, Dong Nai, Vietnam
Tel.: (84) 613936080
Specialty Chemicals Mfr
N.A.I.C.S.: 325998

Ohtomo-chemical Ins., Corp. (1)
4F Kato Bldg 2-1-14 Nihonbashi, Chuo-ku, Tokyo, 103-0027, Japan
Tel.: (81) 362625110
Web Site: https://www.ohtomo-chemical.co.jp
Basic Chemicals Mfr
N.A.I.C.S.: 325180
Plant (Domestic):

Ohtomo-chemical Ins., Corp - Sammu Factory (2)
1454-1 Kibara, Sanmu, 289-1212, Chiba, Japan
Tel.: (81) 298281111
Chemical Products Mfr
N.A.I.C.S.: 327910

PT. Indonesia Nikka Chemicals (1)
Jl Maligi Lot E-3 Kawasan Industri KIIC, Karawang, 41364, Indonesia
Tel.: (62) 218904309
Sales Range: $25-49.9 Million
Emp.: 111
Organic Chemical Mfr
N.A.I.C.S.: 325199

STC Nicca Co., Ltd. (1)
92/30A Sathorn Thani Bldg 2 12th Floor North Sathorn Rd Silom, Bangrak, Bangkok, 10500, Thailand
Tel.: (66) 22668800
Web Site: https://www.stcnicca.co.th
Chemical Product Mfr & Distr
N.A.I.C.S.: 325199
Sumon Suwanpatra (Chm)

STC Nicca Co., Ltd. - Taiban Factory (1)
819 Soi Watrajpothong Moo 5 Sukhumvit Road, Taiban, Bangkok, 10280, Samut Prakan, Thailand
Tel.: (66) 2 395 0505
Web Site: https://www.stcnicca.co.th
Textile Mfr
N.A.I.C.S.: 314999

Solvay Nicca, Ltd. (1)
7th Fl Atago Green Hills Mori Tower Atago 2-5-1, Minato-ku, Tokyo, 105-6207, Japan
Tel.: (81) 354254790
Chemical Equipment Design Services
N.A.I.C.S.: 541330

Taiwan Nicca Chemical Co., Ltd. (1)
No 729 Huannan Rd, Guanyin Dist, Taoyuan, 328, Taiwan
Tel.: (886) 34738289
Web Site: https://www.nicca.com.tw
Organic Chemical Mfr
N.A.I.C.S.: 325199
Emori Yasumasa (Pres)

Taiwan Nicca Chemical Co., Ltd. - Taoyuan Factory (1)
No 729 Huannan Road Datan Vil, Guanyin Township, Taoyuan, 328, Taiwan
Tel.: (886) 34738288
Basic Chemicals Mfr
N.A.I.C.S.: 325180

Yamada Pharmaceutical Co., Ltd. (1)
2-1-14 Nihonbashi Nihonbashi Kato Building 3F, Chuo-ku, Tokyo, 103-0027, Japan
Tel.: (81) 332780390
Web Site: https://www.yamada-seiyaku.com
Emp.: 112
Pharmaceutical Product Mfr & Distr
N.A.I.C.S.: 325412
Kiyotaka Hotta (CEO)

Yamada Pharmaceutical Company - Kasumigaura Factory (1)
24-8 Fukatani, Kasumigaura, 300-0134, Japan
Tel.: (81) 298281111
Pharmaceutical Products Mfr & Distr
N.A.I.C.S.: 325412

Zhejiang Nicca Chemical Co., Ltd. (1)
Building 6 Southern Quarter Yindu Garden No 28 Donghaizhong Rd, Shinan District, Qingdao, 266071, Shandong, China
Tel.: (86) 53268612656
Basic Chemicals Mfr
N.A.I.C.S.: 325180

NICCO CORPORATION LTD.
Nicco House 2 Hare Street, Kolkata, 700 001, India
Tel.: (91) 33 6628 5250
Web Site: http://www.niccogroup.com
Year Founded: 1942
Emp.: 2,000
Cable Mfr
N.A.I.C.S.: 334417
V. R. Moza (Pres-Mktg)

Subsidiaries:

Nicco Corporation Ltd, - BARIPADA WORKS (1)
Hamilton Gardens, Baripada, 757001, Odisha, India
Tel.: (91) 6792 252454
Power Cable Mfr
N.A.I.C.S.: 332618

NICCO PARKS & RESORTS LIMITED
Jheel Meel Sector IV Salt Lake City, Kolkata, 700 106, India
Tel.: (91) 3366285549
Web Site: https://www.niccoparks.com
526721—(BOM)
Rev.: $2,598,796
Assets: $9,291,227
Liabilities: $2,287,071
Net Worth: $7,004,156
Earnings: ($480,221)
Emp.: 229
Fiscal Year-end: 03/31/21
Theme Amusement Park Operating Services
N.A.I.C.S.: 713110
Rahul Mitra (Pres & Sec)

NICCO UCO ALLIANCE CREDIT LIMITED
Nicco House 2 Hare Street 2nd Floor, Kolkata, 700 001, West Bengal, India
Tel.: (91) 3340066499
Web Site: https://nuacl.com
Year Founded: 1989
Rev.: $35,956
Assets: $1,033,883
Liabilities: $96,248,102
Net Worth: ($95,214,219)
Earnings: ($768,670)
Fiscal Year-end: 03/31/18
Business Support Services
N.A.I.C.S.: 561499
S. S. Majumdar (Sec)

NICE CORPORATION
Tsurumi Chuo 4-33-1, Tsurumi-ku, Yokohama, 230-8571, Kanagawa, Japan
Tel.: (81) 455216111
Web Site: https://www.nice.co.jp
Year Founded: 1950
8089—(TKS)
Rev.: $1,492,994,090
Assets: $1,066,245,880
Liabilities: $689,654,350
Net Worth: $376,591,530
Earnings: $27,788,440
Emp.: 2,504
Fiscal Year-end: 03/31/24
Real Estate Development Services
N.A.I.C.S.: 531390

Subsidiaries:

Nice International America Corporation (1)
10300 SW Greenburg Rd Ste 420, Portland, OR 97223
Tel.: (503) 245-9910
Real Estate Development Services
N.A.I.C.S.: 531390

Nice International Canada Corporation (1)
1185 West Georgia Street, Vancouver, V6E 4E6, BC, Canada
Tel.: (604) 681-1273
Real Estate Development Services
N.A.I.C.S.: 531390

SUTEKI EUROPE NV (1)
Pegasuslaan 5, 1831, Diegem, Belgium
Tel.: (32) 2 709 22 75
Web Site: http://www.suteki-europe.be
Civil Engineering Services
N.A.I.C.S.: 541330

NICE D&B CO., LTD.
Credit Center 217 Mapo-daero, Mapo-gu, Seoul, Korea (South)
Tel.: (82) 221222370
Web Site: http://www.nicednb.co.kr
Year Founded: 2002
130580—(KRS)
Rev.: $70,709,645
Assets: $81,753,063
Liabilities: $17,403,452
Net Worth: $64,349,612
Earnings: $10,938,030
Emp.: 356
Fiscal Year-end: 12/31/22
Credit Card Inquiry Services
N.A.I.C.S.: 522320
Jeong Ki Ahn (Dir)

NICE GROUP S.P.A.
Via Callalta 1, 31046, Oderzo, TV, Italy
Tel.: (39) 0422 85 38 38   IT
Web Site: http://www.niceforyou.com
Year Founded: 1990
Holding Company
N.A.I.C.S.: 551112
Lauro Buoro (Chm)

Subsidiaries:

Hy-Security Gate, Inc. (1)
6623 S 228th St, Kent, WA 98032
Tel.: (253) 867-3700
Web Site: http://www.hysecurity.com
Sales Range: $1-9.9 Million
Emp.: 26
Secure Gate Manufacturer
N.A.I.C.S.: 335999
Brian Denault (Pres)

Nice S.p.A. (1)
Via Pezza Alta Via Callalta 1, 31046, Oderzo, TV, Italy   (100%)
Tel.: (39) 0422853838
Web Site: http://www.niceforyou.com
Home Automation System Services
N.A.I.C.S.: 238210
Roberto Griffa (CEO)

NICE HOLDINGS CO., LTD.
17 Eunhaeng-ro, Yeongdeungrp-gu, Seoul, Korea (South)
Tel.: (82) 221224000
Web Site: https://www.nice.co.kr
Year Founded: 2010
034310—(KRS)
Rev.: $2,111,491,235
Assets: $2,591,358,221
Liabilities: $1,578,707,466
Net Worth: $1,012,650,754
Earnings: $52,934,685
Emp.: 49
Fiscal Year-end: 12/31/22
Investment Management Service
N.A.I.C.S.: 523999
Young Choi (CEO)

Subsidiaries:

Bowon Light Metal Co., Ltd. (1)
50-10 Eungbong-ro, Eungbong-myeon, Yesan, Chungcheong, Korea (South)
Tel.: (82) 41 331 6390
Web Site: http://www.bowonmetal.com
Motor Vehicle Parts Mfr
N.A.I.C.S.: 336390

IONE CO., LTD (1)
1336 Seokgok-ri, Dunpo-myeon, Asan, Korea (South)
Tel.: (82) 41 541 7980
Web Site: http://www.ionemetal.com
Motor Vehicle Parts Mfr
N.A.I.C.S.: 336390

ITM Semiconductor Co., Ltd. (1)
112-8 Namchon-Ri, Okson-Myeon, Cheongwon, Chungcheongbuk-do, Korea (South)
Tel.: (82) 43 270 4700
Web Site: http://www.it-m.co.kr
Emp.: 2,000
Semiconductor Product Mfr
N.A.I.C.S.: 334413
Hyuk-Hwi Na (CEO)

KIS Information & Communication, Inc. (1)
Center Point West 22 23rd Fl Semal-ro 97, Guro-gu, Seoul, Korea (South)
Tel.: (82) 15993700
Web Site: https://www.kisvan.co.kr
Investment Management Service
N.A.I.C.S.: 523999

AND PRIVATE COMPANIES / NICE TOTAL CASH MANAGEMENT CO., LTD.

NICE Cash Management & Security Co., Ltd. (1)
Seongsan-dong 5F 137 World cup buk-ro, Mapo-gu, Seoul, Korea (South)
Tel.: (82) 2 366 6211
Web Site: http://www.nicems.co.kr
Escort Services
N.A.I.C.S.: 812990

NICE Combinet Co., Ltd. (1)
507 Woorim E-Biz Bldg 43 Yansan-ro, Yeondeungpo-gu, Seoul, Korea (South)
Tel.: (82) 2 6112 9119
Web Site: http://www.nicecombi.net
Investment Management Service
N.A.I.C.S.: 523999

NICE Data Inc. (1)
36 Chungjeong-ro, Seodaemun-gu, Seoul, 3741, Korea (South)
Tel.: (82) 15885659
Web Site: https://www.nicedata.co.kr
Investment Management Service
N.A.I.C.S.: 541213

NICE Investors Service Co. Ltd. (1)
Tel.: (82) 220146200
Investment Management Service
N.A.I.C.S.: 523999

NICE Pricing & Information Inc. (1)
19 Gukhoe-daero 70-gil, Yeondeungpo-gu, Seoul, Korea (South)
Tel.: (82) 23983900
Web Site: https://www.nicepni.co.kr
Investment Management Service
N.A.I.C.S.: 523999

NICE INFORMATION & TELE-COMMUNICATION, INC.
17 Eunhaeng-ro, Yeongdeungpo-gu, Seoul, Korea (South)
Tel.: (82) 221872700
Web Site: https://www.nicevan.co.kr
Year Founded: 1986
036800—(KRS)
Rev: $617,328,691
Assets: $790,998,954
Liabilities: $524,707,627
Net Worth: $266,291,327
Earnings: $30,839,241
Emp.: 200
Fiscal Year-end: 12/31/22
Financial Services
N.A.I.C.S.: 523999
Seung Hyun Kim (CEO)

Subsidiaries:

NICE Payments Co., Ltd. (1)
Credit Center Building 7th Floor 217 Mapo-daero, Mapo-gu, Seoul, 4117, Korea (South)
Tel.: (82) 16610808
Web Site: https://www.nicepayments.co.kr
Payment Gateway Services
N.A.I.C.S.: 522320
Yoon Kyeong Hwang (CEO)

NICE INFORMATION SERVICE CO., LTD.
17 Eunhaeng-ro, Yeongdeungpo-Gu, Seoul, 07237, Korea (South)
Tel.: (82) 221224000
Web Site: https://www.niceinfo.co.kr
Year Founded: 1985
030190—(KRS)
Rev.: $368,059,210
Assets: $368,997,151
Liabilities: $106,955,617
Net Worth: $262,041,534
Earnings: $40,419,058
Emp.: 916
Fiscal Year-end: 12/31/22
Credit Information Services
N.A.I.C.S.: 541990
Shim Eui-Young (Vice Chm & Exec Dir)

NICE LTD.
13 Zarchin Street, PO Box 690, Ra'anana, 4310602, Israel
Tel.: (972) 97753777
Web Site: https://www.nice.com
Year Founded: 1986
NICE—(NASDAQ)
Rev.: $2,181,294,000
Assets: $4,854,419,000
Liabilities: $1,798,996,000
Net Worth: $3,055,423,000
Earnings: $265,945,000
Emp.: 7,926
Fiscal Year-end: 12/31/22
Digital Recording, Quality Management Solutions & Communications Intelligence Systems Mfr, Developer & Designer
N.A.I.C.S.: 334111
Chris Wooten (Exec VP-NICE Vertical Markets)

Subsidiaries:

Actimize Inc. (1)
1359 Broadway 5th Fl, New York, NY 10018
Tel.: (212) 643-4600
Web Site: http://www.actimize.com
Transactional Risk Management Solutions
N.A.I.C.S.: 541512

Subsidiary (Non-US):

Actimize Japan KK (2)
Holland Mori Tower Rop 1207, 5 11 1 Toranomon Minato Ku, Tokyo, 105-0001, Japan
Tel.: (81) 354089050
Web Site: http://www.actimize.com
Transactional Risk Management Solutions
N.A.I.C.S.: 541512

Actimize UK Limited (2)
18 Mansfeld St, London, E1 8AA, United Kingdom
Tel.: (44) 2079298270
Web Site: http://www.actimize.com
Sales Range: $25-49.9 Million
Emp.: 70
Transactional Risk Management Solutions
N.A.I.C.S.: 541512

LIVEVOX HOLDINGS, INC. (1)
655 Montgomery St Ste 1000, San Francisco, CA 94111
Tel.: (415) 671-6000
Web Site: https://www.livevox.com
Rev.: $136,025,000
Assets: $178,155,000
Liabilities: $80,920,000
Net Worth: $97,235,000
Earnings: ($37,475,000)
Emp.: 627
Fiscal Year-end: 12/31/2022
Holding Company
N.A.I.C.S.: 551112
Linda Esperance (Sr VP-People Ops)

Subsidiary (Domestic):

LiveVox Colombia SAS (2)
655 Montgomery St Ste 1000, San Francisco, CA 94111
Tel.: (415) 671-6000
Software Development Services
N.A.I.C.S.: 541511

LiveVox, Inc. (2)
655 Montgomery St Ste 1000, San Francisco, CA 94111
Tel.: (415) 671-6000
Web Site: http://www.livevox.com
Computer Software Product Mfr
N.A.I.C.S.: 541511
Larry Siegel (Co-Founder & Exec VP-Product Mgmt)

Speech IQ, LLC (2)
1 Marconi Pl Ste 100, Columbus, OH 43215
Web Site: https://www.speechiq.com
Software Development Services
N.A.I.C.S.: 541511

MindTouch, Inc. (1)
101 W Broadway Ste 1500, San Diego, CA 92101
Tel.: (619) 795-8459
Web Site: http://www.mindtouch.com
Custom Computer Programing
N.A.I.C.S.: 541511
Aaron Fulkerson (Co-Founder)

Moxie Software, Inc. (1)
851 Traeger Ave Ste 210, San Bruno, CA 94066
Tel.: (650) 294-4680
Web Site: http://www.moxiesoft.com
Sales Range: $100-124.9 Million
Emp.: 150
Software Developer
N.A.I.C.S.: 513210
David Boyer (Sr VP-Product Dev)

Subsidiary (Non-US):

Moxie Software Germany (2)
Maximilianstrasse 13, 80539, Munich, Germany
Tel.: (49) 89 20 300 6314
Software Developer
N.A.I.C.S.: 513210

Moxie Software UK (2)
9 Greyfriars Rd, Reading, RG1 1NU, United Kingdom
Tel.: (44) 8709041122
Web Site: http://www.gomoxie.com
Software Development Services
N.A.I.C.S.: 513210

NICE APAC Ltd. (1)
16th Floor Allied Kajima Building, 138 Gloucester Road, Wanchai, China (Hong Kong) (100%)
Tel.: (852) 25983838
Web Site: http://www.nice.com
Sales Range: $25-49.9 Million
Emp.: 30
Computer Systems & Services
N.A.I.C.S.: 541512

NICE Actimize, Inc. (1)
221 River St 10th Flr, Hoboken, NJ 07030
Tel.: (551) 256-5130
Web Site: http://www.niceactimize.com
Financial Trading Communication Solution Provider
N.A.I.C.S.: 513210
Barak Eliam (CEO)

Subsidiary (Domestic):

Guardian Analytics, Inc. (2)
2465 Latham St Ste 200, Mountain View, CA 94040-4792
Tel.: (925) 968-9495
Web Site: http://www.guardiananalytics.com
Electronics Stores
N.A.I.C.S.: 449210
Laurent Pacalin (Pres & CEO)

NICE CTI Systems UK Ltd. (1)
Tollbar Way Hedge End, Southampton, S030 2ZP, United Kingdom (100%)
Tel.: (44) 1489771200
Sales Range: $25-49.9 Million
Emp.: 80
Computer Systems & Services
N.A.I.C.S.: 541512

NICE Interactive Solutions India Pvt Ltd. (1)
Umiya Business Bay Tower 1 Marathahalli Sarjapur Ring Road, Koramangala 3rd Block, Bengaluru, 560103, India
Tel.: (91) 8030781600
Web Site: http://www.nice.com
Emp.: 100
Computer Systems & Services
N.A.I.C.S.: 541512

NICE Japan Ltd. (1)
2nd Floor EG Bldg 3-3-2 Nakameguro, Meguro-ku, Tokyo, 153-0061, Japan
Tel.: (81) 357688200
Sales Range: $25-49.9 Million
Emp.: 40
Computer Systems & Services
N.A.I.C.S.: 541512

NICE Switzerland AG (1)
Dammstrasse 19 Suite 128, 6300, Zug, Switzerland
Tel.: (41) 7232323
Software Development Services
N.A.I.C.S.: 541511

NICE Systems (Singapore) Pte. Ltd. (1)
71 Robinson Road 04-02, Singapore, 068895, Singapore
Tel.: (65) 62225123
Web Site: http://www.nice.com

Sales Range: $25-49.9 Million
Emp.: 17
Computer Systems & Services
N.A.I.C.S.: 541512

NICE Systems Australia Pty Ltd. (1)
Level 7 141 Walker Street, Sydney, 2060, NSW, Australia
Tel.: (61) 299271100
Web Site: http://www.nice.com
Sales Range: $25-49.9 Million
Emp.: 35
Computer Systems & Services
N.A.I.C.S.: 541512

NICE Systems GmbH (1)
Grosse Gallusstrass 9, 60311, Frankfurt, Germany (100%)
Tel.: (49) 69971770
Web Site: http://www.nice.com
Computer Systems & Services
N.A.I.C.S.: 541512

NICE Systems Inc. (1)
301 Rt 17 N 10th Fl, Rutherford, NJ 07070
Tel.: (201) 964-2600
Web Site: http://www.nice.com
Sales Range: $25-49.9 Million
Emp.: 100
Computer Systems & Services
N.A.I.C.S.: 334610

Subsidiary (Domestic):

Mattersight Corporation (2)
200 W Madison St Ste 3100, Chicago, IL 60606
Tel.: (877) 235-6925
Web Site: http://www.mattersight.com
Rev.: $46,510,000
Assets: $39,935,000
Liabilities: $47,265,000
Net Worth: ($7,330,000)
Earnings: ($16,320,000)
Emp.: 281
Fiscal Year-end: 12/31/2017
Customer Relationship Management Consulting & Systems Integration Services
N.A.I.C.S.: 541511

Subsidiary (Non-US):

eLoyalty (Canada) Corporation (3)
675 Cochrane Drive East Tower 6th Floor, Markham, L3R 0B8, ON, Canada
Web Site: http://www.eloyalty.com
Sales Range: $100-124.9 Million
Emp.: 5
Designer of Computer Integrated Systems
N.A.I.C.S.: 334610

eLoyalty (UK) Limited (3)
1210 Park View Arlington Business Park, Theele, Reading, RG7 4TY, United Kingdom
Tel.: (44) 8707359526
Web Site: http://www.eloyalty.com
Sales Range: $1-9.9 Million
Emp.: 5
Designer of Computer Integrated Systems
N.A.I.C.S.: 334610

Nexidia Inc. (1)
3565 Piedmont Rd NE Bldg 2 Ste 400, Atlanta, GA 30305 (100%)
Tel.: (404) 495-7220
Web Site: http://www.nexidia.com
Customer Interaction Analytics Software & Services
N.A.I.C.S.: 541511

inContact, Inc. (1)
75 W Towne Rdg Pkwy Tower 1, Sandy, UT 84070
Tel.: (801) 320-3200
Web Site: http://www.incontact.com
Cloud Contact Center Software Solutions
N.A.I.C.S.: 517121

NICE TOTAL CASH MANAGEMENT CO., LTD.
7 Saechang-ro, Mapo-gu, Seoul, 121-709, Korea (South)
Tel.: (82) 221225400
Web Site: https://www.nicetcm.co.kr
Year Founded: 2000
063570—(KRS)
Rev.: $221,596,459
Assets: $381,887,085

5265

NICE TOTAL CASH MANAGEMENT CO., LTD.

NICE Total Cash Management Co., Ltd.—(Continued)

Liabilities: $247,065,064
Net Worth: $134,822,021
Earnings: $6,645,945
Emp.: 490
Fiscal Year-end: 12/31/22
Automatic Teller Machine(ATM) Management Services
N.A.I.C.S.: 238290

NICHE CAPITAL EMAS HOLDINGS BERHAD

Unit 3 1 3rd Floor Wisma Leader, No 8 Jalan Larut, Penang, 10050, Malaysia
Tel.: (60) 42298108
Web Site:
    https://www.nichecapital.com.my
NICE—(KLS)
Rev.: $6,222,290
Assets: $19,544,670
Liabilities: $3,857,657
Net Worth: $15,687,012
Earnings: ($1,394,457)
Emp.: 55
Fiscal Year-end: 06/30/23
Holding Company
N.A.I.C.S.: 551112
Khairul Idham Ismail *(Chm)*

NICHE-TECH SEMICONDUCTOR MATERIALS LIMITED

Unit 208 Lakeside 1 Science Park, Hong Kong, China (Hong Kong)
Tel.: (852) 21153979   Ky
Web Site:
    http://www.nichetech.com.hk
Year Founded: 2006
8490—(HKG)
Rev.: $27,777,023
Assets: $39,738,308
Liabilities: $10,585,050
Net Worth: $29,153,258
Earnings: $1,101,600
Emp.: 179
Fiscal Year-end: 12/31/22
Semiconductor Parts Mfr
N.A.I.C.S.: 334413
Felix Bok Hin Chow *(Co-Founder & Chm)*

Subsidiaries:

Niche-Tech Group Ltd. - Shantou Factory   (1)
No 6 Wanji N St, Wanji Industrial Zone, Shantou, China
Tel.: (86) 75488709888
Semiconductor Product Mfr
N.A.I.C.S.: 334413
Eric Shi *(Gen Mgr)*

NICHENETMARKETING PLC

33 Imperial Square Suite 515, Cheltenham, GL50 1QZ, Glos, United Kingdom
Tel.: (44) 203 468 75 12
Web Site:
    http://www.nichenetmarketing.net
Year Founded: 2010
Online Advertising Services
N.A.I.C.S.: 541890
Edward Logger *(CEO)*

NICHI-IKO PHARMACEUTICAL CO., LTD.

1-6-21 Sogawa, Toyama, 930-8583, Japan
Tel.: (81) 764322121   JP
Web Site: https://www.nichiiko.co.jp
Year Founded: 1965
4541—(NGO)
Rev.: $1,733,300,800
Assets: $2,522,211,120
Liabilities: $2,388,888,480
Net Worth: $133,322,640
Earnings: ($1,016,245,120)
Emp.: 1,954
Fiscal Year-end: 03/31/22
Pharmaceuticals Mfr
N.A.I.C.S.: 325412
Yuichi Tamura *(Pres & CEO)*

Subsidiaries:

ELMED Co., Ltd.   (1)
3-23-5 Diwa Higasi Bukuro, Tokyo, 10070, Toshima Ku, Japan   **(100%)**
Tel.: (81) 339806633
Web Site: http://www.emec.co.jp
Sales Range: $25-49.9 Million
Emp.: 50
Marketer of Generic Pharmaceuticals
N.A.I.C.S.: 424210
Shohei Kanazawa *(Pres)*

Nichi-Iko (Thailand) Co., Ltd.   (1)
57 Park Ventures Ecoplex Room no 1110 11th Floor Wireless Road, Lumpini Patumwan, Bangkok, 10330, Thailand
Tel.: (66) 2 108 5995
Web Site: https://www.nichiiko.co.th
Pharmaceutical Products Distr
N.A.I.C.S.: 424210
Yuichi Tamura *(Co-Pres & CEO)*

Nichi-Iko Gifu Plant Co., Ltd.   (1)
1040-22 Matsunoki-cho, Takayama, 506-0802, Gifu, Japan
Tel.: (81) 57 733 0811
Web Site: https://www.nichiiko.co.jp
Pharmaceutical Product Mfr & Distr
N.A.I.C.S.: 325412

Nichi-Iko Pharmaceutical Co., Ltd. - Aichi Plant   (1)
1212 Aza-teramae Gejo-cho, Kasugai, 486-0923, Aichi, Japan
Tel.: (81) 568814467
Web Site: http://www.nichiiko.co.jp
Pharmaceutical Product Mfr
N.A.I.C.S.: 325412

Nichi-Iko Pharmaceutical Co., Ltd. - Saitama Plant   (1)
51 Sanjyou-machi, Nishi-ku, Saitama, 331-0056, Japan
Tel.: (81) 486233111
Web Site: http://www.nichiiko.co.jp
Pharmaceutical Product Mfr
N.A.I.C.S.: 325412

Nichi-Iko Pharmaceutical Co., Ltd. - Toyama Plant 1   (1)
205-1 Shimo Umezawa, Namerikawa, 936-0857, Toyama, Japan
Tel.: (81) 76 457 5767
Web Site: http://www.nichiiko.co.jp
Pharmaceutical Product Mfr
N.A.I.C.S.: 325412

Nichi-Iko Pharmaceutical Co., Ltd. - Toyama Plant 2   (1)
183-5 Yasuda, Namerikawa, 936-0825, Toyama, Japan
Tel.: (81) 76 457 4775
Web Site: http://www.nichiiko.co.jp
Pharmaceutical Product Mfr
N.A.I.C.S.: 325412

Nichi-Iko Pharmaceutical Co., Ltd. - Yamagata Plant   (1)
2-1-52 Ishidorii, Tendo, 994-0057, Yamagata, Japan
Tel.: (81) 236554335
Web Site: http://www.nichiiko.co.jp
Pharmaceuticals Product Mfr
N.A.I.C.S.: 325412

Sagent Pharmaceuticals, Inc.   (1)
1901 N Roselle Rd Ste 450, Schaumburg, IL 60195
Tel.: (847) 908-1600
Web Site: https://www.sagentpharma.com
Emp.: 200
Holding Company; Pharmaceutical Mfr
N.A.I.C.S.: 325412
Peter Kaemmerer *(CEO)*

Subsidiary (Domestic):

Sagent Pharmaceuticals, Inc.   (2)
1901 N Roselle Rd, Schaumburg, IL 60195
Tel.: (847) 908-1600
Web Site: http://www.sagentpharma.com
Emp.: 200
Pharmaceuticals Mfr
N.A.I.C.S.: 325412

SterRx, LLC
141 Idaho Ave, Plattsburgh, NY 12903
Tel.: (518) 324-7879
Web Site: https://www.sterrx.com
Emp.: 100
Pharmaceutical Preparation Mfr
N.A.I.C.S.: 325412

NICHIA CORPORATION

491 Oka Kaminaka Cho, Anan, 774-8601, Tokushima, Japan
Tel.: (81) 0884222311
Web Site: http://www.nichia.co.jp
Year Founded: 1956
Sales Range: $1-4.9 Billion
Emp.: 8,880
Electronic Components Mfr
N.A.I.C.S.: 334413
Hiroyoshi Ogawa *(Pres)*

Subsidiaries:

NICHIA CHEMICAL (INDIA) Pvt. Ltd.   (1)
203B &204 DLF Galleria Mayur District Centre Mayur Vihar Phase-1, New Delhi, 110091, India
Tel.: (91) 11 47012791
Semiconductor Device Whslr
N.A.I.C.S.: 423690
Ravi Av *(Gen Mgr)*

NICHIA CHEMICAL (THAILAND) CO., Ltd.   (1)
388 Exchange Tower 24th floor Unit 2403 Sukhumvit Road Klongtoey, Bangkok, 10110, Thailand
Tel.: (66) 2663 7640
Semiconductor Device Whslr
N.A.I.C.S.: 423690

NICHIA CHEMICAL HONG KONG., Ltd.   (1)
Suite 23A08-10 23A/F Tower2 The Gateway 25 Canton Road, Tsim Sha Tsui, Kowloon, China (Hong Kong)
Tel.: (852) 2956 3200
Semiconductor Device Whslr
N.A.I.C.S.: 423690
Ketty Tong *(Sr Mgr-Sls)*

NICHIA CHEMICAL Pte Ltd   (1)
78 Shenton Way 26-03, Singapore, 079120, Singapore
Tel.: (65) 63248218
Semiconductor Device Whslr
N.A.I.C.S.: 423690

NICHIA EUROPE B.V.   (1)
Thomas R Malthusstraat 1-3, 1066 JR, Amsterdam, Netherlands
Tel.: (31) 20 5060900
Semiconductor Device Whslr
N.A.I.C.S.: 423690
Alessandro Afeltra *(Key Acct Mgr)*

NICHIA KOREA CORPORATION   (1)
2301 36 Teheran-ro 87-gil, Gangnam-gu, Seoul, 135-973, Korea (South)
Tel.: (82) 2 2016 5750
Semiconductor Device Whslr
N.A.I.C.S.: 423690

NICHIA RUS LLC   (1)
15 Savvinskaya Naberezhnaya, 119435, Moscow, Russia
Tel.: (7) 4957874733
Emp.: 4
Semiconductor Device Whslr
N.A.I.C.S.: 423690
Andrey Vengerov *(Mgr-Sls)*

NICHIA SHANGHAI CORPORATION   (1)
Room 101 Bldg1 622 Song Sheng Road, Song Jiang, Shanghai, China
Tel.: (86) 21 5774 6358
Semiconductor Device Whslr
N.A.I.C.S.: 423690

NICHIA TAIWAN CORPORATION   (1)
No 6 Kwang-Fu North Road Hsinchu Industrial Park Fukou, Taipei, Taiwan

INTERNATIONAL PUBLIC

Tel.: (886) 3 5984468
Semiconductor Device Whslr
N.A.I.C.S.: 423690

Nichia America Corporation   (1)
48561 Alpha Dr Ste 100, Wixom, MI 48393
Tel.: (717) 285-2323
Web Site: http://www.nichia.com
Semiconductor Mfr
N.A.I.C.S.: 334413

Nichia Chemical Europe GmbH   (1)
Westerbachstrasse 28, 61476, Kronberg, Germany
Tel.: (49) 617396700
Web Site: http://www.nichia.com
Sales Range: $25-49.9 Million
Emp.: 10
Semiconductor Components Mfr
N.A.I.C.S.: 334413

Nichia Corporation - A-PLANT   (1)
3 Nyuta Aratano-Cho, Anan, 779-1510, Tokushima, Japan
Tel.: (81) 884 36 3121
Semiconductor Devices Mfr
N.A.I.C.S.: 334413

Nichia Corporation - K-PLANT   (1)
4000-8 Nagasato Chiran-Cho, Minamikyushu, 897-0303, Kagoshima, Japan
Tel.: (81) 993 83 4206
Semiconductor Devices Mfr
N.A.I.C.S.: 334413

Nichia Corporation - N-PLANT   (1)
38-2 Kawamukoichi Ichiba Oasa-Cho, Naruto, 779-0315, Tokushima, Japan
Tel.: (81) 88 641 5252
Semiconductor Devices Mfr
N.A.I.C.S.: 334413

Nichia Corporation - TN-PLANT   (1)
1-19 Tatsumi-Cho, Anan, 774-0001, Tokushima, Japan
Tel.: (81) 884 22 9846
Semiconductor Devices Mfr
N.A.I.C.S.: 334413

Nichia Corporation - TS-PLANT   (1)
1-1 Tatsumi-Cho, Anan, 774-0001, Tokushima, Japan
Tel.: (81) 884 22 9846
Semiconductor Devices Mfr
N.A.I.C.S.: 334413

Nichia Corporation - V-PLANT   (1)
224 Hiraishi Ebisuno Kawauchi-Cho, Tokushima, 771-0132, Japan
Tel.: (81) 88 665 2311
Web Site: http://www.nichia.co.jp
Semiconductor Devices Mfr
N.A.I.C.S.: 334413
Cadanao Kohara *(Gen Mgr)*

NICHIA STEEL WORKS CO., LTD.

6-74 Doi-cho, Amagasaki, 660-0083, Hyogo, Japan
Tel.: (81) 664161021
Web Site:
    https://www.nichiasteel.co.jp
Year Founded: 1952
5658—(TKS)
Rev.: $228,025,170
Assets: $486,529,050
Liabilities: $120,751,480
Net Worth: $365,777,570
Earnings: $8,315,380
Emp.: 329
Fiscal Year-end: 03/31/24
Steel Product Mfr & Distr
N.A.I.C.S.: 331110
Toshinori Onishi *(Pres & CEO)*

Subsidiaries:

J-Witex Corporation   (1)
300 Tsutsumi, Kaizuka, 597-0054, Osaka, Japan
Tel.: (81) 724366802
Web Site: https://www.j-witex.co.jp
Steel Wire Mfr & Distr
N.A.I.C.S.: 331110
Yasushi Ishibashi *(Pres)*

Subsidiary (Domestic):

MRK Corporation   (2)

1-25-19 Harigaya, Utsunomiya, 321-0137, Tochigi, Japan
Tel.: (81) 286883350
Web Site: http://www.jw-mrk.co.jp
Production Facility Construction Services
N.A.I.C.S.: 236210

Nankai Service Corporation (2)
1-12-2 Hori, Kaizuka, 597-0015, Osaka, Japan
Tel.: (81) 724390151
Automobile Parts Mfr
N.A.I.C.S.: 336390

Subsidiary (Non-US):

Yantai J-WITEX Wire Product Co., Ltd (2)
No 8-3 Beijing South Road, Yantai Economic and Technical Development Zone, Shandong, China
Tel.: (86) 5356374975
Wire Product Distr
N.A.I.C.S.: 423510

Yantai J-Witex Metal Products Corporation (2)
Export Processing Zone No 89 Huanhai Road, Yantai, 264000, Shandong, China
Tel.: (86) 5356853095
Wire Product Distr
N.A.I.C.S.: 423510

NICHIAS CORPORATION

6-1 Hatchobori 1-chome, Chuo-ku, Tokyo, 104-8555, Japan
Tel.: (81) 344131111
Web Site: https://www.nichias.co.jp
5393—(TKS)
Rev.: $1,648,474,510
Assets: $1,922,108,680
Liabilities: $594,040,700
Net Worth: $1,328,067,980
Earnings: $178,212,210
Emp.: 6,431
Fiscal Year-end: 03/31/24
Industrial Products & Construction Materials Mfr & Sales
N.A.I.C.S.: 236210
Shoichi Yonezawa (Sr Mng Exec Officer)

Subsidiaries:

Inocrete Co., Ltd. (1)
5th Fl 4-11-10 Minamisenba, Chuo-ku, Osaka, 542-0081, Japan
Tel.: (81) 661201910
Web Site: https://www.inocrete.co.jp
Cooling & Heat Insulation Services
N.A.I.C.S.: 238220

KOKUBU INDUSTRIAL CO., LTD. (1)
1-66 Ishikawa-cho, Kashiwara, 582-0029, Osaka, Japan
Tel.: (81) 729786731
Sales Range: $25-49.9 Million
Emp.: 70
Automotive & Insulation Parts Mfr
N.A.I.C.S.: 441330
Kiyoshi Morita (Pres)

KUMAMOTO NICHIAS Corporation (1)
4000-5 Haramizu, Kikuyo-cho, Kikuchi, 869-1102, Kumamoto Prefecture, Japan
Tel.: (81) 962924046
Web Site: https://www.nichias.co.jp
Emp.: 170
Fluoropolymer Mfr
N.A.I.C.S.: 325211

NICHIAS (Shanghai) TRADING CO., LTD. (1)
Room1701 THE PLACE Tower A No 100 Zun Yi Rd, Shanghai, 200051, China
Tel.: (86) 2162361783
Web Site: http://www.nichias.com.cn
Sales Range: $25-49.9 Million
Emp.: 18
Industrial Products & Building Materials Whslr
N.A.I.C.S.: 423840

NICHIAS (Thailand) CO., LTD. (1)
85 Moo 1 Wellgrow Industrial Estate T Homsin, A Bangpakong, Chachoengsao, 24180, Thailand
Tel.: (66) 38570600
Web Site: http://www.nrc.co.th
Sales Range: $25-49.9 Million
Emp.: 80
Industrial Products Mfr
N.A.I.C.S.: 332911
Kitti Chongrungruang (Gen Mgr)

NICHIAS INDUSTRIAL PRODUCTS PVT. LTD. (1)
No K 3 2 Sipcot Indus Park Mambakkam Kanchipuram Dist, Sriperumbudur, Chennai, 602106, Tamil Nadu, India
Tel.: (91) 4427168035
Sales Range: $25-49.9 Million
Emp.: 40
Automobile Parts Mfr
N.A.I.C.S.: 423110
Ramalingam Krishna (Gen Mgr)

Nichias (Shanghai) Autoparts Trading Co., Ltd. (1)
Room 1702 Building A 100 Zunyi Road, Hongqiao Nanfeng Changning District, Shanghai, China
Tel.: (86) 2162362668
Industrial Product Distr
N.A.I.C.S.: 423840

Nichias Autoparts Europe A.S. (1)
K Vapence 984/10, 69201, Mikulov, Czech Republic
Tel.: (420) 77 575 0311
Web Site: https://www.nichias.cz
Seal & Brake Pad Mfr
N.A.I.C.S.: 336340
Oskar Miskolczy (Mgr-Quality)

Nichias Autoparts Europe GmbH (1)
Prinzenallee 7, 40549, Dusseldorf, Germany
Tel.: (49) 21152391058
Semiconductor Mfr
N.A.I.C.S.: 334413

Nichias Czech, s.r.o. (1)
K Vapence 984/10, Breclav, 69201, Mikulov, Czech Republic
Tel.: (420) 775750311
Web Site: https://www.nichias.cz
Sales Range: $50-74.9 Million
Emp.: 4
Automotive Part Whslr
N.A.I.C.S.: 423110

Nichias Fgs Sdn. Bhd. (1)
Plot 103, Darulaman Industrial Estate Bandar Darulaman, 06000, Jitra, Kedah Darul Aman, Malaysia
Tel.: (60) 49173760
Thermal Sealing Materials Mfr
N.A.I.C.S.: 339991
Hirotsugu Kinugawa (Mng Dir)

Nichias SealTech Corporation (1)
3365 Kitsuneana, Takehana-cho, Hashima, 501-6232, Gifu, Japan
Tel.: (81) 583922080
Cork Mfr
N.A.I.C.S.: 321999

Nichias Singapore Pte. Ltd. (1)
25 International Business Park 01-15/17 German Centre, Singapore, 609916, Singapore
Tel.: (65) 62686568
Web Site: https://www.nichias.co.jp
Emp.: 19
Semiconductor Mfr
N.A.I.C.S.: 334413

Nichias Southeast Asia Sdn. Bhd. (1)
Suite A1102 11th Floor West Wing Wisma Consplant 2 No 7 Jalan SS16/1, 47500, Subang Jaya, Selangor Darul Ehsan, Malaysia
Tel.: (60) 356364067
Sealing Material Mfr
N.A.I.C.S.: 339991

Nichias Vietnam Co., Ltd. (1)
Room 709 Elite Business Center 7th Floor Diamond Flower Building, No 48 Le Van Luong Street Nhan Chinh Ward Thanh Xuan Dist, Hanoi, Vietnam
Tel.: (84) 2466643136
Web Site: https://en.nichias.vn

Semiconductor Mfr
N.A.I.C.S.: 334413

Nippon Reinz Co., Ltd. (1)
1-5-2 Fukami-Nishi, Yamato, 242-0018, Kanagawa, Japan
Tel.: (81) 46 262 1125
Web Site: http://www.nrz.jp
Sales Range: $25-49.9 Million
Gaskets & Other Automotive Components Mfr
N.A.I.C.S.: 339991
Toru Nakano (Pres & CEO)

Nippon Rockwool Corporation (1)
Sumitomo Irifune Building 3F 2-1-1 Irifune, Chuo-ku, Tokyo, 104-0042, Japan
Tel.: (81) 344131221
Web Site: https://www.rockwool.co.jp
Building Materials Whslr
N.A.I.C.S.: 423390

P.T. NICHIAS METALWORKS INDONESIA (1)
Jl Raya Industri Km 2 Kawasan Sarana Terpadu, Cikarang, Bekasi, 17530, Indonesia
Tel.: (62) 2189113526
Web Site: http://www.nichias.com
Sales Range: $50-74.9 Million
Emp.: 125
Gaskets Mfr
N.A.I.C.S.: 339991
Takayuki Takenaka (Pres)

P.T. NICHIAS ROCKWOOL INDONESIA (1)
Jl Jend A Yani 39 Kujang Indus Area, Cikampek, Purwakarta, 41373, West Java, Indonesia
Tel.: (62) 264312730
Insulation Material Mfr
N.A.I.C.S.: 327993

P.T. NICHIAS SUNIJAYA (1)
Sequis Tower 19th Floor Suite 1 and 2 Jln Jend Sudirman, No 71 SCBD Lot 11B, Jakarta, 12190, Indonesia
Tel.: (62) 2122776101
Web Site: https://www.nichiassunijaya.com
Emp.: 340
Insulation & Metal Gaskets Whslr
N.A.I.C.S.: 423610
Tadashi Yamada (Chm)

SUZHOU NICHIAS INDUSTRIAL PRODUCTS CO., LTD. (1)
No 208 Qing Qiu St Suzhou Indus Park, Suzhou, 215116, Jiangsu, China
Tel.: (86) 51262833800
Sales Range: $50-74.9 Million
Emp.: 200
Fluoropolymer Products Mfr
N.A.I.C.S.: 325211

Shanghai Goyu Autoparts Co., Ltd. (1)
No 177 Jizhan Rd Minbei Indus Park, Minhang Qu, Shanghai, China
Tel.: (86) 2162969858
Automobile Parts Mfr
N.A.I.C.S.: 336390

TATSUTA KOGYO Co., Ltd. (1)
6-5-4 Takami-cho, Ikarugacho, Yao, 581-0017, Osaka, Japan
Tel.: (81) 729970255
Sales Range: $50-74.9 Million
Emp.: 130
Building Materials Mfr
N.A.I.C.S.: 444180

Thai Nichias Engineering Co., Ltd. (1)
45 Huaypong-Nongbon rd, Huaypong subdistrict Muang District, Rayong, 21150, Thailand
Tel.: (66) 380260518
Web Site: http://www.thainichias.com
Sales Range: $25-49.9 Million
Emp.: 260
Insulation Engineering Services
N.A.I.C.S.: 541330

Thai Nichias International Co., Ltd. (1)
89 AIA Capital Center 11th Floor Unit 1107 Ratchadaphisek Road, Dindaeng, Bangkok, 10400, Thailand
Tel.: (66) 20012060

Web Site: https://www.thainichias-inter.co.th
Industrial Product Distr
N.A.I.C.S.: 423840

NICHIBAN CO., LTD.

2-3-3 Sekiguchi, Bunkyo-ku, Tokyo, 112-8663, Japan
Tel.: (81) 359785601
Web Site: https://www.nichiban.co.jp
Year Founded: 1918
4218—(TKS)
Rev.: $309,737,990
Assets: $449,737,790
Liabilities: $174,080,960
Net Worth: $275,656,830
Earnings: $12,076,470
Emp.: 1,270
Fiscal Year-end: 03/31/24
Adhesive Product Mfr & Distr
N.A.I.C.S.: 322220
Hironori Sakai (Exec Officer-CSR & Admin)

Subsidiaries:

Nichiban Print Corporation (1)
201 Ooaza Nakazawa, Hidaka, 350-1226, Saitama Prefecture, Japan
Tel.: (81) 429851111
Web Site: https://www.nichibanprint.co.jp
Adhesive Product Mfr
N.A.I.C.S.: 322220

NICHICON CORPORATION

Karasumadori Oike-agaru, Nakagyo-ku, Kyoto, 604-0845, Japan
Tel.: (81) 752318461
Web Site: https://www.nichicon.co.jp
6996—(TKS)
Rev.: $1,200,660,230
Assets: $1,367,853,570
Liabilities: $615,377,780
Net Worth: $752,475,790
Earnings: $54,552,330
Emp.: 5,394
Fiscal Year-end: 03/31/24
Electric Equipment Mfr
N.A.I.C.S.: 334416
Shigeo Yoshida (Pres)

Subsidiaries:

FPCAP Electronics (Suzhou) Co., Ltd. (1)
112 Sutong Rd Suzhou Industrial Park, Suzhou, 215021, Jiangsu, China
Tel.: (86) 51267612423
Web Site: http://www.fpcap.jp
Sales Range: $400-449.9 Million
Emp.: 2,000
Aluminum Electrolytic Capacitors Mfr
N.A.I.C.S.: 334416
Kozaki Kyouyichi (Gen Mgr)

Nichicon (America) Corp. (1)
927 E State Pkwy, Schaumburg, IL 60173
Tel.: (847) 843-7500
Web Site: http://www.nichicon-us.com
Sales Range: $25-49.9 Million
Emp.: 60
Electromechanical Component Mfr
N.A.I.C.S.: 334419

Nichicon (Austria) GmbH (1)
Businesspark Marximum Modecenterstrasse 17 Unit 2-7-A, 1110, Vienna, Austria
Tel.: (43) 17067932
Web Site: http://www.nichicon.co.jp
Electronic Components Mfr
N.A.I.C.S.: 334419

Nichicon (Fukui) Corporation (1)
Nichicon Technology Center 4 Tsuchifugo, Ono, 912-0805, Fukui, Japan
Tel.: (81) 779658800
Web Site: http://www.nichicon.co.jp
Sales Range: $25-49.9 Million
Emp.: 100
Electrolytic Capacitor Mfr
N.A.I.C.S.: 334416

Nichicon (Hong Kong) Ltd. (1)
Unit 308 Harbour Centre Tower 1 1 Hok Cheung Street, Hunghom, Kowloon, China (Hong Kong)

NICHICON CORPORATION

NICHICON CORPORATION—(Continued)
Tel.: (852) 23634331
Web Site: http://www.nichicon.co.jp
Sales Range: $25-49.9 Million
Emp.: 20
Electronic Parts Whslr
N.A.I.C.S.: 423690

Nichicon (Iwate) Corporation (1)
8-17-1 Kubo Iwate-cho, Iwate-gun, Iwate, 028-4305, Japan
Web Site: http://www.nichicon.co.jp
Aluminum Electrolytic Capacitors Mfr
N.A.I.C.S.: 334416

Nichicon (Kameoka) Corporation (1)
15-1 2-chome Kitakose-cho, Kameoka, 621-0811, Kyoto, Japan
Tel.: (81) 771225541
Sales Range: $100-124.9 Million
Emp.: 300
Thermistors Mfr
N.A.I.C.S.: 334416

Nichicon (Kusatsu) Corporation (1)
3-1 Yagura 2-chome, Kusatsu, 525-0053, Shiga, Japan
Tel.: (81) 775620891
Web Site: http://www.nichicon.co.jp
Sales Range: $100-124.9 Million
Emp.: 400
Electric Capacitors Mfr
N.A.I.C.S.: 334416

Nichicon (Malaysia) Sdn. Bhd. (1)
No 4 Jalan P/10 Kawasan Perusahaan Bangi, Hulu Langat Dist, 43650, Bandar Baru Bangi, Selangor, Malaysia
Tel.: (60) 389250678
Web Site: http://www.nichicon.co.jp
Sales Range: $200-249.9 Million
Emp.: 1,000
Aluminum Electrolytic Capacitors Mfr
N.A.I.C.S.: 334416

Nichicon (Ohno) Corporation (1)
1-11-2 Shimoyoro, Ono, 912-0095, Fukui, Japan
Tel.: (81) 779660333
Web Site: http://www.nichicon.co.jp
Aluminum Electrolytic Capacitors Mfr
N.A.I.C.S.: 334416

Nichicon (Singapore) Pte. Ltd. (1)
60 Paya Lebar Road 11-17/18, Paya Lebar Square, Singapore, 409051, Singapore
Tel.: (65) 64815641
Sales Range: $25-49.9 Million
Emp.: 23
Electrolytic Capacitor Mfr
N.A.I.C.S.: 334416

Nichicon (Taiwan) Co., Ltd. (1)
23F No 68 Sec 5 Zhongxiao East Road, Xinyi District, Taipei, 110, Taiwan
Tel.: (886) 227222100
Web Site: http://www.nichicon.co.jp
Sales Range: $25-49.9 Million
Emp.: 30
Electronic Capacitors Distr
N.A.I.C.S.: 423690

Nichicon (Thailand) Co., Ltd. (1)
1 Empire Tower 15th Floor Unit 1506 River Wing West South Sathorn Road, Yannawa Sathorn, Bangkok, 10120, Thailand
Tel.: (66) 2 670 0150
Electric Equipment Mfr
N.A.I.C.S.: 335999

Nichicon (Wakasa) Corporation (1)
35-1-1 Tada, Obama, 917-0026, Fukui, Japan
Tel.: (81) 770562111
Sales Range: $50-74.9 Million
Emp.: 108
Switching Equipment Sales
N.A.I.C.S.: 334419
Takio Sakai (Mng Dir)

Nichicon Corporation - Nagano Factory (1)
4085 Toyoshina, Azumino, 399-8205, Nagano, Japan
Tel.: (81) 263722830
Electrolytic Capacitor Mfr
N.A.I.C.S.: 334416

Nichicon Corporation - Ohmachi Factory (1)
8224-1 Yashiro, Omachi, 398-0003, Nagano, Japan
Tel.: (81) 261213200
Web Site: http://www.nichicon.co.jp
Electrode Foil Mfr
N.A.I.C.S.: 331315

Nichicon Corporation - Power Supply Division (1)
14-9 Nihonbashi Kabuto-cho, Chuo-ku, Tokyo, 103-0026, Japan
Tel.: (81) 336667861
Web Site: http://www.nichicon.co.jp
Emp.: 100
Switching Equipment Distr
N.A.I.C.S.: 335313

Nichicon Corporation - Tomita Factory (1)
Nichicon Technology Center 4 Tsuchifugo, Ono, 912-0805, Fukui, Japan
Tel.: (81) 779658000
Electrode Foil Mfr
N.A.I.C.S.: 331315
Sachihiko Araki (Pres)

Nichicon Electronics (Suqian) Co., Ltd. (1)
No 18 Yangmingshan Avenue, Suzhou Suqian Industrial Park, Suqian, 223800, China
Tel.: (86) 5278 097 8855
Aluminum Solid Electrolytic Capacitor Mfr
N.A.I.C.S.: 334416

Nichicon Electronics (Tianjin) Co., Ltd. (1)
No 4 Xinghua Rd Xiqing Econ Dev Zone, Tianjin, 300381, China
Tel.: (86) 2283968930
Solid Tantalum Electrolytic Capacitors Mfr
N.A.I.C.S.: 334416

Nichicon Electronics (Wuxi) Co. Ltd. (1)
Block 51-B Wuxi National High, New Technology Industrial Development Zone, Wuxi, 214028, Jiangsu, China
Tel.: (86) 51085218222
Sales Range: $200-249.9 Million
Emp.: 1,000
Electrolytic Capacitors Mfr & Sales
N.A.I.C.S.: 334416

Nichicon Electronics Trading (Shanghai) Co., Ltd. (1)
Room 1206 Aetna Tower 107 Zunyi Road, Shanghai, 200051, China
Tel.: (86) 2162375538
Web Site: http://www.nichicon.co.jp
Sales Range: $25-49.9 Million
Emp.: 30
Electronic Capacitors Distr
N.A.I.C.S.: 423690

Nichicon Electronics Trading (Shenzhen) Co., Ltd. (1)
Room A 16 F KK100 No 5016 Shen Nan Road East, Luo Hu District, Shenzhen, 518001, Guangdong, China
Tel.: (86) 75522941800
Electrolytic Capacitors Distr
N.A.I.C.S.: 423690

Nichicon Hi-Tech Foil Corporation (1)
8224-1 Yashiro, Omachi, 398-0003, Nagano, Japan
Tel.: (81) 26 121 3200
Aluminum Electrolytic Capacitors Mfr

Nichicon Tantalum Corporation (1)
690-2 Miosato Adogawa-cho, Takashima, 520-1215, Shiga, Japan
Tel.: (81) 740321250
Web Site: http://www.nichicon.co.jp
Solid Tantalum Electrolytic Capacitors Mfr
N.A.I.C.S.: 334416

Nippon Liniax Co., Ltd. (1)
3-2 Sugahara-cho, Kita-ku, Osaka, 530-0046, Japan
Tel.: (81) 66 362 6470
Pressure Sensor Mfr
N.A.I.C.S.: 334519

Torishima Electric Works Ltd. (1)
3-1 Yagura 2-chome, Kusatsu, 525-0053, Shiga, Japan
Tel.: (81) 775620891
Web Site: http://www.nichicon.co.jp
Sales Range: $50-74.9 Million
Emp.: 200
Power Transformers & Reactors Mfr
N.A.I.C.S.: 335311

Wuxi Nichicon Electronics R&D Center Co., Ltd. (1)
Block 51-B, Wuxi National High & New Technology Industrial Development Zone, Wuxi, 214028, Jiangsu, China
Tel.: (86) 5108 521 8222
Electric Power Distribution Services
N.A.I.C.S.: 423610

Yutaka Electric Mfg. Co., Ltd. (1)
14-9 Nihonbashi Kabuto-cho, Chuo-ku, Tokyo, 103-0026, Japan
Tel.: (81) 33 666 7971
Power Supply Equipment Mfr
N.A.I.C.S.: 335999

NICHIDAI CORPORATION

13 Takigitamachida Kyotanabe City, Kyoto, 610-0341, Japan
Tel.: (81) 774623880
Web Site: https://www.nichidai.jp
6467—(TKS)
Rev.: $74,845,030
Assets: $100,386,070
Liabilities: $28,370,120
Net Worth: $72,015,950
Earnings: $290,840
Emp.: 649
Fiscal Year-end: 03/31/24
Precision Turned Product Mfr
N.A.I.C.S.: 332721
Motonobu Furuya (Pres & CEO)

Subsidiaries:

NICHIDAI CORPORATION - Ujitawara Factory (1)
14 Shiotani Zenjyoji, Ujitawara-cho Tsuzuki-gun, Kyoto, 610-0201, Japan
Tel.: (81) 774886311
Metal Products Mfr
N.A.I.C.S.: 332999

NICHIDAI U.S.A. CORPORATION (1)
15630 E State Route 12 Unit 4, Findlay, OH 45840-9743
Tel.: (419) 423-7511
Web Site: http://www.nichidai.co.jp
Metal Product Mfr & Distr
N.A.I.C.S.: 332999
Kiyoshi Nakagawa (Corp Sec & VP)

NICHIDEN CORPORATION

1-2-16 Uehommachinishi, Chuo-ku, Osaka, 542-8588, Japan
Tel.: (81) 676377000
Web Site: https://www.nichiden.com
Year Founded: 1952
9902—(TKS)
Rev.: $838,888,320
Assets: $843,145,160
Liabilities: $260,189,430
Net Worth: $582,955,730
Earnings: $30,895,140
Emp.: 998
Fiscal Year-end: 03/31/24
Power Transmission Equipment Whslr
N.A.I.C.S.: 423840
Toshikazu Fuke (Pres, Pres & Exec Officer)

Subsidiaries:

NICHIDEN (Shanghai) Co., Ltd. (1)
Unit 803 Building 31 Vanke Hongqiao Cloud No 28 Lane 1333 Xinlong Rd, Minhang District, Shanghai, 201101, China
Tel.: (86) 2154894108
Web Site: http://www.nichiden.com.cn
Industrial Equipment Mfr
N.A.I.C.S.: 333248

NICHIDEN (Thailand) Co., Ltd. (1)
159/18 Serm-Mit Tower 11th Fl Unit 1103/1 Sukhumvit 21 Asoke Rd, Klongtoey Nua Wattana, Bangkok, 10110, Thailand
Tel.: (66) 266527845
Web Site: http://www.nichidenthailand.com
Industrial Machinery Mfr
N.A.I.C.S.: 333248
Akira Nakamura (Mng Dir)

NICHIDEN VIETNAM CO., LTD. (1)
12A Galleria Building Nam Ky Khoi Nghia St, Ward 8 Dist 3, Ho Chi Minh City, Vietnam
Tel.: (84) 2835129975
Web Site: http://www.nichiden.com.vn
Emp.: 22
Industrial Machinery Mfr
N.A.I.C.S.: 333248
Tran Quy Loi (Pres)

NPa System Co., Ltd. (1)
5-11-20 Kitamachi, Warabi, 335-0001, Saitama, Japan
Tel.: (81) 48 446 9614
Web Site: https://www.npasystem.co.jp
Electric Equipment Mfr
N.A.I.C.S.: 335999
Noboru Kurosu (Pres & CEO)

Nichiden Trading (Thailand) Co., Ltd. (1)
159/18 Sermmit Building 11th Floor Room No 1103 Sukhumvit 21 Road, Klongtoey Nuea Sub-district Watthana District, Bangkok, 10110, Thailand
Tel.: (66) 26 652 7845
Web Site: https://www.nichidenthailand.com
Machine Part Mfr
N.A.I.C.S.: 336390

Nichiden USA Corporation (1)
2228 Landmeier Rd, Elk Grove Village, IL 60007
Tel.: (224) 266-2930
Web Site: https://nichidenusa.com
Industrial Machinery Whslr
N.A.I.C.S.: 423830
Shoki Tanaka (Pres)

NICHIDENBO CORPORATION

1F No 4 Aly 1 Siwei Ln Zhongzheng Rd, Xindian Dist, New Taipei City, 231021, Taiwan
Tel.: (886) 222190505
Web Site: https://www.ndb.com.tw
Year Founded: 1993
3090—(TAI)
Rev.: $348,464,914
Assets: $306,850,311
Liabilities: $101,673,105
Net Worth: $205,177,205
Earnings: $23,555,576
Emp.: 360
Fiscal Year-end: 12/31/23
Electronic Components Distr
N.A.I.C.S.: 423690
Yu Yao-Kuo (Pres)

Subsidiaries:

Koho (Taiwan) Co., Ltd. (1)
3F No 2 Aly 1 Siwei Ln Zhongzheng Rd, Xindian Dist, New Taipei City, 231021, Taiwan
Tel.: (886) 222198088
Electronic Parts Mfr & Distr
N.A.I.C.S.: 334419

Lipers Electronic (Shenzhen) Co., Ltd. (1)
Rm 404 Jindi Center 2007 Shennan Ave, Futian Dist, Shenzhen, 518000, China
Tel.: (86) 75582769808
Electronic Component Mfr & Distr
N.A.I.C.S.: 334419

Nichidenbo (Shenzhen) Trading Co., Ltd. (1)
Rm 403 Jindi Center 2007 Shennan Ave, Futian Dist, Shenzhen, 518000, China
Tel.: (86) 75583481177
Electronic Parts Mfr & Distr
N.A.I.C.S.: 334419

Scope Technology Co., Ltd. (1)
2F No 4 Aly 1 Siwei Ln Zhongzheng Rd, Xindian Dist, New Taipei City, 231021, Taiwan
Tel.: (886) 222190805
Electronic Parts Mfr & Distr

AND PRIVATE COMPANIES

N.A.I.C.S.: 334419

Vic-Dawn Enterprise Co., Ltd. (1)
4th Floor No 2 Lane 1 Siwei Lane
Zhongzheng Road, Xindian District, New
Taipei City, 231021, Taiwan
Tel.: (886) 222185115
Web Site: https://www.vic-dawn.com.tw
Aluminum Electrolytic Capacitors Mfr
N.A.I.C.S.: 334416

NICHIFU COMPANY LTD.
1-3-58 Tsurumi, Tsurumi-Ku, Osaka,
538 0053, Japan
Tel.: (81) 669111411
Web Site: http://www.nichifu.co.jp
Year Founded: 1974
Sales Range: $25-49.9 Million
Emp.: 300
Terminals & Connectors Mfr
N.A.I.C.S.: 334417
Yoshio Mori *(Mng Dir)*

Subsidiaries:

NICHIFU EUROPE B.V. (1)
Frans Coenenhove 9, 3438HJ, Nieuwegein,
Netherlands
Tel.: (31) 302 681886
Electronic Connectors Distr
N.A.I.C.S.: 423610

Nichifu America, Inc. (1)
22 Congress Cir W, Roselle, IL 60172
Tel.: (631) 351-1958
Web Site: http://www.nichifu.com
Sales Range: $50-74.9 Million
Emp.: 4
Distribution of Solderless Terminals & Cable Ties
N.A.I.C.S.: 423610

Nichifu Singapore Pte Ltd. (1)
45 Ubi Rd 1 05-03, Singapore Conference
Hall, Singapore, 068810,
Singapore **(100%)**
Tel.: (65) 67413008
Web Site: http://www.mediagalaxy.co.jp
Sales Range: $25-49.9 Million
Emp.: 4
Electrical Contractor
N.A.I.C.S.: 238210
Tepsuyoshi Mitani *(Mng Dir)*

NICHIHA CORPORATION
Mitsui-Sumitomo Bank Nagoya Bldg
2-18-19 Nishiki, Naka-ku, Nagoya,
Japan
Tel.: (81) 522205111
Web Site: http://www.nichiha.co.jp
7943—(NGO)
Rev.: $943,442,088
Assets: $1,160,805,754
Liabilities: $326,296,572
Net Worth: $834,509,182
Earnings: $53,293,675
Emp.: 1,326
Fiscal Year-end: 03/31/24
Building Materials & Household
Equipment Mfr & Sales
N.A.I.C.S.: 324122
Tatsuo Yamanaka *(Pres)*

Subsidiaries:

Nichiha Matex Co., Ltd. (1)
2-10 Sunosaki-cho, Handa, 475-0021, Aichi,
Japan
Tel.: (81) 56 929 3051
Web Site: https://nichiha-matex.co.jp
Ceramic Building Material Mfr & Distr
N.A.I.C.S.: 327120

Nichiha USA, Inc. (1)
6465 E Johns Crossing Ste 250, Johns
Creek, GA 30097
Web Site: https://www.nichiha.com
Building Materials Mfr
N.A.I.C.S.: 327120
Hideto Yoshida *(Pres & CEO)*

Takahagi Nichiha Corporation (1)
160-1 Akahama, Takahagi, 318-0001, Japan
Tel.: (81) 293220461
Building Product Mfr
N.A.I.C.S.: 326199

NICHIMO CO. LTD.
Tennozu Ocean Square 2-2-20 Higashishinagaw, Shinagawa-ku, Tokyo,
140-0002, Japan
Tel.: (81) 334583020
8091—(TKS)
Rev.: $844,467,160
Assets: $536,018,120
Liabilities: $348,631,230
Net Worth: $187,386,890
Earnings: $15,526,890
Emp.: 1,060
Fiscal Year-end: 03/31/24
Fish Products Sales
N.A.I.C.S.: 311710
Kazuaki Matsumoto *(Pres)*

Subsidiaries:

Bibun Corporation (1)
1089-1 Sagata Shinichi-cho, Fukuyama,
729-3102, Hiroshima, Japan
Tel.: (81) 84 751 3558
Web Site: https://bibun.co.jp
Fish Processing Machine Distr
N.A.I.C.S.: 423830

Fukusan Co., Ltd. (1)
4-18-20 Teizukayamaminam, Nara, 631-
0064, Japan
Web Site: http://www.sankakuya.net
Sales Range: $25-49.9 Million
Emp.: 1
Fabric Crafts Whslr
N.A.I.C.S.: 332999

Hokkaido Nichimo Co., Ltd. (1)
29-2 Bentencho, Hakodate, 040-0051, Hokkaido, Japan **(100%)**
Tel.: (81) 138237114
Web Site: https://hokkaido-nichimo.com
Emp.: 61
Fishing Equipment Mfr & Whslr
N.A.I.C.S.: 114119

Marukyu Shokuhin Co., Ltd. (1)
1-8-32 Nakahata, Onojo, 816-0921, Fukuoka, Japan
Tel.: (81) 92 502 8730
Web Site: https://www.marukyu.co.jp
Seafood Mfr & Distr
N.A.I.C.S.: 311710

Nichimo Biotics Co., Ltd. (1)
VORT Hamamatsucho 17th floor 1-6-15
Hamamatsucho, Minato-ku, Tokyo, 105-
0013, Japan
Tel.: (81) 364785051
Web Site: https://www.nichimobiotics.co.jp
Sales Range: $25-49.9 Million
Emp.: 16
Soybean Mfr
N.A.I.C.S.: 111110

Nichimo Foods Co., Ltd. (1)
Tsukiji 3-9-9 round cross Tsukiji 8F, Chuo-ku, Tokyo, 104-0045, Japan
Tel.: (81) 335248886
Web Site: http://www.nichimofoods.co.jp
Emp.: 36
Marine Product Whslr
N.A.I.C.S.: 114119

Nichimo Logistics Co., Ltd. (1)
8-31 Tsunabamachi Hakko Fukuoka Building 6F, Hakata-ku, Fukuoka, 812-0024, Japan
Tel.: (81) 92 273 2567
Web Site: https://www.n-cary.jp
Transportation Services
N.A.I.C.S.: 484110

Nichimo Mariculture Co., Ltd. (1)
2-3-19 Minato, Chuo-ku, Fukuoka, 810-
0075, Japan
Tel.: (81) 92 716 1145
Web Site: https://www.nichimo-mariculture.co.jp
Fishery Material & Equipment Distr
N.A.I.C.S.: 423910

Nishi Nihon Nichimo Co., Ltd. (1)
2-3-17 Kozuki Kojima, Shimonoseki, 750-
1136, Yamaguchi, Japan
Tel.: (81) 832824041
Web Site: http://nishinihon-nichimo.jp
Sales Range: $25-49.9 Million
Emp.: 100
Fishing Nets Mfr

N.A.I.C.S.: 114119

Nor'Eastern Trawl Systems Inc. (1)
7910 NE Day Rd W, Bainbridge Island, WA 98110
Tel.: (206) 842-5623
Web Site: https://www.net-sys.com
Sales Range: $25-49.9 Million
Emp.: 60
Fishing Nets Mfr
N.A.I.C.S.: 114119

Soei Co., Ltd. (1)
Re-35 Kamishimizu-machi, Nomi, 923-1237,
Ishikawa, Japan
Tel.: (81) 761515400
Web Site: http://www.soei-m.com
Sales Range: $25-49.9 Million
Emp.: 40
Tofu Processing Equipments Mfr
N.A.I.C.S.: 333241
Takashi Eriguchi *(Co-Pres)*

Tohei Co., Ltd. (1)
72-1 Shimotogari, Nagaizumi Sunto Dist,
Shizuoka, 411-0943, Japan
Tel.: (81) 559871191
Fishing Equipments Mfr & Whslr
N.A.I.C.S.: 114119

NICHING INDUSTRIAL CORP.
5th Floor No 767 Section 4 Taiwan
Avenue, Xitun, Taichung, 40755, Taiwan
Tel.: (886) 423588966
Web Site: https://www.niching.com.tw
Year Founded: 1993
3444—(TPE)
Rev.: $33,155,051
Assets: $44,700,810
Liabilities: $15,927,305
Net Worth: $28,773,505
Earnings: $6,127,505
Fiscal Year-end: 12/31/22
Semiconductor Product Mfr & Distr
N.A.I.C.S.: 334413
Kun-Hsiang Chang *(Chm)*

NICHIREI CORPORATION
Nichirei Higashi-Ginza Building
6-19-20 Tsukiji, Chuo-ku, Tokyo, 104-
8402, Japan
Tel.: (81) 332482101 JP
Web Site: https://www.nichirei.co.jp
Year Founded: 1945
2871—(TKS)
Rev.: $4,495,401,510
Assets: $3,206,887,770
Liabilities: $1,449,011,150
Net Worth: $1,757,876,620
Earnings: $161,911,950
Emp.: 16,385
Fiscal Year-end: 03/31/24
Frozen Foods Mfr; Real Estate, Biosciences & Agricultural Services
N.A.I.C.S.: 311411
Kunio Otani *(Chm)*

Subsidiaries:

**Amazonas Industrias Alimenticias
S.A.** (1)
Rod Arthur Bernardes 7903 - Pratinha,
Icoaraci, Belem, 66816-000, PA,
Brazil **(100%)**
Tel.: (55) 9132586900
Web Site: https://www.amasa.com.br
Sales Range: $50-74.9 Million
Emp.: 180
Frozen Seafood, Fruit, Juice & Vegetable
Mfr
N.A.I.C.S.: 311411

**GFPT Nichirei (Thailand) Co.,
Ltd.** (1)
77 Mu 4 Hang sung, Nong Yai, Chon Buri,
20190, Thailand
Tel.: (66) 3 893 2900
Web Site: https://www.gfn.co.th
Food Transportation Services
N.A.I.C.S.: 492110
Jedsada Sirimongkolkasem *(Pres & Chm)*

Kyokurei Operation Inc. (1)

NICHIREI CORPORATION

Logistics Consulting Servies
N.A.I.C.S.: 541614

**NL Cold Chain Network (M) Sdn.
Bhd.** (1)
No 3 Jalan Perindustrian Puchong Bandar
Metro Puchong, 47160, Puchong, Selangor,
Malaysia
Tel.: (60) 35 623 5000
Web Site: https://www.coldchain.com.my
Transportation & Logistics Services
N.A.I.C.S.: 488510

Nichirei Australia Pty. Ltd. (1)
Suite 207 7 Railway St, 189 Kent St, Chatswood, 2067, NSW, Australia **(100%)**
Tel.: (61) 294114277
Web Site: http://www.nichirei.com.au
Sales Range: $25-49.9 Million
Emp.: 3
Food Processor
N.A.I.C.S.: 311411

Division (Domestic):

Nichirei Australia Pty (2)
59 / 14 Narabang Way, Belrose, 2085,
NSW, Australia **(100%)**
Tel.: (61) 294114277
Web Site: http://www.nichirei.com.au
Sales Range: $25-49.9 Million
N.A.I.C.S.: 311411

**Nichirei Corporation Shanghai
Ltd.** (1)
Building 3 No 3088 Hechuan Road, Minhang District, Shanghai, 200042, China
Tel.: (86) 2152727475
Web Site: http://www.nichirei.co.jp
Frozen Food Distr
N.A.I.C.S.: 424420

Nichirei Foods Inc. (1)
Nichirei Higashi Ginza Building 6-19-20
Tsukiji, Chuo-ku, Tokyo, 104-8402, Japan
Tel.: (81) 120692101
Web Site: https://www.nichireifoods.co.jp
Emp.: 11,341
Frozen Food Mfr
N.A.I.C.S.: 311412

Plant (Domestic):

**Nichirei Foods inc. - Funabashi
Factory** (2)
2-19-1 Hinode, Funabashi, 273-0015,
Chiba, Japan
Tel.: (81) 474316121
Frozen Food Mfr
N.A.I.C.S.: 311412

**Nichirei Foods inc. - Shiroishi
Factory** (2)
1-16-2 Shiratori, Shiroishi, 989-0734, Miyagi, Japan
Tel.: (81) 224257181
Frozen Food Mfr
N.A.I.C.S.: 311412

Nichirei Foods U.S.A., Inc. (1)
11400 SE 8th St, Bellevue, WA 98004
Tel.: (206) 448-7800
Web Site: https://www.nichireiusa.com
Potato Sticks Mfr
N.A.I.C.S.: 311919

Nichirei Fresh Hong Kong, Ltd. (1)
Unit 3009 30th Floor Saxon Tower 7 Cheung Shun St, Lai Chi Kok, Kowloon, China
(Hong Kong)
Tel.: (852) 2 617 2311
Seafood & Meat Whslr
N.A.I.C.S.: 424460

Nichirei Fresh Inc. (1)
Nichirei Higashi-Ginza Building 6-19-20,
Tsukiji Chuo-ku, Tokyo, 104-0045, Japan
Tel.: (81) 332482204
Web Site: https://www.nichireifresh.co.jp
Emp.: 20
Frozen Seafood Processing Services
N.A.I.C.S.: 311710

Nichirei Fresh Vietnam Co., Ltd. (1)
Floor 3 Room A1 Linco Building 61A-63A
Vo Van Tan Street, Ward 6 Dist 3, Ho Chi
Minh City, Vietnam
Tel.: (84) 283 930 8051
Seafood & Meat Whslr
N.A.I.C.S.: 424460

NICHIREI CORPORATION

Nichirei Corporation—(Continued)

Nichirei Holding Holland B.V. (1)
Tel.: (31) 104292699
Web Site: http://www.nichirei.co.jp
Logistics & Storage Facilities
N.A.I.C.S.: 541614

Subsidiary (Domestic):

Eurofrigo B.V. (2)
PO Box 59021, 3008 PA, Rotterdam,
Netherlands (100%)
Tel.: (31) 10 491 3100
Web Site: https://www.eurofrigo.nl
Sales Range: $25-49.9 Million
Frozen Seafood, Fruit, Juice & Vegetable Mfr
N.A.I.C.S.: 311411
Bergh B. MacKlenberg *(Mng Dir)*

Subsidiary (Domestic):

Eurofrigo Venlo B.V. (3)
Egtenrayseweg 35, 5928 PH, Venlo,
Netherlands (100%)
Tel.: (31) 773231060
Web Site: https://www.eurofrigo.nl
Sales Range: $10-24.9 Million
Emp.: 40
Frozen Seafood, Fruit, Juice & Vegetable Mfr
N.A.I.C.S.: 311411

Subsidiary (Domestic):

Hiwa Rotterdam Port Cold Stores B.V. (2)
Vierhavensstraat 20, 3029 BE, Rotterdam,
Netherlands (100%)
Tel.: (31) 102445222
Web Site: https://www.hiwa.nl
Sales Range: $25-49.9 Million
Emp.: 60
Frozen Seafood, Fruit, Juice & Vegetable Mfr
N.A.I.C.S.: 311411

Subsidiary (Non-US):

Thermotraffic GmbH (2)
Im Industriegelande 60-66, 33775, Versmold, Germany (100%)
Tel.: (49) 5 423 9680
Web Site: https://www.thermotraffic.de
Sales Range: $10-24.9 Million
Cold Storage Transportation
N.A.I.C.S.: 493120
Falko Thomas *(Mng Dir)*

Subsidiary (Domestic):

Thermotraffic Holland B.V. (2)
Abel Tasmanstraat 1 port no 2783, Harbour
No 2783, 3165 AM, Rotterdam,
Netherlands (100%)
Tel.: (31) 850401700
Web Site: http://www.thermotraffic.de
Sales Range: $25-49.9 Million
Emp.: 250
Transportation for the Food Industries
N.A.I.C.S.: 493120

Nichirei Logistics Group Inc. (1)
Web Site: http://www.nichirei-logi.co.jp
Sales Range: $1-4.9 Billion
Emp.: 4,237
Logistics Consulting Servies
N.A.I.C.S.: 541614

Subsidiary (Non-US):

Entrepots De L'Ocean S.A.S (2)
Zi Rue de l'Avenir, Carpiquet, 14650,
France
Tel.: (33) 2 35 26 33 80
Low Temperature Logistics Services
N.A.I.C.S.: 541614

Entrepots Godfroy S.A.S (2)
27 Rue de L Avenir, Carpiquet, 14650,
France
Tel.: (33) 231711313
Logistics & General Storage Services
N.A.I.C.S.: 541614

Frigo Logistics Sp. z o.o. (2)
ul Fabryczna 4, 88-400, Znin, Poland
Tel.: (48) 52 303 3600
Web Site: https://www.frigologistics.pl
Emp.: 300

Food Distr
N.A.I.C.S.: 424420

Subsidiary (Domestic):

Hiroshima Nichirei Service Inc. (2)
1-7-3 Kusatsuko, Nishi-Ku, Hiroshima, 733-0832, Japan
Tel.: (81) 822762345
Logistics Consulting Servies
N.A.I.C.S.: 541614

Kyokurei Inc. (2)
8-110 Honmoku Futo, Naka-ku, Yokohama, 231-0811, Kanagawa, Japan
Tel.: (81) 453071350
Web Site: http://www.kyokurei.com
Warehousing & Storage Services
N.A.I.C.S.: 493110

Subsidiary (Non-US):

Logistics Network Inc. (2)
Sales Range: $300-349.9 Million
Logistics Consulting Servies
N.A.I.C.S.: 541614

Subsidiary (Domestic):

Logistics Planner Inc. (2)
4F Sumitomo Fudosan Tsukiji Building
7-17-1 Tsukiji, Chuo-ku, Tokyo, 104-0045,
Japan
Tel.: (81) 362781560
Web Site: http://www.logiplan.co.jp
Logistics Consulting Servies
N.A.I.C.S.: 541614
Yoshimi Ishikawa *(Pres)*

Subsidiary (Non-US):

NK Trans Inc. (2)
Web Site: http://www.nichirei-logi.co.jp
Logistics Consulting Servies
N.A.I.C.S.: 541614

Subsidiary (Domestic):

Nagoya Nichirei Service Inc. (2)
2-16 Kawanami-cho, Atsuta, Nagoya, 456-0072, Aichi, Japan
Logistics Consulting Servies
N.A.I.C.S.: 541614

Nichirei Logistics Chushikoku Inc. (2)
2F Hiroshima DC 1-7-3 Kusatsu-ko, Nishi-ku, Hiroshima, 733-0832, Japan
Tel.: (81) 82 276 2345
Web Site: http://www.nichirei-logi.co.jp
Emp.: 89
Logistics & Warehousing Services
N.A.I.C.S.: 541614
Oonishi Yoshiaki *(Pres)*

Subsidiary (Non-US):

Nichirei Logistics Engineering Inc. (2)
Web Site: http://nichirei-logieng.co.jp
Emp.: 172
Logistics Consulting Servies
N.A.I.C.S.: 541614
Tsutomu Itou *(Pres)*

Subsidiary (Domestic):

Nichirei Logistics Hokkaido Inc. (2)
14-1076-5 12-jo Hassamu, Nishi-ku, Sapporo, 063-0832, Hokkaido, Japan
Web Site: http://www.nichirei-logi.co.jp
N.A.I.C.S.: 541614
Sano Yoshinori *(Pres)*

Nichirei Logistics Kanto Inc. (2)
Higashi-ginza Bldg 6-19-20, Tsukiji Chuo-ku, Tokyo, 104-0045, Japan
Tel.: (81) 3 5565 7661
Web Site: http://www.nichirei-logi.co.jp
Sales Range: $25-49.9 Million
Logistics Consulting Servies
N.A.I.C.S.: 541614
Kuzuhara Masato *(Pres)*

Subsidiary (Non-US):

Nichirei Logistics Tohoku Inc. (2)
Web Site: http://www.nichirei-logi.co.jp
Logistics Consulting Servies
N.A.I.C.S.: 541614

Subsidiary (Domestic):

Nichirei Logistics Tokai Inc. (2)
2-16 Kawanami-cho, Atsuta-ku, Nagoya, 456-0072, Aichi, Japan
Tel.: (81) 526832561
Web Site: http://www.nichirei-logi.co.jp
Sales Range: $25-49.9 Million
Emp.: 73
Warehousing & Storage Services
N.A.I.C.S.: 493110
Hirohumi Horiuti *(Pres)*

Subsidiary (Non-US):

Osaka Nichirei Service Inc. (2)
Tel.: (81) 666141046
Logistics Consulting Servies
N.A.I.C.S.: 541614

Subsidiary (Domestic):

Sapporo Nichirei Service Inc. (2)
14-1076-5 12jo Hassamu, Nishi, Sapporo, 063-0832, Hokkaido, Japan
Tel.: (81) 116662111
Logistics Consulting Servies
N.A.I.C.S.: 541614

Shikoku Nichirei Service Inc. (2)
796 Gotocho, Takamatsu, 761-8031, Kagawa, Japan
Tel.: (81) 878828811
Logistics Consulting Servies
N.A.I.C.S.: 541614

Subsidiary (Non-US):

Tohoku Nichirei Service Inc. (2)
Logistics Consulting Servies
N.A.I.C.S.: 541614

Transports Godfroy S.A.S (2)
Z I rue de l'Avenir, 14650, Carpiquet, France
Tel.: (33) 231711313
Web Site: http://www.godfroy.fr
Sales Range: $25-49.9 Million
Emp.: 200
Logistics Consulting Servies
N.A.I.C.S.: 541614
Motoyuki Hazu *(Pres)*

Nichirei Proserve Inc. (1)
Nichirei Higashi-Ginza Bldg 6-19-20 Tsukiji, Chuo-ku, Tokyo, 104-8402, Japan
Tel.: (81) 332482137
Web Site: http://www.nichirei.co.jp
Business Support Services
N.A.I.C.S.: 561499

Nichirei Seafoods, Inc. (1)
11400 SE 8th St Ste 345, Bellevue, WA 98004
Tel.: (206) 448-7800
Seafood & Meat Whslr
N.A.I.C.S.: 424460

Nichirei U.S.A., Inc. (1)
2201 6th Ave Ste 1350, Seattle, WA 98121-2594 (100%)
Tel.: (206) 448-7800
Sales Range: $25-49.9 Million
Emp.: 7
Purchase & Exporter of Frozen Sea Food & Vegetables
N.A.I.C.S.: 311710

Subsidiary (Domestic):

InnovAsian Cuisine Enterprises, LLC (2)
116 Andover Park E Ste 200, Tukwila, WA 98188 (51%)
Tel.: (425) 251-3706
Web Site: http://www.innovasiancuisine.com
Sales Range: $25-49.9 Million
Frozen Prepared Food Products Developer & Distr
N.A.I.C.S.: 424420

Branch (Domestic):

Nichirei U.S.A., Inc. (2)
9500 S Dadeland Blvd Ste 703, Miami, FL 33156-2849 (100%)
Tel.: (305) 670-1365
Frozen Fruits & Vegetables Mfr
N.A.I.C.S.: 311411

Nichirei do Brasil Agricola Ltda. (1)
Avenida Luiz de Souza 721 - Quadra H Lotes 14 a 17, Bairro Distrito Industrial, Petrolina, 56308-420, Pernambuco, Brazil (100%)
Tel.: (55) 8721011433
Web Site: http://www.niagro.com.br
Sales Range: $25-49.9 Million
Emp.: 150
Frozen Seafood, Fruit, Juice & Vegetable Mfr
N.A.I.C.S.: 311411

Shandong Nichirei Foods Co., Ltd. (1)
No 60 Huangshan Road, Yantai Economic & Technological Development Zone, Yantai, 264006, Shandong, China
Tel.: (86) 5356373847
Web Site: http://www.nichirei.co.jp
Frozen Foods & Frozen Marine Products Mfr
N.A.I.C.S.: 311710

Shanghai Fresh Line Express Co., Ltd. (1)
8 Hao 3509 Nong Hongmei Nanlu, Minhang-qu, Shanghai, China
Tel.: (86) 2133505301
Food Distr
N.A.I.C.S.: 424410

Shanghai Nichirei Foods Co., Ltd. (1)
333 Tong Hai Rd, Wujing, Shanghai, China
Tel.: (86) 164505708
N.A.I.C.S.: 311411

Shimonoseki Gyoko Unyu Inc. (1)
3-20 Hosoeshinmachi, Shimonoseki, 750-0017, Yamaguchi, Japan
Tel.: (81) 832343309
Logistics Consulting Servies
N.A.I.C.S.: 541614

Surapon Nichirei Foods Co., Inc. (1)
22/5 Moo 4 Theparak Rd, Samut Prakan, 10540, Thailand
Tel.: (66) 2 385 3051
Web Site: https://www.test.surapon.com
Sales Range: $150-199.9 Million
Food Processor; Owned by Nichirei Corporation & by Surapon Foods Public Company Limited
N.A.I.C.S.: 311999

Tokyo Nichirei Service Inc. (1)
Tel.: (81) 3556576611
Logistics Consulting Servies
N.A.I.C.S.: 541614

NICHIREKI CO., LTD.

4-3-29 Kudan-kita, Chiyoda-ku, Tokyo, 102-8222, Japan
Tel.: (81) 332651511
Web Site: https://www.nichireki.co.jp
Year Founded: 1949
5011—(TKS)
Rev.: $488,029,520
Assets: $628,571,340
Liabilities: $133,905,380
Net Worth: $494,665,960
Earnings: $29,665,680
Emp.: 977
Fiscal Year-end: 03/31/24
Asphalt Product Mfr & Whslr
N.A.I.C.S.: 324121
Manabu Obata *(Pres)*

Subsidiaries:

Chongqing Transportation Materials Group Co., Ltd. (1)
No 52 Xinnan Road, Longxi Town Yubei District, Chongqing, 400023, China
Tel.: (86) 2389187895
Web Site: https://www.ccqtm.com
Highway Construction Material Mfr
N.A.I.C.S.: 333120

Premier Structure Pte. Ltd. (1)
15 Gul Crescent, Singapore, 629525, Singapore
Tel.: (65) 68610388
Web Site: https://www.premierstructure.com
Chemical Products Distr
N.A.I.C.S.: 424690

NICHIRIN CO., LTD.
98-1 Edomachi, Chuo-ku, Kobe, 650-0033, Hyogo, Japan
Tel.: (81) 783921471
Web Site: https://www.nichirin.co.jp
Year Founded: 1914
5184—(TKS)
Rev.: $500,773,790
Assets: $552,566,240
Liabilities: $138,886,010
Net Worth: $413,680,230
Earnings: $41,937,350
Emp.: 347
Fiscal Year-end: 12/31/23
Automotive Hose Mfr & Distr
N.A.I.C.S.: 326220
Ryuichi Maeda (Pres)

Subsidiaries:

Hutchinson Nichirin Brake Hoses, S.L. (1)
Paratge la Pietat s/n, Palamos, Gerona, Spain
Tel.: (34) 972613601
Automotive Hose Mfr & Distr
N.A.I.C.S.: 336340

NICHIRIN (THAILAND) CO., LTD. (1)
55/33 Mhutee 13 Nava nakorn Phaholyothin Rd, Klong Luang, Pathumthani, 12120, Thailand
Tel.: (66) 29090550
Automotive Hose Mfr & Distr
N.A.I.C.S.: 336340

NICHIRIN COUPLER TEC MEXICO S.A. de C.V. (1)
9835 Carretera Panamericana, 32690, Ciudad Juarez, Chihuahua, Mexico
Tel.: (52) 6566330356
Automotive Hose Mfr & Distr
N.A.I.C.S.: 336340

NICHIRIN HAKUSAN CO., LTD. (1)
3434 Yamadano, Hakusan-cho, Tsu, 515-2613, Mie, Japan
Tel.: (81) 592622512
Automotive Hose Mfr
N.A.I.C.S.: 336340

NICHIRIN KIKO CO., LTD. (1)
2409-1 Toyotomi Aza Fujinoki, Toyotomi, Himeji, 679-2123, Hyogo, Japan
Tel.: (81) 792640244
Automotive Hose Mfr
N.A.I.C.S.: 336340

NICHIRIN SERVICE CO., LTD. (1)
1118 Sato Bessho-cho, Himeji, 671-0224, Hyogo, Japan
Tel.: (81) 792534338
Automotive Hose Mfr
N.A.I.C.S.: 336340

NICHIRIN TENNESSEE INC. (1)
1620 Old Belfast Rd, Lewisburg, TN 37091
Tel.: (931) 359-5709
Automotive Hose Mfr & Distr
N.A.I.C.S.: 336340

NICHIRIN U.K. LTD (1)
Unit B Hibernia Way Stretford Motorway Estate, Manchester, M32 0ZD, United Kingdom
Tel.: (44) 1618650888
Automotive Hose Mfr & Distr
N.A.I.C.S.: 336340

NICHIRIN-FLEX U.S.A., INC. (1)
9600 Plaza Cir, El Paso, TX 79927
Tel.: (915) 859-1199
Automotive Hose Mfr & Distr
N.A.I.C.S.: 336340

Nichirin Autoparts India Pvt., Ltd. (1)
Plot No 405 Sector-8 IMT Manesar, Gurgaon, 122050, Haryana, India
Tel.: (91) 1244251811
Automotive Hose Distr
N.A.I.C.S.: 423840

Nichirin Co., Ltd. - Himeji Factory (1)
1118 Sazuchi Bessho-cho, Himeji, 671-0224, Hyogo, Japan
Tel.: (81) 792524151
Automotive Related Part Mfr & Retailer
N.A.I.C.S.: 336390

Nichirin Imperial Autoparts India Pvt., Ltd. (1)
Plot No405 Sector-8 IMT Manesar, Gurgaon, 122050, India
Tel.: (91) 1244251811
Automotive Hose Mfr & Retailer
N.A.I.C.S.: 326220

Nichirin Rubber Industrial (Shanghai) Co., Ltd. (1)
Building No 2 No 333 Qianqiao Rd, Qingcun Town Fengxian District, Shanghai, 201407, China
Tel.: (86) 2157599272
Rubber Hose Mfr & Distr
N.A.I.C.S.: 336340

Nichirin Spain S.L.U. (1)
Paratge La Pietat Cami de Bell-Lloc s/n, Palamos, 17230, Gerona, Spain
Tel.: (34) 972613600
Automotive Hose Mfr & Retailer
N.A.I.C.S.: 326220
Emmanuel Joffre (Mng Dir)

Nichirin Vietnam Co., Ltd. (1)
Lot No B4 Quang Chau Industrial Park, Viet Yen, Bac Giang, Vietnam
Tel.: (84) 2403868995
Automotive Hose Mfr & Distr
N.A.I.C.S.: 336340

PT. Nichirin Indonesia (1)
Kawasan Industri Mitra Karawang JI Mitra Timur 1 Blok C6 Parungmulya, Ciampel, Karawang, 41361, Jawa Barat, Indonesia
Automotive Hose Mfr & Distr
N.A.I.C.S.: 336340

SHANGHAI NICHIRIN AUTOMOBILE ACCESSORIES CO., LTD. (1)
825 Xin Chen Rd Beicai, Pudong, Shanghai, 201204, China
Tel.: (86) 2158442698
Web Site: http://www.nichirin.co.jp
Automotive Hose Mfr & Distr
N.A.I.C.S.: 336340

NICHIRYO BAKING CO., LTD.
Tsukisamu Higashi 1-jo 18-chome 5-1, Toyohira Ward, Sapporo, 062-8510, Japan
Tel.: (81) 118518131
Web Site: https://www.nichiryo-pan.co.jp
2218—(SAP)
Sales Range: Less than $1 Million
Bakery Products Mfr
N.A.I.C.S.: 311812
Katsuhiko Yoshida (Pres)

NICHIRYOKU CO., LTD.
1-33-5 Kamiigusa, Suginamo-ku, Tokyo, 167-0023, Japan
Tel.: (81) 333953001 JP
Web Site: http://www.nichiryoku.co.jp
Year Founded: 1966
75780—(TKS)
Rev.: $29,061,454
Assets: $84,948,367
Liabilities: $55,209,892
Net Worth: $29,738,475
Earnings: $1,285,689
Emp.: 183
Fiscal Year-end: 03/31/20
Funeral Service Provider
N.A.I.C.S.: 812210
Koyo Teramura (Dir)

NICHIWA SANGYO CO., LTD.
195 Sumiyoshihamacho, Higashinada-ku, Kobe, 658-0042, Hyogo, Japan
Tel.: (81) 788111221
Web Site: https://www.nichiwasangyo.co.jp
Year Founded: 1924
2055—(TKS)
Rev.: $349,583,070
Assets: $215,704,130
Liabilities: $95,640,090
Net Worth: $120,064,040
Earnings: $3,576,010
Emp.: 149
Fiscal Year-end: 03/31/24
Feed Mfr & Distr
N.A.I.C.S.: 311111
Masatoshi Nakahashi (Chm)

NICHOLS PLC
Overross Industrial Estate Netherton Road, Merseyside, Ross-on-Wye, HR9 7QQ, Herefordshire, United Kingdom
Tel.: (44) 1925222222 UK
Web Site: https://www.nicholsplc.co.uk
Year Founded: 1908
NICL—(AIM)
Rev.: $208,187,326
Assets: $154,197,172
Liabilities: $42,185,054
Net Worth: $112,012,118
Earnings: $14,686,948
Emp.: 308
Fiscal Year-end: 12/31/22
Food & Beverage Mfr
N.A.I.C.S.: 312111
Marnie J. Millard (CEO)

Subsidiaries:

Cariel Soft Drinks Limited (1)
Duckburn Industrial Estate Stirling Road, Dunblane, FK15 0EW, United Kingdom
Tel.: (44) 1786 822 996
Web Site: http://www.cariel.co.uk
Sales Range: $25-49.9 Million
Emp.: 20
Soft Drink Distr
N.A.I.C.S.: 424490
Marnie Millard (CEO)

Nichols Dispense (1)
Laurel House Woodlands Park Ashton Road, Newton-le-Willows, WA12 0HH, Merseyside, United Kingdom (100%)
Tel.: (44) 1925296969
Web Site: http://www.nicholsdispense.co.uk
Sales Range: $25-49.9 Million
Emp.: 80
Independent Supplier of Soft Drinks Using Branded & Own Label Beverages
N.A.I.C.S.: 312111

Subsidiary (Domestic):

Beacon Drinks Limited (2)
Unit B10 Hollingbury Enterprise Estate Crowhurst Road, Brighton, BN1 8AF, East Sussex, United Kingdom
Tel.: (44) 1273506545
Web Site: http://www.beacondrinks.co.uk
Soft Drink Distr
N.A.I.C.S.: 424490

Vimto (Out of Home) Limited (1)
Laurel House 5 Woodlands Park Ashton Road, Newton-le-Willows, WA12 0HH, United Kingdom
Tel.: (44) 8000114010
Web Site: https://vimtooutofhome.co.uk
Soft Drink Distr
N.A.I.C.S.: 424490

NICHOLSON & CATES LIMITED
3060 Mainway Dr Ste 300, Burlington, L7M 1A3, ON, Canada
Tel.: (905) 335-3366
Web Site: http://www.nicholsonandcates.com
Sales Range: $75-99.9 Million
Emp.: 75
Lumber, Building & Industrial Products Distr
N.A.I.C.S.: 423310
Jim Livermore (Pres)

NICK SCALI LIMITED
Level 7 Triniti II 39 Delhi Road, PO Box 6585, North Ryde, 2113, NSW, Australia
Tel.: (61) 297484000 AU
Web Site: https://www.nickscali.com.au
Year Founded: 1962
NCK—(ASX)
Rev.: $312,626,201
Assets: $470,674,410
Liabilities: $298,546,340
Net Worth: $172,128,071
Earnings: $53,827,457
Emp.: 930
Fiscal Year-end: 06/30/24
Furniture Mfr
N.A.I.C.S.: 321912
Anthony J. Scali (Mng Dir)

NICKEL ASIA CORPORATION
28th Floor NAC Tower 32nd Street Bonifacio Global City, Taguig, 1634, Philippines
Tel.: (63) 27987622
Web Site: https://www.nickelasia.com
Year Founded: 2006
NIKL—(PHI)
Rev.: $570,005,592
Assets: $1,075,378,346
Liabilities: $319,730,986
Net Worth: $755,647,360
Earnings: $162,501,560
Emp.: 5,109
Fiscal Year-end: 12/31/21
Nickel Mining Services
N.A.I.C.S.: 212230
Gerard H. Brimo (Chm)

Subsidiaries:

Hinatuan Mining Corporation (1)
4th Floor Nac Building 143 Dela Rosa Corner Adelantado Streets, Legaspi Village, Makati, 1229, Philippines
Tel.: (63) 28140029
Nickel Ore Mining Services
N.A.I.C.S.: 212230

Rio Tuba Nickel Mining Corporation (1)
2nd Floor BMMC Building 143 Dela Rosa Corner Adelantado Street, Legaspi Village, Makati, 1229, Philippines
Tel.: (63) 28921006
Web Site: http://www.riotuba.com
Nickel Ore Mining Services
N.A.I.C.S.: 212230

Taganito Mining Corporation (1)
4th Floor Solid Mills Building 143 Dela Rosa Corner Adelantado Street, Legaspi Village, Makati, 1200, Philippines
Tel.: (63) 28126074
Sales Range: $100-124.9 Million
Emp.: 120
Nickel Ore Mining Services
N.A.I.C.S.: 212230

NICKEL CREEK PLATINUM CORP.
100 King Street West Suite 2550, PO Box 124, Toronto, M5X 1A4, ON, Canada
Tel.: (416) 304-9315 BC
Web Site: https://www.nickelcreekplatinum.com
Year Founded: 2006
NCPCF—(OTCQB)
Rev.: $6,866
Assets: $23,026,134
Liabilities: $763,882
Net Worth: $22,262,253
Earnings: ($1,842,447)
Emp.: 3
Fiscal Year-end: 12/31/20
Metal Mining Services
N.A.I.C.S.: 212290
Myron Manternach (Chm)

NICKEL INDUSTRIES LIMITED
Level 2 66 Hunter Street, Sydney, 2000, NSW, Australia
Tel.: (61) 293003311 AU

NICKEL INDUSTRIES LIMITED

Nickel Industries Limited—(Continued)
Web Site: https://nickelindustries.com
Year Founded: 2007
Rev.: $123,253,263
Assets: $531,934,148
Liabilities: $77,167,270
Net Worth: $454,766,878
Earnings: $71,826,428
Fiscal Year-end: 06/30/19
Mining & Exploration Services
N.A.I.C.S.: 213114
Norman A. Seckold (Deputy Chm)

NICKEL NORTH EXPLORATION CORP.
14881188 West Georgia Street, Vancouver, V6E 4A2, BC, Canada
Tel.: (778) 877-5480 BC
Web Site: https://nnexploration.com
Year Founded: 2007
NNX—(TSXV)
Rev.: $11,694
Assets: $34,904
Liabilities: $1,774,834
Net Worth: ($1,739,930)
Earnings: ($469,561)
Fiscal Year-end: 12/31/23
Mineral Exploration Services
N.A.I.C.S.: 212230
Jingbin Wang (Chm)

NICKEL RESOURCES INTERNATIONAL HOLDINGS COMPANY LIMITED
Room 3501 China Merchants Tower, Shun Tak Centre 168-200 Connaught Road, Central, China (Hong Kong)
Tel.: (852) 2110 0836
Web Site:
http://www.cnrholdings.com
Sales Range: $200-249.9 Million
Emp.: 3,000
Steel Mfr & Sales
N.A.I.C.S.: 331110
Shutong Dong (Founder, Chm & CEO)

NICKELSEARCH LIMITED
Tel.: (61) 61844983 AU
Web Site:
https://www.nickelsearch.com
Year Founded: 2004
NIS—(ASX)
Rev.: $27,118
Assets: $10,408,618
Liabilities: $2,011,738
Net Worth: $8,396,879
Earnings: ($1,355,266)
Fiscal Year-end: 06/30/23
Exploration & Mining Services
N.A.I.C.S.: 213115
Nicole Duncan (Mng Dir)

NICKELX LIMITED
Level 5 191 St Georges Terrace, Perth, 6000, WA, Australia
Tel.: (61) 892614600 AU
Web Site:
https://www.nickelxlimited.com
Year Founded: 2019
NKL—(ASX)
Exploration & Mining Services
N.A.I.C.S.: 213115
Steven Wood (Sec)

NICO HOLDINGS PLC
Chibisa House - 19 Glyn Jones Road, PO Box 501, Blantyre, Malawi
Tel.: (265) 1831902 MW
Web Site: https://www.nicomw.com
Year Founded: 1964
NICO—(MALA)
Rev.: $176,599,056
Assets: $667,325,821
Liabilities: $599,996,335
Net Worth: $67,329,486
Earnings: $21,765,323
Emp.: 1,157
Fiscal Year-end: 12/31/22
Holding Company
N.A.I.C.S.: 551112
Vizenge M. Kumwenda (Mng Dir-Grp)

Subsidiaries:

NBS Bank limted (1)
NBS House Corner Chipembere Highway & Johnstone Roads, PO Box 32251, Ginnery Corner, Blantyre, Malawi
Tel.: (265) 1876222
Web Site: https://www.nbsmw.com
Rev.: $44,740,675
Assets: $267,776,718
Liabilities: $246,270,565
Net Worth: $21,506,153
Earnings: $10,952,489
Fiscal Year-end: 12/31/2022
Banking Services
N.A.I.C.S.: 522110
Vizenge Kumwenda (Chm)

NBS Bank plc (1)
Corner Chipembere Highway and Johnstone Roads Ginnery Corner, PO Box 32251, Chichiri Blantyre 3, Blantyre, Malawi
Tel.: (265) 1812222
Web Site: https://nbs.mw
Banking Services
N.A.I.C.S.: 522110
Vizenge Kumwenda (Chm)

NICO Asset Managers Limited (1)
Chibisa House 19 Glyn Jones Road, PO Box 3173, Blantyre, Malawi
Tel.: (265) 1832085
Web Site: https://nicoassetmanagers.com
Investment Management Service
N.A.I.C.S.: 523150
Daniel Dunga (Chief Investment Officer)

NICO Capital Limited (1)
Michiru House Victoria Avenue, PO Box 501, Blantyre, Malawi
Tel.: (265) 1832085086
Web Site: https://www.nicocapitalmw.com
Financial Services
N.A.I.C.S.: 523999

NICO General Insurance Company Limited (1)
NICO House 3 Stewart Street, PO Box 2592, Blantyre, Malawi
Tel.: (265) 310002222
Web Site: https://nicogeneral.com
General Insurance Services
N.A.I.C.S.: 524210
Chifundo Chiundira (Chm)

NICO Insurance (Zambia) Limited (1)
NICO House Plot No 6106 and 6107 Great East Road, PO Box 32825, Northmead, Lusaka, Zambia
Tel.: (260) 211222862
Web Site: https://nicoinsurance.co.zm
Financial Services
N.A.I.C.S.: 921130
Kennedy N. Njamba (Mgr-Human Resources-Administration)

NICO Life Insurance Company Limited (1)
NICO House 3 Stewart Street, PO Box 3044, Blantyre, Malawi
Tel.: (265) 310002222
Web Site: https://nico-life.com
Fire Insurance Services
N.A.I.C.S.: 524113
Mayamiko Tembo (Mgr-Compliance & Sec)

NICO Pension Services Limited (1)
NICO House 3 Stewart Street, PO Box 1796, Blantyre, Malawi
Tel.: (265) 1822699
Web Site: https://nicopensions.mw
Pension Solution Services
N.A.I.C.S.: 525190

NICO Technologies Limited (1)
Michiru House Victoria Avenue, PO Box 2730, Blantyre, Malawi
Tel.: (265) 1824365
Web Site: https://nicotechnologies.com
Financial Investment Advice Services
N.A.I.C.S.: 523940

Matthews Mtumbuka (Chm)

NICO RESOURCES LIMITED
Level 6 190 St Georges Tce, Perth, 6000, WA, Australia
Tel.: (61) 894810389 AU
Web Site:
https://www.nicoresources.com.au
Year Founded: 2021
NC1—(ASX)
Rev.: $338,142
Assets: $9,153,641
Liabilities: $533,678
Net Worth: $8,619,963
Earnings: ($2,487,625)
Fiscal Year-end: 06/30/23
Exploration & Mining Services
N.A.I.C.S.: 213115
Jonathan Shellabear (CEO)

NICO STEEL HOLDINGS LIMITED
51 Loyang Way, Singapore, 508744, Singapore
Tel.: (65) 65421886
Web Site: http://www.nicosteel.com
Year Founded: 1991
5GF—(SES)
Rev.: $16,418,997
Assets: $20,229,063
Liabilities: $4,117,497
Net Worth: $16,111,566
Earnings: $90,948
Fiscal Year-end: 02/28/23
Holding Company
N.A.I.C.S.: 551112
Tan Chee Khiong Danny (Chm & Pres)

Subsidiaries:

Nico Steel Centre (Thailand) Co., Ltd. (1)
Laem Chabang Industrial Estate EPZII 213/16 Moo 3 Toongsukla, Sriracha, Chon Buri, 20230, Thailand
Tel.: (66) 38495205
Metal Product Distr
N.A.I.C.S.: 423510

Nico Steel Solutions (S) Pte Ltd (1)
51 Loyang Way, Singapore, 508744, Singapore
Tel.: (65) 65421886
Iron & Steel Mill Product Mfr
N.A.I.C.S.: 331110

NICOCCINO HOLDING AB
Gillinge 55 Hus B, Sverige, 186 91, Vallentuna, Sweden
Tel.: (46) 733980474
Web Site: https://www.nicoccino.se
Year Founded: 2013
NICO—(OMX)
Rev.: $14,049
Assets: $2,360,280
Liabilities: $72,120
Net Worth: $2,288,160
Earnings: ($674,366)
Emp.: 1
Fiscal Year-end: 12/31/22
Non-Nicotine Products Mfr
N.A.I.C.S.: 325412
Emil Westgren (Head-Fin)

NICOLA MINING INC.
Suite 12121030 West Georgia Street, Vancouver, V6E 2Y3, BC, Canada
Tel.: (604) 608-6176
Web Site:
https://www.nicolamining.com
Year Founded: 1980
HUSIF—(OTCQB)
Rev.: $699,620
Assets: $8,878,534
Liabilities: $8,722,988
Net Worth: $155,545
Earnings: ($2,261,074)
Fiscal Year-end: 12/31/20

Silver Exploration Services
N.A.I.C.S.: 213114
Peter Espig (Pres & CEO)

NICOLAS CORREA S.A.
Alcalde Martin Cobos 16A, 09007, Burgos, Spain
Tel.: (34) 947288100
Web Site:
https://www.nicolascorrea.com
Year Founded: 1947
NEA—(MAD)
Rev.: $121,272,767
Assets: $151,920,742
Liabilities: $69,369,688
Net Worth: $82,551,054
Earnings: $11,905,288
Emp.: 47
Fiscal Year-end: 12/31/23
Mailing Machine Mfr
N.A.I.C.S.: 333243
Jose I. Nicolas-Correa Barragan (Chm)

Subsidiaries:

APX Technologie Sp. z o.o. (1)
Ul Centralna 27, Opacz k, 05-816, Warsaw, Poland
Tel.: (48) 227596200
Web Site: https://apx.pl
Computer Numerical Control Machine Equipment Mfr & Distr
N.A.I.C.S.: 333517

Binkert AG (1)
Grabenstrasse 1, 8304, Wallisellen, Switzerland
Tel.: (41) 448325555
Web Site: https://www.binkertag.ch
Machine Tools Mfr
N.A.I.C.S.: 333517
Michel Leu (CEO)

CNC Nordic ApS (1)
Aldumvej 11, 8722, Hedensted, Denmark
Tel.: (45) 21711401
Web Site: https://www.cnc-nordic.dk
Machine Tool Distr
N.A.I.C.S.: 423830

Carlstad Machine Tools AB (1)
Zakrisdalsvagen 26, 65342, Karlstad, Sweden
Tel.: (46) 707795159
Web Site: https://www.cmabs.se
Milling Machine Mfr & Distr
N.A.I.C.S.: 333517

Correa India Pvt. Ltd. (1)
A-59 H Block MIDC Pimpri, Aundh, Pune, 411018, Maharashtra, India
Tel.: (91) 2025654891
Mailing Machine Mfr
N.A.I.C.S.: 333517

DEIBAR - Maquinas Ferramenta, Lda. (1)
Zona Industrial do Roligo, Espargo, 4520-115, Santa Maria da Feira, Portugal
Tel.: (351) 256330220
Web Site: https://www.deibar.com
Machine Tool Distr
N.A.I.C.S.: 423830

Delteco S.A. (1)
Pol Joxe Mari Korta Pab 2, Gipuzkoa, 20750, Zumaya, Spain
Tel.: (34) 943707007
Web Site: https://delteco.com
Industrial Machine Tool Distr
N.A.I.C.S.: 423830
Xavier Arambarri (Pres)

Design & Technical Serbices UK Ltd. (1)
Unit C1 Binary Court Western Avenue Matrix Park, Chorley, PR7 7NB, United Kingdom
Tel.: (44) 3302234567
Web Site: https://dtsuk.co.uk
Machine Tool Services
N.A.I.C.S.: 811310

Elif Trading srl (1)
Bulevardul Pipera Nr 1/VI Hyperion Towers Oras, Ilfov, 077190, Voluntari, Romania

Tel.: (40) 722151974
Web Site: https://elifttrading.com
Machine Tool Mfr & Distr
N.A.I.C.S.: 333517

Elliott Mastuura Canada Inc. (1)
2120 Buckingham Road, Oakville, L6H 5X2, ON, Canada
Tel.: (905) 829-2211
Web Site: https://www.elliottmachinery.com
Machine Tool Distr
N.A.I.C.S.: 423830
Vince D'Alessio (Pres)

GCS Machinery Pte Ltd. (1)
50 Tagore Lane 04-10 I Entrepreneur Centre, Singapore, 787494, Singapore
Tel.: (65) 62693208
Mailing Machine Mfr
N.A.I.C.S.: 333517

GNC Manufacturing, S.A (1)
Condado de Trevino 53, 9001, Burgos, Spain
Tel.: (34) 947 29 85 28
Industrial Machinery Mfr
N.A.I.C.S.: 333248
Fernando Huidobro (Gen Mgr)

H. Sukopp Gesellschaft mbH (1)
H Sukopp Am Teich 6, 2452, Bruck an der Leitha, Austria
Tel.: (43) 2168628420
Web Site: https://www.sukopp.at
Machine Tool Distr
N.A.I.C.S.: 423830
Michael Wyhnanek (Mng Dir)

Hypatia Gnc Accesorios S.A. (1)
Calle Condado de Trevino 53, Villalonquejar Industrial Estate, Burgos, Spain
Tel.: (34) 947298528
Web Site: https://gnchypatia.com
Mailing Machine Mfr
N.A.I.C.S.: 333517

Intec Mernoki Kft (1)
Ipari ZonaRepkeny u 7/A, 8000, Szekesfehervar, Hungary
Tel.: (36) 22399167
Mailing Machine Mfr
N.A.I.C.S.: 333517

Minsen Machinery Co., Ltd. (1)
777 Mahachai Road, Wangburapaphirom Pranakorn, Bangkok, 10200, Thailand
Tel.: (66) 26211000
Web Site: https://www.minsen.co.th
Water Pump Distr
N.A.I.C.S.: 423830

NC Mepro S.A. (1)
Via dos Castillas 3, Pozuelo de Alarcon, 28224, Madrid, Spain
Tel.: (34) 917091980
Web Site: http://www.mepro.es
Sales Range: $25-49.9 Million
Emp.: 2
Distribution of Imported Machine-Tools
N.A.I.C.S.: 811310

Nicolas Correa Calderería S.L. (1)
C/ Condado de Trevino 59, 09001, Burgos, Spain
Tel.: (34) 947298244
Web Site: https://www.gnccaldereria.es
Metal Products Mfr
N.A.I.C.S.: 332999

Nicolas Correa China (1)
Flat 2B Block 31 Seaview Garden, Xinzhou S Road, Shenzhen, 518048, Futian, China
Tel.: (86) 75583472116
Web Site: http://www.correaanayak.es
Sales Range: $25-49.9 Million
Emp.: 50
Promotion & Sales of Milling Machines
N.A.I.C.S.: 423830

Nicolas Correa Deutschland GmbH (1)
Im Geisbaum 10, 63329, Egelsbach, Germany
Tel.: (49) 61038330930
Promotion & Sales of Milling Machines
N.A.I.C.S.: 423830

Nicolas Correa Electronica S.A. (1)
C/ Condado de Trevino 69 Nave 1, Poligono ind Villalonquejar, 09001, Burgos, Spain

Tel.: (34) 947473517
Web Site: https://gncelectronica.es
Electrical Design Services
N.A.I.C.S.: 238210

Nicolas Correa India Ltd. (1)
Unit 15 Building No 9, Jojani Industrial Complex, Mumbai, 400 022, Chunabhatti, India
Tel.: (91) 22 25276831
Mechanically Welded & Machined Assemblies & Other Sheet Metal Components Mfr
N.A.I.C.S.: 332322

Nicolas Correa Machine Tools (Kunming) Company Ltd. (1)
11-2-2 Site The Kunming National Economic And Technological, Development Zone, Kunming, Yunnan, China
Tel.: (86) 871 7426788
Industrial Milling Machine & Tools Mfr
N.A.I.C.S.: 333248

Nicolas Correa Portugal Ltd. (1)
Rua Nova do Moinho de Cima 33 A, Albergaria, 2430-011, Marinha Grande, Portugal
Tel.: (351) 244 56 95 53
Promotion & Sales of Milling Machines
N.A.I.C.S.: 423830

Nicolas Correa S.A. (Planta Burgos) (1)
Alcalde Martin Cobos s/n, 09007, Burgos, 09007, Spain
Tel.: (34) 947 28 81 00
Web Site: http://www.correaanayak.eu
Emp.: 150
Machine Sales, Installation & Maintenance
N.A.I.C.S.: 811310
Carmen Pinto (Gen Mgr)

Nicolas Correa S.A. - Burgos plant (1)
Alcalde Martin Cobos 16 A, 09007, Burgos, Spain
Tel.: (34) 947288100
Industrial Machine Tool Mfr
N.A.I.C.S.: 333248
Carmin Pinto (CEO & Gen Mgr)

Nicolas Correa S.A. - Itziar Plant (1)
Poligono Industrial de Itziar, 20820, Deba, Gipuzkoa, Spain
Tel.: (34) 943 606 011
Sales Range: $25-49.9 Million
Emp.: 80
Industrial Machine Tool Mfr
N.A.I.C.S.: 333248
Carmen Pinto (CEO & Mgr)

Overmach SPA. (1)
Via Giuseppe Righi 12, 43122, Parma, Italy
Tel.: (39) 0521771071
Web Site: https://www.overmach.it
Machine Tool Distr
N.A.I.C.S.: 423830

P.A. Bachke AS (1)
Stanseveien 13, Oslo, Norway
Tel.: (47) 21061960
Web Site: https://pabachke.no
Machine Tool Distr
N.A.I.C.S.: 423830

PT Filemon Inti Machinery (1)
Jl Kaliandra 1 Blok F6 N 1E Delta Silicon 2, Lippo Cikarang, Bekasi, 17550, Indonesia
Tel.: (62) 2129288500
Mailing Machine Mfr
N.A.I.C.S.: 333517

PT Yontomo Sukses Abadi (1)
Komplek Daan Mogot Arcadia Blok G4 No 8 Daan Mogot Km 21, Tangerang, 15122, Banten, Indonesia
Tel.: (62) 2155730028
Web Site: https://www.yontomo.com
Mailing Machine Mfr
N.A.I.C.S.: 333517

Passtech Machine Tools M.E. (1)
Plot N D3-003 Saif Zone, PO Box 8493, Sharjah, United Arab Emirates
Tel.: (971) 65529983
Web Site: https://www.passtech-me.com
Machine Tool Distr
N.A.I.C.S.: 423830

Polymeta Co., Ltd. (1)
ul Ilia Beshkov 3 Druzhba 1 Qr, Sofia, 1528, Bulgaria

Tel.: (359) 29732904
Web Site: https://www.polymeta.bg
Sheet Metal Mfr
N.A.I.C.S.: 332322

Secure Equipment Trading Sdn. Bhd. (1)
6 Jalan Sungai Kayu Ara 32/36 Seksyen 32, Taman Perusahaan Berjaya, 40460, Shah Alam, Selangor, Malaysia
Tel.: (60) 195505161
Web Site: https://www.secure.net.my
Cutting Machine Distr
N.A.I.C.S.: 423830
Alby Chong (Founder)

Vallcal S.L. (1)
Merindad de Sotoscueva Street 10, Villalonquejar Industrial Estate, 09001, Burgos, Spain
Tel.: (34) 947484198
Web Site: https://vallcal.com
Cutting Tool Distr
N.A.I.C.S.: 423830

NICOLAS MIGUET & ASSOCIES SA
Moulin de la Tour Grise Verneuil d Avre et d Iton, 27130, Paris, France
Tel.: (33) 144296464
Web Site: https://www.nicolas-miguet-et-associes.fr
MLNMA—(EUR)
Sales Range: $1-9.9 Million
Stock Exchange Consulting Services
N.A.I.C.S.: 523210
Nicolas Miguet (Chm & CEO)

NICOLAY GMBH
Graf Zeppelin Str 21, DE - 72202, Nagold, Germany
Tel.: (49) 74528230
Web Site: http://www.nicolay.de
Year Founded: 1964
Rev.: $35,864,400
Emp.: 230
Plastic Injection Molding Products Mfr
N.A.I.C.S.: 326199
Jan Christmann (Project Mgr)

Subsidiaries:

Nicolay Romania S.R.L. (1)
Str Insulei Nr 1, Targu Mures, Romania
Tel.: (40) 265210095
Plastics Product Mfr
N.A.I.C.S.: 326199
Oliver Muz (Gen Mgr)

NICOMATIC SA
173 rue des Fougeres - Zone industrielle les Bracots, 74890, Bons-en-Chablais, France
Tel.: (33) 450361385
Web Site: http://www.nicomatic.com
Rev.: $21,100,000
Emp.: 162
Electronic Components Mfr
N.A.I.C.S.: 334417
Olivier Nicollin (CEO)

Subsidiaries:

Nicomatic LP (1)
165 Veterans Way Ste 200, Warminster, PA 18974
Tel.: (215) 444-9580
Industrial Machinery Mfr
N.A.I.C.S.: 333120
David Fisher (Mgr)

NICON GROUP OF COMPANIES PLC
Plot 242 Muhammed Buhari Way, Central Business District, PMB 5029, Abuja, FCT, Nigeria
Tel.: (234) 803 320 3414   NG
Year Founded: 1969
Holding Company
N.A.I.C.S.: 551112
Jimoh Ibrahim (Grp CEO & Mng Dir)

Subsidiaries:

NICON PROPERTIES LTD (1)
No 63 Accra Street, Wuse, Abuja, Nigeria
Tel.: (234) 803 320 3414
Property Management Services
N.A.I.C.S.: 531312

Nicon Insurance plc (1)
Plot 242 Muhammed Buhari Way, Central Business District, PMB 5029, Abuja, FCT, Nigeria
Tel.: (234) 09 462 4100 2
Web Site: http://www.niconinsurance.com.ng
Property & Casualty Insurance Product & Services
N.A.I.C.S.: 524126
Alhaji Muhammad Hussein (CEO & Mng Dir)

NICOX S.A.
Sundesk Sophia Antipolis Batiment C Emerald Square rue Evariste Galois, CS 10313, 06410, Sophia-Antipolis, France
Tel.: (33) 497245300   FR
Web Site: https://www.nicox.com
Year Founded: 1996
ALCOX—(EUR)
Rev.: $7,882,769
Assets: $58,483,276
Liabilities: $34,058,947
Net Worth: $24,424,329
Earnings: ($23,050,006)
Emp.: 19
Fiscal Year-end: 12/31/23
Clinical Development & Pharmaceutical Research Services
N.A.I.C.S.: 325412
Michele Garufi (Founder, Chm & CEO)

Subsidiaries:

Nicox Ophthalmics, Inc. (1)
4819 Emperor Blvd Ste 400, Durham, NC 27703
Tel.: (984) 710-5354
Pharmaceutical Preparation Mfr
N.A.I.C.S.: 325412

Nicox Research Institute (1)
Via Ludovico Ariosto 21, 20091, Bresso, MI, Italy
Tel.: (39) 02610361
Web Site: http://www.nicox.com
Emp.: 15
Clinical Development & Pharmaceutical Research Services
N.A.I.C.S.: 325412

NICOZDIAMOND INSURANCE LIMITED
30 Samora Machel Ave, Harare, Zimbabwe
Tel.: (263) 09715324
Web Site: http://www.nicozdiamond.co.zw
NICO—(ZIM)
Sales Range: $25-49.9 Million
Insurance Company
N.A.I.C.S.: 524298
Noel Manika (Gen Mgr-Ops)

Subsidiaries:

Diamond General Insurance Limited (1)
Head Office Base Park Alick Nkhata Road, PO Box 37041, Lusaka, Zambia
Tel.: (260) 211253723
Web Site: http://www.diamond.co.zm
Emp.: 30
General Insurance Services
N.A.I.C.S.: 524210

NICSTECH CO., LTD.
#A-1306 Woorin Blue Nine Building 240-21 Yeomchang-dong, Gangseo-gu, Seoul, 157-861, Korea (South)
Tel.: (82) 2 3497 8900
Web Site: http://www.nicstech.com

NICSTECH CO., LTD.

Nicstech Co., Ltd.—(Continued)
Year Founded: 1995
Emp.: 123
Software Solutions
N.A.I.C.S.: 513210
Dong-Hoon Park (CEO)

NICTUS LIMITED
1st floor Block C The Main Straight Office Park, 392 Main Road, Bryanston, 2191, South Africa
Tel.: (27) 117879019
Web Site: https://nictuslimited.co.za
Year Founded: 1945
NCS—(JSE)
Rev.: $2,454,610
Assets: $45,966,265
Liabilities: $40,020,754
Net Worth: $5,945,511
Earnings: $434,151
Emp.: 42
Fiscal Year-end: 03/31/23
Furniture, Electrical Appliances & Home Electronics Retailer
N.A.I.C.S.: 449110
Barend John Willemse (Chm)

NIDAN LABORATORIES & HEALTHCARE LIMITED
Swapnashil Bunglow Behind Aarti Apt Near Siyaram Showroom Vartak road, Virar West, Virar, 401303, Maharashtra, India
Tel.: (91) 2502500004
Web Site: https://nidanhealthcare.co.in
Year Founded: 1994
NIDAN—(NSE)
Rev.: $3,308,579
Assets: $10,119,489
Liabilities: $1,794,041
Net Worth: $8,325,448
Earnings: $424,387
Emp.: 183
Fiscal Year-end: 03/31/23
Health Care Srvices
N.A.I.C.S.: 621610
Roshan Thorve (CEO)

NIDAROS SPAREBANK
Gryta 2B, Klaebu, 7010, Trondheim, Norway
Tel.: (47) 72830000
Web Site: https://www.nidaros-sparebank.no
Year Founded: 1858
NISB—(EUR)
Commercial Banking Services
N.A.I.C.S.: 522110
Bjorn A. Riise (Mgr)

NIDEC CHAUN-CHOUNG TECHNOLOGY CORPORATION
No 184-3 Zhongxing NSt, Sanchong Dist, New Taipei City, 24158, Taiwan
Tel.: (886) 229952666
Web Site: https://www.ccic.com.tw
Year Founded: 1973
6230—(TAI)
Rev.: $351,845,763
Assets: $337,004,696
Liabilities: $149,445,235
Net Worth: $187,559,462
Earnings: $19,810,196
Fiscal Year-end: 12/31/23
Computer Peripheral Product Mfr
N.A.I.C.S.: 334118
Junich Nagai (Chm)

Subsidiaries:

CCI America, Inc. (1)
333 Cobalt Way Ste 104, Sunnyvale, CA 94085
Tel.: (408) 768-7629
Emp.: 3
Electronic Parts Mfr & Distr
N.A.I.C.S.: 334419

Branch (Domestic):

CCI America, Inc. - Austin Branch (2)
13010 Research Blvd Ste 220, Austin, TX 78750
Tel.: (512) 637-1472
Electronic Parts Mfr
N.A.I.C.S.: 334419

Chaun Choung Technology Corp. - Chung-Shin Plant
No 184 Zhongxing North Street Sanzhong District, New Taipei City, Taiwan
Tel.: (886) 229952369
Electronic Parts Mfr
N.A.I.C.S.: 334419

Chongqing Cyunsiang High-tech Co., Ltd. (1)
No 33 Fengyu Road Jiulongpo District, Chongqing, China
Tel.: (86) 2388260766
Electronic Parts Mfr & Distr
N.A.I.C.S.: 334419

Jue-Chung Electronics Co., Ltd (1)
No 7 Shuanghe Road Dianshanhu Town, Kunshan, Jiangsu, China
Tel.: (86) 51257491288
Electronic Parts Mfr & Distr
N.A.I.C.S.: 334419

Nidec Chaun Choung Technology America Inc. (1)
13010 Research Blvd Ste 220, Austin, TX 78750
Tel.: (512) 637-1472
Web Site: https://www.ncciamerica.com
Plumbing Heating Equipment Mfr
N.A.I.C.S.: 332410

NIDEC CORPORATION
338 Kuzetonoshiro-cho, Minami-ku, Kyoto, 601-8205, Japan
Tel.: (81) 759221111 JP
Web Site: https://www.nidec.com
Year Founded: 1973
NNDNF—(OTCIQ)
Rev.: $15,514,720,990
Assets: $20,885,676,490
Liabilities: $9,924,835,680
Net Worth: $10,960,840,810
Earnings: $827,201,840
Emp.: 101,112
Fiscal Year-end: 03/31/24
Holding Company; Motor & Motor Components Mfr & Distr
N.A.I.C.S.: 551112
Kazuya Hayafune (Sr VP)

Subsidiaries:

ASI Industrial Systems Beijing Co. Ltd. (1)
Room 3206 - 3208 Beijing Silver Tower No 2 Dong San Huan Bei Road, Chaoyang District, Beijing, China
Tel.: (86) 10 6554 4490
Web Site: http://www.asiansaldo.com
Electric Power Control Systems Distr
N.A.I.C.S.: 423610

Automatic Feed Company (1)
476 E Riverview Ave, Napoleon, OH 43545
Tel.: (419) 592-0050
Web Site: http://www.automaticfeed.com
Rolling Mill & Other Metalworking Machinery Mfr
N.A.I.C.S.: 333519
Peter Beck (CEO)

Beijing Embraco Snowflake Compressor Company Limited (1)
No 29 Yuhua Road Area B of Beijing Tianzhu Airport Industrial Zone, Beijing, 101312, China
Tel.: (86) 1080482255
Compressor Mfr
N.A.I.C.S.: 333912

Embraco Industria de Compressores e Solucoes em Refrigeracao Ltda. (1)
Rui Barbosa 1020, PO Box 91, 89219-901, Joinville, SC, Brazil
Tel.: (55) 4734412121
Web Site: http://www.embraco.com
Water Treatment Equipment Whslr
N.A.I.C.S.: 423830

Embraco Mexico, S. de R.L. de C.V. (1)
Av Industrias 501 PIMSA Oriente Industrial Park, CP 66603, Apodaca, Nuevo Leon, Mexico
Tel.: (52) 6788053100
Compressor Mfr
N.A.I.C.S.: 333912

Embraco RUS LLC (1)
BC Lotos - Office 9 Floor Room Office 6 Odesskaya St 2, 117638, Moscow, Russia
Tel.: (7) 4954455506
Web Site: http://www.embraco.com
Household Appliances Mfr
N.A.I.C.S.: 335220
Vladimir Demyachenko (Gen Mgr)

Embraco Slovakia S.r.o. (1)
Odorinska Cesta 2, 052 01, Spisska Nova Ves, Slovakia
Tel.: (421) 534172110
Web Site: http://www.embraco.sk
Home Appliance Services
N.A.I.C.S.: 449210
Marcelo Dorba (Dir Gen)

Fujisoku Corporation - Overseas Sales Division (1)
Nishi-Shinjuku Kimuraya Bldg 7-5-25 Nishi-Shinjuku, Shinjuku-ku, Tokyo, 160-0023, Japan
Tel.: (81) 3 3364 7056
Emp.: 4
Electric Switch Distr
N.A.I.C.S.: 423610

Fujisoku Corporation - System Division (1)
24-12 Sumiyoshi-cho Kizuki, Nakahara-ku, Kawasaki, 211-0021, Kanagawa-ken, Japan
Tel.: (81) 44 433 5721
Measuring Instruments Mfr
N.A.I.C.S.: 334519

Globa Service Inc. (1)
110-1 Araku, Iruma, 358-0031, Saitama, Japan
Tel.: (81) 429653141
Sales Range: $25-49.9 Million
Emp.: 52
Electric Motor & Component Mfr
N.A.I.C.S.: 335312

NIDEC GLOBAL SERVICE CORPORATION (1)
12F Nidec Headquarters Bldg 338 Tonoshiro-cho Kuze, Minami-ku, Kyoto, 601-8205, Japan
Tel.: (81) 75 935 7755
Web Site: http://www.nidec.com
Insurance & Real Estate Management Services
N.A.I.C.S.: 524210

NIDEC SANKYO CORPORATION - Ina Facility (1)
6100 Uenohara, Ina, 396-8511, Nagano, Japan
Tel.: (81) 265 78 5111
Electronic Components Mfr
N.A.I.C.S.: 334419

Nidec (Beijing) Co., Ltd. (1)
Room1506 15F Gateway Bldg 10 Ya Bao Road, Xicheng District, Beijing, 100020, China
Tel.: (86) 1085610580
Web Site: http://www.nidec.co.jp
Electronic Components Distr
N.A.I.C.S.: 423690

Nidec (Dalian) Limited (1)
No 2 Northeast Five Street, Dalian Economic Technical Development Zone, Dalian, 116600, China (100%)
Tel.: (86) 41187310202
Web Site: http://www.nidec.co.jp
Sales Range: $25-49.9 Million
Emp.: 30
Small Precision DC Disk Drive & Fan Motors Mfr
N.A.I.C.S.: 335999

Nidec (Dongguan) Limited (1)
3rd Industrial Zone Gaolong Road, Gaobu, Dongguan, 523273, China (100%)
Tel.: (86) 76988873011
Web Site: http://www.nidec.co.jp
Motor & Motor Components Mfr & Distr
N.A.I.C.S.: 335312

Nidec (H.K.) Co., Ltd. (1)
Units 2608-11 Tower 2 Metroplaza 223 Hing Fong Road, Kwai Chung, China (Hong Kong) (100%)
Tel.: (852) 23175228
Web Site: https://www.nidec.com
Emp.: 30
Sales of Electronic Components
N.A.I.C.S.: 423690
Takeshi Yamada (Gen Mgr)

Nidec (Shanghai) International Trading Co., Ltd. (1)
12/F Tower B 100 Zunyi Road, XuHui District, Shanghai, 200051, China
Tel.: (86) 2180311600
Web Site: http://www.nidec.co.jp
Sales Range: $50-74.9 Million
Emp.: 100
Electric Motor Whslr
N.A.I.C.S.: 423610

Nidec (Shaoguan) Limited (1)
HuangHua Yuan Industrial Zone, Shixing, Shaoguan, Guangdong, China (100%)
Tel.: (86) 7513131111
Web Site: http://www.nidec.co.jp
Direct Current Motors & Precision Motor Components Mfr
N.A.I.C.S.: 335312

Nidec (Shenzhen) Co., Ltd. (1)
Tel.: (86) 75525981929
Web Site: http://www.nidec.co.jp
Electric Motor Mfr
N.A.I.C.S.: 335312

Nidec (Zhejiang) Corporation (1)
Tel.: (86) 57385090777
Web Site: http://www.nidec.co.jp
Sales Range: $400-449.9 Million
Emp.: 1,200
Mfr of Spindle Motors for Hard Disc Drives & Components for Precision Motors
N.A.I.C.S.: 336390

Nidec ASI S.p.A. (1)
Via F Gracchi 39, Cinisello Balsamo, 20092, Milan, Italy
Tel.: (39) 0264451
Web Site: http://www.nidec.com
Sales Range: $100-124.9 Million
Emp.: 1,300
Electric Motor & Generator Mfr
N.A.I.C.S.: 335312

Subsidiary (Non-US):

Ansaldo Sistemi Industriali SA (2)
Z I du Buisson Rue de la Poudriere, 42230, Roche-la-Moliere, France
Tel.: (33) 4 77907600
Web Site: http://www.nidec.com
Sales Range: $25-49.9 Million
Emp.: 10
Electric Motor & Generator Mfr
N.A.I.C.S.: 335312
Franck Girard (Pres)

Subsidiary (Domestic):

Answer Drives S.r.l. (2)
Viale Sarca 336, Milan, 20126, Italy
Tel.: (39) 0444 449268
Web Site: http://www.nidec-asi.com
Electric Motor & Generator Mfr
N.A.I.C.S.: 335312
Giovanni Barra (CEO)

Subsidiary (Non-US):

Nidec ASI GmbH (2)
Im Teelbruch 104, 45219, Essen, Germany
Tel.: (49) 2054104980
Web Site: http://www.nidec-asi.com
Sales Range: $25-49.9 Million
Emp.: 20
Electric Motor & Generator Mfr
N.A.I.C.S.: 335312
Giacomo Dignazio (Mng Dir)

Subsidiary (US):

Nidec ASI LLC (2)

AND PRIVATE COMPANIES — NIDEC CORPORATION

4900 Woodway Dr Ste 680, Houston, TX 77056
Tel.: (832) 214-4185
Web Site: http://www.nidec-asi.com
Electric Power Control Systems Distr
N.A.I.C.S.: 423610
Paolo Osghnac *(VP & Gen Mgr)*

Subsidiary (Non-US):

Nidec ASI RO Srl (2)
235b Darzeii II Street, 137180, Crevedia, Jud Dambovita, Romania
Tel.: (40) 374 00 33 54
Web Site: http://www.nidec-asi.com
Sales Range: $25-49.9 Million
Emp.: 20
Electric Motor & Generator Mfr
N.A.I.C.S.: 335312
Ioan Gauzin *(Mgr)*

Nidec ASI VEI (2)
Neverovskogo st 10 building 4, 121170, Moscow, Russia
Tel.: (7) 4956409003
Web Site: http://nidec-asi-vei.ru
Electric Power Control Systems Distr
N.A.I.C.S.: 423610

Nidec America Corporation (1)
50 Braintree Hill Ofc Park Ste 110, Braintree, MA 02184-8735 **(100%)**
Tel.: (781) 848-0970
Web Site: http://www.nidec.com
Tube Axial Cooling Fans, Electronic Power Supplies & Precision Electric Motors Mfr
N.A.I.C.S.: 333413
Tom Healey *(CFO)*

Subsidiary (Domestic):

Avtron Industrial Automation, Inc. (2)
7555 E Pleasant Valley Rd, Independence, OH 44131-5529
Tel.: (216) 642-1230
Web Site: http://www.avtronautomation.com
Emp.: 70
Industrial Automation Equipments Mfr
N.A.I.C.S.: 334513
John Brock *(VP-Engrg)*

Embraco North America, Inc. (2)
2800 Vista Ridge Dr, Atlanta, GA 30024
Tel.: (770) 814-8004
Web Site: http://www.embraco.com
Wholesale Distr of Compressor & Refrigeration Equipment
N.A.I.C.S.: 423830

Genmark Automation Inc. (2)
46723 Lakeview Blvd, Fremont, CA 94538
Tel.: (510) 897-3400
Web Site: http://www.genmarkautomation.com
Automation Equipment Mfr
N.A.I.C.S.: 334512
Eugene Bonev *(Dir-Software Engrg)*

Subsidiary (Non-US):

Genmark Automation GmbH (3)
Ludwig-Erhard-Str 2E, 85375, Neufahrn, Germany
Tel.: (49) 8165403660
Automation Equipment Mfr
N.A.I.C.S.: 334512

Genmark Taiwan (3)
5F-8 No 65 GAOTIE 7th Rd, Hsinchu County, Zhubei, 302, Taiwan
Tel.: (886) 36683612
Automation Equipment Mfr
N.A.I.C.S.: 333310

Top Tech Inc. (3)
No 1003 1004 Sangdaewon-Dong, Joongwon-Gu, Songnam 13-15, Gyeonggi-Do, Korea (South)
Tel.: (82) 31 777 1250 3
Web Site: http://www.toptechinc.co.kr
Automation Equipment Mfr
N.A.I.C.S.: 333310

Subsidiary (Domestic):

Kato Engineering Inc. (2)
2075 Howard Dr WN, Mankato, MN 56003
Tel.: (507) 625-4011
Web Site: http://www.nidec.com
Broad Line of Alternators, Generators & Motor-Generator Sets Sales & Mfr
N.A.I.C.S.: 335312

Merkle-Korff Industries Inc. (2)
25 NW Point Blvd Ste 900, Elk Grove Village, IL 60007-1044
Tel.: (847) 296-8800
Web Site: http://www.merkle-korff.com
Sales Range: $75-99.9 Million
Emp.: 80
Mfr of Geared Motors & Generators
N.A.I.C.S.: 335312
Bernie Santerre *(Acct Mgr-Strategic)*

Motion Control Engineering (2)
11380 White Rock Rd, Rancho Cordova, CA 95742
Tel.: (916) 463-9200
Web Site: http://www.mceinc.com
Sales Range: $100-124.9 Million
Emp.: 365
Elevator Control Systems
N.A.I.C.S.: 333921
Jeff Yeager *(Reg Mgr-Sls)*

Branch (Domestic):

Nidec America Corp. - Torrington (2)
318 Industrial Ln, Torrington, CT 06790-7704
Tel.: (860) 482-4422
Web Site: http://www.nidec.com
AC/DC Power Supplies & Converters Mfr
N.A.I.C.S.: 335312

Subsidiary (Domestic):

Nidec Vamco Corporation (2)
555 Epsilon Dr, Pittsburgh, PA 15238
Tel.: (412) 963-7100
Web Site: http://www.vamcointernational.com
Sales Range: $1-9.9 Million
Emp.: 24
Mfr of Press Feeding Equipment for Metal Stamping Industry
N.A.I.C.S.: 333514
Scott Welsh *(VP-Sls)*

Roboteq, Inc. (2)
7812 E Acoma Dr Ste 1, Scottsdale, AZ 85260
Tel.: (480) 664-6660
Web Site: http://www.roboteq.com
Relay & Industrial Control Mfr
N.A.I.C.S.: 335314

Shimpo Drives Incorporation (2)
1701 Glenlake Ave, Itasca, IL 60143
Tel.: (630) 924-7138
Web Site: http://www.shimpodrives.com
Emp.: 40
Industrial Drive Product Mfr & Distr
N.A.I.C.S.: 333612
Jeff Williams *(Pres)*

Nidec Automobile Motor (Zhejiang) Corporation (1)
No 288 PingCheng Street, Pinghu Economic Dev Zone, Pinghu, Zhejiang, China **(100%)**
Tel.: (86) 57385093022
Web Site: http://www.nidec.co.jp
Automobile Motor Mfr
N.A.I.C.S.: 335312

Nidec BMS (Suzhou) Co., Ltd. (1)
No 200 Suhong Middle Rd Export Processing Zone Industrial Park, Suzhou, 215021, China
Tel.: (86) 51262587861
Electric Motor Component Mfr
N.A.I.C.S.: 335999

Nidec BMS Pte. Ltd. (1)
36 Loyang Way, Singapore, 508771, Singapore
Tel.: (65) 62618379
Computer Storage Device Mfr
N.A.I.C.S.: 334112

Nidec Component Technology Co., Ltd. (1)
80 Bendemeer Road 03-03, Singapore, 339949, Singapore **(98.9%)**
Tel.: (65) 65422111
Web Site: http://www.nidec-nco.com
Sales Range: $800-899.9 Million
Emp.: 2,950
Computer Disk Drive Contract Manufacturing Services
N.A.I.C.S.: 334112

Subsidiary (Non-US):

Nidec Component Technology Bangpa-In Co., Ltd. (2)
162 Moo 16 Bangpa-In Industrial Estate Tambol Bangkrasan, Amphur, Bangpa-in, 13160, Ayutthaya, Thailand **(100%)**
Tel.: (66) 352583815
Web Site: http://www.nidec-nco.com
Sales Range: $75-99.9 Million
Emp.: 500
Other Computer Peripheral Equipment Mfr
N.A.I.C.S.: 334118

Nidec Control Techniques Ltd. (1)
The Gro, Newtown, Powys, SY16 3BE, United Kingdom
Tel.: (44) 1686612300
Web Site: http://acim.nidec.com
Mechanical Drives Mfr
N.A.I.C.S.: 333992
Tony Pickering *(Pres)*

Subsidiary (Domestic):

CSA Consulting Engineers, Ltd. (2)
Venture House 2 Arlington Square, Bracknell, London, RG12 1WA, Berkshire, United Kingdom
Tel.: (44) 1189641500
Web Site: https://www.nv5.com
Electric Equipment Mfr
N.A.I.C.S.: 334419

Subsidiary (Non-US):

Control Technique Limited (2)
306 Town Centre Blvd, Markham, L3R 0Y6, ON, Canada **(100%)**
Tel.: (905) 513-5615
Web Site: http://acim.nidec.com
Electronic Speed Controls Mfr
N.A.I.C.S.: 335314
Bill Fey *(Reg Dir-Sls)*

Control Techniques Asia-Pacific Pte.Ltd. (2)
36 Lok Yang Way, Singapore, 628641, Singapore
Tel.: (65) 9617 3556
Web Site: http://acim.nidec.com
Electric Equipment Mfr
N.A.I.C.S.: 333992

Subsidiary (Non-US):

Control Techniques Drives(Malaysia) Sdn Bhd (3)
11Jalan PJS 11/18 Bandar Sunway, Petaling Jaya, 46150, Malaysia
Tel.: (60) 162113202
Mfr of AC & DC Variable Speed Drives, Servos & Power Conversion Technologies
N.A.I.C.S.: 335311

Nidec (Thailand) Co Ltd (3)
Tel.: (66) 29622092
Web Site: http://acim.nidec.com
Electrical Equipment Distr
N.A.I.C.S.: 333992

Subsidiary (Domestic):

Nidec Industrial Automation Singapore Pte Limited (3)
36 Lok Yang Way, Singapore, 628641, Singapore
Tel.: (65) 68070473
Web Site: http://acim.nidec.com
Electric Equipment Mfr
N.A.I.C.S.: 333992

Subsidiary (Domestic):

Control Techniques Dynamics Limited (2)
South Way Walworth Business Park, Andover, SP 10 5 AB, Hampshire, United Kingdom
Tel.: (44) 1264387600
Web Site: https://www.controltechniques.com
Fluid Meter & Counting Devices Mfr
N.A.I.C.S.: 335314

Subsidiary (Non-US):

Nidec ACIM Germany GmbH (2)
Meysstrasse 20, 53773, Hennef, Germany
Tel.: (49) 22428770

Web Site: http://acim.nidec.com
Electric Equipment Mfr
N.A.I.C.S.: 333992
Rainer Crevecoeur *(CEO)*

Nidec Industrial Automation Iberia S.A. (2)
Carrer Primer de Maig 41 Pol Ind Pedrosa, Entrada Almacen por C/Rafael Barradas 1 Hospitalet Dec Llobregat, 8908, Barcelona, Spain
Tel.: (34) 936801661
Web Site: http://acim.nidec.com
Electronic Drives for Motor Vehicles Mfr
N.A.I.C.S.: 423110

Nidec Industrial Automation Italy SpA (2)
Via Idiomi 3/6, Assago, 20090, Italy
Tel.: (39) 02575751
Power Drives Reseller
N.A.I.C.S.: 333992

Nidec Industrial Automation Southern Africa (Pty) Limited (2)
Corner Olympic Duel and Angus Crescent Northlands Business Park, Johannesburg, 2162, South Africa
Tel.: (27) 114621740
Motors Mfr & Distr
N.A.I.C.S.: 335312

Subsidiary (Domestic):

Nidec Industrial Automation UK Limited (2)
Stafford Park 4, Telford, TF3 3BA, Shrophire, United Kingdom
Tel.: (44) 1952213705
Web Site: https://www.nidec-industrial.com
Electric Equipment Mfr
N.A.I.C.S.: 334419

Subsidiary (Non-US):

Nidec Netherlands B.V. (2)
Kubus 155, 3364 DG, Sliedrecht, Netherlands
Tel.: (31) 184420555
Web Site: https://www.nidec-netherlands.nl
Motor & Motor Components Mfr, Whslr & Distr
N.A.I.C.S.: 335312

Subsidiary (Non-US):

Control Techniques AG (3)
Lindachesterrasse 1, 5413, Birmenstorf, Switzerland
Tel.: (41) 562014242
Drives & Motors Reseller
N.A.I.C.S.: 335312

Control Techniques Brno s.r.o. (3)
Podnikatelska 2b, CZ 61200, Brno, Czech Republic
Tel.: (420) 511180111
Web Site: https://www.pohony-menice.cz
Electric Equipment Mfr
N.A.I.C.S.: 333992

Control Techniques China Pte. Ltd. (3)
Room B 5 Flr Pionego Bldg No 213 Wai Yip St, Kwun Tong, China (Hong Kong)
Tel.: (852) 29795271
Web Site: http://www.controltechniques.com
Electric Equipment Mfr
N.A.I.C.S.: 333992

Control Techniques Endustriyel Kontrol Sistemerli Sanayi ve Ticaret AS (3)
Icerenkoy Mah Topcu Ibrahim Sk No 13 K 2, 34752, Istanbul, Turkiye
Tel.: (90) 2165131400
Electric Equipment Mfr
N.A.I.C.S.: 333992

Control Techniques India Private Limited (3)
117B Developed Plot, Industrial Estate Perungudi, Chennai, 600096, India
Tel.: (91) 4466918400
Web Site: https://www.nidec.com
Electric Equipment Mfr
N.A.I.C.S.: 333992

Nidec Industrial Automation Belgium NV (3)

NIDEC CORPORATION

Nidec Corporation—(Continued)
Blarenberglaan A23 Z I Mechelen Noord A23, 2800, Mechelen, Belgium
Tel.: (32) 15281010
Web Site: https://www.nidec.com
Speed Changers Mfr
N.A.I.C.S.: 333992

Subsidiary (Non-US):

SKS Control Oy (2)
Martinkylantie 50, 01720, Vantaa, Finland
Tel.: (358) 207 6461
Web Site: http://www.sks.fi
Electric Equipment Mfr
N.A.I.C.S.: 333992
Jouni Kaukonen (Mng Dir)

Nidec Copal Corporation (1)
2-18-10 Shimura, Itabashi-ku, Tokyo, 174-8550, Japan **(100%)**
Tel.: (81) 3 3965 1111
Web Site: http://www.nidec-copal.com
Sales Range: $800-899.9 Million
Emp.: 15,340
Holding Company; Camera Shutter & Other Precision Equipment Component Mfr
N.A.I.C.S.: 551112
Shigenobu Nagamori (Chrm)

Subsidiary (Non-US):

Copal Optical & Electronic Machinery (Shanghai) Co., Ltd. (2)
Room 1010 Suncome Liauws Plaza 738 Shang Cheng Road, New Pu Dong District, Shanghai, 200131, China
Tel.: (86) 2150462603
Web Site: http://www.nidec-copal.com
Sales Range: $25-49.9 Million
Emp.: 13
Camera & Other Precision Components Whslr
N.A.I.C.S.: 423410

Copal Yamada (Vietnam) Co., Ltd. (2)
Group A Lot N 21a-23-25-27a Street No 12, Tan Thuan Epzone, Tan Thuan Dong Ward, Ho Chi Minh City, Vietnam
Tel.: (84) 837700647
Precision Motor & Component Mfr
N.A.I.C.S.: 335312

Subsidiary (Domestic):

Copal Yamada Corporation (2)
80 Oaza Hao, Chikuma, 389-0812, Nagano, Japan
Tel.: (81) 262767534
Web Site: https://www.nidec-precision-yamada.co.jp
Emp.: 50
Special Die Developer & Mfr
N.A.I.C.S.: 333514

Subsidiary (Non-US):

Nidec Copal (Hong Kong) Co., Ltd. (2)
Unit 1601 16th Floor Telford House 16 Wang Hoi Rd, Kowloon Bay, Kowloon, China (Hong Kong)
Tel.: (852) 27506611
Sales Range: $50-74.9 Million
Emp.: 10
Materials Procurement & Camera Parts Whslr
N.A.I.C.S.: 425120

Nidec Copal (Thailand) Co., Ltd. (2)
60/117 Navanakorn Industrial Estate Zone 3 Moo 19 Phaholyothin Road, Tambon Klongnueng Amphur Klongluang, Pathumthani, 12120, Thailand
Tel.: (66) 28349000
Web Site: http://www.nidec-copal.com
Emp.: 2,500
Camera Shutter & Lens Cone Mfr
N.A.I.C.S.: 332721
Yoshitake Matsui (Gen Mgr)

Nidec Copal (Vietnam) Co., Ltd. (2)
Lot I1-N12 Saigon Hi-Tech Park, Tan Phu Ward Thu Duc City, Ho Chi Minh City, Vietnam
Tel.: (84) 2837360075
Emp.: 2,200
Precision Minimotors Mfr

N.A.I.C.S.: 335312
Kumatai Takehiko (Gen Mgr)

Nidec Copal (Zhejiang) Co., Ltd. (2)
1388 Huanbei 2nd Street, Pinghu Economic Dev Zone, Pinghu, Zhejiang, China
Tel.: (86) 57385096222
Camera Shutters, Camera Lens Cones & Other Precision Parts Mfr
N.A.I.C.S.: 332721

Unit (Domestic):

Nidec Copal Corp. - Koriyama (Dies) Technical Center (2)
37 Aza Suwauchi Tomita-machi, Koriyama, 963-8637, Fukushima, Japan
Tel.: (81) 249521111
Web Site: http://www.nidec-copal.com
Precision Parts & Dies Technical Engineering, Development & Support Services
N.A.I.C.S.: 541990

Subsidiary (Non-US):

Nidec Copal GmbH (2)
Charlotton Strasse 51, Dusseldorf, D-40210, Germany
Tel.: (49) 2115504690
Web Site: http://www.nidec-copal.de
Emp.: 55
Precision Minimotors & Electronic Equipment Whslr
N.A.I.C.S.: 423830

Nidec Copal Philippines Corporation (2)
Main Ave cor Binary St Light Industry & Science Park 1, Bo Diezmo Cabuyao, Laguna, Philippines
Tel.: (63) 495430691
Sales Range: $150-199.9 Million
Emp.: 7
Precision Parts Mfr
N.A.I.C.S.: 332721
Joan Alzate (Gen Mgr)

Nidec Copal Precision (Vietnam) Corporation (2)
Lot I-1d-1 N1 Road Saigon Hi-Tech Park, District 9, Ho Chi Minh City, Vietnam
Web Site: http://www.nidec-copal.com
Precision Motor & Component Mfr
N.A.I.C.S.: 335312

Subsidiary (Domestic):

Nidec Copal Precision Parts Corporation (2)
2-18-10 Shimura, Itabashi-ku, Tokyo, 174-0056, Japan
Tel.: (81) 339651111
Web Site: http://www.nidec-cpp.co.jp
Camera Shutter & Other Precision Equipment Component Mfr
N.A.I.C.S.: 332721

Nidec Copal Electronics Corporation (1)
Nishi-shinjuku Prime Square Bldg 7-5-25 Nishi-Shinjuku, Shinjuku-ku, Tokyo, 160-0023, Japan
Tel.: (81) 333647055
Web Site: http://www.nidec-copal-electronics.com
Industrial Electronic Components Mfr & Whslr
N.A.I.C.S.: 334419

Subsidiary (Non-US):

NIDEC COPAL ELECTRONICS (TAIWAN) CO., LTD. (2)
18F-1 No 57 Sec 2 Tun Hwa S Rd, Taipei, 106, Taiwan
Tel.: (886) 227030577
Electronic Components Mfr
N.A.I.C.S.: 334419

NIDEC COPAL ELECTRONICS SINGAPORE PTE. LTD. (2)
180B Bencoolen Street 07-05 The Bencoolen, Singapore, 189648, Singapore
Tel.: (65) 6535 0056
Web Site: http://www.copal-electronics.com
Sales Range: $25-49.9 Million
Emp.: 3
Electronic Components Distr
N.A.I.C.S.: 423690
Masataka Igarashi (Mng Dir)

Nidec Copal Electronics (Korea) Co., Ltd. (2)
2F Jin-il Bldg 52-7 Banpo-Dong, Seocho-Gu, Seoul, 137-040, Korea (South) **(100%)**
Tel.: (82) 234825861
Web Site: http://www.nidec-copal-electronics.com
Industrial Electronics Components Whslr
N.A.I.C.S.: 423690

Nidec Copal Electronics (Shanghai) Co., Ltd. (2)
Unit A 4/F No 4 Bldg No 253 Ai Du Rd, Wai Gao Qiao Free Trade Zone, Shanghai, 200131, China
Tel.: (86) 2150463009
Industrial Electronics Components Whslr
N.A.I.C.S.: 423690

Nidec Copal Electronics (Zhejiang) Co., Ltd. (2)
No 519 Fanrong Road Pinghu Economic Development Zone, Pinghu, 314200, Zhejiang, China
Tel.: (86) 57385096988
Web Site: http://www.nidec.com
Mfr & Sales of Switches, Pressure Sensors, Encoders & Polygon Laser Scanners
N.A.I.C.S.: 335313

Nidec Copal Electronics GmbH (2)
Mergenthalerallee 79-81, 65760, Eschborn, Germany **(100%)**
Tel.: (49) 6196927750
Web Site: http://www.nidec-copal-electronics.com
Industrial Electronics Components Whslr
N.A.I.C.S.: 423690

Subsidiary (US):

Nidec Copal Electronics, Inc. (2)
367 Van Ness Way Ste 601, Torrance, CA 90501
Tel.: (310) 618-0225
Web Site: http://www.nidec-copal-electronics.us
Sales Range: $25-49.9 Million
Emp.: 10
Industrial Electronics Components Whslr
N.A.I.C.S.: 423690
N Kato (Gen Mgr)

Nidec Electronics (Thailand) Co., Ltd. (1)
118 Moo 5 Phaholyothin Road Lamsai, Wangnoi District, Ayutthaya, 13170, Thailand **(99.9%)**
Tel.: (66) 35 271 453
Web Site: http://www.nidec.co.jp
Hard Disk Drive Spindle Motors Mfr
N.A.I.C.S.: 335312

Plant (Domestic):

Nidec Electronics (Thailand) Co., Ltd. - ROJANA FACTORY (2)
Rojana Industrial Park 44 Moo 9 Rojana Road Thanu Sub-district, U-thai District, Ayutthaya, 13210, Thailand
Tel.: (66) 35 330 741
Web Site: http://www.nidec.co.jp
Spindle Motor Mfr
N.A.I.C.S.: 335312

Nidec Electronics (Thailand) Co., Ltd. - Rangsit Factory (2)
199/12 Moo 3 Thanyaburi-Lumlukka Road, Klong 7 Tambol Rangsit, Amphur Thanyaburi Changwat, Pathumthani, 12110, Thailand
Tel.: (66) 2 577 5077
Web Site: http://www.nidec.co.jp
HDD Spindle Motor Mfr
N.A.I.C.S.: 335312

Nidec Electronics GmbH (1)
Seewiesenstrasse 9, Bietigheim-Bissingen, 74321, Germany **(100%)**
Tel.: (49) 71425083700
Web Site: http://www.nidec.co.jp
Sales Range: $25-49.9 Million
Emp.: 18
Motors & Industrial Electronics Distr
N.A.I.C.S.: 423830

Nidec Europe B.V (1)
P J Oudweg 4, 1314 CH, Almere, Netherlands
Tel.: (31) 367603800

INTERNATIONAL PUBLIC

Web Site: https://www.nidec.com
Management Consulting Services
N.A.I.C.S.: 541618

Nidec Global Appliance Italy S.r.l. (1)
Via Pietro Andriano 12, Riva Presso Chieri, 10020, Rivalta di Torino, Italy
Tel.: (39) 0119437111
Automotive Electronic Component Mfr
N.A.I.C.S.: 336320

Nidec India Private Limited (1)
SP2-1 to SP2-4, New Industrial Complex Majrakath, Neemrana, 301 705, Rajasthan, India
Tel.: (91) 1494660300
Web Site: https://www.nidec.com
Automotive Electronic Component Mfr
N.A.I.C.S.: 336320

Nidec Industrial Automation India Pvt. Ltd. - Bangalore (1)
45 Nagarur Huskur Road Off Tumkur Road, Bengaluru, 562162, India
Tel.: (91) 8067264800
Electrical Equipment & Supplies Mfr
N.A.I.C.S.: 335999

Nidec Korea Corporation (1)
16F Keungil Tower Bldg 223 Teheran-ro, Gangnam-gu, Seoul, 06142, Korea (South) **(100%)**
Tel.: (82) 25278760
Web Site: http://www.nidec.com
Sales Range: $1-9.9 Million
Emp.: 22
N.A.I.C.S.: 335311
Manab Yamasati (Pres)

Nidec Laminaciones de Acero, S.A. de C.V. (1)
Calle Sexta 506 Pte Fracc Parque Ind, Apodaca, Nuevo Leon, Mexico
Tel.: (52) 818196750
Automotive Electronic Component Mfr
N.A.I.C.S.: 336320

Nidec Leroy-Somer Holding SA (1)
Boulevard Marcellin Leroy, 10015, Angouleme, Cedex, France
Tel.: (33) 545644564
Web Site: http://acim.nidec.com
Emp.: 6,200
Holding Company; Electromechanical Drive Systems Mfr & Distr
N.A.I.C.S.: 551112

Subsidiary (Domestic):

Girard Transmissions SAS (2)
2 Rue du Bruscos, 64230, Sauvagnon, France
Tel.: (33) 559052940
Web Site: https://www.girard-transmissions.com
Emp.: 75
Gear Box Mfr
N.A.I.C.S.: 335999

Subsidiary (Non-US):

Leroy Somer Elektomekanik Sistemler Ticaret Ltd. STI (2)
Topcu Ibrahim Sok No 13 Kat 2, Atasehir, 34752, Istanbul, Turkiye
Tel.: (90) 2165773107
Electrical Equipment Supplies & Mfr
N.A.I.C.S.: 335999

Leroy-Somer (Pty) Ltd. (2)
PO Box 751103, 2047, Johannesburg, Gardenview, South Africa
Tel.: (27) 114556212
Web Site: http://www.leroy-somer.com
Sales Range: $10-24.9 Million
Emp.: 10
Motors & Generators Distr
N.A.I.C.S.: 335312

Leroy-Somer B.V. (2)
Kubus 155 br, 3364 DG, Sliedrecht, Netherlands
Tel.: (31) 184420555
Relay Mfr
N.A.I.C.S.: 335314

Leroy-Somer Canada Ltd. (2)
3001 Douglas B-Floreani, H4S1Y7, Saint Laurent, QC, Canada
Tel.: (514) 332-1880

AND PRIVATE COMPANIES — NIDEC CORPORATION

Web Site: http://www.usmotors.com
Sales Range: $1-9.9 Million
Emp.: 4
Electric Mfr
N.A.I.C.S.: 335312

Leroy-Somer Denmark A/S (2)
Hollufgards Alle 9, DK-5220, Odense, Denmark
Tel.: (45) 63141463
Web Site: http://www.leroy-somer.dk
Sales Range: $10-24.9 Million
Emp.: 12
Electronic Motors Sales
N.A.I.C.S.: 335312

Leroy-Somer Elektroantriebe GmbH (2)
Durisolstrasse 2, 3 OG TOP 3.4, 4600, Wels, Austria
Tel.: (43) 572720
Web Site: http://www.leroy-somer.com
Sales Range: $25-49.9 Million
Emp.: 8
Electronic Motors Sales
N.A.I.C.S.: 444180

Leroy-Somer Marbaise GmbH (2)
Hesslingsweg 6, 44309, Dortmund, Germany
Tel.: (49) 2319250100
Gear Box Mfr
N.A.I.C.S.: 335999

Leroy-Somer Norden AB (2)
Gransbovagen 6, S 152 42, Sodertalje, Sweden
Tel.: (46) 855424100
Web Site: http://www.leroysomer.com
Sales Range: $25-49.9 Million
Emp.: 14
Electric Motors Sales
N.A.I.C.S.: 335312

Leroy-Somer Norge A/S (2)
Alfheim 7, PO Box 72, N 1371, Asker, Norway
Tel.: (47) 66761110
Web Site: http://www.leroysomer.com
Sales Range: $25-49.9 Million
Emp.: 4
Electronic Motors Sales
N.A.I.C.S.: 335312

Leroy-Somer OY (2)
Insinoorinkatu 7B, PO Box 59, 00811, Helsinki, Finland
Tel.: (358) 9 2536 6600
Web Site: http://www.leroy-somer.com
Sales Range: $1-9.9 Million
Emp.: 4
Electric Mfr
N.A.I.C.S.: 335312

Subsidiary (Domestic):

Moteurs Leroy-Somer S.A. (2)
Boulevard Marcellin Leroy, 16000, Angouleme, France
Tel.: (33) 545644564
Web Site: http://www.leroy-somer.com
Emp.: 6,200
Electric Motor Mfr
N.A.I.C.S.: 335312

Subsidiary (Non-US):

Nidec Schweiz AG
Schaftenholzweg 16, Studen, 2557, Switzerland
Tel.: (41) 323742929
Electric Motors Distr
N.A.I.C.S.: 335312

Subsidiary (Non-US):

Constructions Electriques de Beaucourt SAS (3)
Rue de Dampierre, 90500, Beaucourt, France
Tel.: (33) 384364040
Electronic Product Distr
N.A.I.C.S.: 449210

IMI Elektromos Gepeket Gyarto Kft (3)
Gyartelep Hrsz 03/3, Iklad, H-2181, Hungary
Tel.: (36) 628576100
Web Site: http://www.imi.hu
Electronic Product Distr
N.A.I.C.S.: 449210

Nidec Logistics Corporation (1)
1634 kitahara Minamiminowa-mura, Kamiina-gun, Nagano, 399-4511, Japan (100%)
Tel.: (81) 265787000
Web Site: http://www.nidec-logistics.co.jp
Freight Transportation, Warehousing & Distribution Services
N.A.I.C.S.: 488510

Subsidiary (Non-US):

Nidec Logistics (H.K.) Co., Limited (2)
ATL Bldg, Kwai Chung, China (Hong Kong)
Tel.: (852) 2614 1220
Logistics Management Services
N.A.I.C.S.: 541614

Nidec Machinery Corporation (1)
1-32-2 Chiyomi, Tottori, 680-0911, Japan (76%)
Tel.: (81) 857371721
Web Site: http://www.nidec-machinery.com
Sales Range: $100-124.9 Million
Emp.: 272
Automotive Industry Factory Automation Equipment Mfr & Whslr
N.A.I.C.S.: 333519
Shinichiro Maeta (Pres)

Subsidiary (Non-US):

NIDEC MACHINERY (SHANGHAI) CO., LTD. (2)
Room 904 Building 2 Huayi Mansion No 2020 Zhongshan West Road, Xuhui District, Shanghai, 200235, China
Tel.: (86) 21 3469 1969
Sales Range: $25-49.9 Million
Emp.: 9
Measuring & Testing Device Distr
N.A.I.C.S.: 334519
Shinichiro Maeta (Chm)

NIDEC MACHINERY (ZHEJIANG) CORPORATION (2)
600 Changsheng Road Pinghu Economic Development District, Pinghu, 314200, Zhejiang, China
Tel.: (86) 57385096416
Sales Range: $50-74.9 Million
Emp.: 12
Visual Inspection System Mfr & Distr
N.A.I.C.S.: 334519
Shinichiro Maeta (Pres)

Nidec Machinery (Thailand) Co., Ltd. (2)
40/31-32 Moo 5 Tambol U-Thai, Amphur U-Thai, Ayutthaya, 13210, Thailand
Tel.: (66) 35 227 766
Web Site: http://www.nidec-machinery.com
Automotive Industry Factory Automation Equipment Mfr
N.A.I.C.S.: 333519

Nidec Management Shanghai Corporation (1)
Unit2305 09 23/F Tower A The Place 100 Zunyi Rd, Chang Ning District, Shanghai, 200051, China
Tel.: (86) 2180311610
Electric Motor Mfr
N.A.I.C.S.: 335312

Nidec Mobility Corporation (1)
6368 Nenjozaka Okusa, Komaki, 485-0802, Aichi, Japan
Tel.: (81) 568786160
Emp.: 5,179
Automotive Electronic Component Mfr
N.A.I.C.S.: 336320
Katsuhiro Wada (Pres)

Nidec Motor (Qingdao) Corporation (1)
No 688 Lanzhou E Rd Jiaozhou Economic Development Zone, Qingdao, 266300, China
Tel.: (86) 53287273331
Web Site: http://www.nidecmotor.com
Emp.: 70
Electric Motor Mfr
N.A.I.C.S.: 335312
Peter Murphy (Gen Mgr)

Nidec Motor Holdings Corporation (1)

338 Kuze Tonoshiro-cho, Minami-ku, Kyoto, 601-8205, Japan (100%)
Tel.: (81) 759356666
Web Site: http://www.nidec-motor.com
Holding Company; Electrical Motors & Controls Mfr
N.A.I.C.S.: 551112
Patrick K. Murphy (Pres)

Subsidiary (Non-US):

Compania de Motores Domesticos, S.A. de C.V. (2)
Antigua Carretera A Roma Kilometro 9 7, 66000, Apodaca, Nuevo Leon, Mexico
Tel.: (52) 8181967606
Electric Motor Mfr
N.A.I.C.S.: 335312

Controles Electromecanicos S.A. de C.V. (2)
Viaducto Tlalpan 4777, 1007, Mexico, Mexico
Tel.: (52) 55737819
Web Site: http://www.controleselectromecanicos.com
Electronic Equipment Distr
N.A.I.C.S.: 449210

Motores Reynosa, S.A. de C.V. (2)
Av Industrial Del Norte C/Ave Las Lomas Parque Industral del Norte, Reynosa, 88736, Tamaulipas, Mexico
Tel.: (52) 899921600
Web Site: http://www.motoresreynosa.com
Motor Mfr
N.A.I.C.S.: 335312

Motores U.S. de Mexico, S.A. de C.V. (2)
Blvd.Carlos Salinas de Gortari KM9, Apodaca, Mexico (100%)
Tel.: (52) 8183891302
Web Site: http://www.nidec.com
Electric Motor Mfr
N.A.I.C.S.: 335312

Subsidiary (Domestic):

U.S.E.M. de Mexico S.A. de C.V. (3)
Blvd Carlos Salinas de Gortari Km 9 7, Apodaca, 66600, NL, Mexico
Tel.: (52) 8183891351
Electric Motor Mfr & Whslr
N.A.I.C.S.: 335312

Subsidiary (Non-US):

Nidec Motor Canada Corporation (2)
6617 Boul Thimens, Saint Laurent, H4S 1W8, QC, Canada (100%)
Tel.: (514) 332-1880
Web Site: http://www.usmotors.com
Electrical Motors Whslr
N.A.I.C.S.: 423830

Nidec Motor Colombia SAS (2)
Calle 100 13 76 Pis 5, Bogota, 810810, Colombia
Tel.: (57) 17058000
Electric Motor Mfr
N.A.I.C.S.: 335312

Subsidiary (US):

Nidec Motor Corporation (2)
8050 W Florissant Ave, Saint Louis, MO 63136-1417
Tel.: (314) 521-2727
Web Site: http://www.nidec-motor.com
Electrical Motors & Controls Mfr
N.A.I.C.S.: 335312
Kei Pang (CEO)

Subsidiary (Domestic):

Canton Elevator, Inc. (3)
2575 Greensburg Rd, North Canton, OH 44720
Tel.: (330) 833-3600
Web Site: http://www.cantonelevator.com
Sales Range: $1-9.9 Million
Emp.: 75
Elevator & Moving Stairway Mfr
N.A.I.C.S.: 333921
Michael J. Paschke (Pres)

KB Electronics, Inc. (3)
12095 NW 39th St, Coral Springs, FL 33065
Tel.: (954) 346-4900

Web Site: http://www.kbelectronics.com
Miscellaneous Electrical Equipment & Component Mfr
N.A.I.C.S.: 335999
Alan Bueller (VP-Sls)

Nidec Industrial Automation USA LLC (3)
7078 Shady Oak Rd, Eden Prairie, MN 55344
Tel.: (952) 995-8000
Web Site: http://www.controltechniques.com
High Speed Industrial Drives Mfr
N.A.I.C.S.: 333612

Unit (Domestic):

Nidec Motor Corp. - Hurst Motors (3)
1551 E Broadway St, Princeton, IN 47670-3137
Tel.: (812) 385-2564
Web Site: https://www.hurst-motors.com
Sales Range: $25-49.9 Million
Emp.: 125
Brushless Direct Current Motor Mfr
N.A.I.C.S.: 335312
Greg Davis (Mgr-Ops)

Subsidiary (Non-US):

Switched Reluctance Drives Limited (2)
East Park House Otley Road, Harrogate, HG3 1PR, United Kingdom
Tel.: (44) 1423 845200
Web Site: http://www.srdrives.co.uk
Emp.: 50
Electric Motor Mfr
N.A.I.C.S.: 335312
Steve Cummins (Dir-Bus Dev)

Nidec Motors & Actuators S.A.S. (1)
3bis rue des Archives, 94006, Creteil, Cedex, France (100%)
Tel.: (33) 156701956
Web Site: http://www.nidec-ma.com
Sales Range: $50-74.9 Million
Emp.: 20
Automotive & Industrial Electrical Motor & Actuator Developer, Mfr & Whslr
N.A.I.C.S.: 335312

Subsidiary (Non-US):

Nidec Motors & Actuators (Germany) GmbH (2)
Seewiesenstrasse 9, 74321, Bietigheim-Bissingen, Germany
Tel.: (49) 71425080
Web Site: http://www.nidec-ma.com
Automotive & Industrial Electrical Motor & Actuator Developer, Mfr & Whslr
N.A.I.C.S.: 335312

Nidec Motors & Actuators (Poland), Sp. z o.o. (2)
ul Skarbowa 36, 32 005, Niepolomice, Poland
Tel.: (48) 122972700
Web Site: http://www.nidec-ma.com
Automotive & Industrial Electrical Motor & Actuator Mfr
N.A.I.C.S.: 335312

Nidec Motors & Actuators (Spain) S.A. (2)
Tel.: (34) 935447000
Web Site: http://www.nidec-ma.com
Sales Range: $25-49.9 Million
Automotive & Industrial Airflow Motor Developer, Mfr & Whslr
N.A.I.C.S.: 335312

Subsidiary (US):

Nidec Motors & Actuators (USA), Inc. (2)
1800 Opdyke Ct, Auburn Hills, MI 48326
Tel.: (915) 774-2450
Web Site: https://www.nidec-ma.com
Sales Range: $50-74.9 Million
Emp.: 20
Automotive & Industrial Electrical Motor & Actuator Developer & Whslr
N.A.I.C.S.: 423120
Jon Everart (Mgr-Engrg)

Subsidiary (Non-US):

Nidec Motors & Actuators Mexico S. de R.L. de C.V. (2)

NIDEC CORPORATION

Nidec Corporation—(Continued)
Tel.: (52) 6566293800
Web Site: http://www.nidec-ma.com
Automotive & Industrial Electrical Motor & Actuator Mfr
N.A.I.C.S.: 335312

Nidec Nissin Corporation (1)
2104-1 Yonezawa, Chino, 391-0216, Nagano, Japan
Tel.: (81) 266 72 5300
Web Site: http://www.nidec-nissin.co.jp
Sales Range: $125-149.9 Million
Emp.: 326
Precision-Engineered Plastic Molding, Lens & Optical Equipment Mfr
N.A.I.C.S.: 332721
Shigenobu Nagamori (Chm)

Subsidiary (Non-US):

NIDEC NISSIN (DONGGUAN) CORPORATION (2)
No 213 Bubugao Road Jiangbei Development Zone Wusha Changan, Dongguan, Guangdong, China
Tel.: (86) 769 87085211
Optical Instrument & Lens Mfr
N.A.I.C.S.: 333310

NIDEC NISSIN (HK) Co., Ltd. (2)
Unit 2605-06 Level 26 Metroplaza Tower II N 223 Hing Fong Road, Kwai Chung, New Territories, China (Hong Kong)
Tel.: (852) 2389 4070
Web Site: http://www.nidec-nissin.co.jp
Sales Range: $25-49.9 Million
Emp.: 5
Precision Product Mfr
N.A.I.C.S.: 332721

NIDEC NISSIN Vietnam Corporation (2)
Lot No 7 Quang Minh Industrial Zone, Me Linh District, Hanoi, Vietnam
Tel.: (84) 435 250044
Emp.: 40
Injection Molded Plastic Products Mfr
N.A.I.C.S.: 326199
Hidekazu Oku (Gen Dir)

NIDEC SANKYO (DALIAN) CORPORATION (2)
No 33-31 Industrial Park Economical Development Zone, Dalian, China
Tel.: (86) 411 87651771
Web Site: http://www.nidec-sankyo.co.jp
Injection Molded Plastic Products Mfr
N.A.I.C.S.: 326199

Subsidiary (Domestic):

Nidec Nissin Tohoku Corporation (2)
26 Aza Jamochi Oura, Yurihonjo, 015-0021, Akita, Japan
Tel.: (81) 184 23 3433
Injection Mold Plastic Material Mfr
N.A.I.C.S.: 325211

Nidec Philippines Corporation (1)
136 North Science Avenue Extension, Laguna Technopark Special Economic Zone Binan, Laguna, 4024, Philippines (100%)
Tel.: (63) 495411111
Sales Range: $1-4.9 Billion
Emp.: 7,000
Mfr of Spindle Motors for Hard Disc Drives
N.A.I.C.S.: 335312

Subsidiary (Domestic):

Nidec Precision Philippines Corporation (2)
119 East Main Avenue Laguna Technopark Special Economic Zone, Binan, Laguna, 4024, Philippines
Tel.: (63) 495411126
Web Site: http://www.nidec.co.jp
Sales Range: $700-749.9 Million
Emp.: 2,799
Precision Motor Components Mfr
N.A.I.C.S.: 335999

Nidec Subic Philippines Corporation (2)
Block B Subic Techno Park Argonaut Highway Boton Area, Subic Bay Freeport Zone, Subic, 2222, Philippines (99.9%)
Tel.: (63) 472525828

Web Site: http://www.nidec.co.jp
Emp.: 3,462
Hard Disk Drive Spindle Motors Mfr
N.A.I.C.S.: 335312
Kasahara Toshihiko (Gen Mgr)

Nidec Pigeon Corporation (1)
2-17-3 Kaga, Itabashi-ku, Tokyo, 173-0003, Japan
Tel.: (81) 339625151
Optical, Electronic & Information Equipment Developer & Mfr
N.A.I.C.S.: 335999

Nidec Precision (Thailand) Co., Ltd. (1)
150 Moo 5 Phaholyothin Road, Lamsai Sub-district Wangnoi District, Ayutthaya, 13170, Thailand
Tel.: (66) 35215318
Web Site: http://www.nidec.co.jp
Mfr of Components for Precision Motors
N.A.I.C.S.: 335999

Plant (Domestic):

Nidec Precision (Thailand) Co., Ltd. - ROJANA FACTORY (2)
Rojana Industrial Park 2 29 Moo 2 U-thai-Pachee Road Banchang, Sub-district U-thai District, Ayutthaya, 13210, Thailand
Tel.: (66) 35 746 683
Web Site: http://www.nidec.co.jp
Precision Motor Mfr
N.A.I.C.S.: 335312

Nidec SR Drives Ltd. (1)
East Park House Otley Road, Harrogate, HG3 1PR, United Kingdom
Tel.: (44) 1423 845200
Web Site: http://www.srdrives.com
Emp.: 65
Electric Motor Mfr
N.A.I.C.S.: 335312
Rachel Mills (Mgr-HR)

Nidec Sankyo Corporation (1)
5329 Shimosuwa-machi, Suwa-gun, Nagano, 393-8511, Japan (100%)
Tel.: (81) 266273111
Web Site: http://www.nidec-sankyo.co.jp
Sales Range: $1-4.9 Billion
Emp.: 12,674
Electric Motors, Card Readers, Sensors, Motor Drive Units, Industrial Robots, Precision Ball Screws & Plastic Molded Products Mfr
N.A.I.C.S.: 335312
Shigenobu Nagamori (Chm)

Subsidiary (Non-US):

NIDEC SANKYO (H.K.) CO., LIMITED (2)
Unite 2605-06 Level 26 Metroplaza Tower II No 223 Hing Fong Road, Kwai Fong, New Territories, China (Hong Kong)
Tel.: (852) 2369 6855
Web Site: http://www.nidec-sankyo.co.jp
Injection Molded Plastic Products Mfr
N.A.I.C.S.: 326199

NIDEC SANKYO (THAILAND) CO., LTD. (2)
Room No 805 8th Floor 56 Yada Building Silom Rd Suriyawongse, Bangrak, Bangkok, 10500, Thailand
Tel.: (66) 26329102
Emp.: 5
Electronic Components Mfr
N.A.I.C.S.: 334419

NIDEC SANKYO (ZHEJIANG) CORPORATION (2)
No 888 Xing Ping 2nd Road Pinghu Economic Development Zone, Pinghu, 314200, Zhejiang, China
Tel.: (86) 573 85078861
Electronic Components Mfr
N.A.I.C.S.: 334419

Plant (Domestic):

NIDEC SANKYO CORPORATION - Komagane Facility (2)
5329 Shimosuwa-machi, Suwa-gun, Nagano, 393-8511, Japan
Tel.: (81) 266273111
Emp.: 11,795
Motor Supplies Mfr

N.A.I.C.S.: 335312
Junshi Akama (Gen Mgr)

Subsidiary (Non-US):

NIDEC SANKYO DO BRASIL LTDA. (2)
Rua Amazonas 363 loja 106 Centro, Sao Caetano do Sul, 09520 070, Sao Paulo, Brazil
Tel.: (55) 11 4227 4479
Emp.: 2
Electronic Components Mfr
N.A.I.C.S.: 334419
Valter Santos (Gen Mgr)

NIDEC SANKYO ELECTRONICS (SHAOGUAN) CO., LTD. (2)
National Development-Zone Ruyuán, Shaoguan, 512700, Guangdong, China
Tel.: (86) 751 528 1147
Web Site: http://www.nidec-sankyo.co.jp
Electric Motor & Supplies Mfr
N.A.I.C.S.: 335312

NIDEC SANKYO ELECTRONICS (SHENZHEN) CORPORATION (2)
Room 1005-1008 Excellence Times Square Building 4068 Yitian Road, Futian District, Shenzhen, Guangdong, China
Tel.: (86) 755 8359 2335
Electronic Components Mfr
N.A.I.C.S.: 334419

NIDEC SANKYO EUROPE GmbH (2)
Mollsfeld 1, 40670, Meerbusch, Germany
Tel.: (49) 215969580
Web Site: http://www.nidec-sankyo.co.jp
Emp.: 1
Electronic Components Mfr
N.A.I.C.S.: 334419
Shuhei Fujii (Mng Dir)

NIDEC SANKYO TAIWAN CORPORATION (2)
No 2 S 7th Rd, Qianzhen Dist, Kaohsiung, 806011, Taiwan
Tel.: (886) 783161718
Web Site: https://www.nidecsankyo.com.tw
Sales Range: $25-49.9 Million
Emp.: 7
Stepping Motor Mfr
N.A.I.C.S.: 335312
Eiji Imai (Pres)

NIDEC SANKYO VIETNAM CORPORATION (2)
Lot No I1-N1 Saigon Hi-Tech Park, Dist 9, Ho Chi Minh City, Vietnam
Tel.: (84) 837360075
Digital Camera & Mobile Phone Mfr
N.A.I.C.S.: 333310

Subsidiary (US):

Nidec Sankyo America Corporation (2)
1 International Blvd, Mahwah, NJ 07495
Tel.: (201) 512-8839
Sales Range: $25-49.9 Million
Emp.: 25
Sales of Industrial Robots, Magnetic Card Readers, Musical Movements, DC Motors & Appliance Components
N.A.I.C.S.: 423690

Subsidiary (Domestic):

Nidec Sankyo CMI Corporation (2)
46-1 Senpuku, Susono, 410-1116, Shizuoka, Japan
Tel.: (81) 55 998 6111
Web Site: http://www.nidec-sankyo.co.jp
Emp.: 1,500
Electric Motor & Contact Products Mfr & Distr
N.A.I.C.S.: 335312

Subsidiary (Non-US):

Higashifuji (Malaysia) Sdn. Bhd. (3)
LOT 592 Persiaran Raja Lumu, MIEL Industrial Area Pandamaran, 42000, Port Klang, Selangor, Malaysia
Tel.: (60) 123700500
Web Site: http://www.nidec-sankyo.co.jp
Electric Motor Mfr & Distr
N.A.I.C.S.: 335312

INTERNATIONAL PUBLIC

PT. Higashifuji Indonesia (3)
(100%)
Tel.: (62) 218980144
Synchronous Motor & Motor Assemblies Mfr & Distr
N.A.I.C.S.: 335312

Subsidiary (Non-US):

Nidec Sankyo Korea Corporation (2)
#1410 156 Gwanggyo-ro Yeongtong-gu, Gyeonggi-do, Suwon, 121-812, Korea (South)
Tel.: (82) 3180641990
Electronic Components Distr
N.A.I.C.S.: 423690

Subsidiary (Domestic):

Nidec Sankyo Shoji Corporation (2)
1-20-13 Osaki Shinagawa-ku, Shinagawa-Ku, Tokyo, 141-0032, Japan
Tel.: (81) 3 6893 3112
Musical Instrument Mfr & Distr
N.A.I.C.S.: 339992

Subsidiary (Non-US):

Nidec Sankyo Singapore Pte. Ltd. (2)
No 2 Toh Guan Rd E 02-03, Singapore, 508771, Singapore
Tel.: (65) 62781926
Web Site: http://www.nidec-sankyo.co.jp
Sales Range: $25-49.9 Million
Emp.: 20
Electronic Motor & Control Component Mfr & Whslr
N.A.I.C.S.: 334419
Tanaka Shingo (Mng Dir)

P.T. Nidec Sankyo Precision Indonesia (2)
Delta Silicon Industrial Park Jl Meranti 3 Blok L8-6A Lemahabang, Bekasi, 17550, Indonesia
Tel.: (62) 21 8990 1822
Web Site: http://www.nidec-sankyo.co.jp
Sales Range: $75-99.9 Million
Emp.: 400
Plastic Molded Product Mfr
N.A.I.C.S.: 326199

Nidec Seimitsu Corporation (1)
1771 Nakamaruko, Ueda, 386-0495, Nagano, Japan
Tel.: (81) 268 42 3144
Web Site: http://www.nidec-seimitsu.com
Emp.: 50
Precision Motor Mfr & Distr
N.A.I.C.S.: 335312

Nidec Seimitsu Motor Technology (Dongguan) Co., Ltd. (1)
No 69 Tangxia Section Dongshen Road, Tangxia Town, Dongguan, Guangdong, China
Tel.: (86) 76987907111
Industrial Machinery Mfr
N.A.I.C.S.: 333248

Nidec Seimitsu Singapore Pte. Ltd. (1)
36 Loyang Way, Singapore, 508771, Singapore
Tel.: (65) 62248368
Emp.: 3
Electric Motor Mfr
N.A.I.C.S.: 335312
Kazuhiro Nakamura (Mng Dir)

Nidec Servo Corporation (1)
3-93 Aioi-cho, Kiryu, 376 0011, Japan (53%)
Tel.: (81) 277538811
Web Site: http://www.nidec-servo.com
Rev.: $219,037,000
Emp.: 623
Developer, Mfr & Marketer of Small Motors, Fans, Blowers, Sensors & Motor Application Products
N.A.I.C.S.: 335312

Subsidiary (Non-US):

NIDEC SERVO (HONG KONG) CO., LIMITED (2)
Unit 2607-11 Tower 2 Metroplaza 223 Hing Fong Road, Kwai Chung, New Territories, China (Hong Kong)

Tel.: (852) 2314 0037
Industrial Motor Mfr
N.A.I.C.S.: 335312

NIDEC SERVO (SHANGHAI) CO., LTD (2)
Tower B No 100 ZuiYi Rd Chang Ning, Xu Hui District, Shanghai, 200051, China
Tel.: (86) 21 3356 2977
Web Site: http://www.nidec-servo.com
Industrial Motor Mfr
N.A.I.C.S.: 335312

Plant (Domestic):

NIDEC SERVO CORPORATION - KIRYU TECHNICAL CENTER PLANT (2)
3-93 Aioi-cho, Kiryu, 376-0011, Gunma, Japan
Tel.: (81) 277 53 8811
Web Site: http://www.nidec-servo.com
Emp.: 500
Industrial Motor & Component Mfr
N.A.I.C.S.: 335312
Mr Kobayashi *(Mgr-Human Resources)*

Subsidiary (Non-US):

NIDEC SERVO EUROPE B.V. (2)
P J Oudweg 4, 1314 CH, Almere, Netherlands
Tel.: (31) 367603800
Sales Range: $25-49.9 Million
Emp.: 11
Electronic Components Distr
N.A.I.C.S.: 423690

Subsidiary (Domestic):

NIDEC SERVO HOTAKA CORPORATION (2)
341-1 Hotaka-Kitahotaka, Azumino, 399-8302, Nagano, Japan
Tel.: (81) 263 82 5964
Web Site: http://www.nidec-servo.com
Industrial Motor Mfr
N.A.I.C.S.: 335312

Subsidiary (Non-US):

NIDEC SERVO VIETNAM CORPORATION (2)
Lot No I 1 3-N1 Saigon High-tech Park, District 9, Ho Chi Minh City, Vietnam
Tel.: (84) 8 3736 0912
Web Site: http://www.nidec-servo.com
Sales Range: $150-199.9 Million
Industrial Motor & Component Mfr
N.A.I.C.S.: 335312
Mutsumi Otsuka *(Mgr-Gen Affairs)*

Nidec Singapore Pte. Ltd. (1)
36 Loyang Way, Singapore, 508771, Singapore (100%)
Tel.: (65) 65461111
Web Site: http://www.nidec.com.sg
Sales Range: $25-49.9 Million
Emp.: 80
Research & Development & Mfr of Spindle Motors for Hard Disc Drives
N.A.I.C.S.: 335312

Nidec Taiwan Corporation (1)
Room 1001 10F No 88 Sec 2 Jhongsiao E Road, Jhongjheng District, Taipei, 100, Taiwan (100%)
Tel.: (886) 223928220
Web Site: http://www.nidec.com
Sales Range: $25-49.9 Million
Emp.: 36
Sales of Electronic Components
N.A.I.C.S.: 423690
Seiichi Hattori *(Dir-Sls)*

Nidec Techno Motor Holdings Corporation (1)
36-1-1 Onyu, Minami-ku, Obama, 917-0241, Fukui, Japan (100%)
Tel.: (81) 759356666
Web Site: https://www.nidec.com
Sales Range: $1-4.9 Billion
Emp.: 2,744
Medium-Sized Motors Mfr & Whslr
N.A.I.C.S.: 335312
Tunse Kure *(Chm)*

Subsidiary (Non-US):

Nidec Power Motor (Shanghai) International Trading Co., Ltd. (2)

Room 903 No 2 Area Core Lane 2020 Zhongshan W Rd, Shanghai, 200235, China
Tel.: (86) 21 6428 5865
Electric Motor Mfr

Nidec Shibaura (H.K.) Limited (2)
2607 Tower 2 Metroplaza 223 Hing Fong Rd, Kwai Chung, New Territories, China (Hong Kong)
Tel.: (852) 24276393
Emp.: 9
Industrial Motor Mfr
N.A.I.C.S.: 335312
Seiji Asano *(Gen Mgr)*

Nidec Shibaura (Zhejiang) Corporation (2)
1000 Huanbei 2nd Rd, Pinghu Economic Dev Zone, Pinghu, Zhejiang, China
Tel.: (86) 57385169666
Web Site: http://www.nidec-tecnom.com
Medium-Sized Motors Mfr
N.A.I.C.S.: 335312

Nidec Shibaura Electronics (Thailand) Co., Ltd. (2)
144/4 Moo 5 Bangkadi Industrial Park Tivanon Road, Tivanon Road Tambol Bangkadi, Tambol Bangkadi mphur Muang, Pathumthani, 12000, Thailand
Tel.: (66) 2219000
Web Site: http://www.nidec-tecnom.com
Medium-Sized Motors Mfr & Whslr
N.A.I.C.S.: 335312

Nidec Sole Motor Corporation S.R.L. (2)
Via Consorziale 13, Pordenone, 33170, Italy
Tel.: (39) 04 34 39 31
Emp.: 40
Electric Motor Mfr & Distr
N.A.I.C.S.: 335312

Subsidiary (Non-US):

Nidec Sole Motor Hungary K.F.T. (3)
Szent Istvan Ter 2, Bercel, 2687, Hungary
Tel.: (36) 35384155
Electric Motor Mfr
N.A.I.C.S.: 335312

Nidec Tosok Corporation (1)
2-215 Sobudai, Zama, 252-8570, Kanagawa, Japan (100%)
Tel.: (81) 46 252 3110
Web Site: http://www.nidec-tosok.co.jp
Sales Range: $1-4.9 Billion
Emp.: 594
Precision Automotive Parts, Gauges & Measuring Equipment Mfr & Whslr
N.A.I.C.S.: 332721
Shigenobu Nagamori *(Chm & CEO)*

Subsidiary (Non-US):

Nidec Tosok (Shanghai) Co., Ltd. (2)
12/F Tower B 100 Zunyi Road, Shanghai, 200051, China
Tel.: (86) 2164415792
Web Site: http://www.nidec-tosok.co.jp
Emp.: 13
Precision Automotive Parts, Gauges & Measuring Equipment Whslr
N.A.I.C.S.: 423120
Konji Naito *(Mgr)*

Nidec Tosok (Vietnam) Co., Ltd. (2)
Road 16 Tan Thuan Export Processing Zone, Tan Thuan Dong Ward, District 7, Ho Chi Minh City, Vietnam
Tel.: (84) 837700027
Web Site: http://www.nidec-tosok.co.jp
Precision Automotive Parts, Gauges & Measuring Equipment Mfr
N.A.I.C.S.: 332721

Nidec Tosok (Zhejiang) Corporation (2)
No 550 Fanrong Road Pinghu Economic Development Zone, Pinghu, Zhejiang, China
Tel.: (86) 573 8509 0083
Automobile Parts Distr
N.A.I.C.S.: 423120

Nidec Tosok Akiba (Vietnam) Co., Ltd. (2)

Road 16 Tan Thuan Export Processing Zone, Tan Thuan Dong Ward District 7, Ho Chi Minh City, Vietnam
Tel.: (84) 2837700853
Sales Range: $50-74.9 Million
Emp.: 155
Automotive Parts Mfr & Distr
N.A.I.C.S.: 336390
Masahiko Kojima *(Gen Mgr)*

Plant (Domestic):

Nidec Tosok Corporation - Yamanashi Factory (2)
890 Sudama-cho Anadaira, Hokuto, 408-0111, Yamanashi, Japan
Tel.: (81) 551 42 4600
Web Site: http://www.nidec-tosok.co.jp
Automatic Transmission Equipment Mfr
N.A.I.C.S.: 333613

Nidec Total Service Corporation (1)
338 Kuzetonoshiro-cho, Minami-ku, Kyoto, 617-0833, Japan (100%)
Tel.: (81) 759594191
Web Site: https://www.nidec.com
Sales Range: $50-74.9 Million
Emp.: 125
Insurance, Real Estate, Building Maintenance & Other Corporate Support Services
N.A.I.C.S.: 561499

Nidec Vietnam Corporation (1)
Lot No I1-N2 Saigon High-Tech Park, Tan Phu Ward Thu Duc City, Ho Chi Minh City, 084, Vietnam (100%)
Tel.: (84) 2837360075
Fan Motors & Small Brushless Direct Current Motors Mfr
N.A.I.C.S.: 335312

Nidec-Kyori Corporation (1)
1-7-1 Tsukinowa, Otsu, 520-2152, Shiga, Japan (100%)
Tel.: (81) 775453351
Web Site: http://www.nidec-kyori.co.jp
Sales Range: $50-74.9 Million
Emp.: 127
High Speed Automatic Presses, Feed Devices & Other Industrial Machinery Mfr
N.A.I.C.S.: 333248

Nidec-Read Corporation (1)
10 Tsutsumisoto-cho Nishikyogoku, Ukyo-ku, Kyoto, 615-0854, Japan (100%)
Tel.: (81) 75 315 8001
Web Site: http://www.nidec-read.com
Emp.: 251
Electronics Components Inspection Systems Mfr & Whslr
N.A.I.C.S.: 334515
Michio Kaida *(Chm & CEO)*

Subsidiary (Non-US):

SV Probe Pte. Ltd. (2)
19A Serangoon North Avenue 5 03-00, Singapore, 554859, Singapore (100%)
Tel.: (65) 67698233
Web Site: https://www.svprobe.com
Holding Company; Probe Card Designer, Mfr & Distr
N.A.I.C.S.: 551112
Kevin M. Kurtz *(Pres & CEO)*

Subsidiary (Non-US):

SV Probe (SIP) Co., Ltd (3)
No 99 Suhong West Road Building 3 1st Floor Block B Unit 116 118, Suzhou Industrial Park Pilot Free Trade Zone, Suzhou, 215201, Jiangsu, China
Tel.: (86) 51262752330
Web Site: http://www.svprobe.com
Probe Cards Mfr
N.A.I.C.S.: 334413

SV Probe Tech. Taiwan Co. Ltd (3)
3F No 35 Sintai Road, Jhubei, 302, Taiwan
Tel.: (886) 36565188
Web Site: http://www.svprobe.com
Probe Card Designer, Mfr & Distr
N.A.I.C.S.: 334419

SV Probe Vietnam Co., Ltd (3)
37 A Street 6 Vietnam Singapore Industrial Park, Thuan An, Binh Duong, Vietnam
Tel.: (84) 2743784301
Web Site: http://www.svprobe.com
Electronic Components Mfr
N.A.I.C.S.: 334419

Subsidiary (US):

SV Probe, Inc. (3)
7810 S Hardy Dr Ste 109, Tempe, AZ 85284
Tel.: (480) 635-4700
Web Site: http://www.svprobe.com
Probe Card Designer, Mfr & Distr
N.A.I.C.S.: 334419
Kevin M. Kurtz *(CEO)*

Nidec-Shimpo Corporation (1)
1 Terada Kohtari, Nagaokakyo, 617-0833, Kyoto, Japan (100%)
Tel.: (81) 759583777
Web Site: http://www.nidec-shimpo.co.jp
Sales Range: $150-199.9 Million
Emp.: 1,184
Variable Speed Drives, Control Devices & Factory Automation Systems Mfr
N.A.I.C.S.: 333613
Hitoshi Inoue *(Sr VP)*

Subsidiary (Non-US):

NIDEC-KYORI (SHANGHAI) MACHINERY CORPORATION (2)
Room 5F-A2 Zhao Feng HuanQiu Tower 1800 ZhongShan West Road, Shanghai, China
Tel.: (86) 21 6875 6117
Industrial Machinery Mfr
N.A.I.C.S.: 333248

NIDEC-KYORI MACHINERY (ZHEJIANG) CORPORATION (2)
550 Fanrong Road Pinghu Economic Development Zone, Pinghu, 314200, China
Tel.: (86) 573 8509 6413
Web Site: http://www.nidec-shimpokyoripressmachine.jp
Industrial Machinery Mfr
N.A.I.C.S.: 333248

NIDEC-SHIMPO (SHANGHAI) INT'L TRADING CO., LTD. (2)
Unit 1201 Tower B 100 Zeunyi Road, Shanghai, 200051, China
Tel.: (86) 2164400700
Web Site: http://www.nidec-shimpo.com.cn
Emp.: 2
Power Transmission Equipment Mfr
N.A.I.C.S.: 333613
Stephen Hodson *(Gen Mgr)*

NIDEC-SHIMPO (TAIWAN) CORPORATION (2)
Rm 1 14F No 925 Sec 4 Taiwan Boulevard, Xitun Dist, Taichung, 40767, Taiwan
Tel.: (886) 423582628
Web Site: http://www.nidec-shimpo.co.jp
Power Transmission Equipment Mfr
N.A.I.C.S.: 333613

Subsidiary (US):

NIDEC-SHIMPO AMERICA CORPORATION (2)
1701 Glenlake Ave, Itasca, IL 60143
Tel.: (800) 237-7079
Web Site: http://www.shimpoamerica.com
Sales Range: $25-49.9 Million
Emp.: 40
Industrial Equipment Mfr & Distr
N.A.I.C.S.: 333248
Robert Erickson *(VP)*

Subsidiary (Non-US):

NIDEC-SHIMPO INDIA SALES AND TRADING PRIVATE LIMITED (2)
Raheja Tower 1102 West Wing M G Road, Bengaluru, 560 001, India
Tel.: (91) 80 41640732
Web Site: http://www.nidec-shimpo.co.jp
Sales Range: $25-49.9 Million
Emp.: 5
Power Transmission Equipment Distr
N.A.I.C.S.: 423830
K. S. Vishwanath *(Gen Mgr)*

NIDEC-SHIMPO KOREA CORPORATION (2)
16th Floor Keungil Tower Bldg 223 Teheran-ro, Gangnam-gu, Seoul, 06142, Korea (South)
Tel.: (82) 25278760
Web Site: http://www.nidec-shimpo.co.jp
Power Transmission Equipment Mfr

NIDEC CORPORATION

Nidec Corporation—(Continued)
N.A.I.C.S.: 333613
Subsidiary (US):

Nidec Minster Corporation (2)
240 W 5th St, Minster, OH 45865-1065
Tel.: (419) 628-2331
Web Site: http://www.minster.com
Sales Range: $100-124.9 Million
Emp.: 500
Precision Press Machines & Dies Mfr
N.A.I.C.S.: 333310
Stephen Kill *(VP-HR)*

Subsidiary (Domestic):

Metal Stamping Support Group, LLC (3)
100 Shafer Dr, Romeo, MI 48065
Tel.: (586) 777-7440
Web Site: http://www.chsautomation.com
Sales Range: $10-24.9 Million
Emp.: 45
Coil Handling Equipment Mfr
N.A.I.C.S.: 423830
Eric Werner *(Pres & CEO)*

Subsidiary (Non-US):

Nidec-Shimpo (Zhejiang) Corporation (2)
1858 Ping Cheng Street, Pinghu Economic Development Zone, Pinghu, Zhejiang, China
Tel.: (86) 57385093022
Web Site: http://www.nidec-shimpo-cn.com
Variable Speed Drives, Control Devices & Factory Automation Systems Mfr
N.A.I.C.S.: 334513

P.T. Nidec Indonesia (1)
Lot S58 Bintan Industrial Estate Lobam, Bintan, Riau, Indonesia
Tel.: (62) 770 696 111
Web Site: http://www.nidec.co.jp
Pivot Assembly & Precision Motor Components Mfr
N.A.I.C.S.: 335999

Qingdao EECON Electronic Controls and Appliances Co., Ltd. (1)
No 418 Qianwangang Rd Qingdao Economic Technical Development, Qingdao, 266510, China
Tel.: (86) 53286810682
Household Appliance Whslr
N.A.I.C.S.: 423620

SCD Co., Ltd. (1)
Hyeongje-ro 17 beon-gil Namsamyeon, Cheoin-gu, Yongin, Gyeonggi, Korea (South)
Tel.: (82) 313333371
Web Site: https://www.sscd.co.kr
Rev.: $167,902,984
Assets: $128,058,426
Liabilities: $36,567,665
Net Worth: $91,490,761
Earnings: $6,363,836
Emp.: 397
Fiscal Year-end: 12/31/2022
Electronic Components Mfr
N.A.I.C.S.: 335220
Gil Ho Oh *(CEO)*

Takisawa Machine Tool Co., Ltd. (1)
983 Natsukawa, Kita-ku, Okayama, 701-0164, Japan
(86.14%)
Tel.: (81) 862936111
Web Site: http://www.takisawa.co.jp
Rev.: $270,981,920
Assets: $402,823,520
Liabilities: $181,441,920
Net Worth: $221,381,600
Earnings: $3,223,440
Emp.: 742
Fiscal Year-end: 03/31/2023
Machine Tools Mfr
N.A.I.C.S.: 333517
Kazuhiro Harada *(Pres)*

Subsidiary (Non-US):

SAP Takisawa Machine Tools Private Ltd. (2)
No 33/33/5 Ground First Floor AN-NAPOORNA Kanakapura Road, Jaraganahalli J P Nagar Post, Bengaluru, 560 078, Karnataka, India

Tel.: (91) 8026662386
Web Site: http://www.takisawa.co.jp
Sales Range: $25-49.9 Million
Emp.: 20
Lathes & Machine Tools Distr & Technical Services
N.A.I.C.S.: 423830
P. V. Prasad *(Mgr)*

Shanghi Takisawa Mechatronics Ltd. (2)
Web Site: http://www.takisawa.co.jp
Printed Circuit Board Drilling Machine & CNC Lathes Mfr & Distr
N.A.I.C.S.: 333517

T W Ward CNC Machinery Ltd. (2)
Albion Works Attercliffe Rd, Sheffield, S4 7WW, United Kingdom
Tel.: (44) 1142765411
Web Site: https://www.wardcnc.com
Sales Range: $25-49.9 Million
Emp.: 30
Machine Tools Mfr & Distr
N.A.I.C.S.: 333517
Simon Whitworth *(Mng Dir)*

Plant (Domestic):

TAKISAWA MACHINE TOOL CO. LTD. - Shimosho Factory (2)
268 Shimosho, Kurashiki, 701-0112, Okayama, Japan
Tel.: (81) 864635101
Web Site: http://www.takisawa.co.jp
Emp.: 385
Lathe & Machinery Products Mfr
N.A.I.C.S.: 333517

Subsidiary (Non-US):

Takisawa (Shanghi) Co., Ltd. (2)
Room 1607 XinDa Building No 318-322 Xian Xia Road, Shanghai, 200336, China
Tel.: (86) 2162350938
Web Site: http://www.takisawa-sh.com
Sales Range: $25-49.9 Million
Emp.: 9
Machine Tools & Lathe Machinery Sales & Technical Services
N.A.I.C.S.: 811310
Wakai Shidehide *(Pres)*

Subsidiary (Domestic):

Takisawa Techno Service Inc. (2)
983 Natsukawa, Kita-ku, Okayama, 701-0164, Japan
Tel.: (81) 862936154
Web Site: http://www.takisawa.co.jp
Sales Range: $75-99.9 Million
Emp.: 300
Turning & Milling Machinery Repair & Maintenance Services
N.A.I.C.S.: 811310

The Imperial Electric Company (1)
1503 Exeter Rd, Akron, OH 44306
Tel.: (330) 734-3600
Web Site: http://www.imperialelectric.com
Sales Range: $25-49.9 Million
Emp.: 50
Mfr of Electric Motors, Generators & Controllers
N.A.I.C.S.: 335312
David Molnar *(Pres)*

NIDEK SA

Europarc 13 Rue Auguste Perret, 94042, Creteil, Val-de-Marne, France
Tel.: (33) 149809803
Web Site: http://www.nidek.fr
Sales Range: $25-49.9 Million
Emp.: 80
Drugs, Proprietaries & Sundries
N.A.I.C.S.: 424210
Jean-Paul Boubal *(Gen Mgr)*

NIDHI GRANITES LIMITED

503 Madhu Industrial Park Mogra Cross Road Next to Apollo Chambers, Andheri East, Mumbai, 400069, India
Tel.: (91) 02226491040
Web Site: https://www.nidhigranites.com
Year Founded: 1981

512103—(BOM)
Rev.: $21,088
Assets: $292,075
Liabilities: $2,727
Net Worth: $289,348
Earnings: $9,747
Fiscal Year-end: 03/31/21
Security Brokerage Services
N.A.I.C.S.: 523150
Rajkumar Thard *(Chm & Mng Dir)*

Subsidiaries:

SPNP Paper & Pack Pvt. Ltd. (1)
13th Floor Flt No 1303 Kandivali W Mumbai Veer Tower, Devnagar Derasar Marg Kandivali W Vile Parle West, Mumbai, 400067, Maharashtra, India
Tel.: (91) 7942533191
Web Site: https://www.spnppapernpack.com
Plastic Container Mfr
N.A.I.C.S.: 326160

NIDOCO AB

Sveavagen 21, 111 34, Stockholm, Sweden SE
Web Site: http://nidoco.se
Investment Holding Company
N.A.I.C.S.: 551112
Patrick John Robert Castren *(CEO & Chief Investment Officer)*

NIEN HSING TEXTILE CO., LTD.

13F No 306 Sec 1 Neihu Rd, Neihu District, Taipei, 114, Taiwan
Tel.: (886) 226568888
Web Site: https://www.nhjeans.com
1451—(TAI)
Rev.: $207,947,145
Assets: $262,800,965
Liabilities: $36,808,200
Net Worth: $225,992,764
Earnings: ($11,868,014)
Emp.: 8,606
Fiscal Year-end: 12/31/23
Apparels Mfr
N.A.I.C.S.: 313210
Kuo Chao Chen *(Chm)*

Subsidiaries:

Chentex Garment Co., Ltd. (1)
Kbal Damrey Village, 12406, Phnom Penh, Cambodia
Tel.: (855) 23890555
Denim Jeans Mfr
N.A.I.C.S.: 315210

Formosa Textile Co., (Pty) Ltd. (1)
827 Ha'Thetsane Industrial Area, Maseru, 100, Lesotho
Tel.: (266) 22327679
Fabric Product Mfr & Distr
N.A.I.C.S.: 313230
Vincent Yuan *(Mgr)*

Nien Hsing International Lesotho Pty Ltd. (1)
Site 009 Thetsane Industrial Area, Maseru, 100, Lesotho
Tel.: (266) 22326655
Nonwoven Fabric Product Mfr & Distr
N.A.I.C.S.: 313230
Max Wu *(VP-Sales)*

Nien Hsing International Victoria S.A. DE C. V. (1)
Libramiento Naciones Unidas Km 20, Parque Industrial Nuevo Santander S/N, 87137, Ciudad Victoria, Tamaulipas, Mexico
Tel.: (52) 8343180200
Nonwoven Fabric Product Mfr & Distr
N.A.I.C.S.: 313230

Nien Hsing Ninh Binh Garment Co., Ltd. (1)
Khanh Phu Industrial Zone, Ninh Binh, Vietnam
Jeans Mfr
N.A.I.C.S.: 315210

NIEN MADE ENTERPRISE CO., LTD.

INTERNATIONAL PUBLIC

23F -1 No 98 Shizheng N 7th Rd, Xitun Dist, Taichung, 40878, Taiwan
Tel.: (886) 436000999
Web Site: https://www.nienmade.com
Year Founded: 1974
8464—(TAI)
Rev.: $880,126,557
Assets: $1,066,438,202
Liabilities: $267,524,958
Net Worth: $798,913,244
Earnings: $184,756,460
Emp.: 11,293
Fiscal Year-end: 12/31/23
Curtain Mfr & Distr
N.A.I.C.S.: 314120
Howard Nien *(Chm)*

Subsidiaries:

Bay Blinds Limited (1)
8 Maleme street, Greerton, Tauranga, New Zealand
Tel.: (64) 800229254
Web Site: https://bayblinds.co.nz
Emp.: 39
Shutter & Blind Product Mfr
N.A.I.C.S.: 321918

Dongguan Fanchang Curtain Product Co., Ltd. (1)
International Avenue, Tutang District Changping Town, Dongguan, Guangdong, China
Tel.: (86) 76983393789
Plastic Blind Mfr & Retailer
N.A.I.C.S.: 337920

Norm Pacific Automation Corp. (1)
7F-1 No 31 Sintai Rd, Hsinchu, Jhubei, 30252, Taiwan
Tel.: (886) 36569123
Web Site: https://www.norm.com.tw
Home Appliance Mfr
N.A.I.C.S.: 335220
Horng-Tsann Huang *(Pres)*

Norman Japan Limited (1)
A-PLACE Yoyogi 3F 5-23-15 Sendagaya, Shibuya-ku, Tokyo, 151-0051, Japan
Tel.: (81) 333568688
Web Site: https://www.norman.co.jp
Blind & Shade Mfr
N.A.I.C.S.: 337920

San Feng (Cambodia) Co., Ltd. (1)
Manhattan Svay Rieng Special Economic Zone, Sangkat Bavet, Bavet, Svay Rieng, Cambodia
Tel.: (855) 44712168
Blind Mfr & Distr
N.A.I.C.S.: 337920

Santa Fe Shutters Limited (1)
142 Newton Street, Mount Maunganui, Tauranga, New Zealand
Tel.: (64) 75474042
Web Site: https://www.santafeshutters.co.nz
Emp.: 100
Shutter & Blind Product Mfr
N.A.I.C.S.: 321918

Veneta B.V. (1)
Loggerweg 2, 8042 PG, Zwolle, Netherlands
Tel.: (31) 387600093
Web Site: https://www.veneta.com
Blind Product Mfr
N.A.I.C.S.: 337920
Coen Goorhuis *(Sls Mgr)*

Veneta Blinds Pty Ltd. (1)
13/14 Argyle St, Albion, 4010, QLD, Australia
Tel.: (61) 1800836382
Web Site: https://www.venetablinds.com.au
Emp.: 7,000
Honeycomb Blind Mfr
N.A.I.C.S.: 337920

NIEUWENHUIS BETONRENOVATIE B.V.

Weteringstraat 11, 7391 TX, Twello, Netherlands NL
Tel.: (31) 571260177
Web Site: http://www.nieuwenhuis-br.nl
Sales Range: $1-9.9 Million
Emp.: 35

NIFCO INC.

Concrete Renovation & Plastic Flooring Contractor
N.A.I.C.S.: 238190
Goop Degrip *(Mng Dir)*

NIFCO INC.
Mita Belljuu Building 20F 5-36-7 Shiba
Minato-ku, Tokyo, 108-8522, Japan
Tel.: (81) 354764850 JP
Web Site: http://www.nifco.com
Year Founded: 1967
9WM—(DEU)
Rev.: $2,307,098,070
Assets: $2,575,105,500
Liabilities: $953,774,910
Net Worth: $1,621,330,590
Earnings: $151,788,900
Emp.: 10,169
Fiscal Year-end: 03/31/23
Industrial Plastic Parts & Components Mfr
N.A.I.C.S.: 339993
Masashi Koizumi *(Co-Pres)*

Subsidiaries:

Beijing Nifco Co., Ltd. (1)
Uunction Bo Xing First Street/Tai He Avenue, He Xi District Beijing Economic-Tech Dev Area, Beijing, 100176, China
Tel.: (86) 10 8712 6000
Industrial Plastic Components Mfr
N.A.I.C.S.: 326199

Dongguan Nifco Co., Ltd. (1)
E Fangzheng Rd New City Ctr, Shilong Town, Dongguan, Guangdong, China
Tel.: (86) 76986185767
Injection Molded Plastic Products Mfr
N.A.I.C.S.: 326130

KTW GmbH & Co. KG (1)
Dettenheimer Str 34, D-91781, Weissenburg, Germany
Tel.: (49) 9141 85290
Industrial Plastic Components Mfr
N.A.I.C.S.: 326199

Nifco (Chongqing) Limited Liability Company (1)
No 2 Longshan Road, Changshou Economic and Technology Development Area, Chongqing, China
Tel.: (86) 2340766158
Industrial Mold Mfr
N.A.I.C.S.: 333511

Nifco (HK) Limited (1)
8/F Tai Ping Industrial Centre Blook 3 No 53 Ting Kok Road, Tai Po, New Territories, China (Hong Kong)
Tel.: (852) 26658088
Web Site: http://www.web.nifco.com.hk
Injection Molding Products Mfr
N.A.I.C.S.: 339993

Nifco (Hubei) Co., Ltd. (1)
Baoye Industrial Park ChuangYe Avenue, Gedian Economic & Tech Development Zone, Wuhan, 436070, Hubei, China
Tel.: (86) 711 370 0122
Industrial Plastic Components Mfr
N.A.I.C.S.: 326199

Nifco (Jiangsu) Co., Ltd. (1)
No 9 Chen Xin Road Zhang Jia Gang, Economy Development District, Nanjing, 215637, Jiangsu, China
Tel.: (86) 512 5879 9588
Industrial Plastic Components Mfr
N.A.I.C.S.: 326199

Nifco (Singapore) Pte. Ltd. (1)
11 Woodland 05-38, Singapore, 787853, Singapore
Tel.: (65) 62739123
Web Site: http://www.nifco.com.sg
Sales Range: $25-49.9 Million
Emp.: 4
Industrial Fastener Mfr
N.A.I.C.S.: 339993

Nifco (Thailand) Co., Ltd. (1)
Amata Nakorn Industrial Estate 700/420 Moo 7 Bangna-Trad Road KM 57, Amphur Muang, Chon Buri, 20000, Thailand
Tel.: (66) 38454165

Nifco (Tianjin) Co., Ltd. (1)
No 5 5th Haitaihuake Road Hueyuan Industry Zone, New Technology Industry Park, Tianjin, 300384, China
Tel.: (86) 22 5828 8288
Industrial Plastic Components Mfr
N.A.I.C.S.: 326199

Nifco America Corporation (1)
8015 Dove Pkwy, Canal Winchester, OH 43110-9697
Tel.: (614) 836-3808
Web Site: https://www.nifcousa.com
Sales Range: $100-124.9 Million
Emp.: 275
Mfr of Industrial Resinous Fasteners
N.A.I.C.S.: 333248

Plant (Domestic):

Nifco America Corporation - Kentucky Manufacturing Facility (2)
380 Hudson Blvd, Shelbyville, KY 40065
Tel.: (866) 752-0790
Automotive Plastic Product Mfr
N.A.I.C.S.: 326199

Nifco America Corporation - Tennessee Manufacturing Facility (2)
130 Wheeler Street, La Vergne, TN 37086
Tel.: (877) 218-7507
Automotive Plastic Product Mfr
N.A.I.C.S.: 326199

Nifco Business Service Inc. (1)
Shibaura 4-5-4, Minato-Ku, Tokyo, 108-8522, Japan
Tel.: (81) 354767020
Emp.: 30
Automotive Products Mfr & Distr
N.A.I.C.S.: 339993
Kimura Hiroshi *(Pres)*

Nifco Central Mexico S.de R.L.de C.V. (1)
Avenida Rio San Lorenzo 1117, Parque Technoindustrial Castro del Rio, 36815, Irapuato, Guanajuato, Mexico
Tel.: (52) 14623873700
Industrial Mold Mfr
N.A.I.C.S.: 333511

Nifco Deutschland GmbH (1)
Mergenthaler Allee 77-81, 65760, Eschborn, Hesse, Germany
Tel.: (49) 61967762078
Sales Range: $25-49.9 Million
Emp.: 16
Plastic Fasteners Distr
N.A.I.C.S.: 424610

Nifco Enterprise Management (Shanghai) Co., Ltd. (1)
Room 1603A No 666 Gubei Road, Changning District, Shanghai, China
Tel.: (86) 2162755566
Industrial Plastic Parts Mfr
N.A.I.C.S.: 326199

Nifco India Private Ltd. (1)
Plot No 122 Sector 8 IMT, Manesar, Gurgaon, 122050, Haryana, India
Tel.: (91) 124 499 8225
Web Site: https://www.nifco.com
Industrial Plastic Components Mfr
N.A.I.C.S.: 326199

Nifco KTS GmbH & Co. KG (1)
Lindgesfeld 9, D-42653, Solingen, Germany
Tel.: (49) 212 2583 10
Industrial Plastic Components Mfr
N.A.I.C.S.: 326199

Nifco KTW America Corporation (1)
325 Hammerstone Dr, Toccoa, GA 30577
Tel.: (706) 963-1110
Industrial Mold Mfr
N.A.I.C.S.: 333511

Nifco Kitakanto Inc. (1)
206-10 Agata-cho, Ashikaga, 326-0328, Tochigi, Japan
Tel.: (81) 284708225
Industrial Mold Mfr
N.A.I.C.S.: 333511

Nifco Korea Inc. (1)
1F & 2F 146 Asan Valley Nam-ro Dunpo-myeon, Asan, 31409, Chungcheongnam, Korea
Tel.: (82) 416400100
Web Site: http://www.nifco.co.kr
Sales Range: $125-149.9 Million
Emp.: 500
Industrial Fastener Mfr
N.A.I.C.S.: 332322
Hyun-Don Choi *(Pres & CEO)*

Plant (Domestic):

Nifco Korea Inc. - Cheonan Plant (2)
#185 Gilcheon-ri Sangbuk-Myon Ulj-gun, Ulsan, 689-821, Korea (South)
Tel.: (82) 52 264 4771
Web Site: http://www.nifco.co.kr
Industrial Fastener Mfr
N.A.I.C.S.: 339993

Nifco Korea Inc.- Ulsan plant (2)
185 Gilcheonsaneop-ro Sangbuk-myeon, Ulju-gun, Ulsan, 44905, Korea (South)
Tel.: (82) 522644771
Web Site: http://www.nifco.co.kr
Sales Range: $25-49.9 Million
Emp.: 200
Industrial Fastener Mfr
N.A.I.C.S.: 339993
Hyeon-don Choi *(CEO)*

Nifco Korea Pland Sp. z o.o. (1)
ul Wygoda 8, 44-240, Zory, Poland
Tel.: (48) 32 6211 390
Industrial Plastic Components Mfr
N.A.I.C.S.: 326199

Nifco Korea USA Inc. (1)
647 Industrial Park Blvd, Montgomery, AL 36117
Tel.: (334) 239-8390
Web Site: http://www.nifco.co.jp
Sales Range: $125-149.9 Million
Emp.: 400
Industrial Plastic Materials Mfr
N.A.I.C.S.: 326199

Nifco Kumamoto Inc. (1)
1152-20 Tajima, Shisuimachi, Kikuchi, 861-1214, Kumamoto, Japan
Tel.: (81) 96 841 5400
Web Site: https://www.nifco-kumamoto.co.jp
Emp.: 360
Plastic Parts Mfr
N.A.I.C.S.: 326199

Nifco Manufacturing (Malaysia) Sdn. Bhd. (1)
No 46 Jalan Kelui 1 Taman Perindustrian Utama Bukit Raja, 41720, Kelang, Selangor, Malaysia
Tel.: (60) 333412103
Web Site: http://www.nifco.co.jp
Sales Range: $50-74.9 Million
Emp.: 106
Plastics Product Mfr
N.A.I.C.S.: 339993

Nifco Poland Sp. z o.o. (1)
ul Przemyslowa 41-43, 58-100, Swidnica, Poland
Tel.: (48) 74 649 5500
Web Site: http://www.nifco.co.jp
Sales Range: $50-74.9 Million
Emp.: 130
Industrial Fastener Mfr
N.A.I.C.S.: 339993

Nifco Products Espana, S. L. U. (1)
Bosch I Gimpera 2-4 Pol Ind, Santa Margarita II, 08223, Terrassa, Barcelona, Spain
Tel.: (34) 937361800
Dampers Mfr
N.A.I.C.S.: 332322

Nifco South India Manufacturing Private Ltd. (1)
new No 50 Mannur Vallage Valarpuram Post, Sriperumbudur Taluk Kancheepuram District, Chennai, 602 105, Tamil Nadu, India
Tel.: (91) 44 3718 7003
Industrial Plastic Components Mfr
N.A.I.C.S.: 326199

Nifco Taiwan Corporation (1)
5F No 102 Dunhua N Rd, Songshan District, Taipei, 105, Taiwan
Tel.: (886) 287705225

Web Site: http://www.nifco.com.tw
Sales Range: $25-49.9 Million
Emp.: 40
Plastic Molds & Fasteners Mfr
N.A.I.C.S.: 339993

Plant (Domestic):

Nifco Taiwan Corporation - Chungli Factory (2)
61 Tung Yuan Rd Chungli Industrial Zone, Chung-li, 32063, Taoyuan, Taiwan
Tel.: (886) 34520375
Web Site: http://www.nifco.co.jp
Industrial Fastener Mfr
N.A.I.C.S.: 332722

Nifco U.K. Ltd. (1)
Durham Lane, Stockton-on-Tees, TS16 0PS, Cleveland, United Kingdom (100%)
Tel.: (44) 642672299
Web Site: http://www.nifcoeu.com
Sales Range: $50-74.9 Million
Emp.: 240
Mfr of Injection-Molded Products
N.A.I.C.S.: 326199
Mike Matthews *(Mng Dir)*

Nifco Vietnam Ltd. (1)
Lot 90 Linh Trung 3 Export Processing Zone and Industrial Park, Trang Bang Dist, Tay Ninh, Vietnam
Tel.: (84) 276 389 7451
Web Site: https://www.nifco.com
Industrial Plastic Product Mfr
N.A.I.C.S.: 326199
K. I. Kim *(Gen Dir)*

Nifco Yamagata Inc. (1)
2-3-1 Kiyozumimachi, Yamagata, 990-0834, Japan
Tel.: (81) 236445171
Web Site: http://www.nifco-yamagata.co.jp
Sales Range: $125-149.9 Million
Emp.: 423
Injection Molded Plastic Products Mfr
N.A.I.C.S.: 326121

Nifco Yancheng Co., Ltd (1)
Rm 306 Merchants Bureau Optoelectroniccs Industry, No 69 Donguan Rd Yangcheng Economic Dev Zone, Yancheng, 215600, Jiangsu, China
Tel.: (86) 515 6899 0293
Industrial Plastic Components Mfr
N.A.I.C.S.: 326199

PT Nifco Indonesia (1)
Jl Harapan II Lot KK-5b Kawasan Industri KIIC, Desa Sirnabaya Kec Telukjambe Timur, Karawang, 41361, Jawa Barat, Indonesia
Tel.: (62) 21 8911 4296
Industrial Plastic Components Mfr
N.A.I.C.S.: 326199

Shanghai Nifco Plastic Manufacturer Co., Ltd (1)
305 Shen Xia Road, Ma Lu Town Jiading District, Shanghai, 201818, China
Tel.: (86) 2159903030
Web Site: http://www.nifco.com.hk
Sales Range: $50-74.9 Million
Emp.: 172
Injection Molded Plastic Products Mfr
N.A.I.C.S.: 326130

Simmons Co. Ltd. (1)
24th floor Mita NN Building 4-1-23 Shiba, Minato-ku, Tokyo, 108-0014, Japan
Tel.: (81) 357653121
Web Site: http://www.simmons.co.jp
Emp.: 419
Beds Mfr
N.A.I.C.S.: 337126
Masafumi Ito *(Pres)*

Subsidiary (Non-US):

Shanghai Simmons Bedding & Furniture Sales Ltd. (2)
Tibet Road 168 Headquarters Building 23rd Floor Room 2308, Huangpu District, Shanghai, 200210, China
Tel.: (86) 2162482233
Web Site: http://www.simmons.cn
Sales Range: $25-49.9 Million
Emp.: 60
Mattress Retailer
N.A.I.C.S.: 449110

NIFCO INC.

Nifco Inc.—(Continued)

Simmons (Southeast Asia) Pte. Ltd. (2)
300 Beach Road 25-03 The Concourse, Singapore, 199555, Singapore
Tel.: (65) 62942278
Web Site: http://www.simmons.com.sg
Sales Range: $25-49.9 Million
Emp.: 46
Mattress Retailer
N.A.I.C.S.: 449110

Simmons Bedding & Furniture (HK) Ltd. (2)
Room 2010 - 2015 20/F Tower 2 Grand Century Place 193, Prince Edward Road West Mong Kok, Kowloon, China (Hong Kong)
Tel.: (852) 2 378 4848
Web Site: https://www.simmons.hk
Sales Range: $25-49.9 Million
Emp.: 20
Sale of Bedding, Mattresses, Furniture & Accessories
N.A.I.C.S.: 449110

Simmons Bedding & Furniture (Taiwan) Ltd. (2)
11f-7 81 Hsin Tai Wu Road Section 1, Hsichih, Taipei, 22101, Taiwan
Tel.: (886) 226983391
Web Site: http://www.simmonstaiwan.com.tw
Sales Range: $25-49.9 Million
Emp.: 16
Mattress Retailer
N.A.I.C.S.: 449110

Tifco (Dongguan) Co., Ltd. (1)
No 8 Haiyi Road, Chongtou District Changan Town, Dongguan, 523855, Guangdong, China
Tel.: (86) 76985391205
Industrial Mold Mfr
N.A.I.C.S.: 333511

Union Nifco Co., Ltd. (1)
99/11 Moo 5 Bangna-Trad Road KM 38, Tambol Bangsamak Amphur Bangpakong, Chachoengsao, 24180, Thailand
Tel.: (66) 3845 4165
Industrial Plastic Components Mfr
N.A.I.C.S.: 326199

NIFTYLIFT LIMITED

Fingle Drive Stonebridge, Milton Keynes, MK13 0ER, Buckinghamshire, United Kingdom
Tel.: (44) 1908 223456 UK
Web Site: http://www.niftylift.com
Year Founded: 1985
Sales Range: $75-99.9 Million
Emp.: 250
Monorail System Mfr
N.A.I.C.S.: 333923
Roger Bowden (Founder & Chm)

Subsidiaries:

Nifty Pty Ltd (1)
11 Kennington Drive, Tomago, 2322, NSW, Australia
Tel.: (61) 249649765
Web Site: http://www.niftylift.com.au
Industrial Machinery & Equipment Distr
N.A.I.C.S.: 423830

Niftylift Inc. (1)
1525 S Buncombe Rd, Greer, SC 29651
Tel.: (800) 643-8954
Industrial Machinery & Equipment Mfr
N.A.I.C.S.: 333923

Niftylift SA (1)
Unit 2 Boulevard Park Road, Bellville, 7530, South Africa
Tel.: (27) 219305502
Industrial Machinery & Equipment Distr
N.A.I.C.S.: 423830

NIGBAS NIGDE BETON SANAYI VE TICARET A.S.

Fertek Mah Organized Industrial Zone 8th Street, Outer Door No 2/1 Inner Door No 1 Center, Nigde, Turkiye
Tel.: (90) 2165370000
Web Site: http://www.nigbas.com.tr
Year Founded: 1968
NIBAS—(IST)
Sales Range: Less than $1 Million
Construction Services
N.A.I.C.S.: 236220
Riza Kutlu Isik (Chm & Exec Dir)

Subsidiaries:

Cimtek Cimento Teknolojisi Muhendislik A.S (1)
Anittepe Mahallesi Genclik Caddesi No 9 Isiklar Binasi Tandogan, 06570, Ankara, Turkiye
Tel.: (90) 3122326700
Web Site: http://cimtek.com.tr
Contracting Services
N.A.I.C.S.: 236220
Riza Kutlu Isik (Chm)

HMF Makina ve Servis San. ve Tic. A.S (1)
Icerenkoy Mahallesi Koyarkasi Sokak No 11 Atasehir, 34956, Istanbul, Turkiye
Tel.: (90) 2164888000
Web Site: http://www.hmf.com.tr
Warehouse Equipment Distr
N.A.I.C.S.: 423830

Metemteks Sentetik Iplik San. Tic. A.S. (1)
Cubuklu Mah Yakut Sok No 3 K 2 Eryilmaz Plaza Kavacik, Beykoz, Istanbul, Turkiye
Tel.: (90) 2165370085
Web Site: http://www.metemteks.com.tr
Polyester Material Mfr
N.A.I.C.S.: 325220

NIGER INSURANCE PLC.

48/50 Odunlami Street, Lagos, Nigeria
Tel.: (234) 8133244981
Web Site:
http://www.nigerinsurance.com
Year Founded: 1962
NIGERINS—(NIGE)
Sales Range: $10-24.9 Million
Life Insurance Management Services
N.A.I.C.S.: 524298
Gabriel Tuoyo (Head-Technical Ops)

NIGERIA ENAMELWARE CO. PLC

18 Wempco Road Ogba, Ikeja, Nigeria
Tel.: (234) 8033377285
Year Founded: 1960
ENAMELWA—(NIGE)
Rev.: $168,248
Assets: $4,468,684
Liabilities: $3,113,528
Net Worth: $1,355,156
Earnings: $1,248,016
Emp.: 91
Fiscal Year-end: 04/30/23
House Ware Device Mfr
N.A.I.C.S.: 332215

NIGERIAN AVIATION HANDLING COMPANY PLC.

Nahco aviance House Murtala Muhammed International Airport, Ikeja, Lagos, Nigeria
Tel.: (234) 8097993270 NG
Web Site:
https://www.nahcoaviance.com
Year Founded: 1979
NAHCO—(NIGE)
Rev.: $12,367,171
Assets: $13,861,963
Liabilities: $7,180,751
Net Worth: $6,681,212
Earnings: $1,979,099
Emp.: 1,673
Fiscal Year-end: 12/31/22
Aviation Handling Services
N.A.I.C.S.: 488119

Olatokunbo Adenike Fagbemi (CEO & Mng Dir-Grp)

NIGERIAN NATIONAL PETROLEUM CORPORATION

NNPC Towers Herbert Macaulay Way, Central Business District, PMB 190 Garki, Abuja, Nigeria
Tel.: (234) 9 2348200
Web Site: http://www.nnpcgroup.com
Year Founded: 1977
Sales Range: $25-49.9 Billion
Emp.: 15,000
Petroleum & Natural Gas
N.A.I.C.S.: 211120
Philip O. Chukwu (Exec Dir-Exploration & Production)

Subsidiaries:

Duke Oil Services (UK) Ltd (1)
Capitol House 159 Hammersmith Road, London, W6 8BS, United Kingdom
Tel.: (44) 20 8735 9600
Petroleum Product Distr
N.A.I.C.S.: 424720
Abdulkadir Saidu (Mng Dir)

Eleme Petrochemicals Company Ltd (1)
East West Road Eleme, PMB 1515, Port Harcourt, Rivers State, Nigeria
Tel.: (234) 84239318
Petrochemical Mfr
N.A.I.C.S.: 325110

Integrated Data Services Limited (1)
36 Ogba Road Oko, PO Box 1003, 300-001, Benin City, Edo, Nigeria
Tel.: (234) 528427479
Web Site: http://www.nnpcgroup.com
Petroleum Engineering Services
N.A.I.C.S.: 541330
Ibrahim Y. Bawa (Exec Dir-Svcs)

Kaduna Refining & Petrochemical Company Limited (1)
KM 16 Kachia Road, PMB 2252, Kaduna, Nigeria
Tel.: (234) 9 460 82500
Petrochemical Products Mfr
N.A.I.C.S.: 325110

NNPC Retail Ltd. (1)
Block A 7th Floor Room 25 NNPC Towers Herbert Macaulay Way, Central Business District, Abuja, Nigeria
Tel.: (234) 9 46081715
Petroleum Product Distr
N.A.I.C.S.: 424720
Ladipo Fagbola (Mng Dir)

National Engineering & Technical Company Limited (1)
Stallion House 2 Ajose Adeogun Street, Victoria Island, Lagos, Nigeria
Tel.: (234) 12611232
Oil & Gas Engineering & Technical Services
N.A.I.C.S.: 237990
Philip O. Chukwu (Mng Dir)

National Petroleum Investment & Management Services (1)
8-10 Bayo Kuku Street, Ikoyi, Lagos, Nigeria
Tel.: (234) 14739388
Web Site: http://www.napims.com
Petroleum Industry Management & Consulting Services
N.A.I.C.S.: 541611

Nigerian Petroleum Development Company Ltd. (1)
62/64 Sapele Road, Benin City, Edo, Nigeria
Tel.: (234) 52 251900
Web Site: http://www.npdc-ng.com
Oil & Gas Field Exploration Services
N.A.I.C.S.: 211120
Hamidu A. Namtari (Exec Dir-Engrg & Technical Svcs Div)

Pipelines and Product Marketing Company (1)
Block C 4th Floor NNPC Towers, Central Business District Garki, Abuja, Nigeria
Tel.: (234) 9 460 83426

INTERNATIONAL PUBLIC

Web Site: http://ppmc.nnpcgroup.com
Petroleum Product Distr
N.A.I.C.S.: 424720
Esther Nnamdi Ogbue (Mng Dir)

Port Harcourt Refining Company Limited (1)
Alesa Eleme, PO Box 585, Port Harcourt, Nigeria
Tel.: (234) 84 777848
Petroleum Product Distr
N.A.I.C.S.: 424720

The Nigerian Gas Company Limited (1)
1 Odin Road Ekpan, PMB 1288, Warri, Delta State, Nigeria
Tel.: (234) 8039056001
Web Site: http://www.ngc-nnpcgroup.com
Natural Gas Distr
N.A.I.C.S.: 221210
Babatunde Bakare (Mng Dir)

Warri Refining & Petrochemical Company Limited (1)
Refinery Road Ekpan, PMB 44, Warri, Delta State, Nigeria
Tel.: (234) 53 250812
Web Site: http://www.wrpcnnpcng.com
Petrochemical Product Mfr & Distr
N.A.I.C.S.: 325110
Chinedu Ezeribe (Mng Dir)

NIGERIAN SEWING MACHINE MANUFACTURING PLC

Km 40 Lagos-Abeokuta Road, Sango-Otta, Lagos, Ogun, Nigeria
Tel.: (234) 722196
General Purpose Machinery Mfr
N.A.I.C.S.: 333998

NIGERIAN-GERMAN CHEMICALS PLC.

Plot 144 Oba Akran Avenue Industrial Estate, Ikeja, Lagos, Nigeria
Tel.: (234) 1496 8220 8
Pharmaceutical Mfr & Distr
N.A.I.C.S.: 325412
Alhaji Shehu Idris (Chm)

NIGHTCAP PLC

124 Cornwall Road, London, SE1 8TQ, United Kingdom UK
Web Site:
https://www.nightcapplc.com
Year Founded: 2020
NGHT—(AIM)
Rev.: $48,800,530
Assets: $79,476,856
Liabilities: $57,426,125
Net Worth: $22,050,731
Earnings: $678,860
Emp.: 600
Fiscal Year-end: 07/03/22
Cocktail Product Mfr
N.A.I.C.S.: 311999

NIGHTHAWK ENERGY PLC

6th Floor One London Wall, London, EC2Y 5EB, United Kingdom
Tel.: (44) 20 3582 1350
Year Founded: 2000
Hydrocarbons Exploration Services
N.A.I.C.S.: 211120
Richard Wayne McCullough (Chm)

NIGHTINGALE HEALTH OYJ

Mannerheimintie 164a, 00300, Helsinki, Finland
Tel.: (358) 207301810
Web Site:
https://www.nightingalehealth.com
Year Founded: 2002
HEALTH—(HEL)
Rev.: $4,513,274
Assets: $115,252,536
Liabilities: $10,185,625
Net Worth: $105,066,911
Earnings: ($19,515,433)
Emp.: 82

Fiscal Year-end: 06/30/23
Health Care Srvices
N.A.I.C.S.: 621610
Maximilian LeRoux (Chief Comml Officer)

NIH NORDINVEST HAMBURG GMBH
Teilfeld 5, 20459, Hamburg, Germany
Tel.: (49) 4068875850
Web Site: http://www.nordinvest.de
Year Founded: 1969
Sales Range: $50-74.9 Million
Emp.: 38
Investment Services
N.A.I.C.S.: 523940

NIHAO MINERAL RESOURCES INTERNATIONAL, INC.
7F Peaksun Bldg 1505 Princeton Street Barangay Wack-Wack, Greenhills East Metro Manila, Mandaluyong, 1552, Philippines
Tel.: (63) 288233158   PH
Web Site: https://nihaominerals.com
Year Founded: 1975
NI—(PHI)
Rev.: $25,068
Assets: $5,154,698
Liabilities: $240,135
Net Worth: $4,914,562
Earnings: ($6,621,163)
Emp.: 8
Fiscal Year-end: 12/31/23
Mineral Exploration Services
N.A.I.C.S.: 212390
Jose Francisco E. Miranda (COO & VP)

NIHAR INFO GLOBAL LTD.
Plot No 34 Nihar House Ganesh Nagar West Marredpally, Secunderabad, 500 026, India
Tel.: (91) 4027705389
Web Site: https://nihar.info
531083—(BOM)
Rev.: $385,208
Assets: $1,433,349
Liabilities: $279,641
Net Worth: $1,153,708
Earnings: ($450,604)
Emp.: 5
Fiscal Year-end: 03/31/24
Information Technology Consulting Services
N.A.I.C.S.: 541512
B. S. N. Suryanarayana (Mng Dir)

NIHILENT TECHNOLOGIES LTD.
Weikfield IT Citi Infopark Nagar Road 4th Fl Block D, Pune, 411 014, India
Tel.: (91) 20 39846100
Web Site: http://www.nihilent.com
Year Founded: 2000
Consulting Services
N.A.I.C.S.: 541690

Subsidiaries:

Nihilent Analytics Ltd   (1)
Infinity Benchmark 15th Plot G1 Block GP Sector V Salt Lake, Sector V Salt Lake City, Kolkata, 700091, West Bengal, India
Tel.: (91) 3340097800
Web Site: http://www.nihilentanalytics.com
Financial Investment Services
N.A.I.C.S.: 523940
Vineet Bahal (Mng Dir)

NIHON CANPACK CO. LTD.
Marunouchi Mitsui Building 6 No 2, Tokyo, 100-0005, Japan
Tel.: (81) 3 3201 3181   JP
Web Site: http://www.nihoncanpack.jp
Year Founded: 1973
Beverage Packaging Services
N.A.I.C.S.: 561910

Subsidiaries:

Nihon Canpack Vietnam Co Ltd   (1)
No 17 Dai Lo Doc Lap Vietnam Singapore Industrial Park, Thuan District, Ho Chi Minh City, Vietnam   (100%)
Tel.: (84) 650782292
Corrugated & Solid Fiber Box Mfr
N.A.I.C.S.: 322211

NIHON CHOUZAI CO., LTD.
9F Tamachi Tower 5-33-11, Shiba Minato-ku, Tokyo, 108-0014, Japan
Tel.: (81) 368100800   JP
Web Site: https://www.nicho.co.jp
Year Founded: 1980
3341—(TKS)
Rev.: $2,249,449,100
Assets: $1,289,525,070
Liabilities: $903,824,960
Net Worth: $385,700,110
Earnings: $16,875,330
Emp.: 5,864
Fiscal Year-end: 03/31/24
Pharmacies Operator, Generic Drug Mfr & Medical Professional Staffing Services
N.A.I.C.S.: 456110
Yosuke Mitsuhara (Pres)

Subsidiaries:

Choseido Pharmaceutical Co., Ltd.   (1)
92 Fuchu Kokufu-cho, Tokushima, 779-3122, Japan   (56.97%)
Tel.: (81) 886421101
Web Site: https://www.choseido.com
Sales Range: $100-124.9 Million
Emp.: 385
Generic Pharmaceutical Mfr & Distr
N.A.I.C.S.: 325412

Japan Medical Research Institute Co., Ltd.   (1)
Gran Tokyo North Tower 39th Floor 1-9-1 Marunouchi, Chiyoda-ku, Tokyo, 100-6739, Japan
Tel.: (81) 368100812
Medical Research Development Services
N.A.I.C.S.: 541715

Medical Resources Co., Ltd.   (1)
40th floor Gran Tokyo North Tower 1-9-1 Marunouchi, Chiyoda-ku, Tokyo, 100-6740, Japan
Tel.: (81) 332125580
Employment Placement Services
N.A.I.C.S.: 561311

Nihon Generic Co., Ltd.   (1)
GranTokyo North Tower 1-9-1 Marunouchi, Chiyoda-ku, Tokyo, 100-6739, Japan
Tel.: (81) 368100500
Emp.: 469
Generic Drug Mfr & Whslr
N.A.I.C.S.: 325412
Yosuke Mitsuhara (Pres & CEO)

NIHON DECOLUXE CO., LTD.
10 Maeyashiki Kashimori Fuso-cho, Niwa, 480-0103, Aichi, Japan
Tel.: (81) 587932411
Web Site: https://decoluxe.co.jp
Year Founded: 1958
79500—(NGO)
Sales Range: Less than $1 Million
Chemical Adhesive Mfr
N.A.I.C.S.: 325520
Shigeo Kimura (Pres & CEO)

NIHON DEMPA KOGYO CO LTD
Merkmal Keio Sasazuka Bldg 1-47-1 Sasazuka, Shibuya-ku, Tokyo, 151-8569, Japan
Tel.: (81) 354536711
Web Site: https://www.ndk.com
6779—(TKS)
Rev.: $332,542,490
Assets: $437,390,310
Liabilities: $256,454,780
Net Worth: $180,935,530
Earnings: $15,427,740
Emp.: 2,366
Fiscal Year-end: 03/31/24
Crystal Devices Mfr
N.A.I.C.S.: 334419
Toshiaki Takeuchi (Chm & Chm)

Subsidiaries:

Furukawa NDK Co., Ltd.   (1)
16-1 Shintakayachi, Sakuranome Furukawa, Osaki, 989-6233, Miyagi, Japan
Tel.: (81) 229281611
Web Site: https://www.ndk.com
Sales Range: $200-249.9 Million
Emp.: 600
Crystal Assemblies Mfr
N.A.I.C.S.: 334418

Hakodate NDK Co., Ltd.   (1)
Hakodate Rinkuu Kogyo Danchi, 3-63 Suzuranoka-cho, Hakodate, 042-0958, Oshima, Japan
Tel.: (81) 138323211
Web Site: http://www.ndk.com
Crystal Assemblies Mfr
N.A.I.C.S.: 334419
Hiroshi Takeuchi (Pres)

NDK America, Inc.
425 N Martingale Rd Ste 1330, Schaumburg, IL 60173
Tel.: (847) 852-4165
Web Site: https://www.ndk.com
Sales Range: $25-49.9 Million
Emp.: 25
Crystal Oscillators & Frequency Controls Distr
N.A.I.C.S.: 423690
Shingo Roppongi (Mgr-Sls)

NDK Crystal Asia Pte. Ltd.   (1)
10 Anson Road 14-04 International Plaza, Singapore, 079903, Singapore
Tel.: (65) 62989878
Web Site: https://www.ndk.com
Sales Range: $25-49.9 Million
Emp.: 11
Quartz Crystal Mfr
N.A.I.C.S.: 334419
Tan Teong (Mgr-Sls)

NDK Electronics (HK) Limited   (1)
Unit 1101 11/F Fourseas Building 208-212 Nathan Road, Tsimshatsui, Kowloon, China (Hong Kong)
Tel.: (852) 29563181
Web Site: https://www.ndk.com
Sales Range: $25-49.9 Million
Emp.: 10
Crystal Devices Mfr
N.A.I.C.S.: 334419
Noboru Suzuki (Pres)

NDK Europe Co., Ltd.   (1)
Tel.: (44) 2085470500
Sales Range: $25-49.9 Million
Emp.: 6
Crystal Devices Mfr
N.A.I.C.S.: 332999

NDK Italy SRL   (1)
Via Varese 25/D, 21047, Saronno, Italy
Tel.: (39) 0296702920
Web Site: https://www.ndk.com
Sales Range: $25-49.9 Million
Emp.: 11
Crystal Devices Mfr
N.A.I.C.S.: 334419
Ishikawa Haiami (Mng Dir)

NDK-Electronics Shanghai Co., Ltd   (1)
Rm 3101 3112 New Town Center Building No 83 Lou Shan Guan Rd, Changning District, Shanghai, 200336, China
Tel.: (86) 2162785115
Web Site: https://www.ndk.com
Sales Range: $25-49.9 Million
Emp.: 14
Crystal Devices Distr
N.A.I.C.S.: 334419

Nihon Dempa Kogyo Co., Ltd. - Sayama Plant   (1)
1275-2 Kamihirose, Sayama, 350-1321, Saitama, Japan

Tel.: (81) 4 2952 7211
Web Site: http://www.ndk.com
Crystal Devices Mfr
N.A.I.C.S.: 334419

Suzhou NDK Co., Ltd.   (1)
Building 19 Shishan industrial Belt 855 Zhujiang Road, Suzhou New District, Suzhou, 215129, Jiangsu, China
Tel.: (86) 51268252071
Web Site: https://www.ndk.com
Emp.: 1,000
Crystal Devices Distr
N.A.I.C.S.: 334419
Nobumitsu Fujiwara (Dir-Mktg)

Suzhou NDK Trading Co., Ltd.   (1)
Building 19 Shishan industrial Belt 855 Zhujiang Road, Suzhou New District, Suzhou, 215129, Jiangsu, China
Tel.: (86) 51268252071
Web Site: https://www.ndk.com
Sales Range: $100-124.9 Million
Emp.: 500
Crystal Devices Mfr
N.A.I.C.S.: 334419

NIHON DENGI CO., LTD.
Ryogoku City Core 2-10-14 Ryogoku, Sumida-Ku, Tokyo, 130-8556, Japan
Tel.: (81) 356241100
Web Site: https://www.nihondengi.co.jp
Year Founded: 1959
1723—(TKS)
Rev.: $256,980,437
Assets: $304,069,951
Liabilities: $76,385,839
Net Worth: $227,684,112
Earnings: $30,868,838
Emp.: 860
Fiscal Year-end: 03/31/24
Automatic Control System Mfr
N.A.I.C.S.: 333415
Ryosuke Shimada (Chm & Pres)

NIHON DENKEI CO., LTD.
ND building 5-14-12 ueno, Taito-ku, Tokyo, 110-0005, Japan
Tel.: (81) 358163551
Web Site: https://www.n-denkei.com
Year Founded: 1950
9908—(TKS)
Rev.: $717,442,790
Assets: $436,676,430
Liabilities: $250,287,650
Net Worth: $186,388,780
Earnings: $19,479,670
Emp.: 1,095
Fiscal Year-end: 03/31/24
Electronic Instrument Maintenance & Distr
N.A.I.C.S.: 811210
Yukiya Morita (Pres)

Subsidiaries:

Denkei Measurement and Control Technology (Xiamen) Co., Ltd.   (1)
RM 1710-A 17/F Building B Enjoy Center No 8 Songyue Road, Siming District, Xiamen, 361001, China
Tel.: (86) 5925070669
Electronic Parts Mfr & Distr
N.A.I.C.S.: 332510

Denkei Science & Technology Development (shanghai) Co., Ltd.   (1)
Room 601 Tower 2 Ali Center 1-2 Lane 1398 Shenchang Road, Minhang District, Shanghai, 201107, China
Tel.: (86) 2158208002
Electronic Parts Mfr & Distr
N.A.I.C.S.: 332510

Denkei Technology R&d(suzhou)co., Ltd.   (1)
No 521 Zhujiang Road Suzhou High-Tech Zone, Suzhou, 215002, China
Tel.: (86) 51266902378
Electronic Parts Mfr & Distr
N.A.I.C.S.: 332510

NIHON DENKEI CO., LTD.

NIHON DENKEI CO., LTD.—(Continued)

Denkei Trading (ShangHai) Co., Ltd (1)
Room 601 Tower 2 Ali Center 1-2 Lane 1398 Shenchang Road, Minhang District, Shanghai, 201107, China
Tel.: (86) 2158208002
Electronic Measuring Equipment Distr
N.A.I.C.S.: 423830

ND Korea Co., Ltd. (1)
Digital Empire C-1301 16 Deogyeong-daero 1556 beon-gil, Yeongtong-gu, Suwon, Gyeonggi-do, Korea (South)
Tel.: (82) 312024491
Web Site: https://www.ndkorea.co.kr
Electronic Measuring Equipment Distr
N.A.I.C.S.: 423830

Nihon Denkei (Hong Kong) Limited (1)
Unit 503 5/F Silvercord Tower 2 30 Canton Road, Tsimshatsui, Kowloon, 999077, China (Hong Kong)
Tel.: (852) 83060866
Electronic Measuring Equipment Distr
N.A.I.C.S.: 423830

Nihon Denkei (Malaysia) Sdn Bhd (1)
Unit No A-11-1 North Point Office Mid Valley City No 1, Medan Syed Putra Utara, 59200, Kuala Lumpur, Malaysia
Tel.: (60) 322835702
Web Site: https://www.n-denkei.com
Electronic Measuring Equipment Distr
N.A.I.C.S.: 423830

Nihon Denkei (Thailand) Co., Ltd. (1)
43 Thai CC Tower 30th Fl Room 304-305 South Sathorn Rd, Yannawa Sathorn, Bangkok, 10120, Thailand
Tel.: (66) 26755688
Web Site: https://www.n-denkei.com
Electronic Measuring Equipment Distr
N.A.I.C.S.: 423830
Tadao Itaki (Mng Dir)

Subsidiary (Non-US):

Aikoh Engineering Co., Ltd. (2)
15-7 Hishie 2-chome, Higashi-osaka, 578-0984, Osaka, Japan
Tel.: (81) 729669011
Electronic Measuring Equipment Mfr & Distr
N.A.I.C.S.: 334515
Kazuya Yoshioka (Pres)

Intec Keisoku Co., Ltd. (2)
Nishi-shinjuku 8-17-1 Shinjuku, Sumitomo Fudosan Shinjuku Grand Tower, Tokyo, 160-0023, Japan
Tel.: (81) 5017020500
Electronic Measuring Equipment Distr
N.A.I.C.S.: 423830

System Keisoku Co., Ltd. (2)
2-10-16 Kamiiida, Wakabayashi-ku, Sendai, 984-0838, Miyagi, Japan
Tel.: (81) 222858801
Emp.: 10
Electronic Measuring Equipment Distr
N.A.I.C.S.: 423830

UI Corporation (2)
2-22-20 Kashinodai, Kawagoe, Saitama Prefecture, Japan
Tel.: (81) 492438611
Web Site: https://www.yuai.co.jp
Electrical Measuring Instrument Repair Services
N.A.I.C.S.: 811210

Denkei Science & Technology, Inc. (1)
UNIT 3 Orient Goldcrest Laguna Technopark Bldg 3 East Main Avenue, Lot 3 Phase 5-B Laguna Technopark SEZ, Binan, Laguna, Philippines
Tel.: (63) 495309553
Electronic Measuring Equipment Distr
N.A.I.C.S.: 423830
Cindy Fidel (Coord-Admin & Sls)

Nihon Denkei India Private Limited (1)
Unit 211 2nd Floor Vipul Square Building Sushant Lok - 1 B Block, Gurgaon, 122009, Haryana, India
Tel.: (91) 1244715777
Web Site: https://www.n-denkei.com
Electronic Measuring Equipment Distr
N.A.I.C.S.: 423830
Jyunichiro Hara (Pres)

Nihon Denkei Vietnam Co., Ltd. (1)
Floor 4-5 No 79 Tran Thai Tong street, Dich Vong ward Cau Giay District, 100000, Hanoi, Vietnam
Tel.: (84) 2439516505
Web Site: https://www.n-denkei.com
Electronic Measuring Equipment Distr
N.A.I.C.S.: 423830
Le Ngoc Thai (Deputy Mgr-Sls)

PT Nihon Denkei Indonesia (1)
18 Office Park Building 22nd Floor Jl TB Simatupang No 18, Jakarta Selatan, 12520, Indonesia
Tel.: (62) 2122783422
Electronic Measuring Equipment Distr
N.A.I.C.S.: 423830
Parlon Utama (Engr-Sls)

Taiwan Denkei Solution Co., Ltd. (1)
5F No 413 Ruiguang Rd, Neihu District, Taipei, 11492, Taiwan
Tel.: (886) 226271993
Web Site: https://www.n-denkei.com.tw
Electronic Measuring Equipment Mfr & Distr
N.A.I.C.S.: 334515

NIHON ENTERPRISE CO., LTD.
Matsuoka Shibuya Bldg 1-17-8 Shibuya, Shibuya-ku, Tokyo, 150-0002, Japan
Tel.: (81) 357745730
Web Site: https://www.nihon-e.co.jp
4829—(TKS)
Rev.: $31,040,560
Assets: $39,336,110
Liabilities: $5,836,630
Net Worth: $33,499,480
Earnings: $1,381,490
Emp.: 220
Fiscal Year-end: 05/31/24
Mobile Communications Content & Solutions
N.A.I.C.S.: 517112
Katsunori Ueda (Pres & CEO)

Subsidiaries:

ATIS Corporation (1)
1-17-8 Shibuya Matsuoka Shibuya Building 2F, Shibuya-ku, Tokyo, Japan
Tel.: (81) 364340880
Web Site: http://www.atis.co.jp
Building Design & Planning Services
N.A.I.C.S.: 541310

Aizu Laboratory, Inc. (1)
53 Inter Nishi, Aizuwakamatsu, 965-0059, Fukushima, Japan
Tel.: (81) 242238285
Web Site: https://www.aizulab.com
Emp.: 23
Computer Programming Services
N.A.I.C.S.: 541511
Kunihisa Matsunaga (Pres & CEO)

Promote, Inc. (1)
Matsuoka Shibuya Building 1-17-8 Shibuya, Shibuya-ku, Tokyo, 150-0002, Japan
Tel.: (81) 357745835
Web Site: https://www.pmt-inc.jp
Application & System Development Services
N.A.I.C.S.: 541511

NIHON FALCOM CORPORATION
2-8-18 Akebono-cho, Tachikawa, Tokyo, Japan
Tel.: (81) 425276501
Web Site: http://www.falcom.co.jp
Year Founded: 2001
3723—(TKS)
Sales Range: $10-24.9 Million
Software Game Development Services
N.A.I.C.S.: 541511
Toshihiro Kondo (Pres)

NIHON FLUSH CO., LTD.
5-26 Yokosu-cho, Komatsushima, 773-8504, Tokushima, Japan
Tel.: (81) 885323431
Web Site: https://www.nfnf.co.jp
Year Founded: 1964
7820—(TKS)
Rev.: $171,192,390
Assets: $297,126,110
Liabilities: $80,318,110
Net Worth: $216,808,000
Earnings: $8,784,690
Emp.: 1,477
Fiscal Year-end: 03/31/24
Interior Doors, Door Frames & Furniture Mfr
N.A.I.C.S.: 321911
Eiji Takahashi (Chm, Pres & CEO)

NIHON FORM SERVICE CO., LTD.
4-36-14 Kameido, Koutou-ku, Tokyo, 136-0071, Japan
Tel.: (81) 3 36360011
Web Site: http://www.forvice.co.jp
Year Founded: 1956
Rev.: $28,692,930
Assets: $33,296,270
Liabilities: $15,974,140
Net Worth: $17,322,130
Earnings: ($412,650)
Fiscal Year-end: 09/30/19
Mechanical Equipment Mfr
N.A.I.C.S.: 333613
Takehide Yamashita (Pres)

NIHON HANDA CO., LTD.
Arca Central 16F 1-2-1 Kinshi, Sumida-ku, Tokyo, Japan
Tel.: (81) 336245771
Web Site: http://www.nihonhanda.com
Year Founded: 1910
Soldering Materials Supplier
N.A.I.C.S.: 333992
Makoto Asami (Pres)

Subsidiaries:

Nihon Data Material Co., Ltd. (1)
82-1 Anesaki-kaigan, Ichihara, 299-0107, Chiba, Japan
Tel.: (81) 436 60 7801
Solder Product Mfr
N.A.I.C.S.: 333992

Nihon Handa (HK) Limited (1)
Room V 5 Floor Haribest Industrial Bldg 45-47 Au Pui Wan Street Fotan, Sha Tin, China (Hong Kong)
Tel.: (852) 2690 0678
Solder Product Distr
N.A.I.C.S.: 423610
Koichiro Yoshida (Gen Mgr)

Nihon Handa (Shanghai) Co., Ltd. (1)
635 Huo Cheng Road Jiading Industrial Zone, Shanghai, China
Tel.: (86) 21 3910 8587
Solder Product Mfr
N.A.I.C.S.: 333992
Masatoshi Hirai (Deputy Gen Mgr)

Nihon Handa Co., Ltd. - Funabashi Plant (1)
4-6-1 Narashino, Funabashi, 274-0071, Chiba, Japan
Tel.: (81) 47 479 0611
Solder Product Mfr
N.A.I.C.S.: 333992

Nihon Handa Manufacturing (Malaysia) Sdn. Bhd. (1)
17 Lintang Beringin 6 Jalan Permatang Damar Laut, Diamond Valley Indus Park, Penang, 11960, Malaysia
Tel.: (60) 46262485
Web Site: http://www.nihonhanda.com.my
Sales Range: $25-49.9 Million
Emp.: 20
Mfg. & Sales of Solder
N.A.I.C.S.: 333992

INTERNATIONAL PUBLIC

NIHON HOUSE HOLDINGS CO., LTD.
japan House HD Lidabashi Bldg, 4-3-8 Lidabashi Chiyoda-chome, Tokyo, 102-0072, Japan
Tel.: (81) 352159881
Web Site: https://www.nihonhouse-hd.co.jp
1873—(TKS)
Rev.: $85,202,900
Assets: $285,697,420
Liabilities: $145,228,310
Net Worth: $140,469,110
Earnings: ($8,222,840)
Fiscal Year-end: 04/30/24
Holding Company
N.A.I.C.S.: 551112
Kazuyuki Narita (Pres)

NIHON HOUSING CO. LTD.
1-31-12 Shinjuku, Shinjuku-Ku, Tokyo, 160-8410, Japan
Tel.: (81) 358607565
Web Site: https://www.housing.co.jp
Year Founded: 1966
4781—(TKS)
Rev.: $1,359,304,320
Assets: $719,979,040
Liabilities: $295,859,520
Net Worth: $424,119,520
Earnings: $46,086,480
Emp.: 2,101
Fiscal Year-end: 03/31/23
Building Construction Services
N.A.I.C.S.: 236116
Utena Osano (Pres & CEO)

NIHON ISK COMPANY, LIMITED
1395-1 Teragu, Tsukuba, 300-4297, Ibaraki, Japan
Tel.: (81) 298692001
Web Site: https://www.dental-king.com
Year Founded: 1948
7986—(TKS)
Rev.: $40,278,290
Assets: $41,675,020
Liabilities: $13,272,480
Net Worth: $28,402,540
Earnings: $2,658,750
Fiscal Year-end: 12/31/23
Steel Product Mfr & Distr
N.A.I.C.S.: 331221
Kiyoshi Hirosawa (Chm)

NIHON JYOHO CREATE CO., LTD.
13-18 Uemachi, Miyakonojo, 885-0072, Japan
Tel.: (81) 986252212
Web Site: http://www.n-create.co.jp
Year Founded: 1994
4054—(TKS)
Rev.: $27,591,920
Assets: $34,639,180
Liabilities: $13,080,660
Net Worth: $21,558,520
Earnings: $2,662,160
Emp.: 313
Fiscal Year-end: 06/30/24
Real Estate Development Services
N.A.I.C.S.: 531311
Kenichi Yonedu (Founder & Pres)

NIHON KAGAKU SANGYO CO., LTD.
TIXTOWER UENO Reception 5F 4-8-1 Higashi Ueno, Taito-ku, Tokyo, 110-0015, Japan
Tel.: (81) 352463540
Web Site: https://www.nihonkagakusangyo.com
Year Founded: 1924
4094—(TKS)
Rev.: $148,354,840

Assets: $349,854,080
Liabilities: $48,041,480
Net Worth: $301,812,600
Earnings: $11,514,620
Emp.: 448
Fiscal Year-end: 03/31/24
Chemical & Building Material Mfr
N.A.I.C.S.: 325998
Eiji Yanagisawa *(Chm & Pres)*
Subsidiaries:

Nihon Kagaku Sangyo Co., Ltd. - Aoyagi Plant (1)
1-24 Aoyagi 1-chome, Soka, 340-0002, Saitama, Japan
Tel.: (81) 489315575
Chemical Products Mfr
N.A.I.C.S.: 325998

Nihon Kagaku Sangyo Co., Ltd. - Fukushima No.1 Plant (1)
31-61 Aza Iwasawa Oaza Shimokitaba Hironomachi, Futabagun, Fukushima, 979-0402, Japan
Tel.: (81) 240273347
Chemical Products Mfr
N.A.I.C.S.: 325998

Nihon Kagaku Sangyo Co., Ltd. - Fukushima No.2 Plant (1)
1-1 Aza Nakamaru Oaza Yamadaoka Narahamachi, Futabagun, Fukushima, 979-0513, Japan
Tel.: (81) 240 25 8005
Chemical Products Mfr
N.A.I.C.S.: 325998

Nihon Kagaku Sangyo Co., Ltd. - Otone Plant (1)
567-1 Toyonodai 2-chome, Kazo, 349-1148, Saitama, Japan
Tel.: (81) 480727171
Chemical Products Mfr
N.A.I.C.S.: 325998

Nihon Kagaku Sangyo Co., Ltd. - Saitama Plant (1)
28-13 Nakane 1-chome, Soka, 340-0005, Saitama, Japan
Tel.: (81) 489314291
Chemical Products Mfr
N.A.I.C.S.: 325998

NIHON KEIZAI ADVERTISING CO., LTD.
2-10 Kanda Ogawa-machi, Chiyoda-ku, Tokyo, 101-8323, Japan
Tel.: (81) 352828000   JP
Web Site: http://www.adex.co.jp
Year Founded: 1947
Sales Range: $25-49.9 Million
Emp.: 399
Full Service
N.A.I.C.S.: 541810
Niwa Nobukazu *(Pres)*

NIHON KNOWLEDGE CO., LTD.
JS Building 9th floor 3195 Kotobuki, Taito-ku, Tokyo, 111-0042, Japan
Tel.: (81) 338454781
Web Site: https://www.know-net.co.jp
Year Founded: 1985
5252—(TKS)
Emp.: 331
Software Development Services
N.A.I.C.S.: 541511

NIHON KOGYO CO., LTD.
4614-13 Shido, Sanuki, 769-2101, Kagawa, Japan
Tel.: (81) 878948130
Web Site: https://www.nihon-kogyo.co.jp
Year Founded: 1956
5279—(TKS)
Rev.: $90,340,246
Assets: $103,191,250
Liabilities: $52,580,098
Net Worth: $50,611,152
Earnings: $1,949,124
Fiscal Year-end: 03/31/24
Concrete Product Mfr & Distr
N.A.I.C.S.: 327390
Ayao Tada *(Chm)*

NIHON KOHDEN CORPORATION
1-31-4 Nishiochiai, Shinjuku-ku, Tokyo, 161-8560, Japan
Tel.: (81) 359968036
Web Site: https://www.nihonkohden.com
Year Founded: 1951
6849—(TKS)
Rev.: $1,467,327,460
Assets: $1,541,670,130
Liabilities: $344,718,110
Net Worth: $1,196,952,020
Earnings: $112,541,860
Emp.: 5,891
Fiscal Year-end: 03/31/24
Medical Equipment Mfr
N.A.I.C.S.: 334510
Takashi Tamura *(Exec Operating Officer & Gen Mgr-Sls Ops)*
Subsidiaries:

Advanced Medical Predictive Devices, Diagnostics and Displays, LLC (1)
108 2nd St SW Ste 16, Charlottesville, VA 22902
Tel.: (949) 474-9207
Medical Electronic Equipment Mfr
N.A.I.C.S.: 339112

Beneficks Corporation (1)
5F Nord Building 1-6-11 Kitaueno, Taito-ku, Tokyo, 110-0014, Japan
Tel.: (81) 338431717
Emp.: 27
Medical Equipment Mfr
N.A.I.C.S.: 339112

Defibtech, LLC (1)
741 Boston Post Rd Ste 201, Guilford, CT 06437
Tel.: (203) 453-6654
Medical Equipment Mfr
N.A.I.C.S.: 339112
Dawn Scott *(Mgr-Talent Acquisition)*

E-Staff Insurance Services Corporation (1)
1-31-4 Nishiochiai, Shinjuku-ku, Tokyo, 161-8560, Japan
Tel.: (81) 359968172
Web Site: https://www.nihonkohden.co.jp
Medical Equipment Mfr
N.A.I.C.S.: 339112

NKS Bangkok Co., Ltd. (1)
House No 246 Times Square Building 11th Floor Room No 11-04C, Sukhumvit Road Klongtoey Sub-Area Klongtoey Area, Bangkok, 10110, Thailand
Tel.: (66) 26530051
Medical Equipment Mfr
N.A.I.C.S.: 339112
Wassana Chalermlap *(Product Mgr-Monitoring & IT)*

NKUS Lab Inc. (1)
14 Bunsen, Irvine, CA 92618
Tel.: (949) 474-9207
Web Site: http://www.nklab.com
Medical Equipment Mfr
N.A.I.C.S.: 339112

Neurotronics Inc. (1)
4500 NW 27th Ave Ste C2, Gainesville, FL 32606
Tel.: (352) 372-9955
Web Site: https://www.neurotronics.com
Sleep Diagnostic System Mfr
N.A.I.C.S.: 334510

Nicera Hong Kong Ltd. (1)
Unit L1 5/F Phase 2 Kaiser Estate NOS 47-53 Man Yue Street, Hung Hom, Kowloon, China (Hong Kong)
Tel.: (852) 27957511
Emp.: 6
Ultrasonic Sensors Mfr
N.A.I.C.S.: 334511

Nihon Kohden (Thailand) Co., Ltd. (1)
House No 246 Times Square Building, 11th Floor Room No 11-04C Sukhumvit Road Klongtoey sub-area, Bangkok, 10110, Thailand
Tel.: (66) 26530051
Medical Electronic Equipment Mfr
N.A.I.C.S.: 339112

Nihon Kohden America, Inc. (1)
15353 Barranca Pkwy, Irvine, CA 92618
Tel.: (949) 580-1555
Health Care Srvices
N.A.I.C.S.: 621491
Harsh Dharwad *(CTO & VP)*

Nihon Kohden Chubu Corporation (1)
1-9-12 Shinogashira, Atsuta-Ku, Nagoya, 456-0018, Aichi, Japan
Tel.: (81) 526823239
Medical Electronic Equipment Mfr
N.A.I.C.S.: 423450

Nihon Kohden Chushikoku Corporation (1)
3-15-8 Kusunokicho, Nishi-ku, Hiroshima, 733-0002, Japan
Tel.: (81) 822375200
Web Site: http://www.nihonkohden.co.jp
Medical Equipment Mfr
N.A.I.C.S.: 339112
Kuwahata Naoya *(Pres)*

Nihon Kohden Corporation - International Division (1)
1-31-4 Nishiochia, Shinjuku-ku, Tokyo, 161-8560, Japan
Tel.: (81) 359968000
Web Site: http://www.nihonkohden.com
Sales Range: $250-299.9 Million
Emp.: 3,623
Medical Electronic Equipment Distr
N.A.I.C.S.: 423450

Nihon Kohden Deutschland GmbH (1)
Raiffeisenstrasse 10, 61191, Rosbach vor der Hohe, Germany
Tel.: (49) 60038270
Medical Equipment Mfr
N.A.I.C.S.: 339112
Markus Beilenhoff *(Gen Mgr)*

Nihon Kohden Digital Health Solutions, LLC (1)
14 Bunsen, Irvine, CA 92618
Tel.: (949) 474-9207
Web Site: https://nkdhs.com
Software Services
N.A.I.C.S.: 541714

Nihon Kohden Do Brasil Ltda. (1)
Alameda Jupiter 634 Indaiatuba, American Park Empresarial Nr, Sao Paulo, 13347-397, CEP, Brazil
Tel.: (55) 1130441700
Web Site: https://br.nihonkohden.com
Medical Equipment Mfr
N.A.I.C.S.: 339112
Marcelo Milan *(Acct Mgr)*

Nihon Kohden Europe GmbH (1)
Raiffeisenstrasse 10, 61191, Rosbach vor der Hohe, Germany
Tel.: (49) 60038270
Web Site: http://eu.nihonkohden.com
Sales Range: $25-49.9 Million
Emp.: 100
Electromedical Equipment Mfr
N.A.I.C.S.: 334510

Nihon Kohden Firenze S.r.l. (1)
Via Torta 72/74, Sesto Fiorentino, 50019, Florence, Italy
Tel.: (39) 05530451
Medical Equipment Mfr
N.A.I.C.S.: 339112

Nihon Kohden France S.a.r.l (1)
Centre d'Affaires La Boursidiere Bat C - RDC, 92357, Le Plessis-Robinson, France
Tel.: (33) 149080550
Web Site: http://eu.nihonkohden.com
Sales Range: $25-49.9 Million
Emp.: 20
Medical Electronic Equipment Mfr
N.A.I.C.S.: 334510
Yannick Lecomte *(Mng Dir)*

Nihon Kohden Higashi Kanto Corporation (1)
1-31-4 Nishiochiai Shinjuku-ku, 161-8560, Tokyo, Japan
Tel.: (81) 3 5996 8000
Web Site: http://www.nihonkohden.com
Sales Range: $50-74.9 Million
Emp.: 80
Medical Electronic Equipment Mfr
N.A.I.C.S.: 423450
Shiyoshi Kobayashi *(Pres)*

Nihon Kohden Iberica S.L. (1)
Calle Toronga 23 Oficina 1, 28043, Madrid, Spain
Tel.: (34) 917161080
Web Site: http://eu.nihonkohden.com
Sales Range: $25-49.9 Million
Emp.: 14
Medical Electronic Equipment Mfr
N.A.I.C.S.: 334510

Nihon Kohden India Pvt. Ltd. (1)
308 Tower A Spazedge Sector 47 Sohna Road, Gurgaon, 122 002, Haryana, India
Tel.: (91) 1244931000
Web Site: https://in.nihonkohden.com
Medical Equipment Mfr
N.A.I.C.S.: 339112
Satish Mehta *(Mgr-Sls & Mktg)*

Nihon Kohden Innovation Center, Inc. (1)
271 Cambridge St, Cambridge, MA 02141
Tel.: (617) 318-5900
Medical Equipment Mfr
N.A.I.C.S.: 339112

Nihon Kohden Italia S.r.l. (1)
Via Fratelli Bronzetti 28, 24124, Bergamo, Italy
Tel.: (39) 035219543
Medical Equipment Mfr
N.A.I.C.S.: 339112
Simone Ghilardi *(Product Mgr)*

Nihon Kohden Korea, Inc. (1)
3F Cheongok Bldg 88 Dongmak-ro, Mapo-gu, Seoul, 04075, Korea (South)
Tel.: (82) 232732310
Web Site: https://kr.nihonkohden.com
Medical Equipment Mfr
N.A.I.C.S.: 339112
Eunseok Kim *(Mgr-Svcs)*

Nihon Kohden Latin America S.A.S (1)
Carrera 16 No 93A-36 Of 802, Bogota, Colombia
Tel.: (57) 13001742
Medical Equipment Mfr
N.A.I.C.S.: 339112
Jorge Azuero *(Product Mgr)*

Nihon Kohden Malaysia Sdn. Bhd. (1)
Suite 15-13 Level 15G Tower 199 Jalan Tun Razak, 50400, Kuala Lumpur, Malaysia
Tel.: (60) 321610100
Web Site: http://www.nihonkohden.com.my
Medical Equipment Mfr
N.A.I.C.S.: 339112

Nihon Kohden Mexico S.A. de C.V. (1)
Insurgentes Sur 730 Col Del Valle, Benito Juarez Delegation, 03100, Mexico, Mexico
Tel.: (52) 5588515550
Web Site: https://mx.nihonkohden.com
Medical Equipment Mfr
N.A.I.C.S.: 339112

Nihon Kohden Middle East FZE (1)
JAFZA One Tower A 19th floor Office No 1912, PO Box 261516, Jebel Ali Free Zone, Dubai, United Arab Emirates
Tel.: (971) 48840080
Web Site: https://ae.nihonkohden.com
Medical Equipment Mfr
N.A.I.C.S.: 339112
Alejandro Ravago *(Mktg Mgr)*

Nihon Kohden Minami Kanto Corporation (1)
Yokohama Bus Park High Tech Ctr 2F, Yokohama, 240-0005, Kanagawa, Japan
Tel.: (81) 453339200
Medical Electronic Equipment Mfr
N.A.I.C.S.: 423450

NIHON KOHDEN CORPORATION

Nihon Kohden Corporation—(Continued)

Nihon Kohden OrangeMed, Inc. (1)
1800 E Wilshire Ave, Santa Ana, CA 92705
Tel.: (949) 502-6448
Web Site: https://orange-med.com
Medical Equipment Mfr
N.A.I.C.S.: 339112

Nihon Kohden Singapore Pte Ltd (1)
1 Maritime Square 10-34 HarbourFront
Centre, Singapore, 099253, Singapore
Tel.: (65) 63762210
Web Site: http://sg.nihonkohden.com
Sales Range: $25-49.9 Million
Emp.: 20
Medical Electronic Equipment Mfr
N.A.I.C.S.: 334510

Nihon Kohden Tohoku Co., Ltd. (1)
4-29-7 Izumichuo, Izumi-Ku, Sendai, 981-3133, Miyagi, Japan
Tel.: (81) 5038194782
Web Site: http://www.nihonkohden.co.jp
Medical Electronic Equipment Mfr
N.A.I.C.S.: 423450

Nihon Kohden Tokyo Corporation (1)
1-31-4 Nishiochiai, Shinjuku-ku, Tokyo, 161-8560, Japan
Tel.: (81) 359968000
Web Site: http://www.nihonkohden.com
Emp.: 3,623
Medical Electronic Equipment Mfr
N.A.I.C.S.: 423450

Nihon Kohden Tomioka Corporation (1)
486 Nanokaichi, Tomioka, 370-2343, Gunma, Japan
Tel.: (81) 274623231
Web Site: http://www.nihonkohden.co.jp
Sales Range: $100-124.9 Million
Emp.: 500
Medical Electronic Equipment Mfr
N.A.I.C.S.: 334510
Poshinobu Mayuzumi *(Pres)*

Nihon Kohden Trading (Shanghai) Co., Ltd. (1)
6F Block 2 406 Guilin Road Xuhui District, Shanghai, 200233, China
Tel.: (86) 2162700909
Web Site: http://www.nihonkohden.co.jp
Sales Range: $25-49.9 Million
Emp.: 50
Medical Electronic Equipment Mfr
N.A.I.C.S.: 334510
Y. Yoshitake *(Gen Mgr)*

Nihon Kohden UK Ltd. (1)
Unit 3 Heyworth Business Park Old Portsmouth Road, Peasmarsh, Guildford, GU3 1AF, Surrey, United Kingdom
Tel.: (44) 1483331328
Medical Equipment Mfr
N.A.I.C.S.: 339112
Samantha Cameron *(Mgr-Medical Sls)*

Shanghai Kohden Medical Electronic Instrument Corporation (1)
No 567 Huancheng Bei Road, Shanghai Comprehensive Industrial Development Zone Fengxian District, Shanghai, 201401, China
Tel.: (86) 2157436998
Web Site: http://www.nihonkohden.com.cn
Medical Electronic Equipment Mfr
N.A.I.C.S.: 334510

Software Team S.r.l. (1)
Via Carducci 39, Sesto San Giovanni, 20099, Milan, Italy
Tel.: (39) 0284148166
Web Site: https://www.swt.it
Healthcare Services
N.A.I.C.S.: 621610

NIHON KOLMAR CO., LTD.
Nissei Fushimimachi Main Bldg 4F
4-4-1 Fushimimachi, Chuo-ku, Osaka, 541-0044, Japan
Tel.: (81) 6 6227 5261   JP
Web Site: http://www.kolmar.co.jp
Year Founded: 1912
Emp.: 1,638
Cosmetics Mfr & Distr
N.A.I.C.S.: 325620

Tomoji Kanzaki *(Chm & CEO)*
Subsidiaries:

Kose Cosmetics Co., Ltd. (China) (1)
Baiyulan Square No 501 Dongdaming Road, Hongkou, Shanghai, 200085, China
Tel.: (86) 2163756633
Web Site: http://www.kose.com.cn
Cosmetics Mfr
N.A.I.C.S.: 325620

NIHON M&A CENTER HOLDINGS INC.
24F Tekko Building 1-8-2
Marunouchi, Chiyoda-ku, Tokyo, 100-0005, Japan
Tel.: (81) 352205454
Web Site: https://www.nihon-ma.co.jp
Year Founded: 1991
2127—(TKS)
Rev.: $291,738,960
Assets: $387,610,400
Liabilities: $96,948,870
Net Worth: $290,661,530
Earnings: $70,905,470
Emp.: 1,069
Fiscal Year-end: 03/31/24
Merger & Acquisition Advisory Services
N.A.I.C.S.: 541219
Suguru Miyake *(Pres)*
Subsidiaries:

Japan Private Equity Co., Ltd (1)
2-15-6 Misakicho Kanda K-STAGE 5F, Chiyoda ku, Tokyo, 101-0061, Japan   **(49.8%)**
Tel.: (81) 332381726
Web Site: https://www.private-equity.co.jp
Equity Fund Management Services
N.A.I.C.S.: 525910
Shinichi Hoda *(Pres)*

NIHON PARKERIZING CO., LTD.
1-15-1 Nihonbashi, Chuo-ku, Tokyo, 103-0027, Japan
Tel.: (81) 332784452
Web Site: https://www.parker.co.jp
Year Founded: 1928
4095—(TKS)
Rev.: $826,811,850
Assets: $1,783,503,590
Liabilities: $330,063,740
Net Worth: $1,453,439,850
Earnings: $87,212,340
Emp.: 919
Fiscal Year-end: 03/31/24
Chemical Product Mfr & Distr
N.A.I.C.S.: 325998
Mitsuru Matsumoto *(Pres & COO)*
Subsidiaries:

Chung Jih Metal Treatment Chemicals, Inc. (1)
8F No 136 Section 3 Ren'ai Road, Da'an District, Taipei, Taiwan
Tel.: (886) 22 700 5533
Web Site: https://www.cjm-parker.com.tw
Surface Active Agent Mfr
N.A.I.C.S.: 325613

Dae Han Parkerizing Co., Ltd. (1)
5F Gwangseong Venture Plaza 275 Dokmak-ro, Mapo-gu, Seoul, Korea (South)
Tel.: (82) 2 333 5821
Web Site: https://www.d-parker.co.kr
Metal Surface Treatment Chemical Mfr
N.A.I.C.S.: 325510

Delamin Nitriding Salts U.S. Inc. (1)
134 River Bend Dr, Sevierville, TN 37876
Tel.: (865) 365-4082
High Quality Salt Mfr
N.A.I.C.S.: 311942

Foshan Parker Surface Modification Co., Ltd. (1)
No 1-B Xiaoxiao Road The Auto Parts Industrial Zone, Nanhai Science and Technology Industrial Park Nanhai District, Foshan, China
Tel.: (86) 75786650888
Heat Treatment Services
N.A.I.C.S.: 332811

Guangzhou Parker Auto Parts Co., Ltd. (1)
2 Anyuan Road Jiekou Conghua, Guangzhou, 510900, China
Tel.: (86) 2087910201
Automobile Parts Distr
N.A.I.C.S.: 423120

Guangzhou Parkerizing Co., Ltd. (1)
No 3 Buling Road Yonghe Economic Zone, Guangzhou Economic and Technological Development Zone, Guangzhou, 511356, China
Tel.: (86) 203 222 1855
Web Site: https://www.gzparker.com
Metal Surface Treatment Equipment Mfr
N.A.I.C.S.: 325510

Heisei Corporation (1)
1540-1 O'oka, Numazu, 410-0022, Shizuoka, Japan
Tel.: (81) 559621000
Web Site: https://www.heiseikensetu.co.jp
Emp.: 572
Real Estate Manangement Services
N.A.I.C.S.: 531210
Hisao Akimoto *(Founder & Pres)*

Japan Kanigen Co., Ltd. (1)
1-35-11 Miyagi, Adachi-ku, Tokyo, 120-0047, Japan
Tel.: (81) 3 5959 6701
Web Site: http://www.kanigen.co.jp
Electroless Plating Solution Mfr & Distr
N.A.I.C.S.: 325998
Kiyoshi Fujinaga *(Gen Mgr-Governance Compliance Promo Dept)*
Subsidiary (Non-US):

Kanigen (Shanghai) Trade Co., Ltd. (2)
Room1108 New Town Center Office No 83 Lou Shan Guan Rd, Shanghai, China
Tel.: (86) 2162368533
Chemical Plating Solution Mfr
N.A.I.C.S.: 325998

Kanigen (Thailand) Co., Ltd. (1)
253 16th Floor Sukhumvit 21 Road Asoke, Klongtoey-Nua Wattana, Bangkok, 10110, Thailand
Tel.: (66) 2 260 2670
Web Site: https://www.kanigen.co.th
Metal Surface Treatment Chemical Distr
N.A.I.C.S.: 424690

Komatsu Parkerizing Co., Ltd. (1)
1-6 kougyoudanchi Kushimachi, Komatsu, 923-0965, Ishikawa, Japan
Tel.: (81) 761443610
Chemical Products Mfr
N.A.I.C.S.: 325998

Million Chemicals Co., Ltd. (1)
12-41 Hiroshiba-cho, Suita, 564-0052, Osaka, Japan
Tel.: (81) 64 861 8510
Web Site: https://www.million-k.co.jp
Surface Active Agent Mfr
N.A.I.C.S.: 325613
Hirotaka Yamamoto *(Pres)*

Nihon Parkerizing (India) Pvt. Ltd. (1)
1st Floor Plot No-127 Sector-44, Gurgaon, 122 002, Haryana, India
Tel.: (91) 124 493 8888
Web Site: https://www.nihonparker.in
Metal Surface Treatment Chemical Mfr
N.A.I.C.S.: 325510

Nihon Parkerizing Malaysia Sdn. Bhd. (1)
No 10 Jalan Keluli 2 Kawasan Perindustrian Bukit Raja, 41050, Klang, Selangor, Malaysia
Tel.: (60) 33 341 0227
Metal Surface Treatment Chemical Mfr
N.A.I.C.S.: 325998

P.I of Europe NV. (1)
Schoebroekstraat 46, Paal, 3583, Beringen, Belgium

INTERNATIONAL PUBLIC

Tel.: (32) 11433946
Chemical Products Distr
N.A.I.C.S.: 424690

P.T. Nusantara Parkerizing (1)
Jl Raya Bogor Km 27 Kalisari Pekayon, PO Box 6931, Pasar Rebo, Jakarta, 13710, Indonesia
Tel.: (62) 21 871 1468
Web Site: https://www.parkerizing.co.id
Metal Surface Treatment Equipment Mfr
N.A.I.C.S.: 325510
Abdullah T. Gobel *(Co-Pres & Commissioner)*

P.T. Parker Engineering Indonesia (1)
Perkantoran Hijau Arkadia Tower F 6 Floor Suite 601 Jl, TB Simatupang Kav 88, Jakarta, 12520, Indonesia
Tel.: (62) 217 884 8033
Metal Surface Treatment Equipment Mfr & Distr
N.A.I.C.S.: 325510

P.T. Parker Metal Treatment Indonesia (1)
Kawasan Industri MM-2100 Jl Irian V Blok KK-11 Jatiwangi Kec, Desa Jatiwangi Cikarang Barat Kabupaten, Bekasi, 17530, Jawa Barat, Indonesia
Tel.: (62) 2189982744
Web Site: https://pmti.co.id
Heat Treatment Services
N.A.I.C.S.: 332811

PC Acoustic Co., Ltd. (1)
2-22-1 Ningyocho, Chuo-ku Nihonbashi, Tokyo, 103-0013, Japan
Tel.: (81) 356440655
Web Site: https://pc-acoustic.co.jp
Chemical Products Mfr
N.A.I.C.S.: 325998

Parker Engineering (India) Pvt. Ltd. (1)
Unit No 9051 and 9052 9th Floor Vipul Square B-Block, Sushant Lok Phase-1, Gurgaon, 122009, Haryana, India
Tel.: (91) 124 411 2614
Metal Surface Treatment Equipment Mfr & Distr
N.A.I.C.S.: 325510

Parker Engineering (Shanghai) Co., Ltd. (1)
Room 504-506 No 1699 Gubei Road, Minhang District, Shanghai, 201103, China
Tel.: (86) 216 270 3711
Web Site: https://www.parker-eng.cn
Metal Surface Treatment Equipment Mfr & Distr
N.A.I.C.S.: 325510

Parker Engineering (Thailand) Co., Ltd. (1)
5th Floor Room 501 Thaniya Bldg 62 Silom Road, Suriyawongse Bangrak, Bangkok, 10500, Thailand
Tel.: (66) 2 236 0120
Metal Surface Treatment Equipment Mfr & Distr
N.A.I.C.S.: 325510

Parker Engineering Co., Ltd. (1)
16-8 2 Chome Nihonbashi, Chuo-Ku, Tokyo, 103-0027, Japan
Tel.: (81) 33 278 4800
Web Site: https://www.parker-eng.jp
Metal Surface Treatment Equipment Mfr
N.A.I.C.S.: 325510
Yasuo Satomi *(Pres & CEO)*

Parker Industries, Inc. (1)
4867 Rhoney Rd, Connelly Springs, NC 28612
Tel.: (828) 437-7779
Web Site: http://www.parkerindustriesinc.com
Industrial Machine Mfr & Distr
N.A.I.C.S.: 333248
Jeff Parker *(Exec VP)*

Parker Processing Vietnam Co., Ltd. (1)
Lot C1-2 Thang Long Industrial Park, Kim Chung Commune Dong Anh District, Hanoi, Vietnam
Tel.: (84) 243 881 0973
Web Site: https://parker.com.vn

AND PRIVATE COMPANIES

Metal Surface Treatment Chemical Mfr
N.A.I.C.S.: 325510

Parker Surface Technologies (Shanghai) Co., Ltd.
No 1118 Huatong Road Jinshanwei, Jinshan, Shanghai, 201512, China
Tel.: (86) 2137325086
Web Site: https://www.parker.co.jp
Surface Treatment Chemical Mfr
N.A.I.C.S.: 325998

Parker Trutec Inc.
4700 Gateway Blvd, Springfield, OH 45502
Tel.: (937) 323-8833
Web Site: https://www.parkertrutec.com
Emp.: 500
Heat Treatment Services
N.A.I.C.S.: 332811

Plant (Domestic):

Parker Trutec Inc. - Urbana Plant (2)
4795 Upper Vly Pike, Urbana, OH 43078
Tel.: (937) 653-8500
Metal Coatings Mfr
N.A.I.C.S.: 332812

Parker Trutec MMI Inc. (1)
134 River Bend Dr, Sevierville, TN 37876
Tel.: (865) 453-9186
Heat Treatment Services
N.A.I.C.S.: 332811

Plant (Domestic):

Parker Trutec MMI Inc. - Arkansas Plant (2)
2609 N 12th Ave, Paragould, AR 72450
Tel.: (870) 236-6920
Heat Treatment Services
N.A.I.C.S.: 332811

Parker Trutec Mexicana S.A de C.V. (1)
Av Rio Ota No 628 Parque Tecno Industrial Castro del Rio, 36814, Irapuato, Guanajuato, Mexico
Tel.: (52) 4626228500
Web Site: https://parkertrutec.mx
Heat Treatment Services
N.A.I.C.S.: 332811

Plant (Domestic):

Parker Trutec Mexicana S.A. de C.V. - Aguascalientes Plant (2)
Carolina Villanueva No 408 Ciudad Industrial, 20290, Aguascalientes, Mexico
Tel.: (52) 4499712688
Heat Treatment Services
N.A.I.C.S.: 332811

Philippine Parkerizing Inc. (1)
1148 R Bernal St, Rosario Metro Manila, Pasig, 1609, Philippines
Tel.: (63) 28 571 1311
Metal Surface Treatment Chemical Mfr
N.A.I.C.S.: 325998

Rizhao Parker Surface Treatment Co., Ltd. (1)
No 189 Taizhou Rd, Rizhao Economic and Technological Development Area, Rizhao, Shandong, China
Tel.: (86) 633 836 6880
Web Site: https://www.rzparker.com
Metal Surface Treatment Chemical Mfr
N.A.I.C.S.: 325998

Shanghai Parker M&E Parts Co., Ltd. (1)
No 182 Peng Feng Road Da Kun Industrial Zone, Song Jiang District, Shanghai, 201614, China
Tel.: (86) 2157855685
Chemical Products Distr
N.A.I.C.S.: 424690

Shanghai Parkerizing Co., Ltd. (1)
1588 Xingrong Road, Jiading Industrial Park Jiading District, Shanghai, 201815, China
Tel.: (86) 215 912 2587
Web Site: https://www.shanghaiparker.com
Metal Surface Treatment Equipment Mfr
N.A.I.C.S.: 325510

Shenyang Parkerizing Co., Ltd. (1)
No 21 Xiaoshizi Street, Dadong District, Shenyang, 110042, China
Tel.: (86) 248 431 4501

Web Site: https://www.syparker.com
Metal Surface Treatment Equipment Mfr
N.A.I.C.S.: 325510

Thai Parkerizing Co., Ltd. (1)
570 Moo 4 Bangpoo Industrial Estate Soi 12B Sukumvit Rd Prakasa Maung, Samut Prakan, 10280, Thailand
Tel.: (66) 23246600
Chemical Product Mfr & Distr
N.A.I.C.S.: 325998

Plant (Domestic):

Thai Parkerizing Co., Ltd. - HEAT & SURFACE TREATMENT Factory (2)
500/19 Moo 3 WHA Eastern Seaboard Industrial Estate 1 Tasit, Pluak Daeng, 21140, Rayong, Thailand
Tel.: (66) 33658800
Chemical Products Mfr
N.A.I.C.S.: 325998

Thai Parkerizing Co., Ltd. - HEAT TREATMENT Factory (2)
188 Moo 7 Gateway City Industrial Estate, Hua-Samrong Sub District, Chachoengsao, 24190, Thailand
Tel.: (66) 38575187
Chemical Products Mfr
N.A.I.C.S.: 325998

Vietnam Parkerizing (Hanoi) Co., Ltd. (1)
Tien Son Industrial Park, Dong Nguyen Ward Tu Son town, Bac Ninh, Vietnam
Tel.: (84) 222 374 5525
Metal Surface Treatment Chemical Mfr
N.A.I.C.S.: 325998

Vietnam Parkerizing Co., Ltd. (1)
Vietnam-Singapore Industrial Park 12 Doc Lap Avenue, Thuan An District, Hoa Binh, Binh Duong, Vietnam
Tel.: (84) 274 374 3152
Web Site: https://www.vnparkerizing.com
Emp.: 31
Metal Surface Treatment Chemical Mfr
N.A.I.C.S.: 325510

Wuhan Parkerizing Chemical Co., Ltd. (1)
NO 15 Northwest Lake Se Second Road, Wuhan Econcmic and Technolidical Development Zone, Wuhan, Hubei, China
Tel.: (86) 278 447 2748
Metal Surface Treatment Equipment Mfr
N.A.I.C.S.: 325510

NIHON PLAST CO., LTD.
3507-15 Yamamiya, Fujinomiya, 418-0111, Shizuoka, Japan
Tel.: (81) 544586830
Web Site: https://www.n-plast.co.jp
Year Founded: 1948
7291—(TKS)
Rev.: $821,325,550
Assets: $541,583,740
Liabilities: $336,296,970
Net Worth: $205,286,770
Earnings: $16,379,580
Emp.: 6,112
Fiscal Year-end: 03/31/24
Automotive Plastic Parts Mfr
N.A.I.C.S.: 326199
Makoto Hirose *(Chm)*

Subsidiaries:

NP Service Co., Ltd. (1)
3507-15 Yamamiya, Fujinomiya, 418-0111, Shizuoka, Japan
Tel.: (81) 54 458 7206
Consulting Services
N.A.I.C.S.: 541611

Neaton Auto Mexicana, S.A. de C.V. (1)
De La Condesa 6 Carretas, 76246, Santiago de Queretaro, Queretaro, Mexico
Tel.: (52) 442 256 2000
Web Site: https://www.neaton.com.mx
Automobile Parts Mfr
N.A.I.C.S.: 336390

Neaton Auto Products MFG, Inc. (1)
975 S Franklin St, Eaton, OH 45320
Tel.: (937) 456-7103

Sales Range: $200-249.9 Million
Emp.: 700
Automobile Products Supplier
N.A.I.C.S.: 332510
Takao Watanabe *(Pres)*

Neaton Rome Inc. (1)
1634 Technology Pkwy, Rome, GA 30165
Tel.: (706) 368-9901
Steering Wheel Mfr
N.A.I.C.S.: 336330

Nihon Magnesio S.A de C.V (1)
C P Rafael Sesma Huerta No 7 Parque Industrial Finsa, El Marques, 76246, Queretaro, Mexico
Tel.: (52) 4422963100
Web Site: http://www.n-plast.co.jp
Sales Range: $25-49.9 Million
Emp.: 48
Automotive Components Mfr
N.A.I.C.S.: 441330

Nihon Plast (Wuhan) Co., Ltd. (1)
6 Jing He Wu Lu, Dongxihu District, Wuhan, Hubei, China
Tel.: (86) 278 309 0850
Automobile Airbag Mfr
N.A.I.C.S.: 336390

Nihon Plast (Zhongshan) Co., Ltd. (1)
No 30 Technology West Road, Torch Development Zone, Zhongshan, Guangdong, China
Tel.: (86) 7608 828 7700
Steering Wheel Mfr
N.A.I.C.S.: 336330

Nihon Plast Mexicana S.A de C.V (1)
AV La Canada No 47 Parque Industrial Bernardo Quintana Carr, El Marques, 76246, Queretaro, Mexico
Tel.: (52) 4422961000
Web Site: http://www.n-plast.co.jp
Sales Range: $200-249.9 Million
Emp.: 760
Automobile Parts Mfr
N.A.I.C.S.: 336110

Nihon Plast Thailand Co., Ltd. (1)
7/228 M6 Amata City Industrial Estate T Mabyangporn, Pluak Daeng, 21140, Rayong, Thailand
Tel.: (66) 3 865 0411
Automobile Parts Distr
N.A.I.C.S.: 441330

P.T. Nihon Plast Indonesia P.T. (1)
Jalan Raya Tambun KM 38 2, Bekasi, 17510, Indonesia
Tel.: (62) 218807768
Web Site: http://www.n-plast.co.id
Sales Range: $200-249.9 Million
Emp.: 558
Leather Wrapped Steering Wheels Mfr
N.A.I.C.S.: 336330

NIHON SEIKAN K.K.
2-275 Yoshino-cho, Kita-ku, Saitama, 331-0811, Japan
Tel.: (81) 486651251
Web Site: https://www.nihonseikan.co.jp
Year Founded: 1925
5905—(TKS)
Rev.: $80,959,280
Assets: $100,498,440
Liabilities: $59,827,110
Net Worth: $40,671,330
Earnings: $1,791,310
Emp.: 129
Fiscal Year-end: 03/31/24
Metal Tank Mfr
N.A.I.C.S.: 332431

NIHON SEIMITSU CO., LTD.
8F Kawaguchi Center Building 418 Honmach, Kawaguchi, 332-0012, Saitama, Japan
Tel.: (81) 482255311
Web Site: https://www.nihon-s.co.jp
Year Founded: 1978
7771—(TKS)
Rev.: $44,472,080

NIHON TRIM CO., LTD.

Assets: $38,298,340
Liabilities: $28,581,640
Net Worth: $9,716,700
Earnings: $2,577,900
Emp.: 300
Fiscal Year-end: 03/31/24
Glass Frame Mfr
N.A.I.C.S.: 339115
Hideo Ito *(Pres)*

Subsidiaries:

NISSEY CAMBODIA Co., Ltd (1)
Dragon King SEZ, Prey Angkunh Commune, Bavet, SvayRieng, Cambodia
Tel.: (855) 12270429
Web Site: https://www.nihon-s.co.jp
Watch Parts Distr
N.A.I.C.S.: 423940

Nissey Vietnam Co., Ltd. (1)
6F 31C Ly Tu Trong Street, Ben Nghe Ward District 1, Ho Chi Minh City, Vietnam
Tel.: (84) 2839107093
Web Site: https://www.nisseicorp.co.jp
Plate Work Mfr
N.A.I.C.S.: 332313
Tomiyuki Arai *(Pres)*

NIHON SHOKUHIN KAKO CO., LTD.
20th floor Marunouchi North Exit Building 1-6-5 Marunouchi, Chiyoda-ku, Tokyo, 100-0005, Japan
Tel.: (81) 332129111
Web Site: https://www.nisshoku.co.jp
Year Founded: 1948
2892—(TKS)
Sales Range: $400-449.9 Million
Emp.: 423
Food Products Mfr
N.A.I.C.S.: 311230

NIHON TOKUSHU TORYO CO., LTD
3-23-2 Oji, Kita-ku, Tokyo, 114-8584, Japan
Tel.: (81) 339136131   JP
Web Site: https://www.nttoryo.co.jp
Year Founded: 1929
4619—(TKS)
Rev.: $427,620,730
Assets: $578,084,160
Liabilities: $184,359,510
Net Worth: $393,724,650
Earnings: $26,089,670
Emp.: 625
Fiscal Year-end: 03/31/24
Paint & Automotive Interior Product Mfr
N.A.I.C.S.: 325510

Subsidiaries:

Tianjin Rieter Nittoku Automotive Sound-Proof Co. Ltd (1)
No 9 Saida5 Sub Rd Xiqing Economic Development Zone, Tianjin, 300385, China   (49%)
Tel.: (86) 2223889388
Motor Vehicle Interior Product Mfr
N.A.I.C.S.: 336360

UGN, Inc. (1)
18410 Crossing Dr Ste C, Tinley Park, IL 60487   (50%)
Tel.: (773) 437-2400
Web Site: http://ugn.com
Sales Range: $300-349.9 Million
Automotive Acoustic, Interior Trim & Thermal Management Product Mfr
N.A.I.C.S.: 336390
Peter Anthony *(Pres & CEO)*

NIHON TRIM CO., LTD.
22nd Floor Herbis ENT Office Tower 2-2-22 Umeda, Kita-Ku, Osaka, 530-0001, Japan
Tel.: (81) 664564600   JP
Web Site: https://shop.nihon-trim.co.jp
Year Founded: 1982

NIHON TRIM CO., LTD.

Nihon Trim Co., Ltd.—(Continued)
6788—(TKS)
Rev.: $134,936,540
Assets: $208,505,840
Liabilities: $52,331,370
Net Worth: $156,174,470
Earnings: $14,211,500
Emp.: 663
Fiscal Year-end: 03/31/24
Mfr & Sales of Electrolyzed Reduced Water Systems for Household Use
N.A.I.C.S.: 339999
Shinkatsu Morisawa (Pres & CEO)

Subsidiaries:

PT SUPER WAHANA TEHNO (1)
Green Office Park 9 Wing B 1st floor - Jalan BSD Grand Boulevard, BSD City, Tangerang, 15345, Indonesia
Tel.: (62) 8041001232
Web Site: https://www.superwahanatehno.com
Sales Range: $25-49.9 Million
Emp.: 40
Mineral Water Mfr & Distr
N.A.I.C.S.: 312112
Takafumi Shimizu (Chm)

Trim (Guangzhou) Water & Health Co., Ltd. (1)
Rm 2801 Tower B Bldg 3 No 13 Zhan Jue Xin Jie, Pazhou Haizhu District, Guangzhou, 510335, Guangdong, China
Tel.: (86) 20 32053508
Web Site: http://www.nihon-trim.co.jp
Sales Range: $25-49.9 Million
Emp.: 4
Water Purification Equipment Mfr
N.A.I.C.S.: 333310

Trim Electric Machinery Co., Ltd. (1)
1-5-2 Hotarugaoka, Nangoku, Nankoku, 783-0060, Kochi, Japan
Tel.: (81) 888048510
Web Site: https://www.trim-em.jp
Sales Range: $50-74.9 Million
Emp.: 100
Financial Services
N.A.I.C.S.: 523999

Trim Optimal Health Co., Ltd (1)
2-2-2 Uchisaiwaicho Fukokuseimei Building, Chiyoda-Ku, Tokyo, 100-0011, Japan
Tel.: (81) 355118670
Healthcare Products Sales
N.A.I.C.S.: 424490

NIHON YAMAMURA GLASS CO., LTD.

15-1 Nishimukojima-Cho, Amagasaki, Hyogo, 660-8580, Japan
Tel.: (81) 643006000
Web Site: https://www.yamamura.co.jp
Year Founded: 1914
5210—(TKS)
Rev.: $481,697,140
Assets: $622,291,840
Liabilities: $281,262,110
Net Worth: $341,029,730
Earnings: $81,045,210
Emp.: 750
Fiscal Year-end: 03/31/24
Glass & Plastic Bottle Mfr
N.A.I.C.S.: 327213
Yasuji Iryoda (Exec Officer & Dir-Corp)

Subsidiaries:

Ad Am Co., Ltd. (1)
6F Yotsubashi Nissei Building Annex 1-1-3 Kitahorie, Nishi-ku, Osaka, 550-0014, Japan
Tel.: (81) 665363008
Web Site: http://www.ad-am.co.jp
Sales Range: $25-49.9 Million
Emp.: 4
Marketing & Advertising Agencies
N.A.I.C.S.: 541810

Lam Soon Ball Yamamura Inc. (1)
372 Chien Hsing Rd Sec 2, Hsinfeng Hsiang, Taipei, Taiwan
Tel.: (886) 35983300
Sales Range: $50-74.9 Million
Emp.: 160
Metal Tank Mfr
N.A.I.C.S.: 332431

Nihon Yamamura Glass Co., Ltd. - Amagasaki Plant (1)
111 Nishimukojima-cho, Amagasaki, 660-0857, Hyogo, Japan
Tel.: (81) 664113431
Glass Blanks Mfr
N.A.I.C.S.: 327212

Nihon Yamamura Glass Co., Ltd. - Harima Plant (1)
5 Niijima Harima-cho, Kako-gun, Hyogo, 675-0155, Japan
Tel.: (81) 794352051
Sales Range: $50-74.9 Million
Emp.: 200
Glass Bottle Mfr
N.A.I.C.S.: 327213

Nihon Yamamura Glass Co., Ltd. - Kansai Plant (1)
43-2 Niijima Harima-cho, Kako-gun, Hyogo, 675-0155, Japan
Tel.: (81) 794355801
Sales Range: $25-49.9 Million
Emp.: 20
Plastics Bottle Mfr
N.A.I.C.S.: 326160
Takahiro Chiba (Mgr)

Nihon Yamamura Glass Co., Ltd. - Kawajima Plant (1)
6-8 Hachiman Kawajima-cho, Hiki-gun, Saitama, 350-0151, Japan
Tel.: (81) 492 97 7105
Web Site: http://www.yamamura.co.jp
Plastics Bottle Mfr
N.A.I.C.S.: 326160

Nihon Yamamura Glass Co., Ltd. - Naruohama Plant (1)
2-1-18 Naruohama, Nishinomiya, 663-8142, Hyogo, Japan
Tel.: (81) 798404456
Web Site: http://www.yamamura.co.jp
Glass Blanks Mfr
N.A.I.C.S.: 327212

Nihon Yamamura Glass Co., Ltd. - Osaka Plant (1)
52-2 1-chome Shibo-cho, Osaka, 569-0823, Takatsuki, Japan
Tel.: (81) 72 677 1100
Web Site: http://www.yamamura.co.jp
Glass Bottle Mfr
N.A.I.C.S.: 327213

Nihon Yamamura Glass Co., Ltd. - Saitama Plant (1)
611-10 Shimobayashi Mizugahara, Kumagaya, 360-8558, Saitama, Japan
Tel.: (81) 485337081
Sales Range: $50-74.9 Million
Emp.: 140
Glass Bottle Mfr
N.A.I.C.S.: 327213

Nihon Yamamura Glass Co., Ltd. - Utsunomiya Plant (1)
18-1 Kiyohara-Kogyodanchi, Utsunomiya, 321-3231, Tochigi, Japan
Tel.: (81) 28 667 8631
Web Site: http://www.yamamura.co.jp
Plastics Bottle Mfr
N.A.I.C.S.: 326160

Nissho Seiki Co., Ltd. (1)
4-1-5 Fukaminishi, Yamato, 242-0018, Kanagawa, Japan
Tel.: (82) 462619656
Web Site: http://www.yamamura.co.jp
Industrial Molds Mfr & Distr
N.A.I.C.S.: 331511

Seisho Co.,Ltd. (1)
Kowa Shiba Park Building 1-1-11 Shiba Park, Minato-ku, Tokyo, 105-0011, Japan (93%)
Tel.: (81) 354011741
Web Site: https://www.seisho.co.jp
Emp.: 28
Glass Bottles & Household Goods Distr
N.A.I.C.S.: 423840
Hideto Namerikawa (Pres)

Yamamura Glass Works Co.,Ltd. (1)
2-1-18 Naruohama, Nishinomiya, 663-8142, Hyogo, Japan
Tel.: (81) 798431301
Glass Bottles Mfr & Sales
N.A.I.C.S.: 327213

Yamamura International (Shanghai) Co., Ltd (1)
Suite 1808 Tower B The Place No 100 Zunyi Road, Changning District, Shanghai, 200051, China
Tel.: (86) 2152081258
Web Site: https://www.yamamura-international.com
Emp.: 10
Packaging Machinery & Materials Whslr
N.A.I.C.S.: 423830

Yamamura Kosan Co., Ltd. (1)
15-1 Nishimukojima-cho, Amagasaki, 660-8580, Hyogo, Japan
Tel.: (81) 643006441
Web Site: http://www.yamamura.co.jp
Sales Range: $50-74.9 Million
Emp.: 3
Insurance Services
N.A.I.C.S.: 524114
Makoto Yamashita (Pres)

Yamamura Photonics Co., Ltd. (1)
4207 Ikebe-cho, Tsuzuki-ku, Yokohama, 224-0053, Kanagawa, Japan
Tel.: (81) 459301811
Web Site: https://www.yama-ph.co.jp
Sales Range: $50-74.9 Million
Emp.: 170
Electrical & Electronic Glass Components Mfr
N.A.I.C.S.: 327212

Yamamura Warehouse Co., Ltd. (1)
15-1 Nishimukojimacho, Amagasaki, 660-0857, Hyogo, Japan (100%)
Tel.: (81) 643006400
Web Site: https://www.yamaso-web.co.jp
Emp.: 452
Warehousing & Logistics Services
N.A.I.C.S.: 493110
Toshio Nakajima (Pres)

Zhancheng (Suzhou) Plastic Co., Ltd. (1)
No 306 Zhenghe Middle Road, Economic Development Zone, Taicang, 215400, Jiangsu, China (100%)
Tel.: (86) 51281602158
Web Site: https://www.zhanchengsz.com
PET Beverage Bottles Mfr
N.A.I.C.S.: 326160

NIHONWASOU HOLDINGS, INC.

5F Roppongi Hills North Tower 6-2-31 Roppongi, Minato-ku, Tokyo, 106-0032, Japan
Tel.: (81) 358430097
Web Site: https://www.wasou.com
Year Founded: 1986
2499—(TKS)
Rev.: $31,933,360
Assets: $65,298,900
Liabilities: $40,795,860
Net Worth: $24,503,040
Earnings: $1,219,480
Emp.: 107
Fiscal Year-end: 12/31/23
Kimono Mfr
N.A.I.C.S.: 315250

Subsidiaries:

Main Stage Co., Ltd. (1)
5F Roppongi Hills North Tower, 6-2-31 Roppongi, Minato-ku, Tokyo, 106-0032, Japan
Tel.: (81) 332160014
Web Site: http://www.kimono-model.com
Model & Advertising Services
N.A.I.C.S.: 541810
Shigehisa Yoshida (Pres & CEO)

Nichikure Co., Ltd. (1)
Ginza 1-chome 18-6 Imon Ginza 1-chome Building 7F, Chuo-ku, Tokyo, Japan
Tel.: (81) 355240070
Web Site: https://www.nichicre.co.jp
Financial Services

N.A.I.C.S.: 541611
Yoshio Michibe (Pres)

NIIGATA KOTSU CO., LTD.

1-6-1 Bandai, Chuo-ku, Niigata, 950-8544, Japan
Tel.: (81) 252466323
Web Site: https://www.niigata-kotsu.co.jp
Year Founded: 1943
9017—(TKS)
Rev.: $128,346,370
Assets: $374,582,090
Liabilities: $255,007,190
Net Worth: $119,574,900
Earnings: $7,033,040
Emp.: 581
Fiscal Year-end: 03/31/24
Passenger Transportation Services
N.A.I.C.S.: 485113

NIIIO FINANCE GROUP AG

Elisabethstrasse 4243, 02826, Sachsen, Germany
Tel.: (49) 3581374990
Web Site: https://niiio.finance
Year Founded: 1999
A2G833—(DEU)
Holding Company Financial Technology
N.A.I.C.S.: 513210
Johann Horch (Founder & CEO)

Subsidiaries:

PATRONAS Financial Systems GmbH (1)
Schnewlinstrasse 12 Freiburg, 79098, Baden Wuerttemberg, Germany
Tel.: (49) 761400608
Web Site: https://www.patronas.com
IT Services & IT Consulting
N.A.I.C.S.: 513210

Subsidiary (Domestic):

Aramea Asset Management AG (2)
Kleine Johannisstrasse 4, 20457, Hamburg, Germany
Tel.: (49) 408664880
Web Site: http://www.aramea-ag.de
Emp.: 12
Asset Management Services
N.A.I.C.S.: 523940

NIIT LIMITED

85 Sector 32 Institutional Area, Gurgaon, 122001, Haryana, India
Tel.: (91) 1244293170
Web Site: https://www.niit.com
NIITLTD—(NSE)
Rev.: $195,084,708
Assets: $287,790,185
Liabilities: $80,412,560
Net Worth: $207,377,625
Earnings: $31,376,027
Emp.: 2,200
Fiscal Year-end: 03/31/22
Computer Software Training Services
N.A.I.C.S.: 611420
Vijay Kumar Thadani (Vice Chm & Co-Mng Dir)

Subsidiaries:

Chongqing An Dao Education Consulting Limited (1)
No 2 Floor 5 Block B Neptune Building Star Street 62, Northern New Area District, Chongqing, China
Tel.: (86) 2363065877
Training Center Services
N.A.I.C.S.: 611430

Eagle International Institute Inc. (1)
2165 Brighton Henrietta Townline Rd, Rochester, NY 14623
Web Site: http://www.eagleproductivity.com
Information Technology Consulting Services
N.A.I.C.S.: 541512
Alexander Orlando (Gen Mgr)

AND PRIVATE COMPANIES

NIKKEI INC.

Mindchampion Learning Systems Limited **(1)**
85 Institutional Area Sector 32, Gurgaon, 122001, Haryana, India
Tel.: (91) 18001023233
Web Site: http://www.niitnguru.com
Children School Services
N.A.I.C.S.: 624410
Leena Khokha *(Head-HR-India)*

NIIT (USA) Inc. **(1)**
1050 Crown Pointe Pkwy Ste 300, Atlanta, GA 30338
Tel.: (770) 551-9494
Web Site: http://www.niit.com
Computer & Computer Peripheral Equipment & Software Whslr
N.A.I.C.S.: 423430

NIIT China (Shanghai) Limited **(1)**
7A Long Feng Mansion 1566 Yan An West Road, Shanghai, China
Tel.: (86) 2152581540
Web Site: http://www.niit.com.cn
Software Development Services
N.A.I.C.S.: 541511
Kamal Dhuper *(Head-Country)*

NIIT Institute of Finance Banking & Insurance Training Limited **(1)**
8 Balaji Estate First Floor Guru Ravi Das Marg kalkaji, New Delhi, 110 019, India
Tel.: (91) 1141675000
Training Center Services
N.A.I.C.S.: 611430

NIIT Learning Solutions (Canada) Limited **(1)**
5045 Orbitor Drive Building 11 Suite 100, Mississauga, L4W 4Y4, ON, Canada
Tel.: (770) 551-9494
Training Center Services
N.A.I.C.S.: 611430

NIIT Limited **(1)**
200 Aldersgate Street Suite 129, London, EC1A 4HD, United Kingdom
Tel.: (44) 1582805920
Training Center Services
N.A.I.C.S.: 611430

Ningxia NIIT Education Technology Company Limted **(1)**
4th Floor Building 1 Phase 2 iBi Yucheng Center No 490 Ning'an Avenue, Jinfeng District, Yinchuan, China
Tel.: (86) 9518775770
Training Center Services
N.A.I.C.S.: 611430

NIITAKA CO., LTD.
1-8-10 Niitaka Yodogawa, Osaka, 532-8560, Japan
Tel.: (81) 663952717
Web Site: https://www.niitaka.co.jp
Year Founded: 1963
4465—(TKS)
Rev.: $150,304,790
Assets: $150,318,010
Liabilities: $61,843,160
Net Worth: $88,474,850
Earnings: $4,660,050
Emp.: 239
Fiscal Year-end: 05/31/24
Soap & Detergent Product Mfr & Distr
N.A.I.C.S.: 325611
Yoshiaki Okuyama *(Pres)*

Subsidiaries:

Suisho Petrochemical Industry Co., Ltd. **(1)**
1-11-21 Motomachi, Naniwa-ku, Osaka, 556-0016, Japan
Tel.: (81) 666345290
Web Site: http://www.suisho.co.jp
Chemical Product Mfr & Retailer
N.A.I.C.S.: 325998

Yuho Niitaka Co., Ltd. **(1)**
1-6-35 Shinsuna East Square Tokyo 707, Koto-ku, Tokyo, 136-0075, Japan
Tel.: (81) 356332520
Web Site: http://www.yuhoniitaka.co.jp
Chemical Product Mfr & Retailer
N.A.I.C.S.: 325998

NIJGH INTERPARTNERS B.V.
Spartapark Noord 1, 3027 VW, Rotterdam, Netherlands
Tel.: (31) 10 413 23 60 NI
Web Site: http://www.nijgh.com
Year Founded: 1837
Rev.: $12,116,000
Emp.: 12
N.A.I.C.S.: 541810
Patrick A. van Weel *(Owner)*

NIKHIL ADHESIVES LTD.
9 floor 902 A wing Kaledonia HDIL Building Sahar Rd, Opposite D-Mart Andheri East, Mumbai, 400069, India
Tel.: (91) 2226836558
Web Site: https://www.nikhiladhesives.com
526159—(BOM)
Rev.: $111,154,407
Assets: $43,134,846
Liabilities: $31,470,566
Net Worth: $11,664,280
Earnings: $3,448,550
Emp.: 281
Fiscal Year-end: 03/31/22
Adhesive Mfr
N.A.I.C.S.: 325520
Rajendra Jayantilal Sanghavi *(Chm)*

NIKKAN KOGYO SHIMBUN, LTD.
14-1 Nihonbashi Koami-cho, Chuo-ku, Tokyo, 103-8548, Japan
Tel.: (81) 356447000 JP
Web Site: http://www.corp.nikkan.co.jp
Year Founded: 1915
Sales Range: $100-124.9 Million
Emp.: 523
Advertising & Publishing Services
N.A.I.C.S.: 513110
Haruhiro Imizu *(Pres)*

NIKKATO CORPORATION
3-2-24 Oriono-cho, Sakai-ku, Sakai, 590-0001, Osaka, Japan
Tel.: (81) 722383641
Web Site: https://www.nikkato.co.jp
Year Founded: 1921
5367—(TKS)
Sales Range: $50-74.9 Million
Ceramic Product Mfr & Distr
N.A.I.C.S.: 327110
Takashi Nishimura *(Pres)*

NIKKATSU CORPORATION
3-28-12 Hongo, Bunkyo-ku, Tokyo, 113-0033, Japan
Tel.: (81) 356891018 JP
Web Site: http://www.nikkatsu.com
Year Founded: 1912
Holding Company; Motion Picture & Video Production & Distribution; Television Broadcasting; Movie Theater Operator; Movie Industry School & Talent Agency Operator
N.A.I.C.S.: 551112
Naoki Sato *(Pres & CEO)*

NIKKEI ADVERTISING CO.
4-2 Koraibashi 1-chome, Osaka, 541-0043, Japan
Tel.: (81) 662317421
Year Founded: 1947
Emp.: 380
Advetising Agency
N.A.I.C.S.: 541810
Michio Yamada *(Exec VP)*

Subsidiaries:

Nikkei Advertising Co. **(1)**
1-10-27 Hakata Station East, Hakata-Ku, Fukuoka, 812-0013, Japan
Tel.: (81) 92 431 0080
Advetising Agency
N.A.I.C.S.: 541810

Nikkei Advertising Co. **(1)**
2-20-25 Sakae, Naka-Ku, Nagoya, 460-0002, Japan
Tel.: (81) 52 222 5171
Advetising Agency
N.A.I.C.S.: 541810

NIKKEI INC.
1-3-7 Otemachi, Chiyoda-Ku, Tokyo, 100-8066, Japan
Tel.: (81) 332700251 JP
Web Site: http://www.nikkei.com
Year Founded: 1876
Sales Range: $550-599.9 Million
Emp.: 3,069
Business Information Publisher; Book & Periodical Publishing, Broadcasting, On-Line Information, Databank Services & Industrial & Cultural Exhibitions & Seminars
N.A.I.C.S.: 513110
Tsuneo Kita *(Chm)*

Subsidiaries:

Aichi Television Broadcasting Co., LTD. **(1)**
2-4-8 Osu, Naka-Ku, Nagoya, 460-8325, Japan
Tel.: (81) 522 030250
Television Broadcasting Services
N.A.I.C.S.: 516120

Nihon Keizai Shimbun Europe Ltd. **(1)**
6th Fl Barnald's Inn 86 Fetter Lane, London, EC4A 1EN, United Kingdom **(100%)**
Tel.: (44) 2074217800
Web Site: http://www.nikkeieu.com
Sales Range: $25-49.9 Million
Emp.: 60
Newspaper Publishing, Printing & Sales, Online Databank Services
N.A.I.C.S.: 513110

Nikkei America, Inc. **(1)**
1325 Ave Of The Americas Ste 2500, New York, NY 10019-6055 **(100%)**
Tel.: (212) 261-6200
Web Site: http://www.nikkeius.com
Sales Range: $25-49.9 Million
Emp.: 20
Newspaper Publishing, Printing & Sales, Advertising, Online Databank Services, Marketing & Research
N.A.I.C.S.: 541613
Hitomi Tohyama *(Mgr)*

Subsidiary (Domestic):

Nikkei West Newspaper Printing, Inc. **(2)**
123 E San Carlos St Ste 521, San Jose, CA 95112
Tel.: (408) 998-0920
Newspaper Publishers
N.A.I.C.S.: 513110

Nikkei Business Publications Asia Ltd **(1)**
Suite 1803 18th Floor Chinachem Exchange Square No1 Hoi Wan Street, Quarry Bay, China (Hong Kong)
Tel.: (852) 257 58301
Newspaper Publishers
N.A.I.C.S.: 513110
S. Wong *(Mgr-Admin)*

Nikkei Business Publications, Inc. **(1)**
1 17 3 Shirokane Minato ku, Tokyo, 108 8646, Japan **(100%)**
Tel.: (81) 368118311
Web Site: http://www.nikkeibp.com
Sales Range: $200-249.9 Million
Emp.: 872
Comprehensive Publisher of Magazines & Newsletters that Focus on Business, Marketing, Technology, Services & other Industry-Related Fields
N.A.I.C.S.: 513130
Kohei Osata *(Pres & CEO)*

Subsidiary (Non-US):

BP Advertising (Shanghai) Company Limited **(2)**
Unit G 4Th Floor Zao Fong World Trade Building No 369 Jiang Su Road, Changning District, 200050, Shanghai, China
Tel.: (86) 215 2650273
Newspaper Publishers
N.A.I.C.S.: 513110

Subsidiary (Domestic):

Nikkei BP Ad. Partners, Inc. **(2)**
NBF Platinum Tower 7F 1-17-3 Shirokane, Minato-ku, Tokyo, 108-8646, Japan
Tel.: (81) 368 118880
Web Site: http://www.bpad.co.jp
Advetising Agency
N.A.I.C.S.: 541810
Akira Okamoto *(Co-Mng Dir)*

Subsidiary (Non-US):

Nikkei Business Publications Europe Ltd. **(2)**
Orchard Lea Drift Road Winkfield, Windsor, SL4 4RP, United Kingdom
Tel.: (44) 207 9362855
Web Site: http://www.nikkeibp.com
Emp.: 2
Newspaper Publishers
N.A.I.C.S.: 513110
Math Findel-Hawkins *(Dir-Sls)*

Nikkei-Mutlu Dergi Grubu A.S. **(2)**
Dereboyu Caddesi Meydan Sokak Beybi Giz Plaza Kat 7 Maslak, Istanbul, 34398, Turkiye
Tel.: (90) 212 2902727
Web Site: http://www.nmdg.com.tr
Emp.: 80
Newspaper Publishers
N.A.I.C.S.: 513110
Melis Topaloglu *(Dir-Digital Publ)*

Nikkei China (Hong Kong) Ltd. **(1)**
Level 21 No 28 Hennessy Rd, Hong Kong, Wanchai, China (Hong Kong)
Tel.: (852) 259 81771
Web Site: http://www.nikkei.asia
Newspaper Publishers
N.A.I.C.S.: 513110
Koichi Isobe *(Gen Mgr)*

Nikkei Culture, Inc. **(1)**
Tokyoto Chiyoeadaku Uchikanda 1-6-6 MIF Bldg 2nd Fl, Chiyoda-Ku, Tokyo, 1010047, Japan
Tel.: (81) 352 592666
Newspaper Publishers
N.A.I.C.S.: 513110

Nikkei Europe Ltd. **(1)**
6th Floor Barnards Inn 86 Fetter Lane, London, EC4A 1EN, United Kingdom
Tel.: (44) 207 4217800
Web Site: http://www.nikkeieu.com
Emp.: 20
Newspaper Publishers
N.A.I.C.S.: 513110
Takiya Ma *(Mng Dir)*

Nikkei Group Asia Pte. Ltd. **(1)**
60 Anson Road 06-02 Mapletree Anson, Singapore, 079914, Singapore
Tel.: (65) 6336 4122
Web Site: http://www.nikkei.asia
Emp.: 16
Newspaper Printing & Sales; Online Databank Services
N.A.I.C.S.: 513110
Imai Hidekazu *(Mng Dir)*

Nikkei Human Resources, Inc. **(1)**
3-6-3 Kanda Kajicho, Chiyoda-ku, Tokyo, 101-0045, Japan
Tel.: (81) 368 127300
Web Site: http://www.nikkeihr.co.jp
Human Resource Consulting Services
N.A.I.C.S.: 561311
Kouta Murayama *(Mgr)*

Nikkei Ibaraki Newspaper Printing Center, Inc. **(1)**
2044-10 Kamiinayoshi Kasumigaura, Ibaraki, 315-0056, Japan
Tel.: (81) 298 329625
Newspaper Publishers
N.A.I.C.S.: 513110

Nikkei International Ltd. **(1)**
Nikkei Daini Bekkan 1-6-6 Uchikanda, Chiyoda-ku, Tokyo, 101-0047, Japan **(100%)**

NIKKEI INC.

Nikkei Inc.—(Continued)
Tel.: (81) 352552312
Sales Range: $25-49.9 Million
Emp.: 3
Media Representative Services
N.A.I.C.S.: 541840

Nikkei Media Marketing, Inc. (1)
2 2 1 Uchikanda Kamakura Riverside Building 3rd Fl, Chiyoda Ku, Tokyo, 101 0047, Japan **(100%)**
Tel.: (81) 352956211
Web Site: http://www.nikkeimm.co.jp
Sales Range: $50-74.9 Million
Emp.: 200
Marketing Operations for the Information Products & Services of the NIKKEI Group in Japan
N.A.I.C.S.: 513110

Nikkei Newspaper Printing, Inc. (1)
1-10-5 Shinonome, Koto-ku, Tokyo, 135-0062, Japan
Tel.: (81) 335 366161
Newspaper Publishers
N.A.I.C.S.: 513110
Takehiko Mitena *(Pres)*

Nikkei PR Advertising Co., Ltd. (1)
Kasahara Bldg 1-6-10 Uchikanda, Chiyoda-ku, Tokyo, 101-0047, Japan
Tel.: (81) 368 128694
Web Site: http://www.nikkeipr.co.jp
Advetising Agency
N.A.I.C.S.: 541810

Nikkei Radio Broadcasting Corporation (1)
1 9 15 Akasaka, Minato Ku, Tokyo, 107 8373, Japan **(33%)**
Tel.: (81) 335838151
Web Site: http://www.radionikkei.jp
Sales Range: $25-49.9 Million
Emp.: 79
Private, Nationwide Shortwave Broadcasting (Radio) Station
N.A.I.C.S.: 516120

Nikkei Research, Inc. (1)
Kamakuragashi Bldg 2-1 Uchikanda 2-chome Chiyoda-ku, 2-chome Chiyoda-ku, Tokyo, 101-0047, Japan **(70%)**
Tel.: (81) 352965111
Web Site: http://www.nikkei-r.co.jp
Sales Range: $25-49.9 Million
Emp.: 175
Conducts & Analyzes Surveys on Business & Economics
N.A.I.C.S.: 611710
Toru Yamashita *(Mgr-Intl Dept)*

Nikkei Science, Inc. (1)
1 9 5 Otemachi, Chiyoda Ku, Tokyo, 100 8066, Japan **(50%)**
Tel.: (81) 352552821
Web Site: http://www.nikkei-science.com
Sales Range: $25-49.9 Million
Emp.: 15
N.A.I.C.S.: 513110

Nikkei Visual Images, Inc. (1)
Nihonbashi Kayabacho 261, Chuo Ku, Tokyo, 103 0025, Japan **(66.7%)**
Tel.: (81) 336392901
Web Site: http://www.nikkeivi.jp
Sales Range: $25-49.9 Million
Emp.: 100
Producer of Television Programs, Commercials & Public Relations Videos; Markets NIKKEI's News & Information to CATVs & CCTVs
N.A.I.C.S.: 516210
Teruto Akiyama *(CEO)*

Nikkeisha, Inc. (1)
13-20 Ginza 7-chome, Chuo-ku, Tokyo, 104-8176, Japan
Tel.: (81) 355506544
Web Site: http://www.nks.co.jp
Sales Range: $450-499.9 Million
Emp.: 481
Advetising Agency
N.A.I.C.S.: 541810

Overseas Courier Service Co., Ltd. (1)
(28.2%)
Tel.: (81) 367598665
Web Site: http://www.ocstracking.com
Sales Range: $100-124.9 Million
Emp.: 364
Imports, Exports & Markets Newspapers, Magazines & Books
N.A.I.C.S.: 513110

Quick Corp. (1)
Nihonbashi Mitsui Tower 2-1-1 Nihonbashi Muromachi, Chuo-ku, Tokyo, 103-8317, Japan **(39.8%)**
Tel.: (81) 367300919
Web Site: http://www.corporate.quick.co.jp
Sales Range: $200-249.9 Million
Emp.: 666
Provides Global Security & Financial Information Services
N.A.I.C.S.: 541611

Subsidiary (US):

QUICK AMERICA CORPORATION (2)
708 Third Ave Ste 1320, New York, NY 10017
Tel.: (212) 310-1960
Web Site: http://www.quickamerica.com
Financial Management Services
N.A.I.C.S.: 523999

Rating and Investment Information, Inc. (1)
Nihonbashi 1-Chome Bldg, 1-4-1 Nihonbashi Chuo-ku, Tokyo, 103 0027, Japan **(66%)**
Tel.: (81) 332763400
Web Site: http://www.r-i.co.jp
Sales Range: $100-124.9 Million
Emp.: 188
Credit-Rating Institution that Appraises Japanese Firms, Financial Organizations, Pension-Fund Management, Foreign Governments & Entire Countries
N.A.I.C.S.: 524292

Television Hokkaido Broadcasting Co., Ltd. (1)
12-4 Odori-Higashi 6-chome, Chuo-ku, Sapporo, 060-8517, Japan
Tel.: (81) 112 327152
Web Site: http://www.tv-hokkaido.co.jp
Emp.: 90
Television Broadcasting Services
N.A.I.C.S.: 516120
Naoyuki Sekiguchi *(Pres)*

Television Osaka, Inc. (1)
1-2-18 Otemae, Chuo-ku, Osaka, 540-8519, Japan
Tel.: (81) 669 477777
Television Broadcasting Services
N.A.I.C.S.: 516120

Television Tokyo Channel 12 Ltd. (1)
4-3-12 Toranomon, Tokyo, 105 8012, Minato-ku, Japan **(33.3%)**
Tel.: (81) 334321212
Web Site: http://www.tv-tokyo.co.jp
Sales Range: $200-249.9 Million
Emp.: 800
Television Station
N.A.I.C.S.: 516120

The Financial Times Group Ltd. (1)
Number One Southwark Bridge, London, SE1 9HL, United Kingdom
Tel.: (44) 20 7873 3000
Web Site: http://www.ft.com
Business Newspaper Publishing Services
N.A.I.C.S.: 513110
Jon Slade *(Chief Comml Officer)*

Subsidiary (Domestic):

The Financial Times Ltd. (2)
Number One Southwark Bridge, London, SE1 9HL, United Kingdom
Tel.: (44) 2078733000
Web Site: http://www.ft.com
Printing & Online Publication of the Financial Times, Daily Newspaper, Associated Publications & Provisions of Business Information Services
N.A.I.C.S.: 513110
John Ridding *(CEO)*

Subsidiary (US):

GIS Planning, Inc. (3)
1 Hallidie Plz Ste 760, San Francisco, CA 94102
Tel.: (415) 294-4775
Web Site: http://www.gisplanning.com
Software Services
N.A.I.C.S.: 513210
Anatalio Ubalde *(Co-Founder & Mng Dir)*

Medley Global Advisors (3)
330 Hudson St 8th Fl, New York, NY 10013
Tel.: (212) 941-2700
Web Site: http://www.medleyadvisors.com
Macro Policy Intelligence Services
N.A.I.C.S.: 519290
Erin Blanton *(Head-Natural Gas & Renewables)*

NIKKEL TRADING 392 PROPRIETARY LIMITED
R631 Road Plot 233 Mooiplaats Pretoria, Gauteng, 0081, South Africa
Tel.: (27) 820629570
Web Site: https://nt392.co.za
Year Founded: 2018
Mining Industry
N.A.I.C.S.: 212290

Subsidiaries:

Brikor Limited (1)
3 Marievale Road Vorsterskroon Nigel, Durban, South Africa
Tel.: (27) 117399000
Web Site: https://www.brikor.net
Rev: $19,090,899
Assets: $17,310,819
Liabilities: $11,065,891
Net Worth: $6,244,928
Earnings: $257,541
Emp.: 625
Fiscal Year-end: 02/29/2024
Clay Brick & Aggregate Mfr
N.A.I.C.S.: 327120
Girnie Parkin *(CEO)*

NIKKEN KOGAKU CO., LTD.
17F Nittochi Nishishinjuku Building 6-10-1 Nishishinjuku, Shinjuku-ku, Tokyo, 160-0023, Japan
Tel.: (81) 333446811
Web Site: https://www.nikken-kogaku.co.jp
9767—(TKS)
Rev: $40,929,120
Assets: $47,578,780
Liabilities: $18,514,610
Net Worth: $29,064,170
Earnings: $1,877,240
Emp.: 163
Fiscal Year-end: 03/31/24
Brick, Stone & Related Materials; Equipment Rental & Leasing
N.A.I.C.S.: 423320

NIKKI CO. LTD.
3029 Kamiyochi, Atsugi, 243-0801, Kanagawa, Japan
Tel.: (81) 462850227
Web Site: https://www.nikkinet.co.jp
6042—(TKS)
Rev: $61,836,550
Assets: $152,453,040
Liabilities: $70,522,090
Net Worth: $81,930,950
Earnings: $14,489,120
Fiscal Year-end: 03/31/24
Carburetors & Fuel Equipment Mfr & Sales
N.A.I.C.S.: 336310
Nobuo Tanaka *(Exec Mng Dir)*

Subsidiaries:

Nikki America Fuel Systems, LLC (1)
272 Technology Pkwy, Auburn, AL 36830
Tel.: (334) 321-1001
Motor Vehicle Parts Distr
N.A.I.C.S.: 423120

Nikki America, Inc. (1)
272 Technology Pkwy, Auburn, AL 36830
Tel.: (334) 321-1001
Motor Vehicle Parts Distr
N.A.I.C.S.: 423120

INTERNATIONAL PUBLIC

Nikki India Fuel Systems Private Limited (1)
No135 Ulundhai Village Thandalam-Perambakkam Main Road, Tiruvallur Taluk District, Chennai, 602 105, Tamil Nadu, India
Tel.: (91) 4427658055
Motor Vehicle Parts Distr
N.A.I.C.S.: 423120

Nikki Korea Co., Ltd. (1)
Bukbisan-ro 92, Seo-gu, Daegu, 41757, Korea (South)
Tel.: (82) 535643888
Motor Vehicle Parts Distr
N.A.I.C.S.: 423120

Nikki Soltech Service Co., Ltd. (1)
3029 Kamiechi, Atsugi, 243-0801, Kanagawa, Japan
Tel.: (81) 462842341
Web Site: https://www.nksoltech.co.jp
Emp.: 8
Motor Vehicle Parts Mfr & Distr
N.A.I.C.S.: 336310

Nikki Techno Co., Ltd. (1)
3029 Kamiechi, Atsugi, 243-0801, Kanagawa, Japan
Tel.: (81) 462865837
Motor Vehicle Parts Mfr
N.A.I.C.S.: 336310

Nikki Thailand Co., Ltd. (1)
22/32 Moo 6 Bhudhamondhon 4 Road Krathumlom, Sam Phran, 73220, Nakhonpathom, Thailand
Tel.: (66) 28141079
Motor Vehicle Parts Distr
N.A.I.C.S.: 423120

Shen Yang Rixin Carbureter Corp. (1)
No 26 Zhengliang Road 2, Daoyi Economic Development Zone of Shenbei New District, Shenyang, 110136, China
Tel.: (86) 2489731359
Motor Vehicle Parts Distr
N.A.I.C.S.: 423120

Tai Hua Carbureter Co., Ltd. (1)
10 Kong-Yeh 1st Road Jin-Wu-Industrial Zone, Kaohsiung, 81469, Taiwan
Tel.: (886) 73726807
Motor Vehicle Parts Distr
N.A.I.C.S.: 423120

NIKKI GLOBAL FINANCE LIMITED
3rd Floor Eastern and Central Wing 124 Thapar House Janpath, New Delhi, 110001, Delhi, India
Tel.: (91) 8542836641
Web Site: https://www.nikkiglobal.com
Year Founded: 1986
531272—(BOM)
Rev: $9,273
Assets: $1,252,113
Liabilities: $1,037,650
Net Worth: $214,463
Earnings: ($4,657)
Fiscal Year-end: 03/31/21
Financial Services
N.A.I.C.S.: 523999
Ashesh Agarwal *(Mng Dir)*

NIKKISO CO., LTD.
Yebisu Garden Place Tower 22nd Floor 20-3 Ebisu 4-Chome, Shibuya-ku, Tokyo, 150-6022, Japan
Tel.: (81) 334433711
Web Site: https://www.nikkiso.com
Year Founded: 1953
6376—(TKS)
Rev: $1,365,739,610
Assets: $2,100,256,520
Liabilities: $1,204,874,600
Net Worth: $895,381,920
Earnings: $64,313,390
Emp.: 8,248
Fiscal Year-end: 12/31/23
Fluid Equipment & Aircraft Components Mfr

AND PRIVATE COMPANIES

N.A.I.C.S.: 334511
Toshihiko Kai *(Pres & CEO)*
Subsidiaries:

Geveke B.V. (1)
Kabelweg 51, 1014 BA, Amsterdam, Netherlands
Tel.: (31) 20 582 9111
Web Site: https://www.geveke.com
Air Measuring & Control Equipment Mfr
N.A.I.C.S.: 334519

LEWA GmbH (1)
Ulmer Strasse 10, 71229, Leonberg, Germany
Tel.: (49) 7152140
Web Site: http://www.lewa.de
Sales Range: $150-199.9 Million
Emp.: 600
Mfr of Metering & Process Diaphragm Pumps
N.A.I.C.S.: 333914
Tsunehisa Suita *(CEO)*

M.E. Nikkiso Co., Ltd. (1)
74 Suwintawong Road Saladang Bangnumpeo, Bangkok, 24000, Chacheongsao, Thailand
Tel.: (66) 38593207
Medical Product Mfr & Distr
N.A.I.C.S.: 339112

MicrotracBEL Corp. (1)
8-2-52 Nanko-Higashi, Suminoe-ku, Osaka, 559-0031, Japan
Tel.: (81) 671662161
Web Site: http://www.microtrac-bel.com
Emp.: 120
Measuring Device Mfr
N.A.I.C.S.: 334519
Kazuyuki Nakai *(Pres & CEO)*

Nikkiso (Shanghai) Consulting Co., Ltd. (1)
20 Fl Room 08 No 317 XianXia Rd Far East Intl Plaza Building B, Shanghai, 200051, China
Tel.: (86) 2152399959
Web Site: http://www.nikkiso.co.jp
Sales Range: $25-49.9 Million
Emp.: 2
Business & Investment Management Consulting Services
N.A.I.C.S.: 561499

Nikkiso America, Inc. (1)
7676 Hazard Center Dr Ste 400, San Diego, CA 92108
Tel.: (858) 222-6300
Web Site: http://www.nikkisoamerica.com
Electrical Equipment & Component Mfr
N.A.I.C.S.: 335999

Subsidiary (Domestic):

Cryogenic Industries, Inc. (2)
27710 Jefferson Ave Ste 301, Temecula, CA 92590-4604
Tel.: (951) 677-2081
Web Site: http://www.cryoind.com
Emp.: 300
Cryogenic Gas Processing Equipment Mfr
N.A.I.C.S.: 333248
Russell Higgins *(CFO)*

Subsidiary (Domestic):

ACD, LLC (3)
2321 S Pullman St, Santa Ana, CA 92705
Tel.: (949) 261-7533
Web Site: http://www.acdllc.com
Reciprocating & Centrifugal Pumps Mfr
N.A.I.C.S.: 333914
James Estes *(Mng Dir)*

Cosmodyne, LLC (3)
3010 Old Ranch Pkwy Ste 300, Seal Beach, CA 90740
Tel.: (562) 795-5990
Web Site: https://www.cosmodyne.com
Industrial Machinery Mfr
N.A.I.C.S.: 333248
Peter Sniezynski *(Controller)*

Unit (Domestic):

Cryogenic Industries Service Companies, LLC - Houston (3)
14014 Interdrive S, Houston, TX 77032
Tel.: (281) 590-4800

Web Site: http://www.cryoind.com
Industrial Machinery Mfr
N.A.I.C.S.: 333248

Subsidiary (Domestic):

Cryoquip, LLC (3)
25720 Jefferson Ave, Murrieta, CA 92562
Tel.: (951) 677-2060
Web Site: http://www.cryoquip.com
Cryogenic Vaporizers & Industrial Gas Equipment Fabricator & Mfr
N.A.I.C.S.: 333415
Juan Hernandez *(Mgr-Quality Control)*

Subsidiary (Domestic):

LEWA-Nikkiso America, Inc. (2)
2446 Greens Rd, Houston, TX 77032
Tel.: (713) 577-5392
Web Site: https://www.lewa-inc.com
Pumps Mfr & Sales
N.A.I.C.S.: 333914

Nikkiso Co., Ltd. - Higashimurayama Plant (1)
2-16-2 Noguchi-cho, Higashimurayama, 189-8520, Tokyo, Japan
Tel.: (81) 423923311
Pumps Mfr
N.A.I.C.S.: 333914

Nikkiso Co., Ltd. - Kanazawa Plant (1)
3-1 Hokuyohdai, Kanazawa, 920-0177, Ishikawa, Japan
Tel.: (81) 76 257 4181
Web Site: https://www.nikkiso.com
Sales Range: $400-449.9 Million
Medical Apparatus Mfr
N.A.I.C.S.: 339112

Nikkiso Co., Ltd. - Shizuoka Plant (1)
498-1 Shizutani, Shizuoka, 421-0496, Japan
Tel.: (81) 548510792
Web Site: http://www.nikkiso.com
Medical Equipment Mfr
N.A.I.C.S.: 339112

Nikkiso Critical Care Medical Supplies (Shanghai) Co., Ltd. (1)
Zhaofeng World Trade Plaza No 369 Jiangsu Road, Changning District, Shanghai, 200050, China
Tel.: (86) 2152399959
Medical Product Distr
N.A.I.C.S.: 456199

Nikkiso Cryo, Inc. (1)
4661 Eaker St, North Las Vegas, NV 89081
Tel.: (702) 643-4900
Web Site: http://www.nikkisocryo.com
Motor Pump Mfr & Distr
N.A.I.C.S.: 333996
Daryl Lamy *(Pres & CEO)*

Nikkiso Eiko Co., Ltd. (1)
Seibikyoiku Bunka Kaikan 5th Floor 8-14 Higashihoncho, Higashikurume, 203-0014, Tokyo, Japan
Tel.: (81) 423906540
Water Filtration Product Mfr & Distr
N.A.I.C.S.: 333310

Nikkiso Europe GmbH (1)
Desbrocksriede 1, 30855, Langenhagen, Germany
Tel.: (49) 5116799990
Web Site: http://www.nikkiso-europe.eu
Sales Range: $25-49.9 Million
Emp.: 70
Medical Equipments Mfr & Maintenance Services
N.A.I.C.S.: 339112

Nikkiso Giken Co., Ltd. (1)
1-5-1 Asahigaoka, Hakusan, 924-0004, Ishikawa, Japan
Tel.: (81) 762574141
Pump System Mfr
N.A.I.C.S.: 333914

Nikkiso M.E.S. Co., Ltd. (1)
2-27-10 Nikkiso Bldg Bekkan 3F Ebisu, Shibuya-ku, Tokyo, 1500013, Japan
Tel.: (81) 357912581
Web Site: http://www.nikkiso-mes.co.jp
Medical Equipment Mfr
N.A.I.C.S.: 334510

Nikkiso Medical (Thailand) Co., Ltd. (1)
689 Onnuch Road Onnuch, Suanluang, Bangkok, 10250, Thailand
Tel.: (66) 2 716 2894
Web Site: http://www.nikkiso.com
Medical Equipments Sales & Service
N.A.I.C.S.: 423450

Nikkiso Miyazaki Co., Ltd. (1)
1495-63 Takahama, Takaoka-cho, Miyazaki, 880-2215, Japan
Tel.: (81) 98 582 5600
Web Site: https://www.miyazaki-nikkiso.co.jp
Emp.: 627
Pump System Mfr
N.A.I.C.S.: 333914

Nikkiso Pumps Korea Ltd. (1)
603 6F Ilshin Bldg, 541 Dowha-Dong Mapo-Gu, Seoul, 121 040, Korea (South)
Tel.: (82) 27191446
Web Site: http://www.nikkiso.com
Sales Range: $25-49.9 Million
Emp.: 10
Motor Pumps Mfr & Sales
N.A.I.C.S.: 333914

Nikkiso Vietnam MFG Co., Ltd. (1)
Road 19 Tan Thuan Export Processing Zone, Tan Thuan Dong Ward District 7, Ho Chi Minh City, Vietnam
Tel.: (84) 2837701320
Blood Tubing Equipment Mfr
N.A.I.C.S.: 325413

Nikkiso Vietnam, Inc. (1)
Plot No C6 and C7, Thang Long Industrial Park II Lieu Xa Commune, Yen My, Hung Yen, Vietnam
Tel.: (84) 2213974520
Aircraft Components Mfr
N.A.I.C.S.: 336413

Nikkiso-Therm Co., Ltd. (1)
2-4-24 Sakai, Musashino, 180-0022, Tokyo, Japan
Tel.: (81) 422379811
Web Site: http://www.nktherm.com
Sales Range: $25-49.9 Million
Emp.: 25
Thermistors Mfr & Sales
N.A.I.C.S.: 334513
Akihira Morihara *(Mgr-Admin)*

Shanghai Nikkiso Non-Seal Pump Co., Ltd. (1)
Building 1 No 1359 Huhang Road, Fengxian District, Shanghai, 201400, China
Tel.: (86) 216 710 3258
Web Site: https://www.shnikkisopump.com
Sales Range: $25-49.9 Million
Motor Pumps Mfr & Supplier
N.A.I.C.S.: 333996

Shanghai Nikkiso Trading Co., Ltd. (1)
Room 04b 27F Dawning Center B No 500 Hongbaoshi Road, Changning District, Shanghai, 201103, China
Tel.: (86) 2152393637
Web Site: http://www.nikkiso.com
Sales Range: $25-49.9 Million
Motor Pumps Sales
N.A.I.C.S.: 423120

Sundyne Nikkiso Company (1)
27-10 Ebisu, Shibuya-ku, Tokyo, Japan
Tel.: (81) 334446475
Web Site: http://www.sundyne.com
Sales Range: $25-49.9 Million
Emp.: 25
Pumps & Compressor Sales
N.A.I.C.S.: 423830

Taiwan Nikkiso Co., Ltd. (1)
9F No 184 Sec 4 Xinyi Road, Da'an District, Taipei, 106, Taiwan
Tel.: (886) 227060652
Web Site: http://www.nikkiso.com.tw
Sales Range: $25-49.9 Million
Emp.: 13
Water Conditioning System Mfr & Sales
N.A.I.C.S.: 333310

NIKKO CO., LTD.
1013-1 Eigashima Okubo-cho, Akashi, 674-8585, Hyogo, Japan
Tel.: (81) 789473131   JP

NIKO GROUP N.V.

Web Site: https://www.nikko-net.co.jp
Year Founded: 1919
6306—(TKS)
Rev.: $291,481,170
Assets: $411,333,690
Liabilities: $192,635,230
Net Worth: $218,698,460
Earnings: $8,672,320
Emp.: 1,376
Fiscal Year-end: 03/31/24
Industrial Plant Construction & Machinery Mfr
N.A.I.C.S.: 333120

Subsidiaries:

Nikko Nilkhosol Co., Ltd. (1)
180/1 Moo6 Tambol Bueng, Amphur, Si Racha, 20230, Chonburi, Thailand
Tel.: (66) 33047475
Recycling Services
N.A.I.C.S.: 562920

Tombo Industry Co., Ltd. (1)
Room 1805 18/F Nanyang Plaza No 57 Hung To Road, Kwun Tong, Kowloon, China (Hong Kong)
Tel.: (852) 29510212
Web Site: http://www.tomboind.net
Emp.: 100
Plastics Product Mfr
N.A.I.C.S.: 326199

NIKKO TRAVEL CO., LTD.
1-1-1 Kyobashi 2nd floor Yaesu Daibiru, Chuo-ku, Tokyo, 104-0031, Japan
Tel.: (81) 03 32760111   JP
Web Site: http://www.nikkotravel.co.jp
Year Founded: 1976
Travel Arrangement Services
N.A.I.C.S.: 561510
Tetsuya Furukawa *(Pres)*

NIKKON HOLDINGS CO., LTD.
6-17 Akashi-cho, Chuo-ku, Tokyo, 104-0044, Japan
Tel.: (81) 335415331
Web Site: https://www.nikkon-hd.co.jp
Year Founded: 1950
9072—(TKS)
Rev.: $1,469,561,640
Assets: $2,567,628,060
Liabilities: $938,626,610
Net Worth: $1,629,001,450
Earnings: $109,778,880
Emp.: 12,488
Fiscal Year-end: 03/31/24
Automobile Transportation Services
N.A.I.C.S.: 484110
Yasunori Matsuda *(Exec Officer & Gen Mgr-Accounting Department)*

NIKO GROUP N.V.
Industriepark West 40, Saint-Niklaas, 9100, Belgium
Tel.: (32) 3 778 90 00
Web Site: http://www.niko.be
Year Founded: 1919
Sales Range: $150-199.9 Million
Emp.: 700
Electronic Control Equipment Mfr
N.A.I.C.S.: 334419
Paul Matthijs *(CEO)*

Subsidiaries:

Fifthplay N.V. (1)
Generaal Lemanstraat 47, 2018, Antwerp, Belgium
Tel.: (32) 3 285 97 11
Web Site: http://www.fifthplay.com
Emp.: 45
Electronic Controls Mfr
N.A.I.C.S.: 334419
Kris van Daele *(Mng Dir)*

Servodan A/S (1)
Stenager 5, DK-6400, Sonderborg, Denmark
Tel.: (45) 7442 4726

NIKO GROUP N.V.

INTERNATIONAL PUBLIC

Niko Group N.V.—(Continued)
Web Site: http://www.servodan.com
Lighting Control Equipment Mfr
N.A.I.C.S.: 335139

NIKO RESOURCES LIMITED
1500 205-5th Avenue S W, Calgary, T2P 2V7, AB, Canada
Tel.: (403) 262-1020 **AB**
Web Site:
https://www.nikoresources.com
Year Founded: 1987
NKRSF—(OTCEM)
Rev: $20,000
Assets: $2,178,000
Liabilities: $411,614,000
Net Worth: ($409,436,000)
Earnings: ($1,126,000)
Emp.: 75
Fiscal Year-end: 03/31/23
Producer of Oil & Gas
N.A.I.C.S.: 213112
William T. Hornaday *(CEO)*

NIKO SEMICONDUCTOR CO., LTD.
12F No 368 Gong-Jian Rd, Xizhi District, New Taipei City, 22161, Taiwan
Tel.: (886) 226426789
Web Site: https://www.niko-sem.com
Year Founded: 1998
3317—(TPE)
Rev: $81,714,755
Assets: $107,244,098
Liabilities: $23,608,104
Net Worth: $83,635,994
Earnings: $13,553,825
Emp.: 151
Fiscal Year-end: 12/31/22
Electronic Components Mfr
N.A.I.C.S.: 334419
Hui-Chiang Yang *(Chm, Pres & CEO)*

NIKOLA TESLA ELEKTRONSKA INDUSTRIJA A.D.
Bulevar kralja Aleksanda br 403, Belgrade, Serbia
Tel.: (381) 112862455
Web Site: https://www.ei-ntesla.rs
Year Founded: 1947
NKTS—(BEL)
Assets: $783,922
Liabilities: $317,819
Net Worth: $466,103
Earnings: ($30,991)
Emp.: 1
Fiscal Year-end: 12/31/20
Household Goods Repair & Maintenance Services
N.A.I.C.S.: 811490
Bojan Krstic *(Dir)*

NIKON CORPORATION
Shinagawa Intercity Tower C 2-15-3 Konan, Minato-ku, Tokyo, 108-6290, Japan
Tel.: (81) 364333600 **JP**
Web Site: https://www.nikon.com
Year Founded: 1917
7731—(TKS)
Rev: $4,740,989,450
Assets: $7,582,397,100
Liabilities: $3,053,945,590
Net Worth: $4,528,451,510
Earnings: $215,287,700
Emp.: 19,444
Fiscal Year-end: 03/31/24
Cameras & Photographic Equipment, Binoculars, Microscopes, Telescopes, Ophthalmic Products, Semiconductor Manufacturing Equipment Mfr
N.A.I.C.S.: 333310
Kazuo Ushida *(Co-Chm)*
Subsidiaries:

Aichi Nikon Co., Ltd. **(1)**
2-1-2 Sawakihama Mitocho, Toyokawa, 441-0304, Aichi, Japan **(100%)**
Tel.: (81) 533764800
Web Site: http://www.nikon-essilor.co.jp
Sales Range: $50-74.9 Million
Emp.: 200
Mfr of Ophthalmic Lenses
N.A.I.C.S.: 333310

Beijing Nikon Ophthalmic Products Co., Ltd. **(1)**
301-3 Wangfujing Street, Dongcheng District, Beijing, 100005, China
Tel.: (86) 1065285858
Web Site: https://www.nikonlenswear.cn
Sales Range: $25-49.9 Million
Emp.: 20
Sales, Processing & Repair of Ophthalmic Products
N.A.I.C.S.: 423460

Dong Guan Nikon Surveying Instruments Co., Ltd. **(1)**
Room 101 11 Bei Yuan Street, Chang-An Town, Dongguan, China
Tel.: (86) 76985535435
Surveying Instruments Mfr
N.A.I.C.S.: 333310

Guang Dong Nikon Camera Co., Ltd. **(1)**
Xiao Bian The Second Industry Zone, Chang An Town, Dongguan, 523849, Guan Dong, China
Tel.: (86) 76985313915
Web Site: http://www.nikon.com
Digital Camera Components Mfr
N.A.I.C.S.: 333310

Hang Zhou Nikon Camera Co., Ltd. **(1)**
560 Xi-Xi Road, Hangzhou, China
Tel.: (86) 57185021558
Web Site: http://www.nikon.com
Digital Camera Components Mfr
N.A.I.C.S.: 333310

Hikari Glass (Changzhou) Optics Co., Ltd. **(1)**
No 4 Jinshajiang Road, Xin Bei Zone, Changzhou, Jiangsu, China
Tel.: (86) 5198 513 0777
Web Site: https://www.hikari-g.co.jp
Optic Glass Mfr
N.A.I.C.S.: 327215

Hikari Glass Co., Ltd **(1)**
155 Mimata Shirahata Komagata-cho, Yuzawa, 012-0104, Akita, Japan
Tel.: (81) 183424291
Web Site: https://www.hikari-g.co.jp
Sales Range: $25-49.9 Million
Emp.: 227
Glass Mfr
N.A.I.C.S.: 327212

Kurobane Nikon Co., Ltd. **(1)**
1434 Kurobanemuko-machi, Otawara, Tochigi, 324 0241, Japan **(100%)**
Tel.: (81) 287531111
Web Site: http://www.kurobane-nikon.co.jp
Sales Range: $50-74.9 Million
Emp.: 239
Lenses for Microscopes, Profile Projectors & Surveying Instruments Mfr
N.A.I.C.S.: 333310
Noboru Takashita *(Pres)*

Miyagi Nikon Precision Co., Ltd. **(1)**
20 Shin-oyoke Miya Zao-machi, Katta-gun, Miyagi, 989-0701, Japan
Tel.: (81) 224322336
Liquid Crystal Display Mfr
N.A.I.C.S.: 334419

Morf3D Inc. **(1)**
821 N Nash St, El Segundo, CA 90245
Tel.: (310) 607-0188
Web Site: https://morf3d.com
Additive Mfr
N.A.I.C.S.: 339999

Nanjing Nikon Jiangnan Optical Instrument Co., Ltd. **(1)**
Nanjing Economic & Technical Development Zone 9 Hengda Road, Nanjing, 210038, China
Tel.: (86) 25 8580 0009
Web Site: http://www.nikon.com
Microscopes & Lenses Mfr
N.A.I.C.S.: 333310

Net Work Corporation **(1)**
6-15 Harushinmachi Oitashi, Oita, 870-0912, Japan
Tel.: (81) 97 551 8500
Semiconductor Lithography System Maintenance Services
N.A.I.C.S.: 811210

Nikon (Malaysia) Sdn Bhd **(1)**
Unit 100 7 015 Block J 129 Office Jaya One No72A, Jalan Universiti, 46200, Petaling Jaya, Selangor Darul Ehsan, Malaysia **(100%)**
Tel.: (60) 378093688
Web Site: http://www.nikon.com.my
Sales Range: $10-24.9 Million
Emp.: 30
Sales of Cameras
N.A.I.C.S.: 423410

Nikon (Russia) LLC **(1)**
Premises 77 1F Novinsky bulvar 31, Presnensky municipal district intra-city area, 123242, Moscow, Russia
Tel.: (7) 4952301441
Web Site: http://www.nikon.ru
Sales Range: $25-49.9 Million
Emp.: 100
Import, Sales & Servicing of Cameras
N.A.I.C.S.: 449210

Nikon (Thailand) Co., Ltd. **(1)**
1/42 Moo 5 Rojana Industrial Park Rojana Road Tambol Kanham, Amphur U-Thai, Ayutthaya, 13210, Thailand
Tel.: (66) 35331500
Web Site: http://www.nikon.com.tw
Mfr of Cameras & Camera Lenses
N.A.I.C.S.: 333310

Nikon Americas Inc. **(1)**
1300 Walt Whitman Rd, Melville, NY 11747-3064
Tel.: (631) 547-4200
Web Site: http://www.nikonusa.com
Sales Range: $75-99.9 Million
Emp.: 250
Cameras, Lenses, Accessories, Binoculars, Optical Equipment, Riflescopes, Spotting Scopes & Electronic Imaging Products Wholesale Distr
N.A.I.C.S.: 423410

Branch (Domestic):

Nikon Instrument Inc. **(2)**
1300 Walt Whitman Rd, Melville, NY 11747-3064 **(100%)**
Tel.: (631) 547-8500
Web Site: http://www.microscope.nikon.com
Distr of Nikon Photographic, Ophthalmic, Measuring & Other Equipment
N.A.I.C.S.: 423450
Yoshinobu Ishikawa *(Pres & CEO)*

Nikon Precision Inc. **(2)**
1399 Shoreway Rd, Belmont, CA 94002-4107
Tel.: (650) 508-4674
Web Site: https://www.nikonprecision.com
Sales Range: $75-99.9 Million
Emp.: 250
Mfr of Semiconductors
N.A.I.C.S.: 423830
Hamid Zarringhalam *(Exec VP)*

Nikon Research Corporation of America **(2)**
1399 Shoreway Rd, Belmont, CA 94002
Tel.: (650) 508-4674
Web Site: http://www.nikon.com
Mfr of Semiconductors
N.A.I.C.S.: 334515

Nikon Australia Pty. Ltd. **(1)**
Suite 501 Level 5 5 Rider Boulevard, Rhodes, 2138, NSW, Australia
Tel.: (61) 287676900
Web Site: https://www.nikon.com.au
Sales Range: $50-74.9 Million
Emp.: 60
Camera & Optical Products Sales & Service
N.A.I.C.S.: 423410

Nikon Business Service Co., Ltd. **(1)**
6-3 Nishiohi 1-chome, Shinagawa-ku, Tokyo, 140-0015, Japan
Tel.: (81) 337732122
Business Support Services
N.A.I.C.S.: 561499

Nikon Canada, Inc. **(1)**
1366 Aerowood Drive, Mississauga, L4W 1C1, ON, Canada **(100%)**
Tel.: (905) 625-9910
Web Site: https://www.en.nikon.ca
Sales Range: $50-74.9 Million
Emp.: 100
Photographic Equipment & Supplies Mfr & Sales
N.A.I.C.S.: 333310

Nikon CeLL innovation Co., Ltd. **(1)**
Shinagawa Intercity Tower C 2-15-3, Minato-ku Konan, Tokyo, 108-6290, Japan
Tel.: (81) 36 433 3707
Biological Product Mfr
N.A.I.C.S.: 325414

Nikon Corporation - Glass Division **(1)**
10-1 Asamizodai 1-chome, Minami-ku, Sagamihara, 252-0328, Kanagawa, Japan
Tel.: (81) 42 740 6746
Emp.: 7
Optical Glass Materials Mfr
N.A.I.C.S.: 333310
Hiroyuki Hiraiwa *(Gen Mgr)*

Nikon Engineering Co., Ltd. **(1)**
1-6-3 Nishi-Oi, Shinagawa-ku, Tokyo, 140-0015, Japan **(100%)**
Tel.: (81) 337731620
Web Site: https://www.ave.nikon.co.jp
Sales Range: $10-24.9 Million
Emp.: 64
Designer, Manufacturer & Sales of Precision Laser Processing Devices, Microscopes & Related Equipment
N.A.I.C.S.: 334413

Nikon France S.A. **(1)**
191 rue du Marche Rollay, 94500, Champigny-sur-Marne, France **(100%)**
Tel.: (33) 145164516
Web Site: http://www.nikon.fr
Sales Range: $200-249.9 Million
Emp.: 100
Importer & Sales of Cameras, Microscopes & Measuring Instruments
N.A.I.C.S.: 333310

Nikon GmbH **(1)**
Tiefenbroicher Weg 25, 40472, Dusseldorf, Germany **(100%)**
Tel.: (49) 21194140
Web Site: https://www.nikon.de
Sales Range: $75-99.9 Million
Emp.: 120
Importer & Sales of Cameras, Microscopes & Measuring Instruments
N.A.I.C.S.: 423410

Nikon Holdings Europe B.V. **(1)**
Tripolis 100 Burgerweeshuispad 101, 1076 ER, Amsterdam, Netherlands
Tel.: (31) 207099000
Web Site: http://www.nikon.com
Sales Range: $25-49.9 Million
Emp.: 6
Business & Financial Support Services
N.A.I.C.S.: 561499

Holding (Non-US):

Nikon Europe B.V. **(2)** **(100%)**
Tel.: (31) 9001225564
Web Site: http://www.nikon.nl
Sales Range: $25-49.9 Million
Importer & Sales of Microscopes & Measuring, Surveying & Ophthalmic Instruments
N.A.I.C.S.: 333310

Holding (Domestic):

Nikon Instruments Europe B.V. **(2)**
Tripolis 100 Burgerweeshuispad 101, 1076 ER, Amsterdam, Netherlands
Tel.: (31) 207099000
Web Site: http://www.Nikon.nl
Sales Range: $25-49.9 Million
Microscopes & Measuring Instruments Import, Sales & Service
N.A.I.C.S.: 423450

Holding (Non-US):

Nikon Instruments S.p.A. **(2)**
Via san Quirico 300, Campi Bisenzio,

AND PRIVATE COMPANIES — NIKON CORPORATION

50010, Florence, Italy **(100%)**
Tel.: (39) 0553009601
Web Site: http://www.nikoninstruments.eu
Importer & Sales of Microscopes & Measuring & Surveying Instruments
N.A.I.C.S.: 333310

Nikon Polska Sp. z o.o. **(2)**
Ul Postepu 14 wejscie od Marynarskiej, 02-676, Warsaw, Poland
Tel.: (48) 224608735
Web Site: http://www.nikon.pl
Sales Range: $25-49.9 Million
Camera Import, Sales & Service
N.A.I.C.S.: 423410

Nikon Holdings Hong Kong Limited **(1)**
Unit 2001 Level 20 Tower II Grand Century Place 193, Prince Edward Road West Mongkok, Kowloon, China (Hong Kong)
Tel.: (852) 2 902 9860
Information Technology Services
N.A.I.C.S.: 541219

Nikon Hong Kong Ltd. **(1)**
Room 2001 Tower 2 New Century Plaza 193 Prince Edward Road West, Mongkok, Kowloon, China (Hong Kong) **(100%)**
Tel.: (852) 28823936
Web Site: https://www.nikon.com.hk
Sales Range: $25-49.9 Million
Emp.: 50
Importer & Sales of Cameras
N.A.I.C.S.: 423410

Nikon Imaging (China) Co., Ltd. **(1)**
No 11 Changjiang South Road, New Area, Wuxi, 214028, Jiangsu, China
Tel.: (86) 51085343223
Web Site: http://www.nikon.com
Sales Range: $150-199.9 Million
Emp.: 209
Digital Cameras & Components Mfr
N.A.I.C.S.: 333310
Kamoshida Toshikazu *(Gen Mgr)*

Nikon Imaging (China) Sales Co., Ltd. **(1)**
Room 01-07 12F No 757 Mengzi Road, Huangpu, Shanghai, 200023, China
Tel.: (86) 2153894888
Web Site: http://www.nikon.com
Camera Import, Sales & Service
N.A.I.C.S.: 423410

Nikon Imaging Japan Inc. **(1)**
Shinagawa Intercity Tower C 2-15-3, Minato-ku, Tokyo, 108-6290, Japan
Tel.: (81) 367183010
Sales Range: $150-199.9 Million
Emp.: 30
Digital Camera Distr
N.A.I.C.S.: 423410
Yoshiki Nishikawa *(Pres)*

Nikon Imaging Korea Co., Ltd. **(1)**
22nd floor City Airport Tower 36 Teheran-ro 87-gil, Gangnam-gu, Seoul, 06164, Korea (South)
Tel.: (82) 808006600
Web Site: https://www.nikon-image.co.kr
Camera Import, Sales & Service
N.A.I.C.S.: 423410

Nikon Inc. **(1)**
1300 Walt Whitman Rd, Melville, NY 11747-3064
Tel.: (631) 547-4200
Web Site: https://www.nikonusa.com
Photographic Equipment Distr
N.A.I.C.S.: 423410
Yasuyuki Okamoto *(Pres & CEO)*

Nikon India Private Limited **(1)**
Plot No 71 Sector 32 Institutional Area, Gurgaon, 122001, Haryana, India
Tel.: (91) 1244688500
Web Site: https://www.nikon.co.in
Sales Range: $25-49.9 Million
Emp.: 75
Measuring Instruments Mfr
N.A.I.C.S.: 334515
Sajjan Kumar *(Mng Dir)*

Nikon Instech Co., Ltd. **(1)**
Shinagawa Intercity Tower C 2-15-3 Konan, Minato-ku, Tokyo, 108-6290, Japan **(100%)**
Tel.: (81) 364333980

Web Site: http://www.nikon.co.jp
Sales Range: $50-74.9 Million
Emp.: 100
Sales of Microscopes, Measuring Instruments & Inspection Equipment
N.A.I.C.S.: 423460

Nikon Instruments (Shanghai) Co., Ltd. **(1)**
T5 Jingyao Qiantan No 36 Pingjiaqiao Road, Pudong New District, Shanghai, 200126, China
Tel.: (86) 2168412050
Web Site: https://www.nikon-instruments.com.cn
Sales Range: $25-49.9 Million
Emp.: 20
Microscopes, Measuring Instruments & Semiconductor Measuring Instruments Marketing, Sales & Service
N.A.I.C.S.: 423410

Nikon Instruments Korea Co., Ltd. **(1)**
21F City Air Tower 36 Teheran-ro 87gil, Gangnam-gu, Seoul, 06164, Korea (South)
Tel.: (82) 262881900
Sales Range: $25-49.9 Million
Emp.: 24
Microscopes & Measuring Instruments Sales, Maintenance & Service
N.A.I.C.S.: 423410

Nikon International Trading (Shenzhen) Co., Ltd. **(1)**
No 309 3/F Block 2 Creative Bonded Park 2-1 Binglang Road, Futian Free Trade Zone, Shenzhen, 518017, China
Tel.: (86) 75582821108
Camera Components Mfr
N.A.I.C.S.: 449210

Nikon Kft. **(1)**
Hungaria korut 130, 1143, Budapest, Hungary
Tel.: (36) 12321372
Web Site: https://www.nikon.hu
Sales Range: $25-49.9 Million
Emp.: 15
Importer & Sales of Cameras
N.A.I.C.S.: 423410

Nikon Lao Co., Ltd. **(1)**
KM 28 Savan-Seno Special Economic Zone, Savannakhet, Lao People's Democratic Republic
Tel.: (856) 4 143 1452
Digital Camera Mfr
N.A.I.C.S.: 333310

Nikon Lenswear Experience Center Co., Ltd. **(1)**
LUCE Minami-Aoyama Building 2F 5-5-4 Minami-aoyama, Minato-ku, Tokyo, 107-0062, Japan
Tel.: (81) 36 427 4850
Frame & Lens Distr
N.A.I.C.S.: 423460

Nikon Life Co., Ltd. **(1)**
1-6-3 Nishiohi Shinagawa-ku, Tokyo, 140-0015, Japan
Tel.: (81) 337732122
Web Site: http://www.nikon.com
Sales Range: $75-99.9 Million
Emp.: 300
Employee Services
N.A.I.C.S.: 561499
Nishigaki Takeo *(Pres)*

Subsidiary (Domestic):

Nikon Staff Service Corporation **(2)**
6 Kandasurugadai 4-chome, Chiyoda-ku, Tokyo, 101-0062, Japan
Tel.: (81) 335254079
Web Site: http://www.nikon.co.jp
Sales Range: $25-49.9 Million
Emp.: 150
Staffing & Outsourcing Services
N.A.I.C.S.: 561330

Nikon Logistics Corporation **(1)**
13 17 Ohi 4 Chome, Shinagawa Ku, Tokyo, 140 0014, Japan **(100%)**
Tel.: (81) 337730351
Sales Range: $25-49.9 Million
Emp.: 150
Provider of Logistics Services
N.A.I.C.S.: 561499

Nikon Metrology N.V. **(1)**
Geldenaaksebaan 329, 3001, Leuven, Belgium
Tel.: (32) 16740101
Web Site: http://www.nikonmetrology.com
Sales Range: $100-124.9 Million
Emp.: 544
3D Hardware & Software Inspection Systems Services
N.A.I.C.S.: 333310
Myles Richard *(Mng Dir-North America)*

Subsidiary (Non-US):

Nikon Metrology Canada Inc. **(2)**
60 Northland Dr, Waterloo, N2V 2B8, ON, Canada
Tel.: (519) 884-1376
3D Hardware & Software Inspection Systems Services
N.A.I.C.S.: 333310

Nikon Metrology GmbH **(2)**
Siemensstrasse 24, 63755, Alzenau, Germany
Web Site: http://www.nikonmetrology.com
Sales Range: $25-49.9 Million
Emp.: 20
3D Hardware & Software Inspection Systems Services
N.A.I.C.S.: 333310

Nikon Metrology SARL **(2)**
Rue du Bois Chaland 39, 91090, Lisses, France
Tel.: (33) 160860976
Web Site: http://www.nikonmetrology.com
Sales Range: $25-49.9 Million
Emp.: 20
3D Hardware & Software Inspection Systems Services
N.A.I.C.S.: 333310

Nikon Metrology UK Ltd. **(2)**
Nottingham EMA Argosy Road, Castle Donington, Derby, DE74 2SA, United Kingdom
Tel.: (44) 1332811349
Web Site: http://www.nikon.com
Sales Range: $25-49.9 Million
Emp.: 120
3D Hardware & Software Inspection Systems Services
N.A.I.C.S.: 333310

Subsidiary (US):

Nikon Metrology, Inc. **(2)**
12701 Grand River Ave, Brighton, MI 48116-8506
Tel.: (810) 220-4360
Sales Range: $25-49.9 Million
Emp.: 40
3D Hardware & Software Inspection Systems Services
N.A.I.C.S.: 333310
Hideaki Okamoto *(Mng Dir)*

Subsidiary (Non-US):

X-Tek Systems Ltd **(2)**
Tring Business Centre, Icknield Way, Tring, HP23 4JX, Hertfordshire, United Kingdom
Tel.: (44) 1442828700
Web Site: https://industry.nikon.com
Sales Range: $25-49.9 Million
Emp.: 80
X-Ray Imaging Solutions
N.A.I.C.S.: 541380

Nikon Mexico, S.A. de C.V. **(1)**
Av Paseo de la Reforma 250 Nice Tower 12th Floor, Col Juarez Cuauhtemoc, 06600, Mexico, Mexico
Tel.: (52) 5511025970
Web Site: https://www.nikon.com.mx
Photographic Equipment Sales & Maintenance Services
N.A.I.C.S.: 423410

Nikon Middle East FZE **(1)**
JAFZA View 19-14th Floor Office Nos 1401-1405, PO Box 261908, Downtown Jebel Ali Jebel Ali Freezone, Dubai, United Arab Emirates
Tel.: (971) 48840947
Sales Range: $25-49.9 Million
Emp.: 30
Camera Import & Sales
N.A.I.C.S.: 423410
Takashi Yoshida *(Mng Dir)*

Nikon Nisso Prime Corporation **(1)**
Shin-Yokohama 214 Building 3F 2-14-2 Shin-Yokohama, Kohoku-ku, Yokohama, 222-0033, Kanagawa, Japan
Tel.: (81) 454786127
Web Site: http://www.n-prime.co.jp
Human Resouce Services
N.A.I.C.S.: 541612

Nikon Nordic AB **(1)**
Rasundavagen 12 8 tr, 169 67, Solna, Sweden **(100%)**
Tel.: (46) 859410900
Web Site: https://www.nikon.se
Sales Range: $25-49.9 Million
Emp.: 40
Importer & Sales of Cameras
N.A.I.C.S.: 423410

Nikon Optical Canada, Inc. **(1)**
5075 Fullum St, Montreal, H2H 2K3, QC, Canada **(50%)**
Tel.: (514) 522-3301
Web Site: http://www.nikonlenswear.com
Sales Range: $50-74.9 Million
Emp.: 200
Mfr of Opthalmic Products
N.A.I.C.S.: 339115

Nikon Optical Shop Co., Ltd. **(1)**
5 2 Marunouchi 2 Chome, Chiyoda Ku, Tokyo, 100 0005, Japan **(100%)**
Tel.: (81) 332150725
Web Site: http://www.nikonyashiro.co.jp
Sales Range: $25-49.9 Million
Sales of Ophthalmic Frames & Lenses
N.A.I.C.S.: 339115

Nikon Optical U.K. Ltd. **(1)**
3 Tanners Drive Blakelands, Milton Keynes, MK14 5BU, United Kingdom **(100%)**
Tel.: (44) 1908214100
Sales Range: $50-74.9 Million
Emp.: 120
Processer of Custom-Order Ophthalmic Lenses
N.A.I.C.S.: 339115

Nikon Optical USA Inc. **(1)**
140 Commerce Way, South Windsor, CT 06074
Tel.: (860) 282-0082
Web Site: https://www.nikonlenswear.com
Sales Range: $50-74.9 Million
Emp.: 70
Ophthalmic Lens Distr
N.A.I.C.S.: 423460

Nikon Photo Products, Inc. **(1)**
Shin-Yurakucho Bldg 12-1 Yurakucho 1-chome, Chiyoda-ku, Tokyo, 100-8331, Japan **(100%)**
Tel.: (81) 332145311
Sales of Cameras & Photographic Accessories
N.A.I.C.S.: 423410

Nikon Precision Europe GmbH **(1)**
Robert-Bosch-Str 11, 63225, Langen, Germany **(100%)**
Tel.: (49) 61039730
Web Site: http://www.nikonprecision.com
Sales Range: $50-74.9 Million
Emp.: 70
Importer & Sales of IC Steppers & Scanners
N.A.I.C.S.: 334118
Barry Vaux *(Mng Dir & Sr VP-European Admin)*

Nikon Precision Korea Ltd. **(1)**
17-24 Singal-Dong, Giheung-Gu, Yongin, 16968, Gyeonggi-Do, Korea (South)
Tel.: (82) 312885601
Web Site: http://www.nikon.com
Sales Range: $50-74.9 Million
Emp.: 120
Provider of Service & Maintenance for IC/LCD Steppers
N.A.I.C.S.: 334413

Nikon Precision Shanghai Co., Ltd. **(1)**
Rm 601 Xin Jin Qiao Tower No 28 Xin Jin Qiao Road, Pudong New District, Shanghai, 201206, China
Tel.: (86) 2158990266
Web Site: http://www.nikon.com
Maintenance & Servicing of Semiconductor/FPD Lithography Systems

NIKON CORPORATION

Nikon Corporation—(Continued)
N.A.I.C.S.: 333242

Nikon Precision Singapore Pte Ltd (1)
29 Woodlands Industrial Park E1, Singapore, 757716, Singapore **(100%)**
Tel.: (65) 63674020
Web Site: http://www.nikon.com
Sales Range: $1-9.9 Million
Emp.: 18
Provider of Maintenance & Service for IC/LCD Steppers
N.A.I.C.S.: 334419
Besmonb Sim *(Mgr-Sls)*

Nikon Precision Taiwan Ltd. (1)
3F-1 NO 28 Taiyuan St, Hsinchu County, Zhubei, 302, Taiwan
Tel.: (886) 35525888
Provider of Maintenance & Service of IC/LCD Steppers
N.A.I.C.S.: 333310

Nikon Product Support Corporation (1)
6-3 Nishioi 1-chome, Shinagawa-ku, Tokyo, 140-0015, Japan
Tel.: (81) 33 773 1230
Outsourcing Services
N.A.I.C.S.: 561990

Nikon Sales (Thailand) Co., Ltd. (1)
1 Empire Tower Building 45th Floor River Wing East South Sathorn Road, Yannawa Sathorn, Bangkok, 10120, Thailand
Tel.: (66) 26335100
Web Site: https://www.nikon.co.th
Sales Range: $25-49.9 Million
Emp.: 3
Digital Camera Sales & Maintenance Services
N.A.I.C.S.: 423410

Nikon Singapore Pte. Ltd. (1)
18 Tai Seng Street 04-08, Singapore, 539775, Singapore **(100%)**
Web Site: http://www.nikon.com.sg
Sales Range: $25-49.9 Million
Emp.: 70
Marketer of Cameras & Photographic Equipment
N.A.I.C.S.: 449210

Nikon Solutions Co., Ltd. (1)
6-3 Nishioi 1-chome, Shinagawa-ku, Tokyo, 140-0015, Japan
Tel.: (81) 33 773 8110
Medical Equipment Distr
N.A.I.C.S.: 423450

Nikon Systems, Inc. (1)
Nishioi 1-6-3 Nikon Corporation Ohi Plant, Shinagawa-ku, Tokyo, 140-0015, Japan **(100%)**
Tel.: (81) 337731155
Web Site: http://www.nsi.nikon.com
Sales Range: $100-124.9 Million
Emp.: 468
Developer of Computer Software
N.A.I.C.S.: 334610

Nikon Tec Corporation (1)
5-21 Katsushima 1-chome, Shinagawa-ku, Tokyo, 140-0012, Japan **(100%)**
Sales Range: $25-49.9 Million
Emp.: 100
Maintenance & Service of IC/LCD Steppers; Sales of Used Equipment
N.A.I.C.S.: 334419

Nikon Tsubasa, Inc. (1)
471 Nagaodai-cho, Sakae-ku, Yokohama, 244-8533, Kanagawa, Japan **(100%)**
Tel.: (81) 458538454
Sales Range: $25-49.9 Million
Emp.: 58
Provider of Processing, Assembly & Packing of Optical Instrument Tool Parts
N.A.I.C.S.: 333310

Nikon U.K. Ltd. (1)
1 The Crescent, Surbiton, KT6 4BN, Surrey, United Kingdom **(100%)**
Tel.: (44) 3301230932
Web Site: https://www.nikon.co.uk
Sales Range: $50-74.9 Million
Emp.: 100
Importer & Sales of Cameras, Microscopes & Measuring Instruments
N.A.I.C.S.: 423410

Nikon Vision Co., Ltd. (1)
Shinagawa Intercity Tower C 2-15-3 Konan, Minato-ku, Tokyo, 108-6290, Japan **(100%)**
Tel.: (81) 364333930
Designer, Manufacturer & Sales of Telescopes & Binoculars
N.A.I.C.S.: 333310

Nikon X-Tek Systems Ltd. (1)
Tring Business Centre Icknield Way, Tring, HP23 4JX, Hertfordshire, United Kingdom
Tel.: (44) 144 282 8700
Medical Equipment Mfr
N.A.I.C.S.: 339112

Nikon do Brasil Ltda. (1)
Avenida Paulista No 37 3o Adar Conjuntos 31 e 32 Edificio, Parque Cultural Paulista, 01311-902, Bela Vista, Sao Paulo, Brazil
Tel.: (55) 11 2129 4800
Web Site: http://www.nikon.com.br
Sales Range: $25-49.9 Million
Emp.: 45
Digital Camera Sales & Maintenance Services
N.A.I.C.S.: 423410
Koji Maeda *(Pres)*

Nikon s.r.o. (1)
K Radotin 15, 5 - Zbraslav, 156 00, Prague, Czech Republic
Tel.: (420) 230230100
Web Site: https://www.nikon.cz
Sales Range: $25-49.9 Million
Emp.: 35
Importer & Sales of Cameras
N.A.I.C.S.: 423410

Nikon-Essilor Co., Ltd. (1)
10-8 Ryogoku 2-chome, Sumida-ku, Tokyo, 130-0026, Japan
Tel.: (81) 570025230
Web Site: https://www.nikon-essilor.co.jp
Sales Range: $25-49.9 Million
Developer, Manufacturer & Sales of Ophthalmic Lenses & Related Products; Joint Venture of Essilor International S.A. (50%) & Nikon Corporation (50%)
N.A.I.C.S.: 333310

Subsidiary (Domestic):

Nasu Nikon Co., Ltd. (2)
1956 3 Oaza Kyono Karasuyama Machi, Nasu Gun, Tochigi, 321 0611, Japan **(100%)**
Tel.: (81) 287801122
Sales Range: $75-99.9 Million
Mfr of Ophthalmic Lenses
N.A.I.C.S.: 333310

Nikon-Trimble Co., Ltd. (1)
echnoport Taijuseimei Bldg 2-16-2 Minamikamata, Ota-ku, Tokyo, 144-0035, Japan
Tel.: (81) 357102598
Web Site: https://www.nikon-trimble.co.jp
Sales Range: $25-49.9 Million
Emp.: 240
Surveying Instruments Sales & Mfr
N.A.I.C.S.: 333310
Takashi Tanzawa *(CEO & CEO)*

Optos Australia Pty. Ltd. (1)
10 Myer Court, Beverley, 5009, SA, Australia
Tel.: (61) 88 444 6500
Medical Equipment Distr
N.A.I.C.S.: 423450

Optos plc (1)
Queensferry House Carnegie Campus Enterprise Way, Dunfermline, KY11 8GR, United Kingdom
Tel.: (44) 1383843300
Web Site: http://www.optos.com
Retinal Imaging Devices Designer, Developer, Mfr & Marketer
N.A.I.C.S.: 333310
Robert Kennedy *(CEO)*

Subsidiary (Non-US):

Optos GmbH (2)
Tiefenbroicher Weg 25, 40472, Dusseldorf, Germany
Tel.: (49) 8007236805
Retinal Imaging Devices Mfr
N.A.I.C.S.: 333310

Subsidiary (US):

Optos, Inc. (2)
500 Nickerson Rd Ste 201, Marlborough, MA 01752
Tel.: (508) 787-1400
Web Site: https://www.optos.com
Retinal Imaging Devices Mfr
N.A.I.C.S.: 333310

PT Nikon Indonesia (1)
Gedung Sentra KIIC Unit 02 Lt 01 Jl Permata Raya Lot CA-1, Kawasan Industri KIIC Desa Sukaluyu Kecamatan Telukjambe Timur, Karawang, 41361, Indonesia
Tel.: (62) 267 864 3949
Sales Promotion Activity Services
N.A.I.C.S.: 541810

SLM Solutions Group AG (1)
Estlandring 4, 23560, Lubeck, Germany **(81.98%)**
Tel.: (49) 45140603000
Web Site: http://www.slm-solutions.com
Rev.: $114,082,668
Assets: $196,752,644
Liabilities: $127,408,806
Net Worth: $69,343,838
Earnings: ($26,704,079)
Emp.: 537
Fiscal Year-end: 12/31/2022
Plate Work Mfr
N.A.I.C.S.: 332313
Meddah Hadjar *(CEO & Member-Mgmt Bd)*

Subsidiary (Non-US):

SLM Solutions (India) Private Limited (2)
Embassy Signet 5th Floor Cessna Business Park Kadubeesanahalli, Outer Ring Road-Marathahalli, Bengaluru, 560103, Karnataka, India
Tel.: (91) 9810122192
Laser Melting Machine Mfr
N.A.I.C.S.: 333248

SLM Solutions (Italy) S.R.L. (2)
Largo G Donegani 2, 20121, Milan, Italy
Tel.: (39) 045140603000
Laser Melting Machine Mfr
N.A.I.C.S.: 333248

Subsidiary (US):

SLM Solutions NA, Inc. (2)
48561 Alpha Dr Ste 300, Wixom, MI 48393
Tel.: (248) 243-5400
Web Site: http://www.slm-solutions.us
Laser Melting Machine Mfr
N.A.I.C.S.: 333248

Subsidiary (Non-US):

SLM Solutions Singapore Pte. Ltd. (2)
25 International Business Park 03-57/58 German Centre, Singapore, Singapore
Tel.: (65) 67504595
Laser Melting Machine Mfr
N.A.I.C.S.: 333248

Sendai Nikon Corporation (1)
277 Tako Hara, Natori, 981-1221, Miyagi, Japan **(100%)**
Tel.: (81) 223840011
Web Site: http://www.sendai-nikon.co.jp
Sales Range: $100-124.9 Million
Emp.: 420
Mfr of Cameras, LCD Steppers & Component Devices for IC/LCD Steppers
N.A.I.C.S.: 333310

TNI Industry Corporation (1)
770 Midori, Otawara, 324-0045, Toohigi, Japan
Tel.: (81) 28 728 1919
Industrial Machinery Services
N.A.I.C.S.: 811310

Tochigi Nikon Corporation (1)
770 Mitori, Otawara, 324-8625, Tochigi, Japan **(100%)**
Tel.: (81) 287281111
Web Site: http://www.tochigi-nikon.co.jp
Emp.: 1,087
Mfr of IC/LCD Steppers & Various Optical Lenses
N.A.I.C.S.: 333310

Tochigi Nikon Precision Co., Ltd. (1)
760 Midori, Otawara, 324-8520, Tochigi, Japan
Tel.: (81) 287281177
Emp.: 150
Optical Stepper & Scanner Mfr
N.A.I.C.S.: 334118

NIKOTIANA BT HOLDING AD
39 Knyaginya Klementina Str, 1618, Sofia, Bulgaria
Tel.: (359) 29632888
Web Site: http://www.nicotianabt.com
HNIC—(BUL)
Sales Range: Less than $1 Million
Asset Management Services
N.A.I.C.S.: 523940
Evgeni Evgeniev *(Chm-Mgmt Bd)*

NIKS PROFESSIONAL LTD.
Block 16 Kallang Place 03-27, Singapore, 339156, Singapore
Tel.: (65) 62941802 SG
Web Site: https://www.nikspro.com
Year Founded: 1998
NPL—(SES)
Rev.: $8,226,943
Assets: $19,116,612
Liabilities: $2,561,883
Net Worth: $16,554,729
Earnings: $2,132,554
Emp.: 52
Fiscal Year-end: 12/31/22
Personal Care Product Distr
N.A.I.C.S.: 456199

NIKS TECHNOLOGY LTD.
501 Shiv Laxmi Plaza Opposite Rajendra Nagar, Kankarbagh, Patna, 800020, Bihar, India
Tel.: (91) 9031044450
Web Site: https://www.nikstech.com
543282—(BOM)
Rev.: $249,026
Assets: $358,444
Liabilities: $207,937
Net Worth: $150,507
Earnings: $31,041
Emp.: 8
Fiscal Year-end: 03/31/23
Digital Marketing Services
N.A.I.C.S.: 541890
Pushpendra Patel *(Sec & Compliance Officer)*

NILA INFRASTRUCTURES LTD.
1st Floor Sambhaav House Opp Chief Justice s Bungalow, Bodakdev, Ahmedabad, 380015, India
Tel.: (91) 7940036817
Web Site: https://www.nilainfra.com
Year Founded: 1990
NILAINFRA—(NSE)
Rev.: $15,238,463
Assets: $98,083,772
Liabilities: $82,181,452
Net Worth: $15,902,320
Earnings: ($53,906)
Emp.: 36
Fiscal Year-end: 03/31/23
Real Estate Development Services
N.A.I.C.S.: 531390
Manojbhai Bhupatbhai Vadodaria *(Chm & Mng Dir)*

NILACHAL REFRACTORIES LIMITED
30 - D Jawaharlal Nehru Road, Kolkata, 700 016, India
Tel.: (91) 3322499511
Web Site: https://www.nilachal.in
Year Founded: 1977
502294—(BOM)
Rev.: $130,919
Assets: $5,988,469
Liabilities: $1,174,891
Net Worth: $4,813,578

Earnings: ($215,191)
Fiscal Year-end: 03/31/23
Clay Refractories Mfr
N.A.I.C.S.: 327120

NILAI RESOURCES GROUP SDN BERHAD
Wisma BBN Jalan BBN 1 1A Putra Nilai, 71800, Nilai, Negeri Sembilan, Malaysia
Tel.: (60) 68501888
Web Site:
http://www.nilairesources.com.my
Sales Range: $75-99.9 Million
Emp.: 100
Property Development Services
N.A.I.C.S.: 531311
Eng Hong Gan *(Mng Dir)*

Subsidiaries:

Nilai Landscape Sdn. Bhd. (1)
Lot P T 6367 Jalan BBN 3/1 Putra Nilai, 71800, Nilai, Negeri Sembilan, Malaysia
Tel.: (60) 6 7992882
Web Site: http://www.nlandscape.com.my
Nursery Management Services
N.A.I.C.S.: 444240
Chokyuen Heng *(Mgr-Mktg)*

NILAM RESOURCES, INC.
1480 Benevides Street Sixth Floor B, Miraflores, Lima, 18, Peru
Tel.: (51) 7029409844
Web Site:
https://www.southamerican.com
NILA—(OTCIQ)
Sales Range: Less than $1 Million
Metal Mining Services
N.A.I.C.S.: 213114
Shahin Tabatabaei *(Pres & CEO)*

NILE CITY INVESTMENTS
Nile City Towers Northern Tower 2005 C, Corniche El Nil, Cairo, Egypt
Tel.: (20) 12 22130663
Web Site:
http://www.nilecitytowers.com
Year Founded: 1997
NCIN.CA—(EGX)
Sales Range: Less than $1 Million
Investment Banking Services
N.A.I.C.S.: 523150
Fahd Hussein Ali Shobokshi *(Chm)*

NILE LTD.
Plot No 24 A/A MLA Colony Road No 12 Banjara Hills, Hyderabad, 500 034, Telangana, India
Tel.: (91) 4023606641
Web Site: https://www.nilelimited.com
530129—(BOM)
Rev.: $73,251,810
Assets: $29,743,623
Liabilities: $8,690,778
Net Worth: $21,052,845
Earnings: $1,879,919
Emp.: 131
Fiscal Year-end: 03/31/21
Glass Lined Equipment Mfr
N.A.I.C.S.: 444180
Vuyyuru Ramesh *(Chm)*

NILESAT THE EGYPTIAN SATELLITE COMPANY
PO Box 72, 6th of October City, Egypt
Tel.: (20) 238400145
Web Site: https://nilesat.org
Year Founded: 1996
EGSA.CA—(EGX)
Rev.: $101,824,720
Assets: $660,888,786
Liabilities: $37,981,322
Net Worth: $622,907,464
Earnings: $43,754,499
Emp.: 7,735
Fiscal Year-end: 12/31/23
Satellite Broadcasting Services
N.A.I.C.S.: 516210

NILFISK HOLDING A/S
Kornmarksvej 1, DK-2605, Brondby, Denmark
Tel.: (45) 43238100
Web Site: http://www.nilfisk.com
Holding Company
N.A.I.C.S.: 551112
Hans Henrik Lund *(Pres & CEO)*

Subsidiaries:

Nilfisk A/S (1)
Kornmarksdeg No 1, Brondby, 2605, Denmark
Tel.: (45) 43238100
Web Site: http://www.nilfisk.com
Carpet Cleaners, Vacuum Cleaners & High Pressure Cleaners Mfr
N.A.I.C.S.: 335210

Subsidiary (Non-US):

Nilfisk Ltd. (2)
Nilfisk House Bowerbank Way Gilwilly Industrial Estate, Penrith, CA11 9BQ, Cumbria, United Kingdom
Tel.: (44) 1768868995
Web Site: http://www.new.nilfisk.com
Industrial Cleaning Equipment Distr
N.A.I.C.S.: 423830

Division (Domestic):

Nilfisk-ALTO Danmark A/S (2)
Industrivej 1, 9560, Hadsund, Denmark
Tel.: (45) 72182100
Web Site: http://www.nilfisk.com
Professional Cleaning Equipment Mfr & Whslr
N.A.I.C.S.: 335210

Subsidiary (US):

Nilfisk-Advance, Inc. (2)
9435 Winnetka Ave N, Brooklyn Park, MN 55445
Tel.: (763) 745-3500
Web Site: http://www.advance-us.com
Floor Care Equipment Mfr
N.A.I.C.S.: 333310

Subsidiary (Domestic):

Cyclone Surface Cleaning, Inc. (3)
1845 W 1st St Ste 101, Tempe, AZ 85281
Web Site: http://www.cyclonecleanc.com
Surface Cleaning Equipment Mfr
N.A.I.C.S.: 333310

Hydro Tek Systems, Inc. (3)
2353 Almond Ave, Redlands, CA 92374
Tel.: (909) 799-9222
Web Site: http://www.hydroteksystems.com
Cold, Hot & Steam Pressure Washers Mfr
N.A.I.C.S.: 333310

Subsidiary (Domestic):

Nitodan A/S (2)
H C Orstedsvej 4, 6100, Haderslev, Denmark (100%)
Tel.: (45) 74526363
Web Site: http://www.nito.dk
Sales Range: $1-9.9 Million
Emp.: 30
Vacuum Cleaner Mfr
N.A.I.C.S.: 335210
Dan Nielsen *(Mgr-Sls)*

NILKAMAL LTD
Nilkamal House 77/78 Road No 13/14 MIDC, Andheri East, Mumbai, 400093, India
Tel.: (91) 2242358888
Web Site: https://www.nilkamal.com
NILKAMAL—(NSE)
Rev.: $287,772,617
Assets: $235,298,796
Liabilities: $79,631,561
Net Worth: $155,667,234
Earnings: $15,444,661
Emp.: 2,939
Fiscal Year-end: 03/31/21
Furniture Mfr
N.A.I.C.S.: 238390
Vamanrai V. Parekh *(Co-Founder)*

Subsidiaries:

NILKAMAL Crates & Bins Pvt. Ltd. (1)
77 78 Nilkamal House Rd, 13 14 MIDC Andheri, Mumbai, 400093, Maharashtra, India
Tel.: (91) 2228361366
Web Site: http://www.nilkamal.com
Sales Range: $200-249.9 Million
Emp.: 700
Crates Mfr
N.A.I.C.S.: 321920
Sharad V. Parekh *(Mng Dir)*

NILKAMAL Eswaran Plastics Pvt. Ltd. (1)
Tel.: (94) 114212661
Web Site: https://www.nilkamal.lk
Crates Containers Mfr
N.A.I.C.S.: 321920

NILKANTH ENGINEERING LIMITED
3rd Floor Daulat Bhavan 407 Kalbadevi Road, Mumbai, 400 002, India
Tel.: (91) 2222062108
Web Site:
https://www.nilkanthengineers.com
Year Founded: 1983
512004—(BOM)
Rev.: $21,767
Assets: $1,908,203
Liabilities: $2,056,142
Net Worth: ($147,939)
Earnings: ($106,666)
Fiscal Year-end: 03/31/21
Engineeering Services
N.A.I.C.S.: 541330
Nitin Agrawal *(Mng Dir)*

NILOU TILE COMPANY
Isfahan Hakim Nizami Street Crossroads Mohtashem Kashani, Isfahan, 81758-89771, Iran
Tel.: (98) 3116254127
Year Founded: 1975
Clay Product & Refractory Mfr
N.A.I.C.S.: 327120

NILSSON BROS., INC.
Suite 100 101 Riel Drive, Saint Albert, T8N 3X4, AB, Canada
Tel.: (780) 477-2233
Web Site: https://www.nbinc.com
Sales Range: $10-24.9 Million
Emp.: 40
Livestock & Agricultural Business Owner/Operator
N.A.I.C.S.: 424520
Brian Nilsson *(CEO)*

Subsidiaries:

Heartland Livestock Services (1)
Ste 210 4401 Albert St, Regina, S4S 6P6, SK, Canada
Tel.: (306) 566-4303
Web Site: http://www.hls.ca
Livestock Sales
N.A.I.C.S.: 424520
Stewart Stone *(COO)*

XL Foods Inc. (1)
5883 11 Street SE, Calgary, T2H 1M7, AB, Canada
Tel.: (403) 258-3233
Web Site: http://www.xlfoods.com
Food Packaging
N.A.I.C.S.: 424420

Subsidiary (Domestic):

XL Lakeside Packers, Inc. (2)
Trans Canada Highway 1, PO Box 1868, Brooks, T1R 1C6, Canada
Tel.: (403) 362-3457
Web Site: http://www.xlfoods.com
Cattle Feeding, Slaughtering & Processing; Fertilizer Retailer; Farming Services; Agribusiness Research & Consulting Services
N.A.I.C.S.: 311611

NILSSON SPECIAL VEHICLES AB
Tegelbruksvagen 17, 312 32, Laholm, Sweden
Tel.: (46) 43049050
Web Site: https://www.nilsson.se
Year Founded: 1945
NILS—(OMX)
Rev.: $20,303,090
Assets: $7,196,044
Liabilities: $6,688,396
Net Worth: $507,647
Earnings: ($327,817)
Emp.: 56
Fiscal Year-end: 12/31/22
Automobile Parts Mfr
N.A.I.C.S.: 336110
Ann Hultin *(CFO)*

NIMAG (PTY) LTD
Portion 33 Steenkoppies Farm, PO Box 2, Rustenburg Road, Magaliesburg, 1791, South Africa
Tel.: (27) 10 14 577 1330
Web Site:
http://www.nimaggroup.com
Sales Range: $25-49.9 Million
Emp.: 10
Alloy Metals Mfr
N.A.I.C.S.: 331513
Paul Holm *(Mng Dir)*

NIMANS LTD
Agecroft Road, Pendlebury, Manchester, M27 8SB, United Kingdom
Tel.: (44) 1619251443
Web Site: http://www.nycomm.co.uk
Year Founded: 1984
Telecommunication Servicesb
N.A.I.C.S.: 517810
Julian Nimans *(Founder)*

NIMAX THEATRES LIMITED
11 Maiden Lane, London, WC2E 7NA, United Kingdom
Tel.: (44) 20 7395 0780
Web Site:
http://www.nimaxtheatres.com
Year Founded: 2005
Theater Operator
N.A.I.C.S.: 711310
Nica Burns *(CEO)*

Subsidiaries:

Palace Theater London Limited (1)
Cambridge Circus Shaftesbury Avenue, London, W1D 5AY, United Kingdom (100%)
Tel.: (44) 2074340088
Web Site: http://www.nimaxtheatres.com
Sales Range: $50-74.9 Million
Emp.: 100
Management of the Palace Theatre
N.A.I.C.S.: 531120
Anaa Charles *(Gen Mgr)*

NIMBLE HOLDINGS COMPANY LIMITED
Flat C01 32/F TML Tower 3 Hoi Shing Road Tsuen Wan, New Territories, Hong Kong, China (Hong Kong)
Tel.: (852) 9 237 1885   BM
Web Site:
http://www.nimbleholding.com
0186—(HKG)
Rev.: $25,796,000
Assets: $828,180,580
Liabilities: $763,948,540
Net Worth: $64,232,040
Earnings: ($7,480,840)
Emp.: 141
Fiscal Year-end: 03/31/21
Personal Computer & Consumer Electronics Mfr & Distr
N.A.I.C.S.: 335210

NIMBLE HOLDINGS COMPANY LIMITED

Nimble Holdings Company Limited—(Continued)

Bingzhao Tan *(Chm & CEO)*

NIMBUS B.V.
Driebergseweg 17, 3708 JA, Zeist, Netherlands
Tel.: (31) 306971410
Web Site: http://www.nimbus.com
Emp.: 20
Investment Company
N.A.I.C.S.: 525910
Gert Jan Hubers *(Partner)*

Subsidiaries:

BC Extrusion Holding GmbH (1)
Konigstrasse 53, D-32547, Bad Oeynhausen, Germany
Tel.: (49) 57312420
Web Site: http://www.battenfeld-cincinnati.com
Emp.: 700
Plastic Extrusion Machinery Mfr
N.A.I.C.S.: 333248
Gerold Schley *(Mng Dir)*

Subsidiary (US):

American Maplan Corporation (2)
823 S Bypass, McPherson, KS 67460
Tel.: (620) 241-6843
Web Site: http://www.battenfeld-cincinnati.com
Plastic Extrusion Machinery Mfr
N.A.I.C.S.: 333248
Paul Godwin *(Pres & CEO)*

Gietburg Holding (1)
Deslammert 1220, 5854 MC, Bergen-op-Zoom, Netherlands (100%)
Tel.: (31) 485348226
Web Site: http://www.gietburg.nl
Sales Range: $250-299.9 Million
Emp.: 800
Holding Company
N.A.I.C.S.: 551112
Herman Ten Heuw *(Mng Dir)*

Meneba BV (1)
Brielselaan 115, 3081 AB, Rotterdam, Netherlands
Tel.: (31) 10 42 38 911
Web Site: http://www.meneba.com
Cereal Product Mfr & Distr
N.A.I.C.S.: 311211
Han Boers *(Mgr-Export)*

Nedelko B.V. (1)
Trondheim 1, 2993 LE, Barendrecht, Netherlands
Tel.: (31) 180 64 54 00
Web Site: http://www.nedelko.nl
Light & Electrical Component Distr
N.A.I.C.S.: 423610

Subsidiary (Non-US):

Nedelko N.V.-S.A. (2)
Prins Boudewijn Laan 49, 2650, Edegem, Belgium
Tel.: (32) 3826 99 99
Light & Electrical Component Distr
N.A.I.C.S.: 423610

Nedelko S.R.O. (2)
Purkynova 74/2, 120 00, Prague, Czech Republic
Tel.: (420) 222 563 003
Light & Electrical Component Distr
N.A.I.C.S.: 423610

Nimpon Trade and Services b.v. (1)
Driebergseweg 17, 3708 JA, Zeist, Netherlands (60%)
Tel.: (31) 30 697 1410
Web Site: http://www.nimpon.com
Sales Range: $50-74.9 Million
Emp.: 100
Holding Company
N.A.I.C.S.: 551112
Marc Renne *(CEO)*

Subsidiary (Non-US):

Scanpocon Metric A/S (2)
Aggerhaten 5, Markaervej, 5220, Odense, Denmark
Tel.: (45) 66176260
Web Site: http://www.coromatic.dk

Sales Range: $25-49.9 Million
Emp.: 40
Power Supply Solutions
N.A.I.C.S.: 332410
Micheal Peterson *(Mng Dir)*

Plasticon Europe B.V. (1)
Expolaan 50, 7556BE, Hengelo, Netherlands
Tel.: (31) 541 85 85 00
Web Site: http://www.plasticoncomposites.com
Plastic Tank Mfr
N.A.I.C.S.: 326199

Subsidiary (Non-US):

Plasticon Asia Co., Ltd. (2)
69/3 M00 6 Takham, Bang Pakong, 24130, Chachoengsao, Thailand
Tel.: (66) 38 573 544 5
Web Site: http://www.plasticonasia.com
Plastic Tank Mfr
N.A.I.C.S.: 326199

Plasticon Aubert SAS (2)
13 rue du Perigord, 69330, Meyzieu, France
Tel.: (33) 478 31 00 22
Web Site: http://www.plasticoncomposites.com
Emp.: 15
Plastic Tank Mfr
N.A.I.C.S.: 326199
Martin Mosinkoss *(CEO)*

Plasticon Canada Inc. (2)
1395 Montee Chenier, Les Cedres, J7T 1L9, QC, Canada
Tel.: (450) 455-3311
Web Site: http://www.acplastiques.com
Plastic Tank Mfr
N.A.I.C.S.: 326199

Plasticon China Co., Ltd. (2)
No 11 Tianshan Road E&D Zone, Jiashan, 314100, Zhejiang, China
Tel.: (86) 573 847 525 95
Plastic Tank Mfr
N.A.I.C.S.: 326199
Zhi Jun Xu *(Gen Mgr)*

Plasticon Composites LLC (2)
2 Sovetskaya bld 7 office 110, 191036, Saint Petersburg, Russia
Tel.: (7) 812 332 96 61
Plastic Tank Mfr
N.A.I.C.S.: 326199

Plasticon France SA (2)
16 rue Robert Schuman, 85170, Dompierre-sur-Yon, France
Tel.: (33) 251 341 718
Plastic Tank Mfr
N.A.I.C.S.: 326199

Plasticon Germany GmbH (2)
Dieselstrasse 10, 46539, Dinslaken, Germany
Tel.: (49) 2064 499 0
Plastic Tank Mfr
N.A.I.C.S.: 326199

Subsidiary (US):

Plasticon North America Inc. (2)
6387 Little River Tpke, Alexandria, VA 22312
Tel.: (571) 421-2460
Plastic Tank Mfr
N.A.I.C.S.: 326199

Subsidiary (Domestic):

AC Plastiques USA, LLC (3)
2526 Rome Dr, Baton Rouge, LA 70814
Tel.: (225) 927-1920
Web Site: http://www.acplastiques.net
Plastic Tank Mfr
N.A.I.C.S.: 326199
Drew Rispone *(Gen Mgr)*

Subsidiary (Non-US):

Plasticon Poland S.A. (2)
M Sklodowskiej-Curie 59, 87-100, Torun, Poland
Tel.: (48) 56 658 61 00
Web Site: http://www.plasticoncomposites.com
Plastic Tank Mfr

N.A.I.C.S.: 326199
Plasticon South Africa (PTY) (2)
Central Office Park Unit 5 257 Jean Avenue, Centurion, South Africa
Tel.: (27) 88 85 85 000
Plastic Tank Mfr
N.A.I.C.S.: 326199

Plasticon UK Ltd. (2)
44C Stockholm Road Sutton Fields Industrial Estate, Hull, HU7 OXW, United Kingdom
Tel.: (44) 1482 862194
Web Site: http://www.plasticon.co.uk
Plastic Tank Mfr
N.A.I.C.S.: 326199
Mike Reilly *(Mng Dir)*

Subsidiary (Domestic):

Plasticon the Netherlands B.V. (2)
Havenkade 46, 7553GN, Hengelo, Netherlands
Tel.: (31) 541 85 85 85
Web Site: http://www.plasticoncomposites.com
Emp.: 48
Plastic Tank Mfr
N.A.I.C.S.: 326199
Chris Cekemans *(Gen Mgr)*

Subsidiary (Non-US):

Plasto-tec GmbH (2)
Austrasse 35, 3512, Mautern an der Donau, Austria
Tel.: (43) 2732 81127 0
Web Site: http://www.plasto-tec.at
Plastic Tank Mfr
N.A.I.C.S.: 326199

Subsidiary (Domestic):

Thermopol Kunststoftechniek B.V. (2)
Postbus 343, 4600 AH, Bergen-op-Zoom, Netherlands
Tel.: (31) 164 245446
Web Site: http://www.thermopol.be
Plastic Tank Mfr
N.A.I.C.S.: 326199

Subsidiary (Non-US):

Thermopol Kunststoftechniek NV (3)
Rijkmakerlaan 43, 2910, Essen, Belgium
Tel.: (32) 3 6900340
Emp.: 30
Plastic Tank Mfr
N.A.I.C.S.: 326199
Chris Vekemans *(Mng Dir)*

RCP Ranstadt GmbH (1)
Bahnhofstrasse 25, 63691, Ranstadt, Germany
Tel.: (49) 6041 802 0
Web Site: http://www.rcp-ranstadt.com
Wipe & Sachet Mfr
N.A.I.C.S.: 325620
Karl Koob *(Gen Mgr)*

Rampf Formen GmbH (1)
Altheimer Strasse 1, 89604, Allmendingen, Germany
Tel.: (49) 7391 505 0
Web Site: http://www.rampf.com
Concrete Mold Mfr
N.A.I.C.S.: 327331

Subsidiary (US):

Innovative Polymers, Inc. (2)
208 Kuntz St, Saint Johns, MI 48879
Tel.: (248) 295-0223
Web Site: http://www.innovative-polymers.com
Sales Range: $1-9.9 Million
Emp.: 10
Polyurethane Products Manufacturing
N.A.I.C.S.: 326199
Bill Molitor *(Dir-Sls & Mktg)*

Subsidiary (Non-US):

Rampf Formen (Taicang) Co., Ltd. (2)
No 11 East Qingdao Road, Taicang, 215400, Jiangsu, China
Tel.: (86) 512 5357 9898
Concrete Mold Mfr

INTERNATIONAL PUBLIC

N.A.I.C.S.: 327331
Rampf Formen Kft. (2)
Szekosi ut 58-60, 6791, Szeged, Hungary
Tel.: (36) 62 558585
Web Site: http://www.rampf.hu
Concrete Mold Mfr
N.A.I.C.S.: 327331

Rampf Formen Polska Sp. z o.o. (2)
Al Armii Krajowej 12B/3, 50-541, Wroclaw, Poland
Tel.: (48) 71 79 58 205
Concrete Mold Mfr
N.A.I.C.S.: 327331

Rampf Molds Inc. (2)
270 Saunders Rd, Barrie, L4N 9Y2, ON, Canada
Tel.: (705) 720-7300
Concrete Mold Mfr
N.A.I.C.S.: 327331

Subsidiary (US):

Rampf Molds Industries Inc. (2)
90 Western Maryland Pkwy, Hagerstown, MD 21740
Tel.: (301) 791-6880
Web Site: http://www.rampf-na.com
Concrete Mold Mfr
N.A.I.C.S.: 327331

Remako Paper & Board B.V. (1)
J P Broekhovenstraat 11b, 8081 HB, Elburg, Netherlands
Tel.: (31) 525 68 18 28
Web Site: http://www.remako.com
Paper & Board Distr
N.A.I.C.S.: 424110
Gijs Lindeboom *(Mng Dir)*

Sencio B.V. (1)
Microweg 1-11, 6545 CL, Nijmegen, Netherlands
Web Site: http://www.sencio.nl
Emp.: 70
Semiconductor Assembly Mfr
N.A.I.C.S.: 333242
Oliver Maiwald *(CEO)*

Sitag AG (1)
Simon Frick-Str 3, 9466, Sennwald, Switzerland
Tel.: (41) 817581818
Web Site: http://www.sitag.ch
Sales Range: $50-74.9 Million
Office Furnishings Mfr
N.A.I.C.S.: 337214
Tony Lee *(CEO)*

Branch (Non-US):

Sitag AG - Germany Sales Office (2)
Stiftstrasse 35, 32427, Minden, Germany
Tel.: (49) 571 388 609 30
Web Site: http://www.sitag.de
Office & Household Furniture Distr
N.A.I.C.S.: 423210

Subsidiary (Non-US):

Sitag Buromobel GmbH (2)
Bahnhofstrasse 24, 6850, Dornbirn, Austria
Tel.: (43) 55 72 290 26
Web Site: http://www.sitag.ch
Office Furnishings Mfr
N.A.I.C.S.: 423210

Sitag Formy Siedzenia Sp. z o.o. (2)
ul Sarbinowska 11, Lowecin, 62-020, Swarzedz, Poland
Tel.: (48) 61 817 33 63
Web Site: http://www.sitag.pl
Office & Household Furniture Distr
N.A.I.C.S.: 423210

UnifiedPost SA (1)
Avenue Reine Astrid 92A, 1310, La Hulpe, Belgium
Tel.: (32) 26340628
Web Site: https://www.unifiedpost.be
Emp.: 35
Software Development Services
N.A.I.C.S.: 541511
Tom Totte *(Mgr-Sls)*

Subsidiary (Domestic):

UP-nxt (2)
Vaartstraat 14/1, 3000, Leuven, Belgium
Tel.: (32) 499690571

AND PRIVATE COMPANIES

NINE DRAGONS PAPER HOLDINGS LIMITED

Web Site: http://www.up-nxt.com
Software Development Services
N.A.I.C.S.: 541511
Koen Handekyn *(CEO)*

Subsidiary (Non-US):

UnifiedPost BV (2)
Groene Dijk 2B, 3401 NJ, IJsselstein, Netherlands
Tel.: (31) 20 262 08 30
Web Site: http://www.unifiedpost.com
Emp.: 25
Software Development Services
N.A.I.C.S.: 541511

UnifiedPost SARL (2)
Route de Diekirch 45, 7220, Walferdange, Luxembourg
Tel.: (352) 26 31 32 42
Software Development Services
N.A.I.C.S.: 541511

UnifiedPost SRL (2)
10 Coriolan Brediceanu Street City Business Centre Building D 1st floo, 300011, Timisoara, Romania
Tel.: (40) 766 066 061
Web Site: http://www.unifiedpost.ro
Software Development Services
N.A.I.C.S.: 541511

Vermeer Eemhaven International BV (1)
Bunschotenweg 110, 3089 KC, Rotterdam, Netherlands
Tel.: (31) 10 429 96 66
Web Site: http://www.ve-groep.nl
Emp.: 70
Heat Exchanger Mfr
N.A.I.C.S.: 332410
Paul Blonk *(CEO)*

NIMBUS FOODS INDUSTRIES LTD.
Plot No B-13/14 Phase II, Naroda GIDC Industrial Area, Ahmedabad, 382330, India
Tel.: (91) 7922813445
Web Site: http://www.nimbusfoods.in
Year Founded: 2002
Sales Range: $1-9.9 Million
Food Products Mfr
N.A.I.C.S.: 311999
Faruk H. Diwan *(Officer-Compliance & Sec)*

NIMBUS GROUP AB
Talattagatan 10, Vastra Frolunda, 42676, Gothenburg, Sweden
Tel.: (46) 317267700   SE
Web Site: https://nimbusgroup.se
Year Founded: 1968
BOAT—(OMX)
Rev.: $188,458,716
Assets: $199,683,328
Liabilities: $114,013,145
Net Worth: $85,670,182
Earnings: $4,472,174
Emp.: 492
Fiscal Year-end: 12/31/23
Boat Mfr
N.A.I.C.S.: 336612
Jan-Erik Lindstrom *(CEO)*

Subsidiaries:

Edgewater Power Boats, LLC (1)
211 Dale St, Edgewater, FL 32132
Tel.: (386) 426-5457
Web Site: http://www.ewboats.com
New Boat Dealer
N.A.I.C.S.: 441222
Peter Orlando *(Dir-Sls & Mktg)*

NIMBUS INDUSTRIES LIMITED
B-323 Orchard Mall Royal Palms Aarey Milk Colony, Goregaon East, Mumbai, 400 065, India
Tel.: (91) 22 65258028
Web Site: http://www.nimbusindustries.com
Year Founded: 1975
Rev.: $16,031,468
Assets: $5,979,708
Liabilities: $5,162,808
Net Worth: $816,900
Earnings: $45,124
Fiscal Year-end: 03/31/18
Textile Product Whslr
N.A.I.C.S.: 424990
Nimish B. Thakore *(Chm & Officer-Compliance)*

NIMBUS PROJECTS LTD.
1001-1006 10th Floor Narain Manzil 23 Barakhamba Road, New Delhi, 110001, India
Tel.: (91) 1142878900
Web Site: https://www.nimbusprojectsltd.com
Year Founded: 1993
511714—(BOM)
Rev.: $862,655
Assets: $10,774,215
Liabilities: $18,340,533
Net Worth: ($7,566,318)
Earnings: ($3,030,103)
Emp.: 7
Fiscal Year-end: 03/31/21
Real Estate Development Services
N.A.I.C.S.: 531390
Bipin Agarwal *(Chm & Mng Dir)*

NIMBUS SUPPORT B.V.
Driebergseweg 17, 3708 JA, Zeist, Netherlands
Tel.: (31) 30 697 1410   NI
Web Site: http://nimbus.com
Private Equity & Venture Capital Firm
N.A.I.C.S.: 523999
Ed van Dijk *(Partner)*

NIMES AUTO SPORTS
29 rue de l'Abrivado, 30000, Nimes, France
Tel.: (33) 466029600
Web Site: http://www.nissan-nimes.com
Sales Range: $25-49.9 Million
Emp.: 32
Automobile Sales
N.A.I.C.S.: 441110
Claude Robert *(Pres)*

NIMES VI SAS
1020 avenue Joliot Curie, 30900, Nimes, France
Tel.: (33) 4 66 68 0200
Web Site: http://www.renault-trucks.net
Sales Range: $10-24.9 Million
Emp.: 39
Automobile Dealership
N.A.I.C.S.: 441110
Michel Gabelotaud *(Pres)*

NIMIR INDUSTRIAL CHEMICALS LTD.
14 8 Km Sheikhupura-Faisalabad Road, Mouza Bhikhi District, Sheikhupura, Pakistan
Tel.: (92) 563882199
Web Site: https://www.nimir.com.pk
NICL—(PSX)
Rev.: $221,618,387
Assets: $128,156,938
Liabilities: $92,522,656
Net Worth: $35,634,282
Earnings: $7,975,791
Emp.: 409
Fiscal Year-end: 06/30/23
Oleo Chemicals & Chlor Alkali Chemical Mfr
N.A.I.C.S.: 325998
Zafar Mahmood *(CEO)*

NIMIR RESINS LIMITED
14 5 Km Lahore - Sheikhupura Road, Lahore, Pakistan
Tel.: (92) 4237971512
Web Site: https://www.nimir.com.pk
Year Founded: 1977
NRSL—(KAR)
Rev.: $31,473,196
Assets: $19,657,117
Liabilities: $12,148,900
Net Worth: $7,508,217
Earnings: $991,872
Emp.: 124
Fiscal Year-end: 06/30/19
Paints, Coatings & Resins Mfr
N.A.I.C.S.: 325211
Zafar Mahmood *(CEO)*

Subsidiaries:

Descon Chemicals (Pvt) Limited (1)
18-KM Ferozepur Road, Lahore, Pakistan
Tel.: (92) 4235923721
Web Site: http://www.desconchemicals.com
Chemical Mfr & Distr
N.A.I.C.S.: 325180

Descon Engineering Abu Dhabi (1)
17-Prestige Tower East 2, PO Box 46821, Mohammad Bin Zayed City, 46821, Abu Dhabi, United Arab Emirates
Tel.: (971) 26946074
Web Site: http://www.descon.com
Construction Engineering Services
N.A.I.C.S.: 541330

Descon Engineering Limited (1)
Plot No A 35-36 Eastern Industrial Zone, Port Qasim Industrial Area, Karachi, Pakistan
Tel.: (92) 2134740031
Web Site: http://www.descon.com.pk
Engineering Services
N.A.I.C.S.: 541330
Muhammad Khawar Khan *(Chief Risk & Compliance Officer)*

Subsidiary (Domestic):

Descon Integrated Projects (Private) Limited (2)
18 Km Ferozepur Road, Lahore, 54760, Pakistan
Tel.: (92) 42 3581 2263
Web Site: http://www.descon.com
Engineeering Services
N.A.I.C.S.: 541330

Descon Oxychem Limited (1)
18 km Ferozepur Road, Lahore, 54760, Pakistan
Tel.: (92) 4235923721
Web Site: https://www.descon.com
Rev.: $24,180,069
Assets: $18,113,163
Liabilities: $7,107,531
Net Worth: $11,005,632
Earnings: $5,037,916
Emp.: 115
Fiscal Year-end: 06/30/2023
Chemical Products Mfr
N.A.I.C.S.: 325199

Rousch Pakistan Limited (1)
Corporate Office 43-5-E Block-6, Pechs, Karachi, Pakistan
Tel.: (92) 2134530641
Synthetic Resin Mfr
N.A.I.C.S.: 325211

NIMONIK, INC.
5445 Av de Gaspe Suite 602, Montreal, H2T 3B2, QC, Canada
Tel.: (888) 608-7511
Web Site: https://nimonik.com
Emp.: 100
Software Publr
N.A.I.C.S.: 513210

Subsidiaries:

Document Center Inc (1)
111 Industrial Way, Belmont, CA 94002
Tel.: (650) 591-7600
Web Site: http://www.document-center.com
Rev.: $1,000,000
Emp.: 12
All Other Telecommunications
N.A.I.C.S.: 517810
Claudia Bach *(Owner & Pres)*

NIMY RESOURCES LIMITED
254 Adelaide Terrace, Perth, 6000, WA, Australia
Tel.: (61) 892614600   AU
Web Site: https://www.nimy.com.au
Year Founded: 2012
NIM—(ASX)
Rev.: $95
Assets: $706,741
Liabilities: $218,792
Net Worth: $487,949
Earnings: ($4,006,564)
Fiscal Year-end: 06/30/23
Exploration & Mining Services
N.A.I.C.S.: 213115

NINA INDUSTRIES LIMITED
A/29/A Manghopir Road S I T E, Karachi, Pakistan
Tel.: (92) 21 32575043
Textile Products Mfr
N.A.I.C.S.: 313210

NINE ALLIANCE SCIENCE & TECHNOLOGY GROUP.
40 Lielais prospekts, Ventspils, LV-3601, Latvia
Tel.: (371) 7025091266   NV
Year Founded: 2014
Liabilities: $34,293
Net Worth: ($34,293)
Earnings: ($17,308)
Fiscal Year-end: 09/30/21
Leather Product Mfr
N.A.I.C.S.: 316990
Joseph C. Passalaqua *(Pres, CEO, CFO, Treas & Sec)*

NINE DRAGONS PAPER HOLDINGS LIMITED
Unit 1 22/F One Harbour Square 181 Hoi Bun Road Kwun Tong, Kowloon, China (Hong Kong)
Tel.: (852) 39293800
Web Site: http://www.ndpaper.com
Year Founded: 1995
2689—(OTCIQ)
Rev.: $7,856,036,774
Assets: $16,705,112,428
Liabilities: $10,455,607,831
Net Worth: $6,249,504,597
Earnings: ($328,261,935)
Emp.: 23,079
Fiscal Year-end: 06/30/23
Holding Company
N.A.I.C.S.: 551112
Yan Cheung *(Chm)*

Subsidiaries:

ND Paper Inc. (1)
1901 S Meyers Rd Ste 600, Oakbrook Terrace, IL 60181
Tel.: (937) 528-3870
Web Site: https://us.ndpaper.com
Paper Packaging Services
N.A.I.C.S.: 561910
Ken Liu *(CEO)*

Nine Dragons Paper Industries (Chongqing) Co., Ltd. (1)
Luohuang Building Materials Industrial Park A, Chongqing, Jiangjin, 402279, China
Tel.: (86) 2365558888
Web Site: http://www.ndpaper.com
Paperboard Products & Kraft Pulp Mfr & Sales
N.A.I.C.S.: 322130

Nine Dragons Paper Industries (Hebei) Co., Ltd. (1)
No 88 Cheng Guan Xi Road, Luannan County, Hebei, 063500, China
Tel.: (86) 315 570 8102
Paper Mfr
N.A.I.C.S.: 322299

Nine Dragons Paper Industries (Leshan) Co., Ltd. (1)
Nine Dragons Industrial Park, Qingxi Town

NINE DRAGONS PAPER HOLDINGS LIMITED

Nine Dragons Paper Holdings Limited—(Continued)
Qianwei County, Leshan, 614404, Sichuan, China
Tel.: (86) 833 229 9999
Paper Mfr
N.A.I.C.S.: 322299

Nine Dragons Paper Industries (Quanzhou) Co., Ltd. (1)
Taiwan Business Investment Zone, Quanzhou, 362123, Fujian, China
Tel.: (86) 5952 739 9888
Paper Mfr
N.A.I.C.S.: 322299

Nine Dragons Paper Industries (Shenyang) Co. Ltd. (1)
Dongying Bei Yi Road, Industry Zone of Dongcheng Xinmin, Shenyang, 110300, Liaoning, China
Tel.: (86) 243 178 2611
Paper Mfr
N.A.I.C.S.: 322299

Nine Dragons Paper Industries (Taicang) Co., Ltd. (1)
Jiulong Road, Port Development Zone, Taicang, 215434, Jiangsu, China
Tel.: (86) 51253703888
Web Site: http://www.ndpaper.com
Sales Range: $50-74.9 Million
Emp.: 100
Paperboard Products & Kraft Pulp Mfr & Sales
N.A.I.C.S.: 322130

Nine Dragons Paper Industries (Tianjin) Co., Ltd. (1)
Wuwei Road, Ninghe Economic Development Area, Tianjin, 301500, China
Tel.: (86) 225 932 6666
Paper Mfr
N.A.I.C.S.: 322299

Nine Dragons Paper Industries Co., Ltd. (1)
Xinsha Port Industry Zone, Mayong Town, Dongguan, 523147, Guangdong, China
Tel.: (86) 76988234888
Web Site: http://www.ndpaper.com
Paperboard Products & Kraft Pulp Mfr & Sales
N.A.I.C.S.: 322130

NINE ENTERTAINMENT CO. HOLDINGS LIMITED

1 Denison Street, North Sydney, 2060, NSW, Australia
Tel.: (61) 299069999   AU
Web Site:
    http://www.nineforbrands.com.au
Year Founded: 2006
NEC—(ASX)
Rev.: $1,756,016,286
Assets: $2,673,666,522
Liabilities: $1,481,514,417
Net Worth: $1,192,152,105
Earnings: $90,077,457
Emp.: 4,698
Fiscal Year-end: 06/30/24
Entertainment Holding Company
N.A.I.C.S.: 551112
Michael Stephenson (Chief Sls Officer)

Subsidiaries:

Campaigntrack Pty. Ltd. (1)
Lifestyle Working Building 25 / 117 Old Pittwater Road, Brookvale, 2100, NSW, Australia
Tel.: (61) 1300787220
Web Site: https://www.campaigntrack.com
Real Estate Advertising Services
N.A.I.C.S.: 541810

Domain Holdings Australia Limited (1)
Level 5 100 Harris Street, Pyrmont, 2009, NSW, Australia
Tel.: (61) 292543000
Web Site: https://www.domain.com.au
Rev.: $274,372,639
Assets: $1,171,950,433
Liabilities: $317,492,280
Net Worth: $854,458,153

Earnings: $30,385,563
Emp.: 1,050
Fiscal Year-end: 06/30/2022
Real Estate Development Services
N.A.I.C.S.: 531210
Jason Pellegrino (CEO & Mng Dir)

Fairfax Media Limited (1)
1 Darling Island Rd, Pyrmont, 2009, NSW, Australia
Tel.: (61) 292822833
Web Site: http://www.fairfaxmedia.com.au
Sales Range: $1-4.9 Billion
Newspaper, Magazine & Website Publisher
N.A.I.C.S.: 513110
Gregory Hywood (CEO)

Subsidiary (Domestic):

Agricultural Publishers Pty Limited (2)
1 Darling Island Rd, Pyrmont, 2009, NSW, Australia
Tel.: (61) 292822833
Web Site: http://www.ninenow.com.au
Newspaper Publishing Services
N.A.I.C.S.: 513110

Unit (Domestic):

Australian Financial Review (2)
38 Pirrama Rd, Pyrmont, Sydney, 2009, NSW, Australia (100%)
Tel.: (61) 279666900
Web Site: http://www.afr.com
Sales Range: $25-49.9 Million
Emp.: 100
Business & Financial Newspaper
N.A.I.C.S.: 513110
Michael Stutchbury (Editor-in-Chief)

Subsidiary (Domestic):

Australian Property Monitors Pty Limited (2)
100 Harris Street, Pyrmont, 2009, NSW, Australia
Tel.: (61) 130 066 5177
Web Site: https://www.apm.com.au
Property Management Services
N.A.I.C.S.: 531311

Bridge Printing Office Pty Limited (2)
Unit 8/214 Wellington Road, Mulgrave, 3170, VIC, Australia
Tel.: (61) 395605416
Web Site: http://www.bridgeprinting.com.au
Commercial Printing Services
N.A.I.C.S.: 333248

Bundaberg Broadcasters Pty Limited (2)
38 Crofton Street, Bundaberg, 4670, QLD, Australia
Tel.: (61) 741530800
Web Site: https://www.4bu.com.au
Radio Broadcasting Services
N.A.I.C.S.: 334220

Carpentaria Newspapers Pty Ltd (2)
112 Camooweal Street, PO Box 777, Mount Isa, 4825, QLD, Australia
Tel.: (61) 747433355
Web Site: http://www.northweststar.com.au
Sales Range: $25-49.9 Million
Emp.: 20
Newspaper Publishing Services
N.A.I.C.S.: 513110

Commerce Australia Pty Ltd (2)
Level 2 8 Parliament Place, West Perth, 6005, WA, Australia
Tel.: (61) 892260011
Web Site: http://www.ca.com.au
Emp.: 2
Software Development Services
N.A.I.C.S.: 541511

CountryCars.com.au Pty Ltd (2)
PO Box 2297, Orange, 2800, NSW, Australia
Tel.: (61) 1300737161
Web Site: http://www.countrycars.com.au
Online Advertising Services
N.A.I.C.S.: 541890

Fairfax Business Media (2)
Level 2 469 LaTrobe St, Melbourne, 3000, VIC, Australia (100%)
Tel.: (61) 396033888
Web Site: http://www.brw.com.au

Sales Range: $25-49.9 Million
Emp.: 75
N.A.I.C.S.: 513110
Kevin Chinnery (Mng Dir)

Fairfax Corporation Pty Limited (2)
L 5 1 Darling Island Rd, Pyrmont, 2009, NSW, Australia
Tel.: (61) 292822833
Web Site: http://www.fairfaxmedia.com.au
Emp.: 300
Newspaper Publishing Services
N.A.I.C.S.: 513110

Fairfax Digital Australia & New Zealand Pty Ltd (2)
L 5 1 Darling Island Rd, Pyrmont, 2009, NSW, Australia
Tel.: (61) 292822833
Newspaper Publishing Services
N.A.I.C.S.: 513110
Greg Hywood (CEO)

Fairfax Digital Limited (2)
1 Darling Island Road, Pyrmont, Sydney, NSW, Australia
Tel.: (61) 1800500864
Web Site: http://www.fairfax.com.au
Online News & Classified Advertising Services
N.A.I.C.S.: 513110

Subsidiary (Non-US):

Fairfax Media (UK) Limited (2)
3rd Floor 27-29 Berwick Street, London, W1F 8RQ, United Kingdom
Tel.: (44) 2078519699
Newspaper Publishing Services
N.A.I.C.S.: 513110

Subsidiary (Domestic):

Fairfax Media Group Finance Pty Limited (2)
L 5 Darling Island Rd, Pyrmont, 2000, NSW, Australia
Tel.: (61) 292822833
Financial Management Services
N.A.I.C.S.: 523999

Fairfax Media Management Pty Limited (2)
L5 1 Darling Island Rd, Pyrmont, 2009, NSW, Australia
Tel.: (61) 292822833
Web Site: http://www.fairfaxmedia.com
Newspaper Publishing Services
N.A.I.C.S.: 513110
Brian Cassell (CEO)

Fairfax Media Publications Pty Limited (2)
1 Darling Island Road, Pyrmont, 2009, NSW, Australia
Tel.: (61) 292822833
Web Site: http://www.fairfaxmedia.com.au
Newspaper Publishing Services
N.A.I.C.S.: 513110
Greg Hywood (CEO)

Subsidiary (Non-US):

Fairfax New Zealand Limited (2)
Tel.: (64) 44969800
Web Site: http://www.fairfaxmedia.co.nz
Sales Range: $100-124.9 Million
Emp.: 350
Publisher of Newspapers & Magazines
N.A.I.C.S.: 513110

Subsidiary (Non-US):

Taranaki Newspapers Limited (3) (100%)
Tel.: (64) 67590808
Web Site: http://www.stuff.co.nz
Sales Range: $50-74.9 Million
Emp.: 100
Publisher of Newspapers
N.A.I.C.S.: 513110

The Christchurch Press Co. Ltd. (3) (100%)
Tel.: (64) 33790940
Web Site: http://www.stuff.co.nz
Sales Range: $100-124.9 Million
Publisher of Newspapers
N.A.I.C.S.: 513110

The Manawatu Standard Limited (3)

INTERNATIONAL PUBLIC

Tel.: (64) 63565000
Web Site: http://www.stuff.co.nz
Sales Range: $50-74.9 Million
Emp.: 150
Publisher of Newspapers
N.A.I.C.S.: 513110

The Marlborough Express (3) (100%)
Tel.: (64) 35208900
Web Site: http://www.stuff.co.nz
Emp.: 75
Publisher of Newspapers
N.A.I.C.S.: 513110

The Nelson Mail (3)
Tel.: (64) 35462889
Web Site: http://www.stuff.co.nz
Sales Range: $50-74.9 Million
Emp.: 60
Publisher of Newspapers
N.A.I.C.S.: 513110

The Southland Times (3)
Tel.: (64) 32111130
Web Site: http://www.stuff.co.nz
Sales Range: $50-74.9 Million
Emp.: 150
Publisher of Newspapers
N.A.I.C.S.: 513110

Waikato Times (3)
Tel.: (64) 78496180
Web Site: http://www.stuff.co.nz
Sales Range: $50-74.9 Million
Emp.: 250
Publisher of Newspapers
N.A.I.C.S.: 513110

Subsidiary (Domestic):

Fairfax News Network Pty Limited (2)
L 2 1 Darling Island Rd, Pyrmont, 2009, NSW, Australia
Tel.: (61) 292822833
Web Site: http://www.fairfaxmedia.com.au
Newspaper Publishing Services
N.A.I.C.S.: 513110
Greg Hywood (CEO)

Fairfax Regional Printers Pty Limited (2)
7 Enterprise Dr, Beresfield, Newcastle, 2322, NSW, Australia
Tel.: (61) 249357435
Sales Range: $25-49.9 Million
Emp.: 90
Newspaper Publishing Services
N.A.I.C.S.: 513110

Find a Babysitter Pty Limited (2)
Level 2 1 Darling Island Road, Pyrmont, 2009, NSW, Australia
Tel.: (61) 1300789073
Web Site: http://www.findababysitter.com.au
Babysitting Services
N.A.I.C.S.: 624410
Alicia Melvill (Mgr-Bus Dev)

Hunter Distribution Network Pty Ltd (2)
7 Enterprise Dr, Beresfield, Newcastle, 2322, NSW, Australia
Tel.: (61) 249357488
Emp.: 6
Newspaper Publishing Services
N.A.I.C.S.: 513110
Michael Aubrey (Gen Mgr)

Integrated Publication Solutions Pty Ltd (2)
Media House 655 Collins St, Docklands, 3008, VIC, Australia
Tel.: (61) 1800606477
Web Site:
    http://www.publicationsolutions.com.au
Magazine Publishing Services
N.A.I.C.S.: 513120
Damien Wouda (Gen Mgr)

John Fairfax Limited (2)
1 Darling Island Rd, Pyrmont, 2009, NSW, Australia
Tel.: (61) 292822833
Newspaper Publishing Services
N.A.I.C.S.: 513110

Metro Media Publishing Pty Ltd (2)
214-220 Park Street South, Melbourne,

AND PRIVATE COMPANIES

3205, VIC, Australia **(100%)**
Tel.: (61) 3 9249 5300
Web Site: http://www.mmpgroup.com.au
Newspaper & Magazine Publisher
N.A.I.C.S.: 513110
Antony Catalano *(CEO)*

Milton Ulladulla Publishing Co. Pty Ltd (2)
Suite 29 The Plaza Princes Highway, PO Box 210, Ulladulla, 2539, NSW, Australia
Tel.: (61) 244551244
Web Site: http://www.ulladullatimes.com.au
Sales Range: $25-49.9 Million
Emp.: 13
Newspaper Publishing Services
N.A.I.C.S.: 513110
Freddie Simon *(Mgr)*

Mountain Press Pty Ltd (2)
278 Macquarie Road, Springwood, 2777, NSW, Australia
Tel.: (61) 247511955
Web Site: https://www.bluemountainsgazette.com.au
Emp.: 18
Newspaper Publishing Services
N.A.I.C.S.: 513110

Subsidiary (Non-US):

NZ Rural Press Limited (2)
Level 1 300 Great South Road, PO Box 4233, Auckland, 1140, New Zealand
Tel.: (64) 95235056
Web Site: http://www.ruralpress.com
Sales Range: $25-49.9 Million
Emp.: 12
Commercial Printing Services
N.A.I.C.S.: 323111

Subsidiary (Domestic):

Nine Radio Pty Limited (2)
Ground Floor Building C 33-35 Saunders Street, Pyrmont, 2009, NSW, Australia **(54.4%)**
Tel.: (61) 285700000
Web Site: http://www.mrn.com.au
Rev.: $106,420,592
Assets: $212,741,281
Liabilities: $70,550,052
Net Worth: $142,191,229
Earnings: $11,399,056
Fiscal Year-end: 06/30/2018
Broadcasting Services
N.A.I.C.S.: 334220
Maria Phillips *(CFO)*

Subsidiary (Domestic):

Radio 2GB Sydney Pty Ltd (3)
Radio 2GB Level G Building C 33-35 Saunders St, Pyrmont, 2009, NSW, Australia
Tel.: (61) 283810319
Web Site: https://www.2gb.com
Sales Range: $50-74.9 Million
Emp.: 150
Radio Broadcasting Services
N.A.I.C.S.: 516110
Russell Tate *(Mng Dir)*

Subsidiary (Domestic):

Nine Radio Syndication Pty Limited (2)
Ground Floor Building C 33-35 Saunders Street, Pyrmont, 2009, NSW, Australia
Tel.: (61) 299309810
Web Site: https://www.mmsyndication.com.au
Radio Programs Distribution Services
N.A.I.C.S.: 516110

Port Lincoln Times Pty Ltd (2)
6-8 Washington Street, PO Box 1672, Port Lincoln, 5606, SA, Australia
Tel.: (61) 88 682 1055
Web Site: https://www.portlincolntimes.com.au
Emp.: 20
Newspaper Publishing Services
N.A.I.C.S.: 513110
Billie Harrison *(Editor)*

Queensland Community Newspapers Pty Limited (2)
Cnr Finukane Rd Delance St, Ormiston, Redland, 4160, QLD, Australia
Tel.: (61) 738218333
Emp.: 150

Newspaper Publishing Services
N.A.I.C.S.: 513110

RSVP.com.au Pty Limited (2)
Suite 310 46-56 Kippax St, Surry Hills, 2010, NSW, Australia
Tel.: (61) 28 366 2880
Web Site: https://www.rsvp.com.au
Online Dating Services
N.A.I.C.S.: 812990

Radio 1278 Melbourne Pty Limited (2)
655 Collins St, Docklands, Melbourne, 3008, VIC, Australia
Tel.: (61) 386673600
Web Site: http://www.3aw.com.au
Sales Range: $50-74.9 Million
Emp.: 200
Radio Broadcasting Services
N.A.I.C.S.: 334220

Radio 2UE Sydney Pty Ltd (2)
170 Pacific Hwy, Greenwich, 2065, NSW, Australia
Tel.: (61) 299309954
Web Site: http://www.2ue.com.au
Sales Range: $25-49.9 Million
Emp.: 100
Radio Broadcasting Services
N.A.I.C.S.: 334220
Chris Parker *(Gen Mgr)*

Radio 4BH Brisbane Pty Limited (2)
77 Southgate Avenue, Cannon Hill, Brisbane, 4170, Australia
Tel.: (61) 739088200
Web Site: http://www.4bh.com.au
Emp.: 40
Radio Broadcasting Services
N.A.I.C.S.: 334220
Anthony Franji *(Gen Mgr)*

Radio 6PR Perth Pty Limited (2)
Level 1 169 Hay Street, Perth, 6004, WA, Australia
Tel.: (61) 89 220 1400
Web Site: https://www.6pr.com.au
Sales Range: $25-49.9 Million
Emp.: 50
Radio Station Operating Services
N.A.I.C.S.: 516110

Regional Printers Pty Limited (2)
159 Bells Line Of Rd, North Richmond, Sydney, 2754, NSW, Australia
Tel.: (61) 245704444
Emp.: 200
Commercial Printing Services
N.A.I.C.S.: 323111
Sean Tait *(Gen Mgr)*

Regional Publishers (Western Victoria) Pty Limited (2)
2 Webster Street, Ballarat, 3350, VIC, Australia
Tel.: (61) 35 320 1200
Web Site: https://www.thecourier.com.au
Sales Range: $25-49.9 Million
Emp.: 100
Newspaper Publishing Services
N.A.I.C.S.: 513110

Regional Publishers Pty Ltd (2)
No 12 Elgin St, Maitland, 2320, NSW, Australia
Tel.: (61) 249310100
Web Site: http://www.maitlandmercury.com.au
Sales Range: $25-49.9 Million
Emp.: 40
Newspaper Publishing Services
N.A.I.C.S.: 513110
Sue Prescott *(Mgr)*

Stock Journal Publishers Pty Ltd (2)
123 Greenhill Rd, Unley, Adelaide, 5061, SA, Australia
Tel.: (61) 883725222
Sales Range: $25-49.9 Million
Emp.: 60
Newspaper Publishing Services
N.A.I.C.S.: 513110

The Advocate Newspaper Proprietary Limited (2)
39-41 Alexander Street, PO Box 63, Burnie, 7320, TAS, Australia
Tel.: (61) 36 440 7409
Web Site: https://www.theadvocate.com.au

NINE ENTERTAINMENT CO. HOLDINGS LIMITED

Sales Range: $25-49.9 Million
Emp.: 50
Newspaper Publishing Services
N.A.I.C.S.: 513110
Phil Leersen *(Gen Mgr)*

The Age Company Ltd. (2)
655 Collins St Docklands, Melbourne, 3008, VIC, Australia **(100%)**
Tel.: (61) 279666900
Web Site: https://www.theage.com.au
Sales Range: $25-49.9 Million
Emp.: 100
Newspaper & Magazine Publisher
N.A.I.C.S.: 513110
Alex Lavell *(Editor)*

The Age Print Company Pty Ltd (2)
L 5 1 Darling Island Rd, Pyrmont, 2009, NSW, Australia
Tel.: (61) 292821674
Newspaper Publishing Services
N.A.I.C.S.: 513110
Greg Hywood *(CEO)*

The Border Morning Mail Pty Ltd (2)
1 McKoy Street, PO Box 491, Wodonga, 3689, VIC, Australia
Tel.: (61) 260240555
Newspaper Publishing Services
N.A.I.C.S.: 513110
Debbie Mosbey *(Mgr-Features & Classifieds)*

The Federal Capital Press of Australia Pty Limited (2)
9 Pirie Street, PO Box 186, Fyshwick, 2609, ACT, Australia
Tel.: (61) 262802122
Web Site: http://www.canberratimes.com.au
Sales Range: $100-124.9 Million
Emp.: 400
Newspaper Publishing Services
N.A.I.C.S.: 513110

Unit (Domestic):

The Sun-Herald (2)
40 City Rd HWT Tower, Southbank, Melbourne, 3006, VIC, Australia **(100%)**
Tel.: (61) 39 292 2000
Web Site: https://www.heraldsun.com.au
Sales Range: $50-74.9 Million
Emp.: 200
Sunday Newspaper
N.A.I.C.S.: 513110
Brian Cassell *(CFO)*

The Sydney Morning Herald (2)
1 Darling Island Road, Pyrmont, 2009, NSW, Australia **(100%)**
Tel.: (61) 279666900
Web Site: https://www.smh.com.au
Sales Range: $25-49.9 Million
Emp.: 100
Morning Newspaper
N.A.I.C.S.: 513110
Lisa Davies *(Editor)*

Subsidiary (Domestic):

The Wagga Daily Advertiser Pty Ltd (2)
19 Peter Street, Wagga Wagga, 2650, NSW, Australia
Tel.: (61) 26 938 3300
Web Site: https://www.dailyadvertiser.com.au
Sales Range: $50-74.9 Million
Emp.: 150
Newspaper Publishing Services
N.A.I.C.S.: 513110
Paul McLoughlin *(Editor)*

Unit (Domestic):

Warrnambool Standard (2)
68 Kepler Street, Warrnambool, 3280, VIC, Australia **(100%)**
Tel.: (61) 35 563 1800
Web Site: https://www.standard.net.au
Sales Range: $25-49.9 Million
Emp.: 75
N.A.I.C.S.: 513110

Subsidiary (Domestic):

Western Magazine Pty Ltd (2)
104 Talbragar Street, PO Box 311, Dubbo, 2830, NSW, Australia
Tel.: (61) 268832900

Web Site: https://www.westernmagazine.com.au
Emp.: 1
Magazine Publishing Services
N.A.I.C.S.: 513120

Whyalla News Properties Pty Ltd (2)
T37 Westland Shopping Centre, PO Box 183, Whyalla, 5608, SA, Australia
Tel.: (61) 88 644 9400
Web Site: https://www.whyallanewsonline.com.au
Newspaper Publishing Services
N.A.I.C.S.: 513110

Mi9 New Zealand Limited (1)
GridAKL 12 Madden Street, Wynyard Quarter, Auckland, New Zealand
Tel.: (64) 21 247 1066
Web Site: https://www.mi9.co.nz
Digital Advertising Services
N.A.I.C.S.: 541810
Rhys Heron *(Mng Dir)*

Nine Entertainment Co. Pty. Ltd. (1)
1 Denison Street, North Sydney, 2060, NSW, Australia **(100%)**
Tel.: (61) 129 906 9999
Web Site: https://www.nineforbrands.com.au
Sales Range: $700-749.9 Million
Emp.: 2,000
Holding Company; Multimedia & Entertainment Investments Operator
N.A.I.C.S.: 551112
Simon Kelly *(CFO)*

Subsidiary (Domestic):

Nine Network Australia Pty. Ltd. (2)
24 Artarmon Road, Willoughby, 2068, NSW, Australia **(100%)**
Tel.: (61) 299069999
Web Site: http://www.ninemsn.com.au
Holding Company; Television Programming & Broadcasting Network
N.A.I.C.S.: 551112
David Gyngell *(CEO)*

Subsidiary (Domestic):

General Television Corporation Pty. Limited (3)
717 Bourke Street, PO Box 100, Melbourne, 3008, VIC, Australia **(100%)**
Tel.: (61) 394290201
Web Site: http://www.ninemsn.com.au
Sales Range: $25-49.9 Million
Emp.: 400
Television Broadcasting
N.A.I.C.S.: 516120
Ian Paterson *(Mng Dir)*

Subsidiary (Non-US):

Media Niugini Pty. Limited (3)
2 Floor Garden City, PO Box 443, Boroko National Capital District, 111, Port Moresby, Papua New Guinea **(100%)**
Tel.: (675) 3257322
Web Site: http://www.emtv.com.pg
Sales Range: $10-24.9 Million
Emp.: 100
Television Broadcasting
N.A.I.C.S.: 516120

Publishing and Broadcasting International Holdings Limited (3)
Trident House Dublin Road, Naas, Kildare, Ireland
Tel.: (353) 45856321
Sales Range: $10-24.9 Million
Emp.: 5
Holding Company
N.A.I.C.S.: 551112
Tom Gallagher *(Mng Dir)*

Subsidiary (Domestic):

Queensland Television Ltd. (3)
Sir Samuel Griffith Drive, Mount Coot-tha, Brisbane, 4066, QLD, Australia **(100%)**
Tel.: (61) 732149999
Web Site: http://www.ninemsn.com.au
Emp.: 120
Television Broadcasting
N.A.I.C.S.: 516120
Kylie Blucher *(Gen Mgr)*

TCN Channel Nine Pty. Limited (3)
24 Artarmon Road, PO Box 27, Willoughby, 2068, NSW, Australia **(100%)**

NINE ENTERTAINMENT CO. HOLDINGS LIMITED

Nine Entertainment Co. Holdings Limited—(Continued)
Tel.: (61) 299069999
Web Site: http://www.ninemsn.com.au
Sales Range: $100-124.9 Million
Emp.: 1,100
Television Broadcasting
N.A.I.C.S.: 516120
David Gyngell (CEO)

Territory Television Pty. Limited (3)
Blake Street The Garden, Darwin, 0801, NT, Australia (100%)
Tel.: (61) 889818888
Web Site: http://www.channelnine.ninemsn.com.au
Sales Range: $10-24.9 Million
Emp.: 55
Television Broadcasting
N.A.I.C.S.: 516120
Andrew Bruyn (Gen Mgr)

Subsidiary (Domestic):

Ticketek Pty. Ltd. (2)
Level 19 66-68 Goulburn Street, Sydney, 2000, NSW, Australia (100%)
Tel.: (61) 292664000
Web Site: https://premier.ticketek.com.au
Sales Range: $100-124.9 Million
Emp.: 105
Sports & Entertainment Ticket Services
N.A.I.C.S.: 711310
Geoff Jones (CEO)

Joint Venture (Domestic):

ninemsn Pty. Ltd. (2)
Level 7 Tower Building Australia Square, 264-278 George Street, Sydney, 2000, NSW, Australia (50%)
Tel.: (61) 293836000
Web Site: http://www.ninemsn.com.au
Sales Range: $50-74.9 Million
Emp.: 200
Online Media Publishing & Broadcasting Services
N.A.I.C.S.: 516210

Nine Radio Syndication Pty Limited (1)
Ground Floor Building C 33-35 Saunders Street, Pyrmont, 2009, NSW, Australia
Tel.: (61) 29 134 0260
Web Site: https://www.fxrs.com.au
Radio Broadcasting Services
N.A.I.C.S.: 516210

Pedestrian Group Pty Limited (1)
Level 1 66 Wentworth Avenue, Surry Hills, 2010, NSW, Australia
Tel.: (61) 29 690 1180
Web Site: https://pedestriangroup.com.au
Media Services
N.A.I.C.S.: 541840

Radio 3AW Melbourne Pty Limited (1)
Media House Level 7 655 Collins Street, Docklands, 3008, VIC, Australia
Tel.: (61) 38 667 3600
Web Site: https://www.3aw.com.au
Radio Broadcasting Services
N.A.I.C.S.: 516210

Radio 4BC Brisbane Pty Limited (1)
77 Southgate Ave, Cannon Hill, 4170, QLD, Australia
Tel.: (61) 73 908 8200
Web Site: https://www.4bc.com.au
Radio Broadcasting Services
N.A.I.C.S.: 516210

Realbase Pty. Ltd. (1)
Lifestyle Working Building 25 / 117 Old Pittwater Road, Brookvale, 2100, NSW, Australia
Tel.: (61) 1300787220
Web Site: https://www.realbase.io
Real Estate Management Services
N.A.I.C.S.: 531210

NINE MILE METALS LTD.
1500 800 West Pender St, Vancouver, V6C 2V6, BC, Canada
Tel.: (604) 428-5171
Web Site: https://ninemilemetals.com

VMSXF—(OTCQB)
Rev.: $15,877
Assets: $3,736,921
Liabilities: $128,730
Net Worth: $3,608,191
Earnings: ($2,035,499)
Emp.: 5
Fiscal Year-end: 09/30/23
Mineral Exploration Services
N.A.I.C.S.: 213115
James Bordian (CFO)

NINEBOT LIMITED
Room 101 1/F Bldg A-1 ZGC Dongsheng Science Park No 66 Xixiaokou Road, Haidian District, Beijing, 100192, China
Tel.: (86) 10 8482 8002   Ky
Web Site: http://www.ninebot.com
Holding Company; Personal Transportation Robot Engineering, Mfr & Distr
N.A.I.C.S.: 551112

Subsidiaries:

Ninebot Inc. (1)
Room 101 1/F Bldg A-1 ZGC Dongsheng Science Park No 66 Xixiaokou Road, Haidian District, Beijing, China
Tel.: (86) 10 8482 8002
Web Site: http://www.ninebot.cn
N.A.I.C.S.: 336999
Lufeng Gao (Co-Founder & Co-CEO)

Ninebot Polska Sp. z o.o. (1)
ul Julianowska 37, 05 500, Piaseczno, Poland
Tel.: (48) 784599779
Automobile Parts Distr
N.A.I.C.S.: 423120

SIA NINEBOT LATVIA (1)
Siguldas soseja 11, Garkalne, Latvia
Tel.: (371) 25909030
Web Site: http://www.ninebot-latvia.lv
Automobile Parts Distr
N.A.I.C.S.: 423120

Segway (Thailand) Company Limited (1)
999/2 Moo 6 Teparak Rd A Muang, Samut Prakan, Thailand
Tel.: (66) 3851345
Web Site: http://www.ninebotthailand.com
Automobile Parts Distr
N.A.I.C.S.: 423120

Segway Inc. (1)
14 Technology Dr, Bedford, NH 03110
Tel.: (603) 222-6000
Web Site: http://www.segway.com
Electric Transportation Devices Developer & Mfr
N.A.I.C.S.: 336991
Francis Bridges (VP-Engrg & Supply Chain)

Segway New Zealand Limited. (1)
8 Clarke Road Te Puna R D 6, Tauranga, New Zealand
Tel.: (64) 21669649
Web Site: http://www.segway.co.nz
Automobile Parts Distr
N.A.I.C.S.: 423120

Segwaybooking B.V. (1)
Piet Heinkade 25, 1019 BR, Amsterdam, Netherlands
Tel.: (31) 880123050
Web Site: http://www.segwaybooking.com
Automobile Parts Distr
N.A.I.C.S.: 423120

NINEPOINT PARTNERS LP
Royal Bank Plaza South Tower 200 Bay Street, PO Box 27, Toronto, M5J 2J1, ON, Canada
Tel.: (416) 362-7172
Web Site: http://www.ninepoint.com
Portfolio Management
N.A.I.C.S.: 523940
James Fox (Co-CEO & Mng Partner)

NINETOWNS HOLDINGS LIMITED
22nd Floor Building No 1 Capital A Partners No 20 Gong Ti East Road, Chaoyang District, Beijing, 100020, China
Tel.: (86) 10 6589 9904
Web Site: http://www.ninetowns.com
Sales Range: $10-24.9 Million
Holding Company
N.A.I.C.S.: 551112
Shuang Wang (CEO)

Subsidiaries:

Ninetowns Internet Technology Group Company Limited (1)
22nd Floor Building No 1 Capital A Partners No 20 Gong Ti East Road, Chaoyang District, Beijing, 100020, China
Tel.: (86) 10 65899922
Web Site: http://www.ninetowns.com
Software Publisher
N.A.I.C.S.: 513210
Bolin Wu (CTO)

NINETY ONE PLC
55 Gresham Street, London, EC2V 7EL, United Kingdom
Tel.: (44) 2039382000
Web Site: https://www.ninetyone.com
Year Founded: 1991
N91—(LSE)
Rev.: $778,293,810
Assets: $13,419,269,640
Liabilities: $12,985,008,750
Net Worth: $434,260,890
Earnings: $201,554,640
Emp.: 200
Fiscal Year-end: 03/31/23
Mutual Fund Management Services
N.A.I.C.S.: 523940
Gareth Penny (Chm)

Subsidiaries:

Investec Asset Management Asia Ltd (1)
Suites 2604-06 Tower 2 The Gateway Harbour City, Tsimshatsui, Kowloon, China (Hong Kong)
Tel.: (852) 2861 6888
Asset Management Services
N.A.I.C.S.: 523940
Marco Tang (Head-Advisor Bus-Greater China)

Investec Asset Management Australia Pty Ltd (1)
Level 31 The Chifley Tower 2 Chifley Square, Sydney, 2000, NSW, Australia
Tel.: (61) 2 9293 2346
Sales Range: $50-74.9 Million
Emp.: 4
Asset Management Services
N.A.I.C.S.: 523940
Mark Samuelson (Mng Dir)

Investec Asset Management Guernsey Limited (1)
Glategny Court Glategny Esplanade, PO Box 250, Saint Peter Port, GY1 3QH, Guernsey
Tel.: (44) 20 7597 1900
Asset Management Services
N.A.I.C.S.: 523940

Investec Asset Management Namibia (Pty) Ltd (1)
100 Robert Mugabe Avenue Office 1 Ground Floor, Heritage Square Building, Windhoek, Namibia
Tel.: (264) 61 389 500
Web Site: http://www.investecassetmanagement.com
Emp.: 6
Asset Management Services
N.A.I.C.S.: 523940
Gwynneth Rukoro (Mgr-Bus-Africa)

NINEVEH FOOD INDUSTRIES
Mousel-Al-Resheedia Al-Rashid Camp Al-Taieb Bld, Baghdad, Iraq
Tel.: (964) 60 813498
Year Founded: 1989
Soft Drinks Mfr

INTERNATIONAL PUBLIC

N.A.I.C.S.: 312111
Anmar Khair Al-Dien (Exec Dir)

NING XIA YIN XING ENERGY CO., LTD.
No 166 Liupanshan West Road, Xixia District, Yinchuan, 750021, Ningxia, China
Tel.: (86) 9518887899
Web Site: http://www.nxyxny.com.ch
Year Founded: 1998
000862—(SSE)
Rev.: $163,331,532
Assets: $1,060,191,288
Liabilities: $646,403,004
Net Worth: $413,788,284
Earnings: $17,673,552
Fiscal Year-end: 12/31/22
Power Generation Services
N.A.I.C.S.: 221118
Han Jing (Chm)

NINGBO BAOSI ENERGY EQUIPMENT CO., LTD.
No 18 Shangqiao Road Xiwu Street, Fenghua District, Ningbo, 315505, Zhejiang, China
Tel.: (86) 4001006555
Web Site: https://www.cnbaosi.com
Year Founded: 2005
300441—(CHIN)
Rev.: $288,401,256
Assets: $458,181,360
Liabilities: $167,057,748
Net Worth: $291,123,612
Earnings: $15,570,360
Emp.: 590
Fiscal Year-end: 12/31/22
Screw Compressor Mfr
N.A.I.C.S.: 333912
Jinyue Chen (Chm & Gen Mgr)

NINGBO BIRD CO., LTD.
No 999 Dacheng East Road, Fenghua, 315500, Zhejiang, China
Tel.: (86) 57488953465
Web Site: https://www.chinabird.com
Year Founded: 1992
600130—(SHG)
Rev.: $75,052,350
Assets: $168,649,828
Liabilities: $21,493,218
Net Worth: $147,156,610
Earnings: $2,558,902
Emp.: 1,000
Fiscal Year-end: 12/31/22
Mobile Phone Mfr
N.A.I.C.S.: 334220
Lihua Xu (Chm)

NINGBO BOHUI CHEMICAL TECHNOLOGY CO., LTD.
No 1818 Zhenluo East Road, Zhenhai District, Ningbo, 315207, Zhejiang, China
Tel.: (86) 57486369063
Web Site: http://www.bhpcc.com
Year Founded: 2005
300839—(SSE)
Rev.: $416,315,484
Assets: $318,775,392
Liabilities: $178,108,632
Net Worth: $140,666,760
Earnings: $21,308,508
Fiscal Year-end: 12/31/22
Chemical Product Mfr & Distr
N.A.I.C.S.: 325520
Bihua Jin (Chm)

NINGBO CHANGHONG POLYMER SCIENTIFIC & TECHNICAL, INC.
No 108 Qijiashan Port Road, Beilun District, Ningbo, 315803, Zhejiang, China
Tel.: (86) 13884408500

AND PRIVATE COMPANIES

Web Site:
https://www.changhongpolymer.com
Year Founded: 2012
605008—(SHG)
Rev.: $332,994,683
Assets: $534,941,789
Liabilities: $253,292,762
Net Worth: $281,649,027
Earnings: $25,336,233
Fiscal Year-end: 12/31/22
Plastic Product Mfr & Distr
N.A.I.C.S.: 326199
Chunfeng Tao (Chm)

NINGBO CIXING CO., LTD.
No 708 Binhai 4th Road, Hangzhou Bay New District Ningbo, Cixi, 315336, Zhejiang, China
Tel.: (86) 57463932198
Web Site: https://www.ci-xing.com
300307—(CHIN)
Rev.: $266,879,340
Assets: $620,701,380
Liabilities: $240,133,140
Net Worth: $380,568,240
Earnings: $12,812,904
Emp.: 3,000
Fiscal Year-end: 12/31/22
Computer Knitting Machine Mfr
N.A.I.C.S.: 333248
Pingfan Sun (Chm)

Subsidiaries:

Dongguan Zhongtian Automation Technology Co., Ltd. (1)
Building A1 Dongcheng Silicon Valley Power 2025 Science Park, Dongguan, China
Tel.: (86) 76939016568
Web Site: https://www.en.zt-robot.com
Automation Product Distr
N.A.I.C.S.: 423830

Steiger Participations SA (1)
Route du Simplon 20, 1895, Vionnaz, Switzerland
Tel.: (41) 244822250
Knitting Machine Mfr
N.A.I.C.S.: 333248

NINGBO COLOR MASTER BATCH CO., LTD.
No 168 Jinhui West Road Panhuo Street, Yinzhou District, Ningbo, 315105, Zhejiang, China
Tel.: (86) 57488393338
Web Site: https://www.muli.com.cn
Year Founded: 1999
301019—(CHIN)
Rev.: $65,166,660
Assets: $154,757,304
Liabilities: $8,207,784
Net Worth: $146,549,520
Earnings: $14,105,988
Fiscal Year-end: 12/31/22
Chemical Product Mfr & Distr
N.A.I.C.S.: 327120
Weiqing Ren (Chm & Gen Mgr)

NINGBO CONSTRUCTION CO., LTD.
No 538 Ningchuan Road, Yinzhou District, Ningbo, 315040, Zhejiang, China
Tel.: (86) 57487889898
Web Site:
https://www.jiangong.com.cn
Year Founded: 1951
601789—(SHG)
Rev.: $3,070,108,127
Assets: $3,477,485,494
Liabilities: $2,705,089,482
Net Worth: $772,396,012
Earnings: $48,970,116
Fiscal Year-end: 12/31/22
Housing Construction Services
N.A.I.C.S.: 236115
Wenwei Xu (Chm & Gen Mgr)

Subsidiaries:

Anglorand Securities Limited (1)
3rd Floor 54 Melrose Boulevard Melrose Arch, Melrose North, 2196, Johannesburg, South Africa
Tel.: (27) 110614200
Web Site: http://www.anglorand.com
Financial Services
N.A.I.C.S.: 523999
Richard Bonnichsen (CEO)

Ningbo Preca Construction Technology Co., Ltd. (1)
Economic Development Zone Ning Gulf Recycling, Ningbo, China
Tel.: (86) 57482531216
Web Site: http://www.preca.cn
Building Construction Services
N.A.I.C.S.: 236210

NINGBO DAVID MEDICAL DEVICE CO., LTD.
No 2 Keyuan Road Shi Pu science and Technology Park Xiangshan, Ningbo, 315731, Zhejiang, China
Tel.: (86) 57465983055
Web Site: https://www.nbdavid.com
Year Founded: 1992
300314—(CHIN)
Rev.: $71,048,016
Assets: $175,877,676
Liabilities: $27,151,956
Net Worth: $148,725,720
Earnings: $13,700,232
Emp.: 390
Fiscal Year-end: 12/31/22
Infant Caring Equipment Mfr
N.A.I.C.S.: 339112
Chen Zaihong (Chm & Gen Mgr)

NINGBO DAYE GARDEN MACHINERY CO., LTD.
58 Jinfeng Road, Yuyao, 315403, Zhejiang, China
Tel.: (86) 57462678966
Web Site:
https://www.dayepower.com
Year Founded: 2006
300879—(SSE)
Rev.: $206,609,832
Assets: $367,756,740
Liabilities: $233,837,604
Net Worth: $133,919,136
Earnings: $1,579,500
Emp.: 1,200
Fiscal Year-end: 12/31/22
Agricultural Machinery Mfr & Distr
N.A.I.C.S.: 333112
Xiaobo Ye (Chm & Gen Mgr)

Subsidiaries:

Daye Europe GmbH (1)
Parkstrasse 1 a, 66450, Bexbach, Germany
Tel.: (49) 68269301610
Agricultural Machine Mfr & Whslr
N.A.I.C.S.: 333111

NINGBO DEVELOPMENT CO., LTD.
8-7, Kakuda-cho, Kita-ku, Osaka, 530-8350, Japan
Tel.: (81) 663611381
Emp.: 100
Investment Services
N.A.I.C.S.: 523999

NINGBO DEYE TECHNOLOGY CO., LTD.
No 26 South Yongjiang Road Daqi, Beilun District, Ningbo, 315806, Zhejiang, China
Tel.: (86) 57486222335
Web Site: https://www.deye.com.cn
Year Founded: 2000
605117—(SHG)
Rev.: $836,155,008
Assets: $1,194,450,810
Liabilities: $620,235,828

Net Worth: $574,214,982
Earnings: $213,044,294
Emp.: 5,000
Fiscal Year-end: 12/31/22
Electrical Equipment Mfr & Distr
N.A.I.C.S.: 335999
Hejun Zhang (Chm & Gen Mgr)

Subsidiaries:

Ningbo Deye Daily Electrical Appliance Technology Co., Ltd. (1)
No 26-30 South Yongjiang Road, Beilun, Ningbo, 315806, China
Tel.: (86) 57486120560
Web Site: https://www.deyeinverter.com
Commercial Power Plant Services
N.A.I.C.S.: 561730

NINGBO DONLY CO., LTD.
No 1 Yinhai Road, Jiangbei District, Ningbo, 315033, Zhejiang, China
Tel.: (86) 4001686666
Web Site: https://www.donly.com.cn
Year Founded: 1998
002164—(SSE)
Rev.: $206,164,764
Assets: $324,315,576
Liabilities: $143,172,900
Net Worth: $181,142,676
Earnings: $46,068,048
Fiscal Year-end: 12/31/22
Motor & Gearbox Mfr
N.A.I.C.S.: 333612
Jilong Song (Chm & Gen Mgr)

NINGBO ENERGY GROUP CO., LTD.
7F Block B Development Building No 187 Changle Road, Yinzhou District, Ningbo, 315042, Zhejiang, China
Tel.: (86) 57486897102
Web Site: http://www.nbtp.com.cn
Year Founded: 1995
600982—(SHG)
Rev.: $1,305,341,117
Assets: $1,642,795,198
Liabilities: $983,689,462
Net Worth: $659,105,736
Earnings: $51,066,555
Fiscal Year-end: 12/31/22
Steam & Electricity Supply Services
N.A.I.C.S.: 221330
Ma Yifei (Chm)

NINGBO FANGZHENG AUTOMOBILE MOULD CO., LTD.
Automobile Parts Industrial Park of No 1 Middle Sansheng Road, Ninghai, Ningbo, 315609, Zhejiang, China
Tel.: (86) 57483538525
Web Site: https://www.fzmould.com
Year Founded: 2004
300998—(SSE)
Rev.: $107,508,989
Assets: $182,473,110
Liabilities: $97,846,034
Net Worth: $84,627,076
Earnings: $3,972,735
Fiscal Year-end: 12/31/21
Automotive Parts Mfr & Distr
N.A.I.C.S.: 336390
Song Jian (CFO, Sec & Deputy Gen Mgr)

NINGBO FUBANG JINGYE GROUP CO., LTD.
22F Building D Fubon Center No 188 Ningdong Road, Yinzhou District, Ningbo, 315151, Zhejiang, China
Tel.: (86) 57487410501
Web Site:
https://www.600768.com.cn
Year Founded: 1981
600768—(SHG)
Rev.: $42,557,739
Assets: $78,594,348
Liabilities: $23,487,207

Net Worth: $55,107,140
Earnings: $24,083,500
Fiscal Year-end: 12/31/22
Aluminum Material Mfr
N.A.I.C.S.: 331315

NINGBO FUDA COMPANY LIMITED
Room 1302 Yuyao Chamber of Commerce Building No 2 Nanlei South Road, Yuyao, 315400, Zhejiang, China
Tel.: (86) 57487402545
Web Site: https://www.fuda.com
Year Founded: 1989
600724—(SHG)
Rev.: $457,186,991
Assets: $608,833,438
Liabilities: $126,016,638
Net Worth: $482,816,800
Earnings: $34,289,092
Fiscal Year-end: 12/31/22
Real Estate Development Services
N.A.I.C.S.: 531390
Zhang Chenwei (Sec)

NINGBO GAOFA AUTOMOTIVE CONTROL SYSTEM CO., LTD.
No 717 Xiaying North Road, Yinzhou District, Ningbo, 315105, Zhejiang, China
Tel.: (86) 57488169136
Web Site:
https://www.gaofacable.com
Year Founded: 1999
603788—(SHG)
Rev.: $145,659,679
Assets: $324,965,586
Liabilities: $49,173,864
Net Worth: $275,791,721
Earnings: $16,133,841
Emp.: 120
Fiscal Year-end: 12/31/22
Automobile Parts Mfr & Distr
N.A.I.C.S.: 336350
Gaofa Qian (Chm)

NINGBO GQY VIDEO & TELECOM JOINT-STOCK CO., LTD.
No 131 No 4 Binhai Road Hangzhou Bay New Zone, Ningbo, 315336, China
Tel.: (86) 57463008766
Web Site: https://www.gqy.com.cn
Year Founded: 1992
300076—(CHIN)
Rev.: $22,924,512
Assets: $157,312,584
Liabilities: $15,307,812
Net Worth: $142,004,772
Earnings: $(2,250,612)
Emp.: 130
Fiscal Year-end: 12/31/22
Screen Display Systems & Digital Laboratory Systems Mfr
N.A.I.C.S.: 334310
Jing Yimin (Chm & Gen Mgr)

NINGBO HAITIAN PRECISION MACHINERY CO., LTD.
No 1688 Haitian Road Xiaogang Beilun, Ningbo, 315801, Zhejiang, China
Tel.: (86) 57486182525
Web Site:
https://haitianprecision.com
Year Founded: 2002
601882—(SHG)
Rev.: $446,118,515
Assets: $635,008,393
Liabilities: $356,253,136
Net Worth: $278,755,257
Earnings: $73,099,134
Emp.: 1,900
Fiscal Year-end: 12/31/22
Machine Tool Mfr & Distr
N.A.I.C.S.: 333517

NINGBO HAITIAN PRECISION MACHINERY CO., LTD.

Ningbo Haitian Precision Machinery Co., Ltd.—(Continued)
Zhang Jianming *(Chm)*
Subsidiaries:

Haitian Precision Machinery (Malaysia) Private Limited (1)
Unit 901 Level 9 City Plaza No 21, Jalan Tebrau, 80300, Johor Bahru, Johor, Malaysia
Tel.: (60) 73331898
Industrial Machinery Mfr & Distr
N.A.I.C.S.: 333248

Haitian Precision Machinery (Turkey) Private Limited (1)
Yakuplu Mah Hurriyet Boulevard Skyport No 1 Floor 3 D No 64, Beylikduzu, 34520, Istanbul, Turkiye
Tel.: (90) 13484279882
Machine Tool Mfr & Distr
N.A.I.C.S.: 333511

Haitian Precision Machinery (Vietnam) Company Limited (1)
A1 Room 14 Floor HM Town Building 412 Nguyen Thi Minh Khai, Ward 5 District 3, Ho Chi Minh City, Vietnam
Tel.: (84) 335100022
Web Site: https://hisioncnc.vn
Heavy Machinery Mfr
N.A.I.C.S.: 333248

Haitian Precision Machinery Mexico S.De R.L.De C.V. (1)
Calle 2 Nro 111 - C Colonia Parque Industrial Jurica, Queretaro, Mexico
Tel.: (52) 4427833029
Precision Machinery Mfr
N.A.I.C.S.: 332721

NINGBO HELI TECHNOLOGY CO., LTD.
No 358 Xigu Road Xiangshan Industrial Park, Ningbo, 315700, Zhejiang, China
Tel.: (86) 57465773106
Web Site: http://www.helimould.com
Year Founded: 2000
603917—(SHG)
Rev.: $96,228,658
Assets: $203,647,911
Liabilities: $53,030,596
Net Worth: $150,617,315
Earnings: $8,274,277
Fiscal Year-end: 12/31/22
Mold Product Mfr & Distr
N.A.I.C.S.: 333517
Liangcai Shi *(Chm, Pres & Gen Mgr)*

NINGBO HENGHE PRECISION INDUSTRY CO., LTD.
588 Xinxing Road Zonghan Street, Cixi, 315301, Zhejiang, China
Tel.: (86) 75581728602601
Web Site: https://www.mouldcenter.com
Year Founded: 2001
300539—(CHIN)
Rev.: $95,441,073
Assets: $157,967,331
Liabilities: $81,704,113
Net Worth: $76,263,218
Earnings: $4,771,097
Fiscal Year-end: 12/31/23
Precision Injection Mold Mfr & Distr
N.A.I.C.S.: 331511
Zhijun Hu *(Chm & Gen Mgr)*
Subsidiaries:

Hangzhou Richao Machinery & Electronics Co., Ltd. (1)
South Building of the Standard Factory in Zhige Community, No 1 Hangzhou Economy and Technology Developing Area Xiasha District, Hangzhou, China
Tel.: (86) 57186777636
Precision Injection Molding Product Mfr
N.A.I.C.S.: 333511

Shanghai Hengpeng Electronic Technology Co., Ltd. (1)
No 38 Gucui Road Tanzhi Industrial Park Xinchang Town, Pudong New Area, Shanghai, China
Tel.: (86) 2158145678
Precision Injection Molding Product Mfr
N.A.I.C.S.: 333511

Shenzhen Henghe Xingao Machinery & Electronics Co., Ltd. (1)
Building C Jialongda Industrial Zone No 57 Yanzhao Road, Yanchuan Community Songgang Sub-District, Shenzhen, China
Tel.: (86) 75581728509
Precision Injection Molding Product Mfr
N.A.I.C.S.: 333511

NINGBO HENGSHUAI CO., LTD.
No 399 Tong Ning Road, Ningbo, 315033, China
Tel.: (86) 57487585866
Web Site: https://www.motorpump.com
Year Founded: 2001
300969—(SSE)
Rev.: $89,543,585
Assets: $144,740,551
Liabilities: $24,256,207
Net Worth: $120,484,344
Earnings: $17,711,076
Emp.: 500
Fiscal Year-end: 12/31/21
Automotive Parts Mfr & Distr
N.A.I.C.S.: 336390
Ningning Xu *(Chm, CEO & Gen Mgr)*

NINGBO HOMELINK ECO-ITECH CO., LTD.
No 296 Xingpu Road, Xiepu Town Zhenhai District, Ningbo, 315200, Zhejiang, China
Tel.: (86) 57486360326
Web Site: https://www.nbhomelink.cn
Year Founded: 2009
301193—(CHIN)
Rev.: $242,417,211
Assets: $579,503,350
Liabilities: $320,613,069
Net Worth: $258,890,281
Earnings: $6,388,028
Emp.: 2,200
Fiscal Year-end: 12/31/23
Plastic Product Mfr & Distr
N.A.I.C.S.: 326199
Xiong Wang *(Chm)*

NINGBO HUAXIANG ELECTRONIC CO., LTD.
Xiangxi Development Zone, Xizhou Town Xiangshan County, Ningbo, 201204, China
Tel.: (86) 2168949998
002048—(SSE)
Rev.: $2,755,507,248
Assets: $3,220,781,616
Liabilities: $1,441,342,188
Net Worth: $1,779,439,428
Earnings: $141,402,456
Fiscal Year-end: 12/31/22
Automotive Components Mfr
N.A.I.C.S.: 336390
Subsidiaries:

Changchun Schlemmer Automotive Parts Co., Ltd. (1)
Haoyue Road No 8999, Luyuan, Changchun, China
Tel.: (86) 43184615544
Automobile Spare Parts Mfr
N.A.I.C.S.: 336390

HIB Trim Part Solutions GmbH (1)
Ernst-Blickle Str 21-25, 76646, Bruchsal, Germany
Tel.: (49) 72517220
Automobile Part Mfr & Distr
N.A.I.C.S.: 336360

Mianyang Schlemmer Automotive Parts Co., Ltd. (1)
5 Jiepai Auto Parts Industry Zone, An-County, Mianyang, China
Tel.: (86) 8166155266
Automobile Spare Parts Mfr
N.A.I.C.S.: 336390

NBHX Trim Management Services GmbH (1)
Ernst-Blickle-Str 21-25, 76646, Bruchsal, Germany
Tel.: (49) 72517220
Web Site: https://nbhx-trim.com
Emp.: 4,500
Automobile Part Mfr & Distr
N.A.I.C.S.: 336360

Nbhx Trim Usa Corporation (1)
1020 7 Mile Rd, Comstock Park, MI 49321
Tel.: (616) 785-9400
Automobile Part Mfr & Distr
N.A.I.C.S.: 336360

Ningbo Mile Mould Manufacturing Co., Ltd. (1)
525 Changxing Road, Jiangbei, Ningbo, Zhejiang, China
Tel.: (86) 57483006285
Web Site: https://www.nbml.com.cn
Automotive Trim Mfr
N.A.I.C.S.: 333514

Ningbo Schlemmer Automotive Parts Co., Ltd. (1)
Xizhou Economic Zone, Xiangshan, Ningbo, Zhejiang, China
Tel.: (86) 57465838258
Web Site: https://www.schlemmer.com.cn
Emp.: 900
Plastic Part Mfr & Distr
N.A.I.C.S.: 326199

Northern Automotive Systems Limited (1)
Ty Mawr Road, Gilwern, Abergavenny, NP7 0EB, United Kingdom
Tel.: (44) 1873832263
Web Site: https://www.nasuk.com
Automobile Part Mfr & Distr
N.A.I.C.S.: 326199

P.T. Schlemmer Automotive Indonesia (1)
Kawasan Industri Delta Silicon 3 Jl Johar Blok F8 No 6, Lippo Cikarang Cicau Cikarang Pusat Kab, Bekasi, 17530, Jawa Barat, Indonesia
Tel.: (62) 2189913741
Web Site: https://recruitment.schlemmer.co.id
Wheeled Vehicles Spare Parts Mfr & Distr
N.A.I.C.S.: 336390

Schlemmer Philippines Inc. (1)
Greenfield Automotive Park Special Economic Zone, Laguna, Santa Rosa, 4026, Philippines
Tel.: (63) 495760907
Plastic Part Mfr & Distr
N.A.I.C.S.: 326199

Suzhou Schlemmer Automotive Parts Co., Ltd. (1)
11 Chunwang Road, Panyang Industry Zone Huangdai, Suzhou, China
Tel.: (86) 51265798132
Automobile Spare Parts Mfr
N.A.I.C.S.: 336390

Vietnam Schlemmer Automotive Parts Co. Ltd. (1)
Yen Lich Village, Dan Tien Ward Khoai Chau District, Hung Yen, Vietnam
Tel.: (84) 3213714483
Plastic Part Mfr & Distr
N.A.I.C.S.: 326199

Wuhan Schlemmer Automotive Parts Co., Ltd. (1)
2 Zhangbo Road Jinshan Avenue, Eastwest Lake District, Wuhan, China
Tel.: (86) 2752359233
Automobile Spare Parts Mfr
N.A.I.C.S.: 336390

Yantai Schlemmer Automotive Parts Co., Ltd. (1)
8 Beijing South Road Economic & Development Zone, 18 Factory Building In The East Industrial Park, Yantai, China
Tel.: (86) 5353020061
Automobile Spare Parts Mfr
N.A.I.C.S.: 336390

Zhongshan Schlemmer Automotive Parts Co., Ltd. (1)
6 Qiye North Road Maxin Industry Zone, Huangpu Town, Zhongshan, China
Tel.: (86) 76022500311
Automobile Spare Parts Mfr
N.A.I.C.S.: 336390

NINGBO JIANAN ELECTRONICS CO., LTD.
711 Keji road, Cixi, Ningbo, 315300, China
Tel.: (86) 57423669188
Web Site: https://www.nb-jianan.com
Year Founded: 1999
300880—(SSE)
Rev.: $112,925,124
Assets: $167,314,680
Liabilities: $48,289,176
Net Worth: $119,025,504
Earnings: $19,616,688
Fiscal Year-end: 12/31/22
Electronic Product Mfr & Distr
N.A.I.C.S.: 334419
Guoyao Zhang *(Chm)*

NINGBO JIFENG AUTO PARTS CO., LTD.
No 17 Yingluohe Road Daqi, Bei Lun, Ningbo, Zhejiang, China
Tel.: (86) 57486168228
Web Site: https://www.nb-jf.com
Year Founded: 1996
603997—(SHG)
Rev.: $2,522,538,987
Assets: $2,169,676,974
Liabilities: $1,639,644,510
Net Worth: $530,032,464
Earnings: ($198,999,759)
Emp.: 2,000
Fiscal Year-end: 12/31/22
Automobile Seat Mfr & Distr
N.A.I.C.S.: 336360
Yiping Wang *(Chm)*

NINGBO JINTIAN COPPER (GROUP) CO., LTD.
No 1 Chengxi West Road, Cicheng Jiangbei District, Ningbo, 315034, China
Tel.: (86) 57487597999
Web Site: https://www.jtgroup.com.cn
Year Founded: 1986
601609—(SHG)
Rev.: $14,207,035,551
Assets: $2,809,152,824
Liabilities: $1,718,047,843
Net Worth: $1,091,104,981
Earnings: $59,003,353
Emp.: 5,000
Fiscal Year-end: 12/31/22
Copper Product Mfr & Distr
N.A.I.C.S.: 331420
Guoqiang Lou *(Chm)*
Subsidiaries:

Chongqing Jintian Copper Co., Ltd. (1)
Building 1 Plot 2-7 Anjufang Community, Luohuang Town Jiangjin District, Chongqing, China
Tel.: (86) 13709424801
Copper Material Mfr & Distr
N.A.I.C.S.: 331420

Hongkong Maytime International Industry Co., Ltd. (1)
Flat/Rm 19C Loakhart Centre 301-307 Lockhart Road, Wan Chai, Hong Kong, China (Hong Kong)
Tel.: (852) 57487191177
Copper Material Mfr & Distr
N.A.I.C.S.: 331420

Jintian Copper (Germany) GmbH (1)

Bettinastrasse 30, 60325, Frankfurt am Main, Germany
Tel.: (49) 6990757650
Copper Product Mfr
N.A.I.C.S.: 331420

Jintian Copper (Usa) Co., Ltd. (1)
510 Fairview Ave Apt F, Arcadia, CA 91007
Tel.: (626) 294-9803
Copper Material Mfr & Distr
N.A.I.C.S.: 331420

Jintian Copper (Vietnam) Co., Ltd. (1)
Lot 110A1 110B 110C 110D Long Jiang Industrial Park, Tan Lap 1 Commue, Tan Phuoc, Tien Giang, Vietnam
Tel.: (84) 2733642901
Copper Material Mfr & Distr
N.A.I.C.S.: 331420

Jintian Copper Bar Company Ltd. (1)
No 1 Chengxi West Road, Cicheng, Ningbo, China
Tel.: (86) 18057437999
Copper Bar Mfr & Distr
N.A.I.C.S.: 331420

Jintian Copper Japan Co., Ltd. (1)
404 3-22-1 Toranomon Minato, Tokyo, 105-0001, Japan
Tel.: (81) 364530114
Copper Product Mfr
N.A.I.C.S.: 331420

Jintian Copper Plate Company Ltd. (1)
No 1 Chengxi West Road, Cicheng, Ningbo, China
Tel.: (86) 18057437999
Copper Plate Mfr & Distr
N.A.I.C.S.: 331420

Jintian Copper Rod Company Ltd. (1)
No 1 Chengxi West Road, Cicheng, Ningbo, China
Tel.: (86) 18057437999
Copper Product Mfr & Distr
N.A.I.C.S.: 331420

Ningbo Jiekelong Precision Manufacturing Co., Ltd. (1)
No 1 Chengxi West Road, Cicheng Town jiangbei District, Ningbo, 315034, Zhejiang, China
Tel.: (86) 57487597992
Web Site: https://www.jklong.com
Copper Product Mfr & Distr
N.A.I.C.S.: 332919

Ningbo Jintian Copper Strip Company Ltd. (1)
No 1 Chengxi West Road, Cicheng, Ningbo, China
Tel.: (86) 18057437999
Copper Product Mfr & Distr
N.A.I.C.S.: 331420

Ningbo Jintian Copper Tube Co., Ltd. (1)
No 1 Chengxi West Road, Cicheng, Ningbo, China
Tel.: (86) 18057437999
Copper Product Mfr & Distr
N.A.I.C.S.: 331420

Ningbo Jintian Electric Material Co., Ltd. (1)
No 1 Chengxi West Road, Cicheng, Ningbo, China
Tel.: (86) 18057437999
Copper Product Mfr & Distr
N.A.I.C.S.: 331420

Ningbo Jintian Import & Export Co., Ltd. (1)
Room 1201/12FL Yingting Building Hefeng creative square, Jiangdong North Road, Ningbo, China
Tel.: (86) 57487191177
Copper Material Mfr & Distr
N.A.I.C.S.: 331420

Ningbo Jintian New Material Co., Ltd. (1)
No 1 Chengxi West Road, Cicheng, Ningbo, China
Tel.: (86) 18057437999

Copper Product Mfr & Distr
N.A.I.C.S.: 331420

Ningbo Ketian Magnet Co., Ltd. (1)
Ximenwai, Cicheng, Ningbo, Zhejiang, China
Tel.: (86) 57487574923
Web Site: https://www.ktmagnet.com
Magnet Material Mfr & Distr
N.A.I.C.S.: 332999

NINGBO JOY INTELLIGENT LOGISTICS TECHNOLOGY CO., LTD.

1111 Wushan South Road, Qiaotou, Cixi, 315317, Zhejiang, China
Tel.: (86) 57463559818
Web Site: https://www.joy-nb.com
Year Founded: 2005
301198—(CHIN)
Rev.: $56,787,436
Assets: $182,306,591
Liabilities: $47,901,014
Net Worth: $134,405,577
Earnings: $5,087,423
Fiscal Year-end: 12/31/23
Logistic Services
N.A.I.C.S.: 541614
Zhiqiang Luo *(Chm)*

NINGBO JOYSON ELECTRONIC CORP.

No 99 Qingyi Road High-tech Zone, Ningbo, 315040, Zhejiang, China
Tel.: (86) 43787907001
Web Site: http://www.joyson.cn
Year Founded: 2004
600699.—(SHG)
Rev.: $6,995,965,908
Assets: $7,602,749,116
Liabilities: $5,115,382,403
Net Worth: $2,487,366,713
Earnings: $32,773,225
Emp.: 44,391
Fiscal Year-end: 12/31/22
Motor Vehicle Electrical & Electronic Equipment Mfr
N.A.I.C.S.: 336320
Wang Jianfeng *(Chm)*

Subsidiaries:

Joynext GmbH (1)
Gewerbepark Merbitz 5, 01156, Dresden, Germany
Tel.: (49) 351453550
Software Development Services
N.A.I.C.S.: 541511

Joyson Safety Systems Acquisition LLC (1)
2500 Innovation Dr, Auburn Hills, MI 48326
Tel.: (248) 373-8040
Computer System Design Services
N.A.I.C.S.: 541512

Joyson Safety Systems Aschaffenburg GmbH (1)
Bahnweg 1, 63743, Aschaffenburg, Germany
Tel.: (49) 6021650
Web Site: https://www.joysonsafety.com
Computer System Design Services
N.A.I.C.S.: 541512

Joyson Safety Systems Czech s.r.o. (1)
Na Ohradech 264, Rtyne v Podkrkonosi, 542 33, Trutnov, Czech Republic
Tel.: (420) 499739911
Computer System Design Services
N.A.I.C.S.: 541512

Joyson Safety Systems France Eurl (1)
196 Rue Houdan Immeuble Le Clemencia, 92330, Sceaux, France
Tel.: (33) 141872700
Computer System Design Services
N.A.I.C.S.: 541512

Joyson Safety Systems Hungary Kft. (1)
Joyson Ut 1, 3516, Miskolc, Hungary

Tel.: (36) 46407900
Computer System Design Services
N.A.I.C.S.: 541512

Joyson Safety Systems Ignition GmbH (1)
Wilhelm-Dumling-Strasse 17, Elbe, 39218, Schonebeck, Germany
Tel.: (49) 392842160
Computer System Design Services
N.A.I.C.S.: 541512

Joyson Safety Systems Japan KK (1)
658 Echigawa, Aisho-cho Echi-gun, Shiga, 529-1388, Japan
Tel.: (81) 749426000
Computer System Design Services
N.A.I.C.S.: 541512

Joyson Safety Systems Korea Co., Ltd. (1)
Technological Industrial Development Zone, Kicevo, North Macedonia
Tel.: (389) 45273907
Computer System Design Services
N.A.I.C.S.: 541512

Joyson Safety Systems Maroc S.a r.l. (1)
Lot 17 B 2 Zone Franche d'Exportation Boukhalef Aeroport, Tangiers, Morocco
Tel.: (212) 539394615
Computer System Design Services
N.A.I.C.S.: 541512

Joyson Safety Systems Philippines Corporation (1)
106 East Main Avenue Special Ecozone Laguna Technopark, Binan, 4024, Laguna, Philippines
Tel.: (63) 9175004030
Computer System Design Services
N.A.I.C.S.: 541512

Joyson Safety Systems Poland Sp. z o.o. (1)
Ul Betlejemska 16, 58-405, Krzeszow, Poland
Tel.: (48) 757449110
Computer System Design Services
N.A.I.C.S.: 541512

Joyson Safety Systems Rus LLC (1)
11th Injenerny Proezd No 44, Zavolzhsky Area, 432072, Ulyanovsk, Russia
Tel.: (7) 8422231002
Computer System Design Services
N.A.I.C.S.: 541512

Joyson Safety Systems Sachsen GmbH (1)
Scheibenberger Strasse 88, 09481, Elterlein, Germany
Tel.: (49) 37349185888
Computer System Design Services
N.A.I.C.S.: 541512

Joyson Safety Systems Shanghai Co., Ltd. (1)
No 8000 Songze Avenue, Qingpu Industrial Zone, Shanghai, 201707, China
Tel.: (86) 2169212880
Computer System Design Services
N.A.I.C.S.: 541512

Joyson Safety Systems Sibiu S.R.L. (1)
Str Florian Rieger Nr 3, Sibiu, Romania
Tel.: (40) 269203700
Computer System Design Services
N.A.I.C.S.: 541512

Joyson Safety Systems Tianjin Co., Ltd. (1)
No 10 Saida San Avenue, Xiqing Economic Development Zone, Tianjin, 300385, Hebei, China
Tel.: (86) 2258967888
Computer System Design Services
N.A.I.C.S.: 541512

Joyson Safety Systems Torino S.r.l. (1)
Strada Torino 43, Orbassano, 10043, Turin, Italy
Tel.: (39) 0119691311
Computer System Design Services
N.A.I.C.S.: 541512

Joyson Safety Systems UK Limited (1)
114a High Street, Rayleigh, SS6 BU, Essex, United Kingdom
Tel.: (44) 1268777478
Computer System Design Services
N.A.I.C.S.: 541512

Joyson Safety Systems Uruguay S.A. (1)
KM 46 5 Brigadier Gral Manuel Oribe, Libertad, San Jose, Uruguay
Tel.: (598) 43453629
Computer System Design Services
N.A.I.C.S.: 541512

Key Safety Systems, Inc. (1)
2025 Harmon Rd, Auburn Hills, MI 48326
Tel.: (586) 726-3800
Web Site: http://joysonsafety.com
Sales Range: $1-4.9 Billion
Emp.: 43,000
Automotive Safety Systems & Electronic Components Mfr
N.A.I.C.S.: 336390
Tao Liu *(CEO)*

Holding (Non-US):

Key Safety Systems UK Limited (2)
144a High Street Rayleigh Essex, Rayleigh, SS6 7BU, United Kingdom
Tel.: (44) 1228591711
Web Site: http://www.keysafetyinc.com
Automotive Safety Systems & Electronic Components Mfr
N.A.I.C.S.: 336390

Takata Corporation (2)
Tokyo Front Terrace 2-3-14 Higashishinagawa, Shinagawa-ku, Tokyo, 140-0002, Japan
Tel.: (81) 364558401
Web Site: http://www.takata.com
Motor Vehicle Airbag Mfr & Sales
N.A.I.C.S.: 336390
Yoshihiko Tanaka *(Exec Officer)*

Subsidiary (Non-US):

Joyson PlasTec GmbH (3)
Hauserschlag 1, 97688, Bad Kissingen, Bavaria, Germany
Tel.: (49) 9736900
Web Site: https://joysonplastec.de
Motor Vehicle Parts Mfr
N.A.I.C.S.: 326220
Bin Xu *(Mng Dir)*

Joyson Safety Systems (M) Sdn. Bhd. (3)
No 2 Jalan Sejahtera 25/124 Axis Premier Industrial Park, 40400, Shah Alam, Selangor, Malaysia
Tel.: (60) 351225977
Motor Vehicle Parts, Seat Belts & Air Bags Mfr
N.A.I.C.S.: 336360

Joyson Safety Systems (Philippines) Corporation (3)
106 E Main Ave Special Ecozone Laguna Techno Pk, Binan, 4024, Laguna, Philippines
Tel.: (63) 175004030
Airbag Modules & Seat Belts Mfr
N.A.I.C.S.: 336390

Subsidiary (US):

Joyson Safety Systems Acquisition LLC (3)
2500 Innovation Drive, Auburn Hills, MI 48326
Tel.: (248) 373-8040
Seatbelts, Airbag, Automotive Safety Products Mfr & Supplier
N.A.I.C.S.: 336211

Subsidiary (Non-US):

Equipo Automotriz Americana S.A. DE C.V. (4)
Libramiento Carlos Salinas De Gortari 198 Nte, Ciudad Frontera, 25618, Coahuila, Mexico
Tel.: (52) 8666496500
Airbag Modules & Motor Vehicle Parts Mfr
N.A.I.C.S.: 336390

NINGBO JOYSON ELECTRONIC CORP.

Ningbo Joyson Electronic Corp.—(Continued)

Subsidiary (Non-US):

Joyson Safety Systems Arad S.R.L. (3)
Zona Industriala Vest Str III Nr 9, 310375, Arad, Romania
Tel.: (40) 257203100
Motor Vehicle Parts Mfr
N.A.I.C.S.: 336330

Joyson Safety Systems Aschaffenburg GmbH (3)
Bahnweg 1, 63743, Aschaffenburg, 63743, Germany
Tel.: (49) 6021650
Motor Vehicle Parts, Steering Wheels Mfr
N.A.I.C.S.: 336330

Joyson Safety Systems Brasil Ltda. (3)
Rod Dom Gabriel Paulino, B Couto Km 66, Jundiaí, 13212-240, Sao Paulo, Brazil
Tel.: (55) 1145853700
Sales, Manufacturing, Administration, Engineering, Airbags, Seat Belts, Steering Wheels & Interior Trim
N.A.I.C.S.: 336360

Joyson Safety Systems Czech s.r.o. (3)
Na Ohradech 264, 542 33, Rtyne v Podkrkonosi, Czech Republic
Tel.: (420) 499739911
Airbag Modules & Motor Vehicles Parts Mfr
N.A.I.C.S.: 336330
Frank Haun *(Statutory Member)*

Subsidiary (Domestic):

Joyson Safety Systems Japan G.K. (3)
2195-4 Befu Higasitaku-machi, Taku, 846-0012, Saga, Japan **(100%)**
Tel.: (81) 952763474
Supplier of Automotive Safety Systems; Seat Belts, Airbags & Child Seats
N.A.I.C.S.: 336360

Subsidiary (Non-US):

Joyson Safety Systems Korea Co., Ltd. (3)
22 Jangangongdan 6-gil, Jahgan-myeon, Hwaseong-si, Gyeonggi-do, Korea (South)
Tel.: (82) 318311300
Motor Vehicle Parts, Seat Belts & Air Bags Mfr & Sales
N.A.I.C.S.: 336360

Joyson Safety Systems Poland Sp. z o.o. (3)
Ul Betlejemska 16, 58-405, Krzeszow, Poland
Tel.: (48) 757449110
Motor Vehicle Parts Mfr
N.A.I.C.S.: 336330

Joyson Safety Systems Sibiu S.R.L. (3)
Str Florian Rieger nr 3, 550018, Sibiu, Romania
Tel.: (40) 269203700
Motor Vehicle Parts Mfr
N.A.I.C.S.: 336330

Joyson-TOA Safety Systems Co., Ltd. (3)
159 Mu 5 Wellgrow Industrial Estate Bang Samak Sub-District, Bang Pakong District, Chachoengsao, 24180, Thailand
Tel.: (66) 38562400
Seat Belts & Air Bags & Steering Wheels Mfr & Supplier
N.A.I.C.S.: 336330

Takata (Shanghai) Automotive Component Co., Ltd. (3)
No 8000 Songze Ave Qingpu Indus Zone, Shanghai, 201707, China
Tel.: (86) 2169212880
Seat Belts & Air Bags & Steering Wheels Mfr & Supplier
N.A.I.C.S.: 336330

Takata Asia Pte. Ltd. (3)
101 Thomson Rd 11-05 United Sq, Singapore, 307591, Singapore
Tel.: (65) 62728998

Web Site: http://www.takata.co.jp
Emp.: 17
Automotive Assemblies & Parts Mfr
N.A.I.C.S.: 336330

Takata Automotive Electronics (Shanghai) Co., Ltd. (3)
Bldg 71A 17 Han Cheng Rd Shanghai Waigaoqiao Free Trade Zone, Pudong, Shanghai, 200131, China
Tel.: (86) 21 38556288
Web Site: http://www.takata.com
Sales Range: $50-74.9 Million
Emp.: 130
Crash Sensors & Automotive Parts Mfr
N.A.I.C.S.: 334515

Takata India Private Limited (3)
Unit no 506 Tower B Spazedge Building Sec-47, Gurgaon, 122 002, Haryana, India
Tel.: (91) 1244289603
Web Site: http://www.takata.com
Sales Range: $25-49.9 Million
Emp.: 13
Seat Belts & Air Bags & Steering Wheels Mfr
N.A.I.C.S.: 336330

Plant (Domestic):

Joyson Anand Abhishek Safety Systems Private Limited (4)
Survey No 43 4 215 Thennur Vlg Ammanambakkam Post, Chengalpattu Taluk, Kancheepuram Dist, 603 002, Tamil Nadu, India
Tel.: (91) 4427421312
Motor Vehicle Parts, Airbag & Seat Belt & Steering Wheels Mfr
N.A.I.C.S.: 336330

Subsidiary (Non-US):

Takata-Petri (Sachsen) GmbH (3)
Scheibenberger Strasse 88, 09481, Elterlein, Saxony, Germany
Tel.: (49) 37349185888
Web Site: http://www.takata.com
Sales Range: $100-124.9 Million
Emp.: 400
Airbag Modules & Assemblies Mfr
N.A.I.C.S.: 336330

Logico Design S.r.l. (1)
Piazza Kennedy 4, Tregnago, 37039, Verona, VR, Italy
Tel.: (39) 0456500447
Computer System Design Services
N.A.I.C.S.: 541512

Preh GmbH (1)
Schweinfurter Str 5-9, 97616, Bad Neustadt an der Saale, Germany
Tel.: (49) 9771 92 0
Web Site: http://www.preh.com
Sales Range: $700-749.9 Million
Emp.: 3,430
Motor Vehicle Electrical & Electronic Equipment Mfr
N.A.I.C.S.: 336320
Christoph Hummel *(Chm, Pres, CEO & Exec Dir)*

Subsidiary (Domestic):

IMA Automation Amberg GmbH (2)
Wernher Von Braun Strasse 5, 92224, Amberg, Germany **(100%)**
Tel.: (49) 96216080
Web Site: http://www.ima-automation.de
Emp.: 227
Machining & Assembly Systems & Equipment Mfr
N.A.I.C.S.: 333248

Preh Sweden AB (1)
Backstensgatan 13, Molndal, 431 49, Gothenburg, Sweden
Tel.: (46) 709488522
Electronic Control Equipment Mfr & Distr
N.A.I.C.S.: 335314

Preh de Mexico, S.A. de C.V. (1)
Crio 814, Kalos Guadalupe Industrial Park, 67205, Guadalupe, Nuevo Leon, Mexico
Tel.: (52) 8151025700
Electronic Control Equipment Mfr & Distr
N.A.I.C.S.: 335314

Safety Autoparts Mexico S. de R.L.de C.V. (1)

Carretera Santa Rosa KM 3 5, Apodaca, 66600, Nuevo Laredo, Mexico
Tel.: (52) 8181561100
Computer System Design Services
N.A.I.C.S.: 541512

NINGBO KANGQIANG ELECTRONICS CO., LTD.
No 988 Jinyuan Road Yinzhou Investment and Entrepreneurship Center, Ningbo, 315104, China
Tel.: (86) 57456809777
Web Site:
https://www.kangqiang.com
Year Founded: 1992
002119—(SSE)
Rev.: $239,071,716
Assets: $267,766,668
Liabilities: $95,643,288
Net Worth: $172,123,380
Earnings: $14,317,992
Emp.: 1,000
Fiscal Year-end: 12/31/22
Semiconductor Packaging Material Mfr
N.A.I.C.S.: 334413

NINGBO KBE ELEETRICAL TECHNOLOGY CO., LTD.
No 1726 Kunyang Road, Minhang, Shanghai, 201612, China
Tel.: (86) 2154425422
Web Site: http://www.nbkbe.com
Year Founded: 2004
300863—(CHIN)
Rev.: $486,204,439
Assets: $396,683,630
Liabilities: $226,241,242
Net Worth: $170,442,388
Earnings: $23,373,297
Fiscal Year-end: 12/31/23
Automotive Parts Mfr & Distr
N.A.I.C.S.: 336390
Guangyao Lin *(Chm & Gen Mgr)*

NINGBO LEHUI INTERNATIONAL ENGINEERING EQUIPMENT CO., LTD.
No 1 Chaohui Road, Xizhou Town Xiangshan County, Ningbo, 315722, Zhejiang, China
Tel.: (86) 4008284040
Web Site: https://en.lehui.com
Year Founded: 1991
603076—(SHG)
Rev.: $169,070,214
Assets: $471,797,857
Liabilities: $284,353,636
Net Worth: $187,444,221
Earnings: $3,074,016
Emp.: 500
Fiscal Year-end: 12/31/22
Brewery Equipment Mfr & Distr
N.A.I.C.S.: 333241
Lai Yunlai *(Chm)*

NINGBO LIGONG ONLINE MONITORING TECHNOLOGY CO., LTD.
No 22 Caoejiang Road Bonded, South District, Ningbo, 315806, Zhejiang, China
Tel.: (86) 4008269696
Web Site: https://www.lgom.com.cn
Year Founded: 2000
High Voltage Online Monitoring Services
N.A.I.C.S.: 221122
Zhou Fangjie *(Chm)*

NINGBO MARINE CO., LTD.
Building 1 Beian Fortune Center, Ningbo, 315020, Zhejiang, China
Tel.: (86) 57487659140
Web Site: https://www.nbmc.com.cn
Year Founded: 1950

600798—(SHG)
Rev.: $291,100,193
Assets: $966,504,937
Liabilities: $251,265,526
Net Worth: $715,239,411
Earnings: $15,969,981
Fiscal Year-end: 12/31/22
Inland Water Freight Transportation Services
N.A.I.C.S.: 483211
Dong Jun *(Chm)*

NINGBO MENOVO PHARMACEUTICAL CO., LTD.
12A-14/F Building1 Ningbo R&D Park No 999 Yangfan Rd, Hi-Tech District, Ningbo, 315048, China
Tel.: (86) 57487918601
Web Site:
https://www.menovopharm.com
Year Founded: 2004
603538—(SHG)
Rev.: $204,560,329
Assets: $620,491,973
Liabilities: $315,369,049
Net Worth: $305,122,924
Earnings: $47,559,826
Emp.: 1,900
Fiscal Year-end: 12/31/22
Pharmaceutical Product Mfr & Distr
N.A.I.C.S.: 325412
Chengzhi Yao *(Chm & Gen Mgr)*

Subsidiaries:

Anhui Menovo Pharmaceutical Co., Ltd. (1)
Anhui GuangDe Economic & Technological Development Zone, Xuancheng, China
Tel.: (86) 5636988828
Pharmaceutical Product Mfr & Distr
N.A.I.C.S.: 325412

Biomenovo Research Private Limited (1)
Off No 1403 The Affaires Plot No 9 Sector 17 Sanpada, Navi Mumbai, 400701, Maharashtra, India
Tel.: (91) 8633899116
Pharmaceutical Product Mfr & Distr
N.A.I.C.S.: 325412

Ningbo Menovo TianKang Pharmaceutical Co., Ltd. (1)
Daxie Development Zone West Road No 85, Ningbo, 315812, China
Tel.: (86) 57486778703
Pharmaceutical Product Mfr & Distr
N.A.I.C.S.: 325412

Zhejiang Liaoyuan Pharmaceutical Co., Ltd. (1)
Zhejiang Provincial Chemical & Medical Raw Material Base Linhai Zone, Duqiao Town, Linhai, 317016, Zhejiang, China
Tel.: (86) 57685588211
Web Site: http://www.liaoyuan.com.cn
Pharmaceuticals Product Mfr
N.A.I.C.S.: 325412

Zhejiang Menovo Pharmaceutical Co., Ltd. (1)
Industrial Park by 13 Road No 8 Hangzhou Bay, Shangyu, Zhejiang, China
Tel.: (86) 57582738996
Pharmaceutical Product Mfr & Distr
N.A.I.C.S.: 325412

NINGBO ORIENT WIRES & CABLES CO., LTD.
No 968 Jiangnan East Road, Beilun District, Ningbo, 315100, Zhejiang, China
Tel.: (86) 57486188666
Web Site: http://www.orientcable.com
Year Founded: 1998
603606—(SHG)
Rev.: $984,053,154
Assets: $1,289,968,187
Liabilities: $518,613,732
Net Worth: $771,354,455
Earnings: $118,266,137

AND PRIVATE COMPANIES

Fiscal Year-end: 12/31/22
Electrical Wire & Cable Mfr & Distr
N.A.I.C.S.: 335999
Jun Ke *(CFO, VP & Controller)*

NINGBO PEACEBIRD FASHION CO., LTD
No 258 Xinhui South Road, Ningbo, 315000, Zhejiang, China
Tel.: (86) 57456706588
Web Site: https://www.peacebird.com
Year Founded: 1995
603877—(SHG)
Rev.: $1,207,669,989
Assets: $1,200,567,729
Liabilities: $617,448,958
Net Worth: $583,118,771
Earnings: $25,934,786
Emp.: 12,000
Fiscal Year-end: 12/31/22
Apparel Distr
N.A.I.C.S.: 458110
Jiangping Zhang *(Chm & Gen Mgr)*

NINGBO POWERWAY ALLOY MATERIALS CO., LTD.
No 288 Honggang Rd Yinzhou Economic Development Zone, Yinzhou Dist, Ningbo, 315137, China
Tel.: (86) 57483004690
Web Site: http://www.pwalloy.com
Year Founded: 1993
601137—(SHG)
Rev.: $1,888,076,357
Assets: $2,033,474,751
Liabilities: $1,188,769,229
Net Worth: $844,705,522
Earnings: $75,404,193
Emp.: 3,000
Fiscal Year-end: 12/31/22
Alloy Material Mfr & Whslr
N.A.I.C.S.: 331410

Subsidiaries:

Boviet Solar Technology Co., Ltd. (1)
B5 B6 Song Khe Industrial Zone, Noi Hoang District, Hanoi, Bac Giang, Vietnam
Tel.: (84) 2403766288
Web Site: http://www.boviet.com
Emp.: 700
Solar Cell Mfr
N.A.I.C.S.: 334413

Boviet Solar USA Ltd. (1)
2107 N 1st St Ste 550, San Jose, CA 95131
Web Site: http://www.bovietsolarusa.com
Solar Cell Mfr
N.A.I.C.S.: 334413
Sienna Cen *(Pres)*

Ningbo Powerway Alloy Plate& Strip Co.,Ltd (1)
Address: Binhai Industrial Park, Ningbo, China
Tel.: (86) 574 89016059
Alloy Material Mfr & Whslr
N.A.I.C.S.: 331410

Ningbo Powerway Investment Company (1)
Yunlong Town Yinzhou District, Ningbo, China
Tel.: (86) 574 82829239
Alloy Material Mfr & Whslr
N.A.I.C.S.: 331410

Ningbo Powerway Materialise Co., Ltd. (1)
Yunlong Town Yinzhou District, Ningbo, 315135, China
Tel.: (86) 574 83004302
Alloy Material Mfr & Whslr
N.A.I.C.S.: 331410

Ningbo Powerway New Energy Co., Ltd (1)
Yunlong Town Yinzhou District, Ningbo, China
Tel.: (86) 574 83004999
Alloy Material Mfr & Whslr

N.A.I.C.S.: 331410

NINGBO RONBAY NEW ENERGY TECHNOLOGY CO., LTD.
No 39 East Road of Tanjialong, Yuyao, 315400, Zhejiang, China
Tel.: (86) 57462730999
Web Site: https://www.ronbaymat.com
Year Founded: 2014
688005—(SHG)
Rev.: $4,229,268,512
Assets: $3,602,670,501
Liabilities: $2,401,921,768
Net Worth: $1,200,748,733
Earnings: $189,993,478
Fiscal Year-end: 12/31/22
Energy Distribution Services
N.A.I.C.S.: 221122
You Sang Yul *(Co-Founder)*

Subsidiaries:

Beijing Ronbay Holding Investment Co., Ltd. (1)
No 8FA Shiji Jinyuan Business Center No 69 Banjin Road, Haidian District, Beijing, China
Tel.: (86) 1088466684
Lithium Battery Cathode Material Mfr & Distr
N.A.I.C.S.: 335910

Energy Material Technology Co., Ltd. (1)
85-1 Choemdan Saneop 3-Ro, Daesowon-Myeon, Chungju, Korea (South)
Tel.: (82) 438575533
Lithium Battery Cathode Material Mfr & Distr
N.A.I.C.S.: 335910

Guizhou Ronbay Lithium Battery Materials Co., Ltd. (1)
Longjiang Village, Shenxi Town Honghuagang District, Zunyi, Guizhou, China
Tel.: (86) 85128235587
Lithium Battery Cathode Material Mfr & Distr
N.A.I.C.S.: 335910

Hubei Ronbay Lithium Battery Materials Co., Ltd. (1)
19 Chuangye Avenue, Gedian Development District, Ezhou, Hubei, China
Tel.: (86) 711511598888010
Lithium Battery Cathode Material Mfr & Distr
N.A.I.C.S.: 335910

Ningbo Ronbay Technology Materials Co., Ltd. (1)
No 39 East Road of Tanjialing, Yuyao, Zhejiang, China
Tel.: (86) 57462730999
High Tech Material Research Services
N.A.I.C.S.: 541715

NINGBO RUIYUAN BIOTECHNOLOGY CO., LTD.
No 288 Huangjipu Road, Jiangbei District, Ningbo, China
Tel.: (86) 57427717666
Web Site: http://www.reebio.com
Year Founded: 2005
Medical Equipment Mfr & Distr
N.A.I.C.S.: 334510

NINGBO RUNHE HIGH-TECH MATERIALS CO., LTD.
No 168 Jinhai Road Binhai Zone South of Ninghai, Ningbo, Zhejiang, China
Tel.: (86) 57465554848
Web Site: https://www.chinarunhe.com
Year Founded: 2000
300727—(CHIN)
Rev.: $159,880,060
Assets: $226,088,307
Liabilities: $99,978,443

Net Worth: $126,109,864
Earnings: $11,579,321
Fiscal Year-end: 12/31/23
Chemical Product Mfr & Distr
N.A.I.C.S.: 325998
Jianping Ye *(Pres)*

NINGBO SANXING MEDICAL ELECTRIC CO.,LTD.,
Yinzhou Industrial Park, Jiangshan Town Yinzhou District, Ningbo, 315191, Zhejiang, China
Tel.: (86) 57488072272
Web Site: http://www.sanxingelectric.com
Year Founded: 1986
601567—(SHG)
Rev.: $1,277,387,645
Assets: $2,278,371,734
Liabilities: $927,453,871
Net Worth: $1,350,917,863
Earnings: $133,115,416
Fiscal Year-end: 12/31/22
Electric Power Meter Mfr & Distr
N.A.I.C.S.: 335999
Jianjiang Zheng *(Board of Directors, Founder & Chm)*

Subsidiaries:

Nansen Instrumentos de Precisao Ltda. (1)
Tel.: (55) 3135143100
Web Site: http://www.nansen.com.br
Electric Meter Mfr
N.A.I.C.S.: 334514

Ningbo Sanxing Medical Electric Co., Ltd. - Kareo Factory (1)
Jl Raya Cikande Rangkas Km 7 5 Desa Majasari/Kareo Kec, Jawila, Banten, Indonesia
Tel.: (62) 25448044748
Power Generation & Transmission Mfr & Distr
N.A.I.C.S.: 335311

Ningbo Sanxing Smart Electric Co.,Ltd. (1)
No 17 Fenglin Road, Cicheng Town Jiangbei District, Ningbo, 315034, China
Tel.: (86) 57488072218
Web Site: https://www.sanxingelectric.com
Electrical Equipment Services
N.A.I.C.S.: 811310

NINGBO SHANSHAN CO., LTD.
Shanshan Building No 777 Rili Middle Road, Ningbo, 315100, Zhejiang, China
Tel.: (86) 57488208337
Web Site: https://www.ssgf.net
600884—(SHG)
Rev.: $3,046,907,069
Assets: $6,307,538,964
Liabilities: $2,919,670,889
Net Worth: $3,387,868,076
Earnings: $377,853,269
Fiscal Year-end: 12/31/22
Lithium Battery Mfr
N.A.I.C.S.: 335910

Subsidiaries:

Chenzhou Shanshan New Material Co., Ltd. (1)
No 338 Shanshan Avenue Jiangbei Industrial Park, Zixing, Hunan, China
Tel.: (86) 7353258993
Lithium Battery Material Mfr & Distr
N.A.I.C.S.: 335910

Fujian Shanshan Technology Co., Ltd. (1)
Plot No 1 Phase 10 Dajia Industrial Concentration Zone, Dajia Village Dajia Town Gutian County, Ningde, China
Tel.: (86) 5933973334
Lithium Battery Material Mfr & Distr
N.A.I.C.S.: 335910

Huzhou Shanshan New Energy Technology Co., Ltd. (1)

No 1800 Gangnan Road Economic Development Zone, Huzhou, Zhejiang, China
Tel.: (86) 5722132811
Lithium Battery Material Mfr & Distr
N.A.I.C.S.: 335910

Inner Mongolia Shanshan New Material Co., Ltd. (1)
No 2 Qinghe Road Jiuyuan Industrial Park, 46 kilometers south of Jiuyuan District Inner Mongolia, Baotou, China
Tel.: (86) 4726971615
Lithium Battery Material Mfr & Distr
N.A.I.C.S.: 335910

Inner Mongolia Shanshan Technology Co., Ltd. (1)
No 46 Equipment Avenue Equipment Manufacturing Industrial Park, New Planning Area ingshan District, Baotou, China
Tel.: (86) 4726189689
Lithium Battery Material Mfr & Distr
N.A.I.C.S.: 335910

Ningbo Shanshan New Material Technology Co., Ltd. (1)
No 1 Jucai Road Wangchun Industrial Park, Ningbo, China
Tel.: (86) 57488133066
Lithium Battery Material Mfr & Distr
N.A.I.C.S.: 335910

Shanghai Shanshan Technology Co., Ltd. (1)
No 3158 Jinhai Road, Pudong New Area, Shanghai, China
Tel.: (86) 2158568662
Web Site: https://www.shanshantech.com
Battery Material Mfr
N.A.I.C.S.: 335910

Sichuan Shanshan New Material Co., Ltd. (1)
No 1 Middle Section of Chuangxin 2nd Road, Pengshan Economic Development Zone, Sichuan, China
Tel.: (86) 2837593333
Lithium Battery Material Mfr & Distr
N.A.I.C.S.: 335910

NINGBO SHENGLONG AUTOMOTIVE POWERTRAIN SYSTEM CO., LTD.
No 788 Jinda Road Industrial Park, Yinzhou District, Ningbo, 315104, Zhejiang, China
Tel.: (86) 57488167898
Web Site: http://slpt.sheng-long.com
Year Founded: 2007
603178—(SHG)
Rev.: $207,956,043
Assets: $290,804,370
Liabilities: $114,187,208
Net Worth: $176,617,163
Earnings: $12,510,328
Emp.: 700
Fiscal Year-end: 12/31/22
Automotive Parts Mfr & Distr
N.A.I.C.S.: 336390
Yulong Luo *(Chm)*

NINGBO SHUANGLIN AUTO PARTS CO., LTD.
No 202 Beiying Road, Qingpu District, Shanghai, 201700, China
Tel.: (86) 2139785888
Web Site: https://www.shuanglin.com
Year Founded: 2006
300100—(CHIN)
Rev.: $587,613,312
Assets: $799,471,296
Liabilities: $502,363,836
Net Worth: $297,107,460
Earnings: $10,553,868
Emp.: 2,000
Fiscal Year-end: 12/31/22
Motor Vehicle Parts Mfr
N.A.I.C.S.: 336390
Wu Jianbin *(Chm)*

Subsidiaries:

Ningbo Shuanglin Auto Parts Co., Ltd. - Ningbo Plant (1)

Ningbo Shuanglin Auto Parts Co., Ltd.—(Continued)
666 Jishan Village Huangxikou Xidian Town Ninghai, Ningbo, Zhejiang, China
Tel.: (86) 57465178888
Stamping Die Mfr
N.A.I.C.S.: 333514

NINGBO SINYUAN INDUSTRIAL MATERIAL CO., LTD.
128 Xingyong Road, Jiangbei District, Ningbo, 315021, China
Tel.: (86) 574 87639836
Web Site: http://www.sinyuan.com
Year Founded: 1994
Industrial Material Mfr
N.A.I.C.S.: 339991
Yilin Yuan (Pres)

Subsidiaries:

Ningbo SINYUAN Carbon Material Co., Ltd. (1)
128 XingYong Rd YongJiang Industrial District, 315021, Ningbo, China
Tel.: (86) 57487620575
Sales Range: $25-49.9 Million
Emp.: 81
Graphite Product Mfr
N.A.I.C.S.: 335991
Weigang Xu (Mng Dir)

NINGBO SINYUAN ZM TECHNOLOGY CO., LTD.
No 27 Guantanghe Road Daqi Street, Beilun District, Ningbo, 315806, Zhejiang, China
Tel.: (86) 57486910111
Web Site:
 https://www.sinyuanzm.com
Year Founded: 2003
301398—(CHIN)
Rev.: $37,993,644
Assets: $158,991,768
Liabilities: $18,701,280
Net Worth: $140,290,488
Earnings: $7,894,692
Emp.: 400
Fiscal Year-end: 12/31/22
Magnesium Die Casting Mfr
N.A.I.C.S.: 331523

NINGBO SOLARTRON TECHNOLOGY CO., LTD.
No 999 Qingfeng Road, Jiangbei District, Ningbo, 315000, Zhejiang, China
Tel.: (86) 57456205386
Web Site:
 http://www.solartrontech.com
Year Founded: 2010
688299—(SSE)
Rev.: $161,887,195
Assets: $379,268,192
Liabilities: $88,280,515
Net Worth: $290,987,677
Earnings: $15,925,389
Fiscal Year-end: 12/31/22
Optical Instrument Mfr
N.A.I.C.S.: 333310
Yadong Jin (Chm & Gen Mgr)

NINGBO SUNLIGHT ELECTRICAL APPLIANCE CO., LTD.
Hong Chong Road 515, Jiangbei District, Ningbo, 315032, China
Tel.: (86) 57487522562
Web Site: http://www.nbslt.cn
002473—(SSE)
Rev.: $808,949
Assets: $14,558,014
Liabilities: $16,980,264
Net Worth: ($2,422,250)
Earnings: ($27,989,935)
Fiscal Year-end: 12/31/20
Temperature Control Products Mfr
N.A.I.C.S.: 334512

NINGBO SUNNY ELECTRONIC CO. LTD.
288 Xinjian Nort Road, Yuyao, Zhejiang, China
Tel.: (86) 574 62882396
Web Site: http://www.telescope-binoculars.com.cn
Telescope & Astronomy Accessory Mfr
N.A.I.C.S.: 927110
Junwen Chiu (VP)

Subsidiaries:

Meade Instruments Corporation (1)
27 Hubble, Irvine, CA 92618
Tel.: (949) 451-1450
Web Site: http://www.meade.com
Rev.: $17,428,000
Assets: $10,406,000
Liabilities: $3,816,000
Net Worth: $6,590,000
Earnings: ($3,667,000)
Emp.: 112
Fiscal Year-end: 02/28/2013
Telescope Telescope Accessory Binocular Microscope & Riflescope Mfr
N.A.I.C.S.: 333310
Paul Hobbs (VP-Project Mgmt)

NINGBO SUNRISE ELC TECHNOLOGY CO., LTD.
1511 Luan Road, Changhe, Cixi, 315326, Zhejiang, China
Tel.: (86) 57463411656
Web Site: https://www.zxec.com
Year Founded: 2001
002937—(SSE)
Rev.: $248,105,052
Assets: $267,505,524
Liabilities: $91,244,556
Net Worth: $176,260,968
Earnings: $30,733,560
Fiscal Year-end: 12/31/22
Electrical Component Mfr & Distr
N.A.I.C.S.: 334515
Chen Songjie (Pres & Gen Mgr)

Subsidiaries:

Dongguan Zhongxing Electronics Co., Ltd. (1)
Kaida Industrial City Qiaotouzhen, Dongguan, 523560, Guangdong, China
Tel.: (86) 15013762121
Web Site:
 http://zhongxingmold.gdlekang.com
Electronic Components Mfr
N.A.I.C.S.: 334419

NINGBO TECHMATION CO., LTD.
No 88 Dagang Fifth Road, Beilun District, Ningbo, 315800, Zhejiang, China
Tel.: (86) 57486987281 CN
Web Site:
 http://www.techmation.com.cn
Year Founded: 2001
603015—(SHG)
Rev.: $102,907,416
Assets: $295,379,782
Liabilities: $108,979,491
Net Worth: $186,400,291
Earnings: $6,701,025
Emp.: 700
Fiscal Year-end: 12/31/22
Plastic Machinery Product Mfr
N.A.I.C.S.: 333310
Xiong Yulin (Chm)

Subsidiaries:

Artila Electronics Co., Ltd. (1)
9F No 529-1 Zhongzheng Rd, Xindian Dist, New Taipei City, 23148, Taiwan
Tel.: (886) 286672340
Web Site: https://www.artila.com
Software & Hardware Services
N.A.I.C.S.: 541510

E-Deodar Robot Equipment Co., Ltd. (1)
Cowinn International Industrial Park No7 Xinkai Rd Wusha Area Daliang, Shunde, Foshan, Guangdong, China
Tel.: (86) 75729219061
Web Site: http://www.en.e-deodar.com
Industrial Automation Equipment Mfr & Services
N.A.I.C.S.: 334512

Equipaggiamenti Elettronici Industriali S.p.A. (1)
Viale dell Industria 37, 36100, Vicenza, Italy
Tel.: (39) 0444562988
Web Site:
 http://www.eeipowerelectronics.com
Electronic Components Mfr
N.A.I.C.S.: 334419
Alvaro Brugnoli (VP-Bus Dev)

Subsidiary (Non-US):

EEI India Energy Private Limited (2)
No 2 1st Floor Bajaj Bhavan Nariman Point, Mumbai, 400021, India
Tel.: (91) 2225270383
Electronic Components Mfr
N.A.I.C.S.: 334419

Shanghai E-EE Technologies Co. Ltd. (2)
Room 401 Building No 5 No 138 New Jun-Huan Road, MinHang District, Shanghai, 201114, China
Tel.: (86) 2131009628
Electronic Components Mfr
N.A.I.C.S.: 334419

HDT Srl (1)
Via Sile 8, Monte Di Malo, 36030, Vicenza, Italy
Tel.: (39) 0445602744
Web Site: https://www.hdtlovato.com
Electrical & Electronic Mfr
N.A.I.C.S.: 335999

NINGBO TIANLONG ELECTRONICS CO., LTD.
No 116 Batang Rd Hangzhou Bay New Zone, Ningbo, 315336, Zhejiang, China
Tel.: (86) 57458999888
Web Site: https://www.ptianlong.com
Year Founded: 2000
603266—(SHG)
Rev.: $176,126,675
Assets: $269,376,017
Liabilities: $80,907,255
Net Worth: $188,468,762
Earnings: $17,246,231
Fiscal Year-end: 12/31/22
Plastic Parts Mfr & Distr
N.A.I.C.S.: 326199
Yu Jianfeng (Sec)

Subsidiaries:

Burteck LLC (1)
55 Griffin Rd S, Bloomfield, CT 06002
Tel.: (860) 219-1406
Web Site: https://www.burteckllc.com
Plastic Injection Mold Mfr
N.A.I.C.S.: 333511

Fuzhou Tianlong Electronics Co., Ltd. (1)
Unit D Feitou Industry Zone Mawei Area, Fuzhou, 350015, China
Tel.: (86) 59183970521
Plastics Product Mfr
N.A.I.C.S.: 326199

Jiangsu Livon Automotive Components Technology Co., Ltd (1)
No 9 Jinwen Road Binjiang Development District, Nanjing, 211178, China
Tel.: (86) 2584435237
Plastic Product Mfr & Distr
N.A.I.C.S.: 326199
Johnny Chen (Sls Mgr)

NINGBO TIANYI MEDICAL DEVICES CO., LTD.
No 788 Mozhi North Road, Dongqian lake tourist resort, Ningbo, 315121, Zhejiang, China
Tel.: (86) 57455011010
Web Site:
 https://www.tianyimedical.cn
Year Founded: 1998
301097—(SSE)
Rev.: $63,540,783
Assets: $123,683,369
Liabilities: $51,760,466
Net Worth: $71,922,902
Earnings: $11,994,811
Emp.: 1,998
Fiscal Year-end: 12/31/21
Medical Equipment Mfr
N.A.I.C.S.: 339112
Zhimin Wu (Chm & Gen Mgr)

NINGBO TIP RUBBER TECHNOLOGY CO., LTD.
5 Jinlong Road Taoyuan Street, Ninghai County, Ningbo, 315600, Zhejiang, China
Tel.: (86) 57459973312
Web Site: http://www.tipgroupm.com
Year Founded: 2009
605255—(SHG)
Rev.: $46,250,722
Assets: $127,907,166
Liabilities: $9,604,395
Net Worth: $118,212,771
Earnings: $3,589,073
Fiscal Year-end: 12/31/22
Automobile Parts Mfr
N.A.I.C.S.: 336390
Jianyi You (Chm & Gen Mgr)

NINGBO TUOPU GROUP CO., LTD.
No 268 Yuwangshan Road, Beilun District, Ningbo, 315800, China
Tel.: (86) 57456582888
Web Site: https://www.tuopu.com
601689—(SHG)
Rev.: $2,245,392,167
Assets: $3,862,422,364
Liabilities: $2,155,171,829
Net Worth: $1,707,250,536
Earnings: $238,698,505
Fiscal Year-end: 12/31/22
Automobile Parts Mfr & Distr
N.A.I.C.S.: 336110
Bin Wang (Pres)

NINGBO UNITED GROUP CO., LTD.
United Building No 1 Donghai Road, Ningbo Economic and Technological Development Zone, Ningbo, 315803, Zhejiang, China
Tel.: (86) 57486222256
Web Site: https://www.nug.com.cn
Year Founded: 1988
600051—(SHG)
Rev.: $372,978,595
Assets: $900,354,621
Liabilities: $390,105,444
Net Worth: $510,249,177
Earnings: $21,053,233
Emp.: 850
Fiscal Year-end: 12/31/22
Commercial Goods & Electronics Importer, Exporter & Distr
N.A.I.C.S.: 425120
Shuirong Li (Chm)

Subsidiaries:

Ningbo United Group Import & Export Co., Ltd. (1)
23rd Floor Huijin Building No 77 Heyi Road, Ningbo, Zhejiang, China
Tel.: (86) 5748 730 9067
Web Site: https://www.nbunjon.com
Foreign Trading Services
N.A.I.C.S.: 522299

NINGBO WATER METER CO., LTD.
No 355 Hongxing Road, Jiangbei, Ningbo, 315033, China

AND PRIVATE COMPANIES

Tel.: (86) 57488195854
Web Site:
http://www.nwmwatermeters.com
Year Founded: 1958
603700—(SHG)
Rev.: $218,316,159
Assets: $329,999,151
Liabilities: $114,831,363
Net Worth: $215,167,788
Earnings: $17,744,861
Emp.: 1,500
Fiscal Year-end: 12/31/22
Electronic Control Product Mfr
N.A.I.C.S.: 334514
Lin Zhang *(Chm & Gen Mgr)*

NINGBO WT BEARING CO., LTD.
Industrial Development West Zone
Shengshan, Ningbo, China
Tel.: (86) 574 63549687
Year Founded: 1999
Emp.: 400
Bearing Mfr
N.A.I.C.S.: 332991
Ai Mei Xu *(Pres & CEO)*

NINGBO XIANFENG NEW MATERIAL CO. LTD
Shanxia Village Ji Shigang Town, Yinzhou District, Ningbo, 315127, China
Tel.: (86) 57385637856
Web Site: https://www.aplus.cn
Year Founded: 2003
300163—(CHIN)
Rev.: $42,774,264
Assets: $90,381,096
Liabilities: $7,132,320
Net Worth: $83,248,776
Earnings: ($241,488)
Emp.: 300
Fiscal Year-end: 12/31/22
Sunscreen Fabrics Mfr
N.A.I.C.S.: 313310
Xianfeng Lu *(Founder)*

Subsidiaries:

Kresta Holdings Limited (1)
380 Victoria Road, Malaga, 6090, WA, Australia
Tel.: (61) 63702614
Web Site: https://www.kresta.com.au
Rev.: $59,107,288
Assets: $28,759,496
Liabilities: $18,617,028
Net Worth: $10,142,468
Earnings: ($3,466,156)
Emp.: 415
Fiscal Year-end: 12/31/2017
Window Treatments & Blind Components Mfr & Whslr
N.A.I.C.S.: 449122
Xianfeng Lu *(Chm)*

Subsidiary (Domestic):

Curtain Wonderland Pty Ltd (2)
PO Box 138, Archerfield, 4108, QLD, Australia
Tel.: (61) 732752488
Web Site:
http://www.curtainwonderland.com.au
Home Furnishings Retailer
N.A.I.C.S.: 423220

NINGBO XUSHENG AUTO TECHNOLOGY CO., LTD.
68th Yanshan River North Road, Beilun District, Ningbo, China
Tel.: (86) 57455841801
Web Site: http://www.nbxus.com
603305—(SHG)
Rev.: $625,300,968
Assets: $1,351,168,028
Liabilities: $561,455,795
Net Worth: $789,712,232
Earnings: $98,455,949
Emp.: 2,000
Fiscal Year-end: 12/31/22
Industrial Machinery Mfr & Distr

N.A.I.C.S.: 333248
Xudong Xu *(Chm & Pres)*

NINGBO YONGXIN OPTICS CO., LTD.
No169 Mujin Road Hi-tech Industry Park, Ningbo, 315040, China
Tel.: (86) 57487906088
Web Site: https://www.yxopt.com
Year Founded: 1997
603297—(SHG)
Rev.: $121,815,739
Assets: $262,652,499
Liabilities: $36,263,275
Net Worth: $226,389,224
Earnings: $40,059,819
Emp.: 1,200
Fiscal Year-end: 12/31/21
Optical Component Mfr
N.A.I.C.S.: 333310
Mao Lei *(Co-Chm, Vice Chm, Pres & Gen Mgr)*

NINGBO YUNSHENG CO., LTD.
No 1 Yangtze River Road Ningbo national high tech Zone, Ningbo, 315040, Zhejiang, China
Tel.: (86) 57427862218
Web Site: https://www.yunsheng.com
600366—(SHG)
Rev.: $899,876,798
Assets: $1,361,074,469
Liabilities: $499,787,594
Net Worth: $861,286,875
Earnings: $49,938,918
Fiscal Year-end: 12/31/22
Magnetic Material Mfr & Distr
N.A.I.C.S.: 335999

Subsidiaries:

Ningbo Yunsheng Bonded Magnet Co., Ltd. (1)
No 1 Building 211 MujinRoad, Yinzhou District, Ningbo, 315000, Zhejiang, China
Tel.: (86) 57427861835
Web Site: https://en.ys-magnet.com
Magnetic Material Mfr
N.A.I.C.S.: 334610

Ningbo Yunsheng Co., Ltd. - Servo Control Division (1)
1 Yangfan Road National High-tech Zone, Ningbo, 315040, Zhejiang, China
Tel.: (86) 4006720165
Web Site: http://www.yunsheng-servo.com
Servo Motor Mfr
N.A.I.C.S.: 335312

Ningbo Yunsheng Magnet Devices Technology Co., Ltd. (1)
26 Anju Road, Beilun, Ningbo, China
Tel.: (86) 57426902828
Magnetic Material Mfr
N.A.I.C.S.: 334610

Yunsheng USA Inc. (1)
430 N Canal St Unit 2/3, South San Francisco, CA 94080
Tel.: (650) 827-7928
Web Site: http://www.yunshengusa.com
Magnetic Product Mfr & Distr
N.A.I.C.S.: 327110

NINGBO ZHENYU SCIENCE & TECHNOLOGY CO., LTD.
Xidian Industrial Park, Ninghai County, Ningbo, 315613, Zhejiang, China
Tel.: (86) 57465172919
Web Site:
https://www.zhenyumould.com
Year Founded: 1994
300953—(SSE)
Rev.: $796,457,133
Assets: $1,080,913,865
Liabilities: $749,990,779
Net Worth: $330,923,087
Earnings: $14,349,856
Fiscal Year-end: 12/31/22
Motor Product Mfr

N.A.I.C.S.: 335312
Zhenlin Jiang *(Chm & Gen Mgr)*

NINGBO ZHONGBAI CO., LTD.
21F Huijin Building No 77 Heyi Road, Haishu District, Ningbo, 315000, Zhejiang, China
Tel.: (86) 57487367060
Web Site: http://www.hitsc.com
Year Founded: 1992
600857—(SHG)
Rev.: $127,355,071
Assets: $135,093,442
Liabilities: $25,165,142
Net Worth: $109,928,300
Earnings: $50,848,373
Fiscal Year-end: 12/31/22
Departmental Store Operator
N.A.I.C.S.: 455110
Ying Feijun *(Chm & Gen Mgr)*

NINGBO ZHONGDA LEADER INTELLIGENT TRANSMISSION CO., LTD.
No 185 Xinxing 1st Road Cixi Hightech Industrial Development Zone, Ningbo, 315301, Zhejiang, China
Tel.: (86) 57463530538
Web Site: https://en.zd-motor.com
Year Founded: 2006
002896—(SSE)
Rev.: $126,023,040
Assets: $207,551,916
Liabilities: $60,140,340
Net Worth: $147,411,576
Earnings: $9,316,944
Emp.: 1,400
Fiscal Year-end: 12/31/22
Electromechanical Automation Product Mfr & Distr
N.A.I.C.S.: 333612
Cen Guojian *(Chm & Gen Mgr)*

NINGBO ZHONGJIN PETROCHEMICAL CO., LTD.
Ningbo Petroleum & Chemical Economic Development Zone 1, Rongsheng Road, Ningbo, 315200, Zhenhai, China
Tel.: (86) 688607
Sales Range: $5-14.9 Billion
Emp.: 1,225
Petrochemical Products Mfr
N.A.I.C.S.: 325110
Shui-Rong Li *(Chm)*

NINGBO ZHOUSHAN PORT CO., LTD.
Ningbo Global Shipping Plaza No 269 Ningdong Road, Beilun District, Ningbo, 315800, Zhejiang, China
Tel.: (86) 7427687203
Web Site: https://www.nbport.com.cn
Year Founded: 2008
601018—(SHG)
Rev.: $3,598,969,872
Assets: $15,554,964,693
Liabilities: $4,379,617,994
Net Worth: $11,175,346,699
Earnings: $646,376,689
Fiscal Year-end: 12/31/23
Cargo Transportation Services
N.A.I.C.S.: 488320
Liming Gong *(VP)*

NINGGUO LONCH ELECTRIC CO., LTD.
No 5 ChuangYe Road, Ningguo Economic Dev Zone, Ningguo, Anhui, China
Tel.: (86) 563 418 6838   CN
Web Site: http://www.lonchchina.com
Electronic Capacitor Mfr
N.A.I.C.S.: 334416

NINGXIA DUOWEITAIRUI

NINGXIA XIAOMING AGRICUL

PHARMACEUTICAL CO., LTD.
Wangyuangong Yeyuan 3, Wangyuan, Yinchuan, China
Tel.: (86) 9516149105
Sales Range: $75-99.9 Million
Emp.: 500
Pharmaceuticals Mfr
N.A.I.C.S.: 325412
Wang Yi *(CEO)*

NINGXIA JIAZE RENEWABLES CORPORATION LIMITED
Building 68 District D Enterprise Park Greenland 21 City No 1, Xingshui Road Xingqing District, Yinchuan, 750004, Ningxia, China
Tel.: (86) 9515100532
Web Site: http://www.jzne.net.cn
Year Founded: 2010
601619—(SHG)
Rev.: $258,471,879
Assets: $2,662,902,595
Liabilities: $1,859,207,225
Net Worth: $803,695,370
Earnings: $75,175,762
Fiscal Year-end: 12/31/22
Electric Power Distribution Services
N.A.I.C.S.: 221122
Bo Chen *(Chm)*

NINGXIA QINGLONG PIPES INDUSTRY CO., LTD.
Ningxia Water Conservancy Research and Development Building, Jinfeng District Zhonghai Road, Yinchuan, 750002, China
Tel.: (86) 4006001789
Web Site: https://www.qlgd.com.cn
Year Founded: 1975
002457—(SSE)
Rev.: $361,395,216
Assets: $584,864,280
Liabilities: $231,443,784
Net Worth: $353,420,496
Earnings: $23,618,088
Emp.: 600
Fiscal Year-end: 12/31/22
Concrete Pipe Mfr
N.A.I.C.S.: 327332
Gao Hongbin *(Chm)*

NINGXIA TIANYUAN MANGANESE INDUSTRY GROUP CO., LTD.
Shi Kong Industrial Park Zhong Ning County, Zhongwei, 755103, Ningxia, China
Tel.: (86) 955 5619016
Web Site: http://en.nxtymy.com
Electrolytic Manganese Production Enterprise
N.A.I.C.S.: 212290
Jia Tianjiang *(Pres)*

NINGXIA WESTERN VENTURE INDUSTRIAL CO., LTD.
1F Block C No 168 Beijing Middle Road, Jinfeng District, Yinchuan, 750002, Ningxia, China
Tel.: (86) 9518792651
Web Site:
http://www.guangxia.com.cn
Year Founded: 1994
000557—(SSE)
Rev.: $250,668,756
Assets: $860,862,600
Liabilities: $74,237,904
Net Worth: $786,624,696
Earnings: $33,412,392
Fiscal Year-end: 12/31/22
Beer & Wine Mfr
N.A.I.C.S.: 312140
Liu Jianren *(Chm-Supervisory Bd)*

NINGXIA XIAOMING AGRICUL-

NINGXIA XIAOMING AGRICUL—(CONTINUED)

TURE & ANIMAL HUSBANDRY CO., LTD.
No 36 Chuangye Street, Jinfeng Ningxia Hui Autonomous Region, Yinchuan, 750011, China
Tel.: (86) 4000300967
Web Site: https://www.nxxmqy.com
Year Founded: 2011
300967—(SSE)
Rev.: $110,285,604
Assets: $204,058,764
Liabilities: $91,967,616
Net Worth: $112,091,148
Earnings: $1,027,728
Fiscal Year-end: 12/31/22
Poultry Processing Product Mfr
N.A.I.C.S.: 311615
Xiaoming Wei *(Chm & Gen Mgr)*

NINGXIA YOUNGLIGHT CHEMICALS CO., LTD.
Steel Circuit, Ningxia Hui Autonomous Region Huinong District, Shizuishan, 753202, Ningxia, China
Tel.: (86) 9523689598
Web Site:
    http://www.yinglitechem.com
Year Founded: 1996
000635—(SSE)
Rev.: $263,258,424
Assets: $383,484,348
Liabilities: $64,899,900
Net Worth: $318,584,448
Earnings: ($54,597,348)
Fiscal Year-end: 12/31/22
Industrial Chemical Product Mfr & Distr
N.A.I.C.S.: 325211
Tian Shaoping *(Chm)*

NINGXIA ZHONGKE BIOTECHNOLOGY CO., LTD.
Hebin Street, Huinong District, Shizuishan, 753200, Ningxia, China
Tel.: (86) 9523671243
Web Site:
    http://www.nxhengli.com.cn
Year Founded: 1998
600165—(SHG)
Rev.: $95,631,157
Assets: $460,329,171
Liabilities: $334,800,185
Net Worth: $125,528,986
Earnings: ($19,864,396)
Fiscal Year-end: 12/31/22
Metal Product Mfr & Distr
N.A.I.C.S.: 331110
Hu Chunhai *(Chm)*

NINGXIA ZHONGYIN CASHMERE CO., LTD.
The Cashmere Industry Park, Lingwu, Ningxia, China
Tel.: (86) 9514038950
Web Site:
    http://www.zhongyincashmere.com
000982—(SSE)
Rev.: $88,216,128
Assets: $234,462,384
Liabilities: $57,305,664
Net Worth: $177,156,720
Earnings: $1,443,812
Fiscal Year-end: 12/31/22
Cashmere Clothing Mfr
N.A.I.C.S.: 315120

Subsidiaries:

Todd & Duncan Ltd. (1)
Lochleven Mills, Kinross, KY13 8DH, United Kingdom
Tel.: (44) 1577863521
Web Site: https://www.todd-duncan.co.uk
Sales Range: $25-49.9 Million
Emp.: 200
Cashmere Yarn Spinning Mill

N.A.I.C.S.: 313110

NINH BINH THERMAL POWER JOINT-STOCK COMPANY
01A Hoang Dieu street Thanh Binh ward, Ninh Binh, Ninh Binh, Vietnam
Tel.: (84) 2292210537
Web Site: https://www.nbtpc.com.vn
NBP—(HNX)
Rev.: $93,188,900
Assets: $46,844,900
Liabilities: $20,322,100
Net Worth: $26,522,800
Earnings: $2,426,400
Fiscal Year-end: 12/31/22
Electrical Contractor
N.A.I.C.S.: 238210
Tong Duc Chinh *(Chm-Mgmt Bd)*

NINH VAN BAY TRAVEL REAL ESTATE JOINT STOCK COMPANY
4rd floor Royal Building No 180 Trieu Viet Vuong, Nguyen Du Ward Hai Ba Trung District, Hanoi, Vietnam
Tel.: (84) 2439264950
Web Site: https://www.ninhvanbay.vn
Year Founded: 2006
NVT—(HOSE)
Sales Range: $1-9.9 Million
Real Estate Development Services
N.A.I.C.S.: 531390
Le Xuan Hai *(Vice Chm)*

NINTEC SYSTEMS LIMITED
B-11 Corporate House Bodakdev S G Highway, Ahmedabad, 380 054, Gujarat, India
Tel.: (91) 7940393909
Web Site:
    https://www.nintecsystems.com
NINSYS—(NSE)
Rev.: $4,126,072
Assets: $3,062,934
Liabilities: $741,035
Net Worth: $2,321,899
Earnings: $665,500
Emp.: 249
Fiscal Year-end: 03/31/21
Software Development Services
N.A.I.C.S.: 541511
Niraj Chhaganraj Gemawat *(Chm & Mng Dir)*

NINTENDO CO., LTD.
11-1 Hokotate-cho Kamitoba, Minami-ku, Kyoto, 601 8501, Japan
Tel.: (81) 756629600   JP
Web Site: https://www.nintendo.com
Year Founded: 1889
NTO—(DEU)
Rev.: $11,051,027,650
Assets: $20,830,714,340
Liabilities: $3,611,677,560
Net Worth: $17,219,036,780
Earnings: $3,242,879,220
Emp.: 8,109
Fiscal Year-end: 03/31/24
Electronic Video Games & Console Systems Mfr
N.A.I.C.S.: 339930
Satoshi Yamato *(Sr Exec Officer)*

Subsidiaries:

Brownie Brown Inc. (1)
Daiwa Securities Building 6F, Kichijoji Honmachi 2-1-10, 180-0004, Tokyo, Musashino City, Japan
Tel.: (81) 422238135
Sales Range: $1-9.9 Million
Emp.: 27
Video Game Mfr & Sales
N.A.I.C.S.: 339930

Monolith Software Inc. (1)
2-1-1 Kameguro Nakameguro GT Tower 12F, Meguro-ku, Tokyo, 153-0051, Japan
Tel.: (81) 357217181

Web Site: http://www.monolithsoft.co.jp
Emp.: 109
Gaming Software Development Services
N.A.I.C.S.: 541511

NDCube Co., Ltd. (1)
8-1 Akashi-cho Sacred Road Ka Tower 46F, Chuo-ku, Tokyo, Japan
Tel.: (81) 35 148 1601
Web Site: https://www.ndcube.co.jp
Game Mfr
N.A.I.C.S.: 339930

Nintendo Australia Pty. Ltd. (1)
804 Stud Road, PO Box 804, Scoresby, 3179, VIC, Australia (100%)
Tel.: (61) 397309822
Web Site: http://www.nintendo.com.au
Emp.: 100
Video Game Mfr
N.A.I.C.S.: 336991

Nintendo Benelux B.V. (1)
Zoomstede 21, 3431 HK, Nieuwegein, Netherlands
Tel.: (31) 306097100
Web Site: http://www.nintendo.nl
Sales Range: $25-49.9 Million
Emp.: 40
Game Mfr
N.A.I.C.S.: 339930
Satoru Shibata *(Mng Dir)*

Nintendo France S.A.R.L. (1)
6 Blvd de l'Oise, Immeuble le Montaigne Pontoise, 95031, Cergy, Cedex, France
Tel.: (33) 134354600
Web Site: http://www.nintendo.fr
Sales Range: $25-49.9 Million
Emp.: 55
Video Game Mfr
N.A.I.C.S.: 339930

Nintendo Iberica (1)
Azalea 1 Edificio D 1 Planta Miniparc 1, El Soto de la Moraleja, 28109, Alcobendas, Madrid, Spain
Tel.: (34) 917886498
Web Site: http://www.nintendo.es
Video Game Mfr
N.A.I.C.S.: 339930
Antonio Lopez *(CEO)*

Nintendo Netherlands B.V. (1)
Krijtwal 33, NL 3432 ZT, Nieuwegein, Netherlands (100%)
Tel.: (31) 306097100
Web Site: http://www.nintendo.nl
Sales Range: $25-49.9 Million
Emp.: 25
Video Game Mfr
N.A.I.C.S.: 339930
Vertus Vejong *(Mng Dir)*

Nintendo Phuten Co.,Ltd. (1)
12Floor 1 No 400 Fu Hsing North Road, Taipei, Taiwan
Tel.: (886) 225361216
Web Site: http://www.nintendo.tw
Video Game Development Services
N.A.I.C.S.: 541511

Nintendo Software Technology Corporation (1)
5001 150th Ave Ne, Redmond, WA 98052-5121
Tel.: (425) 497-7500
Gaming Software Development Services
N.A.I.C.S.: 541511

Nintendo of America, Inc. (1)
4600 150th Ave NE, Redmond, WA 98052-5111
Tel.: (425) 882-2040
Web Site: https://www.nintendo.com
Sales Range: $1-4.9 Billion
Emp.: 1,000
Electronic Games & Home Video Systems Whslr
N.A.I.C.S.: 423920
Doug Bowser *(Pres)*

Division (Domestic):

NES Merchandising Inc (2)
4600 150th Ave NE, Redmond, WA 98052
Tel.: (425) 882-2040
Gaming Software Development Services
N.A.I.C.S.: 541511

Subsidiary (Non-US):

Nintendo of Canada Ltd. (2)

INTERNATIONAL PUBLIC

295 Vertuao Way Ste 150, Vancouver, V5M 4X5, BC, Canada
Tel.: (604) 279-1600
Web Site: http://www.nintendo.ca
Sales Range: $25-49.9 Million
Emp.: 45
Video Game Mfr
N.A.I.C.S.: 339930
Ron Bertram *(VP & Gen Mgr)*

Subsidiary (Domestic):

SiRAS .Com Inc (2)
11121 Willows Rd N E, Redmond, WA 98052
Tel.: (425) 497-3300
Web Site: http://www.siras.com
Sales Range: $10-24.9 Million
Emp.: 45
Electronic Products Registration Services
N.A.I.C.S.: 561990
Maridee Maraz *(Dir-Sls & Mktg)*

Nintendo of Europe GmbH (1)
Herriotstrasse 4, 63760, Frankfurt am Main, Germany (100%)
Tel.: (49) 69667747731
Web Site: http://www.nintendo.de
Sales Range: $100-124.9 Million
Emp.: 350
Video Game Mfr
N.A.I.C.S.: 339930
Koji Miyake *(Pres & Mng Dir)*

Retro Studios, Inc. (1)
1835 A Kramer Ln Ste 100, Austin, TX 78758
Tel.: (512) 493-4600
Web Site: http://www.retrostudios.com
Game Development Studio
N.A.I.C.S.: 339930

Wii no Ma Co.,Ltd. (1)
1-3-12 Shiba Koen, Minato-ku, Tokyo, 105-0011, Japan
Tel.: (81) 364303888
Web Site: http://www.wiinoma.co.jp
Sales Range: $25-49.9 Million
Emp.: 20
Online Video Streaming Services
N.A.I.C.S.: 518210

NIO INC.
Building 20 No 56 AnTuo Road, Jiading District, Shanghai, 201804, China
Tel.: (86) 2169082018   Ky
Web Site: https://www.nio.com
Year Founded: 2014
NIO—(NYSE)
Rev.: $7,700,755,012
Assets: $16,252,658,673
Liabilities: $15,718,157,122
Net Worth: $534,501,551
Earnings: $2,868,818,260)
Emp.: 32,820
Fiscal Year-end: 12/31/23
Electric Vehicle Mfr
N.A.I.C.S.: 336320
Lihong Qin *(Co-Founder & Pres)*

NIO STRATEGIC METALS INC.
1 Place Ville Marie Suite 1670, Montreal, H3B 2B6, QC, Canada
Tel.: (514) 288-8506   QC
Web Site:
    https://niometauxstrategiques.com
Year Founded: 1995
NIOCF—(OTCIQ)
Rev.: $9,137
Assets: $1,439,326
Liabilities: $457,149
Net Worth: $982,177
Earnings: ($550,700)
Fiscal Year-end: 12/31/23
Niobium Mining & Metallurgical Production
N.A.I.C.S.: 212290
Hubert Marleau *(Chm, Pres & CEO)*

NIOA NOMINEES PTY. LIMITED
80 Lomandra Dr Brisbane Airport, Brisbane, 4008, QLD, Australia

AND PRIVATE COMPANIES — NIPPN CORPORATION

Tel.: (61) 736219999   AU
Web Site: https://www.nioa.com.au
Year Founded: 1973
Firearms, Weapons & Ammunitions Supplier
N.A.I.C.S.: 332993
Robert Nioa (CEO)

Subsidiaries:

Barrett Firearms Manufacturing, Inc. (1)
PO Box 1077, Murfreesboro, TN 37133
Tel.: (615) 896-2938
Web Site: https://barrett.net
Sales Range: $50-74.9 Million
Emp.: 80
Small Arms Mfr
N.A.I.C.S.: 332994
Ronnie Barret (Co-Founder)

NIOBAY METALS INC.
1100 ave des Canadiens-de-Montreal Suite 300, Montreal, H3B 2S2, QC, Canada
Tel.: (514) 866-6500   Ca
Web Site: https://niobaymetals.com
Year Founded: 1954
NBYCF—(OTCQB)
Rev.: $125,788
Assets: $3,062,618
Liabilities: $116,659
Net Worth: $2,945,959
Earnings: ($1,753,573)
Emp.: 3
Fiscal Year-end: 12/31/23
Gold Development & Exploration Services
N.A.I.C.S.: 212220
Serge Savard (Chm)

NIOX GROUP PLC
Hayakawa Building Edmund Halley Road, The Oxford Science Park, Oxford, OX4 4GB, United Kingdom
Tel.: (44) 3303309356   UK
Web Site: https://www.circassia.com
NIOX—(AIM)
Rev.: $46,452,916
Assets: $115,501,136
Liabilities: $9,719,768
Net Worth: $105,781,368
Earnings: $13,506,690
Emp.: 92
Fiscal Year-end: 12/31/23
Holding Company; Biopharmaceutical Research & Development
N.A.I.C.S.: 551112
Nina Kataria (Sr VP-HR-Global)

Subsidiaries:

Aerocrine AB (1)
Rasundavagen 18 8th floor, SE-169 67, Solna, Sweden
Tel.: (46) 86290780
Web Site: http://www.aerocrine.com
Medical Monitoring Systems Mfr
N.A.I.C.S.: 339112

Circassia (Beijing) Medical Device Co. Limited (1)
Medical Equipment Mfr & Distr
N.A.I.C.S.: 339112

Circassia (Shanghai) Medical Device Co., Limited (1)
Rm 2002A 20F Bld B Dawning Center Hongbaoshi Rd, Changning Dist, Shanghai, China
Tel.: (86) 1065536941
Medical Device Mfr
N.A.I.C.S.: 339112

Circassia AB (1)
Hanselisgatan 13, 754 50, Uppsala, Sweden
Tel.: (46) 18328837
Medical Equipment Mfr & Distr
N.A.I.C.S.: 339112

Circassia Limited (1)
Northbrook House Robert Robinson Avenue, The Oxford Science Park, Oxford,
OX4 4GA, United Kingdom
Tel.: (44) 330 330 9356
Medical Equipment Mfr & Distr
N.A.I.C.S.: 339112

Circassia Pharma Limited (1)
Northbrook House, Oxford Science Park, Oxford, OX4 4GA, Oxon, United Kingdom
Tel.: (44) 1865 405 560
Web Site: http://www.circassia.com
Emp.: 100
Biopharmaceutical Research & Development
N.A.I.C.S.: 541715

NIOX Inc. (1)
1100 Perimeter Park Dr Ste 114, Morrisville, NC 27560
Web Site: https://niox.com
Medical Device Mfr
N.A.I.C.S.: 339112

NIP KOMPANIJA NOVOSTI A.D.
Trg Nikole Pasica 7, 11000, Belgrade, Serbia
Tel.: (381) 11 33 98 130
Web Site: http://www.novosti.rs
Year Founded: 2002
Sales Range: $10-24.9 Million
Emp.: 446
Newspaper Publishing Services
N.A.I.C.S.: 513110

NIP ZRENJANIN A.D.
Kralja Petar Prvo 2, Zrenjanin, Serbia
Tel.: (381) 23562983
Web Site: https://listzrenjanin.com
Year Founded: 1952
NIPZ—(BEL)
Rev.: $503,968
Assets: $244,497
Liabilities: $196,894
Net Worth: $47,603
Earnings: $1,053
Emp.: 19
Fiscal Year-end: 12/31/23
Newspaper Publishing Services
N.A.I.C.S.: 513110
Mira Radulov (Exec Dir-Fin)

NIPCO PLC
1 & 15 Dockyard Road, Apapa, Lagos, Nigeria
Tel.: (234) 811 559 0117
Web Site: http://www.nipcoplc.com
Year Founded: 2001
Petroleum Products Storage & Marketing
N.A.I.C.S.: 424710
Bestman P. Anekwe (Chm)

Subsidiaries:

11 PLC (1)
1 Mobil Road, Apapa, Lagos, Nigeria (74.18%)
Tel.: (234) 1 2801600
Web Site: http://www.11plc.com
Rev.: $525,193,141
Assets: $249,886,038
Liabilities: $141,158,419
Net Worth: $108,727,620
Earnings: $24,341,472
Fiscal Year-end: 12/31/2019
Petroleum Products Marketing & Distr
N.A.I.C.S.: 424720
Adetunji A. Oyebanji (Mng Dir)

NIPPAN RENTAL CO., LTD.
4-5-15 Nishi Katakai-machi, Maebashi, 371-0013, Japan
Tel.: (81) 27 2437711
Web Site: http://www.nippan-r.co.jp
Year Founded: 1979
Rev.: $74,011,070
Assets: $119,274,190
Liabilities: $98,797,580
Net Worth: $20,476,610
Earnings: $2,008,230
Fiscal Year-end: 12/31/19

Construction Machinery Leasing Services
N.A.I.C.S.: 532412
Haruhiko Ishizuka (Pres)

NIPPECRAFT LIMITED
2 Venture Drive 2401 Vision Exchange, Singapore, 629787, Singapore
Tel.: (65) 62622662
Web Site: https://www.nippecraft.com.sg
N32—(CAT)
Rev.: $111,548,000
Assets: $56,421,000
Liabilities: $24,469,000
Net Worth: $31,952,000
Earnings: $1,344,000
Emp.: 50
Fiscal Year-end: 12/31/23
Business Management & Consulting Services
N.A.I.C.S.: 541611
Connie Oi Yan Chan (Chm & CEO)

Subsidiaries:

Collins Debden Limited (1)
Tel.: (44) 1413008500
Web Site: http://uk.collinsdebden.com
Stationery Product Mfr & Distr
N.A.I.C.S.: 322230

Collins Debden Pty. Ltd. (1)
Level 3 93 George Street, PO Box 903, Parramatta, 2150, NSW, Australia
Tel.: (61) 288332900
Web Site: https://www.collinsdebden.com.au
Stationery Product Distr
N.A.I.C.S.: 424120

Collins Debden USA, Inc. (1)
60 Cragmont Ave, San Francisco, CA 94116
Tel.: (415) 255-8843
Dairy Products Distr
N.A.I.C.S.: 424490

Paperich Pte. Ltd. (1)
4th Floor 9 Fan Yoong Road, Singapore, 629787, Singapore
Tel.: (65) 62622662
Stationery Product Mfr
N.A.I.C.S.: 323111

NIPPI. INC.
1-1-1 Senju midori-cho, Adachi, Tokyo, 120-8601, Japan
Tel.: (81) 338885111
Web Site: https://www.nippi-inc.co.jp
Year Founded: 1907
7932—(TKS)
Rev.: $324,194,060
Assets: $478,524,340
Liabilities: $225,334,900
Net Worth: $253,189,440
Earnings: $16,842,280
Fiscal Year-end: 03/31/24
Gelatin Cosmetic Product Mfr & Distr
N.A.I.C.S.: 325998

Subsidiaries:

Daiho Trading Co., Ltd. (1)
3 4 1 Ginza Okura Annex Buildgi 6 Floor, Chuo, 104-0061, Japan
Tel.: (81) 335676731
Emp.: 27
Collagen Casing Product Distr
N.A.I.C.S.: 424610

Nippi (Shanghai) Inc. (1)
Rm B1703 City Center of shanghai Bldg 100 Zunyi Rd Changning Dis, Shanghai, 200051, China
Tel.: (86) 2162370631
Leather Product Distr
N.A.I.C.S.: 424990
Jill Li (Mgr-Bus Dev)

Nippi. Inc. - Fuji Factory (1)
1 Yumizawa-cho Fujinomiya, Shizuoka, 4180073, Japan
Tel.: (81) 544222111
Collagen Casing Product Mfr

N.A.I.C.S.: 326121

Okura Food Sales Co., Ltd. (1)
7F Okura Annex 4-1 Ginza 3-Chome, Chuoku, Tokyo, 104-0061, Japan
Tel.: (81) 335387979
Web Site: https://www.okurafs.co.jp
Emp.: 25
Food Products Distr
N.A.I.C.S.: 424420
Takao Itoh (Chm)

NIPPN CORPORATION
4-8 Kojimachi, Chiyoda-ku, Tokyo, 102-0083, Japan
Tel.: (81) 335115301   JP
Web Site: https://www.nippn.co.jp
Year Founded: 1896
2001—(TKS)
Rev.: $2,647,397,540
Assets: $2,556,034,120
Liabilities: $1,047,070,270
Net Worth: $1,508,963,850
Earnings: $174,285,870
Emp.: 1,173
Fiscal Year-end: 03/31/24
Wheat Miller; Flour & Flour Products, Premixed Foods & Biological Research Products Mfr & Retailer
N.A.I.C.S.: 311824
Hiroshi Sawada (Chm & CEO)

Subsidiaries:

JACS Co., Ltd. (1)
4-3-24 Nishinakajima Samuti Shinosaka Center Building 6f, Yodogawa-Ku, Osaka, 532-0011, Japan
Tel.: (81) 663022446
Information Technology Consulting Services
N.A.I.C.S.: 541512

Junco Flora School Co., Ltd. (1)
2-54-16 Gohonngi, Meguro-ku, Tokyo, 153-0053, Japan
Tel.: (81) 358607516
Web Site: http://www.junco.jp
Sculptural Flower Products Mfr
N.A.I.C.S.: 327110
Junco Hitomi (Founder)

Matsuya Flour Mills Co., Ltd. (1)
3-2-7 Odoori, Utsunomiya, 320-0811, Tochigi, Japan
Tel.: (81) 286346186
Buckwheat Flour Mfr
N.A.I.C.S.: 311211

NIPPN (Shanghai) Trading Co., Ltd. (1)
Room 16EFGH 310 Tianshan Road Near Weining Road, Changning District, Shanghai, China
Tel.: (86) 216 282 0011
Web Site: https://www.shnippn.cn
Farm Product Raw Material Distr
N.A.I.C.S.: 424590

NIPPN (Thailand) Co., Ltd. (1)
101/115 Moo 20 Phaholyothin Road Klong Nueng, Klong Luang, Pathumthani, 12120, Thailand
Tel.: (66) 25296250
Baking Powder Mfr
N.A.I.C.S.: 311999
Hideo Kondo (Mng Dir)

NIPPN California Inc. (1)
2563 W Woodland Dr, Anaheim, CA 92801
Tel.: (562) 404-2456
Web Site: https://www.nippncalifornia.com
Grocery Distr
N.A.I.C.S.: 492210

NIPPN Donut Kansai Co., Ltd. (1)
2-2-30 Nagatanaka, Higashi-osaka, 577-0013, Osaka, Japan
Tel.: (81) 667431701
Doughnut Retailer
N.A.I.C.S.: 722511

NPF Japan Co., Ltd. (1)
229-3 Xingang, Mihama-Ku, Chiba, 261-0002, Chiba, Japan
Tel.: (81) 432035630
Web Site: http://www.nippn.co.jp
Pet Food Mfr & Distr
N.A.I.C.S.: 311111

NIPPN CORPORATION

NIPPN Corporation—(Continued)

Nippn Foods Corporation (Thailand) Ltd. (1)
2034/85 19-01 19 Fl Italthai Tower New Petchburi Rd, Bangkapi Huaykwang, Bangkok, 10320, Thailand
Tel.: (66) 2 716 1780
Web Site: https://www.nippn.co.th
Food Products Mfr
N.A.I.C.S.: 311991

Nippon Daily Health Co., Ltd. (1)
4F Yamato Building 5-27-3 Sendagaya, Shibuya-Ku, Tokyo, 151-0051, Japan
Tel.: (81) 333502580
Web Site: https://www.nippn-lifeinnov.co.jp
Sales Range: $25-49.9 Million
Emp.: 50
Health Foods Distr
N.A.I.C.S.: 424490

Nippon Flour Mills (Shanghai) Co., Ltd. (1)
No 298 Yuyang Road High Technology Park, Songjiang District, Shanghai, 201600, China
Tel.: (86) 2157735566
Web Site: http://www.e-nippn.com
Flour Milling Services
N.A.I.C.S.: 311211

Nippon Flour Mills (Thailand) Co., Ltd. (1)
Khwang Bangkapi Khet, Huai Khwang, Bangkok, 10310, Thailand
Tel.: (66) 27161780
Sales Range: $25-49.9 Million
Emp.: 24
Flour Distr
N.A.I.C.S.: 424490
Narita Atsushi *(Mng Dir)*

Nippon Rich Co., Ltd. (1)
4-8 Kojimachi, Chiyoda-Ku, Tokyo, 102-0083, Japan
Tel.: (81) 332373821
Web Site: http://www.nippn.co.jp
Frozen Food Distr
N.A.I.C.S.: 424420

OHMY Co., Ltd. (1)
5-1-2 Midorigaoka, Atsugi, 243-0041, Kanagawa, Japan
Tel.: (81) 462216660
Pasta Mfr & Sales
N.A.I.C.S.: 311991

OK Food Industry Co., Ltd. (1)
1080-1 Ota, Asakura, 838-0051, Fukuoka, Japan **(51.07%)**
Tel.: (81) 946227131
Web Site: http://www.ok-food.co.jp
Rev.: $77,091,520
Assets: $100,294,480
Liabilities: $80,353,680
Net Worth: $19,940,800
Earnings: ($1,142,240)
Emp.: 447
Fiscal Year-end: 03/31/2021
Food Products Mfr
N.A.I.C.S.: 311991
Toshikatsu Oshige *(Pres)*

PT. NIPPN Foods Indonesia (1)
Menara Global Lantai 6 Suite C Jl Jend Gatot Subroto Kav 27, Kec Setia Budi Kel Kuningan Timur, Jakarta Selatan, 12950, Indonesia
Tel.: (62) 21 527 9662
Web Site: https://nippnfoods.co.id
Farm Product Raw Material Distr
N.A.I.C.S.: 424590

Pasta Montana, LLC (1)
1 Pasta Pl, Great Falls, MT 59401
Tel.: (406) 761-1516
Web Site: http://www.pastamontana.com
Sales Range: $25-49.9 Million
Emp.: 100
Dry Pasta Mfr
N.A.I.C.S.: 311999
Randy Gilbertson *(Gen Mgr)*

SUZUKI Co., Ltd. (1)
1-3-30 Minamiyoshijima, Naka-ku, Hiroshima, 730-0826, Japan
Tel.: (81) 822438321
Wheat Flour Distr
N.A.I.C.S.: 424290

Tofuku Flour Mills Co., Ltd. (1)
Nanotsu 4-chome 9-20, Chuo-ku, Fukuoka, 810-0071, Japan
Tel.: (81) 92 7811661
Web Site: http://www.tofuku.co.jp
Flour Milling Services
N.A.I.C.S.: 311211
Yasunori Tanaka *(Pres)*

NIPPO LTD

MI Terrace Nagoya-Fushimi Bldg 1-10-1 Nishiki, Naka-ku, Nagoya, 460-0003, Japan
Tel.: (81) 52213161
Web Site: https://www.nip.co.jp
9913—(TKS)
Rev.: $277,104,420
Assets: $203,290,550
Liabilities: $105,515,430
Net Worth: $97,775,120
Earnings: $9,630,770
Emp.: 2,830
Fiscal Year-end: 03/31/24
Electrical Equipment & Component Mfr
N.A.I.C.S.: 335999
Yasuchika Iwasa *(Pres)*

Subsidiaries:

NIPPO (HONG KONG) LTD. (1)
26F Two Harvour Square 180 Wai Yip Street, KwunTong, Kowloon, China (Hong Kong)
Tel.: (852) 5211633
Electronic Component Mfr & Distr
N.A.I.C.S.: 334419

NIPPO (SHANGHAI) LTD. (1)
Room 2921 Tower A No 325 Tian Yao Qiao Road, Shanghai, 200030, China
Tel.: (86) 2133632396
Electronic Component Mfr & Distr
N.A.I.C.S.: 334419

NIPPO MECHATRONICS (M) SDN. BHD. (1)
Lot Pt 2499 Kawasan Perindustrian Kecil Sederhana Batu 8, Mukim Setul, 71700, Mantin, Negeri Sembilan, Malaysia
Tel.: (60) 67583930
Electronic Component Mfr & Distr
N.A.I.C.S.: 334419

NIPPO MECHATRONICS (THAILAND) CO., LTD. (1)
55 Moo 18 Suvintawong Road, Tambol Saladaeng Amphur Bang Nam Priao, Chachoengsao, 24000, Thailand
Tel.: (66) 38090950
Electronic Component Mfr & Distr
N.A.I.C.S.: 334419

NIPPO MECHATRONICS (VIETNAM) CO., LTD. (1)
Lot 37 38 39 Noi Bai Industrial Zone, Quang Tien Soc Son, Hanoi, Vietnam
Tel.: (84) 2435820288
Electronic Component Mfr & Distr
N.A.I.C.S.: 334419

NIPPO METAL TECH PHILS., INC. (1)
Unit 12 Phase 4 EZP Business Park Calamba Premiere Industrial Park, Batino, Calamba, Laguna, Philippines
Tel.: (63) 495303355
Electronic Component Mfr & Distr
N.A.I.C.S.: 334419

NIPPO METALTECH CO., LTD. (1)
12-72 Suzaki Okinawa Special Free Trade Zone 8, Uruma, 904-2234, Okinawa, Japan
Tel.: (81) 989212144
Electronic Component Mfr & Distr
N.A.I.C.S.: 334419

NIPPO PRECISION INDUSTRY (SHENZHEN) CO., LTD. (1)
1304 13/F Kerry Center Renmin South Road, Luohu, Shenzhen, China
Tel.: (86) 75582227230
Electronic Component Mfr & Distr
N.A.I.C.S.: 334419

NK MECHATRONICS CO., LTD. (1)
581 Moo 8 Mittraphap Road Tumbol Sungnoen, Amphur Sungnoen, Nakhon Ratchasima, 30170, Thailand
Tel.: (66) 44369718
Electronic Component Mfr & Distr
N.A.I.C.S.: 334419

PT. NIPPO MECHATRONICS INDONESIA (1)
Bekasi International Industrial Estate Blok C4 No 6-7 Desa Sukaresmi, Cikarang Selatan, Bekasi, 17550, Indonesia
Tel.: (62) 2189903233
Electronic Component Mfr & Distr
N.A.I.C.S.: 334419
Ridwan Hasan *(Supvr-Sls & Mktg)*

NIPPON ACCOMMODATIONS FUND, INC.

1-4-1 Nihonbashi, Chuo-Ku, Tokyo, 103-0027, Japan
Tel.: (81) 332463677
Web Site: https://www.naf-r.jp
3226—(TKS)
Sales Range: $100-124.9 Million
Investment Management Service
N.A.I.C.S.: 525990
Takashi Ikeda *(Exec Dir)*

NIPPON AIR CONDITIONING SERVICES CO., LTD.

239-2 Terugaoka, Meito-ku, Nagoya, 465-0042, Aichi, Japan
Tel.: (81) 527732511
Web Site: https://www.nikku.co.jp
Year Founded: 1964
4658—(TKS)
Rev.: $384,913,520
Assets: $283,892,890
Liabilities: $123,851,570
Net Worth: $160,041,320
Earnings: $18,012,250
Emp.: 2,154
Fiscal Year-end: 03/31/24
Air Conditioning Services
N.A.I.C.S.: 811412
Masato Suwa *(Dir & Exec Officer)*

Subsidiaries:

Evar Air-conditioning & Engineering Pte Ltd (1)
51 Ubi Avenue 1 03-31 Paya Ubi Industrial Park, Singapore, 408933, Singapore
Tel.: (65) 67489106
Air Conditioning Equipment Distr
N.A.I.C.S.: 423730

Nippon Air Conditioning Tokai Co., Ltd. (1)
93 Sekishicho Higashi-ku, Hamamatsu, 431-3114, Shizuoka, Japan
Tel.: (81) 534348211
Web Site: http://www.nikku-tokai.co.jp
Air Conditioning Equipment Mfr
N.A.I.C.S.: 333415

Shanghai Nikku Suntec International Trading Co., Ltd. (1)
3F Bldg No 6 1366 Qi Xin Road, MinHang District, Shanghai, 201100, China
Tel.: (86) 2152277857
Building Equipment Maintenance & Repair Services
N.A.I.C.S.: 811310

Suzhou Nikku Suntec Electromechanical Technology Co., Ltd. (1)
No 158-12 Hua Shan Road, Suzhou New District, Jiangsu, 215129, China
Tel.: (86) 5126 536 7251
Web Site: http://www.prc-suns.com
Building Equipment Maintenance & Repair Services
N.A.I.C.S.: 811310

NIPPON ANTENNA CO., LTD

7-49-8 Nishi-Oku, Arakawa-ku, Tokyo, 116-8561, Japan
Tel.: (81) 338935221
Web Site: https://www.nippon-antenna.co.jp
Year Founded: 1953
6930—(TKS)
Rev.: $75,261,460
Assets: $118,504,080
Liabilities: $39,587,290
Net Worth: $78,916,790
Earnings: ($19,208,660)
Emp.: 545
Fiscal Year-end: 03/31/24
Broadcasting & Wireless Services
N.A.I.C.S.: 334220
Yutaka Takizawa *(Chm)*

Subsidiaries:

Ishinomaki Atex Co., Ltd. (1)
36-1 Kaminakazone Hebita, Ishinomaki, 986-0861, Miyagi, Japan
Tel.: (81) 225940517
Web Site: https://www.nippon-antenna.co.jp
Wireless Antenna Mfr & Distr
N.A.I.C.S.: 334220

NIPPON AQUA CO., LTD.

Taiyo Seimei Shinagawa Building 20F 2-16-2 Kounan, Minato-ku, Tokyo, 108-0075, Japan
Tel.: (81) 354631117
Web Site: https://www.n-aqua.jp
Year Founded: 2004
1429—(TKS)
Sales Range: $100-124.9 Million
Emp.: 475
Thermal Insulation Materials Installation & Sales
N.A.I.C.S.: 238310
Fumitaka Nakamura *(Pres)*

NIPPON BEARING CO., LTD.

2833 Chiya, Ojiya, 947-8503, Niigata, Japan
Tel.: (81) 258825709
Web Site: http://www.nb-linear.co.jp
Year Founded: 1959
Rev.: $69,535,200
Emp.: 582
Machinery Products Mfr
N.A.I.C.S.: 333310
Toru Yamazaki *(Pres)*

Subsidiaries:

NB China Co., Ltd. (1)
Room 4001 NanZheng Main Building No 580 Nanjing West Road, Jing an District, Shanghai, 200041, China
Tel.: (86) 2152286811
Engineering Component Mfr
N.A.I.C.S.: 334511
Toru Yamazaki *(Pres)*

NB Corporation of America (1)
930 Muirfield Dr, Hanover Park, IL 60133
Tel.: (630) 295-8880
Web Site: http://www.nbcorporation.com
Emp.: 500
Engineering Component Mfr
N.A.I.C.S.: 334511
Toru Yamazaki *(Pres)*

NB Europe B.V. (1)
Boekweitstraat 21, 2153 GK, Nieuw-Vennep, Netherlands
Tel.: (31) 252463200
Web Site: http://www.nbeurope.com
Engineering Component Mfr
N.A.I.C.S.: 334511
Toru Yamazaki *(Pres)*

NIPPON BEET SUGAR MANUFACTURING CO., LTD.

3-12-14 Mita, Minato-ku, Tokyo, 108-0073, Japan
Tel.: (81) 364145522
Web Site: https://www.nitten.co.jp
Year Founded: 1919
2108—(TKS)
Rev.: $458,053,170
Assets: $680,975,420
Liabilities: $201,519,070
Net Worth: $479,456,350
Earnings: $11,970,710
Emp.: 774

AND PRIVATE COMPANIES

Fiscal Year-end: 03/31/24
Refined & Beet Sugars, Animal Feeds, Seeds, Biodegradable Paper Planters & Raffinose Mfr
N.A.I.C.S.: 311313
Hideo Ishiguri *(Pres & CEO)*

NIPPON BUILDING FUND, INC.
Muromachi Furukawa Mitsui Building 16th Floor 3-1 Nihonbashi Muromachi, Chuo-ku, Tokyo, 103-0022, Japan
Tel.: (81) 335163370
Web Site: https://www.nbf-m.com
8951—(TKS)
Rev.: $353,879,470
Assets: $9,577,835,750
Liabilities: $4,608,245,950
Net Worth: $4,969,589,800
Earnings: $142,245,040
Fiscal Year-end: 06/30/20
Investment Management Service
N.A.I.C.S.: 525990
Koichi Nishiyama *(Exec Dir)*

NIPPON CARBIDE INDUSTRIES CO., INC.
16-2 2-Chome Konan, Minato-ku, Tokyo, 108-8466, Japan
Tel.: (81) 354628200
Web Site: https://www.carbide.co.jp
4064—(TKS)
Rev.: $285,756,910
Assets: $403,342,200
Liabilities: $174,484,170
Net Worth: $228,858,030
Earnings: $6,603,390
Emp.: 3,297
Fiscal Year-end: 03/31/24
Chemical, Electronic & Plastic Products Mfr & Distr
N.A.I.C.S.: 325998
Iguchi Yoshitada *(Sr Mng Exec Officer)*

Subsidiaries:

DIAMOND ENGINEERING (DALIAN) CO., LTD. (1)
No 24 Renmin Road Zhongshan District Ping an Building 2308, Dalian, Lioaning, China
Tel.: (86) 411 82536062
Information Technology Consulting Services
N.A.I.C.S.: 541512

Deck Building Research Institute Inc. (1)
1-7-7 Shakado, Uozu, 9337-0067, Toyama, Japan
Tel.: (81) 765 22 2406
Web Site: http://www.carbide.co.jp
Construction Engineering Services
N.A.I.C.S.: 541330

Diamond Engineering Co., Ltd. (1)
1-7-22 Shakado, Uozu, 937-0067, Toyama, Japan
Tel.: (81) 765245670
Web Site: https://www.diamond-eng.co.jp
Emp.: 144
Engineeering Services
N.A.I.C.S.: 541330
Takahiko Mukai *(Pres)*

Electro-Ceramics (Thailand) Co., Ltd. (1)
65 M 4 T Banklang, A Muang, Lamphun, 51000, Thailand
Tel.: (66) 53581036
Web Site: https://www.ect.co.th
Ceramic Products Mfr & Sales
N.A.I.C.S.: 423830

HAYATSUKI ASUKON CO., LTD. (1)
30-1 Oogake Namerikawa-chi, Toyama, 936-0802, Japan
Tel.: (81) 76 471 2300
Asphalt Concrete Mfr & Distr
N.A.I.C.S.: 327390

HAYATSUKI NAMAKON CO., LTD. (1)
536 Ojima, Namerikawa, 936-0801, Toyama, Japan
Tel.: (81) 764712233
Concrete Mfr & Distr
N.A.I.C.S.: 327320

HOKKAIDO LINER CO., LTD. (1)
7-29 2-chome 1 jyo Shinkononi, Kita-ku, Sapporo, 001-0901, Hokkaido, Japan
Tel.: (81) 117617440
Road Sign Construction & Painting Services
N.A.I.C.S.: 237310

Hokuriku Ceramics Co., Ltd. (1)
143-3 Yokomakura, Uozu, 937-0044, Toyama, Japan
Tel.: (81) 765247387
Web Site: https://hokurikuceramic.co.jp
Emp.: 61
Ceramic Products Mfr
N.A.I.C.S.: 423830

NCI Electronics Co., Ltd. (1)
93 Yokoyama-cho, Sukagawa, 962-0041, Fukushima, Japan
Tel.: (81) 248 76 3155
Print Wiring Boards Mfr & Sales
N.A.I.C.S.: 335999

NCI Holding (Thailand) Co., Ltd. (1)
151/9 Moo 2 Soi Pukmitre Suansom, Samrongtai, Phra Pradaeng, 10130, Thailand
Tel.: (66) 21833513
Business Support Services
N.A.I.C.S.: 561499

NCI Vietnam Co., Ltd. (1)
Lot 4 85 86A Noi Bai IZ Quang Tien, Soc Son District, Hanoi, Vietnam
Tel.: (84) 2435820441
Web Site: https://www.ncivn.vn
Business Support Services
N.A.I.C.S.: 561499

NIIKAWA SANKYO Co., LTD. (1)
3428 Higashiozaki, Uozu, 937-0012, Toyama, Japan
Tel.: (81) 765 31 7321
Aluminum Construction Material Mfr & Distr
N.A.I.C.S.: 333120

NIPPON CARBIDE INDIA PVT. LTD. (1)
Plot Number 10 Sector 30A HSIIDC IMT, Rohtak, 124 001, Haryana, India
Tel.: (91) 1262244500
Printed Sticker Mfr & Distr
N.A.I.C.S.: 323111

NIPPON CARBIDE INDUSTRIES (South Carolina) INC. (1)
179 Perimeter Rd, Greenville, SC 29605
Tel.: (864) 277-7717
Toner Resin Mfr & Distr
N.A.I.C.S.: 325211
Allen Mashburn *(Gen Mgr)*

NIPPON CARBIDE INDUSTRIES CO., INC. - Hayatsuki Factory (1)
530 Ojima, Namerikawa, 936-8555, Toyama, Japan
Tel.: (81) 764710211
Electronic & Chemical Product Mfr
N.A.I.C.S.: 334419

Nippon Carbide Industria Do Brasil Ltda. (1)
Av Buriti 3905 Distrito Industrial, Manaus, 69075-000, Brazil
Tel.: (55) 923 616 3450
Stickers Mfr & Distr
N.A.I.C.S.: 323111

Nippon Carbide Industries (Europe) GmbH (1)
Hanns Martin Schleyer Str 34, 47877, Willich, Germany
Tel.: (49) 2154 428605
Web Site: http://www.carbide.com
Emp.: 2
Business Support Services
N.A.I.C.S.: 561499
Sanjeev Madan *(Gen Mgr)*

Nippon Carbide Industries (Hangzhou) Co., Ltd. (1)
No 99 Hongda Road Xiaoshan Economic Technology Development Zone, Qiaonan-Qu, Hangzhou, Zhejiang, China
Tel.: (86) 5718269666
Sheetings & Film Mfr
N.A.I.C.S.: 326112

Nippon Carbide Industries (Netherlands) B.V. (1)
Eisterweg 5, 6422 PN, Heerlen, Netherlands
Tel.: (31) 455429500
Web Site: https://en.nippon-carbide.eu
Business Support Services
N.A.I.C.S.: 561499

Nippon Carbide Industries (Thailand) Co., Ltd. (1)
151/9 Moo 2 Soi Pukmitre Suansom, Samrongtai Phrapradaeng, Samut Prakan, 10130, Thailand
Tel.: (66) 2 183 3513
Web Site: https://www.ncith.co.th
Emp.: 232
Stickers Mfr & Distr
N.A.I.C.S.: 323111

Nippon Carbide Industries (USA), Inc. (1)
13856 Bettencourt St, Cerritos, CA 90703
Tel.: (562) 777-1810
Web Site: https://www.nikkalite.com
Sales Range: $1-9.9 Million
Emp.: 20
Sign Mfr
N.A.I.C.S.: 339950

Nippon Carbide Industries Espana S.A.U. (1)
Can Gener Nave 18 Poligon Industrial Can Roqueta 2, 08202, Sabadell, Barcelona, Spain
Tel.: (34) 933224109
Business Support Services
N.A.I.C.S.: 561499

Nippon Carbide Industries France s.a.s. (1)
Allee des Joncs, 78353, Lentilly, France
Tel.: (33) 134650000
Business Support Services
N.A.I.C.S.: 561499

Nissetsu Co., Ltd. (1)
1-22-11 Shinkawa, Chuo-ku, Tokyo, 104-0033, Kyoto, Japan
Tel.: (81) 362283600
Web Site: https://www.nissetsu.co.jp
Synthetic Resin Mfr & Distr
N.A.I.C.S.: 325991

PT ALVINY INDONESIA (1)
Kawasan Industri EJIP Park Plot 6L, Sukaresmi Cikarang Selatan Kab, Bekasi, 17530, Jawa Barat, Indonesia
Tel.: (62) 218971177
Web Site: http://mail.alviny.co.id
Aluminum Construction Material Mfr & Distr
N.A.I.C.S.: 333120

Sanwa Chemical Co., Ltd. (1)
9-24-8 Tamura, Hiratsuka, 254-0013, Kanagawa, Japan
Tel.: (81) 463550203
Web Site: https://www.sanwa-chemical.co.jp
Emp.: 50
Chemical Products & Medicine Mfr & Sales
N.A.I.C.S.: 325998

Thai Decal Co., Ltd. (1)
151/9 Moo 2 Soi Pukmitre SuanSom, Samrongtai, Phra Pradaeng, 10130, Thailand
Tel.: (66) 21833513
Sticker Mfr & Sales
N.A.I.C.S.: 325520

USK-Human CO., LTD. (1)
751 Honshin, Uozu, 937-0068, Toyama, Japan
Tel.: (81) 765223620
Web Site: https://www.usk-human.jp
Temporary Employment Services
N.A.I.C.S.: 561320

Vinyframe Industry Co., Ltd. (1)
616 Kitaonie, Uozu, 937-8566, Toyama, Japan
Tel.: (81) 765 24 1032
Web Site: http://www.vinyframe.co.jp
Sales Range: $75-99.9 Million
Emp.: 220
Aluminum Building Materials & Resin Products Mfr & Distr & Property & Casualty Insurance Services
N.A.I.C.S.: 331315

NIPPON CARBON CO., LTD.

Akihiro Ishikura *(Chm)*

NIPPON CARBON CO., LTD.
10-7 Hatchobori 1-Chome Chuo-ku, Tokyo, 104-0032, Japan
Tel.: (81) 368913730
Web Site: https://www.carbon.co.jp
Year Founded: 1915
5302—(TKS)
Rev.: $268,477,030
Assets: $556,323,940
Liabilities: $147,365,650
Net Worth: $408,958,290
Earnings: $28,714,500
Emp.: 650
Fiscal Year-end: 12/31/23
Carbon Product Mfr & Distr
N.A.I.C.S.: 335991
Takafumi Miyashita *(CEO)*

Subsidiaries:

Central Carbon Co., Ltd. (1)
11F No 150 ChangAn West Rd Datong-Dist, Taipei, Taiwan
Tel.: (886) 2 2558 5657
Carbon Product Mfr & Distr
N.A.I.C.S.: 335991

NGS Advanced Fibers Co., Ltd. (1)
1-1 Takauchi, Toyama, 939-2254, Japan
Tel.: (81) 764670178
Web Site: http://www.ngs-advanced-fibers.com
Silicon Carbide Mfr
N.A.I.C.S.: 327910

NTC Machining Co., Ltd. (1)
62-6 Nakasone-yama Kawauchi Osatochou, Kurokawa-gun, Miyagi, 981-3514, Japan
Tel.: (81) 223595207
Carbon & Graphite Product Mfr & Distr
N.A.I.C.S.: 335991

NTC Machining Co., Ltd. - Fukuoka Plant (1)
3-1-10 Yurigaoka Umimachi, Kasuya-gun, Fukuoka, 811-2101, Japan
Tel.: (81) 929320993
Carbon Product Mfr & Whslr
N.A.I.C.S.: 335991

NTC Machining Co., Ltd. - Mie Plant (1)
2309 Kawahigashi, Iga-shi, Mie, 519-1424, Japan
Tel.: (81) 595454388
Carbon Product Mfr & Whslr
N.A.I.C.S.: 335991

NTC Machining Co., Ltd. - Miyagi Plant (1)
62-6 Nakasone-yama Kawauchi Osatochou, Kurokawa-gun, Miyagi, 981-3514, Japan
Tel.: (81) 223595207
Carbon Product Mfr & Whslr
N.A.I.C.S.: 335991

Nikka-en Co., Ltd. (1)
126-1 Takakaicho, Ohmihachiman-shi, Shiga, 523-0891, Japan
Tel.: (81) 748377151
Carbon Product Mfr & Whslr
N.A.I.C.S.: 335991

Nippon Carbon Co., Ltd. - Shiga Plant (1)
126-1 Takakaicho, Shiga, Ohmihachiman, Japan
Tel.: (81) 748 37 7151
Carbon Product Mfr & Distr
N.A.I.C.S.: 335991

Nippon Carbon Co., Ltd. - Shirakawa Plant (1)
1-5 Kakurekubo Aza Omotego, Komatsu, 961-0405, Shirakawa, Japan
Tel.: (81) 248 32 4380
Web Site: http://www.carbon.co.jp
Carbon Product Mfr & Distr
N.A.I.C.S.: 335991

Nippon Carbon Co., Ltd. - Toyama Plant (1)
27 Takauchi, Toyama, 939-2254, Japan
Tel.: (81) 76 467 2291

NIPPON CARBON CO., LTD.

Nippon Carbon Co., Ltd.—(Continued)
Carbon Product Mfr & Distr
N.A.I.C.S.: 335991

Nippon Carbon Co., Ltd. - Yamanashi Plant (1)
647 Shimo-Kanogawa, Yamanashi, 405-0017, Japan
Tel.: (81) 553 22 2411
Carbon Product Mfr & Distr
N.A.I.C.S.: 335991

Nippon Carbon Engineering Co., Ltd. (1)
122 Takauchi, Toyama, 939-2254, Japan
Tel.: (81) 76 467 2355
Carbon Product Mfr & Distr
N.A.I.C.S.: 335991

Nippon Carbon Mersen Co., Ltd. (1)
1-23 Shinjuku 4-chome, Shinjuku-ku, Tokyo, 160-0022, Japan
Tel.: (81) 3 5368 3233
Web Site: http://www.ncmersen.jp
Emp.: 10
Carbon Product Mfr & Distr
N.A.I.C.S.: 335991
Osamu Nakamura (Gen Mgr)

Nippon Carbon Shanghai Co., Ltd. (1)
15/F L'Avenue 99 Xian Xia Rd, Chang Ning, Shanghai, China
Tel.: (86) 822160577007
Carbon Product Mfr & Whslr
N.A.I.C.S.: 335991

Nippon Carbon of America, LLC (1)
17706 Rough River Ct, Humble, TX 77346
Tel.: (832) 799-2006
Carbon Product Mfr & Whslr
N.A.I.C.S.: 335991
Mihoko Alford (Pres)

Nippon Kornmeyer Carbon Group GmbH (1)
Im Nassen 3, 53578, Windhagen, Germany
Tel.: (49) 264595250
Web Site: http://www.carbongroup.de
Carbon Based Material Mfr
N.A.I.C.S.: 335991
Oliver Kruss (Mgr-Sls)

Nippon Techno-Carbon Co., Ltd. (1)
62-6 Nakasoneyama Kawauchi, Kurokawa-gun Osato-cho, Miyagi, 981-3514, Japan
Tel.: (81) 223592611
Web Site: http://www.technocarbon.co.jp
Emp.: 130
Semiconductor Crystal & Mechanical Component Mfr
N.A.I.C.S.: 334513

Toho Tanso Kogyo Co., Ltd. (1)
686-3 Ebisunocho Nishi-iru Shinmachi Sichijo-dori, Shimogyo-ku, Kyoto, 600-8310, Japan
Tel.: (81) 75 371 5141
Carbon Product Mfr & Distr
N.A.I.C.S.: 335991

Zhejiang Nippon Techno-Carbon Co., Ltd. (1)
Tianshan Road 36 Huimin-Street, Jiashan, 314100, Zhejiang Sheng, China
Tel.: (86) 573 84292086
Carbon Product Mfr & Distr
N.A.I.C.S.: 335991

NIPPON CARE SUPPLY CO., LTD.
9F Shiba NBF Tower 1-1-30 Shiba-Daimon, Minato-ku, Tokyo, 105-0012, Japan
Tel.: (81) 357330381
Web Site: https://www.caresupply.co.jp
Year Founded: 1998
2393—(TKS)
Rev.: $188,993,120
Assets: $167,900,610
Liabilities: $58,524,940
Net Worth: $109,375,670
Earnings: $10,430,580
Emp.: 1,295
Fiscal Year-end: 03/31/24
Health Care Equipment Whslr
N.A.I.C.S.: 423990
Hiroomi Kaneko (Pres)

NIPPON CERAMIC CO., LTD.
176-17 Hirooka, Tottori, 689-1193, Japan
Tel.: (81) 857533600   JP
Web Site: https://www.nicera.co.jp
Year Founded: 1975
6929—(TKS)
Rev.: $173,343,410
Assets: $410,652,800
Liabilities: $37,499,010
Net Worth: $373,153,790
Earnings: $26,183,370
Emp.: 1,504
Fiscal Year-end: 12/31/23
Semiconductor Mfr
N.A.I.C.S.: 334413
Kiyoshi Honjo (Exec Officer)

Subsidiaries:

Nicera America Corp. (1)
16461 Sherman Way Ste 248, Van Nuys, CA 91306
Tel.: (818) 779-2100
Ceramic Sensor Mfr & Distr
N.A.I.C.S.: 327120

Nicera European Works Ltd. (1)
25 Copinger Close Totton, Southampton, SO40 8WN, Hants, United Kingdom
Tel.: (44) 2380667908
Web Site: http://www.nicera-european.co.uk
Sales Range: $25-49.9 Million
Emp.: 11
Sensor Mfr
N.A.I.C.S.: 334413

Nicera Philippines Inc. (1)
Lot 46 Blk F Subic Techno Park Subic Bay Freeport Zone, Subic, 2222, Zambales, Philippines
Tel.: (63) 472521044
Web Site: http://www.nicera.ph
Sales Range: $50-74.9 Million
Emp.: 300
Ultrasonic Sensor Products Mfr
N.A.I.C.S.: 334513

Nippon Ceramic Co., Ltd. - Nan-ei Factory (1)
176-17 Hirooka, Tottori, 689-1193, Japan
Tel.: (81) 857533600
Web Site: http://www.nicera.co.jp
Sales Range: $100-124.9 Million
Sensor Mfr
N.A.I.C.S.: 334413

NIPPON CHEMI-CON CORPORATION
5-6-4 Osaki, Shinagawa-ku, Tokyo, 141-8605, Japan
Tel.: (81) 354367711
Web Site: https://www.chemi-con.co.jp
Year Founded: 1931
6997—(TKS)
Rev.: $996,391,400
Assets: $1,143,007,810
Liabilities: $788,645,710
Net Worth: $354,362,100
Earnings: $140,733,510
Emp.: 5,796
Fiscal Year-end: 03/31/24
Electronic Components Mfr
N.A.I.C.S.: 334419
Ikuo Uchiyama (Chm & CEO)

Subsidiaries:

CHEMI-CON (MALAYSIA) SDN. BHD. (1)
FIZ Telok Panglima Garang Km15 Jalan Klang Banting, 42507, Kuala Langat, Selangor, Malaysia
Tel.: (60) 331226239
Emp.: 600
Electronic Component Mfr & Distr
N.A.I.C.S.: 334419
Yoshihisa Narita (Mng Dir)

CHEMI-CON ELECTRONICS (KOREA) CO., LTD. (1)
Lotte IT Castle 2-302 98 Gasan digital 2-ro, Geumcheon-gu, Seoul, 085-06, Korea (South)
Tel.: (82) 220826082
Electronic Components Distr
N.A.I.C.S.: 423690

CHEMI-CON ELECTRONICS (THAILAND) CO., LTD. (1)
183 Regent House Floor 14th Rajdamri Road Lumpini, Pathumwan, Bangkok, 10330, Thailand
Tel.: (66) 26519782
Electronic Components Distr
N.A.I.C.S.: 423690

CHEMI-CON FUKUSHIMA CORP. (1)
185-1 Marunouchi, Yabuki-machi Nishi-Shirakawa, Fukushima, 969-0235, Japan
Tel.: (81) 248424101
Electronic Product Mfr & Distr
N.A.I.C.S.: 334419

CHEMI-CON IWATE CORP. (1)
14-40-1 Shimo-Ezuriko, Kitakami, 024-0073, Iwate, Japan
Tel.: (81) 197772231
Electronic Product Mfr & Distr
N.A.I.C.S.: 334419

CHEMI-CON MACHINERY CORP. (1)
1-7-6 Higashi-Ome, Ome, 198-0042, Tokyo, Japan
Tel.: (81) 428243830
Electronic Components Mfr
N.A.I.C.S.: 334419

CHEMI-CON MATERIAL LOGISTICS LTD. (1)
Unit 603-604 6/F Fourseas Building 208-212 Nathan Road, Kowloon, China (Hong Kong)
Tel.: (852) 2333 2219
Logistics Consulting Servies
N.A.I.C.S.: 541614

CHEMI-CON MATERIALS CORP. (1)
9053 Graham Rd N E, Moses Lake, WA 98837
Tel.: (509) 762-8788
Web Site: http://www.cmc-ml.com
Emp.: 50
Aluminum Foil Mfr
N.A.I.C.S.: 331315
Joseph Akers (VP)

CHEMI-CON MIYAGI CORP. (1)
100-1 Karayashiki Tajirinumabe, Osaki, 989-4308, Miyagi, Japan
Tel.: (81) 229391251
Electronic Component Mfr & Distr
N.A.I.C.S.: 334419

CHEMI-CON NAGAOKA CORP. (1)
3-4-12 Shinsan, Nagaoka, 940-2127, Niigata, Japan
Tel.: (81) 258462244
Web Site: https://www.chemi-con.co.jp
Emp.: 79
Electronic Component Mfr & Distr
N.A.I.C.S.: 334419

CHEMI-CON TECHNICAL CENTER (WUXI) LTD. (1)
A-No 15 Changjiang South Road Xinqu, Wuxi, Jiangsu, China
Tel.: (86) 510 8534 2112
Electronic Component Mfr & Distr
N.A.I.C.S.: 334419

CHEMI-CON TRADING (SHENZHEN) CO., LTD. (1)
Rm 1607 No 1777 Chuangye Road Hisense Southern Building, Nanshan District, Shenzhen, 518041, China
Tel.: (86) 75583476810
Electronic Component Mfr & Distr
N.A.I.C.S.: 334419

CHEMI-CON YAMAGATA CORP. (1)
1-1 Saiwai-cho, Nagai, 993-8511, Yamagata, Japan
Tel.: (81) 238842131
Electronic Component Mfr & Distr
N.A.I.C.S.: 334419

INTERNATIONAL PUBLIC

CHEMI-CON YONEZAWA CORP. (1)
2465 Kami Komatsu, Higashi-Okitama, Kawanishi, 999 0121, Yamagata, Japan
Tel.: (81) 238 42 3135
Electronic Component Mfr & Distr
N.A.I.C.S.: 334419

Chemi-Con (Wuxi) Co., Ltd. (1)
No 15 Changjiang South Road, Xinwu District, Wuxi, Jiangsu, China
Tel.: (86) 51085342112
Electronic Components Mfr
N.A.I.C.S.: 334419

Chemi-Con Americas Holding, Inc. (1)
Continental Towers 1701 Golf Rd 1-1200, Rolling Meadows, IL 60008
Tel.: (847) 696-2000
Electronic Components Mfr
N.A.I.C.S.: 334419

DONG GUANG KDK ALUMINUM FOIL MANUFACTURE LTD. (1)
No 57 Huang Jiang Xing Guang Road, Huang Jiang Town, Dongguan, Guangdong, China
Tel.: (86) 76983624698
Electronic Component Mfr & Distr
N.A.I.C.S.: 334419

Europe Chemi-Con (Deutschland) GmbH (1)
Hamburger Strasse 62, 90451, Nuremberg, Germany
Tel.: (49) 91196340
Electronic Component Mfr & Distr
N.A.I.C.S.: 334419

FUKUSHIMA ELECTROLYTIC INDUSTRY CORP. (1)
8086-1 Shimogawara, Kitakata, 966 0000, Fukushima, Japan
Tel.: (81) 241 23 1251
Electronic Component Mfr & Distr
N.A.I.C.S.: 334419

HONG KONG CHEMI-CON LTD. (1)
Room 2101 21/F Chinachem Exchange Square 1 Hoi Wan Street, Quarry Bay, Hong Kong, China (Hong Kong)
Tel.: (852) 25273066
Electronic Component Mfr & Distr
N.A.I.C.S.: 334419
Brendon Lai (Suprv-Sls)

KDK CORP. (1)
5-4-3 Togoshi, Shinagawa-ku, Tokyo, 142-0041, Japan
Tel.: (81) 357502611
Electronic Component Mfr & Distr
N.A.I.C.S.: 334419
Tsuneo Ohta (Pres)

Nichiei Electronics Corp. (1)
20-90-4 Nameshida, Kitakami, 024 0074, Iwate, Japan
Tel.: (81) 197 77 2471
Electronic Component Mfr & Distr
N.A.I.C.S.: 334419

Nippon Chemi-Con Corporation - Niigata Plant (1)
6-5525-21 Higashikou Seiro-machi, Kita-Kanbara, Niigata, 957-0101, Japan
Tel.: (81) 25 256 1251
Web Site: https://www.chemi-con.co.jp
Electronic Component Mfr & Distr
N.A.I.C.S.: 334419

Nippon Chemi-Con Corporation - Takahagi Plant (1)
363 Arakawa, Takahagi, 318-8505, Ibaraki, Japan
Tel.: (81) 293232511
Electronic Components Mfr
N.A.I.C.S.: 334419

P.T.INDONESIA CHEMI-CON (1)
EJIP Industrial Park Plot 4C Cikarang Selatan, Bekasi, 17550, Indonesia
Tel.: (62) 218970070
Electronic Components Mfr
N.A.I.C.S.: 334419
R. Wijaya (Asst Mgr)

Qingdao Samyoung Electronics Co., Ltd. (1)
No 5 Changjiang Road, Export-oriented In-

dustrial Processing Zone, Pingdu, Shandong, China
Tel.: (86) 53258657000
Web Site: https://www.qsamyoung.com
Electronic Component Mfr & Distr
N.A.I.C.S.: 334419

SHANGHAI CHEMI-CON TRADING CO., LTD. (1)
Room18E New Hua Lian Mansion East Bldg No 755 Huai Hai Mid Road, Shanghai, 200020, China
Tel.: (86) 2164454588
Electronic Component Mfr & Distr
N.A.I.C.S.: 334419

SINGAPORE CHEMI-CON (PTE) LTD. (1)
108 Pasir Panjang Road 04-08/09 Golden Agri Plaza, Jurong, Singapore, 118535, Singapore
Tel.: (65) 62682233
Electronic Component Mfr & Distr
N.A.I.C.S.: 334419
Tony Ting (Mgr-IT & IS)

TAIWAN CHEMI-CON CORP. (1)
87-1 Long Shen Road Chin, Puli, 545, Nantou, Taiwan (100%)
Tel.: (886) 49 299 5101
Web Site: https://www.chemi-con.co.jp
Electronic Component Mfr & Distr
N.A.I.C.S.: 334419

United Chemi-Con, Inc. (1)
1701 Golf Rd 1-1200, Rolling Meadows, IL 60008
Tel.: (847) 696-2000
Sales Range: $25-49.9 Million
Emp.: 40
Electronic Components Mfr
N.A.I.C.S.: 334419

NIPPON CHEMICAL INDUSTRIAL CO LTD
9-11-1 Kameido Koto-ku, Tokyo, 136-8515, Japan
Tel.: (81) 336368111
Web Site: https://www.nippon-chem.co.jp
4092—(TKS)
Rev.: $254,736,180
Assets: $505,684,830
Liabilities: $207,924,160
Net Worth: $297,760,670
Earnings: $10,509,900
Emp.: 667
Fiscal Year-end: 03/31/24
Chemical Products & Electronic Materials Mfr & Sales
N.A.I.C.S.: 423690
Hirota Tanahashi (Pres)

Subsidiaries:

JCI USA Inc. (1)
1311 Mamaroneck Ave Ste 145, White Plains, NY 10605-5221
Tel.: (914) 761-6555
Web Site: http://www.jciusa.com
Sales Range: $50-74.9 Million
Emp.: 3
Industrial Chemicals Supplier
N.A.I.C.S.: 424690

Nippon Puretec Co., Ltd. (1)
2-4-15 Nishiki, Naka-ku, Nagoya, 460-0003, Aichi, Japan
Tel.: (81) 522188511
Web Site: http://www.puretec.co.jp
Sales Range: $25-49.9 Million
Emp.: 50
Chemical Filters Mfr & Supplier
N.A.I.C.S.: 325998
Michinori Hashimoto (Pres & CEO)

NIPPON CHEMIPHAR CO., LTD.
2-2-3 Iwamoto-cho Chiyoda-ku, Tokyo, 101-0032, Japan
Tel.: (81) 338631211   JP
Web Site: http://www.chemiphar.co.jp
Year Founded: 1950
4539—(TKS)
Rev.: $203,244,280

Assets: $327,512,280
Liabilities: $205,491,680
Net Worth: $122,020,600
Earnings: ($1,189,800)
Emp.: 887
Fiscal Year-end: 03/31/24
Pharmaceutical Product Mfr & Distr
N.A.I.C.S.: 325412
Kazushiro Yamaguchi (Pres & CEO)

Subsidiaries:

Nihon Pharmaceutical Industry Co., Ltd. (1)
2-2-3 Iwamoto-cho, Chiyoda-ku, Tokyo, 101-0032, Japan
Tel.: (81) 358335011
Emp.: 365
Pharmaceutical Product Mfr & Distr
N.A.I.C.S.: 325412

Safety Research Institute for Chemical Compounds Co., Ltd. (1)
363-24 Mae, Kiyota-ku, Sapporo, 004-0839, Hokkaido, Japan
Tel.: (81) 118855031
Web Site: https://www.ka-anken.co.jp
Emp.: 80
Medical Study & Research Services
N.A.I.C.S.: 541714
Masao Matsuura (Pres)

NIPPON COKE & ENGINEERING CO., LTD.
3-3-3 Toyosu, Koto-ku, Tokyo, 135-6007, Japan
Tel.: (81) 355601311
Web Site: https://www.n-coke.com
Year Founded: 1889
3315—(TKS)
Rev.: $893,354,720
Assets: $930,112,930
Liabilities: $557,606,380
Net Worth: $372,506,550
Earnings: $12,545,780
Emp.: 1,022
Fiscal Year-end: 03/31/24
Coal Mining; Coke, Coal, Cement, Tile, Petroleum & Construction Materials Mfr; Transportation & Resource Development Services
N.A.I.C.S.: 212115
Akihiko Shimizu (Exec Mng Dir)

Subsidiaries:

Araike Machinery Co.,Ltd. (1)
1-20-1 Nishiminatomachi, Fukuoka, Japan
Tel.: (81) 944573939
Industrial Machinery Equipment Mfr
N.A.I.C.S.: 333248

Araike Materials Co.,Ltd., (1)
15-6 Nihonbashi Kabutocho, Chuo-ku, Tokyo, 103-0026, Japan
Tel.: (81) 336690612
Web Site: http://www.ariake-materials.co.jp
Sales Range: $25-49.9 Million
Emp.: 81
Industrial Machinery Equipment Mfr
N.A.I.C.S.: 333248
Masami Matsukizono (Co-Pres)

NIPPON COMPUTER DYNAMICS CO., LTD.
Tokyo Nissan Nishigotanda Building 32-1 Nishigotanda, Shinagawa-Ku, Tokyo, 141-0031, Nishigotanda, Japan
Tel.: (81) 354371021
Web Site: https://www.ncd.co.jp
Year Founded: 1967
4783—(TKS)
Rev.: $198,924,000
Assets: $115,095,200
Liabilities: $71,844,960
Net Worth: $43,250,240
Earnings: $4,433,440
Emp.: 586
Fiscal Year-end: 03/31/22
Information Technology Consulting Services

N.A.I.C.S.: 541512
Osamu Shimojo (Pres & CEO)

NIPPON CONCEPT CORPORATION
8th floor Fukoku Seimei Building 2-2-2 Uchisaiwaicho, Chiyoda-ku, Tokyo, 100-0011, Japan
Tel.: (81) 335078812
Web Site: https://www.n-concept.co.jp
Year Founded: 1994
9386—(TKS)
Rev.: $122,600,280
Assets: $191,018,780
Liabilities: $61,406,490
Net Worth: $129,612,290
Earnings: $17,235,790
Emp.: 211
Fiscal Year-end: 12/31/23
Multimodal Transportation Services
N.A.I.C.S.: 488999
Yasutoshi Yamanaka (VP)

Subsidiaries:

EURO-CONCEPT B.V. (1)
Oosterparkweg 35, 2985 SX, Ridderkerk, Netherlands
Tel.: (31) 180 470480
Web Site: http://www.n-concept.co.jp
Emp.: 10
Multimodal Transportation Services
N.A.I.C.S.: 488999
Bertus Penters (Mng Dir)

Subsidiary (Domestic):

NICHICON EUROPE B.V. (2)
Ooster Park Weg 35, Ridderkerk, 2985 SX, Netherlands
Tel.: (31) 180 470 480
Emp.: 8
Multimodal Transportation Services
N.A.I.C.S.: 488999
Bertus Pencers (Gen Mgr)

Subsidiary (Non-US):

NICHICON UK LIMITED (2)
Southgate House ST Georges Way, Stevenage, SG1 1HG, Herts, United Kingdom
Tel.: (44) 143 874 2144
Multimodal Transportation Services
N.A.I.C.S.: 488999
Steve Spurling (Gen Mgr)

NIPPON CONCEPT AMERICA, LLC. (1)
Ste 218D 2203 Timberloch Pl The Woodlands, Houston, TX 77380
Tel.: (832) 813-8896
Multimodal Transportation Services
N.A.I.C.S.: 488999
Steve Spurling (Gen Mgr)

NIPPON CONCEPT SINGAPORE PTE. LTD. (1)
182 Cecil Street 20-02 Frasers Tower, Singapore, 069547, Singapore
Tel.: (65) 622 515 87
Web Site: http://www.n-concept.co.jp
Emp.: 30
Multimodal Transportation Services
N.A.I.C.S.: 488999

Subsidiary (Non-US):

NIPPON CONCEPT MALAYSIA SDN. BHD. (2)
Lot 37 Jalan Sungai Pinang 5/1 Section 5 Pulau Indah Industrial Park, 42920, Port Klang, Selangor, Malaysia
Tel.: (60) 33 101 3911
Web Site: http://www.n-concept.co.jp
Multimodal Transportation Services
N.A.I.C.S.: 488999

NIPPON CONCRETE INDUSTRIES CO., LTD.
NC Shibaura Building 4-6-14 Shibaura, Minatoku, Tokyo, 108-8560, Japan
Tel.: (81) 334521026
Web Site: https://www.ncic.co.jp

Year Founded: 1948
5269—(TKS)
Rev.: $354,626,500
Assets: $541,986,950
Liabilities: $274,976,000
Net Worth: $267,010,950
Earnings: $4,058,540
Emp.: 1,428
Fiscal Year-end: 03/31/24
Concrete Product Mfr & Distr
N.A.I.C.S.: 327390
Katsuhiko Amiya (Chm)

Subsidiaries:

NC Kaihara Concrete Co., Ltd. (1)
5-1-26 Oimatsucho, Kurashiki, 710-0826, Japan
Tel.: (81) 864255611
Concrete Product Distr
N.A.I.C.S.: 423320

NC Precon Co., Ltd. (1)
1805 Fujino Wake-cho, Wake-gun, Okayama, 709-0412, Japan
Tel.: (81) 869933511
Concrete Products Mfr
N.A.I.C.S.: 327390

NIPPON CRUCIBLE CO., LTD.
Ebisu NR Building 21-3 Ebisu 1-chome, Shibuya-ku, Tokyo, 150-0013, Japan
Tel.: (81) 334435551
Web Site: https://www.rutsubo.com
Year Founded: 1885
5355—(TKS)
Rev.: $63,522,100
Assets: $70,621,240
Liabilities: $35,641,120
Net Worth: $34,980,120
Earnings: $1,883,850
Emp.: 201
Fiscal Year-end: 03/31/24
Refractory Products Mfr
N.A.I.C.S.: 327120

Subsidiaries:

Asia Refractories Co., Ltd. (1)
995-7 Koshikiya, Ageo, 362-0064, Saitama, Japan
Tel.: (81) 487252628
Refractory Products Mfr
N.A.I.C.S.: 327120

NIPPON DENKO CO., LTD.
1-4-16 Yaesu, Chuo-ku, Tokyo, 103-8282, Japan
Tel.: (81) 368606800   JP
Web Site: https://www.nippondenko.co.jp
Year Founded: 1925
5563—(TKS)
Rev.: $541,718,540
Assets: $714,317,500
Liabilities: $207,836,260
Net Worth: $506,481,240
Earnings: $31,018,750
Fiscal Year-end: 12/31/23
Holding Company
N.A.I.C.S.: 551112

Subsidiaries:

Chuo Denki Kogyo Co., Ltd. (1)
Chiyoda First Bldg 3-2-1 Nishikanda, Chiyoda-ku, Tokyo, 101-0065, Japan
Tel.: (81) 3 3514 0511
Web Site: http://www.chu-den.co.jp
Sales Range: $400-449.9 Million
Emp.: 758
Feroalloy, Graphite & Other Specialty Materials Mfr & Whslr; Industrial Waste Incineration Services
N.A.I.C.S.: 331110
Takao Nishino (Pres)

Subsidiary (Domestic):

Chuden Kosan Co., Ltd. (2)
4 Hikari, Kashima, 314-0014, Ibaraki, Japan
Tel.: (81) 299843420
Web Site: http://www.chu-den.co.jp

NIPPON DENKO CO., LTD.

Nippon Denko Co., Ltd.—(Continued)

Emp.: 36
Industrial Waste Collection Services
N.A.I.C.S.: 562112
Takanori Kikuno (Pres)

Chuden Sangyo Co., Ltd. (2)
684-1 Taguchi, Myoko, 949-2106, Niigata, Japan
Tel.: (81) 255 86 3127
Emp.: 50
Civil Engineering & Construction Services
N.A.I.C.S.: 237990
Yoshitaka Gohdo (Pres)

NIPPON DENSETSU KOGYO CO., LTD.

NDK Daini Ikenohata Building 1-2-23 Ikenohata, Taito-ku, Tokyo, 110-8706, Japan
Tel.: (81) 338228811
Web Site: https://www.densetsuko.co.jp
Year Founded: 1942
1950—(TKS)
Rev.: $1,282,544,910
Assets: $1,867,966,170
Liabilities: $551,816,020
Net Worth: $1,316,150,150
Earnings: $66,377,620
Emp.: 2,546
Fiscal Year-end: 03/31/24
Electric Equipment Mfr
N.A.I.C.S.: 336320
Kentaro Egawa (Chm)

NIPPON DRY-CHEMICAL CO., LTD.

6-1-1 Tabata, Kita-ku, Tokyo, Japan
Tel.: (81) 57673551
Web Site: https://www.ndc-group.co.jp
Year Founded: 1955
1909—(TKS)
Rev.: $369,353,580
Assets: $357,131,690
Liabilities: $178,344,410
Net Worth: $178,787,280
Earnings: $21,727,070
Emp.: 1,104
Fiscal Year-end: 03/31/24
Fire Extinguishing Equipment Mfr
N.A.I.C.S.: 922160
Eiichi Tohyama (Pres)

Subsidiaries:

Hokkaido Dry-Chemical Co., Ltd. (1)
2-5-5 Higashisapporo, Shiroishi-ku, Sapporo, 003-0002, Hokkaido, Japan
Tel.: (81) 118236770
Building Disaster Prevention Equipment Mfr
N.A.I.C.S.: 339999

NIPPON ELECTRIC GLASS CO., LTD.

7-1 Seiran 2-chome, Otsu, 520-8639, Shiga, Japan
Tel.: (81) 775371700 JP
Web Site: https://www.neg.co.jp
Year Founded: 1949
5214—(TKS)
Rev.: $1,985,015,660
Assets: $4,990,771,530
Liabilities: $1,515,749,830
Net Worth: $3,475,021,700
Earnings: ($185,672,920)
Emp.: 1,713
Fiscal Year-end: 12/31/23
Specialty Glass Products & Glass-Making Machinery Mfr & Sales
N.A.I.C.S.: 327215
Masayuki Arioka (Chm)

Subsidiaries:

Electric Glass (Guangzhou) Co., Ltd. (1)
No 1 Bida Street High-Tech Industrial Development Zone of Guangzhou, Guangdong, 510530, China
Tel.: (86) 2082557399
Glass Product Mfr & Distr
N.A.I.C.S.: 327215

Electric Glass (Korea) Co., Ltd. (1)
1675-29 Bangchon-ro, Munsan-eup, Paju, 10816, Gyeonggi-do, Korea (South)
Tel.: (82) 31 935 5077
Glass Product Mfr & Distr
N.A.I.C.S.: 327215

Electric Glass (Nanjing) Co., Ltd. (1)
No 37 Guangzhi Road, Qixia District, Nanjing, 210046, Jiangsu, China
Tel.: (86) 2585551987
Glass Product Mfr & Distr
N.A.I.C.S.: 327215

Electric Glass (Shanghai) Co., Ltd. (1)
No 2009 Zhuanxing Road, Xinzhuang Industrial Park Minhang District, Shanghai, 201108, China
Tel.: (86) 2164427707
Glass Product Mfr & Distr
N.A.I.C.S.: 327215

Electric Glass (Xiamen) Co., Ltd. (1)
No 111 Fang Shan Xi Road, Xiamen Torch Hi-Tech Xiang'an Industrial Zone, Xiamen, 361101, Fujian, China
Tel.: (86) 5926016620
Glass Product Mfr & Distr
N.A.I.C.S.: 327215

Electric Glass Fiber NL, B.V. (1)
Energieweg 3, Westerbroek, 9608 PZ, Hoogezand, Netherlands
Tel.: (31) 59 831 3911
Glass Product Mfr & Distr
N.A.I.C.S.: 327215

Electric Glass Fiber UK, Ltd. (1)
Leigh Road, Hindley Green, Wigan, WN2 4XG, United Kingdom
Tel.: (44) 1942257161
Glass Product Mfr & Distr
N.A.I.C.S.: 327215

Nippon Electric Glass (Fuzhou) Co., Ltd. (1)
7-1 Seiran 2-chome, Otsu, Shiga, Japan
Tel.: (81) 775371700
Web Site: http://www.neg.co.jp
Mfr & Supply of High-Technology Glass Products
N.A.I.C.S.: 327215

Nippon Electric Glass (Korea) Co., Ltd. (1)
145 Kongdan dong Gumi, Kyongbuk, 730 030, Korea (South)
Tel.: (82) 544627200
Web Site: http://www.neg.co.jp
Sales Range: $200-249.9 Million
Emp.: 600
Mfr & Supply of High-Technology Glass Products
N.A.I.C.S.: 327215

Nippon Electric Glass (Malaysia) Sdn. Bhd. (1)
Lot 1-7 Lion Industrial Park Persiaran Jubli Perak, PO Box 7216, 40706, Shah Alam, Selangor, Malaysia
Tel.: (60) 355430000
Web Site: http://www.neg.co.jp
Sales Range: $200-249.9 Million
Emp.: 1,000
Mfr & Supply of High-Technology Glass Products
N.A.I.C.S.: 327215

Nippon Electric Glass America, Inc. (1)
1515 E Woodfield Rd Ste 720, Schaumburg, IL 60173-5468
Tel.: (630) 285-8500
Web Site: http://www.negamerica.com
High-Technology Glass Products Mfr
N.A.I.C.S.: 423220

Subsidiary (Domestic):

Electric Glass Fiber America LLC (2)
1515 E Woodfield Rd Ste 720, Schaumburg, IL 60173-5468
Tel.: (630) 285-8500
Timber Product Mfr
N.A.I.C.S.: 322219

Nippon Electric Glass Co., Ltd - Fujisawa Plant (1)
3-7-6 Kugenuma-shinmei 3 Chome, Fujisawa, 251-0021, Kanagawa, Japan
Tel.: (81) 466261211
Glass Products Mfr
N.A.I.C.S.: 327215

Nippon Electric Glass Co., Ltd - Notogawa Plant (1)
906 Ima-cho, Higashi-omi, 521-1295, Shiga, Japan
Tel.: (81) 74 842 2255
Web Site: https://www.neg.co.jp
Glass Products Mfr
N.A.I.C.S.: 327215

Nippon Electric Glass Co., Ltd - Otsu Plant (1)
7-1 Seiran 2 Chome, Otsu, 520-8639, Shiga, Japan
Tel.: (81) 77 537 1700
Web Site: https://www.neg.co.jp
Sales Range: $450-499.9 Million
Glass Products Mfr
N.A.I.C.S.: 327215

Nippon Electric Glass Co., Ltd - Shiga-Takatsuki Plant (1)
1979 Takatsuki Takatsuki-cho, Nagahama, 529-0292, Shiga, Japan
Tel.: (81) 749852233
Glass Products Mfr
N.A.I.C.S.: 327215

Nippon Electric Glass Co., Ltd - Wakasa-Kaminaka Plant (1)
1-1 Wakasa Techno Valley Wakasa-cho, Mikata Kaminaka-gun, Fukui, 919-1552, Japan
Tel.: (81) 770621800
Web Site: http://www.neg.co.jp
Sales Range: $25-49.9 Million
Emp.: 100
Glass Products Mfr
N.A.I.C.S.: 327215

Nippon Electric Glass Co., Ltd. (1)
4-28 Mita 1-Chome, Minato-Ku, Tokyo, 108-0073, Japan
Tel.: (81) 334563511
Web Site: http://www.neg.co.jp
Sales Range: $450-499.9 Million
Mfr & Supply of High-Technology Glass Products
N.A.I.C.S.: 327215

Nippon Electric Glass Europe GmbH (1)
Am Seestern 8, 40547, Dusseldorf, Germany
Tel.: (49) 21141848890
Glass Product Mfr & Distr
N.A.I.C.S.: 327215

Nippon Electric Glass Taiwan Co., Ltd. (1)
No 6 Wei 6th Road, Wuqi District, Taichung, 435, Taiwan
Tel.: (886) 426570099
Glass Product Mfr & Distr
N.A.I.C.S.: 327215

P. T. Nippon Electric Glass Indonesia (1)
Jl Jababeka IV Block V 10 33 V 44-63, Cikarang Indus Est Lem, Bekasi, 17834, Indonesia
Tel.: (62) 218936007
Web Site: http://www.neg.co.jp
Sales Range: $25-49.9 Million
Emp.: 100
Mfr & Supply of High-Technology Glass Products
N.A.I.C.S.: 327215

Paju Electric Glass Co., Ltd. (1)
1695-35 Bangchon-ro, Munsan-eup, Paju, 10816, Gyeonggi-do, Korea (South)
Tel.: (82) 319341012
Glass Product Mfr & Distr
N.A.I.C.S.: 327215

SGS Engineering Co., Ltd. (1)
2-2-17 Seiran, Otsu, 520-0833, Shiga, Japan
Tel.: (81) 77 534 0618
Web Site: https://www.sgs-e.co.jp

INTERNATIONAL PUBLIC

Emp.: 130
Glass Products Mfr
N.A.I.C.S.: 327215
Yoshimasa Kawamura (Sr Dir)

Techneglas LLC (1)
2100 N Wilkinson Way, Perrysburg, OH 43551
Tel.: (419) 873-2000
Web Site: https://www.techneglas.com
Glass Product Mfr & Distr
N.A.I.C.S.: 327215
Jeff Lowry (Pres)

Techneglas, Inc. (1)
707 E Jenkins Ave, Columbus, OH 43207
Tel.: (614) 445-4700
Web Site: http://www.neg.co.jp
Mfr & Supply of High-Technology Glass Products
N.A.I.C.S.: 327212

NIPPON EXPRESS HOLDINGS, INC.

Kanda-Izumicho 2 Chiyoda-ku, Tokyo, Japan
Tel.: (81) 0358011000 JP
Web Site: https://www.nipponexpress-holdings.com
91470—(TKS)
Rev.: $15,287,654,940
Assets: $14,029,976,070
Liabilities: $8,334,202,230
Net Worth: $5,695,773,840
Earnings: $488,866,620
Emp.: 33,664
Fiscal Year-end: 12/31/21
Investment Services
N.A.I.C.S.: 551112
Satoshi Horikiri (Pres & CEO)

Subsidiaries:

Nippon Express Co., Ltd. (1)
2-Kanda Izumimachi, Chiyoda-ku, Tokyo, 101-8647, Japan
Tel.: (81) 358011111
Web Site: https://www.nittsu.co.jp
Rev.: $20,126,607,600
Assets: $15,796,356,400
Liabilities: $9,981,512,640
Net Worth: $5,814,843,760
Earnings: $543,067,360
Emp.: 72,366
Fiscal Year-end: 03/31/2021
International Freight Forwarding & Transportation Services
N.A.I.C.S.: 488510
Satoshi Horikiri (Pres & CEO)

Subsidiary (Non-US):

APC Logistics AB (2)
Soderbyvagen 13, Arlandastad, Sweden
Tel.: (46) 859513200
Freight Transportation Services
N.A.I.C.S.: 488510

Apc Logistics A/S (2)
Oksenoyveien 10 - Bldg B, PO Box 399, 1366, Lysaker, Norway
Tel.: (47) 67118680
Freight Transportation Services
N.A.I.C.S.: 488510

Apc Logistics AB (2)
Bedrijvenzone Machelen Cargo 705 - Unit 8029, 1830, Machelen, Belgium
Tel.: (32) 474426974
Freight Transportation Services
N.A.I.C.S.: 488510

Apc Logistics AB (2)
Teknobulevardi 3-5, 01530, Vantaa, Finland
Tel.: (358) 942457100
Freight Transportation Services
N.A.I.C.S.: 488510

Subsidiary (Domestic):

Bingo Express Co., Ltd. (2)
2-16-18 Nishimachi, Fukuyama, 720-0067, Japan
Tel.: (81) 849212511
Web Site: https://www.bintsu.co.jp
Sales Range: $200-249.9 Million
Emp.: 600

AND PRIVATE COMPANIES

Railway & Motor Freight Forwarding & Warehousing
N.A.I.C.S.: 488510

Careerroad Co., Ltd. (2)
2nd floor Shiba MONT Building 3-3-15
Shiba, Minato-ku, Tokyo, 105-0014, Japan
Tel.: (81) 352322211
Web Site: https://www.careerroad.co.jp
Emp.: 405
Temporary Staffing & Employee Placement Services
N.A.I.C.S.: 561320
Aranai Takashi *(Pres)*

Subsidiary (Non-US):

Franco Vago SpA (2)
Via 8 Marzo 6 Badia a Settimo, 50018, Florence, Italy
Tel.: (39) 055731711
Web Site: https://www.francovago.com
Sales Range: $200-249.9 Million
Emp.: 60
Freight Forwarding Services
N.A.I.C.S.: 488510
Arnaldo Vivoli *(Pres & CEO)*

Subsidiary (US):

Franco Vago International, Inc. (3)
145-68 228th St 2nd Fl, Springfield Gardens, NY 11413
Tel.: (718) 528-5200
Web Site: https://www.francovago.com
Sales Range: $25-49.9 Million
Emp.: 10
Freight Transportation Arrangement
N.A.I.C.S.: 488510
Mark Schneider *(Mng Dir)*

Subsidiary (Non-US):

Map Cargo S.A.S (2)
AK 97 No 24C-80, Distrito Capital, Bogota, 110911, DC, Colombia
Tel.: (57) 14252600
Freight Transportation Services
N.A.I.C.S.: 488510

Subsidiary (US):

Md Express, LLC (2)
1301 Perry Rd Ste 101, Plainfield, IN 46168
Tel.: (317) 838-8900
Freight Transportation Services
N.A.I.C.S.: 488510

Joint Venture (Domestic):

NEC Logistics, Ltd. (2)
1-403 Kosugi-cho Nakahara-ku, Kawasaki, 211-0063, Kanagawa, Japan (51%)
Tel.: (81) 44 733 4629
Web Site: http://www.necl.co.jp
Emp.: 2,120
Logistic Services
N.A.I.C.S.: 541614
Naoki Yoshimura *(Pres)*

Subsidiary (Non-US):

NEC Logistics (Shenzhen) Ltd. (3)
Room 806 Building B, Shenzhen, 518038, China
Tel.: (86) 755 8348 0034
Logistics & Freight Transportation Services
N.A.I.C.S.: 541614

NEC Logistics Hong Kong Limited
Suite 2002 Exchange Tower 33 Wang Chiu Road Kowloon Bay, Kowloon, China (Hong Kong)
Tel.: (852) 2723 1569
Web Site: http://www.nipponexpress-necl.com.hk
Sales Range: $25-49.9 Million
Emp.: 215
Logistics & Warehousing Services
N.A.I.C.S.: 493110

Subsidiary (Non-US):

NEC Logistics (Thailand) Co., Ltd (4)
12th Floor Thaniya Plaza Building 52 Silom Road Kwaeng Suriyawongse, Bangrak, Bangkok, 10500, Thailand
Tel.: (66) 2238 1370
Web Site: http://www.necl.co.th

Emp.: 70
Logistics Consulting Servies
N.A.I.C.S.: 541614

NEC Logistics Singapore Pte. Ltd. (4)
49 Jalan Pemimpin 02-01 APS Industrial Building, Singapore, 577203, Singapore
Tel.: (65) 66039600
Freight Transportation Services
N.A.I.C.S.: 488510

Subsidiary (Non-US):

NEC Logistics Taiwan Ltd. (3)
15th Floor No 181 Fu Hsing North Road, Songshan District, Taipei, 10596, Taiwan
Tel.: (886) 227122465
Freight Shipping Operation Management Services
N.A.I.C.S.: 483111

Nippon Express NEC Logistics (Shanghai) Ltd. (3)
702 7th Floor No 1189 Changning Road, Shanghai, 200051, China
Tel.: (86) 2164451720
Web Site: http://www.nittsu-necl.co.jp
Logistics & Freight Transportation Services
N.A.I.C.S.: 541614

Subsidiary (Non-US):

NEX GLOBAL LOGISTICS DE MEXICO, S.A. DE C.V. (2)
Blvd Bellas Artes 20240 B & C Ciudad Industrial, Delegacion Mesa de Otay, Tijuana, 22444, Baja California, Mexico
Tel.: (52) 6642314808
Logistics Consulting Servies
N.A.I.C.S.: 541614

NEX Global Logistics Korea Co., Ltd. (2)
11F Kyobo Securities B/D 26-4 Yeouido-Dong, Yeoungdeungpo-Gu, Seoul, 150-737, Korea (South)
Tel.: (82) 237753221
Web Site: https://www.nipponexpress.com
Logistics Consulting Servies
N.A.I.C.S.: 541614

NIPPON EXPRESS (RUSSIA) LIMITED LIABILITY COMPANY (2)
2nd Hutorskaya St 38A Bldg No 8, 127287, Moscow, Russia
Tel.: (7) 4956096023
Sales Range: $25-49.9 Million
Emp.: 40
Marine Freight Transportation Services
N.A.I.C.S.: 488510

NIPPON EXPRESS PORTUGAL S.A (2)
Aeroporto De Lisboa Edificio 125 Piso 3 Gab 6 1700, street cibade de vibolama 18A office 38.2, Lisbon, 1800-079, Portugal
Tel.: (351) 218429520
Web Site: https://www.nipponexpress.com
Sales Range: $25-49.9 Million
Emp.: 17
Transportation Services
N.A.I.C.S.: 488999
Carlos Sousa *(Gen Mgr)*

Nep Logistics, Inc (2)
Unit1 Lot 10 Phase4 East Science Ave cor Trade Ave, Binan, Laguna, Philippines
Tel.: (63) 495412668
Freight Transportation Services
N.A.I.C.S.: 488510

Nex Global Engineering Pte. Ltd. (2)
26 Gul Way, Singapore, 629199, Singapore
Tel.: (65) 68616977
Freight Transportation Services
N.A.I.C.S.: 488510

Nippon Express (Australia) Pty. Ltd. (2)
Airgate Business Park 291 Coward Street, PO Box 343, Mascot, 2020, NSW, Australia (100%)
Tel.: (61) 293133500
Web Site: https://www.nittsu.com.au
Sales Range: $25-49.9 Million
Emp.: 40
International Forwarding & Transportation
N.A.I.C.S.: 488510
Shiro Suehiro *(Mng Dir)*

NIPPON EXPRESS HOLDINGS, INC.

Nippon Express (Belgium) N.V./S.A. (2)
Building 16B Business Park, Grace Hologne, 4460, Liege, Belgium (100%)
Tel.: (32) 27530229
Web Site: https://www.nipponexpress.net
Sales Range: Less than $1 Million
Emp.: 94
International Forwarding & Transportation
N.A.I.C.S.: 488510

Nippon Express (Cambodia) Co., Ltd. (2)
The Great Duke Phnom Penh 2nd Floor Regency Complex C Unit No C2/6, Preah Monireth Blvd Tomnoubteouk Khan Chamkarmon, Phnom Penh, Cambodia
Tel.: (855) 23424867
Freight Transportation Services
N.A.I.C.S.: 488510

Nippon Express (China) Co., Ltd. (2)
Room E508-E513 2nd Building of ACLP International Airport North Street, Nanfaxin Shunyi District, Beijing, 101300, China
Tel.: (86) 1061417777
Web Site: https://www.nipponexpress.com
Sales Range: $200-249.9 Million
Emp.: 868
Freight Transportation & Warehousing Services
N.A.I.C.S.: 488510
Shinya Suto *(Dir)*

Subsidiary (Domestic):

Nippon Express (Jiaxing) Co., Ltd. (3)
Rm 415 BoYuang Bldg No 6 DongFang Rd ZhaPu Development Zone, Jiaxing, 314201, ZheJiang, China
Tel.: (86) 57385582422
Web Site: https://www.nipponexpress.com
Sales Range: $25-49.9 Million
Emp.: 3
Warehousing & Distribution Services
N.A.I.C.S.: 493190

Nippon Express (Shanghai) Co., Ltd. (3)
C-12-11F Shanghai Mart No 2299 West Yan-An Road, Shanghai, 200336, China (100%)
Tel.: (86) 2162361888
Web Site: https://www.nipponexpress.com
Sales Range: $100-124.9 Million
Emp.: 350
Air Freight Transportation & Warehousing Services
N.A.I.C.S.: 488510

Nippon Express (Shenzhen) Co., Ltd. (3)
B 105-36 Futian Free Trade Zone, Shenzhen, 518000, China (100%)
Tel.: (86) 75583590001
Web Site: https://www.nipponexpress.com
Emp.: 868
Global Logistics & Consulting Services
N.A.I.C.S.: 488510
Shinya Suto *(Dir)*

Nippon Express (South China) Co., Ltd. (3)
Room 1312 Hongchang Plaza Shennan East Road, Luohu, Shenzhen, Guangdong, China
Tel.: (86) 75522199021
Sales Range: $100-124.9 Million
Emp.: 314
Transportation Services
N.A.I.C.S.: 488999

Nippon Express (Zhuhai) Co., Ltd. (3)
No 1 Ping Dong 5 Road, Nan Pin High-Technology Industry Area, Zhuhai, 519060, Guangdong, China (100%)
Tel.: (86) 7568675511
Web Site: https://www.nipponexpress.com
Sales Range: $1-9.9 Million
Emp.: 100
Provider of Freight Transportation & Warehousing Services
N.A.I.C.S.: 488510

Nittsu Sinotrans Logistic Dalian Ltd. (3)
No 6 Haitian Rd Free Trade Zone of Dalian,

Dalian, 116600, China (50%)
Tel.: (86) 41187316830
Web Site: https://www.nipponexpress.com
Sales Range: $25-49.9 Million
Emp.: 100
Freight Transportation & Warehousing Services
N.A.I.C.S.: 488510

Subsidiary (Non-US):

Nippon Express (Deutschland) GmbH (2)
Marie-Bernays-Ring 23, 41199, Monchengladbach, Germany (100%)
Tel.: (49) 21669660
Web Site: https://www.nipponexpress.net
Sales Range: $1-9.9 Million
Emp.: 150
Air Freight Consolidation, Ocean Freight Forwarding, Warehousing
N.A.I.C.S.: 488510
Yoshiaki Ishii *(Mng Dir)*

Subsidiary (Domestic):

NEX Logistics Europe GmbH (3)
Marie-Bernays-Ring 23, 41199, Monchengladbach, Germany
Tel.: (49) 227283900
Web Site: https://www.nipponexpress.com
Sales Range: $10-24.9 Million
Emp.: 30
Warehousing Services
N.A.I.C.S.: 493190

Subsidiary (Non-US):

Nippon Express (Deutschland) GmbH (2)
Str Ciprian Porumbescu No 12 2nd Floor, Timisoara, Romania
Tel.: (40) 256223037
Freight Transportation Services
N.A.I.C.S.: 488510

Nippon Express (Deutschland) GmbH (2)
Warsaw Distribution Center Building B ul Szyszkowa 35/37, 02-285, Warsaw, Poland
Tel.: (48) 228783200
Freight Transportation Services
N.A.I.C.S.: 488510

Nippon Express (Deutschland) GmbH (2)
Airport Business Park Unit B4 Lorinci ut 61, 2220, Vecses, Hungary
Tel.: (36) 29553800
Freight Transportation Services
N.A.I.C.S.: 488510

Nippon Express (Deutschland) GmbH (2)
Za Trati 236, 252 19, Chrastany, Czech Republic
Tel.: (420) 255707400
Freight Transportation Services
N.A.I.C.S.: 488510

Nippon Express (Deutschland) GmbH (2)
Obj 293 ALC Nord 2 Bauteil 2, Flughafen, 1300, Vienna, Austria
Tel.: (43) 1700735416
Freight Transportation Services
N.A.I.C.S.: 488510

Nippon Express (H.K.) Co., Ltd. (2)
Room 1101 Chinachem Golden Plaza 77 Mody Road, Tsim Sha Tsui East, Kowloon, 999077, China (Hong Kong) (100%)
Tel.: (852) 27232272
Web Site: https://www.nipponexpress.com
Sales Range: $200-249.9 Million
Emp.: 1,000
Air Freight Consolidation, Ocean Freight Forwarding, Warehousing
N.A.I.C.S.: 488510

Subsidiary (Domestic):

Nippon Express Travel (H.K.) Co., Ltd. (3)
1101 Chinachem Golden Plz 77 Mody Rd Tsim Sha Tsui E, Kowloon, China (Hong Kong) (100%)
Tel.: (852) 27237689
Web Site: https://www.nipponexpress.com

NIPPON EXPRESS HOLDINGS, INC.

Nippon Express Holdings, Inc.—(Continued)
Sales Range: $125-149.9 Million
Emp.: 900
Travel Services
N.A.I.C.S.: 561510

Subsidiary (Non-US):

Nippon Express (India) Private Limited (2)
The Millenia Tower B 3rd Floor Unit No 302 No 1 & 2 Murphy Road, Ulsoor, Bengaluru, 560 008, India
Tel.: (91) 8049475600
Web Site: https://www.nipponexpress.com
Logistics Consulting Servies
N.A.I.C.S.: 541614

Nippon Express (Ireland) Ltd. (2)
Unit 6 Plato Business Park, Damastown Mulhuddart, Dublin, 15, Ireland **(100%)**
Tel.: (353) 12249200
Web Site: https://www.nipponexpress.com
Sales Range: $25-49.9 Million
Emp.: 15
Provider of Freight Transportation Services
N.A.I.C.S.: 488510

Nippon Express (Istanbul) Global Logistics A. S. (2)
Istanbul Dunya Ticaret Merkezi A 2 Blok Kat 3 No 162, Bakirkoy, 34149, Istanbul, Turkiye
Tel.: (90) 2124656934
Sales Range: $25-49.9 Million
Emp.: 9
Logistics Consulting Servies
N.A.I.C.S.: 541614
Yasuo Iwado *(Gen Mgr)*

Nippon Express (Italia) S.R.L. (2)
Via Londra 12, 20090, Segrate, MI, Italy
Tel.: (39) 02216981
Web Site: https://www.nipponexpress.com
Sales Range: $25-49.9 Million
Emp.: 80
Logistics & Transportation Services
N.A.I.C.S.: 541614

Nippon Express (Malaysia) Sdn. Bhd. (2)
Lot 72 Persiaran Jubli Perak Seksyen 22, 40300, Shah Alam, Selangor, Malaysia
Tel.: (60) 350331111
Web Site: https://www.nipponexpress.com
Sales Range: $125-149.9 Million
Emp.: 1,000
Air Freight Consolidation, Ocean Freight Forwarding
N.A.I.C.S.: 488510
Hideaki Shigematsu *(Pres)*

Subsidiary (Domestic):

Nittsu Transport Service (M) Sdn. Bhd. (3)
Lot 4286 Batu 12 Jalan Balakong, 43300, Seri Kembangan, Selangor Darul Ehsan, Malaysia
Tel.: (60) 389433388
Web Site: https://www.nipponexpress.com
Sales Range: $50-74.9 Million
Emp.: 200
Transportation Services
N.A.I.C.S.: 488999

Subsidiary (Non-US):

Nippon Express (Middle East) LLC (2)
Airlink Jebel Ali Logistics Centre, PO Box 17341, Jebel Ali, Dubai, United Arab Emirates
Tel.: (971) 48832688
Web Site: https://www.nipponexpress.com
Logistics Consulting Servies
N.A.I.C.S.: 541614

Nippon Express (Myanmar) Co., Ltd. (2)
Room No 201 Bo Myat Tun Tower B Bo Myat Tun Street, Corner of MahaBandoola Road and Bo Myat Tun Street Botataung Township, Yangon, Myanmar
Tel.: (95) 1290578
Freight Transportation Services
N.A.I.C.S.: 488510

Nippon Express (Nederland) B.V. (2)
Cessnalaan 24, 1119 NL, Schiphol-Rijk, Netherlands
Tel.: (31) 204066500
Sales Range: $25-49.9 Million
Emp.: 60
Air Freight Consolidation, Ocean Freight Forwarding, Warehousing
N.A.I.C.S.: 488510
R. Drejsen *(VP)*

Subsidiary (Domestic):

Nippon Express Euro Cargo B.V. (3)
Cessnalaan 24, 1119 NL, Schiphol-Rijk, Netherlands **(100%)**
Tel.: (31) 205005100
Web Site: https://www.nipponexpress.com
Sales Range: $25-49.9 Million
N.A.I.C.S.: 488510
Eline Imamse *(Mgr-Admin)*

Nippon Express Tours (Nederland) B.V. (3)
Cessnalaan 24, 1119 NL, Amstelveen, Netherlands **(100%)**
Tel.: (31) 206404020
Web Site: https://www.nipponexpresstours.nl
Sales Range: $25-49.9 Million
Emp.: 10
N.A.I.C.S.: 488510

Subsidiary (Non-US):

Nippon Express (New Zealand) Ltd. (2)
37 Andrew Baxter Drive Auckland Int'l Airport, Airport Oaks, Mangere, 2022, Manukau, New Zealand **(100%)**
Tel.: (64) 92560340
Web Site: https://www.nipponexpress.com
Sales Range: $25-49.9 Million
Emp.: 12
Provider of Freight Transportation Services
N.A.I.C.S.: 488510
Hiroyuki Kameyema *(Branch Mgr)*

Nippon Express (Philippines) Corporation (2)
Lot 85 A & B Avocado Road Food Terminal Inc Complex East Service Road, Taguig, 1630, Philippines **(100%)**
Tel.: (63) 288391111
Freight Transportation Services
N.A.I.C.S.: 488510

Nippon Express (Schweiz) AG (2)
Grindelstrasse 19, 8303, Bassersdorf, Switzerland **(100%)**
Tel.: (41) 448369966
Web Site: https://www.nipponexpress.ch
Sales Range: $25-49.9 Million
Emp.: 15
Freight Forwarding & Shipping Services
N.A.I.C.S.: 488510
Beat Hoegger *(Mng Dir)*

Nippon Express (Singapore) Pte., Ltd. (2)
26 Gul Way, Singapore, 629199, Singapore **(100%)**
Tel.: (65) 68616977
Web Site: https://www.nittsu-singapore.com
Sales Range: $125-149.9 Million
Emp.: 505
IT Technology, Logistics, E-Travel, Air & Sea Freight Forwarding
N.A.I.C.S.: 488510
Shuji Kojima *(Mng Dir)*

Nippon Express (South Asia & Oceania) Pte. Ltd. (2)
Level 12 1229 Parkland Building No 33 Park Street, Colombo, 00200, Sri Lanka
Tel.: (94) 117439229
Freight Transportation Services
N.A.I.C.S.: 488510

Nippon Express (South Asia & Oceania) Pte. Ltd. (2)
734 7th Floor Executive Towers Dolmen Mall Clifton, Karachi, Pakistan
Tel.: (92) 2135826135
Freight Transportation Services
N.A.I.C.S.: 488510

Nippon Express (South Asia & Oceania) Pte. Ltd. (2)
Grand Floor SAVAN-SENO SEZ Authority Office Road No 9, Nakae Village Kaisone Phomvihane District, Savannakhet, Lao People's Democratic Republic
Tel.: (856) 2056112470
Freight Transportation Services
N.A.I.C.S.: 488510

Nippon Express (Suzhou) Co., Ltd. (2)
No 622 Changjiang Rd, Suzhou New District, Suzhou, 215011, Jiangsu, China
Tel.: (86) 51266650979
Freight Transportation Services
N.A.I.C.S.: 488510

Nippon Express (Taiwan) Co., Ltd. (2)
14F No 285 Section 4 Chung Hsiao E Rd, Da-an District, Taipei, 10692, Taiwan
Tel.: (886) 227521010
Web Site: https://www.nittsu.com.hk
Sales Range: $50-74.9 Million
Emp.: 150
Freight Transportation Services
N.A.I.C.S.: 488510

Nippon Express (Thailand) Co., Ltd. (2)
2032 3rd Floor 4th Floor 2034/86 19th Floor Italthai Tower New, Petchburi Road Bangkapi Huaykwang, Bangkok, 10310, Thailand **(100%)**
Tel.: (66) 20807555
Web Site: https://www.nipponexpress.co.th
Sales Range: $125-149.9 Million
Emp.: 300
Provider of Freight Transportation Services
N.A.I.C.S.: 488510

Subsidiary (Domestic):

Hi-Tech Nittsu (Thailand) Co., Ltd. (3)
Banwak EPZ Hi Tech 129 Moo 5 Asia Rd Km 60 61 Banwah Bang Pa In, Ayutthaya, 13160, Thailand **(60%)**
Tel.: (66) 35350046
Web Site: https://www.nittsu.co.th
Sales Range: $50-74.9 Million
Emp.: 250
N.A.I.C.S.: 488510

Nippon Express Engineering (Thailand) Co., Ltd. (3)
2032 3rd Floor Italthai Tower New Petchburi Road, Bangkapi Huaykwang, Bangkok, 10310, Thailand
Tel.: (66) 20807698
Web Site: https://www.nipponexpress.com
Sales Range: $10-24.9 Million
Emp.: 30
Construction Engineering Services
N.A.I.C.S.: 541330

Subsidiary (Non-US):

Nippon Express (U.K.), Ltd. (2)
Heathrow 360 2 Millington Road, Hayes, UB3 4AZ, Middlesex, United Kingdom **(100%)**
Tel.: (44) 2087374300
Web Site: https://www.nipponexpress.com
Sales Range: $50-74.9 Million
Emp.: 250
Air Freight Consolidation, Ocean Freight Forwarding, Warehousing
N.A.I.C.S.: 488510

Nippon Express (Vietnam) Co., Ltd. (2)
R 5 2-5 3 Etown 364 Cong Hoa Street, Tan Binh District, 700000, Ho Chi Minh City, Vietnam
Tel.: (84) 2838122922
Web Site: https://www.nipponexpress.com
Sales Range: $25-49.9 Million
Emp.: 90
Transportation Services
N.A.I.C.S.: 488999
Shirai Masakazu *(Gen Mgr)*

Nippon Express (Xiamen) Co., Ltd. (2)
D-202B International Shipping Center NO 97 Xiangyu Road, Xiamen, 361006, China
Tel.: (86) 5925680202
Freight Transportation Services
N.A.I.C.S.: 488510

Nippon Express (Xian) Co., Ltd. (2)
A2-9 Xi'an Integrated Bonded Zone 88 Gangwu Avenue, Xi'an International Trade & Logistics Park, Xi'an, 710026, China
Tel.: (86) 2987203302
Freight Transportation Services
N.A.I.C.S.: 488510

Nippon Express Automotive Logistics (China) Co., Ltd. (2)
2nd Floor Building A3 No 8 Zhishan Road Donggu Street, Huangpu District, Guangzhou, 510530, Guangdong, China
Tel.: (86) 75522199021
Freight Transportation Services
N.A.I.C.S.: 488510

Nippon Express Bangladesh Ltd. (2)
Arzed Chamber 2nd Floor 13 Mohakhali C/A, Dhaka, 1212, Bangladesh
Tel.: (880) 29897759
Overseas Removal Services
N.A.I.C.S.: 484210

Nippon Express Canada, Ltd. (2)
6250 Edwards Boulevard, Mississauga, L5T 2X3, ON, Canada **(100%)**
Tel.: (905) 565-7525
Web Site: https://www.nipponexpress.com
Sales Range: $25-49.9 Million
Emp.: 100
Air Freight Consolidation, Ocean Freight Forwarding, Customs Clearance
N.A.I.C.S.: 488510

Subsidiary (Domestic):

Nippon Express Capital Co., Ltd. (2)
1-9-3 Higashishimbashi, Minato-Ku, Tokyo, 105-0021, Japan
Tel.: (81) 362516570
Financial Management Services
N.A.I.C.S.: 523999

Subsidiary (Non-US):

Nippon Express Cargo Service (Shenzhen) Co.,Ltd. (2)
lock 1 HESC Building Southwest of Mingzhu-Shenyan Intersection, Yantian District, Shenzhen, China
Tel.: (86) 75525281688
Freight Transportation Services
N.A.I.C.S.: 488510

Nippon Express Engineering (Vietnam) Co., Ltd. (2)
Land plot CN5 6B, Dinh Vu Industrial Zone Dong Hai 2 Ward Hai An District, Haiphong, Vietnam
Tel.: (84) 2258830190
Freight Transportation Services
N.A.I.C.S.: 488510

Nippon Express Europe GmbH (2)
4th Floor Laiboni Centre Lenana Road, Kilimani, Nairobi, 00101, Kenya
Tel.: (254) 204938310
Freight Transportation Services
N.A.I.C.S.: 488510

Nippon Express Europe GmbH (2)
Am Wehrhahn 33, 40211, Dusseldorf, Germany
Tel.: (49) 211175400
Freight Transportation Services
N.A.I.C.S.: 488510

Nippon Express France S.A.S. (2)
1 Rue Du Chapelier, BP 18177, Roissy-en-France, 95702, Paris, France **(100%)**
Tel.: (33) 141846363
Web Site: https://www.nipponexpress.net
Sales Range: $50-74.9 Million
Emp.: 200
International Forwarding & Transportation
N.A.I.C.S.: 488510

Nippon Express France, S.A.S (2)
Parc Industrie de la CFCIM de Bouskoura Lot N 94 Etage 1 Bureau N 4, 27182, Bouskoura, Morocco
Tel.: (212) 661934240
Freight Transportation Services
N.A.I.C.S.: 488510

Nippon Express Global SCM (Shanghai) Co. Ltd. (2)
No 168 Xinji Road, Shanghai, 201707, China
Tel.: (86) 3269238811
Freight Transportation Services

AND PRIVATE COMPANIES

N.A.I.C.S.: 488510

Nippon Express Korea Co., Ltd. (2)
11F Kyobo Securities B/D 26-4 Yeouido-Don, Yeoungdeungpo-gu, Seoul, 150-737, Korea (South)
Tel.: (82) 237751211
Freight Transportation Services
N.A.I.C.S.: 488510
Sugi Yasuhiro *(CEO)*

Subsidiary (US):

Nippon Express U.S.A., Inc. (2)
24-01 44th Rd 14th Fl, Long Island City, NY 11101 **(100%)**
Tel.: (212) 758-6100
Web Site: https://www.nipponexpressusa.com
Sales Range: $50-74.9 Million
Emp.: 40
Air Freight Consolidation Ocean Freight Forwarding Customs Clearance
N.A.I.C.S.: 488510

Subsidiary (Domestic):

Associated Global Systems, Inc. (3)
3333 New Hyde Park Rd, New Hyde Park, NY 11042-1205
Tel.: (516) 627-8910
Web Site: https://www.agsystems.com
Sales Range: $100-124.9 Million
Freight Transportation, Logistics, Warehousing & Supply Chain Management
N.A.I.C.S.: 488510
Michael J. Occhicone *(COO & Exec VP)*

MD Logistics, Inc. (3)
1301 Perry Rd Ste 101, Plainfield, IN 46168
Tel.: (317) 838-8900
Web Site: https://www.mdlogistics.com
Sales Range: $500-549.9 Million
Emp.: 270
General Warehousing & Storage
N.A.I.C.S.: 493110
Jeffrey Luthman *(VP-Bus Dev)*

NEX Transport, Inc. (3)
13900 OH-287, East Liberty, OH 43319
Tel.: (937) 642-8333
Web Site: https://nextransportinc.com
Sales Range: $75-99.9 Million
Emp.: 800
Warehousing & Freight Packaging
N.A.I.C.S.: 492210
Bonnie Carver *(Mgr-HR)*

Nippon Express Hawaii, Inc. (3)
3375 Koapaka St D-153, Honolulu, HI 96819
Tel.: (808) 833-0202
Web Site: https://www.nipponexpressusa.com
Sales Range: $25-49.9 Million
International Forwarding & Transportation
N.A.I.C.S.: 488510

Nippon Express Travel U.S.A., Inc. (3)
535 Pacific Avenue Suite B, San Francisco, CA 94123
Tel.: (415) 421-1822
Sales Range: $75-99.9 Million
Emp.: 22
Travel Services
N.A.I.C.S.: 561510

Subsidiary (Non-US):

Nippon Express USA, Inc. (2)
Parque Industrial Sur Flex 3 Oficina 12, Panama, Panama
Tel.: (507) 3020188
Freight Transportation Services
N.A.I.C.S.: 488510

Nippon Express de Espana, S.A. (2)
Centro de Carga Aerea Aeropuerto de Barajas Parcela 2 1 Nave 2, 28042, Madrid, Spain **(100%)**
Tel.: (34) 917480840
Web Site: https://www.nipponexpress.es
Sales Range: $25-49.9 Million
Emp.: 30
Freight Forwarding & Shipping Services
N.A.I.C.S.: 488510
Sumiko Kaku *(Gen Mgr)*

Nippon Express de Mexico, S.A. de C.V. (2)
Insurgentes Sur 1271 Piso 12 Oficina 1201, Col Extremadura Insurgentes Alcaldia Benito Juarez, 03740, Mexico, Mexico **(100%)**
Tel.: (52) 5588821380
Web Site: https://www.nippon.com.mx
Sales Range: $25-49.9 Million
Emp.: 100
N.A.I.C.S.: 488510
Masato Tanave *(Gen Mgr)*

Nippon Express do Brasil (2)
Rua Fortaleza 53, Bela Vista, Sao Paulo, SP, Brazil **(100%)**
Tel.: (55) 1135833850
Web Site: https://www.nipponexpress.com
Sales Range: $25-49.9 Million
Emp.: 50
Air Freight Consolidation, Ocean Freight Forwarding
N.A.I.C.S.: 488510
Taisuke Fujishiro *(Pres)*

Subsidiary (Domestic):

Nippon Shipping Co., Ltd. (2)
12-19 Sotokanda 3-chome Chiyoda-ku, Tokyo, 101-8617, Japan
Tel.: (81) 352945861
Web Site: https://www.nipponexphiress.com
Sales Range: $50-74.9 Million
Emp.: 250
Marine, Harbor & Coastal Transportation
N.A.I.C.S.: 488510

Nittsu Driving School Co., Ltd. (2)
15-1 Miyamae, Suginami-ku, Tokyo, 168-0081, Japan
Tel.: (81) 333352222
Web Site: https://www.nittsu-ds.co.jp
Car Driving School Services
N.A.I.C.S.: 611692

Subsidiary (Non-US):

Nittsu Logistics (India) Private Limited (2)
Logistics Park Plot No 7 Road No 10 Export Promotion Industrial Park, Whitefield, Bengaluru, 560066, India
Tel.: (91) 8041353500
Sales Range: $25-49.9 Million
Emp.: 70
Logistics Consulting Servies
N.A.I.C.S.: 541614

Nittsu Logistics (Thailand) Co., Ltd. (2)
2032 4th Floor Italthai Tower New Petchburi Road, Bangkapi Huaykwang, Bangkok, 10310, Thailand
Tel.: (66) 20807666
Freight Transportation Services
N.A.I.C.S.: 488510

Nittsu Logistics Myanmar Co., Ltd. (2)
Lot No A-9 Thilawa SEZ Zone A Yangon Region, Yangon, Myanmar
Tel.: (95) 12309147
Freight Transportation Services
N.A.I.C.S.: 488510

Subsidiary (Domestic):

Nittsu Real Estate Co., Ltd. (2)
1-9-3 Higashi Shinbashi, Minato-ku, Tokyo, 105-0021, Japan
Tel.: (81) 362516421
Web Site: https://www.nittsufudosan.co.jp
Sales Range: $100-124.9 Million
Emp.: 370
Real Estate, Housing Construction
N.A.I.C.S.: 236220

Nittsu Research Institute and Consulting,Inc. (2)
1-9-3 Higashi-shimbashi, Minato-ku, Tokyo, 105-8322, Japan
Tel.: (81) 362516446
Web Site: https://www.nittsu-soken.co.jp
Emp.: 76
Logistics Research Services
N.A.I.C.S.: 541614

Nittsu Sapporo Unyu Co., Ltd. (2)
5 3 15 Ryutsu Ctr, Shiroishi Ku, Sapporo, 003 0030, Japan
Tel.: (81) 8618111

Sales Range: $200-249.9 Million
Emp.: 670
Motor Freight Forwarding
N.A.I.C.S.: 488510

Nittsu Shoji Co., Ltd. (2)
1-14-22 Kaigan, Minato-ku, Tokyo, 101-8617, Japan
Tel.: (81) 367348800
Web Site: https://www.nittsushoji.co.jp
Sales Range: $450-499.9 Million
Emp.: 2,472
General Trading Company; Sales of Propane Gas & Petroleum, Leasing, Export Packaging, Etc.
N.A.I.C.S.: 457210

Subsidiary (Non-US):

PT. Nex Logistics Indonesia (2)
Jl Teuku Umar KM 44 RT 002 / RW 05 Telaga Asih, Gobel Industrial Estate Cikarang Barat Kab, Bekasi, 17530, West Java, Indonesia
Tel.: (62) 2189527123
Freight Transportation Services
N.A.I.C.S.: 488510

PT. Nittsu Lemo Indonesia Logistik (2)
Jl Roya Cakung Cilincing Kav 14, Cakung Timur, Jakarta, 13910, Indonesia **(95%)**
Tel.: (62) 2146823912
Web Site: https://www.nittsu.com.hk
Sales Range: $50-74.9 Million
Emp.: 150
Freight Transportation & Warehousing Services
N.A.I.C.S.: 488510

Shanghai-Etechnology Co., Ltd. (2)
3rd Floor No 126, Shanghai, 200436, China
Tel.: (86) 2160731437
Web Site: https://www.shanghai-etech.com.cn
Software Development Services
N.A.I.C.S.: 541511

Traconf S.R.L. (2)
Via Dell'Industria 8/10/12, Sona, 37060, Verona, Italy
Tel.: (39) 0456083111
Freight Transportation Services
N.A.I.C.S.: 488510

NIPPON FELT CO., LTD.

1-7-1 Akabane West, Kita-ku, Tokyo, 115-0055, Japan
Tel.: (81) 359932030
Web Site: https://www.felt.co.jp
Year Founded: 1917
3512—(TKS)
Rev.: $66,642,020
Assets: $165,712,700
Liabilities: $31,093,440
Net Worth: $134,619,260
Earnings: $3,219,070
Fiscal Year-end: 03/31/24
Net Mfr
N.A.I.C.S.: 313230

Subsidiaries:

Higashiyama Felt Co., LTD. (1)
88-1 Nozuchi Takozu Higashiyama-cho, Ichinoseki, 029-0301, Iwate, Japan
Tel.: (81) 191472511
Felt Product Mfr
N.A.I.C.S.: 313230

Nippon Felt Co., Ltd. - Saitama Mill (1)
88 Haramamuro, Konosu, 365-0043, Saitama, Japan
Tel.: (81) 485413663
Felt Product Mfr
N.A.I.C.S.: 313230

Nippon Felt Co., Ltd. - Tochigi Mill (1)
1467 Sabui, Otawara, 324-0246, Tochigi, Japan
Tel.: (81) 287544172
Felt Product Mfr
N.A.I.C.S.: 313230

Taiwan Felt Co., LTD. (1)
No 342 Heping Rd, Bade District, Taoyuan, 334, Taiwan
Tel.: (886) 336636637
Pet Product Distr
N.A.I.C.S.: 424990

NIPPON FILCON CO., LTD.

2220 Daimaru, Inagi, Tokyo, 206-8577, Japan
Tel.: (81) 423775711
Web Site: https://www.filcon.co.jp
Year Founded: 1916
5942—(TKS)
Rev.: $198,420,740
Assets: $303,615,070
Liabilities: $139,439,030
Net Worth: $164,176,040
Earnings: $9,004,300
Emp.: 1,281
Fiscal Year-end: 11/30/23
Nonwoven Fabric Product Mfr
N.A.I.C.S.: 313230
Hiroyuki Nagura *(Pres)*

Subsidiaries:

Aqua Product Corporation (1)
2F JS Ichigaya Bldg 5-1 Gobancho, Chiyoda-ku, Tokyo, 102-0076, Japan
Tel.: (81) 352761155
Web Site: https://www.aquaproduct.co.jp
Water Treatment Equipment Mfr
N.A.I.C.S.: 333310
Noriaki Hino *(Chm)*

DIA ENTERPRISE LIMITED (1)
3-26 Shinden-Nakamachi, Daito, Osaka, 574-0056, Japan
Tel.: (81) 728007260
Web Site: http://www.dia-web.com
Steel Wire Mfr & Distr
N.A.I.C.S.: 331110

FILCON Europe SARL (1)
Le Neos 1 rue Icare, 67960, Entzheim, France
Tel.: (33) 388511955
Fabric Product Distr
N.A.I.C.S.: 424310

FILCON FABRICS & TECHNOLOGY CO., LTD. (1)
289 Moo 7 T Thatoom A, Si Maha Phot, Prachinburi, Thailand
Tel.: (66) 37625368
Fabric Product Distr
N.A.I.C.S.: 424310

Filcon America, Inc. (1)
4900 SW Griffith Dr Ste 271, Beaverton, OR 97005
Tel.: (503) 644-0480
Fabric Product Distr
N.A.I.C.S.: 424310

Kansai Wire Netting Co., Ltd. (1)
7-8 Inari 2-chome, Naniwa-ku, Osaka, 556-0023, Japan
Tel.: (81) 6 6562 1281
Web Site: http://www.kwn.co.jp
Wire Mesh Product Mfr
N.A.I.C.S.: 331110
Hideaki Tanikawa *(Pres & CEO)*

Subsidiary (Non-US):

International Mesh Products Pte. Ltd. (2)
60 Paya Lebar Road 10-27 Paya Lebar Square, Singapore, 409051, Singapore
Tel.: (65) 64352425
Web Site: http://www.imp.com.sg
Emp.: 4
Stainless Steel Mfr & Distr
N.A.I.C.S.: 331110
Hideaki Tanikawa *(Pres & CEO)*

Subsidiary (US):

Kansai U.S.A. Corporation (2)
18134 Brookes Bend, Houston, TX 77094
Tel.: (281) 647-6855
Wire Net Product Distr
N.A.I.C.S.: 423390
Naohiko Uehara *(Gen Mgr)*

Plant (Domestic):

Kansai Wire Netting Co., Ltd. - Amagasaki Factory (2)

NIPPON FILCON CO., LTD.

Nippon Filcon Co., Ltd.—(Continued)
2-38 Ohama-cho, Amagasaki, 660-0095, Hyogo, Japan
Tel.: (81) 664307612
Wire Mesh Product Mfr
N.A.I.C.S.: 331110

Kansai Wire Netting Co., Ltd. - Osaka Factory (2)
14-11 Dezaike-cho, Kawanishi, 666-0011, Hyogo, Japan
Tel.: (81) 727591015
72 759 1015
N.A.I.C.S.: 331110

Kansai Wire Netting Co., Ltd. - Tokyo Factory (2)
1489 Koda, Bando, 306-0606, Ibaraki, Japan
Tel.: (81) 297 35 5511
Wire Mesh Product Mfr
N.A.I.C.S.: 331110

Subsidiary (Non-US):

Kansai Wire Netting Technology (Kunshan) Co., Ltd. (2)
No 268 Jinsong Road high-tech zone, yushan, Kunshan, Jiangsu, China
Tel.: (86) 51257562284
Web Site: https://www.en.ktk-cn.com
Industrial Supplies Whslr
N.A.I.C.S.: 423840

Siam Wire Netting Co., Ltd. (2)
Northern Region Industrial Estate 89/2 Moo 4 Highway No 11 Tambol, Amphur Muang, Lamphun, 51000, Thailand
Tel.: (66) 53 581516
Web Site: http://www.swn.co.th
Emp.: 97
Wire Mesh Product Mfr
N.A.I.C.S.: 332618
Hideaki Tanikawa (Pres)

THAI SINTERED MESH CO., LTD. (2)
Saha Group Industrial Park 99/8 Moo 5 Pasak, Muang, Lamphun, 51000, Thailand
Tel.: (66) 53090088
Web Site: https://www.thaisinteredmesh.com
Wire Mesh Product Mfr
N.A.I.C.S.: 331110

TMA Corporation Pty. Ltd. (2)
48 Century Road, PO Box 2466, Malaga, 6944, WA, Australia
Tel.: (61) 892493868
Web Site: https://www.termimesh.com.au
Termite Mesh Product Mfr
N.A.I.C.S.: 331110

Subsidiary (Non-US):

Termi-mesh Singapore Pte Ltd. (3)
40 Jalan Pemimpin 04-10B Tat Ann Building, Singapore, 577185, Singapore
Tel.: (65) 62263343
Web Site: https://www.termi-mesh.com.sg
Termite Mesh Product Distr
N.A.I.C.S.: 423840
Cheng Wai Meng (Founder & CEO)

Termimesh Vietnam (3)
No 109 Tran Duy Hung, Ward 304 Trung Hoa Cau Giay, Hanoi, 026000, Vietnam
Tel.: (84) 368298280
Web Site: https://termimesh.com.vn
Wire Mesh Distr
N.A.I.C.S.: 423840

Subsidiary (US):

Termimesh, LLC (3)
9475 Hwy 290, Austin, TX 78724
Tel.: (512) 997-0066
Web Site: http://www.termistopusa.com
Termite Mesh Product Distr
N.A.I.C.S.: 423840

Nippon Filcon Co., Ltd. - Shizuoka Plant (1)
1780 Atsuhara, Fuji, 419-0201, Shizuoka, Japan
Tel.: (81) 545711312
Web Site: http://www.filcon-fabrics.com
Emp.: 200
Nonwoven Fabric Product Mfr
N.A.I.C.S.: 313230

TEC BRITE TECHNOLOGY CO., LTD. (1)
323 Cheng Kung 3rd Road, Nan-Kang Industrial District, Nant'ou, 54066, Taiwan
Tel.: (886) 492259031
Lead Frames Mfr
N.A.I.C.S.: 332999

NIPPON FINE CHEMICAL CO., LTD.

Nippon Seika Building 4-9 Bingomachi 2-chome, Chuo-ku, Osaka, 541-0051, Japan
Tel.: (81) 662314781
Web Site: http://www.nipponseika.co.jp
Year Founded: 1918
Sales Range: $50-74.9 Million
Emp.: 606
Fine & Industrial Chemical Products, Cosmetic Products Mfr & Sales & Real Estate Leasing
N.A.I.C.S.: 325998
Susumu Yano (Pres & Operating Officer)

Subsidiaries:

Arbos Co., Ltd. (1)
2-4-9 Bingomach Nihonseika Bldg 7f, Chuo, Osaka, 541-0051, Japan
Tel.: (81) 662046767
Web Site: http://www.arbos.co.jp
Household Cleaning Product Mfr
N.A.I.C.S.: 325612

Custom Serve Corporation (1)
2-7 Odenma-cho, Nihonbashi Chuo-ku, Tokyo, 103-0011, Japan
Tel.: (81) 356957811
Web Site: http://www.c-server.co.jp
Sales Range: $25-49.9 Million
Emp.: 27
Sale of plastic resin, products, film, housing materials
N.A.I.C.S.: 326199
Kouji Nishimoto (Pres)

NISSEI PLAS-TECH CORPORATION (1)
2-7 Nihombashiodemmacho Nihombashi No1 Bldg 5f, Chuo, Tokyo, 103-0011, Japan
Tel.: (81) 356957811
Web Site: http://www.c-serve.co.jp
Plastic Product Distr
N.A.I.C.S.: 424610

Nippon Fine Chemical Co., Ltd. - Kakogawa-Higashi Plant (1)
Kitano, Noguchi-cho Hyogo, Kakogawa, 675-0011, Japan
Tel.: (81) 794231771
Chemical Products Mfr
N.A.I.C.S.: 325199

Nippon Fine Chemical Co., Ltd. - Kakogawa-Nishi Plant (1)
671-4 Mizuushi Noguchi-cho, Hyogo, Kakogawa, 675-0019, Japan
Tel.: (81) 794225219
Chemical Products Mfr
N.A.I.C.S.: 325199

Nippon Fine Chemical Co., Ltd. - Kobe Plant (1)
4-55 Motoyama Minamimachi 5-chome, Higashinada-ku, Kobe, 658-0015, Japan
Tel.: (81) 784112961
Chemical Products Mfr
N.A.I.C.S.: 325199

Nippon Fine Chemical Co., Ltd. - Takasago Plant (1)
1-1 Umei 5-chome, Hyogo, Takasago, 676-0074, Japan
Tel.: (81) 794473642
Chemical Products Mfr
N.A.I.C.S.: 325199

Nissei Bilis Co., Ltd. (1)
555 Ukawa Minakuchi, Shiga, Koka, 528-0052, Japan
Tel.: (81) 748622316
Web Site: http://www.nissei-bilis.com
Securities Trading Services
N.A.I.C.S.: 523150

Nissei Kosan Co., Ltd. (1)
2-3721-4 Shinkominami, Ishikari, 061-3244, Japan
Tel.: (81) 133646464
Web Site: http://www.nissei-kosan.co.jp
Industrial Construction & Engineering Services
N.A.I.C.S.: 236210

Oleotrade International Co., Ltd. (1)
4-9 Nihombashikodemmacho Kodemmachoshinnihombashi Bldg 5F, Chuo, Tokyo, 103-0011, Japan
Tel.: (81) 336643751
Specialty Chemicals Distr
N.A.I.C.S.: 424690

Sichuan Nipo Fine Chemical Co., Ltd. (1)
No 349 South Section Of Mianzhou A, Mianyang, 621000, China
Tel.: (86) 8162535665
Web Site: http://www.npcseika.com
Specialty Chemicals Distr
N.A.I.C.S.: 424690

NIPPON GAS CO., LTD.

4-31-8 Yoyogi, Shibuya-ku, Tokyo, 151-8582, Japan
Tel.: (81) 353082111
Web Site: https://www.nichigas.co.jp
Year Founded: 1955
8174—(TKS)
Rev.: $1,284,746,040
Assets: $1,052,437,590
Liabilities: $571,738,560
Net Worth: $480,699,030
Earnings: $71,553,250
Emp.: 2,019
Fiscal Year-end: 03/31/24
Gas Distribution Services
N.A.I.C.S.: 221210
Madoka Yamagishi (Exec Officer & Gen Mgr-Finance Department)

Subsidiaries:

Higashinihon Gas Corporation (1)
32 Ino, Toride, 302-0011, Ibaraki, Japan
Tel.: (81) 29 772 3165
Web Site: http://www.hngas.co.jp
City Gas Mfr
N.A.I.C.S.: 325120

Kitanihon Gas Co., Ltd. (1)
2-11-22 Hanagakicho, Oyama, 323-0027, Tochigi, Japan
Tel.: (81) 120226452
Liquefied Petroleum Gas Distr
N.A.I.C.S.: 424720

Nichigas Butsuryukeisancenter Co., Ltd. (1)
1656-3 Tsuruma, Machida-shi, Tokyo, Japan
Tel.: (81) 42 795 1121
Emp.: 13
Gas Distribution Services
N.A.I.C.S.: 221210

Nihongas Koji, Inc. (1)
Web Site: http://www.nihongas-koji.co.jp
Oil & Gas Pipeline Construction Services
N.A.I.C.S.: 237120

Nippon Gas Co., Ltd. - Tanashi Plant (1)
1-24-22 Shibakubo-cho, Nishitokyo-shi, Tokyo, 188-0011, Japan
Tel.: (81) 42 461 5820
Gas Distribution Services
N.A.I.C.S.: 221210

Nippon Gas Unyuseibi Co., Ltd. (1)
20 Ino, Toride, 302-0011, Ibaraki, Japan
Tel.: (81) 29 773 3524
Web Site: https://nicigas-unyu.co.jp
Gas Transportation Distr
N.A.I.C.S.: 484220

North Eastern States, Inc. (1)
1301 McKinney St 1250, Houston, TX 77010
Tel.: (888) 521-5861
Web Site: http://www.entrustenergy.com
Power Distribution Services
N.A.I.C.S.: 221122
Mike Beck (Pres & CEO)

Shinnihon Gas Corporation (1)
1-5 Furuichiba, Kitamoto, Saitama, Japan
Tel.: (81) 48 592 2411
Gas Distribution Services
N.A.I.C.S.: 221210

Tokyo Energy Alliance Co., Ltd. (1)
4-31-8 Yoyogi, Shibuya-ku, Tokyo, Japan
Tel.: (81) 57 000 2299
Web Site: https://www.tokyo-ea.net
Gas Transportation Distr
N.A.I.C.S.: 484220

Tosai Gas, Inc. (1)
1-14-1 Koshigaya, Koshigaya, 343-0813, Saitama, Japan
Tel.: (81) 12 078 1031
Web Site: https://www.tosaigas.co.jp
Emp.: 384
Gas Distribution Services
N.A.I.C.S.: 221210

NIPPON GEAR CO., LTD.

2F Keihanshin Toranomon Building 1-7-14 Nishi-Shinbashi, Minato-ku, Tokyo, 105-0003, Kanagawa, Japan
Tel.: (81) 363633170
Web Site: https://www.nippon-gear.jp
Year Founded: 1938
6356—(TKS)
Sales Range: Less than $1 Million
Emp.: 417
Gear Mfr & Whslr
N.A.I.C.S.: 333612

NIPPON HEALTHCARE INVESTMENT CORPORATION

6-2-1 Ginza, Chuo-ku, Tokyo, Japan
Tel.: (81) 3 67579600
Web Site: http://www.nippon-healthcare.co.jp
Year Founded: 2013
Sales Range: $1-9.9 Million
Investment Management Service
N.A.I.C.S.: 523999
Hiroshi Fujioka (Exec Dir)

NIPPON HOSO KYOKAI

NHK Broadcasting Center 2-2-1 Jinnan, Shibuya-ku, Tokyo, 150-8001, Japan
Tel.: (81) 334651111
Web Site: http://www.nhk.or.jp
Year Founded: 1925
Sales Range: $5-14.9 Billion
Emp.: 10,318
Television & Radio Broadcasting & Satellite Subscription Services
N.A.I.C.S.: 516120
Yukinori Kida (Exec Dir-Brdcst)

Subsidiaries:

Japan International Broadcasting Inc. (1)
Nihonseimei Shibuya Annex Building 1-19-4 Jinnan, Shibuya-ku, Tokyo, 150-0041, Japan
Tel.: (81) 3 3464 8911
Web Site: http://www.jibtv.com
Emp.: 60
Television Production & Broadcasting Services
N.A.I.C.S.: 516120
Yoshihiko Shimizu (Pres & CEO)

NHK ART, Inc. (1)
1-14-7 Tomigaya, Shibuya-ku, Tokyo, 151-0063, Japan
Tel.: (81) 3 3481 2881
Web Site: http://www.nhk-art.co.jp
Sales Range: $125-149.9 Million
Emp.: 237
Studio Design Services
N.A.I.C.S.: 541430
Atsushi Karube (Pres & CEO)

NHK BUSINESS SERVICES INC. (1)
1-17-10 Tomigaya, Shibuya-ku, Tokyo, 151-0063, Japan
Tel.: (81) 354540511
Web Site: http://www.nhk-nbs.co.jp
Emp.: 871

Television Broadcasting Services
N.A.I.C.S.: 516120
Fuminori Nishida (Pres)

NHK CULTURE CENTER, INC. (1)
1-1-1 Minami-Aoyama, Minato-ku, Tokyo, 107-8601, Japan
Tel.: (81) 3 3475 1359
Web Site: http://www.nhk-cul.co.jp
Emp.: 167
Education Services
N.A.I.C.S.: 611710
Takao Kuroki (Pres & CEO)

NHK Cosmomedia (Europe) Limited (1)
65 Clifton St, London, EC2A 4JE, United Kingdom
Tel.: (44) 2074267330
Web Site: http://www.nhk-cm.co.uk
Sales Range: $10-24.9 Million
Emp.: 30
Satellite Television Broadcasting Services
N.A.I.C.S.: 517410
Fumio Narashima (Mng Dir)

NHK Cosmomedia America, Inc. (1)
100 Broadway 15th Fl, New York, NY 10005
Tel.: (212) 262-3377
Web Site: http://www.nhkcosmomedia.com
Sales Range: $10-24.9 Million
Emp.: 43
Television Broadcasting Services
N.A.I.C.S.: 516120
Yuich Tatsumi (Sec)

NHK ENGINEERING SYSTEM, INC. (1)
1-10-11 Kinuta, Setagaya-ku, Tokyo, 157-8540, Japan
Tel.: (81) 3 5494 2400
Web Site: http://www.nes.or.jp
Emp.: 60
Motion Picture Laboratory Services
N.A.I.C.S.: 512199
Takayuki Ito (Dir)

NHK Educational Corporation (1)
7-13 Udagawa-cho, Shibuya-ku, Tokyo, 150-0042, Japan
Tel.: (81) 3 3462 8101
Web Site: http://www.nhk-ed.co.jp
Sales Range: $150-199.9 Million
Emp.: 255
Education Services
N.A.I.C.S.: 611710
Yoshiaki Kiuchi (Pres)

NHK Enterprises, Inc. (1)
4-14 Kamiyama-cho, Shibuya-ku, Tokyo, 150-0047, Japan
Tel.: (81) 3 5478 8175
Web Site: http://www.nhk-ep.co.jp
Sales Range: $450-499.9 Million
Emp.: 537
Television & Radio Broadcasting Services
N.A.I.C.S.: 516120
Tamaki Imai (Pres & CEO)

NHK Global Media Services, Inc. (1)
9-2 Kamiyama-cho, Shibuya-ku, Tokyo, 150-0047, Japan
Tel.: (81) 334811191
Web Site: http://www.nhk-g.co.jp
Sales Range: $150-199.9 Million
Emp.: 380
Satellite Broadcasting Services
N.A.I.C.S.: 517410
Kenichi Ishida (Pres & CEO)

NHK Integrated Technology Inc. (1)
1-4-1 Jinnan, Shibuya-ku, Tokyo, 150-0041, Japan
Tel.: (81) 3 5456 4711
Web Site: http://www.nhkitec.com
Sales Range: $400-449.9 Million
Emp.: 788
Digital Broadcasting Services
N.A.I.C.S.: 516120
Keiichi Kubota (Pres)

NHK International, Inc. (1)
7-13 Udagawacho, Shibuya-ku, Tokyo, 150-0042, Japan
Tel.: (81) 3 3464 1823
Web Site: http://www.nhkint.or.jp
Sales Range: $10-24.9 Million
Emp.: 33
Television Production & Broadcasting Services

N.A.I.C.S.: 516120
Makoto Harada (Pres & Member-Exec Bd)

NHK MEDIA TECHNOLOGY, INC.
Dai-San Kyodo Bldg 4-14 Kamiyamacho, Shibuya-ku, Tokyo, 150-0047, Japan
Tel.: (81) 3 3481 7820
Web Site: http://www.nhk-mt.co.jp
Sales Range: $250-299.9 Million
Emp.: 1,139
Broadcasting Engineering & Media Technology Services
N.A.I.C.S.: 516120
Akihiko Chigono (Pres)

NHK PROMOTIONS INC. (1)
5-5 Kamiyama-cho, Shibuya-ku, Tokyo, 150-0047, Japan
Tel.: (81) 3 5790 6420
Web Site: http://www.nhk-p.co.jp
Event Organizing Services
N.A.I.C.S.: 711310
Tsunehiko Hatakeyama (Pres & CEO)

NHK Publishing, Inc. (1)
41-1 Udagawa-cho, Shibuya-ku, Tokyo, 150-8081, Japan
Tel.: (81) 3 3464 7311
Web Site: http://www.nhk-book.co.jp
Emp.: 225
Book & Magazine Publisher
N.A.I.C.S.: 513130
Koki Morinaga (Pres)

NHK SERVICE CENTER, INC. (1)
41-1 Udagawa-cho, Shibuya-ku, Tokyo, 150-1687, Japan
Tel.: (81) 3 3464 1687
Web Site: http://www.nhk-sc.or.jp
Sales Range: $75-99.9 Million
Emp.: 231
Broadcasting Services
N.A.I.C.S.: 516120
Yonemoto Shin (Chm)

NHK World Radio Japan (1)
2-2-1 Jinnan, Shibuya-ku, Tokyo, 150-8001, Japan
Tel.: (81) 334651111
Sales Range: $25-49.9 Million
Radio Broadcasting Services
N.A.I.C.S.: 516110

NHK World TV (1)
2-2-1 Jinnan, Shibuya-ku, Tokyo, 150-8001, Japan
Tel.: (81) 334651111
Sales Range: $800-899.9 Million
Emp.: 3,000
Television Broadcasting Services
N.A.I.C.S.: 516120

NIPPON HUME CORPORATION
5-33-11 Shimbashi, Minato-ku, Tokyo, 105-0004, Japan
Tel.: (81) 334334111
Web Site: https://www.nipponhume.co.jp
Year Founded: 1925
5262—(TKS)
Rev.: $222,968,520
Assets: $410,342,190
Liabilities: $135,372,800
Net Worth: $274,969,390
Earnings: $12,638,320
Fiscal Year-end: 03/31/24
Concrete Product Mfr & Distr
N.A.I.C.S.: 325998
Minoru Ohkawauchi (Pres)

NIPPON ICHI SOFTWARE, INC.
3-17 Tsukigaoka-cho, Kakamigahara, 504-0903, Gifu, Japan
Tel.: (81) 583717239
Web Site: https://nippon1.co.jp
Year Founded: 1995
3851—(TKS)
Rev.: $35,290,790
Assets: $71,506,980
Liabilities: $18,071,740
Net Worth: $53,435,240
Earnings: $3,919,730
Emp.: 193
Fiscal Year-end: 03/31/24

Game Development Services
N.A.I.C.S.: 541512
Sohei Niikawa (Pres)

NIPPON INFORMATION DEVELOPMENT CO., LTD.
Harumi Island Triton Square Tower X 29F 1-8-10 Harumi, Chuo-ku, Tokyo, 104-6029, Japan
Tel.: (81) 362216811
Web Site: https://www.nid.co.jp
Year Founded: 1967
2349—(TKS)
Rev.: $149,131,111
Assets: $173,293,642
Liabilities: $43,072,337
Net Worth: $130,221,305
Earnings: $13,927,978
Emp.: 1,720
Fiscal Year-end: 03/31/24
Computer System Design Services
N.A.I.C.S.: 541512
Shuntaro Komori (Pres)

Subsidiaries:

NID-IS Co, Ltd. (1)
2-1-1 Hamacho, Funabashi, 273-0012, Japan
Tel.: (81) 474331000
Web Site: http://www.nidis.co.jp
Software Development Services
N.A.I.C.S.: 541511

NIPPON INSURE CO., LTD.
6th floor Fukuoka Securities Building 2-14-2 Tenjin, Chuo-ku, Fukuoka, 810-0001, Japan
Tel.: (81) 927261080
Web Site: https://www.nipponinsure.jp
Year Founded: 2002
5843—(TKS)
Investment Management Service
N.A.I.C.S.: 523999

NIPPON KANZAI HOLDINGS CO.,LTD.
4th Floor, Yanagiya Building 2-1-10 Nihombashi, Chuo-ku,, Tokyo, 103-0027, Japan
Tel.: (81) 352990863
Web Site: https://www.nkanzaihd.co.jp
Year Founded: 2023
9347—(TKS)
Rev.: $810,875,140
Assets: $612,383,450
Liabilities: $155,288,730
Net Worth: $457,094,720
Earnings: $37,544,800
Emp.: 10,876
Fiscal Year-end: 03/31/24
Real Estate
N.A.I.C.S.: 531390
Takeshi Fukuda (Board of Directors & Founder)

Subsidiaries:

Nippon Kanzai Co., Ltd. (1)
5th Floor Yanagiya Building 2-1-10 Nihombashi, Chuo-ku, Tokyo, 103-0027, Japan
Tel.: (81) 352990850
Web Site: http://www.nkanzai.co.jp
Rev.: $1,004,174,160
Assets: $795,124,880
Liabilities: $198,333,520
Net Worth: $596,791,360
Earnings: $59,793,360
Emp.: 10,278
Fiscal Year-end: 03/31/2022
Real Estate Management & Janitorial Services
N.A.I.C.S.: 561720
Takeshi Fukuda (Chm)

Joint Venture (US):

Hawaiiana Group, Inc. (2)
711 Kapiolani Blvd # 700, Honolulu, HI 96813 (50%)

Tel.: (808) 593-9100
Web Site: http://www.hawaiipottersguild.org
Sales Range: $1-9.9 Million
Emp.: 87
Offices of Real Estate Agents & Brokers
N.A.I.C.S.: 531210
Eiichi Matsumoto (CEO)

Subsidiary (Domestic):

Japan Environmental Solutions, Ltd. (2)
Yanagiya Building 3rd Floor 2-1-10, Nihonbashi Chuo-ku, Tokyo, 103-0027, Japan
Tel.: (81) 35 255 1211
Web Site: https://www.jesol.co.jp
Building Management Services
N.A.I.C.S.: 531312

Japan Housing Management Co. (2)
21 Awajimachi Building 3-1-5 Awajimachi, Chuo-ku, Osaka, 541-0047, Japan
Tel.: (81) 66 223 1771
Web Site: https://www.njk21.co.jp
Residential Management Services
N.A.I.C.S.: 541618

Japan Property Solutions Co., Ltd. (2)
2-4-4 Kanda Jimbocho Daiwa Jimbocho Building 3 4 floor, Chiyoda-ku, Tokyo, 101-0051, Japan
Tel.: (81) 352123800
Web Site: http://www.japan-ps.com
Sales Range: $50-74.9 Million
Emp.: 102
Building Management & Operating Services
N.A.I.C.S.: 531312

K N Facilities Co., Ltd. (2)
3-7 Iidabashi 3-chome, Chiyoda-ku, Tokyo, 102 0072, Japan
Tel.: (81) 352161011
Web Site: https://www.kn-facilities.co.jp
Building Management & Operating Business
N.A.I.C.S.: 531312

NJK Staff Service Co., Ltd. (2)
3-1-5 Awajimachi, Chuo-ku, Osaka, 541-0047, Japan
Tel.: (81) 66 229 6161
Web Site: https://www.njkss.co.jp
Temporary Staffing Services
N.A.I.C.S.: 561320

NS Corporation Co., Ltd. (2)
2-4-1 Shiba Park Shiba Park Building A 4th floor, Minato-ku, Tokyo, 105-0011, Japan
Tel.: (81) 357330201
Web Site: http://www.nscp.co.jp
Sales Range: $50-74.9 Million
Emp.: 105
Building Management Services
N.A.I.C.S.: 236117

Neotrust Co., Ltd. (2)
5-1-5 Higashiueno 8th Floor Nissin Ueno Building, Taito-ku, Tokyo, 110-0015, Japan
Tel.: (81) 508 880 8410
Web Site: https://www.neotrust.co.jp
Consulting Services
N.A.I.C.S.: 541618

Nippon Kanzai Environment Service Co., Ltd. (2)
3-6-3 Awajimachi Midosuji MTR Building 5F, Chuo-ku, Osaka, 541-0047, Japan
Tel.: (81) 66 563 7350
Web Site: https://www.nkks.co.jp
Facility Support Services
N.A.I.C.S.: 561210

Nippon Kanzai Housing Management Co., Ltd. (2)
Awajimachi Building 21 3-1-5 Awajimachi, Chuo-ku, Osaka, 541-0047, Japan
Tel.: (81) 66 229 6600
Web Site: https://www.j.nkanzai.co.jp
Residential Management Services
N.A.I.C.S.: 541618

Okinawa Nippon Kanzai Co., Ltd. (2)
1-12-12 Kumoji Nissei Naha Center Building 9th Floor, Naha, 900-0015, Okinawa, Japan
Tel.: (81) 98 867 5201
Web Site: http://okinawa.nkanzai.co.jp
Facility Support Services
N.A.I.C.S.: 561210

NIPPON KANZAI HOLDINGS CO., LTD.

NIPPON KANZAI Holdings Co., Ltd.—(Continued)

Tokyo Capital Management Co., Ltd. (2)
Shimbashi SY Bldg 9F 1-14-2, Nishishimbashi Minato-ku, Tokyo, 105-0003, Japan
Tel.: (81) 33 503 0100
Web Site: https://www.tokyo-capital.com
Real Estate Services
N.A.I.C.S.: 531390
Akihiko Soga (Pres)

NIPPON KAYAKU CO., LTD.
Meiji Yasuda Seimei Building 19th & 20th Floors 1-1 Marunouchi 2-chome, Chiyoda-ku, Tokyo, 100-0005, Japan
Tel.: (81) 367315200   JP
Web Site:
https://www.nipponkayaku.co.jp
Year Founded: 1916
NP7—(DEU)
Rev.: $1,333,838,510
Assets: $2,400,573,530
Liabilities: $612,251,250
Net Worth: $1,788,322,280
Earnings: $27,186,930
Emp.: 5,950
Fiscal Year-end: 03/31/24
Pharmaceuticals, Functional Chemical Products, Color Chemicals, Agrochemicals, Inflators, Explosives & Catalysts Mfr
N.A.I.C.S.: 325412
Hiroshi Mikami (Mng Dir, Mng Dir, Head-Admin Grp & Head-Admin Grp)

Subsidiaries:

Aero Systems West, Inc. (1)
13025 Murphy Ave, San Martin, CA 95046
Tel.: (408) 599-2791
Web Site: https://aerosystemswest.com
Industrial Drone Mfr
N.A.I.C.S.: 336411

Cultivecs Inc. (1)
5-2 Mitsubishi Building Marunouchi 2-chome, Chiyoda-ku, Tokyo, 100-8324, Japan
Tel.: (81) 33 283 4901
Web Site: https://www.cultivecs.jp
Pharmaceuticals Product Mfr
N.A.I.C.S.: 325412

Euro Nippon Kayaku GmbH (1)
Staufen Strasse 4, 60323, Frankfurt, Germany (100%)
Tel.: (49) 69727800
Web Site: http://www.nipponkayaku.co.jp
Sales Range: $25-49.9 Million
Emp.: 2
Mfr of Pharmaceuticals & Chemicals
N.A.I.C.S.: 325412

Gunnan Sangyo Co., Ltd. (1)
239 Iwahanamachi, Takasaki, 370-1208, Gunma, Japan
Tel.: (81) 273465211
Web Site: http://www.nipponkayaku.co.jp
Construction Engineering Services
N.A.I.C.S.: 541330
Yasuhiro Okabe (Pres)

Indet Safety Systems a.s. (1)
Bobrky 462, 755 01, Vsetin, Czech Republic
Tel.: (420) 571425001
Web Site: http://www.iss-cz.com
Sales Range: $100-124.9 Million
Emp.: 700
Automobile Parts Mfr
N.A.I.C.S.: 336110

JHMS Co.,Ltd. (1)
3-31-12 Shimo, Kita-ku, Tokyo, 115-0042, Japan
Tel.: (81) 335985040
Web Site: https://www.jhms.co.jp
Educational Support Services
N.A.I.C.S.: 611710

Japan Human Resources Medical Science Research Institute Co., Ltd. (1)
3-31-12 Shimo, Kita-ku, Tokyo, 115-0042, Japan
Tel.: (81) 33 598 5040
Web Site: https://www.jhms.co.jp
Medical Research Services
N.A.I.C.S.: 541715

Kayaku (Shanghai) Co., Ltd. (1)
Room 603 Changning Raffles City Tower 3 No 1193 Changning Road, Changning District, Shanghai, 200051, China
Tel.: (86) 2133726028
Chemical Products Mfr
N.A.I.C.S.: 325998

Kayaku Advanced Materials, Inc. (1)
200 Flanders Rd, Westborough, MA 01581
Tel.: (617) 965-5511
Web Site: https://kayakuam.com
Chemical Products Mfr
N.A.I.C.S.: 325998

Kayaku Chemical (Wuxi) Co., Ltd (1)
Xinba Village, Xibei Town Xishan, Wuxi, 214101, Jiangsu, China
Tel.: (86) 51083780313
Web Site: http://www.kayakuwx.com
Emp.: 85
Chemical Products Mfr
N.A.I.C.S.: 325199

Kayaku Japan Co., Ltd. (1)
Kokusai Fashion Center Bldg 9F 6-1 Yokoami 1-choume, Sumida-ku, Tokyo, 130-0015, Japan
Tel.: (81) 356370901
Industrial Machinery Mfr
N.A.I.C.S.: 333248

Kayaku Safety Systems (Huzhou) Co., Ltd. (1)
No 118 YangFuMiao, HuiCheLingVillage HePingTown ChangXingCounty, Huzhou, 313103, ZheJiang, China
Tel.: (86) 5726956007
Web Site: http://www.nipponkayaku.co.jp
Emp.: 300
Chemical Products Mfr & Sales
N.A.I.C.S.: 325998

Kayaku Safety Systems Europe a.s. (1)
Bobrky 2271, 755 01, Vsetin, Czech Republic
Tel.: (420) 57 142 5001
Web Site: https://www.kse-cz.com
Chemical Products Mfr
N.A.I.C.S.: 325998
Petr Foltyn (Mgr-Engrg)

Kayaku Safety Systems Malaysia Sdn. Bhd. (1)
PT12627 PT12628 & PT12629 Jalan Techvalley 4/2 Sendayan Techvalley, Bandar Sri Sendayan, 71950, Negeri Sembilan, Malaysia
Tel.: (60) 67817000
LCD Panel Mfr
N.A.I.C.S.: 334419

Kayaku Safety Systems de Mexico, S.A. de C.V. (1)
Av Ruben J Villarreal S N Col Exhacienda San Isidro, 65503, Salinas Victoria, NL, Mexico
Tel.: (52) 8182883550
Web Site: https://www.nipponkayaku.co.jp
Micro Gas Generator Mfr & Distr
N.A.I.C.S.: 333132

MICROCHEM CORP. (1)
200 Flanders Road, Westborough, MA 01581
Tel.: (617) 965-5511
Web Site: http://www.microchem.com
Semiconductor Machinery Mfr
N.A.I.C.S.: 333242
Jay Cole (Pres & CEO)

NIKKA FINE TECHNO Co., Ltd. (1)
MBR99 Bldg 3F 67, Kandasakumagashi Chiyoda-ku, Tokyo, 101-0026, Japan
Tel.: (81) 366288760
Web Site: http://www.nkft.co.jp
Sales Range: $100-124.9 Million
Emp.: 43
Chemical Products Sales
N.A.I.C.S.: 424690
Shinya Fukuoka (Pres)

Nac Co., Ltd. (1)
31-12 Shimo 3 Chome, Kita-ku, Tokyo, 115-0042, Japan
Tel.: (81) 335985270
Pharmaceutical Testing Services
N.A.I.C.S.: 541380

Nikos Co., Ltd. (1)
11-2 Fujimi 1-chome Tokyo Fujimi Bldg, Chiyoda-ku, Tokyo, 102-8172, Japan
Tel.: (81) 332375372
Sales Range: $50-74.9 Million
Emp.: 11
Real Estate & Travel Management Services
N.A.I.C.S.: 531390

Nippon Kayaku (Thailand) Co., Ltd. (1)
13th Floor Ramaland Building 952 Rama IV Rd, Suriyawongse Bangrak, Bangkok, 10500, Thailand
Tel.: (66) 63 254 2254
Web Site: https://www.kayakuth.co.th
Emp.: 7
Chemical Products Mfr
N.A.I.C.S.: 325998
Tetsuya Tomita (Mng Dir)

Nippon Kayaku America, Inc. (1)
711 Westchester Ave 2nd Fl, White Plains, NY 10604-3530
Tel.: (914) 686-6800
Web Site: http://www.nipponkayaku.co.jp
Sales Range: $25-49.9 Million
Emp.: 6
Mfr of Pharmaceuticals
N.A.I.C.S.: 424690

Nippon Kayaku CZ, s.r.o. (1)
Bobrky 462, 75501, Vsetin, Czech Republic
Tel.: (420) 737206214
Sales Range: $150-199.9 Million
Emp.: 500
Chemical Products Mfr & Sales
N.A.I.C.S.: 325180

Nippon Kayaku Co., Ltd. - Agrochemicals Division (1)
Tokyo Fujimi Building 11-2 Fujimi 1 Chome Chiyoda-ku, Tokyo, 102-8172, Japan
Tel.: (81) 3 3237 5494
Web Site: http://www.nipponkayaku.co.jp
Sales Range: $150-199.9 Million
Emp.: 300
Chemical Products Mfr & Sales
N.A.I.C.S.: 325199

Nippon Kayaku Co., Ltd. - Asa Plant (1)
2300 Kori Sanyoonoda, Yamaguchi, 757-8686, Japan
Tel.: (81) 836720910
Sales Range: $50-74.9 Million
Emp.: 140
Petrochemical Mfr
N.A.I.C.S.: 325110

Nippon Kayaku Co., Ltd. - Corporate Planning Division (1)
Tokyo Fujimi Bldg 11-2 Fujimi 1-chome Chiyoda-ku, 102-8172, Tokyo, Japan
Tel.: (81) 332375043
Sales Range: $125-149.9 Million
Emp.: 400
Chemical Products Mfr
N.A.I.C.S.: 325199

Nippon Kayaku Co., Ltd. - Explosives Research Laboratories (1)
2300 Sanyo Cho, Asa Gun, Yamaguchi, 757 8686, Japan (100%)
Tel.: (81) 836720922
Web Site: http://www.nipponkayaku.co.jp
Sales Range: $50-74.9 Million
Emp.: 450
Mfr of Industrial Explosives
N.A.I.C.S.: 325920

Nippon Kayaku Co., Ltd. - Fukuyama Plant (1)
126 Minookicho, Fukuyama, 721-8567, Hiroshima, Japan
Tel.: (81) 84 954 8111
Web Site: http://www.nipponkayaku.co.jp
Chemical Products Mfr
N.A.I.C.S.: 325180
Masanobu Suzuki (Pres)

Nippon Kayaku Co., Ltd. - Functional Materials Division (1)
Tokyo Fujimi Building 11-2 Fujimi 1 Chome Chiyoda-ku, Tokyo, 102-8172, Japan
Tel.: (81) 332375209
Sales Range: $25-49.9 Million
Emp.: 30
Chemical Products Mfr
N.A.I.C.S.: 325199

Nippon Kayaku Co., Ltd. - Himeji Plant (1)
3903-39 Toyotomi Toyotomicho, Himeji, 679-2123, Hyogo, Japan
Tel.: (81) 792643001
Petrochemical Products Mfr
N.A.I.C.S.: 325110

Nippon Kayaku Co., Ltd. - Kashima Plant (1)
6 Sunayama, Kamisu, 314-0255, Ibaraki, Japan
Tel.: (81) 479 46 2661
Web Site: http://www.nipponkayaku.co.jp
Chemical Products Mfr
N.A.I.C.S.: 325199

Nippon Kayaku Co., Ltd. - Takasaki Plant (1)
239 Iwahanamachi, Takasaki, 370-1208, Gunma, Japan
Tel.: (81) 273461011
Chemical Products Mfr
N.A.I.C.S.: 325199

Nippon Kayaku Food Techno Co., Ltd. (1)
219 Iwahanamachi, Takasaki, 370-1208, Gunma, Japan
Tel.: (81) 27 345 2111
Web Site: http://www.foodtechno.co.jp
Emp.: 78
Frozen Food Products Mfr & Sales
N.A.I.C.S.: 311412

Nippon Kayaku Fukuyama Co., Ltd. (1)
126 Minookicho, Fukuyama, 721-8567, Hiroshima, Japan
Tel.: (81) 849548111
Web Site:
http://www.nipponkayakufukuyama.co.jp
Sales Range: $125-149.9 Million
Emp.: 270
Industrial Chemicals Mfr
N.A.I.C.S.: 325199

Nippon Kayaku Korea Co., Ltd. (1)
1407 Ilsin Building 38 Mapo-daero, Mapo-gu, Seoul, 04174, Korea (South)
Tel.: (82) 27 196 0012
Web Site: https://www.nipponkayaku-korea.co.kr
Touch Panel Material Mfr
N.A.I.C.S.: 334419

Nippon Kayaku Tokyo Co., Ltd. (1)
23-1 Shinden 1 Chome, Adachi-ku, Tokyo, 123-0865, Japan
Tel.: (81) 359595111
Web Site: http://www.nipponkayaku.co.jp
Emp.: 100
Industrial Chemicals Mfr
N.A.I.C.S.: 325199
Akira Saino (Pres)

Nishiminato Driving School Co., Ltd. (1)
15-5 Nishiminatomachi, Kokurakita-ku, Kitakyushu, Japan
Tel.: (81) 12 024 3770
Web Site: https://www.nishiminato-ds.co.jp
Driving School Services
N.A.I.C.S.: 611692

Okiura Golf Center Co., Ltd. (1)
5846 Okiura Hikino-chou, Fukuyama, 721-0942, Hiroshima, Japan
Tel.: (81) 849432225
Golf Goods Sales & Driving Range Management Services
N.A.I.C.S.: 713910

Polatechno (Hong Kong) Co. Limited (1)
Flat D 3rd Floor Yeung Yiu Chung No 8 Ind Bldg 20 Wang Hoi Road, Kowloon Bay, Kowloon, China (Hong Kong)
Tel.: (852) 27581889
LCD Panel Mfr
N.A.I.C.S.: 334419

Polatechno Co., Ltd. (1)

192-6 Inamasu Shimokawara, Itakura-ku, Joetsu, 944-0101, Niigata, Japan
Tel.: (81) 255784700
Web Site: http://www.polatechno.co.jp
Sales Range: $100-124.9 Million
Emp.: 877
Photographic & Photocopying Equipment Mfr
N.A.I.C.S.: 333310
Naosuke Shirasuna *(Mng Exec Officer)*

Subsidiary (Non-US):

DEJIMA OPTICAL FILMS B.V. (2)
Delta 21, 6825 ML, Arnhem, Netherlands
Tel.: (31) 26 384 2060
Web Site: https://www.dejima.nl
Liquid Crystal Display Mfr
N.A.I.C.S.: 334419

Subsidiary (US):

MOXTEK, Inc. (2)
452 W 1260 N, Orem, UT 84057
Tel.: (801) 225-0930
Web Site: https://moxtek.com
Electric Equipment Mfr
N.A.I.C.S.: 334419
Eric Gardner *(Chief Optics Tech Officer & Chief Optics Tech Officer)*

Plant (Domestic):

Polatechno Co., Ltd. - Nakadahara Factory (2)
1 Nakadahara, Joetsu, 943-0882, Niigata, Japan
Tel.: (81) 255 78 7730
Electric Equipment Mfr
N.A.I.C.S.: 334419

RaySpec Ltd. (1)
1 The Valley Centre Gordon Road, High Wycombe, HP13 6EQ, Buckinghamshire, United Kingdom
Tel.: (44) 162 853 3060
Web Site: https://www.rayspec.co.uk
Electrical & Electronic Mfr
N.A.I.C.S.: 335999

Shanghai KAYAKU International Trading Co., Ltd (1)
A B 11th Floor JiaLi Mansion No 2 Lane 1228 Yan an West Road, Shanghai, China
Tel.: (86) 2152581700
Disperse Dyes Sales
N.A.I.C.S.: 424690

Shanghai Nikka Fine Techno Co., Ltd. (1)
507 Victoria Business Center 96 Ronghuadong Road, Gu-bei, Shanghai, China
Tel.: (86) 21 6209 5934
Web Site: http://www.nipponkayaku.co.jp
Chemical Products Mfr & Distr
N.A.I.C.S.: 325199

Taiwan Nippon Kayaku Co., Ltd. (1)
9th FL No 88 Sec 2 Chung-Hsiao East Rd, Sec 2, Taipei, 100, Taiwan **(100%)**
Tel.: (886) 22 396 2923
Web Site: https://www.nipponkayaku.co.jp
Sales Range: $25-49.9 Million
Emp.: 3
Pharmaceuticals Mfr
N.A.I.C.S.: 325412

Teikoku Taping System Co., Ltd. (1)
43-1 Harabuto Kagiyamachi, Tokai, 477-0032, Aichi, Japan
Tel.: (81) 562337172
Web Site: https://www.teikoku-taping.com
Semiconductor Mfr & Distr
N.A.I.C.S.: 333242

Teikoku Taping System(Singapore) Pte. Ltd. (1)
1 Yihshun Industrial Street1 05-07 A POSH Bizhub, Singapore, Singapore
Tel.: (65) 66596462
Web Site: https://www.teikoku-taping.com
Semiconductor Mfr & Distr
N.A.I.C.S.: 333242

Teikoku Taping System,Inc. (1)
Ste 140 5090 N 40th St, Phoenix, AZ 85018
Tel.: (480) 794-1926
Semiconductor Mfr & Distr
N.A.I.C.S.: 334413

Tumor Diagnosis Support Co., Ltd. (1)
Chigayahigashi Building 6 F 1-3 Ichigayatamachi 2-chome, Shinjuku-ku, Tokyo, 162-0843, Japan
Tel.: (81) 352253303
Pharmaceuticals Product Mfr
N.A.I.C.S.: 325412

Wako Toshi Kaihatsu Co., Ltd. (1)
Meiji Yasuda Seimei Building 1-1 Marunouchi 2-chome, Chiyoda-ku, Tokyo, 100-0005, Japan
Tel.: (81) 367315945
Web Site: http://www.nipponkayaku.co.jp
Real Estate Manangement Services
N.A.I.C.S.: 531390

Wuxi Advanced Kayaku Chemical Co., Ltd (1)
No 1 Xinda Road, Xinba Village Xibei Town Xishan, Wuxi, 214192, Jiangsu, China
Tel.: (86) 51083780183
Web Site: http://www.nipponkayaku.co.jp
Mfr & Sales of Water Soluble & Disperse Dyes
N.A.I.C.S.: 325130
Tadayuki Kiyoyanagi *(Gen Mgr)*

NIPPON KINZOKU CO., LTD.
5-29-11 Shiba G-BASE Tamachi 10th and 11th floors, Minato-ku, Tokyo, 108-0014, Japan
Tel.: (81) 357658111
Web Site: https://www.nipponkinzoku.co.jp
Year Founded: 1930
5491—(TKS)
Rev.: $339,826,710
Assets: $496,311,850
Liabilities: $318,747,420
Net Worth: $177,564,430
Earnings: $10,212,450
Fiscal Year-end: 03/31/24
Steel Mfrs
N.A.I.C.S.: 331110
Masanori Hiraishi *(Chm)*

Subsidiaries:

NIPPON KINZOKU (THAILAND) CO., LTD. (1)
Rojana Industrial Park 59 Moo5, Uthai, Ayutthaya, 13210, Thailand
Tel.: (66) 35741621
Steel Product Distr
N.A.I.C.S.: 423510

Nippon kinzoku co., Ltd. - Fukushima Plant (1)
1 Kashima Higashikamako, Shirakawa, Fukushima, 961-0303, Japan
Tel.: (81) 248342961
Steel Mfrs
N.A.I.C.S.: 331110

Nippon kinzoku co., Ltd. - Gifu Plant (1)
2-24 Himegaoka, Kani, Gifu, 509-0249, Japan
Tel.: (81) 574631071
Steel Products Mfr
N.A.I.C.S.: 331110

Nippon kinzoku co., Ltd. - Itabashi Plant (1)
Funato 4-10-1, Itabashi-ku, Tokyo, 174-8560, Japan
Tel.: (81) 339686300
Steel Mfrs
N.A.I.C.S.: 331110

NIPPON KODOSHI CORPORATION
648 Hirooka-kami Haruno-Cho, Kochi, 781-0395, Japan
Tel.: (81) 888942321
Web Site: https://www.kodoshi.co.jp
Year Founded: 1941
3891—(TKS)
Rev.: $98,013,080
Assets: $224,574,750
Liabilities: $76,728,880
Net Worth: $147,845,870
Earnings: $9,776,190
Emp.: 485
Fiscal Year-end: 03/31/24
Electronic Capacitor Manufacturing
N.A.I.C.S.: 334416
Toshinori Yamaoka *(Chm)*

Subsidiaries:

NIPPON KODOSHI CORPORATION - Aki Plant (1)
1 Ueno, Aki, 784-0029, Kochi, Japan
Tel.: (81) 887358500
Electronic Parts Mfr
N.A.I.C.S.: 334419

NIPPON KODOSHI CORPORATION - Nankoku Plant (1)
4465-25 Tochi, Nankoku, 783-0085, Kochi, Japan
Tel.: (81) 888478866
Electronic Parts Mfr
N.A.I.C.S.: 334419

NIPPON KODOSHI CORPORATION - Yonago Plant (1)
220-1 Nihongi, Yonago, 689-3541, Tottori, Japan
Tel.: (81) 859370200
Electronic Parts Mfr
N.A.I.C.S.: 334419

NIPPON KODOSHI KOGYO (MALAYSIA) SDN. BHD. (1)
Pld 683 Jalan Keluli Zone 11, Pasir Gudang Industrial Estate, 81700, Pasir Gudang, Johor, Malaysia
Tel.: (60) 72525270
Electronic Parts Whslr
N.A.I.C.S.: 423690

NIPPON KOEI CO., LTD.
5-4 Kojimachi, Chiyoda-ku, Tokyo, 102-8539, Japan
Tel.: (81) 332388030 JP
Web Site: http://www.n-koei.co.jp
1954—(TKS)
Rev.: $1,264,924,320
Assets: $1,683,603,680
Liabilities: $890,143,760
Net Worth: $793,459,920
Earnings: $64,894,720
Emp.: 6,163
Fiscal Year-end: 06/30/22
Construction Consulting Services
N.A.I.C.S.: 213112
Ryuichi Arimoto *(Pres)*

Subsidiaries:

BDP Holdings Limited (1)
11 Ducie Street Piccadilly Basin, Manchester, M1 2JB, United Kingdom
Tel.: (44) 161 828 2200
Web Site: https://www.bdp.com
Architecture & Planning Services
N.A.I.C.S.: 541310
Robert Ferry *(Principal)*

El Koei Co., Ltd. (1)
4-2-7 Kojimachi Tokyo Kojimachi Mid Square 10th floor, Chiyoda-ku, Tokyo, 102-0083, Japan
Tel.: (81) 332388370
Web Site: https://www.el-koei.co.jp
Sales Range: $25-49.9 Million
Emp.: 315
Recruitment Services
N.A.I.C.S.: 561330
Tetsuro Takehara *(Pres & CEO)*

KRI International Corporation (1)
5-1 Kojimachi, Chiyoda-ku, Tokyo, 102-0083, Japan
Tel.: (81) 332881161
Web Site: http://www.kri-inter.co.jp
Rev.: $14,743,600
Emp.: 80
Socio Economic Research & Development Services
N.A.I.C.S.: 541720

Kisho Kurokawa Architect & Associates Co., Ltd. (1)
Kojimachi 4-chome Kyodo Building 8F 4-2-7, Chiyoda-ku, Tokyo, 102-0083, Japan
Tel.: (81) 33 238 8301
Web Site: https://www.kisho.co.jp
Hydroelectric Power Generation Services
N.A.I.C.S.: 221111

Koei Energy Co., Ltd. (1)
7th Floor Kojimachi 4-chome Joint Building 4-2 Kojimachi, Chiyoda-ku, Tokyo, 102-0083, Japan
Tel.: (81) 35 215 6926
Web Site: https://www.koeienergy.co.jp
Hydroelectric Power Generation Services
N.A.I.C.S.: 221111

Koei Research & Consulting Inc. (1)
Kojimachi Mid Square 9th Floor 4-2-7 Kojimachi, Chiyoda-ku, Tokyo, 102-0083, Japan
Tel.: (81) 33 265 8311
Web Site: https://www.k-rc.co.jp
Emp.: 125
Consulting Services
N.A.I.C.S.: 541611
Akihiko Sasaki *(Pres)*

Koei System Inc. (1)
4-2 Kojimachi Kojimachi 4-chome Joint Building 10th Floor, Chiyoda-ku, Tokyo, 102-0083, Japan
Tel.: (81) 35 215 6630
Web Site: https://www.koeisystem.co.jp
Sales Range: $50-74.9 Million
Emp.: 118
Software Development Services
N.A.I.C.S.: 513210
Katsumi Watanabe *(Pres)*

Myanmar Koei International Ltd. (1)
No 36/A Grand Pho Sein Condominium 1st Floor Pho Sein Road, Tamwe Township, Yangon, Myanmar
Web Site: https://www.myanmar-koei.com
Engineeering Services
N.A.I.C.S.: 541330

NIPPON KOEI Urban Space Co., Ltd. (1)
2-17-14 Higashisakura, Higashi-ku, Nagoya, 461-0005, Japan
Tel.: (81) 529799111
Web Site: https://www.n-koei.co.jp
Sales Range: $150-199.9 Million
Emp.: 812
Engineering Consulting Services
N.A.I.C.S.: 541330
Nobuo Tabei *(Chm)*

Nippon Civic Consulting Engineers Co., Ltd (1)
UC Building 2-26-2 Nishi-Nippori, Arakawa-ku, Tokyo, 116-0013, Japan
Tel.: (81) 35 604 7500
Web Site: https://www.nccnet.co.jp
Sales Range: $50-74.9 Million
Emp.: 166
Subway Infrastructure Designing & Consulting Services
N.A.I.C.S.: 237990
Takayoshi Otsuka *(Pres)*

Nippon Koei LAC, Inc. (1)
5-4 Kojimachi, Chiyoda-ku, Tokyo, 102-8539, Japan
Tel.: (81) 33 238 8030
Web Site: https://www.nklac.com
Consulting Services
N.A.I.C.S.: 541611

Nippon Koei Latin America-Caribbean Co., Ltd. (1)
Torre ADR Piso 9 Avenida Samuel Lewis Urbanizacion Obarrio, Panama, 0823-00864, Panama
Tel.: (507) 300 2010
Web Site: https://www.nklac.com
Environmental Engineering Consulting Services
N.A.I.C.S.: 541620

Nippon Koei Vietnam International Co., Ltd. (1)
19th Floor Peakview Tower No 36 Hoang Cau street, O Cho Dua ward Dong Da District, Hanoi, Vietnam
Tel.: (84) 243 724 6535
Web Site: https://en.nipponkoeivn.com
Consulting Services
N.A.I.C.S.: 541611

PT. Arkora Hydro (1)
Treasury Tower Level 9 Unit G-H, District 8 SCBD Lot 28 Jl Jend Sudirman Kav 52-53,

NIPPON KOEI CO., LTD.

Nippon Koei Co., Ltd.—(Continued)
Jakarta, 12190, Indonesia
Tel.: (62) 2150333144
Web Site: https://www.arkora-hydro.com
Hydroelectric Power Generation Services
N.A.I.C.S.: 221111
Aldo Artoko (Pres)

PT. Indokoei International (1)
Jl Sultan Hasanuddin No 45, Kebayoran Baru, Jakarta, 12160, Indonesia
Tel.: (62) 21 723 7620
Web Site: https://www.indokoei.co.id
Consulting Services
N.A.I.C.S.: 541611

Philkoei International, Inc. (1)
17th Floor The Orient Square F Ortigas Jr Road formerly Emerald Avenue, Ortigas Center Barangay San Antonio, Pasig, 1605, Metro Manila, Philippines
Tel.: (63) 28 534 0325
Web Site: https://www.philkoei.com.ph
Consulting Services
N.A.I.C.S.: 541611
Zenaida N. Abad (VP)

Quadrangle Architects Limited (1)
901 King Street West Suite 701, Toronto, M5V 3H5, ON, Canada
Tel.: (416) 598-1240
Web Site: https://www.bdpquadrangle.com
Emp.: 200
Hydroelectric Power Generation Services
N.A.I.C.S.: 221111
Laura Rachlin (Mng Dir)

Sankoh Machinery Co., Ltd. (1)
3F Daitaku Building 4-6-24 Nishinakajima, Yodogawa-ku, Osaka, 532-0011, Japan
Tel.: (81) 66 305 5470
Web Site: https://www.sankoh-machinery.co.jp
Engineeering Services
N.A.I.C.S.: 541330

NIPPON LIFE INSURANCE COMPANY

3-5-12 Imabashi, Chuo-ku, Osaka, 541-8501, Japan
Tel.: (81) 662094500   JP
Web Site: http://www.nissay.co.jp
Year Founded: 1889
Rev.: $77,930,359,760
Assets: $775,185,725,600
Liabilities: $715,583,932,800
Net Worth: $59,601,792,800
Earnings: $1,859,886,160
Emp.: 92,122
Fiscal Year-end: 03/31/20
Life & Non-Life Insurance, Pension, Mortgage & Other Investment Products & Services
N.A.I.C.S.: 524113
Takeshi Furuichi (Vice Chm)

Subsidiaries:

Bangkok Life Assurance Public Company Limited (1)
23/115-121 Soi Sun Wichai Rama 9 Rd Bangkapi, Huaykwang, Bangkok, 10310, Thailand **(24.4%)**
Tel.: (66) 2 777 8888
Web Site: http://www.bangkoklife.com
Rev.: $1,604,977,452
Assets: $11,566,799,096
Liabilities: $9,968,567,244
Net Worth: $1,598,231,851
Earnings: $106,490,187
Emp.: 1,217
Fiscal Year-end: 12/31/2021
Life Insurance Carrier
N.A.I.C.S.: 524113
Savitri Ramyarupa (Exec Dir)

Hanasaku Life Insurance Co., Ltd. (1)
18th Floor Roppongi Grand Tower 3-2-1 Roppongi, Minato-ku, Tokyo, 106-6218, Japan
Tel.: (81) 120873917
Web Site: https://www.life8739.co.jp
Fire Insurance Services
N.A.I.C.S.: 524113

Japan Pension Service Co., Ltd. (1)
3-5-24 Takaido Nishi, Suginami-ku, Tokyo, 168-8505, Japan
Tel.: (81) 353441100
Web Site: https://www.nenkin.go.jp
Pension Fund Services
N.A.I.C.S.: 525110

LHL Co., Ltd. (1)
4th floor Shinjuku NS Building 2-4-1, Nishi-Shinjuku Shinjuku-ku, Tokyo, 163-0804, Japan
Tel.: (81) 368961350
Web Site: https://www.lhl.co.jp
Fire Insurance Services
N.A.I.C.S.: 524113

Life Plaza Partners Co., Ltd. (1)
6th Floor Shinjuku NS Building 2-4-1, Nishi-Shinjuku Shinjuku-ku, Tokyo, 163-0806, Japan
Tel.: (81) 353227215
Web Site: https://www.lifeplaza.co.jp
Fire Insurance Services
N.A.I.C.S.: 524113

Lifesalon Co., Ltd. (1)
Shinjuku NS Building 4F 2-4-1, Nishi-Shinjuku Shinjuku-ku, Tokyo, 163-0804, Japan
Tel.: (81) 362622780
Web Site: https://lifesalon.jp
Fire Insurance Services
N.A.I.C.S.: 524113

MLC Limited (1)
Ground Floor MLC Building 105 153 Miller Street, Sydney, 2060, NSW, Australia **(80%)**
Tel.: (61) 386344721
Web Site: http://www.mlc.com.au
Sales Range: $5-14.9 Billion
Investment Advice & Services
N.A.I.C.S.: 523940
Suzie Brown (Gen Mgr-Wealth & Corp Partnerships)

Subsidiary (Domestic):

Plum Financial Services Limited (2)
Level 4 500 Bourke Street, Melbourne, 3000, VIC, Australia
Tel.: (61) 392224800
Web Site: http://www.plumfs.com.au
Financial (Superannuation) Services
N.A.I.C.S.: 523999
Geoff Short (Gen Counsel & Sec)

NLI Insurance Agency Inc. (1)
655 3rd Ave 16 Fl, New York, NY 10017
Tel.: (212) 682-3000
Web Site: http://www.nissay.co.jp
Sales Range: $100-124.9 Million
Emp.: 70
Life & Property Insurance Services
N.A.I.C.S.: 524128

Branch (Domestic):

NLI Insurance Agency Inc. - Central Region Office (2)
20 N Martingale Rd Ste 150, Schaumburg, IL 60173
Tel.: (312) 807-1100
Web Site: http://www.nlia.com
Insurance Agents
N.A.I.C.S.: 524210

Division (Domestic):

Nippon Life Benefits (2)
655 3rd Ave 16th Fl, New York, NY 10017-9113
Tel.: (212) 909-9892
Web Site: http://www.nipponlifebenefits.com
Sales Range: $50-74.9 Million
Insurance Services
N.A.I.C.S.: 524298
Francine Young (COO & Exec VP)

Branch (Domestic):

Nippon Life Benefits (3)
515 S Figueroa St Ste 1470, Los Angeles, CA 90071
Tel.: (213) 430-9000
Web Site: http://www.nipponlifebenefits.com
Sales Range: $50-74.9 Million
Emp.: 10
Insurance Agents
N.A.I.C.S.: 524210

Bruce Walker (CFO, Chief Risk Officer, Sec & Sr VP)

NLI Properties West, Inc. (1)
445 S Figueroa St Ste 2850, Los Angeles, CA 90071-1669
Tel.: (213) 623-9307
Real Estate Investment Management Services
N.A.I.C.S.: 531390

NLI Research Institute (1)
4-1-7 Kudankita, Chiyoda-ku Kudan Center Building, Tokyo, 102-0073, Japan **(100%)**
Tel.: (81) 335121800
Web Site: http://www.nli-research.co.jp
Research & Consulting Services
N.A.I.C.S.: 541720
Junichi Noro (Chm & CEO)

Nippon Insurance Service Co., Ltd. (1)
NIS Building 1-6-12 Enokojima, Nishi-ku, Osaka, 550-0006, Japan
Tel.: (81) 664484121
Web Site: http://www.nissay-nis.co.jp
Emp.: 108
Life Insurance Contracts Services
N.A.I.C.S.: 524128

Nippon Life (Deutschland) GmbH (1)
An Der Hauptwache 5, 60313, Frankfurt am Main, Germany **(100%)**
Tel.: (49) 692739990
Sales Range: $75-99.9 Million
Emp.: 4
Life & Property Insurance Services
N.A.I.C.S.: 524128
Keishi Miki (Mgr)

Nippon Life Americas, Inc. (1)
101 Park Ave 33rd Fl, New York, NY 10178
Tel.: (646) 231-4000
Web Site: https://www.nissay.co.jp
Business Support Services
N.A.I.C.S.: 561499

Nippon Life Global Investors Americas, Inc. (1)
277 Park Ave 34th Fl, New York, NY 10172
Tel.: (646) 231-4000
Emp.: 60
Investment Services
N.A.I.C.S.: 523999
Keisuke Kawasaki (CEO)

Nippon Life Global Investors Europe PLC (1)
1-5 Queens Street, London, EC4N 1SW, United Kingdom
Tel.: (44) 2075076011
Investment Services
N.A.I.C.S.: 523999

Nippon Life India Asset Management Limited (1)
4th Floor Tower A Peninsula Business Park Ganapatrao Kadam Marg, Lower Parel W, Mumbai, 400 013, India **(74.99%)**
Tel.: (91) 2268087000
Web Site: https://investeasy.nipponindiaim.com
Rev.: $181,836,820
Assets: $462,911,096
Liabilities: $41,429,171
Net Worth: $421,481,926
Earnings: $86,725,016
Emp.: 1,007
Fiscal Year-end: 03/31/2023
Mutual Fund Services
N.A.I.C.S.: 525910
Sundeep Sikka (CEO)

Subsidiary (Non-US):

Nippon Life India Asset Management (Singapore) Pte. Ltd. (2)
9 Raffles Street 18-05, Singapore, 048619, Singapore **(100%)**
Tel.: (65) 68270120
Financial Investment Services
N.A.I.C.S.: 523999
Jrvisvai Sgue (CEO)

Nippon Life Insurance Co. - Tokyo Office (1)
1-6-6 Marunouchi, Chiyoda-ku, Tokyo, 100-8288, Japan
Tel.: (81) 355335133
Web Site: http://www.nissay.co.jp

INTERNATIONAL PUBLIC

Sales Range: $1-4.9 Billion
Emp.: 10,000
Venture Capital Business
N.A.I.C.S.: 523910

Nippon Life Insurance Company - London Representative Office (1)
1-5 Queen's Street, London, EC4N 1SW, United Kingdom
Tel.: (44) 2076002804
Sales Range: $50-74.9 Million
Emp.: 25
Life & Property Insurance Services
N.A.I.C.S.: 524128

Nippon Life Realty Management Inc. (1)
16th Floor Otemachi Nomura Building 2-1-1 Otemachi, Chiyoda-ku, Tokyo, Japan
Tel.: (81) 362718740
Web Site: https://nissay-realty.co.jp
Real Estate Services
N.A.I.C.S.: 531390

Nippon Life Schroders Asset Management Europe Limited (1)
1 London Wall Place, London, EC2Y 5AU, United Kingdom
Tel.: (44) 2076586000
Fire Insurance Services
N.A.I.C.S.: 524113

Nissay Asset Management Corporation (1)
Nihon Seimei Marunouchi Building 1-6-6 Marunouchi, Chiyoda-ku, Tokyo, 100-8219, Japan
Tel.: (81) 355334920
Web Site: http://www.nam.co.jp
Sales Range: $200-249.9 Million
Emp.: 543
Investment Advisory Services
N.A.I.C.S.: 523940
Hiroyuki Nishi (Pres & CEO)

Nissay Business Service Co., Ltd. (1)
Nissei Yodoyabashi East 12th Floor 3-3-13 Imabashi, Chuo-ku, Osaka, 541-0042, Yubinbango, Japan **(100%)**
Tel.: (81) 676392051
Web Site: http://www.nissay-nbs.co.jp
Clerical & Business Administration Services
N.A.I.C.S.: 561320
Toshifumi Terada (Pres)

Nissay Credit Guarantee Co., Ltd. (1)
1 2 2 Yurakucho, Chiyoda-ku, Tokyo, 100-8488, Japan
Tel.: (81) 335031081
Sales Range: $50-74.9 Million
Emp.: 50
Credit Guarantee Services
N.A.I.C.S.: 522299

Nissay Culture Foundation (1)
1-1-1 Yurakucho, Chiyoda-ku, Tokyo, 100-0006, Japan
Tel.: (81) 335033111
Web Site: http://www.nissaytheatre.or.jp
Sales Range: $25-49.9 Million
Emp.: 40
Nissay Theatre Management & Operations
N.A.I.C.S.: 561311
Yoshikazu Takeda (Mng Dir)

Nissay Green Foundation (1)
1 1 Yurakucho 1 Chome, Minato Ku, Tokyo, 12117, Japan
Tel.: (81) 335019203
Tree Planting Services
N.A.I.C.S.: 561730

Nissay Investment Co., Ltd. (1)
2-2 Yurakucho 1-chome, Chiyoda-ku, Tokyo, 100 8444, Japan
Tel.: (81) 335031081
Investment Strategies & Solutions
N.A.I.C.S.: 523150

Nissay Schroders Asset Management Asia Limited (1)
65 Chulia Street #46-00 OCBC Centre, Singapore, 049513, Singapore
Tel.: (65) 6535 3411
Investment Management Service
N.A.I.C.S.: 523940

Nissay Schroders Asset Management Europe Limited (1)

AND PRIVATE COMPANIES

NIPPON LIGHT METAL HOLDINGS COMPANY, LTD.

31 Gresham Street, London, EC2V 7QA, United Kingdom
Tel.: (44) 20 7658 6739
Investment Management Service
N.A.I.C.S.: 523940

Nissay-Greatwall Life Insurance Co., Ltd. (1)
37th Floor United Plaza 1468, Nanjing Road West, Shanghai, 200 040, China
Tel.: (86) 38999888
Web Site: http://www.nissay.co.jp
Life Insurance Products & Services; Owned 50% by Nippon Life Insurance Co. & 50% by China Great Wall Asset Management Corporation
N.A.I.C.S.: 524113

Reliance Nippon Life Insurance Company Limited (1)
H Block 1st Floor Dhirubhai Ambani Knowledge City, Goregaon East, Mumbai, 400710, India
Tel.: (91) 2230007000
Web Site: http://www.reliancenipponlife.com
Life Insurance Products & Services
N.A.I.C.S.: 524113
Srinivasan Iyengar (COO)

Shinjuku NS Building Co., Ltd. (1)
2-4-1 Nishishinjuku, Tokyo, 163-0813, Japan
Tel.: (81) 333 423755
Building & Construction Services
N.A.I.C.S.: 236116

Taiju Life & I Technology Ltd. (1)
8-18 Higashigamicho Taiju Life Business Center, Kashiwa, 277-0011, Chiba, Japan
Tel.: (81) 471623033
Fire Insurance Services
N.A.I.C.S.: 524113

Taiju Life Insurance Company Limited (1)
1-1-20 Aomi DiverCity Tokyo Office Tower, Koto-ku, Tokyo, 135-8222, Japan
Tel.: (81) 368318000
Web Site: https://www.taiju-life.co.jp
Fire Insurance Services
N.A.I.C.S.: 524113

Taisei Building Management Co, Ltd. (1)
4-22-2 Koishikawa, Bunkyou-Ku, Tokyo, Japan
Tel.: (81) 358045111
Web Site: http://www.taisei.co.jp
Sales Range: $350-399.9 Million
Emp.: 1,250
Building Management
N.A.I.C.S.: 561790

Tokyo Opera City Building Co., Ltd. (1)
Tokyo Opera City Tower 3-20-2, Nishi-Shinjuku Shinjuku-ku, Tokyo, 163-1407, Japan
Tel.: (81) 353530700
Web Site: https://www.tokyooperacity.co.jp
Live Concert Services
N.A.I.C.S.: 711120

NIPPON LIGHT METAL HOLDINGS COMPANY, LTD.
Urbannet Uchisaiwaicho Building
1-1-13 Shimbashi, Minato-ku, Tokyo, 105-8681, Japan
Tel.: (81) 368107100   JP
Web Site:
  https://www.nikkeikinholdings.com
Year Founded: 2012
5703—(TKS)
Rev.: $3,461,756,150
Assets: $3,596,467,950
Liabilities: $2,016,697,780
Net Worth: $1,579,770,170
Earnings: $59,734,570
Fiscal Year-end: 03/31/24
Holding Company; Aluminum Products Mfr & Distr
N.A.I.C.S.: 551112
Kotaro Yasuda (Auditor)

Subsidiaries:

Aluminum Wire Rod Company Ltd. (1)
Kambara 5443, Shimizu-ku, Shizuoka, 421-3203, Japan
Tel.: (81) 54 388 2662
Web Site: https://group.nikkeikin.co.jp
Aluminum Wire Mfr & Distr
N.A.I.C.S.: 335929

CMR Nikkei India Preivate Ltd. (1)
Plot No 65 Sector 15, Bawal, 123501, Haryana, India
Tel.: (91) 128 420 0125
Aluminum Alloy Product Distr
N.A.I.C.S.: 423510

Changchun Nikkei Railway Vehicle Equipment Co., Ltd. (1)
No 8299 Changbai Rd, Lvyuan Economy Development Dist, Changchun, 130113, Jilin, China
Tel.: (86) 4318 785 7889
Aluminum Parts Mfr & Distr
N.A.I.C.S.: 331315

Fruehauf Mahajak Co., Ltd. (1)
67/16 Moo 5 Kokfad, Nongchok, Bangkok, 10530, Thailand
Tel.: (66) 2 988 0900
Web Site: https://www.fruehauf.co.th
Motor Vehicle Body Mfr & Distr
N.A.I.C.S.: 336211

Guangxi Hezhou Nikkei Guiyin Technology Co., Ltd. (1)
11F No 89 Jianshe Mid Road, Hezhou, Guangxi, China
Aluminium Products Mfr
N.A.I.C.S.: 331313

Hunan Ningxiang JiWeiXin Metal Powder Co., Ltd. (1)
No 288 Xieyuan North Road, Ningxiang Economic and Technological Development Zone, Changsha, 410600, Hunan, China
Tel.: (86) 73187890331
Aluminum Powder Mfr
N.A.I.C.S.: 331315

Keinara Co., Ltd. (1)
5th Floor Yokohama Peace Building 3-30-7, Honcho Naka-ku, Yokohama, 231-0005, Japan
Tel.: (81) 4 521 1161
Web Site: https://group.nikkeikin.co.jp
Freight Transportation Services
N.A.I.C.S.: 488510

Kinki Abradant Industry Co., Ltd. (1)
313 Aza-donotani Konan-cho Koji, Koka, 520-3306, Shiga, Japan
Tel.: (81) 748862281
Abrasive Product Mfr
N.A.I.C.S.: 327910

Kinki Kenmazai Kogyo Co., Ltd. (1)
Aza Dounotani 313 Konan-cho Kouji, Koga, 520-3306, Shiga, Japan
Tel.: (81) 74 886 2281
Abrasive Product Mfr
N.A.I.C.S.: 327910

NKS Co., Ltd. (1)
161 Kambara, Shimizu-ku, Shizuoka, 421-3297, Japan
Tel.: (81) 543852282
Fabricated Structural Metal Mfr
N.A.I.C.S.: 332312

Nikkan Co., Ltd. (1)
206 Kambara, Shimizu-ku, Shizuoka, 421-3203, Japan
Tel.: (81) 543852522
Industrial Machinery Mfr
N.A.I.C.S.: 333310

Nikkei (Shanghai) Body Parts Co., Ltd. (1)
No 3 Building No 1368 Song Hua Road Qing Pu Industrial Zone, Shanghai, 201700, China
Tel.: (86) 21 5986 9388
Aluminum Product Mfr & Distr
N.A.I.C.S.: 331313

Nikkei (Shanghai) international Trading Co., Ltd. (1)
Room 1202 Shenggao International Building No 137 Xianxia Road, Changning District, Shanghai, 200051, China
Tel.: (86) 216 236 9658
Web Site: https://cngroup.nikkeikin.com
Marketing Consulting Services
N.A.I.C.S.: 541613

Nikkei (Suzhou) Precision Parts Co., Ltd. (1)
NO 1000 Chunshen Road, Huangcheng Town Xiangcheng District, Suzhou, Jiangsu, China
Tel.: (86) 5126 571 0550
Automobile Parts Aluminum Mfr
N.A.I.C.S.: 331318

Nikkei Engineering Co., Ltd. (1)
Shinnaga Building 2-35-13 Kameido, Koto-ku, Tokyo, 136-0071, Japan
Tel.: (81) 35 628 8510
Web Site: https://www.sne.co.jp
Chemical Engineering Services
N.A.I.C.S.: 541330

Nikkei Hokkaido Co., Ltd. (1)
43-3 Harumi-cho, Tomakomai, 053-0002, Hokkaido, Japan
Tel.: (81) 144557161
Web Site: https://group.nikkeikin.co.jp
Emp.: 191
Aluminum Product Mfr & Distr
N.A.I.C.S.: 331313

Nikkei Inazawa Co., Ltd. (1)
1-11-1 Koike, Inazawa, 492-8144, Aichi, Japan
Tel.: (81) 587329120
Industrial Machinery Mfr & Distr
N.A.I.C.S.: 333310

Nikkei Kambara Co., Ltd. (1)
Extrusion Factory 5617, Kanbara Shimizu-ku, Shizuoka, 421-3297, Japan
Tel.: (81) 54 385 4321
Web Site: https://group.nikkeikin.co.jp
Aluminum Alloys Mfr & Distr
N.A.I.C.S.: 331314

Nikkei MC Aluminium Co., Ltd. (1)
Urbannet Uchisaiwaicho Building 1-1-13, Shimbashi Minato-Ku, Tokyo, 105-8681, Japan
Tel.: (81) 36 810 7360
Web Site: https://www.nmca.jp
Emp.: 514
Aluminum Alloys Mfr & Distr
N.A.I.C.S.: 331314
Masashi Koyama (Pres)

Nikkei MC Aluminum (Kunshan) Co., Ltd. (1)
No 8 ShengXi Road, Kunshan Economic Technology Development Zone, Kunshan, 215334, Jiangsu, China
Tel.: (86) 51257631946
Web Site: https://www.nmak.cn
Aluminum Alloy Mfr
N.A.I.C.S.: 331314

Nikkei New Business Co., Ltd. (1)
1-1-13 Shimbashi Urban Net Uchiyukicho Building, Minato-ku, Tokyo, 140-0002, Japan
Tel.: (81) 36 810 7230
Web Site: https://group.nikkeikin.co.jp
Travel Agency Services
N.A.I.C.S.: 561510

Nikkei Niigata Co., Ltd. (1)
1572-19 Taro-dai, Kita-ku, Niigata, 950-3101, Japan
Tel.: (81) 252553141
Aluminum Extrusion Product Mfr & Distr
N.A.I.C.S.: 331315

Nikkei Panel System Vietnam Company Limited (1)
Unit 1202 12th Floor Dai Minh Convention Tower 77, Hoang Van Thai St Dist 7 Tan Phu Ward, Ho Chi Minh City, Vietnam
Tel.: (84) 285 416 8080
Paper Product Distr
N.A.I.C.S.: 423390

Nikkei Partners Co., Ltd. (1)
5-12 Matsubara-cho, Shimizu-ku, Shizuoka, 424-0825, Japan
Tel.: (81) 54 351 3386
Web Site: https://group.nikkeikin.co.jp
Insurance Services
N.A.I.C.S.: 524210

Nikkei Technology Center Co., Ltd. (1)
1-11 Nishikikitacho, Kaizuka, 597-0092,
Osaka, Japan
Tel.: (81) 724239235
Emp.: 120
Aluminum Fabricated Product Mfr & Distr
N.A.I.C.S.: 332999

Nikkeikin Kakoh Kaihatsu Holdings Company, Ltd. (1)
1-1-13 Urbannet Uchisaiwaicho Building, Shinbashi Minato-ku, Tokyo, 105-8681, Japan
Tel.: (81) 36 810 7300
Web Site: https://group.nikkeikin.co.jp
Aluminum Alloys Mfr & Distr
N.A.I.C.S.: 331314

Nippon Light Metal Company, Ltd. (1)
Urbannet Uchisaiwaicho Building 1-1-13 Shimbashi, Minato-ku, Tokyo, 105-8681, Japan (100%)
Tel.: (81) 368107101
Web Site: http://www.nikkeikin.com
Sales Range: $5-14.9 Billion
Aluminum Products Mfr & Distr
N.A.I.C.S.: 331313
Ichiro Okamoto (Pres & CEO)

Subsidiary (Domestic):

Aluminium Wire & Rod Co., Ltd. (2)
5443 Kambara, Shimizu-ku, Shizuoka, 421-3203, Japan
Tel.: (81) 543882662
Sales Range: $25-49.9 Million
Emp.: 50
Aluminium Products Mfr
N.A.I.C.S.: 331313

Subsidiary (Non-US):

NI Nikkei Shenzhen Co., Ltd. (2)
No 5 South Baozi Road, Pingshan New District, Shenzhen, Guangdong, China
Tel.: (86) 75526505656
Automotive Aluminum Extrusions Mfr
N.A.I.C.S.: 331318

Subsidiary (Domestic):

NLM ECAL Co., Ltd. (2)
161 Kambara, Shimizu-ku, Shizuoka, 421-3203, Japan (100%)
Tel.: (81) 543883555
Emp.: 65
Communication Housings, Power Equipment & Sheet Metal Mfr
N.A.I.C.S.: 333613

Nikkei Extrusions Co., Ltd. (2)
2100 abe, Ochiai-cho, Takahashi, 716-0061, Okayama, Japan
Tel.: (81) 866 22 6021
Web Site: http://www2.nikkeikin.co.jp
Sales Range: $25-49.9 Million
Emp.: 235
Extruded Aluminum Products Mfr
N.A.I.C.S.: 331318
Hiromi Mizu (Chm & CEO)

Joint Venture (Domestic):

Nikkei Heat Exchanger Co., Ltd (2)
161 Kambara, Shimizu-ku, Shizuoka, 421-3297, Japan
Tel.: (81) 543852164
Web Site: https://group.nikkeikin.co.jp
Aluminum Heat Exchange Services
N.A.I.C.S.: 331315

Subsidiary (Domestic):

Nikkei Information System Co., Ltd (2)
Urbannet Uchisaiwaicho Building 1-1-13 Shinbashi, Minato-ku, Tokyo, 105-8681, Japan (100%)
Tel.: (81) 368107320
Development, Sale & Lease of Computer Software & Information Processing Services
N.A.I.C.S.: 541511

Nikkei Logistics Co., Ltd. (2)
1-1-13 Urbannet Uchisaiwaicho, Shimbashi Minato-ku, Tokyo, 105-8681, Japan
Tel.: (81) 368107370
Emp.: 516
Warehousing & Logistics Services
N.A.I.C.S.: 493110

NIPPON LIGHT METAL HOLDINGS COMPANY, LTD.

Nippon Light Metal Holdings Company, Ltd.—(Continued)

Subsidiary (Non-US):

Nikkei MC Aluminum (Thailand) Co., Ltd. (2)
78/1 M 2 Wellgrow Industrial Estate T Pimpa A, Bangpakong, Chachoengsao, 24130, Thailand
Tel.: (66) 38522296
Web Site: https://www.nma-thai.com
Sales Range: $25-49.9 Million
Emp.: 50
Aluminum Alloy Mfr
N.A.I.C.S.: 331313

Subsidiary (Domestic):

Nikkei Matsuo Co., Ltd. (2)
813-1 Shimonogo, Ueda, 386-1211, Nagano, Japan
Tel.: (81) 268380001
Sales Range: $25-49.9 Million
Emp.: 250
Fabricated Aluminum Products Mfr
N.A.I.C.S.: 331315

Nikkei Metal Co., Ltd. (2)
4-20-15 Chiyoda, Naka-ku, Nagoya, 460-0012, Aichi, Japan
Tel.: (81) 523316261
Sale & Processing of Aluminum Ingots & Semis
N.A.I.C.S.: 331315

Nikkei Panel System Co., Ltd. (2)
Urbannet Uchisaiwaicho Building 1-13 Shinbashi, Minato-ku, Tokyo, 105-8681, Japan
Tel.: (81) 368107272
Sales Range: $100-124.9 Million
Emp.: 303
Fabricated Metal & Air Conditioning Products Mfr
N.A.I.C.S.: 332311

Nikkei Sangyo Co., Ltd. (2)
5-12 Matsubara-cho, Shimizu-ku, Shizuoka, 424-0825, Japan
Tel.: (81) 543535271
Sales Range: $50-74.9 Million
Emp.: 229
Steel Product Distr
N.A.I.C.S.: 423510

Subsidiary (Non-US):

Nikkei Siam Aluminium Limited (2)
30 Moo 14 Paholyothin Road KM 47, Tambol Klong 1 Amphur Klongluang, Pathumthani, 12120, Thailand
Tel.: (66) 290973009
Web Site: https://www.nikkeisiam.co.th
Sales Range: $75-99.9 Million
Emp.: 350
Aluminum Sheet & Foil Products Mfr
N.A.I.C.S.: 331315
Yasuhito Tajima *(Mng Dir)*

Nikkei Singapore Aluminium Pte Ltd. (2)
Tel.: (65) 6562933770
Aluminium Products Mfr
N.A.I.C.S.: 331318

Nikkei Taiwan System Engineering Co., Ltd. (2)
Room No 308 3 F 160 Nanjing East Road Section 2, Taipei, 10489, Taiwan
Tel.: (886) 225155233
Web Site: http://www.nikkeitaiwan.com.tw
Sales Range: $25-49.9 Million
Emp.: 6
Metal Products Mfr
N.A.I.C.S.: 332311

Subsidiary (Domestic):

Nikkeikin Aluminium Core Technology Co., Ltd. (2)
Urbannet Uchisaiwaicho Building 1-13 Shinbashi, Minato-ku, Tokyo, 105-8681, Japan
Tel.: (81) 368107300
Web Site: https://group.nikkeikin.co.jp
Sales Range: $25-49.9 Million
Emp.: 175
Extruded Aluminum Products Mfr
N.A.I.C.S.: 331318

Nippon Electrode Co., Ltd. (2)
5600 Kambara, Shimizu-ku, Shizuoka, 421-3203, Japan
Tel.: (81) 543853141
Sales Range: $25-49.9 Million
Emp.: 200
Electrolytic Capacitor Mfr
N.A.I.C.S.: 334416
Hirofumi Mikami *(Pres)*

Nippon Fruehauf Co., Ltd. (2)
3034 Uenohara Kamiechi, Atsugi, 243-0281, Kanagawa, Japan
Tel.: (81) 462853111
Automobile Parts Mfr
N.A.I.C.S.: 336211
Yuji Kato *(Mng Dir)*

Plant (Domestic):

Nippon Fruehauf Co., Ltd. - Atsugi Plant (3)
3034 Kamiechi Uenohara, Atsugi, 243-0281, Kanagawa, Japan
Tel.: (81) 462853111
Web Site: https://www.fruehauf.co.jp
Automobile Bodies Mfr
N.A.I.C.S.: 336211

Subsidiary (Non-US):

Nonfemet International (China-Canada-Japan) Aluminium Co., Ltd. (2)
Block F1-9C TCL International E City No 1001 ZhongShanPark Road, Nanshan, Shenzhen, Guangdong, China
Tel.: (86) 75526611569
Sales Range: $150-199.9 Million
Emp.: 900
Extruded Aluminum Products Mfr
N.A.I.C.S.: 331318
Baoyu Dong *(Chm)*

Subsidiary (Domestic):

Riken Light Metal Industrial Co., Ltd. (2)
2-1 Magarikane 3-chome, Suruga-ku, Shizuoka, 422-8530, Japan
Tel.: (81) 542811111
Sales Range: $25-49.9 Million
Emp.: 330
Fabricated Structural Metal Mfr
N.A.I.C.S.: 332312
Tomio Maeda *(Pres)*

Subsidiary (Non-US):

Thai Nikkei Trading Co., Ltd. (2)
Unit No 23/36 And 23/35 Sukhumvit 63 Road Klongton Nua, Wattana, Bangkok, 10110, Thailand
Tel.: (66) 27269001
Web Site: http://www.nikkei-buturyu.co.jp
Aluminium Product Distr
N.A.I.C.S.: 423510

Subsidiary (Domestic):

Toyo Aluminium Ekco Products Co., Ltd. (2)
1-4-1 Nishihonmachi Orix Honmachi Building 13F, Nishi-ku, Osaka, 550-0005, Japan
Tel.: (81) 661101301
Web Site: https://www.toyoalumi-ekco.jp
Aluminum Foil Containers Mfr
N.A.I.C.S.: 331315

Toyo Aluminium K.K. (2)
6-8 Kyutaromachi 3-chome, Chuo-ku, Osaka, 541-0056, Japan
Tel.: (81) 662713151
Sales Range: $200-249.9 Million
Emp.: 2,607
Aluminium Products Mfr & Distr
N.A.I.C.S.: 331315

Subsidiary (US):

Toyal America Inc. (3)
17401 S Broadway, Lockport, IL 60441-6508
Tel.: (630) 505-2161
Sales Range: $25-49.9 Million
Emp.: 60
Aluminum Products Mfr & Distr
N.A.I.C.S.: 331314
Dan Velkovich *(VP-Sls & Mktg)*

Subsidiary (Domestic):

Toyo Tokai Aluminium Hanbai K.K. (3)

DP Square Honmachi 5F 4-1-10 Minami-honmachi, Chuo-ku, Osaka, 541-0054, Japan
Tel.: (81) 662451071
Web Site: https://www.alumihanbai.co.jp
Emp.: 70
Aluminium Product Distr
N.A.I.C.S.: 331315

Nippon Light Metal Georgia, Inc. (1)
100 Nikkei Way NW, Adairsville, GA 30103
Tel.: (470) 601-5030
Web Site: https://www.nlmga.com
Aluminum Suspension Product Distr
N.A.I.C.S.: 423510

Nippon Light Metal North America, Inc. (1)
485 Metro Pl S 210, Dublin, OH 43017
Tel.: (614) 698-2841
Aluminum Product Mfr & Distr
N.A.I.C.S.: 331315

PT. Nikkei Trading Indonesia (1)
Summitmas II 5th Floor JL Jend Sudirman Kav 61-62, Jakarta, 12190, Indonesia
Tel.: (62) 21 252 1939
Web Site: https://group.nikkeikin.co.jp
Aluminum Materials Distr
N.A.I.C.S.: 423510

Riken Light Metal Industry Company Ltd. (1)
3-2-1 Magarikane, Suruga-ku, Shizuoka, 422-8530, Japan
Tel.: (81) 54 281 1111
Web Site: https://www.rikenkeikinzoku.co.jp
Aluminum Material Mfr & Distr
N.A.I.C.S.: 331314

Sam-A Aluminium Co., Ltd. (1)
5 Nambsunhwan-Ro 289-GIL, Seocho-gu, Seoul, 06699, Korea (South)
Tel.: (82) 23 458 0600
Packaging & Labeling Services
N.A.I.C.S.: 561910

Shandong Conglin Fruehauf Automobile Co., Ltd. (1)
North Second Road, Conglin Industrial Zone, Longkou, 265705, Shandong, China
Web Site: https://www.clfh.com.cn
Truck Trailer Mfr
N.A.I.C.S.: 336212

Shandong Nikkei Conglin Automobile Parts Co., Ltd. (1)
3 North Rd, Conglin Industry Dist, Longkou, Shandong, China
Tel.: (86) 535 856 7839
Automobile Parts Aluminum Mfr
N.A.I.C.S.: 331318

Shizuoka Kosan Co., Ltd. (1)
Nikkei Sangyo Bldg 3F 5-12 Matsubaracho, Shimizu-ku, Shizuoka, 424-0825, Japan
Tel.: (81) 54 355 0166
Chemical Product Mfr & Distr
N.A.I.C.S.: 325998

Sumikei-Nikkei Engineering Co., Ltd. (1)
Shinei Building 2-35-13 Kameido, Koto-ku, Tokyo, 136-0071, Japan
Tel.: (81) 356288510
Web Site: https://www.sne.co.jp
Civil Engineering Services
N.A.I.C.S.: 541330

Suzhou Toyo Aluminium Ekco Household Products Co., Ltd. (1)
No 258 Jinling East Road, Suzhou Industrial Park Weiting Town, Suzhou, Jiangsu, China
Tel.: (86) 5128 227 3091
Converted Paper Product Mfr
N.A.I.C.S.: 322299

Toho Earthtech, Inc. (1)
1450 Kurotori, Nishi-ku, Niigata, 950-1123, Japan
Tel.: (81) 253777131
Emp.: 123
Natural Gas & Iodine Distr
N.A.I.C.S.: 221210

Toyal Europe S.A.S.U. (1)
41 boulevard Vauban, 78280, Guyancourt, France
Tel.: (33) 134931020

Web Site: https://toyal-europe.com
Aluminum Pigment Mfr
N.A.I.C.S.: 331314

Toyal Zhaoqing Co., Ltd. (1)
No 1 Xinglong 5th Street Linjiang Industrial Park, Zhaoqing National High-Tech Industrial Development Zone, Guangdong, 526238, China
Tel.: (86) 758 360 2080
Web Site: https://www.toyalchina.com
Aluminum Paste Mfr & Distr
N.A.I.C.S.: 331314

Toyo Aluminium (Shanghai) Management Co., Ltd. (1)
Room 401 402 A Building Far East International Plaza No 319, Xianxia Road Changning District, Shanghai, 200051, China
Tel.: (86) 213 257 5868
Foil Product Mfr
N.A.I.C.S.: 331315

Toyo Precision Appliance (Kunshan) Co., Ltd. (1)
No 188 Gaoding Road, Economic and Technical Development Zone, Kunshan, Jiangsu, China
Tel.: (86) 5125 033 8039
Electronic Computer Mfr
N.A.I.C.S.: 334111
Hiroharu Miyazaki *(Chm)*

Toyo Rikagaku Kenkyusho Co., Ltd. (1)
1961 Somagi, Tsubame, 959-1284, Niigata, Japan
Tel.: (81) 25 662 5175
Web Site: https://www.toyorikagaku.com
Metal Container Mfr
N.A.I.C.S.: 332439

Toyo Tokai Aluminium Hanbai (Shanghai) Co., Ltd. (1)
Rm 404 Far East International Plaza A-Zone No 319 Xianxia Rd, Changning District, Shanghai, 200051, China
Tel.: (86) 216 278 3200
Marketing Consulting Services
N.A.I.C.S.: 541613

NIPPON LOGISTECH CORPORATION

2-6 Kandasudacho Landic Kanda Building 6F, Chiyoda-ku, Tokyo, 101-0041, Japan
Tel.: (81) 332581276
Web Site: http://www.nippon-logistech.com
Year Founded: 1959
Rev.: $59,600,000
Emp.: 183
Transportation & Warehousing Services
N.A.I.C.S.: 493190
Yugo Suzuki *(Chm)*

Subsidiaries:

Nippon Logistech Support Corporation (1)
12-20 Chidori, Urayasu, Chiba, Japan
Tel.: (81) 473044311
Logistics Consulting Servies
N.A.I.C.S.: 541614

NIPPON MIRAI CAPITAL CO., LTD.

1-3-3 Uchisaiwaicho, Chiyoda-ku, Tokyo, 100-0011, Japan
Tel.: (81) 335004250
Web Site: http://www.miraicapital.co.jp
Year Founded: 2002
Sales Range: $50-74.9 Million
Emp.: 14
Investment Services
N.A.I.C.S.: 523999
Akira Yasujima *(CEO & Partner)*

NIPPON MOLYMER CO., LTD.

Sanko Osaka Hommachi Bldg 7F 2-3-8 Honmachi Chuo-Ku, Osaka, 541-0053, Japan

AND PRIVATE COMPANIES

Tel.: (81) 662671551
Plastics & Chemicals Mfr
N.A.I.C.S.: 325211

Subsidiaries:

Daitai Kako Co., Ltd. (1)
3-11-2 Torikainishi, Settsu, 566-0072, Osaka, Japan
Tel.: (81) 726545121
Web Site: http://www.daitai.co.jp
Paints Mfr
N.A.I.C.S.: 325510

NIPPON PAINT HOLDINGS CO., LTD.

2-1-2 Oyodo Kita, Kita-ku, Osaka, 531-8511, Japan
Tel.: (81) 664581111 JP
Web Site: https://www.nipponpaint-holdings.com
Year Founded: 1881
4612—(TKS)
Rev.: $9,531,377,602
Assets: $17,927,591,675
Liabilities: $8,888,252,395
Net Worth: $9,039,339,280
Earnings: $786,237,199
Emp.: 33,000
Fiscal Year-end: 12/31/23
Holding Company
N.A.I.C.S.: 325510
Seiichiro Shirahata *(Mng Exec Officer)*

Subsidiaries:

Akzo Nobel Industrial Finishes AB (1)
Odensvivagen 32, SE 594 32, Gamleby, Sweden
Tel.: (46) 49314100
Sales Range: $50-74.9 Million
Emp.: 120
Mfr of Coatings; Joint Venture of Akzo Nobel N.V. (75%) & Nippon Paint Company (25%)
N.A.I.C.S.: 325510

Akzo Nobel Nippon Paint Espania SA (1)
14-20 Feixa Llarga, Zona Franca, 08040, Barcelona, Spain
Tel.: (34) 93 484 2541
Sales Range: $25-49.9 Million
Emp.: 6
Mfr of Coatings; Joint Venture of Akzo Nobel N.V. (75%) & Nippon Paint Company (25%)
N.A.I.C.S.: 325510

Akzo Nobel Nippon Paint GmbH (1)
Lochnerstrasse 12, D 90441, Nuremberg, Germany (100%)
Tel.: (49) 91166880
Sales Range: $50-74.9 Million
Emp.: 150
Mfr of Coatings; Joint Venture of Akzo Nobel N.V. (75%) & Nippon Paint Company (25%)
N.A.I.C.S.: 325510

Akzo Nobel Nippon Paint Limited (1)
Hollins Rd, PO Box 37, Darwen, BB3 0BG, Lancashire, United Kingdom (100%)
Tel.: (44) 254760760
Web Site: http://www.akzonobel-ic.co.uk
Sales Range: $25-49.9 Million
Emp.: 20
Mfr & Sales of Coatings; Joint Venture of Akzo Nobel N.V. (75%) & Nippon Paint Company (25%)
N.A.I.C.S.: 325510

Akzo Nobel Nippon Paint Srl (1)
Via Emilia 2, 26861, Fombio, Lo, Italy (100%)
Tel.: (39) 0377410390
Web Site: http://www.akzonobel.it
Sales Range: $25-49.9 Million
Emp.: 11
Mfr of Coatings; Joint Venture of Akzo Nobel N.V. (75%) & Nippon Paint Company (25%)
N.A.I.C.S.: 325510

Betek Boya ve Kimya Sanayi Anonim Sirketi (1)
Zumrutevler Mahallesi Ural Sokak No 38, Maltepe, 34852, Istanbul, Turkiye
Tel.: (90) 2165711000
Web Site: https://www.betek.com.tr
Construction Materials Distr
N.A.I.C.S.: 423390

DP JUB delniska druzba pooblascenka d.d. (1)
Dol pri Ljubljana 28, SI-1262, Ljubljana, Slovenia
Tel.: (386) 15884183
Web Site: https://www.jub.eu
Paint Mfr & Distr
N.A.I.C.S.: 325510

DuluxGroup Limited (1)
1956 Dandenong Rd, Clayton, 3168, VIC, Australia
Tel.: (61) 392635678
Web Site: http://www.duluxgroup.com.au
Rev.: $1,439,000,340
Assets: $1,034,527,788
Liabilities: $690,749,260
Net Worth: $343,778,528
Earnings: $115,925,399
Emp.: 4,000
Fiscal Year-end: 09/30/2018
Holding Company; Paints, Coatings & Other Building Materials & Products Mfr
N.A.I.C.S.: 551112
Patrick Houlihan *(CEO & Mng Dir)*

Subsidiary (Non-US):

B&D Doors (NZ) Limited (2)
46 Braeburn Drive, Hornby, Christchurch, 8042, New Zealand
Tel.: (64) 33845145
Web Site: http://www.bnd.co.nz
Sales Range: $25-49.9 Million
Emp.: 30
Garage Doors & Automatic Door Openers Mfr
N.A.I.C.S.: 339999
Lalit Chand *(Mgr-Mfg Site)*

Concrete Plus Limited (2)
23 Watts Rd, Sockburn, Christchurch, 8042, New Zealand
Tel.: (64) 33430090
Web Site: http://www.concreteplus.co.nz
Sales Range: $25-49.9 Million
Emp.: 7
Construction Products & Equipment Distr
N.A.I.C.S.: 423390
Andy Simpson *(Gen Mgr)*

Countermast Limited (2)
Unit 29-24 Polka Hoi Luen Industrial Center Hoi Yuen Rd, Kwun Tong, Kowloon, China (Hong Kong)
Tel.: (852) 23954257
Sales Range: $10-24.9 Million
Emp.: 8
Engineeering Services
N.A.I.C.S.: 541330
Cyrus Wong *(Mgr-Pur)*

DGL International (Singapore) Pte. Ltd (2)
265 Serangoon Central Drive 02-275, Singapore, 550265, Singapore
Tel.: (65) 68381010
Web Site: http://www.seleys.com.au
Emp.: 8
Adhesive Mfr
N.A.I.C.S.: 325520
Surendran P. Rajendran Nathan *(Mng Dir)*

Dulux Holdings (PNG) Limited (2)
Lot 9 Section 88 Aircorps Rd, Lae, 411, Morobe, Papua New Guinea
Tel.: (675) 4723633
Emp.: 10
Paints Mfr
N.A.I.C.S.: 325510
Andrew Gunn *(Gen Mgr)*

Subsidiary (Domestic):

Dulux Holdings Pty Ltd (2)
1956 Dandenong Road, Clayton, 3168, VIC, Australia
Tel.: (61) 392635678
Web Site: http://www.dulux.com.au
Building Construction Services
N.A.I.C.S.: 236210

NIPPON PAINT HOLDINGS CO., LTD.

Lincoln Sentry Group Pty Limited (2)
48 Weaver St, PO Box 276, Coopers Plains, 4108, QLD, Australia
Tel.: (61) 1300551919
Web Site: http://www.lincolnsentry.com.au
Sales Range: $150-199.9 Million
Emp.: 500
Hardware & Components Distr
N.A.I.C.S.: 423710

Parchem Construction Supplies Pty Limited (2)
7 Lucca Road, Wyong, 2259, NSW, Australia
Tel.: (61) 243505000
Web Site: http://www.parchem.com.au
Sales Range: $25-49.9 Million
Emp.: 100
Construction Products & Equipment Mfr & Distr
N.A.I.C.S.: 333120

Dunn-Edwards Corporation (1)
4885 E 52nd Pl, Los Angeles, CA 90058
Tel.: (323) 771-3330
Web Site: http://www.dunnedwards.com
Full-Service Paint Retailer & Mfr
N.A.I.C.S.: 325510
Tim Bosveld *(VP-Mktg)*

Guangzhou Nippon Paint Co., Ltd. (1)
No 1 Fenghua Second Road Economic Development Zone, Guangzhou, 510530, China
Tel.: (86) 20 2230 1888
Paint Mfr & Distr
N.A.I.C.S.: 325510
Li Guodong *(Plant Mgr)*

Langfang Nippon Paint Co., Ltd. (1)
Fuzhong Road Langfang Economic, Technology Development Zone, Langfang, 65001, Hebei, China
Tel.: (86) 3166088535
Web Site: http://www.nipponpaint.co.jp
Mfr of Coatings
N.A.I.C.S.: 325510

NP Automotive Coatings (Europe) Ltd. (1)
Britannia Trade Park Radway Rd, Swindon, SN3 4ND, Wilts, United Kingdom
Tel.: (44) 793823361
Sales Range: $25-49.9 Million
Emp.: 50
Mfr & Sales of OEM Automotive Coatings
N.A.I.C.S.: 325510

Nippe Home Products Co., Ltd. (1)
4-1-15 Minami-Shinagawa, Shinagawa-ku, Tokyo, 140-0004, Japan
Tel.: (81) 337401132
Web Site: https://www.nippehome.co.jp
Emp.: 70
Color Paint Mfr & Distr
N.A.I.C.S.: 325510

Nippe Trading Co., Ltd (1)
1-22-26 Esaka, Suita, 564-0063, Osaka, Japan
Tel.: (81) 6 6338 5651
Web Site: http://www.nippetrading.co.jp
Rev.: $313,344,000
Emp.: 77
Painting Raw Materials Whslr
N.A.I.C.S.: 424950
Fukuda Masato *(Pres & CEO)*

Nippon Paint (Bangladesh) Private Limited (1)
60/E/2 Dawan Monjeel Purana Paltan, Dhaka, 1000, Bangladesh
Tel.: (880) 9678333444
Web Site: https://www.nipponpaint.com.bd
Color Paint Mfr & Distr
N.A.I.C.S.: 325510

Nippon Paint (Chengdu) Co., Ltd. (1)
No 600 Cheng Long Road Economic Technology Development Zone, Chengdu, 610100, China
Tel.: (86) 2888438188
Web Site: http://www.nipponpaint.co.jp
Paints Mfr
N.A.I.C.S.: 325510

Nippon Paint (China) Co., Ltd. (1)
287 Chuang Ye Road Jinqiao Development Zone, Pudong New District, Shanghai, 201201, China (100%)
Tel.: (86) 2158384799
Web Site: http://www.nipponpaint.com.cn
Sales Range: $200-249.5 Million
Emp.: 1,000
Sales & Marketing of Architectural & Automotive Coatings, Industrial Paints & TU Paints
N.A.I.C.S.: 325510

Nippon Paint (Chongqing) Chemicals Co., Ltd. (1)
75 Panlong the forth Village Jiulong Town, Jiulongpo District, Chongqing, 400051, China
Tel.: (86) 23 6865 7452
Web Site: http://www.nipponpaint.co.jp
Specialty Chemicals Mfr & Distr
N.A.I.C.S.: 325998

Nippon Paint (Europe) Ltd. (1)
Britannia Trade Park Radway Rd, Swindon, SN3 4ND, Wiltshire, United Kingdom (100%)
Tel.: (44) 1793823361
Web Site: http://nipponpainteurope.co.uk
Sales Range: $50-74.9 Million
Emp.: 60
Holding Company; Trading Raw Materials for Paint & Machinery
N.A.I.C.S.: 551112
M. Iwamura *(Mng Dir)*

Nippon Paint (Guangdong) Co., Ltd. (1)
Room 3105 Block 2 Dong Jun Plaza Dong Feng Road East, Guangzhou, Guangdong, China (100%)
Tel.: (86) 2087300868
Web Site: http://www.nipponpaint.com.cn
Sales Range: $125-149.9 Million
Emp.: 400
Mfr of Automotive Coatings
N.A.I.C.S.: 325510

Nippon Paint (H.K.) Co., Ltd. (1)
Suite 3203-4 32/F Tower 2 Nina Tower 8 Yeung Uk Road, Tsuen Wan, New Territories, China (Hong Kong) (100%)
Tel.: (852) 26999333
Web Site: https://www.nipponpaint.com.hk
Sales Range: $25-49.9 Million
Emp.: 40
Mfr of Paints
N.A.I.C.S.: 325510

Nippon Paint (India) Private Limited (1)
No 3 3rd Floor Club House Road, Chennai, 600 002, Tamil Nadu, India
Tel.: (91) 4442982222
Color Paint Mfr & Distr
N.A.I.C.S.: 325510

Nippon Paint (Malaysia) Sdn. Bhd. (1)
Lot I-17 Taman Perindustrian Subang Utama, Jalan SU 4, 40300, Shah Alam, Selangor Darul Ehsan, Malaysia (100%)
Tel.: (60) 351250888
Web Site: https://www.nipponpaint.com.my
Sales Range: $50-74.9 Million
Emp.: 400
Mfr of Paint & Chemicals for Decorative, Automotive, Marine, Automotive Refinish, Industrial & Wood Applications
N.A.I.C.S.: 325510

Nippon Paint (Myanmar) Service Co., Ltd. (1)
Building 14 Ground Floor MICT Park, Hlaing Campus Township, Yangon, Myanmar
Tel.: (95) 9264153025
Web Site: https://www.nipponpaint.com.mm
Emp.: 2,300
Color Paint Mfr & Distr
N.A.I.C.S.: 325510

Nippon Paint (Pakistan) Private Limited (1)
100-G Phase 1 DHA, Cantt, Lahore, Pakistan
Tel.: (92) 111647766
Web Site: https://nipponpaint.com.pk
Emp.: 26,277
Color Paint Mfr & Distr
N.A.I.C.S.: 325510

Nippon Paint (Philippines) Inc. (1)

NIPPON PAINT HOLDINGS CO., LTD.

Nippon Paint Holdings Co., Ltd.—(Continued)
40 Hologram St Light Industry and Science Park, Cabuyao, Laguna, Philippines **(100%)**
Tel.: (63) 28451176
Web Site: http://www.nipponpaint.ph
Sales Range: $50-74.9 Million
Emp.: 150
Mfr of Automotive Coatings
N.A.I.C.S.: 325510

Nippon Paint (Singapore) Co., Pte. Ltd. (1)
1 First Lok Yang Road, Jurong, 629728, Singapore **(100%)**
Tel.: (65) 62655355
Web Site: http://www.nipponpaint.com
Sales Range: $25-49.9 Million
Emp.: 150
Mfr of Paints
N.A.I.C.S.: 325510

Nippon Paint (Thailand) Co., Ltd. (1)
101 Moo 3 Soi Suksawad 76 Suksawad Road, Bangchak Prapradaeng, Samut Prakan, 10130, Thailand **(100%)**
Tel.: (66) 24630032
Web Site: http://www.nipponpaint.co.th
Sales Range: $125-149.9 Million
Emp.: 400
Supplier of Paint
N.A.I.C.S.: 325510

Plant (Domestic):

Nippon Paint (Thailand) Co., Ltd. - BangPakong Factory (2)
700/29 31 Moo6 T Nong Maidaeng 700/33 Moo 5 T Klongtamrhu, A Muang, Chon Buri, 20000, Thailand
Tel.: (66) 38 213 701
Paint & Allied Products Mfr
N.A.I.C.S.: 325510

Nippon Paint (USA) Inc. (1)
Glenpointe Centre E 300 Frank W Burr Blvd, Teaneck, NJ 07666-6895 **(100%)**
Tel.: (201) 692-1111
Web Site: http://www.nipponpaint.com
Sales Range: $50-74.9 Million
Emp.: 7
Provider of Paint Trading & Services
N.A.I.C.S.: 424690

Subsidiary (Domestic):

NB Coatings, Inc. (2)
2701 E 170th St, Lansing, IL 60438-1107
Tel.: (708) 868-7403
Web Site: http://www.nbcoatings.com
Mfr of Paints
N.A.I.C.S.: 325510

NPA Coatings Inc. (2)
11110 Berea Rd, Cleveland, OH 44102-2539
Tel.: (216) 651-5900
Web Site: http://www.nipponpaintamericas.com
Sales Range: $50-74.9 Million
Automotive Coatings Mfr & Whslr
N.A.I.C.S.: 325510
Ken Ternovan (Dir-IT)

Nippon Paint (Vietnam) Co., Ltd. (1)
No 14 3A Road Bien Hoa Industrial Zone II, Long Binh Tan Ward, Bien Hoa, Dong Nai, Vietnam
Tel.: (84) 2513836579
Web Site: https://www.nipponpaint.com.vn
Sales Range: $125-149.9 Million
Emp.: 400
Paint Mfr & Distr
N.A.I.C.S.: 325510

Nippon Paint Automotive Americas, Inc. (1)
2701 E 170th St, Lansing, IL 60438
Web Site: https://www.nipponpaintamericas.com
Automotive Coatings Mfr & Distr
N.A.I.C.S.: 325510

Nippon Paint Automotive Coatings Co., Ltd. (1)
2-14-1 Shodai Otani, Hirakata, 573-1153, Japan
Tel.: (81) 728575530

Web Site: http://www.nipponpaint-automotive.com
Emp.: 790
Chemical Products Mfr
N.A.I.C.S.: 325998
Shinji Takedagawa (Pres)

Nippon Paint Coatings (Taiwan) Co., Ltd. (1)
No 24 Dongyuan Rd, Zhongli Dist, Taoyuan, 320, Taiwan
Tel.: (886) 34529529
Color Paint Mfr & Distr
N.A.I.C.S.: 325510

Nippon Paint Company Ltd. - Tokyo Office (1)
4-7-16 Minamishinagawa, Shinagawa, Tokyo, 140-8675, Japan
Tel.: (81) 354793600
Web Site: http://www.nipponpaint.co.jp
Sales Range: $200-249.9 Million
Emp.: 1,000
Mfr of Paint & Coatings
N.A.I.C.S.: 325510

Nippon Paint Corporate Solutions Co., Ltd. (1)
2-1-2 Oyodo Kita, Kita-ku, Osaka, 531-8511, Japan
Tel.: (81) 664559634
Web Site: https://www.nipponpaint-cs.co.jp
Information Technology Services
N.A.I.C.S.: 541519

Nippon Paint Lanka (private) Limited (1)
Nippolac Towers No 69A Buthgamuwa Road, 10600, Rajagirya, Sri Lanka
Tel.: (94) 114600400
Web Site: https://nipponpaint.lk
Paint Mfr & Distr
N.A.I.C.S.: 325510

Nippon Paint Marine Coatings Co., Ltd (1)
1-26 Komagabayashi Minami-cho, Nagata-Ku, Kobe, 653-0045, Hyogo, Japan
Tel.: (81) 787355384
Web Site: http://www.nippe-marine.co.jp
Sales Range: $50-74.9 Million
Emp.: 150
Marine Coating Paint Mfr & Distr
N.A.I.C.S.: 325510
Yoshiaki Kuroda (Exec VP)

Subsidiary (Non-US):

Nippon Paint Marine (Hong Kong) Co., Ltd. (2)
Room 1708 17/F Tins Enterprise Centre 777 Lai Chi Kok, Kowloon, China (Hong Kong)
Tel.: (852) 23077311
Emp.: 6
Marine Paint Coatings Whslr
N.A.I.C.S.: 424950
Ko Chipo (Gen Mgr)

Nippon Paint Marine (Korea) Co., Ltd. (2)
Rm 201 Taerim Bldg 85-13 Jungang-Dong 4GA, Jung-Gu, Pusan, 600 814, Korea (South)
Tel.: (82) 51 468 2989
Web Site: http://www.nippe-marine.co.jp
Sales Range: $25-49.9 Million
Emp.: 40
Marine Paint Coating Distr
N.A.I.C.S.: 424950
Lee Jaehan (Gen Mgr)

Nippon Paint Marine (Malaysia) Sdn. Bhd. (2)
Lot 1-17 Taman Perindustrian Subang Utama Jalam SU4, 40300, Shah Alam, Selangor, Malaysia
Tel.: (60) 351913388
Sales Range: $25-49.9 Million
Emp.: 7
Marine Coating Paint Whslr
N.A.I.C.S.: 424950

Nippon Paint Marine (Singapore) Pte. Ltd. (2)
No 1 First Lok Yang Road Jurong, Singapore, 629728, Singapore
Tel.: (65) 6268 1161

Sales Range: $25-49.9 Million
Emp.: 17
Marine Coating Paints Mfr & Distr
N.A.I.C.S.: 325510
Bill Phua (Mng Dir)

Nippon Paint Marine (Taiwan) Co., Ltd. (2)
7F 275 Sung Chiang Road, Taipei, 104, Taiwan
Tel.: (886) 2 25185902
Web Site: http://www.nippe-marine.co.jp
Marine Paint Coatings Whslr
N.A.I.C.S.: 424950
Steven Chang (Gen Mgr)

Nippon Paint Surf Chemicals Co., Ltd. (1)
4-1-15 Minamishinagawa, Shinagawa-ku, Tokyo, 140-8675, Japan
Tel.: (81) 337401296
Web Site: https://www.nipponpaint-surf.com
Surface Treatment Product Distr
N.A.I.C.S.: 424690

Nippon Paint Turkey Boya Sanayi Ve Ticaret Anonim Sirketi (1)
Tuzla Kimya Sanayicileri Organize Sanayi Bolgesi Melek Aras Bulvari, No 19 Aydinli Tuzla, Istanbul, Turkiye
Tel.: (90) 2165934520
Web Site: https://www.nipponpaint.com.tr
Color Paint Mfr & Distr
N.A.I.C.S.: 325510

Nippon Paint Vietnam (Hanoi) Co., Ltd. (1)
Lot 39A Quang Minh Industrial Zone, Me Linh District, Hanoi, Vietnam
Tel.: (84) 4 381 82241
Paint Coating Whslr
N.A.I.C.S.: 424950

Nipsea Chemical Korea Co., Ltd. (1)
104 Sandan-ro 19beon-gil, Ansan, 156-10, Gyeonggi-do, Korea (South) **(100%)**
Web Site: http://www.nipsea.co.kr
Sales Range: $25-49.9 Million
Emp.: 50
Mfr & Sales of Surface Treatment Chemicals for Metal
N.A.I.C.S.: 325998

Nipsea Technologies Pte. Ltd. (1)
16 Joo Koon Crescent, Singapore, 629018, Singapore
Tel.: (65) 68622298
Color Paint Mfr & Distr
N.A.I.C.S.: 325510

Noroo Automotive Coatings Co., Ltd. (1)
Jangangongdan-7-gil, Jangan-myeon, Hwaseong, 18579, Gyeonggi-do, Korea (South) **(49%)**
Tel.: (82) 31 8059 9500
Web Site: http://www.norooautocoat.com
Automotive Paints & Coatings Mfr
N.A.I.C.S.: 325510

P.T. Nipsea Paint And Chemicals (1)
Jl Ancol Barat I/A5/C No 12, Jakarta, 14430, Indonesia
Tel.: (62) 216900546
Web Site: https://www.nipponpaint-indonesia.com
Paint Mfr & Distr
N.A.I.C.S.: 325510

Paint Marketing Co (M) Sdn. Bhd. (1)
Lot 2A Taman Perindustrian Subang Utama Jalan SU 4, 40300, Shah Alam, Selangor Darul Ehsan, Malaysia
Tel.: (60) 351016288
Paint Mfr & Distr
N.A.I.C.S.: 325510

Suzhou Nippon Paint Yashili Co., Ltd. (1)
No 14 8 Tonhong Road SIP, Suzhou, 215006, China
Tel.: (86) 512 65931868
Paint Mfr & Distr
N.A.I.C.S.: 325510

Vital Technical Sdn. Bhd. (1)
No 93 Jalan Industri 3/3 Rawang Integrated Industrial Park, 48000, Rawang, Selangor, Malaysia

Tel.: (60) 360942088
Web Site: https://www.vitaltechnical.com
Emp.: 300
Sealant Product Mfr & Distr
N.A.I.C.S.: 325520

NIPPON PALLET POOL CO., LTD.

Kyoei Building 4F 2-8-11 Shibata, Kita-ku, Osaka, 530-0012, Japan
Tel.: (81) 663733231
Web Site: https://www.npp-web.co.jp
Year Founded: 1972
4690—(TKS)
Rev.: $68,675,718
Assets: $100,301,634
Liabilities: $51,284,204
Net Worth: $49,017,429
Earnings: $2,641,169
Emp.: 100
Fiscal Year-end: 03/31/22
Pallet Rental Services
N.A.I.C.S.: 488999
Eiichi Arita (Pres & CEO)

NIPPON PAPER INDUSTRIES CO., LTD.

4-6 Kandasurugadai, Chiyoda-Ku, Tokyo, 101-0062, Japan
Tel.: (81) 366651111 JP
Web Site: https://www.nipponpapergroup.com
Year Founded: 1949
3863—(TKS)
Rev.: $7,715,945,540
Assets: $11,443,529,450
Liabilities: $8,167,296,170
Net Worth: $3,276,233,280
Earnings: $150,357,670
Emp.: 15,557
Fiscal Year-end: 03/31/24
Holding Company; Newsprint, Paper, Packaging Board, Pulp & Other Paper Products Mfr
N.A.I.C.S.: 551112
Fumio Manoshiro (Chm)

Subsidiaries:

Amapa Florestal e Celulose S.A. (1)
Rua Claudio Lucio Monteiro s/n, Caixa Postal 5657, Novo Horizonte, Santana, 68926-000, Amapa, Brazil
Tel.: (55) 9632818000
Web Site: https://www.amcel.com.br
Environmental Consulting Services
N.A.I.C.S.: 541620

Daishowa North America Corporation (1)
2800-666 Burrard Street, Vancouver, V6C 2Z7, BC, Canada
Tel.: (360) 582-6532
Web Site: http://www.np-g.com
Pulp Mill Operators
N.A.I.C.S.: 322110

Daishowa Uniboard Co., Ltd. (1)
111 Fukiagenishi, Iwanuma, 989-2437, Miyagi, Japan **(100%)**
Tel.: (81) 223221521
Web Site: http://www.uniboard.jp
Emp.: 78
Wood Products Mfr
N.A.I.C.S.: 321999

Everwealth Paper Industries (Shanghai) Co., Ltd. (1)
589 QianPu Rd Xin Qiao Industrial Park, Song Jiang, Shanghai, 201612, China
Tel.: (86) 2167760668312
Web Site: http://www.everwealth.com.cn
Sales Range: $50-74.9 Million
Emp.: 200
Paper Products Mfr
N.A.I.C.S.: 322299

FRR Fax Roll (1)
3 Zaytseva St, R 198096, Saint Petersburg, Russia **(100%)**
Tel.: (7) 8121832156
N.A.I.C.S.: 322120

AND PRIVATE COMPANIES

NIPPON PAPER INDUSTRIES CO., LTD.

Graphic Arts Communication Co., Ltd. (1)
2-717-5 Toyonodai, Toyonodai Techno Town, Kazo, 349-1148, Saitama, Japan
Tel.: (81) 480726510
Web Site: http://www.gacnps.co.jp
Paper Product Mfr & Distr
N.A.I.C.S.: 333243

Hotoku Co., Ltd. (1)
84 Kamijuku Uchigomimayamachi, Iwaki, Fukushima, Japan (100%)
Tel.: (81) 246261191
Web Site: http://mimizunotuti.com
Sales Range: $25-49.9 Million
Emp.: 162
Freight Transportation Services
N.A.I.C.S.: 488510
Norikazu Kasamatsu (Dir)

Jujo Thermal Oy (1)
Paperitehtaantie 15, PO Box 92, 27500, Kauttua, Finland
Tel.: (358) 10303200
Web Site: https://www.jujothermal.com
Sales Range: $100-124.9 Million
Emp.: 200
Thermal Paper Mfr & Distr
N.A.I.C.S.: 322299
Toshihiro Sawamura (Pres & CEO)

Kitakami Paper Co., Ltd. (1)
10-1 Asahicho, Ichinoseki, 021-0864, Iwate, Japan
Tel.: (81) 191233366
Web Site: http://www.kitakami-p.jp
Emp.: 90
Paper Products Mfr
N.A.I.C.S.: 322299
Fukudome Yukio (Pres & CEO)

Kokuei Paper Co., Ltd. (1)
3-1-1 Aoyagi, Soka, 340-0002, Saitama, Japan
Tel.: (81) 489353711
Web Site: https://www.kokuei-p.co.jp
Paper Product Distr
N.A.I.C.S.: 424110

Kokusaku Kiko Co., Ltd. (1)
149 Yufutsu, Tomakomai, 059-1372, Hokkaido, Japan (100%)
Tel.: (81) 144560321
Web Site: https://www.kokusakukikou.co.jp
Emp.: 84
Paper Mfr
N.A.I.C.S.: 322299

Koyo Paper Mfg. Co., Ltd. (1)
450 Hina, Fuji, 417-0847, Shizuoka, Japan
Tel.: (81) 545340820
Web Site: http://www.koyopaper.co.jp
Paper Products Mfr
N.A.I.C.S.: 322299

Ky Vy Corporation (1)
B16 Truong son, 15th ward District 10, Ho Chi Minh City, Vietnam
Tel.: (84) 2838683050
Paper Product Mfr & Distr
N.A.I.C.S.: 333243

Kyokushin Transport Co., Ltd. (1)
Logistics Park 1-jo 1-3-1, Asahikawa, 071-8130, Hokkaido, Japan
Tel.: (81) 166587171
Web Site: http://www.kyokushin-unyu.co.jp
General Freight Trucking Services
N.A.I.C.S.: 484122

Kyouei Seitai K.K. (1)
Shinwa Building 2F 2-10-7 Yushima, Bunkyo-ku, Tokyo, 113-0034, Japan
Tel.: (81) 338158241
Web Site: https://www.kyoueiseitai.com
Paper Product Mfr & Distr
N.A.I.C.S.: 333243

NP Trading Co., Ltd. (1)
4-6 Kanda-Surugadai, Chiyoda-ku, Tokyo, 101-8210, Japan
Tel.: (81) 36 665 7032
Web Site: https://www.np-t.co.jp
Emp.: 384
Paper Product Whslr
N.A.I.C.S.: 424110
Harunori Saito (Pres)

Nanko Unyu Co., Ltd. (1)
7-1 Shigeyoshi-cho, Ishinomaki, 986-0844, Miyagi, Japan

Tel.: (81) 225954161
Web Site: http://www.nankou.co.jp
Emp.: 561
Logistics Consulting Servies
N.A.I.C.S.: 541614

Nippon Daishowa Paperboard Co., Ltd. (1)
1-2-2 Hitotsubashi, Chiyoda-ku, Tokyo, 100-0003, Japan
Tel.: (81) 366655000
Web Site: http://www.nichidaiita.co.jp
Sales Range: $450-499.9 Million
Emp.: 1,020
Paperboard Mfr
N.A.I.C.S.: 322130

Plant (Domestic):

Nippon Daishowa Paperboard Co., Ltd. - Akita Mill (2)
2-1-1 Mukaihama, Akita, 010-1601, Japan
Tel.: (81) 188967700
Paperboard Mfr
N.A.I.C.S.: 322130

Nippon Daishowa Paperboard Co., Ltd. - Ashikaga Mill (2)
12-7 Miyakita-cho, Ashikaga, 326-0027, Tochigi, Japan
Tel.: (81) 284415151
Web Site: http://www.np-g.com
Paperboard Mfr
N.A.I.C.S.: 322130

Nippon Daishowa Paperboard Co., Ltd. - Otake Mill (2)
2-1-18 Higashi Sakae, Otake, 739-0601, Hiroshima, Japan
Tel.: (81) 827 52 4131
Paperboard Mfr
N.A.I.C.S.: 322130

Nippon Daishowa Paperboard Co., Ltd. - Soka Mill (2)
4-3-39 Matsue, Soka, 340-0013, Saitama, Japan
Tel.: (81) 489319571
Paperboard Mfr
N.A.I.C.S.: 322130

Nippon Daishowa Paperboard Co., Ltd. - Yoshinaga Mill (2)
798 Hina, Fuji, 417-8520, Shizuoka, Japan
Tel.: (81) 545 57 3212
Web Site: http://www.np-g.com
Paperboard Mfr
N.A.I.C.S.: 322130

Nippon Paper Chemicals Co., Ltd. (1)
4-6 Kanda-Surugadai Chiyoda-ku, Chiyoda-ku, Tokyo, 101-0062, Japan
Tel.: (81) 366655900
Web Site: http://www.npchem.co.jp
Chemical Product Mfr & Distr
N.A.I.C.S.: 325998
Yusuke Makita (Sr Mng Dir)

Subsidiary (Domestic):

Flowric Co., Ltd. (2)
1-10-1 Sumitomo Ikebukuro Ekimae Building 5F Higashiikebukuro, Toshima-ku, Tokyo, 170-0013, Japan
Tel.: (81) 359606911
Web Site: https://www.flowric.co.jp
Emp.: 50
Industrial Chemicals Mfr & Distr
N.A.I.C.S.: 325998

Nippon Paper Chemicals Support Co., Ltd. (2)
1280 Gotsu-cho, Gotsu, 695-0011, Shimane, Japan
Tel.: (81) 855525384
Web Site: http://www.npchem.co.jp
Chemical Products Business Support & Production
N.A.I.C.S.: 325998

Nippon Paper Crecia Co., Ltd. (1)
4-6 Kanda Surugadai, Chiyoda-ku, Tokyo, 101-8215, Japan
Tel.: (81) 366655302
Web Site: https://www.crecia.co.jp
Sales Range: $250-299.9 Million
Emp.: 938
Personal Care Product Mfr & Distr

N.A.I.C.S.: 325620

Plant (Domestic):

Nippon Paper Crecia Co., Ltd. - Iwakuni Mill (2)
1808 Nagano, Iwakuni, 740-0045, Yamaguchi, Japan
Tel.: (81) 827391616
Web Site: http://www.np-g.com
Sales Range: $50-74.9 Million
Emp.: 125
Household Paper Products Mfr
N.A.I.C.S.: 322299

Nippon Paper Crecia Co., Ltd. - Kaisei Mill (2)
500 Yoshidajima Kaisei-machi, Ashigarakami-gun, Kaisei, 258-0021, Kanagawa, Japan
Tel.: (81) 465832311
Household Paper Products Mfr
N.A.I.C.S.: 322299

Nippon Paper Crecia Co., Ltd. - Kyoto Mill (2)
1-54 Osadano-cho, Fukuchiyama, 620-0853, Kyoto, Japan
Tel.: (81) 773276311
Sales Range: $100-124.9 Million
Emp.: 260
Household Paper Products Mfr
N.A.I.C.S.: 322299
Kawa Gutichi (Mgr)

Nippon Paper Crecia Co., Ltd. - Tokyo Mill (2)
4-2-16 Matsue, Soka, 340-0013, Saitama, Japan
Tel.: (81) 489311151
Web Site: http://www.np-g.com
Household Paper Products Mfr
N.A.I.C.S.: 322299

Nippon Paper Development Co., Ltd. (1)
1-1-9 Horifune, Kita-ku, Tokyo, 114-8555, Japan (100%)
Tel.: (81) 339146161
Web Site: http://www.npd.jp
Sales Range: $25-49.9 Million
Emp.: 12
Paper Products Mfr
N.A.I.C.S.: 322299
Tetsuya Yamamoto (Pres)

Nippon Paper Industries Co., Ltd. - Fuji Mill (1)
798 Hina, Fuji, 417-8520, Shizuoka, Japan
Tel.: (81) 545573212
Web Site: http://www.np-g.com
Sales Range: $125-149.9 Million
Emp.: 300
Paper Mfr
N.A.I.C.S.: 322299

Nippon Paper Industries Co., Ltd. - Hokkaido Mill (1)
143 Yufutsu, Tomakomai, 059-1395, Hokkaido, Japan
Tel.: (81) 144560111
Web Site: http://www.np-g.com
Sales Range: $125-149.9 Million
Emp.: 300
Paper Mfr
N.A.I.C.S.: 322299

Nippon Paper Industries Co., Ltd. - Ishinomaki Mill (1)
2-2-1 Nanko-cho, Ishinomaki, 986-8555, Miyagi, Japan
Tel.: (81) 225 95 0111
Web Site: http://www.np-g.com
Paper Mfr
N.A.I.C.S.: 322299

Nippon Paper Industries Co., Ltd. - Iwakuni Mill (1)
2-8-1 Iida-machi, Iwakuni, 740-0003, Yamaguchi, Japan
Tel.: (81) 827246222
Web Site: http://www.np-g.com
Emp.: 543
Paper Mfr
N.A.I.C.S.: 322299

Nippon Paper Industries Co., Ltd. - Iwanuma Mill (1)

1-1 Daishowa, Iwanuma, 989-2492, Miyagi, Japan
Tel.: (81) 223226111
Web Site: http://www.np-g.com
Sales Range: $125-149.9 Million
Emp.: 223
Paper Mfr
N.A.I.C.S.: 322299

Nippon Paper Industries Co., Ltd. - Kushiro Mill (1)
2-1-47 Tottori-Minami, Kushiro, 084-0905, Hokkaido, Japan
Tel.: (81) 154527605
Web Site: http://www.np-g.com
Paper Mfr
N.A.I.C.S.: 322299

Nippon Paper Industries Co., Ltd. - Nakoso Mill (1)
1 Kubota-jujo Nakoso-machi, Iwaki, 979-0141, Fukushima, Japan
Tel.: (81) 246653111
Web Site: http://www.np-g.com
Sales Range: $50-74.9 Million
Emp.: 150
Paper Mfr
N.A.I.C.S.: 322299

Nippon Paper Industries Co., Ltd. - Yatsushiro Mill (1)
1-1 Jujo-machi, Yatsushiro, 866-8602, Kumamoto, Japan
Tel.: (81) 965332111
Web Site: http://www.nipponpapergroup.com
Paper Mfr
N.A.I.C.S.: 322299

Nippon Paper Industries Trading (Shanghai) Co., Ltd. (1)
Room 1805 Building B Hongqiao Nanfengcheng No 100 Zunyi Road, Changning Distric, Shanghai, 200051, China
Tel.: (86) 2161453260
Web Site: https://www.npi-sh.com
Emp.: 15
Paper Product Distr
N.A.I.C.S.: 424130

Nippon Paper Industries USA Co., Ltd. (1)
3001 Industrial Way, Longview, WA 98632
Tel.: (360) 636-6400
Web Site: http://www.npiusa.com
Printing Paper Mfr
N.A.I.C.S.: 322299
Yuji Sato (Pres)

Nippon Paper Logistics Co., Ltd. (1)
2-2-30 Aoyagi, Soka, 340-0002, Saitama, Japan
Tel.: (81) 489322300
Emp.: 410
Logistics Consulting Servies
N.A.I.C.S.: 541614

Nippon Paper Lumber Co., Ltd. (1)
4-6 Kanda Surugadai Ochanomizu Sola City, Chiyoda-ku, Tokyo, 101-8213, Japan
Tel.: (81) 366657500
Web Site: http://www.np-l.co.jp
Sales Range: $50-74.9 Million
Emp.: 188
Paper Mfr
N.A.I.C.S.: 322299

Nippon Paper Papylia Co., Ltd. (1)
4-6-6 Kanda Surugadai, Chiyoda-ku, Tokyo, 101-0062, Japan (100%)
Tel.: (81) 366655800
Web Site: http://www.papylia.com
Sales Range: $1-4.9 Billion
Emp.: 456
Paper Products Mfr
N.A.I.C.S.: 322299
Sumio Miyake (Pres)

Plant (Domestic):

Nippon Paper Papylia Co., Ltd. - Harada Mill (2)
506 Harada, Fuji, 417-0852, Shizuoka, Japan
Tel.: (81) 54 552 4060
Web Site: http://www.np-g.com
Sales Range: $50-74.9 Million
Emp.: 150
Paper Products Mfr
N.A.I.C.S.: 322299

NIPPON PAPER INDUSTRIES CO., LTD.

Nippon Paper Industries Co., Ltd.—(Continued)
Sumio Miyaki (Pres)

Nippon Paper Papylia Co., Ltd. - Kochi Mill (2)
3380 Ino-cho, Agawa-gun, Kochi, 781-2110, Japan
Tel.: (81) 888921122
Web Site: http://www.papylia.com
Paper Products Mfr
N.A.I.C.S.: 322299

Nippon Paper Papylia Co., Ltd. - Suita Mill (2)
11-46 Higashiotabi-cho, Suita, 564-0033, Osaka, Japan
Tel.: (81) 663812255
Web Site: http://www.np-g.com
Paper Products Mfr
N.A.I.C.S.: 322299

Nippon Paper Viet Hoa My JSC (1)
Lot C5-8 Street N8 Block C5 Tan Phu Trung IP, Tan Phu Trung Commune Cu Chi District, Ho Chi Minh City, Vietnam
Tel.: (84) 836204321
Web Site: https://npvhm.com.vn
Paper Product Mfr & Distr
N.A.I.C.S.: 333243

Nippon Paper-Pak Co., Ltd. (1)
J S Kanda Second Central Building 4-1-2 Nishi Kita 1-jo, Chuo-ku, Sapporo, 060-0001, Hokkaido, Japan
Tel.: (81) 112314444
Paper Mfr & Distr
N.A.I.C.S.: 322299

Nippon Seitai Corporation (1)
8F Kanda Second Central Building 7 Kanda Mitoshiro-cho, Chiyoda-ku, Tokyo, 101-0053, Japan
Tel.: (81) 33 518 0380
Web Site: https://www.npseitai.co.jp
Paper Products Mfr
N.A.I.C.S.: 322299
Iwasaki Nobuo (Pres)

Pan Pac Forest Products Limited (1)
1161 State Highway 2 Wairoa Road, Hawke's Bay, Napier, 4182, New Zealand (13%)
Tel.: (64) 6 831 0100
Web Site: https://www.panpac.co.nz
Sales Range: $125-149.9 Million
Emp.: 500
Paper Production
N.A.I.C.S.: 322120
Doug Ducker (Mng Dir)

Paper Australia Pty. Ltd. (1)
Sales Range: $1-4.9 Billion
Emp.: 5,000
Fine Paper & Packaging Paper Products Mfr
N.A.I.C.S.: 322120

Subsidiary (Domestic):

Orora Packaging Australia Pty. Ltd. (2)
109 Burwood Road, Hawthorn, 3122, VIC, Australia (100%)
Tel.: (61) 391161711
Packaging Products Mfr & Distr
N.A.I.C.S.: 322211

Division (Domestic):

Orora Bags (3)
2 Keon Parade, Keon Park, 3073, VIC, Australia
Tel.: (61) 3 9496 8700
Web Site: http://www.orora.com
Emp.: 100
Plastic Bag Mfr & Distr
N.A.I.C.S.: 326111
David Berry (Gen Mgr)

Orora Beverage Cans (3)
109 Burwood Road, Hawthorn, 3122, VIC, Australia
Tel.: (61) 3 9811 7111
Metal Cans Mfr & Distr
N.A.I.C.S.: 332431
Brian Lowe (Gen Mgr-Fibre)

Plant (Domestic):

Orora Beverage Cans - Canning Vale Plant (4)
53-159 Bannister Road, Canning Vale, 6155, WA, Australia
Tel.: (61) 892569300
Metal Can Mfr & Distr
N.A.I.C.S.: 332431
Dee Rust (Mgr-Ops)

Division (Domestic):

Orora Cartons (3)
109 Burwood Road, Hawthorn, 3122, VIC, Australia
Tel.: (61) 391161711
Sales Range: $25-49.9 Million
Emp.: 90
Folding Paperboard Cartons Mfr & Distr
N.A.I.C.S.: 322212
David Berry (Gen Mgr)

Orora Fibre Packaging (3)
109 Burwood Road, Hawthorn, 3122, VIC, Australia
Tel.: (61) 391161711
Corrugated Box Mfr & Distr
N.A.I.C.S.: 322211
Rick Woods (Gen Mgr)

Plant (Domestic):

Orora Fibre Packaging - Smithfield Plant (4)
Cnr Warren & Percival Roads, Smithfield, 2164, NSW, Australia
Tel.: (61) 2 9609 9111
Folding Paperboard Box & Container Mfr
N.A.I.C.S.: 322212

Subsidiary (Non-US):

Orora Packaging New Zealand Ltd. (3)
239 Cavendish Drive, Manukau, 1702, Auckland, New Zealand
Tel.: (64) 398117111
Packaging Products Mfr & Distr
N.A.I.C.S.: 322211

Unit (Domestic):

Orora Packaging New Zealand Ltd. - Kiwi Packaging (4)
239 Cavendish Drive, Wiri, 1702, Auckland, New Zealand
Tel.: (64) 99805500
Sales Range: $100-124.9 Million
Mfr of Corrugated Boxes
N.A.I.C.S.: 322211
Peter McElroy (Gen Mgr)

Paper Products Marketing (Malaysia Branch) Pte. Ltd.
Suite 25-03 Level 25 Centro Office Tower No 8 Jalan Batu Tiga Lama, 43100, Klang, Selangor, Malaysia
Tel.: (60) 333445805
Paper Product Mfr & Distr
N.A.I.C.S.: 333243

Paper Products Marketing (Taiwan) Ltd. (1)
8F-5-2 No 51 Sec 2 Keeiung Rd, Taipei, Taiwan
Tel.: (886) 227398607
Paper Product Mfr & Distr
N.A.I.C.S.: 333243

Paper Products Marketing Europe GmbH (1)
Hellersbergstr 2, 41460, Neuss, Germany
Tel.: (49) 213116980
Paper Product Mfr & Distr
N.A.I.C.S.: 333243

San-Mic Trading Co., (H.K.) Ltd. (1)
Unit 803 8th Floor 68 Yee Wo Street, Causeway Bay, China (Hong Kong)
Tel.: (852) 25045995
Emp.: 5
Paper Product Distr
N.A.I.C.S.: 424130

San-Mic Trading Co., (Shenzhen) Ltd. (1)
Room 3011 News Building 1st NO 1002 Shennanzhong Rd, Futian Area, Shenzhen, China
Tel.: (86) 755 2595 1177
Paper Products Mfr
N.A.I.C.S.: 322299

Shanghai JP Co., Ltd. (1)
No 173 Hongcao Rd, Shanghai, 200233, China
Tel.: (86) 2164089900
Web Site: http://www.shangui.com
Sales Range: Less than $1 Million
Emp.: 5
Paper Products Mfr; Joint Venture of Japan Pulp & Paper Limited & Nippon Paper Industries Co., Ltd.
N.A.I.C.S.: 322120

Shouguang Liben Paper Making Co., Ltd. (1)
Dianqicheng 2-4F Xintiandi Shengcheng Rd, Shouguang, 262700, Shandong, China
Tel.: (86) 536 215 8412
Paper Mills
N.A.I.C.S.: 322120

South East Fibre Exports Pty Ltd (1)
Jews Head Edrom Road, PO Box 189, Eden, 2551, NSW, Australia
Tel.: (61) 264960220
Sales Range: $25-49.9 Million
Emp.: 39
Plywood, Timber & Wood Products
N.A.I.C.S.: 321999
Peter Mitchell (Gen Mgr)

TS Plastics Sdn. Bhd. (1)
PT 30130-30131 Off Jalan Johan 2/1A, Pengkalan 2 Industrial Estate Pusing, 31550, Perak, Malaysia
Tel.: (60) 53652899
Paper Product Mfr & Distr
N.A.I.C.S.: 333243

Volterra S.A. (1)
Calle Cochrane 361, Concepcion, Chile
Tel.: (56) 412244300
Web Site: http://www.volterra.cl
Sales Range: $25-49.9 Million
Emp.: 15
Mfr & Afforestation of Chips
N.A.I.C.S.: 322130

NIPPON PARKING DEVELOPMENT CO., LTD.

Osaka Fukoku Seimei Bldg 2-4 Komatsubara-cho, Kita-ku, Osaka, 530-0018, Japan
Tel.: (81) 663602353
Web Site: https://www.n-p-d.co.jp
2353—(TKS)
Rev.: $203,350,460
Assets: $262,085,920
Liabilities: $146,599,180
Net Worth: $115,486,740
Earnings: $31,746,880
Emp.: 1,012
Fiscal Year-end: 07/31/24
Real Estate & Leasing Business
N.A.I.C.S.: 531110
Kenji Kawamura (Sr VP)

Subsidiaries:

Kashimayari Co., Ltd. (1)
Hirakashimayari Kurosawa Kogen, Omachi, 398-0001, Nagano Prefecture, Japan
Tel.: (81) 261231231
Web Site: https://www.kashimayari.net
Restaurant Services
N.A.I.C.S.: 722511

Kawaba Resort Co., Ltd. (1)
Tel.: (81) 278523345
Web Site: http://www.kawaba.co.jp
Cableway Transportation Services
N.A.I.C.S.: 487110

Nippon Parking Development Sapporo Co., Ltd. (1)
Kita 3-jo Nishi 4-1-1 Nippon Life Sapporo Building, Chuo-ku, Sapporo, Japan
Tel.: (81) 112611630
Web Site: http://www.do-camper.com
Parking Services
N.A.I.C.S.: 812930

Rokuyon Co., Ltd. (1)
2-18-7 Jingumae, Shibuya-ku, Tokyo, 150-0001, Japan
Tel.: (81) 368129318
Web Site: https://www.rokuyon.co.jp
Housing Accommodation Services

INTERNATIONAL PUBLIC

N.A.I.C.S.: 721199

Spicy Co., Ltd. (1)
4672-3 Hokujo Hakuba-mura, Kitaazumi-gun, Nagano, 399-9301, Japan
Tel.: (81) 261727527
Gear Mfr
N.A.I.C.S.: 333612
Masanobu Tsukakoshi (CEO)

TCK Workshop Co., Ltd. (1)
Shin-Marunouchi Building 1-5-1 Marunouchi, Chiyoda-ku, Tokyo, 100-6510, Japan
Tel.: (81) 332181900
Advertising Planning Services
N.A.I.C.S.: 541810

NIPPON PILLAR PACKING CO., LTD.

7-1 Shinmachi 1-chome, Nishi-Ku, Osaka, 550-0013, Japan
Tel.: (81) 671668281
Web Site: https://www.pillar.co.jp
Year Founded: 1924
6490—(TKS)
Rev.: $387,379,050
Assets: $653,299,350
Liabilities: $190,936,460
Net Worth: $462,362,890
Earnings: $71,255,800
Emp.: 1,132
Fiscal Year-end: 03/31/24
Gasket & Mechanical Seal Product Mfr & Distr
N.A.I.C.S.: 339991
Kiyohisa Iwanami (Chm & CEO)

Subsidiaries:

Korea Pillar Packing Co., Ltd. (1)
Room 1703 Namsan Square Bldg 173 Toegye-ro, Jung-gu, Seoul, Korea (South)
Tel.: (82) 222774031
Web Site: https://www.koreapillar.com
Mechanical Seals Mfr
N.A.I.C.S.: 339991
Y. B. Cho (Pres)

Nippon Pillar Corporation of America Co., Ltd. (1)
6630 Roxburgh Dr Ste 171, Houston, TX 77041
Tel.: (281) 529-6367
Web Site: http://www.nipponpillar.com
Mechanical Seal Mfr & Distr
N.A.I.C.S.: 339991

Nippon Pillar Middle East FZE (1)
Office No 6EA-133 Dubai Airport Free Zone, PO Box 371455, Dubai, United Arab Emirates
Tel.: (971) 42952907
Mechanical Seal Distr
N.A.I.C.S.: 423840

Nippon Pillar Packing Co., Ltd. - Kyushu Factory (1)
1-25 Fukuhara Koshi-shi, Kumamoto, 861-1116, Japan
Tel.: (81) 962924511
Precision Product Mfr
N.A.I.C.S.: 332721

Nippon Pillar Packing Co., Ltd. - Sanda Factory (1)
541-1 Aza Uchiba Shimouchigami, Sanda, 669-1333, Hyogo, Japan
Tel.: (81) 795672121
Mechanical Seals Mfr
N.A.I.C.S.: 339991

Shanghai Pillar Trading Co., Ltd. (1)
Tel.: (86) 2162087711
Web Site: http://www.pillar-cn.com
Mechanical Seal Distr
N.A.I.C.S.: 423840

Suzhou Pillar Industry Co., Ltd. (1)
No 1 Dazhong Factory Building 255 Hua Jin Road, Tong An Suzhou New District, Jiangsu, 215153, China
Tel.: (86) 51266070636
Mechanical Seal Distr
N.A.I.C.S.: 423840

Taiwan Pillar Industry Co., Ltd. (1)
8F No 45 Section 1 Minquan East Road

AND PRIVATE COMPANIES

Zhongshan District, Taipei, 104 52, Taiwan
Tel.: (886) 2 2587 1911
Web Site: http://www.taiwanpillar.com
Mechanical Bearing Equipment Mfr & Distr
N.A.I.C.S.: 333613
Ryoichi Katsumi *(Pres)*

NIPPON PNEUMATIC MFG. CO., LTD.
4-11-5 Kamij, Higashinari-ku, Osaka, 537-0003, Japan
Tel.: (81) 6 6973 9104
Web Site: http://www.npk.co.jp
Year Founded: 1916
Construction Equipment Mfr & Distr
N.A.I.C.S.: 333120
Kazuchika Hirota *(VP)*

Subsidiaries:

NPK Construction Equipment, Inc. (1)
7550 Independence Dr, Cleveland, OH 44146
Tel.: (440) 232-7900
Web Site: http://www.npkce.com
Mfr & Distributing & Sales Of Construction & Mining Machinery
N.A.I.C.S.: 423810
Steve Antonini *(Mgr-Div)*

Subsidiary (Domestic):

Genesis Attachments, LLC (2)
1000 Genesis Dr, Superior, WI 54880
Tel.: (715) 395-5252
Web Site: http://www.genesisattachments.com
Construction Machinery Mfr
N.A.I.C.S.: 333120
Justin Palvere *(Mgr-Acct-Demolition-Natl)*

Subsidiary (Non-US):

GENESIS Europe GmbH & Co. KG (3)
Alpenstrasse 71, 87700, Memmingen, Germany
Tel.: (49) 83 31 9 25 98 0
Web Site: http://www.genesis-europe.com
Emp.: 12
Industrial Machinery Mfr
N.A.I.C.S.: 333248

Subsidiary (Non-US):

NPK Demtech B.V. (2)
Oranjelaan 35, 2382 PK, Zoeterwoude, Netherlands
Tel.: (31) 71 5810000
Web Site: http://www.demtech.eu
Construction Equipment Distr
N.A.I.C.S.: 423810
Ton Polak *(Dir-Sls)*

NPK Europe (Holland) BV (2)
World Trade Center Office 403, PO Box 30157, 3001 DD, Rotterdam, Netherlands
Tel.: (31) 10 205 1710
Web Site: http://www.npke.eu
Emp.: 5
Hydraulic Equipment Mfr
N.A.I.C.S.: 333998
Jos Monshouwei *(Mng Dir)*

NPK Europe Manufacturing S.R.O. (2)
Uhrinov 85, 59441, Uhrinov, Czech Republic
Tel.: (420) 566 501 911
Web Site: http://www.npke.cz
Construction Equipment Mfr
N.A.I.C.S.: 333998
Jofef Pokornw *(Gen Mgr)*

Subsidiary (Domestic):

NPK Manufacturing (2)
7550 Independence Dr, Bedford, OH 44146-5541
Tel.: (440) 943-3232
Rev.: $2,600,000
Emp.: 40
Machine Shop, Jobbing & Repair
N.A.I.C.S.: 332710

NPK France S.A.S. (1)
Parc D'Ester 19 Avenue d'Ariane, PO Box 6812, 87088, Limoges, France

Tel.: (33) 555372769
Web Site: http://www.npk-france.fr
Emp.: 6
Hydraulic Equipment Mfr
N.A.I.C.S.: 333998
Hirota Kazuchika *(Gen Mgr)*

Nippon Pneumatic Mfg. Co., Ltd. - Nabari Plant (1)
1300-80 Yabata, Nabari, 518-0605, Mie, Japan
Tel.: (81) 595 64 1722
Web Site: http://www.npk.jp
Construction Equipment Mfr
N.A.I.C.S.: 333120

Shanghai Pneumatic Machinery Co., Ltd. (1)
826 Qing An Road, Qing Pu Town, Shanghai, China
Tel.: (86) 21 5920 9038
Web Site: http://www.npk-chn.com
Pneumatic Equipment Distr
N.A.I.C.S.: 423830

NIPPON PRIMEX INC.
1-5-12 Unoki, Otaku, Tokyo, 146-8650, Japan
Tel.: (81) 337508555
Web Site: https://www.primex.co.jp
Year Founded: 1979
2795—(TKS)
Rev.: $45,853,968
Assets: $66,864,864
Liabilities: $17,178,720
Net Worth: $49,686,144
Earnings: $3,330,029
Fiscal Year-end: 03/31/24
Computer Peripheral Equipment Mfr
N.A.I.C.S.: 334118
Yoshiaki Shiraishi *(Auditor)*

Subsidiaries:

Nippon Printer Engineering, Inc. (1)
2660 Fujikawaguchiko-machi, Minamitsuru-gun, Katsuyama, 401-0310, Yamanashi, Japan
Tel.: (81) 555835678
Printer Distr
N.A.I.C.S.: 423430

NIPPON PROLOGIS REIT, INC.
21F Tokyo Building 273 Marunouch, Chiyoda-ku, Tokyo, 100-6421, Japan
Tel.: (81) 368678585
Web Site: https://www.prologis-reit.co.jp
Year Founded: 2012
3283—(TKS)
Sales Range: Less than $1 Million
Real Estate Related Services
N.A.I.C.S.: 531390
Masahiro Sakashita *(Exec Dir)*

NIPPON RAD INC
Kyodo News Building 2-2-5 Toranomon, Minato-Ku, Tokyo, 105-0001, Japan
Tel.: (81) 355747800
Web Site: https://www.nippon-rad.co.jp
Year Founded: 1971
4736—(TKS)
Sales Range: $25-49.9 Million
Emp.: 283
Custom Computer Programming Services
N.A.I.C.S.: 541511
Ryuichi Ohtsuka *(Chm)*

NIPPON REIT INVESTMENT CORPORATION
Koku Kaikan 3F 181 Shimbashi 1chome, Minato-ku, Tokyo, 105-0021, Japan
Tel.: (81) 355010080
Web Site: https://www.nippon-reit.com
Year Founded: 2010
3296—(TKS)

Sales Range: Less than $1 Million
Real Estate Investment Services
N.A.I.C.S.: 531210
Toshio Sugita *(Exec Officer)*

NIPPON RIETEC CO., LTD.
1-6 Kanda Nishiki-cho, Chiyoda-ku, Tokyo, 101-0054, Japan
Tel.: (81) 368802710
Web Site: https://www.j-rietec.co.jp
Year Founded: 1945
1938—(TKS)
Rev.: $386,962,620
Assets: $577,152,150
Liabilities: $182,039,400
Net Worth: $395,112,750
Earnings: $18,309,700
Emp.: 1,553
Fiscal Year-end: 03/31/24
Construction Engineering Services
N.A.I.C.S.: 541330
Shoji Tanabe *(Chm & Pres)*

Subsidiaries:

Hoansupply Co., Ltd. (1)
3-2-4 Nihonbashi Hongokucho, Chuo-ku, Tokyo, 103-0021, Japan
Tel.: (81) 368951300
Web Site: https://www.hoan-supply.co.jp
Emp.: 106
Engineering Services
N.A.I.C.S.: 541330
Masamitsu Hikawauchi *(Pres)*

NIPPON SANGYO SUISHIN KIKO LTD
2-5-1 Atago Green Hills MORI Tower 17F, Minato-ku, Tokyo, 105-6217, Japan
Tel.: (81) 354015600
Web Site: https://www.nsskjapan.com
Emp.: 100
Investment Services
N.A.I.C.S.: 523999
Jun Tsusaka *(Pres)*

NIPPON SEIKI CO., LTD.
2-2-34 Higashizao, Niigata, Nagaoka, 940-8580, Japan
Tel.: (81) 258243311   JP
Web Site: https://www.nippon-seiki.co.jp
7287—(TKS)
Rev.: $2,064,666,550
Assets: $2,238,357,520
Liabilities: $724,310,580
Net Worth: $1,514,046,940
Earnings: $35,033,000
Emp.: 13,624
Fiscal Year-end: 03/31/24
Instruments & Meters Mfr
N.A.I.C.S.: 334513
Norio Minato *(Sr Operating Officer)*

Subsidiaries:

Car Station Niigata Co., Ltd. (1)
649 Terashimacho, Nagaoka, 940-2101, Niigata, Japan
Tel.: (81) 258213766
Web Site: https://www.cocoselect.jp
Automobile Product Distr
N.A.I.C.S.: 423120

DaNang Nippon Seiki Co., Ltd. (1)
Area C 14F Da Nang Software Park 02 Quang Trung, Thach Thang Ward Hai Chau District, Da Nang, Vietnam
Tel.: (84) 2363888970
Software Services
N.A.I.C.S.: 541511

Dongguan Nissei Electronics Co., Ltd. (1)
No 2A Keyuan 1 Road, Tangxia Town, Dongguan, 224731, Guangdong, China
Tel.: (86) 76986857999
Web Site: http://www.nippon-seiki.co.jp
Remote Control Mfr
N.A.I.C.S.: 334519

Honda Car Sales Nagaoka Co., Ltd. (1)
4-558-2 Inaho cho, Nagaoka, 940-0877, Niigata, Japan
Tel.: (81) 258246688
Web Site: http://www.hondacars-nagaoka.co.jp
Emp.: 184
New & Used Car Dealers
N.A.I.C.S.: 441110
Noguchi Masahiro *(Pres)*

Hong Kong Nippon Seiki Co., Ltd. (1)
Suite 13-15A on 9/F Tower 3 China Hong Kong City 33 Canton Road, Tsim Sha Tsui, Kowloon, China (Hong Kong)
Tel.: (852) 27368038
Web Site: http://www.nippon-seiki.co.jp
Sales Range: $25-49.9 Million
Emp.: 10
Automotive Components Sales
N.A.I.C.S.: 441330

JNS Instruments Ltd. (1)
Plot No 4 Sec-3 IMT Manesar, Gurgaon, Haryana, India
Tel.: (91) 1242290731
Web Site: https://jpmgroup.co.in
Automobile Product Mfr & Distr
N.A.I.C.S.: 336110

Kyoei Engineering Co., Ltd. (1)
1912-2 Yamakura, Agano, 959-1961, Japan
Tel.: (81) 250612400
Web Site: https://www.kyoeieng.co.jp
Emp.: 150
Mould & Precision Component Mfr & Whslr
N.A.I.C.S.: 333511

Mazda Mobility Niigata Co., Ltd. (1)
1-12-17 Meikekiyama, Chuo-ku, Niigata, 950-0945, Japan
Tel.: (81) 252831811
Car Distr
N.A.I.C.S.: 441120

N.S. Computer Service Co., Ltd. (1)
3-3-2 Kanabo, Nagaoka, 940-0045, Niigata, Japan
Tel.: (81) 258371320
Web Site: https://www.nscs.jp
Sales Range: $75-99.9 Million
Emp.: 552
Software Development Services
N.A.I.C.S.: 541511

N.S. Electronics Co., Ltd. (1)
3-2-20 Shirooka, Nagaoka, 940-0021, Niigata, Japan
Tel.: (81) 258247011
Web Site: https://www.nseinet.co.jp
Emp.: 426
Automotive Electronic Circuits & Components Mfr
N.A.I.C.S.: 334419

N.S. International, Ltd. (1)
600 Wilshire Dr, Troy, MI 48084
Tel.: (248) 251-1600
Automobile Product Distr
N.A.I.C.S.: 423120
Jon Donegan *(Mgr-Sys Engrg)*

NS Advantech Co., Ltd. (1)
3-2-20 Shirooka, Nagaoka, 947-0043, Niigata, Japan
Tel.: (81) 258832252
Web Site: https://www.nsadv.co.jp
Sales Range: $75-99.9 Million
Emp.: 852
Automotive Components Mfr
N.A.I.C.S.: 811198

NS India Design & Trading Private Ltd. (1)
Unit No 505 5th Floor Vatika City Point MG Road Sector-25, Gurgaon, 122002, Haryana, India
Tel.: (91) 1244734272
Vehicle Instrument Design Services
N.A.I.C.S.: 541420

NS Instruments India Private Ltd. (1)
No 530 Benjamin Road Sector-24 DTZ SRICITY Varadaiah Palem Post, Sathyavedu Tk Chittoor District, Chittoor, 517 588, AP, India
Tel.: (91) 8576309400
Automobile Product Mfr & Distr

NIPPON SEIKI CO., LTD.

Nippon Seiki Co., Ltd.—(Continued)
N.A.I.C.S.: 336110

NS Sao Paulo Componentes Automotivos Ltda. (1)
Rua Comendador Joao Lucas 675-Distrito Industrial, Vinhedo, 13288-184, Sao Paulo, Brazil
Tel.: (55) 1938268400
Web Site: http://www.nippon-seiki.co.jp
Sales Range: $50-74.9 Million
Emp.: 100
Automotive Components Mfr
N.A.I.C.S.: 336330

NS West Inc. (1)
366-2 Shinjo-cho, Shobara, 727-0004, Hiroshima, Japan
Tel.: (81) 824722033
Web Site: http://www.nswest.co.jp
Sales Range: $25-49.9 Million
Emp.: 250
Automotive Components Mfr
N.A.I.C.S.: 811198
Norio Minato *(Pres)*

Nangtong NS Advantech Co., Ltd. (1)
Guangzhou Road East Minxing Road Shouth, Nantong Economic And technological Development Area, Jiangsu, China
Tel.: (86) 51385981877
Automobile Equipment Mfr
N.A.I.C.S.: 332119

Nantong NS Advantech Co., Ltd. (1)
No 25 Guangzhou Road, Nantong Economic and Technology Development Zone, Jiangsu, 226009, China
Tel.: (86) 51385981877
Web Site: http://www.nsadv.co.jp
Sales Range: $25-49.9 Million
Emp.: 100
Plastics Colouring & Compounding Services
N.A.I.C.S.: 325991

New Sabina Industries, Inc. (1)
12555 E U S Rt 22 St Rt 3, Sabina, OH 45169-9463
Tel.: (937) 584-2433
Sales Range: $125-149.9 Million
Emp.: 400
Automotive Components Mfr & Distr
N.A.I.C.S.: 336390
Hitoshi Nonomura *(Pres)*

Niigata Mazda Co., Ltd. (1)
8-4-15 Yamakido, Higashi-ku, Niigata, 950-0871, Japan
Tel.: (81) 252718111
Automobile Product Distr
N.A.I.C.S.: 423120

Nippon Seiki (Europe) B.V. (1)
Tel.: (31) 237990150
Web Site: http://www.nippon-seiki.eu.com
Sales Range: $25-49.9 Million
Emp.: 7
Automotive Components Mfr
N.A.I.C.S.: 336390

Nippon Seiki Consumer Products (Thailand) Co., Ltd. (1)
Amata City Chonburi Industrial Estate 700/450 Moo 7 T Donhuaroh, Muang, Chon Buri, 20000, Thailand **(80%)**
Tel.: (66) 38320800
Web Site: http://www.nsct.co.th
Sales Range: $125-149.9 Million
Emp.: 270
Printed Circuit Boards Assembly & Remote Controller Mfr
N.A.I.C.S.: 334290
Tsukasa Abe *(Mng Dir)*

Nippon Seiki De Mexico S.A. De C.V. (1)
Av Finsa No 1501 Col Parque Industrial FINSA Monterrey Guadalupe, 67132, Nuevo Leon, Mexico
Tel.: (52) 8181313400
Automotive Products Mfr
N.A.I.C.S.: 336110

Nippon Seiki Do Brasil Ltda. (1)
Palmeira do Miriti 121-GILBERTO MESTRINHO, Manaus, 69006-373, Amazonas, Brazil
Tel.: (55) 9221218900

Web Site: http://www.nippon-seiki.co.jp
Motorcycle Parts Mfr & Sales
N.A.I.C.S.: 336991

Nissei Advantech Mexico S.A. De C.V. (1)
AV Ihlsa NO 1301, Parque Industrial FINSA Monterrey, 67114, Guadalupe, Nuevo Leon, Mexico
Tel.: (52) 8181273400
Web Site: http://www.nippon-seiki.co.jp
Motorcycle Instrument Panel Parts Mfr & Distr
N.A.I.C.S.: 336991

Nissei Display Sales & Development Co., Ltd. (1)
Room 2107 21F No 6088 Humin Road, Shanghai, China
Tel.: (86) 2154428742
Automobile Product Distr
N.A.I.C.S.: 423120

Nissei Kyusyoku Co., Ltd. (1)
188-2 Jyunigata, Nagaoka, 940-0002, Niigata, Japan
Tel.: (81) 258212640
Food Service
N.A.I.C.S.: 722330

Nissei Service Co., Ltd. (1)
188-2 Junigatamachi, Nagaoka, 940-0002, Niigata, Japan
Tel.: (81) 258246344
Web Site: https://www.nissei-service.jp
Emp.: 453
Transportation & Logistic Services
N.A.I.C.S.: 488510
Toshio Bamba *(Pres)*

PT. Indonesia Nippon Seiki (1)
Jl Utama Modern Industri Blok E Kawasan Industri Modern, Cikande, Serang, 42186, Banten, Indonesia
Tel.: (62) 254402166
Web Site: http://www.ins.co.id
Automotive Components Mfr
N.A.I.C.S.: 336390
Takeshi Hayashi *(Pres & Dir)*

Shanghai Nissei Display System Co., Ltd. (1)
No 288 Chunguang Road, Xinzhuang Industrial Zone, Shanghai, 201108, China
Tel.: (86) 2154420803
Web Site: http://www.shns.cn
Emp.: 510
Automobile Accessories Mfr & Distr
N.A.I.C.S.: 334514

Taiwan Nissei Display System Co., Ltd. (1)
2F No 60 Fuxing N Rd, Songshan Dist, Taipei, 104, Taiwan
Tel.: (886) 225457000
Automobile Product Mfr & Distr
N.A.I.C.S.: 336110

Thai Matto NS Co., Ltd. (1)
700/462 Moo 7 Amata City Chonburi Industrial Estate Donhuaroh, Muang Chonburi District, Chon Buri, 20000, Thailand
Tel.: (66) 38450061
Web Site: https://www.thaimatto.co.th
Sales Range: $50-74.9 Million
Emp.: 153
Plastic Pellets Coloring & Compounding Services
N.A.I.C.S.: 325991
Sittidate Janejokwong *(Mgr-Plng & Production Control Department)*

Thai Nippon Seiki Co., Ltd. (1)
Amata City Industrial Estate 700/450 Moo 7 Donhuaroh, Muang, Chon Buri, 20000, Thailand
Tel.: (66) 38456400
Sales Range: $400-449.9 Million
Emp.: 1,300
Automotive Components Mfr
N.A.I.C.S.: 336310

UK-NSI Co., Ltd. (1)
Merse Road North Moons Moat, Redditch, B98 9HL, Worcs, United Kingdom
Tel.: (44) 1527585055
Web Site: https://www.uk-nsi.co.uk
Sales Range: $50-74.9 Million
Emp.: 400
Automotive Components Mfr

N.A.I.C.S.: 336390

Vietnam Nippon Seiki Co., Ltd. (1)
Lot 70B 71 Noibai Industrial Zone, Quang Tien commune Soc Son district, Hanoi, Vietnam
Tel.: (84) 2435823888
Web Site: https://vietnamnipponseiki.com.vn
Sales Range: $150-199.9 Million
Emp.: 400
Motorcycle Parts Distr
N.A.I.C.S.: 423120

Wuhan Nissei Display System Co., Ltd. (1)
No 258 Houguanhu RoadWuhan Economic Technological Development Zone, Wuhan, Hubei, China
Tel.: (86) 2784895388
Automobile Product Mfr & Distr
N.A.I.C.S.: 336110

Zhejiang Nissei Display System Co., Ltd. (1)
84 Shen Wu Nan Lu 315303, Kandun Industrial Zone, Cixi, Zhejiang, China
Tel.: (86) 574 63284462
Web Site: http://www.nippon-seiki.co.jp
Sales Range: $50-74.9 Million
Emp.: 200
Mfr & Sales of Instrument Clusters for Motorcycles
N.A.I.C.S.: 336991

NIPPON SEIRO CO., LTD.

10F Kyobashi Soseikan Bldg 2-5-18 Kyobashi, Chuo-ku, Tokyo, 104-0031, Japan
Tel.: (81) 335383061
Web Site: https://www.seiro.co.jp
Year Founded: 1951
5010—(TKS)
Rev: $153,881,360
Assets: $212,707,090
Liabilities: $185,878,530
Net Worth: $26,828,560
Earnings: ($8,656,890)
Emp.: 221
Fiscal Year-end: 12/31/23
Petroleum Product Mfr & Distr
N.A.I.C.S.: 324199
Tsukasa Ando *(Pres)*

Subsidiaries:

Nippon Seiro (Thailand) Co., Ltd. (1)
700/15 Moo 7 Tambon Khaokhansong Amphur, Si Racha, 20110, Chonburi, Thailand
Tel.: (66) 38950726
Emp.: 40
Petroleum Product Distr
N.A.I.C.S.: 424720
Masuji Yamamoto *(Pres)*

NIPPON SHARYO, LTD.

1-1 Sanbonmatsu-cho, Atsuta-ku, Nagoya, 456-8691, Japan
Tel.: (81) 528823316 JP
Web Site: https://www.n-sharyo.co.jp
Year Founded: 1896
7102—(TKS)
Rev: $581,823,425
Assets: $901,202,258
Liabilities: $490,049,417
Net Worth: $411,152,842
Earnings: $35,559,950
Emp.: 2,263
Fiscal Year-end: 03/31/24
Railway Rolling Stock, Transportation Equipment, Construction Equipment & Steel Structures Mfr
N.A.I.C.S.: 336510
Kazuhiro Igarashi *(Pres & CEO)*

Subsidiaries:

Nippon Sharyo Manufacturing, LLC (1)
1051 Perimeter Dr Ste 270, Schaumburg, IL 60173
Tel.: (847) 228-2700
Web Site: https://www.nipponsharyousa.com
Construction Machinery Mfr

N.A.I.C.S.: 333120
Ted Oshima *(Acct Mgr)*

NIPPON SHEET GLASS CO. LTD.

Sumitomo Fudosan Mita Twin Bldg West Wing 5-27 Mita 3-Chome, Minato-ku, Tokyo, 108-6321, Japan
Tel.: (81) 354439500
Web Site: http://www.nsg.com
Year Founded: 1918
5202—(TKS)
Rev: $5,503,069,570
Assets: $6,660,136,850
Liabilities: $5,643,267,670
Net Worth: $1,016,869,180
Earnings: $70,284,130
Emp.: 25,300
Fiscal Year-end: 03/31/24
Architectural Glass, Building Materials, Transportation Glass & Glass Fiber Mfr & Material Information Technology Services
N.A.I.C.S.: 327211
Koichi Hiyoshi *(Chief Legal Officer, Chief Risk Officer & Sec)*

Subsidiaries:

ARGUS, S.A. (1)
Calle Max Henriquez Urena Nr 33 Edif Kira Apt 201 Ensanche Naco, PO Box 21266, Santo Domingo, Dominican Republic
Tel.: (809) 227 2660
Emp.: 17
Construction Glass Products Mfr
N.A.I.C.S.: 327215
Roos Backheus *(Gen Mgr)*

NGF Canada Limited (1)
255 York Road, Guelph, N1E 8G4, ON, Canada
Tel.: (519) 836-9228
Web Site: http://www.ngfcanada.com
Sales Range: $25-49.9 Million
Emp.: 38
Building Glass Products Mfr
N.A.I.C.S.: 327215

NGF Europe Limited (1)
Lea Green Road, Saint Helens, WA9 4PR, Merseyside, United Kingdom
Tel.: (44) 1744853065
Web Site: http://www.ngfeurope.com
Sales Range: $50-74.9 Million
Emp.: 250
Glass Cord Products Mfr
N.A.I.C.S.: 327215
Alistair Poole *(Mng Dir)*

NSG Assembly Service Co., Ltd. (1)
2125-2 Shimokuzawa, Midori-Ku, Sagamihara, 252-0134, Kanagawa, Japan
Tel.: (81) 427733691
Automotive Glass Mfr
N.A.I.C.S.: 327215

NSG Building Products Co., Ltd. (1)
6 Anesakikaigan Nihonitagarasuchibajigyoshonai, Ichihara, 299-0107, Chiba, Japan
Tel.: (81) 436619030
Construction Glass Products Mfr
N.A.I.C.S.: 327215

NSG Hong Kong Co., Ltd. (1)
Unit 4108 41st Floor Cosco Tower Grand Milennium Plaza 183 Queens Road, Central District, Hong Kong, China (Hong Kong)
Tel.: (852) 2562 4771
Emp.: 23
Glass Products Whslr
N.A.I.C.S.: 423390
Shirley Wong *(Mgr-Sls)*

NSG Precision Co., Ltd. (1)
6-7 Chitose-cho, Yokkaichi, 510-0051, Mie, Japan
Tel.: (81) 593 53 2760
Web Site: http://www.nsgpr.com
Precision Glass Mfr & Distr
N.A.I.C.S.: 327212
Harumi Shima *(Pres)*

NSG Umu Products Co., Ltd. (1)
15 Chikusa Kaigan, Ichihara, 299-0108, Chiba, Japan
Tel.: (81) 436212652

AND PRIVATE COMPANIES — NIPPON SHEET GLASS CO. LTD.

Web Site: https://www.umu.jp
Sales Range: $25-49.9 Million
Emp.: 30
Light Control Glass Mfr
N.A.I.C.S.: 327212

Nanox Corporation (1)
6-7 Nagasone Okajima, Fukushima, 960-8201, Japan
Tel.: (81) 24 531 6178
Web Site: http://www.nanox.co.jp
Sales Range: $900-999.9 Million
Emp.: 4,000
Liquid Crystal Display Panel Mfr & Distr
N.A.I.C.S.: 334419

Nippon Parts Co., Ltd. (1)
425-1 Furukawacho Hazukashi, Fushimi-Ku, Kyoto, 612-8486, Japan
Tel.: (81) 759342837
Sales Range: $50-74.9 Million
Emp.: 13
Automotive Glass Mfr
N.A.I.C.S.: 327215
Nick Takahashi *(Gen Mgr)*

Nishinihon Modular Window Co., Ltd. (1)
29-3 Shintsukijicho, Hofu, 747-0824, Yamaguchi, Japan
Tel.: (81) 835229922
Automotive Glass Mfr
N.A.I.C.S.: 327215

Nissho Co., Ltd. (1)
1-9-10 Namekawa-Cho, Kita-Ku, Hitachi, 317-0053, Ibaraki, Japan
Tel.: (81) 294246301
Web Site: https://nisshoss.co.jp
Emp.: 330
Flat Glass Mfr
N.A.I.C.S.: 327211

Nissho Kako Co., Ltd. (1)
556 Ichishichooyama, Tsu, 515-2514, Mie, Japan
Tel.: (81) 59 293 0153
Web Site: http://www.nisshokako.co.jp
Sales Range: $25-49.9 Million
Emp.: 25
Fiberglass Plastic Products Mfr
N.A.I.C.S.: 326199

Pilkington AGR Czech spol s.r.o. (1)
Prumyslova 1472/11 Hostivar, Prague, 10, Czech Republic
Tel.: (420) 241001281
Web Site: http://www.pilkington.com
Emp.: 9
Automotive Glass Product Mfr
N.A.I.C.S.: 327215

Pilkington AGR Danmark A/S (1)
Ejby Industrivej 124, 2600, Glostrup, Denmark
Tel.: (45) 43270200
Web Site: http://www.pilkington.com
Sales Range: $25-49.9 Million
Emp.: 2
Automotive Glass Mfr
N.A.I.C.S.: 327215

Pilkington Automotive Deutschland GmbH (1)
Otto-Seeling-Strasse 7, 58455, Witten, Germany
Tel.: (49) 23025820
Web Site: http://www.pilkington.de
Automotive Glass Product Mfr
N.A.I.C.S.: 327215

Pilkington Group Limited (1)
Hall Lane, Lathom, Ormskirk, L40 5UF, Lancashire, United Kingdom
Tel.: (44) 169550000
Web Site: http://www.pilkington.com
Sales Range: $1-4.9 Billion
Emp.: 23,800
Glass Producer for the Automotive & Building Products Industries
N.A.I.C.S.: 327211

Subsidiary (Non-US):

Cebrace Cristal Plano Ltda (2)
Presidente Dutra Highway km 136, Santa Luzia, Cacapava, 12286-160, Sao Paulo, Brazil
Tel.: (55) 1232215000
Web Site: http://www.cebrace.com.br

Sales Range: $50-74.9 Million
Emp.: 250
Building Glass Mfr
N.A.I.C.S.: 327211

Changchun Pilkington Safety Glass Co. Ltd. (2)
No 4356 Jilin Rd, Changchun, 130031, Jilin, China
Tel.: (86) 43184855228
Glass Products Mfr
N.A.I.C.S.: 327215

Chiba Sanritsu Konpo Unyu Co., Ltd. (2)
2-12-32 Konan Sosupotoshinagawa, Minato-Ku, Tokyo, 108-0075, Japan
Tel.: (81) 334589631
Glass Products Mfr
N.A.I.C.S.: 327215

Hi-Mirror Co., Ltd. (2)
255-13 Hamada Obashimo, Maizuru, 625-0007, Kyoto, Japan
Tel.: (81) 362798345
Glass Products Mfr
N.A.I.C.S.: 327212

MATEX Co., Ltd. (2)
1-125 Mizukoshi, Yao, 581-0856, Osaka, Japan
Tel.: (81) 729418652
Web Site: https://www.matex-japan.com
Flat Glass Mfr
N.A.I.C.S.: 327211

Subsidiary (Non-US):

Matex Planetary Drive International, Inc. (3)
Light Industry & Science Park II, Calamba, 4027, Laguna, Philippines
Tel.: (63) 495456805
Web Site: http://www.matex-japan.com
Sales Range: $100-124.9 Million
Emp.: 580
Precision Injection Molding Machinery Mfr
N.A.I.C.S.: 333248
Toshiaki Matoba *(Pres)*

Wuxi Matex Precision Co., Ltd. (3)
Furongzhong 2road 294 Xishan Economic Development Zone, Wuxi, 214101, Jiangsu, China
Tel.: (86) 51088267015
Emp.: 210
Gear Reduction System Mfr
N.A.I.C.S.: 333612
Masao Uchida *(Gen Mgr)*

Subsidiary (Non-US):

Maekawa Glass Co., Ltd. (2)
1-1-2 Nakayoshida, Kokuraminami Ward, Kitakyushu, 800-0204, Fukuoka, Japan
Tel.: (81) 934731861
Web Site: https://maekawa-garasu.co.jp
Emp.: 19
Construction Glass Materials Distr
N.A.I.C.S.: 423390

NSG Interior Co., Ltd. (2)
3-13-5 Matsugaya, Taito-Ku, Tokyo, 111-0036, Japan
Tel.: (81) 338436155
Construction Glass Mfr
N.A.I.C.S.: 327215

NSG Purchase & Supply Co., Ltd. (2)
3-5-27 Mita Minato-ku, Minato-ku, Tokyo, 108-6320, Japan
Tel.: (81) 354439495
Emp.: 8
Glass Products Mfr
N.A.I.C.S.: 327215

NSG Techno-Research Co., Ltd. (2)
2-13-12 Konoike, Itami, 664-8520, Hyogo, Japan
Tel.: (81) 72 781 7251
Web Site: http://www.nsg-ntr.com
Glass Products Research & Testing Services
N.A.I.C.S.: 541380

NTT Data Business Brains Corp. (2)
Shiba Park Building A Building 14F 2-4-1 Shiba Park, Minato-Ku, Tokyo, 105-0011, Japan
Tel.: (81) 5034817111

Web Site: http://www.nttd-bb.com
Emp.: 275
Information Technology Consulting Services
N.A.I.C.S.: 541512

Nichifuku Co., Ltd. (2)
6th floor of LUXES Building 2-6-11 Higashisakura, Higashi-Ku, Nagoya, 461-0005, Aichi, Japan
Tel.: (81) 529318581
Web Site: http://www.nichifuku.jp
Flat Glass Mfr
N.A.I.C.S.: 327211

Nissho Kosan Co., Ltd. (2)
1-11-11 Shiba Sumitomofudosan Bldg 12f, Minato-Ku, Tokyo, 105-0014, Japan
Tel.: (81) 354439406
Glass Products Mfr
N.A.I.C.S.: 327212

Oki Glass Co., Ltd. (2)
3rd Floor Honjo Azumabashi DJ Building 4-19-3 Honjo, Sumida-ku, Tokyo, 130-0004, Japan
Tel.: (81) 356377480
Web Site: https://www.oki-glass.co.jp
Emp.: 24
Construction Glass Mfr
N.A.I.C.S.: 327215

Subsidiary (Domestic):

Pilkington (Forex) Limited (2)
Hall Lane, Lathom, Ormskirk, L40 5UF, Lancashire, United Kingdom
Tel.: (44) 169550000
Web Site: http://www.pilkington.com
Flat Glass Mfr
N.A.I.C.S.: 327211

Subsidiary (Non-US):

Pilkington AGR Hungary Kft. (2)
Horog u 14, Budapest, 1107, Hungary
Tel.: (36) 12626268
Web Site: http://www.pilkingtonagr.hu
Sales Range: $25-49.9 Million
Emp.: 50
Automotive Glass Product Mfr
N.A.I.C.S.: 327215
Peter Takacs *(Mng Dir)*

Pilkington Austria GmbH (2)
factory premises 24, 5500, Bischofshofen, Austria
Tel.: (43) 646246990
Web Site: http://www.pilkington.com
Sales Range: $10-24.9 Million
Emp.: 109
Glass Mfr
N.A.I.C.S.: 327211
Hubert Schwarz *(Mng Dir)*

Subsidiary (Domestic):

Pilkington AGR Austria GmbH (3)
Gewerbering 2, 2440, Moosbrunn, Austria
Tel.: (43) 2234799770
Emp.: 18
Automotive Glass Mfr
N.A.I.C.S.: 327215

Pilkington Austria GmbH (3)
Archenweg 54, 6020, Innsbruck, Austria
Tel.: (43) 646246990
Web Site: http://www.pilkington.com
Glass Products Mfr
N.A.I.C.S.: 327212

Subsidiary (Non-US):

Pilkington Automotive Argentina SA (2)
Bernardo Ader 3060, B1605FEX, Munro, Buenos Aires, Argentina
Tel.: (54) 1147212121
Web Site: https://www.pilkington.com
Sales Range: $25-49.9 Million
Emp.: 300
Mfr of Safety Glass
N.A.I.C.S.: 327211

Pilkington Automotive Finland Oy (2)
Pihtisulunkatu 10, PO Box 476, 33330, Tampere, Finland
Tel.: (358) 33499111
Web Site: https://www.pilkington.com
Sales Range: $150-199.9 Million
Emp.: 700
Safety Glass Mfr

N.A.I.C.S.: 327211
Kai Stenvik *(Mgr-Pur)*

Pilkington Automotive France SA (2)
620 Avenue Daniel Dreyfous Ducas, Zone Portuaire de Limay Porcheville, 78520, Limay, France
Tel.: (33) 130983260
Web Site: https://www.pilkington.com
Automotive Glass Mfr
N.A.I.C.S.: 423120

Pilkington Automotive India Private Limited (2)
Plot No 8 Non SEZ of APIIC Atchuthapuram Mandal, Visakhapatnam District, Visakhapatnam, 531011, Andhra Pradesh, India
Tel.: (91) 8924282100
Web Site: https://www.pilkington.com
Flat Glass Mfr
N.A.I.C.S.: 327211

Subsidiary (Domestic):

Pilkington Automotive Limited (2)
7 Old Forge Drive, Kings Norton, Redditch, B98 7AU, Worcestershire, United Kingdom
Tel.: (44) 1527517373
Web Site: http://www.pilkington.com
Sales Range: $50-74.9 Million
Emp.: 200
Safety Glass Mfr
N.A.I.C.S.: 327211

Pilkington Automotive Management Services Limited (2)
Hall Lane, Lathom, Ormskirk, L40 5UF, Lancashire, United Kingdom
Tel.: (44) 169550000
Web Site: http://www.pilkington.com
Automotive Glass Mfr
N.A.I.C.S.: 327215

Subsidiary (Non-US):

Pilkington Automotive Poland Sp. z o.o. (2)
ul Portowa 24, 27-600, Sandomierz, Poland
Tel.: (48) 158330100
Web Site: https://www.pilkington.com
Automotive Glass Product Mfr
N.A.I.C.S.: 327215

Pilkington Benelux AGR B.V. (2)
Schurenbergweg 7, 1105 AP, Amsterdam, Netherlands
Tel.: (31) 206970601
Web Site: http://www.pilkington.com
Sales Range: $25-49.9 Million
Emp.: 50
Glass Products Mfr
N.A.I.C.S.: 327212

Pilkington Benelux BV (2)
De Hoeveler 25, 7547 SB, Enschede, Netherlands
Tel.: (31) 534835835
Web Site: http://www.pilkington.nl
Building Products Whslr
N.A.I.C.S.: 423320

Pilkington Brasil Ltda (2)
Presidente Dutra Highway km 131/133, Santa Luzia, Cacapava, 12286-160, SP, Brazil
Tel.: (55) 1232212100
Web Site: http://www.pilkington.com
Sales Range: $100-124.9 Million
Emp.: 400
Glass Mfr
N.A.I.C.S.: 327211

Pilkington Danmark A/S (2)
Anbolten 14, 6000, Kolding, Denmark
Tel.: (45) 75569811
Web Site: http://www.pilkington.com
Glass Products Mfr
N.A.I.C.S.: 327215

Subsidiary (Domestic):

Pilkington Finance Limited (2)
Prescot Road, Saint Helens, WA10 3TT, Merseyside, United Kingdom
Tel.: (44) 1744692000
Financial Management Services
N.A.I.C.S.: 523999

Subsidiary (Non-US):

Pilkington Floatglas AB (2)

NIPPON SHEET GLASS CO. LTD.

Nippon Sheet Glass Co. Ltd.—(Continued)

Karl XI s vag 61, 302 96, Halmstad, Sweden
Tel.: (46) 35153000
Web Site: http://www.pilkington.com
Sales Range: $100-124.9 Million
Emp.: 25
Mfr Floatglass, Coated, Toughened, Laminated & Decorated Glass
N.A.I.C.S.: 327211

Pilkington Glass India Pvt. Ltd. (2)
501 International Trade Tower Nehru Place, New Delhi, 110 019, India
Tel.: (91) 1141805500
Web Site: http://www.pilkington.com
Sales Range: $25-49.9 Million
Emp.: 6
Building Glass Mfr
N.A.I.C.S.: 327215

Pilkington Glass LLC (2)
Stekolnaya Str 1 Zhukovo Village, Ramensky District, Moscow, Russia
Tel.: (7) 4953699500
Web Site: https://www.firstinglass.ru
Sales Range: $125-149.9 Million
Emp.: 300
Automotive Glass Products Mfr & Whslr
N.A.I.C.S.: 327215
Strygin Alexey (Gen Dir)

Pilkington Glass Service SAS (2)
64/76 rue Charles Heller, 94400, Vitry-sur-Seine, France
Tel.: (33) 155535703
Construction Glass Mfr
N.A.I.C.S.: 327212

Pilkington Glass of Canada Limited (2)
Collingwood Automotive Plant 1000 Hwy 26, Collingwood, L9Y 4V8, ON, Canada
Tel.: (705) 445-4780
Emp.: 300
Automotive Glass Product Mfr
N.A.I.C.S.: 327215
Brian Hammond (Gen Mgr)

Pilkington Holding GmbH (2)
Haydnstrasse 19, 45884, Gelsenkirchen, Germany
Tel.: (49) 2091680
Web Site: https://www.pilkington.com
Fire Protection Glass Mfr
N.A.I.C.S.: 327215

Pilkington IGP Sp. z o.o. (2)
Curtis Plaza - 3rd floor 18 Woloska Str, 02-675, Warsaw, Poland
Tel.: (48) 225487500
Web Site: https://www.pilkington.com
Construction Glass Mfr
N.A.I.C.S.: 327215

Pilkington Italia SpA (2)
Industrial area, 66050, San Salvo, Chieti, Italy
Tel.: (39) 08733481
Web Site: http://www.pilkington.com
Glass Products Mfr
N.A.I.C.S.: 327215

Pilkington Lahden Lasitehdas Oy (2)
Niemenkatu 73, 15140, Lahti, Finland
Tel.: (358) 33499111
Sales Range: $25-49.9 Million
Emp.: 135
Glass Mfr
N.A.I.C.S.: 327211

Pilkington Norge AS (2)
Stanseveien 35, 0976, Oslo, Norway
Tel.: (47) 23335900
Sales Range: $25-49.9 Million
Emp.: 15
Automotive Glass Product Mfr
N.A.I.C.S.: 327215

Subsidiary (US):

Pilkington North America, Inc. (2)
811 Madison Ave, Toledo, OH 43604-5684
Tel.: (419) 467-7245
Web Site: http://www.pilkington.com
Sales Range: $25-49.9 Million
Emp.: 50
Automotive & Building Glass Mfr
N.A.I.C.S.: 327211

Plant (Domestic):

L-N Safety Glass, SA de CV (3)
PO Box 2769, Calexico, CA 92231
Tel.: (419) 247-4560
Safety Glass Mfr
N.A.I.C.S.: 327211

Subsidiary (Domestic):

Pilkington Properties Limited (2)
Prescot Road, Saint Helens, WA10 3TT, Merseyside, United Kingdom
Tel.: (44) 1744 692000
Web Site: http://www.pilkington.com
Sales Range: $1-9.9 Million
Property Development Services
N.A.I.C.S.: 531390
David Pinder (Mng Dir)

Subsidiary (Non-US):

Pilkington Solar (Taicang), Ltd. (2)
Sangang Industrial Zone, Ludu Town, Taicang, 215412, Jiangsu, China
Tel.: (86) 51288898000
Web Site: https://www.appleton.net.cn
Sales Range: $100-124.9 Million
Emp.: 50
Construction Glass Mfr
N.A.I.C.S.: 327215

Subsidiary (Domestic):

Pilkington United Kingdom Ltd. (2)
European Technical Centre, Ormskirk, L40 5UF, Lancashire, United Kingdom
Tel.: (44) 1744692000
Web Site: http://www.pilkington.com
Sales Range: $200-249.9 Million
Emp.: 1,000
Glass Mfr
N.A.I.C.S.: 327211

Subsidiary (Non-US):

UniGlass Ltd (2)
31 Vouliagmenis Av, Glyfada, 166 75, Athens, Greece
Tel.: (30) 2109600920
Web Site: http://www.uniglass.gr
Sales Range: $25-49.9 Million
Emp.: 5
Construction Glass Mfr
N.A.I.C.S.: 327215
Constantin Panaretos (CEO)

Vidrieria Argentina SA (2)
Av Antartida Argentina y Vias del FF CC, Roca Llavallol, BA1836AON, Buenos Aires, Argentina
Tel.: (54) 1142395000
Web Site: https://www.vasa.com.ar
Sales Range: $100-124.9 Million
Emp.: 350
Glass Mfr
N.A.I.C.S.: 327211

Pilkington Polska Sp. z o.o. (1)
ul Portowa 24, 27-600, Sandomierz, Poland
Tel.: (48) 158323041
Web Site: http://www.pilkington.com
Building Glass Mfr
N.A.I.C.S.: 327215

Pilkington Sverige AB (1)
Box 195, 574 22, Vetlanda, Sweden
Tel.: (46) 383762800
Web Site: http://www.pilkington.com
Sales Range: $25-49.9 Million
Emp.: 42
Construction Glass Mfr
N.A.I.C.S.: 327212

Tochigi Nippon Sheet Glass Co., Ltd. (1)
199 Tadacho, Sano, 327-0311, Tochigi, Japan
Tel.: (81) 283626267
Automotive Glass Mfr
N.A.I.C.S.: 327215

Virardi Enterprises Ltd (1)
67 Ayias Zonis Street, 3090, Limassol, Cyprus
Tel.: (357) 25 371501
Web Site: http://www.virardi.com
Sales Range: $25-49.9 Million
Emp.: 45
Catering Equipment Distr
N.A.I.C.S.: 423830

Rolando G. Virardi (Founder & Chm)

NIPPON SHIKIZAI INC
5-3-13 Mita, Minato-ku, Tokyo, Japan
Tel.: (81) 334560561
Web Site: https://www.shikizai.com
Year Founded: 1930
4920—(TKS)
Rev.: $106,704,500
Assets: $121,146,830
Liabilities: $96,147,490
Net Worth: $24,999,340
Earnings: $2,821,820
Emp.: 38
Fiscal Year-end: 02/29/24
Cosmetics & Other Products Mfr
N.A.I.C.S.: 327910
Kouji Okumura (Chm)

Subsidiaries:

Thepenier Pharma Industrie S.A.S. (1)
Route Departementale 912, 61400, Saint-Langis-les-Mortagne, France
Tel.: (33) 233852222
Web Site: https://www.thepenier-pharma.com
Pharmaceutical & Cosmetic Product Mfr
N.A.I.C.S.: 325412

NIPPON SHINDO CO., LTD.
20-1 Takumi-cho, Sakai-ku, Sakai, 590-0908, Osaka, Japan
Tel.: (81) 722290346
Web Site: https://www.nippon-shindo.co.jp
Year Founded: 1938
57530—(TKS)
Sales Range: $125-149.9 Million
Emp.: 110
Metal Products Mfr
N.A.I.C.S.: 332999
Makoto Kubota (Pres)

NIPPON SHINYAKU CO., LTD.
14 Nishinosho-Monguchi-cho Kisshoin, Minami-ku, Kyoto, 601-8550, Japan
Tel.: (81) 753211111
Web Site: https://www.nippon-shinyaku.co.jp
Year Founded: 1919
4516—(TKS)
Rev.: $979,965,550
Assets: $1,741,100,440
Liabilities: $283,370,700
Net Worth: $1,457,729,740
Earnings: $170,875,110
Emp.: 2,213
Fiscal Year-end: 03/31/24
Pharmaceuticals Product Mfr
N.A.I.C.S.: 325412
Shigenobu Maekawa (Chm)

Subsidiaries:

NS Pharma Inc. (1)
140 E Ridgewood Ave Ste 280S, Paramus, NJ 07652
Tel.: (201) 986-3860
Web Site: http://www.nspharma.com
Sales Range: $25-49.9 Million
Emp.: 11
Pharmaceutical Preparation Mfr
N.A.I.C.S.: 325412
Tsugio Tanaka (Pres)

NS Shared Service, Co., Ltd. (1)
14 Kisshoin Nishinosho, Monguchi-cho Minami-ku, Kyoto, 601-8550, Japan
Tel.: (81) 753148258
Web Site: https://www.ns-shared.co.jp
Insurance Agency Services
N.A.I.C.S.: 524210

Nippon Shinyaku Co., Ltd. - Chitose Synthesis Plant & Chitose Functional Food Plant (1)
1007-81 Izumisawa, Chitose, 066-0051, Hokkaido, Japan
Tel.: (81) 123281212

Sales Range: $25-49.9 Million
Emp.: 9
Pharmaceutical & Food Ingredients Mfr
N.A.I.C.S.: 325412

Nippon Shinyaku Co., Ltd. - Odawara Central Factory (1)
676-1 Kuwahara, Odawara, 250-0861, Kanagawa, Japan
Tel.: (81) 465364111
Web Site: http://www.nippon-shinyaku.co.jp
Pharmaceuticals Product Mfr
N.A.I.C.S.: 325412

Sioe Pharmaceutical Co., Ltd. (1)
3-1-11 Shioe, Amagasaki, 661-0976, Hyogo, Japan
Tel.: (81) 664992601
Web Site: https://www.sioe-pharm.co.jp
Sales Range: $50-74.9 Million
Emp.: 32
Pharmaceuticals & Food Ingredients Mfr & Distr
N.A.I.C.S.: 424210

Tajima Shokuhin Kogyo Co., Ltd. (1)
435 Toshiba, Hidaka-cho, Toyooka, 669-5328, Hyogo, Japan
Tel.: (81) 796421095
Web Site: https://www.tajima-shokuhin.co.jp
Sales Range: $25-49.9 Million
Emp.: 85
Vitamin & Mineral Supplements Mfr
N.A.I.C.S.: 325412

NIPPON SHOKUBAI CO., LTD.
Kogin Bldg 4-1-1 Koraibashi, Chuo-ku, Osaka, 541-0043, Japan
Tel.: (81) 662239132   JP
Web Site: https://www.shokubai.co.jp
Year Founded: 1941
4114—(TKS)
Rev.: $2,591,179,490
Assets: $3,596,236,600
Liabilities: $1,001,401,780
Net Worth: $2,594,834,820
Earnings: $72,762,880
Emp.: 129
Fiscal Year-end: 03/31/24
Specialty Chemicals Mfr
N.A.I.C.S.: 325998
Takashi Kobayashi (Mng Exec Officer, Dir-Fin & Acctg Div & Corp Auditor-Statutory)

Subsidiaries:

Catox Co., Ltd. (1)
1-46 Higashikaigancho, Amagasaki, 660-0843, Hyogo, Japan
Tel.: (81) 66 409 1301
Web Site: https://catox.co.jp
Electronic Computer Mfr
N.A.I.C.S.: 334111

Chugoku Kako Co., Ltd. (1)
1575 Mizue, Kurashiki, 710-0802, Okayama, Japan
Tel.: (81) 864653555
Web Site: http://www.chugokukako.co.jp
Emp.: 80
Adhesive Tape Mfr
N.A.I.C.S.: 322220

NA Industries, Inc. (1)
2651 Riverport Rd, Chattanooga, TN 37406-0407   (100%)
Tel.: (423) 624-6496
Sales Range: $25-49.9 Million
Emp.: 122
Mfr of Super Absorbent Polymers, Concrete Admixtures & Water Soluble Polymers
N.A.I.C.S.: 325998

Joint Venture (Domestic):

American Acryl LP (2)
4631 Old Hwy 146 Ste B, Pasadena, TX 77507
Tel.: (281) 909-2600
Web Site: https://www.americanacryl.com
Sales Range: $10-24.9 Million
Mfr of Amines, Acids, Salts & Esters. Joint Venture of Arkema S.A. (50%) & NA Industries, Inc. (50%).
N.A.I.C.S.: 325199

NS Green Co., Ltd. (1)

992-1 Nishioki Okinohama, Aboshi-ku, Himeji, 671-1241, Hyogo, Japan
Plant Maintenance Services
N.A.I.C.S.: 115112

Nippoh Chemicals Co., Ltd. (1)
Neo Kawai Bldg 7F 8-15 4-Chome, Nihonbashi-Honchou Chuo-ku, Tokyo, 103-0023, Japan
Tel.: (81) 332705341
Web Site: https://www.npckk.co.jp
Sales Range: $50-74.9 Million
Emp.: 185
Fine Chemicals Mfr
N.A.I.C.S.: 325411

Plant (Domestic):

Nippoh Chemicals Co., Ltd. - Chimachi Factory (2)
1240 Matsumaru, Isumi, 298-0104, Chiba, Japan
Tel.: (81) 470862211
Sales Range: $50-74.9 Million
Emp.: 200
Fine Chemicals Mfr
N.A.I.C.S.: 325199

Nippon Chemicals Co., Ltd. (1)
Neo Kawai Bldg 7F 8-15 4-Chome, Nihonbashi-Honchou Chuo-ku, Tokyo, 103-0023, Japan
Tel.: (81) 33 270 5341
Web Site: https://www.npckk.co.jp
Emp.: 192
Iodine Chemical Mfr & Distr
N.A.I.C.S.: 325180
Miaki Asakawa (Pres)

Nippon Nyukazai Co., Ltd. (1)
4-1 Kobuna-cho Ibasen Bldg, Nihonbashi Chuo-ku, Tokyo, 103-0024, Japan
Tel.: (81) 356515631
Web Site: https://www.nipponnyukazai.co.jp
Sales Range: $125-149.9 Million
Emp.: 343
Surface Active Agent Mfr
N.A.I.C.S.: 325613
Masakazu Tanaka (Pres)

Nippon Polyester Co., Ltd. (1)
3-4-13 Ishibeguchi, Kita-ku, Konan, 520-3114, Shiga, Japan
Tel.: (81) 748776262
Web Site: https://nippon-polystar.co.jp
Emp.: 80
Polyester Resin Mfr
N.A.I.C.S.: 325211

Nippon Polymer Industries. Co., Ltd. (1)
2114 Kohama, Amihi-ku, Himeji, 671-1241, Japan
Tel.: (81) 79 273 4121
Web Site: https://www.npi-net.co.jp
Synthetic Resins Mfr & Distr
N.A.I.C.S.: 325211

Nippon Shokubai (Asia) Pte. Ltd. (1)
80 Robinson Road 18-02, Singapore, 068898, Singapore (100%)
Tel.: (65) 65320078
Web Site: http://www.shokubai.co.jp
Sales Range: $25-49.9 Million
Emp.: 11
N.A.I.C.S.: 325212

Nippon Shokubai America Industries, Inc. (1)
4631 Old Hwy 146 Ste A, Pasadena, TX 77507
Tel.: (832) 284-4033
Web Site: https://www.shokubai.co.jp
Emp.: 140
Chemical Products Mfr
N.A.I.C.S.: 325998
Yuji Sugiura (Pres)

Nippon Shokubai Europe N.V. (1)
Haven 1053 Nieuwe Weg 1, 2070, Zwijndrecht, Antwerp, Belgium
Tel.: (32) 32503705
Web Site: http://www.shokubai.co.jp
Emp.: 189
Polymer Product Mfr
N.A.I.C.S.: 325211

Nippon Shokubai Korea Co., Ltd. (1)
12F Dowon Bldg3 4 Mapo-daero, Mapo-gu, Seoul, 04174, Korea (South)

Tel.: (82) 2 704 9113
Chemical Products Distr
N.A.I.C.S.: 424690

Nippon Shokubai Trading Co., Ltd. (1)
JP Suitengumae Building 1-14-8, Nihonbasi Ningyo-cho Chuo-Ku, Tokyo, 103-0013, Japan (100%)
Tel.: (81) 356954021
Web Site: https://www.shokubai-trading.co.jp
Minerals & Chemical Products Whslr
N.A.I.C.S.: 424690
Kazuya Watanabe (Pres)

Nisshoku Butsuryu Corporation (1)
6th floor Kogin Building 4-1-1 Koraibashi, Chuo-ku, Osaka, 541-0043, Japan (100%)
Tel.: (81) 662025267
Web Site: http://www.ns-b.jp
Emp.: 191
Warehousing & Freight Forwarding Services
N.A.I.C.S.: 488510
Shu Nakanobu Hata (Pres)

Nisshoku Chemical Industry (Zhangjiagang) Co., Ltd. (1)
No 60 Nanhai Road, Yangtze River International Chemical Industrial Park, Zhangjiagang, 215634, Jiangsu, China (100%)
Tel.: (86) 51258937910
Web Site: http://www.shokubai.co.jp
SAP & Polymers for Concrete Admixture Mfr
N.A.I.C.S.: 327390

Nisshoku Engineering Service Co., Ltd. (1)
992-1 Nishioki Okinohama, Aboshi-ku, Himeji, 671-1241, Japan
Tel.: (81) 79 272 0677
Design Construction Services
N.A.I.C.S.: 236220

Nisshoku Techno Fine Chemical Co., Ltd (1)
9-1 Takayashinmachi, Ichikawa, 272-0011, Chiba, Japan
Tel.: (81) 473281185
Web Site: https://www.ns-technofine.co.jp
Emp.: 110
Chemicals Product Mfr & Whslr
N.A.I.C.S.: 325199
Junichi Tanaka (Pres)

Nisshoku Trading (Shanghai) Co., Ltd. (1)
R/No 3604 The Center 989 Changle Road, Shanghai, 200031, PR, China
Tel.: (86) 2154075959
Web Site: http://www.shokubai.co.jp
Sales Range: $50-74.9 Million
Emp.: 10
Industrial Chemical Whslr
N.A.I.C.S.: 424690

Pt. Nippon Shokubai Indonesia (1)
Kawasan Industri Panca Puri Jl Raya Anyer Km 122 Ciwandan, Cilegon, 42447, Banten, Indonesia
Tel.: (62) 254600660
Acrylic Acid & Esters Mfr
N.A.I.C.S.: 325199

Rena Therapeutics Inc. (1)
Global Business Hub Tokyo Otemachi Financial City, Grand Cube 3F 9-2 Otemachi 1-chome Chiyoda-ku, Tokyo, 100-0004, Japan
Tel.: (81) 34 243 6081
Web Site: https://www.renatherapeutics.com
Emp.: 15
Pharmaceutical Product Mfr & Distr
N.A.I.C.S.: 325412
Shuichi Toriya (Pres & CEO)

Singapore Acrylic Pte Ltd (1)
80 Robinson Road 18-02, Singapore, 068898, Singapore
Tel.: (65) 65320078
Sales Range: $25-49.9 Million
Emp.: 45
Crude Acrylic Acid Mfr & Distr
N.A.I.C.S.: 325130

Singapore Glacial Acrylic Pte. Ltd. (1)
17 Sakra Road, Singapore, 627886, Singapore

Tel.: (65) 62620229
Web Site: http://www.nipponshokubai.com
Sales Range: $25-49.9 Million
Emp.: 42
Glacial Acrylic Acid Mfr & Distr
N.A.I.C.S.: 325130

Sino-Japan Chemical Co., Ltd. (1)
14Fl 99 Sec 2 Jen Ai Rd, Taipei, 100014, Taiwan
Tel.: (886) 22 396 6223
Web Site: https://www.sjc.com.tw
Chemical Products Mfr
N.A.I.C.S.: 325998

Sirrus, Inc. (1)
422 Wards Corner Rd, Loveland, OH 45140
Tel.: (513) 448-0308
Web Site: http://www.sirruschemistry.com
Chemical Products Mfr
N.A.I.C.S.: 325998
Jeffrey Sullivan (Sr VP)

Tokyo Fine Chemical Co., Ltd. (1)
Tel.: (81) 335067666
Web Site: http://www.tokyofine.jp
Sales Range: $25-49.9 Million
Emp.: 61
Chemical Reagent Mfr
N.A.I.C.S.: 325998

NIPPON SIGNAL CO., LTD.
1-5-1 Marunouchi, Chiyoda-ku, Tokyo, 100-6513, Japan
Tel.: (81) 332177200
Web Site: https://www.signal.co.jp 6741—(TKS)
Rev.: $651,322,960
Assets: $1,092,599,950
Liabilities: $452,613,140
Net Worth: $639,986,810
Earnings: $35,337,060
Emp.: 1,261
Fiscal Year-end: 03/31/24
Railway Signal & Traffic Information Systems Mfr
N.A.I.C.S.: 336320
Yohei Furuhata (Chm)

Subsidiaries:

Asahi Electronics Co., Ltd. (1)
1-1-14 Shinjuku, Shinjuku-ku, Tokyo, 160-0022, Japan
Tel.: (81) 72 224 0310
Web Site: https://www.aec.co.jp
Electronic Parts & Equipment Whslr
N.A.I.C.S.: 423690

Fukuoka Nisshin Electronics Co., Ltd. (1)
4-10-5 Meinohama, Nishi-ku, Fukuoka, 819-0002, Japan
Tel.: (81) 92 891 6033
Web Site: https://www.fukuoka-nisshin.co.jp
Construction & Maintenance Services
N.A.I.C.S.: 488210

Hokumei Electric Industry Co., Ltd. (1)
2-2-2 Kikusui 9 Jo, Shiroishi-ku, Sapporo, 003-0809, Hokkaido, Japan
Tel.: (81) 11 821 0931
Web Site: https://www.hokumeidenki.co.jp
Electrical Equipment Mfr & Distr
N.A.I.C.S.: 335999

Nippon Signal Co., Ltd. - Kuki Plant (1)
1836-1 Ooya Aza Ezura, Kuki, 346-8524, Saitama, Japan
Tel.: (81) 480 28 3000
Web Site: http://www.signal.co.jp
Railway Signal & Traffic Information Systems Mfr
N.A.I.C.S.: 336320

Nippon Signal Co., Ltd. - Utsunomiya Plant (1)
11-2 Hiraide Kogyo Danchi, Utsunomiya, 321-8651, Tochigi, Japan
Tel.: (81) 28 660 3000
Web Site: http://www.signal.co.jp
Signal Device Mfr
N.A.I.C.S.: 334515

Nippon Signal India Pvt., Ltd. (1)
Plot No 10 3rd Phase 6th Main Peenya Industrial Area, Bengaluru, 560058, India
Tel.: (91) 802 837 4689
Railway Signal System Mfr
N.A.I.C.S.: 334290

Nisshin Career Service Co., Ltd. (1)
1836-1 Ezura, Kuki, 346-0029, Saitama, Japan
Tel.: (81) 480283315
Signal Device Mfr
N.A.I.C.S.: 334511

Nisshin Electric Construction Co., Ltd. (1)
1-15-13 Kamikizaki, Urawa-ku, Saitama, 330-0071, Japan
Tel.: (81) 48 833 1148
Web Site: https://www.nissindensetu.co.jp
Emp.: 139
Railway Information Control System Services
N.A.I.C.S.: 488210
Oga Hitoshi (Pres)

Nisshin Electronics Service Co., Ltd. (1)
Tokyo Sky Tree East Tower 15F 1-1-2 Oshiage, Sumida-Ku, Tokyo, 131-0045, Japan
Tel.: (81) 35 637 2460
Web Site: https://www.open-nes.co.jp
Medical Equipment Distr
N.A.I.C.S.: 423450

Nisshin IT Field Service Co., Ltd (1)
Higashiueno Building 2-24-1 Higashiueno, Taito-Ku, Tokyo, 110-0015, Japan
Tel.: (81) 362844320
Web Site: https://www.nisshin-it.co.jp
Emp.: 293
Information Technology Services
N.A.I.C.S.: 541512

Nisshin Okabe Nikoh Co., Ltd. (1)
2943-2 Oka, Fukaya, 369-0201, Saitama, Japan
Tel.: (81) 48 585 3361
Web Site: https://www.okabeniko.co.jp
Sheet Metal Work Mfg
N.A.I.C.S.: 332322

Nisshin Software Engineering Co., Ltd. (1)
1836-1 Emen, Kuki, 346-0029, Saitama, Japan
Tel.: (81) 480283870
Web Site: https://www.nisshin-soft.co.jp
Emp.: 243
Software Development Services
N.A.I.C.S.: 541511
Masaki Samukawa (Auditor)

Nisshin TECHNO Engineering Co., Ltd. (1)
1836-1 Otani Ezura, Kuki, 346-8524, Saitama, Japan
Tel.: (81) 48 028 3390
Web Site: https://www.signalntec.co.jp
Electric Device Mfr
N.A.I.C.S.: 334419

Nisshin TECHNO Service Co., Ltd. (1)
Tel.: (81) 480283390
Web Site: http://www.signalnet.co.jp
Sales Range: $25-49.9 Million
Emp.: 48
Transport Signalling System Installation Services
N.A.I.C.S.: 238210

Nisshin Tokki Co., Ltd. (1)
141 Sakusai-cho, Kishiwada, 596-0826, Japan
Tel.: (81) 7 24392921
Web Site: http://www.n-tokki.co.jp
Emp.: 80
Transport Signalling System Installation Services
N.A.I.C.S.: 238210
Mitsuru Suzuki (Pres)

Saitama Union Service Co., Ltd. (1)
756-1 Nakanobayashi, Nishi-ku, Saitama, 331-0057, Japan
Tel.: (81) 48 622 7480
Web Site: https://www.union-e.jp
Highway Street & Bridge Construction Services
N.A.I.C.S.: 237310

NIPPON SIGNAL CO., LTD.

Nippon Signal Co., Ltd.—(Continued)

Sapporo Nisshin Electronics Co., Ltd. (1)
4-8-6-5 Tsukisamu Higashi, Toyohira-ku, Sapporo, 062-0054, Japan
Tel.: (81) 11 855 6781
Web Site: https://www.sapporo-nisshin.co.jp
Electronics Services
N.A.I.C.S.: 449210

Sendai Nisshin Electronics Co., Ltd. (1)
6-1 Shimizukoji East Japan Real Estate Sendai First Building 2nd Floor, Wakabayashi-ku, Sendai, 984-0075, Miyagi, Japan
Tel.: (81) 22 265 5051
Web Site: https://www.sendai-nisshin.co.jp
Eletric Power Generation Services
N.A.I.C.S.: 221118

Tochigi Nisshin Co., Ltd. (1)
141-7 Nogi Nogo-Cho, Shimotsuga-gun, Tochigi, 329-0114, Japan
Tel.: (81) 28 054 1391
Web Site: https://www.tochigi-ns.co.jp
Industrial Machinery Mfr
N.A.I.C.S.: 333248

Yamagata Nisshin Electronics Co., Ltd. (1)
2558-2 Kusaoka Sakaida, Nagai, 993-0063, Yamagata, Japan
Tel.: (81) 23 884 5378
Web Site: https://www.y-nissin.co.jp
Electronic Parts & Equipment Whslr
N.A.I.C.S.: 423690

NIPPON SKI RESORT DEVELOPMENT CO., LTD.

6329-1 Hokujo Hakuba-mura Kitaazumi-gun, Nagano, 399-9301, Japan
Web Site: http://www.nippon-ski.jp
6040—(TKS)
Rev.: $51,283,900
Assets: $68,357,800
Liabilities: $24,450,820
Net Worth: $43,906,980
Earnings: $6,798,460
Fiscal Year-end: 07/31/24
Ski Resort Operations
N.A.I.C.S.: 713920
Shuhei Suzuki *(CEO)*

Subsidiaries:

HAKUBA RESORT DEVELOPMENT, Co., Ltd. (1)
6329-1 Hokujyo, Hakuba-mura Kitaazumi-gun, Nagano, Japan
Tel.: (81) 261723150
Ski Resort Operator
N.A.I.C.S.: 721110

Kitashiga Ryuoo, Co., Ltd. (1)
11700 Yomase, Yamanouchi-machi Shimotakai-gun, Nagano, Japan
Tel.: (81) 81269337131
Ski Resort Operator
N.A.I.C.S.: 721110
Takao Hori *(Mgr)*

Meiho Kogen Kaihatsu Co., Ltd. (1)
3447-1 Mizusawaue, Meiho Okuzumi, Gujo, Japan
Tel.: (81) 575872811
Web Site: https://www.meihoski.co.jp
Ski Resort Operator
N.A.I.C.S.: 721110

NIPPON SODA CO., LTD.

JP Tower 10th Floor 2-7-2 Marunouchi, Chiyoda-ku, Tokyo, 100-7010, Japan
Tel.: (81) 63661920 JP
Web Site: https://www.nippon-soda.co.jp
Year Founded: 1920
4041—(TKS)
Rev.: $1,020,775,690
Assets: $1,920,152,120
Liabilities: $667,728,980
Net Worth: $1,252,423,140
Earnings: $109,805,320
Emp.: 2,446
Fiscal Year-end: 03/31/24
Industrial & Agricultural Chemicals Mfr
N.A.I.C.S.: 325998
Akira Ishii *(Chm)*

Subsidiaries:

Bharat Certis Agriscience Ltd. (1)
Office Unit 301 3rd Floor Worldmark 3 Asset No 7 Aerocity NH-8, Hospitality District, New Delhi, 110037, India
Tel.: (91) 1142262100
Web Site: https://www.bharatcertis.com
Agricultural Chemical Mfr & Distr
N.A.I.C.S.: 325320

Certis Belchim B.V. (1)
Stadsplateau 16, PO Box 607, 3500 AP, Utrecht, Netherlands
Tel.: (31) 302001200
Web Site: https://www.certiseurope.com
Crop Protection Product & Expertise Services
N.A.I.C.S.: 115112

Joetsu Nisso Chemical Co., Ltd. (1)
950 Fujisawa, Nakago, Joetsu, 949-2302, Niigata, Japan
Tel.: (81) 255812390
Sales Range: $25-49.9 Million
Emp.: 55
Caustic Potash & Hydrochloride Chemicals Mfr
N.A.I.C.S.: 325180

NISSO BASF Agro Co., Ltd. (1)
Shinko Building 1-11-4 Kudan-Kita, Chiyoda-ku, Tokyo, 102 0073, Japan
Tel.: (81) 332370655
Herbicide Mfr
N.A.I.C.S.: 325320

Nippon Soda Co., Ltd. - Takaoka Plant (1)
300 Mukainohonmachi, Takaoka, 933-8507, Toyama, Japan
Tel.: (81) 766260206
Chemicals Mfr
N.A.I.C.S.: 325998

Nippon Soda Trading (Shanghai) Co., Ltd. (1)
Room2318 Ruijing Building 205 Maoming South Road, Shanghai, 200020, China
Tel.: (86) 2164731277
Emp.: 10
Chemicals Whslr
N.A.I.C.S.: 424690
Takeshi Koyama *(Gen Mgr)*

Nisso America Inc. (1)
379 Thornall St 5th Fl, Edison, NJ 08837
Tel.: (212) 490-0350
Web Site: https://www.nissoamerica.com
Emp.: 11
Industrial Chemical Whslr
N.A.I.C.S.: 424690
Hiroyasu Yamazaki *(Pres)*

Nisso Brasileira Representa Cao Ltda. (1)
Av Paulista 854-13 andar-cj 135, Bela Vista, 01310-913, Sao Paulo, Brazil
Tel.: (55) 1131451840
Sales Range: $50-74.9 Million
Emp.: 4
Agricultural Chemicals Sales
N.A.I.C.S.: 424910
Helena Omori *(Sec)*

Nisso Chemical Analysis Service Co., Ltd. (1)
345 Takata, Odawara, 250-0216, Kanagawa, Japan
Tel.: (81) 465423115
Web Site: http://www.ncas.co.jp
Agrochemical Research & Development Services
N.A.I.C.S.: 541715

Nisso Chemical Europe GmbH (1)
Berliner Allee 42, 40212, Dusseldorf, Germany
Tel.: (49) 21113066860
Web Site: https://www.nisso-chem.de
Chemical Products Mfr
N.A.I.C.S.: 325998
Tateshi Tsujikawa *(Mng Dir)*

Nisso Construction Co., Ltd. (1)
1169 Fujisawa, Nakago-ku, Joetsu, 949-2302, Niigata, Japan
Tel.: (81) 255 74 2561
Civil Engineering & Construction Services
N.A.I.C.S.: 541330

Nisso Engineering Co., Ltd. (1)
1-6-1 Kanda Jimbocho Takii Tokyo Building, Chiyoda-ku, Tokyo, 101-0051, Japan
Tel.: (81) 332969201
Web Site: https://www.nisso-eng.co.jp
Sales Range: $25-49.9 Million
Emp.: 161
Industrial Engineering Services
N.A.I.C.S.: 541330

Nisso Fine Chemicals Co., Ltd. (1)
3-3-6 Nihonbashi Honcho, Chuo-ku, Tokyo, 103-8422, Japan
Tel.: (81) 362020161
Web Site: http://www.nisso-finechemicals.co.jp
Sales Range: $50-74.9 Million
Emp.: 160
Chemicals Mfr
N.A.I.C.S.: 325199

Nisso Green Co., Ltd. (1)
3-1-2 Ueno Akihabara Shinko Daiichi Seimei Building 5F, Taito-ku, Tokyo, 110-0005, Japan (100%)
Tel.: (81) 358164351
Web Site: https://www.ns-green.com
Emp.: 21
Agricultural Chemicals Whslr
N.A.I.C.S.: 424910

Nisso Korea Co., Ltd. (1)
A-1401 Champs Elysees Center Building 889-5 Daechi-dong, Kangnam-gu, Seoul, 135-712, Korea (South)
Tel.: (82) 220517718
Web Site: http://www.nippon-soda.co.kr
Agrochemicals Whslr
N.A.I.C.S.: 424910
Lee Kansup *(VP)*

Nisso Metallochemical Co., Ltd. (1)
4th floor HF Nihonbashi Kabutocho Building 21-7 Nihonbashi Kabutocho, Chuo-ku, Tokyo, 103-0026, Japan
Tel.: (81) 345867890
Web Site: https://www.nmcc.co.jp
Sales Range: $50-74.9 Million
Emp.: 160
Nonferrous Alloy Mfr
N.A.I.C.S.: 331492

Nisso Shoji Co., Ltd. (1)
3-3-6 Nihonbashi Honmachi Wakasue Building, Chuo-ku, Tokyo, 103-8422, Japan
Tel.: (81) 332700701
Web Site: https://www.nissoshoji.com
Emp.: 150
Chemicals Import & Distr
N.A.I.C.S.: 424690
Tsutomu Sakuma *(Pres-New Bus Mktg Dept & Oversea Bus Promo Dept)*

Sanso Unyu Co., Ltd. (1)
Tamamaenishi1-4-1, Ichihara, 290-0044, Chiba, Japan
Tel.: (81) 436228947
Bulk Chemicals Trucking & Industrial Waste Processing Services
N.A.I.C.S.: 484220

Sanwa Soko Co., Ltd. (1)
Web Site: http://www.sanwasoko.co.jp
Emp.: 166
Warehousing & Freight Forwarding Services
N.A.I.C.S.: 488510

Shinfuji Kaseiyaku Co., Ltd. (1)
313 Koyagicho, Takasaki, 370-0071, Gunma, Japan
Tel.: (81) 273616100
Web Site: https://www.shinfuji-kaseiyaku.co.jp
Emp.: 84
Pesticides & Agricultural Chemicals Mfr
N.A.I.C.S.: 325320

NIPPON STEEL CORPORATION

2-6-1 Marunouchi, Chiyoda-ku, Tokyo, 100-8071, Japan
Tel.: (81) 368674111 JP
Web Site: https://www.nipponsteel.com
Year Founded: 1901
NISTF—(OTCIQ)
Rev.: $54,300,384,250
Assets: $68,270,329,050
Liabilities: $40,791,213,610
Net Worth: $27,479,115,440
Earnings: $3,907,520,400)
Fiscal Year-end: 03/31/20
Holding Company; Steel Foundries & Products Mfr
N.A.I.C.S.: 551112
Kosei Shindo *(Chm)*

Subsidiaries:

AM/NS Calvert (1)
1 Thyssenkrupp Dr, Calvert, AL 36513 (50%)
Tel.: (251) 289-3000
Web Site: http://usa.arcelormittal.com
Sales Range: $900-999.9 Million
Emp.: 4,000
Coiled Carbon Steel Mfr & Distr
N.A.I.C.S.: 332111

Baosteel-Nippon Steel Automotive Steel Sheets Co., Ltd. (1)
Cold Rolling Complex Weiwu Rd Baoshan Steel, Baoshan Dist, Shanghai, China (50%)
Tel.: (86) 21 2664 3800
Automotive Steel Sheet Products Mfr
N.A.I.C.S.: 332322

NS Solutions Corporation (1)
Toranomon Hills Business Tower 1-17-1 Toranomon, Minato-ku, Tokyo, 105-6417, Japan
Tel.: (81) 368996000
Web Site: https://www.nssol.nipponsteel.com
Rev.: $2,053,277,520
Assets: $2,476,350,570
Liabilities: $858,334,940
Net Worth: $1,618,015,630
Earnings: $160,233,010
Emp.: 7,826
Fiscal Year-end: 03/31/2024
Information Technology Services
N.A.I.C.S.: 541512
Tetsuji Fukushima *(Exec Dir)*

Subsidiary (Domestic):

Hokkaido NS Solutions Corporation (2)
2-13-1 Miyukicho, Muroran, 050-0084, Japan
Tel.: (81) 143453220
Information Technology Consulting Services
N.A.I.C.S.: 541512

Subsidiary (Non-US):

NS Solutions Asia Pacific Pte. Ltd. (2)
16 Raffles Quay 17-01 Hong Leong Bldg, Singapore, 048581, Singapore
Tel.: (65) 62209329
Web Site: http://www.nssolutions.nipponsteel.com
Information Technology Consulting Services
N.A.I.C.S.: 541512

Subsidiary (Domestic):

NS Solutions Chubu Corporation (2)
2-13-18 Meiekiminami Ns Bldg 2f, Nakamura-ku, Nagoya, 450-0003, Japan
Tel.: (81) 525895128
Information Technology Consulting Services
N.A.I.C.S.: 541512

NS Solutions Kansai Corporation (2)
7-20-1 Fukushima Kmnishiumeda Bldg 11f, Fukushima-ku, Osaka, 553-0003, Japan
Tel.: (81) 664545270
Information Technology Consulting Services
N.A.I.C.S.: 541512

NS Solutions Nishinihon Corporation (2)
2-3-7-6F Hakataeki-mae, Hakata-ku, Fu-

AND PRIVATE COMPANIES — NIPPON STEEL CORPORATION

kuoka, 810-0801, Japan
Tel.: (81) 924712022
Information Technology Consulting Services
N.A.I.C.S.: 541512

NSSLC Service Corporation (2)
2 Shinnittetsu Bldg Higashikan 2-20-15
Shinkawa, Chuo, 104-0033, Japan
Tel.: (81) 351176100
Information Technology Consulting Services
N.A.I.C.S.: 541512

Network Value Components Ltd. (2)
Nissei Yokosuka Center Bldg 14-1 Ogawa,
Yokosuka, 238-0004, Kanagawa,
Japan (100%)
Tel.: (81) 46 828 1800
Web Site: http://www.nvc.co.jp
Sales Range: $25-49.9 Million
Emp.: 83
Electrical & Electronic Parts Distr
N.A.I.C.S.: 423430
Hiroshi Furukawa (Exec Officer)

Nittetsu Hitachi Systems Engineering, Inc. (2)
St Luke's Tower 26F 8-1 Akashi-cho, Chuo-ku, Tokyo, Japan
Tel.: (81) 335447800
Web Site: https://www.nhs.co.jp
Emp.: 499
Computer Peripheral Equipment Mfr & Distr
N.A.I.C.S.: 334118
Hiroyuki Hori (Exec Dir)

Oita NS Solutions Corporation (2)
1 Oazanishinosu, Oita, 870-0902, Japan
Tel.: (81) 975040900
Information Technology Consulting Services
N.A.I.C.S.: 541512

Subsidiary (Non-US):

PT. NSSOL SYSTEMS INDONESIA (2)
Sentral Senayan II Ground&Mezzanine
Floors Jalan Asia Afrika No 8, Gelora Bung
Karno-Senayan, Jakarta, 10270, Indonesia
Tel.: (62) 2129039210
Information Technology Consulting Services
N.A.I.C.S.: 541512

Thai NS Solutions Co., Ltd. (2)
Boonmitra Building 138 Silom Road Suriyawong, Bang Rak, Bangkok, 10500, Thailand
Tel.: (66) 26345820
Information Technology Consulting Services
N.A.I.C.S.: 541512

Subsidiary (Domestic):

Tohoku NS Solutions Corporation (2)
3-2-1 Chuo Aobadori Plaza 8f, Aoba-ku,
Sendai, 980-0021, Japan
Tel.: (81) 222243325
Information Technology Consulting Services
N.A.I.C.S.: 541512

NS-Siam United Steel Co., Ltd. (1)
12 Soi G2 Pakorn Songkrohraj Road, Map
Ta Phut Muang, Rayong, 21150, Thailand
Tel.: (66) 3 868 5155
Web Site: https://www.ns-sus.com
Emp.: 1,090
Rolled Sheet Product Mfr & Distr
N.A.I.C.S.: 331221

Nippon Steel & Sumikin Crankshaft LLC (1)
1815 E Sandusky St, Fostoria, OH 44830
Tel.: (419) 435-0411
Sales Range: $25-49.9 Million
Emp.: 200
Crankshafts & Camshafts Mfr; Owned 60%
by Sumitomo Metal Industries, Ltd. & 40%
by Sumitomo Corporation
N.A.I.C.S.: 333998
Bob Truscinski (Controller)

Nippon Steel & Sumitomo Metal Consulting (Beijing) Co., Ltd. (1)
Room No 5002 Chang Fu Gong Center
Jian Guo Men Wai Da Jie 26, Chaoyang
District, Beijing, 100022, China
Tel.: (86) 10 6513 8593
Emp.: 10
Steel Products Mfr
N.A.I.C.S.: 331513

Shin Nishiura (Office Mgr)

Nippon Steel & Sumitomo Metal Empreendimentos Siderurgia Ltda. (1)
Avenida Paulista 2300 18 andar conj 181-183, Sao Paulo, 01310-300, SP, Brazil
Tel.: (55) 1135631900
Web Site: http://www.nssmc.com
Emp.: 100
Steel Production
N.A.I.C.S.: 331513

Nippon Steel (Thailand) Co., Ltd. (1)
120 Moo 11 Ample Tower 14th Floor
Bangna-Trad KM 4 Road Khwang Bangna,
Khet Bangna, Bangkok, 10260,
Thailand (100%)
Tel.: (66) 2 744 1480
Steel Products Mfr
N.A.I.C.S.: 331513

Nippon Steel Australia Pty. Limited (1)
Level 24 1 York Street, Sydney, 2000,
NSW, Australia (100%)
Tel.: (61) 292522077
Emp.: 7
Steel Product Distr
N.A.I.C.S.: 423510
Yoshi Nakata (Mng Dir)

Nippon Steel Blast Furnace Slag Cement Co., Ltd. (1)
16 Nishiminato-machi, Kokurakita-ku, Kitakyushu, 803-0801, Fukuoka,
Japan (100%)
Tel.: (81) 93 563 5100
Cement & Steel Slag Mfr
N.A.I.C.S.: 327310

Nippon Steel Chemical & Material Co., Ltd. (1)
13-1 Nihonbashi 1-chome, Chuo-ku, Tokyo,
103-0027, Japan
Tel.: (81) 335100301
Web Site: https://www.nscm.nipponsteel.com
Emp.: 3,206
Chemical & Composite Material Products
Developer, Mfr & Whslr
N.A.I.C.S.: 325998
Sakae Toshiharu (Pres)

Subsidiary (Domestic):

C-Chem Co., Ltd. (2)
13-1 Nihonbashi 1-chome, Chuo-ku, Tokyo,
103-0027, Japan (65%)
Tel.: (81) 335100322
Web Site: http://www.nscm.nipponsteel.com
Sales Range: $400-449.9 Million
Emp.: 120
Manufacture & Sale of Coal Chemicals
N.A.I.C.S.: 325998
Takeshi Hayashi (Pres)

Subsidiary (Non-US):

Harimic (Malaysia) Sdn. Bhd. (2)
Lot 78 Jalan Perusahaan 1, Prai Industrial
Area, Perai, 13600, Penang, Malaysia
Tel.: (60) 43983498
Web Site: http://www.harimic.com
Specialty Chemicals Mfr & Distr
N.A.I.C.S.: 325998

Subsidiary (Domestic):

Nippon Steel Carbon Co., Ltd. (2)
13-1 Nihonbashi 1-chome, Chuo-ku, Tokyo,
103-0027, Japan
Tel.: (81) 3 3510 0324
Emp.: 91
Composite Material Products Developer, Mfr
& Whslr
N.A.I.C.S.: 325211
Miyaki Isao (Pres)

Subsidiary (Non-US):

Nippon Steel Chemical & Material Korea Co., Ltd. (2)
2F CheilPharm Bldg 343 Sapyeong-Daero,
Seocho-gu, Seoul, Korea (South) (100%)
Tel.: (82) 2 541 9004
Web Site: http://www.nscm.nipponsteel.com
Chemical & Composite Products Distr
N.A.I.C.S.: 424690

Nippon Steel Chemical & Material Tradings Hong Kong Co., Ltd. (2)

Rm 1603 16/F Metropolis Tower 10 Metropolis Drive, Hunghom, Kowloon, China
(Hong Kong)
Tel.: (852) 2576 9339
Web Site: http://www.nscc.co.jp
Plastic Product Distr
N.A.I.C.S.: 424610

Nippon Steel Coated Sheet Corporation (1)
1-5-6 Nihonbashi-honcho, Chuo-ku, Tokyo,
103-0023, Japan
Tel.: (81) 3 6848 3900
Web Site: http://www.niscs.nipponsteel.com
Coated Steel Sheet Mfr & Distr
N.A.I.C.S.: 331221

Nippon Steel Corporation - European Representative Office (1)
Am Seestern 8, 40547, Dusseldorf, Germany
Tel.: (49) 2115306680
Web Site: http://www.nssmc.com
Sales Range: $25-49.9 Million
Emp.: 10
Steel Foundries
N.A.I.C.S.: 331513

Nippon Steel Corporation - Hirohata Works (1)
1 Fuji-cho, Hirohata-ku, Himeji, 671-1188,
Hyogo, Japan
Tel.: (81) 79 236 1001
Sales Range: $400-449.9 Million
Emp.: 1,293
Steel Sheet Mfr
N.A.I.C.S.: 331221

Nippon Steel Corporation - Kamaishi Works (1)
23-15 Suzuko-cho, Kamaishi, 026-8567,
Iwate, Japan
Tel.: (81) 193 24 2332
Web Site: http://www.nsc.co.jp
Steel Products Mfr
N.A.I.C.S.: 331110

Nippon Steel Corporation - Kimitsu Works (1)
1 Kimitsu, Kimitsu, 299-1141, Chiba, Japan
Tel.: (81) 439 50 2013
Web Site: http://www.nsc.co.jp
Steel Pole Mfr
N.A.I.C.S.: 331210

Nippon Steel Corporation - Muroran Works (1)
12 Nakamachi, Muroran, 050-8550, Hokkaido, Japan
Tel.: (81) 143 47 2111
Web Site: http://www.nsc.co.jp
Sales Range: $200-249.9 Million
Emp.: 729
Automobile Parts Mfr
N.A.I.C.S.: 336390

Nippon Steel Corporation - Nagoya Works (1)
5-3 Tokaimachi, Tokai, 476-8686, Aichi,
Japan
Tel.: (81) 52 603 7024
Emp.: 3,000
Steel Sheet Mfr
N.A.I.C.S.: 331221
Kodama Shuhei (Mgr-Admin)

Nippon Steel Corporation - Sakai Works (1)
1 Chikkoyawatamachi, Sakai-ku, Sakai,
590-8540, Osaka, Japan
Tel.: (81) 72 233 1108
Web Site: http://www.nssmc.com
Emp.: 300
Steel Sheet Mfr
N.A.I.C.S.: 331221
Kazuhiro Nakashima (Pres)

Nippon Steel Corporation - Tokyo Works (1)
3-1 Funado 4-chome, Itabashi-ku, Tokyo,
174-0041, Japan
Tel.: (81) 3 3968 6801
Web Site: http://www.nssnc.co.jp
Emp.: 150
Steel Pole Mfr
N.A.I.C.S.: 331210
Hirofumi Hori (Gen Mgr)

Nippon Steel Corporation - Yawata Works (1)

1-1 Tobihatacho, Tobata-ku, Kitakyushu,
804-8501, Fukuoka, Japan
Tel.: (81) 93 872 6111
Steel Products Mfr
N.A.I.C.S.: 331110

Nippon Steel Drum Co., Ltd. (1)
5-7 1-chome Kameido, Kotu-ku, Tokyo, 136-0071, Japan (100%)
Tel.: (81) 3 5627 2311
Web Site: http://www.drum.nipponsteel.com
Sales Range: $50-74.9 Million
Emp.: 224
Steel Drum Mfr & Distr
N.A.I.C.S.: 332432
Keiji Ichikawa (Corp Auditor)

Plant (Domestic):

Nippon Steel Drum Co., Ltd. - Chiba Plant (2)
13 Anesakikaigan, Ichihara, 299-0107,
Chiba, Japan
Tel.: (81) 436 61 1291
Steel Drum & Container Products Mfr
N.A.I.C.S.: 332439

Nippon Steel Drum Co., Ltd. - Nagoya Plant (2)
28-2 Shinpomachi, Tokai, 476-0005, Aichi,
Japan
Tel.: (81) 52 603 3411
Steel Drum & Container Products Mfr
N.A.I.C.S.: 332439

Nippon Steel Drum Co., Ltd. - Osaka Plant (2)
1-21 Rinkaicho, Izumiotsu, 595-0075,
Osaka, Japan
Tel.: (81) 725 33 6301
Steel Drum & Container Products Mfr
N.A.I.C.S.: 332439

Nippon Steel Drum Co., Ltd. - Sagamihara Plant (2)
7-1 5-Chome Nishihashimoto, Midori-ku,
Sagamihara, 252-0131, Kanagawa, Japan
Tel.: (81) 42 772 2151
Steel Drum & Container Products Mfr
N.A.I.C.S.: 332439

Subsidiary (Domestic):

Nippon Steel Drum Techno Co., Ltd. (2)
74-1 Kotehashicho, Hanamigawa-ku, Chiba,
Japan (100%)
Tel.: (81) 43 298 5300
Container Filling Systems & Drum Manufacturing Equipment Designer, Mfr & Whslr
N.A.I.C.S.: 333248
Masatake Watanabe (Pres)

Sanyo Steel Drum Industry Co., Ltd. (2)
1230 Nakashima, Kurashiki, 710-0803,
Okayama, Japan (100%)
Tel.: (81) 86 465 3680
Steel Drums Mfr
N.A.I.C.S.: 332439
Tsuyoshi Miyake (Pres)

Nippon Steel Engineering Co., Ltd. (1)
Osaki Center Building 1-5-1 Osaki,
Shinagawa-ku, Tokyo, 141-8604, Japan
Tel.: (81) 3 6665 2000
Web Site: http://www.eng.nssmc.com
Rev.: $3,321,347,000
Emp.: 4,149
Steel Building & Pipeline Construction &
Engineering Services
N.A.I.C.S.: 237990

Affiliate (Non-US):

Nippon Steel & Sumikin Plant Engineering (Shanghai) Co., Ltd (2)
Room 1510 Greenland Commercial Center
1258 Yuyuan Road, Shanghai, 200050,
China
Tel.: (86) 21 5155 3606
Steel Product Distr
N.A.I.C.S.: 423510

Subsidiary (Non-US):

Steinmueller Babcock Environment GmbH (2)

NIPPON STEEL CORPORATION

Nippon Steel Corporation—(Continued)
Fabrikstrasse 1, 51643, Gummersbach, Germany **(100%)**
Tel.: (49) 2261 85 0
Web Site: http://www.steinmueller-babcock.com
Sales Range: $100-124.9 Million
Emp.: 300
Thermal Waste Treatment & Flue Gas Cleaning Plant Engineering & Construction Services
N.A.I.C.S.: 236210
Kai Oberst *(Mgr-Project Svc)*

Subsidiary (Non-US):

Steinmueller Babcock Engineering Co., Ltd. **(3)**
Room 6003B Novel Building 887 Huaihai Road, 200020, Shanghai, China **(100%)**
Tel.: (86) 2164747105
Web Site: http://www.steinmuellerbabcock.com
Emp.: 20
Water Treatment Plant Engineering & Construction Services
N.A.I.C.S.: 237990
Li Ping *(Gen Mgr)*

Affiliate (Non-US):

Thai Nippon Steel & Sumikin Engineering & Construction Corp., Ltd. **(2)**
390 Moo 6 Tai-Ban Road Tambol Tai-Ban, Amphure Muang, Samut Prakan, 10280, Thailand **(47%)**
Tel.: (66) 2 703 5160
Web Site: http://www.thainippon.co.th
Steel Building Construction Engineering Services
N.A.I.C.S.: 237990
Ishiwa Yukito *(Mng Dir)*

Nippon Steel India Pvt. Ltd. **(1)**
Prius Platinum A Wing Ground Floor D-3 Dist Centre, Saket, New Delhi, 110017, India
Tel.: (91) 11 4763 0000
Steel Products Whslr
N.A.I.C.S.: 423510

Nippon Steel Logistics Co., Ltd. **(1)**
23-4 Shinkawa 1-chome, Chuo-ku, Tokyo, Japan **(100%)**
Tel.: (81) 3 3553 1331
Marine Transportation, Harbor Transportation, Freight Transportation & Customs Clearance
N.A.I.C.S.: 541614
Shinya Higuchi *(Pres)*

Nippon Steel Metal Products Co., Ltd. **(1)**
Akihabara UDX 13F Sotokanda 4-14-1, Chiyoda-ku, Tokyo, 101-0021, Japan
Tel.: (81) 366256000
Web Site: https://www.ns-kenzai.co.jp
Cold Formed Steel Products Mfr
N.A.I.C.S.: 331110
Junichi Imade *(Mng Dir)*

Nippon Steel Nisshin Co., Ltd. **(1)**
Shin Kokusai Building 3-4-1 Marunouchi, Chiyoda-ku, Tokyo, 100-8366, Japan **(100%)**
Tel.: (81) 332165511
Holding Company; Steel Products Mfr
N.A.I.C.S.: 551112
Kinya Yanagawa *(Pres & CEO)*

Affiliate (Domestic):

IWATA Specialty Steel, Inc. **(2)**
1-11-2 Kamezawa, Sumida-ku, Tokyo, 130-0014, Japan
Tel.: (81) 3 3624 0531
Web Site: http://www.iwata-koutetsu.co.jp
Steel Product Distr
N.A.I.C.S.: 423510

Subsidiary (Domestic):

Nihon Pipe System Co., Ltd. **(2)**
1390 Ebise 1, Itakura cho Ora gun, Gunma, 374-0111, Japan
Tel.: (81) 276 82 5691
Web Site: http://www.pipesystem.co.jp
Stainless Steel Wire Mfr

N.A.I.C.S.: 331210
Hiroshi Watanabe *(Chm)*

Nisshin Kokan Co., Ltd **(2)**
Shin Kokusai Building 6F 3-4-1 Marunouchi, Chiyoda-ku, Tokyo, 100-0005, Japan
Tel.: (81) 3 3216 5027
Web Site: http://www.nisshin-kokan.co.jp
Steel Pipe & Tubes Mfr & Whslr
N.A.I.C.S.: 331210

Nisshin Metal-Working Co., Ltd. **(2)**
1 Hama-Machi, Hekinan, 447-0853, Aichi, Japan
Tel.: (81) 566 48 3330
Rolled Stainless Steel Products Mfr & Whslr
N.A.I.C.S.: 331221

Nisshin Sanso Co., Ltd. **(2)**
11-1 Showacho, Kure, 737-0027, Hiroshima, Japan
Tel.: (81) 823 22 8080
Industrial Gases Mfr & Whslr
N.A.I.C.S.: 325120

Affiliate (Domestic):

Nitirin Metals Co., Ltd. **(2)**
1-2-1 Shibadaimon Daimon KS Building 4F, Minato-ku, Tokyo, 105-0012, Japan
Tel.: (81) 366284393
Web Site: https://www.nitirin-metals.co.jp
Steel Products Mfr & Whslr
N.A.I.C.S.: 331110
Shozo Tanaka *(Pres & CEO)*

Pro Steel Co., Ltd. **(2)**
1-1908 Daineyama, Midori-ku, Nagoya, 459-8501, Aichi, Japan **(15.2%)**
Tel.: (81) 526291811
Web Site: https://www.prosteel.co.jp
Emp.: 97
Steel Product Distr
N.A.I.C.S.: 423510
Tomoei Hosono *(Pres & CEO)*

Subsidiary (Domestic):

Shinwa Kigyo Co., Ltd. **(2)**
3-9 Kaigandori, Naka-ku, Yokohama, 231-0002, Japan
Tel.: (81) 452262481
Web Site: https://www.shinwa-kigyo.jp
Office Administrative & Facilities Support Services
N.A.I.C.S.: 561110
Masanori Fujita *(Mng Dir)*

Tsukiboshi Art Co., Ltd. **(2)**
2-2-24 Tsugiya, Amagasaki, 661-0965, Hyogo, Japan
Tel.: (81) 6 6499 1157
Web Site: http://www.ms-art.co.jp
Decorative Stainless Steel Sheet Products Mfr & Whslr
N.A.I.C.S.: 332322

Tsukiboshi Logistics Co., Ltd. **(2)**
Yodoyabashi Flex Tower 10F 3-3-11 Koraibashi, Chuo-ku, Osaka, 541-0043, Japan
Tel.: (81) 6 6228 0100
Steel Products Transportation, Warehousing & Logistics Services
N.A.I.C.S.: 488510

Tsukiboshi Shoji Co., Ltd. **(2)**
4-2-4 Hatchobori, Chuo-ku, Tokyo, 104-8533, Japan
Tel.: (81) 3 3551 2122
Web Site: http://www.tsukiboshi-shoji.co.jp
Emp.: 250
Steel Products Whslr
N.A.I.C.S.: 423510

Subsidiary (US):

Wheeling-Nippon Steel, Inc. **(2)**
PO Box 635, Follansbee, WV 26037 **(100%)**
Tel.: (304) 527-2800
Web Site: http://www.wheeling-nisshin.com
Galvanized & Aluminized Steel Sheet Products Mfr & Whslr
N.A.I.C.S.: 331110
Brian Petrella *(Gen Mgr-Comml)*

Nippon Steel North America., Inc. **(1)**
1251 Ave Of The Americas Ste 2320, New York, NY 10020 **(100%)**
Tel.: (212) 486-7150

Sales Range: $50-74.9 Million
Emp.: 11
Provider of Market Research & Investment Management Services
N.A.I.C.S.: 523150
Isao Takenami *(CFO)*

Subsidiary (Domestic):

NS Finance, Inc. **(2)**
1251 Ave of the Americas Ste 2320, New York, NY 10020
Tel.: (212) 486-7150
Sales Range: $50-74.9 Million
Holding Company
N.A.I.C.S.: 523910

NS Kote, Inc. **(2)**
1251 Ave Of the Americas Ste 2320, New York, NY 10020-0088 **(100%)**
Tel.: (212) 486-7150
Web Site: http://www.nsc.co.jp
Sales Range: $50-74.9 Million
Partner of I/N Kote
N.A.I.C.S.: 523910
Nobuhiko Ikura *(Pres & CEO)*

NS Tek **(2)**
1251 Avenue of the Americas Ste 2320, New York, NY 10020
Tel.: (212) 486-7150
Web Site: http://www.nssmc.com
Sales Range: $50-74.9 Million
Emp.: 15
Investment Banking
N.A.I.C.S.: 523150
Steven Wesemann *(Controller)*

Branch (Domestic):

Nippon Steel North America, Inc. - Chicago **(2)**
900 N Michigan Ave Ste 1820, Chicago, IL 60611
Tel.: (312) 751-0800
Web Site: http://www.nssmc.com
Sales Range: $25-49.9 Million
Emp.: 14
Sale of Cold Rolled Sheets
N.A.I.C.S.: 423510
Yoshiro Hori *(Gen Mgr)*

Nippon Steel North America, Inc. - Houston **(2)**
945 Bunker Hill Rd Ste 600, Houston, TX 77024
Tel.: (713) 654-7111
Web Site: http://www.tubular.nssmc.com
Sales Range: $25-49.9 Million
Emp.: 3
Whslr of Iron & Steel Products, Construction Materials, Steel Castings & Forgings
N.A.I.C.S.: 423510
Max Tanida *(Mgr-Tech Svcs)*

Nippon Steel Pipe Co., Ltd. **(1)**
1-1-3 Yurakucho, Chiyoda-ku, Tokyo, 100-0006, Japan
Tel.: (81) 3 6758 0275
Web Site: http://www.nspc.nssmc.com
Sales Range: $600-649.9 Million
Emp.: 4,370
Metal Pipe & Tube Mfr
N.A.I.C.S.: 331210
Rempei Nakanishi *(Pres)*

Nippon Steel SG Wire Co., Ltd. **(1)**
Marunouchi Central Bldg 1-9-1 Marunouchi, Chiyoda-ku, Tokyo, 100-0005, Japan
Tel.: (81) 33 214 4131
Web Site: https://www.sgw.nipponsteel.com
Emp.: 1,551
Steel Products Mfr
N.A.I.C.S.: 331110
Kimitoshi Yonezawa *(Pres & CEO)*

Nippon Steel Southeast Asia Pte. Ltd. **(1)**
16 Raffles Quay Ste 17-01 Hong Leong Bldg, Singapore, 048581, Singapore **(100%)**
Tel.: (65) 62236777
Metals Service Center
N.A.I.C.S.: 423510
Patricia Teng *(Gen Mgr)*

Nippon Steel Spiral Pipe Vietnam Co., Ltd. **(1)**
807 Sunwah Tower 8th Floor 115 Nguyen Hue Blvd District 1, Ben Nghe Ward, Ho

INTERNATIONAL PUBLIC

Chi Minh City, Vietnam **(76.28%)**
Tel.: (84) 83 8278618
Web Site: http://www.nipponsteelpipevn.com
Emp.: 100
Steel Pipe Mfr & Distr
N.A.I.C.S.: 331210
Tokita Yoshifumi *(Gen Dir)*

Nippon Steel Stainless Steel Corporation **(1)**
2-6-1 Otemachi, Chiyoda-Ku, Tokyo, 100-0004, Japan **(100%)**
Tel.: (81) 3 3276 4800
Web Site: http://www.ns-sc.co.jp
Sales Range: $450-499.9 Million
Emp.: 150
Stainless Steel Products Mfr & Distr
N.A.I.C.S.: 331110

Unit (Domestic):

Nippon Steel Stainless Steel Corporation - Hikari Works **(2)**
3434 Ooaza-shimada, Hikari, 743-8550, Yamaguchi, Japan
Tel.: (81) 833 71 5004
Stainless Steel Products Mfr
N.A.I.C.S.: 331513

Nippon Steel Stainless Steel Corporation - Kashima Works **(2)**
2-1 Hikari, Kashima, 314-0014, Ibaraki, Japan
Tel.: (81) 299 84 3702
Stainless Steel Sheet Mfr
N.A.I.C.S.: 331221

Nippon Steel Stainless Steel Corporation - Yawata Works **(2)**
2108-1 Aza-hato Ooaza-maeda, Yawatahigashi-ku, Kitakyushu, 805-0058, Fukuoka, Japan
Tel.: (81) 93 672 2356
Web Site: http://www.nssc-global.com
Stainless Steel Plate Mfr
N.A.I.C.S.: 331221

Nippon Steel Texeng Co., Ltd. **(1)**
Mitsubishi Building 2-5-2 Marunouchi, Chiyoda-ku, Tokyo, 100-0005, Japan **(100%)**
Tel.: (81) 368606600
Web Site: https://www.tex.nipponsteel.com
Emp.: 12,840
Planning, Design, Production & Construction Related to Machinery, Electrical Instrument & Systems; Industrial & Residential Construction; Steel Production Facilities Operations
N.A.I.C.S.: 541330

Subsidiary (Domestic):

Nippon Steel Trading Corporation **(1)**
Tokyo Nihonbashi Tower 23 - 26F 2-7-1 Nihonbashi, Chuo-ku, Tokyo, 103-6025, Japan
Tel.: (81) 367725003
Web Site: https://www.nst.nipponsteel.com
Rev.: $18,061,979,760
Assets: $10,652,268,880
Liabilities: $7,668,912,240
Net Worth: $2,983,356,640
Earnings: $342,836,560
Emp.: 6,584
Fiscal Year-end: 03/31/2022
Holding Company; Steel, Textiles, Foodstuffs, Industrial Supply & Infrastructure Products & Services
N.A.I.C.S.: 551112
Yasumitsu Saeki *(Pres)*

Subsidiary (Domestic):

AGL Corporation **(2)**
8-5-27 Akasaka Nittetsu Bussan Building 4th floor, Minato-ku, Tokyo, 107-0052, Japan
Tel.: (81) 3 5412 5718
Web Site: http://www.aglc.com
Emp.: 10
Marine Freight Transportation Services
N.A.I.C.S.: 488510
Yasuo Ota *(Pres)*

Subsidiary (Non-US):

Aizen SB (Thailand) Co., Ltd. **(2)**
51 Moo 2 A U-Thai, T Banchang, Ayutthaya, 13210, Thailand
Tel.: (66) 35746850
Web Site: http://www.aizen-sb.co.th

AND PRIVATE COMPANIES

NIPPON STEEL CORPORATION

Emp.: 65
Precision Engine Parts Mfr
N.A.I.C.S.: 336310

Subsidiary (Domestic):

Arai Industrial Co., Ltd. (2)
2189 Sue-cho, Aisai, 496-0902, Aichi, Japan
Tel.: (81) 567 28 4171
Web Site: http://www.arais.co.jp
Sales Range: $50-74.9 Million
Emp.: 84
Automotive & Industrial Parts Mfr & Distr
N.A.I.C.S.: 333248
Tokuji Arai *(Pres)*

Awaji Steel Pipe Co., Ltd. (2)
2-10-63 Shibatani, Suminoe-Ku, Osaka, 559-0021, Japan
Tel.: (81) 6 6685 6531
Steel Tubes & Pipes Mfr & Distr
N.A.I.C.S.: 331210
Toshikazu Sonoda *(Acct Mgr)*

Subsidiary (Non-US):

B-Tohin Machine (Jiangsu) Co., Ltd. (2)
Yong'an Road, Industrial Park for Environmental Science & Technology, Yixing, 214205, Jiangsu, China
Tel.: (86) 51087076720
Web Site: http://www.bk.com.cn
Emp.: 300
Rotary Blower Product Mfr
N.A.I.C.S.: 333413

China Steel Sumikin Vietnam Joint Stock Company (2)
My Xuan A2 Industrial Zone, Phu My Town, My Xuan, Ba Ria-Vung Tau, Vietnam
Tel.: (84) 2543931168
Web Site: http://www.csvc.com.vn
Steel Sheet Mfr
N.A.I.C.S.: 331315

Dongguan Sumikinbussan Metal Products Co., Ltd. (2)
Yinghua Industrial Zone Hongmei Town, Dongguan, 523160, Guangdong, China
Tel.: (86) 769 8843 9668
Steel Sheet & Plate Mfr
N.A.I.C.S.: 331315

Subsidiary (Domestic):

Echo Center Co., Ltd. (2)
1-4-26 Shinmachi, Nishi-ku, Osaka, 550-0013, Japan (100%)
Tel.: (81) 6 6536 8870
Web Site: http://www.ecoc.jp
Textile Goods Sales & Storage Services
N.A.I.C.S.: 493190

Fashion Net Inc. (2)
3F 8-11-37 Akasaka, Minato-ku, Tokyo, 107-0052, Japan
Tel.: (81) 3 5412 0234
Web Site: http://www.fashion-net.co.jp
Emp.: 30
Women's Apparel Mfr & Distr
N.A.I.C.S.: 315250

I.T.'S. International Co., Ltd. (2)
3-38-9-5f Sendagaya, Shibuya-Ku, Tokyo, 151-0051, Japan
Tel.: (81) 3 5771 4671
Sales Range: Less than $1 Million
Clothing Accessories Mfr & Distr
N.A.I.C.S.: 315990
Hidetoshi Kurita *(Pres)*

IFC Corp. (2)
1-10-9 Shimmachi Sumikimbussan Bldg 7f, Nishi-Ku, Osaka, 550-0013, Japan
Tel.: (81) 676348282
Fashion Apparels Mfr
N.A.I.C.S.: 315990

Igeta Sunrise Pipe Corp. (2)
WAKITA Fujimura Midosuji Building 4-21 Fushimi-cho, Chuo-ku, Osaka, 541-0044, Japan
Tel.: (81) 645604500
Web Site: http://www.ispkk.co.jp
Emp.: 296
Sales & Processing of Tubes & Pipes, Valves & Fittings
N.A.I.C.S.: 332919

Itoh Kozai Co., Ltd. (2)
2-2-27 Minamikogecho, Imabari, 794-0811, Ehime, Japan
Tel.: (81) 898233800
Web Site: http://www.ito-kouzai.co.jp
Emp.: 26
Steel Products Mfr
N.A.I.C.S.: 331110

Izumi Kohan Co., Ltd. (2)
1-14-45 Higashihama, Higashi-Ku, Fukuoka, 812-0055, Japan
Tel.: (81) 926511721
Steel Sheets & Plates Mfr
N.A.I.C.S.: 331315

Izumi Kohan Industry Inc. (2)
Higashihama 1-chome 14th No 45, Higashi-ku, Fukuoka, 812-0055, Japan
Tel.: (81) 926511721
Web Site: http://www.izumikohan.co.jp
Steel Material Mfr
N.A.I.C.S.: 331110

Subsidiary (US):

JR Manufacturing, Inc. (2)
900 Industrial Dr, Fort Recovery, OH 45846
Tel.: (419) 375-8021
Web Site: http://www.jrmanufacturing.net
Industrial Equipment Mfr
N.A.I.C.S.: 333248
Trent Hamrick *(Plant Mgr)*

Subsidiary (Domestic):

July Star Co., Ltd. (2)
4-3-8 Ebisu Ebisu East 438 Bldg 5f, Tokyo, 150-0013, Japan
Tel.: (81) 3 6277 2148
Womens Clothing Mfr & Distr
N.A.I.C.S.: 315250

Kanaya Knit Co., Ltd. (2)
823 Oechokanaya, Fukuchiyama, 620-0303, Kyoto, Japan
Tel.: (81) 773 56 0022
Knitwear Mfr & Whslr
N.A.I.C.S.: 315250

Subsidiary (Non-US):

Kanpai Co., Ltd. (2)
No 88 Section 2 Zhongxiao East Road, Zhongzheng District, New Taipei City, 100, Taiwan
Tel.: (886) 2 2226 2627
Web Site: http://www.kanpai.com.tw
Emp.: 100
Restaurant Operating Services
N.A.I.C.S.: 722511

Kasco Co., Ltd. (2)
894 Yucheon-ri Sanam-myeon, Sacheon, Gyeongsangnam, Korea (South)
Tel.: (82) 558526102
Web Site: https://www.kascosteel.com
Steel Pipe Product Mfr
N.A.I.C.S.: 331210
Tae-gu Woo *(Pres)*

Subsidiary (Domestic):

Kashii Co., Ltd. (2)
18 Sango, Toyama-shi, Toyama, 939-3548, Japan
Tel.: (81) 76 478 5111
Aluminium Products Mfr
N.A.I.C.S.: 331313
Yoshiaki Kuboki *(Chm, Pres & CEO)*

Subsidiary (Non-US):

Kitagawa Mexico, S.A. de C.V. (2)
Circuito Progreso 102, del Parque Industrial Logistica Automotriz, 20340, Aguascalientes, Mexico
Tel.: (52) 449 917 8825
Web Site: https://www.kiw.com.mx
Casting Product Mfr
N.A.I.C.S.: 331529

Subsidiary (Domestic):

M.I.K. Corp. (2)
5-6-20 Shirahata Minami-ku, Saitama, Japan
Tel.: (81) 488610955
Web Site: http://www.mik-net.co.jp
Household Appliances Mfr
N.A.I.C.S.: 335220

MMI Co., Ltd. (2)
341-1 Kawahira Gonosan-cho, Yatomi, 498-0012, Aichi, Japan
Tel.: (81) 567671161
Web Site: http://www.kk-mmi.co.jp
Design Services
N.A.I.C.S.: 541512

NISC Hanbai Co., Ltd. (2)
3-7-24 Honjonishi, Higashi, Osaka, 578-0965, Japan
Tel.: (81) 667455522
Web Site: http://www.nisc-hanbai.co.jp
Metal Roof & Steel Sheet Mfr
N.A.I.C.S.: 332322

Subsidiary (Non-US):

NS Hanoi Steel Service Co., Ltd (2)
Lot No D1 Que Vo Industrial Park Van Duong Commune, Bac Ninh, Vietnam
Tel.: (84) 2413634255
Web Site: http://www.ns-net.co.jp
Steel Products Mfr & Sales
N.A.I.C.S.: 331110

NS Saigon Coil Center Co., Ltd. (2)
No 3 Street 8 Vietnam Singapore Industrial Park, Thuan An, Binh Duong, Vietnam
Tel.: (84) 6503784460
Web Site: http://www.nssaigon.vn
Sales Range: $25-49.9 Million
Emp.: 40
Steel Products Shearing & Sales
N.A.I.C.S.: 423510

Subsidiary (Domestic):

NS-Stainless Corp. (2)
Takebashi Building 4F 1-2-2 Hitotsubashi, Chiyoda-ku, Tokyo, 100-0003, Japan
Tel.: (81) 368809901
Web Site: http://www.ns-sus.co.jp
Stainless Steel Products Mfr
N.A.I.C.S.: 331110

NSM Coil Center Co., Ltd. (2)
14-12 Ariake 3-Chome, Koto-ku, Tokyo, 135-0063, Japan
Tel.: (81) 335275711
Web Site: http://www.nsmcc.co.jp
Sales Range: $25-49.9 Million
Emp.: 80
Steel Products Mfr & Sales
N.A.I.C.S.: 331110
Satoshi . Kazusa *(Pres)*

NSSB Coil Center Co., Ltd. (2)
27 Higashikaigan-cho, Amagasaki, 660-0843, Hyoho, Japan
Tel.: (81) 6 6409 0201
Web Site: http://www.nssb-cc.com
Sales Range: $125-149.9 Million
Emp.: 80
Steel Sheets, Plates & Coils Processing & Sales
N.A.I.C.S.: 331315
Ishii IsamuOkoshi *(Pres & CEO)*

NSSB Material Co., Ltd. (2)
3-52 Ida-cho, Owariasahi, 488-0024, Japan
Tel.: (81) 561 52 2311
Web Site: http://www.nssb-material.co.jp
Non-Ferrous Metal Processor & Distr
N.A.I.C.S.: 331491

NST Agency Co., Ltd. (2)
8-5-27 Akasaka, Minato-ku, Tokyo, 107-0052, Japan
Tel.: (81) 334789266
Web Site: http://www.nst-agency.co.jp
Insurance Agency Services
N.A.I.C.S.: 524210

Subsidiary (Non-US):

NST Coil Center (Thailand) Ltd. (2)
700/648 Moo-1, Amata City Chonburi Industrial Estate Phase 7, Phan Thong, 20160, Chonburi, Thailand
Tel.: (66) 382101708
Web Site: https://www.nstct.co.th
Emp.: 197
Steel Products Mfr
N.A.I.C.S.: 331110
Shoichi Hamahata *(Pres)*

NST Hanoi Steel Service Co., Ltd. (2)
Lot No D1, Que Vo Industrial Park Van Duong Ward, Bac Ninh, Vietnam

Tel.: (84) 2223634255
Steel Pole Mfr
N.A.I.C.S.: 331221

Subsidiary (Domestic):

NST Information & Communication Systems Co., Ltd. (2)
8-5-26 Akasaka Sumitomo Fudosan Aoyama Building West Building, Minato-ku, Tokyo, 107-0052, Japan
Tel.: (81) 354125187
Web Site: http://www.nsics.co.jp
Emp.: 40
System Integration Services
N.A.I.C.S.: 541512

NST NIHONTEPPAN Co. Ltd. (2)
6th floor Eitaro Building 1-2-5 Nihonbashi, Chuo-ku, Tokyo, 103-8237, Japan (66%)
Tel.: (81) 3 3272 5112
Web Site: http://www.np-nippan.co.jp
Emp.: 217
Metal Housing Construction Products Distr
N.A.I.C.S.: 423510

NST Okuhira Steel Co., Ltd. (2)
7-338-1 Oka, Matsubara, Osaka, Japan
Tel.: (81) 723350500
Web Site: http://www.nsos.co.jp
Steel Roofing Material Mfr
N.A.I.C.S.: 332322

NST Sankohan Co., Ltd. (2)
1-5-7 Kameido Kinshicho Prime Tower 14th floor, Koto-ku, Tokyo, 136-0071, Japan
Tel.: (81) 356281820
Web Site: http://www.nst-skh.co.jp
Emp.: 200
Steel Pipe Product Mfr
N.A.I.C.S.: 331210

NST System Buildings Co., Ltd. (2)
Sumitomo Real Estate Shiba Building No 2 1-5-9 Shiba, Minato-ku, Tokyo, 105-0014, Japan
Tel.: (81) 368661280
Web Site: http://www.nst-sumisys.co.jp
Construction & System Architecture Services
N.A.I.C.S.: 541310

Subsidiary (Non-US):

NST Trading Malaysia Sdn. Bhd. (2)
Suite 33-5 33rd Floor Wisma Uoa II No 21 Jalan Pinang, 50450, Kuala Lumpur, Malaysia
Tel.: (60) 321612511
Steel Products Mfr
N.A.I.C.S.: 331110

Subsidiary (Domestic):

NST Wire & Welding Co., Ltd. (2)
11-10 Nihonbashi Koamicho, Chuo-ku, Tokyo, 103-0016, Japan
Tel.: (81) 336620801
Web Site: http://www.nstww.com
Emp.: 120
Welding Equipment Mfr
N.A.I.C.S.: 333992
Makoto Yasukochi *(Pres)*

Nagoya Nippon Steel Trading Coil Center Co., Ltd (2)
6-2 Chome Shinkataanaike, Chita, 478-0069, Aichi, Japan
Tel.: (81) 562566280
Web Site: http://www.nncc-net.co.jp
Sales Range: $25-49.9 Million
Emp.: 30
Steel Products Mfr & Sales
N.A.I.C.S.: 331110

Nikkyo Foods Co., Ltd. (2)
1-9-12 Nihombashimuromachi Kyodo Bldg 7f, Chuo-Ku, Tokyo, Japan
Tel.: (81) 3 3270 8125
Processed Meats Distr
N.A.I.C.S.: 424470

Subsidiary (Non-US):

Nippon Steel & Sumikin Bussan (M) Sdn. Bhd. (2)
Peti 9 Wisma Selangor Dredging 17th Floor, West Block No 142 C Jalan Ampa, Kuala Lumpur, 50450, Malaysia
Tel.: (60) 321612511
Web Site: http://www.sumikinbussan.co.jp

NIPPON STEEL CORPORATION

Nippon Steel Corporation—(Continued)
Sales Range: $50-74.9 Million
Emp.: 10
Steel Distr
N.A.I.C.S.: 423510
Jogi Psureta *(Mng Dir)*

Subsidiary (US):

Nippon Steel & Sumikin Bussan Americas, Inc. (2)
200 N Martingale Road Ste 801, Schaumburg, IL 60173
Tel.: (847) 882-6700
Web Site: http://www.nssb-us.com
Metals Trading Company, Specializes in Buying & Selling Tin-Free Steel, Tinplate & Aluminum for Large Can Manufacturing Firms
N.A.I.C.S.: 425120

Subsidiary (Domestic):

Kentucky Steel Center, Inc. (3)
1101 Mayde Rd, Berea, KY 40403
Tel.: (859) 986-0572
Web Site: http://www.kentuckysteel.com
Sales Range: $25-49.9 Million
Emp.: 63
Processing of Steel Sheets, Plates & Coils
N.A.I.C.S.: 331210
Seiji Motoni *(Pres & CEO)*

Kitagawa-Northtech Inc. (3)
301 E Commerce Dr, Schaumburg, IL 60173
Tel.: (847) 310-8787
Web Site: http://kitagawa-usa.com
Sales Range: $25-49.9 Million
Emp.: 30
Hydraulic Chucks & Cylinder Distr
N.A.I.C.S.: 423830
Shawn Luschei *(VP-Sls & Mktg)*

Branch (Domestic):

Nippon Steel & Sumikin Bussan Corporation - Tokyo (Otemachi) Head Office (2)
Shin-Otemachi Bldg 2-1 Otemachi 2-chome, Chiyoda-ku, Tokyo, 100-0004, Japan
Tel.: (81) 3 6225 3500
Web Site: http://www.nssb.nssmc.com
Executive Office
N.A.I.C.S.: 921110
Yukio Nakano *(Mng Exec Officer)*

Subsidiary (Non-US):

Nippon Steel Bar & CH Wire (China) Co., Ltd. (2)
Jinling Industrial Park No 88 Jinling East Road, Weiting Town, Suzhou, 215121, China
Tel.: (86) 51262877618
Steel Wires Mfr & Distr
N.A.I.C.S.: 331110

Nippon Steel Trading (China) Co., Ltd. (2)
8th Floor Metro Plaza No 555 Lou Shan Guan Road, Chang Ning District, Shanghai, 200051, China
Tel.: (86) 2180175888
Steel Products Mfr
N.A.I.C.S.: 331110

Nippon Steel Trading (Dongguan) Economy Consultant Co.,Ltd. (2)
Longxi Industrial Zone Zhouxi, Nancheng District, Dongguan, 523077, Guangdong, China
Tel.: (86) 76922400500
Steel Products Sales
N.A.I.C.S.: 423510

Nippon Steel Trading (Europe) S. A. S. (2)
Kohlmarkt 8-10 1F, 1010, Vienna, Austria
Tel.: (43) 1227461049
Steel Products Mfr
N.A.I.C.S.: 331110

Nippon Steel Trading (Europe) S. A. S. (2)
4F 3 Rue du Faubourg, Saint Honore, 75008, Paris, France
Tel.: (33) 142682899
Steel Products Mfr

Nippon Steel Trading (HK) Co., Ltd. (2)
30F Kings Tower 111 King Lam Street Lai Chi Kok, Kowloon, China (Hong Kong)
Tel.: (852) 2629 1111
Web Site: http://www.nssb.nssmc.com
Steel Product Distr
N.A.I.C.S.: 423510

Nippon Steel Trading (HK) Co., Ltd. (2)
30/F Kings Tower 111 King Lam Street, Lai Chi Kok, Kowloon, China (Hong Kong)
Tel.: (852) 26291111
Steel Products Mfr
N.A.I.C.S.: 331110

Nippon Steel Trading (Malaysia) Sdn.Bhd. (2)
Lot 2-113 A 2nd Fl Endah Parade No 1 Jalan 1/149 E, Bander Baru Seri Petaling, 57000, Kuala Lumpur, Malaysia
Tel.: (60) 395434877
Emp.: 3
Iron & Steel Products Whslr
N.A.I.C.S.: 423510

Nippon Steel Trading (Shanghai) Co.,Ltd. (2)
Room 801 United Plaza 1468 Nanjing Road, Shanghai, 200040, China
Tel.: (86) 2162891122
Web Site: http://www.ns-net.co.jp
Steel Products Import & Distr
N.A.I.C.S.: 331221

Nippon Steel Trading (Singapore) Pte. Ltd. (2)
16 Raffles Quay 17-02A Hong Leong Bldg, Singapore, 048581, Singapore
Tel.: (65) 62229814
Sales Range: $50-74.9 Million
Emp.: 6
Steel Products Import & Distr
N.A.I.C.S.: 423510

Nippon Steel Trading (Taiwan) Co., Ltd. (2)
10F -1 No 248 Section 3 Nanjing E Road, Songshan District, Taipei, 105, Taiwan
Tel.: (886) 227721511
Web Site: http://www.ns-net.co.jp
Steel Products Import & Distr
N.A.I.C.S.: 423510

Nippon Steel Trading (Thailand) Co., Ltd. (2)
909 Ample Tower 14th Floor Debaratana Road, Bangna Nuea Bangna, Bangkok, 10260, Thailand
Tel.: (66) 27441844
Web Site: http://www.nst-th.com
Processed Iron & Steel Products Distr
N.A.I.C.S.: 423510

Nippon Steel Trading (Vietnam) Co., Ltd. (2)
Bitexco Financial Tower 2 Hai Trieu St Ben Nghe Ward District 1, Ho Chi Minh City, Vietnam
Tel.: (84) 838221850
Emp.: 10
Iron & Steel Products Distr
N.A.I.C.S.: 423510

Subsidiary (US):

Nippon Steel Trading America, Inc. (2)
444 S Flower St Ste 2320, Los Angeles, CA 90071-5418
Tel.: (213) 485-9072
Sales Range: $200-249.9 Million
Emp.: 10
Metals Trading Company, Specializes in Buying & Selling Tin-Free Steel, Tinplate & Aluminum for Large Can Manufacturing Firms
N.A.I.C.S.: 423510

Nippon Steel Trading Americas, Inc. (2)
200 N Martingale Rd Ste 801, Schaumburg, IL 60173
Tel.: (847) 882-6700
Web Site: http://www.nst-us.com
Steel Products Mfr

N.A.I.C.S.: 331110

Subsidiary (Non-US):

Nippon Steel Trading India Pvt. Ltd. (2)
409 4th Floor DLF South Court District Centre Saket, New Delhi, 110017, India
Tel.: (91) 1142248700
Steel Products Mfr
N.A.I.C.S.: 331110

Nippon Steel Trading Korea Co., Ltd. (2)
10F Kyobo Bldg 1 Jongro, Jongno-gu, Seoul, 03154, Korea (South)
Web Site: http://www.ns-net.co.jp
Steel Products Sales
N.A.I.C.S.: 331110

Subsidiary (Domestic):

Nippon Steel Trading Metals Co., Ltd. (2)
3-52 Ida-cho, Owariasahi, 488-0024, Aichi, Japan
Tel.: (81) 561522311
Web Site: http://www.nst-metals.co.jp
Emp.: 62
Aluminum Plate Mfr
N.A.I.C.S.: 331315

Subsidiary (Non-US):

Nippon Steel Trading Mexico S.A.de.C.V. (2)
Insurgentes Sur 1425-15 Colonia Insurgentes Mixcoac, 03920, Mexico, Mexico
Tel.: (52) 5556622938
Web Site: http://www.ns-net.co.jp
Sales Range: $50-74.9 Million
Emp.: 5
Steel Products Import & Distr
N.A.I.C.S.: 423510
Eduardo Garcia *(Gen Mgr)*

Subsidiary (Domestic):

Nishinippon Kogyo Kaisha, Ltd. (2)
4-8 Hitsujincho, Sasebo, 857-0852, Nagasaki, Japan
Tel.: (81) 956314334
Web Site: https://www.nishinippon-kogyo.co.jp
Emp.: 65
Steel Bar Mfr
N.A.I.C.S.: 331221
Karl Nilsson *(Gen Mgr)*

Ogiwara & Co., Ltd. (2)
22-17 Nishigotanda 7-chome Shinagawa-ku, Tokyo, 141-0031, Japan
Tel.: (81) 3 3491 5951
Web Site: http://www.ogiwara.co.jp
Manufacture & Sales of Women's Wear
N.A.I.C.S.: 315250
Shimamura Takuyu *(Pres)*

Okayama Harada Pipe & Tube Co., Ltd. (2)
86-1 Koshita, Naka-ku, Okayama, 703-8225, Japan
Tel.: (81) 862796673
Web Site: http://www.okayamaharadakokan.jp
Steel Pipe Product Mfr
N.A.I.C.S.: 331210

Subsidiary (Non-US):

PT. Bengawan Solo Garment Indonesia (2)
Dk Butuh 4/2 Ds Butuh, Mojosongo, Boyolali, 276, Indonesia
Tel.: (62) 276 324888
Emp.: 85
Menswear Apparel Mfr
N.A.I.C.S.: 315250
Dursun Parlak *(Gen Mgr)*

PT. IndoJapan Steel Center (2)
Jl Mitra Raya IV Block K4 Parung Mulya, Kawasan Industri Mitra Karawang Ciampel, Karawang, 41361, West Java, Indonesia
Tel.: (62) 2678637840
Web Site: http://www.ijsc.co.id
Emp.: 91
Steel Products Mfr
N.A.I.C.S.: 331110

INTERNATIONAL PUBLIC

PT. IndoJapan Wire Products (2)
Kawasan Industri Mitra Karawang Jl Mitra Raya IV Blok K-3 Parungmulya, Ciampel, Karawang, West Java, Indonesia
Tel.: (62) 2678638010
Web Site: http://www.ijwp.co.id
Steel Pole Mfr
N.A.I.C.S.: 331222

PT. Nippon Steel Trading Indonesia (2)
Gandaria 8 LT 20 Unit D2 JL Sultan Iskandar Muda Kebayoran Lama Utara, Kebayoran Lama Jakarta Selatan Dki, Jakarta, 12240, Indonesia
Tel.: (62) 2129304117
Steel Products Import & Distr
N.A.I.C.S.: 423510

Qingdao Home Fashion Textile Co., Ltd. (2)
Middle Buxi Road, Jimo City, Qingdao, China
Tel.: (86) 53286598310
Web Site: http://www.haofa.com.cn
Emp.: 140
Comforter Cover & Pillow Case Mfr
N.A.I.C.S.: 314120

Subsidiary (Domestic):

Ricwil Japan Ltd. (2)
2-22-5-401 Kasuga, Bunkyo-ku, Tokyo, 112-0003, Japan
Tel.: (81) 358031581
Web Site: http://www.ric-nord.co.jp
Specialty Tubes & Pipes Mfr
N.A.I.C.S.: 331210

Subsidiary (Non-US):

Ruigeng Garments (Dalian) Co., Ltd. (2)
Qianbanlashan Village Ershilipu, Jinzhou, Dalian, 116300, Liaoning, China
Tel.: (86) 411 8738 2505
Emp.: 40
Menswear Mfr
N.A.I.C.S.: 315250

S.B. Saigon Fashion Co., Ltd. (2)
Tan Thuan Processing Zone, Ho Chi Minh City, Vietnam
Tel.: (84) 87701631
Sales Range: $100-124.9 Million
Emp.: 500
Women's Clothing Mfr
N.A.I.C.S.: 315250

Subsidiary (Domestic):

SB Agency Inc. (2)
1-10-9 Shimmachi Sumikimbussan Bldg 9f, Nishi-Ku, Osaka, 550-0013, Japan
Tel.: (81) 6 7634 8286
Web Site: http://www.sumikinbussan.co.jp
Insurance Agency Services
N.A.I.C.S.: 524210

Subsidiary (Non-US):

SB Coil Center (Thailand) Ltd. (2)
5Th Floor Thaniya Bldg 62 Silom Rd Suriyawong, Bangrak, Bangkok, 10500, Thailand
Tel.: (66) 2 2363492
Web Site: http://www.sbct.co.th
Processed Steel Product Mfr
N.A.I.C.S.: 331210

Subsidiary (Domestic):

SB Living Co., Ltd. (2)
Igeta Bldg 9f, Osaka, 550-0013, Japan
Tel.: (81) 6 6539 4920
Household Fabric Mfr & Distr
N.A.I.C.S.: 313310

Subsidiary (Non-US):

SB Pearl Fashion Co., Ltd. (2)
No.8 street 15, Linh Trung ward Thu Duc District, Ho Chi Minh City, Vietnam
Tel.: (84) 2837280741
Web Site: http://www.saigon-pearl.vn
Other Clothing Product Mfr
N.A.I.C.S.: 315990

Subsidiary (Domestic):

SB Planning Co., Ltd. (2)

32-12 Shibuya Property Tokyu Bldg 6th Fl Higashi 1, Shibuya-Ku, Tokyo, 150-0011, Japan
Tel.: (81) 3 5774 8100
Sales Range: $25-49.9 Million
Emp.: 50
Fashion Clothing Apparel Mfr & Distr
N.A.I.C.S.: 315250
Yoshimoto Kazumi *(Gen Mgr)*

SSC Kitakantou Co., Ltd. (2)
14/6 Sakae-cho, Sano, 327-0816, Japan
Tel.: (81) 283 21 4311
Sales Range: $25-49.9 Million
Emp.: 35
Steel Sheet & Plate Mfr & Whslr
N.A.I.C.S.: 331110
Tom Takeuchi *(Mng Dir)*

San-ei Daimaru Corp. (2)
50 Sunami-cho, Minato-ku, Nagoya, 455-0056, Aichi, Japan
Tel.: (81) 526519251
Web Site: http://www.sd-cc.co.jp
Emp.: 74
Electric Equipment Mfr
N.A.I.C.S.: 335999

Sanwa Steel Co., Ltd. (2)
1146 Imazaike, Shikama-ku, Himeji, 672-8079, Hyogo, Japan
Tel.: (81) 792341116
Web Site: https://www.sanwasteel.co.jp
Emp.: 73
Steel Products Mfr
N.A.I.C.S.: 331110
Sato Yasuo *(Mng Dir)*

Subsidiary (Non-US):

Shanghai Echo Fashion Co., Ltd. (2)
166 Tie Shan Road Bao Shan, Shanghai, 200336, China
Tel.: (86) 21 3379 1122
Textile Goods Storage Services
N.A.I.C.S.: 493190

Shanghai Nippon Steel Trading Automotive Parts Co.,Ltd. (2)
No 939 Xinhe Road Jiading Industrial Zone, Shanghai, China
Tel.: (86) 2162891122
Web Site: http://www.ns-net.co.jp
Fabricated Metal Parts Mfr & Sales
N.A.I.C.S.: 332999

Shanghai Sumikin Bussan Co., Ltd. (2)
8th Floor Metro Plaza No 555 Lou Shan Guan Road, Chang Ning District, Shanghai, 200005, China
Tel.: (86) 2122084588
N.A.I.C.S.: 425120

Shanghai Yiyou Metal Products Co., Ltd. (2)
No 132 No 151 Minle Road Xinghuo Development Zone, Fengxian District, Shanghai, 201419, China
Tel.: (86) 2157503094
Web Site: http://www.yiyou-metal.com.cn
Sales Range: $25-49.9 Million
Emp.: 100
Sales & Processing of Steel Sheets, Plates & Coils
N.A.I.C.S.: 331315

Shenzhen NS Steel Centre Co., Ltd. (2)
East Guang Qiao Street Guang Ming Road, Guang Ming, Shenzhen, 518107, Guangdong, China
Tel.: (86) 75523400202
Web Site: http://www.ns-net.co.jp
Sales Range: $75-99.9 Million
Emp.: 148
Steel Products Sales
N.A.I.C.S.: 423510
Yoshiharu Psurummi *(Mng Dir)*

Subsidiary (Domestic):

Shinei Kiko Co., Ltd. (2)
1-34 Shinden Sakaimachi, Daito, 574-0051, Osaka, Japan
Tel.: (81) 72 872 3040
Web Site: http://www.shin-ei-hp.jp
Emp.: 74
Steel Sheet & Plate Mfr & Distr
N.A.I.C.S.: 331315

Subsidiary (Non-US):

Siam Lotus Co., Ltd. (2)
909 Ample Tower 14th Floor Bangna-Trad Road, Bangna, Bangkok, 10260, Thailand
Tel.: (66) 27441844
Steel Products Mfr
N.A.I.C.S.: 331110

Subsidiary (Domestic):

Sumi'saccs Corp. (2)
1-19-4 Nippon Life Shibuya Annex Building 6F Jinnan, Shibuya-ku, Tokyo, 150-0041, Japan
Tel.: (81) 3 5784 3081
Web Site: http://www.sumisaccs.co.jp
Sales Range: $25-49.9 Million
Emp.: 27
Fashion Apparel Mfr & Distr
N.A.I.C.S.: 315990

Sumikin Bussan Business Support Corp. (2)
1-10-9 Shimmachi Sumitomobussan Bldg, Nishi-Ku, Osaka, 550-0013, Japan
Tel.: (81) 6 7634 8036
Business Support Services
N.A.I.C.S.: 561499

Subsidiary (Non-US):

Sumikin Bussan India Pvt. Ltd. (2)
605 Time Tower M G Road Sector-28, Gurgaon, 122 001, Haryana, India
Tel.: (91) 124 4979170
Sales Range: $25-49.9 Million
Emp.: 5
Iron & Steel Products Mfr
N.A.I.C.S.: 331110
Guillermo Ortiz *(Mng Dir)*

Sumikin Bussan International (HK) Ltd. (2)
17th Fl Metropolis Twr 10 Metropolis Dr, Hong Kong, China (Hong Kong) (100%)
Tel.: (852) 26291111
Web Site: http://www.sumikinbussan.com.hk
Sales Range: $50-74.9 Million
Emp.: 50
N.A.I.C.S.: 425120
Yoyo Yaru *(Mgr-Admin)*

Sumikin Bussan International (Korea) Co., Ltd. (2)
Room 705 Marine Center Building No 118 Namdaemuunro 2 Ka Chung, Seoul, 100770, Korea (South) (100%)
Tel.: (82) 27533010
Sales Range: $25-49.9 Million
Emp.: 20
N.A.I.C.S.: 425120

Sumikin Bussan International (M) Sdn. Bhd. (2)
Suite 33-5 33rd Floor Wisma UOA II No 21 Jalan Pinang, Jalan Ampang, Kuala Lumpur, 50450, Malaysia
Tel.: (60) 3 2161 2511
Sales Range: $25-49.9 Million
Emp.: 9
Iron & Steel Products Mfr
N.A.I.C.S.: 331110
Joji Tsuruta *(Gen Mgr)*

Sumikin Bussan International (Thailand) Ltd. (2)
10th Floor Thaniya Building 62 Silom Road, Bangkok, 10500, Thailand (100%)
Tel.: (66) 22369124
Web Site: http://www.sumikinbussan.co.jp
Sales Range: $50-74.9 Million
Emp.: 20
N.A.I.C.S.: 425120

Subsidiary (Domestic):

Sumikin Bussan Kenzai Corp. (2)
Odenmacho 3-2 Nihonbashi, Chuo-ku, Tokyo, 103-0011, Japan
Tel.: (81) 3 3665 4284
Sales Range: $50-74.9 Million
Emp.: 7
Steel Product Distr
N.A.I.C.S.: 423510
Kanji Kudou *(Pres)*

Sumikin Bussan Matex Corp. (2)
3F Sumikin Bussan Bldg 10-9 Shinmachi 1, Nishi-ku, Osaka, 550-0013, Japan
Tel.: (81) 6 6534 8352
Web Site: http://www.sbmatex.co.jp
Industrial Machinery Sales & Maintenance Services
N.A.I.C.S.: 423830
Toshya Yamada *(Gen Mgr)*

Subsidiary (Non-US):

Sumikin Bussan Oceania Pty Ltd (2)
Level 9 564 St Kilda Rd, Melbourne, 3004, Australia (100%)
Tel.: (61) 385170700
Sales Range: $50-74.9 Million
Emp.: 6
N.A.I.C.S.: 425120
Nick Gorgensn *(Mgr)*

Subsidiary (Domestic):

Sumikin Bussan Real Estate Co., Ltd. (2)
1-10-9 Shimmachi Sumikimbussan Bldg 7f, Nishi-Ku, Osaka, 550-0013, Japan
Tel.: (81) 6 6537 1661
Real Estate Manangement Services
N.A.I.C.S.: 531390

Sumikin Bussan Special Steel Co., Ltd. (2)
3-3-41 Nankohigashi Suminoe-Ku, Suminoe-ku, Osaka, 5590031, Japan
Tel.: (81) 6 6612 1123
Emp.: 18
Steel Products Mfr & Distr
N.A.I.C.S.: 331110
Tamesabro Kusaka *(Gen Mgr)*

Sumimetal Mining Co., Ltd (2)
8-5-27 Chome, Minato-ku, Tokyo, 107-8527, Japan
Tel.: (81) 354125001
Web Site: http://www.nssb.nssmc.com
Sales Range: $50-74.9 Million
Emp.: 1,200
Production & Sales of Limestone
N.A.I.C.S.: 212312
Kenji Hiwatari *(CEO)*

Subsidiary (Non-US):

Sumiso International Logistics (Qingdao) Co., Ltd. (2)
No 3 Jiangshan North Road, Qingdao Economic and Technological Development Zone, Qingdao, 266510, China
Tel.: (86) 53286831588
Sales Range: $10-24.9 Million
Warehousing, Inspection, Merchandising, Processing, Packing & Other Distr Services
N.A.I.C.S.: 493190

Taiwan Nippon Steel Trading Co., Ltd. (2)
10F-1 No 248 Section 3 Nanjing E Road, Songshan District, Taipei, 105, Taiwan
Tel.: (886) 227721511
Steel Products Mfr
N.A.I.C.S.: 331110

Subsidiary (Domestic):

Taiyo Shearing Co., Ltd. (2)
No 15 34 Jiangbo South 2 -chome, Naka-ku, Hiroshima, 730-0835, Japan
Tel.: (81) 822935611
Web Site: http://www.taiyo-shr.co.jp
Steel Material Mfr
N.A.I.C.S.: 331110

Takimoto Co., Ltd. (2)
7-4-3 Nishiishikiricho, Higashiosaka, 579-8013, Osaka, Japan
Tel.: (81) 729 86 9800
Web Site: http://www.takimoto.co.jp
Sales Range: $50-74.9 Million
Emp.: 180
School Uniform Mfr & Whslr
N.A.I.C.S.: 315250

Tetsusho Kayaba Corp. (2)
Kanayama Building 7F 1-2-12 Shinkawa, Chuo-ku, Tokyo, 104-0033, Japan
Tel.: (81) 332062031
Web Site: https://www.tetsusho.co.jp
Steel Products Mfr
N.A.I.C.S.: 331110
Tsuneo Fukuda *(Chm)*

Tokyo Seisen Co., Ltd. (2)
9-5 Kouyashinmachi, Ichikawa, 272-0011, Chiba, Japan (100%)
Tel.: (81) 473271131
Web Site: https://www.tokyoseisen.co.jp
Emp.: 29
Low Carbon Steel Wire Products Mfr & Sales
N.A.I.C.S.: 332618
Makoto Watanabe *(Pres)*

Tomakomai Steel Center Co., Ltd. (2)
6 170 Kashiwahara, Tomakomai, Hokkaido, Japan
Tel.: (81) 144845517
Web Site: http://www.tomakomai-sc.com
Rolled Steel Sheet Mfr
N.A.I.C.S.: 331221

Tominaga Sangyo Co., Ltd. (2)
10-12 Takakura-cho, Atsuta-ku, Nagoya, 456-0015, Japan
Tel.: (81) 526815221
Web Site: http://www.tominagasan.co.jp
Emp.: 38
Non Ferrous Metal & Steel Product Distr
N.A.I.C.S.: 423510

Subsidiary (Non-US):

Yawata Electrode (Thailand) Co., Ltd. (2)
82 Moo 5 Kamtalesor-Khoksung Road, Tambon Kamtalesor Aumphur Kamtalesor, Nakhon Ratchasima, 30280, Thailand
Tel.: (66) 44756588
Web Site: http://www.yawata.co.th
Steel Mfrs
N.A.I.C.S.: 331110

Subsidiary (Domestic):

Yoko Industry Co., Ltd. (2)
2-26-3 Shinkawa No 2 3rd floor Sumitomo Real Estate, Kayabacho Building Chuo-ku, Tokyo, 104-0033, Japan
Tel.: (81) 362220600
Web Site: http://www.yokosangyo.co.jp
Sales Range: $50-74.9 Million
Emp.: 7
Nonferrous Metal Distr
N.A.I.C.S.: 423510

Nittetsu Cement Co., Ltd (1)
64 Nakamachi, Muroran, 050-8510, Hokkaido, Japan
Tel.: (81) 1 4344 1693
Blast Furnace Cement Mfr
N.A.I.C.S.: 327310

Nittetsu Tokai Steel Wire Co., Ltd. (1)
7 Nozomigaoka, Seki, 501-3219, Gifu, Japan
Tel.: (81) 575 25 6511
Steel Wire Mfr & Distr
N.A.I.C.S.: 332618

Osaka Steel Co., Ltd. (1)
Keihanshin-Midosuji Building 11F 3-6-1 Dosho-machi, Chuo-ku, Osaka, 541-0045, Japan
Tel.: (81) 662040300
Web Site: https://www.osaka-seitetu.co.jp
Rev.: $775,617,400
Assets: $1,354,283,240
Liabilities: $333,771,950
Net Worth: $1,020,511,290
Earnings: $20,629,810
Fiscal Year-end: 03/31/2024
Steel Product Mfr & Whslr
N.A.I.C.S.: 332111
Masaki Iwasaki *(Pres)*

Subsidiary (Domestic):

Tokyo Kohtetsu Co., Ltd. (2)
2-4-12 Kyobashi 2nd floor of Kyobashi Daiichi Life Building, Chuo-ku, Tokyo, 104-0031, Japan (84.41%)
Tel.: (81) 335480880
Web Site: http://www.kohtetsu.jp
Rolled Steel Product Mfr & Whslr
N.A.I.C.S.: 331221

PT Krakarau Nippon Steel Synergy (1)
Jl Europe I Kav A2 Industrial Estate Krakatau, Cilegon, 42443, Banten, Indonesia

NIPPON STEEL CORPORATION

Nippon Steel Corporation—(Continued)
Tel.: (62) 25 438 6141
Web Site: https://www.knss.co.id
Rolled Steel Products Mfr
N.A.I.C.S.: 331221
Satoshi Hirabaru (Co-Pres)

Sanyo Special Steel Co Ltd (1)
3007 Nakashima, Shikama-ku, Himeji, 672-8677, Hyogo, Japan (51%)
Tel.: (81) 792356003
Web Site: https://www.sanyo-steel.co.jp
Rev.: $2,338,684,100
Assets: $2,635,446,660
Liabilities: $1,124,420,490
Net Worth: $1,511,026,170
Earnings: $59,860,160
Emp.: 6,397
Fiscal Year-end: 03/31/2024
Bearing Steels, Seamless Tubes & Pipes Mfr
N.A.I.C.S.: 324199
Shigehiro Oi (Mng Exec Officer)

Subsidiary (Non-US):

Ningbo Sanyo Special Steel Products Co., Ltd. (2)
Xinxin Industrial Zone Langxia Street, Yuyao, 315482, Zhejiang, China
Tel.: (86) 574 62197730
Web Site: http://www.nssp.cn.452.cn
Sales Range: $25-49.9 Million
Emp.: 524
Steel Foundries
N.A.I.C.S.: 331513

Ovako AB (2)
Kungstradgardsgatan 10, PO Box 1721, 111 87, Stockholm, Sweden
Tel.: (46) 86221300
Web Site: https://www.ovako.com
Steel Products Mfr
N.A.I.C.S.: 331513
Marcus Hedblom (Pres & CEO)

Subsidiary (Domestic):

Ovako Bar AB (3)
Industriomradet Dalarnas, 777 80, Smedjebacken, Sweden
Tel.: (46) 240 668 000
Steel Products Mfr
N.A.I.C.S.: 331513
George Oliver (Mgr)

Subsidiary (Non-US):

P.T. Sanyo Special Steel Indonesia (2)
Kawasan Industri MM2100 Blook T6-2 Gandamekar, Cikarang Barat, Bekasi, Jawa-Barat, Indonesia
Tel.: (62) 218980921
Web Site: http://www.sanyo-steel.co.jp
Sales Range: $25-49.9 Million
Emp.: 43
Steel Foundries
N.A.I.C.S.: 331513
K. Nakayama (Pres)

SANYO SPECIAL STEEL TRADING (SHANGHAI) CO., LTD (2)
Unit1504 TowerC The Place No 150 Zunyi Road, Shanghai, China
Tel.: (86) 21 5396 5666
Web Site: http://www.sanyo-steel.co.jp
Steel Product Distr
N.A.I.C.S.: 423510

Subsidiary (Domestic):

Santoku Computer Service Co., Ltd. (2)
2453-1 Nakashima, Shikama-ku Himeji, Hyogo, 672-8035, Japan
Tel.: (81) 792343530
Information Services
N.A.I.C.S.: 519290

Santoku Seiken Co., Ltd. (2)
5-4-1 Asakusabashi, Daito-ku, Tokyo, 111-0053, Japan
Tel.: (81) 358212330
Web Site: http://www.santokuseiken.co.jp
Steel Products Mfr & Distr
N.A.I.C.S.: 331110

Santoku Tech Co., Ltd. (2)
1676 Nakashima, Shikama-ku, Himeji, 672-8035, Hyogo, Japan
Tel.: (81) 792343530
Web Site: http://santokutech.co.jp
Formed, Fabricated & Special Steel Products Mfr
N.A.I.C.S.: 331513

Subsidiary (US):

Sanyo Special Steel U.S.A., Inc. (2)
445 Park Ave Rm 2104, New York, NY 10022
Tel.: (212) 935-9033
Web Site: http://www.sanyo-steel.co.jp
Sales Range: $25-49.9 Million
Emp.: 3
Rolled Steel Shape Mfr
N.A.I.C.S.: 331221

Subsidiary (Domestic):

Yohkoh Bussan Co., Ltd. (2)
2453-1 Nakashima, Shikama-ku Himeji, 672-8035, Hyogo, Japan
Tel.: (81) 792345476
Web Site: http://www.yohkohb.co.jp
Sales Range: $25-49.9 Million
Emp.: 70
Iron & Steel Mills
N.A.I.C.S.: 331110
Koichi Tajima (Mng Dir)

Standard Steel, LLC (1)
500 N Walnut St, Burnham, PA 17009-1644
Tel.: (717) 248-4911
Web Site: https://www.standardsteel.com
Forged Steel Wheel & Axle Mfr
N.A.I.C.S.: 332111
John M. Hilton (Pres & COO)

Suzuki Metal Industry Co., Ltd. (1)
Marunouchi Central Building 1-9-1 Marunouchi, Chiyoda-ku, Tokyo, 100 0005, Japan (66.4%)
Tel.: (81) 3 3214 4131
Web Site: http://www.suzuki-metal.co.jp
Sales Range: $25-49.9 Million
Emp.: 440
Steel Pole Mfr
N.A.I.C.S.: 331222
Masayuki Shibata (Pres & CEO)

Subsidiary (Non-US):

Thai Special Wire Co., Ltd. (2)
44 Moo 7 Patumthani-Lat Lum Kaeo Road T Kubangluang, A Lat Lum Kaeo, Pathumthani, 12140, Thailand (51%)
Tel.: (66) 2 9794820 9
Web Site: http://www.thaispecialwire.com
Sales Range: $10-24.9 Million
Emp.: 200
Steel Wire Mfr & Distr
N.A.I.C.S.: 331222

NIPPON TECHNO LAB, INC.
Kojimachi 2-1 PMO Hanzomon 9F, Chiyoda-ku, Yokohama, 102-0083, Japan
Tel.: (81) 452638546
Web Site: https://www.ntl.co.jp
Year Founded: 1989
3849—(SAP)
Sales Range: Less than $1 Million
Emp.: 28
Printer Machinery Mfr
N.A.I.C.S.: 333248
Eisei Matsumura (Pres)

NIPPON TELEGRAPH & TELEPHONE CORPORATION
Otemachi First Square East Tower 5-1, Otemachi 1-Chome Chiyoda-ku, Tokyo, 100-8116, Japan
Tel.: (81) 368385111 JP
Web Site: https://group.ntt
Year Founded: 1985
9432—(TKS)
Rev.: $88,405,901,090
Assets: $195,683,914,030
Liabilities: $123,680,794,040
Net Worth: $72,003,119,990
Earnings: $8,457,633,810
Emp.: 338,467
Fiscal Year-end: 03/31/24

Holding Company; Telecommunications Services
N.A.I.C.S.: 551112
Hiromichi Shinohara (Chm)

Subsidiaries:

Agensi Pekerjaan Globesoft Services Sdn. Bhd. (1)
Level 11-3 Menara Mbmr 1 Jalan Syed Putra, 58000, Kuala Lumpur, Malaysia
Tel.: (60) 322761883
Web Site: https://www.globeasia.com.my
Information Technology Consulting Services
N.A.I.C.S.: 541512

Applicable Limited (1)
3120 Great Western Court Stoke Gifford, Bristol, BS34 8HP, United Kingdom
Tel.: (44) 1179152200
Web Site: https://www.applicable.com
Information Technology Solutions Services
N.A.I.C.S.: 541512

Biostock Corporation (1)
Higashi 2 South 4-10, Obihiro, 080-0802, Hokkaido, Japan
Tel.: (81) 155666030
Web Site: https://biostock.co.jp
Livestock & Dairy Farming Services
N.A.I.C.S.: 541940

CS Building Service Corporation (1)
3rd Floor Garden City Shinagawa Gotenyama 3F 6-7-29 Kitashinagawa, Shinagawa-ku, Tokyo, 141-0001, Japan
Tel.: (81) 364564151
Web Site: https://www.csbuilding.co.jp
Emp.: 340
Building Environment Services
N.A.I.C.S.: 541512

Chainalytics B.V. (1)
Beech Avenue 54, 1119 PW, Schiphol, Netherlands
Tel.: (31) 206586010
Truck Transportation Services
N.A.I.C.S.: 811111

Chainalytics Oy (1)
Polttimonkatu 4 4th Floor, 33210, Tampere, Finland
Tel.: (358) 33458228
Truck Transportation Services
N.A.I.C.S.: 811111

Chainalytics S.R.L. (1)
Via Roberto Lepetit 8, 20124, Milan, Italy
Tel.: (39) 0200696437
Mobile Phone Services
N.A.I.C.S.: 517112

Chainalytics Services Private Limited (1)
4th Floor Suite 407 Brigade IRV Centre Nallurahalli Whitefield, Bengaluru, 560066, Karnataka, India
Tel.: (91) 9844605090
Mobile Phone Services
N.A.I.C.S.: 517112

CodeTakt Co.,Ltd. (1)
28-4 Maruyama-cho Tokyo Ohba Building A Building 2F Room b, Shibuya-ku, Tokyo, 150-0044, Japan
Tel.: (81) 344465014
Web Site: https://codetakt.com
Information Technology Consulting Services
N.A.I.C.S.: 541512

Comware Financial Systems Corporation (1)
1-40 Miyamach, Fuchu-shi, Tokyo, 183-0023, Japan
Tel.: (81) 423191608
Web Site: https://www.cw-fsys.co.jp
Emp.: 42
Information Processing Services
N.A.I.C.S.: 519290

Cyber Laboratory Incorporation (1)
Shinkou Chou 38 Hitachinaka Techno Center, Hitachinaka, 312-0005, Ibaraki, Japan
Tel.: (81) 29 265 5600
Web Site: http://www.cyberlab.co.jp
Sales Range: $25-49.9 Million
Emp.: 17
Software Development Services
N.A.I.C.S.: 541511
Yasuyuki Kato (CEO)

INTERNATIONAL PUBLIC

Datacraft (Malaysia) Sdn. Bhd. (1)
Suite 9-1 Tower 2 Wangsa 118 Jalan Wangsa Delima, Wangsa Maju, 53300, Kuala Lumpur, Malaysia
Tel.: (60) 361518666
Web Site: https://www.datakraf.com
Information Technology Services
N.A.I.C.S.: 541512

Day Nite Co,Ltd. (1)
UD Hibiya Building 7F 1-1-2 Uchisaiwaicho, Chiyoda-ku, Tokyo, 100-0011, Japan
Tel.: (81) 362688193
Web Site: https://www.daynite.jp
Food & Beverage Mfr
N.A.I.C.S.: 311421

DearOne, Inc. (1)
4F NTT Toranomon Building 3-8-8 Toranomon, Minato-ku, Tokyo, 105-0001, Japan
Tel.: (81) 363815062
Web Site: https://www.dearone.io
Emp.: 132
Digital Marketing Services
N.A.I.C.S.: 541613

Dimension Data plc (1)
The Campus 57 Sloane Street, Bryanston, Johannesburg, 2021, South Africa
Tel.: (27) 11 575 0000
Web Site: https://www.dimensiondata.com
Sales Range: $1-4.9 Billion
Emp.: 10,000
Business-to-Business Systems Integrator
N.A.I.C.S.: 541512
Jeremy John Ord (Chm)

Subsidiary (Non-US):

AccessKenya Group Limited (2)
Purshottam place 3rd 4th & 6th floor Westlands Road, PO Box 43588, 00100, Nairobi, Kenya
Tel.: (254) 203600000
Web Site: http://www.accesskenya.com
Sales Range: $10-24.9 Million
Emp.: 330
Internet Service Provider
N.A.I.C.S.: 517111

Subsidiary (Domestic):

Broadband Access Limited (3)
Purshottam Pl Building Westlands Road, City Centre, Nairobi, Kenya
Tel.: (254) 203 101 64
Internet Service Provider
N.A.I.C.S.: 517610

Subsidiary (Non-US):

Dimension Data Asia Pacific Pte. Ltd. (2)
8 Kallang Avenue 15-01/09 Aperia Tower 1, Suntec Tower Four, Singapore, 339509, Singapore (100%)
Tel.: (65) 63226688
Sales Range: $450-499.9 Million
Emp.: 700
Business-to-Business Systems Integrator
N.A.I.C.S.: 541512
William Bruce Grahame Padfield (Chm)

Subsidiary (Non-US):

Dimension Data (Beijing) (3)
5A Tower A Pacific Century Place 2A Gong Ti Bei Lu, Chaoyang, Beijing, 100027, China (100%)
Tel.: (86) 10 5737 1800
Web Site: http://www.datacraft-asia.com
Sales Range: $25-49.9 Million
Emp.: 100
Business-to-Business Systems Integrator
N.A.I.C.S.: 541512

Branch (Domestic):

Dimension Data (4)
Room 1802 Tower B Victory Plaza 103 Ti Yu Xi Road, Tianhe District, Guangzhou, 510620, China (100%)
Tel.: (86) 20 2809 2850
Sales Range: $10-24.9 Million
Emp.: 20
Business-to-Business Systems Integrator
N.A.I.C.S.: 541512

Dimension Data (4)
Piyuchemg RD 406 Rm 511 Bldg A, Hangzhou, 310001, China (100%)

AND PRIVATE COMPANIES — NIPPON TELEGRAPH & TELEPHONE CORPORATION

Tel.: (86) 57185271271
Web Site: http://www.datacraft-asia.com
Sales Range: $10-24.9 Million
Emp.: 4
Business-to-Business Systems Integrator
N.A.I.C.S.: 541512

Dimension Data (4)
Room 1602 and 1603 Carlton Building No 21 Huang He Road, Huang Pu, Shanghai, 20003, China **(100%)**
Tel.: (86) 2161713600
Web Site: http://www.dimensiondata.com
Sales Range: $10-24.9 Million
Emp.: 10
Business-to-Business Systems Integrator
N.A.I.C.S.: 541512

Dimension Data (4)
Room 9B01 9/F Jazz Building No 4018 Ji-abin Road, Luohu District, Shenzhen, 518026, Guangdong, China
Tel.: (86) 75582801100
Business-to-Business Systems Integrator
N.A.I.C.S.: 541512

Subsidiary (Domestic):

Dimension Data (Singapore) Pte. Ltd. (3)
2 Kaki Bukit Avenue 1 03-02, Suntec Tower Four, Singapore, 417938, Singapore
Tel.: (65) 65172000
Business-to-Business Systems Integrator
N.A.I.C.S.: 541512
Kim Meng Png *(Gen Mgr)*

Subsidiary (Non-US):

Dimension Data (Thailand) Limited (3)
16th - 17th Floor Column Tower 199 Ratch-adapisek Road, Klongtoey, Bangkok, 10110, Thailand **(100%)**
Tel.: (66) 26250999
Web Site: http://www.dimensiondata.com
Sales Range: $25-49.9 Million
Emp.: 100
Business-to-Business Systems Integrator
N.A.I.C.S.: 541512

Dimension Data China/ Hong Kong Limited (3)
3/F Cityplaza III 14 Taikoo Wan Road, Tai-koo Shing, China (Hong Kong) **(100%)**
Tel.: (852) 25133168
Web Site: http://www.dimensiondata.com
Sales Range: $25-49.9 Million
Emp.: 150
Business-to-Business Systems Integrator
N.A.I.C.S.: 541512
Steve Lam *(Mng Dir)*

Dimension Data India Limited (3)
1701-1704 B-Wing G Block ONE BKC Bandra Kurla Complex, Bandra E, Mumbai, 400 051, India **(100%)**
Tel.: (91) 2261657000
Web Site: http://www.dimensiondata.com
Sales Range: $25-49.9 Million
Emp.: 115
Business-to-Business Systems Integrator
N.A.I.C.S.: 541512
Ulhas Aher *(Head-HR)*

Branch (Domestic):

Dimension Data India (4)
3rd Floor Wing B E2 Block Silver Oak Manyata Embassy Business Park, Outer Ring Road, Nagavara, Bengaluru, 560045, India **(100%)**
Tel.: (91) 8022077000
Sales Range: $10-24.9 Million
Emp.: 85
Business-to-Business Systems Integrator
N.A.I.C.S.: 541512

Dimension Data India (4)
The Oval 7th Floor Old No 57 and 58 New No 10 and 12, Venkatnarayana Road, Chennai, 600017, Tamil Nadu, India **(100%)**
Tel.: (91) 44 4907 5555
Web Site: http://www.dimensiondata.com
Sales Range: $10-24.9 Million
Emp.: 27
Business-to-Business Systems Integrator
N.A.I.C.S.: 541512

Dimension Data India (4)
No 51 Okhla Industrial Estate Phase III, New Delhi, 110020, India **(100%)**
Tel.: (91) 1126936800
Web Site: http://www.dimensiondata.com
Sales Range: $10-24.9 Million
Emp.: 30
Business-to-Business Systems Integrator
N.A.I.C.S.: 541512

Dimension Data India (4)
Sunflower Commercial Building 3rd Floor Banner Road, Pune, 411045, India **(100%)**
Tel.: (91) 20 65005970
Web Site: http://www.dimensiondata.com
Business-to-Business Systems Integrator
N.A.I.C.S.: 541512

Dimension Data India Limited (4)
Ground Floor Humsafar Edifice 8-2-618/2 Banjara Hills Road No 11, Begumpet, Hyderabad, 500 034, India **(100%)**
Tel.: (91) 40 6666 7706
Web Site: http://www.dimensiondata.com
Business-to-Business Systems Integrator
N.A.I.C.S.: 541512

Subsidiary (Non-US):

Dimension Data Japan Inc. (3)
Otemachi Place West Tower 2-3-1 Otemachi, Chiyoda-ku, Tokyo, 100-8019, Japan
Tel.: (81) 367462222
Web Site: http://www.dimensiondata.com
Sales Range: $10-24.9 Million
Emp.: 50
Business-to-Business Systems Integrator
N.A.I.C.S.: 541512

Dimension Data Korea Inc. (3)
International Finance Centre Seoul 28FL Two IFC 10 Gukjegeumyung-ro, Youngdeungpo-gu, Seoul, 07326, Korea (South)
Tel.: (82) 262567000
Web Site: http://www.dimensiondata.com
Sales Range: $25-49.9 Million
Emp.: 180
Business-to-Business Systems Integrator
N.A.I.C.S.: 541512

Dimension Data New Zealand Limited (3)
Level 15 NTT Tower 157, Lambton Quay, Wellington, 6011, New Zealand **(100%)**
Tel.: (64) 44701650
Web Site: http://www.dimensiondata.com
Sales Range: $25-49.9 Million
Emp.: 150
Business-to-Business Systems Integrator
N.A.I.C.S.: 541512
Wayne Yarr *(CEO)*

Dimension Data Philippines, Inc. (3)
26th Floor Zuellig Building Makati Ave cor Paseo De Roxas, Makati, 1223, Philippines **(100%)**
Tel.: (63) 27847000
Web Site: http://www.dimensiondata.com
Sales Range: $10-24.9 Million
Emp.: 200
Business-to-Business Systems Integrator
N.A.I.C.S.: 541512
Ernesto Batungbacal *(CEO)*

Dimension Data Taiwan Limited (3)
14F No 188 Sec 5 Nanjing East Road, Taipei, 10571, Taiwan **(100%)**
Tel.: (886) 221713333
Web Site: http://www.dimensiondata.com
Sales Range: $25-49.9 Million
Emp.: 80
Business-to-Business Systems Integrator
N.A.I.C.S.: 541512

Dimension Data Vietnam Limited (3)
5/F Unit 05-01 Prime Centre Building 53 Quang Trung Street, Hi Ba Trung, Hanoi, Vietnam **(100%)**
Tel.: (84) 49435758
Web Site: http://www.dimensiondata.com
Sales Range: $10-24.9 Million
Emp.: 50
Business-to-Business Systems Integrator
N.A.I.C.S.: 541512

Branch (Domestic):

Dimension Data Vietnam Limited (4)
7/F Centre Point Building 106 Nguyen Van Troi Street, Phu Nhaun District, Ho Chi Minh City, Vietnam **(100%)**
Tel.: (84) 862886768
Web Site: http://www.datacraft-asia.com
Sales Range: $10-24.9 Million
Emp.: 10
Business-to-Business Systems Integrator
N.A.I.C.S.: 541512

Subsidiary (Non-US):

PT Dimension Data Indonesia (3)
DBS Tower 22nd floor Jl Prof Dr Satrio Kav 3 - 5, South Jakarta, 12940, Indonesia **(100%)**
Tel.: (62) 2128548000
Web Site: http://www.datacraft.asia.com
Sales Range: $25-49.9 Million
Emp.: 200
Business-to-Business Systems Integrator
N.A.I.C.S.: 541512

Subsidiary (Non-US):

Dimension Data Australia Pty Limited (2)
Ground Floor Darling Park Tower 3 201 Sussex Street, Sydney, 2000, NSW, Australia
Tel.: (61) 282495000
Sales Range: $600-649.9 Million
Emp.: 1,250
IT Solutions & Services
N.A.I.C.S.: 541512
Haydn Faltyn *(Gen Mgr-IT Outsourcing)*

Branch (Domestic):

Dimension Data Australia (3)
Niveau 22 141 Queen Street, Brisbane, 4000, QLD, Australia **(100%)**
Tel.: (61) 732921300
Web Site: http://www.didata.com.au
Sales Range: $25-49.9 Million
Emp.: 90
Business-to-Business Systems Integrator
N.A.I.C.S.: 541512

Dimension Data Australia (3)
Level 21 25 Grenfell St, Adelaide, 5000, SA, Australia **(100%)**
Tel.: (61) 882918600
Web Site: http://www.didata.com.au
Sales Range: $25-49.9 Million
Emp.: 100
Business-to-Business Systems Integrator
N.A.I.C.S.: 541512

Dimension Data Australia (3)
New Ground Floor 11 17 Dorcas Street, Melbourne, 3205, VIC, Australia **(100%)**
Tel.: (61) 396260770
Web Site: http://www.didata.com.au
Sales Range: $75-99.9 Million
Emp.: 400
Business-to-Business Systems Integrator
N.A.I.C.S.: 541512
Peter Prowse *(Sr VP-Strategic Alliances)*

Dimension Data Australia (3)
Level 4 66 St Georges Terrace, Perth, 6000, WA, Australia **(100%)**
Tel.: (61) 893117111
Web Site: http://www.didata.com.au
Sales Range: $25-49.9 Million
Emp.: 70
Business-to-Business Systems Integrator
N.A.I.C.S.: 541512
Duncan Brown *(Dir-Strategy & Innovation)*

Subsidiary (Domestic):

Oakton Ltd (3)
Level 8 271 Collins Street, Melbourne, 3000, VIC, Australia
Tel.: (61) 396170200
Web Site: http://www.oakton.com.au
Technology & Business Consulting Services
N.A.I.C.S.: 561110
Michael Miers *(Sec)*

Subsidiary (Domestic):

Oakton Contracting and Recruitment Pty Ltd. (4)
2/45 Wentworth Ave, Kingston, 2604, ACT, Australia
Tel.: (61) 261631955
Web Site: http://www.oakton.com.au
Professionals Recruitment Services
N.A.I.C.S.: 541612

Oakton Services Pty. Ltd. (4)
Level 21 35 Collins St, Melbourne, 3000, VIC, Australia
Tel.: (61) 800456122
Web Site: http://www.oakton.com.au
Business Management Services
N.A.I.C.S.: 541611

Subsidiary (Non-US):

Oakton Global Technology Services Centre (India) Pvt Ltd. (5)
No 8-2-293/499 Plot No 499 Road No 36 Jubilee Hills, Hyderabad, 500034, Andhra Pradesh, India
Tel.: (91) 40 23552694
Web Site: http://www.oakton.com.au
Sales Range: $25-49.9 Million
Emp.: 100
Business Consulting & Financial Management Services
N.A.I.C.S.: 541611

Subsidiary (Non-US):

Dimension Data Belgium NV/SA (2)
Telecomlaan 5-7, 1831, Diegem, Belgium **(100%)**
Tel.: (32) 27450445
Web Site: http://www.dimensiondata.com
Sales Range: $25-49.9 Million
Emp.: 200
Business-to-Business Systems Integrator
N.A.I.C.S.: 541512
Andrew Coulsen *(CEO-Europe)*

Dimension Data Brasil (2)
Av Nacoes Unidas 14 401 - 12 Andar - Cj 121, Edificio Parque da Cidade - Torre Aroeira B1 Vila Gertrudes, Sao Paulo, 04794-000, SP, Brazil **(100%)**
Tel.: (55) 1138786500
Web Site: http://www.dimensiondata.com
Sales Range: $10-24.9 Million
Emp.: 30
Business-to-Business Systems Integrator
N.A.I.C.S.: 541512

Dimension Data Espana (2) **(100%)**
Web Site: http://www.dimensiondata.com
Sales Range: $10-24.9 Million
Emp.: 250
Business-to-Business Systems Integrator
N.A.I.C.S.: 541512

Dimension Data Espana SL (2)
C/ Mendez Alvaro 56, 28045, Madrid, Spain **(100%)**
Tel.: (34) 913309300
Web Site: http://www.dimensiondata.com
Sales Range: $25-49.9 Million
Emp.: 63
Business-to-Business Systems Integrator
N.A.I.C.S.: 541512

Dimension Data France SA (2)
20 Avenue Louis Bleriot Orlytech 91550, Paray Vieille Poste, 91781, Paris, Cedex, France **(100%)**
Tel.: (33) 149758600
Web Site: http://www.dimensiondata.com
Business-to-Business Systems Integrator
N.A.I.C.S.: 541512
Andrew Coulsen *(CEO-Europe)*

Branch (Domestic):

Dimension Data France (3)
2 rue Marcel Doret, 31700, Blagnac, Antares, France
Tel.: (33) 5 34 60 63 80
Web Site: http://www.didata.com
Sales Range: $25-49.9 Million
Emp.: 200
Business-to-Business Systems Integrator
N.A.I.C.S.: 541512
Andrew Coulsen *(CEO-Europe)*

Subsidiary (Non-US):

Dimension Data Germany AG & Co. (2)
In Den Schwarzwiesen 8, Oberursel, 61440, Germany **(100%)**
Tel.: (49) 61719770
Web Site: http://www.de.didata.com

NIPPON TELEGRAPH & TELEPHONE CORPORATION

Nippon Telegraph & Telephone Corporation—(Continued)

Sales Range: $150-199.9 Million
Emp.: 600
Business-to-Business Systems Integrator
N.A.I.C.S.: 541512
Andrew Coulsen (CEO-Europe)

Branch (Domestic):

Dimension Data Germany (3)
Brooktorkai 20, Hamburg, 20457, Germany **(100%)**
Tel.: (49) 405201201
Web Site: http://www.dimensiondata.com
Sales Range: $25-49.9 Million
Emp.: 500
Business-to-Business Systems Integrator
N.A.I.C.S.: 541512

Dimension Data Germany (3)
Am Foeldmermoos Rd 17, 85399, Hallbergmoos, Germany **(100%)**
Tel.: (49) 893218160
Sales Range: $25-49.9 Million
Emp.: 20
Business-to-Business Systems Integrator
N.A.I.C.S.: 541512
Herbert Bockers (Mng Dir)

Dimension Data Germany (3)
Ingersheimer Strasse 20, Stuttgart, 70499, Germany **(100%)**
Tel.: (49) 71183840
Web Site: http://www.de.didata.com
Sales Range: $25-49.9 Million
Emp.: 115
Business-to-Business Systems Integrator
N.A.I.C.S.: 541512
Sven Heinsen (Mng Dir)

Subsidiary (Non-US):

Dimension Data Italia SRL (2)
Via S Bovio 3, Segreen Business Park Segrate, 20090, Milan, MI, Italy **(100%)**
Tel.: (39) 025539071
Web Site: http://www.dimensiondata.com
Sales Range: $10-24.9 Million
Emp.: 120
Business-to-Business Systems Integrator
N.A.I.C.S.: 541512
Andrew Coulsen (CEO-Europe)

Branch (Domestic):

Dimension Data Italia (3)
Via Mario Bianchini 51, 00142, Rome, Italy **(100%)**
Tel.: (39) 025539071
Web Site: http://www.didata.it
Business-to-Business Systems Integrator
N.A.I.C.S.: 541512

Subsidiary (Non-US):

Dimension Data Limited (2)
Dimension Data House Building 2 Waterfront Business Park, Fleet Road, Fleet, GU51 3QT, Hamps, United Kingdom
Tel.: (44) 1252779000
Emp.: 40
IT Solutions & Services
N.A.I.C.S.: 541512
Andrew Coulsen (CEO)

Branch (Domestic):

Dimension Data Limited (3)
Fleet Pl House 2 Fleet Pl, London, EC4M 7RT, United Kingdom
Tel.: (44) 2076517000
Web Site: http://www.dimensiondata.com
Sales Range: $25-49.9 Million
Emp.: 130
Business-to-Business Systems Integrator
N.A.I.C.S.: 541512
Andrew Coulsen (CEO-Europe)

Dimension Data Limited (3)
Technology House Monks Way, Abbots Park, Preston Brook, WA7 3GH, Cheshire, United Kingdom
Tel.: (44) 1928793100
Sales Range: $25-49.9 Million
Business-to-Business Systems Integrator
N.A.I.C.S.: 541512
Andrew Coulsen (CEO-Europe)

Subsidiary (Domestic):

Merchants Ltd. (3)
500 Avebury Boulevard, Milton Keynes, MK9 2BE, Buckinghamshire, United Kingdom **(100%)**
Tel.: (44) 1908232323
Web Site: http://www.merchants.co.uk
Sales Range: $100-124.9 Million
Emp.: 35
IT Solutions & Services
N.A.I.C.S.: 541512

Subsidiary (Non-US):

Dimension Data Luxembourg SA (2)
89D rue Pafebruch, 8308, Capellen, Luxembourg **(100%)**
Tel.: (352) 20410700
Web Site: http://www.lu.didata.com
Sales Range: $25-49.9 Million
Emp.: 220
Business-to-Business Systems Integrator
N.A.I.C.S.: 541512
Andrew Coulsen (CEO-Europe)

Dimension Data Mexico (2)
(100%)
Tel.: (52) 5551410470
Web Site: http://www.dimensiondata.com
Sales Range: $10-24.9 Million
Emp.: 40
Business-to-Business Systems Integrator
N.A.I.C.S.: 541512

Dimension Data Nederland BV (2)
Veemweg 23-25, 3771 MT, Barneveld, Netherlands **(100%)**
Tel.: (31) 850004400
Web Site: http://www.dimensiondata.com
Sales Range: $25-49.9 Million
Emp.: 300
Business-to-Business Systems Integrator
N.A.I.C.S.: 541512
Andrew Coulsen (Chm-Supervisory Bd)

Subsidiary (US):

Dimension Data North America, Inc. (2)
1 Penn Plz Ste 1600, New York, NY 10119
Tel.: (212) 613-1220
Web Site: http://www.dimensiondata.com
Sales Range: $25-49.9 Million
Emp.: 100
IT Solutions & Services
N.A.I.C.S.: 541512
Elly Surna (Office Mgr)

Branch (Domestic):

Dimension Data North America (3)
3420 Rochelle Ct, Clearwater, FL 33761-1368 **(100%)**
Tel.: (727) 812-2040
Sales Range: $10-24.9 Million
Emp.: 40
Business-to-Business Systems Integrator
N.A.I.C.S.: 541512

Dimension Data North America, Inc. - Alpharetta (3)
1105 Lakewood Pkwy Ste 100, Alpharetta, GA 30009
Tel.: (770) 360-1040
Sales Range: $10-24.9 Million
Emp.: 30
IT Solutions & Services
N.A.I.C.S.: 541512
Natasha Thomas (Office Mgr)

Dimension Data North America, Inc. - Charlotte (3)
11006 Rushmore Dr Ste 300, Charlotte, NC 28277-1924
Tel.: (704) 969-2200
Business-to-Business Systems Integrator
N.A.I.C.S.: 541512
Patrick King (VP-Fin)

Dimension Data North America, Inc. - Hauppauge (3)
400 Oser Ave Ste 1700 1800 1950, Hauppauge, NY 11788-2012
Tel.: (631) 543-6100
Sales Range: $10-24.9 Million
Emp.: 50
Business-to-Business Systems Integrator
N.A.I.C.S.: 541512

Dimension Data North America, Inc. - Herndon (3)
11730 Plaza America Dr Ste 340, Reston, VA 20190
Tel.: (571) 203-4000
Web Site: http://www.dimensiondata.com
Sales Range: $50-74.9 Million
Computer Integrated Systems Design
N.A.I.C.S.: 541512

Dimension Data North America, Inc. - Raleigh (3)
4101 Lake Boone Trl Ste 200, Raleigh, NC 27607-5243
Tel.: (919) 791-1050
Sales Range: $10-24.9 Million
Emp.: 45
Business-to-Business Systems Integrator
N.A.I.C.S.: 541512
Mark Slaga (CEO-North America)

Dimension Data North America, Inc. - Shelton (3)
3 Corporate Dr Ste 330, Shelton, CT 06484
Tel.: (203) 926-0225
Sales Range: $25-49.9 Million
Emp.: 12
Business-to-Business Systems Integrator
N.A.I.C.S.: 541512

Subsidiary (Domestic):

OpSource, Inc. (3)
5201 Great America Pkwy Ste 120, Santa Clara, CA 95054
Tel.: (408) 567-2000
Web Site: http://www.opsource.net
Sales Range: $50-74.9 Million
Software Publisher
N.A.I.C.S.: 513210
John Rowell (CTO)

Subsidiary (Non-US):

Dimension Data Pty Limited (2)
(100%)
Tel.: (27) 115750000
Web Site: http://www.dimensiondata.com
Sales Range: $25-49.9 Million
Emp.: 57
Business-to-Business Systems Integrator
N.A.I.C.S.: 541512

Branch (Domestic):

Dimension Data (3)
Central Building Black River Park, Observatory, Cape Town, 7925, South Africa **(100%)**
Tel.: (27) 21 486 5500
Web Site: http://www.dimensiondata.com
Emp.: 5,000
Business-to-Business Systems Integrator
N.A.I.C.S.: 541512
John Ell (CEO)

Dimension Data (3)
6 The Boulevard Westway Office Park Spine Road, Westville, 3630, Durban, South Africa **(100%)**
Tel.: (27) 312048400
Sales Range: $25-49.9 Million
Emp.: 150
Business-to-Business Systems Integrator
N.A.I.C.S.: 541512
Marc Jessiman (Gen Mgr)

Dimension Data (3)
Moffet Office Park Cnr Overbaakens Road and William Moffet Express Way, Fairiew, Port Elizabeth, 6070, South Africa **(100%)**
Tel.: (27) 413985300
Web Site: http://www.dimensiondata.com
Sales Range: $75-99.9 Million
Business-to-Business Systems Integrator
N.A.I.C.S.: 541512

Dimension Data (3)
Unit 1 12 Victoria Link Route 21 Office Park 14 Regency Street, Centurion, 0157, Pretoria, South Africa **(100%)**
Tel.: (27) 12 345 2484
Web Site: http://www.deimositalia.com
Business-to-Business Systems Integrator
N.A.I.C.S.: 541512

Subsidiary (Non-US):

Dimension Data Switzerland S.A. (2)

INTERNATIONAL PUBLIC

Rte Du Bois Genoud 1, 1023, Cressier, Switzerland **(100%)**
Tel.: (41) 216310000
Web Site: http://www.dimensiondata.com
Sales Range: $10-24.9 Million
Emp.: 50
Business-to-Business Systems Integrator
N.A.I.C.S.: 541512
Andrew Coulsen (CEO-Europe)

Subsidiary (Domestic):

Internet Solutions Pty Limited (2)
The Campus Le Mans Building 57 Sloane Street, Bryanston, 2020, Gauteng, South Africa
Tel.: (27) 11 575 1000
Web Site: http://www.is.co.za
IT Solutions & Services
N.A.I.C.S.: 541512
Julian Sunker (CFO)

Branch (Domestic):

Internet Solutions (3)
The Terraces 11th Floor 34 Bree Street, Cape Town, 8001, Western Cape, South Africa
Tel.: (27) 21 415 7100
Web Site: http://www.is.co.za
Sales Range: $25-49.9 Million
Emp.: 70
Business-to-Business Systems Integrator
N.A.I.C.S.: 541512

Internet Solutions (3)
314-317 Umahoanga Rocks Dr 2nd Fl E Coast Radio House, Umhlanga, Durban, 4320, South Africa **(100%)**
Tel.: (27) 315660650
Web Site: http://www.is.co.za
Sales Range: $10-24.9 Million
Emp.: 40
IT Solutions & Services
N.A.I.C.S.: 541512
Saki Missaikos (Mng Dir)

Subsidiary (US):

Nexus IS (2)
27202 W Turnberry Ln Ste 100, Valencia, CA 91355
Tel.: (661) 257-1500
Web Site: http://www.nexusis.com
Sales Range: $150-199.9 Million
Emp.: 500
Telecommunication Servicesb
N.A.I.C.S.: 517810
Deron L. Pearson (Co-Founder)

Docomo CS Hokkaido, Inc. (1)
Minami 1-jo Nishi 1-4 Taisei Sapporo Building 1F, Chuo-ku, Sapporo, 060-0061, Japan
Tel.: (81) 120376601
Web Site: https://www.docomo-cs-hokkaido.co.jp
Information Center Services
N.A.I.C.S.: 519290

Docomo Datacom, Inc. (1)
Nikkyohan Building 5F 1-4-25 Koraku, Bunkyo-ku, Tokyo, 112-0004, Japan
Tel.: (81) 338300045
Web Site: https://www.docomo-dc.co.jp
Emp.: 409
Information Technology Development Services
N.A.I.C.S.: 541512

Docomo Gacco, Inc. (1)
1-6-15 Minami-Azabu, Minato-ku, Tokyo, 106-0047, Japan
Tel.: (81) 334568111
Web Site: https://gacco.co.jp
Education Services
N.A.I.C.S.: 923110

Docomo Pacific(Saipan), Inc. (1)
890 S Marine Corps Dr, Tamuning, GU 96913
Tel.: (671) 688-2273
Web Site: https://www.docomopacific.com
Telecommunication Servicesb
N.A.I.C.S.: 541618

Downtown Properties Owner, LLC (1)
818 W 7th St Ste 410, Los Angeles, CA 90017
Tel.: (213) 213-8600
Web Site: https://www.downtown-properties.com

AND PRIVATE COMPANIES

NIPPON TELEGRAPH & TELEPHONE CORPORATION

Real Estate Investment & Management Services
N.A.I.C.S.: 531210

ENNET Corporation (1)
The Front Tower Shiba Koen 2-6-3 Shiba Koen, Minato-ku, Tokyo, 105-0011, Japan
Tel.: (81) 120223379
Web Site: https://www.ennet.co.jp
Energy Power Generation Services
N.A.I.C.S.: 926130

Everis Italia, S.p.A. (1)
Via Calindri 4, 20143, Milan, Italy
Tel.: (39) 02831251
Information Technology Consulting Services
N.A.I.C.S.: 541512

FIT Inversion en Talento, S.A.U. (1)
Camino Fuente de la Mora 1Edificio NOVUS, 28050, Madrid, Spain
Tel.: (34) 917490000
Web Site: https://www.fitalent.es
Venture Capital Services
N.A.I.C.S.: 523910

GISA GmbH (1)
Leipziger Chaussee 191a, 06112, Halle, Germany
Tel.: (49) 3455850
Web Site: https://www.gisa.de
Information Technology Services
N.A.I.C.S.: 541512

Genius-dms GmbH (1)
Herforder Strabe 74, 33602, Bielefeld, Germany
Tel.: (49) 5215577700
Web Site: https://gen-ius.de
Software Development Services
N.A.I.C.S.: 541519

Good Eat Company Inc. (1)
5-27-8 Jingumae, Shibuya-ku, Tokyo, Japan
Tel.: (81) 358607565
Web Site: https://goodeatcompany.com
Food Products Mfr
N.A.I.C.S.: 311412

IMG SRC Inc. (1)
5-2 1F Shioirikoji Shinsen, Shibuya, Tokyo, 150-0045, Japan
Tel.: (81) 354596464
Web Site: https://www.imgsrc.co.jp
Digital Advertising Services
N.A.I.C.S.: 541850

ITMX GmbH (1)
Stuttgarter Strabe 8, 75179, Pforzheim, Germany
Tel.: (49) 7231968250
Web Site: https://www.itmx.de
Software Development Services
N.A.I.C.S.: 541511

InfoCom Research, Inc. (1)
Urbannet Nihonbashi Building 2-14-10 Nihonbashi Ningyocho, Chuo-ku, Tokyo, 103-0013, Japan
Tel.: (81) 336637500
Web Site: http://www.icr.co.jp
Sales Range: $25-49.9 Million
Emp.: 127
Information Technology Research Services
N.A.I.C.S.: 541715
Hiroshi Ohira (Pres)

Intellect Bizware Services Private Limited (1)
Technocity 6th Floor Plot No X-5/3 Opp M B P Mahape M I D C Navi, Mumbai, 400 710, Maharashtra, India
Tel.: (91) 2262646800
Web Site: https://www.intellectbizware.com
Global Consulting Services
N.A.I.C.S.: 541611

Itelligence Software Solutions WLL (1)
Concord Business Centre Building Number, PO Box 39445, 38 Suite 213 Second Floor Al-Rawabi Street 840 Rawadat Al Khail, Doha, Qatar
Tel.: (974) 40326433
Information Technology Consulting Services
N.A.I.C.S.: 541512

JIP Info Bridge Co., Ltd. (1)
2-4-24 Toyo, Koto-ku, Tokyo, 135-0016, Japan
Tel.: (81) 356907733
Web Site: https://www.info-brdg.co.jp
Business Software Development Services
N.A.I.C.S.: 541511

JIP Techno Science Corporation (1)
1-3-1 Kudanminami, Chiyoda-ku, Tokyo, Japan
Tel.: (81) 362728230
Web Site: https://www.jip-ts.co.jp
Emp.: 236
Drafting Services
N.A.I.C.S.: 541340

Japan Information Processing Service Co.,Ltd. (1)
1-3-1 Kudanminami, Chiyoda-ku, Tokyo, 102-8235, Japan
Tel.: (81) 352100131
Web Site: https://www.jip.co.jp
Emp.: 1,455
Information Technology Consulting Services
N.A.I.C.S.: 541512

Japan Infra Waymark Corporation (1)
3-8 Babacho, Chuo Ward, Osaka, 540-0007, Japan
Tel.: (81) 362644649
Web Site: https://www.jiw.co.jp
Infrastructure Services
N.A.I.C.S.: 518210

Jebsen & Jessen Communications (P) Inc. (1)
11th Avenue Corner 38th Street 5th Floor Orion Building, Bonifacio Global City Manila, Taguig, 1634, Philippines
Tel.: (63) 27867700
Fiber Optic Cable Mfr
N.A.I.C.S.: 335921

Jebsen & Jessen Communications (T) Ltd. (1)
23/110-117 Sorachai Building 29th Floor Soi Sukhumvit 63 Ekamai, Sukhumvit Road Klongton Nua Wattana, Bangkok, 10110, Thailand
Tel.: (66) 27878888
Fiber Optic Cable Mfr
N.A.I.C.S.: 335921

Magaseek Corporation (1)
3F Izumikan Sanbancho Building 3-8 Sanbancho, Chiyoda-ku, Tokyo, 102-0075, Japan
Tel.: (81) 352125296
Web Site: https://www.magaseek.co.jp
Emp.: 206
Women & Men Online Clothing Retailer
N.A.I.C.S.: 458110

Meccs Support Co., Ltd. (1)
Isetsune Building 3F 1-9-2 Tsukiji, Chuo-ku, Tokyo, 104-0045, Japan
Tel.: (81) 362643972
Web Site: https://www.meccs-support.com
Emp.: 301
Building Maintenance Services
N.A.I.C.S.: 561790

Meccs Techno Kyushu Co., Ltd. (1)
Hakata Kaisei Building 8F 2-5-28 Hakata Station East, Hakata-ku, Fukuoka, 812-0013, Japan
Tel.: (81) 924323211
Web Site: https://www.meccs-kyushu.com
Emp.: 54
Building Environment Services
N.A.I.C.S.: 541620

Meccs Techno Nishinihon Co., Ltd. (1)
7F Osaka Stock Exchange Building 1-8-16 Kitahama, Chuo-ku, Osaka, 541-0041, Japan
Tel.: (81) 647072010
Web Site: https://www.meccs-nishinihon.com
Emp.: 190
Building Environment Services
N.A.I.C.S.: 541620

Meccs Techno Tohoku Co., Ltd. (1)
Sendai TB Building 1F 4-3-10 Tsutsujioka, Miyagino-ku, Sendai, 983-0852, Miyagi, Japan
Tel.: (81) 222906841
Web Site: https://www.meccs-tohoku.com
Emp.: 58
Building Environment Services
N.A.I.C.S.: 541620

Meccs Techno Tokai Co., Ltd. (1)
3-8-8 Sakae, Naka Ward, Nagoya, 460-0008, Aichi, Japan
Tel.: (81) 522691525
Web Site: https://www.meccs-tokai.com
Emp.: 50
Building Maintenance Services
N.A.I.C.S.: 561790

Merchants SA (Pty.) Ltd. (1)
Merchants Johannesburg Ground floor Roland Garros Building, The Campus 57 Sloane Street, Bryanston, 2191, South Africa
Tel.: (27) 115752000
Web Site: https://www.merchantscx.com
Business Management Consulting Services
N.A.I.C.S.: 541611

Millennium Process Group, Inc. (1)
251 Attwell Drive, Toronto, M9W 7G2, ON, Canada
Tel.: (416) 521-3059
Web Site: https://www.millennium1solutions.com
Information Technology Consulting Services
N.A.I.C.S.: 541512

Mirai Translate, Inc. (1)
Shibuya Higashiguchi Building 2F 2-22-3 Shibuya, Shibuya-ku, Tokyo, 150-0002, Japan
Tel.: (81) 357977042
Web Site: https://miraitranslate.com
Software Development Services
N.A.I.C.S.: 541511

Motomachi Parking Access Co., Ltd. (1)
6-78 Motomachi, Naka-ku, Hiroshima, 730-0011, Japan
Tel.: (81) 822229000
Information Technology Consulting Services
N.A.I.C.S.: 541512

My Supply Chain Group, LLC (1)
2700 Corporate Dr Ste 200, Birmingham, AL 35242
Tel.: (205) 706-4300
Web Site: https://www.mysupplychaingroup.com
Information Technology Consulting Services
N.A.I.C.S.: 541512

N.F.Laboratories Inc. (1)
2-3-1 Otemachi 26th Floor Otemachi Place West Tower, Chiyoda-ku, Tokyo, 100-0004, Japan
Tel.: (81) 364352104
Web Site: https://nflabs.jp
Emp.: 79
Security Services
N.A.I.C.S.: 561612

NIandC Partners Inc. (1)
7th floor Nichirei Akashicho Building 6-4 Akashicho, Chuo-ku, Tokyo, Japan
Tel.: (81) 362786278
Web Site: https://www.nicpartners.co.jp
Emp.: 104
Software Merchant Whslr
N.A.I.C.S.: 423430

NSF Engagement Corporation (1)
6-7-29 Kitashinagawa Garden City Shinagawa Gotenyama 3F, Shinagawa-ku, Tokyo, 141-0001, Japan
Tel.: (81) 120586633
Web Site: https://www.nsf-e.com
Emp.: 500
Insurance Services
N.A.I.C.S.: 524298

NTT Advanced Technology Corporation (1)
Tokyo Opera City Tower 3-20-2 Nishi-shinjuku, Shinjuku-ku, Tokyo, 163-1436, Japan (100%)
Tel.: (81) 353250711
Web Site: https://www.ntt-at.com
Sales Range: $600-649.9 Million
Emp.: 2,113
Network Integration Software Development Services
N.A.I.C.S.: 541511
Akira Nanbu (Sr VP & Gen Mgr-Sls & Mktg)

Subsidiary (Domestic):

NTT-AT IPS Corporation (2)
24th floor Muza Kawasaki Central Tower 1310 Omiya-cho, Saiwai-ku, Kawasaki, 212-0014, Kanagawa, Japan
Tel.: (81) 442016290
Web Site: https://www.ntt-atips.co.jp
Sales Range: $25-49.9 Million
Emp.: 203
Business Outsourcing Services
N.A.I.C.S.: 561499

NTT-AT Mtack Corporation (2)
2-13-12 Shinjuku, Shinjuku-Ku, Tokyo, 160-0022, Japan
Tel.: (81) 33 350 5171
Web Site: https://www.mtack.co.jp
Software Development & Sales
N.A.I.C.S.: 513210
Katsuyuki Okada (Pres & CEO)

NTT-AT SYSTEMS CORPORATION (2)
Musashino Center Building 3F 1-19-18 Nakamachi, Musashino, 180-0006, Tokyo, Japan
Tel.: (81) 422501081
Web Site: https://www.ntt-ats.co.jp
Emp.: 200
Software Development Services
N.A.I.C.S.: 541511

NTT-AT Techno Communications Inc. (2)
2-1-20 Jonan, Mito, 310-0803, Ibaraki, Japan
Tel.: (81) 293028881
Web Site: https://www.ntt-atc.co.jp
Sales Range: $25-49.9 Million
Emp.: 150
Network Consulting Services
N.A.I.C.S.: 541618

NTT Agri Technology Corporation (1)
19-2 Nishi-Shinjuku 3-chome, Shinjuku, Tokyo, Japan
Tel.: (81) 353594831
Web Site: https://www.ntt-agritechnology.com
Telecommunication Technology Services
N.A.I.C.S.: 541618

NTT Art Technology Corporation (1)
3-20-2 Nishi-Shinjuku, Shinjuku-ku, Tokyo, 163-1404, Japan
Tel.: (81) 353530844
Web Site: https://www.ntt-arttechnology.com
Innovative Solution Services
N.A.I.C.S.: 541511

NTT BUSINESS ASSOCIE Co., Ltd. (1)
1-1-1 Hitotsubashi Palace Side Building 7th floor, Chiyoda-ku, Tokyo, 100-0003, Japan
Tel.: (81) 358603300
Web Site: http://www.ntt-ba.co.jp
Emp.: 510
Business Process Outsourcing Services
N.A.I.C.S.: 561499

Subsidiary (Domestic):

NTT BUSINESS ASSOCIE EAST Co., Ltd. (2)
Urbannet Omori Building 2-1-1 Omori Kita, Ota-ku, Tokyo, 143-0016, Japan
Tel.: (81) 357678488
Web Site: https://www.nttba-east.co.jp
Emp.: 683
Business Outsourcing Services
N.A.I.C.S.: 561499

NTT BUSINESS ASSOCIE PARTNERS Co., Ltd. (2)
3-2-4 Nihombashihongokucho Kyodo Nichigimmae Bldg 6f, Chuo-Ku, Tokyo, 103-0021, Japan
Tel.: (81) 335484581
Web Site: http://www.ntt-bap.co.jp
Sales Range: $25-49.9 Million
Emp.: 65
Business Support Services
N.A.I.C.S.: 561499

NTT Broadband Platform, Inc. (1)
Urbannet Kanda Building 3-6-2 Uchikanda, Chiyoda-ku, Tokyo, 101-0047, Japan
Tel.: (81) 120261065
Web Site: https://www.ntt-bp.net
Wireless Consulting Services
N.A.I.C.S.: 517112

NIPPON TELEGRAPH & TELEPHONE CORPORATION

Nippon Telegraph & Telephone Corporation—(Continued)

NTT CLARUTY CORPORATION (1)
3-9-11 Midoricho, Musashino, 180-8585, Tokyo, Japan
Tel.: (81) 422508353
Web Site: https://www.ntt-claruty.co.jp
Sales Range: $25-49.9 Million
Emp.: 461
Handmade Paper Products Mfr
N.A.I.C.S.: 322299

NTT COMWARE Corporation (1)
Ntt Shinagawa Twins Annex Bldg 1-9-1 Konan, Minato-ku, Tokyo, 108-8019, Japan
Tel.: (81) 354635776
Web Site: http://www.nttcom.co.jp
Sales Range: $1-4.9 Billion
Emp.: 5,293
Telecommunication Systems & Software Development
N.A.I.C.S.: 334290
Masato Kuroiwa (Sr Exec VP)

Subsidiary (Domestic):

NTT COMWARE BILLING SOLUTIONS CORPORATION (2)
3-7-10 Nishigotanda Urbannet Gotanda Nn Bldg 4f, Shinagawa-Ku, Tokyo, 141-0031, Japan
Tel.: (81) 337791600
Web Site: http://www.nttbgsol.com
Business Information Services
N.A.I.C.S.: 519290

NTT COMWARE HOKKAIDO CORPORATION (2)
7-3 Odorinishi Ntt Comware Sapporo Bldg, Chuo-Ku, Sapporo, 060-0042, Hokkaido, Japan
Tel.: (81) 112816360
Web Site: http://www.nttcom-hokkaido.co.jp
Communication System Software Development Services
N.A.I.C.S.: 541511

NTT COMWARE WEST CORPORATION (2)
1-2-12 Benten Ntt Comware Benten Bldg, Minato-Ku, Osaka, 552-0007, Japan
Tel.: (81) 665755311
Web Site: http://www.nttcom-west.co.jp
Telecommunication Software Development Services
N.A.I.C.S.: 541511

NTT INTERNET INC. (2)
Gotanda Brick Building 2-11-20 Nishigotanda, Shinagawa-ku, Tokyo, 141-0031, Japan
Tel.: (81) 368036111
Web Site: https://www.ntt-itn.co.jp
Sales Range: $75-99.9 Million
Emp.: 387
Software Development Services
N.A.I.C.S.: 541511

NTT Centerstance, Inc (1)
10200 SW Greenburg Rd Ste 340, Portland, OR 97223
Tel.: (503) 802-1200
Web Site: https://www.centerstance.com
Sales Range: $10-24.9 Million
Emp.: 70
Computer System Design Services
N.A.I.C.S.: 541512
Arne Kainu (Pres)

NTT Com Engineering Corporation (1)
1-2-1 Shibaura Seavans N Bldg, Minato-ku, Tokyo, 105-0023, Japan
Tel.: (81) 367371001
Web Site: https://www.ntteng.com
Network Services
N.A.I.C.S.: 513199

NTT Communications Corporation (1)
Otemachi Place West Tower 2-3-1 Otemachi, Chiyoda-ku, Tokyo, 100-8019, Japan (100%)
Tel.: (81) 36 700 3000
Web Site: https://www.ntt.com
Emp.: 9,000
Domestic & International Telecommunications Services
N.A.I.C.S.: 517111

Tetsuya Shoji (Pres & CEO)

Subsidiary (Non-US):

Arkadin SAS (2)
153 rue de Courcelles, 75017, Paris, France (91.2%)
Tel.: (33) 144652500
Web Site: http://www.arkadin.com
Audio, Web & Video Conferencing Services
N.A.I.C.S.: 517810
Christopher Reyes (Chief Sls & Mktg Officer)

Subsidiary (US):

Arkadin, Inc. (3)
1 Penn Plz Ste 2200, New York, NY 10119
Tel.: (646) 495-7600
Web Site: http://www.arkadin.com
Audio, Web & Video Conferencing Services
N.A.I.C.S.: 517810

Subsidiary (Domestic):

Conference Plus, Inc. (4)
1051 E Woodfield Rd, Schaumburg, IL 60173-4706
Tel.: (847) 413-3311
Web Site: http://www.conferenceplus.com
Sales Range: $25-49.9 Million
Emp.: 150
Audio Conferencing & Online Meeting Services
N.A.I.C.S.: 517810

Subsidiary (Non-US):

Atlas Information Technology, S.A. (2)
Balmes 114 5th Floor, 8008, Barcelona, Spain
Tel.: (34) 93 445 24 61
Web Site: http://www.atlasit.com
Information Technology Consulting Services
N.A.I.C.S.: 541512

Affiliate (Non-US):

Beijing Telecom NTT Engineering Co., Ltd. (2)
Rm 901 Metropolis Tower No 2 Haidian Dongsan Street, Haidian District, Beijing, 100080, China (49%)
Tel.: (86) 10 8286 1166
Web Site: http://www.bnte.com.cn
Sales Range: $25-49.9 Million
Emp.: 30
Telecommunication Services
N.A.I.C.S.: 517111

Subsidiary (Non-US):

Diversified Technology Solutions International, Inc. (2)
12F Zuellig Building Paseo de Roxas cor Makati Avenue, Makati, 1225, Philippines (50.1%)
Tel.: (63) 288568888
Web Site: http://www.dtsigroup.com
Sales Range: $25-49.9 Million
Emp.: 400
Computer System Integration Services
N.A.I.C.S.: 541519
Miguel Antonio C. Garcia (Pres & CEO)

Subsidiary (US):

Diversified Technology Solutions International, Inc. (3)
2415 E Camelback Rd, Phoenix, AZ 85016
Tel.: (602) 508-6128
Web Site: http://www.dtsigroup.com
Sales Range: $25-49.9 Million
Emp.: 4
Computer Systems Design Computer Related Services
N.A.I.C.S.: 541512
Miguel Antonio C. Garcia (Pres & CEO)

Subsidiary (Non-US):

Emerio GlobeSoft Pte. Ltd. (2)
Emerio House 50 Ubi Crescent 01-05 Ubi Tech Park, Singapore, 408568, Singapore
Tel.: (65) 63492999
Web Site: http://www.emeriocorp.com
Emp.: 500
Business Process Outsourcing Services
N.A.I.C.S.: 561499

Subsidiary (Non-US):

Emerio (Malaysia) Sdn. Bhd. (3)
Bangunan Emerio Cyberjaya Lingkaran Teknokrat 3 Barat, 63000, Cyberjaya, Darul Ehsan Selangor, Malaysia
Tel.: (60) 383184908
Web Site: http://www.emeriocorp.com
Business Process Outsourcing Services
N.A.I.C.S.: 561499
Michael Warren (Mng Dir)

Emerio (Thailand) Ltd. (3)
163 Surawongse Road, Bang Rak, Bangkok, 10500, Thailand
Tel.: (66) 263420702
Information Technology Consulting Services
N.A.I.C.S.: 541512

Emerio Australia Pty. Ltd. (3)
L 13 55 Clarence St, Sydney, 2000, NSW, Australia
Tel.: (61) 289158964
Information Technology Consulting Services
N.A.I.C.S.: 541512

Emerio Technologies Private Limited (3)
8th SKCL Central Square 2 Block 20 TVK Industrail Estate Guindy, Teynampet, Chennai, 600 032, India
Tel.: (91) 44 4292 9999
Sales Range: $10-24.9 Million
Emp.: 50
Business Process Outsourcing Services
N.A.I.C.S.: 561499
Sultan Aariff (Gen Mgr)

P.T. Emerio Indonesia (3)
Palma One 7th Floor Suite 707 Jl HR Rasuna Said Kav X-2 No 4, Jakarta, 12950, Indonesia
Tel.: (62) 21 252 5570
Sales Range: $25-49.9 Million
Emp.: 400
Business Process Outsourcing Services
N.A.I.C.S.: 561499
Michael Tanong (Pres)

Subsidiary (Non-US):

Frontline Systems Australia Pty Ltd (2)
Level 3 6 Bridge Street, Sydney, 2000, NSW, Australia
Tel.: (61) 2 9270 3400
Web Site: http://www.frontline.com.au
Sales Range: $25-49.9 Million
Emp.: 150
Information Technology Consulting Services
N.A.I.C.S.: 541512

Subsidiary (US):

NTT America, Inc. (2)
757 3rd Ave 14th Fl, New York, NY 10017 (100%)
Tel.: (212) 661-0810
Web Site: http://www.nttamerica.com
Sales Range: $200-249.9 Million
Emp.: 600
Communications Solutions; Private Network Services, Global IP Network Services & Data Center Services
N.A.I.C.S.: 517810

Branch (Domestic):

NTT America, Inc. (Washington Office) (3)
1100 13th St NW Ste 900, Washington, DC 20005
Tel.: (202) 312-1444
Web Site: http://www.ntt.co.jp
Sales Range: $25-49.9 Million
Emp.: 5
Telecommunication Services
N.A.I.C.S.: 517810

Subsidiary (Domestic):

NTT Multimedia Communications Laboratories, Inc. (3)
101 S Ellsworth Ave Ste 350, San Mateo, CA 94401
Tel.: (650) 579-0800
Sales Range: $25-49.9 Million
Emp.: 25
Developer of Wireless, IP & Security Solutions

INTERNATIONAL PUBLIC

N.A.I.C.S.: 541512

Subsidiary (Non-US):

NTT Australia Pty. Ltd. (2)
Level 13 55 Clarence Street, Sydney, 2000, NSW, Australia (100%)
Tel.: (61) 289158900
Web Site: http://www.au.ntt.com
Sales Range: $25-49.9 Million
Emp.: 100
Telecommunication Services
N.A.I.C.S.: 517111

Subsidiary (Domestic):

NTT BizLink, Inc. (2)
Sumitomo Korakuen Bldg 1-4-1 Koishikawa, Bunkyo-ku, Tokyo, 112-0002, Japan
Tel.: (81) 36 381 2610
Web Site: https://www.nttbiz.com
Emp.: 313
Video Conferencing Services
N.A.I.C.S.: 561499
Osamu Hanasaki (Exec Officer)

Subsidiary (Non-US):

NTT Com Asia Ltd. (2)
12/F Guardian House 32 Oi Kwan Road, Wanchai, China (Hong Kong)
Tel.: (852) 37930288
Web Site: hk.ntt.com
Sales Range: $100-124.9 Million
Emp.: 300
Telecommunication Services
N.A.I.C.S.: 517810
Taylor Man (CTO)

Subsidiary (Domestic):

HKNet Company Limited (3)
6 Chun Kwong Street, Tseung Kwan O Industrial Estate, Wanchai, China (Hong Kong)
Tel.: (852) 3793 0388
Web Site: http://www.hk.ntt.com
Internet Access Services
N.A.I.C.S.: 517810

Subsidiary (Domestic):

NTT Com CHEO Corporation (2)
7F Nippon Life Shinbashi Building 1-18-16 Shinbashi, Minato-Ku, Tokyo, 105-0004, Japan
Tel.: (81) 335395711
Web Site: https://www.nttcheo.com
Business Process Outsourcing Services
N.A.I.C.S.: 561499

Subsidiary (Non-US):

NTT Com Security AG (2) (94.68%)
Tel.: (49) 89 945 73 0
Web Site: http://www.nttcomsecurity.com
Emp.: 624
Holding Company; Computer Network & Data Security Products Mfr
N.A.I.C.S.: 551112

Subsidiary (Non-US):

NTT Com Security (Austria) GmbH (3)
Tel.: (43) 71090190
Web Site: http://www.integralis.co.uk
Computer Network & Data Security Product Mfr
N.A.I.C.S.: 541512

NTT Com Security (France) SAS (3)
Tel.: (33) 155581750
Computer Network & Data Security Product Mfr
N.A.I.C.S.: 541512

NTT Com Security (Germany) GmbH (3)
Tel.: (49) 89945730
Web Site: http://www.nttcomsecurity.com
Sales Range: $25-49.9 Million
Emp.: 220
Computer Network & Data Security Product Mfr
N.A.I.C.S.: 541512

NTT Com Security (Hong Kong) Ltd. (3)
Tel.: (852) 852 3468 8001
Data Security Services

AND PRIVATE COMPANIES **NIPPON TELEGRAPH & TELEPHONE CORPORATION**

N.A.I.C.S.: 541511

NTT Com Security (Japan) KK (3)
Tel.: (81) 3 6800 1533
Data Security Services
N.A.I.C.S.: 541511

NTT Com Security (Singapore) Pte Ltd. (3)
Tel.: (65) 64937650
Data Security Services
N.A.I.C.S.: 541511

NTT Com Security (Sweden) AB (3)
(100%)
Tel.: (46) 8 564 875 00
Computer Network & Data Security Product Mfr
N.A.I.C.S.: 541512

NTT Com Security (Switzerland) AG (3)
Tel.: (41) 43 477 70 10
Web Site: http://www.nttcomsecurity.com
Computer Network & Data Security Product Mfr
N.A.I.C.S.: 541512

NTT Com Security (UK) Limited (3)
Tel.: (44) 1189306060
Emp.: 170
Computer Network & Data Security Product Mfr
N.A.I.C.S.: 541512

NTT Com Security (US) Inc. (3)
Tel.: (860) 761-2900
Computer Network & Data Security Product Mfr
N.A.I.C.S.: 541512

Subsidiary (Domestic):

NTT Com Solution & Engineering Corp. (2)
1-2-1 Shibaura Seavans N-bldg 9th Floor, Minato-ku, Tokyo, 105-0023, Japan
Tel.: (81) 3 6737 1013
Web Site: http://www.nttcse.com
Emp.: 2,000
Communication Equipment Mfr & Whslr
N.A.I.C.S.: 334290

NTT ComTechnology Corporation (2)
3-26-33 Takanawa Shinagawa Bldg, Minato-ku, Tokyo, 108-0074, Japan
Tel.: (81) 3 6734 9100
Web Site: http://www.nttct.co.jp
Information Technology Consulting Services
N.A.I.C.S.: 541512

Subsidiary (Non-US):

NTT Communications (Thailand) Co., Ltd. (2)
946 Rama IV Rd Rm 601 Dusit Thani Bldg, Bangkok, 10500, Thailand (100%)
Tel.: (66) 22367227
Web Site: http://www.ntt.co.th
Sales Range: $25-49.9 Million
Emp.: 100
Telecommunication Servicesb
N.A.I.C.S.: 517111
Manabu Kahara (Pres)

NTT Communications (Vietnam) Ltd. (2)
Unit 1101 & 1102 11F Sailing Tower 51 Nguyen Thi Minh Khai, District 1, Ho Chi Minh City, Vietnam
Tel.: (84) 8 3827 3646
Web Site: http://www.vn.ntt.com
Emp.: 120
Telecommunication System Construction Engineering Services
N.A.I.C.S.: 237130
Tetsuya Shoji (Pres & CEO)

NTT Communications China Co., Ltd. (2)
8th Floor Hongxiang Building No 21 Huanghe Road, Huangpu District, Shanghai, 200003, China
Tel.: (86) 2133663939
Web Site: https://www.ntt.com.cn
Emp.: 350
Information Technology Consulting Services
N.A.I.C.S.: 541512

NTT Communications Deutschland GmbH (2)
Bleidenstr 6-10, Frankfurt am Main, 60311, Hessen, Germany
Tel.: (49) 6950506660
Telecommunication Support Services
N.A.I.C.S.: 517810

NTT Communications Philippines Corporation (2)
17th Floor Philamlife Tower 8767 Paseo de Roxas, 1226, Makati, Philippines
Tel.: (63) 2 403 2450
Web Site: http://www.ph.ntt.com
Sales Range: $25-49.9 Million
Emp.: 19
Information Technology Consulting Services
N.A.I.C.S.: 541512

NTT Communications Russia LLC (2)
Trekhprudny per 9 Bld 2 Business center on Trekhprudny Room 303-305, 123001, Moscow, Russia
Tel.: (7) 4956642356
Web Site: http://www.ru.ntt.com
Emp.: 17
Information Technology Consulting Services
N.A.I.C.S.: 541512
Jun Fujita (Gen Dir)

NTT Communications World Network (S) Pte Ltd (2)
20 West Pasir Panjang Road #11-28 Mapletree Business City, Singapore, 117439, Singapore
Tel.: (65) 64383101
Emp.: 200
Telecommunication System Installation Services
N.A.I.C.S.: 238210
Takeshi Kazami (CEO)

NTT Europe Ltd. (2)
3rd Floor Devon House, 58-60 St Katherines Way, London, E1W 1LB, United Kingdom (100%)
Tel.: (44) 2079771000
Web Site: http://www.eu.ntt.com
Sales Range: $25-49.9 Million
Emp.: 100
Telecommunication Servicesb
N.A.I.C.S.: 517111
Clive Hamilton (Mng Dir)

NTT Europe srl (2)
Avenue Manetorf 62, 28108, Madrid, Spain
Tel.: (34) 902250280
Web Hosting Services
N.A.I.C.S.: 518210

Subsidiary (Domestic):

NTT IF Corporation (2)
7-2-14 Toyo Mk Bldg 2f, Koto-Ku, Tokyo, 135-0016, Japan
Tel.: (81) 358572450
Web Site: http://www.nttif.com
Computer Software Development Services
N.A.I.C.S.: 541511

Subsidiary (Non-US):

NTT Korea Co., Ltd. (2)
28th Floor Two IFC Samsung-Dong, Kangnam-Ku, Seoul, 150-945, Korea (South) (100%)
Tel.: (82) 221569000
Web Site: http://www.kr.ntt.com
Sales Range: $25-49.9 Million
Emp.: 30
Telecommunication Servicesb
N.A.I.C.S.: 517111
Hideaki Niikura (Pres)

NTT MSC Sdn. Bhd. (2)
18th Floor UBN Tower No 10 Jalan P Ramlee, 50250, Kuala Lumpur, Malaysia (100%)
Tel.: (60) 320323208
Sales Range: $25-49.9 Million
Emp.: 80
Telecommunication Servicesb
N.A.I.C.S.: 517111

Subsidiary (Domestic):

NTT NaviSpace Corporation (2)
1-11-1 Nishiikebukuro Metropolitan Plz 12f, Toshima-Ku, Tokyo, 171-0021, Japan
Tel.: (81) 359530630
Web Site: http://www.nttnavi.co.jp
Advertising Agency Services
N.A.I.C.S.: 541810

NTT PC Communications, Inc. (2)
Shuwaonarimon Building 6 1-11 Shinbashi, Minato-ku, 105-0004, Tokyo, Japan (100%)
Tel.: (81) 3 3432 3868
Web Site: http://www.nttpc.co.jp
Sales Range: $5-14.9 Billion
Emp.: 605
IT Services & Solutions
N.A.I.C.S.: 541511
Motoo Tanaka (Pres & CEO)

NTT Resonant Inc. (2)
4-1-8F Granpark Tower Shibaura 3-chome, Minato-ku, Tokyo, 108-0023, Japan
Tel.: (81) 367036911
Web Site: http://www.ntt.co.jp
Sales Range: $100-124.9 Million
Emp.: 350
Business Application Services
N.A.I.C.S.: 518210

Subsidiary (Non-US):

NTT Singapore Pte. Ltd. (2)
20 West Pasir Panjang Road 11-28 Mapletree Business City, Singapore, 117439, Singapore (100%)
Tel.: (65) 68715400
Web Site: http://www.sg.ntt.com
Sales Range: $25-49.9 Million
Emp.: 80
Telecommunication Servicesb
N.A.I.C.S.: 517111
Naoki Wakai (Pres & CEO)

Subsidiary (Domestic):

NTT SmartTrade Inc. (2)
6F Resona Kudan Building 1-5-6 Kudan Minami, Chiyoda-ku, Tokyo, 102-0074, Japan
Tel.: (81) 335150765
Web Site: https://www.nttsmarttrade.co.jp
Online Money Transfer Services
N.A.I.C.S.: 522320

Subsidiary (Non-US):

NTT Taiwan Ltd. (2)
10F Tung Tai Plaza No 28 Ching Cheng St, Taipei, Taiwan (100%)
Tel.: (886) 225472565
Web Site: http://www.tw.ntt.com
Sales Range: $25-49.9 Million
Emp.: 30
Telecommunication Servicesb
N.A.I.C.S.: 517111

Subsidiary (Domestic):

NTT WORLD ENGINEERING MARINE CORPORATION (2)
1 Izuta-cho, Kanagawa-ku, Yokohama, 221-0032, Kanagawa, Japan
Tel.: (81) 45 453 3461
Web Site: https://www.nttwem.co.jp
Sales Range: $25-49.9 Million
Emp.: 120
Marine Engineering Services
N.A.I.C.S.: 541330
Masashi Kino (Pres & CEO)

NTT Worldwide Telecommunications Corporation (2)
4-1 Shibaura 3-chome, Minato-ku, Tokyo, 108-0023, Japan
Tel.: (81) 337981521
Web Site: http://www.nttwt.com
Data Processing Facilities Management Services
N.A.I.C.S.: 541513
Ryuichi Matsuo (Pres & CEO)

Subsidiary (Non-US):

NTT do Brasil Telecomunicacoes Ltda. (2)
Av Paulista 854-13 andar cj 136, Bela Vista, 01310-913, Sao Paulo, SP, Brazil (100%)
Tel.: (55) 1131451466
Web Site: http://www.br.ntt.com

Domestic & International Telecommunications Services
N.A.I.C.S.: 517111
Shinsuke Mizumori (Pres)

PT.NTT Indonesia (2)
Wisma 46 Kota BNI Ste 503, Jl Jend Sudirman Kav 1, Jakarta, 10220, Indonesia
Tel.: (62) 215727777
Web Site: http://www.ntt.co.id
Sales Range: $25-49.9 Million
Emp.: 150
Telecommunication Servicesb
N.A.I.C.S.: 517810
Mizuho Tada (Pres)

Subsidiary (US):

RagingWire Enterprise Solutions Inc (2)
PO Box 348060, Sacramento, CA 95834
Tel.: (916) 286-3000
Web Site: http://www.ragingwire.com
Sales Range: $10-24.9 Million
Emp.: 14
Internet Technology Services & Solutions
N.A.I.C.S.: 541990
Constantine S. Macricostas (Executives, Bd of Dirs)

Secure-24, LLC (2)
26955 NW Hwy Ste 200, Southfield, MI 48033
Tel.: (248) 784-1021
Web Site: http://www.secure-24.com
Information Security & Managed Hosting Services
N.A.I.C.S.: 518210
Shawn Peralta (CFO)

Subsidiary (Domestic):

Symmetry, LLC (3)
1201 N Prospect Ave, Milwaukee, WI 53202
Tel.: (414) 274-3100
Web Site: http://www.sym-corp.com
Sales Range: $10-24.9 Million
Data Processing & Technical Consulting Services
N.A.I.C.S.: 518210
Kevin Knuese (VP-SAP Solutions)

Affiliate (Non-US):

Shanghai NTT Telecommunications Engineering Co., Ltd. (2)
Rm 2202 China Communication Trade Building 357 Songlin Road, Pudong, Shanghai, 200122, China
Tel.: (86) 2158355918
Sales Range: $10-24.9 Million
Emp.: 40
Telecommunication Engineering Services
N.A.I.C.S.: 541330

Subsidiary (US):

Verio Inc. (2)
10 Corporate Dr Ste 300, Burlington, MA 01803
Tel.: (303) 645-1900
Web Site: http://www.verio.com
Sales Range: $1-4.9 Billion
Emp.: 2,900
Global Web Hosting & Internet Services
N.A.I.C.S.: 517810

Subsidiary (Non-US):

Verio Europe GmbH (3)
Neugablonzer Strasse 1, 93073, Neutraubling, Germany
Tel.: (49) 9401784000
Web Site: http://www.verio.de
Web Hosting & Internet Services
N.A.I.C.S.: 518210

Subsidiary (Domestic):

X-LISTING Co., Ltd. (2)
6F Kotobuki Park Building 1-20-8, Dogenzaka Shibuya-ku, Tokyo, 150-0043, Japan
Tel.: (81) 3 5728 1890
Web Site: http://www.xlisting.co.jp
Emp.: 33
Search Engine Optimization Services
N.A.I.C.S.: 519290

NTT DATA Group Corporation (1)
Toyosu Center Building 3-3 Toyosu

NIPPON TELEGRAPH & TELEPHONE CORPORATION

Nippon Telegraph & Telephone Corporation—(Continued)
3-chome, Koto-ku, Tokyo, 135-6033, Japan **(57.73%)**
Tel.: (81) 355468202
Web Site: https://www.nttdata.com
Rev.: $28,868,428,070
Assets: $47,720,425,690
Liabilities: $29,341,889,150
Net Worth: $18,378,536,540
Earnings: $884,874,090
Emp.: 193,500
Fiscal Year-end: 03/31/2024
Information Technology System Integration, Consulting, Network Development & Installation Services
N.A.I.C.S.: 541512
Yo Honma *(Pres & CEO)*

Subsidiary (Non-US):

Atom Technologies Ltd. (2)
FT Tower CTS 256 & 257 Suren Road Chakala, Andheri East, Mumbai, 400 093, Maharashtra, India **(55.35%)**
Tel.: (91) 2271814040
Web Site: http://www.atomtech.in
Sales Range: $100-124.9 Million
Emp.: 120
Mobile & Electronic Payment Services
N.A.I.C.S.: 522320
Dewang Neralla *(CEO)*

Subsidiary (Domestic):

Cats Co., Ltd. (2)
Kawaasa Bldg 2-11-5 Shin-Yokohama, Kohoku-Ku, Yokohama, 222-0033, Japan **(51.5%)**
Tel.: (81) 45 473 2816
Web Site: http://www.zipc.com
Software Development Services
N.A.I.C.S.: 541511
Akifumi Nakai *(CEO)*

Division (Domestic):

CATS CO., LTD - System Business Division (3)
751-2 Katsuta-Cho, Tsuzuki-Ku, Yokohama, 224-0034, Japan
Tel.: (81) 45 592 6581
Software Development Services
N.A.I.C.S.: 541511

Subsidiary (Domestic):

Clinical Support Corporation (2)
9-22-5 Higashigotanda, Shinagawa-ku, Tokyo, 141-0022, Japan
Tel.: (81) 354756111
Hospital Support Services
N.A.I.C.S.: 561499

DACS Co., Ltd. (2)
1-4-8 Kawaramachi, Chuo-ku, Osaka, 541-0048, Japan **(95%)**
Tel.: (81) 66 203 1401
Web Site: https://www.dacs.co.jp
Emp.: 286
Data Processing & Software Development Services
N.A.I.C.S.: 518210
Naofumi Sato *(Pres)*

Intra-mart CSI (2)
4th floor Akasaka Garden City 4-15-1 Akasaka, Minato-ku, Tokyo, 107-0052, Japan
Tel.: (81) 364347811
Web Site: https://www.im-csi.jp
Emp.: 60
Business Support Services
N.A.I.C.S.: 561499

JASTEC Co., Ltd. (2)
3-5-23 Takanawa, Minato-ku, Tokyo, 108-0074, Japan **(86.5%)**
Tel.: (81) 334460295
Web Site: https://www.jastec.co.jp
Sales Range: $125-149.9 Million
Emp.: 1,264
Software & System Sales
N.A.I.C.S.: 423420
Noboru Nakatani *(Pres & CEO)*

Subsidiary (Non-US):

LTU Technologies S. A. S. (3)
192 Rue de Rivoli, 75001, Paris, France
Tel.: (33) 153430168
Web Site: http://www.ltutech.com
Sales Range: $25-49.9 Million
Emp.: 10
Software Development Services
N.A.I.C.S.: 541511

Subsidiary (US):

LTU Technologies, Inc. (3)
232 Madison Ave Ste 1202, New York, NY 10016
Tel.: (646) 434-0273
Web Site: http://www.ltutech.com
Sales Range: $25-49.9 Million
Emp.: 30
Search Engine Optimization Services
N.A.I.C.S.: 519290

Joint Venture (Domestic):

JSOL Corporation (2)
Harumi Center Bldg 2-5-24 Harumi, Chuo-ku, Tokyo, 104-0053, Japan
Tel.: (81) 358596001
Web Site: http://www.jsol.co.jp
Sales Range: $400-449.9 Million
Emp.: 1,300
Information Technology Consulting & Management Services; Owned 50% by Nippon Telegraph & Telephone Corporation & 50% by Sumitomo Mitsui Financial Group, Inc.
N.A.I.C.S.: 541690
Masatoshi Maekawa *(Pres & CEO)*

Subsidiary (Domestic):

Media Drive Corporation (2)
NJK Building 2-3-4 Shintomi, Chuo-ku, Tokyo, 104-0041, Japan
Tel.: (81) 355419660
Web Site: http://www.mediadrive.jp
Software Development Services
N.A.I.C.S.: 541511

NJK Corporation (2)
2-3-4 Shintomi NJK Building, Chuo-ku, Tokyo, 104-0041, Japan **(100%)**
Tel.: (81) 35 117 1900
Web Site: https://www.njk.co.jp
Emp.: 816
Software Development Services
N.A.I.C.S.: 541511
Katsumasa Ishikawa *(Pres)*

Subsidiary (Non-US):

NTT DATA (CHINA) Co., Ltd. (2)
8F Tower A Phoenix Place 5A Shuguang Xili, Chaoyang District, Beijing, 100028, China
Tel.: (86) 1082856466
Web Site: http://china.nttdata.com
Sales Range: $550-599.9 Million
Emp.: 2,620
Strategic Planning, Advancement & Internal Control of Chinese Business; Offshore Development
N.A.I.C.S.: 561499
Yoshio Matsuzaki *(CEO)*

Subsidiary (Non-US):

NTT DATA CHINA OUTSOURCING CORPORATION (3)
3-3-9 Toyosu 26th floor of Toyosu Center Building Annex Toyosu, Koto-Ku, Tokyo, 135-0061, Japan **(100%)**
Tel.: (81) 355469443
Web Site: http://www.nttdata-china.co.jp
Sales Range: $25-49.9 Million
Emp.: 291
Sales & Liaison Functions for Offshore Development & Other Outsourcing Business
N.A.I.C.S.: 561499

Subsidiary (Domestic):

Wuxi NTT DATA Co., Ltd. (3)
No 180-16 Linghu Avenue, New District, Wuxi, 214135, Jiangsu, China
Tel.: (86) 510 8522 8110
Web Site: http://www.wxhx.com
Software Development Services
N.A.I.C.S.: 513210

Subsidiary (Domestic):

NTT DATA 3C Corporation (2)
41st Floor Shinjuku Island Tower 6-5-1 Shinjuku, Shinjuku-ku, Tokyo, 163-1341, Japan **(60%)**
Tel.: (81) 353396200
Web Site: http://www.nttdata3c.com
Information Technology Support Services
N.A.I.C.S.: 541519
Takehiro Yasuda *(Pres & CEO)*

NTT DATA Aurora Corporation (2)
1-14-5 Sendagaya Inte, Shibuya-ku, Tokyo, 151-0051, Japan
Tel.: (81) 367211092
Web Site: https://www.ntt-aurora.com
Emp.: 67
Software Development Services
N.A.I.C.S.: 541511

NTT DATA BILLING SERVICE CORPORATION (2)
NTTDATA Omori Sanno Building 1-3-5 Sanno, Ota-ku, Tokyo, 143-0023, Japan
Tel.: (81) 364518330
Web Site: https://www.nttdatabs.co.jp
Telecommunications Consulting Services
N.A.I.C.S.: 541618

NTT DATA BIZ INTEGRAL CORPORATION (2)
2nd floor Roppongi Yamada Building 3-5-27 Roppongi, Minato-ku, Tokyo, 106-0032, Japan
Tel.: (81) 362341661
Web Site: https://www.biz-integral.com
Emp.: 70
Computer Software Whslr
N.A.I.C.S.: 423430

NTT DATA BUSINESS SYSTEMS CORPORATION (2)
32nd floor Hareza Tower 1-18-1 Higashiikebukuro, Toshima-ku, Tokyo, 170-0013, Japan
Tel.: (81) 5036298209
Web Site: https://www.nttdata-bizsys.co.jp
Emp.: 1,248
Software Development Services
N.A.I.C.S.: 541511

NTT DATA CCS CORPORATION (2)
Shinagawa Seaside South Tower 4-12-1 Higashishinagawa, Shinagawa-ku, Tokyo, 140-0002, Japan
Tel.: (81) 357829500
Web Site: https://www.nttdata-ccs.co.jp
Emp.: 745
Software Development Services
N.A.I.C.S.: 541511

NTT DATA CHUGOKU CORPORATION (2)
NTTDATA Hijiyama Building 11-20 Hijiyamahonmachi, Minami-Ku, Hiroshima, 732-0816, Japan
Tel.: (81) 822523322
Web Site: https://www.nttdata-chugoku.co.jp
Data Communication Software Development Services
N.A.I.C.S.: 541511

NTT DATA CUBIT CORPORATION (2)
4-7-20 Kudamminami Kishisawa Bldg 5f, Chiyoda-Ku, Tokyo, 102-0074, Japan
Tel.: (81) 335125844
Web Site: http://corp.cubit.co.jp
Online Advertising Services
N.A.I.C.S.: 541613

NTT DATA CUSTOMER SERVICE CORPORATION (2)
32nd floor Toyosu Center Building Annex 3-3-9 Toyosu, Koto-Ku, Tokyo, 135-8178, Japan
Tel.: (81) 356902100
Web Site: https://www.nttdatacs.co.jp
Emp.: 1,080
Communication Software Development Services
N.A.I.C.S.: 541511

Subsidiary (Non-US):

NTT DATA EMEA Ltd. (2)
2 Royal Exchange, London, EC3V 3DG, United Kingdom **(100%)**
Tel.: (44) 20 7220 9200
Web Site: http://uk.nttdata.com
IT Management & Consulting Services
N.A.I.C.S.: 541519
Dean Gulzar *(Head-Insurance)*

Subsidiary (Non-US):

Intelligroup Europe Limited (3)

INTERNATIONAL PUBLIC

(100%)
Tel.: (44) 1908524130
Sales Range: $750-799.9 Million
Emp.: 80
Consulting, Information Technology & Outsourcing Services
N.A.I.C.S.: 541690

Subsidiary (Non-US):

NTT DATA Danmark A/S (4)
Tel.: (45) 70251020
Web Site: http://www.dk.nttdata.com
Emp.: 70
Consulting, Information Technology & Outsourcing Services
N.A.I.C.S.: 541690

Subsidiary (Non-US):

NTT DATA Europe GmbH & Co. KG (3)
Immermannstrasse 51-53, 40210, Dusseldorf, Germany
Tel.: (49) 11609370
Web Site: http://www.ntt-data-group.eu
Emp.: 4
Holding Company
N.A.I.C.S.: 551112

Subsidiary (Domestic):

NTT DATA Deutschland GmbH (4)
Hans-Dollgast-Strasse 26, 80807, Munich, Germany
Tel.: (49) 899 9360
Web Site: https://de.nttdata.com
Sales Range: $400-449.9 Million
Information Technology & Technical Consulting Services
N.A.I.C.S.: 541511
Dieter Loewe *(Chief Client Officer & Mng Dir-Clients & Markets)*

Subsidiary (Non-US):

NTT DATA Austria GmbH (5)
Rivergate-Gate 1 2 OG Handelskai 92, 1200, Vienna, Austria
Tel.: (43) 1240400
Web Site: http://at.nttdata.com
Sales Range: $75-99.9 Million
Emp.: 80
Information Technology & Technical Consulting Services
N.A.I.C.S.: 541511
Klaus Schmidt *(CEO)*

NTT DATA Switzerland AG (5)
Europa-Strasse 31, Glattbrugg, 8152, Switzerland
Tel.: (41) 584331111
Web Site: http://www.cirquent.ch
Information Technology & Technical Consulting Services
N.A.I.C.S.: 541512
Thomas Stoecker *(VP-Customer Mgmt)*

NTT DATA UK Consulting & IT Solutions Ltd. (5)
2 Royal Exchange, 58-60 St Katharines Way, London, EC3V 3DG, United Kingdom
Tel.: (44) 20 7220 9200
Web Site: http://www.cirquent.co.uk
Information Technology & Technical Consulting Services
N.A.I.C.S.: 541511
Patrizio Mapelli *(Pres & CEO-EMEA)*

Subsidiary (Domestic):

itelligence AG (4)
Koenigsbreede 1, D 33605, Bielefeld, Germany **(77.7%)**
Tel.: (49) 521914480
Web Site: http://www.itelligence.ag
Information Technology Consulting & Support Services
N.A.I.C.S.: 541690
Norbert Rotter *(CEO)*

Subsidiary (Non-US):

Servicios informaticos itelligence S.A. (5)
Tarragona 161 Planta 19, 08014, Barcelona, Spain
Tel.: (34) 93 4 67 46 90
Web Site: http://www.itelligence.es
Emp.: 93

AND PRIVATE COMPANIES — NIPPON TELEGRAPH & TELEPHONE CORPORATION

IT Services
N.A.I.C.S.: 423430
Juan Carlos Encio *(Dir Gen)*

itelligence AG (5)
The Circle 62, Zurich-Flughafen, 8058, Zurich, Switzerland
Tel.: (41) 447358555
Web Site: https://nttdata-solutions.com
IT Services
N.A.I.C.S.: 423430

itelligence B.V. (5)
Croy 1, NL-5653 LC, Eindhoven, Netherlands
Tel.: (31) 40 296 86 00
IT Services
N.A.I.C.S.: 423430
Camille Dongen *(Dir-Sls)*

itelligence Business Solutions (UK) Ltd. (5)
Unit E Silwood Park Buckhurst Road, Ascot, SL5 7PW, Berks, United Kingdom
Tel.: (44) 1344 297 600
Web Site: http://www.itelligence.ag
Information Technology Consulting & Support Services
N.A.I.C.S.: 541690

itelligence Business Solutions Canada, Inc. (5)
5160 Yonge St Ste 1810, North York, M2N 6L9, ON, Canada
Tel.: (416) 512-6784
IT Services
N.A.I.C.S.: 423430
Jason Mausberg *(Mng Dir)*

itelligence Sp. z o.o. (5)
Postepu Str 17 B, PL-02-676, Warsaw, Poland
Tel.: (48) 22 543 19 00
IT Services
N.A.I.C.S.: 423430
Wojciech Dabski *(Mgr-Sls)*

itelligence a.s
BB Centrum budova Beta 3 patro Vyskocilova 1481, 140 00, Prague, 4, Czech Republic
Tel.: (420) 251 611 921
IT Services
N.A.I.C.S.: 423430
David Krupka *(Dir-Sls)*

itelligence a/s (5)
Erhvervsbyvej 11, DK-8700, Horsens, Denmark
Tel.: (45) 70222166
IT Services
N.A.I.C.S.: 423430
Helle Bo Nielsen *(Mgr-Sls)*

Subsidiary (US):

itelligence, Inc. (5)
10856 Reed Hartman Hwy, Cincinnati, OH 45242
Tel.: (513) 956-2000
Web Site: https://nttdata-solutions.com
Sales Range: $100-124.9 Million
Emp.: 445
Information Technology Consulting & Support Services
N.A.I.C.S.: 541512

Subsidiary (Domestic):

Aster Group, Inc. (6)
434-B Copperfield Blvd, Concord, NC 28025
Tel.: (704) 426-9200
Web Site: http://www.astergroup.com
Business Technology Consulting Services
N.A.I.C.S.: 541690
Richard Cobb *(Co-Founder & CEO)*

Subsidiary (Domestic):

NTT DATA ENGINEERING SYSTEMS CORPORATION (2)
7-37-10 Nishikamata, Ota-ku, Tokyo, 144-8601, Japan
Tel.: (81) 35 711 5300
Web Site: https://www.nttd-es.co.jp
Emp.: 411
Software Development Services
N.A.I.C.S.: 541511
Kazuhisa Higashi *(Pres & CEO)*

NTT DATA FINANCIAL CORE CORPORATION (2)
Shiodome Shibari Palace Building 19th Floor 1-2-3, Kaigan Minato-ku, Tokyo, 105-0022, Japan
Tel.: (81) 343327465
Web Site: http://www.nttdfc.co.jp
Emp.: 616
Telecommunication Software Development Services
N.A.I.C.S.: 541511

NTT DATA FORCE CORPORATION (2)
2nd floor Nisso 18th Building 3-7-18 Shin-Yokohama, Kohoku-ku, Yokohama, 222-0033, Kanagawa, Japan (100%)
Tel.: (81) 454708335
Web Site: https://www.nttdata-force.co.jp
Emp.: 695
Software Development Services
N.A.I.C.S.: 541511

NTT DATA FRONTIER CORPORATION (2)
25th floor Area Shinagawa Building 1-9-36 Konan, Minato-ku, Tokyo, 108-0075, Japan
Tel.: (81) 5055566760
Web Site: https://www.nttd-fr.com
Emp.: 784
Software Development Services
N.A.I.C.S.: 541511

NTT DATA Getronics Corporation (2)
Shuwa Shiba Koen 3-Chome Building, 3-1-38 Shiba Koen Minato-ku, Tokyo, 105-0011, Japan (70%)
Tel.: (81) 354031001
Web Site: http://www.nttdata-getronics.co.jp
Sales Range: $125-149.9 Million
Emp.: 410
Financial Industry Information Technology Solutions
N.A.I.C.S.: 541512
Masashi Yanaka *(Exec VP)*

Subsidiary (Non-US):

NTT DATA HOKKAIDO CORPORATION (2)
(100%)
Tel.: (81) 112817002
Web Site: http://www.nttdata-hokkaido.co.jp
Emp.: 255
Telecommunication Servicesb
N.A.I.C.S.: 517810

Subsidiary (Domestic):

NTT DATA HOKURIKU CORPORATION (2)
Kanazawa Hikozo 111 Building 1-1-1 Hikosancho, Kanazawa, 920-0901, Ishikawa, Japan (100%)
Tel.: (81) 76 232 5000
Web Site: https://www.nttdata-hokuriku.co.jp
Emp.: 168
System Integration & Network Services
N.A.I.C.S.: 541512
Yoshiko Ikeda *(Pres)*

NTT DATA INTELLILINK CORPORATION (2)
1-15-7 Tsukishima Pacific Marks Tsukishma, Chuo-Ku, Tokyo, 104-0052, Japan
Tel.: (81) 358436800
Emp.: 1,401
Information Technology Consulting Services
N.A.I.C.S.: 541512

NTT DATA INTRAMART CORPORATION (2)
5F Akasaka Garden City 4-15-1, Minato-ku, Tokyo, 107-0052, Japan
Tel.: (81) 3 5549 2821
Web Site: http://www.intra-mart.jp
Emp.: 107
Computer Software Whslr
N.A.I.C.S.: 423430
Yoshihito Nakayama *(Pres)*

NTT DATA KANSAI CORPORATION (2)
3-1-21 Dojima NTTDATA Dojima Building, Kita-ku, Osaka, 530-0003, Japan
Tel.: (81) 66 455 3186
Web Site: https://www.nttdata-kansai.co.jp
Emp.: 1,002

Construction Software Development Services
N.A.I.C.S.: 541511
Fuji Koji *(Pres)*

NTT DATA KYUSHU CORPORATION (2)
1-17-21 Hakataekimae, Hakata-Ku, Fukuoka, 812-0011, Japan
Tel.: (81) 92 475 5123
Web Site: https://www.nttdata-kyushu.co.jp
Embedded Software Development Services
N.A.I.C.S.: 541511
Hideki Okada *(Pres)*

NTT DATA MSE CORPORATION (2)
Arena Tower 3-1-9, Shin-yokohama Kohoku-ku, Yokohama, 222-0033, Kanagawa, Japan
Tel.: (81) 454786910
Web Site: https://www.nttd-mse.com
Sales Range: $300-349.9 Million
Emp.: 1,400
Computer Software Development Services
N.A.I.C.S.: 541511
Hidenori Tsuzuki *(Pres)*

NTT DATA SBC Corporation (2)
2nd Nomura Building 6F Bingomachi 2-1-1, Chuo-ku, Osaka, 541-0051, Japan (80%)
Tel.: (81) 6 6221 2088
Web Site: http://www.nttdata-sbc.co.jp
Emp.: 396
Software Developer & Electronic Equipment & Software Evaluation Services
N.A.I.C.S.: 513210
Akiyoshi Nishijima *(Pres & CEO)*

NTT DATA SHIKOKU CORPORATION (2)
NBF Matsuyama Bank of Japan Building 7F 4-9-6, Sanbancho, Matsuyama, 790-0003, Ehime, Japan
Tel.: (81) 899476010
Web Site: https://www.nttdata-shikoku.co.jp
Emp.: 226
Software Development Services
N.A.I.C.S.: 541512
Miwako Akahane *(Pres)*

NTT DATA SHINETSU CORPORATION (2)
161-1 Nanase Nakamachi Harmony Nanase Building Main Building 2F, Nagano, 380-0904, Japan
Tel.: (81) 262237051
Web Site: https://www.nttdata-shinetsu.co.jp
Emp.: 113
Communication Equipment Maintenance Services
N.A.I.C.S.: 811210

NTT DATA SMIS Co,. Ltd. (2)
Sunshine 60 51st floor 3-1-1 Higashiikebukuro, Toshima-Ku, Tokyo, 170-6051, Japan
Tel.: (81) 339883111
Web Site: https://www.nttdata-smis.com
Emp.: 90
Marketing Research Service
N.A.I.C.S.: 541910

NTT DATA SMS CORPORATION (2)
Toyosu Center Building Annex 3F 3-3-9 Toyosu, Koto-Ku, Tokyo, 135-8678, Japan
Tel.: (81) 368035000
Web Site: https://www.nttdata-sms.co.jp
Emp.: 1,052
Telecommunication Construction Engineering Services
N.A.I.C.S.: 237130
Moritaka Watanabe *(CEO)*

NTT DATA SOFIA CORPORATION (2)
1-24-12 Orix Meguro Building 3F, Meguro Meguro-ku, Tokyo, 153-0063, Japan
Tel.: (81) 354373588
Web Site: https://www.nttdsofia.co.jp
Emp.: 638
Software Development Services
N.A.I.C.S.: 541511

Subsidiary (Non-US):

NTT DATA SOLFIS Korea Inc. (2)
NSNCORE Building 3F 1473 U-dong, Haeundae-gu, Busan, 612-020, Korea (South)

Tel.: (82) 51 742 4443
Web Site: http://www.itec-korea.co.kr
Telecommunication Equipment Maintenance Services
N.A.I.C.S.: 811210

Subsidiary (Domestic):

NTT DATA SYSTEM TECHNOLOGIES INC. (2)
4-5-1 Sakura Muromachi Building 10th Floor, Nihonbashi Muromachi Chuo-ku, Tokyo, 103-0022, Japan
Tel.: (81) 3 6202 0811
Web Site: http://www.nttdst.com
Emp.: 947
Communication Software Development Services
N.A.I.C.S.: 541511

NTT DATA TOHOKU CORPORATION (2)
21st floor of Sendai Trust Tower 1-9-1, Ichibancho Aoba-ku, Sendai, 980-0811, Miyagi, Japan
Tel.: (81) 22 721 5533
Web Site: http://www.nttdata-tohoku.co.jp
Emp.: 253
Information Technology Consulting Services
N.A.I.C.S.: 541512

NTT DATA TOKAI CORPORATION (2)
NTTDATA Fushimi Building 2-17-21 Nishiki, Naka-Ku, Nagoya, 460-0003, Aichi, Japan
Tel.: (81) 5055562801
Web Site: https://www.nttdata-tokai.co.jp
Construction Software Development Services
N.A.I.C.S.: 541511

NTT DATA Teranos Co. Ltd. (2)
Shinkawa KT Building 1-28-44 Shinkawa, Chuo-ku, Tokyo, 104-0033, Japan (51%)
Tel.: (81) 335511600
Web Site: http://www.nttd-teranos.com
Sales Range: $25-49.9 Million
Emp.: 97
Information Technology Services
N.A.I.C.S.: 519290
Mutsugu Ono *(Auditor)*

NTT DATA UNIVERSITY CORPORATION (2)
2-18-2 Komaba, Meguro-ku, Tokyo, 153-0041, Japan
Tel.: (81) 357383801
Web Site: https://www.nttdata-univ.co.jp
Sales Range: $10-24.9 Million
Emp.: 100
Computer Training Services
N.A.I.C.S.: 611420

NTT DATA WAVE CORPORATION (2)
Sendagaya Intes 1-14-5 Sendagaya, Shibuya-ku, Tokyo, 151-0051, Japan
Tel.: (81) 36 833 5900
Web Site: https://www.nttd-wave.com
Emp.: 446
Information Technology Consulting Services
N.A.I.C.S.: 541512
Humiharu Hanyuda *(Pres, CEO & Gen Mgr)*

NTT DATA i CORPORATION (2)
Iidabashi Building 1-18 Agebacho, Shinjuku-Ku, Tokyo, 162-0824, Japan (100%)
Tel.: (81) 3 6280 7800
Web Site: http://www.nttd-i.co.jp
Sales Range: $400-449.9 Million
Emp.: 1,950
Information Processing Software Development Services & Distr
N.A.I.C.S.: 541512
Tarou Kutsuna *(Exec VP)*

Subsidiary (US):

NTT DATA, Inc. (2)
100 City Sq, Boston, MA 02129
Tel.: (617) 241-9200
Web Site: http://www.us.nttdata.com
Sales Range: $1-4.9 Billion
Emp.: 18,000
Global IT Consulting & Systems Integration
N.A.I.C.S.: 541690
John M. Dick *(Gen Counsel & Exec VP-Legal)*

Subsidiary (Domestic):

Intelligroup Inc. (3)

NIPPON TELEGRAPH & TELEPHONE CORPORATION

Nippon Telegraph & Telephone Corporation—(Continued)
5 Independence Way Ste 220, Princeton, NJ 08540
Tel.: (646) 810-7400
Sales Range: $125-149.9 Million
Emp.: 2,101
Consulting, Technology & Outsourcing Services
N.A.I.C.S.: 541690

Subsidiary (Domestic):

Empower Solutions, Inc. (4)
5 Concourse Pkwy Ste 1420, Atlanta, GA 30328 (100%)
Tel.: (678) 332-5260
Web Site: http://www.empowersolutions.com
Sales Range: $75-99.9 Million
Management & Technology Consulting Services
N.A.I.C.S.: 541690

Subsidiary (Non-US):

Intelligroup Asia Private, Ltd. (4)
My Home Sarovar Plaza Ground Floor, Secretariat Road, Hyderabad, 500 063, Andhra Pradesh, India (99.8%)
Tel.: (91) 4067010775
Consulting, Information Technology & Outsourcing Services
N.A.I.C.S.: 541690

Unit (Domestic):

Keane Healthcare Solutions (3)
135 Engineers Rd Ste 110, Hauppauge, NY 11788
Tel.: (631) 582-2697
Sales Range: $25-49.9 Million
Emp.: 29
Healthcare IT Consulting Services
N.A.I.C.S.: 513210

Subsidiary (Domestic):

MISICOM, Inc. (3)
45 W 36th St 7th Fl, New York, NY 10018 (100%)
Tel.: (212) 355-5585
Web Site: http://www.misicompany.com
Sales Range: $100-124.9 Million
Emp.: 1,000
Information Technology Consulting & Integration Services; Technical Staffing Services
N.A.I.C.S.: 541690

NTT DATA AgileNet LLC (3)
4005 Miranda Ave Ste 150, Palo Alto, CA 94304 (100%)
Tel.: (650) 687-0635
Web Site: http://www.nttdata-agilenet.com
Sales Range: $25-49.9 Million
Emp.: 14
Market Research & Business Development Services
N.A.I.C.S.: 541715

NTT DATA Enterprise Services, Inc. (3)
5601 Granite Pkwy Ste 100, Plano, TX 75024
Tel.: (972) 915-0123
Web Site: http://americas.nttdata.com
Sales Range: $25-49.9 Million
Emp.: 200
Enterprise Technology Consulting Services
N.A.I.C.S.: 541690
Robb Rasmussen (Pres)

NTT DATA International LLC (3)
45 W 36th St 7th Fl, New York, NY 10018 (100%)
Tel.: (212) 588-8340
Web Site: http://www.nttdatai.com
Sales Range: $250-299.9 Million
Emp.: 700
Holding Company
N.A.I.C.S.: 551112

Unit (Domestic):

NTT DATA, Inc. - Federal Systems (3)
1660 International Dr Ste 300, McLean, VA 22102
Tel.: (703) 848-7200
Web Site: http://americas.nttdata.com

Custom Computer Programming Services
N.A.I.C.S.: 541511
John W. McCain (CEO)

Subsidiary (Domestic):

NTT Data Services, LLC (3)
7950 Legacy Dr Ste 900, Plano, TX 75024
Tel.: (972) 624-7920
Web Site: http://us.nttdata.com
Information Technology Consulting, Business Process Management & Computer Application Development Services
N.A.I.C.S.: 541512
Dan Allison (Pres-Healthcare & Life Sciences)

Subsidiary (Domestic):

Aspirent Consulting LLC (4)
6600 Peachtree Dunwoody Rd NE 400 Embassy Row Ste 260, Atlanta, GA 30328
Tel.: (770) 722-6891
Web Site: http://www.aspirent.com
Sales Range: $1-9.9 Million
Emp.: 53
Information Technology Consulting Services
N.A.I.C.S.: 541512
Andrew Wells (Co-Founder, CEO & Partner)

Net Esolutions Corporation (4)
8180 Greensboro Dr Ste 900, McLean, VA 22102
Tel.: (703) 893-6383
Web Site: http://www.nete.com
Sales Range: $200-249.9 Million
Emp.: 36
Business Management Software Consulting Services
N.A.I.C.S.: 541512
Jolly Vasani (Founder & Pres)

Planet Networks, Inc. (4)
1 Ivy Crest Lane Rockaway, Denville, NJ 07860
Tel.: (862) 300-3100
Web Site: http://www.planet.net
Wired Telecommunications Carriers
N.A.I.C.S.: 518210
Robert Boyle (CEO)

Subsidiary (Non-US):

Sierra Systems Group, Inc. (4)
1177 W Hastings St Ste 2500, Vancouver, V6E 2K3, BC, Canada
Tel.: (604) 688-1371
Web Site: http://www.sierrasystems.com
Sales Range: $100-124.9 Million
Emp.: 700
Holding Company; Information Technology & Management Consulting Services
N.A.I.C.S.: 551112
Patricia Kaiser (Sr VP)

Subsidiary (Domestic):

Sierra Systems Inc. (5)
117 W Hastings St Ste 2500, Vancouver, V6E 2K3, BC, Canada (100%)
Tel.: (604) 688-1371
Web Site: http://www.sierrasystems.com
Sales Range: $50-74.9 Million
Emp.: 100
Information Technology & Management Consulting Services
N.A.I.C.S.: 541611

Branch (US):

Sierra Systems - Austin (6)
901 S Mo-Pac Expy Ste 130, Austin, TX 78746
Tel.: (512) 583-2300
Web Site: http://www.sierrasystems.com
Management Consulting & Systems Integration Services
N.A.I.C.S.: 541611
Shelley Hodgson (Sr VP)

Branch (Domestic):

Sierra Systems - Calgary (6)
833 4th Ave SW 7th Floor, Calgary, T2P 3T5, AB, Canada
Tel.: (403) 264-0955
Web Site: http://www.sierrasystems.com
Sales Range: $50-74.9 Million
Emp.: 20
Management Consulting & Systems Integration Services

N.A.I.C.S.: 541611

Unit (Domestic):

Sierra Systems - Calgary Managed Services (6)
833-4th Avenue SW Canadian Centre 7th Floor, Calgary, T2P 3T5, AB, Canada
Tel.: (403) 264-0955
Web Site: http://www.sierrasystems.com
Sales Range: $10-24.9 Million
Information Technology Support & Staff Augmentation Services
N.A.I.C.S.: 541513

Branch (Domestic):

Sierra Systems - Edmonton (6)
10104 103rd Ave Ste 1300, Edmonton, T5J 0H8, AB, Canada
Tel.: (780) 424-0852
Web Site: http://www.sierrasystems.com
Sales Range: $50-74.9 Million
Emp.: 100
Management Consulting & Systems Integration Services
N.A.I.C.S.: 541611

Branch (US):

Sierra Systems - El Segundo (6)
222 N Sepulveda Blvd Ste 1310, El Segundo, CA 90245-5644
Tel.: (310) 536-6288
Web Site: http://www.sierrasystems.com
Management Consulting & Systems Integration Services
N.A.I.C.S.: 541611

Branch (Domestic):

Sierra Systems - Fredericton (6)
535 Beaverbrook Court Ste 120, Fredericton, E3B 1X6, NB, Canada
Tel.: (506) 451-9293
Management Consulting & Systems Integration Services
N.A.I.C.S.: 541611

Branch (US):

Sierra Systems - Hartford (6)
100 Pearl St 14th Fl, Hartford, CT 06103-4506
Tel.: (860) 249-7008
Management Consulting & Systems Integration Services
N.A.I.C.S.: 541611

Sierra Systems - Kirkland (6)
11109 Slater Ave NE Ste 200A, Kirkland, WA 98033
Tel.: (425) 688-7724
Web Site: http://www.sierrasystems.com
Sales Range: $50-74.9 Million
Emp.: 30
Management Consulting & Systems Integration Services
N.A.I.C.S.: 541611

Sierra Systems - Olympia (6)
111 Market St NE Ste 225, Olympia, WA 98501
Tel.: (360) 357-5668
Web Site: http://www.sierrasystems.com
Sales Range: $50-74.9 Million
Emp.: 20
Management Consulting & Systems Integration Services
N.A.I.C.S.: 541611

Branch (Domestic):

Sierra Systems - Ottawa (6)
275 Slater Street Suite 1800, Ottawa, K1P 5H9, ON, Canada
Tel.: (613) 236-7888
Web Site: http://www.sierrasystems.com
Management Consulting & Systems Integration Services
N.A.I.C.S.: 541611

Sierra Systems - Toronto (6)
150 York Street, Toronto, M5H 3S5, ON, Canada
Tel.: (416) 777-1212
Web Site: http://www.sierrasystems.com
Management Consulting & Systems Integration Services
N.A.I.C.S.: 541611

INTERNATIONAL PUBLIC

Sierra Systems - Victoria (6)
737 Courtney St, Victoria, V8W 1C3, BC, Canada
Tel.: (250) 385-1535
Web Site: http://www.sierrasystems.com
Sales Range: $75-99.9 Million
Emp.: 137
Management Consulting & Systems Integration Services
N.A.I.C.S.: 541611
Carl Yonkers (Pres)

Sierra Systems - Winnipeg (6)
444 St Mary Avenue Suite 1050, Winnipeg, R3C 3T1, MB, Canada
Tel.: (204) 942-2575
Web Site: http://www.sierrasystems.com
Management Consulting & Systems Integration Services
N.A.I.C.S.: 541611

Sierra Systems Group Inc. (6)
1809 Barrington Street Suite M100, Halifax, B3J 3K8, NS, Canada
Tel.: (902) 425-6688
Emp.: 28
Management Consulting & Systems Integration Services
N.A.I.C.S.: 541611

Subsidiary (Domestic):

The Revere Group, Ltd. (3)
325 N LaSalle Dr Ste 325, Chicago, IL 60654-4721 (60.2%)
Tel.: (312) 873-3400
Sales Range: $125-149.9 Million
Emp.: 450
Business Consulting & Information Technology Services
N.A.I.C.S.: 541512

Vectorform LLC (3)
3905 Rochester Rd, Royal Oak, MI 48073-2726
Tel.: (248) 777-7777
Web Site: http://www.vectorform.com
Sales Range: $10-24.9 Million
Emp.: 80
Digital Media Software, Services & Marketing
N.A.I.C.S.: 541519
Kurt Steckling (CEO)

Subsidiary (Domestic):

NTT Data Daichi Corporation (2)
18th floor of Toyosu Center Building 3-3-3 Toyosu, Koto-Ku, Tokyo, 135-6018, Japan
Tel.: (81) 50 5546 8539
Web Site: http://www.nttdata-daichi.co.jp
Emp.: 243
Information Technology Consulting Services
N.A.I.C.S.: 541512

Subsidiary (Non-US):

NTT Data Vertex Software Inc. (2)
130 King St W Exchange Tower Ste 3660, PO Box 366, Toronto, M5X 1E2, ON, Canada
Tel.: (888) 813-2047
Web Site: http://www.vertexsoft.com
Software Testing Services
N.A.I.C.S.: 541511

Subsidiary (Domestic):

Qunie Corporation (2)
Otemachi Place East Tower 11F 2-3-2 Otemachi, Chiyoda-ku, Tokyo, 100-8101, Japan (100%)
Tel.: (81) 33 517 2292
Web Site: https://www.qunie.com
Emp.: 900
Consulting, Technology & Outsourcing Services
N.A.I.C.S.: 541611
Shinya Takagi (Pres & CEO)

Realize Corporation (2)
6F CN-1 Building 5-5-2 Kiba, Koto-ku, Tokyo, 135-0042, Japan
Tel.: (81) 36 734 9888
Web Site: https://www.realize-corp.jp
Emp.: 100
Data Management Services
N.A.I.C.S.: 541512
Hiroshi Onishi (Pres)

XNET Corporation (2)

AND PRIVATE COMPANIES — NIPPON TELEGRAPH & TELEPHONE CORPORATION

4th Floor Sumitomo Fudosan building 13-4
Araki-cho, Shinjuku-ku, Tokyo, Japan
Tel.: (81) 353672201
Web Site: https://www.xnet.co.jp
Sales Range: $25-49.9 Million
Emp.: 183
Business Process Outsourcing Services
N.A.I.C.S.: 561439
Takehiko Motani *(Pres)*

NTT DOCOMO, Inc. (1)
Sanno Park Tower 11-1 Nagata-cho
2-chome, Chiyoda-ku, Tokyo, 100-6150,
Japan **(91.46%)**
Tel.: (81) 35 156 1111
Web Site: https://www.docomo.ne.jp
Wireless Telephone & Internet Services
N.A.I.C.S.: 334220
Seiji Maruyama *(Sr VP)*

Subsidiary (Non-US):

Buongiorno S.p.A. (2)
Borgo Masnovo 2, 43100, Parma, Italy
Tel.: (39) 0521 533111
Web Site: http://www.buongiorno.com
Emp.: 1,099
Mobile Phone Multimedia Distribution & Marketing Services
N.A.I.C.S.: 423430
Pietro De Nardis *(Head-B! Ventures)*

Subsidiary (Non-US):

Buongiorno Deutschland GmbH (3)
Sandstrasse 7-9, 80335, Munich, Germany
Tel.: (49) 89 45205200
Web Site: http://www.buongiorno.com
Mobile Phone Multimedia Distribution & Marketing Services
N.A.I.C.S.: 423430
Alessandro Pieraccini *(Head-Customer Acq-UK & Intl)*

Buongiorno France S.A.S. (3)
10 rue Treilhard, 75008, Paris, France
Tel.: (33) 155065555
Mobile Phone Multimedia Distribution & Marketing Services
N.A.I.C.S.: 423430

Buongiorno Hellas Ltd (3)
Favi 9, 11525, Athens, Greece
Tel.: (30) 2106725191
Sales Range: $25-49.9 Million
Emp.: 4
Mobile Phone Multimedia Distribution & Marketing Services
N.A.I.C.S.: 423430
Lia Mansola *(Country Mgr)*

Buongiorno UK Ltd (3)
57-63 Scrutton Street, London, EC2A 4PF, United Kingdom
Tel.: (44) 2076136000
Web Site: http://www.buongiorno.com
Sales Range: $25-49.9 Million
Emp.: 80
Mobile Phone Multimedia Distribution & Marketing Services
N.A.I.C.S.: 423430
Pietro Catello *(Mng Dir)*

Subsidiary (US):

Dada Entertainment Inc. (3)
757 3rd Ave Ste 16, New York, NY 10016
Tel.: (646) 257-4540
Web Site: http://www.dada-ent.com
Mobile Internet Products & Services
N.A.I.C.S.: 423430
Daniel Cohen *(Pres & CEO)*

Subsidiary (Non-US):

Dada Entertainment Canada Inc. (4)
300 - 150 Ferrand Drive, North York, M3C 3E5, ON, Canada
Tel.: (646) 502-8004
Newspaper Publishing Services
N.A.I.C.S.: 513110

Subsidiary (Non-US):

Tutch Mobile Media B.V. (3)
Sweelinckplein 9-11, 2517 GK, Hague, Netherlands
Tel.: (31) 703605500
Emp.: 30
Mobile Content Services
N.A.I.C.S.: 517810

iTouch Ltd. (3)
2nd Fl Avalon House, 57-63 Scrutton St, London, EC2A 4PF, United Kingdom **(100%)**
Tel.: (44) 2076136000
Web Site: http://www.buongiorno.com
Sales Range: $125-149.9 Million
Emp.: 50
Mobile Phone Information, Entertainment & Messaging Services
N.A.I.C.S.: 517112

Subsidiary (Non-US):

Buongiorno MyAlert S.A. (4)
Calle Javier Ferrero 13-15, Madrid, 28002, Spain
Tel.: (34) 911415100
Web Site: http://www.buongiorno.com
Mobile Phone Multimedia Distribution & Marketing Services
N.A.I.C.S.: 423430
Mabel Bernardo *(Head-Licensing)*

Subsidiary (Non-US):

Axis Mundi SA (5)
Humboldt 2495 Piso 10, C1425FUG, Buenos Aires, Argentina
Tel.: (54) 11 4774 6006
Digital Entertainment & Marketing Services
N.A.I.C.S.: 423430
Matias Martinez Nesi *(Country Mgr)*

Buongiorno MyAlert Brasil Servicios Celulares Ltda. (5)
Av Engenheiro Luis Carlos Berrini no 1748 Cj 2310, Brooklyn Novo, Sao Paulo, 04571-000, SP, Brazil
Tel.: (55) 11 55054595
Web Site: http://www.buongiorno.com
Mobile Phone Multimedia Distribution & Marketing Services
N.A.I.C.S.: 423430

MyAlert Mexico Servicios S.A. de CV (5)
Leon Tolstoi No 18 - PH, Col Anzures, Mexico, 11590, DF, Mexico
Tel.: (52) 5552037531
Mobile Phone Multimedia Distribution & Marketing Services
N.A.I.C.S.: 423430

iTouch Movilisto Portugal Lda (5)
Alameda dos Oceanos Lote 1.07.01 Escritorio Y1.2, Parque da Nacoes, 1990-203, Lisbon, Portugal
Tel.: (351) 21 324 25 70
Web Site: http://www.buongiorno.com
Sales Range: $25-49.9 Million
Emp.: 6
Mobile Phone Multimedia Distribution & Marketing Services
N.A.I.C.S.: 423430

Subsidiary (Non-US):

Buongiorno South Africa (Pty) Limited (4)
9th Floor The Terraces 34 Bree Street, Cape Town, 8001, South Africa
Tel.: (27) 214152100
Web Site: http://www.buongiorno.com
Mobile Phone Multimedia Distribution & Marketing Services
N.A.I.C.S.: 423430

Subsidiary (Domestic):

Business Expert Inc. (2)
3-16-3 Higashiikebukuro Urban Net Ikebukuro 4 Fl, Toshima-Ku, Tokyo, 170-0013, Japan
Tel.: (81) 359540717
Telecommunication Servicesb
N.A.I.C.S.: 517810

Subsidiary (Domestic):

Business Expert Kansai, Inc. (3)
1-4-12 Nonimbashi, Chuo-Ku, Osaka, 540-0011, Japan
Tel.: (81) 669440030
Telecommunication Servicesb
N.A.I.C.S.: 517810

Business Expert Kyushu, Inc. (3)
4-20-1 Chihaya, Higashi-Ku, Fukuoka, 813-0044, Japan
Tel.: (81) 926743311
Telecommunication Servicesb
N.A.I.C.S.: 517810

Business Expert Tokai Inc. (3)
1-14-11 Higashisakura, Higashi-Ku, Nagoya, 461-0005, Aichi, Japan
Tel.: (81) 529551400
Telecommunication Servicesb
N.A.I.C.S.: 517810

Subsidiary (Domestic):

D2C Inc. (2)
Siodome Sumitomo Building 18F 1-9-2
Higashi-Shimbashi, Minato-ku, Tokyo, 105-0021, Japan **(51%)**
Tel.: (81) 362523115
Web Site: http://www.d2c.co.jp
Sales Range: $100-124.9 Million
Emp.: 270
Mobile Marketing Communications Services
N.A.I.C.S.: 541810
Takayuki Hoshuyama *(Pres & CEO)*

Subsidiary (Non-US):

DOCOMO Beijing Communications Laboratories Co., Ltd. (2)
7/F Raycom Infotech Park Tower A No 2
Kexueyuan South Road, Haidian District, Beijing, 100190, China
Tel.: (86) 1082861501
Web Site: http://www.docomolabs.com.cn
Mobile Communication Research & Development Services
N.A.I.C.S.: 541715

Subsidiary (Domestic):

DOCOMO CS, Inc. (2)
Akasaka International Building 4-5 Akasaka, Minato-Ku, Tokyo, 107-0052, Japan **(100%)**
Tel.: (81) 3 5114 7611
Web Site: http://www.docomo-cs.co.jp
Emp.: 7,360
Telecommunication Equipment Maintenance Services
N.A.I.C.S.: 811210
IsaoHiro Kiyoshi *(Pres & CEO)*

Subsidiary (Domestic):

DOCOMO Engineering Chugoku, Inc. (3)
2-6-2 Shoko-Center Docomo Hiroshima
Shoko Bldg 6f, Nishi-Ku, Hiroshima, 733-0833, Japan
Tel.: (81) 825013201
Web Site: http://www.de-chugoku.nttdocomo.co.jp
Telecommunication Equipment Repair & Maintenance Services
N.A.I.C.S.: 811210

DOCOMO Engineering Hokkaido Inc. (3)
14-7 Odorinishi Nttodori 14 Chome Bldg, Chuo-Ku, Sapporo, 060-0001, Hokkaido, Japan
Tel.: (81) 11 252 6700
Web Site: http://www.docomoeng-h.com
Telecommunication Servicesb
N.A.I.C.S.: 517810
Yasukazu Fukushi *(Office Mgr)*

DOCOMO Engineering Kansai, Inc. (3)
1-6-111 Morinomiya Kintetsu Morinomiya Bldg, Joto-Ku, Osaka, 536-0025, Japan
Tel.: (81) 6 6967 1111
Web Site: http://www.docomoeg-kan.co.jp
Telecommunication Construction Engineering Services
N.A.I.C.S.: 237130

DOCOMO Engineering Shikoku Inc. (3)
9-12 Tenjimmae, Takamatsu, 760-0018, Kagawa, Japan
Tel.: (81) 878322112
Telecommunication Engineering Services
N.A.I.C.S.: 541330

DOCOMO Engineering Tokai Inc. (3)
1-10-9 Higashisakura Sakae Plaza Bldg 9f, Higashi-Ku, Nagoya, 461-0005, Aichi, Japan
Tel.: (81) 529592228

Engineering Services
N.A.I.C.S.: 541330

Subsidiary (US):

DOCOMO Capital, Inc. (2)
3240 Hillview Ave, Palo Alto, CA 94304
Tel.: (650) 493-9600
Web Site: http://www.docomocapital.com
Investment Management Service
N.A.I.C.S.: 523999

Subsidiary (Non-US):

DOCOMO Europe Limited (2)
1-King William Street, London, EC4N 7AR, United Kingdom **(100%)**
Tel.: (44) 3305887700
Web Site: https://www.docomo-europe.com
Sales Range: $25-49.9 Million
Emp.: 27
Holding Company; Regional Managing Office
N.A.I.C.S.: 551112

Subsidiary (Non-US):

DOCOMO Communications Laboratories Europe GmbH (3)
Landsberger Strasse 312, 80687, Munich, Germany **(100%)**
Tel.: (49) 8 956 8240
Web Site: https://www.docomolab-euro.com
Mobile Communication Technology Research Services
N.A.I.C.S.: 541715
Takatoshi Okagawa *(Pres, CEO & Mng Dir)*

Subsidiary (US):

DOCOMO Innovations, Inc. (2)
3240 Hillview Ave, Palo Alto, CA 94304
Tel.: (650) 494-2900
Web Site: http://www.docomoinnovations.com
Mobile Telecommunications Support Services
N.A.I.C.S.: 517810
Takashi Suzuki *(Pres & CEO)*

Subsidiary (Domestic):

DOCOMO Mobile Inc. (2)
2-4-5 Akasaka Kokusai Akasaka Bldg 7f, Minato-Ku, Tokyo, 107-0052, Japan
Tel.: (81) 351147111
Web Site: http://www.docomobile.co.jp
Telecommunication Equipment Distr
N.A.I.C.S.: 423690
Fumio Iwasaki *(Pres)*

Subsidiary (Domestic):

DOCOMO Mobile Tokai Inc. (3)
1-1-10 Higashisakura Urban Net Nagoya Bldg 8f, Higashi-Ku, Nagoya, 461-0005, Aichi, Japan
Tel.: (81) 529682006
Telecommunication Servicesb
N.A.I.C.S.: 517810

Subsidiary (Domestic):

DOCOMO Mobilemedia Kansai, Inc. (2)
1-11-4 Umeda Osaka Ekimae No 4 Bldg, Kita-Ku, Osaka, 530-0001, Japan
Tel.: (81) 663438801
Mobile Telecommunications Services
N.A.I.C.S.: 517112

Subsidiary (US):

DOCOMO PACIFIC, INC. (2)
890 S Marine Corps Dr, Tamuning, GU 96913
Tel.: (671) 688-2273
Web Site: https://www.docomopacific.com
Mobile Telecommunications Services
N.A.I.C.S.: 517112

Subsidiary (Domestic):

DOCOMO Service Inc. (2)
3-16-3 Higashiikebukuro Urban Net Ikebukuro Bldg 7f, Toshima-Ku, Tokyo, 170-0013, Japan
Tel.: (81) 359548800
Web Site: http://www.docomo-serv.co.jp
Temporary Staffing Services
N.A.I.C.S.: 561320

NIPPON TELEGRAPH & TELEPHONE CORPORATION

Nippon Telegraph & Telephone Corporation—(Continued)

Subsidiary (Domestic):

DOCOMO Service Chugoku, Inc. (3)
4-1-8 Otemachi Docomo Hiroshima Otemachi Bldg 20f, Naka-Ku, Hiroshima, 730-0051, Japan
Tel.: (81) 825441127
Web Site: http://www.docomo-sv-chugoku.co.jp
Telecommunication Support Services
N.A.I.C.S.: 561499

DOCOMO Service Hokkaido Inc. (3)
9-3-25 Chuodori Tsukisamu Docomo Service Bldg, Toyohira-Ku, Sapporo, 062-0020, Hokkaido, Japan
Tel.: (81) 11 836 6800
Web Site: http://www.docomosrv-h.co.jp
Mobile Communications Services
N.A.I.C.S.: 517112

DOCOMO Service Hokuriku Inc. (3)
12-8 Otemachi, Kanazawa, 920-0912, Ishikawa, Japan
Tel.: (81) 76 234 6070
Web Site: http://www.docomo-service-hokuriku.co.jp
Telecommunication Reseller Support Services
N.A.I.C.S.: 517121

DOCOMO Service Kansai Inc. (3)
1-6-111 Morinomiya Kintetsumorinomiya Bldg, Seongdong-gu, Osaka, 536-8558, Japan
Tel.: (81) 669688800
Web Site: http://www.d-sk.com
Telecommunication Equipment Whslr
N.A.I.C.S.: 423690

DOCOMO Service Kyushu Inc. (3)
4-29-22 Sumiyoshi Ntt Docomo Kyushu Sumiyoshi Bldg, Hakata-Ku, Fukuoka, 812-0018, Japan
Tel.: (81) 924365011
Web Site: http://www.docomo-sq.co.jp
Cellular Telephone Services
N.A.I.C.S.: 517112

DOCOMO Service Shikoku Inc. (3)
2-4-8 Nishikimachi, Takamatsu, 760-0020, Kagawa, Japan
Tel.: (81) 87 811 5811
Web Site: http://www.docomo-ss.co.jp
Telecommunication Data Processing Services
N.A.I.C.S.: 518210

DOCOMO Service Tohoku Inc. (3)
1-4-16 Tsutsujigaoka Docomo Sendai Bldg, Miyagino-Ku, Sendai, 983-0852, Miyagi, Japan
Tel.: (81) 222925322
Web Site: http://www.docomosev-th.co.jp
Communication Equipment Whslr
N.A.I.C.S.: 423690

DOCOMO Service Tokai Inc. (3)
1-1-10 Higashisakura Urban Net Nagoya Bldg 11f, Higashi-Ku, Nagoya, 461-0005, Aichi, Japan
Tel.: (81) 529531541
Web Site: http://www.docomo-st.co.jp
Telecommunication Servicesb
N.A.I.C.S.: 517810

Subsidiary (Domestic):

DOCOMO Support Co., Ltd. (2)
Akasaka Intercity AIR 24th Floor 1-8-1 Akasaka, Minato-Ku, Tokyo, 107-0052, Japan **(100%)**
Tel.: (81) 351147330
Web Site: http://www.docomo-support.co.jp
Sales Range: $150-199.9 Million
Emp.: 1,712
Online Business Support Services
N.A.I.C.S.: 561499
Kumagai Fumiya (Pres)

DOCOMO Systems, Inc. (2)
Kokusai Akasaka Bldg 5F 2-4-5 Akasaka, Minato-Ku, Tokyo, 107-0052, Japan **(100%)**
Tel.: (81) 351147401
Web Site: http://www.docomo-sys.co.jp
Rev.: $569,160,000
Emp.: 702

Development & Maintenance of Internal Information Systems & Sales of Hardware
N.A.I.C.S.: 541519
Seiji Nishikawa (Pres & CEO)

DOCOMO Tametan, Inc. (2)
2-4-5 Akasaka Kokusaiakasaka Bldg, Minato-Ku, Tokyo, 107-0052, Japan **(97.71%)**
Tel.: (81) 335603900
Telecommunication Servicesb
N.A.I.C.S.: 517810

DOCOMO Technology, Inc. (2)
16th floor Sanno Park Tower 2-11-1 Nagata-cho, Chiyoda-ku, Tokyo, 100-6150, Japan **(100%)**
Tel.: (81) 351147949
Web Site: https://www.docomo-tech.co.jp
Sales Range: $75-99.9 Million
Emp.: 593
Research & Development of Mobile Communication
N.A.I.C.S.: 541715

DOCOMO i Kyushu Inc. (2)
4-20-1 Chihaya Docomo Kashii Bldg, Higashi-Ku, Fukuoka, 813-0044, Japan
Tel.: (81) 92 663 7400
Web Site: http://www.docomo-i.co.jp
Mobile Telecommunications Services
N.A.I.C.S.: 517112

Subsidiary (Non-US):

DOCOMO interTouch Pte. Ltd. (2)
30A Kallang Place 12-06, Singapore, 339213, Singapore
Tel.: (65) 2212012
Web Site: https://www.intertouch.com
Sales Range: $25-49.9 Million
Emp.: 80
Internet Video Broadcasting Services
N.A.I.C.S.: 516210
Charles Reed (CEO)

Subsidiary (Non-US):

DOCOMO interTouch Australia Pty. Ltd. (3)
Unit 8 G/F Waterloo Business Park 44-48 O'Dea Avenue, Waterloo, 2017, NSW, Australia
Tel.: (61) 293130400
Web Site: http://www.docomointertouch.com
Emp.: 30
Broadband Internet Services
N.A.I.C.S.: 517810
Grant Wilkins (Gen Mgr)

Subsidiary (US):

Nomadix, Inc. (3)
21600 Oxnard St Fl 19, Woodland Hills, CA 91367 **(100%)**
Tel.: (818) 597-1500
Web Site: http://www.nomadix.com
Network Devices Mfr & Sales
N.A.I.C.S.: 334118
Kelly H. Hughes (Gen Counsel)

Subsidiary (US):

Global Ideas Direct LLC (2)
745 McClintock Dr Ste 220, Burr Ridge, IL 60527
Tel.: (708) 229-2424
Emp.: 20
Trimmer Mfr
N.A.I.C.S.: 332216
Deborah Goc (Mgr-Ops)

Subsidiary (Domestic):

INTAGE HOLDINGS Inc. (2)
INTAGE Akihabara Building 3 Kanda-Neribeicho, Chiyoda-ku, Tokyo, 101-0022, Japan **(51%)**
Tel.: (81) 352947411
Web Site: https://www.intageholdings.co.jp
Rev.: $393,595,380
Assets: $281,877,960
Liabilities: $80,107,380
Net Worth: $201,770,580
Earnings: $15,276,320
Emp.: 3,331
Fiscal Year-end: 06/30/2024
Holding Company; Business Solutions, Marketing, Marketing Research, Consulting & Management Services
N.A.I.C.S.: 561499

Noriaki Ishizuka (Pres)

Subsidiary (Domestic):

ANTERIO Inc. (3)
INTAGE Akihabara Bldg, 3 Kanda-Neribeicho Chiyoda-ku, Tokyo, 101-0022, Japan
Tel.: (81) 3 5294 8393
Web Site: http://www.anterio.co.jp
Sales Range: $25-49.9 Million
Emp.: 60
Healthcare Marketing & Research
N.A.I.C.S.: 541910
Yoshiya Nishi (Pres)

ASKLEP Inc. (3)
INTAGE Akihabara Bldg 3 Kanda-Neribeicho, Chiyoda-ku, 1018202, Tokyo, Japan
Tel.: (81) 359791001
Web Site: http://www.asklep.co.jp
Sales Range: $75-99.9 Million
Emp.: 200
Medical Marketing Research Services
N.A.I.C.S.: 541910
Yahagi Yuichi (Pres)

Subsidiary (Non-US):

A2 Healthcare Corporation (4)
3F No1 Sec 4 Renai Rd, Daan District, Taipei, 106, Taiwan
Tel.: (886) 287736997
Web Site: https://en.a2healthcare.com.tw
Business Support Services
N.A.I.C.S.: 561499

ASKLEP CHINA Inc. (4)
Jinling Haixin Building 14th Floor Suite A, No 666 Fuzhou Road Huangpu District, Shanghai, 200001, China
Tel.: (86) 21 6385 1333
Web Site: http://www.asklep-china.com
Business Support Services
N.A.I.C.S.: 561499

Subsidiary (Domestic):

ASKLEP Inc. (3)
NREG Midousuji Building 3-5-7 Kawaramachi Chuo-ku, 541-0048, Osaka, Japan
Tel.: (81) 6 4706 5088
Web Site: http://www.asklep.co.jp
Sales Range: $25-49.9 Million
Emp.: 35
Medical Marketing & Clinical Trials
N.A.I.C.S.: 541613
Yuichi Yahagi (Pres)

Subsidiary (Non-US):

Consumer Search Hong Kong Limited (3)
5/F Island Place Tower 510 Kings Road, North Point, China (Hong Kong)
Tel.: (852) 2891 6687
Web Site: http://www.csg-worldwide.com
Business Support Services
N.A.I.C.S.: 561499

FTA Research and Consultant, LLC (3)
1st Floor City Light Tower 45 Vo Thi Sau Street, Da Kao Ward District 1, Ho Chi Minh City, Vietnam
Tel.: (84) 8 3820 5558
Business Support Services
N.A.I.C.S.: 561499

INTAGE (Thailand) Co., Ltd. (3)
952 Ramaland Building 15th Floor Rama IV Road, Bangrak, Bangkok, 10500, Thailand
Tel.: (66) 26329945
Web Site: https://www.intage-thailand.com
Emp.: 800
Business Support Services
N.A.I.C.S.: 561499

Subsidiary (Domestic):

INTAGE Associates, Inc. (3)
3 Kanda Neribu-cho, Chiyoda-ku INTAGE Akihabara Building, Tokyo, 101-8204, Japan
Tel.: (81) 352948321
Web Site: https://www.intage-associates.jp
Sales Range: $75-99.9 Million
Emp.: 96
Marketing Research Service
N.A.I.C.S.: 541910

INTERNATIONAL PUBLIC

Subsidiary (Non-US):

INTAGE CHINA Inc. (3)
5th Floor Tower 2 Enterprise Centre 209 Gong He Road, Jing'an District, Shanghai, 200070, China
Tel.: (86) 2180310100
Business Support Services
N.A.I.C.S.: 561499

INTAGE INDIA Private Limited (3)
153 3rd Floor Okhla Industrial Estate Phase 3 Rd Okhla Phase III, Okhla, New Delhi, 110020, Haryana, India
Tel.: (91) 1141810000
Web Site: https://www.intage-india.com
Business Support Services
N.A.I.C.S.: 561499

Subsidiary (Domestic):

INTAGE Real World Inc (3)
13th floor Ochanomizu Sora City 4-6 Kanda, Surugadai Chiyoda-ku, Tokyo, 101-0062, Japan
Tel.: (81) 352945990
Web Site: https://www.intage-realworld.co.jp
Business Support Services
N.A.I.C.S.: 561499

INTAGE Research Inc. (3)
1-4-1 Honcho, Higashikurume, 203-0053, Tokyo, Japan **(100%)**
Tel.: (81) 424765300
Web Site: https://www.intage-research.co.jp
Sales Range: Less than $1 Million
Emp.: 128
Marketing Research Service
N.A.I.C.S.: 541910
Kiyoyuki Murakami (Pres)

Subsidiary (Non-US):

INTAGE SINGAPORE Pte. Ltd. (3)
105 Cecil Street 18-14 The Octagon, Singapore, 069534, Singapore
Tel.: (65) 62259604
Web Site: https://intage.sg
Business Support Services
N.A.I.C.S.: 561499

Subsidiary (Domestic):

INTAGE TECHNOSPHERE Inc. (3)
2-14-11 Yatocho, Nishi-Tokyo, 188-0001, Tokyo, Japan **(100%)**
Tel.: (81) 424231156
Web Site: https://www.intage-technosphere.co.jp
Emp.: 493
Marketing Research Service
N.A.I.C.S.: 541613

Kyowa Kikaku Ltd. (3)
8th Floor World Import Mart Building 1-3-1-3 Higashikebukuro, Toshima-ku, Tokyo, 170-8630, Japan
Tel.: (81) 359791400
Web Site: https://www.kk-kyowa.co.jp
Marketing & Advertising
N.A.I.C.S.: 541810
Atsushi Yamada (Pres)

PLAMED Inc. (3)
Yasaka Shijo Karasuma Building 10th floor 79 Higashiiri, Shijo-dori Muromachi Shimogyo-ku, Kyoto, 600-8009, Japan
Tel.: (81) 752221537
Web Site: https://www.plamed.co.jp
Business Support Services
N.A.I.C.S.: 561499

Subsidiary (Non-US):

PT INTAGE Indonesia (3)
Alamanda Tower 18th Floor Unit H JI TB Simatupang Kav, 23-24 Cilandak Barat, Jakarta, 12430, Indonesia
Tel.: (62) 2129660070
Web Site: https://www.intage-indonesia.com
Business Support Services
N.A.I.C.S.: 561499

Subsidiary (Domestic):

RPS Asklep Inc. (3)
World Import Mart Building 8th Floor, 3-1-1 Higashi-Ikebukuro Toshima-ku, Tokyo, 170-0013, Japan
Tel.: (81) 3 5979 1230
Business Support Services

N.A.I.C.S.: 561499

Subsidiary (Non-US):

Shanghai Harvest Market Consulting Co., Ltd. (3)
Enterprise Residence No 219 Gonghe Road, Jingan District, Shanghai, China
Tel.: (86) 13818186781
Pharmaceutical Mfr & Distr
N.A.I.C.S.: 325412

Subsidiary (Domestic):

dataSpring (3)
7F KOSUGI Building Shinjuku 1-28-11, Shinjuku-ku, Tokyo, 160-0022, Japan
Tel.: (81) 363800564
Web Site: http://www.d8aspring.com
Online Surveying Services
N.A.I.C.S.: 517810
Jun Uematsu (COO)

Subsidiary (Non-US):

MagiNet Interactive Ltd. (2)
Yue Xiu Bldg, Wanchai, China (Hong Kong)
Tel.: (852) 2511 3468
Emp.: 10
Telecommunication Servicesb
N.A.I.C.S.: 517810

May Shyh Corporation (2)
4 Fl No 74 Sec 2 Shinyi Rd Daan Chiu, Taipei, 10641, Taiwan
Tel.: (886) 2 23955818
Wireless Telecommunication Services
N.A.I.C.S.: 517112

Subsidiary (Domestic):

ORIX Credit Corporation (2)
Nissei Hamamatsucho Clare Tower 2-3-1 Hamamatsucho, Minato-ku, Tokyo, 105-0013, Japan (66%)
Tel.: (81) 425285701
Web Site: https://www.orixcredit.co.jp
Sales Range: $250-299.9 Million
Emp.: 300
Consumer Credit & Lending Products & Services; Owned 51% by Sumitomo Mitsui Financial Group, Inc. & 49% by ORIX Corporation
N.A.I.C.S.: 522299

Division (Domestic):

ORIX Club Card (3)
Tachikawa Center 2-22-20 Akebono-cho, Tachikawa, 190-8528, Japan
Tel.: (81) 425281811
Web Site: http://credit.orix.co.jp
Sales Range: $75-99.9 Million
Emp.: 162
Business Executive Loan Card Services
N.A.I.C.S.: 522299

Subsidiary (US):

PacketVideo Corporation (2)
10350 Science Center Dr Ste 210, San Diego, CA 92121-1138 (100%)
Tel.: (858) 731-5300
Web Site: http://www.packetvideo.com
Sales Range: $10-24.9 Million
Emp.: 135
Mobile Video Transmission Services
N.A.I.C.S.: 517810
Dann Wilkens (Sr VP-Design)

Subsidiary (Non-US):

Tecworld Limited (2)
Unit D 7/F Nathan Commercial Building 430 Nathan Road, Yau Ma Tei, Kowloon, China (Hong Kong)
Tel.: (852) 27141333
Telecommunication Servicesb
N.A.I.C.S.: 517810

NTT Data (China) Information Technology Co., Ltd. (1)
No 180-16 Linghu Avenue, Xinwu District, Wuxi, 214135, Jiangsu, China
Tel.: (86) 51085228110
Web Site: https://www.nttdata-it.com.cn
Software Development Services
N.A.I.C.S.: 541511

NTT Data Abic Co., Ltd. (1)
Akasaka Garden City 6F 4-15-1 Akasaka, Minato-ku, Tokyo, 107-0052, Japan
Tel.: (81) 364355980
Web Site: https://www.nttdata.abic.co.jp
Emp.: 66
Financial Management Consulting Services
N.A.I.C.S.: 541611

NTT Data Automobiligence Research Center, Ltd.
Plasteria Building 3rd Floor 3-1-4 Kohoku-ku, Shin-Yokohama, Yokohama, Kanagawa, Japan
Tel.: (81) 454732667
Web Site: https://www.zipc.com
System Development Services
N.A.I.C.S.: 541511

NTT Data BCU, INC. (1)
4911 Canada Way at Iris, Burnaby, V5G 3W3, BC, Canada
Tel.: (604) 291-9611
Web Site: https://www.bcgeu.ca
Information Technology Consulting Services
N.A.I.C.S.: 541512

NTT Data Been (China) Information Technology Co., Ltd. (1)
37F Office Tower 1 Forum66 No 1-1 Qinanian Da jie, Shenhe District, Shenyang, China
Tel.: (86) 2422505580
Web Site: https://www.nttdata-beencn.com
Emp.: 310
Software Design & Development Services
N.A.I.C.S.: 541511

NTT Data Been Corporation (1)
Toyosu Center Building 3-3-3 Toyosu, Koto-ku, Tokyo, 135-6002, Japan
Tel.: (81) 335366617
Web Site: https://nttdata-been.co.jp
Emp.: 430
Business Process Outsourcing Services
N.A.I.C.S.: 561110

NTT Data Been Service Corporation (1)
2-2 Ojikitamachi, Oita, 870-0005, Japan
Tel.: (81) 975378803
Web Site: https://been-service.co.jp
Emp.: 452
Information Technology Services
N.A.I.C.S.: 541512

NTT Data Belgique, SPRL (1)
Rue de Spa 8, 1000, Brussels, Belgium
Tel.: (32) 27885252
Information Technology Consulting Services
N.A.I.C.S.: 541512

NTT Data Business Solution (Thailand) Ltd. (1)
No 323 United Center Building 39th Floor Unit No 3903-4A Silom Road, Silom Subdistrict Bangrak District, Bangkok, 10500, Thailand
Tel.: (66) 22370553
Information Technology Consulting Services
N.A.I.C.S.: 541512

NTT Data Business Solutions AB (1)
Magnus Ladulasgatan 5, 118 65, Stockholm, Sweden
Tel.: (46) 841028320
Information Technology Consulting Services
N.A.I.C.S.: 541512

NTT Data Business Solutions AG (1)
Konigsbreede 1, 33605, Bielefeld, Germany
Tel.: (49) 521914480
Web Site: https://nttdata-solutions.com
Information Technology Development Services
N.A.I.C.S.: 541512

NTT Data Business Solutions B.V. (1)
Bolduc Gebouw A Utopialaan 50, 5232 CE, 's-Hertogenbosch, Netherlands
Tel.: (31) 889644000
Information Technology Consulting Services
N.A.I.C.S.: 541512

NTT Data Business Solutions Bilgi Sistemleri Anonim Sirketi (1)
Nidakule Atasehir Kuzey Is Merkezi Barbaros Mah, Begonya Sok No 3/A Atasehir, TR-34746, Istanbul, Turkiye
Tel.: (90) 2166000500

Information Technology Consulting Services
N.A.I.C.S.: 541512

NTT Data Business Solutions Global Managed Services Co., Ltd. (1)
No 1 Building 46 of Hengsheng Science Park, Tianning, Changzhou, 213017, Jiangsu, China
Tel.: (86) 51988859663
Web Site: https://nttdata-solutions.com
Custom Computer Programming Services
N.A.I.C.S.: 541618

NTT Data Business Solutions Global Managed Services GmbH
Philipp-Reis-Street 2 10, 2625, Bautzen, Germany
Tel.: (49) 359129520
Information Technology Consulting Services
N.A.I.C.S.: 541512

NTT Data Business Solutions Holding B.V. (1)
Bolduc Building A Utopialaan 50, NL-5232 CE, Den Bosch, Netherlands
Tel.: (31) 889644000
Information Technology Solutions Services
N.A.I.C.S.: 541512

NTT Data Business Solutions Inc. (1)
10856 Reed Hartman Hwy, Cincinnati, OH 45242
Tel.: (513) 956-2000
Information Technology Solutions Services
N.A.I.C.S.: 541512

NTT Data Business Solutions Incorporated (1)
2215 Steels Ave W PO, PO Box 304, Toronto, M3J 0J2, ON, Canada
Information Technology Consulting Services
N.A.I.C.S.: 541512

NTT Data Business Solutions International Holding GmbH (1)
Konigsbreede 1, 33605, Bielefeld, Germany
Tel.: (49) 521914480
Information Technology Consulting Services
N.A.I.C.S.: 541512

NTT Data Business Solutions Kft. (1)
Neumann Janos u 1 Infopark A ep, 1117, Budapest, Hungary
Tel.: (36) 14523800
Information Technology Consulting Services
N.A.I.C.S.: 541512

NTT Data Business Solutions Limited (1)
Boole House Beech Hill Office Campus, Clonskeagh, Dublin, Ireland
Tel.: (353) 2078321800
Information Technology Consulting Services
N.A.I.C.S.: 541512

NTT Data Business Solutions Ltd. (1)
12 Gough Square, London, EC4A 3DW, United Kingdom
Tel.: (44) 2078321800
Information Technology Consulting Services
N.A.I.C.S.: 541512

NTT Data Business Solutions MSC Sdn. Bhd. (1)
NTT MSC Momiji West Building No 43000 Persiaran APEC, 63000, Cyberjaya, Selangor, Malaysia
Tel.: (60) 383126200
Information Technology Solutions Services
N.A.I.C.S.: 541512

NTT Data Business Solutions Malaysia Sdn. Bhd. (1)
NTT MSC Momiji West Building No 43000 Persiaran APEC, 63000, Cyberjaya, Selangor, Malaysia
Tel.: (60) 383126200
Information Technology Consulting Services
N.A.I.C.S.: 541512

NTT Data Business Solutions Oy (1)
Alberga Business Park Bertel Jungin Aukio 1, 02600, Espoo, Finland
Tel.: (358) 406528715
Information Technology Consulting Services
N.A.I.C.S.: 541512

NTT Data Business Solutions ParticipaCoes S.A. (1)
100 SCN QD 04 Bloco B 1201, Distrito Federal, Brasilia, 70714-900, Brazil
Tel.: (55) 6135336454
Information Technology Consulting Services
N.A.I.C.S.: 541512

NTT Data Business Solutions Private Limited (1)
Plot No 35 SP 8th Floor Hallmark towers TS No 13, no 5 Alandur Villager Mambalam Thiru Vi Ka Industrial Estate Guindy, Chennai, 600032, India
Tel.: (91) 4461273800
Information Technology Consulting Services
N.A.I.C.S.: 541512

NTT Data Business Solutions S.A. (1)
C/ Tarragona 161 Planta 19, ES-08014, Barcelona, Spain
Tel.: (34) 934674690
Information Technology Solutions Services
N.A.I.C.S.: 541512

NTT Data Business Solutions S.A.S. (1)
Tour EQHO 2 Avenue Gambetta, 92400, Courbevoie, France
Tel.: (33) 140862231
Information Technology Consulting Services
N.A.I.C.S.: 541512

NTT Data Business Solutions Singapore Pte. Ltd. (1)
24 Sin Ming Lane 02-103, Midview City, Singapore, 573970, Singapore
Tel.: (65) 66590123
Information Technology Consulting Services
N.A.I.C.S.: 541512

NTT Data Business Solutions Sp. z o.o. (1)
Ul Pawia 9, 31-154, Krakow, Poland
Tel.: (48) 618167200
Information Technology Consulting Services
N.A.I.C.S.: 541512

NTT Data Business Solutions a.s. (1)
Hlinky 505/118, 603 00, Brno, Czech Republic
Tel.: (420) 543211723
Information Technology Consulting Services
N.A.I.C.S.: 541512

NTT Data Business Solutions s.p.r.l. (1)
Antwerpse Steenweg 330 V3, 2070, Zwijndrecht, Belgium
Tel.: (32) 889644000
Information Technology Consulting Services
N.A.I.C.S.: 541512

NTT Data Business Solutions s.r.o. (1)
Prievozska 4/C Apollo BC 2 Blok D, 821 09, Bratislava, Slovakia
Tel.: (421) 220911111
Information Technology Consulting Services
N.A.I.C.S.: 541512

NTT Data Chile Centers, Ltda. (1)
Rosario Norte 532 Piso 19 Las Condes, 7561185, Santiago, Chile
Tel.: (56) 224215300
Information Technology Consulting Services
N.A.I.C.S.: 541512

NTT Data Enterprise Services Holding, Inc. (1)
7950 Legacy Dr, Plano, TX 75024
Information Technology Consulting Services
N.A.I.C.S.: 541512

NTT Data Financial Technology Corporation (1)
Shiodome Shiba Rikyu Building 19F 1-2-3 Kaigan, Minato-ku, Tokyo, 105-0022, Japan
Tel.: (81) 343327465
Web Site: https://www.nttdft.com
Emp.: 1,906
Educational Consulting Services
N.A.I.C.S.: 611710

NTT Data Global Solutions Corporation (1)
Hamarikyu Mitsui Building 5-6-4 Tsukiji,

NIPPON TELEGRAPH & TELEPHONE CORPORATION

INTERNATIONAL PUBLIC

Nippon Telegraph & Telephone Corporation—(Continued)
Chuo-ku, Tokyo, 104-0045, Japan
Tel.: (81) 367465580
Web Site: https://www.nttdata-gsl.co.jp
System Analysis Program Development Services
N.A.I.C.S.: 541519

NTT Data Italia S.p.A. (1)
Via Calindri 4, 20143, Milan, Italy
Tel.: (39) 02831251
Information Technology Consulting Services
N.A.I.C.S.: 541512

NTT Data Luweave Corporation (1)
Shin-Otemachi Building 2F 2-2-1, Otemachi Chiyoda-ku, Tokyo, 100-0004, Japan
Tel.: (81) 335101091
Web Site: https://www.nttdata-luweave.com
Network Services
N.A.I.C.S.: 513199

NTT Data MCS Corporation (1)
2059 Matsudo, Matsudo, 271-0092, Chiba, Japan
Tel.: (81) 473654820
Web Site: https://www.mcserve.co.jp
Emp.: 114
System Development Services
N.A.I.C.S.: 541511

NTT Data MHI Systems Corporation (1)
NSS-II Building 2-13-34 Konan, Minato-ku, Tokyo, 108-0075, Japan
Tel.: (81) 368721900
Web Site: https://www.nttdata-mhis.co.jp
Emp.: 980
Information Technology Consulting Services
N.A.I.C.S.: 541512

NTT Data MSE Dalian Corporation (1)
11F No 1 Huixianyuan, Dalian, Liaoning, China
Tel.: (86) 41184761771
Web Site: https://www.nttd-mse-dl.com
Emp.: 120
Information Technology Consulting Services
N.A.I.C.S.: 541512

NTT Data Malaysia Sdn. Bhd. (1)
C-06-01 iTech Tower Jalan Impact Cyber 6, 63000, Cyberjaya, Selangor, Malaysia
Tel.: (60) 386010981
Information Technology Consulting Services
N.A.I.C.S.: 541512

NTT Data Management Service Corporation (1)
11th floor Toyosu Center Building 3-3-3 Toyosu, Koto-Ku, Tokyo, 135-6011, Japan
Tel.: (81) 355460868
Web Site: https://www.nttd-ms.co.jp
Emp.: 1,540
Business Process Outsourcing Services
N.A.I.C.S.: 561499

NTT Data Mathematical Systems Inc. (1)
1F Shinanomachi Rengakan 35, Shinanomachiv Shinjuku-ku, Tokyo, 160-0016, Japan
Tel.: (81) 333581701
Web Site: https://www.msi.co.jp
Emp.: 110
Software Consulting Services
N.A.I.C.S.: 541512

NTT Data Myanmar Co., Ltd. (1)
Building No17 1st Floor & 2nd Floor MICT Park University Campus, Hlaing Republic of the Union of Myanmar, Yangon, Myanmar
Tel.: (95) 9421141755
Web Site: https://www.careersnttdatamyanmar.com
Emp.: 200
Information Technology Consulting Services
N.A.I.C.S.: 541512

NTT Data NJK Corporation (1)
NJK Building 2-3-4 Shintomi, Chuo-ku, Tokyo, 104-0041, Japan
Tel.: (81) 351171900
Web Site: https://www.njk.co.jp
System Development Services
N.A.I.C.S.: 541511

NTT Data Newson Corporation (1)
NBF Akasaka Sanno Square 2-2-12 Akasaka, Minato-ku, Tokyo, 107-0052, Japan
Tel.: (81) 355458631
Web Site: https://www.newson.co.jp
Emp.: 526
Information Technology Consulting Services
N.A.I.C.S.: 541512

NTT Data Payment Services India Limited (1)
Plot No 4th Floor Suraksha Ace Building CST No 34/3 Village Chakala, 2-A Andheri-Kurla Rd Andheri East, Mumbai, 400059, Maharashtra, India
Tel.: (91) 2268074100
Web Site: https://www.nttdatapay.com
Digital Payment Solution Services
N.A.I.C.S.: 522320

NTT Data Philippines, Inc. (1)
28th Floor 88 Corporate Center, Salcedo Village, Makati, 1227, Philippines
Tel.: (63) 288896999
Information Technology Consulting Services
N.A.I.C.S.: 541512

NTT Data Sekisui Systems Corporation (1)
Umeda Center Building 2-4-12 Nakazaki Nishi, Kita Ward, Osaka, Japan
Tel.: (81) 663738112
Web Site: https://www.ndis.co.jp
Emp.: 392
Mobile Phone Services
N.A.I.C.S.: 517121

NTT Data Services Colombia S.A.S. (1)
Calle 97A N 13A-57 Building 14-97 Park, 110221, Bogota, Colombia
Tel.: (57) 15190919
Information Technology Consulting Services
N.A.I.C.S.: 541512

NTT Data Services Germany GmbH (1)
Lyoner Strabe 15, 60528, Frankfurt am Main, Germany
Tel.: (49) 69971940010
Information Technology Consulting Services
N.A.I.C.S.: 541512

NTT Data Singapore Pte. Ltd. (1)
9 Raffles Place 18-20/21 Republic Plaza II, Singapore, 048619, Singapore
Tel.: (65) 64884888
Information Technology Consulting Services
N.A.I.C.S.: 541512

NTT Data Smart Sourcing Corporation (1)
Toyosu Center Building Annex 4F 3-3-9 Toyosu, Koto-ku, Tokyo, 135-8677, Japan
Tel.: (81) 5055467860
Web Site: https://www.nttdata-smart.co.jp
Emp.: 2,109
Call Center Services
N.A.I.C.S.: 561422

NTT Data Spain, S.L.U. (1)
Camino Fuente de la Mora numero 1, 28050, Madrid, Spain
Tel.: (34) 917490000
Web Site: https://es.nttdata.com
Business Consulting Services
N.A.I.C.S.: 541611

NTT East Properties, Inc. (1)
2F NTT Toranomon Building 3-8-8 Toranomon, Minato-ku, Tokyo, Japan
Tel.: (81) 364528590
Web Site: https://www.ntt-p.co.jp
Emp.: 20
Real Estate Services
N.A.I.C.S.: 531210

NTT Electronics America, Inc. (1)
226 Airport Pkwy Ste 390, San Jose, CA 95110
Tel.: (408) 827-1633
Information Technology Consulting Services
N.A.I.C.S.: 541512

NTT Electronics Corporation (1)
New Stage Yokohama 1-1-32 Shinurashimacho, Kanagawa-ku, Yokohama, 221-0031, Kanagawa, Japan
Tel.: (81) 454149170
Web Site: http://www.ntt-electronics.com
Emp.: 558
Communication Equipment Mfr
N.A.I.C.S.: 334290
Kazuo Hagimoto (Pres & CEO)

Subsidiary (US):

NEL America, Inc. (2)
250 Pehle Ave Ste 706, Saddle Brook, NJ 07663
Tel.: (201) 556-1770
Web Site: http://www.nel-america.com
Optical Communication Component Whslr
N.A.I.C.S.: 423690
Atsushi Takahara (CEO)

Subsidiary (Domestic):

NTT Electronics Techno Corporation (2)
Aquaria Tower Yokohama 14th floor 1-1-32 Shinurashima-cho, Kanagawa-Ku, Yokohama, 221-0031, Kanagawa Prefecture, Japan
Tel.: (81) 454404281
Web Site: https://www.ntt-et.co.jp
Emp.: 137
Communication Equipment Mfr & Whslr
N.A.I.C.S.: 334290

NTT Electronics Europe S.R.L. (1)
Via Crescenzago 55, 20134, Milan, Italy
Tel.: (39) 0249537430
Information Technology Consulting Services
N.A.I.C.S.: 541512

NTT Electronics Hong Kong Limited (1)
Unit No 1518 15/F The Metropolis Tower No 10 Metropolis Drive HungHom, Kowloon, China (Hong Kong)
Tel.: (852) 31677345
Information Technology Consulting Services
N.A.I.C.S.: 541512

NTT Electronics Shenzhen Limited (1)
Room 705 T2 Kerry Plaza 1 Zhongxin 4th Road, Futian District, Shenzhen, 518048, Guangdong, China
Tel.: (86) 75583206522
Information Technology Consulting Services
N.A.I.C.S.: 541512

NTT FACILITIES, INC. (1)
Granparktower 3-4-1 Shibaura, Minato-ku, Tokyo, 108-0023, Japan (100%)
Tel.: (81) 354445111
Web Site: https://www.ntt-f.co.jp
Emp.: 5,300
General Contracting of Architecture, Building Structure, Telecommunications & Computer Related Power Supplies & Equipment; Facilities Maintenance; Security Services; Real Estate Development
N.A.I.C.S.: 531390
Nagahiro Kuroda (Sr Exec VP)

Subsidiary (Domestic):

NTT FACILITIES CHUGOKU, INC. (2)
14-15 Higashihakushimacho Ntt Kuredo Hakushima Bldg, Naka-Ku, Hiroshima, 730-0004, Japan
Tel.: (81) 82 212 3543
Facilities Support Services
N.A.I.C.S.: 561210

NTT FACILITIES CHUO, INC. (2)
3-4-1 Shibaura Grand Park Tower 28f, Minato-Ku, Tokyo, 108-0023, Japan
Tel.: (81) 3 5444 5282
Telecommunication Servicesb
N.A.I.C.S.: 517810

NTT FACILITIES FM ASSIST, INC. (2)
3-chome Mita MT Building, Minato-ku, Tokyo, 108-0073, Japan
Tel.: (81) 3 5444 2410
Web Site: http://www.ntt-fm.co.jp
Certified Facility Managers, Electrical Engineers & Architects
N.A.I.C.S.: 238210
Yoshifumi Ito (Pres)

NTT FACILITIES HOKKAIDO, INC. (2)
YouNet Bldg 10-1-21 kita 1-jo Nishi, Chuo-Ku, Sapporo, 060-0001, Hokkaido, Japan
Tel.: (81) 112077151
Web Site: http://www.ntt-f.co.jp
Telecommunication Construction Engineering Services
N.A.I.C.S.: 237130

Division (Domestic):

NTT FACILITIES INC - Business Creation Division (2)
Granparktower 3-4-1 Shibaura, Minato-ku, Tokyo, 108-0023, Japan
Tel.: (81) 3 54445080
Web Site: http://www.ntt-f.co.jp
Telecommunication Construction Management Services
N.A.I.C.S.: 237130

Subsidiary (Domestic):

NTT FACILITIES KANSAI, INC. (2)
1-4-14 Tosabori Urban Ace Higobashi Bldg, Nishi-Ku, Osaka, 550-0001, Japan
Tel.: (81) 664467550
Web Site: http://www.ntt-f.co.jp
Facilities Support Services
N.A.I.C.S.: 561210

NTT FACILITIES RESEARCH INSTITUTE Inc. (2)
3-9-11 Midori-cho, Musashino, 180-8585, Tokyo, Japan
Tel.: (81) 422562900
Web Site: http://www.ntt-fsoken.co.jp
Emp.: 121
Telecommunication Servicesb
N.A.I.C.S.: 517810

NTT FACILITIES TOHOKU, INC. (2)
3-2-1 Itsuhashi NTT Itobashi Second Building, Wakabayashi-Ku, Sendai, 984-8519, Miyagi, Japan
Tel.: (81) 22 214 3551
Web Site: http://www.ntt-f.co.jp
Telecommunication Construction Engineering Services
N.A.I.C.S.: 237130

NTT FACILITIES TOKAI, INC. (2)
Atsuta Media Wing 7-30 Gohonmatsu-cho, Atsuta-Ku, Nagoya, 456-0016, Aichi, Japan
Tel.: (81) 526834311
Web Site: http://www.ntt-f.co.jp
Facilities Support Services
N.A.I.C.S.: 561210

Subsidiary (US):

NTT FACILITIES USA, INC. (2)
2099 Gateway Pl Ste 300, San Jose, CA 95110
Tel.: (408) 436-2829
Web Site: http://www.nttf-us.com
Facility Management Services
N.A.I.C.S.: 561210
Soichiro Tsukuda (Pres & CEO)

Subsidiary (Domestic):

NTT GP-ECOcommunication, Inc. (2)
Grand Park Tower 22nd floor 3-4-1 Shibaura, Minato-Ku, Tokyo, 108-0023, Japan (75%)
Tel.: (81) 364363900
Web Site: http://www.ntt-gp.com
Business Consulting Services
N.A.I.C.S.: 541611
Imaizumi Masayoshi (Pres & CEO)

NTT Intelligent Planning & Development Co., Ltd. (2)
3-2-4 Iwamoto-cho, Chiyoda-Ku, Tokyo, 101-0032, Japan
Tel.: (81) 358232621
Web Site: http://www.nttipd.co.jp
Sales Range: $75-99.9 Million
Emp.: 130
Facility Management Services
N.A.I.C.S.: 561210
Hideo Maki (Pres & CEO)

NTT FINANCE CORPORATION (1)
Shinagawa Season Terrace 1-2-70, Konan Minato-ku, Tokyo, 108-0075, Japan
Tel.: (81) 364558810
Web Site: http://www.ntt-finance.co.jp
Emp.: 4,530
Financial Lending Services
N.A.I.C.S.: 522220

AND PRIVATE COMPANIES — NIPPON TELEGRAPH & TELEPHONE CORPORATION

Takahiro Mitsushima *(Exec VP & Exec Mgr-Corp IT Dept)*

NTT Facilities Engineering, Inc. (1)
MS Shibaura Bldg 4-13-23, Shibaura Minato-ku, Tokyo, 108-0023, Japan
Tel.: (81) 364354340
Information Technology Consulting Services
N.A.I.C.S.: 541512

NTT Finance Assets Service Corporation (1)
Aise Kanda Building 4F 1-24-4 Kandasuda-cho, Chiyoda-ku, Tokyo, 101-0041, Japan
Tel.: (81) 335271077
Web Site: https://ntt-fas.co.jp
Emp.: 9
Real Estate Asset Services
N.A.I.C.S.: 531390

NTT Global Data Centers Americas, Inc. (1)
PO Box 348060, Sacramento, CA 95834
Tel.: (916) 286-3000
Web Site: http://www.ragingwire.com
Data Center Services
N.A.I.C.S.: 518210
Douglas Adams *(Pres & CEO)*

NTT Global Data Centers EMEA (Pty.) Ltd. (1)
21 Sterling Road Samrand, Centurion, 0187, Gauteng, South Africa
Tel.: (27) 6978012190
Information Technology Solutions Services
N.A.I.C.S.: 541512

NTT Global Data Centers EMEA GmbH (1)
Voltastrasse 15, DE-65795, Hattersheim, Germany
Tel.: (49) 6978012110
Information Technology Consulting Services
N.A.I.C.S.: 541512

NTT Global Data Centers MAD1 S.L.U. (1)
Calle Aquisgran 2 Las Rozas De, Madrid, Spain
Tel.: (34) 6978012190
Information Technology Solutions Services
N.A.I.C.S.: 541512

NTT Global Data Centers Netherlands B.V. (1)
Aviolanda 1, 1437 ED, Rozenburg, Netherlands
Tel.: (31) 850764500
Information Technology Solutions Services
N.A.I.C.S.: 541512

NTT Global Data Centers Switzerland AG (1)
Hofwisenstrasse 56, PO Box 11, 8153, Rumlang, Switzerland
Tel.: (41) 448176500
Information Technology Solutions Services
N.A.I.C.S.: 541512

NTT Global Networks Inc (1)
5680 Greenwood Plz Blvd, Greenwood Village, CO 80111
Tel.: (720) 475-4000
Web Site: http://www.nttglobal.net
Wired Telecommunications Carriers
N.A.I.C.S.: 517111

NTT IT CORPORATION (1)
2-9-1 Furocho Kannai Waizu Bldg 4F, Naka-Ku, Yokohama, 231-0032, Kanagawa, Japan
Tel.: (81) 45 651 7561
Web Site: http://www.ntt-it.co.jp
Communication Equipment Whslr
N.A.I.C.S.: 423690

NTT Italia S.p.A. (1)
Via San Bovio 1-3, 20054, Segrate, Milan, Italy
Tel.: (39) 025539071
Information Technology Solutions Services
N.A.I.C.S.: 541512

NTT LOGISCO Inc. (1)
1-1-2 Heiwajima, Ota, Tokyo, 143-8530, Japan
Tel.: (81) 36 436 8111
Web Site: https://www.nttlogisco.jp
Emp.: 2,815
Logistics Consulting Servies

N.A.I.C.S.: 541614
Akihiko Higashi *(Pres)*

NTT LePerc Co., Ltd. (1)
NTT Ueno Building 4F 5-24-1 Ueno, Taito-ku, Tokyo, 110-0005, Japan
Tel.: (81) 358178501
Web Site: https://www.le-perc.co.jp
Emp.: 45
Land Utilization Consulting Services
N.A.I.C.S.: 541620

NTT Learning Systems Corporation. (1)
1-6-15 Minami-Azabu, Minato-Ku, Tokyo, 106-8566, Japan
Tel.: (81) 354402716
Web Site: http://www.nttls.co.jp
Emp.: 492
Educational Support Services
N.A.I.C.S.: 611710

NTT MARKETING ACT CORPORATION (1)
NTT West Shinkyo-bashi building 5F 4-15-82 Higashinoda-machi, Miyakojima-ku, Osaka, 534-0024, Japan
Tel.: (81) 120050513
Web Site: http://www.nttact.com
Marketing Consulting Services
N.A.I.C.S.: 541613

NTT Malaysia Solutions Sdn. Bhd. (1)
Level 11 1 First Avenue Bandar Utama, 47800, Petaling Jaya, Selangor, Malaysia
Tel.: (60) 377298966
Information Technology Consulting Services
N.A.I.C.S.: 541512

NTT Managed Services Americas, LLC (1)
4000 Town Ctr Ste 200, Southfield, MI 48075
Tel.: (248) 784-1021
Information Technology Consulting Services
N.A.I.C.S.: 541512

NTT Netherlands B.V. (1)
Veemweg 23-25, 3771 MT, Barneveld, Netherlands
Tel.: (31) 342402400
Information Technology Solutions Services
N.A.I.C.S.: 541512

NTT Nexia Corporation (1)
14-7 Odori Nishi NTT East Japan Odori 14-chome Building 10F, Chuo-ku Hokkaido, Sapporo, 060-0042, Japan
Tel.: (81) 112121111
Web Site: https://www.ntt-nexia.co.jp
Emp.: 6,700
Information Technology Solutions Services
N.A.I.C.S.: 541511

NTT Poland Sp. z o.o. (1)
Sienna 73, 00-833, Warsaw, Poland
Tel.: (48) 225535500
Information Technology Consulting Services
N.A.I.C.S.: 541512

NTT Printing Corporation (1)
Urban Net Irifune Building 3-2-10 Irifune, Chuo-ku, Tokyo, 104-0042, Japan
Tel.: (81) 364537436
Web Site: https://www.nttprint.com
Emp.: 665
Printing Services
N.A.I.C.S.: 513130

NTT Publishing Co., Ltd. (1)
3-4-1 Shibaura Grand Park Tower 14F, Minato-ku, Tokyo, 108-0023, Japan
Tel.: (81) 354341020
Web Site: http://www.nttpub.co.jp
Books Publishing Services
N.A.I.C.S.: 513130

NTT Research, Inc. (1)
940 Stewart Dr, Sunnyvale, CA 94085
Tel.: (650) 579-0800
Web Site: https://www.ntt-research.com
Research Services
N.A.I.C.S.: 541715

NTT Risk Manager Corporation (1)
3-19-2 Nishi-Shinjuku, Shinjuku-ku, Tokyo, 163-8019, Japan
Tel.: (81) 353593711
Web Site: https://ntt-rm.co.jp
Human Resource Consulting Services

N.A.I.C.S.: 541612
NTT Security Corp (1)
Akihabara UDX Building Soto Kanda 4 14 1, Tokyo, Chiyodaku, Japan
Tel.: (81) 362629130
Cyber Security Services
N.A.I.C.S.: 513210
Matthew Gyde *(CEO)*

Subsidiary (Non-US):

NTT Security (Germany) GmbH (2)
Adolf-Grimme-Allee 3, 50829, Cologne, Germany
Tel.: (49) 22196757400
Web Site: http://www.nttsecurity.com
Security Products for Internet & intranet Applications Marketing Network
N.A.I.C.S.: 561621

Subsidiary (Domestic):

NTT Security (Japan) KK (2)
4-14-1 Sotokanda, Chiyoda-ku, Tokyo, 101-0021, Japan
Tel.: (81) 362629130
Web Site: http://www.nttsecurity.com
Emp.: 190
Security Products for Internet & intranet Applications Marketing Network
N.A.I.C.S.: 561621

NTT Security Holdings Corporation (1)
14-1 Soto-Kanda Akihabara UDX Bldg 20th South Floor 4 Chome, Chiyoda-ku, Tokyo, 101-0021, Japan
Tel.: (81) 362629100
Web Site: https://www.security.ntt
Digital Solution Services
N.A.I.C.S.: 541512

NTT Singapore Solutions Pte. Ltd. (1)
12 Kallang Avenue Aperia The Annex 04-28/29, Singapore, 339511, Singapore
Tel.: (65) 62259188
Information Technology Consulting Services
N.A.I.C.S.: 541512

NTT Smile Energy Co., Ltd. (1)
4F Yodoyabashi Square 2-6-18 Kitahama, Chuo-ku, Osaka, 541-0041, Japan
Tel.: (81) 662211234
Web Site: https://nttse.com
Remote Monitoring Equipment Whslr
N.A.I.C.S.: 423450

NTT Software Corporation (1)
2-16-4 Konan Minato-ku, Minato-ku, Tokyo, Japan
Tel.: (81) 357827000
Web Site: http://www.nttsoft.com
Rev.: $450,933,840
Emp.: 1,522
Software Development Services
N.A.I.C.S.: 541511
Shinichi Yamada *(Pres & CEO)*

Subsidiary (Domestic):

NTT SOFT SERVICE Corp. (2)
2-1-6 Tarumachi, Kohoku-Ku, Yokohama, 222-0001, Kanagawa, Japan
Tel.: (81) 45 540 3272
Web Site: http://www.ntts-sv.co.jp
Emp.: 180
Software Development Services
N.A.I.C.S.: 541511
Tajiri Kazuo *(Pres)*

NTT Solutions (Thailand) Limited (1)
16th Floor Column Tower 199 Ratchadapisek Road, Klongtoey, Bangkok, 10110, Thailand
Tel.: (66) 26250988
Information Technology Consulting Services
N.A.I.C.S.: 541512

NTT TC Leasing Co., Ltd. (1)
1-2-70 Konan Shinagawa Season Terrace 13th floor, Minato-ku, Tokyo, Japan
Tel.: (81) 364558511
Web Site: https://www.ntt-tc-lease.com
Emp.: 1,100
Leasing Services
N.A.I.C.S.: 532210

NTT TRAVEL SERVICE CO., LTD. (1)
5-24-11 Ueno NTT Ueno Building 4/5F, Taito-Ku, Tokyo, 110-0005, Japan
Tel.: (81) 35 818 5525
Web Site: https://www.ntt-ts.co.jp
Sales Range: $25-49.9 Million
Emp.: 98
Travel Arrangement Services
N.A.I.C.S.: 561599
Shuji Ota *(Pres & CEO)*

NTT Taiwan Solutions Limited (1)
Floor 14 No 188 Section 5 Nanjing East Road, Taipei, Taiwan
Tel.: (886) 221713333
Information Technology Consulting Services
N.A.I.C.S.: 541512

NTT TechnoCross Corporation (1)
Granpark Tower 15F 3-4-1, Shibaura Minato-ku, Tokyo, 108-8202, Japan
Tel.: (81) 358602900
Web Site: https://www.ntt-tx.com
Emp.: 1,885
Information Technology Solutions Services
N.A.I.C.S.: 541511

NTT Town Page Corporation (1)
NTT Toranomon Building 3-8-8 Toranomon, Minato-ku, Tokyo, 105-0001, Japan
Tel.: (81) 2385240530
Web Site: https://www.ntt-tp.co.jp
Emp.: 1,200
Digital Services
N.A.I.C.S.: 541810

NTT Urban Development Asset Management Corporation (1)
1-5-1 Otemachi, Chiyoda, Tokyo, 100-0004, Japan
Tel.: (81) 362629400
Web Site: https://www.nttud-am.co.jp
Real Estate Manangement Services
N.A.I.C.S.: 531190

NTT Urban Development Corporation (1)
Akihabara UDX 14-1 Sotokanda 4-chome, Chiyoda-ku, Tokyo, 101-0021, Japan
Tel.: (81) 368116300
Web Site: https://www.nttud.co.jp
Emp.: 480
Real Estate Acquisition, Disposition, Management, Leasing, Brokerage & Appraisal Services; Building Design & Construction
N.A.I.C.S.: 531390
Masayuki Kusumoto *(Chief Design Officer & Sr Exec VP-Branch Mgmt)*

Subsidiary (Domestic):

NTT Urban Development Builservice Co. (2)
Grand Park Tower 3-4-1 Shibaura, Minato-ku, Tokyo, 108-0023, Japan
Tel.: (81) 363840600
Web Site: https://www.ntt-uvs.com
Emp.: 560
Construction Management Services
N.A.I.C.S.: 541618

NTT Urban Development Hokkaido BS Co. (2)
7-3-1 Kita1jonishi Nostel Sapporo Bldg, Chuo-Ku, Sapporo, 060-0001, Hokkaido, Japan
Tel.: (81) 112225300
Building Maintenance Services
N.A.I.C.S.: 561730

NTT Urban Solutions Research Institute, Inc. (1)
Akihabara UDX 4-14-1 Sotokanda, Chiyoda-ku, Tokyo, 101-0021, Japan
Tel.: (81) 362607545
Web Site: https://www.ntt-us.com
Information Technology Consulting Services
N.A.I.C.S.: 541512

NTT Urban Solutions, Inc. (1)
11F Akihabara UDX Sotokanda 4-14-1, Chiyoda-ku, Tokyo, 101-0021, Japan
Tel.: (81) 363811111
Web Site: https://www.ntt-us.com
Emp.: 6,500
Business Solutions Services
N.A.I.C.S.: 541611

NTT Urban Value Support, Inc. (1)
Grand Park Tower 3-4-1 Shibaura, Minato-ku, Tokyo, 108-0023, Japan

NIPPON TELEGRAPH & TELEPHONE CORPORATION

Nippon Telegraph & Telephone Corporation—(Continued)
Tel.: (81) 363840600
Web Site: https://www.ntt-uvs.com
Emp.: 560
Building Construction & Design Services
N.A.I.C.S.: 541310

NTTCom Online Marketing Solutions Corporation (1)
4F Osaki Center Building 1-5-1 Osaki, Shinagawa-ku, Tokyo, 141-0032, Japan
Tel.: (81) 343308415
Web Site: https://www.nttcoms.com
Telecommunication Servicesb
N.A.I.C.S.: 517810

Natuvion GmbH (1)
Altrottstrasse 31, 69190, Walldorf, Germany
Tel.: (49) 6227731400
Web Site: https://www.natuvion.com
Emp.: 300
Digital Technology Services
N.A.I.C.S.: 541512

Nihilent Australia Pty. Limited (1)
Level 2 Dimension Data Offices Darling Park Tower 3 201 Sussex Street, Sydney, 2000, NSW, Australia
Tel.: (61) 426188258
Global Consulting Services
N.A.I.C.S.: 541611

Nihilent Limited (1)
4th Floor D Block Weikfield IT Citi Infopark Nagar Road, Pune, 411014, Maharashtra, India
Tel.: (91) 2039846100
Web Site: https://www.nihilent.com
Global Consulting Services
N.A.I.C.S.: 541611

Nihon Meccs Co.,Ltd. (1)
3 Chome-6-3 Irifune, Chuo-ku, Tokyo, 104-0042, Japan
Tel.: (81) 355415511
Web Site: https://www.meccs.co.jp
Emp.: 1,552
Building Construction & Design Services
N.A.I.C.S.: 541310

Nippon Car Solutions Co., Ltd. (1)
Akihabara UDX 9th floor 4-14-1 Sotokanda, Chiyoda-ku, Tokyo, 101-0021, Japan **(40.5%)**
Tel.: (81) 352072000
Web Site: https://www.ncsol.co.jp
Emp.: 1,126
Automobile Leasing Services
N.A.I.C.S.: 532112

Nippon Information & Communication Corporation (1)
St Luke's Garden Tower 15F 8-1 Akashi-cho, Chuo-ku, Tokyo, 104-0044, Japan **(50%)**
Tel.: (81) 362781111
Web Site: http://www.niandc.co.jp
Sales Range: $450-499.9 Million
Emp.: 1,193
Software Development Services
N.A.I.C.S.: 541511
Yujiro Hirose (Pres & CEO)

Subsidiary (Domestic):

NIandC NETSYSTEM Inc. (2)
580 Solid Square West Building 15F 580 Horikawacho, Saiwai-ku, Kawasaki, 212-0013, Japan
Tel.: (81) 44 556 8540
Web Site: http://www.niandcnetsystem.co.jp
Emp.: 171
Information Technology Consulting Services
N.A.I.C.S.: 541512
Hideki Yamauchi (Pres)

NIandC SOFT Inc. (2)
Akashi-cho 6-4 Nichirei Akashi-cho Building 2F, Chuo-ku, Tokyo, 104-0044, Japan
Tel.: (81) 362781212
Web Site: http://www.nicsoft.co.jp
Emp.: 155
Software Development Services
N.A.I.C.S.: 513210
Shiro Yuki (Pres)

Nippon Telegraph & Telephone East Corporation (1)
19-2 Nishi-shinjuku 3-Chome, Shinjuku, Tokyo, 163-8019, Japan **(100%)**
Tel.: (81) 353593711
Web Site: http://www.ntt-east.co.jp
Sales Range: $1-4.9 Billion
Emp.: 6,350
Multimedia, Information & Telecommunications Services
N.A.I.C.S.: 517111
Fukuzo Inoue (Pres)

Subsidiary (Domestic):

AIREC ENGINEERING CORPORATION (2)
Next Sight Asakusa Building 1-4-4 Kaminarimon, Taito-Ku, Tokyo, 111-0034, Japan
Tel.: (81) 338458109
Web Site: https://www.airec.co.jp
Environmental Engineering Services
N.A.I.C.S.: 541330

NIPPON AIRPORT RADIO SERVICE CO., LTD. (2)
2112 Komaino NTT Narita International Airport Building, Narita, 282-0021, Chiba, Japan
Tel.: (81) 476328883
Web Site: https://www.airportradio.co.jp
Emp.: 20
Airport Wireless Telecommunication Services
N.A.I.C.S.: 517112
Yoshikazu Takahashi (Pres & CEO)

NTT CARD SOLUTION CORP. (2)
Higashi 2-2-8 Sphere Tower Tennoz 18F, Shinagawa-ku, Tokyo, 140-0002, Japan
Tel.: (81) 364339490
Web Site: http://www.ntt-card.co.jp
Prepaid Card Mfr & Distr
N.A.I.C.S.: 522210

Subsidiary (Non-US):

NTT EAST-CHIBA CORPORATION (2)
Tel.: (81) 432742129
Web Site: http://www.ntteast-chiba.co.jp
Telecommunication Servicesb
N.A.I.C.S.: 517810

Subsidiary (Domestic):

NTT EAST-GUNMA CORPORATION (2)
3 Takamatsucho, Takasaki, 370-0829, Gunma, Japan
Tel.: (81) 273260646
Web Site: http://www.ntteast-gunma.co.jp
Telecommunication Equipment Maintenance Services
N.A.I.C.S.: 811210

Subsidiary (Non-US):

NTT EAST-HOKKAIDO CORPORATION (2)
Tel.: (81) 112124850
Web Site: http://www.ntteast-hokkaido.co.jp
Telecommunication Equipment Repair & Maintenance Services
N.A.I.C.S.: 811210

Subsidiary (Domestic):

NTT EAST-IBARAKI CORPORATION (2)
8-8 Kitamicho, Mito, 310-0061, Ibaraki, Japan
Tel.: (81) 292312186
Web Site: http://www.ntteast-ibaraki.co.jp
Telecommunication Servicesb
N.A.I.C.S.: 517810

NTT EAST-KANAGAWA CORPORATION (2)
198 Yamashitacho, Naka-Ku, Yokohama, 231-0023, Kanagawa, Japan
Tel.: (81) 452266011
Web Site: http://www.ntteast-kanagawa.com
Telecommunication Servicesb
N.A.I.C.S.: 517810

NTT EAST-NIIGATA CORPORATION (2)
1017-1 Higashiboridori 7 Bancho, Chuo-Ku, Niigata, 951-8519, Japan
Tel.: (81) 252276651
Web Site: http://www.ntteast-niigata.co.jp
Telecommunication Servicesb
N.A.I.C.S.: 517810

NTT EAST-SAITAMA CORPORATION (2)
5-8-17 Tokiwa, Urawa-Ku, Saitama, 330-0061, Japan
Tel.: (81) 486265099
Web Site: http://www.ntteast-saitama.co.jp
Telecommunication Construction Engineering Services
N.A.I.C.S.: 237130

NTT EAST-TOCHIGI CORPORATION (2)
4-3-27 Higashisukugo, Utsunomiya, 321-0953, Tochigi, Japan
Tel.: (81) 286324462
Web Site: http://www.tochigi116.com
Communication Equipment Distr
N.A.I.C.S.: 423690

NTT EAST-TOKYO CORPORATION (2)
1-5-1 Kita-Shinjuku, Shinjuku-Ku, Tokyo, 169-0074, Japan
Tel.: (81) 356889102
Web Site: http://www.ntteast-tokyo.com
Business Support Services
N.A.I.C.S.: 561499

Subsidiary (Non-US):

NTT EAST-YAMAGATA CORPORATION (2)
Tel.: (81) 236219511
Web Site: http://www.ntteast-yamagata.co.jp
Communication Equipment Repair Services
N.A.I.C.S.: 811210

Subsidiary (Domestic):

NTT HOKKAIDO TELEMART CO., LTD. (2)
6-2-22 Minami22jonishi Emuzu Minami22jo No 2 Bldg, Chuo-Ku, Sapporo, 064-0922, Hokkaido, Japan
Tel.: (81) 11 530 5200
Web Site: http://www.telemart.jp
Business Process Outsourcing Services
N.A.I.C.S.: 561499

NTT InfraNet Co., Ltd. (2)
Next Site Higashi Nihonbashi Building 1-8-1 Higashi Nihonbashi, Chuo-ku, Tokyo, 103-0004, Japan
Tel.: (81) 363816400
Web Site: https://www.nttinf.co.jp
Sales Range: $700-749.9 Million
Emp.: 1,530
Engineeering Services
N.A.I.C.S.: 541330

NTT MediaCross, Inc. (2)
8-5-43 Akasaka Futaba Akasaka Bldg, Minato-Ku, Tokyo, 107-0052, Japan
Tel.: (81) 3 5786 6900
Web Site: http://www.nttmc.co.jp
Data Processing Services
N.A.I.C.S.: 518210

NTT Plala Inc. (2)
24th Floor Sunshine 60 3-1-1 Higashi Ikebukuro, Toshima-ku, Tokyo, 170-6024, Japan
Tel.: (81) 359547257
Web Site: http://www.nttplala.com
Sales Range: $50-74.9 Million
Emp.: 394
Telecommunications
N.A.I.C.S.: 517810

NTT RENTAL ENGINEERING CO., LTD. (2)
2-9-7 Iwamotocho, Chiyoda-Ku, Tokyo, 101-0032, Japan
Tel.: (81) 120915809
Web Site: http://www.nttrec.co.jp
Communication Equipment Rental Services
N.A.I.C.S.: 532490

NTT Solco (2)
Sumitomo Fudosan Hibiya Bldg 2-8-6 Nishishimbashi, Minato-ku, Tokyo, 105 0003, Japan
Tel.: (81) 355320120
Web Site: http://www.solco.co.jp
Sales Range: $400-449.9 Million
Emp.: 1,000
Information Retrieval Services
N.A.I.C.S.: 518210

INTERNATIONAL PUBLIC

Hiroshi Makino (VP)

NTT TELECON CO., LTD. (2)
Next Site Asakusa Building 2F 1-4-4 Kaminarimon, Taito-ku, Tokyo, 111-0034, Japan
Tel.: (81) 358066111
Web Site: https://www.ntt-tc.co.jp
Telecommunication Safety System Mfr
N.A.I.C.S.: 334513

NTT Vietnam K.K. (2)
15-5 Kandanishiki-cho 3-chome, Chiyoda-ku, Tokyo, 101 0054, Japan **(100%)**
Tel.: (81) 3 5217 2255
Sales Range: $25-49.9 Million
Emp.: 6
Management Consulting Services
N.A.I.C.S.: 541618

NTT-ME CORPORATION (2)
3-21-14 Higashiikebukuro NTT Shin-Ikebukuro Building, Toshima-Ku, Tokyo, 170-0013, Japan
Tel.: (81) 339852121
Web Site: http://www.ntt-me.co.jp
Emp.: 4,750
Information Technology Consulting Services
N.A.I.C.S.: 541512
Hideo Fujimoto (Pres)

NTT-ME SERVICE CORPORATION (2)
1-21-4 Takadanobaba No 5 Miike Bldg, Shinjuku-Ku, Tokyo, 169-0075, Japan
Tel.: (81) 352861711
Web Site: http://www.ntt-mes.co.jp
Telecommunication Facility Construction Services
N.A.I.C.S.: 237130
Yohei Fukuyama (Gen Mgr)

Nippon Telematique Inc. (2)
4th floor Hatsudai TN Building 1-34-14 Hatsudai, Shibuya-Ku, Tokyo, 151-0061, Japan
Tel.: (81) 353511511
Web Site: https://www.nti.co.jp
Emp.: 108
System Integration Design Services
N.A.I.C.S.: 541512

TelWel East Japan Corporation (2)
5-14-9 Sendagaya, Shibuya-Ku, Tokyo, 151-0051, Japan
Tel.: (81) 33 350 7121
Web Site: https://www.telwel-east.co.jp
Emp.: 5,630
Business Support Services
N.A.I.C.S.: 561499
Kenji Duio (Mng Dir)

Nippon Telegraph & Telephone West Corporation (1)
3-15 Bamba-cho, Chuo-ku, Osaka, 540-8511, Japan **(100%)**
Tel.: (81) 120064337
Web Site: http://www.ntt-west.co.jp
Emp.: 3,000
Holding Company; Telecommunications Services
N.A.I.C.S.: 551112
Shozo Ito (Sr Exec VP)

Subsidiary (Domestic):

Amenity Service Kansai Co., Ltd. (2)
2-1-11 Awaza Ntt Nishinihon Awaza Bldg 2f, Nishi-Ku, Osaka, 550-0011, Japan
Tel.: (81) 6 6578 7713
Web Site: http://www.askansai.jp
Engineeering Services
N.A.I.C.S.: 541330

Data Plus Corporation (2)
1-3-11 Hakataminami Building 5th Floor, Hakata-Ku, Fukuoka, 812-0016, Japan
Tel.: (81) 924513333
Information Technology Consulting Services
N.A.I.C.S.: 541512

DelSol Co., Ltd. (2)
1-6-12 Morinomiyachuo, Chuo-Ku, Osaka, 540-0003, Japan
Tel.: (81) 669447231
Logistic Services
N.A.I.C.S.: 541614

DelSol Kyushu Co., Ltd. (2)
1-4-4 Hakataekimae, Hakata-Ku, Fukuoka, 812-0011, Japan
Tel.: (81) 924521605
Telecommunication Servicesb

AND PRIVATE COMPANIES — NIPPON TELEGRAPH & TELEPHONE CORPORATION

N.A.I.C.S.: 517810

DelSol Tokai Co., Ltd. (2)
3-13-15 Matsubara, Naka-Ku, Nagoya, 460-0017, Aichi, Japan
Tel.: (81) 523311411
Telecommunication Servicesb
N.A.I.C.S.: 517810

DenDen Koukoku Co., Ltd. (2)
3F Matsuo Building 6-5-8 Motomachi-dori, Chuo-ku, Kobe, 650-0022, Hyogo, Japan
Tel.: (81) 783411234
Web Site: https://www.dendenkoukoku.co.jp
Emp.: 23
Outdoor Advertising Services
N.A.I.C.S.: 541850

NTT Media Supply Inc. (2)
Resort Trust Midosuji Building 18F 4-14-3 Nishitenma, Kita-Ku, Osaka, 530-0047, Japan
Tel.: (81) 647090111
Web Site: http://www.nttms.co.jp
Emp.: 96
Broadband Internet Services
N.A.I.C.S.: 517810

NTT NEOMEIT CORPORATION (2)
2-2-5 Uchihommachi, Chuo-Ku, Osaka, 540-0026, Japan
Tel.: (81) 647918000
Web Site: http://www.ntt-neo.com
Emp.: 6,100
Software Development Services
N.A.I.C.S.: 541511
Uehara Ichiro *(Pres & CEO)*

NTT SMART CONNECT CORPORATION (2)
14th Fl Nakanoshima Mitsui Bldg 3-3-3 Nakanoshima, Kita-ku, Osaka, 530-0005, Japan
Tel.: (81) 648038901
Web Site: http://www.nttsmc.com
Sales Range: $25-49.9 Million
Emp.: 85
Telecommunication Equipment Maintenance Services
N.A.I.C.S.: 811210
Akira Shirahase *(Pres)*

NTT Solmare Corporation (2)
No 2 Sumitomo Bldg 4-7-28 Kitahama, Chuo-Ku, Osaka, 541-0041, Japan
Tel.: (81) 662288860
Web Site: http://www.nttsolmare.com
Sales Range: $25-49.9 Million
Emp.: 147
Mobile Comic Services
N.A.I.C.S.: 561990
Akira Tomana *(CEO)*

NTT WEST-CHUGOKU CORPORATION (2)
6-77 Motomachi Nttnishinihommotomachi, Naka-Ku, Hiroshima, 730-0011, Japan
Tel.: (81) 82 226 3763
Web Site: http://www.ntt-west-chugoku.co.jp
Telecommunication Equipment Maintenance Services
N.A.I.C.S.: 811210

NTT WEST-HOKURIKU CORPORATION (2)
4-1 Dewamachi, Kanazawa, 920-0963, Ishikawa, Japan
Tel.: (81) 762204221
Web Site: http://www.ntt-west-hokuriku.co.jp
Telecommunication Servicesb
N.A.I.C.S.: 517810

NTT WEST-HOMETECHNO KYUSHU CORPORATION (2)
2-3-1 Hakataekihigashi NTT Hakata Bldg, Hakata-Ku, Fukuoka, 812-0013, Japan
Tel.: (81) 924810995
Property Development Services
N.A.I.C.S.: 531311

NTT WEST-HYOGO CORPORATION (2)
11 Kaigandori, Chuo-Ku, Kobe, 650-0024, Hyogo, Japan
Tel.: (81) 783266365
Web Site: http://www.ntt-west-hyogo.co.jp
Communication Equipment Maintenance Services
N.A.I.C.S.: 811210

NTT WEST-KANSAI IT-MATE Co., Ltd. (2)
5-3-81 Nakanoshima NTT Nakanoshima Building 7th Floor, Kita-Ku, Osaka, 530-0005, Japan
Tel.: (81) 648038024
Communication Equipment Repair & Maintenance Services
N.A.I.C.S.: 811210

NTT WEST-KYUSHU IT-MATE INC. (2)
2-3-1 Hakataekihigashi, Hakata-Ku, Fukuoka, 812-0013, Japan
Tel.: (81) 92 477 7180
Web Site: http://www.ntt-itmate-kyushu.co.jp
Telecommunication Equipment Repair & Maintenance Services
N.A.I.C.S.: 327910

NTT WEST-SHIKOKU CORPORATION (2)
4-3 Ichibancho, Matsuyama, 790-0001, Ehime, Japan
Tel.: (81) 899362841
Web Site: http://www.ntt-west-shikoku.co.jp
Telecommunications Equipment Repair & Maintenance Services
N.A.I.C.S.: 811210

NTT WEST-SHIKOKU IT-MATE Co Ltd. (2)
4-3 Ichibancho, Matsuyama, 790-0001, Ehime, Japan
Tel.: (81) 899891921
Web Site: http://www.ntt-itmate-shikoku.co.jp
Telecommunications Equipment Repair & Maintenance Services
N.A.I.C.S.: 811210

NTT WEST-TOKAI CORPORATION (2)
4-9-60 Osu Naka-ku, Nagoya, 460-0011, Aichi, Japan
Tel.: (81) 522912191
Web Site: http://www.ntt-west-tokai.co.jp
Information Technology Consulting Services
N.A.I.C.S.: 541512

NTT WEST-TOKAI IT-MATE CORPORATION (2)
No 25 No 8 2-chome Nagoya Sakae Hirokoji Bldg 3F, Naka-ku, Nagoya, 460-0008, Japan
Tel.: (81) 52 209 7757
Web Site: http://www.ntt-itmate-tokai.co.jp
Communication Equipment Maintenance Services
N.A.I.C.S.: 811210

TELTEC Co., LTD. (2)
1489-1 Hamada Shimoagawa, Iyo, 799-3111, Ehime, Japan
Tel.: (81) 899824664
Telecommunication Servicesb
N.A.I.C.S.: 517810

Subsidiary (Non-US):

TelWel West Nippon Corporation (2)
Web Site: http://www.telwel-west.co.jp
Sales Range: $150-199.9 Million
Emp.: 360
Communications Facility Engineering & Logistics
N.A.I.C.S.: 517810

Subsidiary (Domestic):

VIEWTECH TOKAI CO., LTD. (2)
3-2-8 Matsubara Terueru Shimmatsubara Bldg, Naka-Ku, Nagoya, 460-0017, Aichi, Japan
Tel.: (81) 52 331 4171
Web Site: http://www.viewtech-tokai.co.jp
Building Cleaning Services
N.A.I.C.S.: 561720

ViewTech Chugoku Co., Ltd (2)
2-20 Komachi, Naka-Ku, Hiroshima, 730-0041, Japan
Tel.: (81) 822455577
Web Site: http://www.viewtech-c.co.jp
Building Cleaning Services
N.A.I.C.S.: 561720

ViewTech Co., Ltd. (2)
3-2787-7 Yurigaoka, Moriya, 302-0110, Ibaraki, Japan
Tel.: (81) 297459811
Emp.: 10
Telecommunication Servicesb
N.A.I.C.S.: 517810

ViewTech Kyushu Co., Ltd. (2)
1-4-4 Hakataekimae JPR Hakata Bldg, Hakata-Ku, Fukuoka, 812-0011, Japan
Tel.: (81) 924521600
Web Site: http://www.viewtech-k.co.jp
Building Cleaning Services
N.A.I.C.S.: 561720

Oak Lawn Marketing China Co., Ltd. (1)
9G SCC Block A No 88 Haide Yi Road, Nanshan District, Shenzhen, 518002, Guangdong, China
Tel.: (86) 75586321124
Information Technology Consulting Services
N.A.I.C.S.: 541512

Otemachi First Square Inc. (1)
1-5-1 Otemachi, Chiyoda-ku, Tokyo, 100-0004, Japan
Tel.: (81) 332170800
Web Site: https://www.1st.co.jp
Building Construction & Design Services
N.A.I.C.S.: 541310

P.T. Mobile Innovation Indonesia (1)
4Cyber 2 Tower 18th Floor Jl HR Rasuna Said Blok X-5 Kav 13, Kuningan Timur Setiabudi, Jakarta Selatan, 12950, Indonesia
Tel.: (62) 2157998935
Web Site: https://www.mobileinnovation.asia
Vehicle Operation Management Services
N.A.I.C.S.: 561990

P.T. NTT Data Business Solutions (1)
Wisma BCA Wing A PH Floor Jl Kapten Soebijanto Djojohadikusumo, BSD City Kelurahan Lengkong Gudang Kecamatan Serpong, Tangerang, 15321, Banten, Indonesia
Tel.: (62) 2153192000
Information Technology Consulting Services
N.A.I.C.S.: 541512

P.T. NTT Data Indonesia (1)
Wisma 46-Kota BNI 9F J Jend Sudirman Kav 1, Jakarta Pusat, 10220, Indonesia
Tel.: (62) 215746060
Information Technology Consulting Services
N.A.I.C.S.: 541512

P.T. Promatrix Facilities Management (1)
Wisma 46 48th Floor Jl Jend Sudirman Kav, Jakarta Pusat, 10220, Indonesia
Tel.: (62) 215748521
Information Technology Services
N.A.I.C.S.: 541512

Postlight LLC (1)
101 5th Ave 10th Fl, New York, NY 10003
Tel.: (646) 694-8530
Web Site: https://postlight.com
Application Programming Interface Design Services
N.A.I.C.S.: 541512

Pro-Matrix Pte. Ltd. (1)
26 Sin Ming Lane 04-117 Midview, Singapore, 573971, Singapore
Tel.: (65) 68738680
Web Site: https://www.promatrix.sg
Information Technology Services
N.A.I.C.S.: 541512

Quantic Digital GmbH (1)
Loehrstrasse 12, 04105, Leipzig, Germany
Tel.: (49) 3412238720
Web Site: https://www.quantic.de
Information Technology Consulting Services
N.A.I.C.S.: 541512

Riken Suuri Corporation (1)
1-6-5 Kudanminami, Chiyoda-ku Tokyo Kudan Kaikan Terrace Inside JSOL, Tokyo, 102-0074, Japan
Tel.: (81) 367574908
Web Site: https://www.riken-suuri.jp
Construction Engineering Services
N.A.I.C.S.: 541330

SASSOU Co.,Ltd. (1)
4-8-24-203 Nishi-Azabu, Minato-ku, Tokyo, 106-0031, Japan
Tel.: (81) 363161822
Web Site: https://www.sassoujapan.co.jp
Architecture & Interior Design Services
N.A.I.C.S.: 541410

Sistemas de Control Remoto, S.L. (1)
C/Isla de La Palma 36 Naves 8 y 9, San Sebastian de los Reyes, 28703, Madrid, Spain
Tel.: (34) 916518227
Web Site: https://scrdrones.com
Aircraft Mfr
N.A.I.C.S.: 336411

Solutionary, Inc. (1)
9420 Underwood Ave 3rd Fl, Omaha, NE 68114
Tel.: (402) 361-3000
Web Site: http://www.solutionary.com
Information Security Services
N.A.I.C.S.: 541690
Michael Hrabik *(Pres)*

Sybit GmbH (1)
Sankt-Johannis-Str 1 - 5, 78315, Radolfzell, Germany
Tel.: (49) 773295080
Web Site: https://www.sybit.de
Information Technology Consulting Services
N.A.I.C.S.: 541512

Synaq (Pty.) Ltd. (1)
Ballyoaks Office Park Ground Floor Golden Oak House 35 Ballyclare Dr, Johannesburg, 2021, South Africa
Tel.: (27) 112623632
Web Site: https://www.synaq.com
Information Technology Solutions Services
N.A.I.C.S.: 541512

TelTec Sikoku Co.,Ltd. (1)
3-15-15 Yamagoe Ehime Prefecture NTT Yamagoe North Building, Matsuyama, Japan
Tel.: (81) 899895866
Web Site: https://www.teltec.co.jp
Emp.: 30
Information Technology Solutions Services
N.A.I.C.S.: 541512

Tenik Co.,Ltd. (1)
Daiwa Sasazuka Building 5F 1-64-8 Sasazuka, Shibuya-ku, Tokyo, 151-0073, Japan
Tel.: (81) 333729974
Web Site: https://www.tenik.co.jp
Emp.: 29
Video Software Development Services
N.A.I.C.S.: 541511

Transatel SA (1)
49-51 Quai de Dion Bouton, CS 50034, 92806, Puteaux, Cedex, France
Tel.: (33) 174957400
Web Site: http://www.transatel.com
Emp.: 40
Telecommunication Network Operator Services
N.A.I.C.S.: 517121
Jacques Bonifay *(Co-Founder, Chm & CEO)*

UD Hospitality Management Corporation (1)
Akihabara UDX 4-14-1 Sotokanda, Chiyoda-ku, Tokyo, 101-0021, Japan
Tel.: (81) 368116770
Information Technology Consulting Services
N.A.I.C.S.: 541512

Wedge Road Development Pty. Ltd. (1)
Suite 1 04 68 Clarke Street Southbank, Melbourne, 3006, VIC, Australia
Tel.: (61) 473630484
Web Site: https://wedgerd.com.au
Building Construction & Design Services
N.A.I.C.S.: 541310

Xego-it GmbH (1)
Meibner Strabe 31, 01445, Radebeul, Germany
Tel.: (49) 3513144890
Web Site: https://www.xego-it.de
Emp.: 3,000
Software Development Services
N.A.I.C.S.: 541511

Xsfera S.R.L. (1)
Via Romagna 14/16, Milan, 20090, Opera, Italy
Tel.: (39) 03405179482

NIPPON TELEGRAPH & TELEPHONE CORPORATION

Nippon Telegraph & Telephone Corporation—(Continued)

Web Site: https://www.xf-online.it
Professional Training Services
N.A.I.C.S.: 611430

iPay88 (M) Sdn. Bhd. (1)
Suite 2B-20-1 20th Floor Block 2B Plaza Sentral Jalan Stesen Sentral 5, 50470, Kuala Lumpur, Malaysia
Tel.: (60) 322614668
Web Site: https://www.ipay88.com
Financial Services
N.A.I.C.S.: 522110

iPay88 Holding Sdn. Bhd. (1)
Suite 2B-20-1 20th Floor Block 2B Plaza Sentral Jalan Stesen Sentral 5, 50470, Kuala Lumpur, Malaysia
Tel.: (60) 322614668
Financial Services
N.A.I.C.S.: 522110

itelligence Consulting Shanghai Ltd. (1)
Y-602 6/F ShanghaiMart Tower No 2299 West Yanan Road, Changning District, Shanghai, 200336, China
Tel.: (86) 2152080750
Information Technology Solutions Services
N.A.I.C.S.: 541512

NIPPON TELEVISION HOLDINGS INC.
1-6-1 Higashi Shimbashi, Minato-ku, Tokyo, 105-7444, Japan
Tel.: (81) 362154111
Web Site: https://www.ntvhd.co.jp
Year Founded: 1952
9404—(TKS)
Rev.: $2,799,487,030
Assets: $7,821,606,390
Liabilities: $1,559,986,440
Net Worth: $6,261,619,950
Earnings: $229,102,600
Emp.: 220
Fiscal Year-end: 03/31/24
Television & Radio Broadcasting & Production Services
N.A.I.C.S.: 516120
Yoshinobu Kosugi *(Vice Chm)*

Subsidiaries:

Ax-On Inc (1)
NTV Tower 22F 1-6-1, Higashi Shimbashi Minato-Ku, Tokyo, 105-7422, Japan
Tel.: (81) 359628100
Web Site: https://www.ax-on.co.jp
Sales Range: $150-199.9 Million
Emp.: 756
Motion Picture & Video Production
N.A.I.C.S.: 512110

BS Nippon Corporation (1)
Nittele Tower 23rd Floor 1-6-1 Higashi Shimbashi, Minato-ku, Tokyo, 105-8644, Japan
Tel.: (81) 36 228 5624
Web Site: https://www.bs4.jp
Television Broadcasting Services
N.A.I.C.S.: 516120

CS Nippon Corporation (1)
1-6-1 Nittele Tower 22nd Floor Higashi Shimbashi, Minato-ku, Tokyo, Japan
Tel.: (81) 35 962 8225
Web Site: https://www.cs-nippon.com
Television Broadcasting Services
N.A.I.C.S.: 516120

Eiho Produce Corporation (1)
Chome 6-1 days Teretawa 23 Floor Higashi Shimbashi, Minato-ku, Tokyo, 105-7423, Japan
Tel.: (81) 35 962 8249
Web Site: https://www.eiho-pro.co.jp
Television Broadcasting Services
N.A.I.C.S.: 516120

Forecast Communications Inc. (1)
1-2-17 Higashi-Shimbashi Sumitomo Real Estate Wing 5th Floor, Shiodome Minato-ku, Tokyo, 105-0021, Japan **(61.92%)**
Tel.: (81) 362156321
Web Site: http://www.4cast.co.jp
Sales Range: $25-49.9 Million
Emp.: 100
Cross Media, Consumer, Advertising & Solution Services
N.A.I.C.S.: 541519
Takashi Ando *(Pres)*

HJ Holdings, Inc. (1)
Shiodome Wing 13th Floor 1-2-17, Higashi-Shimbashi Minato-ku, Tokyo, 105-0021, Japan
Tel.: (81) 501 741 3358
Web Site: https://www.hjholdings.jp
Video Distribution Services
N.A.I.C.S.: 512120

Ikaros Co., Ltd. (1)
Suzuki Building 2-2-8 Higashi-Shimbashi, Minato-ku, Tokyo, 105-0021, Japan
Tel.: (81) 35 408 3681
Web Site: https://n-ikaros.co.jp
Motion Picture Services
N.A.I.C.S.: 512110

KKT Innovate Corporation (1)
2-1-10 Oe, Chuo-ku, Kumamoto, 862-8504, Japan
Tel.: (81) 96 362 1001
Web Site: https://kkti.jp
Motion Picture Services
N.A.I.C.S.: 512110

Kanazawa Eizo Center Corporation (1)
2-136 Kobu, Kanazawa, 920-0362, Ishikawa, Japan
Tel.: (81) 76 240 9038
Web Site: https://www.kanazawa-eizo.co.jp
Motion Picture Services
N.A.I.C.S.: 512110

Madbox Co., Ltd. (1)
3-23-3 Honcho Shin-Nakano AM1 Building 4F, Nakano-ku, Tokyo, 164-0012, Japan
Tel.: (81) 35 308 3965
Web Site: https://www.madbox.jp
Motion Picture Services
N.A.I.C.S.: 512110

Madhouse Inc. (1)
Shinnakano AM1 Building 3F 3-23-3 Honcho, Nakano-ku, Tokyo, 164-0012, Japan **(84.5%)**
Tel.: (81) 353083960
Web Site: https://www.madhouse.co.jp
Sales Range: $25-49.9 Million
Emp.: 70
Animation Studio & Production Services
N.A.I.C.S.: 512199
Masahiro Takahashi *(Chm)*

NTV America Company (1)
The America 1230 Ave, New York, NY 10020-1513
Tel.: (212) 541-3749
Television Broadcasting Station
N.A.I.C.S.: 516120

NTV EVENTS Inc. (1)
2-5-14 Higashi-Shimbashi 5F, Minato-ku, Tokyo, 105-0021, Japan
Tel.: (81) 359628400
Web Site: http://www.ntve.co.jp
Event Management Services
N.A.I.C.S.: 711320

NTV Group Holdings Inc. (1)
14 Nibancho Nittere Kojimachi Bldg Minamikan 5F, Chiyoda-ku, Tokyo, 102-0084, Japan
Tel.: (81) 332227900
Investment Management Service
N.A.I.C.S.: 523999
Toshiya Sugimoco *(Pres)*

NTV IT Produce Corporation (1)
1-6-1 Higashi-Shimbashi, Minato-ku, Tokyo, 105-7423, Japan
Tel.: (81) 35 962 8240
Web Site: https://www.ntvit.co.jp
Emp.: 104
Information Technology Broadcasting Services
N.A.I.C.S.: 516210
Shigetoshi Suzuki *(Pres)*

NTV International Corporation (1)
645 5th Ave Ste 303, New York, NY 10022
Tel.: (212) 660-6900
Web Site: https://www.ntvic.com
Sales Range: $25-49.9 Million
Emp.: 50
Motion Picture & Video Production
N.A.I.C.S.: 512110

NTV Personnel Center Corp (1)
Tel.: (81) 359628480
Web Site: http://www.ntvpc.co.jp
Emp.: 220
Human Resources & Executive Search Consulting Services
N.A.I.C.S.: 541612

NTV Services Inc. (1)
1-6-1 Higashi Shimbashi Nittele Tower B2F, Minato-ku, Tokyo, 105-7444, Japan
Tel.: (81) 362159686
Web Site: http://www.ntvs.co.jp
Sales Range: $300-349.9 Million
Emp.: 600
Television Production & Program Sales
N.A.I.C.S.: 516120
Toru Horikoshi *(Pres)*

NTV Technical Resources Inc. (1)
19th floor Nippon Television Tower 1-6-1 Higashi-Shinbashi, Minato-ku, Tokyo, 105-7419, Japan
Tel.: (81) 352152106
Web Site: https://www.nitro.co.jp
Emp.: 593
Video Production Services
N.A.I.C.S.: 512110

Nagasaki Vision Corp. (1)
1-14 Dejima Asahi Life Aoki Building 6th Floor, Nagasaki, 850-0862, Japan
Tel.: (81) 95 820 3225
Web Site: https://nvi.ne.jp
Motion Picture Services
N.A.I.C.S.: 512110

Nippon Television Art Corp. (1)
NTV Tower 21F 1-6-1, Higashi Shimbashi Minato-Ku, Tokyo, 105-7422, Japan **(100%)**
Tel.: (81) 359628600
Web Site: https://www.ntvart.co.jp
Business Services
N.A.I.C.S.: 561499
Hiroshi Takeshita *(Pres)*

Nippon Television Music Corporation (1)
5F San Marino Shiodome 2-4-1 Higashi-Shimbashi, Minato-ku, Tokyo, 105-0021, Japan
Tel.: (81) 352751157
Web Site: https://www.ntvm.co.jp
Sales Range: $10-24.9 Million
Emp.: 53
Business Services
N.A.I.C.S.: 561499

Nippon Television Network Europe B.V. (1)
Keizersgracht 555, Strawinskylaan 1251, 1017 DR, Amsterdam, Netherlands
Tel.: (31) 205752014
Web Site: https://ntv-e.com
Sales Range: $25-49.9 Million
Emp.: 5
Television Broadcasting Station
N.A.I.C.S.: 516120

Nippon Television Work 24 Corporation (1)
4th Floor Shimbashi Yamane Building 2-5-14 Higashi-Shimbashi, Minato-ku, Tokyo, 105-0021, Japan
Tel.: (81) 35 962 8470
Web Site: https://www.ntvw24.co.jp
Building Maintenance Services
N.A.I.C.S.: 561790

Nishi Nihon Eizo Corporation (1)
1-9-3 Takasago 4th Floor Mutsukida Building, Chuo-ku, Fukuoka, 810-0011, Japan
Tel.: (81) 92 526 9333
Web Site: https://www.nne.ne.jp
Motion Picture Services
N.A.I.C.S.: 512110

NitteleSeven Co., Ltd (1)
1-6-1 Higashi-Shimbashi Nittele Tower 23F, Minato-ku, Tokyo, 105-7423, Japan
Tel.: (81) 120685210
Web Site: https://www.ntv7.jp
Television Broadcasting Services
N.A.I.C.S.: 516120

INTERNATIONAL PUBLIC

RF Music Publisher Inc. (1)
Azabudai Building 3F 2-2-1, Azabudai Minato-ku, Tokyo, 106-8039, Japan
Tel.: (81) 33 585 6611
Web Site: https://www.rfmp.co.jp
Music Copyright Services
N.A.I.C.S.: 512230

RF Radio Nippon Co., Ltd. (1)
5-85 Chojamachi, Naka-ku, Yokohama, 231-8611, Japan
Tel.: (81) 452311531
Web Site: https://www.jorf.co.jp
Emp.: 32
Radio Broadcasting Network Services
N.A.I.C.S.: 334220

Sound Inn Studios Inc. (1)
5-6 Yonbancho 6th Floor Nittele Yonbancho Building No 1, Chiyoda-ku, Tokyo, 102-0081, Japan
Tel.: (81) 33 234 4311
Web Site: https://sound-inn.com
Music Recording Studio Services
N.A.I.C.S.: 512240
Yoshiro Yasuoka *(Pres)*

Tipness, Ltd. (1)
3rd floor Nippon Television Yobancho Building 1 5-6 Yobancho, Chiyoda-ku, Tokyo, 102-0081, Japan
Tel.: (81) 337698700
Web Site: https://www.tipness.co.jp
Membership Sports Club
N.A.I.C.S.: 711211

VAP Inc. (1)
Tel.: (81) 332345711
Web Site: http://www.vap.co.jp
Movie Videos Distr
N.A.I.C.S.: 512120

Weekday, Inc. (1)
3F 3-18-14 Minami-Aoyama, Minato-ku, Tokyo, 107-0062, Japan
Tel.: (81) 36 803 8131
Web Site: https://weekday.co.jp
Digital Marketing Services
N.A.I.C.S.: 541613
Daisuke Yokota *(Pres)*

NIPPON THOMPSON CO., LTD.
19-19 Takanawa 2-chome, Minato-ku, Tokyo, 108-8586, Japan
Tel.: (81) 334485811   JP
Web Site: https://www.ikont.co.jp
Year Founded: 1950
6480—(TKS)
Rev.: $363,867,280
Assets: $787,826,070
Liabilities: $284,382,030
Net Worth: $503,444,040
Earnings: $17,675,140
Emp.: 2,431
Fiscal Year-end: 03/31/24
Needle Roller Bearings Mfr
N.A.I.C.S.: 336310
Shigeki Miyachi *(Pres)*

Subsidiaries:

Hassei Shokai Co., Ltd. (1)
4-1-3 Higashi Shinagawa, Shinagawa-ku, Tokyo, 140-0002, Japan
Tel.: (81) 35 783 4451
Television Broadcasting Services
N.A.I.C.S.: 516120

IKO International, Inc. (1)
Fox Hill Ind Park 91 Walsh Dr, Parsippany, NJ 07054
Tel.: (973) 402-0254
Sales Range: $25-49.9 Million
Emp.: 11
Industrial Bearings Whslr
N.A.I.C.S.: 423840

IKO Thompson Asia Co., Ltd. (1)
1-7 Zuellig House 3rd Floor Silom Road Silom, Bangrak, 10500, Bangkok, Thailand
Tel.: (66) 2 637 5115
Television Broadcasting Services
N.A.I.C.S.: 516120

IKO Thompson Bearings Canada, Inc. (1)
731-2425 Matheson Boulevard East 7th Floor, Mississauga, L4W 5K4, ON, Canada

Tel.: (905) 361-2872
Motion Picture Services
N.A.I.C.S.: 512110

IKO Thompson Korea Co., Ltd. (1)
201 Worldvision Bldg 77-1 Yeouinaru-ro, Yeongdeungpo-gu, Seoul, 07327, Korea (South)
Tel.: (82) 26 337 5851
Television Broadcasting Services
N.A.I.C.S.: 516120

IKO Thompson Vietnam Co., Ltd. (1)
Plots N5 N6 Japan-Haiphong Industrial Zone, An Hung Commune An Duong District, Haiphong, Vietnam
Tel.: (84) 313743267
Sales Range: $50-74.9 Million
Emp.: 200
Linear Motion Guides & Bearings Mfr
N.A.I.C.S.: 332991

IKO-Thompson (Shanghai) Ltd. (1)
1608-10 MetroPlaza No 555 LouShanGuan Road, ChangNing District, Shanghai, 200051, China
Tel.: (86) 213 250 5525
Motion Picture Services
N.A.I.C.S.: 512110

Kasagami MFG. Co., Ltd. (1)
641-4 Kasagami, Mino, 501-3764, Gifu, Japan
Tel.: (81) 575333888
Linear Motion Guides & Bearings Mfr
N.A.I.C.S.: 332991

Nippon DIC Co., Ltd. (1)
2-12-10 Matsubara, Naka-ku, Nagoya, 460-0017, Aichi, Japan
Tel.: (81) 523223661
Web Site: https://www.n-dic.co.jp
Emp.: 37
Bearings & Hydraulic Equipments Distr
N.A.I.C.S.: 423830

Nippon Thompson Europe B.V. (1)
Keersopstraat 35, 3044 EX, Rotterdam, Netherlands
Tel.: (31) 104626868
Web Site: https://www.ikont.eu
Sales Range: $25-49.9 Million
Emp.: 20
Bearing Distr
N.A.I.C.S.: 423840
Tsutomu Togashi *(Mng Dir)*

Nippon Thompson Sales Co., Ltd. (1)
2-19-19 Takanawa 2-chome, Minato-ku, Tokyo, 108-8586, Japan
Tel.: (81) 334485911
Industrial Bearings Whslr
N.A.I.C.S.: 423840

UBC Precision Bearing Manufacturing Co., Ltd. (1)
Suite 1703 Zhongrong Plaza 1088 South Pudong Road, Pudong New District, Shanghai, 200120, China
Tel.: (86) 216 878 1060
Web Site: https://www.ubc-bearing.com
Liner Motion Rolling Guide Mfr
N.A.I.C.S.: 332991
Ariga Tadayoshi *(Chm)*

NIPPON TUNGSTEN CO., LTD.
2-8 Minoshima 1-chome, Hakata-ku, Fukuoka, 812-8538, Japan
Tel.: (81) 924155507
Web Site: https://www.nittan.co.jp
Year Founded: 1931
6998—(FKA)
Rev.: $116,527,840
Assets: $159,197,280
Liabilities: $55,272,800
Net Worth: $103,924,480
Earnings: $8,421,600
Emp.: 434
Fiscal Year-end: 03/31/22
Tungsten, Molybdenum, Ceramics & Fine Ceramic Products Mfr
N.A.I.C.S.: 327110
Shinji Goto *(Pres)*

Subsidiaries:

Fukuoka Kiki Co., Ltd. (1)
Minoshima No 1-chome No 2 8, Hakata-ku, Fukuoka, 812-0017, Japan
Tel.: (81) 92 437 2303
Web Site: http://www.fukuoka-kiki.co.jp
General Industrial Machinery Mfr
N.A.I.C.S.: 333998

NIPPON TUNGSTEN (SHANGHAI) COMMERCE CO.,LTD
Room 2016 Building B Far East International Plaza No 317 XianXia Road, Shanghai, 200051, China
Tel.: (86) 21 6235 0044
Web Site: http://www.nittansh.com.cn
Emp.: 11
Tungsten Mfr
N.A.I.C.S.: 331491

NIPPON TUNGSTEN USA, INC.
2986 Cyrus Creek Rd, Barboursville, WV 25504
Tel.: (304) 736-6970
Web Site: https://www.nippontungstenusa.com
Emp.: 10
Tungsten Mfr
N.A.I.C.S.: 332999
Kenji Nakahara *(Pres)*

NT. Service Co., Ltd. (1)
2-8 Minoshima 1-Chome, Hakata-ku, Fukuoka, 812-0017, Japan
Tel.: (81) 92 451 3005
Emp.: 4
Tungsten Mfr
N.A.I.C.S.: 325180

Showa Denki Setten Kogyosho.Co.,Ltd (100%)
430 Ushiromuta, Ikisu, Iizuka, 820-0053, Fukuoka, Japan
Tel.: (81) 94 825 8870
Web Site: https://www.showa-dsk.co.jp
Automotive Electrical Products & Brazed Metals Mfr
N.A.I.C.S.: 335999

NIPPON YAKIN KOGYO CO., LTD.
1-5-8 Kyobashi, Chuo-ku, Tokyo, 104-8365, Japan
Tel.: (81) 332721511
Web Site: https://www.nyk.co.jp
5480—(TKS)
Rev.: $1,192,054,010
Assets: $1,454,120,680
Liabilities: $860,641,830
Net Worth: $593,478,850
Earnings: $89,664,650
Emp.: 1,151
Fiscal Year-end: 03/31/24
Stainless Steel Production
N.A.I.C.S.: 331513
Hajime Kimura *(Chm)*

Subsidiaries:

Clean Metals Co., Ltd. (1)
695-5 Shinden Owada, Yachiyo, 276-0046, Chiba, Japan
Tel.: (81) 474507791
Web Site: https://www.cln.co.jp
Emp.: 110
Stainless Steel Whslr
N.A.I.C.S.: 423510

NAS Stainless Steel Strip Manufacturing Co., Ltd. (1)
3rd floor Kogin Building 4-1-1 Koraibashi, Chuo-ku, Osaka, 541-0043, Japan
Tel.: (81) 662281591
Web Site: https://www.nas-kotai.co.jp
Sales Range: $50-74.9 Million
Emp.: 150
Welded Stainless Steel Pipes & Tubes Mfr
N.A.I.C.S.: 331210

Nas Create Co., Ltd. (1)
14-17 Nihonbashi Odenmacho Odenmacho Chitose Building, Chuo- ku, Tokyo, 103-0011, Japan
Tel.: (81) 336658179
Web Site: http://www.nas-create.co.jp
Sales Range: $25-49.9 Million
Emp.: 18
Stainless Steel Pipe & Tubes Mfr
N.A.I.C.S.: 331210

Nas Engineering Co., Ltd. (1)
7th floor Kowa Nitto Building 3-17-9 Tsukiji, Chuo-ku, Tokyo, 104-0045, Japan
Tel.: (81) 368597800
Web Site: https://www.nas-eng.co.jp
Sales Range: $50-74.9 Million
Emp.: 138
Stainless Steel Wire Mfr
N.A.I.C.S.: 331210

Nas Toa (Thailand) Co., Ltd. (1)
555 Soi 9 Moo 4 Pattana 1 Road T Praksa, Bangpoo Industrial Estate A Muang, Samut Prakan, 10280, Thailand
Tel.: (66) 232409359
Web Site: http://www.nastoa.co.th
Sales Range: $50-74.9 Million
Emp.: 220
Welded Stainless Steel Pipe & Tubes Mfr
N.A.I.C.S.: 331210
Kazushi Fujimoto *(Pres)*

Nas Toa Co., Ltd. (1)
1-5-8 Kyobashi 9th floor of Sanei Building, Chuo-ku, Tokyo, 104-0031, Japan
Tel.: (81) 368951370
Web Site: https://www.nastoa.co.jp
Stainless Steel Mfr & Distr
N.A.I.C.S.: 331110

Nas Trading Co., Ltd. (1)
14-17 Nihonbashi Odenmacho, Chuo-ku, Tokyo, 103-0011, Japan
Tel.: (81) 336658181
Web Site: https://www.nas-trd.co.jp
Sales Range: $25-49.9 Million
Emp.: 50
Stainless Steel Whslr
N.A.I.C.S.: 423510

Nippon Yakin America, Inc. (1)
2800 S River Rd Ste 140, Des Plaines, IL 60018
Tel.: (847) 227-9730
Stainless Steel Products Mfr
N.A.I.C.S.: 331110

Nippon Yakin Asia Pte. Ltd. (1)
10 Anson Road 31-09 International Plaza, Singapore, 079903, Singapore
Tel.: (65) 62262376
Stainless Steel Products Mfr
N.A.I.C.S.: 331110

Nippon Yakin Europe Limited (1)
26-28 Hammersmith Grove, Hammersmith, London, W6 7BA, United Kingdom
Tel.: (44) 2088341067
Stainless Steel Products Mfr
N.A.I.C.S.: 331110

Nippon Yakin Shanghai Co., Ltd. (1)
Rm 1018 Shanghai International Trade Centre 2201 Yan An Road W, Shanghai, China
Tel.: (86) 2152392670
Stainless Steel Products Mfr
N.A.I.C.S.: 331110

Nisco Nippon Yakin Kogyo Nanjing Co., Ltd. (1)
3F 35 Puzhou Road Yanjiang Street, Pukou District, Nanjing, 210031, Jiangsu, China
Tel.: (86) 2558207996
Stainless Steel Products Mfr
N.A.I.C.S.: 331110

Yakin Oheyama Co., Ltd. (1)
413 Aza Suzu, Miyazu, 629-2251, Kyoto, Japan
Tel.: (81) 772463121
Web Site: http://www.nyk.co.jp
Sales Range: $25-49.9 Million
Emp.: 100
Metals & Stainless Steel Mfr
N.A.I.C.S.: 331210
Masato Noda *(Pres)*

NIPPON YUSEN KABUSHIKI KAISHA
3-2 Marunouchi 2 Chome, Chiyoda-Ku, Tokyo, 100-0005, Japan
Tel.: (81) 332845151   JP
Web Site: http://www.nyk.com
Year Founded: 1885
9101—(TKS)
Rev.: $15,779,656,400
Assets: $28,124,029,700
Liabilities: $10,320,887,050
Net Worth: $17,803,142,650
Earnings: $1,511,065,830
Emp.: 35,243
Fiscal Year-end: 03/31/24
Transportation Services
N.A.I.C.S.: 488510
Tadaaki Naito *(Chm & Exec Officer)*

Subsidiaries:

Anji-NYK Logistics (Thailand) Co., Ltd. (1)
2525 One FYI Center 7th Floor Rama 4 Road, Klongtoey, Bangkok, 10110, Thailand
Tel.: (66) 2 017 2050
Web Site: https://www.anji-nyk.co.th
Logistic Services
N.A.I.C.S.: 541614
Chatinai Chodokruk *(Mgr-Bus Dev)*

Asahi Unyu Kaisha, Ltd (1)
2-4-6 Irifune, Minato-ku, Nagoya, 455-0032, Japan
Tel.: (81) 526511111
Web Site: https://www.auk.co.jp
Sales Range: $50-74.9 Million
Emp.: 238
Marine Cargo Handling Services
N.A.I.C.S.: 488320

Asia Pacific Marine Corporation (1)
10-16 Hamamachi, Moji-Ku, Kitakyushu, 801-0856, Fukuoka, Japan
Tel.: (81) 933325855
Marine Transportation Services
N.A.I.C.S.: 488390

Camellia Line Co., Ltd. (1)
14-1 Okihama-cho 3rd floor Hakata Port International Terminal, Hakata-ku, Fukuoka, Japan
Tel.: (81) 922622323
Web Site: https://www.camellia-line.co.jp
Emp.: 42
Sea Freight Transportation Services
N.A.I.C.S.: 483111

Chiba Kaiun Sangyo Co., Ltd. (1)
3-1-20 Suehiro, Chuo-ku, Chiba, 260-0843, Japan
Tel.: (81) 43 261 3361
Web Site: https://www.chibamarine.co.jp
Emp.: 25
Shipping Agency Services
N.A.I.C.S.: 488510
Reiko Hamaguchi *(Auditor)*

Csi Logistics Inc. (1)
811 Bond St, Elizabeth, NJ 07201
Tel.: (908) 351-5488
Web Site: http://www.csil.us
Freight Forwarding Services
N.A.I.C.S.: 488510
Carlos Feliu *(Mng Dir)*

Dalian International Container Service Co., Ltd (1)
Room 708 Gold Name Tower No 68 Renmin Road, Zhongshan District, Dalian, 116001, China
Tel.: (86) 41182714848
Harbor Transportation Services
N.A.I.C.S.: 488390

Geneq Corporation (1)
9-11 Minatomachi Mojiko Retro Square Center Building 3F, Moji-Ku, Kitakyushu, 801-0852, Fukuoka, Japan
Tel.: (81) 933312101
Web Site: http://www.geneq.co.jp
Logistics Consulting Servies
N.A.I.C.S.: 541614

Hachiuma Steamship Co., Ltd. (1)
7th floor Kyomachi 74-ban Building 74 Kyomachi, Chuo-ku, Kobe, 650-0034, Japan
Tel.: (81) 78 334 3910
Web Site: https://www.hachiuma.co.jp
Sales Range: $50-74.9 Million
Emp.: 99
Marine Transportation Services
N.A.I.C.S.: 488390
Takashi Sakai *(Pres)*

Hirokura Co., Ltd. (1)
3-9-13 Ujina-Kaigan, Minami-ku, Hiroshima, 734-0011, Japan
Tel.: (81) 822536191

NIPPON YUSEN KABUSHIKI KAISHA

Nippon Yusen Kabushiki Kaisha—(Continued)
Web Site: http://www.hirokura.co.jp
Emp.: 50
International Logistics Services
N.A.I.C.S.: 541614

International Car Operators N.V. (1)
Margareta van Austriastraat 1, 8380, Zeebrugge, Belgium
Tel.: (32) 50725411
Web Site: https://www.icoterminals.com
Terminal Handling Services
N.A.I.C.S.: 488310

Japan Marine Science Inc. (1)
Solid Square West Tower 3F 580 Horikawa-cho, Saiwai-ku, Kawasaki, 212-0013, Kanagawa, Japan
Tel.: (81) 44 548 9130
Web Site: https://www.jms-inc.jp
Emp.: 160
Marine & Shipping Consulting Services
N.A.I.C.S.: 488390
Koichi Akamine (CEO)

K.R.C. Transport & Service Co., Ltd. (1)
96 5 Tambon Thung Suk La Amphoe, Si Racha, 20230, Chonburi, Thailand
Web Site: http://www.krctrans.com
Ship Container Care Services
N.A.I.C.S.: 488390

Kantoeisen Co., Ltd. (1)
8-2 Futatsuya- cho, Kanagawa-ku, Yokohama, 221-0823, Japan
Tel.: (81) 453223080
Web Site: http://www.kantoeisen.co.jp
Emp.: 20
Harbor Transportation Services
N.A.I.C.S.: 488390

Keihin Dock Co., Ltd. (1)
1-2-2 Moriyamachi, Kanagawa-ku, Yokohama, 221-0022, Japan
Tel.: (81) 454616834
Web Site: https://www.keihindock.co.jp
Emp.: 70
Ship Construction & Repair Services
N.A.I.C.S.: 336611

Kinkai Yusen Logistics Co., Ltd. (1)
Nomura Real Estate Development Shiba Daimon Building 7F, 1-9-9 Shiba Daimon Minato-ku, Tokyo, 105-0012, Japan
Tel.: (81) 354058300
Web Site: https://www.kyk.co.jp
Emp.: 51
Transportation & Warehousing Services
N.A.I.C.S.: 488999

Knutsen NYK Offshore Tankers AS (1)
Smedasundet 40, Postbox 2017, 5504, Haugesund, Norway
Tel.: (47) 52704000
Ship Construction Services
N.A.I.C.S.: 336611
Magnus Gudmundsen (VP-Technical Ops)

Laemchabang International Ro-Ro Terminal Ltd. (1)
88/3 Moo 3 LaemChabang Port Rd, ThungSukhla, Si Racha, 20230, Chonburi, Thailand
Tel.: (66) 384900204
Web Site: https://www.lrt-th.com
Ship Construction Services
N.A.I.C.S.: 336611

Logistics International Ltd. (1)
309/15 Negombo Road, Welisara, Sri Lanka
Tel.: (94) 112228224
Web Site: http://www.logisticsinternational.lk
Marine Shipping Services
N.A.I.C.S.: 488510

NYK & BLL of South Africa (Pty) Ltd (1)
16th Avenue Walmer Park House, Walmer, Port Elizabeth, 6045, South Africa
Tel.: (27) 41 503 4400
Web Site: http://www.za.nyklogistics.com
Sales Range: $25-49.9 Million
Emp.: 25
Freight Forwarding Services
N.A.I.C.S.: 488510
Shane Gerber (Mng Dir)

NYK Bulk & Projects Carriers Ltd. (1)
3-2 Marunouchi 2 Chome, Chiyoda-Ku, Tokyo, 100-0005, Japan
Tel.: (81) 33 284 6911
Web Site: https://www.nbpc.co.jp
Emp.: 200
Sea Cargo Shipping Services
N.A.I.C.S.: 483111
Motoyuki Nose (Pres & CEO)

NYK Bulkship (Asia) Pte. Ltd. (1)
1 HarbourFront Place 13-01 HarbourFront Tower One, Singapore, 98633, Singapore
Tel.: (65) 62924342
Freight Transportation Services
N.A.I.C.S.: 483111

NYK Bulkship (Atlantic) N.V. (1)
Avenue Building Noorderplaats 7 3rd floor, 2000, Antwerp, Belgium
Tel.: (32) 3 202 1521
Web Site: http://www.nykeurope.com
Sales Range: $25-49.9 Million
Emp.: 26
Marine Transportation Services
N.A.I.C.S.: 483111

NYK Bulkship (China) Ltd. (1)
1906A 19F Jinbao Tower 89 Jinbao Street, Dongcheng District, Beijing, 100005, China
Tel.: (86) 10 8522 1708
Marine Transportation Services
N.A.I.C.S.: 488390

NYK Bulkship (Europe) Ltd. (1)
Citypoint 1 Ropemaker St, London, EC2 Y9NY, United Kingdom **(100%)**
Tel.: (44) 2070902000
Web Site: http://www.nykline.com
Sales Range: $150-199.9 Million
Emp.: 280
N.A.I.C.S.: 483114

NYK Bulkship (USA) Inc. (1)
300 Lighting Way, Secaucus, NJ 07094 **(100%)**
Tel.: (201) 330-3000
Web Site: http://www.nykline.com
Sales Range: $25-49.9 Million
Emp.: 35
Water Transportation Services
N.A.I.C.S.: 483114

NYK Business Systems Americas Inc. (1)
300 Lighting Way Ste 400, Secaucus, NJ 07094-3647
Tel.: (201) 330-3000
Business Management Consulting Services
N.A.I.C.S.: 541611

NYK Business Systems Co., Ltd. (1)
1-17-21 Shinkawa Kayabacho First Bldg 5f, Chuo-Ku, Tokyo, 104-0033, Japan
Tel.: (81) 3 3537 5200
Web Site: http://www.nykbs.co.jp
Emp.: 92
Computer System Design Services
N.A.I.C.S.: 541612
Norio Nikkuni (Gen Mgr)

NYK Cruises Co., Ltd. (1)
The Landmark Tower Yokohama 2-1 Minatomirai 2-chome, Nishi-ku, Yokohama, 220-8147, Japan
Tel.: (81) 456405301
Web Site: http://www.asukacruise.co.jp
Emp.: 155
Cruise Shipping Services
N.A.I.C.S.: 483112
Fukashi Sakamoto (Pres)

NYK Global Bulk Corporation (1)
Yusen Building 5F 2-3-2 Marunouchi, Chiyoda-ku, Tokyo, 100-0005, Japan
Tel.: (81) 3 3284 6750
Web Site: http://www.nykglobalbulk.com
Rev.: $844,778,000
Emp.: 6
Marine Transportation Services
N.A.I.C.S.: 488390

NYK Group Americas Inc. (1)
300 Lighting Way 5th Fl, Secaucus, NJ 07094
Tel.: (201) 330-3000
Logistic Services
N.A.I.C.S.: 541614
Steven Elmo (Fin Dir)

NYK Group Europe Ltd. (1)
Floor 19 1 Cabot Square, Canary Wharf, London, E14 4QJ, United Kingdom
Tel.: (44) 2034097500
Web Site: http://www.nykeurope.com
Sea Cargo Shipping Services
N.A.I.C.S.: 483111

NYK Group South Asia Pte. Ltd. (1)
1 HarbourFront Place 14-01 HarbourFront Tower One, Singapore, 098633, Singapore **(100%)**
Tel.: (65) 69296388
Web Site: http://www.nykline.com
Sales Range: $150-199.9 Million
Emp.: 350
Water Transportation Services
N.A.I.C.S.: 483114

NYK LNG Shipmanagement (UK) Ltd. (1)
Citypoint 1 Ropemaker Street, London, EC2Y 9NY, United Kingdom
Tel.: (44) 2070902000
Web Site: http://www.nykline.com
Emp.: 238
Freight Transportation Services
N.A.I.C.S.: 483111

NYK Line (Australia) Pty. Ltd. (1)
Level 4 20 Bond St, Sydney, 2000, NSW, Australia **(100%)**
Tel.: (61) 292481000
Web Site: http://www.nykline.com
Sales Range: $50-74.9 Million
Emp.: 78
N.A.I.C.S.: 483114
Robyn Brown (Mgr-Acctg)

NYK Line (Benelux) B.V. (1)
Rotterdam Bldg Aert Van Nesstraat 45, 3012 CA, Rotterdam, 3012 CA, Netherlands **(100%)**
Tel.: (31) 0104031400
Web Site: http://www.nykline.com
Sales Range: $50-74.9 Million
Emp.: 60
N.A.I.C.S.: 483114
Paul Erstemeijer (Mng Dir)

NYK Line (Canada), Inc. (1)
1 Yonge St Ste 1101, Toronto, M5E 1E5, ON, Canada **(100%)**
Tel.: (416) 366-6955
Web Site: http://www.nykline.com
Sales Range: $1-9.9 Million
Emp.: 20
Shipping Services
N.A.I.C.S.: 488330

NYK Line (China) Co., Ltd. (1)
Unit 705 and 706 Raffles City Changning Tower 1 No 1133 Changning Road, Shanghai, 200051, China
Logistic Services
N.A.I.C.S.: 541614

NYK Line (Deutschland) GmbH (1)
Gorch-Fock-Wall 1a, 20354, Hamburg, Germany **(100%)**
Tel.: (49) 40334000
Web Site: http://www.nykeurope.com
Sales Range: $75-99.9 Million
Emp.: 120
Water Transportation Services
N.A.I.C.S.: 483114

NYK Line (Europe) Ltd. (1)
1 Ropemaker St, London, EC2Y 9NY, United Kingdom
Tel.: (44) 2070902000
Web Site: http://www.ne.nykline.com
Sales Range: $150-199.9 Million
Emp.: 300
N.A.I.C.S.: 483114
Morooka Masanichi (Chm)

NYK Line (Hong Kong) Ltd. (1)
Level 35 Tower 1 Kowloon Commerce Ctr 51 Kwai Cheong Rd, 51 Kwai Cheong Rd, Kwai Chung, New Territories, China (Hong Kong) **(100%)**
Tel.: (852) 28645100
Web Site: http://www.nyk.com
Sales Range: $75-99.9 Million
Emp.: 180
N.A.I.C.S.: 483114

NYK Line (New Zealand) Ltd. (1)
Level 22 151 Queen St, PO Box 57, 1010, Auckland, New Zealand
Tel.: (64) 9 358 3840

INTERNATIONAL PUBLIC

Web Site: http://www.nykline.com
Sales Range: $25-49.9 Million
Emp.: 25
Marine Transportation Services
N.A.I.C.S.: 483111
Geoff Davy (Gen Mgr)

NYK Line (North America) Inc. (1)
300 Lighting Way, Secaucus, NJ 07094
Tel.: (201) 330-3000
Web Site: http://www.nykroro.com
Emp.: 250
Marine Transportation Services
N.A.I.C.S.: 488390
Bill Payne (Pres)

NYK Line (Sverige) AB (1)
Forsta Langgatan 28, PO Box 31159, S 400 32, Gothenburg, Sweden **(100%)**
Tel.: (46) 317045400
Web Site: http://www.nykline.com
Sales Range: $50-74.9 Million
Emp.: 25
N.A.I.C.S.: 483114
Yngve Johansson (Pres)

NYK Line (Thailand) Co., Ltd. (1)
163 Ocean Insurance Building G 9-11th Floor Surawongse Road, Suriyawongse Bangrak, Bangkok, 10500, Thailand
Tel.: (66) 2629 7777
Web Site: http://www.nykline.co.th
Sales Range: $25-49.9 Million
Emp.: 25
Logistics Consulting Servies
N.A.I.C.S.: 541614

NYK Line M Sdn Bhd (1)
8th Floor East Wing Wisma Consplant No 2 Jalan SS 16 1, 47500, Subang Jaya, Selango, Malaysia **(70%)**
Tel.: (60) 356286670
Web Site: http://www.nykline.com
Sales Range: $10-24.9 Million
Emp.: 53
N.A.I.C.S.: 483114

NYK Line NZ Ltd (1)
Level 22 151 Queen St, PO Box 57, Auckland, 1010, New Zealand **(100%)**
Tel.: (64) 93583840
Web Site: http://www.nykline.com
Sales Range: $25-49.9 Million
Emp.: 24
N.A.I.C.S.: 483114
Jeff Dave (Mng Dir)

NYK Logistics (China) Co., Ltd. (1)
20F Raffles City No 268 Xizang Road Mid, Shanghai, 200001, China
Tel.: (86) 21 2320 9500
Web Site: http://www.cn.nykfogistics.co
Sales Range: $25-49.9 Million
Emp.: 200
Logistics Consulting Servies
N.A.I.C.S.: 541614

NYK Logistics (India) Ltd. (1)
Trade View Building 3rd Floor Kamala Mills Pandurang Budhkar Marg, Lower Parel, Mumbai, 400 013, India
Tel.: (91) 2230914000
Web Site: http://www.in.nyklogistics.com
Emp.: 125
Logistics Consulting Servies
N.A.I.C.S.: 541614
Koji Shinozaki (Mng Dir)

NYK Logistics (Middle East) L.L.C. (1)
Jebel Ali Free Zone, PO Box 17041, GAC Dubai Building Jebel Ali, Dubai, United Arab Emirates
Tel.: (971) 4 881 8090
Sales Range: $25-49.9 Million
Emp.: 1,600
Freight Forwarding Services
N.A.I.C.S.: 488510

NYK Logistics (Philippines) Inc. (1)
G/F TDG-NYK Harbour Center Building AC Delgado, Cor 23rd & 24th Sts Port Area, Manila, 1018, Philippines
Tel.: (63) 2 527 7057
Web Site: http://www.ph.nyklogistics.com
Sales Range: $50-74.9 Million
Emp.: 18
Freight Forwarding Services
N.A.I.C.S.: 488510

NYK Logistics (Vietnam) Co., Ltd. (1)

AND PRIVATE COMPANIES — NIPPON YUSEN KABUSHIKI KAISHA

Rm 806 HITC Bldg 239 Xuan Thuy Rd, Cau Giay Dist, Hanoi, 10000, Vietnam
Tel.: (84) 4 3768 4641
Web Site: http://www.vn.nyklogistics.com
Freight Forwarding Services
N.A.I.C.S.: 488510

NYK RORO (Thailand) Co., Ltd. (1)
163 Ocean Insurance Building G 9-11th Floor Surawongse Rd, Bangrak, Bangkok, 10500, Thailand
Tel.: (66) 2634 0073
Logistics Consulting Services
N.A.I.C.S.: 541614

NYK Shipmanagement Pte. Ltd. (1)
1 HarbourFront Place 15-01 HarbourFront Tower One, Singapore, 098633, Singapore
Tel.: (65) 64167500
Web Site: https://www.nyksm.com.sg
Sales Range: $50-74.9 Million
Emp.: 200
Marine Transportation Services
N.A.I.C.S.: 488390

NYK Shipping Service (Thailand) Co., Ltd. (1)
10th And 11th Floor Ocean Insurance Building, 163 Surawongse Road, Bangkok, 10500, Thailand **(100%)**
Tel.: (66) 22679900
Web Site: http://www.nykline.com
Sales Range: $75-99.9 Million
Emp.: 250
N.A.I.C.S.: 483114

NYK Sudamerica (Chile) Ltda. (1)
Av Cerro El Plomo 5680 Of 504, Las Condes, Santiago, Chile
Tel.: (56) 22 750 4500
Web Site: https://www.nyk.cl
Logistics Transportation Services
N.A.I.C.S.: 541614
Alejandro Avendano *(Mgr-Logistic Div)*

NYK TDG Philippines Inc. (1)
Bacnotan Drive Bo Real, Calamba, Laguna, Philippines
Tel.: (63) 25208848
Web Site: http://www.nyktdgphil.com
Logistic Services
N.A.I.C.S.: 541614

NYK Terminals (Taiwan), Inc. (1)
67 Chi Chin 1st Rd, Kaohsiung, 80546, Taiwan
Tel.: (886) 75710037
Marine Cargo Terminal Operating Services
N.A.I.C.S.: 488390

NYK Trading (Singapore) Pte. Ltd. (1)
194 Pandan Loop 06-28 Pantech Business Hub, Singapore, 128383, Singapore
Tel.: (65) 6 774 8550
Web Site: https://nyktrading.com.sg
Logistic Services
N.A.I.C.S.: 541614
Soo Koon Chew *(Mgr)*

NYK Trading Corporation (1)
34th floor WTC Bldg 2-4-1 Hamamatsu-cho, Minato-ku, Tokyo, 105-6134, Japan
Tel.: (81) 35 408 7101
Web Site: https://www.nyk-trading.com
Emp.: 141
Marine Equipment Whslr
N.A.I.C.S.: 423860
Shigeru Ohtani *(Exec Officer)*

NYK de Mexico, S.A. de C.V. (1)
Blvd Miguel de la Madrid No 426 Edificio Torre Puerto Piso 5 Local 52, Zona Industrial Fondeport, 28200, Manzanillo, Colima, Mexico
Tel.: (52) 55 5002 6000
Web Site: http://www2.nykline.com
Marine Transportation Services
N.A.I.C.S.: 488390

NYK-Fil Maritime E-Training, Inc. (1)
Knowledge Avenue Carmeltown Canlubang, Calamba, 4037, Laguna, Philippines
Tel.: (63) 495088600
Web Site: https://www.neti.com.ph
Maritime Training Services
N.A.I.C.S.: 541618

NYK-Fil Ship Management, Inc. (1)
Casa Marinero General Luna St, Intramuros, Manila, 1002, Kalakhang Maynila, Philippines
Tel.: (63) 27 908 4900
Web Site: https://www.nykfil.com.ph
Ship Manning Services
N.A.I.C.S.: 488510
Imee Aventurado *(Mgr-Purchasing)*

NYK-Hinode Line, Ltd. (1)
Yusen Bldg 3-2 Marunouchi 2-chome, Chiyoda-ku, Tokyo, 100-0005, Japan
Tel.: (81) 3 5220 5780
Web Site: http://www.nyk-hinode.com
Sales Range: $25-49.9 Million
Emp.: 100
Marine Cargo Handling Services
N.A.I.C.S.: 488320

NYKt Energy & Technology (Shanghai) Corp. (1)
Room606 No 679 Ningxia Road, Putuo District, Shanghai, 200063, China
Tel.: (86) 2163403301
Container & Marine Equipment Distr
N.A.I.C.S.: 423860

NYKt Marine Co., Ltd. (1)
3rd Floor Kannai Arai Bldg 1-8 Onoecho, Naka-ku, Yokohama, 231-0015, Japan
Tel.: (81) 45 226 0021
Web Site: https://www.nyktmarine.com
Emp.: 106
Marine Cargo Handling Services
N.A.I.C.S.: 488320

Naikai Tug Boat Service Co., Ltd (1)
2F Hiroshima Port Ujina Passenger Terminal 1-13-26 Ujikaigan, Minami-ku, Hiroshima, 734-0011, Japan
Tel.: (81) 822536611
Web Site: https://www.naikaitug.co.jp
Marine Transportation Services
N.A.I.C.S.: 488390

Nca Japan Co., Ltd. (1)
Tel.: (81) 476295600
Web Site: http://www.ncajapan.co.jp
Emp.: 204
Air Cargo Handling Services
N.A.I.C.S.: 488119

Nippon Cargo Airlines Co., Ltd. (1)
Narita International Airport, Narita, 282-0011, Chiba, Japan
Tel.: (81) 47 630 3001
Web Site: https://www.nca.aero
Emp.: 882
Air Cargo Transportation Services
N.A.I.C.S.: 488119
Hitoshi Oshika *(Pres & CEO)*

Nippon Container Terminals Co., Ltd. (1)
Mita-Kokusai Bldg 24F 4-28 Mita 1-Chome, Minato-ku, Tokyo, 108-0073, Japan
Tel.: (81) 3 5442 2161
Web Site: http://www.nct-ho.co.jp
Emp.: 177
Harbor Transportation Services
N.A.I.C.S.: 488310
Yasuyuki Usui *(Exec Dir)*

Nippon Container Yuso Co., Ltd. (1)
2-7-8 Yashio, Shinagawa-Ku, Tokyo, 140-0003, Japan
Tel.: (81) 33 790 6471
Web Site: https://www.ncyjp.co.jp
Emp.: 130
Freight Trucking Services
N.A.I.C.S.: 484121
Hiroaki Tsuchiya *(Pres)*

Nishinihon Kaiun Kaisha, Ltd. (1)
Tel.: (81) 933210486
Web Site: http://www.nishi-kai.com
Emp.: 111
Shipping Agency Services
N.A.I.C.S.: 488510

Ocean Network Express Holdings, Ltd. (1)
11F W Building, 1-8-15 Kohnan Minato-ku,, Tokyo, 108-0075, Japan **(38%)**
Tel.: (65) 62200196
Web Site: https://holdco.one-line.com
Marine transportation
N.A.I.C.S.: 713930

Subsidiary (Non-US):

Ocean Network Express Pte. Ltd. (2)
7 Straits View, #16-01 Marina One East Tower,, Singapore, 018936, Singapore
Tel.: (65) 62200196
Web Site: https://www.one-line.com
Container Shipping Businesses
N.A.I.C.S.: 488510
Jeremy Nixon *(CEO)*

Subsidiary (US):

TraPac, LLC (3)
920 West Harry Bridges Blvd, Wilmington, CA 90744
Tel.: (310) 830-2000
Web Site: http://www.trapac.com
Rev.: $7,000,000
Emp.: 50
Freight Transportation Arrangement
N.A.I.C.S.: 488510
Scott Axelson *(VP-Bus Dev)*

Yusen Terminals, LLC (3)
701 New Dock St, Terminal Island, CA 90731
Tel.: (310) 548-8000
Web Site: http://www.yti.com
Marine Cargo Terminal Operating Services
N.A.I.C.S.: 488310
Alan McCorkle *(CEO)*

Oita Rinkai Kogyo K.K. (1)
5F Oita Steel Building 3-1-11 Matsubaracho, Matsubaramachi, Oita, 870-0913, Japan
Tel.: (81) 975589588
Web Site: https://www.oitarinkai.co.jp
Emp.: 42
Maritime Disaster Prevention Services
N.A.I.C.S.: 488390

Okinawa Maritime Industries Co., Ltd. (1)
1 Yonashiro-Hiramiya, Uruma, 900-2428, Okinawa, Japan
Tel.: (81) 98 977 7733
Web Site: https://www.oki-kai.co.jp
Emp.: 30
Shipping Agency Services
N.A.I.C.S.: 488510
Takeshi Ishioka *(Pres)*

P.T. NYK New Wave Logistics Indonesia (1)
MM2100 Industrial Town Blok EE-4 Cikarang, Bekasi, 17520, West Java, Indonesia
Tel.: (62) 21 898 1020
Web Site: http://www.idnwl.nyklogistics.com
Freight Forwarding Services
N.A.I.C.S.: 488510

P.T. NYK New Wave Warehousing (Indonesia) (1)
MM2100 Industrial Town Blok EE-4 Cikarang, Bekasi, 17520, West Java, Indonesia
Tel.: (62) 21 8998 2180
Logistics Consulting Servies
N.A.I.C.S.: 541614

PT. NYK Puninar Logistics Indonesia (1)
Jln Raya Cakung Cilincing KM 1 5, Cakung Jakarta Timur, Jakarta, 13910, Indonesia
Tel.: (62) 21 460 2278
Web Site: https://www.puninar.com
Emp.: 250
Logistics Consulting Servies
N.A.I.C.S.: 541614
Ngono Budijanto *(Pres)*

PT. NYK-Spil Indororo (1)
Sahid Sudirman Centre 16th Floor Unit 16C D H Jl Jend Sudirman No 86, Jakarta, 10220, Indonesia
Tel.: (62) 2180861234
Web Site: http://www.nykspilroro.com
Freight Forwarding Services
N.A.I.C.S.: 488510

PT. Yusen Logistics Solutions Indonesia (1)
Logistic Services
N.A.I.C.S.: 541614

Pegasus Enterprise Co., Ltd. (1)
1-2-5 Mikawaguchicho, Hyogo-Ku, Kobe, 652-0815, Hyogo, Japan
Tel.: (81) 786512951
Marine Transportation Services
N.A.I.C.S.: 488390

Pegasus Maritime Co., Ltd. (1)
74 Kyomachi Dentsu Kobe Bldg 6F, Chuo-Ku, Kobe, 650-0034, Hyogo, Japan
Tel.: (81) 783343922
Marine Transportation Services
N.A.I.C.S.: 488390
Koji Takemura *(Superintendent)*

Rolf Logistic LLC (1)
Altufevskoe sh Building 31 bldg 1, 127410, Moscow, Russia
Tel.: (7) 4952259292
Web Site: http://www.rolfscs.ru
Logistic Services
N.A.I.C.S.: 541614

Saga Shipholding (Norway) AS (1)
Tollbodgaten 22, 3111, Tonsberg, Vestfold, Norway
Tel.: (47) 45377305
Web Site: https://sagashipholding.no
Investment Management Service
N.A.I.C.S.: 523999

Seidopro Global Inc. (1)
20th Floor Four/NEO Building 4th Avenue Corner 30th Street, E-Square Crescent Park West Bonifacio Global City, Taguig, 1634, Philippines
Tel.: (63) 2 859 8888
Web Site: https://www.seidopro.com
BPO & Consulting Firm Services
N.A.I.C.S.: 541611
Jonathan R. Manucat *(Gen Mgr)*

Shenzhen Yusen Logistics Service Co., Ltd (1)
4/F Fubao Building No 2 Hongmian Road Futian Free Trade Zone, Shenzhen, China
Tel.: (86) 75582734772
Logistic Services
N.A.I.C.S.: 541614

Shin-Nipponkaiyosha Corporation (1)
19F Minotomirai Center Building 3-6-1 Minotomirai 3-Chome, Nishi-Ku, Yokohama, 220-0012, Kanagawa, Japan
Tel.: (81) 45 212 4050
Web Site: https://www.snkaiyosha.co.jp
Towing & Tugboat Services
N.A.I.C.S.: 488330

Symphony Creative Solutions Pte. Ltd. (1)
71 Ayer Rajah Crescent 01-03, Singapore, 139951, Singapore
Tel.: (65) 6 352 1371
Web Site: https://www.scs71.com
Shipping & Logistics Services
N.A.I.C.S.: 541614
Akiko Tsurumi *(Mng Dir)*

Taiheiyo Kisen Kaisha, Ltd. (1)
NBF Ogawamachi Bldg 7th Floor 1-3-1 Kanda-Ogawamachi, Chiyoda-ku, Tokyo, 101-0052, Japan
Tel.: (81) 35 217 3050
Web Site: https://www.taiheiyo-kisen.co.jp
Emp.: 23
Sea Cargo Shipping Services
N.A.I.C.S.: 483111
Kenichi Miki *(Pres)*

Tata NYK Shipping Pte. Ltd. (1)
6 Shenton Way 18-08B OUE Downtown 2, Singapore, 068809, Singapore
Tel.: (65) 6 262 2166
Web Site: https://www.tatanykshipping.com
Cargo Shipping Services
N.A.I.C.S.: 488510
Amitabh Panda *(Mng Dir)*

The Cruise Club Tokyo Inc. (1)
1F Seafort Square 2-3-16 Higashi-shinagawa, Shinagawa-ku, Tokyo, 140-0002, Japan
Tel.: (81) 334504300
Web Site: https://www.cctokyo.co.jp
Cruise Shipping Services
N.A.I.C.S.: 483112

Transcontainer (TCL) Philippines, Inc. (1)
Ground Floor TDG-NYK Harbor Center Bldg I A C Delgado St Cor, 23rd and 24th Sts Brgy 653 Zone 068 Port Area, Manila, 1018, Philippines
Tel.: (63) 85277060
Web Site: http://www.tcl.com.ph

NIPPON YUSEN KABUSHIKI KAISHA

Nippon Yusen Kabushiki Kaisha—(Continued)
Logistic Services
N.A.I.C.S.: 541614

Transcontainer Limited (1)
4-10-27 Higashi Shinagawa Sumitomo Fudosan Shinagawa Bldg, Shinagawa-ku, Tokyo, 140-0002, Japan
Tel.: (81) 33 472 4111
Web Site: https://www.tcl.jp
Ocean Transportation Services
N.A.I.C.S.: 483111

Transcontainer Logistics (Thailand) Co., Ltd. (1)
23/11-12 Sorachai Bldg 11th Floor Soi Sukhumvit 63 Sukhumvit Road, Klongton-Nua Wattana, Bangkok, 10110, Thailand
Tel.: (66) 27143080
Freight Transportation Services
N.A.I.C.S.: 488510

Transmeridian S.A.C. (1)
Av Canaval y Moreyra 340 Piso 11, San Isidro, Lima, Peru
Tel.: (51) 16123000
Web Site: http://www.transmeridian.pe
Emp.: 800
Shipping Agency Services
N.A.I.C.S.: 488510

Uni-X Corporation (1)
NT Bldg 1-47-1 Ohi, Shinagawa-ku, Tokyo, 1400014, Japan
Tel.: (81) 3 5742 7700
Web Site: http://www.uni-x.co.jp
Marine Cargo Handling Services
N.A.I.C.S.: 488320
Takamitsu Wakita *(Pres)*

Subsidiary (Non-US):

UNI-X (BOLIVIA) LTDA (2)
Avenida Arce No 2631 Edificio Multicine Piso 4 Of 402, La Paz, Bolivia
Tel.: (591) 2 2912644
Web Site: http://www.unixbol.bo
Sales Range: $25-49.9 Million
Emp.: 8
Marine Transportation Services
N.A.I.C.S.: 488390
Eliana Cabrera *(Gen Mgr)*

Uni-X Nct Corporation (1)
Sumitomo Realty Development Oimachi Station Bldg 4F 13F 1-28-1 Ohi, Shinagawa-ku, Tokyo, 140-0014, Japan
Tel.: (81) 35 742 7700
Web Site: https://www.uni-xnct.com
Emp.: 446
Shipping Freight Transportation Services
N.A.I.C.S.: 488390

United European Car Carriers AS (1)
Karenslyst Alle 49, 0279, Oslo, Norway
Tel.: (47) 90160455
Web Site: https://www.uecc.com
Emp.: 345
Sea Transportation Services
N.A.I.C.S.: 483111

Wing Maritime Service Corporation (1)
13F Landmark Tower Yokohama 2-1 Minatomirai 2-Chome, Nishi-Ku, Yokohama, 220-8113, Kanagawa, Japan
Tel.: (81) 45 212 4050
Web Site: http://www.wingmsc.co.jp
Sales Range: $50-74.9 Million
Emp.: 194
Marine Transportation Services
N.A.I.C.S.: 488390
Takahiro Ota *(Pres)*

YCS Co., Ltd. (1)
Sumitomo Corporation Nishiki-cho Bldg 10F 1-6, Kanda-Nishiki-cho Chiyoda-ku, Tokyo, 101-0054, Japan
Tel.: (81) 367598800
Web Site: https://www.ycsco.com
Emp.: 521
Temporary Staffing Services
N.A.I.C.S.: 561320

Yjk Solutions Co., Ltd., (1)
15th floor Kowa Nishi-Shinbashi Building 2-1-1 Nishi-Shimbashi, Minato-ku, Tokyo, 105-0003, Japan
Tel.: (81) 354257200
Web Site: https://www.yjk.co.jp
Emp.: 137
Software Development Services
N.A.I.C.S.: 541511

Yokohama Kyoritsu Warehouse Co., Ltd. (1)
9-17 Daikoku-cho DPL Yokohama Daikoku 201, Tsurumi-ku, Yokohama, 230-0053, Japan
Tel.: (81) 455063222
Web Site: http://www.kyoritsu-soko.co.jp
Emp.: 62
Warehouse & Logistics Services
N.A.I.C.S.: 541614

Yusen Inci Lojistik Ve Ticaret A.S. (1)
Tel.: (90) 2122593777
Logistic Services
N.A.I.C.S.: 541614

Yusen Koun Co., Ltd. (1)
9th floor Nomura Fudosan Yotsubashi Building 1-4-4 Awaza, Nishi-ku, Osaka, 550-0011, Japan
Tel.: (81) 665382210
Web Site: https://www.yusen-koun.co.jp
Sales Range: $50-74.9 Million
Emp.: 150
Freight Transportation Services
N.A.I.C.S.: 483211

Yusen LogistiCS (Americas) Inc. (1)
300 Lighting Way 5th Fl, Secaucus, NJ 07094-3647 (100%)
Tel.: (201) 553-3800
Web Site: https://www.yusen-logistics.com
Logistics Solutions
N.A.I.C.S.: 483111

Division (Domestic):

GST Corporation (2)
1900 Charles Bryan Rd, Cordova, TN 38017
Tel.: (901) 794-2225
Web Site: http://www.yusen-logistics.com
Sales Range: $100-124.9 Million
Transportation & Logistics Solutions
N.A.I.C.S.: 488999

Yusen Logistics & Kusuhara Lanka Pvt Ltd (1)
West Wing Ground Floor 400 Deans Road, Colombo, Sri Lanka
Tel.: (94) 112167600
Logistic Services
N.A.I.C.S.: 541614

Yusen Logistics (Americas) Inc. (1)
300 Lighting Way, Secaucus, NJ 07094
Tel.: (201) 553-3800
Logistic Services
N.A.I.C.S.: 541614

Subsidiary (Domestic):

Taylored Services Inc. (2)
231 Mill Rd, Edison, NJ 08837
Tel.: (732) 248-7900
Web Site: http://www.tpservices.com
Package Design; Packaging Systems; Packaging Materials
N.A.I.C.S.: 541430
Gladys Perez *(Acct Mgr-Customer Svc)*

Yusen Logistics (Argentina) S.A. (1)
Av Leandro N Alem 1067 15th Floor, Buenos Aires, Argentina
Tel.: (54) 1152176000
Logistic Services
N.A.I.C.S.: 541614

Yusen Logistics (Bangladesh) Ltd. (1)
14th Floor Landview Commercial Center 28 Gulshan North C/A Gulshan 2, Dhaka, 1212, Bangladesh
Freight Transportation Services
N.A.I.C.S.: 488510
Tariqul Islam *(Mng Dir)*

Yusen Logistics (Benelux) B.V. (1)
Middenweg 10, 4782 PM, Moerdijk, Netherlands
Tel.: (31) 885522200
Logistic Services
N.A.I.C.S.: 541614

Yusen Logistics (Cambodia) Co., Ltd. (1)
Logistic Services
N.A.I.C.S.: 541614
Som Soriya *(Mgr-HR & Admin)*

Yusen Logistics (Canada) Inc. (1)
261 Parkhust Square, Brampton, L6T 5H5, ON, Canada
Tel.: (905) 458-2000
Logistic Services
N.A.I.C.S.: 541614
Sunaina Singh *(Coord-Logistics)*

Yusen Logistics (China) Co., Ltd. (1)
8th Floor and Unit 901-05 907-09 9th Floor, Raffles City Changning Office Tower 1 No 1133 Changning Road, Shanghai, 200051, China
Tel.: (86) 2122207500
Freight Forwarding Services
N.A.I.C.S.: 488510

Yusen Logistics (Czech) S.R.O. (1)
Kunice 308, Strancice, 251 63, Prague, Czech Republic
Tel.: (420) 323577222
Logistic Services
N.A.I.C.S.: 541614
Ondrej Rak *(Sr Mgr-Corporate Svcs)*

Yusen Logistics (Deutschland) GmbH (1)
Theodorstr 299, 40472, Dusseldorf, Germany
Tel.: (49) 211418540
Logistic Services
N.A.I.C.S.: 541614
Toshikazu Shiota *(Mng Dir)*

Yusen Logistics (Edam) B.V. (1)
Expeditiestraat 1, 1135 GB, Edam, Netherlands
Tel.: (31) 299372051
Logistic Services
N.A.I.C.S.: 541614
Olaf Tol *(Ops Mgr)*

Yusen Logistics (Europe) B.V. (1)
Taurusavenue 27A Beukenhorst Zuid, 2132 LS, Hoofddorp, Netherlands
Tel.: (31) 884422500
Logistic Services
N.A.I.C.S.: 541614

Yusen Logistics (Hong Kong) Ltd. (1)
Level 31 Tower 1 Kowloon Commerce Centre 51 Kwai Cheong Road, Kwai Chung New Territories, Hong Kong, China (Hong Kong)
Tel.: (852) 22659888
Logistic Services
N.A.I.C.S.: 541614

Yusen Logistics (Hungary) Kft. (1)
Europa u 6 BILK B2 building, 1239, Budapest, Hungary
Tel.: (36) 15552500
Logistic Services
N.A.I.C.S.: 541614

Yusen Logistics (Iberica) S.A. (1)
C/Cal Pi de l'Olla N 37-39, El Prat de Llobregat, 08820, Barcelona, Spain
Tel.: (34) 933287090
Logistic Services
N.A.I.C.S.: 541614
Miriam Maria Calvache *(Fin Mgr)*

Yusen Logistics (India) Pte. Ltd. (1)
Tel.: (91) 2248864000
Logistic Services
N.A.I.C.S.: 541614

Yusen Logistics (Italy) S.P.A. (1)
Via Privata Piemonte 1, 20010, Arluno, MI, Italy
Tel.: (39) 029025171
Logistic Services
N.A.I.C.S.: 541614
Pietro Leanza *(Mgr)*

Yusen Logistics (Korea) Co., Ltd. (1)
17F 361 DMC Iaan Sangam II World Cup buk-ro, Mapo-gu, Seoul, 03908, Korea (South)
Logistic Services
N.A.I.C.S.: 541614

INTERNATIONAL PUBLIC

Yusen Logistics (Lao) Co., Ltd. (1)
Royal Square Office Building 7th Floor 20 Samsenthay Road, Nongduang Nuea Village Sikhottabong District, Vientiane, Lao People's Democratic Republic
Tel.: (856) 21221077
Logistic Services
N.A.I.C.S.: 541614

Yusen Logistics (Mexico), S.A. De C.V. (1)
Av Amistad No 116 Autopista Queretaro-Irapuato KM 35 500, Parque Industrial Amistad Bajio, 38160, Apaseo el Grande, Guanajuato, Mexico
Tel.: (52) 4611591400
Logistic Services
N.A.I.C.S.: 541614

Yusen Logistics (Middle East) L.L.C. (1)
Logistic Services
N.A.I.C.S.: 541614

Yusen Logistics (Myanmar) Co., Ltd. (1)
Logistic Services
N.A.I.C.S.: 541614
Akihiro Azuma *(Mng Dir)*

Yusen Logistics (Philippines) Inc. (1)
Phase 1 Access Road Amvel Business Park Brgy Sucat Road, San Dionisio, Paranaque, 1708, Philippines
Tel.: (63) 288352888
Logistic Services
N.A.I.C.S.: 541614

Yusen Logistics (Polska) Sp.Zo.O. (1)
Domaniewska 34a, 02-672, Warsaw, Poland
Tel.: (48) 225673610
Logistic Services
N.A.I.C.S.: 541614

Yusen Logistics (Romania) Srl (1)
Tel.: (40) 312292700
Emp.: 1,400
Logistic Services
N.A.I.C.S.: 541614

Yusen Logistics (Shenzhen) Co., Ltd. (1)
Tel.: (86) 75536909992
Logistic Services
N.A.I.C.S.: 541614

Yusen Logistics (Singapore) Pte. Ltd. (1)
2 Changi South Avenue 2 05-00, Singapore, 486354, Singapore
Tel.: (65) 65468858
Logistic Services
N.A.I.C.S.: 541614

Yusen Logistics (Taiwan) Ltd. (1)
8F No 88 Sec 2 Chung Hsiao East Road, Taipei, Taiwan
Tel.: (886) 223516310
Logistic Services
N.A.I.C.S.: 541614

Yusen Logistics (Thailand) Co., Ltd. (1)
2525 One Two FYI Center 2nd 6th 7th FL Rama4 Rd, Klongtoey, Bangkok, 10110, Thailand
Tel.: (66) 20348000
Emp.: 1,529
Logistic Services
N.A.I.C.S.: 541614

Yusen Logistics (Vietnam) Co., Ltd. (1)
Room 805 HITC Building 239 Xuan Thuy Road, Cau Giay District, Hanoi, Vietnam
Logistic Services
N.A.I.C.S.: 541614

Yusen Logistics Center, Inc. (1)
1st Avenue Extension MEZ 1, Lapu-Lapu, Cebu, Philippines
Tel.: (63) 324952766
Logistic Services
N.A.I.C.S.: 541614

Yusen Logistics Co., Ltd. (1)
Shinagawa Seaside Park Tower 4-12-4 Higashishinagawa, Shinagawa-ku, Tokyo,

AND PRIVATE COMPANIES

140-0002, Japan
Tel.: (81) 367038111
Web Site: http://www.yusen-logistics.com
Sales Range: $1-4.9 Billion
Emp.: 23,544
Freight Forwarding & Logistics Consulting Services
N.A.I.C.S.: 488510
Minoru Futonaka *(Exec Officer)*

Subsidiary (Non-US):

YUSEN LOGISTICS (AUSTRALIA) PTY. LTD.
1 Entolasia Close, Kemps Creek, Sydney, 2178, NSW, Australia
Tel.: (61) 288629220
Emp.: 305
Logistics Consulting Servies
N.A.I.C.S.: 541614

Yusen Logistics (France) S.A.S. (2)
Tel.: (33) 174372000
Sales Range: $25-49.9 Million
Emp.: 100
Logistics Consulting Servies
N.A.I.C.S.: 541614

Yusen Logistics UK Ltd (2)
Grange Park 1 Cheaney Drive Grange Park, Northampton, NN4 5FB, United Kingdom
Tel.: (44) 1604748500
Sales Range: $350-399.9 Million
Emp.: 2,000
Logistics Consulting Servies
N.A.I.C.S.: 541614

Yusen Logistics Do Brasil Ltda. (1)
Rodovia Anhanguera Km 26 421m, Perus, Sao Paulo, Brazil
Tel.: (55) 1139089740
Logistic Services
N.A.I.C.S.: 541614

Yusen Logistics Pakistan (Pte.) Ltd. (1)
Tel.: (92) 423577749597
Logistic Services
N.A.I.C.S.: 541614

Yusen Logistics Rus LLC (1)
Gamsonovskiy pereulok 5 build 2, Moscow, Russia
Tel.: (7) 4957750739
Logistic Services
N.A.I.C.S.: 541614
Albert Abdulin *(Mng Dir)*

Yusen Real Estate Corporation (1)
1-8-3 Nihonbashi Kayabacho Yusen Kayabacho Building 4th and 5th floors, Chuo-Ku, Tokyo, 103-0025, Japan
Tel.: (81) 3 5644 7421
Web Site: http://www.yfk.co.jp
Real Estate Manangement Services
N.A.I.C.S.: 531390

Yusen Terminal Logopark LLC (1)
Nab Obvodnogo Kanala 138 4th Floor Business center Treugolnik office, 190020, Saint Petersburg, Russia
Tel.: (7) 8126037100
Logistic Services
N.A.I.C.S.: 541614

Yusen Travel (Hong Kong) Ltd. (1)
13/F 88 Lockhart Road, Wanchai, China (Hong Kong)
Tel.: (852) 28653783
Web Site: http://www.yusentravel.com.hk
Travel Agency Services
N.A.I.C.S.: 561510
Naofumi Ota *(CEO)*

Yusen Travel (Singapore) Pte., Ltd. (1)
391 A Orchard Road 09-03 Ngee Ann City Tower A, Singapore, 238873, Singapore
Tel.: (65) 6 732 1511
Web Site: https://www.yusentravel.sg
Tour Operator Services
N.A.I.C.S.: 561520
Masakazu Sagawa *(Mng Dir)*

Yusen Travel (U.S.A.) Inc. (1)
6 East 39th St Ste 305, New York, NY 10016
Tel.: (646) 366-1557
Web Site: http://www.yusentravel.com
Travel Agency Services
N.A.I.C.S.: 561510

Yusen Travel Co., Ltd. (1)
Millene Jimbocho Building 2-2 Kanda-Jimbocho, Chiyoda-ku, Tokyo, 101-8422, Japan
Tel.: (81) 352136705
Web Site: http://www.ytk.co.jp
Emp.: 210
Shipping Agency Services
N.A.I.C.S.: 488510

Yusen Zhongyun Logistics (Dalian) Co., Ltd. (1)
115 Gangxing Avenue Bonded Area, Dalian, China
Tel.: (86) 41187514555
Logistic Services
N.A.I.C.S.: 541614

NIPRESS TBK

Jl Raya Narogong Km 26 Cileungsi, Bogor, 16820, Jawa Barat, Indonesia
Tel.: (62) 218230968
Web Site: https://www.indonesia-investments.com
Year Founded: 1970
Rev.: $75,393,266
Assets: $132,857,371
Liabilities: $71,291,491
Net Worth: $61,565,880
Earnings: $3,087,758
Emp.: 971
Fiscal Year-end: 12/31/17
Battery Mfr
N.A.I.C.S.: 335910

NIPRO CORPORATION

3-26 Senriokashinmachi, Settsu, Osaka, 566-8510, Japan
Tel.: (81) 663106907
Web Site: https://www.nipro.co.jp
Year Founded: 1954
8086—(TKS)
Rev.: $3,878,648,850
Assets: $7,335,916,810
Liabilities: $5,552,618,130
Net Worth: $1,783,298,680
Earnings: $73,430,490
Emp.: 38,117
Fiscal Year-end: 03/31/24
Medical Care Products Developer, Glass Tubes, Electric Light Bulbs & Glass Molded Products Mfr & Marketer
N.A.I.C.S.: 339112
Yoshihiko Sano *(Pres)*

Subsidiaries:

CardioMed Supplies Inc. (1)
199 St David Street, Lindsay, K9V-5K7, ON, Canada
Tel.: (705) 328-2518
Web Site: https://cardiomed.com
Medical Equipment Mfr & Distr
N.A.I.C.S.: 339112

Cell Science & Technology Institute, Inc. (1)
1-16-16 Seikaen, Aoba-ku, Sendai, 982-0262, Miyagi, Japan
Tel.: (81) 22 399 6608
Web Site: https://www.cstimedia.com
Cell Culture Media Product Mfr
N.A.I.C.S.: 325414

Goodman Co., Ltd. (1)
KDX Nagoya Sakae Building 5F 5-3-3 Sakae, Naka-ku, Nagoya, 460-0008, Aichi, Japan
Tel.: (81) 522695300
Web Site: http://www.goodmankk.com
Sales Range: $250-299.9 Million
Emp.: 524
Medical Equipment & Medical Disposables Mfr & Distr
N.A.I.C.S.: 339112
Yasushi Oyama *(Pres)*

Subsidiary (US):

Avantec Vascular Corp. (2)
870 Hermosa Dr, Sunnyvale, CA 94085
Tel.: (408) 329-5400
Web Site: https://www.avantecvascular.com
Sales Range: $25-49.9 Million
Emp.: 35
Mfr& Developer of Products for the Treatment of Vascular Disease
N.A.I.C.S.: 339112
Jack Hoshino *(Pres & CEO)*

Subsidiary (Non-US):

Goodman Medical Ireland Limited (2)
Mervue Business Park, Galway, Connacht, Ireland
Tel.: (353) 91751089
Web Site: https://www.goodmanmedical.ie
Sales Range: $25-49.9 Million
Emp.: 100
Medical Equipment Mfr
N.A.I.C.S.: 339112
Yasushi Oyama *(Pres)*

Subsidiary (Domestic):

Goodtec Co., Ltd. (2)
2-501 Ueshirokane, Seki, 501 3947, Gifu, Japan
Tel.: (81) 575285561
Web Site: http://www.goodtec.co.jp
Medical Equipments Mfr & Sales
N.A.I.C.S.: 339113

Infraredx, Inc. (1)
28 Crosby Dr Ste 100, Bedford, MA 01730
Tel.: (781) 221-0053
Web Site: https://www.infraredx.com
Surgical & Medical Instrument Mfr
N.A.I.C.S.: 339112
Stephen Sum *(Sr VP-Tech Innovation & Regulatory)*

Kagamaiishi Plant (1)
428 Okanouchi Kagamiishi-machi, Iwase-gun, 969-0401, Fukushima, Japan
Tel.: (81) 248622121
Sales Range: $50-74.9 Million
Pharmaceutical Preparation Mfr
N.A.I.C.S.: 325412

Nipro (Shanghai) Co., Ltd. (1)
2555 Bao an Road Ma lu, Jia Ding District, Shanghai, 201801, China
Tel.: (86) 2169154923
Web Site: http://www.nipro.com.cn
Surgical & Medical Instrument Mfr
N.A.I.C.S.: 339112

Nipro (Thailand) Corporation Ltd. (1)
10/2 Moo 8 Bangnomko, Sena, Phra Nakhon Si Ayutthaya, 13110, Thailand
Tel.: (66) 35201618
Web Site: http://www.nipro.co.jp
Sales Range: $800-899.9 Million
Emp.: 3,000
Surgical & Medical Instrument Mfr
N.A.I.C.S.: 339112

Nipro Asia Pte. Ltd. (1)
6 Temasek Boulevard 31-01/02 Suntec Tower Four, Singapore, 038986, Singapore
Tel.: (65) 65882281
Web Site: https://www.niproasia.com.sg
Medical Dental & Hospital Equipment & Supplies Whslr
N.A.I.C.S.: 423450

Nipro Corporation - OHDATE FACTORY (1)
8-7 Hanukiyachi Niida, Odate, 018-5794, Akita, Japan
Tel.: (81) 186 49 5111
Web Site: http://www.nipro.co.jp
Pharmaceuticals Product Mfr
N.A.I.C.S.: 325412

Nipro Corporation - OHTSU FACTORY (1)
2-1-6 Beppo, Otsu, 520-0835, Shiga, Japan
Tel.: (81) 77 537 1473
Pharmaceuticals Product Mfr
N.A.I.C.S.: 325412

Nipro Diagnostics (UK) Limited (1)
Units 12-14 South Point Ensign Way, Hamble, SO31 4RF, Hampshire, United Kingdom
Tel.: (44) 8000858808
Web Site: https://www.nipro-diagnostics.co.uk

NIPRO CORPORATION

Sales Range: $1-9.9 Million
Emp.: 20
Medical Instrument Distr
N.A.I.C.S.: 339112
Christopher J. Avery *(Mng Dir)*

Nipro Europe Group Companies N.V. (1)
Blokhuisstraat 42, 2800, Mechelen, Belgium
Tel.: (32) 1 526 3500
Web Site: https://www.nipro-group.com
Medical Equipment Mfr & Distr
N.A.I.C.S.: 339112

Nipro Europe N.V. (1)
Blokhuisstraat 42, 2800, Mechelen, Belgium
Tel.: (32) 15263500
Web Site: https://www.nipro-group.com
Sales Range: $25-49.9 Million
Emp.: 75
Medical Dental & Hospital Equipment & Supplies Whslr
N.A.I.C.S.: 423450
Kurt Dal *(Mng Dir)*

Nipro India Corporation Pvt. Ltd. (1)
Plot No E-1/2 MIDC Kesurdi Khandala, Taluka - Khandala, Satara, 412 802, Maharashtra, India
Tel.: (91) 2169305050
Web Site: https://niproinindia.com
Sales Range: $50-74.9 Million
Emp.: 150
Medical Device Mfr & Distr
N.A.I.C.S.: 334510

Nipro JMI Pharma Ltd. (1)
Unique Heights Level-6 117 Kazi Nazrul Islam Avenue, Eskaton, Dhaka, 1217, Bangladesh
Tel.: (880) 25 513 8726
Web Site: https://www.niprojmipharma.com
Pharmaceuticals Product Mfr
N.A.I.C.S.: 325412
Yoshihiko Sano *(Pres)*

Nipro Medica de Mexico, S.A. de C.V. (1)
Sierra Candela No 111 Piso 11, Miguel Hidalgo, 11000, Lomas de Chapultepec, Mexico
Tel.: (52) 5553527100
Web Site: https://www.nipromexico.com
Medical Dental & Hospital Equipment & Supplies Whslr
N.A.I.C.S.: 423450

Nipro Medical (India) Pvt. Ltd. (1)
GMR Aero Towers 2nd Floor Rajiv Gandhi International Airport, Shamshabad, Hyderabad, 500 108, Telangana, India
Tel.: (91) 4428250341
Web Site: http://www.niproindia.com
Sales Range: $50-74.9 Million
Emp.: 72
Pharmaceutical Products Mfr & Distr
N.A.I.C.S.: 325412

Nipro Medical Corporation (1)
3150 NW 107 Ave, Miami, FL 33172-2135
Tel.: (305) 599-7174
Web Site: https://www.nipro.com
Medical Dental & Hospital Equipment & Supplies Whslr
N.A.I.C.S.: 423450

Nipro Medical Industries, Ltd. (1)
2-19-64 Matsubara, Tatebayashi, Gunma, 374-8518, Japan
Tel.: (81) 276725117
Sales Range: $200-249.9 Million
Emp.: 500
Surgical & Medical Instrument Mfr
N.A.I.C.S.: 339112
Yoshio Higaki *(CEO)*

Nipro Medical Ltda (1)
Avenida Nipro 451 - Regiao Norte, Sorocaba, Sao Paulo, 18087-127, Brazil
Tel.: (55) 1532387300
Web Site: https://www.nipro.com.br
Sales Range: $100-124.9 Million
Emp.: 360
Surgical & Medical Instrument Mfr
N.A.I.C.S.: 339112

Nipro Medical Panama S.A. (1)
Howard Bodega 9122 Local 1 Pan America Corporate Center, Panama Pacifico, Panama, Panama

5361

NIPRO CORPORATION

Nipro Corporation—(Continued)
Tel.: (507) 3979555
Web Site: https://nipro.com.pa
Sales Range: $50-74.9 Million
Emp.: 4
Medical Dental & Hospital Equipment & Supplies Whslr
N.A.I.C.S.: 423450
George Gomez (Gen Mgr)

Nipro Patch Co., Ltd (1)
8-1 Minamisakae-cho, Kasukabe, 344-0057, Saitama, Japan
Tel.: (81) 48 752 7151
Web Site: http://www.nipro-patch.co.jp
Pharmaceutical Products Mfr & Distr
N.A.I.C.S.: 325412
Koshiro Nakamura (Pres)

Nipro Pharma Corporation (1)
3-26 Senriokashinmachi, settsu, Osaka, 566-8510, Japan
Tel.: (81) 676393190
Web Site: https://www.np.nipro-pharma.co.jp
Emp.: 3,962
Pharmaceutical Preparation Mfr
N.A.I.C.S.: 325412
Kazuto Hanazono (Mng Dir)

Plant (Domestic):

Nipro Pharma Corporation - Ise Plant (2)
647-240 Ureshinotengeji-cho, Matsusaka, 515-2302, Mie, Japan
Tel.: (81) 598426531
Sales Range: $200-249.9 Million
Emp.: 626
Pharmaceuticals Product Mfr
N.A.I.C.S.: 325412

Nipro Pharma Corporation - Odate Plant (2)
5-7 Niida Aza Maedano, Odate, 018-5751, Akita, Japan
Tel.: (81) 186448650
Web Site: https://www.np.nipro-pharma.co.jp
Pharmaceuticals Product Mfr
N.A.I.C.S.: 325412

Nipro Pharma Corporation - Shiki Plant (2)
2-6-19 Furumachi, Kashiwara, 582-0008, Osaka, Japan
Tel.: (81) 729721431
Pharmaceuticals Product Mfr
N.A.I.C.S.: 325412

Nipro Pharma Corporation - Shirokita Plant (2)
2-16-32 Takadono, Asahi-ku, Osaka, 535-0031, Japan
Tel.: (81) 669227801
Pharmaceuticals Product Mfr
N.A.I.C.S.: 325412

Subsidiary (Domestic):

Nipro Pharma Hida Factory Corporation (2)
1-1-27 Furukawachokoreshige, Hida, 509-4244, Gifu, Japan
Tel.: (81) 577732521
Emp.: 71
Pharmaceutical Products Mfr & Distr
N.A.I.C.S.: 325412

Nipro Pharma Vietnam Co., Ltd. (1)
Land Lot IN1-4A and IN1-4B VSIP Hai Phong Township, Industrial and Service Park Dinh Vu - Cat Hai Economic Zone, Haiphong, Vietnam
Tel.: (84) 225 383 2000
Web Site: https://www.np.nipro-pharma.co.jp
Pharmaceutical Products Distr
N.A.I.C.S.: 456110

Nipro Sales (Thailand) Co., Ltd. (1)
89/170 Vibhavadi Rangsit Rd, Talat Bang Khen Lak Si, Bangkok, 10210, Thailand
Tel.: (66) 25512000
Sales Range: $25-49.9 Million
Emp.: 16
Pharmaceutical Products Distr
N.A.I.C.S.: 424210
Sumrit Boonnom (Mng Dir)

Nipro Trading (Shanghai) Co., Ltd. (1)
Room 2001-02 2013-16 Hongqiao Nanfengcheng No 100 Zunyi Road, Changning District, Shanghai, 200051, China
Tel.: (86) 2162370606
Web Site: https://www.nipro-trading.com.cn
Sales Range: $150-199.9 Million
Emp.: 1,000
Marketing Consulting Services
N.A.I.C.S.: 541613

NIPSON SAS
28 Rue E Thierry Mieg, BP 257, F-90005, Belfort, Cedex, France
Tel.: (33) 384545000 FR
Web Site: http://www.nipson.com
Year Founded: 1992
High-Speed Digital Printing Systems Developer, Mfr & Marketer
N.A.I.C.S.: 333248
Ghislain Yves Marie Segard (Pres)

NIRA DYNAMICS AB
Wallenbergs gata 4, Linkoping, 58330, Sweden
Tel.: (46) 13 329800
Web Site: http://www.niradynamics.se
Year Founded: 2001
Automotive Equipment Distr
N.A.I.C.S.: 441330
Johan Hagg (Dir-Mktg & Comm)

NIRAJ CEMENT STRUCTURALS LIMITED
Niraj House Sunder Baug Near Deonar Bus Depot, Chembur, Mumbai, 400 088, India
Tel.: (91) 2225513541
Web Site: https://niraj.co.in
Year Founded: 1972
NIRAJ—(NSE)
Rev.: $73,157,377
Assets: $37,772,208
Liabilities: $16,606,606
Net Worth: $21,165,602
Earnings: $518,734
Emp.: 15
Fiscal Year-end: 03/31/23
Civil Engineering Construction Services
N.A.I.C.S.: 237990
Soni Agarwal (CFO)

Subsidiaries:

Niraj Consulting Group Limited (1)
Niraj house Sundar baug Opp Deonar Bus Depot 88, Deonar Chembur, Mumbai, India
Tel.: (91) 2266027100
Web Site: https://ncgglobal.co.in
Construction Services
N.A.I.C.S.: 541330

NIRAJ ISPAT INDUSTRIES LIMITED
5140/41/34 F/F Chaudhary Market Gali Peti Wali Rui Mandi Sadar Bazar, New Delhi, 110006, India
Tel.: (91) 1125871288 In
Web Site: https://www.nirajispat.in
Year Founded: 1985
Rev.: $1,112,993
Assets: $2,303,644
Liabilities: $1,267,203
Net Worth: $1,036,441
Earnings: $134,041
Fiscal Year-end: 03/31/17
Jute Product Mfr & Distr
N.A.I.C.S.: 313210
Niraj Chaudhry (CFO)

NIRAKU GC HOLDINGS, INC.
1-24 Hohaccho 2-chome, Koriyama, Fukushima, Japan
Tel.: (81) 249923339 JP
Web Site: https://www.ngch.co.jp
Year Founded: 2013
1245—(HKG)
Rev.: $178,097,076
Assets: $434,489,472
Liabilities: $309,078,209
Net Worth: $125,411,263
Earnings: $4,393,788
Emp.: 1,334
Fiscal Year-end: 03/31/24
Holding Company
N.A.I.C.S.: 551112
Hisanori Taniguchi (Chm & CEO)

NIRAS GRUPPEN A/S
Sortemosevej 19, 3450, Allerod, Denmark
Tel.: (45) 4810 4200
Web Site: http://www.niras.com
Year Founded: 1956
Emp.: 1,400
Engineering Consulting Services
N.A.I.C.S.: 541690
Carsten Toft Boesen (CEO)

Subsidiaries:

Lorien Engineering Solutions Limited (1)
Millennium Court First Avenue Centrum 100, First Avenue Centrum 100, Burton-on-Trent, DE14 2WH, Staffordshire, United Kingdom
Tel.: (44) 1283485100
Web Site: https://www.lorienengineering.com
Sales Range: $10-24.9 Million
Emp.: 70
Engineeering Services
N.A.I.C.S.: 541330

Subsidiary (Non-US):

Lorien Engineering Solutions Sp. z.o.o. (2)
Oddzial w Polsce Budynek IItranet II Pietro, Ul Strzegomska 138, 54 429, Wroclaw, Poland
Tel.: (48) 71 881 0117
Engineering Services
N.A.I.C.S.: 541330

NIRAV COMMERCIALS LIMITED
B-1 Tulsi Vihar Dr Annie Besant Road, Worli Naka, Mumbai, 400 018, India
Tel.: (91) 2240457100
Web Site: https://www.associatedgroup.com
512425—(BOM)
Rev.: $1,260,488
Assets: $3,734,980
Liabilities: $242,755
Net Worth: $3,492,225
Earnings: $80,427
Emp.: 11
Fiscal Year-end: 03/31/23
Aluminium Door & Window Mfr
N.A.I.C.S.: 332321
S. K. Sharma (CFO)

NIRBHAY COLOURS INDIA LIMITED
304 Chnakya Building Behind Sales India Income Tax, Ashram Road, Ahmedabad, 380009, Gujarat, India
Tel.: (91) 9825021447
Web Site: https://www.nirbhaycolours.com
526349—(BOM)
Sales Range: Less than $1 Million
Stationery Product Mfr
N.A.I.C.S.: 322230
Mitul Narayanbhai Patel (Exec Dir)

NIRDHAN UTTHAN LAGHUBITTA BITTIYA SANSTHA LIMITED
Nirdhan Bhawan Bhagwatibahal, Naxal -1, Kathmandu, Nepal
Tel.: (977) 714413711
Web Site: http://www.nirdhan.com.np

INTERNATIONAL PUBLIC

Year Founded: 1998
NUBL—(NEP)
Rev.: $30,022,709
Assets: $211,650,545
Liabilities: $176,086,895
Net Worth: $35,563,650
Earnings: $1,288,283
Emp.: 1,136
Fiscal Year-end: 07/16/23
Banking Services
N.A.I.C.S.: 522110
Raj Narayan Das (Asst Gen Mgr)

NIRECO CORPORATION
2951-4 Ishikawa-machi, Hachioji, 192-8522, Tokyo, Japan
Tel.: (81) 426423111
Web Site: https://www.nireco.com
Year Founded: 1950
6863—(TKS)
Rev.: $61,343,703
Assets: $115,539,661
Liabilities: $17,094,868
Net Worth: $98,444,793
Earnings: $6,289,269
Emp.: 450
Fiscal Year-end: 06/30/24
Industrial Valve Mfr
N.A.I.C.S.: 332911
Kouji Hazama (Exec Officer)

Subsidiaries:

NIRECO AUTOMATIC CONTROLLER (SHANGHAI) CO., LTD (1)
Room 101 First Floor Building 7 Erea 8Lane 449 Nujiangbei Rd, Putuo District, Shanghai, 200333, China
Tel.: (86) 2163272000
Web Site: https://www.nirecosh.com
Measuring & Control Equipment Mfr
N.A.I.C.S.: 334519

NIRECO DELTA CO., LTD. (1)
Dangjeong-dong Gunpo IT Valley A-901 17 148 Beongil, Gosan-ro, Gunpo, Gyeonggi-do, Korea (South)
Tel.: (82) 3180851406
Emp.: 6
Electronic Equipment Whslr
N.A.I.C.S.: 423690

NIRECO TAIWAN CORPORATION (1)
No 2 Ln 12 Qingle St, Tu-Cheng Dist, Taipei, 236, Taiwan
Tel.: (886) 222630506
Web Site: https://sites.google.com
Electronic Equipment Whslr
N.A.I.C.S.: 423690

NIRLON LTD
Pahadi Village Off The Western Express Highway, Goregaon E, Mumbai, 400 063, Maharashtra, India
Tel.: (91) 2226852256
Web Site: https://www.nirlonltd.com
500307—(BOM)
Rev.: $69,013,704
Assets: $251,929,992
Liabilities: $203,755,482
Net Worth: $48,174,510
Earnings: $18,933,733
Emp.: 3
Fiscal Year-end: 03/31/23
Nylon Textile Mfr
N.A.I.C.S.: 325220
Jasmin K. Bhavsar (Compliance Officer, Sec & VP-Legal)

Subsidiaries:

Nirlon Ltd - Fabric Division (1)
Plot No D 8 M I D C Tarapur Dist, 401405, Thane, Maharashtra, India
Tel.: (91) 2525272698
Web Site: http://www.nirlonltd.com
Industrial Fabrics Mfr
N.A.I.C.S.: 314994

Nirlon Ltd - Real Estate Division (1)
The Western Express Highway Goregaon E, Pahadi Village, Mumbai, 400 063, Maha-

rashtra, India
Tel.: (91) 2226852256
Web Site: http://www.nirlonltd.com
Sales Range: $50-74.9 Million
Emp.: 75
Real Estate Manangement Services
N.A.I.C.S.: 531390
Haresh Shroff (Sr Mgr-Projects)

NIRMA LIMITED
Nirma House Ashram Road, Ahmedabad, 380 009, Gujarat, India
Tel.: (91) 7927546565
Web Site: http://www.nirma.co.in
Sales Range: $1-4.9 Billion
Emp.: 18,000
Soap & Detergent Mfr
N.A.I.C.S.: 325412
K. K. Patel (Chm)

Subsidiaries:

Glenmark Life Sciences Ltd. (1)
Mohol 141-143 160-165 170-172 Pune - Hyderabad Highway Mohol, Chandramouli Sahakari Audyogik Vasahat Maryadit, Solapur, 413213, Maharashtra, India (75%)
Tel.: (91) 7798882944
Web Site:
https://www.glenmarklifesciences.com
Pharmaceutical Ingredient Mfr & Distr
N.A.I.C.S.: 325412
Yasir Y. Rawjee (CEO & Mng Dir)

Nuvoco Vistas Corp. Ltd. (1)
Equinox Business Park Tower-3 East Wing 4th floor, Off Bandra-Kurla Complex LBS Marg Kurla West, Mumbai, 400070, India (100%)
Tel.: (91) 2267692595
Web Site: http://www.nuvoco.com
Rev.: $1,026,844,455
Assets: $2,717,377,845
Liabilities: $1,717,695,525
Net Worth: $999,682,320
Earnings: ($3,542,175)
Emp.: 3,500
Fiscal Year-end: 03/31/2021
Cement, Aggregates & Ready-Mixed Concrete Mfr
N.A.I.C.S.: 327310
Maneesh Agrawal (CFO)

Searles Domestic Water Company LLC (1)
13217 Main St, Trona, CA 93562
Tel.: (760) 372-5326
Water Supply Services
N.A.I.C.S.: 221310
Audrey Schuyler (Gen Mgr)

Searles Valley Minerals Europe. (1)
164 Avenue Joseph Kessel, 78960, Voisins-le-Bretonneux, France
Tel.: (33) 1 61 08 48 00
Mineral Mining Services
N.A.I.C.S.: 212390

Trona Railway Company LLC (1)
13068 Main St, Trona, CA 93562
Tel.: (760) 372-2053
Rail Transportation Services
N.A.I.C.S.: 488210

NIRMITEE ROBOTICS INDIA LIMITED
C/O Manisha Sales D 3/2 Hingna Midc, Nagpur, 440028, India
Tel.: (91) 9422881677
Web Site:
https://www.nirmiteerobotics.com
Year Founded: 2016
543194—(BOM)
Cleaning Robot Services
N.A.I.C.S.: 811412
Akhilesh Girish Mishra (Sec & Compliance Officer)

Subsidiaries:

Nirmitee Robotics AC Maintenance LLC (1)
M-7 Al Nayieli Building Hor Al Anz East, PO Box 98040, Dubai, United Arab Emirates
Tel.: (971) 543037350
Air Duct Cleaning Services

N.A.I.C.S.: 561790

NIROU TRANS CO.
Unit 1206 Sarve Saei Building Next to Saei Gas Station Vali Asr St, PO Box 14335-899, Tehran, Iran
Tel.: (98) 2188701414
Web Site: https://www.niroutrans.com
Year Founded: 1990
NIRO1—(THE)
Sales Range: Less than $1 Million
Emp.: 155
Electric Equipment Mfr
N.A.I.C.S.: 335999

NIROUMOHAREKE MACHINE TOOLS
No.103 1st Floor Vanak Passage Vanak Ave Vanak Square, Tehran, Iran
Tel.: (98) 21 88797216
Web Site: http://www.nmt-co.com
Industrial Parts Mfr
N.A.I.C.S.: 339999

NIRVANA ASIA LTD.
No 1 Jalan 1/116A Off Jalan Sungai Besi, Kuala Lumpur, Malaysia
Tel.: (60) 800881818 CN
Web Site: http://www.nirvana-asia-ltd.com
Year Founded: 1990
Funeral Services
N.A.I.C.S.: 812210
Kong Hon Kong (Founder & Chm)

Subsidiaries:

Nirvana Memorial Garden Pte. Ltd. (1)
950 Old Choa Chu Kang Road, Singapore, 699816, Singapore
Tel.: (65) 63972272
Web Site: http://www.nirvana.com.sg
Memorial Park Operator
N.A.I.C.S.: 812220
Kong Hon Kong (Chm, Co-CEO, Mng Dir & Exec Dir)

Nirvana Memorial Park Co., Ltd. (1)
65/99-65/100 Chamnan Phenjati Business Center 11th Floor Rama IX Road, Huay Kwang, Bangkok, 10310, Thailand
Tel.: (66) 20266277
Web Site: http://www.nirvana-memorial.co.th
Memorial Park Operator
N.A.I.C.S.: 812220

PT. Nirvana Memorial Nusantara (1)
Groundfloor Tower B The Royal Condominium Jalan Palang Merah, Sukamulia No 1, Medan, 20151, Sumatera Utara, Indonesia
Tel.: (62) 6180512555
Memorial Park Operator
N.A.I.C.S.: 812220

NIRVANA DEVELOPMENT PUBLIC COMPANY LIMITED
343/351 Prasert - Manukitch Road, Nuanchan Buengkum, Bangkok, 10230, Thailand
Tel.: (66) 21056789
Web Site:
https://nirvanadevelopment.co.th
NVD—(THA)
Rev.: $67,422,529
Assets: $429,206,599
Liabilities: $282,025,796
Net Worth: $147,180,802
Earnings: $6,188,076
Emp.: 175
Fiscal Year-end: 12/31/23
Home & Office Product Distr
N.A.I.C.S.: 459410

NIRVANA LIFE SCIENCES INC.
6th Floor 905 West Pender St, Vancouver, V6C 1L6, BC, Canada
Tel.: (604) 401-8100 BC

Web Site:
https://www.nirvanalifescience.com
Year Founded: 2011
NIRV—(CNSX)
Rev.: $40
Assets: $51,021
Liabilities: $750,317
Net Worth: ($699,296)
Earnings: ($1,109,798)
Fiscal Year-end: 04/30/23
Medical Equipment Mfr
N.A.I.C.S.: 339112
Bruce Clark (CEO)

NIS-EKSPRES A.D.
Camurlija br 160, 18000, Nis, Serbia
Tel.: (381) 18 4527 001
Web Site: http://www.nis-ekspres.rs
Year Founded: 1951
NEKS—(BEL)
Sales Range: $25-49.9 Million
Emp.: 1,740
Passenger Transportation Services
N.A.I.C.S.: 485999
Zorica Zlatanovic (Chm-Supervisory Bd)

NISAUTO HOLDING A.D.
Bulevar Nikole Tesle bb, Nis, Serbia
Tel.: (381) 18 575 055
Web Site: http://www.nisauto.co.rs
Year Founded: 1975
Sales Range: Less than $1 Million
Emp.: 11
Holding Company
N.A.I.C.S.: 551112

Subsidiaries:

Wood&Fruits d.o.o (1)
Prvokutinska bb, Prva Kutina, 18110, Nis, Serbia
Tel.: (381) 18 4541 351
Web Site: http://www.woodandfruits.co.rs
Wood Product Mfr; Processed Fruits & Vegetables Mfr
N.A.I.C.S.: 321999
Nebojsa Gatic (CEO)

NISBETS PLC
Fourth Way, Avonmouth, BS11 8TB, Bristol, United Kingdom
Tel.: (44) 8451405555 UK
Web Site: http://www.nisbets.co.uk
Year Founded: 1983
Catering Equipment Supplier
N.A.I.C.S.: 423490
Paul McMahon (Mng Dir)

NISCHER PROPERTIES AB
Upplandsgatan 14, 111 23, Stockholm, Sweden
Tel.: (46) 8763274874
Web Site: https://www.nischer.se
Year Founded: 2015
Real Estate Investment Services
N.A.I.C.S.: 531390
David Aspehult (CEO)

NISHA TECHNOLOGIES INC.
2150 Thurston Dr Ste 202, Ottawa, K1G 5T9, ON, Canada
Tel.: (613) 739-7225
Web Site: http://www.nishatech.com
Sales Range: $50-74.9 Million
Emp.: 12
Computer Products Whslr
N.A.I.C.S.: 423430
Milan Muzar (CFO)

NISHAT CHUNIAN LIMITED
31-Q Gulberg II, Lahore, 54660, Pakistan
Tel.: (92) 4235761730
Web Site: https://www.nishat.net
NCL—(KAR)
Rev.: $394,817,223
Assets: $535,030,338

Liabilities: $337,862,263
Net Worth: $197,168,075
Earnings: $40,053,387
Emp.: 6,007
Fiscal Year-end: 06/30/19
Spinning Product Mfr
N.A.I.C.S.: 313110
Shahzad Saleem (CEO)

Subsidiaries:

Nishat Chunian Power Limited (1)
31-Q Gulberg II, Lahore, 54660, Pakistan
Tel.: (92) 4235761730
Web Site: https://www.nishat.net
Rev.: $65,549,441
Assets: $99,964,633
Liabilities: $12,681,785
Net Worth: $87,282,848
Earnings: $14,233,751
Emp.: 149
Fiscal Year-end: 06/30/2023
Eletric Power Generation Services
N.A.I.C.S.: 221118
Sonia Karim (Dir-Fin & Ops)

Taj Textile Mills Limited (1)
Office-1 First Floor K-1 Commerceial Zone K-Block Model Town, Lahore, Pakistan
Tel.: (92) 425916650
Textile Products Mfr
N.A.I.C.S.: 313110

NISHAT MILLS LTD.
Nishat House 53-A Lawrence Road, Lahore, Pakistan
Tel.: (92) 4236360154 PK
Web Site: https://nishatmillsltd.com
Year Founded: 1951
NML—(KAR)
Rev.: $689,318,212
Assets: $1,075,428,506
Liabilities: $338,598,999
Net Worth: $736,829,507
Earnings: $69,309,215
Emp.: 17,711
Fiscal Year-end: 06/30/19
Mfr & Sales of Yarn, Linen, Cloth & Other Fabrics Made from Raw Cotton, Synthetic Fibre & Cloth
N.A.I.C.S.: 313110
Khalid Mahmood Chohan (Sec)

Subsidiaries:

DG Khan Cement Company Limited (1)
Nishat House 53-A Lawrence Road, Lahore, Pakistan
Tel.: (92) 42111113333
Web Site: https://www.dgcement.com
Rev.: $253,606,771
Assets: $511,731,536
Liabilities: $270,184,746
Net Worth: $241,546,790
Earnings: ($12,109,393)
Emp.: 2,303
Fiscal Year-end: 06/30/2023
Cement Mfr
N.A.I.C.S.: 327310
Raza Mansha (CEO)

Nishat International FZE (1)
Zone MO0741 Northern Region Street 205, Jebel Ali, United Arab Emirates
Tel.: (971) 528250956
Web Site: https://www.nishatlinenuae.com
Textile Products Distr
N.A.I.C.S.: 424350

Nishat Linen (Private) Limited (1)
21 Km Ferozpur Road, Lahore, 54400, Punjab, Pakistan
Tel.: (92) 4238103311
Web Site: https://www.nishatlinen.com
Clothing Retailer
N.A.I.C.S.: 458110

Nishat Power Limited (1)
1-B Aziz Avenue Canal Bank Gulberg V, Lahore, Pakistan
Tel.: (92) 4235717090
Web Site: https://nishatpower.com
Rev.: $82,990,691
Assets: $112,895,487
Liabilities: $5,391,223

NISHAT MILLS LTD.

Nishat Mills Ltd.—(Continued)
Net Worth: $107,504,264
Earnings: $14,717,493
Emp.: 214
Fiscal Year-end: 06/30/2023
Eletric Power Generation Services
N.A.I.C.S.: 221118
Mian Hassan Mansha *(Chm)*

NISHI-NIPPON FINANCIAL HOLDINGS, INC.
3-1-1 Hakataekimae, Hakata-ku, Fukuoka, 812-0011, Japan
Tel.: (81) 924611867
Web Site: https://www.nnfh.co.jp
Year Founded: 2016
7189—(FKA)
Rev.: $1,156,650,060
Assets: $93,103,747,770
Liabilities: $89,235,934,290
Net Worth: $3,867,813,480
Earnings: $189,524,610
Emp.: 3,380
Fiscal Year-end: 03/31/23
Banking Services
N.A.I.C.S.: 522110
Isao Kubota *(Chm)*

Subsidiaries:

NTT Data NCB Corporation (1)
1-17-21 Hakata Ekimae, Hakata-ku, Fukuoka, 812-0011, Japan
Tel.: (81) 924752120
Web Site: https://www.nttdata-ncb.co.jp
Emp.: 169
Bank Information Services
N.A.I.C.S.: 523150
Yoshinori Kano *(Pres & CEO)*

NISHI-NIPPON RAILROAD CO., LTD.
3-5-7 Hakata Ekimae, Hakata-ku, Fukuoka, Japan
Tel.: (81) 927341217
Web Site: https://www.nishitetsu.co.jp
Year Founded: 1908
9031—(TKS)
Rev.: $2,720,999,890
Assets: $4,805,483,220
Liabilities: $3,246,587,430
Net Worth: $1,558,895,790
Earnings: $163,419,030
Emp.: 18,456
Fiscal Year-end: 03/31/24
Transportation Services
N.A.I.C.S.: 484110
Koichi Hayashida *(Pres & CEO)*

Subsidiaries:

Dazaifu Amusement Park. Co. (1)
4-7-8 Zaifu, Dazaifu, 818-0117, Japan
Tel.: (81) 929223551
Web Site: https://www.dazaifuyuuenchi.com
Facility Support Services
N.A.I.C.S.: 561210

Hakata Bus Terminal Co. (1)
2-1 Hakataeki Chuogai, Hakata-ku, Fukuoka, 812-0012, Japan
Tel.: (81) 924311441
Transportation Services
N.A.I.C.S.: 488490

Incube Nishitetsu Co., Ltd. (1)
2-11-3 Tenjin Fukuoka SORA rear stage building, Chuo-ku, Fukuoka, 810-0001, Japan
Tel.: (81) 927131092
Web Site: https://www.incubenews.transer.com
Emp.: 276
Yarn Whslr
N.A.I.C.S.: 424310

Kurume-Nishitetsu Taxi Co. (1)
1596 Gokuden Kokubumachi, Kurume, 839-0863, Fukuoka, Japan
Tel.: (81) 942210011
Web Site: https://www.kurume-nishitaku.co.jp
Taxi Service
N.A.I.C.S.: 485310

Love FM International Broadcasting Co., Ltd. (1)
1-12-23 Nishitetsu Imaizumi Building 5th Floor Imaizumi, Chuo-ku, Fukuoka, 810-8516, Japan
Tel.: (81) 927345462
Web Site: https://lovefm.co.jp
Radio Broadcasting Services
N.A.I.C.S.: 516110

NNR + Dachser GmbH (1)
Global Logistics Admiral-Rosendahl-Str 21, Zeppelinheim, 63263, Neu-Isenburg, Germany
Tel.: (49) 699511850
Web Site: http://www.nnr-dachser.com
Logistic Services
N.A.I.C.S.: 541614
Junichi Ogata *(Mng Dir)*

NNR Global Logistics (Guangzhou) Co., Limited (1)
Room 2201 Kingold Century No 62 Jinsui Road, Zhujiang New Town Tianhe District, Guangzhou, China
Tel.: (86) 2039418900
Logistic Services
N.A.I.C.S.: 541614

NNR Global Logistics (HK) Limited (1)
16/F Grandion Plaza 932 Cheung Sha Wan Road, Cheung Shan Wan, Kowloon, China (Hong Kong)
Tel.: (852) 27538023
Logistic Services
N.A.I.C.S.: 541614

NNR Global Logistics (M) Sdn. Bhd. (1)
Tel.: (60) 378778833
Web Site: http://www.nnr.com.my
Shipping Services
N.A.I.C.S.: 488510

NNR Global Logistics (Philippines) Co., Ltd. (1)
4th Floor Kingsland Bldg Dr A Santos Avenue Brgy, San Isidro, Paranaque, Philippines
Tel.: (63) 88512457
Freight Transportation Services
N.A.I.C.S.: 488510

NNR Global Logistics (S) Pte. Ltd. (1)
10 Changi South Lane 02-01, Singapore, 486162, Singapore
Tel.: (65) 68270888
Logistic Services
N.A.I.C.S.: 541614

NNR Global Logistics (Shanghai) Co., Ltd. (1)
Mainichi Nihonbashi Building 2-5 Nihonbashi 3, Chuo-ku, Tokyo, 103-0027, Japan
Tel.: (81) 343325060
Shipping Services
N.A.I.C.S.: 488510

NNR Global Logistics (Thailand) Co., Ltd. (1)
89 Motor-Way Road Kweang Klongsongtonnoon, Khet Lat Krabang, Bangkok, 10520, Thailand
Tel.: (66) 2184954554
Web Site: https://nnrthailand.com
Freight Transportation Services
N.A.I.C.S.: 488510
Phongthep Tangpinitchit *(Exec Dir)*

NNR Global Logistics India Private Limited (1)
Unit 1007 10Th Floor Magnum Towers Sector 58, Gurgaon, 122001, Haryana, India
Tel.: (91) 1244642100
Logistic Services
N.A.I.C.S.: 541614

NNR Global Logistics Netherlands B.V. (1)
Fokkerweg 300, 1438 AN, Oude Meer, Netherlands
Tel.: (31) 203480070
Logistic Services
N.A.I.C.S.: 541614

NNR Global Logistics Taiwan Inc. (1)
4F No 57 Fu-Hsing N Rd, Songshan District, Taipei, 105404, Taiwan
Tel.: (886) 227408800
Web Site: http://www.nnr.com.tw
Logistics & Transportation Services
N.A.I.C.S.: 541614

Nishitetsu Travel Co., Ltd. (1)
3-16-26 Yakuin Nishitetsu Yakuin Building, Chuo-ku, Fukuoka, 810-0022, Japan
Tel.: (81) 925242211
Freight Transportation Services
N.A.I.C.S.: 488510

Nishitetsu-Plaza Corporation (1)
1-4-1 Daimyo ND Building 4F, Chuo, Fukuoka, Japan
Tel.: (81) 927416264
Web Site: http://www.nishitetsu-plaza.co.jp
Emp.: 141
Restaurant Services
N.A.I.C.S.: 722511

SPINA Co., Ltd. (1)
2-11-1 Hirano, Yahatahigashi-ku, Kitakyushu, 805-8528, Japan
Tel.: (81) 936710344
Web Site: http://www.spina.co.jp
Emp.: 337
Real Estate Services
N.A.I.C.S.: 531390

NISHIKAWA KEISOKU CO., LTD.
Yoyogi 3227 Shinjuku Bunka Quinto Building 5th floor, Shibuya-Ku, Tokyo, 151-8620, Japan
Tel.: (81) 332991331
Web Site: https://www.nskw.co.jp
Year Founded: 1951
75000—(TKS)
Sales Range: Less than $1 Million
Engineering Equipment Mfr
N.A.I.C.S.: 335999
Katsuhiko Tanaka *(Chm & Pres)*

NISHIKAWA RUBBER CO., LTD.
2-2-8 Misasacho, Nishi-Ku, Hiroshima, 733-8510, Japan
Tel.: (81) 822379371
Web Site: https://www.nishikawa-rbr.co.jp
Year Founded: 1949
5161—(TKS)
Rev.: $779,345,440
Assets: $910,408,520
Liabilities: $331,967,420
Net Worth: $578,441,100
Earnings: $33,301,180
Emp.: 1,368
Fiscal Year-end: 03/31/24
Tires & Other Rubber Products Mfr
N.A.I.C.S.: 326211
Masahiro Nishikawa *(Chm)*

Subsidiaries:

DaikyoNishikawa Corporation (1)
5-1 Jike-Sangyodanchi, Higashihiroshima-shi, Hiroshima, 739-0049, Japan
Tel.: (81) 824935600
Web Site: https://www.daikyonishikawa.co.jp
Rev.: $1,051,115,590
Assets: $1,065,697,250
Liabilities: $515,388,310
Net Worth: $550,308,940
Earnings: $38,219,020
Emp.: 5,601
Fiscal Year-end: 03/31/2024
Automobile Parts Mfr
N.A.I.C.S.: 336320
Toshio Hiyama *(VP)*

Guangzhou Nishikawa Sealing Systems Co., Ltd. (1)
No 10 Dongfeng Road Automobile Center, Huadu District, Guangzhou, 510800, Guangdong, China
Tel.: (86) 2086733255
Web Site: http://www.nishikawa-rbr.co.jp
Molded Packings & Seals Mfr
N.A.I.C.S.: 339991

Nishikawa Big Ocean Co., Ltd (1)
3723-1 Oaza-Kuchi Asa-cho, Asakita-Ku, Hiroshima, 731-3362, Japan
Tel.: (81) 828103555
Gasket Packing & Sealing Device Mfr
N.A.I.C.S.: 339991

Nishikawa Bussan Co., Ltd. (1)
Tel.: (81) 828743365
Web Site: http://www.nishikawa-bussan.jp
Emp.: 210
Powder Puffs Mfr
N.A.I.C.S.: 314999

Nishikawa Design Techno Co., Ltd. (1)
2-2-8 Misasa-machi, Nishi-Ku, Hiroshima, 733-8510, Japan
Tel.: (81) 822379379
Web Site: http://www.nishikawa-ndt.com
Automotive Components Mfr
N.A.I.C.S.: 336330

Nishikawa Living Co., Ltd. (1)
51 Suzuenishi Kawauchi-cho, Tokushima, 771-0122, Japan
Tel.: (81) 886650521
Household Furnishings Mfr
N.A.I.C.S.: 314120

Nishikawa Rubber Co., Ltd. - Asa Plant (1)
3723-1 Oaza-kuchi Asa-cho, Asakita-ku, Hiroshima, 731-3362, Japan
Tel.: (81) 828370101
Automotive Rubber Products Mfr
N.A.I.C.S.: 326220

Nishikawa Rubber Co., Ltd. - Mihara Plant (1)
10200-39 Obara Nutanishi-cho, Mihara, 729-0473, Hiroshima, Japan
Tel.: (81) 848865522
Gaskets Mfr
N.A.I.C.S.: 339991

Nishikawa Rubber Co., Ltd. - Shiraki Plant (1)
9531 Oaza-Mita Shiraki-cho, Asakita-ku, Hiroshima, 739-1521, Japan
Tel.: (81) 828281300
Web Site: http://www.nishikawa-rbr.co.jp
Gaskets Mfr
N.A.I.C.S.: 339991

Nishikawa Rubber Co., Ltd. - Yoshida Plant (1)
1489-23 Yoshida-cho, Yoshida, Akitakata, 731-0501, Hiroshima, Japan
Tel.: (81) 826423711
Web Site: http://www.nishikawa-rbr.co.jp
Sales Range: $50-74.9 Million
Emp.: 150
Cosmetic Rubber Products Mfr
N.A.I.C.S.: 314999
Osamu Saito *(Operating Officer)*

Nishikawa Tachaplalert Rubber Co., Ltd. (1)
Suranaree Industrial Zone 399 Village No 3 Ratchasima-Chokchai Road, Nong Bua Sala Sub-district Mueang District, Nakhon Ratchasima, 30000, Thailand
Tel.: (66) 44212974
Web Site: https://www.ntr-th.com
Sales Range: $200-249.9 Million
Emp.: 620
Rubber Mfr
N.A.I.C.S.: 325212

Nishikawa of America Inc. (1)
17197 N Laurel Park Dr Ste 380, Livonia, MI 48152
Tel.: (734) 333-9950
Web Site: http://www.nishikawa-rbr.co.jp
Industrial Machinery Mfr
N.A.I.C.S.: 333248

Joint Venture (Domestic):

Nishikawa Cooper LLC (2)
324 Morrow St, Topeka, IN 46571-9076 (60%)
Tel.: (260) 593-2156
Web Site: https://niscoseals.com
Sales Range: $125-149.9 Million
Emp.: 500
Fabricated Rubber Products
N.A.I.C.S.: 326299
Naoki Masukuni *(Pres)*

AND PRIVATE COMPANIES

Seiwa Butsuryu Co., Ltd. (1)
2-2-8 Misasa-machi, Nishi-Ku, Hiroshima, 733-8510, Japan
Tel.: (81) 822379371
Web Site: http://www.nishikawa-rbr.co.jp
Transportation Support Services
N.A.I.C.S.: 488999

Shanghai Nishikawa Sealing System Co., Ltd.
No 1216 Yushu Road, Songjiang District, Shanghai, 201600, China
Tel.: (86) 2157734608
Sales Range: $200-249.9 Million
Emp.: 700
Automotive Door Seals Mfr
N.A.I.C.S.: 339991

NISHIMATSU CONSTRUCTION CO., LTD.
Toranomon Hills Business Tower 17-1 Toranomon 1-chome, Minato-ku, Tokyo, 105-6407, Japan
Tel.: (81) 335020232 JP
Web Site: https://www.nishimatsu.co.jp
Year Founded: 1937
1820—(TKS)
Rev.: $2,654,794,130
Assets: $3,831,314,640
Liabilities: $2,662,296,480
Net Worth: $1,169,018,160
Earnings: $81,884,680
Emp.: 2,892
Fiscal Year-end: 03/31/24
Buildings, Airports, Factories, Power Plants, Bridges, Tunnels & Elevated Highways Planning, Design & Construction
N.A.I.C.S.: 236220
Yoshiyuki Sawai *(Sr Mng Officer)*

Subsidiaries:

Fan Ling Machine & Mechanical Centre (1)
Room 508 Star House Salisbury Road, PO Box 98612, Tsim Tsa Tsui, Kowloon, China (Hong Kong) (100%)
Tel.: (852) 26747535
Sales Range: $50-74.9 Million
Emp.: 2
Engineeering Services
N.A.I.C.S.: 237110

Lao Nishimatsu Construction Co., Ltd. (1)
Tel.: (856) 41219044
Web Site: http://www.laonishimatsu.com
Construction Services
N.A.I.C.S.: 236220
Eiichi Sakuma *(Mng Dir)*

Nishimatsu Vietnam Co., Ltd. (1)
24th Floor Ngoc Khanh Plaza 1 Pham Huy Thong Street, Ngoc Khanh Ward Ba Dinh District, Hanoi, Vietnam
Tel.: (84) 2437723034
Construction Services
N.A.I.C.S.: 236220

Nishimatsu-Jisho Co., Ltd. (1)
5-12-11 Toranomon, Minato-ku, Tokyo, 105-0001, Japan
Tel.: (81) 354001361
Web Site: https://www.n-jisho.co.jp
Real Estate Development Services
N.A.I.C.S.: 531390

SCI Tech Farm Co., Ltd. (1)
Toranomon Hills Business Tower 1-17-1 Toranomon, Minato-ku, Tokyo, 105-6407, Japan
Tel.: (81) 335020227
Web Site: http://www.scitechfarm.com
Vegetable & Fruit Distr
N.A.I.C.S.: 424480

Thai Nishimatsu Construction Co., Ltd. (1)
19th Floor Sino-Thai Tower 32/48 Sukhumvit 21 Road, Wattana, Bangkok, 10110, Thailand
Tel.: (66) 22589590
Web Site: http://www.thainishimatsu.com
Sales Range: $50-74.9 Million
Emp.: 200
General Construction Engineering Services
N.A.I.C.S.: 236220
Masatoshi Ichi *(Mng Dir)*

NISHIMATSUYA CHAIN CO., LTD.
266-1 Sho Shikito-cho, Himeji, 671-0218, Hyogo, Japan
Tel.: (81) 0792523300 JP
Web Site: https://www.24028.jp
Year Founded: 1956
7545—(TKS)
Sales Range: Less than $1 Million
Accessories Store Operator
N.A.I.C.S.: 424350
Yoshifumi Ohmura *(Pres)*

NISHIMOTO CO., LTD.
Onword Park Building 3-10-5 Nihonbashi, Chuo-ku, Tokyo, 103-0027, Japan
Tel.: (81) 368702180 JP
Web Site: http://www.wismettac.com
Year Founded: 2010
9260—(TKS)
Sales Range: $300-349.9 Million
Emp.: 1,676
Holding Company; Food Wholesale Distr
N.A.I.C.S.: 551112
Yoshiro Susaki *(Chm & CEO)*

Subsidiaries:

IPM Nishimoto Co., Ltd. (1)
2-28-8 Shiba, Minato-ku, Tokyo, Japan
Tel.: (81) 354278860
Web Site: http://www.ipm.co.jp
Fresh Fruit & Vegetable Merchant Whslr
N.A.I.C.S.: 424480

NTC Wismettac Australia Pty Ltd. (1)
Unit 51 A Slough Business Park 2 Slough Ave, Silverwater, 2128, ASW, Australia
Tel.: (61) 8036 4580
Food Trading Business
N.A.I.C.S.: 424480
Kosuke Ishizuka *(Mng Dir)*

NTC Wismettac Europe B.V. (1)
Prof J H Bavinckiaan 5, 1183, Amstelveen, Netherlands
Tel.: (31) 6 5519 5821
Food Trading Business
N.A.I.C.S.: 424480
Yoshitomo Tanaka *(Mng Dir)*

NTC Wismettac Singapore Pte. Ltd. (1)
6 Tuas Bay Walk 01-00, Singapore, 637752, Singapore
Tel.: (65) 6863 4801
Food Trading Business
N.A.I.C.S.: 424480
Kato Takeshi *(Mgr)*

Nishimoto Trading Co., Ltd. (1)
1-30-5 Hamamatsu-cho, Minato-ku, Tokyo, 105-0013, Japan
Tel.: (81) 334385651
Sales Range: $200-249.9 Million
Emp.: 166
Grocery Wholesale Distr
N.A.I.C.S.: 424410

Subsidiary (US):

Nishimoto Trading Co., Ltd. (2)
13409 Orden Dr Bldg J, Santa Fe Springs, CA 90670-6336
Tel.: (562) 802-1900
Web Site: http://www.nishimototrading.com
Sales Range: $150-199.9 Million
Grocery Wholesale Distr
N.A.I.C.S.: 424410
Harold Lee *(Mgr-Natl Sls)*

Nishimoto Trading Foodstuff Shanghai Co., Ltd (1)
Room 1506 No107 Zun Yi Road, Shanghai, 200051, China
Tel.: (86) 6237 5011
Food Trading Business
N.A.I.C.S.: 424480

Wismetac Asian Foods, Inc. (1)
13409 Orden Dr, Santa Fe Springs, CA 90670-6336
Tel.: (562) 802-1900
Food Trading Business
N.A.I.C.S.: 424480

Wismetac Foods, Inc. (1)
Onword Park Building 3-10-5 Nihonbashi Chuou-ku, Tokyo, 103-0027, Japan
Tel.: (81) 6870 3000
Food Trading Business
N.A.I.C.S.: 424480

Subsidiary (Non-US):

Shanghai IPM Co., Ltd. (2)
Heaven road 325 No 3217 rooms, Shanghai, 200030, China
Tel.: (86) 21 33632860
Food Trading Business
N.A.I.C.S.: 424480

NISHIO HOLDINGS CO., LTD.
No 1-11-17 Higashi-Shinsaibashi, Chuo-ku, Osaka, 542-0083, Japan
Tel.: (81) 662517302
Web Site: https://nishio-grp.co.jp
Year Founded: 1959
9699—(TKS)
Rev.: $1,316,329,400
Assets: $1,932,514,210
Liabilities: $1,050,539,480
Net Worth: $881,974,730
Earnings: $72,927,740
Emp.: 4,529
Fiscal Year-end: 09/30/23
Construction Equipment Leasing Services
N.A.I.C.S.: 532412

Subsidiaries:

Japan Speed Shore Co., LTD. (1)
8-2-5 Tawaradai, Shijonawate, Osaka, 575-0013, Japan
Tel.: (81) 743789000
Web Site: https://speedshore.co.jp
Emp.: 272
Industrial Equipment Rental Services
N.A.I.C.S.: 532412

NISHIO RENT ALL HOKKAIDO CO., LTD. (1)
3-4-6 Nagayama 14, Hokkaido, Asahikawa, Japan
Tel.: (81) 166268240
Web Site: https://www.nishio-hokkaido.co.jp
Emp.: 56
Construction Equipment Rental Services
N.A.I.C.S.: 532412

NISHIO RENT ALL VIETNAM CO., LTD. (1)
Unit No 2502 25th Floor Keangnam Hanoi Landmark Tower Plot E6, Cau Giay New Urban Area Me Tri Ward Nam Tu Liem District, Hanoi, Vietnam
Tel.: (84) 432123556
Web Site: http://www.nishio.com.vn
Emp.: 40
Industrial Equipment Rental Services
N.A.I.C.S.: 532412
Yoshihiro Tonomura *(Chm)*

NISHIO WORK SUPPORT CO., LTD (1)
1-11-17 Higashi-Shinsaibashi, Chuo-ku, Osaka, 542-0083, Japan
Tel.: (81) 362222400
Web Site: https://www.opedas.com
Emp.: 102
Engineering Services
N.A.I.C.S.: 541330

Nishio Rent All (M) Sdn. Bhd. (1)
Lot 38 Jalan Delima 1/1 Subang Hi-Tech Industrial Park Batu 3, 40000, Shah Alam, Selangor, Malaysia
Tel.: (60) 356331770
Web Site: https://www.nishio.com.my
Construction Equipment Distr
N.A.I.C.S.: 423810

Nishio Rent All (Thailand) Co., Ltd. (1)
18/8 Fico Place building 12th Floor Unit 1201 Sukhumvit21, Klongtoey-Nua Wattana, Bangkok, 10110, Thailand
Tel.: (66) 266570157
Web Site: https://www.rentall.co.th
Emp.: 228
Construction Equipment Distr
N.A.I.C.S.: 423390
Yoshihiro Tonomura *(Chm)*

Nishio Rent All Shanghai Co., Ltd. (1)
2508/F Jingan China Tower 1701 Beijing West Road, Shanghai, 200041, China
Tel.: (86) 2151501995
Construction Equipment Distr
N.A.I.C.S.: 423390

Nishio Rent All Singapore Pte Ltd (1)
9 Tuas Avenue 18, Singapore, 638893, Singapore
Tel.: (65) 68613939
Web Site: https://www.nishio.com.sg
Industrial Equipment Rental Services
N.A.I.C.S.: 532412

Nishio T&M Company Limited (1)
2-26-1 Karasaki-nishi, Takatsuki, 569-0836, Osaka, Japan
Tel.: (81) 726772137
Web Site: https://www.nishio-tm.co.jp
Emp.: 253
Industrial Equipment Rental Services
N.A.I.C.S.: 532412
Yasuhiko Yagi *(Mng Dir)*

Subsidiary (Non-US):

Nishio T&M (Hong Kong) Co., Ltd (2)
Unit 6 21st Floor Midas Plaza No 1 Tai Yau Street San Po Kong, Kowloon, China (Hong Kong)
Tel.: (852) 23113362
Emp.: 10
Industrial Equipment Rental Services
N.A.I.C.S.: 532412
Shunsuke Kita *(Gen Mgr)*

PT. NISHIO RENT ALL INDONESIA (1)
Sampoerna Strategic Square South Tower Level 18 Jl Jend Sudirman, Kav 45-46 Kav 45-46 Rt 003/004, Jakarta Selatan, 12930, Indonesia
Tel.: (62) 215750846
Construction Equipment Distr
N.A.I.C.S.: 423810

R & R CO., LTD. (1)
16F Prime Tower Shinurayasu 1-5-2 Irifune, Urayasu, 279-0012, Chiba, Japan
Tel.: (81) 473164688
Web Site: https://r-rental.co.jp
Emp.: 200
Industrial Equipment Rental Services
N.A.I.C.S.: 532412
Hideo Harada *(Gen Mgr)*

SACOS CORPORATION (1)
4-5-3 Higashi-Gotanda, Shinagawa-Ku, Tokyo, 141-0022, Japan (86.13%)
Tel.: (81) 334433271
Web Site: http://www.sacos.co.jp
Rev.: $172,855,760
Assets: $215,980,160
Liabilities: $106,712,320
Net Worth: $109,267,840
Earnings: $9,031,440
Fiscal Year-end: 09/30/2021
Industrial Machinery Rental & Distr
N.A.I.C.S.: 532490
Masashi Nishio *(Chm)*

SAN OH CO., LTD. (1)
17-3 Higashishima-machi Nishikujo, Minami-ku, Kyoto, 601-8432, Japan
Tel.: (81) 756627850
Web Site: https://www.san-oh.co.jp
Emp.: 91
Waste Treatment Services
N.A.I.C.S.: 221310
Koji Okumura *(Pres)*

Plant (Domestic):

SAN OH CO., LTD. - Chiba Factory (2)
199-980 Yachimatahe, Yachimata, 289-

NISHIO HOLDINGS CO., LTD.

Nishio Holdings Co., Ltd.—(Continued)
1113, Chiba, Japan
Tel.: (81) 434443010
Waste Treatment Services
N.A.I.C.S.: 221310

SAN OH CO., LTD. - Shiga Factory (2)
650 Ikeshita, Maibara, 521-0221, Shiga, Japan
Tel.: (81) 749552845
Waste Treatment Services
N.A.I.C.S.: 221310

Shin-Tomoe Electric Manufacturing Co., Ltd. (1)
2nd floor JRE Omori Station East Exit Building 1-5-1 Omorikita, Ota-ku, Tokyo, 143-0016, Japan
Tel.: (81) 337623117
Web Site: https://www.s-tomoedenki.co.jp
Emp.: 77
Rolling Stock Mfr
N.A.I.C.S.: 336510

Shoji Co., Ltd. (1)
3-11-15 Yamada, Onojo, 816-0922, Fukuoka, Japan
Tel.: (81) 925749263
Web Site: https://www.shoji-r.co.jp
Emp.: 189
Construction Equipment Distr
N.A.I.C.S.: 423390

Skyreach Group Holdings Pty Ltd. (1)
7-21 Skyreach Street, Caboolture, 4510, QLD, Australia
Tel.: (61) 754314000
Web Site: https://www.skyreach.com.au
Construction Equipment Distr
N.A.I.C.S.: 423390

Skyreach Pty Ltd (1)
7 - 21 Skyreach Street, PO Box 1847, Caboolture, 4510, QLD, Australia
Tel.: (61) 754314000
Web Site: https://www.skyreach.com.au
Emp.: 100
Industrial Equipment Rental Services
N.A.I.C.S.: 532412
Rod Leech (Founder & Mng Dir)

Toyo Service Co., Ltd. (1)
1-11-17 Higashi-Shinsaibashi, Chuo-ku, Osaka, Japan
Tel.: (81) 643977657
Web Site: https://www.toyo-service.co.jp
Car Distr
N.A.I.C.S.: 441120

United Power & Resources Pte. Ltd. (1)
2 Gul Street 4, Singapore, 629234, Singapore
Tel.: (65) 68657333
Web Site: https://www.upr.sg
Construction Equipment Distr
N.A.I.C.S.: 423390

Yamazaki Machinery Co., Ltd. (1)
216-1 Tobihiramatsu, Iwata, 438-0216, Shizuoka, Japan
Tel.: (81) 538661211
Web Site: https://www.y-machinery.jp
Emp.: 60
Automobile Parts Mfr
N.A.I.C.S.: 336390

NISHOKU TECHNOLOGY INC.
No 36 Lane 11 Huacheng Road, Xinzhuang Dist, New Taipei City, 24252, Taiwan
Tel.: (886) 229983578
Web Site:
https://www.nishoku.com.tw
Year Founded: 1980
3679—(TAI)
Rev.: $116,660,416
Assets: $278,933,473
Liabilities: $133,398,962
Net Worth: $145,534,512
Earnings: $15,929,134
Emp.: 2,496
Fiscal Year-end: 12/31/23

Plastic Molds & Plastic Injection Components
N.A.I.C.S.: 333511
Piao-Fu Chen (Chm)

Subsidiaries:

Kunshan Nishoku Plastic Electronic Co., Ltd. (1)
No 308 Yangguang Road Nangang, Zhangpu Town, Kunshan, Jiangsu, China
Tel.: (86) 51257425170
Plastic Forming Tool Mfr
N.A.I.C.S.: 333514

Nishoku Plastic Mold (Shenzhen) Co., Ltd. (1)
No 4 Da Zhong Gang Wanfeng Ind Park Shajing, Shenzhen, Guangdong, China
Tel.: (86) 75529851012
Sales Range: $450-499.9 Million
Emp.: 250
Plastic Injection Component Mfr
N.A.I.C.S.: 326199
Jackson Tsai (Gen Mgr)

Nishoku Technology Vietnam Co., Ltd. (1)
Cn 6 4 Tan Truong Industrial Park, Cam Giang County, Hai Duong, Vietnam
Tel.: (84) 320 3626 339
Web Site: http://www.nishoku.com
Injection Molding Plastic Component Mfr
N.A.I.C.S.: 326199

NISHTHA FINANCE & INVESTMENT (INDIA) LTD.
Unit No 2 Second Floor Narnarayan Complex Near Swastik Cross Road, Navrangpura C G Road, Ahmedabad, 380009, India
Tel.: (91) 7940027017
Web Site: http://www.nfandiltd.com
Rev.: $129,466
Assets: $1,293,766
Liabilities: $53,467
Net Worth: $1,240,299
Earnings: $15,001
Fiscal Year-end: 03/31/18
Financial Investment Services
N.A.I.C.S.: 523999
Chunilal Vrujlal Chovatiya (CFO)

NISKA MLEKARA A.D.
Nikodija Stojanovica Tatka 28 b, 18000, Nis, Serbia
Tel.: (381) 18 265 619
Web Site:
http://www.niskamlekara.co.rs
Year Founded: 1957
Sales Range: $25-49.9 Million
Emp.: 172
Cheese Products Mfr
N.A.I.C.S.: 311513
Zvezdan Gavrilovic (CEO)

NISKOGRADNJA A.D.
Branka Radicevica 1, Smederevo, Serbia
Tel.: (381) 26 621 760
Year Founded: 1975
Sales Range: Less than $1 Million
Hydraulic Structure Construction Services
N.A.I.C.S.: 237990
Borislav Jovanovic (Dir)

NISKOGRADNJA A.D.
Srpskih vladara 16, Pirot, Serbia
Tel.: (381) 10 322 174
Year Founded: 1991
Sales Range: Less than $1 Million
Road Construction Services
N.A.I.C.S.: 237310
Dragan Potic (Exec Dir)

NISKOGRADNJA A.D.
Sime Lozanica 17, 74270, Teslic, Bosnia & Herzegovina
Tel.: (387) 53 411 310

NGRD—(BANJ)
Sales Range: Less than $1 Million
Emp.: 26
Construction Engineering Services
N.A.I.C.S.: 237310
Drago Jovicic (Chm)

NISSAL COMPANY
Bulevar Svetog Cara Konstantina bb, 18 110, Nis, Serbia
Tel.: (381) 18 541 510
Web Site: http://www.nissal.co.rs
Year Founded: 1955
Emp.: 620
Metal Mining
N.A.I.C.S.: 213114
Bratislav Cvetanovic (Dir-Technical)

NISSAN CHEMICAL CORPORATION
5 1 Nihonbashi 2-Chome, Chuo-ku, Tokyo, 103-6119, Japan
Tel.: (81) 344638111   JP
Web Site:
https://www.nissanchem.co.jp
Year Founded: 1887
4021—(TKS)
Rev.: $1,498,520,050
Assets: $2,138,057,380
Liabilities: $611,464,660
Net Worth: $1,526,592,720
Earnings: $251,398,130
Emp.: 3,137
Fiscal Year-end: 03/31/24
Chemical Products Mfr
N.A.I.C.S.: 325998
Mitsunobu Matsumura (Exec Officer)

Subsidiaries:

Chemical Service, Co., Ltd. (1)
12 17 Goiminamikaigan, Ichihara, 290 0045, Chiba, Japan
Tel.: (81) 436222110
Sales Range: $25-49.9 Million
Emp.: 40
Distillation & Refining of Chemical Products
N.A.I.C.S.: 325998

Environmental Technical Laboratories, Ltd. (1)
2-11-17 Kohoku, Adachi-Ku, Tokyo, 123-0872, Japan
Tel.: (81) 338986643
Environmental Consultancy Services
N.A.I.C.S.: 541620

Environmental Technical Laboratory, Ltd. (1)
Kohoku 2 chome 11-17, Adachi-ku, Tokyo, 123-0872, Japan
Tel.: (81) 338986643
Web Site: http://www.etlabo.co.jp
Sales Range: $25-49.9 Million
Emp.: 60
Envirionmental Analysis
N.A.I.C.S.: 541380

Hokkaido Sun Agro Co., Ltd. (1)
9-23 Kitahama-cho, Hakodate, 040-0078, Hokkaido, Japan
Tel.: (81) 138411251
Chemical Products Distr
N.A.I.C.S.: 424690

NC Agro Hakodate Corporation (1)
9-23 Kitahama-Cho, Hakodate, 040-0078, Japan
Tel.: (81) 138411251
Agrochemical Mfr & Distr
N.A.I.C.S.: 325320

NCK Co., Ltd. (1)
127 Chupalsandan-ro Paengseong-eup, Pyeongtaek, 17998, Korea (South)
Tel.: (82) 316917044
Semiconductor Material Distr
N.A.I.C.S.: 423690

Nihon Hiryo Co., Ltd. (1)
1-10-5 Nihonbashihon-cho, Chuo-ku, Tokyo, 103-0023, Japan
Tel.: (81) 332414231
Web Site: http://www.nihonhiryo.co.jp

INTERNATIONAL PUBLIC

Sales Range: $50-74.9 Million
Emp.: 100
Fertilizers & Agrochemicals Mfr
N.A.I.C.S.: 325314

Nippon Phosphoric Acid Co., Ltd. (1)
14 Kitasode, Sodegaura, 299-0266, Japan
Tel.: (81) 438620611
Web Site: https://www.n-rinsan.co.jp
Emp.: 50
Sulphuric Acid Mfr & Distr
N.A.I.C.S.: 325180

Nissan Agro Tech India PVT.Ltd. (1)
502-504 5th Floor Tower B Spazedge Commercial Complex, Sector-47 Sohna Road, Gurgaon, 122002, Haryana, India
Tel.: (91) 1244214446
Agrochemical Mfr & Distr
N.A.I.C.S.: 325320

Nissan Bharat Rasayan PVT.Ltd. (1)
502-504 5th Floor Tower B Spazedge Commercial Complex, Sector-47 Sohna Road, Gurgaon, 122002, Haryana, India
Tel.: (91) 1244214446
Agrochemical Product Mfr & Distr
N.A.I.C.S.: 325320

Nissan Butsuryu Co., Ltd. (1)
Nissan Edobashi Building 10-5 Nihonbashi Honcho 1-chome, Chuo-ku, Tokyo, 103-0023, Japan
Tel.: (81) 35 255 6901
Web Site: https://www.nissan-logi.com
Sales Range: $25-49.9 Million
Emp.: 324
Transportation
N.A.I.C.S.: 488210
Kenji Suzuki (Pres)

Nissan Chemical Agro Korea Ltd. (1)
Room 2001 74 Sejong-daero, Jung-gu, Seoul, 04526, Korea (South)
Tel.: (82) 27746470
Agrochemical Mfr & Distr
N.A.I.C.S.: 325320

Nissan Chemical America Corporation (1)
10333 Richmond Ave Ste 1100, Houston, TX 77042
Tel.: (713) 532-4745
Web Site: https://nissanchem-usa.com
Sales Range: $50-74.9 Million
Emp.: 10
Chemicals
N.A.I.C.S.: 424690
Michael Berg (Mgr-Inside Sls)

Nissan Chemical America Corporation (1)
1100 Arlington Hts Rd, Itasca, IL 60143
Tel.: (630) 775-9654
Web Site: http://www.nissanchem.co.jp
Agrochemical Business
N.A.I.C.S.: 424690

Nissan Chemical Europe S.A.R.L (1)
10A Rue Voie Lactee, 69370, Saint-Didier-au-Mont-d'Or, France
Tel.: (33) 437 64 4020
Emp.: 7
Agricultural Chemical Product Mfr
N.A.I.C.S.: 325320
Tomoya Kakimoto (Gen Mgr)

Nissan Chemical Houston Corporation (1)
12330 Bay Area Blvd, Pasadena, TX 77507
Tel.: (281) 291-0200
Web Site: http://www.nissanchem-usa.com
Chemical Products Mfr
N.A.I.C.S.: 325998

Nissan Chemical Industries Limited - Goi Works (1)
12-17 Goiminamikaigan, Ichihara, 290-0045, Chiba, Japan
Tel.: (81) 436 22 2110
Web Site: http://www.nissanchem.co.jp
Investment Management Service
N.A.I.C.S.: 523999

Nissan Chemical Industries Limited - Nagoya Plant (1)
7 Tsukiji-cho, Minato-ku, Nagoya, 455-0045, Japan
Tel.: (81) 52 661 1676

AND PRIVATE COMPANIES

NISSAN MOTOR CO., LTD.

Web Site: http://www.nissanchem.co.jp
Chemical Products Mfr
N.A.I.C.S.: 325998

Nissan Chemical Industries Limited - Onoda Plant (1)
6903-1 Oaza Onoda, Sanyo-Onoda, 756-0093, Yamaguchi, Japan
Tel.: (81) 836 83 2800
Web Site: http://www.nissanchem.co.jp
Chemical Products Mfr
N.A.I.C.S.: 325998

Nissan Chemical Industries Limited - Saitama Plant (1)
235-1 Aza Nishidai Oaza Jimbohara Kamisato-cho, Saitama, 369-0305, Japan
Tel.: (81) 495 34 2810
Chemical Products Mfr
N.A.I.C.S.: 325998

Nissan Chemical Industries Limited - Sodegaura Plant (1)
11-1 Kitasode, Sodegaura, 299-0266, Chiba, Japan
Tel.: (81) 438 63 2341
Web Site: http://www.nissanchem.co.jp
Chemical Products Mfr
N.A.I.C.S.: 325998

Nissan Chemical Industries Limited - Toyama Plant (1)
635 Sasakura Fuchu-machi, Toyama, 939-2792, Japan
Tel.: (81) 76 433 9602
Chemical Products Mfr
N.A.I.C.S.: 325998

Nissan Chemical Korea Co., Ltd. (1)
401 Chupal Ri, Seoul, 451807, Korea (South) **(100%)**
Tel.: (82) 316917044
Web Site: http://www.nck.co.kr
Sales Range: $25-49.9 Million
Emp.: 50
Chemicals
N.A.I.C.S.: 325998
Hukuro Hiroyuyoshi *(Mng Dir)*

Nissan Chemical Materials Research (Suzhou) Co., Ltd. (1)
Room101 NW-10 Nanopolis Suzhou 99 Jinji Lake Avenue, Suzhou, 215123, China
Tel.: (86) 51262732080
Performance Material Promotional Services
N.A.I.C.S.: 541890

Nissan Chemical Product(Shanghai) Co., Ltd. (1)
Rm 3210 Office Tower 1, Raffles City Changning No 1133 Changning Road, Shanghai, 200051, China
Tel.: (86) 2162368300
Agrochemical Mfr & Distr
N.A.I.C.S.: 325320

Nissan Chemical Taiwan Co., Ltd. (1)
5F No 67 Luke 2nd Rd, Luzhu, Kaohsiung, 82151, Taiwan
Tel.: (886) 76955252
Semiconductor & Electronic Component Distr
N.A.I.C.S.: 423690

Nissan Engineering, Ltd. (1)
634-1 Sasakura, Fuchumachi, Toyama, 939-2753, Japan
Tel.: (81) 76 465 5711
Web Site: https://www.nissaneng.co.jp
Emp.: 26
Plant Engineering Services
N.A.I.C.S.: 541330
Mitsuo Kobayashi *(Dir)*

Nissan Green & Landscape Co., Ltd. (1)
4-4-1 Kanda Surugadai, Chiyoda-Ku, Tokyo, 101-0062, Japan **(100%)**
Tel.: (81) 33 256 4031
Web Site: https://www.nissanryokka.co.jp
Sales Range: $25-49.9 Million
Emp.: 80
Landscaping & Civil Engineering
N.A.I.C.S.: 541320

Nissan Kenzai Co., Ltd. (1)
635 Sasakura Fuchu Mati Nei, Toyama, 939 2753, Japan
Tel.: (81) 764656200

Web Site: http://www.nissanchem.co.jp
Construction Materials
N.A.I.C.S.: 333120

Nissei Corporation (1)
10-5 Nihonbashi-Honcho 1-Chome Nissan Edobashi Building, Chuo-Ku, Tokyo, 103-0023, Japan
Tel.: (81) 332412548
Emp.: 173
Sales of Chemical Products & Insurance
N.A.I.C.S.: 325998
Akihiro Mori *(Pres)*

Sun Agro Company Limited (1)
1-10-5 Nihonbashihon-cho, Chuo-ku, Tokyo, 103-0023, Japan
Tel.: (81) 33 510 3601
Web Site: https://www.nissanchem.co.jp
Fertilizers & Agrochemicals Mfr
N.A.I.C.S.: 212390

NISSAN MEDICAL INDUSTRIES LTD.
11 Harugei Malhut St, Tel Aviv, 69714, Israel
Tel.: (972) 544334461
Year Founded: 1984
NISA—(TAE)
Rev: $202,766,677
Assets: $195,049,313
Liabilities: $97,028,594
Net Worth: $98,020,720
Earnings: $5,260,395
Emp.: 256
Fiscal Year-end: 12/31/23
Nonwoven Fabric Mills
N.A.I.C.S.: 313230
Avraham Harel *(Chm)*

NISSAN MOTOR CO., LTD.
1-1Takashima 1-chome, Nishi-ku, Yokohama, 220-8686, Kanagawa, Japan
Tel.: (81) 455235523
Web Site: https://www.nissan-global.com
Year Founded: 1933
NISA—(DEU)
Rev: $83,852,582,760
Assets: $131,242,548,110
Liabilities: $88,472,258,880
Net Worth: $42,770,289,230
Earnings: $2,820,149,890
Emp.: 133,580
Fiscal Year-end: 03/31/24
Automobile & Truck Mfr
N.A.I.C.S.: 336110
Joji Tagawa *(Sr VP)*

Subsidiaries:

4R Energy Corporation (1)
Queen's Tower C-20F 2-3-5 Minatomirai, Nishi-ku, Yokohama, 220-6220, Kanagawa, Japan
Tel.: (81) 452636718
Lithium-ion Battery Mfr & Distr
N.A.I.C.S.: 335910

Aichi Machine Industry Co., Ltd. (1)
2-12 Kawanami-cho, Atsuta-ku, Nagoya, 456-8601, Japan
Tel.: (81) 526818643
Web Site: http://www.aichikikai.co.jp
Emp.: 1,445
Vehicle Parts Mfr & Distr
N.A.I.C.S.: 336390
Akira Sakurai *(Pres)*

Arabian Automobiles Co. (1)
PO Box 2128, Dubai, United Arab Emirates
Tel.: (971) 43332638
Web Site: http://en.nissan-dubai.com
Car Dealing Services
N.A.I.C.S.: 441110

Autech Japan, Inc. (1)
824-2 Hagisono, Chigasaki, 253-8571, Kanagawa, Japan
Tel.: (81) 467878001
Web Site: http://www.autech.co.jp
Emp.: 443
Vehicle Parts Mfr & Distr
N.A.I.C.S.: 336390

Takao Katagiri *(Pres & CEO)*

Boustead Sdn. Bhd. (1)
Lot No 24 & 29 Beribi Industrial Complex II Jalan Gadong, BE1118, Negara, Brunei Darussalam
Tel.: (673) 2431222
Web Site: https://nissan.com.bn
Motor Vehicles Mfr
N.A.I.C.S.: 332119

Bustami & Saheb Trading Co., Ltd. (1)
Amman-Mecca St-Bldg 53, Amman, 8182, Jordan
Tel.: (962) 65532456
Web Site: http://www.nissan.com.jo
Car Dealing Services
N.A.I.C.S.: 441110

CK KS Engineering (Guangzhou) Tooling Center Corp. (1)
Dongfeng Road Automobile Center, Huadu District, Guangzhou, 510800, China
Tel.: (86) 2086733128
Web Site: http://www.calsonickansei.co.jp
Electronic Components Mfr
N.A.I.C.S.: 334419

Creative Box Inc. (1)
6-34-18 Meijijingumae, Shibuya-ku, Tokyo, 150-0001, Japan
Tel.: (81) 334860798
Web Site: http://www.creative-box.co.jp
Vehicle Parts Mfr
N.A.I.C.S.: 336390
Alfonso Albaisa *(Pres)*

Dongfeng Nissan Auto Finance Co., Ltd. (1)
12th Floor Dongfang Chunyi Building No 50 Eshan Road 17-20 Floors, Pilot Free Trade Zone Pudong New Area, Shanghai, 2001 27, China
Tel.: (86) 4006031188
Web Site: https://www.df-nissanfc.com
Loan Financial Services
N.A.I.C.S.: 522390

Dongfeng Nissan Passenger Vehicle Company (1)
No 8 Fengshen Avenue, Huadu District, Guangzhou, 510800, China
Tel.: (86) 2086872958
Web Site: http://www.dongfeng-nissan.com.cn
Car Dealing Services
N.A.I.C.S.: 441110

JATCO France SAS (1)
Citi Center 19 Le Parvis, La Defence, 92073, Paris, France
Tel.: (33) 1 49 03 72 00
Sales Range: $25-49.9 Million
Emp.: 15
Automatic Transmission Component Mfr
N.A.I.C.S.: 336350

JATCO Korea Engineering Corp. (1)
IT Castle 2-4F 98 Gasan digital 2-ro, Geumcheon-Gu, Seoul, 08506, Korea (South)
Tel.: (82) 264437000
Web Site: http://www.jatco.co.kr
Sales Range: $50-74.9 Million
Emp.: 196
Automatic Transmission Component Mfr
N.A.I.C.S.: 336350

JATCO Korea Service Corp. (1)
IT Castle 2-4F 98 Gasan digital 2-ro, Geumcheon Gu, Seoul, 08506, Korea (South)
Tel.: (82) 264437000
Web Site: http://www.jatco.co.kr
Emp.: 240
Automatic Transmission Component Mfr
N.A.I.C.S.: 336350
Taisuke Naito *(Pres)*

JATCO Ltd (1)
700-1 Imaizumi, Fuji, 417-8585, Shizuoka, Japan
Tel.: (81) 545 51 0047
Web Site: http://www.jatco.co.jp
Emp.: 14,200
Automobile Component Mfr & Distr
N.A.I.C.S.: 336390
William Krueger *(Exec VP)*

Subsidiary (Domestic):

JATCO Engineering Ltd (2)
125-1 Yodabashi, Fuji, 417-0002, Shizuoka, Japan
Tel.: (81) 54 551 5777
Web Site: https://www.jatcoeng.co.jp
Emp.: 957
Automotive Engineering Services
N.A.I.C.S.: 541330
Hiroshi Usuba *(Pres)*

JATCO Plant Tec Ltd (2)
1-1 Yoshiwaratakaracho, Fuji, 417-0023, Shizuoka, Japan
Tel.: (81) 545 57 5510
Web Site: http://www.jatco-plant.co.jp
Power Equipment Maintenance Services
N.A.I.C.S.: 811310

JATCO Tool Ltd (2)
Yoshiharatakara-cho 1-1, Fuji, 417-0023, Shizuoka, Japan
Tel.: (81) 545541159
Web Site: http://www.jatco-tool.co.jp
Sales Range: $25-49.9 Million
Emp.: 95
Cutting Tool Mfr
N.A.I.C.S.: 333515

JSC AVTOVAZ (1)
36 Yuzhnoye Shosse, 445024, Togliatti, Samara, Russia
Tel.: (7) 8007005232
Sales Range: $5-14.9 Billion
Emp.: 112,200
Passenger Car Mfr
N.A.I.C.S.: 336110

Japan Motors Trading Company Ltd. (1)
Graphic Road, PO Box AN 5216, Accra, Ghana
Tel.: (233) 302682220
Web Site: http://www.japanmotors.com
Motor Vehicle Spare Parts Distr
N.A.I.C.S.: 423120
Salem Kalmoni *(Mng Dir)*

Kenya Vehicle Manufacturers Ltd. (1)
Garissa Rd, PO Box 1436, Thika, Kenya
Tel.: (254) 7188090
Web Site: http://www.kvm.co.ke
Automobile Mfr
N.A.I.C.S.: 336110
Martyn Broadfield *(Mng Dir)*

NMKV Co., Ltd. (1)
9F Shinagawa Center Building 3-23-17, Takanawa Minato-ku, Tokyo, 108-0074, Japan
Tel.: (81) 354886055
Web Site: http://www.nmkv.com
Emp.: 52
Vehicle Parts Mfr & Distr
N.A.I.C.S.: 336390
Junichi Endo *(Pres & CEO)*

NR Finance Mexico, S.A. de C.V. (1)
Avenida Insurgentes Sur 2475 20th Floor Mayor's Office, Colonia Barrio Loreto Alvaro Obregon, 01090, Mexico, Mexico
Tel.: (52) 4499944814
Web Site: http://www.nrfm.mx
Vehicle Financing Services
N.A.I.C.S.: 522220

Nissan Arc Ltd. (1)
1 Natsushima-cho, Yokosuka, 237-0061, Kanagawa, Japan
Tel.: (81) 46 867 5280
Web Site: http://www.nissan-arc.co.jp
Sales Range: $25-49.9 Million
Emp.: 131
Automobile Research & Development Services
N.A.I.C.S.: 541715
Takao Asami *(Pres)*

Nissan Argentina S.A. (1)
Av Del Libertador 390, Vicente Lopez, Buenos Aires, Argentina
Tel.: (54) 8102226477
Web Site: https://www.nissan.com.ar
Car Dealing Services
N.A.I.C.S.: 441110

Nissan Asia Pacific Pte. Ltd. (1)

NISSAN MOTOR CO., LTD.

Nissan Motor Co., Ltd.—(Continued)
19 Ubi Road 4 03-01, Singapore, 408623, Singapore
Tel.: (65) 65112300
Web Site: http://www.nissan-global.com
Sales Range: $50-74.9 Million
Emp.: 5
Automotive Distr
N.A.I.C.S.: 423110
Engoo Lim *(Gen Mgr)*

Nissan Automotive Technology Co., Ltd. (1)
Atsugi AXT Main Tower 12F 3050, Okada, Atsugi, 243-0021, Kanagawa, Japan
Tel.: (81) 462204770
Web Site: http://www.nissan-automotive-technology.com
Emp.: 3,084
Vehicle Parts Mfr
N.A.I.C.S.: 336390
Tooru Segoshi *(Pres & CEO)*

Nissan Business Service Co., Ltd. (1)
6-139 Hanasakicho, Nishi-ku, Yokohama, 220-0022, Kanagawa, Japan
Tel.: (81) 45 286 0030
Web Site: http://www.nissan-global.com
Business Process Outsourcing Services
N.A.I.C.S.: 561499

Nissan Canada Inc. (1)
5290 Orbitor Drive, Mississauga, L4W 4Z5, ON, Canada **(100%)**
Tel.: (905) 629-2888
Web Site: http://www.nissan.ca
Sales Range: $100-124.9 Million
Emp.: 300
Car & Truck Distr
N.A.I.C.S.: 441110
Steve Milette *(Pres)*

Nissan Car Rental Solutions Co., Ltd (1)
2-6 Nakase Marib West 20f, Mihama-Ku, Chiba, 261-0023, Japan
Tel.: (81) 433824123
Automotive Distr
N.A.I.C.S.: 423110

Nissan Casting Australia Pty. Ltd. (1)
209-235 Frankston-Dandenong Rd, Dandenong, 3174, VIC, Australia
Tel.: (61) 397974001
Web Site: http://www.nissan.com.au
Sales Range: $50-74.9 Million
Emp.: 170
Automobile Parts Mfr
N.A.I.C.S.: 336390
Peter Jones *(Mng Dir)*

Nissan Center Europe GmbH (1)
Renault-Nissan-Str 6-10, 50321, Bruhl, Germany
Tel.: (49) 2232572079
Web Site: http://www.nissan.de
Car Dealing Services
N.A.I.C.S.: 441110

Nissan Creative Services Co., Ltd. (1)
2384 Kamiyabe-cho, Totsuka-ku, Yokohama, 245-8558, Kanagawa, Japan
Tel.: (81) 45 814 7301
Web Site: http://www.nissan-nics.co.jp
Business Support Services
N.A.I.C.S.: 561499
Toru Takahashi *(CEO)*

Nissan Digital India LLP (1)
Yamuna Building 2101 1st Floor Phase 3 Technopark, Thiruvananthapuram, 695581, India
Tel.: (91) 4714002500
Software Development Services
N.A.I.C.S.: 541511

Nissan Financiacion, S.A. (1)
General Almirante 2, E 08014, Barcelona, Spain
Tel.: (34) 902 11 80 85
Web Site: http://www.nissan.es
Sales Range: $75-99.9 Million
Emp.: 85
Financial Services
N.A.I.C.S.: 523999

Nissan Financial Services Australia Pty. Ltd. (1)
Brandon Park, Locked Bag 2004, Victoria, 3150, VIC, Australia
Tel.: (61) 1800035035
Financial & Loan Services
N.A.I.C.S.: 522310

Nissan Financial Services Co., Ltd. (1)
WBG Malibu West 2-6-1 Nakase, Mihama-ku, Chiba, 261-7114, Japan
Tel.: (81) 43 388 4102
Web Site: http://www.nissan-fs.co.jp
Sales Range: $350-399.9 Million
Emp.: 801
Financial Management Services
N.A.I.C.S.: 523999

Subsidiary (Domestic):

Nissan Plazasol Co., Ltd. (2)
399 Nabasama, Yotsukaido, 284-0034, Chiba, Japan
Tel.: (81) 433825523
Web Site: http://www.nissan-fs.co.jp
Sales Range: $25-49.9 Million
Emp.: 208
Automotive Distr
N.A.I.C.S.: 423110
Shinichi Kai *(Pres)*

Nissan Group Finance Co., Ltd. (1)
1-1 Takashima 1-chome, Nishi-ku, Yokohama, 220-8686, Kanagawa, Japan
Tel.: (81) 455235457
Financial Services
N.A.I.C.S.: 523999

Nissan Human Information Service Co., Ltd. (1)
1-1 Takashima 1-chome, Nishi-ku, Yokohama, 220-8686, Kanagawa, Japan
Tel.: (81) 45 523 5464
Human Resource Consulting Services
N.A.I.C.S.: 541612

Nissan Iberia, S.A. (1)
Avenida Gran Via de L'Hospitalet 149-151, L'Hospitalet de Llobregat, 08014, Barcelona, Spain
Tel.: (34) 900118119
Web Site: http://www.nissan.es
Automobile Mfr & Distr
N.A.I.C.S.: 336110

Nissan International SA (1)
Zone d Activites La Piece 12, 1180, Rolle, Switzerland
Tel.: (41) 218225000
Automobile Mfr
N.A.I.C.S.: 336110

Nissan Italia S.p.A. (1)
Via Tiberina KM 15740, Capena, Rome, 00060, Italy
Tel.: (39) 06908081
Web Site: http://www.nissan.it
Sales Range: $100-124.9 Million
Emp.: 150
Financial Services
N.A.I.C.S.: 523999

Nissan Kohki Co., Ltd. (1)
6-1 Okada 6-chome Samukawa-machi, Koza, 253-0105, Kanagawa, Japan
Tel.: (81) 467 75 1711
Web Site: http://www.nissan-kohki.jp
Sales Range: $200-249.9 Million
Emp.: 900
Automotive Engine Parts Mfr
N.A.I.C.S.: 336310

Nissan Leasing (Thailand) Co., Ltd. (1)
3 Rajanakarn Building Floor 26 South Sathorn Road, Yannawa Sathorn, Bangkok, 10120, Thailand
Tel.: (66) 2 207 4000
Web Site: http://www.nissanleasing.co.th
Automobile Finance Leasing Services
N.A.I.C.S.: 522220

Nissan Manufacturing Russia LLC (1)
140 Komendantski Prospekt, Saint Petersburg, 194362, Russia
Tel.: (7) 8123036300
Web Site: http://www.nissan.ru
Emp.: 200

Automobile Mfr
N.A.I.C.S.: 336110

Nissan Mexicana, S.A. de C.V. (1)
Insurgentes Sur 1958 3rd Floor, Colina Florida, Mexico, 01030, CF, Mexico **(100%)**
Tel.: (52) 5556282727
Web Site: http://www.nissan.com.mx
Sales Range: $250-299.9 Million
Emp.: 560
Mfr of Motor Vehicles & Components
N.A.I.C.S.: 441110
Airton Cousseau *(Vice Chm)*

Nissan Middle East F.Z.E. (1)
Jebel Ali Free Zone, PO Box 61111, Dubai, United Arab Emirates **(100%)**
Tel.: (971) 4600546655
Web Site: http://www.nissan-me.com
Sales Range: $50-74.9 Million
Emp.: 150
Sales & Marketing of Motor Vehicles & Related Products
N.A.I.C.S.: 441227

Nissan Motor (China) Ltd. (1)
G/F Chinachem Century Tower 178 Gloucester Road, Wanchai, China (Hong Kong) **(100%)**
Tel.: (852) 28035333
Web Site: http://www.nissan.com.hk
Motor Vehicles Whslr & Showroom
N.A.I.C.S.: 423120

Nissan Motor (GB) Ltd. (1)
The Rivers Office Park Denham Way, Maple Cross, Rickmansworth, WD3 9YS, Hertfordshire, United Kingdom **(100%)**
Tel.: (44) 3301231231
Web Site: http://www.nissan.co.uk
Sales Range: $100-124.9 Million
Emp.: 285
Distr of Cars & Trucks
N.A.I.C.S.: 441110

Nissan Motor (Schweiz) AG (1)
Bergermoosstrasse 4, 8902, Urdorf, Switzerland
Tel.: (41) 17770200
Web Site: http://www.nissan.ch
Sales Range: $50-74.9 Million
Emp.: 200
Distr of Cars & Trucks
N.A.I.C.S.: 441110

Nissan Motor Co. (Australia) Pty. Ltd. (1)
260 -270 Frankston-Dandenong Rd, Locked Bag 1450, Dandenong South, Dandenong, 3164, VIC, Australia
Tel.: (61) 3 9797 4111
Web Site: http://www.nissan.com.au
Sales Range: $50-74.9 Million
Emp.: 200
Automobile Mfr & Distr
N.A.I.C.S.: 336110
Malcolm Gairns *(Mgr-Fleet Sls)*

Nissan Motor Co., Ltd. - Iwaki Plant (1)
386 Shimokawa-aza-Otsurugi Izumi-cho, Iwaki, 971-8183, Fukushima, Japan
Tel.: (81) 246 75 1123
Web Site: http://www.nissan-global.com
Automobile Mfr
N.A.I.C.S.: 336110

Nissan Motor Co., Ltd. - Kyushu Plant (1)
1-3 Shinhama-cho Kanda-machi, Miyako-gun, Fukuoka, 800-0395, Japan
Tel.: (81) 93 435 1111
Web Site: http://www.nissan-global.com
Automobile Mfr
N.A.I.C.S.: 336110

Nissan Motor Co., Ltd. - Oppama Plant (1)
1 Natsushima-cho, Yokosuka, 237-8523, Kanagawa, Japan
Tel.: (81) 46 867 5000
Web Site: http://www.nissan-global.com
Automotive Products Mfr
N.A.I.C.S.: 336390

Nissan Motor Co., Ltd. - Tochigi Plant (1)
2500 Kamigamou, Kaminokawa-machi Kawachi-gun, Tochigi, 329-0692, Japan

Tel.: (81) 285 56 1204
Web Site: http://www.nissan-global.com
Automotive Products Mfr
N.A.I.C.S.: 336390

Nissan Motor Co., Ltd. - Yokohama Plant (1)
2 Takara-cho, Kanagawa-ku, Yokohama, 220-8623, Kanagawa, Japan
Tel.: (81) 45 461 7304
Web Site: http://www.nissan-global.com
Automobile Mfr
N.A.I.C.S.: 336110

Nissan Motor Espana S.A. (1)
Torre Nissan Plaza Cerda, General Almirante 4-10, E-08014, Barcelona, Spain
Tel.: (34) 902118085
Web Site: http://www.nissan.es
Sales Range: $200-249.9 Million
Emp.: 1,000
Automobile Research & Development
N.A.I.C.S.: 336110

Nissan Motor Iberica, S.A. (1)
P Ind Zona Franca Sector B, 08040, Barcelona, Spain
Tel.: (34) 932908080
Web Site: http://www.nissan.es
Rev.: $3,256,699,904
Emp.: 5,905
Mfr & Distr of Automobiles
N.A.I.C.S.: 336110

Nissan Motor India Private Limited (1)
ASV Ramana Towers 37 & 38 Venkatnarayana Rd, T Nagar, Chennai, 600017, India
Tel.: (91) 44 3088 6000
Web Site: http://www.nissan.in
Sales Range: $50-74.9 Million
Emp.: 200
Automobile Mfr
N.A.I.C.S.: 336110
Abhishek Mahapatra *(Head-Comm & CSR)*

Nissan Motor Kyushu Co., Ltd. (1)
1-3 Shinhama-cho, Kanda-machi Miyako-gun, Fukuoka, 800-0395, Japan
Tel.: (81) 934351111
Vehicle Parts Mfr
N.A.I.C.S.: 336390

Nissan Motor Light Truck Co., Ltd. (1)
V square Omiya Bldg 2-65-2 Nakacho, Omiya-ku, Saitama, 330-0845, Japan
Tel.: (81) 4 8657 9074
Web Site: http://www.nmlt.co.jp
Sales Range: $100-124.9 Million
Emp.: 335
Light Commercial Vehicles Mfr
N.A.I.C.S.: 336110
Hideto Murakami *(COO)*

Nissan Motor Manufacturing (UK) Ltd. (1)
Washington Road, Sunderland, SR5 3NS, Tyne & Wear, United Kingdom **(100%)**
Tel.: (44) 1914150000
Web Site: http://www.nissan.co.uk
Sales Range: $800-899.9 Million
Emp.: 9,000
Automobile Mfr
N.A.I.C.S.: 336110
Samuel Elliot *(CFO)*

Nissan Motor Netherland B.V. (1)
Hornweg 32, 1044 AN, Amsterdam, Netherlands **(100%)**
Tel.: (31) 203549555
Web Site: http://www.nissan.nl
Sales Range: $25-49.9 Million
Emp.: 26
Distr of Cars & Trucks
N.A.I.C.S.: 441110

Nissan Motor Part Center B.V. (1)
Horweg No 32, 1044 AN, Amsterdam, Netherlands **(100%)**
Tel.: (31) 0205162222
Web Site: http://www.nissan.nl
Sales Range: $200-249.9 Million
Emp.: 400
Financial Services
N.A.I.C.S.: 523999

Nissan Motor Philippines, Inc. (1)
Nissan Technopark Brgy Pulong Sta Cruz, Santa Rosa, Laguna, Philippines

AND PRIVATE COMPANIES — NISSAN MOTOR CO., LTD.

Tel.: (63) 495412201
Web Site: http://www.nissan.com.ph
Automobile Mfr
N.A.I.C.S.: 336110
Allen Chen *(Pres & CEO)*

Nissan Motor RUS Ltd. (1)
52 Strasse 3 Kosmoda Mianskaya Nab,
Moscow, 115054, Russia
Tel.: (7) 4959612131
Web Site: http://www.nissan.ru
Automobile Dealers
N.A.I.C.S.: 441110
Philip Seillard *(Pres)*

Nissan Motor Thailand Co., Ltd. (1)
15th Floor Nantawan Building 161 Rajdamri
Road, Lumpini, Pathuwan, Bangkok,
10330, Thailand (75%)
Tel.: (66) 2257420009
Web Site: http://www.nissan.co.th
Automobile Mfr & Distr
N.A.I.C.S.: 336110
Mantana Lau *(Gen Mgr-Corp Comm)*

**Nissan Motorsports & Customizing
Co., Ltd.** (1)
824-2 Hagisono, Chigasaki, 253-8571,
Kanagawa-ken, Japan
Tel.: (81) 467878001
Web Site: https://www.nissan-nmc.co.jp
Emp.: 600
Motor Vehicle Parts Mfr
N.A.I.C.S.: 336211

**Nissan Motorsports International Co.,
Ltd.** (1)
6-1 Daikoku-cho, Tsurumi-ku, Yokohama,
230-0053, Kanagawa, Japan
Tel.: (81) 455058520
Web Site: http://www.nismo.co.jp
Sales Range: $50-74.9 Million
Emp.: 200
Rally Car Mfr
N.A.I.C.S.: 336110
Takao Katagiri *(Pres & CEO)*

**Nissan Network Holdings Co.,
Ltd.** (1)
1-1 Takashima 1-chome, Nishi-ku, Yokohama, 220-8686, Kanagawa, Japan
Tel.: (81) 455235414
Real Estate Development Services
N.A.I.C.S.: 531390

Nissan New Zealand Ltd. (1)
261 Roscommon Road, Private Box 98-888,
Manukau, 2104, Auckland, New Zealand
Tel.: (64) 92690300
Web Site: http://www.nissan.co.nz
New Car Dealers
N.A.I.C.S.: 441110

Nissan Nordic Europe Oy (1)
Keilasatama 5, 02150, Espoo, Finland
Tel.: (358) 107705222
Web Site: http://www.nissan.fi
Car Dealing Services
N.A.I.C.S.: 441110

Nissan North America, Inc. (1)
1 Nissan Way, Franklin, TN 37067
Tel.: (615) 725-1000
Web Site: http://www.nissanusa.com
Sales Range: $5-14.9 Billion
Emp.: 9,000
Cars & Trucks Mfr & Distr
N.A.I.C.S.: 423110
David Kershaw *(VP-Dealer Network Dev)*

Subsidiary (Domestic):

JATCO USA Inc. (2)
30893 Century Dr, Wixom, MI 48393
Tel.: (248) 668-7120
Automatic Transmission Component Mfr
N.A.I.C.S.: 336350
William Krueger *(Exec VP)*

Nissan Design America (2)
9800 Campus Point Dr, San Diego, CA
92121-1514
Tel.: (858) 457-4400
Web Site: http://www.nissanusa.com
Sales Range: $10-24.9 Million
Emp.: 50
Automobile Design Institute
N.A.I.C.S.: 541420

**Nissan Motor Acceptance
Corporation** (2)
One Nissan Way, Franklin, TN 37067
Tel.: (615) 725-1655
Web Site: http://www.nissanfinance.com
Automobile Financing Services
N.A.I.C.S.: 522220
Kevin Cullum *(Pres)*

**Nissan Motor Corporation Hawaii,
Ltd.** (2)
983 Nissan Dr, Smyrna, TN 37167-4405
Web Site: http://www.nissanhawaii.com
Sales Range: $25-49.9 Million
Emp.: 35
Distr of Cars & Trucks
N.A.I.C.S.: 423110

Plant (Domestic):

**Nissan North America, Inc. -
Canton** (2)
300 Nissan Dr, Canton, MS 39046
Tel.: (601) 855-6010
Web Site: http://www.nissanusa.com
Motor Vehicle Parts Mfr
N.A.I.C.S.: 336390

**Nissan North America, Inc.
Decherd** (2)
520 nissan power dr, Decherd, TN 37324
Tel.: (931) 962-5000
Motor Vehicle Engine Parts Mfr
N.A.I.C.S.: 336320

Subsidiary (Domestic):

Nissan Technical Center N.A. (2)
39001 Sunrise Dr, Farmington Hills, MI
48333-9200 (100%)
Tel.: (248) 488-4123
Web Site: http://www.nissandriven.com
Sales Range: $150-199.9 Million
Emp.: 1,000
Automobile Research & Development
N.A.I.C.S.: 541330

**Nissan Technical Center North
America, Inc.** (2)
39001 Sunrise Dr, Farmington Hills, MI
48333-9200
Tel.: (248) 488-4123
Web Site: http://www.nissanusa.com
Sales Range: $150-199.9 Million
Emp.: 1,200
Motor Vehicle Parts Mfr
N.A.I.C.S.: 336390

Nissan Trading Corp., U.S.A. (2)
1974 Midway Ln, Smyrna, TN
37167 (100%)
Tel.: (615) 220-7100
Web Site: http://www.nitco-us.com
Sales Range: $50-74.9 Million
Emp.: 9
Automobile & Automotive Parts Wholesale
Trade Agency
N.A.I.C.S.: 425120
Kizo Tanabe *(Pres)*

Nissan Otomotiv A.S. (1)
Kusbakisi Cad No 11, PK 46, Altunizade,
34662, Istanbul, Turkiye
Tel.: (90) 216 559 8400
Web Site: http://www.nissan.com.tr
Automobile & Motor Vehicle Parts Distr
N.A.I.C.S.: 423110

Nissan Philippines, Inc. (1)
9th Floor Ecoprime Building 32nd Street
corner 9th Avenue, Bonifacio Global City,
Taguig, Metro Manila, Philippines
Tel.: (63) 284036593
Web Site: http://www.nissan.ph
Car Dealing Services
N.A.I.C.S.: 441110

**Nissan Prince Tokyo Motor Sales
Co., Ltd** (1)
Nishigotanda, Shinagawa-Ku, Tokyo,
1418623, Japan
Tel.: (81) 334588123
Automobile Parts Distr
N.A.I.C.S.: 423120

Nissan Saudi Arabia Co., Ltd. (1)
PO Box 21332, Jeddah, Saudi Arabia
Tel.: (966) 126637186
Web Site: http://en.nissan-saudiarabia.com
Car Dealing Services
N.A.I.C.S.: 441110

Nissan Shatai Co., Ltd. (1)
2-1 Tsutsumicho, Hiratsuka, 254-8610, Kanagawa, Japan (43%)
Tel.: (81) 463218001
Web Site: http://www.nissan-shatai.co.jp
Rev.: $1,990,079,310
Assets: $1,707,865,360
Liabilities: $555,524,230
Net Worth: $1,152,341,130
Earnings: $2,690,270
Emp.: 1,681
Fiscal Year-end: 03/31/2024
Passenger & Commercial Vehicles Mfr
N.A.I.C.S.: 336110
Masaaki Ushigome *(Compliance Officer)*

Nissan Shatai Kyushu Co., Ltd. (1)
1-3 Shinhama-cho, Kanda-machi Miyakogun, Fukuoka, 800-0321, Japan
Tel.: (81) 934349645
Emp.: 1,113
Automotive Parts Mfr & Distr
N.A.I.C.S.: 336211

Nissan South Africa Pty. Ltd. (1)
Ernest Oppenheimer Street, PO Box 911-
010, Rosslyn, 0200, South Africa (92%)
Tel.: (27) 125296000
Web Site: http://www.nissan.co.za
Sales Range: $800-899.9 Million
Emp.: 3,500
Mfr & Distr of Cars & Trucks
N.A.I.C.S.: 336120

**Nissan Technical Centre Europe,
Ltd.** (1)
Cranfield Technology Pk Moulsoe Rd, Cranfield, MK43 0DB, Beds, United Kingdom
Tel.: (44) 234755555
Web Site: http://www.nissan.com
Assets: $57,999,000
Emp.: 1,000
Automobile Research & Development
N.A.I.C.S.: 336110

Nissan Techno Co., Ltd. (1)
12F Atsugi Axt Main Tower 3050 Okada,
Atsugi, 243-0021, Kanagawa, Japan
Tel.: (81) 46 220 4770
Web Site: http://www.nissan-techno.com
Automobile Mfr
N.A.I.C.S.: 336110

Nissan Trading Co., Ltd. (1)
91-1 Kawakami-cho, Totsuka-ku, Yokohama, 244-0805, Kanagawa, Japan
Tel.: (81) 5033602021
Web Site: http://www.nitoo.co.jp
Emp.: 1,533
Vehicle Parts Mfr & Distr
N.A.I.C.S.: 336390
Mamoru Kawahara *(CEO)*

Nissan Trading Europe LTD. (1)
Washington Rd, Sunderland, SR5 3NS,
Tyne and Wear, United Kingdom
Tel.: (44) 191 548 9888
Automotive Distr
Akihiro Ishiwatari *(Gen Mgr)*

Nissan West Europe SAS (1)
TSA 60011, 78961, Saint-Quentin-en-
Yvelines, Cedex, France
Tel.: (33) 172676914
Web Site: http://www.nissan.fr
Sales Range: $25-49.9 Million
Emp.: 350
Distr of Automobiles
N.A.I.C.S.: 336110

PT. Nissan Motor Indonesia (1)
Jln Mt Haryono Kav 10, Jakarta, 13330,
Timur, Indonesia
Tel.: (62) 218564760
Web Site: http://www.nissan.co.id
Car Mfr & Distr
N.A.I.C.S.: 336110

Renault Japon Co., Ltd. (1)
1-1-2 Takashima, Nishi-ku, Yokohama, 220-
0011, Japan
Tel.: (81) 120676365
Web Site: http://www.renault.jp
Vehicle Parts Whslr
N.A.I.C.S.: 423120

Saleh Alhamad Almana Co. (1)
Salwa Road, PO Box 91, Doha, Qatar
Tel.: (974) 44283333
Web Site: http://www.shalmana.com
Car Dealing Services
N.A.I.C.S.: 441110

Stallion NMN Ltd. (1)
Plot 1 Block A, Gbagada Industrial Estate
Gbagada, Lagos, Nigeria
Tel.: (234) 805636999
Web Site: http://www.nissan.ng
Car Dealing Services
N.A.I.C.S.: 441110

**Tan Chong Motor (Cambodia) Co.,
Ltd.** (1)
No 131B St 271, Sangkat Beoung Salang
Khan Toul Kork, Phnom Penh, Cambodia
Tel.: (855) 92238318
Web Site: https://www.nissan.com.kh
Car Dealing Services
N.A.I.C.S.: 441110

**Tan Chong Motor (Lao) Sole Co.,
Ltd.** (1)
No 231 Unit 02 Thadeua Road, Chomcheng
Village Sisattanark District, Vientiane, Lao
People's Democratic Republic
Tel.: (856) 2076224494
Web Site: https://www.nissan-lao.la
Car Dealing Services
N.A.I.C.S.: 441110

**Tan Chong Motor Assemblies Sdn.
Bhd.** (1)
249 Jalan Segambut, 51700, Kuala Lumpur, Malaysia
Tel.: (60) 362568888
Automobile Parts Mfr
N.A.I.C.S.: 336390
Loh Chung Ying *(Exec Dir)*

Tokyo Radiator Mfg. Co.,Ltd. (1)
2002-1 Endo, Fujisawa, 252-0816, Kanagawa, Japan
Tel.: (81) 466871231
Web Site: https://www.tokyo-radiator.co.jp
Rev.: $220,780,610
Assets: $209,061,080
Liabilities: $64,288,860
Net Worth: $144,772,220
Earnings: $11,111,410
Emp.: 886
Fiscal Year-end: 03/31/2024
Heat Exchanger Mfr & Distr
N.A.I.C.S.: 332410
Hisao Ochiai *(Chm & Pres)*

Universal Motors Corporation (1)
2232 Don Chino Roces Ave, Makati, 1200,
Philippines
Tel.: (63) 28100151
Web Site: http://www.mynissan.com.ph
Automotive Distr
N.A.I.C.S.: 423110

Vietnam Automobile Industry Development Ltd. (1)
Discovery 302 Dich Vong Street, Cau Giay
County, Hanoi, Vietnam
Tel.: (84) 19001189
Web Site: http://www.nissanvietnam.vn
Car Dealing Services
N.A.I.C.S.: 441110

Y.K. Almoayyed & Sons B.S.C. (1)
PO Box 143, Manama, Bahrain
Tel.: (973) 17211211
Web Site: http://www.almoayyed.com
Automotive Retailer
N.A.I.C.S.: 441110
Farouk Yousuf Almoayyed *(Chm)*

Yokohama Marinos Ltd. (1)
DSM Shinyokohama Bldg 5F 2-6-3, Shinyokohama Kouhoku-ku, Yokohama, 222-0033,
Kanagawa, Japan
Tel.: (81) 452850678
Web Site: http://www.f-marinos.com
Football Club Services
N.A.I.C.S.: 711211

Yulon Motor Co., Ltd. (1)
No 39-1 Bogongkeng, Xihu Village Sanyi
Town, Taipei, Taiwan (100%)
Tel.: (886) 37871801
Web Site: https://www.yulon-motor.com.tw
Rev.: $2,685,525,226
Assets: $12,680,068,392
Liabilities: $9,777,676,337
Net Worth: $2,902,392,055
Earnings: $277,779,838

NISSAN MOTOR CO., LTD.

Nissan Motor Co., Ltd.—(Continued)
Emp.: 10,191
Fiscal Year-end: 12/31/2023
Automobile Mfr
N.A.I.C.S.: 336110
Yen Chen Li-Lien *(Chm)*

Joint Venture (Non-US):

Guangzhou NTN-Yulon Drivetrain Co., Ltd. (2)
No 11 Jun Da Road, East District of Guangzhou Economic and Technological Development Zone, Guangzhou, 510530, Guangdong, China
Tel.: (86) 2082266458
Web Site: http://www.ntn.com.cn
Constant Velocity Joint Mfr
N.A.I.C.S.: 336390

Zhengzhou Nissan Automobile Co., Ltd. (1)
No 3 Lianhu Road, Zhengdong New District, Zhengzhou, China
Tel.: (86) 4006999766
Car Dealing Services
N.A.I.C.S.: 441110

NISSAN SECURITIES GROUP CO., LTD.
2-16-12 Shinkawa, Chuo-Ku, Tokyo, 104-0033, Japan
Tel.: (81) 355438705
Web Site: http://www.okatonissansec-holdings.co.jp
Year Founded: 2005
8705—(TKS)
Rev.: $51,181,230
Assets: $745,713,760
Liabilities: $650,926,360
Net Worth: $94,787,400
Earnings: $3,655,330
Emp.: 289
Fiscal Year-end: 03/31/24
Holding Company
N.A.I.C.S.: 551112
Takashi Ozaki *(Pres)*

NISSAN TOKYO SALES HOLDINGS CO., LTD.
4 32-1 Nishi-Gotanda, Shinagawa-ku, Tokyo, 141-0031, Japan
Tel.: (81) 354965234
Web Site: https://www.nissan-tokyo-hd.co.jp
Year Founded: 1942
8291—(TKS)
Rev.: $984,704,920
Assets: $623,395,710
Liabilities: $243,426,470
Net Worth: $379,969,240
Earnings: $48,497,570
Fiscal Year-end: 03/31/24
Holding Company
N.A.I.C.S.: 551112
Akira Takebayashi *(Pres)*

Subsidiaries:

Ace-Biz-Serv Inc. (1)
7-19-31 Higashisuna, Koto-ku, Tokyo, 136-0074, Japan
Tel.: (81) 366598035
Web Site: https://www.ace-biz-serv.co.jp
Emp.: 44
Industrial Machinery Distr
N.A.I.C.S.: 423830

N.T. Auto Service Inc. (1)
1-5-18 Showajima, Ota-ku, Tokyo, 143-0004, Japan
Tel.: (81) 484562310
Web Site: https://www.nt-auto.co.jp
Vehicle Inspection Services
N.A.I.C.S.: 811198

NTR Transporter Co., Ltd. (1)
5-9-13 Shimorenjaku, Tokyo, Mitaka, 181-0013, Japan
Tel.: (81) 422678623
Web Site: https://www.nt-r.jp
Emp.: 235

General Freight Trucking Services
N.A.I.C.S.: 484110

Nissan PS Field Craft Co., Ltd. (1)
7-35-24 Kitami, Setagaya-ku, Tokyo, 157-0067, Japan
Tel.: (81) 357271523
Web Site: https://www.ps-craft.co.jp
Automotive Retailer
N.A.I.C.S.: 441110

Nissan Tokyo Sales Co., Ltd. (1)
4-32-1 Nishi-Gotanda, Shinagawa, 141-8623, Japan
Tel.: (81) 120238123
Web Site: https://ni-tokyo.nissan-dealer.jp
Emp.: 2,420
Automobile Parts Distr
N.A.I.C.S.: 423110

Shakenkan Co., Ltd. (1)
3-27 Horinouchi, Tokyo, Hachioji, 192-0355, Japan
Tel.: (81) 426754691
Web Site: https://www.shakenkan.co.jp
Automobile Maintenance Services
N.A.I.C.S.: 811111

NISSEI ASB MACHINE CO., LTD.
4586-3 Koo Komoro-Shi, Nagano, 384-8585, Japan
Tel.: (81) 267231560
Web Site: https://www.nisseiasb.co.jp
Year Founded: 1978
6284—(TKS)
Rev.: $246,717,820
Assets: $497,682,550
Liabilities: $140,459,990
Net Worth: $357,222,560
Earnings: $36,052,650
Emp.: 1,977
Fiscal Year-end: 09/30/23
Plastics Product Mfr
N.A.I.C.S.: 326199
Daiichi Aoki *(Chm & CEO)*

Subsidiaries:

ASB INTERNATIONAL PVT. LTD. (1)
E-9 MIDC Industrial Area Anand Nagar, Addl Ambernath Dist, Thane, 421506, Maharashtra, India
Tel.: (91) 2512625000
Web Site: http://www.asbindia.com
Emp.: 1,300
Industrial Machinery Mfr
N.A.I.C.S.: 333248

ASB PTE (Thailand) Co., Ltd. (1)
124 Soi 1 Sukhumvit 62 Sukhumvit Road Bangchak, Prakanong, Bangkok, 10260, Thailand
Tel.: (66) 23117556
Industrial Machinery Mfr & Distr
N.A.I.C.S.: 333248

NISSEI ASB CENTRO AMERICA, S.A. de C.V. (1)
Tel.: (52) 15556692117
Web Site: http://www.nisseiasb.com.mx
Molding Machine Mfr & Distr
N.A.I.C.S.: 333248
Alfas Abae *(Pres)*

NISSEI ASB CO. (1)
1375 Highlands Ridge Rd SE Ste C, Smyrna, GA 30082
Tel.: (404) 699-7755
Web Site: http://www.nisseiasb.co.jp
Emp.: 20
Plastic Container Mfr
N.A.I.C.S.: 326199
Peter Yee *(Treas)*

NISSEI ASB FZEFZE (1)
Jebel Ali Free Zone South Warehouse No FZS1-BH06, PO Box 16789, Dubai, United Arab Emirates
Tel.: (971) 48860919
Emp.: 13
Industrial Machinery Mfr
N.A.I.C.S.: 333248
Cristina Pineda *(Mgr-Logistics)*

NISSEI ASB GmbH (1)
Wahlerstr 8, 40472, Dusseldorf, Germany

Tel.: (49) 211 94104 0
Web Site: http://www.nisseiasb.co.jp
Emp.: 20
Industrial Machinery Mfr
N.A.I.C.S.: 333248

NISSEI ASB LTD. (1)
2 Milnyard Square Bakewell Road Orton Southgate, Peterborough, PE2 6GX, Cambridgeshire, United Kingdom
Tel.: (44) 1733233544
Plastic Container Whslr
N.A.I.C.S.: 424610

NISSEI ASB MEDITERRANEA, S.L.U. (1)
Poligono Industrial Vallegon Pabellon 38, Samano, 39709, Cantabria, Cantabria, Spain
Tel.: (34) 942 87 10 16
Web Site: http://www.nisseiasbmediterranea.com
Emp.: 10
Industrial Machinery Mfr
N.A.I.C.S.: 333248

NISSEI ASB PTE LTD. (1)
1 Boon Leat Terrace 08-03 Harbourside Building 1, Singapore, 119843, Singapore
Tel.: (65) 67784633
Plastic Container Whslr
N.A.I.C.S.: 424610

NISSEI ASB SUDAMERICA LTDA. (1)
Rua Alvaro Rodrigues 429 - Brooklin, Sao Paulo, 04582-000, CEP, Brazil
Web Site: http://www.nisseiasb.com.br
Industrial Machinery Mfr
N.A.I.C.S.: 333248

Nissei ASB Africa Limited (1)
Novel House Plot 3 Block J Otunba Jobi Fele Way Alausa CBD, Ikeja, Lagos, Nigeria
Tel.: (234) 14549208
Industrial Machinery Whslr
N.A.I.C.S.: 423830
Charles Iriogbe *(Mgr-Sls)*

Nissei ASB South Africa (Pty) Ltd. (1)
Tel.: (27) 123454924
Web Site: http://www.nisseiasb.co.jp
Industrial Machinery Whslr
N.A.I.C.S.: 423830

NISSEI BUILD KOGYO CO., LTD.
3-16-10 Kanaiwa-kita, Kanazawa, 920-0396, Ishikawa, Japan
Tel.: (81) 76 2681111
Web Site: http://www.nisseibuild.co.jp
Year Founded: 1961
Rev.: $316,909,440
Emp.: 541
Fiscal Year-end: 03/31/18
Parking Lot & Prefabricated Buildings Mfr, Sale & Installation
N.A.I.C.S.: 236220

Subsidiaries:

Asia Parking Investment Pte. Ltd. (1)
31 Rochester Drive Level 24, Singapore, 138637, Singapore
Tel.: (65) 6659 3628
Parking Structure Construction Services
N.A.I.C.S.: 236220

Nissei Build Asia Pte. Ltd. (1)
31 Rochester Dr Level 24, Singapore, 138637, Singapore
Tel.: (65) 6659 3628
Parking Structure & Prefabricated House Construction
N.A.I.C.S.: 236220

Space Value (Thailand) Co., Ltd. (1)
115 Rimthangrotfaisaipaknum Road, Klongtoey, Bangkok, 10110, Thailand
Tel.: (66) 2671 2145
Parking Structure & Prefabricated Building Construction Services
N.A.I.C.S.: 236220

System House R & C Co., Ltd. (1)

INTERNATIONAL PUBLIC

Keihin Higashi-Ohi Bld. 7F2-13-8 Higashi-Ohi, Shinagawa-Ku, Tokyo, 140-0011, Japan (85%)
Tel.: (81) 357620921
Web Site: http://www.sh-rc.co.jp
Emp.: 294
Module Building Materials Mfr & Construction Services
N.A.I.C.S.: 321992
Noriyuki Sudo *(Pres)*

NISSEI PLASTIC INDUSTRIAL CO., LTD.
2110 Nanjo Sakaki-machi, Hanishina-gun, Sakai, 389-0693, Nagano, Japan
Tel.: (81) 268811068
Web Site: https://www.nisseijushi.co.jp
Year Founded: 1947
6293—(NGO)
Rev.: $310,987,690
Assets: $572,441,201
Liabilities: $306,316,399
Net Worth: $266,124,802
Earnings: $2,484,307
Emp.: 1,353
Fiscal Year-end: 03/31/24
Industrial Machinery Mfr & Whslr
N.A.I.C.S.: 333248
Hozumi Yoda *(Pres)*

Subsidiaries:

NISSEI PLASTIC (HONG KONG) LTD. (1)
Unit 706 7/F Shatin Galleria 18-24 Shan Mei Street, Fotan, NT, China (Hong Kong)
Tel.: (852) 26489833
Industrial Machinery Distr
N.A.I.C.S.: 423830

NISSEI PLASTIC (SHANGHAI) CO., LTD. (1)
Room 108 No 26 Jiafeng Road Pilot Free Trade Zone, Pudong International Trade Building, Shanghai, 200131, China
Tel.: (86) 2288238905
Industrial Machinery Distr
N.A.I.C.S.: 423830

NISSEI PLASTIC (VIETNAM) CO., LTD. (1)
2nd Floor Sun Village Building 31-33 Nguyen Van Dau street, Ward 6 Binh Thanh District, Ho Chi Minh City, Vietnam
Tel.: (84) 838247860
Industrial Machinery Distr
N.A.I.C.S.: 423830

NISSEI PLASTIC MACHINERY (TAICANG) CO., LTD. (1)
No 2 West Qingdao Road, Taicang, 215400, China
Tel.: (86) 51253715656
Industrial Machinery Distr
N.A.I.C.S.: 423830

NISSEI PLASTIC SINGAPORE PTE LTD. (1)
21 Toh Guan Road East 01-13 Toh Guan Centre, Singapore, 608609, Singapore
Tel.: (65) 68614118
Emp.: 9
Industrial Machinery Distr
N.A.I.C.S.: 423830

Subsidiary (Non-US):

NISSEI (MALAYSIA) SDN. BHD. (2)
B1-3-05 Temasya 8 No 13 Jalan Doktor U1/67 Perniagaan Temasya 8, Jalan Segambut Atas, 40150, Shah Alam, Selangor D E, Malaysia
Tel.: (60) 355690911
Industrial Machinery Distr
N.A.I.C.S.: 423830

Nissei America, Inc. (1)
3730 Lyster Rd, San Antonio, TX 78235
Tel.: (714) 693-3000
Web Site: http://www.nisseiamerica.com
Industrial Machinery Distr
N.A.I.C.S.: 423830
Hozumi Yoda *(Pres)*

AND PRIVATE COMPANIES

Nissei Plastic (Thailand) Co., Ltd. (1)
43 Room No 236 23rd Floor Thai C C Tower South Sathorn Road, Yannawa Sathorn, Bangkok, 10120, Thailand
Tel.: (66) 22100910
Industrial Machinery Distr
N.A.I.C.S.: 423830

NISSEI MEXICO, S.A. DE C.V. (1)
Tyrrhenian Sea 58 Col Popotla, Delegacion Cuahutemoc, 11400, Mexico, Mexico
Tel.: (52) 5557404499
Industrial Machinery Distr
N.A.I.C.S.: 423830

PT. NISSEI PLASTIC INDONESIA (1)
Jl Cakung Cilincing Timur Raya KM 2 No 15 RT 00 RW 006, Green Sedayu Bizpark 6 Cakung Timur Cakung Jakarta Timur, Jakarta, 13910, Indonesia
Tel.: (62) 214612682
Emp.: 11
Industrial Machinery Distr
N.A.I.C.S.: 423830
Yukinaga Tada *(Gen Mgr)*

Taiwan Nissei Machinery Corporation (1)
9F-5 No 109 Sec 6 Min-Chuan E Rd, Taipei, Taiwan
Tel.: (886) 287923688
Industrial Machinery Distr
N.A.I.C.S.: 423830

NISSEN CHEMITEC CORPORATION
4 34 Nishibaba Cho 2 Chome Niihamashi, Niihama, 792 8584, Japan
Tel.: (81) 897334171
Web Site: http://www.nissen-chemitec.jp
Rev.: $324,865,306
Emp.: 740
Mfr of Plastic Injection Moulding
N.A.I.C.S.: 333248
Katsuhiro Ichimiya *(Chm)*

Subsidiaries:

Nissen Chemitec America (1)
350 E High St, London, OH 43140-9773 (100%)
Tel.: (740) 852-3200
Web Site: http://www.nissenchemitec.com
Sales Range: $125-149.9 Million
Emp.: 300
Mfr Plastic Injection Moulding
N.A.I.C.S.: 326199
Shawn Hendrix *(Pres)*

NISSEN, INC.
Nissen Kanda 2nd Building 2-6-5 Kandatsukasamachi, Chiyoda-ku, Tokyo, 101-0048, Japan
Tel.: (81) 352097222
Web Site: https://www.nissenad.co.jp
6543—(TKS)
Rev.: $37,038,160
Assets: $32,429,660
Liabilities: $9,181,550
Net Worth: $23,248,110
Earnings: $1,396,730
Emp.: 134
Fiscal Year-end: 02/29/24
Marketing Services
N.A.I.C.S.: 541613
Yuji Otsu *(Pres & CEO)*

NISSHA CO., LTD.
3 Mibu Hanai-cho, Nakagyo-ku, Kyoto, 604-8551, Japan
Tel.: (81) 758118111 JP
Web Site: https://www.nissha.com
7915—(TKS)
Rev.: $1,189,177,340
Assets: $1,544,577,770
Liabilities: $758,637,090
Net Worth: $785,940,680
Earnings: $21,184,920)
Emp.: 5,321
Fiscal Year-end: 12/31/23

Printing Products & Services
N.A.I.C.S.: 323111
Takao Hashimoto *(Co-CTO, Sr Exec VP & Sr Dir-Product & Bus Dev Office)*

Subsidiaries:

AR Metallizing GmbH (1)
Holzhauser Strasse 96-100, 13509, Berlin, Germany
Tel.: (49) 30430080
Paper Products Mfr
N.A.I.C.S.: 332999

AR Metallizing Produtos Metalizados Ltda. (1)
Av Dr Alberto Jackson Byington 2786, Osasco, 05102-100, SP, Brazil
Tel.: (55) 1136014630
Paper Products Mfr
N.A.I.C.S.: 332999

Eimo Technologies Inc. (1)
14320 Portage Rd, Vicksburg, MI 49097-0905
Tel.: (269) 649-5000
Web Site: http://www.nissha.co.jp
Sales Range: $50-74.9 Million
Thermoplastic Components Mfr
N.A.I.C.S.: 326199
Gary Hallam *(CEO)*

FIS Inc. (1)
3-36-3 Kitazono, Itami, 664-0891, Hyogo, Japan
Tel.: (81) 72 780 1800
Web Site: http://www.fisinc.co.jp
Sales Range: $10-24.9 Million
Emp.: 66
Semiconductor Gas Sensory Equipment Mfr
N.A.I.C.S.: 334413
Takao Hashimoto *(Pres & CEO)*

Graphic Controls LLC (1)
400 Exchange St, Buffalo, NY 14204-2064 (100%)
Web Site: http://www.graphiccontrols.com
Recording Supplies & Tickets Mfr
N.A.I.C.S.: 323111

Subsidiary (Non-US):

Crown Graphic NV/SA. (2)
Pijphoekstraat 4, 9041, Gent, Belgium
Tel.: (32) 92 281046
Medical Supplies Whslr
N.A.I.C.S.: 423450

Graphic Controls Canada Co (2)
23 Mill St 201, PO Box 279, Gananoque, K7G 2T8, ON, Canada
Web Site: https://nisshamedical.com
Medical Equipment Whslr
N.A.I.C.S.: 423450

Subsidiary (Domestic):

Vermed, Inc. (2)
9 Lovell Dr, Bellows Falls, VT 05101
Tel.: (802) 463-9976
Web Site: http://www.vermed.com
Medical Electrode & Sensor Equipment Designer, Mfr & Distr
N.A.I.C.S.: 334510
Richard L. Kalich *(Chm & CEO)*

Guangzhou Nissha High Precision Plastics Co., Ltd. (1)
1st-3rd Floor In The West Workshop No 2 Ruifa Road16, Hi-tech industrial development zone, Guangzhou, 510530, Guangdong, China
Tel.: (86) 2082001421
Web Site: http://www.nissha.com
Sales Range: $50-74.9 Million
Plastic Mfr
N.A.I.C.S.: 326199

M Crossing Co., Ltd. (1)
AXIS Bldg B1F 5-17-1 Roppongi, Minato-ku, Tokyo, 106-0032, Japan
Tel.: (81) 367211780
Advanced Material Services
N.A.I.C.S.: 423930

NISSHA PRINTING CO. LTD. - Osaka Division (1)
Nittochi Sakaisuji Bldg 3f 1-7-3 Awajimachi, Chuo-ku, Osaka, 541-0047, Japan

Tel.: (81) 662322701
Web Site: http://www.nissha.co.jp
Industrial Material Design Services
N.A.I.C.S.: 541420

NISSHA PRINTING CO. LTD. - Tokyo Division (1)
Osaki Wiz Tower 22f 2-11-1 Osaki, Shinagawa-ku, Tokyo, 141-0032, Japan
Tel.: (81) 367569600
Web Site: http://www.nissha.com
Sales Range: $150-199.9 Million
Industrial Material Design Services
N.A.I.C.S.: 541420

Nissha (Kunshan) Precision IMD Mold Co., Ltd. (1)
No 489 Yujinxiang Rd Kunshan Developed Region, Kunshan, 215300, Jiangsu, China
Tel.: (86) 51257723737
Web Site: http://www.nissha.co.jp
Sales Range: $50-74.9 Million
Emp.: 200
Injection Molding Plastic Products Mfr
N.A.I.C.S.: 326199
Taro Yoshioka *(Gen Mgr)*

Nissha Back Stickers International B.V. (1)
Grindzuigerstraat 29-31, 1333 MS, Almere, Netherlands
Tel.: (31) 365491020
Web Site: https://www.backstickers.com
Automotive Interior Maintenance Services
N.A.I.C.S.: 811121
Rik de Boer *(Mng Dir)*

Nissha Business Service, Inc. (1)
3 Mibu Hanai-cho, Nakagyo-ku, Kyoto, 604-8551, Japan
Tel.: (81) 758235359
Electronic Services
N.A.I.C.S.: 811210

Nissha Europe GmbH (1)
Immermannstr 65A 1.O.G, 40210, Dusseldorf, Germany
Tel.: (49) 2113004570
Web Site: http://www.nissha.co.jp
Sales Range: $25-49.9 Million
Emp.: 8
Commercial Printing Services
N.A.I.C.S.: 323111
Junya Suzuki *(Chm)*

Nissha F8, Inc. (1)
Web Site: http://www.f-8.co.jp
Digital Services
N.A.I.C.S.: 541613

Nissha FIS, Inc. (1)
2-4-28 Tagawa, Yodogawa-ku, Osaka, 532-0027, Japan
Tel.: (81) 671763910
Web Site: https://www.fisinc.co.jp
Gas Sensor Mfr & Distr
N.A.I.C.S.: 334413

Nissha GSI Technologies, Inc. (1)
311 Shore Dr, Burr Ridge, IL 60527-5859
Tel.: (630) 325-8181
Web Site: http://www.gsitech.com
Industrial Machinery Mfr
N.A.I.C.S.: 333248
Rick Mental *(Gen Mgr)*

Nissha Industrial & Trading (Shenzhen) Co., Ltd. (1)
Room 1701 East Tower Coastal Building Property Service Center, Haide 3 Road Nanshan District, Shenzhen, 518054, China
Tel.: (86) 75521674451
Industrial Material Distr
N.A.I.C.S.: 423840

Nissha Industrial & Trading Malaysia Sdn. Bhd. (1)
Lot7 Jalan P/13 Kawasan Miel Seksyen 10, 43650, Bandar Baru Bangi, Selangor, Malaysia
Tel.: (60) 389280062
Industrial Material Distr
N.A.I.C.S.: 423840
Masayuki Mitamura *(CEO)*

Nissha Industrial and Electronics Trading (Shanghai) Co., Ltd. (1)
Room 1101 Gems Building No 20 487 Tian Lin Road, Shanghai, 200233, China
Tel.: (86) 2134617652

Commercial Printing Services
N.A.I.C.S.: 323111
Tsuneo Nakahara *(Deputy Gen Mgr)*

Nissha Interactive Corporation (1)
Osaki Wiz Tower 22F 2-11-1 Osaki, Shinagawa-ku, Tokyo, 141-0032, Japan
Tel.: (81) 367567500
Web Site: http://www.nissha.co.jp
Marketing Services
N.A.I.C.S.: 541613

Nissha Korea Inc. (1)
12F Seoul City Tower 581 5-ga Namdaemunro, Jung-gu, Seoul, 100-741, Korea (South)
Tel.: (82) 59333317
Sales Range: $25-49.9 Million
Emp.: 48
Injection Molding Products Sales & Management Services
N.A.I.C.S.: 333511

Subsidiary (Domestic):

Nissha Korea High Precision Plastics Inc. (2)
271 Mosi-ri Jiksan-eup, Seobuk-gu, Cheonan, Chungcheongnam-do, Korea (South)
Tel.: (82) 415877470
Web Site: http://www.nissha.co.jp
Injection Molding Products Sales & Mfr
N.A.I.C.S.: 333511

Nissha Medical Technologies GmbH & Co. KG (1)
Willi-Bleicher-Strasse 7 7, 52353, Duren, Germany
Tel.: (49) 242159010
Medical Device Mfr
N.A.I.C.S.: 339112

Nissha Medical Technologies SAS (1)
Z A des Boutries 12 rue des Cayennes, Conflans-Sainte-Honorine, 78700, Yvelines, France
Tel.: (33) 139726666
Medical Device Mfr
N.A.I.C.S.: 339112
David Mace *(Mgr-Quality & Regulatory Affairs)*

Nissha Metallizing Solutions GmbH (1)
Holzhauser Strasse 96-100, 13509, Berlin, Germany
Tel.: (49) 30430080
Metallized Paper Mfr & Distr
N.A.I.C.S.: 331491

Nissha Metallizing Solutions Ltd. (1)
24 National Dr Forge Park, Franklin, MA 02038
Tel.: (508) 541-7700
Metallized Paper Mfr & Distr
N.A.I.C.S.: 331491

Nissha Metallizing Solutions N.V. (1)
Woudstraat 8, 3600, Genk, Belgium
Tel.: (32) 89848000
Web Site: https://www.nisshametallizing.com
Paper Packaging Product Mfr
N.A.I.C.S.: 322220

Nissha Metallizing Solutions Produtos Metalizados Ltda. (1)
Av Dr Alberto Jackson Byington 2786, Sao Paulo, Osasco, 05102-100, Brazil
Tel.: (55) 1136014630
Metallized Paper Mfr & Distr
N.A.I.C.S.: 331491

Nissha Metallizing Solutions S.r.l. (1)
Via Lombriasco 4-16, Casalgrasso, 12030, Cuneo, Italy
Tel.: (39) 011975154
Metallized Paper Mfr & Distr
N.A.I.C.S.: 331491

Nissha PMX Technologies, S.A. de C.V. (1)
Circuito Exportacion No 182 Parque Slp, Industrial Tres Naciones Zona Industrial, 78395, Mexico, Mexico
Tel.: (52) 4441372000
Industrial Machinery Mfr
N.A.I.C.S.: 333248
Hiroyuki Uenishi *(CEO)*

NISSHA CO., LTD.

Nissha Co., Ltd.—(Continued)

Nissha Precision Technologies Malaysia Sdn. Bhd. (1)
Lot7 Jalan P/13 Kawasan Miel Seksyen 10, Bandar Baru Bangi, Selangor, Malaysia
Tel.: (60) 389257288
Industrial Material Distr
N.A.I.C.S.: 423840
Yousuke Sagayama (CEO & Mng Dir)

Nissha Printing Communications, Inc. (1)
3 Mibuhanaicho, Nakagyo-ku, Kyoto, 604-8551, Japan
Tel.: (81) 757776015
Printing Material Mfr & Distr
N.A.I.C.S.: 333248

Nissha SB Poland Sp.zo.o. (1)
Ul Nowodworska 32, 59-220, Legnica, Poland
Tel.: (48) 507737580
Automotive Interior Maintenance Services
N.A.I.C.S.: 811121

Nissha Schuster Kunststofftechnik GmbH (1)
Lauchaer Hohe 13, 99880, Walterhausen, Germany
Tel.: (49) 36224010100
Web Site: http://www.iml-specialist.com
Automotive Interior Maintenance Services
N.A.I.C.S.: 811121

Nissha SiMICS, Inc. (1)
JA Tsukahara Building 6F 3-1 Nakamachi, Chino, 391-0005, Nagano, Japan
Tel.: (81) 266827150
Web Site: https://www.simics.co.jp
Gas Sensor Mfr
N.A.I.C.S.: 334516

Nissha USA Inc. (1)
1051 Perimeter Dr, Schaumburg, IL 60173
Tel.: (847) 413-2665
Web Site: http://www.nissha.co.jp
Sales Range: $25-49.9 Million
Emp.: 9
Commercial Printing Services
N.A.I.C.S.: 323111

Division (Domestic):

HomeMuseum.com (2)
1501 Woodfield Rd Ste 250W, Schaumburg, IL 60173
Tel.: (847) 413-2665
Printing Services
N.A.I.C.S.: 323111

Nissha Vietnam Co., Ltd. (1)
Room 4 Vit Tower 9F 519 Klm Ma, Ba Dinh, Hanoi, Vietnam
Industrial Material Distr
N.A.I.C.S.: 423840
Hien Pham (Asst Mgr)

Nitec Industries, Inc. (1)
1-1 Hinokigaoka, Minakuchi-cho Koka, Shiga, 528-0068, Japan
Tel.: (81) 748655100
Industrial Machinery Mfr
N.A.I.C.S.: 333248

Nitec Precision & Technologies, Inc. (1)
50 Kamiyobe, Yobe-ku, Himeji, 671-1262, Hyogo, Japan
Tel.: (81) 792727630
Industrial Machinery Mfr
N.A.I.C.S.: 333248
Yutaka Nishimoto (CEO)

Rakuhoku Landscape, Inc. (1)
3 Mibu Hanai-cho, Nakagyo-ku, Kyoto, 604-8551, Japan
Tel.: (81) 757781918
Landscaping Services
N.A.I.C.S.: 561730

Southern Nissha Sdn. Bhd. (1)
Lot7 Jalan P 13 Kawasan Miel Seksyen 10, Bandar Baru Bangi, 43650, Selangor, Malaysia
Tel.: (60) 389257288
Web Site: http://www.nissha.co.jp
Sales Range: $125-149.9 Million
Emp.: 400
Plastics Product Mfr
N.A.I.C.S.: 325211

Ng Ming Yee (Gen Mgr)

Taiwan Nissha Co., Ltd. (1)
Web Site: http://www.nissha.co.jp
Sales Range: $25-49.9 Million
Emp.: 7
Commercial Printing Services
N.A.I.C.S.: 323111

Tyrolmed GmbH (1)
Bundesstrasse 25, Rum, 6063, Innsbruck, Austria
Tel.: (43) 51294034
Medical Device Mfr
N.A.I.C.S.: 339112

Zonnebodo Pharmaceutical Co., Ltd. (1)
5-7-14 Sandamachi Hachioji, Tokyo, 193-0832, Japan
Tel.: (81) 426611171
Web Site: https://www.zonnebodo.co.jp
Pharmaceuticals Product Mfr
N.A.I.C.S.: 325412
Toshi Yasui (CEO)

NISSHIN (MYANMAR) CO., LTD.

Room No 702 Danathiha Center No 790 Bogyoke Aung San Road, Lanmadaw Township, Yangon, Myanmar
Tel.: (95) 12301551
Logistic Services
N.A.I.C.S.: 541614

NISSHIN GLOBAL LOGISTICS (SHANGHAI) CO., LTD.

Room 1100-1109 Tomson Commercial Building 710 DongFang Road, Pudong, Shanghai, China
Tel.: (86) 2158303208   CN
Web Site: http://www.en.nisshin-china.com.cn
Year Founded: 2006
Logistic Services
N.A.I.C.S.: 541614

NISSHIN GROUP HOLDINGS COMPANY, LIMITED

5-8-1 Shinjuku, Shinjuku-ku, Tokyo, 160-8411, Japan
Tel.: (81) 353602011
Web Site: https://www.nisshin-hd.co.jp
Year Founded: 1975
8881—(TKS)
Rev.: $535,562,030
Assets: $806,413,390
Liabilities: $360,800,240
Net Worth: $445,613,150
Earnings: $14,297,430
Emp.: 831
Fiscal Year-end: 03/31/24
Real Estate Manangement Services
N.A.I.C.S.: 531390

NISSHIN INTERNATIONAL TRADING CO., LTD.

Room 1105 Tomson Financial Building No 710 Dongfang Road, Pudong New Area, Shanghai, China
Tel.: (86) 2158303208
Logistic Services
N.A.I.C.S.: 541614

NISSHIN SEIFUN GROUP, INC.

1-25 Kanda-Nishiki-cho, Chiyoda-Ku, Tokyo, 101-8441, Japan
Tel.: (81) 352826666   JP
Web Site: https://www.nisshin.com
Year Founded: 2001
2002—(TKS)
Rev.: $5,673,019,280
Assets: $5,464,500,220
Liabilities: $2,051,221,810
Net Worth: $3,413,278,410
Earnings: $209,821,230
Emp.: 9,574
Fiscal Year-end: 03/31/24

Holding Company
N.A.I.C.S.: 551112

Subsidiaries:

Initio Foods Inc. (1)
1-25 Kanda Nishikicho, Chiyoda-ku, Tokyo, 101-8441, Japan
Tel.: (81) 352826258
Web Site: http://www.initio.co.jp
Prepared Food Mfr & Distr
N.A.I.C.S.: 311999

Joyous Foods Co., Ltd. (1)
Tokiwa 1-3-10 Nippon Life Urawa building the Fourth Floor, Urawa-ku, Saitama, 330-0061, Japan
Tel.: (81) 487113901
Web Site: http://www.joyous.co.jp
Prepared Food Mfr & Distr
N.A.I.C.S.: 311999

Miller Milling Company (1)
7808 Creekridge Cir Ste 100, Minneapolis, MN 55439-2612
Tel.: (952) 826-6331
Emp.: 80
Flour & Wheat Milling
N.A.I.C.S.: 311211

NBC (Shanghai) Mesh Co., Ltd. (1)
Room 203 1178-2 Floors Beidi Road, Shanghai, 200335, China
Tel.: (86) 2152161177
Screen Printing Mesh Distr
N.A.I.C.S.: 423690

NBC Meshtec Americas Inc. (1)
512 Kingsland Dr, Batavia, IL 60510
Tel.: (630) 293-5454
Web Site: https://www.nbcmeshtec.com
Screen Printing Mesh Mfr & Distr
N.A.I.C.S.: 323113

NBC Meshtec Thailand Co., Ltd. (1)
369/20 Moo 6 Tambol Bowin, Amphur Sriracha, Chon Buri, 20230, Thailand
Tel.: (66) 38195850
Plastic Filtration Mfr & Distr
N.A.I.C.S.: 333511

NBC Metalmesh Inc. (1)
711-8 Nakatsuno, Aira, 899-5402, Kagoshima, Japan
Tel.: (81) 995735556
Precision Printing Net Mfr & Distr
N.A.I.C.S.: 333248

Nisshin Flour Milling Co., Ltd. (1)
25 Kanda-Nishiki-cho 1-chome, Chiyoda-ku, Tokyo, 101 8441, Japan   (100%)
Tel.: (81) 352826833
Web Site: http://www.nisshin.com
Sales Range: $25-49.9 Million
Emp.: 200
Mfr of Flour & Grain Mill Products
N.A.I.C.S.: 311211
Hiroshi Oeda (Pres)

Subsidiary (Non-US):

Allied Pinnacle Pty Ltd (2)
Level 4 Building G 1 Homebush Bay Drive, Rhodes, 2138, NSW, Australia
Tel.: (61) 293524800
Web Site: http://www.alliedpinnacle.com
Bakery Product Mfr & Distr
N.A.I.C.S.: 311812

Champion Flour Milling Ltd. (2)
Level 2 5 Cryers Road East Tamaki, Auckland, 2013, New Zealand
Tel.: (64) 93771975
Web Site: https://www.championflour.co.nz
Cereal Product Mfr & Distr
N.A.I.C.S.: 311230
Corrine Taylor (Acct Mgr)

Subsidiary (Domestic):

Fresh Food Service Co., Ltd. (2)
7th Floor TT-2 Building 3-8-1 Nihonbashi Ningyocho, Chuo-ku, Tokyo, 103-0013, Japan
Tel.: (81) 356950981
Web Site: http://www.fresh-food.jp
Frozen Product Mfr & Distr
N.A.I.C.S.: 311824

Subsidiary (Non-US):

Nisshin-STC Flour Milling Co., Ltd. (2)

INTERNATIONAL PUBLIC

Thai Sri Tower 23rd Floor, 126/90-91 Krung Thonburi Road, Klong Sarn, Bangkok, 10600, Thailand
Tel.: (66) 24397425
Flour Product Mfr & Distr
N.A.I.C.S.: 311211

Rogers Foods Ltd. (2)
4420 Larkin Cross Road, Armstrong, V0E 1B6, BC, Canada
Web Site: https://www.rogersfoods.com
Cereal Product Mfr & Distr
N.A.I.C.S.: 311230
Brad Duggan (VP-Sls)

Nisshin Foods Inc. (1)
1-25 Kanda Nishikicho, Chiyoda-ku, Tokyo, 101-8441, Japan
Tel.: (81) 352826200
Web Site: http://www.nisshin-foods.com
Processed Food Mfr & Distr
N.A.I.C.S.: 311999
Yuji Koike (Pres)

Oriental Yeast Co., Ltd. (1)
3-6-10 Azusawa, Itabashi-ku, Tokyo, 174-8505, Japan
Tel.: (81) 339681192
Web Site: http://www.oyc.co.jp
Yeast Mfr & Distr
N.A.I.C.S.: 311119
Masashi Nakagawa (Pres)

P.T. NBC Indonesia (1)
Jl Maligi 1 Lot A9-A10, Kawasan Industri Kiic, Karawang, 41361, Jawa Barat, Indonesia
Tel.: (62) 218904245
Screen Printing Mesh Mfr & Distr
N.A.I.C.S.: 323113

Thainak Industries Co., Ltd. (1)
33/1 Moo 10 Teparak Km 16 Bangpra, Bang Phli, 10540, Samut Prakan, Thailand
Tel.: (66) 27507122
Plastic Filtration Mfr & Distr
N.A.I.C.S.: 333511

Tokatsu Foods Co., Ltd. (1)
7-15-14 Hiyoshi, Kohoku-ku, Yokohama, 223-0061, Japan
Tel.: (81) 455645100
Web Site: https://www.tokatsu.co.jp
Emp.: 624
Prepared Food Mfr & Distr
N.A.I.C.S.: 311991

NISSHINBO HOLDINGS INC.

2-31-11 Nihonbashi Ningyo-cho, Chuo-ku, Tokyo, 103-8650, Japan
Tel.: (81) 356958833   JP
Web Site: https://www.nisshinbo.co.jp
Year Founded: 1907
3105—(TKS)
Rev.: $3,837,185,990
Assets: $4,786,047,780
Liabilities: $2,818,863,470
Net Worth: $1,967,184,310
Earnings: ($142,119,050)
Emp.: 19,416
Fiscal Year-end: 12/31/23
Holding Company; Textile Products, Automobile Brakes, Chemical Products, Machine Tools, Tissue & Other Paper Products Mfr
N.A.I.C.S.: 551112
Takeshi Koarai (Sr Exec Mng Officer)

Subsidiaries:

Alphatron Marine Beheer B.V. (1)
Schaardijk 23, 3063 NH, Rotterdam, Netherlands
Tel.: (31) 104534000
Web Site: https://www.alphatronmarine.com
Marine Equipment Distr
N.A.I.C.S.: 423860
Rob Emmers (Mgr-Site-North)

Aries Co. Ltd. (1)
16th Floor 3 No 2 Ln 150 Hsin-Yi Rd, Sec 5, Taipei, Taiwan
Tel.: (886) 223456622
Web Site: http://www.aries-net.com.tw
Real Estate Property Lessors
N.A.I.C.S.: 531190

D-CLUE Technologies Co.,Ltd. (1)

AND PRIVATE COMPANIES — NISSHINBO HOLDINGS INC.

4F Kakiya Building 2-7-17, Shin-Yokohama Kohoku-ku, Yokohama, 222-0033, Japan
Tel.: (81) 454700533
Emp.: 58
Semiconductor Development Services
N.A.I.C.S.: 541715

Goyo Electronics Co., Ltd. (1)
43-224 Tsurunumadai, Tenno, Katakami, 010-0201, Akita, Japan
Tel.: (81) 188785281
Web Site: https://www.hitachi-kokusai.co.jp
Emp.: 392
Electronic Device Mfr & Distr
N.A.I.C.S.: 334419

HYS Engineering Service Inc. (1)
32 Miyukicho, Kodaira City, Tokyo, 187-8512, Japan
Tel.: (81) 423205931
Web Site: https://www.hitachi-kokusai.co.jp
Emp.: 751
Communication Equipment Repair Services
N.A.I.C.S.: 811210

Hitachi Kokusai Electric Comark LLC (1)
104 Feeding Hills Rd, Southwick, MA 01077
Tel.: (413) 998-1100
Web Site: https://comarktv.com
Power Broadcasting Systems Services
N.A.I.C.S.: 541990

Iwao & Co., Ltd. (1)
3-3-9 Hommachi Hommachiiwao Bldg, Chuo-Ku, Osaka, 541-0053, Japan
Tel.: (81) 662511553
Chemical Products Mfr
N.A.I.C.S.: 424690

JRC Mobility Inc. (1)
2-31-11 Nihonbashi Ningyo-cho, Chuo-ku, Tokyo, 103-8650, Japan
Tel.: (81) 368325248
Web Site: https://www.jrc-m.co.jp
Sensor Mfr & Distr
N.A.I.C.S.: 334511
Kinji Kato (Pres)

Japan Radio Co., Ltd. (1)
Nakano Central Park East 10-1 Nakano 4-chome, Nakano-ku, Tokyo, 164-8570, Japan
Tel.: (81) 368321721
Web Site: http://www.jrc.co.jp
Rev.: $1,268,357,040
Emp.: 5,653
Fiscal Year-end: 03/31/2018
Radio Communications Equipment & Information Technology Products Mfr
N.A.I.C.S.: 334220
Kenji Ara (Chm)

Subsidiary (Domestic):

JRC Engineering Co., Ltd. (2)
4th floor MCC Mitaka Building North Building 8-7-2 Shimorenjaku, Mitaka, 181-0013, Japan
Tel.: (81) 422459661
Web Site: https://www.jrce.co.jp
Sales Range: $25-49.9 Million
Emp.: 298
Software Development & Engineering for Information & Data Processing Systems Using General-Purpose Computers, Mini-Computers & Microcomputers
N.A.I.C.S.: 541511

Subsidiary (Non-US):

JRC Shanghai Co., Ltd. (2)
19F/C Yonghua Bldg No 138 Ave, Pudong, Shanghai, China
Tel.: (86) 2120240607
Web Site: http://www.jrc-cn.com
Sales Range: $25-49.9 Million
Emp.: 90
Radio Communication Equipment Mfr
N.A.I.C.S.: 334220
Harry Miyashita (Gen Mgr)

Subsidiary (Domestic):

JRC Tokki Co., Ltd. (2)
3-2-1 Shinyoshida-higashi, Kohoku-ku, Yokohama, 223-8572, Kanagawa, Japan
Tel.: (81) 455478572
Web Site: http://www.jrctokki.co.jp
Sales Range: $75-99.9 Million
Emp.: 359

Repairs & Overhaul of Defense Electronics for Ships & Aircraft, System Support Engineering for Installations on Ships & Manufacture of Peripheral Equipment
N.A.I.C.S.: 811210

Subsidiary (Non-US):

JRC do Brasil Empreendimentos Eletronicos Ltda. (2)
Tel.: (55) 2122208121
Web Site: http://www.jrcbrasil.com.br
Sales Range: $25-49.9 Million
Emp.: 2
Radio Communication Equipment Mfr
N.A.I.C.S.: 334220
Carlos Lito (Gen Mgr)

Plant (Domestic):

Japan Radio Co., Ltd. - Mitaka Plant (2)
1-1 Shimorenjaku 5-chome, Mitaka, 181-8510, Tokyo, Japan
Tel.: (81) 422459111
Radio Communication Equipment Mfr
N.A.I.C.S.: 334220

Japan Radio Co., Ltd. - Saitama Plant (2)
1-4 Fukuoka 2-chome, Fujimino, 356-0011, Saitama, Japan
Tel.: (81) 492665611
Radio Communication Equipment Mfr
N.A.I.C.S.: 334220

Subsidiary (Non-US):

Japan Radio Company (HK) Limited (2)
Suite 1108 11th Floor Two Chinachem Exchange Square 338 King's Road, North Point, China (Hong Kong)
Tel.: (852) 27079170
Web Site: http://www.jrc.co.jp
Radio Communication Equipment Mfr
N.A.I.C.S.: 334220

Subsidiary (Domestic):

Japan Radio Glass Co., Ltd. (2)
2-1-8 Fukuoka, Fujimino, 356-0011, Saitama, Japan
Tel.: (81) 492644411
Web Site: https://www.jrg.co.jp
Emp.: 122
Electrical Glass Bulb Mfr & Distr
N.A.I.C.S.: 335139

Musashino Electric Co., Ltd. (2)
1 33 Shimorenjaku 8 Chome, Mitaka, 181 0013, Japan
Tel.: (81) 422476341
Sales Range: $25-49.9 Million
Emp.: 200
Mfr of Radio Communications, Medical Electronics Equipment & Electronic Parts
N.A.I.C.S.: 334517

Nagano Japan Radio Co., Ltd. (2)
1163 Inasato-machi, Nagano, 381-2288, Japan (26.6%)
Tel.: (81) 26 285 1111
Web Site: http://www.njrc.jp
Sales Range: $250-299.9 Million
Emp.: 1,668
Mfr & Sale of VHF Radio Equipment, Radars, Data Transmission Equipment, Controllers, Public Address Sets, Power Supply Equipment & Capacitors
N.A.I.C.S.: 334220
Toshihiko Fujisawa (Chm)

Subsidiary (Domestic):

Nagano Communications Sales Co., Ltd. (3)
603-7 Aokijima, Nagano, 381-2288, Japan
Tel.: (81) 262851169
Web Site: http://www.njrc.jp
Sales Range: $25-49.9 Million
Emp.: 38
Communication Equipment Distr
N.A.I.C.S.: 423690

Subsidiary (Non-US):

Nagano Japan Radio (HK) Co., Ltd. (3)
20 Floor Suite 1820-21 Level 18 Landmark N No 39 Lung Sum Avenue, Sheung Shui, New Territories, China (Hong Kong)
Tel.: (852) 23446188
Sales Range: $25-49.9 Million
Emp.: 6
Power Supply Unit Mfr & Distr
N.A.I.C.S.: 335313
Hitenali Naoe (Gen Mgr)

Subsidiary (Domestic):

Nagano Japan Radio Engineering Co., Ltd. (3)
1163 Inasato-machi, Nagano, 381-2288, Japan
Tel.: (81) 262851213
Sales Range: $50-74.9 Million
Emp.: 18
Communication Software Development Services & Distr
N.A.I.C.S.: 541511

Nagano Japan Radio Service Co., Ltd. (3)
1163 Inasato-machi, Nagano, Japan
Tel.: (81) 262851207
Web Site: http://www.njrc.jp
Sales Range: $25-49.9 Million
Emp.: 81
Telecommunication Equipment Sales & Maintenance Services
N.A.I.C.S.: 811210

Subsidiary (Domestic):

Nihonmusen Glass Co., Ltd. (2)
1 8 Fukuoka 2 Chome Kamifukuoka, Saitama, 356 0011, Japan
Tel.: (81) 492644411
Sales Range: $50-74.9 Million
Emp.: 150
Mfr & Sale of Glassware for Outdoor Lamps, Mercury-Vapor Lamps, Electron Tubes, Physicochemical Apparatus, Tableware & Other Glass Tubes
N.A.I.C.S.: 327212

Sougou Business Service Co., Ltd. (2)
1-1 Shimorenjaku 5-chome, Mitaka, 181-0013, Tokyo, Japan
Tel.: (81) 422400471
Sales Range: $50-74.9 Million
Emp.: 126
Electronic Equipment Distr
N.A.I.C.S.: 423690

Ueda Japan Radio Co., Ltd. (2)
2-10-19 Fumiiri, Nagano, 386-8608, Ueda, Japan
Tel.: (81) 268262112
Web Site: http://www.ujrc.co.jp
Sales Range: $125-149.9 Million
Emp.: 561
VHF Radio Equipment, Radio Receivers, Measuring Instruments & Electromedical Equipment Mfr
N.A.I.C.S.: 334519
Toru Hasegawa (Auditor)

NJR Shanghai Co., Ltd. (1)
Room H 23rd Floor Huadu Building 838 Zhangyang Road, Pudong New Area, Shanghai, 200122, China
Tel.: (86) 2158202567
Web Site: http://www.njr-shanghai.com.cn
Semiconductor Devices Mfr
N.A.I.C.S.: 334413

Naigai Shirts Co., Ltd. (1)
Textile Products Mfr
N.A.I.C.S.: 314999

New Japan Radio Co., Ltd. (1)
3-10 Nihonbashi Yokoyama-cho, Tokyo, 103-8456, Japan
Tel.: (81) 356428222
Web Site: http://www.njr.com
Rev.: $458,785,200
Assets: $399,591,120
Liabilities: $270,777,840
Net Worth: $128,813,280
Earnings: $33,788,400
Emp.: 2,804
Fiscal Year-end: 03/31/2018
Microwave Products Mfr & Marketer
N.A.I.C.S.: 335999
Ryo Ogura (Chm)

Subsidiary (Non-US):

NJR (Singapore) Pte Ltd. (2)
61 Ubi Avenue 2 07-01 Automobile Megamart, Singapore, 408898, Singapore
Tel.: (65) 67444143
Web Site: http://www.njr.com
Sales Range: $25-49.9 Million
Emp.: 15
Electronic Parts & Equipment Whslr
N.A.I.C.S.: 423690

Subsidiary (Domestic):

NJR Fukuoka Co. Ltd. (2)
1-1-2 Imajuku-higashi, Nishi-ku, Fukuoka, 819-0161, Japan
Tel.: (81) 928054660
Web Site: http://www.njrf.co.jp
Semiconductor & Device Mfr
N.A.I.C.S.: 334413

NJR Trading Co. Ltd. (2)
NB Nihonbashi Building 3-10, Nihonbashi Yokoyama-cho, Chuo-ku, 103-0003, Tokyo, Japan
Tel.: (81) 356428511
Sales Range: $25-49.9 Million
Emp.: 20
Electrical Equipment Wiring Supplies & Construction Material Whslr
N.A.I.C.S.: 423610
Kazuo Hirata (Pres)

Saga Electronics Co. Ltd. (2)
NB Nihonbashi Building 3-10 Yokoyama-Cho, Nihonbashi Chuō-ku, Tokyo, 103-0003, Japan
Tel.: (81) 356428222
Web Site: http://www.sagaelec.co.jp
Sales Range: $75-99.9 Million
Emp.: 2,600
Semiconductor & Device Mfr
N.A.I.C.S.: 334413
Chikara Hayashi (Pres & CEO)

Nippon Kohbunshi Co. Ltd. (1)
1-20-2 Nishiarai-sake-cho, Adachi-ku, 123-0843, Tokyo, Japan
Tel.: (81) 338892631
Web Site: http://www.nisshin.co.jp
Unsupported Plastics Profile Shape Mfr
N.A.I.C.S.: 326121

Nisshin Environmental Planning Inc. (1)
2-18-29 Motoki, Adachi-ku, Tokyo, 123-0853, Japan
Tel.: (81) 338862105
Environmental Research Services
N.A.I.C.S.: 541715

Nisshin Toa Inc. (1)
1-4-8 Nihombashi-Ningyocho, Chuo-ku, Tokyo, 103-0013, Japan
Tel.: (81) 336681861
Web Site: http://www.nisshintoa.co.jp
Rev.: $476,676,490
Emp.: 96
Textile Products Mfr & Distr
N.A.I.C.S.: 314999
Kazuo Manaka (Pres)

Nisshinbo (Shanghai) Co., Ltd. (1)
Rm 2403-2407 Suite B Yuandong International Mansion No 317, Shanghai, 200051, China
Tel.: (86) 2162350420
Web Site: http://www.nisshinbo.com
Sales Range: $25-49.9 Million
Emp.: 27
Textile Products Mfr
N.A.I.C.S.: 314999

Nisshinbo Alps Tech Co., Ltd. (1)
1349 Okubo-cho, Nishi-ku, Hamamatsu, 432-8006, Japan
Tel.: (81) 534822005
Electronic Components Mfr
N.A.I.C.S.: 334419

Nisshinbo Brake Inc. (1)
2-31-11 Ningyo-cho Nihonbashi, Chuo-ku, Tokyo, 103-8650, Japan
Web Site: http://www.nisshinbo-brake.co.jp
Sales Range: $1-4.9 Billion
Emp.: 6,000
Automotive Brake System Mfr
N.A.I.C.S.: 336340
Koji Nishihara (Chm)

Subsidiary (US):

Nisshinbo Automotive Manufacturing Inc. (2)

NISSHINBO HOLDINGS INC.

Nisshinbo Holdings Inc.—(Continued)
14187 Nisshinbo Dr, Covington, GA 30014
Tel.: (770) 787-2002
Sales Range: $25-49.9 Million
Emp.: 230
Motor Vehicle Parts Mfr
N.A.I.C.S.: 336390
Chris Barrett *(Mgr-Mfg)*

Subsidiary (Domestic):

Nisshinbo Brake Sales Co. Ltd. (2)
2-31-11 Ningyo-cho Nihonbashi Chuo-ku, **(100%)**
103-8650, Tokyo, Japan
Tel.: (81) 3 5843 3900
Web Site: http://www.nisshinbo-brake.co.jp
Emp.: 50
Motor Vehicle Brake Mfr & Sales
N.A.I.C.S.: 336340
Shizuka Uzawa *(Chm)*

Subsidiary (Non-US):

Nisshinbo Somboon Automotive Co. Ltd. (2)
Tel.: (66) 3895444451
Web Site: http://www.nsa.co.th
Sales Range: $75-99.9 Million
Emp.: 356
Motor Vehicle Parts Mfr
N.A.I.C.S.: 336390

Saeron Automotive Beijing Corporation (2)
No 69 Keji Rd, Miyun Industrial Development, Beijing, 101509, China
Tel.: (86) 1069076303
Web Site: https://www.saeronauto.co.kr
Sales Range: $75-99.9 Million
Emp.: 309
Automotive Braking System Mfr
N.A.I.C.S.: 336340

TMD Friction Holdings GmbH & Co. KG (2)
Schlebuscher Str 99, 51381, Leverkusen, Germany
Tel.: (49) 21715016
Web Site: http://tmdfriction.com
Sales Range: $800-899.9 Million
Emp.: 5,170
Motor Vehicle Brake Pads & Linings Mfr; Friction Material Mfr
N.A.I.C.S.: 336340
Takaharu Dannoura *(Dir)*

Subsidiary (Non-US):

TMD Friction Espana S.L. (3)
Calle Ciudad de Barcelona 44 Poligono Industrial, Fuente del Jarro 2a fase, 46988, Paterna, Spain
Tel.: (34) 961323612
Web Site: http://www.tmdfriction.com
Emp.: 100
Motor Vehicle Brake Pads & Linings Mfr; Friction Material Mfr
N.A.I.C.S.: 336340
Juan J. Navarro *(Mng Dir)*

TMD Friction France S.A.S. (3)
10 Rue Denis Papin, 57150, Creutzwald, France
Tel.: (33) 387828282
Web Site: http://www.tmdfriction.com
Emp.: 200
Motor Vehicle Brake Pads Mfr
N.A.I.C.S.: 336340

Subsidiary (Domestic):

TMD Friction GmbH (3)
Industriestr 9, 01640, Coswig, Germany
Tel.: (49) 3523960
Web Site: http://www.tmdfriction.com
Motor Vehicle Brake Pads & Linings Mfr; Friction Material Mfr
N.A.I.C.S.: 336340

Subsidiary (Non-US):

TMD Friction Italia S.r.l. (3)
Via Adua 85, I 25034, Brescia, Italy
Tel.: (39) 030 99431
Motor Vehicle Brake Pads & Linings Mfr; Friction Material Mfr
N.A.I.C.S.: 336340

TMD Friction Malaysia (3)
1005 Level 10 Block B, Philio Damansara 1

No 9, Petaling Jaya, 16 11, Jalan, Malaysia
Tel.: (60) 37662 3337
Motor Vehicle Brake Pads & Linings Mfr; Friction Material Mfr
N.A.I.C.S.: 336340

TMD Friction Mexico, S.A. de C.V. (3)
Fracc Ind Benito Juarez, 76120, Queretaro, Mexico
Tel.: (52) 4422384900
Web Site: http://www.tmdfriction.com
Emp.: 200
Motor Vehicle Brake Pads & Linings Mfr; Friction Material Mfr
N.A.I.C.S.: 336340

TMD Friction UK Ltd. (3)
Centurion House Centurion Way, PO Box 18, Cleckheaton, BD19 3UJ, West Yorkshire, United Kingdom
Tel.: (44) 1274854000
Web Site: http://www.tmdfriction.co.uk
Motor Vehicle Brake Pads & Linings Mfr
N.A.I.C.S.: 336340
Rob Sweetnam *(Mng Dir)*

Subsidiary (US):

TMD Friction, Inc. (3)
1035 Crooks Rd, Troy, MI 48084-7119
Tel.: (248) 280-4050
Web Site: http://www.tmdfriction.com
Sales Range: $25-49.9 Million
Emp.: 28
Motor Vehicle Brake Pads & Linings Mfr
N.A.I.C.S.: 336340

Nisshinbo Chemical Inc. (1)
2-31-11 Ningyo-cho Nihonbashi, Chuo-ku, Tokyo, 103-8650, Japan
Tel.: (81) 356958886
Web Site: https://www.nisshinbo-chem.co.jp
Sales Range: $50-74.9 Million
Emp.: 325
Specialty Chemicals Mfr
N.A.I.C.S.: 325998

Plant (Domestic):

Nisshinbo Chemical Inc. - Asahi Plant (2)
9163-13 Kamakazu, Asahi, 289-2505, Chiba, Japan
Tel.: (81) 479603555
Specialty Chemicals Mfr
N.A.I.C.S.: 325199

Nisshinbo Chemical Inc. - Chiba Plant (2)
1-4-1 Onodai, Midori-ku, Chiba, 267-0056, Japan
Tel.: (81) 432057015
Emp.: 100
Specialty Chemicals Mfr
N.A.I.C.S.: 325199
Atsutushi Hagiwara *(Mgr)*

Nisshinbo Chemical Inc. - Tokushima Plant (2)
635 Nakashima Kawauchi-cho, Tokushima, 771-0187, Japan
Tel.: (81) 886529171
Web Site: http://www.nisshinbo-chem.co.jp
Specialty Chemicals Mfr
N.A.I.C.S.: 325199

Nisshinbo Do Brasil Industria Textil Ltda. (1)
Ave Paulista 1009, 11O Andar Cjs 1101-1103, Sao Paulo, Brazil
Tel.: (55) 1132899255
Sales Range: $100-124.9 Million
Emp.: 466
Broadwoven Fabric Finishing Mills
N.A.I.C.S.: 313310

Nisshinbo Europe B.V. (1)
World Trade Center Strawinskylaan B1245, Amsterdam, 1077 XX, Netherlands
Tel.: (31) 205753349
Web Site: http://www.nisshinbo-mechatronics.co.jp
Sales Range: $50-74.9 Million
Emp.: 3
Real Estate Manangement Services
N.A.I.C.S.: 531390
Chikara Iwai *(Mng Dir)*

Nisshinbo Mechatronics Inc. (1)

2-31-11 Nihonbashi Ningyocho, Nihonbashi Chuo-ku, Tokyo, 103-8650, Japan
Tel.: (81) 356958928
Web Site: https://www.nisshinbo-mechatronics.co.jp
Emp.: 360
Photovoltaic Module Mfr & Distr
N.A.I.C.S.: 334413
Masakazu Aitsuki *(Sr Exec Mng Officer)*

Subsidiary (Domestic):

Nanbu Plastics Co., Ltd. (2)
21-1 Ohata Yoshida-cho, Haibara-gun, Shizuoka, 421-0305, Japan
Tel.: (81) 548341801
Web Site: https://www.nanbu.co.jp
Synthetic Resin Mfr & Distr
N.A.I.C.S.: 325211

Subsidiary (Non-US):

Nisshinbo Mechatronics (Shanghai) Co., Ltd. (2)
5828 Shenjiang South Road, Xinchang Town Pudong New Area, Shanghai, 201314, China
Tel.: (86) 2168151086
Web Site: https://en.nisshinbo.com.cn
Emp.: 284
Photovoltaic Module Mfr
N.A.I.C.S.: 334413

Nisshinbo Mechatronics (Thailand) Ltd. (2)
419 Moo 17 Bangplee Industrial Estate Debaratna Road, Bangsaothong Subdistricts Bangsaothong Districts, Bang Sao Thong, 10570, Samutprakarn, Thailand
Tel.: (66) 23153139
Web Site: https://www.nisshinbo.co.th
Sales Range: $350-399.9 Million
Emp.: 950
Industrial Fans Mfr
N.A.I.C.S.: 333413
Tatsuya Shimizu *(Mng Dir)*

Plant (Domestic):

Nisshinbo Mechatronics Inc. - Hamakita Plant (2)
8000 Nakaze, Hamaku-ku, Hamamatsu, 434-0012, Shizuoka, Japan
Tel.: (81) 535883311
Web Site: http://www.nisshinbo-mechatronics.co.jp
Precision Cutting Tools Mfr
N.A.I.C.S.: 333515

Nisshinbo Mechatronics Inc. - Miai Machinery Plant (2)
30 Azukizaka Miai-cho, Okazaki, 444-8560, Aichi, Japan
Tel.: (81) 564551111
Web Site: http://www.nisshinbo-mechatronics.co.jp
Photovoltaic Module Mfr
N.A.I.C.S.: 334413

Subsidiary (Non-US):

Nisshinbo Photovoltaic Korea Corporation (2)
549-10 Uman-dong 401 Asuk Building, Paldal-gu, Suwon, 442-190, Gyeonggi-do, Korea (South)
Tel.: (82) 318987055
Photovoltaic Device Mfr
N.A.I.C.S.: 334413

Nisshinbo-Yawei Precision Instruments & Machinery (Jiangsu) Co., Ltd. (2)
Xiancheng Industrial Zone Lehe Road, Jiangdu, Yangzhou, 225200, Jiangsu, China
Tel.: (86) 51486519139
Semiconductor Devices Mfr
N.A.I.C.S.: 334413

Nisshinbo Micro Devices (Shanghai) Co., Ltd. (1)
Room 403 No 2 Building 690 Bibo Road Zhangjiang Hi-Tech Park, Pudong New District, Shanghai, China
Tel.: (86) 2150273200
Electronic Device Mfr & Distr
N.A.I.C.S.: 334419

INTERNATIONAL PUBLIC

Nisshinbo Micro Devices (Thailand) Co., Ltd. (1)
Northern Region Industrial Estate NRIE 88 Mu 13 Tambol Makhuajae, Amphur Muang, Lamphun, 51000, Thailand
Tel.: (66) 53581260
Web Site: http://www.nisdt.co.th
Emp.: 1,147
Microwave Product Mfr & Distr
N.A.I.C.S.: 334413

Nisshinbo Micro Devices AT Co., Ltd. (1)
950 Tateno Yoshinogari-cho, Kanzaki, 842-0032, Saga, Japan
Tel.: (81) 952523181
Web Site: https://www.nisshinbo-microdevices-at.co.jp
Emp.: 431
Electric Device Mfr
N.A.I.C.S.: 334419

Nisshinbo Micro Devices Americas Inc. (1)
2107 N 1st Ste 520, San Jose, CA 95131
Tel.: (408) 320-2873
Electronic Device Mfr & Distr
N.A.I.C.S.: 334419

Nisshinbo Micro Devices Europe GmbH (1)
Theodor-Heuss-Allee 112, 60486, Frankfurt am Main, Germany
Tel.: (49) 69667741360
Electronic Device Mfr & Distr
N.A.I.C.S.: 334419

Nisshinbo Micro Devices Fukuoka Co., Ltd. (1)
1-1-2 Imajuku-higashi, Nishi-ku, Fukuoka, 819-0161, Japan
Tel.: (81) 928054660
Automobile Parts Mfr & Distr
N.A.I.C.S.: 336320

Nisshinbo Micro Devices Inc. (1)
NB Nihonbashi Bldg 3-10 Nihonbashi Yokoyama-cho, Chuo-ku, Tokyo, 103-8456, Japan
Tel.: (81) 356428222
Web Site: https://www.nisshinbo-microdevices.co.jp
Emp.: 1,921
Electronic Device Mfr & Distr
N.A.I.C.S.: 334419

Nisshinbo Micro Devices Singapore Pte. Ltd. (1)
61 Ubi Avenue 2 07-01 Automobile Megamart, Singapore, 408898, Singapore
Tel.: (65) 67444143
Electronic Device Mfr & Distr
N.A.I.C.S.: 334419

Nisshinbo Mobix Co. Ltd. (1)
63 Mukai Wakayama, Wakayama, Japan
Tel.: (81) 734553128
Yarn Texturizing Throwing & Twisting Mills
N.A.I.C.S.: 313110

Nisshinbo Postal Chemical Co. Ltd. (1)
Nihonbashi Kodenma-cho Chuo-ku, Tokyo, 103-0001, Japan
Tel.: (81) 336658972
Sales Range: $50-74.9 Million
Emp.: 136
Organic Chemical Mfr
N.A.I.C.S.: 325199
Iyata Akira *(Pres)*

Nisshinbo Precision Instrument & Machinery Hiroshima Corporation (1)
1-3-30 Takayadai, Higashi-Hiroshima Core Industrial Park, Higashi-hiroshima, 739-2117, Hiroshima, Japan
Tel.: (81) 824912442
Web Site: http://www.nisshinbo-pim-h.jp
Automotive Brake Parts Mfr & Distr
N.A.I.C.S.: 336390

Nisshinbo Textile Inc. (1)
2-31-11 Ningyo-cho, Nihonbashi Chuo-ku, Tokyo, 103-8650, Japan
Tel.: (81) 356958833
Web Site: http://www.nisshinbo-textile.co.jp
Cloth Mfr & Distr
N.A.I.C.S.: 315250
Kaoru Murata *(Pres)*

AND PRIVATE COMPANIES / NISSIN CORPORATION

Nisshinbo Yarn Dyed Co. Ltd. (1)
1-6-21 Kagoya, Ichinomiya, Japan
Tel.: (81) 586457474
Broadwoven Fabric Finishing Mills
N.A.I.C.S.: 313310

Nisshintoa Iwao Inc. (1)
2-30-8 Nihombashi-Ningyocho, Chuo-ku,
Tokyo, 103-0013, Japan
Tel.: (81) 336681861
Web Site: https://www.nisshintoaiwao.co.jp
Petroleum Product Distr
N.A.I.C.S.: 424720
Hajime Sasaki (Pres)

P.T. Gistex Nisshinbo Indonesia (1)
106 Jl Braga, Bandung, Indonesia
Tel.: (62) 226674531
Broadwoven Fabric Finishing Mills
N.A.I.C.S.: 313310

P.T. Naigai Shirts Indonesia (1)
Jl Mitra Utara I Blok B 5A Ciampel Kawasan Industri Mitra, Karawang Parungmulya Kecamatan Ciampel Kabupaten, Karawang, 41363, Jawa Barat, Indonesia
Tel.: (62) 2678610092
Web Site: http://pt-naigai-shirt-indonesia.business.site
Cloth Mfr & Distr
N.A.I.C.S.: 315250

P.T. Nikawa Textile Industry (1)
10th Fl Jl Jend Sudirman Kav 33 A, Tamahaband, Jakarta, 10220, Indonesia
Tel.: (62) 215721235
Sales Range: $25-49.9 Million
Emp.: 16
Textile Bag Mills
N.A.I.C.S.: 314910
Hiroyuki Suzuki (Pres)

Ricoh Electronic Devices Co., Ltd. (1)
13-1 Himemuro-cho, Ikeda, 563-8501, Osaka, Japan
Tel.: (81) 727486266
Web Site: http://www.n-redc.co.jp
Electronic Device Product Mfr & Retailer
N.A.I.C.S.: 334419
Satoru Taji (Pres)

Saeron Automotive Corp. (1)
133 Gajeon 5-gil Byeongcheon-myeon, Dongnam-gu, Cheonan, Chungcheongnam-do, Korea (South)
Tel.: (82) 415604114
Web Site: https://www.saeronauto.co.kr
Rev.: $105,874,801
Assets: $196,512,887
Liabilities: $20,124,122
Net Worth: $176,388,765
Earnings: ($4,567,474)
Emp.: 312
Fiscal Year-end: 12/31/2022
Automotive Components Mfr
N.A.I.C.S.: 336340
Kumakawa Tetsuya (Exec Dir)

Shanghai Sun-Rich Arts & Crafts Co., Ltd. (1)
No 88 Jiachang Rd Lixin Village Malu Town, Jiading Dist, Shanghai, 201818, China
Tel.: (86) 2159513395
Paper Products Mfr
N.A.I.C.S.: 322299

Taiwan Nisshinbo Photovoltaic Co., Ltd. (1)
Rm 8 7F No 41 Nanjing W Rd, Datong District, Taipei, 10352, Taiwan
Tel.: (886) 225509830
Web Site: http://www.nisshinbo-mechatronics.co.jp
Photovoltaic Device Mfr
N.A.I.C.S.: 334413

Thai NJR Co., Ltd. (1)
88 Mu 13 Tambol Makhuajae, Northern Region Industrial Estate Amphur Muang, Lamphun, 51000, Thailand
Tel.: (66) 53581260
Web Site: http://www.thainjr.co.th
Semiconductor Devices Mfr
N.A.I.C.S.: 334413
Koji Uchiyama (Pres)

Tokyo Shirts Co., Ltd. (1)
Tel.: (81) 358301862
Web Site: http://www.tokyo-shirt.co.jp
Cloth Mfr & Distr
N.A.I.C.S.: 315250

NISSHO SANGYO CO. LTD.
Hulic Kamiyacho Bldg 4F 4-3-13 Toranomon, Minato-Ku, Tokyo, 105-8567, Japan
Tel.: (81) 354721671
Web Site: http://www.nissho.net
Year Founded: 1966
Sales Range: $25-49.9 Million
Emp.: 110
N.A.I.C.S.: 423830
Atsushi Sakata (Chm)

NISSIN CORPORATION
Nissay office building 6-81 Onoe-cho, Naka-ku, Yokohama, Japan
Web Site: http://www.nissin-tw.com
Year Founded: 1938
9066—(TKS)
Rev.: $1,123,263,740
Assets: $1,152,427,060
Liabilities: $476,752,860
Net Worth: $675,674,200
Earnings: $57,169,890
Fiscal Year-end: 03/31/24
Physical Distribution, Warehousing & Logistics Services & Travel Agencies
N.A.I.C.S.: 541614
Masahiro Tsutsui (Pres, Pres & Exec Officer)

Subsidiaries:

Beijing Sanxin Refrigeration Logistics Co., Ltd. (1)
Fuli Nongchang Nanyuan, Daxing District, Beijing, 100076, China
Tel.: (86) 1060221841
Web Site: http://www.nissin-eu.com
Transportation Services
N.A.I.C.S.: 488999

Best Cold Chain Co., Ltd. (1)
131 Moo1 Phahonyothin Road Sanubtueb Km 74, Wang Noi, Phra Nakhon Si Ayutthaya, 13170, Thailand
Tel.: (66) 35958526
Logistic Services
N.A.I.C.S.: 488510

Changshu Nissin-Ninotrans Transportation Co., Ltd. (1)
5FL Customs Building No 7 Haiyu Bei Road, Haiyu Bei Rd, Changshu, 215500, Jiangsu, China
Tel.: (86) 51252885049
Web Site: http://www.nissin-eu.com
Sales Range: $50-74.9 Million
Emp.: 200
Transportation Services
N.A.I.C.S.: 488999

Guangzhou Nissin International Logistics, Ltd. (1)
707-708 Rm Blk A Dongpu Commercial Bldg 282 Zhongshan Main Rd, Tianhe District, 510660, Guangzhou, China
Tel.: (86) 2038796879
Sales Range: $25-49.9 Million
Emp.: 40
Transportation Services
N.A.I.C.S.: 488999

Hokkaido Nissin Co., Ltd. (1)
3rd floor Kitashin Building 1-7-54 Ryutsu Center, Shiroishi-ku, Sapporo, 003-0030, Japan
Tel.: (81) 118685310
Warehousing & Transportation Services
N.A.I.C.S.: 493110

Hokushin Koun Co., Ltd. (1)
5-3 Asanocho, Hakodate, 040-0076, Hokkaido, Japan
Tel.: (81) 138457141
Freight Trucking & Storage Services
N.A.I.C.S.: 484121

Jiangsu Nissin-Sinotrans International Transportation Co., Ltd. (1)
Room No 1002 10 Floor Zhongyi Building No 580 Nanjing Road West, Zhonghua Rd, Shanghai, 200041, Jiangsu, China
Tel.: (86) 2152287700
Sales Range: $50-74.9 Million
Emp.: 200
Transportation Services
N.A.I.C.S.: 488999

Lao Nissin Smt Co., Ltd. (1)
No 9 Ban Oudomvilai Kaisonephomvihan, PO Box 279, Savannakhet, Lao People's Democratic Republic
Tel.: (856) 41260331
Emp.: 13
Logistic Services
N.A.I.C.S.: 488510

Limited Liability Company Nissin Rus (1)
Str Zolotaya 11 Business Center Zoloto 9F 9B11, Moscow, Russia
Tel.: (7) 4957923025
Web Site: http://www.nissin-tw.co.jp
Sales Range: $50-74.9 Million
Emp.: 7
Warehousing & Freight Transportation Services
N.A.I.C.S.: 488510
Ozeki Makoto (Gen Dir)

NR Greenlines Logistics Co., Ltd. (1)
Tel.: (84) 2435772751
Logistic Services
N.A.I.C.S.: 488510

Nissin (Changshu) International Logistics Co., Ltd. (1)
Room 606 Building 1 Huifeng Times Plaza No 22 Huanghe Road, Changshu, 215500, Jiangsu, China
Tel.: (86) 51251927026
Logistic Services
N.A.I.C.S.: 488510

Nissin (Shanghai) Logistics Co., Ltd. (1)
Room 206 and 218 No 340 Houshan Road, Hongkou District, Shanghai, China
Tel.: (86) 21 6541 2530
Web Site: http://www.nissin-tw.co.jp
Sales Range: $25-49.9 Million
Emp.: 50
Transportation & Shipping Services
N.A.I.C.S.: 488999

Nissin ABC Logistics Private Limited (1)
46c Rafi Ahmed Kidwai Road, Via Sutahata Haldia Midnapore, Kolkata, 700 016, India
Tel.: (91) 3322655073
Web Site: http://www.nall.co.in
Sales Range: $125-149.9 Million
Emp.: 270
Transportation Services
N.A.I.C.S.: 488999
Masami Yasuda (Sr Mng Dir)

Nissin Belgium N.V. (1)
Tel.: (32) 27514499
Sales Range: $25-49.9 Million
Emp.: 2
Transportation Services
N.A.I.C.S.: 488999

Nissin France S.A.S. (1)
ZAC du Moulin 1 Rue du Meunier, 95700, Roissy-en-France, France
Tel.: (33) 149385900
Web Site: http://www.nissin-tw.co.jp
Sales Range: $25-49.9 Million
Emp.: 19
Transportation, Truck Freight/Forwarding Services
N.A.I.C.S.: 488999

Nissin International Logistics (M) Sdn. Bhd. (1)
No 5 Jalan Astaka U8/83 Seksyen U8, 40150, Shah Alam, Selangor, Malaysia
Tel.: (60) 327262428
Logistic Services
N.A.I.C.S.: 488510

Nissin International Transport USA, Inc. (1)
172-47 Baisley Blvd, Jamaica, NY 11434
Tel.: (718) 525-2437
Web Site: https://www.nitusa.com
Transportation Services
N.A.I.C.S.: 488999
Hiroshi Tsutsui (Pres)

Nissin Logistics (VN) Co., Ltd. (1)
Room 101 Ocean Park Building No 1 Dao Duy Anh Str, Dong Da Dist, Hanoi, 10000, Vietnam
Tel.: (84) 2435771462
Web Site: https://nissinvn.com.vn
Transportation Services
N.A.I.C.S.: 488999

Nissin Logistics Poland Sp. z o.o. (1)
Ostaszewo 57K, 87-148, Lysomice, Poland
Sales Range: $25-49.9 Million
Emp.: 80
Logistics Consulting Servies
N.A.I.C.S.: 541614

Nissin Logistics Shenzhen Co., Ltd. (1)
Tel.: (86) 75583592811
Logistic Services
N.A.I.C.S.: 488510

Nissin Middle East FZE (1)
Jebel Ali, PO Box 17390, Dubai, United Arab Emirates
Tel.: (971) 48836440
Web Site: http://www.nissin.sg
Sales Range: $25-49.9 Million
Emp.: 25
Transportation Services
N.A.I.C.S.: 488999
Fumisato Nakamura (Mng Dir)

Nissin Middle East L.L.C. (1)
Jafz Warehouse ZH-08 Jebel Ali, PO Box 16883, Dubai, United Arab Emirates
Tel.: (971) 4883644
Web Site: http://www.nissin.sg
Sales Range: $25-49.9 Million
Emp.: 25
Transportation Services
N.A.I.C.S.: 488999
Seiji Torio (Exec Officer)

Nissin Tansportation & Warehousing (H.K.) Ltd. (1)
13/F China Insurance Building 48 Cameron Road, Tsim Sha Tsui, Kowloon, China (Hong Kong)
Web Site: http://www.nissinhkltd.com.hk
Sales Range: $25-49.9 Million
Emp.: 90
Transportation Services
N.A.I.C.S.: 488999

Nissin Transport (Canada) Inc. (1)
5630 Timberlea Blvd, Mississauga, L4W 4M6, ON, Canada
Tel.: (905) 361-0750
Web Site: http://nissincda.com
Sales Range: $25-49.9 Million
Emp.: 20
Import & Export Services, Logistics & Warehousing & Storage
N.A.I.C.S.: 493190

Branch (Domestic):

Nissin Transport (Canada) Inc. (2)
120-1651 Patrick Street, Richmond, V6V 3A7, BC, Canada (100%)
Tel.: (604) 276-9691
Sales Range: $25-49.9 Million
Emp.: 5
Warehousing & Storage
N.A.I.C.S.: 493110

Nissin Transport (S) Pte. Ltd. (1)
No 50 Tuas Avenue 9, Singapore, 639192, Singapore
Tel.: (65) 68612453
Sales Range: $50-74.9 Million
Emp.: 200
Transportation Services
N.A.I.C.S.: 488999
Osamu Koike (Gen Mgr)

Nissin Transport Ges.mbH (1)
Kasernstrasse 5, 2301, Gross-Enzersdorf, Austria
Tel.: (43) 22492896015
Ocean Freight Forwarding Services
N.A.I.C.S.: 483111
Martin Kasak (Gen Mgr)

Nissin Transport GmbH (1)
Habichtweg 1, 41468, Neuss, Germany
Tel.: (49) 21315234331
Web Site: http://www.nissin-eu.com

NISSIN CORPORATION

Nissin Corporation—(Continued)
Sales Range: $25-49.9 Million
Emp.: 30
Transportation Services
N.A.I.C.S.: 488999

Nissin Transport Philippines Corp. (1)
No 14 Cargo Village Complex Ninoy Aquino Avenue, Near Cor Multinational Ave Sto Nino, Paranaque, 1700, Philippines
Tel.: (63) 28515621
Web Site: http://www.nissin-tw.co.jp
Sales Range: $25-49.9 Million
Emp.: 20
Transportation Services
N.A.I.C.S.: 488999
Yoshiki Kikkawa (Gen Mgr)

Nissin Transport Singapore Pte. Ltd. (1)
9 Airline Road 02-08, Cargo Agents Building D, Singapore, 918107, Singapore
Tel.: (65) 65452935
Freight Transportation Services
N.A.I.C.S.: 488510

Nissin Transportation & Warehousing (H.K.) Ltd. (1)
13/F China Insurance Building No 48 Cameron Road, Tsim Sha Tsui, Kowloon, China (Hong Kong)
Tel.: (852) 25201636
Web Site: https://www.nissinhkltd.com.hk
Sea Freight & Logistics Services
N.A.I.C.S.: 541614

Nissin Transportes Espana S.A. (1)
Avda Diagonal 309 5-A, 8013, Barcelona, Spain
Tel.: (34) 932896280
Web Site: http://www.nissinue.com
Transportation Services
N.A.I.C.S.: 488999

Nissin UK Ltd. (1)
Unit 5 Horton Industrial Park Horton Road, West Drayton, UB7 8JD, Middlesex, United Kingdom
Tel.: (44) 1895439555
Sales Range: $50-74.9 Million
Emp.: 150
Freight Transportation Services
N.A.I.C.S.: 488510

Nissin-Sinotrans International Logistics Co., Ltd. (1)
Room 608 The Exchange Beijing No Yi118 Jianguo Road, Chaoyang District, Beijing, 100022, China
Tel.: (86) 1065388766
Web Site: http://www.nissin-sino.cn
Sales Range: $25-49.9 Million
Emp.: 50
Transportation Services
N.A.I.C.S.: 488999

Nistrans (M) Sdn. Bhd. (1)
No 5 Jalan Astaka U8/83 Seksyen U8, 40150, Shah Alam, Selangor, Malaysia
Tel.: (60) 327262428
Web Site: http://www.nistrans.com.my
Sales Range: $50-74.9 Million
Emp.: 180
Transportation Services
N.A.I.C.S.: 488999

Nistrans Internacional De Mexico, S. De r.l. De C.V. (1)
Circuito Productividad Sur 111, Parque Industrial Guadalajara, 45690, El Salto, Jalisco, Mexico
Tel.: (52) 3336885916
Web Site: https://www.nistrans.com.mx
Warehousing & Storage
N.A.I.C.S.: 493190

PT. Nissin Jaya Indonesia (1)
Gedung Mugi Griya 7th Floor Jl MT Haryono Kav 10, Tebet, Jakarta Selatan, 12810, Jakarta, Indonesia
Tel.: (62) 21 830 8446
Web Site: https://www.nissinti.co.id
Emp.: 41
Logistic Services
N.A.I.C.S.: 488510

PT. Nissin Transport Indonesia (1)
Mugi Griya Building 7th Floor Jl MT Haryono Kav 10, Jakarta, 12810, Indonesia
Tel.: (62) 218308446
Web Site: http://www.nissin.co.id
Freight Transportation Services
N.A.I.C.S.: 488510
Hiroaki Okuthu (Mng Dir)

Shanghai Gaosin International Logistics Co., Ltd. (1)
No 288 Fute Road N, Waigaoqiao China Shanghai Pilot Free Trade Zone, Shanghai, 200131, China (25%)
Tel.: (86) 2158662548
Web Site: http://www.gaosin.com.cn
Sales Range: $50-74.9 Million
Emp.: 110
Transportation Services
N.A.I.C.S.: 488999

Siam Nissin & Seo Logistics Co., Ltd. (1)
700/859Moo1, Amata Nakorn Industrial Estate T Panthong A Panthong, Chon Buri, 20160, Thailand
Tel.: (66) 38185150
Logistic Services
N.A.I.C.S.: 488510

Siam Nistrans Co., Ltd. (1)
15th Fl 191/66 68-69 CTI TOWER Ratchadapisek Rd, Kwang Klongtoey Khet Klongtoey, Bangkok, 10110, Thailand
Tel.: (66) 22611080
Web Site: https://www.th.nissin-asia.com
Sales Range: $25-49.9 Million
Emp.: 750
Transportation Services
N.A.I.C.S.: 488999

Tianjin Nissin International Transport Co., Ltd. (1)
B20A International Commercial Trade Center No 59 Machang Road, Hexi District, Tianjin, 300203, China
Tel.: (86) 2283865520
Web Site: http://www.nissin-sino.cn
Sales Range: $25-49.9 Million
Emp.: 20
Transportation Services
N.A.I.C.S.: 488999

NISSIN FOODS HOLDINGS CO., LTD.

28-1 6-chome Shinjuku, Shinjuku-ku, Tokyo, 160-8524, Japan
Tel.: (81) 332055111   JP
Web Site: http://www.nissin.com
Year Founded: 1948
2897—(TKS)
Rev.: $4,844,687,130
Assets: $5,369,845,020
Liabilities: $1,833,428,920
Net Worth: $3,536,416,100
Earnings: $358,063,700
Emp.: 16,509
Fiscal Year-end: 03/31/24
Holding Company; Snack Noodles Mfr
N.A.I.C.S.: 551112
Toshihiko Ijichi (Exec Officer & Pres-Nissin Chilled Foods Co Ltd)

Subsidiaries:

Camino Real Foods, Inc. (1)
2638 E Vernon Ave, Vernon, CA 90058-1825 (100%)
Tel.: (323) 585-6599
Web Site: https://www.caminorealkitchens.com
Sales Range: $50-74.9 Million
Emp.: 25
Mfr & Sales of Frozen Foods
N.A.I.C.S.: 311412
Robert Cross (CEO)

Higashi Nippon Food, Inc. (1)
SE Sapporo Building 1-1-2 Kitashichijo Nishi, Kita-Ku, Sapporo, 060-0807, Hokkaido, Japan
Tel.: (81) 117577281
Web Site: https://www.nfgroup.co.jp
Emp.: 468
Fresh Meat Distr
N.A.I.C.S.: 424470

Kagome Nissin Foods (H.K.) Co., Ltd. (1)
11-13 Tai Shun Street, Tai Po Industrial Estate, Tai Po, New Territories, China (Hong Kong)
Tel.: (852) 34066888
Web Site: https://www.kagome.hk
Vegetable Mixed Juice Mfr
N.A.I.C.S.: 311411

MC Marketing & Sales (Hong Kong) Limited (1)
11-13 Dai Shun Street, Tai Po Industrial Estate, Tai Po, N T, China (Hong Kong)
Tel.: (852) 26627110
Web Site: https://www.mcms.com.hk
Dairy Products Distr
N.A.I.C.S.: 424430

MYOJO FOODS CO., LTD. (1)
3-50-11 Sendagaya, Shibuya-ku, Tokyo, 151-8507, Japan (100%)
Tel.: (81) 334701691
Web Site: https://www.myojofoods.co.jp
Instant Noodle Manufacturing & Marketing
N.A.I.C.S.: 311423

MYOJO U.S.A., INC. (1)
6220 Prescott Ct, Chino, CA 91710
Tel.: (909) 464-1411
Dry Pasta Mfr
N.A.I.C.S.: 311824
Phil Kruse (Mgr-QC)

Mareven Food Central LLC (1)
17 Building World Trade and Exhibition Center, Greenwood 72nd km MKAD Putilkovo Krasnogorsk District, 143441, Moscow, Russia
Tel.: (7) 495 730 1186
Web Site: http://www.marevenfood.ru
Sales Range: $350-399.9 Million
Emp.: 200
Food Products Mfr
N.A.I.C.S.: 311999
Igor Fedorchenko (Mng Dir)

Plant (Domestic):

Mareven Food Central LLC - Serpukhov Plant (2)
Mareven Food Central territory, 142214, Ivanovskoye, Moscow, Russia
Tel.: (7) 4957301186
Web Site: http://mareven.ru
Sales Range: $300-349.9 Million
Emp.: 200
Food Products Mfr
N.A.I.C.S.: 311999
Do Xuan Hoang (Gen Dir)

Mareven Food Holdings Limited (1)
Interlink Hermes Plaza Office 202A Ayois Athanasios Avenue 46, 4102, Limassol, Cyprus
Tel.: (357) 25023800
Web Site: https://mareven.com
Food Production Development Services
N.A.I.C.S.: 541715

NISSIN BUSINESS SUPPORT CO., LTD (1)
6-28-1 Shinjuku Nisshin Shokuhin Holdings Tokyo Honsha Bldg Nai, Shinjuku, Tokyo, 160-0022, Japan
Tel.: (81) 332055111
Business Support Services
N.A.I.C.S.: 561499

NISSIN CHILLED FOODS CO., LTD. (1)
28-1 6-chome Shinjuku, Shinjuku-ku, Tokyo, 160-8524, Japan
Tel.: (81) 332055231
Food Products Mfr
N.A.I.C.S.: 311999

NISSIN CISCO CO., LTD. (1)
80 Ishizukitamachi, Sakai-Ku, Sakai, 590-0823, Osaka, Japan
Tel.: (81) 722410201
Chocolate & Confectionery Mfr
N.A.I.C.S.: 311351

NISSIN FOOD PRODUCTS CO., LTD (1)
1-1 4chome Nishinakajima, Yodogawa-ku, Osaka, 532-8524, Japan
Tel.: (81) 663057711
Food Products Mfr

INTERNATIONAL PUBLIC

N.A.I.C.S.: 311999

NISSIN FROZEN FOODS CO., LTD (1)
28-1 6-chome Shinjuku, Shinjuku-ku, Tokyo, 160-8524, Japan
Tel.: (81) 332055111
Frozen Food Mfr
N.A.I.C.S.: 311412

Nicky Foods Co., Ltd. (1)
5th floor Nissin Foods Holdings Osaka Head Office Building, 4-1-1 Nishinakajima Yodogawa-ku, Osaka, 532-8524, Japan
Tel.: (81) 676683737
Web Site: https://www.nickyfoods.co.jp
Emp.: 286
Frozen Food Mfr
N.A.I.C.S.: 311412

Nippon Food Packer Shikoku, Inc. (1)
838 Takagawahara Aza Takagawara Ishiicho, Myozai, Tokushima, 779-3223, Japan
Tel.: (81) 886744191
Food Packaging Services
N.A.I.C.S.: 561910

Nissin Business Support Plus Co., Ltd. (1)
28-1 6-chome Shinjuku, Shinjuku-ku, Tokyo, 160-8524, Japan
Tel.: (81) 332055111
Building Maintenance Services
N.A.I.C.S.: 561790

Nissin Enterprise Corporation (1)
5-3-20 Torikaikami, Settsu, 566-0062, Osaka, Japan
Tel.: (81) 726533111
Web Site: http://www.nissin.com
General Warehousing & Storage Services
N.A.I.C.S.: 493110

Nissin Foods (Asia) Pte. Ltd. (1)
1 Senoko Avenue 04-06 FoodAxis Senoko, Singapore, 758297, Singapore
Tel.: (65) 62652447
Web Site: http://www.nissinfoods.com.sg
Sales Range: $25-49.9 Million
Emp.: 10
Prepared Food Mfr
N.A.I.C.S.: 311991

Subsidiary (Non-US):

Indo Nissin Foods Limited (2)
3rd Floor SKAV 909 9/1 Lavelle Road, Bengaluru, 560001, Karnataka, India (89.1%)
Tel.: (91) 8043554000
Web Site: http://www.indonissin.in
Sales Range: $1-9.9 Million
Mfr & Sales of Instant Noodles
N.A.I.C.S.: 311824

Nissin Foods (Thailand) Co., Ltd. (2)
2922/287-288 Charn Issara Tower II 25th Floor New Phetchaburi Road, Bangkapi Huaykhwang, Bangkok, 10310, Thailand
Tel.: (66) 23195400
Web Site: https://www.nissinthailand.com
Sales Range: $25-49.9 Million
Emp.: 140
Instant Noodles Mfr & Distr
N.A.I.C.S.: 311824

Nissin Foods Co. Ltd. (2)
11-13 Dai Shun Street, Tai Po Industrial Estate, Tai Po, 4600652, New Territories, China (Hong Kong) (100%)
Tel.: (852) 34066888
Web Site: https://www.nissinfoods.com.hk
Sales Range: $25-49.9 Million
Mfr & Sales of Instant Noodles
N.A.I.C.S.: 311824
K. Anto (Gen Mgr)

Subsidiary (Non-US):

Guangdong Shunde Nissin Foods Co., Ltd. (3)
13 Gang Qian Rd Beijiao Industrial Park, Beijiao County Shunde District, Foshan, 528311, Guangdong, China (100%)
Tel.: (86) 75726330482
Web Site: http://www.nissinfoods.com.cn
Instant Noodles Mfr & Sls
N.A.I.C.S.: 445298

Subsidiary (Domestic):

Nissin Foods (HK) Management Co., Ltd (3)
11-13 Dai Shun Street, Tai Po Industrial Estate, Tai Po, New Territories, China (Hong Kong)
Tel.: (852) 3406 6888
Web Site: http://www.nissinfoods.com.hk
Food Products Mfr
N.A.I.C.S.: 311999

Wing On Foods Co., Ltd. (3)
Tai Po Industrial Estates 9 13 Dai Cheong Street, Tai Po, NT, China (Hong Kong) (100%)
Tel.: (852) 26608418
Web Site: http://www.nissinfoods.com.hk
Sales Range: $75-99.9 Million
Mfr & Sales of Instant Noodles
N.A.I.C.S.: 311824

Winner Food Products Ltd. (3)
11-13 Dai Shun Street, Tai Po Industrial Estate, Tai Po, China (Hong Kong) (74%)
Tel.: (852) 26633992
Web Site: https://www.doll.com.hk
Mfr & Sales of Instant Noodles
N.A.I.C.S.: 311824

Subsidiary (Domestic):

Winner Food Manufacturers Ltd. (4)
Tai Po Industrial Estate 20 Dai Kwai Street, Tai Po, NT, China (Hong Kong) (74%)
Tel.: (852) 34066818
Web Site: http://www.doll.com.hk
Sales Range: $75-99.9 Million
Emp.: 400
Mfr & Sales of Frozen Foods
N.A.I.C.S.: 311411

Joint Venture (Non-US):

Nissin-Universal Robina Corporation (2)
9th floor Tera Tower Bridgetowne C5 Road, Ugong Norte, Quezon City, 1110, Philippines (49%)
Tel.: (63) 26713944
Web Site: http://www.urc.com.ph
Sales Range: $25-49.9 Million
Mfr & Sales of Instant Noodles
N.A.I.C.S.: 311824

Nissin Foods (U.S.A.) Inc. (1)
2001 W Rosecrans Ave, Gardena, CA 90249-2931 (90%)
Tel.: (310) 327-8478
Web Site: http://www.nissinfoods.com
Sales Range: $100-124.9 Million
Emp.: 500
Instant Ramen Noodles Mfr
N.A.I.C.S.: 311824

Nissin Foods GmbH (1)
Ginnheimer Str 6, 65760, Eschborn, Germany (100%)
Tel.: (49) 6196785960
Web Site: http://de.nissin-foods.eu
Sales Range: $25-49.9 Million
Emp.: 9
Sales of Instant Noodles
N.A.I.C.S.: 445298

Nissin Foods India Ltd. (1)
3rd Floor SKAV 909 9/1 Lavelle Road, Bengaluru, 560 001, Karnataka, India
Tel.: (91) 8043554000
Web Site: https://www.indonissin.in
Sales Range: $25-49.9 Million
Emp.: 50
Prepared Food Products Mfr
N.A.I.C.S.: 311999
Gautam Sharma *(Mng Dir)*

Nissin Foods Kft. (1)
Buzakalasz Ut 20, Kecskemet, 6000, Hungary
Tel.: (36) 76485702
Web Site: http://www.nissinfoods.hu
Sales Range: $25-49.9 Million
Emp.: 15
Food Products Mfr
N.A.I.C.S.: 311824
Tsuji Shinji *(Dir-Factory)*

Nissin Foods Vietnam Co., Ltd. (1)
Tel.: (84) 2839300399
Web Site: http://www.nissinfoods.vn

Noodle Product Mfr & Distr
N.A.I.C.S.: 311824
Hidefumi Kawakita *(Gen Dir)*

Nissin Koikeya Foods (China & HK) Co., Ltd. (1)
11-13 Dai Shun Street, Tai Po Industrial Estate, Tai Po, NT, China (Hong Kong)
Tel.: (852) 34066888
Web Site: https://www.nissinkoikeyafoods.com.hk
Snack Product Mfr
N.A.I.C.S.: 311919

Nissin Netcom Co., Ltd. (1)
4-1-1 Nishinakajima, Yodogawa-ku, Osaka, 532-8524, Japan
Tel.: (81) 663052851
Web Site: https://www.nissin-net.com
Insurance Agency Services
N.A.I.C.S.: 524210

Nissin Plastics Co., Ltd. (1)
140-1 Iseki Shimomagari, Ritto, 520-3026, Shiga, Japan
Tel.: (81) 775531611
Sales Range: $125-149.9 Million
Emp.: 400
Plastics Product Mfr
N.A.I.C.S.: 326199

Nissin York Co., Ltd. (1)
6F Nihonbashi-tachibana Bldg 6-11 Higashinihonbashi, Chuo-ku, Tokyo, 103-0004, Japan
Tel.: (81) 356956461
Dairy Products Mfr & Distr
N.A.I.C.S.: 311511

Nissin-Ajinomoto Alimentos Ltda. (1)
Rodovia Bandeirantes Km 57, 18140-000, Ibiuna, SP, Brazil (50%)
Tel.: (55) 15 3145 5900
Web Site: http://www.ajinomoto.com
Sales Range: $25-49.9 Million
Emp.: 100
Instant Noodles Mfr
N.A.I.C.S.: 311423

P.T. Nissinmas (1)
(49%)
Tel.: (62) 218934130
Sales Range: $1-9.9 Million
Emp.: 300
Instant Noodles Mfr & Distr
N.A.I.C.S.: 311999

Uji Kaihatsu Development Co., Ltd. (1)
1 Shinike Todo, Uji, 611-0013, Kyoto, Japan
Tel.: (81) 774315101
Web Site: http://www.nissin.com
Golf Course Management Services
N.A.I.C.S.: 713910

NISSIN SHOJI CO., LTD.
4F Daiwa Shibaura Bldg 1-12-3 Shibaura, Minato-ku, Tokyo, 105-0023, Japan
Tel.: (81) 334576251
Web Site: https://www.nissin-shoji.co.jp
Year Founded: 1947
7490—(TKS)
Rev.: $256,018,520
Assets: $253,044,020
Liabilities: $108,185,870
Net Worth: $144,858,150
Earnings: $1,963,170
Emp.: 374
Fiscal Year-end: 03/31/24
Petroleum Product Mfr & Distr
N.A.I.C.S.: 324191

NISSO CORPORATION
Nisso Kosan NISSO Shin Yokohama Bldg-4-1 Shin Yokohama, Ward Kohoku, Yokohama, 222-0033, Kanagawa, Japan
Tel.: (81) 454764121
Web Site: https://www.nisso.co.jp
Year Founded: 1971
6569—(TKS)
Rev.: $750,674,320
Assets: $265,832,160

Liabilities: $134,581,040
Net Worth: $131,251,120
Earnings: $16,417,280
Fiscal Year-end: 12/31/22
Management Consulting Services
N.A.I.C.S.: 541618

Subsidiaries:

LeafNxT Co., Ltd. (1)
4th floor Honey Gotanda 2nd Building 1-4-1 Higashigotanda, Shinagawa-ku, Tokyo, 141-0022, Japan
Tel.: (81) 354217101
Web Site: https://www.leaf-nxt.co.jp
Media Direction Services
N.A.I.C.S.: 812990

Nisso Brain Co., Ltd. (1)
Nisso Daiichi Building 28-26, Toyooka-cho Tsurumi-ku, Yokohama, 230-0062, Kanagawa, Japan
Tel.: (81) 455756541
Web Site: https://www.nsbrain.jp
Information Technology Services
N.A.I.C.S.: 541519

Nisso Holdings Co Ltd. (1)
1-4-1 Shin Yokohama, Kohoku-ku, Yokohama, 222-0033, Kanagawa, Japan
Tel.: (81) 456203777
Web Site: https://www.nisso-hd.com
Human Resources Solution Services
N.A.I.C.S.: 541612

Nisso Nifty Co., Ltd. (1)
Nisso Kogyo Shin-Yokohama Building 1-4-1, Shin-Yokohama Kohoku-ku, Yokohama, 222-0033, Kanagawa, Japan
Tel.: (81) 454704333
Web Site: https://sweetpea.co.jp
Home Care Services
N.A.I.C.S.: 811411

Nisso Pure Co., Ltd. (1)
1-4-1 Shin-Yokohama Nisso Kosan Shin-Yokohama Building, Kohoku-ku, Yokohama, 222-0033, Kanagawa, Japan
Tel.: (81) 454703920
Web Site: https://www.nisso-pure.co.jp
Beverage Mfr & Distr
N.A.I.C.S.: 311514

Shanghai Nisso Human Resources Service Co., Ltd. (1)
Room 402 No 1996 Zhangyang Road Free Trade Zone, Shanghai, China
Tel.: (86) 2151017955
Information Technology Services
N.A.I.C.S.: 541519

Vector Shinwa Co., Ltd. (1)
3-1 Ikebata, Chiryu, 472-0025, Aichi, Japan
Tel.: (81) 566825783
Web Site: https://vectorshinwa.co.jp
Emp.: 200
Semiconductor Measuring Equipment Mfr & Distr
N.A.I.C.S.: 333242

NISSO PRONITY CO., LTD.
2-10-25 Mukai, Minami-ku, Fukuoka, 815-0035, Japan
Tel.: (81) 925552825
Web Site: https://www.kakou-nisso.co.jp
Year Founded: 1983
3440—(TKS)
Rev.: $110,056,680
Assets: $139,359,100
Liabilities: $64,358,340
Net Worth: $75,000,760
Earnings: $6,804,680
Emp.: 564
Fiscal Year-end: 08/31/24
Metallic Material Products Mfr
N.A.I.C.S.: 332999
Toru Ishida *(Pres & CEO)*

NISSOU CO., LTD.
1-8-17 Kyodo, Setagaya-ku, Tokyo, 156-0052, Japan
Tel.: (81) 334391671
Web Site: https://reform-nisso.co.jp
Year Founded: 1988

Construction Services
N.A.I.C.S.: 236220
Hiroshi Maeda *(Founder, Pres & CEO)*

NISSUI CORPORATION
Nishi-Shimbashi Square 1-3-1 nishi-shimbashi, minato-ku, Tokyo, 105-8676, Japan
Tel.: (81) 362067080   JP
Web Site: https://www.nissui.co.jp
Year Founded: 1911
1332—(TKS)
Rev.: $5,495,388,750
Assets: $4,008,198,240
Liabilities: $2,307,418,800
Net Worth: $1,700,779,440
Earnings: $157,648,500
Emp.: 10,104
Fiscal Year-end: 03/31/24
Seafood & Frozen Food Products Mfr; Frozen Foods Refrigeration & Transportation; Health Food & Pharmaceutical Mfr; Marine Transportation, Engineering, Ship Construction & Repair
N.A.I.C.S.: 311710
Hisami Sakai *(Mng Exec Officer-Intl Bus Dev Dept & Strategic Sls Dept)*

Subsidiaries:

Australian Longline Pty. Ltd. (1)
Ground Floor 85 Macquarie Street, Hobart, 7000, TAS, Australia
Tel.: (61) 36 244 2609
Web Site: https://www.australianlongline.com.au
Fish Product Mfr & Distr
N.A.I.C.S.: 311710
Malcolm McNeill *(Mng Dir)*

BlueWater Seafoods, Inc. (1)
128 Rogers St, Gloucester, MA 01930
Tel.: (978) 283-3000
Web Site: https://www.bluewater.ca
Frozen Food Product Mfr & Distr
N.A.I.C.S.: 311412

CHILLDY CO., LTD (1)
559-6 Kitano-cho, Hachioji, 192-0906, Tokyo, Japan (100%)
Tel.: (81) 42 656 5252
Web Site: https://www.chilldy.co.jp
Processed Foods Mfr & Sales
N.A.I.C.S.: 311412

CITE MARINE S.A.S. (1)
ZI du Porzo, 56700, Kervignac, France
Tel.: (33) 297851939
Web Site: https://www.cite-marine.fr
Frozen Food Products Mfr & Distr
N.A.I.C.S.: 311412

Cap Ocean S.A.S. (1)
Carrefour Industriel du Porzo, 56700, Kervignac, France
Tel.: (33) 29 785 1919
Marine Product Mfr
N.A.I.C.S.: 311710

Empresa de Desarrollo Pesquero de Chile S.A. (1)
Av Providencia 2633 15th Floor Edificio Forum, Providencia, Santiago, Chile
Tel.: (56) 22 414 3600
Web Site: https://www.emdepes.cl
Marine Product Mfr
N.A.I.C.S.: 311710

Farm Choice Co., Ltd. (1)
1-61 Kubara, Yamashiro-cho, Imari, 849-4256, Saga, Japan
Tel.: (81) 95 520 2255
Web Site: https://www.farmchoice-n.jp
Fish Feed Mfr & Distr
N.A.I.C.S.: 311119

Flatfish Ltd. (1)
Unit 5 Stirling Street, Grimsby, DN31 3AE, Lincolnshire, United Kingdom
Tel.: (44) 147 224 0322
Web Site: https://flatfish-ltd.co.uk
Fish Product Mfr & Distr
N.A.I.C.S.: 311710
Steve Stansfield *(CEO)*

NISSUI CORPORATION

INTERNATIONAL PUBLIC

Nissui Corporation—(Continued)

Gorton's, Inc. (1)
128 Rogers St, Gloucester, MA 01930
Web Site: https://www.gortons.com
Frozen Food Product Mfr & Distr
N.A.I.C.S.: 311412

HOKKAIDO NISSUI CO., LTD (1)
2-4-25 2-4-25 Nijuyonken, Nishi-Ku, Sapporo, 063-0801, Hokkaido, Japan
Tel.: (81) 116448601
Processed Seafood Mfr & Sales
N.A.I.C.S.: 311412

Hachikan Co., Ltd. (1)
45-44 Shimoage, Ichikawamachi, Hachinohe, 039-2241, Aomori, Japan
Tel.: (81) 17 852 6235
Web Site: https://www.kabu8kan.jp
Food Product Mfr & Distr
N.A.I.C.S.: 311999

Hakata Marukita Suisan Co., Ltd (1)
4-9-15 Ishimaru, Nishi-Ku, Fukuoka, 819-0025, Japan
Tel.: (81) 928838300
Web Site: http://www.agootoshi.com
Sales Range: $25-49.9 Million
Emp.: 266
Processed Seafood Mfr & Sales
N.A.I.C.S.: 424460
Nobuo Honda *(Pres)*

Halieutis Fish & Co.S.A.S (1)
1 Rue Maurice le Leon, 56100, Lorient, France
Tel.: (33) 29 787 1919
Marine Product Mfr
N.A.I.C.S.: 311710

Hohsui Corporation (1)
5-2-1 Tsukiji, Chuo-ku, Tokyo, 104-0045, Japan
Tel.: (81) 335433536
Web Site: http://www.hohsui.co.jp
Rev: $806,005,200
Assets: $400,635,840
Liabilities: $324,599,440
Net Worth: $76,036,400
Earnings: $7,724,640
Emp.: 285
Fiscal Year-end: 03/31/2021
Seafood Product Whslr
N.A.I.C.S.: 424460
Akitoshi Nomi *(Chm)*

Hokuriku Fresh Foods Co., Ltd (1)
4-8 Shimizu Motomachi, Toyama, 930-0034, Japan
Tel.: (81) 764918181
Web Site: https://www.hoff.co.jp
Emp.: 150
Fresh Food Products Mfr & Distr
N.A.I.C.S.: 311412

KYOWA SUISAN CO., LTD (1)
65 Ei-machi, Sakaiminato, 684-0006, Tottori, Japan
Tel.: (81) 859 44 7171
Sales Range: $10-24.9 Million
Emp.: 30
Fish Farming Services
N.A.I.C.S.: 112511
Kunio Shirasu *(Mgr)*

Kaneko Sangyo Co., Ltd. (1)
5-10-6 Shiba, Minato-ku, Tokyo, 108-0014, Japan
Tel.: (81) 33 455 1411
Web Site: https://kaneko.co.jp
Fish Farming Services
N.A.I.C.S.: 112511
Yosinori Nakamura *(Pres)*

Kaneko Shokuhin Co., Ltd (1)
177-3 Nio-cho Niootsu, Mitoyo, 769-1404, Kagawa, Japan
Tel.: (81) 875823281
Web Site: http://www.kaneko-foods.com
Emp.: 230
Processed Seafood Distr
N.A.I.C.S.: 424420

Kitakyushu Nissui Co., Ltd. (1)
2-3-6 Kawashiro, Tobata-ku, Kitakyushu, 804-0071, Fukuoka, Japan (100%)
Tel.: (81) 938713838
Web Site: https://www.kitakyushunissui.com
Emp.: 134
Frozen Food Products Mfr & Distr

Kunihiro Inc. (1)
15-13 Higashi-Onomichi, Onomichi, Hiroshima, Japan
Tel.: (81) 848643994
Web Site: https://www.kunihiro-jp.com
Emp.: 349
Processed Seafoods Whslr
N.A.I.C.S.: 424460
Ikuzo Kawasaki *(Pres)*

Kurose Suisan Co., Ltd. (1)
2-15-4 Nishihama, Kushima, 888-0012, Miyazaki, Japan
Tel.: (84) 98 772 7700
Web Site: https://www.kurosui.jp
Emp.: 250
Seafoods Distr & Whslr
N.A.I.C.S.: 424460

Maruuo Suisan Co.,Ltd (1)
1920-54 Shirahama-cho Ko, Himeji, 672-8023, Hyogo, Japan
Tel.: (81) 792456120
Web Site: https://www.maruuo-net.co.jp
Emp.: 42
Processed Seafoods Whslr
N.A.I.C.S.: 424460

NIGICO Co., Ltd. (1)
National Road 1A Hamlet 5, Ho Phong Ward GiaRai District, Bac Lieu, Vietnam
Tel.: (84) 781 385 1228
Marine Product Mfr
N.A.I.C.S.: 311710

NIPPO SHOKUHIN KOGYO CO., LTD (1)
624-19 Tsukiji Jonan-cho, Kumamoto, 861-4212, Japan
Tel.: (81) 964287071
Processed Foods Mfr & Sales
N.A.I.C.S.: 311412

NISSUI LOGISTICS CORPORATION (1)
5F Success Shiba Daimon Building 2-8-13 Shiba Daimon, Minato-ku, Tokyo, 105-0012, Japan (100%)
Tel.: (81) 354726100
Web Site: https://www.nissui-logistics.jp
Sales Range: $200-249.9 Million
Emp.: 479
Cold Storage Management & Freight Transportation Services
N.A.I.C.S.: 483111
Hiroshi Suzuki *(Mng Exec Officer & Gen Mgr-Gen Affairs & Acctg)*

Subsidiary (Domestic):

Carry Net Co., Ltd. (2)
1-181 Meisho, Minato-ku, Nagoya, 455-0806, Aichi, Japan (100%)
Tel.: (81) 523818578
Web Site: https://www.carry-net.co.jp
Cargo Handling Services
N.A.I.C.S.: 488320
Tadanori Isayama *(Pres, CEO & Dir)*

NISSUI MARINE INDUSTRIES CO., LTD (1)
2-6-27 Ginza, Tobata-ku, Kitakyushu, 804-0076, Fukuoka, Japan
Tel.: (81) 938842010
Offshore Engineering Services
N.A.I.C.S.: 541330

Nagasaki Shipyard Co., Ltd. (1)
4-2 Naminotaira-cho, Nagasaki, 850-0936, Japan
Tel.: (81) 958260191
Web Site: https://www.nagazou.jp
Ship Building Services
N.A.I.C.S.: 336611

Nakatani Suisan Co., Ltd (1)
1114-59 Koniya Setouti-cho, Oshima-gun, Kagoshima, 894-1508, Japan
Tel.: (81) 997731661
Web Site: http://www.nissui.co.jp
Fish Farming Services
N.A.I.C.S.: 112511

Netuno International S.A. (1)
Avenue Mal Mascarenhas De Morais, 51150-000, Recife, Brazil
Tel.: (55) 81 2121 6868
Web Site: http://www.nissui.co.jp
Fish Farming Services

N.A.I.C.S.: 112511

Nippon Cookery Co., Ltd. (1)
2-20-4 Higashigotanda, Shinagawa-ku, Tokyo, 141-0022, Japan (100%)
Tel.: (81) 334412255
Web Site: http://www.cookery.co.jp
Sales Range: $450-499.9 Million
Emp.: 2,800
Processed Foods Mfr & Distr
N.A.I.C.S.: 311999
Kaneko Teruaki *(Pres)*

Nippon Kayaku Co., Ltd. - Tokyo Plant (1)
23-1 Shinden 1-chome, Adachi-ku, Tokyo, 123-0865, Japan
Tel.: (81) 359595111
Chemical Products Mfr
N.A.I.C.S.: 325180

Nippon Marine Enterprises, Ltd. (1)
Tel.: (81) 468244611
Web Site: http://www.nmeweb.jp
Sales Range: $125-149.9 Million
Emp.: 362
Marine Vessel Operating Services
N.A.I.C.S.: 488390

Nippon Suisan (Europe) B.V. (1)
Hoger Einde-Zuid 6, Amstelveen, 1191 AG, Netherlands
Tel.: (31) 204263800
Web Site: http://www.nissui.co.jp
Holding Company; Regional Managing Office
N.A.I.C.S.: 551112

Nippon Suisan (Singapore) Pte. Ltd. (1)
1 Commonwealth Lane Ste 03-13, Singapore, 149544, Singapore
Tel.: (65) 62220548
Web Site: http://www.nissui.co.jp
Sales Range: $50-74.9 Million
Emp.: 6
Processed Seafood Distr
N.A.I.C.S.: 424460
Sally Tan *(Mgr-Accts)*

Nippon Suisan (U.S.A.), Inc. (1)
15400 NE 90th St Ste 100, Redmond, WA 98052-3507
Tel.: (425) 869-1703
Emp.: 6
Trading Co.
N.A.I.C.S.: 424460

Subsidiary (Domestic):

Fishking Processors, Inc. (2)
1320 Newton St, Los Angeles, CA 90021
Tel.: (213) 746-1307
Sales Range: $75-99.9 Million
Specialty Seafood Processor
N.A.I.C.S.: 311710

Nippon Suisan America Latina S.A. (1)
Providencia Avenue 2653 15th Floor, Santiago, Chile
Tel.: (56) 224143600
Marine Product Whslr
N.A.I.C.S.: 424460

Nippon Suisan Kaisha, Ltd - Anjo Plant (1)
6-6-12 Toei-cho, Anjo, 446-0007, Aichi, Japan
Tel.: (81) 566979151
Frozen Food Product Mfr
N.A.I.C.S.: 311412

Nippon Suisan Kaisha, Ltd - Hachioji General Plant (1)
559-6 Kitano-machi, Hachioji, 192-0906, Tokyo, Japan
Tel.: (81) 426565111
Processed Seafoods Mfr
N.A.I.C.S.: 311710

Nippon Suisan Kaisha, Ltd - Himeji General Plant (1)
1-71 Usazaki-minami Shirahama-cho, Himeji, 672-8022, Hyogo, Japan
Tel.: (81) 79 245 9001
Web Site: http://www.nissui.co.jp
Frozen Food Product Mfr
N.A.I.C.S.: 311412

Nippon Suisan Kaisha, Ltd - Imari Fish Feed and Oil Plant (1)
1-61 Kubara Yamashiro-cho, Imari, 849-4256, Saga, Japan
Tel.: (81) 955202255
Processed Oil Seafoods Mfr
N.A.I.C.S.: 311710

Nippon Suisan Kaisha, Ltd - Kashima Plant (1)
18-2 Higashi-fukashiba, Kamisu, 314-0103, Ibaraki, Japan
Tel.: (81) 299955131
Web Site: http://www.niffui.co.jp
Sales Range: $50-74.9 Million
Emp.: 60
Processed Seafood Distr
N.A.I.C.S.: 424460
Hiroshi Hasegawa *(Plant Mgr)*

Nippon Suisan Kaisha, Ltd - Tobata Plant (1)
2-3-6 Kawashiro Tobata-ku, Kitakyushu, 804-8577, Fukuoka, Japan
Tel.: (81) 93 884 2100
Web Site: http://www.nissui.co.jp
Processed Seafoods Mfr
N.A.I.C.S.: 311710

Nippon Suisan Kaisha, Ltd - Tsukuba Plant (1)
Techno Park Oho 7 Okubo, Tsukuba, 300-2611, Ibaraki, Japan
Tel.: (81) 298 65 1757
Web Site: http://www.nissui.co.jp
Chemical Products Mfr
N.A.I.C.S.: 325199

Nissui (Thailand) Co., Ltd. (1)
118/1 Moo 1 Karnjanavanich Rd Takam, Hat Yai, 90110, Songkhla, Thailand
Tel.: (66) 74 380 2826
Web Site: https://www.nissui.co.th
Marine Product Mfr
N.A.I.C.S.: 311710

Nissui Food System Co., Ltd (1)
Nissui Kayaba-cho Building 2-4-4 Nihonbashi-kayaba-Cho, Chuo-Ku, Tokyo, 103-0025, Japan
Tel.: (81) 336622201
Restaurant Services
N.A.I.C.S.: 722511

Nordic Seafood A/S (1)
Soren Nordbysvej 15, 9850, Hirtshals, Denmark
Tel.: (45) 9 894 1533
Web Site: https://www.nordicseafood.com
Sea Food Product Mfr & Distr
N.A.I.C.S.: 311710

Nordsee Comercial Importadora Y Exportadora, Ltda. (1)
Rua Engenheiro Antonio Jovino 220 - 6 Andar - Cj 62 e 63, Vila Andrade, Sao Paulo, 05727-220, Brazil
Tel.: (55) 113 742 1903
Web Site: https://www.nordsee.com.br
Fish Product Mfr & Distr
N.A.I.C.S.: 311710

Oita Marine Biological Technology Center (1)
508-8 Ariakeura Turumi, Saiki, Oita, 876-1204, Japan
Tel.: (81) 975333311
Web Site: http://www.nissui.co.jp
R&D Promotion of Aquaculture & Efficient High-Quality Farmed Fish Breeding
N.A.I.C.S.: 112511

Qingdao Nissui Food Research & Development Co., Ltd. (1)
Kunlunshan South Road 2089, Qingdao Economic and Technological Development Zone, Qingdao, Shandong, China
Tel.: (86) 5328 683 8990
Consulting Services
N.A.I.C.S.: 541614

SALMONES ANTARTICA S.A (1)
Luis Pasteur 5896, Vitacura, Santiago, Chile
Tel.: (56) 228405292
Web Site: https://tienda-salmonesantartica.cl
Fish Farming Services
N.A.I.C.S.: 112511

AND PRIVATE COMPANIES — NITERRA CO., LTD.

Sasaya Shoten Co., Ltd (1)
19 8 Otanoshike, Kushiro, 084-0917, Hokkaido, Japan
Tel.: (81) 154 57 3594
Web Site: http://www.sasaya-net.co.jp
Seafood Processing Services
N.A.I.C.S.: 311710
Masayuki Sasaya (Dir)

Satsuma Suisan Co., Ltd. (1)
7452-11 Furuecho, Kanoya, 891-2321, Kagoshima, Japan
Tel.: (81) 99 431 8111
Web Site: https://satsuma-suisan.wixsite.com
Fish Farming Services
N.A.I.C.S.: 112511

Suisan Ryutsu Co., Ltd (1)
6-8 Toyomi-cho, Chuo-ku, Tokyo, 104-0055, Japan
Tel.: (81) 362282692
Web Site: https://www.suiryu.co.jp
Emp.: 330
Processed Seafood Distr
N.A.I.C.S.: 424460

TN Fine Chemicals Co., Ltd. (1)
30/2 Mue 8 Sethakit 1 Road, Ampher Muang, Samut Sakhon, 74000, Thailand
Tel.: (66) 3 442 3686
Fish Product Mfr & Distr
N.A.I.C.S.: 311710

Tai Mei Food Industrial Corp. (1)
No 1 Dayou 2nd Street, Daliao District, Kaohsiung, 831, Taiwan
Tel.: (886) 7 787 1179
Web Site: https://taimeifood.com.tw
Food Product Mfr & Distr
N.A.I.C.S.: 311999

Thai Delmar Co., Ltd. (1)
88/8 Moo 4 Asia Industrial Estate Suvarnabhumi Soi Asia Avenue 2, Tambon Khlong Suan Amphoe Bang Bo, Samut Prakan, 10560, Thailand
Tel.: (66) 2 326 1738
Web Site: https://www.delmar.co.th
Frozen Food Product Mfr
N.A.I.C.S.: 311412
Kanokwan Hangsanet (Gen Mgr-Sales)

The Gorton Group (1)
1780 W Horizon Ridge Pkwy 100, Henderson, NV 89012
Tel.: (702) 296-2254
Web Site: http://www.gortonluxury.com
Sales Range: $100-124.9 Million
Emp.: 300
Seafood Processor
N.A.I.C.S.: 311710
Judson Reis (Pres & CEO)

Subsidiary (Domestic):

King & Prince Seafood Corporation (2)
1 King Prince Blvd, Brunswick, GA 31520
Tel.: (912) 265-5155
Web Site: http://www.kpseafood.com
Sales Range: $75-99.9 Million
Frozen & Processed Seafood Products Mfr
N.A.I.C.S.: 311710
Mike Tigani (Dir-Mktg)

Specialty Products (2)
13525 Hummel Rd, Cleveland, OH 44142-2519
Tel.: (216) 362-1050
Sales Range: $25-49.9 Million
Emp.: 36
Fish & Seafood Processing
N.A.I.C.S.: 311999
Sue Spisak (Mgr-Fin)

Tokyosuisanunyu Corporaition (1)
5-3-1 Tokai, Ota-ku, Tokyo, 143-0001, Japan
Tel.: (81) 3 3790 2091
Web Site: http://www.tousuiun.com
Emp.: 131
General Warehousing Services
N.A.I.C.S.: 493110
Yosuke Yamashita (Pres & CEO)

Tomiso Co.,Ltd (1)
2021 Yamadacho, Mizunami, 509-6101, Gifu, Japan
Tel.: (81) 572663777

Web Site: http://www.tomiso.com
Emp.: 200
Food Products Mfr & Distr
N.A.I.C.S.: 311412

UniSea, Inc. (1)
15400 NE 90th St, Redmond, WA 98052
Tel.: (425) 881-8181
Web Site: https://www.unisea.com
Sales Range: $125-149.9 Million
Fish Products Processor
N.A.I.C.S.: 311710
Tom Enlow (Pres & CEO)

YAMATSU SUISAN CO., LTD (1)
711 Myogadani, Konan-ku, Niigata, 950-0114, Japan
Tel.: (81) 252576630
Web Site: https://yamatsu-suisan-saiyo.com
Emp.: 59
Processed Seafood Distr
N.A.I.C.S.: 424460

Yokohama Trading Corp. Ltd. (1)
6-104 Aioi-cho, Naka-ku, Yokohama, 231-0012, Kanagawa, Japan
Tel.: (81) 456417846
Web Site: https://www.ytc-ltd.co.jp
Sales Range: $10-24.9 Million
Emp.: 35
Fishing Equipment Import & Distr
N.A.I.C.S.: 423910
Toshimichi Takada (Pres)

Yumigahama Suisan Co., Ltd. (1)
205 Takenouchi Danchi, Sakaiminato, 684-0046, Tottori, Japan
Tel.: (81) 85 930 2721
Web Site: https://www.yumisui.jp
Fish Farming Services
N.A.I.C.S.: 112511

NISSUI PHARMACEUTICAL CO. LTD.
20th Floor Ueno Frontier Tower
3-24-6 Ueno Taito-ku, Tokyo, 110 8736, Japan
Tel.: (81) 358465611
Web Site: http://www.nissui-pharm.co.jp
4550—(TKS)
Rev.: $161,239,760
Assets: $357,424,320
Liabilities: $41,807,920
Net Worth: $315,616,400
Earnings: $11,093,280
Emp.: 331
Fiscal Year-end: 03/31/22
Pharmaceutical, Clinical Diagnostics Mfr & Drugs Distr
N.A.I.C.S.: 456010
Tokuya Ono (Pres & Pres)

Subsidiaries:

Nissui Pharmaceutical Co., Ltd. - Tsukuba Plant (1)
1500-12 Muko-Ueno, Chikusei, Ibaraki, Japan
Tel.: (81) 296526111
Web Site: http://www.nissui-pharm.co.jp
Solid & Liquid Pharmaceutical Preparations Mfr
N.A.I.C.S.: 325412

NISTEC LTD.
43 Hasivim Street, Petah Tikvah, 4917001, Israel
Tel.: (972) 3 929 2555
Web Site: http://www.nistec.com
Year Founded: 1985
Holding Company; Electronics Designer, Fabricator & Mfr
N.A.I.C.S.: 551112
Yitzhak Nissan (Founder & CEO)

Subsidiaries:

Eltek Ltd. (1)
20 Ben Zion Gelis Street, Petah Tiqwa, 4927920, Israel (50.5%)
Tel.: (972) 39395025
Web Site: https://www.nisteceltek.com
Rev: $39,650,000
Assets: $40,985,000
Liabilities: $19,965,000
Net Worth: $21,020,000
Earnings: $3,194,000
Emp.: 294
Fiscal Year-end: 12/31/2022
Printed Circuit Boards Mfr & Retailer
N.A.I.C.S.: 334412
Yitzhak Nissan (Chm)

Subsidiary (Non-US):

Eltek Europe GmbH (2)
Ferdinand-Porsche-Str 45, 60386, Frankfurt, Germany
Tel.: (49) 69 42002 0
Telecommunication Servicesb
N.A.I.C.S.: 517111
Gunter Schmitt (COO)

Subsidiary (US):

Eltek USA Inc. (2)
250 Commercial St Ste 2022, Manchester, NH 03053
Tel.: (603) 421-0020
Web Site: www.eltek.co.il
Printed Circuit Boards Sales, Engineering & Service
N.A.I.C.S.: 334412
Janice Hock (Mgr-Customer Svc)

Nistec Design Ltd. (1)
43 Hasivim Street, Petah Tiqwa, 4817001, Israel
Tel.: (972) 3 929 2525
Electronics Design Services
N.A.I.C.S.: 541490

Nistec Golan Ltd. (1)
Kazerin Industrial Zone, Kazerin, Qatsrin, 12900, Israel
Tel.: (972) 73 268 8833
Web Site: http://www.nistec.com
Emp.: 100
Printed Circuit Assembly Mfr
N.A.I.C.S.: 334418
Rafi Abbasov (Plant Mgr)

Nistec Merkaz Ltd. (1)
43 Hasivim Street, Petah Tiqwa, 4917001, Israel
Tel.: (972) 3 929 2555
Electronic Assembly Mfr
N.A.I.C.S.: 334418
Elad Nissan (Plant Mgr)

Nistec Zafon Ltd. (1)
Galilee Industrial Zone West, Ma'alot-Tarshiha, 24952, Israel
Tel.: (972) 73 268 8899
Web Site: http://www.nistec.com
Emp.: 14
Surface Mount Electronics Assembly Services
N.A.I.C.S.: 334418
Waspy Armaz (Plant Mgr)

NISUN INTERNATIONAL ENTERPRISE DEVELOPMENT GROUP CO., LTD.
99 Danba Rd Bldg C9, Putuo District, Shanghai, China
Tel.: (86) 2123570055
Web Site: http://www.fintaike.com
Year Founded: 2012
NISN—(NASDAQ)
Rev.: $386,670,899
Assets: $315,898,834
Liabilities: $112,844,313
Net Worth: $203,054,521
Earnings: $17,703,680
Emp.: 206
Fiscal Year-end: 12/31/23
Pipe, Fitting & Valve Mfr & Distr
N.A.I.C.S.: 332919
Changjuan Liang (CFO)

NITCHITSU CO., LTD.
Akasaka 1chome Center Building 13F 11130 Akasaka, Minato-ku, Tokyo, 107-0052, Japan
Tel.: (81) 355616200
Web Site: https://www.nitchitsu.co.jp
Year Founded: 1950

7021—(TKS)
Rev.: $54,770,460
Assets: $101,503,160
Liabilities: $30,564,640
Net Worth: $70,938,520
Earnings: $1,632,670
Emp.: 276
Fiscal Year-end: 03/31/24
Industrial Equipment Mfr & Distr
N.A.I.C.S.: 333248

NITCO LTD.
Plot No 3 Nitco House Kanjur Village Road kanjur Marg East, Mumbai, 400 042, India
Tel.: (91) 2225772800
Web Site: https://www.nitco.in
Year Founded: 1996
NITCO—(NSE)
Rev.: $45,056,439
Assets: $125,992,448
Liabilities: $138,251,322
Net Worth: ($12,258,874)
Earnings: ($19,102,411)
Emp.: 524
Fiscal Year-end: 03/31/21
Ceramic & Marble Tile Mfr & Sales
N.A.I.C.S.: 327120
B. G. Borkar (CFO)

Subsidiaries:

Nitco Ltd - Alibaug Plant (1)
Village Shrigaon Post Poynad Taluka Alibag, Raigad Dist, Alibag, 402108, Maharashtra, India
Tel.: (91) 2141252278
Web Site: http://www.nitcotiles.com
Sales Range: $125-149.9 Million
Emp.: 500
Tiles Mfr
N.A.I.C.S.: 327120

Nitco Ltd - Nitco Marble Plant (1)
Nitco House Seth Govindram Jolly Marg, Kanjur Marg East, Mumbai, 400 042, Maharashtra, India
Tel.: (91) 2225772800
Web Site: http://www.nitco.in
Sales Range: $50-74.9 Million
Emp.: 50
Marbles Mfr
N.A.I.C.S.: 212319

NITERRA CO., LTD.
Urbannet Nagoya Nexta Bldg 1-1-1 Higashisakura, Higashi-ku, Nagoya, 461-0005, Japan
Tel.: (81) 522186095
Web Site: https://www.ngkntk.co.jp
Year Founded: 1936
5334—(TKS)
Rev.: $4,061,752,460
Assets: $6,449,502,590
Liabilities: $2,230,339,590
Net Worth: $4,219,163,000
Earnings: $546,290,060
Emp.: 15,980
Fiscal Year-end: 03/31/24
Automobile Related Products Mfr & Sales
N.A.I.C.S.: 332510
Shinichi Odo (Chm & Chm)

Subsidiaries:

Bujias NGK de Mexico S.A. de C.V. (1)
Carretera Lago de Guadalupe Km 27 5 S/N Lote 2 Bodega 3-A, Colonia San Pedro Barrientos, 54010, Tlalnepantla, Estado de Mexico, Mexico
Tel.: (52) 5553175872
Web Site: http://www.ngkntk.com.mx
Sales Range: $25-49.9 Million
Emp.: 15
Automobile Parts Distr
N.A.I.C.S.: 441330

CAIRE Inc. (1)
2200 Airport Industrial Dr Ste 500, Ball Ground, GA 30107
Tel.: (770) 721-7700

NITERRA CO., LTD.

Niterra Co., Ltd.—(Continued)

Web Site: http://www.cairemedical.com
Respiratory Care Solutions
N.A.I.C.S.: 339113
Brett Townsend (VP-Market Dev)

Subsidiary (Domestic):

AirSep Corporation (2)
260 Creekside Dr, Buffalo, NY 14228-2085
Tel.: (716) 691-0202
Web Site: http://www.chartindustires.com
Oxygen Generating System Mfr
N.A.I.C.S.: 333912

Chart SeQual Technologies, Inc. (2)
11436 Sorrento Valley Rd, San Diego, CA 92121
Tel.: (858) 202-3100
Web Site: http://www.sequal.com
Sales Range: $25-49.9 Million
Medical Oxygen Concentrator Mfr
N.A.I.C.S.: 339112

MGC Diagnostics Corporation (2)
350 Oak Grove Pkwy, Saint Paul, MN 55127-8599
Tel.: (651) 484-4874
Web Site: http://www.mgcdiagnostics.com
Sales Range: $25-49.9 Million
Cardiopulmonary Products Mfr
N.A.I.C.S.: 325412
Todd M. Austin (CEO)

Subsidiary (Domestic):

Medical Graphics Corp. (3)
350 Oak Grove Pkwy, Saint Paul, MN 55127
Tel.: (651) 484-4874
Web Site: http://www.medgraphics.com
Non-Invasive Computerized Diagnostic Systems
N.A.I.C.S.: 339112

Subsidiary (Non-US):

Medisoft SA (3)
Rue du Clairon 5, Sorinnes, 5503, Dinant, Belgium
Tel.: (32) 82223020
Web Site: https://mgcdiagnostics.com
Medical Equipment Mfr & Distr
N.A.I.C.S.: 334510

Cecylls Co., Ltd. (1)
382-1 Hattanda, Honjo, Komaki, 485-0821, Aichi, Japan
Tel.: (81) 56 848 7111
Automotive Sensor Mfr & Distr
N.A.I.C.S.: 336390

Ceramic Sensor Co., Ltd. (1)
391-5 Nakayokouchi Yokouchi, Komaki, 485-0781, Aichi, Japan
Tel.: (81) 568765400
Automotive Sensors Mfr
N.A.I.C.S.: 336390

Ceramica e Velas de Ignicao NGK do Brasil Ltda. (1)
Rodovia Professor Alfredo Rolim de Moura SP-88 km 61 s/n Cocuera, Mogi das Cruzes, 08880-900, Sao Paulo, Brazil
Tel.: (55) 1147938009
Web Site: http://www.ngkntk.com.br
Sales Range: $650-699.9 Million
Emp.: 1,300
Automotive Parts & Technical Ceramics Mfr & Distr
N.A.I.C.S.: 423120

Changshu NGK Spark Plug Co., Ltd. (1)
No 8 Xinhua Port Zone Avenue, Changshu Economic Technology Development Zone, Changshu, Jiangsu, China
Tel.: (86) 5125 226 0700
Automotive Sensor Mfr & Distr
N.A.I.C.S.: 336390

Chart BioMedical (Chengdu) Co., Ltd. (1)
No 48 Qingma Road Chengdu Modern Industrial Park, Pixian Chengdu, 611730, Sichuan, China
Tel.: (86) 2887805257
Liquid Nitrogen Container Research, Development & Production
N.A.I.C.S.: 541714

Maoqi Ran (Dir-HR)

Chart BioMedical Limited (1)
Unit 6 Ashville Way, Wokingham, RG41 2PL, Berkshire, United Kingdom
Tel.: (44) 1189367060
Industrial Gas Equipment Mfr
N.A.I.C.S.: 423830
Paul De Pledge (Sec)

Kamioka Ceramic Co., Ltd. (1)
1100 Azumo Kamiokacho, Hida, 506-1147, Gifu, Japan
Tel.: (81) 578821112
Glow Plugs & Cutting Tools Mfr
N.A.I.C.S.: 334515

Limited Liability Company NGK Spark Plugs (1)
Barklaya Street 6 str 3 of 2 02 Business Centre Barclay Park, 121087, Moscow, Russia
Tel.: (7) 4952690031
Automobile Component Distr
N.A.I.C.S.: 441330

Morimura Sofc Technology Co., Ltd. (1)
2808 Iwasaki, Komaki, 485-8510, Aichi, Japan
Tel.: (81) 56 876 5225
Automotive Sensor Mfr & Distr
N.A.I.C.S.: 336390

NGK Spark Plug (Australia) Pty Ltd. (1)
6 Kingston Park Court, Knoxfield, 3180, VIC, Australia
Tel.: (61) 397304900
Web Site: http://www.ngk.com.au
Sales Range: $25-49.9 Million
Emp.: 40
Spark Plugs Distr
N.A.I.C.S.: 423120

NGK Spark Plug (Shanghai) Co., Ltd. (1)
No 736 Songsheng Road, Songjiang Industrial Zone, Shanghai, 201613, China
Tel.: (86) 2167740987
Web Site: http://www.ngkntk.com.cn
Sales Range: $50-74.9 Million
Emp.: 300
Spark Plugs & Automotive Sensors Mfr & Sales
N.A.I.C.S.: 335999

NGK Spark Plug (Shanghai) Trading Co., Ltd. (1)
No 736 Songsheng Road, Songjiang Industrial Zone, Shanghai, 201613, China
Tel.: (86) 216 774 0987
Automotive Sensor Mfr & Distr
N.A.I.C.S.: 336390

NGK Spark Plug Co., Ltd. - Kagoshima-Miyanojo Factory (1)
2238-1 Tabaru Satsuma-cho, Satsuma-gun, Kagoshima, 895-1802, Japan
Tel.: (81) 996532211
Spark Plugs Mfr
N.A.I.C.S.: 336320

NGK Spark Plug Co., Ltd. - Komaki Factory (1)
2808 Iwasaki, Komaki, 485-8510, Aichi, Japan
Tel.: (81) 568761251
Sales Range: $800-899.9 Million
Emp.: 5,000
Semiconductor Parts Mfr
N.A.I.C.S.: 334413

NGK Spark Plug Europe GmbH (1)
Harkortstrasse 41, 40880, Ratingen, Germany
Tel.: (49) 2102974000
Web Site: https://www.ngkntk.com
Sales Range: $75-99.9 Million
Emp.: 200
Automobile Parts Mfr
N.A.I.C.S.: 423120

NGK Spark Plug Middle East FZE (1)
Office No 1219 1220, PB No 17859, JAFZA One, Dubai, United Arab Emirates
Tel.: (971) 48807244
Sales Range: $25-49.9 Million
Emp.: 16
Spark Plugs Sales

N.A.I.C.S.: 423120

NGK Spark Plugs (Asia) Co., Ltd. (1)
700/1006 Moo 9 Amata City Chonburi Industrial Estate Phase 10, Tambol MapPong Amphur Panthong, Chon Buri, 20160, Thailand
Tel.: (66) 3 810 9305
Web Site: https://ngk-sparkplugs.co.th
Spark Plug Mfr & Distr
N.A.I.C.S.: 334515

NGK Spark Plugs (France) S.A.S. (1)
Centre d'affaires la Boursidiere, Rue de la Boursidiere BP 130, 92357, Le Plessis-Robinson, Cedex, France
Tel.: (33) 155602700
Web Site: http://www.ngkntk.com
Sales Range: $25-49.9 Million
Emp.: 40
Automotive Components & Communication Media Components Whslr
N.A.I.C.S.: 423120

NGK Spark Plugs (India) Pvt. Ltd. (1)
502 Fifth Floor JMD Pacific Square Sector 15, 32nd Milestone National Highway 8, Gurgaon, 122001, Haryana, India
Tel.: (91) 12441 139 6062
Web Site: https://www.ngkntk.in
Automotive Sensor Mfr & Distr
N.A.I.C.S.: 336390

NGK Spark Plugs (Philippines), Inc. (1)
Unit 1207 12th Floor One World Place 32nd Street, Bonifacio Global City, Taguig, 1630, Metro Manila, Philippines
Tel.: (63) 288515106
Sales Range: $25-49.9 Million
Emp.: 6
Spark Plug Distr
N.A.I.C.S.: 336320

NGK Spark Plugs (Thailand) Co., Ltd. (1)
700/864 Moo 1 Amata City Chonburi Industrial Estate Phase 8, Tambol Panthong Amphur Panthong, Chon Buri, 20160, Thailand
Tel.: (66) 38185306
Sales Range: $25-49.9 Million
Emp.: 40
Automotive Components & Technical Ceramics Distr
N.A.I.C.S.: 423120

NGK Spark Plugs (U.K.) Ltd. (1)
Maylands Avenue, Hemel Hempstead, HP2 4SD, Herts, United Kingdom
Tel.: (44) 1442281000
Web Site: http://www.ngkntk.com
Sales Range: $25-49.9 Million
Emp.: 70
Automobile Parts Mfr
N.A.I.C.S.: 336320
Damien Germes (Sr VP-EMEA)

NGK Spark Plugs (U.S.A.), Inc. (1)
46929 Magellan Dr, Wixom, MI 48393
Tel.: (248) 926-6900
Sales Range: $50-74.9 Million
Emp.: 107
Spark Plugs Mfr
N.A.I.C.S.: 336320
Michael Schwab (Pres & CEO)

Plant (Domestic):

NGK Spark Plugs (U.S.A.), Inc. - West Virginia Factory (2)
1 NGK Dr, Sissonville, WV 25320
Tel.: (304) 988-0060
Web Site: http://ngksparkplugs.com
Spark Plugs & Automotive Sensors Mfr
N.A.I.C.S.: 336320

NGK Spark Plugs (Vietnam) Co., Ltd. (1)
Room 601 6th Floor 1060 Nguyen Van Linh Street, Tan Phong Ward District 7, Ho Chi Minh City, Vietnam
Tel.: (84) 283 939 0400
Web Site: https://www.ngkntk.com.vn
Spark Plug Mfr & Distr
N.A.I.C.S.: 334515

NGK Spark Plugs Canada Limited (1)

INTERNATIONAL PUBLIC

275 Renfrew Drive Suite 101, Markham, L3R 0C8, ON, Canada
Tel.: (905) 477-7780
Web Site: http://www.ngksparkplugs.ca
Sales Range: $25-49.9 Million
Emp.: 16
Automobile Parts Distr
N.A.I.C.S.: 441330
Toru Morimoto (Pres)

NGK Spark Plugs Malaysia Ber Had (1)
No 4586 Jalan Permatang Pauh, 13400, Butterworth, Penang, Malaysia
Tel.: (60) 4 332 7555
Web Site: https://ngk.com.my
Spark Plug Mfr & Distr
N.A.I.C.S.: 334515

NGK Spark Plugs SA (Pty) Ltd. (1)
Bantry Park 41 Jansen Road Jet Park, Boksburg, 1459, Gauteng, South Africa
Tel.: (27) 114187900
Web Site: http://www.ngksparkplugs.co.za
Sales Range: $50-74.9 Million
Emp.: 200
Spark Plugs Assembling & Marketing Services
N.A.I.C.S.: 336390
Alexander John Gibson (CEO)

NTK Ceramic Co., Ltd. (1)
2808 Iwasaki, Komaki, 485-8510, Aichi, Japan
Tel.: (81) 568664913
Web Site: http://www.ntktechnicalceramics.com
Emp.: 805
Semiconductors Components Mfr
N.A.I.C.S.: 441330

Subsidiary (Non-US):

NTK Technical Ceramics (Taiwan) Ltd. (2)
3F 102 Tun Hwa North Rd, Taipei, 10595, Taiwan
Tel.: (886) 227173483
Web Site: http://www.ngkntk.co.jp
Communication Media Components Distr
N.A.I.C.S.: 423690
Katsutoshi Umebayashi (Gen Mgr)

NTK Technical Ceramics Korea Co., Ltd. (2)
17 Bodem 6-ro, Seo-gu, Incheon, Korea (South)
Tel.: (82) 324566766
Web Site: http://www.knttool.co.kr
Automobile Parts Mfr
N.A.I.C.S.: 441330
Ogimoto Satinya (Gen Mgr)

Subsidiary (US):

NTK Technologies, Inc. (2)
3979 Freedom Cir Ste 400, Santa Clara, CA 95054
Tel.: (408) 727-5180
Web Site: https://www.ntktech.com
Sales Range: $25-49.9 Million
Emp.: 26
Electronic Components Mfr
N.A.I.C.S.: 334416
Paul Furuya (CEO)

NTK Ceratec Co., Ltd. (1)
3-24-1 Akedori, Izumi-ku, Sendai, 981-3292, Miyagi, Japan
Tel.: (81) 223789231
Emp.: 640
Engineering Ceramics Mfr
N.A.I.C.S.: 334419
Takahiro Suzuki (Pres)

Subsidiary (US):

Ceratec, Inc. (2)
2855 Kifer Rd Ste 215, Santa Clara, CA 95051
Tel.: (408) 567-0347
Web Site: http://www.ceratecinc.com
Sales Range: $10-24.9 Million
Ceramics for Electronics Industry
N.A.I.C.S.: 334413
Takashi Suzuki (Pres)

Nansei Ceramic Co., Ltd. (1)
871-6 Hosokoshi Enza-cho, Watarai-Gun, Ise, 516-1196, Mie, Japan

AND PRIVATE COMPANIES — NITRO CHEMICAL INDUSTRY LTD.

Tel.: (81) 596391690
Electronic Components Mfr
N.A.I.C.S.: 334416

Nichiwa Kiki Co., Ltd. (1)
3-3215 Tochi, Minato-ku, Nagoya, 455-0804, Aichi, Japan
Tel.: (81) 523820511
Automobile Parts Mfr
N.A.I.C.S.: 336390

Nittoku Alpha Service Co., Ltd. (1)
14-18 Takatsuji-cho, Mizuho-ku, Nagoya, 467-8525, Japan
Tel.: (81) 52 872 9989
Office Cleaning Services
N.A.I.C.S.: 561720

Nittoku Seisakusho Co., Ltd. (1)
2808 Iwasaki, Komaki, 485-8510, Aichi, Japan
Tel.: (81) 568769702
Sales Range: $50-74.9 Million
Emp.: 200
Spark Plugs Mfr
N.A.I.C.S.: 336320
Hitoshi Tsuji *(Mng Dir)*

Nittoku Smile Co., Ltd. (1)
2808 Iwasaki, Komaki, 485-8510, Aichi, Japan
Tel.: (81) 56 876 4784
Building Cleaning Services
N.A.I.C.S.: 561720

Nittoku Unyu Co., Ltd. (1)
164 Kamiyoshiike Mamaharashinden, Komaki, 485-0016, Aichi, Japan
Tel.: (81) 568739431
Web Site: http://www.ngkntk.co.jp
Transportation Services
N.A.I.C.S.: 541614

PT NGK Busi Indonesia (1)
Jl Raya Jakarta - Bogor Km 26 6, Jakarta, 13740, Indonesia
Tel.: (62) 21 871 0974
Web Site: https://www.ngkbusi.com
Spark Plug Mfr & Distr
N.A.I.C.S.: 334515

Sharing Factory Co., Ltd. (1)
1-8-23 Shinagawa Heart 13F, Konan Minato-ku, Tokyo, 108-8243, Japan
Tel.: (81) 34 500 1037
Web Site: https://sharingfactory.co.jp
Measuring Instruments Mfr
N.A.I.C.S.: 334515

Siam NGK Spark Plug Co., Ltd. (1)
700/864 Moo 1 Amata City Chonburi Industrial Estate Phase 8, Tambol Panthong Amphur Panthong, Chon Buri, 20160, Thailand
Tel.: (66) 38447155
Sales Range: $100-124.9 Million
Emp.: 300
Spark Plugs & Glow Plugs Mfr & Supplier
N.A.I.C.S.: 336320
Hiroyasu Ogura *(Co-Pres)*

SparkTec Tono Co., Ltd. (1)
2706-3 Minamiyama Nino, Kani, 509-0296, Gifu, Japan
Tel.: (81) 574 60 1350
Web Site: http://www.sparktec-tono.co.jp
Spark Plug Parts Mfr
N.A.I.C.S.: 336110

Sparktec Wks Co., Ltd. (1)
2808 Iwasaki, Komaki, 485-8510, Aichi, Japan
Tel.: (81) 56 876 9702
Web Site: https://sparktec-wks.co.jp
Spark Plug Product Mfr
N.A.I.C.S.: 334515

Taiwan NGK Spark Plug Co., Ltd. (1)
3F No 102 Dun Hua North Rd, Taipei, Taiwan
Tel.: (886) 227176750
Sales Range: $50-74.9 Million
Emp.: 8
Automobile Component Distr
N.A.I.C.S.: 423120

Wells Vehicle Electronics, L.P. (1)
385 W Rolling Meadows Dr, Fond Du Lac, WI 54937-4007
Tel.: (920) 922-5900
Sales Range: $150-199.9 Million
Emp.: 300
Motor Vehicle Electronics Mfr
N.A.I.C.S.: 336320
Matthew R. Wirth *(VP-HR & Gen Affairs)*

Subsidiary (Non-US):

Wells Manufacturing de Mexico S.A. de C.V. (2)
Carretera Laredo Km 9 Maquilpark, Reynosa, Tamaulipas, Mexico
Tel.: (52) 89 9924 9605
Web Site: http://www.wellsve.com
Sales Range: $75-99.9 Million
Emp.: 200
Motor Vehicle Electronics Mfr
N.A.I.C.S.: 336320

NITIN CASTINGS LIMITED
Prestige Precinct 3rd Floor Almeida Road, Panchpakhadi, Thane, 400 601, India
Tel.: (91) 2249748107
Web Site: https://www.nitincastings.com
Year Founded: 1964
508875—(BOM)
Rev.: $8,663,068
Assets: $9,119,019
Liabilities: $2,254,557
Net Worth: $6,864,462
Earnings: $444,549
Emp.: 139
Fiscal Year-end: 03/31/21
Alloy Steel Casting Mfr
N.A.I.C.S.: 331513
Nirmal B. Kedia *(Exec Dir)*

Subsidiaries:

Nitin Alloys Global Limited - Silvassa Works (1)
183/1 Village Surangi, Silvassa, 396 230, India
Tel.: (91) 260 269 9178
Alloy Steel Casting Mfr
N.A.I.C.S.: 331513

NITIN FIRE PROTECTION INDUSTRIES LTD
501 Delta Technology Street Hiranandani Gardens, Powai, Mumbai, 400 076, India
Tel.: (91) 2240457000
Web Site: https://www.nitinfire.com
532854—(BOM)
Sales Range: $125-149.9 Million
Emp.: 127
Fire Protection & Building Management
N.A.I.C.S.: 333414
Nitin M. Shah *(Chm)*

Subsidiaries:

Alert Fire Protection Systems Private Limited (1)
Ranade Rd PLKG Marg Popatlal Chawl, Dadar W, Navi Mumbai, 400705, Maharashtra, India
Tel.: (91) 2265106059
Web Site: http://www.nitinfire.com
Fire Safety Equipment Whslr
N.A.I.C.S.: 922160

Eurotech Cylinders Private Limited (1)
502 Delta Hiranandani Gardens, Tech St, Mumbai, 400 076, Maharashtra, India
Tel.: (91) 2266941030
Sales Range: $25-49.9 Million
Emp.: 45
Cylinder Mfr
N.A.I.C.S.: 333995

Logicon Building Systems Private Limited (1)
101 1st Fl Tulshi Shyam Apt Hwy Jct, 400604, Thane, Maharashtra, India
Tel.: (91) 2225838282
Sales Range: $50-74.9 Million
Emp.: 60
Fire Protection Services
N.A.I.C.S.: 922160

Nitin Cylinders Limited (1)
502 Delta Hiranandani Gardens, Tech St, Mumbai, 400 076, Maharashtra, India
Tel.: (91) 2247457000
Web Site: http://www.nitincylinders.com
Sales Range: $25-49.9 Million
Emp.: 45
Cylinder Mfr
N.A.I.C.S.: 333995
Kunal Shah *(Mgr)*

Nitin Ventures FZE (1)
FZS5 AD 01 02, PO Box 262294, Jebel Ali Free Zone, Dubai, United Arab Emirates
Tel.: (971) 48865858
Web Site: http://www.nitinventures.com
Sales Range: $50-74.9 Million
Emp.: 10
Fire Protection Services
N.A.I.C.S.: 922160

NITIN SPINNERS LIMITED
16-17 Km Stone Chittor Road, Hamirgarh Distt, Bhilwara, 311 025, Rajasthan, India
Tel.: (91) 1482286110
Web Site: https://www.nitinspinners.com
Year Founded: 1993
532698—(BOM)
Rev.: $288,953,528
Assets: $265,929,369
Liabilities: $142,567,328
Net Worth: $123,362,041
Earnings: $19,760,266
Emp.: 5,229
Fiscal Year-end: 03/31/23
Cotton Yarn Mfr
N.A.I.C.S.: 339999
Ratan Lal Nolkha *(Chm)*

NITIRAJ ENGINEERS LTD.
J25/26 MIDC Awdhan, Dhule, 424006, Maharashtra, India
Tel.: (91) 9325309664
Web Site: https://www.nitiraj.net
Year Founded: 1989
NITIRAJ—(NSE)
Rev.: $5,581,164
Assets: $9,570,709
Liabilities: $1,468,089
Net Worth: $8,102,620
Earnings: ($27,552)
Emp.: 259
Fiscal Year-end: 03/31/23
Electric Equipment Mfr
N.A.I.C.S.: 333998

NITOL INSURANCE COMPANY LIMITED
Police Plaza Concord Tower 2 6th Floor Plot 2 Road 144, Gulshan 1, Dhaka, 1212, Bangladesh
Tel.: (880) 255045202
Web Site: https://www.nitolinsurance.com
NITOLINS—(DHA)
Sales Range: $50-74.9 Million
Emp.: 181
General Insurance Services
N.A.I.C.S.: 524126
Md. Mominul Islam *(Mng Dir & Head-Bijoy Nagar Branch)*

NITORI HOLDINGS CO., LTD.
6-20 Kamiya 3-chome, Kita-ku, Tokyo, 115-0043, Japan
Tel.: (81) 367411235
Web Site: https://www.nitorihd.co.jp
Year Founded: 1967
9843—(SAP)
Rev.: $6,264,248,431
Assets: $7,491,053,849
Liabilities: $2,085,728,444
Net Worth: $5,405,325,405
Earnings: $628,536,505
Emp.: 37,329
Fiscal Year-end: 03/31/23
Holding Company
N.A.I.C.S.: 551112
Toshiyuki Shirai *(Pres & COO)*

Subsidiaries:

Home Deco Co., Ltd. (1)
435-2 Iizumi, Kazo, 349-1211, Saitama, Japan
Tel.: (81) 280611089
Web Site: https://home-deco.co.jp
Emp.: 136
Ready Made Curtain Mfr & Whslr
N.A.I.C.S.: 314120
Masanori Takeda *(Pres)*

Home Logistics Co., Ltd. (1)
Tel.: (81) 367411400
Web Site: http://www.homelogi.co.jp
Logistic Services
N.A.I.C.S.: 541614

NITORI Co., Ltd. (1)
No 6-20 Kamiya 3-chome, Kita-ku, Tokyo, 115-0043, Japan
Tel.: (81) 367411235
Web Site: https://www.nitori.co.jp
Emp.: 3,566
Household Furniture Distr
N.A.I.C.S.: 423210

NITORI FURNITURE VIETNAM Co., Ltd (1)
Quang Minh Industrial Zone, Me Linh District, Hanoi, Vietnam
Tel.: (84) 438182983
Emp.: 5,000
Household Furniture Mfr
N.A.I.C.S.: 337126

Nitori China Co., Ltd. (1)
Rm C-F 5th Fl No 1990 Longyang Rd Pudong New Area, Shanghai, 200052, China
Tel.: (86) 2161604600
Sales Range: $25-49.9 Million
Emp.: 4
Household Furniture Distr
N.A.I.C.S.: 423210

Nitori USA, Inc. (1)
4655 Mills Cir, Ontario, CA 91764
Web Site: http://www.aki-home.com
Home Furniture Distr
N.A.I.C.S.: 449110
Akio Nitori *(Founder & Chm)*

Siam Nitori Co., Ltd. (1)
576 Moo 4, Bangpoo Industrial Estate Soi11 Praeksa Muang, Samut Prakan, Thailand
Tel.: (66) 232406702
Web Site: https://www.siam-nitori.com
Polyester Fiber Mfr
N.A.I.C.S.: 325220
Masanori Takeda *(Chm)*

NITRATOS DE CHILE SA
El Trovador 4285 Piso 11, Las Condes, Chile
Tel.: (56) 24294901
Financial Investment Services
N.A.I.C.S.: 523999
Ricardo Moreno *(CEO)*

NITRO CHEMICAL INDUSTRY LTD.
84/2 Moo 4 KM 40 Rama 2, Bangtorad, Mueang Samut Sakhon, 74000, Samut Sakhon, Thailand
Tel.: (66) 3483 9467 TH
Web Site: http://www.nitrochemical.com
Year Founded: 1982
Nitrocellulose Mfr
N.A.I.C.S.: 325211
John Hardy *(Engr)*

Subsidiaries:

Nobel NC Company Limited (1)
24 Rama 1 Road Rongmuang, Pathumwan, Bangkok, 10330, Thailand
Tel.: (66) 26138923
Web Site: https://www.nobelnc.com
Nitrocellulose Mfr
N.A.I.C.S.: 325211

NITRO CHEMICAL INDUSTRY LTD.

Nitro Chemical Industry Ltd.—(Continued)

Subsidiary (Non-US):

Nobel NC Europe Ltd. (2)
Elliott House Kilwinning Rd, Irvine, KA12 8TG, Ayrshire, United Kingdom
Tel.: (44) 1294315243
Sales Range: $25-49.9 Million
Emp.: 9
Nitrocellulose Sales
N.A.I.C.S.: 424950
Don Beck (Mng Dir)

NITTA CORPORATION

4-4-26 Sakuragawa Naniwa-ku, Osaka, 556-0022, Japan
Tel.: (81) 665631211
Year Founded: 1885
5186—(TKS)
Rev.: $585,705,490
Assets: $1,120,421,440
Liabilities: $181,728,730
Net Worth: $938,692,710
Earnings: $65,154,770
Emp.: 2,952
Fiscal Year-end: 03/31/24
Belting & Rubber Mfr
N.A.I.C.S.: 326220
Takeshi Kobayashi (Sr Mng Exec Officer)

Subsidiaries:

Ashihara Driving School Company (1)
1-12-23 Naniwa Nishi, Naniwa-ku, Osaka, 556-0026, Japan
Tel.: (81) 665620771
Web Site: https://www.ashihara-ds.co.jp
Emp.: 100
Driving Training Services
N.A.I.C.S.: 611692

Connect Conveyor Belting Inc. (1)
405 Industrial Drive Units 1-8, Milton, L9T 5B1, ON, Canada
Tel.: (905) 878-5552
Web Site: http://www.connectbelting.com
Conveyor Belt Fabricator Mfr
N.A.I.C.S.: 333922

Gates Unitta Asia Company (1)
4-26 Sakuragawa 4-chome, Naniwa-ku, Osaka, 556-0022, Japan
Tel.: (81) 665631284
Web Site: http://www.unitta.co.jp
Automobile Parts Mfr
N.A.I.C.S.: 336390

KANSAIKAKO CO., LTD. (1)
9-9 Hiroshima-Ku, Nagata-ku, Suita, 564-0052, Osaka, Japan
Tel.: (81) 661925830
Web Site: https://kansaikako.co.jp
Industrial Driving Belts Whslr
N.A.I.C.S.: 423840

KOREA NITTA MOORE CORP (1)
53 Suchul-daero 5-gil, Gumi, 39266, Gyeongsangbuk-do, Korea (South)
Tel.: (82) 544615575
Web Site: http://www.nitta.co.kr
Plastic Hoses Mfr & Distr
N.A.I.C.S.: 326220

Morimitsu Industries Company (1)
3-3-5 Misono 9-jo, Toyohira-ku, Sapporo, 062-0009, Hokkaido, Japan
Tel.: (81) 118120497
Web Site: https://www.morimitu.net
Emp.: 25
Air Filter Distr
N.A.I.C.S.: 423730

NITTA (SHANGHAI) MANAGEMENT CO., LTD (1)
Room2705 Shenggao International Building No 137 Xianxia Road, Changning District, Shanghai, 200051, China
Tel.: (86) 2162296000
Conveyor Belt & Plastic Hose Distr
N.A.I.C.S.: 424610

NITTA CORPORATION INDIA PVT LTD (1)
Gat No 191 192 193-Plot B Village Vadhu Khurd, Taluka Haveli, Pune, 412216, Maharashtra, India
Tel.: (91) 2067313400
Web Site: https://nitta.co.in
Conveyor Belt & Plastic Hose Distr
N.A.I.C.S.: 424610
Vishwanath Labhade (Asst Mgr-Production)

NITTA CORPORATION OF CHANGZHOU
No 1 Ivshu East Road, XueJia XinBei District, Changzhou, 213132, Jiangsu, China
Tel.: (86) 51985166509
Transmission & Conveyor Belt Mfr
N.A.I.C.S.: 326220

NITTA DuPont Incorporated (1)
4-4-26 Sakuragawa, Naniwa-ku, Osaka, 556-0022, Japan (50%)
Tel.: (81) 665631291
Web Site: https://www.nittadupont.co.jp
Emp.: 300
Organic Chemical Product Whslr
N.A.I.C.S.: 424690
Mitsutaka Chiba (Pres & CEO)

NITTA MOORE TECHNOLOGY (CHANGZHOU) CO., LTD (1)
No 21 Syunyun Rd, Xinbei District, Changzhou, 213022, Jiangsu, China
Tel.: (86) 51988222800
Web Site: http://www.cn-nittamoore.com
Plastic Hose Mfr & Distr
N.A.I.C.S.: 326220

NITTA TECHNO COMPANY (1)
2-10-10 Kasumi, Minami-ku, Hiroshima, 734-0037, Japan
Tel.: (81) 822519191
Industrial Driving Belts Whslr
N.A.I.C.S.: 423840

Naniwa Rubber Co., Ltd. (1)
2-6-1 Soone, Yamatotakada, 635-8520, Nara, Japan
Tel.: (81) 745525681
Web Site: http://www.naniwa-rubber.com
Rubber Products Mfr
N.A.I.C.S.: 326299
Yasuhiro Aoki (Pres)

Nitta Air Solutions Company (1)
1-1-8 Nihonbashihoncho, Chuo- ku, Tokyo, 103-0023, Japan
Tel.: (81) 332417188
Web Site: https://www.nitta-air-solutions.co.jp
Air Conditioning Equipment Mfr
N.A.I.C.S.: 333415

Nitta Asocio Company (1)
172 Ikezawa-cho, Yamato-koriyama, 639-1085, Nara, Japan
Tel.: (81) 743561820
Power Transmission & Conveyor Belt Mfr
N.A.I.C.S.: 326220

Nitta Chemical Industrial Products Co., Ltd. (1)
Nitta Bldg 4-4-26 Sakuragawa, Naniwa-ku, Osaka, 556-0022, Japan
Tel.: (81) 665631200
Web Site: https://www.nitta-ci.com
Rail Vehicle Parts Mfr & Distr
N.A.I.C.S.: 336510
Keiji Yoshimura (Chm)

Nitta Corporation (Thailand) Limited (1)
7/472 Moo 6 Tambol Mabyangporn, Amphur, Pluak Daeng, 21140, Rayong, Thailand
Tel.: (66) 38018301
Web Site: https://www.nittathai.com
Hydraulic Hose & Tube Product Distr
N.A.I.C.S.: 423840

Nitta Corporation - Kochi Plant (1)
6th TechnoPark, Tosayamada, Kami, 782-0010, Kochi, Japan
Tel.: (81) 88752337
Web Site: http://www.nitta.co.jp
Belting Products Mfr
N.A.I.C.S.: 326220

Nitta Corporation - Nabari Plant (1)
1300-45 Yabata, Nabari, 518-0494, Mie, Japan
Tel.: (81) 595642921
Machine Tools Mfr
N.A.I.C.S.: 333515

Nitta Corporation - Nara Plant (1)
172 Ikezawa-cho, Yamato-koriyama, 639-1085, Nara, Japan
Tel.: (81) 74356581
Sales Range: $200-249.9 Million
Emp.: 2,000
Conveyor Belts Mfr
N.A.I.C.S.: 326220

Nitta Corporation of America (1)
7605 Nitta Dr, Suwanee, GA 30024
Tel.: (770) 497-0212
Industrial Bearings Distr
N.A.I.C.S.: 423840

Nitta Corporation of Holland B.V. (1)
Berenkoog 25, 1822 BH, Alkmaar, Netherlands
Tel.: (31) 725622234
Sales Range: $25-49.9 Million
Emp.: 50
Conveyor Belts Mfr & Whslr
N.A.I.C.S.: 326220
Hans Froberg (Sls Mgr)

Nitta Corporation of Singapore Pte. Ltd. (1)
120 Lower Delta Road Cendex Centre 05-07/08, Singapore, 169208, Singapore
Tel.: (65) 64388738
Web Site: https://www.nitta.com.sg
Sales Range: $25-49.9 Million
Emp.: 7
Conveyor Belts & Transmission Belts Mfr & Distr
N.A.I.C.S.: 326220

Nitta Do Brazil (1)
Rua Francisco Mommenshon 50B Galpao 02, Laranjeiras, Caieiras, 07743-150, Sao Paulo, Brazil
Tel.: (55) 1144412922
Web Site: http://www.nitta.com.br
Power Transmission Equipment Distr
N.A.I.C.S.: 423830

Nitta Industries Europe GmbH (1)
Heerdter Lohweg 35, 40549, Dusseldorf, Germany
Tel.: (49) 2115375350
Web Site: https://www.nitta.de
Sales Range: $25-49.9 Million
Emp.: 30
Conveyor Belts Mfr
N.A.I.C.S.: 333922

Nitta Mechatronics (Changzhou) Co., Ltd. (1)
15B GDH No 388 Huanghe West Road, Changzhou Airport Industrial Park XinBei District, Changzhou, 213133, Jiangsu, China
Tel.: (86) 51969881818
Power Transmission & Conveyor Belt Mfr
N.A.I.C.S.: 326220

Nitta Moore (Guangzhou) Tube Co., Ltd. (1)
2F 2Building No 257 Junye Road, Eastern Zone of Guangzhou Economic & Technological Development Dist, Guangzhou, 510530, China
Tel.: (86) 2082265087
Power Transmission & Conveyor Belt Mfr
N.A.I.C.S.: 326220

Nitta Moore Company (1)
4-4-26 Sakuragawa, Naniwa-ku, Osaka, 556-0022, Japan
Tel.: (81) 665631270
Web Site: http://www.nitta.co.jp
Hose & Tube Products Mfr
N.A.I.C.S.: 326220

Nitta Moore Mexico S. De R.L. De C.V. (1)
Carretera San Luis Villa de Arriaga KM 6 L2820, La Pila, 78480, San Luis Potosi, Mexico
Tel.: (52) 4447997225
Power Transmission & Conveyor Belt Mfr
N.A.I.C.S.: 326220

Nitta Ranch Corporation (1)
115 Shinmachi Makubetsu-cho, Nakagawa-gun, Hokkaido, 089-0611, Japan
Tel.: (81) 155542207
Web Site: https://www.nittagroup.com
Cattle Breeding & Ranching Services
N.A.I.C.S.: 112111

INTERNATIONAL PUBLIC

Nitta Techno Solutions Company (1)
3-1-23 Nishijiriike-cho, Nagata-ku, Kobe, 653-0031, Japan
Tel.: (81) 786110011
Web Site: https://www.nittats.co.jp
Mechatronics Equipment Mfr & Distr
N.A.I.C.S.: 333248

POWER TECHNO CO., LTD. (1)
4-21-20 Shinkoiwa, Katsushika-ku, Tokyo, 124-0024, Japan
Tel.: (81) 336743991
Web Site: https://www.powertechno.co.jp
Industrial Driving Belts Whslr
N.A.I.C.S.: 423840

SANYU Industry (Hong Kong) Company Limited (1)
17 Floor Tins Enterprises Centre 777 Lai Chi Kok Road, Cheung Sha Wan, Kowloon, China (Hong Kong)
Tel.: (852) 24079829
Sales Range: $25-49.9 Million
Emp.: 15
Tobacco Manufacturing Equipment Whslr
N.A.I.C.S.: 333248

Taiwan Nitta Filter Co., Ltd. (1)
Chia Hsin Building 10 TFL Room No 1005 96 Chung shan N Rd Sec 2, Taipei, 104, Taiwan
Tel.: (886) 225816296
Web Site: https://www.nitta.com.tw
Sales Range: $25-49.9 Million
Emp.: 50
Air Filter Equipment Mfr
N.A.I.C.S.: 333413
Watanabe Koichi (Pres)

Plant (Domestic):

Taiwan Nitta Filter Co., Ltd. - Pinchen Factory (2)
2-1 Industrial 2nd Rd Pinchen Industrial Park, Taoyuan, 324, ROC, Taiwan
Tel.: (886) 346975513
Web Site: http://www.nitta.com.tw
Emp.: 50
Air Filters Mfr
N.A.I.C.S.: 336390
Watanabe Koichi (Pres)

NITTA GELATIN INC.

2-22 Futamata, Yao-city, Osaka, 581-0024, Japan
Tel.: (81) 729495381
Web Site: https://www.nitta-gelatin.co.jp
Year Founded: 1918
4977—(TKS)
Rev.: $267,176,200
Assets: $264,148,820
Liabilities: $116,950,730
Net Worth: $147,198,090
Earnings: ($12,228,500)
Emp.: 946
Fiscal Year-end: 03/31/24
Gelatin Mfr
N.A.I.C.S.: 311999
Takeo Yamaki (Mng Exec Officer)

Subsidiaries:

Nitta Biolab Inc. (1)
4-4-26 Sakuragawa, Naniwa-ku, Osaka, 556-0022, Japan
Tel.: (81) 6 6563 1501
Web Site: http://www.nitta-biolab.co.jp
Food Supplements & Cosmetic Products Distr
N.A.I.C.S.: 456191

Nitta Gelatin Canada Inc. (1)
60 Paton Rd, Toronto, M6H 1R8, ON, Canada
Tel.: (416) 532-5111
Gelatin Mfr
N.A.I.C.S.: 325998

Nitta Gelatin Inc. - NARA PLANT (1)
1596-9 Yuzaki Kawanishi-cho, Shiki-gun, Nara, 636-0202, Japan
Tel.: (81) 745 44 1788
Web Site: https://www.nitta-gelatin.co.jp
Gelatin Products Mfr
N.A.I.C.S.: 311999

AND PRIVATE COMPANIES

Nitta Gelatin Inc. - OSAKA PLANT (1)
22 Futamata 2-chome, Yao, 581-0024, Osaka, Japan
Tel.: (81) 72 949 5381
Web Site: http://www.nitta-gelatin.co.jp
Gelatin Products Mfr
N.A.I.C.S.: 311999

Nitta Gelatin NA Inc. (1)
598 Airport Blvd Ste 900, Morrisville, NC 27560
Tel.: (919) 238-3300
Gelatin & Pharmaceutical Products Mfr
N.A.I.C.S.: 325998

Nitta Gelatin USA Inc. (1)
4341 Production Dr, Fayetteville, NC 28306-9513
Tel.: (910) 484-0457
Chemical Products Mfr
N.A.I.C.S.: 325998

Shanghai Nitta Gelatin Co., Ltd. (1)
Bldg 41 888 Shuangbai Road, Minhang Dist, Shanghai, 201108, China
Tel.: (86) 21 5406 8762
Sales Range: $25-49.9 Million
Emp.: 2
Gelatin Products Distr
N.A.I.C.S.: 311999
Yuki Aka *(Gen Mgr)*

Shinju Service Co., Ltd. (1)
1546-4 Kagawa, Yamaguchi, 754-0897, Japan
Tel.: (81) 729488275
Building Equipment Maintenance Services
N.A.I.C.S.: 811310

NITTA GELATIN INDIA LIMITED
54/1446 SBT Avenue Panampilly Nagar, Cochin, 682 036, India
Tel.: (91) 4842864400
Web Site: https://www.gelatin.in
Year Founded: 1975
506532—(BOM)
Rev.: $54,284,740
Assets: $41,833,046
Liabilities: $17,818,382
Net Worth: $24,014,663
Earnings: $2,447,158
Emp.: 465
Fiscal Year-end: 03/31/21
Pharmeceutical Raw Material Mfr
N.A.I.C.S.: 325412
G. Rajesh Kurup *(Compliance Officer & Sec)*

Subsidiaries:

Bamni Proteins Ltd. (1)
PO Dudholi-Bamni Via, Ballarpur, Chandrapur, 442 701, Maharashtra, India
Tel.: (91) 7172297676
Web Site: https://www.bamniproteins.com
Chemicals Mfr
N.A.I.C.S.: 325998

NITTAN CORPORATION
518 Soya, Hadano, 257-0031, Kanagawa, Japan
Tel.: (81) 463821311
Web Site: https://www.niv.co.jp
Year Founded: 1948
6493—(TKS)
Rev.: $327,049,580
Assets: $416,304,410
Liabilities: $171,436,960
Net Worth: $244,867,450
Earnings: $3,972,610
Fiscal Year-end: 03/31/24
Engine Valves for Internal Combustion Engines
N.A.I.C.S.: 336310
Toshimichi Kimbara *(Pres)*

Subsidiaries:

KN-Tech Co., Ltd. (1)
502-14 Iryeon-ro, Jinryang-eup, Gyeongsan, 38498, Gyeongbuk, Korea (South)
Tel.: (82) 538511390
Marine Engine Valve Mfr & Distr
N.A.I.C.S.: 332911

Nittan (Thailand) Co., Ltd. (1)
700/44 Moo 6 Bangna-trad Rd, Amata City Industrial Estate Donhuaroh, Amphur Muang, 20000, Chonburi, Thailand
Tel.: (66) 387434869
Web Site: https://www.nittan.co.th
Engine Valve Mfr
N.A.I.C.S.: 332911

Nittan Euro Tech Sp. z o.o. (1)
Ul Rudawka 83, Bielsko-Biala, Poland
Tel.: (48) 334993872
Web Site: https://www.nittaneurotech.com
Valve Mfr
N.A.I.C.S.: 332911

Nittan Global Tech Co., Ltd. (1)
Nomura Fudosan Nishi Shinjuku Bldg 2F 8-4-2, Nishi-Shinjuku Shinjuku-ku, Tokyo, 160-0023, Japan
Tel.: (81) 353373248
Valve Mfr
N.A.I.C.S.: 332911
Hiroshi Ono *(Auditor)*

Nittan India Tech Pvt. Ltd. (1)
No 495 Benjamin Road Sector 24, Sri City Tada Varadaiahpalem Mandal, Chittoor, 517 588, Andhra Pradesh, India
Tel.: (91) 8623392222
Engine Valve Mfr & Distr
N.A.I.C.S.: 332911

Nittan Korea Co., Ltd. (1)
560 Samsung-ro, Gangnam-gu, Seoul, 06150, Korea (South)
Tel.: (82) 25651516
Engine Valve Mfr & Distr
N.A.I.C.S.: 332911

Nittan Vietnam Co., Ltd. (1)
No 6 Street15, VSIP Bac Ninh, Tu Son, Bac Ninh, Vietnam
Tel.: (84) 2223765300
Engine Valve Mfr & Distr
N.A.I.C.S.: 332911

PT. Federal Nittan Industries (1)
Jl Halmahera Blok DD-9 Danau Indah, Kawasan Industri MM2100 Cikarang Barat, Bekasi, 17520, Indonesia
Tel.: (62) 218980452
Web Site: http://www.federalnittan.com
Engine Valve Mfr
N.A.I.C.S.: 332911

Rizhao Nittan Valve Co., Ltd. (1)
No 79 Shantou Road, Rizhao, 276826, Shandong, China
Tel.: (86) 6332180777
Engine Valve Mfr & Distr
N.A.I.C.S.: 332911

Rizhao SP Automobile Parts Co., Ltd. (1)
Quanzhou Road No 95, Rizhao, 276800, Shandong, China
Tel.: (86) 6332959678
Valve Lifter Mfr & Distr
N.A.I.C.S.: 332911

Shinhwa Precision Co., Ltd (1)
110-14 Cheomdangieop 5-ro Sandongmyeon, Dalseo-gu, Gumi, 39171, Gyeongsangbuk-do, Korea (South)
Tel.: (82) 546028127
Web Site: http://www.shinhwa.com
Converted Paper Product Mfr
N.A.I.C.S.: 322299

Shinhwa Takahashi Press Co., Ltd. (1)
110-7 Cheomdangieop 5ro Sandong-Myeon, Gumi, 39171, Gyeongsangbuk-do, Korea (South)
Tel.: (82) 546045532
Valve Lifter Raw Material Mfr & Distr
N.A.I.C.S.: 332911

Shune365 Co., Ltd. (1)
183-10 Hirasawa, Hadano, 257-0015, Kanagawa, Japan
Tel.: (81) 463821831
Web Site: https://www.shune365.co.jp
Emp.: 10
Vegetable Product Mfr & Distr
N.A.I.C.S.: 311411

Taiwan Nittan Industrial Co., Ltd. (1)
No 729 Changxing Rd, Bade Dist, Taoyuan, 33453, Taiwan

Tel.: (886) 33651120
Sales Range: $50-74.9 Million
Emp.: 125
Carburetor Piston Piston Ring & Valve Mfr
N.A.I.C.S.: 336310

U.S. Engine Valve Corporation (1)
7039 S Hwy 11, Westminster, SC 29693
Tel.: (864) 647-2061
Web Site: https://www.usenginevalve.com
Sales Range: $75-99.9 Million
Emp.: 400
Engine Valve Mfr
N.A.I.C.S.: 336310

NITTETSU MINING CO., LTD.
Yusen Bldg 3-2 Marunouchi 2-chome, Chiyoda-ku, Tokyo, 100-8377, Japan
Tel.: (81) 332840516
Web Site: https://www.nittetsukou.co.jp
1515—(TKS)
Rev.: $1,103,103,240
Assets: $1,517,503,970
Liabilities: $521,231,550
Net Worth: $996,272,420
Earnings: $43,639,220
Emp.: 2,155
Fiscal Year-end: 03/31/24
Mining & Mineral Resources Sales
N.A.I.C.S.: 212323
Shinya Yamasaki *(Mng Dir)*

Subsidiaries:

AI United Engineering Inc. (1)
1388-1 Yuzukimachi, Sasebo, 857-0112, Nagasaki, Japan
Tel.: (81) 956461121
Construction Consulting Services
N.A.I.C.S.: 541330

Atetsu Lime Co., Ltd. (1)
527-1 Ikura, Niimi, Okayama, Japan
Tel.: (81) 867752401
Quicklime Product Mfr & Distr
N.A.I.C.S.: 327410

Compania Minera Arqueros S.A. (1)
Ruta D-43 901 office 602, Industrial District, Coquimbo, Chile
Tel.: (56) 512427000
Web Site: https://mineraarqueros.cl
Copper Product Mfr
N.A.I.C.S.: 331420

Funao Mining Co., Ltd. (1)
2803-1 Yugeta, Tagawa, Fukuoka, Japan
Tel.: (81) 947420180
Calcium Carbonate Mfr & Distr
N.A.I.C.S.: 327410

Hachinohe Mining Co., Ltd. (1)
9-1 Nagasaka Oaza Matsudate, Hachinohe, 031-0815, Aomori Prefecture, Japan
Tel.: (81) 178254033
Web Site: https://www.hachinohekouzan.co.jp
Emp.: 127
Limestone Distr
N.A.I.C.S.: 424910

Hokkaido Lime Co., Ltd. (1)
3-2-12 Omotemachi, Tomakomai, 053-0022, Japan
Tel.: (81) 144327522
Web Site: https://www.h-sekkaikakou.co.jp
Emp.: 40
Lime Product Distr
N.A.I.C.S.: 423320

Kaho Manufacturing Co., Ltd. (1)
Oita 567, Iizuka, 820-0712, Fukuoka, Japan
Tel.: (81) 948720390
Web Site: http://www.kaho-monorail.com
Industrial Machinery & Electrical Equipment Mfr
N.A.I.C.S.: 333248

Kamaishi Kozan Co., Ltd. (1)
238 3rd Lot, Koshi-cho, Kamaishi, 026-0055, Iwate, Japan
Tel.: (81) 193592221
Web Site: https://www.sennin-hisui.com
Mineral Spring Water Mfr & Distr
N.A.I.C.S.: 312112

Kirishima Geothermal Co., Ltd. (1)

NITTETSU MINING CO., LTD.

1468-45 Gin-yu Manzen Makizono-cho, Kirishima, Kagoshima, Japan
Tel.: (81) 995741400
Geothermal Steam Distribution Services
N.A.I.C.S.: 221330

Kobukuro Techno Co., Ltd. (1)
958-23 Ariyasu, Iizuka, 820-0111, Fukuoka, Japan
Tel.: (81) 948823907
Web Site: https://www.kobukuro.co.jp
Crushing Machine Mfr & Distr
N.A.I.C.S.: 333120

Kuzuu Limestone Aggregate Co., Ltd. (1)
1599 Senba-cho, Sano, Tochigi, Japan
Tel.: (81) 283853715
Limestone Mfr
N.A.I.C.S.: 327410

Nippon Ball Valve Co., Ltd. (1)
5-650 Otoriminamimachi, Nishi-ku, Sakai, 593-8325, Osaka-fu, Japan
Tel.: (81) 722718421
Web Site: https://www.nbv.co.jp
Ball Valve Mfr & Distr
N.A.I.C.S.: 332911
Yuji Tanimura *(Pres & CEO)*

Nittetsu Mining Consultants Co., Ltd. (1)
2-3-2 Marunouchi, Chiyoda-ku, Tokyo, 100-0005, Japan
Tel.: (81) 364142760
Web Site: https://www.nmconsults.co.jp
Emp.: 179
Construction Consulting Services
N.A.I.C.S.: 541330
Shinichiro Okaku *(Pres & CEO)*

Nittetsukou (Shanghai) Co., Ltd. (1)
Room A1101 Oriental International Building No 85 Loushanguan Road, Changning District, Shanghai, China
Tel.: (86) 2162754538
Web Site: http://www.nittetsukou.cn
Machinery Equipment Distr
N.A.I.C.S.: 423830

Nittetsukou Donan Kohatsu Co., Ltd. (1)
64-3 Irie Toyakocho, Abuta-gun, Hokkaido, Japan
Tel.: (81) 142763121
Web Site: http://www.donankohatsu.com
Fresh Concrete Mfr & Distr
N.A.I.C.S.: 327320

Nittetsukoukenzai Co., Ltd. (1)
1-18 Samoncho, Shinjuku-ku, Tokyo, 160-0017, Japan
Tel.: (81) 333515146
Web Site: https://www.nittetsukoukenzai.co.jp
Crushed Stone Distr
N.A.I.C.S.: 423320

Shinwa Shoji Kaisha Ltd. (1)
666 Edakuni, Iizuka, 820-0081, Fukuoka, Japan
Tel.: (81) 948220644
Web Site: https://www.shinwashoji.co.jp
Emp.: 85
Petroleum Distr
N.A.I.C.S.: 486910
Yasuda Seiji *(CFO & Auditor)*

Sociedad Contractual Minera Atacama Kozan S.A. (1)
Parcela Los Olivos S N - Punta Del Cobre, Tierra Amarilla, Copiapo, Chile
Tel.: (56) 52203800
Sales Range: $100-124.9 Million
Emp.: 250
Copper Ore Mining Services
N.A.I.C.S.: 212230

Tamano Refinery, Hibi Kyodo Smelting Co., Ltd. (1)
6-1-1 Hibi, Tamano, Okayama, Japan
Tel.: (81) 863818045
Nonmetallic Mineral Mining Services
N.A.I.C.S.: 212312

Tsukumi Cooperative Mining Co., Ltd. (1)
7-6 Kozono-machi, Tsukumi, Oita, Japan
Tel.: (81) 972823754
Limestone Mining Contracting Services

NITTETSU MINING CO., LTD.

Nittetsu Mining Co., Ltd.—(Continued)
N.A.I.C.S.: 212312

Tsukumi Limestone Co., Ltd. (1)
7-6 Kozono-machi, Tsukumi, Oita, Japan
Tel.: (81) 972824131
Limestone Mfr
N.A.I.C.S.: 327410

Tsukumi Vehicle Repair Co., Ltd. (1)
2-15 Jizo-machi, Tsukumi, Oita, Japan
Tel.: (81) 972822117
Vehicle Distr
N.A.I.C.S.: 423110

Yaguki Aggregate Co., Ltd. (1)
14-1 Aza Motomura Yotsukura-machi, Tamayama, Iwaki, Fukushima, Japan
Tel.: (81) 246332321
Gravel Distr
N.A.I.C.S.: 423320

Youra Silicastone Co., Ltd. (1)
7-6 Kozono-machi, Tsukumi, Oita, Japan
Tel.: (81) 972849349
Silica Distr
N.A.I.C.S.: 424690

NITTO BOSEKI CO., LTD.
2-4-1 Kojimachi, Chiyoda-ku, Tokyo, 102-8489, Japan
Tel.: (81) 345825111 JP
Web Site: https://www.nittobo.co.jp
Year Founded: 1923
3110—(TKS)
Rev.: $616,402,330
Assets: $1,402,060,320
Liabilities: $584,357,050
Net Worth: $817,703,270
Earnings: $48,226,560
Emp.: 2,690
Fiscal Year-end: 03/31/24
Yarn Spinning Mills
N.A.I.C.S.: 313110
Yuichi Tsuji (CEO)

Subsidiaries:

Baotek Industrial Materials Ltd. (1)
No 277 Minfeng Rd, Yangmei, Taoyuan, 326, Taiwan
Tel.: (886) 34754728
Web Site: http://www.baotek.com.tw
Fiberglass Fabric Mfr
N.A.I.C.S.: 313210

Nitto Beverage Co., Ltd. (1)
500 Hirayanagi, Asahi-cho Shimoniikawa-gun, Toyama, 939-0744, Japan
Tel.: (81) 765821133
Web Site: https://nitto-beverage.com
Sales Range: $25-49.9 Million
Emp.: 79
Soft Drinks Mfr & Sales
N.A.I.C.S.: 312111

Nitto Boseki Co., Ltd. - Building Materials Division (1)
4-1-28 Kudan-Kita, Chiyoda-ku, Tokyo, 102-8489, Japan
Tel.: (81) 335148828
Web Site: http://www.nittobo.com
Building Materials Mfr
N.A.I.C.S.: 332311

Nitto Boseki Co., Ltd. - Chiba Factory (1)
Roppocho 210, Inage-ku, Chiba, 263 0004, Japan
Tel.: (81) 43 424 8006
Fiber Glass Mfr
N.A.I.C.S.: 327212

Nitto Boseki Co., Ltd. - Fukushima No.1 Factory (1)
1 Aza Higashi Gonome, Fukushima, 960-8581, Japan
Tel.: (81) 245463131
Web Site: http://www.nittobo.com
Fiber Glass Mfr
N.A.I.C.S.: 327212

Nitto Boseki Co., Ltd. - Fukushima No.2 Factory (1)
20 Ipponsugi Sakurashimo, Fukushima, 960-2154, Japan
Tel.: (81) 245931231

Web Site: http://www.nittobo.co.jp
Fiberglass Materials Mfr
N.A.I.C.S.: 327212

Nitto Boseki Co., Ltd. - New Business Operation & Promotion Division (1)
3-2-11 Kudan-Kita, Chiyoda-ku, Tokyo, 102-0073, Japan
Tel.: (81) 335143738
Web Site: http://www.nittobo.co.jp
Business Research & Development Services
N.A.I.C.S.: 541720

Nitto Boseki Co., Ltd. - Specialty Chemicals Division (1)
Kudan Ist Pl 4-1-28 Kudan-kita, Chiyoda-ku, Tokyo, 142 8489, Japan
Tel.: (81) 335143770
Sales Range: $200-249.9 Million
Emp.: 910
Chemicals Mfr
N.A.I.C.S.: 325998

Nitto Boseki Co., Ltd. - Textiles Division (1)
1-6-1 Kuwazu Hyogo, Itami, 6645801, Japan
Tel.: (81) 345825160
Sales Range: $25-49.9 Million
Emp.: 100
Textile Design Services
N.A.I.C.S.: 541490

Nittobo (China) Co., Ltd. (1)
No 30 Changjiang Road, Xinwu District, Wuxi, 214028, Jiangsu, China
Tel.: (86) 51085214651
Web Site: http://www.nittobo-china.com
Sales Range: $50-74.9 Million
Emp.: 200
Fabrics Interlining Services
N.A.I.C.S.: 332618

Nittobo Acoustic Engineering Co., Ltd. (1)
BR Ryogoku 2 Bldg 1-21-10 Midori Sumida-ku, Tokyo, 130 0021, Japan
Tel.: (81) 336347567
Web Site: http://www.noe.co.jp
Rev.: $39,655,200
Emp.: 94
Architectural & Acoustical Engineering Services
N.A.I.C.S.: 541310
Shinji Ohashi (Mng Dir)

Nittobo America Inc. (1)
25549 Adams Ave, Murrieta, CA 92562
Tel.: (951) 677-5629
Web Site: https://www.nittobous.com
Immunoassay Products Mfr
N.A.I.C.S.: 424720
Susan Wright (Mgr-Admin)

Subsidiary (Domestic):

Kamiya Biomedical Co. (2)
12779 Gateway Dr S, Tukwila, WA 98168-3308
Tel.: (206) 575-8068
Web Site: http://www.kamiyabiomedical.com
Surgical & Medical Instrument Mfr
N.A.I.C.S.: 339112

Nittobo Ecology Co., Ltd. (1)
2-4-1 Kojimachi, Chiyoda-ku, Tokyo, 102-0083, Japan
Tel.: (81) 345825500
Web Site: https://www.ntb-g.co.jp
Building Material Mfr & Sales
N.A.I.C.S.: 444180

Nittobo Interlining Co., Ltd. (1)
Kudan First Pl 4f 4-1-28 Kudankita, Chiyoda-ku, Tokyo, Japan
Tel.: (81) 335148800
Garment Mfr & Sales
N.A.I.C.S.: 424350

Nittobo Macau Glass Weaving Co., Ltd. (1)
Est de Seac Pai Van Parque Ind da Concordia, Quarteirao E1 Coloane, Macau, China (Macau)
Tel.: (853) 28882211
Sales Range: $50-74.9 Million
Emp.: 180
Glass Fiber Whsir
N.A.I.C.S.: 327212

Virigina Yau (Mgr)

Nittobo Medical Co., Ltd. (1)
Koji-Machi O-dori Bldg 7F 2-4-1 Koji-Machi, Chiyoda-ku, Tokyo, 102-0083, Japan
Tel.: (81) 345825430
Web Site: http://www.nittobo-nmd.co.jp
Sales Range: $50-74.9 Million
Emp.: 208
Medicinal Product Mfr
N.A.I.C.S.: 325412
Yutaka Nakamura (Pres)

Nittobo Techno Co., Ltd. (1)
71 Motoki Kubota Fukuyama-machi, Koriyama, 963-8071, Fukushima, Japan
Tel.: (81) 249320185
Web Site: http://www.ntbtec.com
Industrial Machinery Mfr
N.A.I.C.S.: 333248

Paramount Glass Manufacturing Co., Ltd. (1)
24-4 Ogakubo, Kinosaki, Sukagawa, 962-0122, Fukushima, Japan
Tel.: (81) 248681031
Web Site: https://www.pgm.co.jp
Emp.: 270
Glass Wool Product Mfr & Distr
N.A.I.C.S.: 327215

Shinwa Denzai Co., Ltd. (1)
Kojimachi Odori Building 2-4-1 Kojimachi, Chiyoda-ku, Tokyo, 102-0083, Japan
Tel.: (81) 345825360
Web Site: https://www.shinwa-denzai.co.jp
Electrical Materials Whslr
N.A.I.C.S.: 423610

Soyo Co., Ltd. (1)
Rm 304 Phoenix Mansion No 165 Haidian Rd, Haidian Dist, Beijing, China
Tel.: (86) 1062510520
Glass Fiber Products Whslr
N.A.I.C.S.: 327212

NITTO DENKO CORPORATION
33rd Floor Grand Front Osaka 4-20 Ofuka-cho, Kita-ku, Osaka, 530-0011, Japan
Tel.: (81) 676322101 JP
Web Site: https://www.nitto.com
Year Founded: 1918
ND5—(DEU)
Rev.: $6,661,188,120
Assets: $8,271,648,990
Liabilities: $1,795,748,010
Net Worth: $6,475,900,980
Earnings: $782,770,410
Emp.: 28,371
Fiscal Year-end: 03/31/23
Plastics Product Mfr
N.A.I.C.S.: 326199
Toshihiko Omote (Sr Exec VP)

Subsidiaries:

AICHI NITTO DENKO CORPORATION (1)
18 Hirayama, Nakahara-cho, Toyohashi, 441-3106, Aichi, Japan
Tel.: (81) 532 41 8600
Web Site: http://www.nitto.com
Freight Trucking Services
N.A.I.C.S.: 484110

FUKUSHIMA NITTO SHINKO CORPORATION (1)
1-5 Aza Kamifukuzawa Nishigodo, Higashiishirakawa, Hanawa, 963-5407, Fukushima, Japan
Tel.: (81) 247 43 2305
Web Site: http://www.nitto.com
Chemical Products Mfr
N.A.I.C.S.: 325998

KOREA NITTO DENKO CO., LTD. (1)
11th Floor NC TOWER 509 Teheran-Ro, Gangnam-Gu, Seoul, 06169, Korea (South)
Tel.: (82) 2 756 7773
Web Site: http://www.nitto.com
Emp.: 50
Flexible Printed Circuit Mfr
N.A.I.C.S.: 334418

KOREA OPTICAL HIGHTECH CO., LTD. (1)

INTERNATIONAL PUBLIC

53-29 4Gongdan-ro 7-gil, Gumi, 39422, Gyeongsangbuk-do, Korea (South)
Tel.: (82) 544705000
Web Site: http://www.kohtech.kr
Fiber Optic Mfr
N.A.I.C.S.: 335921

KYOSHIN EUROPE LTD. (1)
26 Park Lane Ave, London, United Kingdom
Tel.: (44) 959 603 6035
Web Site: http://www.kyoshineurope.com
Sales Range: $25-49.9 Million
Emp.: 35
Fabricated Rubber Product Mfr
N.A.I.C.S.: 326299

Kinovate Life Sciences, Inc. (1)
501 Via Del Monte, Oceanside, CA 92058
Tel.: (760) 435-7024
Web Site: https://www.kinovate.com
Oligonucleotide Drug Mfr & Distr
N.A.I.C.S.: 325414

Korea Nitto Optical Co., Ltd. (1)
165 Cheongbuksandan-ro Cheongbuk-myeon, Pyeongtaek, 17812, Gyeonggi-do, Korea (South)
Tel.: (82) 31 680 4141
Web Site: http://www.koreno.co.kr
Emp.: 1,050
Polarizing Plastic Film Mfr
N.A.I.C.S.: 326113
Hong-In Kim (Pres & CEO)

L NISSHO CORPORATION (1)
4-3-24 Nishinakajima Samty Shinosaka Center Bldg, Yodogawa-Ku, Osaka, 532-0011, Japan
Tel.: (81) 661010771
Web Site: http://www.l-nissho.co.jp
Building Materials Mfr
N.A.I.C.S.: 326199

MATEX KAKOH CORPORATION (1)
3-77 Tsuchihashi, Toyota, 471-0842, Aichi, Japan
Tel.: (81) 565 28 6192
Plastics Product Mfr
N.A.I.C.S.: 325211

MIE NITTO DENKO CORPORATION (1)
919 Fuke, Kameyama, 519-0166, Mie, Japan
Tel.: (81) 595 84 2898
Automobile Parts Mfr
N.A.I.C.S.: 336390

NISSHO (HONG KONG) LTD. (1)
Unit 3702-06 37 / F Metroplaza Tower 2 223 Hing Fong Road, Kwai Fong, New Territories, China (Hong Kong)
Tel.: (852) 36588588
Web Site: http://www.nissho-group.com
Plastics Films Mfr
N.A.I.C.S.: 325211

NISSHO (TAIWAN) CORPORATION (1)
4F-3 No 129 Sec 2 Zhongshan N Rd, Taipei, 104, Taiwan
Tel.: (886) 2 2541 5000
Plastic Film Products Mfr
N.A.I.C.S.: 326112
Toshimasa Takemoto (Co-Mng Dir)

NISSHO HUNGARY PRECISION KFT. (1)
Japan Fasor 5 M5 Ipari Park, 2367, Ujhartyan, Hungary
Tel.: (36) 29 572 111
Sales Range: $50-74.9 Million
Emp.: 136
Automotive Product Mfr
N.A.I.C.S.: 336350
Hikaru Hayashi (Mng Dir)

NISSHO PRECISION (MALAYSIA) SDN. BHD. (1)
No 1739 Lorong Industri 3 MK7 Taman Industri Bukit Panchor, Seberang Perai Selatan, 14300, Nibong Tebal, Penang, Malaysia
Tel.: (60) 4 593 0118
Web Site: http://www.nissho-group.com
Sales Range: $25-49.9 Million
Emp.: 30
Electronic Components Mfr
N.A.I.C.S.: 334419

AND PRIVATE COMPANIES

NITTO DENKO CORPORATION

Kazuyuki Makino *(Mng Dir)*

NISSHO PRECISION (SUZHOU) CO., LTD. (1)
208 Shanggong Lu Xukou Wu Zhong Zone, Suzhou, 215164, Jiangsu, China
Tel.: (86) 512 6621 8757
Web Site: http://www.nitto.com
Adhesive Tape Mfr & Distr
N.A.I.C.S.: 322220
Atsushi Iwamoto *(Mng Dir)*

NISSHO PRECISION (THAILAND) CO., LTD. (1)
Amatanakorn Industrial Estate 700/825 Moo6 Tambol Nongtamlung, Amphur Panthong, Chon Buri, 20160, Thailand
Tel.: (66) 38 185 185
Web Site: http://www.nitto.com
Rubber Sheet Polyurethane Products Mfr
N.A.I.C.S.: 326299

NISSHO PRECISION (WUXI) CO., LTD. (1)
1F No C Huaren Industrial Area Xixia Rd, Wuxi New District, Wuxi, 214028, Jiangsu, China
Tel.: (86) 510 8520 1848
Adhesive Tape Mfr & Distr
N.A.I.C.S.: 322220
Wei Chen *(Dir)*

NISSHO SANGYO (SHANGHAI) CO., LTD. (1)
11CD Double Dove Building No 438 Pudian Road, Pudong, Shanghai, 200122, China
Tel.: (86) 21 5866 7537
Plastics Films Mfr
N.A.I.C.S.: 322220

NITTO ANALYTICAL TECHNO-CENTER CO., LTD. (1)
1-1-2 Shimohozumi, Ibaraki, 567-8680, Osaka, Japan
Tel.: (81) 72 623 3381
Web Site: http://www.natc.co.jp
Chemical Products Mfr
N.A.I.C.S.: 325998

NITTO BUSINESS SUPPORT CORPORATION (1)
Shimohozumi 1-chome No 1 No 2, Ibaraki, 567-0041, Osaka, Japan
Tel.: (81) 72 627 3502
Web Site: http://www.nitto.co.jp
Industrial Equipment Whsr
N.A.I.C.S.: 423830

NITTO DENKO (FOSHAN) CO., LTD. (1)
No 3 Southshunxiang Rd Wusha Area, Daliang Town Shunde, Foshan, 528300, Guangdong, China
Tel.: (86) 757 2280 2399
Adhesive Tape Whslr
N.A.I.C.S.: 424120
Hideharu Fukushima *(Mng Dir)*

NITTO DENKO (SHANGHAI) ELECTRO-ENERGY CO., LTD. (1)
716-2 Lianyang Rd Songjiang Industrial Zone Songjiang, Shanghai, 201613, China
Tel.: (86) 21 6774 1968
Electronic Component Mfr & Whslr
N.A.I.C.S.: 334419

NITTO DENKO (SHANGHAI) PHARMACEUTICAL CONSULTING CO., LTD. (1)
15 16F The Place Tower C 150 Zunyi Road, Changning District, Shanghai, 200051, China
Tel.: (86) 21 5208 2323
Pharmaceutical Products Consulting Services
N.A.I.C.S.: 541690
Shoukou Nakazawa *(Mng Dir)*

NITTO DENKO (TIANJIN) INTERNATIONAL TRADE CO., LTD. (1)
20F-CDE PingAn Mansion No 59 MaChang Rd, Hexi District, Tianjin, 300203, China
Tel.: (86) 22 5858 1088
Industrial Paper Distr
N.A.I.C.S.: 424130
Tsutomu Tamura *(Gen Mgr)*

NITTO DENKO AMERICA LATINA LTDA. (1)
R Tabapua 1123-cj 67, Sao Paulo, Brazil
Tel.: (55) 11 3791 6065
Electronic Components Distr
N.A.I.C.S.: 423690

NITTO DENKO ASIA TECHNICAL CENTRE PTE. LTD. (1)
3 Biopolis Drive 03-17/18 Synapse, Singapore, 138623, Singapore
Tel.: (65) 6467 7782
Web Site: http://www.nitto.com
Sales Range: $25-49.9 Million
Emp.: 40
Electronic Component Research Services
N.A.I.C.S.: 541715

NITTO DENKO CZECH s.r.o. (1)
Tezebni 1239/4, 627 00, Brno, Czech Republic
Tel.: (420) 548 141 000
Web Site: http://www.nitto.cz
Emp.: 100
Optical Film Mfr
N.A.I.C.S.: 325992

NITTO DENKO FINE CIRCUIT TECHNOLOGY(SHENZHEN) CO., LTD. (1)
Bldg No 1 Weilan Industrial Park Jianan Rd Gaoxin Area, Fuyong Baoan, Shenzhen, 518103, Guangdong, China
Tel.: (86) 755 2730 1614
Flexible Printed Circuits Whslr
N.A.I.C.S.: 423690
Morihisa Eguchi *(Mng Dir)*

NITTO DENKO HIMAWARI CORPORATION (1)
18 Hirayama, Nakahara-cho, Toyohashi, 441-3194, Aichi, Japan
Tel.: (81) 532 41 7207
Web Site: http://www.nitto.com
Optical Film Mfr
N.A.I.C.S.: 325992

NITTO DENKO INDIA PRIVATE LIMITED (1)
Plot No 177-178 Sector-5 IMT-Manesar, Gurgaon, 122 050, Haryana, India
Tel.: (91) 124 422 1600
Web Site: https://www.nitto.com
Sales Range: $25-49.9 Million
Emp.: 20
Adhesive Tape Mfr & Distr
N.A.I.C.S.: 322220
Daisuke Minakata *(Mng Dir)*

NITTO DENKO MATERIALS (SHENZHEN) CO., LTD. (1)
Flat C D 7Fl Teng Fei Ind Bldg No 6 Taohua Rd Futian Free Trade Zone, Shenzhen, 518038, China
Tel.: (86) 755 8349 6600
Sales Range: $50-74.9 Million
Emp.: 160
Adhesive Tape Mfr
N.A.I.C.S.: 322220
Scott Shu *(Mng Dir)*

NITTO DENKO NITOMS KOREA CO., LTD. (1)
11th Floor NC TOWER 509 Teheran-Ro, Gangnam-Gu, Seoul, 06169, Korea (South)
Tel.: (82) 2 3216 8882
Web Site: http://www.nitomskorea.com
Garden Cleaning Equipment Distr
N.A.I.C.S.: 423820

NITTO DENKO TAPE MATERIALS (VIETNAM) CO., LTD. (1)
Lot C Mapletree Logistic Centre No1 VSIP Street 10, Thuan An, Binh Duong, Vietnam
Tel.: (84) 650 3 757988
Adhesive Tape Distr
N.A.I.C.S.: 424130
Katsumi Saito *(Mng Dir)*

NITTO ELECTRONICS KYUSYU CORPORATION (1)
2307-2 Yoshida Yoshinogaricho, Kanzaki-Gun, Saga, 842-0031, Japan
Tel.: (81) 952531166
Web Site: http://www.nitto.co.jp
Semiconductor Epoxy Resin Mfr
N.A.I.C.S.: 325211
Kazuyuki Tanaka *(Pres)*

NITTO LIFETEC CORPORATION (1)
1057-1 Nakanishisoto, Matsuyama, 799-2425, Ehime, Japan
Tel.: (81) 899922333
Web Site: http://www.nitto-lifetec.co.jp
Emp.: 100
Adhesive Tape Mfr
N.A.I.C.S.: 339113

NITTO LOGI-COM CORPORATION (1)
15th Floor Nissay Yodoyabashi East 3-3-13 Imabashi, Chuo-ku, Osaka, 541-0042, Japan
Tel.: (81) 676390012
Web Site: http://www.nitto.co.jp
Logistics Consulting Servies
N.A.I.C.S.: 541614

NITTO MATEX (THAILAND) CO., LTD. (1)
700/611 Moo 7 Bangna-Trad Rd KM 57 Tambol Don Hau Roh, Muang District, Chon Buri, 20000, Thailand
Tel.: (66) 38 04 7015
Web Site: http://www.nitto.com
Adhesive Tape Mfr
N.A.I.C.S.: 325520

NITTO MEDICAL CORPORATION (1)
1-1-2 Shimohozumi, Ibaraki, 567-8680, Osaka, Japan
Tel.: (81) 726 21 8001
Web Site: http://www.ntmed.co.jp
Rev.: $66,193,920
Emp.: 52
Medical Device Distr
N.A.I.C.S.: 423450
Seiji Fujioka *(CEO)*

NITTO SEIKI CO., LTD. (1)
919 Fuke-cho, Kameyama, 519-0193, Mie, Japan
Tel.: (81) 595841021
Web Site: http://www.nitto.co.jp
Emp.: 50
Semiconductor Wafer Tape Mfr
N.A.I.C.S.: 334413

NITTO SHINKO CORPORATION (1)
110-1-1 Funayose Maruokacho, Sakai, 910-0381, Fukui, Japan
Tel.: (81) 776661360
Web Site: http://www.nittoshinko.co.jp
Emp.: 376
Automotive & Electric Wire Parts Mfr
N.A.I.C.S.: 336390

Nissho (Dalian F.T.Z.) International Trading Co., Ltd. (1)
RM No 2708-B Kerren International Mansion, No 1 Building Residential Quarter Wu Cai Cheng Development Zone, Dalian, 116600, China
Tel.: (86) 41187934441
Adhesive Tape Whslr
N.A.I.C.S.: 423990

Nissho (Singapore) Pte. Ltd. (1)
120 Lower Delta Rd 07-15 Cendex Centre, Singapore, 169208, Singapore
Tel.: (65) 62378733
Adhesive Tape Distr
N.A.I.C.S.: 424690

Nissho Corporation - Kyushu Plant (1)
5-7-39 Hakataeki Minami, Hakata, Fukuoka, 812-0016, Japan
Tel.: (81) 92 441 0602
Web Site: http://www.nissho-group.com
Electronic Components Mfr
N.A.I.C.S.: 334419

Nissho Corporation - Nagoya Plant (1)
2-15-5 Kikui Nishi, Nagoya, 451-0044, Aichi, Japan
Tel.: (81) 52 533 1560
Electric Equipment Mfr
N.A.I.C.S.: 334419

Nissho Corporation - Osaka Plant (1)
1-2-3 Torikaishimo, Settsu, 566-0071, Osaka, Japan
Tel.: (81) 72 654 7223
Web Site: http://www.nissho-group.com
Electronic Components Mfr
N.A.I.C.S.: 334419

Nissho Corporation - Shiga Plant (1)
558-1 Deba, Ritto, 520-3041, Shiga, Japan
Tel.: (81) 77 552 1941
Web Site: http://www.nissho-group.com
Electronic Components Mfr
N.A.I.C.S.: 334419

Nissho Corporation - Tohoku Plant (1)
140-1 Shintakayachi Sakuranome Furukawa, Osaki, 989-6233, Miyagi, Japan
Tel.: (81) 229 28 4081
Web Site: http://www.nissho-group.com
Electronic Components Mfr
N.A.I.C.S.: 334419

Nissho Precision (Dongguan) Co., Ltd. (1)
No 8 Chang An Zhen Yuan West Road, Chang An Town, Dongguan, 523875, Guangdong, China
Tel.: (86) 76985645571
Adhesive Tape Mfr & Whslr
N.A.I.C.S.: 325520

Nissho Precision Philippines Incorporated (1)
Lot 5-B-7 Greenfield Automotive Park SEZ, Santa Rosa, 4026, Laguna, Philippines
Tel.: (63) 495083490
Sealing Material Mfr
N.A.I.C.S.: 339991

Nissho Precision Vietnam Co., Ltd. (1)
6A VSIP Street 03, Vietnam - Singapore Industrial Park Binh Hoa Ward, Thuan An, Binh Duong, Vietnam
Tel.: (84) 65033783090
Adhesive Tape Mfr & Whslr
N.A.I.C.S.: 325520

Nitoms Inc. (1)
Kacho Building 7-16-7 Ginza, Chuo-ku, Tokyo, 104-0061, Japan
Tel.: (81) 335440482
Sales Range: $50-74.9 Million
Emp.: 137
Plastics Product Mfr
N.A.I.C.S.: 326199

Nitto (China) New Materials Co., Ltd. (1)
15-16F The Place Tower C 150 Zunyi Road, Changning District, Shanghai, 200051, China
Tel.: (86) 2152081777
Sealing Material Mfr
N.A.I.C.S.: 339991

Nitto (Qingdao)Technology Research Institute, Co., Ltd. (1)
17-D3 Songyuan Road, Qingdao National High-tech Industrial Development zone, Qingdao, 266109, Shandong, China
Tel.: (86) 53266020166
Innovative Research Services
N.A.I.C.S.: 541715

Nitto Belgium N.V. (1)
Eikelaarstraat 22, 3600, Genk, Belgium
Tel.: (32) 89360111
Sealing Material Mfr
N.A.I.C.S.: 339991

Nitto Bento Bantcilik San. ve Tic. A.S. (1)
Akcaburgaz Mah 3097 Sokak No 9, Esenyurt, 34510, Istanbul, Turkiye
Tel.: (90) 2128869040
Sealing Material Mfr
N.A.I.C.S.: 339991

Nitto Business Expert Corporation (1)
1-1-2 Shimohozumi, Ibaraki, 567-0041, Osaka, Japan
Tel.: (81) 726273502
Web Site: http://www.nitto.co.jp
Entrusted Welfare Services
N.A.I.C.S.: 624190

Nitto Denko (Australia) Pty. Ltd. (1)
Caribbean Park Level 1 37 Dalmore Drive, Scoresby, 3179, VIC, Australia (100%)
Tel.: (61) 397993100
Web Site: http://www.nitto.com
Sales Range: $25-49.9 Million
Emp.: 40

NITTO DENKO CORPORATION

Nitto Denko Corporation—(Continued)
Other Chemical & Allied Products Merchant Whslr
N.A.I.C.S.: 424690
Michael Finn *(Mng Dir)*

Nitto Denko (China) Investment Co., Ltd. (1)
24F Maxdo Center No 8 Xingyi Rd, Changning, Shanghai, 200336, China
Tel.: (86) 21 5208 2277
Investment Management Service
N.A.I.C.S.: 523999
Masahiko Arimoto *(Mng Dir)*

Nitto Denko (HK) Co. Ltd. (1)
37/F Metroplaza Tower 2 223 Hing Fong Road, Kwai Fong Rd, Kwai Fong, NT, China (Hong Kong) **(100%)**
Tel.: (852) 24814140
Web Site: http://www.nitto.com.hk
Sales Range: $50-74.9 Million
Emp.: 80
Sales, Marketing & Services of Industrial Products
N.A.I.C.S.: 541519

Nitto Denko (Philippines) Corp. (1)
Lot 5-B-7 Greenfield Automotive Park SEZ, Sta Rosa, Laguna, 4026, Philippines **(100%)**
Tel.: (63) 49 502 8820
Web Site: http://www.nitto.com
Sales Range: $25-49.9 Million
Emp.: 57
Importation, Storage, Processing, Sales & After Sales Servicing of Various Nitto Denko Products & Machines for Automotive Industries
N.A.I.C.S.: 336110
Hiroshi Hanada *(Mng Dir)*

Nitto Denko (Shanghai Pu Dong New Area) Co., Ltd. (1)
D6C 9A Wai Gao Qiao Free Trade Zone, Pu Dong, 200131, Shanghai, China
Tel.: (86) 52801777
Web Site: http://www.nitto.com
N.A.I.C.S.: 424690
Suzuki Sha *(CEO)*

Nitto Denko (Shanghai Songjiang) Co., Ltd. (1)
716 Lianyang Rd, Songjiang Industrial Zone Songjiang, Shanghai, 201613, China **(100%)**
Tel.: (86) 2157742184
Web Site: http://www.nitto.com.cn
Sales Range: $125-149.9 Million
Emp.: 300
Adhesive Mfr
N.A.I.C.S.: 325520

Nitto Denko (Singapore) Pte. Ltd. (1)
438 Alexandra Road 19-01/04 Alexandra Point, Singapore, 119958, Singapore **(100%)**
Tel.: (65) 62238277
Web Site: http://www.nitto.com
Sales Range: $50-74.9 Million
Emp.: 36
Chemicals
N.A.I.C.S.: 424690

Nitto Denko (Taiwan) Corp. (1)
No 1 South 7th Rd KEPZ, Kaohsiung, 80681, Taiwan
Tel.: (886) 7 821 3106
Web Site: http://www.nitto.com
Sales Range: $50-74.9 Million
Emp.: 60
Mfr & Sales of Adhesives & Coatings
N.A.I.C.S.: 325520

Nitto Denko (Taiwan) Corporation (1)
No 1 S 7th Rd Kaohsiung Export Processing Zone, Kaohsiung, 806, Taiwan **(100%)**
Tel.: (886) 78213106
Web Site: http://www.nitto.com
N.A.I.C.S.: 424690

Nitto Denko (Tianjin) Co., Ltd. (1)
52 Wuweilu Dongli Economic Developing Area, Tianjin, 300300, China
Tel.: (86) 2224982105
Adhesive Tape Mfr & Whslr
N.A.I.C.S.: 325520

Nitto Denko (Xiamen) Co., Ltd. (1)
Processing Bldg 26G 2nd Floor Unit B, Xiangyu Free Trade Zone, Xiamen, 361006, China **(100%)**
Tel.: (86) 5925629120
Web Site: http://www.nitto.com
Sales Range: $25-49.9 Million
Emp.: 62
Industrial Tapes Conversion & Sales
N.A.I.C.S.: 339112

Nitto Denko Automotive de Mexico S. de R.L. de C.V. (1)
Street Desarrollo 100 Parque Industrial La Silla Apodaca, Apodaca, 66600, Nuevo Leon, Mexico
Tel.: (52) 81 8625 3550
Plastic Product Distr
N.A.I.C.S.: 424610

Nitto Denko Automotive de Mexico Servicios S. de R.L. de C.V. (1)
Street Desarrollo 100 Parque Industrial La Silla Apodaca, Apodaca, 66600, Nuevo Leon, Mexico
Tel.: (52) 81 8625 3550
Plastics Product Mfr
N.A.I.C.S.: 326199

Nitto Denko CS System Corporation (1)
18 Hirayama, Nakahara-cho, Toyohashi, 441-3194, Aichi, Japan
Tel.: (81) 532431910
Web Site: http://www.nittocs.co.jp
Sales Range: $75-99.9 Million
Emp.: 170
Converted Paper Products & Plastic Products Mfr
N.A.I.C.S.: 322299

Nitto Denko Corporation - Ibaraki Plant (1)
1-1-2 Shimohozumi, Ibaraki, 567-8680, Osaka, Japan
Tel.: (81) 72 622 2981
Black Tape Mfr
N.A.I.C.S.: 322220

Nitto Denko Corporation - Kameyama Plant (1)
919 Fuke-cho, Kameyama, 519-0193, Mie, Japan
Tel.: (81) 595 82 1151
Liquid Crystal Display Mfr
N.A.I.C.S.: 334419

Nitto Denko Corporation - Kanto Plant (1)
1-8-5 Hatara-cho, Fukaya, 366-8521, Saitama, Japan
Tel.: (81) 48 571 3171
Semiconductor Devices Mfr
N.A.I.C.S.: 334413

Nitto Denko Corporation - Onomichi Plant (1)
455-6 Hongo Minogo-cho, Onomichi, 722-0212, Hiroshima, Japan
Tel.: (81) 848 48 2100
Adhesive Tape Mfr
N.A.I.C.S.: 322220

Nitto Denko Corporation - Shiga Plant (1)
61-7 Sasadani Yamadera-cho, Kusatsu, 525-0042, Shiga, Japan
Tel.: (81) 77 562 7711
Liquid Crystal Display Mfr
N.A.I.C.S.: 334419

Nitto Denko Corporation - Tohoku Plant (1)
101 Sunada Shimonome, Iwadeyama, Osaki, 989-6493, Miyagi, Japan
Tel.: (81) 229 72 2211
Semiconductor Devices Mfr
N.A.I.C.S.: 334413

Nitto Denko Corporation - Toyohashi Plant (1)
18 Hirayama Nakahara-cho, Toyohashi, 441-3194, Aichi, Japan
Tel.: (81) 532 41 1121
Semiconductor Devices Mfr
N.A.I.C.S.: 334413

Nitto Denko Electronics (Malaysia) Sdn. Bhd. (1)
No 2 Persiaran Budiman Seksyen 23, Shah Alam, 40300, Malaysia **(100%)**
Tel.: (60) 355417733
Sales Range: $1-9.9 Million
Emp.: 250
Mfr & Sales of Moulding Compounds
N.A.I.C.S.: 334413

Nitto Denko Ltd. (1)
Yeonho Bldg 3rd Floor 135 21-1 Seosumon-Dong Jung-Gu, Seoul, 100 813, Korea (South) **(100%)**
Tel.: (82) 27567773
Web Site: http://www.nitto.co.kr
Sales Range: $25-49.9 Million
Emp.: 50
Product Sales Distribution
N.A.I.C.S.: 339112
Seungjung Yoon *(Gen Mgr)*

Nitto Denko Material (Thailand) Co., Ltd. (1)
Rojana Industrial Park 1/75 Moo5 Rojana Rd T Kanham A U-Thai, Phra Nakhon Si Ayutthaya, 13210, Thailand **(100%)**
Tel.: (66) 35226750
Web Site: http://www.nitto.com
Sales Range: $400-449.9 Million
Emp.: 1,300
Mfr & Sale of Tape & Sealing Materials
N.A.I.C.S.: 334610

Nitto Denko Materials (Malaysia) Sdn. Bhd. (1)
No 2 Persiaran Budiman Seksyen 23, 40300, Shah Alam, Selangor Darul Ehsan, Malaysia **(100%)**
Tel.: (60) 35541 6896
Web Site: http://www.nitto.com.my
Sales Range: $200-249.9 Million
Electronic Components Adhesive Tapes Mfr & Distr
N.A.I.C.S.: 325520

Nitto Denko Medical MFG. Co., Ltd. (1)
101 Sunada Shimonome, Iwadeyama, Osaki, 989-6412, Miyagi, Japan
Tel.: (81) 229 73 4822
Web Site: http://www.nitto.com
Medical Device Mfr
N.A.I.C.S.: 339112

Nitto Denko Turkey Tape Materials Industry and Trade Limited (1)
Tuzla Mermerciler OSB Mermerciler Cad No 39/2, Tuzla, Istanbul, 34953, Türkiye
Tel.: (90) 216 581 7511
Sales Range: $25-49.9 Million
Emp.: 12
Adhesive Tape Distr
N.A.I.C.S.: 424110

Nitto Denko UK Ltd. (1)
Sunrise Building Crown Farm Way, Crown Farm Industrial Park Forest Town, Mansfield, NG19 0FT, Nottinghamshire, United Kingdom
Tel.: (44) 1623415500
Plastics Product Mfr
N.A.I.C.S.: 334419

Nitto Denko Vietnam Co., Ltd. (1)
No6 VSIP Street3, Thuan An, Binh Duong, Vietnam
Tel.: (84) 6503756414
Web Site: http://www.nitto.com
Sales Range: $450-499.9 Million
Emp.: 2,300
Coated & Laminated Paper Mfr
N.A.I.C.S.: 322220

Nitto Denko de Mexico S.de R.L. de C.V. (1)
Street Desarrollo 100, Parque Industrial La Silla Apodaca, 66648, Apodaca, Mexico
Tel.: (52) 8186253550
Sealing Material Mfr
N.A.I.C.S.: 339991

Nitto Emea N.V. (1)
Diestsepoort 1, 3000, Leuven, Belgium
Tel.: (32) 16241770
Sealing Material Mfr
N.A.I.C.S.: 339991

Nitto Europe N.V. (1)
Eikelaarstraat 22 Industrial Park Zuid Zone 12A, Genk, 3600, Belgium
Tel.: (32) 89360111

INTERNATIONAL PUBLIC

Web Site: http://www.nittoeurope.com
Sales Range: $200-249.9 Million
Emp.: 700
Mfr of Adhesive Tapes; Manufacturer & Marketer of Industrial, Electronic & Functional Products
N.A.I.C.S.: 325520
Norikane Nabata *(Pres)*

Subsidiary (Non-US):

Nitto Deutschland GmbH (2)
Schifferstrasse 210, 47059, Duisburg, Germany **(100%)**
Tel.: (49) 203 933 1800
Web Site: http://www.nittoeurope.com
Sales Range: $25-49.9 Million
Emp.: 20
Sales, Marketing & Services of Industrial Products
N.A.I.C.S.: 561990
Stefan Meirsman *(Mng Dir)*

Nitto France S.A.R.L. (2)
Immeuble Le Rabelais 22 Avenue des nations, CS 10024, Villepinte Roissy Ch De Gaulle, 95926, Garges-les-Gonesse, Cedex, France **(100%)**
Tel.: (33) 14 817 8750
Web Site: http://www.nittoeurope.com
Sales Range: $25-49.9 Million
Emp.: 19
Sales, Marketing & Services of Industrial Products
N.A.I.C.S.: 424690
Geoffroy Hue Habrioux *(Mng Dir)*

Nitto Italia S.R.L. (2)
Via Aldo Moro 45, 20060, Gessate, Milano, Italy **(100%)**
Tel.: (39) 029 538 3491
Web Site: http://www.nittoeurope.com
Sales Range: $25-49.9 Million
Emp.: 10
Other Chemical & Allied Product Merchant Wholesalers
N.A.I.C.S.: 424690
Luca Villa *(Mng Dir)*

Nitto Polska Sp. z o.o. (2)
ul Domaniewska 37, 02-672, Warsaw, Poland **(100%)**
Tel.: (48) 22 337 8657
Web Site: http://www.nittoeur.com
Sales Range: $25-49.9 Million
Emp.: 5
Distr of Chemicals, Tapes & Other Sealing & Packaging Products, Medical Products & Electronics
N.A.I.C.S.: 424690
Lidia Rutkowska *(Mng Dir)*

Nitto Scandinavia AB (2)
Heljesvagen 9, 437 36, Lindome, Sweden
Tel.: (46) 31993010
Web Site: http://www.nittoeurope.com
Sales Range: $25-49.9 Million
Emp.: 15
Sales, Marketing & Services of Industrial Products
N.A.I.C.S.: 424690

Nitto U.K. Limited (2)
Unit 2 Berkshire Business Ctr Berkshire Dr, Thatcham, RG19 4EW, Berks, United Kingdom **(100%)**
Tel.: (44) 01635872172
Web Site: http://www.nittoeurope.com
Sales Range: $25-49.9 Million
Emp.: 7
N.A.I.C.S.: 424690

Nitto Himawari Kameyama Corporation (1)
Fukecho Dandruff 919, Kameyama, 519-0193, Mie, Japan
Tel.: (81) 595842810
Plastics Product Mfr
N.A.I.C.S.: 326199

Nitto Himawari Onomichi Corporation (1)
455-6 Minogocho Hongo, Onomichi, 722-0212, Hiroshima, Japan
Tel.: (81) 848486170
Plastics Product Mfr
N.A.I.C.S.: 326199

Nitto L Materials Corporation (1)
4-3-24 Nishinakajima Samty Shin-Osaka

AND PRIVATE COMPANIES

Center Building 5F, Yodogawa-ku, Osaka, 532-0011, Japan
Tel.: (81) 661010771
Web Site: http://www.nitto-lmaterials.com
Sealing Material Mfr
N.A.I.C.S.: 339991

Nitto Material Technology (Chengdu) Co., Ltd.
Building A5-1 Global Logistic Properties No 188, South section Chenxi Road Chongzhou Economic Development Area Chengdu, Sichuan, 611230, China
Tel.: (86) 2882339766
Electric Equipment Mfr
N.A.I.C.S.: 334515

Nitto Matex (Shenzen) Co., Ltd. (1)
Block 16 Cui Hu Industrial Park No 21-9 Xin Tang Rd, Xin Tian Zone Fu Hai Jie Dao Bao An District, Shenzhen, 518103, China
Tel.: (86) 755 2734 2228
Web Site: http://www.nitto.com
Plastics Films Mfr
N.A.I.C.S.: 326112

Nitto Otomotiv San. ve Tic. Ltd. Sti. (1)
Istanbul Anadolu Yakasi OSB Mermerciler Cad No 39/2, Tuzla, Istanbul, 34953, Turkiye
Tel.: (90) 2165817500
Sealing Material Mfr
N.A.I.C.S.: 339991

Nitto Rus LLC (1)
Barclaya str 6 Bld 5 OF C432, 121087, Moscow, Russia
Tel.: (7) 4952690171
Sealing Material Mfr
N.A.I.C.S.: 339991

Nitto Shinko (Suzhou) Co., Ltd. (1)
No 259 Chang Yang Street, Suzhou Industrial Park, Suzhou, 215024, China
Tel.: (86) 51262583330
Sealing Material Mfr
N.A.I.C.S.: 339991

Nitto Switzerland AG (1)
Industriestrasse 18, 3185, Schmitten, Switzerland
Tel.: (41) 264979125
Adhesive Film Material Mfr
N.A.I.C.S.: 325520

Nitto Vietnam Co., Ltd. (1)
RBF Block No 108 Huu Nghi Road, VSIP Bac Ninh Integrated Township and Industrial Park Phu Chan Commune, Tu Son, Bac Ninh, Vietnam
Tel.: (84) 2223765260
Sealing Material Mfr
N.A.I.C.S.: 339991

Nitto, Inc. (1)
400 Frank W Burr Blvd 2nd Fl Ste 66, Teaneck, NJ 07666
Tel.: (201) 371-2122
Sealing Material Mfr
N.A.I.C.S.: 339991

Subsidiary (Domestic):

Hydranautics (2)
401 Jones Rd, Oceanside, CA 92058
Tel.: (760) 901-2500
Web Site: http://www.membranes.com
Sales Range: $100-124.9 Million
Mfr & Sale of Membranes
N.A.I.C.S.: 333310

NISTEM PRECISION INC, (2)
7098 Miratech Dr Ste 110, San Diego, CA 92121
Tel.: (858) 566-5540
Web Site: http://www.nitto.com
Plastic Film Products Distr
N.A.I.C.S.: 424610
Takeo Kishimizu (Mgr)

Nitto Automotive, Inc. (2)
8485 Prospect Ave, Kansas City, MO 64132
Tel.: (816) 444-3611
Web Site: http://www.nittousa.com
Electric Equipment Mfr
N.A.I.C.S.: 334419

Nitto Avecia Pharma Services Inc. (2)
10 Vanderbilt, Irvine, CA 92618

Tel.: (949) 951-4425
Web Site: http://www.aveciapharma.com
Pharmaceutical Development Services
N.A.I.C.S.: 541714

Nitto BioPharma, Inc. (2)
10618 Science Center Dr, San Diego, CA 92121
Tel.: (858) 255-3010
Web Site: http://www.nittobiopharma.com
Pharmaceutical Development Services
N.A.I.C.S.: 541714

Nitto Denko Avecia Inc. (2)
125 Fortune Blvd, Milford, MA 01757
Tel.: (508) 532-2500
Pharmaceutical Product Research & Development Services
N.A.I.C.S.: 541714

Nitto Denko Technical Corporation (2)
501 Via Del Monte, Oceanside, CA 92058 (100%)
Tel.: (760) 435-7011
Web Site: https://www.ndtcorp.com
Sales Range: $25-49.9 Million
Biomedical, Communications & Nanotechnology Materials Research & Development
N.A.I.C.S.: 541714

Nitto Innovations, Inc. (2)
2880 Lakeside Dr Ste 205, Santa Clara, CA 95054
Tel.: (408) 987-9300
Sealing Material Mfr
N.A.I.C.S.: 339991

Plant (Domestic):

Nitto, Inc. - Novi Plant (2)
45880 Dylan Dr, Novi, MI 48377
Tel.: (248) 449-2300
Web Site: http://www.auto.nitto.com
Automobile Parts Mfr
N.A.I.C.S.: 336390

OPTMATE CORPORATION (1)
7-3-46-1 Nojihigashi, Kusatsu, 525-0058, Shiga, Japan
Tel.: (81) 77 532 2926
Web Site: http://www.optmate.co.jp
Microlens Film Mfr
N.A.I.C.S.: 326112

P.T. Nitto Materials Indonesia (1)
Lippo Cikarang Industrial Park Jl Kenari Raya Blok G 3A No 02, Delta Silicon Central Cikarang, Bekasi, 17530, West Java, Indonesia
Tel.: (62) 218971550
Web Site: http://www.nitto.com
Sales Range: $550-599.9 Million
Emp.: 1,550
Sale Marketing & Services of Industrial Product
N.A.I.C.S.: 424690

SAITAMA NITTO DENKO CORPORATION (1)
1-8-5 Hatara, Fukaya, 336-0032, Saitama, Japan
Tel.: (81) 48 573 8911
Fluoroplastic Products Mfr
N.A.I.C.S.: 322220

SUZHOU NITTO MATEX ELECTRONICS CO., LTD. (1)
No 79 Hengshan Rd, New District, Suzhou, 215011, China
Tel.: (86) 512 6813 7040
Web Site: http://www.nitto.com
Sales Range: $150-199.9 Million
Emp.: 300
Adhesive Tape Mfr & Distr
N.A.I.C.S.: 322220

Shanghai Nitto Optical Co., Ltd. (1)
No 210 North Riying Rd Wai Gao Qiao Free Trade Zone, Pudong, Shanghai, 200131, China
Tel.: (86) 21 5046 4133
Web Site: http://www.nitto.com
Optical Film Mfr
N.A.I.C.S.: 423460

Shenzhen Nitto Optical Co., Ltd. (1)
Guangyuan 5th Road Guangming Hi-Tech Park Fenghuang Street, Guangming New District, Shenzhen, 518107, China
Tel.: (86) 75529891668

Sealing Material Mfr
N.A.I.C.S.: 339991

Taiwan Nitto Corporation (1)
14F No 223 Songjiang Rd, Zhongshan Dist, Taipei, 10483, Taiwan
Tel.: (886) 225021212
Sealing Material Mfr
N.A.I.C.S.: 339991

Taiwan Nitto Optical Co., Ltd. (1)
NO 7 Keya W RD, Daya Dist, Taichung, 42882, Taiwan
Tel.: (886) 425658200
Web Site: http://www.nitto.com
Polarizing Film Mfr
N.A.I.C.S.: 326113

NITTO KAKO CO., LTD.
6-1-3 Ichinomiya Sankagawa-cho, Takazado-gun, Yokohama, 253-0111, Kanagawa, Japan
Tel.: (81) 467743111 JP
Web Site: http://www.nitto-kk.co.jp
Year Founded: 1945
51040—(TKS)
Sales Range: Less than $1 Million
Rubber & Plastic Products Mfr & Whslr
N.A.I.C.S.: 326299
Ryohei Arakawa (Pres & CEO)

NITTO KOGYO CORPORATION
2201 Kanihara, Nagakute, 480-1189, Aichi, Japan
Tel.: (81) 561623111
Web Site: https://www.nito.co.jp
Year Founded: 1948
6651—(TKS)
Rev.: $1,062,286,490
Assets: $1,069,114,620
Liabilities: $350,634,060
Net Worth: $718,480,560
Earnings: $57,606,150
Emp.: 4,062
Fiscal Year-end: 03/31/24
Electrical Equipment Mfr & Whslr
N.A.I.C.S.: 335999
Tokio Kato (Co-CEO & Chm)

Subsidiaries:

Aichi Electric Works Co., Ltd. (1)
5953-1 Nenkaesaka, Oaza, Komaki, 485-0802, Aichi Prefecture, Japan
Tel.: (81) 568688623
Web Site: https://www.aichidnk.com
Emp.: 273
Electrical Equipment & Component Mfr
N.A.I.C.S.: 335999

ECAD Solutions Co., Ltd. (1)
6th Floor of Welk Building 4-3 Shintoshin, Chuo-ku, Saitama, 330-0081, Japan
Tel.: (81) 486156350
Web Site: https://www.ecad-sol.com
Software Development Services
N.A.I.C.S.: 541511

ELETTO (Thailand) Co. Ltd. (1)
41 Village No 4 Rojana Industrial Estate 2 Rojana Road, Uthai Subdistrict Uthai District, Phra Nakhon Si Ayutthaya, 13210, Thailand
Tel.: (66) 35746800
Electronic Equipment Distr
N.A.I.C.S.: 423690

Gathergates Group Ltd (1)
16 Senoko Drive, Singapore, 758203, Singapore
Tel.: (65) 65554441
Web Site: http://www.gathergates.com
Switchgear Mfr
N.A.I.C.S.: 335313

Subsidiary (Non-US):

Gathergates Elektrik Sdn Bhd (2)
3A 1st Floor Jalan Suakasih 1/2, Bandar Tun Hussein Onn, 43200, Cheras, Selangor, Malaysia
Tel.: (60) 390802842
Web Site: http://www.gathergates.com
Switchgear Mfr & Distr
N.A.I.C.S.: 335313

NITTO KOHKI CO., LTD.

Gathergates Switchgear (M) Sdn Bhd (2)
16 Jalan Mega 1/8 Taman Perindustrian Nusa Cemerlang, 79200, Iskandar Puteri, Johor, Malaysia
Tel.: (60) 75581323
Web Site: http://www.gathergates.com
Switchgear Mfr
N.A.I.C.S.: 335313

Subsidiary (Domestic):

Gathergates Switchgear Pte Ltd (2)
16 Senoko Drive, Singapore, 758203, Singapore
Tel.: (65) 65554441
Web Site: http://www.gathergates.com
Switchboards & Switchgears Mfr
N.A.I.C.S.: 335313

Subsidiary (Non-US):

Titans Power Holding Pte Ltd (2)
Tel.: (65) 65557666
Web Site: http://www.gathergates.com
Investment Management Service
N.A.I.C.S.: 523999

Subsidiary (Non-US):

Titans Power System Pte Ltd (3)
Tel.: (65) 65557666
Web Site: http://www.gathergates.com
Air Conditioning System Installation Services
N.A.I.C.S.: 238220

Kitagawa Industries Co., Ltd. (1)
695-1 Higashiorido Mukui-cho, Inazawa, 492-8446, Aichi Prefecture, Japan
Web Site: http://www.kitagawa-ind.com
Computer Product Mfr & Distr
N.A.I.C.S.: 334419
Yoshihiro Hirakawa (Pres)

Nankaidensetsu Co., Ltd. (1)
3-12-7 Nipponbashihigashi, Naniwa-ku, Osaka, 556-0006, Japan
Tel.: (81) 666430181
Web Site: http://www.nankai-densetsu.co.jp
Environmental Measure Product Mfr
N.A.I.C.S.: 334512

Nitto Kogyo (China) Corporation (1)
Building 1 No 2 Lushan Road Huimin Street, Huimin Sub-district, Jiashan, 314100, Zhejiang, China
Tel.: (86) 57384295002
Emp.: 39
Electrical Equipment Distr
N.A.I.C.S.: 423610

Nitto Kogyo Bm (Thailand) Co., Ltd. (1)
No 43 Thai CC Tower Building 24th Fl Room No A244 South Sathorn Rd, Yannawa Sathorn, Bangkok, 10120, Thailand
Tel.: (66) 26525156
Web Site: https://th.nito-bm.com
Electrical Equipment Mfr & Distr
N.A.I.C.S.: 335999

SunTelephone Co., Ltd. (1)
Daiwa River Gate 17th floor 36-2 Hakozaki-cho, Chuo-ku, Tokyo, 103-8515, Japan
Tel.: (81) 356513200
Web Site: https://www.suntel.co.jp
Emp.: 552
Telecommunication Device Distr
N.A.I.C.S.: 423690
Masayuki Enomoto (Pres & CEO)

Taiyo Electric Mfg. Co., Ltd. (1)
1-1-8 HiradochO, Nakagawa-ku, Nagoya, 454-0864, Japan
Tel.: (81) 523616006
Web Site: https://www.kk-taiyo-el.co.jp
Control Panel Mfr
N.A.I.C.S.: 335314

Tohoku Nitto Kogyo Corporation (1)
4-3-6 Nimaibashi, Hanamaki, 025-0312, Iwate, Japan
Tel.: (81) 561640112
Web Site: https://www.nito.co.jp
Mechanical Equipment Mfr & Distr
N.A.I.C.S.: 335999
Toru Kurono (Pres & CEO)

NITTO KOHKI CO., LTD.

NITTO KOHKI CO., LTD.

NITTO KOHKI Co., Ltd.—(Continued)
9-4 Nakaikegami 2-chome, Ohta-ku, Tokyo, 146-8555, Japan
Tel.: (81) 337551111
Web Site: https://www.nitto-kohki.co.jp
Year Founded: 1956
6151—(TKS)
Rev.: $178,945,920
Assets: $432,809,580
Liabilities: $52,159,510
Net Worth: $380,650,070
Earnings: $13,550,500
Emp.: 1,014
Fiscal Year-end: 03/31/24
Machine Tools Mfr
N.A.I.C.S.: 333517
Mitsuhiro Inoue (Exec Officer)

Subsidiaries:

Medo Industries Co., Ltd. (1)
2-9-4 Nakaikegami, Ohta-ku, Tokyo, 146-0081, Japan
Tel.: (81) 357485521
Web Site: http://www.medo.co.jp
Sales Range: $250-299.9 Million
Couplings Mfr & Piston Pumps Sales
N.A.I.C.S.: 423830

Medo USA, Inc. (1)
46 Chancellor Dr, Roselle, IL 60172
Tel.: (630) 924-8811
Web Site: http://www.medousa.com
Sales Range: $25-49.9 Million
Emp.: 20
Vacuum Pump Distr
N.A.I.C.S.: 423830
Lance Culli (Mgr-Natl Sls)

Medotech Co., Ltd. (1)
1-36 Wakamiya 1-chome, Yamagata, 990-2453, Japan
Tel.: (81) 236444363
Web Site: http://www.medotech.co.jp
Emp.: 102
Machine Tools Mfr
N.A.I.C.S.: 333517

Nitto Kohki (Shanghai) Co., Ltd. (1)
Room 2602 Shanghai International Trade Center No 2201 West Yan An Road, Changning District, Shanghai, 200336, China
Tel.: (86) 2164153935
Web Site: https://www.nitto-kohki.cn
Industrial Equipment Distr
N.A.I.C.S.: 423830

Nitto Kohki (Thailand) Co., Ltd. (1)
64 64/1 Moo 9 Rojana Industrial Park Rojana Road, Thanu Sub-district Uthai District, Ayutthaya, 13210, Thailand
Tel.: (66) 35227080
Web Site: https://www.nitto-kohki.co.jp
Sales Range: $25-49.9 Million
Emp.: 90
Linear Piston Rings Mfr
N.A.I.C.S.: 336310
K. Ariya (Mgr)

Nitto Kohki Australia Mfg Pty Ltd (1)
77 Brandl Street, Eight Mile Plains, 4113, QLD, Australia
Tel.: (61) 733404680
Web Site: http://www.nitto-kohki.com.au
Sales Range: $25-49.9 Million
Emp.: 25
Annual Cutters Mfr
N.A.I.C.S.: 333515
Steve Tedmanson (COO)

Nitto Kohki Australia Pty Ltd (1)
Building 1 77 Brandl Street, Eight Mile Plains, 4113, QLD, Australia
Tel.: (61) 733404600
Web Site: http://www.nitto-australia.com.au
Sales Range: $25-49.9 Million
Emp.: 20
Machine Tools Import & Distr
N.A.I.C.S.: 423830

Nitto Kohki Coupling (Thailand) Co., Ltd. (1)
64 1 Moo 9 Rojana Indus Park Rojana Rd Thanu Sub-dist, Uthai Dist, Ayutthaya, 13210, Thailand
Tel.: (66) 35227310
Web Site: http://www.nitto-kohki.co.jp
Sales Range: $25-49.9 Million
Emp.: 92
Couplings Mfr
N.A.I.C.S.: 333613
Shigefumi Aita (Pres)

Nitto Kohki Deutschland GmbH (1)
Gottlieb-Daimler-Str 10, 71144, Steinenbronn, Germany
Tel.: (49) 71579895550
Web Site: https://www.nitto-kohki.eu
Sales Range: $50-74.9 Million
Emp.: 14
Vacuum Pump Distr
N.A.I.C.S.: 423610
Peter Hermann (Mng Dir)

Nitto Kohki Europe Co., Ltd. (1)
Unit A5 Langham Park Maple Road, Castle Donington, DE74 2UT, Derbyshire, United Kingdom
Tel.: (44) 1332653800
Web Site: http://www.nitto-kohki.eu
Sales Range: $25-49.9 Million
Emp.: 3
Pumping Systems Mfr
N.A.I.C.S.: 333914
N. Kotake (Pres)

Nitto Kohki Industry (Thailand) Co., Ltd. (1)
64 64/1 Moo 9 Rojana Industrial Park Rojana Road, Thanu Sub-district Uthai District, Ayutthaya, 13210, Thailand
Tel.: (66) 35227080
Machine Tools Mfr
N.A.I.C.S.: 333517

Nitto Kohki USA, Inc. (1)
46 Chancellor Dr, Roselle, IL 60172
Tel.: (630) 924-9393
Sales Range: $25-49.9 Million
Emp.: 20
Machine Tools & Couplings Sales & Services
N.A.I.C.S.: 423830

Division (Domestic):

Nitto Kohki USA, Inc. - Cupla Division (2)
46 Chancellor Dr, Roselle, IL 60172
Tel.: (630) 924-9393
Web Site: https://nittokohki.com
Couplings Distr
N.A.I.C.S.: 333613

Shirakawa Nitto Kohki Co., Ltd. (1)
12 Yokomine Kurabeishi, Shirakawa, 961-0017, Fukushima, Japan
Tel.: (81) 248225511
Web Site: https://www.nitto-kohki.co.jp
Sales Range: $10-24.9 Million
Emp.: 121
Construction Equipment, Electric Driver & Machine Tools Mfr
N.A.I.C.S.: 333120

Tochigi Nitto Kohki Co., Ltd. (1)
3473-2 Ujiie, Sakura, 329-1311, Tochigi, Japan
Tel.: (81) 286828851
Emp.: 149
Couplings & Linear Piston Pumps Mfr
N.A.I.C.S.: 333613

NITTO SEIKO CO., LTD.

20 Umegahata Inokura, Ayabe, 623-0054, Kyoto, Japan
Tel.: (81) 773423111
Web Site: https://www.nittoseiko.co.jp
Year Founded: 1938
5957—(TKS)
Rev.: $317,234,960
Assets: $378,208,960
Liabilities: $120,118,780
Net Worth: $258,090,180
Earnings: $12,294,060
Emp.: 1,940
Fiscal Year-end: 12/31/23
Screw Product Mfr
N.A.I.C.S.: 332722
Masami Zaiki (Pres)

Subsidiaries:

Malaysian Precision Manufacturing Sdn. Bhd. (1)
No 3 Lorong Perak 3 Kawasan Perusahaan, Telok PanglimaGarang, 42500, Kuala Langat, Selangor, Malaysia
Tel.: (60) 331227405
Fastener Product Mfr & Distr
N.A.I.C.S.: 339993

Nitto Precision Screw Industrial (Zhejiang) Co., Ltd. (1)
No 48 Huang Shan Road Huimin Block, Jiashan, Zhejiang, China
Tel.: (86) 57384753988
Web Site: http://www.nitto-nps.com
Emp.: 115
Fastener Product Mfr & Distr
N.A.I.C.S.: 339993
Shyh-An Su (Vice Chm)

Nitto Seiko (Thailand) Co., Ltd. (1)
84/2 Moo 9 Theparak Road, Bangpla, Bang Phli, 10540, Samut Prakan, Thailand
Tel.: (66) 23154142
Web Site: https://www.nittoseikothailand.com
Emp.: 202
Fastener Product Mfr
N.A.I.C.S.: 339993
Praphon Phodhivorakhun (Vice Chm)

Nitto Seiko America Corporation (1)
1301 Rankin Dr, Troy, MI 48083
Tel.: (248) 588-0133
Screw Mfr
N.A.I.C.S.: 332722
Gene Mack (COO & VP)

Nitto Seiko Co., Ltd. - Control System Division (1)
30 Nogamibata Nobu, Ayabe, Kyoto, Japan
Tel.: (81) 773423151
Fastener Product Mfr & Distr
N.A.I.C.S.: 339993

Nitto Seiko Co., Ltd. - Shiroyama Plant (1)
2 Shiroyama, Ayabe, Kyoto, Japan
Tel.: (81) 773431550
Fastener Product Mfr & Distr
N.A.I.C.S.: 339993

Nitto Seiko Co., Ltd. - Yata Plant (1)
10 Bodai Shimoyata, Ayabe, Kyoto, Japan
Tel.: (81) 773423125
Fastener Product Mfr
N.A.I.C.S.: 339993

Nittoseiko Analytech Co., Ltd. (1)
370 Enzo, Chigasaki, 253-0084, Kanagawa, Japan
Tel.: (81) 467 86 3864
Web Site: http://www.dins.jp
Analytical Instrument Mfr & Distr
N.A.I.C.S.: 334516

P.T. Nitto Alam Indonesia (1)
Jl Manis II Kawasan Industri Manis, Tangerang, 15810, Banten, Indonesia
Tel.: (62) 215918691
Web Site: http://www.nittoindonesia.co.id
Fastener Product Mfr & Distr
N.A.I.C.S.: 339993
Takehiko Kyuma (Chm)

PT Indonesia Nitto Seiko Trading (1)
Jl Manis II Kawasan Industri Manis, Tangerang, 15810, Banten, Indonesia
Tel.: (62) 215918691
Screw Mfr
N.A.I.C.S.: 332722

PT Nitto Alam Indonesia - Bekasi Factory (1)
Delta Silicon Industrial Park Lot 7-8/9, Lippo Cikarang, Bekasi, Indonesia
Tel.: (62) 2189915651
Screw Mfr
N.A.I.C.S.: 332722

Shiho Screw Industrial Co., Ltd. (1)
No 12 Yeong Chuen St, Sheau Gaang Dist, Kaohsiung, 00812, Taiwan
Tel.: (886) 78713198
Web Site: http://www.shihoscrew.com
Emp.: 165
Fastener Product Mfr & Distr
N.A.I.C.S.: 339993
Shyh-An Su (Chm)

THAI NITTO SEIKO MACHINERY CO., LTD. (1)
9/158 Moo 5 Phaholyotin Road Klong 1, Klong Luang, Pathumthani, 12120, Thailand
Tel.: (66) 29020916
Industrial Machinery Mfr & Distr
N.A.I.C.S.: 333248

NITTO SEIMO CO., LTD.

Shinbashi Ekimae Building 2-20-15-701 Shinbashi, Minato-ku, Tokyo, 105-0004, Japan
Tel.: (81) 335725376
Web Site: https://www.nittoseimo.co.jp
Year Founded: 1910
3524—(NGO)
Rev.: $127,518,996
Assets: $186,475,058
Liabilities: $143,785,927
Net Worth: $42,689,131
Earnings: $330,360
Emp.: 910
Fiscal Year-end: 04/30/23
Fishing Equipment Mfr & Whslr
N.A.I.C.S.: 314999
Hiroaki Kobayashi (Pres)

Subsidiaries:

CNK Inc. (1)
1-10-8 Kokubu Hirose, Kirishima, 899-4321, Kagoshima, Japan
Tel.: (81) 995461551
Net Mfr
N.A.I.C.S.: 326199

Plant (Domestic):

CNK Inc. - Nagasaki Factory (2)
455-9 Kuroishi Kosaza-cho, Sasebo, Nagasaki, Japan
Tel.: (81) 956682088
Net Mfr
N.A.I.C.S.: 326199

Nippon Turning Co., Ltd. (1)
6280-60 Minoshima-cho, Fukuyama, 721-0957, Hiroshima, Japan
Tel.: (81) 849203359
Web Site: https://n-turning.nittoseimo-group.co.jp
Emp.: 15
Precision Machinery Mfr
N.A.I.C.S.: 333248

Nitto Net Co., Ltd. (1)
3147-1 Horita, Himi, 935-0104, Toyama, Japan
Tel.: (81) 766912474
Net Mfr
N.A.I.C.S.: 326199

Nitto Net Co., Ltd. - Douto Factory (1)
9-9 Heiwa Shibecha-Cho Kawakami-Gun, Hokkaido, Japan
Tel.: (81) 154851671
Net Mfr
N.A.I.C.S.: 326199

Nitto Net Co., Ltd. - Hakodate Factory (1)
1-3-1 Nanaehama, Hokuto, Hokkaido, Japan
Tel.: (81) 138491420
Net Mfr
N.A.I.C.S.: 326199

Nitto Seimo Co., Ltd. - Fukuyama Factory (1)
14-14 Ichimonji-Cho, Fukuyama, Hiroshima, Japan
Tel.: (81) 849531234
Net Mfr
N.A.I.C.S.: 326199

Taku Seimo Co., Ltd. (1)
4248-1 Befu Higash Taku-Cho, Taku, 846-0012, Saga, Japan
Tel.: (81) 952762531
Net Mfr
N.A.I.C.S.: 326199

NITTOBEST CORPORATION

4-27 Saiwai-cho, Sagae, 991-8610, Yamagata, Japan
Tel.: (81) 237862100

AND PRIVATE COMPANIES

Web Site: https://www.nittobest.co.jp
Year Founded: 1948
2877—(TKS)
Rev.: $358,731,310
Assets: $281,665,320
Liabilities: $174,656,030
Net Worth: $107,009,290
Earnings: $2,716,710
Emp.: 1,844
Fiscal Year-end: 03/31/24
Frozen Food Mfr & Distr
N.A.I.C.S.: 311412

NITTOKU CO., LTD.
22921 Higashimachi, Omiya-ku, Saitama, 330-0841, Japan
Tel.: (81) 486152109
Web Site: https://www.nittoku.co.jp
Year Founded: 1972
6145—(TKS)
Rev.: $203,607,830
Assets: $375,348,850
Liabilities: $112,469,150
Net Worth: $262,879,700
Earnings: $18,137,840
Emp.: 993
Fiscal Year-end: 03/31/24
Coil Winding Machine Mfr
N.A.I.C.S.: 333519
Nobushige Kondo *(Pres)*

Subsidiaries:

NITTOKU CO., LTD. (1)
No 715 303 Daedong-ro, Sasang-gu, Busan, Korea (South)
Tel.: (82) 513112978
Web Site: https://nittoku.co.kr
Coil Winding Machine Distr
N.A.I.C.S.: 423830

NITTOKU ENGINEERING CO., LTD. - Nagasaki Factory (1)
2-1306-4 Ikeda, Omura, 856-0026, Nagasaki, Japan
Tel.: (81) 957522109
Coil Winding Machine Mfr
N.A.I.C.S.: 333519

NITTOKU KOIDE CO., LTD. (1)
9-3 Shinkou-cho, Mitsuke, 954-0076, Niigata, Japan
Tel.: (81) 258660063
Coil Winding Machine Distr
N.A.I.C.S.: 423830

NITTOKU KOSEI CO., LTD. (1)
22-1 Umenomachi Kosaka Kunimi-machi, Date, 969-1784, Fukushima, Japan
Tel.: (81) 245855191
Coil Winding Machine Distr
N.A.I.C.S.: 423830

Nittoku (Thailand) Co., Ltd. (1)
1091/335 Citylink Bldg 5th Fl Room 500 Soi Phetchaburi 35, New Phetchaburi Rd Makkasan Ratchathewi, Bangkok, 10400, Thailand
Tel.: (66) 22555432
Coil Winding Machine Distr
N.A.I.C.S.: 423830

Nittoku America Inc. (1)
1224 Race Rd, Baltimore, MD 21237
Tel.: (410) 574-4960
Web Site: http://www.nittokuamerica.com
Coil Winding Machine Mfr & Distr
N.A.I.C.S.: 333519
Masaaki Watanabe *(Pres)*

Nittoku Engineering Co., Ltd. (1)
Turanka 115, 627 32, Brno, Czech Republic
Tel.: (420) 548183182
Coil Winding Machine Distr
N.A.I.C.S.: 423830

Nittoku Engineering Co., Ltd. (1)
2501-2502 Building A No 319 Xian Xia Rd, Far East International Plaza, Shanghai, 200051, China
Tel.: (86) 2168535620
Coil Winding Machine Distr
N.A.I.C.S.: 423830

Nittoku Engineering Co., Ltd. - Iino Factory (1)
17-3 Aza Kanokojima Meiji Iino-Machi, Fukushima, 960-1393, Japan
Tel.: (81) 245624444
Coil Winding Machine Mfr
N.A.I.C.S.: 333519

Nittoku Europe GmbH (1)
Ebentaler Strasse 140, 9020, Klagenfurt, Austria
Tel.: (43) 463931845
Coil Winding Machine Distr
N.A.I.C.S.: 423830

Nittoku Hong Kong Ltd. (1)
Rm 1306-07 Park-In Commercial Centre 56 Dundas Street, Kowloon, China (Hong Kong)
Tel.: (852) 225122942
Web Site: https://www.nittoku.com.hk
Coil Winding Machine Distr
N.A.I.C.S.: 423830

Nittoku Precision(M) SDN. BHD. (1)
Lot 40 Jalan PJS 7/19 Bandar Sunway, 46150, Petaling Jaya, Selangor, Malaysia
Tel.: (60) 356315320
Coil Winding Machine Distr
N.A.I.C.S.: 423830

Nittoku Singapore Pte. Ltd. (1)
BLK 1092 Lower Delta Road No 05 14/15, Tiong Bahru Industrial Estate, Singapore, 169203, Singapore
Tel.: (65) 62783255
Coil Winding Machine Distr
N.A.I.C.S.: 423830

Taiwan Nittoku Advanced Co., Ltd. (1)
2nd Floor No 82 Section 1 Guangfu Road, Taipei, Taiwan
Tel.: (886) 226519388
Web Site: https://www.nittoku.com.tw
Coil Winding Machine Distr
N.A.I.C.S.: 423830

NIU TECHNOLOGIES
No1 Building No 195 Huilongguan East Road, Changping District, Beijing, 102208, China
Tel.: (86) 1064321899
Web Site: http://www.niu.com
Year Founded: 2014
NIU—(NASDAQ)
Rev.: $485,460,798
Assets: $388,647,478
Liabilities: $187,927,382
Net Worth: $200,720,096
Earnings: ($7,578,215)
Emp.: 641
Fiscal Year-end: 12/31/22
Holding Company
N.A.I.C.S.: 551112
Yan Li *(Founder, Chm & CEO)*

NIUM PTE. LTD.
16 Raffles Quay Hong Leong Building #20-05, Singapore, 048581, Singapore
Tel.: (65) 3158 0618
Web Site: http://www.nium.com
Year Founded: 2015
Financial Services Platform
N.A.I.C.S.: 522320
Prajit Nanu *(Founder & CEO)*

NIUMINCO GROUP LIMITED
Suite 50 14 Narabang Way, Belrose, 2085, NSW, Australia
Tel.: (61) 2 9450 0828
Web Site: http://www.niuminco.com.au
Rev.: $221,674
Assets: $2,389,162
Liabilities: $2,734,484
Net Worth: ($345,322)
Earnings: ($2,607,882)
Fiscal Year-end: 06/30/18
Mineral Exploration Services
N.A.I.C.S.: 212290
Tracey Lake *(Mng Dir)*

Subsidiaries:

Niuminco Pty Ltd (1)
ADF Haus Grd Flr Unit 3 Down Town, PO Box 1545, NCD, Port Moresby, Papua New Guinea
Tel.: (675) 320 0820
Mineral Exploration Services
N.A.I.C.S.: 212290

NIUTECH ENVIRONMENT TECHNOLOGY CORPORATION
48th Floor Puli Center, Shizhong, Jinan, 250022, Shandong, China
Tel.: (86) 53186196301
Web Site: https://www.niutech.com
Year Founded: 2006
688309—(SHG)
Rev.: $23,208,597
Assets: $116,436,781
Liabilities: $16,514,031
Net Worth: $99,922,750
Earnings: $2,053,701
Fiscal Year-end: 12/31/22
Waste Management Services
N.A.I.C.S.: 562998
Bin Niu *(Chm & Gen Mgr)*

NIVA AD NOVI SAD
Curuski Put BB, 21230, Zabalj, Serbia
Tel.: (381) 21832684
Web Site: https://www.niva.rs
Year Founded: 1920
Cotton Wool Product Mfr
N.A.I.C.S.: 339999

NIVAKA FASHIONS LIMITED
Harihar Corporation A-12 Gala No 10/11 Mankoli Road, Dapoda Bhiwandi, Thane, 421302, Maharashtra, India
Tel.: (91) 2261642424
Web Site: http://www.nivakafashions.com
Year Founded: 1983
542206—(BOM)
Rev.: $558,324
Assets: $1,817,289
Liabilities: $576,764
Net Worth: $1,240,525
Earnings: $2,722
Emp.: 23
Fiscal Year-end: 03/31/23
Transportation & Logistic Consulting Services
N.A.I.C.S.: 541614
Mitesh Thakkar *(CFO)*

NIVEUS INVESTMENTS LIMITED
Suite 801 76 Regent Road Sea Point, Cape Town, 8005, Western Cape, South Africa
Tel.: (27) 4817560
Web Site: http://www.niveus.co.za
NIV—(JSE)
Rev.: $1,308,466
Assets: $40,621,255
Liabilities: $6,947,784
Net Worth: $33,673,471
Earnings: ($6,523,909)
Fiscal Year-end: 03/31/19
Automobile Parts Mfr
N.A.I.C.S.: 336110

Subsidiaries:

BETcoza Online (RF) Proprietary Limited (1)
Suite 103 1st Floor Block A Sovereign Quay 34 Somerset Road, Green Point, Cape Town, 8000, South Africa
Tel.: (27) 608279633
Web Site: http://www.bet.co.za
Sports Gambling Services
N.A.I.C.S.: 713290

La Concorde Holdings Limited (1)
Suite 801 76 Regent Road, Sea Point, Cape Town, 8005, South Africa
Tel.: (27) 214817560
Web Site: http://www.laconcordeholdings.co.za
Wine & Spirit Mfr
N.A.I.C.S.: 312140
Lael Irene Bethlehem *(CEO)*

NIVI TRADING LIMITED
Uniphos House CD Marg 11th Road, Near Madhu Park Khar West, Mumbai, 400 052, India
Tel.: (91) 26468000
Web Site: https://www.nivionline.com
Year Founded: 1985
Rev.: $20,788
Assets: $244,423
Liabilities: $394
Net Worth: $244,029
Earnings: $16,751
Fiscal Year-end: 03/31/19
Securities Brokerage Services
N.A.I.C.S.: 523150
Sandra R. Shroff *(Mng Dir)*

NIVIKA FASTIGHETER AB
Ringvägen 38 Värnamo,, 331 32, Jonkoping, Sweden
Tel.: (46) 0102636100
Web Site: https://nivika.se
Year Founded: 2000
NIVI-B—(OMX)
Real Estate
N.A.I.C.S.: 531210

NIVS INTELLIMEDIA TECHNOLOGY GROUP, INC.
NIVS Industry Garden No 29-31 Shuikou Road, Huizhou, 516005, Guangdong, China
Tel.: (86) 75582922658
Web Site: http://www.nivsgroup.com
Sales Range: $150-199.9 Million
Emp.: 1,886
Audio & Video Consumer Products Mfr & Sales
N.A.I.C.S.: 334310
Tianfu Li *(Chm & CEO)*

NIVUS GMBH
Im Taele 2, Eppingen, 75031, Germany
Tel.: (49) 726291910
Web Site: http://www.nivus.com
Year Founded: 1967
Rev.: $12,552,540
Emp.: 100
Commercial Equipment Services
N.A.I.C.S.: 423440
Udo Steppe *(Founder)*

Subsidiaries:

NIVUS AG (1)
Hauptstrasse 49, 8750, Glarus, Switzerland
Tel.: (41) 556452066
Measuring Equipment Distr
N.A.I.C.S.: 423830

NIVUS Austria (1)
Muhlbergstrasse 33B, 3382, Loosdorf, Austria
Tel.: (43) 27545676321
Measuring Equipment Distr
N.A.I.C.S.: 423830

NIVUS France (1)
14 rue de la Paix, 67770, Sessenheim, France
Tel.: (33) 388071696
Web Site: http://www.nivus.fr
Measuring Equipment Distr
N.A.I.C.S.: 423830

NIVUS Korea Co. Ltd. (1)
2502 M Dong Technopark IT Center 32 Song-do-gwa-hak-ro, Yeon-su-gu, Incheon, 406-840, Korea (South)
Tel.: (82) 322098588
Web Site: http://www.nivuskorea.com
Measuring Equipment Distr
N.A.I.C.S.: 423830

NIVUS Middle East (1)

NIVUS GMBH

NIVUS GmbH—(Continued)
Building Q1-1 055, PO Box 9217, Sharjah Airport International Free Zone, Sharjah, United Arab Emirates
Tel.: (971) 165578224
Measuring Equipment Distr
N.A.I.C.S.: 423830
Ebrahem Moussa *(Dir-Bus Dev)*

NIVUS Sp. z o.o. (1)
ul Hutnicza 3 / B-18, 81-212, Gdynia, Poland
Tel.: (48) 587602015
Web Site: http://www.nivus.pl
Measuring Equipment Distr
N.A.I.C.S.: 423830
Pawel Wilkoszewski *(Mgr)*

NIVUS U.K. Ltd. (1)
Wedgewood Rugby Road, Weston under Wetherley, Leamington Spa, CV33 9BW, Warwickshire, United Kingdom
Tel.: (44) 1926632470
Measuring Equipment Distr
N.A.I.C.S.: 423830
Allie Southwood *(Reg Mgr-Sls & Innovation)*

NIWAS SPINNING MILLS LIMITED
406/A Chatti Galli West Mangalwar Peth, Solapur, 413002, Maharashtra, India
Tel.: (91) 2172328650
Year Founded: 1984
521009—(BOM)
Rev.: $1,155,797
Assets: $1,454,798
Liabilities: $3,449,098
Net Worth: ($1,994,300)
Earnings: ($259,952)
Fiscal Year-end: 03/31/14
Cotton & Synthetic Yarn Mfr
N.A.I.C.S.: 313110
V. R. Jaju *(Mng Dir)*

NIX, INC.
Queen's Tower B 8F 2-3-3 Minatomirai, Nishi-ku, Yokohama, 220-6108, Japan
Tel.: (81) 452212001
Web Site: https://www.nix.co.jp
Year Founded: 1953
4243—(TKS)
Rev.: $32,018,440
Assets: $40,852,580
Liabilities: $11,372,360
Net Worth: $29,480,220
Earnings: $1,106,040
Emp.: 165
Fiscal Year-end: 09/30/23
Injected Plastic Products Including Fasteners & Precision Components Mfr & Sales
N.A.I.C.S.: 326199
Kazuhide Aoki *(Pres & COO)*

Subsidiaries:

NIX Of America
2055 Junction Ave Ste 230, San Jose, CA 95131
Tel.: (408) 321-8286
Sales Range: $25-49.9 Million
Emp.: 2
Electric Equipment Mfr
N.A.I.C.S.: 334515

NIYOGIN FINTECH LIMITED
Neelkanth Corporate IT Park 311/312 3rd Floor Kirol Road Vidyavihar, Mumbai, 400086, India
Tel.: (91) 2262514604
Web Site: https://www.niyogin.in
Year Founded: 1988
538772—(BOM)
Rev.: $14,049,218
Assets: $41,326,383
Liabilities: $6,902,572
Net Worth: $34,423,812
Earnings: ($3,403,429)
Emp.: 98

Fiscal Year-end: 03/31/23
Finance Management Services
N.A.I.C.S.: 522291
Amit Rajpal *(Co-Founder)*

Subsidiaries:

Iserveu Technology Private Limited (1)
Plot No E-12 SRB Tower, 11th Floor Infocity Area Chandaka Industrial Estate, Bhubaneswar, 751024, Odisha, India
Tel.: (91) 8069649744
Web Site: https://iserveu.in
Banking & Financial Consulting Services
N.A.I.C.S.: 541611

Monemap Investment Advisors Private Limited (1)

NIZHNEKAMSKSHINA PJSC
Promzona, 423580, Nizhnekamsk, Russia
Tel.: (7) 8555497930
Web Site: http://www.dentalclaimsupport.com
NKSH—(MOEX)
Tire Product Mfr
N.A.I.C.S.: 326211
Tsalik Berovich Portnoy *(Dir-Acting)*

NJ HOLDINGS INC.
7F Shibakoen First Building 3-8-2 Shiba, Minato-ku, Tokyo, 105-0014, Japan
Tel.: (81) 354188121
Web Site: https://www.njhd.jp
Year Founded: 1991
9421—(TKS)
Rev.: $60,321,560
Assets: $24,525,460
Liabilities: $14,144,280
Net Worth: $10,381,180
Earnings: $1,704,280
Emp.: 887
Fiscal Year-end: 06/30/24
Mobile Communication Equipment & Games Distr
N.A.I.C.S.: 423690
Toshimitsu Tsutsui *(CEO)*

Subsidiaries:

NEPRO CREATE Co., Ltd. (1)
3-8-2 Shiba Minato, Tokyo, 105-0014, Japan
Tel.: (81) 354275071
Web Site: http://www.nepro.co.jp
Electronic Store Operator
N.A.I.C.S.: 449210

NJS CO., LTD.
1-1-1 Shibaura, Minato-Ku, Tokyo, 105-0023, Japan
Tel.: (81) 363244355
Web Site: https://www.njs.co.jp
Year Founded: 1951
2325—(TKS)
Rev.: $156,171,430
Assets: $209,105,370
Liabilities: $35,031,690
Net Worth: $174,073,680
Earnings: $14,158,730
Emp.: 1,362
Fiscal Year-end: 12/31/23
Environmental Engineering Services
N.A.I.C.S.: 541330
Yuichi Tsuchida *(Exec Dir)*

Subsidiaries:

B&E Engineers Inc. (1)
20 E Foothill Blvd Ste 230, Arcadia, CA 91006-2375
Tel.: (626) 446-4449
Web Site: https://www.beeng.com
Civil Engineering Services
N.A.I.C.S.: 541330
Ramy F. Awad *(Pres)*

NJS Consultants Co., Ltd. (1)
1-1-1 Shibaura, Minato-ku, Tokyo, 105-0023, Japan

Tel.: (81) 3 6324 4344
Web Site: http://www.njs-consultants.com
Water Supply Services
N.A.I.C.S.: 221310
Kengo Fujikawa *(Pres)*

Subsidiary (Non-US):

NJS Engineers India Pvt. Ltd. (2)
18 Shailesh Society, Karvenagar, Pune, 411 052, India
Tel.: (91) 2025459533
Web Site: https://www.njsei.com
Engineering Consulting Services
N.A.I.C.S.: 541330
Uday G. Kelkar *(Mng Dir)*

NJS E&M Co., Ltd. (1)
1-1-1 Shibaura, Minato-ku, Tokyo, 105-0023, Japan
Tel.: (81) 363244350
Web Site: https://www.njs.co.jp
Waste Water Treatment Services
N.A.I.C.S.: 221320
Makoto Tanaka *(Pres & CEO)*

NK BANK JSC
2 Miusskaya Sq, 125047, Moscow, Russia
Tel.: (7) 4954118844
Web Site: http://www.nkbank.ru
Year Founded: 1993
Sales Range: Less than $1 Million
Commercial & Investment Banking Services
N.A.I.C.S.: 523150
Grigoriev Viktor *(Pres)*

NK CO., LTD.
194-11 Gwahaksandan-ro, Gangseo-gu, Busan, Korea (South)
Tel.: (82) 512042211
Web Site: https://www.nkcf.com
Year Founded: 1980
085310—(KRS)
Rev.: $58,819,602
Assets: $142,467,132
Liabilities: $44,113,539
Net Worth: $98,353,593
Earnings: $8,216,157
Emp.: 74
Fiscal Year-end: 12/31/22
Fire Extinguishing System Mfr
N.A.I.C.S.: 339999
D. H. Lee *(Gen Mgr)*

Subsidiaries:

ENK Co., Ltd. (1)
502 Gwahaksandan-ro, Gangseo-gu, Busan, Korea (South)
Tel.: (82) 519747614
Web Site: https://www.enkcf.com
Compressed Gas Cylinder Mfr
N.A.I.C.S.: 325120
Jin Myoung Lee *(CEO)*

NKTECH Co., Ltd. (1)
380 Nambu-daero, 18145, Osan, Gyeonggi-do, Korea (South)
Tel.: (82) 313773311
Web Site: https://www.nktech.co.kr
Emp.: 45
High Pressure Container Mfr
N.A.I.C.S.: 332420
Lee Seung-bok *(CEO)*

The Safety Co., Ltd. (1)
23 Noksansaneopjungro, Gangseo-Gu, Busan, Korea (South)
Tel.: (82) 51 468 0119
Maritime Transport Services
N.A.I.C.S.: 483211

NKB INC.
New International Building 3-4-1 Marunouchi, Chiyoda-Ku, Tokyo, 100-0005, Japan
Tel.: (81) 332155511
Web Site: http://www.nkb.co.jp
Year Founded: 1948
Rev.: $184,320,000
Emp.: 200

INTERNATIONAL PUBLIC

Media Buying Services, Outdoor, Out-of-Home Media
N.A.I.C.S.: 541830
Hisao Taki *(Pres)*

NKHP AO
Elevatornaya st 22, Krasnodar Territory, 353901, Novorossiysk, 353901, Russia
Tel.: (7) 8617678041
Web Site: https://www.novoroskhp.ru
NKHP—(MOEX)
Sales Range: Less than $1 Million
Flour Milling Services
N.A.I.C.S.: 311211
Yuri Medvedev *(Deputy Gen Dir-Economics & Fin)*

NKK SWITCHES CO., LTD.
715-1 Unane, Takatsu-Ku, Kawasaki, 213 8553, Japan
Tel.: (81) 448138001
Web Site: http://www.nkkswitches.com
Year Founded: 1953
Sales Range: $25-49.9 Million
Emp.: 248
Supplier & Mfr of Industrial Switches
N.A.I.C.S.: 333248
Tomoshige Ohashi *(Pres)*

Subsidiaries:

NKK Switches (1)
7850 E Gelding Dr, Scottsdale, AZ 85260-2950
Tel.: (480) 991-0942
Web Site: http://www.nkkswitches.com
Sales Range: $50-74.9 Million
Emp.: 60
Electrical Switches Mfr
N.A.I.C.S.: 423610
Jessica Reimann *(Head-Mktg-North America)*

NKK Switches China Co., Ltd. (1)
Room B 2/F No 1440 Yan An Rd, Shanghai, 200040, China
Tel.: (86) 2162496574
Web Site: http://www.nkkswitches.com.cn
Electronic Components Distr
N.A.I.C.S.: 423690

NKK Switches Hong Kong Co., Ltd. (1)
Room 701-702 7/F Prosperity Centre 77-81 Container Port Rd, Kwai Chung, Hong Kong, China (Hong Kong)
Tel.: (852) 23666634
Web Site: http://www.nkkswitches.com.hk
Electronic Components Distr
N.A.I.C.S.: 423690

NKMAX CO., LTD.
1F/6F SNUH Healthcare Innovation Park 172 Dolma-ro, Bundang-gu, Seongnam, 13605, Gyeonggi-do, Korea (South)
Tel.: (82) 3180178114
Web Site: https://www.nkmax.com
Year Founded: 2002
182400—(KRS)
Rev.: $8,638,483
Assets: $130,156,109
Liabilities: $66,325,533
Net Worth: $63,830,576
Earnings: ($42,650,851)
Emp.: 141
Fiscal Year-end: 12/31/22
Biological Product Mfr
N.A.I.C.S.: 325414
Stephen Chen *(Co-CTO)*

Subsidiaries:

NKGen Biotech, Inc. (1)
19700 Fairchild Rd Ste 300, Irvine, CA 92612
Tel.: (949) 396-6830
Web Site: https://nkgenbiotech.com
Biotechnology Research Services
N.A.I.C.S.: 541714

AND PRIVATE COMPANIES **NMBZ HOLDINGS LIMITED**

NKMax America, Inc. (1)
3001 Daimler St, Santa Ana, CA 92705
Tel.: (949) 396-6830
Web Site: https://www.nkgenbiotech.com
Healtcare Services
N.A.I.C.S.: 621999
Sangwoo Park (Chm & CEO)

NKT A/S
Vibeholms Alle 20, DK 2605,
Brondby, Denmark
Tel.: (45) 43482000   DK
Web Site: https://www.nkt.dk
Year Founded: 1891
NKT—(CSE)
Rev.: $2,243,686,596
Assets: $2,986,617,742
Liabilities: $1,752,212,389
Net Worth: $1,234,405,353
Earnings: $67,342,974
Emp.: 4,000
Fiscal Year-end: 12/31/22
Holding Company
N.A.I.C.S.: 551112
Rene Svendsen-Tune (Deputy Chm)

Subsidiaries:

NKT (Iberica) S.L. (1)
Carrer d'Enric Granados 135 P 5 PTA 2,
08008, Barcelona, Spain
Tel.: (34) 935907017
Voltage Cable Mfr & Distr
N.A.I.C.S.: 335929

NKT (U.K.) Ltd. (1)
Unit 6 Ashbrook Office Park Longstone
Road, Manchester, M22 5LB, United Kingdom
Tel.: (44) 1614370750
Voltage Cable Mfr & Distr
N.A.I.C.S.: 335929

NKT AS (1)
Birkelandsvej 26a, 1081, Oslo, Norway
Tel.: (47) 32817040
Voltage Cable Mfr & Distr
N.A.I.C.S.: 335929

NKT GmbH (1)
Helgolander Damm 75, 26954, Nordenham,
Germany
Tel.: (49) 4731364326
Voltage Cable Mfr & Distr
N.A.I.C.S.: 335929

NKT GmbH & Co. KG (1)
Dusseldorfer Strasse 400 im Chempark,
51061, Cologne, Germany
Tel.: (49) 2216760
Web Site: https://www.nkt.de
Voltage Cable Mfr & Distr
N.A.I.C.S.: 335929

NKT HV Cables AB (1)
Savelundsgatan 2, 441 38, Alingsas, Sweden
Tel.: (46) 32277400
Voltage Cable Mfr & Distr
N.A.I.C.S.: 335929

**NKT Operations India Private
Limited** (1)
7th Floor SKCL Triton Square C3-C7 Thiru-
Vi-Ka Industrial Estate, Guindy, Chennai,
600032, Tamil Nadu, India
Tel.: (91) 9600011050
Cable Wire Mfr & Distr
N.A.I.C.S.: 335921

**NKT Photonics (Zhenzhen) Co.,
Ltd.** (1)
A806 8th Floor Building 5 Shenzhen Bay
Ecological Technology Park, 26 Gaoxin
Nanhuan Road Nanshan District, Shenzhen, 518057, China
Tel.: (86) 75586565376
Fiber Laser Product Distr
N.A.I.C.S.: 423460
Luksun Li (Gen Mgr)

NKT Photonics GmbH (1)
Schanzenstrasse 39 Bldg D9-D13, 51063,
Cologne, Germany
Tel.: (49) 221998870
Fiber Laser Product Distr
N.A.I.C.S.: 423460
Felix Heck (Mgr-Bus Segment)

NKT Photonics Inc. (1)
3514 N Vancouver Ave Ste 310, Portland,
OR 97227
Tel.: (503) 444-8404
Fiber Laser Product Distr
N.A.I.C.S.: 423460
Hector Eduardo Gonzalez-Stahl (Sr Mgr-
Sls-Fiber Optics-Latam)

NKT Photonics Ltd. (1)
20 Compass Point Ensign Way, Southampton, SO31 4RA, United Kingdom
Tel.: (44) 2380458776
Fiber Laser Product Distr
N.A.I.C.S.: 423460

**NKT Photonics Switzerland
GmbH** (1)
Althardstrasse 70, 8105, Regensdorf, Switzerland
Tel.: (41) 435383657
Fiber Laser Product Distr
N.A.I.C.S.: 423460

NKT Pty Ltd (1)
3/789 Kingsford Smith Drive, Eagle Farm,
4009, QLD, Australia
Tel.: (61) 1300458112
Voltage Cable Mfr & Distr
N.A.I.C.S.: 335929

Pressure-Pro, Inc. (1)
7300 Commercial Cir, Fort Pierce, FL
34951
Tel.: (772) 461-4486
Sales Range: $1-9.9 Million
Emp.: 48
Industrial Machinery & Equipment Merchant
Whslr
N.A.I.C.S.: 423830
Dale Reed (Pres)

Ventcroft Ltd. (1)
Faraday Road Astmoor Industrial Estate,
Runcorn, WA7 1PE, Cheshire, United Kingdom
Tel.: (44) 1928581098
Web Site: https://www.ventcroft.co.uk
Electrical & Electronic Mfr
N.A.I.C.S.: 334419

nkt cables group GmbH (1)
Chempark Dusseldorfer Strasse 400,
51061, Cologne, Germany
Tel.: (49) 221 676 0
Web Site: http://www.nktcables.com
Sales Range: $900-999.9 Million
Mfr & Supplier of Cables for Electricity &
Energy Sector
N.A.I.C.S.: 335929

Subsidiary (Non-US):

OOO nkt cables (2)
Rakhmanovsky per 4 bld 1, 127051, Moscow, Russia
Tel.: (7) 495 620 0671
Web Site: http://www.nktcables.ru
Power Cables Sales
N.A.I.C.S.: 423990

nkt cable Italia s.r.l. (2)
Via D Fiasella 3/16, 16121, Genoa, Italy
Tel.: (39) 0108698150
Web Site: http://www.nktcables.es
Emp.: 6
Power Cables Sales
N.A.I.C.S.: 423990

nkt cables AB (2)
Kallviksvagen 18, PO Box 731, 791 29, Falun, Sweden
Tel.: (46) 2368400
Web Site: http://www.nktcables.se
Sales Range: $100-124.9 Million
Emp.: 333
Specialty Power Cables Mfr
N.A.I.C.S.: 335929
Fredrik Dahlstedt (Mng Dir)

nkt cables Ltd. (2)
8a South Preston Office Village Cuerdon
Way, Bamber Bridge, Preston, PR5 6BL,
United Kingdom
Tel.: (44) 77 99 116 477
Web Site: http://www.nktcables.com
Power Cables Sales
N.A.I.C.S.: 423990

nkt cables Ltd., Changzhou (2)
Dongfang Road 128, Qishuyan Development, Changzhou, 213025, Jiangsu, China
Tel.: (86) 519 8840 4180
Web Site: http://www.nktcables.cn
Emp.: 360
Power Cables Mfr & Sales
N.A.I.C.S.: 335929

nkt cables S.A. (2)
ul Gajowa 3, 43 254, Warsaw, Poland
Tel.: (48) 32 757 17 00
Web Site: http://www.nktcables.pl
Emp.: 260
Power Cables Mfr & Sales
N.A.I.C.S.: 335929
Witold Przybyla (Sls Dir)

nkt cables Spain S.L. (2)
Edificio Testa Sant Cugat Alcalde Barnils
64-68, escalera B 3 piso local 3, Sant Cugat de Valles, 08174, Barcelona, Spain
Tel.: (34) 93 59 07 017
Web Site: http://www.nktcables.es
Emp.: 2
Power Cables Sales
N.A.I.C.S.: 423990

nkt cables a/s (2)
Toftegardsvej 25, 4550, Asnaes, Denmark
Tel.: (45) 59661234
Web Site: http://www.nktcables.dk
Emp.: 319
Power Cable Mfr
N.A.I.C.S.: 335929
Jens Peter Johansen (Mgr-Sls)

nkt cables as (2)
Stoperigata 7, NO 3003, Drammen, Norway
Tel.: (47) 32 810 70 40
Web Site: http://www.nktcables.no
Emp.: 12
Power Cables Mfr & Sales
N.A.I.C.S.: 335929

nkt cables s.r.o. (2)
Prumyslova 1130, CZ 272 01, Kladno,
Czech Republic
Tel.: (420) 312 607 111
Web Site: http://www.nktcables.cz
Emp.: 350
Power Cables Mfr & Sales
N.A.I.C.S.: 335929
Zdenek Trejbal (Sls Dir)

NLC INDIA LIMITED
No135 EVR Periyar High Road Kilpauk, Egmore Complex of Food Corporation of India Chetpet, Chennai,
600010, Tamil Nadu, India
Tel.: (91) 4428360027
Web Site: https://www.nlcindia.in
NLCINDIA—(NSE)
Rev.: $1,610,484,330
Assets: $7,358,218,140
Liabilities: $5,174,596,245
Net Worth: $2,183,621,895
Earnings: $183,652,560
Emp.: 11,379
Fiscal Year-end: 03/31/21
Electric Power Generation & Distribution Services
N.A.I.C.S.: 221118
Rakesh Kumar (Chm & Mng Dir)

Subsidiaries:

NLC Tamilnadu Power Limited (1)
Neyveli House No 135 EVR Periyar High
Road, Kilpauk, Chennai, 600 010, India
Tel.: (91) 4428360037
Web Site: http://www.ntplpower.com
Electric Power Generation & Distribution
Services
N.A.I.C.S.: 221118
L. Chandrasekar (Chief Vigilance Officer)

NLINKS CO., LTD.
8F EbisuIS Bldg 1-13-6 Ebisu,
Shibuya-ku, Tokyo, 150-0013, Japan
Tel.: (81) 357937500
Web Site: https://nlinks.co.jp
Year Founded: 1997
6578—(TKS)
Rev.: $27,920,420
Assets: $16,852,930
Liabilities: $9,039,750
Net Worth: $7,813,180
Earnings: $623,920
Fiscal Year-end: 02/29/24
Digital Advertising Services
N.A.I.C.S.: 541850
Kensuke Kuribayashi (Founder &
Pres)

NLS PHARMACEUTICS LTD.
Alter Postplatz 2, CH-6370, Stans,
Switzerland
Tel.: (41) 416188000   CH
Web Site:
https://www.nlspharma.com
Year Founded: 2015
NLSP—(NASDAQ)
Assets: $1,846,641
Liabilities: $10,680,204
Net Worth: ($8,833,563)
Earnings: ($12,172,029)
Emp.: 3
Fiscal Year-end: 12/31/23
Biotechnology Research & Development Services
N.A.I.C.S.: 541714
Ronald Hafner (Chm)

NMB BANK LIMITED
Babarmahal, Kathmandu, Nepal
Tel.: (977) 15346160   NP
Web Site: https://www.nmb.com.np
Year Founded: 2008
NMB—(NEP)
Rev.: $126,559,753
Assets: $1,541,237,307
Liabilities: $1,359,220,544
Net Worth: $182,016,763
Earnings: $15,800,669
Emp.: 1,654
Fiscal Year-end: 07/15/20
Commercial Banking Services
N.A.I.C.S.: 522110
Pawan Kumar Golyan (Chm)

Subsidiaries:

NMB Capital Limited (1)
Baluwatar 4, Kathmandu, Nepal
Tel.: (977) 14437963
Web Site: https://www.nmbcl.com.np
Investment Banking Services
N.A.I.C.S.: 523150
Shreejesh Ghimire (CEO)

NMB BANK PLC
Ohio Street/Ali Hassan Mwinyi Road,
PO Box 9213, Dar es Salaam, Tanzania
Tel.: (255) 222322000   TZ
Web Site: https://www.nmbbank.co.tz
NMB—(DAR)
Rev.: $310,946,760
Assets: $3,035,084,480
Liabilities: $2,548,692,130
Net Worth: $486,392,350
Earnings: $90,429,000
Emp.: 3,465
Fiscal Year-end: 12/31/20
Retail & Commercial Banking Services
N.A.I.C.S.: 522110
Aziz Chacha (Treas)

NMBZ HOLDINGS LIMITED
19207 Liberation Legacy Way, PO
Box 2564, Borrowdale, Harare, Zimbabwe
Tel.: (263) 8688003347   ZW
Web Site: https://www.nmbz.co.zw
NMB—(ZIM)
Rev.: $1,694,757,295
Assets: $4,150,996,985
Liabilities: $2,682,527,035
Net Worth: $1,468,469,950
Earnings: $761,620,279
Emp.: 238
Fiscal Year-end: 12/31/23
Bank Holding Company

NMBZ HOLDINGS LIMITED

NMBZ Holdings Limited—(Continued)
N.A.I.C.S.: 551111
Benson Ndachena *(Fin Dir)*

Subsidiaries:

NMB Bank Limited (1)
Unity Ct Corner First St 1st Fl, Kwame Nkrumah Ave, Harare, 2564, Zimbabwe (100%)
Tel.: (263) 4759651
Provider of Banking Services
N.A.I.C.S.: 522110
Benefit Washaya *(Acting CEO)*

NMC HEALTH PLC

Level 1 Devonshire House One Mayfair Place Mayfair, London, W1J 8AJ, United Kingdom
Tel.: (44) 2032057313
Web Site: http://nmc.ae
Year Founded: 2011
Rev.: $2,057,253,000
Assets: $3,872,415,000
Liabilities: $2,515,652,000
Net Worth: $1,356,763,000
Earnings: $251,909,000
Emp.: 18,000
Fiscal Year-end: 12/31/18
Healthcare Services
N.A.I.C.S.: 621999
Michael Brendon Davis *(CEO & COO)*

Subsidiaries:

Aspen Healthcare Limited (1)
Centurion House 3rd Floor 37 Jewry Street, London, EC3N 2ER, United Kingdom
Tel.: (44) 2079776080
Web Site: http://www.aspen-healthcare.co.uk
Health Care Srvices
N.A.I.C.S.: 622110
David Lewsey *(Dir-Corp Fin)*

NMC Holding Co LLC (1)
Street 5 Warehouse 120, PO Box 6222, Abu Dhabi, 6222, United Arab Emirates
Tel.: (971) 26734300
Web Site: http://www.nmc.ae
Sales Range: $350-399.9 Million
Emp.: 4,000
Diversified Holding Company
N.A.I.C.S.: 551112
B.R. Shetty *(CEO & Mng Dir)*

Subsidiary (Domestic):

Aabharan Jewellery LLC (2)
UAE Exchange Centre Building Hamdan Street, Abu Dhabi, United Arab Emirates
Tel.: (971) 26339433
Web Site: http://www.nmc.ae
Sales Range: $25-49.9 Million
Emp.: 9
Jewelry Retailer
N.A.I.C.S.: 458310

Aabharan Jewellery LLC (2)
Karama Centre Al Kifaf Street, PO Box 6401, Dubai, United Arab Emirates
Tel.: (971) 43356667
Sales Range: $25-49.9 Million
Emp.: 10
Jewelry Retailer
N.A.I.C.S.: 458310

BR Medical Suites FZ LLC (2)
4005 Block B 4th Floor Al Razi Building No 64, PO Box 505162, Dubai, United Arab Emirates
Tel.: (971) 44392305
Web Site: http://www.brms.ae
Healtcare Services
N.A.I.C.S.: 621498
Marc Mueller *(Dir-Medical)*

Bait Al Shifa Pharmacy LLC (2)
Abu Hail Road Opposite Abu Hail Centre Hor Al Anz, Deira, United Arab Emirates
Tel.: (971) 42689800
Healtcare Services
N.A.I.C.S.: 621498

Emilam Industries LLC (2)
Jebel Ali Industrial Area 1 Jebel Ali, PO Box 43794, Dubai, 43794, United Arab Emirates
Tel.: (971) 48801441
Web Site: http://www.emilam.net.ae
Sales Range: $25-49.9 Million
Emp.: 40
Laminated Melamine Faced Medium Density Fiber (MDF) Boards Mfr
N.A.I.C.S.: 325220
Raghava Charaya *(Gen Mgr)*

Focus Optics (2)
New Al Safiya Building, Hor Al Anz Deira, Dubai, United Arab Emirates
Tel.: (971) 42621217
Web Site: http://www.nmc.ae
Sales Range: $25-49.9 Million
Emp.: 20
Optical Retailer
N.A.I.C.S.: 456130

Unit (Domestic):

Foodlands Restaurant (2)
Airport Road Al Manhal Palace, PO Box 200, Abu Dhabi, 46222, United Arab Emirates
Tel.: (971) 26330099
Web Site: http://www.foodlands.com
Sales Range: $10-24.9 Million
Emp.: 100
Restaurant Operators
N.A.I.C.S.: 722511
Abdulla Humaid Al Mazroei *(Chm)*

Foodlands Restaurant (2)
PO Box 7832, Dubai, United Arab Emirates
Tel.: (971) 42683314
Web Site: http://www.foodlands.com
Sales Range: $10-24.9 Million
Emp.: 50
Restaurant Operators
N.A.I.C.S.: 722511

Lotus Boutique Hotel (2)
Burjahar Naif intersection, PO Box 172747, Burj Al Nahar Deira, Deira, United Arab Emirates
Tel.: (971) 42735555
Web Site: http://www.fortunegroupofhotels.com
Sales Range: $10-24.9 Million
Emp.: 80
Hotel Operations
N.A.I.C.S.: 721110
Alok Narula *(Gen Mgr)*

Subsidiary (Domestic):

NMC Day Surgery Centre LLC (2)
PO Box 114621, Abu Dhabi, United Arab Emirates
Tel.: (971) 26911500
Healtcare Services
N.A.I.C.S.: 621498
Laila Abdullah *(Mgr & Head-Nursing)*

NMC Dubai Investment Park LLC (2)
Dubai Investement Park -1, Dubai, United Arab Emirates
Tel.: (971) 48108801
Healtcare Services
N.A.I.C.S.: 621498

NMC Healthcare LLC (2)
104 1st Floor Sama Tower Zayed the first street Electra Street, Abu Dhabi, United Arab Emirates
Tel.: (971) 26179200
Healtcare Services
N.A.I.C.S.: 621498
Ramachandra Manjeshwar *(Mgr-IT Svc Desk)*

Unit (Domestic):

NMC Hearing Care Centre (2)
Airport Road Corner Elektra, PO Box 6222, Abu Dhabi, United Arab Emirates
Tel.: (971) 26332255
Emp.: 1,000
Hearing Services & Products
N.A.I.C.S.: 621340

Division (Domestic):

NMC Hospitals (2)
Electra Street, PO Box 6222, Abu Dhabi, United Arab Emirates
Tel.: (971) 26332255
Sales Range: $550-599.9 Million
Hospitals Owner & Operator
N.A.I.C.S.: 622110

NMC Opticals (2)
PO Box 6222, Abu Dhabi, United Arab Emirates
Tel.: (971) 26332255
Web Site: http://www.nmc.ae
Sales Range: $400-449.9 Million
Emp.: 2,400
Optical Retailer
N.A.I.C.S.: 456130

NMC Pharmacies (2)
Electro St Airport Rd, PO Box 6222, Abu Dhabi, 6000, United Arab Emirates
Tel.: (971) 26332255
Web Site: http://www.nmc.ae
Sales Range: $25-49.9 Million
Emp.: 25
Pharmacies Owner & Operator
N.A.I.C.S.: 456110
Abdulla Humaid Al Mazroei *(Chm)*

NMC Special Medical Services (2)
PO Box 6222, Abu Dhabi, United Arab Emirates
Tel.: (971) 26332255
Web Site: http://www.nmc.ae
Sales Range: $125-149.9 Million
Emp.: 1,000
Ambulatory & Special Medical Sugical Services
N.A.I.C.S.: 621910

Subsidiary (Domestic):

NMC Trading L.L.C. (2)
1st Fl Al Raihan Building Omniyat The Square Apartments 46th Street, Al Mamzar/UAE Ministry Islamic Affairs Office, Dubai, United Arab Emirates
Tel.: (971) 4 2172888
Web Site: http://www.nmctrading.com
Sales Range: $75-99.9 Million
Emp.: 185
Pharmaceuticals, Cosmetics, Medical Products & Food Products Distr
N.A.I.C.S.: 425120
Gopi Kumar *(Mgr-HR)*

Neopharma LLC (2)
Plot A-1 89-95, PO Box 72900, Abu Dhabi, 72900, United Arab Emirates
Tel.: (971) 25501000
Web Site: http://www.neopharma.ae
Sales Range: $125-149.9 Million
Emp.: 200
Pharmaceuticals Mfr
N.A.I.C.S.: 325412
Suresh Pai *(COO-Mfg)*

Subsidiary (US):

Dr. Reddy's Laboratories Tennessee LLC (3)
201 Industrial Dr, Bristol, TN 37620-5413 (100%)
Tel.: (423) 652-3100
Pharmaceuticals Mfr
N.A.I.C.S.: 325412

Subsidiary (Non-US):

Neo Ala Co. Ltd. (3)
4th Floor Iidabashi Grand Bloom 2-10-2 Fujimi, Chiyoda-ku, Tokyo, 1020071, Japan
Tel.: (81) 0362616970
Animal Products Mfr
N.A.I.C.S.: 311119
Atsushi Kawada *(Dir)*

Subsidiary (Domestic):

Kyowa CritiCare Co., Ltd. (4)
4-8-29 Asahicho, Atsugi, 243-0014, Kanagawa, Japan
Tel.: (81) 358405141
Web Site: http://www.kyowacriticare.co.jp
Pharmaceuticals Product Mfr
N.A.I.C.S.: 325412

Division (Domestic):

neo Care L.L.C. (3)
403 4th Floor Aeroflot Airline Building, Maktoum Street, Dubai, United Arab Emirates
Tel.: (971) 42274564
Detergents & Cleaning Products Mfr
N.A.I.C.S.: 325611

INTERNATIONAL PUBLIC

Subsidiary (Domestic):

New Medical Centre LLC (2)
PO Box 25262, Sharjah, United Arab Emirates
Tel.: (971) 65758000
Healtcare Services
N.A.I.C.S.: 621498

New Medical Centre Specialty Hospital LLC (2)
PO Box 84142, Al Ain, United Arab Emirates
Tel.: (971) 37030300
Healtcare Services
N.A.I.C.S.: 621498

New Pharmacy Company Limited (2)
7 Street, Abu Dhabi, United Arab Emirates
Tel.: (971) 26322379
Healtcare Services
N.A.I.C.S.: 621498

Reliance Information Technology LLC (2)
PO Box 107987, Abu Dhabi, United Arab Emirates
Tel.: (971) 26323296
Web Site: http://www.re.ae
Information Technology Consulting Services
N.A.I.C.S.: 541512

Reliance Infotech (2)
Build 2, PO Box 6222, Abu Dhabi, 6222, United Arab Emirates
Tel.: (971) 26323296
Web Site: http://www.nmc.ae
Sales Range: $50-74.9 Million
Emp.: 150
IT Services
N.A.I.C.S.: 541512
H.J. Mark Tompkins *(Chm)*

UAE Exchange Centre LLC (2)
PO Box 44041, Abu Dhabi, United Arab Emirates
Tel.: (971) 43537378
Web Site: http://www.uaeexchange.com
Sales Range: $700-749.9 Million
Emp.: 1,500
Financial Services
N.A.I.C.S.: 525990
B. R. Shetty *(Chm)*

Subsidiary (Non-US):

UAE Exchange Australia Pty Ltd (3)
Level 5 122 Castlereagh Street, Sydney, 2000, NSW, Australia
Tel.: (61) 800 06 05 95
Web Site: http://www.uaeexchange.com
Emp.: 9,000
Financial Services
N.A.I.C.S.: 525990

Subsidiary (Domestic):

UAE Sponsorship Centre (2)
PO Box 6333, Abu Dhabi, United Arab Emirates
Tel.: (971) 26334383
Web Site: http://www.nmc.ae
International Advisory Services
N.A.I.C.S.: 523940

Zari Zardozi (2)
Al Raha Mall - Ground Floor, PO Box 37005, Abu Dhabi, United Arab Emirates
Tel.: (971) 25565188
Web Site: http://www.zarizardozi.com
Indian Restaurant Operations
N.A.I.C.S.: 722511
Abdulla Humaid Al Mazroei *(Chm)*

NMCN PLC

Nunn Close The County Estate, Huthwaite, Sutton in Ashfield, NG17 2HW, Nottinghamshire, United Kingdom
Tel.: (44) 1623515008
Web Site: http://www.nmcn.com
Year Founded: 1946
NMCN—(LSE)
Rev.: $532,310,237
Assets: $184,269,307
Liabilities: $156,796,534
Net Worth: $27,472,774

AND PRIVATE COMPANIES

Earnings: $7,754,179
Emp.: 1,718
Fiscal Year-end: 12/31/19
Construction Engineering Services
N.A.I.C.S.: 541330
Ian Elliott *(Chm-Acting)*

Subsidiaries:

Nomenca Ltd. (1)
Nunn Close The County Estate, Huthwaite, Sutton in Ashfield, NG17 2HW, Notts, United Kingdom
Tel.: (44) 1925281200
Emp.: 50
Civil, Mechanical & Electrical Engineering Services
N.A.I.C.S.: 541330

North Midland Building Ltd. (1)
Nunn Close The County Estate, Huthwaite, Sutton in Ashfield, NG17 2HW, Notts, United Kingdom
Tel.: (44) 1623518860
Web Site: http://www.northmid.co.uk
Sales Range: $25-49.9 Million
Emp.: 200
Construction Services
N.A.I.C.S.: 236220

NMDC LIMITED

Khanij Bhavan Masab Tank, Hyderabad, 500028, India
Tel.: (91) 4023538713   In
Web Site: https://www.nmdc.co.in
Year Founded: 1958
526371—(BOM)
Rev.: $2,725,520,700
Assets: $4,285,728,321
Liabilities: $1,200,368,266
Net Worth: $3,085,360,055
Earnings: $669,669,574
Emp.: 5,713
Fiscal Year-end: 03/31/24
Diamond Mining
N.A.I.C.S.: 212115
Sunil Wadhwani *(Gen Mgr-Comml)*

Subsidiaries:

JK Mineral Development Corporation Limited (1)
143 A, Gandhinagar, 180004, Jammu, India
Tel.: (91) 1912431396
Sales Range: $50-74.9 Million
Emp.: 4
Mineral Development Services
N.A.I.C.S.: 213115
Shakeel Ahamad Rafaqui *(Asst Mgr)*

NMS HOLDINGS CORPORATION

Tokyo Opera City Tower 45F 3-20-2 Nishi-shinjuku, Shinjuku-ku, Tokyo, 163-1445, Japan
Tel.: (81) 353331737   JP
Web Site: https://www.n-ms.co.jp
Year Founded: 1985
2162—(TKS)
Rev.: $481,493,754
Assets: $237,701,235
Liabilities: $215,601,010
Net Worth: $22,100,225
Earnings: ($4,889,995)
Emp.: 12,648
Fiscal Year-end: 03/31/24
Holding Company
N.A.I.C.S.: 551112
Fumiaki Ono *(Pres & CEO)*

Subsidiaries:

NMS International Resources Co., Ltd. (1)
D1 Room 14th Floor Zodiac Building Lane 19 Duy Tan Street, Dich Vong Hau Ward Cau Giay District, Hanoi, Vietnam
Tel.: (84) 2437918157
Electrical & Electronic Product Mfr
N.A.I.C.S.: 335999

NMS Lao Sole Co., Ltd. (1)
No 179 Unit 12 Phonsavanh Tai, Sisattanak, Vientiane, Lao People's Democratic Republic
Tel.: (856) 2055410705
Web Site: https://www.nmslao.com
Electrical & Electronic Product Mfr
N.A.I.C.S.: 335999

NMS Vietnam Co., Ltd. (1)
Lot N Dong Van II Industrial Zone, Duy Minh Ward, Duy Tien, Ha Nam, Vietnam
Tel.: (84) 2263585600
Electrical & Electronic Product Mfr
N.A.I.C.S.: 335999

PST Huanan Electronics Co., Ltd. (1)
2 Shunhe South Rd, Wusha Daljang Town Shunde, Foshan, Guangdong, China
Tel.: (86) 75722915600
Electrical & Electronic Product Mfr
N.A.I.C.S.: 335999

PT NMS Consulting Indonesia (1)
Shophouses Casa De Parco R5 Kelurahan Sampora, Kecamatan Cisauk, Tangerang, 15345, Indonesia
Tel.: (62) 2122235711
Electrical & Electronic Product Mfr
N.A.I.C.S.: 335999

Power Supply Technology (Thailand) Co., Ltd. (1)
2 Jasmine Bldg 12th Fl Room No 39 Soi Prasarnmitr Sukhumvit Rd, North Klongtoey, Bangkok, 10110, Thailand
Tel.: (66) 26127306
Electrical & Electronic Product Mfr
N.A.I.C.S.: 335999

Shima Electronic Industry (Malaysia) Sdn. Bhd. (1)
Building B-1 B-2 and B-3 Plo683 Jalan Keluli Zone 11, Pasir Gudang Industrial Estate, 81700, Pasir Gudang, Johor Darul Takzim, Malaysia
Tel.: (60) 72543466
Electrical & Electronic Product Mfr
N.A.I.C.S.: 335999

Sino Manufacturing Service Corporation (1)
Room 713 7th Floor No 399 Nujiang North Road, Putuo District, Shanghai, China
Tel.: (86) 2162337850
Electrical & Electronic Product Mfr
N.A.I.C.S.: 335999

Sino-Japan Stafftraining & Dispatch Co., Ltd. (1)
Room 151 4th floor 2 west wanshou road, haidian district, Beijing, China
Tel.: (86) 1082191508
Electrical & Electronic Product Mfr
N.A.I.C.S.: 335999

TKR Hong Kong Limited (1)
Suite 1-3 30/F Saxon Tower No 7 Cheung Shun Street, Lai Chi Kok, Kowloon, China (Hong Kong)
Tel.: (852) 27597618
Electrical & Electronic Product Mfr
N.A.I.C.S.: 335999

TKR Huanan Electronics Co., Ltd. (1)
No 4 Xinweixingyuan street, Shilong, Dongguan, China
Tel.: (86) 76986624941
Electrical & Electronic Product Mfr
N.A.I.C.S.: 335999

TKR Manufacturing (Malaysia) Sdn. Bhd. (1)
Lot 11 Kawasan Perindustrian Tangga Batu, 76400, Melaka, Malaysia
Tel.: (60) 63516050
Electrical & Electronic Product Mfr
N.A.I.C.S.: 335999

TKR Manufacturing Vietnam Co., Ltd. (1)
Lot C4 Ba Thien 2 Industrial Park, Thien Ke Commune, Binh Xuyen, Vinh Phuc, Vietnam
Tel.: (84) 2113510861
Electrical & Electronic Product Mfr
N.A.I.C.S.: 335999

TKR Precision (Malaysia) Sdn. Bhd. (1)
No 14 Jalan Gangsa Satu, Perindustrian Kulai II, 81000, Kulai, Johor, Malaysia
Tel.: (60) 76524000
Electrical & Electronic Product Mfr
N.A.I.C.S.: 335999

TKR USA, Inc. (1)
11302 E Point Dr Bldg B Ste 100-B, Laredo, TX 78045
Tel.: (956) 795-4500
Electrical & Electronic Product Mfr
N.A.I.C.S.: 335999

TKR de Mexico S.A de C.V. (1)
Bulevar Luis Donaldo Colosio Km 0 200 Sur, 88277, Nuevo Laredo, Tamaulipas, Mexico
Tel.: (52) 8677113000
Web Site: https://www.tkrdemexico.com
Electrical & Electronic Product Mfr
N.A.I.C.S.: 335999

nms (Thailand) Co., Ltd. (1)
4/222 Harbor Office 6th Floor Room 6D01 Moo 10 Sukhumvit Road Tambon, Tungsukla Amphur Sriracha, Chon Buri, Thailand
Tel.: (66) 381904502
Web Site: https://www.nmsthailand.com
Electrical & Electronic Product Mfr
N.A.I.C.S.: 335999

nms Engineering Co.,Ltd. (1)
Tokyo Opera City Tower 45F3-20-2 Nishi-Shinjuku, Shinjuku-ku, Tokyo, 163-1445, Japan
Tel.: (81) 353331723
Web Site: https://eng.n-ms.co.jp
Software Development Services
N.A.I.C.S.: 541511

NMS RESOURCES GLOBAL LTD.

48 Hasanpur I P Extension, Delhi East, Delhi, 110092, India
Tel.: (91) 1122248139
Web Site: http://www.nmsresourcesglobal.com
Year Founded: 1986
522289—(BOM)
Rev.: $790,276
Assets: $2,272,370
Liabilities: $2,124,645
Net Worth: $147,725
Earnings: $33,259
Emp.: 2
Fiscal Year-end: 03/31/23
Agro & Processed Food Whslr
N.A.I.C.S.: 424480
Om Pal Yadav *(Mng Dir)*

NN GROUP N.V.

Schenkkade 65, 2595 AS, Hague, Netherlands
Tel.: (31) 705130303   Nl
Web Site: https://www.nn-group.com
Year Founded: 1963
NN—(EUR)
Rev.: $23,130,800,777
Assets: $271,514,137,708
Liabilities: $233,830,131,664
Net Worth: $37,684,006,044
Earnings: $3,559,248,867
Emp.: 15,168
Fiscal Year-end: 12/31/21
Holding Company; Insurance & Investment Management Products & Services
N.A.I.C.S.: 551112
Delfin Rueda *(CFO & Member-Mgmt Bd)*

Subsidiaries:

ABN AMRO Verzekeringen B.V. (1)
Prins Bernhardstraat 1, PO Box 100085, 8000 GB, Zwolle, Netherlands (51%)
Tel.: (31) 384992299
Web Site: http://www.abnamro.nl
Sales Range: $350-399.9 Million
Emp.: 800
Insurance
N.A.I.C.S.: 524298

Movir N.V. (1)
Brugwal 1, 3432 NZ, Nieuwegein, Netherlands
Tel.: (31) 30 607 8700
Web Site: https://www.movir.nl
Emp.: 375
Fire Insurance Services
N.A.I.C.S.: 524113

NN Asigurari de Viata S.A. (1)
1-5 Costache Negri St First Floor Sector 5, 050552, Bucharest, Romania
Tel.: (40) 219464
Web Site: https://www.nn.ro
Fire Insurance Services
N.A.I.C.S.: 524113

NN Biztosito Zartkoruen Mukodo Rt. (1)
(100%)
Tel.: (36) 1 255 5757
Web Site: https://www.nn.hu
Sales Range: $250-299.9 Million
Emp.: 300
N.A.I.C.S.: 522210

NN Greek Life Insurance Company S.A. (1)
198 Syngrou Ave, Kallithea, 17671, Athens, Greece
Tel.: (30) 210 950 6000
Web Site: https://www.nnhellas.gr
Sales Range: $150-199.9 Million
Emp.: 400
Fire Insurance Services
N.A.I.C.S.: 524113
Bram Boon *(Chm & Co-CEO)*

NN Hayat ve Emeklilik A.S. (1)
Maslak Mah Sumer Sok Maslak Office Building No 4/92, Sariyer, 34485, Istanbul, Turkiye
Tel.: (90) 212 334 0500
Web Site: https://www.nnhayatemeklilik.com.tr
Sales Range: $125-149.9 Million
Pension Administration Services
N.A.I.C.S.: 524292
Marius Popescu *(Gen Mgr)*

NN Insurance Belgium N.V. (1)
Avenue Fonsny 38, 1060, Brussels, Belgium
Tel.: (32) 24077522
Insurance Services
N.A.I.C.S.: 524210

NN Life Insurance Company Limited (1)
New Otani Garden Court 26Th Floor 4-1 Kioicho, Chiyoda-ku, Tokyo, 102 0094, Japan (100%)
Tel.: (81) 352100300
Web Site: http://www.nnlife.co.jp
Sales Range: $350-399.9 Million
Emp.: 800
Life Insurance Carrier
N.A.I.C.S.: 524113
Mihai Muntean *(CEO-Romania-Interim)*

NN Penzijni spolecnost, a.s. (1)
Nadrazni 344/25, 150 00, Prague, 5, Czech Republic
Tel.: (420) 24 409 0800
Web Site: https://www.nn.cz
Sales Range: $100-124.9 Million
Emp.: 200
Pension Funds
N.A.I.C.S.: 525110

NN Pojistovna a.s. (1)
Nadrazni 344/25, 150 00, Prague, Czech Republic (100%)
Tel.: (420) 244090800
Web Site: http://www.nn.cz
Sales Range: $350-399.9 Million
Insurance Carrier
N.A.I.C.S.: 524298

NN Re (Netherlands) N.V. (1)
Prinses Beatrixlaan 35, 2595AK, Hague, Netherlands
Tel.: (31) 703781615
Sales Range: $25-49.9 Million
Emp.: 45
Reinsurance Services
N.A.I.C.S.: 524130

NN Zivotna Poistovna a.s. (1)
Jesenskeho 4/C, 811 02, Bratislava, Slovakia

NN GROUP N.V.

NN Group N.V.—(Continued)
Tel.: (421) 850111464
Web Site: http://www.nn-group.com
Sales Range: $75-99.9 Million
Fire Insurance Services
N.A.I.C.S.: 524113

Nationale-Nederlanden Bank N.V. (1)
Weena 505, 3013 AL, Rotterdam, Netherlands
Tel.: (31) 105130303
Web Site: https://www.nn.nl
Insurance Financing Services
N.A.I.C.S.: 522299
Marcel Zuidam (CEO)

Nationale-Nederlanden Generales, Compania de Seguros y Reaseguros S.A. (1)
Avenida de Bruselas 16 Parque empresarial Arroyo de la Vega, 28108, Alcobendas, Madrid, Spain
Tel.: (34) 916026000
Web Site: http://www.nnseguros.es
Accident & Health Insurance Services
N.A.I.C.S.: 524114

Nationale-Nederlanden Powszechne Towarzystwo Emerytalne S.A. (1)
ul Topiel 12, 00-342, Warsaw, Poland
Tel.: (48) 225227124
Web Site: https://www.nn.pl
Pension Fund Services
N.A.I.C.S.: 525110
Szymon Ozog (VP)

Nationale-Nederlanden Schadeverzekering Maatschappij N.V. (1)
Prinses Beatrixlaan 35, Hague, 2595 AK, Netherlands
Tel.: (31) 703418080
Property & Casualty Insurance Products & Services
N.A.I.C.S.: 524126

Nationale-Nederlanden Services N.V. (1)
Postbus 225, 6710 DA, Ede, Netherlands
Tel.: (31) 10 513 0303
General Insurance Services
N.A.I.C.S.: 524210

Nationale-Nederlanden Vida, Compania de Seguros y Reaseguros S.A. (1)
Avenida de Bruselas 16 Parque empresarial Arroyo de la Vega, 28108, Alcobendas, Madrid, Spain
Tel.: (34) 916026000
Web Site: http://www.nnseguros.es
Fire Insurance Services
N.A.I.C.S.: 524113

NNE A/S
Vandtarnsvej 108-110, 2860, Soborg, Denmark
Tel.: (45) 44447777
Web Site: http://www.nne.dk
Mfr And Marketing Health Care Products
N.A.I.C.S.:

NNG SOFTWARE DEVELOPING & COMMERCIAL LLC
Szepvolgyi ut 35-37, H 1037, Budapest, Hungary
Tel.: (36) 1 872 0100
Web Site: http://www.nng.com
Emp.: 500
Global Positioning System Software Designer & Developer
N.A.I.C.S.: 513210
Peter Balogh (CEO)

Subsidiaries:

Nfuzion Consulting, Inc. (1)
134 Main St, LaGrange, GA 30240
Tel.: (678) 884-0303
Web Site: http://www.nfuzion.com
Sales Range: $1-9.9 Million
Emp.: 13
Engineering Services
N.A.I.C.S.: 541330

Mark Westcott (Principal)

NO GRAVITY GAMES SA
Ul Dzika 15/lok 13, 00-172, Warsaw, Poland
Tel.: (48) 606720929
Web Site: https://www.nogravitygames.com
Year Founded: 2008
NGG—(WAR)
Software Development Services
N.A.I.C.S.: 541511
Aleksander Sierzega (Pres)

NO SIGNBOARD HOLDINGS LTD.
10 Ubi Crescent 03-02 Ubi Techpark Lobby A, Singapore, 408564, Singapore
Tel.: (65) 67499959   SG
Web Site: https://nosignboardseafood.com
Year Founded: 1981
1G6—(SES)
Rev.: $1,724,846
Assets: $12,291,685
Liabilities: $12,003,075
Net Worth: $288,610
Earnings: ($1,204,657)
Fiscal Year-end: 09/30/21
Restaurant Management Services
N.A.I.C.S.: 722511
Lay Hoon Lim (COO)

NO.1 CO., LTD.
19F Uchisaiwaicho Heiwa Bldg 1-5-2 Uchisaiwaicho Chiyoda-ku, Tokyo, 100-0011, Japan
Tel.: (81) 355108911
Web Site: http://www.number-1.co.jp
Year Founded: 1989
3562—(TKS)
Rev.: $95,374,680
Assets: $57,429,000
Liabilities: $30,749,330
Net Worth: $26,679,670
Earnings: $6,281,740
Emp.: 688
Fiscal Year-end: 02/29/24
Office Equipment Distr
N.A.I.C.S.: 423420
Takayuki Tatsumi (Chm & Pres)

Subsidiaries:

Cube S Co., Ltd. (1)
6 Chome-46-9 Higashikasai, Edogawa-ku, Tokyo, 134-0084, Japan
Tel.: (81) 356591250
Web Site: http://www.cube-s.co.jp
Office Equipment Distr
N.A.I.C.S.: 423420

NOAH EDUCATION HOLDINGS LTD.
33/F NEO Tower A 6011 Shennan Road, Futian District, Shenzhen, 518040, Guangdong, China
Tel.: (86) 755 8288 9100   Ky
Web Site: http://www.noaheducation.com
Year Founded: 2004
Holding Company; Language & Grade Schools Owner & Operator
N.A.I.C.S.: 551112
Qi Du (CEO & Gen Mgr-Wentai Education)

Subsidiaries:

Innovative Noah Electronic (Shenzhen) Co., Ltd (1)
10th Floor B Building Futian Tianan Hi-tech Venture Park, Futian District, Shenzhen, China
Tel.: (86) 75582049267
Electronic Component Mfr & Distr
N.A.I.C.S.: 334419

NOAH HOLDINGS LIMITED
Noah Wealth Center No 1226 Shenbin South Road, Minhang District, Shanghai, 201107, China
Tel.: (86) 2180359221   Ky
Web Site: https://ir.noahgroup.com
NOAH—(NYSE)
Rev.: $459,379,292
Assets: $1,756,393,720
Liabilities: $312,612,843
Net Worth: $1,443,780,876
Earnings: $138,598,665
Emp.: 2,583
Fiscal Year-end: 12/31/23
Wealth Management Services
N.A.I.C.S.: 523940
Jingbo Wang (Co-Founder, Chm & CEO)

Subsidiaries:

Gopher Asset Management Co., Ltd. (1)
Building 2 1687 Changyang Road, Shanghai, 200090, China
Tel.: (86) 2180358600
Web Site: https://www.gopherasset.com
Wealth Management Services
N.A.I.C.S.: 522180
Zhe Yin (Founder, Chm, CEO & Partner)

Noah Holdings (Hong Kong) Limited (1)
Room 903-4 Li Po Chun Chambers 189 Des Voeux Road, Central, China (Hong Kong)
Tel.: (852) 21108118
Web Site: http://www.noahwm.hk
Wealth Management Services
N.A.I.C.S.: 522180
Shirley Yu (Exec Dir)

NOATUM MARITIME HOLDINGS, S.L.U
P Zona Franca 111 Torre Auditori, 08038, Barcelona, Spain
Tel.: (34) 932987717
Web Site: http://www.noatumlogistics.com
Logistics & International Transport Services
N.A.I.C.S.: 541614
Rafael Torres Brinkmann (CEO)

Subsidiaries:

Noatum Logistics, LLC (1)
11501 Outlook St Ste 500, Overland Park, KS 66211
Tel.: (877) 246-4909
Web Site: http://www.miq.com
Global Transportation Logistics Services
N.A.I.C.S.: 488510
John E. Carr (Pres & CEO)

NOBAO RENEWABLE ENERGY HOLDINGS LIMITED
Building 4 150 Yonghe Road, Shanghai, 200072, China
Tel.: (86) 2166520666   Ky
Web Site: http://www.nobaogroup.com
Sales Range: $50-74.9 Million
Emp.: 167
Ground Source Heat Pump (GSHP) Heating, Ventilation, Air Conditioning & Hot Water Supply Systems Designer, Mfr & Installer
N.A.I.C.S.: 333415
Kwok Ping Sun (Chm & CEO)

Subsidiaries:

Danish Renewable Energy A/S (1)
Kogle Alle 5 1st floor, 2970, Horsholm, Denmark
Tel.: (45) 7262 5060
Web Site: http://www.danishrenewable.com
Heat Pump Mfr
N.A.I.C.S.: 333415

INTERNATIONAL PUBLIC

NOBEL DESIGN HOLDINGS PTE LTD
16 Tai Seng Street 07-09, Singapore, 534138, Singapore
Tel.: (65) 63832222   SG
Web Site: http://www.nobel.com.sg
Year Founded: 1981
547—(SES)
Sales Range: $50-74.9 Million
Property Development Services
N.A.I.C.S.: 531311
Adrian Chan Pengee (Chm)

Subsidiaries:

Marquis Furniture Gallery Pte Ltd (1)
6 Raffles Boulevard 02-08/09 & 02-38, Singapore, 039594, Singapore
Tel.: (65) 63830119
Web Site: https://www.marquis.com.sg
Emp.: 50
Home Furniture Retailer
N.A.I.C.S.: 449129
Jean Wee (Mgr)

Marquis HQO Pte Ltd (1)
2 Alexandra Road 02-09 Delta House, Singapore, 159919, Singapore
Tel.: (65) 89233238
Web Site: https://www.marqhqo.com
Indoor & Outdoor Furniture Mfr
N.A.I.C.S.: 337126

Marquis HnC Pte Ltd (1)
16 Tai Seng Street 01-00/C, Singapore, 534138, Singapore
Tel.: (65) 67422386
Web Site: http://www.marquishnc.com
Home Furnishing Product Retailer
N.A.I.C.S.: 423220

Momentum Creations Pte Ltd (1)
16 Tai Seng Street Level 8, Singapore, 368359, Singapore
Tel.: (65) 64570777
Web Site: https://omhome.com.sg
Home Furniture Retailer
N.A.I.C.S.: 449110
Roland Qoh (Gen Mgr)

Nobel Design House (M) Sdn Bhd (1)
Suite 8-11-8 11th Floor Menara Mutiara Bangsar Jalan Liku, 59100, Kuala Lumpur, Malaysia
Tel.: (60) 322840063
Home Furnishing Product Distr
N.A.I.C.S.: 423220

Nobel Design Sdn Bhd (1)
Unit G-4 Ground Floor Gadong Properties Centre Jalan Gadong BSB, BE4119, Negara, Brunei Darussalam
Tel.: (673) 2440993
Home Furnishing Product Distr
N.A.I.C.S.: 423220

Numero Uno Creative Group Pte Ltd (1)
130 Joo Seng Road 07-01, Singapore, 368357, Singapore
Tel.: (65) 62819500
Web Site: https://www.sumisura.asia
Emp.: 15
Household Furniture Retailer
N.A.I.C.S.: 449110
Alson Wee (Mgr-Design)

NOBELIUM TECH CORP.
1969 Upper Water Street Suite 2108, Halifax, B3J 3R7, NS, Canada
Tel.: (519) 374-1834
NBL—(TSXV)
Assets: $213,740
Liabilities: $7,346
Net Worth: $206,394
Earnings: ($31,256)
Fiscal Year-end: 01/31/20
Financial Investment Company
N.A.I.C.S.: 523999
Erroll Treslan (Pres & CEO)

NOBIA AB

NOBIA AB

Blekholmstorget 30 E7, 11164, Stockholm, Sweden
Tel.: (46) 84401600
Web Site: https://www.nobia.com
Year Founded: 1996
NBIAY—(OTCIQ)
Rev.: $1,327,555,764
Assets: $1,351,579,430
Liabilities: $921,933,027
Net Worth: $429,646,403
Earnings: ($34,447,158)
Emp.: 5,315
Fiscal Year-end: 12/31/23
Kitchen Interiors Mfr
N.A.I.C.S.: 337110
Thomas Myringer *(Exec VP & Dir-HR)*

Subsidiaries:

Bribus B.V. (1)
Industriestraat 4, Dinxperlo, 7091 DC, Aalten, Netherlands
Tel.: (31) 315651745
Web Site: https://www.bribus.nl
Emp.: 350
Kitchen Product Mfr
N.A.I.C.S.: 332215

CIE Plc. (1)
237 Queenstown Road, Battersea, London, SW8 3NP, United Kingdom
Tel.: (44) 2077204219
Web Site: https://www.cie.plc.uk
Emp.: 6,000
Building Materials Distr
N.A.I.C.S.: 444180

Commodore Kitchens Ltd. (1)
Acorn House Gumley Road, Grays, RM20 4XP, Essex, United Kingdom
Tel.: (44) 1375382323
Web Site: https://www.commodoredesign.com
Kitchen Furniture Distr
N.A.I.C.S.: 444180
James Heywood *(Mgr-Fin)*

EWE Kuchen GmbH (1)
Dieselstrasse 14, 4600, Wels, Upper Austria, Austria
Tel.: (43) 72422370
Web Site: https://www.ewe.at
Sales Range: $100-124.9 Million
Emp.: 300
Modular Kitchen Installation Services
N.A.I.C.S.: 238350

FM Kuchen GmbH (1)
Galgenau 30, 4240, Freistadt, Upper Austria, Austria
Tel.: (43) 7 942 7010
Web Site: http://www.fm-kuechen.at
Sales Range: $50-74.9 Million
Emp.: 200
Modular Kitchen Installation Services
N.A.I.C.S.: 238350

Gor Det Selv HTH Arhus A/S (1)
Agerovej 29 B, Tilst, 8381, Arhus, Midtjylland, Denmark
Tel.: (45) 87408866
Web Site: http://www.gds-hth.dk
Sales Range: $25-49.9 Million
Emp.: 5
Modular Kitchen Installation Services
N.A.I.C.S.: 337110

Gower Furniture Ltd. (1)
Holmfield Industrial Estate, Halifax, HX2 9TN, West Yorkshire, United Kingdom
Tel.: (44) 1422232200
Web Site: https://www.gower-furniture.co.uk
Sales Range: $100-124.9 Million
Emp.: 400
Kitchen Fixtures Mfr
N.A.I.C.S.: 337110

HTH Ekspert w. Kuchni S.p.z.o.o. (1)
Ziemowita St 53, 00103886, Warsaw, Poland
Tel.: (48) 226351795
Web Site: http://www.hth.pl
Sales Range: $25-49.9 Million
Emp.: 10
Modular Kitchen Design & Installation Services
N.A.I.C.S.: 541490

HTH Gor Det Selv Viborg A.p.S. (1)
Center Vest 8, Viborg, 8800, Midtjylland, Denmark
Tel.: (45) 86601041
Modular Kitchen Installation Services
N.A.I.C.S.: 238350

HTH Gruppen Fyn A/S (1)
Ryttermarken 12, 5700, Svendborg, Denmark
Tel.: (45) 62216000
Modular Kitchen Installation Services
N.A.I.C.S.: 238350

HTH Kokkener A/S. (1)
Industrivej 6, 6870, Olgod, Denmark
Tel.: (45) 7 524 4777
Web Site: http://www.hth-kitchen.com
Emp.: 710
Kitchenware Mfr
N.A.I.C.S.: 321999

HTH Kokkenforum Aabenraa A/S (1)
Vestvejen 155, 6200, Aabenraa, Syddanmark, Denmark
Tel.: (45) 74624211
Web Site: http://www.hth.dk
Sales Range: $25-49.9 Million
Emp.: 16
Modular Kitchen Installation Services
N.A.I.C.S.: 238350

HTH Kokkenforum Arhus A/S (1)
Agerovej 29a, Tilst, 8381, Arhus, Midtjylland, Denmark
Tel.: (45) 8 740 8899
Web Site: http://www.hth.dk
Sales Range: $25-49.9 Million
Emp.: 33
Modular Kitchen Installation Services
N.A.I.C.S.: 337110

HTH Kokkenforum Holstebro A.pS. (1)
Gartnerivej 36, 7500, Holstebro, Midtjylland, Denmark
Tel.: (45) 97429100
Modular Kitchen Design & Installation Services
N.A.I.C.S.: 238350

HTH Kokkenforum Koge A/S (1)
Industrivej 6, Olgod, 6870, Denmark
Tel.: (45) 75244777
Web Site: http://www.hth.dk
Emp.: 650
Prefabricated Kitchen Installation Services
N.A.I.C.S.: 238350

HTH Kokkenforum Naestved A/S (1)
Messebuen 1, 4700, Naestved, Zealand, Denmark
Tel.: (45) 55 73 64 00
Web Site: http://www.hth.dk
Modular Kitchen Design & Installation Services
N.A.I.C.S.: 238350

HTH Kokkenforum Viborg A.p.S. (1)
Alandsvej 1, 8800, Viborg, Denmark
Tel.: (45) 86610822
Web Site: http://www.hth.dk
Prefabricated Kitchen Installation Services
N.A.I.C.S.: 238350

HTH Kuchen GmbH (1)
Griegstrasse 75, 22763, Hamburg, Germany
Tel.: (49) 75244777
Web Site: http://www.hth-kuechen.de
Building Materials Distr
N.A.I.C.S.: 444180

HTH Ost A/S (1)
Hovedvejen 211-217, 2600, Glostrup, Hovedstaden, Denmark
Tel.: (45) 43258000
Web Site: http://www.hth.dk
Sales Range: $25-49.9 Million
Emp.: 100
Modular Kitchen Installation Services
N.A.I.C.S.: 238350

HTH Skive-Silkeborg A/S (1)
Norrevaenget 3, 8600, Silkeborg, Denmark
Tel.: (45) 86 81 19 11
Modular Kitchen Installation Services
N.A.I.C.S.: 238350

Invita Detail & Projekt A/S (1)
Industrivej 6, 6870, Olgod, Syddanmark, Denmark
Tel.: (45) 77887000
Web Site: http://www.invita.dk
Sales Range: $25-49.9 Million
Emp.: 15
Modular Kitchen Installation Services
N.A.I.C.S.: 238350

Invita Kokkener A/S (1)
Agerovej 31, Tilst, 8381, Aarhus, Denmark
Tel.: (45) 7 788 7000
Web Site: https://www.invita.dk
Sales Range: $200-249.9 Million
Emp.: 700
Modular Kitchen Installation Services
N.A.I.C.S.: 238350

Invita Retail A/S (1)
Industrivej 6, 6870, Olgod, Denmark
Tel.: (45) 77887000
Web Site: http://www.nobia.dk
Sales Range: $250-299.9 Million
Emp.: 800
Kitchen Cabinets Retailer
N.A.I.C.S.: 423490

Magnet Kitchens Ltd. (1)
3 Allington Way Yarm Road Business Park, Darlington, Durham, DL1 4XT, United Kingdom
Tel.: (44) 1325744093
Web Site: https://www.magnet.co.uk
Kitchen Product Mfr & Distr
N.A.I.C.S.: 332215

Magnet Limited (1)
Allington Way Yarm Rd Industrial Estate, Darlington, DL1 4XT, United Kingdom
Tel.: (44) 1325469441
Web Site: http://www.magnet.co.uk
Sales Range: $400-449.9 Million
Emp.: 2,200
Retailer of Furniture; Cabinets & Other Home Furnishings; Manufacturer of Kitchen & Bedroom Furniture, Doors & Windows
N.A.I.C.S.: 337110

Marbodal AB (1)
Sagverksgatan 4, 522 30, Tidaholm, Vastergotland, Sweden
Tel.: (46) 5 021 7000
Web Site: https://www.marbodal.se
Sales Range: $150-199.9 Million
Kitchen Designing & Installation Services
N.A.I.C.S.: 541490

Marlin Badmobel GmbH. (1)
Jaka-Strasse 3, 32351, Stemwede, Germany
Tel.: (49) 577 3880
Web Site: https://www.marlinbad.de
Sales Range: $25-49.9 Million
Emp.: 50
Bath Fittings & Household Furnitures Mfr
N.A.I.C.S.: 321999

Mobelwerkstatten Josef Ritter GmbH. (1)
Herringhauser Str 33, Herford, 32051, Nordrhein Westfalen, Germany
Tel.: (49) 52213810
Web Site: http://www.poggenpohl.com
Sales Range: $100-124.9 Million
Emp.: 350
Household Furniture Mfr
N.A.I.C.S.: 337121

Myresjokok AB (1)
PO Box 603, 343 24, Almhult, Smaland, Sweden
Tel.: (46) 47655700
Web Site: http://www.myresjokok.se
Modular Kitchen Design & Installation Services
N.A.I.C.S.: 541490

Nobia Sverige AB (1)
Klarabergsviadukten 70, 111 64, Stockholm, Sweden
Tel.: (46) 84401600
Web Site: http://www.nobia.com
Emp.: 45
Household Furniture Mfr
N.A.I.C.S.: 337121

Norema AS (1)
Rosenholmveien 25, 1414, Trollasen, Akershus, Norway
Tel.: (47) 6 131 8100
Web Site: https://www.norema.no
Sales Range: $25-49.9 Million
Emp.: 40
Modular Kitchen Design & Installation Services
N.A.I.C.S.: 238350
Ole Dalsbo *(CEO)*

Novart OY (1)
Kouvolantie 225, 15560, Nastola, Finland
Tel.: (358) 207730730
Web Site: https://www.novart.fi
Emp.: 345
Kitchenware Mfr
N.A.I.C.S.: 337110
Erkka Lumme *(Mng Dir)*

Optifit Jaka-Mobel GmbH. (1)
Jaka Strasse 3, 32351, Stemwede, Germany
Tel.: (49) 577 3880
Web Site: https://www.optifit.de
Sales Range: $125-149.9 Million
Emp.: 180
Kitchenware Mfr
N.A.I.C.S.: 327110

Poggenpohl GmbH (1)
Poggenpohlstrasse 1, 32051, Herford, Germany
Tel.: (49) 52213810
Web Site: https://www.poggenpohl.com
Sales Range: $100-124.9 Million
Emp.: 380
Kitchen & Bath Cabinets Mfr
N.A.I.C.S.: 337110

Subsidiary (Non-US):

Poggenpohl A/S (2)
Esplanaden 2, 1263, Copenhagen, Denmark
Tel.: (45) 33935559
Web Site: http://www.copenhagen.poggenpohl.com
Modular Kitchen Design & Installation Services
N.A.I.C.S.: 337110

Poggenpohl AB (2)
Birger Jarlsgatan 34, 114 29, Stockholm, Sweden
Tel.: (46) 86796520
Modular Kitchen Design & Installation Services
N.A.I.C.S.: 541490

Poggenpohl Austria GmbH (2)
Schottenring 18, 1010, Vienna, Austria
Tel.: (43) 15351232
Web Site: http://wien.poggenpohl.com
Sales Range: $25-49.9 Million
Emp.: 2
Modular Kitchen Installation Services
N.A.I.C.S.: 238350

Subsidiary (Domestic):

Poggenpohl Forum Gmbh. (2)
Wilfried Kruger Kaiser Wilhelm Platz 9, 45276, Essen, Germany
Tel.: (49) 20154918
Web Site: http://www.poggenpohl.com
Kitchenware & Household Furnitures Mfr
N.A.I.C.S.: 337126

Subsidiary (Non-US):

Poggenpohl France S.A.R.L. (2)
144 Avenue Paul Doumer, 78360, Montesson, Yvelines, France
Tel.: (33) 130537960
Web Site: http://www.poggenpohl.com
Modular Kitchen Design & Installation Services
N.A.I.C.S.: 541490

Poggenpohl Group Schweiz AG (2)
Schachenhof 4, Postfach 642, 6014, Lucerne, Switzerland
Tel.: (41) 412507575
Web Site: http://www.poggenpohl.ch
Sales Range: $25-49.9 Million
Emp.: 12
Modular Kitchen Design & Installation Services
N.A.I.C.S.: 541490

Poggenpohl Group UK Ltd. (2)
100 London Road, Saint Albans, AL1 1NX,

NOBIA AB

Nobia AB—(Continued)
Hertfordshire, United Kingdom
Tel.: (44) 1727738100
Web Site: http://www.poggenpohl.com
Sales Range: $25-49.9 Million
Emp.: 50
Kitchen Cabinet Distr
N.A.I.C.S.: 423440

Poggenpohl Japan Co. Ltd. (2)
5-1-11 Minami Azabu Minato-ku, Tokyo, 106-0047, Japan
Tel.: (81) 3 5798 7950
Web Site: http://www.tokyo.poggenpohl.com
Emp.: 3
Modular Kitchen Design & Installation Services
N.A.I.C.S.: 541490

Poggenpohl Nederland B.V. (2)
Postbus 294, 3840 AG, Harderwijk, Gelderland, Netherlands
Tel.: (31) 341 432 772
Web Site: http://www.poggenpohl.com
Kitchen Cabinets Retailer
N.A.I.C.S.: 423490

Subsidiary (US):

Poggenpohl U.S., Inc. (2)
350 Passaic Ave, Fairfield, NJ 07004
Tel.: (973) 812-8900
Web Site: http://www.poggenpohl.com
Sales Range: $25-49.9 Million
Emp.: 8
Kitchen & Bath Cabinets Distr
N.A.I.C.S.: 337110

Pronorm Einbauküchen GmbH (1)
Hoferfeld 5-7, 32602, Vlotho, Germany
Tel.: (49) 5 733 9790
Web Site: https://www.pronorm.de
Modular Kitchen Design & Installation Services
N.A.I.C.S.: 238350

Rixonway Kitchens Ltd. (1)
Churwell Vale, Shaw Cross Business Park, Dewsbury, WF12 7RD, West Yorkshire, United Kingdom
Tel.: (44) 1924431300
Web Site: http://www.rixonway.co.uk
Kitchen Product Mfr
N.A.I.C.S.: 332215
Dan Francis *(Mgr-Field Ops)*

Sigdal Kjokken AS (1)
Rosenholmveien 25, PO Box 633, 1414, Trollasen, Akershus, Norway
Tel.: (47) 6 682 2300
Web Site: https://www.sigdal.com
Sales Range: $25-49.9 Million
Emp.: 50
Modular Kitchen Design & Installation Services
N.A.I.C.S.: 541490

Ultimate Kitchens (Pimlico) Ltd. (1)
107 Pimlico Road, London, SW1W 8PH, United Kingdom
Tel.: (44) 2077307927
Web Site: http://www.poggenpohl.com
Sales Range: $25-49.9 Million
Emp.: 3
Kitchen Design & Installation Services
N.A.I.C.S.: 541490

Wigmore Street Kitchens Ltd. (1)
118 Wigmore Street, London, W1U 3RT, United Kingdom
Tel.: (44) 2072241986
Web Site: http://www.poggenpohl.com
Sales Range: $50-74.9 Million
Emp.: 50
Kitchen Cabinets Retailer
N.A.I.C.S.: 423440

NOBINA AB

Armegatan 38, Box 6071, SE-171 06, Solna, Sweden
Tel.: (46) 84 106 5000
Web Site: http://www.nobina.com
NOBINA—(OMX)
Rev.: $1,140,824,650
Assets: $1,006,004,790
Liabilities: $858,110,190
Net Worth: $147,894,600
Earnings: $32,686,850
Emp.: 10,526
Fiscal Year-end: 02/29/20
Passenger Transportation Services
N.A.I.C.S.: 485999
Martin Pagrotsky *(Chief Compliance Officer & Gen Counsel)*

Subsidiaries:

Dee Blaa Omnibusser A/S (1)
Skovlytoften 36, Overod, 2840, Holte, Denmark
Tel.: (45) 420177
Web Site: http://www.deblaaomnibusser.dk
Public Transport Services
N.A.I.C.S.: 485999

Nobina A/S (1)
Fabriksparken 18 B, 2600, Glostrup, Denmark
Tel.: (45) 88327327
Public Transport Services
N.A.I.C.S.: 485999

Nobina AS (1)
Schweigaards gate 10, 0185, Oslo, Norway
Tel.: (47) 45488050
Public Transport Services
N.A.I.C.S.: 485999

Nobina Oy (1)
Klovinpellontie 5, 02180, Espoo, Finland
Tel.: (358) 9525711
Public Transport Services
N.A.I.C.S.: 485999

Subsidiary (Domestic):

Nobina Finland East Oy (2)
Pitkasentie 23, 01200, Vantaa, Finland
Tel.: (358) 9525711
Public Transport Services
N.A.I.C.S.: 485999

Nobina Finland South Oy (2)
Tulppatie 14, 00880, Helsinki, Finland
Tel.: (358) 9525711
Public Transport Services
N.A.I.C.S.: 485999

Nobina Finland West Oy (2)
Cableway 1, 01640, Vantaa, Finland
Tel.: (358) 9525711
Public Transport Services
N.A.I.C.S.: 485999

Nobina Sverige AB (1)
Armegatan 38, Box 6071, 171 06, Solna, Sweden
Tel.: (46) 841065000
Public Transport Services
N.A.I.C.S.: 485999

Nobina Technology AB (1)
Fack 401075 R104, 106 54, Stockholm, Sweden
Tel.: (46) 841065000
Public Transport Services
N.A.I.C.S.: 485999

NOBISKRUG GMBH

Kieler Strasse 53, Rendsburg, 24768, Germany
Tel.: (49) 43312070
Web Site: http://www.nobiskrug.com
Year Founded: 1905
Sales Range: $500-549.9 Million
Emp.: 400
Shipbuilding & Ship Repairs
N.A.I.C.S.: 336611
Bertram C. Liebler *(CEO)*

NOBLE CORPORATION PLC

10 Brook Street, London, W1S1BG, United Kingdom
Tel.: (44) 2033002300 UK
Web Site: http://www.noblecorp.com
NE—(NYSE)
Rev.: $2,589,018,000
Assets: $5,507,437,000
Liabilities: $1,586,197,000
Net Worth: $3,921,240,000
Earnings: $481,902,000
Emp.: 3,600
Fiscal Year-end: 12/31/23
Holding Company; Offshore Oil & Gas Well Drilling Services
N.A.I.C.S.: 551112
Robert W. Eifler *(Pres & CEO)*

Subsidiaries:

Frontier Drilling AS (1)
Statsm Michelsensv 38 Paradis, Fjoesanger, Bergen, 5892, Norway
Tel.: (47) 55922820
Sales Range: $50-74.9 Million
Emp.: 2
Oil & Gas Offshore Drilling Contractor Services
N.A.I.C.S.: 213111

NE Drilling Servicos do Brasil Ltda. (1)
Avenida das Americas 3500-BL 04 Edificio Toronto 3000 - Sala 522, Barra da Tijuca, Rio de Janeiro, Brazil
Tel.: (55) 2135012700
Oil & Gas Well Drilling Services
N.A.I.C.S.: 213111

Noble Asset (U.K.) Limited (1)
Farburn Industrial Estate, Dyce, Aberdeen, AB21 7HG, United Kingdom
Tel.: (44) 1224 401600
Asset Management Services
N.A.I.C.S.: 523940

Noble Contracting Offshore Drilling (M) Sdn Bhd (1)
Level 27-02 Menara Prestige 1 Jalan Pinang, 50450, Kuala Lumpur, Malaysia
Tel.: (60) 327211700
Oil & Gas Well Drilling Services
N.A.I.C.S.: 213111

Noble Corporation Holdings Limited (1)
South Chruch Street Ugland House, Georgetown, KY1-1104, Cayman Islands
Tel.: (345) 3459498066
Holding Company
N.A.I.C.S.: 551112

Noble Drilling (Denmark) ApS (1)
Amerika vej 1, Esbjerg, 6700, Denmark
Tel.: (45) 75453044
Web Site: http://www.noblecorp.com
Sales Range: $150-199.9 Million
Deepwater Oil & Gas Contract Drilling
N.A.I.C.S.: 213111

Noble Drilling (Land Support) Limited (1)
Wellheads Road Farburn Industrial Estates, Dyce, Aberdeen, AB21 7HG, United Kingdom
Tel.: (44) 1224 401600
Emp.: 5
Oil Well Drilling Services
N.A.I.C.S.: 213111
Rolf Boje *(Mgr-Ops)*

Noble Drilling (Nederland) II B.V. (1)
Den Helder Branch Office Paleiskade 100, 1781 AR, Den Helder, Netherlands
Tel.: (31) 2033002380
Oil & Gas Well Drilling Services
N.A.I.C.S.: 213111

Noble Drilling (Nigeria) Ltd. (1)
18 Thompson Ave Ikoyi, 2 Mosasejo Ikoyi, Lagos, Nigeria (100%)
Tel.: (234) 14630740
Web Site: http://www.noblecorp.com
Sales Range: $150-199.9 Million
Oil & Gas Drilling Services
N.A.I.C.S.: 213111

Noble Drilling (Norway) AS (1)
Tankbatvegen 2, 4056, Tananger, Norway
Tel.: (47) 48198963
Offshore Oil & Gas Well Drilling Rig Operator
N.A.I.C.S.: 213111
Scott Randell *(Mng Dir)*

Noble Drilling (U.K.) Ltd. (1)
Wellheads Road Farburn Industrial Estate, Dyce, Aberdeen, AB21 7HG, United Kingdom (100%)
Tel.: (44) 1224401600
Web Site: http://www.noblecorp.com
Sales Range: $25-49.9 Million
Emp.: 40

Deepwater Oil & Gas Contract Drilling Services
N.A.I.C.S.: 213111

Noble Drilling Americas LLC (1)
13135 S Dairy Ashford Ste 800, Sugar Land, TX 77478
Tel.: (281) 276-6100
Oil & Gas Well Drilling Services
N.A.I.C.S.: 213111

Noble Drilling Doha W.L.L. (1)
Offices 807 837 Tower II 8th Floor Salem Globex Business Center, PO Box 14023, The Gate Mall West Bay, Doha, Qatar
Tel.: (974) 40206029
Offshore Drilling Services
N.A.I.C.S.: 213111

Noble Drilling International GmbH (1)
Dorfstrasse 19a, Baar, 6340, Switzerland
Tel.: (41) 417616555
Oil & Gas Wells Drilling Services
N.A.I.C.S.: 213111

Noble Drilling Singapore Pte. Ltd. (1)
152 Beach Road 13-07/08 Gateway East, Singapore, 189721, Singapore
Tel.: (65) 68870440
Oil & Gas Well Drilling Services
N.A.I.C.S.: 213111

Noble Holding (U.S.) Corporation (1)
13135 S Dairy Ashford Rd Ste 800, Sugar Land, TX 77478
Tel.: (281) 276-6100
Web Site: http://www.noblecorp.com
Investment Management Service
N.A.I.C.S.: 523999

Subsidiary (Domestic):

Noble Drilling Corporation (2)
13135 S Dairy Ashford Ste 800, Sugar Land, TX 77478
Tel.: (281) 276-6100
Oil & Gas Well Drilling Services
N.A.I.C.S.: 213111
Jessie Jordan *(Superintendent-Drilling)*

Subsidiary (Domestic):

Noble Drilling (U.S.) Inc. (3)
13135 S Dairy Ashford Rd Ste 800, Sugar Land, TX 77478 (100%)
Tel.: (281) 276-6100
Web Site: https://www.noblecorp.com
Drilling Services
N.A.I.C.S.: 213111

Noble Drilling Services Inc. (3)
13135 S Dairy Ashford Ste 800, Sugar Land, TX 77478 (100%)
Tel.: (281) 276-6100
Drilling Services
N.A.I.C.S.: 213111

Noble International Limited (1)
Landmark Square Ste 3D 64 Earth Close, PO Box 31327, Georgetown, KY1-1206, Cayman Islands
Tel.: (345) 1 345 938 0293
Web Site: http://www.noblecorp.com
Oil & Gas Wells Drilling Services
N.A.I.C.S.: 213111

Noble Leasing (Switzerland) GmbH (1)
Dorfstrasse 19a, 6340, Baar, Switzerland
Tel.: (41) 417616580
Web Site: http://www.noblecorp.com
Sales Range: $50-74.9 Million
Emp.: 5
Industrial Machinery Leasing Services
N.A.I.C.S.: 532490

Noble Leasing II (Switzerland) GmbH (1)
Dorfstrasse 19a, 6340, Baar, Zug, Switzerland
Tel.: (41) 417616580
Industrial Machinery Leasing Services
N.A.I.C.S.: 532490

Noble Leasing III (Switzerland) GmbH (1)
Dorfstrasse 19a, 6340, Baar, Zug, Switzerland
Tel.: (41) 417616580

AND PRIVATE COMPANIES

Industrial Machinery Leasing Services
N.A.I.C.S.: 532490

Noble Services (Switzerland) LLC (1)
Rue de lAthenee 8, Geneva, 1205, Switzerland
Tel.: (41) 223182000
Web Site: http://www.noblecorp.com
Oil & Gas Well Drilling Services
N.A.I.C.S.: 213111

Noble Services International Limited (1)
Ste 3D Landmark Square 64 Earth Close, PO Box 31327, Georgetown, KY1-1206, Cayman Islands
Tel.: (345) 3459380293
Oil & Gas Well Drilling Services
N.A.I.C.S.: 213111
Alan Hay *(Dir-Asset Leasing)*

Sedco Dubai LLC (1)
Ubora Tower 13th Fl Business Bay Area 9241, Dubai, United Arab Emirates
Tel.: (971) 47094500
Oil & Gas Well Drilling Services
N.A.I.C.S.: 213111

Triton International de Mexico S.A. de C.V. (1)
Francisco Petrarca Num 223 Desp 503 chapultepec, 11570, Mexico, Mexico
Tel.: (52) 5552540719
Oil & Gas Well Drilling Services
N.A.I.C.S.: 213111

Triton International, Inc (1)
18 Blackjack Rd Ste 101, Fredericksburg, VA 22405
Tel.: (703) 575-8082
Web Site: http://tritonint.com
Packaging Services
N.A.I.C.S.: 561910

WELLDONE EDS GmbH (1)
Braunschweiger Heerstrasse 96, 29227, Celle, Germany
Tel.: (49) 5141 2792 0
Web Site: http://www.welldone.de
Engineering & Drilling Services
N.A.I.C.S.: 541330

NOBLE DEVELOPMENT PUBLIC COMPANY LIMITED
NOBLE Building 1035 Ploenchit Rd Lumpini, Pathumwan, Bangkok, 10330, Thailand
Tel.: (66) 22519955
Web Site:
   https://www.noblehome.com
Year Founded: 1991
NOBLE—(THA)
Rev.: $161,715,104
Assets: $766,846,561
Liabilities: $578,387,172
Net Worth: $188,459,389
Earnings: $26,584,594
Emp.: 689
Fiscal Year-end: 12/31/23
Residential Project Development
N.A.I.C.S.: 236220
Sira Udol *(Co-Chief Bus Dev Officer)*
Subsidiaries:

Ban Suk Sabai Company Limited (1)
Noble Building 1035 Ploenchit Road, Lumpini Pathumwan, Bangkok, 10330, Thailand
Tel.: (66) 22519955
Property Development Services
N.A.I.C.S.: 531312
Kitti Thanakitamnuay *(Mng Dir)*

Noble Furano Godo Kaisha (1)
2-1406 Azabudai 2-chome, Minato-ku, Tokyo, Japan
Tel.: (81) 22519955
Property Development Services
N.A.I.C.S.: 531312
Kitti Thanakitamnuay *(Mng Dir)*

Noble SG Pte. Ltd. (1)
1 Raffles Place 28-02 One Raffles Place, Singapore, 048616, Singapore
Tel.: (65) 22519955
Investment Management Service

N.A.I.C.S.: 523940
Kitti Thanakitamnuay *(Mng Dir)*

NOBLE ENGINEERING GROUP HOLDINGS LIMITED
Room 9 25/F CRE Centre 889 Cheung Sha Wan Road, Cheung Sha Wan, Kowloon, China (Hong Kong)
Tel.: (852) 2 114 3424 Ky
Web Site:
   http://www.nobleengineering.com.hk
Year Founded: 1981
8445—(HKG)
Rev.: $42,132,865
Assets: $16,674,534
Liabilities: $1,855,377
Net Worth: $14,819,157
Earnings: ($1,098,265)
Emp.: 52
Fiscal Year-end: 03/31/21
Building Construction Services
N.A.I.C.S.: 238140
Chun Yuen Tse *(Chm)*

NOBLE EXPLOCHEM LIMITED
54 B Shree Towers West High Court Road, Shankar Nagar E, Nagpur, 440010, India
Tel.: (91) 0712 253 8789 In
Year Founded: 1982
506991—(BOM)
Rev.: $5,726
Assets: $3,084,708
Liabilities: $7,308,983
Net Worth: ($4,224,275)
Earnings: ($85,082)
Fiscal Year-end: 03/31/18
Chemical Product Whslr
N.A.I.C.S.: 424690
Tikamchand Kothari *(Chm)*

NOBLE FINANCIALS SA
Adam Naruszewicza Ul 27, 02-627, Warsaw, Poland
Tel.: (48) 223974343
Web Site: http://www.ppgsa.pl
Year Founded: 2009
IBS—(WAR)
Rev.: $9,428,057
Assets: $19,967,874
Liabilities: $13,433,037
Net Worth: $6,534,837
Earnings: $5,287,130
Fiscal Year-end: 12/31/22
Real Estate Services
N.A.I.C.S.: 531390
Andrzej Malaga *(Chm-Mgmt Bd)*

NOBLE FOODS LTD.
Bridgeway House Icknield Way, Tring, HP23 4JX, Hertfordshire, United Kingdom
Tel.: (44) 1442 891 811
Web Site:
   http://www.noblefoods.co.uk
Year Founded: 1938
Sales Range: $900-999.9 Million
Emp.: 1,824
Egg Product Whslr
N.A.I.C.S.: 424440
Veli Moluluo *(Mng Dir-Shell Div)*

NOBLE GROUP HOLDINGS LIMITED
18th Floor China Evergrande Centre, 38 Gloucester Road, Hong Kong, China (Hong Kong)
Tel.: (852) 28613511 BM
Web Site: http://www.thisisnoble.com
Year Founded: 1987
Holding Company; Industrial Raw Materials Supplier; Agricultural & Transportation Services; Ship Management Services; Trade Finance Services; Insurance Services
N.A.I.C.S.: 551112

James Michael Dubow *(Chm)*
Subsidiaries:

Jamalco (1)
Halse Hall Clarendon, PO Box 64, WI, May Pen, Clarendon, Jamaica (55%)
Tel.: (876) 9862561
Web Site: http://www.jamalco.com
Sales Range: $75-99.9 Million
Emp.: 985
Bauxite Mining & Alumina Production
N.A.I.C.S.: 212290

Noble Carbon Credits Limited (1)
1F Gilford Hall 13 Gilford Road, Sandymount, Dublin, 4, Ireland
Tel.: (353) 12607660
Web Site: http://www.noble.com
Sales Range: $25-49.9 Million
Emp.: 3
Carbon Emission Reduction Systems Distr
N.A.I.C.S.: 423830

Noble Chartering Limited (1)
18F Massmutual Tower 38 Gloucester Road, Wanchai, China (Hong Kong)
Tel.: (852) 28613511
Freight Forwarding Services
N.A.I.C.S.: 488510

Noble Clean Fuels Limited (1)
33 Cavendish Square, London, W1G 0PW, United Kingdom
Tel.: (44) 2079075887
Web Site: http://www.noble.com
Sales Range: $75-99.9 Million
Emp.: 200
Petroleum Product Distr
N.A.I.C.S.: 424720
Tom Sargent *(Mgr-Bus)*

Noble Europe Limited (1)
33 Cavendish Square, London, W1G 0PW, United Kingdom
Tel.: (44) 2079075811
Commodities Trading Services
N.A.I.C.S.: 523160

Noble Netherlands BV (1)
Beechavenue 54-80, Schiphol-Rijk, 1119 PW, Netherlands
Tel.: (31) 206586020
Emp.: 10
Agriculture Product Distr
N.A.I.C.S.: 423820

Noble Paraguay Sociedad Anonima (1)
Parana Country Club Edificio Brisa Del Este Casa 6, Ciudad del Este, 7000, Alto Parana, Paraguay
Tel.: (595) 61571574
Sales Range: $25-49.9 Million
Emp.: 26
Agriculture Product Distr
N.A.I.C.S.: 424910
Hugo Pastore *(Country Mgr)*

Noble Resources Limited (1)
38 Gloucester Road, Wanchai, China (Hong Kong)
Tel.: (852) 22502211
Metals & Minerals Distr
N.A.I.C.S.: 423520

Noble Resources Pte. Ltd (1)
60 Anson Road 19-01 Maple Tree, 079914, Singapore, Singapore
Tel.: (65) 63054890
Agriculture Product Distr
N.A.I.C.S.: 424910

Noble Resources S.A. (1)
207 route serney, Geneva, 1005, Switzerland
Tel.: (41) 213310890
Sales Range: $100-124.9 Million
Emp.: 120
Commodities Trading Services
N.A.I.C.S.: 523160

TOWER Insurance (Fiji) Limited (1)
Level 3 FRCS Building 2, GPO Box 950, Corner of Queen Elizabeth Drive and Ratu Sukuna Road, Suva, Fiji
Tel.: (679) 3315955
Web Site: https://www.towerinsurance.com.fj
Sales Range: $50-74.9 Million
Emp.: 22
Fire & General Insurance Services

N.A.I.C.S.: 524113
Joseph Magnus *(Mgr)*

NOBLE HELIUM LIMITED
Level 10 127 Creek Street, Brisbane, 4000, QLD, Australia
Tel.: (61) 732126299 AU
Web Site:
   https://www.noblehelium.com.au
Year Founded: 2015
NHE—(ASX)
Mineral Exploration Services
N.A.I.C.S.: 212390

NOBLE JEWELRY INVESTMENT LIMITED
Flat M 12/F Phase 3 Kaiser Estate 11 Hok Yuen Street, HungHom, Kowloon, China (Hong Kong)
Tel.: (852) 2722 1132 BM
Web Site: http://www.noble.com.hk
Year Founded: 2011
Emp.: 40
Holding Company; Fine Jewelry Designer, Mfr & Distr
N.A.I.C.S.: 551112
Eddie Sin *(Dir-Admin)*
Subsidiaries:

Chad Allison Corporation (1)
576 Fifth Ave Ste 904, New York, NY 10036 (100%)
Tel.: (212) 278-8669
Web Site: http://www.chadallison.com
Jewelry Designer & Distr
N.A.I.C.S.: 339910

Noble Jewelry Limited (1)
Flat M 12/F Phase 3 Kaiser Estate 11 Hok Yuen St, Hung Hom, Kowloon, China (Hong Kong) (100%)
Tel.: (852) 27221132
Web Site: http://www.noble.com.hk
Sales Range: $25-49.9 Million
Emp.: 50
Fine Jewelry Designer, Mfr & Distr
N.A.I.C.S.: 339910
Johnny Chan *(Chm)*

NOBLE M&B CO., LTD.
1-dong 21-11 Gyeonggidong-ro Namsa-myeon, Cheoin-gu, Yongin, 462-120, Gyeonggi-do, Korea (South)
Tel.: (82) 313655650
Web Site:
   http://www.digitaloptics.co.kr
Year Founded: 2000
106520—(KRS)
Rev.: $11,466,693
Assets: $60,650,499
Liabilities: $23,446,527
Net Worth: $37,203,973
Earnings: ($35,080,892)
Emp.: 69
Fiscal Year-end: 12/31/22
Camera Lenses Mfr
N.A.I.C.S.: 333310
Son Tae Yeol *(CEO)*
Subsidiaries:

Digital Optics Co., Ltd. - Seongnam Factory (1)
Rm 204 Sicox Tower 513-14 Sangdewondong Jungwon-gu, Seongnam, 462-120, Kyonggi-do, Korea (South)
Tel.: (82) 317779361
Lens Mfr
N.A.I.C.S.: 333310

Digital Optics Co., Ltd. - Siwha Factory (1)
Rm 302 2-Da 1263-1 Jungwang-dong, Siheung, 429-923, Kyonggi-do, Korea (South)
Tel.: (82) 7043396800
Lens Mfr
N.A.I.C.S.: 333310

NOBLE METAL GROUP INCORPORATED

NOBLE METAL GROUP INCORPORATED

Noble Metal Group Incorporated—(Continued)
Vedder Crossing 1, PO Box 1145,
Chilliwack, V2R 3N7, BC, Canada
Tel.: (250) 862-9655
Web Site:
http://www.noblemetalgroup.com
Year Founded: 1974
Assets: $4,569,520
Liabilities: $6,905,608
Net Worth: ($2,336,088)
Earnings: ($4,248,122)
Fiscal Year-end: 12/31/17
Mineral Exploration Services
N.A.I.C.S.: 212290
Dorothy Dennis *(CEO)*

NOBLE METALS LIMITED
283 Rokeby Road, Subiaco, 6008,
WA, Australia
Tel.: (61) 8 6141 3500
Web Site:
http://www.noblemetals.com.au
Sales Range: Less than $1 Million
Platinum & Gold Exploration Services
N.A.I.C.S.: 212220
Jay Stephenson *(Sec)*

NOBLE MINERAL EXPLORATION INC.
2500 - 120 Adelaide Street W, Toronto, M5H 1T1, ON, Canada
Tel.: (416) 214-2250
Web Site:
https://www.nobleminerals.com
NOB—(OTCIQ)
Sales Range: Less than $1 Million
Mineral Exploration Services
N.A.I.C.S.: 213114
H. Vance White *(Pres & CEO)*

NOBLE POLYMERS LIMITED
9 Ankur Complex B/h Town Hall, Opp
X-Ray House Ellisbridge, Ahmedabad, 380 006, India
Tel.: (91) 7940329745
Web Site: http://www.noblepoly.com
Rev.: $165,532
Assets: $379,091
Liabilities: $385,490
Net Worth: ($6,399)
Earnings: ($482,281)
Fiscal Year-end: 03/31/17
Plastics Product Mfr
N.A.I.C.S.: 326199

NOBLE VICI GROUP, INC.
45 Ubi Crescent, Singapore, 408590,
Singapore
Tel.: (65) 64917998   DE
Web Site: http://www.noblevici.com
Year Founded: 2010
NVGI—(OTCIQ)
Rev.: $3,074,720
Assets: $8,865,442
Liabilities: $12,113,683
Net Worth: ($3,248,241)
Earnings: ($1,676,479)
Emp.: 8
Fiscal Year-end: 03/31/21
Cutting Edge Technology Products
Mfr
N.A.I.C.S.: 332216
Eldee Wai Chong Tang *(CEO, Interim CFO, Interim Chief Corp Officer & Interim Sec)*

Subsidiaries:

AIM System Pte. Ltd.   (1)
45 Ubi Crescent, Singapore, 408590, Singapore
Tel.: (65) 64917998
Web Site: http://www.aimsystem.cloud
Coffee Product Mfr
N.A.I.C.S.: 311920

Noble Vici Private Limited   (1)
45 Ubi Crescent, Singapore, 408590, Singapore
Tel.: (65) 65216806
Web Site: http://www.noblevici.com.sg
Online Marketplace Services
N.A.I.C.S.: 541511
Eldee Wai Chong Tang *(Founder & CEO)*

VMORE System Pte. Ltd.   (1)
45 Ubi Crescent, Singapore, 408590, Singapore
Tel.: (65) 65216805
Web Site: http://www.vmoresystem.com
Online Marketplace Services
N.A.I.C.S.: 541511
Alfred Tan *(VP-Bus Dev)*

NOBLELIFT INTELLIGENT EQUIPMENT CO.,LTD
No 528 Changzhou Road, Taihu Sub-District, Changxing, 313100, Zhejiang, China
Tel.: (86) 5726210809
Web Site: https://www.noblelift.com
Year Founded: 2000
603611—(SHG)
Rev.: $940,991,281
Assets: $1,264,196,054
Liabilities: $931,588,819
Net Worth: $332,607,235
Earnings: $56,466,788
Emp.: 2,000
Fiscal Year-end: 12/31/22
Industrial Vehicle Mfr & Distr
N.A.I.C.S.: 333924
Ding Yi *(Chm)*

Subsidiaries:

Noblelift Canada Inc.   (1)
850 Ellingham, Pointe-Claire, H9R3S4, QC, Canada
Tel.: (514) 697-0117
Web Site: https://nobleliftcanada.com
Material Handling Equipment Distr
N.A.I.C.S.: 423830

Noblelift Europe GmbH   (1)
Borsigstrasse 9d, 93092, Barbing, Germany
Tel.: (49) 9401607930
Web Site: http://www.noblelifteurope.com
Industrial Equipment Mfr
N.A.I.C.S.: 333310

Noblelift Rus LLC   (1)
Marshal Blucher Ave 78 letter B Premises 1-N Office 1, Saint Petersburg, 195067, Russia
Tel.: (7) 8007002897
Web Site: https://www.noblelift.com.ru
Warehousing Equipment Mfr
N.A.I.C.S.: 333922

Savoye S.A.   (1)
18 boulevard des Gorgets, BP 21898, 21018, Dijon, Cedex, France   **(100%)**
Tel.: (33) 380544000
Web Site: http://www.savoye.com
Automated Logistics Equipment Mfr
N.A.I.C.S.: 333922

Subsidiary (Non-US):

Savoye GmbH   (2)
Wilhelm Strauss 49, 41236, Monchengladbach, Germany
Tel.: (49) 2161567910
Freight Transportation Arrangement
N.A.I.C.S.: 488510

Savoye Logistics SL   (2)
Avinguda de la Verge de Montserrat 116, 08820, El Prat de Llobregat, Spain
Tel.: (34) 933789260
Process Physical Distribution & Logistics Consulting Services
N.A.I.C.S.: 541614

Savoye Ltd.   (2)
17 Charnwood Office Village North Road, Loughborough, LE11 1QJ, England, United Kingdom
Tel.: (44) 1509221000
Web Site: http://www.savoye.com
Industrial Machinery & Equipment Whslr
N.A.I.C.S.: 423830

Wuxi Zhongding Integration Technology Co., Ltd.   (1)
12B Modern International Industrial Design Building, No 801 Hongqiao Road Binhu District, Wuxi, Jiangsu, China
Tel.: (86) 4008044498
Web Site: https://zdintegration.com
Emp.: 900
Lifting Equipment Mfr & Distr
N.A.I.C.S.: 333923

NOBLEOAK LIFE LIMITED
Level 4/44 Market St, Sydney, 2000, NSW, Australia
Tel.: (61) 1300861742   AU
Web Site:
https://www.nobleoak.com.au
NOL—(ASX)
Rev.: $215,385,017
Assets: $222,699,355
Liabilities: $144,562,170
Net Worth: $78,137,185
Earnings: $5,211,580
Fiscal Year-end: 06/30/23
Direct Life Insurance Carriers
N.A.I.C.S.: 524113
Matt Minney *(COO)*

Subsidiaries:

Genus Life Insurance Services Pty Ltd.   (1)
GPO Box 2548, Sydney, 2001, NSW, Australia
Tel.: (61) 1300884488
Web Site:
https://www.genuslifeinsurance.com.au
Fire Insurance Services
N.A.I.C.S.: 524113

NOBUL AI CORP.
130 King Street West Suite 1800, Toronto, ON, Canada
Tel.: (800) 321-5907
Web Site: https://nobul.com
Emp.: 100
Real Estate Services
N.A.I.C.S.: 531210

NOCADIS
Avenue Jules Ferry, 24300, Nontron, Dordogne, France
Tel.: (33) 553609300
Sales Range: $10-24.9 Million
Emp.: 70
Supermarket
N.A.I.C.S.: 445110
Philip Tourre *(Pres)*

NOCERA, INC.
3F No 185 Sec 1 Datong Rd, Xizhi Dist, New Taipei City, 221, Taiwan
Tel.: (886) 910163358   NV
Web Site:
https://www.nocera.company
NCRA—(NASDAQ)
Rev.: $16,338,754
Assets: $8,140,319
Liabilities: $1,958,072
Net Worth: $6,182,247
Earnings: ($4,812,908)
Emp.: 16
Fiscal Year-end: 12/31/22
Aquaculture Consulting Services
N.A.I.C.S.: 112519
David Kugelman *(VP-Fin)*

NOCO-NOCO INC.
3 Temasek Avenue Centennial Tower Level 18, Singapore, 039190, Singapore
Tel.: (65) 69709643   Ky
Web Site: https://www.noco-noco.com
Year Founded: 2019
NCNC—(NASDAQ)
Rev.: $49,084
Assets: $691,195
Liabilities: $4,369,449

INTERNATIONAL PUBLIC

Net Worth: ($3,678,254)
Earnings: ($16,791,770)
Emp.: 12
Fiscal Year-end: 06/30/23
Battery Mfr
N.A.I.C.S.: 335910
Masataka Matsumura *(Founder & CEO)*

NOCTILUCA SA
Jurija Gagarina 7 / 41B, 87-100, Torun, Poland
Tel.: (48) 573821838
Web Site: https://www.noctiluca.eu
Year Founded: 2019
NCL—(WAR)
Chemical Products Mfr
N.A.I.C.S.: 335991

NODA CORPORATION
5136 Asakusabashi, Taito-ku, Tokyo, 111-8533, Japan
Tel.: (81) 356876222
Web Site: https://www.noda-co.jp
Year Founded: 1938
7879—(TKS)
Rev.: $519,179,430
Assets: $541,470,390
Liabilities: $229,219,700
Net Worth: $312,250,690
Earnings: $20,093,060
Emp.: 1,034
Fiscal Year-end: 11/30/23
Housing Material Mfr & Distr
N.A.I.C.S.: 321911
Tsutomu Noda *(Pres)*

Subsidiaries:

Ishinomaki Plywood Mfg. Co., Ltd.   (1)
4-3 Shiomicho, Ishinomaki, 986-0842, Miyagi, Japan
Tel.: (81) 22 596 3111
Web Site: https://www.ishinomaki.co.jp
Plywood Mfr & Distr
N.A.I.C.S.: 321212

Naffics Corporation   (1)
5-13-6 Asakusabashi, Taito-ku, Tokyo, 111-0053, Japan
Tel.: (81) 35 687 6226
Web Site: https://www.naffics-co.jp
Emp.: 12
Building Material Mfr & Distr
N.A.I.C.S.: 321918

NODEN PHARMA DAC
D Olier Chambers 16A D Olier Street, Dublin, Ireland
Tel.: (353) 16778458
Web Site:
http://www.nodenpharma.com
Pharmaceutical Mfr & Whslr
N.A.I.C.S.: 325412
Alan Markey *(CEO)*

NOEL GIFTS INTERNATIONAL LTD.
21 Ubi Road 1 03 01, Singapore, 408724, Singapore
Tel.: (65) 62991133   SG
Web Site: https://www.noelgifts.com
Year Founded: 1975
543—(SES)
Rev.: $13,725,824
Assets: $24,886,254
Liabilities: $1,885,143
Net Worth: $23,001,112
Earnings: $166,728
Emp.: 115
Fiscal Year-end: 06/30/23
Gift & Novelty Distr
N.A.I.C.S.: 459420
Alfred Wong siu Hong *(Chm & Mng Dir)*

NOELL REGGIANE FRANCE SARL

AND PRIVATE COMPANIES

124 Rue Nationale, 57350, Forbach, France
Tel.: (33) 387872800
Sales Range: $25-49.9 Million
Emp.: 29
Professional Equipment Mfr
N.A.I.C.S.: 423490
Claudine Intile *(Sec)*

NOESIS INDUSTRIES LIMITED
1201B 12th Floor Hemkunt Chamber, 89 Nehru Place, New Delhi, 110019, India
Tel.: (91) 1141662674
Web Site: http://www.mvlindustries.in
Year Founded: 1986
Rev.: $363
Assets: $1,131,505
Liabilities: $38,284,357
Net Worth: ($37,152,852)
Earnings: $118,444
Fiscal Year-end: 03/31/17
Consumer Electronics Mfr & Whslr
N.A.I.C.S.: 335220
Prem Adip Rishi *(Chm & Mng Dir)*

NOEVIR HOLDINGS CO., LTD.
7-6-15 Ginza, Chuo-ku, Tokyo, 104-8208, Japan
Tel.: (81) 355680305
Web Site: https://www.noevirholdings.co.jp
Year Founded: 2011
4928—(TKS)
Rev.: $443,493,680
Assets: $547,674,140
Liabilities: $170,450,690
Net Worth: $377,223,450
Earnings: $54,401,570
Emp.: 1,369
Fiscal Year-end: 09/30/23
Holding Company
N.A.I.C.S.: 551112
Takashi Okura *(Pres & CEO)*

Subsidiaries:

Noevir Co., Ltd. (1)
6-13-1 Minatojima Nakamachi, Chuo-ku, Kobe, 650-8521, Japan
Tel.: (81) 783035111
Web Site: https://www.noevir.co.jp
Sales Range: $550-599.9 Million
Cosmetics, Pharmaceuticals & Nutritional Supplements Mfr & Sales
N.A.I.C.S.: 325620

Subsidiary (Domestic):

Bonanza Co., Ltd. (2)
6-13-1 Minatojimanakamachi, Chuo-ku, Kobe, 650-8521, Japan (100%)
Tel.: (81) 783035109
Web Site: https://bonanza.noevir.co.jp
Toilet Preparation Mfr
N.A.I.C.S.: 325620

Noevir Aviation Co., Ltd. (2)
2-12 Kuko, Yao, 581-0043, Osaka, Japan (100%)
Tel.: (81) 729916461
Web Site: https://www.nac.noevir.co.jp
Sales Range: $25-49.9 Million
Emp.: 11
Oil Transportation Services
N.A.I.C.S.: 488190
Mitsuhiro Okazaki *(CEO)*

Subsidiary (US):

Noevir Aviation, Inc. (2)
200 W Grand Ave, Montvale, NJ 07645 (100%)
Tel.: (201) 391-0001
Airport Operations
N.A.I.C.S.: 488119
Masaki Kondo *(Pres)*

Noevir Holding of America, Inc. (2)
1095 SE Main St, Irvine, CA 92614 (100%)
Tel.: (949) 660-1111
Sales Range: $1-9.9 Million
Holding Company
N.A.I.C.S.: 551112

Subsidiary (Non-US):

Noevir Canada, Inc. (3)
c/o Nippon Express Canada Ltd 110-16100 Blundell Rd, Richmond, V6W 0A2, BC, Canada (100%)
Web Site: http://www.noevirusa.com
Sales Range: $1-9.9 Million
Cosmetics, Body Care, Nutritionals & Body Treatments Direct Selling
N.A.I.C.S.: 456120

Subsidiary (Domestic):

Noevir U.S.A. Inc. (3)
1095 Main St, Irvine, CA 92614 (100%)
Tel.: (949) 660-1111
Sales Range: $1-9.9 Million
Cosmetics & Nutritional Supplements Marketer & Sales
N.A.I.C.S.: 424210

Subsidiary (Non-US):

Noevir Taiwan, Inc. (2)
8th Fl-2 No 111 Songjiang Road, Zhongshan District, Taipei, 10486, Taiwan (90.32%)
Tel.: (886) 225163178
Web Site: https://www.noevirtw.com.tw
Sales Range: $25-49.9 Million
Emp.: 20
Cosmetics Beauty Supplies & Perfume Stores
N.A.I.C.S.: 456120
Akemi Nakabo *(Gen Mgr)*

Subsidiary (Domestic):

Noevir Tourist Co., Ltd. (2)
Shin Aoyama Bldg Higashi-kan 18F Minami Aoyama 1-1-1, Minato-ku, Tokyo, 107, Japan (100%)
Tel.: (81) 334033634
Web Site: https://www.tourism.co.jp
Sales Range: $25-49.9 Million
Emp.: 4
Tour Operator
N.A.I.C.S.: 561520

Tokiwa Medical Service Co., Ltd. (1)
Noevia Kobe Building 6-13-1 Minatojima Nakamachi, Chuo-ku, Kobe, 650-8521, Hyogo Prefecture, Japan
Tel.: (81) 783039985
Emp.: 300
Pharmaceutical & Health Care Products Distr
N.A.I.C.S.: 424210

Tokiwa Pharmaceutical Co., Ltd. (1)
Lattice Aoyama Square 1-2-6 Minamiaoyama, Minato-ku, Tokyo, 107-0062, Japan (100%)
Tel.: (81) 367312050
Sales Range: $200-249.9 Million
Emp.: 810
Pharmaceuticals, Cosmetics & Health Food Products Developer, Mfr & Marketer
N.A.I.C.S.: 325412
Masataka Nakano *(Pres)*

NOF CORPORATION
Yebisu Garden Place Tower 20-3 Ebisu 4-chome, Shibuya-ku, Tokyo, 150-6012, Japan
Tel.: (81) 354246600
Web Site: https://www.nof.co.jp
Year Founded: 1937
4403—(TKS)
Rev.: $1,469,085,720
Assets: $2,256,977,890
Liabilities: $499,332,620
Net Worth: $1,757,645,270
Earnings: $224,673,900
Emp.: 1,794
Fiscal Year-end: 03/31/24
Chemical Products Mfr
N.A.I.C.S.: 325199
Kazuhito Maeda *(Sr Exec Operating Officer)*

Subsidiaries:

CACTUS Co., Ltd. (1)
Sengoku Coathouse Bldg 37-4 Sengoku 4-chome, Bunkyo-ku, Tokyo, 112-0011, Japan
Tel.: (81) 359403671
Industrial Products Sales
N.A.I.C.S.: 423830

Changshu NOF Chemical Co., Ltd. (1)
36 Wan Fu Road Riverside Industrial Park, Chang shu Economic Development Zone, Changshu, 215537, Jiang Su, China
Tel.: (86) 51252275252
Fatty Acid Derivatives & Organic Peroxide Producer
N.A.I.C.S.: 325998

Georgia Metal Coatings Co. (1)
3033 Adriatic Ct, Norcross, GA 30071
Tel.: (770) 446-3930
Web Site: http://www.georgiametalcoatings.com
Metal Plating Services
N.A.I.C.S.: 332812
David Billet *(Gen Mgr)*

Hokkaido NOF Corporation (1)
549 Koshunai, Bibai, 079-0167, Hokkaido, Japan
Tel.: (81) 126672211
Web Site: https://www.nof.co.jp
Explosives & Chemical Products Mfr & Sales
N.A.I.C.S.: 325920

JAPEX Corp. (1)
SAPIA Tower 1-7-12 Marunouchi, Chiyoda-ku, Tokyo, 100-0005, Japan
Tel.: (81) 362687000
Web Site: https://www.japex.co.jp
Emp.: 1,617
Industrial Explosives Sales
N.A.I.C.S.: 424690

Jeune Beauty Corporation (1)
Yebisu Garden Place Tower 20-3 Ebisu 4-chome, Shibuya-ku, Tokyo, 150-6019, Japan
Tel.: (81) 3 3442 6331
Web Site: http://www.jeunebeauty.co.jp
Cosmetics & Toiletry Products Mfr
N.A.I.C.S.: 325611

NOF (Shanghai) Co., Ltd. (1)
Room 3405-3406 34F Zhaofeng Plaza No 1027 Changning Road, Changning District, Shanghai, 200050, China
Tel.: (86) 2162101100
Emp.: 11
Chemical Import, Export & Sales
N.A.I.C.S.: 424690
Koji Ozawa *(Mgr)*

NOF AMERICA CORPORATION (1)
1 N Broadway Ste 912, White Plains, NY 10601
Tel.: (914) 681-9790
Web Site: https://www.nofamerica.com
Chemical Products Distr
N.A.I.C.S.: 424210

NOF Corporation - Aichi Works (1)
61-1 Aza-Kitakomatsudani, Chita-gun, Taketoyo, 470-2379, Aichi, Japan
Tel.: (81) 569 72 1221
Web Site: http://www.nof.co.jp
Chemical Products Mfr
N.A.I.C.S.: 325199

NOF Corporation - Amagasaki Plant (1)
56 Ohamacho 1 Chome, Amagasaki, 660-0095, Hyogo, Japan
Tel.: (81) 664161321
Oleo Chemical Product Mfr
N.A.I.C.S.: 325199

NOF Corporation - Display Materials Plant (1)
17-1 Aza-Shimada, Chita-gun, Taketoyo, 470-2373, Aichi, Japan
Tel.: (81) 569 72 1832
Web Site: http://www.nof.co.jp
Display Material Mfr
N.A.I.C.S.: 334419

NOF Corporation - Oita Plant (1)
2 Oaza-Nakanosu, Oita, 870-0111, Japan
Tel.: (81) 97 527 5201
Web Site: http://www.nof.co.jp
Polymer Product Mfr
N.A.I.C.S.: 325211

NOF Corporation - Tanegashima Plant (1)
3138-4 Hirayama, Kumage-gun, Minami, 891-3702, Kagoshima, Japan
Tel.: (81) 997262961
Chemical Products Mfr
N.A.I.C.S.: 325199

NOF Europe (Belgium) N.V. (1)
Bouwelven 1 Industriezone Klein-Gent, 2280, Grobbendonk, Belgium
Tel.: (32) 14259831
Web Site: http://www.nofeurope.com
Emp.: 6
Chemical Import, Export & Sales
N.A.I.C.S.: 424690

NOF Europe GmbH (1)
Hamburger Allee 2-4, 60486, Frankfurt am Main, Germany
Tel.: (49) 6977061000
Web Site: https://www.nofeurope.com
Chemical Products Distr
N.A.I.C.S.: 424690

NOF METAL COATINGS NORTH AMERICA Inc. (1)
275 Industrial Pkwy, Chardon, OH 44024
Tel.: (440) 285-2231
Web Site: http://www.nofmetalcoatings.us
Metal Plating Services
N.A.I.C.S.: 332812

NOF Metal Coatings Asia Pacific Co., Ltd. (1)
3-3 Chidori-Cho, Kawasaki-ku, Kawasaki, 210-0865, Kanagawa, Japan
Tel.: (81) 445201515
Emp.: 350
Anti-Corrosion Agents Mfr & Sales
N.A.I.C.S.: 325510

Subsidiary (US):

Michigan Metal Coatings Co. (2)
2015 Dove St, Port Huron, MI 48060
Tel.: (810) 966-9240
Web Site: http://www.michiganmetalcoatings.com
Sales Range: $1-9.9 Million
Emp.: 70
Paint & Coating Mfr
N.A.I.C.S.: 325510
Kyoji Sato *(Pres)*

Subsidiary (Non-US):

NOF Metal Coatings Europe N.V. (2)
Bouwelven 1 Industriezone Klein-Gent, 2280, Grobbendonk, Belgium
Tel.: (32) 14259831
Web Site: https://www.nofmetalcoatings.com
Emp.: 43
Anti-Corrosion Agents Mfr & Sales
N.A.I.C.S.: 325510

NOF Metal Coatings Europe S.A. (2)
120 rue Galilee, CS 50093, 60106, Creil, Cedex, France
Tel.: (33) 344646362
Anti-Corrosion Agents Mfr & Sales
N.A.I.C.S.: 325510

NOF Metal Coatings Korea Co., Ltd. (2)
9F 22 Saemunan-ro, Jung-gu, Seoul, 04516, Korea (South)
Tel.: (82) 25714051
Web Site: https://www.nofmetalcoatings.com
Emp.: 28
Anti-Corrosion Agents Mfr & Sales
N.A.I.C.S.: 325510

NOF Metal Coatings Shanghai Co., Ltd. (2)
3rd Floor West Gems Building No 487 Tianlin Rd, Xuhui District, Shanghai, 200223, China
Tel.: (86) 2161204020
Anti-Corrosion Agents Sales
N.A.I.C.S.: 424690

NOF CORPORATION

NOF Corporation—(Continued)

NOF Metal Coatings South America Ind. e Com. Ltda. (2)
Rua Minas Gerais No 85 Vila Oriental, Diadema, Sao Paulo, 09941-760, Brazil
Tel.: (55) 1147015651
Anti-Corrosion Agents Mfr & Sales
N.A.I.C.S.: 325510

Nikka Coating Co., Ltd. (2)
Tel.: (81) 489919854
Anti-Corrosion Agents Mfr & Sales
N.A.I.C.S.: 325510

Subsidiary (Domestic):

Nippon C&Z Co., Ltd. (2)
2-25-11 Nagono, Nishiku, Nagoya, 451-0042, Aichi, Japan
Tel.: (81) 525715512
Web Site: https://www.ncz.co.jp
Emp.: 5
Metal Surface Treatment Systems Mfr & Sales
N.A.I.C.S.: 325510

NiGK Corporation (1)
21-2 Matoba-shinmachi, Kawagoe, 350-1107, Saitama, Japan
Tel.: (81) 492312103
Emp.: 340
Thermal Indicator Material Mfr
N.A.I.C.S.: 334513

Nichiyu Giken Kogyo Co., Ltd. (1)
21-2 Matoba-shinmachi, Kawagoe, 350-1107, Saitama, Japan
Tel.: (81) 492312103
Emp.: 340
Chemical Products Mfr & Sales
N.A.I.C.S.: 325998

Nichiyu Kogyo Co., Ltd. (1)
22-1 Dou-cho 4-chome, Takatsuki, Osaka, 569-0011, Japan
Tel.: (81) 726695141
Emp.: 16
Oleochemical Products Mfr
N.A.I.C.S.: 325998
Naoshi Fujita (Pres)

Nichiyu Logistics Co., Ltd. (1)
3-2 Chidoricho, Kawasaki-ku, Kawasaki, 210-0865, Kanagawa, Japan (100%)
Tel.: (81) 44 280 0560
Web Site: http://www.nichiyu.co.jp
Emp.: 356
Transportation, Storage & Freight Handling Services
N.A.I.C.S.: 488510

Nichiyu Techno Co., Ltd. (1)
3-3 Chidori-cho, Kawasaki-ku, Kawasaki, 210-0865, Kanagawa, Japan
Tel.: (81) 44 280 0701
Web Site: http://www.nichiyu-tec.co.jp
Emp.: 45
Analytical Measurement Devices Mfr & Sales
N.A.I.C.S.: 334516
Toshito Shigayama (CEO)

Nichiyu Trading Co., Ltd. (1)
Ebisu Neonato 1-18 Ebisu 4-chome, Shibuya-ku, Tokyo, 150-0013, Japan
Tel.: (81) 357898211
Insurance, Trading & Real Estate Services
N.A.I.C.S.: 531390

Nippo Kogyo Co., Ltd. (1)
1838 Chabatake, Susono, 410-1121, Shizuoka, Japan
Tel.: (81) 55 992 0476
Web Site: http://www.nippokogyo.co.jp
Emp.: 30
Guns & Ammunition Mfr & Sales
N.A.I.C.S.: 332993
Kenji Ito (Pres)

Nippon Koki Co., Ltd. (1)
Nagatanien Bldg 36-1 Nishi-Shinbashi 2-chome, Minato-ku, Tokyo, 105-0003, Japan
Tel.: (81) 334363711
Defense Equipment & Industrial Explosives Mfr
N.A.I.C.S.: 325920

PT. NOF MAS Chemical Industries (1)

Kawasan Industri Bekasi Fajar Block D-1, Mekar Wangi MM2100 Industrial Town Phase III Cikarang Barat, Bekasi, 17530, Indonesia
Tel.: (62) 218980636
Organic Peroxides Mfr & Sales
N.A.I.C.S.: 325998

SIE s.r.l. (1)
Via delle Fabbriche 10A/red, 16158, Genoa, Italy
Tel.: (39) 01061611
Web Site: https://www.sie-srl.net
Emp.: 180
Integrated Design Services
N.A.I.C.S.: 541519

Showa Kinzoku Kogyo Co., Ltd. (1)
Iwase 2120, Sakuragawa, 309-1211, Ibaraki, Japan
Tel.: (81) 296761811
Ammunition & Gas Generators Mfr
N.A.I.C.S.: 332993

Yuka Sangyo Co., Ltd. (1)
7F Ebisu Neonato 4-1-18 Ebisu, Shibuya-ku, Tokyo, 150-0013, Japan
Tel.: (81) 3 5791 4101
Web Site: http://www.yuka-sangyo.co.jp
Emp.: 171
Chemical Products Mfr & Sales
N.A.I.C.S.: 325998

NOFAR ENERGY LTD.
1 Hatachana Street Manivim Building 11th floor, Kfar Saba, Israel
Tel.: (972) 83750060
Web Site: https://www.nofar-energy.com
Year Founded: 2011
NOFR—(TAE)
Rev.: $93,368,310
Assets: $1,536,865,409
Liabilities: $785,517,597
Net Worth: $751,347,812
Earnings: ($27,609,403)
Emp.: 255
Fiscal Year-end: 12/31/23
Solar Electric Power Generation Services
N.A.I.C.S.: 221114
Ofer Yannay (Founder & Chm)

NOGALES RESOURCES CORP.
Unit 1908 Shanghai Mart Tower, 2299 West Yan'an Road Changning District, Shanghai, 200336, China
Tel.: (86) 2123570055 NV
Year Founded: 2014
NLRT—(OTCBB)
Assets: $436
Liabilities: $212,910
Net Worth: ($212,474)
Earnings: ($46,683)
Fiscal Year-end: 04/30/20
Exploration Stage Company; Investment Services
N.A.I.C.S.: 212290
Yang Liu (Pres, CEO & CFO)

NOH & PARTNERS CO., LTD.
6th floor, Geumgang Building 304, Bongeunsa-road Gangnam-gu, Seoul, Korea (South)
Tel.: (82) 025530818
Web Site: http://www.nohnpartners.com
Year Founded: 2015
Private Equity
N.A.I.C.S.: 523940
Sukhee Bae (Mng Dir)

NOHMI BOSAI LTD.
7-3 Kudan-Minami 4-Chome, Chiyoda-ku, Tokyo, 102-8277, Japan
Tel.: (81) 332650231
Web Site: https://www.nohmi.co.jp
6744—(TKS)
Rev.: $783,324,660
Assets: $1,040,975,850

Liabilities: $213,628,590
Net Worth: $827,347,260
Earnings: $56,674,140
Emp.: 2,524
Fiscal Year-end: 03/31/24
Telecom Equipment Mfr
N.A.I.C.S.: 334220
Takeshi Okamura (Pres, Sr Mng Dir & Sr Mng Dir)

Subsidiaries:

Hokkaido Nohmi Co., Ltd. (1)
Kita 13-jo Nishi 1-2-21, Kita-ku, Sapporo, 001-0013, Hokkaido, Japan
Tel.: (81) 117462511
Disaster Prevention Equipment Mfr
N.A.I.C.S.: 334290

Ichibou Co., Ltd. (1)
Koizumi Building 3F1-29-1 Nishigotanda, Shinagawa-ku, Tsukuba, 141-0031, Ibaraki, Japan
Tel.: (81) 33 779 9731
Web Site: https://www.ichibo.com
Fire Alarm Equipment Mfr
N.A.I.C.S.: 334290

Iwate Nohmi Co., Ltd. (1)
2-20-5 Aoyama, Morioka, 020-0133, Iwate, Japan
Tel.: (81) 196450552
Emp.: 46
Disaster Prevention Equipment Mfr
N.A.I.C.S.: 334290

NOHMI Engineering Corporation (1)
Sakura Kameido Building 5-2-3 Kameido, Koto-ku, Tokyo, 136-0071, Japan
Tel.: (81) 356282500
Emp.: 129
Disaster Prevention Equipment Mfr
N.A.I.C.S.: 334290

Nohmi Baoli (Beijing) Intelligent Fire Protection Co., Ltd. (1)
Room 1703 Block M Beichen Huiyuan Hotel Apartment, No 8 Beichen East Road Chaoyang District, Beijing, China
Tel.: (86) 1065501135
Web Site: http://www.anbaoli.net
Disaster Prevention Equipment Distr
N.A.I.C.S.: 423990

Nohmi System Co., Ltd. (1)
10th floor Shinjuku Park Tower 3-7-1 Nishi-Shinjuku, Shinjuku-ku, Tokyo, 163-1010, Japan
Tel.: (81) 362790206
Web Site: https://nohmi-sys.co.jp
Emp.: 38
Disaster Prevention Equipment Mfr
N.A.I.C.S.: 334290

Nohmi Techno Engineering Co., Ltd. (1)
1-14-32 Honmachi, Fuchu, 183-0027, Tokyo, Japan
Tel.: (81) 423109905
Emp.: 37
Disaster Prevention Equipment Mfr
N.A.I.C.S.: 334290

NOHO PARTNERS PLC
Verkatehtaankatu 2, Hatanpaan valtatie 1 B, FI-33100, Tampere, Finland
Tel.: (358) 961286000
Web Site: https://www.noho.fi
Year Founded: 1996
NOHO—(HEL)
Rev.: $337,578,243
Assets: $489,099,935
Liabilities: $400,604,360
Net Worth: $88,495,575
Earnings: $5,288,150
Emp.: 2,300
Fiscal Year-end: 12/31/22
Restaurant, Cafe & Nightclub Owner & Operator
N.A.I.C.S.: 722511
Timo Laine (Founder & Co-Chm)

Subsidiaries:

Bronnum ApS (1)
August Bournonvilles Passage 1, 1055, Copenhagen, Denmark
Tel.: (45) 88440404
Web Site: https://www.bronnumcph.dk
Home Management Services
N.A.I.C.S.: 721110

Cock's & Cows ApS (1)
Gammel Strand 34, 1202, Copenhagen, Denmark
Tel.: (45) 69157001
Web Site: http://www.cloud-kitchen.dk
Catering Services
N.A.I.C.S.: 722320

Friends & Brgrs Ab Oy (1)
Stationsvagen 5, Jakobstad, 68600, Pietarsaari, Finland
Tel.: (358) 442900033
Web Site: https://www.friendsandbrgrs.fi
Food Service
N.A.I.C.S.: 722310
Peter Fagerholm (CEO)

Latitude 25 Oy (1)
Albertinkatu 19, 00120, Helsinki, Finland
Tel.: (358) 961286000
Web Site: https://www.latitude25.fi
Restaurant Services
N.A.I.C.S.: 722511

Lidkoeb ApS (1)
Vesterbrogade 72B, 1620, Copenhagen, Denmark
Tel.: (45) 33112010
Web Site: http://www.lidkoeb.dk
Home Management Services
N.A.I.C.S.: 721110

Royal Ravintolat Oy (1)
Pormestarenrenae 5, 00160, Helsinki, Finland
Tel.: (358) 961286000
Restaurant Services
N.A.I.C.S.: 722511

Subsidiary (Domestic):

Yes Yes Yes Oy (2)
Iso Roobertinkatu 1, 00120, Helsinki, Finland
Tel.: (358) 961285130
Web Site: http://www.yesyesyes.fi
Restaurant Services
N.A.I.C.S.: 722511

Thai Papaya Oy (1)
Yliskylan puistokatu 4, 00840, Helsinki, Finland
Tel.: (358) 449718998
Web Site: http://www.thaipapaya.fi
Restaurant Services
N.A.I.C.S.: 722511

NOIDA MEDICARE CENTRE LTD.
VIMHANS Hospital Campus 1 Institutional Area Nehru Nagar, New Delhi, 110065, India
Tel.: (91) 1129849000
Web Site: http://www.rancanindia.com
Sales Range: $10-24.9 Million
Health Care Srvices
N.A.I.C.S.: 621999
Naveen Chaudhri (Chm & Mng Dir)

NOIDA TOLL BRIDGE COMPANY LIMITED
Toll Plaza Mayur Vihar Link Road, New Delhi, 110091, India
Tel.: (91) 1202516447 In
Web Site: https://www.ntbcl.com
Year Founded: 1996
532481—(BOM)
Rev.: $3,216,642
Assets: $45,831,665
Liabilities: $17,522,822
Net Worth: $28,308,842
Earnings: ($4,212,277)
Emp.: 3
Fiscal Year-end: 03/31/23
Toll Bridge Operator
N.A.I.C.S.: 488999
Rajiv Jain (CFO)

AND PRIVATE COMPANIES

NOIZ GROUP LIMITED
Room 1108 11th Floor Wing On Centre, 111 Connaught Road, Central, China (Hong Kong)
Tel.: (852) 21157600 Ky
Web Site:
http://www.merdeka.com.hk
8163—(HKG)
Rev.: $3,128,723
Assets: $11,333,475
Liabilities: $14,839,088
Net Worth: ($3,505,613)
Earnings: ($3,925,470)
Emp.: 38
Fiscal Year-end: 12/31/21
Financial Trading Services
N.A.I.C.S.: 522299
Wilson Wai Yin Cheung *(Chm, CEO & Officer-Compliance)*

Subsidiaries:

Heng Asset Management Limited (1)
Unit 906 9/F Shui On Centre 6-8 Harbour Road, Wanchai, China (Hong Kong)   (100%)
Tel.: (852) 39710400
Web Site: http://www.heng-asset.com
Investment Management Service
N.A.I.C.S.: 523940
Barry Yu Chak Ip *(Founder & Exec Dir)*

Netgenii Technology Limited (1)
35/F Times Media Center 133 Wanchai Road, Wanchai, China (Hong Kong)
Tel.: (852) 36918369
Web Site: http://www.netgenii.com
Software Development Services
N.A.I.C.S.: 513210

Source Easy Limited (1)
Unit 10 G/F Block B Cambridge Plaza 188 San Wan Road, Sheung Shui, New Territories, China (Hong Kong)
Tel.: (852) 37469355
Web Site: http://www.source-easy.com.hk
Online Product Distr
N.A.I.C.S.: 541612

Veda Corporate Services Limited (1)
Room 1106 11/F Wing On Centre 111 Connaught Road, Central, China (Hong Kong)
Tel.: (852) 21111690
Financial Consulting Services
N.A.I.C.S.: 541611

NOJIMA CORPORATION
JR Yokohama Tower 26F 1-1-1 Minami-Saiwai, Nishi-ku, Yokohama, 220-0005, Japan
Tel.: (81) 452283546
Web Site: https://www.nojima.co.jp
7419—(TKS)
Rev.: $5,032,199,610
Assets: $3,616,608,620
Liabilities: $2,433,947,420
Net Worth: $1,182,661,200
Earnings: $132,061,190
Emp.: 10,317
Fiscal Year-end: 03/31/24
Electronics Retailer
N.A.I.C.S.: 449210
Hiroshi Nojima *(Pres & CEO)*

Subsidiaries:

Business Grand Works, Co., Ltd. (1)
6-12-10 Ginza, Chuo-ku, Tokyo, 104-0061, Japan
Tel.: (81) 355375877
Web Site: https://www.bgw.co.jp
Corporate Education & Training Consulting Services
N.A.I.C.S.: 611710

Conexio Corporation (1)
37FShinjuku Grand Tower 17-1 Nishi-Shinjuku 8-chome, Shinjuku-ku, Tokyo, 160-6137, Japan
Tel.: (81) 353313700
Web Site: http://www.conexio.co.jp
Sales Range: $1-4.9 Billion
Emp.: 5,933
Mobile Phone Terminal Whslr
N.A.I.C.S.: 449210

Hiroo Inoue *(Pres)*

Courts Asia Limited (1)
50 Tampines North Drive 2, Singapore, 528766, Singapore
Tel.: (65) 8002226868
Web Site: http://www.courts.com.sg
Rev.: $533,435,103
Assets: $560,293,150
Liabilities: $388,099,752
Net Worth: $172,193,398
Earnings: $6,022,229
Emp.: 2,410
Fiscal Year-end: 03/31/2018
Electrical & Computer Retailer
N.A.I.C.S.: 449210
Siew Koon Ang *(Sec)*

ITX Communications Inc. (1)
1-1-1 Minamisaiwai, Nishi-ku JR Yokohama Tower 26th Floor Reception 25th Floor, Yokohama, 220-0005, Kanagawa, Japan
Tel.: (81) 5031166600
Web Site: https://www.itx-com.co.jp
Emp.: 1,326
Information & Communication Technology Services
N.A.I.C.S.: 541430

ITX Corporation (1)
1-1-1 Minamisaiwai JR Yokohama Tower 26th floor reception 25th floor, Nishi-ku, Yokohama, 220-0005, Japan   (100%)
Tel.: (81) 5031162300
Emp.: 2,225
Information & Communications Services
N.A.I.C.S.: 517810
Yukihiro Nojiri *(Sr Mng Dir & Exec Officer)*

Nojima (Cambodia) Co., Ltd. (1)
No 432 Preah Monivong Blvd, Sangkat Tonle Bassac Khan Chamkarmo, Phnom Penh, Cambodia
Tel.: (855) 23966233
Web Site: https://nojimacambodia.com
Consumer Electronics & Home Appliances Retailer
N.A.I.C.S.: 423620

Nojima Stella Sports Club Co., Ltd. (1)
478-1 Shindo, Minami-ku, Sagamihara, 252-0326, Kanagawa, Japan
Tel.: (81) 462983881
Web Site:
https://stellakanagawa.nojima.co.jp
Sports Club Facility Operation Services
N.A.I.C.S.: 713940

NOK AIRLINES PUBLIC COMPANY LIMITED
222 Don Mueang International Airport Central Building Room No 4235, 4th Floor Vibhavadi Rangsit Road Sanambin Sub-district Don Mueang, Bangkok, 10210, Thailand
Tel.: (66) 26272000 TH
Web Site: http://www.nokair.com
Year Founded: 2004
NOKPF—(OTCEM)
Rev.: $255,454,955
Assets: $346,598,866
Liabilities: $696,283,471
Net Worth: ($349,684,605)
Earnings: $1,391,258
Fiscal Year-end: 12/31/23
Oil Transportation Services
N.A.I.C.S.: 481111
Wutthiphum Jurangkool *(CEO)*

NOK CORPORATION
1-12-15 Shiba Daimon, Minato-ku, Tokyo, 105-8585, Japan
Tel.: (81) 334324211 JP
Web Site: https://www.nok.co.jp
Year Founded: 1939
7240—(TKS)
Rev.: $4,960,818,220
Assets: $6,295,225,190
Liabilities: $2,071,428,580
Net Worth: $4,223,796,610
Earnings: $208,889,220
Emp.: 38,097
Fiscal Year-end: 03/31/24

Oil Seals, Industrial Mechanical Parts, Hydraulic & Pneumatic Equipment, Nuclear Power Equipment, Synthetic Chemical Products, Flexible Circuit Boards & Electronic Products Mfr & Distr
N.A.I.C.S.: 332999
Mohsen M. Sohi *(Pres & CEO)*

Subsidiaries:

CHUBU NOK SALES CO., LTD. (1)
4-4-1 Otoubashi, Nakagawa-ku, Nagoya, 454-0012, Aichi, Japan
Tel.: (81) 523392752
Emp.: 44
Electronic Components Distr
N.A.I.C.S.: 423690

FUGAKU KOKI CO., LTD. (1)
1256-1 Shimohirakawa, Kikugawa, 437-1594, Shizuoka, Japan
Tel.: (81) 537735151
Industrial Machine Tool Mfr
N.A.I.C.S.: 332216

Freudenberg-NOK General Partnership (1)
47690 E Anchor Ct, Plymouth, MI 48170-2400   (25%)
Tel.: (734) 451-0020
Web Site: http://www.freudenberg-nok.com
Sales Range: $1-4.9 Billion
Emp.: 2,500
Elastomeric Seals, Custom Molded Products & Vibration Control Technologies Mfr
N.A.I.C.S.: 339991
Tom Faust *(VP-Continuous Improvement)*

Plant (Domestic):

Freudenberg NOK (2)
450 Pleasant St, Bristol, NH 03222-0501
Tel.: (603) 744-2281
Web Site: http://www.fngp.com
Sales Range: $150-199.9 Million
Appliance Face, Radial Shaft, Engine Valve Stem Seals, Strut Seals, Oil & Water Pump Seal Caliper Boots
N.A.I.C.S.: 522130
Zean Laughy *(Gen Mgr)*

Freudenberg NOK (2)
50 Ammon Dr, Manchester, NH 03103-3308
Tel.: (603) 669-4050
Web Site: http://www.freudenberg-nok.com
Sales Range: $75-99.9 Million
Sealing Technologies Mfr
N.A.I.C.S.: 339991

Freudenberg NOK (2)
821 S Lk Rd, Scottsburg, IN 47170-6837
Tel.: (812) 752-4232
Web Site: http://www.freudenberg.com
Mfr of Solid Injection Molded Polyurethane Products & Suspension Parts for Automotive Applications
N.A.I.C.S.: 326291

Freudenberg NOK (2)
1618 Lukken Industrial Dr W, Lagrange, GA 30240-5704
Tel.: (706) 884-6111
Web Site: http://www.freudenberg-nok.com
Sales Range: $50-74.9 Million
Emp.: 200
Mfr of Rubber Moulded Products for the Automotive Industry
N.A.I.C.S.: 339991
Scott Thompson *(Mgr-Lean Sys)*

Freudenberg NOK (2)
131 Verner Ave, Newport, TN 37821-8133
Tel.: (423) 623-2366
Web Site: http://www.corteco-usa.com
Sales Range: $25-49.9 Million
Emp.: 37
Mfr of Automotive Engine Gaskets
N.A.I.C.S.: 339991

Freudenberg NOK (2)
1275 Archer Dr, Troy, OH 45373
Tel.: (937) 335-3306
Web Site: http://www.freudenberg-nok.com
Sales Range: $50-74.9 Million
Emp.: 150
Square Cut Seal Rings, Banded Pistons & Various Components For General Industry
N.A.I.C.S.: 326199

NOK CORPORATION

Gary Clyburn *(Plant Mgr)*

Freudenberg NOK-Rubber Products (2)
1700 Miller Ave, Shelbyville, IN 46176-3114
Tel.: (317) 421-3400
Sales Range: $50-74.9 Million
Emp.: 142
Rocker Cover, Electrical Sealing & Extrusion Gaskets; Electrical Connectors; Brake Parts & Transmission Seals
N.A.I.C.S.: 339991

Freudenberg NOK-Rubber Products (2)
487 W Main St, Morristown, IN 46161-9745
Tel.: (765) 763-7246
Sales Range: $25-49.9 Million
Emp.: 215
Mfr of Brake Components, Steering Linkage Components, Electrical Connectors, Oil Seals & Filler Tube Seals & Transmission Seals
N.A.I.C.S.: 339991

Freudenberg NOK-Sealant Products (2)
1 Nok Dr, Cleveland, GA 30528
Tel.: (706) 865-1665
Web Site: http://www.freudenberg-nok.com
Sales Range: $125-149.9 Million
Mfr of Oil Seals, Valve Stem Seals, Boots & Dust Covers & Seal Rings
N.A.I.C.S.: 324110
Gary Vamwambeke *(Exec Dir)*

Subsidiary (Non-US):

Freudenberg-NOK Inc. (2)
65 Spruce Street, Tillsonburg, N4G 5C4, ON, Canada
Tel.: (519) 842-6451
Web Site: http://www.freudenberg-nok.com
Sales Range: $50-74.9 Million
Emp.: 200
Mfr of Silicone Seals
N.A.I.C.S.: 325212
Ped Mansion *(Dir-Mktg)*

Freudenberg-NOK de Mexico (2)
km 1 Carretera Cuautla Las Estacas, 62740, Cuautla, Morelos, Mexico
Tel.: (52) 7353522821
Web Site: http://www.freudenberg-nok.com
Sales Range: $10-24.9 Million
Emp.: 250
Mfr of Oil Seals, Valve Stem Seals, Molded Rubber Products, Polyurethane O-Rings, Engine Mounts
N.A.I.C.S.: 339991

Freudenberg-NOK de Queretaro, S.A. de C.V. (2)
Circuito El Marques Norte No 14, El Marques, 76240, Queretaro, Mexico
Tel.: (52) 4421533270
Automobile Parts Distr
N.A.I.C.S.: 423120

Freudenberg-NOK-Componentes Brasil Ltda. (2)
Av Piraporinha 411 - Vila Oriental, 09950-902, Diadema, Sao Paulo, Brazil
Tel.: (55) 1140728000
Seal Distr
N.A.I.C.S.: 423840
George Rugitsky *(Country Mgr)*

HAKUSAN TEC CO., LTD. (1)
2-20 Asahigaoka, Hakusan, 924-0004, Ishikawa, Japan
Tel.: (81) 76 274 1122
Web Site: http://www.synztec.co.jp
Industrial Equipment Mfr
N.A.I.C.S.: 333248

INTEGRAL ACCUMULATOR GMBH & Co. KG (1)
Sinziger Strasse 47, 53424, Remagen, Germany
Tel.: (49) 26429330
Web Site: http://www.integral-accumulator.com
Emp.: 4
Hydraulic Valve Mfr & Distr
N.A.I.C.S.: 332912

Ishino Gasket Mfg. Co., Ltd. (1)
1257 Kamo, Kikugawa, 439-0031, Shizuoka, Japan

5401

NOK CORPORATION

NOK Corporation—(Continued)
Tel.: (81) 537356146
Packing & Sealing Device Mfr
N.A.I.C.S.: 339991

Isohara Polyurethane Industry Corporation (1)
1212-1 Isohara, Isohara-cho, Kitaibaraki, 319-1541, Ibaraki, Japan
Tel.: (81) 293420559
Web Site: https://www.isohara-ipk.co.jp
Emp.: 192
Industrial Urethane Product Mfr
N.A.I.C.S.: 326150

Isshin Industries Corporation (1)
1884-1 Shiosawa Aza Shinbayashi Tateshina-cho, Kitasaku-gun, Nagano, 384-2303, Japan
Tel.: (81) 267563285
Web Site: http://www.isshin-kogyo.co.jp
Urethane Rubber Mfr & Distr
N.A.I.C.S.: 326299

KANSAI NOK HANBAI Co., LTD. (1)
10-8 Hiroshibacho Esaka Toyu Building 8F, Suita, 564-0052, Osaka, Japan
Tel.: (81) 676326600
Web Site: https://www.kansai-nok.com
Emp.: 25
Industrial Machinery & Equipment Distr
N.A.I.C.S.: 423830

KANTO NOK HANBAI Co., LTD. (1)
Shinjuku L Tower 16F 1-6-1 Nishi-Shinjuku, Shinjuku-ku, Tokyo, 223-0057, Kanagawa, Japan
Tel.: (81) 354478281
Web Site: https://kanto-nok.com
Emp.: 132
Automobile Parts Distr
N.A.I.C.S.: 423120

Kikugawa Seal Industry Co., Ltd. (1)
1257 Kamo, Kikugawa, 439-0031, Shizuoka, Japan
Tel.: (81) 537356146
Web Site: http://www.kikugawa-seal.com
Industrial Rubber Product Mfr
N.A.I.C.S.: 326299

Kumamoto NOK Corporation (1)
2449-1 Ichinomiyamachi Sakanashi, Aso, 869-2611, Kumamoto, Japan
Tel.: (81) 967221191
Web Site: http://www.kumamoto-nok.jp
Industrial Rubber Product Mfr
N.A.I.C.S.: 326299

MEKTEC CORPORATION (H.K.) Limited (1)
Suite 1601 16F Tower 1 China Hong Kong City 33 Canton Road, Tsimshatsui, Kowloon, China (Hong Kong)
Tel.: (852) 27352088
Sales Range: $25-49.9 Million
Emp.: 15
Rubber Rolls Distr
N.A.I.C.S.: 423840
Takahashi Satoru (Gen Mgr)

MEKTEC CORPORATION (SINGAPORE) PTE LTD. (1)
18 Tractor Road Jurong Town, Singapore, 627976, Singapore
Tel.: (65) 6536 6776
Web Site: http://www.mektec.com
Emp.: 12
Printed Circuit Board Mfr
N.A.I.C.S.: 334412
Takashi Kaku (Gen Mgr)

MEKTEC CORPORATION (TAIWAN) LTD. (1)
A-2 Room 2nd Floor No 333 Tun Hua S Road Sec 2, Taipei, Taiwan
Tel.: (886) 223773280
Printed Circuit Board Distr
N.A.I.C.S.: 423690

Plant (Domestic):

MEKTEC CORPORATION (TAIWAN) LTD. - Kaohsiung Plant (2)
No 48 Chiung-Heng St, Hsiao-Kang District, Kaohsiung, 80027, Taiwan
Tel.: (886) 7 872 7777
Web Site: http://www.mektec.com.tw
Printed Circuit Board Mfr

N.A.I.C.S.: 334412

MEKTEC INTERNATIONAL CORPORATION (1)
1731 Technology Dr Ste 840, San Jose, CA 95110
Tel.: (408) 392-4000
Web Site: https://www.mektecusa.com
Printed Circuit Board Mfr
N.A.I.C.S.: 334412
Atsushi Nomoto (Chm & CEO)

MYK Corporation (1)
594-1 Jitogata, Makinohara, 421-0532, Shizuoka, Japan
Tel.: (81) 548580514
Web Site: http://www.kk-myk.com
Industrial Rubber Product Mfr
N.A.I.C.S.: 326299

Mektec Corporation (Shenzhen) Ltd. (1)
Room 503 5/F Tower Three Kerry Plaza1 Zhong Xin si Road, Futian District, Shenzhen, 518048, Guangdong, China
Tel.: (86) 75589803003
Electronic Product Mfr & Distr
N.A.I.C.S.: 334419

Mektec Corporation Korea, Ltd. (1)
905 Opulence Bldg 254, Seocho-daero Seocho-Gu, Seoul, Korea (South)
Tel.: (82) 28683797
Electronic Product Mfr & Distr
N.A.I.C.S.: 334419

Mektec Europe GmbH (1)
Im Technologiepark 1, 69469, Weinheim, Germany
Tel.: (49) 6201807111
Web Site: https://www.mektec.de
Emp.: 1,500
Flexible Printed Circuit Board Mfr
N.A.I.C.S.: 334412
Christian Schrotz (Coord-Internet)

Mektec Manufacturing Corporation (Thailand) Ltd. (1)
560 Moo 2 Bangpa-in Industrial Estate Udomsorayuth Rd Tambol Klong-jik, Amphur Bangpa-in, Ayutthaya, 13160, Thailand
Tel.: (66) 35258888
Web Site: http://www.mektec.co.th
Printed Circuit Board Mfr
N.A.I.C.S.: 334412

Mektec Manufacturing Corporation (Vietnam) Ltd. (1)
Plot No K3 and 4, Thang LongIndustrial Park II Di Su Ward, My Hao, Hung Yen, Vietnam
Tel.: (84) 2213589190
Electronic Product Mfr & Distr
N.A.I.C.S.: 334419

Mektec Manufacturing Corporation (Zhuhai) Ltd. (1)
No 2006 Huangyang Road, Doumen Town Doumen District, Zhuhai, 519110, Guangdong, China
Tel.: (86) 7568917160
Electronic Product Mfr & Distr
N.A.I.C.S.: 334419

Mektec Manufacturing Corporation Europe HU Kft. (1)
Hatar ut 4, 2119, Pecel, Hungary
Tel.: (36) 28548100
Electronic Product Mfr & Distr
N.A.I.C.S.: 334419

Mektec Precision Component (Thailand) Ltd. (1)
189 198 296 Moo 16 Udomsorayuth Rd T Bangkrasan, A Bangpa-in Bangpa-in Industrial Estate, Ayutthaya, 13160, Thailand
Tel.: (66) 35258666
Web Site: http://www.mektec.co.th
Hard Disk Drive Component Mfr
N.A.I.C.S.: 334112

Mektec Trading (Shanghai) Co., Ltd. (1)
The Place Unit 1808 Tower C 150 Zunyi Road, Shanghai, 200051, China
Tel.: (86) 2158366108
Electronic Product Mfr & Distr
N.A.I.C.S.: 334419

Mektec Trading Taiwan Co., Ltd. (1)

A-2 Room 2nd Floor No 333 Tun Hua S Road Sec 2, Taipei, Taiwan
Tel.: (886) 223773280
Electronic Product Mfr & Distr
N.A.I.C.S.: 334419

Miyagi NOK Corporation (1)
4-11 Miyazaki Yashiki Kami-cho, Kami, 981-4401, Miyagi, Japan
Tel.: (81) 229695213
Web Site: https://www.mnok.jp
Oil Seal Mfr
N.A.I.C.S.: 339991

Miyazaki Kogyo Co., Ltd. (1)
1163-13 Nagarayama Nagaramachi, Chosei, Chiba, 297-0234, Japan
Tel.: (81) 436984782
Fabricated Metal Products Mfr
N.A.I.C.S.: 332999

NEOPT CORPORATION (1)
Seiwa Bilding 1-12-15 Shiba Daimon, Minato-ku, Tokyo, 105-8585, Japan
Tel.: (81) 44 200 9150
Web Site: http://www.neopt.co.jp
Inspection Machine & Image Processing Equipment Mfr
N.A.I.C.S.: 334519

NOK (Wuxi) Water Treatment Technology Co., Ltd. (1)
No 217 Fangda Road, Xishan Economic and Technological Development Zone, Wuxi, 214101, Jiangsu, China
Tel.: (86) 51068585333
Web Site: https://www.nokwater.com
Hollow Fiber Membrane Component Mfr
N.A.I.C.S.: 325220

NOK ASIA CO, PTE LTD. (1)
18 Tractor Road, Singapore, 627976, Singapore
Tel.: (65) 62653233
Web Site: http://www.nok.com.sg
Sales Range: $25-49.9 Million
Emp.: 56
Oil Seal Mfr
N.A.I.C.S.: 339991
Kam Yin Cheng (Mng Dir)

NOK Elastomers Processing Co., Ltd. (1)
1651 Okumamachi, Kama, 820-0302, Fukuoka, Japan
Tel.: (81) 948571591
Web Site: http://www.nok-elastomers.jp
Industrial Rubber Product Mfr
N.A.I.C.S.: 326299

NOK PRECISION COMPONENT (THAILAND) LTD. (1)
189 198 296 Moo 16 Bangpa-in Industrial Estate Udomsorayuth Rd, T Bangdrasan A Bangpa-in, Ayutthaya, 13160, Thailand
Tel.: (66) 35258666
Web Site: https://www.mpct.mektec.co.th
Emp.: 437
Hard Disk Drive & Electronic Device Mfr
N.A.I.C.S.: 334112
Tsukasa Furudate (Mng Dir)

NOK PRECISION COMPONENT SINGAPORE PTE LTD. (1)
18 Tractor Road, Jurong, 627976, Singapore
Tel.: (65) 62653233
Sales Range: $50-74.9 Million
Emp.: 16
Precision Turned Product Mfr
N.A.I.C.S.: 332721
Yan Peng Chew (Gen Mgr)

NOK-Freudenberg Group Sales (China) Co., Ltd. (1)
Suite 14-B International Ocean Shipping Building 720 Pudong Avenue, Shanghai, 200120, China
Tel.: (86) 2150366900
Sales Range: $75-99.9 Million
Emp.: 128
Industrial Rubber Products Distr
N.A.I.C.S.: 423840

NOK-Kluber Co., Ltd. (1)
1-12-15 Shiba Daimon, Minato-ku, Tokyo, 105-0122, Japan (51%)
Tel.: (81) 293427319
Web Site: https://www.nokklueber.co.jp

Sales Range: $25-49.9 Million
Emp.: 115
Lubricant Mfr
N.A.I.C.S.: 324191

Nichinan NOK Corporation (1)
3671-1 Gonohara Otsu Kitago-cho, Nichinan, 889-2402, Miyazaki Prefecture, Japan
Tel.: (81) 987553444
Web Site: http://www.nichinan-nok.com
Industrial Rubber Product Mfr & Distr
N.A.I.C.S.: 326299

Nihonmatsu NOK Corporation (1)
30 Miyado, Nihonmatsu, 964-0811, Fukushima, Japan
Tel.: (81) 243220284
Web Site: http://www.nihonmatsu-nok.co.jp
Car Braking Device Parts Mfr
N.A.I.C.S.: 336390

Nippon Mektron, Ltd. (1)
Lila Hijirizaka Bldg 3-4-10 Mita, Tokyo, 108-0073, Japan
Tel.: (81) 363817745
Web Site: http://www.mektron.co.jp
Emp.: 1,342
Electronic Component Mfr & Sales
N.A.I.C.S.: 334418
Toshifumi Kobayashi (Pres)

Subsidiary (Non-US):

Mektec Manufacturing Corporation (Suzhou) Ltd. (2)
No 468 Su Hong Middle Road, Suzhou Industry Park, Suzhou, 215122, Jiang-Su, China
Tel.: (86) 7568917160
Printed Circuit Board Mfr
N.A.I.C.S.: 334412

Plant (Domestic):

NIPPON MEKTRON, LTD. - Fujisawa Plant (2)
4-3-1 Tsujido-Shinmachi, Fujisawa, 251-0042, Kanagawa, Japan
Tel.: (81) 466 35 7441
Web Site: http://www.mektron.co.jp
Electronic Components Mfr
N.A.I.C.S.: 334419

NIPPON MEKTRON, LTD. - Kashima Plant (2)
2626-19 Sunayama, Kamisu, 314-0255, Ibaraki, Japan
Tel.: (81) 479462231
Electronic Products Mfr
N.A.I.C.S.: 334419

NIPPON MEKTRON, LTD. - Minami Ibaraki Plant (2)
757 Amaboki, Tsukuba, 300-1253, Ibaraki, Japan
Tel.: (81) 298712700
Electronic Products Mfr
N.A.I.C.S.: 334419

NIPPON MEKTRON, LTD. - Okuhara Plant (2)
1650-11-1 Okuhara-cho, Ushiku, 300-1283, Ibaraki, Japan
Tel.: (81) 29 830 9150
Web Site: http://www.mektron.co.jp
Electronic Products Mfr
N.A.I.C.S.: 334419

Nittoh Industry (H.K.) Co., Ltd. (1)
Unit 05-6 G/F Fo Tan Industrial Centre 26-28 Au Pui Wan Street, Sha Tin, China (Hong Kong)
Tel.: (852) 2695 1161
Industrial Machinery Mfr
N.A.I.C.S.: 333248

Nokmetal Co., Ltd. (1)
53-2 Osato Mamoru Wakuya-cho, Toda, 987-0281, Miyagi Prefecture, Japan
Tel.: (81) 229452102
Web Site: http://www.nok-metal.jp
Metal Hose Mfr
N.A.I.C.S.: 332999

P.T. NOK Indonesia (1)
MM2100 Industrial Town Jalan Sulawesi II Block F-3 Cibitung Barat, Bekasi, 17520, Jawa Barat, Indonesia
Tel.: (62) 218981041
Oil Seal Mfr & Distr

AND PRIVATE COMPANIES / NOKIA CORPORATION

N.A.I.C.S.: 339991

P.T. NOK Precision Component Batam (1)
Jl Gaharu Lot 101-102, Batamindo Industrial Park Muka Kuning, Batam, 29433, Indonesia
Tel.: (62) 770611634
Rubber Products Mfr
N.A.I.C.S.: 326299

Pyung Hwa Oil Seal Industry Co., Ltd. (1)
42 Nongongjungang-ro 51-gil, Nongong-eup Dalseong-gun, Daegu, Korea (South)
Tel.: (82) 536109000
Oil Seal Mfr
N.A.I.C.S.: 339991

Pyunghwa NOK Drive Train Co., Ltd. (1)
92 Yeongcheonsandan-ro, Yeongcheon, Gyeongsangbuk-do, Korea (South)
Tel.: (82) 543392000
Automobile Parts Distr
N.A.I.C.S.: 423120
Kim Dong Gwan (CEO)

SAGA SEAL INDUSTRY CO., LTD (1)
4646-12 Hei Kuma Shiota-cho, Ureshino, 849-1403, Saga, Japan
Tel.: (81) 954663211
Web Site: https://sagaseal.co.jp
Emp.: 493
Rubber Products Mfr
N.A.I.C.S.: 326299

SYNZTEC (H.K.) CO., LIMITED (1)
Units 05-06 G/F Fo Tan Industrial Centre 26-28 Au Pui Wan Street, Tsim Sha Tsui, Fotan, NT, China (Hong Kong)
Tel.: (852) 24079912
Industrial Equipment Mfr
N.A.I.C.S.: 333248
Gary To Lee (Mng Dir)

SYNZTEC CO., LTD - Kuki Plant (1)
42 Kawarai-cho, Kuki, 346-0028, Saitama, Japan
Tel.: (81) 480 22 9070
Web Site: http://www.synztec.co.jp
Industrial Equipment Mfr
N.A.I.C.S.: 333248

SYNZTEC CO., LTD - Yokosuka Plant A (1)
5-2931 Urago-cho, Yokosuka, 237-0062, Japan
Tel.: (81) 468662172
Web Site: http://www.synztec.co.jp
Emp.: 100
Industrial Equipment Mfr
N.A.I.C.S.: 333248
Akihiro Nakabayashi (Pres)

SYNZTEC CO., LTD - Yokosuka Plant B (1)
5-2931 Urago-cho, Yokosuka, 237-0062, Japan
Tel.: (81) 468690521
Industrial Equipment Mfr
N.A.I.C.S.: 333248

SYNZTEC PRECISION PARTS (SHENZHEN) CO., LTD. (1)
The 11th 13th Industrial building MingKeDa logistics park, NO 19 HuanGuanNan Road GuanLanJunLong community LongHua New district, Shenzhen, 518110, GuanDong, China
Tel.: (86) 75586001549
Industrial Equipment Mfr
N.A.I.C.S.: 333248

Saga NOK Corporation (1)
4646-12 Oaza Kuma Shiota-cho, Ureshino, 849-1403, Saga, Japan
Tel.: (81) 954663211
Web Site: http://www.sagaseal.co.jp
Industrial Rubber Product Mfr & Distr
N.A.I.C.S.: 326299

Shinei Industry Co., Ltd. (1)
1-7-31 Kusune, Kusune, Higashiosaka, 577-0006, Osaka, Japan
Tel.: (81) 667453501
Web Site: https://www.shinei-ind.com
Emp.: 55
Plastic Foam Product Mfr

N.A.I.C.S.: 325211
Kazumasa Watanabe (Pres)

Synztec (Malaysia) Sdn. Bhd. (1)
Lot5 Jalan Lada Sulah 16/11 Seksyen 16, 40000, Shah Alam, Selangor, Malaysia
Tel.: (60) 355100655
Industrial Equipment Mfr & Distr
N.A.I.C.S.: 333248

Synztec Precision Parts (Shanghai) Co., Ltd. (1)
Room 812 Block B Building A No 515 Qifan Road, Pudong District, Shanghai, China
Tel.: (86) 2150480139
Industrial Equipment Mfr & Distr
N.A.I.C.S.: 333248

Synztec Singapore Pte Ltd. (1)
18 Tractor Road, Singapore, 627976, Singapore
Tel.: (65) 68611010
Web Site: http://www.synztec.co.jp
Industrial Equipment Distr
N.A.I.C.S.: 423830

Synztec Vietnam Co., Ltd. (1)
Land P1ot J-12 Km 13, Nomura-Haiphong Industrial Zone An Duong District, Haiphong, Vietnam
Tel.: (84) 2253743292
Industrial Equipment Mfr & Distr
N.A.I.C.S.: 333248

THAI NOK CO., LTD. (1)
Amata City Industrial Estate 700/452 Moo 7 Bangna - Trat Road, Don Hua Lo Subdistrict Mueang Chonburi District, Chon Buri, 20000, Thailand
Tel.: (66) 38456600
Web Site: https://www.nok.co.th
Shock Absorber Mfr
N.A.I.C.S.: 336330

TVC Co., Ltd. (1)
Yoyogi Uehara West Building 45-18 Daisencho, Shibuya-ku, Tokyo, 151-0065, Japan
Tel.: (81) 368587788
Web Site: https://www.tvc.co.jp
Emp.: 75
Image Production Services
N.A.I.C.S.: 512110

Tenei Seal Industry Corporation (1)
10-254 Iitoyo, Tenei-mura Iwase-gun Hightech Oyama Industrial Park, Oyama, 962-0512, Fukushima, Japan
Tel.: (81) 248832211
Web Site: http://www.tenei-s.co.jp
Conveying Machine Mfr
N.A.I.C.S.: 333922

Tokiwa Industry Co., Ltd. (1)
1-1 Akeno Higashi 1-chome, Oita, 870-0161, Japan
Tel.: (81) 975531111
Web Site: https://www.tokiwa-industry.co.jp
Emp.: 1,500
Grocery Products Retailer
N.A.I.C.S.: 445110

UNIMATEC CO., LTD. - Plant No. 1 (1)
831-2 Kamisohda Isohara-cho, Kitaibaraki, 319-1593, Ibaraki, Japan
Tel.: (81) 293 42 2161
Web Site: http://www.unimatec.co.jp
Rubber Products Mfr
N.A.I.C.S.: 326299

UNIMATEC CO., LTD. - Plant No. 2 (1)
8231-2 Isohara-machi, Kitaibaraki, 319-1593, Ibaraki, Japan
Tel.: (81) 293 43 4144
Web Site: http://www.unimatec.co.jp
Rubber Products Mfr
N.A.I.C.S.: 326299

Unimatec Chemicals (China) Co., Ltd. (1)
The Place Unit 1808 Tower C 150 Zunyi Road, Feng Xian District, Shanghai, 200051, China
Tel.: (86) 2162088895
Rubber Products Mfr
N.A.I.C.S.: 326299

Unimatec Chemicals America, Inc. (1)

Ste 164 39555 Orchard Hill Pl, Novi, MI 48375
Tel.: (248) 778-3301
Rubber Products Mfr
N.A.I.C.S.: 326299

Unimatec Chemicals Europe GmbH & Co. KG. (1)
Im Technologiepark 1, 69469, Weinheim, Germany
Tel.: (49) 6201273450
Emp.: 1
Chemical Products Mfr
N.A.I.C.S.: 325998
Hans-Martin Issel (Mng Dir)

Unimatec Chemicals Singapore Pte. Ltd. (1)
30 Sakra View Jurong Island, Singapore, 627745, Singapore
Tel.: (65) 65159331
Synthetic Chemical Product Mfr
N.A.I.C.S.: 325998

NOK9 AB
Citadellsvagen 19, 211 18, Malmo, Sweden
Tel.: (46) 406904900
Web Site: http://www.nok9.com
Year Founded: 1987
Sales Range: $10-24.9 Million
Emp.: 10
Wireless Power Product Mfr
N.A.I.C.S.: 335999
Magnus Wilkstrand (VP-R&D)

Subsidiaries:

AudioDev Far East Ltd. (1)
Flat 1210 12/F Premier Centre, 20 Cheung Shun Street, Cheung Sha Wan, China (Hong Kong)
Tel.: (852) 23148736
Web Site: http://www.audiodev.com
Optical Media Test Systems Sales & Servicing
N.A.I.C.S.: 334610

AudioDev USA (1)
5126 Clareton Dr, Agoura Hills, CA 91301 (100%)
Tel.: (818) 540-3100
Web Site: http://www.audiodev.com
Optical Media Test Systems Sales & Servicing
N.A.I.C.S.: 334610

NOKIA CORPORATION
Karakaari 7, FI-02610, Espoo, Finland
Tel.: (358) 104488000   FI
Web Site: https://www.nokia.com
Year Founded: 1865
NOK—(NYSE)
Rev.: $27,269,384,480
Assets: $49,189,783,760
Liabilities: $27,742,256,880
Net Worth: $21,447,526,880
Earnings: $2,020,454,800
Emp.: 87,927
Fiscal Year-end: 12/31/21
Telecommunications Equipment Mfr
N.A.I.C.S.: 334210
Federico Guillen (Pres-Network Infrastructure)

Subsidiaries:

ALE International (1)
32 avenue Kleber, 92700, Colombes, France (76.01%)
Tel.: (33) 155667000
Web Site: http://www.al-enterprise.com
Holding Company; Wireline & Mobile Telecommunications Infrastructure Design Services
N.A.I.C.S.: 551112
Bernd Stangl (CFO)

Subsidiary (Non-US):

ALE Argentina S.R.L. (2)
3rd floor Guemes Office Building General Guemes 676, Vicente Lopez, CP B1638CJF, Buenos Aires, Argentina
Tel.: (54) 1143408600

Web Site: http://www.al-enterprise.com
Business & Consumer Telecommunications Systems Operator
N.A.I.C.S.: 517810

ALE Austria GmbH (2)
Saturn Tower Leonard-Bernstein-Strasse 10, 1220, Vienna, Austria (100%)
Tel.: (43) 1260220
Telecommunications Equipment, Railway Signalling Equipment & Electronic Components Mfr
N.A.I.C.S.: 334418

ALE Brasil Intermediacao de Negocios Ltda. (2)
Av Paulista 1079 7 and 8 floors, Bela Vista, Sao Paulo, 01311-200, Brazil
Tel.: (55) 1129478133
Communication Equipment Mfr
N.A.I.C.S.: 334290

ALE Deutschland GmbH (2)
Stammheimer Str 10 House 6 3rd floor, 70806, Kornwestheim, Germany
Tel.: (49) 71548035500
Holding Company
N.A.I.C.S.: 551112

Subsidiary (Domestic):

Nokia Solutions and Networks GmbH & Co. KG (3)
St-Martin Strasse 76, 81541, Munich, Germany
Tel.: (49) 89515901
Web Site: http://networks.nokia.com
Switching & Transmission Equipment, Mobile Telephones, Air Navigation, Radar & Air Traffic Control Mfr
N.A.I.C.S.: 333613

Subsidiary (Non-US):

ALE India Pvt. Ltd. (2)
Web Site: http://www.al-enterprise.com
Business & Consumer Telecommunications Systems
N.A.I.C.S.: 517111

ALE International - Czech Republic, odstepny zavod (2)
Podebradska 206/57, 198 00, Prague, 98, Czech Republic
Tel.: (420) 266103111
Business & Consumer Telecommunications Systems
N.A.I.C.S.: 517111

ALE International - Finland Representation Office (2)
Teknopolis Center Teknobulevardi 3-5, 01530, Vantaa, Finland
Tel.: (358) 9804060
Web Site: http://www.al-enterprise.com
Telecommunication & Air Navigation Equipment Mfr
N.A.I.C.S.: 517111

ALE International - Norway Branch (2)
Brynsveien 3, 0667, Oslo, Norway
Tel.: (47) 21419370
Telecommunications Equipment & Services Provider
N.A.I.C.S.: 334290

ALE International - Portugal (2)
Torre de Monsanto Rua Afonso Praca, 1495-061, Alges, Portugal
Tel.: (351) 211214920
Web Site: http://www.al-enterprise.com
Telecommunications Equipment Mfr
N.A.I.C.S.: 517111

ALE International Agency in Chile (2)
Orinoco Street # 90 Building 1 21st Floor Las Condes, Santiago, Chile
Tel.: (56) 2 230 3500
Web Site: http://www.al-enterprise.com
Wired Telecommunication Services
N.A.I.C.S.: 517111

ALE International Belgium (2)
Kievitplein 20 Bus 2, B-2018, Antwerp, Belgium
Tel.: (32) 3 240 40 11
Web Site: http://www.al-enterprise.com

NOKIA CORPORATION

Nokia Corporation—(Continued)
Telecommunications & Electronics Equipment Developer & Mfr
N.A.I.C.S.: 517111

Subsidiary (Domestic):

Nokia Bell NV (3)
Copernicuslaan 50, 2018, Antwerp, Belgium
Tel.: (32) 32404409
Web Site: http://www.bell-labs.com
Communications Technology Research & Development Services
N.A.I.C.S.: 541715

Subsidiary (Domestic):

ALE International, SAS (2)
32 Avenue Kleber, 92700, Colombes, France
Tel.: (33) 155667000
Investment Management Service
N.A.I.C.S.: 523999

Subsidiary (Non-US):

ALE Italia S.r.l. (2)
Via Energy Park 14, 20871, Vimercate, Italy
Tel.: (39) 039 6861
Web Site: http://www.al-enterprise.com
Telecommunication Servicesb
N.A.I.C.S.: 517810

ALE Netherlands B.V. (2)
Van Deventerlaan 31-51, 3528 AG, Utrecht, Netherlands
Tel.: (31) 302228000
Holding Company
N.A.I.C.S.: 551112

Subsidiary (Domestic):

Nokia Solutions and Networks B.V. (3)
Antareslaan 1, 2123 JE, Hoofddorp, Netherlands (100%)
Tel.: (31) 703079111
Web Site: http://networks.nokia.com
Public & Private Telecom Switching & Transmission Systems, Equipment & Components for Voice, Graphics & Television Mfr
N.A.I.C.S.: 334118

Subsidiary (Non-US):

ALE Switzerland GmbH (2)
Friesenbergstrasse 75, 8055, Zurich, Switzerland
Tel.: (41) 583322020
Web Site: http://www.al-enterprise.com
Switching & Transmission Equipment, Mobile Telephones, Air Navigation, Radar & Air Traffic Control Mfr
N.A.I.C.S.: 334210

Subsidiary (Domestic):

Alcatel Submarine Networks S.A. (2)
7 route de Villejust, Villarceaux, 91620, Nozay, Cedex, France
Tel.: (33) 130773077
Web Site: http://networks.nokia.com
Undersea Communications Networks Provider
N.A.I.C.S.: 334290

Subsidiary (Non-US):

Alcatel-Lucent Czech s.r.o (2)
Karolinska 650, 18600, Prague, 8, Czech Republic
Tel.: (420) 266065520
Web Site: http://networks.nokia.com
Telecommunications Equipment & Solutions Provider
N.A.I.C.S.: 334290

Alcatel-Lucent Enterprise (2)
Condesa de Venadito 1, 28027, Madrid, Spain (78.6%)
Tel.: (34) 91 268 12 34
Web Site: http://www.al-enterprise.com
Telecommunication Equipment Mfr
N.A.I.C.S.: 334290

Alcatel-Lucent Enterprise Indonesia (2)
Menara Palma 8th Floor Jl HR Rasuna Sain Kav 6 Block X-2 Kuningan, Jakarta Selatan, 12950, Indonesia

Tel.: (62) 2180644800
Communication Equipment Mfr
N.A.I.C.S.: 334290

Alcatel-Lucent Holding, S.A. de C.V. (2)
Av Ciencia 13 S/N Parque Industrial La Joya, Cuautitlan Izcalli, 54730, Mexico
Tel.: (52) 55 5864 3500
Web Site: http://www.al-enterprise.com
Holding Company
N.A.I.C.S.: 551112

Subsidiary (Domestic):

ALEnterprise Mexico (3)
Av Ciencia 13 S/N Parque Industrial La Joya, Cuautitlan Izcalli, 54730, CP, Mexico
Tel.: (52) 5558643500
Web Site: http://www.al-enterprise.com
Telecommunication Servicesb
N.A.I.C.S.: 517810

Subsidiary (Non-US):

Alcatel-Lucent UK Limited (2)
740 Waterside Drive, Aztec West, Bristol, BS32 4UF, United Kingdom
Tel.: (44) 1454467000
Telecommunication Servicesb
N.A.I.C.S.: 517810

Subsidiary (Domestic):

Nokia UK Limited (3)
740 Waterside Drive, Aztec West Business Park, Bristol, BS32 4UF, United Kingdom (100%)
Tel.: (44) 1454467000
Communication Equipment Mfr
N.A.I.C.S.: 334290

Velocix Limited (3)
3 Ely Road, Milton, CB24 6DD, Cambridge, United Kingdom
Tel.: (44) 1223 435 800
Digital Software Development Services
N.A.I.C.S.: 541511
David Sharpley (CEO)

Subsidiary (Domestic):

Coralec (3)
21 Rue Des Ecoles, Aulnay-sous-Bois, 93600, Seine Saint Denis, France
Tel.: (33) 1 48 66 17 92
Communication Software Development Services
N.A.I.C.S.: 541511

Subsidiary (Non-US):

Nokia Canada Inc. (2)
600 March Road, Ottawa, K2K 2E6, ON, Canada
Tel.: (613) 591-3600
Web Site: http://www.nokia.com
Telecommunications Networking Company
N.A.I.C.S.: 517111

Branch (Domestic):

Nokia Canada Inc. - Markham (3)
1380 Rodick Rd, Markham, L3R 4G5, ON, Canada
Tel.: (905) 943-5000
Web Site: http://www.nokia.com
Cable & Telephone Switches
N.A.I.C.S.: 334210

Nokia Canada Inc. - Montreal (3)
425 de Maisonneuve Blvd West, Montreal, H3A 3G5, QC, Canada
Tel.: (514) 935-7750
Web Site: http://networks.nokia.com
Communications Solutions Provider
N.A.I.C.S.: 334290

Subsidiary (Non-US):

Nokia Denmark A/S (2)
Orestads Boulevard 73 3, 2300, Copenhagen, Denmark
Tel.: (45) 72179000
Web Site: http://networks.nokia.com
Telecommunications Equipment & Services Provider
N.A.I.C.S.: 334290

Nokia Services Limited (2)
5 Rider Boulevard, Rhodes, 2138, NSW, Australia

Tel.: (61) 293703000
Web Site: http://www.al-enterprise.com
Telecommunications & Internet Products & Services
N.A.I.C.S.: 517810

Nokia Shanghai Bell Co., Ltd (2)
388# Ningqiao Road, Jinqiao Pudong, Shanghai, 201206, China (50%)
Tel.: (86) 21 58541240
Web Site: http://www.nokia.com
Telecommunication Servicesb
N.A.I.C.S.: 517810

Nokia Solutions and Network Ecuador S.A. (2)
Av SimonBolivar y Calle Nayon 08th floor, Quito, Ecuador
Tel.: (593) 23982400
Web Site: http://networks.nokia.com
Telecommunication Servicesb
N.A.I.C.S.: 517810

Nokia Solutions and Networks Branch Operations Oy - Brunei (2)
Block B Unit 1 Hassanin Complex Spg 42 Jln Muara Kg Pancha Delima, Bandar Seri Begawan, 4513, Brunei Darussalam
Tel.: (673) 2266 500
Web Site: http://networks.nokia.com
Communication Equipment Mfr
N.A.I.C.S.: 334290

Nokia Solutions and Networks Hellas S.A. (2)
49 Tsiklitira & Karamanli St, Marousi, GR-15125, Athens, Greece
Tel.: (30) 210 8115700
Web Site: http://networks.nokia.com
Telecommunication Servicesb
N.A.I.C.S.: 517810

Nokia Solutions and Networks OU (2)
Ravala pst 2 III floor, 10145, Tallinn, Estonia
Tel.: (372) 665 9966
Web Site: http://networks.nokia.com
Communication Equipment Mfr
N.A.I.C.S.: 334290

Nokia Solutions and Networks Slovakia, s. r. o. (2)
Tel.: (421) 258220661
Web Site: http://networks.nokia.com
Telecommunication Servicesb
N.A.I.C.S.: 517810

Nokia Solutions and Networks Sp. z o.o. (2)
Ulica Rzymowskiego 53, 02 697, Warsaw, Poland
Tel.: (48) 225 155 000
Web Site: http://networks.nokia.com
Business & Consumer Telecommunications Systems
N.A.I.C.S.: 517111

Branch (Domestic):

Nokia Bydgoszcz (3)
Ulica Pilicka 6, 85 776, Bydgoszcz, Poland
Tel.: (48) 523491000
Web Site: http://nokiabydgoszcz.pl
Business & Consumer Telecommunications Systems
N.A.I.C.S.: 517111

Subsidiary (Non-US):

Nokia Solutions and Networks Taiwan Co., Ltd. (2)
7F No 409 Section 2 Tiding Blvd, Nei Hu, Taipei, 114, Taiwan (100%)
Tel.: (886) 221621100
Web Site: http://www.nokia.com
Communication Equipment Mfr
N.A.I.C.S.: 334290

Singapore ALE Pte. Ltd. (2)
Viva Business Park 750E Chai Chee Road 05-01/02, Singapore, 469005, Singapore
Tel.: (65) 68121950
Communication Equipment Mfr
N.A.I.C.S.: 334290

Alcad Limited (1)
1st Floor Unit 5 Area Centre Edinburg Way, Harlow, CM20 2BN, Essex, United Kingdom
Tel.: (44) 1279772555

INTERNATIONAL PUBLIC

Web Site: http://www.alcad.com
Nickel Cadmium Battery Mfr & Distr
N.A.I.C.S.: 335910

Alcatel-Lucent East Africa Limited (1)
Ground Floor Unit A Nairobi Business Park Ngong Road, Karen, 00502, Nairobi, Kenya
Tel.: (254) 202758000
Telecommunication Equipment Distr
N.A.I.C.S.: 423690

Antelec S.A.S. (1)
2 rue du noyer aux perdrix, 77170, Servon, France
Tel.: (33) 185531340
Web Site: https://www.antelec.fr
Electronic Connector Mfr
N.A.I.C.S.: 334417

Beijing Nokia Hang Xing Telecommunications Systems Co. Ltd (1)
11 Dongjie Heping Li, 100013, Beijing, China
Tel.: (86) 1084212288
Web Site: http://www.nokia.com.cn
Sales of Telecommunication Systems & Equipment
N.A.I.C.S.: 517810

IRIS Service Delivery UK Ltd. (1)
Unit 10 Ramsay Court Hinchingbrooke Business Park, Huntingdon, PE29 6FY, United Kingdom
Tel.: (44) 1480274189
Web Site: http://www.iris-services.com
Telecommunication Servicesb
N.A.I.C.S.: 517810
Andy Golby (Mng Dir)

IRIS Telecommunication Austria GmbH (1)
Guglgasse 17, 1110, Vienna, Austria
Web Site: http://www.iris-telco.at
Telecommunication Servicesb
N.A.I.C.S.: 517810
Theresia Sammer (CFO)

IRIS Telecommunication GmbH (1)
Fiete-Schulze-Strasse 14, 06116, Halle, Germany
Tel.: (49) 17676982100
Web Site: http://www.iris-telecommunication.de
Telecommunication Servicesb
N.A.I.C.S.: 517810

IRIS Telecommunication Poland Sp. z o.o. (1)
street Dr Stefana Kopcinskiego 62, 90-032, Lodz, Poland
Tel.: (48) 422807880
Web Site: https://www.iris-telecommunication.pl
Telecommunication Equipment Distr
N.A.I.C.S.: 423690

IRIS Telekomunikasyon Muhendislik Hizmetleri A.S. (1)
Icerenkoy Mah Cayir Cad Haci Zuhre Sayar Is Mer No 11 Floor 5, Atasehir, 34752, Istanbul, Turkiye
Tel.: (90) 2165751840
Web Site: https://www.iris-tele.com
Mobile Broadband Services
N.A.I.C.S.: 517112

Nice-business Solutions Finland Oy (1)
Valimotie 16, 00380, Helsinki, Finland
Tel.: (358) 29302302
Web Site: https://www.nico.fi
Sales Range: $75-99.9 Million
Emp.: 35
Software Services
N.A.I.C.S.: 541512
Jouko Seppa (Mng Dir)

Subsidiary (Domestic):

Nice-business Consulting Oy (2)
Valimotie 16, PO Box 458, 101, Helsinki, Finland
Tel.: (358) 45 78800
Web Site: http://www.nico.fi
Technology Consulting Services
N.A.I.C.S.: 541690
Antria Tarmo (Mng Dir)

Unit (Non-US):

Nice-business Solutions - Brighton (2)

AND PRIVATE COMPANIES / NOKIA CORPORATION

Lees House 21 Dyke Road, Brighton, BN1 3FE, United Kingdom
Tel.: (44) 1273772306
Sales Range: $1-9.9 Million
Emp.: 30
Software Development & Testing Services
N.A.I.C.S.: 513210

Nokia (China) Investment Co., Ltd. (1)
3D Orient International Plaza, 85 Lou Shan Guan Road, Shanghai, 200336, China (100%)
Tel.: (86) 2162786386
N.A.I.C.S.: 812990

Nokia (H.K.) Limited (1)
16 Fl City Plz 4, Taikoo Shing, China (Hong Kong) (100%)
Tel.: (852) 25970100
Web Site: http://www.nokia.com.hk
N.A.I.C.S.: 517112

Nokia (Malaysia) Sdn. Bhd. (1)
Jalan Stesen Sentral 5, 50470, Kuala Lumpur, Malaysia (98%)
Tel.: (60) 327868888
Sales of Telecommunications Equipment
N.A.I.C.S.: 517112

Nokia (Thailand) Ltd. (1)
725 Sukhumvit Road Khlong Tan Nuea, Khlong Tan Nuea Wattana, Bangkok, 10110, Thailand (100%)
Tel.: (66) 26738888
Sales Range: $25-49.9 Million
Emp.: 60
Networking Equipment Dsitr
N.A.I.C.S.: 334210

Nokia (Vietnam) LLC (1)
Tel.: (84) 49743111
Web Site: http://www.nokia.com
Mobile Phone Mfr & Whslr
N.A.I.C.S.: 334220

Nokia Arabia Limited (1)
Tatweer Tower Block 2 King Fahad Road, PO Box 341, Riyadh, Saudi Arabia
Tel.: (966) 112008320
Web Site: https://www.nokiasaudi.com
Telecommunication & Information Technology Services
N.A.I.C.S.: 541512

Nokia Argentina S.A. (1)
Tel.: (54) 1148149665
Web Site: http://www.nokia.com
Sales Range: $25-49.9 Million
Emp.: 50
Sales of Telecommunication Systems & Equipment
N.A.I.C.S.: 517810

Nokia Austria GmbH (1)
Nokia Way 1, 7000, Eisenstadt, Austria (100%)
Tel.: (43) 26827710
Web Site: http://www.nokia.at
Sales Range: $25-49.9 Million
Emp.: 40
Sales of Telecommunication Systems & Equipment
N.A.I.C.S.: 517810

Nokia Benelux N.V./S.A. (1)
Culliganlaan 2 G Park Ln, B 1831, Diegem, Mechelen, Belgium (100%)
Tel.: (32) 27103000
Web Site: http://www.nokia.be
Sales Range: $50-74.9 Million
Emp.: 130
Sales of Telecommunication Systems & Equipment
N.A.I.C.S.: 517810

Nokia Canada Corporation (1)
600 March Road, Ottawa, K2K 2E6, ON, Canada (100%)
Tel.: (905) 427-6654
Web Site: http://www.nokia.ca
Sales Range: $25-49.9 Million
Emp.: 60
Sales of Cellular Mobile Phones
N.A.I.C.S.: 517112

Nokia Colombia S.A (1)
Carrea 7 Nro 76 35 Santa Fe De Bogota Fl 5, Bogota, Colombia
Tel.: (57) 1 640 7979

Sales Range: $25-49.9 Million
Emp.: 50
Communication Equipment Mfr & Whslr
N.A.I.C.S.: 334210

Nokia Communications Turkey (1)
Panbure Ali Esenbi Cad Kat 1 Etiler No 13, 34337, Istanbul, Turkiye (100%)
Tel.: (90) 2123506400
Web Site: http://www.nokia.com.tr
Sales Range: $25-49.9 Million
Emp.: 40
Telecommunications Equipment Distributor
N.A.I.C.S.: 238210

Nokia Costa Rica S.A. (1)
200 East Sports Plaza, La Uruca, San Jose, Costa Rica
Tel.: (506) 22875050
Telecommunication Servicesb
N.A.I.C.S.: 517810

Nokia Czech Republic s.r.o. (1)
Karolinska 654/2, 186 00, Prague, Czech Republic (100%)
Tel.: (420) 221855100
Sales Range: $25-49.9 Million
Emp.: 25
Sales of Telecommunications Equipment & Systems
N.A.I.C.S.: 517112

Nokia Danmark A/S (1)
Orestads Boulevard 73, 2300, Copenhagen, Denmark (100%)
Tel.: (45) 33292929
Sales Range: $400-449.9 Million
Emp.: 1,500
Sales of Telecommunications Equipment & Systems
N.A.I.C.S.: 517112

Nokia Egypt S.A.E. (1)
Nokia Building Building MB4 Maadi Technology Park Maher Abaza St, PO Box 9, New Maadi, 11742, Cairo, Egypt
Tel.: (20) 221605555
Telecommunication Servicesb
N.A.I.C.S.: 517810

Nokia Enterprises Ltd (1)
4F Commercial Plz Radisson Complex National Hwy 8, Mahipalpur, New Delhi, 110 037, India (100%)
Tel.: (91) 1126779000
Sales Range: $100-124.9 Million
Emp.: 300
Sales of Telecommunications Systems & Equipment
N.A.I.C.S.: 517112
V. Sembian *(Dir-Chennai)*

Nokia France (1)
1 Route de Villejust, Saclay, 91620, Paris, France (100%)
Tel.: (33) 153569999
Sales Range: $100-124.9 Million
Emp.: 50
Sales of Telecommunications Equipment & Systems
N.A.I.C.S.: 517112

Nokia Hungary Ltd. (1)
Bokay Janos utca 36-42, 1083, Budapest, Hungary (100%)
Tel.: (36) 34542000
Sales Range: $200-249.9 Million
Emp.: 800
Sales of Telecommunications Systems & Equipment
N.A.I.C.S.: 517112

Nokia Inc. (1)
102 Corporate Park Dr, White Plains, NY 10604
Tel.: (914) 368-0400
Web Site: http://www.nokia.com
Wireless Services
N.A.I.C.S.: 517112

Subsidiary (Domestic):

Intellisync Corporation (2)
2550 N 1st St Ste 500, San Jose, CA 95131-1038
Tel.: (408) 321-7650
Web Site: http://www.intellisync.com
Sales Range: $50-74.9 Million
Emp.: 456
Software Infrastructure Services
N.A.I.C.S.: 334610

Branch (Domestic):

Nokia Inc. (2)
6021 Connection Dr, Irving, TX 75039-2600 (100%)
Tel.: (972) 894-5000
Web Site: http://www.nokiausa.com
Sales Range: $150-199.9 Million
Emp.: 700
Holding Company
N.A.I.C.S.: 517112

Subsidiary (Domestic):

SAC Wireless, LLC (2)
1501 E Woodfield Rd Ste 300E, Schaumburg, IL 60173
Tel.: (847) 944-1600
Web Site: http://www.sacw.com
Emp.: 450
Engineers, Designs, Constructs, Integrates & Maintains Indoor & Outdoor Antenna Systems
N.A.I.C.S.: 541330

Nokia India Private Limited (1)
C/402 Business Square Opposite Apple Heritage Chakala Andheri (E), Mumbai, 400093, India
Tel.: (91) 2267427760
Web Site: http://www.nokia.com
Sales of Telecommunication Systems & Equipment
N.A.I.C.S.: 517112

Nokia Ireland Ltd. (1)
Industrial Park Snugborough Industrial Estate, Campus Beaver Row, Dublin, 15, Ireland (100%)
Tel.: (353) 12602444
Sales Range: $25-49.9 Million
Emp.: 25
Network Infrastructure Services
N.A.I.C.S.: 517112

Nokia Italia S.p.A. (1)
Via Vincenzo Lancetti 43, I 20158, Milan, Italy (100%)
Tel.: (39) 026882101
Web Site: http://www.nokia.it
Sales Range: $50-74.9 Million
Emp.: 250
Sales of Telecommunications Systems & Equipment
N.A.I.C.S.: 517112

Nokia Japan Co. Ltd. (1)
6-10-1 Roppongi, Minato-ku, Tokyo, 106-6141, Japan (100%)
Tel.: (81) 3357597001
Sales Range: $100-124.9 Million
Emp.: 500
Distr of Mobile Communications & Networking Equipment
N.A.I.C.S.: 334220

Nokia Komarom Kft. (1)
Nokia Utca 1 Magyarorszag, Komarom, 2900, Hungary
Tel.: (36) 1 777 4819
Web Site: http://www.nokia.com
Mobile Phone Mfr & Whslr
N.A.I.C.S.: 334220

Nokia Latvija SIA (1)
(100%)
Tel.: (371) 7338427
Web Site: http://www.nokia.lv
Sales Range: $25-49.9 Million
Emp.: 10
Sales of Telecommunications Systems & Equipment
N.A.I.C.S.: 517810

Nokia Mexico S.A. de C.V. (1)
Guillermo Gonzalez Camerena 1200 Piso 15 and 12, Colonia Bosques De Las Lomas, Mexico, 05120, DF, Mexico (100%)
Tel.: (52) 5552617200
Web Site: http://www.nokia.com.mx
Sales Range: $50-74.9 Million
Emp.: 200
Sales of Telecommunications Systems & Equipment
N.A.I.C.S.: 517810

Nokia Nederland B.V. (1)
Laan van Oversteen 14a, 2289 CX, Rijswijk, Netherlands (100%)
Tel.: (31) 703071717

Web Site: http://www.nokia.nl
Sales of Telecommunications Equipment
N.A.I.C.S.: 238210

Nokia Norge AS (1)
Sandakerveien 116 6 etg, PO Box 4332 Nydalen, 0484, Oslo, Norway
Tel.: (47) 41 54 44 00
Web Site: http://www.nokia.no
Sales Range: $25-49.9 Million
Emp.: 50
Telecommunications
N.A.I.C.S.: 517810

Nokia Philippines Inc. (1)
Philamlife Tower 8767 Paseo De Roxas, 1226, Makati, Philippines
Tel.: (63) 27541500
Web Site: http://www.nokia.com
Sales Range: $25-49.9 Million
Emp.: 23
Communication Equipment Mfr & Whslr
N.A.I.C.S.: 334290

Nokia Portugal S.A. (1)
Edificio D Joao I, Quinto Da Fonte, 2780 730, Paco d'Arcos, Portugal (100%)
Tel.: (351) 214465600
Web Site: http://www.nokia.pt
Sales Range: $25-49.9 Million
Emp.: 18
Telecommunication Equipment Whslr
N.A.I.C.S.: 517112

Nokia Research Center (1)
Itamerenkatu 11-133, 00180, Helsinki, Finland (100%)
Tel.: (358) 718008000
Web Site: http://research.nokia.com
Sales Range: $50-74.9 Million
Emp.: 160
Telecommunications Research
N.A.I.C.S.: 541715

Nokia Romania (1)
Regus Primavera 32nd Calea Dorobantilor, 7834331, Bucharest, Romania
Tel.: (40) 214077505
Emp.: 2,000
N.A.I.C.S.: 334418

Nokia Russia (ZAO) (1)
Ul Vozdvizhenka 10, 125000, Moscow, Russia
Tel.: (7) 495 795 0500
Web Site: http://www.nokia.com
Mobile Phone Mfr & Whslr
N.A.I.C.S.: 334220

Nokia Slovakia s.r.o. (1)
Prievozska Street 4A, Apollo Business Center II, 821 09, Bratislava, Slovakia
Tel.: (421) 252923030
Mobile Phone Mfr & Whslr
N.A.I.C.S.: 334220

Nokia Solutions & Networks Argentina S.A. (1)
Av Vieytes 1710, C1275AGT, Buenos Aires, Argentina
Tel.: (54) 1143491111
Telecommunication Servicesb
N.A.I.C.S.: 517810

Nokia Solutions & Networks Bolivia S.A. (1)
Juan Daniel Building Plaza Franz Tamayo, Jose Aguirre Acha 582 corner with Lucas Mendoza de la Tapia, Cochabamba, Bolivia
Tel.: (591) 44681666
Telecommunication Servicesb
N.A.I.C.S.: 517810

Nokia Solutions & Networks Colombia Ltda. (1)
Calle 72 8-56 Torre Vision Building Floors 2 3 4 5 6 7 8, Bogota, Colombia
Tel.: (57) 15875577
Telecommunication Servicesb
N.A.I.C.S.: 517810

Nokia Solutions & Networks Ecuador S.A. (1)
Av Republica del Salvador 34-229 and Moscow 6th Floor, Edifico San Salvador, Quito, Ecuador
Tel.: (593) 23982400
Telecommunication Servicesb
N.A.I.C.S.: 517810

Nokia Solutions & Networks Japan G.K. (1)

5405

NOKIA CORPORATION

Nokia Corporation—(Continued)

6-10-1 Roppongi Hills Mori Tower 41F, Roppongi Minato-ku, Tokyo, 106-6141, Japan
Tel.: (81) 354746400
Telecommunication Equipment Distr
N.A.I.C.S.: 423690

Nokia Solutions & Networks MEA FZ-LLC (1)
2nd Floor Office Park Block B, PO Box 214959, Dubai Internet City, Dubai, United Arab Emirates
Tel.: (971) 43630700
Telecommunication Network Product Distr
N.A.I.C.S.: 423690

Nokia Solutions & Networks Morocco SARL (1)
Route de Meknes Km 8-1000, Sale, 11000, Morocco
Tel.: (212) 537819901
Telecommunication Equipment Distr
N.A.I.C.S.: 423690

Nokia Solutions & Networks Oy (1)
Karaportti 3, Espoo, 02100, Finland
Tel.: (358) 714004000
Web Site: http://www.nsn.com
Telecommunication Servicesb
N.A.I.C.S.: 517112

Subsidiary (Non-US):

Nokia Solutions & Networks (Hangzhou) Co., Ltd (2)
Road 1 Hangzhou Economic & Technological Development Zone, Hangzhou, 310053, China
Tel.: (86) 57186912888
Sales Range: $25-49.9 Million
Emp.: 100
Cellular Equipment Mfr
N.A.I.C.S.: 334220

Nokia Solutions & Networks Hellas AE (2)
18-20 Amaroussiou Chalandriou Avenue, 15125, Maroussi, Greece
Tel.: (30) 2111203600
Web Site: http://www.nsn.com
Sales Range: $50-74.9 Million
Emp.: 105
Supplier of Network &Telecommunications Equipment
N.A.I.C.S.: 517810

Nokia Solutions & Networks Kft. (2)
Koztelek Utca 6, 1092, Budapest, Hungary
Tel.: (36) 20 9777 797
Web Site: http://www.nsn.com
Sales of Telecommunications Systems & Equipment
N.A.I.C.S.: 517810

Nokia Solutions & Networks Norge AS (2)
Fornebuveien 5, 0580, Lysaker, Norway
Tel.: (47) 23891010
Web Site: http://www.nsn.com
Telecommunication Servicesb
N.A.I.C.S.: 517810

Nokia Solutions & Networks Philippines, Inc. (2)
14F Sun Life Centre 5th Ave Cor Rizal Drive, Bonifacio Global City, Taguig, Philippines
Tel.: (63) 2 944 7676
Web Site: http://www.nsn.com
Sales Range: $100-124.9 Million
Emp.: 300
Sales of Telecommunication Systems & Equipment
N.A.I.C.S.: 517810

Nokia Solutions & Networks Poland Sp.z.o.o. (2)
Tel.: (48) 223119000
Web Site: http://www.nsn.com
Sales Range: $100-124.9 Million
Emp.: 300
Sales of Telecommunications Equipment & Systems
N.A.I.C.S.: 517810

Nokia Solutions & Networks Pty Ltd. (2)
Level 5 60 Union Street, Pyrmont, 2009, NSW, Australia

Tel.: (61) 2 9429 9100
Web Site: http://www.nsn.com
Sales Range: $50-74.9 Million
Emp.: 200
Sales of Telecommunications Equipment & Systems
N.A.I.C.S.: 517810

Nokia Solutions & Networks Singapore Pte. Ltd. (2)
438B Alexandra Road, #08-07/10 Alexandra Technopark, Singapore, 119968, Singapore
Tel.: (65) 51 6000
Web Site: http://www.nsn.com
Sales Range: $150-199.9 Million
Emp.: 800
Sales of Telecommunications Equipment & Systems
N.A.I.C.S.: 517810

Subsidiary (US):

Nokia Solutions & Networks US LLC (2)
6000 Connection Dr, Irving, TX 75039
Tel.: (972) 374-3000
Web Site: http://www.nsn.com
Sales Range: $50-74.9 Million
Emp.: 250
Telecommunication Servicesb
N.A.I.C.S.: 517810

Subsidiary (Non-US):

Nokia Networks Inc. (3) **(100%)**
Tel.: (972) 894-5000
Web Site: http://www.nokia.com
Sales Range: $400-449.9 Million
Emp.: 2,500
N.A.I.C.S.: 334418

Unit (Non-US):

Nokia Networks Inc.-ATM Systems R&D (4)
Tel.: (781) 993-4900
Web Site: http://www.nokia.com
Sales Range: $25-49.9 Million
Emp.: 5
N.A.I.C.S.: 334418

Subsidiary (Non-US):

PT Nokia Solutions & Networks (2)
Menara Mulia Building 11th Floor Jalan Jendral Gatot, Subroto Kav 9-11, Jakarta, 12930, Java, Indonesia
Tel.: (62) 2130411000
Web Site: http://www.nsn.com
Sales Range: $25-49.9 Million
Emp.: 50
Telecommunication Servicesb
N.A.I.C.S.: 517112

Nokia Solutions & Networks Schweiz AG (1)
Friesenbergstrasse 75, 8055, Zurich, Switzerland
Tel.: (41) 444652111
Telecommunication Servicesb
N.A.I.C.S.: 517810

Nokia Solutions & Networks Tanzania Limited (1)
Paloma Park 6th Floor Ursino Estate Plot 23 Bagamoyo Road, Dar es Salaam, Tanzania
Tel.: (255) 7547811301
Telecommunication Servicesb
N.A.I.C.S.: 517810

Nokia Solutions & Networks TraffiCOM Kft. (1)
Bokay Janos u 36-42, 1083, Budapest, Hungary
Tel.: (36) 14557199
Web Site: http://www.trafficom.hu
Telecommunication Servicesb
N.A.I.C.S.: 517810
Lazar Zoltan *(Mng Dir-Gen Mgmt & Sls)*

Nokia Solutions and Networks (1)
Edificio Palladio Santiago Ave Providencia #1760, Piso 14 Providencia, Santiago, Chile
Tel.: (56) 2 927 2577
Web Site: http://nsn.com
Sales Range: $25-49.9 Million
Emp.: 25
Mobile Broadband Technologies

N.A.I.C.S.: 517810

Nokia Spain S.A.U (1) **(100%)**
Tel.: (34) 912119300
Sales Range: $50-74.9 Million
Emp.: 180
Sales of Telecommunications Equipment
N.A.I.C.S.: 238210

Nokia TMC Ltd. (1)
8F 705 19 Yeoksam Dong, Gangnam Gu, Seoul, 135 080, Korea (South) **(100%)**
Tel.: (82) 221865000
Web Site: http://www.nokia.co.kr
Mfr of Cellular Mobile Phones
N.A.I.C.S.: 517112

Nokia Taiwan Co. Ltd. (1)
CEC Building No 100 Sec 3, Minsheng East Road, 105, Taipei, Taiwan **(100%)**
Tel.: (886) 227199998
Web Site: http://www.nokia.com.tw
Sales Range: $50-74.9 Million
Emp.: 200
Sales & Marketing of Telecommunications Equipment
N.A.I.C.S.: 517112

Nokia Telecommunications Ltd. (1)
Building 1 No 5 DongHuan Zhong Road BDA, Beijing, 100176, China
Tel.: (86) 10 6787 8899
Mobile Phone Mfr
N.A.I.C.S.: 334220

Nokia Treasury Asia Ltd. (1)
438B Alexandra Road 07-00, Alexandra Techno Pk, Singapore, 119968, Singapore **(100%)**
Tel.: (65) 67232323
Sales Range: $25-49.9 Million
Emp.: 7
N.A.I.C.S.: 334418

Nokia UK Limited (1)
Nokia House Summit Avenue, Southwood, Farnborough, GU14 0NG, Hants, United Kingdom **(100%)**
Tel.: (44) 1252866000
Web Site: http://www.nokia.com
Sales of Telecommunications Equipment & Systems
N.A.I.C.S.: 517112

Nokia Uruguay S.A. (1)
Av Uruguay 1340 esquina Ejido, Montevideo, Uruguay
Tel.: (598) 91633016
Web Site: http://www.nokiauruguay.com.uy
Mobile Retailer
N.A.I.C.S.: 449210

Nokia West & Central Africa SA (1)
Dakar Anta Almadies Immeuble Anta Route de Ngor-Angle Dioulikaye, Dakar, 3879, Senegal
Tel.: (221) 8599797
Telecommunication Servicesb
N.A.I.C.S.: 517810

Nokia de Venezuela, C.A. (1)
Torre Creditcard Piso 14 Av Principal Del Bosque, Chacaito 14th Fl, Caracas, 1050, Venezuela **(100%)**
Tel.: (58) 2129050000
Web Site: http://www.nokia.com
Sales Range: $25-49.9 Million
Emp.: 30
N.A.I.C.S.: 334418

Nokia do Brasil Ltda. (1) **(100%)**
Tel.: (55) 1155086350
Web Site: http://www.nokia.com.br
Sales Range: $50-74.9 Million
Emp.: 150
Sales of Telecommunication Systems & Equipment
N.A.I.C.S.: 517810

Subsidiary (Domestic):

Nokia do Brasil Tecnologia Ltda. (2)
Avenida Torquato Tapajos 7200, Manaus, 69086-660, Amazonas, Brazil
Tel.: (55) 9236527200
Web Site: http://www.nokia.com.br
Cellular Phone Mfr & Whslr
N.A.I.C.S.: 334220

INTERNATIONAL PUBLIC

Nokia of America Corporation (1)
600-700 Mountain Ave, New Providence, NJ 07974
Tel.: (908) 582-3000
Web Site: http://www.nokia.com
Wireline & Mobile Telecommunications Infrastructure Design Services
N.A.I.C.S.: 517810

Subsidiary (Domestic):

Nokia Bell Labs (2)
600-700 Mountain Ave, New Providence, NJ 07974-0636
Tel.: (908) 582-3000
Web Site: http://www.bell-labs.com
Research & Manufacturing
N.A.I.C.S.: 541713

Unit (Non-US):

Nokia Bell Labs - Dublin (3)
Blanchardstown Industrial Park Snugborough Road, Blanchardstown, Dublin, 15, Ireland
Tel.: (353) 18864444
Web Site: http://www.bell-labs.com
Computer & Communications Research & Development
N.A.I.C.S.: 541715

Branch (Domestic):

Nokia of America Corporation - Raleigh (2)
2301 Sugar Bush Rd, Raleigh, NC 27612
Tel.: (919) 867-6453
Web Site: http://networks.nokia.com
Sales Range: $50-74.9 Million
Emp.: 250
Telecommunications Equipment Mfr
N.A.I.C.S.: 334210

Noksel A.S. (1)
Yukari Ovecler Mah Lizbon Cad No 10 Cankaya, Ovecler, 6460, Ankara, Turkiye **(40%)**
Tel.: (90) 3124725959
Sales Range: $200-249.9 Million
Emp.: 50
Spiral Welded Steel Pipe Mfr
N.A.I.C.S.: 331210

Subsidiary (Non-US):

Noksel Espana S.A. (2)
Av Mediterraneo 5 - 1 G, Pozuelo de Alarcon, 28007, Madrid, Spain
Tel.: (34) 915351790
Web Site: https://nokselspain.com
Spiral Welded Steel Pipe Mfr
N.A.I.C.S.: 331210

OOO Nokia (1)
10 Vozdvizhenka Ul, Moscow, Russia
Tel.: (7) 4957950500
Mobile Phone Mfr & Whslr
N.A.I.C.S.: 334220

Original1 GmbH (1)
Mainzer Landstrasse 205, 60326, Frankfurt, Germany
Tel.: (49) 6917536620
Web Site: http://www.original1.net
Sales Range: $25-49.9 Million
Emp.: 12
Supply Chain Integrity & Security Services; Joint Venture of SAP AG, Nokia Corporation & Giesecke & Devrient GmbH
N.A.I.C.S.: 513210

PT. Nokia Indonesia (1)
Menara Mulia Building Jl Jendral Gatot Subroto Kav 9-11, 12930, Jakarta, Indonesia
Tel.: (62) 21 3040 9700
Web Site: http://www.nokia.com
Mobile Phone Mfr & Whslr
N.A.I.C.S.: 334220

Pishahang Communications Networks Development Company (1)
N-27 Corner of 9th Street Gandhi Avenue, PO Box No 15177-63113, Tehran, Iran
Tel.: (98) 2184254000
Telecommunication Servicesb
N.A.I.C.S.: 517810

ZAO Nokia (1)
Sedova Street 12 T Business Centre House

AND PRIVATE COMPANIES

T4, 192019, Saint Petersburg,
Russia **(100%)**
Tel.: (7) 8123240200
Web Site: http://www.nsn.com
Sales Range: $25-49.9 Million
Emp.: 100
Sales of Telecommunication Systems &
Equipment
N.A.I.C.S.: 423690

NOKIAN RENKAAT OYJ
Pirkkalaistie 7, PO Box 20, 37101,
Nokia, Finland
Tel.: (358) 104017000 FI
Web Site:
https://www.nokiantyres.com
Year Founded: 1988
TYRES—(HEL)
Rev.: $1,787,072,588
Assets: $2,612,185,436
Liabilities: $630,369,194
Net Worth: $1,981,816,242
Earnings: $447,832,014
Emp.: 4,942
Fiscal Year-end: 12/31/19
Tires & Retreading Products Mfr
N.A.I.C.S.: 326211
Manu Salmi *(VP-Nokian Heavy Tyres Bus Unit)*

Subsidiaries:

Freibi Reipas SIA (1)
25 Viskalu Iela, LV 1026, Riga,
Latvia **(100%)**
Tel.: (371) 7551883
Web Site: http://www.nokiantyres.com
Sales Range: $25-49.9 Million
Emp.: 20
N.A.I.C.S.: 326211

Levypyora Oy (1)
Kouvolantie 185, PO Box 44, 15561, Nastola, Finland
Tel.: (358) 207929520
Web Site: https://www.levypyora.fi
Wheel Mfr
N.A.I.C.S.: 336330

Nokian Dack AB (1)
Metalvagen 34, PO Box 3002, 19503,
Marsta, Lunda, Sweden **(100%)**
Tel.: (46) 84747440
Sales Range: $25-49.9 Million
Emp.: 32
N.A.I.C.S.: 326211

Nokian Dekk A/S (1)
Leiraveien 17, 2000, Lillestrom,
Norway **(100%)**
Tel.: (47) 64847700
Sales Range: $25-49.9 Million
Emp.: 25
N.A.I.C.S.: 326211
Bjorn Kamphus *(Mng Dir)*

Nokian Portti Oy (1)
Pirkkalaistie 1, 37100, Nokia, Finland
Tel.: (358) 417323716
Web Site: https://nokianportti.fi
Emp.: 30
Real Estate & Management Services
N.A.I.C.S.: 531311

Nokian Reifen AG (1)
Neoa Winterthurarstrause 15 17 Deatlekon,
CH 8305, Zurich, Switzerland **(100%)**
Tel.: (41) 448074000
Web Site: http://www.nokiantyres.com
Sales Range: $25-49.9 Million
Emp.: 12
N.A.I.C.S.: 326211

Nokian Reifen GmbH (1)
Neuwieder Strasse 14, Nuremberg, 90411,
Germany **(100%)**
Tel.: (49) 911527550
Sales Range: $25-49.9 Million
Emp.: 16
N.A.I.C.S.: 326211

Nokian Shina LLC (1)
70 Moiseeva Str Martusivka Village, Boryspil District, Kiev, 8343, Ukraine
Tel.: (380) 44 220 1 220
Web Site: http://www.nokiantyres.ua
Tire Retailer
N.A.I.C.S.: 441340

Nokian Tyres (1)
Russia Leningrad Region Station Kirpichnly
zavod, Industrial Zone Block 6, Saint Petersburg, 188640, Vsevolozhsk,
Russia **(100%)**
Tel.: (7) 8123369000
Web Site: http://www.nokiantyres.ru
Sales Range: $200-249.9 Million
Emp.: 600
Tire Manufacturer
N.A.I.C.S.: 326211
Andrei Pantiouikhov *(Gen Mgr)*

Nokian Tyres Inc., USA (1)
1945 Main St, Colchester, VT
05446 **(100%)**
Tel.: (615) 287-0600
Web Site: http://www.nokiantyres.com
Sales Range: $25-49.9 Million
Emp.: 18
Sales & Distribution of Tires
N.A.I.C.S.: 423130
Hans Dyhrman *(Dir-Mktg-North America)*

Nokian Tyres s.r.o (1)
V Parku 2336-22, 148 00, Prague, Czech
Republic
Tel.: (420) 241932668
Web Site: http://www.nokiantyres.cz
Tiles Mfr
N.A.I.C.S.: 326211

OOO Nokian Shina (1)
Industrial Zone Kirpichniy Zavod Block 6,
Vsevolozhsk, Saint Petersburg, 188640,
Russia
Tel.: (7) 812 336 9000
Web Site: http://www.nokiantyres.ru
Sales Range: $200-249.9 Million
Emp.: 1,000
Tiles Mfr
N.A.I.C.S.: 326211
Andrei Pantiouikhov *(Gen Mgr)*

TOO Nokian Tyres (1)
Office 209 Abai Avenue 151/115, 050059,
Almaty, Kazakhstan
Tel.: (7) 7273901970
Web Site: http://www.nokiantyres.kz
Tiles Mfr
N.A.I.C.S.: 326211

Vianor A/S (1)
Leiraveien 17, PO Box 283, 20 27 Jeller,
2000, Lillestrom, Norway **(100%)**
Tel.: (47) 64847760
Web Site: https://vianor.no
Sales Range: $25-49.9 Million
Emp.: 25
N.A.I.C.S.: 326211

Vianor AB (1)
Box 114, 534 22, Vara, Sweden
Tel.: (46) 512 798000
Web Site: http://www.vianor.se
Tire Retailer
N.A.I.C.S.: 441340

Vianor AG (1)
Neue Winterthurerstrasse 15, 8305, Dietlikon, Switzerland
Tel.: (41) 448357080
Web Site: http://www.vianor.ch
Tire Retailer
N.A.I.C.S.: 441340

Vianor Holding Oy (1)
Pirkkalaistie 7, PO Box 20, 37101, Nokia,
Finland
Tel.: (358) 104017000
Web Site: http://www.vianor.com
Sales Range: $450-499.9 Million
Emp.: 1,409
Tiles Mfr
N.A.I.C.S.: 326211

Subsidiary (Non-US):

Nordicwheels AB (2)
Vaxnasgatan 150, 653 43, Karlstad, Sweden
Tel.: (46) 54141600
Web Site: http://www.nordicwheels.se
Motor Vehicle Parts Retailer
N.A.I.C.S.: 441330

Vianor Oy (1)
Toikansuontie 10, 53500, Lappeenranta,
Finland
Tel.: (358) 104013010
Web Site: http://www.vianor.fi

Car Tires Mfr & Whslr
N.A.I.C.S.: 326211

NOKWON COMMERCIALS & INDUSTRIES, INC.
1 Shin-chon 2-ro, Paju, Gyeonggi-do,
Korea (South)
Tel.: (82) 319582500
Web Site: http://www.cubes.net
Year Founded: 1987
065560—(KRS)
Rev.: $45,533,091
Assets: $92,576,157
Liabilities: $56,659,659
Net Worth: $35,916,498
Earnings: ($19,895,750)
Emp.: 86
Fiscal Year-end: 12/31/22
Software Development Services
N.A.I.C.S.: 513210
Sang Hun Jung *(CEO)*

NOLATO AB

NOLATO AB
Nolatovagen, SE 269 04, Torekov,
Sweden
Tel.: (46) 431442290 SE
Web Site: http://www.nolato.com
NOLAB—(OMX)
Rev.: $1,142,546,720
Assets: $1,060,142,720
Liabilities: $608,568,800
Net Worth: $451,573,920
Earnings: $98,396,480
Emp.: 6,721
Fiscal Year-end: 12/31/20
High-Tech Systems Supplier of Polymer Components
N.A.I.C.S.: 325998
Per-Ola Holmstrom *(CFO & Exec VP)*

Subsidiaries:

A/S Cerbo Norge (1)
Vestvollveien 32F, 2020, Skedsmokorset,
Norway
Tel.: (47) 63878220
Pharmaceutical Products Packaging Services
N.A.I.C.S.: 561910

Cerbo France Sarl (1)
15 Rue Vignon, 75008, Paris, France
Tel.: (33) 147975284
Sales Range: $50-74.9 Million
Emp.: 14
Packaging Plastic Materials Mfr
N.A.I.C.S.: 326112

Cerbo Group AB (1)
Verkmastarevagen 1-3, Box 905, 46129,
Trollhattan, Sweden
Tel.: (46) 520409900
Medical Instrument Mfr
N.A.I.C.S.: 339112

GW Plastics Inc. (1)
239 Pleasant St, Bethel, VT 05032
Tel.: (802) 234-9941
Web Site: http://www.gwplastics.com
Provider of Plastic Products
N.A.I.C.S.: 326199
Brenan Riehl *(Pres & CEO)*

Subsidiary (Non-US):

Avenue Mould Solutions Ltd. (2)
Finisklin Business Park, Sligo, F91 AK63,
Ireland
Tel.: (353) 719169510
Web Site: https://www.nolato.com
Injection Mould Mfr
N.A.I.C.S.: 333248
Anne Chrystal *(Mgr-Quality & Regulatory Affairs)*

GW Plastics (Dongguan) Ltd. (2)
Plastics Product Mfr
N.A.I.C.S.: 326199

GW Plastics Mexicana S de RL de CV (2)
Circuito del Marques Norte 23A Parque Industrial El Marques, 76246, El Marques,
Queretaro, Mexico
Tel.: (52) 4422531069

Plastics Product Mfr
N.A.I.C.S.: 326199

Subsidiary (Domestic):

GW Plastics Southwest Inc. (2)
901 Paulsun St, San Antonio, TX 78219-3125
Tel.: (210) 225-1516
Web Site: http://www.gwplastics.com
Sales Range: $10-24.9 Million
Supplier of Plastic Products
N.A.I.C.S.: 326199

GW Plastics Tucson
Incorporated (2)
2901 E Valencia Rd, Tucson, AZ 85706-5920
Tel.: (520) 294-9400
Web Site: http://www.gwplastics.com
Sales Range: $10-24.9 Million
Supplier of Plastic Products
N.A.I.C.S.: 326199

GW Plastics San Antonio Inc. (1)
901 Paulsun, San Antonio, TX 78219
Tel.: (210) 225-1516
Plastic Material Distr
N.A.I.C.S.: 424610

GW Silicones Inc. (1)
272 Waterman Rd, Royalton, VT 05068
Tel.: (802) 763-2194
Injection Molding Medical Instrument Mfr
N.A.I.C.S.: 339112

Ja-Bar Silicone Corporation (1)
252 Brighton Rd, Andover, NJ 07821
Tel.: (973) 786-5000
Web Site: http://www.jabar.com
Silicone Products Mfr
N.A.I.C.S.: 325212
Gilbert Jacobs *(Pres)*

Lovepac Converting Ltd. (1)
Tel.: (86) 1067805580
Chemical Product & Preparation Mfr
N.A.I.C.S.: 325998

Lovepac Converting Private Ltd (1)
RBF-2 Road R-1 North West 670 Cherivi,
Sri City SEZ, Satyavedu, 517588, Andhra
Pradesh, India
Tel.: (91) 857 6306850
Adhesive Mfr
N.A.I.C.S.: 325520

Lovepac Technology (Shenzhen) Co.,
Ltd. (1)
1st Floor No 3 building No 1 Lirong Rd Dalang St, Changyi Industrial Area Xinshi
Community Longhua District, Shenzhen,
518109, China
Tel.: (86) 75586106065
Automation Equipment Mfr & Distr
N.A.I.C.S.: 336310

Nolato (Malaysia) SDN. BHD. (1)
Plot 368 Lorong Perindustrian Bukit Minyak,
21, Penang Science Park, 14100, Simpang
Empat, Penang, Malaysia
Tel.: (60) 45057830
Emp.: 150
Electrical & Electronic Mfr
N.A.I.C.S.: 334419

Nolato Alpha AB (1)
Tegelbruksvagen 15, PO Box 2072, SE 291
02, Kristianstad, Sweden **(100%)**
Tel.: (46) 441860000
Web Site: http://www.alpha.se
Sales Range: $25-49.9 Million
Emp.: 80
Develops, Injection Molds & Assembles
Plastic Components for the Mobile Phone
Industry
N.A.I.C.S.: 326199

Nolato Automotive Components (Beijing) Co. Ltd. (1)
402 Longsheng Industrial Park 7 Rong
Chang Road East, Beijing Development
Area, Beijing, 100176, China
Tel.: (86) 1067872200
Chemical Product & Preparation Mfr
N.A.I.C.S.: 325998

Nolato Cerbo AB (1)
Verkmastarevagen 1-3, Box 905, 461 29,
Trollhattan, Sweden
Tel.: (46) 520409900

NOLATO AB

INTERNATIONAL PUBLIC

Nolato AB—(Continued)
Emp.: 80
Packaging Plastic Materials Mfr
N.A.I.C.S.: 322220
Ann-Cathrine Petersson (Mgr-Sls)

Nolato Contour Inc. (1)
660 VandeBerg St, Baldwin, WI 54002
Tel.: (715) 684-4614
Web Site: http://www.contour-plastics.com
Sales Range: $25-49.9 Million
Emp.: 110
Plastics Product Mfr
N.A.I.C.S.: 326199
Steve Roth (Mgr-Sls)

Nolato EMC Production Center Sdn Bhd
Lot 39 Jalan SC 2, Pusat Perindustrian Sg Chua, 43000, Kajang, Selangor, Malaysia
Tel.: (60) 3 8739 3603
Silicon Rubber Products Mfr
N.A.I.C.S.: 326299
Nazereen Mazlan (Mng Dir)

Nolato Gota AB (1) **(100%)**
Tel.: (46) 511342100
Web Site: http://www.nolato.com
Sales Range: $25-49.9 Million
Emp.: 150
Develops & Moulds Plastic Components
N.A.I.C.S.: 326199
Peter Holterberg (Mng Dir)

Nolato Hungary Kft (1)
Janossomorjai Utca 3, 9200, Mosonmagyarovar, Hungary
Tel.: (36) 96 578770
Web Site: http://www.nolato.com
Plastic Component Mfr
N.A.I.C.S.: 326199
Arpad Rozsics (Mgr-Sls & Project)

Nolato Jabar LLC (1)
252 Brighton Rd, Andover, NJ 07821
Tel.: (973) 786-5000
Industrial Equipment Distr
N.A.I.C.S.: 423830

Nolato Lovepac AB (1)
Ringvagen 5, 280 40, Skanes Fagerhult, Sweden **(100%)**
Tel.: (46) 43332300
Web Site: http://www.nolatolovepac.com
Rev: $9,552,370
Emp.: 85
Mfr, Developer & Supplier of Gaskets
N.A.I.C.S.: 339991
Henrick Enoksson (Gen Mgr)

Nolato MediTech (1)
Medicingatan 4, PO Box 93, 242 31, Horby, Sweden
Tel.: (46) 4 151 9700
Web Site: http://www.nolato.se
Hoses, Tubes, Gloves & Other Rubber Medical Equipment Mfr
N.A.I.C.S.: 314999

Nolato MediTor AB (1)
Nolatovagen 32, 269 78, Torekov, Sweden
Tel.: (46) 431 442260
Web Site: http://www.nolato.com
Sales Range: $25-49.9 Million
Silicone & Latex Rubber Products Mfr
N.A.I.C.S.: 326299

Nolato Mobile Communication Polymers (Beijing) Co. Ltd. (1)
402 Longsheng Industrial Park 7 Rong Chang Road East, Beijing Development Area, Beijing, 100176, China **(100%)**
Tel.: (86) 1067872200
Web Site: http://www.nolato.com
Sales Range: $450-499.9 Million
Emp.: 1,200
Injection-Mould & Assembly of Polymer Components for Mobile Phones
N.A.I.C.S.: 326199

Nolato Plastteknik AB (1)
Exportgatan 59, Box 4123, 422 04, Hisings Backa, Backa, Sweden **(100%)**
Tel.: (46) 3 158 8400
Web Site: http://www.nolato.com
Sales Range: $50-74.9 Million
Mfr of Industrial Plastics
N.A.I.C.S.: 326199

Nolato Polymer AB (1)
Nolatovagen 32, 269 78, Torekov, Sweden **(100%)**
Tel.: (46) 431442200
Web Site: http://www.nolato.se
Sales Range: $25-49.9 Million
Develop & Manufacture Injection Moulded Parts in Soft Polymer Materials
N.A.I.C.S.: 326199
Jimmy Wallin (Dir-Sls & Mktg)

Nolato Polymer AB (1)
Framtidsgatan 6, 262 73, Angelholm, Sweden **(100%)**
Tel.: (46) 431449050
Web Site: http://www.nolato.se
Sales Range: $25-49.9 Million
Develop Plastic Parts
N.A.I.C.S.: 326199

Nolato STG AB (1)
Hammarevagen 2, 280 70, Lonsboda, Sweden
Tel.: (46) 479252 00
Plastic Product Distr
N.A.I.C.S.: 424610

Nolato Silikonteknik AB (1)
Bergsmansvagen 4, PO Box 62, 694 22, Hallsberg, Sweden **(100%)**
Tel.: (46) 58288900
Web Site: http://www.nolato.se
Sales Range: $25-49.9 Million
Mfr of Injection-Moulded Components in Silicon Rubber
N.A.I.C.S.: 326199
Anders Ericsson (Mng Dir)

Nolato Stargard Sp. z o.o. (1)
ul Uslugowa 1, 73-110, Stargard Szczecinski, Poland
Tel.: (48) 915736362
Medical Device Mfr
N.A.I.C.S.: 339112

Nolato Sunne AB (1)
Sund Gate 21, PO Box 116, SE 686 23, Sunne, Sweden **(100%)**
Tel.: (46) 56517300
Sales Range: $25-49.9 Million
Emp.: 100
Mfr & Developer of Rubber Parts for Automotive Industry
N.A.I.C.S.: 326299
Jan Backstrom (Mgr-Mktg & Sls)

Nolato TEC AB (1)
Tegelbruksvagen 15, PO Box 2072, SE 291 02, Kristianstad, Sweden **(100%)**
Tel.: (46) 441860000
Web Site: http://www.nolato.se
Sales Range: $25-49.9 Million
Emp.: 60
Product Design, Development, Management, Industrializaion; Production of Prototypes & Series Production
N.A.I.C.S.: 326199

Nolato Technology (Dongguan) Co., Ltd. (1)
10 Building Ankang Street, Changan Town, Dongguan, China
Tel.: (86) 76985095789
Automation Equipment Mfr & Distr
N.A.I.C.S.: 336310

Nolato Torekov AB (1)
Nolatovagen 32, 269 78, Torekov, Sweden
Tel.: (46) 431442200
Web Site: http://www.nolato.se
Sales Range: $50-74.9 Million
Rubber & Plastic Products Mfr
N.A.I.C.S.: 326199

Nolato Treff AG (1)
Taastrasse 16, 9113, Degersheim, Switzerland
Tel.: (41) 713725555
Plastic Fabrication Mfr
N.A.I.C.S.: 326199

NOLET HOLDING B.V.
Hoofdstraat 14, Schiedam, 3114, Netherlands
Tel.: (31) 102462929
Web Site:
  https://www.noletdistillery.com
Emp.: 100
Holding Company

N.A.I.C.S.: 551112
Subsidiaries:

Nolet Distillery BV (1)
Hoofdstraat 14, Schiedam, 3114, Netherlands
Tel.: (31) 102462929
Web Site: http://www.noletdistillery.com
Sales Range: $300-349.9 Million
Emp.: 80
Vodka Mfr
N.A.I.C.S.: 312140

Subsidiary (US):

Nolet Spirits USA Inc. (2)
30 Journey, Aliso Viejo, CA 92656
Tel.: (949) 448-5700
Web Site: http://www.noletspirits.com
Rev.: $9,600,000
Emp.: 36
Spirits Distiller & Distributor
N.A.I.C.S.: 312130
Carolus Nolet Sr. (Owner)

NOLIT A.D.
Terazije no 27/II, Belgrade, Serbia
Tel.: (381) 113245017
Web Site: https://www.nolit.rs
Year Founded: 1951
NQLT—(BEL)
Sales Range: Less than $1 Million
Emp.: 37
Books Publishing Services
N.A.I.C.S.: 513130
Slavica Sas (Gen Mgr)

NOMAD FOODS LIMITED
43 Church Street West, Woking, GU21 6HT, Surrey, United Kingdom
Tel.: (44) 2089183200 VG
Web Site:
  https://www.nomadfoods.com
Year Founded: 2014
NOMD—(NYSE)
Rev.: $3,610,657,128
Assets: $7,769,969,064
Liabilities: $4,568,929,976
Net Worth: $3,201,039,088
Earnings: $306,814,352
Emp.: 7,535
Fiscal Year-end: 12/31/22
Investment Holding Company
N.A.I.C.S.: 551112
Noam Gottesman (Co-Founder & Chm)

Subsidiaries:

Birds Eye Ireland Limited (1)
Monread Road, IDA Industrial Estate, Naas, W91 HE67, Kildare, Ireland
Tel.: (353) 14133520
Web Site: https://www.birdseye.ie
Frozen Food Product Mfr & Distr
N.A.I.C.S.: 311412

C'S Three Co., Ltd. (1)
2-3-4 Daiba, Minato-ku, Tokyo, 135-0091, Japan
Tel.: (81) 359621336
Web Site: https://www.cs3.co.jp
Emp.: 63
Temporary Staffing Services
N.A.I.C.S.: 561320

Findus Danmark A/S (1)
Islevdalvej 214, 2610, Rodovre, Denmark
Tel.: (45) 70267670
Web Site: https://www.findusfoodservices.dk
Frozen Food Product Whslr
N.A.I.C.S.: 424420

Findus Espana S.L.U. (1)
Campezo Street 1 Building 4 3rd, Las Mercedes Business Park, 28022, Madrid, Spain
Tel.: (34) 911985300
Web Site: https://www.findus.es
Frozen Food Product Distr
N.A.I.C.S.: 424420

Findus Sverige AB (1)
Billesholmsvaegen 4, 267 40, Bjuv, Sweden
Tel.: (46) 4286000
Web Site: http://www.findus.se

Frozen Food Mfr
N.A.I.C.S.: 311411

Subsidiary (Non-US):

Findus Denmark A/S (2)
Ringager 4A, 2605, Brondby, Denmark
Tel.: (45) 70267670
Web Site: https://www.findusfoodservices.dk
Frozen Foods Mfr & Retailer
N.A.I.C.S.: 311411
Bjorn Zastrow (Sls Mgr)

Findus Finland Oy (2)
Taivaltie 5, 01610, Vantaa, Finland
Tel.: (358) 15581960
Web Site: https://www.findus.fi
Frozen Food Retailer
N.A.I.C.S.: 424420
Kai Makinen (CEO)

Findus France S.A.S. (2)
Jupiter building 11 Boulevard du Mont d'Est, 12 Boulevard du Mont d Est, 93192, Noisy-le-Grand, Cedex, France
Tel.: (33) 800000301
Web Site: https://www.findus.fr
Frozen Food Retailer
N.A.I.C.S.: 424420
Virginie Habermacher (Dir-Mktg)

Findus Norge AS (2)
Ertelokka 7, 1384, Asker, Norway
Tel.: (47) 66 85 40 00
Web Site: https://www.findus.no
Frozen Food Retailer
N.A.I.C.S.: 424420
Frank Hauge (Dir-Sls-Foodservice)

Findus Switzerland AG (1)
Industriestrasse 13/15, 9400, Rorschach, Switzerland
Tel.: (41) 718860111
Web Site: https://www.findus.ch
Frozen Food Product Mfr
N.A.I.C.S.: 311412

Frozen Fish International GmbH (1)
Am Lunedeich 115, 27572, Bremerhaven, Germany
Tel.: (49) 471926520
Web Site: https://www.frozenfish.de
Frozen Food Product Distr
N.A.I.C.S.: 424420
Philipp Kluck (Chm)

Iglo Austria GmbH (1)
Wienerbergstrasse 3, 1100, Vienna, Austria
Tel.: (43) 1608660
Web Site: https://www.iglo.at
Frozen Food Product Distr
N.A.I.C.S.: 424420

Iglo Nederland B.V. (1)
Van Deventerlaan 40, 3528 AE, Utrecht, Netherlands
Tel.: (31) 8002354456
Web Site: https://www.iglo.nl
Frozen Food Product Distr
N.A.I.C.S.: 424420

Iglo Netherlands B.V. (1)
Van Deventerlaan 40, 3528 AE, Utrecht, Netherlands
Tel.: (31) 881303900
Web Site: https://www.iglo.nl
Frozen Seafood Product Grocery Distr
N.A.I.C.S.: 486210

Nomad Foods Europe Holdings Limited (1)
No 1 New Square, Bedfont Lakes Business Park, Feltham, TW14 8HA, Mddx, United Kingdom **(100%)**
Tel.: (44) 2089183200
Holding Company; Frozen Foods Mfr & Whslr
N.A.I.C.S.: 551112

Subsidiary (Non-US):

Iglo Belgium S.A (2)
Techno Center Batiment C Boulevard del Humanite 235, 1620, Drogenbos, Belgium **(100%)**
Web Site: http://www.iglo.be
Frozen Foods Mfr & Distr
N.A.I.C.S.: 311999

Iglo GmbH (2)

Osterbekstrasse 90c, 22083, Hamburg, Germany
Tel.: (49) 401802490
Web Site: https://www.iglo.de
Frozen Food Mfr
N.A.I.C.S.: 424420
Markus Mischko (Mng Dir)

Subsidiary (Domestic):

Nomad Foods Europe Limited (1)
No 1 New Square, Bedfont Lakes Business Park, Feltham, TW14 8HA, Middlesex, United Kingdom
Tel.: (44) 2089183200
Frozen Food Mfr & Distr
N.A.I.C.S.: 311412

Nomura Duo Co., Ltd. (1)
4F Daiba Garden City Building 2-3-5 Daiba, Minato-ku, Tokyo, 135-0091, Japan
Tel.: (81) 364260043
Web Site: http://www.nomura-duo.co.jp
Emp.: 192
Construction Services
N.A.I.C.S.: 236220
Hiroyuki Kametani (Pres)

Nomura Products Co., Ltd. (1)
2-3-5 Daiba Garden City Building 5th Floor, Minato-ku, Tokyo, 135-0091, Japan
Tel.: (81) 364260023
Web Site: http://www.nomuraproducts.co.jp
Construction Services
N.A.I.C.S.: 236220

Nomura Techno Co., Ltd. (1)
2-3-5 Daiba Garden City Building 6th Floor, Minato-ku, Tokyo, 135-0091, Japan
Tel.: (81) 364260198
Web Site: http://www.nomura-techno.co.jp
Exhibition Services
N.A.I.C.S.: 561920

Square Co., Ltd. (1)
2-3-5 Daiba Garden City Building 5th Floor, Minato-ku, Tokyo, 135-0091, Japan
Tel.: (81) 364260164
Web Site: http://www.square-co.net
Architectural & Interior Design Services
N.A.I.C.S.: 541310

TNP Co., Ltd. (1)
1-12-17 Kamirenjaku, Mitaka, 181-0012, Tokyo, Japan
Tel.: (81) 422389031
Web Site: http://www.tnp-co.jp
Construction & Engineering Services
N.A.I.C.S.: 541330

Toppfrys AB (1)
Industrigatan 2, Bralanda, 464 62, Vanersborg, Sweden
Tel.: (46) 521277070
Web Site: https://www.toppfrys.se
Frozen Food Product Mfr
N.A.I.C.S.: 311412

NOMURA CO., LTD.

2-3-4 Daiba, Minato-ku, Tokyo, 135-8622, Japan
Tel.: (81) 359621171
Web Site:
    https://www.nomurakougei.co.jp
Year Founded: 1892
9716—(TKS)
Rev.: $951,038,420
Assets: $614,681,730
Liabilities: $258,012,190
Net Worth: $356,669,540
Earnings: $27,381,580
Emp.: 1,967
Fiscal Year-end: 02/29/24
Investment Management Service
N.A.I.C.S.: 523150
Masahiro Nakagawa (Sr VP)

Subsidiaries:

NOMURA (Beijing) Co., Ltd. (1)
Room 306 Business Building 01 2 Jiuxianqiao Road, Chaoyang District, Beijing, 100015, China
Tel.: (86) 1065667840
Web Site:
    https://www.nomurakougeisha.com.cn
Civil Engineering Services
N.A.I.C.S.: 541330

NOMURA DEVELOPMENT Co., Ltd. (1)
2-3-5 Daiba Daiba Garden City Building 4th floor, Minato-ku, Tokyo, 135-0091, Japan
Tel.: (81) 364260057
Web Site:
    http://www.nomuradevelopment.co.jp
Restaurant Operators
N.A.I.C.S.: 722511

NOMURA Design & Engineering Singapore Pte. Ltd. (1)
46 Craig Road, Singapore, 089684, Singapore
Tel.: (65) 6220 0883
Web Site: http://www.nomuradesign.sg
Event Management Services
N.A.I.C.S.: 711310
Takajiro Sano (Pres & CEO)

Rikuyosha Co., Ltd. (1)
2-3-4 Daiba, Minato-ku, Tokyo, 135-0091, Japan
Tel.: (81) 36 426 0131
Web Site: https://www.rikuyosha.co.jp
Online Book Publisher
N.A.I.C.S.: 513130

NOMURA HOLDINGS, INC.

13-1 Nihonbashi 1-chome, Chuo-ku, Tokyo, 103-8645, Japan
Tel.: (81) 352551000   JP
Web Site:
    https://www.nomuraholdings.com
NMR—(NYSE)
Rev.: $25,861,860,807
Assets: $343,061,926,311
Liabilities: $321,609,278,700
Net Worth: $21,452,647,611
Earnings: $1,102,457,265
Emp.: 26,850
Fiscal Year-end: 03/31/24
Bank Holding Company
N.A.I.C.S.: 551111
Koji Nagai (Chm)

Subsidiaries:

Chugokukogyo Co., Ltd. (1)
11-33 Kawai, Hatsukaichi, 738-0016, Hiroshima, Japan
Tel.: (81) 829311277
Web Site: https://www.chugoku-kogyo.com
Rev.: $88,124,520
Assets: $88,322,820
Liabilities: $51,617,490
Net Worth: $36,705,330
Earnings: $1,361,660
Fiscal Year-end: 03/31/2024
Gas Equipment Mfr & Whlsr
N.A.I.C.S.: 333132
Ryuichi Sakai (Pres & CEO)

Global Funds Management S.A. (1)
Building A-33 rue de Gasperich, 5826, Hesperange, Luxembourg
Tel.: (352) 283 7251
Web Site: https://www.gfmanagement.lu
Financial Investment Services
N.A.I.C.S.: 523999
Alan F. Crutchett (Chm)

Instinet Canada Limited (1)
121 King Street West Suite 1770, Toronto, MH5 3T9, ON, Canada
Tel.: (416) 368-2211
Financial Investment Services
N.A.I.C.S.: 523999

Instinet Pacific Ltd. (1)
31F 2 International Finance Center 8 Finance Street, Central, China (Hong Kong)
Tel.: (852) 2 585 0600
Financial Investment Services
N.A.I.C.S.: 523999

Instinet Singapore Services Pte. Ltd. (1)
Tower 2 10 Marina Boulevard 36-02 Marina Bay Financial Centre, Singapore, 018983, Singapore
Tel.: (65) 6 854 3400
Financial Investment Services
N.A.I.C.S.: 523999

N-Village Co., Ltd. (1)
Shibuya Nomura Building 9F 1-14-16 Shibuya, Shibuya-ku, Tokyo, 150-0002, Japan
Tel.: (81) 36 703 5331
Financial Investment Services
N.A.I.C.S.: 523999
Muneo Yoshihara (Pres)

Nomura Agri Planning & Advisory Co., Ltd. (1)
Urbannet Otemachi Building 20F 2-2-2 Otemachi, Chiyoda-ku, Tokyo, 100-8130, Japan
Tel.: (81) 332810780
Sales Range: $50-74.9 Million
Emp.: 13
Agricultural Financial Advisory Services
N.A.I.C.S.: 523940
Adsuyuki Sutono (Pres)

Subsidiary (Domestic):

Nomura Farm Co., Ltd. (2)
152 Soyama, Nanko-ku, Kochi, 783-0052, Japan
Tel.: (81) 888623205
Agricultural Crop Farming Services
N.A.I.C.S.: 111998
Nomura Katsumi (Gen Mgr)

Nomura America Services, LLC (1)
Worldwide Plz 309 W 49th St, New York, NY 10019-7316
Tel.: (212) 667-9000
Investment Management Service
N.A.I.C.S.: 523940

Nomura Asia Holding N.V. (1)
renbrandt power 94, anstelloin 1, 1096 HA, Amsterdam, Netherlands (100%)
Tel.: (31) 205999000
Sales Range: $1-9.9 Million
Emp.: 100
Investment & Financing Services Including Brokerage, Underwriting, Distribution & Trading Activities
N.A.I.C.S.: 523940

Subsidiary (Non-US):

Capital Nomura Securities Public Company Limited (2)
25 Bangkok Insurance Building 15th-17th Floor South Sathorn Road, Sathorn, Bangkok, 10120, Thailand
Tel.: (66) 26385000
Web Site: http://www.nomuradirect.com
Rev.: $56,944,179
Assets: $393,961,844
Liabilities: $223,251,100
Net Worth: $170,710,744
Earnings: $14,557,953
Emp.: 544
Fiscal Year-end: 12/31/2017
Investment, Securities & Other Financial Services
N.A.I.C.S.: 523150
Suthep Peetakanont (Chm)

Nomura Australia Limited (2)
Level 41 Governor Phillip Tower 1 Farrer Place, 1 Farra Pl, Sydney, 2000, NSW, Australia
Tel.: (61) 280628000
Investment & Financing Services Including Brokerage, Underwriting, Distribution & Trading Activities
N.A.I.C.S.: 523940

Subsidiary (Domestic):

Nomura Asset Management Australia Pty Limited (3)
Level 41 Governor Phillip Tower 1 Farrer Place, Sydney, 2000, NSW, Australia
Tel.: (61) 280628000
Asset Management Services
N.A.I.C.S.: 523940

Subsidiary (Non-US):

Nomura Capital (India) Private Limited (2)
Ceejay House 11th Level Plot F Shivsagar Estate Dr Annie Besant Road, Worli, Mumbai, 400 018, India
Tel.: (91) 2240374037
Consumer Lending Services
N.A.I.C.S.: 522291

Nomura Corporate Advisory (Shanghai) Ltd. (2)
725 7F Shanghai Central Plaza 381 Huai Hai Zhong Road, Shanghai, 200020, China
Tel.: (86) 2163916555
Investment Advisory Services
N.A.I.C.S.: 523940

Nomura Fin Services (India) Private Limited (2)
Nomura Bldg Off High Street Hiranandani Business Park, Powai, Mumbai, 400 076, India
Tel.: (91) 2230534626
Financial Management Services
N.A.I.C.S.: 523999

Nomura Financial Advisory and Securities (India) Private Limited (2)
Ceejay House Level 11 Plot F Shivsagar Estate Dr Annie Besant Road, Worli, Mumbai, 400 018, India
Tel.: (91) 2240374037
Emp.: 115
Financial Advisory Services
N.A.I.C.S.: 523940
Vikas Sharma (Pres & CEO)

Nomura Financial Investment (Korea) Co. Limited (2)
17th Fl Seoul Finance Center 136 Sejongdaero, Jung-gu, Seoul, 04520, Korea (South)
Tel.: (82) 237832000
Financial Investment Services
N.A.I.C.S.: 523999

Nomura Fixed Income Securities Private Limited (2)
Ceejay House Level 11 Plot F Shivsagar Estate Dr Annie Besant Road, Worli, Mumbai, 400 018, India
Tel.: (91) 2240374037
Securities Brokerage Services
N.A.I.C.S.: 523150

Nomura International (Hong Kong) Limited (2)
30/F 2 International Finance Centre, 8 Finance Street, Central, China (Hong Kong) (100%)
Tel.: (852) 25361111
Sales Range: $300-349.9 Million
Emp.: 1,000
International Investment Banking
N.A.I.C.S.: 523150

Subsidiary (Domestic):

Nomura (Hong Kong) Ltd (3)
30/F 2 International Finance Centre, 8 Finance Street, Central, China (Hong Kong) (100%)
Tel.: (852) 25361111
Sales Range: $150-199.9 Million
Emp.: 500
International Investment Banking
N.A.I.C.S.: 523150
Kenji Kimura (Global Head-Mergers & Acq)

Nomura Asia Ltd. (3)
30/F Two International Finance Centre, 8 Finance Street, Central, China (Hong Kong)
Tel.: (852) 25361720
Financial Services
N.A.I.C.S.: 523910

Subsidiary (Non-US):

Nomura Financial Advisory Co., Ltd. (4)
17th Floor No 1 Song Chi, Taipei, 11047, Taiwan
Tel.: (886) 221769999
Sales Range: $50-74.9 Million
Emp.: 55
N.A.I.C.S.: 523910
Amy Tsao (Gen Mgr)

Nomura Securities Investment Advisory Co., Ltd. (4)
14th Fl 109 Min-Sheng E Rd Sec 3, Taipei, Taiwan
Tel.: (886) 225479300
Sales Range: $50-74.9 Million
Emp.: 40
N.A.I.C.S.: 523910

Nomura Securities Philippines, Inc. (4)
18th Fl Tower 2 The Enterprise Ctr, Makati, 1200, Philippines (100%)

NOMURA HOLDINGS, INC.   INTERNATIONAL PUBLIC

Nomura Holdings, Inc.—(Continued)
Tel.: (63) 28865240
Web Site: http://www.nomura.com
Sales Range: $50-74.9 Million
Emp.: 10
Investment & Financing Services Including Brokerage, Underwriting, Distribution & Trading Activities
N.A.I.C.S.: 523940

Subsidiary (Domestic):

Nomura Futures (Hong Long) Limited (3)
30/F Two International Finanace Centre 8 Finance Street, Central, China (Hong Kong)
Tel.: (852) 25361111
Commodity Contracts Brokerage & Dealing Services
N.A.I.C.S.: 523160

Nomura Securities Hong Kong Limited (3)
2 International Finance Center, Central, China (Hong Kong) (100%)
Tel.: (852) 25361111
Web Site: http://www.nomura.com
Sales Range: $150-199.9 Million
Emp.: 255
International Investment Banking
N.A.I.C.S.: 523150

Subsidiary (Non-US):

Nomura Malaysia Sdn. Bhd (2)
Suite 16 3 Level 16 Menara IMC, 8 Jalan Sultan Ismail, 50250, Kuala Lumpur, Malaysia
Tel.: (60) 320276811
Web Site: http://www.nomura.com
Sales Range: $50-74.9 Million
Emp.: 30
Financial Investment Services
N.A.I.C.S.: 525990

Nomura Services India Private Limited (2)
Nomura Bldg Off High Street Hiranandani Business Park, Powai, Mumbai, 400 076, India
Tel.: (91) 2230534626
Financial Investment Services
N.A.I.C.S.: 523999

Nomura Singapore Limited (2)
10 Marina Boulevard Marina Bay Financial Centre Tower 2 36-01, Singapore, 018983, Singapore (100%)
Tel.: (65) 64336288
Sales Range: $75-99.9 Million
Emp.: 200
International Investment Banking
N.A.I.C.S.: 523150
Rig Karkhanis *(Deputy Head-Global Markets)*

Subsidiary (Domestic):

Nomura Commodities Singapore Pte. Ltd. (3)
6 Battery Road 34-01, Singapore, 049909, Singapore (100%)
Tel.: (65) 64201811
Sales Range: $100-124.9 Million
Emp.: 180
Commodity Contracts Brokerage & Dealing Services
N.A.I.C.S.: 523160

Nomura Securities Singapore Pte. Ltd. (3)
10 Marina Boulevard Marina Bay Financial Centre Tower 2 36-01, Singapore, 018983, Singapore (100%)
Tel.: (65) 64336288
Sales Range: $250-299.9 Million
Emp.: 300
N.A.I.C.S.: 523910

Subsidiary (Non-US):

Nomura Structured Finance Services Private Limited (2)
Nomura Bldg Off High Street Hiranandani Business Park, Powai, Mumbai, 400 076, India
Tel.: (91) 2230534626
Financial Management Services
N.A.I.C.S.: 523999

Nomura Trust Company (Singapore) Ltd (2)
10 Marina Boulevard Marina Bay Financial Centre Tower 2 36-01, Singapore, 018983, Singapore
Tel.: (65) 64336288
Financial Services
N.A.I.C.S.: 523999

P.T. Nomura Indonesia (2)
7th Fl The Daiwa Perdania Bank, Jl Jend Sudirman Kav 40 41, Jakarta, 10210, Indonesia (100%)
Tel.: (62) 215718888
Web Site: http://www.nomura.co.id
Sales Range: $25-49.9 Million
Emp.: 30
International Investment Banking
N.A.I.C.S.: 523150

Nomura Asset Management Co., Limited (1)
12th Fl Seoul Finance Center 136 Sejongdaero, Jung-gu, Seoul, 04520, Korea (South)
Tel.: (82) 23 783 2595
Financial Investment Services
N.A.I.C.S.: 523999

Nomura Asset Management Co., Ltd. (1)
2-2-1 Toyosu, Koto-ku, Tokyo, 135-0061, Japan (100%)
Tel.: (81) 363875000
Web Site: https://global.nomura-am.co.jp
Sales Range: $250-299.9 Million
Emp.: 856
Asset Management Services
N.A.I.C.S.: 523940
Akihiro Watanabe *(Sr Mng Dir)*

Subsidiary (Non-US):

Nomura Asset Management (Hong Kong) Limited (2)
30/F Two International Finance Centre 8 Finance Street, Central, China (Hong Kong) (100%)
Tel.: (852) 25248061
Web Site: https://www.nomura-am.co.jp
Sales Range: $50-74.9 Million
Emp.: 100
Asset Management Services
N.A.I.C.S.: 523940
Ogiwara Yasuaki *(Mng Dir)*

Nomura Asset Management (Singapore) Limited (2)
10 Marina Boulevard Marina Bay Financial Centre Tower 2 33-03, Singapore, 018983, Singapore (100%)
Tel.: (65) 64339088
Web Site: https://www.nomura-am.co.jp
Sales Range: $50-74.9 Million
Emp.: 50
Asset Management Services
N.A.I.C.S.: 523940

Nomura Asset Management (U.K.) Limited (2)
1 Angel Lane, London, EC4R 3AB, United Kingdom (100%)
Tel.: (44) 2075213333
Web Site: https://www.nomuraholdings.com
Sales Range: $50-74.9 Million
Emp.: 50
Asset Management Services
N.A.I.C.S.: 523940

Nomura Asset Management Deutschland KAG mbH (2)
Grafstrasse 109, 60487, Frankfurt am Main, Germany
Tel.: (49) 69153093020
Web Site: https://www.nomura-asset.eu
Sales Range: $25-49.9 Million
Emp.: 40
Asset Management Services
N.A.I.C.S.: 523940

Nomura Asset Management Malaysia Sdn. Bhd. (2)
Suite 12 2 12 3 Level 12 Menara IMC 8 Jalan Sultan Ismail, 50250, Kuala Lumpur, Malaysia
Tel.: (60) 320276688
Web Site: https://www.nomura-asset.com.my
Emp.: 32

Asset Management Services
N.A.I.C.S.: 523940
Nor Rejina Rahim *(Mng Dir)*

Subsidiary (US):

Nomura Asset Management U.S.A. Inc. (2)
309 W 49th St 9th Fl, New York, NY 10019-7316
Tel.: (212) 667-1414
Web Site: https://www.nomura-asset.com
Sales Range: $50-74.9 Million
Emp.: 60
Asset Management Services
N.A.I.C.S.: 523940

Nomura Asset Management Europe KVG mbH (1)
Grafstrasse 109, 60487, Frankfurt am Main, Germany
Tel.: (49) 6915 309 3020
Web Site: https://www.nomura-asset.eu
Emp.: 35
Asset Management Services
N.A.I.C.S.: 523940
Magnus Fielko *(CEO & Mng Dir)*

Nomura Babcock & Brown Co., Ltd. (1)
Tornare Nihonbashi Hamacho 5F, 3-3-2 Nihonbashi Hama-cho Chuo-ku, Tokyo, 103 0007, Japan
Tel.: (81) 367572500
Web Site: https://www.nomuraholdings.com
Sales Range: $50-74.9 Million
Emp.: 50
Investment Bank Specializing in Structuring, Arranging & Managing Project Based International Financing with an Emphasis on Lease Financing
N.A.I.C.S.: 523150

Nomura Business Services Co., Ltd. (1)
2-2-1 Toyosu, Koto-ku, Tokyo, 135-0061, Japan (100%)
Tel.: (81) 367415000
Web Site: https://www.nomuraholdings.com
Investment & Financing Services Including Brokerage, Underwriting, Distribution & Trading Activities
N.A.I.C.S.: 523150

Nomura Capital Investment Co., Ltd. (1)
Urbannet Otemachi Building 13 2-2-2 Otemachi, Chiyoda-ku, Tokyo, 100 8130, Japan
Tel.: (81) 367467050
Web Site: https://www.nomuraholdings.com
Sales Range: $75-99.9 Million
Emp.: 45
N.A.I.C.S.: 523910

Nomura Capital Partners Co. Ltd. (1)
2-2-2 Otemachi Urban Net Otemachi Building 14F, Chiyoda-ku, Tokyo, Japan
Tel.: (81) 36 838 4750
Web Site: https://www.nomura-capital.com
Investment Fund Services
N.A.I.C.S.: 523940

Nomura Europe Holdings plc (1)
One Angel Lane, London, EC4R 3AB, United Kingdom (100%)
Tel.: (44) 2071021000
Sales Range: $1-4.9 Billion
Emp.: 4,300
Holding Company; Regional Managing Office
N.A.I.C.S.: 551112
Jonathan Lewis *(CEO, Chief Admin Officer & Head-IT-Grp)*

Subsidiary (Non-US):

Banque Nomura France (2)
7 Place d'Iena, 75773, Paris, Cedex, France (100%)
Tel.: (33) 153893000
Sales Range: $10-24.9 Million
Emp.: 100
Banking Services
N.A.I.C.S.: 522110

Nomura Bank (Deutschland) GmbH (2)
Rathenauplatz 1, 60313, Frankfurt am Main, Germany
Tel.: (49) 69975080
International Banking
N.A.I.C.S.: 522110

Nomura Bank (Luxembourg) S.A. (2)
33 Rue Ge Gasterich, PO Box 2012, 5826, Luxembourg, Luxembourg
Tel.: (352) 4638888
Sales Range: $75-99.9 Million
Emp.: 250
International Banking
N.A.I.C.S.: 522299

Subsidiary (Domestic):

Nomura Advisory Company S.A. (3)
2, Boulevard Royal, L-2449, Luxembourg, Luxembourg
Tel.: (352) 471921
N.A.I.C.S.: 523910

Subsidiary (Non-US):

Nomura Bank (Switzerland) Ltd. (2)
Kasernenstrasse 1, CH-8021, Zurich, Switzerland
Tel.: (41) 442957111
Sales Range: $25-49.9 Million
Emp.: 50
International Banking
N.A.I.C.S.: 522299

Subsidiary (Domestic):

Nomura Bank International PLC (2)
1 Angel Lane, London, EC4R 3AB, United Kingdom (100%)
Tel.: (44) 2071021000
Sales Range: $600-649.9 Million
Emp.: 1,500
International Investment Banking
N.A.I.C.S.: 523150

Nomura International plc (2)
1 Angel Lane, London, EC4R 3AB, United Kingdom (100%)
Tel.: (44) 2071021000
Sales Range: $600-649.9 Million
Emp.: 1,500
International Investment Banking
N.A.I.C.S.: 523150
Arif Merali *(Mng Dir & Head-Swaps Trading)*

Subsidiary (Non-US):

Nomura Corporate Advisory (Central Europe) Ltd. (3)
Eastwest Business Ctr 7th Fl, 1088, Budapest, Hungary (100%)
Tel.: (36) 0012355200
Web Site: http://www.nomura.com
Sales Range: Less than $1 Million
Emp.: 2
Investment Advisory Services
N.A.I.C.S.: 523940

Nomura Corporate Advisory CEE Sp. z o.o. (3)
ul Emilii Plater 53, 00 113, Warsaw, Poland
Tel.: (48) 228500816
Emp.: 4
Investment Advisory Services
N.A.I.C.S.: 523940

Subsidiary (Non-US):

Nomura Investment Banking (Middle East) B.S.C. (2)
7th Floor BMB Centre Diplomatic Area, PO Box 26893, Manama, Bahrain
Tel.: (973) 17 530531
Web Site: http://www.nomuraholdings.com
Investment Banking Services
N.A.I.C.S.: 523150

Nomura Italia S.I.M. p.A. (2)
Via Palestro 2, 20121, Milan, Italy
Tel.: (39) 02 7646 4800
Sales Range: $50-74.9 Million
Emp.: 24
Wealth & Asset Management
N.A.I.C.S.: 523910

Nomura Nederland N.V. (2)
Renbrandd Tower Amstelplein 1 Fl 19, 1096 HA, Amsterdam, Netherlands (100%)
Tel.: (31) 205999000
Web Site: http://www.nomura.com

AND PRIVATE COMPANIES

Sales Range: $1-9.9 Million
Emp.: 26
International Banking
N.A.I.C.S.: 522299

Nomura Saudi Arabia (2)
PO Box 301060, Riyadh, 11372, Saudi Arabia
Tel.: (966) 1215 5902
Financial Management Services
N.A.I.C.S.: 523999

Nomura Sweden AB (2)
Birger Jarlsgatan 27 5th Floor, 111 45, Stockholm, Sweden
Tel.: (46) 8 5056 1800
Emp.: 3
Financial Management Services
N.A.I.C.S.: 523999
Adrian Brady *(Gen Mgr)*

OOO Nomura (2)
21st Floor Block C Naberezhnaya Tower Presnenskaya Nab 10, 123317, Moscow, Russia
Tel.: (7) 4956636000
Web Site: http://www.nomura.com
Financial Advisory Services
N.A.I.C.S.: 523940

Nomura Facilities, Inc. (1)
1 7 2 Nihonbashi Honcho Chuo Ku, Tokyo, 103 0023, Japan (100%)
Tel.: (81) 332316261
Web Site: http://www.nomura-f.co.jp
Emp.: 83
Real Estate Services
N.A.I.C.S.: 531210
Jozuka Junichi *(Pres)*

Nomura Financial Products & Services, Inc. (1)
Urbannet Otemachi Building 18F 2-2-2 Otemachi, Chiyoda-ku, Tokyo, 100-8130, Japan
Tel.: (81) 36 746 7222
Financial Investment Services
N.A.I.C.S.: 523999
Kenji Tsuge *(Pres)*

Nomura Financial Products Europe GmbH (1)
Rathenauplatz 1, 60313, Frankfurt am Main, Germany
Tel.: (49) 6 997 5080
Financial Investment Services
N.A.I.C.S.: 523999

Nomura Funds Research & Technologies Co., Ltd. (1)
16F Nihonbashi Hamacho F-Tower 3-21-1 Nihonbashi Hama-cho, Chuo-ku, Tokyo, 103-0007, Japan
Tel.: (81) 36 367 3260
Web Site: https://www.nfrt.co.jp
Investment Advisory Services
N.A.I.C.S.: 523940
Akikazu Matsuda *(Pres)*

Nomura Global Funding plc (1)
(100%)
Tel.: (44) 2075212000
Web Site: http://www.nomura.com
Sales Range: $50-74.9 Million
Emp.: 100
Financial Services
N.A.I.C.S.: 523999

Subsidiary (Non-US):

Nomura Europe Finance N.V. (2)
Tel.: (31) 205612800
Investment Financing Services
N.A.I.C.S.: 525990

Nomura Greentech Capital Advisors, AG (1)
Bahnhofstrasse 26, 8001, Zurich, Switzerland
Tel.: (41) 44 578 3900
Financial Investment Services
N.A.I.C.S.: 523999

Nomura Healthcare Co., Ltd. (1)
Urbannet Otemachi Building 20F 2-2-2 Otemachi, Chiyoda-ku, Tokyo, 100-8130, Japan (100%)
Tel.: (81) 352551024
Web Site: https://www.nomuraholdings.com
Emp.: 30

Healthcare Financial Management Services
N.A.I.C.S.: 523999

Nomura Holding America Inc. (1)
Pl 309 W 49th St, New York, NY 10019-7316
Tel.: (212) 667-9300
Sales Range: $350-399.9 Million
Emp.: 770
Financial Holding Company; Securities & Investment Banking Services
N.A.I.C.S.: 551111

Subsidiary (Domestic):

Instinet Incorporated (2)
309 W 49th St Worldwide Pl, New York, NY 10019 (100%)
Tel.: (212) 310-9500
Sales Range: $350-399.9 Million
Emp.: 605
Holding Company; Global Equity Markets Trading Technology & Services
N.A.I.C.S.: 551112
Faron Webb *(Gen Counsel)*

Subsidiary (Non-US):

Instinet Europe Ltd. (3)
1 Angel Lane, London, EC4 R3AB, United Kingdom
Tel.: (44) 2071548400
Sales Range: $200-249.9 Million
Emp.: 350
Equity Markets Trading Technology & Services
N.A.I.C.S.: 523150
Richard Parsons *(CEO)*

Subsidiary (Domestic):

Instinet, LLC (3)
309 W 49th St Worldwide Pl, New York, NY 10019 (100%)
Tel.: (212) 310-9500
Sales Range: $200-249.9 Million
Emp.: 300
Equity Markets Trading Technology & Services
N.A.I.C.S.: 523150
Faron Webb *(Gen Counsel)*

Subsidiary (Domestic):

Nomura America Mortgage Finance, LLC (2)
309 W 49th St Worldwide Pl, New York, NY 10019
Tel.: (212) 667-9000
Financial Management Services
N.A.I.C.S.: 523999

Subsidiary (Non-US):

Nomura Canada Inc. (2)
145 King Street West Suite 2701, Toronto, M5H 1J8, ON, Canada
Tel.: (416) 868-1683
Web Site: http://www.nomura.com
International Investment Banking
N.A.I.C.S.: 523150

Subsidiary (Domestic):

Nomura Corporate Research and Asset Management Inc. (2)
309 W 49th St Worldwide Pl, New York, NY 10019
Tel.: (212) 667-9300
Investment Management Service
N.A.I.C.S.: 523940

Nomura Credit and Capital Inc. (2)
309 W 49th St Worldwide Pl, New York, NY 10019
Tel.: (212) 667-9000
Web Site: http://www.nourma.com
Emp.: 1,000
Financial Management Services
N.A.I.C.S.: 523999

Nomura International Trust Company (2)
309 West 49th St, New York, NY 10019
Tel.: (212) 667-9000
Financial Transaction Processing Services
N.A.I.C.S.: 522320

Nomura Securities International, Inc. (2)

309 W 49th St Worldwide Pl, New York, NY 10019
Tel.: (212) 667-9000
Sales Range: $400-449.9 Million
Emp.: 1,000
Securities & Investment Banking Services
N.A.I.C.S.: 523150
James DeNaut *(CEO)*

Subsidiary (Domestic):

Nomura America Securities, LLC (3)
309 W 49th St Worldwide Pl, New York, NY 10019
Tel.: (212) 667-9000
Securities Brokerage Services
N.A.I.C.S.: 523150

Nomura Asset Capital Corporation (3)
309 W 49th St Worldwide Pl, New York, NY 10019
Tel.: (212) 667-9000
Sales Range: $350-399.9 Million
Emp.: 1,000
Asset Management & Investment Services
N.A.I.C.S.: 523150
Koji Nagai *(Mgr)*

Nomura Derivative Products, Inc. (3)
309 W 49th St, New York, NY 10019-7316
Tel.: (212) 667-9416
Sales Range: $50-74.9 Million
Emp.: 2
Structured Financial Services
N.A.I.C.S.: 523150
Richard Lunder *(COO)*

Nomura Funds Research & Technologies America, Inc. (3)
309 W 49th St Worldwide Pl, New York, NY 10019-7316 (100%)
Tel.: (212) 667-9000
Sales Range: $50-74.9 Million
Emp.: 20
Research Funding
N.A.I.C.S.: 523150

Nomura Global Financial Products, Inc. (3)
309 W 49th St Worldwide Pl, New York, NY 10019-7316
Tel.: (212) 667-9000
Sales Range: $75-99.9 Million
Emp.: 100
N.A.I.C.S.: 523910

Subsidiary (Non-US):

Nomura Securities (Bermuda) Ltd. (3)
Wellesley House First Floor 90 Pitts Bay Road, Pembroke, HM 08, Bermuda
Tel.: (441) 2964050
Sales Range: $50-74.9 Million
Emp.: 4
Investment & Financing Services Including Brokerage, Underwriting, Distribution & Trading Activities
N.A.I.C.S.: 523940

Branch (Non-US):

Nomura Securities International, Inc. - Brazil (3)
Av Brigadeiro Faria Lima 4440, 12th Fl I cj, Sao Paulo, 121 04538-132, SP, Brazil
Tel.: (55) 1144801140
Sales Range: Less than $1 Million
Emp.: 3
Investment & Financing Services Including Brokerage, Underwriting, Distribution & Trading Activities
N.A.I.C.S.: 523940

Nomura Infrastructure Investment Advisors Private Limited (1)
Ceejay House Level 11 Plot F Shivsagar Estate Dr Annie Besant Road, Worli, Mumbai, 400 018, India
Tel.: (91) 224 037 4037
Financial Investment Services
N.A.I.C.S.: 523999

Nomura Institute of Capital Markets Research, Ltd. (1)
Urban Net Otemachi Building 18F 2-2-2 Otemachi, Chiyoda-ku, Tokyo, 100-8130, Japan
Tel.: (81) 366367050

NOMURA HOLDINGS, INC.

Web Site: https://www.nomuraholdings.com
Capital Market Research Consulting Services
N.A.I.C.S.: 541910

Nomura Investment Management (Shanghai) Co., Ltd. (1)
Room 725 Shanghai Central Plaza 381 Huaihai Zhong Road, Shanghai, 200020, China
Tel.: (86) 216 081 5000
Financial Investment Services
N.A.I.C.S.: 523999

Nomura Investments (Singapore) Pte. Limited (1)
10 Marina Boulevard Marina Bay Financial Centre Tower 2 36-01, Singapore, 018983, Singapore
Tel.: (65) 6 433 6288
Financial Investment Services
N.A.I.C.S.: 523999

Nomura Investor Relations Co., Ltd. (1)
13th floor Urbannet Otemachi Building 2-2-2 Otemachi, Chiyoda-ku, Tokyo, 100-8130, Japan
Tel.: (81) 332763600
Web Site: https://www.nomura-ir.co.jp
Sales Range: $50-74.9 Million
Emp.: 70
Investment Company
N.A.I.C.S.: 523150

Nomura Islamic Asset Management Sdn. Bhd. (1)
Suite 12 3 Level 12 Menara IMC 8 Jalan Sultan Ismail, 50250, Kuala Lumpur, Malaysia
Tel.: (60) 32 027 6668
Financial Investment Services
N.A.I.C.S.: 523999

Nomura Kagayaki Co., Ltd. (1)
2-2-1 Toyosu, Koto-ku, Tokyo, 135-0061, Japan
Tel.: (81) 36 741 6340
Employment Services
N.A.I.C.S.: 561311
Yasuaki Tanaka *(Pres)*

Nomura Land and Building Co., Ltd. (1)
1-7-2 Nihonbashi-honcho, Chuo-ku, Tokyo, 103-0023, Japan
Tel.: (81) 332311901
Sales Range: $50-74.9 Million
Emp.: 10
Real Estate Development Services
N.A.I.C.S.: 531390

Nomura Mezzanine Partners Co., Ltd. (1)
23rd Floor Otemachi Nomura Building 2-1-1 Otemachi, Chiyoda-ku, Tokyo, 100-0004, Japan
Tel.: (81) 36 838 4650
Web Site: https://www.nomura-mez.com
Investment Fund Services
N.A.I.C.S.: 523940

Nomura Pension Support & Service Co., Ltd. (1)
Urban Net Otemachi Building 18F 2-2-2 Otemachi, Chiyoda-ku, Tokyo, 100 0004, Japan
Tel.: (81) 332750401
Web Site: http://www.n-sas.co.jp
Sales Range: $25-49.9 Million
Emp.: 80
Retirement Benefit Consulting, Pension Plan Administration Services & Support Services for Calculating Projected Benefits
N.A.I.C.S.: 541611

Nomura Philippines, Inc. (1)
18F Tower II The Enterprise Center 6766 Ayala Avenue, Corner Paseo de Roxas, Makati, 1200, Philippines
Tel.: (63) 2 886 5240
Financial Investment Services
N.A.I.C.S.: 523999

Nomura Principal Finance Co., Ltd. (1)
Urban Net Otemachi Bldg 13F 2-2-2 Otemachi, Tokyo, 100-8130, Chiyoda-ku, Japan (100%)

NOMURA HOLDINGS, INC.

Nomura Holdings, Inc.—(Continued)
Tel.: (81) 332780243
Sales Range: $50-74.9 Million
Emp.: 46
Private Investment Firm
N.A.I.C.S.: 523999

Joint Venture (Domestic):

RESOL HOLDINGS Co., Ltd. (2)
6-24-1 Nishi-Shinjuku, Shinjuku-Ku, Tokyo, 160 0023, Japan
Tel.: (81) 333448811
Web Site: http://www.resol.jp
Rev.: $169,989,370
Assets: $284,249,830
Liabilities: $187,307,570
Net Worth: $96,942,260
Earnings: $9,326,710
Emp.: 1,796
Fiscal Year-end: 03/31/2024
Holding Company; Resort Related & Development Business
N.A.I.C.S.: 551112
Hideaki Hirata (Chm & CEO)

Nomura Private Equity Capital Co., Ltd. (1)
1-7-9 Nihonbashi, Chuo-ku, Tokyo, 103-0027, Japan
Tel.: (81) 3 6214 2240
Web Site: http://www.npec.co.jp
Sales Range: $100-124.9 Million
Emp.: 2
Equity Fund Management Services
N.A.I.C.S.: 523940
Kazuo Nishimura (Chief Investment Officer & Co-Mng Dir)

Nomura Properties, Inc. (1)
1-7-2 Nihonbashihoncho, Chuo-ku, Tokyo, 103-0023, Japan
Tel.: (81) 33 231 6261
Web Site: https://www.nomura-p.co.jp
Facility Management Services
N.A.I.C.S.: 561210

Nomura Reinsurance Intermediary Inc. (1)
Worldwide Plz 309 W 49th St, New York, NY 10019-7316
Tel.: (212) 667-1342
Investment Management Service
N.A.I.C.S.: 523940

Nomura Research & Advisory Co., Ltd. (1)
Urbannet Otemachi Building 17F 2-2-2 Otemachi, Chiyoda-ku, Tokyo, 100 8130, Japan (100%)
Tel.: (81) 366367001
Web Site: https://www.nomuraholdings.com
Sales Range: $50-74.9 Million
Emp.: 28
Investment & Financing Services Including Brokerage, Underwriting, Distribution & Trading Activities
N.A.I.C.S.: 523150

Nomura Securities Co., Ltd. (1)
1-13-1 Nihonbashi, Chuo-Ku, Tokyo, 103 8011, Japan (100%)
Tel.: (81) 332111811
Web Site: https://www.nomura.co.jp
Provider of Investment & Financing Services Including Brokerage, Underwriting, Distribution & Trading Activities
N.A.I.C.S.: 523150
Koji Nagai (Chm)

Affiliate (Domestic):

Nippon Clearing Services Co., Ltd. (2)
6 7 Nihonbashi Koamicho, Chuo Ku, Tokyo, 103 0016, Japan
Tel.: (81) 336636751
N.A.I.C.S.: 523910

Subsidiary (Domestic):

Nomura China Investment Co., Ltd. (2)
1-7-2 Nihonbashi-honcho new Edorbasi Bldg, Chuo-ku, Tokyo, 103 0023, Japan
Tel.: (81) 332744608
Sales Range: $50-74.9 Million
Emp.: 7
Investment Company

N.A.I.C.S.: 523150
Kamezo Nakai (Pres)

Nomura Securities Malaysia Sdn. Bhd. (1)
Suite 16 5 Level 16 Menara IMC 8 Jalan Sultan Ismail, 50250, Kuala Lumpur, Malaysia
Tel.: (60) 32 027 6811
Financial Investment Services
N.A.I.C.S.: 523999

P.T. Nomura Sekuritas Indonesia (1)
Suite 209A 9th Floor Sentral Senayan II Building, Jl Asia Afrika No 8 Gelora Bung Karno, Jakarta, 10270, Indonesia
Tel.: (62) 212 991 3300
Financial Investment Services
N.A.I.C.S.: 523999
Masayuki Sekizuka (Co-Pres & Commissioner)

The Nomura Trust & Banking Co., Ltd. (1)
Urban Net Otemachi Building 19F 2-2-2 Otemachi, Chiyoda-ku, Tokyo, 100-0004, Japan
Tel.: (81) 352021600
Web Site: https://www.nomuraholdings.com
Investment Banking Services
N.A.I.C.S.: 523150

Subsidiary (Domestic):

HITO-Communications, Inc. (2)
1-9-6 Higashi-Ikebukuro, Toshima-ku, Tokyo, 170-0013, Japan (83%)
Tel.: (81) 359521111
Web Site: https://hitocom.co.jp
Rev.: $553,419,360
Assets: $172,192,080
Liabilities: $84,599,760
Net Worth: $87,592,320
Earnings: $13,035,840
Emp.: 200
Fiscal Year-end: 08/31/2018
Outsourcing & Staffing Services
N.A.I.C.S.: 561320
Toyomi Yasui (Pres)

Unified Partners, Ltd (1)
13th Floor Urban Net Ootemachi Building 2-2-2 Ootemachi, Chiyoda-ku, Tokyo, 100-8130, Japan
Tel.: (81) 358607201
Real Estate Financial Leasing Services
N.A.I.C.S.: 522220

NOMURA MICRO SCIENCE CO., LTD.
2-9-8 Okata, Atsugi, 243-0021, Kanagawa, Japan
Tel.: (81) 462283946
Web Site: https://www.nomura-nms.co.jp
Year Founded: 1969
6254—(TKS)
Rev.: $482,668,810
Assets: $466,679,220
Liabilities: $275,491,580
Net Worth: $191,187,640
Earnings: $52,734,580
Emp.: 343
Fiscal Year-end: 03/31/24
Water Purification Equipment Mfr
N.A.I.C.S.: 221310
Toyosaku Senda (Chm & Chm)

Subsidiaries:

Agru Plastics Co., Ltd. (1)
2-4-5 Okada, Atsugi, 243-0021, Kanagawa, Japan
Tel.: (81) 462270653
Web Site: https://www.agru-pla.co.jp
Sales Range: $25-49.9 Million
Emp.: 9
Plastic Sales & Services
N.A.I.C.S.: 326199

Nomura Korea Co., Ltd. (1)
5F 105 3 Ace B/D Imae Dong Bundang ku, Seongnam, 463 829, Kyeongki-Do, Korea (South)
Tel.: (82) 317083946
Web Site: http://www.nomura-nms.co.jp

Sales Range: $50-74.9 Million
Emp.: 34
Pure Water Systems Mfr
N.A.I.C.S.: 221310
Saeki Tetsuo (Pres)

Nomura Micro Science U.S.A. Ltd., Co. (1)
1006 E Yager Ln Ste B203, Austin, TX 78753
Tel.: (512) 873-0084
Web Site: http://www.nomura-nms.co
Emp.: 300
Pure Water System Services
N.A.I.C.S.: 221310

Shanghai Nichimura Trading Co.,Ltd. (1)
Rm G08 No 215 Futebei Rd Waigaoqiao Free Trade Zone, Shanghai, 200131, China
Tel.: (86) 2158681571
Sales Range: $50-74.9 Million
Emp.: 30
Pure Water Systems Mfr
N.A.I.C.S.: 221310

Shanghai Nomura Engineering Co., Ltd. (1)
Room 601 Building I Xin Yi Cheng 1618 YiShan Road, Min Hang District, Shanghai, China (100%)
Tel.: (86) 2162625622
Web Site: http://www.nomura-nms.co.jp
Supply & Maintenance of Equipment & Consumables for Ultra Pure Water & Waste Water Disposal Systems
N.A.I.C.S.: 221310
Tsuyoshi Takamori (Pres)

NOMURA REAL ESTATE HOLDINGS, INC.
Shinjuku Nomura Building 1-26-2 Nishi-Shinjuku, Shinjuku-ku, Tokyo, 163-0566, Japan
Tel.: (81) 333488117
Web Site: https://www.nomura-re-hd.co.jp
Year Founded: 1957
3231—(TKS)
Rev.: $4,856,466,150
Assets: $14,882,124,160
Liabilities: $10,305,095,760
Net Worth: $4,577,028,400
Earnings: $450,564,040
Emp.: 7,929
Fiscal Year-end: 03/31/24
Real Estate Holding Company
N.A.I.C.S.: 551112
Seiichi Miyajima (COO & Exec VP)

Subsidiaries:

First Living Assistance Co., Ltd. (1)
6-26-12 Nishi-Shinjuku, Shinjuku-ku, Tokyo, 160-0023, Japan
Tel.: (81) 33 344 3951
Web Site: https://www.f-la.co.jp
Real Estate Services
N.A.I.C.S.: 531390

Lothbury Investment Management Limited (1)
1 Angel Lane, London, EC4R 3AB, United Kingdom
Tel.: (44) 203 551 4900
Web Site: https://www.lothburyim.com
Real Estate Services
N.A.I.C.S.: 531390
Simon Radford (CEO)

MEGALOS Co., Ltd. (1)
Harmony Tower 15th floor 1-32-2 Honmachi, Nakano-ku, Tokyo, 150-0022, Japan (95.52%)
Tel.: (81) 353348600
Web Site: https://www.megalos.co.jp
Emp.: 639
Sports Clubs, Golf Ranges, Tennis & Other Sports Training Schools Owner & Operator; Sports Retailer
N.A.I.C.S.: 713940

NREG Toshiba Building Co., Ltd. (1)
1-1-1 Shibaura, Minato-ku, Tokyo, 105 6691, Japan (95%)
Tel.: (81) 334578800

INTERNATIONAL PUBLIC

Sales Range: $1-4.9 Billion
Emp.: 3,000
Property Development, Leasing & Management Services
N.A.I.C.S.: 531190

Subsidiary (Domestic):

Toshiba Building & Lease Co., Ltd. (2)
1 8 4 Shibakoen, Minato-ku, Tokyo, 105 0011, Japan
Tel.: (81) 354058700
Sales Range: $50-74.9 Million
Emp.: 100
Provider of Real Estate Services
N.A.I.C.S.: 531390

Nomura Real Estate Asset Management Co., Ltd. (1)
Nomura Fudosan Nishi-Shinjuku Kyodo Building 8-5-1, Nishi-Shinjuku Shinjuku-ku, Tokyo, 160-0023, Japan
Tel.: (81) 33 365 8666
Web Site: https://www.nre-am.co.jp
Emp.: 161
Investment Management Service
N.A.I.C.S.: 523940

Nomura Real Estate Development Co., Ltd. (1)
Shinjuku Nomura Building 1-26-2 Nishishinjuku, Shinjuku-ku, Tokyo, 163-0566, Japan (100%)
Tel.: (81) 333488811
Web Site: https://www.nomura-re.co.jp
Sales Range: $650-699.9 Million
Emp.: 1,997
Real Estate
N.A.I.C.S.: 531210

Prime X Co., Ltd. (1)
6-22-1 Shinjuku Square Tower 12th and 17th Floors Reception Desk, Nishi-Shinjuku, Shinjuku-ku, Tokyo, 163-1112, Japan
Tel.: (81) 33 348 0711
Web Site: https://www.prime-x.co.jp
Advertising Agencies Services
N.A.I.C.S.: 541810

Tokio Property Services Pte. Ltd. (1)
20 Kramat Lane 03-12 United House, Singapore, 228773, Singapore
Tel.: (65) 6 737 5187
Web Site: https://www.tokioproperty.com.sg
Real Estate Agency Services
N.A.I.C.S.: 531210
Toru Takano (Mng Dir)

NOMURA REAL ESTATE MASTER FUND, INC.
8-5-1 Nishi-Shinjuku, Shinjuku-ku, Tokyo, Japan
Tel.: (81) 33658708
Web Site: https://www.nre-mf.co.jp
3462—(TKS)
Sales Range: Less than $1 Million
Investment Management Service
N.A.I.C.S.: 525990
Shuhei Yoshida (Exec Dir)

NOMURA RESEARCH INSTITUTE, LTD.
Otemachi Financial City Grand Cube 1-9-2 Otemachi, Chiyoda-ku, Tokyo, 100-0004, Japan
Tel.: (81) 355332111 JP
Web Site: https://www.nri.com
Year Founded: 1965
4307—(TKS)
Rev.: $4,868,635,160
Assets: $6,099,529,530
Liabilities: $3,435,560,720
Net Worth: $2,663,968,810
Earnings: $526,440,230
Emp.: 7,206
Fiscal Year-end: 03/31/24
Information Technology Solutions Services
N.A.I.C.S.: 541512
Hajime Ueda (Sr Exec Mng Dir)

Subsidiaries:

ASG Group Limited (1)

AND PRIVATE COMPANIES

NOMURA RESEARCH INSTITUTE, LTD.

Level 9 167 St George's Terrace, Perth, 6000, WA, Australia **(100%)**
Tel.: (61) 871233190
Web Site: https://www.asggroup.com.au
Emp.: 2,029
IT Services & Business Solutions
N.A.I.C.S.: 541990
Geoffrey Lewis *(Founder)*

Subsidiary (Domestic):

Dowling Consulting Pty Ltd **(2)**
Level 3 312 St Kilda Road, Melbourne, 3056, VIC, Australia **(100%)**
Tel.: (61) 385985569
Web Site: http://dowlingconsulting.net.au
Management Consulting Services
N.A.I.C.S.: 541611

SMS Management & Technology Limited **(2)**
Level 41 140 William Street, Melbourne, 3000, VIC, Australia
Tel.: (61) 396743333
Rev.: $237,631,107
Assets: $101,863,311
Liabilities: $36,608,103
Net Worth: $65,255,208
Earnings: ($32,816,483)
Emp.: 1,400
Fiscal Year-end: 06/30/2017
Management & Technology Consulting Services
N.A.I.C.S.: 541618
Rick Rostolis *(CEO)*

Cutter Associates Europe Ltd. **(1)**
84 Eccleston Square, Pimlico, London, SW1V 1PX, United Kingdom
Tel.: (44) 203 961 9910
Financial Investment Services
N.A.I.C.S.: 523999

DSB Co., Ltd. **(1)**
DSB Group Shiomi Building 2-9-15 Shiomi, Koto-ku, Tokyo, 135-0052, Japan **(100%)**
Tel.: (81) 356653040
Web Site: https://www.daiko-sb.co.jp
Sales Range: $200-249.9 Million
Emp.: 644
Securities Related Services
N.A.I.C.S.: 523150
Etsuo Misonou *(Pres)*

Subsidiary (Domestic):

Fujisoft Dis Co., Ltd. **(2)**
NK Building 2-7 Kanda-Sudacho, Chiyoda-ku, 101-0041, Tokyo, Japan
Tel.: (81) 352097351
Data Processing Hosting & Related Services
N.A.I.C.S.: 518210

KCS Co., Ltd. **(2)**
No 9-15 Shiomi 2-chome, Koto-ku, Tokyo, 135-0052, Japan
Tel.: (81) 356653070
Web Site: https://www.dsb-is.co.jp
Sales Range: $75-99.9 Million
Emp.: 278
Custom Computer Programming Services
N.A.I.C.S.: 541511

Financial Digital Solutions, Ltd. **(1)**
1-5-15 Tower N Building, Kiba Koto-ku, Tokyo, 135-0042, Japan
Tel.: (81) 503 187 0460
Web Site: https://www.financial-ds.jp
Financial Transaction Services
N.A.I.C.S.: 522320

NDIAS, Ltd.
Oshima building 2-4-8 Konan, Minato-ku, Tokyo, 108-0075, Japan
Tel.: (81) 35 656 1913
Web Site: https://ndias.jp
Cyber Security Services
N.A.I.C.S.: 518210
Yukinori Hashimoto *(Pres)*

NRI Cyber Patent Ltd. **(1)**
4th floor Shin-Otemachi Building 2-2-1 Otemachi, Chiyoda-ku, Tokyo, 100-0004, Japan
Tel.: (81) 352995055
Web Site: https://www.patent.ne.jp
Intellectual Property Information Services
N.A.I.C.S.: 519290
Seiji Takano *(Pres)*

NRI Data iTech Ltd. **(1)**
Tower S Building 1-5-25 Kiba, Koto-ku, Tokyo, 135-0042, Japan
Tel.: (81) 366609700
Web Site: https://www.n-itech.com
Information & System Development Services
N.A.I.C.S.: 541511
Makoto Sakurai *(Pres)*

NRI Digital, Ltd. **(1)**
4-4-1 Minatomirai Nomura Building 11F, Nishi-ku, Yokohama, 220-0012, Kanagawa, Japan
Tel.: (81) 45 613 8600
Web Site: https://www.nri-digital.jp
Marketing Consulting Services
N.A.I.C.S.: 541613

NRI Mirai, Ltd. **(1)**
Yokohama Nomura Building 4-4-1, Minato Mirai Nishi-ku, Yokohama, 220-0012, Japan
Tel.: (81) 45 613 7500
Women Healthcare Services
N.A.I.C.S.: 621610
Koichi Nagasaki *(Pres)*

NRI Netcom, Ltd. **(1)**
Nakanoshima Festival Tower West 24F 3-2-4 Nakanoshima, Kita-ku, Osaka, 530-0005, Japan
Tel.: (81) 67 166 1520
Web Site: https://www.nri-net.com
Developing & Operating Services
N.A.I.C.S.: 541511

NRI Process Innovation, Ltd. **(1)**
Osaki Bright Core 5-5-15 Kitashinagawa, Shinagawa-ku, Tokyo, 141-0001, Japan
Tel.: (81) 357898500
Web Site: https://www.nri-pi.com
Emp.: 357
Data Outsourcing Services
N.A.I.C.S.: 518210
Yutaka Yokoshima *(Pres)*

NRI Retail Next, Ltd. **(1)**
134 Godo-cho, Hodogaya-ku, Yokohama, 240-0005, Japan
Tel.: (81) 809 044 7179
Personal Care Stores Distr
N.A.I.C.S.: 456199

NRI SecureTechnologies Ltd. **(1)**
Tokyo Sankei Building 1-7-2 Otemachi, Chiyoda-ku, Tokyo, 100-0004, Japan
Tel.: (81) 9495372957
Web Site: https://www.nri-secure.com
Security Consulting Services
N.A.I.C.S.: 561612
Jun Odashima *(Pres)*

NRI Workplace Services Ltd. **(1)**
Yokohama Nomura Building 4-4-1 Minato Mirai, Nishi-ku, Yokohama, 220-0012, Japan
Tel.: (81) 456137600
Web Site: http://www.nri.co.jp
Real Estate Manangement Services
N.A.I.C.S.: 561110
Katsutoshi Murakami *(Pres)*

NTT Earl Eye Social Information System Co., Ltd. **(1)**
Tower S 1-5-25 Kiba Koto-ku, Tokyo, 135-0042, Japan
Tel.: (81) 3 6660 9766
Web Site: http://www.nri-social.co.jp
Systems Construction & Operations Support Work Activities for Seniors
N.A.I.C.S.: 541511
Takada Ohtake *(Pres)*

Nomura Research Institute (Dailan), Ltd.
602 23th Bldg Software Park No 40 Software Park East Road, Dalian, 116023, Liaoning, China
Tel.: (86) 4113 970 0793
Investment Trust Services
N.A.I.C.S.: 525920
Chiyotaka Kawaguchi *(Pres)*

Nomura Research Institute (Singapore) Pte. Ltd. **(1)**
10 Marina Boulevard MBFC Tower 2 33-02, Singapore, 018983, Singapore
Tel.: (65) 66719800
Web Site: http://www.nrisg.com

Sales Range: $25-49.9 Million
Emp.: 18
Information Technology & Business Development Services
N.A.I.C.S.: 561499
Kazuki Ohara *(Pres)*

Nomura Research Institute America Inc. **(1)**
810 7th Ave 25th Fl, New York, NY 10019
Tel.: (212) 636-0500
Sales Range: $25-49.9 Million
Emp.: 15
Research & Development Services
N.A.I.C.S.: 541720

Subsidiary (Domestic):

Cutter Associates, LLC **(2)**
1050 Hingham St, Hingham, MA 02370
Tel.: (339) 469-0600
Web Site: https://www.cutterassociates.com
Sales Range: $1-9.9 Million
Emp.: 60
Management Consulting Services
N.A.I.C.S.: 541618
John M. Clark *(CEO)*

NRI Pacific Inc. **(2)**
1400 Fashion Island Blvd Ste 1010, San Mateo, CA 94404
Tel.: (650) 638-7250
Web Site: http://www.nri.com
Information Technology Research Services
N.A.I.C.S.: 541715

Nomura Research Institute Asia Pacific Private Limited **(1)**
10 Marina Boulevard MBFC Tower 2 33-02, Singapore, 018983, Singapore
Tel.: (65) 6 671 9800
Management Resources Services
N.A.I.C.S.: 541612
Kazuki Ohara *(Pres)*

Nomura Research Institute Australia, Pty Ltd **(1)**
Suite 3 Level 3 275 George Street, Sydney, 2000, NSW, Australia
Tel.: (61) 2080290526
Web Site: https://www.nri.com
Emp.: 4,000
All Other Business Support Services; Financial Consolidation, M&A & Audit Activities
N.A.I.C.S.: 561499

Subsidiary (Domestic):

Planit Test Management Solutions Pty. Ltd. **(2)**
152 Gloucester St, Sydney, 2000, NSW, Australia
Tel.: (61) 29 464 0600
Web Site: https://www.planittesting.com
Software Testing Services
N.A.I.C.S.: 541511
Chris Carter *(CEO)*

Nomura Research Institute Consulting & Solutions India Private Limited **(1)**
7th Floor/Tower A Building No 5 DLF Cyber City Phase III, Gurgaon, 122002, Haryana, India
Tel.: (91) 124 416 8900
Web Site: https://india.nri.com
Management Consulting Services
N.A.I.C.S.: 541611
Yoshiaki Taguchi *(Pres & Mng Dir)*

Nomura Research Institute Europe Limited **(1)**
1 Angel Lane, London, EC4R 3AB, United Kingdom
Tel.: (44) 2075211600
Web Site: http://www.nomura.com
Investment Banking Services
N.A.I.C.S.: 523150
Yoshihide Sasaki *(Pres)*

Nomura Research Institute Financial Technologies India Pvt. Ltd. **(1)**
PS Srijan Corporate Park 22nd Floor Tower 1 Block EP and GP, Sector V Salt Lake Electronics Complex, Kolkata, 700091, India
Tel.: (91) 336 604 1000
Web Site: https://www.nrifintech.com
Financial Services
N.A.I.C.S.: 523940

Masato Yuasa *(Pres)*

Nomura Research Institute Holdings America, Inc. **(1)**
810 7th Ave Fl 25, New York, NY 10019
Tel.: (212) 636-0500
Business Management Consulting Services
N.A.I.C.S.: 541611
Katsutoshi Murakami *(Pres)*

Nomura Research Institute Hong Kong Limited **(1)**
Suites 1601-03 16/F Prudential Tower The Gateway 21 CantonRoad, Tsim sha tsui, Kowloon, China (Hong Kong)
Tel.: (852) 25350300
Sales Range: $25-49.9 Million
Emp.: 50
System Automation & Integration Services
N.A.I.C.S.: 541512

Nomura Research Institute Seoul Co., Ltd. **(1)**
12F Concordian 76 Saemunan-ro, Jongno-gu, Seoul, Korea (South)
Tel.: (82) 26 744 0850
Web Site: https://www.nri-seoul.co.kr
Management Consulting Services
N.A.I.C.S.: 541611

Nomura Research Institute Shanghai Limited **(1)**
Unit 1110-16 11F Two ICC Shanghai ICC No 288 South Shaanxi Road, Shanghai, 200031, China
Tel.: (86) 2154031122
Web Site: http://www.consulting.nri.com.cn
Information Technology Consulting Services
N.A.I.C.S.: 541611
Y. E. Hua *(Chm)*

Nomura Research Institute Taiwan Co., Ltd. **(1)**
10th Fl -F No 168 Tun-Hwa N Rd, Taipei, Taiwan
Tel.: (886) 22 718 7620
Management Consulting Services
N.A.I.C.S.: 541611
Chang Chengwu *(Pres)*

PT. Nomura Research Institute Indonesia **(1)**
Sahid Sudirman Center Level 11 Unit F Jl Jend Sudirman Kav 86, Jakarta, 10220, Indonesia
Tel.: (62) 21 252 3212
Web Site: https://www.nri.co.id
Digital Transformation Services
N.A.I.C.S.: 518210

UBsecure, Inc. **(1)**
Tsukiji KY bldg 4F 4-7-5, Tsukiji Chuo-ku, Tokyo, 104-0045, Japan
Tel.: (81) 36 264 3811
Web Site: https://www.ubsecure.jp
Emp.: 131
Security System Services
N.A.I.C.S.: 561621
Youko Matsuda *(Pres)*

Ubiqlink Ltd. **(1)**
134 Godo-cho Hodogaya-ku, Yokohama, 240-0005, Japan
Tel.: (81) 453331860
Web Site: http://www.z-an.com
Sales Range: $50-74.9 Million
Emp.: 10
Navigation Support & Traffic Information Services
N.A.I.C.S.: 488330

Zhiming Software Dalian, Ltd. **(1)**
Room 301 NO 18 Software Park Road, Dalian, 116023, China
Tel.: (86) 4113 991 0166
Software Development Services
N.A.I.C.S.: 541511

Zhiming Software Japan, Ltd. **(1)**
1-5-15 Tower N Building, Kiba Koto-ku, Tokyo, 135-0042, Japan
Tel.: (81) 36 660 8300
Web Site: https://www.zhimingsoft.jp
Computer Programming Services
N.A.I.C.S.: 541511

Zhiming Software Jilin, Ltd. **(1)**
Shenzhen Street 98 Jilin Software Service Outsourcing Industry Base, 19-21 Floors High-tech Zone, Jilin, China

NOMURA RESEARCH INSTITUTE, LTD.

Nomura Research Institute, Ltd.—(Continued)
Tel.: (86) 4326 266 5588
Software Development Services
N.A.I.C.S.: 541511

NOMURA SYSTEM CORPORATION CO., LTD.
4F Ebisu Business Tower 11919
Ebisu, Shibuya-ku, Tokyo, 150-0013, Japan
Tel.: (81) 357933330
Web Site: https://www.nomura-system.co.jp
3940—(TKS)
Sales Range: Less than $1 Million
Information Technology Consulting Services
N.A.I.C.S.: 541512
Yasuo Nemoto *(Mng Dir & Dir-Admin)*

NON-STANDARD FINANCE PLC
7 Turnberry Park Road, Gildersome, Morley, Leeds, LS27 7LE, United Kingdom
Tel.: (44) 794 773 5303
Web Site:
  http://www.nsfgroupplc.com
NSF—(LSE)
Rev.: $220,853,524
Assets: $494,726,014
Liabilities: $509,394,820
Net Worth: ($14,668,807)
Earnings: ($184,048,450)
Emp.: 939
Fiscal Year-end: 12/31/20
Investment Firm
N.A.I.C.S.: 551112
John van Kuffeler *(Founder & CEO-Grp)*
Subsidiaries:

George Banco Limited (1)
1st Floor Epsom Court White Horse Business Park, Trowbridge, BA14 0XF, United Kingdom
Tel.: (44) 122 594 1941
Web Site: https://www.georgebanco.com
Financial Investment Services
N.A.I.C.S.: 523999

NONG WOO BIO CO., LTD.
114-8 Central town-ro, Yeongtong-gu, Suwon, 16506, Gyeonggi-do, Korea (South)
Tel.: (82) 312134324
Web Site:
  https://www.nongwoobio.com
Year Founded: 1967
054050—(KRS)
Rev.: $112,213,073
Assets: $251,110,175
Liabilities: $59,257,117
Net Worth: $191,853,058
Earnings: $7,576,943
Emp.: 420
Fiscal Year-end: 12/31/22
Seed Farming Services
N.A.I.C.S.: 111120
Byeonggak Lee *(CEO)*

NONGFU SPRING CO., LTD.
Geyazhuang Road 181, Xihu District, Hangzhou, 310024, China
Tel.: (86) 57187631800 CN
Web Site:
  https://www.nongfuspring.com
Year Founded: 1996
9633—(HKG)
Rev.: $5,907,623,643
Assets: $6,803,435,146
Liabilities: $2,847,561,060
Net Worth: $3,955,874,086
Earnings: $1,672,504,708
Emp.: 20,000
Fiscal Year-end: 12/31/23
Beverage Product Distr

N.A.I.C.S.: 424820
Shanshan Zhong *(Founder, Chm & Gen Mgr)*

NONGHYUP FINANCIAL GROUP, INC.
16 Saemunan-ro, Jung-gu, Seoul, Korea (South)
Tel.: (82) 220805114 KR
Web Site: http://www.nhfngroup.com
Year Founded: 1961
Sales Range: $25-49.9 Million
Holding Company; Financial Products & Services
N.A.I.C.S.: 551112
Yong Hwan Kim *(Chm)*
Subsidiaries:

NH Investment & Securities Co., Ltd. (1)
Parc1 NH Finance Tower Tower2 108 Yeoui-daero, Yeongdeungpo-gu, Seoul, 07335, Korea (South) (49.11%)
Tel.: (82) 27687000
Web Site: https://www.nhqv.com
Rev.: $1,196,713,329
Assets: $42,083,853,896
Liabilities: $36,432,808,070
Net Worth: $5,651,045,826
Earnings: $413,016,047
Emp.: 3,097
Fiscal Year-end: 12/31/2023
Financial Investment Services
N.A.I.C.S.: 523999
Won Kyu Kim *(Chm & Pres)*

NONGSHIM CO., LTD.
112 Yeouidaebang-ro, Dongjak-Gu, Seoul, Korea (South)
Tel.: (82) 28207114
Web Site: https://www.nongshim.com
Year Founded: 1965
004370—(KRS)
Rev.: $2,399,993,015
Assets: $2,327,629,117
Liabilities: $551,763,200
Net Worth: $1,775,865,917
Earnings: $89,065,652
Emp.: 5,243
Fiscal Year-end: 12/31/22
Food Products Mfr
N.A.I.C.S.: 311999
Subsidiaries:

Nongshim America, Inc. (1)
12155 6th St, Rancho Cucamonga, CA 91730
Tel.: (909) 484-1888
Web Site: http://www.nongshimusa.com
Food Products Mfr
N.A.I.C.S.: 311999
Youngchang Kim *(CFO)*

Nongshim Australia Pty, Ltd. (1)
Suite 701A 3 Horwood Place, Parramatta, 2150, NSW, Australia
Tel.: (61) 296333500
Food Products Mfr
N.A.I.C.S.: 311999
Patrick Ro *(Mgr-Sls-Natl)*

Nongshim Co., Ltd - Anseong Plant (1)
28 Gongdan-Ro, Anseong, Gyeonggi-do, Korea (South)
Tel.: (82) 3180466500
Food Products Mfr
N.A.I.C.S.: 311999

Nongshim Co., Ltd - Anyang Plant (1)
35 Nongshim-Ro, Gunpo, Gyeonggi-do, Korea (South)
Tel.: (82) 314505500
Food Products Mfr
N.A.I.C.S.: 311999

Nongshim Co., Ltd - Asan Plant (1)
485 Tangjeongmyeon-Ro, Tangjeong-Myeon, Asan, Chungcheongnam-do, Korea (South)
Tel.: (82) 415404700
Web Site: http://www.nongshim.com

Emp.: 200
Artificial Food Product Mfr
N.A.I.C.S.: 311423

Nongshim Co., Ltd - Busan Plant (1)
46 Sasang-Ro 455beon-Gil, Sasang-Gu, Busan, Korea (South)
Tel.: (82) 513661500
Food Products Mfr
N.A.I.C.S.: 311999

Nongshim Co., Ltd - Gumi Plant (1)
58-11 1Gongdan-Ro 7-Gil, Gumi, Gyeongsangbuk-do, Korea (South)
Tel.: (82) 544621801
Food Products Mfr
N.A.I.C.S.: 311999

Nongshim Co., Ltd - Noksan Plant (1)
48 Noksansandan 261-Ro 73beon-Gil, Gangseo-Gu, Busan, Korea (South)
Tel.: (82) 513294100
Food Products Mfr
N.A.I.C.S.: 311999

Nongshim Communications Co., Ltd. (1)
Nongshim Planning 2nd floor Nongshim Building 112 Yeouidaebang-ro, Dongjak-gu, Seoul, 7057, Korea (South)
Tel.: (82) 28208900
Web Site: https://www.nscom.co.kr
Marketing Communication Services
N.A.I.C.S.: 541613

Nongshim Japan, Inc. (1)
Daido Seimei Kasumigaseki Bldg 4f 1-4-2, Kasumigaseki Chiyoda-Ku, Tokyo, 100-0013, Japan
Tel.: (81) 335950882
Food Products Mfr
N.A.I.C.S.: 311999

Nongshim Vietnam Co., Ltd. (1)
2nd floor Pax sky building 13-15-17 Truong Dinh, Ward 6 District 3, Ho Chi Minh City, Vietnam
Tel.: (84) 2873074979
Food & Beverage Mfr
N.A.I.C.S.: 311991

Qingdao Nongshim Foods Co., Ltd. (1)
Food Products Mfr
N.A.I.C.S.: 311999

Shanghai Nongshim Foods Co., Ltd. (1)
840Hao Langong Road, Jinshangongyek Aifa District, Shanghai, China
Tel.: (86) 2167277711
Food Products Mfr
N.A.I.C.S.: 311999

Shenyang Nongshim Foods Co., Ltd. (1)
Food Products Mfr
N.A.I.C.S.: 311999

Yanbian Nongshim Mineral Water Beverage Co., Ltd. (1)
No 2 Tongchang East Road Bailin Dongqu, Erdao Town, Jilin, Antu, China
Tel.: (86) 4335418002
Bottled Water Mfr
N.A.I.C.S.: 312112

NONGSHIM HOLDINGS CO., LTD.
112 Yeouidaebang-Ro, Dongjak-gu, Seoul, Korea (South)
Tel.: (82) 28207114
Web Site: https://www.nongshim.com
Year Founded: 2003
072710—(KRS)
Rev.: $517,402,247
Assets: $1,065,463,373
Liabilities: $239,199,253
Net Worth: $826,264,119
Earnings: $26,155,728
Emp.: 13
Fiscal Year-end: 12/31/22
Holding Company
N.A.I.C.S.: 551112

NONTHAVEJ HOSPITAL PCL

INTERNATIONAL PUBLIC

432 Ngamwongwan Rd, Bangkhen, Nonthaburi, 11000, Thailand
Tel.: (66) 25967888
Web Site:
  https://www.nonthavej.co.th
Year Founded: 1981
NTV—(THA)
Rev.: $72,534,265
Assets: $87,506,146
Liabilities: $10,613,436
Net Worth: $76,892,710
Earnings: $11,319,074
Fiscal Year-end: 12/31/23
Health Care Srvices
N.A.I.C.S.: 621610
Prompan Siripat *(Chm)*

NOON SUGAR MILLS LIMITED
66-67-A Garden Block New Garden Town, Lahore, Pakistan
Tel.: (92) 4235831462
Web Site: https://noonsugar.net
Year Founded: 1964
NONS—(PSX)
Rev.: $57,067,913
Assets: $27,483,305
Liabilities: $19,238,555
Net Worth: $8,244,750
Earnings: $1,578,085
Emp.: 489
Fiscal Year-end: 09/30/21
Sugar Mfr
N.A.I.C.S.: 311313
Anwar Ali *(Sec)*

NOOR SILK MILLS LIMITED
D/47 S I T E Manghopir Road, Karachi, Pakistan
Tel.: (92) 21 290161 3
Textile Products Mfr
N.A.I.C.S.: 313210

NOPAR FOR TRADING & INVESTMENT COMPANY LTD.
Khalda um al Summaq Shatana str, Crown Comlex Building No 7, PO Box 183533, Amman, 11118, Jordan
Tel.: (962) 65549465
NOTI—(AMM)
Rev.: $2,535
Assets: $1,264,641
Liabilities: $12,252
Net Worth: $1,252,389
Earnings: ($39,908)
Emp.: 2
Fiscal Year-end: 12/31/20
Investment Management Service
N.A.I.C.S.: 523940

NOR-DAT COMPUTER SERVICES, LTD.
12040 149 Street, Edmonton, T5V 1P2, AB, Canada
Tel.: (780) 493-0888
Year Founded: 1974
Rev.: $11,805,955
Emp.: 110
Personal Computer Hardware & Software Solutions
N.A.I.C.S.: 541519
Dan Hinchey *(Pres & CEO)*

NOR-LAN CHRYSLER INC.
12517 100 Street, Grande Prairie, T8V 4H2, AB, Canada
Tel.: (780) 539-5200
Web Site:
  http://www.norlanchrysler.com
Year Founded: 1973
New & Used Car Dealers
N.A.I.C.S.: 441110
Brenan Jones *(Gen Mgr)*

NOR-LOG GRUPPEN AS
Borgeskogen 45, Stokke, 3160, Norway

AND PRIVATE COMPANIES

Tel.: (47) 95754208
Web Site: http://www.nor-log.no
Local Transport Provider
N.A.I.C.S.: 336999
Lars Arne Brottem (CEO)

NORAG RESOURCES INC.
4476 County Road 10 R R 1, Port Hope, ON, Canada
Tel.: (905) 753-1180
Web Site: http://www.norag.ca
Year Founded: 1998
Rev.: $22,683,963
Emp.: 4
Grains & OilSeeds Distr
N.A.I.C.S.: 424590
Ben Currelly (CEO)

NORAM LITHIUM CORP.
Suite 2150 555 West Hastings Street, Vancouver, V6B 4N6, BC, Canada
Tel.: (604) 553-2279   BC
Web Site: https://noramlithiumcorp.com
Year Founded: 2010
NRVTF—(OTCQB)
Rev.: $1,735
Assets: $4,650,069
Liabilities: $430,358
Net Worth: $4,219,711
Earnings: ($4,162,389)
Fiscal Year-end: 01/31/22
Metal Mining Services
N.A.I.C.S.: 212290
Anita Algie (CFO)

Subsidiaries:

Green Energy Resources Inc.   (1)

NORATIS AG
Hauptstrasse 129, 65760, Eschborn, Germany
Tel.: (49) 69170776820
Web Site: https://www.noratis.de
Year Founded: 2002
NUVA—(MUN)
Rev.: $66,430,897
Assets: $521,004,563
Liabilities: $426,833,413
Net Worth: $94,171,150
Earnings: ($12,076,338)
Emp.: 70
Fiscal Year-end: 12/31/23
Real Estate Manangement Services
N.A.I.C.S.: 531210
Igor Christian Bugarski (CEO)

Subsidiaries:

Noratis West GmbH   (1)
Lintorfer Str 7, 40878, Ratingen, Germany
Tel.: (49) 21023700150
Web Site: https://www.noratis-west.de
Portfolio Management Services
N.A.I.C.S.: 525110

NORAUTRON GROUP AS
Nedre vei 8 Bygg 25, 3192, Horten, Norway
Tel.: (47) 33030400
Web Site: http://www.norautron.no
Year Founded: 1967
Emp.: 26
Investment Services
N.A.I.C.S.: 523940
Jorgen C. Broch (Owner & Chm)

Subsidiaries:

Hatteland Display AS   (1)
Stokkastrandvegen 87B, 5578, Nedre Vats, Norway
Tel.: (47) 4814 2200
Web Site: http://www.hatteland-display.com
Computer Peripheral Product Mfr
N.A.I.C.S.: 334111
Jakub Kwiatkowsk (Dir-Product Dev & Project Mgmt)

NORBEN TEA & EXPORTS LIMITED
15-B Hemanta Basu Sarani 3rd Floor, Kolkata, 700 001, India
Tel.: (91) 3322100553
Web Site: https://www.norbentea.com
Year Founded: 1993
NORBTEAEXP—(NSE)
Rev.: $8,236,648
Assets: $32,890,931
Liabilities: $12,951,351
Net Worth: $19,939,580
Earnings: ($363,595)
Emp.: 91
Fiscal Year-end: 03/31/22
Tea Mfr
N.A.I.C.S.: 311920
Manoj Kumar Daga (Chm & Mng Dir)

NORBIT ASA
Stiklestadveien 1, 7041, Trondheim, Norway
Tel.: (47) 73982550
Web Site: http://www.norbit.com
Year Founded: 1980
4NK—(DEU)
Rev.: $107,842,232
Assets: $112,765,564
Liabilities: $57,408,092
Net Worth: $55,357,473
Earnings: $9,855,902
Emp.: 418
Fiscal Year-end: 12/31/22
Information Technology Services
N.A.I.C.S.: 541512
Per Jorgen Weisethaunet (CEO)

Subsidiaries:

Norbit EMS AS   (1)
Oybergvegen 15, Selbu, N-7580, Oslo, Norway
Tel.: (47) 73810081
Electronic Products Mfr
N.A.I.C.S.: 334419

Norbit GmbH   (1)
Rheinstrasse 13, 26506, Norden, Germany
Tel.: (49) 319181750
Web Site: https://www.norbit.de
Software Services
N.A.I.C.S.: 541511

Norbit Kabelpartner AS   (1)
Stiklestadveien 1, N-7041, Trondheim, Norway
Tel.: (47) 73923600
Information Technology Services
N.A.I.C.S.: 541511

Seahorse Geomatics, Incorporated   (1)
2533 NE Clackamas St Ste A, Portland, OR 97232-1726
Tel.: (503) 241-7360
Web Site: http://www.seahorsegeomatics.com
Scientific & Technical Consulting Services
N.A.I.C.S.: 541690
Mike Mutschler (Founder)

NORCOD AS
Thomas Angells Gate 22, 7011, Trondheim, Norway
Tel.: (47) 90537990
Web Site: https://www.norcod.com
Year Founded: 2018
NCOD—(OSL)
Rev.: $26,485,294
Assets: $68,301,779
Liabilities: $46,202,077
Net Worth: $22,099,702
Earnings: ($24,200,779)
Emp.: 93
Fiscal Year-end: 12/31/23
Fish Farming Services
N.A.I.C.S.: 112511
Christian Riber (CEO)

NORCOM INFORMATION TECHNOLOGY GMBH & CO. KGAA
Gabelsbergerstrasse 4, 80333, Munich, Germany
Tel.: (49) 89939480
Web Site: https://www.norcom.de
NC5A—(DEU)
Rev.: $9,758,211
Assets: $7,384,890
Liabilities: $3,311,610
Net Worth: $4,073,280
Earnings: ($507,780)
Emp.: 44
Fiscal Year-end: 12/31/23
Technology & Consulting Services
N.A.I.C.S.: 541618

Subsidiaries:

NSA Sor AS   (1)
Gimlemoen 19, 4630, Kristiansand, Norway
Tel.: (47) 38021020
Information Technology Consulting Services
N.A.I.C.S.: 541512

NorCom Systems Technology GmbH   (1)
Willy-Brandt-Platz 20, 90402, Nuremberg, Bavaria, Germany
Tel.: (49) 91137653200
Sales Range: $25-49.9 Million
Emp.: 20
Clients Consulting & Software Solutions
N.A.I.C.S.: 541511
Tobias Abthoff (Mng Dir)

NORCON PLC
5 Andrea Kalvou Street, PO Box 54843, Limassol, CY 3728, Cyprus
Tel.: (357) 25 736 830   IM
Web Site: http://www.norconplc.com
Year Founded: 2008
Sales Range: $25-49.9 Million
Information Technology Services
N.A.I.C.S.: 541512
Trond Tostrup (Chm)

NORCROS PLC
Ladyfield House Station Road, Wilmslow, SK9 1BU, Cheshire, United Kingdom
Tel.: (44) 1625549010
Web Site: https://www.norcros.com
NXR—(LSE)
Rev.: $538,064,436
Assets: $488,100,340
Liabilities: $216,149,024
Net Worth: $271,951,316
Earnings: $34,893,404
Emp.: 2,196
Fiscal Year-end: 03/31/22
Showers, Ceramic Wall Tiles, Floor Tiles & Related Products Designer, Mfr & Sales
N.A.I.C.S.: 332913
Nick Kelsall (CEO)

Subsidiaries:

Abode Home Products Ltd.   (1)
Unit L Zenith Park Whaley Road, Barnsley, S75 1HT, South Yorkshire, United Kingdom
Tel.: (44) 122 628 3434
Web Site: https://www.abodedesigns.co.uk
Kitchen & Bathroom Design Services
N.A.I.C.S.: 236118

Bathshoponline Ltd.   (1)
Ladyfield House Station Road, Wilmslow, SK9 1BU, Cheshire, United Kingdom
Tel.: (44) 330 041 7190
Web Site: https://www.bathshoponline.co.uk
Homeware Accessories Distr
N.A.I.C.S.: 423220

Croydex Group Ltd.   (1)
Central Way, Andover, SP10 5AW, Hampshire, United Kingdom
Tel.: (44) 126 436 5881
Web Site: https://www.croydex.co.uk
Homeware Accessories Distr
N.A.I.C.S.: 423220

NORD GOLD SE

Johnson Tiles Pty Ltd   (1)
Unit 1 843 Mountain Hwy, Bayswater, 3153, VIC, Australia
Tel.: (61) 397204041
Web Site: http://www.johnsontiles.com.au
Sales Range: $25-49.9 Million
Emp.: 600
Wall & Floor Tiles Mfr
N.A.I.C.S.: 327120

Norcros Adhesives Ltd.   (1)
Harewood Street Tunstall, Stoke-on-Trent, ST6 5JZ, United Kingdom
Tel.: (44) 178 252 4140
Web Site: https://www.nxadh.co.uk
Adhesive Mfr
N.A.I.C.S.: 325520

Norcros SA (Pty) Ltd   (1)
4 Porcelain Road Clayville, Olifantsfontein, 1666, Gauteng, South Africa
Tel.: (27) 112069700
Web Site: http://www.norcros.co.za
Sales Range: $125-149.9 Million
Emp.: 500
Wall & Floor Tiles Mfr
N.A.I.C.S.: 327120
Thomas Wilcox (Mng Dir)

Plumbex UK Ltd.   (1)
Cheddar Business Park Wedmore Road, Cheddar, BS27 3EB, Somerset, United Kingdom
Tel.: (44) 193 474 5160
Web Site: https://www.plumbex.co.uk
Plumbing Accessories Distr
N.A.I.C.S.: 423720

Taps Direct Ltd.   (1)
Grosvenor House 3 Chapel Street, Congleton, CW12 4AB, United Kingdom
Tel.: (44) 126 071 1000
Web Site: https://www.tapsdirect.co.uk
Plumbing Accessories Distr
N.A.I.C.S.: 423720

Tile Africa Group (Pty) Ltd.   (1)
4 Porcelain Road, Olifantsfontein, Midrand, 1666, South Africa
Tel.: (27) 11 455 2607
Web Site: https://www.tileafrica.co.za
Ceramic Tile Mfr & Distr
N.A.I.C.S.: 327110

Triton Plc   (1)
Shepperton Park Triton Road, Nuneaton, CV11 4NR, Warwickshire, United Kingdom
Tel.: (44) 247 637 2222
Web Site: https://www.tritonshowers.co.uk
Shower Product Mfr
N.A.I.C.S.: 326191
Phil Viner (Comml Dir)

Vado UK Ltd.   (1)
Cheddar Business Park Wedmore Road, Cheddar, BS27 3EB, United Kingdom
Tel.: (44) 193 474 4466
Web Site: https://www.vado.com
Shower Product Mfr
N.A.I.C.S.: 326191

NORD CONSTRUCTIONS NOUVELLES
Parc D" Activites Landacres Allee De Lisbonne, Hesdin L Abbe, 62360, Saint Etienne, Pas De Calais, France
Tel.: (33) 321318585
Web Site: http://www.ncn-batiment.com
Sales Range: $25-49.9 Million
Emp.: 200
Nonresidential Construction
N.A.I.C.S.: 236220
Ingrid Morel (Mgr-DP)

NORD GOLD SE
5th Floor 6 St Andrew Street, London, EC 4A 3AE, United Kingdom
Tel.: (44) 2078328914   UK
Web Site: http://www.nordgold.com
Year Founded: 2007
Rev.: $336,953,000
Assets: $2,529,315,000
Liabilities: $1,466,561,000
Net Worth: $1,062,754,000
Earnings: $91,895,000

NORD GOLD SE

Nord Gold SE—(Continued)
Fiscal Year-end: 12/31/18
Gold Mining Services
N.A.I.C.S.: 212220
Nikolai Zelenski (CEO)

NORD HOLDING UNTERNEH-MENSBETEILIGUNGSGESELL-SCHAFT MBH
Villa Venture Walderseestrasse 23, 30177, Hannover, Germany
Tel.: (49) 5112704150 De
Web Site: http://www.nordholding.de
Year Founded: 1969
Emp.: 25
Investment Management Service
N.A.I.C.S.: 523940
Rainer Effinger (Mng Dir)

Subsidiaries:

Dr. Fodisch Umweltmesstechnik AG **(1)**
Zwenkauer Strasse 159, Markranstadt, 4420, Germany
Tel.: (49) 342057550
Web Site: http://www.foedisch.de
Sales Range: $25-49.9 Million
Emp.: 241
Environmental Engineering Services
N.A.I.C.S.: 541330
Holger Fodisch (Founder & Chm)

Subsidiary (Domestic):

AllTec Automatisierungs- und Kommunikationstechnik GmbH **(2)**
Gewerbegebiet Eula-West 11, 04552, Borna, Germany
Tel.: (49) 34332460
Web Site: http://www.alltec-borna.de
Emp.: 150
Switchgear Mfr
N.A.I.C.S.: 335313

DFU Analysenservice GmbH **(2)**
Baukauer Strasse 86, 44653, Herne, Germany
Tel.: (49) 23233990920
Web Site: http://www.dfu-analysenservice.de
Measuring System Distr
N.A.I.C.S.: 423830

DFU Service GmbH **(2)**
In den Gartenwiesen 4, 65830, Kriftel, Germany
Tel.: (49) 61922003009
Web Site: http://www.dfu-service.de
Measuring System Distr
N.A.I.C.S.: 423830

Fanalmatic Gesellschaft fur Umwelttechnik und Industrieautomation mbH **(2)**
Cositzer Weg 2, 06369, Weissandt-Golzau, Germany
Tel.: (49) 349782680
Web Site: http://www.fanalmatic.com
Measuring System Mfr
N.A.I.C.S.: 334513

Peter Nitschke Dosieranlagen und Service GmbH **(2)**
Zwenkauer Strasse 159, 04420, Markranstadt, Germany
Tel.: (49) 3420542780
Web Site: http://www.peter-nitschke.de
Water Treatment Equipment Whslr
N.A.I.C.S.: 423830

GEA Bock GmbH **(1)**
Benzstrasse 7, 72636, Frickenhausen, Germany
Tel.: (49) 702294540
Web Site: http://www.bock.de
Emp.: 340
Refrigeration Compressor Mfr
N.A.I.C.S.: 333415
Thies Hachfeld (Mng Dir)

Subsidiary (Non-US):

Bock (India) Pvt. Ltd. **(2)**
471 Sankarda-Bhadarwa Road Near Moxi Bus Stand Moxi Savli, Vadodara, 391780, India
Tel.: (91) 2667 244 861
Web Site: http://www.bockindia.com
Air Conditioning & Refrigeration Mfr
N.A.I.C.S.: 333415
Uday Sahasrabuddhe (Gen Mgr)

Bock Compressor Technology (Thailand) Co., Ltd. **(2)**
230 Thosapol Land Building 2 15th Fl Ratchadapisek Road, Huay-Kwang, Bangkok, 10320, Thailand
Tel.: (66) 2 274 0396 78
Compressor Equipment Mfr
N.A.I.C.S.: 333912

Bock Compressors (Hangzhou) Co., Ltd. **(2)**
Standard Workshop 4 C 63 Jiuhuan Road, Jianggan District, Hangzhou, Zhejiang, China
Tel.: (86) 57 186730 277
Web Site: http://www.bock.de
Cooling & Ventilation Equipment Mfr & Distr
N.A.I.C.S.: 333415

GEA Bock Asia Pte. Ltd. **(2)**
99 Bukit Timah Road 03-08, Singapore, 229835, Singapore
Tel.: (65) 63388113
Web Site: http://www.bock.de
Sales Range: $25-49.9 Million
Emp.: 1
Air Conditioning Equipment Mfr
N.A.I.C.S.: 333415
Bryan Lim (Mng Dir)

GEA Bock Compressors (Hangzhou) Co., Ltd. **(2)**
Standard Workshop 4 C 63 Jiuhuan Road, Jianggan District, Hangzhou, Zhejiang, China
Tel.: (86) 57 186730 277
Web Site: http://www.bock.de
Air Conditioning Equipment Mfr
N.A.I.C.S.: 423730

GEA Bock Czech s.r.o. **(2)**
Kostelec Ostrov u Stribra 11, 349 01, Stribro, Czech Republic
Tel.: (420) 374 6304 11
Sales Range: $25-49.9 Million
Air Conditioning Equipment Mfr
N.A.I.C.S.: 333415
Jan Hejman (Mng Dir)

GEA Bock GmbH **(2)**
Harterstr 27, 8053, Graz, Austria
Tel.: (43) 316 26 24 27
Web Site: http://www.bock.de
Automotive Air Conditioner Mfr
N.A.I.C.S.: 336390
Peter Pinta (Gen Mgr)

GEA Bock Malaysia SDN. BHD. **(2)**
Unit 516 Block A Damansara Intan No 1 Jalan SS 20/27, 47400, Petaling Jaya, Malaysia
Tel.: (60) 3 7726 1058
Emp.: 6
Air Conditioning Equipment Mfr
N.A.I.C.S.: 333415

Heyform Bramsche GmbH **(1)**
Heywinkelstr 1, 49565, Bramsche, Germany
Tel.: (49) 5468 778 0
Web Site: http://www.heyform.com
Trim Component Mfr
N.A.I.C.S.: 336360
Rolf-Gunther Nieberding (CEO)

Julius Heywinkel GmbH **(1)**
Heywinkel Strasse 1, 49565, Bramsche, Germany
Tel.: (49) 54687780
Web Site: http://www.heytex.com
Sales Range: $150-199.9 Million
Plastic Trim Parts, Vehicle Interior & Coated Fabrics Mfr & Whslr
N.A.I.C.S.: 336360
Hartwig Birszwilks (Dir-Sls & Mktg)

KiKxxl GmbH **(1)**
Mindener Strasse 127, 49084, Osnabruck, Germany
Tel.: (49) 541 3305 0
Web Site: http://www.kikxxl.de
Telecommunication Servicesb
N.A.I.C.S.: 517810

PDS Entwicklungs- und Service GmbH **(1)**
Ettore-Bugatti-Strasse 35, 51149, Cologne, Germany
Tel.: (49) 2203 1888 0
Web Site: http://www.pdsgmbh.de
Software Publisher
N.A.I.C.S.: 513210
Michael Zitzmann (Mng Dir)

RADEMACHER Holding GmbH **(1)**
Buschkamp 7, Rhede, 46414, Germany
Tel.: (49) 28729330
Holding Company
N.A.I.C.S.: 551112

Schoeller-Electronics GmbH **(1)**
Marburger St 65, 35083, Wetter, Germany
Tel.: (49) 64 23 81 295
Web Site: http://www.schoeller-electronics.com
Emp.: 210
Holding Company
N.A.I.C.S.: 551112
Michael Keuthen (Mng Dir)

UHLIG Holding GmbH **(1)**
Innerstetal 16, 38685, Langelsheim, Germany
Tel.: (49) 53 26 5 01 0
Web Site: http://www.uhlig.eu
Emp.: 180
Holding Company
N.A.I.C.S.: 551112
Arne Manzke (Exec Dir)

NORD MASON CO., LTD.
2F 30 Tojeongi-ro 119, Mapo-gu, Seoul, Korea (South)
Tel.: (82) 7071230077
Web Site: https://nordmason.gobizkorea.com
Year Founded: 2013
317860—(KRS)
Cosmetic Product Mfr & Distr
N.A.I.C.S.: 325620
Park Byung Kyu (Dir)

NORD SA
Bld Dacia no 56 floor 1 sector 2, Bucharest, Romania
Tel.: (40) 213129639
Web Site: https://www.nordsa.ro
NORD—(BUC)
Rev.: $135,168
Assets: $9,990,040
Liabilities: $4,993
Net Worth: $9,985,048
Earnings: $16,278
Emp.: 3
Fiscal Year-end: 12/31/23
Home Management Services
N.A.I.C.S.: 721110

NORDA S.P.A.
Via Case Sparse 103 Loc Folzano, 25124, Brescia, Italy
Tel.: (39) 0302165311
Web Site: http://www.nordaspa.com
Metal Forming System Mfr
N.A.I.C.S.: 332431
Gianfranco Sonzogni (Dir-Ops)

NORDAX GROUP AB
Gavlegatan 22, 113 30, Stockholm, Sweden
Tel.: (46) 850880800
Web Site: http://www.nordax.se
Sales Range: Less than $1 Million
Emp.: 200
Consumer Lending Services
N.A.I.C.S.: 522310
Olof Mankert (Chief Risk Officer)

Subsidiaries:

Norwegian Finans Holding ASA **(1)**
PO Box 110, Lysaker, 1325, Oslo, Norway
Tel.: (47) 2929
Sales Range: Less than $1 Million
Holding Company
N.A.I.C.S.: 551111

NORDDEUTSCHE KUNSTST-

INTERNATIONAL PUBLIC

OFF UND ELEKTROGESELL-SCHAFT STACKER MBH & CO. KG
Weidestrasse 122a, 22083, Hamburg, Germany
Tel.: (49) 405130090
Web Site: http://www.norka.de
Year Founded: 1948
Rev.: $93,109,500
Emp.: 266
Light Mfr
N.A.I.C.S.: 335132
Frank Schneider (Mng Dir)

Subsidiaries:

NORKA Lighting Sales Pty. Ltd. **(1)**
14 Knighton Avenue Airport West, Melbourne, 3042, VIC, Australia
Tel.: (61) 393315666
Web Site: http://www.norkalighting.com.au
Lighting Equipment Mfr & Distr
N.A.I.C.S.: 335132

NORDDEUTSCHE LANDES-BANK GIROZENTRALE
Friedrichswall 10, 30159, Hannover, Germany
Tel.: (49) 5113610 De
Web Site: http://www.nordlb.de
Year Founded: 1970
Rev.: $1,146,736,640
Assets: $156,353,733,340
Liabilities: $149,815,990,660
Net Worth: $6,537,742,680
Earnings: ($77,270,340)
Emp.: 5,489
Fiscal Year-end: 12/31/19
Banking & Investment Services
N.A.I.C.S.: 523150
Christoph Schulz (Member-Mgmt Bd)

Subsidiaries:

Bremer Landesbank Kreditanstalt Oldenburg **(1)**
Domshof 26, 28189, Bremen, Germany **(100%)**
Tel.: (49) 4213322443
Web Site: http://www.bremerlandesbank.de
Sales Range: $1-4.9 Billion
Emp.: 1,000
Investment Bank
N.A.I.C.S.: 523150
Stephan-Andreas Kaulvers (CEO)

Subsidiary (Domestic):

BLB Consulting GmbH **(2)**
Kleine Waagestr 3, 28195, Bremen, Germany
Tel.: (49) 421 339270
Banking
N.A.I.C.S.: 522110

BLB Immobilien GmbH **(2)**
Kleine Waagestrasse 3, 28195, Bremen, Germany
Tel.: (49) 421339270
Web Site: http://www.blb-immobilien.de
Banking Services
N.A.I.C.S.: 522110

BLB Leasing GmbH **(2)**
Markt 12, 26122, Oldenburg, Germany
Tel.: (49) 4412371003
Web Site: http://www.blbleasing.de
Banking Services
N.A.I.C.S.: 522110

Subsidiary (Non-US):

Bremer Landesbank Capital Markets Plc **(2)**
71 Queen Victoria Street, London, EC4V 4AY, United Kingdom
Tel.: (44) 2079725450
Web Site: http://www.bremerlb.co.uk
Sales Range: $25-49.9 Million
Banking Services
N.A.I.C.S.: 522110

KreditServices Nord GmbH **(1)**
Friedrich-Wilhelm-Platz, 38100, Braunschweig, Germany
Tel.: (49) 531120400

AND PRIVATE COMPANIES

Web Site: http://www.kreditservices-nord.de
Financial Services
N.A.I.C.S.: 523999

LHI Leasing GmbH (1)
Emil-Riedl-Weg 6, 82049, Pullach,
Germany (50%)
Tel.: (49) 8951200
Web Site: http://www.lhi.de
Sales Range: $75-99.9 Million
Emp.: 260
Estate Agent;Financial Services
N.A.I.C.S.: 531210
Oliver Porr *(Mng Dir)*

Subsidiary (Domestic):

FondsFinance GmbH (2)
Riesstrasse 25, 80992, Munich,
Germany (100%)
Tel.: (49) 891588150
Web Site: http://www.fondsfinanz.de
Sales Range: $50-74.9 Million
Real Estate Finance Services
N.A.I.C.S.: 523940

LHI Leasing GmbH & Co. Immobilien KG (1)
Emil-Riedl-Weg 6, 82049, Pullach, Germany
Tel.: (49) 89 51200
Commercial Banking Services
N.A.I.C.S.: 522110

NORD/FM Norddeutsche Facility Management GmbH (1)
Hans-Bockler-Allee 1, 30173, Hannover, Germany
Tel.: (49) 5113619979
Web Site: http://www.nordfm.de
Commercial Banking Services
N.A.I.C.S.: 522110

NORD/LB Asset Management Holding GmbH (1)
Prinzenstrabe 12, 30159, Hannover, Germany
Tel.: (49) 511 123 540
Web Site: http://www.nordlb-am.de
Commercial Banking Services
N.A.I.C.S.: 522110

NORD/LB COVERED FINANCE BANK S. A. (1)
7 rue Lou Hemmer, 1748, Luxembourg, Luxembourg
Tel.: (352) 4522111
Web Site: http://www.nordlb.lu
Emp.: 300
Commercial Banking Services
N.A.I.C.S.: 522110
Geit Christian *(CEO)*

NORD/LB Luxembourg S.A. Covered Bond Bank (1)
7 rue Lou Hemmer, Findel, 1748, Luxembourg, Luxembourg
Tel.: (352) 4522111
Commercial Banking Services
N.A.I.C.S.: 522110

NORD/LB Project Holding Ltd. (1)
One Wood Street, London, EC2V 7WT, United Kingdom
Tel.: (44) 2079725400
Commercial Banking Services
N.A.I.C.S.: 522110
Tess Jarmolkiewicz *(Mng Dir)*

Norddeutsche Securities PLC (1)
One Wood Street, London, EC2V 7WT,
United Kingdom (100%)
Tel.: (44) 2079725400
Web Site: http://www.nordlb.com
Sales Range: $50-74.9 Million
Banking Services
N.A.I.C.S.: 522320

Offentliche Lebensversicherung Braunschweig (1)
Theodor-Heub-Str 10, Braunschweig, 38122, Germany
Tel.: (49) 531 2020
Commercial Banking Services
N.A.I.C.S.: 522110

Porzellanmanufaktur FURSTENBERG GmbH (1)
Meinbrexener Strasse 2, 37699, Furstenberg, Germany
Tel.: (49) 5271 401 0

Web Site: http://www.fuerstenberg-porzellan.com
Tableware & Gift Products Mfr
N.A.I.C.S.: 459420
Stephanie Saalfeld *(Mng Dir)*

SGK Servicegesellschaft Kreditmanagement mbH (1)
Friedrichswall 10, 30159, Hannover,
Germany (100%)
Tel.: (49) 5113613200
Web Site: http://www.sg-k.de
Commercial Banking Services
N.A.I.C.S.: 522110
Christoph Schroder *(Mng Dir)*

Skandifinanz AG (1)
Muensterhof 13, Zurich, 8001, Switzerland
Tel.: (41) 44 215 16 16
Commercial Banking Services
N.A.I.C.S.: 522110

NORDDEUTSCHE STEINGUT AG
Schonebecker Strasse 101, 28759, Bremen, Germany
Tel.: (49) 42162620
Web Site: http://www.norddeutsche-steingut.de
NST—(BER)
Sales Range: Less than $1 Million
Tile & Ceramic Wall Mfr
N.A.I.C.S.: 327120
Ruediger Grau *(CTO & Member-Mgmt Bd)*

NORDEA BANK ABP
Hamnbanegatan 5, 00020, Helsinki, Finland
Tel.: (358) 20070000   FI
Web Site: https://www.nordea.com
Year Founded: 2017
NBNKF—(OTCQX)
Rev.: $10,398,279,840
Assets: $678,184,998,400
Liabilities: $636,744,180,800
Net Worth: $41,440,817,600
Earnings: $2,781,963,600
Emp.: 28,051
Fiscal Year-end: 12/31/20
Bank Holding Company
N.A.I.C.S.: 551111
Ulrika Romantschuk *(Head-Comm, Mktg, and Grp Brand)*

Subsidiaries:

Danbolig A/S (1)
Sejrogade 9 St Tv, 2100, Copenhagen, Denmark
Tel.: (45) 38400400
Web Site: https://danbolig.dk
Real Estate Development Services
N.A.I.C.S.: 531390

Nordea Bank Danmark A/S (1)
Strandgade 3, PO Box 850, Copenhagen, 900, Denmark
Tel.: (45) 33333333
Web Site: http://www.nordea.dk
Sales Range: $1-4.9 Billion
Emp.: 8,500
Banking Services
N.A.I.C.S.: 522320
Peter Schutze *(Mgr)*

Subsidiary (Domestic):

Nordea Ejendomsinvestering A/S (2)
Ejby Industrivej 38, 2600, Glostrup, Denmark
Tel.: (45) 43338000
Web Site: http://www.nordeaejendomme.dk
Emp.: 50
Real Estate Manangement Services
N.A.I.C.S.: 531390

Nordea Finans Danmark A/S (2)
Helgeshoj Alle 33, 2630, Taastrup, Denmark
Tel.: (45) 70247503
Financial Management Services
N.A.I.C.S.: 523999

Nordea Investment Fund Management A/S (2)

Nyropsgade 17 St, 1602, Copenhagen, Denmark
Tel.: (45) 33360600
Web Site: http://www.nordea.com
Sales Range: $50-74.9 Million
Emp.: 25
Investment Fund Management Services
N.A.I.C.S.: 525910

Nordea Kredit Realkreditaktieselskab (2)
Helgeshoj Alle 33, Taastrup, DK-2630, Denmark
Tel.: (45) 33333636
Web Site: https://www.nordeakredit.dk
Emp.: 120
Mortgage Loan Brokerage Services
N.A.I.C.S.: 522310
Chilarlotte Christensen *(Gen Mgr)*

Nordea Bank Finland Plc (1)
Aleksis Kiven Katu 9, Helsinki, 00020, Finland
Tel.: (358) 91651
Web Site: http://www.nordea.fi
Sales Range: $1-9.9 Million
Emp.: 2,500
International Banking
N.A.I.C.S.: 522299
Sara Mella *(Head-Retail Banking)*

Subsidiary (Domestic):

Fidenta Oy (2)
Nihtisillante 3 Pl 24, 2631, Espoo,
Finland (50%)
Tel.: (358) 900082820
Web Site: http://www.tietopnator.com
Sales Range: $25-49.9 Million
Emp.: 230
N.A.I.C.S.: 522299

Helsingen Pantti-Osakeyhtio (2)
Kaisaniemenkatu 1, FIN 00500, Helsinki,
Finland (100%)
Tel.: (358) 92705301
Web Site: http://www.helsinginpantti.fi
Sales Range: $50-74.9 Million
Emp.: 50
N.A.I.C.S.: 522299

Branch (Non-US):

Nordea Bank Finland Plc - Germany Representative Office (2)
Bockenheimer Landstrasse 33, 60325, Frankfurt am Main, Germany
Tel.: (49) 69710040
Web Site: http://www.nordea.de
Sales Range: $50-74.9 Million
Emp.: 35
Financial Services Group
N.A.I.C.S.: 522299
Gunnar Volkera *(Gen Mgr)*

Nordea Bank Finland Plc - UK Representative Office (2)
55 Basinghall St, London, EC2V 5NB, United Kingdom
Tel.: (44) 2077269000
Web Site: http://www.nordeabank.uk
Sales Range: $50-74.9 Million
Emp.: 70
N.A.I.C.S.: 522299

Branch (US):

Nordea Bank Finland Plc - US Representative Office (2)
437 Madison Ave Fl 21, New York, NY 10022-7001
Tel.: (212) 318-9300
Web Site: http://www.nordea.com
Sales Range: $75-99.9 Million
Emp.: 150
International Banking
N.A.I.C.S.: 523150

Subsidiary (Domestic):

Nordea Corporate Finance Oy (2)
Satamaradankatu 5 6th Fl, 00020, Helsinki,
Finland (100%)
Tel.: (358) 916559771
Sales Range: $50-74.9 Million
Emp.: 20
Financial Advisory Services to Corporations, Government Bodies & Institutional Clients
N.A.I.C.S.: 523999

NORDEA BANK ABP

Nordea Finance Finland Ltd. (2)
Aleksis Kiven katu 9, FI-00020, Helsinki,
Nordea, Finland (100%)
Tel.: (358) 20086210
Web Site: https://www.nordeafinance.fi
Sales Range: $150-199.9 Million
Emp.: 500
Equipment Leasing, Real Estate Leasing, Installment Contracts, Factoring, Contract Financing & Charge Cards
N.A.I.C.S.: 532490

Nordea Investment Fund Company Finland Ltd (2)
Keskuskatu 3, Helsinki, 00020, Finland
Tel.: (358) 9 1651
Web Site: http://www.nordea.fi
Investment Fund Management Services
N.A.I.C.S.: 525910

Tukirahoitus Oy (2)
Kirkkokatu 21 B, 90100, Oulu, Finland
Tel.: (358) 8 880 9800
Sales Range: $50-74.9 Million
Emp.: 20
Financial Management Services
N.A.I.C.S.: 523999
Kari Ollikainen *(Mng Dir)*

Nordea Bank Moscow (1)
9 Prechistenskaya Naberezhnaya, 7th Fl Office 758, 119034, Moscow, Russia
Tel.: (7) 0952587258
Web Site: http://www.unitcreditbank.in
Sales Range: $50-74.9 Million
Emp.: 15
N.A.I.C.S.: 522299

Nordea Bank Norway ASA (1)
Middelthunsgate 17, PO Box 1166, Centrum, 0107, Oslo, Norway
Tel.: (47) 22485000
Web Site: http://www.nordea.no
Sales Range: $1-4.9 Billion
Emp.: 4,300
Provider of International Banking Services
N.A.I.C.S.: 522299
Baard Syrrist *(Head-Retail Banking)*

Subsidiary (Domestic):

Nordea Eiendomskreditt AS (2)
PO Box 1166, Sentrum, 0107, Oslo, Norway
Tel.: (47) 22488400
Commercial Property Financial Services
N.A.I.C.S.: 523999

Nordea Finans A/S (2)
Essendrops Gata 7, PO Box 1166, NO
0107, Oslo, Norway (100%)
Tel.: (47) 22486600
Web Site: http://www.nordeafinans.no
Sales Range: $100-124.9 Million
Emp.: 125
N.A.I.C.S.: 522299

Nordea Finans Norge AS (2)
Essendrops gate 7, PO Box 1166, Sentrum, 0107, Oslo, Norway
Tel.: (47) 23206021
Web Site: https://www.nordeafinance.no
Sales Range: $75-99.9 Million
Emp.: 120
Financial Management Services
N.A.I.C.S.: 523999

Nordea Investment Management (2)
Solkebermadottesvei 38, 1166 Sentrum
0107 Oslo, 5141, Bergen, Norway (100%)
Tel.: (47) 22485000
Web Site: http://www.nordea.no
Sales Range: $50-74.9 Million
Emp.: 50
N.A.I.C.S.: 522299

Nordea Liv Holding Norge AS (2)
Folke Bernadottes Vei 38, Fyllingsdalen, 5147, Bergen, Norway
Tel.: (47) 23254700
Investment Management Service
N.A.I.C.S.: 523999

Nordea Norway A/S (2)
Essendrops Gata No 7, PO Box 1166, NO
0107, Oslo, Norway (100%)
Tel.: (47) 22484500
Web Site: http://www.nordea.no
Sales Range: $350-399.9 Million
Emp.: 1,000
N.A.I.C.S.: 522299

NORDEA BANK ABP

INTERNATIONAL PUBLIC

Nordea Bank Abp—(Continued)

Nordeakreditt A/S (2)
Essendrops Gata 9 No 7, PO Box 1166, Sentrum, NO 0107, Oslo, Norway (100%)
Tel.: (47) 22488400
Web Site: http://www.nordea.no
Sales Range: $200-249.9 Million
Emp.: 300
N.A.I.C.S.: 522299

Privatmegleren AS (2)
Karenslyst Alle 2, PO Box 356, 0213, Oslo, Norway
Tel.: (47) 40002320
Real Estate Brokerage Services
N.A.I.C.S.: 531390
Grethe Wittenberg Meier *(CEO)*

Nordea Bank SA (1)
562 Rue De Neudorf, Luxembourg, 2015, Luxembourg
Tel.: (352) 438871
Web Site: http://www.nordea.lu
Sales Range: $200-249.9 Million
Emp.: 380
Commercial Bank
N.A.I.C.S.: 522110

Nordea Bank SA (1)
Edificio La Bougain Vialle A, Calle El Pulpo 5, 29640, Fuengirola, Spain
Tel.: (34) 952660748
Web Site: http://www.nordea.lu
Sales Range: $75-99.9 Million
Emp.: 3
N.A.I.C.S.: 522299

Nordea Bank Sweden AB (1)
Smalands Gatan 17, Stockholm, 11146, Sweden
Tel.: (46) 86147000
Web Site: http://www.nordea.se
Sales Range: $1-4.9 Billion
Emp.: 9,000
International & Retail Banking
N.A.I.C.S.: 522299

Nordea Danmark, filial af Nordea Bank Aps (1)
Gronjordsvej 10, 2300, Copenhagen, Denmark
Tel.: (45) 70333333
Web Site: https://www.nordea.dk
Investment Banking Services
N.A.I.C.S.: 523999

Nordea Finance Equipment AS (1)
Essendrops Gate 7, 0368, Oslo, Norway
Tel.: (47) 23206021
Web Site: https://www.nordeafinance.no
Emp.: 30,000
Asset Management & Insurance Services
N.A.I.C.S.: 524210

Nordea Fonder AB (1)
Regeringsgatan 59 Smalandsgatan 17, 105 71, Stockholm, Sweden
Tel.: (46) 857942000
Investment Management Service
N.A.I.C.S.: 523999

Nordea Investment Funds S.A. (1)
562 Rue de Neudorf, PO Box 782, 2017, Luxembourg, Luxembourg
Tel.: (352) 27865373
Asset Management & Insurance Services
N.A.I.C.S.: 524210

Nordea Investment Management AB (1)
Master Samuelsgatan 21, 105 71, Stockholm, Sweden
Tel.: (46) 857942000
Sales Range: $350-399.9 Million
Emp.: 520
Investment Management Service
N.A.I.C.S.: 523999

Nordea Life Holding Finland Ltd (1)
Aleksis Kiven Katu 9, Helsinki, 200, Finland
Tel.: (358) 916527601
Sales Range: $75-99.9 Million
Emp.: 145
Investment Management Service
N.A.I.C.S.: 523999

Subsidiary (Domestic):

Nordea Life Assurance Finland Ltd (2)

Aleksis Kiven Katu 9, FI-00020, Helsinki, Nordea, Finland
Tel.: (358) 20070000
Web Site: https://www.nordea.fi
Sales Range: $75-99.9 Million
Emp.: 145
Fire Insurance Services
N.A.I.C.S.: 524113

Nordea Liv AS (1)
Regeringsgatan 59, 10571, Stockholm, Sweden
Tel.: (46) 87876700
Web Site: http://www.nordea.se
Sales Range: $75-99.9 Million
Emp.: 100
N.A.I.C.S.: 522299
Britta Burreau *(Mng Dir)*

Subsidiary (Domestic):

Nordea Livforsakring Sverige AB (2)
Master Samuelsgatan 21, 111 56, Stockholm, Sweden
Tel.: (46) 87876700
Fire Insurance Services
N.A.I.C.S.: 524113

Nordea North America Inc. (1)
437 Madison Ave Fl 22, New York, NY 10022-7001
Tel.: (212) 603-6952
Financial Management Services
N.A.I.C.S.: 523999

Nordea Pension, Livsforsikringsselskab A/S (1)
Gronjordsvej 10, 2300, Copenhagen, Denmark
Tel.: (45) 70331313
Web Site: https://www.nordeapension.dk
Insurance Services
N.A.I.C.S.: 524210

Nordea Private Banking (1)
Smalandgeatan 17, 10571, Stockholm, Sweden
Tel.: (46) 86147520
Web Site: http://www.nordeaprivatebanking.se
Sales Range: $75-99.9 Million
Emp.: 100
N.A.I.C.S.: 522299

Nordea Securities (1)
Smalandstan 17, Stockholm, 105 71, Sweden
Tel.: (46) 86147000
Web Site: http://www.nordea.se
Sales Range: $50-74.9 Million
Emp.: 100
N.A.I.C.S.: 551111
Bjorn Zetterfalk *(Head-Securities)*

Nordea bank estonia (1)
Liivalaia 45, 10145, Tallinn, Estonia
Tel.: (372) 6283300
Web Site: http://www.nordea.ee
Sales Range: $350-399.9 Million
Emp.: 512
Investment Banking Services
N.A.I.C.S.: 523150

Subsidiary (Domestic):

Nordea Pensions Estonia AS (2)
Liivalaia 45, 10145, Tallinn, Estonia
Tel.: (372) 6283300
Pension Fund Management Services
N.A.I.C.S.: 523940

NORDEA BANK JSC

19 3-Ya Ulitsa Yamskogo Polya Building 1, 125124, Moscow, Russia
Tel.: (7) 4957773477
Web Site: http://www.nordea.ru
Year Founded: 1994
Sales Range: $100-124.9 Million
Commercial Banking Services
N.A.I.C.S.: 522110
Mikhail V. Polyakov *(Chm-Mgmt Bd)*

NORDECON AS

Toompuiestee 35, 10149, Tallinn, Estonia
Tel.: (372) 6154400
Web Site: https://www.nordecon.com
Year Founded: 1989

NCN1T—(TAL)
Rev.: $307,298,819
Assets: $133,052,213
Liabilities: $108,173,088
Net Worth: $24,879,126
Earnings: $2,269,566
Emp.: 558
Fiscal Year-end: 12/31/23
Commercial & Institutional Building Construction
N.A.I.C.S.: 236220
Gerd Muller *(Chm)*

Subsidiaries:

Embach Ehitus OU (1)
Turu 34, 51014, Tartu, Estonia
Tel.: (372) 7300020
Web Site: https://embach.ee
Building Construction Services
N.A.I.C.S.: 236220

NORDEN CROWN METALS CORP.

233 West 1st Street Suite 340 North, Vancouver, V7M 1B3, BC, Canada
Tel.: (604) 922-8810
Web Site:
http://www.nordencrownmetals.com
03EA—(DEU)
Assets: $3,356,817
Liabilities: $1,314,689
Net Worth: $2,042,129
Earnings: ($1,526,809)
Fiscal Year-end: 12/31/23
Metals Mfr
N.A.I.C.S.: 332312
Daniel MacNeil *(VP-Exploration)*

NORDEX SE

Langenhorner Chaussee 600, 22419, Hamburg, Germany
Tel.: (49) 40300301000
Web Site: https://www.nordex-online.com
Year Founded: 1985
NDX1—(OTCIQ)
Rev.: $7,163,089,701
Assets: $5,985,216,256
Liabilities: $4,907,176,814
Net Worth: $1,078,039,442
Earnings: ($334,284,952)
Emp.: 9,697
Fiscal Year-end: 12/31/23
Wind Turbine Mfr
N.A.I.C.S.: 333611
Jose Luis Blanco Dieguez *(CEO)*

Subsidiaries:

Corporacion Nordex Energy Spain S.L. (1)
Poligono Industrial Barasoain Parc 2, Barasoain, 31396, Navarra, Spain
Tel.: (34) 948720535
Turbine Generator Mfr
N.A.I.C.S.: 333611

IHI Corporation (1)
1 1 Toyosu 3 Chome, Koto Ku, Tokyo, 135-8710, Japan
Tel.: (81) 362047800
Web Site: https://www.ihi.co.jp
Sales Range: $25-49.9 Million
Emp.: 100
Wind Turbine Mfr
N.A.I.C.S.: 333611

Nordex (Beijing) Wind Power Engineering & Technology Co. Ltd. (1)
Unit 808 First Shanghai Ctr 39 Liangmaqiao Rd, Chaoyang, Beijing, 100125, China
Tel.: (86) 1084535188
Web Site: http://www.nordex.com
Emp.: 70
Wind Turbine Mfr
N.A.I.C.S.: 333611

Nordex (Chile) SpA (1)
Cerro el Plomo 5420 piso 6 oficina 604 Las Condes, Santiago, Chile
Tel.: (56) 942896736
Turbine Generator Mfr

N.A.I.C.S.: 333611

Nordex China (1)
Rm 808 First Shanghai Ctr No 39 Langmaqiao Rd Chaoyang, Beijing, 100125, China
Tel.: (86) 1084535188
Web Site: http://www.nordex-online.com.cn
Sales Range: $25-49.9 Million
Emp.: 80
Wind Turbine Mfr
N.A.I.C.S.: 333611

Nordex Energy Ireland Ltd. (1)
2 Connolly Street, Clonakilty, Cork, Ireland
Tel.: (353) 18970260
Turbine Generator Mfr
N.A.I.C.S.: 333611

Nordex Energy Romania S.r.l. (1)
Maria Rosetti Tower No 6 Maria Rosetti 4th Floor Office 9 Sector 2, 020484, Bucharest, Romania
Tel.: (40) 737088803
Turbine Generator Mfr
N.A.I.C.S.: 333611

Nordex Energy South Africa RF (Pty.) Ltd. (1)
The Towers South 7th Floor 2 Heerengracht Street, Foreshore, Cape Town, 8001, South Africa
Tel.: (27) 214640200
Web Site: https://www.nordex-online.com
Emp.: 140
Turbine Generator Mfr
N.A.I.C.S.: 333611

Nordex Enerji A.S. (1)
B3 Blok Kat 16 No 462, 44149, Istanbul, Turkiye
Tel.: (90) 2124653603
Web Site: http://www.nordex-online.com
Sales Range: $25-49.9 Million
Emp.: 45
Wind Turbine Mfr
N.A.I.C.S.: 333611

Nordex Finland Oy (1)
Hiilikatu 3, 00180, Helsinki, Finland
Tel.: (358) 103230060
Wind Electric Power Generation Services
N.A.I.C.S.: 221115

Nordex France S.A.S. (1)
194 Avenue du President Wilson, 93217, La Plaine Saint-Denis, France
Tel.: (33) 15 593 4343
Web Site: http://www.nordex-france.fr
Turbine Generator Mfr
N.A.I.C.S.: 333611

Nordex Germany GmbH (1)
Langenhorner Chaussee 602, 22419, Hamburg, Germany
Tel.: (49) 40300301000
Wind Turbine Mfr
N.A.I.C.S.: 333611

Nordex Italia S.R.L. (1)
Viale Citta D Europa 679, 00144, Rome, Italy
Tel.: (39) 0683463001
Web Site: http://www.nordex-online.com
Sales Range: $25-49.9 Million
Emp.: 44
Wind Turbine Mfr
N.A.I.C.S.: 333611

Nordex Netherlands B.V. (1)
Herenweg 133-A, 2105 MG, Heemstede, Netherlands
Tel.: (31) 235294494
Web Site: https://nordex.nl
Wind Turbine Mfr
N.A.I.C.S.: 333611

Nordex Pakistan (Private) Ltd. (1)
2nd Floor East Side Low Rise Area Saudi Pak Tower 61-A, Jinnah Avenue Blue Area, Islamabad, 44000, Pakistan
Tel.: (92) 5184411012
Turbine Generator Mfr
N.A.I.C.S.: 333611

Nordex Polska Sp. z o.o. (1)
Plac Bankowy 2, 00-095, Warsaw, Poland
Tel.: (48) 222030140
Web Site: https://www.nordex-online.com
Emp.: 58
Turbine Generator Mfr

AND PRIVATE COMPANIES

N.A.I.C.S.: 333611

Nordex Sverige AB (1)
Bolandsgatan 15G, 753 23, Uppsala, Sweden
Tel.: (46) 1 818 5900
Web Site: http://www.nordex-online.com
Sales Range: $25-49.9 Million
Wind Turbine Mfr
N.A.I.C.S.: 333611

Nordex UK Ltd. (1)
Ste 4 Egerton House Towers Bus Park, Didsbury, Manchester, M20 2DX, United Kingdom
Tel.: (44) 1614459900
Web Site: http://www.nordex-online.com
Sales Range: $25-49.9 Million
Emp.: 100
Wind Turbine Mfr
N.A.I.C.S.: 333611

Nordex USA, Inc. (1)
300 S Wacker Dr Ste 1500, Chicago, IL 60606
Tel.: (312) 386-4100
Sales Range: $25-49.9 Million
Emp.: 50
Wind Turbine Mfr
N.A.I.C.S.: 333611
Ralf Sigrist *(CEO)*

NordexEnergy Uruguay S.A. (1)
Complejo WTC Torre II Oficina 109, Luis A de Herrera 1248, 11300, Montevideo, Uruguay
Tel.: (598) 26245570
Turbine Generator Mfr
N.A.I.C.S.: 333611

NORDFINANZ BANK AG
Martinistrasse 48, Bremen, 28195, Germany
Tel.: (49) 42130750
Web Site: http://www.nf-bank.com
Year Founded: 1927
Rev.: $21,327,377
Emp.: 95
Banking Services
N.A.I.C.S.: 522110
Danyon Llyod *(CEO)*

Subsidiaries:

NF-Leasing GmbH (1)
Martinistr 48, Bremen, 28195, Germany
Tel.: (49) 421 30750
Sales Range: $50-74.9 Million
Emp.: 80
Commercial Banking Services
N.A.I.C.S.: 522110
Marc Horstmann *(Mgr-Fin)*

NORDFYNS BANK A/S
Adelgade 49, Bogense, 5400, Odense, 5400, Denmark
Tel.: (45) 59489300   DK
Web Site:
https://www.nordfynsbank.dk
Year Founded: 1897
NRDF—(CSE)
Rev.: $45,729,334
Assets: $747,653,774
Liabilities: $641,826,916
Net Worth: $105,826,858
Earnings: $15,955,492
Emp.: 103
Fiscal Year-end: 12/31/23
Commercial Banking Services
N.A.I.C.S.: 522110
Per Poulsen *(Deputy Chm)*

NORDHEALTH AS
Eikremsvingen 9, 6422, Molde, Norway
Tel.: (47) 7539032200
Web Site:
https://www.nordhealth.com
Year Founded: 2001
NORDH—(OSL)
Rev.: $39,742,068
Assets: $99,218,649
Liabilities: $9,896,395
Net Worth: $89,322,253

Earnings: ($12,013,814)
Emp.: 395
Fiscal Year-end: 12/31/23
Software Development Services
N.A.I.C.S.: 541511
Hanna Chiorazzo *(Chief People Officer)*

Subsidiaries:

Aspit AS (1)
Steinsrudvegen 1, 3840, Seljord, Norway
Tel.: (47) 35057900
Web Site: https://www.aspit.no
Emp.: 60
Healthcare Software Consulting Services
N.A.I.C.S.: 541618

Navicre Oy (1)
Aleksanterinkatu 30-34, 00100, Helsinki, Finland
Tel.: (358) 445515603
Web Site: https://www.navisec.fi
Information Technology Consulting Services
N.A.I.C.S.: 541512

Nordhealth Oy (1)
Aleksanterinkatu 30-34, 00100, Helsinki, Finland
Tel.: (358) 194251610
Emp.: 400
Healthcare Software Consulting Services
N.A.I.C.S.: 541618

Vetera GmbH (1)
Grosse Hub 1, 65344, Eltville am Rhein, Germany
Tel.: (49) 6123703750
Web Site: https://www.vetera.net
Veterinary Software Consulting Services
N.A.I.C.S.: 541940

NORDIC AMERICAN TANKERS LIMITED
Swan Building 26 Victoria Street, Hamilton, HM12, Bermuda
Tel.: (441) 2927202   BM
Web Site: https://www.nat.bm
Year Founded: 1995
NAT—(NYSE)
Rev.: $339,340,000
Assets: $879,883,000
Liabilities: $339,901,000
Net Worth: $539,982,000
Earnings: $15,101,000
Emp.: 18
Fiscal Year-end: 12/31/22
Tanker Operation & Leasing Services
N.A.I.C.S.: 483111
Herbjorn Hansson *(Pres, CEO & Chm)*

Subsidiaries:

NAT Chartering AS (1)
Fridtjof Nansens Plass 7, 0160, Oslo, Norway
Tel.: (47) 23696900
Crude Oil Transportation Services
N.A.I.C.S.: 486990

Teekay Norway AS (1)
Verven 4, N-4068, Stavanger, Norway   (100%)
Tel.: (47) 51442700
Sales Range: $50-74.9 Million
Owns, Develops, Builds, Converts & Operates Floating Storage, Offloading Units & Tankers
N.A.I.C.S.: 488330

NORDIC AQUA PARTNERS A/S
Hundegade 1, 6760, Ribe, Denmark
Tel.: (45) 8221222   DK
Web Site:
https://www.nordicaquapartners.com
Year Founded: 2016
NOAP—(OSL)
Information Technology Services
N.A.I.C.S.: 541512
Atle Eide *(Chm)*

NORDIC CAPITAL AB
Maester Samuelsgatan 21 9th Fl, 111 44, Stockholm, Sweden
Tel.: (46) 84405050   SE
Web Site:
http://www.nordiccapital.com
Year Founded: 1989
Emp.: 180
Privater Equity Firm
N.A.I.C.S.: 523999
Robert Andreen *(Co-Founder & Sr Partner)*

Subsidiaries:

Acino Holding AG (1)
Dornacherstrasse 114, 4147, Aesch, Switzerland
Tel.: (41) 613386000
Web Site: http://www.acino-pharma.com
Sales Range: $10-24.9 Million
Emp.: 836
Holding Company; Pharmaceuticals Mfr
N.A.I.C.S.: 551112
Jean-Daniel Bonny *(Head-R&D)*

Subsidiary (Domestic):

Acino Pharma AG (2)
Birsweg 2, 4253, Liesberg, Switzerland
Tel.: (41) 617758000
Web Site: http://www.acino-pharma.com
Emp.: 350
Pharmaceuticals Product Mfr
N.A.I.C.S.: 325412
Kalle Kand *(Mng Dir)*

Acino Supply AG (2)
Pfeffingerring 205, 4147, Aesch, Switzerland
Tel.: (41) 61 756 40 00
Pharmaceutical Products Distr
N.A.I.C.S.: 424210

Aditro AB (1)
Landsvagen 66, Sundbyberg, 172 22, Sweden
Tel.: (46) 104511000
Web Site: http://www.aditro.com
Sales Range: $250-299.9 Million
Business Process Outsourcing & Human Resources Management Services
N.A.I.C.S.: 561499
Martin Sjogren *(CEO)*

Aris Global LLC (1)
1266 E Main St, Stamford, CT 06902
Tel.: (203) 588-3000
Web Site: http://www.arisglobal.com
Sales Range: $25-49.9 Million
Emp.: 1,200
Research & Development Software Solutions & Consultancy Services
N.A.I.C.S.: 541690
Ritu Shrivastava *(VP-Corp Dev)*

Britax Childcare Ltd. (1)
3000 Hillswood Drive, Hillswood Business Park, Chertsey, KT16 0RS, United Kingdom
Tel.: (44) 1264 386034
Web Site: http://www.britax.com
Sales Range: $350-399.9 Million
Emp.: 1,020
Childrens Strollers, Car Seats & Bike Seats Mfr
N.A.I.C.S.: 339930

Subsidiary (US):

Britax Child Safety, Inc. (2)
13501 South Ridge Dr, Charlotte, NC 28273
Tel.: (704) 409-1700
Web Site: http://www.britaxusa.com
Sales Range: $75-99.9 Million
Emp.: 190
Distr of Strollers & Child Safety Equipment & Accessories for Motor Vehicles
N.A.I.C.S.: 423120
Kate Clark *(Mgr-PR & Event-Baby Carriers)*

Division (Domestic):

B.O.B. Trailers, Inc. (3)
5475 Gage St, Boise, ID 83706-1547
Tel.: (208) 375-5171
Web Site: http://www.bobgear.com
Bicycle Cargo Trailers & Jogging Strollers Mfr
N.A.I.C.S.: 339930

NORDIC CAPITAL AB

Subsidiary (Non-US):

Britax Childcare Hong Kong Ltd. (2)
Rm 1101-3 11/F Tower II Phase I Enterprise Square, 9 Sheung Yuet Road, Kowloon, China (Hong Kong)
Tel.: (852) 2620 1331
Web Site: http://www.britax.com
Distr of Child Safety Equipment & Accessories for Motor Vehicles & Strollers
N.A.I.C.S.: 423120

Britax Childcare NZ Ltd. (2)
101 Diane Street, Glenfield, New Zealand
Tel.: (64) 9 443 0102
Web Site: http://www.britax.co.nz
Emp.: 4
Distr of Child Safety Equipment & Accessories for Motor Vehicles & Strollers
N.A.I.C.S.: 423120
David Jackson *(CEO)*

Britax Childcare Pty. Ltd. (2)
99 Derby Rd, Sunshine, Melbourne, 3020, VIC, Australia   (100%)
Tel.: (61) 392887288
Web Site: http://www.britax.com.au
Sales Range: $25-49.9 Million
Mfr & Distr of Strollers & Child Safety Equipment & Accessories for Motor Vehicles
N.A.I.C.S.: 339930

Subsidiary (Domestic):

Britax Excelsior Limited (2)
1 Churchill Way West, Andover, SP10 3UW, Hampshire, United Kingdom   (100%)
Tel.: (44) 1264333343
Web Site: http://www.britax.co.uk
Sales Range: $50-74.9 Million
Emp.: 500
Mfr of Strollers & Child Safety Equipment, Seat Belts, Components & Accessories for Motor Vehicles
N.A.I.C.S.: 339930
Rainer Stabler *(Mng Dir)*

Subsidiary (Non-US):

Britax Nordiska Barn AB (2)
Johanneslundsvagen 2 3rd Floor, SE 19461, Upplands Vasby, Sweden
Tel.: (46) 8564 841 00
Web Site: http://www.britax.se
Distr of Child Safety Equipment & Accessories for Motor Vehicles & Strollers
N.A.I.C.S.: 423120

Britax Pohjolan Lapset Oy (2)
Kauppakartanonkatu 15D, 00930, Helsinki, Finland
Tel.: (358) 9 343 6010
Web Site: http://www.britax.fi
Distr of Child Safety Equipment & Accessories for Motor Vehicles & Strollers
N.A.I.C.S.: 423120

Britax Roemer Kindersicherheit GmbH (2)
Blaubeurer Strasse 71, PO Box 3449, 89024, Ulm, Germany   (100%)
Tel.: (49) 73193450
Web Site: http://www.britax-roemer.de
Sales Range: $100-124.9 Million
Mfr of Strollers & Child Safety Equipment, Seat Belts, Components & Accessories for Motor Vehicles
N.A.I.C.S.: 339930
Ian Watson *(Mng Dir)*

Bufab AB (1)
Stenfalksvagen 1, SE-331 41, Varnamo, Sweden
Tel.: (46) 370696900
Web Site: http://www.bufab.com
Rev.: $789,663,473
Assets: $883,793,682
Liabilities: $599,436,155
Net Worth: $284,357,526
Earnings: $57,040,097
Emp.: 1,764
Fiscal Year-end: 12/31/2022
Holding Company; Nuts, Screws, Washers, Bolts, Rivets & Other Fasteners Distr
N.A.I.C.S.: 551112
Jorgen Rosengren *(CEO)*

Subsidiary (US):

American Bolt and Screw Manufacturing Corporation (2)

NORDIC CAPITAL AB

Nordic Capital AB—(Continued)
601 Kettering Dr, Ontario, CA 91761
Tel.: (909) 390-0522
Web Site: http://www.absfasteners.com
Sales Range: $10-24.9 Million
Emp.: 100
Bolts, Nuts & Screws
N.A.I.C.S.: 423710

CameronTec AB (1)
Grev Turegatan 3, Stockholm, 114 46, Sweden
Tel.: (46) 8 506 477 00
Web Site: http://www.camerontecgroup.com
Financial Information Exchange Messaging Software Developer
N.A.I.C.S.: 513210
Anders Henriksson (CEO)

Subsidiary (Non-US):

Cameron Systems (Vic) Pty Ltd (2)
Level 18 56 Pitt St, Sydney, 2000, NSW, Australia
Tel.: (61) 292402400
Emp.: 7
Financial Information Exchange Messaging Software Developer
N.A.I.C.S.: 513210
Torben Munch (CEO)

Subsidiary (US):

CameronTec Americas, Inc. (2)
30 S Wacker Dr Ste 1650, Chicago, IL 60606
Tel.: (312) 235-5600
Web Site: http://www.greenlinetech.com
Sales Range: $1-9.9 Million
Emp.: 38
Developer of Financial Information Exchange Integration, Testing & Management Products
N.A.I.C.S.: 513210
Tim Wilcox (Dir-Sls-Americas)

Cidron IT A/S (1)
Sankt Annae Plads 11, DK-1250, Copenhagen, Denmark
Tel.: (45) 33447750
Information Technology Services
N.A.I.C.S.: 541519

Cint AB (1)
Luntmakargatan 18 1tr, 111 37, Stockholm, Sweden
Tel.: (46) 854638300
Web Site: https://www.cint.com
Software Services & Survey Data
N.A.I.C.S.: 513210

Subsidiary (US):

P2Sample, Inc. (2)
3159 Royal Dr Ste 360, Alpharetta, GA 30022
Tel.: (404) 446-2720
Marketing Consulting Services
N.A.I.C.S.: 541613

Consilium Safety Group AB (1)
Salsmastaregatan 21, 402 76, Gothenburg, Sweden
Tel.: (46) 317107700
Web Site: https://www.consiliumsafety.com
Emp.: 100
Marine Equipments Supply Services
N.A.I.C.S.: 336999

Subsidiary (Domestic):

Consilium Fire & Gas AB (2)
PO Box 8763, 40276, Gothenburg, Sweden
Tel.: (46) 317107700
Sales Range: $75-99.9 Million
Emp.: 240
Fire Alarm Solutions Provider
N.A.I.C.S.: 922160
Carl Adam Rofenblad (Pres-Global Mgmt)

Consilium Marine AB (2)
Salsmastaregatan 21, PO Box 8763, 402 76, Gothenburg, Sweden
Tel.: (46) 317107700
Web Site: http://www.consilium.se
Sales Range: $50-74.9 Million
Emp.: 200
Marine Equipments Supply Services
N.A.I.C.S.: 336999

Consilium Navigation AB (2)
Vastberga alle 36 B, 126 30, Hagersten, Sweden
Tel.: (46) 856305100
Web Site: http://www.consilium.se
Navigational Products Supplier
N.A.I.C.S.: 334511

Consilium Transport Safety AB (2)
Salsmastaregatan 21, PO Box 8763, 40276, Gothenburg, Sweden
Tel.: (46) 317107700
Sales Range: $75-99.9 Million
Emp.: 150
Fire Detection System Suppliers
N.A.I.C.S.: 922160

ConvaTec Ltd. (1)
Centerpointe II 1160 Route 22 E Ste 201, Bridgewater, NJ 08807
Tel.: (908) 231-2179
Web Site: http://www.convatec.com
Sales Range: $1-4.9 Billion
Medicinal Product Mfr
N.A.I.C.S.: 339112
Supratim Bose (Pres-APAC & Exec VP)

Subsidiary (Domestic):

180 Medical, Inc. (2)
8516 NW Expy, Oklahoma City, OK 73162
Tel.: (405) 702-7700
Web Site: https://www.180medical.com
Medical, Dental & Hospital Equipment & Supplies Merchant Whslr
N.A.I.C.S.: 423450
Todd Brown (Founder & CEO)

Ellos AB (1)
Odegardsgatan 6, 504 64, Boras, Sweden
Tel.: (46) 33160000
Web Site: http://www.ellosgroup.com
Sales Range: $200-249.9 Million
Emp.: 550
Online Mail Order General Merchandise Retailer
N.A.I.C.S.: 455219
Hams Ohlffom (Mng Dir)

Subsidiary (Non-US):

Ellos Finland Oy (2)
Tiilitehtaankatu 7, 04250, Kerava, Finland
Tel.: (358) 9476611
Web Site: http://www.ellos.fi
Mail Ordering Shopping Services
N.A.I.C.S.: 425120

IntegriChain Inc. (1)
8 Penn Center 1628 JFK Blvd Ste 300, Philadelphia, PA 19103
Tel.: (609) 806-5005
Web Site: https://www.integrichain.com
Pharmaceutical Information Services
N.A.I.C.S.: 519200
Vickie Bruno (Sr Accountant)

Subsidiary (Domestic):

daVizta, Inc. (2)
750 Route 202 S Ste 110, Bridgewater, NJ 08807
Tel.: (908) 968-0852
Web Site: http://davizta.com
Management Consulting Services
N.A.I.C.S.: 541611

Jotex AB (1)
Udegardsgatan 6, 504 94, Boras, Sweden
Tel.: (46) 33225022
Web Site: http://www.jotex.se
Sales Range: $200-249.9 Million
Home Decor Product Mail Ordering Services
N.A.I.C.S.: 423620
Eric Dubois (Mng Dir)

Keycorp Pty. Limited (1)
22-30 Chifley Drive, Fairfield, Preston, 3072, VIC, Australia
Tel.: (61) 3 9403 1777
Web Site: http://www.keycorp.net
Sales Range: $25-49.9 Million
Secure Electonic Financial Transaction Software & Technologies Development, Implementation & Support Services
N.A.I.C.S.: 541511
Joe Bonin (CEO)

Lock Lower Holding AS (1)
Hoffsveien 70B, 0377, Oslo, Norway
Tel.: (47) 2321 1000
Web Site: http://www.lindorff.com
Rev.: $581,483,280
Assets: $3,341,895,480
Liabilities: $2,482,737,600
Net Worth: $859,157,880
Earnings: ($17,422,720)
Emp.: 4,000
Fiscal Year-end: 12/31/2015
Holding Company; Credit Management Services
N.A.I.C.S.: 551112
Carl Per Eric Sletten Larsson (Chm)

Subsidiary (Domestic):

Lock AS (2)
Hoffsveien 70B, 0377, Oslo, Norway
Tel.: (47) 2321 1000
Credit Management Services
N.A.I.C.S.: 522390
Klaus-Anders Nysteen (CEO)

Subsidiary (Non-US):

Lindorff A/S (3)
Bygholm Sopark 21 E, DK-8700, Horsens, Denmark
Tel.: (45) 76 282828
Web Site: http://www.lindorff.com
Credit Services
N.A.I.C.S.: 522390
Lisbeth Dalum Hansen (Country Mgr)

Lindorff Eesti AS (3)
Sakala 10/Kentmanni 4 5 korrus, EE-10141, Tallinn, Estonia
Tel.: (372) 6118 030
Web Site: http://www.lindorff.ee
Credit Services
N.A.I.C.S.: 522390

Lindorff Netherlands B.V. (3)
Spoetnik 20, 3824 MG, Amersfoort, Netherlands
Tel.: (31) 88 1189900
Web Site: http://www.lindorff.com
Credit Services
N.A.I.C.S.: 522390
Marc Knothe (Country Mgr)

Lindorff Oy (3)
Joukahaisenkatu 6 PL 20, FI-20101, Turku, Finland
Tel.: (358) 10270000
Web Site: http://www.lindorff.com
Credit Intermediation Services
N.A.I.C.S.: 522390
Turkka Kuusisto (Mng Dir)

Lindorff Sverige AB (3)
Kungsgatan 57A, SE-111 22, Stockholm, Sweden
Tel.: (46) 8 587 28100
Web Site: http://www.lindorff.com
Credit Services
N.A.I.C.S.: 522390
Erika Ronnquist Hoh (CEO)

NC Advisory (UK) LLP (1)
3rd Floor 105 Piccadilly, London, W1J 7NJ, United Kingdom
Tel.: (44) 207 355 5700
Financial Investment Management Services
N.A.I.C.S.: 523940
Christof Ratjen (Principal-Capital Markets Team)

NC Advisory AS (1)
Klingenberggaten 5 9th floor, PO Box 2067, 0125, Oslo, Norway
Tel.: (47) 21 09 33 00
Financial Investment Management Services
N.A.I.C.S.: 523940

NC Advisory GmbH (1)
Bockenheimer Landstrasse 2-4, DE-60306, Frankfurt, Germany
Tel.: (49) 699709780
Web Site: http://www.nordiccapital.com
Financial Investment Management Services
N.A.I.C.S.: 523940

NC Advisory Oy (1)
Bulevardi 6 A 8 4th Floor, 00120, Helsinki, Finland
Tel.: (358) 20 7433 250
Financial Investment Management Services
N.A.I.C.S.: 523940

Nordic Capital Limited (1)

INTERNATIONAL PUBLIC

26 Esplanade, Saint Helier, JE2 3QA, Jersey
Tel.: (44) 1534605100
Web Site: http://www.nordiccapital.com
Sales Range: $50-74.9 Million
Emp.: 10
Privater Equity Firm
N.A.I.C.S.: 523999
Ged Kelly (Mng Dir & Grp Head-Fund Ops)

Subsidiary (Non-US):

Max Matthiessen AB (2)
Lastmakargatan 22, Box 3205, 103 64, Stockholm, Sweden
Tel.: (46) 86130200
Web Site: https://www.maxm.se
Insurance Agencies Services
N.A.I.C.S.: 524210

Nordic Capital Sarl (1)
7 Rue Lou Hemmer, Findel, 1748, Luxembourg, Luxembourg
Tel.: (352) 621 200 140
Financial Investment Management Services
N.A.I.C.S.: 523940

Orchid Orthopedic Solutions, LLC (1)
1489 Cedar St, Holt, MI 48842
Tel.: (517) 694-2300
Web Site: http://www.orchid-orthopedics.com
Sales Range: $450-499.9 Million
Surgical Instrument & Supplies Mfr
N.A.I.C.S.: 339112
Louis Pace (CFO)

Subsidiary (Domestic):

Orchid Bio-Coat (2)
21249 Bridge St, Southfield, MI 48034
Tel.: (248) 352-4570
Sales Range: $25-49.9 Million
Medical Instrument Coating & Surface Treatment Services
N.A.I.C.S.: 339112
Bob Naumann (Gen Mgr)

Unit (Domestic):

Orchid Keller (2)
3203 Kashiwa St, Torrance, CA 90505
Tel.: (310) 326-6291
Sales Range: $25-49.9 Million
Emp.: 28
Surgical Appliance & Supplies Mfr
N.A.I.C.S.: 339113
Steven Dragovich (Gen Mgr)

Subsidiary (Domestic):

Orchid Macdee Orthopedic Solutions, LLC (2)
13800 Luick Dr, Chelsea, MI 48118
Tel.: (734) 475-9165
Sales Range: $25-49.9 Million
Plastic Medical Instrument & Supplies Mfr
N.A.I.C.S.: 339112
Patrick Davidson (Gen Mgr)

Subsidiary (Non-US):

Orchid Orthopedic Solutions Sheffield Ltd. (2)
Unit D Beighton Business Park Old Colliery Way, Sheffield, S20 1DJ, United Kingdom (100%)
Tel.: (44) 114 2942300
Web Site: http://www.orchid-ortho.com
Sales Range: $25-49.9 Million
Medical Stainless Steel Products & Materials Mfr & Distr
N.A.I.C.S.: 339112
David Beighton (Gen Mgr)

Unit (Domestic):

Orchid Orthopedic Solutions, LLC - Alabama (2)
331 City Park Dr SE, Arab, AL 35016
Tel.: (256) 586-4534
Web Site: http://www.orchid-ortho.com
Sales Range: $25-49.9 Million
Emp.: 100
Surgical Instrument & Supplies Mfr
N.A.I.C.S.: 339112
Clay Clayton (Gen Mgr)

Reynolds S.A.S. (1)
Immeuble Lumiere 17 Rue Des Deux

AND PRIVATE COMPANIES

Gares, 92565, Rueil-Malmaison, Cedex, France
Tel.: (33) 147145555
Web Site: http://www.reynolds-european.fr
Sales Range: $25-49.9 Million
Emp.: 66
Distr of Semi-Manufactured Products Such as Tubes & Sheets & Wire in Copper, Brass & Aluminum; Joint Venture of Trelleborg AB & Nordic Capital
N.A.I.C.S.: 332439

Subsidiary (Non-US):

Reyton Metals Ltd. (2)
1 Malvern View Business Park, Stella Way, Bishops Cleeve, Cheltenham, GL52 4RP, Glos, United Kingdom
Tel.: (44) 1242631000
N.A.I.C.S.: 326211

Reyton Wire Ltd (2)
Unit 1 Miners Rd Llay Industrial Estate Llay, Wrexham, LL12 0PJ, United Kingdom (100%)
Tel.: (44) 1978855668
Web Site: http://www.reytonwire.co.uk
N.A.I.C.S.: 326211

SafeRoad AS (1)
Strandgata 59, Orsta, 6150, Norway
Tel.: (47) 70064000
Web Site: http://www.saferoad.no
Road Infrastructure Safety Solutions
N.A.I.C.S.: 237310

Unomedical a/s (1)
Aaholmvej 1-3 Osted, 4320, Lejre, Denmark
Tel.: (45) 48167000
Web Site: http://www.infusion-set.com
Subcutaneous Medical Devices Designer & Mfr
N.A.I.C.S.: 334519

Vizrt Group AS (1)
Lars Hilles Gate 30, 5008, Bergen, Norway
Tel.: (47) 55230025
Web Site: http://www.vizrt.com
Rev.: $169,297,000
Assets: $426,718,000
Liabilities: $360,995,000
Net Worth: $65,723,000
Earnings: ($8,578,000)
Emp.: 700
Fiscal Year-end: 12/31/2019
Holding Company; Media Broadcast Graphics, Studio Automation, Sports Analysis & Asset Management Products & Services
N.A.I.C.S.: 551112
Petter Ole Jakobsen (Founder)

Subsidiary (Non-US):

Vizrt (Beijing) Technology Ltd. (2)
Room 1408 No 8 Sandalwood Plaza No 27 Jianguo Road, Chao Yang District, Beijing, China (100%)
Tel.: (86) 1065447691
Web Site: http://www.vizrt.com
Media Broadcast Graphics, Studio Automation, Sports Analysis & Asset Management Products & Services
N.A.I.C.S.: 541430
Lear Tse (Reg Mgr)

Vizrt (Thailand) Limited (2)
99/9 Central Chaengwattana Office Tower 14th Floor Moo 2, Chaengwattana Road Bangtalad Pakkred, Nonthaburi, 11120, Thailand (100%)
Tel.: (66) 21010790
Web Site: http://www.vizrt.com
Media Broadcast Graphics, Studio Automation, Sports Analysis & Asset Management Products & Services
N.A.I.C.S.: 541430
Yupapak Tawanna (Dir & Gen Mgr-Thailand)

Vizrt AG (2)
Elias-Canetti-Strasse 2, 8050, Zurich, Switzerland (100%)
Tel.: (41) 44 277 6500
Web Site: http://www.vizrt.com
Media Broadcast Graphics, Studio Automation, Sports Analysis & Asset Management Products & Services
N.A.I.C.S.: 541430

Vizrt Australia Pty. Ltd. (2)
Suite 2 Level 1 35 Mitchell Street McMahons Point, Sydney, 2060, NSW, Australia (100%)
Tel.: (61) 299222676
Web Site: http://www.vizrt.com
Media Broadcast Graphics, Studio Automation, Sports Analysis & Asset Management Products & Services
N.A.I.C.S.: 541430
Richard Hewitt (Gen Mgr)

Vizrt Austria GmbH (2)
Industriestrasse 2a, Vomp, 6134, Schwaz, Austria (100%)
Tel.: (43) 5242 73225
Web Site: http://www.vizrt.com
Media Broadcast Graphics, Studio Automation, Sports Analysis & Asset Management Products & Services
N.A.I.C.S.: 541430
Armin Kaltenhauser (Pres-EMEA)

Representative Office (Non-US):

Vizrt Hong Kong & Macau (2)
Unit A 9th Floor Great Wall Factory Building No 11 Cheung Shun Street, Lai Chi Kok, Kowloon, China (Hong Kong)
Tel.: (852) 28772170
Web Site: http://www.vizrt.com
Media Broadcast Graphics, Studio Automation, Sports Analysis & Asset Management Products & Services
N.A.I.C.S.: 541430
Danny Chiu (Reg Dir-DMA)

Subsidiary (Non-US):

Vizrt India Private Limited (2)
A-71 3rd Floor FIEE Complex, Okhla Industrial Estate Phase II, New Delhi, 110020, India (100%)
Tel.: (91) 9821013847
Web Site: http://www.vizrt.com
Media Broadcast Graphics, Studio Automation, Sports Analysis & Asset Management Products & Services
N.A.I.C.S.: 541430
Manish Aggarwal (Reg Mgr)

Representative Office (Non-US):

Vizrt Japan (2)
Level 28 Shinagawa Intercity A 2-15-1 Kounan, Minato-ku, Tokyo, 108-6028, Japan
Tel.: (81) 367176050
Web Site: http://www.vizrt.com
Media Broadcast Graphics, Studio Automation, Sports Analysis & Asset Management Products & Services
N.A.I.C.S.: 541430

Vizrt Latin America (2)
Avenida Angelica 2491 CJ105, Sao Paulo, 01227-200, SP, Brazil
Tel.: (55) 11 8274 3344
Web Site: http://www.vizrt.com
Media Broadcast Graphics, Studio Automation, Sports Analysis & Asset Management Products & Services
N.A.I.C.S.: 541430

Vizrt Middle East (2)
Office #1305 13th Floor Al Shatha Tower, PO Box 502472, Dubai Media City, Dubai, United Arab Emirates
Tel.: (971) 50 5528 337
Web Site: http://www.vizrt.com
Media Broadcast Graphics, Studio Automation, Sports Analysis & Asset Management Products & Services
N.A.I.C.S.: 541430
Ian Davis (Reg Mgr)

Subsidiary (Domestic):

Vizrt Norway AS (2)
Lars Hilles Gate 30, 5008, Bergen, Norway (100%)
Tel.: (47) 5523 0025
Web Site: http://www.vizrt.com
Media Broadcast Graphics, Studio Automation, Sports Analysis & Asset Management Products & Services
N.A.I.C.S.: 541430

Representative Office (Non-US):

Vizrt Philippines (2)
4th Floor The West Wing Bldg 107 West Avenue, Quezon City, 1104, Philippines
Tel.: (63) 24110747

Web Site: http://www.vizrt.com
Media Broadcast Graphics, Studio Automation, Sports Analysis & Asset Management Products & Services
N.A.I.C.S.: 541430

Vizrt Singapore (2)
15 Mount Sinai Rise #09-40, Singapore, 276906, Singapore
Tel.: (65) 86131912
Web Site: http://www.vizrt.com
Media Broadcast Graphics, Studio Automation, Sports Analysis & Asset Management Products & Services
N.A.I.C.S.: 541430

Subsidiary (Non-US):

Vizrt Spain & Portugal S.L. (2)
Cedaceros 11 2C, 28014, Madrid, Spain (100%)
Tel.: (34) 687458824
Web Site: http://www.vizrt.com
Media Broadcast Graphics, Studio Automation, Sports Analysis & Asset Management Products & Services
N.A.I.C.S.: 541430
Pablo Herrero Delavenay (Reg Mgr-Southwest Europe & Grp Head-Bus Dev-EMEA)

Vizrt Sweden AB (2)
Kistagangen 12, 164 40, Kista, Sweden (100%)
Tel.: (46) 852227700
Web Site: http://www.vizrt.com
Media Broadcast Graphics, Studio Automation, Sports Analysis & Asset Management Products & Services
N.A.I.C.S.: 541430
Ximena Araneda (Grp Dir-Product Mgmt-Media Workflows)

Vizrt UK Ltd. (2)
1st Floor Building B Ealing Studios, Ealing Green, London, W5 5EP, United Kingdom (100%)
Tel.: (44) 2082800410
Web Site: http://www.vizrt.com
Media Broadcast Graphics, Studio Automation, Sports Analysis & Asset Management Products & Services
N.A.I.C.S.: 541430

Subsidiary (US):

Vizrt USA LLC (2)
352 7th Ave 14th Fl, New York, NY 10001
Tel.: (212) 560-0708
Web Site: http://www.vizrt.com
Media Broadcast Graphics, Studio Automation, Sports Analysis & Asset Management Products & Services
N.A.I.C.S.: 541430
Bill Anderson (VP-Sls)

Branch (Domestic):

Vizrt USA LLC - South Regional Office (3)
1800 Peachtree St NW Ste 335, Atlanta, GA 30309
Tel.: (646) 502-4696
Web Site: http://www.vizrt.com
Media Broadcast Graphics, Studio Automation, Sports Analysis & Asset Management Products & Services
N.A.I.C.S.: 541430
Jose Phon (VP-Ops-America)

eResearchTechnology, Inc. (1)
1818 Market St Ste 1000, Philadelphia, PA 19103-3638
Tel.: (215) 972-0420
Web Site: http://www.ert.com
Medical Diagnostic & Testing Web-Based Software & Consulting Services
N.A.I.C.S.: 513210
Steve Nuckols (Chief Comml Officer & Exec VP)

Subsidiary (Domestic):

APDM, Inc. (2)
2828 SW Corbett Ave Ste 130, Portland, OR 97201-4811
Tel.: (503) 445-7757
Web Site: http://www.apdm.com
Electromedical & Electrotherapeutic Apparatus Mfr

NORDIC ELEMENTS AB

N.A.I.C.S.: 334510
Thomas Rolke (CEO)

BioClinica, Inc. (2)
211 Carnegie Ct Dr, Princeton, NJ 08540
Tel.: (877) 632-9432
Web Site: http://www.bioclinica.com
Medical Imaging Solutions & Cardiac Safety Services for Clinical Trial Sponsors
N.A.I.C.S.: 621511
David S. Herron (Pres & CEO)

Subsidiary (Non-US):

eResearchTechnology GmbH (2)
Sieboldstrasse 3, Estenfeld, 97230, Wurzburg, Germany
Tel.: (49) 9305 720 60
Web Site: http://www.ert.com
Medical Diagnostic & Testing Web-Based Software & Consulting Services
N.A.I.C.S.: 513210

Subsidiary (US):

Biomedical Systems Corp. (3)
77 Progress Pkwy, Maryland Heights, MO 63043
Tel.: (314) 576-6800
Web Site: http://www.biomedsys.com
Sales Range: $1-9.9 Million
Health/Allied Services
N.A.I.C.S.: 621999
Timothy Barrett (Pres)

Subsidiary (Non-US):

eResearchTechnology Limited (2)
Peterborough Business Park, Lynch Wood, Peterborough, PE2 6FZ, Cambs, United Kingdom
Tel.: (44) 1733 374800
Web Site: http://www.ert.com
Medical Diagnostic & Testing Web-Based Software & Consulting Services
N.A.I.C.S.: 513210

Branch (Domestic):

eResearchTechnology, Inc. - Bridgewater (2)
685 US Hwy 202 206 2nd Fl, Bridgewater, NJ 08807-1774
Tel.: (908) 704-8010
Web Site: http://www.ert.com
Medical Diagnostic & Testing Web-Based Software
N.A.I.C.S.: 513210
Tom Devine (CIO, Chief Dev Officer Exec VP)

NORDIC CORPORATE BANK ASA

Inkognitogata 8,, 0285, Oslo, Norway
Tel.: (47) 21032400
Web Site: https://www.ncbank.no
Year Founded: 2019
Emp.: 100
Commercial Bank
N.A.I.C.S.: 522110

NORDIC ELEMENTS AB

City Office World Trade Center Kungsbron 1, 111 22, Stockholm, Sweden
Tel.: (46) 850636251 SE
Web Site: http://www.ferromax.se
Sales Range: $50-74.9 Million
Emp.: 33
Metal Alloy Ores & Metal Production & Consulting Services Distr
N.A.I.C.S.: 423510

Subsidiaries:

AB Ferrolegeringar (1)
Sveavagen 9, Stockholm, 11157, Sweden
Tel.: (46) 84546560
Web Site: http://www.ferrolegeringar.se
Sales Range: $25-49.9 Million
Emp.: 14
Sales & Distribution of Metal Alloys
N.A.I.C.S.: 423510
Robert Idegren (Mgr)

Minpro AB (1)
Odalvagen 8, S 711 77, Strassa, Sweden
Tel.: (46) 58143110

NORDIC ELEMENTS AB

Nordic Elements AB—(Continued)
Web Site: http://www.minpro.se
Sales Range: $25-49.9 Million
Emp.: 28
Ores & Metals Production & Consulting Services; Research & Process Development in Fields of Minerals, Mining & Recycling
N.A.I.C.S.: 541690
Johan Arvidsson (Mng Dir)

NORDIC FIBREBOARD AS
Raama 31, 80044, Parnu, Estonia
Tel.: (372) 4478323
Web Site:
https://www.nordicfibreboard.com
SKN1T—(TAL)
Rev.: $8,504,250
Assets: $9,388,453
Liabilities: $4,529,197
Net Worth: $4,859,256
Earnings: ($752,842)
Emp.: 67
Fiscal Year-end: 12/31/23
Construction Equipment Mfr
N.A.I.C.S.: 333120
Torfinn Losvik (Chm-Mgmt Bd)

Subsidiaries:

Nordic Fibreboard Ltd OU (1)
Raama 31, 80044, Parnu, Estonia
Tel.: (372) 4451800
Web Site: https://www.nordicfibreboard.com
Building Material Mfr & Distr
N.A.I.C.S.: 327120

Suomen Tuulileijona OY (1)
Vuoriukatu 24 b, 18101, Heinola, Finland
Tel.: (358) 5 552 5550
Web Site: https://www.tuulileijona.fi
Drywall & Insulation Services
N.A.I.C.S.: 238310

NORDIC FLANGES GROUP AB
Herkulesgatan 14, 111 52, Stockholm, Sweden
Tel.: (46) 858797900
Web Site:
https://www.nordicflanges.com
Hardware Product Mfr
N.A.I.C.S.: 332510
Frederik Von Sterneck (Pres)

NORDIC GAMES HOLDING AB
Ostanvindsgatan 17, 652 21, Karlstad, Sweden
Tel.: (46) 54 854750   SE
Web Site:
http://www.nordicgamesgroup.com
Year Founded: 2008
Holding Company; Video Game Developer
N.A.I.C.S.: 551112
Lars Wingefors (CEO)

Subsidiaries:

Game Outlet Europe AB (1)
Box 5083, Karlstad, 650 05, Sweden
Tel.: (46) 54 854 750
Web Site: http://www.gameoutlet.se
Video Games Distr
N.A.I.C.S.: 449210
Henrik Westman (Acct Mgr-Key)

Nordic Games GmbH (1)
Landstrasser Hauptstrasse 1/Top 18, A 1030, Vienna, Austria   **(100%)**
Tel.: (43) 664 88 737 20 0
Web Site: http://www.nordicgames.at
Computer Game Software
N.A.I.C.S.: 513210
Reinhard Pollice (Dir-Bus & Product Dev)

NORDIC GROUP LIMITED
2 Tuas Avenue 10, Singapore, 639126, Singapore
Tel.: (65) 68484400   SG
Web Site:
https://www.nordicflowcontrol.com
Year Founded: 1998

MR7—(SES)
Rev.: $60,997,046
Assets: $126,871,954
Liabilities: $59,803,439
Net Worth: $67,068,515
Earnings: $4,138,746
Emp.: 210
Fiscal Year-end: 12/31/20
Marine, Oil & Gas Control Systems Mfr
N.A.I.C.S.: 334513
Yeh Hong Chang (Chm)

Subsidiaries:

Austin Energy (Asia) Pte. Ltd. (1)
2 Tuas Avenue 10, Singapore, 639126, Singapore
Tel.: (65) 68484400
Web Site: https://www.ae.com.sg
Insulation & Fireproofing Services
N.A.I.C.S.: 922160

Austin Energy Offshore Pte. Ltd. (1)
2 Tuas Avenue 10, Singapore, 639126, Singapore
Tel.: (65) 68484400
Insulation & Fireproofing Services
N.A.I.C.S.: 922160

Ensure Engineering Pte. Ltd. (1)
1 Tuas Ave 10, Singapore, 639125, Singapore
Tel.: (65) 68617811
Web Site: https://ensure-engrg.com
Marine Engineering Services
N.A.I.C.S.: 541330

Multiheight Scaffolding Pte. Ltd. (1)
2 Tuas Avenue 10, Singapore, 639126, Singapore
Tel.: (65) 68484400
Web Site: https://www.multiheight.com
Scaffolding Erection Services
N.A.I.C.S.: 532490

Nordic Flow Control Pte. Ltd. (1)
2 Tuas Ave 10, Singapore, 639126, Singapore
Tel.: (65) 68484400
Web Site: https://www.nordicflowcontrol.com
Industrial Valve Mfr
N.A.I.C.S.: 332911
Dorcas Teo Ling Ling (Exec Dir)

Subsidiary (Non-US):

Avitools (Suzhou) Co., Ltd. (2)
Building D No 200 Suhong Middle Road, Integrated Free Trade Zone West Industrial Park, Suzhou, 215021, Jiangsu, China
Tel.: (86) 51262582560
Web Site: https://www.avitools.com
Sales Range: $25-49.9 Million
Emp.: 64
Precision Machine Tools Mfr
N.A.I.C.S.: 333517
Rodney Koh Wei Ming (CEO)

Nordic Flow Control (Suzhou) Co., Ltd. (2)
Building No 2 Lou Feng Chuang Tou Industrial Park, Suzhou, 215022, Jiangsu, China
Tel.: (86) 51269567601
Web Site: http://nordicflowcontrol.com
Industrial Valve Mfr
N.A.I.C.S.: 332911
Samantha Lim Bee Hong (Gen Mgr-Grp Bus Excellence)

Subsidiary (Domestic):

Starburst Holdings Limited (2)
6 Tuas View Circuit, Singapore, 637599, Singapore
Tel.: (65) 68622282
Web Site: http://www.starburst.net.sg
Rev.: $16,437,207
Assets: $42,185,459
Liabilities: $17,924,498
Net Worth: $24,260,961
Earnings: $6,895,141
Emp.: 85
Fiscal Year-end: 12/31/2020
Modern Firearms Training Facilities Designing & Engineering
N.A.I.C.S.: 236220
Edward Chin Wah Lim (Chm)

NORDIC HALIBUT AS
Hendnesveien 124, 6533, Averoy, Norway
Tel.: (47) 41382203
Web Site:
https://www.nordichalibut.com
Year Founded: 1995
NOHAL—(OSL)
Rev.: $9,423,517
Assets: $67,741,179
Liabilities: $21,054,221
Net Worth: $46,686,957
Earnings: ($5,603,547)
Emp.: 64
Fiscal Year-end: 12/31/23
Seafood Product Mfr & Distr
N.A.I.C.S.: 311710
Kenneth Meyer (CFO)

NORDIC INVESTMENT BANK
Fabianinkatu 34, PO Box 249, FI-00171, Helsinki, Finland
Tel.: (358) 10 618 001
Web Site: http://www.nib.int
Year Founded: 1975
Rev.: $341,273,766
Assets: $36,269,203,449
Liabilities: $32,177,232,960
Net Worth: $4,091,970,490
Earnings: $197,885,964
Emp.: 197
Fiscal Year-end: 12/31/18
Investment Banking Services
N.A.I.C.S.: 523150
Henrik Normann (Pres & CEO)

NORDIC IRON ORE AB
Akarevagen 2, SE-772 32, Grangesberg, Sweden
Tel.: (46) 24088300
Web Site:
https://www.nordicironore.se
Year Founded: 2008
Iron Ore Mining Services
N.A.I.C.S.: 212210
Bengt Nilsson (Chm)

NORDIC LEVEL GROUP AB
Vasagatan 12C, 172 67, Sundbyberg, Sweden
Tel.: (46) 86208200
Web Site:
https://www.nordiclevelgroup.com
Year Founded: 1989
LEVEL—(OMX)
Rev.: $35,931,265
Assets: $39,484,187
Liabilities: $20,535,271
Net Worth: $18,948,915
Earnings: ($511,247)
Emp.: 137
Fiscal Year-end: 12/31/23
Security System Services
N.A.I.C.S.: 561621
Anna Abelt (Chief HR Officer)

NORDIC MINING ASA
Munkedamsv 45 A, 0250, Oslo, Norway
Tel.: (47) 22947790
Web Site:
http://www.nordicmining.com
Metal Exploration Services
N.A.I.C.S.: 213114
Ivar S. Fossum (CEO)

NORDIC MORNING PLC
Verkkosaarenkuja 5, 00580, Helsinki, Finland
Tel.: (358) 204502920
Web Site:
http://www.nordicmorning.com
Year Founded: 1859
Rev.: $110,610,046
Assets: $58,444,175
Liabilities: $38,325,575
Net Worth: $20,118,600

INTERNATIONAL PUBLIC

Earnings: ($15,395,698)
Emp.: 653
Fiscal Year-end: 12/31/16
Communication Service
N.A.I.C.S.: 517810
Anne Arneby (CEO)

Subsidiaries:

Citat Oy (1)
Pursimiehenkatu 26, FI-00150, Helsinki, Finland
Tel.: (358) 20 123 121
Web Site: http://www.citat.fi
Publishing Services
N.A.I.C.S.: 513199
Lars Lundstrom (VP)

Edita Prima Oy (1)
Hermannin Rantatie 8, 00580, Helsinki, Finland
Tel.: (358) 20 450 00
Web Site: http://www.editaprima.fi
Publishing Services
N.A.I.C.S.: 513199

Edita Publishing Oy (1)
Porkkalankatu 22A, FI-00043, Helsinki, Finland
Tel.: (358) 20 450 00
Web Site: http://www.editapublishing.fi
Publishing Services
N.A.I.C.S.: 513199

Edita Vastra Aros AB (1)
Elledningsgatan 6, Vasteras, 721 20, Sweden
Tel.: (46) 21 81 55 00
Medical Consulting Services
N.A.I.C.S.: 541840

Subsidiary (Domestic):

Edita Bobergs AB (2)
Matsarvsvagen 7, 791 77, Falun, Sweden
Tel.: (46) 23 79 29 00
Web Site: http://www.editabobergs.se
Commercial Printing Services
N.A.I.C.S.: 323111

JG Communication AB (1)
Gavlegatan 22, Box 49031, 113 30, Stockholm, Sweden
Tel.: (46) 850882800
Web Site: http://www.nordicmorning.com
Publishing Services
N.A.I.C.S.: 513199
Christian Sahlgren (Mgr)

Klikkicom Oy (1)
Verkkosaarenkatu 5, FI-00580, Helsinki, Finland
Tel.: (358) 10 292 0680
Publishing Services
N.A.I.C.S.: 513199

Subsidiary (Non-US):

Klikki AB (2)
Svarvargatan 7, PO Box 49031, SE-100 28, Stockholm, Sweden
Tel.: (46) 8 5500 2174
Publishing Services
N.A.I.C.S.: 513199

Klikki AS (2)
Arbins gate 2, Box 1681 Vika, NO-0120, Oslo, Norway
Tel.: (47) 975 90 962
Publishing Services
N.A.I.C.S.: 513199

Klikki ApS (2)
Todbodgade 18 5al, DK-1253, Copenhagen, Denmark
Tel.: (45) 281 81 279
Publishing Services
N.A.I.C.S.: 513199

Mods Graphic Studio AB (1)
Drottninggatan 59, 111 21, Stockholm, Sweden
Tel.: (46) 8 506 61700
Web Site: http://www.mods.se
Publishing Services
N.A.I.C.S.: 513199

Nordic Morning AB (1)
Svarvargatan 11, PO Box 49031, SE-100 28, Stockholm, Sweden
Tel.: (46) 8 5800 1300

Nordic Morning Sweden AB (1)
Gavlegatan 22 6th floor, 113 30, Stockholm, Sweden
Tel.: (46) 8 58 00 13 00
Medical Consulting Services
N.A.I.C.S.: 541840

Subsidiary (Domestic):

Journalistgruppen, JG AB (2)
Gavleg 12 A, 113 30, Stockholm, Sweden
Tel.: (46) 8 610 20 00
Medical Consulting Services
N.A.I.C.S.: 541840

Seed Digital Media Oy (1)
Teollisuuskatu 21, 00510, Helsinki, Finland
Tel.: (358) 40 860 2402
Web Site: http://www.seedww.com
Marketing Consulting Services
N.A.I.C.S.: 541613
Heikki Autio (CEO)

NORDIC NICKEL LIMITED
Level 12 197 St Georges Tce, Perth, 6000, WA, Australia
Tel.: (61) 861413191 AU
Web Site:
 https://www.nordicnickel.com
Year Founded: 2021
NNL—(ASX)
Rev.: $542,315
Assets: $8,938,440
Liabilities: $1,337,138
Net Worth: $7,601,303
Earnings: ($922,105)
Emp.: 9
Fiscal Year-end: 06/30/23
Mineral Exploration Services
N.A.I.C.S.: 212390
Aaron Bertolatti (CFO)

NORDIC OIL & GAS LTD.
4727 Robin Boulevard, Winnipeg, R3R 0G2, MB, Canada
Tel.: (204) 318-2357 MB
Web Site:
 http://www.nordicoilandgas.ca
Year Founded: 2000
Sales Range: Less than $1 Million
Emp.: 1
Oil & Gas Exploration & Development Services
N.A.I.C.S.: 211120
Donald E. Benson (Chm, Pres & CEO)

NORDIC PAPER HOLDING AB
Tullhusgatan 1B, 652 09, Karlstad, Sweden
Tel.: (46) 55034500
Web Site: https://www.nordic-paper.com
Year Founded: 1871
NPAPER—(OMX)
Rev.: $407,592,000
Assets: $332,866,800
Liabilities: $237,303,000
Net Worth: $95,563,800
Earnings: $51,958,800
Emp.: 672
Fiscal Year-end: 12/31/22
Holding Company
N.A.I.C.S.: 551112
Anita Sjolander (CEO)

Subsidiaries:

Nordic Paper AS (1)
PO Box 155, NO-1720, Greaker, Norway
Tel.: (47) 69138500
Paper Product Mfr & Distr
N.A.I.C.S.: 322220

Nordic Paper Backhammar AB (1)
Ostasgatan 25, SE-681 83, Kristinehamn, Sweden
Tel.: (46) 55034500
Household Paper Mfr & Distr
N.A.I.C.S.: 322299

Nordic Paper Quebec Inc. (1)
1245 Bd Montmorency, Quebec, G1J 5L6, QC, Canada
Paper Product Mfr & Distr
N.A.I.C.S.: 322220

Nordic Paper Seffle AB (1)
PO Box 610, SE-661 29, Saffle, Sweden
Tel.: (46) 53382000
Paper Product Mfr & Distr
N.A.I.C.S.: 322220

NORDIC SEMICONDUCTOR ASA
Otto Nielsens veg 12, 7052, Trondheim, Norway
Tel.: (47) 72898900
Web Site:
 https://www.nordicsemi.com
NOD—(OTCIQ)
Rev.: $405,217,000
Assets: $515,814,000
Liabilities: $113,322,000
Net Worth: $402,492,000
Earnings: $38,391,000
Emp.: 897
Fiscal Year-end: 12/31/20
Semiconductor Devices Mfr
N.A.I.C.S.: 334413
Svenn-Tore Larsen (CEO)

Subsidiaries:

Imagination Technologies Hyderabad Pvt. Ltd. (1)
Level 1 Unit 2A and 2B Octave Block Salarpuria Knowledge City, Hyderabad, 500081, India
Tel.: (91) 404 252 7749
Electric Equipment Mfr
N.A.I.C.S.: 335999

Mobile Semiconductor Corp. (1)
209 1/2 1st Ave S Ste 300, Seattle, WA 98104
Tel.: (206) 971-7439
Web Site: http://www.mobile-semi.com
Semiconductor & Related Device Mfr
N.A.I.C.S.: 334413
Cameron Fisher (Pres & CEO)

Nordic Semiconductor Germany GmbH (1)
Am Wehrhahn 100, 40211, Dusseldorf, Germany
Tel.: (49) 1522 170 8526
Electric Equipment Mfr
N.A.I.C.S.: 335999
Thomas Page (Reg Sls Mgr)

Nordic Semiconductor Inc. (1)
1250 Oakmead Pkwy Ste 210, Sunnyvale, CA 94085-4037
Tel.: (408) 437-7751
Semiconductor Distr
N.A.I.C.S.: 423690

Nordic Semiconductor Japan KK (1)
9F Yokohama Hanasaki Building 6-145 Hanasakicho, Nishi-ku, Yokohama, 220-0022, Kanagawa, Japan
Tel.: (81) 45 620 0162
Electric Equipment Mfr
N.A.I.C.S.: 335999

Nordic Semiconductor Norway AS (1)
Otto Nielsens veg 12, 7052, Trondheim, Norway
Tel.: (47) 7 289 8900
Electric Equipment Mfr
N.A.I.C.S.: 335999

Nordic Semiconductor Poland S.p. z o.o. (1)
Bratyslawska 1A, 31-201, Krakow, Poland
Tel.: (48) 60 043 9203
Electric Equipment Mfr
N.A.I.C.S.: 335999
Maciej Michna (Reg Sls Mgr)

NORDIC SERVICE PARTNERS HOLDING AB
Ranhammarsvagen 20, Bromma, 168 67, Sweden
Tel.: (46) 8 41018950
Web Site:
 http://www.nordicservicepartners.se
Holding Company
N.A.I.C.S.: 551112
Morgan Jallinder (CEO)

NORDIC SHIPHOLDING A/S
Amaliegade 33B 3rd floor, 1256, Copenhagen, Denmark
Tel.: (45) 3 929 1000 DK
Web Site:
 http://www.nordicshipholding.com
Year Founded: 1984
NORDIC—(OMX)
Rev.: $21,519,000
Assets: $44,011,000
Liabilities: $58,323,000
Net Worth: ($14,312,000)
Earnings: ($5,763,000)
Emp.: 1
Fiscal Year-end: 12/31/21
Holding Company
N.A.I.C.S.: 551112
Knud Pontoppidan (Chm)

NORDIC TRANSPORT GROUP HOLDING A/S
Truckvej 5, 4600, Koge, Denmark
Tel.: (45) 76320960
Web Site: http://ntgnordic.dk
Freight Forwarding Services
N.A.I.C.S.: 488510
Kenneth Sorensen (CEO)

Subsidiaries:

NTG Nordic Transport Group A/S (1)
Hammerholmen 47, DK-2650, Hvidovre, Denmark
Tel.: (45) 76340900
Web Site: https://www.ntg.com
Rev.: $1,206,464,962
Assets: $556,785,461
Liabilities: $398,055,302
Net Worth: $158,730,159
Earnings: $58,890,770
Emp.: 1,970
Fiscal Year-end: 12/31/2023
Biopharmaceutical Product Mfr
N.A.I.C.S.: 325412
Michael Larsen (CEO)

Subsidiary (Non-US):

NeuroSearch Sweden AB (2)
Arvid Wallgrens Backe 20, 413 46, Gothenburg, Sweden
Tel.: (46) 317720600
Sales Range: $25-49.9 Million
Drugs Mfr & Whslr
N.A.I.C.S.: 424210

NORDIC UNMANNED ASA
Radhusgata 3, 4306, Sandnes, Norway
Tel.: (47) 51209444 NO
Web Site:
 https://www.nordicunmanned.com
Year Founded: 2005
NUMND—(EUR)
Rev.: $19,771,528
Assets: $56,422,582
Liabilities: $27,490,774
Net Worth: $28,931,809
Earnings: ($24,444,925)
Emp.: 161
Fiscal Year-end: 12/31/22
Aircraft Mfr
N.A.I.C.S.: 336411
Nils Johan Holte (Chm)

Subsidiaries:

AirRobot GmbH & Co. KG (1)
Werler Street 4, 59755, Arnsberg, Germany
Tel.: (49) 2932547740
Micro-UAV System Mfr
N.A.I.C.S.: 336411

DroneMatrix N.V. (1)
Herkenrodesingel 4/1, B-3500, Hasselt, Belgium (55%)
Tel.: (32) 11962731
Web Site: https://www.dronematrix.eu
Aviation & Aerospace Component Mfr
N.A.I.C.S.: 336413

Ecoxy AS (1)
Julsundvegen 4, 6412, Molde, Norway
Tel.: (47) 40003656
Web Site: https://ecoxy.no
Air Emissions Reduction Services
N.A.I.C.S.: 541620

NUAer AS (1)
Radhusgata 3, NO-4306, Sandnes, Norway
Tel.: (47) 96704827
Web Site: https://nuaer.com
Maritime Environmental Monitoring Services
N.A.I.C.S.: 541620

NORDIC VISITOR HF
Bildshofdi 20, 110, Reykjavik, Iceland
Tel.: (354) 578 20 80
Web Site:
 http://www.nordicvisitor.com
Travel Agency
N.A.I.C.S.: 561510

Subsidiaries:

Iceland Travel ehf. (1)
Skogarhlio 12, 105, Reykjavik, Iceland
Tel.: (354) 5854300
Web Site: http://www.icelandtravel.is
Emp.: 150
Travel Tour Operator
N.A.I.C.S.: 561520
Horour Gunnarsson (CEO)

NORDIC WOOD INDUSTRIES A/S
Palsgårdvej 5, 7362, Hampen, Denmark
Tel.: (45) 30237915
Web Site: https://nowi.dk
Year Founded: 2021
Emp.: 500
Prefabricated Woods-based Mfr
N.A.I.C.S.: 321992
Thomas Raunsbaek (CEO & Exec Dir)

Subsidiaries:

Scandi Byg A/S (1)
Himmerlandsvej 3, 9670, Logstor, Nordjylland, Denmark
Tel.: (45) 98672500
Web Site: http://www.scandibyg.com
Sales Range: $50-74.9 Million
Emp.: 120
Prefabricated Modular Buildings Mfr
N.A.I.C.S.: 321992
Jesper F. Hoffmann (Mng Dir)

NORDIC YARDS HOLDING GMBH
Wendorfer Weg 5, 23966, Wismar, Germany
Tel.: (49) 38 41 77 0
Web Site:
 http://www.nordicyards.com
Emp.: 700
Holding Company; Ship Building Services
N.A.I.C.S.: 551112
Vitaly Yusufov (Pres & CEO)

Subsidiaries:

Nordic Yards Stralsund GmbH (1)
An der Werft 5, 18439, Stralsund, Germany
Tel.: (49) 3831660
Web Site: http://www.nordicyards.com
Emp.: 250
Shipyard; Ship Building & Repairing
N.A.I.C.S.: 336611

Nordic Yards Warnemunde GmbH (1)
Werftallee 10, 18119, Rostock, Germany
Tel.: (49) 381 510 0
Web Site: http://www.nordicyards.com

NORDIC YARDS HOLDING GMBH

Nordic Yards Holding GmbH—(Continued)
Ship Building & Repairing
N.A.I.C.S.: 336611

Nordic Yards Wismar GmbH (1)
Wendorfer Weg 5, 23966, Wismar, Germany
Tel.: (49) 38 41 77 0
Web Site: http://www.nordicyards.com
Ship Building & Repairing
N.A.I.C.S.: 336611
Vitaly Yusufov (Mng Dir)

NORDICA LIFE (BERMUDA) LTD.
Swan Building 26 Victoria Street, Hamilton, HM 12, Bermuda
Tel.: (441) 2956548
Web Site: http://www.nordicalife.com
NORD—(BERM)
Rev.: $1,425,128
Assets: $435,159,236
Liabilities: $433,303,040
Net Worth: $1,856,196
Earnings: $530,195
Fiscal Year-end: 12/31/21
Insurance Services
N.A.I.C.S.: 524298

NORDIQUE RESOURCES INC.
Suite 1000 409 Granville Street, Vancouver, V6C 1T2, BC, Canada
Tel.: (236) 521-0626 BC
Web Site:
https://www.brascanresources.com
Year Founded: 2018
V0U—(DEU)
Rev.: $13,242
Assets: $88,824
Liabilities: $49,678
Net Worth: $39,146
Earnings: ($913,236)
Fiscal Year-end: 12/31/23
Mineral Mining Services
N.A.I.C.S.: 213115
Bastien Boulay (VP)

NORDISK BERGTEKNIK AB
Ostra Hamngatan 52, 411 08, Gothenburg, Sweden
Tel.: (46) 103500900
Web Site:
https://www.nordiskbergteknik.se
Year Founded: 1965
NORB.B—(OMX)
Rev.: $334,213,755
Assets: $332,274,954
Liabilities: $218,541,310
Net Worth: $113,733,644
Earnings: $3,624,716
Emp.: 1,195
Fiscal Year-end: 12/31/23
Construction Engineering Services
N.A.I.C.S.: 541330
Johan Lundqvist (CFO)

Subsidiaries:

BGS Svensson AB (1)
Televerksvagen 15, 456 33, Kungshamn, Sweden
Tel.: (46) 52310000
Web Site: https://www.bgssvensson.se
Steel Core Pipes Mfr & Distr
N.A.I.C.S.: 331210

Berg & Betongforstarkning Jarl-Eric Majqvist AB (1)
Asa tallvag 12, 43955, Asa, Sweden
Tel.: (46) 707555588
Web Site: https://www.bergochbetong.se
Rock Pilling Drilling Services
N.A.I.C.S.: 212312

Bohus Bergsprangning AB (1)
Hajums Industriomrade 3, 455 41, Hedekas, Sweden
Tel.: (46) 52430020
Web Site: https://bohusberg.se
Rock Reinforcement & Core Drilling Services
N.A.I.C.S.: 213112

Broderna Anderssons Grus AB (1)
Astraskvagen 17, 937 32, Burtrask, Sweden
Tel.: (46) 91410065
Web Site: https://www.agrus.se
Emp.: 25
Concrete Drilling Services
N.A.I.C.S.: 212321

Fjellsprenger AS (1)
Industriveien 3, 3610, Kongsberg, Norway
Tel.: (47) 91576464
Construction Services
N.A.I.C.S.: 236220

Gjerden Fjellsikring AS (1)
Karen Sogns Vei 49, 3275, Svarstad, Norway
Tel.: (47) 40003780
Web Site: https://www.gjerden-fjellsikring.no
Mountain Safety Services
N.A.I.C.S.: 561730

Grundia AB (1)
Neongatan 5, 431 53, Molndal, Sweden
Tel.: (46) 704031708
Web Site: https://www.grundia.se
Emp.: 40
Pile Drilling Services
N.A.I.C.S.: 237990

Norrbottens Bergteknik AB (1)
Lopevagen 16, SE-906 20, Umea, Sweden
Tel.: (46) 92910910
Web Site: https://www.bergteknik.se
Emp.: 97
Drilling & Mining Services
N.A.I.C.S.: 213113

Norsk Fjellsprengning AS (1)
Bergmannsveien 323, 3614, Kongsberg, Norway
Tel.: (47) 48145484
Mining & Construction Services
N.A.I.C.S.: 532412

Prospekteringsteknik i Norrland AB (1)
Storgatan 125, 935 31, Norsjo, Sweden
Tel.: (46) 910581450
Web Site: https://www.proteknorr.se
Diamond Drilling Services
N.A.I.C.S.: 213113

Rovalin AB (1)
Borrvagen 4, 15593, Nykvarn, Sweden
Tel.: (46) 703017220
Web Site: https://www.rovalin.se
Ground Drilling Services
N.A.I.C.S.: 213113

Rovalin Nord AB (1)
Mavagen 14, 891 55, Arnasvall, Sweden
Tel.: (46) 703334817
Ground Drilling Services
N.A.I.C.S.: 213113

S Blomquist Entreprenad AB (1)
Agnesbergsvagen 12, 424 38, Agnesberg, Sweden
Tel.: (46) 703123844
Web Site: https://www.sblomquist.com
Emp.: 13
Construction Machinery Repair & Maintenance Services
N.A.I.C.S.: 811310

Snemyr Betongsproyting AS (1)
Topdalsveien 23, 4635, Kristiansand, Norway
Tel.: (47) 38029000
Web Site: https://snemyr.no
Rock Drilling Services
N.A.I.C.S.: 237990

Sogndalen Fjellsprenging AS (1)
Mjavannsvegen 285 brennasen, 4628, Kristiansand, Norway
Tel.: (47) 96004040
Web Site: https://fjellsprenging.no
Engineeering Services
N.A.I.C.S.: 238110

Soil Mixing Group AB (1)
Nordansjo 405, SE-776 90, Hedemora, Sweden
Tel.: (46) 727198892
Web Site: https://www.soilmg.com
Soil Reinforcement Services
N.A.I.C.S.: 238910

TSB Borrentreprenad AB (1)
Langgatan 5, 881 33, Solleftea, Sweden
Tel.: (46) 62013540
Web Site: https://tsbab.se
Diamond Drilling Services
N.A.I.C.S.: 237990

Torbjorn Sundh Entreprenad AB (1)
Manusgrand 3, 903 64, Umea, Sweden
Tel.: (46) 90148077
Web Site: https://tsundh.se
Emp.: 100
Transport & Land Construction Services
N.A.I.C.S.: 541614

Vestfold Fjellboring AS (1)
Nordre Kullerod 6, 3241, Sandefjord, Norway
Tel.: (47) 33489550
Web Site: https://nordiskfjellsprengning.no
Concrete Well Drilling & Foundation Services
N.A.I.C.S.: 238110

Visinor AS (1)
Vassdalsveien 17, Pb 23, 8530, Bjerkvik, Norway
Tel.: (47) 80043500
Construction Services
N.A.I.C.S.: 236220

Visinor Rehab AS (1)
Vassdalsveien 17 / Pb 23, 8530, Bjerkvik, Norway
Tel.: (47) 80043500
Web Site: https://visinor.no
Bridge & Building Concrete Rehabilitation Services
N.A.I.C.S.: 237910

NORDITEK GROUP AB
Stora Avagen 21, Askim, 436 34, Gothenburg, Sweden
Tel.: (46) 20111444
Web Site: https://www.norditek.se
Year Founded: 1998
NOTEK—(OMX)
Rev.: $8,412,552
Assets: $12,980,520
Liabilities: $6,445,278
Net Worth: $6,535,242
Earnings: $440,640
Emp.: 13
Fiscal Year-end: 08/31/23
Recycle Equipment Mfr & Distr
N.A.I.C.S.: 325991
Goran Nordlund (Chm)

NORDMARK ARZNEIMITTEL GMBH & CO. KG
Pinnauallee 4, 25436, Uetersen, Germany
Tel.: (49) 41227120
Web Site: http://www.nordmark-pharma.de
Year Founded: 1927
Rev.: $95,441,426
Emp.: 450
Pharmaceuticals Mfr
N.A.I.C.S.: 325412
Peter Tonne (Mng Dir)

Subsidiaries:

Nordix Pharma Vertrieb GmbH (1)
Kurfurstenstr 2, 14467, Potsdam, Germany
Tel.: (49) 331581710
Pharmaceuticals Product Mfr
N.A.I.C.S.: 325412

NORDON INDUSTRIAS METALURGICAS SA
Alameda Roger Adam 169 Escritorio Utinga, Santo Andre, 09080-620, SP, Brazil
Tel.: (55) 30291806 BR
Web Site: https://www.nordon.ind.br
Year Founded: 1956
NORD3—(BRAZ)
Sales Range: Less than $1 Million
Commercial Goods Mfr
N.A.I.C.S.: 311812

INTERNATIONAL PUBLIC

Jussara Do Rocio Gomes Ferreira Lopes (Chief Comml Officer & Member-Exec Bd)

NORDSTJERNAN AB
Stureplan 3, Stockholm, 103 75, Sweden
Tel.: (46) 87885000
Web Site: https://www.nordstjernan.se
Sales Range: $5-14.9 Billion
Emp.: 60,000
Investment Company
N.A.I.C.S.: 523999
Tomas Billing (CEO)

Subsidiaries:

Dacke Industri AB (1)
Stortorget 17, 252 20, Helsingborg, Sweden (100%)
Tel.: (46) 42381550
Web Site: http://www.dackeindustri.se
Hydraulics, Pneumatics, Transmissions, Control Systems; Metrology & Engineering Technology Services
N.A.I.C.S.: 541330
Borje Vernet (CEO)

Subsidiary (Domestic):

Optronic Partner pr AB (2)
Kungsbron 21, 111 22, Stockholm, Sweden
Tel.: (46) 8 610 04 00
Web Site: http://www.optronic.se
Electronic Equipment Distr
N.A.I.C.S.: 423690
Ulrik Stenbacka (CEO)

Subsidiary (Non-US):

PMC Cylinders Oy (2)
Vaakatie 8, 155 60, Nastola, Finland
Tel.: (358) 20 770 8000
Web Site: http://pmccylinders.se
Emp.: 30
Hydraulic Cylinders & Products Mfr
N.A.I.C.S.: 333995
Peter Blomqvist (Mgr-Sls & Supply)

Holding (Domestic):

PMC Hydraulics Group AB (2)
Stortorget 17, 252 20, Helsingborg, Sweden (100%)
Tel.: (46) 42 381550
Web Site: http://www.pmchydraulics.se
Hydraulic Component & System Distr
N.A.I.C.S.: 423830
Mikael Lundgren (Pres & CEO)

Subsidiary (Domestic):

PMC Hydraulics AB (3)
Askims Verkstadsvag 15, Askim, 436 34, Gothenburg, Sweden
Tel.: (46) 31289840
Web Site: http://www.pmchydraulics.com
Hydraulic Mfr
N.A.I.C.S.: 333618
Patrick Olssan (Pres, CEO, Mng Dir, Sls Dir & Mgr-Bus Unit)

Subsidiary (Non-US):

PMC Hydraulics LLC (3)
Vysokovoltny proezd 1 Building 49 office 229, 127566, Moscow, Russia
Tel.: (7) 495 981 80 36
Web Site: http://www.pmchydraulics.com
Hydraulic & Lubrication Systems Mfr & Distr
N.A.I.C.S.: 423830

PMC Hydraulics Oy (3)
Mestarintie 6, 01730, Vantaa, Finland
Tel.: (358) 20 770 9700
Web Site: http://www.pmchydraulics.com
Hydraulic Assemblies & Systems Design & Mfr
N.A.I.C.S.: 333248
Kalle Lindgren (Mgr-Svc)

Subsidiary (Non-US):

PMC Polarteknik AS (4)
Piirimae 8, Tanassilma, 76401, Harjumaa, Estonia
Tel.: (372) 650 6800
Web Site: http://www.pmchydraulics.se
Industrial Machinery & Equipment Mfr

AND PRIVATE COMPANIES

NORDSTJERNAN AB

N.A.I.C.S.: 333248

Subsidiary (Non-US):

PMC Hydraulika Sp.z o.o. (3)
Rosowek 24, 72-001, Kolbaskowo, Poland
Tel.: (48) 91 881 50 20
Web Site: http://www.pmchydraulics.com
Hydraulic & Lubrication System Mfr & Distr
N.A.I.C.S.: 333248
Marek Szczerbo *(Mgr-Quality)*

PMC Qingdao Co. Ltd. (3)
Building C4 No1 Jinhui Road Hongdao Hi-Tech Zone, Licang District, Qingdao, China
Tel.: (86) 532 8766 7711
Web Site: http://www.pmchydraulics.com
Hydraulic Machinery Mfr
N.A.I.C.S.: 333248
Alexander Hahn *(Sls Dir-Sys)*

PMC Winstar Hydraulics Pvt. Ltd. (3)
Bearys Horizon 1st Floor No 21 Wood Street, 560 025, Bengaluru, India
Tel.: (91) 80 2554 3918
Web Site: http://www.pmchydraulics.com
Emp.: 40
Hydraulic Cylinder Mfr
N.A.I.C.S.: 333995
A. K. Kamam *(Mng Dir)*

Subsidiary (Domestic):

Swedrive AB (2)
Prasttorpsvagen 14, 341 51, Lagan, Sweden
Tel.: (46) 372 265 00
Web Site: http://www.swedrive.se
Emp.: 55
Industrial Machinery & Equipment Whslr
N.A.I.C.S.: 423830
Goran Magnusson *(Mgr-Design)*

Etac AB (1)
Kista Science Tower Farogatan 33, 164 51, Kista, Sweden
Tel.: (46) 8 633 47 00
Web Site: http://www.etac.com
Medical Equipment Whslr
N.A.I.C.S.: 423450
Torben Helbo *(CEO)*

Subsidiary (Non-US):

Etac A/S (2)
Egeskovvej 12, 8700, Horsens, Denmark
Tel.: (45) 79 68 58 33
Web Site: http://www.etac.dk
Medical Equipment Whslr
N.A.I.C.S.: 423450

Etac AS (2)
Bratengata 66, PO Box boks 249, 1501, Moss, Norway
Tel.: (47) 815 69 469
Web Site: http://www.etac.no
Medical Equipment Whslr
N.A.I.C.S.: 423450
Maya C. Mikkelrud *(Key Acct Mgr)*

Etac GmbH (2)
Bahnhofstrasse 131, 45770, Marl, Germany
Tel.: (49) 2365 9871 0
Web Site: http://www.etac.de
Medical Equipment Whslr
N.A.I.C.S.: 423450

Etac Holland B.V. (2)
Fluorietweg 16a, 1812RR, Alkmaar, Netherlands
Tel.: (31) 72 547 04 39
Medical Equipment Whslr
N.A.I.C.S.: 423450
Sander May *(Office Mgr)*

Subsidiary (Domestic):

Etac Supply Center AB (2)
Langgatan 12, Box 203, Anderstorp, Sweden
Tel.: (46) 371 58 7200
Web Site: http://www.etac.com
Emp.: 150
Motorcycle & Bicycle Parts Mfr
N.A.I.C.S.: 336991
Torben Helbo *(CEO)*

Etac Sverige AB (2)
Kista Science Tower Farogatan 33, Kista, Sweden

Tel.: (46) 371 58 73 00
Web Site: http://www.etac.se
Medical Equipment Whslr
N.A.I.C.S.: 423450

Subsidiary (Non-US):

Etac UK Limited (2)
Unit D4A Coombswood Business Park, East Coombswood Way, Halesowen, B62 8BH, West Midlands, United Kingdom
Tel.: (44) 121 561 2222
Web Site: http://www.r82.uk
Emp.: 55
Medical Equipment Whslr
N.A.I.C.S.: 423450
Kieron Slocombe *(Mng Dir)*

R82 A/S (2)
Parallelvej 3, Gedved, 8751, Horsens, Denmark
Tel.: (45) 7968 5888
Web Site: http://www.r82.com
Medical Equipment Whslr
N.A.I.C.S.: 423450
Mads Jakob Have *(Key Acct Mgr)*

KMT Precision Grinding AB (1)
Fabriksgatan 2, Box 910, 531 19, Lidkoping, Sweden
Tel.: (46) 510 88 000
Web Site: http://www.kmtgrinding.com
Emp.: 100
Grinding Machine Mfr
N.A.I.C.S.: 333517
Jorgen Moller *(Plant Mgr)*

Subsidiary (Non-US):

KMT Precision Grinding Technology (Beijing) Co., Ltd (2)
Office Room 1812 SCITECH Tower No 22 Jian Guo Men Wai Da Jie, Beijing, 100004, China
Tel.: (86) 1065 2205 15
Medical Equipment Whslr
N.A.I.C.S.: 423450
Li Yang *(Gen Mgr)*

KMT Production Machinery India Private Limited (2)
143 Sector 7 IMT Manesar, Gurgaon, 122050, India
Tel.: (91) 124 43 68 361
Grinding Machine Mfr
N.A.I.C.S.: 333517
Priyank Garg *(Mng Dir)*

Momentum Group AB (1)
Ostermalmsgatan 87 E, PO Box 5900, SE-114 59, Stockholm, Sweden (54.5%)
Tel.: (46) 8929000
Web Site: https://www.momentum.group
Rev.: $837,590,880
Assets: $953,688,960
Liabilities: $581,222,880
Net Worth: $372,466,080
Earnings: $27,956,320
Emp.: 2,670
Fiscal Year-end: 12/31/2020
Holding Company; Industrial Machinery & Equipment Retailer
N.A.I.C.S.: 551112
Ulf Lilius *(Pres & CEO)*

Subsidiary (Domestic):

Gigant AB (2)
Kristineholmsvagen 35D, 441 39, Alingsas, Sweden
Tel.: (46) 322606800
Web Site: http://www.gigant.se
Industrial Equipment Distr
N.A.I.C.S.: 423830
Olof Nyberg *(Mng Dir)*

Subsidiary (Non-US):

Gigant Tyopisteet Oy (2)
Opistokatu 11, 65100, Vaasa, Ostrobothnia, Finland
Tel.: (358) 207570500
Web Site: http://www.gigant.fi
Industrial Component Mfr
N.A.I.C.S.: 339999
Steven Pham *(Mgr)*

Subsidiary (Domestic):

Indoma AB (2)

Fridhemsvagen 25, 55115, Jonkoping, Sweden
Tel.: (46) 36306400
Web Site: http://www.indoma.se
Emp.: 4
Industrial Machinery & Equipment Whslr
N.A.I.C.S.: 423830

Mercus Yrkesklader AB (2)
Kampevagen 31, 553 02, Jonkoping, Sweden
Tel.: (46) 36100120
Web Site: http://www.mercus.se
Clothing Mfr & Distr
N.A.I.C.S.: 315250

Momentum Industrial AB (2)
Von Utfallsgatan 16 B, 415 05, Gothenburg, Sweden
Tel.: (46) 313409900
Web Site: http://www.momentum-industrial.com
Sales Range: $75-99.9 Million
Emp.: 250
Industrial Equipment Resellers
N.A.I.C.S.: 423830

Swedol AB (2)
Vindkraftsvagen 2, Stockholm, 135 70, Sweden
Tel.: (46) 8 7120000
Web Site: http://www.swedol.se
Hardware Retailer
N.A.I.C.S.: 444140

Subsidiary (Domestic):

Grolls AB (3)
Importgatan 23, 422 46, Hisings Backa, Sweden
Tel.: (46) 317421600
Web Site: http://www.grolls.se
Emp.: 365
Helmet Workwear & Worker Glove Mfr
N.A.I.C.S.: 315250
Hans Gustavson *(Mgr-Pur)*

NCC AB (1)
Herrjarva Torg 4, 170 80, Solna, Sweden (63.7%)
Tel.: (46) 858551000
Web Site: https://www.ncc.se
Rev.: $5,076,287,617
Assets: $2,769,114,052
Liabilities: $2,096,340,630
Net Worth: $672,773,422
Earnings: $100,124,570
Emp.: 12,500
Fiscal Year-end: 12/31/2022
Civil Engineering & Building Contractor Services
N.A.I.C.S.: 238290
Tomas Carlsson *(Pres & CEO)*

Subsidiary (Domestic):

NCC Building (2)
Gullbergs Strandgata 2, Gothenburg, 40514, Sweden
Tel.: (46) 317715000
Web Site: http://www.ncc.co.se
Sales Range: $125-149.9 Million
Emp.: 300
N.A.I.C.S.: 237120

Subsidiary (Non-US):

NCC TeleCom A/S (3)
Tutorg Havnevej No 15, 2900 hellerup, Brondby, Denmark
Tel.: (45) 3910395
Web Site: http://www.ncc.dk
Sales Range: $50-74.9 Million
Emp.: 85
N.A.I.C.S.: 237120

Subsidiary (Domestic):

NCC Construction (2)
Vallgatan 3, Solna, 17080, Sweden
Tel.: (46) 858551000
Web Site: http://www.ncc.se
Sales Range: $350-399.9 Million
Emp.: 700
Commercial, Industrial, Bridges & Railway Construction Services
N.A.I.C.S.: 236220

Subsidiary (Domestic):

Hercules Grundlaggning AB (3)

Vallgatan 3, 170 80, Solna, Sweden
Tel.: (46) 858552900
Web Site: http://www.hercules.se
Sales Range: $25-49.9 Million
Emp.: 50
Contractor, Concrete Piles, Pile Driving, Testing & Equipment for Pile Manufacturing
N.A.I.C.S.: 333120
Mats Norberg *(CEO)*

Subsidiary (Non-US):

NCC Denmark A/S (2)
Tobaksvejen 2A, 2860, Soborg, Denmark
Tel.: (45) 39103910
Web Site: http://www.ncc.dk
Sales Range: $125-149.9 Million
Emp.: 500
N.A.I.C.S.: 237120

NCC Deutsche GmbH (2)
Ambahnhof 1, DE 15517, Furstenwalde, Germany
Tel.: (49) 33616700
Web Site: http://www.nccd.de
Sales Range: $150-199.9 Million
Emp.: 730
Construction Purchasing & Subcontractor Services
N.A.I.C.S.: 236220
Olle Boback *(Pres)*

Subsidiary (Domestic):

NCC Forsakrings AB (2)
Vallgatan 3, Solna, 170 80, Sweden
Tel.: (46) 858551000
Web Site: http://www.ncc.se
Sales Range: $250-299.9 Million
Emp.: 800
N.A.I.C.S.: 237120

NCC Hercules (2)
Vallgatan 3, S 170 67, Solna, Sweden
Tel.: (46) 858551000
Web Site: http://www.ncc.se
Sales Range: $200-249.9 Million
Emp.: 900
Construction Operations Outside Sweden
N.A.I.C.S.: 236118

Subsidiary (Non-US):

NCC Immobilien GmbH (2)
Am Nord Stern 1, Furstenwalde, 15517, Germany
Tel.: (49) 33616700
Web Site: http://www.nccd.de
Sales Range: $250-299.9 Million
Emp.: 800
N.A.I.C.S.: 237120
Olle Boback *(Gen Mgr)*

NCC Norway AS (2)
Ostensjoveien 27, 0661, Oslo, Norway
Tel.: (47) 22986800
Web Site: http://www.ncc.no
Sales Range: $500-549.9 Million
Emp.: 1,900
Construction Services
N.A.I.C.S.: 237120
Hakon Tjomsland *(Gen Mgr)*

NCC Rakennus Oy (2)
Mannerheimintie 103a, FI 00281, Helsinki, Finland
Tel.: (358) 1050751
Web Site: http://www.ncc.fi
Sales Range: $50-74.9 Million
Emp.: 200
Engineeering Services
N.A.I.C.S.: 237120
Harri Savolainen *(CEO)*

Subsidiary (Domestic):

NCC Treasury AB (2)
Vallgatan 3, Solna, 17080, Sweden
Tel.: (46) 858552054
Web Site: http://www.ncc.se
Sales Range: $25-49.9 Million
Emp.: 7
N.A.I.C.S.: 237120
Charlotte Lindstedt *(Dir-Fin)*

Nils Hansson Logistics AB (1)
Ragansgatan 3-5, Box 54, SE-260 70, Ljungbyhed, Sweden (100%)
Tel.: (46) 43526900
Web Site: http://www.nilshansson.se
Rev.: $51,190,856

NORDSTJERNAN AB

Nordstjernan AB—(Continued)
Emp.: 400
Freight Forward Transport Services
N.A.I.C.S.: 488510

Rosti A/S (1)
Borupvej 2C 1th, 2750, Ballerup,
Denmark **(100%)**
Tel.: (45) 44201700
Web Site: http://www.rosti.com
Sales Range: $200-249.9 Million
Emp.: 1,800
Plastics Product Mfr
N.A.I.C.S.: 326199
Lars B. Heineke (CFO)

Subsidiary (Non-US):

Rosti (Polska) Sp. z o.o. (2)
Ul Mysliwska 18, 15 569, Bialystok, Poland
Tel.: (48) 856783500
Web Site: http://www.rosti.com
Sales Range: $200-249.9 Million
Emp.: 724
Plastics Product Mfr
N.A.I.C.S.: 326199
Piotr Zehaluk (Sr VP-Eastern Europe)

Rosti GP AB (2)
Baldersvagen 35, 332 35, Gislaved,
Sweden **(100%)**
Tel.: (46) 37184650
Web Site: http://www.rosti.com
Sales Range: $25-49.9 Million
Emp.: 85
Injection Moulded Plastic Components Mfr
N.A.I.C.S.: 326199

Rosti Integrated Manufacturing Solutions (Suzhou) Co.,Ltd (2)
No 1 Huazheng Street, Suzhou Industrial
Park, Suzhou, 215026, Jiangsu, China
Tel.: (86) 51262952000
Web Site: http://www.rosti.com
Sales Range: $100-124.9 Million
Emp.: 1,100
Injection Moulded Plastic Component Mfr
N.A.I.C.S.: 333511
Pat Williams (Sr VP-Asia)

Rosti Technical Plastics (India) Pvt. Ltd. (2)
No 90 2 Madavillagam Village, Thirumazhisai, Chennai, 602 103, India
Tel.: (91) 4426496339
Web Site: http://www.rosti.com
Sales Range: $25-49.9 Million
Emp.: 80
Plastics Product Mfr
N.A.I.C.S.: 326199

Rosti Technical Plastics UK Ltd. (2)
Baird Avenue Strutherhill Industrial Estate,
Strutherhill Industrial Estate, Larkhall, ML9
2 PJ, United Kingdom
Tel.: (44) 1698552200
Web Site: http://www.rosti.com
Emp.: 200
Plastics Product Mfr
N.A.I.C.S.: 326199
Barry Coughlan (COO-Europe)

Subsidiary (Domestic):

Rosti McKechnie Ltd. (3)
Bridge Works Stamford Bridge, York, YO41
1AL, United Kingdom
Tel.: (44) 1759 371 551
Web Site: http://www.rosti.com
Sales Range: $50-74.9 Million
Emp.: 450
Plastics Product Mfr
N.A.I.C.S.: 326199
Nigel Foreman (Gen Mgr)

Plant (Domestic):

Rosti McKechnie Ltd.- Pickering (4)
Westgate Carr Road, Pickering, YO18 8LX,
N Yorkshire, United Kingdom
Tel.: (44) 1751471100
Web Site: http://www.mckechnie-plastics.co.uk
Sales Range: $25-49.9 Million
Emp.: 800
Plastics Product Mfr
N.A.I.C.S.: 326199
Paul Mills (Mgr-Sls)

Rosti Group AB (1)
Vastra Varvsgatan 19, S211 77, Malmo,
Sweden
Tel.: (46) 40 204 701
Web Site: http://www.rosti.com
Plastic Product Mfr & Distr
N.A.I.C.S.: 326199
Nils-Johan Andersson (CFO)

Subsidiary (US):

Plastic Components, Inc. (2)
N116 W18271 Morse Dr, Germantown, WI
53022
Tel.: (262) 253-0353
Web Site: http://www.plasticcomponents.com
Plastics Product Mfr
N.A.I.C.S.: 326199
Gene Mussel (Mgr-Ops)

Subsidiary (Domestic):

Sports Molding, LLC (3)
Z 13 Freeport Ctr, Clearfield, UT 84016
Tel.: (801) 776-4233
Web Site: http://www.smimolding.com
Plastic Injection Mold Mfr
N.A.I.C.S.: 326199
Gordon Blumenfeld (Chm)

Syracuse Plastics of North Carolina, Inc. (3)
100 Falcone Pkwy, Cary, NC 27511
Tel.: (919) 467-5151
Web Site: http://www.syracuseplasticsnc.com
Rev: $9,241,400
Emp.: 100
All Other Plastics Product Mfr
N.A.I.C.S.: 326199

Subsidiary (Non-US):

Rosti GP (2)
Heilbronner Strasse 18, 01189, Dresden,
Germany
Tel.: (49) 351 40 4600
Plastics Product Mfr
N.A.I.C.S.: 326199

Rosti IMS SDN BHD (2)
LOT 177 Jalan Murni9 Taman Perindustrian
Murni Senai, Senai, Johor Bahru, Malaysia
Tel.: (60) 197232366
Plastic Product Distr
N.A.I.C.S.: 424610
Tong Chin Yong (Mgr-Engrg)

Rosti Poland Sp. z o.o. (2)
ul Mysliwska 18, 15-569, Bialystok, Poland
Tel.: (48) 85 66 49 700
Web Site: http://rostipoland.pl
Emp.: 400
Plastic Injection Molding Mfr
N.A.I.C.S.: 326199
Rafael Cybulski (Mng Dir)

Rosti Tebplast Plastik San.Tic.A.S. (2)
Bosb Bakircilar Sitesi Sardunya Cad No 1,
Beylikduzu, Istanbul, 34900, Turkiye
Tel.: (90) 212 875 11 75
Industrial Mold Mfr
N.A.I.C.S.: 333511
Erdem Teber (CEO)

Rosti UK Ltd. (2)
Baird Avenue Strutherhill Industrial Estate,
Larkhall, ML9 2PJ, Lanarkshire, United
Kingdom
Tel.: (44) 1698 552 200
Plastics Product Mfr
N.A.I.C.S.: 326199
Chris Clark (Mgr-Ops)

WinGroup AG (1)
Untermuli 6, 6300, Zug, Switzerland
Tel.: (41) 71 511 11 91
Web Site: http://www.wingroup.ch
Emp.: 400
Residential & Balcony Glazing Services
N.A.I.C.S.: 238150

Subsidiary (Non-US):

ALIMEX Aluminyum San. ve. Tic. Ltd. Sti. (2)
Fabrikalar Caddesi No 45A, Akyazi, 54480,
Sakarya, Turkiye
Tel.: (90) 264 462 48 81
Web Site: http://www.alimex.com.tr
Residential Glazing Services
N.A.I.C.S.: 238150
Oner Tank (Product Mgr)

SUNPARADISE Alutechnik Vertriebs GmbH (2)
Rickenbacher Strasse 1, 88131, Lindau,
Germany
Tel.: (49) 8382 9777 10
Web Site: http://www.sunparadise.com
Residential Glazing Services
N.A.I.C.S.: 238150

Subsidiary (Domestic):

SUNPARADISE Est. (2)
Benderer Strasse 29, 9494, Bern, Switzerland
Tel.: (41) 3 235 54 54
Residential Glazing Services
N.A.I.C.S.: 238150
Felix C. Lavater (CEO)

Subsidiary (Non-US):

WINDOOR Danmark A/S (2)
Ledreborg Alle 130 J, 4000, Roskilde, Denmark
Tel.: (45) 88 18 58 58
Web Site: http://www.windoor.dk
Emp.: 18
Residential Glazing Services
N.A.I.C.S.: 238150
Jens Sloth Nielsen (CEO)

WINDOOR Norge AS (2)
Ringveien 206, 3223, Sandefjord, Norway
Tel.: (47) 33 48 08 80
Web Site: http://www.windoor.no
Residential Glazing Services
N.A.I.C.S.: 238150
Robert Hvass (Project Mgr)

WINDOOR Sverige AB (2)
Hojdrodergatan 18, 21239, Malmo, Sweden
Tel.: (46) 40 63 12 305
Residential Glazing Services
N.A.I.C.S.: 238150

WINDOOR UK Ltd (2)
Unit 16 Menta Business Centre 21-27 Hollands Road, Haverhill, CB9 8PU, Suffolk,
United Kingdom
Tel.: (44) 870 067 88 10
Web Site: http://www.windooruk.co.uk
Residential Glazing Services
N.A.I.C.S.: 238150
Andrew Loader (Mgr-Bus Dev)

NORDTELEKOM TELECOMMUNICATIONS SERVICE PROVIDER PLC

Dohany utca 12-14, Budapest, 1074,
Hungary
Tel.: (36) 14921000
Year Founded: 2009
NORDTELEKOM—(BUD)
Rev: $20,106
Assets: $408,828
Liabilities: $116,568
Net Worth: $292,260
Earnings: ($136,789)
Emp.: 1
Fiscal Year-end: 12/31/21
Internet Services
N.A.I.C.S.: 517112
Mihaly Gacsi (Chm)

NORDVLIES GMBH

Am Redder 7, Bargteheide, 22941,
Germany
Tel.: (49) 453250500
Web Site: http://www.nordvlies.de
Year Founded: 1928
Rev: $15,463,074
Emp.: 45
Sanitary Products Mfr
N.A.I.C.S.: 322291
Bjorn Wasilewski (Mng Dir)

NORDWEST HANDEL AG

Robert-Schuman-Strasse 17, 44263,
Dortmund, Germany
Tel.: (49) 23122223001

INTERNATIONAL PUBLIC

Web Site: https://www.nordwest.com
Year Founded: 1919
NWX—(MUN)
Rev: $759,837,876
Assets: $393,088,107
Liabilities: $274,554,546
Net Worth: $118,533,561
Earnings: $13,886,685
Emp.: 410
Fiscal Year-end: 12/31/23
Industrial Tools Distr
N.A.I.C.S.: 423830

NORDZUCKER AG

Kuchenstrasse 9, Braunschweig,
38100, Germany
Tel.: (49) 53124110
Web Site: http://www.nordzucker.de
Sales Range: $1-4.9 Billion
Emp.: 3,616
Sugar Production
N.A.I.C.S.: 311314
Jochen Johannes Juister (Deputy
Chm-Supervisory Bd)

Subsidiaries:

Mackay Sugar Limited Ltd. (1)
Level 1 Racecourse Mill Peak Downs Highway Racecourse via, MacKay, 4741, QLD,
Australia
Tel.: (61) 749538300
Web Site: http://www.mackaysugar.com.au
Sugar Cane Mfr
N.A.I.C.S.: 311314
Michael Gerloff (Chm)

Norddeutsche Flussigzucker GmbH & Co. KG (1)
Flussigzuckerwerk Gross Munzel Spielburg
9, 30890, Barsinghausen, Germany
Tel.: (49) 503597210
Liquid Sugar Mfr
N.A.I.C.S.: 311314

Nordic Sugar A/S (1)
Langebrogade 1, PO Box 2100, 1014, Copenhagen, Denmark
Tel.: (45) 32662500
Web Site: http://www.nordicsugar.com
Rev: $1,156,618,700
Emp.: 1,550
Sugar Production
N.A.I.C.S.: 311314
Jesper Thomassen (Mng Dir)

Subsidiary (Non-US):

AB Nordic Sugar Kedainiai (2)
Pramones g 6, 1104, Kedainiai, Lithuania
Tel.: (370) 34767730
Emp.: 190
Liquid Sugar Mfr
N.A.I.C.S.: 311314
Jesper Thomassen (Gen Dir)

Plant (Non-US):

Finnsugar Ltd. (2)
Sokeritehtaantie 20, FIN 02460, Kantvik,
Finland
Tel.: (358) 10431010
Web Site: http://www.dansukker.com
Sales Range: $150-199.9 Million
Emp.: 200
Sugar Production
N.A.I.C.S.: 311314

Subsidiary (Non-US):

Nordic Sugar (2)
Sockerbruksgatan Arlov 2, Malmo, 23235,
Sweden
Tel.: (46) 40537000
Web Site: http://www.nordicsugar.com
Sales Range: $100-124.9 Million
Emp.: 500
Sugar Production
N.A.I.C.S.: 311314
Hans Adolfsson (Mng Dir)

Nordic Sugar SIA (2)
Maza Nometnu str 31 office Nr 404, 1002,
Riga, Latvia
Tel.: (371) 67694512
Emp.: 3
Sugar Product Distr

AND PRIVATE COMPANIES

N.A.I.C.S.: 424490
Marika Osite (Mgr-Sls)

Plant (Non-US):

Sucros Ltd. (2)
Sokerikatu 1, FIN 24100, Salo, Finland (80%)
Tel.: (358) 277421
Sales Range: $25-49.9 Million
Emp.: 60
N.A.I.C.S.: 311423

Nordzucker AG Clauen Factory (1)
Zuckerfabrik 3, 31249, Hohenhameln, Germany
Tel.: (49) 5128405135
Liquid Sugar Mfr
N.A.I.C.S.: 311314

Nordzucker AG Klein Wanzleben Factory (1)
Magdeburger Landstrasse 1-5, 39164, Wanzleben-Borde, Germany
Tel.: (49) 3920945130
Liquid Sugar Mfr
N.A.I.C.S.: 311314

Nordzucker AG Nordstemmen Factory (1)
Calenberger Strasse 36, Nordstemmen, 31171, Hildesheim, Germany
Tel.: (49) 5069881102
Liquid Sugar Mfr
N.A.I.C.S.: 311314

Nordzucker AG Schladen Factory (1)
Bahnhofstrasse 13, Schladen, 38315, Wolfenbuttel, Germany
Tel.: (49) 5335802101
Liquid Sugar Mfr
N.A.I.C.S.: 311314

Nordzucker AG Uelzen Factory (1)
An der Zuckerfabrik 1, 29525, Uelzen, Germany
Tel.: (49) 58189156
Liquid Sugar Mfr
N.A.I.C.S.: 311314

Nordzucker Ireland Limited (1)
Arena House Arena Road Sandyford Business Estate, Dublin, Ireland
Tel.: (353) 12130716
Web Site: http://www.nordzuckerireland.ie
Sugar Product Distr
N.A.I.C.S.: 424490

Nordzucker Polska S.A. (1)
Werk Opalenica ul 5 Stycznia 54, 64-330, Opalenica, Poland
Tel.: (48) 614479300
Web Site: http://www.nordzucker.pl
Liquid Sugar Mfr
N.A.I.C.S.: 311314
Jaroslaw Kamieniarz (CEO)

Povazsky Cukor a.s. (1)
Cukrovarska 311/9, Trencianska Tepla, 914 11, Trencin, Slovakia
Tel.: (421) 326558646
Web Site: http://www.nordzucker.sk
Liquid Sugar Mfr
N.A.I.C.S.: 311314

Queensland Commodity Service Pty Ltd. (1)
Level 5 444 Queen Street, Farleigh, Brisbane, 4740, QLD, Australia
Tel.: (61) 800774246
Web Site: http://www.qcs.com.au
Sugar Mfr
N.A.I.C.S.: 311314
Darren Chen (Mgr-Trading)

NOREMAT SAS
Dynapole Ludres Fleville 166 Rue Ampere, 60093, Ludres, France
Tel.: (33) 383256960
Web Site: http://www.noremat.com
Year Founded: 1981
Sales Range: $25-49.9 Million
Farm Machinery & Equipment Mfr.
N.A.I.C.S.: 333111
Christophe Bachmann (Dir)

NORFI ABSAUGTECHNIK GMBH
Kelterstrasse 65, 72669, Unterensingen, Germany
Tel.: (49) 702296650
Web Site: http://www.norfi.de
Year Founded: 2003
Sales Range: $10-24.9 Million
Emp.: 50
Exhaust Extraction Systems Mfr
N.A.I.C.S.: 333413
Alexander Frank (Mng Dir)

NORFOLK METALS LIMITED
Suite 10 85-87 Forrest Street, Cottesloe, 6011, WA, Australia
Tel.: (61) 62558625 AU
Web Site: https://www.norfolkmetals.com.au
Year Founded: 2021
NFL—(ASX)
Rev.: $119
Assets: $4,646,266
Liabilities: $75,529
Net Worth: $4,570,737
Earnings: ($497,982)
Fiscal Year-end: 06/30/22
Metal Exploration Services
N.A.I.C.S.: 213114
Ben Phillips (Chm)

NORGES BANK
Bankplassen 2, 0151, Oslo, Norway
Tel.: (47) 22316000
Web Site: http://www.norges-bank.no
Sales Range: $50-74.9 Million
Emp.: 660
Central Bank
N.A.I.C.S.: 521110
Oystein Olsen (Chm-Exec Bd & Governor)

Subsidiaries:

NBIM S.a r.l. (1)
40 Avenue Monterey, 2163, Luxembourg, Luxembourg
Tel.: (352) 26 38 30 94
Financial Services
N.A.I.C.S.: 523999
Rupert Robinson (Head-Investment Ops)

Norges Bank Investment Management (1)
Bankplassen 2, 0151, Oslo, Norway
Tel.: (47) 2407 3000
Web Site: http://www.nbim.no
Sales Range: $200-249.9 Million
Emp.: 320
Asset Management Services
N.A.I.C.S.: 523940
Yngve Slyngstad (CEO)

Joint Venture (US):

KTR Capital Partners, LLC (2)
1001 Conshohocken State Rd, West Conshohocken, PA 19428-2908 (45%)
Tel.: (484) 530-1280
Web Site: http://www.ktrcapital.com
Emp.: 89
Industrial Real Estate Investment, Development, Property Management & Leasing Services
N.A.I.C.S.: 531390
Jeffrey E. Kelter (Chm)

NORGESGRUPPEN ASA
Karenslyst Alle 12-14, PO Box 300, Skoyen, 0213, Oslo, Norway
Tel.: (47) 2411 3100 NO
Web Site: http://www.norgesgruppen.no
Year Founded: 2000
Sales Range: $5-14.9 Billion
Emp.: 30,000
Holding Company Grocery Whlsr & Retailer Services
N.A.I.C.S.: 551112
Oyvind Andersen (Mng Dir)

Subsidiaries:

ASKO Norge AS (1)
Nedre Kalbakkvei 22, 0950, Oslo, Norway
Tel.: (47) 22169000
Web Site: http://www.asko.no
Sales Range: $5-14.9 Billion
Emp.: 300
Grocery Whlsr, Warehousing, Transportation & Logistics Services
N.A.I.C.S.: 424410

Dagrofa A/S (1)
Krup Industrivej 12, 4100, Ringsted, Denmark (55%)
Tel.: (45) 70 20 02 68
Web Site: http://www.dagrofa.dk
Grocery Distr
N.A.I.C.S.: 445110
Tomas Pietrangeli (CEO)

Subsidiary (Domestic):

Catering Engros A/S (2)
Norremarken 2, Skovlund, 6823, Ansager, Denmark
Tel.: (45) 70808080
Web Site: http://www.cateringengros.dk
Sales Range: $100-124.9 Million
Catering Whlsr & Supplier
N.A.I.C.S.: 722320

Dagrofa Detail A/S (2)
Abakkevej 69, 5210, Odense, Denmark
Tel.: (45) 65941010
Sales Range: $100-124.9 Million
Grocery Stores
N.A.I.C.S.: 424410

Dagrofa S-Engros AS (2)
Stamholmen 175, 2650, Hvidovre, Denmark
Tel.: (45) 43301404
Web Site: http://www.s-engros.dk
Sales Range: $300-349.9 Million
Emp.: 50
Convenience Food Services
N.A.I.C.S.: 722330

ISO Supermarked A/S (2)
Gammelager 11-13, 2605, Brondby, Denmark
Tel.: (45) 43228380
Sales Range: $300-349.9 Million
Grocery Whslr
N.A.I.C.S.: 445110

Lekkerland A/S (2)
Morupvej 2-4, 7400, Herning, Denmark
Tel.: (45) 96 26 69 00
Sales Range: $125-149.9 Million
Emp.: 300
Confectionery Whslr
N.A.I.C.S.: 424450

Nord Data A/S (2)
Ronnevangs Alle 6, DK-3400, Hillerod, Denmark
Tel.: (45) 48 20 03 00
Computer Services
N.A.I.C.S.: 541511

Subsidiary (Non-US):

Pisiffik A/S (2)
Boks 1009, 3911, Sisimiut, Greenland (72%)
Tel.: (299) 862900
Web Site: http://www.pisiffik.gl
Grocery & Shopping Goods Services
N.A.I.C.S.: 424490

Subsidiary (Domestic):

SuperGros A/S (2)
Knud Hojgaards Vej 19, Vejle, 7100, Denmark
Tel.: (45) 70100203
Web Site: http://www.supergros.dk
Emp.: 300
Grocery Supplier
N.A.I.C.S.: 424490
Carsten Christiansen (Mng Dir)

Kiwi Norge AS (1)
Ringeriksveien 4 B, NO-3400, Lier, Norway
Tel.: (47) 3224 4000
Web Site: http://www.kiwi.no
Discount Grocery Stores Operator
N.A.I.C.S.: 445110
Jan Paul Bjorkoy (Gen Mgr)

Meny AS (1)
Karenslyst Alle 12-14, Oslo, 0278, Norway
Tel.: (47) 2161 2000
Web Site: http://www.meny.no
Supermarket Operator
N.A.I.C.S.: 445110
Vegard Kjuus (Mng Dir)

NORGINE B.V.
Antonio VIvaldistraat 150, 1083 HP, Amsterdam, Netherlands
Tel.: (31) 20 567 0900 NI
Web Site: http://www.norgine.com
Year Founded: 1906
Pharmaceuticals Mfr
N.A.I.C.S.: 325412
Sheila Hopkins (Chief Legal Officer)

NORGINE INTERNATIONAL LIMITED
Norgine House Widewater Pl Moorhall Rd, Harefield, UB9 6NS, Mddx, United Kingdom
Tel.: (44) 1895453710
Web Site: http://www.norgine.com
Year Founded: 1906
Sales Range: $10-24.9 Million
Emp.: 1,000
Specialty Pharmaceutical Mfr
N.A.I.C.S.: 325412
Peter Stein (Chm & CEO)

NORINCO INTERNATIONAL COOPERATION LTD.
North International Building No 6 Zhengda Road, Shijingshan District, Beijing, 100040, China
Tel.: (86) 1068137370
Web Site: http://www.norinco-intl.com
Year Founded: 2001
000065—(SSE)
Rev.: $1,886,031,108
Assets: $3,100,099,392
Liabilities: $1,898,504,244
Net Worth: $1,201,595,148
Earnings: $89,295,804
Fiscal Year-end: 12/31/22
Construction Engineering Services
N.A.I.C.S.: 237990
Ji Wei (Chm)

Subsidiaries:

NORINCO International Real Estate Co., Ltd. (1)
Floor 18 NORINCO International Plaza No 6 Zhengda Road, Shijingshan District, Beijing, 100040, China
Tel.: (86) 1068137356
Web Site: http://www.norinco-re.com.cn
Real Estate Development Services
N.A.I.C.S.: 531210

NORINCO-IMC Logistics Co., Ltd. (1)
Floor 15 NORINCO International Plaza No 6 Zhengda Road, Shijingshan District, Beijing, 100040, China
Tel.: (86) 1068137200
Web Site: http://www.norinco-imc.com
Logistics Transportation Services
N.A.I.C.S.: 541614

Shenzhen Huate Packing Co., Ltd. (1)
No 130 Chongqing Road, TongFuYu Ind Zone FuYong Town BaoAn Dist, Shenzhen, 518103, China
Tel.: (86) 75527314282
Web Site: https://en.sz-huate.com
Tinplate Can Mfr
N.A.I.C.S.: 332431

Division (Domestic):

Shenzhen Huate Packing Co., Ltd. - Tin-plate Cutting Division (2)
East of Chongqing Road TongFuYu Ind Zone FuYong Town BaoAn Dist, Shenzhen, 518103, China
Tel.: (86) 75529981298
Tinplate Can Mfr
N.A.I.C.S.: 332431

NORINVEST HOLDING SA

NORINVEST HOLDING SA

Norinvest Holding SA—(Continued)

Avenue de Miremont 20, PO Box 315, 1211, Geneva, Switzerland
Tel.: (41) 582186080 CH
Web Site: http://www.norinvest.ch
Year Founded: 1984
Sales Range: $10-24.9 Million
Emp.: 138
Investment Holding Company
N.A.I.C.S.: 551112
Massimo Esposito-Sporrer *(Chm)*

Subsidiaries:

Banque Cramer & Cie SA (1)
22 Avenue de Miremont, Geneva, 1206, Switzerland
Tel.: (41) 58 218 6000
Web Site: http://www.banquecramer.ch
Investment Banking, Financial Advisory & Wealth Management Services
N.A.I.C.S.: 523150
Marco J. Netzer *(Chm)*

Subsidiary (Domestic):

Cramer Asset Management SA (2)
Via Peri 9a, 6900, Lugano, Switzerland (52%)
Tel.: (41) 91 210 3194
Web Site:
  http://www.cramerassetmanagement.com
Wealth Management Services
N.A.I.C.S.: 523940

Golay Buchel & Cie SA (1)
Avenue de Rhodanie 60, CH-1000, Lausanne, Switzerland (100%)
Tel.: (41) 21 613 7777
Web Site: http://www.golay.com
Sales Range: $25-49.9 Million
Emp.: 30
Jewelry Whslr
N.A.I.C.S.: 423940

NORITAKE CO., LIMITED

3-1-36 Noritake-shinmachi, Nishi-ku, Nagoya, 451-8501, Aichi, Japan
Tel.: (81) 525619837 JP
Web Site: https://www.noritake.co.jp
Year Founded: 1904
5331—(TKS)
Rev.: $911,598,320
Assets: $1,335,676,090
Liabilities: $357,594,390
Net Worth: $978,081,700
Earnings: $75,882,800
Emp.: 4,821
Fiscal Year-end: 03/31/24
Dinnerware, Glassware, Tableware, Grinding Wheels & Machineries; Various New Ceramics; Electronic Parts & Equipment Mfr
N.A.I.C.S.: 327910
Tadashi Ogura *(Chm)*

Subsidiaries:

Dia Resibon (Thailand) Co., Ltd. (1)
1/1 Moo 5 Rojana Industrial Park Rojana Road, Tambol U-Thai Amphur U-Thai, Ayutthaya, 13210, Thailand
Tel.: (66) 35 741-6605
Web Site: https://www.diaresibon.com
Grinding & Polishing Tool Mfr
N.A.I.C.S.: 327910

Subsidiary (Domestic):

Siam Coated Abrasive Co., Ltd. (2)
Amata Nakorn Industrial Estate 7-126 Moo 4, T Mabyangporn A Pluakdaeng, Rayong, 21140, Thailand
Tel.: (66) 3 865 0150
Grinding & Polishing Tool Mfr
N.A.I.C.S.: 327910

Hiroshima Grinding Industries Co., Ltd. (1)
37 Naganoichi Kihoku-cho, Kitauwa-gun, Matsuyama, 798-1333, Ehime, Japan
Tel.: (81) 895 45 1127
Emp.: 60
Grinding Wheel Mfr
N.A.I.C.S.: 327910

Katfuhiro Ishiburo *(Gen Mgr)*

Itron (U.K.) Limited (1)
Vantage House Harfreys Road, Harfreys Industrial Estate, Great Yarmouth, NR31 0LS, Norfolk, United Kingdom (98%)
Tel.: (44) 1493601144
Web Site: http://www.noritake-itron.com
Sales Range: $25-49.9 Million
Emp.: 30
Provider of Electronics Products
N.A.I.C.S.: 449210
Andy Warnes *(Mng Dir)*

KCM Corporation (1)
2-41 Tsukisan-cho, Minato-ku, Nagoya, 455-8668, Aichi, Japan (100%)
Tel.: (81) 526613182
Sales Range: $50-74.9 Million
Emp.: 150
Clay & Non-Clay Refractory Mfr & Distr
N.A.I.C.S.: 327120

Nihon Fureki Sangyo Co., Ltd. (1)
2-13-17 Fuji-cho, Nishi-Tokyo, 202-0014, Tokyo, Japan
Tel.: (81) 42 461 5171
Grinding & Polishing Tool Mfr
N.A.I.C.S.: 327910

Nippon Resibon Corporation (1)
22-10 Kitahorie 1-Chome, Nishi-Ku, Osaka, 550-0014, Japan
Tel.: (81) 66 538 0198
Web Site: https://www.resibon.co.jp
Emp.: 260
Machine Tools Mfr
N.A.I.C.S.: 333517
Kenichi Horaguchi *(Chm)*

Noritake (Australia) Pty Ltd (1)
Unit 4 153 Beauchamp Rd, Matraville, 2036, NSW, Australia (100%)
Tel.: (61) 29 316 7123
Web Site: https://www.noritake.com.au
Sales Range: $25-49.9 Million
Emp.: 15
Provider of Industrial Products
N.A.I.C.S.: 333517
Perry Iwata *(Mgr)*

Noritake (Guam), Inc. (1)
104 Pacifica Plz Bldg Marine Dr, Tamuning, GU 96913
Tel.: (671) 649-7066
Provider of Kitchen & Tableware
N.A.I.C.S.: 327110

Noritake (Siam) Co., Ltd. (1)
(50%)
Tel.: (66) 22351688
Web Site: http://www.noritake.com
Sales Range: $25-49.9 Million
Emp.: 15
Provider of Industrial Products
N.A.I.C.S.: 333517

Noritake Abrasives (Suzhou) Co., Ltd. (1)
688 Taishan Rd, New District of Suzhou, Suzhou, 215129, China
Tel.: (86) 5126 672 6682
Grinding & Polishing Tool Mfr
N.A.I.C.S.: 327910

Noritake Co., Inc. (1)
15-22 Fair Lawn Ave, Fair Lawn, NJ 07410-2322 (100%)
Tel.: (201) 796-2222
Web Site: http://www.noritake.co.jp
Sales Range: $25-49.9 Million
Emp.: 30
Provider of Kitchen & Table Ware
N.A.I.C.S.: 423220

Branch (Domestic):

Noritake Co., Inc. (2)
4990 Alliance Dr, Mason, OH 45040 (100%)
Tel.: (513) 234-0770
Web Site: https://www.noritake-abrasives.com
Sales Range: $25-49.9 Million
Emp.: 24
Provider of Industrial Products
N.A.I.C.S.: 423840
Rene Dillon *(Office Mgr)*

Noritake Co., Limited - Imari Factory (1)
120-3 Nagahama Higashiyamashiro-cho, Imari, 849-4271, Saga, Japan
Tel.: (81) 955228454
Web Site: http://www.noritake.co.jp
Industrial Machinery Mfr
N.A.I.C.S.: 333248

Noritake Co., Limited - Kamori Factory (1)
16-1 Aza-Ninowari Kamori-cho, Tsushima, 496-0005, Aichi-ken, Japan
Tel.: (81) 567285116
Grinding Wheel Mfr
N.A.I.C.S.: 333248

Noritake Co., Limited - Komaki Factory (1)
1780 Oaza-Mitsubuchi, Komaki, 485-0075, Aichi, Japan
Tel.: (81) 568 77 4121
Web Site: http://www.noritake.co.jp
Industrial Machinery & Equipment Mfr
N.A.I.C.S.: 333248

Noritake Co., Limited - Kurume Factory (1)
210 Takeno Tanushimaru-machi, Kurume, 839-1215, Fukuoka-ken, Japan
Tel.: (81) 943 73 0730
Web Site: http://www.noritake.co.jp
Grinding & Polishing Tools Mfr
N.A.I.C.S.: 333248

Noritake Co., Limited - Matsusaka Factory (1)
Matsusaka Core Industrial Park 20 Koyo-cho, Matsusaka, 515-0053, Mie-ken, Japan
Tel.: (81) 598 29 5611
Web Site: http://www.noritake.co.jp
Grinding & Polishing Tools Mfr
N.A.I.C.S.: 333248

Noritake Co., Limited - Minato Factory (1)
2-39 Tsukisan-cho, Minato-ku, Nagoya, 455-0044, Aichi-ken, Japan
Tel.: (81) 526616306
Grinding & Polishing Tools Mfr
N.A.I.C.S.: 333248

Noritake Co., Limited - Yoshida Factory (1)
14-5 Yoshidahigashisakae-cho, Tsubame, 959-0232, Niigata-ken, Japan
Tel.: (81) 256 92 2171
Web Site: http://www.noritake.co.jp
Industrial Machinery Mfr
N.A.I.C.S.: 333248

Noritake Coated Abrasive Co., Limited (1)
20 Shimonagaida Azabu-cho, Nishikamo-gun, Miyoshi, 470-0206, Aichi, Japan
Tel.: (81) 561 32 2235
Emp.: 130
Coated Abrasive Products Mfr & Distr
N.A.I.C.S.: 327910
Yamauchi Ichiro *(Gen Mgr)*

Plant (Domestic):

Noritake Coated Abrasive Co., Limited - Noto Plant (2)
5-7-1 Horimatsu Shika-Machi, Hakui, 925-0157, Ishikawa, Japan
Tel.: (81) 767 32 2717
Coated Abrasive Product Mfr
N.A.I.C.S.: 327910

Noritake Dental Supply Co., Limited (1)
300 Higashiyama Miyoshi-cho, Miyoshi, 470-0293, Aichi, Japan
Tel.: (81) 561 32 8953
Web Site: http://www.noritake-dental.co.jp
Dental Supplies Whslr
N.A.I.C.S.: 423450

Noritake Europe GmbH (1)
Kurhessenstrasse 3, 64546, Morfelden, Germany (100%)
Tel.: (49) 610520920
Web Site: http://www.noritake.de
Sales Range: $25-49.9 Million
Emp.: 10
Provider of Industrial Products
N.A.I.C.S.: 333248
Itsuo Yamashita *(Mng Dir)*

Noritake Garden Co., Ltd (1)

INTERNATIONAL PUBLIC

3-1-36 Noritake-shinmachi, Nishi-ku, Nagoya, 451-8501, Aichi, Japan
Tel.: (81) 525617290
Garden Operating Services
N.A.I.C.S.: 712130
Hitoshi Tanemura *(Pres)*

Noritake Hong Kong Ltd. Electronics Division (1)
Unit 605 Remington Centre 23 Hungpo Rd Kwnpong, Hong Kong, China (Hong Kong) (100%)
Tel.: (852) 25628802
Sales Range: $25-49.9 Million
Emp.: 5
Provider of Kitchen & Tableware
N.A.I.C.S.: 327110

Noritake Itron Corporation (1)
670-5 Uchimi Taiki-cho, Watarai-gun, Ise, 519-2736, Mie, Japan
Tel.: (81) 598832311
Web Site: https://www.noritake-itron.jp
Emp.: 121
Vacuum Fluorescent Displays Mfr & Distr
N.A.I.C.S.: 334419

Noritake Lanka Porcelain (Pvt) Limited (1)
Web Site: http://www.noritake.com
Mfr of Kitchen & Table Ware
N.A.I.C.S.: 327110

Noritake Lanka Porcelain (Pvt) Limited (1)
(100%)
Sales Range: $25-49.9 Million
Emp.: 26
Mfr of Kitchen & Table Ware
N.A.I.C.S.: 327110

Noritake Recycle Center Co., Limited (1)
166-2 Minamikawanami Hayao-cho, Aisai, 496-0931, Aichi, Japan
Tel.: (81) 567282330
Grinding Wheels Recycling Services
N.A.I.C.S.: 562920

Noritake SCG Plaster Co., Ltd. (1)
32 Moo 7 Nongplakradi Rd, Nong Pling Nong Khae, Saraburi, 18140, Thailand
Tel.: (66) 3 637 3578
Grinding & Polishing Tool Mfr
N.A.I.C.S.: 327910

Noritake Sa (Thailand) Co., Ltd. (1)
No 56 Moo7 Nongplakradi Road, Nongpling Nongkhae, Saraburi, 18140, Thailand
Tel.: (66) 3 637 3085
Grinding & Polishing Tool Mfr
N.A.I.C.S.: 327910

Noritake Shanghai Trading Co., Ltd. (1)
Room 701 Aetna Tower No 107 Zun Yi Road, Chang Ning District, Shanghai, 200051, China
Tel.: (86) 2162375667
Emp.: 14
Industrial Supplies Distr
N.A.I.C.S.: 423840
Kataoka Hiroki *(Gen Mgr)*

Noritake TCF Co., Ltd. (1)
7-7 Shimofuji, Ogakie-cho, Kariya, 448-0813, Aichi, Japan
Tel.: (81) 56 625 4300
Web Site: https://www.noritake.co.jp
Emp.: 65
Annealing Furnace & Semiconductor Component Mfr
N.A.I.C.S.: 333994

Noritake Taipei Co., Ltd. (1)
No 37 Alley 105 Lane 514 Zhongzheng Rd, Xinzhuang Dist, Xinbei City, 242, Taiwan
Tel.: (886) 229071221
Sales Range: $25-49.9 Million
Emp.: 20
Ceramic Materials Mfr
N.A.I.C.S.: 327110

Okura Art China, Inc. (1)
20 Akihabachi, Totsuka-ku, Yokohama, 245-0052, Kanagawa, Japan
Tel.: (81) 458112183
Web Site: https://www.okuratouen.co.jp
Tableware Mfr
N.A.I.C.S.: 327110

AND PRIVATE COMPANIES

PT. Noritake INDONESIA (1)
Blok A-II No 9A Kawasan Berikat Kota Bukit Indah, Purwakarta, 41181, Jawa Barat, Indonesia
Tel.: (62) 264351311
Emp.: 130
Electronic Components Mfr
N.A.I.C.S.: 334419

The Siam Moulding Plaster Co., Ltd. (1)
32 Moo 7 Nongplakradi Rd, Nongpling Nonghae, Saraburi, 18140, Thailand
Tel.: (66) 36373578
Web Site: http://www.siammoulding.com
Sales Range: $25-49.9 Million
Emp.: 100
Provider of Ceramics Materials
N.A.I.C.S.: 327110

Tono Grinding Co., Ltd. (1)
2007 Oroshi-cho, Toki, 509-5202, Gifu, Japan
Tel.: (81) 572 57 3300
Grinding Wheel Mfr
N.A.I.C.S.: 333248

Tono Kenma Co., Ltd. (1)
2007 Oroshi-cho, Toki, 509-5202, Gifu, Japan
Tel.: (81) 57 257 3300
Grinding Wheel Mfr
N.A.I.C.S.: 327910

Zen Noritake Co., Ltd. (1)
904 Koibori-cho, Meito-ku, Nagoya, 465-0044, Aichi-ken, Japan
Tel.: (81) 527011193
Grinding & Polishing Tools Distr
N.A.I.C.S.: 423830

NORITSU KOKI CO., LTD.
Joule A 5th Floor 1-10-10 Azabujuban, Minato-ku, Tokyo, 106-0045, Japan
Tel.: (81) 335055053
Web Site: https://www.noritsu.co.jp
7744—(TKS)
Rev.: $649,103,680
Assets: $1,981,449,390
Liabilities: $522,015,430
Net Worth: $1,459,433,960
Earnings: $72,310,910
Emp.: 1,144
Fiscal Year-end: 12/31/23
Photo Finishing Equipment & Peripheral Equipment Mfr
N.A.I.C.S.: 333310
Yukiko Katabe *(Operating Officer)*

Subsidiaries:

Doctor Net, Inc. (1)
Sumitomoshibadaimon Bldg 2-5-5, Shibadaimon Minato-ku, Tokyo, 105-0012, Japan
Tel.: (81) 286578200
Web Site: http://dr-net.co.jp
Emp.: 112
Medical Software Development Services
N.A.I.C.S.: 541511

JLab Audio, LLC (1)
PO Box 43692, Tucson, AZ 85733
Tel.: (866) 358-6640
Web Site: http://www.jlabaudio.com
Sales Range: $1-9.9 Million
Emp.: 6
Portable Audio Products
N.A.I.C.S.: 334310
Josh Rosenfield *(Owner)*

JLab Japan Co., Ltd. (1)
Joule A 5F Azabujuban-1-10-10, Minato-ku, Tokyo, 106-0045, Japan
Tel.: (81) 5017418948
Web Site: https://jlab-audio.jp
Electronic Equipment Mfr & Distr
N.A.I.C.S.: 335311

N&F Techno Service Co., Ltd. (1)
1-67-1 Shibasaki, Chofu, 182-0014, Tokyo, Japan
Tel.: (81) 424447011
Web Site: http://www.nftechno.co.jp
Emp.: 344
Photographic Equipment Maintenance Services

NK Agri Co., Ltd. (1)
579 1 Umehara, Wakayama, 640-8550, Japan **(100%)**
Tel.: (81) 73 453 1000
Web Site: http://www.noritsu.co.jp
Farm Machinery Mfr & Distr
N.A.I.C.S.: 333111

NK Medico Co., Ltd. (1)
5th Fl Place Astle Bldg 1-2-3 Azabu Juban, Minato-ku, Tokyo, 106-0045, Japan **(100%)**
Tel.: (81) 3 3505 5119
Diagnostic Imaging Center Operating Services
N.A.I.C.S.: 621512

NK RELATIONS Co., Ltd. (1)
5th Fl Joule A 1-10-10 Azabu Juban, Minato-ku, Tokyo, 106-0045, Japan **(100%)**
Tel.: (81) 3 3505 0579
Web Site: http://www.noritsu.co.jp
Investigation & Investment Services
N.A.I.C.S.: 561611

Subsidiary (Domestic):

Kidswell Bio Corporation (2)
Kanayama Bldg 3F 1-2-12 Shinkawa Chuo-ku, Tokyo, 104-0033, Japan
Rev.: $15,190,166
Assets: $33,912,283
Liabilities: $17,277,077
Net Worth: $16,635,206
Earnings: ($5,181,307)
Fiscal Year-end: 03/31/2022
Biopharmaceutical Researcher & Developer
N.A.I.C.S.: 325412
Masaharu Tani *(Pres & CEO)*

NK Works Co., Ltd. (1)
2-17-17 Iwamoto-cho, Chiyoda-ku, Tokyo, 101-0032, Japan **(100%)**
Tel.: (81) 3 3864 5411
Web Site: http://www.nk-works.co.jp
Sales Range: $25-49.9 Million
Emp.: 53
Cutting Tool & Machine Tool Mfr
N.A.I.C.S.: 333515
Hirotsugu Nishimoto *(Pres)*

Division (Domestic):

NK Works Co., Ltd. - Domestic Sales Division (2)
2-7-68 Kaigan, Minato-ku, Tokyo, 105-0022, Japan
Tel.: (81) 3 3456 2021
Industrial Machinery Distr
N.A.I.C.S.: 423830

Noritsu (Deutschland) GmbH (1)
Siemensring 87, D-47877, Willich, Germany
Tel.: (49) 215491570
Web Site: http://www.noritsu.de
Sales Range: $50-74.9 Million
Emp.: 65
Photographic Equipment & Supplies Whslr
N.A.I.C.S.: 423410

Noritsu (Far East) Ltd (1)
leadereentid Manhattan Centre 47 wongchapong 513, Kwai Chung, 24, NT, China (Hong Kong)
Tel.: (852) 2873 4788
Web Site: http://www.noritsu.com.hk
Camera & Photographic Supplies Store Operator
N.A.I.C.S.: 449210

Noritsu (Shanghai) Electronics Equipment Manufacturing Co, Ltd (1)
No 343 Meigui Road, Waigaoqiao Free Trade Zone, Shanghai, 200131, China
Tel.: (86) 2150463997
Web Site: http://www.noritsu.co.jp
Sales Range: $50-74.9 Million
Emp.: 100
Photographic Equipment & Supplies Whslr
N.A.I.C.S.: 423410

Noritsu (Shanghai) P.M.E. Co., Ltd. (1)
No 343 Meigui North Road Waigaoqiao Free Trade Zone, Shanghai, 200131, China
Tel.: (86) 2150463997
Photofinishing Equipment Mfr
N.A.I.C.S.: 333310

Noritsu (Shanghai) Photofinishing Equipment Manufacturing Co., Ltd. (1)
No 343 Meigui Road N Waigaoqiao Free Trade Zone, Shanghai, 200131, China
Tel.: (86) 21 5046 3997
Web Site: http://www.noritsu.cn
Photofinishing Equipment Mfr
N.A.I.C.S.: 333310

Noritsu (Shanghai) Precision Machinery Manufacturing Co, Ltd (1)
Jiading Industrial Zone No1631, Ye Cheng Road, 201821, Shanghai, China
Tel.: (86) 2159169898
Specialized Design Services
N.A.I.C.S.: 541490

Noritsu (UK) Ltd (1)
Sherbourne Dr, Milton Keynes, United Kingdom
Tel.: (44) 1908371100
Web Site: http://www.noritsu.co.uk
Durable Goods Whslr
N.A.I.C.S.: 423990

Noritsu America Corporation (1)
6900 Noritsu Ave, Buena Park, CA 90620
Tel.: (954) 385-3775
Web Site: http://www.noritsu.com
Sales Range: $150-199.9 Million
Emp.: 317
Durable Goods Whslr
N.A.I.C.S.: 423990
Go Yoshii *(CEO)*

Noritsu Canada Ltd (1)
102-17750 56th Avenue Suite 501, Cloverdale, Surrey, V3S 1K4, BC, Canada
Tel.: (647) 689-2140
Web Site: https://www.noritsu.com
Photographic Equipment & Supplies Whslr
N.A.I.C.S.: 423410

Noritsu India Private Limited (1)
Noble Heights 2nd Floor NH-II Block C-1 LSC, Janak Puri, New Delhi, 110 058, India
Tel.: (91) 1145089466
Web Site: http://www.noritsuindia.com
Emp.: 16
Digital Photographic Machinery Mfr
N.A.I.C.S.: 333310

Noritsu Italia S.r.l (1)
Largo Donegani 4 A, 28100, Novara, Italy
Tel.: (39) 0321445211
Web Site: http://www.noritsu.co.jp
Sales Range: $25-49.9 Million
Emp.: 14
Photographic Equipment & Supplies Whslr
N.A.I.C.S.: 423410

Noritsu Koki (Malaysia) Sdn. Bhd (1)
Ste G2 Ground Fl Bangunan Thk No 2A jalan 243 sec 51a, Jalan 243 Section 51A, 46100, Petaling Jaya, Selangor, Malaysia
Tel.: (60) 378762733
Sales Range: $25-49.9 Million
Emp.: 26
Photographic Equipment & Supplies Whslr
N.A.I.C.S.: 423410

Noritsu Koki Australia Pty.Ltd (1)
48a Alexander Avenue, Taren Point, 2229, NSW, Australia
Tel.: (61) 285252100
Web Site: http://www.noritsu.com.au
Emp.: 7
Photographic Equipment & Supplies Whslr
N.A.I.C.S.: 423410

Noritsu Mexico, S.A. de C.V. (1)
Horacio Ave No 340 Col Chabuldebc Morales, 11570, Mexico, Mexico
Tel.: (52) 5526266710
Web Site: http://www.noritsu.com.mx
Sales Range: $25-49.9 Million
Emp.: 23
Photographic Equipment & Supplies Whslr
N.A.I.C.S.: 423410

Noritsu Philippines Inc (1)
Unit B 26 Fl Trafalgar Plaza H V De La Costa, Salcedo Village, Makati, 1227, Philippines
Tel.: (63) 28128443
Web Site: http://www.noritsu.com.ph
Sales Range: $25-49.9 Million
Emp.: 15
Photographic Equipment & Supplies Whslr

NORITZ CORPORATION

N.A.I.C.S.: 423410
Joven Suguitan *(Gen Mgr)*

Noritsu Singapore Pte. Ltd. (1)
2 Bukit Batok Street 23 02-13 Bukit Batok Connection, Tradehub 21 East Lobby, Singapore, 659554, Singapore
Tel.: (65) 67788333
Web Site: http://www.noritsu.com.sg
Sales Range: $25-49.9 Million
Emp.: 10
Camera & Photographic Supplies Stores
N.A.I.C.S.: 449210
Pang Seng Heng *(Gen Mgr)*

Noritsu Taiwan Co., Ltd (1)
1st Floor No 7 Alley 2 Lane 75 Section 3 Minquan East Road, Zhongshan District, Taipei, Taiwan
Tel.: (886) 225081908
Web Site: http://www.noritsu.com.tw
Sales Range: $25-49.9 Million
Emp.: 17
Photographic Equipment & Supplies Whslr
N.A.I.C.S.: 423410

Noritsu do Brasil Ltda. (1)
Rua Carlos Villalva no 01 - 10 Andar, Jabaquara, Sao Paulo, 04307-000, Brazil
Tel.: (55) 11 3779 0606
Web Site: http://www.noritsu.com.br
Photographic Equipment & Supplies Whslr
N.A.I.C.S.: 423410

SAIAN Corporation (1)
579 1 Umehara, Wakayama, 640-8550, Japan
Tel.: (81) 73 454 4603
Web Site: http://www.saian-corp.com
Electric Equipment Mfr
N.A.I.C.S.: 334419

NORITZ CORPORATION
93 Edomachi, Chuo-ku, Kobe, 650-0033, Hyogo, Japan
Tel.: (81) 783913361
Web Site: https://form.noritz.co.jp
Year Founded: 1951
5943—(TKS)
Rev.: $1,431,407,190
Assets: $1,473,096,390
Liabilities: $575,027,360
Net Worth: $898,069,030
Earnings: $6,154,120
Emp.: 6,569
Fiscal Year-end: 12/31/23
Household Heater, Air Conditioning, Kitchen & Bathroom Products Mfr
N.A.I.C.S.: 333415
Soichiro Kokui *(Chm)*

Subsidiaries:

Dux Manufacturing Limited (1)
Lackey Road, Moss Vale, 2577, NSW, Australia
Tel.: (61) 300365115
Web Site: http://www.dux.com.au
Hot Water Heater Mfr & Whslr
N.A.I.C.S.: 335220

Kanto Sangyo Co., Ltd. (1)
923-2 Kozakashimachi, Maebashi, 371-0122, Gunma, Japan
Tel.: (81) 272691177
Kitchen Product Mfr
N.A.I.C.S.: 332215

Noritz (China) Co., Ltd. (1)
No 7318 Daye Road, Fengxian, Shanghai, China
Tel.: (86) 21 37186666
Web Site: http://www.noritz.com.cn
Water Heater Mfr
N.A.I.C.S.: 335220

Noritz (HK) Electronics Technology Co Ltd (1)
Unit 1203 Jupiter Tower 9 Jupiter Street, North Point, China (Hong Kong)
Tel.: (852) 2127 7449
Water Heater Mfr
N.A.I.C.S.: 335220

Noritz (Shanghai) Home Appliance Co., Ltd (1)
No 7318 Daye Highway, Fengxian District, Shanghai, 201405, China

NORITZ CORPORATION

Noritz Corporation—(Continued)
Tel.: (86) 2137186666
Web Site: http://www.noritz.com.cn
Emp.: 1,000
Household Appliances Mfr
N.A.I.C.S.: 335220
Shi Wuzhi *(Gen Mgr)*

Noritz America Corporation (1)
11160 Grace Ave, Fountain Valley, CA 92708
Tel.: (714) 433-2905
Web Site: https://www.noritz.com
Sales Range: $25-49.9 Million
Emp.: 35
Water Heaters Mfr & Whslr
N.A.I.C.S.: 423620
Jay Hassel *(Pres & COO)*

Noritz Electronics Technology Corporation (1)
5 Minami Futami Futami-cho, Akashi, 674-0093, Hyogo, Japan
Tel.: (81) 789413270
Web Site: http://www.n-et.co.jp
Sales Range: $100-124.9 Million
Emp.: 253
Electrical Machine Instruments & Parts Mfr & Supplier
N.A.I.C.S.: 334515

Noritz Hong Kong Co., Ltd. (1)
Unit 1203, Jupiter Tower 9 9 Jupiter Street, North Point, China (Hong Kong)
Tel.: (852) 21267026
Web Site: http://www.noritz.com.hk
Sales Range: $25-49.9 Million
Emp.: 10
Water Heater Mfr
N.A.I.C.S.: 335220
Wesley Hung *(Gen Mgr)*

Noritz Hong Kong Holdings Co., Ltd. (1)
Unit 1203 Jupiter Tower 9 Jupiter Street, Hong Kong, China (Hong Kong)
Tel.: (852) 2126 7026
Web Site: http://www.noritz.com.hk
Water Heaters Sales
N.A.I.C.S.: 423620

PB Heat, LLC (1)
131 S Church St, Bally, PA 19503
Tel.: (306) 238-7860
Web Site: http://www.peerlessboilers.com
Power Boiler & Heat Exchanger Mfr
N.A.I.C.S.: 332410
Pete Morgan *(Exec VP)*

S-CORE Corporation (1)
337 Nakao Uozumi Town, Akashi, Hyogo, Japan
Tel.: (81) 789465533
Web Site: http://www.s-core.co.jp
Sales Range: $25-49.9 Million
Emp.: 50
Water Heaters Mfr & Supplier
N.A.I.C.S.: 423620

Sakura Bath & Kitchen Products (China) Co., Ltd. (1)
No 1 Qingyang South Road, Kunshan, 215300, Jiangsu, China
Tel.: (86) 51257710968
Web Site: http://www.sakura.com.cn
Home Appliance Distr
N.A.I.C.S.: 423620

Tada-Smith Company, Ltd. (1)
84-10 Wadayamachokurubuki, Asago, 669-5263, Hyogo, Japan
Tel.: (81) 796742321
Water Heater Mfr
N.A.I.C.S.: 333414

NORMA GROUP SE
Edisonstr 4, 63477, Maintal, Germany
Tel.: (49) 61816102740
Web Site: https://www.normagroup.com
Year Founded: 1949
NOEJ—(MUN)
Rev.: $1,349,790,159
Assets: $1,648,386,994
Liabilities: $883,294,697
Net Worth: $765,092,297
Earnings: $30,720,702

Emp.: 6,094
Fiscal Year-end: 12/31/23
Engineeering Services
N.A.I.C.S.: 541330
Gunter Hauptmann *(Chm-Supervisory Bd)*

Subsidiaries:

Connectors Verbindungstechnik AG (1)
Hertistrasse 29, 8304, Wallisellen, Switzerland
Tel.: (41) 523546868
Pharmaceuticals Product Mfr
N.A.I.C.S.: 325412

Craig Assembly Inc. (1)
1111 Fred W Moore Hwy, Saint Clair, MI 48079
Tel.: (810) 326-1374
Web Site: http://www.normagroup.com
Sales Range: $25-49.9 Million
Emp.: 125
Industrial Molded Products Mfr
N.A.I.C.S.: 333248
Tom Geiser *(Mgr-Plant)*

Fijaciones Norma S.A.U. (1)
Calle Narcis Monturiol 116-118, L'Hospitalet de Llobregat, 08902, Spain
Tel.: (34) 934329955
Web Site: http://www.fijacionesnorma.es
Sales Range: $25-49.9 Million
Emp.: 30
Industrial Equipment Mfr & Distr
N.A.I.C.S.: 333248

Kimplas Piping Systems Ltd. (1)
B-20 MIDC, Ambad, Nashik, 422010, Maharashtra, India
Tel.: (91) 2536622701
Pipe & Pipe Fitting Mfr
N.A.I.C.S.: 332996
Vinod Savale *(Officer-Pur)*

Subsidiary (Non-US):

Kimplas Limited (2)
Suite 310 Lakes Innovation Center Lakes Road, Braintree, CM7 3AN, Essex, United Kingdom
Tel.: (44) 1787473848
Pipe Fitting Mfr
N.A.I.C.S.: 332996

Lifial - Industria Metalurgica de Agueda, Lda. (1)
Rua Ectri n 492 Vale do Grou Apartado 222, 3754-909, Agueda, Portugal
Tel.: (351) 234600040
Web Site: http://www.lifial.pt
Industrial Equipment Whsr
N.A.I.C.S.: 423830
Claudia Lemos *(Sls Mgr)*

NORMA China Co., Ltd. (1)
No 51 Zhouzhou Road, Laoshan District, 266101, Qingdao, Shandong, China
Tel.: (86) 532 80992000
Automobile Parts Mfr
N.A.I.C.S.: 336390

NORMA Czech SRO (1)
Havlickova 28, 693 01, Hustopece, Czech Republic
Tel.: (420) 519440311
Web Site: http://www.normagroup.com
Industrial Equipment Mfr
N.A.I.C.S.: 333248

NORMA Distribution Center GmbH (1)
Unterm Ohmberg 24, 34431, Marsberg, Germany
Tel.: (49) 2992 907 191
Web Site: http://www.normagroup.com
Automobile Parts Distr
N.A.I.C.S.: 423120

NORMA Distribution France SAS (1)
Zac De La Croix St Nicolas 20 Rue Gustave Eiffel, 94510, La Queue-en-Brie, France
Tel.: (33) 1 45 93 18 19
Sales Range: $25-49.9 Million
Emp.: 15
Industrial Equipment Distr
N.A.I.C.S.: 423830

NORMA EJT (Changzhou) Co., Ltd. (1)
No 9 Longyin Road, Wujin National Hi-Tech Industrial Zone, Changzhou, 213167, China
Tel.: (86) 51980588000
Engineeering Services
N.A.I.C.S.: 541330

NORMA EJT (Wuxi) Co., Ltd. (1)
No 50 Chunhui Zhong Road, Xishan Economic Development Zone, Wuxi, 214101, Jiangsu, China
Tel.: (86) 51088266951
Engineeering Services
N.A.I.C.S.: 541330

NORMA France SAS (1)
5 Place Copernic, Evry, 91023, Courcouronnes, Cedex, France
Tel.: (33) 1 607 99240
Web Site: http://www.norma.fr
Discount Supermarket Operators
N.A.I.C.S.: 455211

NORMA Germany GmbH (1)
Edisonstrasse 4, Maintal, 63477, Germany
Tel.: (49) 6181 403 0
Web Site: http://www.norma.de
Clamps & Connectors Mfr
N.A.I.C.S.: 333515

NORMA Group Asia Pacific Holding Pte. Ltd. (1)
10 Jalan Kilang 06-01 Bt Merah Enterprise Centre, Singapore, 159410, Singapore
Tel.: (65) 67597955
Machine Joining Components Mfr
N.A.I.C.S.: 333120

NORMA Group CIS LLC (1)
Borkovskaya St 36, PO Box 4849, Togliatti, 445043, Russia
Tel.: (7) 8482635698
Engineeering Services
N.A.I.C.S.: 541330

NORMA Group Distribution Polska Sp. z.o.o. (1)
ul Dluga 2, Slawniow, 42-436, Pilica, Poland
Tel.: (48) 601887079
Metal Products Mfr
N.A.I.C.S.: 332999

NORMA Group Holding GmbH (1)
Edisonstrasse 4, Maintal, 63477, Hessen, Germany
Tel.: (49) 61814030
Web Site: http://www.normagroup.com
Sales Range: $200-249.9 Million
Emp.: 800
Plastics Product Mfr
N.A.I.C.S.: 326199

NORMA Group Mexico S de RL de C.V. (1)
Avenida Aristoteles 201 Parque Industrial Kalos, Apodaca, 66600, Nuevo Leon, Mexico
Tel.: (52) 81 1247 5770
Web Site: http://www.normagroup.com
Emp.: 190
Automobile Parts Mfr
N.A.I.C.S.: 336390

NORMA Group Products India Pvt. Ltd. (1)
A 13/3 Talegaon MIDC, Talegaon Industrial Area Navlakh Umbre Taluk, Pune, 410507, Maharashtra, India
Tel.: (91) 2114660501
Engineeering Services
N.A.I.C.S.: 541330

NORMA Grupa Jugoistocna Evropa d.o.o. (1)
Batinska 94, 24000, Subotica, Serbia
Tel.: (381) 24644500
Engineeering Services
N.A.I.C.S.: 541330

NORMA Italia SPA (1)
Z I Loc Bolinas, 25085, Gavardo, Italy
Tel.: (39) 0365311412
Industrial Equipment Distr
N.A.I.C.S.: 423830

NORMA Japan Inc. (1)
Tel.: (81) 362068370
Engineeering Services

INTERNATIONAL PUBLIC

N.A.I.C.S.: 541330

NORMA Korea Inc. (1)
1002 A-dong M-state Building 114 Bupwonro, Songpa-gu, Seoul, Korea (South)
Tel.: (82) 7046800381
Engineeering Services
N.A.I.C.S.: 541330

NORMA Michigan, Inc. (1)
2430 E Walton Blvd, Auburn Hills, MI 48326
Tel.: (248) 373-4300
Sales Range: $50-74.9 Million
Emp.: 125
Hose Clamps Mfr
N.A.I.C.S.: 332722
Annette Lebaron *(Mgr-HR)*

NORMA Netherlands BV (1)
Elisabeth Van Zuilenlaan 21, Delft, 2628 LS, Zuid-Holland, Netherlands
Tel.: (31) 152190905
Industrial Hardware Equipment Distr
N.A.I.C.S.: 423830

NORMA Pacific (Thailand) Ltd. (1)
700/709 Moo 1 Amata Nakorn Industrial Estate Tambon Panthong, Amphur Phantong, Chon Buri, 20160, Thailand
Tel.: (66) 380799046
Industrial Equipment Mfr & Distr
N.A.I.C.S.: 333248
Paul Jordan *(Gen Mgr)*

NORMA Pacific Asia Pte Ltd. (1)
No 10 Jalan Kilang 06-01 Sime Darby Enterprise Centre, Singapore, 159410, Singapore
Tel.: (65) 6759 7955
Web Site: http://www.normapacific.com
Industrial Plastic Pipe Distr
N.A.I.C.S.: 423840

NORMA Pacific Pty Ltd. (1)
74 Bazlgette Crescent, Dandenong South, 3175, VIC, Australia
Tel.: (61) 3 9761 4416
Web Site: http://www.normagroup.com.au
Emp.: 40
Industrial Supplies Distr
N.A.I.C.S.: 423840

NORMA Pennsylvania, Inc. (1)
3582 Tunnelton Rd, Saltsburg, PA 15681-9593
Tel.: (724) 639-3571
Sales Range: $50-74.9 Million
Emp.: 250
Hose Clamps Mfr
N.A.I.C.S.: 332722
Sean Gillespie *(Dir-HR)*

NORMA Polska Sp. z.o.o. (1)
Slawniow Dluga 2, Slawniow, Pilica, 42-436, Poland
Tel.: (48) 126227761
Web Site: http://www.normagroup.com
Industrial Equipment Mfr & Distr
N.A.I.C.S.: 333248

NORMA Products Malaysia Sdn. Bhd. (1)
ICT Office 5F-1E Tower 2 PFCC Jalan Puteri 1/2, Bandar Puteri, 47100, Puchong, Selangor, Malaysia
Tel.: (60) 386002500
Engineeering Services
N.A.I.C.S.: 541330

NORMA Sweden AB (1)
Visigatan, Box 100, Anderstorp, 33422, Sweden
Tel.: (46) 371 58 88 00
Web Site: http://www.normagroup.se
Sales Range: $25-49.9 Million
Emp.: 100
Industrial Hardware Products Mfr
N.A.I.C.S.: 333248

NORMA Turkey Baglanti Ye Birlestirme Teknolojiler Sanayi ve Ticaret Limited Sirketi (1)
Kozyatagi Mah Ibrahim Aga Sokak Som Plaza No 8-10 Kat 3, 34742, Istanbul, Turkiye
Tel.: (90) 2165042680
Web Site: http://www.normagroup.com
Industrial Equipment Mfr & Distr
N.A.I.C.S.: 333248

NORMA UK Ltd. (1)

AND PRIVATE COMPANIES

Weber Road Greenham Business Park, Newbury, RG19 6HW, Berkshire, United Kingdom
Tel.: (44) 1635 521880
Web Site: http://www.normagroup.com
Automobile Parts Mfr
N.A.I.C.S.: 336390

NORMA do Brasil Sistemas De Conexao Ltda. (1)
Rua das Moncoes 420 Sala 71/72, 09090-521, Santo Andre, SP, Brazil
Tel.: (55) 1144362577
Engineeering Services
N.A.I.C.S.: 541330

Norma (India) Limited (1)
48 Site-IV Upsidc Industrial Area Sahibabad Industrial Area, Ghaziabad, 201010, Uttar Pradesh, India
Tel.: (91) 9910046941
Web Site: https://www.normaindia.com
Carbon Steel Flange Equipment Mfr
N.A.I.C.S.: 332919

R.G.Ray Corporation (1)
3227 N Wilke Rd, Arlington Heights, IL 60004
Tel.: (847) 459-5900
Web Site: http://www.rgrayclamps.com
Engineered Clamp Mfr & Distr
N.A.I.C.S.: 333515

Statek Stanzerei Technik GmbH
Wilhelm-Roentgen-Str 16-18, 63477, Maintal, Germany
Tel.: (49) 618148894
Web Site: http://www.statek.de
Emp.: 50
Metal Products Mfr
N.A.I.C.S.: 332999

NORMAN BROADBENT PLC
Millbank Tower 21-24 Millbank, London, SW1P 4QP, United Kingdom
Tel.: (44) 2074840000 UK
Web Site:
  https://www.normanbroadbent.com
Year Founded: 1998
NBB—(AIM)
Rev.: $10,978,288
Assets: $5,219,642
Liabilities: $4,373,895
Net Worth: $845,746
Earnings: ($489,775)
Emp.: 56
Fiscal Year-end: 12/31/22
Executive Search, Coaching & Talent Development Services
N.A.I.C.S.: 541612
Michael John Brennan (Grp CEO)

Subsidiaries:

Human Asset Development International Limited (1)
12 St Jamess Square, London, SW1Y 4LB, United Kingdom
Tel.: (44) 2077241041
Web Site: http://www.humanasset.co.uk
Human Resource Consulting Services
N.A.I.C.S.: 541612

Norman Broadbent International Ltd. (1)
12 St James Sq, London, SW1A 4LD, United Kingdom
Tel.: (44) 2074840000
Web Site: http://www.normanbroadbent.com
Sales Range: $25-49.9 Million
Emp.: 50
Executive Search & Human Resource Outsourcing Services
N.A.I.C.S.: 541612

Norman Broadbent Overseas Ltd (1)
12 Street James Square, London, SW1Y 4LB, United Kingdom
Tel.: (44) 2074840000
Executive Recruitment Services
N.A.I.C.S.: 541612

NORMISKA CORPORATION
15 Suffolk St E, Guelph, N1H 2H7, ON, Canada
Tel.: (519) 780-0955 ON

Year Founded: 1997
Sales Range: $10-24.9 Million
Emp.: 30
Horticultural Products Supplier
N.A.I.C.S.: 115310
Fred St. Louis (Treas, Sec, VP & Comptroller)

Subsidiaries:

The Schundler Company (1)
150 Whitman Ave, Edison, NJ 08817
Tel.: (732) 287-2244
Web Site: http://www.schundler.com
Perlite & Vermiculite Producer
N.A.I.C.S.: 113210

NOROFERT S.A.
Justitiei St 63, Bucharest, Romania
Tel.: (40) 727034308
Web Site: https://www.norofert.ro
Year Founded: 2000
NRF—(BUC)
Rev.: $9,971,004
Assets: $14,805,768
Liabilities: $4,603,200
Net Worth: $10,202,568
Earnings: ($850,208)
Emp.: 52
Fiscal Year-end: 12/31/23
Agricultural Product Mfr & Distr
N.A.I.C.S.: 325199
Vlad Popescu (Pres & CEO)

NORONEX LTD
Suite 1 295 Rokeby Road, Subiaco, 6008, WA, Australia
Tel.: (61) 865552950
Web Site:
  https://noronexlimited.com.au
Year Founded: 2015
NRX—(ASX)
Rev.: $27,166
Assets: $2,544,141
Liabilities: $503,751
Net Worth: $2,040,390
Earnings: ($1,679,706)
Fiscal Year-end: 06/30/24
Coal & Mining Services
N.A.I.C.S.: 213113
James Thompson (Exec Dir)

NOROO HOLDINGS CO., LTD.
351 Bakdal-Ro Manan-Gu Anyang-si, Anyang, 13977, Gyeonggi-do, Korea (South)
Tel.: (82) 314676114 KR
Web Site:
  https://www.norooholdings.com
Year Founded: 1945
000320—(KRS)
Rev.: $796,068,970
Assets: $898,915,853
Liabilities: $392,062,730
Net Worth: $506,853,123
Earnings: $19,151,009
Emp.: 57
Fiscal Year-end: 12/31/22
Holding Company; Paint, Coating & Chemical Products Mfr
N.A.I.C.S.: 551112

Subsidiaries:

Noroo Automotive Coatings Co., Ltd. (1)
Jangangongdan-7-gil, Jangan-myeon, Hwaseong, 18579, Gyeonggi-do, Korea (South) (51%)
Tel.: (82) 31 8059 9500
Web Site: http://www.norooautocoat.com
Automotive Paints & Coatings Mfr
N.A.I.C.S.: 325510

Noroo Bee Chemical Co., Ltd (1)
527-6 Baekseok-dong, Seo-gu, Cheonan, Chungcheongnam-do, Korea (South)
Tel.: (82) 416206200
Web Site: https://www.noroobeechem.com
Paints & Coatings for Plastics Mfr & Distr
N.A.I.C.S.: 325510

Noroo Paint Co., Ltd. (1)
615 Bakdal-Dong Manan-Gu, Anyang-Si Gyeonggi-Do, 430-849, Anyang, Korea (South)
Tel.: (82) 314676282
Web Site: http://www.noroologinet.com
Emp.: 84
Paint & Coating Mfr
N.A.I.C.S.: 325510
Ninhyung Lee (Gen Mgr)

Seda Co., Ltd. (1)
351 Bakdal-ro, Manan-gu, Anyang, 150-010, Gyeonggi-do, Korea (South)
Tel.: (82) 313458000
Sales Range: $25-49.9 Million
Emp.: 50
Paint & Coating Mfr
N.A.I.C.S.: 325510

NOROO PAINT & COATINGS CO., LTD.
351 Bakdal-Ro, Manan-Gu, Anyang, Gyeonggi-do, Korea (South)
Tel.: (82) 314676538
Web Site:
  https://www.noroopaint.com
Year Founded: 2006
090350—(KRS)
Rev.: $577,746,746
Assets: $512,491,991
Liabilities: $241,991,480
Net Worth: $270,500,510
Earnings: $8,857,517
Emp.: 768
Fiscal Year-end: 12/31/22
General Paint Mfr
N.A.I.C.S.: 325510
Sung-Kug Cho (CEO)

Subsidiaries:

Colormate Co., Ltd. (1)
658 Nonhyeon-ro, Gangnam-gu, Seoul, Korea (South)
Tel.: (82) 23 443 2080
Paint Product Distr
N.A.I.C.S.: 424950

IPK Co., Ltd. (1)
17F 1000 Jungang-daero, Yeonje-gu, Busan, Korea (South)
Tel.: (82) 515806111
Paint Coating Mfr
N.A.I.C.S.: 325510

Kiban Tech Co., Ltd. (1)
10 Bamgogae-1gil, Samjuk-myeon, Anseong, 17513, Gyeonggi-do, Korea (South)
Tel.: (82) 317859091
Agricultural Research Services
N.A.I.C.S.: 541715

NOROO Holdings(Hong Kong) Co., Ltd. (1)
Rooms 1808 18/F Tower II Admiralty Center 18 Harcourt Road, Hong Kong, China (Hong Kong)
Tel.: (852) 25289899
Paint & Coating Product Mfr & Distr
N.A.I.C.S.: 325510

NOROO Kossan Paint Snd. Bhd. (1)
No 1 Jalan Koporat 1/KU 9, Taman Perindustrian Meru, 42200, Kapar, Selangor, Malaysia
Tel.: (60) 333922799
Web Site: https://www.kossanpaint.com
Paint & Coating Product Mfr & Distr
N.A.I.C.S.: 325510

Noroo Chemicals Co., Ltd. (1)
7 Cheomdan-ro 285beon-gil, Danwon-gu, Ansan, Gyeonggi-do, Korea (South)
Tel.: (82) 315997200
Chemical Product Mfr & Distr
N.A.I.C.S.: 325998

Noroo Coil Coatings Co., Ltd. (1)
Tel.: (82) 542780277
Paint Product Mfr & Distr
N.A.I.C.S.: 325510

Noroo Loginet Co., Ltd. (1)
351 Bakdal-ro, Manan-gu, Anyang, Gyeonggi-do, Korea (South)

Tel.: (82) 314676361
Logistic Services
N.A.I.C.S.: 541614

Noroo Paint (Shanghai) Co., Ltd. (1)
No 199 Xin Tuan Rd, Industrial Estate Qingpu District, Shanghai, China
Tel.: (86) 215 970 5902
Paint Product Mfr & Distr
N.A.I.C.S.: 325510

Noroo R&C Co., Ltd. (1)
351 Bakdal-ro, Manan-gu, Anyang, 13977, Gyeonggi-do, Korea (South)
Tel.: (82) 314676544
Web Site: https://www.norooorrc.com
Emp.: 25
Resin Product Distr
N.A.I.C.S.: 424610
Myung Hee Choi (CEO)

Noroo Vina Co., Ltd. (1)
No 8 TS10 Tien Son Industrial, Noi Due Commune Tien Du Dist, Bac Ninh, Vietnam
Tel.: (84) 241 373 4856
Paint Product Mfr & Distr
N.A.I.C.S.: 325510

Noroo-Nanpao Paint & Coatings (Vietnam) Co., Ltd. (1)
Nhon Trach 2 IZ, Hiep Phuoc Town, Nhon Trach, Dong Nai, Vietnam
Tel.: (84) 251 356 9966
Web Site: https://noroonanpaopaints.com
Surface Treatment Services
N.A.I.C.S.: 325613

The Kiban Co., Ltd. (1)
10 Bamgogae 1-gil, Samjuk-myeon, Anseong, 17513, Gyeonggi-do, Korea (South)
Tel.: (82) 3180539700
Agricultural Research Services
N.A.I.C.S.: 541715

NORRHYDRO GROUP OYJ
Ratavartijankatu 2, Box 8075, 96100, Rovaniemi, Finland
Tel.: (358) 406184054
Web Site: https://www.norrhydro.com
Year Founded: 1985
NORRH—(HEL)
Rev.: $33,519,466
Assets: $27,999,924
Liabilities: $18,206,088
Net Worth: $9,793,836
Earnings: $1,592,498)
Emp.: 166
Fiscal Year-end: 12/31/23
Hydraulic Cylinder Mfr & Distr
N.A.I.C.S.: 333995
Hanne Sarajarvi (CFO)

NORRICH WEST INC
6783 Wellington Road 34 RR 22, Cambridge, N3C 2V4, ON, Canada
Tel.: (519) 658-6656
Web Site:
  http://www.reidsheritagehomes.com
Year Founded: 1978
Rev.: $10,433,394
Emp.: 3
Residential Construction
N.A.I.C.S.: 236117
Scott Reid (VP)

NORRIS FORD SALES LTD
2929 15 Avenue, Wainwright, T9W 0A4, AB, Canada
Tel.: (780) 842-4400
Web Site:
  http://www.norrisbrothersford.ca
Year Founded: 1998
Rev.: $13,710,400
Emp.: 31
New & Used Car Dealers
N.A.I.C.S.: 441110
Blair Pizzey (Mgr-Sls)

NORRIS MEDICINES LTD.
Plot No 801/P 901/3-5 GIDC Industrial Estate, Ankleshwar, 393002, Gujarat, India

NORRIS MEDICINES LTD.

Norris Medicines Ltd.—(Continued)
Tel.: (91) 2646223462
Web Site:
https://www.norrispharma.com
Year Founded: 1990
524414—(BOM)
Rev.: $1,003,853
Assets: $1,640,964
Liabilities: $3,132,875
Net Worth: ($1,491,911)
Earnings: ($209,756)
Emp.: 50
Fiscal Year-end: 03/31/23
Pharmaceuticals Product Mfr
N.A.I.C.S.: 325412
Vimal Shah (Mng Dir)

NORRLAND GOLD CORP.
1055 West Georgia Street Suite 2050, PO Box 11121, Royal Centre, Vancouver, V6E 3P3, BC, Canada
Tel.: (604) 684-2181
Web Site: https://norrlandgold.com
Year Founded: 2019
8VC—(DEU)
Rev.: $9,693
Assets: $568,429
Liabilities: $102,661
Net Worth: $465,769
Earnings: ($301,687)
Fiscal Year-end: 03/31/23
Asset Management Services
N.A.I.C.S.: 523940
Anders West (CEO)

NORS S.A.
Rua Manuel Pinto de Azevedo 711 1, 4149-010, Porto, Portugal
Tel.: (351) 226 150 320
Web Site: http://www.nors.com
Sales Range: $700-749.9 Million
Transport Solutions; Construction, Mining & Forestry Equipment Sales & Rental Services
N.A.I.C.S.: 423810
Tomaz Jervell (Chm)

Subsidiaries:

Strongco Corporation (1)
1640 Enterprise Road, Mississauga, L4W 4L4, ON, Canada
Tel.: (905) 670-5100
Web Site: http://www.strongco.com
Multi-Line Equipment Mfr
N.A.I.C.S.: 333120
William J. Ostrander (VP-Cranes & Material Handling)

Subsidiary (US):

Chadwick-BaRoss, Inc. (2)
160 Warren Ave, Westbrook, ME 04092-4439 **(100%)**
Tel.: (207) 854-8411
Web Site: http://www.chadwick-baross.com
Sales Range: $25-49.9 Million
Emp.: 100
Construction & Mining Machinery Mfr
N.A.I.C.S.: 423810
Stuart Welch (Pres)

NORSE ATLANTIC AIRWAYS AS
Floyveien 14, 4838, Arendal, Norway
Tel.: (47) 91240945 NO
Web Site: https://www.flynorse.com
Year Founded: 2021
NORSE—(OSL)
Rev.: $439,436,000
Assets: $1,083,136,000
Liabilities: $1,172,833,000
Net Worth: ($89,697,000)
Earnings: ($168,746,000)
Emp.: 1,063
Fiscal Year-end: 12/31/23
Airline Services
N.A.I.C.S.: 561599
Ben Boiling (CFO)

NORSE ENERGY CORP. ASA
Munkedamsveien 35 3rd Floor, 0250, Oslo, Norway
Tel.: (47) 22010522 NO
Web Site:
http://www.norseenergycorp.no
Year Founded: 2005
Oil & Gas Exploration & Production
N.A.I.C.S.: 211120
Mark Dice (CEO)

Subsidiaries:

Coplex Petroleo do Brasil Ltda. (1)
Av Epitacio Pessoa 1000 Ap 702, 22410-090, Rio de Janeiro, Brazil **(100%)**
Tel.: (55) 2122479641
Petroleum & Coal Products Mfr
N.A.I.C.S.: 324199

Naftex Energy Corporation (1)
1140 Homer Street Suite 308, Vancouver, V6B 2X6, BC, Canada
Tel.: (604) 689-4498
Oil & Gas Exploration Services
N.A.I.C.S.: 213112

Naftex Holdings Ltd. (1)
920 Wible Rd, Bakersfield, CA 93304-4125 **(100%)**
Tel.: (661) 836-1216
Crude Petroleum & Natural Gas Extraction
N.A.I.C.S.: 211120

Nornew Energy Supply, Inc. (1)
200 Northpointe Cir Ste 200, Mars, PA 16046-7861 **(100%)**
Tel.: (713) 975-1900
Natural Gas Distribution
N.A.I.C.S.: 221210

Nornew, Inc. (1)
200 Northpointe Cir Ste 200, Mars, PA 16046-7861 **(100%)**
Tel.: (713) 975-1900
Web Site: http://www.nornew.com
Natural Gas Distribution
N.A.I.C.S.: 221210

Norse Energy AS (1)
Bryggeg 7, 0250, Oslo, Norway
Tel.: (47) 22010521
Oil & Gas Exploration Services
N.A.I.C.S.: 213112

Norse Energy Corp USA (1)
200 Northpointe Cir Ste 200, Mars, PA 16046-7861
Tel.: (713) 975-1900
Oil & Gas Exploration & Production
N.A.I.C.S.: 211120

Norse Energy Holdings, Inc (1)
2500 Tanglewilde St Ste 250, Houston, TX 77063
Tel.: (713) 975-1900
Web Site: http://www.norseenergy.com
Oil & Gas Exploration Services
N.A.I.C.S.: 213112

Norse Energy do Brasil Ltda. (1)
Praia de Botafogo No 228 Sala 801, Rio de Janeiro, 22250-906, Brazil
Tel.: (55) 2130787475
Web Site: http://www.panoroenergy.com
Oil & Gas Exploration & Production
N.A.I.C.S.: 211120

Norse Exploration, Inc. (1)
2500 Tanglewilde St Ste 250, Houston, TX 77063 **(100%)**
Tel.: (713) 975-1900
Natural Gas Distribution
N.A.I.C.S.: 221210

Norse Pipeline, LLC (1)
200 Northpointe Cir Ste 200, Mars, PA 16046-7861 **(100%)**
Tel.: (713) 975-1900
Natural Gas Distribution
N.A.I.C.S.: 221210

NORSE GOLD CORP.
240 Connemara Rd, Comox, V9M 3T4, BC, Canada
Tel.: (250) 465-1806
Web Site:
http://www.troyenergycorp.com
VKG.H—(TSX)
Assets: $762,696
Liabilities: $99,179
Net Worth: $663,517
Earnings: ($115,917)
Fiscal Year-end: 06/30/21
Gold Exploration Services
N.A.I.C.S.: 212220
Carl G. Verley (Pres & CEO)

NORSEMAN INC.
14545 115 Avenue, Edmonton, T5M 3B8, AB, Canada
Tel.: (780) 451-6828
Web Site: https://www.norseman.ca
Year Founded: 1921
Sales Range: $10-24.9 Million
Fabric & Foam Products Mfr
N.A.I.C.S.: 314999
Shannon Ceron (Mgr-HR)

NORSEMAN SILVER, INC.
Suite 520 - 999 West Hastings Street, PO Box 55, Vancouver, V6C 2W2, BC, Canada
Tel.: (604) 505-4554
Web Site:
https://www.norsemansilver.com
NOC—(OTCIQ)
Rev.: $249
Assets: $4,274,092
Liabilities: $365,760
Net Worth: $3,908,332
Earnings: ($2,451,291)
Fiscal Year-end: 09/30/21
Gold Exploration Services
N.A.I.C.S.: 212220
Sean D. Hurd (Pres & CEO)

NORSEMONT MINING INC.
Suite 610 - 700 West Pender Street, Vancouver, V6C 1G8, BC, Canada
Tel.: (778) 240-7724
Web Site: https://norsemont.com
Year Founded: 2000
NRRSF—(OTCIQ)
Mineral Exploration Services
N.A.I.C.S.: 212290
Jack Currie (VP)

NORSK HYDRO ASA
Drammensveien 264, NO-0283, Oslo, Norway
Tel.: (47) 22538100 NO
Web Site: https://www.hydro.com
Year Founded: 1905
NHYDY—(OTCQX)
Rev.: $17,020,520,090
Assets: $19,184,769,520
Liabilities: $10,147,829,160
Net Worth: $9,036,940,360
Earnings: $215,293,050
Emp.: 34,240
Fiscal Year-end: 12/31/20
Holding Company; Hydroelectric Power Generation
N.A.I.C.S.: 551112
Anne-Lene Midseim (Gen Counsel & Exec VP-Legal & Compliance)

Subsidiaries:

ALUNORTE - Alumina do Norte do Brasil S.A. (1)
Rodovia PA 481 Km 12 Area 73 Distrito De Mucupi, Barcarena, Para, CEP 68 447-000, Brazil **(63.96%)**
Tel.: (55) 8007210794
Web Site: https://www.alunorte.net
Provider of Aluminum Processing Services
N.A.I.C.S.: 331314

Comhlucht Iascaireachta Fanad Teoranta (Fanad Fisheries) (1)
Fanad Fisheries Kindrum, Donegal, Ireland
Tel.: (353) 749159070
Aquaculture & Fish Hatcheries
N.A.I.C.S.: 112511

FTG Cranes (1)
Industrigatan 1, Backefors, 668 40, Vanersborg, Sweden **(100%)**
Tel.: (46) 521262630
Web Site: http://www.ftgforest.com
Sales Range: $25-49.9 Million
Heavy Duty Cranes for Commercial Use
N.A.I.C.S.: 333923

Fundo Aluminium AB (1)
Emterudsvagen 3, PO Box 55, 673 31, Charlottenberg, Sweden **(100%)**
Tel.: (46) 571768300
Web Site: http://www.fundocomponents.com
Sales Range: $25-49.9 Million
Aluminium Extraction & Refining
N.A.I.C.S.: 331313

GA Feral AB (1)
Ostra Ringvagen 4, S-721 88, Vasteras, Sweden
Tel.: (46) 21198490
Alumina Refining
N.A.I.C.S.: 331313

Hueck Aluminium GmbH (1)
Rossakgasse 6-8, 1230, Vienna, Austria
Tel.: (43) 166715290
Web Site: https://www.hueck.at
Aluminium Window Frame System Mfr & Distr
N.A.I.C.S.: 332321

Hueck Aluminium Profieltechniek Benelux B.V. (1)
Windmolen 8, 4751 VM, Oud Gastel, Netherlands
Tel.: (31) 165513955
Aluminium Window Frame System Mfr & Distr
N.A.I.C.S.: 332321

Hueck System GmbH & Co. KG (1)
Loher Strasse 9, 58511, Ludenscheid, Germany
Tel.: (49) 23511510
Web Site: https://www.hueck.com
Aluminium Window Frame System Mfr & Distr
N.A.I.C.S.: 332321

Hueck s.r.o. (1)
Belohorska 662/196, 169 00, Prague, Czech Republic
Tel.: (420) 246083573
Web Site: https://www.hueck.cz
Aluminium Window Frame System Mfr & Distr
N.A.I.C.S.: 332321

Hycast AS (1)
Industriveien 49, 6600, Sunndalsora, Norway **(100%)**
Tel.: (47) 94130411
Web Site: https://www.hycast.no
Sales Range: $10-24.9 Million
Emp.: 50
Aluminum Casting Equipment Mfr
N.A.I.C.S.: 333519

Hydro Alluminio Atessa S.p.A. (1)
Contrada Saletti Zl, 66040, Atessa, 66040, Chieti, Italy
Tel.: (39) 08728941
Web Site: http://www.hydroatessa.com
Sales Range: $50-74.9 Million
Emp.: 170
Aluminium Extraction & Refining
N.A.I.C.S.: 331313

Hydro Alluminio La Roca S.A. (1)
Sta Agnes De Malanyanes Pol Ind Can Font De La Parera, 8430, Laroca, Spain **(100%)**
Tel.: (34) 937078200
Web Site: http://www.hydro.com
Sales Range: $50-74.9 Million
Emp.: 220
Aluminium Extraction & Refining
N.A.I.C.S.: 331313

Hydro Alluminio Ornago S.p.A. (1)
Via A Ciucani 8, 20876, Ornago, Italy
Tel.: (39) 03966581
Sales Range: $50-74.9 Million
Aluminum Production
N.A.I.C.S.: 331313

Hydro Aluminio Azuqueca S.A. (1)
Poligono Industrial Miralcampo C/Pintura No 3, Azuqueca De Henares, 19200, Guadalajara, Spain
Tel.: (34) 94 910 04 00

AND PRIVATE COMPANIES

NORSK HYDRO ASA

Sales Range: $25-49.9 Million
Emp.: 50
Aluminium Products Mfr
N.A.I.C.S.: 331313
Inigo Aranduren *(Mgr)*

Hydro Aluminio La Roca S.A. (1)
Polig Ind Can Font De La Parera S N, Sta Agnes De Malanyanes, E 08430, Barcelona, Spain **(100%)**
Tel.: (34) 937078200
Web Site: http://www.hydro.com
Sales Range: $50-74.9 Million
Emp.: 200
Mfr of Aluminum & Magnesium Extrusions
N.A.I.C.S.: 331313

Hydro Aluminium (Suzhou) Co. Ltd (1)
236 Songbei Road Suzhou Industrial Park, Suzhou, 215024, Jiangsu, China
Tel.: (86) 512 6283 6088
Web Site: http://www.hydro.com
Hydraulic Pumps Mfr
N.A.I.C.S.: 333996

Hydro Aluminium AS (1)
Drammensveien 264, 264, Oslo, Norway **(100%)**
Tel.: (47) 71693000
Sales Range: $1-4.9 Billion
Emp.: 34
Holding Company; Aluminum & Aluminum Products Mfr
N.A.I.C.S.: 551112

Subsidiary (Non-US):

Alumetal S.A. (2)
ul Kosciuszki 111, 32-650, Kety, Poland **(97.65%)**
Tel.: (48) 334707100
Web Site: http://www.alumetal.pl
Rev.: $589,623,050
Assets: $316,149,000
Liabilities: $131,224,310
Net Worth: $184,924,690
Earnings: $40,876,920
Emp.: 613
Fiscal Year-end: 12/31/2021
Aluminum Cast Alloys Mfr
N.A.I.C.S.: 331110
Krzysztof Blasiak *(Vice Chm-Mgmt Bd & Dir-Dev)*

Subsidiary (Domestic):

Alumetal Poland Sp. z o.o. (3)
al Wojska Polskiego 17, 32-650, Kety, Poland
Tel.: (48) 334707157
Web Site: https://alumetal.pl
Aluminum Casting Alloy Mfr
N.A.I.C.S.: 331524

T+S Sp. z o.o. (3)
ul Kosciuszki 111, 32-650, Kety, Poland
Tel.: (48) 334707200
Web Site: https://www.tsalumetal.pl
Auxiliary Material Mfr & Whslr
N.A.I.C.S.: 336413

Subsidiary (Domestic):

Hydro Aluminium AS Karmoy Carbon (2)
Hydroveien 160, N-4265, Havik, Norway
Tel.: (47) 52854000
Primary Aluminum Production
N.A.I.C.S.: 331313

Hydro Aluminium AS Sunndal Carbon (2)
Romsdalsvegen 1, 6600, Sunndalsora, Norway
Tel.: (47) 71693000
Web Site: http://www.hydro.com
Sales Range: $150-199.9 Million
Emp.: 700
Primary Aluminum Production
N.A.I.C.S.: 331313

Hydro Aluminium Ardal (2)
Verksvegen 1, PO Box 303, N-6882, Ovre Ardal, Norway
Tel.: (47) 57649000
Web Site: http://www.hydro.com
Sales Range: $150-199.9 Million
Emp.: 567
Primary Aluminum Production

N.A.I.C.S.: 331313
Subsidiary (Non-US):

Hydro Aluminium Deutschland GmbH (2)
Ettore Bugattistrasse 6-14, D 51109, Cologne, Germany **(100%)**
Tel.: (49) 2285520
Web Site: http://www.hydro.com
Emp.: 140
Secondary Refining of Nonferrous Metals
N.A.I.C.S.: 331314

Subsidiary (Domestic):

Hydro Aluminium Bellenberg GmbH (3)
Am Muhlholz 1, 89287, Bellenberg, Germany **(100%)**
Tel.: (49) 73067830
Web Site: http://www.hydro.at
Sales Range: $25-49.9 Million
Emp.: 100
Aluminum Extraction & Refining

Hydro Aluminium Deutschland GmbH (3)
Aluminiumstr 1, 41515, Grevenbroich, Germany
Tel.: (49) 21816601
Web Site: http://www.hydro.com
Sales Range: $400-449.9 Million
Primary Aluminum Product Mfr
N.A.I.C.S.: 331313

Hydro Aluminium Extrusion Deutschland GmbH (3)
Uphuser Heerstrasse 7, 28832, Achim, Germany **(100%)**
Tel.: (49) 4202570
Web Site: http://www.sapa.com
Sales Range: $100-124.9 Million
Emp.: 250
Aluminum Extrusions
N.A.I.C.S.: 331314
Wilfried Hodel *(Mng Dir)*

Joint Venture (Non-US):

Slovalco AS (2)
Priemyselna 14, 965 48, Ziar nad Hronom, Slovakia **(55.3%)**
Tel.: (421) 456089999
Web Site: https://www.slovalco.sk
Sales Range: $400-449.9 Million
Emp.: 500
Aluminium Products Mfr
N.A.I.C.S.: 331313
Milan Vesely *(CEO)*

Hydro Aluminium Argentina S.A. (1)
Calle 4 S/N Parque Industrial Pilar, B 1629MXA, Pilar, Buenos Aires, Argentina
Tel.: (54) 230 4463 800
Aluminium Products Mfr
N.A.I.C.S.: 331313

Hydro Aluminium Australia Pty. Ltd. (1)
Hart Road, PO Box 1, Kurri Kurri, 2327, NSW, Australia
Tel.: (61) 249370253
Web Site: http://www.hydro.com
Sales Range: $150-199.9 Million
Emp.: 6
Holding Company; Primary Aluminum Production
N.A.I.C.S.: 551112

Subsidiary (Domestic):

Hydro Aluminium Kurri Kurri Pty Ltd. (2)
Lot 435 438 Hart Road, Kurri Kurri, 2326, NSW, Australia **(100%)**
Tel.: (61) 249371555
Web Site: https://www.hydro.com.au
Primary Aluminum Production
N.A.I.C.S.: 331313

Hydro Aluminium Canada, Inc. (1)
2000 McGill College Avenue Suite 2310, Montreal, H3A 3H3, QC, Canada **(100%)**
Tel.: (514) 840-9110
Web Site: https://www.hydro.com
Sales Range: $25-49.9 Million
Aluminium Processing
N.A.I.C.S.: 331313

Hydro Aluminium Chateauroux s.n.c. (1)
Zi Le Buxerious 36 Av Pierre de Coubertin, 36000, Chateauroux, France **(100%)**
Tel.: (33) 254292200
Web Site: http://www.hydro.com
Aluminium Extraction & Refining
N.A.I.C.S.: 331313

Hydro Aluminium Chrzanow Sp. z. o.o. (1)
Hydro 1, 32500, Chrzanow, Poland **(100%)**
Tel.: (48) 326234205
Sales Range: $50-74.9 Million
Emp.: 180
Aluminum Production
N.A.I.C.S.: 331318

Hydro Aluminium Clervaux S.A. (1)
Z I Eselborn-Lenzweiler Op Der Sang 16, Eselborn, L-9779, Clervaux, Luxembourg
Tel.: (352) 9495951
Emp.: 6
Aluminium Products Mfr
N.A.I.C.S.: 333519

Hydro Aluminium Colors srl (1)
Via Amilcare Ponchielli 3, 20063, Cernusco sul Naviglio, 20063, Milan, Italy
Tel.: (39) 02 92 42 94 29
Sales Range: $25-49.9 Million
Emp.: 100
Aluminium Products Mfr
N.A.I.C.S.: 331313

Hydro Aluminium Deeside Ltd. (1)
Bridge Road Wrexham Industrial Estate, Wrexham, LL13 9PS, United Kingdom
Tel.: (44) 1978660231
Sales Range: $25-49.9 Million
Emp.: 41
Aluminium Products Mfr
N.A.I.C.S.: 331313

Hydro Aluminium Dormagen GmbH (1)
Sachtlebenstr 46, 41541, Dormagen, Germany
Tel.: (49) 2133 77 94 00
Aluminium Products Mfr
N.A.I.C.S.: 332999

Hydro Aluminium Fabrication (Taicang) Co. Ltd. (1)
Building No 2 and 4 No 100 Chenmenjing Road, Taicang, Jiangsu, China
Tel.: (86) 2133517200
Aluminium Product Mfr & Distr
N.A.I.C.S.: 331315

Hydro Aluminium France S.A.S. (1)
16 avenue de la Grande Armee, 75017, Paris, France
Tel.: (33) 145729350
Web Site: http://www.hydro.com
Aluminium Extraction & Refining
N.A.I.C.S.: 331313

Hydro Aluminium Giesserei Rackwitz GmbH (1)
Tel.: (49) 34294843100
Emp.: 60
Aluminum Remelting Services
N.A.I.C.S.: 331314

Hydro Aluminium High Purity GmbH (1)
Aluminiumstrasse 2, D-41515, Grevenbroich, Germany
Tel.: (49) 2181662308
Emp.: 60
Aluminium Products Mfr
N.A.I.C.S.: 332999

Hydro Aluminium Hoyanger Verk (1)
PO Box 114, 6991, Hoyanger, Norway **(100%)**
Tel.: (47) 57715000
Web Site: http://www.hydro.com
Sales Range: $50-74.9 Million
Emp.: 156
Aluminum Extraction & Refining
N.A.I.C.S.: 331313

Hydro Aluminium ITC s.n.c. (1)
32 Del Rue De La Beauce, 28111, Luce, France **(100%)**
Tel.: (33) 237304100

Sales Range: $25-49.9 Million
Emp.: 21
Aluminium Extraction & Refining
N.A.I.C.S.: 331313
Luc Graillot *(Gen Mgr)*

Hydro Aluminium International S.A. (1)
Lake Geneva Park Park Route de Luly 5 Bat C, 1131, Tolochenaz, Switzerland
Tel.: (41) 8113141
Aluminium Material Mfr & Distr
N.A.I.C.S.: 331315

Hydro Aluminium Malaysia Sdn. Bhd. (1)
Lot 4 Jalan Pekeliling Pasir Gudang, Industrial Estate, Pasir Gudang, 81700, Johor, Malaysia **(100%)**
Tel.: (60) 72541913
Web Site: http://www.hydro.com
Sales Range: $50-74.9 Million
Emp.: 249
Aluminum Automotive Products Mfr
N.A.I.C.S.: 331318

Hydro Aluminium Metal Products S.r.l. (1)
Via Goffredo Mameli 25, I-21052, Busto Arsizio, Varese, Italy
Tel.: (39) 0331304911
Sales Range: $25-49.9 Million
Aluminium Products Mfr
N.A.I.C.S.: 331313

Hydro Aluminium Nenzing GmbH (1)
Austrasse 16, 6710, Nenzing, Vorarlberg, Austria **(100%)**
Tel.: (43) 5 525 6010
Web Site: https://www.hydro.com
Sales Range: $150-199.9 Million
Emp.: 355
Aluminium Extraction & Refining
N.A.I.C.S.: 331313

Hydro Aluminium Profiler AS (1)
Fabrekk veiem, 2830, Raufoss, Norway **(100%)**
Tel.: (47) 6 115 3000
Web Site: https://www.hap.hydal.com
Sales Range: $100-124.9 Million
Emp.: 300
Aluminum Extruded Product Mfr
N.A.I.C.S.: 331318

Plant (Domestic):

Hydro Aluminium Profiler AS Karmoy (2)
Hydrovegan 160, 4265, Havik, Norway **(100%)**
Tel.: (47) 5 285 4000
Sales Range: $25-49.9 Million
Emp.: 520
Aluminum Extruded Product Mfr
N.A.I.C.S.: 331318

Hydro Aluminium Raeren SA - NV (1)
Waldstrasse 91, 4730, Raeren, Belgium
Tel.: (32) 87 859 211
Web Site: http://www.hydro.com
Sales Range: $100-124.9 Million
Aluminium Extrusion Services
N.A.I.C.S.: 331318

Hydro Aluminium Rolled Products AS Holmestrand (1)
Weidemannsgate 8, PO Box 310, N 3081, Holmestrand, Norway **(100%)**
Tel.: (47) 33054200
Web Site: http://www.hydro.no
Sales Range: $25-49.9 Million
Emp.: 100
Rolled Aluminum Products Mfr
N.A.I.C.S.: 331318

Hydro Aluminium Rolled Products AS Karmoy (1)
Karmoy Rolling Mill, Ringeveien 40, N-4265, Havik, Norway **(100%)**
Tel.: (47) 52854000
Sales Range: $50-74.9 Million
Emp.: 245
Rolled Aluminum Products Mfr
N.A.I.C.S.: 331318

Hydro Aluminium Rolled Products Benelux BV (1)

NORSK HYDRO ASA

Norsk Hydro ASA—(Continued)

Achterbaan 81, 1271 BC, Huizen, Netherlands
Tel.: (31) 35 54 88 444
Web Site: http://www.hydro.com
Sales Range: $25-49.9 Million
Aluminium Products Mfr
N.A.I.C.S.: 331313

Hydro Aluminium Rolled Products Denmark a.s (1)
Smedegade 2A 2 tv, 4200, Slagelse, Denmark
Tel.: (45) 4371 5050
Emp.: 2
Aluminium Products Mfr
N.A.I.C.S.: 332999
Jesper Wienmann Hansen *(Gen Mgr)*

Hydro Aluminium Rolled Products GmbH (1)
Aluminiumstrasse, PO Box 950252, 21129, Hamburg, Germany
Tel.: (49) 40 74 01 10 0
Web Site: http://www.hydro.com
Aluminium Coil & Sheet Mfr
N.A.I.C.S.: 333519

Hydro Aluminium Rolled Products Iberia S.L.U. (1)
Gran Via Carlos Iii 98 6a, 08028, Barcelona, Spain
Tel.: (34) 932 064 320
Web Site: http://www.hydro.com
Sales Range: $25-49.9 Million
Aluminium Products Mfr
N.A.I.C.S.: 331313

Hydro Aluminium Rolled Products Ltd. (1)
4 Newton Ct W Strand Tendesord Business Park, Wolverhampton, WV9 5HB, United Kingdom **(100%)**
Tel.: (44) 1902396630
Web Site: http://www.hydro.com
Sales Range: $25-49.9 Million
Emp.: 4
Alumina Refining
N.A.I.C.S.: 331313

Hydro Aluminium Rolled Products Polska Sp. z o.o. (1)
Ul Grodzka 26/6, 31-044, Krakow, Poland
Tel.: (48) 12 266 42 24
Web Site: http://www.hydro.com
Sales Range: $50-74.9 Million
Aluminium Product Distr
N.A.I.C.S.: 423390

Hydro Aluminium S.A. (1)
Lake Geneva Park Park Route de Luly 5 Bat C, 1131, Tolochenaz, Switzerland **(100%)**
Tel.: (41) 21 811 3160
Web Site: http://www.hydro.com
Sales Range: $10-24.9 Million
Emp.: 35
Aluminium Extraction & Refining
N.A.I.C.S.: 331313

Hydro Aluminium Sales and Trading UK (1)
Garlands Cages Wood Drive, Farnham Common, SL2 3JZ, Bucks, United Kingdom
Tel.: (44) 1 753 669 273
Aluminium Product Distr
N.A.I.C.S.: 423510

Hydro Aluminium Sales and Trading s.n.c. (1)
ZAC Paris Rive Gauche, 118-122 avenue de France, F-75013, Paris, France
Tel.: (33) 146461160
Aluminum Sales
N.A.I.C.S.: 423510

Hydro Aluminium Salko Oy (1)
Salkokatu 3, 30100, Forssa, Finland
Tel.: (358) 34 246 40 00
Sales Range: $25-49.9 Million
Emp.: 46
Aluminium & Fabricated Product Mfr
N.A.I.C.S.: 332311

Hydro Aluminium Seneffe S.A. (1)
Rue Charles Richet 999/R Zoning Industriel Zone C, 7180, Seneffe, Belgium
Tel.: (32) 64 52 04 40
Aluminium Products Mfr

Hydro Aluminium Suomi Oy (1)
Karby, 21710, Korpo, Finland **(100%)**
Tel.: (358) 24643110
Aluminium Extraction & Refining
N.A.I.C.S.: 331313

Hydro Aluminium Sverige AB (Tyreso) (1)
Strandbergsgatan 61 Floor 3, S 114 46, Stockholm, Sweden
Tel.: (46) 86679105
Web Site: http://www.hydroaluminium.se
Sales Range: $25-49.9 Million
Emp.: 2
Aluminium Alloys, Foil & Building Products
N.A.I.C.S.: 331313

Hydro Aluminium Systems Hellas S.A. (1)
Leoforos Nato Thesi Spitharenza Aspropyrgos, GR 193 00, Athens, Greece **(100%)**
Tel.: (30) 2105595923
Sales Range: $25-49.9 Million
Emp.: 100
Aluminum Production
N.A.I.C.S.: 331313

Hydro Aluminium Taiwan Co Ltd (1)
No 122 Sec 3 Yunke Rd, 64064, Douliu, Yunlin, Taiwan
Tel.: (886) 5551 3767
Web Site: http://www.hydro.com
Rev.: $33,979,050
Emp.: 73
Hydraulic Equipment Mfr
N.A.I.C.S.: 333996

Hydro Aluminium UK Ltd (1)
Pantglas Indus Est Bedwas, Caerphilly, CF83 8DR, United Kingdom **(100%)**
Tel.: (44) 1913011200
Sales Range: $25-49.9 Million
Emp.: 100
Primary Production of Aluminum
N.A.I.C.S.: 331313

Hydro Aluminium Vekst (1)
Drammensveien 260 0283, 0240, Oslo, Norway **(100%)**
Tel.: (47) 22538100
Sales Range: $50-74.9 Million
Emp.: 160
Aluminum Alloys, Foil & Building Products
N.A.I.C.S.: 331313

Hydro Aluminium Walzprodukte AG (1)
Rheinweg 21, Postfach 767, 8212, Neuhausen, Switzerland
Tel.: (41) 526246026
Sales Range: $25-49.9 Million
Emp.: 2
Aluminium Products Mfr
N.A.I.C.S.: 331313
Ilan Eisner *(Mgr-Sls)*

Hydro Aluminum AS (1)
Romsdalsvegen 1, PO Box 51, 6600, Sunndalsora, Norway
Tel.: (47) 71 69 30 00
Web Site: http://www.hydro.com
Sales Range: $200-249.9 Million
Aluminium Products Mfr
N.A.I.C.S.: 331313

Hydro Aluminum CIS a.s. Moscow (1)
Testowskaya Str 10 BC Nord Tower, RU 123317, Moscow, Russia **(100%)**
Tel.: (7) 4957084596
Web Site: http://www.hydro.ru
Sales Range: $50-74.9 Million
Emp.: 6
Aluminum Rolled Products Distr
N.A.I.C.S.: 423510

Hydro Aluminum Japan KK (1)
Tekko Building 3F 1-8-2 Marunouchi, Chiyoda-ku, Tokyo, 100-0005, Japan **(100%)**
Tel.: (81) 362122311
Sales Range: $25-49.9 Million
Aluminium Extraction & Refining
N.A.I.C.S.: 331313

Hydro Aluminum Luce s.n.c. (1)
42 rue de la Beauce, PO Box 89, 28112, Luce, Cedex, France

Tel.: (33) 237306400
Web Site: http://www.hydro.com
Emp.: 159
Aluminium Extraction & Refining
N.A.I.C.S.: 331313

Hydro Aluminum Malaysia Sdn. Bhd. (1)
Lot 4 Jalan Besar, Pasir Gudang Industrial Estate, 81700, Pasir Gudang, Johor, Malaysia
Tel.: (60) 72541913
Web Site: http://www.hydro.com
Sales Range: $100-124.9 Million
Emp.: 260
Aluminum Foil Production & Sales
N.A.I.C.S.: 331315

Hydro Aluminum North America Inc. (1)
999 Corporate Blvd Ste 100, Linthicum, MD 21090-2254
Tel.: (410) 487-4500
Sales Range: $25-49.9 Million
Emp.: 30
Aluminum Extrusions
N.A.I.C.S.: 331318

Subsidiary (Domestic):

Hydro Aluminum Metal Products North America Inc. (2)
999 Corporate Blvd Ste 100, Linthicum, MD 21090-2254
Tel.: (410) 487-4500
Web Site: http://www.hydro.com
Metal Products Mfr
N.A.I.C.S.: 332999

Hydro Aluminum USA, Inc. (2)
666 Old Country Rd Ste 705, Garden City, NY 11530
Tel.: (516) 222-1526
Web Site: http://www.hydro.com
Aluminum Products Mfr
N.A.I.C.S.: 331313
Peter Ohlendorf *(Pres)*

Hydro Automotive Structures North America, Inc. (2)
533 Ottawa Ave, Holland, MI 49423-4036
Tel.: (616) 396-6591
Sales Range: $50-74.9 Million
Aluminium Extrusion
N.A.I.C.S.: 331492

Hydro Aluminum Reynosa, S. de R.L. de C.V. (1)
Avenida del Parquet s/n Parque Industrial Villa Florida, 88730, Reynosa, Tamaulipas, Mexico
Tel.: (52) 899 909 6300
Aluminum Products Mfr
N.A.I.C.S.: 331313

Hydro Alunova Logumkloster A/S (1)
Avedvej 7, DK 6240, Logumkloster, Denmark **(100%)**
Tel.: (45) 73745900
Web Site: http://www.hydroaluminiumtubing.com
Sales Range: $25-49.9 Million
Emp.: 8
Alumina Refining
N.A.I.C.S.: 331313

Hydro Automotive Structures Alunord SARL (1)
PO Box 613, F 27406, Louviers, Cedex, France **(100%)**
Tel.: (33) 232093209
Sales Range: $50-74.9 Million
Emp.: 110
Mfr of Heavy Duty Machinery
N.A.I.C.S.: 336120

Hydro Belem (1)
Trav Dom Romualdo de Seixa 1476 Ed Evolution 4 Andar, Umarizal, 66055-200, Belem, Para, Brazil
Tel.: (55) 91 3222 6010
Aluminium Products Mfr
N.A.I.C.S.: 331313

Hydro Building Systems (1)
Jarnvagsgatan 45, PO Box 120, S 360 70, Aseda, Sweden
Tel.: (46) 47448080
Web Site: http://www.hydro.com

Sales Range: $25-49.9 Million
Emp.: 40
Prefabricated Building Systems & Products
N.A.I.C.S.: 332311

Hydro Building Systems (Beijing) Co. Ltd. (1)
Room 2505 25th Floor Block A Fenglian Plaza No.18 Chaoyangmenwai Ave, Chaoyang District, Beijing, 100020, China
Tel.: (86) 13911402551
Web Site: https://www.wicona.cn
Sales Range: $25-49.9 Million
Emp.: 16
Building Materials Distr
N.A.I.C.S.: 423390

Hydro Building Systems Co. Ltd (1)
2106A Xizhang Road No 168, Huangpu, Shanghai, China
Tel.: (86) 21 6107 5017
Web Site: http://www.hydro.com
Building Materials Distr
N.A.I.C.S.: 423390

Hydro Building Systems GmbH (1)
Wallerseestrasse 49, 5201, Seekirchen, Austria
Tel.: (43) 62122000
Web Site: https://www.wicona.at
Building Structural Product Mfr
N.A.I.C.S.: 331318

Hydro Building Systems GmbH (1)
Kozjak Nad Pesnico 34b, Kungota, Slovenia
Tel.: (386) 26 209 070
Building Materials Distr
N.A.I.C.S.: 423390

Hydro Building Systems Iberia (1)
Calle Velazquez N 157 Bajo Izquierda, 28002, Madrid, Spain
Tel.: (34) 91 802 9615
Web Site: http://www.hydro.com
Building Materials Distr
N.A.I.C.S.: 423390

Hydro Building Systems Kft. (1)
Graphisoft Park Zahony u 7 Building D, 1031, Budapest, Hungary
Tel.: (36) 1453 3457
Sales Range: $50-74.9 Million
Emp.: 5
Building Materials Distr
N.A.I.C.S.: 423390
Arnd Brinkmann *(Gen Mgr)*

Hydro Building Systems Ltd. (1)
Unit J1 Baldonnell Business Park Naas Road, Dublin, Ireland
Tel.: (353) 1 410 5766
Sales Range: $50-74.9 Million
Emp.: 8
Building Materials Mfr
N.A.I.C.S.: 423390
Nigel Sissons *(Mng Dir)*

Hydro Building Systems N.V. (1)
Industriezone Roosveld 11, 3400, Landen, Belgium
Tel.: (32) 11690311
Web Site: https://www.wicona.be
Aluminium Product Distr
N.A.I.C.S.: 423510

Hydro Building Systems OU (1)
Parnu Mnt 139 F, EE 11317, Tallinn, Estonia
Tel.: (372) 6576605
Sales Range: $50-74.9 Million
Emp.: 2
Aluminium Material Distr
N.A.I.C.S.: 423390

Hydro Building Systems Private Limited (1)
54 Virgo Nagar Old Madras Road, Bengaluru, 560049, Karnataka, India
Tel.: (91) 80 3060 4000
Web Site: http://www.wicona-int.com
Emp.: 18
Building Structural Product Mfr
N.A.I.C.S.: 331318

Hydro Building Systems S.L. (1)
Representaciones Celso Isla SL Camino de Gandaron N 44, 36214, Vigo, Spain
Tel.: (34) 986 266 085
Building Materials Distr
N.A.I.C.S.: 423390

AND PRIVATE COMPANIES

NORSK HYDRO ASA

Hydro Building Systems SA (1)
270 Rue Leon Joulin, BP 63709, 31037, Toulouse, Cedex, France
Tel.: (33) 56 131 2828
Web Site: https://www.technal.com
Sales Range: $250-299.9 Million
Emp.: 60
Building Materials Distr
N.A.I.C.S.: 423390

Hydro Building Systems SLU (1)
Poligono Ind De Cantabria Avenida De Mendavia N 18, 26009, Logrono, Spain
Tel.: (34) 941 234 133
Web Site: http://www.eural.es
Sales Range: $25-49.9 Million
Emp.: 42
Aluminium Products Mfr
N.A.I.C.S.: 331313

Hydro Building Systems South East Asia (1)
No 56 & 60 2nd Floor Simpang 13 Jalan Berakas Bandar, Jalan Berakas, Bandar Seri Begawan, BB2713, Brunei Darussalam
Tel.: (673) 234 2480
Web Site: http://www.technal.com
Sales Range: $25-49.9 Million
Emp.: 12
Building Materials Distr
N.A.I.C.S.: 423390

Hydro Building Systems Southwest, S.L.U. (1)
Cami de Can Ametller 18, Sant Cugat, 8195, Barcelona, Spain
Tel.: (34) 93 573 77 77
Emp.: 20
Building Materials Distr
N.A.I.C.S.: 423390
Dirk Grunewald *(Gen Mgr)*

Hydro Building Systems Sp. z. o. o. (1)
ul Rokicinska 211/217, 92-620, Lodz, Poland
Tel.: (48) 42 683 6373
Web Site: https://www.wicona.com
Building Materials Distr
N.A.I.C.S.: 423390

Hydro Building Systems SpA (1)
Via Amilcare Ponchielli 3, 20063, Cernusco sul Naviglio, Milan, Italy
Tel.: (39) 02924291
Web Site: http://www.wicona.it
Emp.: 20
Building Materials Distr
N.A.I.C.S.: 423390

Hydro Ellay Enfield Ltd. (1)
Joseph Noble Road Lillyhall Industrial Estate, Workington, CA14 4JX, Cumbria, United Kingdom
Tel.: (44) 1 900 601 166
Sales Range: $25-49.9 Million
Emp.: 5
Industrial Tube Mfr
N.A.I.C.S.: 331210

Hydro Extrusion Denmark A/S (1)
Bygmestervej 7, 6270, Tonder, Denmark
Tel.: (45) 73939313
Aluminium Product Mfr & Distr
N.A.I.C.S.: 331315

Hydro Extrusion Raeren SA (1)
Waldstrasse 91, 4730, Raeren, Belgium
Tel.: (32) 87859211
Aluminium Product Mfr & Distr
N.A.I.C.S.: 331315

Hydro Kapitalforvaltning AS (1)
Drammensveien 264, 0283, Oslo, Norway
Tel.: (47) 22538100
Investment Management Service
N.A.I.C.S.: 523999

Hydro Precision Tubing Tonder A/S (1)
Hydrovej 6, PO Box 50, 6270, Tonder, Denmark
Tel.: (45) 74723313
Aluminium Product Mfr & Distr
N.A.I.C.S.: 331315

Hydro Produits Chimiques (1)
77 ESPLANADE DU GEN DE GAULLE, Paris, F 92751, France
Tel.: (33) 155699600

Sales Range: $25-49.9 Million
Emp.: 100
Alumina Refining
N.A.I.C.S.: 331313
Catherine Nogues *(Asst Mgr)*

Hydro Supra KemiService AB (1)
Morsaregatan 19, PO Box 22081, S-250 22, Helsingborg, Sweden
Tel.: (46) 42183700
Sales Range: $25-49.9 Million
Emp.: 20
Alumina Refining & Production
N.A.I.C.S.: 331313

Industriforsikring A/S (1)
Drammensveien 264, 0283, Oslo, Norway (100%)
Tel.: (47) 22538100
Sales Range: $100-124.9 Million
Emp.: 10
Insurance Services
N.A.I.C.S.: 524113

Korn-og Foderstof Kompagniet (KFK) A/S (1)
Grondalsvej 1, DK-8260, Viby, J, Denmark
Tel.: (45) 86 14 41 11
Sales Range: $400-449.9 Million
Emp.: 2,109
Agricultural Feeds & Fertilizers
N.A.I.C.S.: 325314

Norsk Hydro A/S Brevik Packaging Dept. (1)
Stromtangvn 21, PO Box 44, N-3951, Brevik, Norway
Tel.: (47) 3571122
Aluminum
N.A.I.C.S.: 331313

Norsk Hydro A/S-Development & Commercialization (1)
PO Box 2053, N 4301, Sandnes, Norway
Tel.: (47) 51660622
Alumina Extraction & Refining
N.A.I.C.S.: 331313

Norsk Hydro ASA - Ardal Plant (1)
Verksvegen 1, PO Box 303, Ovre Ardal, 5868, Norway
Tel.: (47) 57 64 90 00
Web Site: http://www.hydro.com
Emp.: 567
Aluminium Products Mfr
N.A.I.C.S.: 331313

Norsk Hydro ASA - Hoyanger Plant (1)
Sturgatt 2, Hoyanger, 6993, Norway
Tel.: (47) 57 71 50 00
Web Site: http://www.hydro.com
Sales Range: $50-74.9 Million
Emp.: 160
Aluminium Products Mfr
N.A.I.C.S.: 331313

Norsk Hydro ASA - Hydro Aluminium Commerce Facility (1)
2000 Economic Dr, Commerce, TX 75428
Tel.: (903) 468-5000
Web Site: http://www.hydroaluminium.com
Emp.: 50
Aluminium Products Mfr
N.A.I.C.S.: 331313

Norsk Hydro ASA - Hydro Aluminium Henderson Facility (1)
5801 Riverport Rd, Henderson, KY 42420
Tel.: (270) 830-0022
Aluminium Products Mfr
N.A.I.C.S.: 331313

Norsk Hydro ASA - Karmoy Plant (1)
Hydrovegen 160, 4265, Havik, Norway
Tel.: (47) 52 85 40 00
Emp.: 90
Aluminium Products Mfr
N.A.I.C.S.: 331313
Thor Olaf *(Gen Mgr)*

Norsk Hydro ASA - Neuss Plant (1)
Koblenzer Strasse 122, 41468, Neuss, Germany
Tel.: (49) 21 31 38 22 00
Emp.: 40
Aluminium Products Mfr
N.A.I.C.S.: 332999

Norsk Hydro Denmark A.S (1)

Bygmestervej 7, PO Box 10, 6270, Tonder, Denmark (100%)
Tel.: (45) 7 393 9393
Web Site: http://www.hydro.dk
Sales Range: $100-124.9 Million
Emp.: 280
Aluminum Production
N.A.I.C.S.: 331313

Norsk Hydro Deutschland GmbH & Co. KG (1)
Ettore Bugatti Strabe 6 14, D 51149, Cologne, Germany (100%)
Tel.: (49) 22038904000
Sales Range: $50-74.9 Million
Emp.: 120
Holding Company
N.A.I.C.S.: 551112

Norsk Hydro Holland B.V. (1)
Groothandelsgebouw Conradstraat 38 Unit D2 139, NL-3013 AP, Rotterdam, Netherlands
Tel.: (31) 102179088
Aluminium Products Mfr
N.A.I.C.S.: 331313

Norsk Hydro Philippines Inc. (1)
Rm 240 Miascor Cargo Ctr, Ninoy Acquino Ave, Paranaque, 1704, Manila, Philippines (30%)
Tel.: (63) 28528892
Web Site: http://www.nordiskph.com
Sales Range: $250-299.9 Million
Emp.: 10
Aluminium Extraction & Refining
N.A.I.C.S.: 331313

Norsk Hydro Produksjon AS (1)
Drammensveien 264, N-0283, Oslo, Norway (100%)
Tel.: (47) 22538100
Web Site: http://www.hydro.com
Holding Company; Hydroelectric & Solar Energy Power Plant Operator
N.A.I.C.S.: 551112

Subsidiary (Domestic):

Hydro Energi Ardal (2)
Verksvegen 1, PO Box 303, N 6882, Ovre Ardal, Norway
Tel.: (47) 57649000
Sales Range: $400-449.9 Million
Emp.: 700
Hydroelectric Power Generation
N.A.I.C.S.: 221111

Hydro Energi Roldal-Suldal (2)
Hydro Olge And Energy Casgplodukson, N 4244, Nesflaten, Norway (100%)
Tel.: (47) 52794700
Sales Range: $50-74.9 Million
Emp.: 50
Hydroelectric Power Generation
N.A.I.C.S.: 221111

Hydro Energi Sogn (2)
Drammensveien 260, PO Box 0240, N 6885, Oslo, Norway
Tel.: (47) 22538100
Hydroelectric Power Generation
N.A.I.C.S.: 221111

Hydro Energy A.S. (2)
Drammensveien 260, N 0240, Oslo, Norway (100%)
Tel.: (47) 22538100
Sales Range: $25-49.9 Million
Emp.: 12
Industrial Organic Chemicals
N.A.I.C.S.: 325199

Norsk Hydro U.K. Ltd. (1)
Bridge House 69 London Rd, Twickenham, TW1 3RH, Middx, United Kingdom (100%)
Tel.: (44) 2082552500
Web Site: http://www.uk.hydro.com
Sales Range: $25-49.9 Million
Emp.: 15
Aluminum Extraction & Refining
N.A.I.C.S.: 331313

Norsk Hydro Zimbabwe Private Ltd. (1)
Regal Star House, 4th Fl George Silundika Ave, PO Box 651, Harare, Zimbabwe
Tel.: (263) 4729441
Aluminum
N.A.I.C.S.: 331313

Norsk Hydro a.s. Hungary (1)
East West Trade Centre Rakoczi ut 1-3, H-1088, Budapest, Hungary
Tel.: (36) 12257615
Aluminium Extraction & Refining
N.A.I.C.S.: 331313

OOO Hydro Building Systems (1)
Berezhkovsk ya embankment 20 E, 123995, Moscow, Russia
Tel.: (7) 4952077530
Web Site: http://www.wicona.ru
Emp.: 4
Aluminium Products Mfr
N.A.I.C.S.: 331313

Precision Tubing, Hydro Aluminium Japan KK (1)
Shin-Otemachi Bldg 2F 2-2-1 Otemachi, Chiyoda-ku, Tokyo, 100-0004, Japan
Tel.: (81) 3 5255 5110
Precision Tubing & Aluminium Product Mfr
N.A.I.C.S.: 332999

Sapa AS (1)
Biskop Gunnerus gate 14 Posthuset 11th Floor, 0185, Oslo, Norway (50%)
Tel.: (47) 2241 6900
Emp.: 23,000
Aluminum Extrusions, Building Systems & Tubing Mfr
N.A.I.C.S.: 331318
Erika Ahlqvist *(Exec VP-Comm)*

Plant (Non-US):

Hydro Aluminium Expa Sa (2)
Siebeponisweg 12, 4700, Eupen, Belgium
Tel.: (32) 87 89 90 90
Construction Product Mfr
N.A.I.C.S.: 327390

Subsidiary (Non-US):

SC Sapa Profiles Srl (2)
Tudor Vladimirescu St, DN79A Km 104 Chisineu Cris, Arad, 315100, Romania
Tel.: (40) 257307802
Sales Range: $25-49.9 Million
Emp.: 200
Aluminum Secondary Smelting & Alloying
N.A.I.C.S.: 331314

Sapa AB (2)
Humlegardsgatan 17, PO Box 5505, Stockholm, 11485, Sweden
Tel.: (46) 84595900
Sales Range: $1-4.9 Billion
Mfr of Aluminum Profiles, Aluminum Building Systems & Aluminium Heat-Exchanger Strip Products
N.A.I.C.S.: 331318

Subsidiary (Domestic):

Sapa Profiler AB (3)
Metallvagen, 574 81, Vetlanda, Sweden
Tel.: (46) 383 941 00
Sales Range: $200-249.9 Million
Emp.: 1,050
Aluminium Products Mfr
N.A.I.C.S.: 331313

Sapa Thermal Management AB (3)
Torsgatan 21, PO Box 6002, 10231, Stockholm, Sweden
Tel.: (46) 87283200
Sales Range: $150-199.9 Million
Emp.: 700
Telecommunications
N.A.I.C.S.: 517810

Subsidiary (Non-US):

Sapa Aluminium Profile AG (2)
Chamerstrasse 176, 6300, Zug, Switzerland
Tel.: (41) 552632777
Metals Service Center
N.A.I.C.S.: 423510

Sapa Aluminium Sp.z o.o. (2)
Powder Coating Plant ul Graniczna 64/66, 93-428, Lodz, Poland
Tel.: (48) 42 683 6300
Aluminium Powder-Coating Plant
N.A.I.C.S.: 331313

Sapa Building System AB (2)
Langhojvej 1 Indgang A, Tilst, 8381, Arhus, Denmark
Tel.: (45) 86 16 00 19

NORSK HYDRO ASA

Norsk Hydro ASA—(Continued)

Web Site: http://www.sapagroup.com
Aluminum Profiles Mfr
N.A.I.C.S.: 331318

Sapa Building System NV (2)
Industrielaan 17, Industriezone Kwakkel
zone C2, 8810, Lichtervelde, West Flanders, Belgium
Tel.: (32) 51729624
Web Site:
  http://www.sapabuildingsystem.com
Aluminium Products Mfr
N.A.I.C.S.: 331318

Sapa Building System Vertriebs GmbH (2)
Pirching 90, 8200, Gleisdorf, Austria
Tel.: (43) 311273660
Web Site: http://www.sapagroup.com
Metals Service Center
N.A.I.C.S.: 423510

Sapa Building Systems (Wakefield) Limited (2)
Albert Drive, Silkwood Park, Wakefield,
WF5 9TG, West Yorkshire, United Kingdom
Tel.: (44) 1924 232 323
Web Site: http://www.technal.co.uk
Sales Range: $50-74.9 Million
Emp.: 62
Fabricated Metal Products Mfr
N.A.I.C.S.: 332999

Sapa Building Systems AG (2)
Gewerbepark, CH 5506, Magenwil, Switzerland
Tel.: (41) 628874141
Web Site: http://www.wicona.com
Sales Range: $25-49.9 Million
Emp.: 20
Aluminium Products Mfr
N.A.I.C.S.: 331313

Sapa Building Systems BV (2)
Alcoalaan1, 5151 RW, Drunen, Netherlands
Tel.: (31) 416 38 6480
Web Site: http://www.sapabuildingsystem.nl
Sales Range: $25-49.9 Million
Aluminum Extruded Product Mfr
N.A.I.C.S.: 331318

Sapa Building Systems GmbH (2)
Einsteinstrasse 61, 89077, Ulm, Germany
Tel.: (49) 73139840
Web Site: http://www.sapagroup.com
Sales Range: $75-99.9 Million
Aluminum Building Products & Design Services
N.A.I.C.S.: 331318

Sapa Building Systems Limited (2)
5300 Tewkesbury Business Park, Severn Drive, Tewkesbury, GL20 8FF, Gloucestershire, United Kingdom
Tel.: (44) 1684 853500
Web Site:
  http://www.sapabuildingsystems.co.uk
Fabricated Metal Products Mfr
N.A.I.C.S.: 332999

Sapa Building Systems SAS (2)
Espace Vernede 4-5 Route des Vernedes, 83488, Puget-sur-Argens, Cedex, France
Tel.: (33) 498125900
Web Site: http://www.sapagroup.com
Emp.: 250
Metals Service Center
N.A.I.C.S.: 423510

Sapa Building Systems spol. s r.o. (2)
Holandska 8, 63900, Brno, Czech Republic
Tel.: (420) 543 422 030
Web Site: http://www.wicona.cz
Sales Range: $50-74.9 Million
Emp.: 6
Building Materials Distr
N.A.I.C.S.: 423390
Jan Stupka (Area Mgr)

Sapa Canada Inc. (2)
7 Alloy Court, North York, M9M 3A2, ON, Canada
Tel.: (416) 743-1080
Sales Range: $25-49.9 Million
Emp.: 60
Aluminium Products Mfr
N.A.I.C.S.: 331318

Wade Ellertson (Plant Mgr)

Sapa Components UK Limited (2)
Spinnaker Park Spinnaker Road, Gloucester, GL2 5DG, United Kingdom
Tel.: (44) 1452 502 502
Web Site: http://www.sapagroup.com
Aluminium Products Mfr
N.A.I.C.S.: 331318

Subsidiary (US):

Sapa Extruder Inc. (2)
2905 Old Oakwood Rd, Gainesville, GA 30504
Tel.: (770) 535-1349
Sales Range: $75-99.9 Million
Emp.: 272
Aluminium Products Mfr
N.A.I.C.S.: 331318

Sapa Extruder Inc. (2)
330 Elmwood Ave, Mountain Top, PA 18707
Tel.: (570) 474-5935
Sales Range: $25-49.9 Million
Emp.: 250
Aluminium Products Mfr
N.A.I.C.S.: 331318

Plant (Non-US):

Sapa Extrusion - Santa Oliva (2)
Pol Industrial l'Albornar c/Montmell Nr 1, 43710, Santa Oliva, Tarragona, Spain
Tel.: (34) 97 716 91 18
Web Site: http://www.sapagroup.com
Emp.: 100
Aluminium Products Mfr
N.A.I.C.S.: 331313

Subsidiary (US):

Sapa Extrusions North America, LLC (2)
9600 Bryn Mawr Ave, Rosemont, IL 60018
Tel.: (877) 710-7272
Web Site: http://www.sapagroup.com
Extruded Aluminum Products Mfr
N.A.I.C.S.: 331318

Plant (Domestic):

Sapa Extrusions - Cressona Operation (3)
53 Pottsville St, Cressona, PA 17929
Tel.: (570) 385-5000
Mfr of Aluminum Alloy, Extruded Shapes & Tubing
N.A.I.C.S.: 331318
Patrick Lawlor (Pres)

Sapa Extrusions North America - Belton (3)
117 Blake Dairy Rd, Belton, SC 29627
Tel.: (864) 338-8000
Aluminium Products Mfr
N.A.I.C.S.: 331313
Kenyon Harper (Plant Mgr)

Sapa Extrusions North America - Kalamazoo (3)
5575 N Riverview Dr, Kalamazoo, MI 49004
Tel.: (269) 349-6626
Aluminium Products Mfr
N.A.I.C.S.: 331313

Sapa Extrusions North America - Monett (3)
808 County Rd, Monett, MO 65708
Tel.: (417) 235-7841
Web Site: http://www.sapagroup.com
Aluminium Products Mfr
N.A.I.C.S.: 331313

Sapa Extrusions North America - North Liberty (3)
400 S Main St, North Liberty, IN 46554
Tel.: (574) 656-8111
Web Site: http://www.sapagroup.com
Aluminium Products Mfr
N.A.I.C.S.: 331313

Sapa Extrusions North America - Phoenix (3)
249 S 51st Ave, Phoenix, AZ 85005
Tel.: (602) 427-1439
Aluminium Products Mfr
N.A.I.C.S.: 331313
Michael Stier (VP & Gen Mgr-West Reg)

Sapa Extrusions North America - Sidney (3)
401 N Stolle Ave, Sidney, OH 45365
Tel.: (937) 492-9194
Aluminium Products Mfr
N.A.I.C.S.: 331313
Brent Taylor (Plant Mgr)

Subsidiary (Non-US):

Sapa H E Tubing Monterrey Operation SA de CV (2)
Ave Tecnologico 1255 Lote 3, Parque Industrial Estrella, 65550, Cienega de Flores, Nuevo Leon, Mexico
Tel.: (52) 8181546440
Web Site: http://www.hydro.com
Purchased Iron & Steel Pipe & Tube Mfr
N.A.I.C.S.: 331210

Sapa Holdings SL (2)
2 Edif Prima Muntadas Esc B 3 A Pl Ofc B3, 08820, Barcelona, Spain
Tel.: (34) 933741698
Sales Range: $25-49.9 Million
Emp.: 12
Aluminum Extruded Product Mfr
N.A.I.C.S.: 331318

Sapa II Perfis SA (2)
Alto da Bela Vista, Estrada das Ligeiras, 2735-337, Cacem, Portugal
Tel.: (351) 214272300
Prefabricated Metal Building & Component Mfr
N.A.I.C.S.: 332311

Subsidiary (US):

Sapa Precision Tubing Rockledge, LLC (2)
100 Gus Hipp Blvd, Rockledge, FL 32955-4701
Tel.: (321) 636-8147
Sales Range: $25-49.9 Million
Emp.: 225
Aluminum Precision Tubing Mfr
N.A.I.C.S.: 331318
Sergio Luiz Vendrasco (VP-Precision Tubing-North America)

Subsidiary (Non-US):

Sapa Precision Tubing Tonder A/S (2)
Hydrovej 6, PO Box 50, DK 6270, Tonder, Denmark
Tel.: (45) 74720304
Web Site: http://www.sapagroup.com
Sales Range: $125-149.9 Million
Emp.: 400
Mfr of Aluminium Extruded & Welded Tubes
N.A.I.C.S.: 331313

Sapa Profiilid AS (2)
Moigu Tehnopark Sara tee 4/6 Peetri kula Rae vald, 75312, Harjumaa, Estonia
Tel.: (372) 6512991
Web Site: http://www.hydro.com
Sales Range: $25-49.9 Million
Primary Aluminum Production
N.A.I.C.S.: 331313

Sapa Profiilit Oy (2)
Sinikalliontie 18 A, 02630, Espoo, Finland
Tel.: (358) 98678280
Sales Range: $25-49.9 Million
Emp.: 10
Construction Materials Whslr
N.A.I.C.S.: 423390
Jussi Heikkimyllo (Mgr-Sls)

Sapa Profiles Albi SAS (2)
ZA du Garric, 81450, Le Garric, France
Tel.: (33) 563 80 10 10
Web Site: http://www.sapagroup.com
Aluminium Products Mfr
N.A.I.C.S.: 331318

Sapa Profiles Banbury Ltd. (2)
Unit 1 Sawpit Lane, Tibshelf, Alfreton, DE55 5NH, Derbyshire, United Kingdom
Tel.: (44) 1773872761
Emp.: 300
Aluminum Rolling & Drawing
N.A.I.C.S.: 331318

Subsidiary (US):

Sapa Profiles Inc. (2)

INTERNATIONAL PUBLIC

7933 NE 21st Ave, Portland, OR 97211
Tel.: (503) 802-3000
Sales Range: $200-249.9 Million
Emp.: 600
Metals Service Center
N.A.I.C.S.: 423510

Subsidiary (Non-US):

Sapa Profiles Kft (2)
Verseci ut 1 15, 8000, Szekesfehervar, Hungary
Tel.: (36) 22532400
Aluminum Extruded Product Mfr
N.A.I.C.S.: 331318

Sapa Profiles NL B.V. (2)
Alcoalaan 1, 5151 RW, Drunen, Netherlands
Tel.: (31) 416 386300
Web Site: http://www.sapagroup.com
Sales Range: $150-199.9 Million
Emp.: 700
Alumina Refining
N.A.I.C.S.: 331313

Branch (Domestic):

Sapa Profiles - Harderwijk (3)
Industrieweg 15, 3846 BB, Harderwijk, Netherlands
Tel.: (31) 341 464411
Web Site: http://www.hydro.com
Sales Range: $25-49.9 Million
Aluminum Extruded Product Mfr
N.A.I.C.S.: 331318

Plant (Non-US):

Sapa Profiles Nord/Ouest - Luce (2)
42 rue de la Beauce, PO Box 89, 28111, Luce, Cedex, France
Tel.: (33) 237 30 64 00
Aluminium Products Mfr
N.A.I.C.S.: 331318

Subsidiary (Non-US):

Sapa Profiles Perifalsa S.r.l. (2)
Po In Sabon Parc 151-154-155, Arteixo, 15142, La Coruna, Spain
Tel.: (34) 981600116
Sales Range: $25-49.9 Million
Emp.: 200
Alumina Refining
N.A.I.C.S.: 331313

Sapa Profiles UK Limited (2)
Unit 1 Sawpit Lane, Tibshelf, Alfreton, DE55 5NH, Derbyshire, United Kingdom
Tel.: (44) 1773 549 300
Web Site: http://www.sapagroup.com
Sales Range: $25-49.9 Million
Emp.: 60
Extruded Aluminum Products Mfr
N.A.I.C.S.: 331318

Plant (Domestic):

Sapa Profiles UK Limited - Birtley (3)
Durham Road, Chester-le-Street, Birtley, DH3 2AH, Durham, United Kingdom
Tel.: (44) 1913011200
Web Site: http://www.hydro.com
Sales Range: $50-74.9 Million
Aluminum Extrusions
N.A.I.C.S.: 331318

Subsidiary (Non-US):

Sapa Profili S.r.l. (2)
Strada Maritima 2 km 5 700, 04014, Latina, Italy
Tel.: (39) 07738561
Aluminum Extruded Product Mfr
N.A.I.C.S.: 331318

Sapa Extrusion Raeren S.A. (1)
Waldstrasse 91, 4730, Raeren, Belgium
Tel.: (32) 8 785 9211
Aluminium Products Mfr
N.A.I.C.S.: 331313

Sor-Norge Aluminium AS (1)
Onarheimsvegen 54, N-5460, Husnes, Norway (100%)
Tel.: (47) 53475000
Web Site: https://www.soral.no
Sales Range: $550-599.9 Million
Emp.: 348

AND PRIVATE COMPANIES

Aluminum Extrusion; Owned 49.9% by
Norsk Hydro ASA & 50% by Rio Tinto Alcan
N.A.I.C.S.: 331313

Speira GmbH (1)
Aluminiumstr 1, 41515, Grevenbroich, Germany
Tel.: (49) 21816601
Web Site: https://www.speira.com
Aluminum Rolling Mfr
N.A.I.C.S.: 331110

Subsidiary (Domestic):

Real Alloy Germany GmbH (2)
Aluminiumstrasse 3, 41515, Grevenbroich, Germany
Tel.: (49) 218116450
Web Site: http://www.realalloy.com
Aluminum Recycling, Smelting & Alloying Services
N.A.I.C.S.: 331314

Plant (Domestic):

Real Alloy Recycling (German Works) Gmbh - Toging Facility (3)
Aluminiumstrasse 8, 84513, Toging, Germany
Tel.: (49) 86313950
Web Site: http://www.realalloy.com
Aluminum Recycler & Magnesium Casting Alloys Mfr
N.A.I.C.S.: 331314
Marcus Heimerl *(Plant Mgr)*

Wicona Benelux N.V. (1)
Welvaartstraat 14 1, B 2200, Herentals, Belgium (100%)
Tel.: (32) 1424999
Web Site: http://www.wicona.be
Sales Range: $10-24.9 Million
Emp.: 25
Alumina Refinery & Production
N.A.I.C.S.: 331313

NORSK SJOMAT AS
Svemorka 26, Stranda, Oslo, N-6200, Norway
Tel.: (47) 70268880
Web Site: http://www.norsksjomat.no
Year Founded: 1996
Frozen Norwegian Salmon Portions & Sashimi Grade Products
N.A.I.C.S.: 311412
Rolleiv Sve *(Mgr-Data)*

Subsidiaries:

Storm Seafood, Inc. (1)
86 Pond Valley Rd, Woodbury, CT 06798-2421
Tel.: (203) 263-6933
Web Site: http://www.stormseafood.com
Fish & Seafood Merchant Whslr
N.A.I.C.S.: 424460

NORSK SOLAR AS
Haakon VIIs gate 8, 4005, Stavanger, Norway
Tel.: (47) 45500840 NO
Web Site:
 https://www.norsksolar.com
Year Founded: 2017
NSOL—(OSL)
Rev: $1,533,365
Assets: $13,641,029
Liabilities: $11,499,843
Net Worth: $2,141,186
Earnings: ($7,002,084)
Emp.: 35
Fiscal Year-end: 12/31/23
Renewable Energy Services
N.A.I.C.S.: 221210
Pal Selboe Valseth *(Chm)*

NORSK TELEGRAMBYRA AS
Langkaia 1 Havnelageret, 0150, Oslo, Norway
Tel.: (47) 22 03 45 45
Web Site: http://www.ntb.no
Sales Range: $25-49.9 Million
Emp.: 185
News Wire Services

N.A.I.C.S.: 516210
Pal Bjerketvedt *(Editor-in-Chief & CEO)*

NORSKE SKOG ASA
Sjolyst Plass 2, 0278, Oslo, Norway
Tel.: (47) 22512020 NO
Web Site:
 http://www.norskeskog.com
Year Founded: 1962
0BQ—(DEU)
Pulp, Paper, Paperboard & Wood Products Mfr & Distr
N.A.I.C.S.: 322299
Sven Ombudstvedt *(Chm)*

Subsidiaries:

A/S Union (1)
Klostergata 33, NO 3730, Skien, Norway (100%)
Tel.: (47) 35585000
Web Site: http://www.norskeskog.com
Sales Range: $75-99.9 Million
Emp.: 400
N.A.I.C.S.: 113310

Follum Industripark AS (1)
Follumveien 100, 3503, Honefoss, Norway
Tel.: (47) 32 11 21 00
Industrial Building Construction Services
N.A.I.C.S.: 236210

International Forest Products (1)
Via della Giustiniana 1120 Private road 700 meters Villa 22, 189, Rome, Italy
Tel.: (39) 0630260640
Web Site: http://www.ifpitaly.com
Sales Range: $50-74.9 Million
Emp.: 3
Sales of Timber
N.A.I.C.S.: 423990

Namsenbygg AS (1)
PO Box 43, N 7800, Namsos, Norway (100%)
Tel.: (47) 74226900
Web Site: http://www.byggern.no
Sales Range: $25-49.9 Million
Emp.: 12
Distr of Building Products
N.A.I.C.S.: 423320

Nor Holz Verkaufsgesellschaft (1)
Fur Holzprodukte MBH Contrescarpe 53, D 28195, Bremen, Germany
Tel.: (49) 421320251
Sales Range: $25-49.9 Million
Emp.: 4
Sales of Chipboard, Timber & Fiberboard
N.A.I.C.S.: 459410

Norske Skog (1)
Sjovegen 108, 7620, Skogn, Norway
Tel.: (47) 74087000
Web Site: http://www.norskeskog.com
Sales Range: $125-149.9 Million
Emp.: 348
Newsprint Mill
N.A.I.C.S.: 322120
Amnud Sazrud *(Gen Mgr)*

Norske Skog (Cyprus) Ltd. (1)
30 Ellados Ave Efkleas Bleg 3 Fl, 8020, Paphos, Cyprus
Tel.: (357) 26950633
Sales Range: $25-49.9 Million
Emp.: 15
Mfr of Publication Papers
N.A.I.C.S.: 322120
Lazi Barbour *(Mgr-Sls)*

Norske Skog (Japan) Ltd. (1)
4th Floor Shibiya Building Shimbashi, Minato Ku, Tokyo, 105 0004, Japan (100%)
Tel.: (81) 335043601
Sales Range: $25-49.9 Million
Emp.: 25
Sales of Printing Paper
N.A.I.C.S.: 424110

Norske Skog (Schweiz) AG (1)
Im Seegarte 18, Landschlacht, 8597, Zolikerberg, Switzerland
Tel.: (41) 443891910
Web Site: https://www.norskeskog.com
Sales Range: $50-74.9 Million
Emp.: 3
Paper Product Distr

N.A.I.C.S.: 424130

Norske Skog (UK) Limited (1)
22 Tudor Street, London, EC4Y 0AY, United Kingdom (100%)
Tel.: (44) 2039254400
Sales Range: $25-49.9 Million
Emp.: 15
Sales of Printing Paper & Pulp
N.A.I.C.S.: 424110

Subsidiary (Domestic):

Respatex International Ltd. (2)
Unit 1 Chiltern Court Asheridge Road, Chesham, HP5 2PX, Buckinghamshire, United Kingdom (100%)
Tel.: (44) 1494771242
Web Site: https://fibo.co.uk
Sales of Laminated Board
N.A.I.C.S.: 459410

Norske Skog Adria d.o.o. (1)
Brodisce 28, 1236, Trzin, Slovenia
Tel.: (386) 1 563 6330
Publication Paper Mfr
N.A.I.C.S.: 322120
Bojan Smole *(Mng Dir)*

Norske Skog Bruck GmbH (1)
Fabriksgasse 10, 8600, Bruck an der Mur, Austria
Tel.: (43) 38628000
Web Site: https://www.norskeskog.at
Sales Range: $200-249.9 Million
Emp.: 270
Newsprint Mfr
N.A.I.C.S.: 322120

Norske Skog Czech & Slovak Republic spol. s.r.o. (1)
Classic 7 Budova C Jankovcova 1037/49, 170 00, Prague, Czech Republic
Tel.: (420) 283 870 072
Sales Range: $25-49.9 Million
Emp.: 7
Newsprint Mfr
N.A.I.C.S.: 322120

Norske Skog Deutschland GmbH (1)
Werner-Haas-Strasse 4, 86153, Augsburg, Germany
Tel.: (49) 821569720
Web Site: http://www.norskeskog.com
Sales Range: $25-49.9 Million
Emp.: 18
Paper Product Distr
N.A.I.C.S.: 327910

Norske Skog Europe Recovered Paper N.V. (1)
Roderveldlaan 5, 2600, Antwerp, Belgium
Tel.: (32) 32200040
Paper Products Mfr
N.A.I.C.S.: 322120

Norske Skog Flooring AS (1)
Alloc As fiboveien 26, 4580, Lyngdal, Norway
Tel.: (47) 38342200
Emp.: 200
N.A.I.C.S.: 113310
John Vonli *(Mng dir)*

Norske Skog Follum AS (1)
Follumveien 100, 3505, Honefoss, Norway
Tel.: (47) 32 11 21 00
Sales Range: $125-149.9 Million
Emp.: 428
Newsprint Mfr
N.A.I.C.S.: 322120
Oddvar Sandvei *(Gen Mgr)*

Norske Skog France sarl. (1)
13 bis rue de l'Abreuvoir, 92400, Courbevoie, France
Tel.: (33) 155619250
Sales Range: $25-49.9 Million
Emp.: 15
Paper Products Mfr
N.A.I.C.S.: 322120
Linda Omland *(Mng Dir)*

Norske Skog Golbey SA (1)
Route Jean-Charles Pellerin, PO Box 109, 88194, Golbey, Cedex, France
Tel.: (33) 329686868
Web Site: https://norskeskog-golbey.com
Sales Range: $125-149.9 Million
Emp.: 350
Newsprint Mfr

NORSKE SKOG ASA

N.A.I.C.S.: 322120
Yves Bailly *(Gen Mgr)*

Norske Skog Holding AS (1)
Oksenoyveien 80, 1326, Lysaker, Norway
Tel.: (47) 67 59 90 00
Investment Management Service
N.A.I.C.S.: 523999

Norske Skog Holdings (No.1) Ltd. (1)
Private Bag 1002, Kawerau, 3169, New Zealand
Tel.: (64) 73233999
Web Site: http://www.norskeskog.com
Sales Range: $125-149.9 Million
Emp.: 18
Paper MfrPeter
N.A.I.C.S.: 322120
Aaron Buist *(Mng Dir)*

Norske Skog Holland B.V. (1)
Kabelweg 61, NL 1014 BA, Amsterdam, Netherlands (100%)
Tel.: (31) 205822710
Web Site: http://www.norskeskog.com
Sales Range: $25-49.9 Million
Emp.: 4
Sales of Chipboard & Fiberboard
N.A.I.C.S.: 459410

Norske Skog Hungary Kft. (1)
Villam U 4, 1089, Budapest, Hungary
Tel.: (36) 14775060
Sales Range: $50-74.9 Million
Emp.: 4
Paper Product Distr
N.A.I.C.S.: 424130
Peter Sipos *(Mng Dir)*

Norske Skog Italia srl (1)
Via Boscovich 14, 20024, Milan, Italy (100%)
Tel.: (39) 0266982233
Sales Range: $25-49.9 Million
Emp.: 10
Sales of Printing Paper & Pulp
N.A.I.C.S.: 424110

Norske Skog Logistics N.V. (1)
Roderveldlaan, Berchem, 2600, Antwerp, Belgium
Tel.: (32) 32200040
Web Site: http://www.norskeskog.com
Paper Products Mfr
N.A.I.C.S.: 322120

Norske Skog Osterreich GmbH (1)
Fabriksgasse 10, 8600, Bruck an der Mur, Austria
Tel.: (43) 3862553110
Web Site: http://www.norskeskog.com
Sales Range: $50-74.9 Million
Emp.: 5
Paper Product Distr
N.A.I.C.S.: 424130
Robert Kirsch *(Mng Dir)*

Norske Skog Papier Recycling GmbH (1)
Industrieg 13a, 8600, Bruck an der Mur, Austria
Tel.: (43) 3862 53595
Paper Products Mfr
N.A.I.C.S.: 322299

Norske Skog Polska Sp. z.o.o. (1)
Ul Dobra 54/95, 00-312, Warsaw, Poland
Tel.: (48) 608 647 648
Web Site: http://www.norskeskog.com
Printing Paper Mfr
N.A.I.C.S.: 322120
Jacek Materkowski *(Mng Dir)*

Norske Skog Presspaier GmbH (1)
Alwinenstrasse 24, PO Box 4569, D 65035, Wiesbaden, Germany
Tel.: (49) 611902220
Web Site: http://www.norskeskog.com
Sales Range: $25-49.9 Million
Emp.: 25
Sales of Printing Paper & Fine Paper; Manufacturer of Pulp
N.A.I.C.S.: 424110

Norske Skog Saugbrugs AS (1)
Tistedalsgata 9-11, 1756, Halden, Norway
Tel.: (47) 69174000
Magazine Paper Mfr
N.A.I.C.S.: 322120
Kjell Arve Kure *(Mng Dir)*

NORSKE SKOG ASA

Norske Skog ASA—(Continued)

Norske Skog Skogn AS (1)
Fiborgtangen, 7620, Skogn, Norway
Tel.: (47) 74087000
Sales Range: $125-149.9 Million
Emp.: 370
Newsprint Mfr
N.A.I.C.S.: 322120
Amun Saxrud *(Gen Mgr)*

Norske Skog Tasman Ltd. (1)
Fletcher Avenue, Kawerau, 3169, New Zealand
Tel.: (64) 73233999
Sales Range: $125-149.9 Million
Emp.: 172
Paper Mfr
N.A.I.C.S.: 327910

Norske Skog US Recovered Paper Inc. (1)
2 N Lk Ave Ste 1025, Pasadena, CA 91101
Tel.: (626) 229-9953
Waste Paper Distr
N.A.I.C.S.: 424130

Norske Skog Walsum GmbH (1)
Theodor-Heuss Strasse 228, 47179, Duisburg, Germany
Tel.: (49) 20349920
Web Site: http://www.norskeskog.com
Sales Range: $200-249.9 Million
Emp.: 520
Paper Idustry Machinery Mfr.
N.A.I.C.S.: 333243
Reitel Sebastian Henneke *(Gen Mgr)*

Norske Skogindustrier ASA - Norske Skog Boyer Unit (1)
1279 Boyer Rd, Boyer, 7140, TAS, Australia
Tel.: (61) 362610111
Sales Range: $125-149.9 Million
Emp.: 355
Newsprint Mfr
N.A.I.C.S.: 322120
Rod Bender *(Gen Mgr)*

Norske Treindustrier AS (1)
Carensylst Alle 49, PO Box 329, Oslo, 1326, Norway
Tel.: (47) 67 59 90 00
Sales Range: $25-49.9 Million
Emp.: 60
Paper Products Mfr
N.A.I.C.S.: 322120

Papeles Norske Skog Bio Bio S.A. (1)
Av Pedro Aguirre Cerda 1054 San Pedro De La Paz, Concepcion, Chile
Tel.: (56) 41 2500000
Sales Range: $50-74.9 Million
Emp.: 20
Pulp Product Mfr
N.A.I.C.S.: 322110
Glen Rybertt *(Gen Mgr)*

Paper Agents Ltd. (1)
42/6 Levi Eshkol Street, PO Box 16092, 6936127, Tel Aviv, Israel
Tel.: (972) 36997041
Web Site: http://www.paperagents.com
Sales Range: $50-74.9 Million
Emp.: 10
Sales of Timber
N.A.I.C.S.: 423990

Saugbrug Trelast A/S (1)
Halden Indus Area, Halden, 1756, Norway (100%)
Tel.: (47) 69174000
Saw & Planing Mills
N.A.I.C.S.: 322120

Saugbrugsforeningen AS (1)
Norskegog Serbooks Ser4kenham Sx, N 1756, Halden, Norway
Tel.: (47) 69174000
Web Site:
 http://www.saugbrugsforeningen.com
Sales Range: $125-149.9 Million
Emp.: 500
Mfr of Magazine Paper; Packaging; Sawn Timber
N.A.I.C.S.: 322299
Kjell-Arve Kure *(Gen Mgr)*

Soder Forestal S.A. (1)
Avenida Diagonal 672, E 08034, Barcelona, Spain (100%)

Tel.: (34) 932801213
Paper Mfr
N.A.I.C.S.: 322220

Sundagardar Ltd. (1)
Sundagardar 10, PO Box 4074, IS-124, Reykjavik, Iceland
Tel.: (354) 5949400
Sales of Printing Paper
N.A.I.C.S.: 424110

Wood and Logistics AS (1)
Karenslyst alle 49, 1326, Oslo, Norway
Tel.: (47) 67 59 90 00
Paper & Cardboard Mfr
N.A.I.C.S.: 322130

n.v. Norske Skog Belgium s.a. (1)
DeVeldekens Roderveldlaan 5, B 2600, Berchem, Oelegem, Belgium
Tel.: (32) 32878140
Web Site: http://www.norskeskog.com
Sales Range: $50-74.9 Million
Emp.: 3
Sales of Printing Paper
N.A.I.C.S.: 424110

NORSTAR HOLDINGS INC.

Ab'A Hilel Silver 16, Ramat Gan, 52506, Israel
Tel.: (972) 36103100
Year Founded: 1962
NSTR—(TAE)
Rev.: $673,573,688
Assets: $10,776,073,875
Liabilities: $7,777,040,906
Net Worth: $2,999,032,969
Earnings: ($380,163,000)
Fiscal Year-end: 12/31/23
Offices of Other Holding Companies
N.A.I.C.S.: 551112
Chaim K. Katzman *(Founder & CEO)*

NORSUN AS

Karenslyst Alle 9C, 278, Oslo, Norway
Tel.: (47) 97415000 NO
Web Site: http://www.norsuncorp.no
Year Founded: 2005
Emp.: 210
Monocrystalline Wafers Mfr
N.A.I.C.S.: 334413
Inge K. Hansen *(Chm)*

NORSYN CROP TECHNOLOGY CO., LTD.

Room 11803 Building B Xiangshu Block No 36 Fenghui South Road, High-tech Zone, Xi'an, 710065, Shaanxi, China
Tel.: (86) 2981777282
Web Site: https://www.norsyn.com
Year Founded: 2006
001231—(SSE)
Rev.: $88,993,944
Assets: $181,361,700
Liabilities: $51,634,908
Net Worth: $129,726,792
Earnings: $13,161,096
Fiscal Year-end: 12/31/22
Agricultural Chemical Product Mfr & Distr
N.A.I.C.S.: 325320
Jingmin Zheng *(Chm & Gen Mgr)*

NORTAL AS

Lootsa St 6c, Tallinn, 11415, Estonia
Tel.: (372) 6101990
Web Site: http://nortal.com
Year Founded: 2000
Multinational Strategic Change & Technology Company
N.A.I.C.S.: 518210
Judy Mirkin *(VP-Client Svcs)*

Subsidiaries:

Dev9, LLC (1)
520 Kirkland Way Ste 200, Kirkland, WA 98033
Tel.: (425) 296-2800

Web Site: http://www.dev9.com
Cloud-first Custom Software Development
N.A.I.C.S.: 541511
Mike Ensor *(VP-Delivery)*

Questers Global Group Limited (1)
141-143 Shoreditch High Street, London, E1 6JE, United Kingdom
Tel.: (44) 2070303762
Web Site: http://www.questers.com
Information Technology Development Services
N.A.I.C.S.: 541519
Alexander Drangajov *(Co-Founder & CEO)*

NORTEC MINERALS CORP.

Suite 915 - 700 West Pender Street, Vancouver, V6C 1G8, BC, Canada
Tel.: (604) 717-6426
Web Site:
 https://www.nortecminerals.com
Year Founded: 1999
NVT—(OTCIQ)
Assets: $2,414,162
Liabilities: $807,752
Net Worth: $1,606,409
Earnings: ($224,053)
Fiscal Year-end: 12/31/19
Mineral Exploration Services
N.A.I.C.S.: 213114
Peter Frederick Tegart *(Exec Dir)*

NORTEC QUIMICA S.A.

Rua Dezessete no 200 - ABCD Distrito Industrial, Duque de Caxias Mantiquira, Duque de Caxias, 25250-612, RJ, Brazil
Tel.: (55) 2136517300
Web Site:
 https://www.nortecquimica.com.br
Year Founded: 1986
NRTQ3—(BRAZ)
Sales Range: Less than $1 Million
Emp.: 157
Pharmaceutical Product Mfr & Whslr
N.A.I.C.S.: 325412
Marcelo Capanema Mansur *(Dir-Investor Relations)*

NORTEL NETWORKS CORPORATION

5495 Airport Road Suite 360, Mississauga, L4V 1R9, ON, Canada
Tel.: (905) 863-7000 Ca
Web Site: http://www.nortel-us.com
Sales Range: $25-49.9 Million
Emp.: 190
Digital Telecommunications Systems & Information Management Systems
N.A.I.C.S.: 334290
Dennis J. Carey *(Exec VP-Corp Ops)*

Subsidiaries:

Guangdong Nortel Telecommunications Switching Equipment Limited (1)
Rongli Industrial Park Liuheng Rd, Shunde, Foshan, 528306, Guangdegong, China (50%)
Tel.: (86) 75726621515
Web Site: http://www.gdnt.com.cn
Sales Range: $25-49.9 Million
Emp.: 100
Wireless Network Equipment Engineer, Installer & Mfr
N.A.I.C.S.: 334220

Nortel China (1)
No 6 Wangjing Dong Lu, Beijing, 100102, Chaoyong, China (60%)
Tel.: (86) 10 6510 8000
Web Site: http://www.nortel.com
Telecommunication Servicesb
N.A.I.C.S.: 517112

Nortel Networks (1)
4000 Veterans Memorial Hwy, Bohemia, NY 11716-1024 (100%)
Tel.: (631) 285-2000
Web Site: http://www.nortelnetworks.com

INTERNATIONAL PUBLIC

Sales Range: $125-149.9 Million
Sales & Service of Voice Response & Audiotex Systems
N.A.I.C.S.: 334210

Subsidiary (Non-US):

Periphonics Corporation (2)
101 Thomson Rd 06 01, United Square, Singapore, 307591, Singapore
Tel.: (65) 62872877
Sales Range: $25-49.9 Million
Emp.: 100
N.A.I.C.S.: 334418

Nortel Networks (Austria) GmbH (1)
Clemens Holzmeister Strasse 4, 1100, Vienna, Austria
Tel.: (43) 1601060
Web Site: http://www.nortel.com
Telecommunication Servicesb
N.A.I.C.S.: 517112

Nortel Networks (India) Private Limited (1)
Orchid Plaza 2nd Floor, Sector 54 Sun City, Gurgaon, 122002, Haryana, India
Tel.: (91) 1244342200
Web Site: http://www.nortel.com
Sales Range: $50-74.9 Million
Emp.: 40
Telecommunication Servicesb
N.A.I.C.S.: 517112

Nortel Networks AG (1)
Wilstrasse 11, 8610, Uster, Switzerland
Tel.: (41) 44943 73 00
Telecommunication Servicesb
N.A.I.C.S.: 517810

Nortel Networks B.V (1)
Siriusdrees 42 2, 2132 WE, Hoofddorp, Netherlands (100%)
Tel.: (31) 235673173
Web Site: http://www.nortel.com
Sales Range: $50-74.9 Million
Emp.: 100
Financial Services
N.A.I.C.S.: 523999

Nortel Networks CALA Inc. (1)
2221 Lakeside Blvd, Richardson, TX 75082-4305
Tel.: (954) 851-8000
Web Site: http://www.nortelnetworks.com
Communications Equipment
N.A.I.C.S.: 423690
Bruce Patterson *(VP)*

Nortel Networks Chile S.A. (1)
Avenida Mariano Sanchez Fontecilla 310, Piso 2 Las Condes, Santiago, Chile
Tel.: (56) 28104500
Web Site: http://www.nortel.com
Telecommunication Servicesb
N.A.I.C.S.: 517112

Nortel Networks Engineering Service Kft (1)
Infopark Research Centre, Infopark Setany 1, I Building 5th Floor, 1117, Budapest, Hungary
Tel.: (36) 1 481 4400
Web Site: http://www.nortel.com
Telecommunication Servicesb
N.A.I.C.S.: 517111

Nortel Networks Hispania, S.A. (1)
Camino De Cerrro De Los Gamos 1 Bldg 56 Edificio 6 Pozuelo De Alarcon, 28224, Madrid, Spain (100%)
Tel.: (34) 917094000
Web Site: http://www.nortelnetworks.com
Sales Range: $100-124.9 Million
Provider of Telecommunications Services
N.A.I.C.S.: 517112

Nortel Networks Inc. (1)
4001 E Chapel Hill Nelson Hwy, Research Triangle Park, NC 27709 (100%)
Tel.: (919) 992-5000
Web Site: http://www.nortel.com
Rev.: $8,000,000,000
Emp.: 24,000
Mfr of Telecommunications & Information Processing Products to Independent Telephone Companies, Government & Military Agencies, Businesses & Institutions & Common Carriers
N.A.I.C.S.: 334210

AND PRIVATE COMPANIES

Division (Domestic):

Nortel Networks (2)
220 Athens Way Fl 3, Nashville, TN 37228-3722 (100%)
Tel.: (615) 432-4000
Mfr, Market & Service a Broad Range of Business & Residential Telephone Sets & Integrated Voice & Data Terminals
N.A.I.C.S.: 334210

Nortel Networks Corporation-Digital Switching Div. (2)
4001 E Chapel Hill Nelson Hwy, Research Triangle Park, NC 27709
Tel.: (919) 992-5000
Web Site: http://www.nortel.com
Mfrs., Markets & Services the DMS-100 Family of Digital Switching Systems
N.A.I.C.S.: 334210

Nortel Networks Japan, Inc. (1)
Gate City Ohsaki E Tower 9th Fl 1-11-2 Ohsaki Shinagawa-ku, Tokyo, 141 0032, Japan (100%)
Tel.: (81) 357401300
Sales Range: $50-74.9 Million
Provider of Telecommunications Services
N.A.I.C.S.: 517810

Nortel Networks Limited (1)
195 The West Mall, Toronto, M9C 5K1, ON, Canada (100%)
Tel.: (905) 863-7000
Web Site: http://www.nortel.com
Telephone Systems, Cable, Wire, Switching Systems, Connectors, Switches
N.A.I.C.S.: 335931

Nortel Networks Malaysia Sdn. Bhd. (1)
Level 2 Annexe Block Menara Milenium, No 8 Jalan Damanlela, Bukit Damansara, Kuala Lumpur, 50490, Malaysia
Tel.: (60) 320808000
Web Site: http://www.nortel.com
Sales Range: $25-49.9 Million
Emp.: 30
Telecommunication Servicesb
N.A.I.C.S.: 517112

Nortel Networks Mauritius Ltd. (1)
Les Cascades Building Edith Cavell Street, Port Louis, Mauritius
Tel.: (230) 2129800
Web Site: http://www.cimglobalbusiness.com
Sales Range: $100-124.9 Million
Emp.: 30
Telecommunication Servicesb
N.A.I.C.S.: 517810

Nortel Networks N.V. (1)
Ikaroslaan 14, 1930, Zaventem, Belgium (100%)
Tel.: (32) 27167511
Web Site: http://www.nortelnetworks.com
Sales Range: $25-49.9 Million
Emp.: 30
Provider of Telecommunications Services
N.A.I.C.S.: 517112

Nortel Networks Netas Telekomunikasyon A.S. (1)
Yenisehir Mah Osmanli Bulvari No 11, Kurtkoy Pendik, 34912, Istanbul, Turkiye (51.85%)
Tel.: (90) 2165222000
Web Site: http://www.netas.com.tr
Telecommunication Servicesb
N.A.I.C.S.: 517112
Ahmet Orel (Gen Counsel & Sec)

Nortel Networks Peru S.A.C. (1)
Avenida Enrique Canaval y Moreyra 380, Urbanizacion Corpac, San Isidro, Lima, 27, Peru
Tel.: (51) 1 411 2261
Web Site: http://www.nortel.com
Telecommunication Servicesb
N.A.I.C.S.: 517112

Nortel Networks Portugal, S.A. (1)
Edificio Tivoli Forum 3rd Fl, PO Box 180 E, 3rd Fl, P 1250 146, Lisbon, Portugal (100%)
Tel.: (351) 213109200
Web Site: http://www.nortelnetworks.com
Sales Range: $25-49.9 Million
Emp.: 30
Networking & Communication Services

N.A.I.C.S.: 517112

Nortel Networks S.A. (1)
Zava Magny Chateaufort, F 78928, Yvelines, Cedex, France (100%)
Tel.: (33) 169554444
Web Site: http://www.nortelnetworks.com
Telecommunications; Joint Venture of EADS (45%) & Nortel Networks (55%)
N.A.I.C.S.: 517112

Nortel Networks Slovensko, s.r.o. (1)
Obchodna 2, 81106, Bratislava, Slovakia
Tel.: (421) 254413000
Web Site: http://www.nortel.com
Telecommunication Servicesb
N.A.I.C.S.: 517112

Nortel Networks de Argentina, S.A. (1)
Larrea 1079 Torre Bouchard Plz, Bouchard 557 599 Piso 17, Buenos Aires, Piso 17, Argentina (100%)
Tel.: (54) 1148277200
Web Site: http://www.nortelnetworks.com
Sales Range: $25-49.9 Million
Emp.: 80
Telecommunications Provider
N.A.I.C.S.: 517111

Nortel Networks de Colombia S.A. (1)
Calle 96 No 13 11, Santafe, Bogota, DC, Colombia (100%)
Tel.: (57) 15220010
Web Site: http://www.nortelnetworks.com
Sales Range: $25-49.9 Million
Emp.: 90
Provider of Telecommunications Services
N.A.I.C.S.: 517112

Nortel Networks de Mexico, S.A. de C.V. (1)
Ave Insurgentes Sur 1605 Piso 30 Ofca, Col San Jose Insurgentes Deleg, 3900, Mexico, DF, Mexico (100%)
Tel.: (52) 55536251011
Web Site: http://www.nortelnetworks.com
Sales Range: $100-124.9 Million
Provider of Telecommunications Services
N.A.I.C.S.: 517112

Nortel Networks do Brasil (1)
Av Das Nacoes Unidas, Andar, 04795 100, Sao Paulo, SP, Brazil (100%)
Tel.: (55) 1156444000
Web Site: http://www.nortelnetworks.com
Sales Range: $50-74.9 Million
Telecommunication Servicesb
N.A.I.C.S.: 517112

Nortel Networks plc (1)
Maidenhead Office Park, Westacott Way, Maidenhead, SL6 3QH, Berkshire, United Kingdom (100%)
Tel.: (44) 1628432000
Web Site: http://nortel.com
Telecommunications Systems
N.A.I.C.S.: 517810

Nortel Technology Excellence Center Private Limited (1)
AMR Tech Park II # 23 / 24 Hongasandra, Bommanahalli Hosur Main Road, Bengaluru, 568868, India
Tel.: (91) 8066472700
Web Site: http://www.nortel.com
Sales Range: $50-74.9 Million
Telecommunications Research & Development
N.A.I.C.S.: 541990

Nortel UK Ltd. (1)
Maiden Head Office Pk, Westacott Way, Maidenhead, SL6 3QH, Berkshire, United Kingdom (100%)
Tel.: (44) 1628432000
Web Site: http://www.nortel.com
Telecommunications Systems
N.A.I.C.S.: 517810

Branch (Domestic):

Nortel UK Ltd. (2)
London Road, Harlow, CM17 9NA, Essex, United Kingdom (100%)
Tel.: (44) 1279429531
Web Site: http://www.nortelnetworks.com
Provider of Telecommunications Services
N.A.I.C.S.: 517810

Nortel Vietnam Limited (1)
Unit 1801 18/F Melinh Point Tower, 2 Ngo Duc Ke Street, District 1, Ho Chi Minh City, Vietnam
Tel.: (84) 8 823 0453
Web Site: http://www.nortel.com
Telecommunication Servicesb
N.A.I.C.S.: 517112

NORTEM BIOGROUP S.A.
C/Alexander Humboldt N 12, El Puerto de Santa Maria, 11500, Cadiz, Spain
Tel.: (34) 856925095
Web Site:
  https://www.nortembiogroup.com
Year Founded: 2015
MLBIO—(EUR)
Biotechnology Research & Development Services
N.A.I.C.S.: 541714

NORTH AMERICAN CONSTRUCTION GROUP LTD.
27287 100 Avenue, Acheson, T7X 6H8, AB, Canada
Tel.: (780) 960-7171 AB
Web Site: https://www.nacg.ca
Year Founded: 1953
NOA—(NYSE)
Rev.: $601,994,969
Assets: $766,253,430
Liabilities: $526,939,114
Net Worth: $239,314,315
Earnings: $52,703,768
Emp.: 205
Fiscal Year-end: 12/31/22
Holding Company; Heavy Construction, Mining, Site Preparation, Piling Services
N.A.I.C.S.: 551112
Martin R. Ferron (Chm)

Subsidiaries:

North American Caisson Ltd. (1)
2820 IIIrd Ave NE, Calgary, T2A 2L5, AB, Canada
Tel.: (403) 503-0599
Web Site: http://www.nacg.com
Sales Range: $10-24.9 Million
Emp.: 50
Construction Services
N.A.I.C.S.: 561499

North American Maintenance Ltd. (1)
53016 Hwy 60 Suite 2, Spruce Grove, T7X 3G7, AB, Canada
Tel.: (780) 960-7171
Web Site:
  http://www.northameciancontrction.ca
Emp.: 20
Oil & Gas Pipeline Construction Services
N.A.I.C.S.: 237120

North American Pipeline Inc. (1)
53016 Hwy 60 Unit 2, Acheson, T7X 5A7, AB, Canada
Tel.: (780) 960-7171
Water Pipeline Construction Services
N.A.I.C.S.: 237110

North American Road Inc. (1)
53016 Hwy 60 Suite 2 Zone 3, Acheson, AB, Canada
Tel.: (780) 960-7171
Highway Construction Engineering Services
N.A.I.C.S.: 237310

NORTH AMERICAN FUR PRODUCERS MARKETING INC
65 Skyway Ave, Toronto, M9W 6C7, ON, Canada
Tel.: (416) 675-9320
Web Site: http://www.nafa.ca
Year Founded: 1670
Sales Range: $350-399.9 Million
Emp.: 70
Auction
N.A.I.C.S.: 424590
Herman Jansen (Mng Dir)

Subsidiaries:

NAFA Polska Sp.z o.o. (1)
ul Granitowa 10 Lozienica, 72-100, Goleniow, Poland
Tel.: (48) 91 350 9520
Web Site: http://www.nafa.ca
Fur Pelt Whslr
N.A.I.C.S.: 424590
Natalia Todryk (Office Mgr)

NAFA USA, INC. (1)
205 Industrial Cir, Stoughton, WI 53589
Tel.: (608) 205-9200
Web Site: http://www.nafa.ca
Fur Pelt Whslr
N.A.I.C.S.: 424590
Chris Vaughan (VP-Ranc Rels)

NORTH AMERICAN INCOME TRUST PLC
PO Box 9023, Chelmsford, CM99 2WB, United Kingdom
Tel.: (44) 1315284000
Web Site:
  https://www.northernincome.co.uk
NAIT—(LSE)
Rev.: $61,586,085
Assets: $621,895,395
Liabilities: $52,299,390
Net Worth: $569,596,005
Earnings: $50,372,190
Fiscal Year-end: 01/31/23
Investment Management Service
N.A.I.C.S.: 525990
Francis Radano (Sr Mgr-Investments)

NORTH ARC CAPITAL PARTNERS
2440 Tedlo Street, Mississauga, L4W 2S7, ON, Canada
Web Site:
  https://www.northarccapital.com
Holding Company
N.A.I.C.S.: 551112
Bryden Richardson (CEO)

Subsidiaries:

Project 321, Inc. (1)
3188 N Marks Ave Ste 104, Fresno, CA 93722-4903
Tel.: (559) 268-7975
Web Site: http://www.project321.com
Mechanical Power Transmission Equipment Mfr
N.A.I.C.S.: 333613
Jake Lilies (Pres)

NORTH ARROW MINERALS INC.
Suite 960 789 West Pender Street, Vancouver, V6C 1H2, BC, Canada
Tel.: (604) 668-8355
Web Site:
  https://www.northarrowminerals.com
Year Founded: 2007
NAR—(TSXV)
Rev.: $25,059
Assets: $15,752,160
Liabilities: $1,409,560
Net Worth: $14,342,600
Earnings: ($1,329,584)
Fiscal Year-end: 04/30/22
Gold Exploration Services
N.A.I.C.S.: 212220
D. Grenville Thomas (Chm)

NORTH ASIA STRATEGIC HOLDINGS LIMITED
18F Shanghai Commercial Bank Tower 12 Queens Road Central, Hong Kong, China (Hong Kong)
Tel.: (852) 2 918 3788 BM
Web Site:
  http://www.nasholdings.com
8080—(HKG)
Rev.: $315,375,447
Assets: $407,833,083
Liabilities: $221,142,014

NORTH ASIA STRATEGIC HOLDINGS LIMITED

North Asia Strategic Holdings Limited—(Continued)
Net Worth: $186,691,069
Earnings: $10,291,701
Emp.: 375
Fiscal Year-end: 03/31/22
Holding Company
N.A.I.C.S.: 551112
Henry Wai Fai Law *(CFO & Sec)*

Subsidiaries:

American Tec Co. Ltd (1)
Unit 1902 03 19 F Futura Plaza No 111 113 How Ming Street, Kwun Tong, Kowloon, China (Hong Kong)
Tel.: (852) 26280288
Web Site: http://www.americantec.com
Sales Range: $25-49.9 Million
Emp.: 40
Surface Mount Technology Electronics Equipment Supplier
N.A.I.C.S.: 334419

Perfect Combo Limited (1)
Room 1001 10F Millennium City 3 370 Kwun Tong Road, Kwun Tong, Kowloon, China (Hong Kong)
Tel.: (852) 21913003
Home Management Services
N.A.I.C.S.: 721110

NORTH ATLANTIC SMALLER COMPANIES INVESTMENT TRUST PLC
6 Stratton Street, London, W1J 8LD, United Kingdom
Tel.: (44) 2076403200
Web Site: https://www.nascit.co.uk
Year Founded: 1973
NAS—(LSE)
Rev.: $26,501,591
Assets: $879,567,158
Liabilities: $852,960
Net Worth: $878,714,198
Earnings: $2,734,564
Fiscal Year-end: 01/31/24
Investment Trust Management Services
N.A.I.C.S.: 523940
Christopher Harwood Bernard Mills *(CEO & Mgr-Investments)*

NORTH AUSTRALIAN CATTLE COMPANY PTY. LTD.
U 1/15 54 Cullen Bay Cres, Larrakeyah, Darwin, 0820, NT, Australia
Tel.: (61) 88981 4033
Web Site: http://www.elders.com.au
Sales Range: $25-49.9 Million
Emp.: 3
Livestock Breeding Services
N.A.I.C.S.: 115210

NORTH BANK FOR FINANCE AND INVESTMENT
Street 99 Karadah Neighborhood Upper Fath Square, PO Box 3377, Baghdad, Iraq
Tel.: (964) 7400148052
Web Site: http://www.northbankiq.com
Year Founded: 2003
Banking Services
N.A.I.C.S.: 522110
Nawzad Dawood Fattah Al Jaff *(Chm)*

NORTH BUD FARMS, INC.
1000 Route 105, Gatineau, J0X 3E0, QC, Canada
Web Site: http://www.northbud.com
NBUD—(CNSX)
Sales Range: Less than $1 Million
Cannabis Product Mfr
N.A.I.C.S.: 325412
Brown *(Chm & CEO-Interim)*

CAIRO MILLS & BAKOMPANY
El-Salam City, Cairo, Egypt
Tel.: (20) 222817233
Web Site: https://www.northcairomills.com
Year Founded: 1967
MILS.CA—(EGX)
Sales Range: Less than $1 Million
Flour Milling Services
N.A.I.C.S.: 311211
Ahmed El-Essawy Abdo Abdo *(Chm & Mng Dir)*

NORTH CASPIAN PETROLEUM JSC
117 b Kulmanov B str, 060011, Atyrau, Kazakhstan
Tel.: (7) 1 222 0219
NCPR—(KAZ)
Assets: $28,465,911
Liabilities: $44,201,050
Net Worth: ($15,735,139)
Earnings: ($4,150,244)
Fiscal Year-end: 12/31/20
Oil & Gas Exploration Services
N.A.I.C.S.: 213112

NORTH CHINA PHARMACEUTICAL COMPANY LTD.
No 388 Heping East Road, Shijiazhuang, 050015, Hebei, China
Tel.: (86) 31186219063
Web Site: http://www.ncpc.com
Year Founded: 1992
600812—(SHG)
Rev.: $1,474,192,573
Assets: $2,979,430,913
Liabilities: $2,104,966,909
Net Worth: $874,464,004
Earnings: ($96,768,103)
Fiscal Year-end: 12/31/22
Pharmaceutical Product Mfr & Distr
N.A.I.C.S.: 325412
Wang Lixin *(Chm & Gen Mgr)*

NORTH COAST S.A.
Al Jerozolimskie 180 street Kopernik Office Buildings A, 02-486, Warsaw, Poland
Tel.: (48) 22 738 31 50
Web Site: http://www.northcoast.com.pl
Year Founded: 1992
NCT—(WAR)
Sales Range: $50-74.9 Million
Food Products Distr
N.A.I.C.S.: 445298
Olivier Savary *(Chm-Mgmt Bd)*

NORTH COPPER CO., LTD.
Dongfeng Mountain, Yuanqu County, Yuncheng, 043700, Shanxi, China
Tel.: (86) 3596031930
Web Site: http://www.nafine.com
Year Founded: 1996
000737—(SSE)
Rev.: $1,499,450,940
Assets: $1,192,304,880
Liabilities: $587,731,248
Net Worth: $604,573,632
Earnings: $85,648,212
Fiscal Year-end: 12/31/22
Chemical Product Mfr & Distr
N.A.I.C.S.: 325998
Wei Yinghui *(Chm)*

NORTH DRILLING COMPANY
No 2127 Corner of Del Afrooz St Valiasr St, Valiasr St, 1511714315, Tehran, Iran
Tel.: (98) 2148610000
Web Site: https://www.ndco.ir
HSHM—(THE)
Sales Range: Less than $1 Million
Oil & Gas Services
N.A.I.C.S.: 213112
Ahmad Khavari *(Chm)*

NORTH EASTERN CARRYING CORPORATION LIMITED
NECC House 9062/47 Ram Bagh Road Azad Market, Delhi, 110 006, India
Tel.: (91) 1123517516
Web Site: https://www.neccgroup.com
Year Founded: 1984
NECCLTD—(NSE)
Rev.: $36,737,642
Assets: $29,183,418
Liabilities: $16,610,947
Net Worth: $12,572,472
Earnings: $691,925
Emp.: 478
Fiscal Year-end: 03/31/23
Transportation Services
N.A.I.C.S.: 488490
Shyam Lal Yadav *(CFO & VP)*

NORTH ELECTRO-OPTIC CO., LTD.
No 35 Changle Middle Road, Xi'an, 710043, Shaanxi, China
Tel.: (86) 2982521712
Web Site: https://www.northeo.com
Year Founded: 2000
600184—(SHG)
Rev.: $352,816,088
Assets: $598,488,022
Liabilities: $248,292,612
Net Worth: $350,195,410
Earnings: $9,980,180
Emp.: 3,600
Fiscal Year-end: 12/31/22
Optoelectronic Device Mfr & Distr
N.A.I.C.S.: 334413
Liang Chen *(VP & Gen Mgr)*

Subsidiaries:

Hubei New Huaguang Information Materials Co., Ltd. (1)
No 67 Changhong North Road, Xiangyang, 441024, Hubei, China
Tel.: (86) 7103349999
Web Site: http://www.hbnhg.com
Optical Component Mfr & Whslr
N.A.I.C.S.: 327212

NORTH ENERGY ASA
Tjuvholmen alle 19, 0252, Oslo, Norway
Tel.: (47) 22017950
Web Site: https://www.northenergy.no
RN2—(DEU)
Rev.: $10,438
Assets: $30,258,637
Liabilities: $1,787,456
Net Worth: $28,471,180
Earnings: ($1,207,464)
Emp.: 3
Fiscal Year-end: 12/31/22
Oil & Gas Exploration & Production Services
N.A.I.C.S.: 211120
Anders Onarheim *(Chm)*

NORTH HAVEN PRIVATE EQUITY ASIA ANGEL CO. LTD.
Sertus Chambers Cassia Court, Camana Bay, Singapore, Singapore
Tel.: (65) 345 943 7700
Privater Equity Firm
N.A.I.C.S.: 523999

NORTH HUAJIN CHEMICAL INDUSTRIES CO., LTD.
Hongqi Street, Shuangtaizi District, Panjin, 124021, Liaoning, China
Tel.: (86) 4275854262
Web Site: https://www.huajinchem.com
Year Founded: 1997
000059—(SSE)
Rev.: $4,663,320,182
Assets: $4,274,505,377
Liabilities: $2,112,415,049
Net Worth: $2,162,090,327
Earnings: $49,715,113
Emp.: 11,779
Fiscal Year-end: 12/31/20
Petrochemical Products Mfr
N.A.I.C.S.: 325110
Ren Yongqiang *(Chm)*

NORTH INDUSTRIES GROUP RED ARROW CO., LTD.
No 1669 Zhongjing North Road, Wolong District, Nanyang, Henan, China
Tel.: (86) 37783880276
000519—(SSE)
Rev.: $942,588,036
Assets: $2,106,447,876
Liabilities: $737,303,580
Net Worth: $1,369,144,296
Earnings: $114,997,428
Emp.: 10,464
Fiscal Year-end: 12/31/22
Automobile Parts Mfr
N.A.I.C.S.: 336110

NORTH MEDIA A/S
Gladsaxe Mollevej 28, DK-2860, Soborg, Denmark
Tel.: (45) 39577000
Web Site: https://www.northmedia.dk
Year Founded: 1965
NORTHM—(CSE)
Rev.: $144,014,701
Assets: $175,268,771
Liabilities: $31,239,600
Net Worth: $144,029,170
Earnings: $303,859
Emp.: 420
Fiscal Year-end: 12/31/22
Newspaper Publishers & Distr; Advertising Services
N.A.I.C.S.: 424920
Kare Stauso Wigh *(CFO; Member-Exec Bd & Exec Dir-Grp)*

Subsidiaries:

Bekey A/S (1)
Gladsaxe Mollevej 28, 2860, Soborg, Denmark
Tel.: (45) 43439990
Web Site: http://bekey.dk
Digital Access Solution Services
N.A.I.C.S.: 518210

Boligmanager ApS (1)
Vestermollevej 32, Klitmoller, DK-7700, Thisted, Denmark
Tel.: (45) 71995380
Newspaper & Magazine Publishing Services
N.A.I.C.S.: 424920

Forbruger-Kontakt A/S (1)
Bredebjergvej 6, 2630, Taastrup, Denmark
Tel.: (45) 43439900
Web Site: http://www.fk.dk
Newspaper Distr
N.A.I.C.S.: 459210

Subsidiary (Domestic):

Tryksagsomdelingen Fyn A/S (2)
Ryttermarken 4 B, 5700, Svendborg, Denmark
Tel.: (45) 62222222
Media Related Advertising Services
N.A.I.C.S.: 541890

North Media Aviser A/S (1)
Gammel Kongevej 60 16 Floor, 1850, Frederiksberg, Denmark
Tel.: (45) 39577500
Media Related Advertising Services
N.A.I.C.S.: 541890

Subsidiary (Domestic):

Helsingor Dagblad A/S (2)
H P Christensens Vej 1A, 3000, Helsingor, Denmark
Tel.: (45) 49222110
Web Site: http://helsingordagblad.dk
Newspaper Publishers
N.A.I.C.S.: 513110

AND PRIVATE COMPANIES
NORTHAMPTON GROUP INC.

Sondagsavisen A/S (2)
Old Kongevej 60 16th Floor, 1850, Frederiksberg, Denmark
Tel.: (45) 39577500
Web Site: http://www.sondagsavisen.dk
Newspaper Publishers
N.A.I.C.S.: 513110

North Media Online A/S (1)
Gladsaxe Mollevej 28, 2860, Soborg, Denmark
Tel.: (45) 3 957 7000
Web Site: https://northmediaonline.ofir.com
Media Related Advertising Services
N.A.I.C.S.: 541890

Subsidiary (Domestic):

BoligPortal.dk ApS (2)
Paludan-Mullers Vej 40 B, 8200, Aarhus, Denmark
Tel.: (45) 7 020 8082
Web Site: https://www.boligportal.dk
Rental Housing Portal Services
N.A.I.C.S.: 721310

Ofir A/S (2)
Gladsaxe Mollevej 28, 2860, Soborg, Denmark
Tel.: (45) 39577800
Web Site: http://www.ofir.dk
Job Placing & Employment Services
N.A.I.C.S.: 561311

Subsidiary (Domestic):

MatchWork Danmark A/S (3)
Gladsaxe Mollevej 26, 2860, Soborg, Denmark
Tel.: (45) 36959595
Web Site: http://www.matchwork.com
Software Development & Design Services
N.A.I.C.S.: 541511

Subsidiary (Non-US):

MatchWork UK Ltd. (3)
Weltech Centre Ridgeway, Welwyn Garden City, AL7 2AA, Herts, United Kingdom
Tel.: (44) 2075201600
Media Related Advertising Services
N.A.I.C.S.: 541890

NORTH MINING SHARES COMPANY LIMITED
Rooms 2009-18 20/F Shui On Centre 6-8 Harbour Road, Wanchai, China (Hong Kong)
Tel.: (852) 2520 8433   BM
Web Site:
    http://www.northmining.com.hk
Year Founded: 1995
Rev.: $108,710,237
Assets: $662,708,216
Liabilities: $320,649,016
Net Worth: $342,059,200
Earnings: ($156,220,139)
Emp.: 693
Fiscal Year-end: 12/31/19
Molybdenum Exploration Services
N.A.I.C.S.: 212290
Yi Dong Qian *(Deputy Chm)*

NORTH NAVIGATION CONTROL TECHNOLOGY CO., LTD.
No 2 Kechuang Fifteenth Street, Beijing Economic and Technological Development Zone, Beijing, 100176, China
Tel.: (86) 1058089788
Web Site: http://www.bfdh.com.cn
Year Founded: 2000
600435—(SHG)
Rev.: $539,058,359
Assets: $888,183,120
Liabilities: $434,040,408
Net Worth: $454,142,712
Earnings: $25,981,118
Fiscal Year-end: 12/31/22
Electronic Communication Equipment Mfr
N.A.I.C.S.: 334290
Li Haitao *(Chm)*

NORTH PACIFIC BANK, LTD.
7 Odori Nishi 3-chome, Chuo-ku, Sapporo, 060-8661, Japan
Tel.: (81) 112611311   JP
Web Site:
    https://www.hokuyobank.co.jp
Year Founded: 1917
8524—(TKS)
Rev.: $879,883,540
Assets: $87,546,634,140
Liabilities: $84,588,526,940
Net Worth: $2,958,107,200
Earnings: $33,050
Emp.: 2,361
Fiscal Year-end: 03/31/24
Commercial Banking Services
N.A.I.C.S.: 522110
Ryosuke Kobayashi *(Mng Exec Officer)*

Subsidiaries:

Hokuyo Business Service Co., Ltd. (1)
8-523 Minami 8 West, Chuo-Ku, Sapporo, 064-0808, Hokkaido, Japan
Tel.: (81) 115335140
Web Site: http://hokuyo-bs.jp
Emp.: 590
Business Management Services
N.A.I.C.S.: 561110
Yasuo In *(Pres)*

Sapporo Hokuyo Card Co., Ltd. (1)
3-11 Odori Nishi Hokuyo Building 5th floor, Chuo-ku, Sapporo, 060-0042, Hokkaido, Japan   (100%)
Tel.: (81) 11 232 8961
Web Site:
    http://www.sapporohokuyocard.co.jp
Emp.: 78
Credit Card Processing Services
N.A.I.C.S.: 522320

Sapporo Hokuyo Lease Co., Ltd. (1)
3-11 Odori Nishi 6th floor of Hokuyo Building, Chuo-ku, Sapporo, 060-0042, Hokkaido, Japan   (100%)
Tel.: (81) 112317135
Web Site: http://www.shls.co.jp
Sales Range: $200-249.9 Million
Emp.: 98
Automobile & Industrial Equipments Leasing Services
N.A.I.C.S.: 532112
Fumio Wada *(Sr Mng Exec Officer)*

NORTH PEAK RESOURCES LTD.
421 7th Avenue S W 30th Floor, Calgary, T2P 4K9, AB, Canada
Tel.: (647) 424-2305   AB
Web Site:
    https://northpeakresources.com
Year Founded: 2011
B9TN—(DEU)
Rev.: $275,288
Assets: $10,692,047
Liabilities: $426,481
Net Worth: $10,265,566
Earnings: ($4,069,253)
Fiscal Year-end: 12/31/23
Investment Services
N.A.I.C.S.: 523999
Robert D. B. Suttie *(CFO)*

Subsidiaries:

North Peak (Nevada) Ltd. (1)
1201 Great Basin Blvd, Ely, NV 89301
Tel.: (775) 405-6764
Coal Mining Services
N.A.I.C.S.: 561730

Xinova, LLC (1)
311 1/2 Occidental Ave S Ste 300, Seattle, WA 98104
Tel.: (206) 800-2678
Web Site: http://www.xinova.com
Marketing Consulting Services
N.A.I.C.S.: 541613
Patrick J. Ennis *(CTO)*

NORTH PLAINS SYSTEMS INC.
600-310 Front Street West, Toronto, M5V 3B5, ON, Canada
Tel.: (416) 345-1900
Web Site: http://www.northplains.com
Digital Asset Management Services
N.A.I.C.S.: 513210
Mark Millar *(CFO)*

Subsidiaries:

Xinet, Inc. (1)
2560 9th St Ste 312, Berkeley, CA 94710
Tel.: (510) 845-0555
Web Site: http://www.xinet.com
Sales Range: $25-49.9 Million
Emp.: 95
Workflow Management Software Developer
N.A.I.C.S.: 513210
Julie Huang *(Mgr-PR)*

NORTH PRAIRIE DEVELOPMENTS LTD.
3030 Louise St, Saskatoon, S7T 0J1, SK, Canada
Tel.: (306) 931-2880
Web Site:
    http://www.northprairiehomes.com
Year Founded: 1987
Rev.: $12,626,965
Emp.: 9
Residential Construction
N.A.I.C.S.: 236115
Bernice Williams *(Founder)*

NORTH RIDGE DEVELOPMENT CORPORATION
3037 Faithfull Avenue, Saskatoon, S7K 8B3, SK, Canada
Tel.: (306) 242-2434
Web Site: http://www.northridge.sk.ca
Year Founded: 1982
Rev.: $34,891,283
Emp.: 110
Building Construction Services
N.A.I.C.S.: 236115

NORTH STAR FORD SALES
505 MacKenzie Blvd, Fort McMurray, T9H 4X3, AB, Canada
Tel.: (780) 791-7911
Web Site:
    http://www.northstarsale.dealer.com
Year Founded: 1995
Sales Range: $25-49.9 Million
Emp.: 80
New & Used Car Dealers
N.A.I.C.S.: 441110
Adeen Bunning *(VP-Sls)*

NORTH WATERLOO FARMERS MUTUAL INSURANCE COMPANY
100 Erb Street East, Waterloo, N2J 1L9, ON, Canada
Tel.: (519) 886-4530
Web Site: http://www.nwfm.com
Year Founded: 1874
Rev.: $55,700,000
Emp.: 100
Insurance Brokers
N.A.I.C.S.: 524298
Les Card *(VP & CFO)*

NORTHAM PLATINUM LIMITED
1st Floor Building 4 Maxwell Office Park Magwa Crescent West, Waterfall City Juskei View, Midrand, 2090, South Africa
Tel.: (27) 117596000   ZA
Web Site: http://www.northam.co.za
NHM—(JSE)
Rev.: $2,226,134,615
Assets: $2,589,387,178
Liabilities: $1,291,971,962
Net Worth: $1,297,415,215
Earnings: $640,199,224
Emp.: 15,358
Fiscal Year-end: 06/30/21

Platinum Ore Mining Services
N.A.I.C.S.: 212290
Paul A. Dunne *(CEO)*

NORTHAMBER PLC
23 Davis Road, Chessington, KT9 1HS, Surrey, United Kingdom
Tel.: (44) 2082967066
Web Site:
    https://www.northamber.com
NAR—(AIM)
Rev.: $89,962,527
Assets: $47,273,095
Liabilities: $14,075,483
Net Worth: $33,197,612
Earnings: ($606,901)
Emp.: 102
Fiscal Year-end: 06/30/22
Office Equipment Distr
N.A.I.C.S.: 423420
David Michael Phillips *(Founder & Chm)*

Subsidiaries:

Audio Visual Material Limited (1)
Ground Floor Front Suite 4 Elmwood-Crockford Lane Chineham Park, Basingstoke, United Kingdom
Tel.: (44) 1276418030
Web Site: https://avmltd.co.uk
Audio Visual Product Distr
N.A.I.C.S.: 423620

NORTHAMPTON GROUP INC.
5830 Campus Road Suite 100, Mississauga, L4V 1G2, ON, Canada
Tel.: (905) 362-9480   ON
Web Site:
    http://www.silverhotelgroup.com
Year Founded: 1974
Sales Range: $25-49.9 Million
Emp.: 20
Hotel Investment Holding Company
N.A.I.C.S.: 551112
Vinod N. Patel *(Pres & CEO)*

Subsidiaries:

Barons Motor Inn (1)
Highway 7 15, Carleton Place, K7C 3P3, ON, Canada
Tel.: (613) 257-4002
Web Site: http://www.baronsmotorinn.ca
Sales Range: $10-24.9 Million
Emp.: 2
Hotel Services
N.A.I.C.S.: 721110

Best Western (1)
730 Old Hespeler Road, Cambridge, N3H 5L8, ON, Canada
Tel.: (519) 623-4600
Web Site: http://www.bwcambridge.com
Sales Range: $10-24.9 Million
Emp.: 55
Hotel Services
N.A.I.C.S.: 721110
Lynda Campbell *(Gen Mgr)*

Best Western (1)
30 Clark Blvd, Brampton, L6W 1X3, ON, Canada
Tel.: (905) 454-1300
Web Site: http://www.bwbrampton.com
Sales Range: $10-24.9 Million
Emp.: 25
Hotel Services
N.A.I.C.S.: 721110
Satyen Pandey *(Gen Mgr)*

Comfort Hotel Airport North (1)
445 Rexdale Boulevard, Toronto, M9W 6K5, ON, Canada
Tel.: (416) 740-9500
Web Site: http://www.choicehotel.com
Sales Range: $10-24.9 Million
Emp.: 25
Hotel Services
N.A.I.C.S.: 721110

Comfort Hotel Toronto (1)
15 Charles Street East, Toronto, M4Y 1S1, ON, Canada
Tel.: (416) 924-1222

NORTHAMPTON GROUP INC.

Northampton Group Inc.—(Continued)
Web Site: http://www.choicehotels.ca
Sales Range: $10-24.9 Million
Emp.: 100
Hotel Services
N.A.I.C.S.: 721110

Country Inn & Suites (1)
578 Terry Fox Drive, Ottawa, K2L 4G1, ON, Canada
Tel.: (613) 599-7767
Web Site:
http://www.countryinnottawawest.com
Sales Range: $10-24.9 Million
Hotel Services
N.A.I.C.S.: 721110
Dave Fowler *(Gen Mgr)*

Holiday Inn - Princeton (1)
100 Independence Way, Princeton, NJ 08540
Tel.: (609) 520-1200
Web Site: http://www.hiprinceton.com
Sales Range: $10-24.9 Million
Emp.: 50
Hotel Services
N.A.I.C.S.: 721110
Victor Nelson *(Gen Mgr)*

Holiday Inn Express - Whitby (1)
180 Consumers Drive, Whitby, L1N 9S3, ON, Canada
Tel.: (905) 665-8400
Web Site: http://www.expresswhitby.com
Sales Range: $10-24.9 Million
Emp.: 30
Hotel Services
N.A.I.C.S.: 721110
Meg Brooke *(Mgr-Front Office)*

Northampton Inns (Oakville East) Inc. (1)
49 Goderich Road, Hamilton, L8E 4W8, ON, Canada
Tel.: (905) 578-1212
Sales Range: $10-24.9 Million
Emp.: 5
Home Management Services
N.A.I.C.S.: 721110

Northampton Inns (Oakville) Inc. (1)
2930 South Sheridan Way, Oakville, L6J 7T4, ON, Canada
Tel.: (905) 829-8020
Web Site: http://www.countryinns.com
Home Management Services
N.A.I.C.S.: 721110

Park Inn & Suites (1)
7300 Cote-de-Liesse, Dorval, H4T 1E7, QC, Canada
Tel.: (514) 733-8818
Web Site:
http://www.travelodgemontrealairport.com
Hotel Services
N.A.I.C.S.: 721110

Quality Hotel & Suites (1)
754 Bronte Road, Oakville, L6L 6R8, ON, Canada
Tel.: (905) 847-6667
Web Site: http://www.gooakville.com
Sales Range: $10-24.9 Million
Emp.: 17
Hotel Services
N.A.I.C.S.: 721110
Satish Palasseri *(Gen Mgr)*

Quality Inn Airport West (1)
50 Britannia Rd E, Mississauga, L4Z 2G2, ON, Canada
Tel.: (289) 277-2423
Web Site:
http://www.qualityinnairportwest.com
Sales Range: $10-24.9 Million
Emp.: 25
Hotel Services
N.A.I.C.S.: 721110
Melissa Guyadeen *(Gen Mgr)*

Radisson Plaza Hotel Admiral (1)
249 Queen's Quay W, Toronto, M5J 2N5, ON, Canada
Tel.: (437) 886-9667
Web Site: http://www.radisson.com
Sales Range: $10-24.9 Million
Emp.: 85
Hotel Services
N.A.I.C.S.: 721110

Dermot Mckeown *(Gen Mgr)*

Shihasi Investment Corporation (1)
5830 Campus Rd Ste 100, Mississauga, L4V 1G2, ON, Canada
Tel.: (905) 629-9992
Web Site: http://www.nhgi.com
Sales Range: $50-74.9 Million
Emp.: 3
Financial Management Services
N.A.I.C.S.: 523999
N. Patel *(CFO)*

Subsidiary (Domestic):

410613 Ontario Limited (2)
50 Britannia Rd E, Mississauga, L4Z 3W7, ON, Canada
Tel.: (905) 890-1200
Home Management Services
N.A.I.C.S.: 721110

NORTHBAZE GROUP AB

Northbaze Group AB Goteborgsvagen 89, 43130, Gothenburg, Sweden
Tel.: (46) 313380000
Web Site:
https://www.northbazegroup.com
Year Founded: 2006
NBZ—(OMX)
Rev.: $15,718,340
Assets: $17,052,085
Liabilities: $8,121,423
Net Worth: $8,930,662
Earnings: ($1,432,090)
Emp.: 277
Fiscal Year-end: 12/31/22
Audio Equipment Mfr
N.A.I.C.S.: 334310

Subsidiaries:

Krusell International AB (1)
Nellickevagen 22, 41263, Gothenburg, Sweden
Tel.: (46) 313380000
Web Site: https://krusell.se
Mobile Accessory Store Services
N.A.I.C.S.: 517122

NORTHCOAST BUILDING PRODUCTS LTD.

14682 66th Avenue, Surrey, V3S 1Z9, BC, Canada
Tel.: (604) 597-8884
Web Site:
http://www.northcoastlumber.com
Year Founded: 1954
Rev.: $17,388,990
Emp.: 30
Building Products Supplier
N.A.I.C.S.: 423390

NORTHCODERS GROUP PLC

Manchester Technology Centre 103 Oxford Road, Manchester, M1 7ED, United Kingdom
Tel.: (44) 3330504368   UK
Web Site:
https://www.northcoders.com
Year Founded: 2021
CODE—(AIM)
Rev.: $7,067,487
Assets: $9,260,191
Liabilities: $3,400,900
Net Worth: $5,859,291
Earnings: $453,848
Emp.: 101
Fiscal Year-end: 12/31/22
Software Development Services
N.A.I.C.S.: 541511

Subsidiaries:

Northcoders Limited (1)
Manchester Technology Centre 103 Oxford Road, Manchester, M1 7ED, United Kingdom
Tel.: (44) 3330504368
Web Site: https://northcoders.com
Software Development Training Services
N.A.I.C.S.: 611420

NORTHCORE RESOURCES INC.

620 St Jacques Suite 110, Montreal, H3C 1C7, QC, Canada
Tel.: (519) 697-6945
Web Site:
http://northcoreresources.com
Year Founded: 1999
Mineral Exploration Services
N.A.I.C.S.: 213114
Francois Desrosiers *(CEO)*

NORTHEAST ELECTRIC DEVELOPMENT COMPANY LIMITED

Internet Finance Building No 3 Guoxing Avenue, Meilan District, Haikou, 570203, Hainan, China
Tel.: (86) 89865315679   CN
Web Site: http://www.nee.com.cn
Year Founded: 1993
0042—(HKG)
Rev.: $18,306,297
Assets: $30,218,987
Liabilities: $55,887,331
Net Worth: ($25,668,344)
Earnings: $2,696,343
Emp.: 651
Fiscal Year-end: 12/31/21
Electrical Component Mfr & Distr
N.A.I.C.S.: 335999
Su Weiguo *(Chm & Pres)*

NORTHEAST PHARMACEUTICAL GROUP CO., LTD.

No 8 Kunminghu Street, Economic Technology Development District, Shenyang, 110027, Liaoning, China
Tel.: (86) 2425807953
Web Site: https://www.nepharm.com
Year Founded: 1946
000597—(SSE)
Rev.: $1,236,775,176
Assets: $1,938,970,332
Liabilities: $1,277,228,628
Net Worth: $661,741,704
Earnings: $49,159,656
Fiscal Year-end: 12/31/22
Pharmaceuticals Mfr
N.A.I.C.S.: 325412
Guo Jianmin *(Chm)*

NORTHEAST RUBBER PUBLIC COMPANY LIMITED

589/156 28th Floor Central City Tower Debaratana Road, Bang Na Nuea Sub-district Bang Na District, Bangkok, 10260, Thailand
Tel.: (66) 830097500
Web Site: https://www.nerubber.com
Year Founded: 2006
NER—(THA)
Rev.: $731,717,505
Assets: $491,566,937
Liabilities: $273,543,919
Net Worth: $218,023,017
Earnings: $337,038,853
Emp.: 442
Fiscal Year-end: 12/31/23
Natural Rubber Product Mfr
N.A.I.C.S.: 326299

NORTHEAST SECURITIES CO., LTD.

No 6666 Shengtai Avenue, Changchun, 130119, Jilin, China
Tel.: (86) 43185096806
Web Site: http://www.nesc.cn
Year Founded: 1993
000686—(SSE)
Rev.: $712,872,576
Assets: $11,077,415,388
Liabilities: $8,457,916,428
Net Worth: $2,619,498,960
Earnings: $32,423,976
Fiscal Year-end: 12/31/22

INTERNATIONAL PUBLIC

Securities Brokerage Services
N.A.I.C.S.: 523150
Fuchun Li *(Chm)*

NORTHEDGE CAPITAL LLP

13th Floor Number One Spinningfields 1 Hardman Square, Spinningfields, Manchester, M3 3EB, United Kingdom
Tel.: (44) 1618326654
Web Site: http://northedge.com
Year Founded: 2009
Investment Management Service
N.A.I.C.S.: 523940
Grant Berry *(Mng Partner)*

Subsidiaries:

Catalis SE (1)
Laan van Diepenvoorde 3, 5582 LA, Waalre, Netherlands
Tel.: (31) 402135930
Web Site: http://www.catalisgroup.com
Digital Media & Entertainment Outsourcing Services
N.A.I.C.S.: 512199
Dominic Wheatley *(CEO & Member-Mgmt Bd)*

Subsidiary (Non-US):

Kuju Limited (2)
63 Gee Street, London, EC1V 3RS, United Kingdom
Tel.: (44) 20 7593 2230
Gaming Software Development Services
N.A.I.C.S.: 541511

Testronic Laboratories Ltd (2)
Suffolk House Suites 1-3 2nd Floor George Street, Croydon, CR0 1PE, United Kingdom
Tel.: (44) 2070 421 700
Web Site: http://www.testroniclabs.com
Product Testing Services
N.A.I.C.S.: 541380
Mike Betti *(Chief Revenue Officer)*

FPE Global Limited (1)
Fairport House 28 Charles Street, Higher Hillgate, Stockport, SK1 3JR, United Kingdom
Tel.: (44) 161 477 4775
Web Site: http://www.fpeglobal.com
Sales Range: $10-24.9 Million
Emp.: 60
Developer & Mfr of Powder Processing Systems for Food, Chemicals, Plastics, Mineral & Pharmaceutical Industries
N.A.I.C.S.: 333310
Ben Howard *(Dir-Fin)*

Phoebus Software Limited (1)
Radcliffe House, Blenheim Court, Solihull, B91 2AA, United Kingdom
Tel.: (44) 8456187070
Web Site: http://www.phoebus.co.uk
Software Developer for Retail Banks & Mortgage Industry
N.A.I.C.S.: 513210
Paul Hunt *(CEO)*

NORTHERN BEAR PLC

A1 Grainger, Prestwick Park, Newcastle upon Tyne, NE20 9SJ, United Kingdom
Tel.: (44) 1661820369
Web Site:
https://www.northernbearplc.com
NTBR—(AIM)
Rev.: $86,583,263
Assets: $49,812,323
Liabilities: $21,788,623
Net Worth: $28,023,701
Earnings: $1,976,946
Emp.: 412
Fiscal Year-end: 03/31/23
Holding Company; Building Services
N.A.I.C.S.: 551112
Keith Soulsby *(Grp Dir-Ops)*

Subsidiaries:

Chirmarn Limited (1)
Newburn Bridge Road, Blaydon, NE21 4NT, Tyne and Wear, United Kingdom
Tel.: (44) 1914148000

AND PRIVATE COMPANIES

NORTHERN IRELAND TRANSPORT HOLDING COMPANY

Web Site: http://www.chirmarn.co.uk
Sales Range: $10-24.9 Million
Emp.: 40
Asbestos Collection & Removal Services
N.A.I.C.S.: 562910
Steve Hampton (Dir-Ops)

Isoler Limited (1)
Northern Bear House 333 Dukesway Court
Team Valley Trading Estate, Gateshead,
NE11 0BH, Tyne and Wear, United Kingdom
Tel.: (44) 1914870295
Web Site: http://www.isoler.co.uk
Sales Range: $25-49.9 Million
Emp.: 30
Building Integrity Services
N.A.I.C.S.: 236210
John Gilstin (Mng Dir)

MGM Limited (1)
Unit 333 Dukesway Court Team Valley
Trading Estate, Gateshead, NE11 0BH,
United Kingdom
Tel.: (44) 1914822100
Sales Range: $25-49.9 Million
Emp.: 80
Building Construction Services
N.A.I.C.S.: 236220

Springs Roofing Limited (1)
Kimblesworth Industrial Estate, Chester-le-Street, DH2 3QT, Durham, United Kingdom
Tel.: (44) 1913711923
Web Site: https://springs-roofing.ltd.uk
Sales Range: $25-49.9 Million
Emp.: 30
Roofing Services
N.A.I.C.S.: 238160
Julie Hall (Office Mgr)

Wensley Roofing Limited (1)
Station House Station Road, Chester-le-Street, DH3 3DU, Durham, United Kingdom
Tel.: (44) 1913871303
Web Site: https://www.wensleyroofing.co.uk
Sales Range: $25-49.9 Million
Emp.: 30
Roofing Services
N.A.I.C.S.: 238160
Keith Soulsby (Co-Mng Dir)

NORTHERN CEMENT COMPANY
Amman Abdali Boulevard AlWeibdeh
Rafic Hariri Avenue, PO Box 961186,
Photographers Square Building No
07 3rd Floor, Amman, 11196, Jordan
Tel.: (962) 62565650777
Web Site: https://www.njcco.net
NCCO—(AMM)
Rev.: $52,457,099
Assets: $124,641,684
Liabilities: $22,752,235
Net Worth: $101,889,449
Earnings: $8,821,068
Emp.: 158
Fiscal Year-end: 12/31/20
Cement Mfr
N.A.I.C.S.: 327310
Sulaiman Saleem Al Harbi (Chm)

NORTHERN DATA AG
An Der Welle 3, 60322, Frankfurt am Main, Germany
Tel.: (49) 6934875225
Web Site:
 https://www.northerndata.de
NB2—(DUS)
Rev.: $122,536,704
Assets: $1,142,602,936
Liabilities: $331,935,092
Net Worth: $810,667,844
Earnings: ($166,745,778)
Emp.: 145
Fiscal Year-end: 12/31/23
Information Technology Services
N.A.I.C.S.: 541512
Aroosh Thillainathan (CEO)

NORTHERN DRILLING LTD.
Par La Ville Place 14th Par La Ville Road, Hamilton, HM 08, Bermuda

Tel.: (441) 7469140012   BM
Web Site:
 http://www.northerndrillingltd.com
Year Founded: 2017
ND6—(DEU)
Rev.: $76,000
Assets: $234,460,000
Liabilities: $1,074,000
Net Worth: $233,386,000
Earnings: ($6,352,000)
Emp.: 1
Fiscal Year-end: 12/31/22
Drilling Services
N.A.I.C.S.: 238990
Scott McReaken (CEO)

NORTHERN DYNASTY MINERALS LTD.
14th Floor 1040 West Georgia Street, Vancouver, V6E 4H1, BC, Canada
Tel.: (604) 684-6365   BC
Web Site:
 https://www.northerndynasty.com
NAK—(NYSEAMEX)
Assets: $106,262,835
Liabilities: $15,190,958
Net Worth: $91,071,877
Earnings: ($15,510,083)
Emp.: 12
Fiscal Year-end: 12/31/23
Copper, Gold & Molybdenum Mining Services
N.A.I.C.S.: 212290
Ronald William Thiessen (Pres & CEO)

Subsidiaries:

Pebble Limited Partnership (1)
Tel.: (907) 339-2600
Web Site: http://www.pebblepartnership.com
Industrial & Mining Engineering Services
N.A.I.C.S.: 541330

NORTHERN FINANCIAL CORPORATION
145 King St Ste 2020, Toronto, M5H 1J8, ON, Canada
Tel.: (416) 644-8180
Web Site: http://www.nfc.ca
Sales Range: $25-49.9 Million
Emp.: 40
Financial Advisory Services
N.A.I.C.S.: 523940
Vic Alboini (Chm & CEO)

Subsidiaries:

Jura Energy Corporation (1)
Tel.: (403) 266-6364
Web Site: https://www.juraenergy.com
Rev.: $9,096,247
Assets: $22,031,768
Liabilities: $18,451,132
Net Worth: $3,580,636
Earnings: ($4,638,324)
Fiscal Year-end: 12/31/2023
Oil & Gas Exploration
N.A.I.C.S.: 211120
Timothy M. Elliott (Chm)

NORTHERN FRONTIER CORP.
400 435 - 4th Avenue SW, Calgary, T2P 3A8, AB, Canada
Tel.: (587) 293-7231   AB
Web Site: http://www.nfcorp.ca
Year Founded: 2011
FFF—(TSXV)
Sales Range: $25-49.9 Million
Investment Services
N.A.I.C.S.: 523999
Trevor Haynes (Chm)

Subsidiaries:

Northern Frontier Facilities LP (1)
209 Pembina Road, Sherwood Park, T8H 2W8, AB, Canada
Tel.: (780) 467-4409
Construction Engineering Services
N.A.I.C.S.: 541330

Mike McClocklin (Sr Project Mgr)

NORTHERN GENERAL INSURANCE CO. LTD.
WW Tower 68, Motijheel,Commercial Area Level 12 & 13, Dhaka, 1000, Bangladesh
Tel.: (880) 29559077
Web Site: http://www.ngicl.com
Year Founded: 1996
Sales Range: Less than $1 Million
Emp.: 585
Insurance Services
N.A.I.C.S.: 524298
Mohiuddin Ahmed (Mng Dir)

NORTHERN GRAPHITE CORPORATION
1000 Innovation Drive Suite 500, Ottawa, K2K 3E7, ON, Canada
Tel.: (613) 271-2124   ON
Web Site:
 https://www.northerngraphite.com
Year Founded: 2002
NGC—(OTCIQ)
Rev.: $9,078
Assets: $11,908,400
Liabilities: $433,120
Net Worth: $11,475,279
Earnings: ($679,122)
Fiscal Year-end: 12/31/20
Graphite Mining Services
N.A.I.C.S.: 212390
Gregory B. Bowes (CEO)

NORTHERN HEAVY INDUSTRIES GROUP CO. LTD.
No 16 Kaifa Road Economic & Technological Development Zone, Shenyang, 110141, China
Tel.: (86) 24 25802222
Web Site: http://www.china-sz.com
Tunnel Boring Machine Mfr
N.A.I.C.S.: 333120

Subsidiaries:

The Robbins Company (1)
29100 Hall St, Solon, OH 44139
Tel.: (440) 248-3303
Web Site:
 http://www.therobbinscompany.com
Underground Construction Machinery Mfr
N.A.I.C.S.: 333120
Lok Home (Pres)

Subsidiary (Non-US):

Robbins (Asia Pacific), Ltd. (2)
Room 4525 45/F The Lee Garden No 33 Hysan Road, Causeway Bay, Hong Kong, China (Hong Kong)
Tel.: (852) 36918611
Web Site:
 http://www.therobbinscompany.com
Underground Construction Machinery Mfr
N.A.I.C.S.: 333120

Robbins (China) Underground Equipment Co., Ltd. (2)
No 295 Bixi Road, Shanghai, 200245, Minhang District, China
Tel.: (86) 21 3402 3238
Web Site:
 http://www.therobbinscompany.com
Underground Construction Machinery Mfr
N.A.I.C.S.: 333120
Biyue Li (VP-Far East Ops)

Robbins Asia Pacific Pte Ltd (2)
No. 3 Upper Aljunied Link Joo Seng Warehouse 07-05, Singapore, 367902, Singapore
Tel.: (65) 962698833
Web Site:
 http://www.therobbinscompany.com
Underground Construction Machinery Mfr
N.A.I.C.S.: 333120
Chao Liu (Mgr)

Robbins Asia Pacific Pty Ltd. (2)
PO Box 480, Wynnum, Brisbane, 4178, QLD, Australia

Tel.: (61) 447050509
Web Site:
 http://www.therobbinscompany.com
Underground Construction Machinery Mfr & Distr
N.A.I.C.S.: 333120

Robbins Chile & Robbins Brazil (2)
Padre Mariano 391 Office 1003, Santiago, Chile
Tel.: (56) 22 4029622
Web Site:
 http://www.therobbinscompany.com
Underground Construction Machinery Mfr
N.A.I.C.S.: 333120
Carlos Lang (Mgr)

Robbins Europe GmbH (2)
Weilheimer Str 34, 73119, Zell, Germany
Tel.: (49) 7164 14940 10
Web Site:
 http://www.therobbinscompany.com
Underground Construction Machinery Mfr
N.A.I.C.S.: 333120
Martin Eckert (Gen Mgr)

Robbins Hispania S.L. (2)
c/ Garcia de Paredes 64 dcha, 28010, Madrid, Spain
Tel.: (34) 91 4445450
Web Site:
 http://www.therobbinscompany.com
Underground Construction Machinery Mfr
N.A.I.C.S.: 333120

Robbins Mexico (2)
Av Patriotism No 229, Col San Pedro de los Pinos, Mexico, 03800, Mexico
Tel.: (52) 55 36 91 7000
Web Site:
 http://www.therobbinscompany.com
Underground Construction Machinery Mfr
N.A.I.C.S.: 333120
Roberto Gonzales (Mgr)

Robbins Norway (2)
Nils Bays Vei 78, 0855, Oslo, Norway
Tel.: (47) 48298792
Web Site:
 http://www.therobbinscompany.com
Underground Construction Machinery Mfr
N.A.I.C.S.: 333120
Sindre Log (Product Mgr)

Robbins TBM Korea (2)
1620 Rosedeil Officetel, 280 Gwangpeongro Kangnamgu, Seoul, 06367, Korea (South)
Tel.: (82) 2 3667 7866
Web Site:
 http://www.therobbinscompany.com
Underground Construction Machinery Mfr
N.A.I.C.S.: 333120
Hoon Kim (Mgr)

Robbins Tunneling and Trenchless Technology (India) Pvt. Ltd. (2)
Suite 8 3rd Floor Yashwant Place, New Delhi, 110021, Chanakyapuri, India
Tel.: (91) 11 24105300
Web Site:
 http://www.therobbinscompany.com
Underground Construction Machinery Mfr
N.A.I.C.S.: 333120

Roboretec (2)
71 A Viilor Str, Mogosoaia, 077135, Romania
Tel.: (40) 21 350 43 75
Web Site:
 http://www.therobbinscompany.com
Underground Construction Machinery Mfr
N.A.I.C.S.: 333120
Sorin Badita (Mgr)

Plant (Domestic):

The Robbins Company - Washington Facility (2)
5866 S 194th St, Kent, WA 98032
Tel.: (253) 872-0500
Web Site: http://www.robbinstbm.com
Tunneling Equipment Mfr
N.A.I.C.S.: 333120

NORTHERN IRELAND TRANSPORT HOLDING COMPANY
22 Great Victoria Street, Belfast, BT2 7LX, United Kingdom

5443

NORTHERN IRELAND TRANSPORT HOLDING COMPANY

Northern Ireland Transport Holding Company—(Continued)
Tel.: (44) 2890666630
Web Site: http://www.translink.co.uk
Year Founded: 1995
Rev.: $302,640,966
Assets: $1,043,032,918
Liabilities: $1,198,632,537
Net Worth: ($155,599,618)
Earnings: ($21,940,087)
Emp.: 4,202
Fiscal Year-end: 03/31/19
Public Transport Services
N.A.I.C.S.: 488210
Philip O'neill *(Chief Bus Change Officer)*

Subsidiaries:

Metro (1)
Short Strand, Belfast, BT5 4BH, Northern Ireland, United Kingdom
Tel.: (44) 2890458345
Web Site: http://www.translink.co.uk
Sales Range: $200-249.9 Million
Emp.: 1,000
Bus Transportation
N.A.I.C.S.: 485210

NI Railways (1)
Central Station, East Bridge St, Belfast, BT1 3PB, Northern Ireland, United Kingdom
Tel.: (44) 2890899400
Sales Range: $50-74.9 Million
Emp.: 100
Railway Transportation
N.A.I.C.S.: 485112

Ulsterbus (1)
Central Station, Bridge Street, Belfast, BT1 3PB, Northern Ireland, United Kingdom
Tel.: (44) 2890899400
Web Site: http://www.ulsterbus.co.uk
Bus Transportation
N.A.I.C.S.: 485210

NORTHERN JUTE MANUFACTURING COMPANY LIMITED

DH Tower Level-14 06 Panthapath, Dhaka, 1215, Bangladesh
Tel.: (880) 255013506
Web Site:
https://www.northernjute.com
Year Founded: 1980
NORTHERN—(DHA)
Rev.: $6,369,597
Assets: $10,631,709
Liabilities: $8,602,670
Net Worth: $2,029,039
Earnings: $281,458
Emp.: 529
Fiscal Year-end: 06/30/20
Jute Yarn Mfr
N.A.I.C.S.: 313110
Uzzal Kumar Nandi *(Chm)*

NORTHERN LIGHT

Assembly Street, Edinburgh, EH6 7RG, United Kingdom
Tel.: (44) 1316229100
Web Site:
http://www.northernlight.co.uk
Year Founded: 1971
Rev.: $12,310,249
Emp.: 80
Electrical Contractor Services
N.A.I.C.S.: 238210
Colin Cuthbert *(Mng Dir)*

NORTHERN LIGHTS RESOURCES CORP.

Suite 1000 355 Burrard Street, Vancouver, V6C 2G8, BC, Canada
Tel.: (604) 602-7166 BC
Web Site:
http://www.northernlights.com
Year Founded: 2007
Metal Mining
N.A.I.C.S.: 212290
Albert Timcke *(Pres & CEO)*

NORTHERN LION GOLD CORP.

488 - 650 Howe St, Vancouver, V6C 2T6, BC, Canada
Tel.: (604) 669-2701
Web Site:
https://www.northernliongold.com
NLGCF—(OTCIQ)
Assets: $849,904
Liabilities: $446,249
Net Worth: $403,655
Earnings: ($161,699)
Fiscal Year-end: 12/31/22
Mineral Exploration Services
N.A.I.C.S.: 213114
Luke Norman *(Pres & CEO)*

NORTHERN MICRO

3155 Swansea Cres, Ottawa, K1G 3J3, ON, Canada
Tel.: (613) 226-1117
Web Site:
http://www.northernmicro.com
Year Founded: 1985
Rev.: $39,469,150
Emp.: 71
IT Solutions & Services
N.A.I.C.S.: 541511

NORTHERN MINERALS LIMITED

Ground Floor 40 Kings Park Road, West Perth, 6005, WA, Australia
Tel.: (61) 894812344
Web Site:
https://www.northernminerals.com
NTU—(ASX)
Rev.: $9,270,969
Assets: $28,936,149
Liabilities: $6,718,824
Net Worth: $22,217,325
Earnings: ($6,534,312)
Emp.: 56
Fiscal Year-end: 06/30/21
Rare Earth Elements Developer & Producer
N.A.I.C.S.: 213115
Robin Wilson *(Mgr)*

NORTHERN PARKLIFE AB

St Goransgatan 66, 112 33, Stockholm, Sweden
Tel.: (46) 84575000
Web Site: http://www.northern.net
Year Founded: 1995
Sales Range: $25-49.9 Million
Emp.: 20
Data Storage Software Publisher
N.A.I.C.S.: 513210
Jonas Areskoug *(CEO)*

Subsidiaries:

NORTHERN PARKLIFE FRANCE SAS (1)
26-28 rue de Londres, 75009, Paris, France
Tel.: (33) 1 78 42 37 59
Software Development Services
N.A.I.C.S.: 541511

Northern Parklife (1)
Via Pio Vii 168, 10127, Turin, Italy
Tel.: (39) 011 19 82 48 45
Software Development Services
N.A.I.C.S.: 541511

Northern Parklife, Inc. (1)
301 Edgewater Pl Ste 100, Wakefield, MA 01880
Tel.: (781) 968-5424
Web Site: http://www.northern.net
Sales Range: $25-49.9 Million
Emp.: 6
Data Storage Software Publisher
N.A.I.C.S.: 513210
Gunnar Bohlin *(VP-Ops)*

NORTHERN POTASH CO.

Olminskogo street 3 office 728, Moscow, Russia
Tel.: (7) 2025967782
Year Founded: 2004
NPTH—(OTCIQ)
Sales Range: Less than $1 Million
Chemical Products Mfr
N.A.I.C.S.: 325320

NORTHERN RECRUITMENT GROUP PLC

Lloyds Ct 56 Grey St, Newcastle upon Tyne, NE1 6AH, United Kingdom
Tel.: (44) 1912321222 UK
Web Site: http://www.nrgplc.com
Year Founded: 1976
Sales Range: $25-49.9 Million
Emp.: 139
Corporate Recruitment Services
N.A.I.C.S.: 561311
Lorna Moran *(Founder & Chm)*

NORTHERN REGION CEMENT COMPANY

Eastern Ring Road Exit 8 Business Gate Building 17B Ground Floor, PO Box 61011, 11565, Riyadh, 11565, Saudi Arabia
Tel.: (966) 112011212
Web Site: https://www.nrc.com.sa
3004—(SAU)
Rev.: $164,766,877
Assets: $909,643,791
Liabilities: $314,235,149
Net Worth: $595,408,642
Earnings: $29,983,008
Emp.: 498
Fiscal Year-end: 12/31/22
Cement Mfr
N.A.I.C.S.: 327310
Suleiman Salim Al Harbi *(Chm)*

NORTHERN SHIELD RESOURCES INC.

150 Elgin Street 10th Floor, Ottawa, K2P 1L4, ON, Canada
Tel.: (613) 232-0459
Web Site: https://www.northern-shield.com
Year Founded: 1999
N9SA—(DEU)
Assets: $4,544,712
Liabilities: $616,648
Net Worth: $3,928,064
Earnings: ($748,499)
Fiscal Year-end: 12/31/23
Mineral Exploration Services
N.A.I.C.S.: 213114
James O'Sullivan *(Sec)*

NORTHERN SOFT DRINKS & MINERAL WATER CO.

Mousel 3rd Bridge Al-Watheq Sequare, Baghdad, Iraq
Tel.: (964) 1 7173240
Year Founded: 1989
Soft Drinks Mfr
N.A.I.C.S.: 312111

NORTHERN SPHERE MINING CORP.

69 Yonge Street Suite 1010, Toronto, M5E 1K3, ON, Canada
Tel.: (416) 427-0382 BC
Web Site:
http://www.northernsphere.com
Year Founded: 2011
Sales Range: Less than $1 Million
Gold & Silver Mining Services
N.A.I.C.S.: 212220
Kelly Malcolm *(CEO-Interim)*

NORTHERN SPIRITS LTD.

Woodburn Central 5-A Woodburn Park Road Suite No 603 6th Floor, Kolkata, 700020, India
Tel.: (91) 3335446094

INTERNATIONAL PUBLIC

Web Site:
https://www.northernspirits.co.in
Year Founded: 1975
542628—(BOM)
Rev.: $108,585,948
Assets: $21,911,264
Liabilities: $11,907,536
Net Worth: $10,003,729
Earnings: $1,334,896
Emp.: 66
Fiscal Year-end: 03/31/23
Alcoholic Beverage Distr
N.A.I.C.S.: 424820
Anuj Bakshi *(Chm)*

NORTHERN STAR RESOURCES LTD

Level 4 500 Hay Street, Subiaco, 6008, WA, Australia
Tel.: (61) 861882100
Web Site: https://www.nsrltd.com
NESRF—(OTCIQ)
Rev.: $3,286,057,679
Assets: $8,734,508,511
Liabilities: $2,864,516,548
Net Worth: $5,869,991,963
Earnings: $426,348,823
Emp.: 840
Fiscal Year-end: 06/30/24
Support Activities for Nonmetallic Minerals (except Fuels) Mining
N.A.I.C.S.: 213115
Stuart Tonkin *(CEO & Mng Dir)*

Subsidiaries:

Kalgoorlie Consolidated Gold Mines Pty Ltd (1)
Black Street, PMB 27, Kalgoorlie, 6433, WA, Australia
Tel.: (61) 890221100
Web Site: http://www.superpit.com.au
Emp.: 1,100
Construction Contracting Services
N.A.I.C.S.: 236220

Saracen Mineral Holdings Limited (1)
Level 11 40 The Esplanade, Perth, 6000, WA, Australia
Tel.: (61) 8 6229 9100
Web Site: http://www.saracen.com.au
Gold & Other Metal Ore Mining Services
N.A.I.C.S.: 212220
Jeremy Ryan *(Sec & Mgr-Legal)*

Subsidiary (Domestic):

Bligh Resources Limited (2)
Unit 5 78 Marine Terrace, Fremantle, 6160, WA, Australia
Tel.: (61) 893363388
Web Site: http://www.bligh-resources.com
Sales Range: Less than $1 Million
Manganese Mining
N.A.I.C.S.: 212290
Lloyd Flint *(Sec)*

Stone Boy Inc. (1)
Tel.: (646) 480-0747
Web Site: http://www.stoneboy.co
Construction Consulting Services
N.A.I.C.S.: 541330
Aditya Arya *(Founder & Mng Dir)*

NORTHERN SUN MINING CORP.

130 Adelaide Street W Suite 3420, Toronto, M5H 3P5, ON, Canada
Tel.: (647) 494-3814 ON
Web Site:
http://www.northernsunmining.ca
Year Founded: 1997
Sales Range: $1-9.9 Million
Metal Exploration Services
N.A.I.C.S.: 212290
James Xiang *(Pres & CEO)*

NORTHERN SUPERIOR RESOURCES INC.

1410-120 Adelaide Street West, Sudbury, M5H 1T1, ON, Canada

AND PRIVATE COMPANIES

Tel.: (705) 525-0992
Web Site: https://www.nsuperior.com
SUP—(OTCIQ)
Rev.: $24,110
Assets: $14,970,930
Liabilities: $1,651,647
Net Worth: $13,319,284
Earnings: ($782,277)
Fiscal Year-end: 12/31/20
Gold Exploration Services
N.A.I.C.S.: 212220
Thomas F. Morris *(Pres & CEO)*

Subsidiaries:

Genesis Metals Corp. (1)
1020 - 800 West Pender Street, Vancouver, V6C 2V6, BC, Canada
Tel.: (604) 484-7855
Web Site:
  http://www.genesismetalscorp.com
Rev.: $721,958
Assets: $3,808,873
Liabilities: $678,836
Net Worth: $3,130,037
Earnings: ($2,458,813)
Fiscal Year-end: 03/31/2021
Gold Mining Services
N.A.I.C.S.: 212220
Jeff Sundar *(Exec Dir)*

NORTHERN TEXTILES & GARMENTS JOINT STOCK COMPANY

79 Lac Trung Street Vnh Tuy Ward, Hai Ba Trung District, Hanoi, Vietnam
Tel.: (84) 39360808
TET—(HNX)
Rev.: $2,299,800
Assets: $11,451,700
Liabilities: $550,700
Net Worth: $10,901,000
Earnings: $975,700
Fiscal Year-end: 12/31/22
Textile Product Mfr & Whslr
N.A.I.C.S.: 313310
Thuy Thi Dieu Nguyen *(Chm-Mgmt Bd)*

NORTHERN TRUST GROUP LTD.

Lynton House Ackhurst Park Foxhole Road, Chorley, PR7 1NY, United Kingdom
Tel.: (44) 1257 238555 UK
Web Site:
  http://www.northerntrust.co.uk
Year Founded: 1962
Rev.: $59,897,744
Assets: $690,598,146
Liabilities: $348,521,115
Net Worth: $342,077,031
Earnings: $36,990,664
Emp.: 1,200
Fiscal Year-end: 03/31/19
Holding Company
N.A.I.C.S.: 551112
John Tootell *(Mgr-Plng)*

Subsidiaries:

Britannia Jinky Jersey Limited (1)
Ainsdale House Shore Road, Ainsdale, Southport, PR8 2PZ, United Kingdom (100%)
Tel.: (44) 8712220201
Web Site: http://www.pontins.com
Sales Range: $10-24.9 Million
Emp.: 70
Short-Break Holiday & Leisure Company
N.A.I.C.S.: 721199

NORTHERN UNITED PUBLISHING & MEDIA (GROUP) COMPANY LIMITED

No 29 Shiyiwei Road, Heping District, Shenyang, 110003, Liaoning, China
Tel.: (86) 2423285500
Web Site: http://www.nupmg.com
Year Founded: 2006

601999—(SHG)
Rev.: $366,606,541
Assets: $590,208,143
Liabilities: $241,666,547
Net Worth: $348,541,596
Earnings: $10,581,751
Fiscal Year-end: 12/31/22
Books Publishing Services
N.A.I.C.S.: 513130
Zhang Dongping *(Chm)*

Subsidiaries:

Volumes Publishing company (1)
907 Frederick Street, Kitchener, N2B 2B9, ON, Canada
Tel.: (519) 571-1908
Books Publishing Services
N.A.I.C.S.: 513130

NORTHERN URANIUM CORP.

203-1634 Harvey Ave, Kelowna, V1Y 6G2, BC, Canada
Tel.: (250) 448-4110 Ca
Web Site:
  http://www.northernuranium.com
Year Founded: 2005
UNO.H—(TSXV)
Assets: $1,472
Liabilities: $727,443
Net Worth: ($725,970)
Earnings: ($70,370)
Fiscal Year-end: 12/31/23
Metal Ore Mining Services
N.A.I.C.S.: 212290
Chad Ulansky *(Pres & CEO)*

NORTHERN VERTEX MINING CORP.

1188 West Georgia St Suite 1920, Vancouver, V6E 4A2, BC, Canada
Tel.: (604) 601-3656
Web Site: https://elevationgold.com
54NA—(DEU)
Rev.: $66,356,000
Assets: $106,764,000
Liabilities: $73,209,000
Net Worth: $33,555,000
Earnings: ($22,544,000)
Fiscal Year-end: 12/31/23
Precious Metal Exploration & Mining Services
N.A.I.C.S.: 212220
Douglas J. Hurst *(Chm & CEO)*

Subsidiaries:

Eclipse Gold Mining Corporation (1)
1400-400 Burrard Street, Vancouver, V6C 3A6, BC, Canada
Tel.: (604) 628-1033
Web Site: http://www.eclipsegoldmining.com
Assets: $10,811,135
Liabilities: $433,080
Net Worth: $10,378,055
Earnings: ($2,222,655)
Mineral Exploration Services
N.A.I.C.S.: 213115
Marcel De Groot *(Chm)*

Golden Vertex Corp. (1)
2011 Plata Caleta, Bullhead City, AZ 86442
Tel.: (928) 763-6252
Gold Mining Services
N.A.I.C.S.: 212220

NORTHFIELD CAPITAL CORPORATION

141 Adelaide St West Suite 301, Toronto, M5H 3L5, ON, Canada
Tel.: (416) 628-5901
Web Site:
  https://www.northfieldcapital.com
NFD.A—(TSXV)
Rev.: $5,133,993
Assets: $59,199,720
Liabilities: $11,925,046
Net Worth: $47,274,674
Earnings: ($6,130,876)
Fiscal Year-end: 12/31/23
Investment Services

N.A.I.C.S.: 523999
Robert D. Cudney *(Founder, Pres & CEO)*

Subsidiaries:

Spirit of York Distillery Inc. (1)
12 Trinity Street, Toronto, M5A 3C4, ON, Canada
Tel.: (416) 777-0001
Web Site: http://www.spiritofyork.com
Spirit Mfr
N.A.I.C.S.: 312140
Germain Gerry Guitor *(Pres & CEO)*

NORTHFIELD GLASS GROUP INC.

230 High Street, Moncton, E1C 6C2, NB, Canada
Tel.: (506) 877-0243
Web Site:
  http://www.economyglass.ca
Rev.: $17,236,825
Emp.: 250
Windows & Doors Mfr
N.A.I.C.S.: 321911

NORTHILL CAPITAL LLP

1 Curzon Street, London, W1J 5HD, United Kingdom
Tel.: (44) 20 7016 4040 UK
Web Site: http://www.northill.com
Year Founded: 2010
Emp.: 1
Private Equity & Venture Capital Firm
N.A.I.C.S.: 523999
Jonathan Little *(Founder & Partner)*

Subsidiaries:

Alpha Strategic PLC (1)
15-17 Grosvenor Gardens, London, SW1W 0BD, United Kingdom (51%)
Tel.: (44) 2072223005
Web Site: http://www.alphastrategic.co.uk
Sales Range: Less than $1 Million
Emp.: 7
Investment Services
N.A.I.C.S.: 523999
Nicola Howe *(Sec)*

Longview Partners (Guernsey) Ltd (1)
Sarnia House Le Truchot, PO Box 559, Saint Peter Port, GY1 6JG, Guernsey
Tel.: (44) 1481 712414
Web Site: http://www.longview-partners.com
Investment Management Service
N.A.I.C.S.: 523940
Peter Crook *(Chm)*

Northill Distribution US Inc. (1)
54 W 40th St, New York, NY 10018
Tel.: (646) 854-3384
Investment Management Service
N.A.I.C.S.: 523940

Riverbridge Partners, LLC (1)
1200 IDS Center 80 S Eighth St, Minneapolis, MN 55402
Tel.: (612) 904-6200
Web Site: http://www.riverbridge.com
Sales Range: $1-4.9 Billion
Emp.: 35
Investment Advisory & Portfolio Management Services
N.A.I.C.S.: 523940
Mark A. Thompson *(Co-Founder & Chief Investment Officer)*

Strategic Investment Group (1)
1001 Nineteenth St N 16th Fl, Arlington, VA 22209
Tel.: (703) 243-4433
Web Site: http://www.strategicgroup.com
Securities Brokerage
N.A.I.C.S.: 523150
Nikki Kraus *(Mng Dir & Head-Client Dev-Global)*

NORTHISLE COPPER AND GOLD INC.

14th Floor 1040 West Georgia Street, Vancouver, V6E 4H1, BC, Canada
Tel.: (604) 638-2515 BC

NORTHLAND POWER INC.

Web Site: https://www.northisle.ca
Year Founded: 2011
0N4—(DEU)
Rev.: $136,394
Assets: $13,593,616
Liabilities: $1,040,259
Net Worth: $12,553,357
Earnings: ($4,038,844)
Emp.: 12
Fiscal Year-end: 12/31/23
Copper & Gold Mining Services
N.A.I.C.S.: 212230
Dale Corman *(Chm)*

NORTHKING INFORMATION TECHNOLOGY CO., LTD.

7th Floor Qingzheng Building No 25 West Third Ring Road North, Haidian, Beijing, 100081, China
Tel.: (86) 1082652688
Web Site: https://www.northking.net
Year Founded: 2009
002987—(SSE)
Rev.: $467,943,175
Assets: $370,500,083
Liabilities: $68,195,303
Net Worth: $302,304,779
Earnings: $35,331,758
Fiscal Year-end: 12/31/21
Information Technology Services
N.A.I.C.S.: 541512
Zhenyong Fei *(Chm & Gen Mgr)*

NORTHLAND CHRYSLER JEEP DODGE

2844 Recplace Drive, Prince George, V2N 0B2, BC, Canada
Tel.: (250) 562-5254
Web Site:
  http://www.northlanddodge.ca
Year Founded: 1984
Sales Range: $25-49.9 Million
New & Used Car Dealers
N.A.I.C.S.: 441110
Kyle Bachman *(Principal-Dealer)*

NORTHLAND FORD SALES LTD.

Highway 10 South, The Pas, R9A 1K9, MB, Canada
Tel.: (204) 623-4350
Web Site:
  http://www.northlandford.dealer.com
Rev.: $22,817,200
Emp.: 150
New & Used Car Dealers
N.A.I.C.S.: 441110
Keith Young *(Gen Mgr)*

NORTHLAND POWER INC.

30 St Clair Avenue West 3th Floor, Toronto, M4V 3A1, ON, Canada
Tel.: (416) 962-6262
Web Site:
  https://www.northlandpower.com
NPIFF—(OTCIQ)
Rev.: $1,649,389,820
Assets: $10,065,965,871
Liabilities: $6,754,505,430
Net Worth: $3,311,460,442
Earnings: ($71,014,257)
Emp.: 1,344
Fiscal Year-end: 12/31/23
Holding Company
N.A.I.C.S.: 551112
John W. Brace *(Chm)*

Subsidiaries:

Iroquois Falls Power Corp. (1)
1 NW Industrial Road, Iroquois Falls, P0K 1E0, ON, Canada
Tel.: (705) 258-4410
Web Site: http://www.northlandpower.com
Sales Range: $75-99.9 Million
Cogeneration Power Plant Services
N.A.I.C.S.: 221118

5445

NORTHLAND POWER INC.

Northland Power Inc.—(Continued)

Kingston CoGen Limited Partnership (1)
5146 Taylor Kidd Blvd, Bath, K0H 1G0, ON, Canada (100%)
Tel.: (613) 384-4388
Sales Range: $10-24.9 Million
Emp.: 20
Gas Powered Electrical Power Producer
N.A.I.C.S.: 335311
Steve Collings (Gen Mgr)

Kirkland Lake Power Corp. (1)
505 Archers Drive, Kirkland Lake, P2N 3M7, ON, Canada
Tel.: (705) 567-9501
Electric Power Services
N.A.I.C.S.: 221118

Nordsee One GmbH (1)
Willinghusener Weg 3, 22113, Oststeinbek, Germany
Tel.: (49) 4046666620
Web Site: https://www.nordseeone.com
Wind Electric Power Services
N.A.I.C.S.: 221115

North Battleford Power L.P. (1)
Balan Hall Road, North Battleford, S9A 3E6, SK, Canada
Tel.: (306) 937-3823
Electric Power Services
N.A.I.C.S.: 221118

Northland Power Preferred Equity Inc. (1)
30 St Clair Avenue West 12th Floor, Toronto, M4V 3A1, ON, Canada
Tel.: (416) 962-6262
Sales Range: $50-74.9 Million
Emp.: 85
Gas Operations
N.A.I.C.S.: 213112

Spy Hill Power L.P. (1)
PO Box 1419, Esterhazy, S0A 0X0, SK, Canada
Tel.: (306) 643-2025
Electric Power Services
N.A.I.C.S.: 221118

Thorold CoGen L.P. (1)
90 Allanburg Road, Thorold, L2V 3Y7, ON, Canada
Tel.: (905) 680-5426
Electric Power Services
N.A.I.C.S.: 221118

NORTHLAND PROPERTIES CORPORATION
310 - 1755 West Broadway, Vancouver, V6J 4S5, BC, Canada
Tel.: (604) 730-6610
Web Site: https://www.northland.ca
Year Founded: 1963
Sales Range: $150-199.9 Million
Emp.: 10,000
Hotel Operator
N.A.I.C.S.: 721110
Bob Gaglardi (Founder)

NORTHLANDER INDUSTRIES
165 Thames Road East Hwy 83, Exeter, N0M 1S3, ON, Canada
Tel.: (519) 235-1530
Web Site: http://www.northlanderindustry.com
Year Founded: 1964
Emp.: 120
Mobile Homes Designing & Building Services
N.A.I.C.S.: 459930

NORTHLEAF CAPITAL PARTNERS LTD.
79 Wellington Street West 6th Floor, PO Box 120, Toronto, M5K 1N9, ON, Canada
Web Site: http://www.northleafcapital.com
Year Founded: 1969
Privater Equity Firm
N.A.I.C.S.: 523999

Stuart Waugh (Mng Partner & Mng Dir)

NORTHLINE FREIGHT PTY LTD
Level 1 62 The Parade, Norwood, 5067, SA, Australia
Tel.: (61) 882737300
Web Site: http://www.northlinefreight.com.au
Year Founded: 1983
Sales Range: $50-74.9 Million
Long-Haul Freight Transportation Management & Services
N.A.I.C.S.: 484121
Craige Whitton (CEO)

NORTHLINK FISCAL & CAPITAL SERVICES LIMITED
86 Mall Road, Ludhiana, 141 001, Punjab, India
Tel.: (91) 1612449890
Web Site: https://www.northlink.co.in
NFCSL—(NSE)
Rev.: $60,122
Assets: $779,170
Liabilities: $58,711
Net Worth: $720,459
Earnings: $6,989
Emp.: 6
Fiscal Year-end: 03/31/23
Financial Support Services
N.A.I.C.S.: 523999
Sunil Dutt Maria (CEO)

NORTHPOWER LIMITED
28 Mt Pleasant Road, Whangarei, 0110, Raumanga, New Zealand
Tel.: (64) 94301803
Web Site: http://www.northpower.com
Rev.: $277,110,509
Assets: $489,012,032
Liabilities: $228,321,326
Net Worth: $260,690,706
Earnings: $19,026,897
Emp.: 1,200
Fiscal Year-end: 03/31/22
Electronic Services
N.A.I.C.S.: 221122
Nikki P. Davies-Colley (Chm)

NORTHSTAR ADVISORS PTE. LTD.
6 Battery Road Unit #35-05, Singapore, 049909, Singapore
Tel.: (65) 6533 3210
Web Site: http://www.nsgroup.com
Year Founded: 2003
Emp.: 50
Privater Equity Firm
N.A.I.C.S.: 523999
Patrick Walujo (Co-Founder & Mng Partner)

Subsidiaries:

INNOVALUES Pte Ltd (1)
Blk 9 #07-08/12 Kallang Place, Singapore, 339154, Singapore
Tel.: (65) 6298 2374
Web Site: http://www.innovalues.com
Precision Machine Parts & Component Mfr
N.A.I.C.S.: 332721
Priscilla Wong (Sr Mgr-Sls & Mktg)

NORTHSTAR ENERGY LIMITED
Level 15 300 Queen Street, Brisbane, 4000, QLD, Australia
Web Site: https://www.northstarenergy.com.au
Year Founded: 2017
NTH—(ASX)
Exploration & Mining Services
N.A.I.C.S.: 213115
Matthew Cooper (CEO)

NORTHSTAR GOLD CORP.
17 Wellington Street North, New Liskeard, P0J 1P0, ON, Canada
Tel.: (604) 646-4527
Web Site: https://northstargoldcorp.com
NSGCF—(OTCIQ)
Assets: $4,691,087
Liabilities: $602,345
Net Worth: $4,088,742
Earnings: ($2,352,403)
Fiscal Year-end: 04/30/21
Metal Mining & Exploration Services
N.A.I.C.S.: 213114
George Pollock (VP-Exploration)

NORTHUMBERLAND CO-OPERATIVE LTD.
256 Lawlor Lane, Miramichi Bay, E1V 3M3, NB, Canada
Tel.: (506) 627-7708
Web Site: http://www.northumberlanddairy.ca
Year Founded: 1942
Sales Range: $50-74.9 Million
Emp.: 270
Fluid Milk Processing Services
N.A.I.C.S.: 311511

NORTHUMBRIAN ROADS LIMITED
Dukes Way Low Prudhoe Industrial Estate, Prudhoe, NE42 6PQ, Northumberland, United Kingdom
Tel.: (44) 1661836377
Web Site: http://www.northumbrianroads.co.uk
Year Founded: 1989
Rev.: $12,302,191
Emp.: 58
Surfacing Material Mfr
N.A.I.C.S.: 237310
Chris Dancer (Mng Dir)

NORTHWATER CAPITAL MANAGEMENT, INC.
161 Bay st 4000, PO Box 794, Toronto, M5J 2F1, ON, Canada
Tel.: (416) 360-5435
Web Site: http://www.northwatercapital.com
Year Founded: 1989
Sales Range: $25-49.9 Million
Emp.: 20
Investment Services
N.A.I.C.S.: 523940
David George Patterson (Founder, Chm & CEO)

NORTHWEST COPPER CORP.
RPO Kingsgate, PO Box 95010, Vancouver, V5T 4T8, BC, Canada
Tel.: (604) 683-7790
Web Site: https://www.northwestcopper.ca
Year Founded: 1973
NWST—(TSXV)
Rev.: $17,034
Assets: $61,222,256
Liabilities: $1,180,825
Net Worth: $60,041,431
Earnings: ($5,575,734)
Emp.: 8
Fiscal Year-end: 12/31/23
Mineral Exploration Services
N.A.I.C.S.: 213114
Vesta Filipchuk (VP)

Subsidiaries:

Sun Metals Corp. (1)
1055 West Hastings Street Suite 1900, Vancouver, V6E 2E9, BC, Canada
Tel.: (604) 683-7790
Web Site: http://www.sunmetals.ca
Rev.: $70,294
Assets: $21,661,100
Liabilities: $1,987,990

Net Worth: $19,673,110
Earnings: ($5,317,141)
Emp.: 4
Fiscal Year-end: 12/31/2019
Investment Services
N.A.I.C.S.: 523999
Donald McInnes (Chm)

Subsidiary (Domestic):

Lorraine Copper Corp. (2)
Suite 110 - 325 Howe Street, Vancouver, V6C 1Z7, BC, Canada
Tel.: (604) 681-7913
Web Site: http://www.lorrainecopper.com
Rev.: $6,554
Assets: $4,048,408
Liabilities: $37,386
Net Worth: $4,011,023
Earnings: ($152,511)
Emp.: 45
Fiscal Year-end: 02/28/2018
Gold, Copper & Precious & Base Metal Mining
N.A.I.C.S.: 213114

Tsayta Resources Corp. (1)

NORTHWEST INVESTMENT GROUP LIMITED
20/F Tower B Yicheng International Centre No 10 Ronghua Zhonglu, Yizhuang Economy & Technology Development Zone, Beijing, 100176, China
Tel.: (86) 10 87246056
Web Site: http://www.northwestinv.com
Year Founded: 2008
Investment Services
N.A.I.C.S.: 523999

NORTHWEST MINING & GEOLOGY GROUP CO., LTD.
No 78 Yanta Middle Road, Xi'an, China
Tel.: (86) 29 85524196
Web Site: http://www.nwme.com.cn
Mining & Mineral Exploration
N.A.I.C.S.: 212290
Feng Sun (Dir)

NORTHWEST VALUE PARTNERS INC.
284 King Street East Suite 200, Toronto, M5A 1K4, ON, Canada
Tel.: (416) 366-8300
Web Site: http://www.nwvp.com
Year Founded: 1994
Emp.: 250
Real Estate Investment & Management Services
N.A.I.C.S.: 531390
Paul Dalla Lana (Pres)

Subsidiaries:

NorthWest Healthcare Properties Real Estate Investment Trust (1)
180 Dundas Street West Suite 1100, Toronto, M5G 1Z8, ON, Canada
Tel.: (416) 366-2000
Web Site: http://www.nwhreit.com
Rev.: $383,597,940
Assets: $5,760,519,759
Liabilities: $3,430,772,187
Net Worth: $2,329,747,572
Earnings: ($363,013,368)
Emp.: 275
Fiscal Year-end: 12/31/2023
Healthcare Facilities Real Estate Investment Trust
N.A.I.C.S.: 525990
Peter Riggin (Mng Dir & COO)

Subsidiary (Non-US):

NorthWest Healthcare Properties Australia REIT (2)
Level 30 101 Collins Street, Melbourne, 3000, VIC, Australia
Tel.: (61) 386561000
Web Site: http://www.nwhreit.com

AND PRIVATE COMPANIES

Sales Range: $50-74.9 Million
Healthcare Real Estate Investment Trust
N.A.I.C.S.: 525990

NorthWest International Healthcare Properties Real Estate Investment Trust (1)
180 Dundas Street West Suite 1100, Toronto, M5G 1Z8, ON, Canada
Tel.: (416) 366-2000
Web Site: http://www.nwhreit.com
Rev.: $256,240,448
Assets: $3,717,365,835
Liabilities: $2,484,108,627
Net Worth: $1,233,257,208
Earnings: $94,362,558
Fiscal Year-end: 12/31/2018
Healthcare Facilities Real Estate Investment Trust
N.A.I.C.S.: 525990
Paul Dalla Lana (CEO)

NORTHWESTERN ENTERPRISES LTD.
Morgan & Morgan Building, Pasea Estate, Road Town, Tortola, Virgin Islands (British)
Tel.: (284) 598 2518 2950   VG
Investment Holding Company
N.A.I.C.S.: 551112
Paulo Carlos de Brito (Owner)

Subsidiaries:

Aura Minerals Inc. (1)
Craigmuir Chambers, PO Box 71, British Virgin Islands, Toronto, VG1110, ON, Canada
Tel.: (305) 239-9332
Web Site: http://www.auraminerals.com
Rev.: $299,874,000
Assets: $536,190,000
Liabilities: $223,476,000
Net Worth: $312,714,000
Earnings: $68,477,000
Emp.: 863
Fiscal Year-end: 12/31/2020
Mining Exploration & Development of Copper, Gold & Iron
N.A.I.C.S.: 212390
Joao Kleber Cardoso (CFO)

Subsidiary (Domestic):

Aura Minerals (Ontario) Inc. (2)
First Canadian Pl, 100 King St W Ste 5700, Toronto, M5X 1C7, ON, Canada
Tel.: (416) 913-0204
Sales Range: $50-74.9 Million
Emp.: 25
Gold Exploration Services
N.A.I.C.S.: 212220

Subsidiary (Non-US):

Big River Gold Limited (2)
Level 29 221 St Georges Terrace, Perth, 6000, WA, Australia   (80%)
Tel.: (61) 8 9480 3708
Web Site: http://www.bigrivergold.com.au
Rev.: $841,815
Assets: $21,456,078
Liabilities: $1,198,996
Net Worth: $20,257,082
Earnings: ($2,240,166)
Emp.: 126
Fiscal Year-end: 12/31/2020
Mineral Mining Services
N.A.I.C.S.: 212220
Andrew Beigel (CFO & Sec)

Subsidiary (Non-US):

Juruena Mineracaeo Ltda. (3)
Av Fernando Correa Da Costa N 400 Ed Avenida Home Center, Galeria Sala 16, Pocao, 78015-600, Pernambuco, Brazil
Tel.: (55) 6530540028
Gold Ore Exploration & Mining Services
N.A.I.C.S.: 212220

Subsidiary (Non-US):

Mineracao Vale Verde Ltda (2)
Stephen Rua Antonio Silva 274 c, Hope Garden, Arapiraca, Alagoas, Brazil
Tel.: (55) 8235303473

Sales Range: $50-74.9 Million
Emp.: 60
Mineral Exploration Services
N.A.I.C.S.: 212220

NORTHWOOD PAPER SALES LTD.
4 Warner House Harrovian Business Village, Bessborough Road, Harrow, HA1 3EX, Middlesex, United Kingdom
Tel.: (44) 20 8423 0100   UK
Year Founded: 1998
Supplies Raw Materials to Tissue Paper Industry
N.A.I.C.S.: 424130
Kishor Vekaria (Controller-Fin)

NORTON MOTORCYCLE (UK) LTD.
Donington Hall, Castle Donington, Derby, DE74 2SG, United Kingdom
Tel.: (44) 1332812119
Web Site: http://www.nortonmotorcycles.com
Year Founded: 1898
Emp.: 32
Motorcycle Mfr
N.A.I.C.S.: 336991
Stuart Garner (Owner)

NORTON ROSE FULBRIGHT LLP
3 More London Riverside, London, SE1 2AQ, United Kingdom
Tel.: (44) 20 7283 6000   UK
Web Site: http://www.nortonrosefulbright.com
Law firm
N.A.I.C.S.: 541110
Martin Scott (Mng Partner)

Subsidiaries:

Norton Rose Fulbright (Germany) LLP (1)
Bleichenbrucke 10, 20354, Hamburg, Germany
Tel.: (49) 409707990
Web Site: http://www.nortonrosefulbright.com
Law firm
N.A.I.C.S.: 541110

Norton Rose Fulbright (Kazakhstan) Limited (1)
3rd floor 32A Manas Street, 50008, Almaty, Kazakhstan
Tel.: (7) 7273311020
Web Site: http://www.nortonrosefulbright.com
Law firm
N.A.I.C.S.: 541110
Yerzhan Kumarov (Mng Partner)

Norton Rose Fulbright (Middle East) LLP (1)
15th Floor Al Sila Tower Abu Dhabi Global Market Square, PO Box 105708, Abu Dhabi, United Arab Emirates
Tel.: (971) 26151700
Web Site: http://www.nortonrosefulbright.com
Law firm
N.A.I.C.S.: 541110

Norton Rose Fulbright (Thailand) Limited (1)
Sindhorn Building Tower 2 Floor 14 130-132 Wireless Road, Bangkok, 10330, Thailand
Tel.: (66) 22058500
Web Site: http://www.nortonrosefulbright.com
Law firm
N.A.I.C.S.: 541110
Somboon Kitiyansub (Partner)

Norton Rose Fulbright Australia (1)
Level 15 RACV Tower 485 Bourke Street, Melbourne, 3000, VIC, Australia
Tel.: (61) 3 8686 6000
Web Site: http://www.nortonrosefulbright.com

Emp.: 900
Law firm
N.A.I.C.S.: 541110
Matthew Croagh (Partner)

Norton Rose Fulbright Canada LLP (1)
1 Place Ville Marie Suite 2500, Montreal, H3B 1R1, QC, Canada
Tel.: (514) 847-4747
Web Site: http://www.nortonrosefulbright.com
Emp.: 665
Law firm
N.A.I.C.S.: 541110
Dominic C. Belley (Partner)

Affiliate (Non-US):

Norton Rose Fulbright Colombia S.A.S. (2)
Edificio K2 7 Piso Calle 97A 9A - 50, Bogota, Colombia
Tel.: (57) 17464666
Law firm
N.A.I.C.S.: 541110
Mauricio Zagarra-Cayon (Mng Partner)

Norton Rose Fulbright Greece (1)
Building K1 1 Palea Leoforos Posidonos &
3 Moraitini Street, Delta Paleo Faliro, 17501, Athens, Greece
Tel.: (30) 2109475300
Web Site: http://www.nortonrosefulbright.com
Law firm
N.A.I.C.S.: 541110

Norton Rose Fulbright Morocco, SARL (1)
Immeuble Merbouha 10 bis rue Ali Abderrazak, Casablanca, Morocco
Tel.: (212) 529090060
Web Site: http://www.nortonrosefulbright.com
Law firm
N.A.I.C.S.: 541110
Alain Malek (Partner)

Norton Rose Fulbright Piotr Strawa and Partners, Limited Partnership (1)
Metropolitan Building Plac Pilsudskiego 2, 00-073, Warsaw, Poland
Tel.: (48) 225814900
Web Site: http://www.nortonrosefulbright.com
Law firm
N.A.I.C.S.: 541110

Norton Rose Fulbright Studio Legale (1)
Piazza San Babila 1, 20122, Milan, Italy
Tel.: (39) 028635941
Web Site: http://www.nortonrosefulbright.com
Law firm
N.A.I.C.S.: 541110

Norton Rose Fulbright Tanzania (1)
3rd Floor 180 Msasani Bay, Msasani, Dar es Salaam, Tanzania
Tel.: (255) 764700900
Web Site: http://www.nortonrosefulbright.com
Law firm
N.A.I.C.S.: 541110
Angela Mndolwa (Partner)

Norton Rose Fulbright US LLP (1)
Fulbright Twr 1301 McKinney Ste 5100, Houston, TX 77010-3095
Tel.: (713) 651-5151
Web Site: http://www.nortonrosefulbright.com
Law firm
N.A.I.C.S.: 541110
Daryl Lansdale (Mng Partner)

NORTRUX INC
18110 118 Ave, Edmonton, T5S 2G2, AB, Canada
Tel.: (780) 452-6225
Web Site: https://www.nortrux.com
Year Founded: 1987
Heavy Truck Distr
N.A.I.C.S.: 336120

NORVIK HF

Arthur S. Langner (Pres, CEO & Dealer Principal)

NORVESTOR EQUITY AS
Hieronymus Heyerdahls Gate 1, 0160, Oslo, Norway
Tel.: (47) 23000700   NO
Web Site: http://www.norvestor.com
Year Founded: 1989
Sales Range: $25-49.9 Million
Emp.: 20
Investment Management Service
N.A.I.C.S.: 523940
Lars A. Grinde (Mng Partner)

Subsidiaries:

Aptilo Networks AB (1)
Tel.: (46) 850898900
Web Site: http://www.aptilo.com
Sales Range: $25-49.9 Million
Developer of Wireless Service Management Platforms
N.A.I.C.S.: 541512
Ulf Stigberg (Founder & CFO)

Subsidiary (US):

Aptilo Networks, Inc. (2)
1700 Alma Dr Ste 360, Plano, TX 75075
Tel.: (972) 767-6901
Web Site: http://www.aptilo.com
Sales Range: $10-24.9 Million
Developer of Wireless Service Management Platforms
N.A.I.C.S.: 541512

BecoTek Metal Group AS (1)
Industriveien 3, NO-3340, Rena, Norway
Tel.: (47) 32782900
Web Site: http://www.becotek.itum.com
Sales Range: $150-199.9 Million
Emp.: 10
Brass Casting
N.A.I.C.S.: 331523

Subsidiary (Non-US):

BecoTek Metal SRL (2)
Industrial Park Brasov, DJ 103 C Building 4, Ghimbav, 507075, Romania   (100%)
Tel.: (40) 368451141
Web Site: http://www.becotek.com
Brass Casting
N.A.I.C.S.: 331523

Subsidiary (US):

BecoTek Mfg. Inc. (2)
1305 Oberlin Ave, Lorain, OH 44052   (100%)
Tel.: (440) 245-6826
Web Site: http://www.becotek.com
Brass Casting
N.A.I.C.S.: 331523
Ronald Bellottie (Pres)

Subsidiary (Non-US):

Johnson Metall AB (2)
Stalgatan 15, 70115, Orebro, Sweden   (100%)
Tel.: (46) 19175100
Web Site: http://www.johnson-metall.com
Sales Range: $25-49.9 Million
Copper Casting
N.A.I.C.S.: 331529
Hans Carlsson (Mng Dir)

Permascand AB (1)
Folkets Husvagen 50, PO Box 42, 840 10, Ljungaverk, Sweden   (88%)
Tel.: (46) 691 355 00
Web Site: http://www.permascand.com
Sales Range: $25-49.9 Million
Electrode & Electrochemical Equipment Mfr
N.A.I.C.S.: 334419
Benny Johansson (Dir-Sls-Oil & Gas & Marine)

NORVIK HF
Vallakor 4, 203, Kopavogur, Iceland
Tel.: (354) 4581000
Web Site: https://www.norvik.is
Emp.: 100
Investment Services
N.A.I.C.S.: 523999

NORVIK HF

Norvik hf—(Continued)

Subsidiaries:

Bergs Timber AB (1)
Stora Torget 3, SE-598 37, Vimmerby, Sweden
Tel.: (46) 101998500
Web Site: http://www.bergstimber.se
Rev.: $262,349,920
Assets: $207,413,920
Liabilities: $54,691,840
Net Worth: $152,722,080
Earnings: $20,631,520
Emp.: 950
Fiscal Year-end: 12/31/2020
Wood Products Whslr
N.A.I.C.S.: 321999
Henrik Egnell *(Head-Bus Area Bitus)*

Subsidiary (Domestic):

Bergs Skog AB (2)
Bergs vag 13, Morlunda, Hultsfred, 57084, Smaland, Sweden
Tel.: (46) 495245550
Web Site: http://www.bergstimber.se
Sales Range: $25-49.9 Million
Emp.: 100
Lumber Mfr
N.A.I.C.S.: 113110
Peter Nilsson *(Pres & CEO)*

Subsidiary (Non-US):

Bergs Timber (UK) Ltd. (2)
Unit 9 Cirencester Office ParkTetbury Road, Cirencester, GL7 6JJ, United Kingdom
Tel.: (44) 1959562181
Web Site: https://www.bergstimber.co.uk
Emp.: 1,000
Wood Product Distr
N.A.I.C.S.: 423310

Subsidiary (Domestic):

Bergs Timber Bitus AB (2)
Orreforsvagen 49, 382 94, Nybro, Sweden
Tel.: (46) 101998500
Web Site: http://www.bergstimber.se
Sales Range: $25-49.9 Million
Lumber Mfr
N.A.I.C.S.: 113110
Henrik Egnell *(Mgr-Product Dev)*

Bergs Timber Morlunda AB (2)
Bergs Vag 13, Morlunda, 570 84, Hultsfred, Smaland, Sweden
Tel.: (46) 495245500
Web Site: http://www.bergstimber.se
Sales Range: $25-49.9 Million
Emp.: 120
Lumber Mfr
N.A.I.C.S.: 113110
Neil Strom *(Gen Mgr)*

Bergs Timber Production AB (2)
Stora Torget 3, Orrefors, 598 37, Vimmerby, Smaland, Sweden
Tel.: (46) 101998500
Web Site: https://www.bergstimber.com
Lumber Mfr
N.A.I.C.S.: 113110

Subsidiary (Non-US):

Laesti AS (2)
Sauga Sawmill Sauga Parish, 85003, Kilksama, Estonia
Tel.: (372) 58558133
Web Site: https://laesti.ee
Timber Export Services
N.A.I.C.S.: 561730

PINUS sp. z o.o. (2)
3-go Maja 76 Street, 37-410, Ulanow, Poland
Tel.: (48) 158763800
Web Site: https://www.pinus-ulanow.com.pl
Emp.: 105
Wood Window & Door Mfr
N.A.I.C.S.: 321911

Subsidiary (Domestic):

Wood Tube Sweden AB (2)
Industrigatan 1, 661 32, Saffle, Sweden
Tel.: (46) 737150155
Web Site: https://wood-tube.com
Furniture Frame & Paper Stud Mfr
N.A.I.C.S.: 337215

Woodworks by Bergs AB (2)
Lundgatan 5, 598 40, Vimmerby, Sweden
Tel.: (46) 101998450
Web Site: https://www.woodworks.se
Windows & Door Mfr
N.A.I.C.S.: 321911

NORVISTA CAPITAL CORP.
82 Richmond Street East, Toronto, M5C 1P1, ON, Canada
Tel.: (416) 504-4171
Web Site: https://olive-resource.com
Year Founded: 2011
DFU—(DEU)
Rev.: $42,518
Assets: $7,169,239
Liabilities: $139,118
Net Worth: $7,030,121
Earnings: ($4,222,903)
Fiscal Year-end: 12/31/19
Financial Consulting Services
N.A.I.C.S.: 541611

NORWALL GROUP INC.
4309 Steeles Avenue West, Toronto, M3N 1V7, ON, Canada
Tel.: (416) 593-4519
Web Site: http://www.norwall.net
Year Founded: 1975
Sales Range: $10-24.9 Million
Residential Wallcovering & Border Mfr
N.A.I.C.S.: 444120

Subsidiaries:

Patton Wallcoverings, Inc. (1)
525 S Central Ave, Columbus, OH 43223
Tel.: (614) 351-7715
Wallcoverings Mfr & Distr
N.A.I.C.S.: 444120
Greg King *(VP)*

NORWEGIAN AIR SHUTTLE ASA
Oksenoyveien 3, Fornebu, Norway
Tel.: (47) 67593000
Web Site: https://www.norwegian.com
NWARF—(OTCIQ)
Rev.: $2,359,070,756
Assets: $2,821,910,216
Liabilities: $2,288,693,885
Net Worth: $533,216,331
Earnings: $160,437,835
Emp.: 4,470
Fiscal Year-end: 12/31/23
Oil Transportation Services
N.A.I.C.S.: 481111
Bjorn Kjos *(Founder)*

Subsidiaries:

Call Norwegian AS (1)
Oksenoyveien 10 A, 1330, Fornebu, Norway
Tel.: (47) 81552369
Web Site: http://www.callnorwegian.no
Mobile Telecommunications Services
N.A.I.C.S.: 517112

Norwegian Air Shuttle Sweden AB (1)
Kungstensgatan 35, 113 57, Stockholm, Sweden
Tel.: (46) 858554400
Airport Shuttle Services
N.A.I.C.S.: 488119

NORWEGIAN BLOCK EXCHANGE AS
Snaroyveien 36, 1364, Fornebu, Norway
Tel.: (47) 93287572
Web Site: https://www.nbx.com
Year Founded: 2018
NBX—(OSL)
Rev.: $728,424
Assets: $11,131,973
Liabilities: $7,529,639
Net Worth: $3,602,334

Earnings: ($2,111,914)
Emp.: 14
Fiscal Year-end: 12/31/23
Investment Management Service
N.A.I.C.S.: 523999
Alex Karpov *(CTO)*

NORWEGIAN PROPERTY ASA
Stoperigata 2, NO-0250, Oslo, Norway
Tel.: (47) 22 83 40 20
Web Site: http://www.norwegianproperty.no
Rev.: $128,078,080
Assets: $2,031,733,056
Liabilities: $1,088,457,472
Net Worth: $943,275,584
Earnings: $115,327,552
Emp.: 47
Fiscal Year-end: 12/31/19
Commercial Property Development & Management Services
N.A.I.C.S.: 531120
Bjorge Aarvold *(Exec VP-Property Mgmt)*

Subsidiaries:

Norwegian Property Holding AS (1)
Bryggegata 9, Oslo, 250, Norway
Tel.: (47) 22834020
Sales Range: $50-74.9 Million
Emp.: 25
Real Estate Development Services
N.A.I.C.S.: 531390

NORWOOD FOUNDRY LTD.
605 18 Avenue, Nisku, T9E 7T7, AB, Canada
Tel.: (780) 955-8844
Web Site: http://www.norwoodfoundry.com
Year Founded: 1922
Rev.: $10,534,386
Emp.: 15
Iron Aluminum Brass & Bronze Foundry Mfr
N.A.I.C.S.: 331524
Jodee Mantai *(Office Mgr)*

NORWOOD SYSTEMS LIMITED
4 Leura St, Nedlands, 6009, WA, Australia
Tel.: (61) 892003500
Web Site: https://www.norwoodsystems.com
Year Founded: 2011
NOR—(ASX)
Rev.: $762,845
Assets: $349,164
Liabilities: $1,168,558
Net Worth: ($819,394)
Earnings: ($1,725,531)
Fiscal Year-end: 06/30/24
Telecommunications Software Platform Development Services
N.A.I.C.S.: 541511
Paul Ostergaard *(Founder, Founder, CEO & CEO)*

NOS SGPS, S.A.
Rua Ator Antonioa Silva 9, Campo Grande, 1600-404, Lisbon, Portugal
Tel.: (351) 217824700
Web Site: https://www.nos.pt
Year Founded: 2014
NOS—(EUR)
Rev.: $1,763,388,895
Assets: $3,829,318,910
Liabilities: $2,731,309,196
Net Worth: $1,098,009,714
Earnings: $200,169,997
Emp.: 1,835
Fiscal Year-end: 12/31/23
Telecommunications, Cable & Internet Services; Cinema Operator
N.A.I.C.S.: 517111

INTERNATIONAL PUBLIC

Jose Pedro Pereira da Costa *(CFO & VP)*

Subsidiaries:

Grafilme - Sociedade Impressora De Legendas, Lda. (1)
R Jonathan Pinto 28 M, 1400146, Lisbon, Portugal
Tel.: (351) 213018187
Emp.: 9
Motion Pictures Subtitling Services
N.A.I.C.S.: 512191

Pluricanal Santarem Televisao por Cabo, S.A. (1)
Rua Conde Ribeira Grande 33, 2005 001, Santarem, Portugal
Tel.: (351) 243 350 400
Cable Television Network Services
N.A.I.C.S.: 516210

TVTel Telecomunicacoes S.A. (1)
Rua Delfim Ferreira 383, 4100 201, Porto, Portugal
Tel.: (351) 22 032 5800
Television Broadcasting & Telecommunications Services
N.A.I.C.S.: 516120

ZON TV Cabo Acoreana S.A. (1)
Av Antero De Quental Nr 9-C Piso 1, 9500 160, Ponta Delgada, Sao Miguel, Portugal
Tel.: (351) 296302401
Television Broadcasting Services
N.A.I.C.S.: 516120

ZON TV Cabo Portugal S.A. (1)
Av 5 de Outubro 208, 1069 203, Lisbon, Portugal
Tel.: (351) 217824800
Cable TV Providers
N.A.I.C.S.: 517111

ZON Televisao por Cabo, S.G.P.S., S.A. (1)
De Outubro Nr 208 Ave, 1069 203, Lisbon, Portugal
Tel.: (351) 217824700
Web Site: http://www.zonlusomundo.pt
Emp.: 200
Television Broadcasting & Telecommunications Services
N.A.I.C.S.: 516120
Rodrigo Costa *(Pres)*

NOSA PLUGS AB
Lastmakargatan 20 7 tr, 111 44, Stockholm, Sweden
Tel.: (46) 771112000
Web Site: https://nosaplugs.com
NOSA—(OMX)
Rev.: $166,883
Assets: $14,191,922
Liabilities: $1,783,833
Net Worth: $12,408,089
Earnings: ($27,970,359)
Emp.: 31
Fiscal Year-end: 12/31/20
Medical Technology Company
N.A.I.C.S.: 621512
Martin Irding *(CEO)*

Subsidiaries:

FRISQ AB (1)
Lastmakargatan 20, 111 44, Stockholm, Sweden
Tel.: (46) 812013121
Web Site: http://www.frisqcare.com
Healtcare Services
N.A.I.C.S.: 621610
George Thaw *(CEO)*

NOSTRA TERRA OIL AND GAS COMPANY PLC
Suite 424 Salisbury House London Wall, London, EC2M 5PS, United Kingdom
Tel.: (44) 4809938933
Web Site: https://www.ntog.co.uk
NTOG—(AIM)
Rev.: $2,820,000
Assets: $4,220,000
Liabilities: $5,730,000

AND PRIVATE COMPANIES

Net Worth: ($1,510,000)
Earnings: ($470,000)
Fiscal Year-end: 12/31/23
Crude Petroleum Extraction Services
N.A.I.C.S.: 211120
Matt Lofgran (CEO)

NOSTROMO ENERGY LTD.
77 Hazorim, Shdema, Gedera, Israel
Web Site:
https://www.nostromo.energy
Year Founded: 2016
NOST—(TAE)
Rev.: $909,754
Assets: $13,748,427
Liabilities: $2,617,348
Net Worth: $11,131,079
Earnings: ($6,790,617)
Fiscal Year-end: 12/31/22
Natural Gas Distribution Services
N.A.I.C.S.: 221210

Subsidiaries:

Somoto Ltd. (1)
10 Habarzel St, Tel Aviv, Israel
Tel.: (972) 732300100
Web Site: http://www.somoto.com
Rev.: $41,048,973
Assets: $42,725,907
Liabilities: $11,708,538
Net Worth: $31,017,370
Earnings: $5,528,431
Fiscal Year-end: 12/31/2019
Software Distribution Services
N.A.I.C.S.: 423430
Assi Itshayek (CEO)

NOSTRUM OIL & GAS PLC
65 Gresham Street, London, EC2V 7NQ, United Kingdom
Tel.: (44) 2074572020
Web Site:
https://www.nostrumoilandgas.com
GB_NTRM—(KAZ)
Rev.: $195,285,000
Assets: $565,308,000
Liabilities: $1,388,561,000
Net Worth: ($823,253,000)
Earnings: ($26,118,000)
Emp.: 559
Fiscal Year-end: 12/31/21
Crude Petroleum Extraction Services
N.A.I.C.S.: 211120
Thomas Hartnett (Chief Legal Officer, Sec & Head-HR & -Acting)

Subsidiaries:

Zhaikmunai LLP (1)
43/1 Alexander Karev str, Oral, 090000, Kazakhstan
Tel.: (7) 7112933900
Oil & Gas Field Exploration Services
N.A.I.C.S.: 213112
Ainagul Kulbayeva (Dir-Contracts & Procurement)

NOTCUTTS LTD.
Ipswich Rd, Woodbridge, IP 12 4AF, United Kingdom
Tel.: (44) 1394383344
Web Site: http://www.notcutts.co.uk
Sales Range: $25-49.9 Million
Emp.: 70
Garden Center Operator
N.A.I.C.S.: 444240
Nicky Dulieu (Chm)

Subsidiaries:

Rivendell Garden Centre Limited (1)
Mill Lane, Widnes, WA8 3UL, United Kingdom
Tel.: (44) 1514232638
Web Site:
http://www.rivendellgardencenter.co.uk
Sales Range: $25-49.9 Million
Emp.: 50
Nursery & Garden Centers
N.A.I.C.S.: 444240
David Cooper (Mgr)

Wheatcroft Garden Centre Limited (1)
Landmere Lane, Edwalton, NG124DE, Nottingham, United Kingdom
Tel.: (44) 1159216061
Web Site: http://www.wheatcroftgc.co.uk
Sales Range: $25-49.9 Million
Emp.: 60
Nursery & Garden Centers
N.A.I.C.S.: 444240
Steve Coles (Gen Mgr)

NOTE AB
Tel.: (46) 856899000
Web Site: https://www.note.eu
Year Founded: 1999
NOTE—(OMX)
Rev.: $345,350,342
Assets: $259,008,870
Liabilities: $156,122,491
Net Worth: $102,886,379
Earnings: $23,812,882
Emp.: 1,366
Fiscal Year-end: 12/31/22
Electronics
N.A.I.C.S.: 334111
Johan Hagberg (Chm)

Subsidiaries:

IONOTE Electronics (Dongguan) Ltd (1)
6 Ling Dong Road Lin Cun Industrial Center, Tangxia, 523710, Dongguan, Guangdong, China
Tel.: (86) 769 8729 0991
Sales Range: $50-74.9 Million
Emp.: 250
Electronic Components Mfr
N.A.I.C.S.: 334419

NOTE Herrljunga AB (1)
OstergArdsgatan 19, 524 33, Herrljunga, Sweden
Tel.: (46) 51354500
Electrical & Electronic Mfr
N.A.I.C.S.: 334419

NOTE Hyvinkaa Oy (1)
Avainkierto 3, 05840, Hyvinkaa, Finland
Tel.: (358) 194266600
Web Site: http://www.note.eu
Electronic Components Mfr
N.A.I.C.S.: 334419

NOTE International AB (1)
Vendevagen 85a, Danderyd, 182 91, Sweden
Tel.: (46) 856899000
Web Site: http://www.note.eu
Sales Range: $100-124.9 Million
Emp.: 400
Electronic Components Mfr
N.A.I.C.S.: 334419

NOTE Norge AS (1)
Jogstadveien 21, 2007, Kjeller, Norway
Tel.: (47) 94 00 24 20
Electronic Components Mfr
N.A.I.C.S.: 334419

NOTE Parnu OU (1)
Laki 2, 80010, Parnu, Estonia
Tel.: (372) 44 485 00
Sales Range: $50-74.9 Million
Emp.: 230
Electronic Components Mfr
N.A.I.C.S.: 334419

Note Components AB (1)
Vendevagen 85 A, PO Box 711, 18217, Danderyd, Sweden (100%)
Tel.: (46) 856899040
Sales Range: $25-49.9 Million
Emp.: 8
Electrical Equipment & Component Mfr
N.A.I.C.S.: 335999

Note Lund AB (1)
Maskinvagen 3, 227 30, Lund, Sweden
Tel.: (46) 462869200
Web Site: http://www.note.se
Sales Range: $25-49.9 Million
Emp.: 50
Electrical Equipment & Component Mfr
N.A.I.C.S.: 335999

Note Norrtelje AB (1)

Vilhelm Mobergs Gata 18, PO Box 185, Norrtaelje, 761 22, Stockholm, Sweden (100%)
Tel.: (46) 17679300
Web Site: http://www.note.eu
Sales Range: $25-49.9 Million
Emp.: 90
Radio & Television Broadcasting & Wireless Communications Equipment Mfr
N.A.I.C.S.: 334220

Note Oslo AS (1)
Jogstadveien 21, 0667, Kjeller, Norway (100%)
Tel.: (47) 22079720
Web Site: http://www.oslo-printdesign.no
Sales Range: $25-49.9 Million
Emp.: 37
Electrical Equipment & Component Mfr
N.A.I.C.S.: 335999

Note Taurage UAB (1)
Pramones G 2A, Taurage, 5900, Klaipeda, Lithuania (100%)
Tel.: (370) 44662504
Web Site: http://www.note.lt
Sales Range: $50-74.9 Million
Emp.: 200
Electronic Components Mfr
N.A.I.C.S.: 334419

Note Torsby AB (1) (100%)
Tel.: (46) 560689300
Web Site: http://www.note.eu
Measuring & Controlling Device Mfr
N.A.I.C.S.: 334519

Note UK Ltd. (1)
Stroudwater Business Park Brunel Way, Stonehouse, GL10 3SX, Gloucestershire, United Kingdom
Tel.: (44) 1453797580
Web Site: http://www.note.eu
Sales Range: $25-49.9 Million
Emp.: 30
Electrical Equipment & Component Mfr
N.A.I.C.S.: 335999

NOTION CAPITAL LIMITED
91 Wimpole Street, Marylebone, London, W1G 0EF, United Kingdom
Tel.: (44) 845 498 9393
Web Site: http://notion.vc
Year Founded: 2009
Holding Company
N.A.I.C.S.: 551112
Ian Milbourn (CFO)

NOTION VTEC BERHAD
Lot 6123 Jalan Haji Salleh Batu 5 1/2 Jalan Meru, 41050, Kelang, Selangor Darul Ehsan, Malaysia
Tel.: (60) 333615615
Web Site:
https://www.notionvtec.com
NOTION—(KLS)
Rev.: $73,070,476
Assets: $108,316,402
Liabilities: $27,677,249
Net Worth: $80,639,153
Earnings: ($9,527,196)
Emp.: 1,949
Fiscal Year-end: 09/30/23
Precision Components & Tools Mfr
N.A.I.C.S.: 332721
Yit Chan Tai (Co-Sec)

NOTORIOUS PICTURES SPA
Largo Brindisi 2, 00182, Rome, Italy
Tel.: (39) 0683600710
Web Site:
https://www.notoriouspictures.it
Year Founded: 2012
NPI—(ITA)
Sales Range: $10-24.9 Million
Oil Distr
N.A.I.C.S.: 512120
Ugo Girardi (VP)

NOTOX TECHNOLOGIES CORP.

95 Mural Street Ste 600, Richmond Hill, L4B 3G2, ON, Canada
Tel.: (519) 421-1900 NV
Year Founded: 2007
NTOX—(OTCIQ)
Rev.: $5,110
Assets: $850,574
Liabilities: $2,922,695
Net Worth: ($2,072,121)
Earnings: ($465,469)
Fiscal Year-end: 08/31/19
Commercial Tanning System Mfr
N.A.I.C.S.: 339112
John Marmora (Pres, CFO, Chief Acctg Officer, Treas & Sec)

NOTREFAMILLE.COM
1 bis Avenue de la Republique, 75011, Paris, France
Tel.: (33) 144849510
Web Site:
http://www.notrefamille.com
Sales Range: $10-24.9 Million
Emp.: 30
Parenting, Genealogy & Other Family Related Services Website Operator
N.A.I.C.S.: 519290
Toussaint Roze (Chm & CEO)

NOTTINGHAM BUILDING SOCIETY
Nottingham House 3 Fulforth Street, Nottingham, NG1 3DL, United Kingdom
Tel.: (44) 344 4814444
Web Site:
http://www.thenottingham.com
Year Founded: 1849
Rev.: $11,017,440
Assets: $5,009,000,400
Liabilities: $4,725,432,480
Net Worth: $283,567,920
Earnings: $9,443,520
Emp.: 510
Fiscal Year-end: 12/31/19
Residential Development & Real Estate Credit Services Organization
N.A.I.C.S.: 925120
David Marlow (CEO)

NOUL CO., LTD.
B-10F 338 Gwanggyojungang-ro, Suji-gu, Yongin, 16942, Gyeonggi-do, Korea (South)
Tel.: (82) 313086310
Web Site: https://noul.com
Year Founded: 2015
376930—(KRS)
Rev.: $415,621
Assets: $19,828,035
Liabilities: $11,087,542
Net Worth: $8,740,492
Earnings: ($10,492,572)
Emp.: 122
Fiscal Year-end: 12/31/22
Medical Device Mfr
N.A.I.C.S.: 339112

NOUMI LIMITED
8a Williamson Road, Ingleburn, 2565, NSW, Australia
Tel.: (61) 295262555 AU
Web Site: https://noumi.com.au
NOU—(ASX)
Rev.: $393,822,782
Assets: $211,139,155
Liabilities: $414,758,278
Net Worth: ($203,619,123)
Earnings: ($65,658,386)
Emp.: 500
Fiscal Year-end: 06/30/24
Nutritional Foods Producer
N.A.I.C.S.: 311224
Timothy Moses (Dir-Strategic Development)

NOUMI LIMITED

Noumi Limited—(Continued)

Subsidiaries:

Crankt Protein International Pty. Limited (1)
80 Box Road, Taren Point, 2229, NSW, Australia
Tel.: (61) 1800646231
Web Site: http://www.crankt.com.au
Protein Shake Mfr
N.A.I.C.S.: 311514

NOURITRANS EXIM PRIVATE LIMITED

101/17 Premier Shopping Centre Nr New Court Complex Mirzapur Road, Ahmedabad, 380 001, Gujarat, India
Tel.: (91) 7698113005   In
Web Site: http://www.neplexport.com
Year Founded: 1995
Rev.: $1,557,434
Assets: $2,216,532
Liabilities: $475,046
Net Worth: $1,741,486
Earnings: $16,913
Fiscal Year-end: 03/31/18
International Goods Trading Services
N.A.I.C.S.: 522299
Asif Iqbal Vohra (Founder, Chm & Mng Dir)

NOUSBO CO., LTD.

6-325 89 Seoho-ro, Gwonseon-gu, Suwon, Korea (South)
Tel.: (82) 15443098
Web Site: https://www.nousbo.com
Year Founded: 2007
332290—(KRS)
Fertilizer Product Mfr & Distr
N.A.I.C.S.: 325314

NOUSOUKEN CORPORATION

4F Teramoto Building II 9912 Kuroda, Wakayama, 640-8341, Japan
Tel.: (81) 734977077
Web Site:
https://www.nousouken.co.jp
3541—(TKS)
Rev.: $28,445,340
Assets: $14,030,100
Liabilities: $8,564,780
Net Worth: $5,465,320
Earnings: $36,680
Fiscal Year-end: 08/31/19
Agriculture Product Distr
N.A.I.C.S.: 424480
Tomomasa Oikawa (Chm & CEO)

NOUVEAU GLOBAL VENTURES LIMITED

401/A Pearl Arcade Opp P K Jewellers Off J P Road, Andheri W, Mumbai, 400 058, India
Tel.: (91) 2226778155
Web Site:
https://www.nouveauglobal.com
531465—(BOM)
Rev.: $22,551
Assets: $1,733,605
Liabilities: $1,468,843
Net Worth: $264,762
Earnings: ($80,548)
Emp.: 8
Fiscal Year-end: 01/25/21
Consumer Electronic Products Distr
N.A.I.C.S.: 423690
Krishan Khadaria (Mng Dir)

NOUVEAU MONDE GRAPHITE INC.

481 Brassard Street, Saint-Michel-des-Saints, J0K 3B0, QC, Canada
Tel.: (450) 757-8905
Web Site: https://nmg.com
NMG—(NYSE)
Assets: $91,555,736
Liabilities: $51,347,418
Net Worth: $40,208,318
Earnings: ($41,355,544)
Emp.: 122
Fiscal Year-end: 12/31/23
Graphite Mining Services
N.A.I.C.S.: 212290
Charles-Olivier Tarte (CFO)

NOUVELLES FRONTIERES

74 rue de Lagny, 93107, Montreuil, Cedex, France
Tel.: (33) 148518939
Web Site: http://www.nouvelles-frontieres.fr
Sales Range: $400-449.9 Million
Emp.: 3,705
Travel Agency
N.A.I.C.S.: 561510
Jean-Marc Siano (Pres)

NOVA ANALITICA LTDA.

Rua Assungui 432, Sao Paulo, Brazil
Tel.: (55) 1121628080   BR
Web Site:
http://www.analiticaweb.com.br
Scientific Product Mfr
N.A.I.C.S.: 334516

NOVA ARGENT CANADA INC.

110 Belfield Rd, Toronto, M9W 1G1, ON, Canada
Tel.: (416) 245-7386
Web Site:
http://www.novacapital.com
Sales Range: $10-24.9 Million
Emp.: 2
Aluminum Mfr
N.A.I.C.S.: 331313
Andrew Boulanger (CFO)

NOVA BANKA A.D.

Ulica Veselina Maslese 1/III, 78000, Banja Luka, Bosnia & Herzegovina
Tel.: (387) 55230300
Web Site: http://www.novabanka.com
Sales Range: $25-49.9 Million
Emp.: 408
Banking Services
N.A.I.C.S.: 522110
Goran Radanovic (Chm-Supervisory Bd)

NOVA BUILDERS INC

200 14020 128 Ave NW, Edmonton, T5L 4M8, AB, Canada
Tel.: (780) 702-6682
Year Founded: 2001
Rev.: $24,860,154
Emp.: 100
Construction & Remodeling Services
N.A.I.C.S.: 236220
Mike Mrdjenovich (Owner)

NOVA CAPITAL MANAGEMENT LIMITED

Octagon Point 5 Cheapside St Pauls, London, EC2V 6AA, United Kingdom
Tel.: (44) 20 7901 1760
Web Site: http://www.nova-cap.com
Year Founded: 2002
Sales Range: $25-49.9 Million
Emp.: 25
Investment Management Service
N.A.I.C.S.: 523940
David Williamson (Founder, Chm & Mng Partner)

Subsidiaries:

Amerock Corporation (1)
3 Glenlake Pkwy, Atlanta, GA 30328 (100%)
Tel.: (704) 987-4555
Web Site: http://www.amerock.com
Emp.: 1,500
Cabinet Hardware, Functional Hardware, Hinges, Storage & Convenience Products Mfr
N.A.I.C.S.: 332999

Bulldog Hardware Co. (1)
8935 N Pointe Executive Park Dr # 200, Huntersville, NC 28078-4857 (100%)
Tel.: (901) 365-0479
Web Site: http://www.bulldoghardware.com
Sales Range: $25-49.9 Million
Emp.: 30
Picture Hanging Hardware, Household Hardware & Fasteners Mfr
N.A.I.C.S.: 493110

Division (Domestic):

Bulldog VSI (2)
2225 S 43rd Ave, Phoenix, AZ 85009-6052
Fasteners
N.A.I.C.S.: 423710

Craig Electronics, Inc. (1)
1160 NW 163rd Dr, Miami, FL 33169-5816
Web Site: https://craigelectronics.com
Sales Range: $1-9.9 Million
Emp.: 23
Electrical & Electronic Appliance, Television & Radio Set Merchant Whsl
N.A.I.C.S.: 423620

Diacom Corporation (1)
5 Howe Dr, Amherst, NH 03031-2315
Tel.: (603) 880-1900
Web Site: http://www.diacom.com
Designer & Mfr of Industrial, Automotive, Commercial & Medical Diaphragms
N.A.I.C.S.: 326299
Scott Rafferty (Pres)

Nova Argent Canada Inc. (1)
172 Belfield Road, Toronto, M9W 1n3, ON, Canada
Tel.: (416) 245-7386
Holding Company; Industrial Products Mfr & Distr
N.A.I.C.S.: 551112

Holding (Domestic):

Exchanger Industries Ltd (2)
140 Quarry Park Blvd SE Suite 120, Calgary, T2C 3G3, AB, Canada (100%)
Tel.: (403) 236-0166
Web Site:
http://www.exchangerindustries.com
Designer & Mfr of Heat Transfer Equipment for Oil, Gas & Petrochemical Industries
N.A.I.C.S.: 332410
John Michelin Jr. (VP)

National Concrete Accessories Ltd (2)
12404 - 184th Street, Edmonton, T5V 1T4, AB, Canada
Tel.: (780) 451-1212
Web Site: http://www.nca.ca
Forming Hardware & Concrete Accessories Mfr & Distr
N.A.I.C.S.: 327390
Vasken Altounian (Pres)

Shur-Line (1)
116 Exmore Rd, Mooresville, NC 28117 (100%)
Tel.: (414) 481-4500
Web Site: http://www.shurline.com
Sales Range: $100-124.9 Million
Emp.: 400
Paint Brushes, Paint Rollers, Painting Pads, Paint Sundries Mfr
N.A.I.C.S.: 339994
Chris Underwood (Mgr-Mktg)

NOVA ENTERTAINMENT PTY. LTD.

Level 5 33 Saunders St, Pyrmont, 2009, NSW, Australia
Tel.: (61) 295649999
Web Site:
http://www.novaentertainment.com
Year Founded: 1996
Radio Broadcasting Services
N.A.I.C.S.: 516110
Nick Wokes (Head-Digital audio-Sydney)

NOVA FURNITURE (DONGGUAN) CO., LTD.

INTERNATIONAL PUBLIC

Nange Industrial Village Nanya Area DaoJiao Town, Dongguan, Guangdong, China
Tel.: (86) 88313441   CN
Year Founded: 2003
Furniture Whslr
N.A.I.C.S.: 423210
XingChang Gu (Mng Dir)

NOVA GROUP HOLDINGS LIMITED

Suites 911-912 Level 9 One Pacific Place 88 Queensway, Hong Kong, China (Hong Kong)
Tel.: (852) 3 588 9688
Web Site: http://www.mega-expo.com
1360—(HKG)
Rev.: $29,416,340
Assets: $113,776,096
Liabilities: $12,795,461
Net Worth: $100,980,635
Earnings: ($702,554)
Emp.: 97
Fiscal Year-end: 06/30/21
Exhibition Organizer
N.A.I.C.S.: 561920
Feng Xu (CEO)

Subsidiaries:

Mega Entertainment & Fair (Hong Kong) Limited (1)
Suites 911-912 Level 9 One Pacific Place 88 Queensway Admiralty, Hong Kong, China (Hong Kong)
Tel.: (852) 26077323
Web Site: http://www.megahk.com
Event Management Services
N.A.I.C.S.: 561920

NOVA HOLDINGS CO., LTD.

Sea Fort Square Center Building 9F 2-3-12 Higashi Shinagawa, Tokyo, 140-0002, Japan
Tel.: (81) 344057075
Web Site: https://nova-holdings.jp
Year Founded: 1994
Holding Company
N.A.I.C.S.: 551112
Masaki Inayoshi (Pres)

Subsidiaries:

Gaba Corporation (1)
2-21-1 Kitashinjuku Shinjuku Front Tower 23rd Floor, Shinjuku, Tokyo, 169-0074, Japan
Tel.: (81) 353385700
Web Site: http://www.gaba.co.jp
Education Management Services
N.A.I.C.S.: 611710
Danish Nazir (CEO)

NOVA IRON & STEEL LTD.

Village Dagori Tehsil, Belha District, Bilaspur, 495224, India
Tel.: (91) 9109107310
Web Site:
https://www.novaironsteel.com
513566—(BOM)
Rev.: $7,539,499
Assets: $57,302,548
Liabilities: $60,333,282
Net Worth: ($3,030,735)
Earnings: ($7,129,500)
Emp.: 271
Fiscal Year-end: 03/31/21
Iron Product Mfr
N.A.I.C.S.: 331110
Hardev Chand Verma (Exec Dir)

NOVA LEAP HEALTH CORP.

7071 Bayers Road Suite 3006, Halifax, B3L 2C2, NS, Canada
Tel.: (902) 401-9480   Ca
Web Site: https://novaleaphealth.com
Year Founded: 2015
NLH—(TSXV)
Rev.: $9,768,378
Assets: $20,895,727

Liabilities: $2,698,956
Net Worth: $18,196,771
Earnings: ($1,054,681)
Emp.: 760
Fiscal Year-end: 12/31/23
Personal Home Care & Support Services
N.A.I.C.S.: 621610
Christopher Dobbin *(Pres & CEO)*

Subsidiaries:

Armistead NH II, Inc. (1)
105 Rt 101A Suite 20, Amherst, NH 03031
Tel.: (603) 546-6060
Web Site: https://www.armisteadinc.com
Women Healthcare Services
N.A.I.C.S.: 621610
Ann Howard *(Coord)*

Division (Domestic):

Armistead Senior Care (2)
1 Kennedy Dr Lowr Level 2, South Burlington, VT 05403
Tel.: (802) 489-5682
Web Site: https://www.armisteadinc.com
Women Healthcare Services
N.A.I.C.S.: 621610
Rachel Lee Cummings *(Founder)*

Living At Home Senior Care (2)
105 Rt 101A Suite 20, Amherst, NH 03031
Tel.: (603) 546-6060
Web Site: http://www.lahseniorcare.com
Women Healthcare Services
N.A.I.C.S.: 621610
Janet Gaynor *(Dir-Client Svcs)*

Comprehensive Home Care (1)
235 Greenfield Rd Ste 6, South Deerfield, MA 01373
Tel.: (413) 665-9058
Web Site: https://www.comprehensive-homecare.com
Women Healthcare Services
N.A.I.C.S.: 621610

NOVA LJUBLJANSKA BANKA D.D.

Trg Republike 2, 1520, Ljubljana, Slovenia
Tel.: (386) 14762139   SI
Web Site: https://www.nlb.si
Year Founded: 1889
N1V2—(DEU)
Rev.: $1,061,751,264
Assets: $27,726,793,568
Liabilities: $24,575,981,856
Net Worth: $3,150,811,712
Emp.: 7,982
Fiscal Year-end: 12/31/23
Commercial, Savings & Investment Banking Services
N.A.I.C.S.: 522110
Archibald Kremser *(Deputy CEO, CFO & Member-Mgmt Bd)*

Subsidiaries:

Adria Bank AG (1)
Gonzagagasse 16, Vienna, 1010, Austria (28%)
Tel.: (43) 1 514 09 0
Web Site: http://www.adriabank.at
Sales Range: $50-74.9 Million
Emp.: 26
Banking Services
N.A.I.C.S.: 522110
Jurij Deticek *(Pres)*

Banka Celje d.d. (1)
Vodnikova 2, 3000, Celje, Slovenia
Tel.: (000) 04221000
Web Site: http://www.nld.si
Sales Range: $350-399.9 Million
Emp.: 571
Banking Services
N.A.I.C.S.: 522110
Dusan Drofenik *(Pres-Mgmt Bd)*

Banka Domzale d.d. (1)
Ljubljanska Cesta 62, 1230, Domzale, Slovenia (100%)
Tel.: (386) 17245300
Web Site: http://www.bankadomzale.si

Sales Range: $50-74.9 Million
Emp.: 50
Banking Services
N.A.I.C.S.: 522110

Bankart d.o.o. (1)
Celovska 150, 1001, Ljubljana, Slovenia
Tel.: (386) 15834202
Web Site: http://www.bankart.si
Banking Services
N.A.I.C.S.: 522110

Convest a.d. (1)
Zlatne grede br 7, 21000, Novi Sad, Serbia
Tel.: (381) 21 422 081
Web Site: http://www.convest.rs
Financial Services
N.A.I.C.S.: 523999

Feniks d.o.o. (1)
Ulica Stefana Kovaca 12, 9000, Murska Sobota, Slovenia
Tel.: (386) 25154180
Web Site: http://www.nlb.si
Banking Services
N.A.I.C.S.: 522110

Koroska banka d.d. (1)
Glavni TRG, 2380, Slovenj Gradec, Slovenia (100%)
Tel.: (386) 28849111
Web Site: http://www.koroska-banka.si
Sales Range: $100-124.9 Million
Emp.: 207
Banking Services
N.A.I.C.S.: 522110

LHB Internationale Handelsbank AG (1)
60014 Frankfurt Main, Grosse Gallusstrasse 16, 60311, Frankfurt, Germany (100%)
Tel.: (49) 6921060
Web Site: http://www.lhb.de
Sales Range: $50-74.9 Million
Emp.: 80
Banking Services
N.A.I.C.S.: 522110

NLB Banka a.d., Banja Luka (1)
Milana Tepica 4, 78000, Banja Luka, Bosnia & Herzegovina (99.85%)
Tel.: (387) 51 245 502
Web Site: http://www.nlb-rs.ba
Sales Range: $25-49.9 Million
Banking Services
N.A.I.C.S.: 522110
Blaz Brodnjak *(Chm-Supervisory Bd)*

NLB Banka a.d., Belgrade (1)
Bulevar Mihajla Pupina 165 v, 11070, Belgrade, Serbia
Tel.: (381) 11 2225 101
Web Site: http://www.nlb.rs
Commericial Banking
N.A.I.C.S.: 522110
Vlastimir Vukovic *(Member-Exec Bd)*

NLB Banka a.d., Podgorica (1)
Boulevard Ivana Crnojevica No 171, 81000, Podgorica, Montenegro (99.83%)
Tel.: (382) 19888
Web Site: https://www.nlb.me
Banking Services
N.A.I.C.S.: 522110
Dino Redzepagic *(Exec Dir)*

NLB Banka a.d., Skopje (1)
st Vodnjanska no 1, Centar Municipality, 1000, Skopje, North Macedonia (86.97%)
Tel.: (389) 215600
Web Site: https://www.nlb.mk
Commericial Banking
N.A.I.C.S.: 522110
Antonio Argir *(Chm-Mgmt Bd)*

NLB Banka d.d., Sarajevo (1)
Ul Kosevo br 3, 71000, Sarajevo, Bosnia & Herzegovina
Tel.: (387) 33720300
Web Site: https://www.nlb-fbih.ba
Rev.: $22,458,925
Assets: $1,438,160,111
Liabilities: $1,343,184,091
Net Worth: $94,976,020
Earnings: $12,101,639
Emp.: 489
Fiscal Year-end: 12/31/2021
Commericial Banking
N.A.I.C.S.: 522110
Peter Andreas Burkhardt *(Chm-Supervisory Bd)*

NLB Banka sh.a., Prishtina (1)
Rr Ukshin Hoti nr 124, 10000, Pristina, Kosovo (81.21%)
Tel.: (383) 38744091
Web Site: https://www.nlb-kos.com
Rev.: $35,473,503
Assets: $916,273,012
Liabilities: $819,134,359
Net Worth: $97,138,653
Earnings: $22,355,376
Emp.: 474
Fiscal Year-end: 12/31/2019
Commericial Banking
N.A.I.C.S.: 522110
Albert Lumezi *(Chm-Mgmt Bd)*

NLB Komercijalna banka AD (1)
Svetog Save 14, 11000, Belgrade, Serbia (83.23%)
Tel.: (381) 113080100
Web Site: https://www.nlbkb.rs
Rev.: $193,548,844
Assets: $4,103,290,404
Liabilities: $3,383,453,282
Net Worth: $719,837,122
Earnings: $84,990,153
Emp.: 27,444
Fiscal Year-end: 12/31/2019
Banking Services
N.A.I.C.S.: 522110
Vlastimir Vukovic *(CEO)*

NLB Nov penziski fond a.d. (1)
Ul Majka Tereza br 1, 1000, Skopje, North Macedonia
Tel.: (389) 25100285
Web Site: http://www.nlbnpf.com.mk
Emp.: 30
Pension Fund Management Services
N.A.I.C.S.: 523940
Davor Vukadinovic *(Co-Pres)*

NLB Srbija d.o.o., Belgrade (1)
Bulevar Mihajla Pupina 165 v, 11070, Belgrade, Serbia (100%)
Tel.: (381) 628032335
Web Site: https://www.nlbsrbija.co.rs
Commercial Real Estate
N.A.I.C.S.: 531390
Vladan Tekic *(Dir)*

Prospera Plus d.o.o. (1)
Smartinska 132, 1520, Ljubljana, Slovenia
Tel.: (386) 15448291
Web Site: http://www.nlb.si
Banking Services
N.A.I.C.S.: 522110

Summit Leasing Slovenija d.o.o. (1)
Flajsmanova Ulica 3, 1000, Ljubljana, Slovenia
Tel.: (386) 15483360
Web Site: https://www.summit-leasing.si
Financial Lending Services
N.A.I.C.S.: 522220

NOVA LTD.

5 David Fikes, PO Box 266, Rehovot, 7610201, Israel
Tel.: (972) 732295600
Web Site: https://www.novami.com
Year Founded: 1993
NVMI—(NASDAQ)
Rev.: $517,922,000
Assets: $1,133,807,000
Liabilities: $383,055,000
Net Worth: $750,752,000
Earnings: $136,310,000
Emp.: 1,202
Fiscal Year-end: 12/31/23
Develops, Produces & Markets Metrology Systems for Process Control
N.A.I.C.S.: 334513
Dror David *(CFO)*

Subsidiaries:

Nova Measuring Instruments B.V.
Jadelaan 4, 2131 XW, Hoofddorp, Netherlands
Tel.: (31) 235698170
Sales, Training & Customer Support for Semiconductor Manufacturing
N.A.I.C.S.: 561499

Nova Measuring Instruments Inc. (1)
3090 Oakmeag Viollage Dr, Santa Clara, CA 95051
Tel.: (408) 200-4344
Web Site: http://www.novameasuring.com
Sales Range: $25-49.9 Million
Emp.: 5
Sales, Training & Customer Support for the Semiconductor Manufacturing Industry
N.A.I.C.S.: 561499

Nova Measuring Instruments K.K. (1)
IOS Gotanda Annex 403 1-7-11 Higashiotanda, Shinagawa-ku, Tokyo, 141-0022, Japan
Tel.: (81) 367219420
Sales Range: $25-49.9 Million
Emp.: 11
Sales, Training & Customer Support for the Semiconductor Manufacturing Industry
N.A.I.C.S.: 561499

Nova Measuring Instruments Taiwan (1)
23F No 118 CiYun Rd, Hsin-chu, Taiwan
Tel.: (886) 35752411
Sales Range: $25-49.9 Million
Emp.: 20
Sales, Training & Customer Support for the Semiconductor Manufacturing Industry
N.A.I.C.S.: 561499
Buck Kim *(Pres-Asia-Pacific)*

ReVera Incorporated (1)
3090 Oakmead Village Dr, Santa Clara, CA 95051
Tel.: (408) 510-7400
Web Site: http://www.revera.com
Sales Range: $1-9.9 Million
Emp.: 25
Materials Metrology Solutions
N.A.I.C.S.: 334413

NOVA MENTIS LIFE SCIENCE CORP.

700-838 West Hasting Street, Vancouver, V6C 0A6, BC, Canada
Tel.: (778) 819-0244   BC
Web Site: https://www.novamentis.ca
Year Founded: 2004
NMLSF—(OTCQB)
Rev.: $426
Assets: $219,240
Liabilities: $188,698
Net Worth: $30,541
Earnings: ($1,821,590)
Emp.: 1
Fiscal Year-end: 12/31/22
Cannabis Products Developer
N.A.I.C.S.: 325412
Rebecca Hudson *(CFO)*

Subsidiaries:

Nova Mentis Biotech Corp. (1)
700-838 West Hasting Street, Vancouver, V6C 0A6, BC, Canada
Tel.: (778) 819-0244
Web Site: http://www.novamentisbiotech.com
Biotechnology Development Services
N.A.I.C.S.: 541714

NOVA MINERALS LIMITED

Suite 5 242 Hawthorn Road, Caulfield, 3161, VIC, Australia
Tel.: (61) 395371238   AU
Web Site: https://www.novaminerals.com.au
Year Founded: 1987
NVA—(ASX)
Rev.: $180,706
Assets: $71,611,926
Liabilities: $5,917,661
Net Worth: $65,694,265
Earnings: ($10,943,705)
Emp.: 1
Fiscal Year-end: 06/30/24
Holding Company; Precious Metals & Rare Earth Elements Exploration & Mining
N.A.I.C.S.: 551112
Avi Kimelman *(Gen Mgr)*

NOVA MINERALS LIMITED

Nova Minerals Limited—(Continued)

Subsidiaries:

Snow Lake Resources Ltd. (1)
242 Hargrave St 1700, Winnipeg, R3C 0V1, MB, Canada
Tel.: (204) 815-5806
Web Site: https://www.snowlakelithium.com
Rev.: $81,874
Assets: $19,708,565
Liabilities: $2,308,142
Net Worth: $17,400,423
Earnings: ($11,471,690)
Emp.: 1
Fiscal Year-end: 06/30/2023
Mineral Mining Services
N.A.I.C.S.: 213115

NOVA MSC BERHAD
A-18-3 Tower A Level 18 Northpoint Mid-Valley City No 1, Medan Syed Putra Utara, 59200, Kuala Lumpur, Malaysia
Tel.: (60) 22836628   MY
Web Site: https://www.nova-hub.com
NOVAMSC—(KLS)
Rev.: $6,993,656
Assets: $12,306,680
Liabilities: $5,794,116
Net Worth: $6,512,564
Earnings: ($1,446,333)
Emp.: 132
Fiscal Year-end: 03/31/24
Healthcare Software Development Services
N.A.I.C.S.: 513210
Kok Aun Tan (Sec)

Subsidiaries:

NovaSolutions (Philippines), Inc. (1)
Unit A and B 11th Floor The JMT Corporate Condominium 27 ADB Avenue, Ortigas Center, Pasig, 1605, Philippines
Tel.: (63) 25350137
Information Technology Services
N.A.I.C.S.: 541512

Novahealth Pte. Ltd. (1)
60 MacPherson Road Block 1 Siemens Centre 05-08, Singapore, 348615, Singapore
Tel.: (65) 65183591
Healthcare Software Development Services
N.A.I.C.S.: 541511

NOVA NET LEASE REIT
200 Bay Street North Tower Suite 1200, Toronto, M5J 2J2, ON, Canada
Tel.: (214) 906-4037   ON
Web Site:
  https://www.novanetleasereit.com
Year Founded: 2021
NNL.U—(CNSX)
Real Estate Manangement Services
N.A.I.C.S.: 531210
Tyson Macdonald (CEO)

NOVA PACIFIC METALS CORP.
Suite 306-1110 Hamilton Street, Vancouver, V6B 2S2, BC, Canada
Tel.: (416) 918-6785   BC
Web Site:
  https://www.novapacificmetals.com
Year Founded: 2017
NVLIF—(OTCIQ)
Assets: $583,273
Liabilities: $59,226
Net Worth: $524,047
Earnings: ($122,780)
Fiscal Year-end: 06/30/22
Mineral Mining Services
N.A.I.C.S.: 213115

NOVA PESCARA A.D.
Brace Buzadjije 156, Deliblato, Serbia
Tel.: (381) 13765713
Year Founded: 1989
NPSC—(BEL)
Rev.: $936,663
Assets: $4,238,757
Liabilities: $787,611
Net Worth: $3,451,147
Earnings: $54,861
Emp.: 12
Fiscal Year-end: 12/31/22
Cereal Crop Farming Services
N.A.I.C.S.: 111998
Leonardo Biskupovic (Gen Mgr)

NOVA RADINOST A.D.
Brace Mazar i majke Marije 19a, 78000, Banja Luka, Bosnia & Herzegovina
Tel.: (387) 51319864
Year Founded: 2002
NRAD-R-A—(BANJ)
Rev.: $11,887
Assets: $354,802
Liabilities: $26,101
Net Worth: $328,701
Earnings: ($11,345)
Emp.: 1
Fiscal Year-end: 12/31/12
Civil Engineering Construction Services
N.A.I.C.S.: 237990
Pero Stojanovic (Chm-Mgmt Bd)

NOVA RESOURCES B.V.
Strawinskylaan 1151, 1077, Amsterdam, Netherlands
Tel.: (31) 20 303 3860   NI
Web Site:
  http://www.novaresourcesbv.com
Investment Services
N.A.I.C.S.: 523999
Oleg Novachuk (Chm)

Subsidiaries:

KAZ Minerals PLC (1)
6th Floor Cardinal Place 100 Victoria Street, London, SW1E 5JL, United Kingdom (100%)
Tel.: (44) 2079017800
Web Site: http://www.kazminerals.com
Rev.: $2,266,000,000
Assets: $6,066,000,000
Liabilities: $3,892,000,000
Net Worth: $2,174,000,000
Earnings: $571,000,000
Emp.: 15,637
Fiscal Year-end: 12/31/2019
Copper, Gold & Petroleum Exploration Services
N.A.I.C.S.: 212230
Eldar Mamedov (Gen Dir-KMM LLP)

Subsidiary (Non-US):

KAZ Minerals Management LLP (2)
85A Dostyk Street, Almaty, 050021, Kazakhstan
Tel.: (7) 7272440353
Copper Mining & Metal Services
N.A.I.C.S.: 212290

KAZ Minerals Russia LLC (2)
1st Krasnogvardeysky Ave 15 Mercury Tower 16th Floor, 123112, Moscow, Russia
Tel.: (7) 4955400125
Web Site: http://www.kazminerals.com
Copper Mining & Metal Services
N.A.I.C.S.: 212290

Kazakhmys Aktogay LLP (2)
Park view office Tower 13th Floor 77 Building Kunaev str, Almaty, 050000, Kazakhstan
Tel.: (7) 727 244 71 60
Copper Mining Services
N.A.I.C.S.: 212230

Kazakhmys LLC (2)
69-A Samal 2, Almaty, 050059, Kazakhstan (99.7%)
Tel.: (7) 7272663317
Web Site: http://www.kazakhmys.com
Copper Mining & Production
N.A.I.C.S.: 212230

Subsidiary (Domestic):

Maikuben West Holding JSC (3)
Bldg 46 corner of Sanatomaya str, Microdistrict Baganashyl, Almaty, 050023, Kazakhstan
Tel.: (7) 727 269 66 54
Web Site: http://www.maikubenholding.kz
Holding Company
N.A.I.C.S.: 551112

Subsidiary (Non-US):

Mansfelder Kupfer und Messing GmbH (2)
Lichtloecherberg 40, Hettstedt, 6333, Germany
Tel.: (49) 3476890
Web Site: http://www.mkm-hett.de
Sales Range: $50-74.9 Million
Emp.: 200
Copper & Copper Alloy Products Mfr
N.A.I.C.S.: 331420
Roland Harings (CEO)

Subsidiary (Non-US):

MKM France s.a.r.l. (3)
53 Avenue de l'Europe, Roncq, 59223, France
Tel.: (33) 320010891
Web Site: http://www.mkm-hett.de
Emp.: 5
Copper & Copper Alloy Products Sales
N.A.I.C.S.: 423510

MKM Italia s.r.l. (3)
Dante Alighieri A 284 Polesella, 45038, Rovigo, Italy
Tel.: (39) 042594593
Web Site: http://www.mkm-hett.de
Sales Range: $50-74.9 Million
Emp.: 3
Copper Products Sales
N.A.I.C.S.: 213114

MKM Mansfelder Copper UK Ltd. (3)
Unit 3 Spire House Waterside Business Park, Ashbourne, DE6 1DG, Derbyshire, United Kingdom
Tel.: (44) 1335300585
Web Site: http://www.mkm-hett.de
Sales Range: $50-74.9 Million
Emp.: 3
Copper Products Sales
N.A.I.C.S.: 213114

Subsidiary (US):

MKM North America Corporation (3)
3056 Earlsmere Ave, Pittsburgh, PA 15216
Tel.: (412) 563-1350
Web Site: http://www.mkm.eu
Sales Range: $50-74.9 Million
Emp.: 1
Copper Products Sales
N.A.I.C.S.: 213114

NOVA SIROVINA A.D.
Dunavska 23a, 78000, Banja Luka, Bosnia & Herzegovina
Tel.: (387) 51310716
Web Site:
  http://www.novasirovina.com
NSRV—(BANJ)
Sales Range: $1-9.9 Million
Emp.: 21
Secondary Raw Material Processing Services
N.A.I.C.S.: 331492
Miso Babic (Chm)

NOVA SRBIJA A.D.
Zeleznicka 26, Odzaci, Serbia
Tel.: (381) 25 742 153
Year Founded: 2003
Sales Range: Less than $1 Million
Emp.: 5
Home Management Services
N.A.I.C.S.: 721110

NOVA STEEL INC.
6001 Irwin Street, La Salle, H8N 1A1, QC, Canada
Tel.: (514) 789-0511   Ca
Web Site: http://www.novasteel.ca
Year Founded: 1979
Sales Range: $800-899.9 Million

INTERNATIONAL PUBLIC

Emp.: 70
Steel Mfrs
N.A.I.C.S.: 331221
Roger Daigneault (VP-Corp Pur)

Subsidiaries:

American Steel & Aluminum Corporation (1)
115 Wallace Ave, South Portland, ME 04106
Tel.: (207) 772-4641
Web Site:
  http://www.americansteelandaluminum.com
Sales Range: $25-49.9 Million
Emp.: 55
Iron & Steel Mills
N.A.I.C.S.: 331110
Peter Brissette (Pres & Gen Mgr)

Cresswell Industries Inc. (1)
424 St-Vallier, Granby, J2G 7Y4, QC, Canada
Tel.: (450) 378-4611
Web Site:
  http://www.cresswellindustries.com
Sales Range: $150-199.9 Million
Emp.: 50
Rolled Steel Shape Mfr
N.A.I.C.S.: 331221

Nova Steel (1)
V830 S Service Rd, Stoney Creek, L8E 5M7, ON, Canada
Tel.: (905) 643-3300
Sales Range: $25-49.9 Million
Emp.: 40
Iron & Steel Mills
N.A.I.C.S.: 331110
Rayan Taberner (Gen Mgr)

Nova Steel - Baie d'Urfe (1)
19460 Clark Graham, Baie-d'Urfe, H9X 3R8, QC, Canada
Tel.: (514) 789-0511
Web Site: http://www.novasteel.ca
Tubular & Flat Rolled Steel Products Mfr
N.A.I.C.S.: 331210

Nova Tube Indiana, LLC (1)
1195 Port Rd, Jeffersonville, IN 47130-8478
Tel.: (812) 285-9796
Web Site: http://www.novamerican.com
Sales Range: $10-24.9 Million
Emp.: 30
Iron, Steel Pipe & Tube Mfr
N.A.I.C.S.: 331210

NOVA STOKOVNA KUKA AD
Ul Blagoj Jankov-Muceto br 25, Strumica, North Macedonia
Tel.: (389) 34323190
NOSK—(MAC)
Rev.: $556,093
Assets: $3,695,802
Liabilities: $1,651,771
Net Worth: $2,044,032
Earnings: $286,643
Fiscal Year-end: 12/31/23
Clothing Apparel Distr
N.A.I.C.S.: 458110

NOVA SYSTEM CO., LTD.
Shin Ishihara Building 9th Floor 1-3-15 Edobori, Nishi-ku, Osaka, 550-0002, Japan
Tel.: (81) 664798100
Web Site: https://www.nova-system.com
Year Founded: 1982
5257—(TKS)
Emp.: 480
Information Technology Services
N.A.I.C.S.: 541512
Masayasu Yoshiyama (Pres & CEO)

NOVA TECHNOLOGY CORPORATION LIMITED
16Floor Building A Shenzhen International Innovation Center No 1006, Shennan Road, Shenzhen, 518040, Guangdong, China
Tel.: (86) 75582720666
Web Site: https://www.nova.net.cn

AND PRIVATE COMPANIES

Year Founded: 1996
300921—(CHIN)
Rev.: $79,648,920
Assets: $135,566,028
Liabilities: $19,529,640
Net Worth: $116,036,388
Earnings: $8,005,608
Fiscal Year-end: 12/31/22
Network Communication Services
N.A.I.C.S.: 516210
Shulin Chen *(Chm)*

NOVA TRANSPORTADORA DO SUDESTE S.A.
Praia do Flamengo 200 23rd Floor, Rio de Janeiro, 22210-901, Brazil
Tel.: (55) 2132509200 BR
Web Site: http://www.ntsbrasil.com
Oil & Gas Services
N.A.I.C.S.: 213112
Alex Sandro Monteiro Barbosa da Silva *(CFO & Chief IR Officer)*

NOVA VAROS A.D.
Trg Petra Bojovica 2, Nova Varos, Serbia
Tel.: (381) 33 61793
Web Site: http://www.inex.co.rs
Year Founded: 1945
INNV—(BEL)
Sales Range: Less than $1 Million
Farming Services
N.A.I.C.S.: 111998
Ratomir Obucina *(Exec Dir)*

NOVA VISION ACQUISITION CORP.
Room 602 6/F168 Queens Road Central, Central, China (Hong Kong)
Tel.: (852) 93385690 VG
Year Founded: 2021
NOVV—(NASDAQ)
Rev.: $638,020
Assets: $19,026,721
Liabilities: $20,288,528
Net Worth: ($1,261,807)
Earnings: ($75,807)
Emp.: 1
Fiscal Year-end: 12/31/22
Investment Services
N.A.I.C.S.: 523999
Eric Ping Hang Wong *(CEO & CFO)*

NOVA WELLNESS GROUP BHD
Lot 708 Nova Avenue, Sungai Pelek, 43950, Sepang, Malaysia
Tel.: (60) 331413181
Web Site: https://nova.my
Year Founded: 2017
NOVA—(KLS)
Rev.: $9,636,929
Assets: $25,072,179
Liabilities: $2,646,774
Net Worth: $22,425,404
Earnings: $3,172,994
Fiscal Year-end: 06/30/23
Nutraceutical Product Mfr
N.A.I.C.S.: 325411
Phang Yeen Nung *(Exec Dir)*

Subsidiaries:

Nova Laboratories Sdn. Bhd. (1)
Lot 708 Nova Avenue 4th Mile, Sungai Pelek, 43950, Sepang, Selangor, Malaysia
Tel.: (60) 133569832
Web Site: http://www.nova.my
Wellness & Fitness Services
N.A.I.C.S.: 713940

NOVAAGRO GROUP
Chernyshevska Street Building 66, 61000, Kharkiv, Ukraine
Tel.: (380) 573414321
Web Site: https://novaagro.com.ua
Year Founded: 2009
Emp.: 100
Agricultural Industry
N.A.I.C.S.: 325320

Subsidiaries:

NOVAAGRO Ukraine LLC (1)
Chernyshevska Street Building 66 Kharkiv 61000, 61000, Kharkiv, Ukraine
Tel.: (380) 500133333
Web Site: https://novaagro.com.ua
Agricultural Industry
N.A.I.C.S.: 424440
Sergii Polumysnyi *(Bd of Dirs & Exec Dir)*

Subsidiary (Non-US):

AgroGeneration SA (2)
19 boulevard Malesherbes business center REGUS, 75008, Paris, France (56.9%)
Tel.: (33) 155273840
Web Site: https://www.agrogeneration.com
Rev.: $27,912,799
Assets: $39,273,689
Liabilities: $24,175,480
Net Worth: $15,098,209
Earnings: ($34,097,777)
Emp.: 615
Fiscal Year-end: 12/31/2022
Grain & Oilseed Farming
N.A.I.C.S.: 111191
Olga Shantyr *(CEO)*

NOVABASE SGPS, SA
Av D Joao II n 34 Parque das Nacoes, 1998-031, Lisbon, Portugal
Tel.: (351) 213836300
Web Site: https://www.novabase.pt
Year Founded: 1989
NBA—(EUR)
Rev.: $146,325,201
Assets: $195,018,214
Liabilities: $98,875,152
Net Worth: $96,143,062
Earnings: $3,779,667
Emp.: 1,317
Fiscal Year-end: 12/31/23
Information Technology Services
N.A.I.C.S.: 541512
Luis Paulo Cardoso Salvado *(Chm & CEO)*

Subsidiaries:

COLLAB - Sol. I. Com. e Colab., S.A. (1)
Avenida D Joao II No 51-Bloco B 2nd Floor C, 1990-085, Lisbon, Portugal
Tel.: (351) 21 092 7840
Web Site: http://collab.com
Software Publisher
N.A.I.C.S.: 513210
Paulo Porto *(Exec VP-Sales-Global)*

Novabase Neotalent Espana S.A.U. (1)
Avda De Burgos 12 Planta 5 DCHA, 28036, Madrid, Spain
Tel.: (34) 91 344 3850
Web Site: https://www.neotalent.es
Managed Network Services
N.A.I.C.S.: 811210

Novabase Solutions Middle East FZ-LLC (1)
Dubai Internet City EIB 05 Alfa Builiding Office 206, PO Box 500035, Dubai, 500035, United Arab Emirates
Tel.: (971) 44542997
Computer Software Development Services
N.A.I.C.S.: 541512
Maribel Perez *(Coord-Admin)*

NOVABEV GROUP
Yakimanskaya emb 4 building 1, Moscow, 119180, Russia
Tel.: (7) 4955102695
Web Site: https://novabev.com
Year Founded: 1999
BELU—(MOEX)
Rev.: $1,390,602,390
Assets: $1,057,246,830
Liabilities: $705,895,350
Net Worth: $351,351,480
Earnings: $52,007,670
Emp.: 12,000
Fiscal Year-end: 12/31/21
Distilled Spirits Mfr
N.A.I.C.S.: 424820

NOVACAP MANAGEMENT INC.
3400 rue de l Eclipse Bureau 700, Brossard, J4Z 0P3, QC, Canada
Tel.: (450) 651-5000 Ca
Web Site: http://www.novacap.ca
Year Founded: 1981
Privater Equity Firm
N.A.I.C.S.: 523999
Pascal Tremblay *(Pres, CEO & Mng Partner)*

Subsidiaries:

All West Communications Inc. (1)
50 W 100 N, Kamas, UT 84036
Tel.: (435) 783-4361
Web Site: http://www.allwest.net
Sales Range: $50-74.9 Million
Emp.: 200
Local Telephone Communications
N.A.I.C.S.: 517121
Jenny Prescott *(VP-Fin)*

Subsidiary (Domestic):

Sweetwater Television Company (2)
602 Broadway St, Rock Springs, WY 82901
Tel.: (307) 362-3773
Web Site: http://www.allwest.com
All Other Telecommunications
N.A.I.C.S.: 517810

Bentley Leathers, Inc. (1)
6125 Court Dellias Road, Saint Laurent, H4T 1C8, QC, Canada
Tel.: (514) 341-9333
Web Site: http://www.shopbentley.com
Sales Range: $50-74.9 Million
Retailer of Handbags, Luggage & Leather Products
N.A.I.C.S.: 458320

Bestar Inc. (1)
4220 Villeneuve, Lac Megantic, G6B 2C3, QC, Canada
Tel.: (819) 583-1017
Web Site: http://www.bestar.ca
Sales Range: $1-9.9 Million
Emp.: 209
Ready-to-Assemble Home Office & Home Entertainment Furniture Designer & Mfr
N.A.I.C.S.: 337126
Roger Charbonneau *(CEO & CFO)*

Subsidiary (US):

Bush Industries Inc. (2)
1 Mason Dr, Jamestown, NY 14702-0460
Tel.: (716) 665-2000
Web Site: http://www.bush.co
Sales Range: $650-699.9 Million
Emp.: 2,750
Ready-To-Assemble Office & Home Furniture Mfr & Designer
N.A.I.C.S.: 337122
Steven Thaelan *(Exec VP-Sls & Mktg)*

Subsidiary (Non-US):

Bush Europe Ltd. (3)
Interchange Business Centre Howards Way, Newport Pagnell, MK16 9PY, United Kingdom
Tel.: (44) 1908 299046
Furniture Whslr
N.A.I.C.S.: 423210

Business Interactions, LLC (1)
3454 Douglas Rd, South Bend, IN 46635
Tel.: (574) 314-9302
Web Site: https://www.harmonyhit.com
Software Development Services
N.A.I.C.S.: 513210
Tom Liddell *(CEO)*

Subsidiary (Domestic):

Trinisys, LLC (2)
750 Old Hickory Blvd Ste 268, Brentwood, TN 37027
Tel.: (615) 515-8891
Web Site: http://www.trinisys.com
Sales Range: $1-9.9 Million
Emp.: 16
Computer Management Services
N.A.I.C.S.: 518210
Chuck Harris *(Mgr-Bus Solutions)*

Cadent, LLC (1)
1675 Broadway 22nd Fl, New York, NY 10019
Tel.: (212) 796-1960
Web Site: http://www.cadent.tv
Media Telecommunication & Television Advertising
N.A.I.C.S.: 516120
Nick Troiano *(CEO)*

Subsidiary (Domestic):

4info, Inc. (2)
4 North 2nd St Ste 1150, San Jose, CA 95113
Tel.: (650) 350-4800
Web Site: http://www.4info.com
Media Representatives
N.A.I.C.S.: 541840
Tim Jenkins *(CEO)*

Dialogic Inc. (1)
4 Gatehall Dr, Parsippany, NJ 07054
Tel.: (973) 967-6000
Web Site: http://www.dialogic.com
Rev.: $132,081,000
Assets: $66,724,000
Liabilities: $133,721,000
Net Worth: ($66,997,000)
Earnings: ($53,935,000)
Emp.: 539
Fiscal Year-end: 12/31/2013
Internet Protocol, Media Gateways & Digital Compression Products Mfr
N.A.I.C.S.: 334220

Subsidiary (Non-US):

Dialogic (UK) Limited (2)
85 King Street, Maidenhead, SL6 1DU, Berks, United Kingdom
Tel.: (44) 1628641770
Web Site: http://www.dialogic.com
Sales Range: $25-49.9 Million
Communications Applications Sales & Service
N.A.I.C.S.: 423430
James Besley *(VP-Sls & Support & Gen Mgr-EMEA)*

Dialogic Corporation (2)
6700 Chemin de la Cote-de-Liesse Suite 100, Montreal, H4T 2B5, QC, Canada
Tel.: (514) 745-5500
Web Site: http://www.dialogic.com
Media Processing Hardware & Software Developer & Mfr
N.A.I.C.S.: 332510

Dialogic Distribution Limited (2)
Unit O3 North Ring Business Park, Santry, Dublin, 9, Ireland
Tel.: (353) 1 630 9000
Communications Applications Distr
N.A.I.C.S.: 423430

Dialogic Japan, Inc. (2)
2F Ichiban-cho M-Building 10-2 Ichiban-cho, Chiyoda-ku, Tokyo, 102-0082, Japan
Tel.: (81) 3 3234 2176
Communications Applications Sales & Service
N.A.I.C.S.: 423430

Dialogic Manufacturing Limited (2)
Unit O3 North Ring Business Park, Santry, Dublin, 9, Ireland
Tel.: (353) 16309000
Sales Range: $10-24.9 Million
Emp.: 20
Telephone Apparatus Mfr
N.A.I.C.S.: 334210

Dialogic Networks (Israel) Ltd. (2)
43 Hasivim Street, PO Box 7073, Petah Tiqwa, 49170, Israel
Tel.: (972) 39709000
Communications Applications Sales & Service
N.A.I.C.S.: 423430
Marjan Torkar *(VP-Sls-Europe, Israel, Russia & CIS, Turkey)*

Dialogic Networks Espana SRL (2)
Gran Via Carlos III 84-3 Planta Edifici Trade, 08028, Barcelona, Spain
Tel.: (34) 934965722
Web Site: http://www.dialogic.com

NOVACAP MANAGEMENT INC.

Novacap Management Inc.—(Continued)
Emp.: 10
Communications Applications Sales
N.A.I.C.S.: 423430
Lola Massanet Amer *(Reg Mgr-Sls)*

Dialogic Networks Sdn Bhd (2)
Ground Floor Block C Peremba Square
Saujana Resort, Seksyen U2, Shah Alam,
40150, Selangor, Malaysia
Tel.: (60) 378476100
Emp.: 2
Communications Applications Sales & Service
N.A.I.C.S.: 423430
Chew Weng Hock *(Reg Dir-Sls)*

Dialogic RUS LLC (2)
9 Zemlyanoy Val, 103064, Moscow, Russia
Tel.: (7) 495 287 1322
Communications Applications Sales & Service
N.A.I.C.S.: 423430
Marjan Torkar *(VP-Sls-Europe, Israel, Russia & CIS & Turkey)*

Dialogic SARL (2)
52 rue Paul Vaillant Couturier, 92240, Malakoff, France
Tel.: (33) 146570505
Sales Range: $10-24.9 Million
Emp.: 12
Communications Applications Sales & Service
N.A.I.C.S.: 423430

Dialogic Singapore Pte. Limited (2)
60 Anson Road No 09-04 MapleTree Anson, Singapore, 079914, Singapore
Tel.: (65) 64964660
Communications Applications Development & Sales
N.A.I.C.S.: 423430

Dialogic d.o.o. (2)
Dunajska cesta 156, 1000, Ljubljana, Slovenia
Tel.: (386) 15687020
Communications Applications & Solutions
N.A.I.C.S.: 423430
Marjan Torkar *(VP-Sls-Europe, Israel, Russia & CIS & Turkey)*

Dialogic do Brasil Comercio de Equipamentos Para Telecomunicacao Ltda. (2)
Av Luis Carlos Berrini 1297,8 andar Conjunto 82, Sao Paulo, 04571-010, SP, Brazil
Tel.: (55) 11 4563 8130
Sales Range: $100-124.9 Million
Emp.: 12
Communications Applications Distr & Services
N.A.I.C.S.: 423430

Horizon Telecom Inc. (2)
68 E Main St, Chillicothe, OH 45601-2503
Tel.: (740) 772-8200
Web Site: http://www.horizontel.com
Sales Range: $25-49.9 Million
Emp.: 200
Holding Company for Telecommunications
N.A.I.C.S.: 517121
Bill Melcow *(Pres)*

Subsidiary (Domestic):

Horizon Chillicothe Telephone (2)
68 E Main St, Chillicothe, OH 45601-2503
Tel.: (740) 772-8200
Provider of Telephone Communication Services
N.A.I.C.S.: 517121
Robert K. McKell *(Chm)*

Horizon Telecom Inc. (2)
68 E Main St, Chillicothe, OH 45601
Tel.: (740) 772-8200
Web Site: http://www.horigonconnects.com
Sales Range: $25-49.9 Million
Emp.: 190
Personal Communication Services
N.A.I.C.S.: 517112
William A. McKell *(Pres)*

Host.net (1)
3500 NW Boca Raton Blvd Bldg 900, Boca Raton, FL 33431
Tel.: (561) 869-6100
Web Site: http://www.host.net

Software Development Services
N.A.I.C.S.: 541511
Jeffrey Davis *(Founder)*

Mailhot Industries USA, Inc. (1)
3 Capitol St, Nashua, NH 03063
Tel.: (603) 880-9380
Web Site: http://www.mailhotindustries.com
Sales Range: $1-9.9 Million
Emp.: 14
Electronic & Precision Equipment Repair & Maintenance
N.A.I.C.S.: 811210

Nitrex Metal Inc. (1)
3474 Poirier Boulevard, Saint Laurent, H4R 2J5, QC, Canada
Tel.: (514) 335-7191
Web Site: http://www.nitrex.com
Metal Heat Treating Services
N.A.I.C.S.: 332811
Jean-Francois Cloutier *(CEO)*

Subsidiary (US):

Jhawar Industries, Inc. (2)
525 Klug Cir, Corona, CA 92880
Tel.: (951) 340-4646
Web Site: http://www.gmenterprises.com
Industrial Process Furnace & Oven Mfr
N.A.I.C.S.: 333994
Suresh Jhawar *(Pres & CEO)*

Rosmar Litho, Inc. (1)
19500 Ave Clark Graham, Baie-d'Urfe, H9X 3R8, QC, Canada
Tel.: (450) 651-5000
Web Site: http://www.rosmarlitho.com
Cardboard Packaging Printing & Manufacturing Services
N.A.I.C.S.: 322220

The Knowlton Development Corporation (1)
375 Blvd Roland-Therrien Suite 210, Longueuil, J4H 4A6, QC, Canada
Tel.: (450) 243-2000
Web Site: https://www.kdc-one.com
Rev.: $2,143,800,000
Assets: $3,574,100,000
Liabilities: $2,638,700,000
Net Worth: $935,400,000
Earnings: ($125,800,000)
Emp.: 11,200
Fiscal Year-end: 04/30/2020
Consumer Goods Custom Formulator & Contract Mfr
N.A.I.C.S.: 325620
Nicholas Whitley *(Pres & CEO)*

Subsidiary (US):

Aerofil Technology, Inc. (2)
225 Industrial Park Dr, Sullivan, MO 63080
Tel.: (573) 468-5551
Web Site: http://www.aerofil.com
Aerosol & Liquid Packaging
N.A.I.C.S.: 561910
Steve Engler *(VP-Tech Svcs)*

Kolmar Laboratories, Inc. (2)
20 W King St, Port Jervis, NY 12771
Tel.: (845) 856-5311
Web Site: http://www.kolmar.com
Private Label Cosmetics Producer
N.A.I.C.S.: 325620
Robert E. Theroux *(CEO)*

Subsidiary (Domestic):

Acupac Packaging, Inc. (3)
55 Ramapo Vly Rd, Mahwah, NJ 07430
Tel.: (201) 529-3434
Web Site: http://www.acupac.com
Single Use & Unit Dosage Products Mfr
N.A.I.C.S.: 326112
Laurie Koppe *(Project Mgr)*

Subsidiary (US):

Northern Labs, Inc. (2)
5800 W Dr, Manitowoc, WI 54220-4168
Tel.: (920) 684-7137
Web Site: http://www.kdc-one.com
Hair Care & Bath Products, Automotive Care Products, Household Products, Silver, Jewelry, Metal, Fabric, Leather & Furniture Care Products & Car Polishes, Waxes & Cleaners Mfr
N.A.I.C.S.: 325612

Thibiant International Inc. (2)
20320 Prairie St, Chatsworth, CA 91311-6026
Tel.: (818) 709-1345
Web Site: http://www.thibiant.com
Toilet Preparation Mfr
N.A.I.C.S.: 325620
Janine Hofer *(Dir-Acctg)*

The Master Group, Inc (1)
1675 boul de Montarville, Boucherville, J4B 7W4, QC, Canada
Tel.: (514) 527-2301
Web Site: http://www.master.ca
Heating Exchanger Distr
N.A.I.C.S.: 423730

Subsidiary (US):

Refrigeration Sales Corporation (2)
9450 Allen Dr Ste A, Cleveland, OH 44125-4602
Tel.: (216) 525-8200
Web Site: http://www.refrigerationsales.net
Refrigeration Equipment & Supplies
N.A.I.C.S.: 423740
Rhonda Wight *(Pres)*

NOVACON TECHNOLOGY GROUP LIMITED

Office E 17th Floor EGL Tower No 83 Hung To Road, Kwun Tong, Kowloon, China (Hong Kong)
Tel.: (852) 3 412 3636
Web Site:
  http://www.novacontechgroup.com
Year Founded: 2006
8635—(HKG)
Rev.: $5,813,258
Assets: $16,865,812
Liabilities: $2,170,217
Net Worth: $14,695,594
Earnings: $1,680,867
Emp.: 31
Fiscal Year-end: 03/31/21
Software Development Services
N.A.I.C.S.: 541511
Ming Wei *(Chm)*

Subsidiaries:

Global eSolutions (HK) Limited (1)
Office E 17th Floor EGL Tower No 83 Hung To Road, Kwun Tong, Kowloon, China (Hong Kong)
Tel.: (852) 34123636
Web Site: https://www.ges.com.hk
Financial Trading Services
N.A.I.C.S.: 523999

Max Online Limited (1)
Unit 4510 45th Floor Metroplaza Tower 2 223 Hing Fong Road, Kwai Chung, New Territories, China (Hong Kong)
Tel.: (852) 28820100
Web Site: https://www.maxonline.io
Precious Metals Trading Services
N.A.I.C.S.: 523160

Real Logic Technology Company Limited (1)
Office E 17th Floor EGL Tower No 83 Hung To Road, Kwun Tong, Kowloon, China (Hong Kong)
Tel.: (852) 34123636
Web Site: https://www.reallogictech.com
Software Development Services
N.A.I.C.S.: 541511

NOVACYT SA

13 Avenue Morane Saulnier, 78140, Velizy-Villacoublay, France
Tel.: (33) 139465104
Web Site: https://www.novacyt.com
Year Founded: 2005
ALNOV—(EUR)
Rev.: $22,706,670
Assets: $152,062,379
Liabilities: $27,719,620
Net Worth: $124,342,758
Earnings: ($27,768,185)
Emp.: 222
Fiscal Year-end: 12/31/22

INTERNATIONAL PUBLIC

Cancer & Infectious Disease Products & Services
N.A.I.C.S.: 339112
Graham Mullis *(CEO)*

Subsidiaries:

Lab21 Healthcare Ltd. (1)
Unit 1 Watchmoor Point Watchmoor Road, Camberley, GU15 3AD, Surrey, United Kingdom
Tel.: (44) 1276600081
Plasmatec & Biotech Product Mfr & Distr
N.A.I.C.S.: 325414

Lab21 Ltd. (1)
Park House Winship Road, Milton, Cambridge, CB24 6BQ, United Kingdom
Tel.: (44) 1223 395450
Web Site: http://lab21.com
Sales Range: $10-24.9 Million
Emp.: 25
Health Care Diagnostic Services
N.A.I.C.S.: 621511
Graham Mullis *(CEO)*

Microgen Bioproducts Ltd. (1)
Unit 1 Watchmoor Point, Camberley, GU15 3AD, Surrey, United Kingdom
Tel.: (44) 127 660 0081
Web Site:
  https://www.microgenbioproducts.com
Bio Product Mfr & Distr
N.A.I.C.S.: 325414
Thomas Brown *(Product Mgr)*

Primerdesign Ltd. (1)
York House School Lane, Chandlers Ford, SO53 4DG, United Kingdom
Tel.: (44) 238 074 8830
Web Site: https://www.primerdesign.co.uk
Bio Product Mfr & Distr
N.A.I.C.S.: 325414
Simon King *(Head-Customer Care)*

NOVAE AEROSPACE SERVICES SA

3 rue Teheran, 75008, Paris, France
Tel.: (33) 1 4450 3945
Emp.: 300
Aircraft Part Mfr
N.A.I.C.S.: 336413
Sebastien Taveau *(Pres)*

NOVAGANT CORP.

Suite 2006 AIA Kowloon Tower Landmark East 100 How Ming Street, Kwun Tong, 999077, China (Hong Kong)
Tel.: (852) 94079401
Year Founded: 1987
NVGT—(OTCIQ)
Rev.: $50,913
Assets: $51,944
Liabilities: $325,778
Net Worth: ($273,834)
Earnings: ($50,913)
Emp.: 3
Fiscal Year-end: 03/31/23
Logistic Services
N.A.I.C.S.: 541614
HongZhen Xu *(Treas)*

NOVAGOLD PETRORESOURCES LIMITED

A 202 Vrindavan Town Ship Iskon Mandir Road Gotri Road, Baroda, 390021, Gujarat, India
Tel.: (91) 265 2326998
Web Site:
  http://www.novagoldpetro.com
Sales Range: Less than $1 Million
Shares Brokerage Services
N.A.I.C.S.: 523150
Sharmila Amin *(Compliance Officer)*

NOVALPINA CAPITAL LLP

The Caxton Building, London, SW1H 0RH, United Kingdom
Tel.: (44) 20 3907 4444
Web Site: http://www.novalpina.pe
Year Founded: 2017

AND PRIVATE COMPANIES

Privater Equity Firm
N.A.I.C.S.: 523999
Stephen Peel *(Co-Founder & Partner)*

Subsidiaries:

Odyssey Europe AS (1)
c/o Olympic Entertainment Group Pronksi
Road 19, Tallinn, 10124, Estonia (100%)
Tel.: (372) 667 1250
Web Site: http://www.odyssey-europe.eu
Investment Holding Company
N.A.I.C.S.: 551112
Stefan Kowski *(Member-Mgmt Bd)*

Holding (Domestic):

Olympic Entertainment Group AS (2)
Pronksi 19, Tallinn, 10124, Estonia (100%)
Tel.: (372) 6671250
Web Site: http://www.olympic-casino.com
Sales Range: $250-299.9 Million
Casinos & Gaming Services
N.A.I.C.S.: 713210
Marje Braunbruck *(Mgr-Mktg)*

Subsidiary (Non-US):

Olympic Casino Group Baltija UAB (3)
Konstitucijos pr 12, LT-09308, Vilnius, Lithuania
Tel.: (370) 52638638
Web Site: http://lt.olympic-casino.com
Casino Operation Services
N.A.I.C.S.: 713210
Saulius Petravicius *(Mng Dir)*

NOVAMEDIA GROUP

Beethovenstraat 200, 1077 JZ, Amsterdam, Netherlands
Tel.: (31) 206640978
Web Site: http://www.novamedia.nl
Year Founded: 1983
Sales Range: $25-49.9 Million
Emp.: 50
Holding Company
N.A.I.C.S.: 551112
Boudewijn Poelmann *(CEO)*

Subsidiaries:

Independent Media (1)
Bolshoy Savvinsky Pereulok 12/6 Moscow Silk Business Area, 119435, Moscow, Russia
Tel.: (7) 4952520999
Web Site: http://www.imedia.ru
Newspaper Publishers
N.A.I.C.S.: 513110
Mbuso Khoza *(Acting CEO-Conde Nast Independent Magazines)*

Subsidiary (Domestic):

The Moscow Times (2)
Ulitsa Polkovaya 3 Bldg 1, 127018, Moscow, Russia
Tel.: (7) 4952343223
Web Site: http://www.themoscowtimes.com
Sales Range: $25-49.9 Million
Emp.: 10
Newspapers
N.A.I.C.S.: 513110
Igor Grishin *(Mgr-Production)*

The St. Petersburg Times (2)
4 Konnogvardeisky Blvd Entrance 7 3rd Fl, Saint Petersburg, 190000, Russia (100%)
Tel.: (7) 8123256080
Web Site: http://www.sptimes.ru
Emp.: 20
Newspapers
N.A.I.C.S.: 513110
Tatyana Turikova *(Gen Dir)*

NOVAMEX SA

Le Moulin de Saint-Pierre, 84300, Taillades, France
Tel.: (33) 490787070
Web Site: http://www.novamex.fr
Sales Range: $25-49.9 Million
Ecological Cleaning Product Mfr &Distr
N.A.I.C.S.: 325998
Bruno Carnevali *(CEO)*

NOVAMIND INC.

10 Wanless Avenue Suite 201, Toronto, M4N 1V6, ON, Canada
Tel.: (647) 953-9512
Web Site: http://www.novamind.ca
Year Founded: 1997
NM—(DEU)
Sales Range: Less than $1 Million
Mineral Exploration Services
N.A.I.C.S.: 213114
Yaron Conforti *(Co-Founder & CEO)*

NOVAREX CO., LTD.

80 Osongsaengmyeong 14-ro Osong-eup, Heungdeok-gu, Cheongju, Chungcheongbuk-do, Korea (South)
Tel.: (82) 432180510
Web Site: https://www.novarex.co.kr
Year Founded: 1995
194700—(KRS)
Rev.: $216,044,879
Assets: $207,535,868
Liabilities: $68,427,293
Net Worth: $139,108,575
Earnings: $15,295,239
Emp.: 412
Fiscal Year-end: 12/31/22
Health Care Srvices
N.A.I.C.S.: 621999
Kwon Suk Hyung *(Chm)*

NOVARISE RENEWABLE RESOURCES INTERNATIONAL LTD

Suite 5 Level 1 325 Pitt Street, Sydney, 2000, NSW, Australia
Tel.: (61) 292831338
Web Site: http://www.novarise.com.au
Year Founded: 1998
Sales Range: $75-99.9 Million
Emp.: 480
Polypropylene Filament Yarn Producer
N.A.I.C.S.: 325998
Qingyue Su *(Chm & Mng Dir)*

NOVARTIS AG

Fabrikstrasse 2, CH-4056, Basel, Switzerland
Tel.: (41) 613241111   CH
Web Site: https://www.novartis.com
Year Founded: 1996
NVS—(NYSE)
Rev.: $45,440,000,000
Assets: $99,945,000,000
Liabilities: $53,195,000,000
Net Worth: $46,750,000,000
Earnings: $14,854,000,000
Emp.: 76,057
Fiscal Year-end: 12/31/23
Holding Company; Pharmaceuticals, Preventive Vaccines, Eye Care & Diagnostic Tools
N.A.I.C.S.: 551112
Joerg Reinhardt *(Chm)*

Subsidiaries:

1 A Pharma GmbH (1)
Keltenring 1 3, 82041, Oberhaching, Germany
Tel.: (49) 89 6138825 0
Web Site: http://www.1apharma.de
Pharmaceuticals Product Mfr
N.A.I.C.S.: 325412

Abadia Retuerta S.A. (1)
Sardon de Duero, 47340, Valladolid, Spain
Tel.: (34) 98 368 0368
Web Site: https://www.abadia-retuerta.com
Pharmaceutical Product Mfr & Distr
N.A.I.C.S.: 325412

Advanced Accelerator Applications (UK & Ireland) Limited (1)
Edison House 223-231 Old Marylebone Road, Marylebone, London, NW1 5QT, United Kingdom
Tel.: (44) 207 258 5200

Nuclear Medicine Mfr
N.A.I.C.S.: 325412

Advanced Accelerator Applications S.A. (1)
20 rue Diesel, 01630, Saint-Genis-Pouilly, France (98.7%)
Tel.: (33) 4 50 99 30 70
Web Site: http://www.adacap.com
Pharmaceuticals Mfr
N.A.I.C.S.: 325412
Gerard Ber *(Co-Founder)*

Subsidiary (Non-US):

Advanced Accelerator Applications (UK & Ireland) Limited (2)
2nd Floor The WestWorks Building White City Place 195 Wood Lane, Chilcompton, London, W12 7FQ, United Kingdom
Tel.: (44) 2072585200
Web Site: http://www.imagingequipment.co.uk
Pharmaceutical Products Distr
N.A.I.C.S.: 424210

Advanced Accelerator Applications GmbH (2)
Saime-Genc-Ring 18, 53121, Bonn, Germany
Tel.: (49) 2289258830
Web Site: http://www.adacap.com
Pharmaceutical Products Distr
N.A.I.C.S.: 424210

Advanced Accelerator Applications Iberica S.L. (2)
Poligono Industrial La Cuesta, 50100, La Almunia de Dona Godina, Spain
Tel.: (34) 97 6600 126
Web Site: http://www.adacap.com
Pharmaceutical Products Distr
N.A.I.C.S.: 424210
Giovanni Tesoriere *(Mng Dir)*

Advanced Accelerator Applications International SA (2)
4 rue de la Tour de lille, 1204, Geneva, Switzerland
Tel.: (41) 22 519 0700
Web Site: http://www.adacap.com
Pharmaceutical Products Distr
N.A.I.C.S.: 424210

Subsidiary (Non-US):

Advanced Accelerator Applications Canada, Inc. (3)
Suite 700 7th Floor 2810 Matheson Blvd East, Mississauga, L4W 4X7, ON, Canada
Tel.: (905) 206-0690
Web Site: http://www.adacap.com
Pharmaceutical Products Distr
N.A.I.C.S.: 424210

Subsidiary (Non-US):

Advanced Accelerator Applications Italy, S.r.l. (2)
Via dellIndustria Prima Traversa, 86077, Rome, Isernia, Italy
Tel.: (39) 0865 91231
Web Site: http://www.adacap.com
Pharmaceutical Products Distr
N.A.I.C.S.: 424210

Advanced Accelerator Applications Portugal Lda. (2)
Edificio Mar Vermelho Av Dom Joao II lote1 06 2 5B, 1998-028, Lisbon, Portugal
Tel.: (351) 211212078
Web Site: http://www.adacap.com
Pharmaceutical Products Distr
N.A.I.C.S.: 424210

Subsidiary (US):

Advanced Accelerator Applications USA, Inc. (2)
57 E Willow St, Millburn, NJ 08108
Tel.: (862) 263-0820
Web Site: http://www.adacap.com
Pharmaceutical Products Distr
N.A.I.C.S.: 424210

Aeropharm GmbH (1)
Francois-Mitterrand-Allee 1, 07407, Rudolstadt, Germany
Tel.: (49) 3 672 4790
Pharmaceuticals Product Mfr

NOVARTIS AG

N.A.I.C.S.: 325412

Alcon Laboratories Inc. (1)
6201 S Freeway, Fort Worth, TX 76134-2001
Tel.: (817) 293-0450
Web Site: http://www.alconlabs.com
Sales Range: $1-4.9 Billion
Emp.: 25,000
Pharmaceutical Preparations
N.A.I.C.S.: 325412
Christel Vogel *(Mgr)*

Subsidiary (Non-US):

Alcon (China) Ophthalmic Product Co., Ltd. (2)
12th Floor Beijing Towercrest Plaza No 3 West Maizidian Road, Chaoyang District, Beijing, 100016, China
Tel.: (86) 10 6467 6688
Web Site: http://www.alcon.com
Sales Range: $100-124.9 Million
Emp.: 253
Ophthalmic Surgical Device Mfr & Distr
N.A.I.C.S.: 339112

Subsidiary (Domestic):

Alcon (Puerto Rico) Inc. (2)
Royal Industrial Park Bldg C Barrio Palmas, Catano, PR 00962 (100%)
Tel.: (787) 788-6800
Web Site: http://www.alcon.com
Sales Range: $25-49.9 Million
Emp.: 35
Ophthalmic Product Distr
N.A.I.C.S.: 423460

Subsidiary (Non-US):

Alcon Bulgaria Eood (2)
10 Dimitar Manov Street 1st floor, 1408, Sofia, Bulgaria
Tel.: (359) 29 50 15 65
Eye Care Product Distr
N.A.I.C.S.: 423450

Alcon Canada, Inc. (2)
2665 Meadowpine Blvd, Mississauga, L5N 8C7, ON, Canada (100%)
Tel.: (905) 826-6700
Web Site: http://www.alcon.ca
Sales Range: $50-74.9 Million
Emp.: 220
Ophthalmic Surgical Equipment & Supplies, Pharmaceutical Products for Eyes & Ears & Vision Care Products Developer & Marketer
N.A.I.C.S.: 423460

Alcon Deutschland GmbH (2)
Heinrich-von-Stephan-Strasse 17, 79100, Freiburg, Germany (100%)
Tel.: (49) 76113040
Web Site: https://www.de.alcon.com
Sales Range: $50-74.9 Million
Emp.: 250
Ophthalmic Surgical Equipment & Supplies, Pharmaceuticals & Vision Care Products Mfr & Distr
N.A.I.C.S.: 339115
Benedict Hoffmann *(Mng Dir)*

Subsidiary (Domestic):

CIBA Vision GmbH (3)
Industriering 1, 63868, Grosswallstadt, 63868, Germany (100%)
Tel.: (49) 6022 240 0
Web Site: http://www.cibavision.de
Vision Care Products Research, Mfr & Sales
N.A.I.C.S.: 339115

Unit (Domestic):

Alcon Distribution Center - Elkridge (2)
6740 Business Pkwy, Elkridge, MD 21075-6340
Tel.: (410) 796-5400
Web Site: http://www.alcon.com
Sales Range: $25-49.9 Million
Emp.: 47
Pharmaceuticals Distr
N.A.I.C.S.: 424210

Subsidiary (Non-US):

Alcon Division of Pharmaco Ltd. (2)
109 Carlton Gore Road, Mount Wellington,

NOVARTIS AG

Novartis AG—(Continued)
Auckland, 1023, New Zealand
Tel.: (64) 9 270 4360
Web Site: http://www.alcon.com
Emp.: 15
Eye Care Products Mfr
N.A.I.C.S.: 325412

Alcon EyeCare (UK) Ltd. (2)
Park View Riverside Way, Watchmoor Park, Camberley, GU15 3YL, Surrey, United Kingdom **(100%)**
Tel.: (44) 127 667 3311
Web Site: http://www.uk.alcon.com
Vision Care Products Marketer
N.A.I.C.S.: 423460

Alcon Farmacevtika LLC (2)
Naberezhnaya Tower Presnenskaya nab 10 Block B, Moscow, 123317, Russia
Tel.: (7) 495 258 5278
Web Site: http://www.alcon.com
Sales Range: $25-49.9 Million
Emp.: 100
Eye Care Products Mfr
N.A.I.C.S.: 339115

Alcon Hong Kong, Ltd (2)
Suites 1201-2 625 Kings Road, North Point, China (Hong Kong)
Tel.: (852) 2568 0636
Eye Care Product Distr
N.A.I.C.S.: 423450

Alcon Hungaria Kft (2)
Bartok Bela ut 43-47, 1114, Budapest, Hungary
Tel.: (36) 1 463 9080
Web Site: http://www.novartis.hu
Pharmaceutical Product Mfr & Distr
N.A.I.C.S.: 325412

Alcon Hungary Pharmaceuticals Trading Ltd (2)
Bartok Bela ut 43-47, Budapest, Hungary
Tel.: (36) 1 463 9080
Web Site: http://www.alcon.com
Pharmaceuticals Product Mfr
N.A.I.C.S.: 325412

Alcon Italia S.p.A. (2)
Viale Giulio Richard 1/B, 20143, Milan, Italy **(100%)**
Tel.: (39) 02818031
Web Site: http://www.alcon.com
Sales Range: $50-74.9 Million
Emp.: 180
Ophthalmic Products Supplier
N.A.I.C.S.: 423460

Alcon Japan Ltd. (2)
Akasaka Tameike Tower 2-17-7 Akasaka, Minato-ku, Tokyo, 107 0052, Japan **(100%)**
Tel.: (81) 335883200
Web Site: http://www.alcon.com
Sales Range: $250-299.9 Million
Emp.: 932
Marketing & Sale of Ophthalmic Surgical Equipment & Supplies, Pharmaceuticals & Contact Lens Care Solutions
N.A.I.C.S.: 423460

Alcon Korea Ltd (2)
6th Floor Glass Tower 946-1 Daechi-dong, Gangnam-gu, Seoul, 135-708, Korea (South)
Tel.: (82) 2 200 75000
Web Site: http://www.alcon.co.kr
Sales Range: $25-49.9 Million
Emp.: 100
Eye Care Product Mfr & Distr
N.A.I.C.S.: 339112

Alcon Laboratories (Australia) Pty. Ltd. (2)
10/25 Frenchs Forest Road East, French's Forest, 2086, NSW, Australia **(100%)**
Tel.: (61) 294529200
Web Site: http://www.alcon.com
Sales Range: $50-74.9 Million
Emp.: 100
Ophthalmic Surgical Equipment, Pharmaceuticals & Contact Lens Care Products Sales
N.A.I.C.S.: 423460

Alcon Laboratories (India) Private Limited (2)
Unit No 502 Tower D 5th Floor RMZ Infinity Benniganahalli, Old Madras Road, Bengaluru, 560 016, India
Tel.: (91) 80 4006 4600
Web Site: http://www.alcon.com
Sales Range: $50-74.9 Million
Emp.: 200
Surgical Equipment & Supplies Distr
N.A.I.C.S.: 423450

Alcon Laboratories (Pty.) Ltd. (2)
65 Peter Place, Extension 13, Bryanston, 2021, Gauteng, South Africa **(100%)**
Tel.: (27) 11 840 2300
Web Site: http://www.alcon.com
Sales Range: $25-49.9 Million
Emp.: 90
Ophthalmic Product Distr
N.A.I.C.S.: 423460

Alcon Laboratories (Thailand) Ltd (2)
191 Silom Road 18th Floor Silom Complex Building, Bangrak, Bangkok, 10500, Thailand
Tel.: (66) 2 235 5430
Web Site: http://www.alcon.com
Sales Range: $25-49.9 Million
Emp.: 85
Eye Care Products Mfr
N.A.I.C.S.: 325412

Alcon Laboratories (UK) Ltd. (2)
Pentagon Park, Boundary Way, Hemel Hempstead, HP2 7UD, Herts, United Kingdom **(100%)**
Tel.: (44) 1442 341100
Web Site: http://www.uk.alcon.com
Sales Range: $75-99.9 Million
Emp.: 130
Ophthalmic Surgical Equipment, Supplies & Pharmaceutical Products Sales & Distribution
N.A.I.C.S.: 423460

Alcon Laboratories Hellas Commercial & Industrial S.A. (2)
18 Kifissias Avenue, 15125, Maroussi, Athens, Greece **(100%)**
Tel.: (30) 2106800811
Sales Range: $25-49.9 Million
Emp.: 65
Eye Care Products Distr
N.A.I.C.S.: 423460

Alcon Laboratories Ireland Limited (2)
Cork Business & Technology Park Model Farm Road, Cork, Ireland
Tel.: (353) 21 486 5100
Sales Range: $25-49.9 Million
Emp.: 200
Contact Lens Mfr
N.A.I.C.S.: 339115
Oonagh Kellegher (Mgr-Mfg)

Alcon Laboratories SDN. BHD. (2)
No 1001A & 1001D Wisma Glomac 3 9th Floor Kompleks Kelana Centre Point, Kelana Jaya, Petaling Jaya, 47302, Selangor Darul Ehsan, Malaysia
Tel.: (60) 3 7880 0650
Sales Range: $25-49.9 Million
Emp.: 40
Eye Care Product Distr
N.A.I.C.S.: 423450

Alcon Laboratories, Inc. (2)
Scientific Office Flat No 19 3rd Floor Alkamal Building Corner Al, PO Box 405, Jazira Rayat Al Ittihad Street, Jeddah, 21411, Saudi Arabia
Tel.: (966) 2 657 0957
Pharmaceuticals Product Mfr
N.A.I.C.S.: 325412

Alcon Laboratorios Argentina S.A. (2)
Alicia Moreau de Justo 240 2 Piso, Buenos Aires, C1107AAF, Argentina **(100%)**
Tel.: (54) 11 4318 7200
Web Site: http://www.alcon.com
Sales Range: $50-74.9 Million
Emp.: 90
Supplier of Ophthalmic Surgical Equipment, Pharmaceuticals & Vision Care Products & Services
N.A.I.C.S.: 423460

Alcon Laboratorios Chile Limitada (2)
Avenida Los Leones 1459 Providencia, Casilla 343-V Correo 21, Santiago, Chile **(100%)**
Tel.: (56) 24106400
Web Site: http://www.alconlabs.com
Sales Range: $25-49.9 Million
Emp.: 40
Eye Care Products Distr
N.A.I.C.S.: 423460

Alcon Laboratorios Uruguay, S.A. (2)
Constituyente 1891, 11200, Montevideo, Uruguay
Tel.: (598) 2 400 4000
Eye Care Product Distr
N.A.I.C.S.: 423450

Alcon Laboratorios do Brasil Ltda. (2)
Av Prof Vicente Rao 90 122 1 andar Brooklin, Sao Paulo, 04636 000, SP, Brazil **(100%)**
Tel.: (55) 11 3732 4000
Web Site: http://www.alcon.com
Sales Range: $125-149.9 Million
Emp.: 423
Ophthalmic Surgical, Pharmaceutical & Vision Care Products Mfr & Distr
N.A.I.C.S.: 339115

Alcon Laboratorios, S.A. de C.V. (2)
Adolfo Prieto 1644, Entre Jose Maria Rico y Parroquia, Col Del Valle, Mexico, CP 03100, DF, Mexico **(100%)**
Tel.: (52) 55 52001100
Web Site: http://www.alcon.mx
Sales Range: $75-99.9 Million
Emp.: 200
Ophthalmic Surgical Equipment, Pharmaceuticals & Contact Lens Care Products Mfr & Distr
N.A.I.C.S.: 423460

Alcon Laboratuvarlari Ticaret A.S. (2)
Kavacik Ticaret Merkezi Kavak Sokak No 18, 34805, Istanbul, Turkiye **(100%)**
Tel.: (90) 2164256870
Web Site: http://www.alcon.com
Sales Range: $25-49.9 Million
Emp.: 90
Ophthalmic Product Distr
N.A.I.C.S.: 423460

Alcon Nederland B.V. (2)
Claudius Prinsenlaan 142, 4818 CP, Breda, Netherlands **(100%)**
Tel.: (31) 183654321
Web Site: http://be.alcon.com
Sales Range: $50-74.9 Million
Emp.: 70
Ophthalmic Surgical Equipment & Supplies, Pharmaceuticals & Vision Care Products
N.A.I.C.S.: 423460

Alcon Nordic A/S (2)
Edvard Thomsens Vej 14 2nd Story, 2300, Copenhagen, Denmark
Tel.: (45) 36364360
Web Site: https://www.alcon.dk
Emp.: 130
Eye Treatment Drug Mfr & Whslr
N.A.I.C.S.: 325412

Alcon Norge AS (2)
Hoffsveien 1 A, PO Box 618, Skoyen, 0214, Oslo, Norway
Tel.: (47) 23 25 25 50
Web Site: http://www.alcon.no
Sales Range: $25-49.9 Million
Emp.: 20
Eye Care Product Mfr & Distr
N.A.I.C.S.: 339115

Alcon Pharmaceuticals (Czech Republic) s.r.o. (2)
Gemini Building B Na Pankraci 1724/129, 140 00, Prague, Czech Republic
Tel.: (420) 225 775 111
Web Site: http://www.cz.alcon.com
Sales Range: $25-49.9 Million
Emp.: 40
Pharmaceuticals Product Mfr
N.A.I.C.S.: 325412

Alcon Pharmaceuticals Ltd (2)
Ave Dubrovnikik 16, Zagreb, 10000, Croatia
Tel.: (385) 1 461 1988
Web Site: http://www.alcon.com

Emp.: 20
Pharmaceuticals Product Mfr
N.A.I.C.S.: 325412

Alcon Pharmaceuticals Ltd. (2)
8 Paronyan Str Off 11, Yerevan, 0015, Armenia
Tel.: (374) 10 53 82 47
Web Site: http://www.alcon.com
Emp.: 6
Pharmaceuticals Product Mfr
N.A.I.C.S.: 325412

Alcon Pharmaceuticals Ltd. (2)
Hitachi Center Baouchrieh Sin-El-Fil Highway Bloc A 4 Floor, Beirut, Lebanon
Tel.: (961) 1 490 553 4
Web Site: http://www.alcon.com
Sales Range: $25-49.9 Million
Emp.: 10
Pharmaceuticals Product Mfr
N.A.I.C.S.: 325412

Alcon Pharmaceuticals Taiwan Ltd (2)
4F 119 Pao-Chung Road, Hsin Tien, 23141, Taipei, Taiwan
Tel.: (886) 2 2917 2468
Web Site: http://www.alcon.com
Sales Range: $25-49.9 Million
Emp.: 100
Pharmaceutical Product & Surgical Equipment Mfr
N.A.I.C.S.: 325412

Alcon Portugal, Produtos e Equipamentos Oftalmologicos, LDA (2)
Quinta da Fonte-Edificio D Sancho I Rua dos Malhoes N 4-Piso 3, Paco d'Arcos, 2770-071, Porto Salvo, Portugal
Tel.: (351) 214 400 300
Web Site: http://www.alcon.com
Sales Range: $25-49.9 Million
Emp.: 40
Pharmaceuticals Product Mfr
N.A.I.C.S.: 325412

Plant (Domestic):

Alcon Research, Ltd. (2)
714 Columbia Ave, Sinking Spring, PA 19608-1405
Tel.: (610) 670-3500
Web Site: http://www.alcon.com
Sales Range: $150-199.9 Million
Emp.: 700
Ophthalmic Medical Devices & Instruments Mfr
N.A.I.C.S.: 339112

Alcon Research, Ltd. (2)
9965 Buffalo Speedway, Houston, TX 77054-5008 **(100%)**
Tel.: (713) 668-9100
Web Site: http://www.alcon.com
Sales Range: $150-199.9 Million
Emp.: 750
Ophthalmic Surgical Products Mfr
N.A.I.C.S.: 339115

Alcon Research, Ltd. (2)
6065 Kyle Ln, Huntington, WV 25702-9795
Tel.: (304) 736-5230
Web Site: http://www.alcon.com
Sales Range: $150-199.9 Million
Emp.: 800
Intraocular Lenses Mfr & Distr
N.A.I.C.S.: 339115

Subsidiary (Non-US):

Alcon Romania S.R.L. (2)
Baneasa Business Center - 1st Floor 17-21 Sos Bucuresti-Ploiesti, Sector 1, Bucharest, 7000, Romania
Tel.: (40) 212039301
Web Site: http://www.alcon.com
Sales Range: $25-49.9 Million
Emp.: 30
Ophthalmic Product Distr
N.A.I.C.S.: 423460

Alcon Switzerland SA (2)
Bosch 69, 6331, Hunenberg, Switzerland
Tel.: (41) 41 785 8888
Web Site: http://www.alcon.com
Ophthalmic Goods Whslr
N.A.I.C.S.: 423460

Alcon-Cusi S.A. (2)
Camil Fabra 58 Apartado 2, El Masnou,

AND PRIVATE COMPANIES   NOVARTIS AG

08320, Barcelona, Spain **(100%)**
Tel.: (34) 934977000
Web Site: http://www.alcon.es
Sales Range: $200-249.9 Million
Emp.: 600
Ophthalmic Surgical Equipment, Supplies, Pharmaceuticals & Vision Care Products Research, Development & Mfr
N.A.I.C.S.: 339112

Laboratoires Alcon S.A. (2)
4 rue Henri Sainte-Claire Deville, 92563, Rueil-Malmaison, France **(100%)**
Tel.: (33) 147104710
Web Site: http://www.alcon.fr
Sales Range: $150-199.9 Million
Emp.: 1,000
Ophthalmic Surgical Instruments, Pharmaceuticals & Vision Care Products Mfr & Distr
N.A.I.C.S.: 325412

PT CIBA Vision Batam (2)
Jalan Beringin Kav 204 Batamindo Industrial Park, Muka Kuning, Batam, 29433, Pulau Batam, Indonesia **(100%)**
Tel.: (62) 770611048
Web Site: http://www.id.novartis.com
Vision Care Products Mfr
N.A.I.C.S.: 339115

S.A. Alcon-Couvreur N.V. (2)
Rijksweg 14, Puurs, 2870, Belgium **(100%)**
Tel.: (32) 38902711
Web Site: http://www.alcon.com
Sales Range: $500-549.9 Million
Emp.: 1,300
Ophthalmic Surgical Equipment & Supplies, Pharmaceuticals & Vision Care Products Mfr & Distr
N.A.I.C.S.: 325412

Cellerys AG (1)
Wagistrasse 21, 8952, Schlieren, Switzerland
Tel.: (41) 445449880
Web Site: https://www.cellerys.com
Biotechnological Research Services
N.A.I.C.S.: 541714

CellforCure SASU (1)
3 avenue des Tropiques Z A de Courtaboeuf, 91940, Les Ulis, France
Tel.: (33) 1 69 82 70 10
Web Site: http://www.cellforcure.com
Pharmaceutical Product Mfr & Distr
N.A.I.C.S.: 325412

China Novartis Institutes for BioMedical Research Co., Ltd. (1)
4218 Jinke Road, Zhang Jiang Hi-Tech Park Pudong, Shanghai, 201203, China
Tel.: (86) 216 160 6000
Pharmaceuticals Product Mfr
N.A.I.C.S.: 325412
Jay Bradner *(Pres)*

Chinook Therapeutics, Inc. (1)
400 Fairview Ave N Ste 900, Seattle, WA 98109
Tel.: (206) 485-7241
Web Site: https://www.chinooktx.com
Rev.: $6,128,000
Assets: $574,084,000
Liabilities: $132,143,000
Net Worth: $441,941,000
Earnings: ($187,865,000)
Emp.: 214
Fiscal Year-end: 12/31/2022
Pharmaceutical Mfr, Researcher & Developer
N.A.I.C.S.: 325412
Valerie Fauvelle *(Sr VP)*

Subsidiary (Non-US):

Aduro Biotech, Europe B.V. (2)
Pivot Park - RX1101 Kloosterstraat 9, 5349 AB, Oss, Netherlands
Tel.: (31) 880121400
Pharmaceuticals Product Mfr
N.A.I.C.S.: 325412

Elanco Centre de Recherche Sante Animale SA (1)
1566 Saint-Aubin, Saint-Aubin, Switzerland
Tel.: (41) 266791111
Pharmaceuticals Product Mfr
N.A.I.C.S.: 325412

Endocyte, Inc. (1)
3000 Kent Ave Ste A1-100, West Lafayette, IN 47906
Tel.: (765) 463-7175
Web Site: http://www.endocyte.com
Rev.: $70,000
Assets: $100,762,269
Liabilities: $5,278,124
Net Worth: $95,484,145
Earnings: ($55,064,150)
Emp.: 44
Fiscal Year-end: 12/31/2017
Biopharmaceutical Mfr
N.A.I.C.S.: 325412

Farmanova Saglik Hizmetleri Ltd. (1)
Suryapi and Akel Is Merkezi Rzgarlibahe, Mah Sehit Sinan Eroglu Cad No 6 Kavacik-Beykoz, 34805, Istanbul, Turkiye
Tel.: (90) 216 681 2000
Pharmaceuticals Product Mfr
N.A.I.C.S.: 325412

Gyroscope Therapeutics Limited (1)
Stevenage Bioscience Catalyst Gunnels Wood Road, Stevenage, SG1 2FX, Herts, United Kingdom
Tel.: (44) 1438906770
Web Site: http://www.gyroscopetx.com
Therapy Services
N.A.I.C.S.: 621340
Chris Hollowood *(Chm)*

JSC Sandoz (1)
Leningradskiy prospect 70, Moscow, 125315, Russia
Tel.: (7) 4956607509
Web Site: https://www.sandoz.ru
Pharmaceuticals Mfr
N.A.I.C.S.: 325412

Lek S.A. (1)
ul Podlipie 16, 95-010, Strykow, Poland
Tel.: (48) 427106100
Web Site: http://www.sandoz.pl
Generic Drug Mfr & Distr
N.A.I.C.S.: 325412

MorphoSys AG (1)
Semmelweisstr 7, 82152, Planegg, Germany
Tel.: (49) 89899270
Web Site: https://www.morphosys.com
Rev.: $341,778,664
Assets: $2,944,008,083
Liabilities: $2,750,671,378
Net Worth: $193,336,704
Earnings: ($185,535,711)
Emp.: 629
Fiscal Year-end: 12/31/2022
Biotechnology Research & Development Services
N.A.I.C.S.: 541714
Marc Cluzel *(Chm-Supervisory Bd)*

Subsidiary (US):

Constellation Pharmaceuticals, Inc. (2)
215 First St Ste 200, Cambridge, MA 02142
Tel.: (617) 714-0555
Web Site: http://www.constellationpharma.com
Rev.: $2,851,000
Assets: $441,854,000
Liabilities: $31,130,000
Net Worth: $410,724,000
Earnings: ($126,357,000)
Emp.: 154
Fiscal Year-end: 12/31/2020
Biopharmaceutical Product Mfr & Distr
N.A.I.C.S.: 325411
Danny Reinberg *(Co-Founder)*

MorphoSys US Inc. (2)
4350 Lassiter at N Hills Ave Ste 250, Raleigh, NC 27609
Tel.: (919) 878-7978
Web Site: http://www.abdserotec.com
Emp.: 15
Biotechnology Research & Development Services
N.A.I.C.S.: 541714
Jennifer L. Herron *(Pres)*

Navigate BioPharma Services, Inc. (1)
1890 Rutherford Rd, Carlsbad, CA 92008
Tel.: (760) 602-1400
Web Site: https://www.navigatebp.com

Pharmaceutical Product Mfr & Distr
N.A.I.C.S.: 325412
Arkadius Pichota *(Pres & Gen Mgr)*

Novartis (Bangladesh) Ltd. (1)
House 50 Road 2A Dhanmondi RA, Dhaka, 1209, Bangladesh **(60%)**
Tel.: (880) 28615302
Web Site: http://www.novartis.com.bd
Sales Range: $250-299.9 Million
Emp.: 900
Pharmaceuticals Mfr & Sales; Joint Venture of Novartis International AG (60%) & Bangladesh Chemical Industries Corporation (40%)
N.A.I.C.S.: 325412

Novartis (Hellas) S.A.C.I. (1)
National Road No 1 12th km, Metamorphosis, GR 144 51, Athens, Greece **(100%)**
Tel.: (30) 2102811712
Web Site: http://www.novartis.gr
Sales Range: $150-199.9 Million
Emp.: 350
Pharmaceuticals Sales & Marketing
N.A.I.C.S.: 424210

Novartis (Singapore) Pte Ltd. (1)
20 Pasir Panjang Rd Ste 10-25/28 Mapletree Business City, Singapore, 117439, Singapore **(100%)**
Tel.: (65) 67226010
Web Site: http://www.novartis.com
Pharmaceuticals Mfr & Marketer
N.A.I.C.S.: 325412

Novartis (Taiwan) Co., Ltd. (1)
11th Floor No 99 Section 2 Jen-Ai Road, Taipei, 10062, Taiwan **(100%)**
Tel.: (886) 2 2341 6580
Web Site: http://www.novartis.com.tw
Sales Range: $50-74.9 Million
Emp.: 64
Pharmaceuticals Mfr & Sales
N.A.I.C.S.: 325412

Novartis (Thailand) Ltd. (1)
622 Emporium Tower 15th Floor Sukhumvit Road Kwaeng Klongton, Khet Klongtoey, Bangkok, 10110, Thailand **(100%)**
Tel.: (66) 26850999
Web Site: http://www.th.novartis.com
Sales Range: $150-199.9 Million
Emp.: 300
Pharmaceuticals Sales & Marketing
N.A.I.C.S.: 424210

Novartis Argentina S.A. (1)
Ramallo 1851, 1429, Buenos Aires, Argentina **(100%)**
Tel.: (54) 1147037000
Web Site: http://www.ar.novartis.com
Sales Range: $50-74.9 Million
Emp.: 150
Pharmaceuticals Research & Sales
N.A.I.C.S.: 541715

Novartis Asia Pacific Pharmaceuticals Pte Ltd. (1)
10 Hoe Chiang Road No 15-02A Keppel Towers, Singapore, 89315, Singapore
Tel.: (65) 6722 6132
Pharmaceutical Products Distr
N.A.I.C.S.: 424210

Novartis Australia Pty Ltd. (1)
54 Waterloo Rd, North Ryde, 2113, NSW, Australia
Tel.: (61) 2 9805 3555
Web Site: http://www.novartis.com.au
Sales Range: $250-299.9 Million
Emp.: 700
Pharmaceutical Product Mfr & Distr
N.A.I.C.S.: 325412

Novartis Austria GmbH (1)
Stella-Klein-Low-Weg 17, Vienna, 1020, Austria
Tel.: (43) 1 8665 7 0
Web Site: http://www.novartis.at
Emp.: 200
Pharmaceutical Product Mfr
N.A.I.C.S.: 325412

Novartis Baltics SIA (1)
Gustava zemgala gatve 76, Riga, LV-1039, Latvia
Tel.: (371) 6 788 7070
Web Site: https://www.novartis.lv
Pharmaceutical Product Mfr & Distr

N.A.I.C.S.: 325412

Novartis Biociencias S.A. (1)
Professor Vicente Rao Avenue 90 Predio 111 Sala 0036, Sao Paulo, BR 04706 900, SP, Brazil **(100%)**
Tel.: (55) 11 5532 4446
Web Site: http://www.novartis.com.br
Sales Range: $250-299.9 Million
Emp.: 1,000
Pharmaceuticals Mfr & Marketing
N.A.I.C.S.: 325412

Novartis Biosciences Peru S.A. (1)
Car Carretera Central Nro 1315 Santa Anita, Lima, Peru
Tel.: (51) 14942788
Pharmaceuticals Product Mfr
N.A.I.C.S.: 325412

Novartis Chile S.A. (1)
Rosario Norte 615 Las Condes, Edificio Mistral - Las Condes, Santiago, Chile **(100%)**
Tel.: (56) 2 350 0200
Web Site: http://www.novartis.cl
Sales Range: $25-49.9 Million
Emp.: 20
Pharmaceuticals Sales & Marketing
N.A.I.C.S.: 424210

Novartis Consumer Health S.A. (1)
Route de l'Etraz, PO Box 1279, Prangins, 1260, Nyon, 1260, Switzerland **(100%)**
Tel.: (41) 223633111
Web Site: http://www.consumer-health.ch
Sales Range: $75-99.9 Million
Emp.: 1,000
Consumer Self-Medication Products Mfr & Distr
N.A.I.C.S.: 325412
Tobias Hestler *(CFO)*

Subsidiary (Non-US):

N.V. Novartis Consumer Health S.A. (2)
Medialaan 40, 1800, Vilvoorde, Belgium **(100%)**
Tel.: (32) 22649700
Web Site: http://www.novartis.be
Sales Range: $25-49.9 Million
Emp.: 30
Pharmaceuticals Sales & Marketing
N.A.I.C.S.: 424210

Novartis Consumer Health Australasia Pty Ltd. (2)
327 - 333 Police Road, Mulgrave, Melbourne, 3170, VIC, Australia
Tel.: (61) 397012711
Sales Range: $25-49.9 Million
Emp.: 40
Pharmaceuticals Product Mfr
N.A.I.C.S.: 325412
Violeta Delgado *(Head-Bus Unit)*

Novartis Consumer Health GmbH (2)
Zielstattstrasse 40, Munich, 81379, Germany **(100%)**
Tel.: (49) 8978770
Web Site: http://www.novartis-consumerhealth.de
Sales Range: $50-74.9 Million
Emp.: 200
Pharmaceuticals Research, Mfr & Marketing
N.A.I.C.S.: 325412
Erhard Heck *(Mng Dir)*

Novartis Consumer Health LLC (2)
10/10 Starokonushenny Lane Bld 1, Moscow, 119002, Russia
Tel.: (7) 495 969 21 65
Web Site: http://www.novartis.net
Emp.: 3,000
Pharmaceuticals Product Mfr
N.A.I.C.S.: 325412
Irina Romanova *(Gen Mgr)*

Novartis Consumer Health Nederland B.V (2)
Claudius Prinsenlaan 142, Postbus 2014, Breda, 4818 CP, Netherlands
Tel.: (31) 76 533 00 00
Web Site: http://www.novartisconsumerhealth.nl
Pharmaceuticals Product Mfr
N.A.I.C.S.: 325412

NOVARTIS AG

Novartis AG—(Continued)

Subsidiary (Domestic):

Novartis Consumer Health Schweiz AG (2)
Monbijoustr 118, Postfach 3001, 3007, Bern, Switzerland
Tel.: (41) 31 377 61 11
Web Site: http://www.consumer-health.ch
Pharmaceuticals Product Mfr
N.A.I.C.S.: 325412

Subsidiary (Non-US):

Novartis Consumer Health UK Limited (2)
Park View Riverside Way Watchmoor Park, Camberley, GU15 3YL, Surrey, United Kingdom
Tel.: (44) 1276687300
Pharmaceuticals Product Mfr
N.A.I.C.S.: 325412

Subsidiary (US):

Novartis Consumer Health, Inc. (2)
200 Kimball Dr, Parsippany, NJ 07054
Tel.: (973) 503-8000
Web Site: http://www.us.novartis.com
OTC Pharmaceutical Preparations Research, Mfr, Sales & Marketing
N.A.I.C.S.: 325412

Subsidiary (Domestic):

Ex-Lax, Inc. (3)
Rte 909 Km 13 Mariana Ward, Humacáo, PR 00791 (100%)
Tel.: (787) 852-3190
Web Site: http://www.novartis.com
Sales Range: $50-74.9 Million
Emp.: 230
Laxatives Mfr
N.A.I.C.S.: 325412

Plant (Domestic):

Novartis Consumer Health, Inc. (3)
10401 Hwy 6, Lincoln, NE 68517-9626 (100%)
Tel.: (402) 464-6311
Web Site: http://www.us.novartis.com
Sales Range: $450-499.9 Million
Pharmaceutical Preparation Mfr
N.A.I.C.S.: 325412

Subsidiary (Non-US):

Novartis Consumer Health, S.A. (2)
Marina 206, Barcelona, 08003, Spain
Tel.: (34) 93 306 47 00
Pharmaceuticals Product Mfr
N.A.I.C.S.: 325412

Novartis Corporation (1)
608 5th Ave, New York, NY 10020-2303 (100%)
Tel.: (212) 307-1122
Web Site: http://www.novartis.com
Sales Range: $25-49.9 Million
Emp.: 52
Administration, Communications & Sales & Marketing Services
N.A.I.C.S.: 561499

Subsidiary (Domestic):

Novartis Capital Corporation (2)
608 5th Ave, New York, NY 10020
Tel.: (212) 307-1122
Pharmaceuticals Product Mfr
N.A.I.C.S.: 325412
David Richardson (Mgr-Talent Acq)

Novartis Finance Corporation (2)
230 Park Ave, New York, NY 10169
Tel.: (212) 307-1122
Web Site: http://www.us.novartis.com
Sales Range: $25-49.9 Million
Emp.: 25
Investment Holding Companies, Except Banks
N.A.I.C.S.: 551112
William McHugh (Treas)

Novartis Institute For Functional Genomics, Inc. (2)
10675 John J Hopkins Dr, San Diego, CA 92121-1127
Tel.: (858) 812-1500
Web Site: http://www.gnf.org
Pharmaceutical Research & Development Services
N.A.I.C.S.: 541715

Novartis Institutes for BioMedical Research, Inc. (2)
250 Massachusetts Ave, Cambridge, MA 02139
Tel.: (617) 871-8000
Web Site: http://www.nibr.com
Pharmaceuticals Research & Development
N.A.I.C.S.: 541715
Fiona H. Marshall (Pres)

Branch (Domestic):

Novartis Institutes for BioMedical Research, Inc. (3)
1 Health Plz, East Hanover, NJ 07936
Tel.: (862) 778-8300
Web Site: http://www.nibr.com
Research & Development of Pharmaceutical Products
N.A.I.C.S.: 541715

Subsidiary (Domestic):

Novartis Pharmaceuticals Corporation (2)
1 Health Plz, East Hanover, NJ 07936-1016
Tel.: (862) 778-8300
Web Site: http://www.pharma.us.novartis.com
Sales Range: $125-149.9 Million
Pharmaceuticals Mfr
N.A.I.C.S.: 325412

Subsidiary (Domestic):

Falcon Pharmaceuticals, Ltd. (3)
6201 S Freeway, Fort Worth, TX 76134-2099
Tel.: (800) 343-2133
Web Site: http://www.falconpharma.com
Pharmaceutical Products Distr
N.A.I.C.S.: 424210

Branch (Domestic):

Novartis Pharmaceuticals (3)
2010 Cessna Dr, Vacaville, CA 95688-8712
Tel.: (707) 453-2200
Web Site: http://www.us.novartis.com
Sales Range: $50-74.9 Million
Emp.: 150
Pharmaceuticals Mfr
N.A.I.C.S.: 325412

Novartis Pharmaceuticals Corp. (3)
25 Old Mill Rd, Suffern, NY 10901-4106
Tel.: (845) 368-6000
Web Site: http://www.pharma.us.novartis.com
Pharmaceuticals Mfr
N.A.I.C.S.: 325412

Novartis Pharmaceuticals Corp. (3)
909 Lake Carolyn Pkwy Ste 1700, Irving, TX 75039-3911
Tel.: (972) 409-0626
Sales Range: $25-49.9 Million
Emp.: 13
Pharmaceuticals Marketing
N.A.I.C.S.: 424210

Subsidiary (Domestic):

Novartis Vaccines & Diagnostics, Inc. (2)
350 Massachusetts Ave, Cambridge, MA 02139
Tel.: (617) 871-7000
Web Site: http://www.novartis-vaccines.com
Vaccines & Blood Testing & Molecular Diagnostics Mfr
N.A.I.C.S.: 325412
Andrin Oswald (Head-Novartis Vaccines & Diagnostics Div)

Subsidiary (Non-US):

Novartis Vaccines & Diagnostics GmbH (3)
Emil von Behring Strasse 76, 35041, Marburg, Germany
Tel.: (49) 6421 39 15
Web Site: http://www.novartis-vaccines.de
Sales Range: $900-999.9 Million
Emp.: 3,000
Vaccines Mfr
N.A.I.C.S.: 325414

Novartis Vaccines & Diagnostics Limited (3)
Frimley Business Park, Frimley, Camberley, GU16 7SR, Surrey, United Kingdom
Tel.: (44) 1276694490
Web Site: http://www.novartis.co.uk
Vaccines & Diagnostic Products Mfr & Marketer
N.A.I.C.S.: 325414

Novartis Vaccines & Diagnostics S.A.S. (3)
10 Rue Chevreul, 92150, Suresnes, France
Tel.: (33) 155490030
Web Site: http://www.novartis.fr
Sales Range: $25-49.9 Million
Emp.: 30
Sales & Marketing of Vaccines
N.A.I.C.S.: 424210

Novartis Vaccines & Diagnostics S.r.l. (3)
Via Fiorentina 1, Siena, 53100, Italy
Tel.: (39) 0577243111
Web Site: http://www.novartisvaccines.it
Sales Range: $300-349.9 Million
Emp.: 1,000
Pharmaceuticals Research, Sales & Mfr
N.A.I.C.S.: 325412
Francesco Gulli (Mng Dir & Head-Cluster South)

Novartis Vaccines and Diagnostics, S.L. (3)
Gran Via de les Corts Catalanes 764, Barcelona, 08013, Spain
Tel.: (34) 933 06 42 00
Pharmaceuticals Product Mfr
N.A.I.C.S.: 325412

Novartis Corporation (Malaysia) Sdn. Bhd. (1)
Level 15 Crest 3 Two Sq No 2 Jln 19/1, Petaling Jaya, Selangor, Malaysia
Tel.: (60) 3 7948 1888
Sales Range: $125-149.9 Million
Emp.: 400
Pharmaceuticals Product Mfr
N.A.I.C.S.: 325412

Novartis Deutschland GmbH (1)
Oeflingerstrasse 44, D 79664, Wehr, Germany (100%)
Web Site: http://www.novartis.de
Rev.: $216,500,000
Emp.: 400
Holding Company; Pharmaceuticals
N.A.I.C.S.: 551112

Novartis Ecuador S.A. (1)
Av Republica del Salvador N34-107 y Suiza, Edificio Brescia I Piso 5, Quito, Ecuador (100%)
Tel.: (593) 22464111
Sales Range: $10-24.9 Million
Emp.: 200
Pharmaceuticals Sales & Marketing
N.A.I.C.S.: 424210
Joao Carlos Deretto (Gen Mgr)

Novartis Finance S.A. (1)
20 rue Eugene Ruppert, Luxembourg, 2453, Luxembourg
Tel.: (352) 26 29 42 01
Pharmaceuticals Product Mfr
N.A.I.C.S.: 325412

Novartis Finland Oy (1)
Metsanneidonkuja 10, Espoo, 02130, Finland
Tel.: (358) 10 6133 200
Web Site: http://www.novartis.fi
Pharmaceuticals Product Mfr
N.A.I.C.S.: 325412

Novartis Groupe France S.A. (1)
14 Boulevard Richelieu, F 92500, Rueil-Malmaison, Cedex, France (100%)
Tel.: (33) 155478100
Web Site: http://www.novartis.fr
Sales Range: $1-4.9 Billion
Emp.: 3,169
Management & Financial Services; Holding Company
N.A.I.C.S.: 551112

Subsidiary (Domestic):

Novartis Sante Familiale S.A.S. (2)
14 Bd Richelieu, BP 440, 92845, Rueil-Malmaison, France
Tel.: (33) 155478000
Pharmaceuticals Product Mfr
N.A.I.C.S.: 325412

Novartis Healthcare A/S (1)
Edvard Thomsensvej 14, Copenhagen, 2300, Denmark (100%)
Tel.: (45) 39168400
Web Site: http://www.novartis.dk
Rev.: $50,000,000
Emp.: 100
Pharmaceuticals Sales & Marketing
N.A.I.C.S.: 424210

Novartis Healthcare Private Limited (1)
Sandoz House 8th Fl Dr Annie Besant Rd, Worli, Mumbai, 400 018, India
Tel.: (91) 22 24958888
Pharmaceutical Product Research & Development Services
N.A.I.C.S.: 541715

Novartis Holding AG (1)
Lichtstrasse 35, Basel, 4056, Switzerland
Tel.: (41) 616971111
Investment Management Service
N.A.I.C.S.: 523940

Novartis Holding Japan K.K. (1)
Midori-ku Hakusan 1-18-2, Yokohama, Japan
Tel.: (81) 45 931 8900
Investment Management Service
N.A.I.C.S.: 523940

Novartis Hungary Healthcare Limited Liability Company (1)
Bartok Bela ut 43-47, 1114, Budapest, Hungary (100%)
Tel.: (36) 14576500
Web Site: http://www.novartis.hu
Sales Range: $75-99.9 Million
Emp.: 150
Pharmaceuticals Sales & Marketing
N.A.I.C.S.: 424210

Novartis India Limited (1)
Inspire BKCPart of 601 & 701 Bandra Kurla Complex, Bandra East, Mumbai, 400 051, India (76%)
Tel.: (91) 2250243000
Web Site: https://www.novartis.com
Rev.: $47,570,325
Assets: $110,899,107
Liabilities: $21,595,189
Net Worth: $89,303,918
Earnings: $10,214,281
Emp.: 62
Fiscal Year-end: 03/31/2024
Pharmaceuticals Mfr, Sales & Marketing
N.A.I.C.S.: 325412
Amitabh Dube (Pres-Country)

Novartis International AG (1)
Forum 1 Novartis Campus, CH 4056, Basel, Switzerland (100%)
Tel.: (41) 613241111
Web Site: http://www.novartis.ch
Corporate Environmental & Safety Management, Industrial Technology, Patents & Trademarks, Information Services
N.A.I.C.S.: 561499

Subsidiary (US):

Novartis Gene Therapies, Inc. (2)
2275 Half Day Rd Ste 200, Bannockburn, IL 60015
Tel.: (847) 572-8280
Web Site: http://www.avexis.com
Gene Therapy Company
N.A.I.C.S.: 541714

PowerVision, Inc. (2)
298 Harbor Blvd, Belmont, CA 94002
Tel.: (650) 620-9948
Professional Equipment & Supplies Merchant Whslr
N.A.I.C.S.: 423490

Selexys Pharmaceuticals (2)
840 Research Pkwy, Oklahoma City, OK 73104-3611 (100%)
Tel.: (405) 319-8195

AND PRIVATE COMPANIES — NOVARTIS AG

Web Site:
http://medinfo.novartispharmaceuticals.com
Emp.: 50
Biopharmaceutical Mfr
N.A.I.C.S.: 325412

Novartis International Pharmaceutical Ltd. (1)
131 Front Street, Hamilton, HM 12, Bermuda
Tel.: (441) 296 8025
Web Site: http://www.novartis.com
Sales Range: $50-74.9 Million
Emp.: 9
Financial Management Services
N.A.I.C.S.: 523999

Novartis Investments S.a.r.l. (1)
Rue Eugene Ruppert 20, 2453, Luxembourg, Luxembourg
Tel.: (352) 26294211
Pharmaceuticals Product Mfr
N.A.I.C.S.: 325412

Novartis Ireland Limited (1)
Merrion Road, Clonskeagh, Dublin, 4, Ireland **(100%)**
Tel.: (353) 12601255
Web Site: http://www.ie.novartis.com
Sales Range: $25-49.9 Million
Emp.: 100
Pharmaceuticals Sales & Marketing
N.A.I.C.S.: 424210

Novartis Israel Ltd. (1)
36 Shacham Street-4th Floor Kiryat Matalon, 4951729, Petach Tikva, Israel
Tel.: (972) 3 920 1111
Pharmaceuticals Product Mfr
N.A.I.C.S.: 325412

Novartis Korea Ltd. (1)
18th Fl Yonsei Jaedan Severance Bldg 84-11 5-GA Namdaemunro, Joong-gu, Seoul, 100 753, Korea (South) **(99%)**
Tel.: (82) 27689000
Web Site: http://www.novartis.co.kr
Sales Range: $125-149.9 Million
Emp.: 500
Pharmaceuticals Sales & Marketing
N.A.I.C.S.: 325412

Novartis Middle East FZE (1)
5th Floor Limitless Building, PO Box 23510, Jumeirah Village Triangle Al Khail Road, Dubai, United Arab Emirates
Tel.: (971) 4 435 7002
Pharmaceutical Products Distr
N.A.I.C.S.: 456199

Novartis Netherlands B.V. (1)
Raapopseweg 1, Arnhem, 6824 DP, Netherlands
Tel.: (31) 263782100
Web Site: http://www.novartis.nl
Sales Range: $150-199.9 Million
Emp.: 300
Pharmaceuticals Sales & Marketing
N.A.I.C.S.: 424210

Novartis Neva LLC (1)
Road to Kamenka 40 Bldg 3, 194362, Saint Petersburg, Russia
Tel.: (7) 8123369891
Web Site: https://www.novartis.ru
Pharmaceutical Product Mfr & Distr
N.A.I.C.S.: 325412

Novartis New Zealand Ltd. (1)
Building G 5 Orbit Drive, Rosedale, Auckland, 0632, New Zealand **(100%)**
Tel.: (64) 9 361 8100
Web Site: http://www.novartis.com
Sales Range: $25-49.9 Million
Emp.: 15
Pharmaceuticals Sales & Marketing
N.A.I.C.S.: 424210

Novartis Norge AS (1)
Nydalen Alle 37 A, 0484, Oslo, Norway **(100%)**
Tel.: (47) 23052000
Web Site: http://www.novartis.no
Sales Range: $75-99.9 Million
Emp.: 115
Pharmaceuticals Sales & Marketing
N.A.I.C.S.: 424210

Novartis Ophthalmics AG (1)
Fadrikstrasse 2, 4002, Basel, Switzerland **(100%)**
Tel.: (41) 613241111
Sales Range: $25-49.9 Million
Emp.: 100
Mfr of Ophthalmologic Preparations, Sterile Eye Drops & Ointments
N.A.I.C.S.: 325412

Novartis Pharma (Pakistan) Limited (1)
15 W Wharf Rd, West Wharf Karachi, Karachi, 74000, Sindh, Pakistan
Tel.: (92) 213 231 3386
Web Site: https://www.novartis.pk
Pharmaceutical Product Mfr & Distr
N.A.I.C.S.: 325412
Christopher Snook *(Chm)*

Novartis Pharma AG (1)
Fabrikstrasse 2, CH 4056, Basel, Switzerland **(100%)**
Tel.: (41) 613241111
Web Site: http://www.novartis.ch
Pharmaceuticals Mfr & Distr
N.A.I.C.S.: 325412

Subsidiary (Non-US):

Beijing Novartis Pharma Co., Ltd. (2)
14th Fl China World Tower 2 No 1 Jian Guo Men Wai Ave, Chao Yang District, Beijing, 100004, China
Tel.: (86) 1065058833
Web Site: http://www.novartis.com.cn
Sales Range: $50-74.9 Million
Emp.: 100
Pharmaceuticals Mfr & Sales
N.A.I.C.S.: 325412

N.V. Novartis Pharma S.A. (2)
Medialaan 40, B 1800, Vilvoorde, Belgium **(100%)**
Tel.: (32) 22461611
Web Site: http://www.novartis.be
Sales Range: $150-199.9 Million
Emp.: 300
Pharmaceuticals Sales & Marketing
N.A.I.C.S.: 424210

Novartis Farma - Produtos Farmaceuticos S.A. (2)
Rua do Centro Empresarial Edf 8 Quinta da Beloura-Linho, 2710-444, Sintra, Portugal
Tel.: (351) 21 000 86 00
Web Site: http://www.novartis.pt
Pharmaceuticals Product Mfr
N.A.I.C.S.: 325412

Novartis Farma S.p.A. (2)
Largo Umberto Boccioni 1, I 21040, Origgio, VA, Italy **(100%)**
Tel.: (39) 0296541
Web Site: http://www.novartis.it
Sales Range: $600-649.9 Million
Emp.: 2,000
Pharmaceuticals Research, Mfr, Sales & Marketing
N.A.I.C.S.: 325412

Novartis Farma SA (2)
Avenida Professor-Doutor Cavaco Silva 10E Tugaspark, Porto Salvo, 2740-255, Portugal
Tel.: (351) 21 000 86 00
Web Site: http://www.novartis.pt
Pharmaceutical Products Distr
N.A.I.C.S.: 424210

Novartis Farmaceutica, S.A. (2)
Gran Via de les Corts Catalanes 764, E 08013, Barcelona, Spain **(100%)**
Tel.: (34) 933064200
Web Site: http://www.novartis.es
Sales Range: $600-649.9 Million
Emp.: 1,050
Pharmaceuticals Mfr, Sales & Marketing
N.A.I.C.S.: 325412

Novartis Farmaceutica, S.A. (AC) (2)
Anillo Periferico 30-31 Zona 11, PO Box 1115, 01011, Guatemala, Guatemala **(100%)**
Tel.: (502) 24228400
Web Site: http://www.novartis.com
Sales Range: $75-99.9 Million
Emp.: 120
Pharmaceuticals Mfr, Sales & Marketing
N.A.I.C.S.: 424210

Novartis Farmaceutica, S.A. de C.V. (2)
Calzada Tlalpan No 1779, Col San Diego Churubusco, Delegacion Coyoacan, Mexico, 04120, Mexico **(100%)**
Tel.: (52) 55 5420 8600
Web Site: http://www.novartis.com.mx
Sales Range: $250-299.9 Million
Emp.: 1,000
Pharmaceuticals Mfr & Distr
N.A.I.C.S.: 325412

Novartis Pharma (Logistics), Inc. (2)
Costa del Este Business Park, Panama, Panama
Tel.: (507) 3002033
Pharmaceutical Products Distr
N.A.I.C.S.: 424210

Novartis Pharma B.V. (2)
Hullenbergweg 83-85, 1101 CL, Amsterdam, Netherlands
Tel.: (31) 205640564
Sales & Marketing of Vaccines
N.A.I.C.S.: 424210

Novartis Pharma GmbH (2)
Roonstrasse 25, 90429, Nuremberg, Germany **(100%)**
Tel.: (49) 9112730
Web Site: http://www.novartis.de
Sales Range: $150-199.9 Million
Emp.: 500
Pharmaceuticals Research & Sales
N.A.I.C.S.: 325412
Patrick Boeuf *(Chm-Supervisory Bd)*

Novartis Pharma GmbH (2)
Stella-Klein-Low-Weg 17, Vienna, 1020, Austria **(100%)**
Tel.: (43) 1866570
Web Site: http://www.novartis.at
Pharmaceuticals Sales & Marketing
N.A.I.C.S.: 325412

Novartis Pharma K.K. (2)
4-17-30 Nishi-Azabu, Minato-ku, Tokyo, 106 8616, Japan **(100%)**
Tel.: (81) 337978000
Web Site: http://www.novartis.jp
Sales Range: $300-349.9 Million
Emp.: 700
Pharmaceuticals Research & Sales
N.A.I.C.S.: 424210
Leo Lee *(Pres-Japan)*

Novartis Pharma LLC (2)
Leningradsky pr-t 70, 125315, Moscow, Russia
Tel.: (7) 4959671270
Web Site: http://www.novartis.ru
Pharmaceuticals Product Mfr
N.A.I.C.S.: 325412

Novartis Pharma Maroc SA (2)
BMCI Building Lot 3 La Colline II, Sidi Maarouf, 20190, Casablanca, Morocco **(100%)**
Tel.: (212) 522349292
Web Site: http://www.novartis.com
Sales Range: $75-99.9 Million
Emp.: 212
Pharmaceuticals Sales & Marketing
N.A.I.C.S.: 424210

Novartis Pharma Produktions GmbH (2)
Oeflingerstrasse 44, Wehr, 79664, Germany
Tel.: (49) 7762 820
Pharmaceutical Products Distr
N.A.I.C.S.: 424210

Novartis Pharma S.A.S. (2)
2 et 4 rue Lionel Terray, Rueil-Malmaison, F 92500, France **(100%)**
Tel.: (33) 155476000
Web Site: http://www.novartis.fr
Researcher, Mfr & Sales of Pharmaceuticals
N.A.I.C.S.: 325412

Subsidiary (Domestic):

Novartis Pharma Schweiz AG (2)
Suurstoffi 14, CH 3007, Rotkreuz, Switzerland **(100%)**
Tel.: (41) 313775111
Web Site: http://www.novartispharma.ch
Sales Range: $25-49.9 Million
Emp.: 125

Pharmaceuticals Research, Sales & Marketing
N.A.I.C.S.: 541715

Subsidiary (Domestic):

Novartis Pharma Schweizerhalle AG (3)
Rheinfelderstrasse Pratteln 1, 4133, Liestal, Switzerland
Tel.: (41) 61 324 11 11
Pharmaceuticals Product Mfr
N.A.I.C.S.: 325412

Novartis Pharma Services AG (3)
Monbijoustrasse 118, Bern, 3001, Switzerland
Tel.: (41) 31 377 51 11
Pharmaceuticals Product Mfr
N.A.I.C.S.: 325412

Novartis Pharma Stein AG (3)
Schaffhauserstrasse 101, Stein am Rhein, 4332, Switzerland
Tel.: (41) 62 868 61 11
Pharmaceuticals Product Mfr
N.A.I.C.S.: 325412

Subsidiary (Non-US):

Novartis Pharmaceuticals (HK) Limited (2)
27/F 1063 King's Road, Quarry Bay, China (Hong Kong) **(100%)**
Tel.: (852) 2882 5222
Web Site: http://www.novartis.com
Sales Range: $50-74.9 Million
Emp.: 95
Pharmaceuticals Sales & Marketing
N.A.I.C.S.: 424210

Novartis Pharmaceuticals Australia Pty Ltd. (2)
54 Waterloo Road, North Ryde, 2113, NSW, Australia **(100%)**
Tel.: (61) 298053555
Web Site: http://www.novartis.com.au
Sales Range: $150-199.9 Million
Emp.: 330
Pharmaceuticals Research & Sales
N.A.I.C.S.: 424210

Novartis Pharmaceuticals Canada Inc. (2)
385 Bouchard Blvd, Dorval, H9S 1A9, QC, Canada **(100%)**
Tel.: (514) 631-6775
Web Site: http://www.novartis.ca
Sales Range: $125-149.9 Million
Emp.: 380
Pharmaceuticals Research & Sales
N.A.I.C.S.: 325412

Novartis Pharmaceuticals UK Limited (2)
200 Frimley Business Park, Frimley, Camberley, GU16 7SR, Surrey, United Kingdom **(100%)**
Tel.: (44) 1276692255
Web Site: http://www.novartis.co.uk
Sales Range: $150-199.9 Million
Emp.: 500
Pharmaceuticals Research, Mfr, Sales & Marketing
N.A.I.C.S.: 325412

Salutas Pharma GmbH (2)
Otto-von-Guericke Allee 1, Barleben, 39179, Germany
Tel.: (49) 3 92 03 71 0
Pharmaceuticals Product Mfr
N.A.I.C.S.: 325412

Saudi Pharmaceutical Distribution Co. Ltd. (2)
Saphad Building Prince Mohammed Bin Abdulaziz Street Salamaniya Area, 16032, Riyadh, Saudi Arabia
Tel.: (966) 1 465 8882
Pharmaceuticals Product Mfr
N.A.I.C.S.: 325412

Suzhou Novartis Pharma Technology Co. Ltd. (2)
18 Tonglian road Riverside Industrial Park, Changshu Economic Development Zone, Changshu, 215537, Jiangsu, China
Tel.: (86) 512 52256666
Pharmaceutical Products Distr
N.A.I.C.S.: 424210

NOVARTIS AG

Novartis AG—(Continued)

Novartis Pharma N.V. (1)
Medialaan 40, 1800, Vilvoorde, Belgium
Tel.: (32) 2 246 1611
Web Site: https://www.novartis.be
Pharmaceutical Product Mfr & Distr
N.A.I.C.S.: 325412

Novartis Pharma Services Romania S.R.L. (1)
Equilibrium Complex Building 1 Floor 10, Section E10 02 2 Gara Herastrau St District 2, 020334, Bucharest, Romania
Tel.: (40) 21 312 9901
Web Site: https://www.novartis.com.ro
Pharmaceutical Product Mfr & Distr
N.A.I.C.S.: 325412

Novartis Poland Sp. z o.o. (1)
Marynarska 15, Warsaw, 02-674, Poland **(100%)**
Tel.: (48) 223754888
Web Site: http://www.novartis.pl
Sales Range: $75-99.9 Million
Emp.: 225
Pharmaceuticals Sales & Marketing
N.A.I.C.S.: 424210

Novartis Portugal SGPS Lda (1)
Rua C Empresarial Qt Beloura-Ed 8, Linho, 2710-693, Sintra, Portugal
Tel.: (351) 210 008 600
Pharmaceuticals Product Mfr
N.A.I.C.S.: 325412

Novartis Research Foundation (1)
Klybeckstrasse 141, 4002, Basel, Switzerland
Tel.: (41) 61 696 23 00
Pharmaceutical Research & Development Services
N.A.I.C.S.: 541715

Novartis Saglik, Gida ve Tarim Urunleri Sanayi ve Ticaret A.S. (1)
Suryapi & Akel Is Merkezi Ruzgarlibahce Mah, Sehit Sinan Eroglu Cad No 6, Kavicik-Beykoz, TR 34805, Istanbul, Turkiye **(100%)**
Tel.: (90) 2166812000
Web Site: http://www.novartis.com.tr
Sales Range: $50-74.9 Million
Emp.: 100
Pharmaceuticals Mfr & Sales
N.A.I.C.S.: 325412

Novartis Saudi Ltd. (1)
Tamkeen Tower Olaya Street, Al Yasmin District, Riyadh, 11425, Saudi Arabia
Tel.: (966) 11 265 8100
Pharmaceuticals Product Mfr
N.A.I.C.S.: 325412

Novartis Securities Investment Ltd. (1)
131 Front Street, Hamilton, HM 12, Bermuda
Tel.: (441) 296 8025
Investment Management Service
N.A.I.C.S.: 523999

Novartis Services, Inc. (1)
1 Health Plz, East Hanover, NJ 07936-1080
Tel.: (862) 778-8300
Pharmaceuticals Product Mfr
N.A.I.C.S.: 325412

Novartis Singapore Pharmaceutical Manufacturing Pte. Ltd. (1)
20 Pasir Panjang Road 10-25/28 West Tower, Mapletree Business City, Singapore, 117439, Singapore
Tel.: (65) 6 722 6010
Web Site: https://www.novartis.com.sg
Pharmaceuticals Product Mfr
N.A.I.C.S.: 325412

Novartis Slovakia s.r.o. (1)
Galvaniho 15/A, Bratislava, 82104, Slovakia
Tel.: (421) 2 5070 6111
Web Site: http://www.novartis.com
Pharmaceutical Products Distr
N.A.I.C.S.: 424210

Novartis South Africa (Pty) Ltd. (1)
72 Steel Road, Spartan, Kempton Park, 1619, Gauteng, South Africa **(100%)**
Tel.: (27) 119299111
Web Site: http://www.novartis.com

Sales Range: $150-199.9 Million
Emp.: 400
Pharmaceuticals Sales & Marketing
N.A.I.C.S.: 424210

Novartis Sverige AB (1)
Kemistvagen 1B, S 183 79, Taby, Sweden **(100%)**
Tel.: (46) 87323200
Web Site: http://www.novartis.se
Sales Range: $75-99.9 Million
Emp.: 200
Pharmaceuticals Sales & Marketing
N.A.I.C.S.: 424210
Niklas Karlberg *(Mng Dir)*

Subsidiary (Domestic):

Novartis Sverige Participations AB (2)
Kemistvagen 1B, Box 1150, Taby, Stockholm, 183 11, Sweden
Tel.: (46) 8732 32 00
Web Site: http://www.novartis.com
Pharmaceutical Products Distr
N.A.I.C.S.: 424210

Novartis Tiergesundheit GmbH (1)
Zielstattstrabe 40, Munich, 81379, Germany
Tel.: (49) 897877710
Web Site: http://www.ah.novartis.de
Sales Range: $25-49.9 Million
Emp.: 60
Pharmaceuticals Product Mfr
N.A.I.C.S.: 325412
Thomas Weers *(Gen Mgr)*

Novartis UK Limited (1)
Frimley Business Park, Frimley, Camberley, GU16 7SR, Surrey, United Kingdom **(100%)**
Tel.: (44) 1276692255
Web Site: http://www.novartis.co.uk
Sales Range: $900-999.9 Million
Emp.: 500
Holding Company
N.A.I.C.S.: 551112

Subsidiary (Domestic):

Novartis Grimsby Ltd. (2)
Pyewipe, Grimsby, DN31 2SR, Lincs, United Kingdom **(100%)**
Tel.: (44) 1472355221
Web Site: http://www.novartis.co.uk
Sales Range: $75-99.9 Million
Emp.: 500
Pharmaceuticals Mfr
N.A.I.C.S.: 325412

Unit (Domestic):

Novartis Horsham Research Centre (2)
Wimblehurst Road, Horsham, RH12 5AB, W Sussex, United Kingdom **(100%)**
Tel.: (44) 1403272827
Sales Range: $200-249.9 Million
Emp.: 400
Pharmaceutical Research Services
N.A.I.C.S.: 325412

Novartis Uruguay S.A. (1)
Av Luis Alberto de Herrera 1248 Torre 3 Piso 11 Oficina 1174, 11300, Montevideo, Uruguay
Tel.: (598) 26231916
Web Site: http://www.novartis.com
Pharmaceuticals Producut Sales
N.A.I.C.S.: 424210

Novartis de Colombia S.A. (1)
Calle 93B No 16-31, Bogota, DC, Colombia **(100%)**
Tel.: (57) 16544444
Web Site: http://www.novartis.com.co
Sales Range: $125-149.9 Million
Emp.: 400
Mfr & Distr of Pharmaceuticals
N.A.I.C.S.: 325412

Novartis s.r.o. (1)
Gemini Building B, Na Pankraci 1724/129, 140 00, Prague, Czech Republic **(100%)**
Tel.: (420) 225775111
Web Site: http://www.novartis.cz
Emp.: 350
Pharmaceuticals Sales & Marketing
N.A.I.C.S.: 424210

Novista Insurance Limited (1)

Suite 913 Europort, Gibraltar, Gibraltar
Tel.: (350) 20043882
General Insurance Services
N.A.I.C.S.: 524298

PT Novartis Indonesia (1)
AXA Tower 25th-26th Floor Jl Prof Dr Satrio Kav 18, Kuningan, 12940, Indonesia
Tel.: (62) 21 3048 0600
Web Site: http://www.id.novartis.com
Pharmaceutical Products Distr
N.A.I.C.S.: 424210

Sandoz Philippines Corporation (1)
7/F Asian Reinsurance Bldg Salcedo and Gamboa Streets, Legaspi Village, Makati, 1229, Metro Manila, Philippines
Tel.: (63) 2 368 7888
Biomedical Research Services
N.A.I.C.S.: 541715

Sandoz Private Limited (1)
iThink Techno Campus Phase 1 Alpha Building Ground Floor Off, Jogeshwari Vikroli Link Road Kanjurmarg East, Mumbai, 400 042, India
Tel.: (91) 226 152 9700
Biomedical Research Services
N.A.I.C.S.: 541715

Sandoz S.p.A. (1)
Largo Umberto Boccioni 1, 21040, Origgio, Varese, Italy
Tel.: (39) 0296541
Web Site: https://www.sandoz.it
Pharmaceutical Product Mfr & Distr
N.A.I.C.S.: 325412

Sandoz Ukraine LLC (1)
Stepana Bandera Avenue Bldg 28-A Letter G, SP Hall Business Center 7th Floor, 04073, Kiev, Ukraine
Tel.: (380) 44 495 2866
Web Site: https://www.sandoz.ua
Pharmaceuticals Product Mfr
N.A.I.C.S.: 325412

Shanghai Novartis Trading Ltd. (1)
801 Huai Hai Plaza 1045 Mid-Huai Hai Road, Shanghai, 200031, China
Tel.: (86) 21 2411 6688
Web Site: http://www.novartis.com.cn
Pharmaceutical Products Distr
N.A.I.C.S.: 424210

Suzhou Novartis Technical Development Co., Ltd. (1)
18-1 Tonglian Road, Bixi Subdistrict, Changshu, 215537, China
Tel.: (86) 5125 225 6666
Pharmaceuticals Product Mfr
N.A.I.C.S.: 325412

The Medicines Company (1)
8 Sylvan Way, Parsippany, NJ 07054
Tel.: (973) 290-6000
Web Site:
  http://www.themedicinescompany.com
Rev: $6,138,000
Assets: $841,686,000
Liabilities: $863,950,000
Net Worth: ($22,264,000)
Earnings: ($123,156,000)
Emp.: 62
Fiscal Year-end: 12/31/2018
Biopharmaceutical Products Developer
N.A.I.C.S.: 325412
Mark Timney *(CEO)*

Subsidiary (Domestic):

Annovation BioPharma, Inc. (2)
25 1st St Ste 303, Cambridge, MA 02141
Tel.: (617) 588-2644
Pharmaceuticals Product Mfr
N.A.I.C.S.: 325412

Subsidiary (Non-US):

ProFibrix B.V. (2)
Darwinweg 24, Leiden, 2333 CR, Netherlands
Tel.: (31) 887308301
Web Site: http://www.profibrix.com
Pharmaceuticals Product Mfr
N.A.I.C.S.: 325412

Subsidiary (Domestic):

ProFibrix, Inc. (2)

INTERNATIONAL PUBLIC

1144 Eastlake Ave E Ste 700, Seattle, WA 98109
Tel.: (973) 290-6000
Pharmaceuticals Product Mfr
N.A.I.C.S.: 325412
Martijn Meijer *(VP-Fin)*

Rempex Pharmaceuticals, Inc. (2)
3033 Science Park Rd, San Diego, CA 92121
Tel.: (858) 875-2840
Web Site: http://www.rempexpharma.com
Emp.: 40
Antibacterial Pharmaceutical Research & Development
N.A.I.C.S.: 325412
Michael N. Dudley *(Chief Scientific Officer & Sr VP-R&D)*

Subsidiary (Non-US):

The Medicines Company (Australia) Pty Limited (2)
Suite 1 Level 8 North Tower 1-5 Railway Street, Chatswood, 2067, NSW, Australia
Tel.: (61) 294131808
Web Site:
  http://www.themedicinescompany.com
Emp.: 3
Biopharmaceutical Products Developer & Mfr
N.A.I.C.S.: 325412

The Medicines Company (Belgium) SPRL/BVBA (2)
Square de Meeus 37-4th Floor, Brussels, 1000, Belgium
Tel.: (32) 27917732
Biopharmaceutical Product Developer & Mfr
N.A.I.C.S.: 325412

The Medicines Company (Deutschland) GmbH (2)
Nymphenburger Strasse 5, Munich, Germany
Tel.: (49) 89244180860
Sales Range: $25-49.9 Million
Emp.: 8
Biopharmaceutical Products Developer
N.A.I.C.S.: 325412

The Medicines Company (Netherlands) BV (2)
Zekeringstraat 46, 1001 NS, Amsterdam, Netherlands
Tel.: (31) 203469960
Biopharmaceutical Products Developer & Mfr
N.A.I.C.S.: 325412

The Medicines Company (Schweiz) GmbH (2)
Balsberg Balz-Zimmermannstrabe 7, Zurich, Switzerland
Tel.: (41) 448281071
Pharmaceutical Preparation Mfr
N.A.I.C.S.: 325412

The Medicines Company (Spain) S.L. (2)
Pinar 5, Madrid, 28006, Spain
Tel.: (34) 917456600
Pharmaceutical Preparation Mfr
N.A.I.C.S.: 325412

Branch (Domestic):

The Medicines Company -Indianapolis (2)
225 S East St, Indianapolis, IN 46202-4002
Tel.: (973) 290-6000
Sales Range: $200-249.9 Million
Emp.: 600
Biopharmaceutical Products
N.A.I.C.S.: 325412

Branch (Non-US):

The Medicines Company -Montreal (2)
6100 Ave Royalmount, Montreal, H4P 2R2, QC, Canada
Tel.: (514) 496-6667
Web Site:
  http://www.themedicinescompany.com
Sales Range: $200-249.9 Million
Emp.: 10
Biopharmaceutical Products
N.A.I.C.S.: 325412

AND PRIVATE COMPANIES

The Medicines Company
-Quebec (2)
2901 Rue Rachel E, Montreal, H1W 4A4, QC, Canada
Tel.: (514) 523-2825
Sales Range: $150-199.9 Million
Emp.: 11
Antibiotics Developer
N.A.I.C.S.: 325412

The Medicines Company -Saint Laurent
7170 Frederick Banting 2nd floor, Saint Laurent, H4S 2A1, QC, Canada
Tel.: (514) 332-1008
Sales Range: $150-199.9 Million
Antibiotics Developer
N.A.I.C.S.: 325412

Subsidiary (Non-US):

The Medicines Company UK Limited (2)
Suite J & L 115L Milton Park, Abingdon, OX14 4SA, Oxfordshire, United Kingdom
Tel.: (44) 1235448500
Web Site:
http://www.themedicinescompany.com
Emp.: 10
Pharmaceutical Preparation Mfr
N.A.I.C.S.: 325412

Subsidiary (Domestic):

Vita Solutions, Inc. (2)
7203 Anaquitas Creek Ct, Richmond, TX 77407
Tel.: (281) 239-8881
Pharmaceuticals Product Mfr
N.A.I.C.S.: 325412

WaveLight GmbH (1)
Am Wolfsmantel 5, 91058, Erlangen, Germany
Tel.: (49) 91 31 61 86 0
Web Site: http://www.wavelight.de
Surgical Equipment Mfr & Distr
N.A.I.C.S.: 339112

Zhejiang Tianyuan Bio-Pharmaceutical Co., Ltd (1)
Tianhe Road 56 Linping, Yuhang, 311100, Hangzhou, China
Tel.: (86) 571 26286888
Pharmaceutical Products Distr
N.A.I.C.S.: 424210

NOVATECH APS
Skudehavnsvej 30, 9000, Aalborg, Denmark
Tel.: (45) 98165009 DK
Web Site: http://www.novatech.dk
Transport Equipment for Shipping Industry & Industrial Application Design & Mfr
N.A.I.C.S.: 333924
Poul Nordby Jensen (Rreg Sls Mgr-USA, Australia & New Zeland & Dir-Special Projects)

Subsidiaries:

NT Liftec Oy (1)
Sorkkalantie 394, Tampere, 33980, Pirkkala, Finland
Tel.: (358) 331401400
Web Site: http://www.ntliftec.com
Trailers, Translifters, Straddle Carriers & Marine Cargo Handling Machinery Mfr
N.A.I.C.S.: 333924
Ari Ranta (Product Mgr-Sls Support)

NOVATECH INDUSTRIES SA
1 rue Paul Sabatier, 22300, Lannion, France
Tel..: (33) 296482440
Web Site: https://www.novatech-groupe.com
Year Founded: 1985
MLNOV—(EUR)
Sales Range: $25-49.9 Million
Emp.: 100
Electronic Components Mfr
N.A.I.C.S.: 334419
Jocelyne Madec (CEO)

Subsidiaries:

Novatech Technologies SA (1)
Route de Quimper, 29590, Pont-de-Buis-les-Quimerch, France
Tel.: (33) 298813200
Emp.: 220
Electrical & Electronic Equipment Mfr
N.A.I.C.S.: 335999

NOVATEK MICROELECTRONICS CORPORATION
2F No 13 Innovation Rd I Hsinchu Science Park, Hsin-chu, 30076, Taiwan
Tel.: (886) 35670889 TW
Web Site:
https://www.novatek.com.tw
Year Founded: 1997
3034—(TAI)
Rev.: $3,591,141,259
Assets: $3,396,471,498
Liabilities: $1,210,582,398
Net Worth: $2,185,889,100
Earnings: $758,285,393
Emp.: 3,464
Fiscal Year-end: 12/31/23
Wafers, Display & Digital Imaging Systems Mfr
N.A.I.C.S.: 334419
Tai-Shung Ho (Chm)

Subsidiaries:

NTK International Limited (1)
18F Po Shau Centre 115 How Ming Street, Kwun Tong, Kowloon, China (Hong Kong)
Tel.: (852) 27662083
Electric Equipment Mfr
N.A.I.C.S.: 334419

Novatek (Shanghai) Co., Ltd. (1)
Room 505 15# No 498 Guo Shou Jing Rd, Shanghai, 201203, China
Tel.: (86) 2161637088
Web Site: http://www.novatek.com.tw
Integrated Circuits Design & Services
N.A.I.C.S.: 334419

Novatek (Shenzhen) Co., Ltd. (1)
32F Tower A KINGKEY TIMEMARK Building No 9289 Binhe Blvd, Futian District, Shenzhen, 518048, China
Tel.: (86) 75533353399
Electric Equipment Mfr
N.A.I.C.S.: 334419

Novatek (Suzhou) Co., Ltd. (1)
Unit 304 Building 1 No 5 Xing Han Street, Suzhou Industrial Park, Suzhou, 215021, China
Tel.: (86) 51287172138
Electric Equipment Mfr
N.A.I.C.S.: 334419

Novatek Japan Kabushiki-Kaisha (1)
6F Eishin Building 6-1 3Chome Kanda-Ogawamachi, Chiyoda-Ku, Tokyo, 101-0052, Japan
Tel.: (81) 352598222
Electric Equipment Mfr
N.A.I.C.S.: 334419

NOVATEOR RESEARCH LABORATORIES LTD.
1026 Dev Atelier 100 Feet Road, Anand Nagar Cross Road Opp Dev Aurum Prahlad Nagar, Ahmedabad, 380015, India
Tel.: (91) 9979961759
Web Site: https://novateor.com
Year Founded: 2011
542771—(BOM)
Rev.: $209,807
Assets: $1,067,252
Liabilities: $122,365
Net Worth: $944,888
Earnings: $4,395
Emp.: 13
Fiscal Year-end: 03/31/23
Developing Novel Personal Services
N.A.I.C.S.: 456199

Navdeep Subhashbhai Mehta (Mng Dir)

NOVATEX GMBH
Werner-von-Siemens-Strasse 14, 30982, Pattensen, Germany
Tel.: (49) 510191950
Web Site: http://www.novatex.de
Year Founded: 1984
Rev.: $20,691,000
Emp.: 120
Baby Products Mfr
N.A.I.C.S.: 339930
Armin Struckmeier (Co-Mng Dir)

Subsidiaries:

NOVATEX North America Inc. (1)
1070 Faultless Dr, Ashland, OH 44805
Tel.: (419) 282-4264
Web Site: http://www.novatex.us
Baby Care Product Mfr
N.A.I.C.S.: 325620

NOVATOR PARTNERS LLP
25 Park Lane, Mayfair, London, W1K 1RA, United Kingdom
Tel.: (44) 2076471500 UK
Web Site: http://www.novator.is
Year Founded: 2004
Sales Range: $1-4.9 Billion
Emp.: 20
Privater Equity Firm
N.A.I.C.S.: 523999
Thor Bjorgolfsson (Chm & Partner)

Subsidiaries:

NOVATOR (Luxembourg) S.a.r.l. (1)
25 C Boulevard Royal, 2449, Luxembourg, Luxembourg
Tel.: (352) 2747201
Investment Management Service
N.A.I.C.S.: 523940

Novator ehf (1)
Odinsgata 7, 101, Reykjavik, Iceland
Tel.: (354) 4146000
Web Site: http://www.novator.is
Sales Range: $50-74.9 Million
Emp.: 2
Privater Equity Firm
N.A.I.C.S.: 523999
Thor Bjorgolfsson (Founder)

NOVATTI GROUP LIMITED
Level 3 461 Bourke Street, Melbourne, 3000, VIC, Australia
Tel.: (61) 390118490 AU
Web Site: https://www.novatti.com
Year Founded: 2015
NOV—(ASX)
Rev.: $14,120,116
Assets: $48,872,962
Liabilities: $42,055,403
Net Worth: $6,817,559
Earnings: ($9,073,988)
Fiscal Year-end: 06/30/21
Financial Process Technology
N.A.I.C.S.: 561499
Peter Cook (CEO, Mng Dir & Exec Dir)

Subsidiaries:

Emersion Systems Pty Ltd (1)
Level 3 461 Bourke Street, Melbourne, 3001, VIC, Australia
Tel.: (61) 386589400
Web Site: https://www.emersion.com
Real Time Billing Services
N.A.I.C.S.: 561110
Paul Dundas (Founder & CEO)

Vasco Pay Pty Ltd (1)
100 Harris St, Pyrmont, 2009, NSW, Australia
Tel.: (61) 291586047
Web Site: https://www.vascopay.com
Electronic Payment Services
N.A.I.C.S.: 522320
Leo Borovilas (CEO)

NOVATURAS AB
A Mickeviciaus Str 27, LT-44245, Kaunas, Lithuania
Tel.: (370) 37321264
Web Site:
https://www.novaturasgroup.com
NTU1L—(RSE)
Rev.: $40,401,727
Assets: $55,715,423
Liabilities: $38,813,612
Net Worth: $16,901,811
Earnings: ($7,062,380)
Emp.: 119
Fiscal Year-end: 12/31/20
Travel Tour Operator
N.A.I.C.S.: 561520
Tomas Staskunas (CFO)

NOVAVEST REAL ESTATE AG
Feldeggstrasse 26, 8008, Zurich, Switzerland
Tel.: (41) 442764040
Web Site: https://www.novavest.ch
NREN—(SWX)
Sales Range: Less than $1 Million
Real Estate Development Services
N.A.I.C.S.: 531390
Peter Mettler (CEO & Member-Mgmt Bd)

NOVAVIS GROUP SA
Park Avenue ul Wspolna 70 5 Pietro, 00-687, Warsaw, Poland
Tel.: (48) 222099800
Web Site: https://novavisgroup.pl
NVG—(WAR)
Rev.: $2,698,933
Assets: $7,912,856
Liabilities: $5,807,165
Net Worth: $2,105,691
Earnings: $1,199,949
Fiscal Year-end: 12/31/23
Investment Services
N.A.I.C.S.: 523940
Piotr Karmelita (Chm-Mgmt Bd & Pres)

NOVEKO INTERNATIONAL INC.
1190 Place Nobel Suite 300, Boucherville, J4B 5L2, QC, Canada
Tel.: (514) 875-0606 Ca
Web Site: http://www.noveko.com
Year Founded: 1983
Sales Range: $10-24.9 Million
Emp.: 100
Medical Equipment Mfr & Marketer
N.A.I.C.S.: 339112
Andre Leroux (Chm & CEO)

Subsidiaries:

Epurair Inc. (1)
3140 Rue Nor Star, Saint-Hubert, J3Y 3W6, QC, Canada
Tel.: (514) 316-4368
Web Site: http://www.epurair.com
Air Exchangers Mfr
N.A.I.C.S.: 333912

S.A.S. E.C.M., (1)
126 Boulevard de La Republique, 16 000, Angouleme, Charente, France
Tel.: (33) 545920357
Web Site: http://www.ecmscan.com
Ultrasound Scanners Mfr & Sales
N.A.I.C.S.: 334510
Emere Patrica (Gen Mgr)

NOVEL APPAREL (BVI) LTD.
1F Novel Industrial Bldg 850-870 Lai Chi Kok Rd, Cheung Sha, Kowloon, K3, China (Hong Kong)
Tel.: (852) 27855988
Mfr of Denim Apparel
N.A.I.C.S.: 315990

Subsidiaries:

Novel Denim Holdings Limited (1)
1F Novel Industrial Building 85-870 Lai Chi

NOVEL APPAREL (BVI) LTD.

Novel Apparel (BVI) Ltd.—(Continued)
Kok Road, Cheung Sha Wan, Kowloon, K3, China (Hong Kong)
Tel.: (852) 27855988
Sales Range: $1-4.9 Billion
Emp.: 7,700
Mfr of Denim Apparel
N.A.I.C.S.: 315990

NOVEM GROUP S.A.
19 rue Edmond Reuter, 5326, Contern, Luxembourg
Tel.: (352) 20213055   LU
Web Site: https://www.novem.com
Year Founded: 1947
NVM—(DEU)
Rev.: $685,850,420
Assets: $649,812,216
Liabilities: $552,804,877
Net Worth: $97,007,338
Earnings: $37,536,154
Emp.: 4,887
Fiscal Year-end: 03/31/24
Motor Vehicle Product Mfr
N.A.I.C.S.: 336360
Gnter Brenner (CEO)

Subsidiaries:

Novem Car Interior Design GmbH (1)
Industriestrasse 45, 95519, Vorbach, Germany
Tel.: (49) 9205180
Automobile Parts Mfr & Distr
N.A.I.C.S.: 336390

Novem Group GmbH (1)
Industriestrasse 45, 95519, Vorbach, Germany
Tel.: (49) 9205181399
Vehicle Parts Mfr & Distr
N.A.I.C.S.: 332321

NOVEMBER AG
Hansaring 97, 50670, Cologne, Germany
Tel.: (49) 221820052010
Web Site: http://www.november.de
Sales Range: $1-9.9 Million
Emp.: 34
Medical & Biotechnology Investing Services
N.A.I.C.S.: 523940
Dr Dirk Zurek (Chm-Mgmt Bd & CEO)

Subsidiaries:

IBL Gesellschaft fur Immunchemie und Immunbiologie m.b.H. i.l. (1)
Flughafenstrasse 52a, 22335, Hamburg, Germany
Tel.: (49) 405328910
Diagnostic Test Substance Mfr
N.A.I.C.S.: 325413

NOVEXCO, INC.
950 Place Paul-Kane, Laval, H7C 2T2, QC, Canada
Tel.: (514) 335-8521
Web Site: http://www.novexco.ca
Emp.: 250
Office Supplies & Furniture Whslr
N.A.I.C.S.: 424120
Denis Mathieu (Pres & CEO)

Subsidiaries:

S.P. Richards Co. Canada, Inc. (1)
Unit 4 820 Cliveden Pl, Delta, V3M 6C7, BC, Canada
Tel.: (604) 540-0444
Web Site: http://www.iteminfo.ca
Sales Range: $75-99.9 Million
Emp.: 85
Business Furniture & Office Supplies Whslr
N.A.I.C.S.: 459410
Peter R. Dalglish (Partner)

NOVEXIA

210 Rue Leon Jouhaux, 69400, Villefranche-sur-Saone, France
Tel.: (33) 474656161
Web Site: http://www.ensto.com
Rev.: $26,100,000
Emp.: 179
Noncurrent-carrying Wiring Devices
N.A.I.C.S.: 335932
Dominique Blanc (Dir-Sls)

NOVI CENTAR D.D.
Marsala Tita br 7, 72 220, Zavidovici, Bosnia & Herzegovina
Tel.: (387) 32868090
NCTZRK1—(SARE)
Rev.: $121,363
Assets: $1,397,855
Liabilities: $759,625
Net Worth: $638,229
Earnings: $25,371
Emp.: 2
Fiscal Year-end: 12/31/20
Food Products Distr
N.A.I.C.S.: 445298
Ismet Mujanovic (Pres)

NOVI DOM - PROMET A.D.
Industrijska bb, Debeljaca, Serbia
Tel.: (381) 13 664 050
Year Founded: 1991
Sales Range: Less than $1 Million
Wood Container Mfr
N.A.I.C.S.: 321920

NOVI PAZAR PUT A.D.
Sabana Koce 67, 36300, Novi Pazar, Serbia
Tel.: (381) 20 314 911
Web Site: http://www.np-put.rs
Year Founded: 2004
Sales Range: $10-24.9 Million
Emp.: 296
Road Construction & Maintenance Services
N.A.I.C.S.: 237310

NOVICLEAN INC.
Suite 2 1303 45th Ave NE, Calgary, T2E 2P3, AB, Canada
Tel.: (587) 997-6040
Web Site: https://www.noviclean.ca
Sales Range: $10-24.9 Million
Commercial Motor Vehicle Washing Equipment & Supplies Distr
N.A.I.C.S.: 423850
Kirk Ylinen (Co-Owner-Sls & Mktg-Western US)

Subsidiaries:

NoviClean, LLC (1)
65 Via Athena, Aliso Viejo, CA 92656
Tel.: (949) 681-6041
Web Site: http://www.noviclean.ca
Commercial Motor Vehicle Washing Equipment & Supplies Distr
N.A.I.C.S.: 423850
Kirk Ylinen (Pres)

NOVIKOMBANK JSCB
50/1 Bld 1 Polyanka Bolshaya Str, 119180, Moscow, Russia
Tel.: (7) 4959747187
Web Site: http://www.novikom.ru
Year Founded: 1993
Sales Range: Less than $1 Million
Commercial Banking Services
N.A.I.C.S.: 522110
Ilya Nikolaevich Gubin (Chm-Mgmt Bd & Pres)

NOVISOURCE N.V.
Hoogoorddreef 56L, 1101 BE, Amsterdam, Netherlands
Tel.: (31) 308504444
Web Site: https://www.novisource.nl
NOVI—(EUR)
Sales Range: $25-49.9 Million

Emp.: 80
Business Consulting Services
N.A.I.C.S.: 541611
Willem van der Vorm (CEO)

NOVITET A.D.
Futoski put 51, Novi Sad, Serbia
Tel.: (381) 21401944
Web Site: https://www.novitet.co.rs
Year Founded: 1947
NOVT—(BEL)
Sales Range: Less than $1 Million
Emp.: 146
Apparel & Accessory Mfr
N.A.I.C.S.: 315990
Srdan Kizdobranski (Gen Mgr)

NOVMETAPHARMA CO., LTD.
727 Eonju-ro Trees Bldg 13F, Gangnam-gu, Seoul, 06050, Korea (South)
Tel.: (82) 25381893
Web Site: https://www.novmeta.com
Year Founded: 2010
Medicine Mfr & Distr
N.A.I.C.S.: 325412
Sun-Wook Hwang (CEO)

NOVO BANCO, S.A.
Avenida da Liberdade 195, 1250-142, Lisbon, Portugal
Tel.: (351) 213 501 000   PT
Web Site: http://www.novobanco.pt
Year Founded: 2014
Commericial Banking
N.A.I.C.S.: 522110
Antonio Ramalho (Pres)

Subsidiaries:

BEST - Banco Electronico de Servico Total, S.A. (1)
Praca Marques de Pombal 3 - 3rd andar, 1250-161, Lisbon, Portugal (75%)
Tel.: (351) 218839252
Web Site: http://www.bancobest.pt
Emp.: 300
Banking, Asset Management & Securities, Brokerage Services
N.A.I.C.S.: 523150
Isabel Maria Ferreira Possantes Rodrigues Cascao (Vice Chm & CEO)

Banco Economico S.A. (1)
Rua do 1 Congresso no 27, Bairro Ingombotas, Luanda, Angola
Tel.: (244) 222693600
Web Site: http://www.bancoeconomico.ao
Sales Range: $300-349.9 Million
Emp.: 500
Retail, Commercial & Investment Banking
N.A.I.C.S.: 522110
Marcos Erwin Mariscal Sachse (Deputy Mgr-Micro & Small Bus Banking-Natl)

Banco Internacional de Cabo Verde (1)
Avenida Cidade de Lisboa, CP 35, Praia, Santiago, Cape Verde
Tel.: (238) 260 26 26
Web Site: http://www.bancointernacional.cv
Emp.: 25
Commercial Banking Services
N.A.I.C.S.: 522110
Bengt Ino Martens (Gen Mgr)

ESAF - Espirito Santo Activos Financeiros S.G.P.S., S.A. (1)
Avenida Alvares Cabral 41, 1249-140, Lisbon, 1250015, Portugal
Tel.: (351) 213810800
Web Site: http://www.esaf.pt
Asset Management & Private Banking Services
N.A.I.C.S.: 523940

Espirito Santo Informatica, ACE (1)
Rua da Barruncheira 4, 2790-034, Carnaxide, Portugal
Tel.: (351) 21 42168000
Web Site: http://www.gnbsi.pt
Information Technology Services
N.A.I.C.S.: 541513

INTERNATIONAL PUBLIC

Espirito Santo Ventures - Sociedade de Capital de Risco, S.A. (1)
Rua Alexandre Herculano 38 5th piso, 1250-011, Lisbon, Portugal (100%)
Tel.: (351) 213106490
Web Site: http://www.es-ventures.com
Rev.: $343,362,500
Venture Capital Investment Firm
N.A.I.C.S.: 523999
Jose Guerreiro de Sousa (Principal)

Subsidiary (Domestic):

ES Tech Ventures, S.G.P.S., S.A. (2)
Avenida Da Liberdade 195, 1250-142, Lisbon, Portugal
Tel.: (351) 213106490
Web Site: http://www.f-ventuers.com
Emp.: 12
Venture Capital Management Services
N.A.I.C.S.: 523940
Julian Rodriguez (CEO)

ImoInvestimento - Fundo Especial de Investimento Imobiliario Fechado (1)
Flua de S Caetano a Lapa n 6 Bloco C 1 Piso, 1200-829, Lisbon, Portugal
Tel.: (351) 213942960
Commercial Banking Services
N.A.I.C.S.: 522110

Novo Banco Banco dos Acores, S.A. (1)
Rua Hintze Ribeiro 2 A 8, 9500-049, Ponta Delgada, Sao Miguel - Acores, Portugal
Tel.: (351) 296309000
Web Site: http://www.novobancodosacores.pt
Retail & Commercial Banking
N.A.I.C.S.: 522110
Maria Lopes Estrela (Gen Mgr)

Novo Banco, S.A. - Sucursal en Espana (1)
Calle Serrano 88 7th Planta, Madrid, 28006, Spain
Tel.: (34) 914005000
Web Site: http://www.bes.es
Sales Range: $200-249.9 Million
Emp.: 500
Commericial Banking
N.A.I.C.S.: 522110
Pedra Escudero (Pres)

OBLOG Consulting S.A. (1)
Avenida Dr Mario Soares Lote 4, 2740-119, Porto Salvo, Portugal
Tel.: (351) 21 425 86 86
Web Site: http://www.oblog.pt
Sales Range: $25-49.9 Million
Emp.: 4
Information Technology Consulting Services
N.A.I.C.S.: 541512
Miroslav Krpec (Gen Mgr)

Socur, S.A. (1)
Avenida 18 De Julio, 1317, Montevideo, Uruguay
Tel.: (598) 2908 0000
Web Site: http://www.creditel.com.uy
Emp.: 450
Consumer Lending Services
N.A.I.C.S.: 522291
Gustavo Trelles (Gen Mgr)

NOVO NORDISK FONDEN
Tuborg Havnevej 19, 2900, Hellerup, Denmark
Tel.: (45) 35276600
Web Site: https://novonordiskfonden.dk
Commercial & Scientific Research Grantmaking Foundation
N.A.I.C.S.: 813211
Lars Rebien Sorensen (Chm)

Subsidiaries:

Novo Holdings A/S (1)
Krogshoejvej 41, DK-2880, Bagsvaerd, Denmark (100%)
Tel.: (45) 88248824
Web Site: https://novoholdings.dk
Investment Holding Company
N.A.I.C.S.: 551112
Thorkil Kastberg Christensen (CFO)

AND PRIVATE COMPANIES

Subsidiary (Non-US):

BBI Diagnostics Group Limited (2)
Golden Gate 73 Ty Glas Av, Cardiff, CF14 5DX, United Kingdom
Tel.: (44) 2920747232
Web Site: http://www.bbigold.com
Sales Range: $10-24.9 Million
Emp.: 130
Holding Company
N.A.I.C.S.: 551112

Subsidiary (US):

BBI Detection Inc. (3)
2312 Vondron Rd, Madison, WI 53718
Tel.: (608) 310-4105
Web Site: http://www.bbidetection.com
Pharmaceuticals Product Mfr
N.A.I.C.S.: 325412

Subsidiary (Domestic):

BBI Detection Limited (3)
Haywood House South Dumfries Place, Cardiff, CF10 3GA, South Glamorgan, United Kingdom
Tel.: (44) 1382569900
Web Site: http://www.bbisolutions.com
Emp.: 75
Pharmaceuticals Product Mfr
N.A.I.C.S.: 325412

BBI Enzymes (UK) Limited (3)
Unit 6 Gilchrist Thomas Ind Est, Gwent, NP4 9RL, United Kingdom
Tel.: (44) 1495790678
Web Site: http://www.bbienzymes.com
Pharmaceuticals Product Mfr
N.A.I.C.S.: 325412
Liam Taylor (Mng Dir)

Subsidiary (US):

BBI Enzymes (USA) Limited (3)
2312-2314 Vondron Rd, Madison, WI 53718
Tel.: (608) 310-4105
Pharmaceuticals Product Mfr
N.A.I.C.S.: 325412

Subsidiary (Non-US):

BBI Enzymes SA (Pty) Limited (3)
19 Packer Avenue Epping 2, PO Box 441, 7475, Cape Town, South Africa
Tel.: (27) 215344531
Web Site: http://www.bbisolutions.com
Emp.: 51
Pharmaceuticals Product Mfr
N.A.I.C.S.: 325412

Subsidiary (US):

BBI Research Inc. (3)
2312-2314 Vondron Rd, Madison, WI 53718
Tel.: (608) 310-4105
Web Site: http://www.britishbiocell.co.uk
Medical Diagnostic Chemical & Equipment Mfr & Distr
N.A.I.C.S.: 339112

Subsidiary (Domestic):

BBI Solutions OEM, Limited (3)
73 Ty Glas Avenue, Cardiff, CF14 5DX, United Kingdom
Tel.: (44) 2920747232
Web Site: http://www.bbisolutions.com
Pharmaceuticals Product Mfr
N.A.I.C.S.: 325412

Subsidiary (Non-US):

IBEX Technologies Inc. (4)
5485 Rue Pare Suite 100, Montreal, H4P 1P7, QC, Canada
Tel.: (514) 344-4004
Web Site: https://www.ibex.ca
Rev.: $3,296,899
Assets: $6,417,867
Liabilities: $1,387,343
Net Worth: $5,030,513
Earnings: ($970,081)
Fiscal Year-end: 07/31/2019
Biopharmaceutical Product Mfr
N.A.I.C.S.: 325414
Paul Baehr (Chm, Pres & CEO)

Subsidiary (Domestic):

Technologies IBEX R&D Inc. (5)
5485 Pare St, Mont Royal, H4P 1P7, QC, Canada
Tel.: (514) 344-4004
Pharmaceutical Research & Development Services
N.A.I.C.S.: 325412

Subsidiary (Domestic):

The BBI Group (3)
The Courtyard 73 Ty Glas Avenue Llanishen, Cardiff, CF14 5DX, United Kingdom
Tel.: (44) 2920 747 232
Web Site: http://www.bbisolutions.com
Medical Diagnostic Chemical & Equipment Mfr & Distr
N.A.I.C.S.: 339112

Subsidiary (Domestic):

NNIT A/S (2)
Weidekampsgade 14, DK -2300, Copenhagen, Denmark (51%)
Tel.: (45) 70244242
Web Site: https://www.nnit.com
Rev.: $250,032,556
Assets: $286,061,553
Liabilities: $166,398,981
Net Worth: $119,662,572
Earnings: $4,340,843
Emp.: 1,773
Fiscal Year-end: 12/31/2023
IT Consulting & Solutions
N.A.I.C.S.: 541519
Per Kogut (Pres & CEO)

Subsidiary (US):

Valiance Partners, LLC (3)
75 Claremont Rd Ste 206, Bernardsville, NJ 07924
Tel.: (908) 334-2300
Web Site: http://www.valiancepartners.com
Sales Range: $1-9.9 Million
Emp.: 30
Software & Technical Services for Data Migration
N.A.I.C.S.: 513210
Richard Higger (Founder & Pres)

Subsidiary (Domestic):

Novo Nordisk A/S (2)
Novo Alle 1, DK-2880, Bagsvaerd, Denmark (75.5%)
Tel.: (45) 44448888
Web Site: http://www.novonordisk.com
Rev.: $19,030,474,860
Assets: $21,725,257,020
Liabilities: $12,232,206,270
Net Worth: $9,493,050,750
Earnings: $6,316,907,580
Emp.: 44,723
Fiscal Year-end: 12/31/2020
Healthcare Services & Pharmaceutical Products Mfr
N.A.I.C.S.: 325412
Helge Lund (Chm)

Subsidiary (Non-US):

Alkermes plc - Athlone Facility (3)
Monksland, Athlone, Westmeath, Ireland
Tel.: (353) 906495000
Web Site: https://www.alkermes.com
Emp.: 320
Pharmaceuticals Product Mfr
N.A.I.C.S.: 325412
Declan O'Connor (Sr VP-Ops, Quality, and Safety)

Biocorp SA (3)
Parc Technologique Lavaur-la-Bechade, 63500, Issoire, France
Tel.: (33) 473557050
Web Site: http://www.biocorpsys.com
Sales Range: $10-24.9 Million
Pharmaceutical Product Delivery Device Mfr
N.A.I.C.S.: 339112
Jacques Gardette (Founder & CEO)

Subsidiary (US):

Emisphere Technologies, Inc. (3)
4 Becker Farm Rd Ste 103, Roseland, NJ 07068
Tel.: (973) 532-8000
Web Site: http://www.emisphere.com
Sales Range: $1-9.9 Million
Emp.: 6
Drug Delivery Systems Mfr

N.A.I.C.S.: 325412
Timothy G. Rothwell (Chm)

Forma Therapeutics Holdings, Inc. (3)
500 Arsenal St Ste 100, Watertown, MA 02472
Tel.: (617) 679-1970
Web Site: http://www.formatherapeutics.com
Rev.: $1,176,000
Assets: $561,061,000
Liabilities: $62,705,000
Net Worth: $498,356,000
Earnings: ($172,964,000)
Emp.: 166
Fiscal Year-end: 12/31/2021
Holding Company
N.A.I.C.S.: 551112
David N. Cook (Chief Scientific Officer & Sr VP)

Representative Office (Non-US):

Novo Nordisk A/S - Algeria (3)
Cooperative Immobiliere El Bouroudj section N2, Ilot de propriete N 428, Algiers, 16000, Algeria
Tel.: (213) 21919290
Web Site: https://www.novonordisk.dz
Mfr of Industrial Enzymes & Insulin, Recovery & Purification of Fermentation Products; Protein Technology
N.A.I.C.S.: 325411

Novo Nordisk A/S - Kazakhstan (3)
Seiphulina Prospect 534 Office 28-30, 480072, Almaty, Kazakhstan
Tel.: (7) 3272615735
Web Site: https://www.novonordisk.kz
Mfr of Industrial Enzymes & Insulin, Recovery & Purification of Fermentation Products; Protein Technology
N.A.I.C.S.: 325199

Novo Nordisk A/S - Kenya (3)
Mosemiaque Plz 3rd Fl W Wing, PO Box 59117, Westlands, Nairobi, Kenya
Tel.: (254) 2224744483
Web Site: https://www.novonordisk.co.ke
Provider of Pharmaceuticals
N.A.I.C.S.: 325412

Novo Nordisk A/S - North Macedonia (3)
Bul Jane Sandanski br 111, 1000, Skopje, North Macedonia
Tel.: (389) 2400202
Web Site: https://www.novonordisk.mk
Mfr of Industrial Enzymes & Insulin, Recovery & Purification of Fermentation Products; Protein Technology
N.A.I.C.S.: 325411

Novo Nordisk A/S - Russia (3)
Lomonosovsky Prospect 38, 117 330, Moscow, Russia
Tel.: (7) 4959561132
Web Site: https://www.novonordisk.ru
Sales Range: $25-49.9 Million
Emp.: 10
Mfr of Industrial Enzymes & Insulin, Recovery & Purification of Fermentation Products; Protein Technology
N.A.I.C.S.: 325199

Novo Nordisk A/S - Serbia (3)
Milutina Milankovica 9b, 11070, Belgrade, Serbia
Tel.: (381) 112222700
Web Site: https://www.novonordisk.rs
Sales Range: $25-49.9 Million
Emp.: 20
Mfr of Industrial Enzymes & Insulin, Recovery & Purification of Fermentation Products; Protein Technology
N.A.I.C.S.: 325411

Novo Nordisk A/S - Ukraine (3)
29 1 Sagaychogo St, 04070, Kiev, Ukraine
Tel.: (380) 442346102
Web Site: https://www.novonordisk.ua
Sales Range: $25-49.9 Million
Emp.: 30
Mfr of Industrial Enzymes & Insulin, Recovery & Purification of Fermentation Products; Protein Technology
N.A.I.C.S.: 325199

Novo Nordisk A/S - Uzbekistan (3)
Ctr 5 Bldg 57 Ofc 3, 100017, Tashkent, Uzbekistan

NOVO NORDISK FONDEN

Tel.: (998) 711206690
Web Site: https://www.novonordisk.uz
Sales Range: $25-49.9 Million
Emp.: 3
Mfr of Industrial Enzymes & Insulin, Recovery & Purification of Fermentation Products; Protein Technology
N.A.I.C.S.: 325199

Subsidiary (Non-US):

Novo Nordisk Asia Pacific Pte. Limited (3)
238 A Thompson Road 16 06 08, Novena Square Tower A, Singapore, 307684, Singapore (100%)
Tel.: (65) 63539555
Sales Range: $25-49.9 Million
Emp.: 50
Mfr of Pharmaceuticals
N.A.I.C.S.: 325412

Novo Nordisk B.V. (3)
Flemingweg 18, 2408 AV, Alphen aan den Rijn, Netherlands (100%)
Tel.: (31) 172449494
Web Site: http://www.novonordisk.nl
Sales Range: $100-124.9 Million
Emp.: 140
Pharmaceuticals Mfr
N.A.I.C.S.: 325412
G. Segers (Dir-Fin)

Novo Nordisk Canada, Inc. (3)
101-2476 Argentia Road, Mississauga, L5N 6M1, ON, Canada (100%)
Tel.: (905) 629-4222
Web Site: http://www.novonordisk.ca
Sales Range: $50-74.9 Million
Emp.: 200
Mfr of Pharmaceutical Chemicals
N.A.I.C.S.: 325412

Novo Nordisk China (3)
Unit 3112 Level 31 China World Tower 2, No 1 Jian Guo Men Wai Ave, Beijing, 100004, China (100%)
Tel.: (86) 65058787
Web Site: http://www.novonordisk.com.cn
Sales Range: $25-49.9 Million
Emp.: 100
Mfr of Industrial Enzymes & Insulin, Recovery & Purification of Fermentation Products; Protein Technology
N.A.I.C.S.: 325411

Novo Nordisk Comercio Produtos Farmaceuticos, Lda (3)
Quinta Da Fonte Edif D Jose Q54 Piso 1, Paco De Arcos, 2780 730, Lisbon, Portugal (100%)
Tel.: (351) 214404000
Web Site: http://www.novonordisk.pt
Sales Range: $25-49.9 Million
Emp.: 45
Mfr of Pharmaceuticals & Pharmaceutical Chemicals
N.A.I.C.S.: 325412
Mads Watson (Mng Dir)

Novo Nordisk Farmaceutica do Brasil Ltda. (3)
Av Francisco Matarazzo 1 500 Ed New York 13th Fl Agua Braca, 05001 400, Sao Paulo, SP, Brazil (100%)
Tel.: (55) 138689100
Web Site: http://www.novonordisk.com
Sales Range: $25-49.9 Million
Emp.: 100
Mfr of Industrial Enzymes & Insulin, Recovery & Purification of Fermentation Products; Protein Technology
N.A.I.C.S.: 325199

Novo Nordisk Farmaceutici S.p.A. (3)
Via Elio Vittorini 129, 00144, Rome, Italy (100%)
Tel.: (39) 06500881
Web Site: http://www.novonordisk.it
Sales Range: $25-49.9 Million
Emp.: 100
Mfr of Pharmaceutical Chemicals
N.A.I.C.S.: 325412

Novo Nordisk Health Care AG (3)
Thurgauerstrasse 36/38, 8050, Zurich, Switzerland
Tel.: (41) 44 914 1111
Web Site: http://www.novonordisk.ch

NOVO NORDISK FONDEN

Novo Nordisk Fonden—(Continued)
Health Care Products Mfr & Whslr
N.A.I.C.S.: 424210

Novo Nordisk Hellas Ltd. (3)
Ag triados 65 Al Panagouli, 153 43, Athens,
Greece **(100%)**
Tel.: (30) 2106071600
Web Site: http://www.novonordisk.gr
Sales Range: Less than $1 Million
Emp.: 53
Mfr of Industrial Enzymes & Insulin, Recovery & Purification of Fermentation Products; Protein Technology
N.A.I.C.S.: 325411
Olympios Pipadimitrou *(Gen Mgr)*

Novo Nordisk Hrvatska d.o.o. (3)
Oreskovic Vie 20 A, 10 000, Zagreb,
Croatia **(100%)**
Tel.: (385) 016651900
Web Site: http://www.novonordisk.hr
Sales Range: $25-49.9 Million
Emp.: 30
Mfr of Industrial Enzymes & Insulin, Recovery & Purification of Fermentation Products; Protein Technology
N.A.I.C.S.: 325411
Martina Troglic *(Mgr-HR)*

Novo Nordisk Hungaria Kft. (3)
Felsozoldmali U 35, Budapest, 1025,
Hungary **(100%)**
Tel.: (36) 13259161
Web Site: http://www.novonordisk.hu
Sales Range: $25-49.9 Million
Emp.: 50
Mfr of Industrial Enzymes & Insulin, Recovery & Purification of Fermentation Products; Protein Technology
N.A.I.C.S.: 325411
Zsolt Jozsa *(Gen Mgr)*

Novo Nordisk India Pvt. Ltd. (3)
8th Fl Raheja Towers East Wing No 26 And 27 MG Rd, 560 001, Bengaluru,
India **(100%)**
Tel.: (91) 8025327447
Web Site: http://www.novonordisk.co.in
Sales Range: $25-49.9 Million
Emp.: 50
Industrial Enzymes & Insulin, Recovery & Purification of Fermentation Products; Protein Technology Mfr
N.A.I.C.S.: 325411

Novo Nordisk Ltd. (3)
3 City Place Beehive Ring Road, Gatwick,
RH6 0PA, West Sussex, United
Kingdom **(100%)**
Tel.: (44) 1293613555
Web Site: http://www.novonordisk.co.uk
Sales Range: $125-149.9 Million
Emp.: 400
Pharmaceuticals Mfr
N.A.I.C.S.: 325412

Novo Nordisk Maroc (3)
2 Rue Hassan Souktani Residence Bellevue, 4eme Etage, Casablanca, 20000, Morocco
Tel.: (212) 2200631
Web Site: http://www.novonordisk.com
Mfr of Industrial Enzymes & Insulin, Recovery & Purification of Fermentation Products; Protein Technology
N.A.I.C.S.: 325199

Novo Nordisk Pharma (3)
Itatuulentie 1, 02100, Espoo,
Finland **(100%)**
Tel.: (358) 93482500
Web Site: http://www.novonordisk.fi
Sales Range: $50-74.9 Million
Emp.: 110
Mfr of Industrial Enzymes & Insulin, Recovery & Purification of Fermentation Products; Protein Technology
N.A.I.C.S.: 325199

Novo Nordisk Pharma (Taiwan) Ltd. (3)
7F-1 216 Tun Hua South Road Sec 2, Taipei, 106, Taiwan **(100%)**
Tel.: (886) 223772566
Web Site: http://www.novonordisk.com.tw
Sales Range: $50-74.9 Million
Emp.: 145
Mfr of Industrial Enzymes & Insulin, Recovery & Purification of Fermentation Products; Protein Technology

N.A.I.C.S.: 325411

Novo Nordisk Pharma (Thailand) Ltd. (3)
139 Sethiwan Tower 4th Fl Pan Rd, Silom District, Bangkok, 10500, Thailand **(100%)**
Tel.: (66) 22379263
Web Site: http://www.novonordisk.co.th
Sales Range: $25-49.9 Million
Emp.: 45
Mfr of Industrial Enzymes & Insulin, Recovery & Purification of Fermentation Products; Protein Technology
N.A.I.C.S.: 325412
Chin Lan Limpuang *(Gen Mgr)*

Novo Nordisk Pharma AG (3)
Untere Heslibachstrasse 46, CH-8700, Kusnacht, Switzerland **(100%)**
Tel.: (41) 449141111
Web Site: http://www.novonordisk.ch
Rev.: $5,000,000
Emp.: 35
Mfr of Pharmaceuticals
N.A.I.C.S.: 325412

Novo Nordisk Pharma Argentina S.A. (3)
Av del Libertador 350 Piso 3 Vicente Lopez, B1638BEP, Buenos Aires,
Argentina **(100%)**
Tel.: (54) 1151986686
Web Site: http://www.novonordisk.com.ar
Sales Range: $10-24.9 Million
Emp.: 100
Provider of Pharmaceuticals
N.A.I.C.S.: 325412

Novo Nordisk Pharma Ead (3)
20 22 Zlaten Rog Str, Sofia, 1407, Bulgaria
Tel.: (359) 29627471
Web Site: http://www.novonordisk.bg
Sales Range: $50-74.9 Million
Emp.: 30
Mfr of Industrial Enzymes & Insulin, Recovery & Purification of Fermentation Products; Protein Technology
N.A.I.C.S.: 325411
Krum Kassabov *(Gen Mgr)*

Novo Nordisk Pharma GmbH (3)
DC Tower Donau-City-Str 7, 1220, Vienna,
Austria **(100%)**
Tel.: (43) 14051501
Web Site: http://www.novonordisk.at
Sales Range: $25-49.9 Million
Emp.: 45
Pharmaceutical Chemicals Mfr
N.A.I.C.S.: 325412
Thomas Aumer *(Product Mgr)*

Novo Nordisk Pharma GmbH (3)
Brucknerstrasse 1, 55127, Mainz,
Germany **(100%)**
Tel.: (49) 61319030
Web Site: http://www.novonordisk.de
Sales Range: $50-74.9 Million
Emp.: 210
Pharmaceutical Chemicals Mfr
N.A.I.C.S.: 325412

Novo Nordisk Pharma Korea Limited (3)
16 Floor Korea Advertising Culture Ctr Olympic Road 35 Gill Songpa gu, Seoul, 138 921, Korea (South) **(100%)**
Tel.: (82) 25642057
Web Site: http://www.novonordisk.co.kr
Sales Range: $10-24.9 Million
Emp.: 100
Provider of Pharmaceuticals
N.A.I.C.S.: 325412
Hangu Kang *(CEO)*

Novo Nordisk Pharma Limited (3)
139 Sethiwan Tower 4th Fl Pan Rd Silom District, Bangkok, 10500, Thailand **(100%)**
Tel.: (66) 22379263
Web Site: http://www.novonordisk.co.th
Sales Range: $25-49.9 Million
Emp.: 40
Provider of Pharmaceuticals
N.A.I.C.S.: 325412

Novo Nordisk Pharma Ltd. (3)
Meiji Yasuda Seimei Bldg 2-1-1 Marunouchi, Chiyoda-ku, Tokyo, 100-0005, Japan **(100%)**
Tel.: (81) 362661000
Web Site: http://www.novonordisk.co.jp

Sales Range: $125-149.9 Million
Emp.: 350
Provider of Pharmaceuticals
N.A.I.C.S.: 325412

Novo Nordisk Pharma Private Limited (3)
113 Shahrah-e-Iran, Clifton, Karachi, 75300,
Pakistan **(100%)**
Tel.: (92) 21 35360920
Web Site: http://www.novonordisk.pk
Sales Range: $25-49.9 Million
Emp.: 40
Mfr of Industrial Enzymes & Insulin, Recovery & Purification of Fermentation Products; Protein Technology
N.A.I.C.S.: 325411

Novo Nordisk Pharma S.A. (3)
Via De Los Poblabos 3 Bldg 6, Madrid,
28033, Spain **(100%)**
Tel.: (34) 913349800
Web Site: http://www.novonordisk.es
Sales Range: $50-74.9 Million
Emp.: 250
Mfr of Pharmaceuticals
N.A.I.C.S.: 325412

Novo Nordisk Pharma Sdn. Bhd. (3)
A-9-2 Level 9 Tower A 5 Menara UOA Bangsar, Jalan Bangsar Utama 1, Kuala Lumpur, 59000, Malaysia **(100%)**
Tel.: (60) 379577527
Web Site: http://www.novonordisk.com
Sales Range: $25-49.9 Million
Emp.: 40
Mfr of Industrial Enzymes & Insulin, Recovery & Purification of Fermentation Products; Protein Technology
N.A.I.C.S.: 325411

Novo Nordisk Pharma Sp. z.o.o. (3)
ul Krakowiakow 46, 02-255, Warsaw,
Poland **(100%)**
Tel.: (48) 224444900
Web Site: http://www.novonordisk.pl
Sales Range: $50-74.9 Million
Emp.: 200
Medicinal & Botanical Manufacturing
N.A.I.C.S.: 325411

Novo Nordisk Pharmaceuticals Ltd. (3)
3 4 Upper Pembroke St, Dublin, 2,
Ireland **(100%)**
Tel.: (353) 16785989
Web Site: http://www.novonordisk.ie
Sales Range: $25-49.9 Million
Emp.: 22
Provider of Pharmaceuticals
N.A.I.C.S.: 325412

Novo Nordisk Pharmaceuticals Ltd. (3)
58 Richard Pearse Drive Airport Oaks, Mangere, 2022, Manukau, New
Zealand **(100%)**
Tel.: (64) 95790653
Web Site: http://www.novodisk.com
Sales Range: $25-49.9 Million
Emp.: 4
Mfr of Pharmaceuticals
N.A.I.C.S.: 325412
Kevin Anderson *(Mgr)*

Novo Nordisk Pharmaceuticals Pty. Ltd. (3)
Level 3 21 Solent Circuit, Baulkham Hills, 2153, NSW, Australia **(100%)**
Tel.: (61) 288583600
Web Site: http://www.novonordisk.com.au
Sales Range: $25-49.9 Million
Emp.: 100
Pharmaceuticals Mfr
N.A.I.C.S.: 325412

Novo Nordisk Pharmaceutique S.A. (3)
100 Esplanade Charles De Gaulle Coeur Defense, 92932, Paris, Cedex, La Defense, France **(100%)**
Tel.: (33) 141976600
Web Site: http://wwwlab-novonordisk.fr
Sales Range: $25-49.9 Million
Emp.: 100
Mfr of Pharmaceutical Chemicals
N.A.I.C.S.: 325412

Novo Nordisk Pty Ltd. (3)

INTERNATIONAL PUBLIC

PO Box 783155, Sandton, 2146, South
Africa **(100%)**
Tel.: (27) 112020500
Web Site: http://www.novonordisk.co.za
Sales Range: $50-74.9 Million
Emp.: 140
Pharmaceuticals Mfr
N.A.I.C.S.: 325412

Novo Nordisk Regional Office Latin America (LARO) (3)
Av Francisco Matarazzo 1 500 Ed New York 13th Fl, Sao Paulo, 05001-100,
Brazil **(100%)**
Tel.: (55) 1138689100
Web Site: http://www.novonordisk.com.br
Sales Range: $50-74.9 Million
Emp.: 150
Mfr of Pharmaceutical Chemicals
N.A.I.C.S.: 325412
Gustavo Nizraje *(CEO)*

Novo Nordisk Saglik Urunleri Tic Ltd Sti (3)
Nisbetiye Cad Akmerkez E3 Blok Kat 7, Etiler, 80600, Istanbul, Turkiye **(100%)**
Tel.: (90) 2122822110
Web Site: http://www.novoturk.com
Sales Range: $25-49.9 Million
Emp.: 100
Mfr of Industrial Enzymes & Insulin, Recovery & Purification of Fermentation Products; Protein Technology
N.A.I.C.S.: 325411

Novo Nordisk Scandinavia AB (3)
Carlsgatan 3, PO Box 50587, 202 15,
Malmo, Sweden **(100%)**
Tel.: (46) 40388900
Web Site: http://www.novonordisk.se
Sales Range: $50-74.9 Million
Emp.: 125
Pharmaceuticals Mfr
N.A.I.C.S.: 325412

Novo Nordisk Scanvinavia A/S (3)
Baker Osteusuei No 5, PO Box 24, 1351,
Rud, Norway **(100%)**
Tel.: (47) 67178500
Web Site: http://www.novonordisk.no
Sales Range: $25-49.9 Million
Emp.: 47
Mfr of Pharmaceuticals
N.A.I.C.S.: 325412

Novo Nordisk d.o.o. (3)
Smartinska Cesta 140, SL-1000, Ljubljana,
Slovenia **(100%)**
Tel.: (386) 1 810 8700
Web Site: http://www.novonordisk.com
Sales Range: $25-49.9 Million
Emp.: 20
Mfr of Industrial Enzymes & Insulin, Recovery & Purification of Fermentation Products; Protein Technology
N.A.I.C.S.: 325411

Subsidiary (US):

Novo Nordisk, Inc. (3)
800 Scudders Mill Rd, Plainsboro, NJ 08536
Tel.: (609) 987-5800
Web Site: http://www.novonordisk-us.com
Sales Range: $150-199.9 Million
Emp.: 900
Mfr of Pharmaceuticals
N.A.I.C.S.: 561110

Subsidiary (Domestic):

Novo Nordisk Pharmaceuticals Industries, Inc. (4)
3612 Powhatan Rd, Clayton, NC 27527 **(100%)**
Tel.: (919) 550-2200
Web Site: http://www.novonordisk-clayton.com
Sales Range: $125-149.9 Million
Emp.: 1,000
Mfr of Insulin for Diabetics
N.A.I.C.S.: 325411

Branch (Domestic):

Novo Nordisk, Inc. - Puerto Rico (4)
Metro Office Pk 14 Calle 2 Ste 212, Guaynabo, PR 00968-1706
Tel.: (787) 775-6666
Web Site: http://www.novonordisk-us.com

AND PRIVATE COMPANIES — NOVOKRAMATORSKY MASHINOSTROITELNY ZAVOD, PJSC

Sales Range: $25-49.9 Million
Emp.: 13
Mfr of Industrial Enzymes & Insulin, Recovery & Purification of Fermentation Products; Protein Technology
N.A.I.C.S.: 541810

Subsidiary (Non-US):

Novo Nordisk, s.r.o. (3)
Evropska 33C, 160 00, Prague, 6, Czech Republic
Tel.: (420) 233089611
Web Site: http://www.novonordisk.cz
Sales Range: $25-49.9 Million
Emp.: 50
Industrial Enzymes & Insulin, Recovery & Purification of Fermentation Products Mfr; Protein Technology
N.A.I.C.S.: 325411
Daniel White *(Gen Mgr)*

S.A. Novo Nordisk Pharma N.V. (3)
Riverside Business Pk, International Land 55/6, 1070, Brussels, Belgium (100%)
Tel.: (32) 25560580
Web Site: http://www.novonordisk.be
Sales Range: $50-74.9 Million
Emp.: 50
Mfr of Pharmaceuticals
N.A.I.C.S.: 325412
Peter Meeus *(Gen Mgr)*

Subsidiary (Domestic):

Steno Diabetes Center (3)
Niels Steensensvej 2, 2820, Gentofte, Denmark (100%)
Tel.: (45) 39680800
Web Site: http://www.steno.com
Sales Range: $800-899.9 Million
Emp.: 2,000
Diabetes Care, Research & Prevention
N.A.I.C.S.: 525120
Knut Borch Johnsen *(Mng Dir)*

Joint Venture (US):

Paratek Pharmaceuticals, Inc. (2)
75 Park Plz, Boston, MA 02116
Tel.: (617) 807-6600
Web Site: https://www.paratekpharma.com
Rev.: $160,268,000
Assets: $172,538,000
Liabilities: $343,580,000
Net Worth: ($171,042,000)
Earnings: ($63,566,000)
Emp.: 268
Fiscal Year-end: 12/31/2022
Holding Company; Specialty Pharmaceutical Develpment & Marketing Services
N.A.I.C.S.: 551112
Walter A. Gilbert *(Founder)*

Subsidiary (Domestic):

Paratek Pharmaceuticals, LLC (3)
75 Park Plz 3rd Fl, Boston, MA 02116
Tel.: (617) 807-6600
Web Site: https://www.paratekpharma.com
Specialty Pharmaceutical Develpment & Marketing Services
N.A.I.C.S.: 325412

Subsidiary (Domestic):

Sonion A/S (2)
Byleddet 12-14, DK 4000, Roskilde, Denmark
Tel.: (45) 4630 6666
Web Site: http://www.sonion.com
Sales Range: $125-149.9 Million
Emp.: 3,500
Micro Acoustical & Micro Mechanical Components Mfr
N.A.I.C.S.: 334419
Christian Nielsen *(CFO & Exec VP)*

Subsidiary (US):

Sonion US, Inc. (3)
12455 Ridgedale Dr Ste 104, Minnetonka, MN 55305-1786
Tel.: (952) 543-8100
Web Site: http://www.sonion.com
Emp.: 9
Medical, Dental & Hospital Equipment & Supplies Merchant Whslr
N.A.I.C.S.: 423450
William J. Taylor *(Pres)*

Subsidiary (Non-US):

Sonion Vietnam Co Ltd. (3)
Lot I3-9 Saigon Hi-Tech Park District 9, Ho Chi Minh City, 700000, Vietnam
Tel.: (84) 8 3736 2222
Web Site: http://www.sonion.com
Mfr of Micro-Acoustic & Micro-Mechanical Components for Hearing Instruments
N.A.I.C.S.: 334419
Torben Axelsen *(Gen Dir & VP-Ops)*

Subsidiary (Domestic):

Xellia Pharmaceuticals ApS (2)
Dalslandsgade 11, Copenhagen, 2300, Denmark (100%)
Tel.: (45) 32 64 5500
Web Site: http://www.xellia.com
Sales Range: $250-299.9 Million
Emp.: 600
Pharmaceuticals Mfr
N.A.I.C.S.: 325412
Carl-Ake Carlsson *(Pres & CEO)*

Subsidiary (Non-US):

Xellia (Taizhou) Pharmaceuticals Co., Ltd. (3)
108 Binhai Road, Jiaojiang District, Taizhou, 318000, Zhejiang, China (100%)
Tel.: (86) 57688827026
Web Site: http://www.xellia.com
Sales Range: $50-74.9 Million
Emp.: 195
Pharmaceuticals Mfr
N.A.I.C.S.: 325412
Lei Zhao *(Gen Mgr)*

Xellia Pharmaceuticals AS (3)
Harbitzalleen 3, 0212, Oslo, Norway
Tel.: (47) 22529000
Web Site: http://www.xellia.com
Sales Range: $250-299.9 Million
Emp.: 850
Pharmaceuticals Mfr
N.A.I.C.S.: 325412
Carl-Ake Carlsson *(Pres & CEO)*

Xellia Pharmaceuticals Ltd. (3)
Szallas u 3, Budapest, 1107, Hungary (100%)
Tel.: (36) 1 2604130
Web Site: http://www.xellia.com
Sales Range: $50-74.9 Million
Emp.: 152
Pharmaceuticals Mfr
N.A.I.C.S.: 325412
Attila Mile *(Gen Mgr)*

Joint Venture (US):

eResearchTechnology, Inc. (2)
1818 Market St Ste 1000, Philadelphia, PA 19103-3638
Tel.: (215) 972-0420
Web Site: http://www.ert.com
Medical Diagnostic & Testing Web-Based Software & Consulting Services
N.A.I.C.S.: 513210
Steve Nuckols *(Chief Comml Officer & Exec VP)*

Subsidiary (Domestic):

APDM, Inc. (3)
2828 SW Corbett Ave Ste 130, Portland, OR 97201-4811
Tel.: (503) 445-7757
Web Site: http://www.apdm.com
Electromedical & Electrotherapeutic Apparatus Mfr
N.A.I.C.S.: 334510
Thomas Rolke *(CEO)*

BioClinica, Inc. (3)
211 Carnegie Ct Dr, Princeton, NJ 08540
Tel.: (877) 632-9432
Web Site: http://www.bioclinica.com
Medical Imaging Solutions & Cardiac Safety Services for Clinical Trial Sponsors
N.A.I.C.S.: 621511
David S. Herron *(Pres & CEO)*

Subsidiary (Non-US):

eResearchTechnology GmbH (3)
Sieboldstrasse 3, Estenfeld, 97230, Wurzburg, Germany
Tel.: (49) 9305 720 60
Web Site: http://www.ert.com

Medical Diagnostic & Testing Web-Based Software & Consulting Services
N.A.I.C.S.: 513210

Subsidiary (US):

Biomedical Systems Corp. (4)
77 Progress Pkwy, Maryland Heights, MO 63043
Tel.: (314) 576-6800
Web Site: http://www.biomedsys.com
Sales Range: $1-9.9 Million
Health/Allied Services
N.A.I.C.S.: 621999
Timothy Barrett *(Pres)*

Subsidiary (Non-US):

eResearchTechnology Limited (3)
Peterborough Business Park, Lynch Wood, Peterborough, PE2 6FZ, Cambs, United Kingdom
Tel.: (44) 1733 374800
Web Site: http://www.ert.com
Medical Diagnostic & Testing Web-Based Software & Consulting Services
N.A.I.C.S.: 513210

Branch (Domestic):

eResearchTechnology, Inc. - Bridgewater (3)
685 US Hwy 202 206 2nd Fl, Bridgewater, NJ 08807-1774
Tel.: (908) 704-8010
Web Site: http://www.ert.com
Medical Diagnostic & Testing Web-Based Software
N.A.I.C.S.: 513210
Tom Devine *(CIO, Chief Dev Officer Exec VP)*

NOVO ONBOARD RETAIL LIMITED

Crown Chambers Princess Street, Harrogate, HG1 1NJ, United Kingdom
Tel.: (44) 7768 145226 UK
Web Site: http://www.onboard-retail.com
In-Flight Point-of-Sale Software Products
N.A.I.C.S.: 513210
Jon Simpson Hall *(CEO)*

NOVO RESOURCES CORP.

Suite 1100 1199 West Hastings Street, Vancouver, V6E 3T5, BC, Canada
Tel.: (604) 562-4854 BC
Web Site: https://www.novoresources.com
Year Founded: 2009
NSRPF—(OTCQX)
Metal Mining Services
N.A.I.C.S.: 212290
Leo Karabelas *(VP-Corp Comm)*

NOVO TELLUS CAPITAL PARTNERS PTE. LTD.

43 Mosque Street #04 03, Singapore, 059521, Singapore
Tel.: (65) 6438 8074
Web Site: http://www.novotellus.com
Year Founded: 2010
Private Equity Firm Services
N.A.I.C.S.: 523999
Wai San Loke *(Founder & Mng Partner)*

Subsidiaries:

Smartflex Technology Pte. Ltd. (1)
No 27 Ubi Rd 4 #04-04, Singapore, 408618, Singapore
Tel.: (65) 67877133
Web Site: http://www.smartflex.com.sg
Semiconductor Equipment Mfr
N.A.I.C.S.: 334413

NOVOCURE LIMITED

No 4 The Forum Grenville Street, Saint Helier, JE2 4UF, Jersey
Tel.: (44) 1534756700 JE

Web Site: http://www.novocure.com
Year Founded: 2000
NVCR—(NASDAQ)
Rev.: $509,338,000
Assets: $1,146,129,000
Liabilities: $783,633,000
Net Worth: $362,496,000
Earnings: ($207,043,000)
Emp.: 1,453
Fiscal Year-end: 12/31/23
Surgical & Medical Device Mfr
N.A.I.C.S.: 339112
Wilhelmus Groenhuysen *(COO)*

Subsidiaries:

Novocure GmbH (1)
Business Village D4 Park 6/Platz 10, 6039, Root, Switzerland
Tel.: (41) 414553600
Web Site: https://www.novocure.com
Biological Product Mfr
N.A.I.C.S.: 325414

NOVOGENE CO., LTD.

Building 301 Zone A10 Jiuxianqiao North Road, Chaoyang, Beijing, China
Tel.: (86) 4006581585
Web Site: https://www.novogene.com
Year Founded: 2011
688315—(SHG)
Rev.: $270,359,028
Assets: $427,977,726
Liabilities: $150,588,800
Net Worth: $277,388,926
Earnings: $24,883,134
Emp.: 1,000
Fiscal Year-end: 12/31/22
Research & Development Biotechnology Services
N.A.I.C.S.: 541714
Ruiqiang Li *(Chm & Gen Mgr)*

Subsidiaries:

Guangzhou Novogene Med LAB Co., Ltd. (1)
Unit 701 West Elevator Building C6 Enterprise Accelerator Fayuan Road, Huangpu District, Guangzhou, Guangdong, China
Tel.: (86) 4006581585
Genetic Research Services
N.A.I.C.S.: 541714

Nanjing Novogene Bio Technology Co., Ltd. (1)
Industrial Technology Research and Innovation Park, Nanjing, China
Tel.: (86) 400 658 1585
Testing Lab Operator Services
N.A.I.C.S.: 541380

Novogene Corporation Inc. (1)
8801 Folsom Blvd Ste 290, Sacramento, CA 95628
Tel.: (916) 252-0068
Testing Lab Operator Services
N.A.I.C.S.: 541380

Novogene Japan K.K. (1)
Nagaoka BLDG3-7F 2-7-10 Nihonbashi-Kayabacho, Chuo-ku, Tokyo, 103-0025, Japan
Tel.: (81) 368108588
Testing Lab Operator Services
N.A.I.C.S.: 541380

NovogeneAIT Genomics Singapore Pte. Ltd. (1)
25 Pandan Crescent 05-15 TIC Centre, Singapore, 128477, Singapore
Tel.: (65) 65134308
Testing Lab Operator Services
N.A.I.C.S.: 541380

NOVOKRAMATORSKY MASHINOSTROITELNY ZAVOD, PJSC

Ordzhonikidze str 5, Kramatorsk, 84305U, Ukraine
Tel.: (380) 6264 3 70 80
Web Site: http://www.nkmz.com
Engineering Services
N.A.I.C.S.: 541330

Novokramatorsky Mashinostroitelny Zavod, PJSC—(Continued)

Georgy M. Skudar *(Pres)*

NOVOLIPETSKI METALLURGICHESKI KOMB OAO
40 Bolshaya Ordynka str bldg 3, 119017, Moscow, 119017, Russia
Tel.: (7) 4955040504
Web Site: https://www.nlmk.com
NLMK—(MOEX)
Rev.: $9,245,000,000
Assets: $9,862,000,000
Liabilities: $5,121,000,000
Net Worth: $4,741,000,000
Earnings: $1,237,000,000
Emp.: 51,900
Fiscal Year-end: 12/31/20
Steel Producer
N.A.I.C.S.: 331110
Vladimir Lisin *(Chm)*

Subsidiaries:

Altai-Koks (1)
2 Pritayozhnaya st, Altay region, 659107, Zarinsk, Russia
Tel.: (7) 3859553180
Web Site: http://www.altai-koks.ru
Emp.: 3,000
Production & Sales of Coke & Chemical Products
N.A.I.C.S.: 325180
Pavel Lizogub *(Gen Dir)*

DanSteel A/S (1)
Havnevej 33, 3300, Frederiksvaerk, Denmark **(100%)**
Tel.: (45) 47770333
Web Site: http://www.dansteel.dk
Sales Range: $125-149.9 Million
Emp.: 400
Steel Rolling
N.A.I.C.S.: 331221
Igor Sarkits *(CEO & Dir-Industrial Dev-Intl)*

Dolomit JSC (1)
1 Sverdlova St, Dankov, 399854, Lipetsk, Russia
Tel.: (7) 4746528552
Emp.: 600
Steel Mfrs
N.A.I.C.S.: 331110

Independent Transport Company (1)
Leninsky Prospekt D 32a Suite 1003, 119991, Moscow, Russia **(100%)**
Tel.: (7) 4959385727
Web Site: http://www.ntcorp.ru
Cargo Transportation & Forwarding Services
N.A.I.C.S.: 488510

Jsc Nlmk-Ural (1)
3 K Libkhneta, Revda, Sverdlovskaya, Russia
Tel.: (7) 3439726754
Web Site: http://ural.nlmk.com
Emp.: 1,900
Steel Mfrs
N.A.I.C.S.: 331110

LLC NLMK Long Products (1)
3 Ul Novinskaya, Ekaterinburg, Russia
Tel.: (7) 3432537507
Steel Product Mfr & Distr
N.A.I.C.S.: 331511

LLC Nlmk-Kaluga (1)
20 Lyskina st, Vorsino, 249020, Kaluga, Russia
Tel.: (7) 4843829898
Web Site: http://kaluga.nlmk.com
Steel Mfrs
N.A.I.C.S.: 331110

LLC Nlmk-Metalware (1)
5 Koltsevaya St, Beryozovskiy, 623704, Sverdlovskaya, Russia
Tel.: (7) 3436962400
Emp.: 750
Steel Mfrs
N.A.I.C.S.: 331110
Sergei Kim *(Gen Dir)*

LLC Viz-Steel (1)
28 Kirova St GSP-714, 620108, Yekaterinburg, Russia
Tel.: (7) 3432632195
Emp.: 360
Steel Mfrs
N.A.I.C.S.: 331110

LLC Vtorchermet Nlmk (1)
st Novinskaya 3, Sverdlovsk, 620024, Yekaterinburg, Russia
Tel.: (7) 3432531344
Web Site: http://www.uvchm.ru
Steel Mfrs
N.A.I.C.S.: 331110

NLMK Indiana LLC (1)
6500 S Boundary Rd, Portage, IN 46368
Tel.: (219) 787-8200
Web Site: http://www.us.nlmk.com
Steel Product Mfr & Distr
N.A.I.C.S.: 331511
Joseph Gazarkiewicz *(Dir-HR & Labor Rels)*

NLMK Pennsylvania LLC (1)
15 Roemer Blvd, Farrell, PA 16121
Tel.: (724) 983-6464
Web Site: http://www.us.nlmk.com
Steel Product Distr
N.A.I.C.S.: 423510
Robert D. Miller *(Pres & CEO)*

Nlmk - Ural Service OOO (1)
6 Klubnaya Str, Revda, 623281, Sverdlovskaya, Russia
Tel.: (7) 3439726989
Emp.: 630
Steel Mfrs
N.A.I.C.S.: 331110
Pavel Miroshnikov *(Gen Mgr)*

Nlmk Clabecq S.A. (1)
Rue de Clabecq 101, Ittre, 1460, Wavre, Belgium
Tel.: (32) 23919100
Emp.: 530
Steel Mfrs
N.A.I.C.S.: 331110
Arnaud Lust *(Plant Mgr)*

Nlmk Engineering JSC (1)
1 Kalinina street, 398008, Lipetsk, Russia
Tel.: (7) 4742771757
Web Site: http://engineering.nlmk.com
Emp.: 530
Engineeering Services
N.A.I.C.S.: 541330
Igor Baikov *(Head-Dev)*

Nlmk La Louviere S.A. (1)
Rue des Rivaux 2, 7100, La Louviere, Belgium
Tel.: (32) 64272711
Emp.: 500
Steel Mfrs
N.A.I.C.S.: 331110
Jean-Francois Lagaly *(Acct Mgr)*

Nlmk Verona Spa (1)
Via Antonio Salieri 22, Verona, VR, Italy
Tel.: (39) 0456997911
Emp.: 260
Steel Mfrs
N.A.I.C.S.: 331110
Marco Strambini *(Mgr-ICT)*

Novex Trading (Swiss) S.A. (1)
Riva Paradiso 2, Paradiso, 6902, Switzerland
Tel.: (41) 91 985 30 60
Steel Product Mfr & Distr
N.A.I.C.S.: 331511

Novexco (Cyprus) Ltd. (1)
Egypt Street 12 P C, Nicosia, 1097, Cyprus
Tel.: (357) 22875646
Emp.: 13
Steel Product Mfr & Distr
N.A.I.C.S.: 331511
Stefan Jenkins *(CEO & Mng Dir)*

Novolipetsk Steel Pjsc (1)
40 Bolshaya Ordynka Str Bldg 3, 119017, Moscow, Russia
Tel.: (7) 4955040504
Web Site: https://lipetsk.nlmk.com

Sharon Coating, LLC (1)
277 N Sharpsville Ave, Sharon, PA 16146
Tel.: (724) 981-3545
Web Site: http://www.nlmk.com
Emp.: 110
Steel Product Mfr & Distr
N.A.I.C.S.: 331511

Stagdok OAO (1)
4 Arkadiya Gaidara, 398020, Lipetsk, Russia
Tel.: (7) 4742328502
Emp.: 780
Steel Mfrs
N.A.I.C.S.: 331110

Stoilensky GOK (1)
4 proezd, Stary Oskol, 309500, Belgorod, Russia **(96.98%)**
Tel.: (7) 4725449435
Web Site: http://sgok.nlmk.com
Sales Range: $1-4.9 Billion
Emp.: 6,000
Iron Ore Mining
N.A.I.C.S.: 212210
Alexander Gorshkov *(Gen Dir)*

Tuapse Commercial Seaport (1)
Morskoy Boulevard 2, Tuapse, 352800, Krasnodar, Russia **(69.41%)**
Tel.: (7) 8616771030
Web Site: http://www.tmtp.ru
Cargo Handling
N.A.I.C.S.: 488320

VIZ-Stal LLC (1)
28 Kirova Str GSP-714, 620108, Ekaterinburg, Russia **(100%)**
Tel.: (7) 3432632195
Web Site: http://www.viz.ru
Sales Range: $400-449.9 Million
Emp.: 2,500
Electrical Steel Production & Sales
N.A.I.C.S.: 331110

NOVOLOG (PHARM-UP 1966) LTD.
55 HaMaayan Street, Modi'in-Maccabim-Re'ut, 717131, Israel
Tel.: (972) 86604400
Web Site: https://novolog.co.il
Year Founded: 1966
NVLG—(TAE)
Rev.: $454,065,195
Assets: $770,430,710
Liabilities: $660,989,905
Net Worth: $109,440,805
Earnings: ($10,881,613)
Emp.: 800
Fiscal Year-end: 12/31/23
Surgical & Medical Instrument Manufacturing
N.A.I.C.S.: 339112
Aviad Bussi *(CEO)*

NOVOMATIC AG
Wiener Strasse 158, 2352, Gumpoldskirchen, Austria
Tel.: (43) 2252 606 0
Web Site: http://www.novomatic.com
Year Founded: 1980
Holding Company; Gaming Machines & Equipment Supplier & Operator
N.A.I.C.S.: 551112
Bernd Oswald *(Chm)*

Subsidiaries:

ADMIRAL Sportwetten GmbH (1)
Novomatic Strasse 5, 2352, Gumpoldskirchen, Austria
Tel.: (43) 2252 60 70 90 999
Web Site: http://www.admiral.ag
Gaming Concession Management Services
N.A.I.C.S.: 713290
Jurgen Irsigler *(Co-CEO)*

Subsidiary (Non-US):

Admiral Sports Betting Ltd. (2)
11 Allard Way, Broxbourne, EN10 7ER, Hertfordshire, United Kingdom
Tel.: (44) 1992429860
Gaming Concession Management Services
N.A.I.C.S.: 713290

AGI Africa (Pty) Ltd. (1)
Unit 1 Coventry Park 675 Old Main Pretoria Road Halfway House, Midrand, 1685, Gauteng, South Africa
Tel.: (27) 11 847 9700
Web Site: http://www.agiafrica.co.za

Casino & Gaming Services
N.A.I.C.S.: 721120
Deon Valkenborgh *(Mgr-Sls & Mktg)*

AGI Gaming Colombia S.A.S. (1)
Cra 43a No 34 - 95 Of 106B CC Almacentro, Bogota, Colombia
Tel.: (57) 4 2323315
Web Site: http://www.agigamingcolombia.com
N.A.I.C.S.: 713290

AGI Hungaria Kft. (1)
Infopark walkway 3, 1117, Budapest, Hungary
Tel.: (36) 1 299 0666
Gaming Concession Management Services
N.A.I.C.S.: 713290
Krisztina Nagy *(Office Mgr)*

Admiral d.o.o. (1)
Bazoviska 23, 6240, Kozina, Slovenia
Tel.: (386) 5 689 07 00
Web Site: http://www.admiral.si
Hotel & Casino Operations
N.A.I.C.S.: 721120
Karl Thoene *(Mgr-Hotel & Casino Ops)*

Adria Gaming Vicenza S.r.l. (1)
Via Roma 188/m, Castelgomberto, 36070, Italy
Tel.: (39) 0445 947399
Web Site: http://www.admiralclub.it
Gaming Concession Management Services
N.A.I.C.S.: 713290

Ainsworth Game Technology Limited (1)
10 Holker Street, Newington, 2127, NSW, Australia
Tel.: (61) 297398000
Web Site: https://www.agtslots.com
Rev.: $194,034,466
Assets: $285,026,906
Liabilities: $70,072,883
Net Worth: $214,954,022
Earnings: ($4,456,100)
Emp.: 500
Fiscal Year-end: 12/31/2023
Gaming Machines Mfr
N.A.I.C.S.: 713290
Daniel Eric Gladstone *(Chm)*

Subsidiary (US):

Ainsworth Game Technology Inc (2)
5800 Rafael Rivera Way, Las Vegas, NV 89118
Tel.: (702) 954-3000
Web Site: http://www.agtslots.com
Gaming Machine Mfr & Sales
N.A.I.C.S.: 339930

AuTec AutomatenbetriebsgmbH (1)
Sechtergasse 16, 1120, Vienna, Austria
Tel.: (43) 1 817 17 65
Gaming Concession Management Services
N.A.I.C.S.: 713290

Austrian Gaming Industries GmbH (1)
Wiener Strasse 158, 2532, Gumpoldskirchen, Austria
Tel.: (43) 2252606234
Web Site: http://www.novomatic.com
Emp.: 3,000
Holding Company; Designer, Developer, Mfr & Distr of Electronic Gaming Machines
N.A.I.C.S.: 713290
Harald Neumann *(Mng Dir)*

Subsidiary (Non-US):

Astra Games Ltd. (2)
Astra House 1 Kingsway, Bridgend Industrial Estate, Bridgend, CF31 3RY, United Kingdom
Tel.: (44) 1656 658658
Web Site: http://www.astra-games.com
Gaming Machines Developer & Mfr
N.A.I.C.S.: 713290
Zane Mersich *(CEO)*

Subsidiary (Domestic):

Gamestec Leisure Limited (3)
Wira House West Park Ring Road, Horsforth, Leeds, LS16 6EB, West Yorkshire, United Kingdom
Tel.: (44) 113 258 9495
Web Site: http://www.gamestec.co.uk

AND PRIVATE COMPANIES

Sales Range: $50-74.9 Million
Emp.: 700
Gaming & Amusement Machine Supplier
N.A.I.C.S.: 713290
Neil Lancaster *(Dir-HR)*

Subsidiary (Non-US):

NOVO RS d.o.o. (2)
Urosa Predica Br 1, Banja Luka, Bosnia & Herzegovina
Tel.: (387) 51250610
Gaming Concession Management Services
N.A.I.C.S.: 713290

Novo Invest Bulgaria EOOD (2)
Ovcha Kupel Distr Fl 12 136 Tsar Boris, Sofia, Bulgaria
Tel.: (359) 888330641
Gaming Concession Management Services
N.A.I.C.S.: 713290

Novo Invest Co SRL (2)
Calea Bucurestilor 275-277, 075100, Otopeni, Romania
Tel.: (40) 374 159 000
Gaming Concession Management Services
N.A.I.C.S.: 713290

Subsidiary (Domestic):

Fenikss Slots SRL (3)
Str Stadionului 2 E, 500064, Brasov, Romania
Tel.: (40) 748135395
Gaming Concession Management Services
N.A.I.C.S.: 713290

BPA Freizeit- und Unterhaltungsbetriebe GmbH (1)
Triebstr 14, 80993, Munich, Germany
Tel.: (49) 89 15 92 56 88 0
Gaming Concession Management Services
N.A.I.C.S.: 713290

Bell-Fruit Group Ltd. (1)
Leen Gate, Lenton, Nottingham, NG7 2LX, United Kingdom
Tel.: (44) 115 970 6707
Web Site: http://www.bellfruitgames.co.uk
Gaming Machinery Mfr
N.A.I.C.S.: 339999

Subsidiary (Domestic):

RLMS Sales Ltd. (2)
Unit C4 Beeches Park Eastern Avenue, Burton-on-Trent, DE13 0BB, Staffordshire, United Kingdom
Tel.: (44) 8456036666
Web Site: http://www.rlms-sales.com
Gaming Machine Distr
N.A.I.C.S.: 423990
Tony Glanville *(Mng Dir)*

Crown Gaming Mexico S.A. de C.V. (1)
Monte Elbruz 132 Int 804 Colonia Polanco II Seccion, Miguel Hidalgo, 11530, Mexico, Mexico
Tel.: (52) 55 5281 5687
Web Site: http://www.crown-gaming.mx
Gaming Concession Management Services
N.A.I.C.S.: 713290

Crown Technologies GmbH (1)
Adlerstrasse 48-56, 25462, Rellingen, Germany
Tel.: (49) 4101 3024 0
Web Site: http://www.crown-tec.de
Money Changing Machine Mfr
N.A.I.C.S.: 339999
Uwe Christiansen *(Pres)*

Subsidiary (Domestic):

Hirscher Moneysystems GmbH (1)
Lange Strasse 51, 29664, Walsrode, Germany
Tel.: (49) 5161609200
Web Site: http://www.hirscher-ms.de
Gaming Concession Management Services
N.A.I.C.S.: 713290

Eurocoin Gaming B.V. (1)
van Liemptstraat 16, 5145 RB, Waalwijk, Netherlands
Tel.: (31) 885840010
Web Site: http://www.eurocoingaming.nl
Gaming Concession Management Services
N.A.I.C.S.: 713290

Extra Games Entertainment GmbH (1)
Theuerbach 30, 88630, Pfullendorf, Germany
Tel.: (49) 7552 9286 0
Web Site: http://www.extra-games.net
Gaming Concession Management Services
N.A.I.C.S.: 713290

G.Matica S.r.l. (1)
Via Amsterdam, Rome, 00144, Italy
Tel.: (39) 06 894681
Gaming Concession Management Services
N.A.I.C.S.: 713290

Games Network Ltd. (1)
1 Grand Parade, Brighton, BN2 9QB, United Kingdom
Tel.: (44) 1273 746 864
Web Site: http://www.gamer-network.com
Gaming Concession Management Services
N.A.I.C.S.: 713290

Gastronomie- u. Unterhaltungsselektronik Betriebs GmbH (1)
Thomas Bohrer Strasse 7, Klagenfurt, 9020, Austria
Tel.: (43) 4634107870
Gaming Concession Management Services
N.A.I.C.S.: 713290

GiGames S.L. (1)
Pol Ind Sta Margarida II - Avda Can Jofresa 69, 08223, Terrassa, Spain
Tel.: (34) 937 845 670
Web Site: http://www.gigames.es
Gaming Concession Management Services
N.A.I.C.S.: 713290

Subsidiary (Domestic):

GiGames Norte S.L. (2)
Paduleta n 55 Oficina 102 Centro de Servicios Jandiz, 01015, Vitoria-Gasteiz, Spain
Tel.: (34) 945139098
Gaming Concession Management Services
N.A.I.C.S.: 713290

Greentube Internet Entertainment Solutions GmbH (1)
Zieglergasse 6/ Stiege 3, 1070, Vienna, Austria
Tel.: (43) 1 494 5056
Web Site: http://www.greentube.com
Gaming Concession Management Services
N.A.I.C.S.: 713290
Thomas Graf *(CEO)*

Subsidiary (Non-US):

BeatYa Online Entertainment p.l.c. (2)
W Business Centre Level 4 Dun Karm Street, Birkirkara, BKR 9033, Malta
Tel.: (356) 21341680
Web Site: http://www.beatya.com
Gaming Concession Management Services
N.A.I.C.S.: 713290

Subsidiary (Domestic):

Cervo Media GmbH (2)
Burggasse 4, 8010, Graz, Austria
Tel.: (43) 316228764
Web Site: http://www.cervomedia.com
Gaming Concession Management Services
N.A.I.C.S.: 713290
Christian Baumgartner *(Mng Dir)*

Platogo Interactive Entertainment GmbH (2)
Sechskrugelgasse 10/17, 1030, Vienna, Austria
Tel.: (43) 6502141333
Web Site: http://www.platogo.com
Mobile Software Development Services
N.A.I.C.S.: 513210
Jakob Sommerhuber *(CEO)*

Subsidiary (Non-US):

Stakelogic B.V. (2)
De Regent 8, 5611 HW, Eindhoven, Netherlands
Tel.: (31) 408080328
Web Site: http://www.stakelogic.com
Gaming Concession Management Services
N.A.I.C.S.: 713290

Hotel & Casino Resort Admiral (1)
Bazoviska 23, 6240, Kozina, Slovenia

Tel.: (386) 5 689 07 00
Web Site: http://www.admiral.si
Hotel & Casino Resort
N.A.I.C.S.: 721120
Karl Thoene *(Mgr-Hotel & Casino Ops)*

JVH exploitatie B.V. (1)
Maidstone 56, 5026 SK, Tilburg, Netherlands
Tel.: (31) 13 595 32 00
Web Site: http://www.jvhexploitatie.nl
Gaming Concession Management Services
N.A.I.C.S.: 713290

LOWEN Entertainment GmbH (1)
Saarlandstrasse 240, 55411, Bingen am Rhein, Germany
Tel.: (49) 6721 4070
Web Site: http://www.loewen.de
Gaming Machinery Mfr
N.A.I.C.S.: 339999

Subsidiary (Domestic):

Admiral Play GmbH (2)
Erkrather Str 372, Dusseldorf, 40231, Germany
Tel.: (49) 2115421480
Gaming Concession Management Services
N.A.I.C.S.: 713290

Loontjens Automaten B.V. (1)
Loontjens Automaten Dam 21, Middelburg, 4331 GE, Netherlands
Tel.: (31) 118 634400
Web Site: http://www.loontjensautomaten.nl
Casino & Gaming Services
N.A.I.C.S.: 721120

Luxury Leisure ltd. (1)
362C Dukesway Team Valley Trading Estate, Gateshead, NE11 0PZ, United Kingdom
Tel.: (44) 191 497 8200
Web Site: http://www.luxuryleisure.co.uk
Gaming Machine Mfr & Distr
N.A.I.C.S.: 339999

Memorija Turizem d.o.o. (1)
Vinarski trg 5, 2250, Ptuj, Slovenia
Tel.: (386) 2779 82 11
Web Site: http://www.hotel-poetovio.si
Casino & Gaming Services
N.A.I.C.S.: 721120

NGE Oud B.V. (1)
Tulpenhof 31, 1648 KL, De Goorn, Netherlands
Tel.: (31) 229 542241
Gaming Concession Management Services
N.A.I.C.S.: 713290

NOVOMATIC Gaming Spain S.A. (1)
Galileo Galilei 28 Poligono Industrial La Garena, Alcala de Henares, 28806, Madrid, Spain
Tel.: (34) 91 877 6262
Web Site: http://www.novomatic-spain.com
Gaming Concession Management Services
N.A.I.C.S.: 713290

NOVOMATIC Italia S.p.A. (1)
Via Galla Placidia 2, Rimini, 47922, Italy
Tel.: (39) 0541 420 611
Web Site: http://www.novomatic.it
Gaming Concession Management Services
N.A.I.C.S.: 713290

Novogaming Ghana Ltd. (1)
9 Sir Arku Korsah Road Roman Ridge, Accra, Ghana
Tel.: (233) 302 733 188
Web Site: http://www.novogaming-ghana.com
Gaming Concession Management Services
N.A.I.C.S.: 713290
John Kivinen *(Mng Dir)*

OOO United Gaming Industries (1)
Ul A Nevskogo 238, 236029, Kaliningrad, Russia
Tel.: (7) 401 258 5951
Gaming Concession Management Services
N.A.I.C.S.: 713290

Octavian de Argentina S.A. (1)
San jose 83 Piso 3, C1076AAA, Buenos Aires, Argentina
Tel.: (54) 11 4307 6101
Web Site: http://www.octavian.com.ar

Gaming Concession Management Services
N.A.I.C.S.: 713290

Recreatieprojecten Zeeland B.V. (1)
Nieuwstraat 83-A, 4524 EG, Sluiskil, Netherlands
Tel.: (31) 117 461000
Gaming Concession Management Services
N.A.I.C.S.: 713290

SIM Spielbanken Investitions-, Beteiligungs- und Management GmbH & CO. KG (1)
Burnitzstr 42-44, 60596, Frankfurt, Germany
Tel.: (49) 69 6780320
Gaming Concession Management Services
N.A.I.C.S.: 713290

Subsidiary (Domestic):

Kurhessische Spielbank Kassel/BadWildungen GmbH & CO. KG (2)
Wall Street 11, 34117, Kassel, Germany
Tel.: (49) 561930850
Web Site: http://www.spielbank-kassel.de
Casino & Gaming Services
N.A.I.C.S.: 721120
Gerhard Wilhelm *(CEO)*

UAB Azarto Technika (1)
Pramones g 31, 62175, Alytus, Lithuania
Tel.: (370) 315 77303
Web Site: http://www.atech.lt
Gaming Machinery Mfr
N.A.I.C.S.: 339999

Wett Cafe Betriebs GmbH (1)
Karlauer Strase 43, Graz, 8020, Austria
Tel.: (43) 316766766
Gaming Concession Management Services
N.A.I.C.S.: 713290

NOVOMED GROUP

7 rue de Thionville, Paris, 75019, France
Tel.: (33) 1 42 03 96.78
Web Site: http://www.novomedgroup.com
Year Founded: 1993
Disposable Dressing Kits Mfr
N.A.I.C.S.: 339113
Aurelie Descubes *(Mng Dir)*

Subsidiaries:

Mediq France SA (1)
200 Avenue des Gresillons, 92601, Asnieres, Cedex, France
Tel.: (33) 141324050
Web Site: http://www.nmmedical.fr
Medical Equipment & Supplies Distr
N.A.I.C.S.: 423450
Antoine Laforgue *(Dir Gen)*

NOVONESIS A/S

Krogshoejvej 36, DK-2880, Bagsvaerd, Denmark
Tel.: (45) 44460000
Web Site: https://www.novonesis.com
Year Founded: 2000
NSIS-B—(CSE)
Rev.: $2,650,329,452
Assets: $4,203,894,266
Liabilities: $2,078,922,035
Net Worth: $2,124,972,231
Earnings: $449,988,893
Emp.: 6,397
Fiscal Year-end: 12/31/23
Biotechnology Company
N.A.I.C.S.: 541714

Subsidiaries:

Novozymes A/S (1)
Krogshoejvej 36, DK-2880, Bagsvaerd, Denmark
Tel.: (45) 44460000
Web Site: http://www.novozymes.com
Rev.: $2,312,960,840
Assets: $3,385,585,700
Liabilities: $1,531,354,390
Net Worth: $1,854,231,310
Earnings: $466,322,750
Emp.: 6,369

NOVONESIS A/S

Novonesis A/S—(Continued)

Fiscal Year-end: 12/31/2020
Enzyme Mfr
N.A.I.C.S.: 325199
Thomas Videbaek *(Exec VP-Strategy, Bus Transformation, People & Sustainability)*

Subsidiary (Domestic):

Chr. Hansen Holding A/S (2)
Boge Alle 10-12, 2970, Horsholm, Denmark
Tel.: (45) 45747474
Web Site: https://www.chr-hansen.com
Rev.: $201,055,260
Assets: $547,504,176
Liabilities: $246,433,003
Net Worth: $301,071,173
Earnings: $37,157,257
Emp.: 3,834
Fiscal Year-end: 08/31/2022
Holding Company; Biological Products & Food Additive Chemicals Mfr
N.A.I.C.S.: 551112
Winnie Hoejvang Buegel *(Gen Counsel & VP-Compliance, Corp Affairs & Sustainability)*

Subsidiary (Non-US):

AKAY Flavours & Aromatics Pvt. Ltd. (3)
Malaidamthuruthu PO, South Vazhakkulam, 683561, Cochin, Kerala, India
Tel.: (91) 484 2686111
Sales Range: $25-49.9 Million
Mfr of Natural Flavors & Fragrances
N.A.I.C.S.: 311930

Subsidiary (Domestic):

Chr. Hansen A/S (3)
Boege Alle 10-12, 2970, Horsholm, Denmark
Tel.: (45) 45747474
Sales Range: $100-124.9 Million
Emp.: 500
Mfr of Natural Colors, Flavors & Cultures for Food Industry; Provider of Biotechnological Services for Dairy, Agriculture & Health Food Industries; Manufacturer of Vaccines & Diagnostic Products
N.A.I.C.S.: 325414

Subsidiary (Non-US):

Chr. Hansen Argentina S.A.I.C. (3)
Cecilia Grierson 422 4 Piso, Casilla De Correo 20, 1107, Buenos Aires, BA, Argentina
Tel.: (54) 1150707700
Sales Range: $25-49.9 Million
Provider of Natural Colors, Flavors & Cultures for Food Industry; Provider of Biotechnological Services for Dairy, Agriculture & Health Food Industries; Provider of Vaccines & Diagnostic Products
N.A.I.C.S.: 325414

Chr. Hansen Czech Republic, s.r.o (3)
C P 215, PO Box 28, 693 01, Starovice, Czech Republic
Tel.: (420) 724868855
Web Site: https://www.chr-hansen.com
Sales Range: $1-9.9 Million
Emp.: 30
Natural Colors, Flavors & Cultures for Food Industry; Biotechnological Services for Dairy, Agriculture & Health Food Industries; Vaccines & Diagnostic Products
N.A.I.C.S.: 325414
Petr Hartman *(Mgr-Fin)*

Chr. Hansen GmbH (3)
Grosse Drakenburger Strasse 93-97, 31582, Nienburg, Germany
Tel.: (49) 50219630
Sales Range: $25-49.9 Million
Food Enzyme Mfr
N.A.I.C.S.: 325199

Chr. Hansen GmbH (3)
Giessener Str 94, 35415, Pohlheim, Germany
Tel.: (49) 640395010
Sales Range: $25-49.9 Million
Culture for Food Industry Mfr
N.A.I.C.S.: 325414

Chr. Hansen Industria e Comercio Ltda. (3)
Rodovia Visconde de Porto Seguro 2860, Valinhos, 13278-327, SP, Brazil
Tel.: (55) 1938818300
Web Site: https://www.chr-hansen.com
Sales Range: $50-74.9 Million
Provider of Natural Colors, Flavors & Cultures for Food Industry; Provider of Biotechnological Services for Dairy, Agriculture & Health Food Industries; Provider of Vaccines & Diagnostic Products
N.A.I.C.S.: 325414

Chr. Hansen Ireland Limited (3)
Office 1 Building A3, Fota Business Park, T45 T924, Carrigtwohill, Co Cork, Ireland
Tel.: (353) 214538216
Web Site: https://www.chr-hansen.com.ie
Sales Range: $25-49.9 Million
Emp.: 6
Mfr of Natural Colors, Flavors & Cultures for Food Industry; Provider of Biotechnological Services for Dairy, Agriculture & Health Food Industries; Manufacturer of Vaccines & Diagnostic Products
N.A.I.C.S.: 325414

Chr. Hansen Poland Sp. z.o.o. (3)
st Gdanska 4, Czastkow Mazowiecki, 05-152, Czosnow, Poland
Tel.: (48) 727606202
Web Site: https://pl.chr-hansen.com
Sales Range: $25-49.9 Million
Emp.: 30
Natural Colors, Flavors & Cultures for Food Industry; Biotechnological Services for Dairy, Agriculture & Health Food Industries; Vaccines & Diagnostic Products
N.A.I.C.S.: 325414

Chr. Hansen Pty. Ltd. (3)
49 Barry Street, PO Box 591, Bayswater, 3153, VIC, Australia
Tel.: (61) 397629600
Sales Range: $10-24.9 Million
Emp.: 30
Mfr & Sales of Natural Food Ingredients
N.A.I.C.S.: 311999

Chr. Hansen de Mexico, S.A. de C.V. (3)
Avenida Insurgentes Sur No 1431 Piso 11, Colonia Insurgentes Mixcoac, 03920, Mexico, Mexico
Tel.: (52) 5558047400
Web Site: https://www.chr-hansen.com
Natural Food Ingredients Mfr & Distr
N.A.I.C.S.: 325414
Gustavo Pimentel *(Mgr-Technical Applications)*

Christian Hansen (UK) Ltd. (3)
2 Tealgate Rd, Hungerford, RG17 0YT, Berkshire, United Kingdom
Tel.: (44) 1488689800
Web Site: https://www.chr-hansen.com
Sales Range: $10-24.9 Million
Natural Food Color & Rennet Manufacturer
N.A.I.C.S.: 311942
Mark Hurley *(Mng Dir)*

Christian Hansen France S.A. (3)
Le Moulin Daulnay Rte DaAulnay, Saint Germain Les Arpajon, 91290, Arpajon, France
Tel.: (33) 0169883636
Web Site: https://www.chf-hansen.com
Sales Range: $50-74.9 Million
Provider of Biotechnological Services for Dairy, Agriculture & Health Food Industries
N.A.I.C.S.: 325414

Christian Hansen Italy (3)
Canosa, I 42026, Reggio nell'Emilia, RE, Italy
Tel.: (39) 0522872302
Sales Range: $25-49.9 Million
Emp.: 15
Mfr of Natural Colors for Food Products
N.A.I.C.S.: 311942

Christian Hansen S.p.A. (3)
Via Quintino Sella 3/A, Parma, 43123, Italy
Tel.: (39) 0521497211
Web Site: http://www.christianhansen.com
Sales Range: $25-49.9 Million
Mfr of Natural Colors, Flavors & Cultures for Food Industry; Provider of Biotechnological Services for Dairy, Agriculture & Health Food Industries; Manufacturer of Vaccines & Diagnostic Products

Hansen Hellas a/s (3)
39 Sigrou St, Athens, 117 43, Greece
Tel.: (30) 2109233660
Web Site: https://www.chr-hansen.com
Sales Range: $50-74.9 Million
Emp.: 3
Dairy Sales & Technical Support; Meat & Prepared Food Applications; Food & Beverage Applications
N.A.I.C.S.: 424430

Division (Domestic):

Hansen Hellas Abee (4)
2 Drakou Str 70 Sygrou Av, PO Box 1385, 11742, Athens, Greece
Tel.: (30) 2109233660
Sales Range: $50-74.9 Million
Emp.: 1
Dairy Sales & Support, Logistics & Warehouse & Customer Service
N.A.I.C.S.: 424430
Argiris Leveneos *(Mgr-Customer Svc)*

Subsidiary (Non-US):

Peyma Chr. Hansen's Peynir Mayasi Sanayi Ve Ticaret A.S. (3)
Mevlut Pehlivan Sok Yilmaz Ishani No 24 Kat 2, Gayrettepe, Istanbul, 34394, Sisli, Turkiye
Tel.: (90) 2122755253
Web Site: https://www.peyma-chr.hansen.com
Sales Range: $25-49.9 Million
Emp.: 25
Natural Colors, Flavors & Cultures for Food Industry; Provider of Biotechnological Services for Dairy, Agriculture & Health Food Industries; Provider of Vaccines & Diagnostic Products
N.A.I.C.S.: 325414

Subsidiary (Non-US):

Medipharm Hungary Kft (4)
Temeto u 10, Budapest, 1222, Hungary
Tel.: (36) 12266061
Dairy Products
N.A.I.C.S.: 311511

Subsidiary (US):

Medipharm USA (4)
10215 Dennis Dr, Des Moines, IA 50322
Tel.: (515) 254-1280
Dairy Products Provider
N.A.I.C.S.: 311511

Subsidiary (US):

UAS Laboratories, Inc. (3)
555 N 72nd Ave, Wausau, WI 54401
Tel.: (715) 849-3333
Web Site: http://www.uaslabs.com
Emp.: 230
Pharmaceutical Preparation Mfr
N.A.I.C.S.: 325412
Kevin Mehring *(Pres & CEO)*

Subsidiary (Non-US):

Novozymes (China) Biotechnology Co., Ltd. (2)
No 150 Nanhai Road, Tianjin, 300457, China
Tel.: (86) 2225322063
Bio Technology Services
N.A.I.C.S.: 541714

Novozymes (China) Investment Co., Ltd. (2)
No 14 Xinxi Road, Shangdi Zone, Beijing, 100085, China
Tel.: (86) 1062987888
Bio Technology Services
N.A.I.C.S.: 541714

Novozymes (Shenyang) Biologicals Co., Ltd. (2)
Canghai Road 39-1, Shenyang Economic & Technical Development Zone, Shenyang, 110141, China
Tel.: (86) 2425813137
Bio Technology Services
N.A.I.C.S.: 541714

INTERNATIONAL PUBLIC

Novozymes Australia Pty Ltd. (2) **(100%)**
Tel.: (61) 296308466
Web Site: https://www.novozymes.com
Sales Range: $25-49.9 Million
Emp.: 8
Mfr of Industrial Biochemicals
N.A.I.C.S.: 325998
Tony Bryan *(Gen Mgr)*

Novozymes Austria GmbH (2)
Karolinengasse 5 9, 1040, Vienna, Austria **(100%)**
Tel.: (43) 015054757
Sales Range: $25-49.9 Million
Emp.: 10
Mfr of Industrial Biochemicals
N.A.I.C.S.: 325998
Michael Brennan *(Dir-Sls)*

Novozymes Belgium B.V. (2)
Chaussee de la Hulpe 166, Watermael-Boitsfort, 1170, Brussels, Belgium
Tel.: (32) 27354145
Bio Technology Services
N.A.I.C.S.: 541714

Novozymes Berlin GmbH (2)
Gustav-Meyer-Allee 25, 13355, Berlin, Germany
Tel.: (49) 30921076550
Bio Technology Services
N.A.I.C.S.: 541714

Subsidiary (Domestic):

Novozymes BioAg A/S (2)
Krogshoejvej 36, 2880, Bagsvaerd, Denmark
Tel.: (45) 44460000
Food Production Services
N.A.I.C.S.: 541714

Subsidiary (Non-US):

Novozymes BioAg Limited (2)
3935 Thatcher Ave, Saskatoon, S7R 1A3, SK, Canada
Tel.: (306) 657-8200
Bio Technology Services
N.A.I.C.S.: 541714

Novozymes BioAg Productos Para Agricultura Ltda. (2)
Rua Aristeu Luciano Adamoski 12, Jardim Menino Deus, Quatro Barras, 83420-000, PR, Brazil
Tel.: (55) 4136721292
Bio Technology Services
N.A.I.C.S.: 541714

Novozymes BioAg S.A. (2)
Planta Industrial - Calle 10 No 753 - Parque Industrial Pilar, 1629, Buenos Aires, Argentina
Tel.: (54) 2304496100
Food Production Services
N.A.I.C.S.: 541714

Subsidiary (Domestic):

Novozymes Bioindustrial A/S (2)
Krogshoejvej 36, 2880, Bagsvaerd, Denmark
Tel.: (45) 44460000
Food Production Services
N.A.I.C.S.: 541714

Subsidiary (Non-US):

Novozymes Biologicals France S.A. (2)
Parc Technologiq des Grillions 60 route de Sartrouville Bat, 78230, Le Pecq, France **(100%)**
Tel.: (33) 130152840
Web Site: https://www.novozymes.com
Mfr of Industrial Biochemicals
N.A.I.C.S.: 325998

Subsidiary (US):

Novozymes Biologicals Inc. (2)
5400 Corporate Cir, Salem, VA 24153 **(100%)**
Tel.: (540) 389-9361
Web Site: https://www.novozymesbiologicals.com
Sales Range: $50-74.9 Million
Emp.: 166
Mfr of Biochemicals

AND PRIVATE COMPANIES

N.A.I.C.S.: 325414
Patrick Patterson (Pres)

Subsidiary (Domestic):

Novozymes Biopharma DK A/S (2)
Krogshojvej 36, 2880, Bagsvaerd, Denmark
Tel.: (45) 44460000
Biopharmaceutical Product Mfr & Distr
N.A.I.C.S.: 325414

Subsidiary (US):

Novozymes Blair, Inc. (2)
1209 Orange St, Wilmington, DE 19801
Tel.: (402) 426-5518
Biopharmaceutical Product Mfr & Distr
N.A.I.C.S.: 325414

Subsidiary (Non-US):

Novozymes Canada Limited (2)
300 Hunt Club Road East, Ottawa, K1V 1C1, ON, Canada
Tel.: (613) 482-8880
Food Production Services
N.A.I.C.S.: 541714

Novozymes China (2)
14 Xinxi Lu Shangdi Zone, Haidin District, Beijing, 100085, China (100%)
Tel.: (86) 1062987888
Web Site: https://www.novozymes.com.cn
Sales Range: $50-74.9 Milllion
Emp.: 100
Biochemical & Petrochemical Mfr
N.A.I.C.S.: 325110

Novozymes Deutschland GmbH (2)
Hasenrecher Weg 25, 55543, Bad Kreuznach, Germany
Tel.: (49) 61529613545
Bio Technology Services
N.A.I.C.S.: 541714

Novozymes Eenzim Dis Ticaret Limited Sirketi (2)
Buyukhanli Konutlari B1Blok Kat 5 Daire 17, 81070 Suadiye, Istanbul, Turkiye
Tel.: (90) 163733000
Mfr of Enzymes
N.A.I.C.S.: 325411

Novozymes Enzim Dis Ticaret Ltd. (2)
Worldwide Business Center Barbaros Mah Mor Sumbul Sok No 9/41, Atasehir, 34746, Istanbul, Turkiye
Tel.: (90) 2163733000
Bio Technology Services
N.A.I.C.S.: 541714

Novozymes France S.A.S. (2)
Le Montreal Parc du Saint Laurent 54 Rte de Sartrouville, 78230, Le Pecq, France
Tel.: (33) 130152840
Bio Technology Services
N.A.I.C.S.: 541714

Novozymes Hong Kong Ltd. (2)
14th Floor One Taikoo Place 979 King's Road, Quarry Bay, China (Hong Kong)
Tel.: (852) 28461061
Bio Technology Services
N.A.I.C.S.: 541714

Novozymes Japan, Ltd. (2)
Makuhari Techno Garden CB 5 3 Nakase 1 Chome, Mihama ku, Chiba, 261 8501, Japan (100%)
Tel.: (81) 432966767
Web Site: https://www.novozymes.co.jp
Sales Range: $25-49.9 Million
Emp.: 50
Mfr of Industrial Biochemicals
N.A.I.C.S.: 325998

Novozymes Korea, Limited (2)
(100%)
Tel: (82) 27950880
Sales Range: $10-24.9 Million
Emp.: 9
Mfr of Industrial Biochemicals
N.A.I.C.S.: 325998

Novozymes Latin America Ltda. (2)
Rua Professor Francisco Ribeiro 683, Araucaria, Parana, 83707-660, Brazil
Tel.: (55) 4136411000
Biopharmaceutical Product Mfr & Distr
N.A.I.C.S.: 325414

Novozymes Malaysia Sdn. Bhd. (2)
Jalan Inovasi 1 Technology Park Malaysia, Bukit Jalil, 57000, Kuala Lumpur, Malaysia
Tel.: (60) 389918688
Sales Range: $25-49.9 Million
Emp.: 18
Industrial Biochemicals Sales
N.A.I.C.S.: 424690

Novozymes Mexicana, S.A. de C.V. (2)
Av De Los Angeles 303 1-B, 02120, Mexico, Mexico
Tel.: (52) 5553189680
Biopharmaceutical Product Mfr & Distr
N.A.I.C.S.: 325414

Novozymes Mexico, S.A. de C.V. (2)
Av De Los Angeles 303 1-B DF, 02120, Mexico, Mexico
Tel.: (52) 5553189680
Bio Technology Services
N.A.I.C.S.: 541714

Novozymes Nederland B.V. (2)
Beukenstraat 43, 2023 TA, Haarlem, Netherlands
Tel.: (31) 44460000
Bio Technology Services
N.A.I.C.S.: 541714

Subsidiary (US):

Novozymes North America, Inc. (2)
77 Perry Chapel Church Rd, Franklinton, NC 27525 (100%)
Tel.: (919) 494-3000
Web Site: https://www.novozymes.com
Sales Range: $125-149.9 Million
Emp.: 400
Mfr of Enzymes
N.A.I.C.S.: 325199

Subsidiary (Non-US):

Novozymes OneHealth Biotechnology (Shanghai) Co., Ltd. (2)
Unit 2604A 99 Xianxia Road, Changning District, Shanghai, China
Tel.: (86) 2225322062
Food Production Services
N.A.I.C.S.: 541714

Novozymes S.A. (Pty) Ltd. (2)
23 14th St, Marlboro, Sandton, 2010, Johannesburg, South Africa (100%)
Tel.: (27) 114448124
Web Site: https://www.novozymes.com
Sales Range: $1-9.9 Million
Emp.: 16
Mfr of Industrial Biochemicals
N.A.I.C.S.: 325998

Novozymes SA Oddzial W Polsce (2)
Ul Messynska 16, 02 761, Warsaw, Poland (100%)
Tel.: (48) 226420540
Web Site: https://www.novozymes.com
Sales Range: $25-49.9 Million
Emp.: 2
Mfr of Enzymes
N.A.I.C.S.: 325411

Novozymes Singapore Pte. Ltd. (2)
80 Robinson Road 02-00, Singapore, 068898, Singapore
Tel.: (65) 62363333
Food Production Services
N.A.I.C.S.: 541714

Novozymes South Africa (Pty.) Ltd. (2)
Block E Lincolnwood Office Park 6-8 Woodlands Drive, Woodmead, Johannesburg, South Africa
Tel.: (27) 116564200
Bio Technology Services
N.A.I.C.S.: 541714

Novozymes South Asia Pacific Pte. Ltd. (2)
No 16 7th Fl Innovator Intl Tech Pk, Whitefield Rd, Bengaluru, 560 066, India (100%)
Tel.: (91) 8028418275
Web Site: https://www.teckcominco.com
Sales Range: $25-49.9 Million
Emp.: 19
Industrial Biochemicals Mfr
N.A.I.C.S.: 325998

Novozymes South Asia Pvt. Ltd. (2)
Plot No 32 47-50 EPIP Area, Bengaluru, 560066, Karnataka, India
Tel.: (91) 8069033000
Bio Technology Services
N.A.I.C.S.: 541714

Novozymes Switzerland AG (2)
Neumatt, 4243, Dittingen, Switzerland (100%)
Tel.: (41) 617656111
Sales Range: $100-124.9 Million
Emp.: 55
Mfr of Industrial Biochemicals
N.A.I.C.S.: 325998

Novozymes Switzerland Holding AG (2)
Gewerbestrasse 7A, 4147, Aesch, Switzerland
Tel.: (41) 796955338
Biopharmaceutical Product Mfr & Distr
N.A.I.C.S.: 325414

Novozymes UK Ltd. (2)
11 The Office Village North Road, Loughborough, LE11 1QJ, Leicestershire, United Kingdom
Tel.: (44) 212066012
Food Production Services
N.A.I.C.S.: 541714

Subsidiary (US):

Novozymes US, Inc. (2)
77 Perrys Chapel Church Rd, Franklinton, NC 27525
Tel.: (919) 494-3000
Bio Technology Services
N.A.I.C.S.: 541714

Subsidiary (Non-US):

Novozymes do Brasil Ltda. (2)
R Prof Francisco Ribeiro 683, CEP 83701 000, Araucaria, Parana, Brazil (100%)
Tel.: (55) 4136411000
Web Site: https://www.novozymes.com
Sales Range: $50-74.9 Million
Emp.: 200
Mfr of Enzymes
N.A.I.C.S.: 325411
Pedro Fernandez (VP)

Subsidiary (US):

Novozymes, Inc. (2)
1445 Drew Ave, Davis, CA 95618 (100%)
Tel.: (530) 757-8100
Web Site: https://www.novozymes.com
Sales Range: $25-49.9 Million
Emp.: 75
Mfr & Supplier of Enzymes
N.A.I.C.S.: 325199

Physicians Exclusive LLC (2)
1332 Waukegan Rd, Glenview, IL 60025
Tel.: (904) 940-2208
Web Site: https://www.microbiomelabs.com
Medical Research & Development Services
N.A.I.C.S.: 541713

Subsidiary (Non-US):

PrecisionBiotics Group Ltd. (2)
Building 4400 Cork Airport Business Park Kinsale Road, Cork, T12 N84F, Ireland
Tel.: (353) 212066012
Web Site: https://www.precisionbiotics.ie
Biotechnology Research & Development Services
N.A.I.C.S.: 541715

Riata Life Sciences Pvt. Ltd. (2)
141-B Tundav Raniya Road Near Anjesar, Tundav Savli, Vadodara, 391780, Guajarat, India
Tel.: (91) 2667262020
Biopharmaceutical Product Mfr & Distr
N.A.I.C.S.: 325414

Suzhou Hongda Enzyme Co., Ltd. (2)
Sha Xi Town, Jiangsu, China
Tel.: (86) 51253211506
Bio Technology Services
N.A.I.C.S.: 541714

Synergia Life Sciences Pvt. Ltd. (2)
6/312 Jogani Industrial Complex, V N Purav Marg Chunabhatti East, Mumbai, 400 022, India
Tel.: (91) 2262669600
Biopharmaceutical Product Mfr & Distr
N.A.I.C.S.: 325414

NOVONIX LIMITED

Level 8 46 Edward Street, Brisbane, 4000, QLD, Australia
Tel.: (61) 439310818
Web Site: https://www.novonixgroup.com
Year Founded: 2015
NVX—(NASDAQ)
Rev.: $6,449,606
Assets: $336,787,551
Liabilities: $57,631,343
Net Worth: $279,156,208
Earnings: ($54,737,398)
Emp.: 165
Fiscal Year-end: 06/30/22
Electrical & Electronic Mfr
N.A.I.C.S.: 334419
Anthony Bellas (Chm & Deputy Chm)

Subsidiaries:

PUREgraphite LLC (1)
353 Corporate Pl, Chattanooga, TN 37419
Tel.: (423) 541-6874
Graphite Product Mfr
N.A.I.C.S.: 335991

NOVONOR S.A.

Av Luis Viana 2841 Paralela Edificio Odebrecht, 41730-900, Salvador, Bahia, Brazil
Tel.: (55) 7121051111 BR
Web Site: https://novonor.com
Year Founded: 1944
Sales Range: $5-14.9 Billion
Emp.: 28,000
Holding Company
N.A.I.C.S.: 551112

Subsidiaries:

Bento Pedroso Construcoes S.A. (1)
Quinta da Fonte Rua Quinta da Quinta Edificio D Joao I n 4 Piso 1B, 2770-203, Lisbon, Paco de Arcos, Portugal
Tel.: (351) 214407400
Web Site: http://www.odebrecht.com
Sales Range: $200-249.9 Million
Emp.: 1,000
Civil Engineering Construction
N.A.I.C.S.: 237990

Braskem S.A. (1)
Rua Lemos Monteiro 120 22 andar Pinheiros One, Butanta, Sao Paulo, 05501-050, SP, Brazil (50.1%)
Tel.: (55) 1135769000
Web Site: https://www.braskem.com.br
Rev.: $14,072,988,334
Assets: $18,295,144,082
Liabilities: $17,641,240,403
Net Worth: $653,903,679
Earnings: ($975,172,001)
Emp.: 8,569
Fiscal Year-end: 12/31/2023
Petrochemicals, Including Ethylene, Propylene, Benzene, Butadiene, Toluene & Xylenes Mfr
N.A.I.C.S.: 325199
Marcelo de Oliveira Cerqueira (Exec Officer & Head-Chemicals & Vinyl Unit)

Subsidiary (US):

Braskem America, Inc. (2)
1735 Market St 28th Fl, Philadelphia, PA 19103-7583
Tel.: (215) 841-3100
Web Site: http://www.braskem.com
Polypropylene, Thermoplastic Resins & Other Petrochemical Products Mfr
N.A.I.C.S.: 325110
Gustavo Valverde (VP-Legal & Corp Affairs & Head-External Affairs)

Subsidiary (Domestic):

Ipiranga Quimica S.A. (2)
Rua Antonio Carlos 434-4 andar, Sao Paulo, 01309 905, Brazil (60%)

NOVONOR S.A.

Novonor S.A.—(Continued)
Tel.: (55) 1121959132
Web Site:
http://www.ipirangaquimica.com.br
Chemicals & Petrochemical Products Distr
N.A.I.C.S.: 424690

Quattor Petroquimica SA (2)
Rua Joaquim Floriano 960 14 andar, Sao Paulo, Brazil (60%)
Tel.: (55) 11 37075993
Web Site: http://www.quattor.com.br
Sales Range: $1-4.9 Billion
Emp.: 475
Petrochemical Products Mfr
N.A.I.C.S.: 325110

CBPO Engenharia Ltda. (1)
Av Alvares Cabral 1777 19 Andar, Santo Agostinho, 30170 001, Belo Horizonte, MG, Brazil (100%)
Tel.: (55) 3132996700
Web Site: http://www.odebrecht.com.br
N.A.I.C.S.: 541330

CBPO Ingenieria de Venezuela C.A. (1)
Centro Empresarial Torre Humboldt Piso 10 Oficina, 10-13 - Avenida Rio Caura, Caracas, Venezuela
Tel.: (58) 212 976 4333
Civil Engineering Construction
N.A.I.C.S.: 237990

Constructora Norberto Odebrecht Peru S.A. (1)
Avda la Floresta 497 Ofc 104, Chacarilla Del Estanque, San Borja, Lima, Peru (100%)
Tel.: (51) 12172800
Web Site: http://www.odebrecht.com.pe
Sales Range: $25-49.9 Million
Emp.: 50
N.A.I.C.S.: 236220
Brimonu Farra *(Mng Dir)*

Constructora Norberto Odebrecht S.A. (1)
Calle Pedro Henriquez Urena 152 Edificio Torre Professional, Diandy Century Loca 8B Piso 8, Santo Domingo, Dominican Republic
Tel.: (809) 5494000
Civil Engineering Construction
N.A.I.C.S.: 237990

Constructora Norberto Odebrecht S.A. (1)
Punta Pacifica - Torres de las Americas, Panama, Panama
Tel.: (507) 204 5742
Web Site: http://www.odebrecht.com
Civil Engineering Construction
N.A.I.C.S.: 237990

Constructora Norberto Odebrecht de Venezuela C.A. (1)
Centro Empresarial Torre Humboldt Piso 10 Oficina 10-13, Avenida Rio Caura, Urbanizacion Parque Humboldt, Caracas, Venezuela
Tel.: (58) 212 976 4333
Construction Services
N.A.I.C.S.: 236220

Constructora Odebrecht Argentina S.A. (1)
Av Leandro N Alme 855 Piso 32, Torre Alem Plaza, Capital Federal, C1001AAD, Buenos Aires, Argentina (100%)
Tel.: (54) 11 4319 5300
Web Site: http://www.odebrecht.com.ar
Sales Range: $50-74.9 Million
Emp.: 5
N.A.I.C.S.: 236220

Constructora Odebrecht Chile S.A. (1)
Av Bernardine Lib O Higgins N 292 Ofc 21 Meter U, Catolica, Santiago, 6501242, Chile (100%)
Tel.: (56) 24202419
Web Site: http://www.debrecht.com
Sales Range: $50-74.9 Million
Emp.: 3
N.A.I.C.S.: 236220

Construtora Norberto Odebrecht S.A. (1)
Praia de Botafogo 300-10 andar, Botafogo, 22250-040, Rio de Janeiro, Brazil
Tel.: (55) 21 2559 3000
Web Site: http://www.odebrecht.com
Construction & Engineering Services
N.A.I.C.S.: 236220

Branch (Domestic):

Construtora Norberto Odebrecht S.A. (2)
SAS Qd 5 BL N 9 Andar, Edificio OAB, Brasilia, 70438 900, DF, Brazil
Tel.: (55) 61 3316 2525
Web Site: http://www.odebrecht-ec.com
Sales Range: $25-49.9 Million
Emp.: 30
Construction & Engineering Services
N.A.I.C.S.: 236220

Construtora Norberto Odebrecht S.A. (2)
Reboucas Ave 3970, Sao Paulo, 05402 600, SP, Brazil
Tel.: (55) 1130968000
Web Site: http://www.odebrecht.com
Sales Range: $25-49.9 Million
Emp.: 2,000
Construction & Engineering Services
N.A.I.C.S.: 236220
Marcelo Odebrecht *(Mng Dir)*

Construtora Norberto Odebrecht S.A. (2)
Av Luiz Viana 2841 Paralela Fl 1, Odebrecht Bldg, 41730 900, Salvador, BA, Brazil (100%)
Tel.: (55) 71 2105 1111
Web Site: http://www.odebrecht-ec.com
Engineering & Construction Services
N.A.I.C.S.: 541330

Construtora Norberto Odebrecht S.A. (1)
Salam Street, Mezzanine 1 & 2, Abu Dhabi, United Arab Emirates
Tel.: (971) 26679911
Web Site: http://www.odebrecht.com
Sales Range: $25-49.9 Million
Emp.: 75
Civil Engineering Construction
N.A.I.C.S.: 237990
Eduardo Badin *(Mng Dir)*

Construtora Norberto Odebrecht S.A. (1)
Odebrecht Oil & Gas, Mexico, S de R.L de C.V., Homero 418 - 6 Piso, Polanco, Mexico
Tel.: (52) 55 5545 8551
Web Site: http://www.odebrecht.com.br
Civil Engineering Construction
N.A.I.C.S.: 237990

ENSEADA (1)
Rua A Fazenda Boa Vista do Gurjao e Dende Anexo 2 Estaleiro, 44420-000, Maragojipe, Brazil
Tel.: (55) 75 3527 6800
Web Site: http://www.enseada.com
Offshore Construction Services
N.A.I.C.S.: 336611

Fundacao Odebrecht (1)
Mundo Plaza Empresarial Building Av Tancredo Neves 620 room 408, Caminho das Arvore, Salvador, Bahia, Brazil
Tel.: (55) 71 32061752
Web Site:
http://www.fundacaoodebrecht.org.br
Education, Financial & Development Programs
N.A.I.C.S.: 523940

Instituto de Hospitalidade (1)
Rua Frei Vicente 16, Pelourinho Centro Historico, 40025 130, Salvador, BA, Brazil (100%)
Tel.: (55) 713200700
Sales Range: $25-49.9 Million
Emp.: 20
N.A.I.C.S.: 561520

ODEPREV Odebrecht Previdencia (1)
Av Luiz Viana Av 2841 Paralela, Edificio Odebrecht, 41730 900, Salvador, BA, Brazil (100%)
Tel.: (55) 7132061656
Web Site: http://www.odeprev.org

Sales Range: $75-99.9 Million
Emp.: 100
Insurance
N.A.I.C.S.: 524298

Odebrecht Administradora e Corretora de Seguros Ltda. (1)
Avenida Luis Viana 2841 Paralela, Edificio Odebrecht, 41730 900, Salvador, BA, Brazil (100%)
Tel.: (55) 7121051861
Sales Range: $75-99.9 Million
Emp.: 50
N.A.I.C.S.: 524298

Odebrecht Angola - Projectos e Servicos Ltda (1)
Parque Empresarial Odebrecht Rua Eng. Pedro, de Castro Van-Dunem, Luanda, Luanda Sul, Angola
Tel.: (244) 1 67 5000
Web Site: http://www.odebrecht.com.br
Engineeering Services
N.A.I.C.S.: 541330

Odebrecht Angola LTDA. (1)
Via A1 Av Talatona Condominio Belas Business Pk Torre Bengo 7 andar, Luanda, Angola (100%)
Tel.: (244) 222 67 8000
Web Site: http://www.odebrecht.com
Construction & Mineral Exploration
N.A.I.C.S.: 327992

Odebrecht Angola Ltd. (1)
Parque Operacional Odebrecht Estrada Do Futungo S N, Luanda Sul, Luanda, Angola (100%)
Tel.: (244) 2399392
Web Site: http://www.odebrecht.com.br
Sales Range: $25-49.9 Million
Emp.: 35
Engineering & Construction Services
N.A.I.C.S.: 541330

Odebrecht Construction, Inc (1)
201 Alhambra Cir Ste 1400, Coral Gables, FL 33134-5108 (100%)
Tel.: (305) 341-8800
Web Site: http://www.odebrecht.com
Engineeering Services
N.A.I.C.S.: 236220

Odebrecht Engenharia de Projetos (1)
Av Paulista 2064-2 andar Bela Vista, 01310-200, Sao Paulo, Brazil
Tel.: (55) 11 4573 0100
Environmental Engineering Services
N.A.I.C.S.: 541330

Odebrecht Oil and Gas S.A. (1)
Avenida Pasteur n 154 Botafogo, Rio de Janeiro, 22290240, Brazil
Tel.: (55) 2138506757
Web Site: http://www.odebrecht.com
Oil Field Drilling Services
N.A.I.C.S.: 213111
Carlos Brandt *(Mgr-Engrg)*

Odebrecht Peru Ingenieria y Construccion S.A.C. (1)
Av La Floresta 497 - 601, Chacarilla del Estanque, Lima, Peru
Tel.: (51) 12172800
Web Site: http://www.odebrecht.com.pe
Civil Engineering Construction
N.A.I.C.S.: 237990

Odebrecht Realizacoes Imobiliarias (1)
Avda Nacoes Unidas 4 777 1st & 3rd Floors Edificio Villa Lobos, Alto De Pinheiros, 05477 000, Sao Paulo, SP, Brazil (100%)
Tel.: (55) 1130257301
Web Site: http://www.orealizacoes.com.br
Sales Range: $75-99.9 Million
Emp.: 300
Engineeering Services
N.A.I.C.S.: 541330

NOVOPAK A.D.
Industrijska 25A, Vrcin, Belgrade, Serbia
Tel.: (381) 21 443 824
Year Founded: 1922
Sales Range: Less than $1 Million

Hardware Product Whslr
N.A.I.C.S.: 423710

NOVOPAN INDUSTRIES LIMITED
IDA Phase II Patancheru, Medak, Medak, 502 319, Andhra Pradesh, India
Tel.: (91) 8455242624
Web Site: http://www.novopan.in
Sales Range: $10-24.9 Million
Prelaminated Particle Board Mfr
N.A.I.C.S.: 339999
Syed Ali Naqui *(Exec Dir)*

NOVORAY CORP.
No 6 Zhujiang Road, Lianyungang, 222346, Jiangsu, China
Tel.: (86) 51885846000
Web Site: https://www.novoray.com
Year Founded: 2002
688300—(SHG)
Rev.: $92,938,370
Assets: $215,882,297
Liabilities: $43,185,861
Net Worth: $172,696,437
Earnings: $26,428,966
Fiscal Year-end: 12/31/22
Silica Powder Mfr
N.A.I.C.S.: 327120
Xiaodong Li *(Chm & Gen Mgr)*

NOVOSADSKI SAJAM A.D.
Hajduk Veljkova 11, 21137, Novi Sad, Serbia
Tel.: (381) 214830000
Web Site: https://www.sajam.net
Year Founded: 1956
NSSJ—(BEL)
Rev.: $7,260,101
Assets: $61,243,113
Liabilities: $5,867,449
Net Worth: $55,375,664
Earnings: ($288,201)
Emp.: 125
Fiscal Year-end: 12/31/23
Meeting & Trade Show Organizing Services
N.A.I.C.S.: 561920
Andrea Knezy *(Member-Exec Bd & Exec Dir-Congressional Activity)*

NOVOSIBIRSKENERGO OJSC
Sverdlova 7, Novosibirsk, 630007, Russia
Tel.: (7) 383 2891959
Web Site: http://www.nske.ru
Year Founded: 1993
Sales Range: $450-499.9 Million
Emp.: 2,669
Electric Power Generation, Transmission & Distribution Services
N.A.I.C.S.: 221111
Dmitry Vladimirovich Mamontov *(Gen Dir)*

NOVOTECHNIK MESSWERTAUFNEHMER OHG
Horbstrasse 12, 73760, Ostfildern, Germany
Tel.: (49) 71144890
Web Site: http://www.novotechnik.de
Rev.: $59,314,200
Emp.: 200
Position Transducer Mfr
N.A.I.C.S.: 335999
Torsten Wegner *(Gen Mgr)*

Subsidiaries:

Novotechnik Sensors Trading (Shanghai) Co., Ltd. (1)
Room 204 No 7 Building JinLinZhiDu No 100 Jin Hai Road, Pu Dong, 201206, Shanghai, China
Tel.: (86) 2158997738
Web Site: http://www.novotechnik.cn
Electronic Components Distr

Novotechnik U.S., Inc. (1)
155 Northboro Rd Ste 5, Southborough, MA 01772
Tel.: (508) 485-2244
Web Site: http://www.novotechnik.com
Electronic Components Distr
N.A.I.C.S.: 423690

NOVOTEK AB
Hojdrodergatan 18, 212 39, Malmo, Sweden
Tel.: (46) 40316900
Web Site: https://www.novotek.com
Year Founded: 1986
NTEK.B—(OMX)
Rev.: $38,949,624
Assets: $34,012,709
Liabilities: $16,810,416
Net Worth: $17,202,293
Earnings: $3,471,955
Emp.: 152
Fiscal Year-end: 12/31/20
Information Technology & Automation Services
N.A.I.C.S.: 541512
Goran Andersson (Chm)

Subsidiaries:
Novotek A/S (1)
Naverland 2 8 sal, 2600, Glostrup, Denmark
Tel.: (45) 43433717
Web Site: https://www.novotek.dk
Electrical & Electronic Mfr
N.A.I.C.S.: 334419

Novotek B.V. (1)
Paardeweide 2, 4824 EH, Breda, Netherlands
Tel.: (31) 765871010
Web Site: https://www.novotek.nl
Industrial Automation Services
N.A.I.C.S.: 541330

Novotek B.V.B.A. (1)
Mechelsesteenweg 277, 1800, Vilvoorde, Belgium
Tel.: (32) 22548550
Web Site: https://www.novotek.be
Electrical & Electronic Mfr
N.A.I.C.S.: 334419

Novotek OY (1)
Ayritie 24, 01510, Vantaa, Finland
Tel.: (358) 207959450
Web Site: https://www.novotek.fi
Electrical & Electronic Mfr
N.A.I.C.S.: 334419

Novotek Sverige AB (1)
Hojdrodergatan 18, 212 39, Malmo, Sweden
Tel.: (46) 40316900
Web Site: https://www.novotek.se
Electrical & Electronic Mfr
N.A.I.C.S.: 334419

Novotek Switzerland AG (1)
Glutz-Blotzheim-Strasse 3, 4500, Solothurn, Switzerland
Tel.: (41) 582553232
Web Site: https://www.novotek.ch
Industrial Automation Services
N.A.I.C.S.: 541330

Novotek UK & Ireland Ltd. (1)
Cartelli House 3 Hawthorn Park, Seacroft, Leeds, LS14 1PQ, United Kingdom
Tel.: (44) 1135312400
Electrical & Electronic Mfr
N.A.I.C.S.: 334419

ROB-EX A/S (1)
Billedskaerervej 17, 5230, Odense, Denmark
Tel.: (45) 70220170
Web Site: https://www.rob-ex.com
Electrical & Electronic Mfr
N.A.I.C.S.: 334419

SecuriOT ApS (1)
Agro Food Park 13, 8200, Aarhus, Denmark
Tel.: (45) 61761775
Web Site: https://securiot.dk
Electrical & Electronic Mfr
N.A.I.C.S.: 334419

NOVRA TECHNOLOGIES INC.
210-100 Innovation Drive, Winnipeg, R3T 6G2, MB, Canada
Tel.: (204) 989-4724
Web Site: https://www.novra.com
7CV—(DEU)
Rev.: $5,622,312
Assets: $5,521,351
Liabilities: $7,497,497
Net Worth: ($1,976,146)
Earnings: $102,875
Emp.: 29
Fiscal Year-end: 12/31/23
Video Broadcasting Services
N.A.I.C.S.: 516210
Harris Liontas (Pres & CEO)

Subsidiaries:
International Datacasting Corporation (1)
10 Breware Hunt Way, Kanata, K2K 2B5, ON, Canada (100%)
Tel.: (613) 596-4120
Web Site: https://www.datacast.com
Broadband Satellite Distribution Services
N.A.I.C.S.: 517410
Steven Archambault (CEO-Interim & CFO)

Subsidiary (Non-US):
PROFline B.V. (2)
Westerveldsestraat 50, 6842 BV, Arnhem, Netherlands (100%)
Tel.: (31) 263236969
Web Site: http://www.profline.nl
Digital Equipments Mfr
N.A.I.C.S.: 334515
Rob Katsma (CEO)

NOVUS LEISURE LTD.
Clareville House 26-27 Oxendon Street, London, SW1Y 4EL, United Kingdom
Tel.: (44) 20 7968 2400 UK
Web Site: http://www.novusbars.com
Year Founded: 1999
Sales Range: $400-449.9 Million
Emp.: 1,300
Holding Company; Bar Owner & Operator
N.A.I.C.S.: 551112

NOVUS PROPERTY SOLUTIONS LIMITED
Five Towns House Hillside Festival Way, Fenton, Stoke-on-Trent, ST1 5SH, United Kingdom
Tel.: (44) 1782237249
Web Site: http://www.novussolutions.co.uk
Year Founded: 1987
Sales Range: $150-199.9 Million
Emp.: 1,000
Facilities Support Services
N.A.I.C.S.: 561210
Neil Hand (CEO)

NOVUS ROBOTICS INC.
7669 Kimbal Street, Mississauga, L5S 1A7, ON, Canada
Tel.: (905) 672-7669 NV
Web Site: http://www.novusrobotics.com
Year Founded: 2005
NRBT—(OTCIQ)
Rev.: $1,369,000
Assets: $1,216,000
Liabilities: $237,000
Net Worth: $979,000
Earnings: $7,000
Emp.: 13
Fiscal Year-end: 12/31/20
Industrial Services
N.A.I.C.S.: 339999
Berardino Paolucci (Pres, CEO, CFO, Treas & Sec)

NOVX21 INC.
c/o Lavery de Billy 4000 1 Place Ville Marie, Montreal, H3B 4M4, QC, Canada
Tel.: (514) 282-2110
Web Site: http://www.novx21.com
Year Founded: 1986
NOV—(TSXV)
Sales Range: Less than $1 Million
Metal Recycling Services
N.A.I.C.S.: 423510
Rene Branchaud (Sec)

NOW CORPORATION
Unit 5-I 5th Floor OPL Building 100 C Palanca St, Legaspi Village, Makati, 1229, Philippines
Tel.: (63) 277500211
Web Site: https://now-corp.com
Year Founded: 1996
NOW—(PHI)
Rev.: $4,085,203
Assets: $58,737,898
Liabilities: $13,793,021
Net Worth: $44,944,876
Earnings: $165,282
Emp.: 70
Fiscal Year-end: 12/31/21
Telecommunication Servicesb
N.A.I.C.S.: 517810
Thomas G. Aquino (Vice Chm)

Subsidiaries:
I-Professional Search Network, Inc. (1)
NowPlanet TV Building 2244 Espana Boulevard, Manila, 1008, Philippines
Tel.: (63) 277997700
Web Site: http://www.iprofessional.ph
Information Technology Recruitment Services
N.A.I.C.S.: 561312

I-Resource Consulting International, Inc. (1)
NowPlanet TV Building 2244 Espana Boulevard, Sampaloc, Manila, 1008, Philippines
Tel.: (63) 277997700
Web Site: http://iresourceconsulting.com
Information Technology Recruitment Services
N.A.I.C.S.: 561312

NOW PREPAY CORP.
365 Evans Ave Ste 310, Toronto, M8Z 1K2, ON, Canada
Web Site: http://www.nowprepay.ca
Sales Range: $50-74.9 Million
Prepaid Long Distance & Internet Processing Services
N.A.I.C.S.: 522320
George DeMarchi (Pres)

NOWAK S.A.S.
Zone Artisanale, 35320, Pance, France
Tel.: (33) 299430197
Web Site: http://www.nowak.fr
Year Founded: 1984
Sales Range: $50-74.9 Million
Emp.: 130
Precision Casting Products Mfr
N.A.I.C.S.: 331524
Thierry Avrons (Pres)

NOWCOS CO., LTD.
220 Sandan-Gil Jeonui-Myeon, Jeonui-Myeon, Sejong, Korea (South)
Tel.: (82) 448622791
Web Site: https://www.nowcos.com
Year Founded: 2000
257990—(KRS)
Personal Care Product Mfr & Distr
N.A.I.C.S.: 325620
Hyang-Seon Ro (CEO)

NOWNEWS DIGITAL MEDIA TECHNOLOGY CO. LTD.
4F No 32 Lane 407 Sec 2 Tiding Road, Neihu District, Taipei, 114, Taiwan
Tel.: (886) 2 87978775 NV
Web Site: http://www.nownews.com
Year Founded: 2010
NDMT—(OTCIQ)
Sales Range: $1-9.9 Million
Emp.: 103
Online Advertising & Marketing Services & News Content Licensing
N.A.I.C.S.: 541890
Chi-Yi Lan (CEO)

NOWTRANSIT, INC.
20 Ayres Road, Manchester, M16 9NB, United Kingdom
Tel.: (44) 1618841268 NV
Year Founded: 2019
Assets: $6,314
Liabilities: $19,106
Net Worth: ($12,792)
Earnings: ($25,610)
Fiscal Year-end: 08/31/21
Online Passenger Car Rental Booking Services
N.A.I.C.S.: 532111
Ivan Homici (Founder)

NOWVERTICAL GROUP INC.
545 King Street West, Toronto, M5V 1M1, ON, Canada
Tel.: (416) 364-4039 ON
Web Site: https://www.nowvertical.com
Year Founded: 2018
NOWVF—(OTCQB)
Rev.: $27,009,266
Assets: $34,167,963
Liabilities: $32,351,814
Net Worth: $1,816,149
Earnings: ($9,547,527)
Emp.: 432
Fiscal Year-end: 12/31/22
Software Development Services
N.A.I.C.S.: 541511
Alim Virani (CFO)

Subsidiaries:
CoreBI S.A. (1)
Juan Del Campillo 932 Floor 4, X5000GUM, Cordoba, Argentina
Tel.: (54) 3514734840
Web Site: https://corebi.com.ar
Emp.: 300
Data & Analytic Services
N.A.I.C.S.: 518210

Integra Data & Analytic Solutions Corp. (1)
100 111-5 Ave SW, Calgary, T2P 3Y6, AB, Canada
Web Site: https://www.integradas.ca
Data & Analytic Services
N.A.I.C.S.: 518210

Signafire Technologies Inc. (1)
15 Watts St, New York, NY 10012
Tel.: (212) 302-0868
Web Site: https://signafire.com
Big Data Fusion & Content Analytic Services
N.A.I.C.S.: 518210

NOX CORPORATION
KD Center355 Hyoryeong-ro, Seocho-gu, Seoul, 06643, Korea (South)
Tel.: (82) 25207600
Web Site: http://www.noxprime.com
Year Founded: 1994
Luxury Vinyl Tile Flooring Mfr
N.A.I.C.S.: 238330
Dan Koh (Pres & CEO)

NOXOPHARM LIMITED
Level 20 Tower A The Zenith, 821 Pacific Highway, Chatswood, 2067, NSW, Australia
Tel.: (61) 291442223 AU

NOXOPHARM LIMITED

Noxopharm Limited—(Continued)
Web Site:
https://www.noxopharm.com
Year Founded: 2015
NOX—(ASX)
Rev.: $1,607,376
Assets: $4,529,753
Liabilities: $860,453
Net Worth: $3,669,300
Earnings: ($2,389,234)
Fiscal Year-end: 06/30/24
Drug Mfr
N.A.I.C.S.: 325412
David Franks *(Sec)*
Subsidiaries:

Pharmorage Pty. Limited **(1)**
BIO101 Financial Advisory Suite 201 697
Burke Road, Camberwell, VIC, Australia
Tel.: (61) 459022445
Web Site: https://www.pharmorage.com
Inflammatory Disease Treatment Services
N.A.I.C.S.: 622310

NOXXON PHARMA N.V.
Max-Dohrn-Str 8-10, 10589, Berlin, Germany
Tel.: (49) 30 726247 0   NL
Web Site: http://www.noxxon.com
Year Founded: 2015
Biopharmaceutical Research & Development Services
N.A.I.C.S.: 541714
Aram Mangasarian *(CEO)*

NOYEN CONSTRUCTION LTD.
8309 - 113 Street, PO Box 3329, Fort Saskatchewan, T8L 4K7, AB, Canada
Tel.: (780) 998-3974
Web Site:
http://www.noyenconstruction.ca
Year Founded: 1964
Highway & Railway Industrial Construction
N.A.I.C.S.: 237310
Peter Noyen *(Gen Mgr)*

NOZAKI INSATSU SHIGYO CO., LTD.
54-5 Oyama Shimousa-cho, Kita-ku, Kyoto, 603-8151, Japan
Tel.: (81) 754516130
Web Site:
https://www.nozakiinsatu.co.jp
Year Founded: 1868
7919—(TKS)
Rev.: $93,577,770
Assets: $71,070,720
Liabilities: $42,819,580
Net Worth: $28,251,140
Earnings: $3,787,530
Emp.: 413
Fiscal Year-end: 03/31/24
Printing & Packaging Services
N.A.I.C.S.: 323111
Takao Nozaki *(Pres)*

NOZAWA CORPORATION
15 Naniwamachi, Chuo Ward, Kobe, 650-0035, Japan
Tel.: (81) 783334111
Web Site: https://www.nozawa-kobe.co.jp
Year Founded: 1913
5237—(TKS)
Rev.: $152,519,140
Assets: $194,842,970
Liabilities: $63,905,480
Net Worth: $130,937,490
Earnings: $5,777,140
Emp.: 377
Fiscal Year-end: 03/31/24
Construction Materials Mfr
N.A.I.C.S.: 327991
Toshiya Nozawa *(Pres)*

NP INC.
8 9th Floor 128 Dosan-daero, Gangnam-gu, Seoul, Korea (South)
Tel.: (82) 25559288
Web Site: https://npinc.co.kr
291230—(KRS)
Asset Management Services
N.A.I.C.S.: 523940

NP3 FASTIGHETER AB
Gardevagen 5A, 856 50, Sundsvall, Sweden
Tel.: (46) 607770300
Web Site:
https://www.np3fastigheter.se
Year Founded: 2010
NP3—(OMX)
Rev.: $145,269,606
Assets: $2,046,887,147
Liabilities: $1,329,156,013
Net Worth: $717,731,134
Earnings: $116,515,403
Emp.: 58
Fiscal Year-end: 12/31/22
Commercial Property Owner & Rental Services
N.A.I.C.S.: 531312
Andreas Wahlen *(CEO)*

NPC CO., LTD.
785-17 Sinsu-ro Suji-gu, Danwon-gu, Yongin, Gyeonggi-do, Korea (South)
Tel.: (82) 3151748800   KR
Web Site: https://www.npc.co.kr
Year Founded: 1965
004250—(KRS)
Rev.: $430,219,366
Assets: $416,547,798
Liabilities: $144,460,403
Net Worth: $272,087,395
Earnings: $22,269,452
Emp.: 234
Fiscal Year-end: 12/31/22
Plastics Product Mfr
N.A.I.C.S.: 326199
Doo Shik Park *(CEO)*
Subsidiaries:

NPC Industrial De Monterrey S. A. de C. V. **(1)**
Av Dal Parque 2020 Airport Technology Park, 66650, Pesqueria, NL, Mexico
Tel.: (52) 8115372507
Sells Plastic Product Mfr
N.A.I.C.S.: 326199

NPC Sangseng Pte. Ltd. **(1)**
110 Tuas South Avenue 3 03-13 The Index, Singapore, 637369, Singapore
Tel.: (65) 62612830
Sells Plastic Product Mfr
N.A.I.C.S.: 326199

NPC Siam Co., Ltd. **(1)**
7/397 Moo 6 Mabyangporn, Pluakdaeng, Rayong, 21140, Thailand
Tel.: (66) 386505434
Sells Plastic Product Mfr
N.A.I.C.S.: 326199

NPC Vina Co., Ltd. **(1)**
11th Floor 194 Golden Building 473 Dien Bien Phu St W 25, Binh Thanh, Ho Chi Minh City, Vietnam
Tel.: (84) 2862973877
Sells Plastic Product Mfr
N.A.I.C.S.: 326199

NPS USA Inc. **(1)**
510 Callaway Church Rd, LaGrange, GA 30241
Tel.: (762) 323-9794
Plastic Container Mfr
N.A.I.C.S.: 326199

Rizhao NPC Plastic Co., Ltd. **(1)**
NO 568 Rizhao South Road Rizhao Economic Development Zone City, Shandong, China
Tel.: (86) 6338774688
Plastic Container Mfr
N.A.I.C.S.: 326199

NPC INCORPORATED
5th Floor Hulic Higashi-ueno 1-chome Building 1-7-15 Higashi-ueno, Taito-ku, Tokyo, 110-0015, Japan
Tel.: (81) 358178830
Web Site: https://www.npcgroup.net
Year Founded: 1992
6255—(TKS)
Rev.: $67,157,340
Assets: $96,011,920
Liabilities: $35,777,440
Net Worth: $60,234,480
Earnings: $10,424,720
Emp.: 171
Fiscal Year-end: 08/31/24
Solar Cell Equipment & Vacuum Packaging Machine Developer, Mfr & Sales
N.A.I.C.S.: 333248
Yasuhisa Sera *(Auditor)*
Subsidiaries:

NPC America Automation Inc. **(1)**
Beck Business Ctr 28317 Beck Rd Ste E2, Wixom, MI 48393
Tel.: (248) 773-7947
Photovoltaic Module Mfr
N.A.I.C.S.: 334413

NPC America Corporation **(1)**
560 Sylvan Ave, Englewood Cliffs, NJ 07632
Tel.: (201) 227-9400
Web Site: http://www.npcgroup.net
Sales Range: $25-49.9 Million
Emp.: 1
Photovoltaic Equipment Mfr
N.A.I.C.S.: 334413

NPC RESOURCES BERHAD
Lot 9 T3 Taman Tshun Ngen Mile 5 North Road, 90000, Sandakan, Sabah, Malaysia
Tel.: (60) 89274488
Web Site: https://www.npc.com.my
NPC—(KLS)
Rev.: $87,469,206
Assets: $282,792,804
Liabilities: $163,274,497
Net Worth: $119,518,307
Earnings: $234,497
Fiscal Year-end: 12/31/22
Palm Oil Mills
N.A.I.C.S.: 311224
Vun Su Tan *(Co-Sec)*
Subsidiaries:

Ballerina Sdn. Bhd. **(1)**
No 1034 1st Floor Jalan Utara Taman Tshun Ngen, 90000, Sandakan, Sabah, Malaysia
Tel.: (60) 89217111
Sales Range: $25-49.9 Million
Emp.: 250
Oil Palm Cultivation Services
N.A.I.C.S.: 115112

Berkat Setia Sdn. Bhd. **(1)**
Jalan Tengku Mahkota Ismail No 19 1st Floor, 86000, Keluang, Johor, Malaysia
Tel.: (60) 77722172
Sales Range: $25-49.9 Million
Emp.: 2
Oil Palm Plantation Services
N.A.I.C.S.: 115112

Better Prospects Sdn. Bhd. **(1)**
Lot 9 T3 Taman Tshun Ngen Mile 5 North Road, 90000, Sandakan, Sabah, Malaysia
Tel.: (60) 89271502
Sales Range: $25-49.9 Million
Emp.: 60
Fish Hatcheries & Farming Services
N.A.I.C.S.: 112511

Growth Enterprise Sdn. Bhd. **(1)**
Lot 9 Taman Tshun Ngen Mile 5 North Road WDT 514, 90009, Sandakan, Sabah, Malaysia
Tel.: (60) 89274488
Emp.: 54
Oil Palm Cultivation Services
N.A.I.C.S.: 115112

INTERNATIONAL PUBLIC

NPF MICROFINANCE BANK PLC.
Aliyu Atah House 1 Ikoyi Road, Obalende, Lagos, Nigeria
Tel.: (234) 8074550514   NG
Web Site:
http://www.npfmicrofinancebank.com
Year Founded: 1993
NPFMCRFBK—(NIGE)
Rev.: $11,135,927
Assets: $53,659,385
Liabilities: $39,060,832
Net Worth: $14,598,553
Earnings: $2,182,205
Emp.: 349
Fiscal Year-end: 12/31/19
Commercial Banking Services
N.A.I.C.S.: 522110
Azubuko Joel Udah *(Chm)*

NPG TECHNOLOGY S.A.
C/ Ecuador 14, Torrejon de Ardoz, 28850, Madrid, Spain
Tel.: (34) 916794790
Web Site: http://www.npgtech.com
Year Founded: 2001
NPG—(MAD)
Sales Range: $10-24.9 Million
Telecommunication, Electronics & IT Products Mfr
N.A.I.C.S.: 334220
Enrique Cosio Sanchez *(Chm & CEO)*

NPK CO., LTD.
A-708 Keumkang Penterium 333-7 Sangdaewon-Dong, Jungwon-Gu, Seongnam, 462901, Gyeonggi-do, Korea (South)
Tel.: (82) 317300650
Web Site: https://www.npk.co.kr
Year Founded: 1987
048830—(KRS)
Rev.: $50,009,164
Assets: $55,522,982
Liabilities: $21,925,804
Net Worth: $33,597,178
Earnings: $1,134,852
Emp.: 284
Fiscal Year-end: 12/31/22
Plastic Materials & Products Mfr
N.A.I.C.S.: 326112
Choi Woon Pil *(Sls Dir)*
Subsidiaries:

NPK Co., Ltd. - Nano Division **(1)**
389-1 Chupal-ri, Pangseong-eup, Pyeongtaek, 451-805, Gyeonggi-do, Korea (South)
Sales Range: $25-49.9 Million
Emp.: 100
Plastic Mfr
N.A.I.C.S.: 326199

NPK Co., Ltd. - Plastics Division **(1)**
622-21 Gupo-dong, Gumi, 730-400, Gyeongsangbukdo, Korea (South)
Tel.: (82) 544753001
Plastic Mfr
N.A.I.C.S.: 326199

Nippon Pigment (M) Sdn. Bhd. **(1)**
No 2479 Mk 1 Lorong Perusahaan 8B Prai Industrial Estate, 13600, Prai, Pulau Pinang, Malaysia
Tel.: (60) 43997261
Web Site: https://www.npm.com.my
Plastic Product Distr
N.A.I.C.S.: 424610

Nippon Pigment (S) Pte. Ltd. **(1)**
1 Pioneer Place, Singapore, 627866, Singapore
Tel.: (65) 2681590
Plastic Product Distr
N.A.I.C.S.: 424610

Nippon Pigment Co., Ltd. **(1)**
3-20 Kanda Nishikicho, Chiyoda-ku, Tokyo, 101-0054, Japan
Tel.: (81) 363628801
Web Site: http://www.pigment.co.jp

AND PRIVATE COMPANIES — NRJ GROUP SA

Plastics Product Mfr
N.A.I.C.S.: 326199

P.T. Nippisun Indonesia (1)
Tel.: (62) 218980018
Inorganic Pigments Mfr
N.A.I.C.S.: 325130

Tianjin Pigment Engineering Plastics Co., Ltd. (1)
G1 Hongtai Industrial Estate No 78 Taihua Rd, TEDA Dist, Tianjin, 300457, China
Tel.: (86) 22 5981 3950
Plastic Product Mfr & Distr
N.A.I.C.S.: 326199

NPO FIZIKA AO
Varshavskoe shosse 125Zh str1 PAO NPO Fizika, Moscow, 117587, Russia
Tel.: (7) 4953814565
Web Site: https://www.npofizika.ru
Year Founded: 1985
NPOF—(MOEX)
Sales Range: Less than $1 Million
Electronic Components Mfr
N.A.I.C.S.: 334419
Gulyaev Igor Mikhailovich *(Gen Mgr)*

NPO SATURN JSC
163 Lenin Ave Rybinsk, 152903, Yaroslavl, Russia
Tel.: (7) 4855 296 100
Web Site: http://www.npo-saturn.ru
Year Founded: 1916
Aircraft Engine Mfr
N.A.I.C.S.: 336412
Sergey V. Antropov *(Dir-Quality)*

NPPG (THAILAND) PUBLIC COMPANY LIMITED
283/99 Home Place Office Building 20th Floor, Soi Sukhumvit 55 Sukhumvit Road Klong ton Nua Wattana, Bangkok, 10110, Thailand
Tel.: (66) 2712 5487
Web Site: http://nppg.co.th
Year Founded: 1987
Rev.: $39,889,716
Assets: $47,001,036
Liabilities: $12,700,996
Net Worth: $34,300,040
Earnings: ($1,986,620)
Emp.: 244
Fiscal Year-end: 12/31/19
Flexible Packaging Services
N.A.I.C.S.: 333993
Anant Sirisaengtaksin *(Co-Chm)*

Subsidiaries:

Thai Flexible Co., Ltd. (1)
302 Pracha-u-tid Rd Bangmod, Tungkru, Bangkok, 10140, Thailand
Tel.: (66) 2426232830
Web Site: http://www.thaiflex.com
Metal Hose Mfr
N.A.I.C.S.: 423510

NPR FINANCE LIMITED
Todi Mansion 9th Floor 1 Lu Shun Sarani, Kolkata, 700073, India
Tel.: (91) 3322377201
Web Site: https://www.nprfinance.com
Year Founded: 1989
530127—(BOM)
Rev.: $789,348
Assets: $8,273,002
Liabilities: $914,969
Net Worth: $7,358,033
Earnings: ($145,024)
Emp.: 58
Fiscal Year-end: 03/31/21
Financial Lending Services
N.A.I.C.S.: 522220
Sarika Mehra *(Exec Dir)*

NPX CO., LTD.
14 Tapsil-ro 58beon-gil Giheung-gu, 17084, Yongin, 17084, Gyeonggi-do, Korea (South)
Tel.: (82) 3180055155
Web Site: https://www.bioptro.co.kr
Year Founded: 2000
222160—(KRS)
Rev.: $9,466,796
Assets: $19,728,242
Liabilities: $1,606,117
Net Worth: $18,122,125
Earnings: $92,532
Emp.: 45
Fiscal Year-end: 03/31/23
Factory Automation Equipment Mfr
N.A.I.C.S.: 334519
Samuel Hwang *(Co-CEO)*

NQ MINERALS PLC
Finsgate 5-7 Cranwood Street, London, EC1V 9EE, United Kingdom
Tel.: (44) 77380763004
Web Site: http://www.nqminerals.com
NQMLF—(OTCIQ)
Rev.: $35,709,622
Assets: $63,703,100
Liabilities: $137,648,485
Net Worth: ($73,945,385)
Earnings: ($47,138,904)
Fiscal Year-end: 12/31/19
Metal Exploration Services
N.A.I.C.S.: 213114
David Anthony Lenigas *(Chm)*

NR 21 SA
176-178 rue dEstienne dOrves, BP 39, 92700, Colombes, France
Tel.: (33) 147690097
Web Site: http://www.nr21.eu
Women & Children Apparel Distr
N.A.I.C.S.: 458110
Lionnel Rainfray *(Chm & CEO)*

NR INSTANT PRODUCE PUBLIC COMPANY LIMITED
99/1 Moo4, Kaerai Kratumbaen, Samut Sakhon, 74110, Thailand
Tel.: (66) 3484957680
Web Site: https://www.nrinstant.com
Year Founded: 1991
NRF—(THA)
Rev.: $89,872,694
Assets: $190,432,026
Liabilities: $104,916,260
Net Worth: $85,515,765
Earnings: ($1,585,985)
Emp.: 886
Fiscal Year-end: 12/31/23
Food Product Mfr & Distr
N.A.I.C.S.: 311423
Kesara Manchusree *(Chm)*

NR MOTORS LTD.
805 1st Avenue, Prince George, V2L 2Y4, BC, Canada
Tel.: (250) 563-8891
Web Site: http://www.nrmotors.ca
Year Founded: 1967
Rev.: $19,040,944
Emp.: 46
Motor Vehicle Dealers
N.A.I.C.S.: 441227
Greg Nikkel *(Asst Gen Mgr)*

NRB BEARINGS LIMITED
Dhannur 15 SIR PM Road, Fort, Mumbai, 400001, Maharashtra, India
Tel.: (01) 2222604100
Web Site: https://www.nrbbearings.com
Year Founded: 1965
530367—(BOM)
Rev.: $106,126,020
Assets: $130,562,250
Liabilities: $58,370,130
Net Worth: $72,192,120
Earnings: $7,603,050
Emp.: 1,436
Fiscal Year-end: 03/31/21
Ball & Roller Bearing Mfr
N.A.I.C.S.: 332991
Harshbeena S. Zaveri *(Vice Chm & Mng Dir)*

Subsidiaries:

SNL Bearings Limited (1)
Dhannur 15 Sir P M Road, Fort, Mumbai, 400 001, India
Tel.: (91) 2222663698
Web Site: https://www.snlbearings.in
Rev.: $5,079,165
Assets: $6,397,755
Liabilities: $799,890
Net Worth: $5,597,865
Earnings: $844,935
Emp.: 156
Fiscal Year-end: 03/31/2021
Bearing Mfr
N.A.I.C.S.: 336350
Krishna kant Prasad Sinha *(CEO & Gen Mgr)*

NRB INDUSTRIAL BEARINGS LIMITED
Dhannur 2nd Floor 15 sir P M Road, Fort, Mumbai, 400001, India
Tel.: (91) 2222704206
Web Site:
  https://www.nrbindustrial.com
Year Founded: 2012
NIBL—(NSE)
Rev.: $7,883,571
Assets: $17,517,222
Liabilities: $17,368,997
Net Worth: $148,225
Earnings: $576,071
Emp.: 260
Fiscal Year-end: 03/31/21
Bearing Mfr & Whslr
N.A.I.C.S.: 332991
Devesh Singh Sahney *(Chm & Mng Dir)*

NRC GROUP ASA
Lysaker Torg 25, 1366, Lysaker, Norway
Tel.: (47) 90407097 NO
Web Site: http://www.nrcgroup.no
NRC—(OSL)
Rev.: $703,215,150
Assets: $615,781,650
Liabilities: $384,934,500
Net Worth: $230,847,150
Earnings: ($8,175,600)
Emp.: 2,070
Fiscal Year-end: 12/31/19
Geographic Information & Transportation Services
N.A.I.C.S.: 541370
Helge Midttun *(Chm)*

Subsidiaries:

Blom CGR S.p.A. (1)
Via Cremonese 35/A, 43100, Parma, Italy
Tel.: (39) 0521994948
Sales Range: $75-99.9 Million
Emp.: 150
Aircraft Maintenance & Aerial Surveying Services
N.A.I.C.S.: 488190

Blom Czech Republic (1)
Olomoucka 1158/164A, 627 00, Brno, Czech Republic
Tel.: (420) 513033050
Web Site: http://www.blom.com
Sales Range: $25-49.9 Million
Emp.: 5
Geophysical Surveying Services
N.A.I.C.S.: 541360

Blom Data AS (1)
PO Box 34, Skoyen, 0212, Oslo, Norway
Tel.: (47) 22131920
Sales Range: $25-49.9 Million
Emp.: 60
Geophysical Surveying Services
N.A.I.C.S.: 541360
Lennart Flem *(Head-Geo Div)*

Blom Deutschland GmbH (1)
Oskar-Frech-Strasse 15, 73614, Schorndorf, Germany
Tel.: (49) 7181980210
Web Site: https://www.blom-deutschland.de
Sales Range: $25-49.9 Million
Emp.: 20
Aerial Photography & Digital Mapping Services
N.A.I.C.S.: 541370
Ralf Schroth *(Mng Dir)*

Blom Portugal Lda. (1)
Av do Forte N 8 Edificio Pujol Fraccao K, 2795 503, Carnaxide, Portugal
Tel.: (351) 214253830
Geophysical Surveying Services
N.A.I.C.S.: 541360

Compagnia Aeronautica Emiliana S.r.l. (1)
Via Cremonese 35/a, 43126, Parma, Italy
Tel.: (39) 0521982261
Web Site: https://www.caeitalia.com
Aircraft & Parts Distr
N.A.I.C.S.: 423860
Giovanni Banchini *(Pres)*

LTD BlomInfo Ukraine (1)
43 Demiivska Str, Kiev, Ukraine
Tel.: (380) 444675622
Web Site: http://www.blominfo-ukraine.com.ua
Geophysical Surveying Services
N.A.I.C.S.: 541360

PT. Blom Nusantara (1)
CCSL Building 8th Floor Suite 8004 Jl Asia Afrika No 133-137, Bandung, 40112, West Java, Indonesia
Tel.: (62) 224221985
Web Site: http://www.blom.co.id
Geophysical Mapping Services
N.A.I.C.S.: 541360
Trisnawati Nurhayati *(Accountant)*

Signal & Banebyggarna i Dalarna AB (1)
Hafenstrasse 10, 78462, Konstanz, Germany (100%)
Tel.: (49) 7531915109
Web Site: https://www.sbb-deutschland.de
Line-Haul Railroads
N.A.I.C.S.: 482111

NRG DRILLING LTD.
PO Box 2804, Wakatipu, Queenstown, 9349, New Zealand
Tel.: (64) 274 366 769 NZ
Sales Range: $10-24.9 Million
Emp.: 40
Contract Oil Drilling Services
N.A.I.C.S.: 213111
Stacey Redford *(Mgr)*

NRGENE TECHNOLOGIES LTD.
5 Golda Meir St, Ness Ziona, 7403649, Israel
Tel.: (972) 722203750
Web Site: http://www.nrgene.com
Year Founded: 2009
NRGN—(TAE)
Rev.: $2,001,000
Assets: $10,787,000
Liabilities: $3,573,000
Net Worth: $7,214,000
Earnings: ($5,243,000)
Fiscal Year-end: 06/30/23
Computer Programming Services
N.A.I.C.S.: 541511
Ehud Belder *(CFO)*

NRJ GROUP SA
22 Rue Boileau, 75203, Paris, Cedex 16, France
Tel.: (33) 140714000
Web Site: https://www.nrjgroup.fr
NRG—(EUR)
Sales Range: $400-449.9 Million
Radio Station Operator; Television Broadcasting; Music Publishing Services

NRJ GROUP SA

NRJ Group SA—(Continued)
N.A.I.C.S.: 516210
Jean-Paul Baudecroux *(Chm & CEO)*

Subsidiaries:

Cherie FM SAS **(1)**
22 Rue Boileau, Paris, 75203, France
Tel.: (33) 0140714000
Radio Broadcasting Services
N.A.I.C.S.: 516210

Subsidiary (Domestic):

Reseau Cherie FM **(2)**
17 rue Claude Chappe, Metz, 57070, France
Tel.: (33) 387222233
Web Site: http://www.cheriefm.fr
Sales Range: $25-49.9 Million
Emp.: 2
Radio Broadcasting Services
N.A.I.C.S.: 516210
Stefan Gine *(Mgr)*

Subsidiary (Domestic):

CHERIE FM Aquitaine Sud **(3)**
22 Rue Boileau, 75016, Paris, France
Tel.: (33) 892680050
Radio Broadcasting Services
N.A.I.C.S.: 516110

Communication 2000 SAS **(3)**
22 Rue Boileau, 75016, Paris, France
Tel.: (33) 147439486
Radio Broadcasting Services
N.A.I.C.S.: 516110

Energy Media GmbH **(1)**
Winter Marktplatz 6-7, 22299, Hamburg, Germany
Tel.: (49) 4048001953
Web Site: http://www.energy-media.de
Sales Range: $25-49.9 Million
Emp.: 18
Radio Broadcasting Services
N.A.I.C.S.: 516210

Energy Zurich (Radio Z AG) **(1)**
Kreuz St 26, Zurich, 8008, Switzerland
Tel.: (41) 442509000
Web Site: http://www.energyzueri.ch
Sales Range: $25-49.9 Million
Emp.: 65
Radio Broadcasting Services
N.A.I.C.S.: 516210
Manuel Schaub *(Mng Dir)*

NRJ 12 SARL **(1)**
46 Ave Theophile Gautier, Paris, 75016, France
Tel.: (33) 140717805
Web Site: http://www.nrjgroup.fr
Emp.: 1,700
Picture & Video Production Services
N.A.I.C.S.: 512110
Jean Paul Baudecroux *(Gen Mgr)*

NRJ Boileau 1 SAS **(1)**
22 Rue Boileau, 75016, Paris, France
Tel.: (33) 140714000
Web Site: http://www.nrj.fr
Television Broadcasting Services
N.A.I.C.S.: 516120

NRJ Boileau 2 SAS **(1)**
22 Rue Boileau, 75016, Paris, France
Tel.: (33) 140714000
Television Broadcasting Services
N.A.I.C.S.: 516120
Bouog Crouh *(Gen Mgr)*

NRJ Boileau 3 SAS **(1)**
22 Rue Boileau, 75016, Paris, France
Tel.: (33) 140714000
Television Broadcasting Services
N.A.I.C.S.: 516120

NRJ ENTERTAINMENT SARL **(1)**
22 Rue Boileau, 75016, Paris, France
Tel.: (33) 140714000
Web Site: http://www.nrj.fr
Entertainment Services
N.A.I.C.S.: 711410

NRJ EVENTS SARL **(1)**
22 Rue Boileau, 75016, Paris, France
Tel.: (33) 140714000
Entertainment Services
N.A.I.C.S.: 711410

NRJ Media AB **(1)**
Nybrogatan 34, 114 39, Stockholm, Sweden
Tel.: (46) 86706536
Radio Broadcasting Services
N.A.I.C.S.: 516210

NRJ SAS **(1)**
22 Rue Boileau, 75203, Paris, France
Tel.: (33) 140714000
Web Site: http://www.nrj.com
Radio Broadcasting Services
N.A.I.C.S.: 516210

Subsidiary (Non-US):

Energy Holding Norway AS **(2)**
Trondheimsveien 184, 0570, Oslo, Norway
Tel.: (47) 22797500
Web Site: http://www.nrj.no
Sales Range: $25-49.9 Million
Emp.: 20
Radio & TV Broadcasting Services
N.A.I.C.S.: 516210
Richard Edouard Arvid Mazeres *(Mgr)*

Subsidiary (Domestic):

NRJ Norge AS **(3)**
Trondheimsveien 184, 0570, Oslo, Norway
Tel.: (47) 22797500
Web Site: http://www.nrj.no
Sales Range: $25-49.9 Million
Emp.: 12
Radio Broadcasting Services
N.A.I.C.S.: 516210

Radio Melodi Norge AS **(3)**
Trondheimsveien 184, Oslo, 0570, Norway
Tel.: (47) 22797500
Web Site: http://www.mrj.no
Sales Range: $25-49.9 Million
Emp.: 12
Radio Broadcasting Services
N.A.I.C.S.: 516210

Subsidiary (Domestic):

NRJ Audio SAS **(2)**
22 Rue Boileau, 75016, Paris, France
Tel.: (33) 140714000
Web Site: http://www.nrj.com
Sales Range: $550-599.9 Million
Emp.: 1,500
Office Equipment Rental & Leasing Services
N.A.I.C.S.: 532420

Subsidiary (Non-US):

NRJ Belgique S.A **(2)**
Chaussee de Louvain 775/1, Brussels, Belgium **(99.9%)**
Tel.: (32) 25132808
Web Site: http://www.nrj.be
Sales Range: $25-49.9 Million
Emp.: 40
Radio Broadcasting Services
N.A.I.C.S.: 516210
Marc Vossen *(CEO & Mng Dir)*

Subsidiary (Domestic):

Regie Networks Belgium SA **(3)**
Chaussee De Louvain 775, Brussels, 1140, Belgium
Tel.: (32) 25132808
Web Site: http://www.nrj.be
Sales Range: $25-49.9 Million
Emp.: 40
Radio Broadcasting Services
N.A.I.C.S.: 516210

Subsidiary (Domestic):

NRJ Global SAS **(2)**
22 Rue Boileau, 75016, Paris, France
Tel.: (33) 140714000
Web Site: http://www.nrj.fr
Media Representative Services
N.A.I.C.S.: 541840

Subsidiary (Non-US):

NRJ Holding Switzerland SA **(2)**
7 rue du Valais c/o Diffusia SA, 1202, Geneva, Switzerland
Tel.: (41) 229096969
Business Management Services
N.A.I.C.S.: 541618

Subsidiary (Domestic):

NRJ Network SAS **(2)**
25 Ave Clemenceau, 68100, Mulhouse, France
Tel.: (33) 389466111
Web Site: http://www.nrj.com
Sales Range: $25-49.9 Million
Emp.: 8
Radio Broadcasting Services
N.A.I.C.S.: 516210

Subsidiary (Non-US):

NRJ Nordic AB **(2)**
Nybrogatan 34, 10245, Stockholm, Sweden
Tel.: (46) 86706536
Business Management Services
N.A.I.C.S.: 541618

Subsidiary (Domestic):

Radio Nostalgie SAS **(2)**
51 Av De La Cote De Nacre, 14000, Caen, France
Tel.: (33) 2 31 53 66 22
Radio Broadcasting Services
N.A.I.C.S.: 516210

Regie Networks SAS **(2)**
134 Ave of the 25th Regiment, 69009, Lyon, France
Tel.: (33) 472531717
Radio Broadcasting Services
N.A.I.C.S.: 516210
Pierre Todeschini *(Pres)*

Subsidiary (Domestic):

Regie Networks Leman SAS **(3)**
4th Ave, 74160, Archamps, France
Tel.: (33) 450820084
Public Relations Services
N.A.I.C.S.: 541820

Subsidiary (Domestic):

Reseau NRJ **(2)**
4e Blvd, 74160, Archamps, France
Tel.: (33) 450952891
Radio Broadcasting Services
N.A.I.C.S.: 516210

Subsidiary (Non-US):

Telemast Nordic OY **(2)**
Teknobulevardi 3-5, Vantaa, 530, Finland
Tel.: (358) 95657600
Web Site: http://www.telemast.com
Sales Range: $25-49.9 Million
Emp.: 5
Radio Broadcasting Services
N.A.I.C.S.: 516110
Rose Marie Skogster *(Gen Mgr)*

Subsidiary (Domestic):

Vive la Prod **(2)**
22 Rue Boileau, 75016, Paris, France
Tel.: (33) 140714000
Web Site: http://www.nrj.fr
Radio Broadcasting Services
N.A.I.C.S.: 516210
Jean Pierre Trelat *(Mng Dir)*

e-NRJ SARL **(2)**
22 Rue Boileau, 75203, Paris, France
Tel.: (33) 140714000
Internet Entertainment Services
N.A.I.C.S.: 516210

RBDS Broadcasting AB **(1)**
Nybrogatan 34, 114 39, Stockholm, Sweden
Tel.: (46) 86706536
Sales Range: $25-49.9 Million
Emp.: 1
Radio Broadcasting Services
N.A.I.C.S.: 516210

RBG Broadcasting AB **(1)**
Nybrogatan 34, 11439, Stockholm, Sweden
Tel.: (46) 86706536
Sales Range: $25-49.9 Million
Emp.: 1
Radio Broadcasting Services
N.A.I.C.S.: 516210

RBKR Broadcasting AB **(1)**
Nybrogatan 34, PO Box 5216, 10245, Stockholm, Sweden
Tel.: (46) 86706536
Radio Broadcasting Services

INTERNATIONAL PUBLIC

N.A.I.C.S.: 516210

RIRE ET CHANSONS SAS **(1)**
22 Rue Boileau, 75016, Paris, France
Tel.: (33) 140714000
Radio Broadcasting Services
N.A.I.C.S.: 516210

RMR Radiobetriebs und Beteiligungsgesellschaft mbH **(1)**
Naststr 31, 70376, Stuttgart, Germany
Tel.: (49) 7119330350
Web Site: http://www.energy.de
Sales Range: $25-49.9 Million
Emp.: 25
Radio Broadcasting Services
N.A.I.C.S.: 516210

Radio 106.9 Mhz Nuremberg GmbH **(1)**
Outer Bayreuther St 76, Outer Bayreuthe, Nuremberg, Germany
Tel.: (49) 911544440
Web Site: http://www.energy.de
Sales Range: $25-49.9 Million
Emp.: 25
Radio Broadcasting Services
N.A.I.C.S.: 516210
Kai Maltz Kummer *(Mgr)*

Radio 2000 Gesellschaft mbH **(1)**
Hardenbergstr 5, Berlin, 10236, Germany
Tel.: (49) 30254350
Web Site: http://www.energy.de
Sales Range: $25-49.9 Million
Emp.: 30
Radio Broadcasting Services
N.A.I.C.S.: 516210
Martin Liss *(Mng Dir)*

Radio 93.3 Mhz Munchen GmbH Produktion und Verbreitung von Rundfunkprogrammen **(1)**
Liebherr Strasse 5, 80538, Munich, Germany
Tel.: (49) 892319070
Web Site: http://www.energy.de
Sales Range: $25-49.9 Million
Emp.: 35
Radio Broadcasting Services
N.A.I.C.S.: 516210
Engrid Katzenberger *(CEO)*

Radio 97.1 Mhz Hamburg GmbH **(1)**
Winterhuder Marktplatz 6-7, 22299, Hamburg, Germany
Tel.: (49) 404800190
Web Site: http://www.energy.de
Sales Range: $25-49.9 Million
Emp.: 40
Radio Broadcasting Services
N.A.I.C.S.: 516210

Radio NRJ Berlin und Brandenburg GmbH **(1)**
Westenriederstr. 19, 80331, Munich, Germany
Tel.: (49) 89242970
Business Management Services
N.A.I.C.S.: 541611

SW Radiodiffusion SAS **(1)**
22 Rue Boileau, Paris, 75016, France
Tel.: (33) 140714000
Web Site: http://www.nrj.fr
Sales Range: $100-124.9 Million
Emp.: 500
Radio Broadcasting Services
N.A.I.C.S.: 516210
Jeantaul Baudecroux *(Gen Mgr)*

Societe de Television Locale SAS **(1)**
46-50 Avenue Throphile Gautier, 75016, Paris, France
Tel.: (33) 140714000
Sales Range: $100-124.9 Million
Emp.: 300
Television Broadcasting Services
N.A.I.C.S.: 516120

NRL GROUP LTD

Building 5 Glasshouse Business Park, Wigan, WN3 6GL, Lancashire, United Kingdom
Tel.: (44) 1942323277
Web Site: http://www.nrl.co.uk
Human Resouce Services

AND PRIVATE COMPANIES

N.A.I.C.S.: 541612
Subsidiaries:

Intec (UK) Limited (1)
Brunel House 9 Penrod Way, Heysham, LA3 2UZ, Lancashire, United Kingdom
Tel.: (44) 1524865555
Web Site: http://www.velosi-intec.com
Recruitment & Training & Consultancy Services
N.A.I.C.S.: 541612
Linda McConville (Gen Mgr)

NRW HOLDINGS LIMITED

181 Great Eastern Highway, Belmont, 6104, WA, Australia
Tel.: (61) 892324200   AU
Web Site: https://www.nrw.com.au
NWH—(ASX)
Rev.: $1,963,753,998
Assets: $1,076,561,160
Liabilities: $640,826,653
Net Worth: $435,734,507
Earnings: $70,176,282
Emp.: 7,400
Fiscal Year-end: 06/30/24
Civil Contracting & Mining Services
N.A.I.C.S.: 541330
Michael Arnett (Chm)

Subsidiaries:

Action Drill & Blast Pty. Ltd. (1)
181 Great Eastern Highway, Belmont, 6104, WA, Australia
Tel.: (61) 89 232 4306
Web Site: https://www.actiondb.com.au
Emp.: 500
Mining Services
N.A.I.C.S.: 213114
Andrew Broad (Exec Gen Mgr)

DIAB Engineering Pty. Ltd. (1)
20 Foskew Way, Geraldton, 6532, WA, Australia
Tel.: (61) 89 956 8000
Web Site: https://diabengineering.com.au
Mining Services
N.A.I.C.S.: 213112
Glen Payne (CEO)

Golding Contractors Pty. Ltd. (1)
Level 2 40 McDougall Street, PO Box 1643, Milton, Brisbane, 4064, QLD, Australia
Tel.: (61) 73 510 3400
Web Site: https://www.golding.com.au
Mining Services
N.A.I.C.S.: 213113

NRW Contracting Pty. Ltd. (1)
20 Walters Dr, Osborne Park, Australia
Tel.: (61) 6189260230
Web Site: http://www.bgc.cc
Mining, Construction & Engineering Services
N.A.I.C.S.: 541330
Greg Heylen (CEO)

Subsidiary (US):

Diab Engineering Consultants (2)
5851 San Felipe St, Houston, TX 77057
Tel.: (713) 706-6336
Web Site: http://www.decprojects.com
Sales Range: $1-9.9 Million
Engineeering Services
N.A.I.C.S.: 541330
Talal Diab (Owner)

NRW Pty Ltd (1)
181 Great Eastern Highway, Belmont, 6104, WA, Australia
Tel.: (61) 892324200
Sales Range: $25-49.9 Million
Emp.: 70
Earthmoving & Mining Contract Services
N.A.I.C.S.: 238910

Primero Group Limited (1)
78 Hasler Road, Osborne Park, 6017, WA, Australia
Tel.: (61) 865009500
Web Site: http://www.primero.com.au
Rev.: $144,128,892
Assets: $81,921,649
Liabilities: $49,225,166
Net Worth: $32,696,482
Earnings: $3,250,765
Fiscal Year-end: 06/30/2020
Construction Engineering Services
N.A.I.C.S.: 541330
Cameron Henry (Mng Dir)

RCR Heat Treatment (1)
73 Industrial Avenue, Wacol, 4076, QLD, Australia
Tel.: (61) 738793344
Sales Range: $25-49.9 Million
Emp.: 50
Thermal Engineering & Heat-Treatment Services
N.A.I.C.S.: 541330
S. L. Lee (Mgr)

RCR Mining Technologies (1)
21 Wilson Rd, Bunbury, 6230, WA, Australia
Tel.: (61) 897264555
Emp.: 240
Design & Manufacture of Materials Handling & Process Equipment for Mining Industries
N.A.I.C.S.: 333131

Subsidiary (Domestic):

RCR Mining (Spliceline) Pty Ltd (2)
Lot 522 McCombe Road, Bunbury, 6230, WA, Australia
Tel.: (61) 897264546
Sales Range: $25-49.9 Million
Emp.: 15
Conveyor System Repair Services
N.A.I.C.S.: 811310

RCR Mining Technologies Pty Ltd (1)
239 Planet Street, Welshpool, 6106, WA, Australia
Tel.: (61) 893558101
Web Site: http://www.promac.net.au
Sales Range: $25-49.9 Million
Emp.: 12
Heavy Machineries & Truck Sales
N.A.I.C.S.: 423810
Andrew McAdam (Gen Mgr)

NRW.BANK

Kavalleriestrasse 22, 40213, Dusseldorf, Germany
Tel.: (49) 211 91741 0   De
Web Site: http://www.nrwbank.com
Year Founded: 2002
Rev.: $4,391,603,109
Assets: $167,122,228,785
Liabilities: $146,982,200,093
Net Worth: $20,140,028,692
Earnings: $9,142,318
Emp.: 1,428
Fiscal Year-end: 12/31/19
Institutional Banking
N.A.I.C.S.: 521110
Michael Stolting (Member-Mgmt Bd)

Subsidiaries:

NRW.BANK Munster (1)
Friedrichstrasse 1, 48145, Munster, Germany
Tel.: (49) 251 91741 0
Web Site: http://www.nrwbank.com
Sales Range: $200-249.9 Million
Institutional Banking
N.A.I.C.S.: 521110

NRW.Bank (1)
Rue Montoyer 47, 1000, Brussels, Belgium
Tel.: (32) 2 504 79 71
Web Site: http://www.nrwbank.de
Emp.: 2
Corporate Communications, European Affairs, Business Management & Banking Services
N.A.I.C.S.: 541618
Henning Treder (Mng Dir)

NRW.Bank (1)
Kavalleriestrasse 22, 40213, Dusseldorf, Germany
Tel.: (49) 211917410
Web Site: http://www.nrwbank.de
Business & Banking Management & European Affairs
N.A.I.C.S.: 522110

NS BANK JSC

20 Dobrovolcheskaya St Building 2, Moscow, 109004, Russia
Tel.: (7) 8005554324
Web Site: http://www.nsbank.ru
Year Founded: 1994
Sales Range: Less than $1 Million
Mortgage Banking Services
N.A.I.C.S.: 522292

NS HOME SHOPPING CO., LTD.

NS Home Shopping Bldg 15 Pangyo-ro 228beon-gil, Bundang-gu, Seongnam, 463-400, Gyeonggi-do, Korea (South)
Tel.: (82) 263361234
Web Site: http://pr.nsmall.com
Year Founded: 2001
138250—(KRS)
Rev.: $447,782,947
Assets: $869,589,283
Liabilities: $578,915,564
Net Worth: $290,673,720
Earnings: ($27,382,759)
Emp.: 422
Fiscal Year-end: 12/31/21
Online Shopping Service Provider
N.A.I.C.S.: 459999
Sang Cheol Do (CEO)

NS TOOL CO., LTD.

6F Sumitomo fudosan oimachi ekimae Bldg 1-28-1 Oi, Shinagawa-ku, Tokyo, 140-0014, Japan
Tel.: (81) 364231135
Web Site: https://www.ns-tool.com
Year Founded: 1954
6157—(TKS)
Rev.: $59,729,088
Assets: $127,129,135
Liabilities: $9,990,086
Net Worth: $117,139,049
Earnings: $8,721,504
Fiscal Year-end: 03/31/24
Agricultural Handtools Products Mfr
N.A.I.C.S.: 332216
Hiroji Goto (Pres)

Subsidiaries:

NS TOOL CO., LTD. - Sendai Plant (1)
2-11 Matsusakadaira Taiwa-cho, Kurokawa-gun, Sendai, 981-3408, Miyagi, Japan
Tel.: (81) 223442201
Web Site: https://www.ns-tool.com
Cutting Tool Mfr
N.A.I.C.S.: 333515

NS UNITED KAIUN KAISHA, LTD.

Otemachi First Square West Tower 21F 22F 5-1 Otemachi 1-chome, Chiyoda-ku, Tokyo, 100-8108, Japan
Tel.: (81) 368956400   JP
Web Site: https://www.nsuship.co.jp
Year Founded: 1950
9110—(TKS)
Rev.: $1,540,791,000
Assets: $1,892,733,840
Liabilities: $903,983,600
Net Worth: $988,750,240
Earnings: $118,887,460
Emp.: 649
Fiscal Year-end: 03/31/24
Shipping Equipment Sales
N.A.I.C.S.: 423840
Shin Yaguchi (Mng Exec Officer)

Subsidiaries:

International Marine Consulting Co., Ltd. (1)
Otemachi First Square West Tower 21F 5-1 Otemachi 1-chome, Chiyoda-ku, Tokyo, 100-0004, Japan
Tel.: (81) 368956365
Web Site: http://www.shinwaship.co.jp
Sales Range: $25-49.9 Million
Emp.: 10
Marine Transportation Services
N.A.I.C.S.: 488320
Tadashi Sekine (Pres)

Ns United Bulk Pte. Ltd. (1)
65 Chulia Street 21-08 OCBC Centre, Singapore, 049513, Singapore
Tel.: (65) 62249138
Marine Services
N.A.I.C.S.: 488390

Ns United Business Co., Ltd. (1)
Otemachi First Square West Tower 22F 5-1 Otemachi 1-chome, Chiyoda-ku, Tokyo, 100-0004, Japan
Tel.: (81) 368956630
Marine Services
N.A.I.C.S.: 488390

Ns United Coastal Tanker Kaisha, Ltd. (1)
1-5-1 Otemachi First Square West Tower, Chiyoda-ku, Tokyo, 100-0004, Japan
Tel.: (81) 368956580
Emp.: 66
Shipping Brokerage Services
N.A.I.C.S.: 488510

Ns United Kaiun Kaisha, Ltd. (1)
201 A5 Building Main Campus VIETNAM MARITIME UNIVERSITY, No 484 Lach Tray St Kenh Duong Ward Le Chan Dist, Haiphong, Vietnam
Tel.: (84) 2253829609
Marine Services
N.A.I.C.S.: 488390

Ns United Kaiun Kaisha, Ltd. (1)
RM 1103 Ruijin Building 205 Mao Ming Nan Lu, Shanghai, 200020, China
Tel.: (86) 2164153557
Marine Services
N.A.I.C.S.: 488390

Ns United Marine Service Corporation (1)
Otemachi First Square West Tower 22F 5-1 Otemachi 1-chome, Chiyoda-ku, Tokyo, 100-0004, Japan
Tel.: (81) 368956770
Marine Services
N.A.I.C.S.: 488390

Ns United Naiko Kaiun Kaisha, Ltd. (1)
1-5-1 Otemachi Otemachi First Square West Tower 22nd floor, Chiyoda-ku, Tokyo, 100-0004, Japan
Tel.: (81) 368956500
Web Site: https://www.nsu-naiko.co.jp
Emp.: 316
Limestone Transportation Services
N.A.I.C.S.: 485999

Ns United Shipping (H.K.) Co., Ltd. (1)
Room 1002 Ocean Centre Harbour City 5 Canton Road, Tsimshatsui, Kowloon, China (Hong Kong)
Tel.: (852) 21101228
Marine Services
N.A.I.C.S.: 488390

Ns United Shipping (U.K.) Ltd. (1)
1st Floor 1 Knightrider Court, London, EC4V 5BJ, United Kingdom
Tel.: (44) 2072481227
Marine Services
N.A.I.C.S.: 488390

Ns United Shipping (U.S.A.) Inc. (1)
1055 Washington Blvd Ste 620, Stamford, CT 06901
Tel.: (203) 514-4773
Marine Services
N.A.I.C.S.: 400390

Ns United Systems Co., Ltd. (1)
1-5-1 Otemachi First Square West Tower 22F, Chiyoda-ku, Tokyo, 100-0004, Japan
Tel.: (81) 368956670
Emp.: 16
Marine Services
N.A.I.C.S.: 488390

Philippine Standard Shipmanagement Inc. (1)
5F New Solid Bldg 357 Sen Gil Puyat Ave,

NS UNITED KAIUN KAISHA, LTD.

NS United Kaiun Kaisha, Ltd.—(Continued)
Makati, 1200, Philippines
Tel.: (63) 284241188
Marine Services
N.A.I.C.S.: 488390

Shinsho Senpaku Kaisha, Ltd. (1)
Otemachi First Square West Tower 21F 5-1 Otemachi 1-chome, Chiyoda-ku, Tokyo, 100-0004, Japan
Tel.: (81) 368956368
Sales Range: $25-49.9 Million
Emp.: 100
Marine Shipping Services
N.A.I.C.S.: 488320

Shinwa (U.K.) Ltd. (1)
1st Floor 1 Knightrider Court, London, EC4V 5BJ, United Kingdom
Tel.: (44) 2072481227
Ship Broking Services
N.A.I.C.S.: 488320

Shinwa Agency Co., Ltd. (1)
Marine Shipping Services
N.A.I.C.S.: 488510

Shinwa Business Management Kaisha, Ltd. (1)
KDDI Otemachi Bldg 14F 8-1 Otemachi 1-chome, Chiyoda-ku, Tokyo, 100-0004, Japan
Tel.: (81) 352906633
Real Estate Manangement Services
N.A.I.C.S.: 531390

Shinwa Chartering Corp. (1)
KDDI Otemachi Bldg 15F 8-1 Otemachi 1-chome, Chiyoda-ku, Tokyo, 100-8108, Japan
Tel.: (81) 352906365
Web Site: http://www.shinwaship.co.jp
Marine Shipping Services
N.A.I.C.S.: 488320

Shinwa Chemical Tanker Co., Ltd. (1)
KDDI Otemachi Bldg 13F 8-1 Otemachi 1-chome, Chiyoda-ku, Tokyo, 100-0004, Japan
Tel.: (81) 352906500
Gas & Chemical Products Transportation Services
N.A.I.C.S.: 486210

Shinwa Engineering Services Co., Ltd. (1)
Matsumura Bldg 2F 2-64 Minami-Saiwai-cho, Saiwai-ku, Kawasaki, 212-0016, Kanagawa, Japan
Tel.: (81) 445436815
Web Site: http://www.nsuship.co.jp
Sales Range: $25-49.9 Million
Emp.: 39
Generators Maintenance Services
N.A.I.C.S.: 811114
Masami Mochizuki (Mgr)

Shinwa Marine Corp. (1)
KDDI Otemachi Bldg 15F 8-1 Otemachi 1-chome, Chiyoda-ku, Tokyo, 100-0004, Japan
Tel.: (81) 352906600
Sales Range: $25-49.9 Million
Emp.: 50
Marine Shipping Services
N.A.I.C.S.: 488510

Shinwa Shipping (H.K.) Co., Ltd. (1)
Rm 1002 Ocean Ctr Harbour City 5 Canton Rd, Kowloon, China (Hong Kong)
Tel.: (852) 2110 1228
Web Site: http://www.shinwaship.com.hk
Emp.: 5
Marine Shipping Services
N.A.I.C.S.: 488510

Shinwa Systems Co., Ltd. (1)
KDDI Otemachi Bldg 13F 8-1 Otemachi 1-chome, Chiyoda-ku, Tokyo, 100-0004, Japan
Tel.: (81) 3 5290 6670
Information Processing Services
N.A.I.C.S.: 519290

NSC GROUPE SA

170 rue de la Republique, 68500, Guebwiller, Cedex, France
Tel.: (33) 389744019 FR
Web Site: https://www.nsc-groupe.com
Year Founded: 1808
ALNSC—(EUR)
Sales Range: $75-99.9 Million
Emp.: 1,400
Machinery & Equipment for Textile & Packaging Industries Designer & Mfr
N.A.I.C.S.: 333993
Bruno Ameline (Chm & CEO)

Subsidiaries:

Asselin-Thibeau Site d'Elbeuf (1)
Rue Camille Randoing 41, PO Box 421, 76504, Elbeuf, France (100%)
Tel.: (33) 232964242
Sales Range: $50-74.9 Million
Emp.: 175
Textile Machinery Mfr
N.A.I.C.S.: 333248
Johannes Haep (CEO)

Asselin-Thibeau Site de Tourcoing (1)
191 Rue Des Cinq-Voies, BP 363, 59336, Tourcoing, Cedex 191, France
Tel.: (33) 320116464
Web Site: http://www.nsa.fr
Sales Range: $50-74.9 Million
Emp.: 150
Textile Machinery Mfr
N.A.I.C.S.: 333248

Fonderie Schlumberger SAS (1)
3 Rue Du 17 Novembre, 68500, Guebwiller, France
Tel.: (33) 3 89 74 41 33
Iron Products Distr
N.A.I.C.S.: 423510
Georges Chapelier (Dir-Tech)

Subsidiary (Non-US):

Monomatic Italia S.r.l. (2)
Via Salvo D Aquisto 45 Interno 17, Castellare Di Pescia, 51012, Pescia, Italy (100%)
Tel.: (39) 0572444208
Web Site: http://www.monomatic.it
Sales Range: $25-49.9 Million
Emp.: 4
Textile Machinery Mfr
N.A.I.C.S.: 333248

Monomatic (1)
48 Rue De lEngelbreit, PO Box BP54, 67034, Strasbourg, France (100%)
Tel.: (33) 388309300
Web Site: http://www.monomatic.fr
Sales Range: $25-49.9 Million
Emp.: 4
Retailer of Non-stop Winders & Unwinders for the Manufacture of Wall Papers, Industrial & Consumer Product Packaging & Paper
N.A.I.C.S.: 333248
Bernard Muller (Pres)

N. Schlumberger (U.K.) Ltd. (1)
Hillam Road Industrial Estate, Canal Road, Bradford, BD2 1QN, West Yorkshire, United Kingdom (99.9%)
Tel.: (44) 1274394641
Sales Range: $25-49.9 Million
Emp.: 4
Textile Machinery Mfr
N.A.I.C.S.: 333248

N. Schlumberger Deutschland Gmbh (1)
Kreuzberger Ring 44 A, 65205, Wiesbaden, Germany (100%)
Tel.: (49) 611609390
Sales Range: $25-49.9 Million
Emp.: 4
Textile Machinery Mfr
N.A.I.C.S.: 333248

N. Schlumberger Japan KK (1)
Level 5 Dojima Building, 2-6-8- Nishitemma Kitaku, Osaka, 530 0047, Japan
Tel.: (81) 663632886
Sales Range: $25-49.9 Million
Emp.: 2
Textile Machinery Mfr
N.A.I.C.S.: 333248

NSC Florival (1)
170 Rue De La Republique, 68500, Guebwiller, France
Tel.: (33) 389744141
Web Site: http://www.nsc-schlumberger.com
Sales Range: $100-124.9 Million
Emp.: 200
Financial Management Services
N.A.I.C.S.: 523999
Bruno Ameline (COO)

NSC USA Inc. (1)
1299 Schlumberger Dr, Fort Mill, SC 29715
Tel.: (803) 548-7233
Web Site: http://www.nscusa.com
Packaging Textile Machinery Distr
N.A.I.C.S.: 423830
James Kerns Jr. (Mgr-Parts & IT)

NSC environnement SAS (1)
170 rue de la Republique, Guebwiller, 68500, France
Tel.: (33) 389744141
Web Site: http://www.nsc-environment.com
Emp.: 200
Solid Waste Collection Services
N.A.I.C.S.: 562111
David Vermelle (Gen Mgr)

Nsc Packaging SAS (1)
Argonne Activity Center Rue Albert Caquot, 08400, Vouziers, France
Tel.: (33) 389542733
Web Site: http://www.nscpackaging.com
Industrial Equipment Distr
N.A.I.C.S.: 423840

Pack'Industrie (1)
Rue Gutenberg, PO Box 109, 68172, Rixheim, Cedex, France (100%)
Tel.: (33) 389542733
Web Site: http://www.pakea.eu
Sales Range: $10-24.9 Million
Emp.: 45
Supplier of Production Equipment in Packaging & Board Conversion Markets
N.A.I.C.S.: 333993
Gascal Buzon (Gen Mgr)

Pakea (1)
Rue Gutenberg, BP 109, 68170, Rixheim, France
Tel.: (33) 3 89 54 27 33
Web Site: http://www.pakea.eu
Sales Range: $25-49.9 Million
Emp.: 4
Paper Tube Machine Mfr
N.A.I.C.S.: 333243
Charles Ochsenbein (Gen Mgr)

Plant (Domestic):

Pakea - RIXHEIM PLANT (2)
Rue Gutenberg, 68172, Rixheim, France
Tel.: (33) 3 89 54 27 33
Web Site: http://www.pakea.eu
Emp.: 4
Paper Tube Machine Mfr
N.A.I.C.S.: 333243
Podsekina Julia (Gen Mgr)

Pakea - TRAINEL PLANT (2)
Zi - Rue Des Maucourants, 10400, Trainel, France
Tel.: (33) 3 25 39 46 70
Web Site: http://www.pakea.eu
Sales Range: $25-49.9 Million
Paper Tube Machine Mfr
N.A.I.C.S.: 333243
Buzon Pascal (Gen Mgr)

SBA (1)
Rue Du Calvaire 40, Herve, 4650, Liege, Belgium (100%)
Tel.: (32) 87306553
Web Site: http://www.nsc-groupe.com
Sales Range: $25-49.9 Million
Emp.: 3
Process Control & Monitoring Systems
N.A.I.C.S.: 334513

Sant'Andrea Textiles Machines Srl (1)
Via L Da Vinci 18, 28100, Novara, Italy
Tel.: (39) 03213721
Web Site: http://www.santandreatm.it
Cloth & Fabric Product Mfr
N.A.I.C.S.: 315990

Servitex Ltda (1)
Rio Negro 1530, 11000, Montevideo, Uruguay (100%)
Tel.: (598) 9025702
Web Site: http://servitex.com.uy
Sales Range: $25-49.9 Million
Textile Machinery Mfr
N.A.I.C.S.: 333248
Mario Neumann (Dir)

Seydel GmbH (1)
Kracksen Strasse 12, 33659, Bielefeld, Germany
Tel.: (49) 52114590
Web Site: http://www.seydel-germany.com
Spinning Flax Machinery Mfr
N.A.I.C.S.: 333248

Wuxi NSC Hongyuan (1)
No 105-2 Xinjin Road Supporting Zone Phase 2, Wuxi New District, Wuxi, 214112, Jiangsu, China
Tel.: (86) 51085361269
Sales Range: $25-49.9 Million
Emp.: 60
Mfr of Cross-lappers
N.A.I.C.S.: 333248
Rakesh Kumar (Gen Mgr)

NSCOMPANY CO., LTD.

127 Gueo2sandan-ro, Oedong-eup, Gyeongju, Gyeongsangbuk-do, Korea (South)
Tel.: (82) 522892888
Industrial Machinery Maintenance Services
N.A.I.C.S.: 811310
Chang-Jo Hwang (Sr Mng Dir)

NSD CO., LTD.

Kanda Awajicho 2-101 Waterras Tower, Chiyoda-ku, Tokyo, 101-0063, Japan
Tel.: (81) 332571130
Web Site: https://www.nsd.co.jp
9759—(TKS)
Rev.: $669,348,430
Assets: $571,137,050
Liabilities: $147,885,530
Net Worth: $423,251,520
Earnings: $67,831,820
Emp.: 4,380
Fiscal Year-end: 03/31/24
System Solution Services
N.A.I.C.S.: 541513
Masataka Komatsu (Mng Exec Officer)

Subsidiaries:

Chengdu Renbenxindong Technology Ltd. (1)
No 1201 Block A Building 6 No 300, Tianfu Fourth Street High-tech Zone, Chengdu, 610041, Sichuan, China
Tel.: (86) 286 767 0090
Web Site: https://www.rxcsoft.cn
Software Development Services
N.A.I.C.S.: 541511

NSD Advanced Technology Research Institute Co., Ltd. (1)
2-101 Kanda Awajicho Wateras Tower, Chiyoda-ku, Tokyo, 101-0063, Japan
Tel.: (81) 33 257 1120
Web Site: https://www.natric.co.jp
Advanced Technology Development Services
N.A.I.C.S.: 541715

NSD International, Inc. (1)
50 Main St Ste 910, White Plains, NY 10606
Tel.: (914) 333-6810
Web Site: https://www.nsdintl.com
System Integration Services
N.A.I.C.S.: 541512
Hidenori Tomioka (Pres)

Subsidiary (Domestic):

Mkg Global Technology, Inc. (2)
50 Main St Ste 910, White Plains, NY 10606
Tel.: (201) 476-0964
Web Site: https://www.japantech.com
Computer & Computer Peripheral Equipment & Software Merchant Whslr
N.A.I.C.S.: 423430

AND PRIVATE COMPANIES

NSK LTD.

Goichi Ikeda (Owner)

Renbenxindong Technology Ltd. (1)
1103 Baiyan building NO 238 North Fourth Ring Road, Haidian District, Beijing, 100191, China
Tel.: (86) 108 233 5821
Software Development Services
N.A.I.C.S.: 513210

Shareholders Relation Service, Inc. (1)
2-chome 105 Address Wa Terrace Annex, Awajicho Chiyoda-ku, Tokyo, 101-0063, Japan
Tel.: (81) 33 257 1260
Web Site: https://www.sr-s.co.jp
Information Technology Services
N.A.I.C.S.: 523999

StellaS Co., Ltd. (1)
6th Floor Sotetsu Manseibashi Building 1-5-10 Kanda Sudacho, Chiyoda-ku, Tokyo, 101-0041, Japan
Tel.: (81) 33 257 6201
Web Site: https://stellas.co.jp
Human Resource Management Services
N.A.I.C.S.: 541612

Winnersoft Co., Ltd. (1)
2-105 Kanda Awajicho Waterras Annex 6th Floor, Chiyoda-ku, Tokyo, 101-0063, Japan
Tel.: (81) 33 257 1202
Web Site: https://www.winnersoft.co.jp
Software Services
N.A.I.C.S.: 541511

NSE INDUSTRIES SA
65 bis avenue de l'Europe, 77184, Emerainville-Malnoue, France
Tel.: (33) 470584390
Web Site: https://www.nse-groupe.com
Year Founded: 1983
ALNSE—(EUR)
Sales Range: $25-49.9 Million
Aviation Electronic Equipment Mfr
N.A.I.C.S.: 334511
Pierre Maillard (Deputy CEO)

Subsidiaries:

NSE Aero North America Inc. (1)
3544 Ashby, Saint-Laurent, Montreal, H4R 2C1, QC, Canada
Tel.: (514) 335-5205
Electrical Equipment Distr
N.A.I.C.S.: 423610

NSE Automatech Inc. (1)
520 Rutherford, Granby, J2G 0B2, QC, Canada
Tel.: (450) 378-7207
Emp.: 75
Electrical Equipment Distr
N.A.I.C.S.: 423610

NSE Brasil (1)
Rodovia Geraldo Scavone 2080, Jacarei, 12305490, Sao Paulo, Brazil
Tel.: (55) 1239538713
Web Site: http://www.nsegroup.com
Emp.: 50
Electrical Equipment Distr
N.A.I.C.S.: 423610
Stephane Delafoy (Mgr)

NSFOCUS TECHNOLOGIES GROUP CO., LTD.
5th Floor Yitai Building No 4 Beiwa Road, Haidian District, Beijing, 100089, China
Tel.: (86) 1068438880
Web Site: http://www.nsfocus.com
Year Founded: 2000
300369—(CHIN)
Rev.: $369,089,136
Assets: $688,469,652
Liabilities: $174,810,636
Net Worth: $513,659,016
Earnings: $3,983,148
Emp.: 5,000
Fiscal Year-end: 12/31/22
Network Security Communications Equipment

N.A.I.C.S.: 334220
Jiye Shen (Founder & CEO)

Subsidiaries:

NSFOCUS Japan K.K. (1)
East Tower 4th Floor Otemachi First Square 1-5-1 Otemachi, Chiyoda-ku, Tokyo, 100-0004, Japan
Tel.: (81) 352191339
Security Software Development Services
N.A.I.C.S.: 541511

NSFOCUS Technologies (S) Pte. Ltd. (1)
7500A Beach Road 08-308 The Plaza, Singapore, 119591, Singapore
Tel.: (65) 65098500
Security Software Development Services
N.A.I.C.S.: 541511

NSFOCUS Technologies (UK), Limited (1)
Lakeside House 1 Furzeground Way Stockley Park, Uxbridge, United Kingdom
Tel.: (44) 2034766758
Security Software Development Services
N.A.I.C.S.: 541511

NSFOCUS, Inc. (1)
3979 Freedom Cir Ste 900, Santa Clara, CA 95054
Tel.: (408) 907-6638
Security Software Development Services
N.A.I.C.S.: 541511

NSFOCUS, Inc. (1)
Rua Funchal 418 - 35 andar - E-Tower Building, Sao Paulo, 04551-060, Brazil
Tel.: (55) 1135217124
Security Software Development Services
N.A.I.C.S.: 541511

NSI ASSET AG
Heidenkampsweg 75, 20097, Hamburg, Germany
Tel.: (49) 040524737994
Web Site: https://www.nsi-asset.de
Year Founded: 1993
VMR1—(DEU)
Assets: $131,038,204
Liabilities: $124,347,075
Net Worth: $6,691,129
Earnings: ($1,651,198)
Emp.: 33
Fiscal Year-end: 12/31/22
Investment Management Service
N.A.I.C.S.: 523940
Eugen Fleck (Member-Mgmt Bd)

Subsidiaries:

4 Free AG (1)
Heidenkampsweg 75, 20097, Hamburg, Germany
Tel.: (49) 4052473790
Web Site: http://www.4free.de
Investment Fund Services
N.A.I.C.S.: 523940

NSI N.V.
Hoogoorddreef 62 1101 BE Amsterdam, PO Box 3044, 2130 KA, Amsterdam, Netherlands
Tel.: (31) 207630300 NI
Web Site: https://www.nsi.nl
NIUWF—(OTCIQ)
Rev.: $78,594,768
Assets: $1,200,601,612
Liabilities: $416,980,903
Net Worth: $783,620,709
Earnings: ($157,158,627)
Emp.: 61
Fiscal Year-end: 12/31/23
Property Investment Services
N.A.I.C.S.: 523999
L. A. S. van der Ploeg (Chm-Supervisory Bd)

Subsidiaries:

NSI Bedrijfsgebouwen B.V. (1)
Antareslaan 69-75, Hoofddorp, 2132JE, Netherlands (100%)
Tel.: (31) 229295050

Web Site: http://www.nsi.nl
Sales Range: $25-49.9 Million
Emp.: 46
Other Real Estate Property Lessors
N.A.I.C.S.: 531190

NSI Beheer B.V. (1)
Nieuwe Steen 27, 1625, Hoorn, Netherlands (100%)
Tel.: (31) 229295050
Web Site: http://www.nsi.nl
Sales Range: $25-49.9 Million
Emp.: 40
Other Real Estate Property Lessors
N.A.I.C.S.: 531190

NSI Development BV (1)
Antareslaan 69-75, Hoofddorp, 2132 NC, Netherlands
Tel.: (31) 207630300
Web Site: http://www.nsi.nl
Sales Range: $50-74.9 Million
Emp.: 72
Real Estate Investment Services
N.A.I.C.S.: 531390
G. Buegs (CEO)

NSI Hoorn B.V. (1)
Antaras Laan 69, 1625, Hoofddorp, Netherlands (100%)
Tel.: (31) 229295050
Web Site: http://www.nsi.nl
Sales Range: $50-74.9 Million
Emp.: 70
Real Estate Investment Trust
N.A.I.C.S.: 525990
J. Buijs (CEO)

NSI Kantoren B.V. (1)
Antareslaan 69-75, 2132JE, Hoofddorp, Netherlands (100%)
Tel.: (31) 229295050
Web Site: http://www.nsi.nl
Sales Range: $25-49.9 Million
Emp.: 60
Other Real Estate Property Lessors
N.A.I.C.S.: 531190
Johan Buys (Dir)

NSI Management B.V. (1)
Antareslaan 69-75 Pobox 3044, 1625, Hoofddorp, Netherlands (100%)
Tel.: (31) 229295050
Web Site: http://wwwnsi.nl
Sales Range: $50-74.9 Million
Emp.: 40
Securities Brokerage
N.A.I.C.S.: 523150
Johan Buijs (CEO)

NSI Monument B.V. (1)
Nieuwe Steen 27, 1625HV, Hoorn, Netherlands (100%)
Tel.: (31) 229295050
Web Site: http://www.nsi.nl
Sales Range: $50-74.9 Million
Emp.: 100
Museums
N.A.I.C.S.: 712110

NSI Overig B.V (1)
Antareslaan 69, Hoofddorp, 2132JE, Netherlands (100%)
Tel.: (31) 229295050
Web Site: http://www.nsi.nl
Sales Range: $50-74.9 Million
Emp.: 74
Trusts Estates & Agency Accounts
N.A.I.C.S.: 525920
Johan Buijs (CEO)

NSI Volumineuze Detailhandel B.V. (1)
Antareslaan 69-75, 1621 C, Hoofddorp, Netherlands (100%)
Tel.: (31) 229295050
Web Site: http://www.nsi.nl
Other Real Estate Property Lessors
N.A.I.C.S.: 531190

NSI Winkels B.V. (1)
Nieuwe Steen 27, 1625, Hoorn, Netherlands (100%)
Tel.: (31) 229244744
Web Site: http://www.nsi.nl
Securities Brokerage
N.A.I.C.S.: 523150

NSI Woningen B.V. (1)
Nieuwe Steen 27, 1625 HV, Hoorn, Netherlands (100%)

Tel.: (31) 229244744
Sales Range: $50-74.9 Million
Emp.: 40
Securities Brokerage
N.A.I.C.S.: 523150
Johan Buijs (CEO)

VastNed Offices/Industrial N.V. (1)
De Boelelaan 7, 1083 HJ, Amsterdam, Netherlands
Tel.: (31) 202424300
Rev.: $158,123,509
Assets: $1,913,952,687
Liabilities: $795,852,195
Net Worth: $1,118,100,492
Earnings: $127,702,657
Emp.: 42
Fiscal Year-end: 12/31/2017
Property Investment Services
N.A.I.C.S.: 531390
Taco T. J. de Groot (Chm, CEO & Member-Mgmt Bd)

Subsidiary (Domestic):

VastNed Industrial B.V. (2)
KpVan Per Man De Le laan 43, 3062 MB, Rotterdam, Netherlands (100%)
Tel.: (31) 102424300
Web Site: http://www.vastnedretail.nl
Sales Range: $25-49.9 Million
Emp.: 50
Other Real Estate Property Lessors
N.A.I.C.S.: 531190
Reinier A. van Gerrevink (CEO)

NSJ GOLD CORP.
101-17565-58 Avenue, Surrey, V3S 4E3, BC, Canada
Tel.: (778) 218-9638 BC
Web Site: https://www.nsjgold.com
Year Founded: 2020
NSJ—(CNSX)
Assets: $632,098
Liabilities: $46,762
Net Worth: $585,336
Earnings: ($233,168)
Fiscal Year-end: 11/30/23
Gold Exploration Services
N.A.I.C.S.: 212220
Jag Sandhu (Founder)

NSJ-US. CO., LTD.
Kitahama Bldg 2F 1-7-19 Imabashi Chuo-ku, Osaka, Japan
Tel.: (81) 6 43910370 NV
Year Founded: 2011
Security Systems & Related Software Products
N.A.I.C.S.: 561621
Joko Toshikazu (Chm, Pres, Treas & Sec)

NSK LTD.
Nissei Building 1-6-3 Ohsaki, Shinagawa-ku, Tokyo, 141-8560, Japan
Tel.: (81) 337797111 JP
Web Site: https://www.nsk.com
Year Founded: 1916
6471—(TKS)
Rev.: $5,214,410,870
Assets: $8,580,288,970
Liabilities: $4,099,013,030
Net Worth: $4,481,275,940
Earnings: $56,198,220
Emp.: 25,632
Fiscal Year-end: 03/31/24
Ball & Roller Bearings Mfr
N.A.I.C.S.: 332991
Shigeyuki Suzuki (Auditor-NSK-Warner)

Subsidiaries:

AKS EAST JAPAN CO., LTD. (1)
12 Kirihara-cho, Fujisawa, 252-0811, Kanagawa, Japan
Tel.: (81) 466446631
Emp.: 10
Ball & Roller Bearing Manufacturing
N.A.I.C.S.: 332991
Yuichi Hasegawa (Mgr)

NSK LTD.

INTERNATIONAL PUBLIC

NSK Ltd.—(Continued)

Subsidiary (Domestic):

AKS SALES CO., LTD. (2)
3-1-5 Tagawa, Yodogawa-ku, Osaka, 532-0027, Japan
Tel.: (81) 6 6301 7535
Emp.: 80
Steel Product Distr
N.A.I.C.S.: 423510

AMATSUJI INDUSTRIAL CO., LTD. (2)
3-1-5 Tagawa, Yodogawa-ku, Osaka, 532-0027, Japan
Tel.: (81) 6 6301 8751
Web Site: http://www.aksball.co.jp
Ball Bearing Mfr
N.A.I.C.S.: 332991

AKS PRECISION BALL (HANGZHOU) CO., LTD. (1)
No 189 Hongda Road Xiaoshan Area of Economic, Technological Development Zone, Hangzhou, 311231, Zhejiang, China
Tel.: (86) 57122801288
Steel Ball Mfr & Distr
N.A.I.C.S.: 331110
Toru Sakai (Gen Mgr)

ASAHI SEIKI CO., LTD. (1)
3-7 Tenjinmae Kamo-cho, Toyohashi, 441-1101, Aichi, Japan
Tel.: (81) 532880810
Web Site: https://www.asahi-seiki.co.jp
Emp.: 185
Bearing Parts Mfr
N.A.I.C.S.: 332991

Adtech Corporation (1)
13th Floor Nissei Bldg 1-6-3 Ohsaki, Shinagawa-ku, Tokyo, 141-0032, Japan
Tel.: (81) 35 434 9052
Automobile Parts Mfr
N.A.I.C.S.: 336390
Osamu Miyoshi (Pres)

Amatsuji Steel Ball Mfg. Co., Ltd. (1)
1-1 Kaminoguchi-cho, Kadoma, 571-0070, Osaka, Japan (32%)
Tel.: (81) 669082261
Web Site: https://www.aksball.co.jp
Sales Range: $200-249.9 Million
Emp.: 700
Mfr & Sales of Steel Balls
N.A.I.C.S.: 331110
Hirohide Ishida (Mng Dir)

Subsidiary (Non-US):

AKS Precision Ball Europe Ltd. (2)
Davy Drive, North West Industrial Estate, Peterlee, SR8 2PP, Durham, United Kingdom (100%)
Tel.: (44) 1915870000
Web Site: https://www.aksball.com
Sales Range: $25-49.9 Million
Emp.: 75
Mfg. & Sales of Steel Balls
N.A.I.C.S.: 331110

Plant (Domestic):

Amatsuji Steel Ball Mfg. Co., Ltd. - Shiga Works (2)
50 Ueda-cho, Omihachiman, 523-0015, Shiga, Japan
Tel.: (81) 748376761
Sales Range: $25-49.9 Million
Emp.: 20
Ball Bearing Mfr
N.A.I.C.S.: 332991
Minami Hata (Plant Mgr)

Subsidiary (Domestic):

SAKAI AMATSUJI STEEL BALL MFG. CO., LTD. (2)
2-7 Matsuya-cho, Sakai-ku, Sakai, 590-0903, Osaka, Japan
Tel.: (81) 722322031
Web Site: http://www.aksball.co.jp
Sales Range: $25-49.9 Million
Steel Mfrs
N.A.I.C.S.: 331110

Changshu NSK Needle Bearing Co., Ltd. (1)
No 666 Dongnan Road, Changshu Southeast Economic Development Zone, Changshu, 215500, Jiangsu, China
Tel.: (86) 5125 230 1111
Automobile Parts Mfr
N.A.I.C.S.: 336390

Chitose Sangyo Co., Ltd. (1)
561 Hatsuuma, Kakegawa, 436-0081, Shizuoka, Japan (100%)
Tel.: (81) 537223135
Web Site: https://chitose-kakegawa.com
Sales Range: $50-74.9 Million
Emp.: 138
Processing of Bearing Parts
N.A.I.C.S.: 336350
Isogai Kihichi (Gen Mgr)

Delphi Chassis NSK do Brasil Ltda. (1)
Ave Vereador Joao Batista Fitipaldi 66, Vila Maluf, 08685 000, Suzano, SP, Brazil
Tel.: (55) 1147442527
Mfg. & Sales of Bearings
N.A.I.C.S.: 332991

Delphi Saginaw NSK Co., Ltd. (1)
1 6 3 Ohsaki, Shinagawa-ku, Tokyo, 141-0032, Japan
Tel.: (81) 37796581
Design & Sales of Automotive Components
N.A.I.C.S.: 441330

Hefei NSK Co., Ltd. (1)
No 89 Chuangxin Avenue, Boyan Science and Technology Park High-tech Zone, Hefei, 230088, Anhui, China
Tel.: (86) 5516 856 2811
Automobile Parts Mfr
N.A.I.C.S.: 336390

ISC Micro Precision Sdn. Bhd. (1)
No 108 Jalan Taming Lima, Taman Taming Jaya, 43300, Balakong, Selangor Darul Ehsan, Malaysia
Tel.: (60) 123385221
Web Site: http://www.nskmicro.co.jp
Sales Range: $50-74.9 Million
Emp.: 250
Mfr of Bearings
N.A.I.C.S.: 332991

Inoue Jikuuke Kogyo Co., Ltd. (1)
1640-1 Oaza Sabi, Tondabayashi, 590-0052, Osaka, Japan (40%)
Tel.: (81) 721351551
Web Site: https://www.ijics.co.jp
Sales Range: $100-124.9 Million
Emp.: 300
Mfr & Sales of Bearings & Machine Parts
N.A.I.C.S.: 332991

KURIBAYASHI SEISAKUSHO CO., LTD. (1)
4860 Minamijo Sakaki-Machi, Hanishina-Gun, Nagano, 389-0695, Japan
Tel.: (81) 268823150
Web Site: https://www.k-kuri.jp
Emp.: 330
Bearing Parts Mfr
N.A.I.C.S.: 332991

Kaiki Sangyo Kabushiki Kaisha (1)
3-6-13, Oroshimachi, Wakabayashi-ku, Sendai, 984-0015, Miyagi, Japan
Tel.: (81) 2 2232 4391
Sales of Bearings, Automotive Components, Precision Machinery & Parts
N.A.I.C.S.: 441330

Kunshan NSK Co., Ltd. (1)
NO 1268 Middle Huang Pu Jiang Rd, Kunshan Economic Technology Development Zone, Kunshan, 215335, Jiangsu, China
Tel.: (86) 51257715654
Emp.: 1,120
Bearings Mfr & Sales
N.A.I.C.S.: 332991

NISSEI BLDG. MANAGEMENT LTD. (1)
1-6-3 Ohsaki, Shinagawa-ku, Tokyo, 141-0032, Japan
Tel.: (81) 3 3779 7488
Web Site: http://www.nsk.com
Building Construction Engineering Services
N.A.I.C.S.: 236210

NOMURA TEKKOSHO CO., LTD. (1)
449 Miyadera, Iruma, 358-0014, Saitama, Japan

Tel.: (81) 429346235
Bearing Parts Mfr
N.A.I.C.S.: 332991

NSK (China) Investment Co., Ltd. (1)
No 8 NSK Rd, Huaqiao Economic Development Zone, Kunshan, 215332, Jiangsu, China
Tel.: (86) 5125 796 3000
Automobile Parts Mfr
N.A.I.C.S.: 336390

NSK (China) Research & Development Co., Ltd. (1)
No 8 Ensk Road, Huaqiao Economic Development Zone, Kunshan, 215332, Jiangsu, China
Tel.: (86) 5125 796 3000
Machine Part Mfr
N.A.I.C.S.: 333248

NSK Argentina S.R.L. (1)
Garcia del Rio 2477 Piso 7 Oficina A, 1429, Buenos Aires, Argentina
Tel.: (54) 1147045100
Web Site: http://www.la.nsk.com
Sales of Bearings, Automotive Components, Precision Machinery & Parts
N.A.I.C.S.: 332991

NSK Asia Pacific Technology Centre (Thailand) Co., Ltd. (1)
700/430 Moo 7 Amata City, Chonburi Industrial Estate T Donhualor A Muangchonburi, Chon Buri, 20000, Thailand
Tel.: (66) 38454611
Web Site: http://www.nsk.co.th
Sales Range: $25-49.9 Million
Emp.: 30
Automotive Engineering Services
N.A.I.C.S.: 541330

NSK Australia Pty. Ltd. (1)
100 Logis Boulevard, Dandenong South, 3175, VIC, Australia
Tel.: (61) 397654400
Web Site: http://www.aus.nsk.com
Sales Range: $25-49.9 Million
Emp.: 50
Sales of Bearings, Automotive Components, Precision Machinery & Parts
N.A.I.C.S.: 441330

Subsidiary (Non-US):

NSK New Zealand Limited (2)
Unit F 70 Business Parade South Highbrook Business Park, Auckland, New Zealand
Tel.: (64) 92764992
Bearing Parts Distr
N.A.I.C.S.: 423840

Subsidiaries:

NSK Bearings (Malaysia) Sdn. Bhd. (1)
Web Site: http://www.nsk.com.my
Sales Range: $50-74.9 Million
Emp.: 55
Sales of Bearings, Automotive Components, Precision Machinery & Parts
N.A.I.C.S.: 423840

NSK Bearings (Thailand) Co., Ltd. (1)
26 Soi On Nut 55/1, Prawet Subdistrict Prawet District, Bangkok, 10250, Thailand (79%)
Web Site: http://www.nsk.co.th
Sales Range: $25-49.9 Million
Emp.: 70
Sales of Bearings, Automotive Parts, Precision Machinery & Parts
N.A.I.C.S.: 441330

NSK Bearings India Private Limited (1)
TVH Belicia Towers 2nd Floor Block I No 71/1, MRC Nagar Main Road, Chennai, 600 028, India
Tel.: (91) 442 847 9600
Machine Part Mfr
N.A.I.C.S.: 333248

NSK Bearings Manufacturing (Thailand) Co., Ltd. (1)
700/430 Moo 7 Amata City Chonburi Industrial Estate, T Donhualor A Muangchonburi, Chon Buri, 20000, Thailand
Tel.: (66) 38454010

Bearing Parts Mfr
N.A.I.C.S.: 332991

NSK Bearings Manufacturing, Mexico, S.A. de C.V. (1)
Circuito Mexiamora Oriente No 331, Parque Industrial Santa Fe V Col Puerto Interior, 36275, Silao, Guanajuato, Mexico
Tel.: (52) 472 103 9400
Automobile Parts Mfr
N.A.I.C.S.: 336390

NSK Bearings Middle East Trading Co., Ltd. (1)
Ulya Engin Is Merkezi No 68 Kat 6, Kozyatagi, 34734, Istanbul, Turkiye (100%)
Tel.: (90) 2163550398
Web Site: http://www.nskeurope.com
Sales Range: $50-74.9 Million
Emp.: 9
Sales of Bearings, Automotive Parts, Precision Machinery & Parts
N.A.I.C.S.: 423840
Emrah Takir (Gen Mgr)

NSK Bearings New Zealand Ltd. (1)
3 Te Apunga Place, Auckland, 1060, New Zealand (100%)
Tel.: (64) 92764992
Web Site: http://www.nsk.com
Sales Range: $50-74.9 Million
Emp.: 10
Sales of Bearings, Automotive Components, Precision Machinery & Parts
N.A.I.C.S.: 423840
Tony Wilson (Gen Mgr)

NSK Brasil Ltda. (1)
Av Vereador Joao Batista Fitipaldi 66, Suzano, Sao Paulo, 08685-000, SP, Brazil (100%)
Tel.: (55) 47442500
Web Site: https://www.nsk.com.br
Sales Range: $10-24.9 Million
Emp.: 100
Mfr & Sales of Bearings; Sales of Precision Machinery & Parts
N.A.I.C.S.: 332991

NSK Canada, Inc. (1)
317 Rutherford Road South, Brampton, L6W 3R5, ON, Canada (100%)
Tel.: (905) 890-0740
Web Site: http://www.ca.nsk.com
Sales Range: $25-49.9 Million
Emp.: 65
Mfr & Sales of Bearings Automotive Components Precision Machinery & Parts
N.A.I.C.S.: 441330

NSK Europe Limited (1)
Belmont Place Belmont Road, Maidenhead, SL6 6TB, Berks, United Kingdom (100%)
Tel.: (44) 1628509800
Web Site: http://www.eu.nsk.com
Sales Range: $25-49.9 Million
Emp.: 25
Bearings, Automotive Components, Precision Machinery & Parts Sales
N.A.I.C.S.: 441330
Ulrich Nass (CEO)

Subsidiary (Non-US):

AKS PRECISION BALL POLSKA SP. Z.O.O. (2)
ul Przemyslowa 12, 58-130, Zarow, Poland
Tel.: (48) 746499200
Web Site: https://www.aksball.com.pl
Sales Range: $25-49.9 Million
Emp.: 16
Ball Bearing Mfr
N.A.I.C.S.: 332991
Rafal Wierzbicki (Plant Mgr)

Subsidiary (Domestic):

NSK Bearings Europe Ltd. (2)
Northern Road, Newark, NG24 2JF, Nottinghamshire, United Kingdom (100%)
Tel.: (44) 1636605123
Web Site: http://www.nsk.co.uk
Research & Development of Bearings & Automotive Components
N.A.I.C.S.: 332991

Plant (Domestic):

NSK Bearings Europe Ltd. - Peterlee Plant (3)

3 Brindley Road, SW Industrial Estate, Peterlee, SR8 2JD, Co Durham, United Kingdom
Tel.: (44) 1915866111
Web Site: http://www.nsk.co.uk
Emp.: 600
Bearings, Precision Machinery & Parts Mfr
N.A.I.C.S.: 332991

Subsidiary (Non-US):

NSK Bearings Polska S.A. (2)
ul Jagiellonska 109, 25-734, Kielce, Poland (100%)
Tel.: (48) 413670502
Web Site: http://www.nsk.com.pl
Emp.: 1,257
Mfr & Sales of Bearings
N.A.I.C.S.: 332991

NSK Deutschland GmbH (2)
Harkortstrasse 15, 40880, Ratingen, Germany (100%)
Tel.: (49) 21024810
Web Site: http://www.nskeurope.de
Sales Range: $25-49.9 Million
Sales of Bearings, Automotive Components, Precision Machinery & Parts
N.A.I.C.S.: 441330

NSK EUROPEAN DISTRIBUTION CENTRE B.V. (2)
Brakman 54, 5047 SW, Tilburg, Netherlands
Tel.: (31) 134647647
Web Site: http://www.nsk.com
Sales Range: $50-74.9 Million
Emp.: 15
Bearing Parts Distr
N.A.I.C.S.: 423840

NSK Europa Holding GmbH (2)
Harkortstrasse 15, 40880, Ratingen, Germany (100%)
Tel.: (49) 21024810
Web Site: http://www.nskeurope.de
Sales Range: $25-49.9 Million
Emp.: 20
Holding Company
N.A.I.C.S.: 551112

NSK France S.A.S. (2)
Quartier de l'Europe 2 Rue Georges Guynemer, 78283, Guyancourt, Cedex, France
Tel.: (33) 130573939
Web Site: https://www.nskeurope.fr
Sales Range: $25-49.9 Million
Sales of Bearings, Automotive Components, Precision Machinery & Parts
N.A.I.C.S.: 441330
Zean Yves Chapelet (Dir-Sales-Western Europe)

NSK Italia S.p.A. (2)
Via Garibaldi 215, Garbagnate, 20024, Milan, MI, Italy (100%)
Tel.: (39) 02995191
Web Site: http://www.nskeurope.it
Sales Range: $25-49.9 Million
Sales of Bearings, Automotive Parts, Precision Machinery & Parts
N.A.I.C.S.: 441330

NSK Nederland B.V. (2)
De Kroonstraat 38, 5048 AP, Tilburg, Netherlands
Tel.: (31) 13464764
Sales of Bearings, Automotive Products, Precision Machinery & Parts
N.A.I.C.S.: 441330

Subsidiary (Domestic):

NSK PRECISION UK LTD. (2)
Belmont Place Belmont Road, Maidenhead, SL6 6TB, Berkshire, United Kingdom
Tel.: (44) 1628509800
Web Site: http://www.nskeurope.com
Emp.: 3
Roller Bearing Mfr
N.A.I.C.S.: 332991

Subsidiary (Non-US):

NSK Polska Sp. z.o.o. (2)
Ul Migdalowa 4/73, 02-796, Warsaw, Poland (100%)
Tel.: (48) 226451525
Web Site: http://www.nskeurope.pl

Sales Range: $25-49.9 Million
Emp.: 20
Bearings Mfr & Distr
N.A.I.C.S.: 332991

NSK STEERING SYSTEMS EUROPE (POLSKA) SP. Z.O.O. (2)
ul M Jachimowicza 17, 58-306, Walbrzych, Poland
Tel.: (48) 746644100
Web Site: http://www.nssp.com.pl
Roller Bearing Mfr
N.A.I.C.S.: 332991
Sarah Ouakim (Gen Mgr)

NSK Spain S.A. (2)
C/ Tarragona 161 Cuerpo Bajo 2a Planta, 08014, Barcelona, Spain
Tel.: (34) 932892763
Web Site: http://www.nskeurope.es
Sales of Bearings, Automotive Components, Precision Machinery & Parts
N.A.I.C.S.: 423840

Subsidiary (Domestic):

NSK Steering Systems (2)
Silverstone Dr, Rowieys Green, Coventry, CV6 6PA, United Kingdom (100%)
Tel.: (44) 2476588588
Web Site: http://www.nsk.co.uk
Sales Range: $25-49.9 Million
Mfr & Sales of Automotive Components
N.A.I.C.S.: 336330

NSK UK Ltd. (2)
Northern Road, Newark, NG24 2JF, Notts, United Kingdom
Tel.: (44) 1636605123
Emp.: 867
Sales of Bearings, Automotive Components, Precision Machinery & Parts
N.A.I.C.S.: 441330

Subsidiary (Non-US):

Neuweg Fertigung GmbH (2)
Ehinger Strasse 5, 89597, Munderkingen, Germany (100%)
Tel.: (49) 7393540
Web Site: http://www.neuweg-nsk.com
Sales Range: $25-49.9 Million
Emp.: 150
Mfr & Sales of Bearings
N.A.I.C.S.: 332991

NSK Hangzhou Automotive Components Co., Ltd. (1)
No 308 Gaoxin 11th Road Qiaonan Block, Xiaoshan Economic and Technological Development Zone Xiaoshan District, Hangzhou, 311231, Zhejiang, China
Tel.: (86) 5718 231 4818
Machine Part Mfr
N.A.I.C.S.: 333248

NSK Hong Kong Limited (1)
Suite 705 7th Floor South Tower World Finance Centre, Harbour City T S T, Kowloon, China (Hong Kong) (100%)
Tel.: (852) 27399933
Web Site: http://www.nsk.com.hk
Sales Range: $25-49.9 Million
Emp.: 8
Sales of Bearings, Automotive Components, Precision Machinery & Parts
N.A.I.C.S.: 441330

NSK Human Resource Services Ltd. (1)
1 6 3 Ohsaki, Shinagawa Ku, Tokyo, 141 0032, Japan (100%)
Tel.: (81) 354872448
Web Site: http://www.nsk.com
Sales Range: $75-99.9 Million
Emp.: 30,000
Personal Support Services
N.A.I.C.S.: 812990
Norio Otsuka (Pres)

NSK INDIA SALES CO. PVT. LTD. (1)
No 321 A Wing Ahura Centre 82 Mahakali Caves Road, Andheri East, Mumbai, 400 093, India
Tel.: (91) 2228387787
Web Site: http://www.nsk.com
Emp.: 8
Bearing Parts Distr
N.A.I.C.S.: 423840

NSK International (Singapore) Pte. Ltd. (1)
238A Thomson Road 24-01/02 Novena Square Tower A, Singapore, 307684, Singapore (70%)
Tel.: (65) 64968000
Web Site: http://www.nsk-singapore.com.sg
Sales Range: $25-49.9 Million
Emp.: 28
Bearing Manufacturer
N.A.I.C.S.: 332991

NSK Korea Co., Ltd. (1)
Posco Center West Wing 9F Western-wing 440 Teheran-ro, Gangnam-gu, Seoul, 06194, Korea (South) (100%)
Tel.: (82) 232870300
Web Site: http://www.kr.nsk.com
Sales Range: $100-124.9 Million
Emp.: 80
Mfr & Sales of Bearings, Automotive Components, Precision Machinery & Parts
N.A.I.C.S.: 332991

Plant (Domestic):

NSK KOREA CO., LTD. - CHANGWON PLANT (2)
53 Gongdan-ro 474 beon-gil, Seongsan-gu, Changwon, 51575, Gyeongsangnam-do, Korea (South)
Tel.: (82) 552876001
Emp.: 300
Roller Bearing Mfr
N.A.I.C.S.: 332991

NSK Kyushu Co., Ltd. (1)
774 Aza Nissei Furukawa, Ukiha-machi, Ukiha, 839-1405, Fukuoka, Japan
Tel.: (81) 943773110
Web Site: https://www.nsk.com
Emp.: 529
Bearings, Automotive Components, Precision Machinery & Parts Mfr
N.A.I.C.S.: 332991

NSK Logistics Co., Ltd. (1)
1-5-50 Kugenumashimei, Fujisawa, 251-8501, Kanagawa, Japan (100%)
Tel.: (81) 466213111
Web Site: http://www.jp.nsk.com
Sales Range: $25-49.9 Million
Emp.: 100
Distribution of Bearings, Automotive Components, Precision Machinery & Parts
N.A.I.C.S.: 332991

NSK Ltd. - Automotive Business Division (1)
Nissei Bldg 1-6-3 Ohsaki, Shinagawa-ku, Tokyo, 141-8560, Japan
Tel.: (81) 3 3779 7189
Emp.: 70
Bearing Parts Mfr
N.A.I.C.S.: 332991
Norio Otsuke (CEO)

NSK Ltd. - FUJISAWA PLANT (1)
1-5-50 Kugenumashinmei, Fujisawa, 251-8501, Kanagawa, Japan
Tel.: (81) 466213111
Emp.: 989
Bearing Parts Mfr
N.A.I.C.S.: 332991
Fumio Ogiso (Pres)

NSK Ltd. - FUKUSHIMA PLANT (1)
180-1 Nikaki Tsutsumi Tanagura-machi, Higashishirakawa-gun, Fukushima, 963-6101, Japan
Tel.: (81) 247333210
Web Site: https://www.nsk.com
Sales Range: $200-249.9 Million
Emp.: 566
Bearing Parts Mfr
N.A.I.C.S.: 332991

NSK Ltd. - Industrial Machinery Business Division (1)
Nissei Bldg 1-6-3 Ohsaki, Shinagawa-ku, Tokyo, 141-8560, Japan
Tel.: (81) 3 3779 7227
Web Site: http://www.nsk.com
Industrial Machinery Mfr
N.A.I.C.S.: 333248

NSK Ltd. - Ishibe Plant (1)
1-1-1 Ishibegaoka, Konan, 520-3180, Japan
Tel.: (81) 748 77 3161
Web Site: http://www.jp.nsk.com

Emp.: 759
Ball Bearing Mfr
N.A.I.C.S.: 332991

NSK Ltd. - MAEBASHI PRECISION MACHINERY & PARTS PLANT (1)
78 Toriba-machi, Maebashi, 371-8527, Gunma, Japan
Tel.: (81) 27 251 1511
Automobile Parts Mfr
N.A.I.C.S.: 336390

NSK Ltd. - OHTSU PLANT (1)
1-16-1 Seiran, Otsu, 520-0833, Shiga, Japan
Tel.: (81) 775371600
Web Site: https://www.nsk.com
Emp.: 566
Bearing Parts Mfr
N.A.I.C.S.: 332991

NSK Ltd. - SAITAMA PLANT (1)
1-1 Ohnuma, Hanyu, 348-8506, Saitama, Japan
Tel.: (81) 485651111
Emp.: 814
Bearing Parts Mfr
N.A.I.C.S.: 332991

NSK Machinery Co., Ltd. (1)
5 Showanuma Shobucho, Kuki, 346-0198, Saitama, Japan
Tel.: (81) 480853131
Web Site: https://www.nsk.com
Emp.: 163
Industrial Machinery Mfr
N.A.I.C.S.: 333248

NSK Micro Precision (M) Sdn. Bhd. (1)
No 43 Jalan Taming Dua Taman Taming Jaya, 43300, Balakong, Selangor, Malaysia
Tel.: (60) 389616288
Web Site: http://www.nskmicro.co.jp
Sales Range: $200-249.9 Million
Emp.: 700
Mfr of Bearings
N.A.I.C.S.: 332991

NSK Micro Precision Co., Ltd. (1)
6F Hirose Bldg 3-17 Kanda-nishiki cho, Chiyoda-ku, Tokyo, 101-0054, Japan (51%)
Tel.: (81) 352837420
Web Site: https://www.nskmicro.co.jp
Sales Range: $25-49.9 Million
Emp.: 1,300
Mfr & Sales of Bearings
N.A.I.C.S.: 332991
Kazuo Ishii (Chm)

Plant (Domestic):

NSK Micro Precision Co., Ltd. - Matsukawa Plant (2)
2953 Motoojima Matsukawa-cho, Shimoina-gun, Nagano, 399-3303, Japan
Tel.: (81) 265486022
Web Site: http://www.nskmicro.co.jp
Mechanical Bearing Mfr
N.A.I.C.S.: 332991

NSK NEEDLE BEARING KOREA CO., LTD. (1)
60 Seongsan-Dong, Changwon, 642-315, Kyungsangnam-Do, Korea (South)
Tel.: (82) 55 279 1590
Roller Bearing Mfr
N.A.I.C.S.: 332991

NSK Needle Bearing Ltd. (1)
358 Yawata Machi, Takasaki, 370 0884, Gunma, Japan (100%)
Tel.: (81) 273436431
Web Site: http://www.jp.nsk.com
Sales Range: $400-449.9 Million
Emp.: 1,100
Mfr of Bearings
N.A.I.C.S.: 332991
Tonotsuka Takashi (Pres)

Plant (Domestic):

NSK NEEDLE BEARING LTD. - HARUNA PLANT (2)
941-2 Nakazatomi-machi, Takasaki, 370-3344, Gunma, Japan
Tel.: (81) 27 360 8511
Web Site: http://www.jp.nsk.com
Bearing Parts Mfr

NSK LTD.

NSK Ltd.—(Continued)
N.A.I.C.S.: 332991

NSK NEEDLE BEARING LTD. - TAKASAKI PLANT (2)
358 Yawata-machi, Takasaki, 370-0884, Gunma, Japan
Tel.: (81) 27 343 6431
Web Site: http://www.jp.nsk.com
Sales Range: $150-199.9 Million
Emp.: 600
Bearing Parts Mfr
N.A.I.C.S.: 332991
Takashi Tonotsuka (Pres)

NSK Needle Bearing Poland Sp. z o.o. (1)
UL Jagiellonska 109, 25-734, Kielce, Poland
Tel.: (48) 41 345 2469
Automobile Parts Mfr
N.A.I.C.S.: 336390

NSK Real Estate Co., Ltd. (1)
1 6 3 Ohsaki, Shinagawa Ku, Tokyo, 141 8575, Japan (100%)
Tel.: (81) 337797111
Sales Range: $150-199.9 Million
Emp.: 400
Real Estate Management & Rental
N.A.I.C.S.: 531210
Ken Kajikawa (Mgr-Gen Affairs)

NSK Rodamientos Mexicana, S.A. de C.V. (1)
Circuito Mexiamora Oriente No 331 Parque Industrial Santa Fe I, Puerto Interior, 36275, Silao, Guanajuato, Mexico (100%)
Tel.: (52) 4725009500
Web Site: http://www.mx.nsk.com
Sales Range: $25-49.9 Million
Emp.: 14
Sales of Bearings, Automotive Components, Precision Machinery & Parts
N.A.I.C.S.: 441330

NSK STEERING SYSTEMS DONGGUAN CO., LTD. (1)
High-tech Park Shilong Road Guanlong Section, Dongguan, 523119, Guangdong, China
Tel.: (86) 76922620960
Sales Range: $100-124.9 Million
Emp.: 430
Steering Parts Mfr
N.A.I.C.S.: 336330

NSK Sales Co., Ltd. (1)
163 Ohsaki, Tokyo, 141 8575, Shinagawa Ku, Japan (100%)
Tel.: (81) 334958200
Web Site: http://www.nsksales.com
Sales Range: $50-74.9 Million
Emp.: 250
Sales of Bearing, Automotive Components, Precision Machinery & Parts
N.A.I.C.S.: 332991

NSK Singapore (Private) Ltd. (1)
238A Thomson Road 24 - 01/02 Novena Square Tower A, Singapore, 307684, Singapore (70%)
Tel.: (65) 64968000
Web Site: http://www.nsk-singapore.com.sg
Sales Range: $50-74.9 Million
Emp.: 80
Sales of Bearings, Automotive Parts, Precision Machinery & Parts
N.A.I.C.S.: 441330
Makoto Kizuka (Mng Dir)

NSK South Africa (Pty) Ltd. (1)
25 Galaxy Avenue Linbro Business Park, Sandton, 2146, Gauteng, South Africa (100%)
Tel.: (27) 114583600
Web Site: http://www.nskeurope.com
Sales Range: $25-49.9 Million
Emp.: 25
Sales of Bearings, Automotive Parts, Precision Machinery & Parts
N.A.I.C.S.: 423840

NSK Steering Systems Co., Ltd. (1)
1-8-1 Soja-machi, Maebashi, 371-8528, Gunma, Japan (100%)
Tel.: (81) 272531331
Web Site: http://www.jp.nsk.com
Emp.: 835
Mfr of Automotive Components
N.A.I.C.S.: 336330

Plant (Domestic):

NSK STEERING SYSTEMS CO., LTD. - AKAGI PLANT (2)
1240-1 Idoimachi, Maebashi, 379-2111, Gunma, Japan
Tel.: (81) 27 268 1000
Web Site: http://www.jp.nsk.com
Emp.: 835
Bearing Parts Mfr
N.A.I.C.S.: 332991

NSK STEERING SYSTEMS CO., LTD. - SOJA PLANT (2)
1-8-1 Soja-machi, Maebashi, 371-8528, Gunma, Japan
Tel.: (81) 272531331
Emp.: 1,000
Automobile Parts Mfr
N.A.I.C.S.: 336390

NSK Steering Systems Europe Ltd. (1)
6 Doxford Dr SW Industrial Estate, Peterlee, SR8 2JD, United Kingdom
Tel.: (44) 783 493 3078
Automobile Parts Mfr
N.A.I.C.S.: 336390

NSK Toyama Co., Ltd. (1)
796-1 Toidekasuga, Takaoka, 939-1112, Toyama, Japan
Tel.: (81) 76 663 7132
Web Site: https://www.nsk-toyama.co.jp
Machine Part Mfr
N.A.I.C.S.: 333248

NSK VIETNAM CO., LTD. (1)
Techno Center Room 204-205 Thang Long Industrial Park, Dong Anh District, Hanoi, Vietnam
Tel.: (84) 439550159
Web Site: https://www.nsk.com
Automobile Parts Mfr
N.A.I.C.S.: 336390

NSK-CHUGAI, LTD. (1)
Nissei Building 16F 1-6-3 Osaki, Shinagawa Ku, Tokyo, 141-8608, Japan (45%)
Tel.: (81) 37799522
Web Site: https://www.nsk.com
Sales Range: $50-74.9 Million
Emp.: 147
Insurance Agent; Sales of Electric Parts
N.A.I.C.S.: 524298

NSK-WANDA ELECTRIC POWER ASSISTED STEERING SYSTEMS CO., LTD. (1)
No 1833 Yatai Rd Wenyan Town, Xiaoshan Dist, Hangzhou, 311258, China
Tel.: (86) 571 8231 4818
Automobile Parts Mfr
N.A.I.C.S.: 336390

NSK-Warner (Shanghai) Co., Ltd. (1)
No 2518 Huancheng Road West, Fengxian District, Shanghai, 201401, China
Tel.: (86) 2133655757
Web Site: http://www.nsk-warner.com
Motor Vehicle Transmission Systems Parts Mfr
N.A.I.C.S.: 336350

NSK-Warner Kabushiki Kaisha (1)
2345 Aino, Fukuroi, 437-8545, Shizuoka, Japan
Tel.: (81) 538431121
Web Site: http://www.nsk-warner.com
Sales Range: $200-249.9 Million
Emp.: 988
Motor Vehicle Transmission Systems Parts Mfr; Joint Venture Owned 50% by BorgWarner Inc. & 50% by NSK Limited
N.A.I.C.S.: 336350

NSK-Warner U.S.A., Inc. (1)
3001 W Big Beaver Rd, Troy, MI 48084-3101
Tel.: (248) 822-8888
Sales Range: $25-49.9 Million
Emp.: 40
Sales of Automotive Components; Joint Venture Owned 50% by BorgWarner Inc. & 50% by NSK Ltd.
N.A.I.C.S.: 423120

Michael Madley (Dir-Sls)

Nissei Biru Kanri K.K. (1)
1 6 3 Ohsaki Shinagawa Ku, Tokyo, 141 0032, Japan (100%)
Tel.: (81) 337797488
Sales Range: $50-74.9 Million
Emp.: 7
Management of Nissei Building
N.A.I.C.S.: 531210
Takao Yamamoto (Mgr-Gen Affairs)

Nsk Peru S.A.C.
Calle Teniente Enrique Palacious 360 Oficina 311, Miraflores, Lima, Peru
Tel.: (51) 493 4385
Automobile Parts Mfr
N.A.I.C.S.: 336390

PT. AKS Precision Ball Indonesia (1)
MM2100 Industrial Estate Blok N8-9 Gandamekar, Cikarang Barat, Bekasi, 17520, Indonesia
Tel.: (62) 218 998 2248
Web Site: https://aks-ball.co.id
Emp.: 230
Steel Bar Mfr
N.A.I.C.S.: 331110
Kiyohito Fujimoto (Pres)

PT. NSK BEARINGS MANUFACTURING INDONESIA (1)
Blok M4 Kawasan Berikat MM2100, Industrial Town Cikarang Barat, Bekasi, 17520, Jawa Barat, Indonesia
Tel.: (62) 218980155
Bearing Mfr
N.A.I.C.S.: 332991

Plant (Domestic):

PT. NSK BEARINGS MANUFACTURING INDONESIA - JAKARTA PLANT (2)
Kawasan MM 2100 Blok M 4 Desa Gandamekar, Kecamatan Cikarang Barat, Bekasi, 17520, Indonesia
Tel.: (62) 21 898 0155
Web Site: http://www.jp.nsk.com
Bearing Parts Mfr
N.A.I.C.S.: 332991

PT. NSK INDONESIA (1)
Summitmas II 6th Floor Jl Jend Sudirman Kav 61-62, Jakarta, 12190, Indonesia
Tel.: (62) 218980155
Emp.: 33
Roller Bearing Mfr
N.A.I.C.S.: 332991

Subsidiary (Domestic):

P.T. NSK Precision Ball Indonesia (2)
Blok N-4 Kawasan Berikat Industrial Town Cibitung, Jawa Barat, Bekasi, 20100, Indonesia
Tel.: (62) 218980155
Mfr of Steel Balls
N.A.I.C.S.: 331110

Rane Nastech Limited (1)
Maithri 132 Cathedral Road, Chennai, 600086, India (50%)
Tel.: (91) 4428112472
Web Site: http://www.rane.co.in
Mfr & Sales of Automotive Components
N.A.I.C.S.: 336330
V. Usha (Dir-Bus Dev)

SIAM NSK STEERING SYSTEMS CO., LTD. (1)
90 Moo 9 Wellgrow Industrial Estate Km 36 Bangna-Trad Rd Bangwao, Bangpakong, Chachoengsao, 24180, Thailand
Tel.: (66) 38522343
Web Site: http://www.nsk.com
Emp.: 360
Automobile Parts Distr
N.A.I.C.S.: 423120

SUZHOU NSK BEARINGS CO., LTD. (1)
No 22 Taishan Road, Suzhou New District, Suzhou, 215129, Jiangsu, China
Tel.: (86) 51266655666
Web Site: https://www.nsk.com.cn
Sales Range: $100-124.9 Million
Emp.: 350
Bearing Parts Mfr

INTERNATIONAL PUBLIC

N.A.I.C.S.: 332991
Seiji Kobayashi (Gen Mgr)

Shenyang NSK Co., Ltd. (1)
No 5 15 Street, Shenyang Economic and Technological Development Area, Shenyang, 110141, Liaoning, China
Tel.: (86) 242 532 6080
Automobile Parts Mfr
N.A.I.C.S.: 336390

Shenyang NSK Precision Co., Ltd. (1)
No 7 15 Street, Shenyang Economic & Technological Development Area, Shenyang, 110141, Liaoning, China
Tel.: (86) 242 550 5017
Automobile Parts Mfr
N.A.I.C.S.: 336390

Shinwa Seiko Co., Ltd. (1)
1727 Nippa-cho, Kohoku-ku, Yokohama, 223-0057, Kanagawa, Japan
Tel.: (81) 455422337
Web Site: http://www.shinwa-seiko.co.jp
Sales Range: $25-49.9 Million
Emp.: 45
Processing of Bearing Parts
N.A.I.C.S.: 336350
Masato Ono (Owner)

TAIWAN NSK TECHNOLOGY CO., LTD. (1)
11F No 87 Song Jiang Rd, Jhongshan District, Taipei, 10486, Taiwan
Tel.: (886) 2 2509 3305
Web Site: http://www.jp.nsk.com
Automobile Parts Distr
N.A.I.C.S.: 423120
Sagara Norio (Gen Mgr)

Taiwan NSK Precision Co., Ltd. (1)
10F-A6 No 168 Sec 3 Nanjing East Rd, Zhongshan Dist, Taipei, 104, Taiwan (100%)
Tel.: (886) 227723355
Web Site: http://www.jp.nsk.com
Sales Range: $25-49.9 Million
Emp.: 10
Sales of Precision Machinery & Parts
N.A.I.C.S.: 441330

Zhangjiagang NSK Precision Machinery Co., Ltd. (1)
No 134 Zhenxing Road, Yangshe Town, Zhangjiagang, 215600, Jiangsu, China
Tel.: (86) 51258676496
Web Site: https://www.nsk.com.cn
Emp.: 585
Bearing Parts Mfr
N.A.I.C.S.: 332991

NSV CORPORATION

592-9 Hwajeon-dong, Gangseo-gu, Busan, Korea (South)
Tel.: (82) 51 832 1560
Web Site: http://www.nsvcorporation.com
Year Founded: 1984
Rev.: $14,368,745
Assets: $31,250,812
Liabilities: $17,252,700
Net Worth: $13,998,112
Earnings: ($567,727)
Emp.: 107
Fiscal Year-end: 12/31/16
Valve Mfr
N.A.I.C.S.: 332919
Jeong-Min Kim (Exec Dir)

NSW INC.

31-11 Sakuragaokacho, Shibuya-ku, Tokyo, 150-8577, Japan
Tel.: (81) 337701111   JP
Web Site: https://www.nsw.co.jp
9739—(TKS)
Rev.: $332,476,390
Assets: $291,752,180
Liabilities: $72,472,040
Net Worth: $219,280,140
Earnings: $28,337,070
Emp.: 2,428
Fiscal Year-end: 03/31/24
Software Reproducing Services
N.A.I.C.S.: 334610

AND PRIVATE COMPANIES

Shoji Tada *(Pres)*
Subsidiaries:

Kohwa System Corporation (1)
3398-1 Noborito Taiki Seimei Noborito Building, Tama-ku, Kawasaki, 214-0014, Kanagawa, Japan
Tel.: (81) 44 900 2876
Web Site: https://www.kohwa-system.co.jp
Automation System Services
N.A.I.C.S.: 541511

NSW China Co., Ltd. (1)
C317 3rd Floor Building 2 No 12 Jingan Dongli, Chaoyang District, Beijing, 100028, China
Tel.: (86) 106 409 4320
Web Site: https://www.nsw.co.jp
Information Technology Solutions Services
N.A.I.C.S.: 541519

NSW Techno Service Co., Ltd. (1)
31-10 Sakuragaoka-cho NSW Shibuya CI Building, Shibuya-ku, Tokyo, 150-0031, Japan (100%)
Tel.: (81) 337701063
Web Site: http://www.nswt.co.jp
Emp.: 415
Business Software Distr
N.A.I.C.S.: 541511
Hisato Nakayama *(Pres)*

NSW Technoservices Co., Ltd. (1)
31-10 NSW Shibuya CI Building, Sakuragaoka-cho Shibuya-ku, Tokyo, 150-0031, Japan
Tel.: (81) 33 770 1063
Web Site: https://www.nswt.co.jp
Software Services
N.A.I.C.S.: 541511

Nippon Systemware Co., Ltd. - Product Solution Division (1)
2-15 Nanpeidai-cho, Shibuya-ku, Tokyo, 150-0036, Japan
Tel.: (81) 343352610
Web Site: https://www.nsw.co.jp
Sales Range: $350-399.9 Million
Software Development Services
N.A.I.C.S.: 541511

NSX LIMITED

1 Bligh Street, Sydney, 2000, NSW, Australia
Tel.: (61) 292330100 AU
Web Site: https://www.nsx.com.au
NSX—(ASX)
Rev.: $983,166
Assets: $2,881,358
Liabilities: $3,486,479
Net Worth: ($605,121)
Earnings: ($2,742,703)
Emp.: 12
Fiscal Year-end: 06/30/24
Holding Company; Securities Exchange
N.A.I.C.S.: 551112
Scott Francis Evans *(Sec)*
Subsidiaries:

BSX Services Pty Limited (1)
Level 3 45 Exhibition Street, Melbourne, 3000, VIC, Australia
Tel.: (61) 390010300
Securities Trading Services
N.A.I.C.S.: 523150

NSX Services Pty Limited (1)
Level 2 117 Scott St, PO Box 283, Newcastle, 2300, NSW, Australia
Tel.: (61) 249296377
Web Site: http://www.nsxa.com.au
Sales Range: $50-74.9 Million
Emp.: 10
Securities Trading Services
N.A.I.C.S.: 523150
Scott Evans *(Gen Mgr & Sec)*

National Stock Exchange of Australia Limited (1)
Level 2 117 Scott Street, PO Box 283, Newcastle, 2300, NSW, Australia (100%)
Tel.: (61) 249296377
Web Site: http://www.nsxa.com.au

Sales Range: $50-74.9 Million
Securities Exchange
N.A.I.C.S.: 523210
Scott Francis Evans *(Mng Dir)*

NSYS CO., LTD.

117-10 2 Gongdan 5-Ro Jiksan-Eup, Seobuk-Gu, Cheonan, Chungcheongnam-do, Korea (South)
Tel.: (82) 415687222
Web Site: https://www.n-sys.co.kr
Year Founded: 2002
333620—(KRS)
Rev.: $39,273,663
Assets: $64,222,027
Liabilities: $13,867,006
Net Worth: $50,355,021
Earnings: $4,442,660
Emp.: 129
Fiscal Year-end: 12/31/21
Electric Equipment Mfr
N.A.I.C.S.: 335999
Jin Kee Soo *(CEO)*

NTACO CORPORATION

99 Hung Vuong street Industrial Zone My Quy Ward, Long Xuyen, An Giang, Vietnam
Web Site: http://www.ntacocorp.com.vn
Year Founded: 2000
Sales Range: $10-24.9 Million
Seafood Product Mfr
N.A.I.C.S.: 311710
Nguyen Thanh *(Chm)*

NTC INDUSTRIES LTD.

149 BT Road PO Kamarhati, Kolkata, 700 058, India
Tel.: (91) 7595046807
Web Site: https://www.ntcind.com
Year Founded: 1931
28044—(KOL)
Rev.: $6,622,337
Assets: $13,593,753
Liabilities: $2,942,318
Net Worth: $10,651,436
Earnings: $758,288
Emp.: 64
Fiscal Year-end: 03/31/23
Tobacco Product Mfr
N.A.I.C.S.: 312230
Upmanyu Pathak *(Mng Dir)*
Subsidiaries:

RDB Group (1)
8/1 Lalbazar Street, Kolkata, 700 001, West Bengal, India
Tel.: (91) 3344500500
Web Site: http://www.rdbindia.com
Sales Range: $25-49.9 Million
Emp.: 40
Real Estate Agencies
N.A.I.C.S.: 531210
Sunder Lal Dugar *(Mng Dir)*

Subsidiary (Domestic):

RDB Realty & Infrastructure Limited (2)
8/1 Lalbazar Street, Kolkata, 700 001, India
Tel.: (91) 3344500500
Web Site: https://www.rdbindia.com
Rev.: $17,019,543
Assets: $119,800,300
Liabilities: $98,164,678
Net Worth: $21,635,621
Earnings: $2,023,644
Emp.: 13
Fiscal Year-end: 03/31/2023
Real Estate Management Services
N.A.I.C.S.: 531390
Pradeep Kumar Pugallia *(Exec Dir)*

NTEGRATOR INTERNATIONAL LTD

4 Leng Kee Road 06-04 SIS Building, Singapore, 159088, Singapore
Tel.: (65) 64796033
Web Site: http://www.ntegrator.com

5HC—(SES)
Rev.: $57,716,191
Assets: $60,561,690
Liabilities: $57,251,575
Net Worth: $3,310,115
Earnings: ($4,645,424)
Emp.: 54
Fiscal Year-end: 12/31/22
System Integration Services
N.A.I.C.S.: 541512
Meng Siew Han *(Chm)*
Subsidiaries:

Fiber Reach Pte. Ltd. (1)
4 Leng Kee Road 06-04 Sis Building, Singapore, 159088, Singapore
Tel.: (65) 64796033
Construction Services
N.A.I.C.S.: 236220

Ntegrator (Thailand) Limited (1)
Na Nakorn Building 4th Floor 99 349 Moo 2 Chaengwattana Road, Thungsonghong Laksi, Bangkok, 10210, Thailand
Tel.: (66) 29822173
Web Site: http://www.ntegrator.com
System Integration Services
N.A.I.C.S.: 541512

Ntegrator Pte. Ltd. (1)
4 Leng Kee Road 06-04 SIS Building, Singapore, 159088, Singapore
Tel.: (65) 64796033
System Integration Services
N.A.I.C.S.: 541512

NTELS CO., LTD.

Geumha Bldg 8th Floor Hakdong-ro 401, Gangnam-gu, Seoul, 06069, Korea (South)
Tel.: (82) 232181200
Web Site: https://www.ntels.com
Year Founded: 2000
069410—(KRS)
Rev.: $41,097,641
Assets: $50,759,105
Liabilities: $10,657,560
Net Worth: $40,101,545
Earnings: $88,010
Emp.: 229
Fiscal Year-end: 12/31/22
Software Development Services
N.A.I.C.S.: 541511
Kim Jin Cheol *(Dir)*

NTG CLARITY NETWORKS INC.

2820 Fourteenth Avenue Suite 202, Markham, L3R 0S9, ON, Canada
Tel.: (905) 305-1325
Web Site: https://www.ntgclarity.com
Year Founded: 1992
NCI—(OTCIQ)
Rev.: $6,601,289
Assets: $2,118,290
Liabilities: $11,379,340
Net Worth: ($9,261,050)
Earnings: ($6,743,092)
Emp.: 400
Fiscal Year-end: 12/31/19
Telecommunication Servicesb
N.A.I.C.S.: 517810
Ashraf Zaghloul *(Chm & CEO)*

NTH AG

Waaghaus-Passage 8, CH-3011, Bern, Switzerland
Tel.: (41) 44 581 60 07
Web Site: http://www.nth.ch
Year Founded: 1999
Emp.: 200
Applications & Infrastructure Services
N.A.I.C.S.: 334220
Subsidiaries:

NTH Media d.o.o. (1)
Petrovaradinsk ul 7, 10000, Zagreb, Croatia
Tel.: (385) 42204094
Applications & Infrastructure Services
N.A.I.C.S.: 334220

NTN CORPORATION

NTH Media d.o.o. (1)
Jurija Gargarina 14lj, 11070, Belgrade, Serbia
Tel.: (381) 11 63 00 242
Applications & Infrastructure Services
N.A.I.C.S.: 334220

NTN CORPORATION

Daibiru-Honkan Bldg 3-6-32 Nakanoshima, Kita-Ku, Osaka, 530-0005, Japan
Tel.: (81) 664435001 JP
Web Site: http://www.ntn.co.jp
Year Founded: 1918
6472—(TKS)
Rev.: $5,527,843,850
Assets: $6,016,765,720
Liabilities: $4,160,532,300
Net Worth: $1,856,233,420
Earnings: $69,854,480
Emp.: 22,617
Fiscal Year-end: 03/31/24
Ball & Roller Bearings & Constant Velocity Joints Mfr
N.A.I.C.S.: 332991
Koji Takahashi *(Exec Officer)*
Subsidiaries:

HIKARI SEIKI Industry Co., Ltd. (1)
8 Motohigashi Sanmaidamachi, Tenri, 632-0046, Nara, Japan
Tel.: (81) 743660285
Web Site: https://www.hikariseiki.co.jp
Emp.: 69
Bearing Products Mfr
N.A.I.C.S.: 332991
Kondo Hiromitsu *(Pres)*

NIN Mie Corp. (1)
3601-2 Mizono, Tado-cho, Kuwana, 511-0118, Mie, Japan
Tel.: (81) 59 448 6711
Web Site: https://www.ntn-mie.co.jp
Automotive Parts Mfr & Distr
N.A.I.C.S.: 336390

NTA PRECISION AXLE CORP. (1)
795 Kimberly Dr, Carol Stream, IL 60188
Tel.: (630) 690-6300
Web Site: http://www.ntn.co.jp
Roller Bearing Mfr
N.A.I.C.S.: 332991

NTN (China) Investment Corporation (1)
Building 6 No 1666 Nanle Road, Songjiang Industrial Zone Songjiang District, Shanghai, 201611, China
Tel.: (86) 2157745500
Web Site: https://www.ntn.com.cn
Holding Company
N.A.I.C.S.: 551112

Affiliate (Domestic):

Beijing NTN-Seohan Driveshaft Co., Ltd. (2)
No 3 Zhengfu Rd, Opto-Mechatronics Indus Park, Beijing, 101111, China
Tel.: (86) 1069507324
Constant Velocity Joint Mfr
N.A.I.C.S.: 336390

Changzhou NTN-Guangyang Corp. (2)
52 Hanjiang Road New District, Changzhou, 213022, Jiangsu, China
Tel.: (86) 519 5158888
Web Site: http://www.ntn.co.jp
Sales Range: $25-49.9 Million
Emp.: 51
Automotive Products Mfr
N.A.I.C.S.: 336390

Joint Venture (Domestic):

Guangzhou NTN-Yulon Drivetrain Co., Ltd. (2)
No 11 Jun Da Road, East District of Guangzhou Economic and Technological Development Zone, Guangzhou, 510530, Guangdong, China
Tel.: (86) 2082266458
Web Site: http://www.ntn.com.cn
Constant Velocity Joint Mfr
N.A.I.C.S.: 336390

NTN CORPORATION

NTN Corporation—(Continued)

Subsidiary (Non-US):

NTN China Limited (2)
Room 2003-2005 Gala Place 56 Dundas Street, Mongkok, Kowloon, China (Hong Kong)
Tel.: (852) 23855097
Web Site: https://www.ntnchina.com
Bearing Products Sales
N.A.I.C.S.: 423840
Joynie Wong (Mng Dir)

Affiliate (Domestic):

Shanghai NTN Corp. (2)
No 666 Nanle Road Songjiang Industrial Zone, Songjiang, Shanghai, 201611, China
Tel.: (86) 2157744666
Automotive Components Mfr
N.A.I.C.S.: 336390

Joint Venture (Non-US):

Taiway Industry Co., Ltd. (2)
No 14 Kwang Fu Rd, Hukou, 303, Hsian-chu, Taiwan
Tel.: (886) 35983601
Web Site: http://www.roc-spicer.com.tw
Automotive Front-wheel Drive Shaft, Hub Bearings & Other Precision Mechanical Parts & Components Mfr
N.A.I.C.S.: 336390

Affiliate (Non-US):

Tung Pei Industrial Co., Ltd. (2)
10th Fl No 142 Chung Hsiao E Rd Sec 4, Taipei, 106, Taiwan
Tel.: (886) 227417321
Web Site: https://tungpei.en.taiwantrade.com
Sales Range: $350-399.9 Million
Emp.: 1,157
Bearing Products Mfr
N.A.I.C.S.: 332991

Affiliate (Non-US):

Shanghai Tung Pei Enterprise Co., Ltd. (3)
No 1555 Rongle Road E, Songjiang Industrial Zone, Shanghai, 201613, China
Tel.: (86) 2157744698
Web Site: http://www.ntn.co.jp
Bearing Products Mfr
N.A.I.C.S.: 332991

NTN Akaiwa Corp. (1)
100-43 Tsurui, Akaiwa, 709-0718, Okayama, Japan
Tel.: (81) 86 995 9541
Automobile Parts Mfr
N.A.I.C.S.: 336390

NTN Antriebstechnik GmbH (1)
Buschstuckenstrasse 6, 39638, Gardelegen, Germany
Tel.: (49) 3 907 7770
Web Site: https://www.ntn-at.de
Emp.: 185
Auto Parts Mfr
N.A.I.C.S.: 336390

NTN Bearing Corp. of Canada Ltd. (1)
305 Courtneypark Drive West, Mississauga, L5W 1Y4, ON, Canada
Tel.: (905) 564-2700
Web Site: http://www.ntn.ca
Sales Range: $25-49.9 Million
Emp.: 60
Bearing Products Mfr
N.A.I.C.S.: 332991

Division (Domestic):

NTN Bearing Mfg. Canada (2)
6740 Kitimat Road, Mississauga, L5N 1M6, ON, Canada
Tel.: (905) 826-5500
Web Site: http://www.ntn.ca
Sales Range: $25-49.9 Million
Emp.: 130
Bearing Products Mfr
N.A.I.C.S.: 332991

NTN Bearing India Private Ltd. (1)
Polyhose Towers SPIC Annexe No 86 Mount Road, Guindy, Chennai, 600032, India
Tel.: (91) 446 686 7700
Web Site: https://www.ntnbearing.in
Auto Parts Mfr
N.A.I.C.S.: 336390

NTN Bearing Service Corporation (1)
3-1-3 Shiba-kouen, Minato-Ku, Tokyo, 105-0011, Japan
Tel.: (81) 357766003
Web Site: http://www.ntn-bs.co.jp
Rev: $74,800,000
Emp.: 73
Roller Bearing & Other Precision Equipments Mfr
N.A.I.C.S.: 332991
Araki Toshihiko (Pres & CEO)

NTN Bearing-Malaysia Sdn. Bhd. (1)
No 2 Jalan Arkitek U 1/22 Section U1, Hicom Glenmarie Industrial Park, 40150, Shah Alam, Selangor Darul Ehsan, Malaysia
Tel.: (60) 355696088
Web Site: http://www.ntn.co.jp
Sales Range: $25-49.9 Million
Emp.: 60
Bearing Products Sales
N.A.I.C.S.: 423840

NTN Bearing-Singapore (Pte). Ltd. (1)
9 Clementi Loop, Singapore, 12981, Singapore
Tel.: (65) 64698066
Web Site: https://www.ntn.com.sg
Sales Range: $75-99.9 Million
Emp.: 62
Bearing Products Sales
N.A.I.C.S.: 423840

NTN Bearing-Thailand Co., Ltd. (1)
29th Floor Panjathani Tower 127/34 Nonsee Road Chongnonsee, Yannawa, Bangkok, 10120, Thailand
Tel.: (66) 26810401
Web Site: http://www.ntn.co.th
Sales Range: $50-74.9 Million
Emp.: 70
Bearing Products Sales
N.A.I.C.S.: 423840

NTN Bearings (UK) Ltd. (1)
Wellington Crescent Fradley Park, Lichfield, WS13 8RZ, Staffordshire, United Kingdom
Tel.: (44) 1543445000
Web Site: http://www.ntn-snr.com
Sales Range: $50-74.9 Million
Emp.: 60
Bearing Products Sales
N.A.I.C.S.: 423840

NTN Bizen Corp. (1)
2139-2 Yamaguchi, Akaiwa, 701-2225, Okayama, Japan
Tel.: (81) 869573101
Web Site: http://www.ntnglobal.com
Bearing Products Mfr
N.A.I.C.S.: 332991

NTN Casting Corp. (1)
475-1 Nadabucho, Izumo, 691-0003, Shimane, Japan
Tel.: (81) 853633108
Web Site: https://www.ntn-casting.co.jp
Emp.: 173
Bearing Products Mfr
N.A.I.C.S.: 332991

NTN Driveshaft Anderson, Inc. (1)
7625 Layton Rd, Anderson, IN 46011
Tel.: (765) 635-2500
Roller Bearing Mfr
N.A.I.C.S.: 332991

NTN Driveshaft do Brasil (1)
Estrada Municipal 400 Bairro Jardim Santo Afonso, Sao Paulo, 07215-040, Brazil
Tel.: (55) 1120855000
Web Site: http://www.ntn.com.br
Sales Range: $25-49.9 Million
Emp.: 230
Automobile Drive Shaft Mfr
N.A.I.C.S.: 336350
Hiroshi Fuhee (Pres)

NTN Engineering Plastics Corp. (1)
970 Ano Toin-cho, Inabe-gun, Mie, 511-0243, Japan
Tel.: (81) 594767221
Web Site: http://www.ntn-epc.com
Sales Range: $50-74.9 Million
Emp.: 190
Bearing Products Mfr
N.A.I.C.S.: 332991
Tetsuji Goto (Pres)

NTN FUKUROI CORP. (1)
1959 Midori, Fukuroi-shi, Shizuoka, 437-0005, Japan
Tel.: (81) 538301800
Roller Bearing Mfr
N.A.I.C.S.: 332991

NTN France S.A. (1)
ZI Sabliere, BP 338, Schweighouse sur Moder, 67507, Haguenau, Cedex, France
Tel.: (33) 388532222
Web Site: http://www.ntn-snr.com
Sales Range: $25-49.9 Million
Emp.: 50
Bearing Products Sales
N.A.I.C.S.: 423840
Konath Gainpheleppa (Mgr)

NTN HOUDATSUSHIMIZU CORP. (1)
1-1 Futakuchiho Houdatsushimizu-cho, Hakui-gun, Ishikawa, 929-1421, Japan
Tel.: (81) 767225111
Web Site: https://ntn-houdatsushimizu.jp
Emp.: 64
Ball Bearing Mfr
N.A.I.C.S.: 332991

NTN KUGELLAGERFABRIK (DEUTSCHLAND) G.m.b.H. (1)
NTN Strasse 1-3, 40822, Mettmann, Germany
Tel.: (49) 210414090
Sales Range: $50-74.9 Million
Emp.: 20
Bearing Mfr
N.A.I.C.S.: 332991
Takahashi Fujee (Gen Mgr)

NTN Kamiina Corp. (1)
522-2 Nakazone Minowa-machi, Kamiina-gun, Nagano, 399-4605, Japan
Tel.: (81) 265797877
Web Site: http://www.ntnglobal.com
Sales Range: $100-124.9 Million
Emp.: 260
Bearing Products Mfr
N.A.I.C.S.: 332991

NTN Kamina Corp. (1)
522-2 Nakazone Minowa-machi, Kamiina-gun, Nagano, 399-4605, Japan
Tel.: (81) 26 579 7877
Automobile Parts Mfr
N.A.I.C.S.: 336390

NTN Kinan Corp. (1)
2504-1 Ikuma Kamitonda-chou, Nishimuro-gun, Wakayama, 649-2103, Japan
Tel.: (81) 739471801
Web Site: https://www.ntn-kinan.com
Sales Range: $50-74.9 Million
Emp.: 230
Bearing Products Mfr
N.A.I.C.S.: 332991

NTN Kongo Corporation (1)
1-3-13 Kidonishi-machi, Kawachi, Nagano, 586-0009, Osaka, Japan
Tel.: (81) 721531317
Web Site: http://www.ntn-kongo.co.jp
Sales Range: $100-124.9 Million
Emp.: 452
Bearing Products Mfr
N.A.I.C.S.: 332991
Yamanata Kaguhiko (Pres)

NTN Korea Co., Ltd. (1)
10th Fl 124 Sejong-Daero, Jung-Gu, Seoul, 04520, Korea (South)
Tel.: (82) 27203666
Web Site: http://www.ntnkorea.co.kr
Sales Range: $25-49.9 Million
Emp.: 23
Bearing Products Sales
N.A.I.C.S.: 423840
Takaishi Shinya (CEO)

NTN Logistics Co., Ltd. (1)
1092-1 Maeda Higashiyurlage, Kuwana, 511-0806, Mie, Japan
Tel.: (81) 59 424 3516
Automobile Parts Mfr
N.A.I.C.S.: 336390

NTN Manufacturing (Thailand) Co., Ltd. (1)
111/2 Moo 4 Tambol Pluakdaeng, Amphur Pluakdaeng, Rayong, 21140, Thailand
Tel.: (66) 38955185
Web Site: http://www.ntn.co.jp
Bearing Products Mfr
N.A.I.C.S.: 332991

NTN Manufacturing de Mexico, S.A. de C.V. (1)
Circuito Progreso 120, Parque Industrial de Logistica Automotriz, 20340, Aguascalientes, Mexico
Tel.: (52) 449 922 6200
Roller Bearing Mfr
N.A.I.C.S.: 332991

NTN Mettmann (Deutschland) GmbH (1)
NTN Strasse 1-3, 40822, Mettmann, Germany
Tel.: (49) 21 041 4090
Automobile Parts Mfr
N.A.I.C.S.: 336390

NTN Mie Corp. (1)
3601-25 Miino Tado-cho, Kuwana, 511-0118, Mie, Japan
Tel.: (81) 594486711
Web Site: https://www.ntn-mie.com
Sales Range: $200-249.9 Million
Emp.: 700
Bearing Products Mfr
N.A.I.C.S.: 332991

NTN Mikumo Company Ltd. (1)
750-1 Onoe Matusaka-shi, Mie, 515-2109, Japan
Tel.: (81) 598563311
Web Site: http://www.ntn.co.jp
Sales Range: $50-74.9 Million
Emp.: 125
Bearing Products Mfr
N.A.I.C.S.: 332991

NTN NEI Manufacturing India Pvt. Ltd. (1)
Plot No 131 Sector 7 HSIIDC IMT, BAWAL Distt, Rewari, 123 501, Haryana, India
Tel.: (91) 1284264191
Web Site: http://www.ntn.co.jp
Bearing Products Mfr
N.A.I.C.S.: 332991

Plant (Domestic):

NTN NEI Manufacturing India Private LTD. - Chennai Plant (2)
Plot P48/1 8th Avenue DTA Mahindra World City, Chengalpattu Taluk Kancheepuram District, Chennai, 603 004, Tamil Nadu, India
Tel.: (91) 4437483600
Web Site: http://www.ntn.co.jp
Automotive Bearing Mfr
N.A.I.C.S.: 332991

NTN Net Manufacturing India Private Ltd. (1)
Plot No 131 Sector 7 Hssidc Imt Bawal, Distt, Rewari, 123501, India
Tel.: (91) 128 426 4191
Automotive Parts Mfr & Distr
N.A.I.C.S.: 336390

NTN Noto Corp. (1)
Wakabadai 38, Shika Hakui-gun, Ishikawa, 925-0375, Japan
Tel.: (81) 76 738 8020
Web Site: https://ntn-noto.jp
Roller Bearing Mfr
N.A.I.C.S.: 332991

NTN Omaezaki Corp. (1)
4681-3 Sakura, Omaezaki, 437-1604, Shizuoka, Japan
Tel.: (81) 537862480
Web Site: http://www.ntn.co.jp
Sales Range: $50-74.9 Million
Emp.: 170
Bearing Products Mfr
N.A.I.C.S.: 332991

NTN Powder Metal Corp. (1)
101 Katsutaba Kanie-cho Ama-gun, Na-

AND PRIVATE COMPANIES — NTN CORPORATION

goya, 497-8541, Japan
Tel.: (81) 567953913
Web Site: http://www.ntn-goukin.com
Sales Range: $50-74.9 Million
Emp.: 148
Production & Sales of Sintered Products Using Metal Powder
N.A.I.C.S.: 332117

NTN Sales Japan Corp. (1)
2-16-2 Konan Taiyo Life Shinagawa Building 24th Floor, Minato- ku, Tokyo, 108-0075, Japan
Tel.: (81) 35 780 7903
Web Site: https://www.ntn-sj.co.jp
Steel Bar Mfr
N.A.I.C.S.: 331110

NTN Sudamericana, S.A. (1)
World Trade Center Panama Piso 16 Oficina 1601 Urbanizacion Marbella, Calle 53 Este Apartado, 0832-0487, Panama, Panama
Tel.: (507) 2694777
Web Site: http://www.ntnsudamericana.com
Sales Range: $25-49.9 Million
Emp.: 44
Bearing Products Mfr
N.A.I.C.S.: 332991
Kensaku Hata *(Pres)*

Subsidiary (Non-US):

NTN do Brasil Ltda. (2)
Av Moema 94-9 Andar-conj 92a94, Indianopolis, 04077-020, Sao Paulo, Brazil
Tel.: (55) 1150510600
Web Site: http://www.ntn.com.br
Sales Range: $25-49.9 Million
Emp.: 9
Bearing Products Sales
N.A.I.C.S.: 423840

NTN Tado Corp. (1)
1077 Yui Tado-cho, Kuwana, 511-0101, Mie, Japan
Tel.: (81) 594482383
Web Site: https://www.ntn-tado.com
Sales Range: $25-49.9 Million
Emp.: 100
Bearing Products Mfr
N.A.I.C.S.: 332991

NTN Technical Service Corp. (1)
Daibiru Main Building 3-6-32 Nakanoshima, Kita, Osaka, 530-0005, Japan
Tel.: (81) 664495461
Web Site: https://www.ntn-ts.co.jp
Sales Range: $200-249.9 Million
Emp.: 654
Welfare Facility Management, Insurance Agency Services & Technical Support Services
N.A.I.C.S.: 524298

NTN Transmissions Europe (1)
Z A des Tremelieres Communaute Urbaine du Mans, 72704, Allonnes, Cedex, France
Tel.: (33) 243839000
Web Site: http://www.ntn.co.jp
Sales Range: $200-249.9 Million
Emp.: 534
Automotive Transmission Mfr
N.A.I.C.S.: 336350

NTN Transmissions Europe Crezancy S.A.S. (1)
ZA des Tremelieres Communaute Urbaine du Mans, 72704, Allonnes, Cedex, France
Tel.: (33) 24 383 9000
Roller Bearing Mfr
N.A.I.C.S.: 332991

NTN USA Corporation (1)
1600 E Bishop Ct, Mount Prospect, IL 60056-7604
Tel.: (847) 298-7500
Web Site: http://www.ntnamerica.com
Bearing Products Mfr
N.A.I.C.S.: 332991
Tetsuya Sogo *(Pres)*

Subsidiary (Domestic):

American NTN Bearing Mfg. Corp. (2)
9515 Winona Ave, Schiller Park, IL 60176
Tel.: (847) 671-5450
Sales Range: $25-49.9 Million
Emp.: 30
Bearing Products Mfr

N.A.I.C.S.: 332991
Marty Fukuda *(Plant Mgr)*

Affiliate (Domestic):

Asahi Forge of America Corp. (2)
5030 Corporate Way, Richmond, KY 40475
Tel.: (859) 626-4100
Web Site: http://www.asahiforge.co.jp
Sales Range: $25-49.9 Million
Emp.: 50
Forged Parts Mfr
N.A.I.C.S.: 332111

NTK Precision Axle Corp. (2)
741 S County Rd 200 W, Frankfort, IN 46041
Tel.: (765) 656-1000
Web Site: https://www.ntkaxle.com
Sales Range: $10-24.9 Million
Emp.: 200
Joints, Shafts & Hub Bearings Mfr
N.A.I.C.S.: 332991
Hirofumi Tsuji *(Pres)*

Subsidiary (Domestic):

NTN-Bower Corp. (2)
711 N Bower Rd, Macomb, IL 61455-2511
Tel.: (309) 837-0440
Web Site: http://www.ntnbower.com
Sales Range: $150-199.9 Million
Emp.: 700
Bearing Products Mfr
N.A.I.C.S.: 332991
Kunio Kamo *(Pres)*

Subsidiary (Domestic):

NTN Bearing Corporation of America (3)
1600 E Bishop Ct, Mount Prospect, IL 60056-7604
Tel.: (847) 298-7500
Web Site: http://www.ntnamerica.com
Emp.: 175
Bearing Products Sales
N.A.I.C.S.: 423840
Pete Eich *(Pres)*

Plant (Domestic):

NTN BEARING CORP OF AMERICA-Schiller Park Plant (4)
9515 Winona Ave, Schiller Park, IL 60176
Tel.: (847) 671-5450
Web Site: http://www.ntn.co.jp
Sales Range: $10-24.9 Million
Emp.: 35
Roller Bearing Mfr
N.A.I.C.S.: 332991

NTN BEARING CORP.OF AMERICA-Elgin Plant (4)
1500 Holmes Rd, Elgin, IL 60123
Tel.: (847) 741-4545
Web Site: http://www.ntn.co.jp
Bearing Mfr
N.A.I.C.S.: 332991

Subsidiary (Domestic):

NTN Driveshaft, Inc. (3)
8251 S International Dr, Columbus, IN 47201
Tel.: (812) 342-7000
Web Site: http://www.ntndriveshaft.com
Sales Range: $50-74.9 Million
Bearing Products Mfr
N.A.I.C.S.: 332991

NTN-BCA Corp. (3)
1600 Bishop Ct, Mount Prospect, IL 60056-6033
Tel.: (717) 627-3623
Web Site: http://www.ntnamerica.com
Sales Range: $50-74.9 Million
Emp.: 400
Bearing Products Mfr
N.A.I.C.S.: 332991

Plant (Domestic):

NTN-Bower Corp-Hamilton Plant (3)
2086 Military St S, Hamilton, AL 35570
Tel.: (205) 921-2173
Web Site: http://www.ntnamerica.com
Constant Velocity Joint Mfr
N.A.I.C.S.: 336350

NTN-Bower Corp-Macomb Plant (3)
711 N Bower Rd, Macomb, IL 61455-2511
Tel.: (309) 833-4541
Web Site: http://www.ntnamerica.com
Constant Velocity Joint Mfr
N.A.I.C.S.: 336350

NTN Walzlager (Europa) GmbH (1)
Max-Planck-Str 23, 40699, Erkrath, Germany
Tel.: (49) 21125080
Web Site: http://www.ntn-snr.com
Sales Range: $75-99.9 Million
Emp.: 150
Bearing Products Sales
N.A.I.C.S.: 423840

NTN de Mexico, S.A. (1)
Calle Emilio Cardenas No 158 Fracc Industrial, San Nicolas, 54030, Tlalnepantla, Mexico
Tel.: (52) 5555655562
Web Site: http://www.ntn.com
Sales Range: $25-49.9 Million
Emp.: 50
Bearing Products Mfr
N.A.I.C.S.: 332991
Enrique Jaime Alexanderson Conde *(Pres)*

Division (Domestic):

NTN de Mexico, S.A. (2)
Emilio cardenas No 158 Apdo 124, 54030, Tlalnepantla, Edo de Mexico, Mexico
Tel.: (52) 3331451490
Web Site: http://www.ntnamericas.com
Bearing Products Mfr
N.A.I.C.S.: 332991

NTN do Brasil Producao de Semi-Eixos Ltda. (1)
Av das Industrias 380 Eucaliptos Fazenda, Rio Grande, 83820-332, Brazil
Tel.: (55) 413 627 8000
Web Site: https://www.ntn.com.br
Bearing Mfr
N.A.I.C.S.: 332991

NTN-CBC (Australia) Pty. Ltd. (1)
18 Worth Street, Chullora, 2190, NSW, Australia
Tel.: (61) 299479200
Web Site: http://www.conbear.com.au
Sales Range: $75-99.9 Million
Emp.: 500
Bearing Products Sales
N.A.I.C.S.: 423840

NTN-LYC (Luoyang) Precision Bearing Corporation (1)
No 1 Zhangheng Street Luolong Science & Technology Park, Luolong, Luoyang, 471023, Henan, China
Tel.: (86) 37964989602
Web Site: http://www.ntnlyc.com
Roller Bearing Mfr
N.A.I.C.S.: 332991

NTN-RAB (Changzhou) Corp (1)
31 ShengLi Road, ChunJiang Town XinBei District, Changzhou, 213034, Jiangsu, China
Tel.: (86) 51968195888
Web Site: http://www.ntn.com.cn
Roller Bearing Mfr & Distr
N.A.I.C.S.: 332991

NTN-SNR Iberica S.A. (1)
C/ Basauri 17 Edificio-A Planta Baja Drcha, 28023, Madrid, Spain
Tel.: (34) 916718913
Web Site: http://www.ntn-snr.com
Sales Range: $25-49.9 Million
Emp.: 15
Ball Bearing Mfr
N.A.I.C.S.: 332991

NTN-SNR Maroc S.A (1)
Espace Paquet Angle Bvd Smiha et Rue Pierre Parent 6 ieme E, Etage Bureau N 603, 20110, Casablanca, Morocco
Tel.: (212) 522667680
Web Site: http://www.ntn-snr.com
Sales Range: $25-49.9 Million
Emp.: 5
Ball Bearing Mfr
N.A.I.C.S.: 332991
Rachid Dannoun *(Gen Mgr)*

NTN-SNR ROULEMENTS SA (1)
1 rue des Usines, BP 2017, 74010, Annecy, France

Tel.: (33) 450653000
Web Site: http://www.ntn-snr.com
Ball Bearing Mfr
N.A.I.C.S.: 332991

NTN-SNR RULMENTI S.R.L (1)
6 Strada Salzburg, Zona Industriala-Vest, 550018, Sibiu, Romania
Tel.: (40) 269203500
Web Site: http://www.ntn-snr.com
Sales Range: $200-249.9 Million
Emp.: 600
Ball Bearing Mfr
N.A.I.C.S.: 332991

NTPT Co., Ltd. (1)
789/171 Moo1 Tambon, Nongkham Amphur Sriracha, Chon Buri, 20230, Thailand
Tel.: (66) 3 834 8580
Automotive Parts Mfr & Distr
N.A.I.C.S.: 336390

Nanjinh NTN Corp. (1)
No 1 Yangjiabian Road, Nanjing Economic and Technological Development Zone, Nanjing, 210033, Jiangsu, China
Tel.: (86) 258 528 5000
Automobile Parts Mfr
N.A.I.C.S.: 336390

PT. NTN Bearing Indonesia (1)
Midplaza 1 7th Floor Jl Jend Sudirman Kav 10-11, Jakarta, 10220, Indonesia
Tel.: (62) 21 570 7676
Web Site: https://ntnbearing.co.id
Auto Parts Mfr
N.A.I.C.S.: 336390

SNR Argentina S.A (1)
Viamonte 1145-Piso, 11-1053, Buenos Aires, Argentina
Tel.: (54) 1143721272
Web Site: http://www.ntn-snr.com
Sales Range: $25-49.9 Million
Emp.: 14
Ball Bearing Mfr
N.A.I.C.S.: 332991

SNR Italia Spa (1)
Via Ricardo Lombardi 19/4, 20153, Milan, Italy
Tel.: (39) 024799861
Bearing Mfr
N.A.I.C.S.: 332991

SNR ROULEMENTS SA (1)
Przedstawicielstwo w Polsce Ul Rafii 22, 04 241, Warsaw, Poland
Tel.: (48) 227402985
Web Site: http://www.ntn-snr.com
Sales Range: $25-49.9 Million
Emp.: 6
Ball Bearing Mfr
N.A.I.C.S.: 332991

SNR Waelzlager GmbH (1)
Max-Planck-Strasse 23, 40699, Erkrath, Germany
Tel.: (49) 21125080
Web Site: http://www.ntn-snr.com
Sales Range: $25-49.9 Million
Emp.: 150
Metal Screws Mfr
N.A.I.C.S.: 332722

SNR Walzlager GmbH (1)
Friedrich-Hagemann-Strasse 66, 33719, Bielefeld, Germany
Tel.: (49) 521924000
Sales Range: $25-49.9 Million
Emp.: 100
Ball Bearing Mfr
N.A.I.C.S.: 332991
Friedel Morsch *(Mgr-Sls)*

Seohan-NTN Driveshaft USA Corp (1)
264 Teague Ct, Auburn, AL 36832
Tel.: (334) 321-3200
Web Site: http://www.ntn.co.jp
Roller Bearing Mfr
N.A.I.C.S.: 332991

Shangai NTN Corp. (1)
No 1666 Nanle Road, Songjiang Industrial Zone Songjiang, Shanghai, 201611, China
Tel.: (86) 215 774 8666
Automotive Parts Mfr & Distr
N.A.I.C.S.: 336390

Unidrive Pty. Ltd. (1)

NTN CORPORATION

NTN Corporation—(Continued)
45 49 McNaughton Rd, Clayton, 3168, VIC, Australia
Tel.: (61) 395424100
Sales Range: $100-124.9 Million
Emp.: 120
Automotive Transmission Product Mfr; Owned 60% by GKN plc & 40% by NTN Corporation
N.A.I.C.S.: 336350

Xiangyang NTN-Yulon Drivetrain Co., Ltd. (1)
No 36 Shenzhen Ave, Shenzhen Industrial Park Hi-tech Development Zone, Xiangyang, 441000, Hubei, China
Tel.: (86) 710 282 8836
Automotive Parts Mfr & Distr
N.A.I.C.S.: 336390

NTPC LIMITED
NTPC Bhawan SCOPE Complex Institutional Area Lodhi Road, New Delhi, 110003, Delhi, India
Tel.: (91) 1124360100   In
Year Founded: 1975
NTPC—(BOM)
Rev.: $15,772,142,295
Assets: $54,458,887,665
Liabilities: $36,814,600,095
Net Worth: $17,644,287,570
Earnings: $2,043,323,100
Emp.: 21,941
Fiscal Year-end: 03/31/21
Electricity Distribution Services
N.A.I.C.S.: 221112
Vinod Choudhary *(Exec Dir-PP & M)*

Subsidiaries:

Jhabua Power Limited (1)
Village - Barela PO- Attaria Tahsil - Ghansore, Seoni, 480997, Madhya Pradesh, India
Tel.: (91) 7693 298223
Thermal Power Generation Services
N.A.I.C.S.: 221116

Kanti Bijlee Utpadan Nigam Ltd. (1)
Kanti Thermal, Distt - Muzaffarpur, Bihar, 843130, India
Tel.: (91) 622 326 7519
Web Site: https://www.kbunl.co.in
Thermal Power Services
N.A.I.C.S.: 221116
V. Ramesh Babu *(Chm)*

NTPC Electric Supply Company Ltd. (1)
2nd Fl R&D Building A-8A Sector 24, Noida, 201301, India
Tel.: (91) 01202410333
Electric Power Supplier
N.A.I.C.S.: 221122

NTPC GE Power Services Private Limited (1)
6th Floor Tower-B Indian Glycols Limited Building Plot No2B, Near Lotus Valley School Sector 126, Noida, 201304, Uttar Pradesh, India
Tel.: (91) 1206937700
Web Site: https://ngsl.co.in
Electric Power Distr
N.A.I.C.S.: 221122
Anand Mohan Awasthy *(Mng Dir)*

NTPC SAIL Power Company Pvt. Ltd (1)
4th Fl NBCC Tower 15 Bhikaiji Cama Place, Bikaji Kama Place, New Delhi, 110 066, India
Tel.: (91) 112 671 7379
Web Site: https://www.nspcl.co.in
Sales Range: $5-14.9 Billion
Emp.: 120
Electric Power Supply; Owned 50% by National Thermal Power Corp. Ltd & 50% by Steel Authority of India Limited
N.A.I.C.S.: 221122
Saptarshi Roy *(Chm)*

NTPC Vidyut Vyapar Nigam Limited (1)
2nd Floor Core-5 SCOPE Complex 7 Lodhi Rd Institutional Area, New Delhi, 110003, India
Tel.: (91) 1124387741
Web Site: http://www.nvvn.co.in
Emp.: 60
Eletric Power Generation Services
N.A.I.C.S.: 221113

THDC India Ltd. (1)
Rishikesh Pragatipuram By Pass Road, Rishikesh, 249201, Uttarkhand, India
Tel.: (91) 135 243 9450
Web Site: https://www.thdc.co.in
Eletric Power Generation Services
N.A.I.C.S.: 221118
R. K. Vishnol *(Mng Dir & Chm)*

TUSCO Limited (1)
4th Floor UP Neda Building Vibhuti Khand Gomti Nagar, Lucknow, 226010, Uttar Pradesh, India
Tel.: (91) 5223515962
Web Site: https://www.tuscoltd.co.in
Solar & Wind Power Structure Installation Services
N.A.I.C.S.: 238220

NTPM HOLDINGS BERHAD
No 886 Jalan Bandar Baru Sungai Kecil, Nibong Tebal SPS, 14300, Penang, Malaysia
Tel.: (60) 45931296
Web Site: https://www.ntpm.com.my
NTPM—(KLS)
Rev.: $183,764,852
Assets: $228,909,522
Liabilities: $120,894,669
Net Worth: $108,014,853
Earnings: ($1,244,743)
Emp.: 3,640
Fiscal Year-end: 04/30/23
Paper Mfr
N.A.I.C.S.: 322120
Sook Fun Thum *(Co-Sec)*

Subsidiaries:

NTPM (Singapore) Pte. Ltd. (1)
1783 Geylang Bahru 01-01 Kallang Distripark, Singapore, 339708, Singapore
Tel.: (65) 62930811
Web Site: http://www.ntpm.com
Emp.: 30
Tissue Paper Import & Distr
N.A.I.C.S.: 424130
Philip Hai Foo Say *(Mng Dir)*

Nibong Tebal Enterprise Sendirian Berhad (1)
Lot 7278 Jalan Perusahan 3 Kawasan Perindustrian, 34200, Parit Buntar, Perak, Malaysia
Tel.: (60) 57160333
Tissue Paper Product Mfr
N.A.I.C.S.: 322291

Nibong Tebal Paper Mill Sdn. Bhd. (1)
No 886 Jalan Bandar Baru Jalan Sungai Kechil, 14300, Nibong Tebal, Penang, Malaysia
Tel.: (60) 45931296
Web Site: https://www.ntpm.com.my
Paper Products Mfr & Distr
N.A.I.C.S.: 322299

Nibong Tebal Technology Sdn. Bhd. (1)
No 886 Jalan Bandar Baru SPS, Sungai Kecil, 14300, Nibong Tebal, Malaysia
Tel.: (60) 45931296
Web Site: https://www.en.china.cn
Emp.: 1,000
Consumer Product Mfr
N.A.I.C.S.: 322291

NTR HOLDING A/S
Bredgade 30, DK-1260, Copenhagen, Denmark
Tel.: (45) 70251056
Web Site: https://www.ntr.dk
NTR.B—(OMX)
Rev.: $12,495,799
Assets: $25,107,147
Liabilities: $3,416,949
Net Worth: $21,690,198
Earnings: $1,155,490
Emp.: 56
Fiscal Year-end: 12/31/20
Holding Company
N.A.I.C.S.: 551112
Niels T. Heering *(Chm)*

NTR PLC
Burton Court Burton Hall Drive, Sandyford, Dublin, D18 Y2T8, Ireland
Tel.: (353) 1 206 3700   IE
Web Site: http://www.ntrplc.com
Year Founded: 1978
Renewable Energy & Sustainable Waste Management Investments
N.A.I.C.S.: 523999
Rosheen McGuckian *(CEO)*

Subsidiaries:

Wind Capital Group, LLC (1)
1310 Papin St Ste 107, Saint Louis, MO 63103
Tel.: (314) 685-3000
Web Site: http://www.windcapitalgroup.com
Sales Range: $10-24.9 Million
Emp.: 4
Wind Power Turbine Construction, Operation & Investment
N.A.I.C.S.: 237130
Casandra Carney *(CFO)*

NTS GROUP
Dillenburgstraat 9, PO Box 7093, Eindhoven, 5652 AM Eindhov, Netherlands
Tel.: (31) 40 259 7200
Web Site: http://www.nts-group.nl
Year Founded: 2005
Sales Range: $125-149.9 Million
Emp.: 700
Develops, Manufactures & Optimizes Opto-Mechatronic Systems, Modules & Components for International Machine Builders
N.A.I.C.S.: 334419
Marc Hendrikse *(CEO)*

Subsidiaries:

NTS Botech (1)
Korte Dijk 2, 5705 CV, Helmond, Netherlands
Tel.: (31) 492 551875
Web Site: http://www.nts-group.nl
Sales Range: $25-49.9 Million
Emp.: 33
Precision Machine Components & Assemblies Mfr
N.A.I.C.S.: 332710
Frank Theuws *(Interim Mng Dir)*

NTS CombiMetaal (1)
Standerdmolen 5, 5571 RN, Bergeijk, Netherlands
Tel.: (31) 497 552552
Emp.: 12
Part Supplier for Sheet Metal Work Assemblies & Mfr of Sheet Metal Work Solutions
N.A.I.C.S.: 332322
Ramesh Gopal *(Mng Dir)*

NTS Components (Suzhou) Ltd. (1)
39 Shuang Jing Street Suzhou Industrial Park, Suzhou, 215121, China
Tel.: (86) 51262746728
Electronic Equipment Distr
N.A.I.C.S.: 423690
John Sun *(Gen Mgr)*

NTS Components Singapore Pte Ltd (1)
11 Woodlands Walk, Singapore, 738265, Singapore
Tel.: (65) 67537135
Electronic Equipment Distr
N.A.I.C.S.: 423690
Sunny Wang Xin Chun *(Mng Dir)*

NTS Finish (1)
Stoekskesweg 30, 5571 TJ, Bergeijk, Netherlands
Tel.: (31) 497 552581
Emp.: 45

INTERNATIONAL PUBLIC

Priming, Coating & Printing Metal & Plastic Products
N.A.I.C.S.: 332812
Jan Vercoelen *(Mng Dir)*

NTS Hermus (1)
Metaalweg 12, 5804 CG, Venray, Netherlands
Tel.: (31) 478 521500
Emp.: 80
Thin Sheet Metal Mfr
N.A.I.C.S.: 332322
John Dirks *(Mng Dir)*

NTS Mechatronics (1)
Dillenburgstraat 9, 5652 AM, Eindhoven, Netherlands
Tel.: (31) 40 259 7200
Assembles Mechatronic Systems
N.A.I.C.S.: 333998
Rene van Wijk *(Mng Dir)*

NTS Mechatronics Brno, s.r.o. (1)
Turanka 1313/108, 62 700, Brno, Czech Republic
Tel.: (420) 511157400
Web Site: http://www.nts-mechatronics.cz
Industry Machinery Assembling Services
N.A.I.C.S.: 333519
David Cadik *(Mng Dir)*

NTS Mechatronics Shanghai (1)
11-A 227 North Fu Te Road, Waigaoqiao Free Trade Zone, Shanghai, 200131, China
Tel.: (86) 21 5064 0060
Web Site: http://www.nts-group.nl
Emp.: 50
Mechatronic Assemblies Mfr
N.A.I.C.S.: 333998
Bas Kreukniet *(Mng Dir)*

NTS Optel (1)
Kerkenbos 1303, 6546 BG, Nijmegen, Netherlands
Tel.: (31) 24 3221558
Web Site: http://www.optel.nl
Emp.: 15
Solutions & Engineering for Optics, Opto-Electronics & Laser Technology
N.A.I.C.S.: 541690
Eric Hezemans *(Mng Dir)*

NTS Precision (1)
Esp 400, 5633 AJ, Eindhoven, Netherlands
Tel.: (31) 40 84 85 900
Mfr of Turned & Milled Stainless Steel, Aluminum & Plastic Technical Products
N.A.I.C.S.: 332710
Twan Bussers *(Mng Dir)*

NTS Prometal Machining, s.r.o. (1)
Divnicka 222, 763 21, Slavicin, Czech Republic
Tel.: (420) 577 343054
Web Site: http://www.nts-prometal.cz
Sales Range: $50-74.9 Million
Emp.: 11
Milling, Turning, Sheet-Metal Work, Frame Construction, Finishing, Assembly & Engineering
N.A.I.C.S.: 332322
Otto van Leuven *(Mng Dir)*

NTS Shemer Motion (1)
Barlev Industrial Park, Misgav, Israel   (100%)
Tel: (972) 4 9911196
Web Site: http://www.nts-group.nl
Sales Range: $25-49.9 Million
Emp.: 43
Motion Control Systems Mfr
N.A.I.C.S.: 335314

NTS Systems Development (1)
Dillenburgstraat 9, 5652 AM, Eindhoven, Netherlands
Tel.: (31) 40 402 7500
Emp.: 200
Support Services for Development & Engineering of Complex High-Tech Equipment
N.A.I.C.S.: 541690
Eric Hezemans *(Mng Dir)*

NTT ADVERTISING, INC.
3-1-1 Kamiosaki, Shinagawa-ku, Tokyo, 141-8661, Japan
Tel.: (81) 3 5745 7637   JP
Web Site: http://www.ntt-ad.co.jp

AND PRIVATE COMPANIES

Year Founded: 1985
Rev.: $1,163,630,000
Emp.: 446
Full Service
N.A.I.C.S.: 541810
Toshiharu Hasebe *(Pres & CEO)*

Subsidiaries:

NTT Advertising, Inc. (1)
4-1-21 Kitahama, Chuoh-ku, Osaka, 541-0041, Japan
Tel.: (81) 6 6209 0100
Web Site: http://www.ntt-ad.co.jp
N.A.I.C.S.: 541810

NTT Advertising, Inc. (1)
3-5-27 Nishiki, Naka-ku, Nagoya, 460-0003, Aichi, Japan
Tel.: (81) 52 973 4711
Web Site: http://www.ntt-ad.co.jp
N.A.I.C.S.: 541810

NTT Advertising, Inc. (1)
2-10 Sati Chuou, Sendai, 980-0021, Miyagi, Japan
Tel.: (81) 22 266 3434
Web Site: http://www.ntt-ad.co.jp
Emp.: 15
N.A.I.C.S.: 541810

NTT Advertising, Inc. (1)
7-3-1 Oodohri-nishi, Chuoh-ku, Sapporo, 060-0042, Japan
Tel.: (81) 11 272 3721
Web Site: http://www.ntt-ad.co.jp
N.A.I.C.S.: 541810

Nippon Computer Arts, Inc. (1)
3-1-1 Kamiosaki, Shinagawa-ku, Tokyo, 141-0021, Japan
Tel.: (81) 3 5434 8800
Web Site: http://www.nc-arts.co.jp
N.A.I.C.S.: 541810

NTT SYSTEM S.A.
Trakt Brzeski Street 89, 05-077, Warsaw, Poland
Tel.: (48) 227736298
Web Site: http://www.ntt.pl
NTT—(WAR)
Rev.: $421,089,176
Assets: $117,891,006
Liabilities: $67,866,870
Net Worth: $50,024,136
Earnings: $6,239,329
Emp.: 140
Fiscal Year-end: 12/31/23
Computer Equipment, Peripherals & Electronics Mfr & Distr
N.A.I.C.S.: 334118
Tadeusz Kurek *(Pres & CEO)*

NTT UD REIT INVESTMENT CORPORATION
8-4-14 Akasaka, Minato Ward, Tokyo, 107-0052, Japan
Tel.: (81) 357728554
Web Site: http://www.pic-reit.co.jp
Year Founded: 2002
8956—(TKS)
Sales Range: $50-74.9 Million
Real Estate Investment Services
N.A.I.C.S.: 523999
Takeshi Oodera *(Exec Dir)*

NTUC FAIRPRICE CO-OPERATIVE LTD.
680 Upper Thomson Road, Singapore, 787103, Singapore
Tel.: (65) 64560233
Web Site: http://www.fairprice.com.sg
Year Founded: 1973
Sales Range: $1-4.9 Billinn
Emp.: 7,000
Grocery Stores
N.A.I.C.S.: 445110
Kian Peng Seah *(CEO)*

Subsidiaries:

Cheers Holdings (2004) Pte Ltd (1)
82 Genting Lane, Singapore, Singapore
Tel.: (65) 65015650
Investment Management Service
N.A.I.C.S.: 523940

Grocery Logistics of Singapore Pte Ltd (1)
37 Joo Koon Circle, 629062, Singapore, Singapore
Tel.: (65) 68625411
Grocery Logistics & Warehousing Services
N.A.I.C.S.: 541614

Interstates Market (2007) Pte Ltd (1)
Mountbatten Square Ste 03-01 229 Mountbatten Road, Singapore, 398007, Singapore
Tel.: (65) 92 1473
Sales Range: $25-49.9 Million
Emp.: 3
Procurement & Product Sourcing Services
N.A.I.C.S.: 561990
Robert Yong *(Mgr)*

NU HOLDINGS LTD.
Floor 4 Willow House Cricket Square, Grand Cayman, Georgetown, KY1-9010, Cayman Islands
Tel.: (345) 9492648 Ky
Web Site: https://www.investidores.nu
Year Founded: 2016
NU—(NYSE)
Rev.: $8,028,976,000
Assets: $43,498,449,000
Liabilities: $37,092,064,000
Net Worth: $6,406,385,000
Earnings: $1,030,530,000
Emp.: 7,686
Fiscal Year-end: 12/31/23
Holding Company
N.A.I.C.S.: 551112
David Velez Osorno *(CEO, Co-Founder & Chm)*

NU-WORLD HOLDINGS LTD.
3rd Street Wynberg, Sandton, 2199, Gauteng, South Africa
Tel.: (27) 113212111
Web Site: https://www.nuworld.co.za
NWL—(JSE)
Rev.: $160,900,805
Assets: $114,558,102
Liabilities: $21,596,228
Net Worth: $92,961,874
Earnings: $9,695,074
Emp.: 401
Fiscal Year-end: 08/31/21
Home Electronics & Appliances Mfr & Distr
N.A.I.C.S.: 449210
Michael Stanley Goldberg *(Chm)*

Subsidiaries:

Yale Appliance Group Pty., Ltd. (1)
12/20 St Albans Road, Kingsgrove, 2208, NSW, Australia (65%)
Tel.: (61) 295771700
Web Site: http://www.yaleprima.biz
Sales Range: $25-49.9 Million
Emp.: 20
Distr of Home Electronics & Appliances
N.A.I.C.S.: 449210

Yale Prima Proprietary Limited (1)
12/20 St Albans Road, Kingsgrove, NSW, Australia
Tel.: (61) 295771700
Web Site: https://www.yaleprima.biz
Audio Visual Equipment Mfr
N.A.I.C.S.: 334310

NUBIAN RESOURCES LTD.
Suite 3680 130 King Street, Abbotsford, V2S 8G9, BC, Canada
Tel.: (604) 870-4988
Web Site: https://www.nubianr.com
Year Founded: 2004
IVHN—(DEU)
Assets: $8,318,392
Liabilities: $216,672
Net Worth: $8,101,720
Earnings: ($267,036)
Fiscal Year-end: 07/31/24
Mineral Exploration Services
N.A.I.C.S.: 213114
David A. Fynn *(CFO)*

NUCANA PLC
3 Lochside Way, Edinburgh, EH12 9DT, United Kingdom
Tel.: (44) 1313571111 UK
Web Site: https://www.nucana.com
Year Founded: 1997
NCNA—(NASDAQ)
Assets: $35,106,034
Liabilities: $16,314,062
Net Worth: $18,791,972
Earnings: ($34,880,081)
Emp.: 25
Fiscal Year-end: 12/31/23
Biotechnology Research & Development Services
N.A.I.C.S.: 541714
Donald Munoz *(CFO)*

NUCAP INDUSTRIES INC.
3370 Pharmacy Avenue, Toronto, M1W 3K4, ON, Canada
Tel.: (416) 494-1444
Web Site: http://www.nucap.com
Year Founded: 1994
Sales Range: $75-99.9 Million
Emp.: 350
Brake Parts Mfr
N.A.I.C.S.: 336340

Subsidiaries:

Nucap US Inc. (1)
238 Wolcott Rd, Wolcott, CT 06716
Tel.: (203) 879-2823
Automobile Component Distr
N.A.I.C.S.: 423120

Nucap Vehicle Components (Shanghai) Company (1)
Building No 3 558 Tai Bo Rd Anting, Jiading District, Shanghai, 201814, China
Tel.: (86) 21 6957 5817
Automotive Component Mfr & Distr
N.A.I.C.S.: 336390
Kevin Aike Wang *(Mng Dir)*

NUCHEM LIMITED
54 Industrial Area NIT, Faridabad, 121001, Haryana, India
Tel.: (91) 129 4184000
Sales Range: $10-24.9 Million
Fertilizer Mfr
N.A.I.C.S.: 325311
B. J. Shah *(Sec & VP-Fin)*

NUCHEV LIMITED
Level 12 636 St Kilda Road, Melbourne, 3004, VIC, Australia
Tel.: (61) 422266570 AU
Web Site: https://www.nuchev.com.au
Year Founded: 2013
NUC—(ASX)
Rev.: $5,732,282
Assets: $9,991,915
Liabilities: $1,634,211
Net Worth: $8,357,704
Earnings: ($5,742,123)
Emp.: 20
Fiscal Year-end: 06/30/23
Biotechnology Research & Development Services
N.A.I.C.S.: 541714

NUCLETRON ELECTRONIC AG
Riesstrasse 8, 80992, Munich, Germany
Tel.: (49) 8914900220
Web Site: https://www.nucletron.ag
Year Founded: 1954
NUC—(DEU)
Sales Range: $10-24.9 Million
Emp.: 40

Electronic Components Distr
N.A.I.C.S.: 423690
Bernd Luft *(Chm-Mgmt Bd)*

NUCLEUS FINANCIAL PLATFORMS LIMITED
Dunn's House St Paul's Road, Salisbury, SP2 7BF, United Kingdom
Tel.: (44) 1312269800 UK
Web Site: https://www.nucleusplatforms.com
Financial Planning & Retirement Services
N.A.I.C.S.: 524292
Richard Rowney *(CEO)*

Subsidiaries:

Curtis Banks Group PLC (1)
3 Temple Quay, Bristol, BS1 6DZ, United Kingdom
Tel.: (44) 1179107910
Web Site: http://www.curtisbanks.co.uk
Rev.: $84,520,633
Assets: $4,471,796,308
Liabilities: $4,385,662,576
Net Worth: $86,133,732
Earnings: ($8,336,203)
Emp.: 802
Fiscal Year-end: 12/31/2022
Pension Services
N.A.I.C.S.: 524292
Ian Stone *(Chief Risk Officer)*

James Hay Holdings Limited (1)
Dunns House Saint Pauls Road, Salisbury, SP2 7BF, United Kingdom
Tel.: (44) 8458504455
Web Site: http://www.jameshay.co.uk
Sales Range: $200-249.9 Million
Emp.: 300
Financial Advisory Services
N.A.I.C.S.: 523940

Subsidiary (Domestic):

James Hay Administration Company Limited (2)
Dunns House Saint Pauls Rd, Salisbury, SP2 7BF, United Kingdom
Tel.: (44) 8458504455
Web Site: http://www.jameshay.co.uk
Pension Fund Management Services
N.A.I.C.S.: 524292

James Hay Pension Trustees Limited (2)
Dunns House Saint Pauls Rd, Salisbury, SP2 7BF, United Kingdom
Tel.: (44) 1722338333
Web Site: http://www.jameshay.co.uk
Emp.: 500
Pension Fund Management Services
N.A.I.C.S.: 524292

James Hay Wrap Managers Limited (2)
Trinity House Anderson Road, Swavesey, CB24 4UQ, Cambridgeshire, United Kingdom
Tel.: (44) 844 809 4024
Web Site: http://www.jameshay.co.uk
Portfolio Management Services
N.A.I.C.S.: 523940

NUCLEUS SOFTWARE EXPORTS LIMITED
A-39 Sector-62, Noida, 201307, Uttar Pradesh, India
Tel.: (91) 1204031400
Web Site: https://www.nucleussoftware.com
NUCLEUS—(NSE)
Rev.: $75,490,785
Assets: $120,756,090
Liabilities: $29,025,360
Net Worth: $91,730,730
Earnings: $16,100,175
Emp.: 1,932
Fiscal Year-end: 03/31/21
Banking & Financial Software Development Services
N.A.I.C.S.: 541511
Vishnu R. Dusad *(Mng Dir)*

NUCLEUS SOFTWARE EXPORTS LIMITED

Nucleus Software Exports Limited—(Continued)

Subsidiaries:

Nucleus Software Japan Kabushiki Kaisha (1)
Mitsubishi Building - 1171 2-5-2 Marunouchi, Chiyoda-ku, Tokyo, 100-0005, Japan
Tel.: (81) 362699990
Banking Software Development Services
N.A.I.C.S.: 541511

Nucleus Software Netherlands B.V. (1)
Cuserstraat 93 floor 2 and 3th, 1081 CN, Amsterdam, Netherlands
Tel.: (31) 206763600
Software Development Services
N.A.I.C.S.: 541511

Nucleus Software Solutions Pte. Ltd. (1)
300 Tampines Avenue 5 04-06 Tampines Junction, Singapore, 529653, Singapore
Tel.: (65) 67859024
Web Site: https://www.nucleussoftware.com
Sales Range: $25-49.9 Million
Emp.: 100
Banking Software Development Services
N.A.I.C.S.: 541511

Nucleus Software South Africa Pty. Ltd. (1)

VirStra i-Technology (Singapore) Pte. Ltd. (1)
300 Tampinies Avenue 5 04-06 NTUC Income Tampines Junction, Singapore, 529653, Singapore
Tel.: (65) 6785 9024
Sales Range: $25-49.9 Million
Emp.: 100
Banking Software Development Services
N.A.I.C.S.: 541511

VirStra i-Technology Services Limited (1)
6th Flr Marisoft-I Marigold Premises Kalyani Nagar, Pune, 411 014, India
Tel.: (91) 20 66033641
Web Site: http://www.nucleussoftware.com
Emp.: 82
Information Technology Consulting Services
N.A.I.C.S.: 541512

NUENERGY GAS LIMITED

Unit 3 39 Brook Street, 300 Barangaroo Avenue, Sunbury, 3429, VIC, Australia
Tel.: (61) 280767600   AU
Web Site: https://www.nuenergygas.com
Year Founded: 1985
NGY—(ASX)
Rev.: $4,737
Assets: $28,369,523
Liabilities: $10,529,816
Net Worth: $17,839,707
Earnings: ($675,662)
Fiscal Year-end: 06/30/23
Gas & Ancillary Power Generation Services
N.A.I.C.S.: 221112
Kong Kok Keong (Chm)

NUERA INC.

1980 Dagenais Boulevard West, Laval, H7L 5W2, QC, Canada
Tel.: (450) 625-1466   Ca
Web Site: http://www.nuera-inc.com
Emp.: 35
Vacuum System, Industrial Conveyor & Automotive Trailer Component Mfr & Retailer
N.A.I.C.S.: 335210
Claude Brochu (Pres & CEO)

Subsidiaries:

Nuera Air Inc (1)
3695 Desserte des Laurentides, Laval, H7L 3H7, QC, Canada
Tel.: (450) 622-9000
Web Site: http://www.nuera-air.com

Emp.: 200
Vacuum System Mfr & Distr
N.A.I.C.S.: 335210

Nuera Transport, Inc. (1)
7100 Roberts Matthews Hwy, Cookeville, TN 38506
Tel.: (931) 739-4055
Web Site: http://www.nuera-transport.com
Sales Range: $50-74.9 Million
Trailer Parts & Accessories Mfr & Retailer
N.A.I.C.S.: 423120
Michael Perna (Pres & CEO)

NUERNBERGER BETEILI-GUNGS AG

Ostendstrasse 100, D 90334, Nuremberg, Germany
Tel.: (49) 9115315
Web Site: https://www.nuernberger.de
Year Founded: 1884
NBG6—(DEU)
Assets: $38,629,632,605
Liabilities: $37,580,812,602
Net Worth: $1,048,820,003
Earnings: $46,064,495
Emp.: 4,383
Fiscal Year-end: 12/31/23
Financial Investment Services
N.A.I.C.S.: 551112
Werner Rupp (Chm)

NUEVA GENERACION MANUFACTURAS S.A DE C.V.

Tezozomoc 239 Fracc Industrial San Antonio, Mexico, 02760, Mexico
Tel.: (52) 5553525244
Web Site: http://www.ngm.com.mx
Year Founded: 1960
Sales Range: $10-24.9 Million
Emp.: 900
Capacitor Mfr
N.A.I.C.S.: 334416
Enrique Sanchez Aldunate (Pres)

Subsidiaries:

Commonwealth Sprague Capacitor Inc. (1)
865 S Church St, North Adams, MA 01247   (100%)
Tel.: (413) 664-4461
Mfr of Motor Run Capacitors, Power Factor Correction Assemblies & Harmonic Filters
N.A.I.C.S.: 334416

NUEVOLUTION A/S

Ronnegade 8, Copenhagen, 2100, Denmark
Tel.: (45) 70200987
Year Founded: 2001
Pharmaceuticals Product Mfr
N.A.I.C.S.: 325412
Alex Haahr Gouliaev (CEO)

NUFARM LIMITED

103-105 Pipe Road, Melbourne, 3026, VIC, Australia
Tel.: (61) 392821000   AU
Web Site: https://nufarm.com
NUF—(ASX)
Rev.: $2,370,826,919
Assets: $3,150,375,996
Liabilities: $1,576,988,625
Net Worth: $1,573,387,371
Earnings: $75,703,290
Emp.: 3,059
Fiscal Year-end: 09/30/23
Holding Company; Crop Protection & Specialty Chemicals Mfr & Distr
N.A.I.C.S.: 551112
Greg Hunt (CEO & Mng Dir)

Subsidiaries:

Agrimax Ltd. (1)
NE 33 27 26 W4M, PO Box 9, Irricana, T0M 1B0, AB, Canada   (100%)
Tel.: (403) 935-8800

Sales Range: $25-49.9 Million
Emp.: 10
Mfr of Elemental Plant Nutrient Sulphur
N.A.I.C.S.: 325314

Agrow Australia Pty Ltd (1)
10 McLennan Ave, Randwick, 2031, NSW, Australia   (100%)
Tel.: (61) 418246460
Sales Range: $25-49.9 Million
Emp.: 6
Provider of Farm Supplies
N.A.I.C.S.: 444240

Croplands Equipment Pty Ltd (1)
50 Cavan Road, Dry Creek, Adelaide, 5094, SA, Australia   (100%)
Tel.: (61) 883599300
Sales Range: $25-49.9 Million
Emp.: 44
Chemical Spray Equipment
N.A.I.C.S.: 333111

Subsidiary (Non-US):

Croplands Equipment Pty Ltd (2)
1422 Omahu Rd, PO Box 2004, Stortford Lodge, Hastings, 4120, New Zealand   (100%)
Tel.: (64) 43872453
Web Site: http://www.croplands.com.au
Sales Range: $25-49.9 Million
Emp.: 6
Chemical Spray Equipment
N.A.I.C.S.: 333111
Sean Mulvaney (Gen Mgr)

Mastra Corporation Pty. Ltd. (1)
17 Raymond Road, Laverton, 3026, VIC, Australia
Tel.: (61) 39 369 7848
Agricultural Chemical Product Mfr & Distr
N.A.I.C.S.: 325320

Nufarm (Asia) Pte Ltd (1)
391B Orchard Rd 23-01 Ngee Ann City, 68808, Singapore, Singapore   (100%)
Tel.: (65) 62275575
Web Site: http://www.nufarm.com
Sales Range: $50-74.9 Million
Emp.: 1
Marketer of Agricultural Chemicals throughout Asia
N.A.I.C.S.: 424910

Nufarm Agriculture, Inc. (1)
5101 333-96th Ave NE, Calgary, T3K 0S3, AB, Canada   (100%)
Tel.: (403) 692-2500
Sales Range: $25-49.9 Million
Emp.: 35
Mfr & Marketing of Agricultural Chemicals
N.A.I.C.S.: 325320

Nufarm Americas Inc. (1)
11901 S Austin Ave, Alsip, IL 60803
Tel.: (708) 377-1330
Web Site: https://nufarm.com
Sales Range: $50-74.9 Million
Emp.: 60
Agricultural & Turf & Vegetation Management Chemicals Mfr
N.A.I.C.S.: 325320
Ken Barham (VP-Customer & Brand Mktg)

Nufarm Australia Limited (1)
103-105 Pipe Road, Laverton, 3026, VIC, Australia
Tel.: (61) 39 282 1000
Web Site: https://nufarm.com
Crop Protection & Specialty Chemicals Mfr & Distr
N.A.I.C.S.: 325199

Nufarm B.V. (1)
Rivium Quadrant 75- 7, Botlek, 2909 LC, Capelle aan den IJssel, Netherlands   (100%)
Tel.: (31) 103037700
Web Site: https://nufarm.com
Sales Range: $25-49.9 Million
Emp.: 60
Mfr of MCPA & Related Agricultural Products
N.A.I.C.S.: 325320

Nufarm Chemical (Shanghai) Co., Ltd. (1)
2505 Litong Plaza 1350 North Sichuan Road, Hongkou District, Shanghai, 200080, China

Tel.: (86) 215 036 7200
Agricultural Chemical Product Mfr
N.A.I.C.S.: 325320

Nufarm Deutschland GmbH (1)
Im MediaPark 4e, 50670, Cologne, Germany
Tel.: (49) 221 179 1790
Web Site: https://nufarm.com
Agricultural Chemical Product Mfr
N.A.I.C.S.: 325320

Nufarm Espana S.A. (1)
Balmes 200 1-4, 08006, Barcelona, Spain   (100%)
Tel.: (34) 932389890
Web Site: https://nufarm.com
Sales Range: $25-49.9 Million
Emp.: 18
Formulator & Marketer of Agricultural Chemicals
N.A.I.C.S.: 325320

Nufarm Europe GmbH (1)
Parsevalstrasse 11, 40468, Dusseldorf, Germany
Tel.: (49) 2215 180 6011
Agricultural Product Mfr & Distr
N.A.I.C.S.: 333111

Nufarm GmbH & Co KG (1)
St-Peter-Str 25, 4021, Linz, Austria   (100%)
Tel.: (43) 73269180
Web Site: https://nufarm.com
Sales Range: $25-49.9 Million
Emp.: 200
Mfr & Marketer of Phenoxy Herbicides & Other Agricultural Chemicals
N.A.I.C.S.: 325320

Nufarm Grupo Mexico S de R.L. de C.V. (1)
Hotel Presidente Intercontinental Av Moctezuma 3515, Planta Baja Local 5 C Col. Ciudad del Sol, 45050, Zapopan, Jalisco, Mexico
Tel.: (52) 333 121 4108
Web Site: https://nufarm.com
Agricultural Chemical Product Mfr
N.A.I.C.S.: 325320

Nufarm Hungaria Kft (1)
Dayka Gabor u 3, 1118, Budapest, Hungary
Tel.: (36) 1 248 2140
Web Site: https://nufarm.com
Agricultural Chemical Product Mfr
N.A.I.C.S.: 325320

Nufarm Italia S.R.L. (1)
Via Guelfa 5, 40138, Bologna, Italy
Tel.: (39) 051 039 4022
Web Site: https://nufarm.com
Agricultural Chemical Product Mfr
N.A.I.C.S.: 325320

Nufarm KK (1)
21st Fukokuseimei Building 2-2 Uchisaiwaicho 2-Chome, Chiyoda-ku, Tokyo, 100-0011, Japan
Tel.: (81) 35 511 7561
Agricultural Chemical Product Mfr
N.A.I.C.S.: 325320

Nufarm Malaysia (1)
35-2 Jalan Setia Prima S U13/S, Setia Alam Sek U13, 40170, Shah Alam, Selangor Darul Ehsan, Malaysia   (100%)
Tel.: (60) 333437188
Web Site: https://nufarm.com
Emp.: 153
Marketer of Crop Protection & Crop Nutrition Products
N.A.I.C.S.: 115112
Lee Siak Choon (Bus Mgr)

Nufarm NZ Limited (1)
6 Manu Street, Otahuhu, Auckland, New Zealand
Tel.: (64) 9 270 4157
Fertilizer Mfr
N.A.I.C.S.: 325314

Nufarm New Zealand Trading Division (1)
Unit 11- 9 Manu Street, Otahuhu, Auckland, 2024, New Zealand   (100%)
Tel.: (64) 9 270 4150
Web Site: https://www.nufarm.com
Emp.: 35
Mfr of Pharmaceutical Products
N.A.I.C.S.: 325412

AND PRIVATE COMPANIES

Nufarm Polska Sp. z o.o. (1)
ul Grojecka 1/3, 02-019, Warsaw, Poland
Tel.: (48) 22 620 3252
Web Site: https://nufarm.com
Agricultural Chemical Product Mfr
N.A.I.C.S.: 325320

Nufarm Portugal Lda. (1)
Praca de Alvalade 7 - 6 Esq, 1700-036, Lisbon, Portugal
Tel.: (351) 21 799 8440
Web Site: https://nufarm.com
Agricultural Chemical Product Mfr
N.A.I.C.S.: 325320

Nufarm Romania S.R.L. (1)
Str Poet Andrei Muresanu 11-13 ap 3 et 2 Sector 1, Bucharest, 011841, Romania
Tel.: (40) 21 224 6320
Web Site: https://www.nufarm.com
Agricultural Chemical Product Mfr
N.A.I.C.S.: 325320
Ileana Ungureanu *(Mgr)*

Nufarm SA (1)
Immeuble West Plaza 11 rue du Debarcadere, PO Box 75, 92700, Colombes, France (100%)
Tel.: (33) 140855050
Web Site: https://www.nufarm.com
Sales Range: $50-74.9 Million
Emp.: 200
Mfr & Marketer of Chemicals
N.A.I.C.S.: 325998
Gambon Yzonneck *(Mng Dir)*

Nufarm SA (1)
(100%)
Tel.: (33) 232647400
Web Site: https://www.nufarm.com
Sales Range: $50-74.9 Million
Emp.: 150
Mfr of Specialty Industrial Chemicals
N.A.I.C.S.: 325998
Cosneau Pascal *(Mng Dir)*

Nufarm Suisse S.A.R.L. (1)
Business Centre Chemin du Canal 5, 1260, Nyon, Switzerland
Tel.: (41) 22 363 9111
Agricultural Chemical Product Mfr
N.A.I.C.S.: 325320

Nufarm UK Ltd. (1)
Wyke Lane Wyke, Bradford, BD12 9EJ, West Yorkshire, United Kingdom (100%)
Tel.: (44) 127 469 1234
Web Site: https://www.nufarm.com
Sales Range: $25-49.9 Million
Emp.: 100
Wholesales Farm Supplies
N.A.I.C.S.: 444240

Nufarm Ukraine LLC (1)
Horizon Park 4 M Hrinchenka Street, 03038, Kiev, Ukraine
Tel.: (380) 44 495 5360
Web Site: https://www.nufarm.com
Agricultural Chemical Product Mfr
N.A.I.C.S.: 325320

Nuseed Pty. Ltd. (1)
103-105 Pipe Road, Laverton, 3026, VIC, Australia
Tel.: (61) 39 282 1000
Web Site: https://nuseed.com
Emp.: 15
Agricultural Seed Bioengineering & Distr
N.A.I.C.S.: 424910

Unit (US):

Nuseed Americas (2)
1000 Burr Ridge Pkwy Ste 200, Burr Ridge, IL 60527
Tel.: (630) 455-2019
Web Site: http://www.nuseed.com
Agricultural Seed Distr
N.A.I.C.S.: 424910

Subsidiary (Domestic):

Nuseed Central US (3)
115 N 3rd St, Breckenridge, MN 56520
Tel.: (218) 643-2410
Web Site: http://www3.nuseed.com
Sunflower Seed Bioengineering & Whslr
N.A.I.C.S.: 424910
Tim Birkel *(Gen Mgr-Americas)*

Nuseed Ukraine LLC (1)
Regus Business Center Mykoly Grynchenka Str 4, 03680, Kiev, Ukraine
Tel.: (380) 44 4495 391 5333
Farm Whslr
N.A.I.C.S.: 424910
Mykola Shepeliya *(Mgr-Commercial)*

PT Nufarm Indonesia (1)
Plaza Aminta Suite 802 8th Floor Jl Let Jend TB Simatupang Kav 10, South Jakarta, 12310, Indonesia (100%)
Tel.: (62) 2175904844
Web Site: https://nufarm.com
Sales Range: $25-49.9 Million
Emp.: 30
Mfr, Formulator & Marketer of Glyphosate, 2, 4-D, Diuron & Other Agricultural Chemicals
N.A.I.C.S.: 325320

Pharma Pacific Management Pty. Ltd. (1)
376 Bay Street, Brighton-Le-Sands, Sydney, 2216, NSW, Australia
Tel.: (61) 295976199
Pharmaceutical Products
N.A.I.C.S.: 325412

SEAC (1)
28 Boulevard Camelinat, PO Box 77, 92233, Gennevilliers, France (100%)
Tel.: (33) 140855055
Web Site: http://www.seac.fr
Sales Range: $25-49.9 Million
Emp.: 12
Fine Chemicals Mfr
N.A.I.C.S.: 325998

NUFFIELD HEALTH
Epsom Gateway Ashley Avenue, Epsom, KT18 5AL, Surrey, United Kingdom
Tel.: (44) 3001236200
Web Site: http://www.nuffieldhealth.com
Year Founded: 1957
Sales Range: $900-999.9 Million
Emp.: 9,311
Hospital & Health Care Services
N.A.I.C.S.: 524114
Russell Hardy *(Chm)*

Subsidiaries:

Greens Health & Fitness Ltd (1)
Epsom Gateway Ashley Avenue, Epsom, KT18 5AL, United Kingdom
Tel.: (44) 1603760600
Consumer Fitness Center Services
N.A.I.C.S.: 713940

Health Club Acquisitions Ltd (1)
Highfield Park Drive, Saint Albans, Hertfordshire, United Kingdom
Tel.: (44) 1727 816 100
Emp.: 200
Holding Company
N.A.I.C.S.: 551112

Nuffield Haywards Heath Hospital (1)
Burrell Road, Haywards Heath, RH16 1UD, West Sussex, United Kingdom
Tel.: (44) 1444847916
Web Site: http://www.nuffieldhealth.com
Sales Range: $25-49.9 Million
Emp.: 150
Hospital Services
N.A.I.C.S.: 622110
Graeme Stacey *(Mgr-Fin)*

Nuffield Health Chichester Hospital (1)
78 Broyle Road, Chichester, PO19 6WB, West Sussex, United Kingdom
Tel.: (44) 1243530600
Web Site: http://www.nuffieldhealth.com
Sales Range: $10-24.9 Million
Emp.: 100
Hospital Services
N.A.I.C.S.: 622110
Karen Jowett *(Mgr-Fin)*

Nuffield Health Taunton Hospital (1)
Staplegrove Elm, Taunton, TA2 6AN, United Kingdom
Tel.: (44) 1823 476266
Web Site: http://www.nuffieldhealth.com

Hospital & Surgical Services
N.A.I.C.S.: 622110
David Mobbs *(Grp CEO)*

Nuffield Health Tees Hospital (1)
Junction Road, Norton, Stockton-on-Tees, TS20 1PX, United Kingdom
Tel.: (44) 1642919446
Web Site: http://www.nuffieldhealth.com
Sales Range: $25-49.9 Million
Emp.: 200
Hospital Services
N.A.I.C.S.: 622110
David Richardson *(Gen Mgr)*

Nuffield Hospital Brighton (1)
Warren Road, Woodingdean, Brighton, BN2 6DX, East Sussex, United Kingdom
Tel.: (44) 1273624488
Web Site: http://www.nuffieldhealth.com
Sales Range: $25-49.9 Million
Emp.: 200
Hospital Services
N.A.I.C.S.: 622110
Cath Anderson *(Head-Clinical Svcs)*

Nuffield Hospital Cambridge (1)
4 Trumpington Road, Cambridge, CB2 8AF, United Kingdom
Tel.: (44) 1223853595
Web Site: http://www.nuffieldhealth.com
Hospital Services
N.A.I.C.S.: 622110
Victoria Pangratiou *(Mgr-Clinical Svcs)*

Nuffield Hospital Exeter (1)
Wonford Road, Exeter, EX2 4UG, United Kingdom
Tel.: (44) 1392276591
Web Site: http://www.nuffieldhealth.com
Sales Range: $50-74.9 Million
Emp.: 400
Hospital Services
N.A.I.C.S.: 622110
Paul Taylor *(Gen Mgr)*

Nuffield Hospital Leeds (1)
2 Leighton Street, Leeds, LS1 3EB, United Kingdom
Tel.: (44) 01133882000
Web Site: http://www.nuffieldhospitals.org.uk
Sales Range: $25-49.9 Million
Emp.: 250
Hospital Services
N.A.I.C.S.: 622110

Nuffield Hospitals York (1)
Haxby Road, York, YO31 8TA, United Kingdom
Tel.: (44) 01904715000
Web Site: http://www.nuffieldhealth.com
Hospital Services
N.A.I.C.S.: 622110

Nuffield Proactive Health (1)
40-44 Coomba Rd, KT3 4QS, New Malden, Surrey, United Kingdom - England
Tel.: (44) 2083296200
Sales Range: $100-124.9 Million
Emp.: 1,000
Employee Wellness Solutions
N.A.I.C.S.: 622110

The Bournemouth Nuffield Hospital (1)
67 Lansdowne Road, Bournemouth, BH1 1RW, United Kingdom
Tel.: (44) 1202291866
Web Site: http://www.nuffieldhealth.com
Hospital Services
N.A.I.C.S.: 622110
T. McNair *(Mng Dir)*

The Bristol Nuffield Hospital (1)
3 Clifton Hill, Bristol, BS8 1BN, United Kingdom
Tel.: (44) 1179872727
Web Site: http://www.nuffieldhealth.com
Sales Range: $10-24.9 Million
Emp.: 100
Hospital Services
N.A.I.C.S.: 622110
Angela Appiah Shippey *(Mgr-Comml)*

The Bristol Nuffield Hospital (1)
3 Clifton Hill, Bristol, BS8 1BN, United Kingdom
Tel.: (44) 1179872727
Web Site: http://www.nuffieldhealth.com
Sales Range: $25-49.9 Million
Emp.: 150
Hospital Services

NUFFIELD HEALTH

N.A.I.C.S.: 622110
Sheryl Krause *(Dir-Hospital)*

The Cheltenham & Gloucester Nuffield Hospital (1)
Hatherley Lane, Cheltenham, GL51 6SY, Gloucestershire, United Kingdom
Tel.: (44) 1242809691
Web Site: http://www.nuffieldhealth.com
Sales Range: $25-49.9 Million
Emp.: 130
Hospital Services
N.A.I.C.S.: 622110
Michelle Stone *(Dir-Hospital)*

The Essex Nuffield Hospital (1)
Shenfield Road, Brentwood, CM15 8EH, Essex, United Kingdom
Tel.: (44) 1277695695
Web Site: http://www.nuffieldhealth.com
Sales Range: $10-24.9 Million
Hospital Services
N.A.I.C.S.: 622110

The Glasgow Nuffield Hospital (1)
Beaconsfield Rd, Glasgow, G12 0PJ, United Kingdom
Tel.: (44) 1413349441
Web Site: http://www.nuffieldhealth.com
Sales Range: $25-49.9 Million
Emp.: 150
Hospital Services
N.A.I.C.S.: 622110
Christine Boner *(Mgr-Ward)*

The Grosvenor Nuffield Hospital (1)
Wrexham Road, Chester, CH4 7QP, Cheshire, United Kingdom
Tel.: (44) 1244680444
Web Site: http://www.nuffieldhealth.com
Sales Range: $10-24.9 Million
Emp.: 40
Hospital Services
N.A.I.C.S.: 622110
Geraldine Woods *(Mgr-Fin)*

The Guildford Nuffield Hospital (1)
Stirling Rd, Guildford, GU2 7RF, Surrey, United Kingdom
Tel.: (44) 1483555800
Sales Range: $10-24.9 Million
Hospital Services
N.A.I.C.S.: 622110

The Leicester Nuffield Hospital (1)
Scraptoft Lane, Leicester, LE5 1HY, United Kingdom
Tel.: (44) 1162769401
Web Site: http://www.nuffieldhealth.com
Sales Range: $25-49.9 Million
Emp.: 150
Hospital Services
N.A.I.C.S.: 622110
Simon George *(Mgr-Fin)*

The Manor Hospital Oxford (1)
Beech Road, Oxford, OX3 7RP, United Kingdom
Tel.: (44) 1865307777
Web Site: http://www.nuffieldhouse.com
Emp.: 500
Hospital Services
N.A.I.C.S.: 622110
Louis Sullivan *(Gen Mgr)*

The Newcastle Nuffield Hospital (1)
Clayton Road, Newcastle upon Tyne, NE2 1JP, United Kingdom
Tel.: (44) 1912816131
Web Site: http://www.nuffieldhealth.com
Sales Range: $25-49.9 Million
Emp.: 187
Hospital Services
N.A.I.C.S.: 622110
Graham Chapman *(Mng Dir)*

The North Staffordshire Nuffield Hospital (1)
Clayton Road, Newcastle-under-Lyme, ST5 4DB, United Kingdom
Tel.: (44) 1782625431
Web Site: http://www.nuffieldhealth.com
Sales Range: $10-24.9 Million
Emp.: 100
Hospital Services
N.A.I.C.S.: 622110

The Nuffield Hospital Derby (1)
Rykneld Road, Derby, DE23 4SN, United Kingdom

NUFFIELD HEALTH

Nuffield Health—(Continued)
Tel.: (44) 1332540100
Sales Range: $25-49.9 Million
Emp.: 200
Hospital Services
N.A.I.C.S.: 622110

The Nuffield Hospital Ipswich (1)
Foxhall Road, Ipswich, IP4 5SW, Suffolk, United Kingdom
Tel.: (44) 1473858446
Web Site: http://www.nuffieldhealth.com
Hospital Services
N.A.I.C.S.: 622110
Malcolm Nunn (Mgr-Fin)

The Plymouth Nuffield Hospital (1)
Derriford Road, Plymouth, PL6 8BG, Devon, United Kingdom
Tel.: (44) 01752775861
Web Site: http://www.nuffieldhealth.com
Sales Range: $25-49.9 Million
Emp.: 200
Hospital Services
N.A.I.C.S.: 622110

The Purey Cust Nuffield Hospital (1)
Precentors Court, Nuffield Hospital Haxpy road Y, York, YO1 2EL, United Kingdom
Tel.: (44) 01904715000
Sales Range: $25-49.9 Million
Emp.: 200
Physiotherapy Services
N.A.I.C.S.: 621999

The Shropshire Nuffield Hospital (1)
Longden Road, Shrewsbury, SY3 9DP, Shropshire, United Kingdom
Tel.: (44) 1743282500
Web Site: http://www.nuffieldhealth.com
Sales Range: $10-24.9 Million
Emp.: 100
Hospital Services
N.A.I.C.S.: 622110
Michael S. Haffenden (Gen Mgr)

The Thames Valley Nuffield Hospital Slough (1)
Wexham Street, Slough, SL3 6NH, Buckinghamshire, United Kingdom
Tel.: (44) 1753662241
Hospital Services
N.A.I.C.S.: 622110

The Tunbridge Wells Nuffield Hospital (1)
Kingswood Road, Kingswood Road, Tunbridge Wells, TN2 4UL, United Kingdom
Tel.: (44) 1892531111
Web Site: http://www.nuffieldhospitals.com
Sales Range: $25-49.9 Million
Emp.: 200
Hospital Services
N.A.I.C.S.: 622110
Joe Hazel (Gen Mgr)

The Warwickshire Nuffield Hospital (1)
The Chase Old Milverton Ln, Leamington Spa, CV32 6RW, Warwickshire, United Kingdom
Tel.: (44) 1926427971
Sales Range: $25-49.9 Million
Emp.: 200
Hospital Services
N.A.I.C.S.: 622110
Andrew Whithorn (Dir-Hospital)

The Wessex Nuffield Hospital (1)
Winchester Road, Chandlers Ford, Eastleigh, SO53 2DW, Hampshire, United Kingdom
Tel.: (44) 2380266377
Web Site: http://www.nt6511.vs.netbenefit.co.uk
Sales Range: $25-49.9 Million
Emp.: 250
Hospital Services
N.A.I.C.S.: 622110
Peter Howgrave-Graham (Dir-Hospital)

The Woking Nuffield Hospital (1)
Shores Road, Woking, GU21 4BY, Surrey, United Kingdom
Tel.: (44) 1483227800
Web Site: http://www.nuffield.co.uk
Sales Range: $25-49.9 Million
Emp.: 150
Hospital Services

N.A.I.C.S.: 622110

The Wolverhampton Nuffield Hospital (1)
Wood Road Tettenhall, Wolverhampton, WV6 8LE, West Midlands, United Kingdom
Tel.: (44) 1902754177
Hospital Services
N.A.I.C.S.: 622110
Tony Avery (Gen Mgr)

The Wye Valley Nuffield Hospital (1)
Venns Lane, Hereford, HR1 1DF, United Kingdom
Tel.: (44) 01432355131
Hospital Services
N.A.I.C.S.: 622110

Vale Health Partners Ltd (1)
Hensol Castle Park, Pontyclun, CF72 8JX, Mid Glamorgan, United Kingdom
Tel.: (44) 1443 449 220
Emp.: 100
Holding Company
N.A.I.C.S.: 551112
Simon Roger (Gen Mgr)

NUFORMIX PLC

6th Floor 60 Gracechurch Street, London, EC3V 0HR, United Kingdom
Tel.: (44) 1223627222 UK
Web Site: https://www.nuformix.com
Year Founded: 2008
NFX—(LSE)
Rev.: $62,090
Assets: $6,178,977
Liabilities: $295,376
Net Worth: $5,883,601
Earnings: ($1,377,148)
Emp.: 4
Fiscal Year-end: 03/31/22
Pharmaceutical Preparation Manufacturing
N.A.I.C.S.: 325412
Anne Brindley (CEO)

NUH CIMENTO SANAYI A.S.

Hac Akif Mahallesi D100 Karayolu Caddesi No 92, Korfez, Kocaeli, Turkiye
Tel.: (90) 2623162000
Web Site: https://www.nuhcimento.com.tr
Year Founded: 1966
NUHCM—(IST)
Rev.: $239,041,262
Assets: $214,446,922
Liabilities: $74,141,775
Net Worth: $140,305,148
Earnings: $64,450,463
Emp.: 968
Fiscal Year-end: 12/31/22
Cement Mfr
N.A.I.C.S.: 327310
Tevfik Bilgin (Chm)

Subsidiaries:

Cim-Nak Tasimacilik Limited Sirketi (1)
Haci Akif Mh D-100 Karayolu Cd No 92, Hereke Korfez, 1 41800, Kocaeli, Turkiye
Tel.: (90) 2623162000
Web Site: https://www.cimnak.com.tr
Ship Agency Services
N.A.I.C.S.: 532411

Nuh Beton A.S. (1)
Buyukbakkalkoy Mah Mezarlik Yolu Sk No 35, Maltepe, Istanbul, Turkiye
Tel.: (90) 2165640000
Web Site: https://www.nuhbeton.com.tr
Ceramics & Concrete Mfr
N.A.I.C.S.: 327211

Nuh Yapi Urunleri A.S. (1)
Haci Akif Mh Nuh Cimento Cd No 32, Hereke, Kocaeli, Turkiye
Tel.: (90) 2623105000
Web Site: https://www.nuhyapi.com.tr
Building Materials Whslr
N.A.I.C.S.: 423390

NUHEARA LIMITED

190 Aberdeen Street, Northbridge, 6003, WA, Australia
Tel.: (61) 865559999
Web Site: https://www.nuheara.com
NUH—(ASX)
Rev.: $1,289,312
Assets: $8,690,512
Liabilities: $5,278,632
Net Worth: $3,411,879
Earnings: ($8,424,934)
Fiscal Year-end: 06/30/23
Audio Technology Services
N.A.I.C.S.: 339113
Justin Miller (Co-Founder & Mng Dir)

NUI NHO STONE JOINT STOCK COMPANY

Binh Thung 2 Hamlet, Binh An Ward, Di An, Binh Duong, Vietnam
Tel.: (84) 2743751515
Web Site: https://www.nuinho.vn
NNC—(HOSE)
Sales Range: Less than $1 Million
Nonmetallic Mineral Mining Services
N.A.I.C.S.: 212390
Doan Minh Quang (Chm)

NUINSCO RESOURCES LIMITED

80 Richmond St W 18th Floor, Toronto, M5H 2A4, ON, Canada
Tel.: (416) 626-0470 ON
Web Site: http://www.nuinsco.ca
Year Founded: 1989
Sales Range: Less than $1 Million
Emp.: 8
Gold, Copper, Nickel & Uranium Mining Services
N.A.I.C.S.: 212220
Rene R. Galipeau (Chm)

NUINTEK CO., LTD.

243 Eumbongmyeon-ro Eumbongmyeon, Asan, Chungcheongnam-do, Korea (South)
Tel.: (82) 415418100 KR
Web Site: http://www.nuin.co.kr
Year Founded: 1968
012340—(KRS)
Rev.: $57,771,865
Assets: $62,457,384
Liabilities: $48,354,889
Net Worth: $14,102,495
Earnings: ($7,388,104)
Emp.: 274
Fiscal Year-end: 12/31/22
Electronic Components Mfr
N.A.I.C.S.: 334419
Andy Seo (Dir)

Subsidiaries:

NUINTEK CO., LTD. - China Plant (1)
6 Fengin Road Wuzhon Zone, Suzhou, Jiangsu, China
Tel.: (86) 512 562 2980
Electronic Components Mfr
N.A.I.C.S.: 334419

NUINTEK CO., LTD. - Damyang Plant (1)
143 Dogae Road, Wolsan, Jeollanam-do, Korea (South)
Tel.: (82) 61 383 0053
Electronic Components Mfr
N.A.I.C.S.: 334419

NUINTEK CO., LTD. - Mexico Plant (1)
Caizada Coltongo 162 Coltongo, Azcapotzalco, 26304, Mexico, Mexico
Tel.: (52) 55 5719 2881
Electronic Components Mfr
N.A.I.C.S.: 334419

NUINTEK CO., LTD. - Thailand Plant (1)
192-4 Mhu 10 Petchkasem Road T Nong-or A Rachaburi Tollom, Bangkok, Thailand
Tel.: (66) 3 236 8241

INTERNATIONAL PUBLIC

Electronic Components Mfr
N.A.I.C.S.: 334419

NUIX LIMITED

Level 2 10 Rudd Street, Canberra, 2601, ACT, Australia
Tel.: (61) 292800699 AU
Web Site: https://www.nuix.com
Year Founded: 2000
NXL—(ASX)
Rev.: $118,970,464
Assets: $247,485,167
Liabilities: $70,891,309
Net Worth: $176,593,858
Earnings: ($3,644,129)
Emp.: 400
Fiscal Year-end: 06/30/23
Software Development Services
N.A.I.C.S.: 541511
Alexis Rouch (CIO)

Subsidiaries:

Nuix USG Inc. (1)
13755 Sunrise Valley Dr Ste 300, Herndon, VA 20171
Technology Services
N.A.I.C.S.: 541512

NULEGACY GOLD CORPORATION

300-1055 W Hastings Street, Vancouver, V6E 2E9, BC, Canada
Tel.: (604) 639-3640 BC
Web Site: https://www.nulegacygold.com
NULGF—(OTCQB)
Rev.: $180
Assets: $34,902,733
Liabilities: $124,108
Net Worth: $34,778,625
Earnings: ($1,113,633)
Emp.: 10
Fiscal Year-end: 03/31/23
Gold Mining Services
N.A.I.C.S.: 212220
Albert J. Matter (CEO)

Subsidiaries:

NuLegacy Gold N.V. (1)
5450 Riggins Ct Ste 1B, Reno, NV 89502-6577
Tel.: (775) 825-0494
Gold Mining Services
N.A.I.C.S.: 212220

NUM AG

Battenhusstrasse 16, 9053, Teufen, Switzerland
Tel.: (41) 713350411
Web Site: http://www.num.com
Sales Range: $10-24.9 Million
Emp.: 250
Developer of Production Process Optimization Software & Hardware
N.A.I.C.S.: 561210
Peter Von Rueti (Pres, CEO & Chief Scientific Officer)

Subsidiaries:

NUM (UK) Ltd. (1)
Unit 5 Fairfield Court Seven Stars Industrial Estate Wheler Road, Coventry, CV3 4LJ, United Kingdom
Tel.: (44) 2476 301 259
Software Development Services
N.A.I.C.S.: 541511
Colin Reader (Mgr-Engrg)

NUM CNC HighEnd Applications S.A. (1)
Errementari Plaza 8, Post Box 55, 20560, Onati, Spain
Tel.: (34) 943 78 02 65
Software Development Services
N.A.I.C.S.: 541511

NUM CNC KOREA Co. Ltd. (1)
A-503 Hangang Xi-Tower Yangcheon-ro 401, Gangseo-gu, 157801, Seoul, Korea (South)

NUM Corporation (1)
603 E Diehl Rd Ste 115, Naperville, IL 60563-4800
Tel.: (630) 505-7722
Web Site: http://www.num-usa.com
Rev.: $2,399,795
Emp.: 10
Mfr of Numerical Controls
N.A.I.C.S.: 561210
Steve Schilling (Gen Mgr)

NUM GmbH (1)
Zeller Strasse 18, 73271, Holzmaden, Germany
Tel.: (49) 7023 7440 0
Web Site: http://www.num.com
Software Development Services
N.A.I.C.S.: 541511

NUM Numerical Control Technology (Beijing) CO LTD. (1)
Room 904 No 4 Building Brilliancy International Plaza, Haidian District, Beijing, China
Tel.: (86) 10 6266 9458
Software Development Services
N.A.I.C.S.: 541511

NUM Numerical Control Technology (Changzhou) Co. Ltd (1)
The 5th floor Haiye building No 1-2 Guihua Road, Zhonglou District, 213023, Changzhou, China
Tel.: (86) 519 8585 0766
Software Development Services
N.A.I.C.S.: 541511
Arno Mueller (Gen Mgr)

NUM S.A.S. (1)
Immeuble le Naxos 56 rue des Hautes Patures, 92 737, Nanterre, Cedex, France
Tel.: (33) 1 56 47 58 06
Software Development Services
N.A.I.C.S.: 541511

NUM Servis Turkiye (1)
Feyzullah Caddesi Kirli APT B Blok No 17/4, Maltepe, 34840, Istanbul, Turkiye
Tel.: (90) 542 265 80 54
Software Development Services
N.A.I.C.S.: 541511

NUM SpA (1)
Sede Legale Via F Somma 62, Cuggiono, 20012, Milan, Italy
Tel.: (39) 02 97 969 350
Software Development Services
N.A.I.C.S.: 541511
Massimiliano Menegotto (Mng Dir)

NUM Taiwan Ltd. (1)
7F-2 No 536 Sec 2 Taiwan Boulevard, Taichung, 40353, Taiwan
Tel.: (886) 4 2316 9600
Software Development Services
N.A.I.C.S.: 541511
Peter Lee (Mgr-R&D)

NUMIKO
46 The Calls, Leeds, LS2 7EY, United Kingdom
Tel.: (44) 1132021400
Web Site: http://www.numiko.com
Year Founded: 2000
Sales Range: $10-24.9 Million
Emp.: 18
Digital/Interactive, Graphic Design, Internet/Web Design, Production (Ad, Film, Broadcast)
N.A.I.C.S.: 541810
David Eccles (Founder & Mng Dir)

NUMINUS WELLNESS INC.
250 - 997 Seymour St, Vancouver, V6B 3M1, BC, Canada
Tel.: (604) 649-3229 BC
Web Site: https://investors.numinus.com
Year Founded: 1962
LR23—(DEU)
Rev.: $17,292,652
Assets: $18,151,692
Liabilities: $7,671,357
Net Worth: $10,480,335
Earnings: ($22,571,258)
Emp.: 200
Fiscal Year-end: 08/31/23
Metal Mining Services
N.A.I.C.S.: 212290
Michael Tan (COO)

Subsidiaries:

Cedar Clinical Research Inc. (1)
154 E Myrtle Ave Ste 202, Murray, UT 84107
Tel.: (801) 369-4219
Web Site: https://www.cedarclinicalresearch.com
Mental Health Care Services
N.A.I.C.S.: 621330

Foundations for Change Inc. (1)
3115 S Grand Blvd Ste 450, Saint Louis, MO 63118
Tel.: (314) 577-0444
Web Site: https://foundationsforchange.net
Mental Health Care Services
N.A.I.C.S.: 621330

Mindspace Services Inc. (1)
6-80 Citizen Court, Markham, L6G 1A7, ON, Canada
Tel.: (905) 284-1000
Web Site: https://www.mindspace.ca
Safety Equipment Distr
N.A.I.C.S.: 423840

NUMULAE GESTION DE SERVICIOS SOCIMI SA
C/Goya N 23 1 Planta, 28001, Madrid, Spain
Tel.: (34) 913101161
Web Site: https://www.numulae.com
YNUM—(MAD)
Sales Range: Less than $1 Million
Real Estate Services
N.A.I.C.S.: 531390

NUNAMINERALS A/S
Issortarfimmut 1, 3905, Nuuk, Greenland
Tel.: (299) 362000 GL
Web Site: http://www.nunaminerals.com
Year Founded: 1998
Sales Range: Less than $1 Million
Emp.: 14
Mineral Exploration & Mining Services
N.A.I.C.S.: 213115
Ole Christian Anthon Christiansen (Pres & CEO)

NUNASI CORPORATION
611 Paunna Place, PO Box 1559, Iqaluit, X0A 0H0, NU, Canada
Tel.: (867) 979-2175 NT
Web Site: http://www.nunasi.com
Year Founded: 1976
Sales Range: $350-399.9 Million
Emp.: 10
Investment Holding Company
N.A.I.C.S.: 551112
Clint Davis (Pres)

Subsidiaries:

Larga Kitikmeot Ltd. (1)
5602-50th Avenue, Yellowknife, X1A 1E7, NT, Canada
Tel.: (867) 766-3410
Boarding Services
N.A.I.C.S.: 721310

Nunasi Corporation - Corporate Office (1)
Ste 301 5109 48th St, Yellowknife, X1A 1N5, NT, Canada
Tel.: (867) 920-4587
Web Site: http://www.nunasi.com
Sales Range: $25-49.9 Million
Executive Office
N.A.I.C.S.: 921140
Fred Hunt (CEO)

Subsidiary (Domestic):

Arctic Spirit Promotions (2)
Ste 5112 48th St, Yellowknife, X1A 1N5, NT, Canada (100%)
Tel.: (867) 873-6909
Sales Range: $50-74.9 Million
Emp.: 4
Promotional Products Including Sportswear, Mugs, Clocks, Office Supplies, Electronics, Toys & Novelty Items
N.A.I.C.S.: 423990

Pan Arctic Inuit Logistics Corporation (1)
75 Albert St, Ottawa, K1P 5E7, ON, Canada
Tel.: (613) 234-3344
Logistics Consulting Servies
N.A.I.C.S.: 541614

Polar Vision Centres Ltd. (1)
Suite 113 5109 48th Street, Yellowknife, X1A 1N5, NT, Canada
Tel.: (867) 920-4500
Web Site: https://www.polarvision.ca
Optical Product Distr
N.A.I.C.S.: 456130
Malaya Rheaume (Sec)

Subsidiary (Domestic):

Baffin Optical (2)
-, PO Box 891, Building 1088 Block E, Iqaluit, X0A 0H0, NU, Canada
Tel.: (867) 979-4300
Optical Product Distr
N.A.I.C.S.: 423460

NUNWOOD
7 Airport W, Lancaster Way, Leeds, LS19 7ZA, Yeadon, United Kingdom
Tel.: (44) 845 372 0101
Web Site: http://www.nunwood.com
Emp.: 150
Advetising Agency
N.A.I.C.S.: 541810
Clare Bruce (CEO)

NUODE INVESTMENT CO., LTD.
No 1666 Hangkong Street North Area, Hi-tech Industrial Development Zone, Changchun, 518000, Jilin, China
Tel.: (86) 75588911333
Web Site: http://www.kinwa.com.cn 600100—(SHG)
Rev.: $661,190,732
Assets: $1,961,712,900
Liabilities: $873,946,055
Net Worth: $1,087,766,845
Earnings: $49,457,753
Fiscal Year-end: 12/31/22
Electric Wire & Cable Mfr & Whslr
N.A.I.C.S.: 331222

NUPUR RECYCLERS LIMITED
Plot no 03 Funtional Industrial Estate Patparganj, Delhi, 110092, India
Tel.: (91) 9555101552
Web Site: https://www.nupurrecyclers.com
Year Founded: 2019
NRL—(NSE)
Rev.: $22,273,101
Assets: $10,069,373
Liabilities: $1,451,855
Net Worth: $8,617,518
Earnings: $2,576,014
Fiscal Year-end: 03/31/22
Metal Products Mfr
N.A.I.C.S.: 332119

NUR INK INNOVATIONS LTD.
20 Hamelacha Street Afek Industrial Park, Rosh Ha'Ayin, 4809154, Israel
Tel.: (972) 747973081
Web Site: https://www.nur-ink.com
Year Founded: 2018
NURI—(TAE)
Assets: $6,032,325
Liabilities: $1,590,827
Net Worth: $4,441,497
Earnings: ($3,553,253)
Fiscal Year-end: 12/31/23
Printing Ink Mfr
N.A.I.C.S.: 325910
Moshe Nur (Chm & Co-Founder)

NURAN WIRELESS, INC.
2150 Cyrille-Duquet Suite 100, Quebec, G1N 2G3, QC, Canada
Tel.: (418) 914-7484 BC
Web Site: https://www.nuranwireless.com
Year Founded: 2014
NRRWF—(OTCQB)
Rev.: $2,415,710
Assets: $15,261,352
Liabilities: $19,163,552
Net Worth: ($3,902,200)
Earnings: ($9,304,723)
Emp.: 50
Fiscal Year-end: 12/31/23
Telephone Equipment Mfr
N.A.I.C.S.: 334210
David Parsons (CTO)

NURANI DYEING & SWEATER LTD.
Janata Housing Road 03 213 214 Sah Ali Bag, Mirpur 02, Dhaka, 1216, Bangladesh
Tel.: (880) 28391790
Web Site: http://www.ndsl-bd.com
Year Founded: 2005
NURANI—(DHA)
Rev.: $13,732,059
Assets: $24,857,806
Liabilities: $9,847,401
Net Worth: $15,010,405
Earnings: $1,388,044
Fiscal Year-end: 06/30/19
Garments Mfr
N.A.I.C.S.: 315990
Rehana Alam (Chm)

NURBANK JSC
10 Abay Avenue, Bostandyk district, A15E2D3, Almaty, Kazakhstan
Tel.: (7) 7272500000 KZ
Web Site: https://nurbank.kz
Year Founded: 1992
NRBN—(KAZ)
Rev.: $115,928,597
Assets: $1,011,659,227
Liabilities: $888,181,236
Net Worth: $123,477,990
Earnings: $16,975,953
Emp.: 1,360
Fiscal Year-end: 12/31/23
Banking Services
N.A.I.C.S.: 522110
Irina Telegina (Mng Dir & Member-Mgmt Bd)

Subsidiaries:

JSC OOIUPA Nur-Trust (1)
173 Zheltoksan St, 050013, Almaty, Kazakhstan
Tel.: (7) 727 250 67 82
Web Site: http://www.nurbank.kz
Sales Range: $50-74.9 Million
Emp.: 10
Banking Services
N.A.I.C.S.: 523150

SB JSC Nurbank Money Experts JSC (1)
Republic Square 13, 050013, Almaty, Kazakhstan (100%)
Tel.: (7) 7272502016
Web Site: https://www.moneyexperts.kz
Portfolio Management, Brokerage & Other Financial Consulting Services
N.A.I.C.S.: 523940
Lyazzat Shaikhiyeva (Chm-Mgmt Bd)

NURCAPITAL CORPORATION LTD.

Nurbank JSC—(Continued)

NURCAPITAL CORPORATION LTD.
1585 Markham Road Suite 209, Toronto, M1B 2W1, ON, Canada
Tel.: (416) 754-4135 ON
Web Site: http://www.nurcapital.ca
Year Founded: 2015
Assets: $297,291
Liabilities: $102,903
Net Worth: $194,388
Earnings: ($81,307)
Fiscal Year-end: 12/31/18
Financial Investment Services
N.A.I.C.S.: 523999
Barry M. Polisuk *(Sec)*

NURECA LIMITED
Sco 6-7-8 1St Floor Sector-9D, Madhya Marg, Chandigarh, 160009, India
Tel.: (91) 9356658436
Web Site: https://www.nureca.com
Year Founded: 2017
NURECA—(NSE)
Rev.: $14,199,149
Assets: $24,768,299
Liabilities: $1,402,554
Net Worth: $23,365,745
Earnings: ($9,891,493)
Emp.: 102
Fiscal Year-end: 03/31/23
Healtcare Services
N.A.I.C.S.: 621999
Aryan Goyal *(Co-Founder & CEO)*

NURIFLEX CO., LTD.
Nuri Building 16 Sapyeong-daero, Seocho-gu, Seoul, Korea (South)
Tel.: (82) 27810700
Web Site: https://www.nuritelecom.com
Year Founded: 1992
040160—(KRS)
Rev.: $95,659,937
Assets: $117,963,555
Liabilities: $57,009,015
Net Worth: $60,954,540
Earnings: $480,573
Emp.: 135
Fiscal Year-end: 12/31/22
Measuring Instruments Mfr
N.A.I.C.S.: 334513
Song-Man Cho *(Founder & Chm)*

Subsidiaries:

Apivio Systems Inc. (1)
Unit 270 - 2985 Virtual Way, Vancouver, V5M 4X7, BC, Canada
Tel.: (604) 343-4200
Web Site: https://www.apivio.com
Communication Equipment Mfr
N.A.I.C.S.: 334290
S. H. Shin *(CTO-Moimstone Korea)*

NURI Telecom Co., Ltd. (1)
4F Resona Kudan Building 1-5-6, Chiyoda-ku, Tokyo, 102-0074, Japan
Tel.: (81) 3 3512 2882
Web Site: http://www.nuritelecom.co.jp
Emp.: 10
Telecommunication Servicesb
N.A.I.C.S.: 517111
Masayuki Suzuki *(CEO)*

NURI Telecom USA Co., Inc. (1)
8 Corporate Park Ste 300, Irvine, CA 92606
Tel.: (949) 442-8347
Telecommunication Servicesb
N.A.I.C.S.: 517111

NURIPLAN CO., LTD.
3291 Songmari Daegodmyeon, Gyeonggi-do, Gimpo, Korea (South)
Tel.: (82) 319979097
Web Site: https://www.nuriplan.com
069140—(KRS)
Rev.: $100,594,307
Assets: $109,279,400
Liabilities: $85,485,320
Net Worth: $23,794,080
Earnings: ($7,090,993)
Emp.: 75
Fiscal Year-end: 12/31/22
Steel & Lighting Structures
N.A.I.C.S.: 332999

NURMINEN LOGISTICS PLC
Satamakaari 24, 00980, Helsinki, Finland
Tel.: (358) 1054500 FI
Web Site: https://www.nurminenlogistics.com
Year Founded: 1886
NLG1V—(HEL)
Rev.: $132,215,627
Assets: $75,197,496
Liabilities: $49,137,708
Net Worth: $26,059,788
Earnings: $1,588,603
Emp.: 141
Fiscal Year-end: 12/31/22
Logistics Consulting Servies
N.A.I.C.S.: 541614
Olli Pohjanvirta *(Chm & CEO)*

Subsidiaries:

Nurminen Maritime Latvia SIA (1)
17A Duntes Street, Riga, 1005, Latvia
Tel.: (371) 67517948
Web Site: https://www.nurminen.lv
Emp.: 15
Transportation Services
N.A.I.C.S.: 488999
Andrey Dobrynin *(Mgr-Comml)*

OOO Huolintakeskus (1)
Ul Dnepropetrovskaya 31 Ofis 301, Saint Petersburg, 191119, Russia
Tel.: (7) 8123 25 31 51
Logistics Consulting Servies
N.A.I.C.S.: 541614

RW Logistics Oy (1)
Pasilankatu 2, Helsinki, 00240, Uusimaa, Finland
Tel.: (358) 1054500
Logistics Consulting Servies
N.A.I.C.S.: 541614

UAB Nurminen Maritime (1)
Minijos str 19 3 floor, Klaipeda, 91207, Lithuania
Tel.: (370) 46477712
Web Site: http://www.nurminen.lt
Sales Range: $50-74.9 Million
Emp.: 7
Ship Transport & Logistics Services
N.A.I.C.S.: 488390
Romas Zimkus *(Mng Dir)*

NUROL GAYRIMENKUL YATIRIM ORTAKLIGI AS
Maslak Mah Buyukdere Cad Nurol Plaza Sitesi NO 255 ic Kapi NO 103, Sariyer, Istanbul, Turkiye
Tel.: (90) 2122868240
Web Site: http://www.nurolgyo.com
Year Founded: 1997
NUGYO—(IST)
Sales Range: Less than $1 Million
Real Estate Investment Services
N.A.I.C.S.: 531390
Nurdogan Topuz *(Gen Mgr)*

NUROL HOLDING A.S.
Arjantin Cad No 7 GOP, Cankaya, 6700, Ankara, Turkiye
Tel.: (90) 3124551000
Web Site: http://www.nurol.com.tr
Year Founded: 1966
NRHOL—(IST)
Rev.: $827,763,865
Assets: $2,443,440,904
Liabilities: $1,826,793,285
Net Worth: $616,647,619
Earnings: $307,266,822
Emp.: 11,634
Fiscal Year-end: 12/31/22
Building Construction Services
N.A.I.C.S.: 236116
Kerim Kemahli *(CFO)*

Subsidiaries:

BNA Nurol BAE Systems Air Systems Inc. (1)
Universiteler Mah 1605 Cad E Blok No 3/1-3, Bilkent Cankaya, 06800, Ankara, Turkiye
Tel.: (90) 3122100220
Web Site: https://www.nurolbaesystems.com
Flight Control System Services
N.A.I.C.S.: 488190
Mehmet Oguz Carmikli *(Chm)*

Bosfor Tourism Management Inc. (1)
Bogaz Sokak No 21-1, Gaziosmanpasa, 06700, Ankara, Turkiye
Tel.: (90) 3124551020
Web Site: http://www.bosforucakbileti.com
Tourism Travel Services
N.A.I.C.S.: 561510

Bosfor Turizm Isletmecilik A.S. (1)
Bogaz Sokak No 21-1, Gaziosmanpasa, 06700, Ankara, Turkiye
Tel.: (90) 3124551020
Web Site: https://www.bosforucakbileti.com
Travel Agency Services
N.A.I.C.S.: 561510

Botim Business Management & Trading Inc. (1)
Emin Anter Bulvari Kibris Sehitleri Cad Oasis Alisveris, Kultur ve Eglence Merkezi No 316 Bodrum, 48400, Mugla, Turkiye
Tel.: (90) 2523170002
Construction Services
N.A.I.C.S.: 236220
Mazhar Vardar *(Mng Dir)*

Enova Elektrik Enerjisi Toptan Satis A.S. (1)
Guvenevler Mahallesi Gelincik Sk No 2 D 3, Cankaya, 06690, Ankara, Turkiye
Tel.: (90) 312 428 1125
Hydroelectric Power Generation Services
N.A.I.C.S.: 221111

Enova Energy Production Inc. (1)
Guvenevler Mahallesi Gelincik Sk No 2 D 3, Cankaya, 06690, Ankara, Turkiye
Tel.: (90) 3124281125
Web Site: http://www.enovaenerji.com.tr
Hydroelectric Power Generation Services
N.A.I.C.S.: 221111

Enova Enerji Uretim A.S. (1)
Guvenevler Mahallesi Gelincik Sk No 2 D 3, Cankaya, 06690, Ankara, Turkiye
Tel.: (90) 3124281125
Web Site: https://www.enovaenerji.com.tr
Hydroelectric Power Generation Services
N.A.I.C.S.: 221111

FNSS Savunma Sistemleri A.S. (1)
Ogulbey Mahallesi Kumludere Caddesi No 11, Golbasi, 06830, Ankara, Turkiye
Tel.: (90) 3124974300
Web Site: http://www.fnss.com.tr
Armored Combat Vehicle Mfr & Distr
N.A.I.C.S.: 336992
Nusret Duyar *(Dir-Mechanical Design)*

Nurol Aviation Inc. (1)
Arjantin Cad No 7, Gaziosmanpasa, 06700, Ankara, Turkiye
Tel.: (90) 3124551890
Web Site: http://www.nurolair.com
Aircraft Services
N.A.I.C.S.: 488190

Nurol BAE Systems Hava Sistemleri A.S. (1)
Universiteler Mah 1605 Cad E Blok No 3/1-3 Bilkent, Cankaya, 06800, Ankara, Turkiye
Tel.: (90) 312 210 0220
Web Site: https://www.nurolbaesystems.com
Aircraft Services
N.A.I.C.S.: 488190
Mehmet Oguz Carmikli *(Chm)*

Nurol Construction & Trading Co. Inc. (1)
Nurol Plaza Buyukdere Caddesi No 255 Kat 19, Maslak Sariyer, 34485, Istanbul, Turkiye
Tel.: (90) 2122868010
Web Site: http://www.nurolinsaat.com.tr

INTERNATIONAL PUBLIC

Construction Services
N.A.I.C.S.: 236220
Nurettin Carmikli *(Chm)*

Nurol Energy Generation & Marketing Inc. (1)
Karum Is ve Alisveris Merkezi Iran Cad No 21/430, Gaziosmanpasa, 06680, Ankara, Turkiye
Tel.: (90) 3124551880
Construction Services
N.A.I.C.S.: 236220

Nurol Enerji Uretim Ve Pazarlama A.S. (1)
Karum Is Merkezi Iran Cad No 21/430 GOP, Gop, 06680, Ankara, Turkiye
Tel.: (90) 3124551880
Web Site: https://www.nurolenerji.com.tr
Hydroelectric Power Generation Services
N.A.I.C.S.: 221111
Nurettin Carmikli *(Chm)*

Nurol Georgia LLC (1)
Luka Asatiani Street No 1/1, 6000, Batumi, Georgia
Tel.: (995) 422276058
Construction Services
N.A.I.C.S.: 236220
Lutfu Bilgin *(Gen Mgr)*

Nurol Goksu Elektrik Uretim A.S. (1)
Arjantin Cad No 7, GOP, Ankara, Turkiye
Tel.: (90) 3124281880
Hydroelectric Power Distr
N.A.I.C.S.: 423610

Nurol Havacilik A.S. (1)
Arjantin Cad No 7 GOP, 06700, Ankara, Turkiye
Tel.: (90) 3124551891
Web Site: https://www.nurolair.com
Aircraft Services
N.A.I.C.S.: 488190

Nurol Insaat ve Ticaret A.S. (1)
Nurol Plaza Buyukdere Caddesi No 255 Kat 19, Sariyer, 34485, Maslak, Istanbul, Turkiye
Tel.: (90) 2122868010
Web Site: https://www.nurolinsaat.com
Building Construction Services
N.A.I.C.S.: 236220
Nurettin Carmikli *(Chm)*

Nurol Insurance Brokerage Serviıves Inc. (1)
Karum Is Merkezi D Blok Kat 3 No 367, Kavaklidere, 06690, Ankara, Turkiye
Tel.: (90) 3124551420
Web Site: http://www.nurolsigorta.com.tr
Insurance Brokerage Services
N.A.I.C.S.: 524210

Nurol Isletme ve Gayrimenkul Yonetim A.S. (1)
Karum Is Merkezi No 21/433 Kat 5, Kavaklidere, 06680, Ankara, Turkiye
Tel.: (90) 3124551440
Web Site: http://www.nurolisletme.com
Real Estate Rental Services
N.A.I.C.S.: 531110

Nurol Kontrol ve Aviyonik Sistemleri A.S. (1)
Universiteler Mah 1605 Cad E Blok No 3/1-3, Bilkent Cankaya, 06800, Ankara, Turkiye
Tel.: (90) 3122100220
Web Site: https://www.nurolcas.com.tr
Control Panel Mfr
N.A.I.C.S.: 335314

Nurol LLC (1)
Building No 3 Office No 202 and 203 Zayed The First Street, PO Box 46254, Khalidiya, Abu Dhabi, United Arab Emirates
Tel.: (971) 26666810
Web Site: https://www.nuroluae.com
Highway Construction Services
N.A.I.C.S.: 237210
Ali Mirza Ozbek *(Gen Mgr)*

Nurol Makina Sanayi A.S. (1)
Organize Sanayi Bolgesi Avrupa Hun Cad No 6, Sincan, 06935, Ankara, Turkiye
Tel.: (90) 3124703000
Web Site: https://www.nurolmakina.com.tr
Armored Vehicle Mfr
N.A.I.C.S.: 336992

AND PRIVATE COMPANIES

Nurol Makina ve Sanayi A.S. (1)
Organize Sanayi Bolgesi Avrupa Hun Cad No 6, Sincan, 06935, Ankara, Turkiye
Tel.: (90) 312470300005
Web Site: http://www.nurolmakina.com.tr
Steel Construction Machinery Mfr
N.A.I.C.S.: 333120

Nurol Sigorta Aracilik Hizmetleri A.S. (1)
Karum Is Merkezi D Blok Kat 3 No 367, Kavaklidere, 06690, Ankara, Turkiye
Tel.: (90) 3124551420
Web Site: https://www.nurolsigorta.com.tr
Insurance Services
N.A.I.C.S.: 524210

Nurol Solar Enerji Uretim A.S. (1)
Ogulbey Mah 3060 Ave No 5, Golbasi, 06830, Ankara, Turkiye
Tel.: (90) 3124551960
Web Site: https://www.nurolsolar.com.tr
Solar Electric Power Generation Services
N.A.I.C.S.: 221114

Nurol Teknoloji Sanayi Ve Madencilik ticaret A.S. (1)
Ogulbey Mah 3060 Cad No 5, Golbasi, 06830, Ankara, Turkiye
Tel.: (90) 3126155511
Web Site: https://www.nurolteknoloji.com
Ceramic Products Mfr
N.A.I.C.S.: 327110

Otoyol Yatirim ve Isletme A.S. (1)
Universiteler Mah 1598 Caddesi Bilkent Plaza A-3 Apt No 3/44, Cankaya, Ankara, Turkiye
Tel.: (90) 8503993505
Web Site: http://www.isletme.otoyolas.com.tr
Highway Construction Services
N.A.I.C.S.: 237210

TUMAD Mining Industry & Trade Inc. (1)
Bugday Sokak No 9, Kavaklidere, Ankara, Turkiye
Tel.: (90) 3124551600
Web Site: http://www.tumad.com.tr
Metal Mining Services
N.A.I.C.S.: 213114

Tumad Madencilik Sanayi Ve Ticaret A.S. (1)
Bugday Sokak No 9 Kavaklidere, Barbaros Mahallesi cankaya, 06680, Ankara, Turkiye
Tel.: (90) 3124551600
Web Site: https://www.tumad.com.tr
Gold Product Mfr
N.A.I.C.S.: 331410
Hasan Yucel (Gen Mgr)

Turser Tourism Publishing and Trade Inc. (1)
Karum Is Merkezi D Blok Kat 3 No 368, Kavaklidere, 06680, Ankara, Turkiye
Tel.: (90) 312455140001
Web Site: http://www.turser.com.tr
Tourism Investment Services
N.A.I.C.S.: 523940

Turser Turizm Servis Ve Ticaret A.S. (1)
Karum Is Merkezi D Blok Kat 3 No 368, Kavaklidere, 06680, Ankara, Turkiye
Tel.: (90) 3124551400
Web Site: https://www.turser.com.tr
Hotel Operator
N.A.I.C.S.: 721110

NUROL VARLIK KIRALAMA A.S.
Maslak Mah Buyukdere Cad Nurol Plaza No 255 Ic Kapi No 1502, Sariyer, Istanbul, Turkiye
Tel.: (90) 2122868153
Web Site: http://www.nurolvarlikkiralama.com
NURVK—(IST)
Financial Investment Services
N.A.I.C.S.: 523999
Murat Cimen (Chm)

NUROL YATIRIM BANKASI A.S.
Buyukdere Cad Nurol Plaza No 255 Kat 15/1502, Maslak Sariyer, 34485, Istanbul, Turkiye
Tel.: (90) 2122868100
Web Site: http://www.nurolbank.com.tr
NRBNK—(IST)
Rev.: $64,112,060
Assets: $539,121,898
Liabilities: $467,132,739
Net Worth: $71,989,158
Earnings: $45,044,308
Emp.: 97
Fiscal Year-end: 12/31/22
Banking Services
N.A.I.C.S.: 522110
Ziya Akkurt (Chm)

Subsidiaries:

Nurol Portfoy Yonetim Anonim Sirketi (1)
Buyukdere Cad No 255 Nurol Plaza A blok Kat 8, Maslak, Turkiye
Tel.: (90) 2122868255
Web Site: https://www.nurolportfoy.com.tr
Investment Management Service
N.A.I.C.S.: 523940

Ortak Varlik Yonetim Anonim Sirketi (1)
Sultan Selim Mahallesi Lalegul Sokak Levent, No 5 Plaza Ic Kapi No 58-59-60 PK Kagithane, 34415, Istanbul, Turkiye
Tel.: (90) 2122731000
Web Site: https://ortakvarlik.com.tr
Investment Management Service
N.A.I.C.S.: 523940

NURTURE LANDSCAPES HOLDINGS LIMITED
Nursery Court London Road, Windlesham, GU20 6LQ, Surrey, United Kingdom
Tel.: (44) 8007555265
Web Site: https://www.nurture-group.co.uk
Year Founded: 2008
Landscape Maintenance Services
N.A.I.C.S.: 561730
Peter Fane (Founder & Exec Chm)

Subsidiaries:

Nurture Landscapes Limited (1)
Nursery Court London Road, Windlesham, GU20 6LQ, Surrey, United Kingdom
Tel.: (44) 8007555265
Landscaping Services
N.A.I.C.S.: 561730

NUSANTARA RESOURCES LIMITED
Level 4 100 Albert Road, South Melbourne, 3205, VIC, Australia
Tel.: (61) 894608600   AU
Web Site: http://www.nusantararesources.com
NUS—(ASX)
Rev.: $314,135
Assets: $79,135,921
Liabilities: $12,764,576
Net Worth: $66,371,345
Earnings: ($2,877,374)
Fiscal Year-end: 12/31/20
Mining & Mineral Exploration Services
N.A.I.C.S.: 213114
Colin McMillian (Gen Mgr-Geology)

NUSASIRI PUBLIC COMPANY LIMITED
2922/209-214 Chan Issara Tower 2 Building, New Petchaburi Road Bangkapi Huai Khwang, Bangkok, 10310, Thailand
Tel.: (66) 20301399
Web Site: https://www.nusasiri.com
Year Founded: 1960
NUSA—(THA)
Rev.: $52,216,890

Assets: $458,547,681
Liabilities: $168,904,069
Net Worth: $289,643,612
Earnings: ($21,822,262)
Emp.: 660
Fiscal Year-end: 12/31/23
Real Estate Investment & Management Services
N.A.I.C.S.: 531190
Visanu Thepcharoen (Chm & CEO)

NUSCO S.P.A.
S S 7 bis km 50 500, Nola, 80035, Naples, Italy
Tel.: (39) 0815122234
Web Site: https://www.nuscospa.com
Year Founded: 1960
NUS—(EUR)
Building Product Mfr
N.A.I.C.S.: 332321

NUSEP HOLDINGS LTD.
30 Richmond Road, Homebush, 2140, NSW, Australia
Tel.: (61) 2 8415 7300
Web Site: http://www.nusep.com
Emp.: 20
Plasma Protein Research Services
N.A.I.C.S.: 541715
Alison Coutts (Chm)

Subsidiaries:

Prime Biologics Pte Ltd (1)
61 Robinson Centre 15-01 Robinson Road, Singapore, 068893, Singapore
Tel.: (65) 612 8415 7300
Web Site: http://www.primebiologics.com
Plasma Product Mfr
N.A.I.C.S.: 325414
Hari Nair (Chm)

NUTECH ENGINEERING INC.
200 Chisholm Drive, Milton, ON, Canada
Tel.: (905) 878-6923
Web Site: http://www.nutech-engineering.com
Year Founded: 1988
Rev.: $15,500,674
Emp.: 100
Welding & Thermal Cutting Automation
N.A.I.C.S.: 333992
Mark Amlinger (Pres)

NUTECH GLOBAL LTD.
E-149 Riico Industrial Area, Bhilwara, 311001, Rajasthan, India
Tel.: (91) 1482260508
Web Site: https://www.nutechglobal.com
531304—(BOM)
Rev.: $3,486,637
Assets: $2,650,167
Liabilities: $1,832,631
Net Worth: $817,535
Earnings: ($146,855)
Emp.: 26
Fiscal Year-end: 03/31/21
Textile Products Mfr
N.A.I.C.S.: 314999
Shyam Sunder Mukhija (Chm)

NUTEX INVESTMENTS PUBLIC LIMITED COMPANY
Cziraki Street 24-32 Building A II em 141, 1163, Budapest, Hungary
Tel.: (36) 18017081
Web Site: https://www.nutex.hu
Year Founded: 1983
NUTEX—(BUD)
Rev.: $1,233
Assets: $15,017,790
Liabilities: $24,003
Net Worth: $14,993,788
Earnings: $468,936
Emp.: 1

Fiscal Year-end: 12/31/23
Dietary Supplements Mfr
N.A.I.C.S.: 325412
Vilmos Galamb (Chm)

NUTRAPLUS INDIA LIMITED
405 Matharu Arcade, Subhash Road Vile Parle East Above Axis Bank, Mumbai, 400057, India
Tel.: (91) 22 40140442
Web Site: http://www.nutraplusindia.com
Rev.: $17,000,638
Assets: $26,737,153
Liabilities: $16,274,998
Net Worth: $10,462,155
Earnings: $21,660
Emp.: 36
Fiscal Year-end: 03/31/18
Pharmaceuticals Product Mfr
N.A.I.C.S.: 325412
Mukesh Dhirubhai Naik (Chm & Mng Dir)

NUTRASTAR INTERNATIONAL INC.
4/F Yushan Plaza 51 Yushan Road, Nangang District, Harbin, 150090, China
Tel.: (86) 451 82287746   NV
Web Site: http://www.nutrastarintl.com
Year Founded: 2002
Sales Range: Less than $1 Million
Emp.: 336
Holding Company; Agricultural & Nutraceutical Product Researcher, Developer & Mfr
N.A.I.C.S.: 551112
Cosimo Borrelli (Pres-Interim)

NUTRI-ASIA INC.
JY Campos Centre 9th Ave, Bonifacio Global City, Taguig, 1634, Metro Manila, Philippines
Tel.: (63) 2 662 2888
Web Site: http://www.nutriasia.com
Condiment, Sauce & Cooking Oil Mfr & Distr
N.A.I.C.S.: 311941
Joselito D. Campos Jr. (Chm & CEO)

Subsidiaries:

Del Monte Pacific Limited (1)
c/o 17 Bukit Pasoh Road, Singapore, 089831, Singapore   (67%)
Tel.: (65) 63246822
Web Site: https://www.delmontepacific.com
Rev.: $2,421,313,000
Assets: $3,139,669,000
Liabilities: $2,753,911,000
Net Worth: $385,758,000
Earnings: $25,377,000
Emp.: 6,300
Fiscal Year-end: 04/30/2023
Beverages Mfr
N.A.I.C.S.: 311421
Ma Bella B. Javier (Chief Scientific Officer)

Subsidiary (US):

Del Monte Foods, Inc. (2)
205 N Wiget Ln, Walnut Creek, CA 94598
Tel.: (925) 949-2772
Web Site: https://www.delmontefoods.com
Canned Fruit, Vegetables, Seafood, Broth & Pet Food Producer
N.A.I.C.S.: 311421
Gregory N. Longstreet (Pres & CEO)

Joint Venture (Non-US):

FieldFresh Foods Pvt. Ltd. (2)
ower C-2 First Floor Plot No 16 Udyog Vihar Phase IV, Gurgaon, 122 015, India
Tel.: (91) 1244109400
Web Site: http://www.fieldfreshfoods.in
Sales Range: $75-99.9 Million
Emp.: 200

NUTRI-ASIA INC.

Nutri-Asia Inc.—(Continued)
Fresh & Processed Fruits & Vegetable
Bharti Enterprise & Del Monte Food Joint Venture Distr
N.A.I.C.S.: 424480
Yogesh Billani (CEO)

NUTRIART INC.
550 Avenue Godin, Quebec, G1M 2K2, QC, Canada
Tel.: (418) 687-5320 Ca
Web Site: http://www.nutriart.ca
Year Founded: 2009
Sales Range: $75-99.9 Million
Emp.: 200
Chocolate Mfr
N.A.I.C.S.: 311351
Jacques Leclerc (Co-Owner)

Subsidiaries:

Laura Secord (1)
550 Godin Ave, Ste 800 East Tower, Quebec, G1M 2K2, QC, Canada
Tel.: (905) 629-5059
Web Site: https://www.laurasecord.ca
Sales Range: $75-99.9 Million
Emp.: 20
Candy Mfr; Chocolates
N.A.I.C.S.: 311352

NUTRICIRCLE LIMITED
5-8-272 Ayesha Residency Opp City Convention Centre Public Garden Road, Nampally, Hyderabad, 500 001, India
Tel.: (91) 9030528805
Web Site: https://nutricircle.in
530219—(BOM)
Rev.: $239,830
Assets: $190,956
Liabilities: $559,492
Net Worth: ($368,535)
Earnings: ($41,330)
Fiscal Year-end: 03/31/23
Pharmaceutical Preparation Mfr
N.A.I.C.S.: 325412
Hitesh Mohanbhai Patel (Mng Dir)

NUTRIDAR PLC
Rabieh Sharif Nassir Street AlWathiq Building no 37 4th floor, PO Box 9695, Amman, 11191, Jordan
Tel.: (962) 65563578 JO
Web Site: https://www.nutridar.com
Year Founded: 1994
NDAR—(AMM)
Rev.: $17,441,274
Assets: $18,227,764
Liabilities: $9,380,337
Net Worth: $8,847,426
Earnings: $112,425
Emp.: 128
Fiscal Year-end: 12/31/20
Baby Food Product Mfr
N.A.I.C.S.: 311999

NUTRIEN LTD.
211 19th Street East, Saskatoon, S7K 5R6, SK, Canada
Tel.: (306) 933-8500 Ca
Web Site: https://www.nutrien.com
Year Founded: 2018
NTR—(NYSE)
Rev.: $29,056,000,000
Assets: $52,749,000,000
Liabilities: $27,548,000,000
Net Worth: $25,201,000,000
Earnings: $1,282,000,000
Emp.: 25,900
Fiscal Year-end: 12/31/23
Chemical Products Mfr
N.A.I.C.S.: 551112
Russell K. Girling (Chm)

Subsidiaries:

Actagro, LLC (1)
4516 N Howard, Biola, CA 93606
Tel.: (559) 369-2222
Web Site: http://www.actagro.com
Sales Range: $1-9.9 Million
Emp.: 29
Nitrogenous Fertilizer Mfr
N.A.I.C.S.: 325311
Carl Ueland (Pres)

Agrium Inc. (1)
13131 Lake Fraser Drive SE, Calgary, T2J 7E8, AB, Canada
Tel.: (403) 225-7000
Fertilizer, Seed Treatment, Plant Nutrition & Farm Management Products Mfr & Distr
N.A.I.C.S.: 325311

Subsidiary (US):

Agrium U.S. Inc. (2)
4582 S Ulster St Ste 1700, Denver, CO 80237-2636
Tel.: (303) 804-4400
Fertilizer, Seed Treatment, Plant Nutrition & Crop Protection Product Retailer
N.A.I.C.S.: 424910

Joint Venture (Domestic):

Interprovincial Cooperative Limited (2)
945 Marion Street, Winnipeg, R2J 0K7, MB, Canada
Tel.: (204) 233-3461
Web Site: https://www.ipco.ca
Agricultural Chemicals Mfr & Whslr
N.A.I.C.S.: 325320

Subsidiary (Non-US):

Nutrien Ag Solutions Limited (2)
Level 10/737 Bourke St, Docklands, 3008, VIC, Australia
Tel.: (61) 392092000
Web Site: https://www.nutrienagsolutions.com.au
Agriculture Merchandise & Fertilizer Distr
N.A.I.C.S.: 424910

Subsidiary (Domestic):

Arcadian Wool Brokers Limited (2)
151 Yarra Street, Geelong, 3220, VIC, Australia
Tel.: (61) 352221022
Wool Retailer
N.A.I.C.S.: 314999

Subsidiary (US):

Nutrien Ag Solutions, Inc. (2)
3005 Rocky Mountain Ave, Loveland, CO 80538
Tel.: (970) 685-3300
Web Site: https://www.nutrienagsolutions.com
Agronomic Consulting Services & Supplies Distr
N.A.I.C.S.: 424910
Kaye Reitzenstein (VP-Fin)

Subsidiary (Domestic):

Loveland Products, Inc. (3)
3005 Rocky Mountain Ave, Loveland, CO 80538-9001
Tel.: (970) 356-8920
Web Site: https://www.lovelandproducts.com
Fertilizer, Plant Nutrition, Seed Treatment & Crop Protection Products Distr
N.A.I.C.S.: 424910

Subsidiary (Non-US):

United Agri Products Canada Inc. (3)
789 Donnybrook Drive, Dorchester, N0L 1G5, ON, Canada
Tel.: (519) 268-8001
Agricultural Chemical, Fertilizer & Seed Distr
N.A.I.C.S.: 424910

Subsidiary (Non-US):

Nutrien Europe S.A. (2)
Avenue Louise 326/36, 1050, Brussels, Belgium
Tel.: (32) 26467000
Fertilizer Distr
N.A.I.C.S.: 424690

Subsidiary (Non-US):

Agro Baltic GmbH (3)
Rungestrasse 17, 18107, Rostock, Germany
Tel.: (49) 381497870
Web Site: https://agro-baltic.de
Fertilizer Materials Whslr
N.A.I.C.S.: 424910

Nutrien Deutschland GmbH (3)
Mullerstrasse 13a, 21244, Buchholz, Germany
Tel.: (49) 418130060
Fertilizer Materials Whslr
N.A.I.C.S.: 424910

Nutrien Italia S.p.A. (3)
Via delle Cataratte 68, 57122, Livorno, Italy
Tel.: (39) 0586249999
Web Site: https://www.nutrienitalia.com
Fertilizer Distr
N.A.I.C.S.: 424690

Joint Venture (Non-US):

Profertil S.A. (2)
Manuela Saenz 323 Piso 8 - Of 803, Puerto Madero, 1107, Buenos Aires, Argentina (50%)
Tel.: (54) 91141212000
Web Site: https://www.profertil.com.ar
Fertilizer Production & Whslr
N.A.I.C.S.: 325311

Subsidiary (Non-US):

Ruralco Holdings Limited (2)
Level 5 Building A 26 Talavera Road, Macquarie Park, 2113, NSW, Australia (100%)
Tel.: (61) 299526555
Web Site: http://www.ruralco.com.au
Rev.: $1,493,465,274
Assets: $741,200,133
Liabilities: $506,482,595
Net Worth: $234,717,538
Earnings: $24,722,801
Emp.: 1,955
Fiscal Year-end: 09/30/2018
Agricultural Services
N.A.I.C.S.: 926140
Travis Dillon (CEO & Mng Dir)

Subsidiary (Domestic):

Ag Concepts Unlimited Pty. Ltd. (3)
200 Skipton Street, Ballarat, 3350, VIC, Australia
Tel.: (61) 1300987742
Web Site: http://www.agconcepts.com.au
Emp.: 5
Agricultural Advisory Services
N.A.I.C.S.: 926140
Robert Herrmann (Mng Dir)

Agfarm Pty. Ltd. (3)
Level 7 56 Clarence Street, Sydney, 2000, NSW, Australia
Tel.: (61) 283051000
Farm Product Whslr
N.A.I.C.S.: 424910
Anthony Hall (Mgr-NSW & QLD)

Archards Irrigation Pty. Ltd. (3)
22 Leitchville Rd, Cohuna, 3568, VIC, Australia
Tel.: (61) 354562664
Web Site: http://www.archards.com.au
Sales Range: $50-74.9 Million
Emp.: 45
Irrigation & Water Supply Equipments Whslr
N.A.I.C.S.: 221310

B.J. Underwood Pty. Ltd. (3)
137-143 Fitzgerald Road, Laverton North, Melbourne, 3026, VIC, Australia
Tel.: (61) 392404700
Web Site: http://www.ruralco.com.au
Emp.: 2
Commercial Wool Broking Services
N.A.I.C.S.: 425120

BR&C Agents Pty. Ltd. (3)
209 Karinie St, Swan Hill, 3585, VIC, Australia
Tel.: (61) 350329911
Web Site: https://www.brcagents.com.au
Emp.: 40
Livestock Broking Services
N.A.I.C.S.: 424520
Lee McNab (Gen Mgr)

INTERNATIONAL PUBLIC

CRT Real Estate Pty Ltd (3)
8a Murdoch Circuit, Brisbane, 4110, QLD, Australia (100%)
Tel.: (61) 732725400
Web Site: http://www.crtrealestate.com.au
Sales Range: $50-74.9 Million
Emp.: 1
Real Estate Services
N.A.I.C.S.: 531390

Combined Rural Traders Pty Limited (3)
Level 5 Building A 26 Talavera Road, Macquarie Park, 2113, NSW, Australia
Tel.: (61) 299526555
Web Site: https://www.crt.com.au
Sales Range: $25-49.9 Million
Emp.: 40
Organic Fertilizers Distr
N.A.I.C.S.: 424910

Dairy Livestock Services Pty. Ltd. (3)
Unit 11 85-91 Keilor Park Drive, PO Box 462, Tullamarine, 3043, VIC, Australia
Tel.: (61) 393389259
Web Site: https://www.dairylivestockservices.com.au
Sales Range: $50-74.9 Million
Emp.: 5
Livestock Auction Services
N.A.I.C.S.: 424520
Merryn Anderson (Office Mgr)

Davidson Cameron & Co. Narrabri Pty. Ltd. (3)
135 Maitland Street, Narrabri, 2390, NSW, Australia
Tel.: (61) 267922000
Web Site: https://www.dcco.com.au
Sales Range: $50-74.9 Million
Emp.: 5
Livestock Retailer
N.A.I.C.S.: 424520
Hunter Harley (Mgr-Livestock)

Davidson Cameron Board & Simmons Pty. Ltd. (3)
92 Erskine Street, Dubbo, 2830, NSW, Australia
Tel.: (61) 268848355
Web Site: http://www.graemeboard.com
Emp.: 100
Livestock Auction Services
N.A.I.C.S.: 424520

Davidson Cameron Clydsdale & Co. Pty. Ltd. (3)
Shop 2 Campbells Corner 177 Kelly Street, Scone, 2337, NSW, Australia
Tel.: (61) 265459070
Sales Range: $50-74.9 Million
Emp.: 3
Livestock Auction Services
N.A.I.C.S.: 424520
Warick Clydsdale (Mgr)

Davidson Cameron McCulloch Pty. Ltd. (3)
288 Peel Street, Tamworth, 2340, NSW, Australia
Tel.: (61) 267624440
Sales Range: $50-74.9 Million
Emp.: 4
Livestock & Property Auctioneers
N.A.I.C.S.: 424520

Davidson Cameron Pty. Ltd. (3)
207 George Street, Quirindi, 2343, NSW, Australia
Tel.: (61) 267462177
Sales Range: $50-74.9 Million
Emp.: 4
Livestock Auction Services
N.A.I.C.S.: 424520

Ensil Pty. Ltd. (3)
3 Lady Carrington Road, Otford, Wollongong, 2508, NSW, Australia
Tel.: (61) 242942442
Fencing Contract Services
N.A.I.C.S.: 238910

GDL Real Estate Pty. Ltd. (3)
83-89 Marshall St, PO Box 450, Goondiwindi, 4390, QLD, Australia
Tel.: (61) 746715025
Real Estate Property Management Services
N.A.I.C.S.: 531210

AND PRIVATE COMPANIES

Andrew McCallum *(Mgr)*

Grant Daniel Long Pty. Ltd. (3)
Warrego Centre Shop 2/8 Drayton St, PO Box 1016, Dalby, 4405, QLD, Australia
Tel.: (61) 746696955
Sales Range: $25-49.9 Million
Emp.: 15
Livestock & Property Management Services
N.A.I.C.S.: 115210

Ingham Farm Centre Pty. Ltd. (3)
49506 Townsville Rd, Ingham, 4850, QLD, Australia
Tel.: (61) 747761566
Web Site: http://www.ingham.ruralco.com.au
Sales Range: $50-74.9 Million
Emp.: 7
Agricultural Support Services
N.A.I.C.S.: 926140

Merredin Rural Supplies Pty Limited (3)
106 Barrack Street East, Merredin, 6415, WA, Australia
Tel.: (61) 890415574
Sales Range: $50-74.9 Million
Emp.: 6
Agricultural Products & Accessories Distr
N.A.I.C.S.: 424910
Nick Carlson *(Mgr)*

NT Rural Pty. Ltd. (3)
Shop 8/235 Musgrave St, Berserker, Rockhampton, 4701, QLD, Australia
Tel.: (61) 749211084
Property Management Services
N.A.I.C.S.: 531312

Primaries of WA Pty. Ltd. (3)
18 Wellard Street, Bibra Lake, 6163, WA, Australia
Tel.: (61) 894341622
Web Site: http://www.primaries.com.au
Emp.: 50
Agricultural Support Services
N.A.I.C.S.: 926140

Queensland Rural Pty. Ltd. (3)
129 Walsh Street, PO Box 1234, Mareeba, 4880, QLD, Australia
Tel.: (61) 740923522
Web Site: http://www.qldrural.com.au
Livestock Management, Real Estate & Insurance Services
N.A.I.C.S.: 424520

Rawlinson & Brown Pty Ltd (3)
50-56 Banna Avenue, Griffith, 2680, NSW, Australia (72%)
Tel.: (61) 269641933
Web Site: http://www.rawbrown.com.au
Sales Range: $25-49.9 Million
Emp.: 45
Real Estate, Insurance, Agribusiness & Livestock Stock & Station Services
N.A.I.C.S.: 531390
Renee J. James *(Property Officer)*

Roberts Don Mac Pty. Ltd. (3)
200 Argyle St, Hobart, 7000, TAS, Australia
Tel.: (61) 362344322
Web Site: https://www.robertsdonmac.com.au
Emp.: 7
Garden Equipments Distr
N.A.I.C.S.: 423820

Roberts Hawkins Pty. Ltd. (3)
Ground Floor 441 St Kilda Road, Melbourne, 3004, VIC, Australia
Tel.: (61) 398665588
Web Site: http://www.prh.com.au
Sales Range: $50-74.9 Million
Emp.: 8
Property Management Services
N.A.I.C.S.: 531312

Roberts Limited (3)
52 Kennedy Dr, Cambridge, 7170, TAS, Australia
Tel.: (61) 0023 1444
Web Site: http://www.robertsltd.com.au
Sales Range: $300-349.9 Million
Emp.: 700
Agricultural & Real Estate Management Services
N.A.I.C.S.: 926140

Roberts Shearwater Pty. Ltd. (3)
2 Quinlan Crescent, Shearwater, Port Sorell, 7307, TAS, Australia
Tel.: (61) 364286700
Web Site: https://www.robertsre.com.au
Emp.: 5
Real Estate Manangement Services
N.A.I.C.S.: 531390
Corinne Price *(Principal)*

Rodwells & Co NSW Pty. Ltd. (3)
174 Hardinge St, Deniliquin, 2710, NSW, Australia
Tel.: (61) 358818744
Emp.: 7
Livestock Breeding & Wool Broking Services
N.A.I.C.S.: 115210

Rodwells & Co Pty. Ltd. (3)
29 Aitken Street, Alexandra, 3714, VIC, Australia
Tel.: (61) 357722444
Web Site: http://www.rodwells.com.au
Sales Range: $25-49.9 Million
Emp.: 6
Livestock Breeding & Wool Broking Services
N.A.I.C.S.: 115210

Ruralco Finance Pty. Ltd. (3)
4/100 Simpson Street, Ballarat North, Ballarat, 3350, VIC, Australia
Tel.: (61) 407 604582
Web Site: http://www.ruralcofinance.com.au
Business Finance Lending Services
N.A.I.C.S.: 522299

Southern Australian Livestock Pty. Ltd. (3)
2 Smith Street, PO Box 23, Naracoorte, 5271, SA, Australia
Tel.: (61) 887601300
Sales Range: $10-24.9 Million
Emp.: 30
Livestock Breeding Services
N.A.I.C.S.: 115210
Will Nolan *(Mgr-Livestock)*

Southern Wool Warehousing Pty. Ltd. (3)
137-143 Fitzgerald Road, Laverton North, Melbourne, 3026, VIC, Australia
Tel.: (61) 392404700
Sheep Farming, Wool Handling & Logistics Services
N.A.I.C.S.: 112410

Stevens Egan Johnston Pty. Ltd. (3)
26 Anderson St, Leongatha, 3953, VIC, Australia
Tel.: (61) 356624033
Sales Range: $25-49.9 Million
Emp.: 30
Real Estate Management Services & Live Stock Agents
N.A.I.C.S.: 531210

Tasmania Farm Equipment Pty. Ltd. (3)
1 Ferguson Drive, Quoiba, 7310, TAS, Australia
Tel.: (61) 364241511
Web Site: http://www.tfe.com.au
Sales Range: $25-49.9 Million
Emp.: 32
Agricultural Machinery Distr
N.A.I.C.S.: 423820
Ian Hayes *(Mgr-State Svc)*

Terra Firma Fertilisers Pty Limited (3)
17-19 Enterprise Drive, Beaudesert, 4285, QLD, Australia
Tel.: (61) 755412322
Web Site: https://www.tff.com.au
Sales Range: $25-49.9 Million
Emp.: 10
Organic Pellets Mfr
N.A.I.C.S.: 325311

Territory Rural McPherson Pty Ltd. (3)
293 Stuart Highway, Alice Springs, 0870, NT, Australia
Tel.: (61) 889534255
Livestock & Real Estate Management Services
N.A.I.C.S.: 112990

Total Eden McCrackens Group Pty Limited (3)
71 F Mathews Ave Airport W, Airport W, Melbourne, 3042, VIC, Australia
Tel.: (61) 393356666
Holding Company; Water Management Services
N.A.I.C.S.: 551112

Subsidiary (Domestic):

Total Eden Pty Limited (4)
6 Port Kembla Drive, Bibra Lake, 6163, WA, Australia
Tel.: (61) 894347575
Web Site: http://www.totaleden.com.au
Sales Range: $50-74.9 Million
Emp.: 400
Waste Management Services
N.A.I.C.S.: 221310

Subsidiary (Non-US):

Elegant Landscapes Pty Limited (5)
Tel.: (61) 402572452
Web Site: http://www.elegantlandscapes.net.au
Commercial & Residential Landscaping Services
N.A.I.C.S.: 561730
Jason Chapman *(Founder)*

Subsidiary (Domestic):

Town & Country Agrimerchants Pty Limited (3)
1-5 Bantlay St Waithill Park, Girraween, 2164, NSW, Australia
Tel.: (61) 297690777
Web Site: http://www.tc.ruralco.com.au
Sales Range: $50-74.9 Million
Emp.: 80
Farm Products Retailer
N.A.I.C.S.: 424910
Sharmila Shankar *(Mgr-Comml)*

Wesfal Pty Limited (3)
8 Camp Street, Forbes, 2871, NSW, Australia (62%)
Tel.: (61) 268514200
Sales Range: $50-74.9 Million
Emp.: 8
Farm & Garden Machinery Distr
N.A.I.C.S.: 423820
Greg Rout *(Mng Dir)*

Canpotex Limited (1)
Suite 700 409 - Third Avenue South, Saskatoon, S7K 5R5, SK, Canada (66.67%)
Tel.: (306) 931-2200
Web Site: https://www.canpotex.com
Potash Export, Marketer & Distr
N.A.I.C.S.: 424590
Kendra Kuse *(VP-HR & Admin)*

Subsidiary (Non-US):

Canpotex (Japan) Limited (2)
Suite 1908 East Tower Shin Aoyama Building, 1 1 1 Minami Aoyama Minato ku, Tokyo, 107 0062, Japan
Tel.: (81) 334788260
Web Site: http://www.canpotex.com
Potash Products Exporter, Marketer & Distr
N.A.I.C.S.: 424590

Canpotex International Pte. Limited (2)
38 Beach Road 17-13 South Beach Tower, Singapore, 189767, Singapore
Tel.: (65) 67330221
Potash Product Exporter, Marketer & Distr
N.A.I.C.S.: 424590

Nutrien Ag Solutions (Canada) Inc. (1)
3735 East Quance Street, Regina, S4V 3A4, SK, Canada
Web Site: https://www.nutrienagsolutions.ca
Agricultural Services
N.A.I.C.S.: 115116

Potash Corporation of Saskatchewan Inc. (1)
Suite 1700 211 19th Street East, Saskatoon, S7K 5R6, SK, Canada
Tel.: (306) 933-8500
Web Site: http://www.nutrien.com
Phosphate & Nitrogen Chemicals & Fertilizers Distr & Mfr
N.A.I.C.S.: 325312

NUTRIEN LTD.

Plant (Domestic):

Nutrien Potash - Allan (2)
Highway 397 N, PO Box 301, Allan, S0K 0C0, SK, Canada
Tel.: (306) 257-3312
Web Site: http://www.nutrien.com
Potash Mining
N.A.I.C.S.: 212390

Nutrien Potash - Cory (2)
PO Box 1320, Saskatoon, S7K 3N9, SK, Canada
Tel.: (306) 382-0525
Web Site: http://www.nutrien.com
Potash Mining
N.A.I.C.S.: 212390

Nutrien Potash - Lanigan (2)
PO Box 3100, Lanigan, S0K 2M0, SK, Canada
Tel.: (306) 365-2030
Web Site: http://www.nutrien.com
Potash Mining
N.A.I.C.S.: 212390

Nutrien Potash - Patience Lake (2)
Box 509, Patience Lake, Saskatoon, S7K 3L6, SK, Canada
Tel.: (306) 667-4300
Web Site: http://www.nutrien.com
Potash Mining
N.A.I.C.S.: 212390

Nutrien Potash - Rocanville (2)
PO Box 460, Rocanville, S0A 3L0, SK, Canada
Tel.: (306) 645-2870
Web Site: http://www.nutrien.com
Potash Mining
N.A.I.C.S.: 212390

Subsidiary (US):

PCS Administration (USA), Inc. (2)
500 Lk Cook Rd Ste 150, Deerfield, IL 60015
Tel.: (847) 849-4200
Phosphate Fertilizer Materials, Potash, Sulphur, Sulphuric Acid & Feed Ingredients Mfr & Distr
N.A.I.C.S.: 325312

Subsidiary (Domestic):

PCS Nitrogen, Inc. (3)
500 Lk Cook Rd Ste 150, Deerfield, IL 60015
Tel.: (847) 849-4200
itrogen Chemicals & Fertilizers for Agricultural & Industrial Uses Mfr & Distr
N.A.I.C.S.: 325311

Subsidiary (Domestic):

PCS Nitrogen Fertilizer, L.P. (4)
PO Box 1483, Augusta, GA 30903
Tel.: (706) 469-1200
Potash Mining
N.A.I.C.S.: 212390

Subsidiary (Domestic):

PCS Nitrogen Fertilizer Operations, Inc. (5)
PO Box 307, Geismar, LA 70734
Tel.: (504) 621-1500
Web Site: http://www.nutrien.com
Nitrogenous Fertilizer Mfr
N.A.I.C.S.: 325311

Subsidiary (Domestic):

PCS Nitrogen Ohio, L.P. (4)
1900 Fort Amanda Rd, Lima, OH 45804
Tel.: (419) 879-8989
Web Site: http://www.nutrien.com
Potash Mining
N.A.I.C.S.: 212390

PCS Nitrogen Trinidad Corporation (4)
1101 Skokie Blvd 400, Northbrook, IL 60062-4123
Tel.: (847) 849-4200
Nitrogenous Fertilizer Mfr
N.A.I.C.S.: 325311

Unit (Non-US):

PCS Nitrogen Trinidad Limited (5)

NUTRIEN LTD.

Nutrien Ltd.—(Continued)
Mediterranean Drive, PO Bag 201, Point Lisas, Couva, Trinidad & Tobago
Tel.: (868) 6362205
Web Site: https://www.nutrien.com
Anhydrous Ammonia, Nitrogen & Granular Urea Production
N.A.I.C.S.: 325311

Subsidiary (Domestic):

PCS Phosphate Company, Inc. (3)
500 Lk Cook Rd Ste 150, Deerfield, IL 60015
Tel.: (847) 849-4200
Phosphate Mining Services
N.A.I.C.S.: 212390

Unit (Domestic):

Nutrien Phosphate - Aurora (4)
1530 Hwy 306 S, Aurora, NC 27806-0048
Tel.: (252) 322-4111
Sales & Marketing of Phosphate Fertilizer Products
N.A.I.C.S.: 325180

Nutrien Phosphate - Marseilles (4)
2660 E US Rte 6, Marseilles, IL 61341-0088
Tel.: (815) 795-5111
Phosphatic Fertilizer Mfr & Distr
N.A.I.C.S.: 325312

Nutrien Phosphates - Cincinnati (4)
10818 Paddys Run Rd, Harrison, OH 45030
Tel.: (513) 738-1261
Phosphate Fertilizer Mfr
N.A.I.C.S.: 325312

Subsidiary (Domestic):

White Springs Agricultural Chemicals, Inc. (4)
15843 SE 78th St, White Springs, FL 32096
Tel.: (386) 397-8101
Web Site: http://www.nutrien.com
Phosphate Fertilizer & Feed Producer
N.A.I.C.S.: 325312

Subsidiary (Domestic):

PCS Sales (USA), Inc. (3)
500 Lk Cook Rd Ste 150, Deerfield, IL 60015
Tel.: (847) 849-4200
Potash, Soda & Borate Mineral Mining
N.A.I.C.S.: 212390

Van Horn Inc. (1)
94 E 150 N Rd, Cerro Gordo, IL 61818
Tel.: (217) 677-2131
Web Site: http://www.vanhorninc.com
Fertilizers & Agricultural Chemicals Mfr & Distr
N.A.I.C.S.: 325314

NUTRIGOLD LIMITED

Unit 7 Tidwell Ct Liverton Bus Park, PO Box 217, Exmouth, EX8 2NR, Devon, United Kingdom
Tel.: (44) 845 603 5690
Web Site: http://www.nutrigoldsupplements.uk
Year Founded: 1999
Nutraceutical Products Sales
N.A.I.C.S.: 424210
Andrew Wren (Mng Dir)

NUTRINOR COOPERATIVE AGRO-ALIMENTAIRE DU SAGUENAY LAC ST-JEAN

425 Melancon, Saint-Bruno, G0W 2L0, QC, Canada
Tel.: (418) 343-2470
Web Site: http://www.nutrinor.com
Year Founded: 1949
Rev.: $246,855,372
Emp.: 400
Dairy Products Mfr
N.A.I.C.S.: 311514
Sylvain Martel (Pres)

NUTRIPLANT INDUSTRIA E COMERCIO S.A.

388 Arnaldo Street Barueri, Sao Paulo, 06415-110, Brazil
Tel.: (55) 41617600
Web Site: https://www.nutriplant.com.br
Year Founded: 1970
NUTR3—(BRAZ)
Rev.: $32,007,650
Assets: $18,462,844
Liabilities: $12,227,883
Net Worth: $6,234,962
Earnings: $627,089
Fiscal Year-end: 12/31/23
Chemical Products Mfr
N.A.I.C.S.: 325320
Emilio Pansa (Co-CEO)

NUTRITION SC PUBLIC COMPANY LIMITED

47/2 Moo 6 Phutthamonthon Sai 4 Road, Krathum Lom Sampran, Nakhon Pathom, 73220, Thailand
Tel.: (66) 28404333
Web Site: https://www.nutritionsc.co.th
Year Founded: 1981
NTSC—(THA)
Rev.: $28,086,470
Assets: $34,734,357
Liabilities: $6,814,573
Net Worth: $27,919,784
Earnings: $2,030,593
Fiscal Year-end: 12/31/23
Food Additives Mfr
N.A.I.C.S.: 325199
Darunee Edwards (Co-Chm)

NUTRITIONAL GROWTH SOLUTIONS LTD.

3 Hanechoshet Street, Tel Aviv, 6971068, Israel
Web Site: https://www.ngsolutions.co
Year Founded: 2013
NGS—(ASX)
Rev.: $2,984,000
Assets: $936,000
Liabilities: $1,113,000
Net Worth: ($177,000)
Earnings: $2,893,000
Fiscal Year-end: 12/31/23
Biotechnology Research & Development Services
N.A.I.C.S.: 541714
Moshe Phillip (Chief Scientific Officer)

Subsidiaries:

NG Solutions Inc. (1)
4801 S University Dr 134, Davie, FL 33328
Tel.: (954) 367-2781
Web Site: https://ngsolutionsproducts.com
Information Technology Consulting Services
N.A.I.C.S.: 541512

NUTRITIONAL HOLDINGS LIMITED

Unit 20 Boulevade Business Park 14 Belladona Road Unit 5 1 Randworth Close Parkhill, Durban, 4319, South Africa
Tel.: (27) 718853203   ZA
Web Site: https://nutritionalholdings.co.za
Year Founded: 2004
NUT—(JSE)
Rev.: $2,903,758
Assets: $3,415,254
Liabilities: $1,758,584
Net Worth: $1,656,669
Earnings: $422,524
Emp.: 36
Fiscal Year-end: 02/29/20
Pharmaceutical Product Mfr & Whslr
N.A.I.C.S.: 325412

NUTRYFARM INTERNATIONAL LIMITED

Victoria Place 5th Floor 31 Victoria Street, Hamilton, HM 10, Bermuda
Tel.: (441) 2948000
Year Founded: 2014
AZT—(SES)
Rev.: $7,941,041
Assets: $23,837,052
Liabilities: $22,888,404
Net Worth: $948,648
Earnings: ($6,257,078)
Fiscal Year-end: 09/30/20
Investment Services
N.A.I.C.S.: 523999
Meng Cheng (CEO)

Subsidiaries:

Huge Hill Beijing Technology Development Co., Ltd (1)
Room 2611 Lanbao International Center No A3 Xidawanglu, Chaoyang District, Beijing, 100026, China
Tel.: (86) 10 85999322
Surveillance System Installation Services
N.A.I.C.S.: 238210

LottVision (Hong Kong) Limited (1)
Unit 3606 7 36 F AIA Tower 183 Electric Rd, North Point, China (Hong Kong)
Tel.: (852) 2110 3162
Business Support Services
N.A.I.C.S.: 561499

NUUO, INC.

10F No 909 Zhongzheng Rd, Zhonghe Dist, New Taipei City, Taiwan
Tel.: (886) 277392260
Web Site: https://www.nuuo.com
6419—(TPE)
Rev.: $5,597,911
Assets: $15,427,852
Liabilities: $5,128,506
Net Worth: $10,299,347
Earnings: $2,242,848
Fiscal Year-end: 12/31/22
Hardware Product Mfr
N.A.I.C.S.: 332510
Yang Wen-Pin (Chm)

NUUVERA INC.

5 Hazelton Avenue Suite 300, Toronto, M5R 2E1, ON, Canada
Tel.: (416) 972-6294   ON
Year Founded: 2015
Holding Company
N.A.I.C.S.: 551112
Ronald D. Schmeichel (Pres, CEO, CFO & Sec)

NUVEI CORPORATION

1100 Boulevard Rene-Levesque O Suite 900, Montreal, H3B 4N4, QC, Canada
Tel.: (514) 313-1190
Web Site: https://www.nuvei.com
NVEI—(NASDAQ)
Rev.: $843,323,000
Assets: $3,524,669,000
Liabilities: $1,545,179,000
Net Worth: $1,979,490,000
Earnings: $61,955,000
Emp.: 1,990
Fiscal Year-end: 12/31/22
Electronic Payment Processing Services
N.A.I.C.S.: 522320
Philip Fayer (Chm & CEO)

Subsidiaries:

Base Commerce, LLC (1)
5055 E Washington St Ste 300, Phoenix, AZ 85034
Web Site: http://www.BaseCommerce.com
Sales Range: $10-24.9 Million
Emp.: 17
Financial Planning Services
N.A.I.C.S.: 523940
Jason E. Kafer (CTO)

INTERNATIONAL PUBLIC

Paya Holdings Inc. (1)
303 Perimeter Ctr N Ste 600, Atlanta, GA 30346
Tel.: (800) 261-0240
Web Site: https://paya.com
Rev.: $282,743,000
Assets: $744,260,000
Liabilities: $487,366,000
Net Worth: $256,894,000
Earnings: $8,262,000
Emp.: 300
Fiscal Year-end: 12/31/2022
Financial Services
N.A.I.C.S.: 522320
Jeff Hack (CEO)

Subsidiary (Domestic):

Paya, Inc. (2)
11710 Plz America Dr Ste 900, Reston, VA 20190
Web Site: https://paya.com
Credit Card Processing Services
N.A.I.C.S.: 522320
Jeff Hack (CEO)

NUVISTA ENERGY LTD.

2500 525 8th Ave SW, Calgary, T2P 1G1, AB, Canada
Tel.: (403) 538-8500   AB
Web Site: https://nvaenergy.com
Year Founded: 2003
NVA—(TSX)
Rev.: $332,185,032
Assets: $1,688,027,252
Liabilities: $783,012,214
Net Worth: $905,015,038
Earnings: ($154,796,784)
Emp.: 86
Fiscal Year-end: 12/31/20
Oil & Natural Gas Exploration
N.A.I.C.S.: 211120
Ryan Paulgaard (VP-Production & Facilities)

Subsidiaries:

NuVista Resources (1)
Bronson N Plant, Paradise Hill, S0M 2G0, SK, Canada
Tel.: (306) 344-4900
Oil & Gas Services
N.A.I.C.S.: 237120

NUVOTEC CO., LTD.

42-4 Taejang Industrial Complex-gil, Wonju, 220962, Gangwon-do, Korea (South)
Tel.: (82) 337346001
Web Site: https://www.nuvotec.co.kr
Year Founded: 1990
060260—(KRS)
Rev.: $35,269,595
Assets: $40,174,220
Liabilities: $27,179,192
Net Worth: $12,995,028
Earnings: ($2,071,821)
Emp.: 125
Fiscal Year-end: 12/31/22
Plastic Pipe Mfr & Whslr
N.A.I.C.S.: 326122
Hwang Moon-Ki (Chm & CEO)

NUVOTON TECHNOLOGY CORPORATION

No 4 Creation Rd III Hsinchu Science Park, Hsin-chu, 00300, Taiwan
Tel.: (886) 35770066
Web Site: https://www.nuvoton.com
Year Founded: 2008
4919—(TAI)
Rev.: $1,155,961,531
Assets: $1,037,973,537
Liabilities: $490,831,925
Net Worth: $547,141,612
Earnings: $79,153,468
Emp.: 3,660
Fiscal Year-end: 12/31/23
Semiconductor Equipment Mfr
N.A.I.C.S.: 334413
Sean Tai (Pres)

AND PRIVATE COMPANIES — NV BEKAERT SA

Subsidiaries:

Atfields Manufacturing Technology Corporation (1)
800 Higashiyama, Uozu, 937-8585, Japan
Tel.: (81) 765223138
Web Site: https://atfields.com
Emp.: 222
Information Technology Services
N.A.I.C.S.: 541512

Nuvoton Electronics Technology (H.K.) Ltd. (1)
Unit 9-11 22F Millennium City 2 378 Kwun Tong Road, Kowloon, China (Hong Kong)
Tel.: (852) 27513100
Web Site: http://www.nuvoton.com
Semiconductor & Electronic Component Distr
N.A.I.C.S.: 423690

Subsidiary (Non-US):

Nuvoton Electronics Technology (Shenzhen) Ltd. (2)
8F Microprofit Building Gaoxinnan 6 Road High-Tech Industrial Park, Nanshan Dist, Shenzhen, 518057, China
Tel.: (86) 75583515350
Semiconductor & Electronic Component Distr
N.A.I.C.S.: 423690

Nuvoton Electronics Technology (Shanghai) Ltd. (1)
Unit 2701 27F 2299 Yan An Road West, Shanghai, 200336, China
Tel.: (86) 2162365999
Semiconductor & Electronic Component Distr
N.A.I.C.S.: 423690

Nuvoton Technology Corp. (1)
2727 N 1st St, San Jose, CA 95134
Tel.: (408) 544-1718
Semiconductor & Electronic Component Distr
N.A.I.C.S.: 423690

Nuvoton Technology India Private Limited (1)
Suite 2 Tech Park Business Centre Ground Floor Innovator Bldg, International Tech Park Whitefield, Bengaluru, India
Tel.: (91) 8041880600
Semiconductor & Electronic Component Distr
N.A.I.C.S.: 423690

Nuvoton Technology Israel Ltd. (1)
8 Hasadnaot Street, Herzliyya, 4672835, Israel
Tel.: (972) 99702000
Semiconductor & Electronic Component Distr
N.A.I.C.S.: 423690

NUWAY ORGANIC NATURALS INDIA LIMITED
N H 1 Mile Stone 232 Delhi-Amritsar Village Devi Nagar, Rajpura, 140401, Punjab, India
Tel.: (91) 1762644334   In
Web Site:
   https://www.nuwaycare.com
Year Founded: 1995
531819—(BOM)
Rev.: $40,585
Assets: $2,836,628
Liabilities: $6,958,396
Net Worth: ($4,121,767)
Earnings: $24,867
Emp.: 9
Fiscal Year-end: 03/31/23
Vodka & Cosmetic Product Mfr
N.A.I.C.S.: 312130

NV BEKAERT SA
Bekaertstraat 2, BE-8550, Zwevegem, Belgium
Tel.: (32) 56766100   BE
Web Site: https://www.bekaert.com
Year Founded: 1880
BEKAY—(OTCIQ)
Rev.: $4,633,380,642
Assets: $5,266,815,944
Liabilities: $3,381,399,991
Net Worth: $1,885,415,953
Earnings: $181,824,965
Emp.: 27,455
Fiscal Year-end: 12/31/20
Steel Wire, Wire Products, Steel Cord & Advanced Materials Mfr
N.A.I.C.S.: 331222
Matthew Taylor *(CEO)*

Subsidiaries:

Acma SA (1)
Maruri 1942, Renca, Santiago, Chile
Tel.: (56) 223506610
Web Site: http://www.acma.cl
Electro-Welded Product Mfr
N.A.I.C.S.: 333992

BBRG Finance (UK) Ltd. (1)
Ground Floor Icon Building Balby Carr Bank, Doncaster, DN4 5JQ, South Yorkshire, United Kingdom
Tel.: (44) 7452391966
Web Site: http://www.bbrgfinanceuk.com
Financial Services
N.A.I.C.S.: 523999
Vinay Jha *(Mgr-IT)*

BOSFA Pty. Ltd. (1)
48B Kewdale Road, Kewdale, 6105, WA, Australia
Tel.: (61) 894517533
Steel Cord & Advanced Material Mfr
N.A.I.C.S.: 331222

Bekaert (China) Technology Research and Development Co Ltd (1)
No 98 Hongtong Rd, Changshan Town, Jiangyin, 214400, China
Tel.: (86) 51086009666
Drawn Steel Wire Product Mfr
N.A.I.C.S.: 331222

Bekaert (Qingdao) Wire Products Co Ltd (1)
East Of Guanjiada Village Fuyuan Industrial Park Development Zone, Qingdao, 266555, China
Tel.: (86) 53280983069
Wire Product Mfr
N.A.I.C.S.: 332618

Bekaert (Schweiz) AG (1)
Mellingerstrasse 1, CH-5400, Baden, Switzerland   (100%)
Tel.: (41) 562036040
Sales Range: $10-24.9 Million
N.A.I.C.S.: 332618

Bekaert (Shandong) Tire Cord Co Ltd (1)
No 1 Bekaert Road Economic Technology Development Zone, 264205, Weihai, Shandong, China
Tel.: (86) 6315969800
Textile Machinery Mfr
N.A.I.C.S.: 333248

Bekaert (Thailand) Co., Ltd. (1)
No 64/26 Moo 4 Amphur Pluakdaeng, Eastern Seaboard Industrial Estate Tambol, Pluak Daeng, 21140, Rayong, Thailand
Tel.: (66) 38923558
Steel Cord & Advanced Material Mfr
N.A.I.C.S.: 331222

Bekaert A/S (1)
Ladegaardsvej 2, 7100, Vejle, Denmark   (100%)
Tel.: (45) 70209618
Web Site: http://www.bekaert.com
Sales Range: Less than $1 Million
Emp.: 5
N.A.I.C.S.: 332618

Bekaert Advanced Products (Shanghai) Co Ltd (1)
No 555 North Riying Road Shanghai Waigaoqiao Free Trade Zone, 200131, Shanghai, China
Tel.: (86) 21 5064 35 49
Web Site: http://www.bekaert.com
Drawn Steel Wire Product Mfr
N.A.I.C.S.: 331222

Bekaert Asia Shanghai Office (1)
1603 Shartex Plaza, 88 Zun Yi Nan Lu, 200336, Shanghai, China   (100%)
Tel.: (86) 162952233
Sales Range: $25-49.9 Million
Emp.: 80
N.A.I.C.S.: 332618

Bekaert Benelux N.V. (1)
Financial Services Ctr Bekaertstraat 2, B 8550, Zwevegem, Belgium   (100%)
Tel.: (32) 56766999
Web Site: http://www.bekaert.com
Sales Range: $250-299.9 Million
Emp.: 1,000
N.A.I.C.S.: 332618

Bekaert Binjiang Advanced Products Co Ltd (1)
No 1 Botong Rd Jiangyin Economic Development Zone Development, Jiangyin, 214434, China
Tel.: (86) 51086199280
Steel Wire Drawing Services
N.A.I.C.S.: 331222
Qiu Aimin *(Engr-IT)*

Bekaert Binjiang Steel Cord Co Ltd (1)
No 358 Binjiang East Rd Hi-Tech Industrial Park, Economic Development Zone, Jiangyin, 214434, China
Tel.: (86) 51086198658
Drawn Steel Wire Mfr
N.A.I.C.S.: 331222

Bekaert Bradford UK Ltd. (1)
Park House Road GB, Low Moor, Bradford, BD12 0PX, West Yorkshire, United Kingdom
Tel.: (44) 1274696700
Steel Cord & Advanced Material Mfr
N.A.I.C.S.: 331222

Bekaert Combustion Technology BV (1)
J C van Markenstraat 19, NL-9403 AR, Assen, Netherlands
Tel.: (31) 592345145
Web Site: https://www.bekaert.com
Gas Burner Mfr
N.A.I.C.S.: 333414

Bekaert Coordinatiecentrum N.V. (1)
Financial Services Ctr Bekaertstraat 2, Zwevegem, 8550, Belgium   (100%)
Tel.: (32) 56766783
Sales Range: $25-49.9 Million
Emp.: 30
In-House Banking Services
N.A.I.C.S.: 522110
Frank Vromant *(CFO)*

Bekaert Corporation (1)
3200 W Market St Ste 303, Akron, OH 44333-3326   (100%)
Tel.: (330) 867-3325
Web Site: http://www.bekaert.com
Sales Range: $25-49.9 Million
Emp.: 30
Sales & Marketing Office
N.A.I.C.S.: 331222

Subsidiary (Domestic):

Bekaert Contours Ltd. (2)
510 Collins Blvd, Orrville, OH 44667-9796
Tel.: (330) 683-5060
Web Site:
   http://www.bekaertshapedwire.com
Sales Range: $75-99.9 Million
Emp.: 200
Rolled Steel Wires & Rods Mfr
N.A.I.C.S.: 331221
Otto Simmerman *(Plant Mgr)*

Plant (Domestic):

Bekaert Corporation (2)
1881 Bekaert Dr, Van Buren, AR 72956-6807   (100%)
Tel.: (479) 474-5211
Web Site: http://www.bekaert.com
Sales Range: $75-99.9 Million
Mfr of Farm Fences & Industrial Steel Wires
N.A.I.C.S.: 332618

Bekaert Corporation (2)
12TW Alexander Dr, Research Triangle Park, NC 27709
Tel.: (919) 485-8995
Web Site: http://www.bekaert.com
Sales Range: $50-74.9 Million
Emp.: 5
N.A.I.C.S.: 332618

Bekaert Corporation (2)
1395 S Marietta Pkwy SE Bldg 500, Marietta, GA 30067-4440   (100%)
Tel.: (770) 421-8520
Web Site: http://www.bekaertna.com
Sales Range: $25-49.9 Million
Emp.: 60
N.A.I.C.S.: 332618
Rick McWhirt *(Pres)*

Subsidiary (Domestic):

Bekaert Specialty Films LLC (2)
4540 Viewridge Ave, San Diego, CA 92123
Tel.: (858) 576-0200
Solar Film Distr
N.A.I.C.S.: 423330

Bekaert Trade Latin America N.V. (2)
1400 NW 107th Ave Ste 420, Miami, FL 33172   (100%)
Tel.: (305) 463-8979
Web Site: http://www.bekaert.com
Sales Range: $50-74.9 Million
Emp.: 4
N.A.I.C.S.: 332618

Bekaert Engineering (1)
Meuleekestraat 139, Ingelmunster, 8770, Belgium   (100%)
Tel.: (32) 51333411
Web Site: http://www.bekaert.com
Sales Range: $75-99.9 Million
Emp.: 250
Engineering Activities
N.A.I.C.S.: 541330
Willem Dewild *(VP)*

Bekaert France S.A. (1)
Parc De Haute Technologie, 4 Rue Alexis da Doucaville, F-92183, Antony, Cedex, France   (100%)
Tel.: (33) 140962626
Web Site: http://www.bekaert.com
Sales Range: $25-49.9 Million
Emp.: 25
Wire Product Sales
N.A.I.C.S.: 332618

Bekaert GmbH (1)
Grungasse 16, 1050, Vienna, Austria   (100%)
Tel.: (43) 223645180
Web Site: http://www.bekaert.com
Sales Range: $50-74.9 Million
Wire Product Mfr
N.A.I.C.S.: 332618

Bekaert GmbH (1)
Siemensstrase 24, 61267, Neu-Anspach, Germany
Tel.: (49) 6081445610
Web Site: http://www.bekaert.com
Wire Product Mfr
N.A.I.C.S.: 332618

Bekaert Guatemala SA (1)
18 Calle 24-69 Zona 10 Torre III Nivel 6 Ofc 604, Empresarial Zona Pradera, Guatemala, Guatemala
Tel.: (502) 22617592
Steel Cord & Advanced Material Mfr
N.A.I.C.S.: 331222

Bekaert Heating Technology (Suzhou) Co., Ltd. (1)
No 9 Xi Xin Road, Taicang, China
Tel.: (86) 51233069302
Steel Cord & Advanced Material Mfr
N.A.I.C.S.: 331222

Bekaert Iberica Holding SL (1)
Calle Lopez Bravo Pg Ind De Villalonqueja 94, Burgos, 9001, Spain
Tel.: (34) 947298536
Investment Management Service
N.A.I.C.S.: 523999

Bekaert Ideal SL (1)
Calle Lopez Bravo Pg Ind De Villalo 94, Burgos, 9001, Spain
Tel.: (34) 947298536
Web Site: http://www.bekaert.com
Sales Range: $100-124.9 Million
Emp.: 100
Wire Product Mfr

NV BEKAERT SA

NV Bekaert SA—(Continued)
N.A.I.C.S.: 332618

Bekaert Industries Pvt Ltd (1)
IndiQube Orchid 6th Floor Next to Don Bosco School Loop Road, Yerawada, Pune, 411006, Maharastra, India
Tel.: (91) 2066276600
Web Site: https://www.bekaert.com
Sales Range: $200-249.9 Million
Emp.: 600
Wire Product Mfr
N.A.I.C.S.: 332618

Subsidiary (Domestic):

Bekaert Mukand Wire Industries Pvt Ltd (2)
B-21 Lonand MIDC MIDC Road Lonand Tal Khandala, Satara, 415 521, Maharastra, India
Tel.: (91) 21 69 30 47 00
Web Site: http://www.bekaert.com
Sales Range: $50-74.9 Million
Emp.: 250
Stainless Steel Wire Mfr
N.A.I.C.S.: 332618

Bekaert Izmit Celik Kord Sanayi ve Ticaret AS (1)
Alikahya Fatih Mah Sanayi Cad No 88, TR-41310, Izmit, Kocaeli, Turkiye
Tel.: (90) 2623168500
Sales Range: $150-199.9 Million
Emp.: 40
Steel Building Materials Distr
N.A.I.C.S.: 423320
Jerome Lebecque (Gen Mgr)

Bekaert Japan (1)
Kyobashi TD Bldg 4F 1-2-5 Kyobashi, Chuo-ku, Tokyo, 104-0031, Japan (100%)
Tel.: (81) 332432525
Sales Range: $1-9.9 Million
N.A.I.C.S.: 332618

Bekaert Korea Ltd (1)
3F Changwoo Bldg Dogok-Dong 130 Dogok-ro, Gangnam-gu, Seoul, 06259, Korea (South)
Tel.: (82) 25398760
Sales Range: $25-49.9 Million
Emp.: 6
Wire Product Mfr
N.A.I.C.S.: 332618
Jan Chun (Gen Mgr)

Bekaert Management (Shanghai) Co Ltd (1)
7F block 3 East Hongqiao Hub No 29 Suhong Road, Shanghai, 201106, China
Tel.: (86) 13918243096
Web Site: http://www.bekaert.com.cn
Wire Product Mfr
N.A.I.C.S.: 332618

Bekaert Norge AS (1)
Forsta Langgatan 28b, 413 27, Gothenburg, Sweden
Tel.: (46) 317041640
Web Site: http://www.bekaert.com
Wire Product Mfr
N.A.I.C.S.: 332618

Bekaert North America Management Corporation (1)
1395 S Marietta Pkwy Bldg 500 Ste 100, Marietta, GA 30067-4440
Tel.: (770) 421-8520
Steel Cord & Advanced Material Mfr
N.A.I.C.S.: 331222

Bekaert Poland Sp. z o.o. (1)
ul Ku Wisle 7, PL-00707, Warsaw, Poland
Tel.: (48) 228514163
Steel Cord & Advanced Material Mfr
N.A.I.C.S.: 331222

Bekaert Portugal-Importacao Comercializacao de Arames e Seus Derivados, Ltda. (1)
Ave Almirante Gago Coutinho No 56 2 Esq Frente, 1700 031, Lisbon, Portugal (100%)
Tel.: (351) 218470040
Web Site: http://www.bekaert.com
Sales Range: $50-74.9 Million
Emp.: 4
N.A.I.C.S.: 332618

Bekaert Sardegna SpA (1)
Strada Macchiareddu Grogastu, Assemini, 9032, Cagliari, Italy
Tel.: (39) 07024781
Emp.: 221
Steel Wire Drawing Services
N.A.I.C.S.: 331222

Bekaert Shah Alam Sdn. Bhd. (1)
No 7 Jalan Utas 15/7 Seksyen 15, 40200, Shah Alam, Selangor, Malaysia
Tel.: (60) 355191501
Steel Cord & Advanced Material Mfr
N.A.I.C.S.: 331222

Bekaert Singapore Pte. Ltd. (1)
7 Temasek Boulevard 14-07 Suntec City Tower 1, Singapore, 038987, Singapore (100%)
Tel.: (65) 65464611
Sales Range: $400-449.9 Million
Emp.: 16
N.A.I.C.S.: 332618

Bekaert Slovakia sro (1)
Velkoulanska Cesta 1332, 925 21, Sladkovicovo, Slovakia
Tel.: (421) 317881601
Sales Range: $200-249.9 Million
Emp.: 60
Steel Wire Products Mfr
N.A.I.C.S.: 331222
Marc Gombeer (Gen Mgr)

Bekaert Specialty Films Canada (1)
760 Pacific Road Unit 1, Oakville, L6L 6M5, ON, Canada
Tel.: (905) 847-2790
Web Site: http://www.bekaer.com
Sales Range: $50-74.9 Million
Emp.: 10
N.A.I.C.S.: 332618

Bekaert Specialty Films Nordic AB (1)
Stockholmsvagen 21, 762 21, Stockholm, Sweden
Tel.: (46) 175 748 80
Sales Range: $25-49.9 Million
Emp.: 5
Plastics Films Mfr
N.A.I.C.S.: 322220
Anna Bilger (Office Mgr)

Bekaert Specialty Wire Products Hong Kong Ltd (1)
Unit 902 19/F Central Plaza 18 Harbour Road, Wanchai, China (Hong Kong)
Tel.: (852) 29209000
Web Site: https://www.bekaert.com
Wire Product Mfr
N.A.I.C.S.: 332618

Bekaert Svenska A/B (1)
Drottninggatan 69 van 6, SE-411-07, Gothenburg, Sweden (100%)
Tel.: (46) 317041640
N.A.I.C.S.: 332618

Bekaert Svenska A/S (1)
Drottninggatan 69 Van 6, 411-07, Gothenburg, Sweden (100%)
Tel.: (46) 317041640
Web Site: http://www.bekaert.com
Sales Range: $50-74.9 Million
Emp.: 10
Wire Product Mfr
N.A.I.C.S.: 332618

Bekaert Taiwan Co., Ltd. (1)
6F 200 No Gangqian Road, TW-Neihu District, Taipei, 11494, Taiwan
Tel.: (886) 287514999
Steel Cord & Advanced Material Mfr
N.A.I.C.S.: 331222

Bekaert Tarak Aksesuarlari ve Makinalari Ticaret AS (1)
Turgutreis Mah Barbados Cad Tekstilkent Sitesi B10 Blok No 71, 34200, Istanbul, Turkiye
Tel.: (90) 2124384947
Web Site: http://www.bekaert.com
Sales Range: $100-124.9 Million
Emp.: 330
Mfr of Steel Cord; Joint Venture of Sabanci Holdings A.S. (50%) & Bekaert (50%)
N.A.I.C.S.: 314994

Bekaert Toko Metal Fiber Co Ltd (1)
5749 Shishikura, Kasumigaura, 300-0121, Ibaraki, Japan
Tel.: (81) 298301715
Metal Products Mfr
N.A.I.C.S.: 332999

Bekaert Trade Mexico S de RL de CV (1)
Avenida Rio Churubusco 601 Floor 8 Office 145, Colonia Xoco Delegación Benito Juarez, CP 03330, Mexico, Mexico
Tel.: (52) 5556511311
Web Site: http://www.bekaert.com.mx
Sales Range: $25-49.9 Million
Emp.: 1
Wire Product Mfr
N.A.I.C.S.: 332618

Bekaert do Brasil Ltda (1)
Avenida Marechal Rondon 1215 - Predio Administrativo 2 Andar, Osasco, 06093-900, Sao Paulo, Brazil
Tel.: (55) 1121478523
Sales Range: $100-124.9 Million
Emp.: 40
Drawn Steel Wire Mfr
N.A.I.C.S.: 331222
Rubens do Nascimento (Mgr-Mktg)

Bekaert-Jiangyin Wire Products Co Ltd (1)
Binjiang Economic Development Zone, 214434, Jiangyin, Jiangsu, China
Tel.: (86) 510 8619 54 00
Wire Product Mfr
N.A.I.C.S.: 332618

Bekintex N.V. (1)
Industriepark Kwatrecht Neerhonderd 16, BE-9230, Wetteren, Belgium (100%)
Tel.: (32) 93657111
Sales Range: $25-49.9 Million
Emp.: 80
Metal Fiber Technology & Weaving Textiles
N.A.I.C.S.: 333248

Betasenze Deustchland GmbH (1)
Eickener Street 29, 41366, Hamburg, Germany (100%)
Tel.: (49) 21633390
Web Site: http://www.betafence.com
Sales Range: $50-74.9 Million
Emp.: 130
N.A.I.C.S.: 332618

Cold Drawn Products Ltd (1)
Park House Road Low Moor, Bradford, BD12 0PX, West Yorkshire, United Kingdom
Tel.: (44) 1274 697697
Web Site: http://www.cdpltd.co.uk
Sales Range: $50-74.9 Million
Emp.: 15
Fabricated Wire Product Mfr
N.A.I.C.S.: 332618

Flintstone Technology Limited (1)
Constable Works Fowler Road, West Pitkerro Industrial Estate, Dundee, DD5 3RU, United Kingdom (75%)
Tel.: (44) 1382725120
Web Site: https://www.flint-tech.com
Software Management Services
N.A.I.C.S.: 541511
Andrew Clayson (Mng Dir)

Ideal Alambrec SA (1)
Calle S60 No E3-423 and Calle E3E, Sector Parque Industrial del Sur, Quito, Ecuador
Tel.: (593) 23342056
Web Site: http://idealalambrec.bekaert.com
Wire Product Mfr
N.A.I.C.S.: 332618

Industrias Chilenas de Alambre - Inchalam SA (1)
Great Britain 2675 Bio Bio, Talcahuano, Hualpen, Chile
Tel.: (56) 412267602
Web Site: http://www.inchalam.cl
Home & Construction Product Mfr
N.A.I.C.S.: 321992

Industrias del Ubierna S.A. (1)
Traversera de Gracia 30 2rd Fl, E 08021, Barcelona, Spain (100%)
Tel.: (34) 932419000
Sales Range: $25-49.9 Million
Emp.: 15
Wire Products

INTERNATIONAL PUBLIC

N.A.I.C.S.: 332618
Jose Perez (Gen Mgr)

Industrias del Ubierna, S.A. (1)
Traversa de Gracia No 30, 08021, Barcelona, Spain (100%)
Tel.: (34) 932419000
Web Site: http://www.bekaert.com
Emp.: 12
Mfr Steel Fibers
N.A.I.C.S.: 332618

Leon Bekaert S.p.A. (1)
Via G Fantoli 11/2, IT-20138, Milan, Italy (100%)
Tel.: (39) 02484811
Sales Range: $50-74.9 Million
Emp.: 10
Wire Products
N.A.I.C.S.: 332618

N.V. Bekaert S.A. - Zwevegem (1)
Bekaertstraat 2, B 8550, Zwevegem, Belgium
Tel.: (32) 596095161
Web Site: http://www.bekaert.com
Metal Fiber Technology
N.A.I.C.S.: 332618

OOO Bekaert Lipetsk (1)
Lipetsk Oez Ppt, 399071, Kazinka, Russia
Tel.: (7) 4742519363
Web Site: http://www.bekaert.com
Sales Range: $50-74.9 Million
Emp.: 20
Steel Wire Drawing Services
N.A.I.C.S.: 332618

OOO Bekaert Wire (1)
Business Center Diagonal Butyrskaya street 77 8th floor, Moscow, RU-127015, Russia
Tel.: (7) 4999290138
Emp.: 1
Wire Product Mfr
N.A.I.C.S.: 332618
Hitachi Tatsumi (Mgr-Bus Dev)

PT Bekaert Advanced Filtration (1)
Jl Raya Surya Madya Kav I-29 K Kawasan Industri Suryacipta, Jakarta, Indonesia
Tel.: (62) 21 5704508
Filtration Equipment Mfr
N.A.I.C.S.: 333998

PT Bekaert Indonesia (1)
ID-Telukjambe, Karawang, 41361, West Java, Indonesia
Tel.: (62) 267440287
Wire Product Mfr
N.A.I.C.S.: 332618

PT Bekaert Trade Indonesia (1)
Jalan Surya Utama Kavling I-14, Kota Industri Suryacipta ID-Telukjambe, Karawang, 41361, Indonesia
Tel.: (62) 267440288
Steel Cord & Advanced Material Mfr
N.A.I.C.S.: 331222

Prodalam SA (1)
Alberto Pepper 1610, Renca, Santiago, Chile
Tel.: (56) 26851000
Web Site: https://www.prodalam.cl
Steel Cord & Advanced Material Mfr
N.A.I.C.S.: 331222

Prodinsa SA (1)
El Milagro 455, Maipu, Santiago, Chile
Tel.: (56) 225658110
Web Site: https://www.prodinsa.cl
Steel Cable Mfr
N.A.I.C.S.: 331222

Productos de Acero Cassado SA (1)
Av Nestor Gambetta 6429, Callao, Peru
Tel.: (51) 1 613 6666
Steel Wire Products Mfr
N.A.I.C.S.: 332618

Shanghai Bekaert-Ergang Co Ltd (1)
No 555 North Riying Road Shanghai Waigaoqiao Free Trade Zone, 200131, Shanghai, China
Tel.: (86) 21 5046 06 10
Emp.: 100
Wire Product Mfr
N.A.I.C.S.: 332618
Robert Sun (Mng Dir)

Solaronics AB (1)

AND PRIVATE COMPANIES

Nygatan 100, Box 1530, 462 28, Vanersborg, Sweden
Tel.: (46) 521 27 80 30
Burner Parts Mfr
N.A.I.C.S.: 333414

Webster And Horsfall Ltd. (1)
Haymills, Birmingham, B25 8DW, W Midland, United Kingdom (100%)
Tel.: (44) 1217722555
Web Site: http://www.horsfall.co.uk
Sales Range: $25-49.9 Million
Emp.: 100
N.A.I.C.S.: 332618

NV BEVER HOLDING
Rijksstraatweg 324 C, Postbus 2114, 2242 AB, Wassenaar, Zuid-Holland, Netherlands
Tel.: (31) 705121810
Web Site:
 https://www.beverholding.nl
BEVER—(EUR)
Sales Range: $1-9.9 Million
Emp.: 1
Holding Company
N.A.I.C.S.: 551112
Willy J. Simon (Chm)

NV GOLD CORPORATION
750 West Pender Street Suite 250, Vancouver, V6C 2T7, BC, Canada
Tel.: (604) 245-0054
Web Site:
 https://www.nvgoldcorp.com
Year Founded: 2007
NVGLF—(OTCQB)
Rev.: $54,771
Assets: $5,232,007
Liabilities: $141,613
Net Worth: $5,090,394
Earnings: ($4,337,827)
Fiscal Year-end: 08/31/21
Mineral Exploration Services
N.A.I.C.S.: 213114
John E. Watson (Chm)

NV MICHEL VAN DE WIELE
Michel Vandewielestraat 7, B-8510, Kortrijk, Belgium
Tel.: (32) 56 24 32 11
Web Site: http://www.vandewiele.com
Emp.: 1,500
Textile Machinery Mfr
N.A.I.C.S.: 314999
Stefaan Logie (Mgr-Pur)

Subsidiaries:

Cobble - Van de Wiele Limited (1)
Gate Street, Blackburn, BB1 3AH, Lancashire, United Kingdom
Tel.: (44) 1254 55121
Web Site: http://www.cobble.co.uk
Sales Range: $25-49.9 Million
Emp.: 40
Textile Machinery Mfr
N.A.I.C.S.: 333248
Jason Kent (Mng Dir)

NV MULTI ASIA SDN. BHD.
Level 3A Wisma NV Multi No 1 Jalan 1/116A Off Jalan Sungai Besi, Kuala Lumpur, 57100, Malaysia
Tel.: (60) 379818899
Web Site: http://www.nvasia.com.my
Sales Range: $75-99.9 Million
Bereavement Care Services
N.A.I.C.S.: 812220
Huey Jiuan Chen (Sec)

Subsidiaries:

Eight Eleven Services Sdn. Bhd. (1)
139A Bt 3 1/2 Jalan Klang Lama, Kuala Lumpur, 58100, Wilayah Persekutuan, Malaysia
Tel.: (60) 379831366
Web Site: http://www.8eleven.com.my
Sales Range: $25-49.9 Million
Emp.: 20
Funeral Support Services

N.A.I.C.S.: 812210
Lee Kim Kiong (Mgr)

NV Care Sdn. Bhd. (1)
Mezzanine Floor Nirvana Memorial Center No 1 Jalan 1/116A, Off Jalan Sungai Besi, Kuala Lumpur, 57100, Malaysia
Tel.: (60) 379818899
Web Site: http://www.nvasia.com.my
Emp.: 100
Funeral Support Services
N.A.I.C.S.: 812210
Bhan Coi (Gen Mgr)

NV Multi (Cambodia) Co., Ltd. (1)
Building 338 Mao Tse Toung Boulevard Sangkat Boeng Salang, Khan Tuol Kork, Phnom Penh, Cambodia
Tel.: (855) 17686613
Web Site: http://www.nvmc.com.my
Funeral Support Services
N.A.I.C.S.: 812210

Nirvana Memorial Park Sdn. Bhd. (1)
No 1 Jalan 1/116A Nirvana Memorial Center Off Jalan Sungai Besi, 57100, Kuala Lumpur, Wilayah Persekutuan, Malaysia
Tel.: (60) 379818899
Web Site: http://www.nvasia.com.my
Memorial Center Management Services
N.A.I.C.S.: 812220
Kong Hon Kong (Mng Dir)

Subsidiary (Domestic):

Nirvana Memorial Park (Johor) Sdn. Bhd. (2)
Lot 2966 KM3 Jalan Gelang Patah, Skudai, Johor Bahru, 81300, Johor, Malaysia
Tel.: (60) 75586666
Web Site: http://www.nvasia.com.my
Sales Range: $10-24.9 Million
Emp.: 50
Funeral & Cemetery Support Services
N.A.I.C.S.: 812220

Nirvana Memorial Park (Shah Alam) Sdn. Bhd. (2)
Tmn Perkuburan Seksyen 21 Jalan Pusaka 21/1 Off Persiaran Jubli Pera, 40300, Shah Alam, Selangor, Malaysia
Tel.: (60) 122213424
Cemetery Plot Care Services
N.A.I.C.S.: 561730
Gary Hiew (Mgr)

Nirvana Memorial Park (Sibu) Sdn. Bhd. (2)
No 48 Lane 1 Lanang, 96000, Sibu, Sarawak, Malaysia
Tel.: (60) 128925656
Web Site: http://www.nirvana.com.my
Cemetery Plot Care Services
N.A.I.C.S.: 561730

PT Alam Hijau Lestari (1)
Pusat Niaga Roxy Mas Block D3/34-35 Jl K H Hasyim Ashari, 10510, Jakarta, Indonesia
Tel.: (62) 216332227
Sales Range: $25-49.9 Million
Emp.: 100
Funeral Support Services
N.A.I.C.S.: 812210

NV NEDERLANDSE SPOORWEGEN
Laan van Puntenburg 100, PO Box 2812, 3500 GV, Utrecht, Netherlands
Tel.: (31) 30 751 51 55 NI
Web Site: http://www.ns.nl
Year Founded: 1937
Sales Range: $1-9.9 Million
Emp.: 33,000
Holding Company; Passenger Railway Operator
N.A.I.C.S.: 551112
Gerard van de Aast (Chm-Supervisory Bd)

Subsidiaries:

Abellio (1)
Laan van Puntenburg 100, 3511 ER, Utrecht, Netherlands (100%)
Tel.: (31) 302354706
Web Site: http://www.abellio.com

Sales Range: $75-99.9 Million
Emp.: 10
Passenger Railway Operator
N.A.I.C.S.: 485112

Subsidiary (Non-US):

Abellio Greater Anglia Ltd (2)
18-20 St Andrews Street, London, EC4A 3AG, United Kingdom (60%)
Tel.: (44) 345 600 7245
Web Site: http://www.greateranglia.co.uk
Passenger Railway Operator
N.A.I.C.S.: 488210

Abellio London & Abellio Surrey (2)
301 Camberwell New Road, London, SE5 0TF, United Kingdom
Tel.: (44) 2077888550
Web Site: http://www.abellio.co.uk
Bus Transportation Services
N.A.I.C.S.: 485113

NedRailways Ltd. (2)
1 Ely Pl 2nd Floor, London, EC1N 6RY, United Kingdom
Tel.: (44) 2074308270
Web Site: http://www.abellio.com
Emp.: 20
Passenger Railway Operator
N.A.I.C.S.: 485112

Abellio GmbH (1)
Essen, 45133, Essen, Germany
Tel.: (49) 201 1858 0
Web Site: http://www.abellio.de
Passenger Railway Operator
N.A.I.C.S.: 488210

Abellio London Limited (1)
1 Ely Place Second Floor, London, EC1N 6RY, United Kingdom
Tel.: (44) 20 7430 8270
Web Site: http://www.abellio.com
Passenger Railway Operator
N.A.I.C.S.: 488210

Abellio Transport Holdings Ltd (1)
5 Fleet Place, London, EC4M 7RD, United Kingdom
Tel.: (44) 20 7430 8270
Web Site: http://www.abellio.com
Holding Company
N.A.I.C.S.: 551112

NS Financial Services (Holdings) Ltd. (1)
Behan House 10 Lower Mount Street, Dublin, Ireland
Tel.: (353) 1 638 1380
Web Site: http://www.nsfsc.com
Holding Company
N.A.I.C.S.: 551112

NS Opleidingen BV (1)
Gebouw Eempolis Piet Mondriaanplein 19, Amersfoort, 3812 GZ, Netherlands
Tel.: (31) 88 671 1000
Web Site: http://www.nsopleidingen.nl
Passenger Railway Operator
N.A.I.C.S.: 488210

NS Stations Retailbedrijf BV (1)
Stationsplein 19 B, Rotterdam, 3013 AJ, Zuid-Holland, Netherlands
Tel.: (31) 886711200
Passenger Railway Operator
N.A.I.C.S.: 488210

NedTrain Ematech BV (1)
Stationshal 15, Utrecht, 3511 CE, Netherlands
Tel.: (31) 886711834
Passenger Railway Operator
N.A.I.C.S.: 488210
Joost Kruiswijk (Project Mgr)

Qbuzz BV (1)
Piet Mondriaanplein 1, 3812 GZ, Amersfoort, Netherlands
Tel.: (01) 33 460 1580
Web Site: http://www.qbuzz.nl
Emp.: 30
Passenger Railway Operator
N.A.I.C.S.: 488210

NVC INTERNATIONAL HOLDINGS LIMITED
NVC Industrial Park Huizhou Ruhu, Huizhou, Guangdong, China

Tel.: (86) 7522786675
Web Site: http://www.nvc-international.com
2222—(HKG)
Rev.: $265,137,959
Assets: $575,963,060
Liabilities: $115,006,554
Net Worth: $460,956,506
Earnings: ($5,262,754)
Emp.: 2,246
Fiscal Year-end: 12/31/22
Lighting Product Mfr
N.A.I.C.S.: 335132
Donglei Wang (Chm)

Subsidiaries:

ETI Solid State Lighting Inc. (1)
720 Northgate Pkwy, Wheeling, IL 60090-2660
Tel.: (847) 821-6550
Electric Equipment Mfr
N.A.I.C.S.: 335999

NVC LED Lighting Aps (1)
Viborgvei 221, Hojslev, 7840, Skive, Denmark
Tel.: (45) 71995071
Lighting Product Distr
N.A.I.C.S.: 423610

NVC Lighting & Electrical Technology (S) Pte. Ltd. (1)
55 Kim Chuan Drive Precise Tree 07-09, Singapore, 537098, Singapore
Tel.: (65) 64937388
Web Site: https://www.nvc-international.com.sg
Lighting Equipment Distr
N.A.I.C.S.: 423610

NVC Lighting & Electrical Technology (Singapore) Private Limited (1)
55 Kim Chuan drive Ste 07-09 Precise Tree, Singapore, 537098, Singapore
Tel.: (65) 64937388
Electric Equipment Mfr
N.A.I.C.S.: 335999

NVC Lighting & Electrical Technology (Vietnam) Pte. Ltd. (1)
1602 Indochina Park Tower 4 Nguyen Dinh Chieu Street, Da Kao Ward Distrist 1, Ho Chi Minh City, Vietnam
Tel.: (84) 2862988569
Electric Equipment Mfr
N.A.I.C.S.: 335999

NVC Lighting (Brazil) Commercial Import & Export Co., Ltd. (1)
R Maratona 00252 LT 26 QD M VL, Alexandria, 04635-041, Sao Paulo, Brazil
Tel.: (55) 1144352603
Electric Equipment Mfr
N.A.I.C.S.: 335999

NVC Lighting Japan Co., Ltd. (1)
9F Mihama Building 3-16-5 Taito, Taito-ku, Tokyo, 110-0016, Japan
Tel.: (81) 358124092
Web Site: https://www.nvc-lighting.co.jp
Electric Equipment Mfr
N.A.I.C.S.: 335999

NVC Lighting Limited (1)
NVC Park 201 Hollymoor Way Rubery, Birmingham, B31 5HE, United Kingdom
Tel.: (44) 1214576340
Web Site: https://www.nvcuk.com
Emp.: 120
Electric Equipment Mfr
N.A.I.C.S.: 335999

Subsidiary (Non-US):

NVC Lighting AB (2)
Albybergsringen 3b, Osterhaninge, 137 69, Stockholm, Sweden
Tel.: (46) 87355540
Web Site: https://www.nvclighting.se
Electric Equipment Mfr
N.A.I.C.S.: 335999

NVC Lighting Middle East FZE (1)
Techno Hub 2 Dubai Silicon Oasis, PO Box 342146, Dubai, United Arab Emirates
Tel.: (971) 585865908
Electric Equipment Mfr
N.A.I.C.S.: 335999

NVC INTERNATIONAL HOLDINGS LIMITED

NVC International Holdings Limited—(Continued)
James Hunter Johnston (Gen Mgr)

NVC Lighting for Electrical Equipment & Machines Trading & Contracting Company WLL (1)
Tunis Street Madar Complex Opposite to Rehab Complex Ground floor, Hawalli, Kuwait
Tel.: (965) 67687278
Electric Equipment Mfr
N.A.I.C.S.: 335999

New Vision China Lighting W.L.L (1)
Building 03 No 29, Barwa Village, Doha, Qatar
Tel.: (974) 44151527
Electric Equipment Mfr
N.A.I.C.S.: 335999

PT Rise Electronic Indonesia (1)
Perwata Tower Lt 5 Unit F Jalan Pluit Selatan Raya Kav 1, Penjaringan, Jakarta Utara, 14440, Indonesia
Tel.: (62) 2122669073
Electric Equipment Mfr
N.A.I.C.S.: 335999

West Asia For Lightings NVC LLC (1)
Shop No 1 Building No 33 Block No 29SE Plot No 153 Way S 238 Ghubra, 999046, Muscat, Oman
Tel.: (968) 22021282
Electric Equipment Mfr
N.A.I.C.S.: 335999

Zhejiang Jiangshan Sunny Electron Co., Ltd (1)
No 201 Tongda Road Chengnan Economic Development Zone, Jiangshan, 324100, Zhejiang, China
Tel.: (86) 5704221838
Sales Range: $800-899.9 Million
Emp.: 3,500
Commercial Lighting Fixtures Mfr
N.A.I.C.S.: 335132

Zhejiang NVC Lamps Co., Ltd. (1)
No 21 Kaiyuan Road Shanhai Xiezuo Area Economic Development Zon, Jiangshan, Zhejiang, China
Tel.: (86) 5704221032
Web Site: http://www.zjnvc.com
Sales Range: $200-249.9 Million
Emp.: 1,000
Fluorescent Lamp Mfr
N.A.I.C.S.: 335139

NVENT ELECTRIC PLC

The Mille 1000 Great West Road 8th Floor East, London, TW8 9DW, United Kingdom
Tel.: (44) 2039660279   IE
Web Site: https://www.nvent.com
Year Founded: 2018
NVT—(NYSE)
Rev.: $3,263,600,000
Assets: $6,161,700,000
Liabilities: $3,019,600,000
Net Worth: $3,142,100,000
Earnings: $567,100,000
Emp.: 11,300
Fiscal Year-end: 12/31/23
Electrical Equipment Mfr & Distr
N.A.I.C.S.: 335999
Lynnette R. Heath (Chief HR Officer & Exec VP)

Subsidiaries:

ECM Industries, LLC (1)
16250 W Woods Edge Rd, New Berlin, WI 53151
Tel.: (800) 624-4320
Web Site: http://www.ecmindustries.com
Electrical Products Mfr & Distr
N.A.I.C.S.: 335999
Mike Masino (CEO)

Subsidiary (Domestic):

Briscon Electric Manufacturing Corporation (2)
PO Box 145, Auburn, MA 01501-0145
Tel.: (508) 832-3481
Web Site: http://www.brisconelectric.com
Fabricated Wire Product Mfr
N.A.I.C.S.: 332618
Bill Rogers (Pres)

Division (Domestic):

Gardner Bender (2)
16250 W Woods Edge Rd, New Berlin, WI 53151
Web Site: http://www.gardnerbender.com
Electrical Tools, Supplies for Electrical Contracting Industry & Construction
N.A.I.C.S.: 335999

Subsidiary (Domestic):

ILSCO Corporation (2)
4730 Madison Rd, Cincinnati, OH 45227-1426
Tel.: (513) 533-6200
Web Site: http://www.ilsco.com
Sales Range: $150-199.9 Million
Emp.: 500
Electrical Connectors, Screw Machine Products, Tool & Die & Specialty Machines Mfr
N.A.I.C.S.: 335931
Kevin Jenkins (VP-Ops)

Subsidiary (Domestic):

FTZ Industries, Inc. (3)
515 Palmetto Dr, Simpsonville, SC 29681-6142   (100%)
Tel.: (864) 963-5000
Web Site: http://www.ftzind.com
Sales Range: $10-24.9 Million
Emp.: 35
Mfr of Connectors
N.A.I.C.S.: 335910
Dave Wood (Gen Mgr)

Eldon Holding AB (1)
Paseo de la Finca 1 - Edif 3 - Bajo Pozuelo de Alarcon, 28223, Madrid, Spain
Tel.: (34) 917997135
Web Site: http://www.eldon.com
Sales Range: $150-199.9 Million
Emp.: 700
Holding Company
N.A.I.C.S.: 551112

Subsidiary (Non-US):

ELDON A/S (2)
Energivegen 8, 2069, Jessheim, Norway
Tel.: (47) 67792140
Web Site: http://www.eldon.com
Emp.: 5
Mild & Stainless Steel Mfr
N.A.I.C.S.: 331110

ELDON Danmark (2)
Bogovej 15, 8382, Hinnerup, Denmark
Tel.: (45) 702 769 60
Web Site: http://www.eldon.com
Steel Products Mfr
N.A.I.C.S.: 332311

ELDON Electric Ltd (2)
Unit 1 Innovation Way, Sheffield, S13 9AD, United Kingdom
Tel.: (44) 1709918510
Web Site: https://www.eldon.com
Electric Appliance Mfr & Distr
N.A.I.C.S.: 335220
Brett Bedford (Sls Mgr-UK & Ireland)

Eldon AB (2)
Mogelsvagen 22, 555 93, Jonkoping, Sweden
Tel.: (46) 105559500
Web Site: https://www.eldon.com
Sales Range: $100-124.9 Million
Emp.: 424
Electronic Enclosures, Relays, Timers, Electric Housing, Electric Boxes, Electric Cabinets & Switchgear Mfr
N.A.I.C.S.: 335313

Subsidiary (Non-US):

Eldon Espana S.A.U. (3)
C/ Esteban Ramirez Martinez 2 3 A, Poligono Industrial, 23009, Jaen, Spain   (100%)
Tel.: (34) 953551000
Web Site: https://www.eldon.com
Sales Range: $25-49.9 Million
Emp.: 75

Electronic Enclosures, Relays, Timers, Electric Housing, Electric Boxes, Electric Cabinets & Switchgear Mfr
N.A.I.C.S.: 335991

Eldon GmbH (3)
Darmstadter Str 59, 64572, Buttelborn, Germany   (100%)
Tel.: (49) 61529789827
Web Site: http://www.eldon.de
Sales Range: $25-49.9 Million
Emp.: 18
Electronic Enclosures, Relays, Timers, Electric Housing, Electric Boxes, Electric Cabinets & Switchgear Mfr
N.A.I.C.S.: 335991

Eldon N.V. (3)
Beechavenue 133, PO Box 38 9200, 1119 RB, Schiphol-Rijk, Netherlands   (100%)
Tel.: (31) 512744100
Web Site: https://www.eldon.com
Sales Range: $25-49.9 Million
Emp.: 35
Electronic Enclosures, Relays, Timers, Electric Housing, Electric Boxes, Electric Cabinets & Switchgear Mfr
N.A.I.C.S.: 335991
David Ramos (Product Mgr)

Subsidiary (Non-US):

Eldon CS Enclosures Pvt Limited (2)
A 1/ 285/1 GIDC, Umbergaon, Valsad, 396171, Gujarat, India
Tel.: (91) 260 6532709
Stainless Steel Product Mfr & Distr
N.A.I.C.S.: 332311
Mitul Shukla (Mgr-Natl Sls)

Eldon International S.A. (2)
Bedrijvenzone Planet 1 6C Tollaan 103, Sint-Stevens-Woluwe, 1932, Brussels, Belgium
Tel.: (32) 2 3891610
Electronic Components Mfr
N.A.I.C.S.: 334419
Marcel de Boer (Dir-Sls)

SC ELDON SRL (2)
Str Bruxelles no 4 Parcul Industrial Graells Llonch Prejmer, Prejmer, 507165, Brasov, Romania
Tel.: (40) 268308200
Electronic Components Mfr
N.A.I.C.S.: 334419
Remus Dinu (Chief Accountant)

Trachte LLC (1)
422 N Burr Oak Ave, Oregon, WI 53575
Tel.: (608) 835-5707
Web Site: http://www.trachteusa.com
Prefabricated Metal Building & Component Mfr
N.A.I.C.S.: 332311
Aaron Ingham (Product Mgr-T-RAMS Product Grp)

Vynckier Enclosure Systems, Inc. (1)
271 McCarty St, Houston, TX 77029
Tel.: (713) 374-7850
Web Site: http://www.enclosuresonline.com
Rev.: $8,722,990
Emp.: 35
Sheet Metal Work Mfg
N.A.I.C.S.: 332322
Jay Lambdin (Mgr-MIS)

WBT LLC (1)
115 Harting Dr, Centralia, IL 62801-5903
Tel.: (618) 918-3821
Web Site: http://www.wbtray.com
Emp.: 40
Miscellaneous Fabricated Metal Product Mfr
N.A.I.C.S.: 332999

NVEST FINANCIAL HOLDINGS LIMITED

NFB House 42 Beach Road Nahoon, PO Box 8132, East London, 5210, South Africa
Tel.: (27) 437352000
Web Site: http://www.nvestholdings.co.za
NVE—(JSE)
Rev.: $22,060,416
Assets: $47,209,622

INTERNATIONAL PUBLIC

Liabilities: $12,615,656
Net Worth: $34,593,967
Earnings: $4,726,481
Emp.: 151
Fiscal Year-end: 02/29/20
Bank Holding Company
N.A.I.C.S.: 551111
Anthony Denis Godwin (CEO)

Subsidiaries:

Independent Executor & Trust (Pty) Limited (1)
49 Beach Road Nahoon, East London, 5241, South Africa
Tel.: (27) 437354633
Web Site: http://www.iet.co.za
Financial Services
N.A.I.C.S.: 523210
Debbie Jacobs (Mgr-Estates)

NFB Private Wealth Management (Pty) Ltd (1)
Office No 1101 68 Melville Road, Illovo, Sandton, 2196, South Africa
Tel.: (27) 118958000
Web Site: http://www.nfb.co.za
Financial Services
N.A.I.C.S.: 523210
Andrew Duvenage (Mng Dir & Mgr-Private Wealth)

NVest Securities (Pty) Limited (1)
NFB House 42 Beach Road Nahoon, East London, 5241, South Africa
Tel.: (27) 437351270
Web Site: http://www.nvestsecurities.co.za
Investment Management Service
N.A.I.C.S.: 523210
Chris Lemmon (Mng Dir)

NVH KOREA INC.

44 Munsangongdanan-gil Oedongeup, Gyeongju, Gyeongsanbuk-do, Korea (South)
Tel.: (82) 547791822
Year Founded: 1984
067570—(KRS)
Rev.: $943,415,102
Assets: $816,997,266
Liabilities: $588,058,845
Net Worth: $228,938,421
Earnings: $5,823,132
Emp.: 554
Fiscal Year-end: 12/31/22
Automotive Components Mfr
N.A.I.C.S.: 336390

Subsidiaries:

NVH Rus, LLC (1)
Gorskoye shosse 165 lit D, Levashovo Village, 194361, Saint Petersburg, Russia
Tel.: (7) 8126407160
Web Site: http://www.nvhrus.com
Motor Vehicle Parts Mfr
N.A.I.C.S.: 336390

NVM PRIVATE EQUITY LIMITED

Time Central 32 Gallowgate, Princess Square, Newcastle upon Tyne, NE1 4SN, United Kingdom
Tel.: (44) 191 244 6000
Web Site: http://www.nvm.co.uk
Year Founded: 1984
Sales Range: $25-49.9 Million
Emp.: 20
Privater Equity Firm
N.A.I.C.S.: 523999
Mauro Biagioni (Dir-Investment)

Subsidiaries:

Volumatic Limited (1)
Taurus House, Endemere Road, Coventry, CV6 5PY, Warwickshire, United Kingdom   (100%)
Tel.: (44) 2476684217
Web Site: http://www.volumatic.com
Sales Range: $25-49.9 Million
Mfr of Cash Handling Equipment & Other Related Cash Storage Products
N.A.I.C.S.: 333310

AND PRIVATE COMPANIES

Colin Amos *(Mng Dir)*

NVP S.P.A.
Via G Grande 1, San Piero Patti, 98068, Messina, Italy
Tel.: (39) 0941660301
Web Site: https://www.nvp.it
Year Founded: 2007
Television Broadcasting Services
N.A.I.C.S.: 516120
Ivan Pintabona *(Co-CEO)*

NWF GROUP PLC
MHP Communications 60 Great Portland Street, London, W1W 7RT, Cheshire, United Kingdom
Tel.: (44) 1829260260
Web Site: https://www.nwf.co.uk
NWF—(LSE)
Rev.: $917,275,632
Assets: $253,757,868
Liabilities: $172,973,528
Net Worth: $80,784,340
Earnings: $10,590,216
Emp.: 1,263
Fiscal Year-end: 05/31/21
Agriculture & Garden Industries
N.A.I.C.S.: 337127
Stephen Robert Andrew *(Sec)*

Subsidiaries:

Bassett Fuels Limited (1)
Wardle, Nantwich, CW5 6AF, Cheshire, United Kingdom
Tel.: (44) 1793849666
Web Site: http://www.nwffuels.co.uk
Sales Range: $25-49.9 Million
Emp.: 7
Retail Stores
N.A.I.C.S.: 459999
Kevin Kennerley *(Mng Dir)*

Boughey Distribution Limited (1)
Nantwich Road, Wardle, Rochdale, CW56RS, Cheshire, United Kingdom
Tel.: (44) 1829260704
Web Site: http://www.boughey.co.uk
Sales Range: $75-99.9 Million
Emp.: 400
General Warehousing & Storage
N.A.I.C.S.: 493110
Keith Forster *(Mng Dir)*

Evesons Fuels Ltd (1)
Eveson House Birmingham Road, Kenilworth, CV8 1PT, United Kingdom
Tel.: (44) 1676 531100
Web Site: http://www.evesons.co.uk
Emp.: 30
Fuel & Lubricants Distr
N.A.I.C.S.: 424720
Ian Taplin *(Gen Mgr)*

Knutsford Domestic Fuel Oil Company Limited (1)
Nantwich Road, Chester, CW8 2DN, United Kingdom
Tel.: (44) 1565634488
Web Site: http://www.nwffuels.co.uk
Emp.: 100
Retail Stores
N.A.I.C.S.: 459999

NWF Agriculture Holdings Limited (1)
Nantwich Road, Nantwich, United Kingdom
Tel.: (44) 1829200980
Web Site: http://www.nwfagriculture.co.uk
Animal Feed Mfr
N.A.I.C.S.: 311119

NWF Agriculture Limited (1)
Nantwich Road, CW56AQ, Chester, United Kingdom
Tel.: (44) 1800262397
Web Site: http://www.nwfagriculture.co.uk
Animal Aquaculture
N.A.I.C.S.: 112519
Rob Thomas *(Dir-Fin)*

NWF Fuels Limited (1)
Wardle, Nantwich Road, Chester, CW5 6BP, United Kingdom
Tel.: (44) 1829260900
Web Site: http://www.nwffuels.co.uk

Emp.: 300
Activities for Nonmetallic Minerals
N.A.I.C.S.: 213115
Kevin Kennerley *(Mng Dir)*

NWM SOLUTIONS LIMITED
Merchant Court Milburn Road, Bournemouth, BH4 9HJ, United Kingdom
Tel.: (44) 330 333 4240
Web Site: http://www.nwmsolutions.co.uk
Year Founded: 2007
Sales Range: $75-99.9 Million
Emp.: 203
Payroll Processing Services
N.A.I.C.S.: 541214
Graham Williams *(Founder)*

NX FILTRATION N.V.
Josink Esweg 44, 7545 PN, Enschede, Netherlands
Tel.: (31) 850479900 NI
Web Site: https://www.nxfiltration.com
Year Founded: 2016
NXFIL—(EUR)
Rev.: $8,889,502
Assets: $150,169,997
Liabilities: $18,309,968
Net Worth: $131,860,029
Earnings: ($25,711,447)
Emp.: 166
Fiscal Year-end: 12/31/23
Application Development Services
N.A.I.C.S.: 541511
Erik Roesink *(CTO)*

NXERA PHARMA CO., LTD.
Midtown East 9-7-2 Akasaka, Minato-ku, Tokyo, 107-0052, Japan
Tel.: (81) 352103290 JP
Web Site: https://www.nxera.life
Year Founded: 1990
4565—(TKS)
Rev.: $90,510,940
Assets: $1,114,533,820
Liabilities: $640,850,920
Net Worth: $473,682,900
Earnings: ($50,998,370)
Emp.: 350
Fiscal Year-end: 12/31/23
Pharmaceuticals & Drugs Mfr
N.A.I.C.S.: 325412
Shinichi Tamura *(Founder & Chm)*

Subsidiaries:

Heptares Therapeutics Ltd. (1)
Steinmetz Building Granta Park, Great Abington, Cambridge, CB21 6DG, United Kingdom
Tel.: (44) 122 394 9100
Web Site: http://www.heptares.com
Pharmaceutical Research & Development Services
N.A.I.C.S.: 541715
Malcolm Weir *(Chm & CEO)*

Sosei CVC Ltd. (1)
PMO Hanzomon 11F 2-1 Kojimachi, Chiyoda-ku, Tokyo, 102-0083, Japan
Tel.: (81) 366792044
Pharmaceutical Preparation Mfr
N.A.I.C.S.: 325412

Sosei Co. Ltd. (1)
PMO Hanzomon 11F 2-1 Kojimachi, Chiyoda-ku, Tokyo, 102-0083, Japan
Tel.: (81) 35 210 3290
Web Site: http://www.soseiheptares.com
Sales Range: $25-49.9 Million
Pharmaceutical Preparation Mfr & Supplier
N.A.I.C.S.: 325412

Sosei R&D Ltd. (1)
3rd Fl London BioScience Innovation Ctr, 2 Royal College St, London, NW1 0NH, United Kingdom
Tel.: (44) 2076912081
Web Site: http://www.sosei.com

Sales Range: $25-49.9 Million
Emp.: 4
Biopharmaceutical Services
N.A.I.C.S.: 325412

NXP SEMICONDUCTORS N.V.
High Tech Campus 60, 5656 AG, Eindhoven, Netherlands
Tel.: (31) 402729999 NI
Web Site: https://www.nxp.com
Year Founded: 2006
NXPI—(NASDAQ)
Rev.: $13,276,000,000
Assets: $24,353,000,000
Liabilities: $15,393,000,000
Net Worth: $8,960,000,000
Earnings: $2,797,000,000
Emp.: 34,200
Fiscal Year-end: 12/31/23
Semiconductors, Wireless Communication Components, Audio & Video Components, Radio Frequency Identification Technologies & Mobile Handset Software Mfr
N.A.I.C.S.: 334413
Jeff Palmer *(VP-IR)*

Subsidiaries:

Freescale Semiconductor Hong Kong Limited (1)
7/F No 8 Science Park West Avenue, Hong Kong Science Park, Sha Tin, China (Hong Kong)
Tel.: (852) 26668333
Web Site: http://www.freescale.com
Sales Range: $150-199.9 Million
Emp.: 500
Semiconductor Whslr & Distr
N.A.I.C.S.: 423690

Freescale Semiconductor Israel Ltd. (1)
1 Shenkar Street Industrial Zone, Herzliyya, 46120, Israel
Tel.: (972) 99522333
Web Site: http://www.freescale.com
Sales Range: $125-149.9 Million
Emp.: 600
Semiconductor Product Mfr
N.A.I.C.S.: 334413

Freescale Semiconductor Malaysia Sdn. Bhd. (1)
No 2 Jalan SS 8-2 Free Industrial Zone Sungai Way, Petaling Jaya, 47300, Malaysia
Tel.: (60) 378731133
Web Site: http://www.freescale.com
Sales Range: $600-649.9 Million
Emp.: 4,000
Semiconductor Mfr
N.A.I.C.S.: 334413

NXP Semiconductors Austria GmbH & Co. KG (1)
Mikron-Weg 1, 8101, Gratkorn, Austria
Tel.: (43) 312 429 9160
Semiconductor Product Mfr
N.A.I.C.S.: 334413

NXP Semiconductors France S.A.S. (1)
Parc Les Algorithmes-Immeuble Thales, Saint-Aubin Saclay, 91190, Paris, France
Tel.: (33) 16 910 4809
Semiconductor Material Mfr
N.A.I.C.S.: 334413

NXP Semiconductors GmbH (1)
Schatzbogen 7, 81829, Munich, Germany
Tel.: (49) 8962706100
Web Site: http://www.nxp.com
Sales Range: $1-9.9 Million
Emp.: 40
Marketer of Semiconductors
N.A.I.C.S.: 334413

NXP Semiconductors Netherlands B.V. (1)
High Tech Campus 60, 5656 AG, Eindhoven, Netherlands
Tel.: (31) 40 272 9999
Emp.: 700
Semiconductor Product Mfr
N.A.I.C.S.: 334413

NXP Semiconductors Singapore Pte. Ltd. (1)
1 Fusionopolis Walk 02-11 North Tower Solaris, Singapore, 138628, Singapore
Tel.: (65) 6 434 8688
Semiconductor Product Mfr
N.A.I.C.S.: 334413

NXP Semiconductors USA, Inc. (1)
1109 McKay Dr, San Jose, CA 95131
Tel.: (408) 434-3000
Web Site: http://www.nxp.com
Sales Range: $600-649.9 Million
Emp.: 700
Semiconductor Mfr
N.A.I.C.S.: 334413

Subsidiary (Domestic):

Freescale Semiconductor, Inc. (2)
6501 William Cannon Dr W, Austin, TX 78735
Tel.: (800) 521-6274
Web Site: http://www.freescale.com
Semiconductor Designer & Mfr
N.A.I.C.S.: 334413

Subsidiary (Domestic):

Zenverge, Inc. (3)
3960 Freedom Cir Ste 100, Santa Clara, CA 95054
Tel.: (408) 350-5052
Web Site: http://www.zenverge.com
Electrical Equipment & Component Mfr
N.A.I.C.S.: 335999

Plant (Domestic):

NXP Semiconductors USA, Inc. - Cary (2)
15501 Weston Pkwy, Cary, NC 27513
Tel.: (919) 677-7900
Sales Range: Less than $1 Million
Emp.: 30
Mfr & Marketer of Semiconductors & Related Devices
N.A.I.C.S.: 334413

NXP Semiconductors USA, Inc. - Tempe (2)
8375 S River Pkwy, Tempe, AZ 85284-2616
Tel.: (480) 752-8574
Web Site: http://www.nxp.com
Sales Range: $1-9.9 Million
Mfr of Semiconductors
N.A.I.C.S.: 334413

NXP Software B.V. (1)
High Tech Campus 41, 5656 AE, Eindhoven, Netherlands
Tel.: (31) 4027000
Web Site: http://www.nxpsoftware.com
Sales Range: $25-49.9 Million
Mobile Communications Software
N.A.I.C.S.: 513210

NXT ENERGY SOLUTIONS INC.
Suite 302 3320 - 17th Avenue SW, Calgary, T3E 0B4, AB, Canada
Tel.: (403) 264-7020 AB
Web Site: https://www5.nxtenergy.com
NSFDF—(OTCQB)
Rev.: $2,451,862
Assets: $16,885,022
Liabilities: $2,679,752
Net Worth: $14,205,270
Earnings: ($2,443,686)
Emp.: 10
Fiscal Year-end: 12/31/21
Surveying & Mapping Services
N.A.I.C.S.: 541360
George Liszicasz *(Pres, CEO & Chm)*

NYCO CO., LTD.
77 Cheongam-ro, Nam-gu, Pohang, Gyeongsangbuk-do, Korea (South)
Tel.: (82) 54 705 6900
Web Site: http://www.nyco.or.kr
Steel Products Mfr
N.A.I.C.S.: 331513
Ji-Young Kim *(Pres & CEO)*

NYCOMM HOLDINGS LIMITED

Nyco Co., Ltd.—(Continued)

NYCOMM HOLDINGS LIMITED
Agecroft Road, Pendlebury, Manchester, M27 8SB, United Kingdom
Tel.: (44) 1619251443
Web Site: http://www.nycomm.co.uk
Year Founded: 1996
IT Equipment Retailer & Telecommunications Distr
N.A.I.C.S.: 423420

Subsidiaries:

Rocom Ltd. (1)
Thorpe Park Business Park 1200 Century Way, Leeds, LS15 8ZA, United Kingdom
Tel.: (44) 1937847777
Web Site: http://www.rocom.co.uk
Sales Range: $75-99.9 Million
Emp.: 175
IT Equipment Retailer
N.A.I.C.S.: 423420

NYESA VALORES CORP SA
Calle de Madre Vedruna 18 3 Izquierda, 50008, Zaragoza, Spain
Tel.: (34) 976232744
Web Site: https://nyesa.com
Year Founded: 1950
NYE—(MAD)
Sales Range: Less than $1 Million
Residential Real Estate Management Services
N.A.I.C.S.: 531311
Juan Manuel Vallejo Montero (Chm)

NYFOSA AB
Hastholmsvagen 28, 131 30, Nacka, Sweden
Tel.: (46) 84066400   SE
Web Site: https://www.nyfosa.se
Year Founded: 2009
NYF—(OMX)
Rev.: $295,129
Assets: $4,246,162
Liabilities: $2,521,285
Net Worth: $1,724,878
Earnings: $158,663
Emp.: 80
Fiscal Year-end: 12/31/22
Real Estate Manangement Services
N.A.I.C.S.: 531210
Stina Lindh Hok (CEO)

NYGARD INTERNATIONAL PARTNERSHIP
1 Niagara Street, Toronto, M5V 1C2, ON, Canada
Tel.: (416) 598-6900
Web Site: http://www.nygard.com
Year Founded: 1967
Sales Range: $1-4.9 Billion
Emp.: 2,600
Sportswear & Clothing Mfr
N.A.I.C.S.: 315210
Peter J. Nygard (Chm)

Subsidiaries:

Nygard Cay (1)
E P Teller Drive, CR54697, Nassau, Bahamas
Tel.: (242) 6774000
Women's Clothing Store
N.A.I.C.S.: 458110

Nygard Inc. (1)
14401 S San Pedro St, Gardena, CA 90248 **(100%)**
Tel.: (310) 776-8900
Web Site: http://www.nygard.com
Sales Range: $50-74.9 Million
Emp.: 120
Women's Clothing Store
N.A.I.C.S.: 458110

Nygard International (1)
1771 Inkster Blvd, Winnipeg, R2X 1R3, MB, Canada
Tel.: (204) 982-5000
Retail & IT Distribution Services
N.A.I.C.S.: 459999

Division (Domestic):

Jayset (2)
1771 Inkster Blvd, Winnipeg, R2X 1R3, MB, Canada **(100%)**
Tel.: (204) 982-5000
Web Site: http://www.nygard.com
Emp.: 450
Women's Clothing Store
N.A.I.C.S.: 458110
John Joba (Mgr-HR)

Nygard International Limited, Inc. (1)
312 E Rosecrans Ave, Gardena, CA 90248-2021
Tel.: (310) 329-4000
Web Site: http://www.nygard.com
Sales Range: $25-49.9 Million
Emp.: 60
Mfr of Women's & Children's Clothing
N.A.I.C.S.: 459999

NYKREDIT A/S
Kalvebod Brygge 1-3, 1780, Copenhagen, Denmark
Tel.: (45) 44551000   DK
Web Site: http://www.nykredit.dk
Year Founded: 1985
Sales Range: $1-4.9 Billion
Emp.: 4,400
Mortgage Credit Institution
N.A.I.C.S.: 522390
Anders Jensen (CFO)

Subsidiaries:

Nykredit Bank A/S (1)
Kalvebod Brygge 1 3, 1780, Copenhagen, Denmark **(100%)**
Tel.: (45) 33421471
Web Site: http://www.nykredit.com
Sales Range: $200-249.9 Million
Emp.: 4,000
Corporate Banking
N.A.I.C.S.: 522299

Nykredit Ejendomme A/S (1)
Kalvebod Brygge 1-3, 1780, Copenhagen, Denmark **(100%)**
Tel.: (45) 33772000
Real Estate Agents & Brokers Offices
N.A.I.C.S.: 531210

Nykredit Forsikring A/S (1)
Kalvebod Brygge 1, 1780, Copenhagen, Denmark **(100%)**
Tel.: (45) 70159633
Sales Range: $200-249.9 Million
Emp.: 400
Mortgage & Nonmortgage Loan Brokers
N.A.I.C.S.: 522310

Nykredit Maegler A/S (1)
Aahave Parkveda 29, 8260, Viby, Denmark **(100%)**
Tel.: (45) 89386350
Web Site: http://www.nykredit.com
Sales Range: $75-99.9 Million
Emp.: 60
N.A.I.C.S.: 522390

Nykredit Pantebrevsinvestering A/S (1)
Kalvebod Brygge 1-3, 1780, Copenhagen, Denmark **(100%)**
Tel.: (45) 33772000
Credit Intermediation Services
N.A.I.C.S.: 522390

Nykredit Portefolje Adm. A/S (1)
Otto Monsteds Plads 9, 1780, Copenhagen, Denmark **(100%)**
Tel.: (45) 33759200
Sales Range: $1-4.9 Billion
Emp.: 3,000
Nondepository Credit Intermediation
N.A.I.C.S.: 522299

Nykredit Portefolje Bank A/S (1)
Otto Moristeds Plads 9, 1780, Copenhagen, Denmark **(100%)**
Tel.: (45) 33759200
Nondepository Credit Intermediation
N.A.I.C.S.: 522299

Pantebrevsselskabet af 8/8 1995 A/S (1)

Kampmannsgade 1 4th Floor, Copenhagen, Denmark **(100%)**
Tel.: (45) 33767400
Mortgage & Nonmortgage Loan Brokers
N.A.I.C.S.: 522310

Totalkredit A/S (1)
Kalvebod Brygge 1-3, 1780, Copenhagen, V, Denmark **(100%)**
Tel.: (45) 44555400
Web Site: http://www.totalkredit.dk
Sales Range: $50-74.9 Million
Emp.: 100
Mortgage & Nonmortgage Loan Broker Services
N.A.I.C.S.: 522310

NYLEX (MALAYSIA) BERHAD
Lot 16 Persiaran Selangor Section 15, 40200, Shah Alam, Selangor Darul Ehsan, Malaysia
Tel.: (60) 355191706
Web Site: https://www.nylex.com
NYLEX—(KLS)
Rev.: $44,656
Assets: $4,655,238
Liabilities: $139,259
Net Worth: $4,515,979
Earnings: ($319,153)
Fiscal Year-end: 05/31/23
Vinyl Coated Fabrics Mfr
N.A.I.C.S.: 313320
Stephen Geh Sim Whye (Co-Sec)

Subsidiaries:

CKG Chemicals Pte Ltd
51 Goldhill Plaza 11-03, Singapore, 308900, Singapore
Tel.: (65) 63194680
Web Site: http://www.nylex.com
Sales Range: $25-49.9 Million
Emp.: 15
Petrochemical Distr
N.A.I.C.S.: 424690
Edwin Koh (Mgr-Distr)

Dynamic Chemical Trading Pte Ltd
3 International Business Park 03-04 Nordic European Centre, Singapore, 609927, Singapore
Tel.: (65) 62244142
Web Site: http://www.dynamicchemical.com.sg
Emp.: 5
Petrochemical Solvents Distr
N.A.I.C.S.: 424690
Keen Seng Chow (Gen Mgr)

Kumpulan Kesuma Sdn Bhd (1)
No 6 Lorong SS13/6A, Subang Jaya Industrial Estate, 47500, Subang Jaya, Selangor, Malaysia
Tel.: (60) 356336229
Web Site: http://www.nylex.com
Sales Range: $25-49.9 Million
Emp.: 24
Industrial Adhesives & Sealants Mfr & Distr
N.A.I.C.S.: 325520
Lim Liang Tan (Mng Dir)

Nylex Specialty Chemicals Sdn Bhd (1)
Lot 593 and 624 Persiaran Raja Lumu Kawasan Perusahaan, Pandamaran, 42000, Port Klang, Selangor, Malaysia
Tel.: (60) 331688282
Web Site: http://www.nylexsc.com.my
Sales Range: $25-49.9 Million
Emp.: 32
Industrial Chemicals Mfr
N.A.I.C.S.: 325312
William Tan (Mng Dir)

PT Nylex Indonesia (1)
Desa Sumengko KM-31 Wringinanom, Gresik, 61176, East Java, Indonesia
Tel.: (62) 318982626
Web Site: http://nylexindonesia.co.id
Sales Range: $25-49.9 Million
Emp.: 75
Plastics Product Mfr
N.A.I.C.S.: 325211

PT PKG Lautan Indonesia (1)
Gedung Graha Indramas Jl AIPDA K S Tu-

bun Raya No 77, Jakarta, 11410, Indonesia
Tel.: (62) 2153673269
Web Site: http://www.nylex.com
Sales Range: $50-74.9 Million
Emp.: 10
Industrial Chemicals Import & Distr
N.A.I.C.S.: 424690

Perusahaan Kimia Gemilang (Vietnam) Company Ltd. (1)
7 Floor 205B Hoang Hoa Tham Street, Ward 6 Binh Thanh District, Ho Chi Minh City, Vietnam
Tel.: (84) 835163115
Web Site: http://www.nylex.com
Industrial Chemical Distr
N.A.I.C.S.: 424690

NYLEX LIMITED
50-70 Stanley Dr, Somerton, 3062, VIC, Australia
Tel.: (61) 3 9303 1444   AU
Year Founded: 1987
Sales Range: $200-249.9 Million
Emp.: 2,095
Plastic & Automotive Products Mfr & Distr
N.A.I.C.S.: 326199
Desmond J. Kelly (Sec)

Subsidiaries:

Ajax Technology Centre Pty Ltd. (1)
Level 1 88 Albert Road, Melbourne, 3205, VIC, Australia **(100%)**
Tel.: (61) 386460999
Sales Range: $25-49.9 Million
Emp.: 15
Commercial Equipment Whslr
N.A.I.C.S.: 423440

Celrets Pty Ltd. (1)
Level 1 88 Albert Road, Melbourne, 3205, VIC, Australia **(100%)**
Tel.: (61) 386460999
Sales Range: $25-49.9 Million
Emp.: 15
Fabricated Metal Products Mfr
N.A.I.C.S.: 332999

Champion Environmental Technologies Pty Ltd. (1)
Level 1 88 Albert Road, Melbourne, 3205, VIC, Australia **(100%)**
Tel.: (61) 386460999
Refrigeration Equipment & Supplies Whslr
N.A.I.C.S.: 423740

Eilloc Pty Ltd. (1)
Level 1 88 Albert Road, Melbourne, 3205, VIC, Australia **(100%)**
Tel.: (61) 386460999
Sales Range: $25-49.9 Million
Emp.: 15
Holding Company
N.A.I.C.S.: 551112

Hawker Richardson Ltd. (1)
75 - 77 West Gate Dr, Altona, 3025, VIC, Australia
Tel.: (61) 383696600
Web Site: http://www.hrltd.com.au
Sales Range: $500-549.9 Million
Emp.: 20
Industrial Supplies, Machinery & Equipment Mfr
N.A.I.C.S.: 423830
Rob Plageman (Gen Mgr)

Nylex Consumer Products (1)
50-70 Stanley Dr, Somerton, VIC, Australia
Tel.: (61) 393031444
Web Site: http://www.ilcaustralia.org.au
Fabricated Metal Products Mfr
N.A.I.C.S.: 332999

Nylex Industrial Products Pty Ltd. (1)
Unit 11 Healey Road, Dandenong, 3175, VIC, Australia
Tel.: (61) 3 9213 4444
Rev.: $257,200,000
Administrative Management & General Management Consulting Services
N.A.I.C.S.: 541611

Nylex Water Solutions Pty Ltd. (1)
80 Hattnatt Dr, Pakenham, VIC, Australia

AND PRIVATE COMPANIES

Tel.: (61) 359414967
Web Site: http://www.nylex.com.au
Sales Range: $25-49.9 Million
Emp.: 100
Plastics Product Mfr
N.A.I.C.S.: 326199

Ormsray Corporation Pty Ltd. (1)
Level 1 88 Albert Road, Melbourne, 3205, VIC, Australia **(100%)**
Tel.: (61) 386460999
Sales Range: $25-49.9 Million
Emp.: 15
Fabricated Metal Products Mfr
N.A.I.C.S.: 332999

Spurway Cooke Industries Pty Ltd. (1)
Level 1 88 Albert Road, Melbourne, 3205, VIC, Australia **(100%)**
Tel.: (61) 386460999
Sales Range: $25-49.9 Million
Emp.: 15
Fabricated Metal Products Mfr
N.A.I.C.S.: 332999

NYMOX PHARMACEUTICAL CORPORATION
Bay and Deveaux Streets, Nassau, Bahamas
Tel.: (242) 8009369669   BS
Web Site: http://www.nymox.com
Year Founded: 1995
NYMXF—(OTCIQ)
Rev.: $7,000
Assets: $627,000
Liabilities: $3,800,000
Net Worth: ($3,173,000)
Earnings: ($8,844,000)
Fiscal Year-end: 12/31/23
Diagnostic Test Products Mfr
N.A.I.C.S.: 325412
Paul Averback (Founder, Chm, Pres & CEO)

NYNOMIC AG
Am Marienhof 2, 22880, Wedel, Germany
Tel.: (49) 410393080
Web Site: https://www.nynomic.com
Year Founded: 1995
M7U—(DEU)
Rev.: $130,240,645
Assets: $167,250,248
Liabilities: $52,520,146
Net Worth: $114,730,103
Earnings: $11,626,007
Emp.: 535
Fiscal Year-end: 12/31/23
Measuring Instruments Mfr
N.A.I.C.S.: 334515
Heist Hans Wormcke (Chm-Supervisory Bd)

Subsidiaries:

APOS GmbH (1)
Am Marienhof 4, 22880, Wedel, Germany
Tel.: (49) 4103187830
Web Site: https://www.apos.biz
Spectrometer & Optical Sensor Instrument Mfr
N.A.I.C.S.: 334516

Avantes B.V. (1)
Oude Apeldoornseweg 28, 7333 NS, Apeldoorn, Netherlands
Tel.: (31) 313670170
Web Site: https://www.avantes.com
Spectrometer & Optical Sensor Instrument Mfr
N.A.I.C.S.: 334516

Avantes China Ltd. (1)
Room 1209 1210 2609 Building E Youlehui Wangjing Park, Chaoyang District, Beijing, 100102, China
Tel.: (86) 1084574045
Web Site: https://www.avantes.cn
Spectrometer & Optical Sensor Instrument Mfr
N.A.I.C.S.: 334516

Avantes Inc. (1)
500 S Arthur Ave Ste 500, Louisville, CO 80027
Tel.: (303) 410-8668
Web Site: http://www.avantesusa.com
Spectrometer & Optical Sensor Instrument Mfr
N.A.I.C.S.: 334516

LayTec AG (1)
Seesener Str 10-13, 10709, Berlin, Germany
Tel.: (49) 308900550
Web Site: https://www.laytec.de
Metrology Thin Film Product Mfr
N.A.I.C.S.: 334413
J. Thomas Zettler (Pres & CEO)

LemnaTec GmbH (1)
Nerscheider Weg 170, 52076, Aachen, Germany
Tel.: (49) 2408981850
Web Site: https://www.lemnatec.com
Digital Phenotyping Technology Services
N.A.I.C.S.: 541715

M-u-t GmbH (1)
Am Marienhof 2, 22880, Wedel, Germany
Tel.: (49) 410393080
Web Site: https://www.mut-group.com
Emp.: 120
Industrial Automation Equipment Mfr & Distr
N.A.I.C.S.: 334513

Sensortherm GmbH (1)
Weisskirchener Strasse 2-6, 61449, Steinbach, Germany
Tel.: (49) 61718870980
Web Site: https://www.sensortherm.de
Infrared Radiation Thermometers Mfr & Distr
N.A.I.C.S.: 334513

Shenzhen Image Engineering Co., Ltd. (1)
Room 1508 Chengshi Shanhai Pingji Center Pingxin North Road No 51, Pinghu Street Longgang District, Shenzhen, China
Tel.: (86) 15889619096
Image Quality Test Equipment Mfr
N.A.I.C.S.: 334220

Spectral Engines Oy (1)
Kutomotie 18 B, 00380, Helsinki, Finland
Tel.: (358) 504090204
Web Site: http://www.spectralengines.com
Power Material Sensing & Spectral Mfr
N.A.I.C.S.: 334515
Uula Kantojarvi (CTO)

tec5 AG (1)
Weisskirchener Strasse 2-6, 61449, Steinbach, Germany
Tel.: (49) 617197580
Web Site: https://www.tec5.com
Spectrometer & Optical Sensor Instrument Mfr
N.A.I.C.S.: 334516
Steffen Piecha (Head-Sls)

Subsidiary (US):

tec5 USA Inc. (2)
80 Skyline Dr, Plainview, NY 11803
Tel.: (516) 653-2000
Web Site: https://www.tec5usa.com
Spectrometer & Optical Sensor Instrument Mfr
N.A.I.C.S.: 334516
Dileep Mathew (Head-Production)

tec5 Technology Co. Ltd. (1)
Room 1210 ULO Park No 601 Apartment of Wangjing Yuan, Chaoyang District, Beijing, 100102, China
Tel.: (86) 1084574045
Spectrometer & Optical Sensor Instrument Mfr
N.A.I.C.S.: 334516
Henry Zhang (Gen Mgr)

NYOCOR CO., LTD.
No 290 Heping Road, Heping District, Tianjin, 100044, China
Tel.: (86) 1050950528
Web Site: http://www.qyc.com.cn
Year Founded: 1992
600821—(SHG)
Rev.: $432,749,655
Assets: $4,590,208,411

Liabilities: $3,350,567,278
Net Worth: $1,239,641,133
Earnings: $102,775,580
Emp.: 301
Fiscal Year-end: 12/31/22
Departmental Store Operator
N.A.I.C.S.: 455110
You Mingyang (Chm)

NYOTA MINERALS LTD.
Suite 2 47 Havelock Street, West Perth, 6005, WA, Australia
Tel.: (61) 893242955
Web Site: http://www.nyotaminerals.com
Sales Range: Less than $1 Million
Gold Mining & Exploration Services
N.A.I.C.S.: 212220
Michael J. Langoulant (Sec)

Subsidiaries:

Nyota Minerals (UK) Limited (1)
Suite 5 Sicilian House 7 Sicilian Avenue, London, WC1A 2QH, United Kingdom
Tel.: (44) 20 7400 5740
Gold Mining Services
N.A.I.C.S.: 212220

NYQUEST TECHNOLOGY CO., LTD.
7F-1 No 81 Shuili Road, Hsinchu, 30059, Taiwan
Tel.: (886) 35169077
Web Site: https://www.nyquest.com.tw
Year Founded: 2006
6494—(TPE)
Rev.: $55,555,295
Assets: $50,793,422
Liabilities: $12,853,078
Net Worth: $37,940,343
Earnings: $9,415,815
Emp.: 140
Fiscal Year-end: 12/31/22
Electronic Components Mfr
N.A.I.C.S.: 334419
Chiu-Li Kuo (Chm)

NYRADA INC.
Suite 2 Level 3 828 Pacific Highway, Gordon, 2072, NSW, Australia
Tel.: (61) 294983390
Web Site: https://www.nyrada.com
Year Founded: 2017
NYR—(ASX)
Rev.: $1,029,355
Assets: $3,367,492
Liabilities: $590,913
Net Worth: $2,776,578
Earnings: ($5,073,803)
Fiscal Year-end: 06/30/23
Pharmaceutical Product Mfr & Distr
N.A.I.C.S.: 325412
Benny Evison (Chief Scientific Officer)

NYRSTAR NV
Hoofdstraat 1, 6024 AA, Budel, Netherlands
Tel.: (31) 495512920
Web Site: https://www.nyrstar.com
Year Founded: 2007
NYRSY—(OTCEM)
Sales Range: $1-9.9 Million
Emp.: 4,024
Zinc, Silver & Lead Producer
N.A.I.C.S.: 212230
Daniel Vanin (CEO)

Subsidiaries:

Budelco BV (1)
Hoofdstraat 1, Budel-Dorplein, Cranendonck, 2001, Noord-Brabant, Netherlands
Tel.: (31) 495512911
Web Site: http://www.nyrstar.com
Emp.: 450
Zinc Products Mfr

N.A.I.C.S.: 331529
Francis Terwinghe (Plant Mgr)

Galva 45 S.A. (1)
rue de la Gare 17 Zone Industrielle, 45300, Escrennes, France
Tel.: (33) 238340091
Web Site: http://www.galvaunion.com
Sales Range: $50-74.9 Million
Emp.: 137
Metal Galvanization Services
N.A.I.C.S.: 332812

Nyrstar Belgium NV (1)
Zinkstraat 1, Balen, 2490, Antwerp, Belgium
Tel.: (32) 14449500
Web Site: http://www.nyrstar.com
Sales Range: $200-249.9 Million
Emp.: 400
Zinc Refining Services
N.A.I.C.S.: 331410
Virginie Lietaer (Sec)

Nyrstar Budel BV (1)
Hoofdstraat 1, Budel-Dorplein, Cranendonck, 6024 AA, Netherlands
Tel.: (31) 495 512911
Web Site: http://www.nyrstarbudel.nl
Sales Range: $125-149.9 Million
Emp.: 450
Zinc Products Mfr
N.A.I.C.S.: 325180

Nyrstar Clarksville Inc. (1)
1800 Zinc Plant Rd, Clarksville, TN 37040
Tel.: (931) 552-4200
Sales Range: $50-74.9 Million
Emp.: 230
Zinc Smelting Services
N.A.I.C.S.: 331410
Kelly Strong (VP-Mining Ops)

Nyrstar Finance International NV (1)
Zinkstraat 1, 2490, Balen, Antwerpen, Belgium
Tel.: (32) 14 44 95 00
Financial Support Services
N.A.I.C.S.: 561990

Nyrstar France SAS (1)
Rue Jean-Jacques Rousseau, 59950, Auby, Nord, France
Tel.: (33) 3 2793 5000
Sales Range: $100-124.9 Million
Emp.: 300
Industrial Chemicals Mfr
N.A.I.C.S.: 339999
Zinc Nestas (CEO)

Nyrstar Germany GmbH (1)
Gladbecker Street 413, 45326, Essen, Nordrhein-Westfalen, Germany
Tel.: (49) 201364740
Metal Galvanization Services
N.A.I.C.S.: 332812

Nyrstar Hobart Pty Ltd (1)
Risdon Road, Lutana, Hobart, 7009, TAS, Australia
Tel.: (61) 362784444
Web Site: http://nyrstarhobart.com
Sales Range: $100-124.9 Million
Emp.: 471
Zinc Smelting Services
N.A.I.C.S.: 331492

Nyrstar Holdings Inc (1)
1800 Zinc Plant Rd, Clarksville, TN 37041-1104
Tel.: (931) 552-4200
Precious Metal Smelting Services
N.A.I.C.S.: 331410

Nyrstar Metals Pty Ltd (1)
Riverside Quay Level 2/1 Southbank Boulevard, Southbank, 3006, VIC, Australia
Tel.: (61) 386990600
Zinc Refining Services
N.A.I.C.S.: 331410

Nyrstar Netherlands (Holdings) BV (1)
Hoofdstraat 1, Budel-Dorplein, Cranendonck, 6024 AA, Netherlands
Tel.: (31) 495512911
Zinc Refining & Alloying Services
N.A.I.C.S.: 331410

Nyrstar Port Pirie Pty Ltd (1)
Ellen St, PO Box 219, Port Pirie, 5540, SA, Australia

NYRSTAR NV

Nyrstar NV—(Continued)
Tel.: (61) 886381500
Web Site: http://www.nyrstar.com
Sales Range: $200-249.9 Million
Emp.: 700
Zinc Refining Services
N.A.I.C.S.: 331410
Bertus De Villiers *(Gen Mgr)*

Nyrstar Sales & Marketing NV (1)
Zinkstraat 1, Balen, 2490, Antwerpen, Belgium
Tel.: (32) 14449500
Web Site: http://www.nyrstar.com
Emp.: 570
Seal Products Distr
N.A.I.C.S.: 423510
Daniel Vanin *(CEO)*

Nyrstar Tennessee Mines - Gordonsville LLC (1)
120 Zinc Mine Cir, Gordonsville, TN 38563
Tel.: (615) 683-4900
Web Site: http://www.nyrstar.com
Sales Range: $100-124.9 Million
Emp.: 300
Zinc Smelting & Alloying Services
N.A.I.C.S.: 331410

Nyrstar Tennessee Mines - Strawberry Plains LLC (1)
2421 W Old Andrew Johnson Hwy, Strawberry Plains, TN 37871
Tel.: (865) 932-8200
Zinc Smelting Services
N.A.I.C.S.: 331410

NYSSA CORPORATION LIMITED

Office No 002 Gulmohar Complex Opposite Anupam Cinema Station Road, Goregaon East, Mumbai, 400063, Maharashtra, India
Tel.: (91) 2260502425
Web Site:
 https://www.nyssacorporation.com
Year Founded: 1981
504378—(BOM)
Rev.: $1,482,664
Assets: $3,901,736
Liabilities: $528,051
Net Worth: $3,373,685
Earnings: $77,484
Emp.: 5
Fiscal Year-end: 03/31/21
Real Estate Development Services
N.A.I.C.S.: 531390
Prasanna Shirke *(Chm & CFO)*

NYXOAH SA

Rue Edouard Belin 12, 1435, Mont-Saint-Guibert, Belgium
Tel.: (32) 10222355 **BE**
Web Site: https://www.nyxoah.com
Year Founded: 2009
NYXH—(NASDAQ)
Rev.: $3,787,892
Assets: $179,410,245
Liabilities: $31,623,495
Net Worth: $147,786,750
Earnings: ($38,351,794)
Emp.: 137
Fiscal Year-end: 12/31/22
Medical Device Mfr
N.A.I.C.S.: 334510
David Demartino *(Chief Strategy Officer)*

NZ WINDFARMS LIMITED

376 North Range Road, PO Box 20031, Summerhill, Palmerston North, 4448, New Zealand
Tel.: (64) 62802773
Web Site:
 https://www.nzwindfarms.co.nz
NWF—(NZX)
Rev.: $6,912,693
Assets: $28,530,801
Liabilities: $6,650,978
Net Worth: $21,879,822
Earnings: ($3,169,875)
Emp.: 11
Fiscal Year-end: 06/30/23
Renewable Electricity Generation
N.A.I.C.S.: 221118
Adam Radich *(Gen Mgr-Ops)*

Subsidiaries:

TRH Services Limited (1)
23-140 McGovern Drive, Cambridge, N3H 4R7, ON, Canada
Tel.: (519) 893-9488
Web Site: https://www.trhservices.ca
Medical Equipment Maintenance Services
N.A.I.C.S.: 811210

NZX LIMITED

Level 2 NZX Centre 11 Cable Street, PO Box 2959, Wellington, 6011, New Zealand
Tel.: (64) 44727599
Web Site: https://www.nzx.com
NZX—(NZX)
Rev.: $46,742,515
Assets: $142,866,843
Liabilities: $99,908,195
Net Worth: $42,958,649
Earnings: $9,842,758
Emp.: 226
Fiscal Year-end: 12/31/19
Stock Exchange
N.A.I.C.S.: 523210
James Miller *(Chm)*

Subsidiaries:

SuperLife Limited (1)
Level 15 45 Queen Street, Auckland, 1010, New Zealand
Tel.: (64) 93759800
Web Site: https://www.superlife.co.nz
Fire Insurance Services
N.A.I.C.S.: 524113

NZZ-MEDIENGRUPPE

Falkenstrasse 11, 8021, Zurich, Switzerland
Tel.: (41) 44 258 11 11
Web Site:
 http://www.nzzmediengruppe.ch
Newspaper Publishers
N.A.I.C.S.: 513110
Veit V. Dengler *(CEO)*

Subsidiaries:

St. Galler Tagblatt AG (1)
Furstenlandstrasse 122, 9001, Saint Gallen, Switzerland
Tel.: (41) 712727211
Web Site: http://www.tagblatt.ch
Newspaper Publishers
N.A.I.C.S.: 513110
Christine Bolt *(Head-Mktg & Reader Market & Deputy Dir)*

Unit (Domestic):

Thurgauer Zeitung (2)
Schmidgasse 7, 8501, Frauenfeld, Switzerland (100%)
Tel.: (41) 52 728 32 32
Web Site: http://www.thurgauerzeitung.ch
Newspaper Publishers
N.A.I.C.S.: 513110

O SORBET D'AMOUR SA

250 avenue du parc des expositions, 33260, La Teste, France
Tel.: (33) 557152839 **FR**
Web Site:
 http://www.osorbetdamour.fr
Year Founded: 1935
MLOSA—(EUR)
Sales Range: $1-9.9 Million
Ice Cream Mfr & Distr
N.A.I.C.S.: 311520
Pascal Hamon *(Pres)*

O TWELVE ESTATES LIMITED

1st Floor Royal Chambers St Julian's Avenue, PO Box 650, Saint Peter Port, GY1 3JX, Guernsey
Tel.: (44) 1481 810100 **GY**
Web Site:
 http://www.otwelveestates.com
Sales Range: $10-24.9 Million
Real Estate Investment Trust
N.A.I.C.S.: 525990
Phillip Rhodes *(Chm)*

O'CONNOR DODGE CHRYSLER JEEP

45730 Hocking Ave, PO Box 190, Chilliwack, V2P 6J1, BC, Canada
Tel.: (604) 792-2754
Web Site:
 http://www.oconnorchrysler.com
Year Founded: 1976
Rev.: $15,139,765
Emp.: 60
New & Used Car Dealers
N.A.I.C.S.: 441110
Shane O'Connor *(Gen Mgr)*

O'KEY GROUP S.A.

Kirovogradskaya Ulitsa 23A/1 Street, 117534, Moscow, 117534, Russia
Tel.: (7) 4956636677 **LU**
Web Site: http://okeygroup.lu
Year Founded: 2001
OKEY—(LSE)
Rev.: $2,323,244,834
Assets: $1,307,831,496
Liabilities: $1,183,832,594
Net Worth: $123,998,902
Earnings: ($32,167,293)
Emp.: 19,230
Fiscal Year-end: 12/31/23
Hypermarket & Supermarket Operators
N.A.I.C.S.: 445110
Heigo Kera *(Chm)*

O'LEARY AUTO GROUP

1165 Hanwell Road, Fredericton, E3C 1A5, NB, Canada
Tel.: (506) 450-0800
Car Dealership Operator
N.A.I.C.S.: 441110
Gerald O'Leary *(Owner)*

O'REGAN'S CHEVROLET BUICK GMC CADILLAC

2477 Robie St, Halifax, B3K 4N2, NS, Canada
Tel.: (902) 422-8551
Web Site: http://www.oregans.com
Sales Range: $50-74.9 Million
Emp.: 125
New & Used Car Dealers
N.A.I.C.S.: 441110
Paul O Regan *(Pres)*

O'WILL CORPORATION

12F Aoyoma Building 1-2-3 Kita Aoyama, Minatoku, Tokyo, Japan
Tel.: (81) 357724488
Web Site: http://www.owill.co.jp
Year Founded: 1987
3143—(TKS)
Rev.: $302,548,400
Assets: $110,787,600
Liabilities: $70,480,080
Net Worth: $40,307,520
Earnings: $5,614,400
Emp.: 102
Fiscal Year-end: 03/31/23
Food, Pharmaceutical Products, Chemical Equipment & Materials Importer, Exporter & Sales
N.A.I.C.S.: 425120
Hideki Oguchi *(Chm & CEO)*

Subsidiaries:

J.S. O'will, Inc. (1)
34004 9th Ave S Ste A4, Federal Way, WA 98003 (51%)
Tel.: (360) 226-3637
Sales Range: $1-9.9 Million
Emp.: 7
Industrial Heating & Cooling Machinery Wholesale Distr
N.A.I.C.S.: 423730
Jerry Kono *(Pres)*

O-NET TECHNOLOGIES (GROUP) LIMITED

35 Cuijing Road Pingshan New District, Shenzhen, 518118, China
Tel.: (86) 755 26710000 **Ky**
Web Site: http://www.o-netcom.com
Rev.: $331,421,202
Assets: $448,604,701
Liabilities: $148,385,074
Net Worth: $300,219,627
Earnings: $13,968,440
Emp.: 2,969
Fiscal Year-end: 12/31/19
Fibber Optic Components Mfr
N.A.I.C.S.: 335921
Qinglin Na *(Chm & CEO)*

Subsidiaries:

3SP Technologies S.A.S. (1)
Route de Villejust, 91625, Nozay, Cedex, France
Tel.: (33) 169805750
Web Site: http://www.3sptechnologies.com
Telecommunication Equipment Whslr
N.A.I.C.S.: 423690
Guang-Hua Duan *(Gen Mgr)*

ITF Technologies Inc. (1)
400 boul, Montpellier, Montreal, H4N 2G7, QC, Canada
Tel.: (514) 748-4848
Web Site: https://www.itftechnologies.com
Fiber Optic Component Mfr & Distr
N.A.I.C.S.: 334417
Julien Tremblay *(Mgr-Product Line-Industrial)*

O-Net Communications (HK) Limited (1)
Unit 1608 West Tower Shun Tak Centre 168-200 Connaught Road, Central, China (Hong Kong)
Tel.: (852) 23074100
Optical Component Distr
N.A.I.C.S.: 423690

O-Net Communications (USA), Inc. (1)
756 San Aleso Ave, Sunnyvale, CA 94085
Tel.: (408) 900-8825
Optical Component Distr
N.A.I.C.S.: 423690

O-Net Technologies (Thailand) Co., Ltd. (1)
221/3 Moo 6 Pinthong Industrial Estate 3 Soi 4, Sriracha District, Ban Bueng, 20230, Chon Buri, Thailand
Tel.: (66) 3 313 6060
Fiber Optic Cable Mfr
N.A.I.C.S.: 335921

O-TA PRECISION INDUSTRY CO., LTD.

No 8 Jianfu Road, Toyota Village Neipu Township, Ping-tung, Taiwan
Tel.: (886) 87783855
Web Site: https://www.o-ta.com.tw
Year Founded: 1988
8924—(TPE)
Rev.: $240,762,968
Assets: $197,868,868
Liabilities: $56,531,501
Net Worth: $141,337,367
Earnings: $56,065,472
Fiscal Year-end: 12/31/22
Iron & Wooden Golf Product Mfr
N.A.I.C.S.: 339920
Kung-Wen Li *(Chm)*

O-WELL CORPORATION

5-13-9 Mitejima, Nishiyodogawa-ku, Osaka, 555-0012, Japan
Tel.: (81) 66 473 0138
Web Site: http://www.owell.co.jp
Year Founded: 1943
7670—(TKS)
Rev.: $551,227,600
Assets: $403,133,280
Liabilities: $228,012,400
Net Worth: $175,120,880
Earnings: $2,526,480
Emp.: 646
Fiscal Year-end: 03/31/22
Electronic Equipment Mfr & Distr
N.A.I.C.S.: 336320
K. Tobito *(Pres)*

Subsidiaries:

O-A-C Corporation (1)
3-6-17 Kitashinagawa, Shinagawa-ku, Tokyo, 140-0001, Japan
Tel.: (81) 367129650
Paint & Coating Equipment Distr
N.A.I.C.S.: 423830

O-Well (Dalian) Corporation (1)
International Business Buildings of Gugeng 9F-904 No 138 Jin Ma Road, Dalian Economic and Technological Development Area, Dalian, 116600, China
Tel.: (86) 41187189041
Paint & Coating Equipment Distr
N.A.I.C.S.: 423830

O-Well (Shanghai) Corporation (1)
609-610 Dazhong Building No 1515 Zhong Shan Road W, Shanghai, 200235, China
Tel.: (86) 2160438858
Paint & Coating Equipment Distr
N.A.I.C.S.: 423830

O-Well (Thailand) Company Limited (1)
89 AIA Capital Center Unit 1106 11th Floor Ratchadaphisek Road, Dindaeng, Bangkok, 10400, Thailand
Tel.: (66) 20018900
Paint & Coating Equipment Distr
N.A.I.C.S.: 423830

O-Well Color Center Corporation (1)
1503 Mefuki, Noda, 278-0001, Chiba, Japan
Tel.: (81) 471238686
Paint & Coating Equipment Distr
N.A.I.C.S.: 423830

O-Well Germany GmbH (1)
Marie-Bernays-Ring 23a, 41199, Monchengladbach, Germany
Tel.: (49) 21661339050
Paint & Coating Equipment Distr
N.A.I.C.S.: 423830

O-Well Korea Corporation (1)
Heungdeok IT valley A-1505 13 Heungdeok 1-road, Giheung-gu, Yongin, 16954, Gyeonggi-do, Korea (South)
Tel.: (82) 312264927
Paint & Coating Equipment Distr
N.A.I.C.S.: 423830

O-Well Mexico Coatings & Electronics S.A. De C.V. (1)
Carretera A Santa Ana del Conde No 2102-A Localidad Los Lopez, Col Guadalupe Victoria, 37680, Leon, Guanajuato, Mexico
Tel.: (52) 4771002839
Paint & Coating Equipment Distr
N.A.I.C.S.: 423830

O-Well Super Build Corporation (1)
2F Shinbonishimura Bldg 1107-2 Shinbo, Minami-ku, Okayama, 700-0945, Japan
Tel.: (81) 862061666
Paint & Coating Equipment Distr
N.A.I.C.S.: 423830

O-Well Vietnam Company Limited (1)
22nd Floor Vinaconex 9 Tower Pham Hung Road, Me Tri Ward Nam Tu Liem District, Hanoi, Vietnam
Tel.: (84) 2432565123
Paint & Coating Equipment Distr
N.A.I.C.S.: 423830

PT. O Well Indonesia (1)
Japanese SME's Centre JI Kenari Raya Blok G6-01 Kav 17A, Delta Silicon VI Kel Jayamukti Kec Cikarang Pusat, Bekasi, 17530, Jawa Barat, Indonesia
Tel.: (62) 2128085173
Paint & Coating Equipment Distr
N.A.I.C.S.: 423830

Sun Maruko Co., Ltd. (1)
Sagamihara Incubation Center 5-4-30 Nishi-hashimoto, Midori-ku, Sagamihara, 252-0131, Kanagawa, Japan
Tel.: (81) 42 770 9457
Chemical Products Distr
N.A.I.C.S.: 424990

Uni-Electronics (Hong Kong) Ltd. (1)
Unit 01 8/F Laford Centre 838 Lai Chi Kok Road, Cheung Sha Wan, Kowloon, China (Hong Kong)
Tel.: (852) 3 154 9546
Electronic Equipment Distr
N.A.I.C.S.: 423690

Uni-Electronics Pte. Ltd. (1)
2 Jurong East Street 21 03-188A IMM Building, Singapore, Singapore
Tel.: (65) 6 375 3612
Electronic Equipment Distr
N.A.I.C.S.: 423690

Uni-Electronics, Inc. (1)
3-6-17 Kita-Shinagawa, Shinagawa-ku, Tokyo, 140-0001, Japan
Tel.: (81) 36 811 7477
Web Site: https://www.uni-elec.co.jp
Electronic Equipment Distr
N.A.I.C.S.: 423690
Kazunori Sugimura *(Pres)*

O. P. CHAINS LTD.
8/16 A Seth Gali, Agra, 282003, Uttar Pradesh, India
Tel.: (91) 5623059117
Web Site: https://www.opchainsltd.com
539116—(BOM)
Rev.: $445,269
Assets: $3,901,593
Liabilities: $2,884
Net Worth: $3,898,708
Earnings: $276,798
Emp.: 8
Fiscal Year-end: 03/31/23
Precious Metal Distr
N.A.I.C.S.: 423940
Om Prakash Agarwal *(Mng Dir)*

O.B.SYSTEM INC.
Urban Ace Kitahama Bldg 2-3-7 Hiranocho, Chuo-ku, Osaka, 541-0046, Japan
Tel.: (81) 662283411
Web Site: https://www.obs.co.jp
Year Founded: 1972
5576—(TKS)
Asset Management Services
N.A.I.C.S.: 523999
Toshio Toyoda *(Pres & CEO)*

O.J. COMPANY
294 Rang St Paul, Sherrington, J0L 2N0, QC, Canada
Tel.: (514) 990-2050
Web Site: http://www.ojcompagnie.com
Year Founded: 1950
Rev.: $15,765,149
Emp.: 30
Golf Course Equipment Supplier
N.A.I.C.S.: 713910
Corey Young *(Mgr-Admin, Inventory & Logistics)*

O.K. INDUSTRIES LTD.
6702 Rajpur Pl, Saanichton, V8M 1Z5, BC, Canada
Tel.: (250) 652-9211
Web Site: http://www.islandpaving.com
Year Founded: 1944
Sales Range: $25-49.9 Million
Emp.: 150
Asphalt Pavement Contractor
N.A.I.C.S.: 324121
Jason Waldron *(Controller)*

Subsidiaries:

O.K. Industries Ltd. - Duncan Paving Division (1)
6357 Cowichan Valley Hwy, PO Box 815, Duncan, V9L 3Y2, BC, Canada
Tel.: (250) 748-2531
Asphalt Pavement Contracting Services
N.A.I.C.S.: 238990
Ken Wright *(Mgr)*

O.K. Industries Ltd. - Haylock Bros. Paving Division (1)
1301 Alberni Highway, Parksville, V9P 2B9, BC, Canada
Tel.: (250) 248-8011
Asphalt Pavement Contracting Services
N.A.I.C.S.: 238990
Darrell McKay *(Pres)*

O.K. Industries Ltd. - O.K. Paving Division (1)
6075 Bronze Road, Port Hardy, V0N 2P0, BC, Canada
Tel.: (250) 949-6711
Asphalt Pavement Contracting Services
N.A.I.C.S.: 238990

O.O.M. ONDERLINGE VERZEKERING-MAATSCHAPPIJ U.A
Jan Thijssenweg 2, 2289 AA, Rijswijk, Netherlands
Tel.: (31) 703532100
Web Site: http://www.oominsurances.com
Year Founded: 1961
Sales Range: $25-49.9 Million
Emp.: 25
Insurance Providing Services
N.A.I.C.S.: 524113
Marga Purcis *(CEO)*

Subsidiaries:

O.O.M Global Care N.V. (1)
Nassaukave 1, PO Box 3036, 2280 GA, Hague, Netherlands
Tel.: (31) 703532100
Sales Range: $50-74.9 Million
Insurance Services
N.A.I.C.S.: 524298

Schadeverzekeringmaatschappij Zevenwouden U.A. (1)
22 Van Maasdijkstraat, 8441 CM, Heerenveen, Netherlands
Tel.: (31) 513622514
Web Site: http://www.zavenwauden.nl
Sales Range: $50-74.9 Million
Emp.: 15
Insurance Services
N.A.I.C.S.: 524298

O.T.E INGENIERIE
1 Rue De La Lisiere, BP 40110, 67403, Illkirch-Graffenstaden, CEDEX, France
Tel.: (33) 388675555
Web Site: http://www.ote-ingenierie.com
Year Founded: 1962
Emp.: 205
Engineering & Construction Services
N.A.I.C.S.: 541330
Patrick Lullin *(Chm)*

O1 GROUP LIMITED
Office centre Lighthouse Valovaya str 26, Moscow, 115054, Russia
Tel.: (7) 495 980 5550
Web Site: http://www.o1group.ru
Year Founded: 2004
Investment Holding Company
N.A.I.C.S.: 551112
Boris Mints *(Chm)*

O1 PROPERTIES PLC
26 Valovaya Str, 115054, Moscow, Russia
Tel.: (7) 4957885575
Web Site: http://www.o1properties.ru
Emp.: 100
Owns & Manages Office Space
N.A.I.C.S.: 531312
Dmitry Mints *(Chm)*

O2 CAPITAL PARTNERS B.V.
Utrechtseweg 181, 6862 AJ, Oosterbeek, Netherlands
Tel.: (31) 263342302
Web Site: https://o2capital.nl
Emp.: 100
Investment Services
N.A.I.C.S.: 523999

O2 MARKETING COMMUNICATIONS
Office 508 5th Floor Latifa Tower, Seikh Zayed Road, 39746, Dubai, United Arab Emirates
Tel.: (971) 43 889802
Web Site: http://www.o2.ae
Year Founded: 2005
Sales Range: $1-9.9 Million
Emp.: 100
Multidisciplinary Design Advertising
N.A.I.C.S.: 541810
Mohammed Johmani *(Founder & CEO)*

O2GOLD INC.
65 Queen Street West Unit 900, Toronto, M5H 2M5, ON, Canada
Tel.: (416) 861-5888 Ca
Web Site: http://otugold.com
Year Founded: 2012
OTGO.H—(TSXV)
Assets: $111,176
Liabilities: $256,965
Net Worth: ($145,789)
Earnings: ($273,746)
Emp.: 250
Fiscal Year-end: 12/31/23
Investment Services
N.A.I.C.S.: 523999
Scott Moore *(Pres & CEO)*

O3 MINING INC.
1440 - 155 University Ave, Toronto, M5H 3B7, ON, Canada
Tel.: (873) 381-2014
Web Site: https://o3mining.com
15A—(DEU)
Rev.: $3,946,257
Assets: $197,756,111
Liabilities: $25,401,482
Net Worth: $172,354,630
Earnings: ($25,757,898)
Emp.: 48
Fiscal Year-end: 12/31/23
Metal Mining
N.A.I.C.S.: 212390
Louis Gariepy *(VP-Exploration)*

Subsidiaries:

Alexandria Minerals Corp. (1)
1 Toronto St Suite 201, PO Box 10, Toronto, M5C 2V6, ON, Canada
Tel.: (416) 363-9372
Web Site: http://www.azx.ca
Gold Mining Services
N.A.I.C.S.: 212220

OAK WOODS ACQUISITION CORPORATION
101 Roswell Drive, Nepean, K2J 0H5, ON, Canada
Tel.: (403) 561-7750 Ky
Web Site: https://www.oakwoodsacquisition.com
Year Founded: 2022

OAK WOODS ACQUISITION CORPORATION

Oak Woods Acquisition Corporation—(Continued)
OAKU—(NASDAQ)
Rev.: $2,337,439
Assets: $61,199,425
Liabilities: $61,835,600
Net Worth: ($636,175)
Earnings: $1,308,097
Fiscal Year-end: 12/31/23
Investment Management Service
N.A.I.C.S.: 523999

OAKBAY INVESTMENTS (PTY) LTD.
144 Katherine Street, Sandton, 2031, South Africa
Tel.: (27) 11 542 2000
Web Site: http://www.ioakbay.co.za
Year Founded: 2006
Emp.: 4,500
Investment Holding Company
N.A.I.C.S.: 551112
Ronica Ragavan *(Acting CEO)*

OAKBAY RESOURCES & ENERGY LIMITED
Grayston Ridge Office Park Block A Lower Ground Floor, 144 Katherine Street Sandown Sandton, Johannesburg, South Africa
Tel.: (27) 11 430 7640   ZA
Web Site: http://www.oakbay.co.za
Year Founded: 2009
Sales Range: $25-49.9 Million
Gold & Uranium Product Mining Services
N.A.I.C.S.: 212290
Trevor Scott *(CFO & Dir-Fin)*

OAKLEIGH CONSULTING LIMITED
Suite 626 Sunlight House Quay Street, Manchester, M3 3JZ, United Kingdom
Tel.: (44) 1618354100
Web Site: http://www.oakleigh.co.uk
Rev.: $10,200,000
Emp.: 60
Management Consulting Services
N.A.I.C.S.: 541611
Jim Young *(Mng Dir)*

OAKLEY CAPITAL LIMITED
3 Cadogan Gate, London, SW1X 0AS, United Kingdom
Tel.: (44) 2077666900   UK
Web Site: http://www.oakleycapital.com
Year Founded: 2002
Private Equity, Asset Management & Financial Advisory Services
N.A.I.C.S.: 523940
Peter Dubens *(Founder & Mng Partner)*

Subsidiaries:

Career Partner GmbH (1)
Newton Ridlerstrasse 57, D-80339, Munich, Germany
Tel.: (49) 89 125 99 96 90
Web Site: http://www.careerpartner.eu
Vocational Training Services
N.A.I.C.S.: 624310
Sven Schutt *(CEO & Member-Exec Bd)*

Oakley Capital Corporate Finance Limited (1)
3 Cadogan Gate, London, SW1X 0AS, United Kingdom
Tel.: (44) 20 7766 6900
Web Site: http://www.oakleyadvisory.com
Emp.: 20
Financial Advisory Services
N.A.I.C.S.: 523940
Chris Godsmark *(Partner)*

Oakley Capital Investments Limited (1)
Mintflower Place 3rd Floor 8 Par-la-Ville Road, Hamilton, HM08, Bermuda
Tel.: (441) 5426330
Web Site: http://www.oakleycapitalinvestments.com
Rev.: $72,679,566
Assets: $1,547,709,391
Liabilities: $11,062,978
Net Worth: $1,536,646,413
Earnings: $60,458,094
Fiscal Year-end: 12/31/2023
Closed-End Investment Fund
N.A.I.C.S.: 525990
Caroline Foulger *(Chm)*

Pelican Midco Limited (1)
2nd Floor The Place 175 High Holborn, London, WC1 V7AA, United Kingdom
Tel.: (44) 207 299 1800
Web Site: http://www.oceantechnologiesgroup.com
Holding Company; Maritime Learning & Training Services
N.A.I.C.S.: 551112
Roger Ringstad *(Chm)*

Subsidiary (Domestic):

Marlins Training Limited (2)
1st Floor Skypark 8 Elliot Place, Glasgow, G3 8EP, United Kingdom
Tel.: (44) 1413051370
Web Site: http://www.marlins.co.uk
Sales Range: $10-24.9 Million
Emp.: 150
Shipping Industry Training Solutions
N.A.I.C.S.: 611710
Catherine Logie *(Mgr)*

Subsidiary (Non-US):

Seagull Maritime AS (2)
Gamleveien 36, PO Box 1062, 3194, Horten, Norway
Tel.: (47) 33 03 0910
Web Site: http://www.seagull.no
Software Training Services
N.A.I.C.S.: 611420
Frank Stefan Pete *(Dir-Customer Svcs)*

Subsidiary (Non-US):

Seagull K.K. (3)
Terada Bldg 3D 4-29-6 Shinbashi, Minato-Ku, Tokyo, 105-0004, Japan
Tel.: (81) 3 6450 1595
Software Training Services
N.A.I.C.S.: 611420
Hea Won Kim *(Mgr-Sls)*

Seagull Maritime AS Sp. z o.o. (3)
ul Falista 7, 81-331, Gdynia, Poland
Tel.: (48) 58 620 51 90
Software Training Services
N.A.I.C.S.: 611420
Andrzej Biedrawa *(Mng Dir)*

Seagull Maritime Information Technologies Ltd. (3)
The Quadrus Centre Wood stock Way, Boldon Business Park, Boldon, NE35 9PF, Tyne and Wear, United Kingdom
Tel.: (44) 191 519 7346
Software Training Services
N.A.I.C.S.: 611420
Aidan Osmialowski *(Area Mgr-Sls)*

Seagull Maritime Information Technology (3)
8-10 Sachtouri Str, 185-37, Piraeus, Greece
Tel.: (30) 210 4510013
Web Site: http://www.seagull.no
Emp.: 3
Software Training Services
N.A.I.C.S.: 611420
Loannis Athanasopoulos *(Mng Dir)*

Seagull Maritime Information Technology GmbH (3)
Katharinenstr 30A, 20457, Hamburg, Germany
Tel.: (49) 40 80 79 178 21
Software Training Services
N.A.I.C.S.: 611420
Jens Hansen *(Mng Dir)*

Seagull Maritime Information Technology Pte Ltd (3)
315 Outram Road, 15-03 Tan Boon Liat Building, Singapore, 169074, Singapore
Tel.: (65) 62201218

Software Training Services
N.A.I.C.S.: 611420
Lim Soo Hock *(Mng Dir)*

Subsidiary (Domestic):

Videotel Marine International Ltd. (2)
84 Newman St, Fitzrovia, London, W1T 3EU, United Kingdom
Tel.: (44) 2072991800
Web Site: http://www.videotel.com
Mobile Satellite Communications & Television Antenna Systems Provider
N.A.I.C.S.: 517410

Subsidiary (Non-US):

Videotel Marine Asia Ltd. (3)
Room 401 Yu Sung Boon Building 107-111 Des Voeux Road, Central, China (Hong Kong)
Tel.: (852) 28150266
Mobile Satellite Communication Services
N.A.I.C.S.: 517410

Plesk International GmbH (1)
Vordergasse 59, 8200, Schaffhausen, Switzerland
Tel.: (41) 52 539 10 00
Web Site: http://www.plesk.com
Software Publisher
N.A.I.C.S.: 513210
Nils Hueneke *(CEO)*

Subsidiary (US):

cPanel, LLC (2)
2550 N Loop W Ste 4006, Houston, TX 77092
Tel.: (570) 443-7700
Web Site: http://www.cpanel.net
Web Hosting Services
N.A.I.C.S.: 541511
J. Nick Koston *(CEO)*

TechInsights Inc. (1)
1891 Robertson Road Suite 500, Ottawa, K2H 5B7, ON, Canada
Tel.: (613) 599-6500
Web Site: http://www.techinsights.com
Consulting & Management Software Solutions
N.A.I.C.S.: 513210
Mike McLean *(Sr VP-Intellectual Property Rights)*

Subsidiary (US):

Strategy Analytics, Inc. (2)
199 Wells Ave Ste 108, Newton, MA 02459
Tel.: (617) 614-0700
Web Site: http://www.strategyanalytics.com
Marketing Research & Consulting Services
N.A.I.C.S.: 541910
Harvey Cohen *(Founder & Pres)*

Subsidiary (Non-US):

Strategy Analytics (3)
19 Rue Pierre Lescot, 75001, Paris, France
Tel.: (33) 1 53 40 99 50
Marketing Research & Consulting Services
N.A.I.C.S.: 541910

Strategy Analytics GmbH (3)
Sebastiansplatz 5, Munich, 80331, Germany
Tel.: (49) 89 51 51 35 0
Marketing Research & Consulting Services
N.A.I.C.S.: 541910

Strategy Analytics Inc. (3)
59-2-102 Beijing Suncity No 30 Litang Road, Xiaotangshan Changping District, Beijing, 102209, China
Tel.: (86) 10 8975 5246
Marketing Research & Consulting Services
N.A.I.C.S.: 541910

Strategy Analytics Inc. (3)
Level 18 Yebisu Garden Place Tower 4-20-3 Ebisu, Shibuya-ku, Tokyo, 150-6018, Japan
Tel.: (81) 3 5789 5935
Marketing Research & Consulting Services
N.A.I.C.S.: 541910

Strategy Analytics Inc. (3)
14F 631 Gangam-daero, Seocho-gu, Seoul, 06524, Korea (South)
Tel.: (82) 2 310 9122
Marketing Research & Consulting Services
N.A.I.C.S.: 541910

INTERNATIONAL PUBLIC

Strategy Analytics Ltd. (3)
Bank House 171 Midsummer Boulevard, Milton Keynes, MK9 1EB, United Kingdom
Tel.: (44) 1908 423600
Web Site: http://www.strategyanalytics.com
Marketing Research & Consulting Services
N.A.I.C.S.: 541910
Chris Webber *(VP-Global Automotive Practice)*

Subsidiary (US):

VLSI Research, Inc. (2)
2880 Lakeside Dr Ste 350, Santa Clara, CA 95054
Tel.: (408) 453-8844
Web Site: http://www.vlsiresearch.com
Sales Range: $1-9.9 Million
Emp.: 23
Marketing Research & Public Opinion Polling
N.A.I.C.S.: 541910
Dan G. Hutcheson *(Chm & CEO)*

Time Out New York (1)
475 10th Ave 12th Fl, New York, NY 10018
Tel.: (646) 432-3000
Web Site: http://www.timeout.com
Entertainment Services
N.A.I.C.S.: 516210
Aaron David *(Sr VP)*

UNIT4 Business Software Iberica S.A. (1)
Avenida Castell De Barbera 22-24, Barbera del Valles, 08210, Barcelona, Spain
Tel.: (34) 937489600
Web Site: http://www.ekon.es
Business Administration Software Development Services
N.A.I.C.S.: 541511
Juan Antonio Fernandez *(CEO)*

Via-Online GmbH (1)
Kimplerstr 296, 47807, Krefeld, Germany
Tel.: (49) 21516501940
Web Site: http://www.afterbuy.de
Data Processing Services
N.A.I.C.S.: 518210
Daliah Salzmann *(CEO)*

WindStar Medical GmbH (1)
Bessie-Coleman-Strasse 13, 60549, Frankfurt am Main, Germany
Tel.: (49) 69654 027 2101
Web Site: https://www.windstar-medical.com
Emp.: 100
Pharmaceutical Product Mfr & Distr
N.A.I.C.S.: 325412
Rene Flaschker *(CEO & Mng Dir)*

Subsidiary (Domestic):

Districon GmbH (2)
At Joseph 15, Wehrheim, 61273, Hessen, Germany
Tel.: (49) 608157610
Vitamin & Supplement Retailer
N.A.I.C.S.: 456191

Dr. Kleine Pharma GmbH (2)
Heidsieker Heide 114, 33739, Bielefeld, Germany
Tel.: (49) 5206997250
Vitamin & Supplement Retailer
N.A.I.C.S.: 456191

vLex Networks, SL (1)
Almogavers 119-123, 08017, Barcelona, Spain
Tel.: (34) 93272268
Web Site: https://vlex.com
Online Marketing & Legal Publishing Services
N.A.I.C.S.: 518210

Subsidiary (US):

Fastcase (2)
711 D St NW Ste 200, Washington, DC 20004-2806
Tel.: (202) 999-4777
Web Site: http://www.fastcase.com
Law firm
N.A.I.C.S.: 541110
Ed Walters *(Co-Founder & CEO)*

OAKMONT CAPITAL CORP.
Suite 910 355 Burrard Street, Vancouver, V6C 2G8, BC, Canada

Tel.: (604) 220-8048 BC
Year Founded: 2010
Investment Services
N.A.I.C.S.: 523999
Gregory P. Hannon *(VP)*

OAKRIDGE INTERNATIONAL LIMITED
Level 6 412 Collins St, Melbourne, 3000, VIC, Australia
Tel.: (61) 396420655 AU
Web Site:
https://www.oakridgeint.com
OAK—(ASX)
Rev.: $785,944
Assets: $1,207,125
Liabilities: $518,663
Net Worth: $688,462
Earnings: ($508,312)
Fiscal Year-end: 06/30/24
Communication Service
N.A.I.C.S.: 517810
Con Unerkov *(Exec Chm & CEO)*

OAKVILLE HYDRO CORPORATION
861 Redwood Sq, Oakville, L6J 5E3, ON, Canada
Tel.: (905) 825-9400
Web Site:
http://www.oakvillehydro.com
Sales Range: $100-124.9 Million
Emp.: 103
Electricity Power Services
N.A.I.C.S.: 221122
Rob Lister *(Pres & CEO)*

OAKVILLE VOLKSWAGEN INC.
1355 North Service Rd W, Oakville, L6M 2W2, ON, Canada
Tel.: (905) 844-3285
Web Site: http://www.oakville-vw.ca
Year Founded: 1967
Rev.: $21,214,568
Emp.: 45
New & Used Car Dealers
N.A.I.C.S.: 441110
Gorette Gregorio *(Mgr-Guest Svcs)*

OAKWELL DISTRIBUTION (S) PTE. LTD.
No 8 Aljunied Avenue 3 Oakwell Building, Singapore, 389933, Singapore
Tel.: (65) 67428000
Web Site: http://www.oakwell.com.sg
Sales Range: $125-149.9 Million
Engineering Products Distr
N.A.I.C.S.: 423810
Derick Chien Joo Lim *(Sec & Controller-Fin)*

Subsidiaries:

OID Pte. Ltd. (1)
8 Aljunied Avenue 3, Singapore, 389933, Singapore
Tel.: (65) 67428000
Sales Range: $100-124.9 Million
Emp.: 150
Investment Management Service
N.A.I.C.S.: 523940
Beng Tin Low *(Mng Dir)*

Subsidiary (Non-US):

Oakwell International Trading (Shanghai) Co., Ltd. (2)
Shanghai Everwin Garden Tower B Room 804 521 South Wan Ping Road, Shanghai, 200032, China
Tel.: (86) 2164325985
Electric Wiring Supplies Distr
N.A.I.C.S.: 423610

Oakwell Engineering (M) Sdn Bhd (1)
No 6-3 Jalan Puteri 2/3 Bandar Puteri, 47100, Puchong, Selangor Darul Ehsan, Malaysia
Tel.: (60) 380631630
Web Site: http://www.oakwell.com.sg
Sales Range: $50-74.9 Million
Emp.: 8
Electronic Product Distr
N.A.I.C.S.: 423690
Derick Lim *(Sec)*

Oakwell Engineering International Pte Ltd (1)
No 8 Aljunied Avenue 3 Oakwell Building, Singapore, 389933, Singapore
Tel.: (65) 6741 9000
Web Site: http://www.oakwell.com.sg
Sales Range: $25-49.9 Million
Emp.: 150
Engineeering Services
N.A.I.C.S.: 541330
Bengtin Low *(Mng Dir)*

Oakwell Shipbuilding Engineering and Construction Pte. Ltd. (1)
No 8 Aljunied Avenue 3 Oakwell Building, Singapore, 389933, Singapore
Tel.: (65) 67428000
Engineering Products Distr
N.A.I.C.S.: 423830
Per Lindeberg *(CEO)*

OANDO PLC
2 Ajose Adeogun Street, Victoria Island, Lagos, Nigeria
Tel.: (234) 2014656000
Web Site: https://www.oandoplc.com
Year Founded: 1956
OAO—(JSE)
Rev.: $4,446,072,227
Assets: $2,792,696,973
Liabilities: $3,232,465,835
Net Worth: ($439,768,863)
Earnings: ($181,144,720)
Emp.: 154
Fiscal Year-end: 12/31/22
Petroleum Products
N.A.I.C.S.: 213112
Jubril Adewale Tinubu *(CEO)*

Subsidiaries:

Gaslink Nigeria Limited (1)
Stallion House 8th Floor 2 Ajose Adeogun Street, Victoria Island, Lagos, Nigeria
Tel.: (234) 12702794
Web Site: http://www.oandoplc.com
Natural Gas Pipeline Distr
N.A.I.C.S.: 221210

Nigerian Agip Oil Co. Ltd. (1)
No 40/42 Aguiyi Ironsi Street, Maitama Federal Capital Territory, Abuja, Nigeria
Tel.: (234) 946119006
Natural Gas Producer
N.A.I.C.S.: 221210

Oando Energy Services Ltd. (1)
Stallion House 10th Floor 2 Ajose Adeogun Street, Victoria Island, Lagos, Nigeria
Tel.: (234) 12622311
Web Site: http://www.oandoplc.com
Oil & Gas Rig Support Services
N.A.I.C.S.: 213112

Oando Exploration & Production Limited (1)
Stallion House 10th Floor 2 Ajose Adeogun Street, Victoria Island, Lagos, Nigeria
Tel.: (234) 12601290
Web Site: http://www.oandoplc.com
Oil & Gas Producer & Developer
N.A.I.C.S.: 211120

OAO AK TRANSNEFT
4 bldg 2 Presnenskaya Embankment, 123112, Moscow, Russia
Tel.: (7) 4959508178 RU
Web Site: http://www.transneft.ru
Year Founded: 1992
TRNFP—(MOEX)
Rev.: $17,159,561,770
Assets: $53,704,867,260
Liabilities: $18,719,187,600
Net Worth: $34,985,679,660
Earnings: $3,179,287,520
Emp.: 117,772
Fiscal Year-end: 12/31/19
Holding Company; Oil Pipeline Operator
N.A.I.C.S.: 551112
Nikolay Petrovich Tokarev *(Chm-Mgmt Bd & Pres)*

Subsidiaries:

Chernomortransneft, JSC (1)
Sheskharis, 353911, Novorossiysk, Krasnodar Territory, Russia
Tel.: (7) 8617603451
Web Site:
http://www.en.chernomor.transneft.ru
Oil Transporting Services
N.A.I.C.S.: 486110
Alexandr Vladimirovich Zlenko *(Gen Dir)*

Giprotruboprovod, JSC (1)
24-1 Vavilova St, 119334, Moscow, Russia
Tel.: (7) 4959508650
Web Site:
http://www.en.giprotruboprovod.transneft.ru
Oil Transporting Services
N.A.I.C.S.: 486110
Kopaseva Lyudmila Anatolyevna *(Gen Dir)*

JSC Uralsibnefteprovod (1)
ul Krupskaya 10, 450077, Ufa, Russia
Tel.: (7) 347 279 2525
Web Site: http://usmn.transneft.ru
Oil & Gas Pipeline Operator
N.A.I.C.S.: 486110

NPF Transneft, JSC (1)
5/7 ul Shchipok Str 23, 115054, Moscow, Russia
Tel.: (7) 4997998569
Web Site: http://www.npf-transneft.ru
Oil Transporting Services
N.A.I.C.S.: 486110

OAO Energoterminal (1)
St 4 Bld 1, Moscow, 115094, Russia
Tel.: (7) 4997998695
Web Site: http://www.energoterminal.ru
Emp.: 20
Customs Brokerage Services
N.A.I.C.S.: 488510
Alek Skov *(CEO)*

OAO MN Druzhba (1)
113 ul Uralskaya, Bryansk, 241020, Russia
Tel.: (7) 4832747708
Web Site: http://www.druzhbamn.ru
Pipeline Oil Transportation Services
N.A.I.C.S.: 486110

OAO SZMN (1)
26a ul Nikolaya Ershova, Kazan, 420061, Russia
Tel.: (7) 843 279 04 20
Web Site: http://www.szmn.ru
Oil & Gas Pipeline Transportation Services
N.A.I.C.S.: 486110

OAO Sibnefteprovod (1)
139 ul Respubliki, Tyumen, 625048, Russia
Tel.: (7) 3452 32 27 10
Web Site: http://www.sibnefteprovod.ru
Oil Pipeline Transportation Services
N.A.I.C.S.: 486110

OAO Transsibneft (1)
111 Korp 1 ul Krasny Put, Omsk, 644033, Russia
Tel.: (7) 3812691456
Web Site: http://www.transsibneft.com
Crude Oil Pipeline Transportation Services
N.A.I.C.S.: 486110

QOO DSD (1)
163 ul Volochaevskaya, Khabarovsk, 680000, Russia
Tel.: (7) 4212311594
Oil & Gas Pipeline Transportation Services
N.A.I.C.S.: 486110

OOO TransPress (1)
16 K 1 Dobrolyubova ul, Moscow, 127254, Russia
Tel.: (7) 4959508724
Oil & Gas Pipeline Transportation Services
N.A.I.C.S.: 486110

OOO Transneft Finance (1)
Vavilova St 24 Bldg 1, 119334, Moscow, Russia
Tel.: (7) 4959508135
Web Site: http://www.transneftfinance.ru
Financial Management Services
N.A.I.C.S.: 523999

OOO Transneft-Servis (1)
19/2 B Sukharevskiy Lane, Moscow, 127051, Russia
Tel.: (7) 495 950 85 15
Web Site: http://www.tns-s.ru
Electric Power Distribution Services
N.A.I.C.S.: 221122
Aleksander Zaprudnov *(Gen Dir)*

Subsidiary (Domestic):

JSC Nizhniy Novgorod Retail Company (2)
3B Beketova, Nizhniy Novgorod, 603950, Russia (52.9%)
Tel.: (7) 831 2430799
Web Site: http://www.nsk.elektra.ru
Emp.: 1,014
Electric Power Distribution Services
N.A.I.C.S.: 221122
Dmitry Aleksandrovich Arzhanov *(Chm)*

OOO Vostoknefteprovod (1)
14 ul Olimpiskaya, Bratsk, 665734, Russia
Tel.: (7) 3953300743
Web Site: http://www.vostoknefteprovod.ru
Oil & Gas Pipeline Construction Services
N.A.I.C.S.: 237120

PMC ESPO, LLC (1)
2-b ul Gorkogo, Angarsk, Irkutsk, Russia
Tel.: (7) 3955691854
Oil Transporting Services
N.A.I.C.S.: 486110

REM, JSC (1)
8-i Eniseyskaya st, 454010, Chelyabinsk, Russia
Tel.: (7) 3512044060
Web Site: http://www.en.red.transneft.ru
Oil Transporting Services
N.A.I.C.S.: 486110

Sredne-Volzhsky Transnefteproduct, JSC (1)
4 Zinina Str, 420097, Kazan, Russia
Tel.: (7) 8432366634
Web Site: http://www.en.sv-transnefteproduct.transneft.ru
Oil Transporting Services
N.A.I.C.S.: 486110
Gabbasov Rinat Flyurovich *(Chief Engr)*

Svyaztransneft, JSC (1)
12/1 Nametkina Str, 117420, Moscow, Russia
Tel.: (7) 4959508500
Web Site: http://www.en.svyaz.transneft.ru
Oil Transporting Services
N.A.I.C.S.: 486110

TNT, JSC (1)
37 Lenina Avenue, 353913, Novorossiysk, Krasnodar Territory, Russia
Tel.: (7) 8617308141
Web Site: http://www.en.ttr.transneft.ru
Oil Transporting Services
N.A.I.C.S.: 486110
Sergey Georgievich Kireev *(Gen Dir)*

TOMZEL, JSC (1)
14 Prichalnaya Str, 634024, Tomsk, Russia
Tel.: (7) 3822530671
Web Site: http://www.en.tomzel.transneft.ru
Oil Transporting Services
N.A.I.C.S.: 486110
Odushev Oleg Nikolaevich *(Deputy Dir-Quality)*

The Pipeline Transport Institute, LLC (1)
47a Sevastopolskiy Prospect, 117186, Moscow, Russia
Tel.: (7) 4959508295
Web Site: http://www.en.niitn.transneft.ru
Oil Transporting Services
N.A.I.C.S.: 486110
Yakov Mikhailovich Fridlyand *(Gen Dir)*

Transneft Baltic, LLC (1)
11-A Arsenalnaya Embankment, 195009, Saint Petersburg, Russia
Tel.: (7) 8123806225
Web Site: http://en.baltic.transneft.ru
Oil Transporting Services
N.A.I.C.S.: 486110

OAO AK TRANSNEFT

OAO AK Transneft—(Continued)

Transneft Diascan, JSC (1)
7 Kuybysheva Str, Lukhovitsy, 140501, Moscow, Russia
Tel.: (7) 4966324036
Web Site: http://www.en.dlascan.transneft.ru
Oil Transporting Services
N.A.I.C.S.: 486110
Igor Vladimirovich Pavlov *(Gen Dir)*

Transneft Druzhba, JSC (1)
Uralskaya ulitsa 113, 241020, Bryansk, Russia
Tel.: (7) 4832747652
Web Site: http://www.en.druzhba.transneft.ru
Oil Transporting Services
N.A.I.C.S.: 486110
Roman Valeryevich Kamozin *(Dir Gen)*

Transneft East, LLC (1)
14 Olimpiyskaya St, Energetik District, 665734, Bratsk, Irkutsk Region, Russia
Tel.: (7) 3953300774
Web Site: http://www.en.vostok.transneft.ru
Oil Transporting Services
N.A.I.C.S.: 486110
Aleksandr Fedorovich Puzikov *(Gen Dir)*

Transneft Energy, LLC (1)
4 Str 2 Presnenskaya Nab, 123112, Moscow, Russia
Tel.: (7) 4997998688
Web Site: http://www.en.transneftenergo.transneft.ru
Oil Transporting Services
N.A.I.C.S.: 486110
Sergey Mikhailovich *(Gen Dir)*

Transneft Far East, LLC (1)
1 Zaparina Str, 680020, Khabarovsk, Khabarovsk Territory, Russia
Tel.: (7) 4212401101
Web Site: http://www.en.fareast.transneft.ru
Oil Transporting Services
N.A.I.C.S.: 486110
Vitaliy Valeryevich Stepanov *(Dir Gen)*

Transneft Invest Management Company, LLC (1)
Vernadsky Avenue 8 A, 119311, Moscow, Russia
Tel.: (7) 4997998555
Web Site: http://www.tn-invest.ru
Oil Transporting Services
N.A.I.C.S.: 486110

Transneft Kama Region, JSC (1)
20/1 P Lumumby St, 420081, Kazan, Russia
Tel.: (7) 8432790420
Web Site: http://www.en.kama.transneft.ru
Oil Transporting Services
N.A.I.C.S.: 486110
Robert Anisovich Galiev *(Dir Gen)*

Transneft Kozmino Port, LLC (1)
78 Nizhne-Naberezhnaya St, Vrangel City District, 692941, Nakhodka, Primorsky Territory, Russia
Tel.: (7) 4236771000
Web Site: http://www.en.kozmino.transneft.ru
Oil Transporting Services
N.A.I.C.S.: 486110
Denis Petrovich Cheplyanskiy *(Gen Dir)*

Transneft Media, LLC (1)
4 bld 2 Presnenskaya Embankment, 123112, Moscow, Russia
Tel.: (7) 4959508074
Web Site: http://www.en.media.transneft.ru
Oil Transporting Services
N.A.I.C.S.: 486110
Sergey Vladimirovich Vyhuholev *(Gen Dir)*

Transneft Metrology, JSC (1)
4 Bld 2 Presnenskaya Embankment, 123112, Moscow, Russia
Tel.: (7) 4959508700
Web Site: http://www.en.metrology.transneft.ru
Oil Transporting Services
N.A.I.C.S.: 486110

Transneft North, JSC (1)
1 A I Zeryunov Avenue, 169313, Ukhta, Komi Republic, Russia
Tel.: (7) 8216771300
Web Site: http://www.en.north.transneft.ru

Oil Transporting Services
N.A.I.C.S.: 486110
Rustem Riljevich Islamov *(Gen Dir)*

Transneft Oil Pumps, JSC (1)
8-i Eniseyskaya St, 454010, Chelyabinsk, Russia
Tel.: (7) 3512044060
Web Site: http://www.en.pumps.transneft.ru
Oil Transporting Services
N.A.I.C.S.: 486110

Transneft PCD, LLC (1)
39 Chernovskaya Magistral Str, 443067, Samara, Russia
Tel.: (7) 8463743894
Web Site: http://www.en.tsd.transneft.ru
Oil Transporting Services
N.A.I.C.S.: 486110

Transneft Primorsk Port, LLC (1)
Leningrad Region, Vyborg District, 188910, Saint Petersburg, Russia
Tel.: (7) 8137878778
Web Site: http://www.en.primorsk.transneft.ru
Oil Transporting Services
N.A.I.C.S.: 486110
Andrey Vitalievich Kulishin *(Gen Dir)*

Transneft Service, JSC (1)
205 Ofice 37 Lenina Avenue, 353913, Novorossiysk, Krasnodar Territory, Russia
Tel.: (7) 8617717215
Web Site: http://www.en.atns.transneft.ru
Oil Transporting Services
N.A.I.C.S.: 486110
Maksim Gennadievich Murashko *(Gen Dir)*

Transneft Supervision, LLC (1)
57 Bolshaya Polyanka str, 119180, Moscow, Russia
Tel.: (7) 4997998450
Web Site: http://www.en.supervision.transneft.ru
Oil Transporting Services
N.A.I.C.S.: 486110
Sregey Alexandrovich Reutov *(Gen Dir)*

Transneft Technology, LLC (1)
2A 3rd Peschanaya Str, 125252, Moscow, Russia
Tel.: (7) 4952529370
Web Site: http://www.en.tt.transneft.ru
Oil Transporting Services
N.A.I.C.S.: 486110
Andrey Valeryevich Trusov *(Dir Gen)*

Transneft Telecom, LLC (1)
12 ulitsa Nametkina Bldg 1, 117420, Moscow, Russia
Tel.: (7) 4997070742
Web Site: http://www.en.telecom.transneft.ru
Telecommunication Servicesb
N.A.I.C.S.: 517112
Chuvashina Natalia Vladimirovna *(Dir Gen)*

Transneft UW Service, JSC (1)
19-A Larina Str, 603152, Nizhniy Novgorod, Russia
Tel.: (7) 8314377763
Web Site: http://www.en.tps.transneft.ru
Oil Transporting Services
N.A.I.C.S.: 486110

Transneft Upper Volga, JSC (1)
4/1 Granitny Lane, 603950, Nizhniy Novgorod, Russia
Tel.: (7) 8314382265
Web Site: http://www.en.uppervolga.transneft.ru
Oil Transporting Services
N.A.I.C.S.: 486110
Yury Leonidovich Levin *(Gen Dir)*

Transneft Urals, JSC (1)
10 Krupskoy Str, 450008, Ufa, Russia
Tel.: (7) 3472792525
Web Site: http://www.en.ural.transneft.ru
Oil Transporting Services
N.A.I.C.S.: 486110

Transneft Ust-Luga Port, LLC (1)
40 Pulkovskoe Shosse Bldg 4 D, 196158, Saint Petersburg, Russia
Tel.: (7) 8123835363
Web Site: http://www.en.ust-luga.transneft.ru
Oil Transporting Services
N.A.I.C.S.: 486110
Olga Aleksandrovna Shevchenko *(Gen Dir)*

Transneft Volga Region, JSC (1)
100 Leninskaya St, 443020, Samara, Russia
Tel.: (7) 8462500241
Web Site: http://www.en.volga.transneft.ru
Oil Transporting Services
N.A.I.C.S.: 486110

Transneft Western Siberia, JSC (1)
111 Krasny Put Str Bldg 1, 644033, Omsk, Russia
Tel.: (7) 3812653502
Web Site: http://www.en.westernsiberia.transneft.ru
Oil Transporting Services
N.A.I.C.S.: 486110
Oleg Vyacheslavovich Chepurnoy *(Gen Dir)*

Transneft security services, LLC (1)
57 Bolshaya Polyanka Str, 119180, Moscow, Russia
Tel.: (7) 4959508109
Web Site: http://www.en.security.transneft.ru
Oil Transporting Services
N.A.I.C.S.: 486110
Alla Nikolaevna Akzhigitova *(Deputy Dir Gen-Economics & Fin)*

Transneft-Logistics, LLC (1)
24 Building 2 Radio Str, 105005, Moscow, Russia
Tel.: (7) 4956443238
Web Site: http://www.en.logistics.transneft.ru
Oil Transporting Services
N.A.I.C.S.: 486110

Transneft-Service, LLC (1)
37 Lenina Avenue, 353913, Novorossiysk, Krasnodar Territory, Russia
Tel.: (7) 8617717101
Web Site: http://www.en.otns.transneft.ru
Oil Transporting Services
N.A.I.C.S.: 486110
Roman Vladimirovich Fedotov *(Gen Dir)*

Transnefteproduct, JSC (1)
Vishnyakovskaya 2 Street, 115184, Moscow, Russia
Tel.: (7) 4959159807
Web Site: http://www.en.transnefteprod.transneft.ru
Oil Transporting Services
N.A.I.C.S.: 486110

ZAO SK Transneft (1)
2 3rd Pavlovsky Per, 115093, Moscow, Russia
Tel.: (7) 495 995 0123
Web Site: http://eng.sktransneft.ru
Sales Range: $15-24.9 Billion
Insurance Services
N.A.I.C.S.: 524298

OAO GROUP OF COMPANIES PIK

19 bld 1 Barrikadnaya street, Moscow, 123242, Russia
Tel.: (7) 4955059733   RU
Web Site: https://pik-group.com
Sales Range: $1-4.9 Billion
Emp.: 11,000
Residential Property Developer; Mortgage Services
N.A.I.C.S.: 236115
Marina Zinovina *(Member-Mgmt Bd & First VP)*

Subsidiaries:

Evroproekt OOO (1)
31 Karla Marksa ul, Kursk, 305029, Russia
Tel.: (7) 4712562482
Architectural Design Services
N.A.I.C.S.: 541310

LLC Pik-Comfort (1)
St Barrikadnaya House 19 Building 1 Floor 3 Room II Part of Room 7, 123242, Moscow, Russia
Tel.: (7) 88002342222
Web Site: http://www.pik-comfort.ru
Structural Management Services
N.A.I.C.S.: 236220

PIK Profile OOO (1)
Ul Lobnenskaya D 18 Kor 4, 127644, Moscow, Russia

Tel.: (7) 495442 83 29
Property Management Services
N.A.I.C.S.: 531311

PIK-Zapad ZAO (1)
72 kv 182 ul Kurchatova, Obninsk, 249039, Russia
Tel.: (7) 4843923350
Property Development Services
N.A.I.C.S.: 531390

ZDZHB Volga FORM ZAO (1)
46 Zaitseva ul, Nizhniy Novgorod, 603074, Russia
Tel.: (7) 8312231113
Property Management Services
N.A.I.C.S.: 531311

OAO IRKUTSKENERGO

3 Sukhe-Batora Street, Irkutsk, 664011, Russia
Tel.: (7) 3952790201
Web Site:
    https://www.irkutskenergo.ru
Year Founded: 1992
IRGZ—(MOEX)
Sales Range: $1-9.9 Million
Power Generation Services
N.A.I.C.S.: 221118
Evgeniy A. Novikov *(Member-Mgmt Bd, Chief Engr & Dir-Power Mfr)*

OAO KUZBASSKAYA TOPLIVNAYA COMPANY OJSC

50 let Octyabrya 4, 650000, Kemerovo, 650000, Russia
Tel.: (7) 3842771880
Web Site: https://ktk.company
Year Founded: 2000
KBTK—(MOEX)
Sales Range: $400-449.9 Million
Emp.: 4,400
Thermal Coal Mfr & Distr
N.A.I.C.S.: 324199
Igor Yurievich Prokudin *(Gen Dir)*

Subsidiaries:

LLC Novosibirsk Fuel Corporation (1)
ul Kirova 27, Novosibirsk, 630008, Federal Territory, Russia   (51%)
Tel.: (7) 383 206 37 85
Web Site: http://www.oaoktk.ru
Coal Sales & Services to Various Utility Sectors
N.A.I.C.S.: 213113
Alexeev Alexey Yuryevich *(Dir)*

OJSC Kuzbasstoplivosbyt (1)
ul 50-let Oktyabrya 4, Kemerovo, 650991, Russia
Tel.: (7) 3842 58 66 50
Coal Sales
N.A.I.C.S.: 457210

OAO NPO PROMAVTOMATIKA

156 Garazhnaya Str, 350051, Krasnodar, Russia
Tel.: (7) 8612794800
Web Site:
    http://www.promavtomatika.com
Emp.: 200
Oil & Gas Machinery Mfr
N.A.I.C.S.: 333132
Alexander Nikolaevich Lipko *(Gen Dir)*

OAO OTKRITIE BROKERAGE HOUSE

19/10 Protopopovsky Pereulok, Prospect Mira metro station, Moscow, 129010, Russia
Tel.: (7) 495 232 0300
OPEN—(SPBE)
Securities Brokerage & Dealership Services
N.A.I.C.S.: 523150
Alexander Nikolayevich Bukharin *(CEO)*

AND PRIVATE COMPANIES

OAO RASPADSKAYA
106 Mira Street, Mezhdurechensk, 652870, Kemerovo, 652870, Russia
Tel.: (7) 4953631966
Web Site: https://raspadskaya.com
Year Founded: 1973
RASP—(MOEX)
Rev.: $996,000,000
Assets: $1,632,000,000
Liabilities: $421,000,000
Net Worth: $1,211,000,000
Earnings: $208,000,000
Emp.: 9
Fiscal Year-end: 12/31/19
Coal Mining & Transportation Services
N.A.I.C.S.: 212115
Eric Hugh John Stoyell *(Chm)*

OAO SIBUR HOLDING
Krzhizhanovsky st 16/1, 117218, Moscow, Russia
Tel.: (7) 4957775500 RU
Web Site: http://www.sibur.ru
Year Founded: 1995
Sales Range: $5-14.9 Billion
Emp.: 30,500
Holding Company; Petrochemical Mfr & Distr
N.A.I.C.S.: 551112
Alexander V. Dyukov *(Deputy Chm)*

Subsidiaries:

Biaxplen LLC (1)
17 Administrativnaya St Gidrotorf Settlement, Balakhna District, 606425, Nizhniy Novgorod, Russia (100%)
Tel.: (7) 831 243 0169
Web Site: http://www.biaxplen.ru
Biaxially Oriented Polypropylene Films Mfr
N.A.I.C.S.: 326112

Subsidiary (Domestic):

Biaxplen K LLC (2)
10 Ob'ezdnaya, 305045, Kursk, Russia (100%)
Tel.: (7) 471 232 8455
Web Site: http://www.biaxplen.ru
Biaxially Oriented Polypropylene Films Mfr
N.A.I.C.S.: 326112

Biaxplen M LLC (2)
35 Promishlennaya St, Zheleznodorozhny, 143985, Russia (100%)
Tel.: (7) 495 987 4560
Web Site: http://www.biaxplen.ru
Biaxially Oriented Polypropylene Films Mfr
N.A.I.C.S.: 326112

Biaxplen NK LLC (2)
1 Zheleznodorozhniy Str, 446201, Novokuybyshevsk, Samara, Russia (100%)
Tel.: (7) 846 357 1077
Web Site: http://www.biaxplen.ru
Biaxially Oriented Polypropylene Films Mfr
N.A.I.C.S.: 326112

JSC Polief (1)
71 Socialist St, Blagoveshchensk, 453434, Bashkortostan, Russia
Tel.: (7) 3472797524
Purified Terephthalic Acid Mfr
N.A.I.C.S.: 325199

JSC SIBUR-PET (1)
Pl Gagarina 1 Bldg 77 Office 1, 170100, Tver, Russia
Tel.: (7) 4822336700
Plastic & Organic Synthesis Mfr
N.A.I.C.S.: 326199

OAO Sibur-PETF (1)
Ploshchad Gagarina d 1, Tver, 170100, Russia
Tel.: (7) 4822 49 87 00
Plastics Bottle Mfr
N.A.I.C.S.: 326160

OAO Voronezhsintezkauchuk (1)
Lenin avenue 2, 394014, Voronezh, Russia
Tel.: (7) 4732206709
Thermoplastic Product Mfr
N.A.I.C.S.: 325211

OOO SIBUR (1)
16/1 Krzhizhanovskogo St, GSP 7, 117218, Moscow, Russia (100%)
Tel.: (7) 4957805500
Web Site: http://www.sibur.ru
Petrochemical Mfr & Distr
N.A.I.C.S.: 325110
Dmitry Konov *(Chm-Mgmt Bd & CEO)*

RusVinyl LLC (1)
RusVinyl neighbourhood Nizhegorodskiy region, Western microdistrict, 607650, Kstovo, Russia (100%)
Tel.: (7) 8314559400
Web Site: http://www.rusvinyl.ru
Emp.: 500
Polyvinyl Chloride Mfr
N.A.I.C.S.: 325180

SIBUR International GmbH (1)
Prinz Eugen Str 8-10, Vienna, 1040, Austria
Tel.: (43) 1 370 8000
Web Site: http://www.sibur-int.com
Natural & Liquified Petroleum Gas Distr
N.A.I.C.S.: 221210
Andrey Frolov *(CEO)*

SIBUR-Kstovo LLC (1)
Passage 4 Industrial Area Building 2, Kstovsky District, 607650, Kstovo, Nizhny Novgorod, Russia
Tel.: (7) 8314549400
Chemical Products Mfr
N.A.I.C.S.: 325998

ZapSibNeftekhim LLC (1)
Eastern Industrial area Block 9 House 1/1, 626150, Tobolsk, Tyumen, Russia
Tel.: (7) 3456398111
Chemical Products Mfr
N.A.I.C.S.: 325998

OAO VOLGOGRADENERGOSBYT
Ul Kozlovskaya 14, 400001, Volgograd, Russia
Tel.: (7) 8442262626
Web Site: http://www.energosale34.ru
Year Founded: 2005
VGSB—(MOEX)
Sales Range: Less than $1 Million
Electric Power Distribution Services
N.A.I.C.S.: 221122
Petr Bronislavovich Zakharov *(Chm)*

OAR RESOURCES LIMITED
Unit 3/32 Harrogate Street, West Leederville, 6007, WA, Australia
Tel.: (61) 861174797
Web Site: https://www.oarresources.com.au
OAR—(ASX)
Rev.: $99,608
Assets: $2,440,351
Liabilities: $2,074,537
Net Worth: $365,814
Earnings: ($4,243,398)
Fiscal Year-end: 06/30/24
Metal Ore Mining Services
N.A.I.C.S.: 212290
Christopher Gale *(Chm)*

Subsidiaries:

Ozinca Peru SAC (1)
Calle Cura Bejar 190 Oficina 303, San Isidro, Lima, Peru
Tel.: (51) 14212009
Gold Mining Services
N.A.I.C.S.: 212220

OAS AG
Caroline Herschel-Strasse 1, Bremen, 28359, Germany
Tel.: (49) 42122060
Web Site: http://www.oas.de
Year Founded: 1982
Sales Range: $25-49.9 Million
Emp.: 186
Automatic Control Systems Mfr
N.A.I.C.S.: 334512
Otto A. Schwimmbeck *(Pres & CEO)*

OASIS BEVERAGES
Amathountos Street 50E Agios Tychonas, Pearl Building Office 1 3rd Floor, 4532, Limassol, Cyprus
Tel.: (357) 25591196
Web Site: http://www.oasisdrinks.com
Year Founded: 2008
Brewery Operator
N.A.I.C.S.: 312120
Nicholas Henderson-Stewart *(Chm & CFO)*

Subsidiaries:

Oasis Kazakhstan (1)
No 289 industrial Area Mukhametzhan Tuimebayev village, Aschibulak rural district Ili district, 040702, Almaty, Kazakhstan
Tel.: (7) 7273210000
Web Site: http://www.pivzavod1.kz
Beverage Distr
N.A.I.C.S.: 424810
Tatyana Konopelko *(CFO)*

Oasis Russia (1)
12 Volkovskoe Shosse, Mytishchi, Russia
Tel.: (7) 4957885433
Web Site: http://www.mosbrew.ru
Beverage Distr
N.A.I.C.S.: 424810
Igor Dementive *(CEO)*

Oasis Ukraine (1)
29 Myronositskaya St, 61002, Kharkiv, Ukraine
Tel.: (380) 503230235
Web Site: http://www.oasis.ua
Beverage Distr
N.A.I.C.S.: 424810

OASIS CRESCENT MANAGEMENT COMPANY LTD.
4th Floor West Office Tower Nelson Mandela Square, Sandton, Johannesburg, South Africa
Tel.: (27) 112637860
Holding Company
N.A.I.C.S.: 551112
Mohamed Shaheen Ebrahim *(Chm)*

OASIS ENERGY CO. LLC
PO Box 1125, PC 114, Jibroo, Oman
Tel.: (968) 24 705 830
Web Site: http://www.oasisenergy.net
Emp.: 100
Bulk Petroleum Operations
N.A.I.C.S.: 424710
Daniel George *(Gen Mgr)*

OASIS SECURITIES LIMITED
Raja Bahadur Compound Bldg No 5 2nd floor 43 Tamarind Lane, Fort, Mumbai, 400 001, India
Tel.: (91) 2240463500
Web Site: https://www.oasiscaps.com
Year Founded: 1986
512489—(BOM)
Rev.: $148,145
Assets: $1,348,540
Liabilities: $30,790
Net Worth: $1,317,751
Earnings: ($49,973)
Emp.: 8
Fiscal Year-end: 03/31/23
Securities Brokerage Services
N.A.I.C.S.: 523150
Indra Kumar Bagri *(Chm)*

OASMIA PHARMACEUTICAL AB
Vallongatan 1, SE-752 28, Uppsala, Sweden
Tel.: (46) 18505440
Web Site: https://www.vivesto.com
OMAX—(DEU)
Rev.: $378,767
Assets: $34,021,746
Liabilities: $2,911,211
Net Worth: $31,110,534
Earnings: ($34,102,336)
Emp.: 18
Fiscal Year-end: 12/31/22
Pharmaceuticals Mfr
N.A.I.C.S.: 325412
Nina Heldring *(Chief Medical Officer)*

OAT AGRIO CO., LTD.
NBF Ogawamachi Building 8F 1-3-1 Kanda Ogawamachi, Chiyoda-ku, Tokyo, 101-0052, Japan
Tel.: (81) 352830262
Web Site: https://www.oat-agrio.co.jp
4979—(TKS)
Rev.: $205,524,920
Assets: $241,060,000
Liabilities: $135,617,520
Net Worth: $105,442,480
Earnings: $17,639,920
Emp.: 585
Fiscal Year-end: 12/31/23
Pesticides & Fertilizers Mfr
N.A.I.C.S.: 325320
Hisashi Oka *(Pres & CEO)*

Subsidiaries:

Asahi Chemical Manufacturing Co., Ltd. (1)
500 Oaza Takayasu Ikaruga-cho, Ikomagun, Nara, 636-0104, Japan
Tel.: (81) 745741131
Web Site: https://www.asahichem-mfg.co.jp
Fertilizer Mfr & Distr
N.A.I.C.S.: 325311

CAPA Ecosystems, S.L. (1)
Camino De Borboto A Godella 3, 46016, Valencia, Spain
Tel.: (34) 96 176 7149
Web Site: https://www.capaecosystems.com
Agricultural Product Whslr
N.A.I.C.S.: 424910

Drip Fertigation Research Co., Ltd. (1)
3-4-13 Higashi Ishioka, Ishioka, Ibaraki, Japan
Tel.: (81) 299566752
Fertilizer Distr
N.A.I.C.S.: 424910

Inplanta Innovations Inc. (1)
Urban Plaza Tsurumi 4F 4-5-11 Namamugi, Tsurumi-ku, Yokohama, 230-0054, Japan
Tel.: (81) 455000538
Web Site: https://www.inplanta.jp
Biotechnology Research Services
N.A.I.C.S.: 541714

LIDA Plant Research, S.L. (1)
Parque Industrial Rey Juan Carlos I C/Granja n 12, Almussafes, 46440, Valencia, Spain
Tel.: (34) 961767033
Web Site: https://www.lidaplantresearch.com
Biotechnology Research Services
N.A.I.C.S.: 541714

OAT Agri Frontier Co., Ltd. (1)
84-6 Uchino Fukuda Ami-chou, Inashiki-gun, Ibaraki, Japan
Tel.: (81) 298867272
Nitrogenous Fertilizer Mfr
N.A.I.C.S.: 325311

PT. Oat Mitoku Agrio (1)
Jl Bendungan Asahan II No 8 Bendungan Hilir, Jakarta Pusat, Indonesia
Tel.: (62) 215701909
Web Site: https://oatmitokuagrio.com
Fertilizer Distr
N.A.I.C.S.: 424910

OATLY GROUP AB
Tel.: (46) 418475500 SE
Web Site: https://oatly.com
Year Founded: 1994
OTLY—(NASDAQ)
Rev.: $783,348,000
Assets: $1,116,971,000
Liabilities: $781,190,000
Net Worth: $335,781,000
Earnings: ($417,060,000)
Emp.: 1,548

OATLY GROUP AB

Oatly Group AB—(Continued)
Fiscal Year-end: 12/31/23
Holding Company
N.A.I.C.S.: 551112
Eric Melloul (Chm)

Subsidiaries:

Oatly AB (1)
PO Box 588, 201 25, Malmo, Sweden
Tel.: (46) 418475500
Web Site: https://www.oatly.com
Drink Mfr
N.A.I.C.S.: 312111

Oatly UK Ltd. (1)
78 Cowcross St, London, United Kingdom
Tel.: (44) 418475100
Food Mfr
N.A.I.C.S.: 311991

OBARA GROUP INCORPORATED

3-2-10 Chuo-Rinkan, Yamato, 242-0007, Kanagawa, Japan
Tel.: (81) 462712111
Web Site: https://www.obara-g.com
Year Founded: 1957
6877—(TKS)
Rev.: $391,431,810
Assets: $670,877,070
Liabilities: $145,430,080
Net Worth: $525,446,990
Earnings: $51,125,990
Emp.: 1,711
Fiscal Year-end: 09/30/23
Welding Equipment Mfr
N.A.I.C.S.: 333992
Yasushi Obara (Pres)

Subsidiaries:

LLC Obara Rus (1)
Babushkina street 3 letter A office 215, 192029, Saint Petersburg, Russia
Tel.: (7) 8124497337
Web Site: http://www.obara-rus.ru
Welding Equipment Distr
N.A.I.C.S.: 423830

OBARA S.A.S. (1)
ZAE Les Dix Muids Rue Blaise Pascal, 59770, Marly, France
Tel.: (33) 327237616
Web Site: https://www.obara.fr
Welding Equipment Repair & Maintenance Services
N.A.I.C.S.: 811310

OBARA TECNOLOGIAS E PRODUTOS DE SOLDAGEM LTDA. (1)
57 Mario Zampieri Street room 37 Downtown, Sao Bernardo do Campo, 09720-450, Sao Paulo, Brazil
Tel.: (55) 11983055257
Welding Equipment Distr
N.A.I.C.S.: 423830

Obara (Malaysia) SDN. BHD. (1)
Lot 6 Jalan Lada Hitam Satu 16/12A Seksyen16, 40200, Shah Alam, Selangor Darul Ehsan, Malaysia
Tel.: (60) 355118898
Welding Equipment Distr
N.A.I.C.S.: 423830

Obara (Nanjing) Machinery & Electric CO. LTD. (1)
No 28 Renjie Road, Jiangning District, Nanjing, 211111, China
Web Site: http://www.obara.com.cn
Welding Equipment Mfr & Distr
N.A.I.C.S.: 333992

Obara (Shanghai) CO., LTD. (1)
17 Ai Du Road Pilot Free Trade Zone, Pu Dong New Area, Shanghai, 200131, China
Tel.: (86) 2150462668
Welding Equipment Distr
N.A.I.C.S.: 423830

Obara (Thailand) Co., Ltd. (1)
90/1 Moo 5 Wellgrow Industrial Estate Soi 6, Bangsamak Bangpakong, Chachoengsao, 24180, Thailand
Tel.: (66) 3857192829
Web Site: https://www.obarathailand.com
Emp.: 62
Welding Equipment Mfr & Distr
N.A.I.C.S.: 333992
Ikuo Nakamura (Pres)

Obara Corporation (1)
4151 Fujisa, Sakaigawa, Fuefuki, 406-0853, Yamanashi, Japan
Tel.: (81) 552665432
Web Site: https://www.obara.co.jp
Emp.: 211
Welding Equipment Mfr & Distr
N.A.I.C.S.: 333992
Mitsuhisa Yamashita (Pres)

Obara Corporation (1)
26800 Meadowbrook Rd Ste 111, Novi, MI 48377
Tel.: (586) 755-1250
Web Site: http://www.obarausa.com
Welding Equipment Mfr & Distr
N.A.I.C.S.: 333992

Subsidiary (Domestic):

Obara Corporation - Kentucky Plant (2)
1346 Jamike Ave, Erlanger, KY 41018
Tel.: (859) 283-5490
Welding Equipment Mfr
N.A.I.C.S.: 333992

Obara Corporation (1)
Unit 1 Tomlinson Industrial Estate Alfreton Road, Derby, DE21 4ED, United Kingdom
Tel.: (44) 1332297868
Web Site: http://www.obara.co.uk
Welding Equipment Distr
N.A.I.C.S.: 423830
Pete Preston (Branch Mgr)

Obara India PVT. LTD. (1)
W-17 F-2 Block MIDC, Pimpri, 411 018, Pune, India
Tel.: (91) 2030688551
Welding Equipment Distr
N.A.I.C.S.: 423830
Vinod Pattan (Mgr-Production & Design Dept)

Obara Korea Corp. (1)
97-23 Barangongdan-ro4-gil Hyangnam-eup, Hwaseong, Gyeonggi-do, Korea (South)
Web Site: http://www.obara.co.kr
Emp.: 230
Industrial Equipment Mfr
N.A.I.C.S.: 333248

Obara Mexico S. De R.L. De C.V. (1)
Roberto Diaz Rodriguez 212 Ciudad Industrial, 20290, Aguascalientes, Mexico
Tel.: (52) 4499711525
Welding Equipment Distr
N.A.I.C.S.: 423830

SpeedFam Clean System Co., Ltd. - Yamagata Factory (1)
160-7 Chuo-kogyodanchi, Sagae, Yamagata, Japan
Tel.: (81) 237861500
Precision Product Mfr
N.A.I.C.S.: 332721

SpeedFam Company Limited (1)
4-2-37 Ogami, Ayase, 252-1104, Kanagawa, Japan
Tel.: (81) 467763131
Web Site: https://www.speedfam.com
Emp.: 125
Polishing Equipment Mfr & Distr
N.A.I.C.S.: 333517
Yasushi Obara (Pres)

Subsidiary (Non-US):

Melchiorre S.r.l. (2)
Via Raffaello Sanzio 58, Bollate, 20021, Milan, Italy
Tel.: (39) 0266046522
Web Site: https://www.melchiorre.net
Precision Machine Tool Mfr & Distr
N.A.I.C.S.: 332721

SpeedFam (India) Pvt. Ltd. (2)
B 87 Addl MIDC Anand Nagar, Ambernath District Thane, Mumbai, 421 506, Maharashtra, India
Tel.: (91) 2512620403
Polishing Machinery Mfr & Distr
N.A.I.C.S.: 333517

SpeedFam Co., Ltd. (2)
5E Gambas Crescent Nordcom 1, Singapore, 757041, Singapore
Tel.: (65) 65617997
Polishing Machinery Mfr & Distr
N.A.I.C.S.: 333517

Subsidiary (US):

SpeedFam Corporation (2)
1544 Barclay Blvd, Buffalo Grove, IL 60089
Tel.: (847) 499-3400
Web Site: http://www.speedfamusa.com
Industrial Equipment Mfr & Distr
N.A.I.C.S.: 333248

Subsidiary (Non-US):

SpeedFam Inc. (2)
No 56 Guangfu S Rd, Hukou Township, Hsinchu, 303, Taiwan
Tel.: (886) 35983411
Polishing Equipment Mfr & Distr
N.A.I.C.S.: 333517

SpeedFam Korea Ltd. (2)
50 Dolmugae-Gil, Gwacheon, 13820, Gyeonggi, Korea (South)
Tel.: (82) 25033888
Web Site: http://www.speedfam.co.kr
Polishing Equipment Distr
N.A.I.C.S.: 423830

SpeedFam Mechatronics (Shanghai) Ltd. (2)
390 Middle Fute Road Wai Gao Qiao Bonded Area, Pudong New Area, Shanghai, 200131, China
Tel.: (86) 2150462888
Polishing Equipment Mfr & Distr
N.A.I.C.S.: 333517

Subsidiary (Domestic):

SpeedFam Nagano Co., Ltd. (2)
553-12 Seto, Saku-shi, Nagano, 385-0035, Japan
Tel.: (81) 267621333
Polishing Equipment Mfr
N.A.I.C.S.: 333517

OBAYASHI CORPORATION

Shinagawa Intercity Tower B 2-15-2 Konan, Minato-ku, Tokyo, 108-8502, Japan
Tel.: (81) 357691111   JP
Web Site: https://www.obayashi.co.jp
Year Founded: 1892
1802—(FKA)
Rev.: $18,613,517,120
Assets: $23,445,782,800
Liabilities: $13,873,104,960
Net Worth: $9,572,677,840
Earnings: $378,749,360
Emp.: 9,026
Fiscal Year-end: 03/31/22
Commercial Building Contractor
N.A.I.C.S.: 236220
Takeo Obayashi (Chm)

Subsidiaries:

Ibaraki Green Co., Ltd. (1)
686-3 Torihata Ibaraki-machi, Ibaraki-machi Higashi Ibaraki District, Ibaraki, 311-3142, Japan
Tel.: (81) 292927777
Golf Club Services
N.A.I.C.S.: 713910

JS Builders, LLC (1)
2600 Old Crow Canyon Rd Ste 200, San Ramon, CA 94583
Tel.: (925) 399-8811
Web Site: https://www.jsbuilders.com
Construction Services
N.A.I.C.S.: 236220
Greg Butler (Project Engr)

Kenaidan Group Ltd. (1)
7080 Derrycrest Dr, Mississauga, L5W 0G5, ON, Canada
Tel.: (905) 670-2660
Construction Services
N.A.I.C.S.: 236220

Kraemer North America, LLC (1)
1 Plainview Rd, Plain, WI 53577-0220
Tel.: (608) 546-2311
Web Site: https://www.kraemerna.com
Civil Engineering Construction Services
N.A.I.C.S.: 541330

Naigai Technos Corporation (1)
Sumitomo Ichigaya Building 5F 1-1 Ichigaya-honmuracho, Shinjyuku-ku, Tokyo, 162-0845, Japan
Tel.: (81) 352613410
Web Site: http://www.naigai-technos.co.jp
Construction Equipment Distr
N.A.I.C.S.: 423390

OAK Information System Corporation (1)
2-2-20 Higashi-Shinagawa Tennozu Ocean Square 10th floor reception, 11th floor Shinagawa-ku, Tokyo, 140-0002, Japan
Tel.: (81) 368443900
Web Site: http://www.oakis.co.jp
Emp.: 194
Electronic Equipment Distr
N.A.I.C.S.: 449210

OAK Setsubi Corporation (1)
1-16-3 Shinkawa, Chuo-ku, Tokyo, 104-0033, Japan
Tel.: (81) 335532911
Web Site: http://www.oaksetsubi.co.jp
Emp.: 1,963
Construction Services
N.A.I.C.S.: 236220

OC Finance Corporation (1)
Shinagawa Intercity Tower B 2-15-2 Konan, Minato-ku, Tokyo, 108-8502, Japan
Tel.: (81) 357691067
Financial Management Services
N.A.I.C.S.: 523910

Obayashi Clean Energy Corporation (1)
Shinagawa Intercity Tower B 2-15-2 Konan, Minato-ku, Tokyo, 108-8502, Japan
Tel.: (81) 357691700
Civil Engineering Services
N.A.I.C.S.: 541330

Obayashi Energy Construction, LLC (1)
577 Airport Blvd Ste 600, Burlingame, CA 94010
Tel.: (650) 952-4910
Construction Services
N.A.I.C.S.: 236220

Obayashi Facilities Corporation (1)
Sumitomo Corporation Nishikicho Building 1-6, Kanda Nishikicho Chiyoda-ku, Tokyo, 101-0054, Japan
Tel.: (81) 352818311
Web Site: http://www.obayashi-f.co.jp
Facility Management Services
N.A.I.C.S.: 561210

Obayashi Middle East Construction, LLC (1)
Twin Tower 804 Baniyas Road Deira, PO Box 182845, Dubai, United Arab Emirates
Tel.: (971) 42212121
Construction Services
N.A.I.C.S.: 236220
Saad Daghestani (CEO)

Obayashi Properties UK Limited (1)
Bracken House One Friday Street, London, EC4M 9JA, United Kingdom
Tel.: (44) 2072368338
Civil Engineering Construction Services
N.A.I.C.S.: 541330

Obayashi Qatar, LLC (1)
Office 110 1st Floor Regus Business Center Al-Jaidah Square Building, PO Box 55743, Area 63 Airport Road Umm Ghuwailina, Doha, Qatar
Tel.: (974) 44267414
Construction Services
N.A.I.C.S.: 236220

Obayashi Real Estate Corporation (1)
3-4 Kandasurugadai Ryumeikanhonten Bldg 10/F, Chiyoda-ku, Tokyo, 101-0062, Japan
Tel.: (81) 3 5256 0611
Web Site: http://www.orec.co.jp
Real Estate Investment & Management Services

AND PRIVATE COMPANIES

N.A.I.C.S.: 531390

Obayashi Road Corporation (1)
Sumitomo Realty & Development Sarugaku-cho Building 2-8-8, Kanda-sarugakucho Chiyoda-ku, Tokyo, 101-8228, Japan
Tel.: (81) 332958861
Web Site: http://www.obayashi-road.co.jp
Sales Range: $900-999.9 Million
Assets: $864,924,000
Liabilities: $456,564,000
Net Worth: $408,360,000
Earnings: $604,429,000
Emp.: 1,142
Road & Infrastructure Construction & Engineering Services; Asphalt Paving Mixture Mfr
N.A.I.C.S.: 237310
Katsuji Fukumoto (Pres)

Obayashi Singapore Private Limited (1)
1 Paya Lebar Link 06-03 Paya Lebar Quarter-PLQ1, Singapore, 408533, Singapore **(100%)**
Tel.: (65) 62206333
Web Site: https://www.obayashi.com.sg
Sales Range: $50-74.9 Million
Emp.: 100
Construction & Related Services
N.A.I.C.S.: 532412
Aik Seng Lee (Mng Dir)

Obayashi Technical Research Institute (1)
4-640 Shimokiyoto, Kiyose, 204-8558, Tokyo, Japan
Tel.: (81) 424951111
Web Site: http://www.obayashi.go.gp
Construction & Related Services
N.A.I.C.S.: 532412

Obayashi USA, LLC (1)
5000 Shoreline Ct Ste 201, South San Francisco, CA 94080-1956
Tel.: (213) 687-8700
Sales Range: $10-24.9 Million
Emp.: 7
Holding Company; Building Construction
N.A.I.C.S.: 551112

Subsidiary (Domestic):

E.W. Howell Company, Inc. (2)
37 W 37th St 7th Fl 48 W 37th St 2nd Fl, New York, NY 10018 **(100%)**
Tel.: (212) 930-1050
Web Site: http://www.ewhowell.com
Institutional, Commercial & Industrial Buildings Contractor
N.A.I.C.S.: 236220
Dominic Paparo (VP)

Affiliate (Domestic):

James E. Roberts-Obayashi Corporation (2)
20 Oak Ct, Danville, CA 94526-4006
Tel.: (925) 820-0600
Web Site: https://www.jerocorp.com
Multi-Family Housing & Commercial Facility Construction Services
N.A.I.C.S.: 236116
Larry Smith (Chm & CEO)

Subsidiary (Domestic):

John S. Clark Company, LLC (2)
210 Airport Rd, Mount Airy, NC 27030-7950
Tel.: (336) 789-1000
Web Site: http://www.jsclark.com
Nonresidential Construction
N.A.I.C.S.: 236220

OC Real Estate Management, LLC (2)
5901 Coastal Hwy Ste C, Ocean City, MD 21842 **(100%)**
Tel.: (410) 524 5701
Real Estate Development & Property Asset Management
N.A.I.C.S.: 531210

Obayashi Construction, Inc. (2)
5000 Shoreline Ct Ste 201, South San Francisco, CA 94080-1956 **(100%)**
Tel.: (213) 687-8700
Management of Construction Projects
N.A.I.C.S.: 236220

Webcor, LP (2)
951 Mariners Island Blvd 7th Fl, San Mateo, CA 94404-1561
Tel.: (650) 349-2727
Web Site: http://www.webcor.com
Sales Range: $1-4.9 Billion
Emp.: 2,010
Commercial Building Contractor Services
N.A.I.C.S.: 236220
Greg Chauhan (Sr VP)

Obayashi Vietnam Corporation (1)
24th Floor Unit 2401 37 Ton Duc Thang Street, District 1, Ho Chi Minh City, Vietnam
Tel.: (84) 2839105523
Web Site: http://www.obayashivn.com
Sales Range: $25-49.9 Million
Emp.: 10
Construction Engineering Services
N.A.I.C.S.: 541330
Tran Huu Ninh (Member-Mgmt Bd & Dir-Hanoi Branch Office)

Obayashi-Shinseiwa Real Estate Corporation (1)
Kojimachi Building 3-3-6 Kudan-minami, Chiyoda-ku, Tokyo, 102-0074, Japan
Tel.: (81) 335117520
Real Estate Services
N.A.I.C.S.: 531390

P.T. Jaya Obayashi (1)
Jl Pancoran Timur II No 3 Pancoran, Jakarta, 12780, Indonesia **(85%)**
Tel.: (62) 217982223
Web Site: https://www.jayaobayashi.co.id
Emp.: 250
Engineeering Services
N.A.I.C.S.: 237310
Koichiro Minami (Chm)

Taiwan Obayashi Corporation (1)
16F-1 No 57 Fuxing N Rd, Songshan Dist, Taipei, 105, Taiwan **(100%)**
Tel.: (886) 227812024
Web Site: http://www.obayashi.co.jp
Sales Range: $25-49.9 Million
Emp.: 100
Management of Construction Projects
N.A.I.C.S.: 237990

Thai Obayashi Corporation Limited (1)
11th Fl Nantawan Bldg 161 Ratchadamri Rd, Lumpini Pathumwan, Bangkok, 10330, Thailand **(49%)**
Tel.: (66) 22525200
Web Site: http://www.thaiobayashi.co.th
Sales Range: $200-249.9 Million
Emp.: 962
Engineeering Services
N.A.I.C.S.: 236220
Sompong Chintawongvanich (Vice Chm)

OBB-HOLDING AG
Clemens Holzmeister street 6, Vienna, 1020, Austria
Tel.: (43) 1930000
Web Site: http://www.oebb.at
Year Founded: 1837
Sales Range: $5-14.9 Billion
Emp.: 45,352
Passenger & Freight Transportation
N.A.I.C.S.: 485999
Roman Hebenstreit (Deputy Chm-Supervisory Bd)

Subsidiaries:

AgroFreight Spedition CZ s.r.o. (1)
Srbska 53, 612 00, Brno, Czech Republic
Tel.: (420) 5 49437584
Web Site: http://www.railcargologistics.com
Freight Forwarding & Logistics Consulting Services
N.A.I.C.S.: 488510

CI&M Werbeagontur GmbH (1)
Elisabethstrasse 9, 1010, Vienna, Austria
Tel.: (43) 19300033380
Sales Range: $25-49.9 Million
Emp.: 7
Advertising Services
N.A.I.C.S.: 541870

CRL Car Rail Logistics GmbH (1)
Wiedner Hauptstrasse 120 124, A 1040, Vienna, Austria

Tel.: (43) 7105280222
Web Site: http://www.carrail.com
Sales Range: $50-74.9 Million
Emp.: 6
N.A.I.C.S.: 485999

Express-Interfracht Polska Sp. z.o.o. (1)
Ul Siemonska 3, 42500, Bedzin, Poland
Tel.: (48) 327622770
Freight Transportation Services
N.A.I.C.S.: 481212
Rafael Klimkiewicz (Mng Dir)

OBB-Infrastruktur Aktiengesellschaft (1)
Praterstern 3, 1020, Vienna, Austria
Tel.: (43) 1 93000 0
Railway Construction Services
N.A.I.C.S.: 236220
Andreas Mattha (Member-Mgmt Bd)

Subsidiary (Domestic):

Guterterminal Werndorf Projekt GmbH (2)
Lassallestrasse 9b, 1020, Vienna, Austria
Tel.: (43) 1 8127343
Railway Infrastructure Maintenance Services
N.A.I.C.S.: 488210

Mungos Sicher & Sauber GmbH & Co KG (2)
Langauergasse 1, 1150, Vienna, Austria
Tel.: (43) 19300035901
Web Site: http://www.mungos.at
Janitorial Services
N.A.I.C.S.: 561720

Netz- und Streckenentwicklung GmbH (2)
Praterstern 3, 1020, Vienna, Austria
Tel.: (43) 1 930 00 33002
Web Site: http://www.oebb.at
Emp.: 300
Railway Construction Services
N.A.I.C.S.: 236220
Kaar Hans (Gen Mgr)

OBB Telekom Service GmbH (2)
Brunnerstrasse 20, 1210, Vienna, Austria
Tel.: (43) 1 93000 39000
Web Site: http://www.oebbtel.at
Railway Transportation Services
N.A.I.C.S.: 482112

OBB-Immobilienmanagement Gesellschaft mbH (2)
Nordbahnstrasse 50, 1020, Vienna, Austria
Tel.: (43) 193000 44020
Web Site: http://www.oebb-immobilien.at
Emp.: 740
Real Estate Manangement Services
N.A.I.C.S.: 531210
Herbert Logar (Co-CEO)

Rail Equipment GmbH (2)
Operngasse 24/5, 1040, Vienna, Austria
Tel.: (43) 1 93000 33500
Railway Infrastructure Maintenance Services
N.A.I.C.S.: 488210

Rail Equipment GmbH & Co KG (2)
Operngasse 24/4, 1040, Vienna, Austria
Tel.: (43) 1 93000 32016
Railway Infrastructure Maintenance Services
N.A.I.C.S.: 488210

OBB-Personenverkehr Aktiengesellschaft (1)
PO Box 222, 1020, Vienna, Austria
Tel.: (43) 1930000
Web Site:
http://www.personenverkehr.oebb.at
Emp.: 2,900
Transportation Services
N.A.I.C.S.: 488490
Siegfried Stumpf (Member-Mgmt Bd)

Subsidiary (Domestic):

OBB-Postbus GmbH (2)
Wagramer Strasse 17-19, 1220, Vienna, Austria
Tel.: (43) 1 79 444 0
Web Site: http://www.postbus.at
Transportation Services

N.A.I.C.S.: 488490
Alois Ometzberger (Reg Mgr)

Subsidiary (Non-US):

CSAD AUTOBUSY Ceske Budejovice a.s. (3)
Zizkova tr 1321/1, 370 27, Ceske Budejovice, Czech Republic
Tel.: (420) 386 100 111
Web Site: http://www.csadcbas.cz
Transportation Services
N.A.I.C.S.: 488490

Probat Bahnhof Linz Projektentwicklungs-GmbH (1)
Elisabethstrasse 9, 1010, Vienna, Austria
Tel.: (43) 930000
Provider of Transit Services
N.A.I.C.S.: 485999

RAIL SERVICE HUNGARIA KFT. (1)
Bajcsy-Zsilinszky ut 25, 1065, Budapest, Hungary
Tel.: (36) 1 334 1174
Web Site: http://www.railservice.hu
Logistics Consulting Servies
N.A.I.C.S.: 541614
Istvan Bajtai (Mng Dir)

Subsidiary (Domestic):

LOGISZTAR Kft. (2)
Vasarhelyi ut 7, 8000, Szekesfehervar, Hungary
Tel.: (36) 22 522 201
Web Site: http://www.logisztar.hu
Logistics Consulting Servies
N.A.I.C.S.: 541614

Rail Cargo Austria Aktiengesellschaft (1)
Erdberger Lande 40-48, 1030, Vienna, Austria
Tel.: (43) 5 7750
Web Site: http://www.railcargo.at
Railway Freight Transportation Services
N.A.I.C.S.: 482111
Reinhard Bamberger (Member-Mgmt Bd)

Subsidiary (Non-US):

BIHATEAM d.o.o. (2)
Tresnje 1, 71000, Sarajevo, Bosnia & Herzegovina
Tel.: (387) 33 775 450
Web Site: http://www.railcargologistics.ba
Emp.: 40
Rail & Road Transportation Services
N.A.I.C.S.: 482112
Hamed Sivsic (Gen Mgr)

Subsidiary (Domestic):

EC LOGISTIK GmbH (2)
Wagramerstr 17-19 IZD-Tower, 1220, Vienna, Austria
Tel.: (43) 1 93000 36340
Web Site: http://www.ec-logistics.net
Logistics Consulting Servies
N.A.I.C.S.: 541614
Gunter Birnstingl (Co-Mng Dir)

Subsidiary (Non-US):

EXPRESS-INTERFRACHT CROATIA d.o.o. (2)
Radnicka cesta 39, 10000, Zagreb, Croatia
Tel.: (385) 14002290
Web Site: http://www.express-interfracht.hr
Rail & Road Transportation Services
N.A.I.C.S.: 482112
Damir Vukic (Exec Mgr)

European Contract Logistics - Czech Republic spol.s.r.o. (2)
Nerudova 107, 500 02, Hradec Kralove, Czech Republic
Tel.: (420) 495 772 111
Web Site: http://www.ec-logistics.cz
Freight Forwarding & Logistics Consulting Services
N.A.I.C.S.: 488510
Petr Bartel (Mgr-IT)

European Contract Logistics d.o.o. (2)
Cesta k Tamu 24, 2000, Maribor, Slovenia
Tel.: (386) 2 320 12 78
Web Site: http://www.ec-logistics.si

OBB-HOLDING AG

OBB-Holding AG—(Continued)
Emp.: 7
Freight Forwarding & Logistics Consulting Services
N.A.I.C.S.: 488510
Robert Pihlar (Gen Mgr)

Express Polska Sp. z o.o. (2)
Ul Wawozowa 11, 02-796, Warsaw, Poland
Tel.: (48) 22 853 20 53
Web Site: http://www.expresspolska.pl
Freight Forwarding & Trucking Services
N.A.I.C.S.: 488510
Rafal Klimkiewicz (Mng Dir)

Express-Interfracht Bulgaria Speditionsgesellschaft EOOD (2)
11 AP Chekhov Str, 1113, Sofia, Bulgaria
Tel.: (359) 2 9805240
Web Site: http://www.express-bg.com
Freight Forwarding & Logistics Consulting Services
N.A.I.C.S.: 488510
Christo Dyakov (Mgr)

Express-Interfracht Hungaria Kft. (2)
Montevideo u 4, 1037, Budapest, Hungary
Tel.: (36) 1 4308500
Web Site: http://www.railcargologistics.hu
Rail & Road Transportation Services
N.A.I.C.S.: 482112
Vernes Andras (Co-Mng Dir)

Express-Interfracht Romania s.r.l. (2)
Judetul Ilfov Sos Odaii 62-68, 75100, Otopeni, Romania
Tel.: (40) 21 3503762
Freight Forwarding & Logistics Management Services
N.A.I.C.S.: 488510

OOO "Rail Cargo Logistics - RUS" (2)
Volokolamskoe shosse 73 office 609, 125424, Moscow, Russia
Tel.: (7) 495 7756057
Web Site: http://www.railcargologistics.ru
Transportation & Logistics Services
N.A.I.C.S.: 488510

RAIL CARGO ROMANIA S.R.L. (2)
Sos Odaii NR 62-68, Otopeni, 075100, Romania
Tel.: (40) 74 114 4957
Rail & Road Transportation Services
N.A.I.C.S.: 482112

Rail Cargo Italia S.R.L. (2)
Via Girardengo 60, 15067, Novi Ligure, Italy
Tel.: (39) 0143418626
Web Site: http://www.lineaferroviaria.it
Railway Transportation Services
N.A.I.C.S.: 482112
Leo Herze (Dir-Sls)

Rail Cargo Logistics - Czech Republic s.r.o. (2)
Mickova 64, CZ-61400, Brno, Czech Republic
Tel.: (420) 548 426 411
Web Site: http://www.railcargo.com
Freight Forwarding & Logistics Management Services
N.A.I.C.S.: 488510

Rail Cargo Operator - Hungaria Kft. (2)
Vaci ut 92, 1133, Budapest, Hungary
Tel.: (36) 1 421 4093
Web Site: http://www.railcargooperator.hu
Railway Freight Transportation Services
N.A.I.C.S.: 482111
Gabor Spellenberg (Co-Mng Dir)

Wagon Service s.r.o. (2)
Cajakova 18, 811 05, Bratislava, Slovakia
Tel.: (421) 2 44 64 50 31
Web Site: http://www.wagonservice.sk
Railway Transportation Services
N.A.I.C.S.: 482112

Rail Cargo Terminal - BILK Zrt. (1)
Europa utca 4, 1239, Budapest, Hungary
Tel.: (36) 6 1 289 6000
Web Site: http://www.bilkkombi.hu
Freight Forwarding Services
N.A.I.C.S.: 488510
Istvan Fuller (CEO)

Speditions Holding AG (1)
Wohllebengasse 18, 1040, Vienna, Austria
Tel.: (43) 0501560
Transit Services
N.A.I.C.S.: 485999

TS-MAV Gepeszet Services Kft. (1)
Fek Utca 8, Budapest, 1087, Hungary
Tel.: (36) 209451793
Rail & Road Transportation Services
N.A.I.C.S.: 482112

Technical Services Hungaria Kft. (1)
Kando K ter 1, Miskolc, 3527, Hungary
Tel.: (36) 46 340 233
Web Site: http://www.tshungaria.hu
Railway Transportation Services
N.A.I.C.S.: 482112

Technical Services Slovakia, s.r.o. (1)
Koniarekova 19, 917 21, Trnava, Slovakia
Tel.: (421) 335567111
Web Site: http://www.railcargo.com
Railway Transportation Services
N.A.I.C.S.: 488210

OBDUCAT AB

Scheelevagen 2, 223 63, Lund, Sweden
Tel.: (46) 46101600
Web Site: https://www.obducat.com
Year Founded: 1989
OBD—(DEU)
Sales Range: $1-9.9 Million
Lithography Equipment Mfr
N.A.I.C.S.: 333242

Subsidiaries:

Obducat Europe GmbH (1)
Robert-Gerwig-Strasse 9, 78315, Radolfzell, Germany
Tel.: (49) 7732978980
Medical Device Distr
N.A.I.C.S.: 423450

OBEGI CHEMICALS GROUP

Seaside Express Road, PO Box 11 2652, Dora District, 11072110, Beirut, Riad El Solh, Lebanon
Tel.: (961) 1901880   LB
Web Site: http://www.obegichem.com
Year Founded: 1905
Sales Range: $25-49.9 Million
Emp.: 100
Chemical Distr
N.A.I.C.S.: 424690

Subsidiaries:

Obegi Chemicals (L.L.C.) (1)
City Tower 1 Offc 1002, PO Box 28098, Dubai, 28098, United Arab Emirates **(100%)**
Tel.: (971) 43322440
Sales Range: $25-49.9 Million
Emp.: 25
Distr of Chemicals
N.A.I.C.S.: 424690
Yordan Obegi (CEO)

Obegi Chemicals (R) (1)
PO Box 6983, Hawalli, 32044, Kuwait **(100%)**
Web Site: http://www.obegichem.com
Rev.: $45,000,000
Emp.: 40
Chemical Distr
N.A.I.C.S.: 424690

Obegi Chemicals S.A.S. (1)
Old El Bab Road, PO Box 89, Aleppo, Syria **(100%)**
Tel.: (963) 214469731
Web Site: http://www.obegichem.com
Sales Range: $25-49.9 Million
Emp.: 18
Distr of Chemicals
N.A.I.C.S.: 424690

Obegi Chemicals S.A.S. (1)
Mazraa 1 Al Zonhair Bin El Awwam St 24 Bldg 7, PO Box 343, Damascus, Syria **(100%)**
Tel.: (963) 114428210
Web Site: http://www.obegichem.com

Sales Range: $25-49.9 Million
Emp.: 25
Distribuor of Chemicals
N.A.I.C.S.: 325998

Tibah Chemicals (1)
6th Of October City 2nd Industrial Zone, Plots 192 193, Cairo, Egypt **(100%)**
Tel.: (20) 28326993
Web Site: http://www.obegichem.com
Sales Range: $25-49.9 Million
Emp.: 20
Distr of Chemicals
N.A.I.C.S.: 424690

Western Chemical (R) (1)
Baghaffar Ctr Office No 25 2nd Fl, PO Box 127722, Al Sitteen St, Jeddah, 21332, Saudi Arabia **(100%)**
Tel.: (966) 26530238
Web Site: http://www.obegichem.com
Distr of Chemicals
N.A.I.C.S.: 424690

Western Chemical Company S.A. (1)
Ave louise 54, Brussels, 1050, Belgium
Tel.: (32) 25125906
Web Site: http://www.obegigroup.com
Sales Range: $50-74.9 Million
Emp.: 4
Distr of Chemicals
N.A.I.C.S.: 424690
Chanpel Schoonjans (Gen Mgr)

OBEN HOLDING GROUP SAC

Av San Pedro Mz B Lote 48 A Lurin, Lima, Peru
Tel.: (51) 1 715 7000   Pe
Web Site: http://www.obengroup.com
Year Founded: 1991
Emp.: 1,800
Holding Company; Polypropylene Sheets & Thermo-Formed Products Mfr
N.A.I.C.S.: 551112
Alfredo Barreda (VP & Dir-Strategy)

Subsidiaries:

Bopp del Ecuador S.A. (1)
Jaime Roldos Aguilera E3-37 e Isidro Ayora, Carcelen Bajo, Quito, Ecuador
Tel.: (593) 2 247861
Polypropylene Film Mfr
N.A.I.C.S.: 326113

Opp Film Argentina S.A. (1)
Ruta Panamericana KM 60 Calle 9 esquina 23, Parque Industrial Pilar, Buenos Aires, Argentina
Tel.: (54) 230 449 6469
Polypropylene Sheets & Thermo-Formed Products Mfr
N.A.I.C.S.: 326130

Opp Film Chile S.a. (1)
Guacolda 215 Casilla 2, Quilicura, Santiago, Chile
Tel.: (56) 2 26170300
Polypropylene Film Mfr
N.A.I.C.S.: 326113
Cesar Augusto Pena Herrera (Mgr-Mfg)

Opp Film S.A. (1)
Av San Pedro Mz B Lote 48 A Lurin, Peru
Tel.: (51) 1 715 7000
Web Site: http://www.obengroup.com
Emp.: 1,000
Polypropylene Sheets & Thermo-Formed Products Mfr
N.A.I.C.S.: 326130
Bruno Mosto (Reg Mgr-Bopp & Cast)

Packfilm Ltda (1)
Autopista Bogota-Medellin Km 7 0 Celta Trade Park Lote D - 45, Cundinamarca, Colombia
Tel.: (57) 1 7467700
Polypropylene Film Mfr
N.A.I.C.S.: 326113

Sigdopack Argentina S.A. (1)
Parque Industrial Campana Ruta Nacional Nro 9 Km 70, 2804, Campana, Buenos Aires, Argentina
Tel.: (54) 3489507000
Polypropylene Film Mfr

N.A.I.C.S.: 326130
Sergio Sanchez (Head-Logistics & Customer Svcs)

Sigdopack S.A. (1)
Guacolda 2151 casilla 4, Quilicura, Santiago, Chile
Tel.: (56) 2 837 2200
Web Site: http://www.sigdopack.cl
Polypropylene Film Mfr
N.A.I.C.S.: 326130
Jose Ramon Aboitiz (Gen Mgr)

Terphane, Ltda. (1)
Av Eng Luis Carlos Berrini 1645 - 9 andar, Brooklin Novo, Sao Paulo, 04571-011, Brazil
Tel.: (55) 127143965
Web Site: http://www.terphane.com
Sales Range: $75-99.9 Million
Polyester Packaging Films Mfr
N.A.I.C.S.: 326113

Subsidiary (US):

Terphane Inc. (2)
2754 W Park Dr, Bloomfield, NY 14469-9385
Tel.: (585) 657-5800
Web Site: http://www.terphane.com
Sales Range: $25-49.9 Million
Emp.: 55
Polyester Packaging Films Mfr
N.A.I.C.S.: 326113

OBER S.A.

31 Rue de Bar, Tremont-sur-Saulx, 55000, Haironville, France
Tel.: (33) 3 29 76 77 78
Web Site: http://www.groupe-ober.fr
ALOBR—(EUR)
Sales Range: $25-49.9 Million
Interior Product Mfr & Distr
N.A.I.C.S.: 337212
Etienne La Thebeaudiere (Chm, CEO & Dir-IR)

OBEROI REALTY LIMITED

Commerz 3rd Floor International Business Park Oberoi Garden City, Off Western Express Highway Goregaon East, Mumbai, 400 063, India
Tel.: (91) 2266773333
Web Site:
https://www.oberoirealty.com
533273—(NSE)
Rev.: $285,365,057
Assets: $1,645,319,417
Liabilities: $366,431,397
Net Worth: $1,278,888,020
Earnings: $100,913,331
Emp.: 636
Fiscal Year-end: 03/31/21
Residential, Commercial & Retail Property Developer & Manager
N.A.I.C.S.: 531311
Vikas Oberoi (Chm & Mng Dir)

Subsidiaries:

Encase Realty Private Limited (1)

Oberoi Mall Limited (1)
Mall Management Office Oberoi Garden City Off Western Express Highway, Goregaon East, Mumbai, 400063, India
Tel.: (91) 2240990824
Web Site: https://www.oberoimall.com
Shopping Mall Construction Services
N.A.I.C.S.: 236220

OBERON INVESTMENTS GROUP PLC

Nightingale House 65 Curzon Street, London, W1J 8PE, United Kingdom
Tel.: (44) 2031795300   UK
Web Site:
https://oberoninvestments.com
Year Founded: 2017
Financial Investment Services
N.A.I.C.S.: 523940
Rodger Sargent (Founder & Fin Dir)

OBEROSTERREICHISCHE VERSICHERUNG AG
Gruber Strasse 32, A-4020, Linz, Austria
Tel.: (43) 57891710 AT
Web Site: http://www.ooev.at
Year Founded: 1811
Sales Range: $700-749.9 Million
Emp.: 691
Property & Casualty Insurance Products & Services
N.A.I.C.S.: 524126
Wolfgang Weidl *(Chm-Mgmt Bd & CEO)*

OBI PHARMA, INC.
6F No 508 Sec 7 Zhongxiao E Rd, Nangang District, Taipei, 115, Taiwan
Tel.: (886) 226558799
Web Site: https://www.obipharma.com
Year Founded: 2002
4174—(TPE)
Rev.: $147,297
Assets: $207,413,345
Liabilities: $15,557,265
Net Worth: $191,856,080
Earnings: ($59,385,424)
Emp.: 267
Fiscal Year-end: 12/31/22
Pharmaceuticals Product Mfr
N.A.I.C.S.: 325412

OBIC BUSINESS CONSULTANTS CO., LTD.
Sumitomo Fudosan Shinjuku Oak Tower 6-8-1 Nishi-Shinjuku, Shinjuku-ku, Tokyo, 163-6027, Japan
Tel.: (81) 333421880
Web Site: https://pages.obc.co.jp
Year Founded: 1980
4733—(TKS)
Sales Range: $100-124.9 Million
IT Consulting Services
N.A.I.C.S.: 541512
Masahiro Noda *(Chm)*

OBIC CO LTD
Obic Building 2-4-15 Kyobashi, Chuo-ku, Tokyo, 104-8328, Japan
Tel.: (81) 332456500
Web Site: https://www.obic.co.jp
Year Founded: 1968
4684—(TKS)
Rev.: $737,609,900
Assets: $3,054,910,650
Liabilities: $419,556,530
Net Worth: $2,635,354,120
Earnings: $383,426,270
Emp.: 2,107
Fiscal Year-end: 03/31/24
Software Maintenance & System Operational Support Services
N.A.I.C.S.: 541511
Masahiro Noda *(CEO & Chm)*

Subsidiaries:

OBIC Business Solution Co., Ltd. (1)
1-2-5 Hakataekimae, Hakata-Ku, Fukuoka, 812-0011, Japan
Tel.: (81) 924724337
Web Site: http://www.obs.obic.co.jp
Software Development Services
N.A.I.C.S.: 541511

OBIC Office Automation Co., Ltd. (1)
2-2-1 Kyobashi Edgran 8F, Chuo-ku, Tokyo, 104-0031, Japan
Tel.: (81) 332456780
Web Site: http://www.oa.obic.co.jp
Sales Range: $25-49.9 Million
Emp.: 195
Computer Peripheral Equipment Whslr
N.A.I.C.S.: 423440
Shoichi Tachibana *(Pres)*

OBIGO INC.
3rd Fl 338 Pangyo-ro, Bundang-gu, Seongnam, 13493, Gyeonggi-do, Korea (South)
Tel.: (82) 3180333000
Web Site: https://www.obigo.com
Year Founded: 2003
352910—(KRS)
Rev.: $9,269,308
Assets: $30,081,215
Liabilities: $3,207,315
Net Worth: $26,873,900
Earnings: ($1,998,199)
Emp.: 110
Fiscal Year-end: 12/31/22
Software Development Services
N.A.I.C.S.: 541511
Jason Oh *(CFO)*

OBIZ SA
41 quai Fulchiron, 69005, Lyon, France
Tel.: (33) 469554659
Web Site: https://espace-partenaire.obiz.fr
Year Founded: 2010
ALBIZ—(EUR)
Emp.: 73
Management Consulting Services
N.A.I.C.S.: 541618
Brice Chambard *(Chm)*

Subsidiaries:

Adelya S.A.S. (1)
Green Park 11 298 Allee du Lac, 31670, Labege, France
Tel.: (33) 562249304
Web Site: https://www.adelya.com
Loyalty Card Processing Services
N.A.I.C.S.: 522320

OBJECT SOFTWARE LIMITED
Suite 4A No 6 Knutsford Terrace Tsimshatsui, Kowloon, China (Hong Kong)
Tel.: (852) 2956 0576
Web Site: http://www.objectsw.com
Year Founded: 1995
Video Game Development Services
N.A.I.C.S.: 513210
Richard Wallis *(CEO)*

Subsidiaries:

Object Software (Beijing) Co., Ltd. (1)
College Rd Haidian District, Beijing Hong Yu Bldg 7, 100083, Beijing, China
Tel.: (86) 1082306880
Web Site: http://www.object.com.cn
Sales Range: $150-199.9 Million
Emp.: 400
Entertainment Software Developing Services
N.A.I.C.S.: 711410

OBJECTIVE CORPORATION LIMITED
Level 30 177 Pacific Highway, North Sydney, 2060, NSW, Australia
Tel.: (61) 299552288 AU
Web Site: https://www.objective.com
Year Founded: 1987
OCL—(ASX)
Rev.: $78,458,867
Assets: $115,450,053
Liabilities: $53,817,441
Net Worth: $61,632,612
Earnings: $20,920,139
Emp.: 450
Fiscal Year-end: 06/30/24
Information Technology Software & Services Supply
N.A.I.C.S.: 541511
Tony Walls *(Founder, Chm & CEO)*

Subsidiaries:

Objective Corporation Singapore Pte Limited (1)
146 Robinson Road 07-01 Overseas Union Trust Building, Singapore, 068909, Singapore
Tel.: (65) 65833474
Software Development Services
N.A.I.C.S.: 541511

Objective Corporation UK Limited (1)
Level 10 Thames Tower, Reading, RG1 1LX, Berks, United Kingdom
Tel.: (44) 1182072300
Software Development Services
N.A.I.C.S.: 541511

OBJECTONE INFORMATION SYSTEMS LIMITED
8-3-988/34/7/2/1 and 2 Kamalapuri Colony, Hyderabad, 500073, Telangana, India
Tel.: (91) 4023757192
Web Site: https://www.objectinfo.com
Year Founded: 1996
535657—(BOM)
Rev.: $7,226,185
Assets: $4,618,428
Liabilities: $2,534,620
Net Worth: $2,083,808
Earnings: $547,929
Emp.: 87
Fiscal Year-end: 03/31/23
Software Development Services
N.A.I.C.S.: 541511
K. Himabindu *(Exec Dir)*

Subsidiaries:

Stiaos Technologies Inc.
12345 Jones Rd Ste 214, Houston, TX 77070
Tel.: (832) 510-8455
Web Site: https://www.stiaos.com
IT Services
N.A.I.C.S.: 541513

OBJECTWAY FINANCIAL SOFTWARE SPA
Via Giovanni da Procida 24, 20149, Milan, Italy
Tel.: (39) 02 89800 1 IT
Web Site: http://www.objectway.it
Year Founded: 1990
Emp.: 700
Financial Software Developer
N.A.I.C.S.: 513210

Subsidiaries:

Objectway Limited (1)
25 Canada Square, Canary Wharf, London, E14 5LQ, United Kingdom (100%)
Tel.: (44) 20 7071 3000
Web Site: http://www.objectway.com
Software Products Distr
N.A.I.C.S.: 513210

OBM INTERNATIONAL (OBMI)
Woodbourne Hall 1 Gorham Road, Hamilton, HM 08, Bermuda
Tel.: (441) 278 3550
Web Site: http://www.obmi.com
Sales Range: $25-49.9 Million
Emp.: 16
Architecture, Town Planning, Interior Design, Resort Design & Development Services
N.A.I.C.S.: 541310
Michele D. Smith *(Mng Dir)*

Subsidiaries:

OBM Limited (1)
1st Floor Caribbean Maritime Building, PO Box 000, Scott's Hill, Saint John's, Antigua & Barbuda
Tel.: (268) 4621047
Web Site: http://www.obmi.com
Sales Range: $50-74.9 Million
Emp.: 10
Architecture Town Planning Interior Design Resort Design & Development Services
N.A.I.C.S.: 541310
Brian A. D'Ornellas *(Mgr-Reg)*

OBM Limited (1)
PO Box 132, Road Town, 33134, Tortola, Virgin Islands (British)
Tel.: (284) 4942148
Sales Range: $25-49.9 Million
Emp.: 3
Architecture, Town Planning, Interior Design, Resort Design & Development Services
N.A.I.C.S.: 541310
Tim Peck *(Chm)*

OBM Limited (1)
59 McLendon Drive Concord Centre, PO Box 10693, Georgetown, Grand Cayman, Cayman Islands
Tel.: (345) 9498115
Sales Range: $25-49.9 Million
Emp.: 1
Architecture, Town Planning, Interior Design, Resort Design & Development Services
N.A.I.C.S.: 541310
Colin Campbell *(Reg Dir)*

OBM Miami Inc. (1)
806 Douglas Rd 4th Fl, Coral Gables, FL 33134
Tel.: (305) 445-7811
Web Site: http://www.obmi.com
Sales Range: $25-49.9 Million
Architecture, Town Planning, Interior Design, Resort Design & Development Services
N.A.I.C.S.: 541310
Douglas A. Kulig *(Pres & COO)*

OBNOVA A.D. ADA
Trg oslobodenja 11, Ada, Serbia
Tel.: (381) 24853222 RS
Year Founded: 2003
OBNA—(BEL)
Sales Range: $1-9.9 Million
Emp.: 47
Building Construction Services
N.A.I.C.S.: 236220
Goran Masulovic *(Exec Dir)*

OBNOVA A.D. BEOGRAD
Dunavska 17-19, Belgrade, Serbia
Tel.: (381) 112621766 RS
Web Site: https://www.obnova.co.rs
Year Founded: 1948
OBNV—(BEL)
Rev.: $6,462
Assets: $93,285
Liabilities: $780,197
Net Worth: ($686,912)
Earnings: $30,662
Fiscal Year-end: 12/31/20
Material Recycling Services
N.A.I.C.S.: 562920
Igor Markicevic *(Exec Dir)*

OBNOVA PROMET MALESEV A.D.
Branislava Nusica 26/a, Odzaci, Serbia
Tel.: (381) 255743678
Year Founded: 1977
OBNO—(BEL)
Sales Range: Less than $1 Million
Material Recycling Services
N.A.I.C.S.: 562920
Zoran Malesev *(Exec Dir)*

OBOS BBL
Hammersborg Torg 1, 0129, Oslo, Norway
Tel.: (47) 22 86 55 00 NO
Web Site: http://www.obos.no
Year Founded: 1929
Sales Range: $1-1.0 Billion
Emp.: 2,661
Cooperative Housing Association
N.A.I.C.S.: 813990
Arne Baumann *(Exec VP-Residential Dev)*

Subsidiaries:

BWG Homes ASA (1)

OBOS BBL

OBOS BBL—(Continued)

Vika Atrium Munkedamsveien 45 Entrance D 5th Floor, PO Box 1817 Vika, 0123, Oslo, Norway
Tel.: (47) 23246000
Web Site: http://www.bwghomes.no
Sales Range: $650-699.9 Million
Emp.: 1,039
Home Construction & Land Development
N.A.I.C.S.: 236115
Ole Feet *(CEO)*

Subsidiary (Non-US):

BWG Homes AB (2)
Stationsvagen Myresjo, 574 85, Vetlanda, Sweden **(100%)**
Tel.: (46) 104341690
Web Site: http://www.smalandsvillan.se
Sales Range: $150-199.9 Million
Emp.: 300
House Component & Load-Bearing Structure Services
N.A.I.C.S.: 236117

Subsidiary (Domestic):

Myresjohus AB (3)
Scateonvagen 4, SE 574 85, Vetlanda, Sweden **(100%)**
Tel.: (46) 38396000
Web Site: http://www.myresjohus.se
Sales Range: $125-149.9 Million
Emp.: 400
Prefabricated Wooden Houses Mfr
N.A.I.C.S.: 321992
David Carlsson *(COO)*

SmalandsVillan AB (3)
Vaxjovagen, Vrigstad, 570 03, Savsjo, Jonkoping, Sweden **(100%)**
Tel.: (46) 38234550
Web Site: http://www.smalandsvillan.se
Prefabricated Wooden Houses Mfr
N.A.I.C.S.: 321992
David Carlsson *(COO)*

Subsidiary (Domestic):

Block Watne AS (2)
PO Box 1817 Vika, 0123, Oslo, Norway **(100%)**
Tel.: (47) 23246000
Web Site: http://www.blockwatne.no
Sales Range: $25-49.9 Million
Emp.: 50
Land Acquisition & Development & Housing Construction
N.A.I.C.S.: 236115
Ole Feet *(CEO)*

Hetlandhus AS (2)
PO Box 1817 Vika, 0123, Oslo, Norway **(100%)**
Tel.: (47) 22012000
Web Site: http://www.hetlandhus.no
Prefabricated Module Housing Mfr
N.A.I.C.S.: 321992
Stein Ivar Lysberg *(Mgr-Sls & Construction)*

Fornebu Utvikling ASA (1)
Wideroeveien 5, 1360, Fornebu, Norway
Tel.: (47) 67107800
Web Site: http://www.fornebuutvikling.no
Sales Range: $200-249.9 Million
Emp.: 31
Property Development Services
N.A.I.C.S.: 531311

OBOUR LAND FOR FOOD INDUSTRIES S.A.E

1st Industrial Zone-Block 13012-Area 12/13/14/15, Obour, Egypt
Tel.: (20) 244812019
Web Site: http://www.obourland.com
Year Founded: 1995
OLFI.CA—(EGX)
Rev.: $161,030,026
Assets: $81,155,657
Liabilities: $27,862,646
Net Worth: $53,293,011
Earnings: $18,375,874
Fiscal Year-end: 12/31/19
Diary Product Mfr & Distr
N.A.I.C.S.: 311511
Mohamed Hamed Sherif *(Chm)*

OBSERVE MEDICAL ASA

Dronning Eufemias gate 16, 191, Oslo, Norway
Tel.: (47) 41104345
Web Site: https://observemedical.com
Year Founded: 2019
OM5A—(DEU)
Rev.: $1,803,159
Assets: $19,934,602
Liabilities: $7,159,246
Net Worth: $12,775,356
Earnings: ($4,692,500)
Emp.: 17
Fiscal Year-end: 12/81/22
Health Care Srvices
N.A.I.C.S.: 621610
Bjorn Larsson *(CEO)*

OBSEVA SA

Chemin des Aulx 12, Plan-les-Ouates, 1228, Geneva, Switzerland
Tel.: (41) 225523840 CH
Web Site: https://www.obseva.com
Year Founded: 2012
OBSVF—(OTCIQ)
Rev.: $19,637,000
Assets: $16,544,000
Liabilities: $8,061,000
Net Worth: $8,483,000
Earnings: ($29,879,000)
Emp.: 6
Fiscal Year-end: 12/31/22
Biotechnology Research & Development Services
N.A.I.C.S.: 541714
Ernest Loumaye *(Co-Founder & Interim Chm)*

OBSIDIAN ENERGY LTD.

207 - 9th Avenue SW Calgary Calgary, Calgary, T2P 1K3, AB, Canada
Tel.: (403) 777-2500 AB
Web Site: https://www.obsidianenergy.com
Year Founded: 1979
OBE—(NYSEAMEX)
Rev.: $505,207,949
Assets: $1,402,406,737
Liabilities: $448,105,193
Net Worth: $1,214,301,544
Earnings: $79,781,340
Emp.: 198
Fiscal Year-end: 12/31/23
Oil & Natural Gas Explorer & Producer
N.A.I.C.S.: 211120
Stephen E. Loukas *(Pres & Interim & CEO)*

OC OERLIKON CORPORATION AG

Churerstrasse 120, 8808, Pfaffikon, Switzerland
Tel.: (41) 583609696 CH
Web Site: https://www.oerlikon.com
Year Founded: 1973
OERL—(OTCIQ)
Rev.: $3,200,618,031
Assets: $4,871,642,522
Liabilities: $3,636,795,832
Net Worth: $1,234,846,689
Earnings: $27,335,394
Emp.: 12,620
Fiscal Year-end: 12/31/23
Holding Company; Field of Surface Solutios, Manmade Fibers, Drive Systems & Vacuum Generation Services
N.A.I.C.S.: 551112
Gerhard Pegam *(Vice Chm)*

Subsidiaries:

AUTEFA Solutions Germany GmbH (1)
Paul-Lenz-Str 1b, 86316, Friedberg, Germany
Tel.: (49) 821 2608 0

Web Site: http://www.autefa.de
Industrial Machinery Mfr
N.A.I.C.S.: 333248

InnoDisc AG (1)
Dorfstrasse 69, Brugg, 5210, Windisch, Switzerland
Tel.: (41) 564511355
Textile Products Mfr
N.A.I.C.S.: 314999

OC Oerlikon Balzers AG (1)
Iramali 18, 9496, Balzers, Liechtenstein **(100%)**
Tel.: (423) 388 5701
Web Site: https://www.oerlikon.com
Emp.: 4,600
Coating Technology Solutions
N.A.I.C.S.: 332812
Helmut Rudigier *(CTO)*

Subsidiary (Non-US):

Balzers Balinit do Brasil Ltda. (2)
Caixa Postal 3092, 132 15990, Sao Paulo, Brazil
Tel.: (55) 45850044
Web Site: http://www.balzers.com.br
Producer & Distributor of Wear Preventative Coatings
N.A.I.C.S.: 332812

Balzers Korea Coating Co., Ltd. (2)
Eyon-Hansan Industrial Park 5B-3 4 5, 833 Hansan-Ri Chongbuk-Myeon, 451833, Kyongki, Korea (South)
Tel.: (82) 316809900
Web Site: http://www.oerlikon.com
Sales Range: $25-49.9 Million
Emp.: 173
Producer & Distributor of Wear Preventative Coatings
N.A.I.C.S.: 332812

Balzers Ltd. (2)
Bradbourne Drive, Tilbrook, Milton Keynes, MK7 8AT, United Kingdom **(100%)**
Tel.: (44) 1908377277
Web Site: http://www.balzers.com
Sales Range: $25-49.9 Million
Emp.: 50
Producer & Distributor of Wear Preventative Coatings
N.A.I.C.S.: 332812

Balzers Revetements LA (2)
Erlenstrasse 39, PO Box 1000, Balzers, 9496, Switzerland **(100%)**
Tel.: (41) 323657474
Web Site: http://www.balzers.com
Sales Range: $25-49.9 Million
Emp.: 24
Producer & Distributor of Wear Preventative Coatings
N.A.I.C.S.: 332812

Balzers S.A. (2)
4 Rue Louis De Broglie Parc D Activites De IEsplanade, Saint Thibault Des Vignes, F 77462, Lagny, Cedex, France **(100%)**
Tel.: (33) 0164124900
Web Site: http://www.balzers.com
Sales Range: $25-49.9 Million
Emp.: 56
Producer & Distributor of Wear Preventative Coatings
N.A.I.C.S.: 332812
Boghe Willy *(Mgr)*

Balzers Verschleissschutz GmbH (2)
Am Ockenheimer Graben 41, D 55441, Bingen, Germany **(100%)**
Tel.: (49) 67217930
Web Site: http://www.oerlikon.com
Sales Range: $50-74.9 Million
Emp.: 250
N.A.I.C.S.: 334413

Nihon Balzers Co. Ltd.. (2)
7 2 2 Shinomiya, Hiratsuka, 254 0014, Kanagawa, Japan **(100%)**
Tel.: (81) 463542220
Web Site: http://www.oerlikon.com
Sales Range: $25-49.9 Million
Emp.: 90
Total Coating Service
N.A.I.C.S.: 332812

OOO Oerlikon Balzers Rus (2)
Lesnaya St 8A, Moscow Region, 144011, Elektrostal, Russia

Tel.: (7) 4956468851
Web Site: http://www.oerlikon.com
Precision Turned Product Mfr
N.A.I.C.S.: 332721

Oerlikon Balzers Argentina SA (2)
Av Pablo Richieri 4240, Cordoba, 5014, Argentina
Tel.: (54) 351 464 8999
Mechanical Power Transmission Component Mfr
N.A.I.C.S.: 333613
Alberto Blangine *(Mgr)*

Oerlikon Balzers Coating (2)
El-22 J Block MIDC, Bhosari, Pune, 411 026, India **(100%)**
Tel.: (91) 2061326000
Web Site: http://www.balzers.com
Sales Range: $25-49.9 Million
Emp.: 50
Producer & Distributor of Wear Preventative Coatings
N.A.I.C.S.: 332812

Oerlikon Balzers Coating (Suzhou) Co. Ltd (2)
No 9 Changyang Street, Suzhou Industrial Park, Suzhou, 215024, Jiangsu, China
Tel.: (86) 5126 762 0369
Web Site: https://www.oerlikon.com
Precision Component Mfr
N.A.I.C.S.: 332721

Oerlikon Balzers Coating (Thailand) Co. Ltd (2)
Amatanakorn Industrial Estate Phase 4 700/538 M 6 T Donhualoh, A Muang, 20000, Chon Buri, Thailand
Tel.: (66) 3 845 4201
Web Site: https://www.oerlikon.com
Precision Component Coating Services
N.A.I.C.S.: 238990

Oerlikon Balzers Coating Austria GmbH (2)
Burgstallweg 27, 8605, Kapfenberg, Austria
Tel.: (43) 38 623 4144
Web Site: https://www.oerlikon.com
Emp.: 5
Precision Turned Product Mfr
N.A.I.C.S.: 332721

Oerlikon Balzers Coating Benelux N.V. (2)
Nijverheidslaan 5470, 3800, Sint-Truiden, Belgium
Tel.: (32) 1 169 3040
Web Site: http://www.oerlikon.com
Sales Range: $25-49.9 Million
Emp.: 45
Precision Products Coating Distr
N.A.I.C.S.: 423840

Oerlikon Balzers Coating France SAS (2)
16 Avenue James De Rothschild, 77164, Ferrieres en Brie, France
Tel.: (33) 164124900
Sales Range: $25-49.9 Million
Emp.: 15
Textile Machinery Mfr
N.A.I.C.S.: 333248
Gilles Widawski *(Gen Mgr)*

Oerlikon Balzers Coating Germany GmbH (2)
Hohe Flum Strasse 22, 79650, Schopfheim, Germany
Tel.: (49) 7622 3999 0
Web Site: http://www.oerlikon.com
Sales Range: $25-49.9 Million
Emp.: 6
Precision Turned Product Mfr
N.A.I.C.S.: 332721
Henrick Alster *(Gen Mgr)*

Oerlikon Balzers Coating India Limited (2)
EL-22 J Block MIDC, Bhosari, Pune, 411 026, India
Tel.: (91) 2030616000
Web Site: http://www.oerlikon.com
Sales Range: $25-49.9 Million
Emp.: 220
Coating Tools & Components
N.A.I.C.S.: 325510
Pravin Shirse *(Mng Dir)*

Oerlikon Balzers Coating Korea Co. Ltd. (2)

AND PRIVATE COMPANIES

OC OERLIKON CORPORATION AG

Eyon-Hansan Industrial Park 5B-3 4 5
833-2 Hansan-Ri, Chongbuk-Myeon, Pyeongtaek, 451-833, Kyonggi-Do, Korea (South)
Tel.: (82) 31 680 9900
Web Site:
http://www.oerlikonbalzerscoating.com
Emp.: 200
Precision Turned Product Mfr
N.A.I.C.S.: 332721

Oerlikon Balzers Coating Luxembourg S.a r.l. (2)
Route de Bascharage, Zone Industrielle Haaneboesch, 4513, Niedercorn, Luxembourg
Tel.: (352) 26580891
Web Site:
http://www.oerlikonbalzerscoating.com
Sales Range: $25-49.9 Million
Emp.: 15
Precision Turned Product Mfr
N.A.I.C.S.: 332721

Oerlikon Balzers Coating Mexico, S.A. de C.V. (2)
Acceso III No 304 y 306, 76150, Queretaro, Mexico
Tel.: (52) 442 209 6800
Web Site: http://www.oerlikon.com
Sales Range: $25-49.9 Million
Producer & Distr of Wear Preventative Coatings
N.A.I.C.S.: 332812

Oerlikon Balzers Coating Poland Sp. z.o.o. (2)
ul Fabryczna 4, 59-101, Polkowice, Poland
Tel.: (48) 767464800
Sales Range: $25-49.9 Million
Emp.: 67
Precision Turned Product Mfr
N.A.I.C.S.: 332721
Marek Danis *(Gen Mgr)*

Oerlikon Balzers Coating SA (2)
Erlenstrasse 39, 2555, Brugg, Switzerland
Tel.: (41) 323657474
Precision Turned Product Mfr
N.A.I.C.S.: 332721

Oerlikon Balzers Coating Singapore Pte. Ltd. (2)
21 Kian Teck Drive, Singapore, 628838, Singapore **(100%)**
Tel.: (65) 62686227
Web Site: http://www.oerlikon.com
Sales Range: $25-49.9 Million
Producer & Distr of Wear Preventative Coatings
N.A.I.C.S.: 332812

Oerlikon Balzers Coating UK Ltd. (2)
Bradbourne Drive, Tilbrook, Milton Keynes, MK7 8AT, United Kingdom
Tel.: (44) 190 837 7277
Web Site: https://www.oerlikon.com
Industrial Coating Mfr
N.A.I.C.S.: 325510
Sara Deering *(CFO)*

Subsidiary (US):

Oerlikon Balzers Coating USA, Inc. (2)
1475 E Woodfield Rd Ste 201, Schaumburg, IL 60173 **(99.8%)**
Tel.: (847) 844-1753
Web Site: http://www.oerlikon.com
Rev.: $43,000,000
Emp.: 316
Coatings Supplier
N.A.I.C.S.: 424950

Subsidiary (Non-US):

Oerlikon Balzers Hartec GmbH (2)
Schmeienstrasse 51, 72510, Stetten, Germany
Tel.: (49) 757395140
Web Site: http://www.hartec-pvd.com
Physical Vapor Deposition Coating Equipment Mfr
N.A.I.C.S.: 333310

Oerlikon Balzers Kaplama Sanayi ve Ticaret Limited (2)
Nosab 120 Sokak No 7, Nilufer, 16140, Bursa, Turkiye
Tel.: (90) 224 411 00 77

Emp.: 49
Precision Turned Product Mfr
N.A.I.C.S.: 332721
Uhur Urkut *(Gen Mgr)*

Oerlikon Balzers Revestimentos Metalicos Ltda (2)
Av Pablo Richieri 4240, Cordoba, 5014, Argentina
Tel.: (54) 351 464 8999
Sales Range: $25-49.9 Million
Emp.: 7
Metal Processing Machinery Mfr
N.A.I.C.S.: 333248

Joint Venture (Non-US):

Oerlikon Balzers Sandvik Coating AB (2)
Arstaangsvagen 31 D-E, 117 43, Stockholm, Sweden
Tel.: (46) 86814140
Web Site: http://www.oerlikon.com
Rev.: $53,743,200
Emp.: 25
PVD Coatings Whslr; Owned 51% by OC Oerlikon Corporation AG & 49% by Sandvik AB
N.A.I.C.S.: 424950
Sara Deering *(CFO)*

Subsidiary (Non-US):

Oerlikon Balzers Sandvik Coating Oy (3)
Vaittintie 10, 33960, Pirkkala, Finland
Tel.: (358) 102398080
Industrial Coating Machinery Distr
N.A.I.C.S.: 423830

Subsidiary (Non-US):

Oerlikon Balzers-ELAY Coating S.A. (2)
Antigua 2, 20577, Antzuola, Gipuzkoa, Spain
Tel.: (34) 943766208
Sales Range: $25-49.9 Million
Emp.: 5
Precision Turned Product Mfr
N.A.I.C.S.: 332721
Alberto Biana *(Gen Mgr)*

Oerlikon Coating Services Austria (2)
Burgstallweg 27, Kapfenberg, 8650, Austria
Tel.: (43) 3862341440
Web Site: http://www.oerlikon.com
Sales Range: $25-49.9 Million
Emp.: 50
Coating Components
N.A.I.C.S.: 325510
Johann Zechner *(Gen Mgr)*

Oerlikon Metco AG (2)
Rigackerstrasse 16, 5610, Wohlen, Switzerland **(100%)**
Tel.: (41) 566188181
Web Site: http://www.oerlikon.com
Sales Range: $700-749.9 Million
Surface Engineering Products & Services
N.A.I.C.S.: 325510
Markus Tacke *(CEO-Surface Solutions Div)*

Subsidiary (Non-US):

Oerlikon Eldim (NL) B.V. (3)
Spikweien 24 Components - ELDIM, 5943 AD, Lomm, Netherlands **(100%)**
Tel.: (31) 774731919
Web Site: http://www.oerlikon.com
Sales Range: $75-99.9 Million
Mfr of Components for the Aircraft Engine & the Industrial Gas Turbine OEM's
N.A.I.C.S.: 336412

Subsidiary (Non-US):

Oerlikon Eldim (HU) Kft. (4)
Hatar str 1/C, 4031, Debrecen, Hungary
Tel.: (00) 56501270
Web Site: http://www.oerlikon.com
Sales Range: $25-49.9 Million
Mfr of Components for the Aircraft Engine & the Industrial Gas Turbine OEM's
N.A.I.C.S.: 336412

Subsidiary (Non-US):

Oerlikon Friction Systems (Germany) GmbH (3)

Bremer Heerstrasse 39, 28719, Bremen, Germany **(100%)**
Tel.: (49) 421638930
Web Site: http://www.oerlikon.com
Thermal Spraying Coatings Mfr
N.A.I.C.S.: 332812

Subsidiary (US):

Oerlikon Friction Systems (US) Inc. (3)
240 Detrick St, Dayton, OH 45404-0277
Tel.: (937) 449-4000
Web Site: http://www.oerlikon.com
Friction Lining & Power Transmission Equipment Mfr
N.A.I.C.S.: 333613

Subsidiary (Non-US):

Oerlikon Friction Systems India Limited (3)
K17 & K18 SIPCOT Industrial Park, Irungattukottai Sriperumbudur Tk Kancheepuram District, Chennai, 602117, Tamil Nadu, India
Tel.: (91) 784 201 7331
Web Site: https://www.oerlikon.com
Sales Range: $25-49.9 Million
Emp.: 70
Electrical Equipment Mfr & Distr
N.A.I.C.S.: 335999

Oerlikon Friction Systems do Brasil Ltda. (3)
Rua Tupiniquins 70 Vila Conceicao, Diadema, 09990-300, Sao Paulo, Brazil
Tel.: (55) 11 4044 55 88
Web Site: http://www.oerlikon.com
Electric Equipment Mfr
N.A.I.C.S.: 335999

Oerlikon Metaplas GmbH (3)
Am Boettcherberg 30-38, 51427, Bergisch Gladbach, Germany
Tel.: (49) 22042990
Sales Range: $50-74.9 Million
Emp.: 160
Industrial Coating & Thin Film & Heat Treatments
N.A.I.C.S.: 332812
Thomas Guttwiller *(Exec VP-Components)*

Branch (Domestic):

Oerlikon Metaplas GmbH (4)
Theodor-Heuss-Strasse 63, 38228, Salzgitter, Germany
Tel.: (49) 534185870
Web Site:
http://www.oerlikonbalzerscoating.com
Industrial Coating Mfr
N.A.I.C.S.: 332812

Subsidiary (Non-US):

Oerlikon Metco (Australia) Pty. Ltd. (3)
14 Lexington Drive Unit 411, Bella Vista, 2153, NSW, Australia **(100%)**
Tel.: (61) 29 796 2011
Web Site: http://www.sulzermetco.com.au
Sales Range: $25-49.9 Million
Emp.: 3
Industrial Coatings Sales
N.A.I.C.S.: 423840

Oerlikon Metco (Canada) Inc. (3)
10108 - 114 Street, Fort Saskatchewan, T8L 4R1, AB, Canada
Tel.: (780) 992-5100
Industrial Machinery Mfr
N.A.I.C.S.: 333248
Mitch Regnier *(Mgr-Ops)*

Oerlikon Metco (Japan) Ltd. (3)
3-4-2 Hikawadai, Nerima-ku, Tokyo, 179-0084, Japan **(100%)**
Tel.: (81) 35 920 3301
Web Site: http://www.sulzer-metco.co.jp
Sales Range: $25-49.9 Million
Emp.: 43
Industrial Coatings Mfr & Distr
N.A.I.C.S.: 325510
Nick Yumiba *(Pres)*

Oerlikon Metco (Singapore) Pte Ltd. (3)
2 Loyang Lane 06-01/02, Singapore, 508913, Singapore **(100%)**
Tel.: (65) 65450870

Emp.: 16
Industrial Coatings Sales
N.A.I.C.S.: 423840
Ling Phua Lin *(Controller-Asia Pacific)*

Oerlikon Metco (UK) Limited (3)
Brecon House William Brown Close, Llantarnam Industrial Park, Cwmbran, NP44 3AB, Gwent, United Kingdom **(100%)**
Tel.: (44) 1633 488090
Emp.: 16
Industrial Coatings Sales
N.A.I.C.S.: 423840
Andrew Coomber *(Gen Mgr)*

Subsidiary (US):

Oerlikon Metco (US) Inc. (3)
1101 Prospect Ave, Westbury, NY 11590-2724 **(100%)**
Tel.: (516) 334-1300
Web Site: http://www.oerlikon.com
Sales Range: $100-124.9 Million
Thermal Sprays & Coating Materials Mfr
N.A.I.C.S.: 325510

Plant (Domestic):

Oerlikon Metco (US) Inc. (4)
1972 Meijer Dr, Troy, MI 48084
Tel.: (248) 288-1200
Web Site: http://www.oerlikon.com
Surface Engineering Products & Services
N.A.I.C.S.: 325510

Oerlikon Metco (US) Inc. (4)
1303 Long St, Barboursville, WV 25504
Tel.: (304) 733-9350
Web Site: http://www.oerlikon.com
Surface Engineering Products & Services
N.A.I.C.S.: 325510

Subsidiary (Non-US):

Oerlikon Metco Coatings GmbH (3)
Gottfried-Linke-Strasse 205, 38223, Salzgitter, Germany
Tel.: (49) 5341 243 0
Web Site: http://www.oerlikon.com
Surface Solutions & Coatings Mfr
N.A.I.C.S.: 325510

Oerlikon Metco Coatings Ltd. (3)
9-14 Newton Wood Road, Globe Lane Industrial Estate, Dukinfield, SK16 4XF, Cheshire, United Kingdom
Tel.: (44) 161 343 6220
Web Site: http://www.oerlikon.com
Emp.: 40
Coating Surface Services
N.A.I.C.S.: 325510

Oerlikon Metco Europe GmbH (3)
Spreestrasse 2, 65451, Kelsterbach, Germany **(100%)**
Tel.: (49) 6142 6033 0
Web Site: http://www.oerlikon.com
Sales Range: $25-49.9 Million
Emp.: 70
Industrial Coatings Mfr & Sales
N.A.I.C.S.: 325510

Branch (Non-US):

Oerlikon Metco Europe GmbH (4)
Botkyrkavagen 4, Varby, 143 30, Stockholm, Sweden **(100%)**
Tel.: (46) 86807580
Emp.: 6
Sales & Servicer of Industrial Coatings
N.A.I.C.S.: 423840
Rikard Zaar *(Branch Mgr-Sls)*

Oerlikon Metco Europe GmbH (4)
rue Maryse Bastie Les Citadelles, BP 319, 69671, Bron, France **(100%)**
Tel.: (33) 4 72 81 60 80
Sales Range: $25-49.9 Million
Emp.: 12
Industrial Coatings Sales
N.A.I.C.S.: 423840
Farnand Bisquert *(Gen Mgr)*

Subsidiary (Non-US):

Oerlikon Metco Surface Technology (Shanghai) Co. Ltd. (3)
Bai An Road B1 & B2 539 Anting, Jiading District, Shanghai, 201814, China
Tel.: (86) 21 6708 7000
Web Site: http://www.oerlikon.com

OC OERLIKON CORPORATION AG

INTERNATIONAL PUBLIC

OC Oerlikon Corporation AG—(Continued)
Sales Range: $25-49.9 Million
Thermal Spray & Thin Film Material Mfr
N.A.I.C.S.: 325613

Oerlikon Metco WOKA GmbH (3)
Im Vorwerk 25, 36456, Barchfeld, Germany
Tel.: (49) 369618610
Sales Range: $25-49.9 Million
Emp.: 100
Mfr of Carbides for Tools & Machinery
N.A.I.C.S.: 325998
Salvatore Musso *(Head-Matls Bus)*

Oerlikon Neomet Ltd. (3)
Cross Lane 92, Marple, Stockport, SK6 7PZ, Cheshire, United Kingdom
Tel.: (44) 161 427 7741
Web Site: http://www.oerlikon.com
Sales Range: $25-49.9 Million
Emp.: 35
Fabricated Metal Products Mfr & Whslr
N.A.I.C.S.: 332999
Danny Molloy *(Acct Mgr-Sls)*

Subsidiary (Non-US):

Oerlikon Nihon Balzers Coating Co. Ltd. (2)
7-2-2 Shinomiya, Hiratsuka, 254-0014, Kanagawa, Japan
Tel.: (81) 463 54 2220
Web Site:
  http://www.oerlikonbalzerscoating.com
Precision Turned Product Mfr
N.A.I.C.S.: 332721

Oerlikon (China) Technology Co. Ltd. (1)
No 9 Chang Yang Street, Suzhou Industrial Park, Suzhou, 215024, Jiangsu, China
Tel.: (86) 51281855380
Emp.: 500
Textile Machinery Mfr
N.A.I.C.S.: 333248
Joachim Dietzel *(Gen Mgr)*

Oerlikon Czech s.r.o. (1)
Lhota 261, Cerveny Kostelec, 549 41, Czech Republic
Tel.: (420) 491 469 111
Textile Machinery Mfr
N.A.I.C.S.: 333248

Oerlikon Deutschland Holding GmbH (1)
Bonner Str 498, Cologne, 50968, Germany
Tel.: (49) 2213470
Web Site: http://www.oerlikon.com
Investment Management Service
N.A.I.C.S.: 523999

Subsidiary (Domestic):

Oerlikon Deutschland Vertriebs GmbH (2)
Karl-Hammerschmidt-Strasse 34, Dornach, 85609, Aschheim, Germany
Tel.: (49) 8975505100
Emp.: 40
Semiconductor Devices Mfr
N.A.I.C.S.: 334413
Rals Eichert *(Pres)*

Oerlikon France Holding SAS (1)
Parc D'Activite Des Trois Noyers 16 Avenue James De Rothschild, Ferrieres-en-Brie, Torcy, 77164, France
Tel.: (33) 164124900
Web Site: http://www.oerlikon.com
Emp.: 80
Investment Management Service
N.A.I.C.S.: 523999

Oerlikon Graziano Group S.p.A. (1)
Via Cumiana 14, Rivoli, 10098, TO, Italy
Tel.: (39) 0119570206
Sales Range: $300-349.9 Million
Emp.: 800
Holding Company; Power Transmission Components Mfr
N.A.I.C.S.: 551112
Gary Lehman *(CEO)*

Subsidiary (US):

Fairfield Manufacturing Company, Inc. (2)
US 52 S, Lafayette, IN 47903
Tel.: (765) 772-4000
Web Site: http://www.fairfieldmfg.com
Custom Gears & Drive Solutions
N.A.I.C.S.: 333612

Subsidiary (Non-US):

Fairfield Atlas Ltd. (3)
Sry No 157, Devarwadi Village Dist Kolhapur, Belgaum, 416 507, India
Tel.: (91) 2320236605
Web Site: http://www.oerlikon.com
Rev.: $64,796,569
Assets: $58,207,512
Liabilities: $15,685,597
Net Worth: $42,521,915
Earnings: $5,136,080
Fiscal Year-end: 03/31/2017
Industrial Machinery Mfr
N.A.I.C.S.: 333248

Subsidiary (Non-US):

Graziano Trasmissioni India Pvt. Ltd. (2)
Plot 14 Udyog Kendra Greater Noida, Gautam Budh Nagar, New Delhi, 201 304, Uttar Pradesh, India
Tel.: (91) 1206625500
Sales Range: $25-49.9 Million
Emp.: 150
Gear Mfr
N.A.I.C.S.: 333612

Oerlikon Graziano Czech Republic (2)
Lhota 261, CZ 54941, Cerveny Kostelec, Czech Republic
Tel.: (420) 491413401
Power Transmissions
N.A.I.C.S.: 333613

Subsidiary (Domestic):

Oerlikon Graziano S.p.A. (2)
Via Cumiana 14, 10090, Rivoli, 10090, TO, Italy
Tel.: (39) 01195701
Web Site: http://www.oerlikon.com
Sales Range: $150-199.9 Million
Mfr of Industrial Machinery
N.A.I.C.S.: 333248
Luciano Viaro *(CFO & VP)*

Plant (Domestic):

Oerlikon Graziano SpA (3)
Frazione Grinzano, Cervere, Cuneo, 12040, Italy
Tel.: (39) 0172471511
Web Site: http://www.oerlikon.com
Sales Range: $50-74.9 Million
Gear Mfr
N.A.I.C.S.: 333612

Subsidiary (Non-US):

Oerlikon Graziano United Kingdom (2)
9 Harley Industrial Park, Paxton Hill Saint Neots, Huntingdon, P19 6TA, United Kingdom
Tel.: (44) 1480403453
Web Site: http://www.oerlikon.com
Sales Range: $25-49.9 Million
Emp.: 7
Gear Mfr
N.A.I.C.S.: 333612

Oerlikon IT Solutions AG (1)
Churerstrasse 120, 8808, Pfaffikon, Switzerland
Tel.: (41) 583609696
Information Technology Consulting Services
N.A.I.C.S.: 541512

Oerlikon Real Estate GmbH (1)
Bonner Str 498, Cologne, 50968, Germany
Tel.: (49) 2213471300
Web Site: http://www.oerlikon.com
Real Estate Manangement Services
N.A.I.C.S.: 531390

Oerlikon SEA Pte. Ltd. (1)
8 Commonwealth Lane, Singapore, 149555, Singapore
Tel.: (65) 6303 7030
Web Site: http://www.oerlikon.com
Holding Company; Regional Managing Office
N.A.I.C.S.: 551112

Oerlikon Textile GmbH & Co. KG (1)
Leverkuser Strasse 65, 42897, Remscheid, Germany
Tel.: (49) 2191670
Web Site: http://www.oerlikontextile.com
Emp.: 1,000
Holding Company; Textile Machinery Mfr & Textile Plant Engineering
N.A.I.C.S.: 551112

Subsidiary (Domestic):

Oerlikon Barmag (2)
Leverkuser Strasse 65, Remscheid, 42967, Germany
Tel.: (49) 2191670
Web Site: http://www.oerlikon.com
Sales Range: $350-399.9 Million
Textile Machinery
N.A.I.C.S.: 333248

Subsidiary (Non-US):

Barmag Czech Republic S.r.o. (3)
U Veze 8, CZ 46107, Liberec, Czech Republic
Tel.: (420) 482427841
Textile Machinery
N.A.I.C.S.: 333248

Subsidiary (Domestic):

Barmag Liegenschaften GmbH & Co. KG (3)
Leverkuser Str 65, 42897, Remscheid, Germany
Tel.: (49) 2191670
Sales Range: $300-349.9 Million
Emp.: 800
Real Estate Agency Services
N.A.I.C.S.: 531210

Oerlikon Barmag-Spinnzwirn (3)
Zwickauer Strasse 247, 09116, Chemnitz, Germany
Tel.: (49) 37123880
Web Site: http://www.oerlikon.de
Sales Range: $50-74.9 Million
Emp.: 150
Textile Machinery
N.A.I.C.S.: 333248

Affiliate (Non-US):

Oerlikon Segment Manmade Fibers China (3)
No 100 Yutong Road 48F Intercontinental Business Center, 200070, Shanghai, Zhabei, China
Tel.: (86) 2152 88 588 85 968
Web Site: http://www.oerlikon.com
Sales Range: $25-49.9 Million
Emp.: 10
Textile Machinery
N.A.I.C.S.: 333248

Subsidiary (Domestic):

Oerlikon Neumag Zweigniederlassung der Oerlikon Textile GmbH & Co. KG (2)
Christianstrasse 168-170, 24536, Neumunster, Germany
Tel.: (49) 43213050
Web Site:
  http://www.neumag.oerlikontextile.com
Sales Range: $75-99.9 Million
Emp.: 350
Textile Machinery
N.A.I.C.S.: 333248

Subsidiary (Non-US):

Oerlikon Saurer Arbon AG (2)
Textilstrasse 2, CH 9320, Arbon, Switzerland
Tel.: (41) 714475111
Web Site: http://www.arbon.com
Sales Range: $25-49.9 Million
Emp.: 100
Industrial Machinery Mfr
N.A.I.C.S.: 333248

Subsidiary (Domestic):

Aktiengesellschaft Adolph Saurer (3)
Bruhlstrasse 57, 2503, Biel/Bienne, Switzerland
Tel.: (41) 323410004
Trucks Mfr

N.A.I.C.S.: 336212

Subsidiary (Non-US):

Allma Volkmann Zweigniederlassung der Saurer Germany GmbH & Co. KG (3)
Leonhardstrasse 19, D 87437, Kempten, Germany
Tel.: (49) 8316880
Web Site: http://www.allma.saurer.com
Sales Range: $25-49.9 Million
Emp.: 70
Embroidery
N.A.I.C.S.: 313110

Subsidiary (Domestic):

Oerlikon Saurer Arbon AG (3)
Textilstrasse 2, 9320, Arbon, Switzerland
Tel.: (41) 714475111
Web Site: http://www.saurer.com
Emp.: 10
Textile Machinery Mfr
N.A.I.C.S.: 333248

Subsidiary (Non-US):

Oerlikon Vacuum Japan (3)
5-13, Kawagishi-cho, Osaka, 562, Suita-Shi, Japan
Tel.: (81) 6 4860 2212
Web Site: http://www.oerlikon.com
Vacuum Components
N.A.I.C.S.: 333298

SAC Saurer Automotive Components B.V. (3)
Westblaak 89, Rotterdam, 3012 KG, Netherlands
Tel.: (31) 102245333
Automotive Components Mfr
N.A.I.C.S.: 336390

Subsidiary (Domestic):

Saurer AG (3)
Textilstrasse 2, 9320, Arbon, Switzerland
Tel.: (41) 714475111
Web Site: http://saurer.com
Textile Machinery Mfr
N.A.I.C.S.: 333248
Carsten Voigtlander *(Vice Chm)*

Subsidiary (Non-US):

Saurer Far East Ltd. (3)
Room 2806 China Resources Building 26 Harbour Road, 213 Queens Road E Wanchai, Wanchai, China (Hong Kong)
Tel.: (852) 28274314
Web Site: http://www.oerlikon.com
Sales Range: $25-49.9 Million
Emp.: 15
Textile Machinery
N.A.I.C.S.: 333248

Subsidiary (Domestic):

Saurer Management AG (3)
Bahnhofplatz 12, CH 8401, Winterthur, Switzerland
Tel.: (41) 522640911
Sales Range: $25-49.9 Million
Emp.: 20
Textile Machinery
N.A.I.C.S.: 333248

Subsidiary (Non-US):

Saurer Textile Systems (Suzhou) Co. Ltd. (3)
9 Chang Yang St, Suzhou Industrial Pk, Suzhou, 215024, Jiangsu, China
Tel.: (86) 51281885998
Web Site:
  http://www.saurer.oerlikontextile.com
Mfr of Textile Solutions
N.A.I.C.S.: 333248

Subsidiary (Domestic):

Oerlikon Schlafhorst Zweigniederlassung der Saurer GmbH & Co.KG (2)
Blumenberger Strasse 143-145, D 41061, Monchengladbach, Germany
Tel.: (49) 2161280
Web Site:
  http://www.schlafhorst.oerlikontextile.com

AND PRIVATE COMPANIES

Sales Range: $350-399.9 Million
Textile Machinery
N.A.I.C.S.: 333248

Subsidiary (Domestic):

Schlafhorst Autocoro GmbH (3)
Blumenberger Strasse 143 145, 41061,
Monchengladbach, Germany
Tel.: (49) 2161280
Web Site: http://www.schlafhorst.de
Sales Range: $350-399.9 Million
Emp.: 1,500
Mfr of Industrial Machinery
N.A.I.C.S.: 333248

Subsidiary (Non-US):

Schlafhorst Marketing Company Ltd.
Jyoti Studio's Compound, 1st Floor, K.B.A.
Irani Bridge, Mumbai, 400 007, India
Tel.: (91) 223860350
Mfr of Industrial Machinery
N.A.I.C.S.: 333248

Subsidiary (Domestic):

Schlafhorst Winding Systems GmbH (3)
Carlstrasse 60, D 52531, Ubach-Palenberg,
Germany
Tel.: (49) 2161280
Web Site: http://www.schlafhorst.de
Sales Range: $100-124.9 Million
Emp.: 500
Mfr of Industrial Machinery
N.A.I.C.S.: 333248

Schlafhorst Zweigniederlassung der Saurer Germany GmbH & Co. KG (3)
Hans-Zinser-Strasse 1-3, 73061, Ebersbach, Germany
Tel.: (49) 7163140
Web Site: http://schlafhorst.saurer.com
Industrial Machinery Mfr
N.A.I.C.S.: 333248

s.e.t. electronics AG (3)
Waldnieler Strasse 73, 41068, Monchengladbach, Germany
Tel.: (49) 21615761500
Web Site: http://www.set-electronics.com
Sales Range: $25-49.9 Million
Electronic Components, Devices & Systems Mfr
N.A.I.C.S.: 334419
Mehmet Cirik (Mng Dir)

Subsidiary (Non-US):

Oerlikon Textile Far East Ltd. (2)
Room 2806 China Resources Building 26
Harbour Road, Wanchai, China (Hong Kong)
Tel.: (852) 2527 4314
Web Site: http://www.oerlikontextile.com
Textile Software Development Services
N.A.I.C.S.: 541511

Subsidiary (US):

Oerlikon Textile Inc. (2)
8801 S Blvd, Charlotte, NC 28273
Tel.: (980) 465-6262
Web Site: https://www.oerlikon.com
Sales Range: $25-49.9 Million
Emp.: 110
Textile Machinery
N.A.I.C.S.: 333248

Subsidiary (Non-US):

Oerlikon Textile India Pvt. Ltd. (2)
Empire Industries Complex 414 Senapati
Bapat Marg Lower Parel West, Mumbai,
400013, India
Tel.: (91) 223 351 7900
Web Site: http://www.oerlikontextile.com
Textile Products Mfr
N.A.I.C.S.: 314999

Oerlikon Textile do Brasil Maquinas Ltda (2)
Av Theodomiro Porto da Fonseca 2123
Bairro Christo Rei, Sao Leopoldo, 93020-080, Brazil
Tel.: (55) 5135798503

Web Site:
http://www.barmag.oerlikontextile.com
Sales Range: $25-49.9 Million
Emp.: 36
Textile Machinery Distr
N.A.I.C.S.: 423830

Zinser Textile Systems Pvt. Ltd. (2)
Plot No 1685 Survey No 1517 Opposite
Telco Cargo NH No 8 Post Aslali, Ahmedabad, 382 427, Gujarat, India
Tel.: (91) 2266766100
Web Site: http://www.ateindia.com
Textile Machinery Mfr
N.A.I.C.S.: 333248

Oerlikon Trading AG (1)
Hauptstrasse 1a, 9477, Trubbach, Switzerland
Tel.: (41) 81 784 40 40
Textile Machinery Distr
N.A.I.C.S.: 423830

Oerlikon USA Holding Inc. (1)
5700 Mellon Rd, Export, PA 15632-8900
Tel.: (724) 327-5700
Web Site: http://www.oerlikon.com
Emp.: 100
Investment Management Service
N.A.I.C.S.: 523999

Vocis Limited (1)
Unit 1 Technology Centre Nw03 Mira Technology Park Lindley, Warwick, CV10 0TU,
United Kingdom
Tel.: (44) 1926650308
Web Site: http://www.vocis.co.uk
Sales Range: $25-49.9 Million
Mechanical Power Transmission Mfr
N.A.I.C.S.: 333613

OC&C STRATEGY CONSULTANTS
6 New Street Square, London, EC4A 3AT, United Kingdom
Tel.: (44) 2070108000
Web Site:
http://www.occstrategy.com
Year Founded: 1987
Sales Range: $100-124.9 Million
Emp.: 350
Management & Strategy Consulting Services
N.A.I.C.S.: 541611
Michael Jary (Mng Partner-Worldwide)

OCADO GROUP PLC
Buildings 1 & 2 Trident Place Hatfield
Business Park Mosquito Way, Hatfield, AL10 9UL, United Kingdom
Tel.: (44) 1707227800
Web Site:
https://www.ocadogroup.com
Year Founded: 2000
OCDO—(LSE)
Rev.: $3,596,435,406
Assets: $5,638,446,872
Liabilities: $3,714,831,333
Net Worth: $1,923,615,539
Earnings: $492,679,824)
Emp.: 18,869
Fiscal Year-end: 12/31/23
Groceries Internet Retailer
N.A.I.C.S.: 424490
Neill Abrams (Grp Gen Counsel & Sec)

Subsidiaries:

Ocado Cell in Atlas Insurance PCC Limited (1)
48 50 Ta Xbiex Seafront, Ta' Xbiex, MSD11, Malta
Tel.: (356) 23435255
General Insurance Services
N.A.I.C.S.: 524298

Ocado Limited (1)
Apollo Court 2 Bishop Square Hatfield Business Park, PO BOX 362, Hatfield, AL10
9NE, Hertfordshire, United Kingdom
Tel.: (44) 2073534200
Grocery Retailer

N.A.I.C.S.: 445110

Ocado Retail Limited (1)
Apollo Court 2 Bishop Square, Hatfield
Business Park, Hatfield, AL10 9NE, Herefordshire, United Kingdom
Tel.: (44) 1707228080
Web Site: https://ocadoretail.com
Online Food Retailer
N.A.I.C.S.: 445110

OCB BERHAD
2B-5 Level 5 Jalan SS 6/6 Kelana
Jaya, 47301, Petaling Jaya, Selangor Darul Ehsan, Malaysia
Tel.: (60) 378807539
Web Site: https://www.ocbb.com.my
OCB—(KLS)
Rev.: $53,947,937
Assets: $63,775,873
Liabilities: $27,935,026
Net Worth: $35,840,847
Earnings: ($797,460)
Emp.: 528
Fiscal Year-end: 12/31/22
Consumer Foods Mfr
N.A.I.C.S.: 311710
Heng Leong Fong (Exec Dir)

Subsidiaries:

Agrow Corporation Sdn. Bhd. (1)
2C-4 Level 3 Jalan SS6/6, Kelana Jaya,
47301, Petaling Jaya, Selangor, Malaysia
Tel.: (60) 378054748
Web Site: https://www.agrow.com.my
Sales Range: $25-49.9 Million
Emp.: 70
Building Materials Distr
N.A.I.C.S.: 444180

Agrow Healthtech Sdn. Bhd. (1)
2C-4 Level 3 Jalan SS6/6, Kelana Jaya,
47301, Petaling Jaya, Selangor, Malaysia
Tel.: (60) 378054748
Web Site: https://agrowhealthtech.com
Healthcare Product Distr
N.A.I.C.S.: 423450

Biz-Allianz International (M) Sdn. Bhd. (1)
Wisma King Koil 2C-3 Level 2 Jalan SS
6/6, Kelana Jaya, 47301, Petaling Jaya,
Selangor, Malaysia
Tel.: (60) 378054728
Web Site: http://www.biz-allianz.com
Sales Range: $25-49.9 Million
Emp.: 43
Convenience Food & Spreads Mfr
N.A.I.C.S.: 311511

Kingkoil Corporation (M) Sdn. Bhd. (1)
2C-5 Level 5 Jalan SS6 / 6 Kelana Jaya,
Kelana Jaya, 47301, Petaling Jaya, Selangor, Malaysia
Tel.: (60) 378054766
Web Site: http://www.kingkoil.com.my
Emp.: 28
Bedroom Furnishings Mfr & Distr
N.A.I.C.S.: 313210

Spices & Seasonings Specialities Sdn. Bhd. (1)
Lot 1956 Jalan Bangi Lama Batu 1 1/2,
43500, Semenyih, Selangor Darul Ehsan,
Malaysia
Tel.: (60) 387239588
Web Site: https://www.telly.com.my
Sales Range: $50-74.9 Million
Emp.: 150
Spices & Seasonings Mfr
N.A.I.C.S.: 311941

OCC PUBLIC COMPANY LIMITED
729/4-7 Radchadaphisek Road,
Bangpongpang District Yannawa,
Bangkok, 10120, Thailand
Tel.: (66) 22954545
Web Site: https://www.occ.co.th
Year Founded: 1973
OCC—(THA)
Rev.: $26,718,739
Assets: $36,350,483

Liabilities: $6,513,838
Net Worth: $29,836,645
Earnings: ($183,034)
Emp.: 773
Fiscal Year-end: 12/31/23
Cosmetics, Women's Lingerie,
Sportswear & Swimsuit Distr
N.A.I.C.S.: 456120

OCEAN & OIL HOLDINGS LIMITED
8th Floor The Octagon 13A A J
Marinho Drive Victoria Island, Lagos,
Nigeria
Tel.: (234) 146033601
Web Site:
http://www.oandoholdings.com
Year Founded: 1994
Sales Range: $25-49.9 Million
Emp.: 24
Investment Services
N.A.I.C.S.: 523940
Lanre Osinoiki (Grp CEO)

Subsidiaries:

Avante Property Asset Management Services (1)
10th Floor The Octagon, 13A AJ Marinho
Drive, Victoria Island, Lagos, Nigeria
Tel.: (234) 23414616223
Web Site: http://www.avantepams.com
Real Estate Services
N.A.I.C.S.: 531390

OPSL Human Capital (1)
2nd Floor Riz Plaza Plot 19 Stadium Road,
Port Harcourt, Rivers State, Nigeria
Tel.: (234) 1 460 3360
Web Site: http://www.opslhumancapital.com
General Management Services
N.A.I.C.S.: 541611
Lanre Osinoiki (CEO & Mng Dir)

OCEAN AGRO (INDIA) LIMITED
76-77 GIDC Nandesari, Vadodara,
391 340, Gujarat, India
Tel.: (91) 02652840307
Web Site: http://www.oceanagro.com
Rev.: $2,914,992
Assets: $2,213,489
Liabilities: $1,232,409
Net Worth: $981,080
Earnings: ($1,589,774)
Emp.: 113
Fiscal Year-end: 03/31/19
Fertilizer Mfr
N.A.I.C.S.: 325311
Kaushikbhai B. Parikh (Co-Mng Dir)

Subsidiaries:

Ocean Agro LLC (1)
6150 Mission St Ste 204, San Francisco,
CA 94105
Tel.: (888) 203-8468
Web Site: http://www.oceanagrollc.com
Fertilizer Mfr & Distr
N.A.I.C.S.: 325314

OCEAN BRIDGE CO LTD
49 Donghanggongdan-gil Yangseongmyeon, Anseong, Gyeonggi-do, Korea (South)
Tel.: (82) 3180529090
Web Site:
https://www.oceanbridge.co.kr
Year Founded: 2012
241790—(KRS)
Rev.: $126,531,428
Assets: $105,552,120
Liabilities: $26,114,197
Net Worth: $79,437,923
Earnings: $12,106,316
Emp.: 168
Fiscal Year-end: 12/31/22
Semiconductor Equipment Mfr & Distr
N.A.I.C.S.: 334515
Dong-Jun Lee (CEO)

OCEAN CONTRACTORS LIMITED

Ocean Bridge Co Ltd—(Continued)

OCEAN CONTRACTORS LIMITED
PO Box 604, Dartmouth, B2Y 3Y9, NS, Canada
Tel.: (902) 435-1291
Web Site: https://www.oceancontractors.ca
Year Founded: 1974
Rev.: $29,173,420
Emp.: 200
Roadways Constructors & Building Materials Mfr
N.A.I.C.S.: 237310
John M. Flemming (Pres)

OCEAN GEOLOOP AS
Neptunvegen 6, 7652, Verdal, Norway
Tel.: (47) 47456601
Web Site: https://www.oceangeoloop.com
Year Founded: 2020
OCEAN—(OSL)
Rev.: $16,992,450
Assets: $30,220,106
Liabilities: $7,042,586
Net Worth: $23,177,520
Earnings: ($4,858,539)
Emp.: 47
Fiscal Year-end: 12/31/23
Natural Gas Distribution Services
N.A.I.C.S.: 221210
Odd-Geir Lademo (CEO)

OCEAN GLASS PUBLIC COMPANY LIMITED
75/88 91 34th Fl Ocean Tower II Sukhumvit 19 Road Soi Wattana, NorthKlongtoey Wattana, Bangkok, 10110, Thailand
Tel.: (66) 26616556
Web Site: https://www.oceanglass.com
Year Founded: 1979
OGC—(THA)
Rev.: $58,584,898
Assets: $112,389,522
Liabilities: $54,969,239
Net Worth: $57,420,284
Earnings: $409,242
Emp.: 544
Fiscal Year-end: 12/31/23
Glass Products Mfr
N.A.I.C.S.: 327215
Chakri Chanruangvanich (Chm)

Subsidiaries:

Ocean Glass Trading (Shanghai) Co., Ltd. (1)
Room 1902 Jin Hang Tower 83 Wan Hang Du Road Jing An District, Shanghai, China
Tel.: (86) 21 6135 9505
Glass Products Mfr
N.A.I.C.S.: 327213

Ocean Glass Trading India Private Limited (1)
9H 25-Gopala Tower Rajendra Place, New Delhi, 110008, India
Tel.: (91) 999 908 3383
Glassware Mfr
N.A.I.C.S.: 327215

OCEAN GROUP JOINT STOCK COMPANY
23rd Floor TNR Building 54A Nguyen Chi Thanh, Dong Da, Hanoi, Vietnam
Tel.: (84) 437727252 VN
Web Site: https://www.oceangroup.vn
OGC—(HOSE)
Rev.: $40,569,022
Assets: $196,434,761
Liabilities: $132,282,282
Net Worth: $64,152,479
Earnings: $5,819,953
Emp.: 1,140

Fiscal Year-end: 12/31/23
Financial Investment Company;Real Estate Management Services
N.A.I.C.S.: 531390
Huu Mai (Chm-Mgmt Bd)

OCEAN LINE PORT DEVELOPMENT LTD.
Room 2715-16 27/F Hong Kong Plaza, 188 Connaught Road West, Hong Kong, China (Hong Kong)
Tel.: (852) 21190648 Ky
Web Site: http://www.oceanlineport.com
8502—(HKG)
Rev.: $26,307,731
Assets: $114,167,102
Liabilities: $26,280,774
Net Worth: $87,886,328
Earnings: $12,278,401
Emp.: 216
Fiscal Year-end: 12/31/22
Bulk Cargo Transportation Services
N.A.I.C.S.: 484230
Sze Hoi Kwai (Co-Founder, Chm & Compliance Officer)

OCEAN ONE HOLDING LTD.
Unit B Goodwill Industrial Bl 5th Floor 36-44 Pak Tin Par S, Tsuen Wan, China (Hong Kong)
Tel.: (852) 21495266 Ky
Web Site: https://www.oceanoneholding.com
8476—(HKG)
Rev.: $42,272,679
Assets: $23,061,624
Liabilities: $2,358,786
Net Worth: $20,702,838
Earnings: $3,527,087
Emp.: 17
Fiscal Year-end: 03/31/21
Food Products Distr
N.A.I.C.S.: 424420

OCEAN OUTDOOR LIMITED
25 Argyll Street, London, W1F 7TU, United Kingdom
Tel.: (44) 20 7292 6161 VG
Web Site: http://www.oceanoutdoor.com
Year Founded: 2007
OOUT—(LSE)
Rev.: $116,996,090
Assets: $681,730,220
Liabilities: $415,617,100
Net Worth: $266,113,120
Earnings: ($243,717,529)
Fiscal Year-end: 12/31/20
Holding Company; Digital Outdoor Advertising Services
N.A.I.C.S.: 551112
Tim Bleakley (CEO)

Subsidiaries:

Ocean Outdoor UK Limited (1)
25 Argyll Street, London, W1F 7TU, United Kingdom
Tel.: (44) 2072926161
Web Site: http://www.oceanoutdoor.com
Digital Outdoor Advertising Services
N.A.I.C.S.: 541850

OCEAN PARK FORD SALES LTD.
3050 King George Highway, Surrey, V4P1A2, BC, Canada
Tel.: (604) 531-6100
Web Site: http://www.oceanparkford.com
Year Founded: 1987
Rev.: $43,385,530
Emp.: 85
Used & New Car Dealers
N.A.I.C.S.: 441110

OCEAN PLASTICS CO., LTD.

5-6F No 310 Juguang Rd, Wanhua District, Taipei, Taiwan
Tel.: (886) 223081188
Web Site: https://www.opc.com.tw
1321—(TAI)
Rev.: $160,716,695
Assets: $390,192,438
Liabilities: $187,632,976
Net Worth: $202,559,461
Earnings: $6,315,903
Fiscal Year-end: 12/31/23
Plastic Cloths Mfr
N.A.I.C.S.: 315250
Fan-Chu Chen (Founder)

Subsidiaries:

Fine Environment Technologies Co., Ltd. (1)
No 539 Lungshing Rd, Chung-li, 320, Taoyuan, Taiwan
Tel.: (886) 3 438 4626
Web Site: http://www.fetech.com.tw
Research, Design & Production of Wood Plastic Composites, WPC Compound & Rooftile Fixed Strip
N.A.I.C.S.: 321212

Fuzetec Technology Co., Ltd. (1)
No 60 Wu-Gong 5 Road, Wu-Gu Dist, New Taipei City, 24890, Taiwan
Tel.: (886) 289902113
Web Site: http://www.fuzetec.com.tw
Sales Range: $25-49.9 Million
Emp.: 100
Electronic Components Mfr
N.A.I.C.S.: 334419

Subsidiary (Non-US):

Fuzetec Technology (Suzhou) Co., Ltd. (2)
Room 805 B No 1039 Cai Lian Road, Xiang Cheng District, Suzhou, 215000, Jiangsu, China
Tel.: (86) 512 65860239
Web Site: http://www.fuzetec.com.tw
Circuit Protection Components Mfr
N.A.I.C.S.: 334417

Ocean Plastics (Hui Zhou) Co., Ltd. (1)
Folong Industrial District, Huiyang District, Huizhou, 516086, Guang Dong, China
Tel.: (86) 7523728989
Web Site: http://www.opc.com.tw
Polyvinyl Chloride Products Mfr
N.A.I.C.S.: 326122

Ultra-Pak Industries Co. Ltd. (1)
No 240 Bo'ai St, Shulin Dist, New Taipei City, 238, Taiwan
Tel.: (886) 286868897
Web Site: http://www.upak.com.tw
Sales Range: $25-49.9 Million
Electronic Packing Materials Mfr
N.A.I.C.S.: 334419

Plant (Non-US):

Ultra-Pak Industries Co. Ltd. - Kun Shan Factory (2)
No 1885 Yingbin West Road, Bacheng, Kunshan, 215311, Jiangsu, China
Tel.: (86) 51257658686
Web Site: http://www.upak.com.tw
Electronic Packing Materials Mfr
N.A.I.C.S.: 339991

Ultra-Pak Industries Co. Ltd. - Philippine Factory (2)
First Cavite Industrial Estate SEPZ Unit 2 Orient Goldcrest Building, Langkaan, Dasmarinas, 4114, Cavite, Philippines
Tel.: (63) 464020323
Sales Range: $25-49.9 Million
Emp.: 40
Electronic Packing Materials Mfr
N.A.I.C.S.: 339991

OCEAN SKY INTERNATIONAL LIMITED
29 Tuas South Street 1, 638036, Singapore
Tel.: (65) 67899988

Web Site: https://www.oceanskyintl.com
1B6—(SES)
Rev.: $22,547,532
Assets: $55,634,004
Liabilities: $23,492,945
Net Worth: $32,141,059
Earnings: ($540,554)
Fiscal Year-end: 12/31/22
Holding Company
N.A.I.C.S.: 551112
Yau Leong Chia (Sec & Controller-Fin)

Subsidiaries:

Ang Tong Seng Brothers Enterprises Pte. Ltd. (1)
29 Tuas South Street 1, Singapore, 638036, Singapore
Tel.: (65) 67498998
Web Site: https://www.angtongseng.com
Engineeering Services
N.A.I.C.S.: 541330
Wong Siew Hui (Mng Dir)

Ang Tong Seng Construction Pte. Ltd. (1)
29 Tuas South Street 1, Singapore, 638036, Singapore
Tel.: (65) 67498998
Web Site: https://www.angtongseng.com
Engineeering Services
N.A.I.C.S.: 541330
Ang Boon Cheow Edward (Exec Dir)

OCEAN STAR TECHNOLOGY GROUP LIMITED
1/F Lok Kui Industrial Building 6-8 Hung To Road Kwun Tong, Kowloon, China (Hong Kong)
Tel.: (852) 23304669
Web Site: http://www.bodibra.com
8297—(HKG)
Rev.: $6,008,791
Assets: $12,316,558
Liabilities: $11,464,903
Net Worth: $851,655
Earnings: ($2,425,469)
Emp.: 110
Fiscal Year-end: 03/31/22
Women Apparel Mfr
N.A.I.C.S.: 315250

OCEAN SUN AS
Snaroyveien 20, 1360, Fornebu, Norway
Tel.: (47) 90195778 NO
Web Site: https://www.oceansun.no
Year Founded: 2016
OSUN—(OSL)
Rev.: $1,554,314
Assets: $4,880,935
Liabilities: $708,664
Net Worth: $4,172,270
Earnings: ($1,724,090)
Emp.: 14
Fiscal Year-end: 12/31/23
Solar Component Distr
N.A.I.C.S.: 423720
Borge Bjorneklett (CEO)

OCEAN SYSTEM CORPORATION
2-26-57 Nishihonjoji, Sanjo, 955-0845, Niigata, Japan
Tel.: (81) 256333987
Web Site: https://www.ocean-system.com
Year Founded: 1955
3096—(TKS)
Rev.: $567,551,873
Assets: $156,247,066
Liabilities: $87,822,902
Net Worth: $68,424,163
Earnings: $8,833,826
Fiscal Year-end: 03/31/24
Seafood Processing
N.A.I.C.S.: 311710

Katsuhito Higuchi *(Pres & CEO)*

OCEAN TANKERS HOLDINGS PUBLIC COMPANY LIMITED
Blue Anchor House 4R Parou Street, 1082, Nicosia, Cyprus
Tel.: (357) 22 813030   CY
Year Founded: 2005
Oil & Tankers Management Services
N.A.I.C.S.: 213112
Michael G. Ioannides *(Chm, Pres & CEO)*

OCEAN VANTAGE HOLDINGS BERHAD
Lot 6073 & 6074 1st & 2nd Floor, Jalan Tudan Bandar Baru Permyjaya Block 11 Kuala Baram land District, 98000, Miri, Malaysia
Tel.: (60) 85491780   MY
Web Site: https://ovbhd.com
Year Founded: 2018
OVH—(KLS)
Rev.: $32,826,311
Assets: $21,025,916
Liabilities: $8,106,329
Net Worth: $12,919,586
Earnings: ($234,931)
Fiscal Year-end: 12/31/22
Holding Company
N.A.I.C.S.: 551112
Martin Philip King Ik Piau *(Exec Dir)*

OCEAN WILSONS HOLDINGS LIMITED
Richmond House 5th Floor 12 Par-la-Ville Road, PO Box HM 2250, Hamilton, HM JX, Bermuda
Tel.: (441) 2951309   BM
Web Site: https://www.oceanwilsons.bm
OCN—(BERM)
Rev.: $486,646,000
Assets: $1,521,865,000
Liabilities: $706,051,000
Net Worth: $815,814,000
Earnings: $103,072,000
Emp.: 3,849
Fiscal Year-end: 12/31/23
Holding Company; Port & Harbor Services, Small Vessel Construction & Maintenance, Container Terminal Operations, Freight Logistics & Shipping Support Services
N.A.I.C.S.: 551112
Jose Francisco Gouvea Vieira *(Vice Chm)*

Subsidiaries:

Brasco Logistica Offshore Ltda. (1)
Av Rio Branco 25 17o andar, 20090, Rio de Janeiro, Brazil
Tel.: (55) 21 2516 5575
Shipping Services
N.A.I.C.S.: 488510

Ocean Wilsons Investments Limited (1)
504 International Ctr, Bermudiana Rd, HMJX, Hamilton, Bermuda
Tel.: (441) 2951422
Water Transportation Services
N.A.I.C.S.: 488320

Tecon Rio Grande S.A. (1)
Av Portuaria S N, 4th Seccao Toolbar, Rio Grande, 96204-040, Brazil
Tel.: (55) 5332343000
Web Site: http://www.tecon.com.br
Sales Range: $250-200.0 Million
Emp.: 900
Container Terminal Services
N.A.I.C.S.: 488320

Tecon Salvador S.A. (1)
Avda Engenheiro Oscar Pontes 97, Agua de Meninos, Salvador, 40460 130, Bahia, Brazil
Tel.: (55) 7121061522
Web Site: http://www.wilsonsons.com.br
Sales Range: $25-49.9 Million
Emp.: 50
Water Transportation & Maritime Services
N.A.I.C.S.: 488320

Wilson Sons Agencia Maritima Ltd. (1)
Avenida Nossa Senhora dos Navegantes 451 9th Fl, Vitoria, Espirito Santo, Brazil
Tel.: (55) 2732321422
Web Site: http://www.wilsonsons.com
Sales Range: $50-74.9 Million
Emp.: 108
Shipping Agency Services
N.A.I.C.S.: 488510

Wilson Sons S.A., Comercio, Industria, e Agencia de Navegacao Ltda. (1)
Rua Jardim Botanico 518 3rd floor, Rio de Janeiro, 22461-000, Brazil
Tel.: (55) 2121264122
Web Site: http://www.wilsonsons.com.br
Sales Range: $25-49.9 Million
Emp.: 50
Ship Building Services
N.A.I.C.S.: 336611

OCEAN'S KING LIGHTING SCIENCE & TECHNOLOGY CO., LTD.
Oceans King Science & Technology Tower No 1601 Gaoxin Road, Guangming New District, Shenzhen, 518107, Guangdong, China
Tel.: (86) 75526492666
Web Site: https://www.oceansking.com
Year Founded: 1995
002724—(SSE)
Rev.: $243,480,276
Assets: $542,637,576
Liabilities: $106,719,444
Net Worth: $435,918,132
Earnings: $19,525,428
Fiscal Year-end: 12/31/22
Lighting Equipment Mfr
N.A.I.C.S.: 335139
Li Caifen *(Chm)*

Subsidiaries:

Ocean's King Tech Limited (1)
Flat/Rm 1107 11/F Sun Hung Kai Center 30 Harbour Rd, Wanchai, China (Hong Kong)
Tel.: (852) 28779168
Lighting Product Mfr & Distr
N.A.I.C.S.: 335139

OCEAN8
Talstrasse 38, 40271, Dusseldorf, Germany
Tel.: (49) 211498780
Web Site: http://www.ocean8.de
Year Founded: 1972
Sales Range: $10-24.9 Million
Emp.: 5
N.A.I.C.S.: 541810
Harald Kuhlmeier *(Co-Chm & Co-CEO)*

OCEANA GROUP LIMITED
9th Floor Oceana House 25 Jan Smuts Street Foreshore, Cape Town, 8001, South Africa
Tel.: (27) 214101400
Web Site: http://www.oceana.co.za
Year Founded: 1918
OCE—(JSE)
Rev.: $566,878,106
Assets: $823,630,326
Liabilities: $415,619,361
Net Worth: $408,010,965
Earnings: $55,710,818
Emp.: 4,450
Fiscal Year-end: 09/30/20
Fishing & Allied Services
N.A.I.C.S.: 114119
Suleiman Salie *(Mng Dir-Lucky Star Ops)*

Subsidiaries:

Blue Atlantic Trading (1)
4 Vibra Street, Philippi, Cape Town, 7785, South Africa
Tel.: (27) 216901400
Web Site: http://www.blueatlantic.co.za
Sales Range: $25-49.9 Million
Emp.: 17
Seafood Product Whslr
N.A.I.C.S.: 424460
Robert Zive *(Mng Dir)*

Blue Continent Products (Pty) Ltd. (1)
25 Jan Mug Road Fore Shore, Paarden Eiland, Cape Town, 8000, South Africa
Tel.: (27) 215089600
Web Site: http://www.oceana.co.za
Sales Range: $25-49.9 Million
Emp.: 60
Marine Products Processing
N.A.I.C.S.: 114119
Barrie James King *(Mgr-Risk)*

CCS Logistics (1)
Vrystaat Road Paarden Eiland, 7405, Cape Town, South Africa
Tel.: (27) 873507350
Web Site: http://www.ccslogistics.co.za
Emp.: 53
Refrigerated Warehousing Services
N.A.I.C.S.: 493120
Juan Swanepoel *(Mgr-Customer)*

Calamari Fishing (Pty) Limited (1)
Oakworth Rd, Port Elizabeth, 6001, Eastern Cape, South Africa
Tel.: (27) 415085200
Sales Range: $25-49.9 Million
Emp.: 15
Squid & Mackerel Fishing Services
N.A.I.C.S.: 114119
Anton Gerber *(Mgr-Ops)*

Commercial Cold Storage (Namibia) (Pty) Limited (1)
Commercial Cold Storage Port of Walvis Bay, PO Box 59, Walvis Bay, Namibia
Tel.: (264) 64 213300
Web Site: http://www.oceana.co.za
Sales Range: $10-24.9 Million
Emp.: 50
Commercial Refrigerated Warehousing Services
N.A.I.C.S.: 493120
Willie Venter *(Gen Mgr)*

Commercial Cold Storage (Ports) (Pty) Limited (1)
18 Davey Road, PO Box 29110, Maydon Wharf, Durban, 4057, South Africa
Tel.: (27) 31 2742800
Commercial Refrigerated Warehousing Services
N.A.I.C.S.: 493120
Kevin Atkinson *(Branch Mgr-Fruit)*

Desert Diamond Fishing (Pty) Limited (1)
25 Jan Smuts Fore Shore, Cape Town, 8012, Western Cape, South Africa
Tel.: (27) 215089600
Web Site: http://www.oceana.co.za
Emp.: 30
Marine Fishing Services
N.A.I.C.S.: 114119

Erongo Marine Enterprises (Pty) Limited (1)
25 Jan Smuts Street - Foreshore, Cape Town, 8012, Western Cape, South Africa
Tel.: (27) 21 410 1400
Web Site: http://www.oceana.co.za
Emp.: 100
Marine Fishing Services
N.A.I.C.S.: 114119

Oceana Brands (1)
Oceana House, 25 Jan Smuts Street, 7 Coen Steytler Ave, Cape Town, 8001, South Africa
Tel.: (27) 214158500
Web Site: http://www.oceanabrands.co.za
Sales Range: $25-49.9 Million
Emp.: 50
Canned Food Mfr
N.A.I.C.S.: 311710

Oceana Lobster Abalone & Squid (1)
Vrystaat Road, 25 Jan Smuts St Foreshore, Cape Town, 8000, Paarden Eiland, South Africa
Tel.: (27) 215089600
Sales Range: $25-49.9 Million
Emp.: 200
Seafood Product Mfr
N.A.I.C.S.: 311710
Neville Donovan Brink *(Mng Dir)*

Oceana Lobster Limited (1)
7th Floor Oceana House 25 Jan Smuts Street, Cape Town, 8001, Western Cape, South Africa
Tel.: (27) 215089600
Web Site: http://www.oceana.co.za
Emp.: 300
Lobster Fishing Services
N.A.I.C.S.: 114112

OCEANA LITHIUM LIMITED
Level 8 99 St Georges Tce, Perth, 6000, WA, Australia
Tel.: (61) 894864036   AU
Web Site: https://www.oceanalithium.com.au
Year Founded: 2021
OCN—(ASX)
Exploration & Mining Services
N.A.I.C.S.: 213115
Dan Smith *(Sec)*

OCEANAA BIOTEK INDUSTRIES LIMITED
No 4B-1 Eastern Portion 4th Floor Centre Point Appointment, Sadhullah Street T Nagar, Chennai, 600 017, Tamilnadu, India
Tel.: (91) 4430241900
Web Site: http://www.oceanaabiotek.com
538019—(BOM)
Rev.: $3,505,479
Assets: $5,599,939
Liabilities: $1,848,485
Net Worth: $3,751,455
Earnings: $302,604
Emp.: 28
Fiscal Year-end: 03/31/20
Food Testing Laboratory Services
N.A.I.C.S.: 541380
Thomas Xavier Jeyaraj *(Mng Dir)*

OCEANAGOLD CORPORATION
Tel.: (61) 396565300   AU
Web Site: https://www.oceanagold.com
OGC—(TSX)
Rev.: $967,400,000
Assets: $2,290,600,000
Liabilities: $617,300,000
Net Worth: $1,673,300,000
Earnings: $132,600,000
Emp.: 2,523
Fiscal Year-end: 12/31/22
Gold & Copper Exploration & Mining Services
N.A.I.C.S.: 212220
Michael Holmes *(Pres & CEO)*

Subsidiaries:

Haile Gold Mine Inc. (1)
6911 Snowy Owl Rd, Kershaw, SC 29067
Tel.: (803) 475-1220
Emp.: 550
Gold Mining Services
N.A.I.C.S.: 212220

Oceana Gold Holdings (New Zealand) Limited (1)
22 Maclaggan Street, Dunedin, 9016, New Zealand (100%)
Tel.: (64) 34794700
Web Site: http://www.oceanagold.com
Emp.: 30
Holding Company
N.A.I.C.S.: 551112

OCEANAGOLD CORPORATION

OceanaGold Corporation—(Continued)
Subsidiary (Domestic):

Oceana Gold (New Zealand) Ltd. (2)
Golden Point Road RD3 Macraes Flat
9483, Dunedin, 9483, New
Zealand **(100%)**
Tel.: (64) 34792922
Web Site: http://www.oceanagold.com
Emp.: 20
Gold Mining Services
N.A.I.C.S.: 212220

Subsidiary (Domestic):

Oceana Gold (Waihi) Limited (3)
43 Moresby Avenue, Waihi, 3610, New Zealand
Tel.: (64) 78638192
Gold Ore Mining
N.A.I.C.S.: 212220

Oceana Gold Limited (1)
Level 3 154 Melbourne St, South Brisbane,
4101, QLD, Australia
Tel.: (61) 396565300
Gold Ore Mining Services
N.A.I.C.S.: 212220

OceanaGold (Philippines) Holdings Inc. (1)
2nd floor CJV Building 108 Aguirre Street,
Legaspi Village, Makati, 1229,
Philippines **(100%)**
Tel.: (63) 2 892 6643
Holding Company
N.A.I.C.S.: 551112

Subsidiary (Domestic):

OceanaGold (Philippines) Inc. (2)
2nd Floor CJV Building, 108 Aguirre Street
Legaspi Vi, 1229, Makati,
Philippines **(100%)**
Tel.: (63) 28926643
Gold & Copper Exploration & Mining Services
N.A.I.C.S.: 212220

OCEANCASH PACIFIC BERHAD
Lot 73 Jalan P10/21 Taman Industri
Selaman, 43650, Bandar Baru Bangi,
Selangor, Malaysia
Tel.: (60) 389250000 **MY**
Web Site: https://oceancash.com
Year Founded: 1996
OCNCASH—(KLS)
Rev.: $16,950,787
Assets: $32,784,502
Liabilities: $6,061,369
Net Worth: $26,723,132
Earnings: $672,666
Fiscal Year-end: 12/31/23
Investment Holding Services
N.A.I.C.S.: 551112
Siew Chin Tan *(Chm & CEO)*

OCEANEX INC.
Suite 701 Baine Johnston Centre 10
Fort William Place, PO Box 5097,
Saint John's, A1C 1K4, NL, Canada
Tel.: (709) 758-0382
Web Site: https://www.oceanex.com
Year Founded: 1990
Emp.: 425
Holding Company; Intermodal Transportation Services
N.A.I.C.S.: 551112
Sidney J. Hynes *(Chm)*

Subsidiaries:

Oceanex Inc. - Montreal (1)
630 Boul Rene-Levesque W Suite 2550,
Montreal, H3B 1S6, QC, Canada
Tel.: (514) 875-9595
Web Site: http://www.oceanex.com
Intermodal Freight Distr
N.A.I.C.S.: 488510

OCEANIA CAPITAL PARTNERS LIMITED
Suite 57 Level 3 14 Narabang Way,
Belrose, 2085, NSW, Australia
Tel.: (61) 2 9986 3867
Web Site:
  http://www.oceaniacapital.com.au
Rev.: $42,507,046
Assets: $95,211,975
Liabilities: $17,854,489
Net Worth: $77,357,486
Earnings: $3,288,204
Emp.: 5,500
Fiscal Year-end: 03/31/18
Privater Equity Firm
N.A.I.C.S.: 523999
Brian Scheiner *(Exec Dir)*

Subsidiaries:

Crimsafe Security Systems Pty. Ltd. (1)
Warehouse C 14 Dixon Street, Yatala,
4207, QLD, Australia
Tel.: (61) 75 540 7588
Web Site: https://www.crimsafe.com.au
Security System Services
N.A.I.C.S.: 561621

Proline Quality Finishing Pty. Ltd. (1)
183 Magnesium Dr, Crestmead, 4132, QLD,
Australia
Tel.: (61) 73 803 0016
Web Site:
  https://www.prolinepowdercoating.com.au
Powder Coating Product Mfr
N.A.I.C.S.: 332812

Radio 2CH Pty Limited (1)
Level 1 Bldg C 33-35 Saunders St, Pyrmont, 2009, NSW, Australia **(85.5%)**
Tel.: (61) 29302 0255
Web Site: http://www.2ch.com
Radio Broadcasting Services
N.A.I.C.S.: 516110
Rod Rice *(Dir-Content & Officer-Privacy)*

OCEANIA GAS LIMITED
Vetaia St Lam, Suva, Fiji
Tel.: (679) 3361011
Web Site:
  http://www.oceaniagas.com
Year Founded: 1965
Industrial Gas Mfr
N.A.I.C.S.: 325120
Ronald Raju *(Mktg Mgr)*

OCEANIA HEALTHCARE LIMITED
Tel.: (64) 800333688 **NZ**
Web Site:
  https://www.oceaniahealthcare.com
Year Founded: 2008
OCA—(NZX)
Rev.: $171,034,689
Assets: $1,522,093,301
Liabilities: $946,578,947
Net Worth: $575,514,354
Earnings: $9,239,234
Emp.: 2,919
Fiscal Year-end: 03/31/23
Assisted Living Facility Services
N.A.I.C.S.: 623312
Elizabeth Coutts *(Chm)*

OCEANIC BEVERAGES CO., INC.
No 410 South East Road Nanshili,
2nd Neighborhood Nanshi Vil
Pingzhen District, Taoyuan, 324015,
Taiwan
Tel.: (886) 229820061
Web Site:
  https://www.applesidra.com.tw
1213—(TAI)
Rev.: $3,947,219
Assets: $26,793,714
Liabilities: $19,363,582
Net Worth: $7,430,132
Earnings: ($4,535,433)
Fiscal Year-end: 12/31/23
Beverage Mfr & Distr
N.A.I.C.S.: 312111

Su Yunle *(Chm)*

OCEANIC FOODS LIMITED
Opp Brooke Bond Factory Pandit
Nehru Marg, Jamnagar, 361 002, Gujarat, India
Tel.: (91) 2882757355 **In**
Web Site:
  https://www.oceanicfoods.com
Year Founded: 1972
540405—(BOM)
Rev.: $10,677,310
Assets: $5,012,805
Liabilities: $1,259,565
Net Worth: $3,753,240
Earnings: $361,585
Emp.: 98
Fiscal Year-end: 03/31/23
Grocery Product Mfr & Distr
N.A.I.C.S.: 311942
Ajesh Vinodrai Patel *(Chm)*

OCEANIC INVESTMENT CORPORATION
Eldon Court, Percy Street, Newcastle
upon Tyne, NE99 1TD, United Kingdom
Tel.: (44) 1912112799
Sales Range: $25-49.9 Million
Emp.: 30
Holding Company; Marine Transportation Services
N.A.I.C.S.: 551112

Subsidiaries:

Burness, Corlett Three Quays Ltd. (1)
Beresford Ho/Town Quay, Southampton,
SO14 2AQ, United Kingdom
Tel.: (44) 2079292299
Web Site: http://www.bctq.com
Sales Range: $25-49.9 Million
Emp.: 15
Marine Design, Engineering & Consulting Services
N.A.I.C.S.: 541330
Graeme Armstrong *(Gen Mgr)*

OCEANIC IRON ORE CORP.
3083 Three Bentall Centre 595 Burrard Street, Vancouver, V7X 1L3, BC,
Canada
Tel.: (604) 566-9080 **BC**
Web Site:
  https://www.oceanicironore.com
FEOVF—(OTCIQ)
Assets: $34,593,339
Liabilities: $3,321,668
Net Worth: $31,271,671
Earnings: $2,421,244
Fiscal Year-end: 12/31/21
Iron Ore Mining Services
N.A.I.C.S.: 212210
Steven G. Dean *(Chm)*

OCEANIC WIND ENERGY INC.
720 - 999 West Broadway Street,
Vancouver, V5Z 1K5, BC, Canada
Tel.: (604) 631-4483
Web Site:
  https://www.oceanicwind.ca
NKW.H—(TSXV)
Assets: $52,820
Liabilities: $888,184
Net Worth: ($835,363)
Earnings: ($314,400)
Fiscal Year-end: 09/30/22
Wind Energy Services
N.A.I.C.S.: 221118
Michael J. O'Connor *(Pres & CEO)*

OCEANO SEAFOOD SA
Calle Manuel Olguín 211 Oficina 401,
Santiago de Surco, Lima, 15023,
Peru
Tel.: (51) 17166601 **Pe**
Web Site: https://osf.pe

INTERNATIONAL PUBLIC

Year Founded: 1997
Emp.: 1,100
Fish & Seafood Merchant Whslr & Distr
N.A.I.C.S.: 424460
Ignacio Tirado *(Pres)*

Subsidiaries:

Sea Fresh USA Inc. (1)
45 All American Way, North Kingstown, RI
02852
Tel.: (401) 583-0200
Web Site: http://www.seafreshusa.com
Rev.: $45,000,000
Emp.: 100
Cured Fish
N.A.I.C.S.: 424460

Unit (Domestic):

Sea Fresh USA, Inc. (2)
11 Portland Fish Pier, Portland, ME 04101
Tel.: (207) 773-6799
Web Site: http://www.seafreshusa.com
Fresh & Frozen Seafood Processing
N.A.I.C.S.: 311710

OCEANUS GROUP LIMITED
25 Ubi Rd 4 03-05 UBIX, Singapore,
408621, Singapore
Tel.: (65) 6562850500 **SG**
Web Site: https://oceanus.com.sg
Year Founded: 1998
579—(SES)
Rev.: $264,518,670
Assets: $139,844,732
Liabilities: $93,362,115
Net Worth: $46,482,618
Earnings: ($1,699,614)
Emp.: 250
Fiscal Year-end: 12/31/23
Aquaculture Production & Abalone
Processing Services
N.A.I.C.S.: 112512
Peter Heng Kang Koh *(CEO-Grp)*

Subsidiaries:

Ap Media Pte. Ltd. (1)
39 Ubi Rd 1 04-01 World Publication building, Singapore, 408695, Singapore
Tel.: (65) 67174466
Web Site: https://apmedia.asia
Marketing Agent Services
N.A.I.C.S.: 541613
Nick Tan *(Mng Dir)*

Oceanus Aquaculture Group Pte. Ltd. (1)
Unit 10-01 Robinson Road, Singapore,
68853, Singapore
Tel.: (65) 68370568
Emp.: 10
Aquaculture Services
N.A.I.C.S.: 112519
Cher Yew Ng *(Mng Dir)*

OCH HOSPITALITY AND SERVICE JOINT STOCK COMPANY
3rd Floor VNT Building 19 Nguyen
Trai, Thanh Xuan, Hanoi, Vietnam
Tel.: (84) 2437830101
Web Site: https://www.och.vn
OCH—(HNX)
Rev.: $99,553,100
Assets: $229,850,200
Liabilities: $96,055,300
Net Worth: $133,794,900
Earnings: $9,466,700
Fiscal Year-end: 12/31/22
Hotel Owner & Operator
N.A.I.C.S.: 721110
Trung Thanh Nguyen *(Chm-Mgmt Bd)*

OCHI HOLDINGS CO., LTD.
Tenmayacho 3-22, Hakata Ward, Fukuoka, 810-0071, Japan
Tel.: (81) 927328959
Web Site:
  http://www.ochiholdings.co.jp
Year Founded: 2010

AND PRIVATE COMPANIES — OCIMUM BIOSOLUTIONS LTD.

3166—(TKS)
Rev.: $749,349,260
Assets: $438,487,570
Liabilities: $284,177,120
Net Worth: $154,310,450
Earnings: $13,834,730
Emp.: 1,624
Fiscal Year-end: 03/31/24
Housing Construction Materials & Equipment Distr
N.A.I.C.S.: 423320
Michihiro Ochi *(Pres & CEO)*

Subsidiaries:

Taiyo Industry Co., Ltd. (1)
107 Shiga, Suwa, 392-8585, Nagano, Japan
Tel.: (81) 266587000
Web Site: http://www.taiyo-ind.co.jp
Emp.: 250
Automobile Equipment Mfr
N.A.I.C.S.: 336390
Naofumi Kodaira *(Pres)*

OCI CO., LTD.
OCI Building 94 Sogong-ro, Jung-gu, Seoul, 04532, Korea (South)
Tel.: (82) 027279500
Web Site: https://oci.co.kr
Year Founded: 1959
456040—(KRS)
Emp.: 1,621
Basic Chemicals Mfr
N.A.I.C.S.: 325998
Teak Joung Kim *(Vice Chm)*

Subsidiaries:

OCI Dream Co., Ltd. (1)
2F OCI Building 94 Songong-ro, Jung-go, 04532, Seoul, Korea (South) (55%)
Tel.: (82) 2 776 7511
Staff Recruitment Services
N.A.I.C.S.: 561311

OCI HOLDINGS CO., LTD.
OCI Bldg 94 Sogong-ro Jung-gu, Seoul, 100-718, Korea (South) KR
Year Founded: 1959
010060—(KRS)
Sales Range: $1-4.9 Billion
Emp.: 2,403
Basic, Fine & Petrochemicals Mfr
N.A.I.C.S.: 325998
Woo Hyun Lee *(Pres & CEO)*

Subsidiaries:

DCC (SHANGHAI) CO., LTD. (1)
Lippo Plaza Suite 2501-03 222 Huaihai Middle Road, Luwan District, Shanghai, 200021, China
Tel.: (86) 21 5396 6655
Chemical Distr
N.A.I.C.S.: 424690
Eric Li *(Mgr)*

DCRE Co., Ltd. (1)
587-46 Hakik 1-dong, Nam-gu, Incheon, 402-865, Korea (South)
Tel.: (82) 328302512
Sales Range: $25-49.9 Million
Emp.: 12
Industrial Chemical Whslr
N.A.I.C.S.: 424690

Ma Steel OCI Chemical Co., Ltd. (1)
West Side Liqingchi Road, Chemical Industry Area Yushan Economic Development Zone, Ma'anshan, Anhui, China
Tel.: (86) 555 822 8239
Carbon Black Oil Mfr
N.A.I.C.S.: 325998

Mission Solar Energy LLC (1)
8303 S New Braunfels Ave, San Antonio, TX 78235
Tel.: (210) 531-8600
Web Site: https://www.missionsolar.com
Solar Panel Mfr
N.A.I.C.S.: 334413

OCI Alabama LLC (1)
1455 Red Hat Rd, Decatur, AL 35603
Tel.: (256) 301-5200

Utility-Scale Solar Distribution Services
N.A.I.C.S.: 221114
Richard Kalber *(Pres & CEO)*

OCI Chemical Corporation (1)
1800 West Oak Commons Ct Ste 100, Marietta, GA 30062
Tel.: (770) 261-0336
Web Site: http://www.ocichemical.com
Sales Range: $150-199.9 Million
Emp.: 500
Mfr & Distributor of Soda Ash
N.A.I.C.S.: 212390

Subsidiary (Domestic):

OCI Wyoming, L.P. (2)
254 Country Rd 4-6, Green River, WY 82935
Tel.: (307) 875-2600
Web Site: http://www.ocichemical.com
Sales Range: $150-199.9 Million
Emp.: 400
Holding Company; Soda Ash Mfr
N.A.I.C.S.: 551112
Terrell Johnson *(Engr-Principal Environmental)*

Affiliate (Domestic):

OCI Wyoming Co. (3)
254 Country Rd 4-6, Green River, WY 82935
Tel.: (307) 875-2600
Web Site: http://www.ocichemical.com
Sales Range: $125-149.9 Million
Soda Ash Mfr
N.A.I.C.S.: 325180
Craig Rood *(Plant Mgr)*

OCI China Co., Ltd. (1)
Room 806 No 11 Yujinggang Road, Jingan District, Shanghai, China
Tel.: (86) 213 372 2600
Polysilicon Chemical Product Distr
N.A.I.C.S.: 424690

OCI Co., Ltd. - Gunsan Plant (1)
233-1 Soryong-dong, Gunsan, 573-879, Jeollabuk-do, Korea (South)
Tel.: (82) 634606000
Web Site: http://www.oci.co.kr
Polycrystalline Silicon Mfr
N.A.I.C.S.: 325180

OCI Co., Ltd. - Gwangyang Plant (1)
109 Sanup-Ro, Gwangyang, 545-885, Jeollanam-do, Korea (South)
Tel.: (82) 61 798 6114
Web Site: http://www.oci.co.kr
Petrochemical Mfr
N.A.I.C.S.: 324110

OCI Co., Ltd. - Iksan Insulation Plant (1)
740-27 Shinhung-Dong, Iksan, 570 978, Jeollabuk, Korea (South)
Tel.: (82) 5 645 21 56
Silicon Wafers Mfr
N.A.I.C.S.: 334413

OCI Co., Ltd. - Iksan Plant (1)
107 4Gill Bosoek Ro, Iksan, 570-978, Jeollabuk-do, Korea (South)
Tel.: (82) 638305212
Web Site: http://www.oci.co.kr
Rubber Compounds & Sealants Mfr
N.A.I.C.S.: 325520

OCI Co., Ltd. - Pohang Plant (1)
1 Cheongrim-dong Nam-gu, Pohang, 790-340, Gyeongsangbuk-do, Korea (South)
Tel.: (82) 542908000
Web Site: http://www.oci.co.kr
Sales Range: $125-149.9 Million
Emp.: 300
Petrochemical Mfr
N.A.I.C.S.: 324110
Lee Chang-Hee *(Mgr-Production)*

OCI Information & Communication Co., Ltd. (1)
OCI Building 8F 94 Sogong-ro, Jung-gu, Seoul, Korea (South)
Tel.: (82) 26 288 1000
Information Technology Services
N.A.I.C.S.: 541512

OCI Japan Co., Ltd. (1)
3rd Floor Mita Kokusai Building 1-4-28 Mita, Minato, Tokyo, 108-0073, Japan

Tel.: (81) 36 400 5800
Web Site: https://www.ocijapan.co.jp
Chemical Products Mfr
N.A.I.C.S.: 325998

OCI Power Co., Ltd. (1)
4th OCI Bldg 94 Sogong-ro, Jung-gu, Seoul, 04532, Korea (South)
Tel.: (82) 23 016 1100
Web Site: https://www.ocipower.co.kr
Inverter Mfr
N.A.I.C.S.: 335999

OCI Se Co., Ltd. (1)
213 Saemangeumsandan 3-ro, 54002, Gunsan, Jeollabuk, Korea (South)
Tel.: (82) 63 440 9110
Electric Power Distribution Services
N.A.I.C.S.: 221122

OCI Specialty Co., Ltd. (1)
110 Tancheonsaneopdanji-gil Tancheon-myeon, 32611, Gongju, Chungcheongnam, Korea (South)
Tel.: (82) 41 851 7000
Web Site: https://www.ocis.co.kr
Silicon Wafers Mfr
N.A.I.C.S.: 334413
Jeong Chang Hyun *(Pres & CEO)*

OCI Vietnam Co., Ltd. (1)
Km 24 DT 743 Street, Binh An Village, Di An, Binh Doung, Vietnam
Tel.: (84) 6503750461
Web Site: http://www.oci.co.kr
Sales Range: $50-74.9 Million
Emp.: 60
Agricultural Chemical Distr
N.A.I.C.S.: 325320

OCIM Sdn.Bhd. (1)
Lot 600 6th Floor Wisma Bukit Mata Kuching Jalan Tunku Abdul Rahma, 93100, Kuching, Sarawak, Malaysia (100%)
Tel.: (60) 82422705
Web Site: http://ocim.com.my
Polysilicon Mfr
N.A.I.C.S.: 325998
Teak Joung Kim *(Pres & CEO)*

Philko Peroxide Corporation (1)
Unit 81 8th Floor Citibank Center 8741 Paseo de Roxas, 8741, Makati, Philippines
Tel.: (63) 28896120
Web Site: www.mixmedicine.com
Chemicals Mfr & Distr
N.A.I.C.S.: 325180
July Mac *(Mgr)*

Shandong OCI Co., Ltd. (1)
No 1 Hengshan Road, Chemical Industrial Complex Xuecheng District, Zaozhuang, 277000, Shandong, China
Tel.: (86) 1846 326 7444
Carbon Black Oil Mfr
N.A.I.C.S.: 325998

Shandong OCI-Jianyang Carbon Black Co., Ltd. (1)
East Side of Shugang Road West Side of Zhuqiao Road, Xuecheng Economic Development Zone, Zaozhuang, 277000, Shandong, China
Tel.: (86) 632 768 0763
Carbon Black Oil Mfr
N.A.I.C.S.: 325998

OCI INTERNATIONAL HOLDINGS LIMITED
Suite 811 Level 8 One Pacific Place 88 Queensway, Hong Kong, China (Hong Kong)
Tel.: (852) 29720200 Ky
Web Site: http://www.oci-intl.com
0329—(HKG)
Rev.: $3,907,238
Assets: $53,239,155
Liabilities: $15,800,055
Net Worth: $37,439,100
Earnings: ($9,971,903)
Emp.: 26
Fiscal Year-end: 12/31/22
Tobacco & Pharmaceutical Products Mfr & Sales
N.A.I.C.S.: 532490
Hai Feng *(Exec Dir)*

Subsidiaries:

Real Treasure Investment Limited (1)
Level 23 28 Hennessy Road, Wanchai, China (Hong Kong)
Tel.: (852) 29720211
Web Site: https://www.rt-wines.com
Vineyard & Winery Wine Distr
N.A.I.C.S.: 424820

OCI N.V.
Honthorststraat 19, 1071 DC, Amsterdam, Netherlands
Tel.: (31) 207234500 Nl
Web Site: https://oci-global.com
OIC—(DEU)
Rev.: $2,118,066,048
Assets: $9,685,409,022
Liabilities: $7,580,509,389
Net Worth: $2,104,899,633
Earnings: ($512,626,808)
Emp.: 4,141
Fiscal Year-end: 12/31/23
Infrastructure, Commercial & Industrial Construction; Fertilizer Mfr
N.A.I.C.S.: 236220
Nassef Onsi Naguib Sawiris *(Chm)*

Subsidiaries:

Egyptian Fertilizers Company (1)
Nile City Towers, Corniche El Nil, Cairo, Egypt (100%)
Tel.: (20) 2 2461 1897
Sales Range: $200-249.9 Million
Emp.: 650
Fertilizer Mfr
N.A.I.C.S.: 325314
Hossam Khattab *(Mng Dir)*

OCI Agro BV (1)
Mijnweg 1, PO Box 601, 6160 AP, Geleen, Netherlands (100%)
Tel.: (31) 46 7020 111
Web Site: http://www.ociagro.com
Sales Range: $100-124.9 Million
Emp.: 375
Nitrogen-Based Fertilizer Mfr & Distr
N.A.I.C.S.: 325311

OCI International Cyprus (1)
15 Nafpliou Street 1st 2nd And 4th Floor, Limassol, 3025, Cyprus
Tel.: (357) 25960000
Fertilizer Mfr
N.A.I.C.S.: 325312

OCI Melamine B.V. (1)
Mijnweg 1, PO Box 601, Geleen, 6160 AP, Netherlands (100%)
Tel.: (31) 46 7020 111
Web Site: http://www.ocimelamine.com
Sales Range: $25-49.9 Million
Emp.: 45
Melamine Resin Mfr
N.A.I.C.S.: 325211

Subsidiary (US):

OCI Melamine Americas Inc. (2)
320 Somerulos St Ste 217, Baton Rouge, LA 70802
Tel.: (225) 685-3020
Sales Range: $25-49.9 Million
Melamine Distr
N.A.I.C.S.: 424690

OCI Partners LP (1)
5470 N Twin City Hwy, Nederland, TX 77627 (100%)
Tel.: (409) 723-1900
Web Site: http://www.ocipartnerslp.com
Rev.: $343,325,000
Assets: $624,104,000
Liabilities: $483,783,000
Net Worth: $140,321,000
Earnings: $24,479,000
Fiscal Year-end: 12/31/2017
Methanol & Ammonia Production
N.A.I.C.S.: 325120
Hans Zayed *(Dir-IR)*

OCIMUM BIOSOLUTIONS LTD.
6th Floor Reliance Classic Road No 1 Banjara Hills, Hyderabad, 500 034, India

OCIMUM BIOSOLUTIONS LTD.

Ocimum Biosolutions Ltd.—(Continued)
Tel.: (91) 4066986700
Web Site: http://www.ocimumbio.com
Sales Range: $10-24.9 Million
Emp.: 150
Life Sciences Research & Development Company; Genomic Products & Services; Software for Biotechnology & Pharmaceutical Industries
N.A.I.C.S.: 541714
Anuradha Acharya (Co-Founder)

Subsidiaries:

Ocimum Biosolutions Inc. (1)
Fortune Park VI 8765 Guion Rd Ste G, Indianapolis, IN 46268 **(100%)**
Tel.: (317) 228-0600
Life Sciences
N.A.I.C.S.: 541715

OCION WATER SCIENCES GROUP LTD.
350-3771 Jacombs Road, Richmond, V6V 2L9, BC, Canada
Tel.: (604) 270-2639
Web Site: http://www.ocion.com
Emp.: 20
Water Disinfecting Mineral Mfr
N.A.I.C.S.: 221310
Frank Varseveld (Chm, Pres & CTO)

OCK GROUP BERHAD
No 18 Jalan Jurunilai U1/20 Seksyen U1 HICOM Glenmarie Industrial Park, 40150, Shah Alam, Selangor, Malaysia
Tel.: (60) 355659688
Web Site: https://www.ock.com.my
OCK—(KLS)
Rev.: $130,604,444
Assets: $348,924,233
Liabilities: $195,499,259
Net Worth: $153,424,974
Earnings: $8,137,989
Emp.: 3,789
Fiscal Year-end: 12/31/22
Telecommunications Network Services & Telecommunications Equipment Distr
N.A.I.C.S.: 517810
Abdul Halim Abdul Hamid (Deputy Chm)

Subsidiaries:

Avion Drone (Malaysia) Sdn. Bhd. (1)
No 18 Jalan Jurunilai U1/20 Seksyen U1, 40150, Shah Alam, Selangor, Malaysia
Tel.: (60) 355659688
Web Site: https://aviondrone.com
Drone Product Distr
N.A.I.C.S.: 423990

Dynasynergy Services Sdn. Bhd. (1)
Block A Lot 8 2nd Floor Lintas Square, Jalan Lintas, Kota Kinabalu, 88300, Sabah, Malaysia
Tel.: (60) 88246133
Web Site: http://www.dynasynergy.com
Industrial Engineering Services
N.A.I.C.S.: 541330
Mohamed Zulfikar Ahmad (Mng Dir)

El Power Technologies Sdn. Bhd. (1)
No 2 Jalan Anggerik Mokara 31/49, Kota Kemuning, 40460, Shah Alam, Selangor, Malaysia
Tel.: (60) 351229908
Web Site: https://www.eipt.com.my
Wind Electric Power Generation Services
N.A.I.C.S.: 221115

Firatel Sdn. Bhd. (1)
18 Jalan Jurunilai U1/20 Seksye U1, Hicom Glenmarie Industrial Park, 40150, Shah Alam, Selangor, Malaysia
Tel.: (60) 355659688
Web Site: https://www.firatel.net
Telecommunication Equipment Whslr
N.A.I.C.S.: 423610

Fortress Distribution Sdn. Bhd. (1)
No 11 & 13 Jalan Puteri 2/6 Bandar Puteri, 47100, Puchong, Selangor, Malaysia
Tel.: (60) 3 8065 6868
Telecommunication Servicesb
N.A.I.C.S.: 517810

Fortress Pte. Ltd. (1)
110 Robinson Road 02-00, Singapore, 068901, Singapore
Tel.: (65) 62251703
Web Site: https://www.fortress-ap.com
Telecommunication Servicesb
N.A.I.C.S.: 517810
Charles Fong (Founder & CEO)

Frontier Integrator (Sabah) Sdn. Bhd. (1)
17 Jalan Anggerik Mokara 31/51 Kota Kemuning Seksyen 31, 40460, Shah Alam, Selangor, Malaysia
Tel.: (60) 355258502
Web Site: https://www.frontier-integrator.com
Industrial Machinery Mfr & Distr
N.A.I.C.S.: 333248

OCK Phnom Penh Pte. Ltd. (1)
No 35b St 456 Sangkat Toul Tom Poung 2, Khan Chamkarmorn, Phnom Penh, Cambodia
Tel.: (855) 962993487
Telecommunication Servicesb
N.A.I.C.S.: 517121

PT. Harapan Utama Prima (1)
Graha Surveyor Level 15 Unit 1503 Jl Jend Gatot Subroto Kav 56, Jakarta Selatan, 12950, Indonesia
Tel.: (62) 2129492253
Web Site: https://www.harapanutama.co.id
Telecommunication Servicesb
N.A.I.C.S.: 517121

Smartbean Systems Sdn. Bhd. (1)
No 20-2 Jalan DU2 Taman Damai Utama, 47180, Puchong, Selangor, Malaysia
Tel.: (60) 3 80826020
Information Technology Consulting Services
N.A.I.C.S.: 541512
Chan Chow Hoo (Exec Dir)

OCL IRON AND STEEL LIMITED
Village Lamloi, PO Garvana, Rajgangpur, 770 017, Orissa, India
Tel.: (91) 6624 222562
Web Site: http://www.oclsteel.in
Rev.: $67,755,095
Assets: $343,884,543
Liabilities: $387,105,848
Net Worth: ($43,221,305)
Earnings: ($23,422,727)
Emp.: 409
Fiscal Year-end: 03/31/19
Iron & Steel Products Mfr
N.A.I.C.S.: 331110
Sanjay Tiku (Chm)

OCORIAN LIMITED
26 New Street, Saint Helier, JE2 3RA, CI, Jersey
Tel.: (44) 1534 507 000 JE
Web Site: http://www.ocorian.com
Year Founded: 1971
Fiduciary & Investment Administration Services
N.A.I.C.S.: 523991
Anthony Zarmakoupis (CFO)

Subsidiaries:

Ocorian (UK) Ltd. (1)
5th Floor 20 Fenchurch Street, London, EC3M 3BY, United Kingdom
Tel.: (44) 2073678300
Web Site: http://www.ocorian.com
Fiduciary & Investment Administration Services
N.A.I.C.S.: 523991
Jason Gerlis (Reg Head-America)

Holding (US):

Emphasys Technologies, Inc. (2)
261 York Rd, Jenkintown, PA 19046
Tel.: (215) 572-8827
Web Site: http://www.e-t-i.com
Administrative Management & General Management Consulting Service
N.A.I.C.S.: 541611
Jeff Stone (Founder & Pres)

Ocorian Administration (Guernsey) Limited (1)
Floor 2 Trafalgar Court Les Banques, PO Box 286, Saint Peter Port, GY1 4LY, Guernsey
Tel.: (44) 1481742742
Equity Investment Services
N.A.I.C.S.: 523150

OCP SA
Boulevard Al Abtal, Casablanca, Morocco
Tel.: (212) 522230025
Web Site: http://www.ocpgroup.ma
Fertilizer Mfr
N.A.I.C.S.: 325314
Mostafa Terrab (Chm & CEO)

Subsidiaries:

Zuari Maroc Phosphates Limited (1)
Jai Kissan Bhawan, PO Zuarinagar, Goa, 403726, India **(50%)**
Tel.: (91) 832 2592180
Fertilizer & Phosphate Chemicals Mfr
N.A.I.C.S.: 325199
Saroj Kumar Poddar (Chm)

Subsidiary (Domestic):

Paradeep Phosphates Ltd (2)
5th Floor Bayan Bhavan Pandit Jawaharlal Nehru Marg, Bhubaneswar, 751 001, India **(80.45%)**
Tel.: (91) 6746666100
Web Site: http://www.paradeepphosphates.com
Fertilzer & Phospate Mfr
N.A.I.C.S.: 325312
Suresh Krishnan (Mng Dir)

OCP SENIOR CREDIT FUND
95 Wellington Street West Suite 1400, Toronto, M5J 2N7, ON, Canada
Tel.: (647) 260-4055 ON
Web Site: http://www.ocpseniorcredit.com
Year Founded: 2010
Sales Range: Less than $1 Million
Investment Services
N.A.I.C.S.: 523999
Stuart Kovensky (CEO & Chief Investment Officer)

OCR GROUP BERHAD
Level 5 Block B Dataran PHB, Saujana Resort Section U2, 40150, Shah Alam, Selangor, Malaysia
Tel.: (60) 378900638 MY
Web Site: https://www.ocrbhd.com
Year Founded: 1997
OCR—(KLS)
Rev.: $44,095,983
Assets: $103,392,429
Liabilities: $61,443,108
Net Worth: $41,949,321
Earnings: $1,153,144
Fiscal Year-end: 12/31/22
Property Development
N.A.I.C.S.: 531390
Tze Chern Tee (Exec Dir)

Subsidiaries:

Takasa Rubber Products Sdn. Bhd. (1)
K55 Kawasan Perindustrian Tg Ags, 84000, Johor, Ledang, Malaysia
Tel.: (60) 69510988
Sales Range: $125-149.9 Million
Emp.: 254
Rubber Products Mfr
N.A.I.C.S.: 326299
Tee Tze Chern (Mng Dir)

INTERNATIONAL PUBLIC

OCRA (ISLE OF MAN) LIMITED
Grosvenor Court Tower Street, Ramsey, IM8 1 JA, Isle of Man
Tel.: (44) 1624 811000
Web Site: http://www.ocra.com
Sales Range: $50-74.9 Million
Emp.: 350
International Corporate & Trust Services
N.A.I.C.S.: 561499
Bart Dekker (Grp Mng Dir-Asia Pacific)

Subsidiaries:

4 Business Limited (1)
3rd Floor 14 Hanover Street, Mayfair, London, W1S 1YH, United Kingdom
Tel.: (44) 207 514 9901
Web Site: http://www.4business.com
Business Consultants
N.A.I.C.S.: 541618

E-Solutions Limited (1)
Level 2 MaxCity Building Remy Ollier Street, Port Louis, 11602, Mauritius
Tel.: (230) 217 5100
Web Site: http://www.e-solutionslimited.com
Emp.: 5
Internet Solutions
N.A.I.C.S.: 541519
Dharmesh Naik (Dir)

OCRA (Australia) Holdings Pty Ltd (1)
Level 9 St Martins Tower 31 Market Street, Sydney, 2000, NSW, Australia
Tel.: (61) 2 9251 5822
Financial Consulting Services
N.A.I.C.S.: 541611
Bart Dekker (Grp Mng Dir)

OCRA (Brunei) Limited (1)
21 Britannia House 2nd Floor Cator Road, Raigad, BS 8811, Bandar Seri Begawan, Brunei, Brunei Darussalam
Tel.: (673) 222 0872
Financial Consulting Services
N.A.I.C.S.: 541611
Wuei Chua (Mgr-Bus Dev)

OCRA (Cyprus) Limited (1)
15 Agiou Pavlou Str, Ledra House Ayios Andreas, 1105, Nicosia, Cyprus
Tel.: (357) 22 556666
Financial Consulting Services
N.A.I.C.S.: 541611

OCRA (Hong Kong) Limited (1)
3908 Two Exchange Square 8 Connaught Place, Central, China (Hong Kong)
Tel.: (852) 2522 0172
Financial Consulting Services
N.A.I.C.S.: 541611
Iris Lee (Head-Company Secretarial-Asia Pacific)

OCRA (London) Limited (1)
3rd Floor 14 Hanover Street, Mayfair, London, W1S 1YH, United Kingdom
Tel.: (44) 20 7317 0600
Financial Consulting Services
N.A.I.C.S.: 541611
Franco Gjolleshi (Mgr-Corp)

OCRA (Luxembourg) S.A. (1)
Parc d'Activite Syrdall 2 18-20 rue Gabriel Lippmann, L-5365, Munsbach, Luxembourg
Tel.: (352) 224 286
Web Site: http://www.ocra.com
Emp.: 10
Financial Consulting Services
N.A.I.C.S.: 541611
Joah Ferreira (Mng Dir)

OCRA (Malta) Limited (1)
The Penthouse Tower Business Centre Tower Street, BKR3013, Swatar, Malta
Tel.: (356) 2557 2333
Financial Consulting Services
N.A.I.C.S.: 541611
Tony Zammit (Chm)

OCRA (Mauritius) Limited (1)
2nd Floor Max City Building Remy Ollier Street, Port Louis, Mauritius
Tel.: (230) 217 5100
Web Site: http://www.ocra-mauritius.com
Financial Consulting Services

AND PRIVATE COMPANIES

N.A.I.C.S.: 541611
Dharmesh Naik *(Mng Dir)*

OCRA (Seychelles) Limited (1)
303 Aarti Chambers Mont Fleuri, PO Box 983, Mahe, Victoria, Seychelles
Tel.: (248) 248 422 5555
Financial Consulting Services
N.A.I.C.S.: 541611
Dharmesh Naik *(Mng Dir)*

OCRA (Singapore) Pte Limited (1)
8 Temasek Boulevard 35-03 Suntec Tower 3, 38988, Singapore, Singapore
Tel.: (65) 6535 3382
Financial Consulting Services
N.A.I.C.S.: 541611

OCRA Aerospace (Isle of Man) Limited (1)
Grosvenor Court Tower Street, Ramsey, IM8 1JA, Isle of Man
Tel.: (44) 1624 818888
Web Site: http://www.ocra.aero
Aircraft Registration & Business Management Services
N.A.I.C.S.: 488190

OCRA Marine (Isle of Man) Limited (1)
Grosvenor Court Tower Street, Ramsey, IM8 1JA, Isle of Man
Tel.: (44) 1624 818888
Web Site: http://www.ocramarine.com
Emp.: 60
Ship Registry & Business Management Services
N.A.I.C.S.: 488390
James Potter *(Gen Mgr)*

OCRA Switzerland Sarl (1)
Place St Francois 12 bis, 1003, Lausanne, Switzerland
Tel.: (41) 21 643 10 26
Financial Consulting Services
N.A.I.C.S.: 541611

OCS GROUP LIMITED
79 Limpsfield Road, Sanderstead, CR2 9LB, Surrey, United Kingdom
Tel.: (44) 8448467606   UK
Web Site: http://www.ocs.co.uk
Sales Range: $1-4.9 Billion
Emp.: 63,000
Property Support Services Including Auditing, Inventory Management, Document Management, Catering, Cleaning, HVAC, Security, Electrical Maintenance & Waste Disposal
N.A.I.C.S.: 561210
David Gratton *(Dir-Fin)*

Subsidiaries:

Absotherm Facility Management Pvt. Limited (1)
Basement Tara Nivas Vishnu Nagar, Naupada, Thane, 400602, Maharashtra, India
Tel.: (91) 22 40081717
Web Site: http://www.absotherm.com
Emp.: 6,000
Facility Management Services
N.A.I.C.S.: 561210
Pradip Menon *(Mng Dir)*

Cannon Hygiene (S.A.) (Pty) Limited (1)
Unit D12 Connaught Park Riley rd, Beaconvale, Parow, South Africa
Tel.: (27) 21 931 8228
Web Site: http://www.cannonhygiene.co.za
Cleaning Product Mfr
N.A.I.C.S.: 325612

Cannon Hygiene Australia Pty Limited (1)
Level 3 233 Adelaide Terrace, Perth, 6000, WA, Australia
Tel.: (61) 1300 781 666
Web Site: http://www.cannonhygiene.com.au
Cleaning Product Distr
N.A.I.C.S.: 424690

Cannon Hygiene Ltda (1)
Rua Mandaguari 1752 Bairro Emiliano Perneta, 83325-015, Pinhais, Parana, Brazil
Tel.: (55) 41 3551 1500

Web Site: http://www.cannonhygiene.com.br
Cleaning Product Distr
N.A.I.C.S.: 424690

Don-Thaker Cleaning Services Pte. Limited (1)
8 Boon Lay Way 08-16 TradeHub 21, Singapore, 609964, Singapore
Tel.: (65) 6863 0500
Web Site: http://www.donthaker.com
Janitorial Services
N.A.I.C.S.: 561720
Jinny Tan *(Mgr-Bus Dev)*

Envirocomp Limited (1)
PO Box 1849, Christchurch, 8140, New Zealand
Tel.: (64) 3 345 5589
Web Site: http://www.envirocomp.co.nz
Sanitary Products Distr
N.A.I.C.S.: 424130

Fountains America Inc. (1)
175 Barnstead Rd Ste 4, Pittsfield, NH 03263 (100%)
Tel.: (603) 435-8234
Web Site: http://www.fountainsamerica.com
Sales Range: $25-49.9 Million
Emp.: 8
Forest Management, Land Brokerage & Geographic Information System Services
N.A.I.C.S.: 115310
Philip A. Bryce *(Pres)*

Subsidiary (Domestic):

Fountains Forestry Inc. (2)
7 Green Mountain Dr Ste 3, Montpelier, VT 05602-2715
Tel.: (802) 223-8644
Web Site: http://www.fountainsamerica.com
Sales Range: $25-49.9 Million
Forest Management Services
N.A.I.C.S.: 115310
Michael Tragner *(Pres)*

Fountains Land Inc. (2)
7 Green Mountain Dr Ste 3, Montpelier, VT 05602-2708
Tel.: (802) 223-8644
Web Site: http://www.fountainsland.com
Sales Range: $50-74.9 Million
Land Brokerage & Consulting Services
N.A.I.C.S.: 531210
Michael Tragner *(Pres)*

Fountains Spatial Inc. (2)
137 Jay St, Schenectady, NY 12305 (100%)
Tel.: (518) 346-0942
Web Site: http://www.fountainsspatial.com
Sales Range: $25-49.9 Million
Geographic Information System (GIS) Services
N.A.I.C.S.: 541370
Larry Spraker *(Pres)*

Integrated Premises Services Pty Limited (1)
Suite F Level 1 82 Waterloo Road, Macquarie Park, 2133, NSW, Australia
Tel.: (61) 2 9432 8000
Web Site: http://www.ipsl.com.au
Emp.: 2,000
Janitorial Services
N.A.I.C.S.: 561720
Brett Giffen *(Officer-Compliance)*

Integris Management Services Limited (1)
Unit 11/12 North Link Business Park Mallow Road, Cork, Ireland
Tel.: (353) 21 2386360
Web Site: http://www.integris.ie
Engineeering Services
N.A.I.C.S.: 541330
Aine Mulcahy *(Mng Dir)*

Limpotecnica Sociedade de Limpeza Tecnica e Mecanica Lda (1)
R D Joao V 2 A 1 Andar, 1250-090, Lisbon, Portugal
Tel.: (351) 210 451 962
Janitorial Services
N.A.I.C.S.: 561720

O.C.S. Forestry UK Limited (1)
Blenheim Court George Street, Banbury, OX16 5BH, Oxfordshire, United Kingdom
Tel.: (44) 1295 753250

Cleaning Product Distr
N.A.I.C.S.: 424690

OCS Group International Limited (1)
79 Limpsfield Road, Sanderstead, CR2 9LB, Surrey, United Kingdom
Tel.: (44) 844 846 7606
Web Site: http://www.ocsinternational.com
Management Activities of Holding Companies
N.A.I.C.S.: 551112

OCS Group Ireland Ltd. (1)
Century House Richmond Industrial Estate, North Richmond Street, Dublin, 1, Ireland
Tel.: (353) 1850 67 57 47
Web Site: http://www.ocsireland.com
Sales Range: $250-299.9 Million
Emp.: 1,000
Facilities Services
N.A.I.C.S.: 561210
Evelyn Daly *(Dir-Mktg)*

OCS Group UK Ltd. (1)
79 Limpsfield Road, Sanderstead, CR2 9LB, Surrey, United Kingdom
Tel.: (44) 844 846 7606
Web Site: http://www.ocs.co.uk
Facilities Support Services
N.A.I.C.S.: 561210

Subsidiary (Domestic):

Legion Group plc (2)
Hanover House, Queensgate, Britannia Road, Waltham Cross, EN8 7TF, Herts, United Kingdom
Tel.: (44) 1992701940
Web Site: http://www.legion-group.co.uk
Sales Range: $25-49.9 Million
Emp.: 2,800
Security & Parking Facility Management Services
N.A.I.C.S.: 561612

OCS Netherlands BV (1)
Heulweg 25, 2288 GN, Rijswijk, Netherlands
Tel.: (31) 15 214 3640
Web Site: http://www.ocs-nederland.nl
Facilities Support Services
N.A.I.C.S.: 561210

OCS New Zealand Ltd. (1)
Level 4 26 Virginia Avenue East, Auckland, 1021, New Zealand
Tel.: (64) 93775317
Web Site: http://www.ocs.co.nz
Sales Range: $650-699.9 Million
Emp.: 3,000
Facilities Management Services
N.A.I.C.S.: 561210

OCS One Complete Solution Limited (1)
Bromley House Bulwer Avenue, Saint Sampson's, GI2 41Q, Guernsey
Tel.: (44) 1481 244048
Web Site: http://www.ocs.com
Cleaning Product Distr
N.A.I.C.S.: 424690
Andre De Vasconcelos *(Asst Mgr-Property Support)*

OCS One Complete Solution Limited (1)
Unit 38 Airways Industrial Estate, Dublin, Ireland
Tel.: (353) 1 704 7700
Cleaning Product Distr
N.A.I.C.S.: 424690
Annie Mulchay *(Owner)*

OCS One Complete Solution Limited (1)
32-38 Apsley Road, Saint Helier, JE2 4LR, Jersey
Tel.: (44) 1534 888906
Janitorial Services
N.A.I.C.S.: 327910
Gorete Estevao *(Supvr-Contracts)*

OCS Services Pty Limited (1)
level 3 233 Adelaide Terrace, Perth, 6000, WA, Australia
Tel.: (61) 8 9318 2000
Web Site: http://www.ocsservisec.com
Emp.: 700
Janitorial Services
N.A.I.C.S.: 561720

Ivan Ashby *(Gen Mgr-Ops)*

PWB (M) Sdn. Bhd. (1)
No 412A 414A Jalan 5/132 Along Jalan 5/46 Gasing Indah, 46000, Petaling Jaya, Selangor, Malaysia
Tel.: (60) 3 7784 1396
Janitorial Services
N.A.I.C.S.: 561720

Property Care Services (Thailand) Limited (1)
234 Soi Sukhumvit 101 Punnavithi Sukhumvit Road, Bangchak Prakanong, Bangkok, 10260, Thailand
Tel.: (66) 2 741 8800
Web Site: http://www.pcs.co.th
Janitorial Services
N.A.I.C.S.: 561720
Thana Thiramanus *(Mng Dir)*

Radiant Hospitality Services Pvt. Limited (1)
4th & 5th Floor Simran Center Parsi Panchayat Road, Andheri East, Mumbai, 400069, India
Tel.: (91) 2240620513
Web Site: http://www.radianthospitality.com
Janitorial Services
N.A.I.C.S.: 561720
Govind Kokare *(Mgr-Payroll)*

OCTAGON 88 RESOURCES, INC.
Hochwachstrasse 4, CH 6312, Steinhausen, Switzerland
Tel.: (41) 792376218   NV
Web Site: http://www.octagon-88.com
Year Founded: 2008
OCTX—(OTCBB)
Sales Range: $25-49.9 Million
Petroleum & Natural Gas Exploration & Mining Services
N.A.I.C.S.: 211120
Feliciano Tighe *(Sec)*

OCTAGONAL PLC
2nd Floor 2 London Wall Buildings, London, EC2M 5PP, United Kingdom
Tel.: (44) 20 7048 9400
Web Site: http://www.octagonalplc.com
Year Founded: 2002
Rev.: $6,739,765
Assets: $12,697,814
Liabilities: $1,387,039
Net Worth: $11,310,775
Earnings: $1,176,382
Emp.: 18
Fiscal Year-end: 03/31/19
Investment Services
N.A.I.C.S.: 523999
Samantha Dru Esqulant *(CEO)*

Subsidiaries:

Global Investment Strategy UK Limited (1)
2nd Floor 2 London Wall Buildings, London, EC2M 5PP, United Kingdom
Tel.: (44) 2070489400
Web Site: http://www.gisukltd.com
Financial Investment Services
N.A.I.C.S.: 523999
John Gunn *(Founder & Chm)*

Synergis Capital Plc (1)
2nd Floor 2 London Wall Buildings, London, EC2M 5PP, United Kingdom
Tel.: (44) 2037349030
Financial Investment Services
N.A.I.C.S.: 523999

OCTAL CREDIT CAPITAL LIMITED
16A Shakespeare Sarani Unit II 2nd floor, Kolkata, 700 071, West Bengal, India
Tel.: (91) 3322826815
Web Site: https://www.occl.co.in
538894—(BOM)
Rev.: $46,634
Assets: $1,876,406

Octal Credit Capital Limited—(Continued)
Liabilities: $198,282
Net Worth: $1,678,124
Earnings: ($147,560)
Emp.: 4
Fiscal Year-end: 03/31/20
Financial Support Services
N.A.I.C.S.: 523999
Arihant Patni *(Exec Dir)*

OCTANE PR
Millbank Tower, Millbank, London, SW1P 4RS, United Kingdom
Tel.: (44) 2078022662
Web Site: http://www.octanepr.com
Sales Range: $25-49.9 Million
Emp.: 50
N.A.I.C.S.: 541810
David Brown *(Head-Editorial)*

OCTANEX LTD
Level 1 10 Yarra Street, South Yarra, 3141, VIC, Australia
Tel.: (61) 3 8610 4724
Web Site: http://www.octanex.com.au
OXX—(ASX)
Rev.: $303,906
Assets: $4,861,368
Liabilities: $273,741
Net Worth: $4,587,627
Earnings: ($230,009)
Fiscal Year-end: 06/30/21
Oil & Gas Exploration Services
N.A.I.C.S.: 211120
Ernest Geoffrey Albers *(Chm)*

Subsidiaries:

Goldsborough Pty Ltd (1)
120 Greenhill Road, Unley, 5061, SA, Australia
Tel.: (61) 883784000
Web Site: http://www.goldsborough.com.au
Financial Planning Services
N.A.I.C.S.: 523940

OCTANTE SECURITIZADORA S.A.
Rua Beatriz 226, Alto de Pinheiros, Sao Paulo, 05445-040, Brazil
Tel.: (55) 1130605250
Web Site: http://www.octante.com.br
Year Founded: 2008
Financial Management Services
N.A.I.C.S.: 523999
William Trosman *(Founder & Partner)*

OCTAPHARMA AG
Seidenstrasse 2, 8853, Lachen, Switzerland
Tel.: (41) 554512121
Web Site: http://www.octapharma.com
Year Founded: 1983
Sales Range: $1-4.9 Billion
Emp.: 6,000
Developer & Producer of Plasma Derivatives
N.A.I.C.S.: 325414
Wolfgang Marguerre *(Chm)*

Subsidiaries:

Deutsche Gesellschaft fur Humanplasma mbH (1)
Elisabeth-Selbert-Strasse 11, 40764, Langenfeld, Germany
Tel.: (49) 2173917107
Web Site: http://www.octapharmaplasma.de
Plasma Products Developer
N.A.I.C.S.: 325412
Johannes Hafer *(Gen Mgr)*

Octapharma AG, o.z.z.o. (1)
Zochova 6/8, 811 03, Bratislava, Slovakia
Tel.: (421) 254646701
Sales Range: $25-49.9 Million
Emp.: 3
Sales of Human Proteins
N.A.I.C.S.: 325414

Octapharma AS (1)
Industrivegen 23, 2050, Jessheim, Norway
Tel.: (47) 6398 8860
Plasma Products Developer
N.A.I.C.S.: 325412

Octapharma Australia Pty. Ltd (1)
Jones Bay Wharf 42/26-32 Pirrama Road, Pyrmont, 2009, NSW, Australia
Tel.: (61) 285725800
Web Site: http://www.octapharma.com.au
Sales Range: $50-74.9 Million
Emp.: 10
Sales of Human Proteins & Plasma Derivatives
N.A.I.C.S.: 423450

Octapharma Benelux S.A./N.V. (1)
Rue de Stalle 63, 1180, Brussels, Belgium
Tel.: (32) 1 41 31 80 02
Sales of Human Proteins
N.A.I.C.S.: 325414

Octapharma Biopharmaceuticals GmbH (1)
Im Neuenheimer Feld 590, 69120, Heidelberg, Germany
Tel.: (49) 62211852500
Web Site: http://www.octapharma-biopharmaceuticals.com
Emp.: 85
Plasma Products Research Services
N.A.I.C.S.: 541715
Christoph Kannicht *(Gen Mgr)*

Octapharma Brasil Ltda (1)
Av Ayrton Senna 1850 salas 322 & 323 Barra da Tijuca, 22775-003, Rio de Janeiro, RJ, Brazil
Tel.: (55) 2124211681
Sales Range: $50-74.9 Million
Emp.: 5
Sales of Human Proteins & Plasma Derivatives
N.A.I.C.S.: 423450
Samuel Mauricio *(Gen Mgr)*

Octapharma CZ s.r.o. (1)
Argentinska 38, 170 00, Prague, 7, Czech Republic
Tel.: (420) 2 6679 4310
Plasma Products Developer
N.A.I.C.S.: 325412

Octapharma Canada Inc. (1)
308-214 King Street West, Toronto, M5H 3S6, ON, Canada
Tel.: (416) 531-5533
Web Site: https://www.octapharma.ca
Human Protein Mfr
N.A.I.C.S.: 325414
Sri Adapa *(Gen Mgr)*

Octapharma France S.A.S. (1)
62 B avenue Andre Morizet, Boulogne-Billancourt, 92100, France
Tel.: (33) 141318000
Web Site: http://www.octapharma.com
Rev.: $24,200,000
Emp.: 18
Developer & Producer of Plasma Derivatives
N.A.I.C.S.: 325414

Octapharma Gestao Estrategica e Operacional, Lda. (1)
Quinta do Lamas Lote 5 Cave Zona Industrial da Paia, 1675-076, Pontinha, Portugal
Tel.: (351) 21 810 7000
Plasma Products Developer
N.A.I.C.S.: 325412

Octapharma GmbH (1)
Elisabeth-Selbert-Strasse 11, Langenfeld, 40764, Germany
Tel.: (49) 21739170
Web Site: http://www.octapharma.de
Sales Range: $25-49.9 Million
Emp.: 50
Sales of Human Proteins
N.A.I.C.S.: 325414
Johannes Hafer *(Mng Dir)*

Octapharma Handelsgesellschaft m.b.H. (1)
Oberlaaer Strasse 235, 1100, Vienna, Austria
Tel.: (43) 1 61032 0
Web Site: http://www.octapharma.com
Emp.: 900

Plasma Products Sales
N.A.I.C.S.: 424210

Octapharma Hella SA (1)
60 Posidonos Ave, 166 75, Glyfada, Attiki, Greece
Tel.: (30) 210 8986500
Plasma Products Developer
N.A.I.C.S.: 325412

Octapharma Italy Spa (1)
Via Cisanello 145, 56124, Pisa, Italy
Tel.: (39) 050549001
Sales of Human Proteins
N.A.I.C.S.: 325414

Octapharma Latin America (1)
Oficina J4 Piso 49 Torre Mil Claro PH Oceania Business Plaza Calle 56D, Panama, Panama
Tel.: (507) 203 77 77
Pharmaceutical Products Distr
N.A.I.C.S.: 424210

Octapharma Limited (1)
The Zenith Building, 26 Spring Gardens, Manchester, M2 1AB, United Kingdom
Tel.: (44) 1618373770
Web Site: http://www.octapharma.co.uk
Sales Range: $25-49.9 Million
Emp.: 18
Plasma Products Developer
N.A.I.C.S.: 325414
Sue Griffin *(Gen Mgr)*

Octapharma Nordic AB (1)
Lyngbyvez 20, 2100, Copenhagen, Denmark
Tel.: (45) 702 00354
Plasma Products Developer
N.A.I.C.S.: 325412

Octapharma Nordic AB (1)
Rajatorpantie 41 C, 01640, Vantaa, Finland
Tel.: (358) 9 8520 2701
Plasma Products Developer
N.A.I.C.S.: 325412

Octapharma Nordic AB (1)
Elersvagen 40, 11275, Stockholm, Sweden
Tel.: (46) 8 5664 3000
Plasma Products Sales
N.A.I.C.S.: 424210

Octapharma Pharmazeutika Produktionsges.m.b.H (1)
Oberlaaer Strasse 235, A 1100, Vienna, Austria
Tel.: (43) 1610320
Web Site: http://www.octapharma.com
Sales Range: $250-299.9 Million
Emp.: 800
Production of Human Proteins
N.A.I.C.S.: 325414
Juergen Roemisch *(Dir-Plasma R&D)*

Octapharma Plasma, Inc. (1)
2588 Hubbell Ave, Des Moines, IA 50317
Tel.: (515) 263-2192
Pharmaceutical Products Distr
N.A.I.C.S.: 424210

Octapharma Poland Sp. z o.o. (1)
39A Domaniewska Street, 02-672, Warsaw, Poland
Tel.: (48) 22 2082734
Pharmaceutical Products Distr
N.A.I.C.S.: 424210

Octapharma Produktionsgesellschaft Deutschland mbH (1)
Eldagsener Strasse 38, 31832, Springe, Germany
Tel.: (49) 504177918190
Production & Sales of Human Proteins
N.A.I.C.S.: 325414

Octapharma Produtos Farmaceuticos, Lda. (1)
Rua dos Lagares d'el Rei 21-C, 1700-268, Lisbon, Portugal
Tel.: (351) 218160820
Sales Range: $25-49.9 Million
Emp.: 15
Sales of Human Proteins
N.A.I.C.S.: 325414
Paulo Pastro *(Gen Mgr)*

Octapharma Pte Ltd (1)
143 Cecil Street 16-04 GB Building, Singapore, Singapore
Tel.: (65) 6225 7225
Pharmaceutical Products Distr
N.A.I.C.S.: 424210

Octapharma Russia LLC (1)
Northern Tower 19th Floor 10 Testovskaya Street, Moscow, 123317, Russia
Tel.: (7) 495 662 1815
Plasma Products Developer
N.A.I.C.S.: 325412

Octapharma S.A. de C.V. (1)
Calzada Mexico Tacuba No 1419, Col Argentina Poniente, Mexico, CP 11230, Mexico
Tel.: (52) 5553995644
Sales Range: $50-74.9 Million
Emp.: 100
Production & Sales of Human Proteins & Plasma Derivatives
N.A.I.C.S.: 325414

Octapharma S.A.S. (1)
70-72 rue du Marechal Foch, 67380, Lingolsheim, France
Tel.: (33) 3 8878 8989
Plasma Products Mfr
N.A.I.C.S.: 325412

Octapharma South Africa (Pty) Ltd (1)
Building 3 Design Quarter District Cnr William Nicol and Leslie Avenue, Fourways, 2191, South Africa
Tel.: (27) 11 465 4269
Emp.: 3
Pharmaceutical Products Distr
N.A.I.C.S.: 424210
Sean Hancock *(Gen Mgr)*

Octapharma USA, Inc. (1)
121 River St 12th Fl, Hoboken, NJ 07032
Tel.: (201) 604-1130
Web Site: http://www.octapharmausa.com
Sales Range: $250-299.9 Million
Emp.: 1,000
Sale of Human Proteins Including Plasma Derivatives & Recombinant Products
N.A.I.C.S.: 325414
Flemming Nielsen *(Pres)*

Octapharma s.a. (1)
Parque Empresarial de San Fernando Edif Berlin - Planta Baja, San Fernando de Henares, 28830, Madrid, Spain
Tel.: (34) 916487298
Sales of Human Proteins
N.A.I.C.S.: 325414

OCTAVA MINERALS LIMITED
Suite 1 234 Churchill Ave, Subiaco, 6008, WA, Australia
Tel.: (61) 892188878
Web Site: https://www.octavaminerals.com
Year Founded: 2020
OCT—(ASX)
Rev.: $260,807
Assets: $3,808,864
Liabilities: $69,713
Net Worth: $3,739,150
Earnings: ($490,791)
Fiscal Year-end: 06/30/23
Mineral Exploration Services
N.A.I.C.S.: 212390

OCTAVA S.A.
Twarda Street 18, 00-105, Warsaw, Poland
Tel.: (48) 223506245
Web Site: https://www.octava.com.pl
Year Founded: 1997
08N—(WAR)
Rev.: $1,633,130
Assets: $20,659,045
Liabilities: $6,265,498
Net Worth: $14,393,547
Earnings: $939,533
Fiscal Year-end: 12/31/23
Real Estate Financial Services
N.A.I.C.S.: 522292
Piotr Rymaszewski *(Chm/Pres-Mgmt Bd)*

OCTAVIUS PLANTATIONS LTD.
E-40/3 Okhla Industrial Area Phase -2, New Delhi, 110020, India
Tel.: (91) 1145542200
Web Site: https://www.octaviusplantations.com
Year Founded: 1984
542938—(BOM)
Rev.: $2,665,536
Assets: $2,857,479
Liabilities: $893,747
Net Worth: $1,963,731
Earnings: $227,037
Emp.: 15
Fiscal Year-end: 03/31/23
Export Agricultural Distr
N.A.I.C.S.: 424910
Nagraj Ramachandra Rao *(CFO)*

OCTAWARE TECHNOLOGIES LIMITED
204 Timmy Arcade Makwana Road Marol Off Andheri-Kurla, Mumbai, 400 059, India
Tel.: (91) 2240231431
Web Site: https://www.octaware.com
540416—(BOM)
Rev.: $2,076,099
Assets: $2,303,987
Liabilities: $2,302,512
Net Worth: $1,475
Earnings: ($163,060)
Emp.: 75
Fiscal Year-end: 03/31/23
Software Development Services
N.A.I.C.S.: 541512
Mohammed Aslam Khan *(Chm & Mng Dir)*

Subsidiaries:

Octaware Gulf FZE (1)
Office 236 2nd Floor Regus Building D-Ring, PO Box 32522, Doha, Qatar
Tel.: (974) 44231209
Software Development Services
N.A.I.C.S.: 513210

Octaware Technologies Limited - Kent Branch (1)
24298 103rd Ave SE D306, Kent, WA 98030
Tel.: (206) 293-0786
Software Development Services
N.A.I.C.S.: 513210

OCTOBER PHARMA
Piece 190 St 25 1st industrial zone 6 october city, Cairo, Egypt
Tel.: (20) 238201832
Web Site: http://www.octoberpharma.com
Year Founded: 1987
OCPH.CA—(EGX)
Sales Range: Less than $1 Million
Pharmaceutical Preparation Mfr
N.A.I.C.S.: 325412

OCTODEC INVESTMENTS LIMITED
CPA House 101 Du Toit Street, Pretoria, 0002, South Africa
Tel.: (27) 123198781 ZA
Web Site: https://www.octodec.co.za
OCT—(JSE)
Rev.: $104,697,821
Assets: $606,814,552
Liabilities: $260,400,564
Net Worth: $346,413,988
Earnings: $32,238,564
Emp.: 191
Fiscal Year-end: 08/31/23
Real Estate Property Investment Services
N.A.I.C.S.: 531390
Jeffrey P. Wapnick *(Mng Dir)*

Subsidiaries:

Elarduspark Shopping Centre (Pty) Limited (1)
CNR Delmas Barnard Street, PO Box 15, Elardus Park, Pretoria, 0181, South Africa
Tel.: (27) 123454813
Web Site: https://theparkcentre.co.za
Shopping Mall Operation Services
N.A.I.C.S.: 236220

OCTOPUS AIM VCT PLC
33 Holborn, London, EC1N 2HT, United Kingdom
Tel.: (44) 8003162295 UK
Year Founded: 1997
OOA—(LSE)
Rev.: $2,622,533
Assets: $165,288,352
Liabilities: $922,979
Net Worth: $164,365,373
Earnings: ($22,576,703)
Emp.: 250
Fiscal Year-end: 02/29/24
Investment Management Service
N.A.I.C.S.: 523940
Neal Ransome *(Chm)*

OCTOPUS APOLLO VCT PLC
33 Holborn, London, EC1N 2HT, United Kingdom
Tel.: (44) 8003162295 UK
Year Founded: 2006
OAP3—(LSE)
Rev.: $63,502,294
Assets: $369,536,472
Liabilities: $15,303,056
Net Worth: $354,233,416
Earnings: $42,379,766
Fiscal Year-end: 01/31/22
Investment Management Service
N.A.I.C.S.: 523940
Murray Steele *(Chm)*

OCTOPUS CAPITAL LTD
6Th Floor 33 Horborn, London, EC1N 2HT, United Kingdom
Tel.: (44) 0808 164 1088
Web Site: http://www.octopus.energy
Privater Equity Firm
N.A.I.C.S.: 523999
Simon Rogerson *(Co-Founder & CEO)*

Subsidiaries:

Octopus Energy Ltd (1)
6th Floor 33 Holborn, London, EC1N 2HT, United Kingdom
Tel.: (44) 0808 164 1088
Energy Mfr
N.A.I.C.S.: 335929
Greg Jackson *(CEO)*

Subsidiary (Domestic):

Co-operative Energy Limited (2)
Co-operative House Warwick Technology Park, Warwick, CV34 6DA, United Kingdom
Tel.: (44) 1926 516152
Web Site: http://www.cooperativeenergy.coop
Electric Power Distribution Services
N.A.I.C.S.: 221122
David Bird *(CEO)*

OCTOPUS FUTURE GENERATIONS VCT PLC
6th Floor 33 Holborn, London, EC1N 2HT, United Kingdom
Tel.: (44) 8003162295 UK
Year Founded: 2021
OFG—(LSE)
Rev.: $535,218
Assets: $57,985,357
Liabilities: $653,875
Net Worth: $57,331,482
Earnings: ($982,075)
Emp.: 750
Fiscal Year-end: 06/30/23
Investment Management Service
N.A.I.C.S.: 523999

OCTOPUS ROBOTS SA
29 Rue Saint Pierre, 49300, Cholet, France
Tel.: (33) 290380180
Web Site: https://www.octopusrobots.com
Year Founded: 1987
MLOCT—(EUR)
Sales Range: Less than $1 Million
Industrial Robot Mfr & Distr
N.A.I.C.S.: 334513
Bertrand Vergne *(Chm & CEO)*

OCTOPUS TITAN VCT PLC
33 Holborn, London, EC1N 2HT, United Kingdom
Tel.: (44) 8003162295 UK
Year Founded: 2007
OTV2—(LSE)
Rev.: $1,090,634
Assets: $1,359,741,227
Liabilities: $32,096,693
Net Worth: $1,327,644,534
Earnings: ($402,947,488)
Emp.: 750
Fiscal Year-end: 12/31/22
Investment Management Service
N.A.I.C.S.: 523999
Tom Leader *(Chm)*

OCULIS HOLDING AG
Bahnofstrasse 7, 6300, Zug, Switzerland
Tel.: (41) 588100182 CH
Web Site: https://www.oculis.com
Year Founded: 2016
OCS—(NASDAQ)
Emp.: 28
Holding Company
N.A.I.C.S.: 551112
Pall Ragnar Johannesson *(Chief Strategy Officer)*

Subsidiaries:

Oculis Operations Sarl (1)
EPFL Innovation Park Building D, Route J-D. Colladon, 1015, Lausanne, Switzerland
Tel.: (41) 217113970
Web Site: https://oculis.com
Pharmaceutical Preparation Mfr
N.A.I.C.S.: 325412

OCULUS VISIONTECH INC.
837 West Hastings Street Suite 507, Vancouver, V6C 3N6, BC, Canada
Tel.: (604) 685-1017 WY
Web Site: https://www.ovtz.com
Year Founded: 1986
OVTZ—(OTCQB)
Rev.: $5,153
Assets: $717,840
Liabilities: $302,423
Net Worth: $415,417
Earnings: ($1,649,589)
Emp.: 3
Fiscal Year-end: 12/31/22
Streaming Video & Video-on-Demand Systems, Services & Source-To-Destination Digital Media Solutions Designer & Marketer
N.A.I.C.S.: 541512
Rowland Perkins *(Pres & CEO)*

OCUMENSION THERAPEUTICS (SHANGHAI) CO., LTD.
Room 502-1 Want Want Plaza No 211 Shimen Yi Road, Jingan, Shanghai, China
Tel.: (86) 2161493800 Ky
Web Site: http://www.ocumension.com
Year Founded: 2017
1477—(HKG)
Emp.: 100
Pharmaceutical Product Mfr & Distr
N.A.I.C.S.: 325412
Ye Liu *(CEO)*

OD6 METALS LIMITED
Level 1 50 Kings Park Road, West Perth, 6005, WA, Australia
Tel.: (61) 861898515 AU
Web Site: https://www.od6metals.com.au
Year Founded: 2021
OD6—(ASX)
Rev.: $352
Assets: $7,196,462
Liabilities: $513,497
Net Worth: $6,682,965
Earnings: ($1,026,081)
Fiscal Year-end: 06/30/22
Metal Exploration Services
N.A.I.C.S.: 213114

ODAKYU ELECTRIC RAILWAY CO., LTD.
1-8-3 Nishi-Shinjuku, Shinjuku-ku, Tokyo, 163-0706, Japan
Tel.: (81) 333492526 JP
Web Site: https://www.odakyu.jp
Year Founded: 1948
9007—(TKS)
Rev.: $2,709,022,570
Assets: $8,603,430,580
Liabilities: $5,561,667,220
Net Worth: $3,041,763,360
Earnings: $538,873,640
Emp.: 3,712
Fiscal Year-end: 03/31/24
Railway Transportation Services
N.A.I.C.S.: 485112
Koji Hoshino *(Pres & CEO)*

Subsidiaries:

Enoshima Electric Railway Co., Ltd (1)
1-8-16 KataseKaigan, Fujisawa, 251-0035, Japan
Tel.: (81) 466242711
Web Site: http://www.enoden.co.jp
Emp.: 230
Rail Transportation Operating Services
N.A.I.C.S.: 488210

Giraud Restaurant System Co., Ltd (1)
2-12-24 Totate-Nagai Bld 4F, Shibuya-ku, Tokyo, 150-0002, Japan
Tel.: (81) 364185222
Web Site: http://www.giraud.co.jp
Emp.: 477
Restaurant Operating Services
N.A.I.C.S.: 722511
Yasuyuki Asahi *(Pres)*

Hakone Ropeway Co., Ltd (1)
1-15-1 Shiroyama, Odawara, 250-0045, Kanagawa, Japan
Tel.: (81) 465322207
Web Site: http://www.hakoneropeway.co.jp
Ropeway Operating Services
N.A.I.C.S.: 488999

Hakone Tozan Railway Co., Ltd. (1)
1-15-1 Shiroyama, Odawara, 250-0045, Japan
Tel.: (81) 465326821
Web Site: http://www.hakone-tozan.co.jp
Emp.: 302
Tourist & Mountain Railway Transportation Services
N.A.I.C.S.: 482112

Hokuo Tokyo Co., Ltd (1)
4-26-1 Hibarigaoka, Zama, 228-0003, Kanagawa, Japan (100%)
Tel.: (81) 462530909
Web Site: http://www.hokuo-tokyo.jp
Emp.: 938
Frozen Sweet Mfr
N.A.I.C.S.: 311813

Kanagawa Chuo Kotsu Co., Ltd. (1)
6-18 Yaezaki-cho, Hiratsuka, 254-0811, Kanagawa, Japan
Tel.: (81) 463228800
Web Site: http://www.kanachu.co.jp
Rev.: $773,812,870
Assets: $1,052,252,510
Liabilities: $657,595,850
Net Worth: $394,656,660

ODAKYU ELECTRIC RAILWAY CO., LTD.

Odakyu Electric Railway Co., Ltd.—(Continued)
Earnings: $21,561,820
Fiscal Year-end: 03/31/2024
Transportation & Real Estatate Management Services
N.A.I.C.S.: 485999
Yasunori Hori (Pres & Chm)

Odakyu Agency Co., Ltd. (1)
1-8-3 Nishi-Shinjuku Odakyu Meiji Yasuda Seimei Building, Shinjuku-ku, Tokyo, 160-0023, Japan **(100%)**
Tel.: (81) 333460664
Web Site: https://www.odakyu-ag.co.jp
Emp.: 189
Advetising Agency
N.A.I.C.S.: 541890
Takao Oishi (Auditor)

Odakyu Building Service Co., Ltd (1)
No 1 West Exit Underground Mall Nishi-Shinjuku 1-chome, Shinjuku-ku, Tokyo, 160-0023, Japan
Tel.: (81) 333428117
Web Site: https://www.nishiguchi-chushajyo.jp
Transportation Equipment Maintenance Services
N.A.I.C.S.: 811198

Odakyu Department Store Co., Ltd. (1)
1-5-1 Nishi-Shinjuku, Shinjuku, Tokyo, 160-8001, Japan
Tel.: (81) 570025888
Web Site: https://www.odakyu-dept.co.jp
Sales Range: $1-4.9 Billion
Emp.: 3,570
Department Stores
N.A.I.C.S.: 455110

Odakyu Hakone Highway Bus Co., Ltd (1)
3-1-60 Miyasaka, Setagaya-ku, Tokyo, 156-0051, Japan
Tel.: (81) 334283133
Web Site: http://www.odakyu-hakonehighway.co.jp
Sales Range: $25-49.9 Million
Emp.: 100
Rail Transportation Operating Services
N.A.I.C.S.: 488210

Odakyu Hotels Co., Ltd. (1)
2-7-2 Nishishinjuku, Shinjuku, Tokyo, 160-0023, Japan
Tel.: (81) 333481234
Web Site: http://www.hyattregencytokyo.com
Home Management Services
N.A.I.C.S.: 721110

Odakyu Housing Co., Ltd. (1)
8F Odakyu Nishi-Shinjuku Building 1-47-1 Hatsudai, Shibuya-ku, Tokyo, 151-0061, Japan
Tel.: (81) 333796182
Web Site: https://www.odakyuhousing.co.jp
Housing Services
N.A.I.C.S.: 925110

Odakyu Koutsu Co., Ltd. (1)
1-8-3 Nishi-Shinjuku, Shinjuku, Tokyo, Japan
Tel.: (81) 333492526
Web Site: http://www.odakyu.co.jp
Automotive Distr
N.A.I.C.S.: 423110
Toshimitsu Yamaki (Mgr)

Odakyu Real Estate Co., Ltd (1)
Odakyu Nishi-Shinjuku Building 1-47-1 Hatsudai, Shibuya-ku, Tokyo, 151-0061, Japan
Tel.: (81) 333701110
Web Site: https://www.odakyu-fudosan.co.jp
Emp.: 389
Real Estate Manangement Services
N.A.I.C.S.: 531390

Odakyu Resorts Co., Ltd (1)
2-7-25 Sakae-cho 2nd floor, Minami-Ku, Odawara, 250-0011, Kanagawa, Japan
Tel.: (81) 465241230
Web Site: https://www.odakyu-hotel.co.jp
Emp.: 517
Home Management Services
N.A.I.C.S.: 721110

Odakyu Shoji Co., Ltd (1)
3-1-2 Manpukuji, Aso-ku, Kawasaki, 215-0004, Kanagawa, Japan
Tel.: (81) 449671711
Web Site: http://www.odakyu-shoji.jp
Railway Transportation Services
N.A.I.C.S.: 488210
Michinobu Fujinami (Pres)

Odakyu Sightseeing Service Center Odawara (1)
Odawara-shi Shiroyama 1-1-1, Odakyu Line Counter, Odawara, Japan **(100%)**
Web Site: http://www.odakyu.jp
Travel Services
N.A.I.C.S.: 561599

Okinawa UDS Co., Ltd. (1)
2-16-8 Makishi Bit Plaza Building 3F 5 Minutes, Walk From Miebashi Station, Naha, 900-0013, Okinawa, Japan
Tel.: (81) 98 894 8655
Web Site: https://www.okinawa-uds.co.jp
Architectural Services
N.A.I.C.S.: 541310

Tachikawa Bus Co., Ltd (1)
2-27-27 Takamatsucho, Tachikawa, 190-0011, Tokyo, Japan
Tel.: (81) 425243111
Web Site: http://www.tachikawabus.co.jp
Rail Transportation Operating Services
N.A.I.C.S.: 488210

Tokai Jidosha Co., Ltd (1)
2-28 Nagisacho, Ito, 414-0023, Shizuoka, Japan
Tel.: (81) 557361111
Rail Transportation Operating Services
N.A.I.C.S.: 488210

ODAS ELEKTRIK URETIM VE SANAYI TICARET AS

Barbaros Mh Basak Cengiz St Varyap Meridian Site, No1/D Villa 4 West Atasehir Istanbul, Istanbul, Turkiye
Tel.: (90) 2164741474
Web Site: https://www.odas.com.tr
Year Founded: 2010
ODAS—(IST)
Rev.: $236,001,194
Assets: $353,629,377
Liabilities: $154,312,421
Net Worth: $199,316,957
Earnings: $88,335,318
Emp.: 1,040
Fiscal Year-end: 12/31/22
Electricity Distr
N.A.I.C.S.: 221122

ODAWARA AUTO-MACHINE MFG. CO., LTD.

1-13-1 Nakachi, Odawara, 250-0005, Kanagawa, Japan
Tel.: (81) 465230121
Web Site: https://www.odawarakiki.com
7314—(TKS)
Rev.: $27,863,700
Assets: $54,380,300
Liabilities: $26,452,790
Net Worth: $27,927,510
Earnings: $1,354,190
Emp.: 185
Fiscal Year-end: 12/31/23
Bus Fare Machine Mfr & Sales
N.A.I.C.S.: 333310
Akiyoshi Maruyama (Pres)

ODAWARA ENGINEERING CO., LTD.

1577 Matsudasoryo Matsuda Ashigarakami, Kaisei, 258-0003, Kanagawa, Japan
Tel.: (81) 465831122
Web Site: https://www.odawara-eng.co.jp
Year Founded: 1950
6149—(TKS)
Rev.: $104,244,270
Assets: $189,508,610
Liabilities: $78,365,770
Net Worth: $111,142,840
Earnings: $10,840,610
Fiscal Year-end: 12/31/23
Heating Equipment Mfr Equipment
N.A.I.C.S.: 333414
Takayuki Tsugawa (Chm)

Subsidiaries:

Odawara Automation Nagaoka Co., Ltd. (1)
2-949-7 Nanyo, Nagaoka, 940-1164, Niigata, Japan
Tel.: (81) 258231660
Web Site: https://odawara-automation.co.jp
Emp.: 35
Winding Motor Equipment Mfr & Distr
N.A.I.C.S.: 423120
Masahiko Hoshina (Pres)

Odawara Automation, Inc. (1)
4805 S County Rd 25A, Tipp City, OH 45371
Tel.: (937) 667-8433
Web Site: https://odawara.com
Motor Winding Mfr & Distr
N.A.I.C.S.: 335312

Odawara Engineering (Guangzhou) Co., Ltd. (1)
Room No 2743 Vili International Building No 167 Linhe West Road, Tianhe, Guangzhou, 510610, Guangdong, China
Tel.: (86) 2084454782
Motor Winding Equipment Mfr & Distr
N.A.I.C.S.: 335312

Royal Electric Co., Ltd. (1)
Takanawa JEBL 6F 7F, Minato-ku, Tokyo, 108-0074, Japan **(100%)**
Tel.: (81) 3 54241860
Web Site: http://www.royal-elec.co.jp
Sales Range: $25-49.9 Million
Electrical Equipment Mfr & Distr
N.A.I.C.S.: 335999

Royal Electric Trading (Shenzhen) Co., Ltd. (1)
3A07 Building 13 No 1 Pingan Avenue Pinghu Street, Tiedong Logistics District Pinghu Community Longgang District, Shenzhen, China
Tel.: (86) 75584686041
Motor Winding Equipment Mfr & Distr
N.A.I.C.S.: 335312

ODD BURGER CORPORATION

Western University UCC Building 1151 Richmond Street, London, N6A 2K5, ON, Canada BC
Web Site: https://www.oddburger.com
Year Founded: 2014
ODDAF—(OTCQB)
Rev.: $2,202,213
Assets: $3,897,150
Liabilities: $3,113,262
Net Worth: $783,889
Earnings: ($3,197,159)
Emp.: 15
Fiscal Year-end: 09/30/22
Food Product Mfr & Distr
N.A.I.C.S.: 311813
James McInnes (CEO)

ODDITY TECH LTD.

8 Haharash Street, Tel Aviv, 6761304, Israel
Tel.: (972) 5517517495 IL
Year Founded: 2013
ODD—(NASDAQ)
Rev.: $324,520,000
Assets: $216,408,000
Liabilities: $117,703,000
Net Worth: $98,705,000
Earnings: $21,728,000
Fiscal Year-end: 12/31/22
Information Technology Services
N.A.I.C.S.: 541512
Jonathan Truppman (Chief Legal Officer)

ODDO BHF SCA

INTERNATIONAL PUBLIC

12 boulevard de la Madeleine, 75009, Paris, France
Tel.: (33) 1 4451 8500 FR
Web Site: http://www.oddo.eu
Year Founded: 1849
Rev.: $66,424,120,000
Investment Banking & Asset Management Services
N.A.I.C.S.: 523150
Philippe Oddo (Mng Partner)

Subsidiaries:

Landolt & Cie SA (1)
Chemin de Roseneck 6, PO Box 6739, 1006, Lausanne, Switzerland
Tel.: (41) 21 320 33 11
Web Site: http://www.landoltetcie.ch
Provide Various Banking Services
N.A.I.C.S.: 522110

Subsidiary (Domestic):

Degroof Banque Privee S.A. (2)
18 Avenue Louis Casai, CH-1209, Geneva, Switzerland **(100%)**
Tel.: (41) 228173500
Web Site: http://www.degroof.ch
Sales Range: $50-74.9 Million
Emp.: 30
Commericial Banking
N.A.I.C.S.: 522110
Clode Roensli (CEO)

ODDO BHF Aktiengesellschaft (1)
Bockenheimer Landstrasse 10, 60323, Frankfurt am Main, Germany
Tel.: (49) 69 718 0
Web Site: http://www.bhf-bank.com
Merchant & Commercial Bank
N.A.I.C.S.: 522110
Frank Behrends (Mng Dir)

Subsidiary (Domestic):

BHF Immobilien-GmbH (2)
Bockenheimer Landstrasse 10, 60323, Frankfurt am Main, Germany
Tel.: (49) 69 718 3285
Web Site: http://www.bhf-bank.com
Institutional Asset Management & Real Estate Services
N.A.I.C.S.: 525990
Gerhard Opitz (Member-Mgmt Bd)

BHF Private Equity Management GmbH (2)
Bockenheimer Landstrasse 10, 60323, Frankfurt am Main, Germany
Tel.: (49) 697183621
Web Site: http://www.bhf-bank.com
Financial Investment Services
N.A.I.C.S.: 523999
Kirsten von Langenthal (Member-Mgmt Bd)

BHF Private Equity Treuhand- und Beratungsgesellschaft mbH (2)
Bockenheimer Landstrasse 10, 60323, Frankfurt, Germany
Tel.: (49) 69 718 3621
Web Site: http://www.bhf-bank.com
Investment Banking & Securities Dealing Services
N.A.I.C.S.: 523150
Ulrich Lingenthal (Member-Mgmt Bd)

BHF Trust Management Gesellschaft fur Vermogensverwaltung mbH (2)
Bockenheimer Landstrasse 10, 60323, Frankfurt, Germany
Tel.: (49) 697182130
Web Site: http://www.bhf-bank.com
Management of Securities for Private Investors & Foundations
N.A.I.C.S.: 523150
Wolfgang Baums (Member-Mgmt Bd)

Subsidiary (Non-US):

BHF-Bank (Schweiz) AG (2)
Schulhausstrasse 6, Postfach 8027, Zurich, Switzerland **(100%)**
Tel.: (41) 44 209 7511
Web Site: http://www.bhf-bank.ch
Investment Advisory, Securities Dealing & Portfolio Management Services
N.A.I.C.S.: 523940
Hans-Peter Fornoff (Member-Mgmt Bd)

AND PRIVATE COMPANIES

Subsidiary (Domestic):

BHF Zurich Family Office AG (3)
Schulhausstrasse 6, Zurich, 8002, Switzerland
Tel.: (41) 44 2097567
Web Site: http://www.oddo-bhf.com
Emp.: 2,500
Fund Management Services
N.A.I.C.S.: 523940

Subsidiary (Domestic):

Frankfurt-Trust Investment-Gesellschaft mbH (2)
Bockenheimer Landstrasse 10, 60323, Frankfurt am Main, Germany (100%)
Tel.: (49) 69920500
Web Site: http://www.frankfurt-trust.de
Employee Benefits, Trust Services, Institutional Asset Mannagement, Saving & Investing Services
N.A.I.C.S.: 525910
Karl Stacker *(Member-Mgmt Bd)*

Subsidiary (Non-US):

Frankfurt - Trust Invest Luxembourg AG (3)
534 rue de Neudorf, 2220, Luxembourg, Luxembourg (100%)
Tel.: (352) 4576761
Web Site: http://www.frankfurt-trust.lu
Portfolio Management Services
N.A.I.C.S.: 523940
Monika Anell *(Mng Dir)*

ODEA BANK AS
Levent 199 Buyukdere Caddesi No 199 Kat 33-40, Sisli, Istanbul, 34394, Turkiye
Tel.: (90) 2123048444
Web Site:
   http://www.odeabank.com.tr
ODEA—(IST)
Sales Range: Less than $1 Million
Banking Services
N.A.I.C.S.: 522110
Mert Oncu *(CEO & Gen Mgr)*

ODELIC COMPANY LIMITED
1-17-5 Miyamae, Suginami-ku, Tokyo, 168-0081, Japan
Tel.: (81) 333321111
Web Site: http://www.odelic.co.jp
Year Founded: 1951
Rev.: $333,690,735
Assets: $378,557,749
Liabilities: $83,174,161
Net Worth: $295,383,588
Earnings: $29,996,518
Fiscal Year-end: 03/31/19
Electric Lighting Fixture Mfr
N.A.I.C.S.: 335131
Masato Ito *(Pres)*

Subsidiaries:

Yamada Shomei Lighting Co., Ltd. (1)
3-8-11 Sotokanda, Chiyoda-ku, Tokyo, 101-0021, Japan
Tel.: (81) 332535161
Web Site: http://www.yamada-shomei.co.jp
Lighting Equipment Mfr & Retailer
N.A.I.C.S.: 335139

ODELO GMBH
Hedelfinger Strasse 137, 70329, Stuttgart, Germany
Tel.: (49) 711185630
Web Site: http://www.odelo.de
Year Founded: 1935
Sales Range: $250-299.9 Million
Emp.: 1,800
Motor Signal Light Mfr
N.A.I.C.S.: 336390
Klaus Holeczek *(CEO)*

Subsidiaries:

Odelo LED GmbH (1)
Carl-Friedrich-Gauss-Strasse 1, 47475, Kamp-Lintfort, Germany
Tel.: (49) 28 42 985 0
Automobile Parts Mfr
N.A.I.C.S.: 336390

odelo Deutschland GmbH (1)
Robert-Bosch-Srasse 3, 73312, Geislingen, Germany
Tel.: (49) 73 31 26 0
Automobile Parts Mfr
N.A.I.C.S.: 336390

odelo Slovenija d.o.o. (1)
Tovarniska c12, 3312, Prebold, Slovenia
Tel.: (386) 3 703 45 00
Automobile Parts Distr
N.A.I.C.S.: 423120
Simon Sarlah *(Mgr-Quality)*

ODESSA CABLE PLANT ODESKABEL PJSC
Mykolaivska doroga 144, 65102, Odessa, Ukraine
Tel.: (380) 487161123
Web Site:
   https://www.odeskabel.com
Year Founded: 1949
OCAB—(UKR)
Sales Range: Less than $1 Million
Cable Products Mfr
N.A.I.C.S.: 335921

ODESSA MINERALS LIMITED
Suite 1 295 Rokeby Road, Subiaco, 6008, WA, Australia
Tel.: (61) 865552950 AU
Web Site:
   https://odessaminerals.com.au
Year Founded: 1986
ODE—(ASX)
Rev.: $78,612
Assets: $4,463,198
Liabilities: $98,398
Net Worth: $4,364,800
Earnings: ($531,791)
Fiscal Year-end: 06/30/24
Investment Services
N.A.I.C.S.: 523999
Zane Lewis *(Bd of Dirs & Sec)*

Subsidiaries:

Flamingo Ventures Pty. Ltd. (1)
204 Clarence Street Level 1, Sydney, 2000, NSW, Australia
Tel.: (61) 1300556368
Telephone & Data Communication Services
N.A.I.C.S.: 561421

ODESSOS SHIPREPAIR YARD S.A.
Island Zone, 9000, Varna, Bulgaria
Tel.: (359) 52601107
Web Site: https://www.odessos-yard.bg
Year Founded: 1963
ODES—(BUL)
Sales Range: Less than $1 Million
Equipment Repair Services
N.A.I.C.S.: 811114

ODEWALD & COMPAGNIE GESELLSCHAFT FUR BETEILIGUNGEN MBH
Franzosische Strasse 8, 10117, Berlin, Germany
Tel.: (49) 302017230 De
Web Site: http://www.odewald.com
Year Founded: 1997
Sales Range: $25-49.9 Million
Emp.: 20
Privater Equity Firm
N.A.I.C.S.: 523999
Ernst-Moritz Lipp *(Mng Dir)*

Subsidiaries:

OYSTAR Holding GmbH (1)
Lorenzstrasse 6, Stutensee, 76297, Germany
Tel.: (49) 72447470
Web Site: http://www.oystar-group.com
Sales Range: $500-549.9 Million
Holding Company; Packaging Machinery Mfr
N.A.I.C.S.: 551112
Markus Ehl *(CEO)*

ODFJELL DRILLING LTD.
Kokstadflaten 35, Kokstad, NO-5257, Bergen, Norway
Tel.: (47) 55998900
Web Site:
   https://www.odfjelldrilling.com
OD3—(DEU)
Rev.: $649,500,000
Assets: $2,219,300,000
Liabilities: $1,010,800,000
Net Worth: $1,208,500,000
Earnings: $129,600,000
Emp.: 1,358
Fiscal Year-end: 12/31/22
Holding Company; Drilling, Well Service & Engineering
N.A.I.C.S.: 551112
Simen Lieungh *(CEO-Odfjell Drilling AS)*

Subsidiaries:

Deep Sea Management FZE Ltd. (1)
Suite 3201 32nd Floor Tiffany Tower W Cluster, PO Box 17354, Dubai, United Arab Emirates
Tel.: (971) 4 8865884
Oil & Gas Field Drilling Services
N.A.I.C.S.: 213111

Odfjell Drilling (UK) Ltd. (1)
Bergen House Crawpeel Road, Altens, Aberdeen, AB12 3LG, United Kingdom
Tel.: (44) 1 224 856000
Oil & Gas Field Drilling Services
N.A.I.C.S.: 213111
Gail Farquhar *(Mgr-HR)*

Odfjell Drilling Philippines Corporation (1)
27th Floor Zuellig Building Makati Avenue corner Paseo de Roxas, Makati, 1225, Philippines
Tel.: (63) 2 858 2800
Drilling Oil & Gas Services
N.A.I.C.S.: 213111

Odfjell Offshore Ltd. (1)
Sandslimarka 63, NO-5863, Bergen, Norway
Tel.: (47) 55998900
Web Site: http://www.odfjelloffshore.com
Offshore Drilling Rigs Owner & Operator
N.A.I.C.S.: 333132

Odfjell Well Service (UK) Ltd. (1)
Bergen House Crawpeel Road, Altens, Aberdeen, AB12 3LG, United Kingdom
Tel.: (44) 122 485 6000
Tubular Running Services
N.A.I.C.S.: 213112

Odfjell Well Services AS (1)
Hammaren 19, PO Box 152, 4098, Tananger, Norway
Tel.: (47) 51648400
Web Site:
   https://www.odfjellwellservices.com
Tubular Running Services
N.A.I.C.S.: 213112

Odfjell Well Services Cooperatief U.A. (1)
Stephensonweg 18A, 7741 KW, Coevorden, Netherlands
Tel.: (31) 524527000
Tubular Running Services
N.A.I.C.S.: 213112

Odfjell Well Services Europe AS (1)
Tvaerkaj 4, Esbjerg, Ribe, 6700, Denmark
Tel.: (45) 76129012
Oil & Gas Field Drilling Services
N.A.I.C.S.: 213111

Odfjell Well Services Ltd. (1)
B56CR01 Al Hesah Street N600 Junction 9, Post Box 17354, Before exit gate 8 Jafza North Jebel Ali Freezone, Dubai, United Arab Emirates
Tel.: (971) 4 807 7800
Tubular Running Services
N.A.I.C.S.: 213112

Odfjell Well Services S.R.L. (1)
Ploiesti West Park SME Building Modules 13 and 15 Office 3B, Aricestii Rahtivani Village Aricestii Rahtivani Commune Prahova County, Ploiesti, 107025, Romania
Tel.: (40) 34 422 0102
Tubular Running Services
N.A.I.C.S.: 213112

ODFJELL SE
Conrad Mohrsv 29, PO Box 6101, Postterminalen, 5892, Bergen, Norway
Tel.: (47) 55270000 NO
Web Site: http://www.odfjell.com
Year Founded: 1916
ODF—(OSL)
Rev.: $42,324,000
Assets: $1,994,323,000
Liabilities: $1,195,813,000
Net Worth: $798,510,000
Earnings: $203,304,000
Emp.: 2,303
Fiscal Year-end: 12/31/23
Holding Company; Chemicals & Other Specialty Liquids Transportation, Storage & Related Logistics Services
N.A.I.C.S.: 551112
Laurence Ward Odfjell *(Chm)*

Subsidiaries:

Flumar Transportes de Quimicos e Gases Ltda (1)
Av Paulista 460, Sao Paulo, 01310-000, Brazil
Tel.: (55) 1135495800
Emp.: 100
Deep Sea Freight Transportation
N.A.I.C.S.: 483111
Roberto Ferreira *(Mng Dir)*

Norfra Shipping AS (1)
Conrad Mohrsv 29, PO Box 6101, Postterminalen, 5892, Bergen, Norway (100%)
Tel.: (47) 55270000
Web Site: http://www.odfjell.com
Freight Transportation Arrangement
N.A.I.C.S.: 488510

Odfjell Ahrenkiel Europe GmbH (1)
Admiralitatstr 45, Hamburg, Germany (49%)
Tel.: (49) 4024838307
Web Site: http://www.odfjell.com
Deep Sea Freight Transportation
N.A.I.C.S.: 483111

Odfjell Argentina SA (1)
Alicia Moreau de Justo 1960 Office 202, Puerto Madero, 1107, Buenos Aires, Argentina
Tel.: (54) 1143137837
Web Site: https://www.odfjell.com
Sales Range: $25-49.9 Million
Emp.: 12
Freight Transportation Arrangement
N.A.I.C.S.: 488510

Odfjell Asia II Pte. Ltd. (1)
6 Shenton Way 27-08/09 Dbs Tower 2, OUE Downtown 2, Singapore, 68809, Singapore (100%)
Tel.: (65) 63491300
Web Site: http://www.odfjell.com
Sales Range: $25-49.9 Million
Freight Transportation Arrangement
N.A.I.C.S.: 488510

Odfjell Australia Pty Ltd. (1)
Suite 4 Level 1 443 Little Collins Street, PO Box 1279, Melbourne, 3001, VIC, Australia (100%)
Tel.: (61) 396422210
Web Site: http://www.odfjell.com
Sales Range: $25-49.9 Million
Emp.: 2
Freight Transportation Arrangement
N.A.I.C.S.: 488510
Adam Kuner *(Mng Dir)*

Odfjell Brasil-Representacoes Ltda (1)
Av Paulista 460 - 18 andar, Sao Paulo,

ODFJELL SE

Odfjell SE—(Continued)
01310-000, Brazil **(100%)**
Tel.: (55) 1135495800
Web Site: http://www.odfjell.com
Sales Range: $25-49.9 Million
Emp.: 60
Freight Transportation Arrangement
N.A.I.C.S.: 488510

Odfjell Chemical Tankers AS (1)
Conrad Mohrsv 29, PO Box 6101, Postterminalen, Bergen, 5892, Norway **(100%)**
Tel.: (47) 55270000
Web Site: http://www.odfjell.com
Sales Range: $50-74.9 Million
Emp.: 250
Water Transportation
N.A.I.C.S.: 488390

Subsidiary (Non-US):

Odfjell Chemical Tankers Netherlands BV (2)
Oude Maasweg 6, PO Box 5010, 3197 KJ, Rotterdam, Netherlands **(100%)**
Tel.: (31) 102953666
Sales Range: $75-99.9 Million
Emp.: 10
Trusts Estates & Agency Accounts
N.A.I.C.S.: 525920

Odfjell Chemical Tankers II AS (1)
Conrad Mohrs Vei 29, PO Box 6101, Postterminalen, 5892, Bergen, Norway **(100%)**
Tel.: (47) 55270000
Web Site: http://www.odfjell.com
Water Transportation
N.A.I.C.S.: 488390

Odfjell Holdings (US) Inc. (1)
13100 Space Center Blvd Ste 600, Houston, TX 77059
Tel.: (713) 844-2200
Web Site: http://www.odfjell.com
Emp.: 100
Holding Company; Chemical Storage Terminal Operator & Deep Sea Freight Transportation Arrangement Services
N.A.I.C.S.: 551112
Joe Nassif *(Pres)*

Subsidiary (Domestic):

Odfjell USA (Houston) Inc. (2)
13100 Space Ctr Blvd Ste 600, Houston, TX 77059
Tel.: (713) 844-2200
Web Site: https://www.odfjell.com
Deep Sea Chemical Transportation Arrangement
N.A.I.C.S.: 488510

Odfjell Japan Ltd. (1)
Ogawa Bldg 8f 2-2 Uchikanda 1-chome, Chiyoda-ku, Tokyo, 101-0047, Japan **(100%)**
Tel.: (81) 332598555
Web Site: http://www.odfjell.com
Sales Range: $25-49.9 Million
Freight Transportation Arrangement
N.A.I.C.S.: 488510

Odfjell Korea Ltd. (1)
Room 1815 Gwanghwaumun Officia Bldg 92 Saemoonan-ro, Jongno-gu, Seoul, 03186, Korea (South)
Tel.: (82) 27759760
Web Site: http://www.odfjell.com
Sales Range: $25-49.9 Million
Warehousing & Storage
N.A.I.C.S.: 493190
Dh Chong *(Mgr-Chartering)*

Odfjell Management Consultancy (Shanghai) Co Ltd (1)
Suit B 13F Huamin Empire Plaza 728 Yan An West, Shanghai, 200050, China
Tel.: (86) 2152399469
Sales Range: $25-49.9 Million
Emp.: 7
Business Management Consulting Services
N.A.I.C.S.: 541611
Zhu Guohe *(Gen Mgr)*

Odfjell Management Philippines Inc. (1)
5F Unit 501 W Mall Building Diosdado Macapagal, Avenue corner Coral Way, Pasay, Philippines
Tel.: (63) 284055020
Marine Transportation Services
N.A.I.C.S.: 541614

Odfjell Maritime Services AS (1)
Conrad Mohrsv 29, PO Box 6101, 5892, Bergen, Norway
Tel.: (47) 55270000
Chemical Transportation & Storage Services
N.A.I.C.S.: 493110

Odfjell Netherlands BV (1)
Oude Maasweg 6, PO Box 5010, Rotterdam, 3197 KG, Netherlands **(100%)**
Tel.: (31) 102953666
Sales Range: $25-49.9 Million
Emp.: 10
Deep Sea Freight Transportation
N.A.I.C.S.: 483111

Odfjell Peru S.A.C. (1)
Av Enrique Meiggs 240, Callao, Peru
Tel.: (51) 16140800
Sales Range: $25-49.9 Million
Emp.: 40
Deep Sea Transportation Services
N.A.I.C.S.: 483111

Odfjell Projects AS (1)
Conrad Mohrs Veg 29, Bergen, 5072, Norway
Tel.: (47) 55 27 00 00
Chemical Products Logistics Services
N.A.I.C.S.: 541614

Odfjell Seachem AS (1)
Conrad Mohrs Vei 29, PO Box 6101, Postterminalen, 5892, Bergen, Norway **(100%)**
Tel.: (47) 55270000
Web Site: http://www.odfjell.com
Water Transportation
N.A.I.C.S.: 488390

Subsidiary (Non-US):

Odfjell Seachem South Africa (Pty) Ltd. (2)
The Sharaf House La Lucia Ridge, 2 Sinembe Crescent, 4051, Durban, South Africa **(100%)**
Tel.: (27) 315834470
Web Site: http://odfjell.com
Sales Range: $25-49.9 Million
Emp.: 10
Freight Transportation Arrangement
N.A.I.C.S.: 488510

Odfjell Ship Management (Philippines) Inc (1)
2315 Leon Guinto St, Malate, Manila, 1004, Philippines
Tel.: (63) 2 52 80341
Marine Transportation Services
N.A.I.C.S.: 483111
Agnes Enesio *(Head-Crew & Family Affairs-Legal)*

Odfjell Singapore Pte. Ltd. (1)
6 Shenton Way 27-08/09 OUE Downtown 2, Singapore, 068809, Singapore
Tel.: (65) 63491300
Web Site: http://www.odfjell.no
Sales Range: $25-49.9 Million
Emp.: 60
Deep Sea Chemical Transportation Arrangement; Petroleum & Chemical Terminal Operator
N.A.I.C.S.: 488510

Odfjell Tankers Europe AS (1)
Conrad Mohrsv 29, PO Box 6101, 5892, Bergen, Norway
Tel.: (47) 5 527 0000
Web Site: https://www.odfjell.com
Bulk Liquid Transportation Services
N.A.I.C.S.: 484230

Odfjell Terminals AS (1) **(51%)**
Tel.: (47) 55270000
Holding Company; Chemical & Petroleum Storage Terminal Operator
N.A.I.C.S.: 551112

Subsidiary (Non-US):

Odfjell Terminals B.V. (2)
Oude Maasweg 6, Rotterdam, 3197 KJ, Netherlands
Tel.: (31) 102954700
Holding Company; Chemical & Petroleum Storage Terminal Operator; Corporate Office
N.A.I.C.S.: 551112
Ake Henrik Gregertsen *(Interim Pres)*

Joint Venture (Non-US):

Advario Singapore Chemical Pte, Ltd. (3)
1 Seraya Avenue, Jurong Island, Singapore, 628208, Singapore
Tel.: (65) 64731700
Web Site: https://advario.com
Petroleum & Chemical Storage Terminal Operator
N.A.I.C.S.: 493190

Subsidiary (Non-US):

Odfjell Terminals (Dalian) Co Ltd. (3)
New Port Economy & Technology Development Zone, Zhongshan District, Dalian, 116601, China
Tel.: (86) 41187595500
Web Site: http://www.odfjell.com
Freight Transportation Arrangement
N.A.I.C.S.: 488510

Subsidiary (US):

Odfjell Terminals (Houston) Inc. (3)
13100 Space Ctr Blvd Ste 600, Houston, TX 77059
Tel.: (713) 844-2300
Chemical & Petroleum Storage Terminal Operator
N.A.I.C.S.: 493190
Koert Schouten *(CFO)*

Subsidiary (Domestic):

Odfjell Terminals (Rotterdam) B.V. (3)
Oude Maasweg 6, Rotterdam, 3197 KJ, Netherlands
Tel.: (31) 10 295 3400
Web Site: http://www.odfjell.com
Sales Range: $10-24.9 Million
Petroleum & Chemical Storage Terminal Operator
N.A.I.C.S.: 493190

Odfjell Terminals EMEA B.V. (3)
Oude Maasweg 6, 3197 KJ, Rotterdam, Netherlands
Tel.: (31) 10 2953666
Holding Company; Regional Managing Office; Chemical Storage Terminals Operator
N.A.I.C.S.: 551112

Joint Venture (Non-US):

Oiltanking Odfjell Terminals & Co. LLC (4)
322 Falaj Al Qabail, PO Box 369, Plot 28 Sohar Industrial Port, Sohar, Oman
Tel.: (968) 2670 0300
Web Site: http://www.oiltanking.com
Petroleum & Chemical Storage Terminal Operator
N.A.I.C.S.: 493190

ODFJELL TECHNOLOGY LTD.

Lower Ground Floor, Prime View Prime Four Business Park Kingswells, Aberdeen, AB15 8PU, United Kingdom
Tel.: (44) 1224856000
Web Site: https://www.odfjelltechnology.com
Year Founded: 1973
OTL—(OSL)
Rev.: $463,827,822
Assets: $341,271,014
Liabilities: $241,825,236
Net Worth: $99,445,779
Earnings: $31,793,830
Emp.: 2,398
Fiscal Year-end: 12/31/23
Engineeering Services
N.A.I.C.S.: 541330
Elisabeth Haram *(Exec VP)*

Subsidiaries:

Odfjell Arabia Drilling Services LLC (1)
Eastern Province-Al Khobar 3599, At Taawun Dist, Al Khobar, 34632-7343, Saudi Arabia
Tel.: (966) 138107850
Engineeering Services
N.A.I.C.S.: 541330

Odfjell Technology AS (1)
Kokstadflaten 35, NO-5257, Kokstad, Norway
Tel.: (47) 55998900
Well Drilling & Engineering Services
N.A.I.C.S.: 213111

ODIN ENERGY LIMITED

Suite 2 16 Ord Street, West Perth, 6005, WA, Australia
Tel.: (61) 894292900
Web Site:
http://www.odinenergy.com.au
Year Founded: 2007
Sales Range: Less than $1 Million
Oil & Gas Exploration Services
N.A.I.C.S.: 213112
Alexander S. Bajada *(Chm)*

ODIN METALS LIMITED

35 Richardson Street, West Perth, 6005, WA, Australia
Tel.: (61) 861170447
Web Site:
http://www.odinmetals.com.au
G11—(ASX)
Rev.: $22,181
Assets: $5,661,719
Liabilities: $238,214
Net Worth: $5,423,506
Earnings: $(704,993)
Fiscal Year-end: 06/30/24
Gold & Silver Mining Services
N.A.I.C.S.: 212220
Jason Bontempo *(Exec Dir)*

ODISHA HYDRO POWER CORPORATION LTD.

Odisha State Police Housing & Welfare, Corporation Building Vanivihar Chowk Janpath, Bhubaneswar, India
Tel.: (91) 674 2542983
Web Site: http://www.ohpcltd.com
Year Founded: 1995
Hydroelectric Power Generation
N.A.I.C.S.: 221111

Subsidiaries:

Odisha Power Generation Corporation Limited (1)
Zone-a 7th Floor Fortune Towers, Chandrasekharpur, Bhubaneswar, 751023, Odisha, India **(51%)**
Tel.: (91) 6742303765
Web Site: http://www.opgc.co.in
Eletric Power Generation Services
N.A.I.C.S.: 221118
Indranil Dutta *(Mng Dir)*

ODK SOLUTIONS COMPANY, LTD.

6-7 Doshomachi 1-chome, Chuo-ku, Osaka, 541-0045, Japan
Tel.: (81) 662020413
Web Site: https://www.odk.co.jp
Year Founded: 1963
3839—(TKS)
Rev.: $53,240,000
Assets: $77,730,400
Liabilities: $22,215,600
Net Worth: $55,514,800
Earnings: $1,877,920
Emp.: 637
Fiscal Year-end: 03/31/22
Information Processing & Outsourcing Services
N.A.I.C.S.: 519290
Katsune Hidekazu *(Pres)*

Subsidiaries:

Fplus, Inc. (1)
Gakken Building 5F 2-11-8 Nishigotanda,

AND PRIVATE COMPANIES

Shinagawa-ku, Tokyo, 141-0031, Japan
Tel.: (81) 357596080
Mobile Application Development Services
N.A.I.C.S.: 541511
Sadamu Okuchi (Pres)

ODLANDER FREDRIKSON & CO. AB
Engelbrektsplan 1, 114 34, Stockholm, Sweden
Tel.: (46) 84425850
Web Site: http://www.healthcap.eu
Year Founded: 1996
Sales Range: $25-49.9 Million
Emp.: 23
Investment Services
N.A.I.C.S.: 523999
Bjorn Odlander (Founder & Mng Partner)

Subsidiaries:

HealthCap GP SA (1)
18 Avenue D'Ouchy, 1006, Lausanne, Switzerland
Tel.: (41) 216143500
Medical Device Distr
N.A.I.C.S.: 423450

Odlander Fredrikson SA (1)
18 Avenue D'Ouchy, CH-1006, Lausanne, Switzerland
Tel.: (41) 216143500
Web Site: http://www.healthcape.ch
Investment Services
N.A.I.C.S.: 523999
Peder Fredrikson (Mng Dir)

ODLEWNIE POLSKIE S.A.
inz Wladyslawa Rogowskiego 22, 27-200, Starachowice, Poland
Tel.: (48) 412758600
Web Site: https://ww.odlewniepolskie.pl
Year Founded: 1899
ODL—(WAR)
Rev.: $67,910,315
Assets: $46,856,961
Liabilities: $10,108,486
Net Worth: $36,748,476
Earnings: $8,876,778
Fiscal Year-end: 12/31/23
Iron Mfr
N.A.I.C.S.: 331511
Zbigniew Ronduda (Chm-Mgmt Bd & CEO)

ODONTOPREV S.A.
Av Dr Marcos Penteado de Ulhoa Rodrigues, 939-14 andar Edificio Jatoba Torre II Tambore, Barueri, 06460-040, Sao Paulo, Brazil
Tel.: (55) 1148788200   BR
Web Site: http://www.odontoprev.com.br
Sales Range: $300-349.9 Million
Dental Care Services
N.A.I.C.S.: 541715
Manoel Antonio Peres (Vice Chm)

Subsidiaries:

Adcon Administradora de Convenios Odontologicos Ltda. (1)
Rua Parana 29, Pituba, 41830-170, Salvador, Bahia, Brazil
Tel.: (55) 82 21215416
Dental Insurance Services
N.A.I.C.S.: 524114

Bradesco Dental SA (1)
Barao De Itapagipe 225, Anexo Parte, Rio de Janeiro, 20261-901, Brazil
Tel.: (55) 3132739936
Web Site: http://www.bradescodental.com.br
Dental Insurance Services
N.A.I.C.S.: 524114

Prontodente Odontologia Integral Ltda (1)
Largo de Sao Francisco, Centro, Rio de Janeiro, 20051 070, Brazil
Tel.: (55) 21 3523 2465

Web Site: http://www.prontodente.com.br
Dental Care Services
N.A.I.C.S.: 339116

Rede Dental (1)
Rua Padre Rolim 523Rua Padre Rolim 523, Santa Efigenia, Belo Horizonte, 30141 970, Minas Gerais, Brazil
Tel.: (55) 31 2105 7225
Web Site: http://www.rededental.com.br
Dental Care Services
N.A.I.C.S.: 339116

ODS ELEKTRO-BIJELJINA A.D. BIJELJINA
Majevicka 97, 76 300, Bijeljina, Bosnia & Herzegovina
Tel.: (387) 55226700   BA
Web Site: https://www.elektrobijeljina.com
Year Founded: 2006
ELBJ—(BANJ)
Sales Range: $50-74.9 Million
Emp.: 920
Electric Power Distr
N.A.I.C.S.: 221122
Milorad Solakovic (Deputy Chm-Supervisory Bd)

ODU STECKVERBINDUNGS-SYSTEME GMBH & CO. KG
Pregelstrsse 11, 84453, Muhldorf, Germany
Tel.: (49) 863161560   De
Web Site: http://www.odu.de
Year Founded: 1942
Sales Range: $100-124.9 Million
Emp.: 1,500
Connector System Distr
N.A.I.C.S.: 423690
Kurt Woelfl (Mng Dir)

Subsidiaries:

ODU (Shanghai) International Trading Co., Ltd. (1)
Level3 Unit T15-3 No 999 Ningqiao Road, Shanghai, 201 206, China
Tel.: (86) 21583478280
Web Site: http://www.odu-china.com
Electronic Parts Distr
N.A.I.C.S.: 423690

ODU Denmark ApS (1)
Lergravsvej 53, 2300, Copenhagen, Denmark
Tel.: (45) 22335335
Web Site: http://www.odu-denmark.dk
Electronic Parts Distr
N.A.I.C.S.: 423690
Mads Haastrup (Reg Mgr-Sls)

ODU France SARL (1)
16 Rue de la Republique, 95570, Bouffemont, France
Tel.: (33) 139354690
Web Site: http://www.odu.fr
Electronic Parts Distr
N.A.I.C.S.: 423690

ODU Italia S.R.L. (1)
Leonardo da Vinci 12, 39100, Bolzano, Italy
Tel.: (39) 03318708847
Electronic Parts Distr
N.A.I.C.S.: 423690

ODU Scandinavia AB (1)
Hantverkaregatan 18, 761 30, Norrtalje, Sweden
Tel.: (46) 17618261
Web Site: http://www.odu.se
Electronic Parts Distr
N.A.I.C.S.: 423690

ODU-UK Ltd. (1)
The Technology Centre Epinal Way, Loughborough, LE11 3GE, United Kingdom
Tel.: (44) 1509266433
Web Site: http://www.odu-uk.co.uk
Electronic Parts Distr
N.A.I.C.S.: 423690

ODU-USA Inc. (1)
4010 Adolfo Rd, Camarillo, CA 93012
Tel.: (805) 484-0540
Web Site: http://www.odu-usa.com

Electronic Parts Distr
N.A.I.C.S.: 423690
Joe Vigil (Mgr-Bus Dev)

ODYSIGHT.AI INC.
Suite 7A Industrial Park, PO Box 3030, Omer Industrial Park, Omer, 8496500, Israel
Tel.: (972) 733704691   NV
Web Site: https://odysight.ai
Year Founded: 2013
ODYS—(OTCQB)
Rev.: $3,033,000
Assets: $22,829,000
Liabilities: $5,022,000
Net Worth: $17,807,000
Earnings: ($9,445,000)
Emp.: 49
Fiscal Year-end: 12/31/23
Internet Food Retailer
N.A.I.C.S.: 541511
Benad Goldwasser (Chm)

ODYSSEAN INVESTMENT TRUST PLC
Frostrow Capital LLP 25 Southampton Buildings, London, WC2A 1AL, United Kingdom
Tel.: (44) 2030084910
Web Site: https://www.oitplc.com
OIT—(LSE)
Rev.: $2,769,503
Assets: $238,788,185
Liabilities: $2,033,577
Net Worth: $236,754,608
Earnings: ($8,481,444)
Fiscal Year-end: 03/31/24
Portfolio Management & Investment Advice
N.A.I.C.S.: 523940
Jane Tufnell (Chm)

ODYSSEY CORPORATION LTD.
102 Haridarshan Building Bhogilal Phadia Road Kandivali West, Vile Parle West, Mumbai, 400056, India
Tel.: (91) 2226241111
Web Site: https://www.odysseycorp.in
531996—(BOM)
Rev.: $3,846,423
Assets: $8,774,609
Liabilities: $260,856
Net Worth: $8,513,753
Earnings: $858,419
Fiscal Year-end: 03/31/21
Corporate Finance Advisory Services
N.A.I.C.S.: 523940
Hiten Ramniklal Mehta (Chm)

ODYSSEY GOLD LTD
Level 9 28 The Esplanade, Perth, 6000, WA, Australia
Tel.: (61) 893226322   AU
Web Site: https://odysseygold.com.au
ODY—(ASX)
Rev.: $87,794
Assets: $8,006,023
Liabilities: $110,138
Net Worth: $7,895,885
Earnings: ($1,363,821)
Fiscal Year-end: 06/30/24
Oil & Gas Producer
N.A.I.C.S.: 336611
Ian P. Middlemas (Chm)

ODYSSEY RESOURCES LIMITED
101-1111 St-Charles St West, West Tower, Longueuil, J4K 5G4, QC, Canada
Tel.: (450) 677-1233
Web Site: https://www.odysseyresources.com
ODX.H—(TSXV)

Assets: $23,813
Liabilities: $1,995
Net Worth: $21,818
Earnings: $522,319
Fiscal Year-end: 12/31/23
Silver Mining & Exploration Services
N.A.I.C.S.: 212220
Alain Krushnisky (CFO)

ODYSSEY TECHNOLOGIES LTD.
5th Floor Dowlath Towers 63 Taylors Road Kilpauk, Chennai, 600 010, India
Tel.: (91) 4426450082
Web Site: https://www.odysseytec.com
530175—(BOM)
Rev.: $3,115,065
Assets: $6,006,055
Liabilities: $324,417
Net Worth: $5,681,638
Earnings: $523,482
Emp.: 161
Fiscal Year-end: 03/31/23
Information Technology Services
N.A.I.C.S.: 519290
B. Robert Raja (Chm & Mng Dir)

ODZACAR A.D.
Apatinski put 16, Sombor, Serbia
Tel.: (381) 25482880
Year Founded: 1991
ODZS—(BEL)
Sales Range: Less than $1 Million
Building Cleaning Services
N.A.I.C.S.: 561790
Zlatoslav Vranjes (Board of Directors & Exec Dir)

ODZACAR A.D.
Marsala Tita 116, Vrbas, Serbia
Tel.: (381) 21705041
Year Founded: 2002
ODZV—(BEL)
Sales Range: Less than $1 Million
Emp.: 8
Building Cleaning Services
N.A.I.C.S.: 561790
Mrkoje Tomovic (Exec Dir)

OE SOLUTIONS CO., LTD.
53 Cheomdanyeonsinro 30beongil, Buk-Gu, Gwangju, 61080, Korea (South)
Tel.: (82) 629605252
Web Site: https://www.oesolutions.com
Year Founded: 2003
138080—(KRS)
Rev.: $59,023,706
Assets: $144,134,510
Liabilities: $30,882,737
Net Worth: $113,251,774
Earnings: ($4,584,185)
Emp.: 362
Fiscal Year-end: 12/31/22
Optoelectronic Transceiver Mfr
N.A.I.C.S.: 334220
Yong Kwan Park (Co-Founder, Chm & CEO)

OEM INTERNATIONAL AB
PO Box 1009, 573 28, Tranas, Sweden
Tel.: (46) 752424000
Web Site: http://www.oem.se
Year Founded: 1074
OEM.B—(OMX)
Rev.: $400,764,224
Assets: $243,146,736
Liabilities: $76,397,664
Net Worth: $166,749,072
Earnings: $38,735,984
Emp.: 895
Fiscal Year-end: 12/31/20

OEM INTERNATIONAL AB

OEM International AB—(Continued)

Automated Components & Systems Mfr
N.A.I.C.S.: 335999
Urban Malm *(Mng Dir-OEM Electronics AB)*

Subsidiaries:

AB Ernst Hj Rydahl Bromsbandfabrik (1)
Brisgatan 19, 652 21, Karlstad, Sweden
Tel.: (46) 105509400
Web Site: https://www.rydahls.com
Brake System Mfr
N.A.I.C.S.: 336340

ATC Adhesive Tape Converting AB (1)
Matarvagen 17A, 196 37, Kungsangen, Sweden
Tel.: (46) 856470880
Web Site: https://atc.se
Tape Mfr & Distr
N.A.I.C.S.: 322230

Agolux AB (1)
Dalagatan 4, 573 42, Tranas, Sweden
Tel.: (46) 752424550
Web Site: https://www.agolux.se
Lighting Design Services
N.A.I.C.S.: 541490

Akkupojat OY (1)
Satakunnankatu 38, 28130, Pori, Finland
Tel.: (358) 26318600
Web Site: https://www.akkupojat.fi
Battery Material Mfr & Distr
N.A.I.C.S.: 335910

All Motion Technology AB (1)
Tumstocksvagen 11B, Taby, 187 66, Sweden
Tel.: (46) 84 46 37 70
Web Site: http://www.allmotion.se
Sales Range: $25-49.9 Million
Emp.: 25
Precision Turned Component Distr
N.A.I.C.S.: 423830
Fredrik Falkenstrom *(Gen Mgr)*

Apex Dynamics Sweden AB (1)
Fredriksbergsgatan 2, 573 92, Tranas, Sweden
Tel.: (46) 752424444
Web Site: https://www.apexdyna.se
Mechanical Product Mfr & Distr
N.A.I.C.S.: 333612

Elektro Elco AB (1)
Tallvagen 5, 564 35, Bankeryd, Sweden
Tel.: (46) 362906000
Web Site: https://www.elco.se
Emp.: 70
Electrical Equipment Installation Services & Lighting Mfr
N.A.I.C.S.: 238210

Flexitron AB (1)
Sidensvansvagen 8, PO Box 7117, 187 12, Sollentuna, Sweden
Tel.: (46) 87328560
Sales Range: $50-74.9 Million
Emp.: 10
Electronic Equipment Distr
N.A.I.C.S.: 423690
Jonas Liljedahl *(Gen Mgr)*

IBEC B.V. (1)
Aartsdijkweg 111, 2676 LE, Maasdijk, Netherlands **(100%)**
Tel.: (31) 174525100
Sales Range: $50-74.9 Million
Industrial Machinery & Equipment Whslr
N.A.I.C.S.: 423830
Jun Geng *(Mng Dir)*

IBEC Bearings AB (1)
Lerbacksgatan 3, PO Box 105, 57122, Nassjo, Sweden **(100%)**
Tel.: (46) 752424960
Web Site: http://www.ibec.biz
Real Estate Property Lessors
N.A.I.C.S.: 531190

Intermate Electronics AB (1)
Forradsvagen, Tranas, Sweden **(100%)**
Tel.: (46) 14069900
Real Estate Property Lessors
N.A.I.C.S.: 531190

Internordic Bearings AB (1)
Lerbacksgatan 3 Brana Industriomrade, 571 38, Nassjo, Sweden **(100%)**
Tel.: (46) 752424940
Web Site: https://www.internordic.com
Sales Range: $10-24.9 Million
Iron & Steel Forging
N.A.I.C.S.: 332111

OEM Automatic (Shanghai) Ltd. (1)
Room 117 Building 8 No 787 Kangqiao Rd, Shanghai Zhongtian Science & Technology Business Park Pudong district, Shanghai, 201315, China
Tel.: (86) 2133070588
Vehicle Components Mfr & Distr
N.A.I.C.S.: 336320

OEM Automatic A/S (1)
Engholm Parkvej 4, 3450, Allerod, Denmark **(100%)**
Tel.: (45) 70270527
Web Site: http://www.oemklitso.dk
Sales Range: $25-49.9 Million
Emp.: 28
Electrical Appliance Television & Radio Set Whslr
N.A.I.C.S.: 423620

OEM Automatic AB (1)
Dalagatan 4, 573 42, Tranas, Sweden **(100%)**
Tel.: (46) 752424100
Web Site: https://www.oemautomatic.se
Sales Range: $75-99.9 Million
Electrical Apparatus & Equipment Wiring Supplies & Related Equipment Whslr
N.A.I.C.S.: 423610

OEM Automatic AS (1)
Bjornstjerne Bjornsonsgate 110, 3044, Drammen, Norway **(100%)**
Tel.: (47) 32210505
Web Site: https://www.oem.no
Sales Range: $25-49.9 Million
Emp.: 25
Electrical Apparatus & Equipment Wiring Supplies & Related Equipment Whslr
N.A.I.C.S.: 423610

OEM Automatic Kft (1)
Gyar u 2, PF 111, 2040, Budaors, Hungary
Tel.: (36) 23880895
Web Site: https://www.oemautomatic.hu
Sales Range: $25-49.9 Million
Industrial Automation Equipment Mfr & Distr
N.A.I.C.S.: 333248

OEM Automatic Klitso A/S (1)
Engholm Parkvej 4, 3450, Allerod, Denmark
Tel.: (45) 70106400
Web Site: https://www.oemklitso.dk
Emp.: 3
Industrial Machinery & Equipment Distr
N.A.I.C.S.: 423830
Mads Salling *(Dir-Admin)*

OEM Automatic Ltd. (1)
Whiteacres, Whetstone, Leicester, LE86ZG, United Kingdom **(100%)**
Tel.: (44) 1164271395
Web Site: https://www.oem.co.uk
Sales Range: $25-49.9 Million
Emp.: 40
Industrial Machinery & Equipment Whslr
N.A.I.C.S.: 423830

OEM Automatic OU (1)
Aia 8, 80010, Parnu, Estonia **(100%)**
Tel.: (372) 5295114
Web Site: http://www.oem.ee
Sales Range: $50-74.9 Million
Industrial Machinery & Equipment Whslr
N.A.I.C.S.: 423830

OEM Automatic OY (1)
Fiskarsinkatu 3, 20750, Turku, Finland **(100%)**
Tel.: (358) 20 749 9499
Web Site: https://www.oem.fi
Sales Range: $25-49.9 Million
Electrical Apparatus & Equipment Wiring Supplies & Related Equipment Whslr
N.A.I.C.S.: 423610

OEM Automatic SIA (1)
Vilandes 3-3, Riga, LV-1010, Latvia
Tel.: (371) 3725059849
Web Site: https://www.oem.ee
N.A.I.C.S.: 531190

Industrial Components Supplier
N.A.I.C.S.: 423840

OEM Automatic Sp. z o. o. (1)
street Dzialkowa 121 A, 02-234, Warsaw, Poland **(100%)**
Tel.: (48) 228632722
Web Site: https://www.oemautomatic.pl
Sales Range: $25-49.9 Million
Emp.: 50
Electrical Apparatus & Equipment Wiring Supplies & Related Equipment Merchant Whslr
N.A.I.C.S.: 423610

Division (Domestic):

OEM Electronics PL (2)
ul Dzialkowa 121 A, 02-234, Warsaw, Poland **(100%)**
Tel.: (48) 228632722
Web Site: http://www.oemelectronics.pl
Sales Range: $25-49.9 Million
Electrical Apparatus & Equipment Wiring Supplies & Related Equipment Merchant Whslr
N.A.I.C.S.: 423610

OEM Automatic UAB (1)
Raudondvario pl 101, 47184, Kaunas, Lithuania **(100%)**
Tel.: (370) 64015878
Web Site: https://www.oem.ee
Industrial Machinery & Equipment Merchant Whslr
N.A.I.C.S.: 423830

OEM Automatic s.r.o. (1)
Bratislavska 8356, 917 01, Trnava, Slovakia
Tel.: (421) 33 240 0160
Web Site: https://www.oemautomatic.sk
Sales Range: $50-74.9 Million
Electronic Components Distr
N.A.I.C.S.: 423690

OEM Automatic spol. s r.o. (1)
Prazska 239, Zdiby, 25066, Prague, Czech Republic
Tel.: (420) 241484940
Web Site: https://www.oemautomatic.cz
Sales Range: $25-49.9 Million
Emp.: 30
Electronic Components Distr
N.A.I.C.S.: 423690

OEM China Development B.V. (1)
Aartsdijkweg 111, 2676LE, Maasdijk, Netherlands **(100%)**
Tel.: (31) 174525100
Web Site: http://www.ibec.cn
Sales Range: $50-74.9 Million
Emp.: 5
Industrial Machinery & Equipment Whslr
N.A.I.C.S.: 423830
Jun Geng *(Mng Dir)*

OEM Eesti Ou (1)
Aia 8, 80010, Parnu, Estonia
Tel.: (372) 5059849
Web Site: https://www.oem.ee
Industrial Components Supplier
N.A.I.C.S.: 423840

OEM Electronics AB (1)
Dalagatan 4, 573 42, Tranas, Sweden **(100%)**
Tel.: (46) 752424500
Web Site: https://oemelectronics.se
Sales Range: $10-24.9 Million
Sales of Electronic Equipment
N.A.I.C.S.: 449210

OEM Electronics OY (1)
Telekatu 6, 20360, Turku, Finland **(100%)**
Tel.: (358) 207499402
Web Site: http://www.oemelectronics.fi
Sales Range: $25-49.9 Million
Emp.: 15
Electrical Apparatus & Equipment Wiring Supplies & Related Equipment Merchant Whslr
N.A.I.C.S.: 423610

OEM Motor AB (1)
Fredriksbergsgatan 2, Box 1011, 57392, Tranas, Sweden **(100%)**
Tel.: (46) 752424400
Web Site: https://www.oem-motor.se
Sales Range: $25-49.9 Million
Emp.: 15

INTERNATIONAL PUBLIC

Electrical Apparatus & Equipment Wiring Supplies & Related Equipment Merchant Whslr
N.A.I.C.S.: 423610

OEM Trading (Shanghai) Co., Ltd. (1)
Room 117 Building 8 Shanghai 787 Kangqiao Rd, Zhongtian Science & Technology Business Park, Shanghai, 201315, China
Tel.: (86) 2133311200
Web Site: http://www.oemautomatic.cn
Electrical Component Distr
N.A.I.C.S.: 423690

Rauheat OY (1)
Kirvestie 1, 26510, Rauma, Finland
Tel.: (358) 25490400
Web Site: https://www.rauheat.com
HAVC Installation Services
N.A.I.C.S.: 423730

Sitek-Palvelu OY (1)
Fiskarsinkatu 3, 20750, Turku, Finland
Tel.: (358) 207499499
Web Site: https://www.sitek.fi
Manifolds Mfr
N.A.I.C.S.: 332996

Svenska Batteripoolen AB (1)
Fredriksbergsgatan 2, 573 92, Tranas, Sweden
Tel.: (46) 752424300
Web Site: https://www.batteripoolen.se
Vehicle Accessories Battery Mfr & Distr
N.A.I.C.S.: 335910

Svenska Helag AB (1)
Connection Technology Component Mfr & Distr
N.A.I.C.S.: 335999
Mattias Wressel *(CEO)*

Telfa AB (1)
Fredriksbergsgatan 2, Box 1011, 573 28, Gothenburg, Sweden **(100%)**
Tel.: (46) 752424450
Web Site: https://www.telfa.se
Sales Range: $25-49.9 Million
Emp.: 50
Industrial Machinery & Equipment Whslr
N.A.I.C.S.: 423830

OEMETA CHEMISCHE WERKE GMBH

Ossenpadd 54, 25436, Uetersen, Germany
Tel.: (49) 41229240
Web Site: http://www.oemeta.com
Year Founded: 1916
Rev.: $22,070,400
Emp.: 100
Lubricating Oil Services
N.A.I.C.S.: 324191

Subsidiaries:

Oemeta (UK) Limited (1)
Bramley House 39 Main Road, Middleton, OX 17 2ND, United Kingdom
Tel.: (44) 1295713280
Lubricant Oil Distr
N.A.I.C.S.: 424720

Oemeta (Wuhan) Co., Ltd. (1)
Tangxun-lake Industrial Park Miaoshan Economic Development Zone, Jiangxia District, Wuhan, 430223, Hubei, China
Tel.: (86) 2781800911
Lubricant Oil Distr
N.A.I.C.S.: 424720

Oemeta CR s.r.o. (1)
Jana Babaka 11, 612 00, Brno, Czech Republic
Tel.: (420) 778057487
Lubricant Oil Distr
N.A.I.C.S.: 424720

Oemeta Inc. (1)
2125 Center Ave Ste 507, Fort Lee, NJ 07024
Tel.: (201) 720-2829
Lubricant Oil Distr
N.A.I.C.S.: 424720

Oemeta North America Inc. (1)

265 Ingersoll St, Ingersoll, N5C 3J7, ON, Canada
Tel.: (519) 485-1800
Lubricant Oil Distr
N.A.I.C.S.: 424720

Oemeta Polska Sp. z o. o. (1)
ul Przeskok 6/2, 50-319, Wroclaw, Poland
Tel.: (48) 713433082
Lubricant Oil Distr
N.A.I.C.S.: 424720

Oemeta Singapore Pte Ltd (1)
10 Admiralty Street 03-03 Northlink Building, Singapore, 757695, Singapore
Tel.: (65) 64810560
Lubricant Oil Distr
N.A.I.C.S.: 424720

OENEO SA
21 boulevard Haussmann, 75009, Paris, France
Tel.: (33) 158361093
Web Site: https://www.oeneo.com
SBT—(EUR)
Rev.: $329,946,039
Assets: $541,486,077
Liabilities: $201,575,653
Net Worth: $339,910,425
Earnings: $31,133,175
Emp.: 1,196
Fiscal Year-end: 03/31/24
Wine Mfr & Distr
N.A.I.C.S.: 312130
Francois Heriard Dubreuil *(CEO)*

Subsidiaries:

Piedade Pietec S.A. (1)
Zona Industrial Monte Grande 140, 4535, Fiaes, Portugal
Tel.: (351) 256910510
Wine Distr
N.A.I.C.S.: 424820

Vivelys USA (1)
1260 N Dutton Ave Ste 190, Santa Rosa, CA 95401
Tel.: (707) 546-2213
Web Site: http://us.boise.vivelys.com
Wine Mfr
N.A.I.C.S.: 312130
Francois Margot *(Sls Mgr)*

OENON HOLDINGS INC
1-17-6 Higashikomagata, Sumida-ku, Tokyo, 130-0005, Japan
Tel.: (81) 367574584
Web Site: https://www.oenon.jp
Year Founded: 1924
2533—(TKS)
Rev.: $602,274,230
Assets: $393,005,790
Liabilities: $235,416,360
Net Worth: $157,589,430
Earnings: $24,056,370
Emp.: 787
Fiscal Year-end: 12/31/23
Beverages Mfr
N.A.I.C.S.: 312120
Yukio Nagai *(Chm)*

Subsidiaries:

Akitakenhakko Kogyo Co., Ltd. (1)
120-8 Nakagawara, Fukahori, Yuzawa, 012-8511, Akita, Japan
Tel.: (81) 183733106
Alcoholic Beverage Mfr & Distr
N.A.I.C.S.: 312140

Fukumusume Sake Brewery Co., Ltd. (1)
2 28 Shinzaike Minami Machi 3 Chome Nada ku Kobe shi, Hyogo, Japan
Tel.: (81) 362158841
Web Site: http://www.asahi-kasei.co.jp
Alcoholic Beverages & Foods Distr
N.A.I.C.S.: 424820

Fukutokucho Co., Ltd. (1)
250 Nakahara Kamihongo, Matsudo, 271-0064, Chiba, Japan
Tel.: (81) 473155020
Alcoholic Beverage Mfr & Distr

N.A.I.C.S.: 312140

Godo Shusei Co., Ltd. (1)
1-17-6 Higashikomagata, Sumida-ku, 130-0005, Japan
Tel.: (81) 367574020
Sales Range: $250-299.9 Million
Alcoholic Beverages & Foods Distr
N.A.I.C.S.: 424820

Gotech Co., Ltd. (1)
250 Nakahara Kamihongo, Matsudo, 271-0064, Chiba, Japan
Tel.: (81) 473611271
Warehousing Services
N.A.I.C.S.: 531130

Oenon Asset Corporation (1)
6 2 10 Ginza Chuo ku, Tokyo, 104 0061, Japan
Tel.: (81) 335752893
Web Site: http://www.oenon.jp
Emp.: 150
Real Estate Brokerage Services
N.A.I.C.S.: 531390

Oenon Product Support Co., Ltd. (1)
3-2-28 Shinzaike, Minami-cho Nada-ku, Kobe, 657-0864, Hyogo, Japan
Tel.: (81) 788027800
Alcoholic Beverage Mfr & Distr
N.A.I.C.S.: 312140

Sunny Maize Co., Ltd. (1)
No 1 No 2 Shizuoka, Shimizu Ku Cho, Shizuoka, 424 0035, Japan (50%)
Tel.: (81) 543655180
Web Site: http://www.sunny-maize.co.jp
Starch Mfr & Distr
N.A.I.C.S.: 311221
Tori Yamaguchi *(Pres)*

Taisetsu no Kura Co., Ltd. (1)
19 2182 103 Hokkaido, Asahikawa, 078 8336, Japan
Tel.: (81) 166393788
Web Site: http://www.taisetsunokura.jp
Alcoholic Beverages & Foods Whslr
N.A.I.C.S.: 424820

OERMESTER VAGYONVEDELMI NYRT
Ogyalla square 8-9, Budapest, 1142, Hungary
Tel.: (36) 13682002
Web Site: http://www.ormester.hu
Year Founded: 1989
Security Services
N.A.I.C.S.: 561612
Gergely Kincs *(Chm)*

OESTERREICHISCHE KONTROLLBANK AG
Am Hof 4 Strauchgasse 3, 1010, Vienna, Austria
Tel.: (43) 1531270
Web Site: http://www.oekb.at
Year Founded: 1946
Rev.: $106,425,895
Assets: $37,349,931,315
Liabilities: $36,445,596,211
Net Worth: $904,335,104
Earnings: $57,612,318
Emp.: 366
Fiscal Year-end: 12/31/19
Banking Services
N.A.I.C.S.: 522110
Helmut Bernkopf *(Member-Exec Bd)*

Subsidiaries:

CCP Austria Abwicklungsstelle fur Borsengeschafte GmbH (1)
Strauchgasse 1-3, A-1010, Vienna, Austria (50%)
Tel.: (43) 5332244
Web Site: http://www.ccpa.at
Banking Services
N.A.I.C.S.: 522110
Wolfgang Aubrunner *(Mng Dir)*

OeKB Business Services GmbH (1)
Strauchgasse 3, 1011, Vienna, Austria
Tel.: (43) 1531272800
Web Site: http://www.oekb-bs.at
Banking Services

N.A.I.C.S.: 522110

OeKB Sudosteuropa Holding Ges.m.b.H. (1)
Am Hof 4, 1011, Vienna, Austria (100%)
Tel.: (43) 1531272712
Web Site: http://www.oekb-see.at
Sales Range: $50-74.9 Million
Emp.: 2
Banking Services; Limited Liability Company
N.A.I.C.S.: 522110

OeKB Versicherung AG (1)
Strauchgasse 3, Vienna, 1010, Austria
Tel.: (43) 1531272664
Web Site: http://www.oekbversicherung.at
Sales Range: $50-74.9 Million
Emp.: 40
Credit Insurance Services
N.A.I.C.S.: 524210

PRISMA Kreditversicherungs-Aktiengesellschaft (1)
Heiligenstadter Str 201, A-1190, Hannover, Germany
Tel.: (49) 1 379 00 0
Banking Services
N.A.I.C.S.: 522110

OESTERREICHISCHE NATIONALBANK
Otto-Wagner-Platz 3, Vienna, 1090, Austria
Tel.: (43) 1404200
Web Site: http://www.oenb.at
Sales Range: $1-4.9 Billion
Emp.: 984
Banking Services
N.A.I.C.S.: 521110

Subsidiaries:

IG Immobilien Invest GmbH (1)
Stadion Center / 4 OG / Top 15 Olympiaplatz 2, 1020, Vienna, Austria
Tel.: (43) 1 5320140 0
Web Site: http://www.ig-immobilien.com
Real Estate Manangement Services
N.A.I.C.S.: 531390
Hermann Klein *(Co-Mng Dir)*

Subsidiary (Domestic):

IG Dobling Herrenhaus-Bautrager GmbH (2)
Doblinger Hauptstr 52A, 1190, Vienna, Austria
Tel.: (43) 1 3692828
Real Estate Manangement Services
N.A.I.C.S.: 531390

Munze Osterreich Aktiengesellschaft (1)
Am Heumarkt 1, 1030, Vienna, Austria
Tel.: (43) 1 717 15 200
Coin Mfr & Distr
N.A.I.C.S.: 339910
Gerhard Starsich *(CEO)*

Subsidiary (Domestic):

Schoeller Munzhandel GmbH (2)
Renngasse 14, 1010, Vienna, Austria
Tel.: (43) 1 5333 606 0
Web Site: http://www.smh.net
Coin Mfr & Distr
N.A.I.C.S.: 339910
Alexander Schwab-Trau *(Dir-Sls-Retail)*

Oesterreichische Banknoten- und Sicherheitsdruck GmbH (1)
Garnisongasse 15, 1090, Vienna, Austria
Tel.: (43) 1 316 90 0
Web Site: http://www.oebs.at
Banknote & Security Paper Printing Services
N.A.I.C.S.: 323111
Norbert Feist *(Exec Dir)*

OETIKER SCHWEIZ AG
Spatzstrasse 11, PO Box 358, 8810, Horgen, Switzerland
Tel.: (41) 44 728 55 55
Web Site: http://www.oetiker.com
Year Founded: 1942

Emp.: 1,370
Clamps, Rings, Straps & Connectors Mfr
N.A.I.C.S.: 332999
Thomas Meier-Bickel *(CEO)*

Subsidiaries:

Oetiker NY Inc. (1)
4437 Walden Ave, Lancaster, NY 14086
Tel.: (716) 681-7200
Web Site: http://www.oetiker.com
Quick Connect Fittings
N.A.I.C.S.: 332510

Oetiker, Inc. (1)
6317 Euclid St, Marlette, MI 48453
Tel.: (989) 635-3621
Web Site: http://www.oetiker.com
Industrial Clamp Mfr
N.A.I.C.S.: 332722
Dawn Prieskorn *(Dir-Fin-Americas)*

OETTINGER IMEX AG
Hochbergerstrasse 15, CH 4002, Basel, Switzerland
Tel.: (41) 612793636
Web Site: http://www.davidoff.com
Sales Range: $550-599.9 Million
Emp.: 3,000
Holding Company; Mfr & Distr of Tobacco & Confectionery Products
N.A.I.C.S.: 551112

Subsidiaries:

A. Durr & Co. AG (1)
Nauenstrasse 73, 4052, Basel, Switzerland
Tel.: (41) 58 219 3636
Emp.: 64
Tobacco Product Mfr & Distr
N.A.I.C.S.: 312230
Sebastian Marten *(Mng Dir)*

Agroindustrias Diadema Zona Franca Honduras SA (1)
El Paraiso, Danli, Honduras
Tel.: (504) 2 704 3020
Emp.: 535
Tobacco Product Mfr & Distr
N.A.I.C.S.: 312230
Manuel Batista *(Mng Dir)*

Cruspi S.A. (1)
Huttenwiesenstrasse 10, 8108, Dallikon, Switzerland
Tel.: (41) 448472626
Web Site: http://www.cruspi.ch
Sales Range: $50-74.9 Million
Emp.: 85
Sweet & Snack Importer & Distr
N.A.I.C.S.: 424450

Davidoff & Cie. SA (1)
2 Rue de Rive, 1206, Geneva, Switzerland
Tel.: (41) 22 310 9041
Emp.: 6
Tobacco Product Mfr & Distr
N.A.I.C.S.: 312230
Thomas Mathys *(Gen Mgr)*

Davidoff Distribution (UK) Ltd. (1)
Office 304 3rd Floor The Pinnacle Station Way, Crawley, RH10 1JH, West Sussex, United Kingdom
Tel.: (44) 129 386 3591
Emp.: 4
Tobacco Product Mfr & Distr
N.A.I.C.S.: 312230
Roy Sommer *(Mng Dir)*

Davidoff of Geneva (CC) Inc. (1)
10 Columbus Cir, New York, NY 10019
Tel.: (212) 823-6383
Emp.: 5
Tobacco Product Mfr & Distr
N.A.I.C.S.: 312230
Dylan Austin *(Mng Dir)*

Davidoff of Geneva (NY) Inc. (1)
515 Madison Ave, New York, NY 10022
Tel.: (212) 751-9060
Emp.: 9
Tobacco Product Mfr & Distr
N.A.I.C.S.: 312230
Dylan Austin *(Pres & Mng Dir)*

Davidoff of Geneva Austria GmbH (1)
Heiligenstadter Strasse 41 - 43, 1190, Vi-

OETTINGER IMEX AG

Oettinger IMEX AG—(Continued)
enna, Austria
Tel.: (43) 1 236 3040
Emp.: 4
Tobacco Product Mfr & Distr
N.A.I.C.S.: 312230
Stefanie Birtel *(Mng Dir)*

Davidoff of Geneva Benelux SA/NV (1)
Chaussee de Dielegheim 33, 1090, Brussels, Belgium
Tel.: (32) 2 478 1716
Emp.: 22
Tobacco Product Mfr & Distr
N.A.I.C.S.: 312230
Pascal Lorie *(Mng Dir & Gen Mgr)*

Davidoff of Geneva France S.a.r.l. (1)
165 Boulevard de Valmy, 92700, Colombes, Cedex, France
Tel.: (33) 14 780 4081
Emp.: 17
Tobacco Product Mfr & Distr
N.A.I.C.S.: 312230
Jerome Aubert *(Gen Mgr)*

Davidoff of Geneva Germany GmbH (1)
Wendenstrasse 377, 20537, Hamburg, Germany
Tel.: (49) 40 280 0200
Emp.: 22
Tobacco Product Mfr & Distr
N.A.I.C.S.: 312230

Davidoff of Geneva Hong Kong Ltd. (1)
21/F dorset House Taikoo Place 979 Kings Road, Hong Kong, China (Hong Kong)
Tel.: (852) 2 968 1188
Tobacco Product Mfr & Distr
N.A.I.C.S.: 312230

Davidoff of Geneva Iberia SL (1)
C/ Nunez de Balboa 114 Piso 3 Oficina 14, 28006, Madrid, Spain
Tel.: (34) 91 196 0760
Emp.: 14
Tobacco Product Mfr & Distr
N.A.I.C.S.: 312230
Carlos Martinez *(Mng Dir, VP & Gen Mgr)*

Davidoff of Geneva Japan K.K. (1)
2-2-3 Minami Aoyama M-Square, Minato-ku, Tokyo, 107-0062, Japan
Tel.: (81) 35 413 1370
Web Site: https://davidoffgeneva.jp
Tobacco Product Mfr & Distr
N.A.I.C.S.: 312230

Davidoff of Geneva Luxembourg Sarl (1)
33-39 Rue du Puits Romain, 8070, Bertrange, Luxembourg
Tel.: (352) 2 711 3017
Tobacco Product Mfr & Distr
N.A.I.C.S.: 312230
Pascal Lorie *(Mng Dir)*

Davidoff of Geneva Malaysia Sdn. Bhd. (1)
Office Suite No 28-9 10 and 11 Level 28 Wisma UOA II, No 21 Jalan Pinang, 50450, Kuala Lumpur, Malaysia
Tel.: (60) 32 166 3836
Tobacco Product Mfr & Distr
N.A.I.C.S.: 312230

Davidoff of Geneva Russia LLC (1)
Trubnaya Street 12 Business Centre Millenium House Office U, 107045, Moscow, Russia
Tel.: (7) 4957879927
Tobacco Product Mfr & Distr
N.A.I.C.S.: 312230
Bora Buladi *(Mng Dir & VP)*

Davidoff of Geneva Singapore Pte. Ltd. (1)
435 Orchard Road 10-15 Wisma Atria, Singapore, 238877, Singapore
Tel.: (65) 6 737 3677
Tobacco Product Mfr & Distr
N.A.I.C.S.: 312230

Davidoff of Geneva USA, Inc. (1)
3001 Gateway Center Pkwy, Pinellas Park, FL 33782-6124
Tel.: (727) 828-5400
Web Site: http://www.davidoff.com
Tobacco Product Distr
N.A.I.C.S.: 424940

Pronk Import B.V. (1)
Van Baerlestraat 80, 1071 BB, Amsterdam, Netherlands
Tel.: (31) 20 695 5001
Tobacco Product Mfr & Distr
N.A.I.C.S.: 312230
Pascal Lorie *(Mng Dir)*

Tabadom Holding Inc. (1)
Zona Franca Industrial Palmarejo AP, Villa Gonzalez, 1162, Santiago, Dominican Republic
Tel.: (809) 580 0291
Emp.: 1,340
Tobacco Product Mfr & Distr
N.A.I.C.S.: 312230
Hamlet Spinal *(Mng Dir & Gen Mgr)*

Wolsdorff Tobacco GmbH (1)
Wendenstrasse 377, 20537, Hamburg, Germany
Tel.: (49) 40 253 0230
Web Site: https://wolsdorff.shop
Tobacco Product Mfr & Distr
N.A.I.C.S.: 312230

OEX S.A.
ul Klimczaka 1, 02-797, Warsaw, Poland
Tel.: (48) 223956133
Web Site: https://www.oex.pl
OEX—(WAR)
Rev.: $188,397,103
Assets: $121,389,990
Liabilities: $65,824,441
Net Worth: $55,565,549
Earnings: $7,826,728
Fiscal Year-end: 12/31/23
Mobile Telecommunications Products Sales
N.A.I.C.S.: 449210
Jerzy Motz *(Pres)*

OFER GROUP
Ramat Aviv Tower 40 Einstein St, PO Box 11, 69102, Tel Aviv, Israel
Tel.: (972) 37456060
Web Site: http://www.oferg.com
Holding & Investment Company
N.A.I.C.S.: 551112
Udi Angel *(Chm)*

Subsidiaries:

Ofer Hi-Tech Ltd. (1)
Ramat Aviv Tower 6th Fl 40 Einstein St, Ramat Aviv, 69102, Tel Aviv, Israel
Tel.: (972) 37456000
Web Site: http://www.oferhitech.com
Sales Range: $50-74.9 Million
Emp.: 20
Investment Services
N.A.I.C.S.: 523999

OFFCN EDUCATION TECHNOLOGY CO., LTD.
Block B Hanhua Shiji Building No 23 Xueqing Road, Haidian District, Wuhu, 100089, China
Tel.: (86) 1083433677
Web Site: http://www.yaxia.com
002607—(SSE)
Rev.: $677,403,324
Assets: $1,127,048,364
Liabilities: $1,017,551,808
Net Worth: $109,496,556
Earnings: ($154,729,224)
Fiscal Year-end: 12/31/22
Automobile Sales & Service
N.A.I.C.S.: 423110
Hui Zhou *(Pres)*

OFFICE BRANDS LIMITED
Unit 2A Level 2 25 Ryde Road, Pymble, 2073, NSW, Australia
Tel.: (61) 285996866
Web Site: http://www.officebrands.com.au
Year Founded: 1999
Office Furniture Distr
N.A.I.C.S.: 423210
Gavin Ward *(CEO)*

OFFICINA STELLARE S.P.A.
Via Della Tecnica 87/89, Sarcedo, 36030, Vicenza, Italy
Tel.: (39) 0445370540
Web Site: https://www.officinastellare.com
Year Founded: 2009
OS—(ITA)
Sales Range: Less than $1 Million
Aerospace Instrument Mfr
N.A.I.C.S.: 334511
Giovanni Dal Lago *(Founder, Vice Chm & CEO)*

OFFICINE PICCOLI S.P.A
Via G Verdi, 37060, Castel D'Azzano, VR, Italy
Tel.: (39) 0458206540
Web Site: https://www.officinepiccoli.it
Industrial Equipment Distr
N.A.I.C.S.: 423830

OFFIZIN ANDERSEN NEXO LEIPZIG GMBH
Spenglerallee 26-30, 04442, Zwenkau, Germany
Tel.: (49) 3420337800
Web Site: http://www.oan.de
Book Printing Services
N.A.I.C.S.: 323117
Stephan Treuleben *(CEO)*

Subsidiaries:

Sachsendruck GmbH (1)
Paul Schneider Strasse 12, 08525, Plauen, Germany
Tel.: (49) 37412130
Web Site: http://www.sachsendruck.ge
Sales Range: $10-24.9 Million
Emp.: 200
Printer
N.A.I.C.S.: 323111

OFFSET PRESS INC.
8 4th Km of Ab-Ali Road, PO Box 11155-4979, 17468 53171, Tehran, Iran
Tel.: (98) 2177339093
Web Site: https://www.offset.ir
Year Founded: 1957
OFST—(THE)
Sales Range: Less than $1 Million
Printing Services
N.A.I.C.S.: 323111

OFFSHORE OIL ENGINEERING COMPANY LIMITED
No 199 Haibin 15 Road TianjinPort Free Trade Zone, Tianjin, 300461, China
Tel.: (86) 2259898808
Web Site: https://www.cnoocengineering.com
Year Founded: 2000
600583—(SHG)
Rev.: $4,121,914,909
Assets: $5,986,469,956
Liabilities: $2,380,635,710
Net Worth: $3,605,834,246
Earnings: $204,620,238
Emp.: 9,000
Fiscal Year-end: 12/31/22
Offshore Oil & Gas Exploration Services
N.A.I.C.S.: 213112
Wang Zhangling *(Chm, Pres & Sec-Party)*

INTERNATIONAL PUBLIC

Subsidiaries:

A.E.S. Destructive & Non-destructive Testing Ltd. (1)
Flat F 2/F Block 2 Kwai Tak Industrial Centre 15-33 Kwai Tak Street, Kwai Chung, New Territories, China (Hong Kong)
Tel.: (852) 24226898
Web Site: https://aes.hk
Calibration Instrument Testing Services
N.A.I.C.S.: 541380

COOEC Canada Company Ltd. (1)
Ste 2100 777-8th Ave SW, Calgary, T2P 3R5, AB, Canada
Tel.: (587) 393-2080
Web Site: https://www.cooec.ca
Engineering Services
N.A.I.C.S.: 541330

COOEC Subsea Technology Co., Ltd. (1)
Unit C/D 4th Floor Technology Bldg No 1067 Nanhai Rd, Shekou, Shenzhen, 518067, Guangdong, China
Tel.: (86) 75526850218
Emp.: 500
Engineering Consulting Services
N.A.I.C.S.: 541330
Xingchao Wei *(Bus Mgr)*

COOEC-ENPAL Engineering Co., Ltd. (1)
HaiKou Road 277, Laoshan, Qingdao, 266061, China
Tel.: (86) 532 89090666
Web Site: http://www.enpal.cn
Emp.: 200
Petrochemical Products Mfr
N.A.I.C.S.: 325110
Zeng Ferris *(Mgr-Design)*

OFFTEC HOLDING GROUP, PLC.
Third Circle 12 Queen Misbah Street, PO Box 383, Amman, 11118, Jordan
Tel.: (962) 64642724
Web Site: https://www.offtec.com
Year Founded: 1910
OFTC—(AMM)
Rev.: $33,887,851
Assets: $87,187,013
Liabilities: $24,552,093
Net Worth: $62,634,920
Earnings: $1,034,037
Emp.: 165
Fiscal Year-end: 12/31/20
Information Technology Services
N.A.I.C.S.: 519290

Subsidiaries:

World Axis Trading Company (1)
12 Queen Misbah Street 3rd circle 1st floor, PO Box 383, Amman, 11118, Jordan
Tel.: (962) 64642724
Architectural Services
N.A.I.C.S.: 541310

OFU CO., LTD.
5th floor One4U Building 222 Dogokro, Gangnam-Gu, Seoul, 06272, Korea (South)
Tel.: (82) 25691414
Web Site: https://ofu.co.kr
Year Founded: 1998
122830—(KRS)
Information Technology Services
N.A.I.C.S.: 541519
Dong Ho Jeon *(Board of Directors & CEO)*

OFX GROUP LIMITED
Level 19 60 Margaret Street, Locked Bag 1800, Royal Exchange, Sydney, 2000, NSW, Australia
Tel.: (61) 286678091 AU
Web Site: https://www.ofx.com
Year Founded: 1998
OZFRY—(OTCIQ)
Rev.: $150,214,673
Assets: $441,570,000
Liabilities: $345,362,164

AND PRIVATE COMPANIES

Net Worth: $96,207,836
Earnings: $20,969,984
Emp.: 715
Fiscal Year-end: 03/31/23
Foreign Exchange Services
N.A.I.C.S.: 522320
John Alexander Skander Malcolm *(CEO & Mng Dir)*

Subsidiaries:

CanadianForex Limited (1)
Suite 1002 145 King Street, Toronto, M5H 1J8, ON, Canada
Web Site: https://www.ofx.com
Foreign Exchange Services
N.A.I.C.S.: 522320

OFX (SNG) PTE. Limited (1)
Capital Tower 168 Robinson Road 12-01 to 12-04, Singapore, 068812, Singapore
Tel.: (65) 68178747
Foreign Currency Exchange Services
N.A.I.C.S.: 522390

OFX Payments Ireland Limited (1)
Fitzwilliam Court 2 Leeson Close, Dublin, D02 YW24, Ireland
Tel.: (353) 1800948364
Financial Services
N.A.I.C.S.: 541611

OzForex Limited (1)
Level 9 10 Bridge Street, Sydney, 2000, NSW, Australia
Tel.: (61) 2 8667 8091
Foreign Exchange Services
N.A.I.C.S.: 522320

UKForex Limited (1)
1st Floor 85 Gracechurch Street, London, EC3V 0AA, United Kingdom
Tel.: (44) 207 614 4195
Foreign Exchange Services
N.A.I.C.S.: 522320

OGAWA SMART HEALTHCARE TECHNOLOGY GROUP CO., LTD.

No 168 Qianpu Road, Siming District, Xiamen, 361000, Fujian, China
Tel.: (86) 5925569658
Web Site: http://www.ogawaworld.net.cn
Year Founded: 1996
002614—(SSE)
Rev.: $845,817,336
Assets: $1,222,572,312
Liabilities: $545,935,572
Net Worth: $676,636,740
Earnings: $14,323,608
Fiscal Year-end: 12/31/22
Specialty Massage & Lounge Furniture Designer, Mfr & Distr
N.A.I.C.S.: 337121
Zou Jianhan *(Chm)*

Subsidiaries:

OGAWA World Berhad (1)
No 22 Jalan Anggerik Mokara 31/47 Kota Kemuning, 40460, Shah Alam, Selangor Darul Ehsan, Malaysia
Tel.: (60) 351214286
Web Site: http://www.ogawaworld.net
Health & Wellness Retail Store Owner & Operator; Health & Wellness Products Mfr & Marketer
N.A.I.C.S.: 456110
Eric Yew Kong Cheah *(Deputy Chm & CEO)*

OGCC KAZSTROYSERVICE JSC

Grand Alatau Business Center, 28 V Timiryazev Str, Almaty, 050040, Kazakhstan
Tel.: (7) 727 266 9696
Web Site: http://www.kazstroyservice.kz
Sales Range: $450-499.9 Million
Emp.: 5,000
Oil & Gas Construction & Engineering Services
N.A.I.C.S.: 237990
Sabit Zhanassov *(Gen Dir)*

Subsidiaries:

KSS ISKER (1)
Kulmanov Str 23, Atyrau, 060011, Kazakhstan
Tel.: (7) 7122 58 66 86
Construction Engineering Services
N.A.I.C.S.: 541330

KazStroyService Global B.V. (1)
Strawinskylaan 411, 1077 XX, Amsterdam, Netherlands
Tel.: (31) 20 575 2738
Construction Engineering Services
N.A.I.C.S.: 541330
Lyudmila Pavlova *(Head-Fin & Acct)*

KazStroyService Infrastructure India Pvt. Ltd. (1)
Vatika Towers 1st Fl Sector 54, Haryana, Gurgaon, 122002, India
Tel.: (91) 1123362414
Pipeline Construction Services
N.A.I.C.S.: 237120

KazStroyService Middle East (1)
302 Al Otaiba Building Airport Road, PO Box 30471, Abu Dhabi, United Arab Emirates
Tel.: (971) 2 622 75 66
Oil & Gas Construction & Engineering Services
N.A.I.C.S.: 237990

LLP "Engineering Procurement Services" (1)
Timiryazev str 28 V 9th Floor, Almaty, Kazakhstan
Tel.: (7) 727 258 10 33
Oil & Gas Engineering & Procurement Services
N.A.I.C.S.: 237120
Kamar Bastarova *(Deputy Gen Dir-Estimates & Tenders Calculations)*

OGI GROUP LTD

Level 1 566 Elizabeth Street, Melbourne, 3000, VIC, Australia
Tel.: (61) 3 9349 1488
Web Site: http://www.ggpl.com.au
Sales Range: $1-9.9 Million
Emp.: 4
Oil & Gas Exploration
N.A.I.C.S.: 211120

Subsidiaries:

Kindee Oil & Gas Louisiana LLC (1)
800 Wilcrest Dr Ste 214, Houston, TX 77042
Tel.: (713) 334-0966
Web Site: http://www.ggpl.com
Oil & Gas Exploration Services
N.A.I.C.S.: 213112
James Sloan *(Pres)*

Kindee Oil & Gas Texas LLC (1)
800 Wilcrest Dr Ste 214, Houston, TX 77042
Tel.: (713) 334-2830
Oil & Gas Exploration Services
N.A.I.C.S.: 213112

OGIER GROUP L.P.

Ogier House The Esplanade, JE4 9WJ, Saint Helier, Jersey
Tel.: (44) 1534 504 000 JE
Web Site: http://www.ogier.com
Year Founded: 1995
Sales Range: $100-124.9 Million
Emp.: 850
Holding Company; Legal & Administrative Services
N.A.I.C.S.: 551112
Marcus Leese *(Partner-Practice-Guernsey)*

Subsidiaries:

Ogier Hong Kong (1)
11th Floor Central Tower 28 Queen's Road, Central, China (Hong Kong)
Tel.: (852) 3656 6000
Financial Investment Services
N.A.I.C.S.: 523150
Anthony Oakes *(Head-Fin)*

Ogier Legal Limited Partnership (1)
44 The Esplanade Ogier House, The Esplanade, Saint Helier, JE4 9WG, Jersey
Tel.: (44) 1534514000
Web Site: http://www.ogier.com
Law firm
N.A.I.C.S.: 541110
Nick Kershaw *(CEO & Partner)*

Ogier Luxembourg (1)
2-4 rue Eugene Ruppert, PO Box 2078, 1020, Luxembourg, Luxembourg
Tel.: (352) 2712 2000
Financial Investment Services
N.A.I.C.S.: 523150

Ogier Services (Cayman) Limited (1)
89 Nexus Way, Camana Bay, Camana Bay, KY1-9007, Grande Cayman, Cayman Islands
Tel.: (345) 949 9876
Web Site: http://www.ogier.com
Emp.: 120
Law firm
N.A.I.C.S.: 541110
Nick Rogers *(Mng Partner)*

Ogier Shanghai (1)
Room 904B 21st Century Tower No 210 Century Avenue Pudong New Area, Shanghai, 200120, China
Tel.: (86) 21 6075 6525
Financial Investment Services
N.A.I.C.S.: 523150
Kristy Calvert *(Mng Dir)*

OGILVIE MOTORS LIMITED

1110 St Laurent Blvd, Ottawa, K1K 3B6, ON, Canada
Tel.: (613) 745-9000
Web Site: http://www.mercedes-benz-ogilvie.ca
Year Founded: 1972
Sales Range: $10-24.9 Million
New & Used Car Dealers
N.A.I.C.S.: 441110
Leslie Mise *(Gen Mgr-Sls)*

OGLESBY & BUTLER GROUP PLC

Industrial Estate O'Brien Rd, Carlow, Ireland
Tel.: (353) 599143333 IE
Web Site: http://www.portasol.com
Year Founded: 1984
Portable Gas Powered Hand Tools Mfr
N.A.I.C.S.: 333414
John Bailey *(Head-Fin)*

OGUNSEN AB

Tel.: (46) 84075500
Web Site: https://ogunsen.se
Year Founded: 1993
OGUN.B—(OMX)
Rev.: $43,248,061
Assets: $14,702,094
Liabilities: $6,613,074
Net Worth: $8,089,021
Earnings: $1,348,984
Emp.: 485
Fiscal Year-end: 12/31/20
Management Consulting Services
N.A.I.C.S.: 541618
Kent Sangler *(Mng Dir)*

OGURA CLUTCH CO., LTD.

2-678 Aioi-cho, Kiryu, 376-0011, Gumma, Japan
Tel.: (81) 277547101
Web Site: https://www.oguraclutch.co.jp
Year Founded: 1938
6408—(TKS)
Rev.: $287,475,510
Assets: $321,239,390
Liabilities: $219,729,620
Net Worth: $101,509,770
Earnings: ($3,952,780)

OHASHI TECHNICA, INC.

Emp.: 2,013
Fiscal Year-end: 03/31/24
Automotive Parts Mfr & Distr
N.A.I.C.S.: 336390
Yasuhiro Ogura *(Pres)*

Subsidiaries:

Ogura Clutch do Brasil LTDA. (1)
Rua Ettore Soliani 568-Distrito Industrial Nova Era Indaiatuba, Sao Paulo, Brazil
Tel.: (55) 1938856000
Clutch Distr
N.A.I.C.S.: 423120

Toyo Clutch Co., Ltd. (1)
2-12-6 Higashi-Gotanda, Shinagawa-ku, Tokyo, 141-0022, Japan
Tel.: (81) 334493221
Web Site: https://www.toyoclutch.com
Emp.: 37
Automobile Parts Distr
N.A.I.C.S.: 423120
Yasuhiro Ogura *(Pres)*

OGUS NETZE- UND WIRKWAREN GMBH & CO. KG

Sachsenstrasse 30, D-41063, Monchengladbach, Germany
Tel.: (49) 216124580
Web Site: http://www.ogus.de
Rev.: $14,748,014
Emp.: 48
Camouflage Nets Mfr
N.A.I.C.S.: 339999
Markus Schmitz *(Co-Mng Dir)*

OHARA INC.

1-15-30 Oyama, Chuo-ku, Sagamihara, 252-5286, Kanagawa, Japan
Tel.: (81) 427722101 JP
Web Site: https://www.ohara-inc.co.jp
Year Founded: 1935
5218—(TKS)
Rev.: $199,392,070
Assets: $438,445,600
Liabilities: $103,010,610
Net Worth: $335,434,990
Earnings: $11,145,480
Emp.: 475
Fiscal Year-end: 10/31/23
Lenses & Special Glass Mfr
N.A.I.C.S.: 333310
Hirokazu Saito *(Pres & CEO)*

Subsidiaries:

OHARA GmbH (1)
Im Langgewann 4, 65719, Hofheim, Germany
Tel.: (49) 6192965050
Web Site: https://www.ohara-gmbh.com
Optical Lens Mfr
N.A.I.C.S.: 333310

Ohara Corporation (1)
23141 Arroyo Vista Ste 200, Rancho Santa Margarita, CA 92688-2609
Tel.: (949) 858-5700
Web Site: https://www.oharacorp.com
Sales Range: $25-49.9 Million
Emp.: 3
Precision Optical Glasses Mfr
N.A.I.C.S.: 423460
Brion Hoffman *(Pres)*

OHARA TECHNOLOGIES

20 Kinnear Court, Richmond Hill, L4B 1K8, ON, Canada
Tel.: (905) 707-3286
Web Site: http://www.oharatech.com
Year Founded: 1976
Rev.: $14,439,636
Emp.: 80
Processing Equipment Mfr
N.A.I.C.S.: 333310
Gil O Hara *(Founder)*

OHASHI TECHNICA, INC.

Hulic Kamiyacho Building 10F 4-3-13 Toranomon, Minato-ku, Tokyo, 105-0001, Japan

OHASHI TECHNICA, INC.

Ohashi Technica, Inc.—(Continued)
Tel.: (81) 354044411
Web Site: https://www.ohashi.co.jp
Year Founded: 1953
7628—(TKS)
Rev.: $259,191,320
Assets: $307,510,420
Liabilities: $61,221,820
Net Worth: $246,288,600
Earnings: $6,649,660
Emp.: 756
Fiscal Year-end: 03/31/24
Automotive Parts Mfr & Distr
N.A.I.C.S.: 336390
Mamoru Shibasaki (Pres)

Subsidiaries:

OHASHI LOGISTICS, INC. (1)
6-7-9 Yaho, Kunitachi-shi, Tokyo, 186-0011, Japan
Tel.: (81) 425019681
Warehousing & Storage Services
N.A.I.C.S.: 493110

Ohashi Giken, Inc. (1)
266-21 Tonowari Minamishibata-machi, Tokai, 476-0001, Aichi, Japan
Tel.: (81) 526041451
Emp.: 114
Industrial Machinery Parts Mfr
N.A.I.C.S.: 333248

Plant (Domestic):

Ohashi Giken, Inc. - SENDAI PLANT (2)
3-19 Akedori, Izumi-ku, Sendai, 981-3206, Miyagi, Japan
Tel.: (81) 22 342 6446
Automobile Parts Mfr
N.A.I.C.S.: 336390

Ohashi Nakahyo Precision Parts (Guangzhou) Co., Ltd. (1)
No 7 of Yongsheng Road, Yonghe Subdistrict Guangzhou Economic & Technological Development, Guangzhou, China
Tel.: (86) 2032225184
Automotive Spare Parts Distr
N.A.I.C.S.: 423120

Ohashi Nakahyo USA, Inc. (1)
111 Burrer Dr, Sunbury, OH 43074
Tel.: (740) 965-5115
Automobile Parts Mfr & Distr
N.A.I.C.S.: 336390

Ohashi Sato (Thailand) Co., Ltd. (1)
304 Industrial Park 232Moo7 Tambol Tatoom Amphur, Si Maha Phot, 25140, Prachinbury, Thailand
Tel.: (66) 37208576
Automobile Parts Distr
N.A.I.C.S.: 423120

Ohashi Technica (Shanghai) Co., Ltd. (1)
Bldg 3 558 Chuantu Road, Pu Dong New Area, Shanghai, China
Tel.: (86) 2158382211
Automobile Parts Distr
N.A.I.C.S.: 423120

Ohashi Technica (Thailand) Co., Ltd. (1)
9/9 Moo 13 Soi Kingkaew Tambol Bangpleeyai, Amphur, Bang Phli, 10540, Samutprakarn, Thailand
Tel.: (66) 23171339
Automobile Parts Distr
N.A.I.C.S.: 423120

Ohashi Technica Mexico S.A. DE .C.V. (1)
Circuito San Roque Poniente 263-D Col Puerto Interior, 36275, Silao, Guanajuato, Mexico
Tel.: (52) 4721032100
Automobile Parts Distr
N.A.I.C.S.: 423120
Gerardo Linares Segovia (Sr Mgr-Admin & Acctg)

Ohashi Technica Precision Parts (Shanghai) Co., Ltd. (1)
B16 4th Floor No 231 North Fute Road, China Pilot Free Trade Zone, Shanghai, China
Tel.: (86) 2158382661
Automobile Spare Parts Mfr
N.A.I.C.S.: 336390

Ohashi Technica Taiwan Co., Ltd. (1)
3F No 899 Xinsheng Rd, Qianzhen Dist, Kaohsiung, 80672, Taiwan
Tel.: (886) 7 821 1971
Automobile Parts Mfr & Distr
N.A.I.C.S.: 336390

Ohashi Technica U.S.A. Manufacturing Inc. (1)
99 Burrer Dr, Sunbury, OH 43074
Tel.: (740) 965-9002
Automobile Spare Parts Mfr
N.A.I.C.S.: 336390

Ohashi Technica U.S.A., Inc. (1)
111 Burrer Dr, Sunbury, OH 43074
Tel.: (740) 965-5115
Emp.: 80
Industrial Supplies Whslr
N.A.I.C.S.: 423840
Ian McGregor (Sr Mgr)

Ohashi Technica UK, Ltd. (1)
Unit 30 Bentall Business Park, Washington, NE37 3JD, United Kingdom
Tel.: (44) 1914162038
Automobile Parts Mfr
N.A.I.C.S.: 336390

OHB SE

Manfred-Fuchs-Platz 2-4, 28359, Bremen, Germany
Tel.: (49) 42120208
Web Site: https://www.ohb.de
Year Founded: 1981
OHB—(STU)
Rev.: $1,156,634,986
Assets: $1,479,274,110
Liabilities: $1,027,780,241
Net Worth: $451,493,869
Earnings: $78,694,892
Emp.: 3,292
Fiscal Year-end: 12/31/23
Space Technology Developer & Mfr
N.A.I.C.S.: 336414
Heinz Stoewer (Deputy Chm-Supervisory Bd)

Subsidiaries:

Aerotech Czech s.r.o. (1)
Dr Sedlaka 763, Klatovy, 33901, Czech Republic
Tel.: (420) 376339910
Emp.: 80
Aerospace Equipment Mfr
N.A.I.C.S.: 336414
Miroslav Vich (Mgr-Quality & Production)

Aerotech France S.A.S. (1)
29 Boulevard D Anvaux, 36000, Chateauroux, France
Tel.: (33) 2 54 08 12 12
Emp.: 33
Aerospace Equipment Mfr
N.A.I.C.S.: 336414
Eric Matias (Mgr-Sls)

Antwerp Space N.V. (1)
Berkenrodelei 33, Hoboken, 2660, Antwerp, Belgium
Tel.: (32) 38295050
Web Site: https://www.antwerpspace.be
Emp.: 3,000
Satellite Equipment Mfr
N.A.I.C.S.: 334220

GEOSYSTEMS Gesellschaft fur Vertrieb und Installation von Fernerkundungs- und Geoinformationssystemen mbH (1)
Friedrichshafener Str 1, 82205, Gilching, Germany
Tel.: (49) 81053988350
Web Site: https://www.geosystems.de
Information Technology Services
N.A.I.C.S.: 541519

LuxSpace Sarl (1)
9 rue Pierre Werner, 6832, Betzdorf, Luxembourg
Tel.: (352) 2678904000
Web Site: https://www.luxspace.lu
Emp.: 40
Aerospace Application Development Services
N.A.I.C.S.: 541511
Thomas Goerlach (Member-Exec Bd)

M2M Europe Network & Solutions Ges.mbH (1)
Brielgasse 21, 6900, Bregenz, Austria
Tel.: (43) 557420723
Web Site: http://www.m2m-ens.com
Logistic Services
N.A.I.C.S.: 541614

MT Aerospace AG (1)
Franz-Josef-Strauss St 5, 86153, Augsburg, Germany (70%)
Tel.: (49) 82150501
Web Site: http://www.mt-aerospace.de
Sales Range: $150-199.9 Million
Emp.: 600
Space Systems; Lightweight Engineering & Apparatuses; Electronic Systems & Material Technologies
N.A.I.C.S.: 336414
Marco R. Fuchs (Chm-Supervisory Bd)

MT Mecatronica SpA (1)
Limache 3405 Of 94, Vina del Mar, Chile
Tel.: (56) 232027910
Web Site: http://www.mt-mecatronica.cl
Business Support Services
N.A.I.C.S.: 561499

OHB Hellas mon.E.P.E (1)
Ifestou 3, 15124, Maroussi, Greece
Tel.: (30) 2106100600
Web Site: https://www.ohb-hellas.gr
Logistic Services
N.A.I.C.S.: 541614
Katerina Panopoulou (Mng Dir)

OHB Logistic Solutions GmbH (1)
Lise-Meitner-Str 6, 28359, Bremen, Germany
Tel.: (49) 42189768317
Web Site: http://www.ohb-ls.de
Logistic Services
N.A.I.C.S.: 541614

OHB Sweden AB (1)
Viderogatan 6, 164 40, Kista, Sweden
Tel.: (46) 812140100
Web Site: https://www.ohb-sweden.se
Emp.: 100
Aeronautical Product Mfr
N.A.I.C.S.: 336419
Gierth Olsson (Mng Dir)

OHB System AG (1)
Universitatsallee 27-29, 28359, Bremen, Germany
Tel.: (49) 42120208
Web Site: https://www.ohb.de
Space Technology Developer
N.A.I.C.S.: 927110

TeleConsult Austria GmbH (1)
Rettenbacher Strasse 22, 8044, Graz, Austria
Tel.: (43) 3168909710
Web Site: http://www.tca.at
Tele Consulting Services
N.A.I.C.S.: 541890
Andreas Lesch (CEO)

OHBA CO., LTD.

Kouwa hitotsubashi Building 3-7-1 Kanda Nishikicho, Chiyoda-ku, Tokyo, 101-0054, Japan
Tel.: (81) 334600111
Web Site: https://www.k-ohba.co.jp
Year Founded: 1922
9765—(TKS)
Rev.: $108,965,850
Assets: $118,755,260
Liabilities: $35,310,620
Net Worth: $83,444,640
Earnings: $8,850,790
Emp.: 519
Fiscal Year-end: 05/31/24
Construction Surveying Services
N.A.I.C.S.: 541370

INTERNATIONAL PUBLIC

Shigeru Tsujimoto (Pres)

OHISHI SANGYO CO., LTD.

2-7-1 Taoyuan, Yahatahigashi-ku, Kitakyushu, 805-0068, Fukuoka, Japan
Tel.: (81) 936616511
Web Site: https://www.osk.co.jp
Year Founded: 1947
3943—(TKS)
Rev.: $145,182,040
Assets: $172,335,920
Liabilities: $55,074,520
Net Worth: $117,261,400
Earnings: $7,039,650
Emp.: 579
Fiscal Year-end: 03/31/24
Industrial Packaging Material Mfr & Distr
N.A.I.C.S.: 326112
Hiroaki Yamaguchi (Pres & CEO)

Subsidiaries:

Corepax (M) Sdn. Bhd. (1)
Plo 204 Jalan Tembaga, Kawasan Perindustrian, 81700, Pasir Gudang, Johor, Malaysia
Tel.: (60) 72510846
Web Site: http://www.corepax.com.my
Emp.: 130
Paper Bag Mfr
N.A.I.C.S.: 322220

Encore Lami Sdn. Bhd. (1)
Plo 793 Jalan Nikel 2 Zone 12C Kaw, Perindustrain, 81700, Pasir Gudang, Johor, Malaysia
Tel.: (60) 72512054
Web Site: http://www.encore-lami.com.my
Lamination Paper Product Mfr
N.A.I.C.S.: 322220

OHKI HEALTHCARE HOLDINGS CO., LTD.

2-1-4 Otowa, Bunkyo-ku, Tokyo, 112-0013, Japan
Tel.: (81) 368920710 JP
Web Site: https://www.ohki-net.co.jp
Year Founded: 2015
3417—(TKS)
Rev.: $2,212,109,210
Assets: $915,987,360
Liabilities: $731,574,970
Net Worth: $184,412,390
Earnings: $14,608,100
Fiscal Year-end: 03/31/24
Holding Company; Pharmaceutical Mfr & Whslr
N.A.I.C.S.: 551112
Hideo Matsui (Chm & Pres)

Subsidiaries:

Liv Laboratories Co., Ltd. (1)
2-1-4 Otowa, Bunkyo-ku, Tokyo, 112-0013, Japan
Tel.: (81) 33 947 2228
Web Site: https://www.liv-net.co.jp
Cosmetic Product Distr
N.A.I.C.S.: 456120

Ohki Co., Ltd. (1)
2-1-4 Otowa, Bunkyo-ku, Tokyo, 112-0013, Japan
Tel.: (81) 339472228
Web Site: http://www.ohki-net.co.jp
Pharmaceutical Mfr & Whslr
N.A.I.C.S.: 325412
Hideo Matsui (Chm, Pres & CEO)

OHL LOGISTIK GMBH & CO. KG

Hittfelder Kirchweg 1-5, Maschen, 21220, Seevetal, Germany
Tel.: (49) 41 05 6 91 0 De
Web Site: http://www.ohl.de
Print & Media Logistics Services
N.A.I.C.S.: 541614
Jochen Claussen (Mng Partner)

Subsidiaries:

Logwin Solutions Media GmbH (1)

AND PRIVATE COMPANIES

Weichertstrasse 5, 63741, Aschaffenburg, Germany
Tel.: (49) 6021 343 0
Sales Range: $75-99.9 Million
Emp.: 113
Logistic Services
N.A.I.C.S.: 541614

Ohl Logistics A/S (1)
Plantagevej 7-9, 6330, Padborg, Denmark
Tel.: (45) 74 30 36 00
Web Site: http://www.ohllogistics.com
Print & Media Logistics Services
N.A.I.C.S.: 541614

Subsidiary (Non-US):

Ohl Logistics AB (2)
Hemsogatan 6, SE 21124, Malmo, Sweden
Tel.: (46) 40 18 20 70
Web Site: http://www.ohllogistics.com
Print & Media Logistics Services
N.A.I.C.S.: 541614

Ohl Logistics AS (2)
Ostre Aker Vei 95, NO 0598, Oslo, Norway
Tel.: (47) 23 100 300
Web Site: http://www.ohllogistics.com
Print & Media Logistics Services
N.A.I.C.S.: 541614

Omnidata GmbH & Co. KG (1)
Luruper Chaussee 125, Businesspark Bahrenfeld, 22761, Hamburg, Germany
Tel.: (49) 40 89 80 5 0
Web Site: http://www.omnidata.de
Printing & Logistics Mfr
N.A.I.C.S.: 323111
Michael Hoffmann (Mng Dir)

OHLTHAVER & LIST GROUP OF COMPANIES
Alexander Forbes House 7th Floor South Block 23-33 Fidel Castro St, Windhoek, Khomas, Namibia
Tel.: (264) 61 2075111
Web Site: http://www.ol.na
Year Founded: 1919
Holding Company
N.A.I.C.S.: 551112
Gunni Hanke (COO)

Subsidiaries:

CRONIMET Mining Power Solutions GmbH (1)
Maximilianstr 2 a, 82319, Starnberg, Germany
Tel.: (49) 8151 7463 261
Web Site: http://www.crm-ps.com
Steel & Ferroalloy Distr
N.A.I.C.S.: 423510
Rollie Armstrong (Mng Dir)

OHMORI CO., LTD.
15-8 Mizumoto 3-chome, Katsushika-ku, Tokyo, 125-0032, Japan
Tel.: (81) 336273260
Web Site: https://www.ohmori.co.jp
Year Founded: 1967
1844—(TKS)
Rev.: $37,201,820
Assets: $74,210,820
Liabilities: $39,273,080
Net Worth: $34,937,740
Earnings: $2,575,080
Fiscal Year-end: 07/31/24
Construction Engineering Services
N.A.I.C.S.: 541330
Mikio Kuriki (Pres & CEO)

OHMORIYA CO., LTD.
1-1-60 Nishikujo, Konohana-ku, Osaka, 554-0012, Japan
Tel.: (01) 664641108
Web Site: https://ohmoriya-inc.co.jp
Year Founded: 1927
2917—(TKS)
Rev.: $100,954,510
Assets: $105,194,330
Liabilities: $23,326,100
Net Worth: $81,868,230
Earnings: $1,729,960
Emp.: 371

Fiscal Year-end: 09/30/23
Seaweed Product Mfr
N.A.I.C.S.: 311999
Taro Inano (Pres)

OHMOTO GUMI CO., LTD.
Aoyama OHMOTO Building 5-9-15 Minamiaoyama, Minato-ku, Tokyo, 107-8514, Japan
Tel.: (81) 367527007
Web Site: https://www.ohmoto.co.jp
Year Founded: 1937
1793—(TKS)
Sales Range: $700-749.9 Million
Civil Engineering Construction Services
N.A.I.C.S.: 541330
Mampei Ohmoto (Pres)

OHMURA SHIGYO CO., LTD.
163-1 Amanuma, Chigasaki, 253-0004, Kanagawa, Japan
Tel.: (81) 467521032
Web Site: https://www.ohmurashigyo.co.jp
Year Founded: 1981
3953—(TKS)
Sales Range: Less than $1 Million
Paper Container Mfr
N.A.I.C.S.: 322211
Hideo Omura (Chm, Pres & CEO)

OHMYHOME LIMITED
11 Lorong 3 Toa Payoh Jackson Square Proptech Innovation Centre, Block B 04-17, Singapore, 319579, Singapore
Tel.: (65) 68869009   Ky
Web Site: https://www.ohmyhome.com
Year Founded: 2015
OMH—(NASDAQ)
Rev.: $3,308,039
Assets: $1,883,313
Liabilities: $1,230,432
Net Worth: $652,881
Earnings: ($1,377,675)
Emp.: 49
Fiscal Year-end: 12/31/21
Property Management Services
N.A.I.C.S.: 531311
David Kim Kang Loh (Chm)

OHRLINGS PRICEWATERHOUSECOOPERS
Kyrkangsgatan 8, 503 38, Boras, Sweden
Tel.: (46) 102125500   SE
Web Site: http://www.pwc.se
Emp.: 3,600
Accounting & Business Consulting Services
N.A.I.C.S.: 541211
Oskar Ebbinghaus (Partner & Head-Consulting-Sweden)

OHRMANN MONTAGETECHNIK GMBH
An der Haar 27 29, 59519, Soest, Germany
Tel.: (49) 292497140
Web Site: http://www.ohrmann.de
Year Founded: 1986
Emp.: 140
Assembly & Moulding System Mfr
N.A.I.C.S.: 336110
Colestin Ohrmann (Co-Owner & Mng Dir)

OHSHO FOOD SERVICE CORP.
294-1 Ibanoue-cho Nishinoyama, Yamashina-ku, Kyoto, 607-8307, Japan
Tel.: (81) 755921411
Web Site: https://www.ohsho.co.jp

Year Founded: 1974
9936—(TKS)
Rev.: $670,260,610
Assets: $604,563,820
Liabilities: $150,886,470
Net Worth: $453,677,350
Earnings: $52,291,710
Emp.: 2,290
Fiscal Year-end: 03/31/24
Restaurant Operators
N.A.I.C.S.: 722511
Hiroshi Kadobayashi (Sr Mng Dir)

OHTO CO., LTD.
4-5-9 Kuramae, Taito-ku, Tokyo, 111-0051, Japan
Tel.: (81) 338647441   JP
Web Site: http://www.ohto.jp
Year Founded: 1929
Emp.: 100
Pen Mfr
N.A.I.C.S.: 339940
Hideki Niwa (Pres)

OI ELECTRIC CO., LTD.
7-3-16 Kikuna Kanagawa Prefecture, Kohoku-ku, Yokohama, 222-0011, Japan
Tel.: (81) 454331361
Web Site: https://www.ooi.co.jp
Year Founded: 1950
6822—(TKS)
Rev.: $185,774,642
Assets: $157,786,543
Liabilities: $104,975,194
Net Worth: $52,811,350
Earnings: $5,014,865
Emp.: 420
Fiscal Year-end: 03/31/24
Telecommunication Servicesb
N.A.I.C.S.: 517121
Kou Ishida (Pres)

Subsidiaries:

Create Oi Co., Ltd. (1)
7-3-16 Kikuna, Kohoku-ku, Yokohama, 222-0011, Kanagawa, Japan
Tel.: (81) 454331360
Building Maintenance Services
N.A.I.C.S.: 561790

NF Service KK (1)
1F TF Nishidai Bldg 3-17-1 Hasune, Itabashi-ku, Tokyo, 174-0046, Japan
Tel.: (81) 363712730
Communication Device Installation Services
N.A.I.C.S.: 238210

Nippon Field Engineering Co., Ltd. (1)
Nishigotanda TF Bldg 1-14-8, Nishigotanda Shinagawa-ku, Tokyo, 141-0031, Japan
Tel.: (81) 363712000
Communication Device Mfr & Distr
N.A.I.C.S.: 334290

Nippon Technical Service Co., Ltd. (1)
Mitsubishi Electric Setagaya Bldg 3-10-3 Ikejiri, Setagaya-ku, Tokyo, 154-0001, Japan
Tel.: (81) 334138500
Communication Device Mfr & Distr
N.A.I.C.S.: 334290

Oi-Techno. Co., Ltd. (1)
7-3-16 Kikuna, Kohoku-ku, Yokohama, 222-0011, Kanagawa, Japan
Tel.: (81) 454332257
Software Development Services
N.A.I.C.S.: 541511

OI S.A.
Rua do Lavradio n 71 2 andar - Centro, Leblon, Rio de Janeiro, 22280-004, RJ, Brazil
Tel.: (55) 8000010031   BR
Web Site: https://www.oi.com.br
Year Founded: 1998
OIBR4—(BRAZ)
Rev.: $2,002,623,616

OIL & GAS DEVELOPMENT

Assets: $5,383,625,883
Liabilities: $11,006,187,924
Net Worth: ($5,622,562,042)
Earnings: ($1,230,275,343)
Fiscal Year-end: 12/31/23
Telecommunication Servicesb
N.A.I.C.S.: 517121
Eleazar de Carvalho Filho (Chm)

Subsidiaries:

Dommo Empreendimentos Imobiliarios SA (1)
Av Das Nacoes Unidas 12901 - 27 Floor, 4578903, Sao Paulo, Brazil
Tel.: (55) 21 3131 2918
Real Estate Development Services
N.A.I.C.S.: 531390

PT Inovacao Brasil Ltda. (1)
Rua Cubatao 320 3 Paraiso, Sao Paulo, 04013-001, Brazil
Tel.: (55) 11 3888 2644
Web Site: http://www.ptinovacao.com.br
Telecommunication Servicesb
N.A.I.C.S.: 517810

Telemar Norte Leste S.A. (1)
Rua General Polidoro 99 5th Floor, 22280001, Rio de Janeiro, RJ, Brazil   (81.9%)
Tel.: (55) 2131311208
Web Site: http://www.oi.com.br
Sales Range: $5-14.9 Billion
Fixed-Line Communications Services
N.A.I.C.S.: 517111
Jose Mauro Mettrau Carneiro de Cunha (Chm)

OI WAH PAWNSHOP CREDIT HOLDINGS LIMITED
Rooms 2302-2303 Kwan Chart Tower, No 6 Tonnochy Rd, Wanchai, China (Hong Kong)
Tel.: (852) 28332065
Web Site: http://www.pawnshop.com.hk
1319—(HKG)
Rev.: $21,390,172
Assets: $148,787,459
Liabilities: $15,932,255
Net Worth: $132,855,204
Earnings: $11,106,081
Emp.: 50
Fiscal Year-end: 02/28/23
Financial Lending Services
N.A.I.C.S.: 522291
Edward Kai Ho Chan (Chm & CEO)

OIE SANGYO CO., LTD.
6-11-27 Toyosaki, Kita-ku, Osaka, 531-8534, Japan
Tel.: (81) 663750151
Web Site: https://www.oie.co.jp
Year Founded: 1961
7481—(TKS)
Rev.: $736,188,750
Assets: $234,066,710
Liabilities: $150,159,370
Net Worth: $83,907,340
Earnings: $20,193,550
Emp.: 885
Fiscal Year-end: 03/31/24
Food Products Distr
N.A.I.C.S.: 424420
Makoto Oie (Chm)

OIG OFFSHORE INSTALLATION GROUP ASA
Drammensveien 127, N-0212, Oslo, Norway
Tel.: (17) 22560360
Web Site: http://www.oig-offshore.com
Offshore Subsea Installation & Logistics Services
N.A.I.C.S.: 237990
Heiko Felderhoff (CEO)

OIL & GAS DEVELOPMENT

OIL & GAS DEVELOPMENT

OIL & GAS DEVELOPMENT —(CONTINUED)

COMPANY LTD.
OGDCL House Plot No 3 F-6 G-6
Blue Area Jinnah Avenue, Islamabad,
Pakistan
Tel.: (92) 519209811
Web Site: https://www.ogdcl.com
Year Founded: 1961
OGDC—(KAR)
Rev.: $1,877,434,930
Assets: $5,504,167,824
Liabilities: $1,014,045,344
Net Worth: $4,490,122,481
Earnings: $850,009,958
Emp.: 11,956
Fiscal Year-end: 06/30/19
Oil & Gas Exploration & Development
N.A.I.C.S.: 211120
Masood Nabi (Exec Dir-Joint Venture)

OIL & NATURAL GAS CORPORATION LIMITED
Plot No 5A-5B Nelson Mandela Road
Vasant Kunj, New Delhi, 110070,
India
Tel.: (91) 1126750998
Web Site: https://www.ongcindia.com
Year Founded: 1961
ONGC—(BOM)
Rev.: $83,076,950,183
Assets: $73,680,082,249
Liabilities: $37,560,540,855
Net Worth: $36,119,541,394
Earnings: $3,929,932,858
Emp.: 25,993
Fiscal Year-end: 03/31/23
Refined Petroleum Mfr
N.A.I.C.S.: 324110
Ajay Kumar Dwivedi (Dir-Exploration)

Subsidiaries:

HPCL Middle East FZCO (1)
1 W 101 Dubai Airport Free Zone Al Twar 2,
PO Box 54618, Dubai, United Arab Emirates
Tel.: (971) 4 214 6862
Petroleum Product Distr
N.A.I.C.S.: 424720

Hindustan Petroleum Corporation Limited (1)
Petroleum House 17 Jamshedji Tata Road,
Mumbai, 400 020, India **(51.1%)**
Tel.: (91) 2222863900
Web Site: https://www.hindustanpetroleum.com
Rev.: $37,294,760,685
Assets: $18,312,800,415
Liabilities: $13,114,763,025
Net Worth: $5,198,037,390
Earnings: $1,455,484,485
Emp.: 9,448
Fiscal Year-end: 03/31/2021
Oil & Gas Operations
N.A.I.C.S.: 211120
K. Radhakrishnan (CEO-Hindustan Colas)

Subsidiary (Domestic):

HPCL Biofuels Limited (2)
No 271 Road No 3E Holding No 437 & 438
Ward No 22, New Patliputra Colony, Patna,
800013, Bihar, India **(100%)**
Tel.: (91) 6122220559
Web Site: http://www.hpclbiofuels.co.in
Rev.: $33,730,720
Assets: $118,726,567
Liabilities: $112,326,396
Net Worth: $6,400,171
Earnings: ($9,686,899)
Fiscal Year-end: 03/31/2019
Biofuels Mfr
N.A.I.C.S.: 325199
Raja Kishor Barik (CEO)

Joint Venture (Domestic):

Hindustan Colas Pvt. Ltd. (2)
HINCOL House B-601 6th Floor Marathon
Futurex, N M Joshi Marg Lower Parel,
Mumbai, 400013, India **(50%)**
Tel.: (91) 222 302 3250
Web Site: https://www.hincol.com
Sales Range: $100-124.9 Million
Bitumen Emulsions Mfr & Marketer
N.A.I.C.S.: 325110
K. Radhakrishnan (CEO)

Mangalore Refinery & Petrochemicals Limited (1)
Kuthethoor PO Via Katipalla, Mangalore,
575 030, India **(71.63%)**
Tel.: (91) 8242270400
Web Site: https://www.mrpl.co.in
Rev.: $12,639,241,954
Assets: $4,248,060,957
Liabilities: $2,655,487,388
Net Worth: $1,592,573,668
Earnings: $431,287,494
Emp.: 2,569
Fiscal Year-end: 03/31/2024
Petroleum Refiner & Petrochemical Mfr
N.A.I.C.S.: 325110
Dinesh Mishra (Officer-Compliance & Sec)

Mansarovar Energy Colombia Ltd. (1)
Calle 100 No 13 - 76 Piso 11, Bogota, Colombia
Tel.: (57) 1 485 1212
Web Site: https://www.mansarovar.com.co
Crude Petroleum Production & Transportation Services Owned by Oil & Natural Gas Corporation & by China Petrochemical Services
N.A.I.C.S.: 211120
Sidhartha Sur (Mgr-Ops)

ONGC Campos Ltda. (1)
Av Das Americas 3500 Block 01 Room 518
and 519 Barra-de-Tijuca, Rio de Janeiro,
22640-102, Brazil
Tel.: (55) 213 553 7853
Petroleum Product Distr
N.A.I.C.S.: 424720

ONGC Mangalore Petrochemicals Ltd. (1)
Mangalore SEZ, Permude Village, Mangalore, 574509, Karnataka, India
Tel.: (91) 824 287 2000
Web Site: https://www.ompl.co.in
Oil & Gas Exploration Services
N.A.I.C.S.: 213112
Subhash Kumar (Chm)

ONGC Nile Ganga (San Cristobal) B.V. (1)
Kingsfordweg 151 Office 13 04, 1043 GR,
Amsterdam, Noord-Holland, Netherlands
Tel.: (31) 204919821
Sales Range: $50-74.9 Million
Emp.: 4
Oil & Gas Exploration Services
N.A.I.C.S.: 211120

ONGC Videsh Atlantic Inc. (1)
Ste 1230 2200 Post Oak Blvd, Houston, TX 77056
Tel.: (713) 228-7576
Petroleum Product Distr
N.A.I.C.S.: 424720

ONGC Videsh Ltd. (1)
Deendayal Urja Bhawan Tower B 5 Nelson
Mandela Marg, Vasant Kunj, New Delhi,
110070, India
Tel.: (91) 1126129344
Web Site: http://www.ongcvidesh.com
Rev.: $2,474,955,620
Assets: $15,966,006,693
Liabilities: $8,347,557,855
Net Worth: $7,618,448,838
Earnings: $203,919,944
Emp.: 1,854
Fiscal Year-end: 03/31/2022
Oil & Natural Gas Exploration & Extraction Services
N.A.I.C.S.: 211120
Shashi Shanker (Chm & Mng Dir)

Subsidiary (Non-US):

Imperial Energy Corporation PLC (2)
6/8 York Place, Leeds, LS1 2DS, United Kingdom
Tel.: (44) 2072557714
Web Site: http://www.imperialenergy.com
Sales Range: $150-199.9 Million
Emp.: 415
Oil & Gas Exploration Services
N.A.I.C.S.: 211120

Jarpeno Limited (2)
4th Floor 12 Esperidon Street, Nicosia, Cyprus
Tel.: (357) 22458700
Oil & Gas Exploration Services
N.A.I.C.S.: 213112

ONGC Nile Ganga B.V. (2)
Kingsfordweg 151 Regus Telepo, Amsterdam, 1043 GR, North Holland, Netherlands
Tel.: (31) 204919821
Oil & Gas Exploration Services
N.A.I.C.S.: 213112

OOO Imperial Energy (2)
Prospekt Kirova d 51 a str 15, 634041,
Tomsk, Russia
Tel.: (7) 3822556868
Web Site: http://www.imperialenergy.com
Oil & Gas Exploration Services
N.A.I.C.S.: 213112

Subsidiary (Domestic):

OOO Imperial Energy Tomsk Gas (3)
51 A Korp 15 Prospekt Kirova, Tomsk,
634041, Russia
Tel.: (7) 3822556868
Sales Range: $350-399.9 Million
Emp.: 800
Oil & Gas Exploration Services
N.A.I.C.S.: 213112
S. K. Thamilselvam (CEO)

ONGC Videsh Singapore Pte. Ltd. (2)
8 Temasek Boulevard 23-01 Suntec Tower 3, Singapore, 038988, Singapore
Tel.: (65) 6 235 2251
Petroleum Product Distr
N.A.I.C.S.: 424720

OOO Nord Imperial (1)
Prospekt Kirova 51, Tomskaya Oblast,
634041, Tomsk, Russia
Tel.: (7) 4959089718
Web Site: http://www.nord-imperia.com
Sales Range: $200-249.9 Million
Emp.: 500
Oil & Gas Exploration Services
N.A.I.C.S.: 213112
Ranbir Singh Butola (Chm)

OOO Sibinterneft (1)
Kirova avenue 51a-15, 634041, Tomsk, Russia
Tel.: (7) 9164676781
Web Site: http://sibinterneft.com
Oil & Natural Gas Refining Services
N.A.I.C.S.: 324110

OVL Overseas IFSC Limited (1)

Petro Carabobo Ganga B.V. (1)
Kingsfordweg 151 Office 13 04, 1043 GR,
Amsterdam, Noord-Holland, Netherlands
Tel.: (31) 204919813
Petroleum Product Distr
N.A.I.C.S.: 424720

Petronet MHB Ltd. (1)
Corporate Miller 2nd Floor Block B 332/1
Thimmaiah Road Vasanth Nagar, Bengaluru, 560052, Karnataka, India
Tel.: (91) 802 226 2317
Web Site: https://www.petronetmhbl.com
Oil & Gas Mfr
N.A.I.C.S.: 333132
Subhash Kumar (Chm)

Prize Petroleum Company Ltd. (1)
3rd Floor UCO Bank Building Parliament
Street, New Delhi, 110 001, India
Tel.: (91) 112 331 2996
Web Site: https://www.prizepetroleum.com
Oil & Gas Operation Services
N.A.I.C.S.: 213112
M. K. Surana (Chm)

OIL COUNTRY TUBULAR LIMITED
KAMINENI 3rd Floor King Koti,
Hyderabad, 500 001, Telangana, India
Tel.: (91) 4024785555
Web Site: https://www.octlindia.com
500313—(BOM)
Rev.: $681,231

INTERNATIONAL PUBLIC

Assets: $31,042,598
Liabilities: $41,251,965
Net Worth: ($10,209,367)
Earnings: ($6,944,547)
Fiscal Year-end: 03/31/21
Tool Mfr
N.A.I.C.S.: 333515
Sridhar Kamineni (Mng Dir)

Subsidiaries:

Oil Country Tubular Limited - Nalgonda Works (1)
Sreepuram, Narketpally, Nalgonda, 508 254, Andhra Pradesh, India
Tel.: (91) 8682 272531
Web Site: http://www.octlindia.com
Tubular Pipe Mfr
N.A.I.C.S.: 331210

OIL FACTORY BANAT AD
Magazinska bb, Nova Crnja, Serbia
Tel.: (381) 23 815 210
Web Site: http://www.uljarabanat.rs
Year Founded: 1961
Emp.: 170
Oil Processing
N.A.I.C.S.: 311224

OIL INDIA LIMITED
Plot 19 Near Flim City Sector 16A,
Noida, 201301, India
Tel.: (91) 1202419000
Web Site: https://www.oil-india.com
Year Founded: 1959
533106—(BOM)
Rev.: $5,006,689,047
Assets: $8,858,344,224
Liabilities: $3,840,348,900
Net Worth: $5,017,995,324
Earnings: $1,181,510,701
Emp.: 6,759
Fiscal Year-end: 03/31/23
Oil & Gas Exploration, Development & Production Services
N.A.I.C.S.: 211120
Pramod Kumar Sharma (Dir-Ops)

OIL INSURANCE LIMITED
3 Bermudiana Road, Hamilton, HM 08, Bermuda
Tel.: (441) 295 0905
Web Site: http://www.oil.bm
Year Founded: 1972
Sales Range: $1-9.9 Million
Mutual Insurance Services
N.A.I.C.S.: 524298
Ricky E. Lines (CFO & Sr VP)

Subsidiaries:

Oil Casualty Insurance, Ltd. (1)
3 Bermudiana Rd, Hamilton, HM 08, Bermuda **(100%)**
Tel.: (441) 295 0905
Web Site: http://www.ocil.bm
Emp.: 50
Insurance & Reinsurance Services
N.A.I.C.S.: 524130
Robert D. Stauffer (Pres & CEO)

Oil Investment Corporation Ltd. (1)
3 Bermudiana Road, Hamilton, HM08, Bermuda
Tel.: (441) 295 0905
Web Site: http://www.oil.bm
Oil Industries Investment Services
N.A.I.C.S.: 523940
Ricky E. Lines (Pres & Treas)

Oil Management Services Ltd. (1)
3 Bermudiana Rd, PO Box HM 1751, Hamilton, HM 08, Bermuda **(100%)**
Tel.: (441) 295 0905
Web Site: http://www.oil.bm
Emp.: 47
Insurance Consultants, Managers & Advisors to Energy Operations
N.A.I.C.S.: 541620
Marlene J. Cechini (Controller & Asst Sec)

OIL OPTIMIZATION INC.

AND PRIVATE COMPANIES

300-714 1st Street SE, Calgary, T2G 2G8, AB, Canada
Tel.: (416) 848-9888   AB
Web Site: http://www.oilop.com
Year Founded: 2007
Investment Services
N.A.I.C.S.: 523999
Luc Desmarais *(Pres & CEO)*

OIL REFINERY BELGRADE
Pancevacki put 83, 11210, Belgrade, Serbia
Tel.: (381) 11 2711433
Web Site: http://www.rnb.rs
Year Founded: 1934
Lubricant & Anti-corrosion Mfr
N.A.I.C.S.: 213112
Karmila Boskovic *(Dir-Laboratory)*

OIL REFINERY J.S.C. BROD
Svetog Save bb, 74450, Brod, Bosnia & Herzegovina
Tel.: (387) 53 626 001
Web Site: http://www.rafinerija.com
Year Founded: 1892
Sales Range: $50-74.9 Million
Emp.: 1,299
Producing Oil Derivatives
N.A.I.C.S.: 457210

OIL REFINERY MODRICA
Vojvode Stepe Stepanovica br 49, 74480, Modrica, Bosnia & Herzegovina
Tel.: (387) 53810111
Web Site: http://modricaoil.com
Year Founded: 1954
RFUM—(BANJ)
Rev.: $7,709,008
Assets: $122,709,234
Liabilities: $770,920
Net Worth: $121,938,314
Earnings: ($6,431,725)
Emp.: 521
Fiscal Year-end: 12/31/19
Petroleum Product Mfr
N.A.I.C.S.: 324199
Zoran Jovanovic *(Chief Technical Officer)*

OIL SPILL RESPONSE LIMITED
One Great Cumberland Place, London, W1H 7AL, United Kingdom
Tel.: (44) 20 7724 0102   UK
Web Site: http://www.oilspillresponse.com
Year Founded: 1985
Oil Spill Remediation Services
N.A.I.C.S.: 562910
Robert Limb *(CEO)*

Subsidiaries:

Oil Spill Response (Americas) Limited (1)
2381 Stirling Rd, Fort Lauderdale, FL 33312
Tel.: (954) 983-9880
Web Site: http://www.oilspillresponse.com
Emp.: 20
Oil Spill Remediation Services
N.A.I.C.S.: 562910

PT Oil Spill Response Indonesia (1)
Indonesia Stock Exchange Building Tower II 17th Floor, Jl Jend Sudirman Kav 52-53, Jakarta, 12190, Indonesia
Tel.: (62) 21 5291 7494
Oil Spill Remediation Services
N.A.I.C.S.: 562910

OIL TERMINAL S.A
Str Caraiman no 2, 900117, Constanta, Romania
Tel.: (40) 241702600
Web Site: https://www.oil-terminal.com
OIL—(BUC)
Rev.: $1,418,720,685
Assets: $3,055,764,494
Liabilities: $942,478,991
Net Worth: $2,113,285,503
Earnings: $53,273,827
Emp.: 943
Fiscal Year-end: 12/31/22
Crude Oil Producer
N.A.I.C.S.: 324110
Gabriel Daraban *(Dir-Comml)*

OILCORP BERHAD
No 2-2 Jalan SS 6/6 Kelana Jaya, 47301, Petaling Jaya, Selangor Darul Ehsan, Malaysia
Tel.: (60) 378044843   MY
Sales Range: $50-74.9 Million
Emp.: 482
Oil & Gas Facilities Construction & Engineering Services
N.A.I.C.S.: 237120
Sunny Huat Tian Ng *(Mng Dir)*

Subsidiaries:

Azdaman Sdn. Bhd. (1)
No 5A & 5B Jalan Ss 24/8 Daman Negah, Petaling Jaya, 47301, Selangor, Malaysia
Tel.: (60) 378054597
Web Site: http://www.azdaman.com
Sales Range: $50-74.9 Million
Emp.: 10
Oil & Gas Drilling Services
N.A.I.C.S.: 213111
Edna Encarnation *(Gen Mgr)*

Oil-Line Engineering & Associates Sdn. Bhd. (1)
No 2 2 Jalan SS 6 6, Kelana Jaya, 47301, Petaling Jaya, Selangor Darul Ehsan, Malaysia
Tel.: (60) 378044843
Sales Range: $25-49.9 Million
Emp.: 30
Engineeering Services
N.A.I.C.S.: 541330

Oilfab Sdn. Bhd. (1)
No 2-2 Jalan SS 6/6, Petaling Jaya, 47301, Selangor Darul Ehsan, Malaysia
Tel.: (60) 378044843
Web Site: http://www.oilfab.com.my
Investment Holding Services
N.A.I.C.S.: 551112
Mohamed Hazali bin Tan Sri Abu Hassan *(CEO & Mng Dir)*

Tiara Bay Resorts Bhd. (1)
No 1 PD Tiara Batu 13 Jalan Pantai Pasir Panjang, Port Dickson, 71250, Malaysia
Tel.: (60) 66628888
Web Site: http://www.tbr.com.my
Resort
N.A.I.C.S.: 721110

Town and Country Properties Sdn. Bhd (1)
No 2 1 Jalan SS 6/6 Kelana Jaya, 47301, Petaling Jaya, Selangor, Malaysia
Tel.: (60) 378052022
Resort Management & Investment Services
N.A.I.C.S.: 541618

OILES CORPORATION
8 Kirihara-cho, Fujisawa, 252-0811, Kanagawa, Japan
Tel.: (81) 466444823
Web Site: https://www.oiles.co.jp
Year Founded: 1952
6282—(TKS)
Rev.: $454,536,650
Assets: $628,445,750
Liabilities: $133,356,750
Net Worth: $495,089,000
Earnings: $36,196,360
Emp.: 2,577
Fiscal Year-end: 03/31/24
Bearing Mfr & Whslr
N.A.I.C.S.: 333248
Toshio Okayama *(Chm)*

Subsidiaries:

OILES (Thailand) Co., Ltd. (1)
Amata City Industrial Estate 7/261 Moo 6 Tambol Mabyangporn, Amphur Pluakdaeng, Rayong, 21140, Thailand
Tel.: (66) 38640200
Web Site: http://www.oiles.com
Emp.: 115
Bearing Mfr & Whslr
N.A.I.C.S.: 332991

OILES Deutschland GmbH (1)
Schorbachstr 9, 35510, Butzbach, Germany
Tel.: (49) 6033928800
Web Site: https://www.oiles.de
Emp.: 30
Bearing Whslr
N.A.I.C.S.: 423840

Oiles America Corporation (1)
44099 Plymouth Oaks Blvd Ste 109, Plymouth, MI 48170
Tel.: (734) 414-7400
Web Site: http://www.oilesglobal.com
Emp.: 205
Bearing Mfr & Whslr
N.A.I.C.S.: 333248

Oiles Corporation - Ashikaga Plant (1)
1000 Hakari-cho, Ashikaga, 326-0327, Tochigi, Japan
Tel.: (81) 284701811
Bearing Mfr
N.A.I.C.S.: 333248

Oiles Corporation - Oita Plant (1)
264-1 O-aza-Inumaru, Nakatsu, 879-0105, Oita, Japan
Tel.: (81) 979325511
Bearing Mfr
N.A.I.C.S.: 333248

Oiles Corporation - Shiga Plant (1)
1118 Deba, Ritto, 520-3041, Shiga, Japan
Tel.: (81) 775524581
Bearing Mfr
N.A.I.C.S.: 333248

Oiles Czech Manufacturing s.r.o. (1)
Kralovsky vrch 1966, 432 01, Kadan, Czech Republic
Tel.: (420) 477101611
Web Site: https://www.oiles.cz
Bearing Whslr
N.A.I.C.S.: 423840

Oiles Eco Corporation (1)
4th floor Okura 2 Building 2-28-5 Nishigotanda, Shinagawa-ku, Tokyo, 141-0031, Japan
Tel.: (81) 354355462
Web Site: https://www.oiles-eco.co.jp
Emp.: 178
Industrial Supplies Whslr
N.A.I.C.S.: 423840

Oiles France SAS (1)
189 Route Nationale 10, Coignieres, 78310, Yvelines, France
Tel.: (33) 130 490 682
Bearing Whslr
N.A.I.C.S.: 423840
Vincent Remond *(Acct Mgr)*

Oiles India Private Limited (1)
11th Floor Unit No 1149 to 1152 JMD Megapolis Sohna Road Sector-48, Gurgaon, 122018, Haryana, India
Tel.: (91) 1244947250
Web Site: https://www.oilesglobal.com
Bearing Whslr
N.A.I.C.S.: 423840
Rajat Agarwal *(Mgr-Sls)*

Plant (Domestic)

Oiles India Private Limited - Rajasthan Plant (2)
SP-2-36 New Industrial Complex Majrakath Japanese Zone, Neemrana, Alwar, 301 705, Rajasthan, India
Tel.: (91) 149 467 0900
Bearing Mfr
N.A.I.C.S.: 333248

Oiles Suzhou Corporation (1)
No 1111 Xiang Jiang Rd, New District, Suzhou, 215129, Jiangsu, China
Tel.: (86) 51266670228
Bearing Whslr
N.A.I.C.S.: 423840

Shanghai Oiles Bearing Inc. (1)
No 81 Xinge Rd, Xinqiao Town Songjiang, Shanghai, 201612, China
Web Site: https://www.oiles.cn
Bearing Mfr & Whslr
N.A.I.C.S.: 333248

TAIWAN OILES INDUSTRY COMPANY LIMITED (1)
No 236 Nanshang Rd, Guishan Shiang, Taoyuan, 00333, Taiwan
Tel.: (886) 33218596
Bearing Distr
N.A.I.C.S.: 423840

OILFIELD SERVICES & SUPPLIES PTE. LTD.
No 20 Tuas Avenue 10, Singapore, 639144, Singapore
Tel.: (65) 6542 5933   SG
Web Site: http://www.ossapi.com
Year Founded: 1999
Gas & Oilfield Equipment Mfr
N.A.I.C.S.: 333132
Peter Ong See Kong *(Founder)*

Subsidiaries:

Oilfield Services & Supplies (India) Pvt Ltd (1)
L-39 MIDC Taloja, Raigad, Navi Mumbai, 410208, India
Tel.: (91) 22274 01944
Web Site: http://www.ossapi.com
Emp.: 30
Oil Field Drilling Machinery Mfr
N.A.I.C.S.: 333132
Shakthivel Murthy *(Asst Mgr-QA)*

Oilfield Services & Supplies (Thailand) Co., Ltd. (1)
295/1 Kanjanavanit Road Moo 2 Tambol Pawong, Amphur Muang, Songkhla, 90100, Thailand
Tel.: (66) 74 333587
Oil Field Drilling Machinery Mfr
N.A.I.C.S.: 333132

Oilfield Services & Supplies (Tianjin) Co. Ltd (1)
No 49 Muning Road, Tianjin Economic & Technological Development Area Tanggu, Tianjin, 300457, China
Tel.: (86) 22 25321691
Oil Field Drilling Machinery Mfr & Distr
N.A.I.C.S.: 333132

Oilfield Services & Supplies Pte Ltd. - Kakinada Facility (1)
Plot No 16 Phase II Industrial Park, Dist East Godvari, Peddapuram, 533437, Andhra Pradesh, India
Tel.: (91) 92470 09992
Oil Field Drilling Machinery Mfr
N.A.I.C.S.: 333132

Olio Oilfield Services Sdn Bhd (1)
Jalan Rancha Rancha, 87000, 87000, Labuan, Malaysia
Tel.: (60) 87 582885
Web Site: http://www.oliocompanies.com
Emp.: 18
Oil Field Drilling Machinery Distr
N.A.I.C.S.: 423840
Kay Ong *(Mng Dir)*

PT Oilfield Services & Supplies (1)
Jl Cikunir Raya RT 003/011, Kel Jatimekar - Kec Jatiasih, Bekasi, Indonesia
Tel.: (62) 21 8211257
Oil Field Drilling Machinery Mfr
N.A.I.C.S.: 333132

OILKO KDA
No 152 10 Str, Miladinovci, 1042, Ilinden, North Macedonia
Tel.: (389) 22520693
Web Site: https://www.oilco.com.mk
Year Founded: 2007
OILK—(MAC)
Rev.: $12,041,499
Assets: $36,419,106
Liabilities: $1,043,974
Net Worth: $35,375,132
Earnings: $4,285,579
Fiscal Year-end: 12/31/23
Oil Product Distr

Oilko KDA—(Continued)
N.A.I.C.S.: 424720
Makpetrol A. D. *(Founder)*

OILMAX ENERGY PVT. LTD.
3-A Runwal & Omkar Esquare Chunabhatti Signal Eastern Express Highway, Sion East, Mumbai, 400 022, India
Tel.: (91) 22 4244 1100
Web Site: http://www.oilmax.in
Year Founded: 2008
Oil & Gas Exploration & Extraction Services
N.A.I.C.S.: 211120
Kapil Garg *(Chm & Mng Dir)*

Subsidiaries:

Asian Energy Services Ltd. (1)
3B 3rd Floor Omkar Esquare Chunabhatti Signal, Eastern Express Highway, Mumbai, 400022, Maharashtra, India (62.67%)
Tel.: (91) 2242441138
Web Site: https://www.asianenergy.com
Rev.: $31,969,679
Assets: $47,277,458
Liabilities: $19,508,307
Net Worth: $27,769,151
Earnings: $3,081,010
Emp.: 269
Fiscal Year-end: 03/31/2021
Oil & Gas Exploration Services
N.A.I.C.S.: 213112
Ashutosh Kumar *(CEO)*

OILTEK INTERNATIONAL LIMITED
Lot 6 Jalan Pasaran 23/5 Kawasan MIEL Phase 10 Section 23, 40300, Shah Alam, Selangor, Malaysia
Tel.: (60) 355428288   SG
Web Site: https://www.oiltek.com.my
Year Founded: 1980
HQU—(CAT)
Rev.: $43,777,536
Assets: $40,320,636
Liabilities: $25,574,445
Net Worth: $14,746,191
Earnings: $4,161,950
Emp.: 81
Fiscal Year-end: 12/31/23
Construction Services
N.A.I.C.S.: 237990
Yong Khai Weng *(CEO)*

OIMEX ELECTRODE LTD.
90/3 Pragati Sarani North Badda Level 11, Dhaka, 1212, Bangladesh
Tel.: (880) 29665272
Web Site: https://www.oimexelectrodes.com
Year Founded: 2008
OIMEX—(CHT)
Rev.: $1,685,684
Assets: $4,819,483
Liabilities: $3,033,479
Net Worth: $1,786,004
Earnings: ($504,490)
Emp.: 103
Fiscal Year-end: 06/30/23
Nail & Galvanized Wire Mfr
N.A.I.C.S.: 332618

OIO HOLDINGS LIMITED
14 Arumugam Road 02-06 LTC Building C, Singapore, 409959, Singapore
Tel.: (65) 69098155   SG
Web Site: https://oio.holdings
Year Founded: 2017
KUX—(CAT)
Rev.: $1,036,317
Assets: $4,270,733
Liabilities: $7,077,320
Net Worth: ($2,806,586)
Earnings: ($781,534)
Emp.: 6
Fiscal Year-end: 12/31/23

Electrical & Mechanical Engineering Services
N.A.I.C.S.: 541330
Chee Seng Fan *(Founder & Chm)*

OISIX RA DAICHI INC.
Gate City Osaki East 5F 1 11 2 Osaki, Shinagawa-ku, Tokyo, 141-0032, Japan
Tel.: (81) 120016916
Web Site: https://www.oisixradaichi.co.jp
Year Founded: 2018
3182—(TKS)
Rev.: $980,976,880
Assets: $950,042,080
Liabilities: $702,695,880
Net Worth: $247,346,200
Earnings: $27,233,200
Emp.: 2,093
Fiscal Year-end: 03/31/24
Internet Food Retailer
N.A.I.C.S.: 424490
Kohey Takashima *(CEO)*

Subsidiaries:

Radishbo-ya Co., Ltd. (1)
5th floor Gate City Osaki East Tower 1-11-2 Osaki, Shinagawa ku, Tokyo, 141-0032, Osaki, Japan
Tel.: (81) 120831375
Web Site: https://www.radishbo-ya.co.jp
Food Whslr
N.A.I.C.S.: 424410

OIZUMI CORPORATION
Oizumi Atsugi Bldg 2-7-10 Nakamachi, Atsugi, 243 0018, Kanagawa, Japan
Tel.: (81) 462972111   JP
Web Site: https://www.oizumi.co.jp
Year Founded: 1968
6428—(TKS)
Rev.: $141,407,730
Assets: $277,223,400
Liabilities: $155,890,240
Net Worth: $121,333,160
Earnings: $3,490,080
Emp.: 421
Fiscal Year-end: 03/31/24
Arcade & Coin-Operated Machines Mfr
N.A.I.C.S.: 713990
Seiji Ohizumi *(Founder & Chm)*

OJI HOLDINGS CORPORATION
7-5 Ginza 4-chome, Chuo-ku, Tokyo, 104-0061, Japan
Tel.: (81) 335631111   JP
Web Site: https://www.ojiholdings.co.jp
Year Founded: 1873
OJIPF—(OTCIQ)
Rev.: $11,212,331,480
Assets: $16,144,806,020
Liabilities: $8,902,909,850
Net Worth: $7,241,896,170
Earnings: $335,867,320
Emp.: 35,608
Fiscal Year-end: 03/31/24
Printing, Writing, Packaging, Wrapping & Carbonless Papers, Household Products, Containerboard, Boxboard, Disposable Paper Diapers & Reforestation Products Mfr & Sales
N.A.I.C.S.: 322120
Susumu Yajima *(Chm)*

Subsidiaries:

APICA Co., Ltd. (1)
3174 Osawa, Koshigaya, 343-0025, Saitama, Japan
Tel.: (81) 489630111
Web Site: http://www.apica.co.jp
Paper Products Mfr
N.A.I.C.S.: 322230
Michisei Buntachi *(Pres)*

Albany Plantation Export Company Pty. Ltd. (1)
Lot 100 Down Road, Albany, Albany, 6330, WA, Australia
Tel.: (61) 898453888
Harvesting & Transport Services
N.A.I.C.S.: 484230

Albany Plantation Forest Company of Australia Pty. Ltd. (1)
Lot 100 Down Road, Albany, 6330, WA, Australia
Tel.: (61) 898453777
Tree Plantation Services
N.A.I.C.S.: 561730

Celulose Nipo-Brasileira S.A. (1)
Br 381 Km 172 Oriente, Belo Oriente, 35196-000, Minas Gerais, Brazil
Tel.: (55) 3138295112
Web Site: http://www.cenibra.com.br
Emp.: 1,700
Bleached Eucalyptus Pulp Mfr
N.A.I.C.S.: 325199
Robinson Felix *(Dir-Technical)*

Chuetsu Co., Ltd. (1)
Kamihonmachi Building 3-16 Kamihonmachi, Toyama, 930-0057, Japan
Tel.: (81) 76 495 1300
Web Site: https://chuetsu-web.jp
Emp.: 192
Commercial Printing Services
N.A.I.C.S.: 323111

GS Paperboard & Packaging Sdn. Bhd. (1)
Lot 7090 Mukim Kapar 12, Daerah Kuala Langat, 42700, Banting, Selangor, Malaysia
Tel.: (60) 33 182 5000
Web Site: https://www.gspp.com.my
Paper Board Packaging Mfr
N.A.I.C.S.: 322212
Eric Tan *(Mgr-IT)*

Green Triangle Plantation Forest Company of Australia Pty. Ltd. (1)
Level 7 303 Collins Street, Melbourne, 3000, VIC, Australia
Tel.: (61) 396293773
Tree Plantation Services
N.A.I.C.S.: 561730

Guangxi Oji Plantation Forest Co., Ltd. (1)
21 Floor Wukuang Building 32 Yuanhu Road, Nanning, Guangxi, China
Tel.: (86) 7715852376
Web Site: http://www.ojipaper.co.jp
Sales Range: $25-49.9 Million
Emp.: 9
Eucalyptus Plantation Services
N.A.I.C.S.: 115112

Gunma Mori Shigyo Co., Ltd. (1)
1588-4 Serada-cho, Ota, 370-0426, Gunma, Japan
Tel.: (81) 27 652 6111
Web Site: http://www.morishigyo-gr.co.jp
Paper Products Mfr & Sales
N.A.I.C.S.: 322220

Hitachi Mori Shigyo Co., Ltd. (1)
1025 Obata Itabashi Ibaraki-cho, Higashiibaraki-gun, Ibaraki, 311-3157, Japan
Tel.: (81) 29 292 1234
Web Site: http://www.morishigyo-gr.co.jp
Paper Products Mfr & Sales
N.A.I.C.S.: 322220

Hokuriku Mori Shigyo Co., Ltd. (1)
600 Oka, Oyabe, 932-0031, Toyama, Japan
Tel.: (81) 766683131
Paper Products Mfr
N.A.I.C.S.: 322220

Hotel New Oji Co., Ltd. (1)
4-3-1 Omotemachi, Tomakomai, 053-0022, Hokkaido, Japan
Tel.: (81) 144313111
Web Site: http://www.newoji.co.jp
Sales Range: $25-49.9 Million
Emp.: 10
Home Management Services
N.A.I.C.S.: 561110

Huizhou Nanyou Forest Development Co., Ltd. (1)
Huayang Mansion 13A Yandayi Rd, Huizhou, Guangdong, China
Tel.: (86) 7522526326
Web Site: http://www.ojipaper.co.jp
Sales Range: $25-49.9 Million
Emp.: 100
Eucalyptus Plantation Services
N.A.I.C.S.: 115310

Hyper-Region Labels Sdn. Bhd. (1)
18 Jalan Istimewa 5, Taman Perindustrian Cemerlang, 81800, Ulu Tiram, Johor, Malaysia
Tel.: (60) 78631988
Web Site: http://www.hyper-region.com.my
Label Product Mfr
N.A.I.C.S.: 323111
Steven Jn Tan *(Fin Mgr)*

Japan Brazil Paper and Pulp Resources Development Co., Ltd. (1)
2-16-11 Ginza Kataho Building 8f, Chuo-Ku, Tokyo, 104-0061, Japan
Tel.: (81) 335433411
Web Site: http://www.jbp.co.jp
Sales Range: $25-49.9 Million
Emp.: 10
Pulp & Paper Mfr
N.A.I.C.S.: 322299

Japan Paper Technology (VN) Co., Ltd. (1)
U 33b-35 Road No 20 Tan Thuan Epz, Tan Thuan Dong Ward Dist 7, Ho Chi Minh City, Vietnam
Tel.: (84) 2837701915
Web Site: http://www.jptvn.com
Kraft Paper Mfr & Distr
N.A.I.C.S.: 322120

Japan Paper Technology Dong Nai (VN) Co., Ltd. (1)
B1 Road D2 Long Duc IP, Long Thanh District, Dong Nai, Vietnam
Tel.: (84) 613681214
Kraft Paper Mfr & Distr
N.A.I.C.S.: 322120

Jiangsu Oji Paper Co., Ltd. (1)
No 18 Tongda Road Economic & Technological Development Area, Nantong, 226017, Jiangsu, China
Tel.: (86) 51385996555
Coated Paper Mfr
N.A.I.C.S.: 322220

Kanzaki Specialty Papers Inc. (1)
20 Cummings St, Ware, MA 01082 (100%)
Tel.: (413) 967-6204
Web Site: http://www.kanzakiusa.com
Sales Range: $50-74.9 Million
Emp.: 200
Mfr of Specialty Paper
N.A.I.C.S.: 322220
Josh Polak *(VP-HR)*

Kanzan Spezialpapiere GmbH (1)
Nippesstrasse 5, 52349, Duren, Nordrhein-Westfalen, Germany
Tel.: (49) 242159240
Web Site: http://www.kanzan.de
Rev.: $141,580,000
Emp.: 315
Thermal Papers Mfr
N.A.I.C.S.: 322299
Matthias Simon *(CEO)*

Kyushu Mori Shigyo Co., Ltd. (1)
1310 Uekimachi Shosei, Kita-ku, Kumamoto, 861-0117, Japan
Tel.: (81) 96 274 7121
Web Site: http://www.kyu-mori.co.jp
Paper Products Mfr
N.A.I.C.S.: 322211

Mori Shigyo Co., Ltd. (1)
61 Nanden-cho Nishikujyo, Minami-ku, Kyoto, 601-8441, Japan
Tel.: (81) 756812111
Web Site: http://www.morishigyo-gr.co.jp
Sales Range: $600-649.9 Million
Emp.: 2,200
Paper Products Mfr & Sales
N.A.I.C.S.: 322211

Subsidiary (Domestic):

Aipax Co., Ltd. (2)
6722-91 Yamamoto, Iida, 395-0244, Nagano, Japan
Tel.: (81) 265252511

AND PRIVATE COMPANIES

OJI HOLDINGS CORPORATION

Web Site: http://www.morishigyo-gr.co.jp
Paper Products Mfr
N.A.I.C.S.: 322211

Fukuyama Mori Shigyo Co., Ltd. (2)
90-2 Minooki-cho, Fukuyama, 721-0956,
Hiroshima, Japan
Tel.: (81) 849541288
Web Site: http://www.morishigyo-gr.co.jp
Paper Products Mfr
N.A.I.C.S.: 322299

Hokkaido Mori Shigyo Co., Ltd. (2)
947-2 Kamiosatsu, Chitose, 066-8512, Hokkaido, Japan
Tel.: (81) 123278111
Paper Products Mfr
N.A.I.C.S.: 322211

Iwate Mori Shigyo Co., Ltd. (2)
2-20 Kita Kogyodanchi, Kitakami, 024-0002,
Iwate, Japan
Tel.: (81) 197662216
Paper Products Mfr
N.A.I.C.S.: 322220

Kuga Co., Ltd. (2)
1-401-1 Miyuki-cho, Sabae, 916-0015, Fukui, Japan
Tel.: (81) 778514650
Paper Products Mfr
N.A.I.C.S.: 322211

Mori Kamihanbai, Co., Ltd. (2)
12-1 Nanden-cho Nishikujo, Minami-ku,
Kyoto, 601-8441, Japan
Tel.: (81) 756717700
Cardboard Products Whslr
N.A.I.C.S.: 424130

Plant (Domestic):

**Mori Kamihanbai Co., Ltd. - Tokyo
Shiki Plant** (3)
898 Minamiushiroya, Yashio, 340-0831, Saitama, Japan
Tel.: (81) 48 995 6811
Web Site: http://www.morishigyo-gr.co.jp
Paper Products Mfr
N.A.I.C.S.: 322211

Plant (Domestic):

Mori Shigyo Co., Ltd. - Wrapping Paper Plant (2)
63 Kamitoba Minamishimada-cho, Minamiku, Kyoto, 601-8183, Japan
Tel.: (81) 75 681 3511
Web Site: http://www.morishigyo-gr.co.jp
Wrapping Paper Mfr
N.A.I.C.S.: 322120

**Mori Shigyo Co., Ltd. - Yokkaichi
Plant** (2)
8-5 Mitsuya-cho, Yokkaichi, 510-0802, Mie,
Japan
Tel.: (81) 593321117
Paper Products Mfr
N.A.I.C.S.: 322211

Subsidiary (Domestic):

Moriha Shigyo Co., Ltd. (2)
28-1 Sakuragi Ubayachi, Goshogawara,
037-0015, Aomori, Japan
Tel.: (81) 173352646
Paper Products Mfr
N.A.I.C.S.: 322211

Nagano Mori Shigyo Co., Ltd. (2)
2001 Takaide Hirooka, Shiojiri, 399-0703,
Nagano, Japan
Tel.: (81) 263521291
Paper Products Mfr & Sales
N.A.I.C.S.: 322211
Yoshiyuki Pfudigaito (Gen Mgr)

Nihon Hoso Yoki Co., Ltd. (2)
5-26-1 Haginosho, Takatsuki, 569-0093,
Osaka, Japan
Tel.: (81) 726695093
Web Site: http://www.morishigyo-gr.co.jp
Sales Range: $25-49.9 Million
Emp.: 10
Paper Product Whslr
N.A.I.C.S.: 424130
Hugo Maruyama (Pres)

Niigata Morishigyo Co., Ltd. (2)
801-4 Kyogase-Kogyodanchi, Agano, 959-2136, Niigata, Japan

Tel.: (81) 250673110
Web Site: http://www.morishigyo-gr.co.jp
Emp.: 80
Paper Products Mfr
N.A.I.C.S.: 322220

Sendai Mori Shigyo Co., Ltd. (2)
1 Shinmeido Nakanomyo Shibata-machi,
Shibata-gun, Miyagi, 989-1612, Japan
Tel.: (81) 224553311
Web Site: http://www.morishigyo-gr.co.jp
Sales Range: $25-49.9 Million
Emp.: 85
Paper Products Mfr
N.A.I.C.S.: 322211
Kuniaki Shoya (Pres)

Shikoku Mori Shigyo Co., Ltd. (2)
1 of 698 Inari Kitada, Iyo, 799-3121, Ehime,
Japan
Tel.: (81) 89 982 1235
Web Site: http://www.morishigyo-gr.co.jp
Paper Products Mfr & Sales
N.A.I.C.S.: 322299

Shimane Mori Shigyo Co., Ltd. (2)
453 Hama-cho, Izumo, 693-0054, Shimane,
Japan
Tel.: (81) 853215120
Paper Products Mfr
N.A.I.C.S.: 322211

Tohoku Mori Shigyo Co., Ltd. (2)
2 of 28 Uwano Hiruba, Hachinohe, 039-1108, Aomori, Japan
Tel.: (81) 17 827 3101
Web Site: http://www.morishigyo-gr.co.jp
Corrugated Paper Products Mfr & Sales
N.A.I.C.S.: 322220

Torika Hoso Shizai Co., Ltd. (2)
1075-107 Outsuka Kotoura-cho, Tohakugun, Tottori, 689-2304, Japan
Tel.: (81) 858 53 0221
Web Site: http://www.morishigyo-gr.co.jp
Paper Products Mfr
N.A.I.C.S.: 322211
Maruyama Jun (Pres)

Yamada Danboru, Co., Ltd. (2)
1-2-8 Shirasuka, Yokkaichi, 510-0018, Mie,
Japan
Tel.: (81) 593311151
Paper Products Mfr
N.A.I.C.S.: 322211

Yamagata Shiki Co., Ltd. (2)
2-851-5 Tachiyagawa, Yamagata, 990-2251,
Japan
Tel.: (81) 236866036
Web Site: http://www.morishigyo-gr.co.jp
Paper Products Mfr
N.A.I.C.S.: 322211

Yamanashi Mori Shigyo Co., Ltd. (2)
2443-11 Yagoshima, Minami-Alps, 400-0205, Yamanashi, Japan
Tel.: (81) 55 285 1131
Web Site: http://www.morishigyo-gr.co.jp
Paper Products Mfr
N.A.I.C.S.: 322220

**Mori Shigyo Co., Ltd. - Kansai
Plant** (1)
15th place near 2chome Hidakata, Hirakata,
573-1132, Osaka, Japan
Tel.: (81) 728573161
Web Site: http://www.morishigyo-gr.co.jp
Sales Range: $50-74.9 Million
Emp.: 100
Paper Products Mfr
N.A.I.C.S.: 322211

**Mori Shigyo Co., Ltd. - Tokyo
Plant** (1)
2--11 Kandanishikicho, Chiyoda-ku, Tokyo,
101-0054, Japan
Tel.: (81) 332955421
Web Site: http://www.morishigyo-gr.co.jp
Emp.: 320
Paper Products Mfr & Sales
N.A.I.C.S.: 322299

**Mori Shigyo Co., Ltd.- Kanto
Plant** (1)
628 Kashio Cho, Totsuka-Ku, Yokohama,
244-0812, Kanagawa, Japan
Tel.: (81) 458227001
Paper Products Mfr & Sales
N.A.I.C.S.: 322211

**Nagano Mori Shigyo Co., Ltd. -
Kawanakajima Plant** (1)
238 Otsuka Minami Aokijima-machi, Nagano, 381-2205, Japan
Tel.: (81) 262853424
Web Site: http://www.morishigyo-gr.co.jp
Sales Range: $25-49.9 Million
Emp.: 26
Paper Products Mfr
N.A.I.C.S.: 322130

New Tac Kasei Co., Ltd. (1)
4148 Kamitakano Toyonaka-ch, Mitoyo,
769-1504, Kagawa, Japan
Tel.: (81) 875621080
Web Site: http://www.tack.co.jp
Adhesive Product Mfr
N.A.I.C.S.: 339113

Oi Seishi Co., Ltd. (1)
920 Shoge Osashima Cho, Ena, 509-7203,
Gifu, Japan
Tel.: (81) 573255331
Paper Products Mfr & Sales
N.A.I.C.S.: 322220

**Oji Asia Household Product Sdn.
Bhd.** (1)
Lot 7090 Mukim Tanjung 12, Daerah Kuala
Langat, 42700, Banting, Selangor, Malaysia
Tel.: (60) 331823588
Baby Diaper Mfr & Distr
N.A.I.C.S.: 322291
Hooiyin Lim (Reg Dir-Mktg)

Oji Asia Management Sdn. Bhd. (1)
Lot 7090 Mukim Tanjung 12, Daerah Kuala
Langat, 42700, Banting, Selangor, Malaysia
Tel.: (60) 731825114
Industrial Material Distr
N.A.I.C.S.: 423840
Kawahara Kazuhiro (Gen Mgr-Forestry Div)

Oji Chiyoda Container Co., Ltd. (1)
5-12-8 Ginza Ojiseishi 1go-Kan 5F, Chuoku, Tokyo, 104-0061, Japan
Tel.: (81) 355503027
Web Site: http://www.e-occ.jp
Beverage Containers Mfr
N.A.I.C.S.: 339999

Subsidiary (Non-US):

Kunshan Oji Filter Co., Ltd. (2)
No 28 Fengxia Road, Lujia Town, Kunshan,
2153311, Jiangsu, China
Tel.: (86) 5125 787 9118
Web Site: http://www.ojiholdings.co.jp
Heat Exchanger Equipment Parts Mfr &
Whslr
N.A.I.C.S.: 335999

Oji Cornstarch Co., Ltd. (1)
4-7-5 Ginza, Chuo-ku, Tokyo, 104-0061,
Japan
Tel.: (81) 335637230
Web Site: http://www.oji-cs.co.jp
Corn Starch Mfr
N.A.I.C.S.: 311221

Oji Eco Materials Co., Ltd. (1)
4-7-5 Ginza Ojiseishihonkannai, Chuo-ku,
Tokyo, 104-0061, Japan
Tel.: (81) 335637011
Sales Range: $25-49.9 Million
Emp.: 20
Paper Processing Services
N.A.I.C.S.: 322120
Kawabe Azumi (Pres)

Oji Engineering Co., Ltd. (1)
4-7-5 Ginza, Chuo-ku, Tokyo, 104-0061,
Japan
Tel.: (81) 363115400
Web Site: http://www.homepage.ojieng.co.jp
Paper Making & Packaging Machinery Mfr
N.A.I.C.S.: 333243

Oji Fibre Solutions (NZ) Ltd. (1)
289 Great South Road Ellerslie, Auckland,
1051, New Zealand
Tel.: (64) 9 633 0000
Web Site: http://www.ojifs.com
Emp.: 800
Pulp & Paperboard Mfr
N.A.I.C.S.: 322130
Jon Ryder (CEO)

Subsidiary (Non-US):

**Oji Fibre Solutions Hong Kong
Ltd** (2)

Unit 2902 29/F Bayfield Building 99 Hennessy Road, Wanchai, China (Hong Kong)
Tel.: (852) 2834 7333
Emp.: 3
Pulp & Paperboard Mfr
N.A.I.C.S.: 322130
Eling Mok (Mgr-Sls)

**Oji Fibre Solutions Malaysia Sdn
Bhd** (2)
Suite A303 3rd Floor West Wing Wisma
Consplant 2, No 7 Jalan SS16/1, 47500,
Subang Jaya, Selangor, Malaysia
Tel.: (60) 3 589 10118
Pulp & Paperboard Mfr
N.A.I.C.S.: 322130

Oji Fibre Solutions Pty. Ltd. (1)
440 Princes Highway, Noble Park, 3174,
VIC, Australia
Tel.: (61) 397976000
Paper Products Mfr
N.A.I.C.S.: 322299

Oji Forest & Products Co., Ltd. (1)
4-7-5 Ginza, Chuo-ku, Tokyo, 104-0061,
Japan
Tel.: (81) 335634177
Web Site: http://www.oji-ryokka.co.jp
Timber Products Distr
N.A.I.C.S.: 423990

**Oji Forest Products Vietnam Co.,
Ltd.** (1)
Room No 601 V-Tower Building 39 Ly Thai
To Street, Vo Cuong Ward, Bac Ninh, Vietnam
Tel.: (84) 2223895099
Procuring Woodchip Services
N.A.I.C.S.: 113310

**Oji GS Packaging (Yangon) Co.,
Ltd.** (1)
Plot B-1 2 No 3 Highway Road, Mingalardon Industrial Park Mingalardon Township,
Yangon, Myanmar
Tel.: (95) 1639069
Paper Board Packaging Mfr
N.A.I.C.S.: 322212

Oji Hall Co., Ltd. (1)
7-5 Ginza 4-chome, Chuo-ku, Tokyo, 104-0061, Japan
Tel.: (81) 335640200
Web Site: http://www.ojihall.jp
Sales Range: $50-74.9 Million
Emp.: 14
Concert Hall Operation Services
N.A.I.C.S.: 711310
Momoko Hoshino (Pres)

Oji India Packaging Pvt. Ltd. (1)
No SP4 -78, New Industrial Complex
Majrakath Dist Alwar, Neemrana, Rajasthan, India
Tel.: (91) 1494674722
Web Site: http://www.ojpack.in
Corrugated Container Mfr & Distr
N.A.I.C.S.: 322211
Yasuki Shigesaka (Mng Dir)

Oji Interpack Co., Ltd. (1)
5-12-8 Ginza, Chuo-ku, Tokyo, 104-0061,
Japan
Tel.: (81) 363271021
Web Site: http://www.hipl.co.jp
Sales Range: $25-49.9 Million
Emp.: 30
Packaging Materials Mfr & Sales
N.A.I.C.S.: 326112

Oji Interpack India Pvt. Ltd. (1)
Plot No I-74 Site-V, Kasna Industrial Area
Surajpur, Raipur, UP, India
Tel.: (91) 9643034012
Industrial Chemical Product Mfr & Distr
N.A.I.C.S.: 325998

Oji Interpack Korea Ltd. (1)
6th Floor Cheonji Building 115 Yanghwa-ro,
Mapo-gu, Seoul, Korea (South)
Tel.: (82) 2 715 4524
Web Site: https://www.hiplkorea.com
Triple Wall Corrugated Board Mfr & Distr
N.A.I.C.S.: 322211

Oji Intertech, Inc. (1)
906 W Hanley Rd, North Manchester, IN
46962
Tel.: (260) 982-1544

OJI HOLDINGS CORPORATION

INTERNATIONAL PUBLIC

Oji Holdings Corporation—(Continued)
Web Site: http://www.ojiintertech.com
Automotive Interior Material Mfr & Distr
N.A.I.C.S.: 336360
Rick Sereno (Pres)

Oji Kinocloth Co., Ltd. (1)
Iriyamase 1-2-5, Fuji, 419-0204, Shizuoka, Japan
Tel.: (81) 54 571 3132
Web Site: https://www.kinocloth.co.jp
Air Laid Nonwoven Fabrics Mfr
N.A.I.C.S.: 313230

Subsidiary (Non-US):

Oji Kinocloth (Shanghai) Co., Ltd. (2)
34F Shanghai International Trade Centre No 2201 Yan An Road West, Changning District, Shanghai, 200336, China
Tel.: (86) 2162375200
Web Site: http://www.kinocloth.cn
Wet & Dry Tissue Mfr & Whslr
N.A.I.C.S.: 322120

Oji Label (Thailand) Ltd. (1)
130-132 Sindhorn Building Tower3 12th Floor Wireless Road Lumpini, Pathumwan, Bangkok, 10330, Thailand
Tel.: (66) 2 263 2600
Web Site: https://www.ojilabel.com
Self-Adhesive Label Product Mfr
N.A.I.C.S.: 325520

Oji Logistics Co., Ltd. (1)
5-12-8 Ginza, Chuo-ku, Tokyo, 104-0061, Japan
Tel.: (81) 35 550 3110
Web Site: http://www.oji-logistics.co.jp
Logistics & Warehousing Services
N.A.I.C.S.: 493110

Oji Myanmar Packaging Co., Ltd. (1)
Plot A14 Thilawa Special Economic Zone A, Thanlyin, Yangon, Myanmar
Tel.: (95) 9445340109
Paper Board Packaging Mfr & Distr
N.A.I.C.S.: 322212

Oji Nepia Co., Ltd. (1)
5-12-8 Ginza, Chuo-ku, Tokyo, 104-0061, Japan
Tel.: (81) 33 248 3111
Web Site: https://www.nepia.co.jp
Tissue & Diapers Mfr
N.A.I.C.S.: 322120
Noriyuki Shimizu (Pres & Dir)

Oji Packaging (Shanghai) Co., Ltd. (1)
No 1818 Shengli Road, Industrial Park Qingpu District, Shanghai, China
Tel.: (86) 216 922 5881
Web Site: https://www.ojipack.sh.cn
Coated Paper Mfr
N.A.I.C.S.: 322220

Oji Packaging Co., Ltd. (1)
2-3-2 Higashishinozaki, Edogawa-ku, Tokyo, 133-8580, Japan
Tel.: (81) 336704441
Web Site: http://www.oji-pkg.co.jp
Sales Range: $125-149.9 Million
Emp.: 400
Corrugated Paperboard Mfr
N.A.I.C.S.: 322211

Oji Papeis Especiais Ltda. (1)
Via Comendador Pedro Morganti 3393 Bairro Monte Alegre, Piracicaba, 13415-900, SP, Brazil
Tel.: (55) 1921069609
Paper Products Mfr
N.A.I.C.S.: 322299

Oji Paper (Thailand) Ltd. (1)
130-132 Wireless Road, Pathumwan, Bangkok, 10330, Thailand
Tel.: (66) 22632705
Paper Mfr
N.A.I.C.S.: 322120

Oji Paper Co., Ltd. (1)
666 Burrard St Ste 1088, Vancouver, V6C 2X8, BC, Canada
Tel.: (604) 683-0787
Paper Whslr
N.A.I.C.S.: 424110

Oji Paper International Trading (Shanghai) Co., Ltd. (1)
Room 3402 Shanghai International Trade Centre No 2201 Yan an West Road, Changning District, Shanghai, 200336, China
Tel.: (86) 2162703350
Chemical Products Distr
N.A.I.C.S.: 424690
Xie Rachel (Sls Mgr)

Oji Paper Management (Shanghai) Co., Ltd. (1)
Room 3401 Shanghai International Trade Center No 2201 Yan'an West Road, Changning District, Shanghai, 200336, China
Tel.: (86) 216 219 5555
Web Site: https://www.ojiholdings.cn
Consulting Services
N.A.I.C.S.: 541618

Oji Paper Nepia (Suzhou) Co., Ltd. (1)
98 Jin Shan Rd, Suzhou New District, Suzhou, 215129, Jiangsu, China
Tel.: (86) 512 6825 8526
Web Site: http://www.nepia.com.cn
Sales Range: $75-99.9 Million
Emp.: 200
Production, Conversion & Sales of Household Products, Paper Container Products & Industrial Papers
N.A.I.C.S.: 322299

Oji Paperboard Co., Ltd. (1)
5-12-8 Ginza Ojiseishi 1 Go Kan, Chuo-Ku, Tokyo, 104-0061, Japan
Tel.: (81) 335431112
Web Site: http://www.ojipaperboard.co.jp
Sales Range: $550-599.9 Million
Emp.: 1,450
Paper Mfr & Whslr
N.A.I.C.S.: 322120

Oji Real Estate Co., Ltd. (1)
5-12-8 Prince Holdings 1 Building 7F, Chuo-ku, Tokyo, 104-0061, Japan
Tel.: (81) 335429411
Web Site: http://www.ojire.co.jp
Emp.: 195
Real Estate Manangement Services
N.A.I.C.S.: 531210
Hironaka Naofumi (Auditor)

Oji Salmon Co., Ltd. (1)
3-7-12 Ginza, Chuo-Ku, Tokyo, 104-0061, Japan
Tel.: (81) 33 561 2331
Web Site: https://www.oji-salmon.co.jp
Emp.: 120
Seafood Processing Services
N.A.I.C.S.: 311710

Oji South Lao Plantation Forest Co., Ltd. (1)
Ban Saphanthong Kang Unit 9 House No 197, PO Box 8832, Sisatanak District, Vientiane, Lao People's Democratic Republic
Tel.: (856) 21 35 3511
Web Site: http://www.lpfi.la
Sales Range: $25-49.9 Million
Emp.: 130
Forest Management Services
N.A.I.C.S.: 115310

Oji Specialty Paper Co., Ltd. (1)
5-12-8 Ginza Oji Seishi Ichigo Kan Building 3F, Chuo-ku, Tokyo, 104-0061, Japan
Tel.: (81) 355503041
Web Site: http://www.ojispecialtypaper.co.jp
Sales Range: $50-74.9 Million
Emp.: 150
Pulp & Paper Mfr
N.A.I.C.S.: 322120

Oji Tac Co., Ltd. (1)
5-12-8 Ginza Ojiseishi 1go-Kan 2F, Chuo-ku, Tokyo, 104-0061, Japan (100%)
Tel.: (81) 332483450
Web Site: http://www.ojitac.co.jp
Sales Range: $125-149.9 Million
Emp.: 413
Adhesives Mfr & Whslr
N.A.I.C.S.: 325520
Kosuke Hamada (Pres)

Oji Timely Co., Ltd. (1)
1-2-5 Iriyamase, Fuji, 419-0204, Shizuoka, Japan
Tel.: (81) 54 572 2400

Web Site: https://www.ojitimely.co.jp
Paper Towel Mfr
N.A.I.C.S.: 322120

Ojitex (Vietnam) Co., Ltd. (1)
No 12 Road 9A Bien Hoa Industrial Zone 2, Bien Hoa, Dong Nai, Vietnam
Tel.: (84) 613835800
Web Site: http://www.ojipaper.oo.jp
Corrugated Containers Mfr & Sales
N.A.I.C.S.: 322211

Ojitex Haiphong Co., Ltd. (1)
Land Plot B 1 B 2 B 7 B 8 Nomura Haiphong Industrial Zone, An Duong District, Haiphong, Vietnam
Tel.: (84) 313743020
Corrugated Containers Mfr
N.A.I.C.S.: 322211

PT Indo Oji Sukses Pratama (1)
Sudirman Plaza-Indofood Tower Lt 9 Jl Jend Sudirman Kav 76-78, Setiabudi, Jakarta Selatan, Indonesia
Tel.: (62) 2157958822
Baby Diapers Distr
N.A.I.C.S.: 424350

PT. Korintiga Hutani (1)
Wisma Korindo Jalan MT Haryono Kavling 62, Pancoran, Jakarta, Indonesia
Tel.: (62) 217975959
Sales Range: $75-99.9 Million
Emp.: 500
Forest Management Services
N.A.I.C.S.: 115310

Pan Pac Forest Products Ltd. (1)
1161 SH2 Wairoa Rd, Napier, 4182, New Zealand
Tel.: (64) 68310100
Web Site: http://www.panpac.co.nz
Sales Range: $75-99.9 Million
Emp.: 350
Forestry Services; Joint Venture between Oji Paper & Nippon Paper; Oji Paper owns 87%
N.A.I.C.S.: 113210
Doug Ducker (Mng Dir)

People & Grit (M) Sdn. Bhd. (1)
No 10 Jalan Sepadu 25/123 Section 25, Taman Perindustrian Axis, 40400, Shah Alam, Selangor, Malaysia
Tel.: (60) 351219881
Baby Diaper Mfr & Distr
N.A.I.C.S.: 322291

Quy Nhon Plantation Forest Company of Vietnam Ltd. (1)
2nd Floor 259 Le Hong Phong street, Quy Nhon, Binh Dinh, Vietnam
Tel.: (84) 2563892866
Tree Plantation Services
N.A.I.C.S.: 327910

S. Pack & Print Public Company Limited (1)
119 Moo 1 Karnjanavanich Road Tambol Takarm, Amphoe Hat Yai, Songkhla, 90110, Thailand
Tel.: (66) 74260602
Web Site: http://www.spack.co.th
Rev.: $36,283,996
Assets: $39,193,561
Liabilities: $20,901,791
Net Worth: $18,291,770
Earnings: $511,712
Emp.: 305
Fiscal Year-end: 12/31/2023
Paper Products Mfr
N.A.I.C.S.: 322299
Akio Hasebe (Chm)

Shanghai Eastern Oji Packaging Co., Ltd. (1)
525 Xumin Road Shanghai Xijiao Economic & Technological Development, Area Xujing Qingpu Ward, Shanghai, 201702, China
Tel.: (86) 2159765071
Web Site: http://www.ojiholdings.co.jp
Sales Range: $125-149.9 Million
Emp.: 300
Mfr of Paper-based Packaging Materials
N.A.I.C.S.: 322220

Southland Plantation Forest Company of New Zealand Ltd. (1)
45 Kekeno Place, PO Box 7010, Invercargill, New Zealand

Tel.: (64) 32141912
Web Site: http://www.spfl.co.nz
Sales Range: $25-49.9 Million
Emp.: 2
Forest Management Services
N.A.I.C.S.: 115310
Shaun Foster (Mgr-Establishment)

Sunshine Oji (Shouguang) Specialty Paper Ltd. (1)
69 Wenchang Road, Shouguang, China
Tel.: (86) 5362235300
Web Site: http://www.en.sunshineoji.com
Decorative Paper Distr
N.A.I.C.S.: 424130

Suzhou Oji Packaging Co., Ltd. (1)
No 235 Yangjia Road, Lujia Town, Kunshan, Jiangsu, China
Tel.: (86) 51257671181
Web Site: http://www.hipl.szbnet.com
Packaging Materials Mfr & Whslr
N.A.I.C.S.: 322211

Tele-Paper (M) Sdn. Bhd. (1)
Lot 2C Jalan Keluli 15/16 Section 15, 40200, Shah Alam, Selangor Darul Ehsan, Malaysia
Tel.: (60) 35 525 6777
Web Site: https://www.telepaper.com
Thermal Paper Product Mfr
N.A.I.C.S.: 325992

Tokai Mori Shigyo Co., Ltd. (1)
451 Gonori Sanbayashi Ono-cho, Ibi-gun, Gifu, 501-0596, Japan
Tel.: (81) 58 532 3711
Web Site: http://www.morishigyo-gr.co.jp
Paper Products Mfr & Sales
N.A.I.C.S.: 322220

Union & Oji Interpack Co., Ltd. (1)
79-79/1 Moo 6 Rama II Road, Tambol Kokkham, Amphur Muang, 74000, Samutsakorn, Thailand
Tel.: (66) 3 481 2956
Web Site: https://www.uoi.co.th
Triple Wall Corrugated Board Mfr
N.A.I.C.S.: 322212

United Kotak Berhad (1)
No 9 Jalan Seroja 4, Indahpura Industrial Area Bandar Indahpura, 81000, Kulai, Johor, Malaysia
Tel.: (60) 7 661 3588
Web Site: https://www.ukb.com.my
Sales Range: $10-24.9 Million
Corrugated Carton & Board Mfr & Sales
N.A.I.C.S.: 322211

United Packaging Co., Ltd. (1)
Plot A5-1 Block A5 Road D4, Tan Phu Trung Industrial Zone Tan Phu Trung Ward Cu Chi District, Ho Chi Minh City, Vietnam
Tel.: (84) 2837157102
Paper Cup Product Mfr & Distr
N.A.I.C.S.: 322299

Walki Group Oy (1)
Ahventie 4 A 15, Fin-02170, Espoo, Finland
Tel.: (358) 205363111
Web Site: http://www.walki.com
Paper Product Services
N.A.I.C.S.: 322230
Leif Frilund (Pres & CEO)

Subsidiary (Non-US):

Walki GmbH (2)
Dieselstrasse 26 Postfach 1625, D-48546, Steinfurt, Germany
Tel.: (49) 2551680
Web Site: http://www.walki.com
Packaging Materials
N.A.I.C.S.: 561910

Walki Ltd. (2)
Ray Ln, Garstang, Preston, PR3 1GB, United Kingdom
Tel.: (44) 995604227
Web Site: http://www.walki.com
Wrappings for the Paper, Steel & Mechanical Wood-Processing Industries & Composite Materials for the Packaging Industry & Technical Purposes Mfr
N.A.I.C.S.: 322299

Subsidiary (Domestic):

Walki Oy (2)
P O Box 33, 37601, Valkeakoski, Finland

Tel.: (358) 205363111
Web Site: http://www.walki.com
Printing Solutions
N.A.I.C.S.: 322120

OJIBWAY OF THE PIC RIVER FIRST NATION
78 Pic River Rd, PO Box 193, Heron Bay, P0T 1R0, ON, Canada
Tel.: (807) 229-1749
Web Site: http://www.picriver.com
Sales Range: $50-74.9 Million
Emp.: 1,200
Community Centre
N.A.I.C.S.: 925120

Subsidiaries:

Pic River Development Corp (1)
7 Lynx Rd, PO Box 220, Heron Bay, P0T 2E0, ON, Canada
Tel.: (807) 229-8695
Web Site: https://prdc.picriver.com
Rural & Urban Development Services
N.A.I.C.S.: 925120
Robert Starr *(Gen Mgr)*

OJJUS MEDICARE PRIVATE LIMITED
D-141 A&B Sec 40, Noida, 201303, India
Tel.: (91) 120 4635777
Web Site: http://www.ojjus.org
Sales Range: $10-24.9 Million
Emp.: 150
Hospital Owner & Operator
N.A.I.C.S.: 622110
Namrata Chawla *(Mng Dir)*

Subsidiaries:

Goodwill Hospital and Research Centre Limited (1)
D-141 A&B Sec 40, Noida, 201303, India
Tel.: (91) 120 4635777
Web Site: http://www.ojjus.org
Hospital
N.A.I.C.S.: 622110
Namrata Chawla *(Mng Dir)*

OJSC AK BARS BANK
1 Dekabristov str, 420066, Kazan, Russia
Tel.: (7) 8432303303   RU
Web Site: http://www.akbars.ru
Year Founded: 1993
Banking Services
N.A.I.C.S.: 522110

Subsidiaries:

AO AK Bars Leasing (1)
Meridiannaya st 1A, 420124, Kazan, Russia
Tel.: (7) 8435909501
Web Site: http://www.akbars-leasing.ru
Leasing Services
N.A.I.C.S.: 532490

IC AK BARS Finance JSC (1)
15 B 2 Lubyansky Passage, Moscow, 101000, Russia
Tel.: (7) 495 644 29 95
Web Site: http://www.akbf.ru
Investment Banking Services
N.A.I.C.S.: 523150
Elena Vasileva-Korzyuk *(Head-Analytical)*

OJSC ARMADA
15 c6 5-y Donskoy proyezd, Moscow, 119334, Russia
Tel.: (7) 495 797 6020   RU
Sales Range: $125-149.9 Million
Information Technology Software & Services
N.A.I.C.S.: 541511

OJSC BANK SAINT PETERSBURG
64A Maloohtinskij pr, 195112, Saint Petersburg, 195112, Russia
Tel.: (7) 8123295050
Web Site: https://www.bspb.ru
BSPB—(MOEX)
Rev.: $878,635,784
Assets: $11,435,048,894
Liabilities: $9,554,353,007
Net Worth: $1,880,695,887
Earnings: $511,726,393
Fiscal Year-end: 12/31/23
Banking Services
N.A.I.C.S.: 522110
Vladimir P. Skatin *(Deputy Chm-Mgmt Bd)*

OJSC CHERKIZOVO GROUP
Lesnaya str 5B White Square Office Center 12th floor, 125047, Moscow, Russia
Tel.: (7) 4956602440
Web Site: http://www.cherkizovo.com
Rev.: $1,937,358,170
Assets: $2,329,946,240
Liabilities: $1,341,435,320
Net Worth: $988,510,920
Earnings: $107,280,630
Emp.: 30,355
Fiscal Year-end: 12/31/19
Veal Product Mfr
N.A.I.C.S.: 311612
Evgeny Mikhailov *(Chm)*

OJSC CONCERN KALASHNIKOV
Deryabina driveway 3, Udmurtia, Izhevsk, Russia
Web Site: http://www.kalashnikovconcern.ru
Year Founded: 1807
Aircraft Equipment Mfr
N.A.I.C.S.: 336412
Alexey Krivoruchko *(CEO)*

Subsidiaries:

JSC Izhevsky Mekhanichesky Zavod (1)
8 Promyshlennaya str, 426063, Izhevsk, Russia
Tel.: (7) 3412573838
Web Site: http://www.baikalinc.ru
Aircraft Equipment Mfr
N.A.I.C.S.: 336412

JSC NITI Progress (1)
268 Pushkinskaya Str, 426008, Izhevsk, Russia
Tel.: (7) 3412439535
Web Site: http://www.niti-progress.ru
Aircraft Equipment Mfr
N.A.I.C.S.: 336412

OJSC FEDERAL GRID COMPANY OF UNIFIED ENERGY SYSTEM
5A Akademika Chelomeya str, 117630, Moscow, Russia
Tel.: (7) 4957109333
Web Site: http://www.fsk-ees.ru
Rev.: $3,659,837,390
Assets: $17,422,295,220
Liabilities: $5,329,970,800
Net Worth: $12,092,324,420
Earnings: $1,337,896,450
Emp.: 22,052
Fiscal Year-end: 12/31/18
Energy Transmission Services
N.A.I.C.S.: 221121
Maria Tikhonova *(Deputy Chm-Mgmt Bd & Sec)*

Subsidiaries:

JSC Mobile GTES (1)
St Belovezhskaya St 4 Block B, 121353, Moscow, Russia
Tel.: (7) 4957823960
Web Site: http://www.mobilegtes.ru
Electric Energy Distribution Services
N.A.I.C.S.: 221122
Anna Grafova *(Head-Protocol Support)*

OJSC GLOBALSTROY-ENGINEERING
15 Ibragimova St Bldg 2, 105318, Moscow, Russia
Tel.: (7) 4999737522
Web Site: http://www.globse.com
Sales Range: $1-4.9 Billion
Emp.: 30,000
Oil & Gas Field Engineering & Construction Services
N.A.I.C.S.: 237990
Marat Ingilievich Gizatullin *(First VP-Economy)*

Subsidiaries:

LLC GSE Giprokauchuk (1)
Ul Ibragimova 15 korp 1, 105318, Moscow, Russia
Tel.: (7) 4999737575
Web Site: http://www.gpkauchuk.ru
Civil Engineering Services
N.A.I.C.S.: 541330
Vladimir A. Manenkov *(Gen Dir)*

LLC GSE Surgutnefte-chimmontazh (1)
Ul October Revolution d39 of 10, Republic of Bashkortostan, Ufa, 450077, Russia
Tel.: (7) 3472462979
Web Site: http://www.gse-snhm.com
Oil & Gas Industry Construction Services
N.A.I.C.S.: 237120

LLC GSE Volgograd Firm NZM (1)
ul them Mozart 19, 400029, Volgograd, Russia
Tel.: (7) 8442402730
Web Site: http://nzm.globse.com
Oil & Gas Pipeline Installation Services
N.A.I.C.S.: 237120

LLC GSE Yug-Stroy (1)
Volgograd st Pugachevskaya 7, Volgograd, 400001, Russia
Tel.: (7) 8442253236
Web Site: http://www.gsi-ugstroy.ru
Oil & Gas Industry Construction Services
N.A.I.C.S.: 237120

LLC GSE-Neftechim-montazh (1)
Ul Groznenskaya d 55, Samara, 443004, Russia
Tel.: (7) 8463742101
Web Site: http://www.nhm-globse.ru
Industrial Pipeline Construction & Installation Services
N.A.I.C.S.: 238290

LLC GSE-Permnefte-gazstroy (1)
Ul Industrial 84B, Perm, 614055, Russia
Tel.: (7) 3422201424
Web Site: http://www.gse-pngs.ru
Oil & Gas Industry Construction Services
N.A.I.C.S.: 237120

LLC GSE-Snema (1)
St October Revolution 39, Republic of Bashkortostan, Ufa, Russia
Tel.: (7) 3472735452
Web Site: http://www.snema.ru
Oil & Gas Construction & Installation Services
N.A.I.C.S.: 237120

LLC GSE-Volgonefte-gazstroy (1)
Tsentralnoe Highway 13 Nizhny Novgorod Region, Kstovsky District, 607650, Kstovo, Russia
Tel.: (7) 8314553490
Web Site: http://www.gse-vngs.com
Oil Refining & Chemical Industry Construction Services
N.A.I.C.S.: 237120

LLC Global-Flot (1)
Kaliningrad Region St Gagarina d 61, 238340, Svetly, Russia
Tel.: (7) 4012560454
Web Site: http://www.global-flot.com
Marine Fleet & Transportation Services
N.A.I.C.S.: 488390

LLC Global-Neftegazstroy (1)
Ul Ibragimova House 15 Building 2, 105318, Moscow, Russia
Tel.: (7) 4999737500
Web Site: http://gngs.globse.com
Oil & Gas Equipment Maintenance Services
N.A.I.C.S.: 811310

LLC TNS-RU (1)
Str Ibrahimova d 15 corp 2, 105318, Moscow, Russia
Tel.: (7) 4999737475
Web Site: http://www.tns-ru.com
Network & Telecommunication Development Services
N.A.I.C.S.: 517810

OJSC IG Spasskie Vorota (1)
Ul Mayakovsky 4, Yamalo-Nenets Autonomous Okrug, Salekhard, 629003, Russia
Tel.: (7) 4994028902
Web Site: http://www.spasskievorota.msk.ru
Corporate Insurance Services
N.A.I.C.S.: 524210
Tatyana Kostika *(Head-Sls)*

OJSC HUMAN STEM CELL INSTITUTE
Bld 2 3 Gubkina Str, PO Box 373, 119333, Moscow, Russia
Tel.: (7) 4956468076
Web Site: http://hsci.ru
Year Founded: 2003
Stem Cell Mfr & Researcher
N.A.I.C.S.: 325413
Isaev Artur Alexandrovich *(Gen Dir)*

OJSC KUZBASSENERGO
Brilliantovaya Street 2, 656037, Barnaul, Russia
Tel.: (7) 3842 453350   RU
Web Site: http://www.kuzbassenergo.ru
Year Founded: 1943
Sales Range: $1-4.9 Billion
Emp.: 6,361
Electric & Thermal Power Distr
N.A.I.C.S.: 221122
Mikhail V. Kuznetsov *(Gen Dir)*

OJSC MAGNITOGORSK IRON & STEEL WORKS
93 Kirov St Magnitogorsk, Chelyabinsk, 455000, Russia
Tel.: (7) 3519242388   RU
Web Site: https://mmk.ru
MAGN—(MOEX)
Rev.: $7,566,000,000
Assets: $8,284,000,000
Liabilities: $2,765,000,000
Net Worth: $5,519,000,000
Earnings: $856,000,000
Emp.: 56,088
Fiscal Year-end: 12/31/19
Steel Products Mfr
N.A.I.C.S.: 331110
Victor F. Rashnikov *(Chm)*

Subsidiaries:

CJSC Intercos-IV (1)
Volkhonskoye Shosse 4, 198323, Gorelovo, Leningrad, Russia
Tel.: (7) 812 320 54 03
Web Site: http://www.intercos-iv.ru
Steel & Iron Casting Mfr
N.A.I.C.S.: 331110

CJSC Profit (1)
Prospekt Pushkina 6A, Magnitogorsk, 455019, Chelyabinsk, Russia
Tel.: (7) 3519 25 49 00
Web Site: http://www.profit.ru
Steel & Iron Casting Mfr
N.A.I.C.S.: 331110

CJSC Tamozhenny Broker (1)
Ul Kirova 72 Magnitogorsk, Magnitogorsk, 455002, Chelyabinsk, Russia
Tel.: (7) 3519 24 91 35
Steel & Iron Casting Mfr
N.A.I.C.S.: 331110

LLC Abzakovo (1)
Novoabzakovo, 453565, Beloretsk, Russia
Tel.: (7) 3479270860
Web Site: http://www.abzakovo.ru
Resort Operator
N.A.I.C.S.: 721110

OJSC MAGNITOGORSK IRON & STEEL WORKS

OJSC Magnitogorsk Iron & Steel Works—(Continued)

LLC Aquapark (1)
Ul Naberezhnaya 9, Magnitogorsk, 455023, Chelyabinsk, Russia
Tel.: (7) 3519 27 94 01
Resort Operator
N.A.I.C.S.: 721110

LLC Berezki (1)
Ul Kurortnaya 15, Zelyonaya Polyana, 453613, Bashkortostan, Russia
Tel.: (7) 3519 25 55 95
Web Site: http://www.berezki.net
Resort Operator
N.A.I.C.S.: 721110
Pudovkin Yevgenia (Mgr-Mktg & Adv)

LLC Buskul (1)
ul Zelenaya 24, Chesmensky District, 457225, Chelyabinsk, Russia
Tel.: (7) 3516923504
Steel & Iron Casting Mfr
N.A.I.C.S.: 331110

LLC CherMetInvest (1)
Pl Lenina D 2, 367000, Makhachkala, Russia
Tel.: (7) 928 528 68 93
Steel & Iron Casting Mfr
N.A.I.C.S.: 331110

LLC GLC Metallurg-Magnitogorsk (1)
Zelyenaya Polyana, 453613, Zelyonaya Polyana, Russia
Tel.: (7) 3519 255 601
Web Site: http://www.ski-bannoe.mgn.ru
Resort Operator
N.A.I.C.S.: 721110

LLC IK MMK-Finance (1)
Ul Kirova 70, Magnitogorsk, 455019, Chelyabinsk, Russia
Tel.: (7) 3519253222
Web Site: http://www.mmk-finance.mmk.ru
Emp.: 10
Financial Management Services
N.A.I.C.S.: 523999

LLC MAGSTORN (1)
Ul Malaya Yakimanka 8, Moscow, 119180, Russia
Tel.: (7) 499 238 13 66
Steel & Iron Casting Mfr
N.A.I.C.S.: 331110
Shileaev Pavel (CEO)

LLC MMK-Informservice (1)
Prospekt Pushkina 2, Magnitogorsk, 455019, Chelyabinsk, Russia
Tel.: (7) 3519240111
Web Site: http://is-mmk.ru
Steel & Iron Casting Mfr
N.A.I.C.S.: 331110

LLC MMK-Vtormet (1)
ul Metiznikov d 3 of 34 Chelyabinsk Region, 455000, Magnitogorsk, Russia
Tel.: (7) 3519254900
Web Site: http://www.profit.ru
Scrap Metal Distr
N.A.I.C.S.: 423930

LLC Mekhanoremontny Kompleks (1)
Ul Kirova 93 Chelyabinsk Region, 455000, Magnitogorsk, Russia
Tel.: (7) 3519243283
Web Site: http://www.metal-expo.ru
Iron & Steel Mfr
N.A.I.C.S.: 332111

LLC Ogneupor (1)
Ul Kirova 93, Magnitogorsk, 455019, Chelyabinsk, Russia
Tel.: (7) 3519247157
Web Site: http://www.oup.ru
Refractory Products Mfr
N.A.I.C.S.: 327120

LLC Profit-Center (1)
ul Novoostapovskaya 4 korp 2, 115088, Moscow, Russia
Tel.: (7) 495 280 04 61
Steel & Iron Casting Mfr
N.A.I.C.S.: 331110

LLC Region (1)
Ul Zavenyagina 9 Chelyabinsk Region, Magnitogorsk, 455049, Russia
Tel.: (7) 3519256007
Iron & Steel Mfr
N.A.I.C.S.: 332111

LLC SUTK (1)
Ul Ordzhonikidze d 39, Kusa, Chelyabinsk, 456940, Russia
Tel.: (7) 3515433254
Steel & Iron Casting Mfr
N.A.I.C.S.: 331110

LLC Sanatorii Metallurg (1)
Stavropol Territory the St Lenin 30, Yessentuki, 357601, Russia
Tel.: (7) 8793455324
Web Site: http://www.metallurgess.ru
Iron & Steel Mfr
N.A.I.C.S.: 332111

LLC Sanatorii Ybileyny (1)
Ul Kurortnaya 1 Zelyenaya Polyana, Abzelilovsky District, 453613, Bashkortostan, Russia
Tel.: (7) 3519243580
Iron & Steel Mfr
N.A.I.C.S.: 332111

LLC Shakhta Chertinskaya-Yuzhnaya (1)
Ul Rudnichnaya 5 YA d 90, Belovo, Kemerovo, 652607, Russia
Tel.: (7) 3845231434
Steel & Iron Casting Mfr
N.A.I.C.S.: 331110

LLC Shlakservis (1)
Ul Kirova 93 Chelyabinsk Region, Magnitogorsk, 455000, Russia
Tel.: (7) 3519247271
Iron & Steel Mfr
N.A.I.C.S.: 332111

LLC TFC of OJSC MMK (1)
Office 803 Ul Gertsena 6, Magnitogorsk, 455001, Chelyabinsk, Russia
Tel.: (7) 3519 42 14 53
Steel Product Distr
N.A.I.C.S.: 423510

LLC Tamozhenny Broker (1)
Ul Kirova 72 Chelyabinsk region, 455002, Magnitogorsk, Russia
Tel.: (7) 3519249135
Iron & Steel Mfr
N.A.I.C.S.: 332111

LLC Torgovy dom MMK (1)
Ul Kirova 76, Magnitogorsk, 455000, Chelyabinsk, Russia
Tel.: (7) 3519 24 24 19
Web Site: http://www.tdmmk.ru
Steel & Iron Casting Mfr
N.A.I.C.S.: 331110

LLC Torgovy dom MMK Ural (1)
ul Sovetskaya d 162, 455008, Magnitogorsk, Russia
Tel.: (7) 3519 34 1863
Steel Product Distr
N.A.I.C.S.: 423510

LLC UralKontrakt (1)
Ul Tolstogo 36 kv 6, Udmurtia, 427600, Glazov, Russia
Tel.: (7) 3414133150
Steel & Iron Casting Mfr
N.A.I.C.S.: 331110

MMK Atakas Metalurji Sanayi ve Liman Isletmecilgi A.S. (1)
Ozerli Mahallesi Alparslan Turkes Bulvari No 346, Dortyol, 31600, Hatay, Turkiye
Tel.: (90) 3267701000
Web Site: http://www.mmk-atakas.com.tr
Sales Range: $200-249.9 Million
Emp.: 600
Steel Products Mfr
N.A.I.C.S.: 331110

MMK Steel Trade AG (1)
Via Adamini 10A, Lugano, 6900, Switzerland (100%)
Tel.: (41) 919753960
Sales Range: $50-74.9 Million
Emp.: 10
Metal Service Centers & Metal Merchant Whslr
N.A.I.C.S.: 423510
George Bochorishvili (Mng Dir)

MMK Trading AG (1)
Gartenstrasse 6, Zug, Switzerland (99.6%)
Tel.: (41) 417260535
Metal Service Centers & Metal Merchant Whslr
N.A.I.C.S.: 423510

OJSC Bashmetalloptorg (1)
Ul Elektrozavodskaya D 2, Zubovo, 450520, Bashkortostan, Russia
Tel.: (7) 3472730574
Web Site: http://www.bmet.ru
Steel Product Distr
N.A.I.C.S.: 423510

OJSC MCRW (1)
Beloratskoye Shosse 11, Magnitogorsk, 455022, Chelyabinsk, Russia
Tel.: (7) 3519 22 81 69
Steel & Iron Casting Mfr
N.A.I.C.S.: 331110

OJSC MMK-METIZ (1)
5 Metiznikov Str, Magnitogorsk, 455002, Chelyabinsk, Russia
Tel.: (7) 3519241701
Web Site: http://www.mmk-metiz.ru
Steel & Iron Casting Mfr
N.A.I.C.S.: 331110

OSK LLC (1)
Ul Kirova house 93 ABK Building Office 209, Magnitogorsk, 455019, Chelyabinsk, Russia
Tel.: (7) 3519245325
Web Site: http://www.usc-service.ru
Steel & Iron Casting Mfr
N.A.I.C.S.: 331110

OJSC MOSCOW EXCHANGE MICEX-RTS

Tel.: (7) 4953633232 RU
Web Site: https://www.moex.com
Year Founded: 2011
MOEX—(MOEX)
Rev.: $903,027,747
Assets: $71,589,583,773
Liabilities: $69,678,066,006
Net Worth: $1,911,517,767
Earnings: $392,499,581
Emp.: 2,339
Fiscal Year-end: 12/31/22
Investment Management Service
N.A.I.C.S.: 551112
Dmitry Shcheglov (COO & Member-Exec Bd)

Subsidiaries:

CJSC MICEX Stock Exchange (1)
Bolshoy Kislovsky Per 13, 125009, Moscow, Russia (100%)
Tel.: (7) 4953633232
Web Site: http://www.moex.com
Sales Range: $250-299.9 Million
Securities & Commodities Exchange Operator
N.A.I.C.S.: 523210

CJSC National Clearing Center (1)
Bolshoy Kislovsky pereulok 13, 125009, Moscow, Russia
Tel.: (7) 4953633232
Web Site: http://www.nationalclearingcentre.com
Security Entitled Services
N.A.I.C.S.: 523150
Alexey S. Khavin (Chm)

Closed Joint-Stock Company DCC (1)
12 Spartakovskaya St, Moscow, 105066, Russia (99.99%)
Tel.: (7) 495 956 0999
Web Site: http://www.dcc.ru
Depository Clearing Services
N.A.I.C.S.: 522320

JSC National Settlement Depository (1)
12 Spartakovskaya St, 105066, Moscow, Russia
Tel.: (7) 4952344827
Web Site: http://www.nsd.ru
Settlement & Depository Services
N.A.I.C.S.: 522180

Moscow Exchange International Ltd. (1)

INTERNATIONAL PUBLIC

1 King Street, London, EC2V 8AU, United Kingdom
Tel.: (44) 2037131522
Security & Commodity Exchange Services
N.A.I.C.S.: 523210

NCO CJSC National Settlement Depository (1)
Spartakovskaya str 12, 105066, Moscow, Russia
Tel.: (7) 4952344827
Stock Analysis & Research Services
N.A.I.C.S.: 523150

OJSC MYRONIVSKY HLIBOPRODUCT

158 Ak Zabolotnogo Str, Kiev, 3143, Ukraine
Tel.: (380) 442070000
Web Site: http://www.mhp.com.ua
Year Founded: 1998
Sales Range: $900-999.9 Million
Emp.: 20,000
Agricultural & Livestock Farming Services
N.A.I.C.S.: 111998
Yuriy Kosiuk (CEO)

Subsidiaries:

LLC Katerynopilsky Elevator (1)
47 Lenina Street Urban-type Settlement, Katerynopil, 20505, Cherkassy, Ukraine
Tel.: (380) 474222607
Emp.: 586
Poultry Farming Services
N.A.I.C.S.: 112990

LLC Tavriysky Plant (1)
13 Promyslova Street, 74988, Tavriisk, Kherson Oblast, Ukraine
Tel.: (380) 554974732
Emp.: 159
Animal Feed Mfr
N.A.I.C.S.: 311119

LLC Urozhayna Kraina (1)
72 Maiakovskoho street office 15, Romny, Sumy Oblast, Ukraine
Tel.: (380) 544857716
Emp.: 440
Crop Fertilizer Services
N.A.I.C.S.: 115112

OJSC Myronivsky Hliboproduct Lehko Plant (1)
16 Frunze St, Myronivka, Kiev, Ukraine
Tel.: (380) 457442050
Emp.: 390
Food Products Mfr
N.A.I.C.S.: 311991

PRJSC UROZHAI (1)
193 Blahovisna Street, 18000, Cherkassy, Ukraine
Tel.: (380) 472455103
Emp.: 1,800
Crop Fertilizer Services
N.A.I.C.S.: 115112

PrJSC Agrofort (1)
22 Nezalezhnosti Street office 30, Kaharlyk, 09200, Kiev, Ukraine
Tel.: (380) 457354804
Emp.: 368
Crop Fertilizer Services
N.A.I.C.S.: 115112

PrJSC Myronivska Poultry Farm (1)
177 Lenina street, Kaniv, Cherkassy, Ukraine
Tel.: (380) 473638523
Emp.: 3,277
Poultry Farming Services
N.A.I.C.S.: 112990

PrJSC Oril Leader (1)
1 Khmelnytskoho street Yelyzavetivka, Petrykivka, 51831, Dnipropetrovsk, Ukraine
Tel.: (380) 563423160
Emp.: 1,520
Poultry Farming Services
N.A.I.C.S.: 112990

PrJSC Zernoproduct MHP (1)
164 Vynnychenka Street, Horodenka, 78100, Ivano-Frankivs'k, Ukraine
Tel.: (380) 343028437

AND PRIVATE COMPANIES

Emp.: 272
Crop Fertilizer Services
N.A.I.C.S.: 115112

PrJSc Ukrainian Bacon (1)
1a Zelena St Vodyane-2, Kostyantinivsky, 85180, Donetsk, Ukraine
Tel.: (380) 627261061
Emp.: 1,450
Poultry Meat Mfr
N.A.I.C.S.: 311615

Starynska Breeding Farm Agricultural LLC (1)
1 Lenin St Myrne village, Boryspil, 8361, Kiev, Ukraine
Tel.: (380) 459531545
Emp.: 1,280
Poultry Farming Services
N.A.I.C.S.: 112990

OJSC OLMA INVESTMENT FIRM
7/1 Maliy Karetniy per, 127051, Moscow, Russia
Tel.: (7) 495 699 03 04   RU
Web Site: http://eng.olma.ru
Year Founded: 1992
Privater Equity Firm
N.A.I.C.S.: 523999
Oleg Yachnik *(Gen Dir)*

OJSC ORIENBANK
Rudaki Avenue 95 1, Dushanbe, 734001, Tajikistan
Tel.: (992) 372210568
Web Site: http://www.orienbank.com
Sales Range: $200-249.9 Million
Emp.: 350
Banking Services
N.A.I.C.S.: 522110
Davlatzod Umed Davlatovich *(First Vice Chm)*

OJSC PAVA
Choros-Gurkina Street 39/1 Office 4, 649002, Gorno-Altaysk, Altay, Russia
Tel.: (7) 3822 226990
Web Site: http://www.apkhleb.ru
Sales Range: $150-199.9 Million
Emp.: 1,552
Grain Processing & Trading Services
N.A.I.C.S.: 311212
Sergey Stolbov *(VP)*

Subsidiaries:

Agrofirma Niva LLC (1)
38 Pushkina Street, Barnaul, Altai, Russia
Tel.: (7) 3852 63 65 57
Web Site: http://www.apkhleb.ru
Vegetable Farming Services
N.A.I.C.S.: 111211

Korporatsiya Transagro OJSC (1)
68a Ul Molodezhnaya, Barnaul, 656031, Altai Krai, Russia
Tel.: (7) 3852636557
Grain Storage Services
N.A.I.C.S.: 493130

PAVA-Export LLC (1)
68a Ul Molodezhnaya, Barnaul, 656031, Altai Krai, Russia
Tel.: (7) 3852636557
Wheat Whslr
N.A.I.C.S.: 424590

OJSC PHARMACY CHAIN 36.6
10-2-1 Ochakovskoe shosse, Moscow, 119530, Russia
Tel.: (7) 495 797 86 86   RU
Web Site: http://www.pharmacychain366.com
Year Founded: 1991
APTK—(MOEX)
Sales Range: $550-599.9 Million
Emp.: 5,000
Pharmaceutical Preparation Whslr
N.A.I.C.S.: 456110
Sergey Krivosheev *(Chm)*

OJSC RESO GARANTIA
6 Nagorny proezd, 117105, Moscow, Russia
Tel.: (7) 4957303000   RU
Web Site: http://www.reso.ru
Year Founded: 2004
Insurance Products & Services
N.A.I.C.S.: 524298
Sarkisov Sergey Eduardovich *(Chm-Supervisory Bd)*

OJSC ROSINTER RESTAURANTS HOLDING
Dushinskaya str 7 bld 1, 111024, Moscow, Russia
Tel.: (7) 4957884488
Web Site: http://www.rosinter.com
ROST—(MOEX)
Sales Range: $250-299.9 Million
Emp.: 7,441
Restaurant Owner, Operator & Franchiser
N.A.I.C.S.: 722511
Valeria Silina *(Sr VP-Mktg)*

OJSC ROSNEFTEGAZ
18/1 Ovchinnikovskaya, Embankment, Moscow, 115324, Russia
Tel.: (7) 4952259721   RU
Year Founded: 2001
Sales Range: Less than $1 Million
Holding Company
N.A.I.C.S.: 551112
Igor Ivanovich Sechin *(Chm)*

Subsidiaries:

OAO Rosneft Oil Company (1)
26/1 Sofiyskaya Embankment, 117997, Moscow, 117997, Russia   **(69.5%)**
Tel.: (7) 4995178899
Web Site: https://www.rn-card.ru
Rev.: $102,412,285,360
Assets: $209,977,038,640
Liabilities: $115,936,116,560
Net Worth: $94,040,922,080
Earnings: $17,089,204,880
Fiscal Year-end: 12/31/2023
Oil & Gas Exploration & Production Services
N.A.I.C.S.: 211120
Igor Ivanovich Sechin *(Chm-Mgmt Bd, Deputy Chm & CEO)*

Subsidiary (Non-US):

Anglo-Siberian Oil Company (Cyprus) Limited (2)
2 Agapinoros St, Nicosia, Cyprus   **(100%)**
Tel.: (357) 22717777
Web Site: http://www.mscyprus.com
Sales Range: $25-49.9 Million
Emp.: 40
Management Consulting Services
N.A.I.C.S.: 541618
George Stylianou *(CEO)*

Subsidiary (Domestic):

CJSC Penzanefteprodukt (2)
104 Ul Neitralnaya, Penza, 440013, Russia
Tel.: (7) 8412593914
Oil & Gas Exploration Services
N.A.I.C.S.: 324110

CJSC Sakhalinmorneftegaz Shelf (2)
Sakhalinskaya Ul 4, Yuzhno-Sakhalinsk, 693010, Russia
Tel.: (7) 4242499305
Oil Refining Services
N.A.I.C.S.: 213112

CJSC Vankorneft (2)
19 Prospekt Mira, Krasnoyarsk, 660049, Russia
Tel.: (7) 3912745644
Web Site: http://www.rosneft.com
Oil & Gas Field Development Services
N.A.I.C.S.: 211120

ITERA Oil and Gas Company Ltd. (2)
Sevastopolsky Prospekt 28 Bldg 1, 117209, Moscow, Russia   **(100%)**
Tel.: (7) 4954118500
Web Site: http://www.itera.ru
Sales Range: $150-199.9 Million
Emp.: 400
Natural Gas Producer & Marketer
N.A.I.C.S.: 211130
Igor V. Makarov *(Pres, Founder & Chm-ITERA Int'l Grp)*

Subsidiary (Domestic):

Investment Development Group LLC (IDG) (3)
28 Building 1 Sevastopolsky Prospekt, 117209, Moscow, Russia
Tel.: (7) 495 727 05 98
Web Site: http://www.idgcompany.ru
Real Estate, Construction & Investment Management Services
N.A.I.C.S.: 236220
Igor V. Makarov *(Chm & Founder & Pres-ITERA Intl Grp)*

Joint Venture (Non-US):

Nayara Energy Limited (2)
5th Floor Jet Airways Godrej BKC Plot No C-68 G Block, Bandra East Kurla Complex, Mumbai, 400 051, Maharashtra, India   **(49.13%)**
Tel.: (91) 2833661444
Web Site: http://www.nayaraenergy.com
Rev.: $14,384,912,880
Assets: $10,700,264,220
Liabilities: $7,944,618,120
Net Worth: $2,755,646,100
Earnings: $98,730,900
Fiscal Year-end: 03/31/2019
Oil & Gas Exploration, Production & Marketing Services
N.A.I.C.S.: 211120
Chakrapany Manoharan *(Dir-Refinery)*

Subsidiary (Domestic):

OJSC Dagneftegaz (2)
Generala Tankaeva St 75A, Makhachkala, 367008, Russia
Tel.: (7) 8722 680269
Web Site: http://www.rosneft.com
Oil & Gas Field Development Services
N.A.I.C.S.: 211120

OJSC East-Siberian Oil and Gas Company (2)
36 Mira Street, Krasnoyarsk, 660049, Russia
Tel.: (7) 391 252 46 01
Web Site: http://www.vsnk.ru
Oil & Gas Exploration Services
N.A.I.C.S.: 211120

OJSC Kuybyshev Refinery (2)
25 Groznenskaya St, Samara, 443004, Russia
Tel.: (7) 846 377 32 09
Web Site: http://www.rosneft.com
Sales Range: $450-499.9 Million
Emp.: 2,000
Petroleum Refining Services
N.A.I.C.S.: 324110
Oleg Druzhinin *(Gen Mgr)*

OJSC Rosneft-Karachaevo-Cherkessknefteproduct (2)
1 Korp B Ul Mira S, Znamenka, Russia
Tel.: (7) 8782275799
Oil Refining Services
N.A.I.C.S.: 324110

OJSC Rosneft-Smolenskneftteproduct (2)
3 Ul Volodarskogo, Smolensk, 214014, Russia
Tel.: (7) 4812382833
Emp.: 1,500
Oil Refining Services
N.A.I.C.S.: 324110
Angrey Myachev *(Mng Dir)*

OJSC Samaraneftegaz (2)
50 Volzhsky Avenue, Oktyabrsky region, 443071, Samara, Russia
Tel.: (7) 8463330232
Oil Refining Services
N.A.I.C.S.: 324110
Vladimir Nozhin *(Gen Dir)*

PJSOC Bashneft (2)
ul Karl Marx 30 building 1, 450077, Ufa, Russia   **(71%)**
Tel.: (7) 3472616161
Web Site: http://www.bashneft.ru
Oil Exploration & Production Services
N.A.I.C.S.: 213112
Lazeev Andrey Nikolaevich *(Member-Mgmt Bd & VP-Geology & Dev)*

RN-Burenie LLC (2)
26/1 Nab Sofiskaya, Moscow, 115035, Russia
Tel.: (7) 4952259784
Oil & Gas Exploration Services
N.A.I.C.S.: 213112

RN-Kaigannetegaz LLC (2)
26 Korp 1 Nab Sofiskaya, Moscow, 115035, Russia
Tel.: (7) 4959673293
Oil Field Survey & Exploration Services
N.A.I.C.S.: 211120

RN-Purneftegaz LLC (2)
3 District 10, Gubkinsky, 629830, Russia
Tel.: (7) 3493651272
Oil & Gas Field Development Services
N.A.I.C.S.: 213112

Rosneft-Tuapsenefteprodukt OJSC (2)
4 Industrialnaya St, 350063, Krasnodar, Russia
Tel.: (7) 08616731755
Crude Petroleum & Natural Gas Extraction
N.A.I.C.S.: 211120

Samara Terminal LLC (2)
70 Kv 1 Ul Tovarnaya, Samara, 443044, Russia
Tel.: (7) 8463302607
Oil Refining Services
N.A.I.C.S.: 324110

ZAO Rosnefteflot (2)
7 Dunayevskogo Str, Moscow, 121165, Russia
Tel.: (7) 495 225 59 95
Web Site: http://www.rosnefteflot.ru
Sea Freight Transportation Services
N.A.I.C.S.: 483111

OJSC SAMARAENERGO
Georgy Mitirev passage 9, 443079, Samara, 443079, Russia
Tel.: (7) 8001000763
Web Site: https://www.samaraenergo.ru
Year Founded: 1932
SAGO—(MOEX)
Sales Range: $900-999.9 Million
Emp.: 1,028
Electric Energy Distribution Services
N.A.I.C.S.: 221122

OJSC SBERBANK OF RUSSIA
Tel.: (7) 4959575731   RU
Web Site: https://www.sberbank.ru
Year Founded: 1841
SBER—(MOEX)
Rev.: $30,055,029,000
Assets: $483,237,057,000
Liabilities: $410,866,586,000
Net Worth: $72,370,471,000
Earnings: $13,629,850,000
Emp.: 281,000
Fiscal Year-end: 12/31/19
International Banking Services
N.A.I.C.S.: 522110
Lev Khasis *(Member-Exec Bd)*

Subsidiaries:

Auction LLC (1)
14 Entuziastov Highway, Moscow, 111024, Russia
Tel.: (7) 4959748462
Real Estate Manangement Services
N.A.I.C.S.: 531390

Insurance Company Sberbank Insurance Life LLC (1)
St Shabolovka d 31G 3rd Entrance, Moscow, 115162, Russia
Tel.: (7) 4997070737
Web Site: http://www.sberbank-insurance.ru

OJSC SBERBANK OF RUSSIA

OJSC Sberbank of Russia—(Continued)
Investment Life Insurance Services
N.A.I.C.S.: 524113

Intertech Bilgi Islem ve Pazarlama Ticaret AS (1)
Sanayi Mahallesi Teknopark Bulvari 1/3C
Kurtkoy, Pendik, 34906, Istanbul, Türkiye
Tel.: (90) 2166642000
Web Site: http://www.intertech.com.tr
Emp.: 1,100
Information Technology Services
N.A.I.C.S.: 541511
Duygu Meydan (Acct Mgr)

KORUS Consulting CIS LLC (1)
Derbenevskaya emb 11 Business Center Pollars building A office 401, 115114, Moscow, Russia
Tel.: (7) 4958773020
Web Site: http://www.korusconsulting.com
IT Consulting Services
N.A.I.C.S.: 541618

Rublevo Archangelskoe JSC (1)
Poklonnaya str 3 Floor 3 Office 1, 121170, Moscow, Russia
Tel.: (7) 4957304488
Web Site: http://www.mfc-city.com
Real Estate Services
N.A.I.C.S.: 531110
Andrey Likhachev (Gen Dir)

SB JSC Sberbank (1)
13/1 Al-Farabi Ave Pfc Nurlytau Block 3 B, Kaldayakova St, 050059, Almaty, Kazakhstan
Tel.: (7) 7272503020
Web Site: http://www.sberbank.kz
Sales Range: $10-24.9 Million
Emp.: 540
Banking Services
N.A.I.C.S.: 522110

SBERBANK CZ A.S. (1)
U Trezorky 921/2, 158 00, Prague, Czech Republic
Tel.: (420) 221969911
Web Site: http://www.sberbankcz.cz
Commercial Banking Services
N.A.I.C.S.: 522110
Edin Karabeg (Chm & CEO)

SIB (CYPRUS) Limited (1)
Alpha Business Centre 1st Floor Block B 27 Pindarou Street, 1060, Nicosia, Cyprus
Tel.: (357) 22419000
Web Site: http://www.sib.com.cy
Security & Exchange Commission Services
N.A.I.C.S.: 523999
Aleksander Kuzin (Sr Mgr-IT)

Sberbank (Switzerland) AG (1)
Gartenstrasse 24, Postfach 2136, CH-8027, Zurich, Switzerland **(99.15%)**
Tel.: (41) 442505656
Web Site: http://www.aberbank.ch
Sales Range: $50-74.9 Million
Emp.: 15
Banking Services
N.A.I.C.S.: 522110
Thomas Frick (Deputy Chm)

Sberbank Asset Management JSC (1)
Presnenskaya nab 8 bld 1 City of Capitals South Tower 13th Floor, 123112, Moscow, Russia
Tel.: (7) 4955000100
Web Site: http://www.sberbank-am.ru
Asset Management Services
N.A.I.C.S.: 523940
Andrey Makarov (Dir-Sls)

Sberbank BH DD (1)
Fraa Andela Zvizdovica 1, 71000, Sarajevo, Bosnia & Herzegovina
Tel.: (387) 33294700
Web Site: http://www.sberbank.ba
Financial Institution Services
N.A.I.C.S.: 522110

Sberbank CIB (UK) Limited (1)
85 Fleet Street 4th Floor, London, EC4Y 1AE, United Kingdom
Tel.: (44) 2075833257
Investment Banking Services
N.A.I.C.S.: 523150

Sberbank CIB JSC (1)
ul Vavilova d 19, 117312, Moscow, Russia
Tel.: (7) 4952580500
Web Site: http://www.sbrf-cib.ru
Investment Banking Services
N.A.I.C.S.: 523150

Sberbank CIB USA, Inc. (1)
Carnegie Tower 152 W 57th St 46 Fl, New York, NY 10019
Tel.: (212) 300-9600
Investment Banking Services
N.A.I.C.S.: 523150

Sberbank Capital LLC (1)
37A bld 4 Leningradsky avenue Arcus III Business Centre, 125167, Moscow, Russia
Tel.: (7) 4952803484
Commercial Real Estate Services
N.A.I.C.S.: 531390
Levon Melikov (Project Mgr)

Sberbank Europe AG (1)
Schwarzenbergplatz 3, Vienna, 1010, Austria **(100%)**
Tel.: (43) 1 22732 0
Web Site: http://www.sberbank.at
Sales Range: $50-74.9 Million
Emp.: 60
Bank Holding Company
N.A.I.C.S.: 551111
Sonja Sarkozi (CEO & Member-Mgmt Bd)

Subsidiary (Non-US):

Magyarorszagi Volksbank Zrt. (2)
Rakoczi ut 7, 1088, Budapest, Hungary
Tel.: (36) 13286666
Web Site: http://www.sberbank.hu
Sales Range: $300-349.9 Million
Emp.: 650
Commercial Banking Services
N.A.I.C.S.: 522110

Sberbank Banka d.d. (2)
Dunajska 128a, 1000, Ljubljana, Slovenia
Tel.: (386) 15307400
Web Site: http://www.sberbank.si
Sales Range: $75-99.9 Million
Emp.: 179
Commericial Banking
N.A.I.C.S.: 522110

Volksbank BH d.d. (2)
Fra Andela Zvizdovica 1, 71 000, Sarajevo, Bosnia & Herzegovina
Tel.: (387) 33295601
Web Site: http://www.volksbank.ba
Sales Range: $150-199.9 Million
Emp.: 353
Commericial Banking
N.A.I.C.S.: 522110
Reinhold Kolland (CEO)

Volksbank CZ, a.s. (2)
Na Pankrati 1724, Prague, 14000, Czech Republic
Tel.: (420) 221969911
Web Site: http://www.volksbank.cz
Sales Range: $300-349.9 Million
Emp.: 610
Commercial Banking Services
N.A.I.C.S.: 522110
Frank Guthan (Gen Mgr)

Volksbank Slovensko, a.s. (2)
Vysoka 9, SK 810 01, Bratislava, Slovakia
Tel.: (421) 259651111
Web Site: http://www.volksbank.sk
Sales Range: $300-349.9 Million
Emp.: 644
Commericial Banking
N.A.I.C.S.: 522110

Volksbank a.d. (2)
Bulevar Mihaila Pupina 165g, RS 11070, Belgrade, Serbia
Tel.: (381) 11 201 3200
Web Site: http://www.volksbank.com
Sales Range: $150-199.9 Million
Emp.: 456
Commericial Banking
N.A.I.C.S.: 522110

Branch (Non-US):

Sberbank a.d. Banja Luka (3)
Jevrejska 71, 78 000, Banja Luka, Bosnia & Herzegovina
Tel.: (387) 51246441
Web Site: http://www.sberbankbl.ba

Sales Range: $75-99.9 Million
Emp.: 237
Commericial Banking
N.A.I.C.S.: 522110
Aleksandar Kesic (Chm-Mgmt Bd)

Subsidiary (Non-US):

Volksbank d.d. (2)
Varsavska 9, HR 10000, Zagreb, Croatia
Tel.: (385) 14801300
Web Site: http://www.volksbank.hr
Sales Range: $150-199.9 Million
Emp.: 390
Commericial Banking
N.A.I.C.S.: 522110

Sberbank Leasing JSC (1)
6 Vorobyevskoe Highway, 119285, Moscow, Russia
Tel.: (7) 4956171026
Real Estate Lending Services
N.A.I.C.S.: 531110
Andrey Pavlov (Head-Compliance)

Sberbank Magyarorszag Zrt (1)
Rakoczi ut 1-3, 1088, Budapest, Hungary
Tel.: (36) 613268666
Web Site: http://www.sberbank.hu
Commercial Banking Services
N.A.I.C.S.: 522110

Sberbank Srbija AD (1)
Mihail Pupina Boulevard 165g, 11070, Novi Beograd, Serbia
Tel.: (381) 112257498
Web Site: http://www.sberbank.rs
Commercial Banking Services
N.A.I.C.S.: 522110
Marijana Vasilescu (CEO)

Strategy Partners Group JSC (1)
Kosmodamianskaya Nab 52 Bld 2, 115054, Moscow, Russia
Tel.: (7) 4957307747
Web Site: http://www.strategy.ru
Emp.: 100
Strategic Consulting Services
N.A.I.C.S.: 541618
Aleksander Idrisov (Mng Partner-Strategic Plng)

United Credit Bureau CJSC (1)
9 Bolshaya Tatarskaya Str Office 51, 115184, Moscow, Russia
Tel.: (7) 4956655173
Web Site: http://www.bki-okb.ru
Credit Bureau Services
N.A.I.C.S.: 561450

OJSC SOLLERS

Victory Park Plaza 1 Build 1 2 Kiyevskoye MZD 5 km, 119590, Moscow, 119590, Russia
Tel.: (7) 4952283045
Web Site: https://www.sollers-auto.com
Year Founded: 2002
SVAV—(MOEX)
Rev.: $1,235,320,230
Assets: $973,099,740
Liabilities: $599,576,640
Net Worth: $373,523,100
Earnings: $61,221,150
Fiscal Year-end: 12/31/21
Automobile Parts Mfr
N.A.I.C.S.: 336110
Sobolev A. Nikolay (Dir Gen)

Subsidiaries:

JSC Isuzu Rus (1)
St Azovskaya 97A, 432061, Ulyanovsk, Russia **(74%)**
Tel.: (7) 4957837035
Web Site: https://www.isuzu.ru
Truck Whslr
N.A.I.C.S.: 423110

Ulyanovsk Automobile Plant PJSC (1)
Moscow Highway 92, 432034, Ulyanovsk, Russia **(66.07%)**
Tel.: (7) 8422409100
Web Site: http://www.uaz.ru
Automobile Mfr
N.A.I.C.S.: 336110

OJSC SVYAZINVEST

55 Bldg 2 Plyushchikha Street, 119121, Moscow, Russia
Tel.: (7) 4957270402
Web Site: http://www.svyazinvest.ru
Sales Range: $5-14.9 Billion
Emp.: 187,018
Holding Company; Telecommunications Services
N.A.I.C.S.: 551112
Mikhail Aleksandrovich Leschenko (Deputy Gen Dir)

Subsidiaries:

JSC Central Telegraph (1)
7 Tverskaya Street, 103375, Moscow, Russia **(51%)**
Tel.: (7) 4955044444
Web Site: http://www.cnt.ru
Sales Range: $200-249.9 Million
Emp.: 900
Provider of Data Transmission, Commercial Telecommunications & Pre-Paid Long Distance Services
N.A.I.C.S.: 517111
Egovikt Zabolotme (Gen Dir)

OAO Artelekom Arkhangelsk Region (1)
45 Troitsky pr, 163061, Arkhangelsk, Russia **(51%)**
Tel.: (7) 8182 20 50 20
Web Site: http://www.arkhangelsk.nwtelecom.ru
Emp.: 4,512
Telecommunications & Data Transmission Services
N.A.I.C.S.: 517111

OAO Elektrosvyaz Kaliningrad Region (1)
32 Leninskiy Pr, 236006, Kaliningrad, Russia **(50.66%)**
Tel.: (7) 4012214214
Web Site: http://www.kaliningrad.nwtelecom.ru
Sales Range: $1-4.9 Billion
Emp.: 2,700
Telecommunications & Data Transmission Services
N.A.I.C.S.: 517111

OAO Elektrosvyaz Kaluga Region (1)
Ul Teatralnaya 38, 248600, Kaluga, Russia **(50.66%)**
Tel.: (7) 842531112
Web Site: http://www.kaluga.ru
Sales Range: $800-899.9 Million
Emp.: 3,000
Provider of Telecommunication, Internet & Data Transmission Services
N.A.I.C.S.: 517111

OAO Elektrosvyaz Kareliya Republic (1)
Ul Dzerzhinskogo 5, 185000, Petrozavodsk, Russia **(50.66%)**
Tel.: (7) 8142765111
Sales Range: $1-4.9 Billion
Emp.: 3,000
Telecommunications & Data Transmission Services
N.A.I.C.S.: 517111

OAO Elektrosvyaz Kostroma Region (1)
Ul Podlipaeva 1, 156601, Kostroma, Russia **(50.66%)**
Tel.: (7) 942558082
Web Site: http://www.kosnet.ru
Sales Range: $400-449.9 Million
Emp.: 2,100
Provider of Telecommunications Services
N.A.I.C.S.: 517111

OAO Elektrosvyaz Kurgan Region (1)
Ul Gogolya 44, 640000, Kurgan, Russia **(50.66%)**
Tel.: (7) 3522233555
Web Site: http://www.zaural.ru
Sales Range: $800-899.9 Million
Emp.: 2,900
Provider of Telecommunication & Data Transmission Services

AND PRIVATE COMPANIES

OAO Elektrosvyaz Kursk Region (1)
Red Square 8, 305000, Kursk, Russia (50.66%)
Tel.: (7) 122561318
Web Site: http://www.kursknet.ru
Sales Range: $800-899.9 Million
Emp.: 3,600
Provider of Telecommunication, Broadcasting & Data Transmission Services
N.A.I.C.S.: 517111

OAO Elektrosvyaz Orel Region (1)
Ul Lenina 43, 302000, Orel, Russia (50.66%)
Tel.: (7) 862431111
Web Site: http://www.orel.ru
Sales Range: $800-899.9 Million
Emp.: 2,600
Provider of Telecommunication, Internet & Data Transmission Services
N.A.I.C.S.: 517111

OAO Elektrosvyaz Pskov Region (1)
Oktyabrskiy PR 5, 180000, Pskov, Russia (50.66%)
Tel.: (7) 8112165481
Web Site: http://www.pskov.nwtelecom.ru
Sales Range: $450-499.9 Million
Emp.: 2,300
Telecommunications & Data Transmission Services
N.A.I.C.S.: 517111

OAO Elektrosvyaz Ryazan Region (1)
Ul Shedrina 43, 390006, Ryazan, Russia (50.66%)
Tel.: (7) 912216166
Web Site: http://www.esv.ryazan.ru
Sales Range: $800-899.9 Million
Emp.: 3,600
Provider of Telecommunication, Internet & Data Transmission Services
N.A.I.C.S.: 517111

OAO Elektrosvyaz Tver Region (1)
Ul Novotorzhskaya 24, 170000, Tver, Russia (50.66%)
Tel.: (7) 822427466
Sales Range: $800-899.9 Million
Emp.: 3,900
Telecommunication & Internet Services
N.A.I.C.S.: 517111

OAO Elektrosvyaz Vladimir Region (1)
Ul Gorkogo 42, 600000, Vladimir, Russia (50.66%)
Tel.: (7) 922 25 35 44
Web Site: http://www.wladimir.ru
Sales Range: $800-899.9 Million
Emp.: 4,000
Telecommunication Servicesb
N.A.I.C.S.: 517111

OAO Kamchatsvyazinform (1)
Ul Leninskaya 56, 683001, Petropavlovsk-Kamchatsky, Russia (50.66%)
Tel.: (7) 952093007
Web Site: http://www.kamchatka.ru
Sales Range: $400-449.9 Million
Emp.: 2,100
Telecommunication & Data Transmission Services
N.A.I.C.S.: 517111

OAO Smolensksvyazinform (1)
Ul Octyabrskoi Revolutsii 6, Smolensk, Russia (50.66%)
Tel.: (7) 812163311
Web Site: http://www.sci.ru
Sales Range: $800-899.9 Million
Emp.: 4,100
Telecommunication, Internet & Data Transmission Services
N.A.I.C.S.: 517111

OAO Uraltelecom Sverdlovsk Region (1)
Ul Moskovskaya 11, 620014, Ekaterinburg, Russia (50.54%)
Tel.: (7) 3432768555
Web Site: http://www.uraltelecom.ru
Sales Range: $800-899.9 Million
Emp.: 5,000
Telecommunication & Data Transmission Services
N.A.I.C.S.: 517111

OAO Yartelecom (1)
Ul Komsomolskaya 22, 150000, Yaroslavl, Russia (50.66%)
Tel.: (7) 852729721
Web Site: http://www.yartelecom.ru
Sales Range: $800-899.9 Million
Emp.: 5,000
Telecommunication Servicesb
N.A.I.C.S.: 517111

OJSC URALSIB FINANCIAL CORPORATION
8 Efremova St, 119048, Moscow, Russia
Tel.: (7) 4957237777 RU
Web Site: http://www.uralsib.com
Bank Holding Company
N.A.I.C.S.: 551111
Nikolai A. Tsvetkov *(Chm & Pres)*

Subsidiaries:

Bank UralSib PAO (1)
ul Ephraim 8, 119048, Moscow, Russia (15.2%)
Tel.: (7) 4957237777
Web Site: http://www.bankuralsib.ru
Sales Range: $1-4.9 Billion
Commerical Banking
N.A.I.C.S.: 522110

OJSC VYSOCHAISHY
14/3 Kadashevskya Nab, 119017, Moscow, Russia
Tel.: (7) 4957804995
Web Site: http://www.gvgold.ru
Year Founded: 1998
Sales Range: $50-74.9 Million
Emp.: 647
Gold Mining Services
N.A.I.C.S.: 212220
Sergey A. Vasiliev *(CEO & Gen Dir)*

Subsidiaries:

SAKHA Gold Mining, CJSC (1)
Dostavalova Str 30, Sakha Republic, Aldan, 678900, Russia
Tel.: (7) 41145 34 509
Gold Mining Services
N.A.I.C.S.: 212220
Igor A. Menshikov *(CEO & Gen Dir)*

Subsidiary (Domestic):

Taryn Gold Mining Company, CJSC (2)
8 office 34 Lenina Str, Ust-Nera Settlement, Oymyakon, 678730, Russia
Tel.: (7) 41154 2 08 78
Gold Mining Services
N.A.I.C.S.: 212220
Alexeiy A. Reshtanenko *(CEO & Gen Dir)*

OK BIOTECH CO., LTD.
No 91 Sec 2 Gongdao 5th Rd, Hsinchu, 30070, Taiwan
Tel.: (886) 35160258
Web Site: https://www.okbiotech.com
Year Founded: 2006
4155—(TAI)
Rev.: $38,980,508
Assets: $100,309,293
Liabilities: $21,984,498
Net Worth: $78,324,795
Earnings: ($52,127)
Fiscal Year-end: 12/31/23
Diagnostic Products Mfr
N.A.I.C.S.: 325413
James Lai *(Founder & CEO)*

OK BLOCKCHAIN CENTRE SDN. BHD.
G-04 Medini 7 Jalan Medini Sentral 5, Bandar Medini Iskandar, 79250, Iskandar Puteri, Johor, Malaysia
Tel.: (60) 75102930 MY
Web Site: http://www.okwave.global
Emp.: 100
Software Development Services
N.A.I.C.S.: 541511

OK PLAY INDIA LTD
124 New Manglapuri Mehrauli, New Delhi, 110030, India
Tel.: (91) 1146190000
Web Site: https://www.okplay.in
Year Founded: 1990
526415—(BOM)
Rev.: $21,784,509
Assets: $28,663,509
Liabilities: $24,313,075
Net Worth: $4,350,435
Earnings: ($234,722)
Emp.: 116
Fiscal Year-end: 03/31/23
Molded Plastic Product Mfr
N.A.I.C.S.: 339930
Rajan Wadhera *(Exec Dir)*

OK PROPERTIES I SOCIMI, S.A.U.
2 Planta Calle Costa de Can Santacilia 9, Pozuelo de Alarcon, ES-07001, Palma de Mallorca, Spain
Tel.: (34) 682271754
Web Site: https://www.okbusinessproperty.es
Year Founded: 2022
MLOKP—(EUR)
Rev.: $4,155,674
Assets: $83,063,567
Liabilities: $51,793,061
Net Worth: $31,270,506
Earnings: $623,561
Fiscal Year-end: 12/31/23
Real Estate Investment Services
N.A.I.C.S.: 531190
Lorenzo Ramon Bagur Munar *(Sec)*

OK SCIENCE & TECHNOLOGY CO., LTD.
Lutang project area xiushui industrial park, Jiujiang, 332400, Jiangxi, China
Tel.: (86) 7927627466
Web Site: https://www.nicepacker.com
Year Founded: 2011
001223—(SSE)
Rev.: $72,572,760
Assets: $272,606,256
Liabilities: $23,875,020
Net Worth: $248,731,236
Earnings: $25,724,088
Fiscal Year-end: 12/31/22
Paper Machinery Mfr & Distr
N.A.I.C.S.: 333243
Fusheng Hu *(Vice Chm)*

OK TRANSPORTATION LIMITED
130 Belfield Road, Etobicoke, M9W 1G1, ON, Canada
Tel.: (416) 291-5414
Year Founded: 1919
Rev.: $19,562,614
Emp.: 185
Freight Transportation Services
N.A.I.C.S.: 484110
Peter A. Lobraico *(Pres)*

OK ZIMBABWE LIMITED
OK House 7 Ramon Road, PO Box 3081, Graniteside, Harare, Zimbabwe
Tel.: (263) 242757311
Web Site: https://www.okziminvestor.com
Year Founded: 1942
OKZ—(ZIM)
Rev.: $2,213,225
Assets: $841,406
Liabilities: $377,716
Net Worth: $463,691
Earnings: $135,851
Emp.: 4,740
Fiscal Year-end: 03/31/19
Supermarket Operator
N.A.I.C.S.: 445110

Albert R. Katsande *(Dir-Comml)*

OKABE CO., LTD.

OKA CORPORATION BHD
No 6 Lebuhraya Chateau Off Persiaran Kampar, 30250, Ipoh, Perak, Malaysia
Tel.: (60) 52542741
Web Site: https://www.oka.com.my
Year Founded: 1981
OKA—(KLS)
Rev.: $29,865,637
Assets: $47,032,589
Liabilities: $6,940,514
Net Worth: $40,092,076
Earnings: $1,964,792
Fiscal Year-end: 03/31/24
Precast Concrete Mfr
N.A.I.C.S.: 327331
Choo Ian Ong *(CEO-Grp)*

OKA DIRECT LIMITED
166 Purchas Road, Didcot, OX11 7BF, Oxfordshire, United Kingdom
Tel.: (44) 1235 433930
Web Site: http://www.oka.com
Year Founded: 1999
Emp.: 250
Furnitures & Home Accessories Retailer
N.A.I.C.S.: 423210
Annabel Astor *(Co-Founder)*

OKA-BUROMOBEL GMBH & CO. KG
Eibauer Strasse 1-5, 02727, Ebersbach, Germany
Tel.: (49) 35867110
Web Site: http://www.oka.de
Year Founded: 1858
Rev.: $28,763,183
Emp.: 148
Office Furniture Mfr
N.A.I.C.S.: 337214
Mathias Lenaif *(Mgr-Sls & Mktg)*

OKAB CONVERT AB
Gyllngs Vag 7, Oskarshamn, 572 36, Oskarshamn, Sweden
Tel.: (46) 491767300
Web Site: http://www.okabconvert.com
Paper Products
N.A.I.C.S.: 322299
Dan Erlandsson *(Mng Dir)*

Subsidiaries:

OKAB France SAS (1)
31 Rue du Commandant Cousteau, 26800, Portes-les-Valence, France
Tel.: (33) 475 578 710
Web Site: http://www.okabconvert.com
Emp.: 19
Paper Product Mfr & Distr
N.A.I.C.S.: 322299
Laurent Labbe *(Mng Dir)*

OKAB Germany GmbH (1)
Steinbruckerstrasse 8, 23556, Lubeck, Germany
Tel.: (49) 451 89 90 10
Emp.: 50
Paper Products Mfr
N.A.I.C.S.: 322299
Juha Turunen *(Mng Dir)*

OKABE CO., LTD.
2-8-2 Oshiage, Sumida-ku, Tokyo, Japan
Tel.: (81) 336245111 JP
Web Site: https://www.okabe.co.jp
Year Founded: 1917
5959—(TKS)
Rev.: $554,097,680
Assets: $637,284,650
Liabilities: $197,279,250
Net Worth: $440,005,400
Earnings: ($38,796,480)
Emp.: 915

OKABE CO., LTD.

Okabe Co., Ltd.—(Continued)
Fiscal Year-end: 12/31/23
Construction & Civil Engineering Products Mfr
N.A.I.C.S.: 333120
Makoto Hirowatari *(Pres & CEO)*

Subsidiaries:

FUJI BOLT Manufacturing Co., Ltd. (1)
2-8-2 Oshiage, Sumida-ku, Tokyo, 131-8505, Japan
Tel.: (81) 35 637 7192
Web Site: https://www.fujibolt.co.jp
Construction Machinery Mfr
N.A.I.C.S.: 333120

Plant (Domestic):

FUJI BOLT Manufacturing Co., Ltd. - Shiroi Plant (2)
2638-8 Hiratsuka, Shiroishi, 270-1402, Chiba-ken, Japan
Tel.: (81) 474971062
Construction Machinery Mfr
N.A.I.C.S.: 333120

Subsidiary (Domestic):

FUJI KIZAI Co., Ltd. (2)
36-3 Kanda-Konya-cho, Chiyoda-ku, Tokyo, 101-0035, Japan
Tel.: (81) 33 252 8515
Web Site: https://www.fujikizai.jp
Fastener Product Mfr & Distr
N.A.I.C.S.: 339993
Akihide Nakazato *(CEO)*

Huizhou Golf & Resort Co., Ltd. (1)
12 Tuo Da Ling Town, Huizhou, 516300, Guangdong, China
Tel.: (86) 7528909999
Web Site: http://www.okabe.co.jp
Golf Course & Resort Operation Services
N.A.I.C.S.: 721110

Naoe Bussan Co., Ltd. (1)
23-5-10 Kita 35 Jo Higashi, Higashi-ku, Sapporo, 007-0835, Hokkaido, Japan
Tel.: (81) 117826716
Temporary Building & Formwork Products Distr
N.A.I.C.S.: 423310

OCM, Inc. (1)
1120 Peterson Rd, Grayslake, IL 60030
Tel.: (847) 462-4258
Web Site: http://www.ocm-inc.com
Sales Range: $25-49.9 Million
Emp.: 15
Construction Material Mfr & Distr
N.A.I.C.S.: 325998

Okabe Company, Inc. (1)
1120 E Peterson Rd, Grayslake, IL 60030 **(100%)**
Tel.: (847) 541-9200
Web Site: https://www.okabe-inc.com
Sales Range: $10-24.9 Million
Emp.: 16
Metal Fastener Mfr
N.A.I.C.S.: 332722
Nada Bursac *(Mng Dir)*

Okabe Kaiyo Engineering Co., Ltd. (1)
4-21-15 Mukojima, Sumida-ku, Tokyo, 1318535, Japan
Tel.: (81) 336249207
Web Site: http://www.okabe-marine.co.jp
Sales Range: $25-49.9 Million
Emp.: 150
Law firm
N.A.I.C.S.: 541199
Makoto Hirowatari *(CEO)*

Okabe Lease Co., Ltd. (1)
4-33-6 Fukuei, Ichikawa, Japan
Tel.: (81) 473976101
Heavy & Civil Engineering Construction
N.A.I.C.S.: 237990

PT Fujibolt Indonesia - Bogor Factory (1)
JI Wanaherang RT04 RW01, Kecamatan Gunung Putri, Bogor, 16965, Jawa Barat, Indonesia
Tel.: (62) 2186862907

Construction Machinery Mfr
N.A.I.C.S.: 333120

Water Gremlin Aquila Company S.p.A. (1)
Via Firenze 1C/3, 25060, Cellatica, Brescia, Italy
Tel.: (39) 030 2522416
Web Site: http://www.watergremlinaquila.com
Sales Range: $25-49.9 Million
Lead Bushings Mfr
N.A.I.C.S.: 333613

OKADA AIYON CORPORATION

4-1-18 Kaigan-dori, Minato-ku, Osaka, 552-0022, Japan
Tel.: (81) 665761268
Web Site: https://www.okada-aiyon.com
Year Founded: 1938
6294—(TKS)
Rev.: $179,097,950
Assets: $224,792,880
Liabilities: $118,907,290
Net Worth: $105,885,590
Earnings: $12,466,460
Fiscal Year-end: 03/31/24
Construction Machinery Mfr & Distr
N.A.I.C.S.: 333120
Yuji Okada *(Pres)*

Subsidiaries:

Aiyon Tech. Co., Ltd. (1)
357-1 Oaza-Uchimagi, Asaka, 351-0001, Saitama, Japan
Tel.: (81) 484581295
Hydraulic Equipment Mfr
N.A.I.C.S.: 333998

Okada America, Inc. (1)
12950 SE Highway 212 Bldg D, Clackamas, OR 97015
Tel.: (503) 557-7033
Web Site: https://www.okadaamerica.com
Hydraulic Equipment Mfr & Distr
N.A.I.C.S.: 333998
Jim Brown *(Pres)*

Thoesen Tractor & Equipment Inc. (1)
3142 E Lincoln Hwy, Chicago Heights, IL 60411-7728
Tel.: (708) 758-2060
Rev.: $4,000,000
Emp.: 20
Construction & Mining, except Oil Well, Machinery & Equipment Merchant Whslr
N.A.I.C.S.: 423810
Peter Thoesen *(Pres)*

Subsidiary (Domestic):

Chicago Machinery Co (2)
3142 E Lincoln Hwy, Lynwood, IL 60411
Tel.: (708) 758-2060
Web Site: https://www.chicagomachineryinc.com
Rev.: $3,020,000
Emp.: 20
General Freight Trucking, Long-Distance, Truckload
N.A.I.C.S.: 484121

OKAI INFORMATION SYSTEM CONSULTATION

1-18-9 Sakae, Naka-ku, Nagoya, 460-0008, Japan
Tel.: (81) 522221000
Web Site: https://www.kktisc.co.jp
Year Founded: 1974
4349—(NGO)
Sales Range: Less than $1 Million
System Consulting & Leasing Services
N.A.I.C.S.: 532420
Hajime Umeda *(Pres)*

OKAMOTO GLASS CO., LTD

380 Toyo Kashiwa City, Chiba, 277-0872, Japan
Tel.: (81) 471373111
Web Site: https://www.ogc-jp.com

Year Founded: 1928
7746—(TKS)
Rev.: $30,293,630
Assets: $52,794,070
Liabilities: $41,603,340
Net Worth: $11,190,730
Earnings: $667,610
Emp.: 253
Fiscal Year-end: 03/31/24
Electronic Components Mfr
N.A.I.C.S.: 334419
Tsuyoshi Okamoto *(Chm & CEO)*

Subsidiaries:

Niigata Okamoto Glass Co., Ltd. (1)
7587-1 Oaza-Yasuda, Kashiwazaki, 945-1352, Niigata, Japan
Tel.: (81) 257233111
Industrial Glass Mfr
N.A.I.C.S.: 327211

OKAMOTO OPTECH Co., Ltd. (1)
No77 Sec 1 Xintai 5th Rd RM B 6F-7, Xizhi Dist, Taipei, 221432, Taiwan
Tel.: (886) 226982200
Glass Mfr
N.A.I.C.S.: 327211

SUZHOU OKAMOTO TRADING Co., Ltd. (1)
Tian Xiang Garden 6-1201C Industrial park, Suzhou, China
Tel.: (86) 51262881879
Glass Mfr
N.A.I.C.S.: 327211

OKAMOTO INDUSTRIES, INC.

3-27-12 Hongo, Bunkyo-ku, Tokyo, 113-8710, Japan
Tel.: (81) 338174111
Web Site: https://www.okamoto-inc.jp
Year Founded: 1934
5122—(TKS)
Rev.: $701,473,030
Assets: $950,901,380
Liabilities: $345,550,970
Net Worth: $605,350,410
Earnings: $48,834,680
Emp.: 2,775
Fiscal Year-end: 03/31/24
Rubber Products Mfr
N.A.I.C.S.: 326299
Toshio Tamura *(Pres & CEO)*

Subsidiaries:

APOLLOTEX, CO. LTD (1)
108 Moo 18 Navana Korn Estate Zone 3 Phaholyothin Road, Khlong Luang, 12120, Pathumthani, Thailand
Tel.: (66) 2 529 1420
Rubber Products Mfr
N.A.I.C.S.: 326299

OKAMOTO SANDUSKY MANUFACTURING LLC. (1)
3130 W Monroe St, Sandusky, OH 44870
Tel.: (419) 626-1633
Rubber Products Mfr
N.A.I.C.S.: 326299

Okamoto Industries (Hong Kong) Ltd. (1)
16/F Fortis Tower 77-79 Gloucester Road, Wanchai, China (Hong Kong)
Tel.: (852) 25201683
Rubber Products Mfr
N.A.I.C.S.: 326299

Okamoto Industries (Shenzhen) Co., Ltd (1)
World Financial Center A 32F CD 4003 Shen Nan Dong Lu Luohu-qu, Shenzhen, Guangdong, China
Tel.: (86) 75525981267
Rubber Products Mfr
N.A.I.C.S.: 326299

Okamoto Rubber Products Co., Ltd. (1)
60/50 Navanakorn Industrial Estate Zone 2 Phaholyothin Road, Khlong Luang, 12120, Pathum Thani, Thailand
Tel.: (66) 25200729
Rubber Products Mfr

INTERNATIONAL PUBLIC

N.A.I.C.S.: 326299

Okamoto Vietnam Co., Ltd. (1)
Lot 105/2 Amata Road Amata Industrial Zone Long Binh, Bien Hoa, Dong Nai, Vietnam
Tel.: (84) 61993445
Rubber Products Mfr
N.A.I.C.S.: 326299

Riken Corundum Co., Ltd. (1)
547-1 Miyamae, Konosu, 365 0051, Saitama, Japan **(100%)**
Tel.: (81) 485963550
Web Site: https://www.rikencorundum.co.jp
Rev.: $29,671,650
Assets: $45,432,720
Liabilities: $10,961,140
Net Worth: $34,471,580
Earnings: $680,640
Emp.: 115
Fiscal Year-end: 12/31/2023
Manufacture of Variety of Abrasive Papers & Cloths & Office Automation Equipment Parts
N.A.I.C.S.: 327910
Masuda Tomio *(CEO)*

Plant (Domestic):

Riken Corundum Co., Ltd. - Gunma Niiharu Factory (2)
915-1 Sukawa, Tone-gun Minakami, Gunma, 379-1418, Japan
Tel.: (81) 278642345
Coated Abrasive Paper Mfr
N.A.I.C.S.: 327910

Riken Corundum Co., Ltd. - Gunma Numata Factory (2)
418 Yanagimachi, Numata, 378-0055, Gunma, Japan
Tel.: (81) 278224327
Coated Abrasive Paper Mfr
N.A.I.C.S.: 327910

Siam Okamoto Co., Ltd. (1)
108 Moo Navanakorn Estate Zone 3 Phaholythin Road, Khlong Nueng, Khlong Luang, 12120, Pathum Thani, Thailand
Tel.: (66) 2 529 1420
Automotive Material Mfr
N.A.I.C.S.: 336110

Vina Okamoto Co., Ltd. (1)
Land Plot 14-15 Namsach Industrial Zone, Hai Duong, Haidong, Vietnam
Tel.: (84) 3203574680
Rubber Products Mfr
N.A.I.C.S.: 326299

OKAMOTO MACHINE TOOL WORKS, LTD.

2993 Gohara, Annaka, 379-0135, Gunma, Japan
Tel.: (81) 273855800
Web Site: https://www.okamoto.co.jp
Year Founded: 1926
6125—(TKS)
Rev.: $331,808,780
Assets: $397,684,040
Liabilities: $199,536,070
Net Worth: $198,147,970
Earnings: $30,115,160
Emp.: 1,677
Fiscal Year-end: 03/31/24
Industrial Machinery Mfr & Whslr
N.A.I.C.S.: 333248
Tsuneyuki Ishii *(Pres & CEO)*

Subsidiaries:

Okamoto (Singapore) Pte, Ltd. (1)
10 Riverside Road Entrance at Marsiling Lane, Woodlands Newtown, Singapore, 739082, Singapore
Tel.: (65) 62696426
Emp.: 230
Machine Tool Distr
N.A.I.C.S.: 423830

Okamoto (Thai) Company Ltd. (1)
174 Mu2 Tambol Chamaeb Amphur, Wangnoi, Ayutthaya, 13170, Thailand
Tel.: (66) 35958499
Emp.: 1,000
Industrial Machinery Distr
N.A.I.C.S.: 423830

AND PRIVATE COMPANIES

Okamoto Corporation (1)
370 Corporate Woods Pkwy, Vernon Hills, IL 60061
Tel.: (847) 235-3500
Industrial Machinery Distr
N.A.I.C.S.: 423830

Okamoto Machine Tool Europe GmbH (1)
Raiffeisenstrasse 7b, 63225, Langen, Germany
Tel.: (49) 6103201100
Commercial Machinery Maintenance Services
N.A.I.C.S.: 811310
Akihiro Takesada *(Mng Dir)*

Okamoto Machinery Co., Ltd. (1)
2050 Kanami Kanae-cho, Fukuyama, 720-0541, Hiroshima, Japan
Tel.: (81) 849359191
Web Site: https://www.okamoto-kouki.co.jp
Emp.: 321
Machine Tools Mfr
N.A.I.C.S.: 333517
Masato Kikuchi *(Co-Pres)*

Plant (Non-US):

Okamoto Machinery Co., Ltd. - Chinese Plant (2)
No 65-9 Xtng Gang Road Zhonglou Economic Development Zone, Changzhou, 213023, China
Tel.: (86) 519 83903057
Machine Tools Mfr
N.A.I.C.S.: 333517

Plant (Domestic):

Okamoto Machinery Co., Ltd. - Matsunaga Plant (2)
1-7-41 Yanaizu-cho, Fukuyama, 729-0114, Hiroshima, Japan
Tel.: (81) 84 934 1774
Machine Tools Mfr
N.A.I.C.S.: 333517

Okamoto Machinery Co., Ltd. - Onomichi Plant (2)
1-220-55 Chojohara, Onomichi, 720-0221, Hiroshima, Japan
Tel.: (81) 848482882
Machine Tools Mfr
N.A.I.C.S.: 333517

OKAMURA CORPORATION
2-7-18 Kitasaiwai, Nishi-ku, Yokohama, 220-0004, Japan
Tel.: (81) 453193401   JP
Web Site: https://www.okamura.com
Year Founded: 1945
7994—(TKS)
Rev.: $1,971,729,950
Assets: $1,864,799,980
Liabilities: $709,405,030
Net Worth: $1,155,394,950
Earnings: $134,050,800
Emp.: 3,940
Fiscal Year-end: 03/31/24
Office Furniture, Store Displays, Industrial Machinery, Public Interiors Products Development & Material Handling Support Mfr
N.A.I.C.S.: 337211
Sakae Fukuda *(CFO, Exec Dir & Dir)*

Subsidiaries:

FM Solution Corporation (1)
2-14-3 Nagata- cyo, Chiyoda-ku, Tokyo, 100-0014, Japan
Tel.: (81) 335934601
Web Site: https://www.fm-solution.co.jp
Sales Range: $25-49.9 Million
Emp.: 30
Management Consulting Services
N.A.I.C.S.: 541618
Tomoyuki Ota *(Pres)*

Fuji Seiko Honsha Co., Ltd (1)
25 Ohama-cho, Nomi, 929-0198, Ishikawa, Japan
Tel.: (81) 761550600
Web Site: http://www.fujiseiko.co.jp
Sales Range: $50-74.9 Million
Emp.: 190
Office Equipments Mfr
N.A.I.C.S.: 333310

Kansai Okamura Manufacturing Co., Ltd (1)
2-8-63 Inadauemachi, Higashi-osaka, 577-0002, Osaka, Japan
Tel.: (81) 667445151
Web Site: http://www.kansai.okamura.co.jp
Production of Work Stations & Storage Cabinets
N.A.I.C.S.: 337214
Shigeji Kikuchi *(Mng Dir)*

NS Okamura Corporation (1)
23-15 Suzuko -cho, Kamaishi, Iwate, 026-0031, Japan
Tel.: (81) 193226551
Web Site: https://www.nso.okamura.co.jp
Sales Range: $25-49.9 Million
Emp.: 130
Metal Household Furniture Mfr
N.A.I.C.S.: 337126

Okamura Business Support Corporation (1)
Tenri Bldg 34th Floor 1-4-1 Kitasaiwai, Nishi-ku, Yokohama, 220-0004, Kanagawa, Japan
Tel.: (81) 453193410
Sales Range: $25-49.9 Million
Emp.: 10
Business Support Services
N.A.I.C.S.: 561499

Okamura International (Singapore) Pte Ltd. (1)
137 Cecil St ste 01-01/04 Cecil Building, Singapore, 069537, Singapore
Tel.: (65) 62247995
Web Site: https://www.okamura.com.sg
Sales Range: $25-49.9 Million
Emp.: 25
Wood Office Furniture Mfr
N.A.I.C.S.: 337211
Nomura Kazuhiro *(Mng Dir)*

Okamura Logistics Corporation (1)
14F Tenri Building 1-4-1 Kitako, Nishi-ku, Yokohama, 220-0004, Japan
Tel.: (81) 455236967
Web Site: http://www.okl.co.jp
General Warehousing & Storage
N.A.I.C.S.: 493110

Okamura Support & Service Corporation (1)
1-8-10 Akasaka No 9 Kowa Bldg 3f, Minato-ku, Tokyo, 107-0052, Japan
Tel.: (81) 335682831
Office Equipments Mfr
N.A.I.C.S.: 333310

SANYO Okamura Corporation (1)
1 Ainomachi, Takahashi, 716-0009, Okayama, Japan
Tel.: (81) 866220700
Web Site: https://www.sanyo.okamura.co.jp
Emp.: 136
Office Equipments Mfr
N.A.I.C.S.: 333310

Seeder Co., Ltd. (1)
2-2-17 Suehirocho, Tsurumi-ku, Yokohama, 230-0045, Kanagawa, Japan
Tel.: (81) 455086901
Web Site: http://www.okamura.co.jp
Sales Range: $1-4.9 Billion
Emp.: 23
Conveyor System Distr
N.A.I.C.S.: 423830

Shanghai Okamura Furniture and Logistic System Co., Ltd (1)
19F Cloud Nine Shopping Mall 1018 Changning Road, Shanghai, 200042, China
Tel.: (86) 21 6074 6000
Web Site: http://www.okamura.cn
Office Environmental Equipment Mfr
N.A.I.C.S.: 337214

OKAMURA FOODS CO., LTD.
1-6-11 Yaeda, Aomori, 030-0912, Japan
Tel.: (81) 177367777
Web Site: https://www.okamurashokuhin.co.jp
Year Founded: 1971
2938—(TKS)
Rev.: $203,176,300
Assets: $243,637,400
Liabilities: $155,618,180
Net Worth: $88,019,220
Earnings: $12,240,960
Emp.: 852
Fiscal Year-end: 06/30/24
Packaged Frozen Food Distr
N.A.I.C.S.: 424420
Koichi Okamura *(Pres & CEO)*

OKANO VALVE MFG. CO.LTD.
1-14 Nakamachi, Moji-ku, Kitakyushu, 800-8601, Japan
Tel.: (81) 933729244
Web Site: https://www.okano-valve.co.jp
Year Founded: 1926
6492—(TKS)
Rev.: $52,515,630
Assets: $90,092,630
Liabilities: $19,114,640
Net Worth: $70,977,990
Earnings: $4,941,730
Emp.: 364
Fiscal Year-end: 11/30/23
Industrial Valve Mfr & Whslr
N.A.I.C.S.: 332911
Takeharu Okano *(Pres & Dir-Res)*

Subsidiaries:

OKANO VALVE MFG. CO. - Yukuhashi Steel Foundry Works (1)
4-4-1 Nishiizumi, Yukuhashi, 824-0038, Japan
Tel.: (81) 930230026
Industrial Valve Mfr
N.A.I.C.S.: 332911

OKAPI RESOURCES LIMITED
Level 2 8 Colin Street, West Perth, 6005, WA, Australia
Tel.: (61) 861179338   AU
Web Site: http://www.okapiresources.com
Year Founded: 2017
GUELF—(OTCQB)
Rev.: $347,516
Assets: $26,860,584
Liabilities: $486,521
Net Worth: $26,374,063
Earnings: ($1,058,369)
Emp.: 4
Fiscal Year-end: 06/30/24
Mineral Exploration Services
N.A.I.C.S.: 213114
Andrew Shearer *(Exec Dir)*

OKASAN SECURITIES GROUP INC.
2-2-1 Nihonbashi Muromachi, Chuo-ku, Tokyo, 103-0022, Japan
Tel.: (81) 332722222
Web Site: https://www.okasan.jp
Year Founded: 1944
8609—(NGO)
Rev.: $558,367,865
Assets: $7,980,037,409
Liabilities: $6,565,065,886
Net Worth: $1,414,971,523
Earnings: $89,659,704
Emp.: 2,458
Fiscal Year-end: 03/31/24
Holding Company; Securities, Asset Management & Support Services
N.A.I.C.S.: 551112
Hiroyuki Shinshiba *(Pres & Exec Officer)*

Subsidiaries:

Oishi Securities Co., Ltd. (1)
1 Kuriya-cho, Ogaki-shi, Gifu, 503-0902, Japan
Tel.: (81) 584753111
Web Site: http://www.oishi-sec.co.jp
Securities Services
N.A.I.C.S.: 523210

Okasan Asset Management Co., Ltd. (1)
21F Kyobashi Edogrand 2-2-1 Kyobashi, Chuo-ku, Tokyo, 104-0031, Japan
Tel.: (81) 335161188
Web Site: http://www.okasan-am.jp
Sales Range: $75-99.9 Million
Emp.: 167
Asset Management Services
N.A.I.C.S.: 531390

Okasan Business Service Co., Ltd. (1)
5th floor Sumitomo Fudosan Nihonbashi Honcho Building, 4-11-5 Nihonbashi Honcho Chuo-ku, Tokyo, 103-0023, Japan (65%)
Tel.: (81) 363858200
Web Site: https://www.obs-okasan.co.jp
Emp.: 92
Business Outsourcing Services
N.A.I.C.S.: 561499

Okasan International (Asia) Limited (1)
Tel.: (852) 25253045
Sales Range: $50-74.9 Million
Emp.: 34
Financial Services
N.A.I.C.S.: 523210
Keiichi Okuzawa *(Pres & Mng Dir)*

Okasan Kogyo Co., Ltd. (1)
3rd Floor Koami-cho Yasuda Building 9-9 Koami-cho, Nihonbashi Chuo-ku, Tokyo, 103-0016, Japan
Tel.: (81) 336653500
Web Site: http://www.okasan.jp
Insurance Agency Services
N.A.I.C.S.: 524210
Shinji Iida *(Pres)*

Okasan Niigata Securities Co., Ltd. (1)
1-5-5 Ote-dori, Nagaoka, Niigata, 940-0062, Japan
Tel.: (81) 258350290
Web Site: https://www.okasan-niigata.co.jp
Sales Range: $25-49.9 Million
Emp.: 209
Securities Brokerage Services
N.A.I.C.S.: 523150
Kenjiro Takemiya *(Chm, Pres & CEO)*

Okasan Online Securities Co., Ltd. (1)
3-9-7 Ginza, Chuo-ku, Tokyo, 104-0061, Japan
Tel.: (81) 120146890
Web Site: http://www.okasan-online.co.jp
Emp.: 77
Online Securities Brokerage Services
N.A.I.C.S.: 523150
Yoshihiro Ikeda *(Pres)*

Okasan Securities Co., Ltd. (1)
1-17-6 Nihonbashi, Chuo-ku, Tokyo, 103-8278, Japan
Tel.: (81) 332722211
Web Site: https://www.okasan.jp
Sales Range: $700-749.9 Million
Emp.: 2,470
Securities Dealing Services
N.A.I.C.S.: 523150
Mitsuru Tanaka *(Sr Mng Exec Officer)*

Sanko Securities Co., Ltd. (1)
3-2-2 Nihonbashi Kayabacho, Chuo-ku, Tokyo, 103-0025, Japan
Tel.: (81) 356140700
Web Site: http://sanko-sec.co.jp
Financial Securities Services
N.A.I.C.S.: 523999
Shinichi Koga *(Pres)*

OKAYA & CO., LTD.
2-4-18 Sakae, Naka-ku, Nagoya, 460-8666, Aichi, Japan
Tel.: (81) 522048121   JP
Web Site: https://www.okaya.co.jp
Year Founded: 1669
74850—(NGO)
Rev.: $7,346,772,382

OKAYA & CO., LTD.

Okaya & Co., Ltd.—(Continued)
Assets: $5,530,260,984
Liabilities: $2,858,790,882
Net Worth: $2,671,470,102
Earnings: $165,127,189
Emp.: 5,626
Fiscal Year-end: 02/29/24
Steel Products Whslr; General Merchandise Mfr & Whslr
N.A.I.C.S.: 423510
Tokuichi Okaya *(Chm & Pres)*

Subsidiaries:

Chubu Plastics Molding Co., Ltd. (1)
3-2-5 Honohara, Toyokawa, 442-0061, Aichi, Japan
Tel.: (81) 533807001
Web Site: https://chubu-gousei.co.jp
Emp.: 164
Synthetic Resin Mfr
N.A.I.C.S.: 325211
Yukiteru Hosokawa *(Pres)*

Chuetsu Precision Works Co., Ltd. (1)
1-1 Nishiashiharashin Tateyama-cho, Nakaniikawa, Toyama, 930-0298, Japan
Tel.: (81) 764629534
Web Site: http://www.okaya.co.jp
Automobile Parts Mfr & Sales
N.A.I.C.S.: 336390

Chuhbu Plastics Molding Co., Ltd. (1)
3-2-5 Honohara, Toyokawa, 442-0061, Japan
Tel.: (81) 533807001
Plastic Molded Products Mfr & Sales
N.A.I.C.S.: 326199

H.O. Engineering Co., Ltd. (1)
1900 Sukaguchi, Kiyosu, Nagoya, 452-0905, Japan
Tel.: (81) 524083050
Machinery Maintenance & Mfr
N.A.I.C.S.: 333248

Hattori Koun Co., Ltd. (1)
27 Sorami-cho, Minato-ku, Nagoya, 455-0847, Japan
Tel.: (81) 523981554
Logistic Services
N.A.I.C.S.: 488510

Hitachi Steel Center Co., Ltd. (1)
1227-1 Kasamatsu Mukoyama, Naka, Ibaraki, 311-0102, Japan
Tel.: (81) 292983211
Sales Range: $100-124.9 Million
Emp.: 300
Metal Products Mfr
N.A.I.C.S.: 332999
Patricia Huppermans *(Gen Mgr)*

INTERNATIONAL MOLD STEEL, INC. (1)
1155 Victory Pl, Hebron, KY 41048
Tel.: (859) 342-6000
Web Site: https://www.imsteel.com
Sales Range: $25-49.9 Million
Emp.: 35
Steel Molding & Forging Services
N.A.I.C.S.: 332111
Paul W. Britton *(Mgr-Natl Sls-Mold Products Div)*

Iwai & Okaya Machinery Co., Ltd. (1)
148-1 Shimoyama Uchikoshi, Nishikamogun, Miyoshi, 470-0213, Aichi, Japan
Tel.: (81) 561341633
Web Site: https://www.iwai-okaya.co.jp
Machinery Maintenance & Mfr
N.A.I.C.S.: 333248
Yasuo Iwai *(Pres)*

Makishima Farm Co., Ltd. (1)
22 Higashihara Isozaki, Matsushima-machi, Miyagi, 981-0212, Miyagi, Japan
Tel.: (81) 227628117
Web Site: https://makishimafarm.com
Tomato Farming Services
N.A.I.C.S.: 111219
Takanori Utsumi *(CEO)*

Miwa Kozai Co., Ltd. (1)
12-24 Fujimi-cho, Naka-ku, Nagoya, 460-0008, Japan
Tel.: (81) 523311616
Metal & Consumer Goods Trading Services
N.A.I.C.S.: 425120

NaITO & Co. Ltd. (1)
2-1-11 Showamachi, Kita-ku, Tokyo, 114-8516, Japan
Tel.: (81) 338008651
Web Site: http://www.naito.net
Sales Range: $150-199.9 Million
Emp.: 340
Machinery & Tool Sales
N.A.I.C.S.: 423830

Naito Vietnam Co., Ltd. (1)
5th Floor Phuong Long Building 506 Nguyen Dinh Chieu Street, Ward 4 District 3, Ho Chi Minh City, Vietnam
Tel.: (84) 2839153971
Web Site: https://www.naito.com.vn
Machine Tools Mfr
N.A.I.C.S.: 333517
Keisuke Harada *(Gen Dir)*

Nakamura Kozai Co., Ltd. (1)
5F Shinkawa City Building 1-25-9 Shinkawa, Chuo-Ku, Tokyo, 104-0033, Japan
Tel.: (81) 335518161
Web Site: https://www.nakashow.co.jp
Emp.: 28
Steel Product & Equipment Distr
N.A.I.C.S.: 423510
Shuichi Sugito *(Pres)*

Nishifu Meat Co., Ltd. (1)
10th floor Asahi Life Insurance Fuchu Building 1-14-1 Fuchu-cho, Fuchu-shi, Tokyo, 183-0055, Japan
Tel.: (81) 423683142
Web Site: https://www.nishifu.co.jp
Sales Range: $25-49.9 Million
Emp.: 13
Imports, Processes & Distributes Fresh & Frozen Chicken Meat Products
N.A.I.C.S.: 311615
Tatsumine Kitada *(Pres)*

OKAYA (CANADA) CO., LTD. (1)
250 Thompsons Dr Unit 8, Cambridge, N1T 2E3, ON, Canada
Tel.: (519) 623-0303
Web Site: http://www.okaya-canada.ca
Emp.: 2
Automotive Distr
N.A.I.C.S.: 423110
Kenichi Watanabe *(Office Mgr)*

OKAYA (THAILAND) CO., LTD. (1)
Asia Centre Bldg 23rd Floor 173/25 South Sathorn Road, Khwaeng Thungmahamek Khet Sathorn, Bangkok, 10120, Thailand
Tel.: (66) 21636333
Automobile Parts Distr
N.A.I.C.S.: 423120

OKAYA SHINNICHI CORPORATION OF AMERICA (1)
300 Crompton St, Charlotte, NC 28273
Tel.: (704) 588-3131
Web Site: http://www.osa-usa.com
Sales Range: $25-49.9 Million
Emp.: 45
Precision Stainless Tube Mfr & Distr
N.A.I.C.S.: 331210

Okaya & Co., India Pvt. Ltd. (1)
Suite 426 Level 4 Rectangle No 1, District Commercial Complex, D-4 Saket, New Delhi, 110017, India
Tel.: (91) 1140514171
Sales Range: $50-74.9 Million
Emp.: 7
Metal & Consumer Goods Trading Services
N.A.I.C.S.: 425120

Okaya (Beijing) Co., Ltd. (1)
Jing Guang Centre Room No 2612A Hu Jia Lou, Chao Yang Qu, 10020, Beijing, China
Tel.: (86) 1065973811
Web Site: http://www.okayausa.com
Sales Range: $50-74,9 Million
Emp.: 10
Metal & Consumer Goods Trading Services
N.A.I.C.S.: 425120

Okaya (Guangzhou) Co., Ltd. (1)
Room 313 Tianan Science and Technology Innovation Building, No 555 North Panyu Avenue Panyu District, Guangzhou, 511400, China
Tel.: (86) 2039993399
Web Site: https://www.okayagz.cn
Sales Range: $25-49.9 Million
Emp.: 30
Metal & Consumer Goods Trading Services
N.A.I.C.S.: 425120
Tsuyuki Keiji *(Gen Mgr)*

Okaya (Korea) Co., Ltd. (1)
Room No 416 Korean Air Terminal Bldg No 159-6 Samsung-Dong, Kangnam-ku, Seoul, 135728, Korea (South)
Tel.: (82) 25518466
Sales Range: $50-74.9 Million
Emp.: 8
Metal & Consumer Goods Trading Services
N.A.I.C.S.: 425120

Okaya (Shanghai) Co., Ltd. (1)
Hang Seng Bank Tower 24F, 1000 Lujiazui Ring Rd, Pudong New Area, Shanghai, China
Tel.: (86) 2168415058
Emp.: 42
Metal & Consumer Goods Trading Services
N.A.I.C.S.: 425120
Nishiguchi Nolikadu *(Gen Mgr)*

Okaya (Taiwan) Co., Ltd. (1)
11th Floor-2 No 87, Song Chiang Road, Taipei, 104, Taiwan
Tel.: (886) 225152733
Sales Range: $25-49.9 Million
Emp.: 15
Metal & Consumer Goods Trading Services
N.A.I.C.S.: 425120

Okaya (Tianjin) Co., Ltd. (1)
The Exchange Tower 1 18th Floor No 1807 Nanjing Road 189, Heping District, Tianjin, 300051, China
Tel.: (86) 2283192050
Sales Range: $25-49.9 Million
Emp.: 21
Metal & Consumer Goods Trading Services
N.A.I.C.S.: 425120
Yamaea Kunihiro *(Mng Dir)*

Okaya (U.S.A.), Inc. (1)
64 W Seegers Rd, Arlington Heights, IL 60005 (100%)
Tel.: (847) 621-5530
Web Site: http://www.okayausa.com
Sales Range: $50-74.9 Million
Emp.: 60
Metals Trading
N.A.I.C.S.: 423510
Nobuo Tsukioka *(Gen Mgr)*

Okaya Australia Pty. Ltd. (1)
Suite 1002 Level 10 80 Mount Street, Sydney, 2060, NSW, Australia
Tel.: (61) 299594177
Web Site: http://www.okaya.co.jp
Sales Range: $50-74.9 Million
Emp.: 2
Metal & Consumer Goods Trading Services
N.A.I.C.S.: 425120
Tokio Shigeishi *(Mng Dir)*

Okaya Building Co., Ltd. (1)
9th Floor Okaya Koki Building 2-4-18, Sakae Naka-ku, Nagoya, 460-0008, Japan
Tel.: (81) 522041701
Sales Range: $50-74.9 Million
Emp.: 3
Real Estate Services
N.A.I.C.S.: 531390

Okaya Business Support Co., Ltd. (1)
7F Green Building 1-16-20 Nishiki, Naka-Ku, Nagoya, 460-0003, Aichi, Japan
Tel.: (81) 522320090
Real Estate Manangement Services
N.A.I.C.S.: 531311

Okaya Consultant Co., Ltd. (1)
6th Floor Okaya Koki Building 2-4-18 Sakae, Naka-Ku, Nagoya, 460-0008, Aichi, Japan
Tel.: (81) 522048491
Management Consulting & Accounting Services
N.A.I.C.S.: 541611

Okaya Do Brasil Comercio Ltda. (1)
Rua Pirapitingui 80-apartment 802-Room E, Liberdade, Sao Paulo, 01508-020, Brazil
Tel.: (55) 114 328 4804
Web Site: https://www.okayadobrasil.com
Import & Export Services
N.A.I.C.S.: 425120

Okaya Eco-Assort Corp. (1)
265-27 Yufutsu, Tomakomai, 059-1372, Hokkaido, Japan
Tel.: (81) 144561800
Web Site: https://www.okaya-oea.co.jp
Emp.: 48
Raw Materials Processing, Treatment & Sales for Steel Production
N.A.I.C.S.: 423510
Shoichi Kawata *(Dir-Rep)*

Okaya Electronics (H.K.) Ltd. (1)
Unit 1906-7 19th Floor FWD Financial Centre 308 Des Voeux Road, Central, China (Hong Kong)
Tel.: (852) 25660077
Electronic Component & Semiconductor Distr
N.A.I.C.S.: 423690

Okaya Electronics (Shenzhen) Ltd. (1)
0929 Tower B East Pacific International Center 7888 Shennan Avenue, Futian District, Shenzhen, 518040, Guangdong, China
Tel.: (86) 75582778615
Electronic Component & Semiconductor Distr
N.A.I.C.S.: 423690

Okaya Electronics Corp. (1)
Prime Shin-Yokohama Bldg 8f 2-3-19 Shin-yokohama, Kohoku-ku, Yokohama, 222-0033, Kanagawa, Japan
Tel.: (81) 454751502
Web Site: https://www.oec.okaya.co.jp
Emp.: 204
Semiconductors, Electric Application Equipment & Software Sales
N.A.I.C.S.: 423690
Osamu Mizuno *(Pres)*

Okaya Europe GmbH (1)
Konigs-Allee 66, Dusseldorf, 40212, Germany
Tel.: (49) 2113004590
Web Site: http://www.okaya.de
Sales Range: $50-74.9 Million
Emp.: 100
Metal & Consumer Goods Trading Services
N.A.I.C.S.: 425120

Okaya Hokkaido Co., Ltd. (1)
266-7 Yufutsu, Tomakomai, 059-1372, Hokkaido, Japan
Tel.: (81) 144563006
Web Site: https://hkd.okaya.co.jp
Sales Range: $50-74.9 Million
Emp.: 16
Metal & Consumer Goods Trading Services
N.A.I.C.S.: 425120
Yasuhiro Nakajima *(Pres)*

Okaya Homes Co., Ltd. (1)
3rd Floor Okaya Koki Building 2-4-18 Sakae, Nagoya, 460-0008, Japan
Tel.: (81) 522048124
Sales Range: $25-49.9 Million
Emp.: 15
Housing Construction & Real Estate Services
N.A.I.C.S.: 236117

Okaya International (H.K.) Ltd. (1)
Unit 2401-24 ING Tower Shun Tak Centre, 168 Connaught Road, Central, China (Hong Kong)
Tel.: (852) 25488227
Sales Range: $25-49.9 Million
Emp.: 22
Metal & Consumer Goods Trading Services
N.A.I.C.S.: 425120
Toshiyuki Akiya *(Pres)*

Okaya International (Malaysia) Sdn. Bhd. (1)
Level 15-06 1 Mont Kiara No 1 Jalan Kiara, Mont Kiara, 50480, Kuala Lumpur, Malaysia
Tel.: (60) 36 411 0726
Metal Product Distr
N.A.I.C.S.: 423510

Okaya Iwai Hokkaido Co., Ltd. (1)
266-7 Yufutsu, Tomakomai, 059-1372, Hok-

AND PRIVATE COMPANIES OKAYA & CO., LTD.

kaido, Japan
Tel.: (81) 144522751
Web Site: https://www.oih.co.jp
Emp.: 20
Machine Tool Designer & Mfr
N.A.I.C.S.: 333517
Koji Sato *(CEO)*

Okaya Kenzai Co., Ltd. (1)
6F Arca Central 1-2-1 Kinshicho, Sumida-ku, Tokyo, 130-0013, Japan
Tel.: (81) 356379373
Web Site: https://www.okaya-kenzai.co.jp
Construction Materials Lease, Repair & Sales
N.A.I.C.S.: 423390
Takeshi Komatsu *(Dir-Rep)*

Okaya Kenzai Tech Construction Co., Ltd. (1)
6F Arca Central 1-2-1 Kinshicho, Sumida, Tokyo, 130-0013, Japan
Tel.: (81) 356377325
Steel Structure Construction Services
N.A.I.C.S.: 238190
Junji Otsuki *(Dir-Rep)*

Okaya Kiden Co., Ltd. (1)
6th Floor Tokai Building 1-16-30 Meiekiminami, Nakamura-ku, Nagoya, 450-0003, Aichi, Japan (100%)
Tel.: (81) 525862577
Web Site: https://www.kiden.okaya.co.jp
Electrical Appliances & Equipment Mfr & Sales
N.A.I.C.S.: 335999

Okaya Kihan Co., Ltd. (1)
2F Okaya Tomifune Logistics Center 4-1 Tomifune-cho, Nakagawa-ku, Nagoya, 454-0823, Aichi, Japan (100%)
Tel.: (81) 523517325
Web Site: https://www.okaya-kihan.co.jp
Machine Tools & Machinery Maintenance & Sales
N.A.I.C.S.: 423510
Takao Kama *(Pres)*

Okaya Kyushu Co., Ltd. (1)
7F 3rd Myojo Building 1-7 Tenjin 4-chome, Tenjin Chuo-ku, Fukuoka, 810-0001, Japan
Tel.: (81) 927813211
Web Site: https://www.okk-okaya.co.jp
Emp.: 40
Logistics Services & Industrial Machinery Sales
N.A.I.C.S.: 488510
Kazuki Uchida *(Chm-Exec)*

Okaya Logistics Co., Ltd. (1)
4-1 Tomifunecho, Nakagawa-ku, Nagoya, 454-0823, Aichi, Japan
Tel.: (81) 523624111
Web Site: https://www.okaya-logi.jp
Logistic Services
N.A.I.C.S.: 488510
Shinichi Kurumiya *(Pres)*

Okaya Mart Co., Ltd. (1)
No 6 Amado 1-28, Koto-ku, Tokyo, 136-0071, Japan
Tel.: (81) 358365588
Web Site: https://www.okaya-mart.jp
Emp.: 130
Construction & Plumbing Equipment Sales
N.A.I.C.S.: 423720
Mitsunori Sakata *(Chm)*

Okaya Mexico S.A. de C.V. (1)
Piso 10 Del Edificio Hotel Hampton Inn Blvd, Lopez Mateos Numero 1717 Col Los Gavilanes, 37270, Leon, Guanajuato, Mexico
Tel.: (52) 477 763 1687
Metal Product Distr
N.A.I.C.S.: 423510

Okaya Seiritsu Engineering Co., Ltd. (1)
1-18-1 Senjumidori-cho, Adachi ku, Tokyo, 120 0044, Japan
Tel.: (81) 368120201
Web Site: https://www.okaya-seiritsu.co.jp
Sales Range: $25-49.9 Million
Emp.: 93
Automatic Controller, Electro Hydraulic Actuator & Automatic Bottle Inspector Designer & Mfr
N.A.I.C.S.: 333248
Toshiyuki Sakamoto *(Pres)*

Okaya Service & Homes Co., Ltd. (1)
3F Okaya Koki Building 2-4-18 Sakae, Naka-Ku, Nagoya, 460-0008, Aichi, Japan
Tel.: (81) 522042782
Real Estate Manangement Services
N.A.I.C.S.: 531311

Okaya Service Co., Ltd. (1)
3th Floor Okaya Koki Building 2-4-18 Sakae, Naka-ku, Nagoya, 460-0008, Japan
Tel.: (81) 522042782
Sales Range: $25-49.9 Million
Emp.: 9
Metal & Consumer Goods Trading Services
N.A.I.C.S.: 425120

Okaya Singapore Pte. Ltd. (1)
20 Seiesee Park Road 02-16 & 17 Teoe Tech Park, Singapore, 117674, Singapore
Tel.: (65) 63230311
Web Site: http://www.okaya.com
Sales Range: $25-49.9 Million
Emp.: 20
Metal & Consumer Goods Trading Services
N.A.I.C.S.: 423510
Cakaya Wava *(Mng Dir)*

Okaya Special Steel Center Co., Ltd. (1)
1-45-1 Hagishima Oguchi-cho, Niwa-gun, Niwa, 480-0124, Aichi, Japan
Tel.: (81) 587952315
Web Site: https://www.kotc.co.jp
Sales Range: $25-49.9 Million
Emp.: 46
Steel Processing Services
N.A.I.C.S.: 423510
Hideto Konishi *(CEO)*

Okaya Steel Co., Ltd. (1)
Tokai Building 5F 1-16-30 Meiekiminami, Nakamura-ku, Nagoya, 450-0003, Aichi, Japan (100%)
Tel.: (81) 525272311
Web Site: https://www.okaya-steel.co.jp
Sales Range: $150-199.9 Million
Iron & Steel Products Sales
N.A.I.C.S.: 423510
Tsukasa Murase *(Pres)*

Okaya Steel Sheet Sales Co., Ltd. (1)
8F Tokai Building 1-16-30 Meiekiminami, Nakamura-ku, Nagoya, 450-0003, Aichi, Japan
Tel.: (81) 528756081
Web Site: https://www.okayauh.co.jp
Sales Range: $25-49.9 Million
Emp.: 15
Metal & Consumer Goods Trading Services
N.A.I.C.S.: 425120
Eiji Ito *(Pres)*

Okaya System Co., Ltd. (1)
6F Okaya Koki Building 2-4-18 Sakae, Naka-ku, Nagoya, 460-0008, Japan
Tel.: (81) 522220718
Web Site: https://www.okaya-system.co.jp
Emp.: 215
Office Computers & Software Sales, Design & Development of Computer Work Systems
N.A.I.C.S.: 334111
Takashi Urushibara *(CEO)*

Okaya Trade Service Co., Ltd. (1)
8th Floor Marunouchi Chuo Building 1-9-1 Marunouchi, Chiyoda-ku, Tokyo, 100-0005, Japan
Tel.: (81) 332140755
Sales Range: $25-49.9 Million
Emp.: 15
Metal & Consumer Goods Trading Services
N.A.I.C.S.: 425120

Okuda Kinzoku Co., Ltd. (1)
19-2 Tamazukuri-Motomachi, Tennoji-ku, Osaka, 543-0014, Japan
Tel.: (81) 729673700
Web Site: https://www.okuda-kinzoku.co.jp
Copper Tube Processing & Sales
N.A.I.C.S.: 423510
Kodai Okuda *(Pres)*

POLAND TOKAI OKAYA MANUFAC-TURING SP. Z O.O. (1)
Ostaszewo 57/G, 87-148, Lysomice, Poland
Tel.: (48) 566524612
Web Site: https://ptom.com.pl
Liquid Crystal Display Television Mfr
N.A.I.C.S.: 334419

PT. OKAYA INDONESIA (1)
Mid Plaza 2 24th Floor Jl Jend Sudirman Kav 10-11, Jakarta, 10220, Indonesia
Tel.: (62) 21 571 9725
Web Site: http://www.okaya.co.id
Emp.: 12
Electronic Components Distr
N.A.I.C.S.: 423690
Honda Yoshitaka *(Pres)*

Rokugo Elemec (Thailand) Co., Ltd. (1)
253 Asoke 12th Floor Sukhumvit21 Road, Klongtoey Nua Wattana, Bangkok, 10110, Thailand
Tel.: (66) 26127380
Metal Product Distr
N.A.I.C.S.: 423510

Rokugo Elemec Co., Ltd. (1)
3-18-11 Shirakabe, Higashi-ku, Nagoya, 461-8560, Japan
Tel.: (81) 529315875
Web Site: https://www.rokugo-g.co.jp
Emp.: 110
Electronic Equipment Distr
N.A.I.C.S.: 423690
Goro Takeda *(Pres)*

Rokugo Service Techno Co., Ltd. (1)
3-18-11 Shirakabe, Higashi-Ku, Nagoya, 461-8560, Aichi, Japan
Tel.: (81) 529315875
Metal Product Distr
N.A.I.C.S.: 423510

Rokugo System Electronics Ind. Co., Ltd. (1)
13-11 Shirakabe 3-chome, Higashi-Ku, Nagoya, 461-0011, Japan
Tel.: (81) 529792265
Web Site: https://rdk.rokugo-g.co.jp
Electric Equipment Mfr
N.A.I.C.S.: 334419
Goro Takeda *(Pres)*

SIAM OKAYA CHEMICAL CO., LTD. (1)
60/18 Moo 3 Tambon Mabyangporn, Amphur, Pluak Daeng, 21140, Rayong, Thailand
Tel.: (66) 388913003
Resin Coloring Compound Distr
N.A.I.C.S.: 424690

SIAM SURIYA CO., LTD. (1)
No 1 Md Tower 15fl Room C3 E Soi Bangna-Trad 25 Kwang Bangna Nua, Khet Bangna, Bangkok, 10260, Thailand
Tel.: (66) 23993623
Plastic Materials Mfr
N.A.I.C.S.: 326199

Shin-Ikeda Co., Ltd. (1)
74-6 Uchitamoto Shimoshimizu, Tsuruoka, 997-0845, Yamagata, Japan
Tel.: (81) 235242111
Steel Product & Equipment Distr
N.A.I.C.S.: 423510

Shin-Kanaya Co., Ltd. (1)
670-1 Fukuhashi, Hoetsu, Niigata, 942-0033, Japan
Tel.: (81) 255438585
Web Site: https://www.kanaya-web.com
Emp.: 29
Metal & Equipment Sales
N.A.I.C.S.: 423510
Tsuyoshi Kanaya *(Pres)*

Shin-Tanigaki Co., Ltd. (1)
1-4-11 Haradanaka, Toyonaka, 561-0807, Osaka, Japan
Tel.: (81) 668553521
Web Site: https://www.tanigaki.co.jp
Emp.: 40
Metal & Consumer Goods Trading Services
N.A.I.C.S.: 425120
Toshihiro Tanigaki *(Proc)*

Shizuokachubu Plastics Molding Co., Ltd. (1)
16-38 Nakayoshida, Suruga-ku, Shizuoka, 422-8001, Japan
Tel.: (81) 542626671
Web Site: https://www.okaya.co.jp
Plastic Molded Products Mfr & Sales
N.A.I.C.S.: 326199

Sorami Steel Service Co., Ltd. (1)
1-11 Sorami-cho Minato-ku, Nagoya, 455-0847, Japan
Tel.: (81) 523981633
Web Site: https://www.sorami-steel.jp
Emp.: 92
Slitting & Shearing Steel Sheets Mfr
N.A.I.C.S.: 332322
Masaji Okumura *(Pres)*

Tetsuso Butsuryu Co., Ltd. (1)
1-1-20 Shiohama, Koutou-ku, Tokyo, 135-0043, Japan
Tel.: (81) 336440161
General Warehousing Services
N.A.I.C.S.: 493190

Tohoku Okaya Co., Ltd. (1)
Sendai Daiichi Life Tower Building 9F 4-6-1 Ichibancho, Aoba-ku, Sendai, 980-0811, Japan
Tel.: (81) 222211387
Web Site: https://www.tok-okaya.com
Metal & Consumer Goods Trading Services
N.A.I.C.S.: 425120

Tokai Okaya Kizai Co., Ltd. (1)
207 Harazakicho 4-chome, Kariya, 448-0039, Aichi, Japan (100%)
Tel.: (81) 566214554
Web Site: https://www.tokai-okaya.co.jp
Sales Range: $25-49.9 Million
Machines, Tools & Precision Components Sales
N.A.I.C.S.: 423510
Takanori Moriya *(Pres)*

Tokai Pressing Co., Ltd. (1)
25 Kobe 9-chome, Yatomi, 490-1405, Aichi, Japan
Tel.: (81) 567522291
Web Site: https://www.tokai-press.co.jp
Emp.: 90
Specialty Machinery Mfr
N.A.I.C.S.: 333248
Hiroki Tanaka *(Pres)*

Tsurumi Kozai Center Co., Ltd. (1)
1-1 Anzen-cho, Tsurumi-ku, Yokohama, 230-0035, Kanagawa, Japan
Tel.: (81) 455055031
Warehouse Rental Services
N.A.I.C.S.: 493110

UNION AUTOPARTS MANUFAC-TURING CO., LTD. (1)
102 Moo 6 Poochaosamingprai Rd Samrongtai, Phra Pradaeng, 10130, Samutprakarn, Thailand
Tel.: (66) 21833872
Web Site: https://www.uam.co.th
Emp.: 1,200
Automobile Parts Mfr
N.A.I.C.S.: 336390

Plant (Domestic):

UNION AUTOPARTS MANUFAC-TURING CO., LTD. - Factory II (2)
51/6 Moo 15 Poochaosamingprai Rd Bangyapreak, Phra Pradaeng, 10130, Samutprakarn, Thailand
Tel.: (66) 722516873
Web Site: http://www.uam.co.th
Automobile Parts Mfr
N.A.I.C.S.: 336390

UNION AUTOPARTS MANUFAC-TURING CO., LTD. - Factory III (2)
60/75 Moo 3 Mabyangporn, Pluak Daeng, 21140, Rayong, Thailand
Tel.: (66) 38 891999
Automobile Parts Mfr
N.A.I.C.S.: 336390

Subsidiary (Non-US):

UPI PHILIPPINES, INC. (2)
Lot 33 Second Street Corner Road Lot No Fpip, Tanauan, Batangas, Philippines
Tel.: (63) 43 405 5459
Sales Range: $25-49.9 Million
Emp.: 92
Automobile Parts Mfr
N.A.I.C.S.: 336390
Yasuyuki Isoda *(Gen Mgr)*

Uam Philippines, Inc. (1)
Lot 33 Second St Corner Road Lot 8, First Philippine Industrial Park, Tanauan, 4232,

OKAYA & CO., LTD.

Okaya & Co., Ltd.—(Continued)
Batangas, Philippines
Tel.: (63) 9399870804
Web Site: https://www.upi.com.ph
Emp.: 185
Auto Parts Mfr
N.A.I.C.S.: 336390

Vina Okaya International Co., Ltd (1)
No 1403 2A-4A Ton Duc Thang Street, District 1, Ho Chi Minh City, Vietnam
Tel.: (84) 8 3823 2457
Sales Range: $50-74.9 Million
Emp.: 6
Industrial Machine Tool Distr
N.A.I.C.S.: 423830

Yanagi Kanzai Inc. (1)
3-1-55 Midoricho, Kasukabe, 344-0063, Saitama, Japan (100%)
Tel.: (81) 487356225
Web Site: https://www.yanagikanzai.co.jp
Emp.: 37
Piping Materials Distr
N.A.I.C.S.: 423830

OKAYA ELECTRIC INDUSTRIES CO., LTD.
6-16-9 Todoroki, Setagaya-ku, Tokyo, 158-8543, Japan
Tel.: (81) 345447000
Web Site:
https://www.okayaelec.co.jp
Year Founded: 1939
6926—(TKS)
Rev.: $94,675,030
Assets: $112,759,990
Liabilities: $53,025,420
Net Worth: $59,734,570
Earnings: $793,200
Emp.: 1,115
Fiscal Year-end: 03/31/24
Electrical Equipment Mfr & Whslr
N.A.I.C.S.: 335999
Naoto Yamada (Chm & Pres)

Subsidiaries:

OKAYA (HONG KONG) LIMITED (1)
Rm 908 9/F Empire Centre 68 Mody Rd Tsim Sha Tsui, Kowloon, China (Hong Kong)
Tel.: (852) 27440628
Electrical Equipment Distr
N.A.I.C.S.: 423610

Plant (Non-US):

OKAYA (HONG KONG) LIMITED - DONGGUAN DONGKENG OKAYA ELECTRONIC FACTORY (2)
No 11 Shuixiang Rd, Huangwu Dongkeng Town, Dongguan, 523447, Guangdong, China
Tel.: (86) 76983384416
Electric Equipment Mfr
N.A.I.C.S.: 335999

OKAYA ELECTRIC (THAILAND) CO., LTD. (1)
319 Chamchuri Square Bldg Rm 2011 20F Phayathai Rd, Pathumwan Dist, Bangkok, 10330, Thailand
Tel.: (66) 21605230
Electrical Equipment Distr
N.A.I.C.S.: 423610

OKAYA ELECTRIC SINGAPORE PTE LTD. (1)
175A Bencoolen St 10-10 Burlington Square, Singapore, 189650, Singapore
Tel.: (65) 67486063
Electrical Equipment Distr
N.A.I.C.S.: 423610

OKAYA LANKA (PVT) LTD. (1)
Spur Rd 4 Phase I E P Z, Katunayake 1, 11450, Negombo, Sri Lanka
Tel.: (94) 112252957
Electrical Equipment Distr
N.A.I.C.S.: 423610

Okaya Electric America, Inc. (1)
52 Marks Rd Ste 1, Valparaiso, IN 46383
Tel.: (219) 477-4488

Web Site: https://www.okaya.com
Emp.: 14
Electrical Equipment Distr
N.A.I.C.S.: 423610
Aman Alagh (Mgr-Sls)

OKAYAMA ELECTRONIC DATA PROCESSING SYSTEM CENTER CO., LTD.
3 23 18 Omote-cho, Okayama, 700 0822, Japan
Tel.: (81) 862271121 JP
Web Site: http://www.oec-o.co.jp
Year Founded: 1969
Sales Range: $50-74.9 Million
Emp.: 337
Data Processing; Computer Equipment Whslr
N.A.I.C.S.: 518210

OKAYAMA PAPER INDUSTRIES CO., LTD.
1-4-34 Hamano, Minami-ku, Okayama, 700-0845, Japan
Tel.: (81) 862621101
Web Site:
https://www.okayamaseishi.co.jp
Year Founded: 1907
38920—(TKS)
Sales Range: $75-99.9 Million
Emp.: 182
Paperboard Mfr
N.A.I.C.S.: 322130
Kotaro Tsugawa (Chm, Pres & CEO)

OKAYAMAKEN FREIGHT TRANSPORTATION CO., LTD.
4-31 Seishin-cho, Kita-ku, Okayama, 700-0027, Japan
Tel.: (81) 862522111
Web Site: https://www.okaken.co.jp
Year Founded: 1943
9063—(TKS)
Rev.: $249,150,730
Assets: $306,869,250
Liabilities: $158,018,660
Net Worth: $148,850,590
Earnings: $16,491,950
Fiscal Year-end: 03/31/24
Freight Transportation Services
N.A.I.C.S.: 484110
Toshio Endo (Board of Directors & Chm)

OKE PRECISION CUTTING TOOLS CO., LTD.
Chuangye Rd, Chuangye Park for SMEs Yanling County, Zhuzhou, Hunan, China
Tel.: (86) 73127577393
Web Site: https://www.oke-carbide.com.cn
Year Founded: 1996
688308—(SHG)
Rev.: $148,167,307
Assets: $445,425,641
Liabilities: $98,982,014
Net Worth: $346,443,627
Earnings: $33,988,664
Fiscal Year-end: 12/31/22
Cutting Tool Mfr
N.A.I.C.S.: 333515
Meihe Yuan (Chm)

OKEA ASA
Kongens gate 8, 7011, Trondheim, Norway
Tel.: (47) 73525222 NO
Web Site: https://www.okea.no
Year Founded: 2015
3SX—(DEU)
Rev.: $614,504,803
Assets: $1,442,927,028
Liabilities: $1,250,978,940
Net Worth: $191,948,088
Earnings: $61,851,838

Emp.: 383
Fiscal Year-end: 12/31/22
Oil & Gas Exploration Services
N.A.I.C.S.: 213112
Erik Haugane (CEO)

OKEANIS ECO TANKERS CORP.
Ethnarchou Makariou av and 2 D Falireos str N Faliro, 185 47, Palaion Faliron, 185 47, Greece
Tel.: (30) 2104804200
Web Site:
https://www.okeanisecotankers.com
Year Founded: 2018
ECO—(NYSE)
Rev.: $270,972,421
Assets: $1,183,355,242
Liabilities: $761,111,981
Net Worth: $422,243,261
Earnings: $84,559,995
Emp.: 5
Fiscal Year-end: 12/31/22
Freight Forwarding & Logistics Consulting Services
N.A.I.C.S.: 488510

OKH GLOBAL LTD.
171 Chin Swee Road 0201 CES Centre, Singapore, 387383, Singapore
Tel.: (65) 63450544
Web Site: https://www.okh.com.sg
S3N—(SES)
Rev.: $10,765,469
Assets: $93,573,916
Liabilities: $52,333,457
Net Worth: $41,240,459
Earnings: $1,865,135
Emp.: 17
Fiscal Year-end: 06/30/23
Property Development & Real Estate Services
N.A.I.C.S.: 236220
Wai Han Lock (CEO)

OKI ELECTRIC INDUSTRY CO., LTD.
1-7-12 Toranomon, Minato-ku, Tokyo, 105-8460, Japan
Tel.: (81) 335013111
Web Site: https://www.oki.com
Year Founded: 1881
OKI—(DEU)
Rev.: $2,646,418,320
Assets: $2,799,347,250
Liabilities: $2,087,516,820
Net Worth: $711,830,430
Earnings: ($20,076,000)
Emp.: 14,452
Fiscal Year-end: 03/31/23
Telecommunication Systems, Information Systems & Electronic Devices Mfr & Sales
N.A.I.C.S.: 517810
Shinya Kamagami (Chm)

Subsidiaries:

Business Logistics (Thailand) Co., Ltd. (1)
1168/32 Lumpini Tower 16th Fl Rama IV Road Tungmahamek, Sathon, Bangkok, 10120, Thailand
Tel.: (66) 2 285 5998
Web Site: http://www.blt.th.com
Sales Range: $10-24.9 Million
Emp.: 43
Packaging Services
N.A.I.C.S.: 561910
Masanori Wada (Pres)

Japan Business Operations Co., Ltd. (1)
Lucid Square Toyocho 2-7-5 Minamisuna 5th floor, Koto-ku, Tokyo, 136-0076, Japan
Tel.: (81) 3 5621 3171
Web Site: http://www.jbo.co.jp

INTERNATIONAL PUBLIC

Automatic Teller Machine Operational Status Monitoring Services
N.A.I.C.S.: 541512

Kyushu OKI Telecommunication Systems (1)
3-2-3 Aioimachi, Hakata-ku, Fukuoka, 812-0885, Japan
Tel.: (81) 92 584 5111
Web Site: http://www.oki.com
Telecommunication Devices Mfr & Whslr
N.A.I.C.S.: 334290

Marubeni OKI Network Solutions Inc (1)
1-16-8 Chuo Oki System Center, Warabi, 335-0004, Saitama, Japan
Tel.: (81) 484207011
Network Systems Integration Services
N.A.I.C.S.: 541512

Nagano Oki Electric Co., Ltd. (1)
965 Minori, Komoro, 384-0084, Nagano, Japan (75%)
Tel.: (81) 267221881
Web Site: http://www.naganooki.co.jp
Sales Range: $100-124.9 Million
Emp.: 146
Wire Harnessing; Exchange Parts
N.A.I.C.S.: 332618

Nikko Denki Seisakusho Co., Ltd. (1)
3-12-15 Chuo, Warabi, 335, Saitama, Japan (22%)
Tel.: (81) 4 8431 4711
Sales Range: $25-49.9 Million
Emp.: 94
Switchboards; Terminal Blocks; Distribution Boxes; Exchange Parts
N.A.I.C.S.: 335313

OKI Customer Adtech Co., Ltd. (1)
Dai-ichi Biru 2-7-23 Kiba, Koto-ku, Tokyo, 135-0042, Japan
Tel.: (81) 356211311
Web Site: http://www.oca.co.jp
Sales Range: $400-449.9 Million
Emp.: 2,500
Telecommunication System Installation Services
N.A.I.C.S.: 517810
Seiji Mouri (Pres)

OKI Electric Cable Service (1)
2-10-1 Osachigosho, Okaya, 394-0082, Nagano, Japan
Tel.: (81) 266 27 0433
Electric Cable Recycling & Packaging Services
N.A.I.C.S.: 562920

OKI Electric Cable Wire Harness (1)
3344-1 Sakaliyoku, Isesaki, 370-0105, Gunma, Japan
Tel.: (81) 270767865
Web Site: http://www.oki.com
Wire & Cable Processing Services
N.A.I.C.S.: 238210

OKI Networks Co., Ltd. (1)
10-16 Shibaura 4-chome, Minato-ku, Tokyo, 108-8551, Japan
Tel.: (81) 3 3451 9071
Telecommunications Equipment Mfr
N.A.I.C.S.: 334290

OKI Precision (Thailand) Co Ltd (1)
Northern Region Industrial Estate 89/3 Moo 4 Tambol Banklang, Amphur Muang, Lamphun, 51000, Thailand
Tel.: (66) 53554605
Sales Range: $50-74.9 Million
Emp.: 200
Print Heads Mfr & Whslr
N.A.I.C.S.: 334118

OKI Printed Circuits Co., Ltd. (1)
1 Fukudacho, Joetsu, 942-0032, Niigata, Japan
Tel.: (81) 25 544 5300
Web Site: http://www.oki-printed.co.jp
Sales Range: $125-149.9 Million
Emp.: 260
Printed Circuit Board Mfr & Whslr
N.A.I.C.S.: 334412
Masahiko Morioka (Pres)

OKI Proserve Co., Ltd. (1)
4-10-16 Shibaura, Minato-ku, Tokyo, 108-

AND PRIVATE COMPANIES

8551, Japan
Tel.: (81) 356358292
Web Site: https://www.oki-ops.jp
Business Management Consulting Services
N.A.I.C.S.: 561499

OKI Sistem ve Yazici Cozumleri Ticaret Ltd Sti (1)
Harman Sok Duran Is Merkezi No 4 Kat 6, 34394, Istanbul, Turkiye
Tel.: (90) 212 279 2393
Web Site: http://www.oki.com.tr
Emp.: 25
Printers & Faxes Whslr
N.A.I.C.S.: 423430

OKI Software Expert Service (1)
1-16-8 Chuou Warabi, Saitama, 335-8510, Japan
Tel.: (81) 48 420 5290
Web Site: http://www.oki.com
Computer Software Consulting Services
N.A.I.C.S.: 541512

OKI Systems (Rus) (1)
14 Sadovnicheskaya Street 2 building, 115035, Moscow, Russia
Tel.: (7) 4952586065
Printers & Faxes Whslr
N.A.I.C.S.: 423430

OKI Systems Korea Co., Ltd. (1)
11F Daeyun Blue Tower 1338-11 Seochodong, Seocho-gu, Seoul, Korea (South)
Tel.: (82) 25625211
Web Site: http://www.okiprinting.co.kr
Computer Printer Distr
N.A.I.C.S.: 423430

Oki Communication Systems Co., Ltd. (1)
1 Kamiyamaguchi, Tokorozawa, 359-1153, Saitama, Japan **(100%)**
Tel.: (81) 4 2922 0211
Web Site: http://www.o-cms.co.jp
Communication Equipment Mfr
N.A.I.C.S.: 334290
Fumio Goto *(Pres & Dir)*

Oki Comtec Co., Ltd. (1)
1-16-8 Central OKI System Center 5F, Warabi, 335-8510, Saitama, Japan
Tel.: (81) 484207141
Web Site: https://www.ocom.co.jp
Telecommunication Engineering Services
N.A.I.C.S.: 541330

Oki Consulting Solutions Co., Ltd. (1)
4-11-15 Shibaura, Minato-ku, Tokyo, 108-8551, Japan
Tel.: (81) 354456015
Computer Software Consulting Services
N.A.I.C.S.: 541512

Oki Data (Singapore) Pte. Ltd. (1)
438A Alexandra Road 02-11/12 Lobby 3 Alexandra Technopark, Singapore, 119967, Singapore
Tel.: (65) 62213722
Web Site: http://www.oki.com
Emp.: 17
Printing & Office Equipment Sales & Support Services
N.A.I.C.S.: 423430

Oki Data Americas, Inc. (1)
2000 Bishops Gate Blvd, Mount Laurel, NJ 08054-4620
Tel.: (856) 235-2600
Web Site: http://www.okidata.com
Rev.: $30,000,000
Emp.: 600
Printing & Imaging Equipment Mfr & Whslr
N.A.I.C.S.: 333248
Akio Samata *(CFO & Exec VP)*

Subsidiary (Non-US):

Oki Data de Mexico, S.A. de C.V. (2)
Mariano Escobedo 748 Piso 8 Colonia Nueva Anzures, 11590, Mexico, Mexico
Tel.: (52) 5552638780
Web Site: http://www.oki.com
Sales Range: $50-74.9 Million
Emp.: 55
Printing & Imaging Equipment Sales & Support Services
N.A.I.C.S.: 423430

Oki Data do Brasil, Ltda. (2)
Av Alfredo Egidio de Souza Aranha, 100 Bloco C 4 andar, Sao Paulo, 04726-170, Brazil
Tel.: (55) 1134443500
Web Site: http://www.okidata.com
Printing & Imaging Equipment Mfr & Whslr
N.A.I.C.S.: 333248
Sergio Horikawa *(Deputy Pres)*

Oki Data Dalian Co., Ltd. (1)
Room 301B 15 NO 23 Soft Park East Road, Dalian, 116023, China
Tel.: (86) 411 8475 6680
Web Site: http://www.oki.com
Computer Software Development Services
N.A.I.C.S.: 541511

Oki Data Manufacturing (Thailand) Co., Ltd. (1)
Rojana Industrial Park 1/39 Moo 5 Tambol Kanham Amphur U-Thai, Ayutthaya, 13210, Thailand
Tel.: (66) 35330943
Web Site: http://www.oki.com
Printer Mfr
N.A.I.C.S.: 334419

Oki Electric Cable Co., Ltd. (1)
2 12 8 Shimokodanaka, Nakahara-ku, Kawasaki, 211-8585, Kanagawa, Japan **(86.75%)**
Tel.: (81) 447544369
Web Site: http://www.okidensen.co.jp
Sales Range: $125-149.9 Million
Emp.: 150
Mfr & Sales of Cables, Wires, Connectors & Printed Circuit Boards
N.A.I.C.S.: 334412

Oki Electric Technology (Kunshan) Co., Ltd. (1)
Kunshan Hi-tech Industrial Park Yucheng Road, Kunshan, 215300, Jiangsu, China
Tel.: (86) 512 5775 9068
Web Site: http://www.oki.com
Keyboard Mfr & Whslr
N.A.I.C.S.: 334118

Oki Engineering Co., Ltd. (1)
3-20-16 Hikawadai, Nerima-ku, Tokyo, 179-0084, Japan
Tel.: (81) 35 920 2300
Web Site: https://www.oeg.co.jp
Sales Range: $25-49.9 Million
Emp.: 150
Environmental Engineering Services
N.A.I.C.S.: 541330
Yasunori Shibata *(Pres & CEO)*

Oki Europe Ltd. (1)
Blays House Wick Road, Egham, TW20 0HJ, United Kingdom **(100%)**
Tel.: (44) 1784274300
Web Site: http://www.oki.com
Sales Range: $125-149.9 Million
Emp.: 500
Mfr of Printers
N.A.I.C.S.: 423430
Shigeru Ogasawara *(VP-Fin)*

Subsidiary (Non-US):

Oki Europe Ltd. - Spain (2)
Avenida de Bruselas 15 2, Alcobendas, 28108, Madrid, Spain
Tel.: (34) 910470449
Web Site: http://www.oki.com
Printers & Facsimile Products Distr
N.A.I.C.S.: 423430
Carlos Sousa *(Dir Gen)*

Oki Systems (Deutschland) GmbH (2)
Hansaalee 187, D-40549, Dusseldorf, Germany **(100%)**
Tel.: (49) 021152660
Web Site: http://www.okiprintingsolutions.de
Marketing of Printers & Facsimile Products
N.A.I.C.S.: 423430

Oki Systems (Holland) b.v. (2)
Neptunusstraat 29, 2132 JA, Hoofddorp, Netherlands
Tel.: (31) 235563740
Web Site: http://www.oki.nl
Sales Range: $25-49.9 Million
Emp.: 10
Printers & Faxes Marketing
N.A.I.C.S.: 423430

Ervin Bader *(Mng Dir)*

Oki Systems (Ireland) Ltd. (2)
A7 Calmount Park Ballymount, Dublin, 12, Ireland **(100%)**
Tel.: (353) 014049590
Web Site: http://www.oki.ie
Rev.: $3,567,000
Emp.: 10
Marketing of Printers & Facsimile Products
N.A.I.C.S.: 423430
Martin Deignan *(Dir-Sls & Mktg)*

Oki Systems (Italia) S.p.A. (2)
Centro Direzionale Milanofiori Strada 4 Palazzo A10, Assago, 20090, Milan, Italy
Tel.: (39) 02900261
Web Site: http://www.oki.com
Emp.: 35
Marketing of Printers & Facsimile Products
N.A.I.C.S.: 423430

Oki Systems (Norway) A/S (2)
Tevlingveiem 33, PO Box 174, 1081, Oslo, Norway **(100%)**
Tel.: (47) 63893600
Web Site: http://www.oki.no
Rev.: $12,286,000
Emp.: 10
Marketer of Printers & Facsimile Products
N.A.I.C.S.: 423430
Romar Hoff *(Mgr-Sls)*

Oki Systems (Sweden) AB (2)
Box 1193, 164 26, Kista, Sweden
Tel.: (46) 86343700
Web Site: http://www.oki.com
Emp.: 20
Marketing of Printers & Facsimile Products
N.A.I.C.S.: 423430

Oki Hong Kong Limited (1)
Suite 1909 Tower 3 China Hong Kong City 33 Canton Road, Tsim Tsa Tsui, Kowloon, China (Hong Kong)
Tel.: (852) 23177151
Web Site: http://www.oki.com
Emp.: 21
Financial Investment Management Services
N.A.I.C.S.: 523999

Oki Information Systems Co., Ltd. (1)
3-1 Futaba-machi, Takasaki, 370-8585, Gunma, Japan
Tel.: (81) 27 325 1525
Web Site: http://www.okijoho.co.jp
Computer Software Development Services
N.A.I.C.S.: 541511

Oki Powertech Hong Kong Co., Ltd. (1)
Suite 1909 19/F Tower 3 China Hong Kong City 33 Canton Road, Tsim Tsa Tsui, Kowloon, China (Hong Kong)
Tel.: (852) 2148 7333
Electronic Component Procurement Services
N.A.I.C.S.: 561499

Oki Seatec Co., Ltd. (1)
537-5 Uchiuramito, Numazu, 410-0223, Shizuoka, Japan
Tel.: (81) 55 946 1111
Web Site: http://www.seatec.jp
Marine Engineering Services
N.A.I.C.S.: 541330

Oki Systems (Czech and Slovak), s.r.o. (1)
Futurama Business Park-Sokolovska 651/136A, 186 00, Prague, Czech Republic
Tel.: (420) 224890158
Web Site: http://www.czech.oki.com
Sales Range: $25-49.9 Million
Emp.: 15
Printer Whslr
N.A.I.C.S.: 423430

Oki Systems (Hong Kong) Ltd (1)
Suite 1908 Tower 3 China Hong Kong City 33 Canton Road, Tsim Tsa Tsui, Kowloon, China (Hong Kong)
Tel.: (852) 3543 9200
Web Site:
   http://www.okiprintingsolutions.com.hk
Printers & Fax Machine Distr
N.A.I.C.S.: 423430

Oki Systems (Magyarorszag) Kft. (1)
Vaci ut 76, Budapest, 1133, Hungary

Tel.: (36) 18148000
Web Site: http://www.okihu.hu
Sales Range: $50-74.9 Million
Emp.: 7
Printers & Fax Machine Whslr
N.A.I.C.S.: 423430
Ujlaki Andrea *(Mgr-Mktg)*

Oki Trading (Beijing) Co., Ltd. (1)
22nd Floor Tower B Global Trade Center 36th North 3rd Ring East Road, Dongcheng District, Beijing, 100013, China
Tel.: (86) 10 5825 7100
Web Site: http://www.okidata.com.cn
Printer Whslr
N.A.I.C.S.: 423430

Oki Vietnam Company Limited (1)
P-1 4 Factory Lot P-1 Trang Due Industrial Park a part of Dinh Vu, Cat Hai Economic Zone An Hoa Commune An Duong District, Haiphong, Vietnam
Tel.: (84) 225 359 7770
Automatic Teller Machine Mfr
N.A.I.C.S.: 334118

Oki Workwel Co., Ltd. (1)
4-11-17 Shibaura, Minato-ku, Tokyo, 108-8551, Japan
Tel.: (81) 3 5445 6805
Web Site: http://www.okiworkwel.co.jp
Emp.: 87
Information Technology Consulting Services
N.A.I.C.S.: 541512

Shizuoka Oki Electric Co., Ltd. (1)
681-1 Ozuwa, Numazu, 410-0873, Shizuoka, Japan **(100%)**
Tel.: (81) 559232381
Web Site: http://www.s-oki.co.jp
Sales Range: $50-74.9 Million
Emp.: 174
Mfr of Telecommunications Equipment, Control Equipment; Measuring Equipment & Acoustic Equipment
N.A.I.C.S.: 334290

Taiko Electric Work, Ltd. (1)
6 10 13 Nakanobe, Shinagawa Ku, Tokyo, 142 8639, Japan **(20%)**
Tel.: (81) 337889011
Web Site: http://www.taiko-ew.co.jp
Sales Range: $200-249.9 Million
Emp.: 600
Mfr of PABX & Key Telephone Systems
N.A.I.C.S.: 334210

Toho Electronics, Inc. (1)
1-13-21 Tanashioda, Chuo-ku, Sagamihara, 252-0245, Kanagawa, Japan **(100%)**
Tel.: (81) 42 777 3311
Web Site: https://www.toho-inc.co.jp
Emp.: 190
Mfr of Transmission Equipment & Parts
N.A.I.C.S.: 334418
Satoru Kawamoto *(CEO)*

Yamako Electric Manufacture Co., Ltd. (1)
4-3-3 Higashishinagawa, Shinagawu-ku, Tokyo, 140, Japan **(22%)**
Tel.: (81) 3 3474 2511
Sales Range: $50-74.9 Million
Emp.: 103
Steel Structures for Switchboards
N.A.I.C.S.: 335313

OKINAWA CELLULAR TELEPHONE COMPANY

1-2-1 Matsuyama Naha City, Okinawa, 900-8540, Japan
Tel.: (81) 988691001
Web Site: https://okinawa-cellular.jp
Year Founded: 1991
9436—(TKS)
Rev.: $515,513,900
Assets: $763,937,530
Liabilities: $119,588,120
Net Worth: $644,349,410
Earnings: $80,172,690
Fiscal Year-end: 03/31/24
Telecommunications Resellers
N.A.I.C.S.: 517121
Hiroki Kuniyoshi *(Mng Exec Officer, Exec Officer & Dir)*

OKINAWA COCA-COLA BOT-

OKINAWA COCA-COLA BOT

OKINAWA COCA-COLA BOT—(CONTINUED)

TLING CO., LTD.
5-14-1 Iso, Urasoe, 901-2555, Okinawa, Japan
Tel.: (81) 98 877 5255   JP
Web Site:
  http://www.okinawa.ccbc.co.jp
Year Founded: 1968
Emp.: 271
Soft Drinks Mfr
N.A.I.C.S.: 312111
Takahashi Toshio *(Pres & CEO)*

OKINAWA FINANCIAL GROUP, INC.
3-10-1 Kumoji, Naha, Okinawa, 900-0015, Japan
Tel.: (81) 988641354
Web Site:
  https://www.okinawafg.co.jp
Year Founded: 2021
7350—(FKA)
Rev.: $354,117,530
Assets: $19,393,217,810
Liabilities: $18,355,976,610
Net Worth: $1,037,241,200
Earnings: $41,391,820
Fiscal Year-end: 03/31/24
Investment Management Service
N.A.I.C.S.: 523999
Yoshiaki Tamaki *(Chm)*

Subsidiaries:

Future Okinawa Co., Ltd. (1)
Inside Okinawa Innovation Lab 3-10-1 Kumoji, Naha, 900-0015, Okinawa, Japan
Tel.: (81) 988600960
Web Site: https://www.big-advance.site
Emp.: 18
Channel Development & Consulting Services
N.A.I.C.S.: 541618

OKINS ELECTRONICS CO., LTD.
501 13 OjeonGongup-gil, Uiwang, 16072, Gyeonggi, Korea (South)
Tel.: (82) 314675580
Web Site: https://okinsglobal.com
Year Founded: 1998
080580—(KRS)
Rev.: $49,223,376
Assets: $63,323,087
Liabilities: $38,032,391
Net Worth: $25,290,696
Earnings: $2,307,494
Emp.: 146
Fiscal Year-end: 12/31/22
Semiconductor Electronic Components Mfr
N.A.I.C.S.: 334419
Jun Jin Kook *(CEO)*

Subsidiaries:

Neverg Co., Ltd. (1)
2-9-16 Casa Asakawa 301 Minamiyukigaya, Ohta-ku, Tokyo, Japan
Tel.: (81)-364257315
Electronic Component Semiconductor Distr
N.A.I.C.S.: 423690

New Intelligence Co., Ltd. (1)
Tsu Yu Building 5F-2 NO 67 Tsu Yu Road, Hsinchu, Taiwan
Tel.: (886) 35346339
Electronic Component Semiconductor Distr
N.A.I.C.S.: 423690

OKins USA INC. (1)
3003 N 1st St Ste 333, San Jose, CA 95134
Tel.: (408) 232-5480
Electronic Component Semiconductor Distr
N.A.I.C.S.: 423690

Okins Electronics Co., Ltd. - Songsan Factory (1)
San Sin Samjon-ri Songsan-myeon, Hwaseong, Gyeonggi-do, Korea (South)
Tel.: (82) 313578371

Electronic Component Semiconductor Distr
N.A.I.C.S.: 423690

ZenVoce Technology Pte Ltd (1)
23D Cadena de Amor St Bahayang Pagasa, Maysan, Valenzuela, 1440, Philippines
Tel.: (63) 9228172410
Electronic Component Semiconductor Distr
N.A.I.C.S.: 423690

OKK CORPORATION
8-10d Kita-itami, Itami, 664-0831, Hyogo, Japan
Tel.: (81) 72 782 5121
Web Site: http://www.okkcorp.com
Year Founded: 1915
6205—(TKS)
Rev.: $133,496,880
Assets: $317,349,120
Liabilities: $191,557,520
Net Worth: $125,791,600
Earnings: ($12,622,720)
Fiscal Year-end: 03/31/22
Machinery Tool Mfr & Whlsr
N.A.I.C.S.: 333517
Yoshitsugu Miyajima *(Pres)*

Subsidiaries:

OKK (Shanghai) Co., Ltd. (1)
Room 2506 2201 Yan An Road W, Changning District, Shanghai, 200336, China
Tel.: (86) 2162700930
Web Site: http://www.okk.com.cn
Machine Tool Distr
N.A.I.C.S.: 423830

OKK Europe GmbH (1)
Hansemannstr 33, 41468, Neuss, Germany
Tel.: (49) 213 129 8680
Web Site: https://www.okkeurope.com
Machine Tool Distr
N.A.I.C.S.: 423830

OKK USA Corporation (1)
100 Regency Dr, Glendale Heights, IL 60139
Tel.: (630) 924-9000
Web Site: https://okkcorp.com
Machine Tool Distr
N.A.I.C.S.: 423830
Takahiro Kawano *(Pres)*

PT. OKK INDONESIA (1)
Ruko Podium Mataram Jl Mataram Blok B No 22 Cibatu Cikarang Selatan, Bekasi, 17530, Jawa Barat, Indonesia
Tel.: (62) 2189911214
Machine Tool Distr
N.A.I.C.S.: 423830

Thai OKK Machinery Co., Ltd. (1)
36/49 Moo 7 Suksawut Rd Bangjak, Phra Pradaeng, 10130, Samutprakarn, Thailand
Tel.: (66) 28177027
Web Site: http://www.okkth.com
Emp.: 66
Machine Tool Distr
N.A.I.C.S.: 423830

OKMETIC OYJ
Piitie 2, Koivuhaka, 01510, Vantaa, Finland
Tel.: (358) 9502800
Web Site: http://www.okmetic.com
Sales Range: $75-99.9 Million
Emp.: 387
Semiconductor Components Mfr
N.A.I.C.S.: 334413
Markus Virtanen *(Sr VP-HR & Quality)*

Subsidiaries:

Okmetic Inc. (1)
307 S Jupiter Rd Ste 210, Allen, TX 75002
Tel.: (972) 747-8600
Web Site: http://www.okmetic.com
Sales Range: $25-49.9 Million
Emp.: 45
Semiconductor Component Whlsr
N.A.I.C.S.: 423690

Okmetic K.K. (1)
Sunrise Mita 8F 3-16-12, Shiba Minato-ku, Tokyo, 105-0014, Japan (100%)

Tel.: (81) 337981400
Web Site: http://www.okmetic.com
Semiconductor & Related Device Mfr
N.A.I.C.S.: 334413
Sheynsuke Yoshi *(Pres)*

Okmetic Limited (1)
Level 3A Causeway Corner 18 Percival Street, Causeway Bay, China (Hong Kong)
Tel.: (852) 3656 7858
Semiconductor Product Whlsr
N.A.I.C.S.: 423690

OKOMU OIL PALM PLC
Okomu-Udo Ovia South West LGA, PO Box 1449, Benin City, Nigeria
Tel.: (234) 8060361068
Web Site:
  https://www.okomunigeria.com
Year Founded: 1976
OKOMUOIL—(NIGE)
Rev.: $43,911,297
Assets: $53,663,084
Liabilities: $28,471,287
Net Worth: $25,191,797
Earnings: $12,014,009
Emp.: 390
Fiscal Year-end: 12/31/22
Oil Palm Mfr
N.A.I.C.S.: 311225
Gbenga Oyebode Okomu *(Chm)*

OKONG CORPORATION
341 Hambakmoe-ro, Namdong-gu, Incheon, 405-806, Korea (South)
Tel.: (82) 328225050
Web Site: https://www.okong.com
Year Founded: 1962
045060—(KRS)
Rev.: $130,714,878
Assets: $104,907,529
Liabilities: $25,283,030
Net Worth: $79,624,499
Earnings: $5,786,236
Emp.: 150
Fiscal Year-end: 12/31/22
Adhesive Mfr
N.A.I.C.S.: 325520
Kim Yoon Jung *(CEO)*

Subsidiaries:

Okong TS Co., Ltd. (1)
341 Hambakmoe-ro, Namdong-gu, Incheon, 21630, Korea (South)
Tel.: (82) 328102030
Adhesive Product Distr
N.A.I.C.S.: 424690

OKOV A.D.
Filipa Visnjica 2A, Novi Sad, Serbia
Tel.: (381) 21 527 787
Year Founded: 1958
Sales Range: Less than $1 Million
Emp.: 9
Metal Products Mfr
N.A.I.C.S.: 331110

OKOWORLD AG
Itterpark 1, 40724, Hilden, Germany
Tel.: (49) 21039290
Web Site: http://www.oekoworld.com
Year Founded: 1975
VVV3—(MUN)
Rev.: $70,184,055
Assets: $175,239,362
Liabilities: $18,522,939
Net Worth: $156,716,424
Earnings: $23,810,476
Emp.: 64
Fiscal Year-end: 12/31/23
Financial Investment Services
N.A.I.C.S.: 523940

OKP HOLDINGS LIMITED
No 30 Tagore Lane, Singapore, 787484, Singapore
Tel.: (65) 64567667
Web Site: https://www.okph.com
Year Founded: 2002

INTERNATIONAL PUBLIC

5CF—(SES)
Rev.: $121,481,689
Assets: $196,527,798
Liabilities: $68,176,196
Net Worth: $128,351,603
Earnings: $35,938,185
Emp.: 871
Fiscal Year-end: 12/31/23
Civil Engineering Services
N.A.I.C.S.: 541330
Daniel Lay Huat Or *(Exec Dir)*

OKUMA CORPORATION
Oguchi-cho Niwa-gun, Nagoya, 480-0193, Aichi, Japan
Tel.: (81) 587957825   JP
Web Site: https://www.okuma.co.jp
Year Founded: 1898
6103—(NGO)
Rev.: $1,506,401,957
Assets: $1,967,452,373
Liabilities: $395,956,282
Net Worth: $1,571,496,091
Earnings: $129,256,654
Emp.: 4,012
Fiscal Year-end: 03/31/24
Machining Centers, Lathes & Grinders & Industrial Machinery Mfr
N.A.I.C.S.: 333517
Atsushi Ieki *(Pres)*

Subsidiaries:

BYJC-Okuma (Beijing) Machine Tool Corporation (1)
16 Shuanghe Dajie Linhe Industrial Development Zone, Shunyi District, Beijing, 101300, China
Tel.: (86) 1089498551
Web Site: http://www.okuma-byjc.com
Sales Range: $125-149.9 Million
Emp.: 300
Industrial Machinery Mfr & Distr
N.A.I.C.S.: 333248

Nippon Seiki Shokai Co., Ltd. (1)
800 Nagata 1 Komaki, Tomakomai, 485-0825, Aichi, Japan
Tel.: (81) 568733557
Web Site: http://www.nss-co.co.jp
Emp.: 60
Metal Cutting Machinery Distr
N.A.I.C.S.: 423830

OTR Makina Sanayi ve Ticaret Ltd Sti. (1)
Halkali Merkez Mah Basin Ekspres Cad No 5/B Ayaz Plaza Kat, Kucukcekmece, 34303, Istanbul, Turkiye
Tel.: (90) 4448237
Emp.: 20
Metalworking Machines Mfr
N.A.I.C.S.: 333517

Okuma (Changzhou) Machine Tool Co., Ltd. (1)
Floor 1 west section of Building 18 377 Wuyi South Road, Innovation Industrial Park Wujin National Hi-Tech Industrial Zone, Changzhou, Jiangsu, China
Tel.: (86) 51983668990
NC Machine Tool Mfr & Distr
N.A.I.C.S.: 333517

Okuma America Corporation (1)
11900 Westhall Dr, Charlotte, NC 28278-7127 (100%)
Tel.: (704) 588-7000
Web Site: http://www.okuma.com
Sales Range: $150-199.9 Million
Emp.: 200
CNC Machining Centers, Lathes & Grinders Mfr
N.A.I.C.S.: 423830
Jim King *(Pres & COO)*

Okuma Australia Pty Ltd (1)
3 Tampe Road, Rowville, 3178, VIC, Australia
Tel.: (61) 397575888
Web Site:
  https://www.okumaaustralia.com.au
Sales Range: $25-49.9 Million
Emp.: 15
Lathe Accessories Mfr & Distr

AND PRIVATE COMPANIES

OLATECH SOLUTIONS LIMITED

N.A.I.C.S.: 333120
Dean A. McCarroll *(Mng Dir)*

Okuma Benelux B.V. (1)
Weerschip 7 cr, 3991, Houten, Netherlands
Tel.: (31) 302412541
Web Site: https://www.okuma.nl
Computer Numerically Controlled Machine Distr
N.A.I.C.S.: 423830

Okuma Corporation - Kani Plant (1)
3-6 Himegaoka, Kani, 509-0249, Gifu, Japan
Tel.: (81) 574 63 5630
Machine Tools Mfr
N.A.I.C.S.: 333998

Okuma Europe GmbH (1)
Europark Fichtenhain A20, 47807, Krefeld, Germany (100%)
Tel.: (49) 2 151 3740
Web Site: https://www.okuma.eu
Emp.: 125
N.A.I.C.S.: 333517
Nobert Teeuwen *(Mng Dir)*

Subsidiary (Domestic):

Okuma Deutschland GmbH (2)
Donatusstrasse 24, 50767, Cologne, Germany
Tel.: (49) 221 5989 0
Web Site: https://www.okuma.eu
Computer Numerical Control Machinery Mfr
N.A.I.C.S.: 335314

Subsidiary (Non-US):

Okuma Europe RUS LLC (2)
Entuziastov Street House 56 Bldg 32, 111123, Moscow, Russia
Tel.: (7) 4952292652
Web Site: http://www.okuma.co.jp
Machine Tool Distr
N.A.I.C.S.: 423830

Okuma India Pvt Ltd (1)
Plot No 89 Udyog Vihar Phase-1, Gurgaon, 122016, Haryana, India
Tel.: (91) 1244250229
Web Site: http://www.okumaindia.com
NC Machine Tool Mfr & Distr
N.A.I.C.S.: 333517

Okuma Korea Corporation (1)
16 Cheomdan-daero 60beon-gil, Yeonsu-gu, Incheon, Korea (South)
Tel.: (82) 324689000
Web Site: http://www.okuma.kr
NC Machine Tool Mfr & Distr
N.A.I.C.S.: 333517

Okuma Latino Americana Comercio Ltda (1)
Av dos Bandeirantes 513, Vila Olimpia, 04553-010, Sao Paulo, Brazil
Tel.: (55) 1130495600
Web Site: https://www.okuma.com.br
Sales Range: $25-49.9 Million
Emp.: 23
Industrial Machinery Mfr & Distr
N.A.I.C.S.: 333517

Okuma Machine Tool (Shanghai) Corporation (1)
No 8 Lane 2915 Huaning Road, Xinzhuang Industrial Zone, Shanghai, 201108, China
Tel.: (86) 2131373100
Web Site: https://www.okuma-sh.com.cn
Emp.: 150
Industrial Machinery Mfr & Distr
N.A.I.C.S.: 333517

Okuma New Zealand Ltd (1)
Auckland Christchurch Unit F 47 Mount Wellington Highway, Mount Wellington, Auckland, 1060, New Zealand
Tel.: (64) 9 570 7025
Web Site: http://www.okuma.co.jp
Sales Range: $50-74.9 Million
Emp.: 3
Industrial Machinery Mfr & Sales
N.A.I.C.S.: 333517
Fred De Jong *(Gen Mgr)*

Okuma Techno (Thailand) Ltd. (1)
38 Motorway Road, Prawet Subdistrict Prawet District, Bangkok, 10250, Thailand
Tel.: (66) 23222445
Web Site: https://www.okumathai.com
Sales Range: $25-49.9 Million
Emp.: 50
Lathe Machinery & Accessories Mfr & Distr
N.A.I.C.S.: 333243

Branch (Non-US):

Okuma Techno (Thailand) Ltd. (2)
275 Kakibukit Avenue 1, Shun Li Industrial Park, Singapore, 416072, Singapore
Tel.: (65) 62140112
NC Machine Tool Mfr & Distr
N.A.I.C.S.: 333517

Okuma Techno (Thailand) Ltd. - Singapore Branch (2)
275 Kaki Bukit Avenue 1 Shun Li Industrial Park, Loyang Industrial Est, Singapore, 416072, Singapore
Tel.: (65) 62140112
Web Site: http://www.okuma.co.jp
Sales Range: $25-49.9 Million
Emp.: 15
N.A.I.C.S.: 333517
Mark Liew *(Mgr-Marketing)*

Okuma Vietnam Co., Ltd. (1)
LANT building 6th 56-58-60 Hai Ba Trung Street, Ben Nghe Ward District 1, Ho Chi Minh City, Vietnam
Tel.: (84) 2839103861
NC Machine Tool Mfr & Distr
N.A.I.C.S.: 333517

PT. Okuma Indonesia (1)
Rukan The Walk No 3 5 Jakarta Garden City Kel Cakung Timur, Kec Cakung Kota ADM Jakarta Utara, Jakarta, 13910, Indonesia
Tel.: (62) 2146833458
Sales Range: $25-49.9 Million
Emp.: 7
Cutting Tool & Machine Tool Mfr
N.A.I.C.S.: 333515

Tatung-Okuma Co., Ltd. (1)
No14-2 Donghu Rd, Yingge Dist, New Taipei City, 239, Taiwan
Tel.: (886) 226788688
Web Site: http://www.tatung-okuma.com.tw
Computer Numeric Control Machine & Lathe Mfr
N.A.I.C.S.: 333243

OKUMURA ENGINEERING CORP.
446-1 Ichimiyake, Yasu, 520-2362, Shiga, Japan
Tel.: (81) 775181260
Web Site: https://www.okm-net.jp
Year Founded: 1902
6229—(TKS)
Rev.: $62,689,240
Assets: $83,272,780
Liabilities: $19,717,630
Net Worth: $63,555,150
Earnings: $3,377,710
Emp.: 345
Fiscal Year-end: 03/31/24
Rubber Product Mfr & Distr
N.A.I.C.S.: 326299
Keiichi Okumura *(Chm)*

Subsidiaries:

OKM Valve (Jiangsu) Co., Ltd. (1)
No 38 Xinggang Road, Economic Development Zone, Changshu, Jiangsu, China
Tel.: (86) 51265688537
Web Site: www.jsokm.com
Industrial Valve Mfr & Distr
N.A.I.C.S.: 332911

OKM Valve (M) Sdn. Bhd. (1)
Lot 7 Jalan Sungai Kayu Ara 32/31, Berjaya Industrial Park, 40460, Shah Alam, Malaysia
Tel.: (60) 357408250
Web Site: http://www.okmvalve.com
Industrial Valve Mfr
N.A.I.C.S.: 332911

OKURA INDUSTRIAL CO., LTD.
1515 Nakazu-cho, Marugame, 763-8508, Kagawa, Japan
Tel.: (81) 877561111
Web Site: https://www.okr-ind.co.jp
Year Founded: 1947
4221—(TKS)
Rev.: $559,138,670
Assets: $710,928,480
Liabilities: $279,367,270
Net Worth: $431,561,210
Earnings: $30,593,350
Emp.: 1,904
Fiscal Year-end: 12/31/23
Plastics Product Mfr
N.A.I.C.S.: 326112
Kazunori Takahama *(Chm)*

Subsidiaries:

Kansai Okura Co., Ltd. (1)
90 Misonocho, Higashi-omi, 527-0056, Japan
Tel.: (81) 748226151
Web Site: http://www.kansaiokura.co.jp
Plastics Product Mfr
N.A.I.C.S.: 326112

Kanto Okura Co., Ltd. (1)
2158 Kamo, Kikugawa, 439-0031, Shizuoka, Japan
Tel.: (81) 537353151
Web Site: http://www.kantookura.co.jp
Plastics Product Mfr
N.A.I.C.S.: 326112

Kyushu Okura Co., Ltd. (1)
1694-6 Yamamoto Ueki-cho, Kita-ku, Kumamoto, 861-0101, Japan
Tel.: (81) 96272673
Web Site: https://www.kyushuokura.co.jp
Emp.: 118
Plastics Product Mfr
N.A.I.C.S.: 326112

O.L.S. Co., Ltd. (1)
2-7-1 Nihonbashi, Chuo-ku, Tokyo, 763-8508, Japan
Tel.: (81) 877561183
Emp.: 176
Polarizing Plate Mfr & Distr
N.A.I.C.S.: 332313

Okura House Co., Ltd. (1)
3529-1 Gungecho, Marugame, 763-0093, Kagawa Prefecture, Japan
Tel.: (81) 877561133
Web Site: https://www.okurahouse.co.jp
Property Management Services
N.A.I.C.S.: 531311

Okura Industrial Co., Ltd. - Chunan Plant (1)
773-6 Sabumi Mannou, Nakatado, Kagawa, 769-0301, Japan
Tel.: (81) 877 75 6350
Plastics Films Mfr
N.A.I.C.S.: 326112

Okura Industrial Co., Ltd. - Marugame No. 4 Plant (1)
52 Horai-cho, Marugame, 763-0062, Kagawa, Japan
Tel.: (81) 877 24 1717
Plastics Films Mfr
N.A.I.C.S.: 326112

Okura Industrial Co., Ltd. - Marugame No. 5 Plant (1)
23 Horai-cho, Marugame, 763-0062, Kagawa, Japan
Tel.: (81) 877 25 5800
Plastics Films Mfr
N.A.I.C.S.: 326112

Okura Industrial Co., Ltd. - Saitama Plant (1)
58 Ohara, Kashiwazaki, Higashimatsuyama, 355-0034, Saitama, Japan
Tel.: (81) 493 22 3735
Plastics Films Mfr
N.A.I.C.S.: 326112

Okura Industrial Co., Ltd. - Takuma Plant (1)
2102-4 Takuma, Mitoyo, 769-1101, Kagawa, Japan
Tel.: (81) 875 83 2511
Plastics Product Mfr
N.A.I.C.S.: 326112

Okura Sangyo Co., Ltd. (1)
422-5 Makabechohanawaze, Sakuragawa, 300-4423, Ibaraki, Japan
Tel.: (81) 296551141
Plastics Product Mfr
N.A.I.C.S.: 326112
Kiyoshi Hayashi *(Gen Mgr)*

Okura Vietnam Co., Ltd. (1)
Lot 6 - Road No 2 Ho Nai Industrial Park, Trang Bom, Dong Nai Province, Vietnam
Tel.: (84) 2513671056
Web Site: http://okura.com.vn
Emp.: 140
Metal Parts Mfr
N.A.I.C.S.: 336991

Wuxi Okura Packing Material Co., Ltd. (1)
No 9 Minshan Road Wuxi National Hi-New Tech Industry Development Zone, Wuxi, 214028, Jiangsu, China
Tel.: (86) 51085212364
Web Site: http://www.wxokura.com
Packaging Services
N.A.I.C.S.: 561910

OKUWA CO., LTD.
185-3 Nakajima, Wakayama, 641-8501, Japan
Tel.: (81) 734252481
Web Site: https://www.okuwa.net
Year Founded: 1969
8217—(TKS)
Rev.: $1,753,910,020
Assets: $939,396,640
Liabilities: $381,562,530
Net Worth: $557,834,110
Earnings: $7,090,000
Emp.: 15,895
Fiscal Year-end: 02/29/24
Supermarket Store Operator
N.A.I.C.S.: 445110

OKWAVE INC.
3-11-8 Shinbashi Oizumi Shinbashi 2nd Building 702, Minato-ku, Tokyo, 105-0004, Japan
Tel.: (81) 368417672
Web Site: https://www.okwave.co.jp
Year Founded: 1999
38080—(NGO)
Rev.: $21,257,280
Assets: $92,356,880
Liabilities: $37,122,800
Net Worth: $55,234,080
Earnings: $39,213,680
Emp.: 109
Fiscal Year-end: 06/30/21
Education Services
N.A.I.C.S.: 611710
Gen Matsuda *(Pres)*

OKYO PHARMA LIMITED
14/15 Conduit St Floor 4, London, W1S 2XJ, United Kingdom
Tel.: (44) 2074952379 UK
Web Site: https://www.okyopharma.com
OKYO—(NASDAQ)
Assets: $5,203,920
Liabilities: $7,257,157
Net Worth: ($2,053,237)
Earnings: ($13,271,685)
Emp.: 3
Fiscal Year-end: 03/31/23
Metals & Rare Earth Elements Mining & Trading Services
N.A.I.C.S.: 212290
Gary Jacob *(CEO)*

OLATECH SOLUTIONS LIMITED
310 3rd floor Rupa Solitaire Millennium Business Park, Thane-Belapur Road Mahape, Navi Mumbai, 400710, Maharashtra, India
Tel.: (91) 2227780129
Web Site: https://www.olatechs.com
Year Founded: 1956

OLATECH SOLUTIONS LIMITED

Olatech Solutions Limited—(Continued)
543578—(BOM)
Rev.: $357,840
Assets: $303,645
Liabilities: $79,399
Net Worth: $224,246
Earnings: $47,780
Fiscal Year-end: 03/31/22
Software Development Services
N.A.I.C.S.: 541511

OLAV THON EIENDOMSSELSKAP ASA
Stenersgata 2, PO Box 489, 105,
Oslo, 105, Norway
Tel.: (47) 23080000
Web Site: https://www.olt.no
Year Founded: 1982
OLT—(OSL)
Rev.: $365,892,029
Assets: $5,947,564,115
Liabilities: $2,955,448,134
Net Worth: $2,992,115,981
Earnings: ($162,498,529)
Emp.: 237
Fiscal Year-end: 12/31/23
Real Estate Manangement Services
N.A.I.C.S.: 531390
Dag Tangevald Jensen (CEO)

Subsidiaries:

Gardermoen Park AS (1)
Museumsvegen 15, 2060, Gardermoen, Norway
Tel.: (47) 63949596
Web Site: https://www.gardermoenparkering.no
Real Estate Services
N.A.I.C.S.: 531390

Jessheim Storsenter AS (1)
Storgata 6, 2050, Jessheim, Norway
Tel.: (47) 63996960
Web Site: https://www.jessheimstorsenter.no
Shopping Mall Operator
N.A.I.C.S.: 531120

Sartor Storsenter AS (1)
Sartorvegen 12, 5353, Straume, Norway
Tel.: (47) 56315500
Web Site: https://www.sartorstorsenter.no
Shopping Mall Operator
N.A.I.C.S.: 531120

Vestkanten AS (1)
Loddefjordveien 2, 5171, Loddefjord, Norway
Tel.: (47) 55507700
Web Site: https://www.vestkanten.no
Shopping Mall Operator
N.A.I.C.S.: 531120

OLBA HEALTHCARE HOLDINGS INC
8F Nippon Life Insurance Okayama Dai-ni Building 1-1-3 Shimoishii, Kitaku, Okayama, 700-0907, Japan
Tel.: (81) 862505940
Web Site: https://olba.co.jp
Year Founded: 1967
2689—(TKS)
Rev.: $737,468,080
Assets: $268,934,140
Liabilities: $198,194,080
Net Worth: $70,740,060
Earnings: $9,330,000
Fiscal Year-end: 06/30/24
Holding Company
N.A.I.C.S.: 551112
Taira Takai (Vice Chm)

OLD CHANG KEE LTD
2 Woodlands Terrace, Singapore, 738427, Singapore
Tel.: (65) 63032400
Web Site: https://www.oldchangkee.com
5ML—(CAT)
Rev.: $74,807,706
Assets: $68,219,340
Liabilities: $32,496,480
Net Worth: $35,722,860
Earnings: $7,164,135
Fiscal Year-end: 03/31/24
Food & Beverage Products Mfr & Distr
N.A.I.C.S.: 311999
Adrian Chan Pengee (Co-Sec)

Subsidiaries:

Old Chang Kee UK Limited (1)
15A New Row, London, WC2N 4LA, United Kingdom
Tel.: (44) 2073799235
Emp.: 6
Food Mfr
N.A.I.C.S.: 311999

Ten & Han Trading Pte Ltd (1)
2 Woodlands Terrace, Singapore, 738427, Singapore
Tel.: (65) 63032400
Food Mfr
N.A.I.C.S.: 311999

OLD GRANGONIAN CLUB S.A.
Av Del Valle 11300, PO Box 13, Chicureo Colina, Santiago, Chile
Tel.: (56) 999669511
Web Site: https://www.ogclub.cl
Year Founded: 1938
OLDBOYS—(SGO)
Sales Range: Less than $1 Million
Golf Club Operator
N.A.I.C.S.: 713910
Hernan Ortiz Pereda (CEO)

OLD MUTUAL LIFE ASSURANCE COMPANY (SOUTH AFRICA) LTD.
Mutualpark, Jan Smuts Dr, Pinelands, South Africa
Tel.: (27) 215099111
Web Site: http://www.oldmutual.co.za
Insurance Company
N.A.I.C.S.: 524298

Subsidiaries:

Commercial Cold Strorage Group Ltd. (1)
7 Toulon & Rotterdam Roads, Durban, 4001, South Africa
Tel.: (27) 312057277
Web Site: http://www.comcold.co.za
Emp.: 60
Cold Storage & Transportation Services
N.A.I.C.S.: 493120
Sharon Gabellone (Mgr-Admin)

OLD MUTUAL LIMITED
Mutualpark Jan Smuts Drive, Pinelands, Cape Town, 7405, South Africa
Tel.: (27) 215099111   ZA
Web Site: https://www.oldmutual.com
Year Founded: 1845
OMU—(MALA)
Rev.: $568,288,638
Assets: $61,079,119,974
Liabilities: $57,985,772,980
Net Worth: $3,093,346,994
Earnings: $403,098,892
Emp.: 31,032
Fiscal Year-end: 12/31/23
Financial Investment Services
N.A.I.C.S.: 523999
Casper Troskie (CFO)

Subsidiaries:

Faulu Microfinance Bank Limited (1)
Ngong Lane off Ngong Road, PO Box 60240-00200, Nairobi, Kenya
Tel.: (254) 711074000
Web Site: https://www.faulukenya.com
Investment Finance Services
N.A.I.C.S.: 523999

Old Mutual Insure Limited (1)
Wanooka Place St Andrews Road, Parktown, Johannesburg, 2193, South Africa
Tel.: (27) 113749111
Web Site: https://www.oldmutual.co.za
Financial Processing & Insurance Services
N.A.I.C.S.: 522320

Old Mutual Zimbabwe Limited (1)
100 The Chase Mutual Gardens Emerald Hill, Harare, Zimbabwe
Tel.: (263) 242308400
Web Site: https://www.oldmutual.co.zw
Investment Finance Services
N.A.I.C.S.: 523999

OLD OAK HOLDINGS LIMITED
7th Floor 90 Long Acre, London, WC2E 9RA, United Kingdom
Tel.: (44) 207 845 6100   UK
Year Founded: 2004
Holding Company; Private Equity & Investment Management Services
N.A.I.C.S.: 551112
Martin Hughes (Founder & CEO)

Subsidiaries:

Toscafund Asset Management LLP (1)
7th Floor 90 Long Acre, London, WC2E 9RA, United Kingdom
Tel.: (44) 207 845 6100
Web Site: http://www.toscafund.com
Hedge Fund Investment Management Services
N.A.I.C.S.: 523940
Martin Gilbert (Chm)

Holding (Domestic):

Avanta Serviced Office Group plc (2)
1 Lyric Square, London, W6 0NB, United Kingdom
Tel.: (44) 2030086000
Web Site: http://www.avanta.co.uk
Office Building Operation & Maintenance Services
N.A.I.C.S.: 561790
Tom Sleigh (Head-Acq & Portfolio Mgmt)

Joint Venture (Domestic):

Healthcare Locums Plc (2)
10 Old Bailey, London, EC4M 7NG, United Kingdom
Tel.: (44) 2074511451
Web Site: http://www.hclwiforc.com
Sales Range: $350-399.9 Million
Emp.: 10
Holding Company; Healthcare Recruitment & Employment Placement Services
N.A.I.C.S.: 551112
Andy McRae (Exec Dir)

Subsidiary (Domestic):

Allied Health Professionals Limited (3)
Garden Flat 28 Clifton Park Road, Bristol, BS8 3HL, Essex, United Kingdom
Tel.: (44) 8453892299
Web Site: http://www.ahp-ltd.com
Medical Staff Recruitment Services
N.A.I.C.S.: 561311

HCL BBL Medical Limited (3)
10 Old Bailey, London, EC4M 7NG, United Kingdom
Tel.: (44) 845 222 3223
Web Site: http://www.healthcarelocums.com
Doctor Recruitment Services
N.A.I.C.S.: 561311

HCL GPS Limited (3)
Nesfield House Broughton, Skipton, BD23 3AE, North Yorkshire, United Kingdom
Tel.: (44) 8453661133
Web Site: http://www.healthcarelocums.com
Medical Staff Recruitment Services
N.A.I.C.S.: 561311

HCL Healthcare Limited (3)
33 Soho Square, London, W1D 3QU, United Kingdom
Tel.: (44) 8450639639
Medical Staff Recruitment Services
N.A.I.C.S.: 561311

HCL Thames Medics Limited (3)
Nesfield House Broughton Hall, Skipton,
BD23 3AN, North Yorkshire, United Kingdom
Tel.: (44) 8450613613
Medical Staff Recruitment Services
N.A.I.C.S.: 561311

Holding (Domestic):

TalkTalk Telecom Group PLC (2)
11 Evesham Street, London, W11 4AR, United Kingdom
Tel.: (44) 20 3417 1000
Web Site: http://www.talktalkgroup.com
Rev.: $2,071,040,640
Assets: $2,164,948,120
Liabilities: $1,799,470,360
Net Worth: $365,477,760
Earnings: $40,608,640
Emp.: 2,187
Fiscal Year-end: 03/31/2019
Holding Company; Television, Broadband & Telephone Services
N.A.I.C.S.: 551112

Subsidiary (Domestic):

TalkTalk Communications Limited (3)
West Wing Cameron House Metro Centre, Gateshead, NE11 9XW, United Kingdom
Tel.: (44) 845 330 3456
Web Site: http://www.talktalkbusiness.co.uk
Internet Service Provider
N.A.I.C.S.: 517111
Ruth Kennedy (Dir-Carrier & Sys Integrators)

TalkTalk Telecom Limited (3)
11 Evesham Street, London, W11 4AR, United Kingdom
Tel.: (44) 20 3417 1000
Web Site: http://www.talktalk.co.uk
Television, Broadband & Telephone Services
N.A.I.C.S.: 517810
Tristia Harrison (Mng Dir)

OLD OAK PROPERTIES INC.
Suite 600 465 Richmond Street, London, N6A 5P4, ON, Canada
Tel.: (519) 661-0215
Web Site: http://www.oldoakproperties.com
Year Founded: 1955
Rev.: $31,548,172
Emp.: 75
Real Estate Services
N.A.I.C.S.: 236117
Keith McAlister (Office Mgr-Leasing)

OLD TOWN S.A.
22-24 Blvd Royale, L-2449, Luxembourg, Luxembourg
Tel.: (352) 227840
Holding Company
N.A.I.C.S.: 551112
Gilbert Cahen d'Anvers (Chm)

OLDFIELDS HOLDINGS LIMITED
25 Helles Avenue, Moorebank, 2170, NSW, Australia
Tel.: (61) 1300306888   AU
Web Site: https://www.oldfields.com.au
Year Founded: 1916
OLH—(ASX)
Rev.: $18,699,920
Assets: $13,944,979
Liabilities: $17,477,297
Net Worth: ($3,532,318)
Earnings: ($4,843,082)
Fiscal Year-end: 06/30/24
Paint Equipment & Storage Sheds Mfr
N.A.I.C.S.: 424950
Brendan Coyle (Natl Sls Mgr)

Subsidiaries:

Adelaide Garden Sheds Pty Limited (1)
125 Cavan Rd, Gepps Cross, 5094, SA, Australia
Tel.: (61) 883495555

Painting Equipment Mfr
N.A.I.C.S.: 339994

Adelaide Scaffold Solutions Pty Limited (1)
5-7 Peekarra Street Regency Park, Adelaide, 5010, SA, Australia
Tel.: (61) 882613344
Painting Equipment Mfr
N.A.I.C.S.: 339994

Foshan Advcorp Scaffold Limited (1)
108 Ming Er Road MingCheng Town, GaoMing District, Foshan, 528518, Guangdong, China
Tel.: (86) 757 8883 9990
Web Site: http://www.scaffoldtheworld.com
Painting Equipment Mfr
N.A.I.C.S.: 339994

H & O Products Pty Limited (1)
U F 25 Fairfield St, Fairfield, 2165, NSW, Australia
Tel.: (61) 296320200
Painting Equipment Mfr
N.A.I.C.S.: 339994

Oldfields Pty Limited (1)
5/18 28 Gray St, Kilkenny, 5009, SA, Australia
Tel.: (61) 246270777
Painting Equipment Mfr
N.A.I.C.S.: 339994

OLE MEDIA MANAGEMENT LP
120 Bremner Blvd Suite 2900, Toronto, M5J 0A8, ON, Canada
Tel.: (416) 850-1163
Web Site:
   http://www.majorlyindie.com
Year Founded: 2004
Emp.: 100
Music Publishing & Licensing Services
N.A.I.C.S.: 512230
Gilles Godard *(VP-Corp Affairs & Dev)*

Subsidiaries:

Jingle Punks Music, LLC (1)
20 W 22nd St Ste 905, New York, NY 10010
Tel.: (646) 478-7472
Web Site: http://www.jinglepunks.com
Emp.: 20
Music Publishing & Licensing Services
N.A.I.C.S.: 512230
Justin Fantasia *(Dir-Ops)*

OLECTRA GREENTECH LTD
S-22 3rd Floor Technocrat Industrial Estate, Balanagar, Hyderabad, 500 037, Telangana, India
Tel.: (91) 4046989999
Web Site: https://www.olectra.com
Year Founded: 1992
532439—(BOM)
Rev.: $131,985,301
Assets: $186,667,298
Liabilities: $85,827,301
Net Worth: $100,839,998
Earnings: $8,020,275
Emp.: 348
Fiscal Year-end: 03/31/23
Polymer Insulator Mfr & Sales
N.A.I.C.S.: 339999
P. Hanuman Prasad *(Compliance Officer & Sec)*

Subsidiaries:

Goldstone Infratech Limited - Unit I (1)
Plot No 1 & 9 Phase-II IDA, Cherlapally, Hyderabad, 500 051, Andhra Pradesh, India
Tel.: (91) 40 27266783
Web Site: http://www.goldstonepower.com
Composite Insulator Mfr
N.A.I.C.S.: 335932

OLEEO, PLC
5 7 Bridgeworks The Crescent, London, SW19 8DR, United Kingdom
Tel.: (44) 2089469876 UK
Web Site: http://www.oleeo.com
Year Founded: 1995
Rev.: $9,981,563
Assets: $13,166,909
Liabilities: $3,047,312
Net Worth: $10,119,597
Earnings: $392,271
Emp.: 115
Fiscal Year-end: 07/31/18
Human Resouce Services
N.A.I.C.S.: 923130
David K. Moore *(Dir-Technical)*

Subsidiaries:

World Careers Network Plc - New York Branch (1)
200 Park Ave 17th Fl, New York, NY 10166
Tel.: (212) 686-7733
Recruitment Software Consulting Services
N.A.I.C.S.: 541512

OLEREX AS
Voru 79, Tartu, Estonia
Tel.: (372) 6100105
Web Site: http://www.olerex.ee
Year Founded: 1994
Fuel Company
N.A.I.C.S.: 811191
Andres Linnas *(Owner)*

Subsidiaries:

Oiltanking Tallinn AS (1)
Port of Muuga Oli tn 7, 74115, Tallinn, Estonia
Tel.: (372) 6 319 403
Web Site: http://www.oiltanking.com
Petroleum Product Distr
N.A.I.C.S.: 424710

OLICAR S.P.A
Via Don Orione 39, 12042, Bra, Italy
Tel.: (39) 0172419911
Web Site: http://www.olicar.it
Sales Range: $75-99.9 Million
Emp.: 200
Energy Facility Management Services
N.A.I.C.S.: 561210
Paolo Fusaro *(COO)*

OLIDATA S.P.A.
Via Fossalta 3055, 47522, Cesena, Forli Cesena, Italy
Tel.: (39) 0547419111
Web Site: http://www.olidata.it
Year Founded: 1982
Sales Range: $100-124.9 Million
Emp.: 135
Computer Mfr
N.A.I.C.S.: 334111

OLIE, INC.
300 Jameson House 838 West Hastings Street, Vancouver, V6C 0A6, BC, Canada
Tel.: (604) 669-9000 DE
Year Founded: 2010
Music Production Services
N.A.I.C.S.: 512250
Robert Gardner *(CEO & CFO)*

Subsidiaries:

MVP Financial, LLC (1)
75 Wall St 9th Fl, New York, NY 10005
Tel.: (212) 962-2100
Web Site: http://www.mvpfinancial.com
Sales Range: Less than $1 Million
Emp.: 5
Securities Brokerage Services
N.A.I.C.S.: 523150
Steven Perlstein *(CEO)*

OLIMPO REAL ESTATE PORTUGAL, SIGI, S.A.
Place of Espido North Road, 4470-177, Maia, Portugal
Tel.: (351) 229401700
Web Site: https://www.ores-portugal.com
Year Founded: 2019
MLORE—(EUR)
Real Estate Investment Services
N.A.I.C.S.: 531190
Alberto Jorge Reis de Oliveira Ramos *(Chm)*

OLIMPO REAL ESTATE SOCIMI SA
Calle Goya 22 - 3 planta, 28001, Madrid, Spain
Tel.: (34) 915758986
Web Site: https://www.ores-socimi.com
YORE—(MAD)
Sales Range: Less than $1 Million
Real Estate Investment Services
N.A.I.C.S.: 531390
Jaime Inigo Guerra Azcona *(Gen Dir)*

OLIPASS CORPORATION
Ace Dongbaek Tower 20th Floor 16 Beon-gil 16-4 Dongbaek Jungang-ro, Giheung-Gu, Yongin, 17015, Gyeonggi-do, Korea (South)
Tel.: (82) 264882232
Web Site: https://www.olipass.com
Year Founded: 2006
244460—(KRS)
Rev.: $1,761,054
Assets: $19,130,254
Liabilities: $12,053,821
Net Worth: $7,076,433
Earnings: ($18,536,723)
Emp.: 86
Fiscal Year-end: 12/31/22
Medicinal Chemical Mfr
N.A.I.C.S.: 325411
Youngyoup Park *(Mng Dir)*

OLIVE BUSINESS SOLUTIONS LIMITED
Bishops Court 15-17 The Broadway, Hatfield, AL9 5HZ, United Kingdom
Tel.: (44) 203 675 3030
Web Site: http://olive.co.uk
Year Founded: 2003
Sales Range: $10-24.9 Million
Emp.: 58
Wireless Telecommunication Services
N.A.I.C.S.: 517112
Mark Geraghty *(Founder)*

OLIVE TREE ESTATES LIMITED
65 Chulia Street 49-06 OCBC Centre, Singapore, 049513, Singapore
Tel.: (65) 68096176
Web Site:
   https://www.olivetreeestates.com
1H2—(CAT)
Rev.: $908,127
Assets: $15,791,108
Liabilities: $8,048,928
Net Worth: $7,742,180
Earnings: ($579,414)
Emp.: 7
Fiscal Year-end: 12/31/23
Property Development Services
N.A.I.C.S.: 531312
Daniel Chee Tim Long *(CEO)*

OLIVEIRA ENERGIA GERACAO E SERVICOS LTDA.
7203 Av do Turismo, 6923 - Taruma, Manaus, Brazil
Tel.: (55) 92 3321 5900
Web Site:
   http://www.oliveiraenergia.com.br
Year Founded: 1972
Thermal Electric Power Generation Services
N.A.I.C.S.: 221122
Orsine Oliveira *(CEO)*

Subsidiaries:

Boa Vista Energia S.A. (1)
Av Capitao Julio Bezerra Forest, Rio de Janeiro, Brazil (90%)
Tel.: (55) 32125700
Web Site: http://www.boavistaenergia.gov.br
Electric Company
N.A.I.C.S.: 926130

OLIVER HUME CORPORATION PTY. LTD.
Level 2 4 Riverside Quay, Southbank, 3006, VIC, Australia
Tel.: (61) 3 9669 5999 AU
Web Site:
   http://www.oliverhume.com.au
Residential Property Research & Advisory Services
N.A.I.C.S.: 531390
Michael Duster *(Mng Dir & Chm-Property Funds)*

OLIVER J. NILSEN (AUSTRALIA) LIMITED
Unit 1 18-22 Lexia Place, Heidelberg W, Mulgrave, 3170, VIC, Australia
Tel.: (61) 392713900
Web Site: http://www.nilsen.com.au
Year Founded: 1916
Sales Range: $100-124.9 Million
Emp.: 1,000
Electronic Services
N.A.I.C.S.: 221122
Oliver Mark Nilsen *(Founder)*

Subsidiaries:

Nilsen (NSW) Pty. Ltd. (1)
Unit 29 38-46 S St, Rydalmere, 2116, NSW, Australia
Tel.: (61) 298989355
Web Site: http://www.nilsen.com.au
Sales Range: $75-99.9 Million
Emp.: 100
Electric Power Generation
N.A.I.C.S.: 221118
Mark Nilsen *(Mng Dir)*

Nilsen (NT) Pty. Ltd. (1)
Berrimah 41 Rd, Berrimah, 0828, NT, Australia
Tel.: (61) 889471134
Web Site: http://www.nilsen.com.au
Sales Range: $25-49.9 Million
Emp.: 50
Electrical Equipment & Component Mfr
N.A.I.C.S.: 335999
Mark Nilsen *(Mng Dir)*

Nilsen (QLD) Pty. Ltd. (1)
379 Thynne Road, Morningside, Brisbane, 4170, QLD, Australia
Tel.: (61) 738998866
Web Site: http://www.nilsen.com.au
Sales Range: $25-49.9 Million
Emp.: 100
Electrical Contractor
N.A.I.C.S.: 238210

Nilsen (SA) Pty. Ltd. (1)
100 Regency Road, Ferryden Park, Adelaide, 5010, SA, Australia
Tel.: (61) 884405300
Web Site: http://www.nilsen.com.au
Sales Range: $25-49.9 Million
Emp.: 400
Electrical Contractor Services
N.A.I.C.S.: 238210

Nilsen (VIC) Pty. Ltd. (1)
43 Sheehan Road Heidelberg West, Heidelberg, 3081, VIC, Australia
Tel.: (61) 394501300
Web Site: http://www.nilsen.com.au
Sales Range: $50-74.9 Million
Emp.: 200
Electrical Contractor
N.A.I.C.S.: 238210
Mark Nilsen *(Mng Dir)*

Nilsen (WA) Pty. Ltd (1)
12 Efficiency Way, Bibra Lake, 6163, WA, Australia
Tel.: (61) 894342311
Web Site: http://www.nilsen.com.au

Oliver J. Nilsen (Australia) Limited—(Continued)
Sales Range: $100-124.9 Million
Emp.: 300
Electrical Contractor Services
N.A.I.C.S.: 238210

Nilsen Electric (WA) Pty Limited (1)
4 Park Place, Bibra Lake, 6163, WA, Australia
Tel.: (61) 894342311
Electrical Contractor
N.A.I.C.S.: 238210

Nilsen Networks Pty.Ltd. (1)
Unit 4/3-5 Gilda Court, Mulgrave, 3170, VIC, Australia
Tel.: (61) 1300 734 766
Web Site: http://www.nilsen.com.au
Electrical Equipment Installation Services
N.A.I.C.S.: 238210
Anthony Tenson (Acct Mgr-Natl)

OLIVER JAMES ASSOCIATES
1st Floor No 1 Bartholomew Lane, London, EC2N 2AX, United Kingdom
Tel.: (44) 2038619120
Web Site: http://www.ojassociates.com
Year Founded: 2002
Sales Range: $50-74.9 Million
Emp.: 74
Recruitment Consultancy Services
N.A.I.C.S.: 561311
James Rogers (Mng Dir)

Subsidiaries:

Oliver James Associates (Switzerland) AG (1)
Muhlebachstrasse 20, 8032, Zurich, Switzerland
Tel.: (41) 435080444
Employee Recruitment Services
N.A.I.C.S.: 561311
Audrey Dadon (Mgr-Underwriting & Broking)

OLIVER SCHROTT KOMMUNIKATION GMBH
An den Dominikanern 11-27, 50668, Cologne, Germany
Tel.: (49) 221 3390 0
Web Site: http://www.osk.de
Year Founded: 1993
Sales Range: $25-49.9 Million
Emp.: 130
Public Relation Agency Services
N.A.I.C.S.: 541820
Andre Kau-Gravert (Mng Dir-Content)

OLIVER VALVES LIMITED
Parkgate Industrial Estate, Knutsford, WA16 8DX, Cheshire, United Kingdom
Tel.: (44) 1565 632 636
Web Site: http://www.valves.co.uk
Year Founded: 2000
Sales Range: $25-49.9 Million
Emp.: 142
Industrial Valve Mfr
N.A.I.C.S.: 332911
Michael Oliver (Chm)

OLIVER'S REAL FOOD LIMITED
10 Amsterdam Circuit, Wyong, 2259, NSW, Australia
Tel.: (61) 2 4353 8055
Web Site: http://www.oliversrealfood.com.au
Full-Service Organic Restaurant & Store
N.A.I.C.S.: 722511
Jason Gunn (Founder)

OLIVUT RESOURCES LTD.
PO Box 6690, Hinton, T7V 1X8, AB, Canada
Tel.: (780) 866-2226
Web Site: https://www.olivut.ca

OLVRF—(OTCIQ)
Rev.: $13,527
Assets: $345,696
Liabilities: $947,894
Net Worth: ($602,198)
Earnings: ($291,745)
Fiscal Year-end: 10/31/22
Mineral Exploration Services
N.A.I.C.S.: 213114
Leni F. Keough (Pres & CEO)

OLIX PHARMACEUTICALS, INC.
Ace Gwanggyo Tower1 Suite 1014 17 Daehak 4-ro, Yeongtong-gu, Suwon, 16226, Gyeonggi-do, Korea (South)
Tel.: (82) 317798400
Web Site: https://olixpharma.com
Year Founded: 2010
Pharmaceuticals Product Mfr
N.A.I.C.S.: 325412
Lee Dong-Ki (CEO)

OLLOO JOINT STOCK COMPANY
Suite 201 Lveel Company Building,11th Khoroo, Ulaanbaatar, Mongolia
Tel.: (976) 7 720 1100
Web Site: http://www.olloo.mn
OLL—(MONG)
Rev.: $20,368
Assets: $431,896
Liabilities: $15,467
Net Worth: $416,429
Earnings: ($57,668)
Fiscal Year-end: 12/31/20
Internet Publishing & Broadcasting Services
N.A.I.C.S.: 516210

OLMA INVESTMENT COMPANY OJSC
7/1 Maliy Karetniy Per, 127051, Moscow, Russia
Tel.: (7) 4956642321
Web Site: http://www.olma.ru
Sales Range: Less than $1 Million
Financial Brokerage Services
N.A.I.C.S.: 523999

OLMIX S.A.
ZA du Haut du Bois Le Lintan, 56580, Brehan, France
Tel.: (33) 297388103
Web Site: http://www.olmix.com
Year Founded: 1995
MLOLM—(EUR)
Sales Range: $50-74.9 Million
Animal Nutrition & Litter Product Mfr
N.A.I.C.S.: 325998
Herve Balusson (Founder, Chm & CEO)

Subsidiaries:

Melspring International B.V. (1)
Arnhemsestraatweg 8, 6880 AG, Velp, Netherlands
Tel.: (31) 26 384 20 00
Web Site: http://www.melspring.com
Chemical Product Mfr & Distr
N.A.I.C.S.: 325998

Subsidiary (Non-US):

Melspring Agro India Pvt. Ltd. (2)
1-A Kondhawa Khurd, Krishnakeval Nagar, Pune, 411048, India
Tel.: (91) 20 2698 0226
Chemical Products Distr
N.A.I.C.S.: 424690

Melspring France Sarl (2)
1 Rue de la Grosse Pierre, 02220, Brenelle, France
Tel.: (33) 323 74 10 35
Chemical Products Distr
N.A.I.C.S.: 424690

Melspring GMBH (2)

Johannastr 1, 26954, Nordenham, Germany
Tel.: (49) 473196950
Chemical Products Distr
N.A.I.C.S.: 424690
Ralf Keunecke (Mng Dir)

Melspring Romania Srl (2)
Punct de lucru Free zone Giurgiu Str Portului no 1, Giurgiu, 80013, Romania
Tel.: (40) 246 211 070
Web Site: http://www.olmix.com
Chemical Products Distr
N.A.I.C.S.: 424690

Olmix B.V. (1)
Industrieweg 37, Rogat, 7949 AJ, Meppel, Netherlands
Tel.: (31) 263842000
Antibiotic & Chemical Product Mfr
N.A.I.C.S.: 325998

Olmix China Co., Ltd. (1)
Rm Bei 206 Yinhai Dasha No Jia 10 Zhongguancun Nan Street, 100081, Beijing, 100081, China
Tel.: (86) 1062158713
Chemical Products Distr
N.A.I.C.S.: 424690

Olmix Do Brasil SC (1)
Rua Sao Joaquim n 378-E Bairro, Eldorado, Chapeco, Santa Catarina, Brazil
Tel.: (55) 1124493359
Antibiotic & Chemical Product Mfr
N.A.I.C.S.: 325998

Olmix Iberica, S.L. (1)
Rda de la Industria Poligono Sepes parcela 22 nave 6, Mutilva Baja, 22006, Huesca, Spain
Tel.: (34) 747721183
Web Site: http://www.olmix-iberica.pymes.com
Chemical Products Distr
N.A.I.C.S.: 424690

Olmix Indonesia Nutrition P.T. (1)
Menara Thamrin Suite 310 Jl M H Thamrin Kav 3, Jakarta, Indonesia
Tel.: (62) 212302602
Animal Nutrition Additive Mfr & Distr
N.A.I.C.S.: 311119

Olmix Mexico (1)
Av Luis Pasteur sur 10322-A Col Vistas del Cimatario Delegacion Josefa, Vergara y Hernandez, 76085, Queretaro, Mexico
Tel.: (52) 4422455860
Chemical Products Distr
N.A.I.C.S.: 424690
Edgar Chi Moreno (Territory Mgr)

Olmix North America (1)
805 Red Iron Rd, Black River Falls, WI 54615
Tel.: (715) 284-3360
Web Site: http://www.olmix.com
Emp.: 9
Chemical Products Distr
N.A.I.C.S.: 424690

Olmix Ooo (1)
Krivokolenniy pereulok 12 bld 1 room I, 101000, Moscow, Russia
Tel.: (7) 4952681517
Antibiotic & Chemical Product Mfr
N.A.I.C.S.: 325998

Olmix SA (1)
Menara Thamrin Suite 310 Jl M H Thamrin Kav 3, Jakarta, 10250, Indonesia
Tel.: (62) 212302602
Antibiotic & Chemical Product Mfr
N.A.I.C.S.: 325998

Olmix Sa Site de Brains (1)
ZA Les Houssais, Brains, 44830, Chateau-Gontier, France
Tel.: (33) 240326847
Antibiotic & Chemical Product Mfr
N.A.I.C.S.: 325998

Olmix Sa Site de Brenelle (1)
1 rue de la Grosse Pierre, 02220, Brenelle, France
Tel.: (33) 323741035
Antibiotic & Chemical Product Mfr
N.A.I.C.S.: 325998

Olmix Suisse SA (1)
Chemin de la Voie Ferree 5, 1580,

Avenches, Switzerland
Tel.: (41) 266760666
Antibiotic & Chemical Product Mfr
N.A.I.C.S.: 325998

OLRAC SPS (PTY) LTD.
Silvermine House Steenberg Office Park, 9 Silverwood Close, Cape Town, 7945, South Africa
Tel.: (27) 217024666   ZA
Web Site: http://www.olsps.com
Year Founded: 1989
Sales Range: $1-9.9 Million
Emp.: 12
Predictive Analytics & Data Mining Software Distr
N.A.I.C.S.: 423430

OLSBERG HERMANN EVERKEN GMBH
Huettenstrasse 38, Olsberg, 59939, Germany
Tel.: (49) 29628050
Web Site: http://www.olsberg.com
Rev.: $110,777,244
Emp.: 300
Electric Heating Products Mfr
N.A.I.C.S.: 333414
Christoph Bosing (Head-Sls)

OLTCHIM S.A.
1 Uzinei Street, 240050, Ramnicu Valcea, Romania
Tel.: (40) 250701200   RO
Web Site: http://www.oltchim.ro
Year Founded: 1966
Sales Range: $150-199.9 Million
Emp.: 2,345
Organic Basic Chemicals Mfr
N.A.I.C.S.: 325211

OLVI OYJ
Olvitie I-IV, 74100, Iisalmi, Finland
Tel.: (358) 290001050
Web Site: http://www.olvi.fi
Year Founded: 1878
OLVAS—(HEL)
Rev.: $1,353,099,504
Assets: $528,463,199
Liabilities: $224,399,957
Net Worth: $304,063,242
Earnings: $8,122,167
Emp.: 2,335
Fiscal Year-end: 12/31/22
Alcoholic & Non-Alcoholic Beverages Mfr & Whslr
N.A.I.C.S.: 312130
Ilkka Auvola (Dir-Sls)

Subsidiaries:

A/S Bryggeriet Vestfyen (1)
Faborgvej 4, DK-5610, Assens, Denmark
Tel.: (45) 64711041
Web Site: https://bryggeriet-vestfyen.dk
Wine Beverage Distr
N.A.I.C.S.: 424820

A/S Cesu Alus (1)
Aldaru laukums 1, Cesis, 4101, Latvia
Tel.: (371) 25955537
Web Site: https://www.cesualus.lv
Beverage Mfr & Distr
N.A.I.C.S.: 312120
Eva Sietinsone (Chm)

AS A. Le Coq (1)
Laulupeo Pst 15, 50050, Tartu, Estonia
Tel.: (372) 7449711
Web Site: https://www.alecoq.ee
Alcoholic Beverages Mfr
N.A.I.C.S.: 312130
Martin Kutsar (Mgr-Product Dev)

JSC Lidskoe Pivo (1)
St Mickiewicz 32, 231300, Lida, Belarus
Tel.: (375) 154535300
Web Site: http://www.lidskae.by
Beverage Mfr & Distr
N.A.I.C.S.: 312120

OAO Lidskoe Pivo (1)

Mitskevicha Street 32, Grodno region, 231300, Lida, Belarus
Tel.: (375) 154535300
Web Site: https://lidskae.by
Alcoholic Beverage Mfr & Distr
N.A.I.C.S.: 312120

SIA Piebalgas Alus (1)
Ulbrokas Street 19a, Riga, 1021, Latvia
Tel.: (371) 67511377
Web Site: https://www.piebalgasalus.lv
Alcoholic Beverages Whslr
N.A.I.C.S.: 424820

Servaali Oy (1)
Hameentie 3 B 6krs, 00530, Helsinki, Finland
Tel.: (358) 94542350
Web Site: https://servaali.fi
Wine Beverage Distr
N.A.I.C.S.: 424820

Volfas Engelman, AB (1)
Kaunakiemio st 2, 44354, Kaunas, Lithuania
Tel.: (370) 7324345
Web Site: https://www.volfasengelman.lt
Beverage Mfr & Distr
N.A.I.C.S.: 312120
Mantas Matukaitis *(Head-Mktg Dept)*

OLYMPIA CAPITAL HOLDINGS LIMITED
Avon Center Enterprise Road Industrial Area, PO Box 30102, 100, Nairobi, Kenya
Tel.: (254) 203517137 KE
Web Site: https://ochl.co.ke
Year Founded: 1968
OCH—(NAI)
Rev.: $3,757,889
Assets: $11,745,858
Liabilities: $1,371,607
Net Worth: $10,374,251
Earnings: $268,384
Emp.: 40
Fiscal Year-end: 02/28/23
Holding Company
N.A.I.C.S.: 551112
Christopher W. Obura *(Chm)*

Subsidiaries:

Mather & Platt (K) Ltd. (1)
Addis Ababa Road off Enterprise Road, Nairobi, Kenya
Tel.: (254) 724255645
Web Site: https://mplattkenya.com
Engineeering Services
N.A.I.C.S.: 541330

OLYMPIA FINANCIAL GROUP INC.
4000 520 3rd Ave SW, Calgary, T2P 0R3, Canada
Tel.: (403) 770-6350 AB
Web Site: https://www.olympiacgp.com
Year Founded: 1996
OLY—(TSX)
Rev.: $38,034,576
Assets: $23,979,870
Liabilities: $9,192,050
Net Worth: $14,787,820
Earnings: $6,153,583
Emp.: 200
Fiscal Year-end: 12/31/20
Holding Company; Trust Management, Foreign Exchange & Other Financial Services
N.A.I.C.S.: 551112
Rick Skauge *(Pres & CEO)*

Subsidiaries:

Olympia Benefits Inc. (1)
Olympia Trust Company (1) (100%)
Tel.: (587) 774-2340
Web Site: https://www.olympiatrust.com
Holding Company
N.A.I.C.S.: 523991
Rick Skauge *(Pres & CEO)*

OLYMPIA GROUP SINGLE MEMBER HOLDING CO. S.A.
22 Thivaidos Kifissia, 14564, Athens, Greece
Tel.: (30) 2108181111
Web Site: https://www.groupolympia.com
Year Founded: 1980
Investment Services
N.A.I.C.S.: 523999
Ioannis Karagiannis *(Chm)*

OLYMPIA INDUSTRIES BERHAD
Level 23 Menara Olympia No 8 Jalan Raja Chulan, 50200, Kuala Lumpur, Malaysia
Tel.: (60) 320700033
Web Site: https://www.oib.com.my
Year Founded: 1980
OLYMPIA—(KLS)
Rev.: $18,284,868
Assets: $117,439,788
Liabilities: $42,851,005
Net Worth: $74,588,783
Earnings: ($2,721,693)
Emp.: 50
Fiscal Year-end: 12/31/22
Property Development & Stockbroking Services
N.A.I.C.S.: 523150
Yoke Si Lim *(Co-Sec)*

OLYMPIA INDUSTRIES LIMITED
C/205 Synthofine Industrial Estate Behind Virwani Industrial Estate, Goregoan East, Mumbai, 400 063, Maharashtra, India
Tel.: (91) 2242138333
Web Site: https://eolympia.com
Year Founded: 1987
521105—(BOM)
Rev.: $45,369,678
Assets: $15,551,358
Liabilities: $9,415,623
Net Worth: $6,135,735
Earnings: $118,086
Emp.: 165
Fiscal Year-end: 03/31/23
Yarn Mfr
N.A.I.C.S.: 313110
Navin Kumar Pansari *(Chm & Mng Dir)*

OLYMPIA MANAGEMENT SERVICES LIMITED
Hammersmith Road, Kensington, London, W14 8UX, United Kingdom
Tel.: (44) 2073851200 UK
Web Site: http://olympia.london
Year Founded: 1886
Exhibition Centers; Convention Exhibit Services
N.A.I.C.S.: 611620

OLYMPIA MILLS LIMITED
H-23 3 Landhi Industrial Area, Karachi, Pakistan
Tel.: (92) 2135080923 PK
Web Site: https://www.olympiaspinning.com
Year Founded: 1960
OML—(PSX)
Rev.: $363,051
Assets: $2,500,170
Liabilities: $1,909,129
Net Worth: $591,041
Earnings: $61,088
Emp.: 36
Fiscal Year-end: 06/30/23
Yarn Spinning Mills
N.A.I.C.S.: 313110
M. Waqar Monnoo *(Bd of Dirs & CEO)*

OLYMPIA TILE INTERNATIONAL, INC.
1000 Lawrence Ave W, Toronto, M6B 4A8, ON, Canada
Tel.: (416) 785-6666
Web Site: http://www.olympiatile.com
Year Founded: 1956
Sales Range: $200-249.9 Million
Emp.: 831
Ceramic Tiles Distr
N.A.I.C.S.: 327120

OLYMPIC ACCESSORIES LTD.
Saiham Sky View Tower 5th floor 45 Bijoy Nagar, Dhaka, 1000, Bangladesh
Tel.: (880) 28392458
Web Site: https://www.olympicaccessory.com
Year Founded: 2003
OAL—(CHT)
Rev.: $5,004,308
Assets: $29,327,028
Liabilities: $2,499,427
Net Worth: $26,827,602
Earnings: ($651,577)
Emp.: 170
Fiscal Year-end: 06/30/21
Carton Product Mfr
N.A.I.C.S.: 322130
Mohammad Abu Sayam *(CFO)*

OLYMPIC CARDS LIMITED
195 NSC Bose Road, Chennai, 600001, India
Tel.: (91) 4442921000
Web Site: https://www.olympicweddings.com
Year Founded: 1962
534190—(BOM)
Rev.: $1,991,895
Assets: $6,830,106
Liabilities: $6,023,104
Net Worth: $807,002
Earnings: ($508,519)
Emp.: 44
Fiscal Year-end: 03/31/23
Invitation Cards Mfr
N.A.I.C.S.: 513191
Noor Mohamed Faizal *(Mng Dir)*

OLYMPIC CATERING S.A.
Athens International Airport Building 14B, Spata, 19019, Greece
Tel.: (30) 210 3541500
Web Site: http://www.olympic-catering.gr
Year Founded: 1970
Sales Range: $75-99.9 Million
Emp.: 581
Catering Services
N.A.I.C.S.: 722320
Athanasios E. Papanikolaou *(VP)*

OLYMPIC CIRCUIT TECHNOLOGY CO., LTD.
8 Shiyun Road Gonghe, Heshan, Guangdong, China
Tel.: (86) 7508911888 CN
Web Site: https://www.olympicpcb.com
Year Founded: 1985
603920—(SHG)
Rev.: $622,253,979
Assets: $823,174,733
Liabilities: $364,359,439
Net Worth: $458,815,294
Earnings: $60,938,233
Emp.: 6,000
Fiscal Year-end: 12/31/22
Printed Circuit Board Mfr & Distr
N.A.I.C.S.: 334412

OLYMPIC GROUP
Ramsis Street Extension, Nasr City, Cairo, Egypt
Tel.: (20) 224880880
Web Site: http://www.olympicgroup.com
Household Appliances & Electronics Mfr & Distr
N.A.I.C.S.: 335220
Ahmed El Bakry *(Chm & CEO)*

OLYMPIC GROUP CORPORATION
4-12-1 Honmachi, Kokubunji, 185-0012, Tokyo, Japan
Tel.: (81) 423007200
Web Site: https://www.olympic-corp.co.jp
Year Founded: 1973
8289—(TKS)
Rev.: $644,743,330
Assets: $460,871,270
Liabilities: $278,062,710
Net Worth: $182,808,560
Earnings: ($3,381,930)
Emp.: 1,362
Fiscal Year-end: 02/29/24
Retail Store Operator
N.A.I.C.S.: 445110
Toru Ohshita *(Pres & Co-CEO)*

Subsidiaries:

Animal General Medical Center Corporation (1)
510 E 62nd St, New York, NY 10065
Tel.: (212) 838-8100
Web Site: https://www.amcny.org
Pet Care Services
N.A.I.C.S.: 812910

Avance Corporation (1)
1-8-26 Nakamachi, Ichinomiya, 491-0913, Aichi, Japan
Tel.: (81) 586434511
Web Site: https://www.avance-corp.com
Industrial Supplies Whslr
N.A.I.C.S.: 423840

OSC Golf World Corporation (1)
290 Shimohirama, Saiwai ward, Kawasaki, 212-0053, Kanagawa, Japan
Tel.: (81) 445424841
Web Site: https://www.golfworld.co.jp
Golf Equipment Distr
N.A.I.C.S.: 423910

OLYMPIC INDUSTRIES LIMITED
Amin Court 6th Floor 62-63 Motijheel C/A, Dhaka, 1000, Bangladesh
Tel.: (880) 9606565228
Web Site: https://www.olympicbd.com
Year Founded: 1979
OLYMPIC—(CHT)
Rev.: $238,719,823
Assets: $130,353,688
Liabilities: $37,577,004
Net Worth: $92,776,685
Earnings: $14,407,643
Fiscal Year-end: 06/30/23
Cookie Mfr
N.A.I.C.S.: 311821
Mubarak Ali *(Mng Dir)*

OLYMPIC INTERNATIONAL LTD.
344 Harbor Avenue, North Vancouver, V7J 2E9, BC, Canada
Tel.: (604) 986-1400
Web Site: http://www.olympicinternational.com
Year Founded: 1963
Rev.: $39,131,024
Emp.: 175
Warm Air Heating & Air-Conditioning Equipment & Supplies Merchant Wholesalers
N.A.I.C.S.: 423730
Julian Howitt *(Principal)*

OLYMPIC MANAGEMENT &

OLYMPIC MANAGEMENT &

OLYMPIC MANAGEMENT & —(CONTINUED)

FINANCIAL SERVICES LIMITED
42 Gopal Bhavan 199 Princess Street, Mumbai, 400002, India
Tel.: (91) 2222093908
Web Site:
  https://www.corporatementors.in
Year Founded: 1984
511632—(BOM)
Rev.: $29,035
Assets: $319,474
Liabilities: $1,575
Net Worth: $317,899
Earnings: ($21,568)
Fiscal Year-end: 03/31/14
Financial Services
N.A.I.C.S.: 523999
Akhilesh Tiwari (Officer-Compliance)

OLYMPIC OIL INDUSTRIES LIMITED
709 C Wing One BKC Near Indian Oil Petrol Pump G Block Bandra-Kurla, Complex Bandra East, Mumbai, 400051, India
Tel.: (91) 2226540901
Web Site:
  https://www.olympicoil.co.in
Year Founded: 1980
507609—(BOM)
Rev.: $100,503
Assets: $50,203,478
Liabilities: $53,079,203
Net Worth: ($2,875,725)
Earnings: $23,265
Emp.: 7
Fiscal Year-end: 03/31/21
Edible Oil Mfr
N.A.I.C.S.: 311224
Atul Rastogi (Officer-Compliance)

OLYMPUS CORPORATION
2951 Ishikawa-machi, Hachioji-shi, Tokyo, 192-8507, Japan
Tel.: (81) 426422111   JP
Web Site: https://www.olympus-global.com
Year Founded: 1919
7733—(TKS)
Rev.: $6,188,348,100
Assets: $10,141,167,760
Liabilities: $5,136,168,300
Net Worth: $5,004,999,460
Earnings: $1,603,361,260
Emp.: 28,838
Fiscal Year-end: 03/31/24
Cameras, Endoscopic Instruments, Microscopes, Analyzers & Ion Printers Mfr
N.A.I.C.S.: 333310
Akihiro Taguchi (CTO & Exec Officer)

Subsidiaries:

AVS Co., Ltd. (1)
Daiwa Sasazuka Tower 1-50-1 Sasazuka, Shibuya-Ku, Tokyo, 151-0073, Japan
Tel.: (81) 35 738 3940
Medical Equipment Distr
N.A.I.C.S.: 423450

Aizu Olympus Co., Ltd. (1)
3-1-1 Niiderakita, Aizuwakamatsu, 965-8520, Fukushima, Japan
Tel.: (81) 24 228 2111
Web Site: https://www.aizu.olympus.co.jp
Medical Equipment Mfr
N.A.I.C.S.: 339112

Aomori Olympus Co., Ltd. (1)
2-248-1 Oikonogi, Kuroishi, 036-0357, Aomori, Japan
Tel.: (81) 172528511
Web Site: https://www.aomori.olympus.co.jp
Emp.: 600
Medical Equipment Mfr
N.A.I.C.S.: 339112

Gyrus Group Limited (1)
Fortran Road, Cardiff, CF3 0LT, South Glamorgan, United Kingdom
Tel.: (44) 29 2077 6300
Web Site: http://www.olympus-oste.eu
Sales Range: $50-74.9 Million
Emp.: 15
Surgical & Medical Instrument Mfr
N.A.I.C.S.: 339112
Simon Edwards (Mng Dir)

Mishima Olympus Co., Ltd. (1)
128 Shimotogari Nagaizumi Machi, Sunto, Shizuoka, 411-0943, Japan (100%)
Tel.: (81) 559731311
Web Site:
  http://www.olympuscorporation.com
Sales Range: $25-49.9 Million
Emp.: 200
Mfr of Clinical Analyzers
N.A.I.C.S.: 621330

Nagano Olympus Co., Ltd. (1)
6666 Inatomi Tatsuno-cho, Kamiina-gun, Nagano, 399-0495, Japan
Tel.: (81) 26 641 4111
Web Site: https://www.nagano.olympus.co.jp
Medical Equipment Mfr
N.A.I.C.S.: 339112

Okaya Olympus Co., Ltd. (1)
6666 Inatomi Tatsuna Machi, Nagano, 399 0495, Japan (100%)
Tel.: (81) 266415505
Web Site: http://www.okaya.olympus.co.jp
Sales Range: $50-74.9 Million
Emp.: 150
Mfr of Magneto-Optical Disk Drives & Barcode Data Processing Devices
N.A.I.C.S.: 334112
Yamada Yoshihiro (Gen Mgr)

Olympus (China) Co., Ltd. (1)
A8F Ping An International Financial Center No 1-3 Xinyuan South Road, Chaoyang District, Beijing, 100027, China
Tel.: (86) 105 819 9000
Photocopying Equipment Mfr
N.A.I.C.S.: 333310

Olympus (Schweiz) AG (1)
Richtiring 30, 8304, Wallisellen, Switzerland (100%)
Tel.: (41) 449476662
Web Site: https://www.olympus.ch
Sales Range: $10-24.9 Million
Emp.: 100
Sales of Cameras, Recorders, Endoscopes & Microscopes
N.A.I.C.S.: 449210
Stephen Kausnau (Gen Mgr)

Olympus (Shenzhen) Industrial Ltd. (1)
North District High-Tech Industrial Park Nan Tou Nan Shan, Shenzhen, 518052, Guangdong, China
Tel.: (86) 755 2698 0118
Web Site: http://www.olympus-global.com
Sales Range: $1-4.9 Billion
Emp.: 10,000
Imaging Products Mfr
N.A.I.C.S.: 621512

Olympus (Thailand) Company Limited (1)
33/4 The Nine Tower Building A 32nd Floor Rama 9 Road, Huai Khwang Subdistrict Huai Khwang District, Bangkok, 10310, Thailand (100%)
Tel.: (66) 20007700
Web Site: https://www.olympus.co.th
Sales Range: $25-49.9 Million
Emp.: 51
Sales of Endoscopes
N.A.I.C.S.: 325414

Olympus America de Mexico S.A. de C.V. (1)
Insurgentes Sur 859 6th Floor Office 601, Col Napoles Delegacion Benito Juarez, 03810, Mexico, DF, Mexico (100%)
Tel.: (52) 5590002255
Web Site:
  http://www.olympusmexico.com.mx
Sales Range: $50-74.9 Million
Emp.: 60
Servicer of Medical Endoscopes
N.A.I.C.S.: 423450

Olympus America, Inc. (1)
3500 Corporate Pkwy, Center Valley, PA 18034-0610 (100%)
Tel.: (484) 896-5000
Web Site: http://www.learnandsupport.com
Sales Range: $300-349.9 Million
Emp.: 800
Cameras, Endoscopes, Microscopes, Clinical Analyzers & Other Products Mfr & Marketer
N.A.I.C.S.: 423410
Donna Miller (Gen Counsel & Corp VP)

Subsidiary (Domestic):

Spiration, Inc. (2)
6675 185th Ave NE, Redmond, WA 98052
Tel.: (425) 497-1700
Web Site: http://www.spiration.com
Sales Range: $25-49.9 Million
Emp.: 44
Medical Device Mfr
N.A.I.C.S.: 339112
Gregory Sessler (COO)

Olympus Asian Pacific Limited (1)
35 Twr 6 Gtwy, Tsui Sha Tsam, Kowloon, China (Hong Kong)
Tel.: (852) 27301505
Holding Company
N.A.I.C.S.: 551112

Olympus Australia Pty. Ltd. (1)
3 Acacia Place, Notting Hill, 3168, VIC, Australia (100%)
Tel.: (61) 1300132992
Web Site: https://www.olympus.com.au
Sales Range: $75-99.9 Million
Emp.: 200
Sales of Endoscopes
N.A.I.C.S.: 423450

Olympus Austria Ges.m.b.H. (1)
Shuttleworthstrasse 25, 1210, Vienna, Austria (100%)
Tel.: (43) 1291010
Web Site: http://www.olympus.at
Sales Range: $25-49.9 Million
Emp.: 88
Sales of Cameras, Endoscopes & Microscopes
N.A.I.C.S.: 449210

Olympus C&S Spol. s.r.o. (1)
Evrobska 176, 160 41, Prague, Czech Republic (100%)
Tel.: (420) 221985111
Web Site: http://www.olympus.cz
Sales Range: $50-74.9 Million
Emp.: 175
Sales of Cameras, Endoscopes, Microscopes & Other Products
N.A.I.C.S.: 449210
Jiri Bartla (Dir-Fin)

Olympus Co. (Europa) GMBH (1)
(100%)
Tel.: (49) 40237730
Web Site: http://www.olympus-europa.com
Sales Range: $200-249.9 Million
Emp.: 1,000
Sales of Cameras, Endoscopes, Microscopes & Information Related Peripheral Equipment
N.A.I.C.S.: 449210
Stefan Kaufman (Gen Mgr)

Subsidiary (Domestic):

Olympus Deutschland GmbH (2)
Wendenstrasse 20, 20097, Hamburg, Germany (100%)
Tel.: (49) 40237730
Web Site: http://www.olympus.de
Mfr of Reagents & Clinical Analyzers
N.A.I.C.S.: 334516

Olympus Corporation of Asia Pacific Limited (1)
L26 Tower 1 Kowloon Commerce Centre 51 Kwai Cheong Road, Mongkok, Kwai Chung, New Territories, China (Hong Kong)
Tel.: (852) 24817812
Sales Range: $25-49.9 Million
Emp.: 7
Imaging & Medical Instrument Mfr
N.A.I.C.S.: 334510
Atnes Loeunt (Mgr-HR)

Olympus Corporation of the Americas (1)

INTERNATIONAL PUBLIC

3500 Corporate Pkwy, Center Valley, PA 18034-0610
Tel.: (484) 896-5000
Web Site: https://www.olympusamerica.com
Imaging & Medical Products Sales, Service & Marketing
N.A.I.C.S.: 621512
Mark Miller (VP- Corp & Medical Comm)

Subsidiary (Domestic):

Image Stream Medical, Inc. (2)
1 Monarch Dr, Littleton, MA 01460
Tel.: (978) 486-8494
Web Site:
  http://www.imagestreammedical.com
Medical Imaging Management Software & Hardware Products Developer & Whslr
N.A.I.C.S.: 423450
Eddie E. Mitchell (CEO)

Olympus Danmark A/S (1)
Tempovej 48-50, 2750, Ballerup, Denmark
Tel.: (45) 44734700
Web Site: https://www.olympus.dk
Sales Range: $25-49.9 Million
Emp.: 74
Sales of Cameras, Microscopes & Microcassette Recorders
N.A.I.C.S.: 449210
Harald Dremmel (Mng Dir)

Olympus Digital System Design Corp (1)
8F Nihon-Seimei Tachikawa Bldg 2-20-5 Akebono-cho, Tachikawa-shi, Tokyo, 190-0012, Japan
Tel.: (81) 426423953
Digital System Software Development Services
N.A.I.C.S.: 541511

Olympus Engineering Co., Ltd. (1)
4-29-16 Owada-cho, Hachioji, 192-0045, Tokyo, Japan
Tel.: (81) 42 645 9161
Web Site: http://www.olympus-global.com
Sales Range: $25-49.9 Million
Emp.: 20
Industrial Equipment Mfr
N.A.I.C.S.: 333248
Hitoshi Yamazaki (Gen Mgr)

Olympus Europa GmbH (1)
Wendenstrasse 20, 20097, Hamburg, Germany (100%)
Tel.: (49) 40237730
Web Site: http://www.olympuseuropa.com
Sales Range: $150-199.9 Million
Emp.: 700
Servicer of Endoscopes
N.A.I.C.S.: 811210
Frank Drewalowski (Mng Dir-Medical Sys Div)

Olympus Europa Holding GmbH (1)
Wendenstrasse 20, 20097, Hamburg, Germany
Tel.: (49) 40237730
Web Site: http://www.olympus-europa.com
Sales Range: $200-249.9 Million
Emp.: 700
Optical & Digital Equipment Mfr
N.A.I.C.S.: 334419
Frank Drewalowski (Mng Dir)

Olympus Finland Oy (1)
Vanrikinkuja 3, 02600, Espoo, Finland (100%)
Tel.: (358) 9875810
Web Site: https://www.olympus.fi
Sales Range: $25-49.9 Million
Emp.: 50
Medical Equipment & Cameras Sales & Distr
N.A.I.C.S.: 423450
Arni Ekholm (Mng Dir)

Olympus France S.A.S. (1)
19 rue d'Arcueil, CS 700014, 94593, Rungis, Cedex, France (100%)
Tel.: (33) 145602300
Web Site: https://www.olympus.fr
Sales Range: $100-124.9 Million
Emp.: 450
Sales of Cameras, Endoscopes, Microscopes, Clinical Analyzers & Other Products
N.A.I.C.S.: 333310
Didier Quilain (Gen Mgr)

AND PRIVATE COMPANIES

OLYMPUS CORPORATION

Olympus Hong Kong and China Ltd. (1)
26th Floor Tower 1 Kowloon Trade Centre 51 Kwai Cheong Road, Kwai Chung, China (Hong Kong) **(100%)**
Tel.: (852) 24817812
Web Site: http://hk.olympus.com
Sales Range: $200-249.9 Million
Emp.: 790
Mfr of Cameras & Microcassette Recorders
N.A.I.C.S.: 333310

Olympus Hungary Kft. (1)
Papirgyar u 58-59, 1038, Budapest, Hungary **(100%)**
Tel.: (36) 16960721
Web Site: http://www.olympus.hu
Sales Range: $25-49.9 Million
Emp.: 60
Sales & Servicer of Endoscopes, Microscopes & Cameras
N.A.I.C.S.: 811210

Olympus Imaging America Inc. (1)
3500 Corporate Pkwy, Center Valley, PA 18034-0610
Tel.: (484) 896-5000
Digital & Professional Camera Mfr & Distr
N.A.I.C.S.: 333310

Olympus Imaging Corp. (1)
Shinjuku Monolith 2-3-1 Nishi-Shinjuku, Shinjuku-ku, Tokyo, 163-0914, Japan
Tel.: (81) 3 3340 2210
Web Site: http://www.olympus-global.com
Sales Range: $250-299.9 Million
Emp.: 1,000
Imaging & Information Equipment Whslr
N.A.I.C.S.: 423910
Haruo Ogawa *(Pres)*

Plant (Domestic):

Olympus Imaging Corp - Ishikawa Facility (2)
2951 Ishikawa-machi, Hachioji, 192-8507, Tokyo, Japan
Tel.: (81) 42 642 2111
Web Site: http://www.olympus-global.com
Medical Instrument Mfr
N.A.I.C.S.: 339112

Olympus Imaging Corp - Utsugi Facility (2)
2-3 Kuboyamacho, Hachioji, 192-8512, Tokyo, Japan
Tel.: (81) 42 691 7111
Web Site: http://www.olympus.co.jp
Medical Equipment Mfr
N.A.I.C.S.: 339112

Olympus Imaging India Private Limited (1)
8th Floor Corporate Park 2 Sion Trombay Rd, Chembur, Mumbai, 400 071, Maharashtra, India
Tel.: (91) 22 61420400
Web Site: http://www.olympus-imaging.co.in
Sales Range: $25-49.9 Million
Emp.: 27
Digital Camera & Accessories Distr
N.A.I.C.S.: 423410
Kenichiro Mori *(Mng Dir)*

Olympus Imaging Singapore Pte. Ltd. (1)
491B River Valley Road 13-03 Valley Point Office Tower, Singapore, 248373, Singapore
Tel.: (65) 6834 0010
Web Site: http://www.olympus-global.com
Medical Imaging Products Distr
N.A.I.C.S.: 423450
Jimmy Loh *(Gen Mgr)*

Olympus Italia S.R.L. (1)
Via San Bovio 1-3, 20054, Segrate, MI, Italy
Tel.: (39) 02269721
Web Site: https://www.olympus.it
Sales Range: $50-74.9 Million
Emp.: 175
Sales of Microscopes
N.A.I.C.S.: 334516
Andrea Bernardini *(Mng Dir)*

Olympus Keymed Group Limited (1)
KeyMed House Stock Rd, Southend-on-Sea, SS2 5QH, United Kingdom **(100%)**
Tel.: (44) 1702616333
Web Site: http://www.olympus.com

Sales Range: $550-599.9 Million
Emp.: 1,200
Sales of Cameras & Microscopes
N.A.I.C.S.: 423410
Constantin Zangemeister *(Mng Dir)*

Subsidiary (Domestic):

KeyMed (Medical & Industrial Equipment) Ltd. (2)
KeyMed House, Stock Road, Southend-on-Sea, SS2 5QH, Essex, United Kingdom **(100%)**
Tel.: (44) 1702616333
Web Site: http://www.keymed.co.uk
Sales Range: $150-199.9 Million
Emp.: 900
Mfr & Sales of Endoscopes
N.A.I.C.S.: 334510

Subsidiary (Domestic):

Algram Group Ltd. (3)
Eastern Wood Road, Langage Business Park Plympton, Plymouth, PL7 5ET, Devon, United Kingdom **(100%)**
Tel.: (44) 1752320000
Web Site: https://www.algram.net
Sales Range: $25-49.9 Million
Emp.: 180
Plastics Product Mfr
N.A.I.C.S.: 326199
Catherine Harris *(Mng Dir)*

Subsidiary (Non-US):

KeyMed Ireland Ltd. (3)
KeyMed House Calmount Park, Ballymount, Dublin, Ireland **(100%)**
Tel.: (353) 14260100
Web Site: http://www.keymed.co.uk
Sales Range: $25-49.9 Million
Emp.: 30
Sales of Endoscopes
N.A.I.C.S.: 334517
Alison Harvey *(Dir-Medical Bus & Mng Dir)*

Olympus Ireland (3)
KeyMed House Calmount Park, Ballymount, Dublin, Ireland
Tel.: (353) 14260100
Web Site: http://www.olympus.ie
Sales Range: $25-49.9 Million
Emp.: 23
Medical Equipment Distr
N.A.I.C.S.: 423450
Philip Cullinan *(Gen Mgr)*

Subsidiary (Domestic):

Olympus (U.K.) Ltd. (2)
KeyMed House Stock Road, Southend-on-Sea, SS2 5QH, United Kingdom **(100%)**
Tel.: (44) 1702616333
Web Site: https://www.olympus.co.uk
Sales Range: $50-74.9 Million
Emp.: 200
Holding Company for Manufacturers of Dictation Equipment, Digital Voice Recorders & Digital Dictation
N.A.I.C.S.: 551112

Olympus Korea Co., Ltd. (1)
3rd floor 12 Seocho-daero 38-gil Seocho-dong Majesta City Tower One, Seocho-gu, Seoul, 06655, Korea (South)
Tel.: (82) 15443200
Web Site: https://www.olympus.co.kr
Sales Range: $75-99.9 Million
Emp.: 200
Medical Equipment Distr
N.A.I.C.S.: 423450

Olympus Latin America Inc. (1)
5301 Blue Lagoon Dr Ste 290, Miami, FL 33126
Tel.: (305) 266-2332
Web Site: http://www.olympusamericalatina.com
Business Support Services
N.A.I.C.S.: 561499

Olympus Logitex Co., Ltd. (1)
1-13-1 Asamizodai, Minami-ku, Sagamihara, 252-0328, Kanagawa, Japan **(100%)**
Tel.: (81) 427019800
Web Site: http://www.logitex.olympus.co.jp
Emp.: 99
Provider of Transportation Services
N.A.I.C.S.: 488210

Olympus Medical Engineering Co., Ltd. (1)
Shinjuko Monolith 3-1 Nishi Shinjuku 2-Chome Shinjuku-Ku, Tokyo, 163 0914, Japan
Tel.: (81) 369014080
Web Site: http://www.olympus.co.jp
Sales Range: $400-449.9 Million
Emp.: 1,400
Maintainer of Clinical Analyzers
N.A.I.C.S.: 334516

Olympus Medical Science Sales Corp. (1)
Tower 12F 3-20-2 Nishi Shinjuku, Shinjuku-ku, Tokyo, 163-1412, Japan
Tel.: (81) 3 3379 600
Web Site: http://www.olympus.co.jp
Medical Equipment Whslr
N.A.I.C.S.: 423450

Olympus Medical Systems Corp. (1)
2951 Ishikawa-machi, Hachioji, 192-8507, Tokyo, Japan
Tel.: (81) 426422111
Web Site: http://www.olympus.co.jp
Medical Equipment Mfr & Whslr
N.A.I.C.S.: 339112

Plant (Domestic):

Olympus Medical Systems Corp - Hinode Plant (2)
34-3 Hirai Hinode-cho, Nishitama-gun, Tokyo, 190-0182, Japan
Tel.: (81) 42 597 7111
Web Site: http://www.olympus-global.com
Medical Equipment Mfr
N.A.I.C.S.: 339112

Olympus Medical Systems Corp - Ishikawa Facility (2)
2951 Ishikawa-machi, Hachioji, 192-8507, Tokyo, Japan
Tel.: (81) 42 642 2111
Web Site: http://www.olympus.co.jp
Medical Equipment Mfr
N.A.I.C.S.: 334510

Olympus Medical Systems Corp - Shirakawa Facility (2)
3-1 Oaza-Odakura-Aza-Okamiyama, Nishigo-mura Nishishirakawa-gun, Fukushima, 961-8061, Japan
Tel.: (81) 248 27 2211
Web Site: http://www.olympus-global.com
Medical Equipment Mfr
N.A.I.C.S.: 339112
Kazuhisa Otani *(Gen Mgr)*

Olympus Medical Systems Corp - Utsugi Facility (2)
2-3 Kuboyama-cho, Hachioji, 192-8512, Tokyo, Japan
Tel.: (81) 426917111
Web Site: https://www.olympus-global.com
Medical Camera Equipments Mfr
N.A.I.C.S.: 339112

Olympus Medical Systems India Private Limited (1)
Ground Floor Tower-C SAS Tower The Medicity Complex Sector- 38, Gurgaon, 122001, Haryana, India
Tel.: (91) 1244999191
Web Site: https://www.olympus.in
Sales Range: $25-49.9 Million
Emp.: 160
Medical Equipment Mfr
N.A.I.C.S.: 339112

Olympus Medical Systems Vietnam Co., Ltd. (1)
Unit 305-307 3rd Floor V Tower 649 Kim Ma Street, Ba Dinh District, Hanoi, Vietnam
Tel.: (84) 243 766 5831
Web Site: https://olympusmedical.com.vn
Medical Equipment Distr
N.A.I.C.S.: 423450

Olympus Memory Works Corp. (1)
Daiwa Sasazuka Tower 1-50-1 Sasazuka, Shibuya-ku, Tokyo, 151-0073, Japan
Tel.: (81) 357383550
Web Site: http://www.olympus.co.jp
Sales Range: $25-49.9 Million
Emp.: 8
Network Storage Device Mfr
N.A.I.C.S.: 334112

Olympus NDT Canada Inc. (1)
3415 rue Pierre-Ardouin, Quebec, G1P 0B3, QC, Canada
Tel.: (418) 872-1155
Web Site: http://www.olympus-global.com
Sales Range: $100-124.9 Million
Emp.: 400
Analytical Instrument Mfr
N.A.I.C.S.: 334516
Alaian Laboissonniere *(Gen Mgr)*

Olympus NDT Corporation (1)
48 Woerd Ave, Waltham, MA 02453
Tel.: (484) 896-5000
Web Site: http://www.olympus-global.com
Ultrasonic Testing Instruments Mfr & Whslr
N.A.I.C.S.: 335999

Olympus New Zealand Limited (1)
28 Corinthian Drive, Albany, Auckland, 0632, New Zealand **(100%)**
Tel.: (64) 98369993
Web Site: https://www.olympus.co.nz
Sales Range: $25-49.9 Million
Emp.: 25
Distr of Endoscopes & Microscopes
N.A.I.C.S.: 334517

Olympus Norge A/S (1)
Drengsrudbekken 12, 1383, Asker, Norway **(100%)**
Tel.: (47) 23005050
Web Site: https://www.olympus.no
Sales Range: $25-49.9 Million
Emp.: 50
Sales of Cameras, Microcassette Recorders & Microscopes
N.A.I.C.S.: 449210
Roberto Cartadnano *(Mng Dir)*

Olympus Optical Polska Sp. z.o.o. (1)
ul Suwak 3, 00-676, Warsaw, Poland
Tel.: (48) 228600077
Endoscopes, Microscopes & Other Products Whslr
N.A.I.C.S.: 334516

Olympus Optical Technology Philippines, Inc. (1)
Mactan Economic ZoneII, 6015, Lapu-Lapu, Cebu, Philippines
Tel.: (63) 32 341 3160
Web Site: http://www.olympus.co.jp
Sales Range: $25-49.9 Million
Emp.: 50
Microscope Mfr
N.A.I.C.S.: 333310

Olympus Opto-Technology Co., Ltd (1)
6666 Inatomi Tatsuno-Machi, Kamiina-Gun, Nagano, 399 0495, Japan **(100%)**
Tel.: (81) 266414111
Sales Range: $50-74.9 Million
Emp.: 600
Mfr of Cameras, Endoscopes & Other Products
N.A.I.C.S.: 333310
Hiro Okda *(Mng Dir)*

Branch (Domestic):

Olympus Opto-Technology Co., Ltd.-Sakaki (2)
1355 Nakanojo, Sakaki, Nagano, 398 0004, Japan **(100%)**
Tel.: (81) 268822361
Mfr of Optical Products
N.A.I.C.S.: 333310

Olympus Scientific Solutions Americas Inc. (1)
48 Woerd Ave, Waltham, MA 02453
Tel.: (781) 419-3900
Web Site: http://www.olympus-ims.com
Sales Range: $25-49.9 Million
Emp.: 109
X-Ray Devices Mfr
N.A.I.C.S.: 334513
Michael Drummy *(VP Engrg & Product Dev)*

Olympus Singapore Pte Ltd. (1)
438B Alexandra Road 03-07/12 Alexandra Technopark Blk B, Singapore, 119968, Singapore **(100%)**
Tel.: (65) 68340010
Web Site: https://www.olympus.com.sg
Sales Range: $10-24.9 Million
Emp.: 100

OLYMPUS CORPORATION

Olympus Corporation—(Continued)
Sales of Endoscopes, Microscopes, Cameras & Microcassette Recorders
N.A.I.C.S.: 423450

Olympus Slovenia d.o.o. (1)
Baznikova 2, 1000, Ljubljana, Slovenia (100%)
Tel.: (386) 012363310
Web Site: http://www.olympus.se
Sales Range: $25-49.9 Million
Emp.: 15
Distr of Cameras, Voice Processing Equipment, Flexible Endoscopy Equipment & Digital Imaging Equipment
N.A.I.C.S.: 333310

Olympus Soft Imaging Solutions GmbH (1)
Johann-Krane-Weg 39, 48149, Munster, Germany
Tel.: (49) 251798000
Web Site: http://www.olympus-sis.com
Sales Range: $50-74.9 Million
Emp.: 120
Imaging Solutions
N.A.I.C.S.: 323111

Olympus Software Technology Corp. (1)
14f Tokyo Opera City Bldg 3-20-2 Nishi-Shinjuku, Shinjuku-ku, Tokyo, 163-1414, Japan
Tel.: (81) 3 3374 9179
Web Site: http://www.olympus-soft.jp
Sales Range: $150-199.9 Million
Emp.: 581
Healthcare Software Development Services
N.A.I.C.S.: 541511

Olympus Surgical Technologies Europe (1)
Web Site: http://www.olympus.co.uk
Sales Range: $100-124.9 Million
Emp.: 277
Endoscopic Medical Equipment Mfr
N.A.I.C.S.: 339113
Andre Roggan (Exec Mng Dir & Chm)

Subsidiary (US):

Olympus Surgical Technologies America (2)
800 W Park Dr, Westborough, MA 01581
Tel.: (508) 804-2600
Web Site: http://www.gyrusacmi.com
Diagnostic & Therapeutic Endoscopic Instrumentation Products Mfr & Whslr
N.A.I.C.S.: 334510

Division (Domestic):

Gyrus ACMI ENT (3)
2925 Appling Rd, Bartlett, TN 38133
Tel.: (901) 373-0200
Web Site: http://www.gyrus-acmi.com
Sales Range: $50-74.9 Million
Emp.: 150
Specialized Medical Products for Ear, Nose & Throat
N.A.I.C.S.: 339112

Gyrus ACMI Stamford Division (3)
300 Stillwater Ave, Stamford, CT 06902-3695
Tel.: (203) 357-8300
Sales Range: $125-149.9 Million
Emp.: 340
Diagnostic & Therapeutic Endoscopic Instrumentation Products Mfr & Whslr
N.A.I.C.S.: 334510

Gyrus ACMI-Surgical Division (3)
6655 Wedgwood Rd Ste 160, Maple Grove, MN 55311-3602
Tel.: (763) 416-3000
Web Site: http://www.olympusamerica.com
Sales Range: $50-74.9 Million
Emp.: 250
Endoscopic Medical Instrument Mfr
N.A.I.C.S.: 334510

Olympus Sverige AB (1)
Rasundavagen 12, 169 67, Solna, Sweden (100%)
Tel.: (46) 87353400
Web Site: http://www.olympus.se
Sales Range: $25-49.9 Million
Emp.: 63
Sales of Cameras & Recorders
N.A.I.C.S.: 449210

Olympus Systems Corporation (1)
1-53-6 Hatsudai, Shibuya, Tokyo, Japan
Tel.: (81) 353500620
Information Technology Consulting Services
N.A.I.C.S.: 541512
Stephen Kneebone (Pres)

Olympus Systems Corporation - Enterprise Division (1)
Hatsudai Kouyama Bldg 1-53-6 Hatsudai, Shibuya-ku, Tokyo, 151-0061, Japan
Tel.: (81) 3 3350 0620
Sales Range: $25-49.9 Million
Emp.: 20
Information Support Services
N.A.I.C.S.: 561990

Olympus Systems Corporation - UVAS Division (1)
Hatsudai Kouyama Bldg 1-53-6 Hatsudai, Shibuya-ku, Tokyo, 151-0061, Japan
Tel.: (81) 3 3350 0620
Information System Services
N.A.I.C.S.: 519290

Olympus Taiwan Co., Ltd. (1)
2nd Floor No 6 No 210 38 Road Technology Building, Taichung Industrial Zone, Taichung, Taiwan
Tel.: (886) 42 350 8668
Web Site: https://www.olympus.com.tw
Medical Equipment Mfr
N.A.I.C.S.: 339112

Olympus Technologies Singapore Pte. Ltd. (1)
41 Science Pk Rd 04-17-18 The Gemini Singapore Science Pk II, Singapore, 117610, Singapore (100%)
Tel.: (65) 67778978
Sales Range: $25-49.9 Million
Emp.: 49
Mfr of Information Peripheral Equipment
N.A.I.C.S.: 334118
Hockngee Lim (Mng Dir)

Olympus Terumo Biomaterials Corp. (1)
Daiwa Sasazuka Tower 1-50-1 Sasazuka, Shibuya-ku, Tokyo, 151-0073, Japan
Tel.: (81) 357383950
Web Site: https://www.biomaterial.co.jp
Sales Range: $25-49.9 Million
Emp.: 135
Biomaterial Products Research & Development Services
N.A.I.C.S.: 541715

Olympus Trading (Shanghai) Limited (1)
Unit E F 3F 185 Taigu Rd Pilot FTZ, Shanghai, 200131, China
Tel.: (86) 2158667171
Web Site: http://www.olympuschina.com
Medical Equipment Distr
N.A.I.C.S.: 423450

Olympus Vietnam Co., Ltd. (1)
8 Street, Long Thanh Industrial Zone Tam An Commune Long Thanh District, Dong Nai, Vietnam
Tel.: (84) 251 351 4555
Web Site: https://www.olympus-vn.com
Medical Equipment Mfr
N.A.I.C.S.: 339112

Olympus Winter & Ibe GmbH (1)
Kuehnstrasse 61, 22045, Hamburg, Germany (100%)
Tel.: (49) 40669660
Web Site: http://www.olympus-oste.eu
Sales Range: $100-124.9 Million
Emp.: 1,245
Mfr & Sales of Endoscopes
N.A.I.C.S.: 334517

Olympus d.o.o. za trgovinu (1)
Avenia Veceslava Holjevea 40, 10000, Zagreb, Croatia (100%)
Tel.: (385) 14899000
Web Site: http://www.olympus.hr
Sales Range: $25-49.9 Million
Emp.: 32
Sales of Cameras, Endoscopes & Microscopes
N.A.I.C.S.: 449210

Olympus-Supportmate Corp. (1)
2951 Ishikawacho, Hachioji, 192-8507, Tokyo, Japan
Tel.: (81) 426422111
Web Site: https://www.olympus-supportmate.jp
Cleaning Service
N.A.I.C.S.: 561720

Shirakawa Olympus Co., Ltd. (1)
3-1 Okamiyama Odakura Nishigo-mura, Nishishirakawa, Fukushima, 961-8061, Japan (100%)
Tel.: (81) 248272211
Web Site: http://www.shirakawa.olympus.co.jp
Sales Range: $100-124.9 Million
Emp.: 300
Mfr of Endoscope Light Sources & Accessories
N.A.I.C.S.: 334517

Sony Olympus Medical Solutions Inc. (1)
4-7-1 Koyasu-machi, Hachioji, Tokyo, 192-0904, Japan
Tel.: (81) 42 655 7232
Web Site: https://www.sony-olympus-medical.com
Emp.: 130
Medical Product Mfr & Distr
N.A.I.C.S.: 339112
Katsunori Ogawa (Pres)

Tmedix Corporation (1)
2-3-1 Shinjuku Monolith, Shinjuku Nishi-Shinjuku-Ku, Tokyo, 163-0914, Japan
Tel.: (81) 33 349 8590
Web Site: https://www.tmedix.com
Medical Equipment Mfr & Distr
N.A.I.C.S.: 339112

Veran Medical Technologies, Inc. (1)
1938 Innerbelt Business Ctr Dr, Saint Louis, MO 63114
Tel.: (314) 659-8500
Web Site: http://www.veranmedical.com
Electromedical & Electrotherapeutic Apparatus Mfr
N.A.I.C.S.: 334510
Jason Pesterfield (Pres & CEO)

OLYMPUS DIGITAL KG
Hopfigheimer Str 19, 74321, Bietigheim-Bissingen, Germany
Tel.: (49) 71425920
Web Site: http://www.olymp.com
Year Founded: 1951
Sales Range: $75-99.9 Million
Emp.: 759
Men's Clothing Stores
N.A.I.C.S.: 458110
Eugen Bezner (Founder, Owner & CEO)

OM FINANCIAL LIMITED
Level 2 37 Galway Street Britomart, Auckland, New Zealand
Tel.: (64) 9 520 9310
Web Site: http://www.omf.co.nz
Year Founded: 1987
Rev.: $13,462,217
Assets: $182,681,839
Liabilities: $172,664,882
Net Worth: $10,016,957
Earnings: $699,419
Emp.: 200
Fiscal Year-end: 03/31/18
Brokerage Services
N.A.I.C.S.: 523160
Lance Jones (COO)

OM HOLDINGS LIMITED
10 Eunos Road 8 09-03A Singapore Post Centre, Singapore, 408600, Singapore
Tel.: (65) 63465515   BM
Web Site:
  https://www.omholdingsltd.com
Year Founded: 1998
5298 (KLS)
Rev.: $589,235,000
Assets: $940,942,000
Liabilities: $526,316,000
Net Worth: $414,626,000
Earnings: $18,360,000
Emp.: 2,371
Fiscal Year-end: 12/31/23
Manganese Mining, Trading & Production Services
N.A.I.C.S.: 212290
Ngee Tong Low (Chm)

Subsidiaries:

OM (Manganese) Ltd (1)
Suite 13B 420 Bagot Road, Subiaco, 6008, WA, Australia
Tel.: (61) 863111500
Sales Range: $200-249.9 Million
Mineral Services
N.A.I.C.S.: 213115

OM Materials (Qinzhou) Co Ltd (1)
JinguJiang Industrial Garden Qinzhou Port, Qinzhou, 535008, Guangxi, China
Tel.: (86) 7773887800
Sales Range: $75-99.9 Million
Marketing Services
N.A.I.C.S.: 541613
Yang Li Zhong (Chm)

OM Materials (S) Pte Ltd (1)
10 Eunos Road 8 09-03A Singapore Post Centre, Singapore, 408600, Singapore
Tel.: (65) 63465515
Sales Range: $50-74.9 Million
Emp.: 24
Investment Management Service
N.A.I.C.S.: 523999

OM INFRA LTD.
NBCC Plaza Tower-III 4th Floor Sector 5 Pushp Vihar, Saket, New Delhi, 110 017, India
Tel.: (91) 1129565552
Web Site: https://www.ommetals.com
Year Founded: 1969
OMINFRAL—(NSE)
Rev.: $34,042,895
Assets: $157,875,368
Liabilities: $72,936,987
Net Worth: $84,938,381
Earnings: $1,493,747
Emp.: 259
Fiscal Year-end: 03/31/21
Hydro Mechanical Equipment Mfr
N.A.I.C.S.: 333613
Sunil Kothari (Mng Dir)

Subsidiaries:

Om Metals Auto Pvt. Ltd (1)
F 99A Rd No 7 VKI Area, Sikkar Rd, Jaipur, 302013, Rajasthan, India
Tel.: (91) 1415150789
Web Site: http://www.ommetals.com
Sales Range: $25-49.9 Million
Emp.: 100
Hydro Mechanical Equipment Mfr
N.A.I.C.S.: 336320

OM PHARMA SA
22 rue du Bois-du-Lan, Meyrin, 1217, Geneva, Switzerland
Tel.: (41) 22 783 11 11
Web Site:
  http://www.viforpharma.com
Emp.: 200
Pharmaceuticals Product Mfr
N.A.I.C.S.: 325412
Frederic Zwahlen (Mgr)

OM RESIDUAL UK LIMITED
5th Floor Millennium Bridge House, 2 Lambeth Hill, London, EC4V 4GG, United Kingdom
Tel.: (44) 2070027000   UK
Web Site: http://www.oldmutual.com
Year Founded: 1927
Rev.: $23,440,857,840
Assets: $215,110,242,720
Liabilities: $201,107,916,000
Net Worth: $14,002,326,720
Earnings: $1,059,452,550
Emp.: 64,043

AND PRIVATE COMPANIES

Fiscal Year-end: 12/31/16
International Financial Services
N.A.I.C.S.: 523940
Trevor Manuel *(Chm)*

Subsidiaries:

Mutual & Federal Insurance Company Limited (1)
75 Helen Joseph Street, 2001, Johannesburg, South Africa
Tel.: (27) 113749111
Web Site: http://www.mf.co.za
Sales Range: $900-999.9 Million
Emp.: 3,000
Insurance Services
N.A.I.C.S.: 524126

Quilter Cheviot Limited (1)
One Kingsway, London, WC2B 6AN, United Kingdom
Tel.: (44) 20 7150 4000
Web Site: http://www.quiltercheviot.com
Investment Management Service
N.A.I.C.S.: 523940
Duncan Gwyther *(CIO)*

OM2NETWORK CO., LTD.
2-4-7 Shiba Daimon, Minato-Ku, Tokyo, 105-0012, Japan
Tel.: (81) 354059541
Web Site: https://www.om2.co.jp
Year Founded: 1966
7614—(TKS)
Rev.: $287,728,320
Assets: $176,708,400
Liabilities: $35,119,040
Net Worth: $141,589,360
Earnings: $9,408,960
Fiscal Year-end: 01/31/22
Meat Retailer
N.A.I.C.S.: 424470
Tsutomu Ogoe *(Pres)*

OMA SAASTOPANKKI OYJ
Valtakatu 32, 53100, Lappeenranta, 53100, Finland
Tel.: (358) 207640600
Web Site: https://www.omasp.fi
Year Founded: 2009
OMASP—(HEL)
Rev.: $155,881,718
Assets: $6,412,443,341
Liabilities: $6,018,573,279
Net Worth: $393,870,063
Earnings: $59,766,890
Emp.: 463
Fiscal Year-end: 12/31/22
Commercial Banking Services
N.A.I.C.S.: 522110
Pasi Sydänlammi *(Pres & CEO)*

Subsidiaries:

Handelsbanken Rahoitus Oy (1)
Tel.: (358) 104442800
Web Site: http://www.handelsbanken.fi
Commercial Banking Services
N.A.I.C.S.: 522110

SAV-Rahoitus Oyj (1)
Mikonkatu 8 A 7th Floor, 00100, Helsinki, Finland
Tel.: (358) 932993200
Web Site: http://www.sav-rahoitus.fi
Vehicle Financing Services
N.A.I.C.S.: 522220
Jyri Niemi *(Sls Mgr)*

OMAI GOLD MINES CORP.
401 Bay Street Suite 2704, Toronto, M5H 2Y4, ON, Canada
Tel.: (416) 815-9777
Web Site: https://omaigoldmines.com
Year Founded: 1969
OMG—(TSXV)
Rev.: $33,747
Assets: $4,277,122
Liabilities: $883,603
Net Worth: $3,393,519
Earnings: ($3,392,775)
Emp.: 6

Fiscal Year-end: 12/31/23
Precious Metal Exploration Services
N.A.I.C.S.: 212390
Denis Clement *(Chm)*

OMAN & EMIRATES INVESTMENT HOLDING COMPANY SAOG
PO Box 2205, Ruwi, 112, Oman
Tel.: (968) 24489458
Web Site: http://www.omanemirates.com
Year Founded: 1993
OEIO—(MUS)
Rev.: $5,714,885
Assets: $123,985,739
Liabilities: $60,352,123
Net Worth: $63,633,616
Earnings: $4,782,907
Emp.: 8
Fiscal Year-end: 12/31/21
Holding Company
N.A.I.C.S.: 551112
Mohamed Darwish Al Khoori *(Chm)*

Subsidiaries:

Omani Euro Food Industries SAOG (1)
PO Box 23, 134, Muscat, Oman
Tel.: (968) 24691266
Web Site: http://www.babyfoodoman.com
Rev.: $5,306,634
Assets: $8,156,877
Liabilities: $10,944,933
Net Worth: ($2,788,056)
Earnings: ($456,039)
Emp.: 53
Fiscal Year-end: 12/31/2021
Food Products Mfr
N.A.I.C.S.: 311999
Hussain Mohammed Hassan Al Lawati *(Gen Mgr)*

OMAN AIR S.A.O.C.
Muscat International Airport, PO Box 58, Muscat, 111, Oman
Tel.: (968) 24531111
Web Site: http://www.omanair.com
Year Founded: 1993
Sales Range: $1-4.9 Billion
Emp.: 7,633
Airline Transportation Services
N.A.I.C.S.: 488119
Salim Mohammed Al Kindy *(Deputy CEO & Exec VP-Change)*

OMAN CHLORINE S.A.O.G.
Bldg No 708 Way No 2114, Madinat Al Sultan Qaboos, Muscat, Oman
Tel.: (968) 24695839
Web Site: https://www.omanchlorine.com
Year Founded: 1998
OCHL—(MUS)
Rev.: $83,572,197
Assets: $237,763,879
Liabilities: $155,852,531
Net Worth: $81,911,348
Earnings: $5,290,410
Emp.: 104
Fiscal Year-end: 12/31/23
Chemical Products Mfr
N.A.I.C.S.: 325998
Sulaiman Mohammed Al Yahyai *(Chm)*

Subsidiaries:

Gulf Chlorine W.L.L (1)
Zone No 93 -Street number 303- Building No 68, PO Box 55627, Mesaieed Industrial City MIC - Medium Industries Area, Doha, 93020007, Qatar
Tel.: (974) 44147100
Web Site: https://www.gulfchlorine.com
Chemical Products Mfr
N.A.I.C.S.: 325180
Sulaiman Mohamad Hamed Al Yahyai *(Chm)*

Union Chlorine L.L.C (1)
Tarif Road-ICAD 3, PO Box 42387, Abu-Dhabi, United Arab Emirates
Tel.: (971) 24475231
Web Site: https://www.unionchlorine.com
Chemical Products Mfr
N.A.I.C.S.: 325180
Sulaiman Mohamad Hamed Al Yahyai *(Chm)*

OMAN CHROMITE COMPANY (SAOG)
Tel.: (968) 26845115
Web Site: https://www.omanchromite.com
Year Founded: 1991
OCCI—(MUS)
Rev.: $15,547,495
Assets: $19,737,022
Liabilities: $4,339,222
Net Worth: $15,397,800
Earnings: $4,238,487
Emp.: 84
Fiscal Year-end: 12/31/23
Chromite Mining Services
N.A.I.C.S.: 212290
Ali Abdullah Al Badi *(Deputy Chm)*

OMAN EDUCATION & TRAINING INVESTMENTS
Al Batinah Govern, PO Box 553, 311, Sohar, Oman
Tel.: (968) 26850160
Web Site: http://www.en.oeti.om
OETI—(MUS)
Rev.: $41,867,739
Assets: $113,991,878
Liabilities: $58,818,440
Net Worth: $55,173,438
Earnings: $7,579,713
Emp.: 665
Fiscal Year-end: 08/31/23
Education Services
N.A.I.C.S.: 611710
Hassan Ehsan Naseeb Al Naseeb *(Chm)*

OMAN FIBER OPTIC CO. S.A.O.G.
Road No 4C Al Rusayl, PO Box 5, 124, Muscat, Oman
Tel.: (968) 2444 1000 OM
Web Site: http://www.omanfiber.com
Year Founded: 1995
Sales Range: $75-99.9 Million
Emp.: 256
Fiber Optic Cable Mfr
N.A.I.C.S.: 335921
Mohammed Khamis Al Sinaidy *(CFO)*

OMAN FILTERS INDUSTRY COMPANY SAOG
Oman Filters Industry Building St 23 Industrial Estate Area, PO Box 45, Muscat, 124, Oman
Tel.: (968) 24446420
Year Founded: 1995
OFII—(MUS)
Sales Range: $1-9.9 Million
Emp.: 65
Automotive & Industrial Filters Mfr & Marketer
N.A.I.C.S.: 333248
Issa Ali Al-Hawqani *(Chm)*

OMAN FISHERIES CO. SAOG
PO Box 2900, Ruwi, 112, Oman
Tel.: (968) 24509500
Web Site: https://www.omanfisheries.com
Year Founded: 1987
OFCI—(MUS)
Rev.: $33,738,637
Assets: $31,777,421
Liabilities: $12,952,919
Net Worth: $18,824,502
Earnings: ($8,002,068)

Emp.: 494
Fiscal Year-end: 12/31/20
Seafood Product Mfr
N.A.I.C.S.: 311710
Khalid Mansoor Sabil Al Zadjali *(CEO)*

OMAN FLOUR MILLS CO SAOG
PO Box 566, Ruwi, 112, Oman
Tel.: (968) 24717300
Web Site: http://www.omanflourmills.com
Year Founded: 1977
OFMI—(MUS)
Rev.: $252,212,821
Assets: $362,341,028
Liabilities: $170,724,373
Net Worth: $191,616,655
Earnings: $12,287,138
Emp.: 260
Fiscal Year-end: 12/31/21
Flour Mills
N.A.I.C.S.: 311211
Salah Hilal Al Mawali *(Chm)*

Subsidiaries:

Atyab Bakery LLC (1)
PO Box 638, Barka, 320, Oman
Tel.: (968) 26881444
Web Site: http://www.atyabfoodindustries.com
Bakery Services
N.A.I.C.S.: 311811

Atyab Foodtech LLC (1)
PO Box 566, 112, Ruwi, Oman
Tel.: (968) 24717210
Web Site: http://www.atyabfoodtech.com
Food Mfr
N.A.I.C.S.: 311999

Atyab Investments LLC (1)
Tel.: (968) 24717200
Web Site: https://www.atyabinvestments.com
Food Mfr
N.A.I.C.S.: 311999

Modern Poultry Farms Co. SAOC (1)
PB 2598, Near Barka, 112, Ruwi, Wadi Al Maawal, Oman
Tel.: (968) 269839008
Web Site: https://www.modernpoultry.com
Egg Production Services
N.A.I.C.S.: 112310
Ali Salman Al Balushi *(Mgr-HR & Admin)*

OMAN FOODS INTERNATIONAL SAOG
PO Box 137, Rusayl, 124, Oman
Tel.: (968) 24446213 OM
Web Site: http://www.omanfoodsintl.com
Year Founded: 1996
Basmati Rice Mfr
N.A.I.C.S.: 311212
Jaikumar Menon *(CFO)*

OMAN HOLDINGS INTERNATIONAL COMPANY SAOG
PO Box 889, Muscat, 100, Oman
Tel.: (968) 24489789
Web Site: http://www.ohigroup.com
Sales Range: $300-349.9 Million
Investment Management Service
N.A.I.C.S.: 523999
Ammar Maqbool Al Saleh *(Vice Chm)*

Subsidiaries:

Eihab Travels LLC (1)
Hala Fm Building, PO Box 889, Al Khuwair, 100, Muscat, Oman
Tel.: (968) 24683900
Web Site: http://www.eihabtravels.com
Travel & Tour Operator
N.A.I.C.S.: 561510

OMAN HOLDINGS INTERNATIONAL COMPANY SAOG INTERNATIONAL PUBLIC

Oman Holdings International Company SAOG—(Continued)

Subsidiary (Domestic):

Travel & Allied Services LLC (2)
Street No 49 Hala Building, Al Khuwair Building No 84, Muscat, 100, Oman
Tel.: (968) 24683999
Web Site: http://www.budgetoman.com
Emp.: 60
Car Rental Services
N.A.I.C.S.: 532111
Shabbir Wala *(Gen Mgr)*

Falcon Air Services & Transport Co. LLC (1)
PO Box 889, 100, Muscat, Oman
Tel.: (968) 24683960
Web Site: http://www.fastcooman.com
Sales Range: $25-49.9 Million
Emp.: 25
Logistics Consulting Servies
N.A.I.C.S.: 541614
Ramanathan Ramesh *(Gen Mgr)*

International Information Technology Co. LLC (1)
PO Box 889, Muscat, 100, Oman
Tel.: (968) 24609400
Web Site: http://www.iitcoman.com
Information Technology Consulting Services
N.A.I.C.S.: 541512

OHI Petroleum and Energy Services LLC (1)
Street No 3341 OHI House, PO Box 889, Al-Khuwair, 100, Muscat, Oman
Tel.: (968) 24478655
Oil, Gas & Energy Consulting Services
N.A.I.C.S.: 213112

OHI Telecommunications Company LLC (1)
OHI Telecom House 87 Dohat Al Adab St, PO Box 889, Al Khuwair, 100, Muscat, Oman
Tel.: (968) 24609400
Web Site: http://www.ohiomantelecom.com
Sales Range: $100-124.9 Million
Emp.: 400
Telecommunication Servicesb
N.A.I.C.S.: 517810
J. Kumar *(Gen Mgr)*

Overseas Projects and Equipment Co. LLC (1)
Al Khuwair 1st Fl OHI House, PO Box 261, 131, Muscat, Oman
Tel.: (968) 24478655
Oil & Gas Field Equipment Mfr
N.A.I.C.S.: 333132

Sagar Polyclinic LLC (1)
PO Box 889, Muscat, 100, Oman
Tel.: (968) 24393601
Web Site: http://www.sagarpolyclinic.com
Sales Range: $10-24.9 Million
Emp.: 100
Health Care Srvices
N.A.I.C.S.: 621999
Murali Dharan *(Gen Mgr)*

OMAN HOTELS & TOURISM COMPANY SAOG

PO Box 2031, 112, Ruwi, Oman
Tel.: (968) 24702311
Web Site: http://www.omanhotels.com
Year Founded: 1991
OHTS—(MUS)
Sales Range: $10-24.9 Million
Emp.: 267
Hotel Operator
N.A.I.C.S.: 721110
Awad Mohammed Bamkhalif *(Vice Chm)*

OMAN INTERNATIONAL DEVELOPMENT & INVESTMENT COMPANY SAOG

Madinat Al Erfaan Muscat Hills Block No 9993 Building No 95, PO Box 3886, Seventh Floor Sultanate of Oman, 112, Ruwi, 112, Oman
Tel.: (968) 24769500
Web Site: https://ominvest.com
Year Founded: 1983
OMVS—(MUS)
Rev.: $514,531,049
Assets: $2,069,185,728
Liabilities: $1,253,391,768
Net Worth: $815,793,960
Earnings: $74,777,421
Emp.: 47
Fiscal Year-end: 12/31/21
Investment Management Service
N.A.I.C.S.: 523999
Khalid Muhammad Al Zubair *(Chm)*

Subsidiaries:

Jabreen International Development Company SAOC (1)
Block No 9993 Building No 95 Madinat Al Efraan, Airport Heights, Muscat, Oman
Tel.: (968) 24252500
Web Site: https://www.jabreencapital.com
Financial Investment Services
N.A.I.C.S.: 523999

National Life & General Insurance Company SAOC (1)
Al Aman Building CBD Area, PO Box 798, Wadi Kabir, 117, Muscat, Oman
Tel.: (968) 24730999
Web Site: http://www.nlicgulf.com
Sales Range: $100-124.9 Million
Emp.: 130
General Insurance Services
N.A.I.C.S.: 524210
S. Venkatachalam *(CEO)*

Oman Arab Bank S.A.O.C. (1)
Sultan Qaboos Street, PO Box 2010, Ghubrah, 112, Ruwi, Oman (51%)
Tel.: (968) 24544444
Web Site: http://www.oman-arabbank.com
Sales Range: $50-74.9 Million
Emp.: 100
Banking Services; Owned 51% by Oman International Development & Investment Co. SAOG & 49% by Arab Bank plc
N.A.I.C.S.: 522110
Rashad Al Musafir *(CEO)*

Subsidiary (Domestic):

alizz islamic bank SAOG (2)
Alizz Tower, PO Box 753, CBD Area, 112, Ruwi, Oman
Tel.: (968) 80072265
Web Site: https://www.alizzislamic.com
Rev.: $106,593,986
Assets: $2,243,075,665
Liabilities: $1,982,332,795
Net Worth: $260,742,870
Earnings: ($19,669,395)
Emp.: 236
Fiscal Year-end: 12/31/2020
Commercial Banking Services
N.A.I.C.S.: 522110
Mohammed Shukri Ghanem *(Vice Chm)*

Shamel Plastic Industries LLC (1)
Po Box-31, Sohar Industrial Estate, 327, Sohar, Oman
Tel.: (968) 26751174
Web Site: https://www.shamalplastics.com
Plastic Thermoplastic Sheet Services
N.A.I.C.S.: 561910

OMAN INVESTMENT & FINANCE CO. SAOG

PO Box 2476, 112, Ruwi, 112, Muscat, Oman
Tel.: (968) 24817878 OM
Web Site: https://eservice.oifcoman.com
Year Founded: 1979
OIFC—(MUS)
Rev.: $48,045,639
Assets: $308,379,795
Liabilities: $236,014,221
Net Worth: $72,365,574
Earnings: $8,360,703
Emp.: 894
Fiscal Year-end: 12/31/21
Financial Investment Services
N.A.I.C.S.: 523999

Said Ahmed Safrar *(CEO)*

Subsidiaries:

Gulf Investment Services Holding Company SAOG (1)
Building No 1540 Way No 2724 Hayy Souq El Mal Muscat, PO Box 974, 112, Ruwi, 112, Oman
Tel.: (968) 22350700
Web Site: http://www.gisoman.net
Rev.: $1,299,030
Assets: $49,137,778
Liabilities: $10,893,876
Net Worth: $38,243,903
Earnings: ($5,797,115)
Emp.: 11
Fiscal Year-end: 12/31/2019
Investment Management Service
N.A.I.C.S.: 523999

OMAN INVESTMENT AUTHORITY

Beach One Building Level 5 and Level 4, Shati Al Qurum, Ruwi, 100, Muscat, Oman
Tel.: (968) 24745100
Web Site: https://www.oia.gov.om
Emp.: 100
Investment Services
N.A.I.C.S.: 523999

OMAN NATIONAL ENGINEERING & INVESTMENT CO. S.A.O.G

Way 3520 Plot 689 Area 2/17, PO Box 1393, Al Khuwair, 112, Muscat, Oman
Tel.: (968) 24396222
Web Site: https://www.oneic.com.om
Year Founded: 1978
ONES—(MUS)
Rev.: $155,902,263
Assets: $373,062,728
Liabilities: $303,825,905
Net Worth: $69,236,823
Earnings: $3,829,633
Emp.: 3,029
Fiscal Year-end: 12/31/21
Engineering & Investment Services
N.A.I.C.S.: 541330

OMAN REFRESHMENT COMPANY SAOG

PO Box 30, CPO Airport, 111, Seeb, 111, Oman
Tel.: (968) 24589100
Web Site: https://www.pepsioman.com
Year Founded: 1974
ORCI—(MUS)
Rev.: $190,930,596
Assets: $336,879,217
Liabilities: $146,504,379
Net Worth: $190,374,837
Earnings: $18,318,281
Emp.: 941
Fiscal Year-end: 12/31/21
Soft Drink Distr
N.A.I.C.S.: 722515
Buti Obaid Al Mulla *(Chm)*

OMAN TELECOMMUNICATIONS COMPANY

PO Box 789, 112, Ruwi, Oman
Tel.: (968) 24242424
Web Site: http://www.omantel.om
QTEL—(MUS)
Rev.: $6,240,200,241
Assets: $19,608,257,083
Liabilities: $12,438,463,043
Net Worth: $7,169,794,040
Earnings: $605,293,150
Emp.: 2,240
Fiscal Year-end: 12/31/21
Telecommunication Servicesb
N.A.I.C.S.: 517111

Saud Ahemed Al-Nahari *(Deputy Chm)*

Subsidiaries:

Oman Data Park LLC (1)
Zone 2 3rd Floor KOM4 Knowledge Oasis, 135, Muscat, Oman
Tel.: (968) 24171111
Web Site: https://www.omandatapark.com
Information Technology Services
N.A.I.C.S.: 541512
Maqbool Al Wahaibi *(CEO)*

Oman Data Park LLC (1)
Zone 2 3rd Floor KOM4 Knowledge Oasis, 135, Muscat, Oman
Tel.: (968) 24171111
Web Site: https://www.omandatapark.com
Information Technology Services
N.A.I.C.S.: 541512
Maqbool Al Wahaibi *(CEO)*

Oman Data Park LLC (1)
Zone 2 3rd Floor KOM4 Knowledge Oasis, 135, Muscat, Oman
Tel.: (968) 24171111
Web Site: https://www.omandatapark.com
Information Technology Services
N.A.I.C.S.: 541512
Maqbool Al Wahaibi *(CEO)*

Oman Data Park LLC (1)
Zone 2 3rd Floor KOM4 Knowledge Oasis, 135, Muscat, Oman
Tel.: (968) 24171111
Web Site: https://www.omandatapark.com
Information Technology Services
N.A.I.C.S.: 541512
Maqbool Al Wahaibi *(CEO)*

Oman Data Park LLC (1)
Zone 2 3rd Floor KOM4 Knowledge Oasis, 135, Muscat, Oman
Tel.: (968) 24171111
Web Site: https://www.omandatapark.com
Information Technology Services
N.A.I.C.S.: 541512
Maqbool Al Wahaibi *(CEO)*

Oman Mobile Telecommunications Company LLC (1)
PO Box 789, 112, Ruwi, Oman
Tel.: (968) 24241999
Web Site: http://www.omanmobile.om
Mobile Telecommunications Services
N.A.I.C.S.: 517112
Amer bin Awad Al-Rawas *(CEO)*

OMAN UNITED INSURANCE COMPANY SAOG

Oman United Insurance Company SAOG, PO Box 1522, 112, Ruwi, 112, Oman
Tel.: (968) 24477300
Web Site: https://www.omanutd.com
Year Founded: 1985
OUIS—(MUS)
Rev.: $78,921,576
Assets: $281,874,038
Liabilities: $201,990,057
Net Worth: $79,883,981
Earnings: $10,260,382
Emp.: 234
Fiscal Year-end: 12/31/21
Insurance Management Services
N.A.I.C.S.: 524298
R. Muthukumar *(CEO)*

OMANI PACKAGING COMPANY (S.A.O.G)

Al Rusayl, PO Box 99, 124, Muscat, Oman
Tel.: (968) 24446652
Web Site: https://www.omanipackaging.com
Year Founded: 1992
OPCI—(MUS)
Rev.: $29,363,211
Assets: $28,305,380
Liabilities: $8,236,407
Net Worth: $20,068,973
Earnings: $2,100,891
Emp.: 167
Fiscal Year-end: 12/31/21
Paper & Packaging Products Mfr
N.A.I.C.S.: 322229
Bakhit Said Al Shanfari *(Chm)*

OMANSH ENTERPRISES LIMITED

Shop No 37 QD DDA Market, Pitam-

pura, New Delhi, 110 034, India
Tel.: (91) 119891408133
Web Site:
http://www.omanshenterprises.com
Year Founded: 1974
538537—(BOM)
Rev.: $438,319
Assets: $2,489,918
Liabilities: $2,086,471
Net Worth: $403,447
Earnings: ($33,256)
Fiscal Year-end: 03/31/22
Steel & Electrical Product Distr
N.A.I.C.S.: 423390
Manoj Ramesh Kumar Chauhan (CFO)

OMAR ZAWAWI ESTABLISHMENT LLC
PO Box 879, Muscat, 100, Oman
Tel.: (968) 24719500
Web Site: http://www.omzest.com
Year Founded: 1978
Sales Range: $1-4.9 Billion
Emp.: 4,000
Holding Company
N.A.I.C.S.: 551112
Omar Abdul Muniem Al Zawawi (Chm & Pres)

Subsidiaries:

Advertising International Company LLC (1)
Al Harthy Complex, PO Box No 407, 118, Muscat, Oman
Tel.: (968) 24564614
Telecommunication Servicesb
N.A.I.C.S.: 517111

Advertising and Publicity Company SAOC (1)
PO Box 889, Muscat, Oman
Tel.: (968) 2460 7490
Advertising & Publicity Services
N.A.I.C.S.: 541810

Al Amal Industries Co. SAOC (1)
Rd No 8 Rusayl Industrial Zone, PO Box 47, Rusayl, Muscat, 124, Oman
Tel.: (968) 24446905
Web Site: http://www.omzest.com
Sales Range: $25-49.9 Million
Emp.: 20
Diapers & Sanitary Paper Products Mfr
N.A.I.C.S.: 322291
Siva Rama Krishna (Gen Mgr)

Al Khuwair Development & Services Co. SAOC (1)
Jameat Duwal Al Arabia Street Bldg 1012, PO Box 879, Way 3613 Areej Estate, Muscat, 100, Al Khuwair, Oman
Tel.: (968) 24699130
Web Site: http://www.omzest.com
Sales Range: $25-49.9 Million
Emp.: 4
Business Services & Investments
N.A.I.C.S.: 561499

Al Wardha Footwear & Leather Products Co. LLC (1)
Road No 8 Rusayl Industrial Estate, PO Box No 4, Rusayl, 124, Oman
Tel.: (968) 24446567
Footwear Mfr
N.A.I.C.S.: 316210
Vijaybhai Mehta (Acct Mgr)

Areej Vegetable Oils & Derivatives SAOG (1)
PO Box 22, Rusayl, Muscat, Oman
Tel.: (968) 24446458
Web Site: http://www.omzest.com
Sales Range: $100 124.0 Million
Emp.: 285
Edible Oil Mfr
N.A.I.C.S.: 311225

Bishara Establishment LLC (1)
PO Box No 541, 112, Ruwi, Oman
Tel.: (968) 24700224
Web Site: http://www.bishara.com
Information Technology Consulting Services
N.A.I.C.S.: 541512

Madhur Bhatnagar (Sr Mgr-Sls)

Medical & Scientific Supplies LLC (1)
PO Box No 737, 100, Muscat, Oman
Tel.: (968) 24497844
Pharmaceutical Products Distr
N.A.I.C.S.: 325412

Mezoon Travel LLC (1)
Ruwi Street Block No 131 Building No 335, PO Box 629, Muscat, 100, Oman
Tel.: (968) 2486 3200
Web Site: http://www.mezoontravel.com
Tourism Management Services
N.A.I.C.S.: 561520

Subsidiary (Domestic):

Mezoon Cargo (2)
Cargo Complex 1st floor Shop No 88, Seeb, Oman
Tel.: (968) 2451 0105
Web Site:
http://www.mezooninternational.com
Logistics Consulting Servies
N.A.I.C.S.: 541614
Pramod Nair (Mgr-Cargo)

Muscat Finance Co. Ltd. SAOG (1)
PO Box 108, Ruwi, Oman
Tel.: (968) 24625300
Web Site: https://muscatfinance.com
Sales Range: $25-49.9 Million
Emp.: 85
Financial Services
N.A.I.C.S.: 561499
Maneesh Srivastava (CEO)

National Heaters Industries Co. LLC (1)
Factory No 1605 Road No 16 Rusayl Industrial Estate, PO Box No 58, Rusayl, 124, Oman
Tel.: (968) 24446302
Electric Water Heater Mfr
N.A.I.C.S.: 333310

National Oilfield Supply Co. LLC (1)
PO Box No 2670, 112, Ruwi, Oman
Tel.: (968) 24595271
Oilfield Machinery Distr
N.A.I.C.S.: 423830
Deepak Bradoo (Gen Mgr)

Office Supplies Co. LLC (1)
PO Box 1437, 112, Ruwi, Oman
Tel.: (968) 24829400
Web Site: http://www.officesuppliesllc.com
Office Equipment Distr
N.A.I.C.S.: 423420

Oman Agriculture Development Comany SAOG (1)
PO Box 604, Ruwi, 112, Oman
Tel.: (968) 24592947
Web Site: http://www.omangriculture.com
Sales Range: $75-99.9 Million
Emp.: 300
Milk & Vegetable Producer
N.A.I.C.S.: 112120

Oman Mechanical Services Co, Ltd. LLC (1)
PO Box 1199, 112, Ruwi, Oman
Tel.: (968) 24597705
Web Site: http://www.omsc.co.om
Engine Oil Distr
N.A.I.C.S.: 457210

Oman Methanol Holding Co. LLC (1)
PO Box No 474, 322, Falaj Al Qabail, Oman
Tel.: (968) 26865800
Web Site: http://www.omanmethanol.com
Holding Company
N.A.I.C.S.: 551112

Oman Services & Supply Organication LLC (1)
PO Box 437, 133, Muscat, Oman
Tel.: (968) 24797954
Web Site: http://www.omzest.com
Sales Range: $25-49.9 Million
Emp.: 30
Industrial Systems Marketer
N.A.I.C.S.: 423990
Kamlesh Mehta (Gen Mgr)

Oman Textile Mills Co. LLC (1)
Road No 14 Rusayl Industrial Estate, 124, Muscat, Oman
Tel.: (968) 24446129
Web Site: http://www.omzest.com
Textile Mfr
N.A.I.C.S.: 314999
Karan Sadana (CEO)

Protein Products International LLC (1)
PO Box No 1668, 114, Muttrah, Oman
Tel.: (968) 24815512
Meat & Seafood Processing Services
N.A.I.C.S.: 311612

Reem Batteries & Power Appliances Company SAOC (1)
Rusayl Industrial Area, PO Box 3, Muscat, Oman
Tel.: (968) 24446191
Web Site: http://www.reembatteries.com
Sales Range: $50-74.9 Million
Emp.: 249
Battery Mfr
N.A.I.C.S.: 335910

Riyam Computer Services LLC (1)
Way No 2108 Building 387 Al Inshirah Street, Madinat Al Sultan Qaboos, Muscat, 117, Oman
Tel.: (968) 2469 1230
Web Site: http://www.riyamcomputers.com
Emp.: 25
Software Development Services
N.A.I.C.S.: 541511
Manoj Shah (COO)

Waleed Catering & Services Co. LLC (1)
Building No 150 Genserv Building 1st Floor Way No 4457, Azaiba, Muscat, Oman
Tel.: (968) 24493124
Emp.: 1,500
Catering Services
N.A.I.C.S.: 722320

Waleed Communications Co. (WACOM) Ltd. (1)
PO Box No 2805, 112, Ruwi, Oman
Tel.: (968) 2450 2412
Telecommunication Servicesb
N.A.I.C.S.: 517121
Sanjay Kondalkar (Gen Mgr)

Waleed Pharmacy & Stores LLC (1)
PO Box 437, 100, Muscat, Oman
Tel.: (968) 24494766
Pharmaceutical Products Distr
N.A.I.C.S.: 424210

Zawawi Business Machines LLC (1)
PO Box No 9, Ruwi, Oman
Tel.: (968) 24489923
Information Technology Consulting Services
N.A.I.C.S.: 541512

Zawawi Trading Company LLC (1)
PO Box No 58, 100, Muscat, Oman
Tel.: (968) 24659200
Home Appliance Distr
N.A.I.C.S.: 423620
Pranesh Jebabhushanam (Mgr-HR)

OMATEK VENTURES PLC
11 Kudirat Abiola way, Oregun, Lagos, Nigeria
Tel.: (234) 70066283572537
Web Site: https://www.omatek.ng
Sales Range: Less than $1 Million
Electronic Appliance Distr
N.A.I.C.S.: 449210
Timothy Farinre (Chm-Grp)

OMAX AUTOS LTD
Plot No B-26 Institutional Area Sector-32, Gurgaon, 122001, Haryana, India
Tel.: (91) 1244343000
Web Site: https://www.omaxauto.com
OMAXAUTO—(NSE)
Rev.: $25,052,145
Assets: $80,975,840
Liabilities: $41,823,423
Net Worth: $39,152,418
Earnings: ($1,379,169)
Emp.: 229
Fiscal Year-end: 03/31/21
Sheet Metal Mfr
N.A.I.C.S.: 332322
Jatender Kumar Mehta (Vice Chm & Co-Mng Dir)

OMAXE LTD
Omaxe House 7 LSC Kalkaji, New Delhi, 110019, India
Tel.: (91) 1141893100
Web Site: https://www.omaxe.com
532880—(BOM)
Rev.: $70,241,535
Assets: $1,507,279,410
Liabilities: $1,340,499,615
Net Worth: $166,779,795
Earnings: ($32,106,165)
Emp.: 751
Fiscal Year-end: 03/31/21
Construction Services
N.A.I.C.S.: 236220
Rohtas Goel (Founder, Chm & Mng Dir)

Subsidiaries:

Advaita Properties Private Limited (1)
Ramachandrapuram Mandal, Osman Nagar Village Tellapur Municipality Sanga Reddy District, Hyderabad, 502032, TS, India
Tel.: (91) 7837445566
Web Site:
https://www.advaitaproperties.com
Real Estate Manangement Services
N.A.I.C.S.: 531390

OMC GROUP CO. LTD.
479 481 Preah Monivong Blvd, Phnom Penh, Cambodia
Tel.: (855) 23224866
Web Site: http://www.omc.com.kh
Year Founded: 1995
Rev.: $13,000,000
Emp.: 75
Mfr of Motorcycles
N.A.I.C.S.: 441227
Siv Thay (Pres)

OMDA AS
Drammensveien 288, 0283, Oslo, Norway
Tel.: (47) 22941590
Web Site: https://omda.com
OMDA—(OSL)
Rev.: $34,145,206
Assets: $64,062,812
Liabilities: $61,405,043
Net Worth: $2,657,768
Earnings: ($12,155,736)
Emp.: 317
Fiscal Year-end: 12/31/22
Healthcare Solutions & Services
N.A.I.C.S.: 621999
Sverre Flatby (CEO)

Subsidiaries:

CSAM Carmenta Technologies, S.L. (1)
Calle Profesor Beltran Baguena 4 109, 46009, Valencia, Spain
Tel.: (34) 96 122 9771
Health Care Srvices
N.A.I.C.S.: 621610

CSAM Denmark A/S (1)
Ejby Industrivej 38, 2600, Glostrup, Denmark
Tel.: (45) 7 022 1011
Health Care Srvices
N.A.I.C.S.: 621610

CSAM Health UK Ltd. (1)
15 Warwick Road, Stratford-upon-Avon, CV37 6YW, Warwickshire, United Kingdom
Tel.: (44) 788 556 7667
Health Care Srvices
N.A.I.C.S.: 621610

CSAM New Zealand Ltd. (1)
Suite 8948 17B Farnham St, Parnell, Auck-

Omda AS—(Continued)

land, 1052, New Zealand
Tel.: (64) 9 379 8240
Health Care Srvices
N.A.I.C.S.: 621610

CSAM Philippines Inc. (1)
14F/1400B Apple One Tower Mindanao Ave Cor Biliran Road, Cebu Business Park Brgy Luz, Cebu, Philippines
Tel.: (63) 32 233 4416
Health Care Srvices
N.A.I.C.S.: 621610

CSAM Sweden AB (1)
Telegrafgatan 4, 169 72, Solna, Sweden
Tel.: (46) 8 640 9005
Health Care Srvices
N.A.I.C.S.: 621610

CSAM UAB MedSciNet LT (1)
Konstitucijos pr 9-24, 09038, Vilnius, Lithuania
Tel.: (370) 5 273 6968
Health Care Srvices
N.A.I.C.S.: 621610

OMDURMAN NATIONAL BANK
Al Qasr Street, Khartoum, Sudan
Tel.: (249) 183770400
Web Site: http://www.onb-sd.com
Year Founded: 1993
OMNB—(KHAR)
Sales Range: $25-49.9 Million
Banking Services
N.A.I.C.S.: 522110
Abdelhameed Mohammed Gameel (Gen Mgr)

OMEGA AG-SEEDS (PUNJAB) LIMITED
SY No 115 Brig Sayeed Hanumanji Colony Bowenpally Picket, Secunderabad, Hyderabad, 500009, India
Tel.: (91) 9866272052   In
Web Site: https://www.omegaagseeds.co.in
Year Founded: 1992
Rev.: $23,099
Assets: $1,492,076
Liabilities: $239,719
Net Worth: $1,252,357
Earnings: $91
Fiscal Year-end: 03/31/18
Agriculture Seed Mfr
N.A.I.C.S.: 111199
Veera Venkata Satyanarayana Aakana (CFO)

OMEGA GERACAO S.A.
Avenue Pres Juscelino Kubitschek 1830 6 Floor Andar, Itaim Bibi, Sao Paulo, 04543-900, Brazil
Tel.: (55) 1132549810
Web Site: http://www.omegageracao.com.br
Year Founded: 2008
SEGE—(BRAZ)
Rev.: $605,495,104
Assets: $3,542,502,000
Liabilities: $2,462,286,238
Net Worth: $1,080,215,762
Earnings: $12,813,601
Fiscal Year-end: 12/31/23
Eletric Power Generation Services
N.A.I.C.S.: 221111
Jose Carlos Reis de Magalhaes Neto (Chm)

OMEGA OIL & GAS LIMITED
Level 3A 243 Edward Street, Brisbane, 4000, QLD, Australia
Tel.: (61) 737783861   AU
Web Site: https://www.omegaoilandgas.com
Year Founded: 2020
OMA—(ASX)
Rev.: $51,153
Assets: $16,570,120
Liabilities: $3,507,147
Net Worth: $13,062,973
Earnings: ($3,480,773)
Fiscal Year-end: 06/30/23
Oil & Gas Exploration Services
N.A.I.C.S.: 213112
Luke Manos (CFO)

OMEGA PACIFIC RESOURCES INC.
750 West Pender Street Suite 401, Vancouver, V6C 2T7, BC, Canada
Tel.: (778) 828-8085
Web Site: https://www.omegapacific.ca
Year Founded: 2022
OMGA—(CNSX)
Mineral Exploration Services
N.A.I.C.S.: 212390

OMER S.P.A.
Via della Moscova 18, 20121, Milan, Italy
Web Site: https://www.iubenda.com
Year Founded: 1972
OMER—(EUR)
Railway Component Mfr
N.A.I.C.S.: 335312
Giuseppe Russello (CEO)

OMER-DECUGIS & CIE SA
1 place Paul Omer-Decugis BP 70131, 94538, Rungis, France
Tel.: (33) 145122960
Web Site: https://www.omerdecugis.com
Year Founded: 1850
ALODC—(EUR)
Fruit & Vegetable Distr
N.A.I.C.S.: 445230

OMESTI BERHAD
Ho Hup Tower Aurora Place 20901 Level 9 Plaza Bukit Jalil, 1 Persiaran Jalil 1 Bandar Bukit Jalil, 57000, Kuala Lumpur, Malaysia
Tel.: (60) 397791700
Web Site: https://www.omesti.com
OMESTI—(KLS)
Rev.: $24,598,051
Assets: $131,746,001
Liabilities: $62,610,372
Net Worth: $69,135,630
Earnings: ($13,211,267)
Fiscal Year-end: 03/31/23
Information Technology Services
N.A.I.C.S.: 541511
Xian-zhen Mah (Exec Dir)

Subsidiaries:

Continuous Network Advisers Sdn. Bhd. (1)
9th Floor Menara Smi 6 Lorong P Ramlee, Kuala Lumpur, 50250, Malaysia
Tel.: (60) 327132899
Web Site: http://www.formis.net
Sales Range: $25-49.9 Million
Emp.: 50
Communication Networking Services
N.A.I.C.S.: 517810

Formis Holdings Berhad (1)
16th Floor Kh Tower 8 Lorong P Ramlee, Kuala Lumpur, 50250, Malaysia
Tel.: (60) 320784488
Web Site: http://www.omesti.com
Sales Range: $50-74.9 Million
Emp.: 50
Financial Management Services
N.A.I.C.S.: 523999
Tansri Megat (Pres)

Subsidiary (Domestic):

Com-Line Systems Sdn. Bhd. (2)
Level 3 Unit A-3-5 & A-3-6 TTDI Plaza Jalan Wan Kadir 3, Taman Tun Dr Ismail, 60000, Kuala Lumpur, Malaysia
Tel.: (60) 377101848
Web Site: http://www.comline.com.my
Sales Range: $10-24.9 Million
Emp.: 30
Application Software Development Services
N.A.I.C.S.: 541511

Subsidiary (Domestic):

Comline Dotcom Sdn. Bhd. (3)
4th Floor Bangunan Tan Kim Onn 48 Jalan Sungai Besi, 57100, Kuala Lumpur, Wilayah Persekutuan, Malaysia
Tel.: (60) 392228848
Sales Range: $10-24.9 Million
Emp.: 30
Application Software Development Services
N.A.I.C.S.: 541511

Subsidiary (Domestic):

Formis Media Teknologi Sdn. Bhd. (2)
Unit No 302 Level 3 Uptown 2 No 2 Jalan SS21/37 Damansara Uptown, Petaling Jaya, 47400, Selangor, Malaysia
Tel.: (60) 376608787
Sales Range: $25-49.9 Million
Emp.: 15
Application Software Development & Educational Consulting Services
N.A.I.C.S.: 541511

Subsidiary (Non-US):

Formis Network Services Sdn. Bhd. (2)
Sales Range: $25-49.9 Million
Emp.: 67
Communication Technology Services
N.A.I.C.S.: 517810
Suhaily Sarmani (Sec)

Subsidiary (Domestic):

Microlink Solutions Berhad (2)
Ho Hup Tower Aurora Place 02-08-01 Level 8 Plaza Bukit Jalil, No 1 Persiaran Jalil 1 Bandar Bukit Jalil, 57000, Kuala Lumpur, Malaysia (95.6%)
Tel.: (60) 397791700
Web Site: https://www.microlink.com.my
Rev.: $54,031,769
Assets: $74,689,773
Liabilities: $24,759,916
Net Worth: $49,929,856
Earnings: $6,301,103
Emp.: 265
Fiscal Year-end: 03/31/2022
Information Technology Solutions for the Banking Industry
N.A.I.C.S.: 541519
Monteiro Gerard Clair (Exec Dir)

Subsidiary (Domestic):

Applied Business Systems Sdn. Bhd. (3)
Ho Hup Tower - Aurora Place 02-08-01 Level 8 Plaza Bukit Jalil No 1, Persiaran Jalil 1 Bandar Bukit Jalil, 57000, Kuala Lumpur, Malaysia
Tel.: (60) 397791700
Web Site: https://www.abs.com.my
Sales Range: $25-49.9 Million
Emp.: 70
Application Software Development & Educational Consulting Services
N.A.I.C.S.: 541511

CA IT Infrastructure Solutions Sdn Bhd (3)
L15-01-02 PJX-HM Shah Tower, No 16A Persiaran Barat, 46050, Petaling Jaya, Selangor, Malaysia
Tel.: (60) 374932060
Computer Services
N.A.I.C.S.: 541519

CSA Servis (M) Sdn Bhd (3)
6th Floor Menara Atlan 161B Jalan Ampang, 50450, Kuala Lumpur, Malaysia
Tel.: (60) 321712200
Computer Services
N.A.I.C.S.: 541519

Formis Systems & Technology Sdn. Bhd. (3)
7th & 10th Fl Menara SMI 6 Lorong P Ramlee, Kuala Lumpur, 50250, Malaysia
Tel.: (60) 320703388
Web Site: http://www.fst.com.my
Sales Range: $25-49.9 Million
Emp.: 15
Computer Hardware & Software Distr
N.A.I.C.S.: 423430
Alvin Chong (Mgr-Tech Support-Consultancy & Svc Delivery Div)

Microlink Innovation Sdn Bhd (3)
6th Floor Menara Atlan 161B Jalan Ampang, 50450, Kuala Lumpur, Malaysia (60%)
Tel.: (60) 321712200
Computer Services
N.A.I.C.S.: 541519

Microlink Software Sdn Bhd (3)
6th Floor Menara Atlan 161B Jalan Ampang, 50450, Kuala Lumpur, Malaysia
Tel.: (60) 321712200
Software Development Services
N.A.I.C.S.: 513210

Microlink Systems Sdn Bhd (3)
6th Floor Menara Atlan 161B Jalan Ampang, 50450, Kuala Lumpur, Malaysia
Tel.: (60) 321712200
Computer Services
N.A.I.C.S.: 541519

Subsidiary (Non-US):

PT Microlink Indonesia (3)
The City Tower Level 12 Unit 1-N, JL MH Thamrin No 81, Jakarta, 10310, Pusat, Indonesia
Tel.: (62) 2130499589
Computer Services
N.A.I.C.S.: 541519

Nostalgic Properties Sdn. Bhd. (1)
No 57 Northam Tower Jalan Sultan Ahmad Shah, 10050, George Town, Penang, Malaysia
Tel.: (60) 4 818 2122
Web Site: http://www.northamtower.com
Property Management & Development Services
N.A.I.C.S.: 531390

Yakimbi ICT Sdn Bhd (1)
Ho Hup Tower - Aurora Place 2-07-01 Level 7 Plaza Bukit Jalil, No 1 Persiaran Jalil 1 Bandar Bukit Jalil, 57000, Kuala Lumpur, Malaysia
Tel.: (60) 397791700
Information Technology Services
N.A.I.C.S.: 541519

OMFURN INDIA LTD.
109 Gundecha Industrial Complex Akurli Road Kandivali East, Mumbai, 400 101, India
Tel.: (91) 2242108900
Web Site: https://www.omfurnindia.com
Year Founded: 1975
OMFURN—(NSE)
Rev.: $8,522,391
Assets: $6,855,680
Liabilities: $3,772,795
Net Worth: $3,082,885
Earnings: $468,305
Emp.: 176
Fiscal Year-end: 03/31/23
Furniture Repair Services
N.A.I.C.S.: 811420
Rajendra Chitbahal Vishwakarma (Mng Dir)

OMICO CORPORATION
Suite 1109 East Tower Tektite Towers, Pasig, Philippines
Tel.: (63) 286376923   PH
Web Site: https://www.omico.com.ph
Year Founded: 1968
OM—(PHI)
Rev.: $821,920
Assets: $13,492,188
Liabilities: $662,210
Net Worth: $12,829,978
Earnings: ($316,951)
Emp.: 10
Fiscal Year-end: 12/31/21
Real Estate Development Services
N.A.I.C.S.: 236117

Tommy Kin Hing Tia (Chm)

OMID INVESTMENT BANK CO.
No 2 Shokouh Alley Khoramshahr St North Sohrevardi St Tehran, Tehran, 1557746511, Iran
Tel.: (98) 2154906
Year Founded: 2011
OMID1—(THE)
Sales Range: Less than $1 Million
Financial Services
N.A.I.C.S.: 523999

OMID INVESTMENT MANAGEMENT CORPORATION
No 2 on the corner of Isar St Shahid Taheri St, Nelson Mandela Blvd, Tehran, Iran
Tel.: (98) 2126207066
Web Site: https://omidinvestment.ir
Year Founded: 2002
Sales Range: $200-249.9 Million
Investment Management Service
N.A.I.C.S.: 523940

OMIKENSHI CO., LTD.
4-1-1 Minami-honmachi, Chuo-ku, Osaka, 541-8541, Japan
Tel.: (81) 662057300
Web Site: https://www.omikenshi.co.jp
Year Founded: 1917
3111—(TKS)
Rev.: $20,008,470
Assets: $120,467,250
Liabilities: $109,805,320
Net Worth: $10,661,930
Earnings: ($15,976,370)
Emp.: 321
Fiscal Year-end: 03/31/24
Textile Products Mfr
N.A.I.C.S.: 313220
Yoshihide Ishihara (Pres)
Subsidiaries:

Omi do Brasil Textil S.A. (1)
Av Osaka 85-Bairro da Prata, Lencois Paulista, 18682-903, Sao Paulo, Brazil
Tel.: (55) 1432691233
Web Site: https://www.omitextil.com.br
Textile Products Distr
N.A.I.C.S.: 424310

Omikenshi Co., Ltd. - Kakogawa Plant (1)
850 Ikeda Onoecho, Kakogawa, 675-0023, Hyogo, Japan
Tel.: (81) 794223891
Textile Products Mfr
N.A.I.C.S.: 313220

Omikenshi Shanghai Co., Ltd. (1)
Room2216 Building-B Far Eastern International Plaza NO317 Xian, Xia Road Chang-Ning, Shanghai, 200051, China
Tel.: (86) 2162350584
Emp.: 5
Textile Products Distr
N.A.I.C.S.: 424310
Nobuo Ryuho (Pres)

Omikenshi Solution Co., LTD. (1)
2-6-33 Edohori Nishi-ku, Osaka, 540-0002, Japan
Tel.: (81) 664792801
Web Site: http://www.omic-net.com
Textile Products Distr
N.A.I.C.S.: 424310

OMIKRON SYSTEMHAUS GMBH & CO.
Von Hunefeld-Strasse 55, 50829, Cologne, Germany
Tel.: (49) 2215956990
Web Site: http://www.omikron.de
Year Founded: 1983
Sales Range: $10-24.9 Million
Emp.: 60
Electronic Banking Solutions, Products & Software Developer & Distr

N.A.I.C.S.: 334610
Werner Zimmermann (Mng Dir)
Subsidiaries:

Omkiron Hungary Ltd. (1)
Vaci ut 49, 1134, Budapest, Hungary
Tel.: (36) 12373040
Web Site: http://www.omikron-mo.hu
Software Development Services
N.A.I.C.S.: 513210
Gabor Csuros (Mng Dir)

OMINECA MINING AND METALS LTD.
602-224 4th Avenue South, Saskatoon, S7K 5M5, SK, Canada
Tel.: (306) 653-2692   AB
Web Site: https://ominecaminingandmetal.com
OMMSF—(OTCIQ)
Rev.: $8,370
Assets: $13,003,791
Liabilities: $8,192,820
Net Worth: $4,810,971
Earnings: ($1,586,272)
Fiscal Year-end: 12/31/23
Gold Mining Services
N.A.I.C.S.: 212220

OMISE CO. LTD.
2-1-10 Sendagaya, Shibuya, Tokyo, Japan
Tel.: (81) 6622528777
Web Site: http://www.omise.co
Financial Services
N.A.I.C.S.: 523999
Amnat Anantapien (Mgr-Bus Dev)
Subsidiaries:

PaySbuy Co., Ltd. (1)
Phayathai Plaza Bld Phayathai Road, Ratchathewi, Bangkok, 10400, Thailand
Tel.: (66) 26121314
Web Site: http://www.paysbuy.com
Electronic Money Transfer Services
N.A.I.C.S.: 522390

OMKAR OVERSEAS LIMITED
304 Shoppers Plaza-V Govt Servant Co-Op Hsg Soc, Opp Municipal Market C G Road Navrangpura, Ahmedabad, 380009, India
Tel.: (91) 7926464153
Web Site: https://www.omkaroverseasltd.com
Year Founded: 1994
531496—(BOM)
Rev.: $42,066
Assets: $129,922
Liabilities: $12,847
Net Worth: $117,076
Earnings: ($12,167)
Emp.: 3
Fiscal Year-end: 03/31/23
Fabric Mfr & Distr
N.A.I.C.S.: 313240
Ramesh G. Deora (Chm & CEO)

OMKAR PHARMACHEM LIMITED
310 Wall Street-1 Near Gujarat College Cross Road, Ellisbridge, Ahmedabad, 380006, Gujarat, India
Tel.: (91) 7930071411
Web Site: https://www.omkarpharma.com
Year Founded: 1995
532167—(BOM)
Rev.: $65,104
Assets: $1,166,585
Liabilities: $82,273
Net Worth: $1,084,311
Earnings: $23,716
Emp.: 3
Fiscal Year-end: 03/31/23
Pharmaceutical Preparation Mfr
N.A.I.C.S.: 325412

Anurag Sharma (Mng Dir)

OMKAR SPECIALITY CHEMICALS LTD.
B-34 MIDC Badlapur E, Thane, 421503, Maharashtra, India
Tel.: (91) 2512690651
Web Site: https://www.omkarchemicals.com
Year Founded: 1983
OMKARCHEM—(NSE)
Rev.: $6,276,898
Assets: $11,788,495
Liabilities: $33,401,304
Net Worth: ($21,612,809)
Earnings: $274,856
Emp.: 59
Fiscal Year-end: 03/31/21
Chemicals Mfr
N.A.I.C.S.: 325998
Pravin S. Herlekar (Chm & Mng Dir)

OMNI AX'S SOFTWARE LIMITED
New No 32 Old No 106 Dr Ranga Road Mylapore, Chennai, 600004, Tamil Nadu, India
Tel.: (91) 9003113372
532340—(BOM)
Assets: $1,463,054
Liabilities: $42,539
Net Worth: $1,420,514
Earnings: ($20,335)
Fiscal Year-end: 03/31/22
Software Development Services
N.A.I.C.S.: 541511
K. Ramakrishnan (Exec Dir)

OMNI BANCO & FINANCEIRA
Av Sao Gabriel 555 1 Andar, Jardim Paulista, 01435-001, Sao Paulo, Brazil
Tel.: (55) 40043500
Web Site: http://www.omni.com.br
Banking Services
N.A.I.C.S.: 551111
Guilherme Salge Tenorio (Comml Dir)

OMNI SYSTEM CO., LTD.
Ganam Samseung-ri 413-14, Yeoju, Gyeonggi, Korea (South)
Tel.: (82) 318835400
Web Site: https://www.omnisystem.co.kr
Year Founded: 1997
057540—(KRS)
Rev.: $75,202,805
Assets: $82,375,019
Liabilities: $15,094,492
Net Worth: $67,280,526
Earnings: $437,206
Emp.: 240
Fiscal Year-end: 12/31/22
Digital Meters Mfr
N.A.I.C.S.: 334515

OMNI-PLUS SYSTEM LIMITED
994 Bendemeer Road 01-03 B-Central, Singapore, 339943, Singapore
Tel.: (65) 62960326
Web Site: https://www.omniplussystem.com
Year Founded: 2002
7699—(TKS)
Rev.: $310,157,170
Assets: $206,662,915
Liabilities: $130,896,974
Net Worth: $75,765,941
Earnings: $10,491,553
Emp.: 242
Fiscal Year-end: 03/31/24
Plastics Material & Resin Mfr
N.A.I.C.S.: 325211

Subsidiaries:

Cepco Trading Sdn. Bhd. (1)
Plot 40 Jalan Perindustrian Bukit Minyak Kawasan Bukit, Minyak Simpang Ampat, 14000, Pulau Penang, Malaysia
Tel.: (60) 45086388
Plastic Product Distr
N.A.I.C.S.: 423720

DP Chemicals Co., Ltd. (1)
994 Bendemeer Road 01-03 B-Central, Singapore, 339943, Singapore
Tel.: (65) 62960326
Plastic Resin Mfr & Distr
N.A.I.C.S.: 325211

DP Chemicals Vietnam Co., Ltd. (1)
Sunwah Pearl Unit S-09 90 Nguyen Huu Canh Street, Ward 22 Binh Tanh District, Ho Chi Minh City, Vietnam
Tel.: (84) 2838221641
Raw Polymer Material Mfr & Distr
N.A.I.C.S.: 325211

Nihan Pigment Sdn. Bhd. (1)
No 7 Jalan Hasil 2 Kawasan Perindustrian Hasil, 81200, Johor Bahru, Johor, Malaysia
Tel.: (60) 72359177
Plastic Resin Mfr & Distr
N.A.I.C.S.: 325211

OPS Technologies Sdn. Bhd. (1)
No 37 Plot 27 Jalan I-Park Sac 4 Taman Perindustrian I-Park Sac, 81400, Senai, Johor, Malaysia
Tel.: (60) 75951696
Plastic Product Distr
N.A.I.C.S.: 423720

Omni Plus System (Thailand) Co., Ltd. (1)
723 Supakarn Tower Room No L1 L Floor Charoennakorn Road, Klongtonsai Klongsan, Bangkok, 10600, Thailand
Tel.: (66) 2122677301
Raw Polymer Material Mfr & Distr
N.A.I.C.S.: 325211

Omni-Plus System Philipines, Inc. (1)
Lot 6 Blk 9 Units C&D of Orient Goldcrest Building Light Industry, Science Park III Brgy San Rafael & Sta Anastacia Santo Tomas, Batangas, 4234, Philippines
Tel.: (63) 437030005
Raw Polymer Material Mfr & Distr
N.A.I.C.S.: 325211

Omni-Plus System Shanghai Limited (1)
Room 608 & 610 6/F No 2 Huajing Road Waigaoqiao Free Trade Zone Pudong, Shanghai, 200131, China
Tel.: (86) 2161405875
Raw Polymer Material Mfr & Distr
N.A.I.C.S.: 325211

P.T. Omni Plus System (1)
Jalan Pluit Sakti Raya 28 Blok B Nomor 5, Kawasan Sentra Bisnis Pluit RT 004 RW 006 Kel Pluit Kec Penjaringan, Jakarta, 14450, Jakarta Utara, Indonesia
Tel.: (62) 2122677301
Plastic Resin Mfr & Distr
N.A.I.C.S.: 325211

OMNIA METALS GROUP LIMITED
22 Townshend Rd, Subiaco, 6008, WA, Australia
Tel.: (61) 893880051
Web Site: https://www.omniametals.com.au
Year Founded: 2021
OM1—(ASX)
Metal Exploration Services
N.A.I.C.S.: 213114
Anna MacKintosh (Sec)

OMNIA NETWORK SPA
Via C Colombo 6, 20094, Corsico, MI, Italy
Tel.: (39) 02450541
Web Site: http://www.omnianetwork.it
Year Founded: 1995
Sales Range: $300-349.9 Million

OMNIA NETWORK SPA

Omnia Network SpA—(Continued)

Emp.: 2,500
Outsourcing Services
N.A.I.C.S.: 561499
Luigino Bellusci (Chm)

Subsidiaries:

Omnia Group Service Srl (1)
Via Cristoforo Colombo 6, 20094, Corsico, Italy
Tel.: (39) 02450541
Outsourcing Services
N.A.I.C.S.: 541611

Omnia Service Center Spa (1)
Via Cristoforo Colombo 6A, 20094, Corsico, Italy
Tel.: (39) 02450541
Business Consulting Services
N.A.I.C.S.: 541611

Web Global Renting Spa (1)
Via C Colombo 6, 20094, Corsico, Milan, Italy
Tel.: (39) 02450541
Web Site: http://www.wgr.it
Renting Services
N.A.I.C.S.: 531210

OMNIBRIDGE HOLDINGS LIMITED

Suit 506 5/F Admiralty Centre Tower 2 18 Harcourt Road, Admirally, Hong Kong, China (Hong Kong)
Tel.: (852) 21173066
Web Site: http://www.omnibridge.com.hk
8462—(HKG)
Rev.: $70,341,656
Assets: $21,593,222
Liabilities: $7,980,765
Net Worth: $13,612,457
Earnings: $693,303
Emp.: 54
Fiscal Year-end: 12/31/22
Professionals Recruitment Services
N.A.I.C.S.: 541612
Chee Kian Chew (Founder, Chm, CEO & Officer-Compliance)

Subsidiaries:

A Very Normal Company Pte. Ltd. (1)
298 Tiong Bahru Road 12-03 Central Plaza, Singapore, 168730, Singapore
Tel.: (65) 65570707
Web Site: https://avnc.asia
Cyber Security Services
N.A.I.C.S.: 541511

BGC Group (HK) Limited (1)
Suite 506 Admiralty Centre Tower 2 18 Harcourt Road Admiralty, Hong Kong, China (Hong Kong)
Tel.: (852) 21175922
Human Resource Consulting Services
N.A.I.C.S.: 541612

BGC Group Pte. Ltd. (1)
298 Tiong Bahru Road 12-03 Central Plaza, Singapore, 168730, Singapore
Tel.: (65) 65359696
Web Site: https://www.bgc-group.com
Human Resource Consulting Services
N.A.I.C.S.: 541612
Weilis Lua (Asst Mgr-HR)

OMNICANE LTD

Omnicane House Mon Tresor Business Gateway, New Airport Access Road, 51521, Plaine Magnien, 51521, Mauritius
Tel.: (230) 6600600
Web Site: https://www.omnicane.com
Year Founded: 2009
MTMD—(MAU)
Rev.: $172,869,342
Assets: $382,350,162
Liabilities: $230,428,713
Net Worth: $151,921,449
Earnings: $13,006,602

Emp.: 1,243
Fiscal Year-end: 12/31/23
Sugar Mfr
N.A.I.C.S.: 311313
Nelson Mirthil (CFO)

OMKAS SPECIAL CHEMICALS LTD.

OMNIJOI MEDIA CORP

Building 28 No 8 Yuanhua Road, No 8 Yuanhua Road Qixia District, Nanjing, 210033, Jiangsu, China
Tel.: (86) 2583188552
Web Site: http://www.omnijoi.com
Year Founded: 2005
300528—(CHIN)
Rev.: $154,868,420
Assets: $355,924,725
Liabilities: $252,941,754
Net Worth: $102,982,970
Earnings: ($3,105,165)
Fiscal Year-end: 12/31/23
Movie Theatre Operator
N.A.I.C.S.: 512131
Ren Tong (Chm)

OMNIPOTENT INDUSTRIES PVT. LTD.

1/11 Damji Nenshi Estate Station Road, Bhandup West, Mumbai, 400078, Maharashtra, India
Tel.: (91) 7400152424
Web Site: https://www.omnipotent.co.in
Year Founded: 2016
543400—(BOM)
Petroleum Product Distr
N.A.I.C.S.: 424720
Punit Popat (Pres)

OMNITECH INFOSOLUTIONS LTD

Omnitech House A-13 Cross Road No 5 Kondivita Road MIDC, Andheri E, Mumbai, 400 093, India
Tel.: (91) 22 4095 6666
532882—(BOM)
Computer Softwares Mfr
N.A.I.C.S.: 541511
Avinash Pitale (CFO & Mng Dir)

OMNITEX INDUSTRIES (INDIA) LIMITED

Sabnam House Ground Floor Plot No A 15/16 Central Cross Road B, MIDC Andheri East, Mumbai, 400 093, India
Tel.: (91) 2240635100
Web Site: https://www.omnitex.com
Year Founded: 1987
514324—(BOM)
Rev.: $44,722
Assets: $646,844
Liabilities: $1,055
Net Worth: $645,789
Earnings: $24,807
Emp.: 2
Fiscal Year-end: 03/31/23
Fabrics Whslr
N.A.I.C.S.: 424310
Narendra Kumar Dalmia (Mng Dir)

OMNIUM ET REALISATION D'EMBALLAGES PLASTIQUES

Z I de Vauzelle, 37600, Loches, France
Tel.: (33) 247911414
Web Site: http://www.orep-packaging.com
Emp.: 160
Plastic Film Packaging Mfr & Services
N.A.I.C.S.: 326199

OMPHALOS CORP.

Unit 2 15 Fl 83 Nankan Rd Sec 1, Luchu, Taoyuan, Taiwan
Tel.: (886) 33229658
Year Founded: 1991

OMPS—(OTCIQ)
Rev.: $186,299
Assets: $165,341
Liabilities: $2,004,152
Net Worth: ($1,838,811)
Earnings: ($226,870)
Emp.: 7
Fiscal Year-end: 12/31/19
Electronic Equipment Distr & Servicer
N.A.I.C.S.: 423690

OMRON CORPORATION

Shiokoji Horikawa, Shimogyo-ku, Kyoto, 600-8530, Japan
Tel.: (81) 753447000
Web Site: https://www.omron.com
Year Founded: 1933
6645—(TKS)
Rev.: $5,412,010,210
Assets: $8,954,758,690
Liabilities: $2,668,694,960
Net Worth: $6,286,063,730
Earnings: $53,574,050
Emp.: 28,450
Fiscal Year-end: 03/31/24
Electrical Eqiupment Mfr
N.A.I.C.S.: 551112
Fumio Tateishi (Chm)

Subsidiaries:

3A Health Care S.R.L. (1)
Via Marziale Cerutti 90 F/G, Lonato del Garda, 25017, Brescia, Italy
Tel.: (39) 030 913 3177
Web Site: https://www.3-a.it
Medical Devices
N.A.I.C.S.: 622110

Automation Investment Europe B.V. (1)
Wegalaan 67-69, 2132 JD, Hoofddorp, Netherlands
Tel.: (31) 23 568 1300
Web Site: http://www.omron.com
Business Support Services
N.A.I.C.S.: 561990
Shizuto Yukumoto (Gen Mgr)

Delta Tau Data Systems Inc. (1)
21314 Lassen St, Chatsworth, CA 91311 (100%)
Tel.: (818) 998-2095
Web Site: http://www.deltatau.com
Motion Control Products
N.A.I.C.S.: 333998
Curtis S. Wilson (VP-R&D)

Development and Engineering Netherlands B.V. (1)
Zilverenberg 2, 5234 GM, 's-Hertogenbosch, Netherlands
Tel.: (31) 73 6481811
Sales Range: $25-49.9 Million
Emp.: 100
Engineering Services
N.A.I.C.S.: 541330

Inneos LLC (1)
5700 Stoneridge Dr Ste 200, Pleasanton, CA 94588
Tel.: (925) 226-0138
Web Site: http://www.inneos.com
Electronic Components Mfr
N.A.I.C.S.: 334419

JMDC, Inc. (1)
12th floor Sumitomo Shibadaimon Building 255 Shibadaimon, Minato-ku, Tokyo, 105-0012, Japan. (54.57%)
Tel.: (81) 357335010
Web Site: https://www.jmdc.co.jp
Rev.: $214,038,410
Assets: $809,407,720
Liabilities: $342,173,260
Net Worth: $467,234,460
Earnings: $30,452,270
Emp.: 431
Fiscal Year-end: 03/31/2024
Information Technology Services
N.A.I.C.S.: 541512
Matsushima Yosuke (Pres & CEO)

Ns Industria De Aparelhos Medicos Ltda. (1)
Rua Francisco Pedroso de Toledo 437 -

Vila Liviero, Sao Paulo, 04185-150, Brazil
Tel.: (55) 112 336 8000
Medical Device Mfr
N.A.I.C.S.: 339112

O.M.S, Servicos de Programacao, Lda. (1)
Edificio Mar do Oriente-Rua do Polo Norte nr 18-3 2, 1990-266, Lisbon, Portugal
Tel.: (351) 219429400
Industrial Automation Component Mfr
N.A.I.C.S.: 333248

OMRON (China) Co., Ltd. (1)
Room 1212 2 Tower China Overseas Plaza No8 Guanghua Dongli, Chaoyang District Jianguomenwai Ave, Beijing, 100020, China (100%)
Tel.: (86) 1065951906
Sales Range: $25-49.9 Million
Emp.: 8,500
Marketing & Retail of Systems Equipment
N.A.I.C.S.: 423850

OMRON (China) Group Co., Ltd. (1)
1504B-09B Tower 3 China Hong Kong City 33 Canton Road, Tsim Sha Tsui, Kowloon, China (Hong Kong) (100%)
Tel.: (852) 23753827
Web Site: http://www.omron.com.hk
Sales Range: $250-299.9 Million
Emp.: 60
Electronics Mfr
N.A.I.C.S.: 334220

OMRON (Guangzhou) Automotive Electronics Co., Ltd. (1)
No 52 Nanxiang Yi Lu Guangzhou Science City, Hi-Tech Industrial Development Zone, Guangzhou, 510663, China
Tel.: (86) 2082075333
Sales Range: $200-249.9 Million
Emp.: 785
Automotive Electronic Component Mfr & Distr
N.A.I.C.S.: 336320

OMRON (Shanghai) Co., Ltd. (1)
No 789 Jinji Road Jinqiao Export Processing Zone, Pudong, Shanghai, 201206, China
Tel.: (86) 2150509988
Sales Range: $200-249.9 Million
Emp.: 600
Marketing & Manufacturing of Control Components & Systems
N.A.I.C.S.: 335314

OMRON (Shanghai) Co., Ltd. (1)
No 789 Jinji Road Jinqiao Economic and Technological Development Zone, Pudong New Area, Shanghai, 201206, China (100%)
Tel.: (86) 2150509988
Sales Range: $25-49.9 Million
Emp.: 40
Trading of Industrial Automation Components & Systems
N.A.I.C.S.: 238990

OMRON AUTOMOTIVE TECHNOLOGIES, INC. (1)
2440 Winston Park Dr, Oakville, L6H 7V2, ON, Canada
Tel.: (905) 829-0143
Web Site: http://www.omron.com
Automotive Electronic Component Research & Development Services
N.A.I.C.S.: 541715

OMRON Amusement Hong Kong Co., Ltd. (1)
1504B-09B Tower 3 China Hong Kong City 33 Canton Road, Tsim Sha Tsui, Kowloon, China (Hong Kong)
Tel.: (852) 23753827
Web Site: http://www.omron.com
Electric Component Whslr
N.A.I.C.S.: 423690

OMRON Asia Pacific Pte. Ltd. (1)
No 438A Alexandra Road 05-05/08 Lobby 2, Alexandra Technopark, Singapore, 119967, Singapore (100%)
Tel.: (65) 68353011
Web Site: http://www.omron.asia.com
Sales Range: $1-9.9 Million
Emp.: 55
Sales & Marketing of Electronic Control Components & Systems in Asian Countries

AND PRIVATE COMPANIES

N.A.I.C.S.: 449210

OMRON Automation PVT Ltd. (1)
The Qube 5th Floor Unit No 501-504 M V Road, Marol Andheri East, Mumbai, 400 059, India
Tel.: (91) 2271288400
Web Site: http://www.omron-ap.co.in
Industrial Automation Component Distr
N.A.I.C.S.: 423830

OMRON Automotive Components India PVT. LTD (1)
Web Site: http://www.omronauto.com
Automotive Component Mfr & Distr
N.A.I.C.S.: 336390

OMRON Automotive Electronics Europe GmbH (1)
Schulze-Delitzsch-Str 43 70565, 70565, Stuttgart, Germany
Tel.: (49) 711 6868 76 20
Sales Range: $50-74.9 Million
Emp.: 7
Electronic Automotive Component Distr
N.A.I.C.S.: 423120
Joerg Primus (Mgr-Sls)

OMRON Automotive Electronics Inc. (Manufacturing) (1)
3709 Ohio Ave, Saint Charles, IL 60174-5437
Tel.: (630) 443-6800
Web Site: http://www.omronauto.com
Marketing & Manufacturing of Control Components & Systems
N.A.I.C.S.: 335314

OMRON Automotive Electronics Inc. (Marketing) (1)
29185 Cabot Dr, Novi, MI 48377 **(100%)**
Tel.: (248) 893-0200
Web Site: http://www.omronauto.com
Sales Range: $25-49.9 Million
Emp.: 30
Marketing & Manufacturing of Automotive Components
N.A.I.C.S.: 334419
David Hoffman (Dir-Sls)

OMRON Automotive Electronics Italy S.r.l. (1)
Via delle Centurie 20-22, 03100, Frosinone, Italy
Tel.: (39) 077544771
Electronic Automotive Component Mfr & Distr
N.A.I.C.S.: 336390
Marco Gallinaro (Mng Dir)

OMRON Automotive Electronics Korea, Co., Ltd. (1)
Kyobo-tower B-dong 18F 465 Gangnam-daero, Seocho-gu, Seoul, 06611, Korea (South) **(100%)**
Tel.: (82) 234837789
Web Site: http://www.omron.com
Sales Range: $25-49.9 Million
Emp.: 50
Marketing & Manufacturing of Automotive Components
N.A.I.C.S.: 336340

OMRON Automotive European Service, Ltd. (1)
Opal Drive Fox Milne, The Pensnett Estate, Milton Keynes, MK15 0DG, W Midlands, United Kingdom
Tel.: (44) 1908258258
Web Site: http://www.omron.com
Automotive Electronic Component Sales & Services
N.A.I.C.S.: 423120

OMRON Automotive Technologies, Inc. (1)
2030 Bristol Circle Suite 100, Oakville, L6H 0H2, ON, Canada
Tel.: (905) 829-0143
Web Site: http://www.automotive.omron.com
Automotive Components Research & Development Svcs
N.A.I.C.S.: 811198
Patrick Edmiston (Program Mgr)

OMRON Canada, Inc. (1)
100 Consilium Place Suite 802, Toronto, M1H 3E3, ON, Canada **(100%)**
Tel.: (416) 286-6465
Web Site: http://www.automation.omron.com
Sales Range: $1-9.9 Million
Emp.: 50
Sales & Marketing of ECR & POS
N.A.I.C.S.: 423420

OMRON Componentes Automotivos Ltda. (1)
Estrada Aldeia da Serra 711-A, Itapevi, 06696 050, Brazil
Tel.: (55) 11 4789 8250
Web Site: http://www.omronauto.com.br
Electronic Automotive Parts Mfr & Sales
N.A.I.C.S.: 336390

OMRON Dalian Co., Ltd. (1)
Song Jiang Lu 3-hao, Economic and Technological Development Zone, Dalian, 116600, China **(100%)**
Tel.: (86) 41187614222
Sales Range: $400-449.9 Million
Emp.: 8,500
Mfr of Healthcare Equipment & Computer Peripherals
N.A.I.C.S.: 456199

OMRON Electronic Components (Hong Kong) Ltd. (1)
16038-04 33 Canton Road, Tsim Sha Tsui, Kowloon, China (Hong Kong)
Tel.: (852) 2375 3827
Electronic Components Distr
N.A.I.C.S.: 423690

OMRON Electronic Components (Shenzhen) Ltd. (1)
OMRON Industrial Park, Taiyang Village Pingshan Town Longgang District, Shenzhen, 518118, China
Tel.: (86) 75584620000
Web Site: http://www.omron.com
Sales Range: $1-4.9 Billion
Emp.: 5,878
Electronic Component Mfr & Distr
N.A.I.C.S.: 334419

OMRON Electronic Components Canada, Inc. (1)
100 Consilium Place Suite 802, Toronto, M1H 3E3, ON, Canada
Tel.: (416) 286-6465
Web Site: http://www.omron.ca
Electronic Components Mfr
N.A.I.C.S.: 334419

OMRON Electronic Components Co., Ltd. (1)
Kyobo-tower A-dong 18F 465, Gangnam-daero Seocho-Gu, Seoul, Korea (South)
Tel.: (82) 25675020
Web Site: http://www.omron-ecb.co.kr
Sales Range: $25-49.9 Million
Emp.: 24
Electronic Components Distr
N.A.I.C.S.: 423690

OMRON Electronic Components Co., Ltd. (OCB-TH) (1)
Phaholythin Place Building 41st Floor 408/166 Phaholythin Road, Samsen-nai Phayathai, Bangkok, 10400, Thailand
Tel.: (66) 26190292
Sales Range: $25-49.9 Million
Emp.: 30
Electronic Components Distr
N.A.I.C.S.: 423690

OMRON Electronic Components Europe B.V. (1)
Wegalaan 57, 2132 JD, Hoofddorp, Netherlands
Tel.: (31) 235681200
Web Site: http://www.omron.eu
Electronic Components Distr
N.A.I.C.S.: 423690

OMRON Electronic Components France S.a.r.l. (1)
14 Ruo do Lisbonne, 93110, Rosny-sous-Bois, France
Tel.: (33) 156631900
Web Site: http://www.omron.com
Sales Range: $25-49.9 Million
Emp.: 9
Electronic Components Distr
N.A.I.C.S.: 423690

OMRON Electronic Components LLC (1)
2895 Greenspoint Pkwy Ste 300, Hoffman Estates, IL 60169-7257
Tel.: (847) 882-2288
Web Site: http://www.components.omron.com
Electronic Components Distr
N.A.I.C.S.: 423690

OMRON Electronic Components Pte. Ltd. (1)
438A Alexandra Road 05-05/08 Lobby 2 Alexandra Technopark, Singapore, 119967, Singapore
Tel.: (65) 63763200
Web Site: http://www.ecb.omron.com.sg
Sales Range: $25-49.9 Million
Emp.: 20
Electronic Components Distr
N.A.I.C.S.: 423690

OMRON Electronic Components Sdn. Bhd. (1)
3A Lot 4 Bangunan TH Uptown 3 Damansara Uptown No 3 Jalan SS21/39, 47400, Petaling Jaya, Selangor, Malaysia
Tel.: (60) 37 623 6300
Medical Device Mfr
N.A.I.C.S.: 339112

OMRON Electronic Components Trading (Shanghai) Ltd. (1)
27F Xin Mei Union Square 999 Pudong South Road, Pudong New Area, Shanghai, 200120, China
Tel.: (86) 2168595919
Electronic Components Distr
N.A.I.C.S.: 423690

OMRON Electronics A.B. (1)
Knarrarnasgatan 15, PO Box 1275, 164 40, Kista, Sweden **(100%)**
Tel.: (46) 86323500
Web Site: http://www.industrial.omron.se
Sales Range: $25-49.9 Million
Emp.: 20
Sales & Marketing of Control Components & Systems
N.A.I.C.S.: 238210

OMRON Electronics A/S (1)
Theilgaards Torv 3 1st floor, 4600, Køge, Denmark **(100%)**
Tel.: (45) 43440011
Web Site: http://www.omron.dk
Sales Range: $25-49.9 Million
Emp.: 45
Sales, Marketing & Manufacturing of Control Components & Systems
N.A.I.C.S.: 335314

OMRON Electronics AG (1)
Blegistrasse 3, PO Box 4319, Baar, 6340, Zug, Switzerland **(100%)**
Tel.: (41) 417481313
Web Site: http://www.industrial.omron.ch
Sales Range: $25-49.9 Million
Emp.: 23
Sales & Marketing of Electronic Control Components & Systems
N.A.I.C.S.: 449210

OMRON Electronics Asia Ltd. (1)
1603A-04 Tower 5 China Hong Kong City 33 Canton Road Tsim Sha Tsui, Kowloon, New Territories, China (Hong Kong) **(100%)**
Tel.: (852) 23753827
Web Site: http://www.omron.com.hk
Sales Range: $25-49.9 Million
Emp.: 20
Sales & Marketing of Electronic Control Components, Retail Systems & Financial Systems
N.A.I.C.S.: 449210

OMRON Electronics B.V. (1)
Wegalaan 61, PO Box 582, 2132 JD, Hoofddorp, Netherlands **(100%)**
Tel.: (31) 235681100
Web Site: http://www.industrial.omron.nl
Sales Range: $25-49.9 Million
Emp.: 80
Sales & Marketing of Electronic Control Components & Systems in Europe
N.A.I.C.S.: 449210

OMRON Electronics Co., Ltd. (1)
Rasa Tower 2 16th Floor 555 Phaholyothin Road, Chatuchak, Bangkok, 10900, Thailand **(100%)**

OMRON CORPORATION

Tel.: (66) 2 937 0500
Web Site: http://www.omron-at.com
Sales Range: $25-49.9 Million
Emp.: 100
Marketing & Manufacturing of Control Components & Systems
N.A.I.C.S.: 335314
Seiki Yamazaki (Mng Dir)

OMRON Electronics Ges.m.b.H. (1)
Liebermannstrasse A01 118/116, 2345, Brunn am Gebirge, Austria
Tel.: (43) 223 637 7800
Web Site: https://industrial.omron.at
Sales Range: $25-49.9 Million
Emp.: 25
Industrial Automation Component Distr
N.A.I.C.S.: 423830
Micheal David Winkler (Mng Dir)

OMRON Electronics GmbH (1)
Elisabeth-Selbert-Str 17, 40764, Langenfeld, Germany
Tel.: (49) 217368000
Web Site: https://industrial.omron.de
Sales Range: $10-24.9 Million
Emp.: 70
Sales & Marketing of Electronic Control Components & Systems in Germany
N.A.I.C.S.: 449210
Klaus Oklraffka (Mng Dir)

OMRON Electronics GmbH (1)
Liebermannstrasse A01 118/116, A-2345, Brunn am Gebirge, Austria **(100%)**
Tel.: (43) 2236377800
Web Site: http://www.industrial.omron.at
Sales Range: $25-49.9 Million
Emp.: 16
Sales & Marketing of Electronic Automation Components & Systems
N.A.I.C.S.: 334419

OMRON Electronics Iberia SA. (1)
C/Arturo Soria 95, 28027, Madrid, Spain
Tel.: (34) 913 777 900
Web Site: http://www.industrial.omron.es
Industrial Automation Component Distr
N.A.I.C.S.: 423830

OMRON Electronics Iberia SAU (1)
Mar do Oriente Building-Rua do Polo Norte nr 18-3 2, 1990-266, Lisbon, Portugal
Tel.: (351) 219429400
Web Site: http://www.industrial.omron.pt
Sales Range: $75-99.9 Million
Emp.: 150
Industrial Automation Component Distr
N.A.I.C.S.: 423830

OMRON Electronics Korea Co., Ltd. (1)
21F Kyobo Tower B Wing 1303-22 Seocho-Dong, Seocho-Gu, Seoul, Korea (South)
Tel.: (82) 2 3483 7789
Web Site: http://www.ia.omron.co.kr
Industrial Automation Machinery Distr
N.A.I.C.S.: 423830

OMRON Electronics LLC (1)
2895 Greenspoint Pkwy Ste 200, Hoffman Estates, IL 60169
Tel.: (847) 843-7900
Web Site: http://www.omron.com
Emp.: 350
Marketing & Manufacturing of Control Components & Systems
N.A.I.C.S.: 423690
Nigel Blakeway (Chm & CEO)

OMRON Electronics Ltd. (1)
Opal Drive Fox Milne, Milton Keynes, MK15 0DG, United Kingdom **(100%)**
Tel.: (44) 1908258258
Web Site: http://industrial.omron.co.uk
Sales Range: $50-74.9 Million
Emp.: 200
Marketing & Manufacturing of Control Components & Systems
N.A.I.C.S.: 335314

OMRON Electronics Ltd. (1)
Burhaniye Mah Tunuslu Mahmut Pasa Cad No 10, Uskudar, 34676, Istanbul, Turkiye **(100%)**
Tel.: (90) 2165565130
Web Site: http://www.industrial.omron.com.tr
Sales Range: $25-49.9 Million
Emp.: 25
Sales & Marketing of Control Components & Systems

OMRON CORPORATION

OMRON Corporation—(Continued)
N.A.I.C.S.: 238210

OMRON Electronics Ltd. (1)
65 Boston Road Mt Eden, Auckland, 1023,
New Zealand (100%)
Tel.: (64) 93584400
Web Site: http://www.omron-ap.co.nz
Sales Range: $1-9.9 Million
Emp.: 15
Marketing & Manufacturing of Control Components & Systems
N.A.I.C.S.: 335314

OMRON Electronics Manufacturing of Germany GmbH (1)
Carl Benz St 4, PO Box 1165, D 71154,
Nufringen, Germany (100%)
Tel.: (49) 70328110
Web Site: http://www.omron.com
Sales Range: $50-74.9 Million
Emp.: 120
Mfr of Control Components & Systems
N.A.I.C.S.: 335314
Ingo Kirmes *(Mgr-Site)*

OMRON Electronics N.V./S.A. (1)
Oktrooiplein 1 B 601, 9000, Gent, Diobeek,
Belgium (100%)
Tel.: (32) 24662480
Web Site: http://www.industrial.omron.be
Sales Range: $10-24.9 Million
Emp.: 30
Sales & Marketing of Electronic Control Components & Systems
N.A.I.C.S.: 449210

OMRON Electronics Norway A/S (1)
Ole Deviks Vei 6 B, PO Box 109, 0666,
Oslo, Norway
Tel.: (47) 2 265 7500
Web Site: https://www.industrial.omron.no
Sales Range: $1-9.9 Million
Emp.: 21
Sales & Marketing of Electronic Control Components & Systems
N.A.I.C.S.: 449210
Erik Tordhol *(Mng Dir)*

OMRON Electronics O.Y. (1)
Bertel Jungin aukio 7 b, 02600, Espoo,
Finland (100%)
Tel.: (358) 207464200
Web Site: http://www.omron.fi
Sales Range: $25-49.9 Million
Emp.: 40
Marketing & Manufacturing of Control Components & Systems
N.A.I.C.S.: 335314

OMRON Electronics Pte. Ltd. (1)
438B Alexandra Road 08-01/02 Alexandra Technopark, Singapore, 119968, Singapore
Tel.: (65) 68353011
Industrial Automation Component Distr
N.A.I.C.S.: 423830

OMRON Electronics Pty. Ltd. (1)
Unit 6 108 Silverwater Road, Silverwater,
2128, NSW, Australia (100%)
Tel.: (61) 1300766766
Web Site: http://www.omron.com.au
Sales Range: $25-49.9 Million
Emp.: 60
Marketing & Manufacturing of Control Components & Systems
N.A.I.C.S.: 335314

OMRON Electronics S.A. (1)
c/Arturo Soria 95, 28027, Madrid,
Spain (100%)
Tel.: (34) 913777900
Web Site: http://www.industrial.omron.es
Sales Range: $75-99.9 Million
Emp.: 100
Sales & Marketing of Electronic Control Components & Systems
N.A.I.C.S.: 449210

OMRON Electronics S.A.S. (1)
3 Parvis de la Gare, 94130, Nogent-sur-
Marne, Cedex, France (100%)
Tel.: (33) 825825679
Web Site: http://www.industrial.omron.fr
Sales Range: $25-49.9 Million
Emp.: 100
Sales & Marketing of Electronic Control Components & Systems
N.A.I.C.S.: 449210

OMRON Electronics S.a.r.l. (1)
14 rue de Lisbonne, 93561, Rosny-sous-
Bois, France
Tel.: (33) 156637000
Web Site: http://www.industrial.omron.fr
Industrial Automation Component Distr
N.A.I.C.S.: 423830

OMRON Electronics S.p.A. (1)
Viale Certosa 49, 20149, Milan, Italy
Tel.: (39) 02 32681
Web Site: http://www.industrial.omron.it
Sales Range: $25-49.9 Million
Emp.: 10
Industrial Automation Component Mfr
N.A.I.C.S.: 333248

OMRON Electronics S.r.l. (1)
Viale Certosa 49, 20149, Milan,
Italy (100%)
Tel.: (39) 0232681
Web Site: http://www.industrial.omron.it
Sales Range: $25-49.9 Million
Emp.: 200
Sales & Marketing of Electronic Control Components & Systems
N.A.I.C.S.: 449210

OMRON Electronics Sdn. Bhd. (1)
Unit 1101 Level 11 Uptown 1 No 1 Jalan
SS21/58 Damansara Uptown, 47400, Petaling Jaya, Selangor, Malaysia
Tel.: (60) 37 688 2888
Industrial Machinery Mfr
N.A.I.C.S.: 333998

OMRON Electronics Sdn. Bhd. (OEP-MY) (1)
Unit 1101 Level 11 Uptown 1 No 1 Jalan
SS21/58 Damansara Uptown, 47400, Petaling Jaya, Selangor, Malaysia
Tel.: (60) 376882888
Web Site: http://www.omron-ap.com
Sales Range: $25-49.9 Million
Emp.: 50
Marketing & Manufacturing of Control Components & Systems
N.A.I.C.S.: 335314

OMRON Electronics Sp.Z.O.O. (1)
ul Zwirki i Wigury 16A Budynek 5B, 02-092,
Warsaw, Poland (100%)
Tel.: (48) 224586666
Web Site: http://www.industrial.omron.pl
Sales Range: $25-49.9 Million
Emp.: 18
Sales & Marketing of Electronic Control Components & Systems
N.A.I.C.S.: 238210

OMRON Electronics Spol. s.r.o. (1)
Boudnikova 2506/1, 180 00, Prague, Czech
Republic (100%)
Tel.: (420) 234076010
Web Site: http://www.omron.cz
Sales Range: $25-49.9 Million
Emp.: 17
Sales & Marketing of Control Components & Systems
N.A.I.C.S.: 238210

OMRON Electronics, KFT (1)
Vaci ut 45 C/6, 1134, Budapest,
Hungary (100%)
Tel.: (36) 13993050
Web Site: http://www.omron.hu
Sales Range: $10-24.9 Million
Emp.: 25
Sales & Marketing of Control Components & Systems
N.A.I.C.S.: 238210

OMRON Eletronica do Brasil Ltda. (1)
Alameda Vicente Pinzon 51-14 andar, Vila
Olimpia, Sao Paulo, 04547-130, SP,
Brazil (100%)
Tel.: (55) 1151718920
Web Site: http://automation.omron.com
Sales Range: $10-24.9 Million
Emp.: 35
Electronic Control Components Sales & Marketing
N.A.I.C.S.: 449210

OMRON Europe B.V. (1)
Wegalaan 67-69, 2132 JD, Hoofddorp,
Netherlands (100%)
Tel.: (31) 235681300
Web Site: http://www.omron.nl

Sales Range: $25-49.9 Million
Emp.: 75
Provider of Electronic Components
N.A.I.C.S.: 334419

OMRON Finance Canada, Inc. (1)
885 Milner Avenue, Scarborough, M1B 5V8,
ON, Canada
Tel.: (416) 286-6465
Web Site: http://www.omron.com
Sales Range: $50-74.9 Million
Emp.: 70
Financial Services
N.A.I.C.S.: 525990

OMRON Healthcare (China) Co., Ltd. (1)
23rd Floor Jinlinghaixin Building 666 Fuzhou Road, Shanghai, China
Tel.: (86) 216 391 7557
Healthcare Services
N.A.I.C.S.: 621610

OMRON Healthcare (Thailand) Co., Ltd. (1)
Rasa Tower 2 22nd Floor Unit 2202-1 2203
No 555 Phahonyothin Road, Kwaeng
Chatuchak Khet Chatuchak, Bangkok,
10900, Thailand
Tel.: (66) 2 021 5555
Healtcare Services
N.A.I.C.S.: 621610

OMRON Healthcare Bangladesh Ltd. (1)
Plot-17/A Ground Floor Road-6 Dhanmondi
R/A, Dhaka, 1205, Bangladesh
Tel.: (880) 2 961 2558
Healtcare Services
N.A.I.C.S.: 621610

OMRON Healthcare Co., Ltd. (1)
53 Kunotsubo Terado-cho, Muko, 617-0002,
Kyoto, Japan
Tel.: (81) 759252000
Web Site: http://www.healthcare.omron.co.jp
Sales Range: $650-699.9 Million
Emp.: 696
Health Equipment Mfr
N.A.I.C.S.: 339112

Subsidiary (Non-US):

OMRON Healthcare Brazil (2)
Av Paulista 967 - 5o andar - Bela Vista,
Sao Paulo, 01311-100, Brazil
Tel.: (55) 1131492035
Web Site: http://www.omronbrasil.com
Sales Range: $25-49.9 Million
Emp.: 15
Health Care Device Distr
N.A.I.C.S.: 423450

OMRON Healthcare Europe B.V. (2)
Scorpius 33, 2132 LR, Hoofddorp, Netherlands
Tel.: (31) 23 554 4700
Web Site: https://www.omron.com
Sales Range: $25-49.9 Million
Emp.: 40
Mfr & Marketer of Healthcare Equipment
N.A.I.C.S.: 456199
Andre Van Gils *(Pres & CEO)*

OMRON Healthcare India Pvt Ltd. (2)
6th Floor B-Block Sewa Tower Plot no 19
Sector -18, Udyog Vihar Maruti Industrial
complex, Gurgaon, 122008, Haryana, India
Tel.: (91) 1247122700
Web Site: http://www.omronhealthcare-ap.com
Medical Device Distr
N.A.I.C.S.: 423450

OMRON Healthcare Manufacturing Vietnam Co., Ltd. (2)
28 VSIP II Street 2 VSIP II, Hoa Phu, Thu
Dau Mot, Binh Duong, Vietnam
Tel.: (84) 2743589357
Web Site: http://vn.omron.asia
Healthcare Device Mfr
N.A.I.C.S.: 339112

OMRON Healthcare Product Development Dalian Co., Ltd. (2)
No 18 Software Park Road Software Park,
Dalian, 116023, Liaoning, China
Tel.: (86) 41184768080

Sales Range: $25-49.9 Million
Emp.: 88
Healthcare Device Mfr
N.A.I.C.S.: 339112

OMRON Healthcare Singapore Pte Ltd. (2)
438B Alexandra Road 08-01/02 Alexandra
Technopark Block B, Singapore, 119968,
Singapore (100%)
Tel.: (65) 6376 3500
Web Site: http://www.omronhealthcare-ap.com
Sales Range: $25-49.9 Million
Emp.: 11
Marketing of Healthcare Equipment
N.A.I.C.S.: 456199

OMRON Healthcare U.K. Ltd. (2)
Opal Drive Fox Milne, Milton Keynes, MK15
0DG, United Kingdom
Tel.: (44) 1908258285
Web Site: http://www.omron-healthcare.co.uk
Sales Range: $25-49.9 Million
Emp.: 7
Health Care Devices Sales
N.A.I.C.S.: 423450

Subsidiary (US):

OMRON Healthcare, Inc. (2)
1925 W Field Ct, Lake Forest, IL 60045
Tel.: (847) 680-6200
Web Site: http://www.omronhealthcare.com
Sales Range: $75-99.9 Million
Emp.: 180
Health Care Equipment Mfr
N.A.I.C.S.: 423450
Ranndy Kellogg *(Pres & CEO)*

OMRON Healthcare Korea Co., Ltd. (1)
Kyobo-tower A-dong 18F 465, Gangnam-
daero Seocho-gu, Seoul, 06611, Korea
(South)
Tel.: (82) 22 038 4210
Healtcare Services
N.A.I.C.S.: 621610

OMRON Healthcare Mexico S.A De C.V. (1)
Lamartine 238 Piso 4 Col, Chapultepec Morales, 11570, Mexico, Mexico
Healtcare Services
N.A.I.C.S.: 621610

OMRON Healthcare Taiwan Co., Ltd. (1)
9F No 367 Fusing N Rd, Songshan Dist,
Taipei, 10543, Taiwan
Tel.: (886) 28 770 7733
Healtcare Services
N.A.I.C.S.: 621610

OMRON Hong Kong Limited (1)
1504B-09B Tower 3 China Hong Kong City
33 Canton Road, Tsim Sha Tsui, Kowloon,
China (Hong Kong)
Tel.: (852) 2 375 3827
Web Site: https://www.omron.com.hk
Industrial Automation Products Mfr
N.A.I.C.S.: 333998

OMRON Immobiliare S.r.l. (1)
Viale Certosa 49, 20149, Milan, Italy
Tel.: (39) 0232681
Building Management Services
N.A.I.C.S.: 236220

OMRON Industrial Automation (China) Co., Ltd. (1)
Room 2211 Bank of China Tower 200
Yincheng Middle Road, Pu Dong New Area,
Shanghai, 200120, China
Tel.: (86) 216 023 0333
Web Site: https://www.fa.omron.com.cn
Industrial Automation Products Mfr
N.A.I.C.S.: 333998

OMRON Industry & Trade (Dalian) Co., Ltd. (1)
IC-45-1 Free Trade Zone, Dalian, 116600,
China
Tel.: (86) 411 8731 7201
Web Site: http://www.omron.com
Sales Range: $75-99.9 Million
Emp.: 160
Health Care Device Distr
N.A.I.C.S.: 423450

AND PRIVATE COMPANIES

OMRON Laserfront Korea Inc. (1)
A-902 Bundang Technopark Yatap-dong,
Bundang-gu, Seongnam, 463-760, Kyeonggi, Korea (South)
Tel.: (82) 31 607 3311
Web Site: http://www.omron.com
Laser Fabrication Equipment Distr
N.A.I.C.S.: 423830

OMRON Malaysia Sdn. Bhd. (1)
Lot 15 SS8/4 Sg Way F I Z, 47300, Petaling Jaya, Selangor, Malaysia (100%)
Tel.: (60) 37 884 8000
Web Site: https://www.omron.com
Sales Range: $25-49.9 Million
Emp.: 800
Marketing & Manufacturing of Control Components & Systems
N.A.I.C.S.: 335314
Ezaki Masahiko (Pres)

OMRON Management Center Of India (1)
6th Floor B-Block Sewa Tower Plot no 19 Sector-18, Udyog Vihar Maruti Industrial Complex, Gurgaon, 122008, Haryana, India
Tel.: (91) 124 712 2700
Industrial Automation Products Mfr
N.A.I.C.S.: 333998

OMRON Management Center of America, Inc. (1)
2895 Greenspoint Pkwy Ste 100, Hoffman Estates, IL 60169
Tel.: (224) 520-7650
Web Site: http://www.omron.com
Sales Range: $650-699.9 Million
Emp.: 1,500
Research & Development
N.A.I.C.S.: 423420

OMRON Manufacturing of America, Inc. (1)
3632 Stern Ave, Saint Charles, IL 60174-5437 (100%)
Tel.: (630) 513-0400
Web Site: http://www.omron.com
Sales Range: $25-49.9 Million
Emp.: 50
Mfr of Industrial Control Components & Systems
N.A.I.C.S.: 335314

OMRON Manufacturing of the Netherlands B.V. (1)
Zilverenberg 2, 5234 GM, 's-Hertogenbosch, Netherlands (100%)
Tel.: (31) 73 648 1811
Web Site: https://www.omron.com
Sales Range: $50-74.9 Million
Emp.: 250
Marketing & Manufacturing of Control Components & Systems
N.A.I.C.S.: 335314
Hugo Sintnicolaas (CEO)

OMRON Medical (Beijing) Co., Ltd. (1)
Rm509-511 TowerB Focus square No 6 Futong East Street, Wangjing, Beijing, 100102, Chaoyang, China
Tel.: (86) 108 472 0008
Healtcare Services
N.A.I.C.S.: 621610

OMRON Medizintechnik Handelsgesellschaft mbH (1)
Konrad-Zuse-Ring 28, 68163, Mannheim, Germany (100%)
Tel.: (49) 621833480
Web Site: http://www.omron-healthcare.de
Sales Range: $25-49.9 Million
Emp.: 50
Mfr, Sales & Servicer of Healthcare Equipment
N.A.I.C.S.: 456199

OMRON Mexico, S.A. de C.V. (1)
Miguel de Cervantes Saavedra No 169 Piso 1 Colonia Granada, 11520, Mexico, Mexico
Tel.: (52) 811 156 9910
Web Site: https://automation.omron.com
Industrial Automation Products Mfr
N.A.I.C.S.: 333998

OMRON Microscan Systems Inc. (1)
700 SW 39th St Ste 100, Renton, WA 98057
Tel.: (425) 226-5700
Web Site: http://www.microscan.com
Bar Coding Products & Machine Vision Hardware Mfr
N.A.I.C.S.: 561499
Andy Zosel (Sr VP-Engrg & Comml Ops)

OMRON Precision Tech Hong Kong (1)
Unit 218-220 2/F Photonics Center No 2 Science Park East Avenue, Hong Kong Science Park, Sha Tin, New Territories, China (Hong Kong)
Tel.: (852) 23148403
Emp.: 3
Electronic Components Mfr & Distr
N.A.I.C.S.: 334419

OMRON Precision Technology Korea Co., Ltd. (1)
Pacific Tower 10F 941-1 Daechi-dong, Gannam-gu, Seoul, 135-280, Korea (South)
Tel.: (82) 2 563 8212
Web Site: http://www.omron.com
Electronic Components Distr
N.A.I.C.S.: 423690

OMRON Robotics & Safety Technologies, Inc. (1)
4225 Hacienda Dr, Pleasanton, CA 94588
Tel.: (925) 245-3400
Web Site: https://www.robotics.omron.com
Industrial Automation Products Mfr
N.A.I.C.S.: 333998

OMRON Sante France SAS (1)
14 Rue de Lisbonne, 93561, Rosny-sous-Bois, Cedex, France
Tel.: (33) 15 963 7000
Healtcare Services
N.A.I.C.S.: 621610

OMRON Taiwan Electronics, Inc. (1)
6F Home Young Bldg No 363 Fu-Shing North Rd, Taipei, 105, Taiwan (100%)
Tel.: (886) 22 715 3331
Web Site: http://www.omron.com.tw
Sales Range: $1-9.9 Million
Emp.: 100
Sales & Marketing of Electronic Control Components in Taiwan
N.A.I.C.S.: 449210
Takashi Ikezoe (Chm)

OMRON Vietnam Co., Ltd. (1)
6th Floor 789 Tower 147 Hoang Quoc Viet, Cau Giay, Hanoi, Vietnam
Tel.: (84) 243 556 3444
Industrial Equipment Distr
N.A.I.C.S.: 423830

OOO OMRON Electronics (1)
26 Pravdy Street, 125040, Moscow, Russia
Tel.: (7) 4956489450
Web Site: https://www.industrial.omron.ru
Industrial Automation Products Mfr
N.A.I.C.S.: 333998

OOO OMRON Electronics (OEE-RUS) (1)
26 Pravdy Street, 125040, Moscow, Russia
Tel.: (7) 4956489450
Web Site: http://www.industrial.omron.ru
Emp.: 30
Sales & Marketing of Control Components & Systems
N.A.I.C.S.: 423830

Omron Adept Technologies, Inc. (1)
4550 Norris Canyon Rd Ste 150, San Ramon, CA 94583
Tel.: (925) 245-3400
Web Site: http://www.adept.com
Robotics, Motion Controllers & Machine Vision Mfr
N.A.I.C.S.: 334513
Nigel Blakeway (Chm & CEO)

Subsidiary (Domestic):

Omron Adept MobileRobots, LLC (2)
10 Columbia Dr, Amherst, NH 03031
Tel.: (603) 881-7960
Web Site: http://www.mobilerobots.com
Autonomous Mobile Robotic System Developer
N.A.I.C.S.: 333922

Subsidiary (Non-US):

Omron Adept Technologies France (2)
Parc Altais 25 rue Vega, FR-74650, Chavanod, France
Tel.: (33) 450028116
Web Site: http://www.adept-technology.fr
Robotics, Motion Controllers & Machine Vision Mfr
N.A.I.C.S.: 333310
Bruno Adam (Dir)

Omron Adept Technologies GmbH (2)
Revierstrasse 5, 44379, Dortmund, Germany
Tel.: (49) 231758940
Web Site: http://www.adept.de
Robotics, Motion Controllers & Machine Vision Mfr
N.A.I.C.S.: 333310
Olaf Trimpop-Dietz (Engr-Sls)

P.T. OMRON Healthcare Indonesia (1)
Menara Bidakara 1 Lt 22 Jl Jend Gatot Subroto Kav 71-73, Pancoran, 12870, South Jakarta, Indonesia
Tel.: (62) 212 949 7500
Healtcare Services
N.A.I.C.S.: 621610

PT OMRON Electronics (1)
Menara Bidakara 1 Lantai 22 Jl Jend Gatot Subroto Kav 71-7, Selatan, Jakarta, 12810, Indonesia
Tel.: (62) 2129497500
Web Site: http://www.omron.co.id
Industrial Automation Component Distr
N.A.I.C.S.: 423830

PT OMRON Manufacturing of Indonesia (1)
EJIP Industrial Park Plot 5C, Cikarang Selatan, Bekasi, 17530, W Java, Indonesia (100%)
Tel.: (62) 21 897 0111
Web Site: https://www.omron.com
Sales Range: $400-449.9 Million
Emp.: 1,800
Marketing & Manufacturing of Control Components & Systems
N.A.I.C.S.: 335314
Irawan Santoso (Pres)

Shanghai OMRON Automation System Co., Ltd. (1)
1600 Jinsui Road Pudong New Area, Shanghai, 201206, China
Tel.: (86) 2150504535
Marketing & Manufacturing of Control Components & Systems
N.A.I.C.S.: 335314

Shanghai OMRON Control Components Co., Ltd. (1)
11 Chuangye Road Jinqiao Economic Technological Development Zone, Pudong New Area, Shanghai, 201201, China (100%)
Tel.: (86) 2160360188
Sales Range: $25-49.9 Million
Emp.: 30
Control Components & Systems Mfr & Marketer
N.A.I.C.S.: 335314

OMV AKTIENGESELLSCHAFT

Trabrennstrasse 6-8, 1020, Vienna, Austria
Tel.: (43) 14044023760 AT
Web Site: https://www.omv.com
Year Founded: 1956
OMVJF—(OTCIQ)
Rev.: $45,551,736,880
Assets: $66,076,855,520
Liabilities: $39,060,488,480
Net Worth: $27,016,367,040
Earnings: $3,443,984,960
Emp.: 22,434
Fiscal Year-end: 12/31/21
Crude Oil & Natural Gas Explorer, Refiner, Importer & Transporter
N.A.I.C.S.: 213112
Alyazia Ali Saleh Al Kuwaiti (Deputy Chm-Supervisory Bd)

Subsidiaries:

AGGM Austrian Gas Grid Management AG (1)
Floridsdorfer Hauptstrasse 1 Peak Vienna, 1210, Vienna, Austria
Tel.: (43) 127560
Web Site: https://www.aggm.at
Natural Gas Distribution Services
N.A.I.C.S.: 221210
Stefan Wagenhofer (Chm)

Adria-Wien Pipeline Gesellschaft m.b.H. (1)
St Ruprechter strabe 113, 9020, Klagenfurt, Austria (55%)
Tel.: (43) 463569900
Web Site: http://www.awp.at
Sales Range: $50-74.9 Million
Emp.: 40
Petroleum Services
N.A.I.C.S.: 213112
Stefan Tuman (Mng Dir)

Borealis Chile SpA (1)
Piso 4 Oficina 413 Alonso de Cordova, Las Condes, 5870, Santiago, Chile
Tel.: (56) 226660770
Web Site: https://www.borealis.cl
Software Development Services
N.A.I.C.S.: 541511

Borealis Colombia S.A.S. (1)
Calle 77 11-91 Oficina 502, Bogota, Colombia
Tel.: (57) 3122650878
Web Site: https://www.borealis.com.co
Software Development Services
N.A.I.C.S.: 541511

Borealis L.A.T France S.A.S. (1)
Tour Ciel 20 Ter Rue de Bezons, 92400, Courbevoie, France
Tel.: (33) 147969766
Software Development Services
N.A.I.C.S.: 541511

Borealis L.A.T Hrvatska d.o.o. (1)
Setaliste Petra Preradovica 8, 31000, Osijek, Croatia
Tel.: (385) 98382983
Software Development Services
N.A.I.C.S.: 541511

Borealis L.A.T Italia s.r.l. (1)
Via Filippo Turati 40, 20121, Milan, Italy
Tel.: (39) 0392042268
Software Development Services
N.A.I.C.S.: 541511

Borealis L.A.T Polska Sp. z o.o. (1)
Ul Obro ncow 26 Lok 3, 03-927, Warsaw, Poland
Tel.: (48) 437326915
Software Development Services
N.A.I.C.S.: 541511

Borealis Produits et Engrais Chimiques du Rhin S.A.S. (1)
Z I Mulhouse Rhin Route CD 52, CS 10028, 68490, Ottmarsheim, France
Tel.: (33) 389265326
Polyolefin Plastic Distr
N.A.I.C.S.: 424610

Diramic Insurance Limited (1)
Suite 827 Europort, PO Box 708, Gibraltar, Gibraltar
Tel.: (350) 20051801
General Insurance Services
N.A.I.C.S.: 524210
Deborah Schembri (Acct Mgr)

Gas Connect Austria GmbH (1)
Floridsdorfer Hauptstrasse 1, Floridsdorfer Hauptstrasse 1, 1210, Vienna, Austria (51%)
Tel.: (43) 1275000
Web Site: https://www.gasconnect.at
Sales Range: $75-99.9 Million
Emp.: 240
Petroleum Services
N.A.I.C.S.: 213112
Harald Stindl (Mng Dir)

ICS PETROM MOLDOVA SA (1)
Str Calea Iesilor Nr 8 Zity Mall, Chisinau, MD-2069, Moldova
Tel.: (373) 69600257
Web Site: http://www.petrom.md
Oil Terminal Operating Services
N.A.I.C.S.: 424710

OMV (BAYERN) Exploration GmbH (1)

OMV AKTIENGESELLSCHAFT
INTERNATIONAL PUBLIC

OMV Aktiengesellschaft—(Continued)
Trabrennstrasse 628, Vienna, 1020, Austria
Tel.: (43) 1404400
Web Site: http://www.omv.com
Sales Range: $1-4.9 Billion
Emp.: 4,000
Crude Petroleum & Natural Gas Extraction Services
N.A.I.C.S.: 211120

Subsidiary (Non-US):

OMV (NORGE) AS (2)
Fjordpiren Laberget 22, 4020, Stavanger, Norway
Tel.: (47) 52977000
Web Site: https://www.omv.no
Emp.: 150
Oil & Gas Exploration Services
N.A.I.C.S.: 213112
Knut Egil Mauseth *(Mng Dir & Sr VP-North Sea)*

Subsidiary (Domestic):

OMV (Tunesien) Exploration GmbH (2)
Trabrennstrasse 6-8, Vienna, 1020, Austria
Tel.: (43) 1404400
Web Site: http://www.omv.com
Oil & Gas Exploration Services
N.A.I.C.S.: 213112

OMV (YEMEN) Al Mabar Exploration GmbH (2)
Trabrennstrasse 6-8, Vienna, 1020, Austria
Tel.: (43) 1404400
Web Site: http://www.omv.com
Fuel Extraction Services
N.A.I.C.S.: 213112

OMV (YEMEN) South Sanau Exploration GmbH (2)
Trabrennstrasse 6-8, Vienna, 1020, Austria
Tel.: (43) 1404400
Sales Range: $200-249.9 Million
Emp.: 40
Natural Gas Distr
N.A.I.C.S.: 221210

OMV (Yemen Block S 2) Exploration GmbH (2)
Trabrennstrasse 6-8, 1020, Vienna, Austria
Tel.: (43) 1404400
Oil & Gas Exploration Services
N.A.I.C.S.: 213112

OMV Oil Production GmbH (2)
Trabrennstra 6-8, Vienna, 1020, Austria
Tel.: (43) 1404400
Oil & Gas Exploration Services
N.A.I.C.S.: 213112

OMV Oil and Gas Exploration GmbH (2)
Trabrennstrasse 6-8, 1020, Vienna, Austria
Tel.: (43) 1404400
Oil & Gas Exploration Services
N.A.I.C.S.: 213112

OMV Petroleum Exploration GmbH (2)
Trabrennstrasse 6-8, Vienna, 1020, Austria
Tel.: (43) 1404400
Web Site: http://www.omv.com
Oil & Gas Exploration Services
N.A.I.C.S.: 213112

OMV Southeast Caspian Upstream GmbH (2)
Trabrennstrasse 6-8, Vienna, 1020, Austria
Tel.: (43) 1 404 40 0
Natural Gas Distr
N.A.I.C.S.: 221210

OMV Australia Pty Ltd (1)
Level 29 St Martins Tower, 44 St George Terrace, Perth, 6000, WA, Australia **(100%)**
Tel.: (61) 892235000
Web Site: https://www.omv.com
Sales Range: $25-49.9 Million
Emp.: 22
Lubricating Oil & Grease Mfr
N.A.I.C.S.: 324191

OMV BULGARIA OOD (1)
2 Donka Ushlinova Str Office building 4 1st floor, 1766, Sofia, Bulgaria
Tel.: (359) 29329710
Web Site: https://www.omv.bg
Fuels Whslr
N.A.I.C.S.: 457210

OMV Bulgarien OOD Einmanngesellschaft mbH (1)
Bul Tsarigradsko shose 90, Capital Fort Business Center Building A Fl 20, Sofia, 1784, Bulgaria **(100%)**
Tel.: (359) 29329710
Web Site: http://www.omv.bg
Sales Range: $50-74.9 Million
Petroleum Services
N.A.I.C.S.: 213112

OMV Czech Republic spol. s.r.o. (1)
Stetkova 1638/18, 140 00, Prague, Czech Republic **(100%)**
Tel.: (420) 261392111
Web Site: http://www.omv.cz
Sales Range: $50-74.9 Million
Emp.: 40
Petroleum Services
N.A.I.C.S.: 213112

OMV Deutschland GmbH (1)
Haiminger Strasse 1, 84489, Burghausen, Germany **(100%)**
Tel.: (49) 86779600
Web Site: https://www.omv.de
Sales Range: $125-149.9 Million
Emp.: 700
Petroleum Products
N.A.I.C.S.: 324199

OMV Exploration & Production GmbH (1)
Trabrennstrasse 6-8, 1020, Vienna, Austria **(100%)**
Tel.: (43) 1404400
Sales Range: $800-899.9 Million
Emp.: 1,500
Oil & Gas Exploration, Development & Production
N.A.I.C.S.: 211120

Subsidiary (Domestic):

OMV Austria Exploration & Production GmbH (1)
Protteser Strasse 40, 2230, Ganserndorf, Austria
Tel.: (43) 140 4400
Web Site: http://www.omv.com
Oil & Gas Exploration Services
N.A.I.C.S.: 213112

Subsidiary (Domestic):

OMV (SLOVAKIA) Exploration GmbH (3)
Protteserstrasse 40, 2230, Ganserndorf, Austria
Tel.: (43) 140 4400
Web Site: http://www.omv.com
Oil & Gas Exploration Services
N.A.I.C.S.: 213112

Subsidiary (Non-US):

OMV New Zealand Limited (2)
Level 20 The Majestic Centre 100 Willis Street, PO Box 2621, Wellington, 6140, New Zealand
Tel.: (64) 4 910 2500
Web Site: https://www.omv.nz
Oil & Gas Exploration & Extraction Services
N.A.I.C.S.: 213112

Subsidiary (Domestic):

OMV Taranaki Limited (3)
Level 20 The Majestic Centre 100 Willis Street, Wellington, New Zealand
Tel.: (64) 4 910 2500
Petroleum Extraction
N.A.I.C.S.: 211120

OMV Gas & Power GmbH (1)
Trabrennstrasse 6-8, 1020, Vienna, Austria
Tel.: (43) 140440
Sales Range: $50-74.9 Million
Emp.: 80
Investment Management Service
N.A.I.C.S.: 523999
Harald Stindl *(Office Mgr)*

Subsidiary (Domestic):

Central European Gas Hub AG (2)
Peak Vienna Floridsdorfer Hauptstrasse 1, 1210, Vienna, Austria
Tel.: (43) 127027 002 8501
Web Site: https://www.cegh.at
Natural Gas Distribution Services
N.A.I.C.S.: 221210
Gottfried Steiner *(CEO)*

OMV Gas Marketing & Trading GmbH (2)
Trabrennstrasse 6-8, 1020, Vienna, Austria
Tel.: (43) 1404400
Natural Gas Distribution Services
N.A.I.C.S.: 221210

OMV Gaz Ve Enerji Limited Sirketi (1)
Maslak Mahallesi Maslak Meydan Sokak Veko Giz Plaza No 3 Kat 16, Maslak Sisli, 34396, Istanbul, Türkiye
Tel.: (90) 212 329 10 00
Sales Range: $75-99.9 Million
Emp.: 4
Electric Power & Natural Gas Distribution Services
N.A.I.C.S.: 221122
Hilmar Kroat-Reder *(Gen Mgr)*

OMV Global Oil & Gas GmbH (1)
Trabrennstrasse 6-8, 1020, Vienna, Austria
Tel.: (43) 1404400
Web Site: http://www.omv.com
Oil & Gas Exploration Services
N.A.I.C.S.: 213112

OMV Insurance Broker GmbH (1)
Trabrennstrasse 6-8, 1020, Vienna, Austria
Tel.: (43) 14044021794
Natural Gas Distribution Services
N.A.I.C.S.: 221210

OMV PETROM GAS SRL (1)
Petrom City 22 Coralilor sector 1, 013329, Bucharest, Romania
Tel.: (40) 21 402 2201
Web Site: https://www.omvpetrom.com
Oil & Gas Exploration Services
N.A.I.C.S.: 213112

OMV PETROM SA (1)
Petrom City Coralilor Street 22 Sector 1, 013329, Bucharest, Romania
Tel.: (40) 214022201
Web Site: https://www.omvpetrom.com
Natural Gas Distribution Services
N.A.I.C.S.: 221210
Alfred Stern *(Pres)*

OMV Power & Gas GmbH (1)
Trabrennstrasse 6-8, 1020, Vienna, Austria
Tel.: (43) 14044021600
Web Site: http://www.omv.com
Gas & Power Distribution
N.A.I.C.S.: 221210

Subsidiary (Non-US):

S.C. OMV Petrom S.A. (2)
Petrom City 22 Coralilor sector 1, 013329, Bucharest, Romania **(51.01%)**
Tel.: (40) 214022201
Web Site: https://www.omvpetrom.com
Rev.: $8,566,631,915
Assets: $12,631,458,917
Liabilities: $4,078,456,159
Net Worth: $8,553,002,758
Earnings: $875,324,168
Emp.: 7,714
Fiscal Year-end: 12/31/2023
Exploration & Production of Oil & Natural Gas
N.A.I.C.S.: 211120
Rainer Seele *(Chm-Supervisory Bd)*

OMV Proterra GmbH (1)
Trabrennstrasse 6-8, Vienna, 1020, Austria **(100%)**
Tel.: (43) 1404400
Web Site: http://www.omv.co.at
Sales Range: $25-49.9 Million
Emp.: 100
Petroleum Services
N.A.I.C.S.: 541330

OMV Refining & Marketing GmbH (1)
Trabrennstrasse 6-8, A 1020, Vienna, Austria **(100%)**
Tel.: (43) 1 40 440 0
Web Site: http://www.omv.com

Petroleum Refining & Marketing
N.A.I.C.S.: 424720

Subsidiary (Domestic):

Avanti GmbH (2)
Franz-Brotzner-Strasse 11, Wals bei, 5071, Salzburg, Austria
Tel.: (43) 662276705
Web Site: http://www.avanti.at
Natural Gas Distribution Services
N.A.I.C.S.: 221210

Borealis AG (2)
Wagramer Strasse 17-19, 1220, Vienna, Austria **(75%)**
Tel.: (43) 122400300
Web Site: https://www.borealisgroup.com
Rev.: $9,074,082,238
Assets: $11,331,064,880
Liabilities: $4,099,286,725
Net Worth: $7,231,778,155
Earnings: $976,516,800
Emp.: 6,869
Fiscal Year-end: 12/31/2019
Holding Company; Petrochemical Mfr
N.A.I.C.S.: 551112
Thomas Gangl *(CEO & Member-Exec Bd)*

Subsidiary (Non-US):

Borealis A/S (3)
Parallelvej 16, DK 2000, Kongens Lyngby, Denmark
Tel.: (45) 45966000
Web Site: http://www.borealisgroup.com
Sales Range: $5-14.9 Billion
Emp.: 4,639
Plastic Industry Materials Mfr; Owned 65% by International Petroleum Investment Company & 35% by OMV AG
N.A.I.C.S.: 325211

Borealis AB (3)
Industrivagen 3, 444 86, Stenungsund, Sweden
Tel.: (46) 303 860 00
Petrochemical Product Distr
N.A.I.C.S.: 424690

Subsidiary (Non-US):

Borealis Group Services AS (4)
Asdalstrand 291, 3960, Stathelle, Norway
Tel.: (47) 35578337
Petrochemical Product Distr
N.A.I.C.S.: 424690

Subsidiary (Non-US):

Borealis AG Moscow (3)
Representative Office World Trade Center 12 Krasnopresnenskaya emb, Entrance 6 4th Fl Office 420, 123610, Moscow, Russia **(100%)**
Tel.: (7) 4952581897
Web Site: http://www.borealisgroup.com
Sales Range: $25-49.9 Million
Emp.: 7
Agricultural & Industrial Petrochemical Refinement
N.A.I.C.S.: 325110

Subsidiary (Domestic):

Borealis Agrolinz Melamine GmbH (3)
St-Peter-Strasse 25, 4021, Linz, Austria **(100%)**
Tel.: (43) 73269140
Sales Range: $200-249.9 Million
Emp.: 800
Agricultural & Industrial Petrochemical Refinement
N.A.I.C.S.: 325110

Subsidiary (Non-US):

Borealis Agrolinz Melamine Deutschland GmbH (4)
Mollensdorfer Strasse 13, 06886, Lutherstadt Wittenberg, Germany
Tel.: (49) 3491 68 2200
Petrochemical Product Distr
N.A.I.C.S.: 424690

Subsidiary (Non-US):

Borealis Brasil S.A. (3)
Av Osvaldo Berto 700 - Bairro do Pinhal, 13255-405, Itatiba, Brazil

AND PRIVATE COMPANIES

Tel.: (55) 11 4524 9100
Petrochemical Product Distr
N.A.I.C.S.: 424690
Leonardo Harsch *(Mng Dir)*

Borealis Chimie S.A.S. (3)
Usine de Grandpuits, CS 20798, 77720, Mormant, France **(100%)**
Tel.: (33) 16 460 3500
Web Site: https://www.borealisgroup.com
Sales Range: $650-699.9 Million
Emp.: 725
Nitrogen Fertilizer & Nitrogen Oxide Reducer Mfr
N.A.I.C.S.: 325311
Benoit Anet *(Dir-HR & Comm)*

Plant (Domestic):

Borealis Chimie S.A.S. - Grand-Quevilly Plant (4)
30 Rue de l'Industrie, BP 204, 76121, Grand Quevilly, Cedex, France
Tel.: (33) 23 567 4141
Web Site: https://www.borealisgroup.com
Emp.: 300
Fertilizer Mfr
N.A.I.C.S.: 325311

Borealis Chimie S.A.S. - Grandpuits Plant (4)
Usine de Grandpuits, CS 20798, Grandpuits, 77720, Mormant, France
Tel.: (33) 16 460 3500
Web Site: https://www.borealisgroup.com
Fertilizer Mfr
N.A.I.C.S.: 325311

Subsidiary (Domestic):

Borealis L.A.T. Sobelagro S.A.S. (4)
8 Rue des Anciens Combattants AFN, 28300, Clevilliers, France
Tel.: (33) 237239612
Petrochemical Product Distr
N.A.I.C.S.: 424690

Subsidiary (US):

Borealis Compounds Inc. (3)
176 Thomas Rd, Port Murray, NJ 07865
Tel.: (908) 850-6200
Petrochemical Product Distr
N.A.I.C.S.: 424690
Peter Nielsen *(Gen Mgr-Sls)*

Subsidiary (Non-US):

Borealis Financial Services N.V. (3)
Industriepark Noord-Campus Mechelen Schalienhoevedreef 20G, 2800, Mechelen, Belgium
Tel.: (32) 15 47 97 11
Financial Management Services
N.A.I.C.S.: 551112

Borealis France S.A.S. (3)
9/11 rue Benoit Malon, 95156, Suresnes, France
Tel.: (33) 546557000
Petrochemical Product Distr
N.A.I.C.S.: 424690

Borealis Italia S.p.A. (3)
Via Ercolano 8/10, 20900, Monza, Italy
Tel.: (39) 039 2042 1
Petrochemical Product Distr
N.A.I.C.S.: 424690

Borealis Kallo N.V. (3)
Haven 1568, Sing-Jansweg 2, BE-9130, Kallo, Belgium **(100%)**
Tel.: (32) 35705211
Agricultural & Industrial Petrochemical Refinement
N.A.I.C.S.: 325110

Borealis L.A.T Beograd d.o.o. (3)
Bulevar Zorana Dindica 64a, 11070, Belgrade, Serbia
Tel.: (381) 11 260 88 31
Fertilizer Product Mfr
N.A.I.C.S.: 325312

Borealis L.A.T Bulgaria EOOD (3)
13 Tintyava Str ent A 3rd floor office 3-5, 1113, Sofia, Bulgaria
Tel.: (359) 2 442 5368
Web Site: https://www.borealis-lat.com
Fertilizer Product Mfr
N.A.I.C.S.: 325312

Borealis L.A.T Czech Republic spol. s.r.o. (3)
Nemanicka ul 440/14, 37010, Ceske Budejovice, Czech Republic
Tel.: (420) 387 221 613
Web Site: http://www.borealis-lat.com
Fertilizer Product Mfr
N.A.I.C.S.: 325312

Borealis L.A.T Hungary Kft. (3)
Futo utca 37-45, 1082, Budapest, Hungary
Tel.: (36) 1 479 5959
Web Site: https://www.borealis-lat.com
Fertilizer Product Mfr
N.A.I.C.S.: 325312
Andras Hajdu *(Mng Dir)*

Borealis L.A.T Romania s.r.l. (3)
St-Maria Rosetti 6 et 8 sector 2, 020485, Bucharest, Romania
Tel.: (40) 212123268
Web Site: https://www.borealis-lat.com
Emp.: 12
Fertilizer Product Mfr
N.A.I.C.S.: 325312
Stephen Porsos *(Gen Mgr)*

Borealis L.A.T Slovakia s.r.o. (3)
Pri zeleznicnej stanici, 94631, Chotin, Slovakia
Tel.: (421) 35 77 86 305
Fertilizer Product Mfr
N.A.I.C.S.: 325312
Oto Jommeke *(Mng Dir)*

Borealis L.A.T d.o.o. za trgovinu (3)
Ivana Gundulica 28, 31000, Osijek, Croatia
Tel.: (385) 3 154 0260
Web Site: https://www.borealis-lat.com
Fertilizer Product Mfr
N.A.I.C.S.: 325312
Borna Sikora *(Mgr-Sls)*

Borealis PEC-Rhin SAS (3)
ZI Mulhouse Rhin Route CD 52, PO Box 28, 68490, Ottmarsheim, France
Tel.: (33) 38 926 5326
Web Site: http://www.borealisgroup.com
Sales Range: $50-74.9 Million
Emp.: 180
Ammonia, Nitric Acid & Fertilizers Mfr
N.A.I.C.S.: 325998

Borealis Plasticos S.A. de C.V. (3)
1041 Gabriel Mancera Col Del Valle Centro Distrito Federal, 03100, Mexico, Mexico
Tel.: (52) 39 2042 1
Petrochemical Product Distr
N.A.I.C.S.: 424690
Angel Rodrigo Morales Valle *(Mgr-Sls)*

Borealis Plastik ve Kimyasal Maddeler Ticaret Limited Sirketi (3)
Ayazma Deresi Cad Saral Is Merkezi No 5 Kat 3, Gayrettepe, 34349, Istanbul, Türkiye
Tel.: (90) 212 275 76 27
Petrochemical Product Distr
N.A.I.C.S.: 424690

Borealis Plastomers B.V. (3)
Koolwaterstofstraat 1, PO Box 606, Sittard, 6161 RA, Geleen, Netherlands
Tel.: (31) 46 4768280
Petrochemical Product Distr
N.A.I.C.S.: 424690

Borealis Polska Sp Z.o.o. (3)
Wachocka street, 03-934, Warsaw, Poland
Tel.: (48) 22 6290955
Petrochemical Product Distr
N.A.I.C.S.: 424690
Jerzy Pawlicki *(Mng Dir)*

Borealis Polymere GmbH (3)
Haiminger Strasse 1, 84489, Burghausen, Germany
Tel.: (49) 86 77 977 0
Petrochemical Product Distr
N.A.I.C.S.: 424690

Borealis Polymers N.V. (3)
Industrieweg 148, 3583, Beringen, Belgium
Tel.: (32) 11 45 90 11
Petrochemical Product Distr
N.A.I.C.S.: 424690

Subsidiary (Domestic):

Borealis Antwerpen Compounding N.V. (4)
Haven 1053 Nieuwe Weg 1, 2070, Zwijndrecht, Belgium
Tel.: (32) 3 250 88 11
Emp.: 230
Petrochemical Product Distr
N.A.I.C.S.: 424690

Subsidiary (Non-US):

Borealis Polymers Oy (3)
Muovintie 19, 06101, Porvoo, Finland
Tel.: (358) 9 3949 00
Petrochemical Product Distr
N.A.I.C.S.: 424690

Subsidiary (Domestic):

Borealis Polyolefine GmbH (3)
St-Peter-Strasse 25, 4021, Linz, Austria **(100%)**
Tel.: (43) 7 326 9810
Web Site: https://www.borealisgroup.com
Sales Range: $125-149.9 Million
Emp.: 400
Agricultural & Industrial Petrochemical Refinement
N.A.I.C.S.: 325110
Thomas Abel *(Mng Dir)*

Subsidiary (Non-US):

Poliolefinas Borealis Espana S.A. (3)
110-112 Office 5 Vilamari Calle, 08015, Barcelona, Spain
Tel.: (34) 933 71 03 86
Petrochemical Product Distr
N.A.I.C.S.: 424690

Rosier S.A. (3)
Route de Grandmetz 11A, B7911, Frasnes-lez-Anvaing, Belgium **(98.09%)**
Tel.: (32) 69 87 15 10
Web Site: http://www.rosier.eu
Rev.: $246,351,282
Assets: $152,579,805
Liabilities: $117,644,653
Net Worth: $34,935,153
Earnings: ($8,793,141)
Emp.: 251
Fiscal Year-end: 12/31/2019
Mineral Fertilizer Mfr
N.A.I.C.S.: 325314
Willy Raymaekers *(Chm)*

Subsidiary (Non-US):

Rosier Nederland B.V. (4)
Westkade 38a, 4551 BV, Sas-van-Gent, Netherlands
Tel.: (31) 115456000
Web Site: https://www.rosier.eu
Sales Range: $25-49.9 Million
Emp.: 100
Fertilizer Mfr
N.A.I.C.S.: 325311
Willy Van Overfelt *(Gen Mgr)*

Subsidiary (Domestic):

Union pour le Negoce en Produits Chimiques S.A. (4)
Grand-Vivier 2, 7911, Frasnes-lez-Anvaing, Belgium
Tel.: (32) 69859925
Petrochemical Product Distr
N.A.I.C.S.: 424690

Subsidiary (Domestic):

OMV - International Services Ges.m.b.H. (2)
TrabrennStrasse No0628, 1020, Vienna, Austria
Tel.: (43) 140440
Oil & Gas Exploration Services
N.A.I.C.S.: 213112

OMV Warme VertriebsgmbH (2)
Trabrenn Strasse 628, Vienna, 1020, Austria
Tel.: (43) 140 44 02 76 60
Web Site: http://www.omv.com
Heating Oil Whslr
N.A.I.C.S.: 424720

VIVA International Marketing- und Handels-GmbH (2)
Trabrennstrasse 6-8, 1020, Vienna, Austria
Tel.: (43) 140 440 27408

OMV AKTIENGESELLSCHAFT

Sales Range: $1-4.9 Billion
Emp.: 3,000
Oil & Gas Exploration Services
N.A.I.C.S.: 213112

Subsidiary (Non-US):

OMV Ceska republika, s.r.o. (3)
Stetkova 1638/18, 14000, Prague, Czech Republic
Tel.: (420) 261392111
Web Site: https://www.omv.cz
Sales Range: $50-74.9 Million
Emp.: 50
Oil & Gas Exploration Services
N.A.I.C.S.: 213112

OMV SLOVENIJA trgovina z nafto in naftnimi derivati, d.o.o. (1)
Ulica 15 Maja 19, 6000, Koper, Slovenia
Tel.: (386) 5 663 33 00
Oil & Petroleum Products Whslr
N.A.I.C.S.: 424720

OMV SRBIJA d.o.o. (1)
90 A Omladinskih Brigada, Airport City, 11070, Novi Beograd, Serbia
Tel.: (381) 112071500
Web Site: https://www.omv.co.rs
Petroleum Product Distr
N.A.I.C.S.: 424720

OMV Slovensko s.r.o. (1)
Einsteinova c 25, 851 01, Bratislava, Slovakia **(100%)**
Tel.: (421) 268720500
Web Site: https://www.omv.sk
Emp.: 200
Petroleum Products
N.A.I.C.S.: 324199

OMV Solutions GmbH (1)
Trabennstrasse 6 8, 1020, Vienna, Austria **(100%)**
Tel.: (43) 1404400
Web Site: https://www.omv.at
Sales Range: $650-699.9 Million
Emp.: 6,000
Business Support Services; Shared Services
N.A.I.C.S.: 561499

OMV Supply & Trading AG (1)
Poststrasse 14, PO Box 14, 6300, Zug, Switzerland **(100%)**
Tel.: (41) 41 712 0855
Web Site: http://www.omv.ch
Sales Range: $1-9.9 Million
Emp.: 8
Oil & Gas Services
N.A.I.C.S.: 213112

OMV Trading GmbH (1)
Trabrennstrasse 6-8, 1020, Vienna, Austria
Tel.: (43) 1404400
Web Site: https://www.omv.com
Sales Range: $50-74.9 Million
Emp.: 5
Natural Gas Distr
N.A.I.C.S.: 221210
Olivir Dillenz *(Head-Trading)*

OMV Trading Services Limited (1)
14 Ryder St 5th Fl, London, SW1Y 6QB, United Kingdom **(100%)**
Tel.: (44) 74512300
Web Site: http://www.omvtsl.co.uk
Sales Range: $50-74.9 Million
Emp.: 12
Petroleum Services
N.A.I.C.S.: 213112

OMV of Libya Limited ('OLIB') (1)
Corinthia Hotel Commercial Centre Ground Level, PO Box 91867, Tripoli, Libya **(100%)**
Tel.: (218) 213350367
Web Site: http://www.omv.com
Petroleum Services
N.A.I.C.S.: 213112

PETROM DISTRIBUTIE GAZE SRL (1)
Popasavu St 77 4th Fl, District 1, Bucharest, 11432, Romania
Tel.: (40) 726159436
Web Site: http://www.petromdistributiegaze.ro
Sales Range: $50-74.9 Million
Emp.: 246
Fuels Whslr

OMV AKTIENGESELLSCHAFT

INTERNATIONAL PUBLIC

OMV Aktiengesellschaft—(Continued)
N.A.I.C.S.: 457210

PETROM NADLAC SRL (1)
Fn Calea Aradului, Nadlac, 315500, Romania
Tel.: (40) 257473552
Fuels Whslr
N.A.I.C.S.: 457210

Petrom-Moldova S.R.L. (1)
Calea Lesilor Str No 8 Zity Mall, 2069, Chisinau, Moldova
Tel.: (373) 69600257
Web Site: https://www.petrom.md
Fuel Distr
N.A.I.C.S.: 424710

Rosier France S.A.S. (1)
13 Rue Sigmund Freud, 69120, Vaulx-en-Velin, France
Tel.: (33) 472046861
Web Site: https://rosier.fr
Electric Actuator & Cylinder Mfr
N.A.I.C.S.: 333995

SC OMV Romania Mineraloel s.r.l. (1)
Alex Serbanescu 85, 78118, Bucharest, Romania **(100%)**
Tel.: (40) 212030505
Petroleum Services
N.A.I.C.S.: 213112
Rainer Sjhlak *(Mng Dir)*

SapuraOMV Block 30, S. de R.L. de C.V. (1)
Camino a Santa Teresa 187-C 3 Piso Parques del Pedregal, Tlalpan, 14010, Mexico, Mexico
Tel.: (52) 5554248460
Petrochemical Mfr & Distr
N.A.I.C.S.: 325110

SapuraOMV Upstream (Western Australia) Pty Ltd. (1)
4/109 St George S Terrace, Perth, 6000, WA, Australia
Tel.: (61) 861184990
Petrochemical Mfr & Distr
N.A.I.C.S.: 325110

OMYA (SCHWEIZ) AG

Baslerstrasse 42, Oftringen, 4665, Switzerland
Tel.: (41) 627892929
Web Site: http://www.omya.com
Year Founded: 1880
Sales Range: $1-4.9 Billion
Emp.: 8,000
Calcium Carbonates & Industrial Raw Materials
N.A.I.C.S.: 424590
Riener Fiedler *(Dir-Mktg & Sls)*

Subsidiaries:

Al Faltas Group for Carbonate & Coloring Material Co. (1)
10th Ramadan, Cairo, Egypt
Tel.: (20) 15 410 625
Web Site: http://www.greenegyptgroup.com
Calcium Carbonate & Raw Material Distr
N.A.I.C.S.: 424690

Bjorka Mineral AB (1)
Bjorkaverken, Glanshammar, 705 97, Orebro, Sweden
Tel.: (46) 40206700
Web Site: https://www.omya.com
Calcium Carbonate & Raw Material Distr
N.A.I.C.S.: 424690
Pertunnar Leverfen *(Mng Dir)*

COMITAL Uruguay S.A. (1)
Rbla Rpca Argentina s/n, 70001, Juan Lacaze, Uruguay
Tel.: (598) 586 5636 5693
Calcium Carbonate & Raw Material Distr
N.A.I.C.S.: 424690

Eduard Merkle GmbH & Co KG (1)
Altental, Blaubeuren, 89143, Germany
Tel.: (49) 7344 9601 0
Web Site: http://www.eduard-merkle.de
Calcium Carbonate & Raw Material Distr
N.A.I.C.S.: 424690

Gasgruvan Kalcit AB (1)
Hogbergsvagen 55, 682 40, Filipstad, Sweden
Tel.: (46) 40 206 700
Calcium Carbonate & Raw Material Distr
N.A.I.C.S.: 424690

Industrochem d.o.o. (1)
Buzinski prilaz 10, 10010, Zagreb, Croatia
Tel.: (385) 1 66 0 6677
Chemical Products Distr
N.A.I.C.S.: 424690

Jordan Carbonate Co. (1)
15 Abdulwehab Al-Majali St, Shmeasani, Amman, 11118, Jordan
Tel.: (962) 6 566 5517
Web Site: http://www.jordancarbonate.com
Calcium Carbonate & Raw Material Mfr & Distr
N.A.I.C.S.: 325199

K.Z. Kalsium Sdn. Bhd. (1)
Pt No 3672 Kg Keramat Pulai Mukim Sungai Raia, Simpang Pulia, Ipoh, 31300, Perak Darul Ridzuan, Malaysia
Tel.: (60) 5 357 7866
Calcium Carbonate & Raw Material Distr
N.A.I.C.S.: 424690

Kimberly Carbonates LLC (1)
339 N Wilson St, Kimberly, WI 54136
Tel.: (800) 451-4468
Calcium Carbonate & Raw Material Distr
N.A.I.C.S.: 424690

Lih-Hsiang Omya Corp. (1)
Room 804 130 Chung Hsiao E Road Section 2, Taipei, Taiwan
Tel.: (886) 2 33221212
Chemical Product Whslr
N.A.I.C.S.: 424690

Massa Minerali S.r.L. (1)
Via Longobarda s n c, 54100, Massa, Italy
Tel.: (39) 0585 852 020
Calcium Carbonate & Raw Material Distr
N.A.I.C.S.: 424690

Muhlendorfer Kreidefabrik Margit Hoffman-Ostenhof kg (1)
Fabrikstrasse 3, 7052, Mullendorf, Austria
Tel.: (43) 2682 627 45
Web Site: http://www.kreide.at
Calcium Carbonate & Raw Material Distr
N.A.I.C.S.: 424690

OOO Omya Ukraine (1)
87a Mezhigorskaya Str, 04080, Kiev, Ukraine
Tel.: (380) 44 536 9973
Web Site: http://www.omya.com
Chemical Product Mfr & Whslr
N.A.I.C.S.: 424690

OOO Omya Ural (1)
Ovchinnikovskaya Nab House 20 Bld 2 4 Floor, 115035, Moscow, Russia
Tel.: (7) 495 786 63 30
Web Site: http://www.omya.ru
Emp.: 100
Limestone Product Mfr
N.A.I.C.S.: 327991
Popo Muksim *(Mgr)*

Plant (Domestic):

OOO Omya Ural - Subutak Plant (2)
ul Shkolnaya 55, Chelyabinsk oblast, 457430, Subutak, Russia
Tel.: (7) 3519 22 00 54
Calcium Carbonate & Raw Material Mfr
N.A.I.C.S.: 325199

OOO Omya Ural - Svetogorsk Plant (2)
Zabodskaja Ulitsa 17, 188991, Svetogorsk, Russia
Tel.: (7) 3519 22 00 54
Calcium Carbonate & Raw Material Mfr
N.A.I.C.S.: 325199

OOO UNIKRISTALL KOMI (1)
Bumazhnikov pr 2, 167026, Syktyvkar, Russia
Tel.: (7) 8212 66 86 42
Calcium Carbonate & Raw Material Mfr
N.A.I.C.S.: 325199

Omya A/S (1)
Stevns Kridtbrud Harvejen 58 A, 4660, Store Heddinge, Denmark
Tel.: (45) 56560300
Calcium Carbonate & Raw Material Distr
N.A.I.C.S.: 424690

Omya AB (1)
Kalendegatan 18, 211 35, Malmo, Sweden
Tel.: (46) 40 206 700
Building Materials Whslr
N.A.I.C.S.: 423390
Ola Lindstrom *(Mgr-Market & Dev)*

Omya Andina S.A. (1)
Autopista Medellin-Bogota km 30, Antioquia, Guarne, Colombia **(100%)**
Tel.: (57) 4 562 7676
Emp.: 110
Calcium Carbonate & Raw Material Distr
N.A.I.C.S.: 424690
Gabriel Longono *(Gen Mgr)*

Omya Argentina S.A. (1)
Av Del Libertador 7270 P 11 B, Capital Federal, Buenos Aires, Argentina
Tel.: (54) 11 5195 8983
Building Materials Whslr
N.A.I.C.S.: 423390
Adriana Ristaino *(Head-Fin & Controller)*

Omya Arizona Inc. (1)
6 N Mesquite Rd, Superior, AZ 85173
Tel.: (520) 689-2500
Web Site: http://www.omya-na.com
Calcium Carbonate & Chemical Product Mfr
N.A.I.C.S.: 325199

Omya Australia Pty. Ltd. (1)
Level 2 280 Pacific Highway, PO Box 430, Lindfield, 2070, NSW, Australia
Tel.: (61) 2 9416 6077
Web Site: http://www.omya.com.au
Emp.: 100
Chemical Product Mfr & Distr
N.A.I.C.S.: 325998
Bill Hudson *(Plant Mgr)*

Omya Bulgaria EOOD (1)
Str Stratzin Nr 12 wh 1 et 1 ap 1, 1407, Sofia, Bulgaria
Tel.: (359) 2 962 63 80
Building Materials Whslr
N.A.I.C.S.: 423390

Omya CZ, s.r.o. (1)
C p 765 Olomoucky, Lipova - lazne, 790 61, Olomouc, Czech Republic
Tel.: (420) 584 492 116
Web Site: http://www.omya.cz
Calcium Carbonate & Raw Material Mfr
N.A.I.C.S.: 325199

Omya Calcita S.r.l. (1)
Ploiesti no 15 Sector 1, 013682, Bucharest, Romania
Tel.: (40) 212009500
Web Site: http://www.omya.ro
Building Materials Whslr
N.A.I.C.S.: 423390

Omya Canada Inc. (1)
18595 HWY 7 West, Perth, K7H 3C6, ON, Canada
Tel.: (613) 267-5367
Calcium Carbonate & Raw Material Mfr
N.A.I.C.S.: 325199

Plant (Domestic):

Omya Canada Inc. - St. Armand Plant (2)
1500 Chemin des Carrieres Suite 2040, St-Armand, Quebec, J0J 1T0, QC, Canada
Tel.: (450) 248-2931
Calcium Carbonate & Raw Material Mfr
N.A.I.C.S.: 325199

Omya Chemical Merchants Inc. (1)
17th Floor BDO Plaza 8737 Paseo de Roxas, 1226, Makati, Philippines
Tel.: (63) 2 813 0301
Web Site: http://www.omya.com
Emp.: 34
Chemical Product Whslr
N.A.I.C.S.: 424690
Prexy Longasa *(Mgr-Indus-Paints)*

Omya Chile S.A. (1)
San Sebastian 2750 Oficina 203, Las Condes, Santiago, 5697539969, Chile
Tel.: (56) 2 334 5101
Emp.: 20

Building Materials Mfr
N.A.I.C.S.: 326199
Roberto Duran *(Controller)*

Omya Clariana S.L.U. (1)
Poligono 7 Parcela 84, L'Arboc, 43720, Tarragona, Spain
Tel.: (34) 977 67 01 75
Emp.: 150
Calcium Carbonate & Raw Material Mfr & Distr
N.A.I.C.S.: 325199

Omya Egypt S.A.E. (1)
El-Fasakhany Street, 10th of Ramadan City, Cairo, Egypt
Tel.: (20) 2 291 0935
Limestone Product Mfr
N.A.I.C.S.: 327991
Yasser Ghazy *(Plant Mgr)*

Omya GmbH (1)
Siegburger Strasse 229 c, 50679, Cologne, Germany
Tel.: (49) 221 3775 0
Web Site: http://www.omya.de
Chemical Products Distr
N.A.I.C.S.: 424690

Plant (Domestic):

Omya GmbH - Emden Plant (2)
Eichstr, 26725, Emden, Germany
Tel.: (49) 4921 95 80 0
Web Site: http://www.omya.com
Calcium Carbonate & Raw Material Mfr
N.A.I.C.S.: 325199

Subsidiary (Domestic):

Omya Hamburg GmbH (2)
Kanalstrasse 44, 22085, Hamburg, Germany
Tel.: (49) 40 658 72 0
Web Site: http://www.omya-hamburg.de
Chemical Product Whslr
N.A.I.C.S.: 424690
Nico Duehrkop *(Bus Dir)*

Omya Weil GmbH (2)
Hafenstr 16, 79576, Weil am Rhein, Germany
Tel.: (49) 7621 422 045 0
Chemical Products Distr
N.A.I.C.S.: 424690
Wolfgant Stark *(Mgr)*

Omya GmbH (1)
Gersheim Strasse 1-2, 9722, Gummern, Austria
Tel.: (43) 4258 855 0
Web Site: http://www.omya.com
Calcium Carbonate & Raw Material Distr
N.A.I.C.S.: 424690

Plant (Domestic):

Omya GmbH - Golling Plant (2)
Taggerstrasse 273, 5440, Golling an der Salzach, Austria
Tel.: (43) 6244 4657 0
Calcium Carbonate & Raw Material Mfr
N.A.I.C.S.: 325199

Omya GmbH - Neu Pirka Plant (2)
Sandgrubenstr 16, 8073, Feldkirchen bei Graz, 8073, Austria
Tel.: (43) 316 296 919 0
Calcium Carbonate & Raw Material Mfr
N.A.I.C.S.: 325199

Omya GmbH - Ulmerfeld-Hausmening Plant (2)
Theresienthalstrasse 50, 3363, Ulmerfeld-Hausmening, Austria
Tel.: (43) 7475 90 465
Calcium Carbonate & Raw Material Mfr
N.A.I.C.S.: 325199

Omya Haiming (Nanchang) Chemical Co. Ltd. (1)
Bei Sui Hu Industry Zone Nanchang Economic and Technology, Nanchang, China
Tel.: (86) 791 395 1802
Calcium Carbonate & Raw Material Distr
N.A.I.C.S.: 424690

Omya Hellas S.A. (1)
Industrial Zone of Thessaloniki, PO Box 1255, Sindos, Greece
Tel.: (30) 2310 569 565

AND PRIVATE COMPANIES

Calcium Carbonate & Raw Material Distr
N.A.I.C.S.: 424690

Omya Hungaria Kft. (1)
Lesret utca 71, 3300, Eger, Hungary
Tel.: (36) 36531510
Web Site: http://www.omya.com
Calcium Carbonate & Raw Material Mfr
N.A.I.C.S.: 325199

Omya Hustadmarmor AS (1)
Langebakken 31, N-5355, Knarrevik, Norway
Tel.: (47) 56 313 100
Web Site: http://www.omya.com
Calcium Carbonate & Raw Material Mfr & Distr
N.A.I.C.S.: 424690

Omya Hustadmarmor AS (1)
Plant Hammerfall, 8220, Rosvik, Norway
Tel.: (47) 75698000
Calcium Carbonate & Raw Material Mfr
N.A.I.C.S.: 325199

Omya India Pvt. Ltd. (1)
302 3rd floor Windsor House Off CST road
Kalina, Santacruz EE, 40059, Mumbai, India
Tel.: (91) 22 40631475
Limestone Product Mfr
N.A.I.C.S.: 327991
Tushar Mehta *(Mgr-Ops)*

Omya International AG (1)
Baslerstrasse 42, PO Box 335, 4665, Oftringen, Aargau, Switzerland
Tel.: (41) 62 789 29 29
Chemical Product Whslr
N.A.I.C.S.: 424690
Charles-Etienne Houssa *(VP-Key Acct Mgmt)*

Omya Japan K.K. (1)
Level 16 Shiroyama Trust Tower 4-3-1 Toranomon, Minato-ku, Tokyo, Japan
Tel.: (81) 3 5403 4735
Chemical Product Whslr
N.A.I.C.S.: 424690
Heikki Markkanen *(Project Mgr)*

Omya Korea Inc. (1)
12F SIMPAC Building 52 Gukjegeumyung-ro, Yeongdeungpo-gu, 150-730, Seoul, Korea (South)
Tel.: (82) 2 7684811
Web Site: http://www.omya.co.kr
Limestone Product Mfr & Distr
N.A.I.C.S.: 327991
Chaewoo Lee *(Dir-Sls)*

Subsidiary (Domestic):

Omya Hankuk Chemical Inc. (2)
40 Wonsan-ro Onsan-eup, Ulju-gun, 689-892, Ulsan, Korea (South)
Tel.: (82) 52 237 6693
Limestone Product Mfr
N.A.I.C.S.: 327991

Plant (Domestic):

Omya Korea Inc. - Chechon Plant (2)
194 Bukbu-ro 11-gil Bongyang-eup, Jecheon, 390-875, Chungcheongbuk-do, Korea (South)
Tel.: (82) 43 648 0103
Calcium Carbonate & Raw Material Mfr
N.A.I.C.S.: 325199

Omya Korea Inc. - Gangwon-do Plant (2)
420 Hambaek-ro Sindong-eup, Jeongseon, 233-826, Gangwon-do, Korea (South)
Tel.: (82) 33 378 2311
Calcium Carbonate & Raw Material Mfr & Distr
N.A.I.C.S.: 325199

Omya Korea Inc. - Gyeongsangbuk do Plant (2)
2 Saemdeulwit-gil Namseon-myeon, Andong, 760-862, Gyeongsangbuk-do, Korea (South)
Tel.: (82) 54 822 8100
Web Site: http://www.omya.co.kr
Calcium Carbonate & Raw Material Mfr
N.A.I.C.S.: 325199

Omya Korea Inc. - Jeollabuk-do Plant (2)
133 -10 Sandan-ro, Gunsan, 573-879, Jeollabuk-do, Korea (South)
Tel.: (82) 63 467 4001
Calcium Carbonate & Raw Material Mfr & Distr
N.A.I.C.S.: 325199

Omya Madencilik A.S. (1)
Metrocity D Blok Kirgulu Sokak 4/1A Esentepe, Sisli, 34394, Istanbul, Turkiye
Tel.: (90) 212 337 4646
Web Site: http://www.omya.com.tr
Chemical Products Mfr
N.A.I.C.S.: 325998
Yucel Comert *(Product Mgr-Aluminium Finishing)*

Omya Madencilik Sanayi ve Ticaret A.S. (1)
Ataturk Mahallesi No 10, Kemalpasa, 35175, Izmir, Turkiye
Tel.: (90) 232 877 0151
Web Site: http://www.omya.com.tr
Calcium Carbonate & Raw Material Mfr
N.A.I.C.S.: 325199
Cagatay Yilmaz *(Plant Mgr)*

Plant (Domestic):

Omya Madencilik Sanayi ve Ticaret A.S. - Gebze Factory (2)
Tavsanli Koyu, 41400, Gebze, Kocaeli, Turkiye
Tel.: (90) 262 724 9145
Calcium Carbonate & Raw Material Mfr
N.A.I.C.S.: 325199

Omya Madencilik Sanayi ve Ticaret A.S. - Karabiga Factory (2)
Ortuluce Koyu, Canakkale, 17204, Karabiga, Turkiye
Tel.: (90) 286 372 1802
Calcium Carbonate & Raw Material Mfr
N.A.I.C.S.: 325199

Omya Madencilik Sanayi ve Ticaret A.S. - Kirsehir Factory (2)
Kaman Yolu Ayrimi 24 km, Kirsehir, Turkiye
Tel.: (90) 286 372 1802
Web Site: http://www.omya.com
Emp.: 50
Calcium Carbonate & Raw Material Mfr
N.A.I.C.S.: 325199
Erhan Yasar *(Plant Mgr)*

Omya Malaysia Sdn. Bhd. (1)
No 29-2 Jalan PJS 11/2, Subang Jaya, 46000, Petaling Jaya, Malaysia
Tel.: (60) 3 5634 7991
Chemical Product Whslr
N.A.I.C.S.: 424690

Plant (Domestic):

Omya Malaysia Sdn. Bhd. - Keramat Plant (2)
Lot PT 166135 Kawasan Perindustrian Kampung Tanjung, 31300, Ipoh, Malaysia
Tel.: (60) 53575227
Calcium Carbonate & Raw Material Mfr
N.A.I.C.S.: 325199

Omya Malaysia Sdn.Bhd. - Bercham Plant (2)
Lot PT 115755 Bercham Industrial Area, Kampung Bercham, 31250, Ipoh, Perak, Malaysia
Tel.: (60) 5 545 9115
Web Site: http://www.omya.com
Calcium Carbonate & Raw Material Mfr
N.A.I.C.S.: 325199

Omya Malaysia Sdn.Bhd. - Ipoh Plant (2)
Jalan Keramat Pulai KA 23173 Teluk Liat Mukim Sungai Raia PT 1089 HS D, Simpang Pulai, 31300, Ipoh, Perak Darul Ridzuan, Malaysia
Tel.: (60) 5 3106 868
Calcium Carbonate & Raw Material Mfr
N.A.I.C.S.: 325199

Omya Mexico SA de CV (1)
Edificio Centro Corporativo Av Lomas Verdes 750 Of 203 Col, Lomas Verdes - 1 Seccion, 53120, Naucalpan, Mexico
Tel.: (52) 55 5343 9442
Chemical Product Whslr
N.A.I.C.S.: 424690

Plant (Domestic):

Omya Mexico S.A. de C.V. - Mpio Tlajomulco Jalisco Plant (2)
Km 2 Carretera Guadalajara a El Salto s/n, 45685, Tlajomulco de Zuniga, Jalisco, Mexico
Tel.: (52) 33 3688 0204
Web Site: http://www.omya.com
Emp.: 20
Calcium Carbonate & Raw Material Mfr
N.A.I.C.S.: 325199
Andres Torres *(Gen Mgr)*

Omya Mexico S.A. de C.V. - San Juan del Rio Plant (2)
Km 7 5 Carr San Juan del Rio Tequisquiapan Apartado, Postal No 54, 76800, San Juan del Rio, Mexico
Tel.: (52) 427 271 8400
Calcium Carbonate & Raw Material Mfr
N.A.I.C.S.: 325199

Omya Mineral (Vietnam) Inc. (1)
Nam Cam Industrial Zone, Nighi Loc distribt Hung Binh Ward, Vinh, Vietnam
Tel.: (84) 38 3791547
Calcium Carbonate & Raw Material Mfr
N.A.I.C.S.: 325199

Omya Mineral Portuguesa Lda. (1)
Rua da Cova da Moura 2-6, 1399-033, Lisbon, Portugal
Tel.: (351) 21 392 0130
Chemical Product Whslr
N.A.I.C.S.: 424690
Isabel Nunes *(Controller-Fin)*

Omya Minerals (Changshu) Co., Ltd. (1)
Riverside Industrial Park, 215537, Changshu, China
Tel.: (86) 512 5264 9708
Calcium Carbonate & Raw Material Distr
N.A.I.C.S.: 424690

Omya Netherlands BV (1)
Grasweg 47, 1031 HX, Amsterdam, Netherlands
Tel.: (31) 20 636 2222
Web Site: http://www.omya.nl
Calcium Carbonate & Raw Material Mfr & Distr
N.A.I.C.S.: 325199

Plant (Domestic):

Omya Netherlands BV - Moerdijk Plant (2)
Haven-Nr Port No M 312 Middenweg 47, 4782 PM, Moerdijk, Netherlands
Tel.: (31) 168 334 000
Calcium Carbonate & Raw Material Mfr
N.A.I.C.S.: 325199

Omya New Zealand Ltd. (1)
Ground Floor Building 2 Central Park 666 Great South Road, Greenlane, Auckland, 1051, New Zealand
Tel.: (64) 9 573 2950
Web Site: http://www.omya.co.nz
Emp.: 30
Limestone Quarrying Services
N.A.I.C.S.: 212312
Ian Campbell *(Dir-Sls-Distr Svcs & Life Sciences)*

Plant (Domestic):

Omya New Zealand Ltd. - Te Kuiti Plant (2)
Hangatiki East Road, PO Box 372, Te Kuiti, New Zealand
Tel.: (64) 7 878 8260
Calcium Carbonate & Raw Material Mfr
N.A.I.C.S.: 325199

Omya Oy (1)
Itamerenkatu 1, 00180, Helsinki, Finland
Tel.: (358) 10 235 0300
Web Site: http://www.omya.fi
Limestone Product Mfr
N.A.I.C.S.: 327991

Plant (Domestic):

Omya Oy - Forby Plant (2)
Tehtaantie 100, 25640, Forby, Finland
Tel.: (358) 2 7757 1

Web Site: http://www.omya.com
Calcium Carbonate & Raw Material Mfr
N.A.I.C.S.: 325199
Antti Salminen *(Office Mgr)*

Omya Oy - Imatra Plant (2)
Keattelatia 15, 55800, Imatra, Finland
Tel.: (358) 204 62 48 85
Web Site: http://www.omya.com
Emp.: 3,000
Calcium Carbonate & Raw Material Mfr
N.A.I.C.S.: 325199
Antti Salminen *(Gen Mgr)*

Omya Oy - Kemi Plant (2)
PO Box 168, 94101, Kemi, Finland
Tel.: (358) 204 63 4719
Calcium Carbonate & Raw Material Mfr
N.A.I.C.S.: 325199

Omya PCC USA Inc. (1)
499 Glen Ave, Johnsonburg, PA 15845
Tel.: (814) 965-3400
Calcium Carbonate & Raw Material Mfr
N.A.I.C.S.: 325199

Plant (Domestic):

Omya PCC USA Inc, - Hawesville Plant (2)
58 Wescor Rd, Hawesville, KY 42348
Tel.: (270) 927-1001
Calcium Carbonate & Raw Material Mfr
N.A.I.C.S.: 325199

Omya PCC USA Inc. - Kingsport Plant (2)
100 Clinchfield St, Kingsport, TN 37660
Tel.: (423) 392-3758
Calcium Carbonate & Raw Material Mfr
N.A.I.C.S.: 325199

Omya S.A. (1)
Rua C Lote 22 Zona Industrial de Soure, Baixo Mondego, 3130-551, Soure, Portugal
Tel.: (351) 239 506 100
Web Site: http://www.omya.com
Emp.: 44
Calcium Carbonate & Raw Material Distr
N.A.I.C.S.: 424690

Omya S.P.A (1)
Localita Bagnara Nocera Umbra, Perugia, 06025, Italy
Tel.: (39) 0742813774
Web Site: http://www.omya.it
Chemical Product Mfr & Distr
N.A.I.C.S.: 325998

Plant (Domestic):

Omya SPA - Avenza Plant (2)
Via Antica di Massa 67, Avenza, 54031, Carrara, Italy
Tel.: (39) 0585 852 020
Calcium Carbonate & Raw Material Mfr
N.A.I.C.S.: 325199

Omya SPA - Nocera Umbra Plant (2)
Localita Bagnara, 06025, Nocera Umbra, Italy
Tel.: (39) 0742 813 774
Calcium Carbonate & Raw Material Mfr
N.A.I.C.S.: 325199

Omya SPA - Vipiteno Plant (2)
Unterackern/Campi di Sotto, Sterzing, 39049, Vipiteno, BZ, Italy
Tel.: (39) 0472 761 500
Web Site: http://www.omya.com
Emp.: 39
Calcium Carbonate & Raw Material Mfr
N.A.I.C.S.: 325199
Christian Graf *(Plant Mgr)*

Omya SA (1)
Route d'El Jadida - rp 8 km 16, 20400, Casablanca, Morocco
Tel.: (212) 22 65 10 01
Limestone Product Mfr
N.A.I.C.S.: 327991
Samir El Khadir *(Plant Mgr)*

Omya SA/NV (1)
Brussels Office Place Communale Chaussee de Wavre 1789, 1160, Brussels, Belgium
Tel.: (32) 2 674 23 11
Web Site: http://www.omya.be
Chemical Products Mfr

OMYA (SCHWEIZ) AG

Omya (Schweiz) AG—(Continued)
N.A.I.C.S.: 325998

Plant (Domestic):

Omya SA/NV - Harmignies Plant (2)
Chaussee de Beaumont 401A, 7022, Harmignies, Belgium
Tel.: (32) 65 58 63 05
Calcium Carbonate & Raw Material Mfr & Distr
N.A.I.C.S.: 325199

Omya SAS (1)
19 Rue De L abbaye, 88480, Etival-Clairefontaine, France
Tel.: (33) 3 29 42 01 66
Emp.: 340
Calcium Carbonate & Raw Material Distr
N.A.I.C.S.: 424690

Plant (Domestic):

Omya SAS - Entrains-sur-Nohain Plant (2)
RD 168, 58410, Entrains-sur-Nohain, France
Tel.: (33) 3 86 29 53 00
Web Site: http://www.omya.com
Calcium Carbonate & Raw Material Mfr
N.A.I.C.S.: 325199

Omya SAS - Omey Plant (2)
6 rue Pierre Semard, 51240, Omey, France
Tel.: (33) 3 2669 2900
Calcium Carbonate & Raw Material Mfr
N.A.I.C.S.: 325199

Omya SAS - Onyx & Marbres Granules Plant (2)
Siege social, 31440, Saint-Beat, France
Tel.: (33) 5 6194 6650
Web Site: http://www.omg-sa.com
Emp.: 44
Calcium Carbonate & Raw Material Mfr
N.A.I.C.S.: 325199

Omya SAS - Orgon Plant (2)
Rte d Eygalirres, BP 10, 13660, Orgon, France
Tel.: (33) 4 9073 3800
Calcium Carbonate & Raw Material Mfr
N.A.I.C.S.: 325199

Omya SAS - Salses le Chateau Plant (2)
Chemin du Mas-Fages, BP 3, 66600, Salses-le-Chateau, France
Tel.: (33) 4 68 38 23 50
Calcium Carbonate & Raw Material Mfr
N.A.I.C.S.: 325199

Omya Shunda (Linkou) Fine Chemical Co., Ltd. (1)
27 Daging Street, Mudanjiang, Heilongjiang, China
Tel.: (86) 453 6825 399
Calcium Carbonate & Raw Material Mfr
N.A.I.C.S.: 325199

Omya Slovakia s.r.o. (1)
Tomasikova 30, 821 01, Bratislava, Slovakia
Tel.: (421) 24 825 0881
Chemical Products Distr
N.A.I.C.S.: 424690

Omya Sp. z o.o. (1)
Ul Krucza 16/22, 00 526, Warsaw, Poland
Tel.: (48) 22 5258900
Web Site: http://www.omya.pl
Limestone Product Mfr
N.A.I.C.S.: 327991

Plant (Domestic):

Omya Sp. z o.o. - Mielnik Plant (2)
ul Przemyslowa 1, 17-307, Mielnik, Poland
Tel.: (48) 85 656 50 80
Calcium Carbonate & Raw Material Mfr
N.A.I.C.S.: 325199

Omya Sp. z o.o. - Romanowo Plant (2)
Ul Bystrzycka 21, 57-360, Oldrzychowice Klodzkie, Poland
Tel.: (48) 74 8651 700
Web Site: http://www.omya.pl
Calcium Carbonate & Raw Material Mfr
N.A.I.C.S.: 325199

Omya Sp. z o.o. - Wojciechowice Plant (2)
Przemialownia Jasice, 27-532, Wojciechowice, Poland
Tel.: (48) 15 861 80 50
Calcium Carbonate & Raw Material Mfr
N.A.I.C.S.: 325199

Omya UAE FZC (1)
Plot 4K-05 & 06 Hamriyah Free Zone Phase II Near Hamriyah Cement Co, PO Box 49057, Sharjah, 4905, United Arab Emirates
Tel.: (971) 6 526 9414
Web Site: http://www.omyauae.ae
Calcium Carbonate & Raw Material Mfr & Distr
N.A.I.C.S.: 325199

Omya UK Ltd. (1)
Ashwood Dale Plant, Buxton, SK17 9TB, Derbyshire, United Kingdom
Tel.: (44) 1298 213 840
Web Site: http://www.omya.co.uk
Chemical Products Mfr
N.A.I.C.S.: 325998
Nigel Barratt *(Gen Mgr)*

Plant (Domestic):

Omya UK Ltd. - Ballymena Plant (2)
Demesne Quarry 17 Munie Road, Glenarm, Ballymena, BT44 0BG, United Kingdom
Tel.: (44) 28 2884 1333
Calcium Carbonate & Raw Material Mfr & Distr
N.A.I.C.S.: 325199

Omya UK Ltd. - Hartlepool plant (2)
Hartlepool, Hartlepool, TS24 0RA, United Kingdom
Tel.: (44) 1429 892 000
Calcium Carbonate & Raw Material Mfr
N.A.I.C.S.: 325199

Omya UK Ltd. - Humber Plant (2)
Humber Industrial Estate Gibson Lane, North Ferriby East Yorkshire, Melton, HU14 3LJ, United Kingdom
Tel.: (44) 1482 635 800
Web Site: http://www.omya.com
Emp.: 32
Calcium Oxide & Raw Material Distr
N.A.I.C.S.: 424690

Omya UK Ltd. - Steeple Morden Plant (2)
75 Station Road Steeple Morden, Hertfordshire, Royston, SG8 0NX, United Kingdom
Tel.: (44) 1763 852 181
Calcium Carbonate & Raw Material Mfr
N.A.I.C.S.: 325199

Omya Vencac d.o.o. (1)
Vencacki put bb, 34300, Arandelovac, Serbia
Tel.: (381) 34 617 0345
Calcium Carbonate & Raw Material Distr
N.A.I.C.S.: 424690
Mihajlo Hadzistevic *(Mgr-Sls)*

Omya do Brasil Importacao, Exportacao e Comercio de Minerais Ltda. (1)
Rua L s/n Bloco 2 Sala 08 Ilha 001 Rodovia MS 395 km 21, 79601-970, Tres Lagoas, Brazil
Tel.: (55) 67 2105 9400
Web Site: http://www.omya.com
Emp.: 8
Limestone Product Mfr
N.A.I.C.S.: 327991
Guillermo Schanck *(Mgr)*

Omya s.r.o. (1)
Hany Melickovej 1e, Bratislava, 82105, Slovakia
Tel.: (421) 265 316 965
Emp.: 5
Chemical Product Whslr
N.A.I.C.S.: 424690
Mato Kral *(Mgr-Sls-Polymers)*

Omya, Inc. (1)
9987 Carver Rd Ste 300, Cincinnati, OH 45242
Tel.: (513) 387-4600
Web Site: http://www.omya-na.com
Sales Range: $50-74.9 Million
Emp.: 100
Calcium Carbonates
N.A.I.C.S.: 325180
Michael Phillips *(CFO)*

Subsidiary (Domestic):

Lipscomb Chemical Company Inc. (2)
5150 E Pacific Coast Hwy Ste 600, Long Beach, CA 90804
Tel.: (562) 961-3333
Web Site: http://www.lipscombchemical.com
Chemical Product Mfr & Distr
N.A.I.C.S.: 325998
Kimberlee Norton *(Mgr-Acctg)*

Omya Alabama Inc. (2)
2071 Sylacauga-Fayetteville Hwy, Sylacauga, AL 35151
Tel.: (256) 245-1777
Web Site: http://www.omya-na.com
Sales Range: $50-74.9 Million
Emp.: 70
Calcium Carbonate Slurry Processing
N.A.I.C.S.: 325180
Alex Hardy *(Mgr-Ops)*

Plant (Domestic):

Omya Inc. - Columbia River Carbonates Plant (2)
300 N Pekin Rd, Woodland, WA 98674
Tel.: (360) 225-6505
Web Site: http://www.carbonates.com
Furniture Distr
N.A.I.C.S.: 423210
Bernie Schockelt *(Gen Mgr)*

Omya Inc. - Verpol Plant (2)
Whipple Hollow Rd, Pittsford, VT 05744
Tel.: (800) 451-4468
Calcium Carbonate & Raw Material Mfr
N.A.I.C.S.: 325199

Subsidiary (Domestic):

Omya Industries, Inc. (2)
9987 Carver Rd Ste 300, Cincinnati, OH 45242
Tel.: (802) 459-3311
Web Site: http://www.omya-na.com
Industrial Minerals, Trading, Marble Manufacturer
N.A.I.C.S.: 325180

Omya, California, Inc. (2)
7225 Crystal Creek Rd PO Box 825, Lucerne Valley, CA 92356 **(100%)**
Tel.: (760) 248-7306
Sales Range: $25-49.9 Million
Emp.: 85
Calcium Carbonates
N.A.I.C.S.: 325180

Otto Hauenstein Samen AG (1)
Bahnhofstrasse 92, PO Box 138, 8197, Rafz, Switzerland
Tel.: (41) 44 879 17 17
Web Site: http://www.hauenstein.ch
Emp.: 30
Landscaping Services
N.A.I.C.S.: 561730
Vincent Vuille *(Mgr)*

PLASTOCHEM KIEV t.o.v. (1)
Solomjanskij R N, 03110, Kiev, Ukraine
Tel.: (380) 44 249 2411
Plastic Product Whslr
N.A.I.C.S.: 424610

PT Omya Indonesia (1)
Desa Tanjungsari, 61257, Trosobo, Indonesia
Tel.: (62) 31 788 1982
Calcium Carbonate & Raw Material Mfr & Distr
N.A.I.C.S.: 325199

Plant (Domestic):

PT Omya Indonesia - East Java Plant (2)
Jl Raya Daendless Km 62, Sentul, East Java, Indonesia
Tel.: (62) 31 77550071
Calcium Carbonate & Raw Material Mfr
N.A.I.C.S.: 325199

PT Omya Indonesia - Paciran Plant (2)
Jl Raya Kandang Semangkon Km 76 3, 62264, Paciran, Indonesia

INTERNATIONAL PUBLIC

Tel.: (62) 322 662204 08
Calcium Carbonate & Raw Material Mfr
N.A.I.C.S.: 325199

PT United Chemicals Inter Aneka (1)
Jl Kesehatan No 21, Jakarta, 10160, Indonesia
Tel.: (62) 21 380 3805
Web Site: http://www.unitedchemicals.com
Logistics Consulting Services
N.A.I.C.S.: 541614

Plastochem Brno, spol. s r.o. (1)
Olomoucka 63, 627 00, Brno, Czech Republic
Tel.: (420) 532 190 635
Web Site: http://www.plastochem.cz
Plastic Product Whslr
N.A.I.C.S.: 424610
Pavel Zemene *(Head-Sls & Proxy)*

Saudi Carbonate Co. Ltd. (1)
PO Box 25679, 11476, Riyadh, Saudi Arabia
Tel.: (966) 1 265 1947
Web Site: http://www.saudicarbonate.com
Calcium Carbonate & Raw Material Mfr & Distr
N.A.I.C.S.: 325199

Surint Omya (Vietnam) Co. Ltd. (1)
192 Phan Xich Long St Ward 2, Phu Nhan District, Ho Chi Minh City, Dong Nai, Vietnam
Tel.: (84) 8 3517 8396
Calcium Carbonate & Raw Material Mfr & Distr
N.A.I.C.S.: 325199

Vereinigte Kreidewerke Dammann KG (1)
Hildesheimer Strasse 3, 31185, Sohlde, Germany
Tel.: (49) 5129 78 0
Web Site: http://www.calcium-carbonat.de
Chemical Products Mfr
N.A.I.C.S.: 325998
Anastasios Neofitidis *(Head-Sls Feed-Europe)*

Plant (Domestic):

Vereinigte Kreidewerke Dammann KG - Lagerdorf Plant (2)
Schinkeler Weg, 25566, Lagerdorf, Germany
Tel.: (49) 4828 690
Chemical Products Mfr
N.A.I.C.S.: 325998
Heiner Gers *(Plant Mgr)*

Vereinigte Kreidewerke Dammann KG - Rugen Plant (2)
Klementelvitz, 18546, Sassnitz, Germany
Tel.: (49) 38392 3110
Chemical Products Mfr
N.A.I.C.S.: 325998
Lars Notzel *(Plant Mgr)*

ZAO Karat Polevskoy (1)
Volodarskogo St 111, Sverdlovsk Region, 623391, Polevskoy, Russia
Tel.: (7) 34350 205 86
Calcium Carbonate & Raw Material Mfr
N.A.I.C.S.: 325199
Sergey Uzhegov *(Gen Mgr)*

ON DOOR CONCEPTS LIMITED

1st and 2nd Floor Plot No 13 Railway Colony, E-8 Arera Colony, Bhopal, 462039, Madhya Pradesh, India
Tel.: (91) 7024505050
Web Site: https://www.ondoor.com
Year Founded: 2014
ONDOOR—(NSE)
Rev.: $21,832,532
Assets: $10,919,466
Liabilities: $4,713,080
Net Worth: $6,206,385
Earnings: $1,552,293
Fiscal Year-end: 03/31/23
Online Shopping Services
N.A.I.C.S.: 425120

ON HOLDING AG

AND PRIVATE COMPANIES

Forrlibuckstrasse 190, 8005, Zurich, Switzerland
Tel.: (41) 442251555 CH
Year Founded: 2012
ONON—(NYSE)
Rev.: $1,986,807,095
Assets: $1,766,075,388
Liabilities: $574,833,703
Net Worth: $1,191,241,685
Earnings: $88,248,337
Emp.: 2,353
Fiscal Year-end: 12/31/23
Holding Company
N.A.I.C.S.: 551112

ON SIDE RESTORATION SERVICES LTD.
3157 Grandview Hwy, Vancouver, V5M 2E9, BC, Canada
Tel.: (604) 293-1596 Ca
Web Site: https://www.onside.ca
Year Founded: 1979
Emp.: 1,200
Home & Businesses Restoration Services
N.A.I.C.S.: 236220
Alain Fortin *(Pres)*

ON THE BEACH GROUP PLC
Aeroworks 5 Adair Street, Manchester, M1 2NQ, United Kingdom
Tel.: (44) 2037271000 UK
Web Site: https://www.onthebeachplc.com
Year Founded: 2004
OTB—(LSE)
Rev.: $163,150,020
Assets: $392,760,180
Liabilities: $215,231,220
Net Worth: $177,528,960
Earnings: $1,811,520
Fiscal Year-end: 09/30/22
Online Travel Ticketing Services
N.A.I.C.S.: 561599
William Allen *(Chief Supply Officer)*

Subsidiaries:

Classic Collection Holidays Limited (1)
Saxon House Little High Street, Worthing, BN11 1DH, West Sussex, United Kingdom
Tel.: (44) 190 383 6621
Web Site: https://www.classic-collection.co.uk
Tourism Services
N.A.I.C.S.: 561520
Claire Stafa *(Sls Mgr-Agency)*

On The Beach Limited (1)
5 Adair Street, Manchester, M1 2NQ, United Kingdom
Tel.: (44) 161 509 3700
Web Site: https://www.onthebeach.co.uk
Travel Arrangement Services
N.A.I.C.S.: 561599
Simon Cooper *(CEO)*

Sunshine.co.uk Limited (1)
5 Adair Street, Manchester, M1 2NQ, United Kingdom
Tel.: (44) 371 512 2004
Web Site: https://www.sunshine.co.uk
Tourism Services
N.A.I.C.S.: 561520
Belinda Jenkins *(Ops Mgr)*

ON TRACK INNOVATIONS, LTD.
Hatnufa 5 Yokneam Industrial Zone, Box 372, Yokneam, 2069200, Israel
Tel.: (972) 46868000 Il
Web Site: http://www.otiglobal.com
Year Founded: 1990
OTIVF—(OTCQX)
Rev.: $12,742,000
Assets: $16,986,000
Liabilities: $14,280,000
Net Worth: $2,706,000
Earnings: ($6,133,000)
Emp.: 121

Fiscal Year-end: 12/31/20
Contactless Microprocessor Based Smart Card Systems Designer & Developer
N.A.I.C.S.: 334413
Amir Eilam *(CEO)*

Subsidiaries:

OTI Africa (Pty) Ltd. (1)
10th Floor Park On Long, 64 Long Street, Cape Town, 8001, Western Cape, South Africa
Tel.: (27) 214221940
Web Site: http://www.za.oti.ag
Smart Card Solutions
N.A.I.C.S.: 519290

OTI America Inc. (1)
13809 Research Blvd Ste 605, Austin, TX 78750
Tel.: (732) 429-1900
Web Site: http://www.otiamerica.com
Sales Range: $25-49.9 Million
Emp.: 7
Smart Card Solutions
N.A.I.C.S.: 519290

OTI PetroSmart (Pty) Ltd. (1)
The Forum North Bank Lane Century City, Cape Town, South Africa
Tel.: (27) 215269100
Web Site: http://www.otipetrosmart.com
Petroleum Product Whslr
N.A.I.C.S.: 423830
Charlotte Hambly-Nuss *(Mng Dir)*

ON-BRIGHT ELECTRONICS, INC.
Bldg 3 Business Center 168 Hua Tuo Road, Zhangjiang Hi-Tech Park, Shanghai, 201203, China
Tel.: (86) 2150271718
Web Site: http://www.on-bright.com
4947—(TPE)
Rev.: $151,847,630
Assets: $187,087,409
Liabilities: $54,330,001
Net Worth: $132,757,408
Earnings: $21,933,130
Fiscal Year-end: 12/31/19
Electronic Components Mfr
N.A.I.C.S.: 334419
Chih-Liang Chen *(Pres)*

ONAMBA CO., LTD.
3-1-27 Fukae-Kita, Higashinari-ku, Osaka, 537-0001, Japan
Tel.: (81) 669766101
Web Site: https://www.onamba.co.jp
Year Founded: 1941
5816—(TKS)
Rev.: $317,334,220
Assets: $262,861,750
Liabilities: $96,473,630
Net Worth: $166,388,120
Earnings: $14,066,560
Emp.: 4,000
Fiscal Year-end: 12/31/23
Electrical Wire Mfr & Whslr
N.A.I.C.S.: 335929
Seiji Endo *(Pres)*

Subsidiaries:

Arneses Y Conexiones, S. A. De C.V (1)
Calle Uno Norte 1108 Ciudad Industrial, 22444, Tijuana, BC, Mexico
Tel.: (52) 6646233700
Web Site: http://www.osca-arcosa.com
Emp.: 1,300
Electrical Wire Distr
N.A.I.C.S.: 423610

Asle Electronics Co., Ltd (1)
10th floor Yuizumi Shinyoko Building 3-17-2 Shinyokohama, Kohoku-ku, Yokohama, 222-0033, Kanagawa, Japan
Tel.: (81) 454709201
Web Site: https://www.asle.co.jp
Emp.: 50
Electrical Wire Mfr & Distr
N.A.I.C.S.: 335929

Subsidiary (Non-US):

ASLE Corporation Singapore Pte. Ltd. (2)
No 2 Toh Guan Road East 03-02, Singapore, 608837, Singapore
Tel.: (65) 6272 8682
Emp.: 12
Electrical Wire Distr
N.A.I.C.S.: 423610

ASLE Electronics (Cambodia) Co., Ltd. (2)
No 23 Longitude Road 5 Sihanoukville Special Economic Zone, Prey Nob, Sihanoukville, 181000, Cambodia
Tel.: (855) 34 637 0071
Electrical Wire Distr
N.A.I.C.S.: 423610
Dok Soktheng *(Officer-Pur)*

Czech Republic Onamba s.r.o. (1)
Technologicka 842/8, 779 00, Olomouc, Czech Republic
Tel.: (420) 585153570
Web Site: https://www.cronamba.cz
Emp.: 25
Electrical Wire Distr
N.A.I.C.S.: 423610
Michal Galas *(Officer-Sls)*

Hangzhou ASLE E. Co. Ltd. (1)
No 107 Dalingshan Road, Yinhu Sub-district Fuyang District, Hangzhou, 311402, Zhejiang, China
Tel.: (86) 57188855530
Emp.: 300
Electrical Wire Distr
N.A.I.C.S.: 423610

Intelligent Solar System Co., Ltd. (1)
3-1-27 Fukaekita, Higashinari-ku, Osaka, 537-0001, Japan
Tel.: (81) 667857334
Web Site: https://www.i-solar.co.jp
Solar Electric Power Services
N.A.I.C.S.: 221114

Onamba (M) Sdn. Bhd. (1)
Lot 37 & 38 Jalan Timah, Pasir Gudang, 81700, Johor, Malaysia
Tel.: (60) 7 251 4741
Emp.: 110
Electrical Wire Distr
N.A.I.C.S.: 423610

Onamba (Shanghai) Trading Co., Ltd. (1)
No 1606 Heng Ji Building No 99 Huai Hai Dong Road, Shanghai, 200021, China
Tel.: (86) 2154662526
Emp.: 22
Electrical Wire Distr
N.A.I.C.S.: 423610

Onamba Electronic Parts (Kunshan) Co., Ltd. (1)
1255-14 15 Jinmao Road Zhoushi Town, Kunshan, 215313, Jiangsu, China
Tel.: (86) 51257641701
Emp.: 350
Electronic Components Distr
N.A.I.C.S.: 423690

Onamba Interconnect Technology Co., Ltd. (1)
1-5-39 Teradacho, Izumi-shi, Osaka, 594-0062, Japan
Tel.: (81) 725455711
Electrical Wire Mfr & Distr
N.A.I.C.S.: 335929

Division (Domestic):

Onamba Interconnect Technology Co., Ltd. - Electric Cable Division (2)
Azanakaodani 2292-1, Saimyoji, Iga, 518-0809, Mie, Japan
Tel.: (81) 595 24 2351
Electrical Cables Mfr
N.A.I.C.S.: 335929

PT. Onamba Indonesia (1)
Jl Maligi II Lot C-5B Kawasan Industri KIIC Desa Sukaluyu, Kec Teluk Jambe, Karawang, 41361, Jawa Barat, Indonesia
Tel.: (62) 218902554
Emp.: 400
Electrical Wire Distr
N.A.I.C.S.: 423610

SD Vietnam Industries Ltd. (1)
Plot H2-a Thang Long Industrial Park, Vong La Commune Dong Anh, Hanoi, Vietnam
Tel.: (84) 438811184
Emp.: 1,250
Electrical Wire Distr
N.A.I.C.S.: 423610

UMA Manufacturing (HuiZhou) Co., Ltd. (1)
No 81 JiangBei, Xiao JinKou Subdistrict HuiCheng District, Huizhou, GuangDong, China
Tel.: (86) 7522836520
Emp.: 300
Electrical Wire Distr
N.A.I.C.S.: 423610

UMA Manufacturing CO., Ltd. (1)
Unit 18 7/F GoldField Industrial Centre No1 Sui Wo Road, Fotan, Sha Tin, NT, China (Hong Kong)
Tel.: (852) 26627099
Emp.: 2
Electrical Wire Distr
N.A.I.C.S.: 423610

UMAC Manufacturing (HuiZhou) CO., Ltd. (1)
No 81 JiangBei, Xiao JinKou HuiCheng, Huizhou, China
Tel.: (86) 7522836520
Emp.: 300
Wire Mfr & Distr
N.A.I.C.S.: 335921

UMT International Co., Ltd. (1)
Rangsit Prosper Estate 9/69 Moo 5 Paholyothin Rd Klong 1, Klongluang, Pathumthani, Thailand
Tel.: (66) 3811 0141
Electronic Equipment Distr
N.A.I.C.S.: 423690

Union Machinery Co., Ltd. (1)
1936-19 Kamimizo, Chuo-ku, Sagamihara, Kanagawa, Japan
Industrial Machinery Mfr & Distr
N.A.I.C.S.: 333998

Subsidiary (Non-US):

UMT (Thailand) (2)
219/26 Moo 6 T Borwin, Si Racha, 20230, Chonburi, Thailand
Tel.: (66) 38 110 141
Industrial Machinery Distr
N.A.I.C.S.: 423830

Vietnam Onamba Co., Ltd. (1)
No 22 Street 9 Vietnam-Singapore Industrial Park II, Hoa Phu, Thu Dau Mot, Binh Duong, Vietnam
Tel.: (84) 6503635305
Emp.: 400
Electrical Wire Distr
N.A.I.C.S.: 423610

ONANO CORPORATION
No 18 Beiyuan Rd, Zhongli Dist, Taoyuan, 32063, Taiwan
Tel.: (886) 34335831
Web Site: https://www.onano-nm.com
6405—(TAI)
Rev.: $6,835,279
Assets: $83,545,011
Liabilities: $2,590,111
Net Worth: $80,954,901
Earnings: $2,812,453
Fiscal Year-end: 12/31/23
Optical Glass Product Mfr
N.A.I.C.S.: 327215
Bill Liao *(Dir-Process Integration Dept)*

ONARA - INDUSTRIA E COMERCIO DE TEXTEIS LDA
Rua Delfim Ferreira 698, 4100-199, Porto, Portugal
Tel.: (351) 226192960
Year Founded: 1976
Sales Range: $1-9.9 Million
Emp.: 35

Onara - Industria e Comercio de Texteis Lda—(Continued)
Women's Clothing Designer & Retailer
N.A.I.C.S.: 315250
Maria Luisa Barros *(CEO)*

ONCE UPON A TIME LONDON LTD.
17 Bowling Green Ln, Clerkenwell, London, EC1R 0QH, United Kingdom
Tel.: (44) 2075348800
Web Site: http://www.onceuponlondon.com
Year Founded: 2012
Digital Marketing Services
N.A.I.C.S.: 541613
Mark Benjamin Carbeck *(Dir)*

Subsidiaries:

Ideawork Studios, Inc. (1)
7 West Figeuroa St, Santa Barbara, CA 93101
Tel.: (805) 962-2468
Web Site: http://www.ideawork.com
Advertising Services
N.A.I.C.S.: 541890
Caitlin Reese *(Project Mgr)*

ONCIMMUNE HOLDINGS PLC
1 Park Row, Leeds, LS1 5AB, United Kingdom
Tel.: (44) 1157840500 UK
Web Site: https://www.oncimmune.com
Year Founded: 2015
ONC—(AIM)
Rev.: $4,730,678
Assets: $12,681,712
Liabilities: $11,857,900
Net Worth: $823,812
Earnings: ($14,216,998)
Fiscal Year-end: 08/31/22
Pharmaceutical Product Mfr & Distr
N.A.I.C.S.: 325412
Adam Mark Hill *(CEO)*

Subsidiaries:

Oncimmune Germany GmbH (1)
Otto-Hahn-Strasse 15, 44227, Dortmund, Germany
Tel.: (49) 23197426300
Cancer Diagnostic & Treatment Services
N.A.I.C.S.: 622310

ONCOARENDI THERAPEUTICS S.A.
Zwirki i Wigury 101, 02-089, Warsaw, Poland
Tel.: (48) 225526724
Web Site: https://molecure.com
OAT—(WAR)
Sales Range: Less than $1 Million
Biotechnology Research & Development Services
N.A.I.C.S.: 541714
Marcin Szumowski *(Chm-Mgmt Bd & CEO)*

ONCODESIGN PRECISION MEDICINE SACA
18 rue Jean Mazen, 21000, Dijon, France
Tel.: (33) 310451820
Web Site: https://www.oncodesign.com
Year Founded: 1995
ALOPM—(EUR)
Biotechnology Research & Development Services
N.A.I.C.S.: 541714
Sylvie Fernandes Forster *(Chief Legal Officer)*

ONCOLYS BIOPHARMA INC.
Toranomon Towers Office 4-1-28
Toranomon, Tokyo, 105-0001, Japan
Tel.: (81) 354721578
Web Site: https://www.oncolys.com
Year Founded: 2004
4588—(TKS)
Sales Range: $1-9.9 Million
Emp.: 20
Pharmaceutical Researcher, Developer & Mfr
N.A.I.C.S.: 325412
Yasuo Urata *(Pres & CEO)*

ONCOLYTICS BIOTECH INC.
Suite 210 1167 Kensington Crescent N W, Calgary, T2N 1X7, AB, Canada
Tel.: (403) 670-7377 AB
Web Site: https://www.oncolyticsbiotech.com
Year Founded: 1998
ONCY—(NASDAQ)
Rev.: $413,044
Assets: $29,205,642
Liabilities: $8,473,657
Net Worth: $20,731,985
Earnings: ($19,427,924)
Emp.: 29
Fiscal Year-end: 12/31/22
Cancer Therapy Research & Development Services
N.A.I.C.S.: 325412
Matthew C. Coffey *(Founder, Pres & CEO)*

ONCOPEPTIDES AB
Luntmakargatan 46, 111 37, Stockholm, Sweden
Tel.: (46) 86152040
Web Site: https://www.oncopeptides.se
Year Founded: 2000
ONCO—(OMX)
Rev.: $782,545
Assets: $36,090,084
Liabilities: $8,526,043
Net Worth: $27,564,041
Earnings: ($31,653,133)
Emp.: 41
Fiscal Year-end: 12/31/22
Pharmaceuticals Product Mfr
N.A.I.C.S.: 325412
Monica Shaw *(CEO)*

Subsidiaries:

Oncopeptides, Inc. (1)
4940 El Camino Real Ste 100, Los Altos, CA 94022
Pharmaceuticals Product Mfr
N.A.I.C.S.: 325412

ONCOSIL MEDICAL LIMITED
Level 5 7 Eden Park Drive, Macquarie Park, Sydney, 2113, NSW, Australia
Tel.: (61) 289359629
Web Site: https://www.oncosil.com
OSL—(ASX)
Rev.: $1,089,709
Assets: $4,486,113
Liabilities: $1,323,447
Net Worth: $3,162,666
Earnings: ($7,955,150)
Fiscal Year-end: 06/30/24
Pharmaceutical Mfr, Researcher & Developer
N.A.I.C.S.: 325412
Daniel Kenny *(CEO & Mng Dir)*

Subsidiaries:

NeuroSolutions Limited (1)
PO Box 3517, Coventry, CV4 7ZS, United Kingdom
Tel.: (44) 8454500171
Web Site: https://www.nsolns.com
Sales Range: $25-49.9 Million
Emp.: 13
Electrophysiological Research Services
N.A.I.C.S.: 541715
David Spanswick *(Co-Founder)*

ONCOTHERAPY SCIENCE, INC.
1-2 Higashida-cho, Kawasaki-ku, Kawasaki, 210-0005, Kanagawa, Japan
Tel.: (81) 442016429
Web Site: https://www.oncotherapy.co.jp
Year Founded: 2001
4564—(TKS)
Rev.: $4,032,100
Assets: $5,730,870
Liabilities: $3,397,540
Net Worth: $2,333,330
Earnings: ($8,513,680)
Fiscal Year-end: 03/31/24
Drug Mfr
N.A.I.C.S.: 325412
Hatsuo Kato *(Chm)*

ONCOZENGE AB
Gustavslundsvagen 34, 167 51, Bromma, Sweden
Tel.: (46) 8311420
Web Site: https://www.oncozenge.se
Year Founded: 2020
ONCOZ—(OMX)
Assets: $2,019,179
Liabilities: $168,761
Net Worth: $1,850,418
Earnings: ($1,578,414)
Emp.: 2
Fiscal Year-end: 12/31/23
Pharmaceutical Product Mfr & Distr
N.A.I.C.S.: 325412
Mark Beveridge *(CFO)*

ONDECK CO., LTD.
Bingomachi Yamaguchi Gen Building 3F, Chuo Ward, Osaka, 541-0051, Japan
Tel.: (81) 649632034
Web Site: https://www.ondeck.jp
Year Founded: 2005
7360—(TKS)
Investment Brokerage Services
N.A.I.C.S.: 524210
Ryosuke Kubo *(Founder, Chm & Pres)*

ONDINE BIOMEDICAL INC.
888-1100 Melville Street, Vancouver, V6E 4A6, BC, Canada
Tel.: (604) 669-0555 BC
Web Site: https://www.ondinebio.com
Sales Range: $1-9.9 Million
Emp.: 16
Biopharmaceutical Researcher, Developer & Mfr
N.A.I.C.S.: 325412
Carolyn Cross *(Chm & CEO)*

Subsidiaries:

Ondine Research Laboratories, Inc. (1)
19017 120th Ave NE Ste 102, Bothell, WA 98011-9510
Tel.: (425) 489-1100
Anti Microbial Technology Research & Development Services
N.A.I.C.S.: 541715
Saran Baskaran *(Project Mgr)*

ONDO INSURTECH PLC
6th Floor 60 Gracechurch Street, London, EC3V 0HR, United Kingdom
Web Site: https://www.ondoplc.com
Year Founded: 2021
ONDO—(LSE)
Assets: $2,397,192
Liabilities: $129,188
Net Worth: $2,268,003
Earnings: ($787,831)
Emp.: 5
Fiscal Year-end: 02/28/22
Insurance Agencies & Brokerages
N.A.I.C.S.: 524210

Kevin Withington *(CFO)*

ONE BANK PLC
HRC Bhaban 46 Kawran Bazar C/A, Dhaka, 1215, Bangladesh
Tel.: (880) 255012505
Web Site: https://www.onebank.com.bd
ONEBANKPLC—(CHT)
Rev.: $147,723,662
Assets: $2,874,152,350
Liabilities: $2,702,498,218
Net Worth: $171,654,131
Earnings: $14,217,193
Emp.: 2,701
Fiscal Year-end: 12/31/22
Commercial Banking Services
N.A.I.C.S.: 522110
Zahur Ullah *(Vice Chm)*

Subsidiaries:

ONE Bank Limited - Retail Banking Division (1)
45 Dilkusha C/A Zaman Court, Dhaka, 1000, Bangladesh
Tel.: (880) 2 9564249
Commercial Banking Services
N.A.I.C.S.: 522110

ONE Securities Limited (1)
4/F 45 Dilkusha CA, Dhaka, 1000, Bangladesh
Tel.: (880) 2223389665
Web Site: https://www.onesecuritiesbd.com
Banking Services
N.A.I.C.S.: 522110
Aminul Islam *(CEO)*

ONE CARIBBEAN MEDIA LIMITED
Express House 35 37 Independence Square, Port of Spain, Trinidad & Tobago
Tel.: (868) 6231711
Web Site: https://www.onecaribbeanmedia.net
Year Founded: 2006
OCM—(BARB)
Rev.: $48,422,854
Assets: $130,461,722
Liabilities: $32,380,770
Net Worth: $98,080,953
Earnings: $4,218,953
Emp.: 573
Fiscal Year-end: 12/31/22
Newspaper Publishing & Television & Radio Broadcasting Services
N.A.I.C.S.: 513110
Dawn Thomas *(CEO)*

Subsidiaries:

Starcom Network Inc (1)
River Road, Bridgetown, Barbados
Tel.: (246) 430-7300
Web Site: https://starcomnetwork.net
Emp.: 50
Radio Broadcasting Services
N.A.I.C.S.: 516110
Dominic Beaubrun *(Gen Mgr)*

ONE COMMUNICATION TECHNOLOGY CORPORATION
135 Hoang Ngan Road Trung Hoa Ward, Cau Giay district, Hanoi, Vietnam
Tel.: (84) 49765086
Web Site: https://www.one.com.vn
ONE—(HNX)
Rev.: $72,581,900
Assets: $51,199,400
Liabilities: $41,165,900
Net Worth: $10,033,500
Earnings: $603,900
Emp.: 80
Fiscal Year-end: 12/31/22
Telecommunication & Data Network Equipments Distr
N.A.I.C.S.: 517810
Dang Anh Phuong *(Mmeber-Mgmt Bd & Gen Dir)*

AND PRIVATE COMPANIES

ONEALL INTERNATIONAL LIMITED

ONE COMMUNICATIONS LTD.
30 Victoria Street, Hamilton, HM 12, Bermuda
Tel.: (441) 295 5009 BM
Web Site: http://www.onecomm.bm
Year Founded: 1998
Holding Company; Telecommunication Services
N.A.I.C.S.: 551112
Gary L. Phillips (Chm)

Subsidiaries:

Bermuda Digital Communications, Ltd. (1)
30 Victoria Street 2nd Floor, Hamilton, HM 12, Bermuda
Tel.: (441) 7007300
Web Site: http://www.onecomm.bm
Wireless Telecommunication Services
N.A.I.C.S.: 517112

Bermuda Yellow Pages Limited (1)
Swan Building 26 Victoria Street, Hamilton, HM 12, Bermuda
Tel.: (441) 297 9355
Web Site: http://www.bermudayp.com
Online Directory Publisher
N.A.I.C.S.: 513140
Anthony Richardson (Mgr-Ops)

Cable Co. Ltd. (1)
19 Laffan Street, Hamilton, HM 09, Bermuda
Tel.: (441) 292 5544
Web Site: http://www.cablevision.bm
Cable Television Telecommunication Services
N.A.I.C.S.: 517121
Mike Jones (Sr Dir-Technical Ops)

Logic Communications Ltd. (1)
30 Victoria Street, Hamilton, HM 12, Bermuda (100%)
Tel.: (441) 2969600
Web Site: http://www.onecomm.bm
Telecommunication Servicesb
N.A.I.C.S.: 517111

ONE EXPERIENCE S.A.
8 Rue Barthelemy Danjou, 92100, Boulogne-Billancourt, France
Tel.: (33) 146999780
Web Site: https://www.one-experience.fr
MLOEX—(EUR)
Sales Range: $1-9.9 Million
Telecommunication Servicesb
N.A.I.C.S.: 517810
Pascal Chevalier (Chm & CEO)

ONE GLOBAL SERVICE PROVIDER LTD.
1205 1206 12th Floor Raheja Chambers 213 Free Press Journal Marg, Nariman Point, Mumbai, 400021, Gujarat, India
Tel.: (91) 2652981195
Web Site: https://www.1gsp.in
Year Founded: 1992
514330—(BOM)
Rev.: $2,172,088
Assets: $1,537,702
Liabilities: $663,521
Net Worth: $874,180
Earnings: $165,362
Emp.: 1
Fiscal Year-end: 03/31/23
Textile Products Mfr
N.A.I.C.S.: 314999
Kamal R. Aggarwal (Mng Dir)

ONE GLOVE GROUP BERHAD
lot 73 86 Jalan Logam 5 Perindustrian Kamunting 3, Kamunting Raya Industrial Estate, 34600, Kamunting, Perak, Malaysia
Tel.: (60) 58913333 MY
Web Site: https://www.onelovegroup.com
Year Founded: 2002

ONEGLOVE—(KLS)
Rev.: $9,047,509
Assets: $128,664,508
Liabilities: $72,182,156
Net Worth: $56,482,352
Earnings: ($16,591,206)
Emp.: 383
Fiscal Year-end: 03/31/23
Express Bus Services
N.A.I.C.S.: 336211
Azizuddin Ismail (Mng Dir)

Subsidiaries:

Konsortium Bas Ekspres Semenanjung (M) Sdn. Bhd. (1)
Lot 73 & 86 Jalan Logam 5 Kamunting Industrial Estate, 34600, Kamunting, Perak, Malaysia
Tel.: (60) 58918888
Online Transportation Support Services
N.A.I.C.S.: 561599

ONE HERITAGE GROUP PLC
80 Mosley Street, Manchester, M2 3FX, United Kingdom
Tel.: (44) 1618061498 UK
Web Site: https://www.oneheritageplc.com
Year Founded: 2020
OHG—(LSE)
Rev.: $19,681,808
Assets: $24,301,247
Liabilities: $25,019,142
Net Worth: ($717,894)
Earnings: ($3,017,233)
Emp.: 28
Fiscal Year-end: 06/30/23
Real Estate Development Services
N.A.I.C.S.: 531190
Anthony Unsworth (CFO)

ONE MEDIA GROUP LIMITED
16th Floor Block A Ming Pao Industrial Centre 18 Ka Yip Street, Chai Wan, China (Hong Kong)
Tel.: (852) 3 605 3705
Web Site: http://www.corp.omghk.com
0426—(HKG)
Rev.: $5,809,130
Assets: $13,235,025
Liabilities: $14,400,617
Net Worth: ($1,165,592)
Earnings: ($1,590,581)
Emp.: 106
Fiscal Year-end: 03/31/22
Magazine Publishing Services
N.A.I.C.S.: 513120
Pak Cheong Lam (CEO)

ONE MEDIA IP GROUP PLC
623 East Props Building, Goldfinger Avenue Pinewood Studios, Iver Heath, SL0 0NH, Buckinghamshire, United Kingdom
Tel.: (44) 1753785500
Web Site: https://omip.co.uk
Year Founded: 2005
OMIP—(AIM)
Rev.: $6,963,529
Assets: $24,573,457
Liabilities: $4,106,219
Net Worth: $20,467,238
Earnings: $595,021
Emp.: 21
Fiscal Year-end: 10/31/22
Digital Content; Music & Video Intellectual Property Rights
N.A.I.C.S.: 533110
Michael Infante (CEO)

ONE NORTH ENTERTAINMENT LIMITED
1 Kim Seng Promenade 17-04 Great World City East Tower, Singapore, 237994, Singapore
Tel.: (65) 67377959 AU

Year Founded: 1982
Sales Range: $1-9.9 Million
Media & Artist Representation Services
N.A.I.C.S.: 711410
Christopher Taylor (COO)

ONE POINT ONE SOLUTIONS LIMITED
C/42 Ttc Industrial Area Midc, Village Pawane Navi Mumbai, Mumbai, 400705, India
Tel.: (91) 2261656363
Web Site: https://www.1point1.in
Year Founded: 2008
ONEPOINT—(NSE)
Rev.: $17,293,903
Assets: $16,306,960
Liabilities: $9,688,760
Net Worth: $6,618,200
Earnings: $1,053,846
Emp.: 3,125
Fiscal Year-end: 03/31/23
Business Consulting Services
N.A.I.C.S.: 541611
Akshay Chhabra (Founder, Chm & Mng Dir)

ONE REIT, INC.
1-5-5 Otemachi, Chiyoda-ku, Tokyo, 100-8176, Japan
Tel.: (81) 352203804
Year Founded: 2013
3290—(TKS)
Sales Range: Less than $1 Million
Real Estate Related Services
N.A.I.C.S.: 531390
Hirofumi Nabeyama (Exec Dir)

ONE SA
ul Adama Naruszewicza 27 lok 2, 02-627, Warsaw, Poland
Tel.: (48) 224802727
Web Site: https://onesa.pl
FMG—(WAR)
Sales Range: Less than $1 Million
Holding Company; Telecommunications
N.A.I.C.S.: 551112
Piotr Zietek (CEO)

ONE SOFTWARE TECHNOLOGIES LTD.
17 Yagia Kapayim St, P O B 3961, Petach Tikva, 4913000, Israel
Tel.: (972) 39767800
Web Site: https://www.one1.co.il
Year Founded: 1973
ONE—(TAE)
Rev.: $1,020,942,932
Assets: $587,619,828
Liabilities: $397,549,655
Net Worth: $190,070,172
Earnings: $52,826,356
Emp.: 7,000
Fiscal Year-end: 12/31/23
Software Publisher
N.A.I.C.S.: 513210
Nitzan Sapir (Chm)

Subsidiaries:

CallUp Net Ltd. (1)
One1 Building 1 Amal St Afeq Park, Rosh Ha'Ayin, Israel
Tel.: (972) 39767481
Web Site: https://www.callup.net
Emp.: 25
Telecommunication Servicesb
N.A.I.C.S.: 517111
Alon Roth (CEO)

Tescom Software Systems Testing Ltd. (1)
1st Ha'amal Street Afek Park, Rosh Ha'Ayin, 48092, Israel
Tel.: (972) 3 9767930

Sales Range: $25-49.9 Million
Emp.: 600
IT Quality Assurance Consulting & Services
N.A.I.C.S.: 541511

Branch (US):

Tescom USA (2)
400 Perimeter Ctr NE Ste 900, Atlanta, GA 30346
Tel.: (678) 250-1166
Sales Range: $25-49.9 Million
Emp.: 20
Independent Software Testing Services
N.A.I.C.S.: 513210

ONE WORLD LITHIUM INC.
Suite 615 - 800 West Pender Street, Vancouver, V6C 2V6, BC, Canada
Tel.: (604) 564-2017 BC
Web Site: https://www.oneworldlithium.com
Year Founded: 1982
OWRDF—(OTCQB)
Assets: $2,535,386
Liabilities: $1,299,003
Net Worth: $1,236,384
Earnings: ($2,577,034)
Fiscal Year-end: 12/31/19
Investment Services
N.A.I.C.S.: 523999
Douglas Fulcher (Pres & CEO)

ONE97 COMMUNICATIONS LIMITED
B 121 Sector 5, Noida, 201 301, India
Tel.: (91) 1204770770
Web Site: http://www.one97world.com
Year Founded: 2000
PAYTM—(BOM)
Sales Range: $150-199.9 Million
Emp.: 1,000
Mobile Content, Messaging & Network Applications
N.A.I.C.S.: 517112
Vijay Shekhar Sharma (Co-CEO-Paytm Money & Mng Dir-Paytm Money)

Subsidiaries:

Nearbuy India Private Limited (1)
Building No 22 Mezzanine Floor Pushp Vihar Commercial Complex, Lsc Madangir Saket, New Delhi, 110062, India
Tel.: (91) 7303390416
Web Site: https://www.nearbuy.com
Online Platform Services
N.A.I.C.S.: 561311

Paytm Insurance Broking Private Limited (1)
136 1st Floor Devika Tower Nehru Place, Delhi, 110019, India
Tel.: (91) 8826390016
Web Site: https://paytminsurance.co.in
Health & Bike Insurance Services
N.A.I.C.S.: 524114

Paytm Money Limited (1)
The Hub 3Rd Floor SY No 8 & 8/2 Varthur Hobli Sarjapura Main Road, Ambalipura Village, Bengaluru, 560103, Karnataka, India
Tel.: (91) 7612796277
Web Site: https://www.paytmmoney.com
Investment Fund Services
N.A.I.C.S.: 525910

ONEALL INTERNATIONAL LIMITED
Suite 54 Level 8 591 George Street, Sydney, 2000, NSW, Australia
Tel.: (61) 2 9267 3855
Web Site: http://www.oneallinternational.com
Rev.: $38,087,819
Assets: $30,039,278
Liabilities: $12,681,861
Net Worth: $17,357,417
Earnings: $6,467,900

5575

ONEALL INTERNATIONAL LIMITED

OneAll International Limited—(Continued)
Fiscal Year-end: 12/31/18
Outdoor Furniture Manufacturer
N.A.I.C.S.: 337126
Huatang Li *(Co-Founder, Chm & CEO)*

ONEAPEX LIMITED
38 Jalan Pemimpin 06-06, Singapore, 577178, Singapore
Tel.: (65) 68179118
Web Site:
  https://oneapex.wixsite.com
5SY—(CAT)
Rev.: $765,458
Assets: $49,035,945
Liabilities: $39,897,139
Net Worth: $9,138,806
Earnings: ($615,874)
Emp.: 10
Fiscal Year-end: 09/30/23
Egg Producer
N.A.I.C.S.: 112310
Alex Pei Hong Tan *(CEO)*

Subsidiaries:

Chew s Agriculture Pte Ltd (1)
150 Neo Tiew Road, Singapore, 719032, Singapore
Tel.: (65) 67937678
Web Site: https://www.chewsegg.com
Fresh Egg Mfr
N.A.I.C.S.: 112310

ONECLICK LOGISTICS INDIA LIMITED
5th Floor Goldcrest Business Park 511 Lal Bahadur Shastri Marg, Nityanand Nagar Ghatkopar Ghatkopar West, Mumbai, 400086, Maharashtra, India
Tel.: (91) 9082247302
Web Site: https://1click.co.in
Year Founded: 2017
OLIL—(NSE)
Emp.: 19,544
Logistic Services
N.A.I.C.S.: 541614
Mahesh Bhanushali *(Mng Dir)*

ONECONNECT FINANCIAL TECHNOLOGY CO., LTD.
21/24F Ping An Financial Center PAFC No 5033 Yitian Rd, Futian District, Shenzhen, Guangdong, China
Tel.: (86) 237579718   Ky
Web Site: https://www.ocft.com
Year Founded: 2015
OCFT—(NYSE)
Rev.: $683,929,746
Assets: $1,360,869,746
Liabilities: $858,638,940
Net Worth: $502,230,807
Earnings: ($142,182,863)
Emp.: 2,832
Fiscal Year-end: 12/31/22
Holding Company
N.A.I.C.S.: 551112
Wangchun Ye *(Chm & CEO)*

ONEE TAX LIMITED
Springfield House Springfield Court Summerfield Road, Bolton, BL3 2NT, Greater Manchester, United Kingdom
Tel.: (44) 1204 559914
Web Site: http://www.oneetax.com
Year Founded: 2006
Sales Range: $25-49.9 Million
Emp.: 33
Tax Planning Services
N.A.I.C.S.: 541213
Sufyan Gulam Ismail *(Chm & CEO)*

ONEFLOW AB
Gavlegatan 12a, 113 30, Stockholm, Sweden
Tel.: (46) 851729770
Web Site: https://www.oneflow.com
Year Founded: 2012
ONEF—(OMX)
Rev.: $8,877,519
Assets: $28,440,466
Liabilities: $7,270,744
Net Worth: $21,169,723
Earnings: ($6,177,406)
Emp.: 122
Fiscal Year-end: 12/31/22
Software Development Services
N.A.I.C.S.: 541511
Anders Hamnes *(CEO)*

Subsidiaries:

Oneflow B.V. (1)
Brouwersgracht 167-1, 1015 GH, Amsterdam, Netherlands
Tel.: (31) 205321633
Software Development Services
N.A.I.C.S.: 541511

Oneflow England Ltd. (1)
35 Luke Street, London, EC2A 4LH, United Kingdom
Tel.: (44) 851729770
Software Development Services
N.A.I.C.S.: 541511

Oneflow Norge AS (1)
Universitetsgata 10, 0164, Oslo, Norway
Tel.: (47) 81503026
Software Development Services
N.A.I.C.S.: 541511

Oneflow S.A.S. (1)
20 rue des Petits Champs, 75002, Paris, France
Tel.: (33) 189881571
Information Technology Services
N.A.I.C.S.: 541512

ONEFORCE HOLDINGS LTD.
Level 54 Hopewell Centre 183 Queens Road East, Hong Kong, China (Hong Kong)
Tel.: (852) 2 980 1639   Ky
Web Site:
  http://www.oneforce.com.cn
Year Founded: 2016
1933—(HKG)
Rev.: $44,992,568
Assets: $55,721,405
Liabilities: $23,010,610
Net Worth: $32,710,795
Earnings: $3,195,195
Emp.: 111
Fiscal Year-end: 03/31/21
Electric Power System Parts Mfr & Distr
N.A.I.C.S.: 335311
Dongbin Wang *(Founder & Chm)*

ONEJOON CO., LTD.
174-29 Saneop-ro, Gwonseon-gu, Suwon, Gyeonggi-do, Korea (South)
Tel.: (82) 312970594
Web Site: https://www.onejoon.de
Year Founded: 2008
382840—(KRS)
Rev.: $109,834,429
Assets: $120,665,546
Liabilities: $35,187,375
Net Worth: $85,478,171
Earnings: $11,643,472
Emp.: 96
Fiscal Year-end: 12/31/22
Industry Machinery Mfr
N.A.I.C.S.: 333310

ONELIFE CAPITAL ADVISORS LIMITED
Plot No A 356 Road No 26 Wagle Industrial Estate, Mumbai, 400604, Maharashtra, India
Tel.: (91) 2225833206
Web Site:
  https://www.onelifecapital.in
Year Founded: 2007

533632—(NSE)
Rev.: $895,740
Assets: $12,342,371
Liabilities: $752,893
Net Worth: $11,589,478
Earnings: ($7,439)
Emp.: 30
Fiscal Year-end: 03/31/21
Investment Advisory Services
N.A.I.C.S.: 523940
Thiruvidaimarudur Krishna Prab Naig *(Chm)*

Subsidiaries:

Dealmoney Distribution & E-marketing Private Limited (1)
Plot No A356/357 Road No 26 Wagle Industrial Estate, Thane, 400 604, Maharashtra, India
Tel.: (91) 8657566377
Web Site: https://www.dealtravel.in
Travel Support Services
N.A.I.C.S.: 624190

Dealmoney Real Estate Private Limited (1)

ONELOGIX GROUP LIMITED
46 Tulbagh Road, Pomona, Kempton Park, 1620, South Africa
Tel.: (27) 113969040   ZA
Web Site: http://www.onelogix.com
Year Founded: 2000
OLG—(JSE)
Rev.: $168,042,302
Assets: $181,424,048
Liabilities: $115,111,720
Net Worth: $66,312,328
Earnings: $2,897,387
Emp.: 2,216
Fiscal Year-end: 05/31/21
Freight Trucking & Logistics Services
N.A.I.C.S.: 484121
Ian K. Lourens *(CEO)*

Subsidiaries:

Buffelshoek Transport SA Proprietary Limited (1)
Plot 14 4th Street, PO Box 525, Naboomspruit, Pretoria, 0560, South Africa
Tel.: (27) 147430683
Logistic Services
N.A.I.C.S.: 541614
Athol Saunders *(Mng Dir)*

Cranbourne Panel Beaters & Spray Painters Proprietary Limited (1)
11 Cranbourne Ave, Benoni, 1501, South Africa
Tel.: (27) 11 421 9445
Web Site: https://www.cranbourne.co.za
Vehicle Repair Services
N.A.I.C.S.: 811111

Jackson Transport Proprietary Limited (1)
224 4th Rd, Witpoort, Brakpan, 1540, South Africa
Tel.: (27) 11 743 2960
Web Site: https://jackson-transport.business.site
Transportation Services
N.A.I.C.S.: 485999

OneLogix Cargo Solutions Proprietary Limited (1)
3rd Floor Dunlop House 265 Sydney Road, Durban, 4000, South Africa
Tel.: (27) 103500224
Logistic Services
N.A.I.C.S.: 541614
Andre Niemand *(Mng Dir)*

OneLogix Warehousing Proprietary Limited (1)
3 Clydebank Road Bayhead, Durban, 4052, South Africa
Tel.: (27) 312062299
Logistic Services
N.A.I.C.S.: 541614

Quasar Software Development Proprietary Limited (1)

INTERNATIONAL PUBLIC

80 Sovereign Drive Route 21 Business Park, Irene, 1620, South Africa
Tel.: (27) 119209175
Logistic Services
N.A.I.C.S.: 541614
Vincent Kaufman *(Mng Dir)*

United Bulk Proprietary Limited (1)
16 Barrage Road, Vereeniging, 1939, South Africa
Tel.: (27) 164241130
Web Site: http://www.unitedbulk.co.za
Liquid Transportation Services
N.A.I.C.S.: 484230
Patrick Pols *(Mng Dir)*

Subsidiary (Domestic):

Cryogas Express Proprietary Limited (2)
9 Angus Crescent Longmeadow East, Longmeadow Business Estate, Edenvale, 1610, South Africa
Tel.: (27) 11 579 6700
Web Site: https://www.cryogasexpress.co.za
Cryogenic Gas Delivery Services
N.A.I.C.S.: 492110

ONEMEDIA FRANCE SARL
Parc d'Activite Gruber 91 b route des Romains, 67200, Strasbourg, France
Tel.: (33) 3 6867 6867
Mobile Marketing Services
N.A.I.C.S.: 541890
Laurent Krugell *(Pres & Dir Gen)*

ONEMEDNET CORPORATION
Trident Court 1 Oakcroft Road, Chessington, KT91BD, Surrey, United Kingdom
Tel.: (44) 2080902009   DE
Year Founded: 2021
ONMD—(NASDAQ)
Assets: $29,060,286
Liabilities: $37,866,724
Net Worth: ($8,806,438)
Earnings: $336,658
Emp.: 2
Fiscal Year-end: 12/31/22
Investment Services
N.A.I.C.S.: 523999
Aaron Green *(Pres & CEO)*

Subsidiaries:

OneMedNet Solutions Corporation (1)
3774 LaVista Rd Ste 200, Tucker, GA 30084
Web Site: http://www.onemednet.com
Computer System Design Services
N.A.I.C.S.: 541512
Brian Frake *(VP-Product Dev)*

ONENERGY INC.
155 Gordon Baker Road Suite 301, Toronto, M2H 3N5, ON, Canada
Tel.: (416) 444-4848   Ca
Web Site:
  http://www.onenergyinc.com
Year Founded: 1999
OEG—(TSXV)
Sales Range: $1-9.9 Million
Energy Products Supply to Residential, Industrial & Commercial Customers
N.A.I.C.S.: 335929
Ray de Ocampo *(CFO)*

Subsidiaries:

0867893 B.C. Ltd. (1)
1631 Powell Street, Vancouver, V5L 1H5, BC, Canada
Tel.: (604) 558-0441
Web Site: http://pvlprojects.ca
Energy Saving Equipment Installation Services
N.A.I.C.S.: 238220

Sunwave Gas & Power Inc. (1)
263 Tresser Blvd 9th Fl, Stamford, CT 06901
Tel.: (855) 478-6928

AND PRIVATE COMPANIES

Web Site: http://www.gosunwave.com
Electric Power Distribution Services
N.A.I.C.S.: 221122

ONENESS BIOTECH CO., LTD.
35F No 66 Sec 1 Zhongxiao W Rd,
Zhongzheng Dist, Taipei, 106, Taiwan
Tel.: (886) 227031098
Web Site:
  https://www.onenessbio.com
Year Founded: 2008
4743—(TPE)
Rev.: $33,316,262
Assets: $487,145,827
Liabilities: $21,898,540
Net Worth: $465,247,288
Earnings: $11,002,626
Emp.: 180
Fiscal Year-end: 12/31/22
Biotechnology Research & Development Services
N.A.I.C.S.: 541714
Shan-Ney Huang *(Chm & Pres)*

ONEPOINT SOFTWARE GMBH
Arche Noah 9/I, Graz, 8010, Austria
Tel.: (43) 699 17 17 17 22
Web Site: http://www.onepoint-projects.com
Emp.: 10
Software Publisher
N.A.I.C.S.: 513210
Gerald Aquila *(Founder & CEO)*

ONESANO S.A.
Ul Dyrekcyjna 6, 41-506, Chorzow, Poland
Tel.: (48) 327937271
Web Site: http://www.skotansa.pl
Year Founded: 1999
SKT—(WAR)
Sales Range: Less than $1 Million
Oil Field Operating Services
N.A.I.C.S.: 213112
Jacek Kostrzewa *(Chm-Mgmt Bd)*

ONESAVINGS BANK PLC
Reliance House Sun Pier, Chatham, ME4 4ET, United Kingdom
Tel.: (44) 1634848944 UK
Web Site: http://www.osb.co.uk
Year Founded: 2011
OSB—(LSE)
Rev.: $966,560,868
Assets: $30,758,467,740
Liabilities: $28,481,707,072
Net Worth: $2,276,760,668
Earnings: $266,520,436
Emp.: 1,816
Fiscal Year-end: 12/31/20
Commercial Banking Services
N.A.I.C.S.: 522110
Andy Golding *(CEO)*

Subsidiaries:

Charter Court Financial Services Group plc (1)
1 Charter Court Broadlands, Wolverhampton, WV10 6TD, United Kingdom
Tel.: (44) 3330143477
Web Site: http://www.chartercourtfs.co.uk
Rev.: $285,402,598
Assets: $9,881,224,230
Liabilities: $9,309,784,524
Net Worth: $571,439,706
Earnings: $153,297,616
Emp.: 577
Fiscal Year-end: 12/31/2018
Investment Banking Services
N.A.I.C.S.: 523150
Ian Lonergan *(Co-Founder & CEO)*

Heritable Development Finance Limited (1)
85 Newman St, Fitzrovia, London, W1T 3EU, United Kingdom
Tel.: (44) 2070425070
Web Site: http://www.heritable.co
Finance Development Services
N.A.I.C.S.: 522220

Interbay Asset Finance Limited (1)
Sentinel House Ancells Business Park Harvest Crescent, Fleet, GU51 2UZ, United Kingdom
Tel.: (44) 345 120 2007
Web Site:
  https://www.interbayassetfinance.co.uk
Asset Finance Services
N.A.I.C.S.: 522220
Paul Fazakerley *(Head-Asset Fin)*

OSB India Private Limited (1)
Salarpuria Magnificia No 78 9th and 10th Floor Dooravaninagar, Old Madras Road, Bengaluru, 560016, Karnataka, India
Tel.: (91) 806637470107
Web Site: http://www.osb-india.com
Home Loan & Mortgage Services
N.A.I.C.S.: 522310
Ranjit Nair *(Asst Mgr-HR)*

Prestige Finance Limited (1)
Prestige House 16 Melbourne Road, Bushey, WD23 3LN, Hertfordshire, United Kingdom
Tel.: (44) 333 240 6114
Web Site: https://www.prestigefinance.co.uk
Home Loan & Mortgage Services
N.A.I.C.S.: 522310

ONESHOP RETAIL SDN. BHD.
4th Floor 1 Utama Shopping Centre Lebuh Bandar Utama, Bandar Utama, 47800, Petaling Jaya, Selangor, Malaysia
Tel.: (60) 37 726 4788 MY
Web Site:
  https://www.oneshop.com.my
Emp.: 100
Fashion Product Retailer
N.A.I.C.S.: 458110

ONESOURCE IDEAS VENTURE LTD.
F4 4th Floor Sindur Pantheon Plaza No 346 Pantheon Road Egmore, Chennai, 600 008, India
Tel.: (91) 9685634568
Web Site: https://www.osivl.com
Year Founded: 1994
530805—(BOM)
Rev.: $46,652
Assets: $392,003
Liabilities: $49,865
Net Worth: $342,138
Earnings: $17,217
Emp.: 4
Fiscal Year-end: 03/31/23
Financial Consulting Services
N.A.I.C.S.: 541611
Fathima Jalal *(Mng Dir)*

ONESTAT INTERNATIONAL B.V.
Lemelerberg 13, Alphen, 2402 ZN, Rijn, Netherlands
Tel.: (31) 172 244 043
Web Site: http://www.onestat.com
Web Analytics Solutions
N.A.I.C.S.: 513210
Niels Brinkman *(Co-Founder & Head-Mktg & Sls)*

ONET SA
36 Boulevard de l'Océan, 13009, Marseille, France
Tel.: (33) 49123222 FR
Web Site:
  https://www.groupeonet.com
Emp.: 100
Engineeering Services
N.A.I.C.S.: 541330

Subsidiaries:

ISS Abilis France S.A.S. (1)
65-67 rue Ordener, F-75899, Paris, Cedex 18, France
Tel.: (33) 144924848
Web Site: http://www.fr.issworld.com
Commercial Facility Maintenance & Support Services
N.A.I.C.S.: 561210

ONEVIEW GROUP PLC
Suite 25 6-8 Revenge Road Lordswood, Chatham, ME5 8UD, Kent, United Kingdom
Tel.: (44) 1634 673172 UK
Web Site:
  http://www.oneviewcommerce.com
Sales Range: Less than $1 Million
Business Support Services
N.A.I.C.S.: 561499
Richard Abraham *(Chm)*

ONEVIEW HEALTHCARE PLC
2nd Floor Avoca Court Temple Road Blackrock, Dublin, A94 R7W3, Ireland
Tel.: (353) 15241677 IE
Web Site:
  https://www.oneviewhealthcare.com
Year Founded: 2012
ONE—(ASX)
Rev.: $10,087,348
Assets: $23,527,441
Liabilities: $13,716,727
Net Worth: $9,810,714
Earnings: ($9,590,566)
Emp.: 79
Fiscal Year-end: 12/31/23
Healtcare Services
N.A.I.C.S.: 621491
Mark McCloskey *(Pres & Founder)*

Subsidiaries:

Oneview Healthcare Inc (1)
444 N Michigan Ave Ste 3310, Chicago, IL 60611
Tel.: (312) 763-6800
Software Distribution Services
N.A.I.C.S.: 513210

Oneview Healthcare Pty Limited (1)
Level 7 176 Wellington Parade, Melbourne, 3002, VIC, Australia
Tel.: (61) 391142210
Software Distribution Services
N.A.I.C.S.: 513210

Oneview Middle East DMCC (1)
Unit No AG-PF-38 AG Tower Plot No JLT-PH1-I1A Jumeirah Lakes Towers, Dubai, United Arab Emirates
Tel.: (971) 585687680
Software Distribution Services
N.A.I.C.S.: 513210

ONEWO INC.
Meilin Vanke Center No 63 Meilin Road, Futian District, Shenzhen, China CN
Web Site: https://www.onewo.com
Year Founded: 1990
2602—(HKG)
Rev.: $4,594,519,550
Assets: $5,452,912,744
Liabilities: $2,930,172,242
Net Worth: $2,522,740,502
Earnings: $281,877,077
Emp.: 101,284
Fiscal Year-end: 12/31/23
Property Management Services
N.A.I.C.S.: 531311
Guanghui Yang *(Chief Customer Officer)*

ONEWORLD HOTEL DESTINATION SERVICE INC.
3115-8788 Mckim Way, Richmond, V6X 4E2, BC, Canada
Tel.: (604) 606-9080
Year Founded: 1999
Travel Agency Services
N.A.I.C.S.: 561510

ONEX CORPORATION
161 Bay Street, Toronto, M5J 2S1, ON, Canada
Tel.: (416) 362-7711 ON
Web Site: https://www.onex.com
Year Founded: 1984
ONE—(DEU)
Rev.: $1,126,000,000
Assets: $9,025,000,000
Liabilities: $461,000,000
Net Worth: $8,564,000,000
Earnings: $529,000,000
Fiscal Year-end: 12/31/23
Privater Equity Firm
N.A.I.C.S.: 523999
Gerald W. Schwartz *(Co-Founder & Chm)*

Subsidiaries:

Celestica, Inc. (1)
Celestica 1900-5140 Yonge Street, Toronto, M2N 6L7, ON, Canada (81%)
Tel.: (416) 448-5800
Web Site: https://www.celestica.com
Rev.: $7,250,000,000
Assets: $5,628,000,000
Liabilities: $3,950,300,000
Net Worth: $1,677,700,000
Earnings: $145,500,000
Emp.: 26,324
Fiscal Year-end: 12/31/2022
Electronic Components Mfr
N.A.I.C.S.: 334412
Michael M. Wilson *(Chm)*

Subsidiary (Non-US):

Celestica (Romania) S.R.L. (2)
88 Sos Borsului, Bors, 417075, Bihor, Romania
Tel.: (40) 359403500
Electronic Components Mfr
N.A.I.C.S.: 334419
Codruta Bala *(Dir-HR)*

Celestica AG (2)
Thurgauer Strasse 40 3 Fl, 8050, Zurich, Switzerland
Tel.: (41) 443064300
Web Site: http://www.celestica.com
Sales Range: $25-49.9 Million
Emp.: 6
International Purchasing
N.A.I.C.S.: 928120

Celestica Automation Technology (Wuxi) Co., Ltd. (2)
287 Gaolang East Road J3-4 Export Processing Zone, Wuxi New District, Wuxi, 214028, Jiangsu, China (100%)
Tel.: (86) 51085203888
Web Site: http://www.celestica.com
Sales Range: $125-149.9 Million
Emp.: 400
Semiconductor Equipment Mfr
N.A.I.C.S.: 334413

Celestica Electronics (Malaysia) Sdn Bhd. (2)
No 10 & 10A Jalan Bayu Kawasan, Perindustrian Hasil, 81200, Johor Bahru, Malaysia
Tel.: (60) 72371007
Printed Circuit Board & Systems Assemblies & Laboratory Testing
N.A.I.C.S.: 334418

Celestica Electronics (S) Pte. Ltd. (Woodlands) (2)
Blk 35 Marsiling Industrial Ests Rd 3, 02 05 Woodlands Ave 5, Singapore, 739257, Singapore
Tel.: (65) 63666022
Web Site: http://www.celestica.com
Sales Range: $25-49.9 Million
Emp.: 100
Mfr of Electronic Components
N.A.I.C.S.: 334419

Celestica Holdings Pte Limited (2)
Peace Centre 05-03 1 Sophia Road, Singapore, 228149, Singapore
Tel.: (65) 63666022
Investment Management Service
N.A.I.C.S.: 523940

Celestica Hong Kong Limited (2)
4/F Goldlion Holdings Ctr 13 - 15 Yuen Shun Circuit Siu Lek Yuen, Sha Tin, New Territories, China (Hong Kong)

ONEX CORPORATION

ONEX Corporation—(Continued)
Tel.: (852) 2727 5461
Supply Chain Management Services
N.A.I.C.S.: 541614

Celestica Inc.-China (2)
Mai Yuen Guan Li Qu Changping, Dongguan, 523576, China
Tel.: (86) 7693394581
Mfr of Electronic Components
N.A.I.C.S.: 334419

Celestica Inc.-China (2)
448 Su Hong Middle Rd, Suzhou, 215051, Jiangsu, China
Tel.: (86) 51262588111
Web Site: http://www.celestica.com
Sales Range: $350-399.9 Million
Emp.: 2,000
Mfr of Electronic Components
N.A.I.C.S.: 334419

Celestica Malaysia Sdn. Bhd. (2)
Plot 15 Jalan Hi-Tech 2/3 Phase 1, Kulim Hi-Tech Park, Kulim, 09000, Kedah, Malaysia
Tel.: (60) 44033288
Web Site: http://www.celestica.com
Sales Range: $350-399.9 Million
Emp.: 2,000
Mfr of Electronic Components
N.A.I.C.S.: 334419

Celestica Philippines (2)
Mactan Economic Zone MEZ 1, Lapu-Lapu, 6015, Cebu, Philippines
Tel.: (63) 323040451
Sales Range: $350-399.9 Million
Emp.: 2,000
Mfr of Communications Equipment
N.A.I.C.S.: 334290

Celestica Singapore Pte Ltd. (2)
53 Serangoon N Ave 4 # 02-00, 555852, Singapore, Singapore
Tel.: (65) 64858629
Other Electronic Component Mfg
N.A.I.C.S.: 335999

Celestica de Monterrey S.A. de C.V. (2)
Calle Octava 102, Parque Industrial Monterrey, Apodaca, 66600, NL, Mexico
Tel.: (52) 8181561500
Web Site: http://www.celestica.com
Sales Range: $25-49.9 Million
Emp.: 25
Mfr of Electronic Components
N.A.I.C.S.: 334419

Celestica do Brazil (2)
Rodovia SP 340 S N Km 128 7 B, Jaguariuna, 13820-000, Sao Paulo, Brazil
Tel.: (55) 1938475400
Sales Range: $75-99.9 Million
Emp.: 500
Mfr of Electronic Components
N.A.I.C.S.: 334419

Celestica, Inc.-Japan (2)
Teito Misakicho Bldg 6F 7 10 Misakicho 2 Chome, Tokyo, 101 0061, Japan
Tel.: (81) 352122581
Web Site: http://www.celestica.co.jp
Sales Range: $75-99.9 Million
Emp.: 465
Mfr of Electronic Components
N.A.I.C.S.: 334419
Robert L. Crandall *(Chm)*

Celestica, Inc.-Thailand (2)
49-18 Moo 5 Laem Chabang Industrial Est Tungsukla, Chon Buri, 20230, Thailand
Tel.: (66) 38493561
Web Site: http://www.celestica.com
Sales Range: $700-749.9 Million
Emp.: 5,000
Mfr of Electronic Components
N.A.I.C.S.: 334419

Celestica, Kawasaki SRC (2)
Sakuramoto 2-chome, Kawasaki-ku, Kawasaki, 210-0833, Kanagawa, Japan
Tel.: (81) 442703360
Web Site: http://www.celestica.co.jp
Sales Range: $25-49.9 Million
Emp.: 60
After-Market, Repair & Related Services on Electronic Components
N.A.I.C.S.: 334419

Subsidiary (US):

D&H Manufacturing Company (2)
49235 Milmont Dr, Fremont, CA 94538
Tel.: (510) 770-5100
Web Site: http://www.celestica.com
Sales Range: $10-24.9 Million
Emp.: 118
Precision Machinery Parts Mfr
N.A.I.C.S.: 332710
Mark Morse *(Gen Mgr)*

Subsidiary (Non-US):

SC Celestica (Romania) SRL (2)
400 Sos Borsului 88, Oradea, 410605, Bors Bihor, Romania
Tel.: (40) 359403500
Web Site: http://www.celestica.com
Sales Range: $150-199.9 Million
Emp.: 1,000
Mfr of Electronic Components
N.A.I.C.S.: 334111

Falcon Investment Advisors, LLC (1)
21 Custom House St, Boston, MA 02110
Tel.: (617) 412-2700
Web Site: http://www.onexfalcon.com
Privater Equity Firm
N.A.I.C.S.: 523999
Sandeep D. Alva *(Founder, Mng Partner & Portfolio Mgr)*

Holding (Domestic):

Dearborn Midwest Conveyor Co. (2)
20334 Superior Rd, Taylor, MI 48180-6301
Tel.: (734) 288-4400
Web Site: http://www.dmwcc.com
Sales Range: $25-49.9 Million
Heavy-Duty Conveyor Systems Mfr
N.A.I.C.S.: 333922
Tony Rosati *(Pres)*

Branch (Domestic):

Falcon Investment Advisors, LLC - New York Office (2)
600 Lexington Ave 35th Fl, New York, NY 10022
Tel.: (212) 300-0200
Web Site: http://www.falconinvestments.com
Sales Range: $50-74.9 Million
Emp.: 9
Privater Equity Firm
N.A.I.C.S.: 523999
Eric Y. Rogoff *(Partner)*

Joint Venture (Domestic):

Protect America, Inc. (2)
3800 Quick Hill Rd Bldg 1-100, Austin, TX 78728
Tel.: (512) 218-8833
Web Site: http://www.protectamerica.com
Security Systems Services; Owned by RockBridge Growth Equity LLC, Falcon Investment Advisors, LLC & Protect America, Inc.
N.A.I.C.S.: 561621
Ryan Pombrio *(VP-Bus Dev)*

Gluskin Sheff + Associates Inc. (1)
Bay Adelaide Centre 333 Bay Street Suite 5100, Toronto, M5H 2R2, ON, Canada
Tel.: (416) 681-6000
Web Site: http://www.gluskinsheff.com
Wealth Management Services
N.A.I.C.S.: 541618
Jeff Moody *(Pres & CEO)*

Moran Foods, LLC (1)
100 Corporate Ofc Dr, Earth City, MO 63045-1528
Tel.: (314) 592-9100
Web Site: http://www.save-a-lot.com
Emp.: 500
Holding Company; Food Distr & Discount Grocery Stores Operator
N.A.I.C.S.: 551112
Rob ANderson *(CFO & VP-Corp Dev)*

Subsidiary (Domestic):

Save-A-Lot Food Stores, Ltd. (2)
100 Corporate Ofc Dr, Earth City, MO 63045
Tel.: (314) 592-9100
Web Site: http://www.save-a-lot.com
Food Distr & Discount Grocery Stores Operator
N.A.I.C.S.: 445110
John Gerber *(VP-Distr SAL)*

National Action Financial Services, Inc. (1)
3587 Pkwy Ln, Norcross, GA 30092-2827
Tel.: (770) 248-4577
Web Site: http://www.sitel.com
Sales Range: $75-99.9 Million
Emp.: 300
Adjustment & Collection Services
N.A.I.C.S.: 561440

ONCAP Management Partners L.P. (1)
161 Bay Street 49th Floor, Toronto, M5J 2S1, ON, Canada
Tel.: (416) 214-4300
Web Site: https://www.oncap.com
Privater Equity Firm
N.A.I.C.S.: 523999
Michael Lay *(Mng Partner)*

Holding (US):

Davis-Standard, LLC (2)
1 Extrusion Dr, Pawcatuck, CT 06379-2313
Tel.: (860) 599-1010
Web Site: http://www.davis-standard.com
Sales Range: $100-124.9 Million
Emp.: 1,400
Extrusion Systems & Process Controls Developer & Mfr
N.A.I.C.S.: 333248
Mike Newhall *(VP-Mfg)*

Subsidiary (Domestic):

Davis-Standard, LLC - Egan (3)
36 S Adamsville Rd, Bridgewater, NJ 08807
Tel.: (908) 722-6000
Web Site: http://www.davis-standard.com
Sales Range: $50-74.9 Million
Converting Machinery Mfr
N.A.I.C.S.: 333248

Davis-Standard, LLC - Fulton (3)
46 N 1st St, Fulton, NY 13069
Tel.: (315) 598-7121
Web Site: http://www.davis-standard.com
Rubber Processing Machine Mfr
N.A.I.C.S.: 333248

Thermoforming Systems, LLC (3)
1601 W Pine St, Union Gap, WA 98903
Tel.: (509) 454-4578
Web Site: http://www.tslusa.biz
Sales Range: $1-9.9 Million
Emp.: 24
Packaging Machinery Mfr
N.A.I.C.S.: 333993
Roger Underwood *(VP-Sls)*

Holding (US):

Enertech Resources LLC (2)
1820 Watson Ln E, New Braunfels, TX 78130-7259
Tel.: (830) 387-4502
Web Site: http://www.enertechresources.com
Power & Communication Line Construction
N.A.I.C.S.: 237130
Eric Chase *(CEO)*

Hopkins Manufacturing Corporation (2)
428 Peyton St, Emporia, KS 66801
Tel.: (620) 342-7320
Web Site: http://www.hopkinsmfg.com
Sales Range: $50-74.9 Million
Automotive Aftermarket Products Mfr & Distr
N.A.I.C.S.: 336390
Bradley T. Kraft *(Pres & CEO)*

Joint Venture (Domestic):

Paradise Road LLC (3)
5872 Engineer Dr, Huntington Beach, CA 92649
Tel.: (714) 894-1779
Web Site: http://www.paradiseroadcarcare.com
Sales Range: $1-9.9 Million
Motor Vehicle Detailing Products Mfr & Distr
N.A.I.C.S.: 325612

Holding (Domestic):

Laces Group, Inc. (2)

INTERNATIONAL PUBLIC

9150 Parc Avenue, Montreal, H2N 1Z2, QC, Canada
Tel.: (514) 384-2910
Home Fashion Products Mfr & Distr
N.A.I.C.S.: 423220

Subsidiary (US):

Maytex Mills, Inc. (3)
261 5th Ave #1701 17th Fl, New York, NY 10016
Tel.: (212) 684-1191
Web Site: http://www.maytex.com
Home Furnishings Mfr & Distr
N.A.I.C.S.: 423220
David Baines *(Pres)*

Zenith Products Corporation (3)
400 Lukens Dr, New Castle, DE 19720-2728
Tel.: (302) 326-8200
Web Site: http://www.zenith-products.com
Bathroom Storage & Organization Products Mfr & Distr
N.A.I.C.S.: 332510

Holding (US):

Precision Concepts International LLC (2)
136 Fairview Rd Ste 320, Mooresville, NC 28117
Tel.: (704) 360-8923
Web Site: https://pcinternational.com
Packaging Product Distr
N.A.I.C.S.: 424610
Ray Grupinski *(CEO)*

Subsidiary (Domestic):

Precision Concepts (Mebane) LLC (3)
135 Fairview Rd Ste 320, Mooresville, NC 28117
Tel.: (704) 360-8923
Web Site: https://pcinternational.com
Plastics Product Mfr
N.A.I.C.S.: 326199
Michael Mims *(Gen Mgr)*

Onex Partners LP (1)
161 Bay Street, Toronto, M5J 2S1, ON, Canada
Tel.: (416) 362-7711
Web Site: http://www.onex.com
Privater Equity Firm
N.A.I.C.S.: 523999
Anthony Munk *(Mng Dir & Co-Head)*

Holding (US):

Carestream Health, Inc. (2)
150 Verona St, Rochester, NY 14608 (100%)
Tel.: (585) 627-1800
Web Site: http://www.carestream.com
Sales Range: $1-4.9 Billion
Emp.: 8,000
Diagnostic Imaging Products Mfr
N.A.I.C.S.: 339112
Bruce Leidal *(Chm)*

Cosmetic Essence Inc. (2)
2182 Rte 35 S, Holmdel, NJ 07733
Tel.: (732) 888-7788
Web Site: http://www.cosmeticessence.com
Sales Range: $250-299.9 Million
Emp.: 1,100
Personal Care & Household Product Supply Chain Management Services
N.A.I.C.S.: 325620
John F. Croddick *(CEO)*

Emerald Holding, Inc. (2)
100 Broadway 14th Fl, New York, NY 10005
Tel.: (949) 226-5700
Web Site: https://www.emeraldx.com
Rev: $325,900,000
Assets: $1,098,400,000
Liabilities: $1,131,500,000
Net Worth ($33,100,000)
Earnings: $31,800,000
Emp.: 759
Fiscal Year-end: 12/31/2022
Trade Fair Management Services
N.A.I.C.S.: 561920
Herve Sedky *(Pres & CEO)*

Subsidiary (Domestic):

Centerstone Technologies, Inc. (3)

AND PRIVATE COMPANIES

1675 Larimer St Ste 550, Denver, CO 80202
Tel.: (303) 763-7325
Computer System Design Services
N.A.I.C.S.: 541512

Emerald Expositions, Inc. (3)
31910 Del Obispo St Ste 200, San Juan Capistrano, CA 92675-3182
Tel.: (949) 226-5744
Web Site: http://www.emeraldexpositions.com
Sales Range: $150-199.9 Million
Emp.: 100
Trade Show Organizer, Periodicals Publisher & Marketing Services
N.A.I.C.S.: 561920
Joe Randall *(Exec VP)*

Branch (Domestic):

Emerald Expositions, Inc. - Alpharetta (4)
1145 Sanctuary Pkwy Ste 450, Alpharetta, GA 30009-4793
Tel.: (770) 569-1540
Sales Range: $25-49.9 Million
Emp.: 45
Publisher
N.A.I.C.S.: 518210

Unit (Domestic):

Hospitality Design Group (4)
200 W Jackson Blvd 2700, Chicago, IL 60606
Tel.: (312) 583-5600
Web Site: http://www.hdmag.com
Sales Range: $25-49.9 Million
Emp.: 5
Magazine Publisher & Website Operator
N.A.I.C.S.: 513120

Subsidiary (Domestic):

G3 Communications (3)
411 State Route 17 S Suite 410, Hasbrouck Heights, NJ 07604
Tel.: (888) 603-3626
Web Site: http://www.gthreecom.com
Digital Media Firm Specializing in B2B Marketing
N.A.I.C.S.: 541613
Jeff Walcoff *(Owner & Specialist-Mktg & Dev)*

Affiliate (US):

JELD-WEN Holding, Inc. (2)
2645 Silver Crescent Dr, Charlotte, NC 28273
Tel.: (704) 378-5700
Web Site: https://www.jeld-wen.com
Rev.: $5,129,179,000
Assets: $3,501,361,000
Liabilities: $2,777,813,000
Net Worth: $723,548,000
Earnings: $45,727,000
Emp.: 23,400
Fiscal Year-end: 12/31/2022
Holding Company; Window & Door Mfr
N.A.I.C.S.: 551112
Mark Dixon *(Sr VP-Global Procurement)*

Subsidiary (Domestic):

American Building Supply Inc. (3)
8360 Elder Creek Rd, Sacramento, CA 95828
Tel.: (916) 503-4100
Web Site: http://www.abs-abs.com
Construction Materials Mfr
N.A.I.C.S.: 423310

Subsidiary (Non-US):

Breezway Australia Pty Ltd (3)
35 Cambridge Street, Coorparoo, Brisbane, 4151, QLD, Australia
Tel.: (61) 7 3847 0500
Web Site: http://www.breezway.com
Metal Door & Window Mfr
N.A.I.C.S.: 332321

Subsidiary (Non-US):

Breezway (Malaysia) Sdn Bhd. (4)
No 39 Jalan Wawasan 3/KU 7, Sungai Kapar Indah, 42200, Klang, Selangor Darul Ehsan, Malaysia
Tel.: (60) 3 3291 4885

Web Site: http://www.breezway.com.my
Metal Door & Window Distr
N.A.I.C.S.: 423220
Karen Law *(Mgr-Comm)*

Subsidiary (US):

Breezway North Amercia (4)
99-1451 Koaha Pl Ste 1, Aiea, HI 96701
Tel.: (808) 484-5999
Web Site: http://www.breezway.com
Emp.: 9
Metal Door & Window Distr
N.A.I.C.S.: 423220
Darryl Demello *(Gen Mgr)*

Subsidiary (Non-US):

JELD-WEN A/S (3)
Danmarksvej 9, 9670, Logstor, Denmark
Tel.: (45) 96 66 22 11
Web Site: http://www.jeld-wen.biz
Sales Range: $50-74.9 Million
Emp.: 23
Wood Window & Door Mfr
N.A.I.C.S.: 321911

JELD-WEN Deutschland GmbH & Co. KG (3)
Barmbeker Strasse 4a, 22303, Hamburg, Germany
Tel.: (49) 40 854 09 0
Web Site: http://www.kilsgaard.de
Wood Door Mfr
N.A.I.C.S.: 321911

JELD-WEN Eesti AS (3)
Arkna Tee 1, EE-44317, Rakvere, Estonia
Tel.: (372) 3229 130
Web Site: http://www.jeld-wen.biz
Sales Range: $200-249.9 Million
Emp.: 700
Wooden Window & Door Mfr
N.A.I.C.S.: 321911
Keijo Erkheikki *(Mng Dir)*

JELD-WEN France S.A.S (3)
35 Avenue de la Tenareze, 32800, Eauze, France
Tel.: (33) 562 08 1010
Web Site: http://www.jeld-wen.fr
Emp.: 500
Wood Door Mfr
N.A.I.C.S.: 321911
Peter Maxwell *(Gen Mgr)*

JELD-WEN Latvija SIA (3)
Rupniecibas Iela 13, Aizkraukle, 5010, Latvia
Tel.: (371) 651 21623
Emp.: 10
Wood Window & Door Mfr
N.A.I.C.S.: 321911
Same Leananen *(Gen Mgr)*

JELD-WEN Magyarorszag Kft. (3)
Gyar u 4, 8961, Lenti, Hungary
Tel.: (36) 92 551 920
Emp.: 120
Wood Window & Door Mfr
N.A.I.C.S.: 321911
Bernd Kressmann *(Gen Mgr)*

JELD-WEN Norge AS (3)
Gjerdrumsvei 10 D, PO Box 4443, 402, Oslo, Norway
Tel.: (47) 22 02 72 00
Wood Window & Door Mfr
N.A.I.C.S.: 321911

JELD-WEN Polska Sp. z.o.o. (3)
ul Konduktorska 39 B, 40-155, Katowice, Poland
Tel.: (48) 32 781 21 20
Wood Window & Door Mfr
N.A.I.C.S.: 321911

JELD-WEN Suomi Oy (3)
Jyvaskylantie 288, PO Box 300, 17201, Vaaksy, Finland
Tel.: (358) 201 100 200
Sales Range: $125-149.9 Million
Emp.: 30
Wood Window & Door Mfr
N.A.I.C.S.: 321911

JELD-WEN Turen GmbH (3)
Gleinkerau 70, 4582, Spital am Pyhrn, Austria
Tel.: (43) 7562 5522 0

Sales Range: $250-299.9 Million
Emp.: 55
Wood Window & Door Distr
N.A.I.C.S.: 423310
Horst Kogl *(Mgr-Sls & Mktg)*

JELD-WEN UK LTD. (3)
Retford Road Woodhouse Mill, Sheffield, S13 9WH, S Yorkshire, United Kingdom
Tel.: (44) 114 254 2000
Web Site: http://www.jeld-wen.co.uk
Sales Range: $125-149.9 Million
Emp.: 45
Wood Window & Door Mfr
N.A.I.C.S.: 321911

JELD-WEN of Canada Ltd. (3)
485 Watt Street, Winnipeg, R2K 2R9, MB, Canada
Tel.: (204) 694-6012
Web Site: http://en.jeld-wen.ca
Sales Range: $25-49.9 Million
Emp.: 25
Wood Window & Door Mfr
N.A.I.C.S.: 321911

Plant (Domestic):

JELD-WEN of Canada Ltd. - Saint Apollinaire Window Plant (4)
90 Rue Industrielle, Saint-Apollinaire, G0S 2E0, QC, Canada
Tel.: (418) 881-3974
Web Site: http://en.jeld-wen.ca
Wood Window & Door Mfr
N.A.I.C.S.: 321911

JELD-WEN of Canada Ltd. - Saint-Henri Door Plant (4)
115 Rue De La Gare, Saint-Henri-de-Levis, G0R 3E0, QC, Canada
Tel.: (418) 882-2223
Web Site: http://www.en.jeld-wen.ca
Wood Window & Door Mfr
N.A.I.C.S.: 321911

JELD-WEN of Canada Ltd. - Toronto Window Plant (4)
90 Stone Ridge Road, Vaughan, L4H 3G9, ON, Canada
Tel.: (905) 265-5700
Wood Window & Door Mfr
N.A.I.C.S.: 321911
Carlos Domingues *(Gen Mgr)*

JELD-WEN of Canada Ltd. - Winnipeg Window Plant (4)
550 Munro Avenue, Winnipeg, R2K 4H3, MB, Canada
Tel.: (204) 668-8230
Wood Window & Door Mfr
N.A.I.C.S.: 321911

Subsidiary (Domestic):

JELD-WEN, Inc. (3)
401 Harbor Isles Blvd, Klamath Falls, OR 97601
Tel.: (541) 882-3451
Web Site: http://www.jeld-wen.com
Sales Range: $1-4.9 Billion
Emp.: 20,000
Windows, Doors, Millwork, Building Products, Metal Doors, Wood Pallets, Sash & Trim Mfr & Distr
N.A.I.C.S.: 321999

Subsidiary (Domestic):

Craftmaster Manufacturing, Inc. (4)
500 W Monroe St Ste 2010, Chicago, IL 60661
Tel.: (312) 382-8701
Web Site: http://www.cmicompany.com
Sales Range: $150-199.9 Million
Emp.: 650
Wood Door & Window Mfr
N.A.I.C.S.: 321911

Plant (Domestic):

JELD-WEN, Inc. Hawkins (4)
811 Factory St, Hawkins, WI 54530
Tel.: (715) 585-6311
Web Site: http://www.jeldwen.com
Sales Range: $100-124.9 Million
Emp.: 360
Vinyl & Wood Windows Mfr
N.A.I.C.S.: 321911

JELD-WEN, Inc. - Plymouth (4)

ONEX CORPORATION

541 N Oak Dr, Plymouth, IN 46563
Web Site: http://www.jeld-wen.com
Sales Range: $25-49.9 Million
Emp.: 160
Wood Door Mfr
N.A.I.C.S.: 321911

Subsidiary (Domestic):

Karona, Inc. (4)
4100 Karona Ct, Caledonia, MI 49316
Tel.: (616) 554-3551
Web Site: http://www.karonadoor.com
Sales Range: $1-9.9 Million
Emp.: 150
Millwork Mfr
N.A.I.C.S.: 321918

Subsidiary (Domestic):

Milliken Millwork Inc. (3)
6361 Sterling Dr N, Sterling Heights, MI 48312
Tel.: (586) 722-0104
Web Site: http://www.mmidoor.com
Lumber, Plywood & Millwork Supplier
N.A.I.C.S.: 423310

Joint Venture (US):

PowerSchool Group LLC (2)
150 Parkshore Dr, Folsom, CA 95630
Web Site: http://www.powerschool.com
Assessment Tools & Student Information Systems Solutions
N.A.I.C.S.: 611710
Rich Gay *(Chief Information Security Officer & VP-Dev)*

Subsidiary (Domestic):

PeopleAdmin, Inc. (3)
805 Las Cimas Pkwy Ste 400, Austin, TX 78746
Web Site: http://www.peopleadmin.com
Human Resource Software for Schools & Government Agencies
N.A.I.C.S.: 334610
Tony Montoya *(VP-Sls)*

Holding (Non-US):

SIG Combibloc Group Ltd. (2)
Laufengasse 18, CH 8212, Neuhausen, Rheinefall, Switzerland
Tel.: (41) 526746111
Web Site: http://www.sig.biz
Emp.: 5,000
Packaging Systems Mfr
N.A.I.C.S.: 333993
Rolf Stangl *(CEO)*

Subsidiary (Non-US):

SIG Combibloc France (3)
1 rue d'Anjou, 92604, Asnieres, France
Tel.: (33) 141114242
Web Site: http://www.sig.biz
Packaging Systems & Products Mfr
N.A.I.C.S.: 333993
Victor Cordoba *(Head-Cluster)*

SIG Combibloc GmbH (3)
Rurstrasse 58, 52441, Linnich, Germany
Tel.: (49) 2462790
Web Site: http://www.sig.biz
Aseptic Packaging Systems & Products Mfr
N.A.I.C.S.: 561910

SIG Combibloc S.A. (3)
Calle de Valportillo II n 14 2 planta, 28108, Alcobendas, Madrid, Spain
Tel.: (34) 914841330
Web Site: http://www.sig.biz
Packaging Products & Systems Mfr
N.A.I.C.S.: 333993

SIG Combibloc S.r.l. (3)
Viale Mentana 45, 43121, Parma, Italy
Tel.: (39) 0521 270 791
Web Site: http://www.sig.biz
Packaging Systems Mfr
N.A.I.C.S.: 333993

SIG Combibloc Taiwan Ltd. (3)
4F-3 37 Zhongyang S Rd Sec 2, Beitou District, 11270, Taipei, Taiwan
Tel.: (886) 228976000
Web Site: http://www.sig.biz
Emp.: 20

ONEX CORPORATION

ONEX Corporation—(Continued)
Food & Beverages Packaging Products & Machines Mfr & Distr
N.A.I.C.S.: 333993

Holding (US):

Spirit AeroSystems Holdings, Inc. (2)
3801 S Oliver, Wichita, KS 67210 (73%)
Tel.: (316) 526-9000
Web Site: https://www.spiritaero.com
Rev.: $6,047,900,000
Assets: $6,950,100,000
Liabilities: $7,446,000,000
Net Worth: ($495,900,000)
Earnings: ($616,200,000)
Emp.: 20,655
Fiscal Year-end: 12/31/2023
Aerostructures OEM Designer & Mfr
N.A.I.C.S.: 336411
Patrick M. Shanahan *(Pres & CEO)*

Subsidiary (Domestic):

Spirit AeroSystems Finance, Inc. (3)
3801 S Oliver St, Wichita, KS 67210
Tel.: (316) 526-9000
Financial Management Services
N.A.I.C.S.: 523999

Spirit AeroSystems, Inc. (3)
3801 S Oliver St, Wichita, KS 67210-2112 (89.6%)
Tel.: (316) 526-9000
Web Site: http://www.spiritaero.com
Sales Range: $1-9.9 Million
Emp.: 10,500
Commercial Aircraft Equipment & Structures Mfr
N.A.I.C.S.: 336413
Stacy Cozad *(Chief Compliance Officer & Sr VP)*

Subsidiary (Non-US):

Spirit AeroSystems (Europe) Limited (4)
Building 90 Prestwick International Airport, Prestwick, KA9 2RW, United Kingdom
Tel.: (44) 12 9247 9888
Emp.: 3,000
Aerospace Component Distr
N.A.I.C.S.: 423860
John Kelly *(Mgr-Ops)*

Subsidiary (Domestic):

Spirit AeroSystems International Holdings, Inc. (4)
3801 S Oliver St, Wichita, KS 67210
Tel.: (316) 526-9000
Web Site: http://www.spiritaero.com
Investment Management Service
N.A.I.C.S.: 551112
Larry A. Lawson *(CEO)*

Subsidiary (Non-US):

Spirit AeroSystems Malaysia Sdn Bhd (4)
Lot 1210 Section U3 Malaysia International Aerospace Centre, Subang Jaya, 40150, Selangor, Malaysia
Tel.: (60) 378419000
Emp.: 600
Well Drilling Equipment Distr
N.A.I.C.S.: 423810
Eiko Abe *(Mng Dir)*

Subsidiary (Domestic):

Spirit AeroSystems North Carolina, Inc. (4)
2600 Aerosystems Blvd, Kinston, NC 28504-7356
Tel.: (252) 208-4645
Aircraft Equipment Distr
N.A.I.C.S.: 423860

Spirit AeroSystems Operations International, Inc. (4)
3801 S Oliver St, Wichita, KS 67210
Tel.: (316) 526-9000
Aircraft Equipment Distr
N.A.I.C.S.: 423860

Subsidiary (Non-US):

Spirit AeroSystems Singapore Pte. Ltd. (4)
392 Havelock Road 03-12 / 14, Singapore, 169663, Singapore
Tel.: (65) 6737 0512
Web Site: http://www.spiritaero.com
Aircraft Component Distr
N.A.I.C.S.: 423860

Subsidiary (Domestic):

Spirit Defense, Inc. (4)
3801 S Olive St, Wichita, KS 67210-2112
Tel.: (316) 523-8840
Financial Management Services
N.A.I.C.S.: 523999

Holding (Non-US):

Survitec Group Limited (2)
1-5 Beaufort Road Birkenhead, Birkenhead, CH41 1HQ, England, United Kingdom
Tel.: (44) 2890301531
Web Site: http://www.survitecgroup.com
Sales Range: $350-399.9 Million
Emp.: 2,000
Safety & Survival Equipment Designer, Mfr, Distr & Servicer
N.A.I.C.S.: 336612
Chris Bates *(CFO)*

Unit (Domestic):

Crewsaver (3)
Survitec House Lederle Lane, Gosport, PO13 0FZ, Hants, United Kingdom
Tel.: (44) 1329 820 000
Web Site: http://www.crewsaver.co.uk
Marine Safety Equipment Mfr & Distr
N.A.I.C.S.: 339999

Subsidiary (Non-US):

DBC Marine Safety Systems Ltd. (3)
1689 Cliveden Avenue, Delta, V3M 6V5, BC, Canada
Tel.: (604) 278-3221
Web Site: https://www.dbcmarine.com
Liferaft & Marine Passenger Evacuation Systems Mfr & Whslr
N.A.I.C.S.: 339920

Deutsche Schlauchboot GmbH & Co. KG (3)
Angerweg 5, Eschershausen, 37632, Germany
Tel.: (49) 55343010
Web Site: http://survitecgroup.com
Inflatable Boat Mfr
N.A.I.C.S.: 336612

Eurovinil S.p.A (3)
Via Genova 5, 58100, Grosseto, Italy
Tel.: (39) 0564 487300
Web Site: http://www.eurovinil.it
Inflatable Safety & Survival Equipment Mfr
N.A.I.C.S.: 336612

RFD New Zealand Limited (3)
30 Hargreaves St, Ponsonby, Auckland, 1140, New Zealand
Tel.: (64) 93732019
Web Site: http://www.rfd.nz
Emp.: 15
Marine Safety Equipment Mfr
N.A.I.C.S.: 336612

Subsidiary (Domestic):

Survitec Service & Distribution Limited (3)
1-5 Beaufort Road, Merseyside, Birkenhead, CH41 1HQ, England, United Kingdom
Tel.: (44) 0151 670 9009
Web Site: http://survitecgroup.com
Marine Safety, Rope, Rigging, Lifting & Fire Fighting Equipment Mfr & Distr
N.A.I.C.S.: 423490

Subsidiary (Non-US):

Survitec Service & Distribution B.V. (4)
Sheffieldstraat 89, 3047 AN, Rotterdam, Netherlands
Tel.: (31) 10 2380380
Web Site: http://survitecgroup.com
Emp.: 15
Marine Safety Equipment Distr
N.A.I.C.S.: 423490

Survitec Service & Distribution GmbH (4)
Winsbergring 8, Hamburg, 22525, Germany
Tel.: (49) 406750960
Web Site: http://survitecgroup.com
Emp.: 25
Industrial Marine Safety Equipment Distr
N.A.I.C.S.: 423490

Survitec Service & Distribution N.V. (4)
Vosseschynstraat 44, 2030, Antwerp, Belgium
Tel.: (32) 3 213 86 70
Web Site: http://survitecgroup.com
Emp.: 27
Industrial Marine Safety Equipment Distr
N.A.I.C.S.: 423490

Subsidiary (Domestic):

Survival-One Limited (3)
Kirkton Dr Tyce, Aberdeen, AB21 OBG, United Kingdom
Tel.: (44) 1224214444
Web Site: http://www.survitecgroup.com
Emp.: 200
Survival Equipment Rental, Servicing & Repair
N.A.I.C.S.: 213112

Holding (Non-US):

Tes Global Limited (2)
26 Red Lion Square, London, WC1R4HQ, United Kingdom
Tel.: (44) 2031943000
Web Site: http://www.tsleducation.com
Sales Range: $25-49.9 Million
Emp.: 250
Educational Support Services
N.A.I.C.S.: 611710
Louise Rogers *(CEO)*

Subsidiary (Non-US):

Schrole Group Limited (3)
First Floor 142 Hasler Road, Osborne Park, 6017, WA, Australia
Tel.: (61) 892307000
Web Site: https://www.schrole.com
Rev.: $3,901,489
Assets: $4,200,583
Liabilities: $2,623,970
Net Worth: $1,576,614
Earnings: ($1,205,736)
Fiscal Year-end: 12/31/2022
Portfolio Management & Investment Advice
N.A.I.C.S.: 523940
Robert Graham *(CEO & Mng Dir)*

Holding (Domestic):

WestJet Airlines Ltd. (2)
22 Aerial Place NE, Calgary, T2E 3J1, AB, Canada
Tel.: (403) 444-2600
Web Site: http://www.westjet.com
Rev.: $3,469,485,642
Assets: $4,953,451,573
Liabilities: $3,265,739,039
Net Worth: $1,687,712,534
Earnings: $67,041,101
Emp.: 11,624
Fiscal Year-end: 12/31/2018
Oil Transportation Services
N.A.I.C.S.: 481111
Clive J. Beddoe *(Founder & Chm)*

Subsidiary (Domestic):

WestJet Vacations Inc. (3)
22 Aerial Place NE, Calgary, T2E 3J1, AB, Canada
Web Site: https://www.westjet.com
Passenger Air Transportation Services
N.A.I.C.S.: 481111

Holding (US):

WireCo WorldGroup Inc. (2)
2400 W 75th St, Prairie Village, KS 66208
Tel.: (816) 270-4700
Web Site: http://www.wireco.com
Steel Wire Rope, Wire Slings & Assemblies Mfr
N.A.I.C.S.: 332618
Richard Humiston *(VP-Sls)*

Subsidiary (Non-US):

Aceros Camesa, S.A. de C.V. (3)
Margarita Maza de Juarez 154, Col Nueva Industrial Vallejo, 07700, Mexico, DF, Mexico
Tel.: (52) 5557474700
Web Site: http://www.grupocamesa.com.mx
Steel Wire Rope & Electromechanical Cables Mfr
N.A.I.C.S.: 332618

Subsidiary (US):

Camesa, Inc. (4)
1615 Spur 529, Rosenberg, TX 77471
Tel.: (281) 342-4494
Web Site: http://www.camesawire.com
Electromechanical Steel Wire Cable Mfr
N.A.I.C.S.: 335929

Plant (Domestic):

WireCo WorldGroup (3)
24150 Oak Grove Ln, Sedalia, MO 65301-9540
Tel.: (660) 827-3131
Web Site: http://www.wireco.com
Steel Wire Rope & Wire Rope Slings Mfr
N.A.I.C.S.: 332618

WireCo WorldGroup (3)
601 Corporate Dr, Chillicothe, MO 64601
Tel.: (660) 646-3572
Web Site: http://www.wireco.com
Steel Wire Rope Mfr & Whslr
N.A.I.C.S.: 332618

WireCo WorldGroup (3)
12200 NW Ambassador Dr, Kansas City, MO 64163
Tel.: (816) 233-0287
Web Site: http://www.wireco.com
Steel Wire Rope Mfr
N.A.I.C.S.: 332618

Onex Real Estate Partners (1)
620 8th Ave 22nd Fl, New York, NY 10018
Tel.: (212) 755-8566
Web Site: http://www.onex.com
Sales Range: $50-74.9 Million
Emp.: 10
Real Estate Services
N.A.I.C.S.: 531210
Michael Dana *(Pres & CEO)*

Sport Supply Group, Inc. (1)
1901 Diplomat Dr, Dallas, TX 75234-8914 (62%)
Tel.: (972) 484-9484
Web Site: http://www.sportsupplygroup.com
Sales Range: $250-299.9 Million
Emp.: 760
Sporting Goods, Equipment, Team Uniforms, Physical Education, Recreational & Leisure Products Marketer & Distr
N.A.I.C.S.: 423910

Subsidiary (Domestic):

Kesslers Sport Shop Inc. (2)
930 E Main St, Richmond, IN 47374
Tel.: (765) 935-2595
Web Site: http://www.kesslersteamsports.com
Sales Range: $10-24.9 Million
Emp.: 200
Sporting Goods Retailer
N.A.I.C.S.: 459110
Phil Dickman *(Pres)*

VPI Quality Windows, Inc. (1)
3420 East Ferry Ave, Spokane, WA 99202
Web Site: http://www.vpiwindows.com
Emp.: 7
Metal Window & Door Mfr
N.A.I.C.S.: 332321

ONEX CORPORATION
3012-3 Uenohara Kamiechi, Atsugi, 243-0801, Kanagawa, Japan
Tel.: (81) 462850600 JP
Web Site: https://www.onex.co.jp
Year Founded: 1951
5987—(TKS)
Rev.: $30,894,740
Assets: $55,270,920
Liabilities: $22,454,200
Net Worth: $32,816,720
Earnings: ($2,344,940)
Emp.: 207
Fiscal Year-end: 06/30/24

AND PRIVATE COMPANIES

Metal Material Mfr
N.A.I.C.S.: 332811
Kazuo Oya *(Pres)*

Subsidiaries:

ONEX Corporation - Higashi Matsuyama Plant (1)
88-23 Shingo, Higashimatsuyama, 355-0071, Saitama, Japan
Tel.: (81) 493242931
Metal Heat Treatment Services
N.A.I.C.S.: 332811

ONEX Corporation - Nagano Plant (1)
2416-10 Fujiyama, Ueda, 386-1212, Nagano, Japan
Tel.: (81) 268388010
Metal Heat Treatment Services
N.A.I.C.S.: 332811

ONEX Corporation - Yamaguchi Plant (1)
1366-2 Yamanoi, Sanyo-Onoda, 757-0003, Yamaguchi, Japan
Tel.: (81) 836731311
Metal Heat Treatment Services
N.A.I.C.S.: 332811

Onex Technology Center Co., Ltd. (1)
60-28 Shirakicho, Kameyama, 519-0169, Mie, Japan
Tel.: (81) 595973270
Web Site: https://www.onex-tec.jp
Metal Heat Treatment Services
N.A.I.C.S.: 332811

ONEXIM GROUP LIMITED
13/1 Tverskoy Blvd, 123104, Moscow, Russia
Tel.: (7) 4952292939
Web Site: http://www.onexim.org
Year Founded: 2007
Sales Range: $25-49.9 Million
Emp.: 100
Investment Management Service
N.A.I.C.S.: 523940
Mikhail Dmitrievich Prokhorov *(Founder)*

Subsidiaries:

Brooklyn Nets (1)
15 MetroTech Ctr 11th Fl, Brooklyn, NY 11201 (51%)
Tel.: (718) 933-3000
Sales Range: $75-99.9 Million
Professional Basketball Team
N.A.I.C.S.: 711211
Leo Ehrlire *(Chief Admin Officer, Chief Relationship Officer & Exec VP)*

Unit (Domestic):

Barclays Center (2)
620 Atlantic Ave, Brooklyn, NY 11217
Tel.: (917) 618-6100
Web Site: http://www.barclayscenter.com
Emp.: 25
Sports & Entertainment Arena Operator
N.A.I.C.S.: 711310

JSC OPIN (1)
13 Tverskoy Boulevard Bldg 1, 123104, Moscow, Russia (83.17%)
Tel.: (7) 495 363 14 57 58
Web Site: http://www.opin.ru
Sales Range: Less than $1 Million
Real Estate Development Services
N.A.I.C.S.: 531390

Subsidiary (Domestic):

Agroprom LLC (2)
ul Sovetskaya d 191, 392000, Tambov, Russia
Tel.: (7) 4752 63 35 07
Vegetable & Fruit Distr
N.A.I.C.S.: 424180

Agrosistema LLC (2)
ul Yuzhnaya d 25, 350007, Krasnodar, Russia
Tel.: (7) 918 255 19 05
Agricultural Machinery & Equipment Distr
N.A.I.C.S.: 423820

Militta LLC (2)
ul Tayginskaya d 6, Novosibirsk, Russia
Tel.: (7) 383 215 00 12
Furniture Distr
N.A.I.C.S.: 423210

Ostara LLC (2)
ul Lenina d 94 kv 81, 636000, Seversk, Tomskaya, Russia
Tel.: (7) 3823 56 84 53
Apparel Whslr
N.A.I.C.S.: 458110

Pestovo LLC (2)
rp Selizharovo ul selskaya d 8, 172200, Tverskaya, Russia
Tel.: (7) 909 931 34 62
Mining Equipment Distr
N.A.I.C.S.: 423810

Proekt Stroy LLC (2)
ul 50 LET Oktyabrya d 62A korp 2, 625023, Tyumen, Russia
Tel.: (7) 3452 69 54 43
Oil & Gas Transportation Services
N.A.I.C.S.: 486210

RozInvest LLC (2)
ul Navaginskaya d 14, Krasnodar Krai, 354000, Sochi, Russia
Tel.: (7) 8622 60 85 10
Leasing Services
N.A.I.C.S.: 533110

Russkaya zemlya LLC (2)
Kuznetskiy Most st 21/5 office 600, 107996, Moscow, Russia
Tel.: (7) 4956260727
Web Site: http://www.rz-agro.com
Emp.: 1,000
Investment Management Service
N.A.I.C.S.: 523940
Stehanie MacFarlane *(Gen Mgr)*

Tanais LLC (2)
ul Novorossyskaya d 61, 400087, Volgograd, Russia
Tel.: (7) 905 333 94 80
Food Products Distr
N.A.I.C.S.: 424490

Veres LLC (2)
Myasnitskaya ul d 22/2/5 str 1 AB, Moscow, 101000, Russia
Tel.: (7) 495 233 17 65
Home Management Services
N.A.I.C.S.: 721110

JSCB International Financial Club JSC (1)
Presnenskaya Nab 10, 123112, Moscow, Russia
Tel.: (7) 4952870260
Web Site: http://www.mfk-bank.ru
Financial Insurance Services
N.A.I.C.S.: 524210
Nikolay Evtikhiev *(Mng Dir-Fin Markets Transactions)*

Renaissance Capital Holdings Limited (1)
Naberezhnaya Tower block C 10 Presnenskaya nab, 123112, Moscow, Russia
Tel.: (7) 4952587777
Web Site: http://www.rencap.com
Sales Range: $250-299.9 Million
Emp.: 500
Investment Banking, Merchant Banking & Asset Management Services
N.A.I.C.S.: 523150
Christophe Francois Charlier *(Chm)*

SOGLASIE Insurance Company Ltd. (1)
bld 42 Gilyarovskogo str, 129110, Moscow, Russia
Tel.: (7) 4957390101
Web Site: http://www.soglasie.ru
General Insurance Services
N.A.I.C.S.: 524210

ONFIDO LTD
14-18 Finsbury Square, London, EC2A 1AH, United Kingdom
Tel.: (44) 2081525321
Web Site: https://onfido.com
Identity Verification & IT Consulting Services
N.A.I.C.S.: 518210

Mike Tuchen *(CEO)*

Subsidiaries:

Airside Mobile Inc. (1)
1545 22nd St N, Arlington, VA 22201
Tel.: (202) 253-2301
Web Site: http://www.airsidemobile.com
Software Publisher
N.A.I.C.S.: 513210
Adam Tsao *(COO)*

ONI HOLDINGS AD
103 James Bourchier Blvd 1st floor, 1407, Sofia, Bulgaria
Tel.: (359) 2 962 14 88
Web Site: http://www.oni.gr
Sales Range: Less than $1 Million
Pharmaceuticals Mfr
N.A.I.C.S.: 325412

ONION GLOBAL LIMITED
No 309 3-05 Huangfu Avenue Zhong, Tianhe District, Guangzhou, Guangdong, China
Tel.: (86) 203 826 2863 Ky
Year Founded: 2018
OG—(NYSE)
Rev.: $391,735,908
Assets: $224,169,518
Liabilities: $72,205,422
Net Worth: $151,964,096
Earnings: ($54,576,007)
Emp.: 855
Fiscal Year-end: 12/31/21
Holding Company
N.A.I.C.S.: 551112
Cong Li *(CEO)*

ONIVA ONLINE GROUP EUROPE AB
Gustavslundsvagen 151G, 167 51, Stockholm, Sweden
Tel.: (46) 8320360
Web Site: https://binero.com
Year Founded: 1999
Sales Range: $10-24.9 Million
Emp.: 130
Internet Marketing & Search Engine Optimization Services
N.A.I.C.S.: 541890
Thomas Broberger *(CEO)*

Subsidiaries:

Digital Next (1)
Gold 157 The Sharp Project Thorp Road, Manchester, M40 5BJ, United Kingdom (51%)
Tel.: (44) 845 539 0642
Web Site: http://www.digitalnext.co.uk
Emp.: 40
Digital Advertising Agency
N.A.I.C.S.: 541810
Justin Blackhurst *(Co-Founder)*

Getupdated Sverige AB (1)
Brahegatan 10, 114 37, Stockholm, Sweden
Tel.: (46) 8 410 96100
Web Site: http://www.getupdated.se
Internet Advertising Services
N.A.I.C.S.: 541810

Just Search Italia S.R.L (1)
Via Tirone 11, Rome, Italy
Tel.: (39) 0645213326
Web Site: http://www.justsearch.it
Search Engine Operators
N.A.I.C.S.: 519290

Justsearch Ireland Limited (1)
Unit 3 Grand Canal Wharf Grand Canal Dock, Ringsend, Dublin, Ireland
Tel.: (353) 16349660
Web Site: http://www.justsearch.ie
Search Engine Operators
N.A.I.C.S.: 519290

S.A.R.L Just Search (1)
42 Boulevard De Sebastopol, Paris, 75003, France
Tel.: (33) 175438078
Web Site: http://www.justsearch.fr
Search Engine Optimization Services

N.A.I.C.S.: 519290

The Interactive Circuit in Stockholm AB (1)
Brahegatan 10, 114 37, Stockholm, Sweden
Tel.: (46) 8 410 96 200
Web Site: http://www.circuit.se
Digital Marketing Services
N.A.I.C.S.: 541613

ONKYO HOME ENTERTAINMENT CORP.
Kitahama Chuo Bldg 2-2-22 Kitahama, Chuo-ku, Osaka, 541-0041, Japan
Tel.: (81) 662267343
Web Site: http://www.onkyo.com
6628—(TKS)
Rev.: $199,979,360
Assets: $89,765,130
Liabilities: $120,530,480
Net Worth: ($30,765,350)
Earnings: ($90,599,600)
Emp.: 400
Fiscal Year-end: 03/31/20
Audio Equipment & Speakers Mfr & Sales
N.A.I.C.S.: 334310
Munenori Ohtsuki *(Pres & CEO)*

Subsidiaries:

Onkyo U.S.A. Corporation (1)
38701 7 Mile Rd, Livonia, MI 48152
Tel.: (734) 293-0530
Sales Range: $1-9.9 Million
Emp.: 38
Audio & Video Equipment Mfr
N.A.I.C.S.: 334310

ONLINE BLOCKCHAIN PLC
Suite 27 Essex Technology Centre, The Gables Fyfield Road, Ongar, CM5 0GA, Essex, United Kingdom
Tel.: (44) 2070700961
Web Site: http://www.onlineblockchain.io
Year Founded: 1989
OBC—(AIM)
Rev.: $145,276
Assets: $2,624,473
Liabilities: $40,732
Net Worth: $2,583,741
Earnings: ($1,382,159)
Emp.: 4
Fiscal Year-end: 06/30/22
Holding Company; Internet Content Development Services
N.A.I.C.S.: 551112
Jonathan B. Mullins *(Dir-Technical)*

ONLINE BRANDS NORDIC AB
Exportgatan 28, Blekinge County Soelvesborg, 422 46, Hisings Backa, Sweden
Tel.: (46) 313202200
Web Site: https://onlinebrands.se
OBAB—(OMX)
Rev.: $26,872,536
Assets: $27,545,965
Liabilities: $12,486,068
Net Worth: $15,059,897
Earnings: ($1,714,013)
Emp.: 2
Fiscal Year-end: 12/31/22
Online Shopping Retailer
N.A.I.C.S.: 423620
Magnus Skoglund *(CEO)*

ONLINE MARKETING SOLUTIONS AG
Niederurseler Allee 8-10, 65760, Eschborn, Germany
Tel.: (49) 6196 7808 00 De
Web Site: http://www.omsag.de
Year Founded: 2004
Marketing & Search Engine Optimization Services
N.A.I.C.S.: 541613

ONLINEFORMAPRO S.A.

Onlineformapro S.A.—(Continued)

ONLINEFORMAPRO S.A.
Espace de la Motte, 70000, Vesoul, France
Tel.: (33) 384765244
Web Site:
https://www.onlineformapro.com
Year Founded: 1999
MLONL—(EUR)
Sales Range: $1-9.9 Million
Emp.: 40
Online Training & Education
N.A.I.C.S.: 611430
Michele Guerrin *(Chm & CEO)*

ONLY CORPORATION
6F TFT Bldg Tokan 3-6-11 Ariake, Kyoto, 600-8427, Japan
Tel.: (81) 753544129
Web Site: http://www.only.co.jp
Year Founded: 1976
3376—(TKS)
Rev.: $45,292,720
Assets: $86,103,600
Liabilities: $21,460,560
Net Worth: $64,643,040
Earnings: ($309,760)
Emp.: 329
Fiscal Year-end: 08/31/21
Apparel Product Mfr & Whslr
N.A.I.C.S.: 315250
Koichi Nakanishi *(Chm)*

ONLY WORLD GROUP HOLDINGS BERHAD
No 10 Jalan Pelukis U1/46 Section U1 Temasya Industrial Park, Glenmarie, 40150, Shah Alam, 40150, Selangor Darul Ehsan, Malaysia
Tel.: (60) 355668000
Web Site: https://www.owg.com.my
Year Founded: 1973
OWG—(KLS)
Rev.: $15,607,697
Assets: $95,336,736
Liabilities: $45,930,884
Net Worth: $49,405,851
Earnings: ($3,819,175)
Fiscal Year-end: 06/30/22
Investment Holding Company; Leisure, Entertainment & Hospitality Management
N.A.I.C.S.: 551112
Richard Cheng Keong Koh *(Founder, CEO-Grp & Mng Dir)*

Subsidiaries:

Tower Club Penang Berhad (1)
Level 67 No 1 Jalan Penang, 10000, George Town, Penang, Malaysia
Tel.: (60) 43759898
Web Site:
https://www.towerclubpenang.com
Dining & Entertainment Services
N.A.I.C.S.: 722310

ONMOBILE GLOBAL LIMITED
Tower 1 94/1C and 94/2 Veerasandra Village Attibele Hobli, Anekal Taluk Electronic City Phase-1, Bengaluru, 560100, Karnataka, India
Tel.: (91) 8040096000
Web Site: https://www.onmobile.com
ONMOBILE—(NSE)
Rev.: $76,625,367
Assets: $123,703,262
Liabilities: $38,240,066
Net Worth: $85,463,196
Earnings: $6,277,089
Emp.: 686
Fiscal Year-end: 03/31/21
Products & Services for Mobile, Landline & Media Service Providers
N.A.I.C.S.: 517810
Sanjay Bhambri *(Pres & COO)*

Subsidiaries:

OnMobile Bangladesh Private Limited (1)
Star Center Plot SE C 2 Road 138 4th floor Gulshan Avenue Gulshan-1, Dhaka, 1212, Bangladesh
Tel.: (880) 29882691
Products & Services for Mobile, Landline & Media Service Providers
N.A.I.C.S.: 517810

OnMobile Global Limited - Australia (1)
Level 34 100 Miller Street, North Sydney, 2060, NSW, Australia
Tel.: (61) 2 9657 1342
Telecommunication Servicesb
N.A.I.C.S.: 517112
Brody Kenrick *(Dir-R&D)*

OnMobile Global S.A. (1)
Av Pte Roque Saenz Pena 788 Piso 9, C1035AAP, Buenos Aires, Argentina
Tel.: (54) 1143948091
Web Site: http://www.onmobile.com/Mobile, Landline & Media Services
N.A.I.C.S.: 517112

OnMobile Global Solutions Canada Limited (1)
460 McGill Street Suite 500, Montreal, H2Y 2H2, QC, Canada
Tel.: (514) 834-3571
Products & Services for Mobile, Landline & Media Service Providers
N.A.I.C.S.: 517810

OnMobile Live Inc. (1)
One Monarch Dr, Littleton, MA 01460
Tel.: (978) 742-3100
Web Site: http://www.livewiremobile.com
Sales Range: $10-24.9 Million
Emp.: 168
Technology-Leading Systems & System Building Blocks Designer for Voice, Video & Data Services on Wireless & Wireline Networks
N.A.I.C.S.: 334290
Dean Foulis *(CTO)*

OnMobile S.A. (1)
6 rue Duret, 75116, Paris, France
Tel.: (33) 173442722
Web Site: http://www.onmobile.com
Sales Range: $25-49.9 Million
Emp.: 40
Speech Recognition Software Development Services
N.A.I.C.S.: 513210

OnMobile Servicios Corporativos De Telefonia S.A. DE C.V. (1)
Av Santa Fe Torre A Piso 8, Col Zedec Santa Fe, Mexico, 01210, DF, Mexico
Tel.: (52) 305 716 4139
Products & Services for Mobile, Landline & Media Service Providers
N.A.I.C.S.: 517112

OnMobile Singapore Pte. Ltd (1)
78 Shenton Way 26-02A, Singapore, 079120, Singapore
Tel.: (65) 62234355
Products & Services for Mobile, Landline & Media Service Providers
N.A.I.C.S.: 517810

OnMobile USA LLC (1)
2222 Ponce De Leon Blvd, Miami, FL 33134
Tel.: (786) 309-2890
Products & Services for Mobile, Landline & Media Service Providers
N.A.I.C.S.: 517112

Branch (Domestic):

OnMobile USA (2)
5401 Old Redwood Hwy Ste 100, Petaluma, CA 94954
Tel.: (707) 792-3900
Sales Range: $25-49.9 Million
Emp.: 20
Mobile Video Infrastructure Solutions
N.A.I.C.S.: 513210

PT. OnMobile Indonesia (1)
Mayapada Tower 11th Floor Suite 01B Jl Jend Sudirman Kav 28, Jakarta, 12920, Indonesia
Tel.: (62) 21 5289 7330
Products & Services for Mobile, Landline & Media Service Providers
N.A.I.C.S.: 517810

ONO PHARMACEUTICAL CO., LTD.
8-2 Kyutaromachi 1-chome, Chuo-ku, Osaka, 541-8564, Japan
Tel.: (81) 662635670
Web Site: https://www.ono-pharma.com
Year Founded: 1717
OPHLF—(OTCIQ)
Rev.: $3,564,039,988
Assets: $6,478,079,717
Liabilities: $815,825,622
Net Worth: $5,662,254,095
Earnings: $907,381,246
Emp.: 3,853
Fiscal Year-end: 03/31/24
Pharmaceutical & Biotechnology Mfr
N.A.I.C.S.: 325414
Toichi Takino *(Sr Exec Officer & Exec Dir-Discovery & Res)*

Subsidiaries:

Bee Brand Medico Dental Co., Ltd. (1)
Nishiawaji 5-20-19 Yubinbango, Higashi-Yodogawa-ku, Osaka, 533-0031, Japan
Tel.: (81) 663704182
Web Site: http://www.bee.co.jp
Pharmaceuticals Product Mfr
N.A.I.C.S.: 325412

Deciphera Pharmaceuticals, Inc. (1)
200 Smith St, Waltham, MA 02451
Tel.: (781) 209-6400
Web Site: https://www.deciphera.com
Rev.: $163,356,000
Assets: $473,566,000
Liabilities: $122,650,000
Net Worth: $350,916,000
Earnings: ($194,942,000)
Emp.: 355
Fiscal Year-end: 12/31/2023
Biotechnology Research & Development Services
N.A.I.C.S.: 541714
Ron Squarer *(Chm)*

Namicos Corporation (1)
Lions Bldg Ohtemaye 8F 2-3-14 Uchihiranomachi, Chuo-ku, Osaka, 540-0037, Japan
Tel.: (81) 669449544
Web Site: http://www.namicos.co.jp
Sales Range: $50-74.9 Million
Emp.: 180
Packaging Materials Mfr
N.A.I.C.S.: 322220
Kazunori Ashida *(Pres)*

ONO Pharma Korea Co., Ltd. (1)
19th floor Yeoksam POSCO Tower 134 Teheran-ro, Gangnam-gu, Seoul, Korea (South)
Tel.: (82) 29288423
Web Site: http://www.onopharma.co.kr
Pharmaceuticals Product Mfr
N.A.I.C.S.: 325412

ONO Pharma Taiwan Co., Ltd. (1)
12F No 68 Sec 5 Zhongxiao E Rd, Xinyi Dist, Taipei, 110, Taiwan
Tel.: (886) 287869750
Pharmaceuticals Product Mfr
N.A.I.C.S.: 325412

Ono Pharma UK Ltd. (1)
Midcity Place 71 High Holborn London, London, W1H 7AA, United Kingdom
Tel.: (44) 20742149
Pharmaceuticals Product Mfr
N.A.I.C.S.: 325412

Ono Pharma USA, Inc. (1)
2000 Lenox Dr Ste 101, Lawrenceville, NJ 08648
Tel.: (609) 219-1010
Sales Range: $25-49.9 Million
Emp.: 30
Pharmaceutical & Biotechnology Mfr
N.A.I.C.S.: 325414
David R. Trexler *(Chief Comml Officer)*

Oriental Pharmaceutical & Synthetic Chemical Co., Ltd. (1)
2-1-5 Doshomachi, Chuo-ku, Osaka, 541-0045, Japan
Tel.: (81) 662311581
Pharmaceuticals Product Mfr
N.A.I.C.S.: 325412

Tokai Capsule Co., Ltd. (1)
Kuzawa 168, Fuji, 419-0202, Shizuoka, Japan
Tel.: (81) 545713488
Web Site: https://www.tokai-cap.co.jp
Sales Range: $50-74.9 Million
Emp.: 130
Capsules & Pharmaceutical Products Mfr
N.A.I.C.S.: 325998
Fumito Wakao *(Pres)*

ONO SOKKI CO., LTD.
12F Yokohama Connect Square 3-3-3 Minatomirai, Nishi-ku, Yokohama, 220-0012, Japan
Tel.: (81) 459353888
Web Site: https://www.onosokki.co.jp
Year Founded: 1954
6858—(TKS)
Rev.: $81,811,510
Assets: $148,911,270
Liabilities: $48,871,370
Net Worth: $100,039,900
Earnings: $3,105,420
Emp.: 596
Fiscal Year-end: 12/31/23
Measuring Equipment Mfr & Whslr
N.A.I.C.S.: 334515
Hitoshi Hamada *(Mng Exec Officer & Mng Exec Officer)*

Subsidiaries:

Ono Sokki (Thailand) Co., Ltd. (1)
1/293-4 Moo 9, T Bangphud, Pak Kret, 11120, Nonthaburi, Thailand
Tel.: (66) 2 584 6735
Web Site: https://www.onosokki.co.th
Measuring Instrument Mfr & Distr
N.A.I.C.S.: 334519
Kiyoshi Sato *(Mng Dir)*

Ono Sokki India Private Ltd. (1)
Plot No 20 Ground Floor Sector-3, IMT Manesar, Gurgaon, 122050, Haryana, India
Tel.: (91) 8047631493
Web Site: https://www.onosokki.in
Emp.: 25
Measuring Instruments Mfr
N.A.I.C.S.: 334519
Gireesh Nambiar *(Mgr)*

Ono Sokki Shanghai Technology Co., Ltd. (1)
Room 506 No 47 Zhengyi Road, Yangpu District, Shanghai, 200433, China
Tel.: (86) 2165032656
Web Site: https://www.onosokki-china.com
Measuring Instrument Distr
N.A.I.C.S.: 423830

Ono Sokki Technology Inc. (1)
2171 Executive Dr Ste 400, Addison, IL 60101
Tel.: (630) 627-9700
Web Site: http://www.onosokki.net
Emp.: 10
Measuring Instrument Mfr & Distr
N.A.I.C.S.: 334519

ONODERA GROUP CO., LTD.
16th Floor Ote Center Building 1-1-3 Otemachi, Chiyoda-ku, Tokyo, 100-0004, Japan
Tel.: (81) 352208550 JP
Web Site: https://www.onodera-group.jp
Year Founded: 1983
Emp.: 10,805
Restaurants & Food Chain Stores Operator
N.A.I.C.S.: 722511
Yuji Onodera *(CEO)*

AND PRIVATE COMPANIES / ONTARIO MUNICIPAL EMPLOYEES RETIREMENT SYSTEM

Subsidiaries:

Nadaman Co., Ltd. (1)
Asahi Group Calpis Ebisu Building 2F 2-4-1 Ebisu Minami, Shibuya-ku, Tokyo, 150-0022, Japan
Tel.: (81) 120635877
Web Site: https://www.nadaman.co.jp
Emp.: 1,300
Restaurant Services
N.A.I.C.S.: 722511
Kazutoshi Onuki (Pres)

ONOKEN CO., LTD.
12-1 Nishi-Minatomachi, Kokura Kita-ku, Kitakyushu, 803-0801, Japan
Tel.: (81) 935610036
Web Site: https://www.onoken.co.jp
Year Founded: 1949
7414—(FKA)
Rev.: $2,156,307,120
Assets: $1,650,130,240
Liabilities: $844,028,240
Net Worth: $806,102,000
Earnings: $78,843,600
Emp.: 618
Fiscal Year-end: 03/31/22
Steel Products Whslr
N.A.I.C.S.: 423510
Tetsuji Ono (Exec Mng Dir-Mgmt Control Div)

Subsidiaries:

Nishi-nippon Steel Center Co., Ltd. (1)
13-1 Nishiminato-cho, Kokurakita-ku, Kitakyushu, 803-0801, Fukuoka, Japan
Tel.: (81) 935812131
Web Site: https://www.s-center.co.jp
Emp.: 15
Steel Product Distr
N.A.I.C.S.: 423510

Onoken Okinawa Co., Ltd. (1)
8th floor Kokuba Building 3-21-1 Kumoji, Naha, 900-0015, Okinawa, Japan
Tel.: (81) 988609015
Emp.: 44
Steel Product Distr
N.A.I.C.S.: 423510

Sankyo Noritake Steel Co., Ltd. (1)
4-543-2 Miyakenishi, Matsubara-shi, Osaka, 580-0045, Japan
Tel.: (81) 72 332 5891
Steel Product Distr
N.A.I.C.S.: 423510
Daisuke Teramoto (Pres)

ONPRESS PCB LIMITED
9/F, Block B, Eldex Industrial Building, 21 Ma Tau Wai Road, Hung Hom,, Kowloon, China (Hong Kong)
Tel.: (852) 23428207
Web Site: https://www.onpress.com
Year Founded: 1987
Printed Circuit Board Mfr
N.A.I.C.S.: 334412

Subsidiaries:

Gainbase Industrial Limited (1)
No 3-4 6/F Worldwide Industrial Centre 43-47 Shan Mei Street, Fo Tan, Sha Tin, N T, China (Hong Kong)
Tel.: (852) 2 601 1286
Web Site: https://www.gainbase.com
Sales Range: $400-449.9 Million
Emp.: 1,800
Printed Circuit Board Mfr
N.A.I.C.S.: 334412

Plant (Non-US):

Gainbase Industrial Limited - China Factory (2)
Block No 3 Wan Le Road North Sha Jing Street, TongFuYu Industrial District Bao An Country, Shenzhen, China
Tel.: (86) 75527234702
Web Site: https://www.gainbase.com
Control Measuring Machine Mfr
N.A.I.C.S.: 334519

ONQUEST LABORATORIES LTD.
B2 1A Africa Avenue Road opp St Thomas Chruch, Safdarjung Enclave, New Delhi, 110029, India
Tel.: (91) 1130611432 67
Web Site: http://www.oncquest.net
Oncology & Pathology Services
N.A.I.C.S.: 621512
Ravinder Sethi (COO)

ONSITE ELECTRO SERVICES PVT. LTD.
Skyline Icon G-3A 86/92 Andheri - Kurla Rd, Chimatpada Marol Andheri East, Mumbai, 400059, India
Tel.: (91) 9920599206
Web Site: https://onsitego.com
Emp.: 100
Device Care Service Provider; Appliance Repair & Maintenance Services
N.A.I.C.S.: 811412

Subsidiaries:

Qdigi Services Limited (1)
B-1/I-1 1st Floor Mohan Cooperative Industrial Estate, New Delhi, 110044, India
Tel.: (91) 8005721144
Web Site: https://www.digicare.com
Gadgets, Appliances & Electronics Support Services
N.A.I.C.S.: 811412

ONTARIO DRIVE & GEAR LIMITED
3551 Bleams Rd, New Hamburg, N3A 2J1, ON, Canada
Tel.: (519) 662-2840
Web Site: https://www.odg.com
Year Founded: 1962
Precision Gears, Shafts & Power Transmission Parts Design & Mfr
N.A.I.C.S.: 333612
Stephen Brown (Mgr)

Subsidiaries:

ARGO (1)
220 Bergey Court, New Hamburg, N3A 2J5, ON, Canada
Tel.: (519) 662-2840
Web Site: https://www.argoxtv.com
All-Terrain Vehicle Mfr
N.A.I.C.S.: 441227
Brad Darling (Pres)

ONTARIO LOTTERY & GAMING CORPORATION
4120 Yonge Street Suite 500, Toronto, M2P 2B8, ON, Canada
Tel.: (416) 224-1772 ON
Web Site: http://www.olg.ca
Year Founded: 1975
Lottery, Casino & Related Gambling Operator
N.A.I.C.S.: 713290
Stephen Rigby (Pres & CEO)

ONTARIO MUNICIPAL EMPLOYEES RETIREMENT SYSTEM
EY Tower 900-100 Adelaide St W, Toronto, M5H 0E2, ON, Canada
Tel.: (416) 369-2400
Web Site: http://www.omers.com
Year Founded: 1962
Assets: $95,829,300,000
Liabilities: $13,240,089,000
Net Worth: $82,589,211,000
Earnings: $2,976,575,400
Emp.: 1,023
Fiscal Year-end: 12/31/20
Pension & Investment Services
N.A.I.C.S.: 525110
Jonathan Simmons (Chief Fin & Strategy Officer)

Subsidiaries:

OMERS Infrastructure Management Inc. (1)
EY Tower 900 - 100 Adelaide St W, Toronto, M5H 0E2, ON, Canada
Tel.: (416) 361-1011
Web Site: http://www.omersinfrastructure.com
Sales Range: $50-74.9 Million
Emp.: 50
Infrastructure Investment & Portfolio Management Services
N.A.I.C.S.: 523940
Jenine Krause (Mng Dir-Asset Mgmt)

Holding (Domestic):

407 International Inc. (2)
6300 Steeles Avenue West, Woodbridge, L4H 1J1, ON, Canada (50.1%)
Tel.: (905) 265-4070
Web Site: http://www.407etr.com
Sales Range: $300-349.9 Million
Emp.: 600
Toll Highway Operation, Management & Maintenance Services
N.A.I.C.S.: 488490

Joint Venture (Non-US):

Associated British Ports Holdings Ltd. (2)
25 Bedford Street, London, WC2E 9ES, United Kingdom (33.33%)
Tel.: (44) 2074301177
Web Site: https://www.abports.co.uk
Holding Company; Marine Ports Operator & Cargo Handling Activities
N.A.I.C.S.: 551112
Harm van Weezel (CIO)

Unit (Domestic):

ABP Ayr (3)
Port Office North Harbour Street, Ayr, KA8 8AH, United Kingdom
Tel.: (44) 1292281687
Sales Range: $100-124.9 Million
Emp.: 30
Marine Cargo Handling
N.A.I.C.S.: 488320

ABP Barrow (3)
Port Office Ramsey Way, Barrow-in-Furness, LA14 2GR, Cumbria, United Kingdom
Tel.: (44) 1229822911
Sales Range: $25-49.9 Million
Emp.: 30
Marine Cargo Handling Distr
N.A.I.C.S.: 488320
Paul Jervis (Mgr-Port)

ABP Cardiff (3)
QA House Cargo Road, Cardiff, CF10 4LY, United Kingdom
Tel.: (44) 8706096699
Sales Range: $25-49.9 Million
Emp.: 100
Marine Cargo Handling
N.A.I.C.S.: 488320
Matthew Kennerley (Dir-Ports-South Wales)

ABP Fleetwood (3)
Dock Office, Fleetwood, FY7 6PP, Lancs, United Kingdom
Tel.: (44) 1253872323
Sales Range: $100-124.9 Million
Emp.: 15
Marine Cargo Handling
N.A.I.C.S.: 488320
Nick Ridehalgh (Dir-Short-Sea Ports)

ABP Garston (3)
Port Office Garston, Liverpool, L19 2JW, United Kingdom
Tel.: (44) 1514275971
Sales Range: $25-49.9 Million
Emp.: 20
Marine Cargo Handling
N.A.I.C.S.: 488320
Paul Jervis (Mgr-Port)

ABP Goole (3)
Port Office East Parade, Goole, DN14 5RB, East Yorkshire, United Kingdom
Tel.: (44) 1482327171
Web Site: http://www.abport.co.uk
Sales Range: $50-74.9 Million
Emp.: 250
Marine Cargo Handling
N.A.I.C.S.: 488320
Phil Coombes (Mgr-Comml)

ABP Hull (3)
Port House Northern Gateway, PO Box 1, Hull, HU9 5PQ, Yorkshire, United Kingdom
Tel.: (44) 1482327171
Sales Range: $25-49.9 Million
Emp.: 125
Port & Harbor Operations
N.A.I.C.S.: 488310

ABP Ipswich (3)
Old Custom House Key Street, Ipswich, IP4 1BY, United Kingdom
Tel.: (44) 1473231010
Sales Range: $25-49.9 Million
Emp.: 23
Marine Cargo Handling
N.A.I.C.S.: 488320
Alastair MacFarlane (Mgr-Port)

ABP Plymouth (3)
Port Office Millbay Docks, Plymouth, PL1 3EF, Devon, United Kingdom
Tel.: (44) 1752662191
Sales Range: $25-49.9 Million
Emp.: 22
Passenger Ferry & Marine Cargo Handling Services
N.A.I.C.S.: 488320

Holding (Domestic):

Bruce Power, Inc. (2)
177 Tie Rd R R 2, PO Box 1540, Tiverton, Kincardine, N0G 2T0, ON, Canada (61.38%)
Tel.: (519) 361-2673
Web Site: https://www.brucepower.com
Nuclear Electric Power Generation
N.A.I.C.S.: 221113
Cathy Sprague (Exec VP-HR)

CEDA International Corporation (2)
Suite 625 11012 Macleod Trail SE, Calgary, T2J 6A5, AB, Canada
Tel.: (403) 253-3233
Web Site: https://www.ceda.com
Sales Range: $50-74.9 Million
Oil Refinery & Petrochemical Plant Support Services
N.A.I.C.S.: 213112

Joint Venture (Non-US):

Fortum Distribution AB (2)
Hangovagen 19, 115 77, Stockholm, Sweden (50%)
Tel.: (46) 8 671 70 00
Electric Power Distr
N.A.I.C.S.: 221122

Holding (Domestic):

LifeLabs Inc. (2)
100 International Blvd, Toronto, M9W 6J6, ON, Canada
Tel.: (416) 675-4530
Web Site: https://www.lifelabs.com
Medical Laboratory Testing & Diagnostic Services
N.A.I.C.S.: 621512
Michael Rolland (Chm)

Subsidiary (Domestic):

CML HealthCare Inc. (3)
60 Courtneypark Dr West Unit 1, Mississauga, L5W 0B3, ON, Canada
Tel.: (905) 565-0043
Web Site: http://cmlhealthcare.com
Sales Range: $350-399.9 Million
Emp.: 100
Provider of Diagnostic Laboratory Services
N.A.I.C.S.: 621512

Subsidiary (Domestic):

DC DiagnostiCare, Inc. (4)
6560 Kennedy Rd, Mississauga, L5T 2X4, ON, Canada (100%)
Tel.: (905) 565-0043
Sales Range: $10-24.9 Million
Emp.: 30
Medical Imaging Organization
N.A.I.C.S.: 621512

ONTARIO MUNICIPAL EMPLOYEES RETIREMENT SYSTEM

Ontario Municipal Employees Retirement System—(Continued)

Pharma Medica Research Inc. (4)
6100 Belgrave Rd, Mississauga, L5R 0B7, ON, Canada
Tel.: (905) 624-9115
Web Site: http://www.pharmamedica.com
Medical Laboratories
N.A.I.C.S.: 621511

Joint Venture (Non-US):

NET4GAS, s.r.o. (2)
Na Hrebenech II 1718/8, 140 21, Prague, Czech Republic
Tel.: (420) 220221111
Web Site: http://www.net4gas.cz
Sales Range: $50-74.9 Million
Natural Gas Transportation Services
N.A.I.C.S.: 486210
Andreas Rau (CEO & Mng Dir)

OMERS Private Equity Inc. (1)
EY Tower 900-100 Adelaide St W, Toronto, M5H 0E2, ON, Canada
Tel.: (416) 369-2400
Web Site: https://www.omersprivateequity.com
Privater Equity Firm
N.A.I.C.S.: 523999
Michael Graham (Sr Mng Dir & Head-Global)

Joint Venture (Non-US):

Autobahn Tank & Rast GmbH (2)
Andreas Hermes Strasse 729, 53175, Bonn, Germany
Tel.: (49) 2289220
Web Site: http://www.tank.rast.de
Gas Station Operator
N.A.I.C.S.: 457110
Karl-H. Rolfes (CEO)

Subsidiary (Domestic):

AXXE Reisegastronomie GmbH (3)
Clevischer Ring 127, 51063, Cologne, Germany
Tel.: (49) 2219647670
Web Site: http://www.axxe.de
Motorway Restaurant & Hotel Services
N.A.I.C.S.: 722511
Wolfgang Fritze (Mng Dir)

Joint Venture (Non-US):

BridgeTex Pipeline Company, LLC (2)

Environmental Resources Management Limited (2)
2nd Floor Exchequer Court 33 St Mary Axe, London, EC3A 8AA, United Kingdom
Tel.: (44) 20 3206 5200
Web Site: http://www.erm.com
Emp.: 300
Environmental Consulting Services
N.A.I.C.S.: 541620
Shawn Doherty (Dir-Digital Bus & Transformation-US)

Subsidiary (US):

The ERM Group, Inc. (3)
75 Vly Stream Pkwy Ste 200, Malvern, PA 19355
Tel.: (484) 913-0300
Web Site: http://www.erm.com
Sales Range: $900-999.9 Million
Emp.: 4,500
Environmental Engineering & Consulting Services
N.A.I.C.S.: 541620
Rachel Agnew (Sr Engr-Honolulu)

Holding (US):

Epiq Systems, Inc. (2)
501 Kansas Ave, Kansas City, KS 66105-1300
Tel.: (913) 621-9500
Web Site: http://www.epiqsystems.com
Business & Legal Software
N.A.I.C.S.: 513210
Greg Wildisen (Mng Dir-Intl)

Subsidiary (Domestic):

Epiq Bankruptcy Solutions, LLC (3)
777 3rd Ave 12rd Fl, New York, NY 10017
Tel.: (212) 225-9200
Web Site: http://www.epiqsystems.com
Case Management & Consulting Services
N.A.I.C.S.: 541611

Epiq Class Action & Claims Solutions, Inc. (3)
10300 SW Allen Blvd, Beaverton, OR 97005
Tel.: (503) 350-5800
Web Site: http://www.epiqglobal.com
Class Action Litigation Case Management Services
N.A.I.C.S.: 541199

Subsidiary (Non-US):

Epiq Systems Ltd. (3)
Epiq Systems 11 Old Jewry 4th Fl, London, EC2R 8DU, United Kingdom
Tel.: (44) 2073679191
Web Site: http://www.epiqsystems.co.uk
Emp.: 55
Business & Legal Software
N.A.I.C.S.: 513210
Christine Flores (Gen Mgr)

Epiq Systems, Limited (3)
1102-1004 Central Plaza 18 Harbour Road, 183 Queens Road East, Wanchai, China (Hong Kong)
Tel.: (852) 21107600
Web Site: http://www.epiqglobal.com
Computer & Software Store Services
N.A.I.C.S.: 541519

Subsidiary (Domestic):

Epiq eDiscovery Solutions, Inc. (3)
777 3rd Ave 11th & 12th Fl, New York, NY 10017
Tel.: (212) 225-9200
Web Site: http://www.epiqglobal.com
Cloud-based Data Collection, Processing, Review & Production Platform Developer & Services
N.A.I.C.S.: 518210
Edward Burke (Sr VP-Document Review Solutions)

The Garretson Resolution Group, Inc. (3)
6281 Tri-Rdg Blvd Ste 300, Cincinnati, OH 45140
Tel.: (513) 794-0400
Web Site: http://www.garretsongroup.com
Healthcare Lien Resolution Services
N.A.I.C.S.: 524292
Matthew L. Garretson (Founder)

Joint Venture (Non-US):

Eurolife ERB Insurance Group Holdings S.A. (2)
33-35 El Venizelou (Panepistimiou) & Korai Str, 10564, Athens, Greece (40%)
Tel.: (30) 2109303800
Web Site: http://www.eurolife.gr
Holding Company; Insurance Products & Services
N.A.I.C.S.: 551112

Subsidiary (Domestic):

Eurolife ERB General Insurance S.A. (3)
Panepistimiou 33-35 Korai, 10564, Athens, Greece
Tel.: (30) 2109303800
Web Site: https://www.eurolife.gr
General Insurance Products & Services
N.A.I.C.S.: 524126

Holding (US):

Great Expressions Dental Centers, P.C. (2)
29777 Telegraph Rd Ste 3000, Southfield, MI 48034
Tel.: (248) 203-1134
Web Site: http://www.greatexpressions.com
Sales Range: $200-249.9 Million
Emp.: 2,000
Healtcare Services
N.A.I.C.S.: 621210
Richard Beckman (CEO)

Inmar, Inc. (2)
1 W 4th St Ste 500, Winston Salem, NC 27101-3818
Tel.: (336) 770-1200
Web Site: http://www.inmar.com
Holding Company; Promotion & Reverse Logistics Services
N.A.I.C.S.: 551112
Rich Schmidt (CFO & Exec VP)

Subsidiary (Domestic):

Collective Bias, Inc (3)
1750 S Osage Springs Dr Ste 100, Rogers, AR 72758 (100%)
Tel.: (479) 268-3232
Web Site: http://www.CollectiveBias.com
Online Advertising & Marketing Services
N.A.I.C.S.: 541890

Inmar Scanner Applications, LLC (3)
400 Milford Pkwy, Milford, OH 45150
Tel.: (513) 248-5588
Promotion Management & Consulting Services
N.A.I.C.S.: 541618

Inmar Supply Chain Solutions, LLC (3)
2601 Pilgrim Ct, Winston Salem, NC 27106
Tel.: (336) 770-3500
Web Site: http://www.inmar.com
Reverse Logistics & Product Reclamation Services
N.A.I.C.S.: 561990

ownerIQ, Inc. (3)
27-43 Wormwood St Fl 6, Boston, MA 02210
Tel.: (866) 870-2295
Web Site: https://www.owneriq.com
Advertising Services
N.A.I.C.S.: 541810

Joint Venture (Non-US):

London City Airport Limited (2)
London City Airport City Aviation House, Royal Docks, London, E16 2PB, United Kingdom
Tel.: (44) 20 7646 0088
Web Site: http://www.londoncityairport.com
Airport Operator
N.A.I.C.S.: 488119
Alison FitzGerald (COO)

Holding (US):

Premise Health Employer Solutions, LLC (2)
5500 Maryland Way Ste 200, Brentwood, TN 37027-4973
Tel.: (615) 468-5500
Sales Range: $125-149.9 Million
Worksite-Based Health & Wellness Centers Management
N.A.I.C.S.: 621498
Stuart Clark (CEO)

Subsidiary (Domestic):

IMWell Health, LLC (3)
616 S 17th St, Fort Smith, AR 72901
Tel.: (479) 434-3333
Web Site: http://www.imwhealth.com
Health Care Srvices
N.A.I.C.S.: 621999
Eric Simpson (COO)

Sonic Boom Wellness, Inc. (3)
5963 La Pl Ct Ste 100, Carlsbad, CA 92008
Tel.: (760) 438-1600
Web Site: http://www.sonicboomwellness.com
Software Development Services
N.A.I.C.S.: 541511
Danna Van Noy (Co-Founder & CEO)

Holding (US):

Pueblo Mechanical & Controls, LLC (2)
3930 East Watkins Street Suite 300, Phoenix, AZ 85034
Tel.: (800) 840-9170
Web Site: http://www.pueblo-mechanical.com
Plumbing Heating & Air-Conditioning Contractor Services
N.A.I.C.S.: 238220
Dan Bueschel (CEO)

INTERNATIONAL PUBLIC

Subsidiary (Domestic):

Infinity Contractors, Inc. (3)
1400 Everman Pkwy Ste 134, Fort Worth, TX 76140-5006
Tel.: (817) 838-8700
Web Site: http://www.infinitycontractors.com
Provider of Mechanical Contracting Services
N.A.I.C.S.: 238220
Jim Salter (CEO)

Niemeyer Brothers Plumbing, Inc. (3)
21408 N 11th Ave, Phoenix, AZ 85027
Tel.: (623) 582-5775
Plumbing, Heating & Air-Conditioning Contractors
N.A.I.C.S.: 238220

Travers Mechanical Services (3)
6609 Edith Boulevard Northeast, Albuquerque, NM 87113
Tel.: (505) 994-9788
Web Site: http://www.site.traversmechanics.com
Plumbing, Heating & Air-Conditioning Contractors
N.A.I.C.S.: 238220
Mike Travers Jr (Pres)

Holding (US):

The Kenan Advantage Group, Inc. (2)
4366 Mt Pleasant St NW, North Canton, OH 44720
Web Site: http://www.thekag.com
Sales Range: $1-4.9 Billion
Emp.: 10,000
Fuel Transportation Services
N.A.I.C.S.: 213112
Becky Perlaky (Exec VP-Safety, Security & Compliance)

Subsidiary (Domestic):

Advantage Tank Lines LLC (3)
4366 Mt Pleasant St NW, North Canton, OH 44720
Tel.: (800) 969-5419
Web Site: http://www.thekag.com
Fuel Transportation Services
N.A.I.C.S.: 484121
Doug Allen (VP-Ops)

BXI (3)
3000 Calumet Pl, Hammond, IN 46320
Tel.: (800) 937-3490
Web Site: http://www.thekag.com
Heated Product Trucking Services
N.A.I.C.S.: 484230
Dick Widdicombe (Gen Mgr)

Cryogenic Transportation, LLC (3)
100 W Main St Ste 207, Lansdale, PA 19446
Tel.: (800) 228-8257
Web Site: http://www.cryotran.com
Industrial Gas Transportation
N.A.I.C.S.: 484220
Vernon Ingham (Pres & COO)

DistTech, LLC (3)
4366 Mt Pleasant St NW, North Canton, OH 44720
Tel.: (800) 969-5419
Web Site: http://www.thekag.com
Transportation & Logistic Services
N.A.I.C.S.: 484121
John Rakoczy (Sr VP-Sls & Mktg)

Fort Transfer Co. (3)
225 South Maple Ave, Morton, IL 61550
Tel.: (309) 263-2000
Web Site: http://www.forttransfer.com
Rev.: $10,000,000
Emp.: 50
General Freight Trucking, Long-Distance, Truckload
N.A.I.C.S.: 484121
Brad Kahler (Pres & CEO)

Idaho Milk Transport, Inc. (3)
745 W Bedke Blvd, Burley, ID 83318-3318
Tel.: (208) 878-5000
Web Site: http://www.idahomilktransport.com
General Freight Trucking
N.A.I.C.S.: 484121

AND PRIVATE COMPANIES

Gene Brice *(CEO)*

Jack B. Kelley, Inc. (3)
801 Fillmore St Ste 505, Amarillo, TX 79101
Tel.: (800) 225-5525
Web Site: http://www.jackbkelley.com
Trucking Service
N.A.I.C.S.: 484121
Mark Davis *(Pres)*

KAG Logistics, Inc. (3)
4366 Mt Pleasant St NW, North Canton, OH 44720
Tel.: (800) 969-5419
Web Site: http://www.kaglogistics.com
Petroleum Supply Chain Solutions
N.A.I.C.S.: 424710
Kevin Spencer *(Exec VP-Logistics)*

Division (Domestic):

KAG Ethanol Logistics (4)
4366 Mt Pleasant St NW, North Canton, OH 44720
Tel.: (877) 279-8205
Web Site: http://www.thekag.com
Ethanol Logistics Services
N.A.I.C.S.: 541614

Subsidiary (Domestic):

KAG West, LLC (3)
4076 Seaport Blvd, West Sacramento, CA 95691
Tel.: (800) 547-1587
Web Site: http://www.thekag.com
Fuel Transportation Services
N.A.I.C.S.: 424720
Phil Stewart *(Dir-IT)*

Kenan Transport Company (3)
100 Europa Dr Ste 190, Chapel Hill, NC 27516
Tel.: (800) 343-8804
Web Site: http://www.thekag.com
Bulk Transportation Services
N.A.I.C.S.: 484230
Dennis Walker *(VP-Ops)*

Northern Dry-Bulk, Inc. (3)
805 Industrial Dr, Clare, MI 48617
Tel.: (989) 386-2389
Web Site: http://www.northerndrybulk.com
Sales Range: $1-9.9 Million
Emp.: 20
Refuse Systems, Nsk
N.A.I.C.S.: 562920
Janet Kunse *(VP)*

Holding (Non-US):

Trescal S.A. (2)
Parc d'affaires Silic 8 rue de l'Esterel, BP 30441, Rungis, 94593, France
Tel.: (33) 156703636
Web Site: http://www.trescal.com
Test & Measuring Equipment Calibration, Maintenance & Repair Services
N.A.I.C.S.: 811210
Olivier Delrieu *(Chm & CEO)*

Subsidiary (US):

AcuCal, Inc. (3)
11090 Industrial Rd, Manassas, VA 20109-3923
Tel.: (703) 369-3090
Web Site: http://www.acucal.com
Testing Laboratories
N.A.I.C.S.: 541380
Thomas Efaw *(Pres & CEO)*

Integrated Service Solutions, Inc. (3)
1565 Bustard Rd, Lansdale, PA 19446
Tel.: (610) 287-3433
Web Site: http://www.integratedservicesolutions.com
Other Electronic & Precision Equipment Repair & Maintenance
N.A.I.C.S.: 811210
Catherine Peetros *(Dir-Bus Dev & Ops)*

New York Callibration Lab (3)
80 Orville Dr Ste 115, Bohemia, NY 11716
Tel.: (631) 563-3520
Web Site: http://trescal.us
Electrical Apparatus & Equipment, Wiring Supplies & Related Equipment Merchant Whslr
N.A.I.C.S.: 423610
William Lutz *(Sls Mgr-Acct)*

Precision Metrology, Inc. (3)
7350 N Teutonia, Milwaukee, WI 53209 **(100%)**
Tel.: (414) 351-7420
Web Site: http://www.precisionmetrology.com
Laboratory Calibration Services
N.A.I.C.S.: 811210
Jon Shipley *(Branch Mgr-Ops)*

Subsidiary (Non-US):

Trescal A/S (3)
Mads Clausens Vej 12, Silkeborg, 8600, Denmark
Tel.: (45) 87206969
Web Site: http://www.trescal.dk
Test & Measuring Equipment Calibration, Maintenance & Repair Services
N.A.I.C.S.: 811210
Jin Wang *(Mng Dir)*

Trescal B.V. (3)
Storkstraat 2-4, 2722 NN, Zoetermeer, Netherlands
Tel.: (31) 793430000
Web Site: http://www.trescal.nl
Test & Measuring Equipment Calibration, Maintenance & Repair Services
N.A.I.C.S.: 811210

Trescal Espana de Metrologia SLU (3)
C/ Traastrania 21, 28022, Madrid, Spain
Tel.: (34) 916250900
Web Site: http://www.trescal.es
Test & Measuring Equipment Calibration, Maintenance & Repair Services
N.A.I.C.S.: 811210
Tomas Estrada *(Mng Dir)*

Trescal GmbH (3)
Borsigstrasse 11, 64291, Darmstadt, Germany **(100%)**
Tel.: (49) 615130940
Web Site: http://www.trescal.de
Test & Measuring Equipment Calibration, Maintenance & Repair Services
N.A.I.C.S.: 811210

Subsidiary (US):

Trescal Inc. (3)
1200 N Old US 23, Hartland, MI 48353-0559
Tel.: (810) 225-4601
Web Site: http://www.trescal.com
Metrology Services
N.A.I.C.S.: 541330

Subsidiary (Non-US):

Trescal Limited (3)
Saxony Way, Blackbushe Business Park, Yateley, GU46 6GT, United Kingdom
Tel.: (44) 1252533300
Web Site: http://www.trescal.co.uk
Test & Measuring Equipment Calibration, Maintenance & Repair Services
N.A.I.C.S.: 811210

Trescal s.r.l. (3)
Via dei Metalli 1, IT-25039, Travagliato, BS, Italy
Tel.: (39) 0306842501
Web Site: http://www.trescal.it
Test & Measuring Equipment Calibration, Maintenance & Repair Services
N.A.I.C.S.: 811210

Holding (US):

Turnpoint Services, LLC (2)
3416 Robards Ct, Louisville, KY 40218
Web Site: http://turnpointservices.com
Plumbing, HVAC & Electrical Services
N.A.I.C.S.: 238220
Kurt Bratton *(CEO)*

Subsidiary (Domestic):

Cool Air Mechanical, LLC (3)
1950 Guffin Ln, Marietta, GA 30066-7016
Tel.: (770) 266-5247
Web Site: http://www.770coolair.com
Heating, Cooling, Ventilation & Water Heater Services
N.A.I.C.S.: 238220
Jake Mazhar *(Founder)*

Meetze Plumbing Co, Inc. (3)
10009 Broad River Rd, Irmo, SC 29063
Tel.: (803) 973-6691
Web Site: http://www.meetzeplumbing.com
Plumbing, Heating & Air-Conditioning Contractors
N.A.I.C.S.: 238220
Kevin Meetze *(Pres)*

Oxford Properties Group, Inc. (1)
100 Adelaide Street West Suite 2100, Toronto, M5H 0E2, ON, Canada
Tel.: (416) 865-8300
Web Site: https://www.oxfordproperties.com
Sales Range: $400-449.9 Million
Emp.: 2,000
Investment, Development & Management of Properties
N.A.I.C.S.: 531390
Paul A. Brundage *(Sr Mng Dir & Head-Europe & Asia Pacific)*

ONTARIO NORTHLAND TRANSPORTATION COMMISSION

555 Oak Street East, North Bay, P1B 8L3, ON, Canada
Tel.: (705) 472-4500
Web Site: http://www.ontarionorthland.ca
Year Founded: 1902
Rev.: $147,821,448
Emp.: 1,000
Transportation, Telecommunication & Rail Freight Services
N.A.I.C.S.: 488510
Chad Evans *(Pres)*

ONTARIO POWER GENERATION, INC.

700 University Avenue, Toronto, M5G 1X6, ON, Canada
Tel.: (416) 592-2555 Ca
Web Site: http://www.opg.com
Year Founded: 1998
Rev.: $4,608,275,280
Assets: $42,397,356,960
Liabilities: $31,473,555,960
Net Worth: $10,923,801,000
Earnings: $861,660,240
Emp.: 10,001
Fiscal Year-end: 12/31/19
Electricity Generation & Distribution Services
N.A.I.C.S.: 221112
Kenneth M. Hartwick *(Pres & CEO)*

Subsidiaries:

Lower Mattagami Energy Limited Partnership (1)
700 University Avenue, Toronto, M5G 1X6, ON, Canada
Tel.: (416) 592-4463
Hydroelectric Power Generation Services
N.A.I.C.S.: 221111

TransCanada Energy Ltd. - Halton Hills Plant (1)
7870 6 Line, Halton Hills, Halton Hills, L7G 0E9, ON, Canada
Tel.: (905) 864-7725
Natural Gas Generation Services
N.A.I.C.S.: 211130

ONTARIO SEED COMPANY LTD.

PO Box 7, Waterloo, N2J 3Z6, ON, Canada
Tel.: (519) 886-0557
Web Site: http://www.oscseeds.com
Year Founded: 1894
Rev.: $14,367,170
Emp.: 40
Horticultural Products Store
N.A.I.C.S.: 424910
Scott Uffelman *(Pres)*

ONTARIO TEACHERS' PENSION PLAN

5650 Yonge Street 3rd Floor, Toronto, M2M 4H5, ON, Canada

ONTARIO TEACHERS' PENSION PLAN

Tel.: (800) 668-0105
Web Site: http://www.otpp.com
Year Founded: 1990
Private Pension Fund Administrator
N.A.I.C.S.: 525110
David McGraw *(CFO)*

Subsidiaries:

24-7 Intouch, Inc. (1)
240 Kennedy Street 2nd Floor, Winnipeg, R3C 1T1, MB, Canada
Web Site: https://www.intouchcx.com
Business Process Outsourcing Services
N.A.I.C.S.: 561499
Jeff Fettes *(Co-Founder)*

Subsidiary (US):

Knoah Solutions, Inc. (2)
140 N Stephanie St, Henderson, NV 89074
Tel.: (702) 722-5005
Web Site: http://www.knoah.com
Telecommunications Resellers
N.A.I.C.S.: 517121
Sri Myneni *(Pres)*

Abano Healthcare Group Limited (1)
Level 11 AMP Centre 29 Customs Street West, Auckland, 1010, New Zealand
Tel.: (64) 93001410
Web Site: http://www.abano.co.nz
Rev.: $187,084,877
Assets: $231,012,159
Liabilities: $127,358,165
Net Worth: $103,653,994
Earnings: $5,132,487
Emp.: 1,700
Fiscal Year-end: 05/31/2019
Healthcare & Medical Services
N.A.I.C.S.: 621410
Richard G. Keys *(CEO)*

Subsidiary (Non-US):

1300 Smiles Limited (2)
Ground Floor 105 Denham Street, Townsville, 4810, QLD, Australia **(84%)**
Tel.: (61) 747201300
Web Site: http://www.1300smiles.com.au
Rev.: $34,436,410
Assets: $55,755,646
Liabilities: $21,762,861
Net Worth: $33,992,786
Earnings: $7,375,345
Emp.: 338
Fiscal Year-end: 06/30/2021
Dentistry Services
N.A.I.C.S.: 621210
Daryl Shane Holmes *(Mng Dir)*

Subsidiary (Domestic):

Plaza Central Dentists Pty. Ltd. (3)
Shop 7 Plaza Central 31-33 Plaza Parade, Maroochydore, Sunshine Coast, 4558, QLD, Australia
Tel.: (61) 754794499
Web Site: http://www.plazacentraldentists.com.au
Dental Care Services
N.A.I.C.S.: 621210
David Mcfall *(Principal)*

Subsidiary (Domestic):

Aotea Pathology Limited (2)
Level 6 CMC Building 89 Courtenay Place, Wellington, 6011, New Zealand
Tel.: (64) 43815900
Web Site: http://www.apath.co.nz
Sales Range: $25-49.9 Million
Emp.: 230
Pathological Laboratory Services
N.A.I.C.S.: 621511

Auckland Dental Group (2)
134 Remuera Road, Remuera, Auckland, New Zealand
Tel.: (64) 95206609
Web Site: http://www.akldental.co.nz
Sales Range: $10-24.9 Million
Emp.: 25
Dental Services
N.A.I.C.S.: 621210

Subsidiary (Non-US):

Dental Partners Pty Limited (2)
Suite 30901 Southport Central 3 Level 9/9 Lawson St, Southport, 4215, QLD, Australia

5585

ONTARIO TEACHERS' PENSION PLAN

Ontario Teachers' Pension Plan—(Continued)
Tel.: (61) 755917772
Web Site: http://www.dentalpartners.com.au
Sales Range: $10-24.9 Million
Emp.: 40
Dental Care Services
N.A.I.C.S.: 621491
Alan Clarke (Chm)

Subsidiary (Domestic):

Greenlane Imaging Ltd (2)
Ascot Central Bldg Ground Fl, 7 Ellerslie
Racecourse Dr, Auckland, 1051, Remuera,
New Zealand
Tel.: (64) 9 555 9556
Web Site: http://www.ascotrad.co.nz
Sales Range: $10-24.9 Million
Emp.: 8
Health Care Srvices
N.A.I.C.S.: 621999
David Milne (Dir-Clinical)

Insight Radiology Limited (2)
20 Titoki Street, Parnell, 1052, Auckland,
New Zealand
Tel.: (64) 93735988
Web Site: http://www.insightrad.co.nz
Sales Range: $10-24.9 Million
Emp.: 15
Diagnostic Radiology Services
N.A.I.C.S.: 621512

Kidz Teeth Limited (2)
21 St Johns Rd, Meadowbank, Auckland,
1072, New Zealand
Tel.: (64) 95219003
Web Site: http://www.kidz-teeth.com
Dental Care Services
N.A.I.C.S.: 621999

Lumino Care Dental (2)
AMP Tower 29 Customs St West, PO Box
106514, Auckland, 1010, New Zealand
Tel.: (64) 93617100
Web Site: http://www.lumino.co.nz
Sales Range: $50-74.9 Million
Emp.: 400
Dental Services
N.A.I.C.S.: 621210
Andrew Tappar (Mng Dir)

Lumino Dental Limited (2)
40 Panama St Wellington Central, Wellington, 6011, New Zealand
Tel.: (64) 4 384 8481
Web Site: http://www.lumino.co.nz
Emp.: 15
Dental Care Services
N.A.I.C.S.: 339116

Medical Laboratory Wellington (2)
CMC Building, 89 Courtenay Place, Wellington, New Zealand
Tel.: (64) 48015111
Pathology Laboratory Diagnostics
N.A.I.C.S.: 621511

Nelson Diagnostic Laboratory (2)
1 Harley Street, Nelson, New Zealand
Tel.: (64) 35487395
Pathology Laboratory Diagnostics
N.A.I.C.S.: 621511

Allworth Financial Group LP (1)
8775 Folsom Blvd Ste 100, Sacramento,
CA 95826
Tel.: (888) 242-6766
Web Site: https://allworthfinancial.com
Management Consulting Services
N.A.I.C.S.: 541611

Subsidiary (Domestic):

Allworth Financial Holdings, LLC (2)
340 Palladio Pkwy Ste 501, Folsom, CA 95630
Tel.: (916) 357-5287
Web Site: https://allworthfinancial.com
Financial Services
N.A.I.C.S.: 541611

Allworth Financial, LP (2)
8775 Folsom Blvd Ste 100, Sacramento,
CA 95826
Tel.: (916) 482-2196
Web Site: http://www.allworthfinancial.com
Management Consulting Services
N.A.I.C.S.: 541611
Patrick McClain (Co-Founder & Sr Partner)

Subsidiary (Domestic):

Blueprint Financial LLC (3)
4320 44th St SW 102, Grandville, MI 49418
Tel.: (616) 988-1180
Web Site: http://www.walkaboutcamp.com
Investment Advice
N.A.I.C.S.: 523940

Houston Asset Management, Inc. (3)
1800 West Loop S Ste 1980, Houston, TX 77027
Tel.: (713) 629-5490
Web Site:
http://www.houstonassetmgmt.com
Securities Brokerage
N.A.I.C.S.: 523150
Kristian Taylor (COO & Chief Compliance Officer)

Red Rock Wealth Management (3)
9480 S Eastern Ave Ste 251, Las Vegas,
NV 89123-8037
Tel.: (702) 987-1607
Web Site: http://www.redrockwealth.com
Investment Advice
N.A.I.C.S.: 523940
Greg Phelps (Mgr)

Subsidiary (Domestic):

McDaniel Knutson Finanicial, Inc. (2)
3705 Clinton Pwy Ste 200, Lawrence, KS 66047
Tel.: (785) 841-4664
Web Site: http://www.mcdanielknutson.com
Investment Advice
N.A.I.C.S.: 523940

Constellation Insurance Holdings Inc. (1)
1211 Avenue of the Americas 30th floor,
New York, NY 10036
Web Site: https://www.constellationih.com
Emp.: 100
Holding Company
N.A.I.C.S.: 551111
Anurag Chandra (Founder & CEO)

Subsidiary (Domestic):

Ohio National Holdings, Inc. (2)
1 Financial Way, Cincinnati, OH 45242
Tel.: (513) 794-6100
Web Site: http://www.ohionational.com
Rev.: $2,388,716,000
Assets: $39,178,667,000
Liabilities: $36,713,380,000
Net Worth: $2,465,287,000
Earnings: $72,649,000
Fiscal Year-end: 12/31/2018
Mutual Insurance Holding Company; Insurance & Financial Products & Services
N.A.I.C.S.: 551112

Subsidiary (Domestic):

Ohio National Equities, Inc. (3)
1 Financial Way Ste 100, Cincinnati, OH 45242
Tel.: (513) 794-6100
Web Site: http://www.ohionational.com
Sales Range: $50-74.9 Million
Emp.: 40
Wholesale Securities Brokerage & Dealing Services
N.A.I.C.S.: 523150
Laurens N. Sullivan (VP-Institutional Sls)

Ohio National Financial Services, Inc. (3)
One Financial Way, Cincinnati, OH 45242 (100%)
Tel.: (513) 794-6100
Web Site: http://www.ohionational.com
Sales Range: $75-99.9 Million
Emp.: 700
Holding Company
N.A.I.C.S.: 551112
Pamela A. Webb (Sr VP-HR & Corp Svcs)

Ohio National Investments, Inc. (3)
1 Financial Way, Montgomery, OH 45242
Tel.: (513) 794-6336
Emp.: 30
Investment Advisory Services
N.A.I.C.S.: 523940

Ohio National Life Assurance Corporation (3)

1 Financial Way ste100, Cincinnati, OH 45242
Tel.: (513) 794-6100
Fire Insurance Services
N.A.I.C.S.: 524210

The O.N. Equity Sales Company (3)
1 Financial Way, Cincinnati, OH 45242
Tel.: (513) 794-6794
Web Site: http://www.joinonesco.com
Investment Management Service
N.A.I.C.S.: 523940
Patrick H. McEvoy (Pres)

Lendmark Financial Services, Inc. (1)
229 Village At Glynn Pl, Brunswick, GA 31525
Tel.: (912) 262-1100
Web Site: http://www.lendmarkfinancial.com
Sales Range: $25-49.9 Million
Emp.: 3
Financial & Mortgage Lending Services
N.A.I.C.S.: 522310
Robert Aiken (Founder, Pres & CEO)

Mitratech Holdings, Inc. (1)
5001 Plaza On The Lk Ste 111, Austin, TX 78746
Tel.: (512) 382-7322
Web Site: http://www.mitratech.com
Corporate Legal Automation Software Developer & Sales
N.A.I.C.S.: 513210
Jason Parkman (Chm & Co-CEO)

Subsidiary (Domestic):

Applied Training Systems Inc (2)
113 Cherry ST, PMB 57615, Seattle, WA 98104
Tel.: (800) 516-5849
Web Site: https://appliedtraining.com
Performance Management System
N.A.I.C.S.: 541512

Subsidiary (Domestic):

Mindflash Technologies, Inc. (3)
2825 El Camino Real, Palo Alto, CA 94306
Tel.: (805) 963-8417
Web Site: http://www.mindflash.com
Custom Computer Programming Services
N.A.I.C.S.: 541511

Subsidiary (Domestic):

CMPG Inc. (2)
2620 Concord Ave Ste 100, Alhambra, CA 91803-1235
Tel.: (626) 782-9999
Web Site: http://www.cmpg.com
Marketing Consulting Services
N.A.I.C.S.: 541613
Terry Pan (Owner)

Subsidiary (Non-US):

HotDocs Limited (2)
14 South Charlotte Street, Edinburgh, EH2 4AX, Scotland, United Kingdom
Tel.: (44) 1312263999
Web Site: http://www.hotdocs.co.uk
Automated Document Processing Software & Services
N.A.I.C.S.: 513210

Subsidiary (US):

HotDocs Corporation (3)
4850 Eastgate Mall, San Diego, CA 92121
Tel.: (800) 828-8328
Web Site: http://www.hotdocs.com
Legal Information Software Publisher
N.A.I.C.S.: 513210

Subsidiary (Domestic):

Prevalent Power, Inc (2)
11811 N. Tatum Boulevard, Phoenix, AZ 85028
Corporate Legal Automation Software Developer & Sales
N.A.I.C.S.: 423430

Syntrio, Inc. (2)
500 Lake Cook Rd Ste #350, Deerfield, IL 60015
Tel.: (888) 289-6670
Web Site: http://www.syntrio.com
Custom Computer Programming Services

INTERNATIONAL PUBLIC

N.A.I.C.S.: 541511
Madan Joshi (Gen Mgr-Ops-India)

Subsidiary (Domestic):

Lighthouse Services LLC (3)
630 Freedom Business Ctr, 3rd Fl, King of Prussia, PA 19406
Tel.: (215) 884-6150
Web Site: http://www.lighthouse-services.com
All Other Support Services
N.A.I.C.S.: 561990

Subsidiary (Domestic):

The Infosoft Group LLC (2)
1000 N Water St Ste 1200, Milwaukee, WI 53202
Tel.: (414) 278-0700
Web Site: http://www.circaworks.com
Sales Range: $1-9.9 Million
Emp.: 24
Computer System Design Services
N.A.I.C.S.: 541511
Patrick Sheahan (CEO)

Subsidiary (Domestic):

America's Job Exchange LLC (3)
200 Minuteman Rd Ste 203, Andover, MA 01810
Web Site:
http://www.americasjobexchange.com
Recruitment Services
N.A.I.C.S.: 561311

Subsidiary (Domestic):

ThinkSmart LLC (2)
530 Jackson St 3rd Fl, San Francisco, CA 94133
Digital Transaction Management Services
N.A.I.C.S.: 541618

talentReef, Inc. (2)
210 University Blvd Ste 300, Denver, CO 80206
Tel.: (303) 974-4835
Web Site: http://www.jobappplus.com
Sales Range: $1-9.9 Million
Recruiting & Talent Management System
N.A.I.C.S.: 513210
Joe Poxson (Exec VP-Sls)

Nvision Laser Eye Center, Inc. (1)
75 Enterprise Ste 200, Aliso Viejo, CA 92656
Tel.: (866) 257-2851
Web Site: http://www.nvisioncenters.com
Offices of Other Health Practitioners
N.A.I.C.S.: 621399
Tom Tooma (Founder & Chief Medical officer)

RSA Security LLC (1)
174 Middlesex Tpke, Bedford, MA 01730
Tel.: (781) 515-5000
Web Site: http://www.rsa.com
Security Management Services
N.A.I.C.S.: 561621
Zulfikar Ramzan (CTO)

Subsidiary (Non-US):

RSA Security GmbH (2)
Osterfeldstrasse 84, 85737, Ismaning, Germany
Tel.: (49) 89930910
Web Site: http://www.rsa.com
Network Security Systems & Risk Solutions
N.A.I.C.S.: 541512

RSA Security UK Limited (2)
Rsa House Western Road, Bracknell, RG12 1RT, Berkshire, United Kingdom
Tel.: (44) 1344781000
Web Site: http://www.rsa.com
Network Security Systems
N.A.I.C.S.: 541512

Seven Investment Management LLP (1)
55 Bishopsgate, London, EC2N 3AS, United Kingdom
Tel.: (44) 2077608777
Investment Advice Services
N.A.I.C.S.: 523940
Dean Proctor (CEO)

Teachers' Private Capital (1)

AND PRIVATE COMPANIES — ONTARIO TEACHERS' PENSION PLAN

5650 Yonge Street, Toronto, M2M 4H5, ON, Canada
Tel.: (416) 228-5900
Web Site: http://www.otpp.com
Privater Equity Firm
N.A.I.C.S.: 523999
Romeo Leemrijse *(Mng Dir & Head-Global Group Sector)*

Joint Venture (US):

24 Hour Fitness USA, Inc. (2)
12647 Alcosta Blvd 5th Fl, San Ramon, CA 94583
Tel.: (925) 543-3100
Web Site: http://www.24hourfitness.com
Fitness Centers Owner & Operator
N.A.I.C.S.: 713940
Patrick Flanagan *(CFO)*

Subsidiary (Domestic):

Lady Fitness Inc. (3)
2231 Rutherford Rd, Carlsbad, CA 92008-8815
Tel.: (760) 931-0880
Sales Range: $10-24.9 Million
Emp.: 25
Provider of Physical Fitness Services
N.A.I.C.S.: 713940

Holding (US):

APCO Holdings, LLC (2)
6010 Atlantic Blvd, Norcross, GA 30071
Tel.: (678) 225-1000
Holding Company; Automotive Warranty Insurance Products & Services
N.A.I.C.S.: 551112
John Lee *(Pres)*

Subsidiary (Domestic):

Automobile Protection Corporation (3)
6010 Atlantic Blvd, Norcross, GA 30071-1303
Tel.: (678) 225-1000
Web Site: http://www.easycare.com
Sales Range: $150-199.9 Million
Emp.: 450
Automobile Extended Warranty & Service Contract Insurance Products & Services
N.A.I.C.S.: 524128
Larry I. Dorfman *(Founder, Chm & CEO)*

Subsidiary (Domestic):

The Aegis Group, Inc. (4)
6010 Atlantic Blvd, Norcross, GA 30071-1303 (100%)
Tel.: (770) 394-7070
Web Site: http://www.easycare.com
Sales Range: $150-199.9 Million
Emp.: 300
Insurance & Financial Services
N.A.I.C.S.: 524298

Subsidiary (Domestic):

Automotive Development Group, LLC (3)
123 Sailview Rd, Mooresville, NC 28117
Tel.: (571) 235-4951
Web Site: http://www.adgonline.net
Emp.: 100
Innovative Theft Deterrent Products & Finance & Insurance Services
N.A.I.C.S.: 524298
Greg English *(Pres)*

GWC Warranty Corporation (3)
Showroom Level 40 Coal St, Wilkes Barre, PA 18702-5236
Web Site: http://www.gwcwarranty.com
Used Automobile Extended Warranty & Service Contract Insurance Products & Services
N.A.I.C.S.: 524128
Rob Glander *(Pres & CEO)*

Holding (Domestic):

Arterra Wines Canada, Inc. (2)
441 Courtneypark Drive East, Mississauga, L5T 2V3, ON, Canada
Tel.: (905) 564-6906
Web Site: http://www.arterracanada.com
Wine & Wine Coolers Producer
N.A.I.C.S.: 312130
Jay Wright *(Pres & CEO)*

Subsidiary (Domestic):

InnisKillin Wines, Inc. (3)
1499 Line 3 Niagara Pkwy, Niagara-on-the-Lake, L0S 1J0, ON, Canada
Tel.: (905) 468-2187
Web Site: http://www.inniskillin.com
Wine Mfr
N.A.I.C.S.: 312130

NkMip Cellars Inc. (3)
1400 Rancher Creek Road, Osoyoos, V0H 1V6, BC, Canada
Tel.: (250) 495-2985
Web Site: https://www.nkmipcellars.com
Liquor Store Operator
N.A.I.C.S.: 445320

Division (Domestic):

Wine Rack (3)
441 Courtneypark Drive East, Mississauga, L5T 2V3, ON, Canada
Tel.: (888) 793-9999
Web Site: http://www.winerack.com
Wine Retail Outlet
N.A.I.C.S.: 312130

Holding (Domestic):

Atlantic Aqua Farms, Ltd. (2)
10 Borden Avenue, Orwell Cove, Borden-Carleton, C0B 1X0, PE, Canada
Tel.: (902) 437-2700
Web Site: https://atlanticaquafarms.com
Mussel Farming & Processing
N.A.I.C.S.: 112512
Jeff MacPherson *(CFO)*

BayBridge Seniors Housing Inc. (2)
120 Adelaide St W Ste 202, Toronto, M5H 1T1, ON, Canada (100%)
Tel.: (416) 487-2020
Web Site: http://www.baybridgeseniorliving.com
Holding Company; Senior Living Communities Operator
N.A.I.C.S.: 551112
Amy R. Holland *(VP-Sls & Mktg)*

Subsidiary (Domestic):

Amica Mature Lifestyles Inc. (3)
20 Queen St West Suite 2700, Toronto, M5H 3R4, ON, Canada
Tel.: (416) 487-2020
Web Site: http://www.amica.ca
Retirement & Nursing Residence Operator
N.A.I.C.S.: 623311
Kieran Hess *(Reg Dir-Ops)*

Holding (Non-US):

Bridon International Limited (2)
Balby Carr Bank, Doncaster, DN4 5JQ, United Kingdom
Tel.: (44) 1302565100
Web Site: http://www.bridon.com
Sales Range: $250-299.9 Million
Emp.: 300
Fabricated Wire Product Mfr
N.A.I.C.S.: 332618
Chris Dugan *(Mng Dir-Bridon American Corporation)*

Subsidiary (US):

Bridon American Corporation (3)
C280 New Commerce Blvd, Wilkes Barre, PA 18706
Tel.: (800) 521-5555
Web Site: http://www.bridon.com
Sales Range: $100-124.9 Million
Fabricated Wire Product Mfr
N.A.I.C.S.: 332618
Chris Dugan *(Mng Dir)*

Subsidiary (Non-US):

Bridon Hangzhou Ropes Co. Ltd. (3)
No 57 Yonghua Street, Xiacheng District, Hangzhou, 310022, China
Tel.: (86) 57185818780
Web Site: http://www.bridon.com
Fabricated Wire Product Mfr
N.A.I.C.S.: 332618

Bridon Hong Kong Ltd. (3)
Unit B G/F Roxy Industrial Centre, 58-66 Tai Lin Pai Road, Kwai Chung, China (Hong Kong)
Tel.: (852) 852 240 11 166
Web Site: http://www.bridon.com
Fabricated Wire Product Mfr
N.A.I.C.S.: 332618

Bridon International GmbH (3)
Magdeburger Strasse 14 A, D-45881, Gelsenkirchen, Germany
Tel.: (49) 20980010
Web Site: http://www.bridon-bekaert.com
Fabricated Wire Product Mfr
N.A.I.C.S.: 332618

Bridon International Moscow (3)
Ivovaya Street 2/8 Building 1 Office 215, 129329, Moscow, Russia
Tel.: (7) 9163296516
Web Site: http://www.bridon.com
Sales Range: $25-49.9 Million
Emp.: 6
Fabricated Wire Product Mfr
N.A.I.C.S.: 332618

Bridon Middle East (3)
PO Box 16931, Dubai, United Arab Emirates
Tel.: (971) 48835129
Web Site: http://www.bridon.com
Sales Range: $25-49.9 Million
Emp.: 20
Fabricated Wire Product Mfr
N.A.I.C.S.: 332618
Steve Hodgkins *(Gen Mgr)*

Bridon New Zealand Limited (3)
6-10 Greenmount Drive, East Tamaki, Auckland, Panmure, New Zealand
Tel.: (64) 2744299
Web Site: http://bridon.co.nz
Fabricated Wire Product Mfr
N.A.I.C.S.: 332618

Bridon Singapore (Pte) Ltd. (3)
Loyang Offshore Supply Base (SOPS Way), Loyang Cresent, Singapore, 508988, Singapore
Tel.: (65) 65464611
Web Site: http://www.bridon.com
Sales Range: $25-49.9 Million
Emp.: 20
Fabricated Wire Product Mfr
N.A.I.C.S.: 332618

Guangzhou Bridon Ropes & Lifting (3)
139 Gang Wan Road, Hoangpu District, Guangzhou, 510700, China
Tel.: (86) 2082298698
Fabricated Wire Product Mfr
N.A.I.C.S.: 332618

PT Bridon (3)
Jl Raya Bekasi Km 43, Cibitung Bekasi, Jakarta, 17520, Indonesia
Tel.: (62) 21 883 1566
Web Site: http://www.bridon.com
Fabricated Wire Product Mfr
N.A.I.C.S.: 332618

Holding (Non-US):

Bristol Airport Limited (2)
Bristol Airport, Bristol, BS48 3DY, United Kingdom (100%)
Tel.: (44) 207 8692
Web Site: http://www.bristolairport.co.uk
Airport
N.A.I.C.S.: 488111
Jim McAuliffe *(Dir-Fin)*

Burton's Foods Ltd. (2)
Charter Court 74-78 Victoria Street, 74-78 Victoria Street, Saint Albans, AL1 3XH, United Kingdom
Tel.: (44) 1727899700
Web Site: http://www.burtonsfoods.com
Sales Range: $750-799.9 Million
Emp.: 200
Cookies & Crackers Mfr
N.A.I.C.S.: 311821
Ben Clark *(CEO)*

Busy Bees Holdings Limited (2)
St Matthews Shaftsbury Drive, Burntwood, WS7 9QP, Staffs, United Kingdom
Tel.: (44) 870 380 6614
Web Site: http://www.busybeeschildcare.co.uk
Educational Learning & Child Care Services
N.A.I.C.S.: 624410
Simon Irons *(CEO)*

Subsidiary (Non-US):

BrightPath Early Learning Inc. (3)
200 Rivercrest Drive SE Suite 201, Calgary, T2C 2X5, AB, Canada
Tel.: (403) 705-0362
Web Site: http://www.brightpathkids.com
Educational Learning & Child Care Center Services
N.A.I.C.S.: 624410
Dale Kearns *(Pres)*

Subsidiary (Domestic):

Appleby Learning and Child Care Centre Inc. (4)
E112 - 676 Appleby Line, Burlington, L7L 5Y1, ON, Canada
Tel.: (905) 637-5437
Web Site: http://www.brightpathkids.com
Child Care Services
N.A.I.C.S.: 624410
Simardeep Panesar *(Dir-Centre)*

Edleun, Inc. (4)
30 Glendeer Circle SE, Calgary, T2H 2Z7, AB, Canada
Tel.: (403) 705-0362
Child Care Services
N.A.I.C.S.: 624410

Little Scholars Montessori Learning Centre Inc. (4)
4100 Strandherd Dr, Nepean, K2J 0V2, ON, Canada
Tel.: (613) 843-4100
Child Care Services
N.A.I.C.S.: 624410

Subsidiary (Non-US):

Marlborough Day Nursery Ltd. (4)
Jackson Street, Coalville, LE67 3LT, Leics, United Kingdom
Tel.: (44) 1530 814 051
Web Site: http://www.marlboroughnursery.co.uk
Child Care Services
N.A.I.C.S.: 624110

Subsidiary (US):

Skills Development Inc. (4)
2923 Saint Marys Ave, Hannibal, MO 63401
Tel.: (573) 221-3282
Child Care Services
N.A.I.C.S.: 624410

Subsidiary (Domestic):

Strandherd Montessori Daycare Inc. (4)
4100 Strandherd Drive, Nepean, K2J 0V2, ON, Canada
Tel.: (613) 843-4100
Child Care Services
N.A.I.C.S.: 624410

Subsidiary (Non-US):

Busy Bees Early Learning Australia Pty. Ltd. (3)
34 Station St, Nundah, 4012, QLD, Australia
Tel.: (61) 1300 851 331
Web Site: http://www.busybees.edu.au
Childcare Services & Kindergarten Schools
N.A.I.C.S.: 624110
Robert Hughes *(CEO)*

Subsidiary (Domestic):

Think Childcare Limited (4)
Suite 3 1 Park Avenue, Drummoyne, 2047, NSW, Australia
Tel.: (61) 297127444
Web Site: http://www.thinkchildcare.com.au
Child Care Services
N.A.I.C.S.: 624410
Mathew Edwards *(CEO & Mng Dir)*

Holding (Domestic):

CFM Corporation (2)
2695 Meadowvale Blvd, Mississauga, L5N 8A3, ON, Canada
Tel.: (905) 819-4777
Sales Range: $500-549.9 Million
Home Products & Related Accessories Mfr
N.A.I.C.S.: 333414

ONTARIO TEACHERS' PENSION PLAN

Ontario Teachers' Pension Plan—(Continued)

Subsidiary (Non-US):

CFM Europe Limited (3)
Trentham Lakes, Stoke-on-Trent, ST4 4TJ, United Kingdom
Tel.: (44) 1782339000
Web Site: http://www.cfm-europe.com
Sales Range: $25-49.9 Million
Emp.: 100
Heating & Warming Products Mfr
N.A.I.C.S.: 333414

Affiliate (US):

CareerBuilder, LLC (2)
200 N LaSalle St Ste 1100, Chicago, IL 60601
Tel.: (773) 527-3600
Web Site: http://www.careerbuilder.com
Online Job Portal Publisher
N.A.I.C.S.: 518210
Farhan Yasin (Pres-HCM Software & Intl Grp)

Subsidiary (Non-US):

CareerBuilder Germany GmbH (3)
Hanns-Schwindt-Strasse 8, 81829, Munich, Germany
Tel.: (49) 80062824464
Web Site: http://www.jobs.de
Online Services
N.A.I.C.S.: 541519
Karsten Borgmann (Mng Dir)

Subsidiary (Domestic):

Monster Worldwide, Inc. (3)
133 Boston Post Rd, Weston, MA 02493
Tel.: (978) 461-8000
Job Posting Website Publisher
N.A.I.C.S.: 513140
Scott Gutz (CEO)

Subsidiary (Domestic):

Military Advantage, Inc. (4)
133 Boston Post Rd, Weston, MA 02493
Tel.: (978) 461-8000
Web Site: https://www.military.com
Online Military & Veteran Membership Services
N.A.I.C.S.: 513199
Gregory J. Smith (Pres)

Subsidiary (Non-US):

Monster Belgium NV (4)
Medialaan 28B, 1800, Vilvoorde, Belgium
Tel.: (32) 27531100
Web Site: http://www.monster.com
Employment Placement Services
N.A.I.C.S.: 561311

Monster Executive Services Limited (4)
Chancery House 53-64 Chancery Lane, London, WC2A 1QS, United Kingdom
Tel.: (44) 2073456000
Web Site: http://info.monster.co.uk
Employment Placement Services
N.A.I.C.S.: 561311
Andrew Summer (Mng Dir)

Subsidiary (Domestic):

Monster Government Solutions, LLC (4)
133 Boston Post Rd, Weston, MA 02493
Tel.: (703) 269-4900
Web Site: https://monstergovernmentsolutions.com
Employment Placement Services
N.A.I.C.S.: 561311

Subsidiary (Non-US):

Monster Worldwide Austria GmbH (4)
Neubaugasse 43/1/1-2, A-1070, Vienna, Austria
Tel.: (43) 800880880
Web Site: https://www.monster.at
Employment Placement Services
N.A.I.C.S.: 561311

Monster Worldwide Deutschland GmbH (4)
Frankfurter Strasse 100, 65760, Eschborn, Germany
Tel.: (49) 619699920
Web Site: https://www.monster.de
Employment Placement Services
N.A.I.C.S.: 561311
Andrea Bertone (Mng Dir-Europe Boss)

Subsidiary (Domestic):

Trovix Inc. (4)
55 2nd St Ste 300, San Francisco, CA 94105
Tel.: (650) 605-4300
Employment Placement Services
N.A.I.C.S.: 561311

Joint Venture (Non-US):

Cushman & Wakefield plc (2)
125 Old Broad Street, London, EC2N 1AR, United Kingdom
Tel.: (44) 2032963000
Web Site: http://www.cushmanwakefield.com
Rev.: $10,105,700,000
Assets: $7,949,300,000
Liabilities: $6,287,200,000
Net Worth: $1,662,100,000
Earnings: $196,400,000
Emp.: 52,000
Fiscal Year-end: 12/31/2022
Holding Company
N.A.I.C.S.: 551112
Matthew Miller (Vice Chm)

Subsidiary (US):

Colvill Office Properties, LLC (3)
5847 San Felipe St Ste 600, Houston, TX 77057-3008
Tel.: (713) 877-1550
Web Site: http://www.colvilloffice.com
Offices of Real Estate Agents & Brokers
N.A.I.C.S.: 531210
Chip Colvill (Owner)

Cresa Partners of Los Angeles, Inc. (3)
11726 San Vicente Blvd, Los Angeles, CA 90049
Tel.: (310) 207-1700
Sales Range: $10-24.9 Million
Emp.: 41
Management Consulting Services
N.A.I.C.S.: 541618
Nancy Ryan (Controller)

Cushman & Wakefield, Inc. (3)
225 W Wacker Dr Ste 3000, Chicago, IL 60606
Tel.: (312) 470-1800
Web Site: http://www.cushmanandwakefield.com
Sales Range: $5-14.9 Billion
Emp.: 45,000
Real Estate Brokerage & Property Management Services
N.A.I.C.S.: 531210
Brian R. Corcoran (Exec VP-Phoenix)

Subsidiary (Domestic):

C&W Facility Services, Inc. (4)
275 Grove St Ste 3-200, Auburndale, MA 02466
Tel.: (888) 751-9100
Web Site: http://cwservices.com
Maintenance Services
N.A.I.C.S.: 811490
Paul Bedborough (CEO)

Subsidiary (Domestic):

Pyramid Building Maintenance Corporation (5)
2175 Martin Ave, Santa Clara, CA 95050
Tel.: (408) 727-9393
Web Site: http://www.pacificmaintenance.com
Sales Range: $25-49.9 Million
Emp.: 600
Building Maintenance & Janitorial Services
N.A.I.C.S.: 561210
Kari Hus (Pres)

Subsidiary (Non-US):

Cushman & Wakefield (Bahrain) W.L.L. (4)
The Lagoon Amwaj Island Office #306
Building 2648, Road 5720 Area 257, Manama, Bahrain
Tel.: (973) 17692476
Web Site: http://www.cushmanwakefield.com
Management Consulting Services
N.A.I.C.S.: 541618
Kelvin Crutchlow (Dir & Gen Mgr)

Cushman & Wakefield (HK) Limited (4)
16/F Jardine House, Central, China (Hong Kong)
Tel.: (852) 2956 3888
Web Site: http://www.cushmanwakefield.com
Real Estate Services
N.A.I.C.S.: 531390
Eric Chong (Sr Mgr-Research)

Cushman & Wakefield (India) Pvt. Ltd. (4)
14th Floor Building 8 Tower C DLF Cyber City, Gurgaon, 122002, Haryana, India
Tel.: (91) 1244695555
Web Site: http://www.cushmanwakefield.co.in
Real Estate Services
N.A.I.C.S.: 531390
Anshul Jain (Mng Dir & Country Mgr)

Cushman & Wakefield (NSW) Pty Limited (4)
Level 22 1 O'Connell Street, Sydney, 2000, NSW, Australia
Tel.: (61) 2 8243 9999
Web Site: http://www.cushmanwakefield.com.au
Real Estate Services
N.A.I.C.S.: 531390
James Patterson (CEO-Australia & New Zealand)

Cushman & Wakefield (S) Pte Ltd (4)
3 Church Street 09-03 Samsung Hub, Singapore, 49483, Singapore
Tel.: (65) 65353232
Web Site: http://www.cushmanwakefield.com
Real Estate Services
N.A.I.C.S.: 531390
Christine Li (Dir-Res)

Cushman & Wakefield (Shanghai) Co. Ltd. (4)
42-43/F Tower 2 Plaza 66 1366 Nanjing West Road, Shanghai, 200040, China
Tel.: (86) 21 2208 0088
Web Site: http://www.cushmanwakefield.com.cn
Real Estate Services
N.A.I.C.S.: 531390
Mimie Lau (Mng Dir-East China)

Cushman & Wakefield (U.K.) Ltd. (4)
43-45 Portman Square, London, W1A 3BG, United Kingdom
Tel.: (44) 2079355000
Web Site: http://www.cushmanwakefield.co.uk
Emp.: 1,200
Real Estate Brokerage & Property Management Services
N.A.I.C.S.: 531390
James Heyworth-Dunne (Partner-Central London)

Cushman & Wakefield (VIC) Pty Ltd (4)
Level 9 385 Bourke Street, Melbourne, 3000, VIC, Australia
Tel.: (61) 3 9631 7500
Web Site: http://www.cushmanwakefield.com.au
Real Estate Services
N.A.I.C.S.: 531390
Dominic Long (Mng Dir-Comml Real Estate)

Branch (Non-US):

Cushman & Wakefield - Brussels (4)
Chaussee de la Hulpe 166 Terhulpsesteenweg, Brussels, 1170, Belgium
Tel.: (32) 26290200
Web Site: http://www.cushmanwakefield.be
Real Estate Services
N.A.I.C.S.: 531390

INTERNATIONAL PUBLIC

Koen Nevens (Mng Partner & Head-Northern Europe Reg)

Cushman & Wakefield - Madrid (4)
Edificio Beatriz Jose Ortega y Gasset 29 6th Floor, 28006, Madrid, Spain
Tel.: (34) 91 781 0010
Web Site: http://www.cushmanwakefield.es
Real Estate Services
N.A.I.C.S.: 531390
Jenny Pizarro (Partner)

Cushman & Wakefield - Sao Paulo (4)
Praca Jose Lannes 40-3rd Floor, Sao Paulo, Brazil
Tel.: (55) 1155015464
Web Site: http://www.cushmanwakefield.us
Real Estate Services
N.A.I.C.S.: 531390
Celina Antunes (Pres-South America)

Subsidiary (Non-US):

Cushman & Wakefield K.K. (4)
Sanno Park Tower 13F 2-11-1 Nagatacho, Chiyoda-ku, Tokyo, 100-6113, Japan
Tel.: (81) 3 3596 7070
Web Site: http://www.cushmanwakefield.jp
Real Estate Services
N.A.I.C.S.: 531390
Todd Olson (Exec Mng Dir)

Cushman & Wakefield LLP (4)
125 Old Broad Street, London, EC2N 1AR, United Kingdom
Tel.: (44) 20 3296 3000
Web Site: http://www.cushmanwakefield.com
Emp.: 200
Real Estate Services
N.A.I.C.S.: 531390
Colin Wilson (CEO-EMEA)

Cushman & Wakefield Ltd. (4)
161 Bay Street Suite 1500, PO Box 602, Toronto, M5J 2S1, ON, Canada
Tel.: (416) 862-0611
Web Site: https://www.cushmanwakefield.com
Real Estate Services
N.A.I.C.S.: 531390
Bradley S. Anderson (Vice Chm)

Cushman & Wakefield Sweden AB (4)
Regeringsgatan 59, Stockholm, 11156, Sweden
Tel.: (46) 8 545 677 0
Web Site: http://www.cushmanwakefield.com
Real Estate Services
N.A.I.C.S.: 531390
Agneta Jakobsson (Head-Sweden & Nordics)

Cushman & Wakefield de Mexico (4)
Paseo de las Tamarindos N60-B 2 Floor, Col Bosques de las Lomas, Mexico, 5120, Mexico
Tel.: (52) 55 8525 8000
Web Site: http://www.cushmanwakefield.com
Emp.: 80
Real Estate Services
N.A.I.C.S.: 531390
Victor M. Lachica (Pres & CEO)

Subsidiary (Domestic):

Cushman & Wakefield of Arizona, Inc. (4)
2555 E Camelback Rd Ste 400, Phoenix, AZ 85016
Tel.: (602) 954-9000
Web Site: http://www.cushwakephoenix.com
Emp.: 260
Real Estate Services
N.A.I.C.S.: 531210
Phil Jones (Mng Dir)

Cushman & Wakefield of California, Inc. (4)
425 Market St Ste 2300, San Francisco, CA 94105
Tel.: (415) 397-1700
Web Site: http://www.cushwakesanfrancisco.com
Emp.: 125

AND PRIVATE COMPANIES / ONTARIO TEACHERS' PENSION PLAN

Real Estate Services
N.A.I.C.S.: 531210
Joe Cook *(Mng Principal-Northern CA & OR)*

Cushman & Wakefield of Connecticut, Inc. (4)
107 Elm St 4 Stamford Plz 8th Fl, Stamford, CT 06902
Tel.: (203) 326-5800
Real Estate Services
N.A.I.C.S.: 531210
Steve Baker *(Exec Mng Dir)*

Cushman & Wakefield of Florida, Inc. (4)
333 SE 2nd Ave, Miami, FL 33131-2662
Tel.: (305) 371-4411
Web Site: http://www.cushwakesouthfl.com
Real Estate Services
N.A.I.C.S.: 531210
Larry Richey *(Mng Principal-Florida)*

Branch (Domestic):

Cushman & Wakefield, Inc. - Tampa (5)
1 Tampa City Ctr Ste 3300, Tampa, FL 33602
Tel.: (813) 223-6300
Web Site: http://www.cushwaketampa.com
Emp.: 135
Real Estate Brokerage, Property Management & Leasing Services
N.A.I.C.S.: 531210
Doug Rothschild *(Exec Mng Dir)*

Subsidiary (Domestic):

Cushman & Wakefield of Georgia, Inc. (4)
1180 Peachtree St Ste 3100, Atlanta, GA 30309
Tel.: (404) 875-1000
Web Site: http://www.cushwakeatlanta.com
Emp.: 350
Real Estate Services
N.A.I.C.S.: 531210
Bryan Berthold *(Mng Dir-Workplace Strategies)*

Cushman & Wakefield of Illinois, Inc. (4)
225 W Wacker Dr Ste 3000, Chicago, IL 60606
Tel.: (312) 470-1800
Web Site: http://www.cushwakechicago.com
Emp.: 640
Real Estate Services
N.A.I.C.S.: 531210
Brian Adelstein *(Sr VP)*

Cushman & Wakefield of Long Island, Inc. (4)
401 Broad Hollow Rd Ste 301, Melville, NY 11747-4711
Tel.: (631) 425-1241
Web Site: http://www.cushmanwakefield.com
Emp.: 20
Real Estate Services
N.A.I.C.S.: 531210
Robert Sheehy *(Exec Mng Dir)*

Cushman & Wakefield of Maryland, Inc. (4)
1 E Pratt St Ste 700, Baltimore, MD 21202
Tel.: (410) 752-4285
Web Site: http://www.cushwakebaltimore.com
Emp.: 75
Commercial Real Estate Services
N.A.I.C.S.: 531210
Robert Shovan *(VP-Ops)*

Cushman & Wakefield of Massachusetts, Inc. (4)
225 Franklin St Ste 300, Boston, MA 02110
Tel.: (617) 330-6966
Web Site: http://www.cushwakeboston.com
Emp.: 120
Real Estate Services
N.A.I.C.S.: 531210
Linda McDonough *(Dir-Mktg)*

Cushman & Wakefield of New Jersey, Inc. (4)
1 Meadowlands Plz 7th Fl, East Rutherford, NJ 07073-1605
Tel.: (201) 935-4000
Web Site: http://www.cushmanwakefield.us
Real Estate Services
N.A.I.C.S.: 531210
Richard Baumstein *(Exec Mng Dir)*

Cushman & Wakefield of Oregon, Inc. (4)
200 SW Market St Ste 200, Portland, OR 97201-5730
Tel.: (503) 279-1700
Web Site: http://www.cushmanwakefield.us
Real Estate Services
N.A.I.C.S.: 531210
Judy Howard *(Dir-Ops)*

Cushman & Wakefield of Texas, Inc. (4)
1330 Post Oak Blvd Ste 2700, Houston, TX 77056
Tel.: (713) 877-1700
Web Site: http://www.cushmanwakefield.com
Emp.: 140
Real Estate Services
N.A.I.C.S.: 531210
Scott Wegmann *(Vice Chm)*

Branch (Domestic):

Cushman & Wakefield of Texas, Inc. - Austin (4)
200 W Cesar Chavez Ste 250, Austin, TX 78701
Tel.: (512) 474-2400
Web Site: http://www.cushwakeaustintx.com
Emp.: 50
Commercial Real Estate Broker
N.A.I.C.S.: 531210
Spencer Hayes *(Exec Mng Dir & Mng Principal)*

Subsidiary (Domestic):

Cushman & Wakefield of Washington D.C., Inc. (4)
2101 L St NW Ste 700, Washington, DC 20037
Tel.: (202) 463-2100
Web Site: http://www.cushwakedc.com
Emp.: 650
Real Estate Services
N.A.I.C.S.: 531210
Peter Carroccio *(Mng Principal)*

Cushman & Wakefield of Washington, Inc. (4)
1420 5th Ave Ste 2600, Seattle, WA 98101
Tel.: (206) 682-0666
Web Site: http://www.cushmanwakefield.com
Emp.: 22
Real Estate Services
N.A.I.C.S.: 531210
Janice Davis *(Sr Mgr-Property)*

Branch (Domestic):

Cushman & Wakefield, Inc. - Indianapolis (4)
1 American Sq Ste 1300, Indianapolis, IN 46282
Tel.: (317) 634-6363
Web Site: http://www.cushwakeindianapolis.com
Emp.: 145
Commercial Real Estate Services
N.A.I.C.S.: 531210
Patrick B. Lindley *(Exec Mng Dir)*

Subsidiary (Non-US):

DTZ Zadelhoff v.o.f. (4)
Gustav Mahlerlaan 362, Amsterdam, 1082 ME, Netherlands
Tel.: (31) 206644644
Web Site: http://www.dtz.nl
Emp.: 400
Real Estate & Property Management Services
N.A.I.C.S.: 531311
Marcel Akkerman *(Controller-Credit)*

Joint Venture (Domestic):

Quality Solutions Inc. (4)
128 N First St, Colwich, KS 67030
Tel.: (316) 721-3656
Web Site: http://www.qsifacilities.com
Specialty Trade Contractors
N.A.I.C.S.: 238990
Chad Pore *(Pres)*

Subsidiary (Domestic):

Emcon Associates, Inc. (5)
74 Brick Blvd, Brick, NJ 08723-7984
Tel.: (800) 545-4866
Web Site: http://www.emconfm.com
Facilities Support Services
N.A.I.C.S.: 561210
Michael Cocuzza *(CEO)*

Holding (US):

EXAL Corporation (2)
1 Performance Pl, Youngstown, OH 44502
Tel.: (330) 744-2267
Web Site: http://www.exal.com
Sales Range: $300-349.9 Million
Emp.: 400
Aluminum Container Mfr
N.A.I.C.S.: 332431
Delfin Gibert *(Founder)*

Subsidiary (Non-US):

Boxal (Suisse) SA (3)
Rte De Lossy 20, Belfaux, 1782, Switzerland
Tel.: (41) 264759111
Web Site: http://www.boxal.com
Sales Range: $25-49.9 Million
Emp.: 70
Fabricated Metal Products Mfr
N.A.I.C.S.: 331313
Romuald De Sereys *(Gen Mgr)*

Boxal Netherlands B.V. (3)
Rozenstraat 19, 3905 BM, Veenendaal, Netherlands
Tel.: (31) 8559800
Web Site: http://www.boxal.com
Sales Range: $100-124.9 Million
Emp.: 350
Bottles & Containers Mfr
N.A.I.C.S.: 332431
Deark Schwung *(Mng Dir)*

Joint Venture (US):

Flexera Software LLC (2)
300 Park Blvd Ste 500, Itasca, IL 60143
Tel.: (847) 466-4000
Web Site: http://www.flexerasoftware.com
Sales Range: $50-74.9 Million
Emp.: 250
Software Developer
N.A.I.C.S.: 513210
Jim Ryan *(Pres & CEO)*

Subsidiary (Non-US):

Flexera Software Ltd. (3)
Vision House Wellfield Road, Preston Brook, Runcorn, WA7 3FR, Cheshire, United Kingdom
Tel.: (44) 8708736300
Sales Range: $25-49.9 Million
Software Developer
N.A.I.C.S.: 513210

Subsidiary (Domestic):

Palamida, Inc. (3)
215 2nd St 2nd Floor, San Francisco, CA 94105
Tel.: (415) 777-9400
Web Site: http://www.palamida.com
Sales Range: $1-9.9 Million
Emp.: 200
Application Software Security Solutions
N.A.I.C.S.: 423430
Jeffrey Luszcz *(VP-Svcs & Support)*

RightScale, Inc. (3)
402 E Gutierrez St, Santa Barbara, CA 93101
Tel.: (805) 500-4164
Web Site: http://www.rightscale.com
Sales Range: $10-24.9 Million
Emp.: 110
Software Applications
N.A.I.C.S.: 513210
Michael Crandell *(Co-Founder & CEO)*

Subsidiary (Non-US):

RightScale Asia Pacific (4)
9 Battery Road 11-00, The Straits Trading Building, Singapore, 49910, Singapore
Tel.: (65) 3158 2491
Software Applications
N.A.I.C.S.: 513210

RightScale Australia (4)
100 Walker Street, North Sydney, 2060, NSW, Australia
Tel.: (61) 2 8607 8266
Software Applications
N.A.I.C.S.: 513210

RightScale UK Ltd (4)
1 Lyric Square, Hammersmith, London, W6 0NB, United Kingdom
Tel.: (44) 203 3184425
Software Applications
N.A.I.C.S.: 513210

Joint Venture (US):

GNC Holdings Inc. (2)
300 6th Ave, Pittsburgh, PA 15222
Tel.: (412) 288-4600
Web Site: http://www.gnc.com
Rev: $2,068,188,000
Assets: $1,650,587,000
Liabilities: $1,646,455,000
Net Worth: $4,132,000
Earnings: ($35,112,000)
Emp.: 4,400
Fiscal Year-end: 12/31/2019
Holding Company; Nutritional Supplements Retailer
N.A.I.C.S.: 551112
Cameron W. Lawrence *(Chief Acctg Officer)*

Subsidiary (Domestic):

GNC Parent LLC (3)
300 6th Ave, Pittsburgh, PA 15222
Tel.: (412) 288-4600
Web Site: http://www.gnc.com
Sales Range: $125-149.9 Million
Emp.: 600
Holding Company
N.A.I.C.S.: 551112

Subsidiary (Domestic):

GNC Corporation (4)
300 6th Ave, Pittsburgh, PA 15222
Tel.: (412) 288-4600
Web Site: http://www.gnc.com
Holding Company; Vitamins & Nutritional Supplements Mfr, Distr & Retailer
N.A.I.C.S.: 551112

Subsidiary (Non-US):

GNC Hong Kong Limited (5)
8/F Devon House Taikoo Place 979 King's Road, Quarry Bay, China (Hong Kong)
Tel.: (852) 22993390
Web Site: https://gnclivewell.com.hk
Health Supplements Distr
N.A.I.C.S.: 424210

Subsidiary (Domestic):

General Nutrition Centers, Inc. (5)
300 6th Ave, Pittsburgh, PA 15222
Tel.: (412) 288-4600
Web Site: http://www.gnc.com
Sales Range: $1-4.9 Billion
Nutritional Supplements Mfr, Distr & Retailer
N.A.I.C.S.: 456191
Thomas Dowd *(Exec VP-Store Ops & Dev)*

Subsidiary (Non-US):

General Nutrition Centres Company (5)
6299 Airport Rd Suite 201, Mississauga, L4V 1N3, ON, Canada
Tel.: (905) 612-1016
Web Site: http://www.gnc.ca
Nutritional Supplements Retailer
N.A.I.C.S.: 456191

Subsidiary (Domestic):

General Nutrition Investment Company (5)
1011 Centre Rd, Wilmington, DE 19805
Tel.: (302) 573-3895
Investment Management Service
N.A.I.C.S.: 523940

Nutra Manufacturing, Inc. (5)
1050 Woodruff Rd, Greenville, SC 29607
Tel.: (864) 987-3400

ONTARIO TEACHERS' PENSION PLAN

Ontario Teachers' Pension Plan—(Continued)
Web Site: https://www.nutramfg.com
Sales Range: $25-49.9 Million
Emp.: 600
Vitamins & Nutritional Supplement Mfr
N.A.I.C.S.: 325411
Joseph M. Fortunato (CEO)

Holding (Domestic):

Heritage Resource LP (2)
710 215 2nd Street SW, Calgary, T2P 1M4, AB, Canada
Tel.: (587) 956-1500
Web Site: https://www.heritageroyalty.ca
Sales Range: $250-299.9 Million
Oilfield Royalties Holding Company
N.A.I.C.S.: 551112
Glenn McNamara (Pres & CEO)

Joint Venture (Non-US):

London City Airport Limited (2)
London City Airport City Aviation House, Royal Docks, London, E16 2PB, United Kingdom
Tel.: (44) 20 7646 0088
Web Site: http://www.londoncityairport.com
Airport Operator
N.A.I.C.S.: 488119
Alison FitzGerald (COO)

Joint Venture (US):

National Bedding Co. (2)
2600 Forbs Ave, Hoffman Estates, IL 60192
Tel.: (847) 645-0200
Web Site: http://www.serta.com
Sales Range: $1-4.9 Billion
Emp.: 125
Holding Company; Mattress Mfr & Whslr
N.A.I.C.S.: 551112
Burton Kaplan (Co-Founder)

Subsidiary (Domestic):

Serta, Inc. (3)
2600 Forbs Ave, Hoffman Estates, IL 60192
Tel.: (847) 645-0200
Web Site: http://www.serta.com
Sales Range: $25-49.9 Million
Mattress Mfr
N.A.I.C.S.: 337910
Kevin Bayer (Dir-Acctg)

Subsidiary (Domestic):

Serta Mattress Company (4)
61 Leona Dr, Middleboro, MA 02346-1404
Tel.: (508) 946-4700
Web Site: http://www.serta.com
Sales Range: $25-49.9 Million
Emp.: 120
Mattress Mfr
N.A.I.C.S.: 337910
Tom McCue (VP & Controller)

Plant (Domestic):

Serta Mattress Company (5)
2050 Cessna Dr, Vacaville, CA 95688-8712
Tel.: (707) 446-7999
Web Site: http://www.serta.com
Sales Range: $25-49.9 Million
Emp.: 100
Mattress Mfr
N.A.I.C.S.: 337910

Subsidiary (Domestic):

Simmons Company (3)
1 Concourse Pkwy Ste 800, Atlanta, GA 30328-6188
Tel.: (770) 512-7700
Web Site: http://www.simmons.com
Sales Range: $1-4.9 Billion
Bed & Mattress Mfr & Retailer
N.A.I.C.S.: 337910

Joint Venture (US):

Northern Star Generation Services Company LLC (2)
2929 Allen Pkwy Ste 3275, Houston, TX 77019
Tel.: (713) 580-6250
Web Site: https://northernstargeneration.com
Emp.: 30
Power Generation Services

N.A.I.C.S.: 324199
Joe M. Stevens Jr. (VP-HR & Dev)

Subsidiary (Domestic):

Cambria Cogen Inc. (3)
243 Rubisch Rd, Ebensburg, PA 15931-4500
Tel.: (814) 472-1120
Web Site: http://www.northernstargeneration.com
Rev.: $310,000
Emp.: 45
Electric Power Generation
N.A.I.C.S.: 221118
David Simms (Co-Pres)

Holding (Non-US):

OGF, S.A. (2)
31 rue de Cambrai, 75946, Paris, Cedex 19, France
Tel.: (33) 155265400
Web Site: http://www.ogf.fr
Emp.: 6,400
Holding Company; Funeral Services; Funeral Parlor & Crematorium Operator; Coffin, Headstone & Monument Mfr
N.A.I.C.S.: 551112
Philippe Lerouge (Pres & CEO)

Holding (US):

PODS Enterprises, LLC (2)
13535 Feather Sound Dr, Clearwater, FL 33762
Tel.: (727) 538-6300
Web Site: http://www.pods.com
Moving & Storage Services
N.A.I.C.S.: 493110
John Koch (Pres & CEO)

Plano Molding Company, Inc. (2)
431 E South St, Plano, IL 60545-1676
Tel.: (630) 552-3111
Web Site: http://www.planomolding.com
Sales Range: $100-124.9 Million
Mfr of Plastic Tackle Boxes, Utility Boxes, Tool Boxes, Paramedic Boxes, Cosmetic & Home Organizers
N.A.I.C.S.: 326199
Ben Rand (Mgr-Mktg)

SeaCube Container Leasing Ltd. (2)
1 Maynard Dr, Park Ridge, NJ 07656
Tel.: (201) 391-0800
Web Site: http://www.seacubecontainer.com
Rev.: $198,915,000
Assets: $1,728,891,000
Liabilities: $1,473,085,000
Net Worth: $255,806,000
Earnings: $46,436,000
Emp.: 77
Fiscal Year-end: 12/31/2012
Container Leasing Services
N.A.I.C.S.: 532411
David F. Doorley (CFO)

Subsidiary (Domestic):

Container Leasing International LLC. (3)
1 Maynard Dr, Park Ridge, NJ 07656
Tel.: (201) 391-0800
Refrigerated & Dry Container Leasing Services
N.A.I.C.S.: 532490

Holding (US):

Sterling & Sterling, Inc. (2)
135 Crossways Park Dr Ste 300, Woodbury, NY 11797
Tel.: (516) 487-0300
Web Site: http://www.sterlingrisk.com
Sales Range: $50-74.9 Million
Emp.: 150
Insurance Brokers
N.A.I.C.S.: 524210
David A. Sterling (CEO)

Techem GmbH (1)
Hauptstrasse 89, 65760, Eschborn, Germany
Tel.: (49) 61965220
Web Site: http://www.techem.de
Energy Billing & Energy Management Services
N.A.I.C.S.: 561499
Robert Woggon (Head-Corp Comm)

Subsidiary (Non-US):

Danuvius EOOD (2)
bul Ovtscha kupel 72 Et 2, 1618, Sofia, Bulgaria
Tel.: (359) 2 955 04 11
Energy & Water Metering Equipment Mfr
N.A.I.C.S.: 334515
Asya Angelova (Country Mgr)

Subsidiary (US):

Metron Sustainable Services Inc. (2)
5661 Airport Blvd, Boulder, CO 80301
Tel.: (303) 217-5990
Web Site: http://www.metronsubmetering.com
Energy Billing & Energy Management Services
N.A.I.C.S.: 561499
Rick Minogue (Mng Dir)

Subsidiary (Non-US):

Techem (Schweiz) AG (2)
Steinackerstrasse 55, 8902, Urdorf, Switzerland
Tel.: (41) 43 455 65 00
Web Site: http://www.techem.ch
Energy Billing & Energy Management Services
N.A.I.C.S.: 561499
Marcel Sporrer (Mng Dir & Head-Fin)

Techem Danmark A/S (2)
Trindsovej 7A-B, 8000, Arhus, Denmark
Tel.: (45) 87 44 77 00
Web Site: http://www.techem.dk
Energy Billing & Energy Management Services
N.A.I.C.S.: 561499
Carsten Hejgaard (Mgr)

Techem Energy Services B.V. (2)
Takkebijsters 17 A1, 4817 BL, Breda, Netherlands
Tel.: (31) 76 57 25 800
Web Site: http://www.techem.nl
Energy Billing & Energy Management Services
N.A.I.C.S.: 561499
Maikel van Loo (Mng Dir)

Techem Energy Services Middle East FZCO (2)
Dubai Silicon Oasis Headquaters Building, PO Box 341002, Office 603 D-Wing, Dubai, United Arab Emirates
Tel.: (971) 4 5015516
Web Site: http://www.techem.me
Energy Billing & Energy Management Services
N.A.I.C.S.: 561499

Techem Energy Services S.R.L. (2)
Strada Ronda nr 8 Sector 2, 024102, Bucharest, Romania
Tel.: (40) 21 323 21 21
Web Site: http://www.techem.ro
Energy Billing & Energy Management Services
N.A.I.C.S.: 561499

Techem Enerji Hizmetleri Sanayi ve Ticaret Limited Sirketi (2)
Gulbahar Mah Avni Dilligil Sok Celik Is Merkezi, No 11/A Daire 5 Sisli, 34394, Istanbul, Turkiye
Tel.: (90) 212 447 07 47
Web Site: http://www.techem.com.tr
Energy Billing & Energy Management Services
N.A.I.C.S.: 561499

Techem Norge A/S (2)
Dicks vei 10b, 1366, Lysaker, Norway
Tel.: (47) 22 02 14 59
Web Site: http://www.techem.no
Energy Billing & Energy Management Services
N.A.I.C.S.: 561499

Techem S.r.l. (2)
Via dei Buonvisi 61/D, 00148, Rome, Italy
Tel.: (39) 06 65191810
Web Site: http://www.techem.it
Energy Billing & Energy Management Services
N.A.I.C.S.: 561499
Octavio Manuel Prieto (Mng Dir)

INTERNATIONAL PUBLIC

Techem SAS (2)
Gay Lussac building 20 avenue Edouard Herriot, CS 9002, 92356, Le Plessis-Robinson, Cedex, France
Tel.: (33) 1 46 01 59 70
Web Site: http://www.techem.fr
Energy Billing & Energy Management Services
N.A.I.C.S.: 561499
Bruno Macre (Dir)

Techem Services e.o.o.d. (2)
jk Geo Milev Prof Georgi Pavlov No 3, 1111, Sofia, Bulgaria
Tel.: (359) 700 1 28 28
Web Site: http://www.techem.net
Energy Billing & Energy Management Services
N.A.I.C.S.: 561499

Techem Sverige AB (2)
Foretagsgatan 9, Box 5, 233 51, Svedala, Sweden
Tel.: (46) 102022800
Web Site: http://www.techem.se
Energy Billing & Energy Management Services
N.A.I.C.S.: 561499
Carsten Hejgaard (CEO)

Techem Techniki Pomiarowe Sp. z o.o. (2)
os Lecha 121, 61 298, Poznan, Poland
Tel.: (48) 61 623 35 00
Web Site: http://www.techem.pl
Energy Billing & Energy Management Services
N.A.I.C.S.: 561499
Wojciech Lubiniecki (Chm-Mgmt Bd)

Techem do Brasil Servicos de Medicao de Agua Ltda. (2)
Av Brig Luis Antonio 2 729, 13 andar Jardim Paulista, Sao Paulo, 01401 000, Brazil
Tel.: (55) 11 3059 3030
Web Site: http://www.techem.com.br
Energy Billing & Energy Management Services
N.A.I.C.S.: 561499
Eduardo Lacerda Soares (Mng Dir)

Techem spol. s. r. o. (2)
Hattalova 12, 831 03, Bratislava, Slovakia
Tel.: (421) 2 49 10 64 11
Web Site: http://www.techem.sk
Energy Billing & Energy Management Services
N.A.I.C.S.: 561499
Eliana Kostolany (Mng Dir)

Techem spol. s. r. o. (2)
Pocernicka 96, Malesice, 108 00, Prague, Czech Republic
Tel.: (420) 272 088 777
Web Site: http://www.techem.cz
Energy Billing & Energy Management Services
N.A.I.C.S.: 561499
Jiri Zerzan (Mng Dir)

TricorBraun Inc. (1)
6 City Pl Dr St 1000, Saint Louis, MO 63141
Tel.: (855) 754-3728
Web Site: http://www.tricorbraun.com
Plastic, Glass & Metal Rigid Packaging Product Services
N.A.I.C.S.: 423990
Keith Strope (Chm)

Subsidiary (Domestic):

CanSource, LLC (2)
2120 Miller Dr Ste G, Longmont, CO 80501
Web Site: http://www.cansource.com
Sales Range: $1-9.9 Million
Emp.: 200
Beverage Product Mfr
N.A.I.C.S.: 312140
Paige Sopcic (CEO)

Package All Corp. (2)
655 Church St, Bayport, NY 11705
Tel.: (631) 472-7200
Web Site: https://www.packageall.com
Packaging Industry Services
N.A.I.C.S.: 561910

Price Container & Packaging Corporation (2)

8850 S Hwy 89, Willard, UT 84340
Tel.: (801) 786-1509
Web Site: http://www.pricecontainers.com
Sales Range: $1-9.9 Million
Emp.: 22
Plastic Container, Bottle & Jar Distr
N.A.I.C.S.: 423840
Ryan Price *(Pres)*

SGB Packaging Group, Inc. (2)
401 Hackensack Ave Ste 7 Fl, Hackensack, NJ 07601-6426
Tel.: (201) 488-3030
Web Site: http://www.sgbpackaging.com
Landscape Architectural Services
N.A.I.C.S.: 541320
Shoshanna Gibli *(Founder & Pres)*

Division (Domestic):

TricorBraun Design & Engineering (2)
3011 Butterfield Rd Ste 200, Oak Brook, IL 60523
Tel.: (630) 645-1200
Rigid Packaging Design Services
N.A.I.C.S.: 541490

ONTERRAN LIMITED
27/10 Eagle St, Brisbane, 4000, QLD, Australia
Tel.: (61) 73 054 4570   AU
Web Site:
http://www.onterran.com.au
OTR—(ASX)
Sales Range: $150-199.9 Million
Construction & Property Development Services
N.A.I.C.S.: 531312
Heather Gardner *(CEO)*

Subsidiaries:

Halley Homes Pty Ltd. (1)
43 Lear Jet Dr, Caboolture, Brisbane, 4510, QLD, Australia
Tel.: (61) 754283647
Web Site: http://www.halleyhomes.com.au
Sales Range: $400-449.9 Million
Modular House Building Services
N.A.I.C.S.: 236117

Rapley Wilkinson Property Pty Ltd. (1)
33 Walters Dr, Osborne Park, 6017, WA, Australia
Tel.: (61) 892048700
Web Site: http://www.rapley.com.au
Sales Range: $25-49.9 Million
Emp.: 35
Property Development Services
N.A.I.C.S.: 237210

Rapley Wilkinson Pty Ltd. (1)
33 Walters Dr, Osborne Park, 6017, WA, Australia
Tel.: (61) 892048700
Web Site: http://www.rapley.com.au
Sales Range: $25-49.9 Million
Emp.: 30
Property Development & Building Services
N.A.I.C.S.: 236117

ONTEX GROUP N.V.
Korte Keppestraat 21, 9320, Erembodegem, Belgium
Tel.: (32) 53333600   BE
Web Site: https://ontex.com
ONTEX—(EUR)
Rev.: $2,563,091,232
Assets: $3,767,012,080
Liabilities: $2,418,036,088
Net Worth: $1,348,975,992
Earnings: $66,324,960
Emp.: 10,000
Fiscal Year-end: 12/31/20
Holding Company; Disposable Hygienic & Sanitary Products Mfr & Whslr
N.A.I.C.S.: 551112
Annick De Poorter *(Exec VP-R&D & Sustainability)*

Subsidiaries:

Active Industria De Cosmeticos S.A. (1)
R Contorno Oeste 1/16 quadra 1 lote 1/16 Modulo 2 Distrito, Agroindustrial de Senador Canedo, 74252-900, Goiania, Brazil
Tel.: (55) 6236044001
Disposable Baby Diaper Mfr
N.A.I.C.S.: 322291

Chicolastic Chile, S.A. (1)
La Conception 65 703, 8320000, Providencia, Chile
Tel.: (56) 222362767
Disposable Baby Diaper Mfr
N.A.I.C.S.: 322291

Eutima bvba (1)
Korte Moeie 53, 9900, Eeklo, Belgium
Tel.: (32) 93767711
Disposable Baby Diaper Mfr
N.A.I.C.S.: 322291

Moltex Baby-Hygiene GmbH (1)
Robert-Bosch-Strasse 8, 56727, Mayen, Germany
Tel.: (49) 26514040
Web Site: http://www.moltex.de
Disposable Baby Diaper Mfr
N.A.I.C.S.: 322291

Ontex CZ Sro (1)
Vesecko 491, 511 01, Turnov, Czech Republic
Tel.: (420) 481319600
Emp.: 800
Disposable Baby Diaper Mfr
N.A.I.C.S.: 322291
Michal Kapralek *(Mgr-Plng)*

Ontex France SAS (1)
Parc Affaires - Batiment A 586 Boulevard Albert Camus CS 50433, 69655, Villefranche-sur-Saone, France
Tel.: (33) 474656565
Emp.: 30
Disposable Baby Diaper Mfr
N.A.I.C.S.: 322291

Ontex Healthcare Deutschland GmbH (1)
Hansaring 6, 49504, Lotte, Germany
Tel.: (49) 54049995300
Disposable Baby Diaper Mfr
N.A.I.C.S.: 322291

Ontex Hygienartikel Deutschland GmbH (1)
Fabrikstrasse 30, Grosspostwitz, 02692, Bautzen, Germany
Tel.: (49) 359385820
Disposable Baby Diaper Mfr
N.A.I.C.S.: 322291

Ontex Hygienic Disposables (Shanghai) Ltd. (1)

Ontex Hygienic Disposables Plc (1)
Tracon Tower 7th Floor Office Number 08-03, Churchill Road in Front of Black Lion School, Addis Ababa, Ethiopia
Tel.: (251) 111734021
Disposable Baby Diaper Mfr
N.A.I.C.S.: 322291
Elias Dinagde *(Mgr-Quality)*

Ontex International BVBA (1)
Spinnerijstraat 12, 9240, Zele, Belgium
Tel.: (32) 52 454 611
Web Site: http://www.ontexglobal.com
Holding Company
N.A.I.C.S.: 551112

Subsidiary (Domestic):

Ontex BVBA (2)
Spinnerijstraat 12, 9140, Zele, Belgium
Tel.: (32) 52 454 611
Web Site: http://www.ontexglobal.com
Disposable Hygienic & Sanitary Products Mfr & Whslr
N.A.I.C.S.: 322291

Ontex Italia S.r.l. (1)
Via Guglielmo Oberdan 140, 25127, Brescia, Provincia di Brescia, Italy
Tel.: (39) 0302400676
Disposable Baby Diaper Mfr
N.A.I.C.S.: 322291

Ontex Manufacturing Italy S.r.l. (1)
Localita Cucullo, 66026, Ortona, CH, Italy
Tel.: (39) 0859032184
Emp.: 180

Disposable Baby Diaper Mfr
N.A.I.C.S.: 322291

Ontex Manufacturing Pty Ltd (1)
5 Wonderland Drive, Eastern Creek, 2766, NSW, Australia
Tel.: (61) 298325300
Disposable Baby Diaper Mfr
N.A.I.C.S.: 322291

Ontex Mayen GmbH (1)
Industriegebiet Mayener Tal/Robert-Bosch-Strasse 8, 56727, Mayen, Germany
Tel.: (49) 26514040
Emp.: 750
Disposable Baby Diaper Mfr
N.A.I.C.S.: 322291

Ontex Mexico Operations S.A. de C.V. (1)
Ejercito Nacional 453 1er Piso Col Granda, 11520, Acuamanala de Miguel Hidalgo, Mexico
Tel.: (52) 5583116100
Financial Services
N.A.I.C.S.: 522390

Ontex Operations USA, LCC (1)
9300 NC Hwy 65, Stokesdale, NC 27357
Tel.: (336) 916-0201
Baby Care Product Mfr
N.A.I.C.S.: 325620

Ontex Pakistan Ltd. (1)
Suite No 402 4th Floor Parsa Tower Main Shahrah-e-Faisal, Karachi, Pakistan
Tel.: (92) 213415087172
Disposable Baby Diaper Mfr
N.A.I.C.S.: 322291

Ontex RU LLC (1)
9 Zemlyanoy Val Street Business centre Citydel tenth floor premise I, 105064, Moscow, Russia
Tel.: (7) 4956469221
Emp.: 70
Disposable Baby Diaper Mfr
N.A.I.C.S.: 322291

Ontex Retail UK Ltd. (1)
Unit 5 First Floor-Grovelands Business Park-Boundary Way-Hemel, Hemel Hempstead, HP2 7TE, Hertfordshire, United Kingdom
Tel.: (44) 5601091300
Emp.: 20
Disposable Baby Diaper Mfr
N.A.I.C.S.: 322291

Ontex Tuketim. Urn. San. ve Tic. AS (1)
Oruc Reis Mah Tekstilkent cad Koza Plaza A, Esenler, 34225, Istanbul, Turkiye
Tel.: (90) 2124110900
Disposable Baby Diaper Mfr
N.A.I.C.S.: 322291

Ontex Ukraine LLC (1)
Building 7 C 13 Pimonenko St, 04050, Kiev, Ukraine
Tel.: (380) 444619712
Emp.: 11
Disposable Baby Diaper Mfr
N.A.I.C.S.: 322291

Valor Brands LLC (1)
960 North Point Pkwy Ste 100, Alpharetta, GA 30005
Web Site: http://www.valorbrands.com
Textile Products Mfr
N.A.I.C.S.: 314999

ONTHEHOUSE HOLDINGS LIMITED
Level 2 200 Adelaide Street, Brisbane, 4000, QLD, Australia
Tel.: (61) 7 3136 9841   AU
Web Site:
http://www.onthehouse.com.au
Sales Range: $10-24.9 Million
Emp.: 100
Holding Company; Online Real Estate Brokerage Services
N.A.I.C.S.: 551112
Chris Meehan *(CEO)*

Subsidiaries:

Portplus Pty Limited (1)
Suite 310 546 Collins Street, Melbourne, 3000, VIC, Australia
Tel.: (61) 3 9800 7777
Web Site: http://www.portplus.com.au
Real Estate Software Development Services
N.A.I.C.S.: 541511
Chris Meehin *(CEO)*

Subsidiary (Non-US):

Portplus (NZ) Limited (2)
Level 1 14 Ruapehu Street, PO Box 354, Taupo, 3330, New Zealand
Tel.: (64) 7 377 1797
Web Site: http://www.portplus.com
Real Estate Software Development Services
N.A.I.C.S.: 541511

Residex Pty. Ltd. (1)
121 Walker Street, North Sydney, 2060, NSW, Australia   (50%)
Tel.: (61) 2 9409 0333
Web Site: http://www.residex.com.au
Real Estate Consulting Service
N.A.I.C.S.: 531390
John Edwards *(Founder)*

ONTIC FINSERVE LIMITED
311 Madhupura Commercial Center Madhupura Chowk, Madhupura, Ahmedabad, 380004, India
Tel.: (91) 7929292956
Web Site: https://onticfinserve.in
Year Founded: 1995
540386—(BOM)
Rev.: $60,680
Assets: $552,044
Liabilities: $6,767
Net Worth: $545,277
Earnings: $5,383
Fiscal Year-end: 03/31/23
Financial Advisory Services
N.A.I.C.S.: 523940
Hiteshbhai Mistry *(Exec Dir)*

ONTOR LTD.
12 Leswyn Road, Toronto, M6A 1K3, ON, Canada
Tel.: (416) 781-5286
Web Site: http://www.ontor.com
Year Founded: 1948
Rev.: $20,900,000
Emp.: 100
Industrial Product Distr
N.A.I.C.S.: 333415

ONTRACK SYSTEMS LTD
Plot Y-18 EP-Block Sector-V Salt Lake, Kolkata, 700 091, India
Tel.: (91) 33 2357 2555
Sales Range: $10-24.9 Million
Emp.: 145
Software & Network Technology
N.A.I.C.S.: 513210
S. V. Ramani *(Sec & Exec Dir)*

Subsidiaries:

Ontrack Global Services Ltd. (1)
Plot Y 18 Block EP Sector 5, Salt Lk, 700091, Kolkata, West Bengal, India
Tel.: (91) 3323572555
Information Technology Services
N.A.I.C.S.: 541511

Ontrack Systems (Aust.) Pty. Ltd. (1)
Level 14 309 Kent St, 2000, Sydney, New South Wales, Australia
Tel.: (61) 292480162
Web Site: http://www.ontrackaus.com
Information Technology Services
N.A.I.C.S.: 541511

Ontrack Systems (UK) Ltd (1)
Abbey House 18-24 Stoke Rd, Slough, SL2 5AG, Berkshire, United Kingdom
Tel.: (44) 1753722160
Web Site: http://www.ontrackuk.com
Information Technology Services
N.A.I.C.S.: 541511
Manik Dey *(VP-Sls)*

ONTRACK SYSTEMS LTD

Ontrack Systems Ltd—(Continued)

Ontrack Systems BV. (1)
Leyenseweg 111 D, 3721 BC, Bilthoven, Netherlands
Tel.: (31) 302287310
Information Technology Services
N.A.I.C.S.: 541511

ONVEST OY

Teollisuuskatu 33, 00510, Helsinki, Finland
Tel.: (358) 201115100
Web Site: http://www.onvest.fi
Year Founded: 1913
Electric Equipment Mfr
N.A.I.C.S.: 335999
Maarit Toivanen-Koivisto *(Chm)*

Subsidiaries:

Are Oy (1)
Kaivokselantie 9, Vantaa, 01610, Finland
Tel.: (358) 20 5305500
Renovation Services
N.A.I.C.S.: 561210

Subsidiary (Domestic):

Lemminkainen Talotekniikka Oy (2)
Laturinkuja 8, 02650, Espoo, Finland
Tel.: (358) 2071 5003
Web Site: http://www.lemminkainentalotekniikka.fi
Sales Range: $300-349.9 Million
Emp.: 1,700
Construction & Engineering Services
N.A.I.C.S.: 541330

ONWARD HOLDINGS CO., LTD.

Onward Park Building 10-5 Nihonbashi 3-chome, Chuo-ku, Tokyo, 103-8239, Japan
Tel.: (81) 345121020
Web Site: https://www.onward-hd.co.jp
Year Founded: 1947
OKASF—(OTCIQ)
Rev.: $1,630,625,040
Assets: $1,526,797,360
Liabilities: $778,949,600
Net Worth: $747,847,760
Earnings: $82,918,880
Emp.: 6,377
Fiscal Year-end: 02/28/22
Clothing Mfr & Distr
N.A.I.C.S.: 315210
Michinobu Yasumoto *(Pres & CEO)*

Subsidiaries:

Across Transport Co., Ltd. (1)
Distribution & Logistics Services
N.A.I.C.S.: 541614

Bien Co., Ltd. (1)
ONWARD Bay Park Building 3-9-32 Kaigan, Minato-ku, Tokyo, 108-8439, Japan
Tel.: (81) 354765738
Web Site: http://www.onward-hd.co.jp
Real Estate Management
N.A.I.C.S.: 541618

Birz Association Ltd. (1)
BIRZ Building 3-26-8 Sendagaya, Shibuya-ku, Tokyo, 151-0051, Japan
Tel.: (81) 3 5786 3655
Web Site: http://www.birz.jp
Apparel Mfr & Distr
N.A.I.C.S.: 315990
Toru Hashizume *(Dir-Fin)*

Booklet Co., Ltd. (1)
1-5-26 Shinkita, Joto-ku, Osaka, 536-0015, Japan
Tel.: (81) 6 6939 3345
Book Retailer
N.A.I.C.S.: 459210

Bus Stop Co., Ltd. (1)
Onda Imaizumi Building 7-4 Jingumae 5-chome, Shibuya-ku, Tokyo, 150-0001, Japan
Tel.: (81) 357782391
Web Site: http://www.onward-hd.co.jp

Sales Range: $25-49.9 Million
Emp.: 30
Imported Apparel & Accessories Retailer
N.A.I.C.S.: 459999
Kazunori Ogura *(Pres)*

Candela International Co., Ltd. (1)
5-7-4 Jingumae, Shibuya-Ku, Tokyo, 150-0001, Japan
Tel.: (81) 3 5766 3507
Web Site: http://www.croon-a-song.com
Sales Range: $25-49.9 Million
Emp.: 40
Apparel Mfr & Whslr
N.A.I.C.S.: 315250
Hiroyuki Honda *(Gen Mgr)*

Chacott Co., Ltd. (1)
1-20-8 Jinnan, Shibuya-ku, Tokyo, 150-0041, Japan
Tel.: (81) 120919031
Web Site: http://www.chacott-jp.com
Sales Range: $25-49.9 Million
Stage, Theater & Ballet Goods Mfr
N.A.I.C.S.: 315990
Akinori Baba *(Chm)*

Corporate s.r.l. (1)
Via Robuschi 3, 43126, Parma, Italy
Tel.: (39) 0521292961
Textile & Fabric Products Mfr
N.A.I.C.S.: 314999

Creative Yoko Co., Ltd. (1)
667-16 Takada, Nagano, 381-8545, Japan
Tel.: (81) 262262001
Web Site: http://www.creativeyoko.co.jp
Sales Range: $25-49.9 Million
Emp.: 179
Pet Related Merchandise Mfr
N.A.I.C.S.: 315990
Kazuyuki Suematsu *(Pres)*

Erika s.r.l. (1)
Via Bosche 42 Bis 37060, Verona, Italy
Tel.: (39) 0442 56666
Knitwear Mfr
N.A.I.C.S.: 315990

Frassineti s.r.l. (1)
Via E Fermi 7, Loc Scopeti, 50068, Florence, Italy
Tel.: (39) 055 839 73 85
Luxury Handbag Mfr
N.A.I.C.S.: 316990

Freed of London Ltd. (1)
94 St Martins Lane, London, WC2N 4AT, United Kingdom
Tel.: (44) 2072400432
Web Site: https://www.freedoflondon.com
Dance Related Merchandise Mfr
N.A.I.C.S.: 458110

Gallardo Dance S.L. (1)
Cabestreros 10, 28012, Madrid, Spain
Tel.: (34) 915270100
Web Site: https://www.gallardodance.com
Shoe Product Mfr
N.A.I.C.S.: 316210

Gino Co. S.p.A. (1)
Via Cassia 69, Tavarnuzza, 50029, Florence, Italy
Tel.: (39) 0552372020
Apparel & Accessories Mfr
N.A.I.C.S.: 315990

Horlge Saint Benoit S.A. (1)
22 Rue Sant Benoit, 75006, Paris, France
Tel.: (33) 145441118
Web Site: http://www.onward-hd.co.jp
Sales Range: $10-24.9 Million
Restaurant Management Services
N.A.I.C.S.: 722511

Horloge Saint Benoit S.A.S. (1)
22 Rue Sant Benoit, 75006, Paris, France
Tel.: (33) 145441118
Restaurant Services
N.A.I.C.S.: 722511

Intimates Co., Ltd. (1)
ONWARD Bay Park Building 3-9-32 Kaigan, Minato-ku, Tokyo, 108-8439, Japan
Tel.: (81) 354286611
Women Infant Product Mfr & Distr
N.A.I.C.S.: 315250

Iris S.p.A. (1)
Via Pampagnina 42 Fisse D'Artico, 30032,

Venice, Italy
Tel.: (39) 0415169911
Apparel & Accessories Mfr
N.A.I.C.S.: 315990

Island Co., Ltd. (1)
3-30-12 Ikejiri, Setagaya-ku, Tokyo, 154-0001, Japan
Tel.: (81) 364160828
Women Apparel Mfr
N.A.I.C.S.: 315250

J. Direction Co., Ltd. (1)
12-1 Yakumo 3-Chome, Meguro-ku, Tokyo, 152 0023, Japan
Tel.: (81) 357316239
Web Site: http://www.onward-hd.co.jp
Imported Apparel & Accessories Retailer
N.A.I.C.S.: 459999

J. PRESS, INC. (1)
1801 L St NW, Washington, DC 20036
Tel.: (202) 857-0120
Web Site: http://jpressonline.com
Apparels Mfr
N.A.I.C.S.: 315990

JIL SANDER AMERICA INC. (1)
8 Crosby St 3rd Fl, New York, NY 10013
Tel.: (212) 447-9200
Apparel Distr
N.A.I.C.S.: 424310
Gena Starr *(Mgr-Men's Wholesale)*

Jil Sander AG (1)
Foro Buonaparte 71, 20121, Milan, Italy
Tel.: (39) 028069131
Web Site: http://www.jilsander.com
Sales Range: $700-749.9 Million
Emp.: 700
Clothing Mfr
N.A.I.C.S.: 315210
Alessandra Bettari *(CEO)*

Jil sander Japan Co., Ltd. (1)
313 Minami-Aoyama bldg 3-13-18 Minami-Aoyama, Minato-ku, Tokyo, 107-0062, Japan
Tel.: (81) 36406 0350
Apparel Distr
N.A.I.C.S.: 424310

Joseph Ltd. (1)
90 Peterborough Road, London, SW6 3HH, United Kingdom
Tel.: (44) 2076108438
Web Site: https://www.joseph-fashion.com
Sales Range: $25-49.9 Million
Apparel & Accessories Mfr
N.A.I.C.S.: 315990

Kashiyama (Dalian) Co., Ltd. (1)
North Tie Shan Xi Rd, Economic and Technical Development Zone, Dalian, 116601, China
Tel.: (86) 41187612098
Textile Products Mfr
N.A.I.C.S.: 314999

Kashiyama Daikanyama Co., Ltd. (1)
14-18 Daikanyama-cho, Shibuya-ku, Tokyo, 150-0034, Japan
Tel.: (81) 357841670
Web Site: http://www.kashiyamadaikanyama.com
Restaurant Services
N.A.I.C.S.: 722511

Kashiyama Saga Co., Ltd. (1)
6656 Tachibanacyo Nagasima, Takeo, 843-0014, Saga, Japan
Tel.: (81) 954232118
Men & Women Clothing Product Mfr
N.A.I.C.S.: 315990

Kokobuy Inc. (1)
6th Floor Daikanyama Front 16-2 Daikanyama-cho, Shibuya-ku, Tokyo, 150-0034, Japan
Tel.: (81) 366963547
Cosmetic Product Mfr & Distr
N.A.I.C.S.: 325620

La Maison Moreau S.A.S. (1)
14 Rue de Savoie, 75006, Paris, France
Tel.: (33) 185658410
Bag Product Mfr & Distr
N.A.I.C.S.: 316990

Maglificio Erika s.r.l. (1)

INTERNATIONAL PUBLIC

Via Boschi N 42 Bis, Gazzo Veronese, 37060, Verona, VR, Italy
Tel.: (39) 044256666
Web Site: https://maglificioerikasrl.gruppoflorence.it
Knitwear Product Mfr & Distr
N.A.I.C.S.: 313240

Maison Moreau Japan Co., Ltd. (1)
3-26-8 Sendagaya, Shibuya-ku, Tokyo, 151-0051, Japan
Tel.: (81) 357705339
Bag Product Mfr & Distr
N.A.I.C.S.: 316990

Mulberry Japan Co., Ltd. (1)
3rd Floor ONWARD Bay Park Building 3-9-32 Kaigan, Minato-ku, Tokyo, 108-8439, Japan
Tel.: (81) 354765040
Women Clothing & Leather Bag Distr
N.A.I.C.S.: 458110

O & K Co., Ltd. (1)
2-8-81 Nakajima, Nishiyodogawa-ku, Osaka, 555-0041, Japan
Tel.: (81) 664710110
Web Site: https://www.oandk-co.com
Emp.: 324
Steel Pole Mfr
N.A.I.C.S.: 331222
Kazuta Oku *(Pres)*

ONWARD BEACH RESORT GUAM, INC. (1)
445 Governor Carlos G Camacho Rd, Tamuning, GU 96913
Tel.: (671) 647-7777
Web Site: http://www.onwardguam.com
Sales Range: $50-74.9 Million
Emp.: 250
Home Management Services
N.A.I.C.S.: 721110

ONWARD KASHIYAMA SINGAPORE PTE. CO., LTD. (1)
150 Orchard Road 07-18, Singapore, 238841, Singapore
Tel.: (65) 68380690
Sales Range: $25-49.9 Million
Emp.: 30
Apparel Whslr
N.A.I.C.S.: 315210
Jun Murakami *(Gen Mgr)*

Onward Creative Center Co., Ltd. (1)
2-10-10 Iidabashi, Chiyoda-ku, Tokyo, 102-8115, Japan
Tel.: (81) 352261358
Web Site: https://www.onwardcc.jp
Emp.: 25
Store Operation & Management Services
N.A.I.C.S.: 541611

Onward Fashion Trading Co., Ltd. (1)
5F No 55 Loushanguan Rd, 400 Changle Road, Shanghai, 200336, China
Tel.: (86) 2164723660
Sales Range: $25-49.9 Million
Emp.: 50
Apparel & Accessories Mfr
N.A.I.C.S.: 315990

Onward Golf Resort Guam, Inc. (1)
825 Route 4A, Talofofo, GU 96915
Tel.: (671) 789-5555
Golf Resort Operator
N.A.I.C.S.: 713910
Tamotsu Ito *(Gen Mgr)*

Onward International Fashion Co., Ltd. (1)
3-26-8 Sendagaya, Shibuya-ku, Tokyo, 151-0051, Japan
Tel.: (81) 357705370
Web Site: http://www.onward-if.com
Emp.: 223
Online Clothing Services
N.A.I.C.S.: 458110
Hitoshi Futamura *(Chm)*

Onward Italia S.p.A. (1)
Via Della Spiga 9, 20121, Milan, Italy
Tel.: (39) 02783667
Sales Range: $25-49.9 Million
Emp.: 4
Apparel & Accessories Mfr
N.A.I.C.S.: 315990

AND PRIVATE COMPANIES

Onward J Bridge Co., Ltd. (1)
3-9-32 Kaigan, Minato-ku, Tokyo, 108-8439, Japan
Tel.: (81) 354765370
Clothing Product Mfr & Distr
N.A.I.C.S.: 315250

Onward Kashiyama Co., Ltd. (1)
3-10-5 Nihonbashi, Chuo-ku, Tokyo, 103-8239, Japan
Tel.: (81) 345121020
Web Site: https://www.onward.co.jp
Emp.: 3,086
Clothing Mfr
N.A.I.C.S.: 315990

Onward Kashiyama Hong Kong Ltd. (1)
Units 1208-9 Lippo Sun Plaza 28 Canton Road T S T, Kowloon, China (Hong Kong)
Tel.: (852) 23672055
Sales Range: $25-49.9 Million
Emp.: 15
Apparel & Accessories Mfr
N.A.I.C.S.: 315990

Onward Kashiyama Korea Co., Ltd. (1)
Seochojungang-Ro 61, Seoul, 06651, Korea (South)
Tel.: (82) 25485841
Web Site: http://www.onward.co.kr
Emp.: 50
Apparel & Accessories Mfr
N.A.I.C.S.: 315990
H. K. Park *(Mgr)*

Onward Kashiyama Vietnam Ltd. (1)
5th Floor 60 Nguyen Van Thu Street, Da Kao Ward District 1, Ho Chi Minh City, Vietnam
Tel.: (84) 839118857
Apparel Distr
N.A.I.C.S.: 424310

Onward Life Design Network Co., Ltd. (1)
10-5 Nihonbashi 3-chome, Chuo-ku, Tokyo, 103 8239, Japan
Tel.: (81) 332722748
Web Site: http://www.onward-hd.co.jp
Sales Range: $25-49.9 Million
Emp.: 20
Travel, Culture, Hotel & Restaurant Information Services
N.A.I.C.S.: 519290

Onward Personal Style Co, Ltd (1)
ONWARD Bay Park Building 3-9-32 Kaigan, Minato-ku, Tokyo, 108 8439, Japan
Tel.: (81) 354766131
Web Site: http://www.onward-hd.co.jp
Men's Clothing Mfr
N.A.I.C.S.: 424350

Onward Personal Style Co., Ltd. (1)
ONWARD Bay Park Building 3-9-32 Kaigan, Minato-ku, Tokyo, 108-8439, Japan
Tel.: (81) 354766131
Men Infant Product Mfr & Distr
N.A.I.C.S.: 315250

Onward Resort & Golf Co., Ltd. (1)
3-10-5 Nihonbashi, Chuo-ku, Tokyo, 103-8239, Japan
Tel.: (81) 345121130
Web Site: http://www.onward-hd.co.jp
Rental Facilities Services
N.A.I.C.S.: 532310

Onward Retail L.L.C. (1)
530 7th Ave 29th Fl, New York, NY 10018
Tel.: (212) 997-3600
Apparel Mfr & Distr
N.A.I.C.S.: 315990
Chinatsu Kato-Samuel *(Sr Dir-ICB Product Dev & Licensing)*

Onward Trading (Shanghai) Co., Ltd. (1)
5F No 55 Loushanguan Rd, Shanghai, 200336, China
Tel.: (86) 2162713535
Uniform Textile Product Mfr
N.A.I.C.S.: 315150

Onward Trading Co., Ltd. (1)
2-10-10 Iidabashi, Chiyoda-ku, Tokyo, 102-8115, Japan
Tel.: (81) 352261333

Web Site: https://www.onward-shoji.co.jp
Uniform, Sales Promotion Goods, Men's Wear, Jewelry, Ladies' Wear, Sundry Goods & Health Related Product Mfr
N.A.I.C.S.: 315990

Onward U.S.A. L.L.C. (1)
8 W 38th St Ste 200, New York, NY 10018
Tel.: (212) 997-3600
Men Suit Distr
N.A.I.C.S.: 424350

Project Sloane Ltd. (1)
50 Carnwath Road, London, SW6 3JX, United Kingdom
Tel.: (44) 2077362522
Apparel Whslr
N.A.I.C.S.: 424350

Shanghai Across Apparel Processing Co., Ltd. (1)
Building 6 No 258 Jinglian Road, Minhang, Shanghai, China
Tel.: (86) 21 6434 3099
Web Site: http://www.onward-hd.co.jp
Apparels Mfr
N.A.I.C.S.: 315990

Shanghai Onward Fashion Co., Ltd. (1)
5F No 55 Loushanguan Rd, Putuo District, Shanghai, 200336, China
Tel.: (86) 2164666466
Web Site: http://www.chinaonward.net
Apparel & Accessoies Mfr
N.A.I.C.S.: 315990

Taicang Onward High Fashion Co., Ltd. (1)
28 Group of Taixi Village Shaxi Town, Taicang, Jiangsu, China
Tel.: (86) 51253254297
Web Site: http://www.onward-hd.co.jp
Apparels Mfr
N.A.I.C.S.: 315990

Tiaclasse Inc. (1)
1-5-3 Shinsenri Higashimachi, Toyonaka, 560-0082, Osaka, Japan
Tel.: (81) 668735566
Web Site: https://www.tiaclasse.com
Online Clothing Services
N.A.I.C.S.: 458110

Vina Birz Co., Ltd. (1)
C6 C7 Dinh TRAM Industrial Zone, Viet Yen, Bac Giang, Vietnam
Tel.: (84) 240 3661410
Apparels Mfr
N.A.I.C.S.: 315990

ONWARD LUXURY GROUP S.P.A.
Via Cassia 69 Tavarnuzze, 50029, Florence, Italy
Tel.: (39) 0552372020 IT
Shoe Product Mfr
N.A.I.C.S.: 316210

ONWARD MEDICAL N.V.
Schimmelt 2, 5611 ZX, Eindhoven, Netherlands
Tel.: (31) 402882830
Web Site: https://www.onwd.com
Year Founded: 2015
ONWD—(EUR)
Rev.: $587,261
Assets: $48,160,945
Liabilities: $28,367,369
Net Worth: $19,793,575
Earnings: ($39,939,287)
Emp.: 108
Fiscal Year-end: 12/31/23
Medical Technology Services
N.A.I.C.S.: 541512
Andy Dolan *(VP)*

ONWARD TECHNOLOGIES LTD.
2nd Floor Sterling Centre Dr A B Road, Worli, Mumbai, 400018, India
Tel.: (91) 2224926570
Web Site:
   https://www.onwardgroup.com

ONWARDTEC—(NSE)
Rev.: $53,513,662
Assets: $29,045,297
Liabilities: $8,199,029
Net Worth: $20,846,268
Earnings: $1,376,428
Emp.: 2,798
Fiscal Year-end: 03/31/23
Mechanical Engineering Design & IT Consulting Services
N.A.I.C.S.: 541690
Harish Shantilal Mehta *(Founder & Chm)*

Subsidiaries:

Onward Technologies GmbH (1)
Taunusanlage 8, 60329, Frankfurt am Main, Germany
Tel.: (49) 611188900
Engineering Design Services
N.A.I.C.S.: 541330

ONXEO S.A.
49 Boulevard du General Martial Valin, 75015, Paris, France
Tel.: (33) 145587600 FR
Web Site: https://www.orpha.net
Year Founded: 1997
ALVIO—(EUR)
Rev.: $1,986,974
Assets: $38,938,073
Liabilities: $22,595,209
Net Worth: $16,342,863
Earnings: ($22,457,225)
Emp.: 19
Fiscal Year-end: 12/31/23
Biopharmaceutical Product Mfr
N.A.I.C.S.: 325412
Nicolas Fellmann *(CFO)*

Subsidiaries:

Onxeo US Inc. (1)
315 Madison Ave Ste 3006, New York, NY 10017
Tel.: (646) 979-3657
Pharmaceuticals Product Mfr
N.A.I.C.S.: 325412

ONYX INTERNET LIMITED
9 Cheltenham Road Portrack Interchange Business Park, Stockton-on-Tees, TS18 2AD, United Kingdom
Tel.: (44) 1642 216 200
Web Site: http://www.onyx.net
Year Founded: 1996
Sales Range: $10-24.9 Million
Emp.: 85
IT Services
N.A.I.C.S.: 541512
Neil Stephenson *(CEO)*

ONZIMA VENTURES PLC
190 High Street, Tonbridge, TN9 1BE, Kent, United Kingdom
Tel.: (44) 1732 366561
Web Site:
   http://www.onzimaventures.com
Sales Range: $1-9.9 Million
Emp.: 29
Investment Services
N.A.I.C.S.: 523999

Subsidiaries:

Cognito Software Limited (1)
Cognito House, Fordton Trading Estate, Crediton, EX17 3BZ, Devon, United Kingdom
Tel.: (44) 1363771044
Web Site: http://www.cognitosoftware.co.uk
Sales Range: $25-49.9 Million
Emp.: 7
Computer Application Software Support & Marketing Services
N.A.I.C.S.: 513210
Kerry Frater *(Gen Mgr)*

Integrated Publishing Systems Limited (1)
Akhter House Perry Road, Harlow, CM18

OOH HOLDINGS LIMITED

7PN, Essex, United Kingdom
Tel.: (44) 1279821200
Web Site: http://www.ultima-networks.co.uk
Sales Range: $25-49.9 Million
Computer Application Software Support Services
N.A.I.C.S.: 513210
Humayun Mughal *(CEO)*

UTN Solutions (North) Limited (1)
Akhter House Perry Rd, Harlow, CM18 7PN, Essex, United Kingdom
Tel.: (44) 1279821200
Web Site: http://www.ultimanetworks.co.uk
Sales Range: $50-74.9 Million
Emp.: 6
Electronic Products Merchandiser
N.A.I.C.S.: 423620
Wassim Mughal *(Mgr)*

OO. LANDESHOLDING GMBH
Landhausplatz 1, A-4021, Linz, Austria
Tel.: (43) 73277200 AT
Web Site:
   http://www.landesholding.com
Year Founded: 2005
Holding Company
N.A.I.C.S.: 551112
Dieter Widera *(CEO)*

Subsidiaries:

HYPO Oberosterreich (1)
Landstrasse 38, 4010, Linz, Austria
Tel.: (43) 73276390
Web Site: http://www.hypo.at
Sales Range: $250-299.9 Million
Emp.: 459
Retail & Commercial Banking, Real Estate, Leasing & Other Financial Services
N.A.I.C.S.: 522110

OO. Gesundheits- und Spitals-AG (1)
Goethestrasse 89, 4020, Linz, Austria (100%)
Tel.: (43) 50554600
Web Site: http://www.gespag.at
Sales Range: $700-749.9 Million
General Hospital & Specialty Hospital Operator
N.A.I.C.S.: 561110
Harald Geck *(CEO)*

OO. Technologie- und Marketinggesellschaft m.b.H. (1)
Hafenstrasse 47-51, 4020, Linz, Austria (56%)
Tel.: (43) 732798100
Web Site: http://www.tmg.at
Business Location & Technology Marketing Services
N.A.I.C.S.: 541613
Bruno Lindorfer *(Mng Dir & Member-Mgmt Bd)*

OOEDO ONSEN REIT INVESTMENT CORPORATION
3-3-4 Nihonbashihoncho Chuo-ku, Tokyo, 103-0023, Japan
Tel.: (81) 362625200
Year Founded: 2016
3472—(TKS)
Sales Range: Less than $1 Million
Real Estate Investment Services
N.A.I.C.S.: 531210
Fuminori Imanishi *(Exec Dir)*

OOH HOLDINGS LIMITED
A5 9/F Jumbo Building 189 Wai Yip Street, Kwun Tong, Kowloon, China (Hong Kong)
Tel.: (852) 27516666 Ky
Web Site: https://mediasavvy.com.hk
Year Founded: 2015
8091—(HKG)
Rev.: $5,596,995
Assets: $11,555,070
Liabilities: $6,380,865
Net Worth: $5,174,205
Earnings: ($1,206,405)
Emp.: 30

OOH HOLDINGS LIMITED

OOH Holdings Limited—(Continued)
Fiscal Year-end: 03/31/23
Advertising Display Services
N.A.I.C.S.: 541850

OOH!MEDIA LIMITED
Level 2 73 Miller Street, North Sydney, 2060, NSW, Australia
Tel.: (61) 299275555 AU
Web Site: https://www.oohmedia.com.au
Year Founded: 2014
OML—(ASX)
Rev.: $395,635,115
Assets: $1,156,213,102
Liabilities: $618,899,915
Net Worth: $537,313,187
Earnings: $21,040,082
Emp.: 776
Fiscal Year-end: 12/31/22
Holding Company; Out-of-Home Advertising Services
N.A.I.C.S.: 551112
Brendon Cook (CEO)

Subsidiaries:

Adshel Street Furniture Pty Ltd **(1)**
The Forum Level 9 205 Pacific Highway, Saint Leonards, 2065, NSW, Australia
Tel.: (61) 284257200
Web Site: http://www.adshel.com.au
Outdoor Advertising Services
N.A.I.C.S.: 541850
Myke Tyquin (CEO)

Subsidiary (Non-US):
Adshel New Zealand Ltd **(2)**
Level 1 22 Pollen Street Grey Lynn, Auckland, 1021, New Zealand
Tel.: (64) 93775595
Web Site: http://www.adshel.com.au
Outdoor Advertising Services
N.A.I.C.S.: 541890

oOh!media Group Limited **(1)**
Level 2 73 Miller Street, North Sydney, 2060, NSW, Australia
Tel.: (61) 299275555
Web Site: https://www.oohmedia.com.au
Holding Company
N.A.I.C.S.: 551112

Subsidiary (Domestic):
oOh!media Operations Pty. Ltd. **(2)**
Level 2 76 Berry Street, North Sydney, 2060, NSW, Australia **(100%)**
Tel.: (61) 299275555
Web Site: http://www.oohmedia.com.au
Out-of-Home Advertising Services
N.A.I.C.S.: 541850

oOh!media Regional Pty. Limited **(2)**
Level 2 76 Berry Street, North Sydney, 2060, NSW, Australia
Tel.: (61) 294500945
Sales Range: $25-49.9 Million
Emp.: 1
Billboard Advertising Services
N.A.I.C.S.: 541810

OOKAMI LIMITED
108 Outram Street, West Perth, 6005, WA, Australia
Tel.: (61) 8 9486 7244
Web Site: http://ookami.com.au
Rev.: $92,330
Assets: $2,430,508
Liabilities: $70,426
Net Worth: $2,360,082
Earnings: ($883,846)
Emp.: 40
Fiscal Year-end: 06/30/18
Software Development Services
N.A.I.C.S.: 513210
Faldi Ismail (Chm)

Subsidiaries:

AEC China Limited **(1)**
Heqiao Dasha A407 8A Guanghua Rd, Beijing, 100026, Chaoyang, China

Tel.: (86) 1065814430
Engine Mfr
N.A.I.C.S.: 333618

OOMITSU CO., LTD.
227 1 Furumiya cho, Ogaki, 503-0947, Gifu, Japan
Tel.: (81) 584897777
Web Site: https://www.oomitsu.com 3160—(TKS)
Rev.: $466,038,050
Assets: $157,238,680
Liabilities: $117,122,590
Net Worth: $40,116,090
Earnings: $5,023,600
Emp.: 1,045
Fiscal Year-end: 05/31/24
Food Service Contractors
N.A.I.C.S.: 722310
Takeshi Kanamori (Pres & CEO)

OOO MORGAN STANLEY BANK
21 1st Tverskaya-Yamskaya Street, Moscow, 125047, Russia
Tel.: (7) 495 287 2100
Web Site: http://www.morganstanley.ru
Year Founded: 1994
Investment Banking Services
N.A.I.C.S.: 523150
Mikhail Soloviev (Chm-Mgmt Bd & Pres)

OOO MORON
1-Neopalimovski Pereulok 16/13, 119021, Moscow, Russia
Tel.: (7) 4957280291 RU
Pharmaceuticals Product Mfr
N.A.I.C.S.: 325412

OOO NOVGORODPRODUKT
St North 17, Velikiy Novgorod, Russia
Tel.: (7) 9116300698
Web Site: http://nowgorodprodukt.ru
Year Founded: 1994
Feed Mfr
N.A.I.C.S.: 311119
Angela Savcenco (Dir-European Ops)

OOO PONSSE
Ponsse Street 4 Ter, Southern Part of The Industrial Zone Lomonosov District, Gorelovo, 188508, Russia
Tel.: (7) 8127771211
Emp.: 100
Construction Equipment Distr
N.A.I.C.S.: 423610

OOO RUUKKI RUS
100 Km Kievskoe Shosse, Obninsk, 249030, Kaluzhskaya, Russia
Tel.: (7) 4843860035
Metal Component Distr
N.A.I.C.S.: 423510
Jussi Tuisku (Gen Dir)

OOO SEVERGRUPP
2 Clara ul Zetkin, Moscow, Russia
Tel.: (7) 495 926 77 66 RU
Web Site: http://www.severgroup.ru
Year Founded: 1993
Investment Holding Company
N.A.I.C.S.: 551112
Alexey Mordashov (CEO)

Subsidiaries:

OJSC Power Machines **(1)**
25A Protopopovsky Perulok, Moscow, 129010, Russia **(100%)**
Tel.: (7) 812 346 7037
Web Site: http://www.power-m.ru
Sales Range: $1-4.9 Billion
Emp.: 20,844
Hydro, Steam, Gas & Nuclear Power Plants Turbine & Generator Mfr & Supplier
N.A.I.C.S.: 333611
Maxim Rumyantsev (Dir-HR)

Subsidiary (Non-US):
Enermasch Handels GmbH **(2)**
Habersaath-Strasse 58, 10115, Berlin, Germany **(96%)**
Tel.: (49) 302835234
Web Site: http://www.enermasch.com
Sales Range: $25-49.9 Million
Emp.: 4
Business Support Services
N.A.I.C.S.: 561499

Subsidiary (Domestic):
Kaluga Turbine Works OJSC **(2)**
Moskovskaia str h 241, 248021, Kaluga, Russia
Tel.: (7) 4842706566
Web Site: http://www.paoktz.ru
Wind Power Generation Services
N.A.I.C.S.: 221115

PJSC TKZ Krasny Kotelshchik **(2)**
220 Lenina str, 347910, Taganrog, 347910, Rostov, Russia
Tel.: (7) 8634313601
Web Site: https://www.tkz.su
Sales Range: Less than $1 Million
Steam Generator Mfr
N.A.I.C.S.: 335312
Alexander Podkalyuk (Dir-Technical)

Plant (Domestic):

Power Machines Reostat Plant LLC **(2)**
65 Tretyei Udarnoi Armii St, Velikiye Luki, Pskov, 182100, Russia
Tel.: (7) 8115338103
Web Site: http://www.reostat.ru
Automotive Components Mfr
N.A.I.C.S.: 336330

OOOOO ENTERTAINMENT COMMERCE LTD.
595 Burrard Street Suite 700, Vancouver, V7X 1S8, BC, Canada
Tel.: (604) 339-7688
Year Founded: 2012
OOOOF—(OTCQB)
Rev.: $275,037
Assets: $2,040,929
Liabilities: $3,568,722
Net Worth: ($1,527,794)
Earnings: ($9,027,821)
Fiscal Year-end: 10/31/22
Asset Management Services
N.A.I.C.S.: 523940
Jin Kuang (CFO-Interim)

OOREDOO PALESTINE
PO Box 4236, Sateh Marhaba, Al-Bireh, Palestine
Tel.: (970) 568003000
Web Site: https://www.ooredoo.ps
Year Founded: 2009
OOREDOO—(PAL)
Rev.: $109,001,985
Assets: $220,209,316
Liabilities: $70,425,070
Net Worth: $149,784,246
Earnings: $16,139,027
Emp.: 630
Fiscal Year-end: 12/31/23
Mobile Telecommunications Services
N.A.I.C.S.: 517112
Mohammed Abu Ramadan (Chm)

OOREDOO Q.S.C.
West Bay, PO Box 217, Doha, Qatar
Tel.: (974) 44400400 QA
Web Site: https://www.ooredoo.qa
Year Founded: 1987
ORDS—(QE)
Rev.: $6,352,312,903
Assets: $15,962,827,917
Liabilities: $7,578,253,119
Net Worth: $8,384,574,798
Earnings: $962,988,071
Emp.: 12,604
Fiscal Year-end: 12/31/23
Telecommunication Servicesb

INTERNATIONAL PUBLIC

N.A.I.C.S.: 551112
Najib Khan (Chief Bus Svcs Officer-Grp)

Subsidiaries:

Asiacell Communications PJSC **(1)**
Salem Street, Sulaymaniyah, Kurdistan, Iraq **(53.9%)**
Tel.: (964) 7701195811
Web Site: https://www.asiacell.com
Rev.: $1,024,649,715
Assets: $1,551,501,025
Liabilities: $616,265,730
Net Worth: $935,235,295
Earnings: $181,755,845
Fiscal Year-end: 12/31/2022
Wireless Telecommunication Services
N.A.I.C.S.: 517112
Faruk Mustafa Rasool (Chm)

FAST Telecommunication Company **(1)**
287 5th Floor Salhiya Building Abdullah Al Salem Street, Kuwait, 15453, Kuwait
Tel.: (965) 2225 6666
Web Site: http://www.fasttelco.net
Telecommunication Servicesb
N.A.I.C.S.: 517112

Intaleq Technology Consulting & Services W.L.L. **(1)**
PO Box - 23833, Doha, Qatar
Tel.: (974) 4 413 6320
Web Site: https://intaleq.qa
Information Technology Services
N.A.I.C.S.: 541519

Ooredoo Maldives PLC **(1)**
Ooredoo Maldives H Sunleet 5th Floor, PO Box 2196, Boduthakurufaanu Magu, Male, Maldives
Tel.: (960) 961 3929
Web Site: https://www.ooredoo.mv
Telecommunication Servicesb
N.A.I.C.S.: 517810
Najib Khan (CEO & Mng Dir)

Ooredoo Myanmar Ltd. **(1)**
Myanmar Centre Tower 1 192 Kaba Aye Pagoda Road, Bahan Township, Yangon, Myanmar
Tel.: (95) 997 000 0234
Web Site: https://ooredoo.com.mm
Telecommunication Servicesb
N.A.I.C.S.: 517810

Ooredoo Oman **(1)**
PO Box 874, 111, Muscat, Oman
Tel.: (968) 22002200
Web Site: http://www.ooredoo.om
Rev.: $734,741,282
Assets: $1,069,185,143
Liabilities: $401,416,569
Net Worth: $667,768,574
Earnings: $108,500,347
Emp.: 1,000
Fiscal Year-end: 12/31/2018
Telecommunication Servicesb
N.A.I.C.S.: 517810
Sultan Al Wahaibi (Chief Bus & Wholesale Officer)

Ooredoo Qatar **(1)**
West Bay Area, PO Box 217, Doha, Qatar
Tel.: (974) 4440 0400
Web Site: http://www.ooredoo.qa
Telecommunication Servicesb
N.A.I.C.S.: 517111
Yousuf Abdulla Al Kubaisi (COO)

P.T. Indosat Mega Media **(1)**
Jl Kebagusan Raya No 36, Pasar Minggu, Jakarta, 12550, Indonesia
Tel.: (62) 217 854 6900
Web Site: https://indosatm2.id
Media Services
N.A.I.C.S.: 541840

PT Indosat Tbk **(1)**
Jalan Medan Merdeka Barat No 21 Jakarta Pusat, Jakarta, 10110, Indonesia **(65%)**
Tel.: (62) 2130003001
Web Site: https://www.ioh.co.id
Rev.: $3,326,797,103
Assets: $7,450,062,850
Liabilities: $5,261,013,898
Net Worth: $2,189,048,952
Earnings: $310,136,621
Emp.: 2,699

Fiscal Year-end: 12/31/2023
Satellite Telecommunications & Television Programming Services
N.A.I.C.S.: 517410
Indar Atmanto *(Chief Corp Svcs Officer)*

Subsidiary (Non-US):

Indosat Singapore Pte Ltd (2)
8 Temasek Boulevard, 038988, Singapore, 038988, Singapore (100%)
Tel.: (65) 62355155
Web Site: http://www.indosatsingapore.com
Sales Range: $25-49.9 Million
Emp.: 10
Telecommunications
N.A.I.C.S.: 517810

OOTOYA HOLDINGS CO., LTD.
4F Ekinia Yokohama 1-1-8 Kitasaiwai, Nishi-ku, Yokohama, 220-0004, Kanagawa, Japan
Tel.: (81) 455770357
Web Site: https://www.ootoya.jp
Year Founded: 1977
2705—(TKS)
Rev.: $184,379,340
Assets: $71,711,890
Liabilities: $38,999,000
Net Worth: $32,712,890
Earnings: $9,267,220
Emp.: 629
Fiscal Year-end: 03/31/24
Holding Company
N.A.I.C.S.: 551111
Hisami Mitsumori *(Founder)*

Subsidiaries:

Hong Kong Ootoya Co., Ltd. (1)
Unit 102B 1 / F Mirror Tower 61 Mody Road, Tsim Sha Tsui, Kowloon, China (Hong Kong)
Tel.: (852) 21423130
Restaurant Services
N.A.I.C.S.: 722511

M Ootoya (Thailand) Co., Ltd. (1)
47/1 Sukhumvit Soi 23, Klongtoey Nua Wattana, Bangkok, 10110, Thailand
Tel.: (66) 26408283
Restaurant Services
N.A.I.C.S.: 722511

Ootoya Co., Ltd. (1)
Equinia Yokohama 4F 1-1-8 Kitasaiwai, Nishi-ku, Yokohama, Kanagawa, Japan
Tel.: (81) 455770357
Restaurant Services
N.A.I.C.S.: 722511

Three Forest (Thailand) Co., Ltd. (1)
47/1 Sukhumvit Soi 23, Klongtoey Nua Wattana, Bangkok, 10110, Thailand
Tel.: (66) 26408280
Restaurant Services
N.A.I.C.S.: 722511

OP FINANCIAL GROUP
Teollisuuskatu 1b, 00510, Helsinki, Finland
Tel.: (358) 10252011
Web Site: http://www.op.fi
Year Founded: 1981
Sales Range: $1-4.9 Billion
Emp.: 12,130
Financial Services Holding Company
N.A.I.C.S.: 551111
Reijo Karhinen *(Chm & Pres)*

Subsidiaries:

Pohjola Bank plc (1)
Teollisuuskatu 1b, 00510, Helsinki, Finland (100%)
Tel.: (358) 50 523 9904
Web Site: http://www.pohjola.fi
Banking & Insurance Services
N.A.I.C.S.: 522110
Jouko Polonen *(Pres & CEO)*

Subsidiary (Domestic):

A-Insurance Ltd (2)
, Lapinmaentie 1, FIN-00350, Helsinki, Finland

Tel.: (358) 105040
Web Site: http://www.a-vakuutus.fi
Insurance Related Activities
N.A.I.C.S.: 524298
Tomi Ylikynmy *(Mng Dir)*

OKO Venture Capital Ltd (2)
Teollisuuskatu 1B, PO Box 308, FI-00013, Helsinki, Finland
Tel.: (358) 10252011
Web Site: http://www.op.fi
Emp.: 5,000
Mortgage & Nonmortgage Loan Brokers
N.A.I.C.S.: 522310
Reijo Karhinen *(Gen Mgr)*

OP Asset Management Ltd (2)
Gebhardinaukio 1, PO Box 1068, FI-00013, Helsinki, Finland
Tel.: (358) 10252011
Web Site: http://www.pohjola.fi
Financial Investment Activities
N.A.I.C.S.: 523999

OP Fund Management Company Ltd (2)
Teollisuuskatu 1B, PO Box 308, 00101, Helsinki, Finland
Tel.: (358) 10252010
Open-End Investment Funds
N.A.I.C.S.: 525910

OP-Kotipankki Oyj (2)
Mikonkatu 13, PO Box 1020, Teollisuuskatu 1B, 00101, Helsinki, Finland
Tel.: (358) 10252010
Web Site: http://www.pohjola.fi
Commericial Banking
N.A.I.C.S.: 522110
Mika Kibimaki *(Mng Dir)*

Pohjola Insurance Company Ltd (2)
Lapinmaentie 1, 00350, Helsinki, Finland
Tel.: (358) 10253000
Web Site: http://www.pohjola.fi
Sales Range: $600-649.9 Million
Insurance Related Activities
N.A.I.C.S.: 524298
Carina Geber-Teir *(Chief Comm Officer)*

Subsidiary (Domestic):

Excenta Oy (3)
Kutomotie 18, 00380, Helsinki, Finland
Tel.: (358) 10 839 6900
Web Site: http://www.excenta.fi
Corporate & Personal Training Services
N.A.I.C.S.: 624310

OPAL BALANCE INVESTMENTS LTD.
4 Arik Einstein St, BBQ Star Center, Ashdod, 65180, Israel
Tel.: (972) 88531531
Web Site:
https://www.opalbalance.co.il
Year Founded: 2005
OPAL—(TAE)
Rev.: $25,514,297
Assets: $102,870,561
Liabilities: $44,737,947
Net Worth: $58,132,614
Earnings: $7,287,471
Fiscal Year-end: 12/31/23
Consumer Lending
N.A.I.C.S.: 522291
Nagel Dror *(Chm)*

OPAL HORIZON LIMITED
Level 2 87 Wickham Terrace, Spring Hill, 4000, QLD, Australia
Tel.: (61) 738395088
Web Site:
http://www.opalhorizon.com
Year Founded: 2001
Sales Range: Less than $1 Million
Emp.: 4
Opal Exploration & Mining Services
N.A.I.C.S.: 212311
David John Horton *(Founder)*

OPAL LUXURY TIME PRODUCTS LIMITED
Plot 31 1st Floor Shree Ganesh Shivaji Housing Society, Senapati Bapat Road, Pune, 411 016, India
Tel.: (91) 2025631919
Web Site: http://www.opalclocks.com
Emp.: 150
Clock Mfr
N.A.I.C.S.: 339910
Sameer Subhash Gujar *(Mng Dir)*

OPASNET CO LTD
512 Teheran-ro 10F, Gangnam-gu, Seoul, Korea (South)
Tel.: (82) 221938600
Web Site: https://opasnet.co.kr
Year Founded: 2004
173130—(KRS)
Rev.: $130,839,007
Assets: $91,496,474
Liabilities: $64,398,883
Net Worth: $27,097,591
Earnings: $4,654,572
Emp.: 349
Fiscal Year-end: 12/31/22
Information Technology Services
N.A.I.C.S.: 541511
Han Yong Jin *(Deputy Gen Mgr)*

OPAWICA EXPLORATIONS INC.
Suite 488 - 625 Howe Street, Vancouver, V6C 2T6, BC, Canada
Tel.: (604) 681-3170
Web Site: https://www.opawica.com
OE5—(DEU)
Rev.: $780
Assets: $3,823,851
Liabilities: $851,543
Net Worth: $2,972,307
Earnings: ($1,495,423)
Fiscal Year-end: 08/31/23
Gold Exploration & Mining Services
N.A.I.C.S.: 212220
Blake Morgan *(CEO)*

OPC PHARMACEUTICAL JOINT-STOCK COMPANY
1017 - Hong Bang, Dist 6, Ho Chi Minh City, Vietnam
Tel.: (84) 2837517111
Web Site: https://opcpharma.com
Year Founded: 1977
OPC—(HOSE)
Rev.: $41,401,344
Assets: $51,945,825
Liabilities: $15,518,268
Net Worth: $36,427,557
Earnings: $5,039,543
Fiscal Year-end: 12/31/23
Pharmaceuticals Product Mfr
N.A.I.C.S.: 325412
Trinh Xuan Vuong *(Chm)*

OPCAPITA LLP
2 Park Street, London, W1K 2HX, United Kingdom
Tel.: (44) 2076477300 UK
Web Site: http://www.opcapita.com
Year Founded: 2006
Privater Equity Firm
N.A.I.C.S.: 523999
Henry Jackson *(CEO)*

Subsidiaries:

Maurices Incorporated (1)
425 W Superior St, Duluth, MN 55802
Tel.: (218) 727-8431
Web Site: http://www.maurices.com
Women's Clothing Retailer
N.A.I.C.S.: 458110
Jennifer Lansing *(Asst VP & Assoc Mgr-Divisional Mdse-Tops)*

Reiner Appelrath Cuepper Nachf. GmbH (1)
Zeppelinstrasse 2, 50667, Cologne, Germany
Tel.: (49) 22130065000

Web Site: http://www.appelrath.com
Emp.: 1,000
Womens Clothing & Accessories Merchant Whslr
N.A.I.C.S.: 458110
Frank Rheinboldt *(Chm)*

The Football Pools Limited (1)
Walton House 55 Charnock Road, Liverpool, L67 1AA, Merseyside, United Kingdom (100%)
Tel.: (44) 1515253677
Web Site: http://www.footballpools.com
Gambling Industries
N.A.I.C.S.: 713290
Ian Nicholls *(Mgr-Digital Mktg)*

Subsidiary (Domestic):

Football Pools 1923 Limited (2)
55 Charnock Road Walton House, Liverpool, L67 1AA, Merseyside, United Kingdom (100%)
Tel.: (44) 1515253677
Gambling Industries
N.A.I.C.S.: 713290

Sportech Pools Competitions Limited (2)
Icarus House Hawkfield Close, Hawkfield Business Park, Bristol, BS14 0BN, United Kingdom (100%)
Tel.: (44) 1515253677
Gambling Industries
N.A.I.C.S.: 713290

OPCOM HOLDINGS BERHAD
11 Jalan Utas 15/7, 40200, Shah Alam, Selangor Darul Ehsan, Malaysia
Tel.: (60) 355195599 MY
Web Site:
https://www.opcom.com.my
Year Founded: 1994
OPCOM—(KLS)
Rev.: $46,038,735
Assets: $65,533,852
Liabilities: $22,790,771
Net Worth: $42,743,082
Earnings: $675,836
Fiscal Year-end: 09/30/23
Holding Company; Fiber Optic Cables & Cable Related Products Mfr
N.A.I.C.S.: 551112
Yusree Putra Alias *(CEO-Opcom Engineering Services Sdn Bhd)*

Subsidiaries:

OPCOM NIAGA SDN BHD (1)
11 Jalan Utas 15/7, Shah Alam, Selangor, Malaysia
Tel.: (60) 355195599
Sales Range: $50-74.9 Million
Emp.: 150
Fiber Optic Cable Mfr
N.A.I.C.S.: 334417
Eric Chhoa Kwang *(Mng Dir)*

Opcom Cables Sdn. Bhd. (1)
11 Jalan Utas 15/7, Shah Alam Industrial Estate, Shah Alam, 40200, Selangor Darul Ehsan, Malaysia
Tel.: (60) 355195599
Web Site: http://www.opcom.com.my
Emp.: 120
Fiber Optic Cables & Systems Mfr; Owned 70% by Opcom Holdings Berhad & 30% by Telefonaktiebolaget LM Ericsson
N.A.I.C.S.: 335921
Yusree Putra Alias *(COO)*

Opcom VC Sdn. Bhd. (1)
11 Jalan Utas 15/7, 40200, Shah Alam, Selangor Darul Ehsan, Malaysia (100%)
Tel.: (60) 355195599
Fiber Optic Cables & Cable Related Products Mfr
N.A.I.C.S.: 335921

OPEL BRUN AUTOMOBILES S.A.
710 Avenue De L'Europe, 69400, Villefranche-sur-Saone, France
Tel.: (33) 474620085

OPEL BRUN AUTOMOBILES S.A.

Opel Brun Automobiles S.A.—(Continued)
Web Site: http://www.opel-brun-auto.com
Rev.: $12,300,000
Emp.: 23
Automobile Dealer for Opel
N.A.I.C.S.: 441110
Daniel Brun (Pres)

OPEN AIRWAY DENTAL SOLUTIONS LTD
5 Moorak St, 4068, Taringa, QLD, Australia
Tel.: (61) 1300533159
Web Site: https://openairway.com
Emp.: 100
Pharmaceuticals Product Mfr
N.A.I.C.S.: 325412

Subsidiaries:

Oventus Medical Limited (1)
1 Swann Road, Indooroopilly, Brisbane, 4068, QLD, Australia
Tel.: (61) 300533159
Rev.: $834,791
Assets: $11,553,086
Liabilities: $1,885,226
Net Worth: $9,667,861
Earnings: ($7,532,844)
Fiscal Year-end: 06/30/2021
Oral Device Mfr & Distr
N.A.I.C.S.: 339114

Subsidiary (US):

Oventus Medical USA, Inc. (2)
600 B St Ste 300, San Diego, CA 92101
Tel.: (425) 681-1894
Web Site: http://www.oventusmedical.com
Sleep Disorder Medical Equipment Mfr
N.A.I.C.S.: 339113

OPEN DOOR INC.
Akasaka Tameike Tower 6th floor
2-17-7 Akasaka, Minato-ku, Tokyo, 107-0052, Japan
Tel.: (81) 335868707
Web Site: https://www.opendoor.co.jp
Year Founded: 1997
3926—(TKS)
Rev.: $16,928,210
Assets: $37,432,430
Liabilities: $3,648,720
Net Worth: $33,783,710
Earnings: ($1,123,700)
Emp.: 187
Fiscal Year-end: 03/31/24
Travel Related Services
N.A.I.C.S.: 561599
Daisuke Sekine (Pres & CEO)

OPEN GROUP, INC.
Toranomon Hills Mori Tower 8F
1-23-1 Toranomon, Minato-ku, Tokyo, 105-6308, Japan
Tel.: (81) 351576388
Web Site: https://open-group.co.jp
Year Founded: 2000
6572—(TKS)
Rev.: $43,709,850
Assets: $136,432,870
Liabilities: $53,713,840
Net Worth: $82,719,030
Earnings: $1,176,940
Fiscal Year-end: 02/29/24
Holding Company
N.A.I.C.S.: 551112

Subsidiaries:

Open Associates Japan, Inc. (1)
1-23-1 Toranomon Toranomon Hills Mori Tower 8F, Minato-ku, Tokyo, 105-6308, Japan
Tel.: (81) 35 157 6381
Web Site: https://www.open-associates.com
Marketing Services
N.A.I.C.S.: 541613

RPA Engineering Inc. (1)
400 Spring Ridge Dr, Wyomissing, PA 19610
Web Site: https://rpaengr.com
Engineering Services
N.A.I.C.S.: 541330
Richard P. Aulenbach (Pres & CEO)

Segment, Inc. (1)
1-23-1 Toranomon Toranomon Hills Mori Tower 8F, Minato-ku, Tokyo, 105-6390, Japan
Tel.: (81) 35 157 6372
Web Site: https://segment.co.jp
Web Marketing Services
N.A.I.C.S.: 541613

OPEN HOUSE GROUP CO., LTD.
JP TOWER 20F 21F 2-7-2 Marunouchi, Chiyoda-ku, Tokyo, 100-7020, Japan
Tel.: (81) 362130775 JP
Web Site: https://openhouse-group.co.jp
Year Founded: 1997
3288—(TKS)
Rev.: $7,588,265,610
Assets: $7,919,841,427
Liabilities: $4,745,635,943
Net Worth: $3,174,205,484
Earnings: $608,192,930
Emp.: 4,904
Fiscal Year-end: 09/30/23
Holding Company; Real Estate Development, Management & Brokerage Services
N.A.I.C.S.: 551112
Tsugumasa Sekiguchi (Pres & CEO)

Subsidiaries:

Open House Architect Co., Ltd. (1)
15F Nakano Central Park South 4-10-2 Nakano, Nakano-ku, Tokyo, Japan
Tel.: (81) 366270200
Web Site: https://oha.openhouse-group.com
Real Estate & Housing Services
N.A.I.C.S.: 531210

Pressance Corporation (1)
27F Crystal Tower 1-2-27 Shiromi, Chuo-ku, Osaka, 540-6027, Japan (62.5%)
Tel.: (81) 647931650
Web Site: https://www.pressance.co.jp
Rev.: $1,156,599,870
Assets: $1,952,527,230
Liabilities: $688,700,010
Net Worth: $1,263,827,220
Earnings: $125,553,870
Fiscal Year-end: 09/30/2023
Apartment Building Construction Services
N.A.I.C.S.: 236116
Shinobu Yamagishi (Pres)

OPEN ORPHAN PLC
18 Fitzwilliam Place, Dublin, D02 HH29, Ireland
Tel.: (353) 16440007
Web Site: http://www.openorphan.com
Year Founded: 2017
Pharmaceutical Services
N.A.I.C.S.: 424210
Trevor Phillips (CEO)

Subsidiaries:

Venn Life Sciences Holdings PLC (1)
19 Railway Rd, Dalkey, Dublin, Ireland
Tel.: (353) 1 537 3269
Web Site: http://www.vennlifesciences.com
Rev.: $20,848,753
Assets: $14,629,464
Liabilities: $4,142,200
Net Worth: $10,487,264
Earnings: ($1,842,309)
Emp.: 149
Fiscal Year-end: 12/31/2017
Pharmaceutical Researcher & Developer
N.A.I.C.S.: 325412

Subsidiary (Domestic):

Venn Life Sciences (Ireland) Limited (2)
19 Railway Rd, Dalkey, Dublin, Ireland
Tel.: (353) 1 537 3269
Pharmaceutical Research & Development Services
N.A.I.C.S.: 541715

Subsidiary (Non-US):

Venn Life Sciences UK Limited (2)
4 Lombard St, London, EC3V 9HD, United Kingdom
Tel.: (44) 28 90 737 900
Pharmaceutical Research & Development Services
N.A.I.C.S.: 541715

Venn Synergie S.A.S (2)
Tour Albert 1er 65 ave de, Colmar, 92500, Rueil Malmaison, France
Tel.: (33) 130 82 67 07
Pharmaceutical Research & Development Services
N.A.I.C.S.: 541715

hVIVO Services Limited (1)
Queen Mary BioEnterprises Innovation Centre 42 New Road, London, E1 2AX, United Kingdom
Tel.: (44) 20 7756 1300
Web Site: http://www.hvivo.com
Sales Range: $10-24.9 Million
Emp.: 164
Holding Company; Biotechnology Research & Development & Human Disease Diagnostics
N.A.I.C.S.: 551112
Reid Tripp (Exec VP-Bus Dev & Mktg)

Subsidiary (Domestic):

Activiomics Limited (2)
24 Cornhill, London, EC3V 3ND, United Kingdom
Tel.: (44) 845 5195 091
Web Site: http://www.activiomics.com
Medical Product Mfr & Distr
N.A.I.C.S.: 325412
Kevin FitzGerald (CEO)

Retroscreen Virology Limited (2)
Queen Mary BioEnterprises Innovation Centre 42 New Road, London, E1 2AX, United Kingdom
Tel.: (44) 20 7756 1300
Web Site: http://www.retroscreen.com
Biotechnology Research & Development
N.A.I.C.S.: 541714

OPEN TEXT CORPORATION
275 Frank Tompa Drive, Waterloo, N2L 0A1, ON, Canada
Tel.: (519) 888-7111 ON
Web Site: https://www.opentext.com
Year Founded: 1991
OTEX—(NASDAQ)
Rev.: $5,769,577,000
Assets: $14,205,707,000
Liabilities: $10,006,026,000
Net Worth: $4,199,681,000
Earnings: $465,284,000
Emp.: 22,900
Fiscal Year-end: 06/30/24
Enterprise Content Management Software Solutions
N.A.I.C.S.: 513210
Mark J. Barrenechea (Vice Chm- & CTO)

Subsidiaries:

Actuate Canada Corporation (1)
95 Mural St Suite 201, Toronto, L4B 3G2, ON, Canada
Tel.: (905) 709-1020
Software Development Services
N.A.I.C.S.: 541511
Philip Watkinson (Sr Engr-Softwrae)

Captaris (Hong Kong) Limited (1)
Unit F 9th Floor China Overseas Bldg 139 Hennessey Rd, Wanchai, China (Hong Kong)
Tel.: (852) 2824 8223
Software Development & Information Technology Solutions
N.A.I.C.S.: 541511

Carbonite, Inc. (1)
2 Avenue de Lafayette, Boston, MA 02111
Tel.: (617) 587-1102
Web Site: http://www.carbonite.com
Rev.: $296,408,000
Assets: $561,091,000
Liabilities: $303,881,000
Net Worth: $257,210,000
Earnings: $7,562,000
Emp.: 959
Fiscal Year-end: 12/31/2018
Online Data Backup Services
N.A.I.C.S.: 334112
Larry Friedman (Chief Info Security Officer)

Subsidiary (Non-US):

Double-Take Software SAS (2)
116-118 avenue Paul Doumer, Rueil-Malmaison, 92500, France
Tel.: (33) 147770500
Sales Range: $10-24.9 Million
Emp.: 80
Data-Protection Software
N.A.I.C.S.: 513210
Jo Murciano (Pres)

MailStore Software GmbH (2)
Clorather Str 1-3, 41748, Viersen, Germany
Tel.: (49) 2162502990
Web Site: https://www.mailstore.com
Software Development Services
N.A.I.C.S.: 541511

Subsidiary (Domestic):

Webroot Software, Inc. (2)
385 Interlocken Cres Ste 800, Broomfield, CO 80021-8062
Tel.: (303) 442-3813
Web Site: http://www.webroot.com
Sales Range: $25-49.9 Million
Emp.: 450
Developer of Internet Utilities & Privacy Software & Tools
N.A.I.C.S.: 541511
David Bennett (Chief Revenue Officer)

Subsidiary (Non-US):

Webroot BV (3)
Vlietweg 17w, 2266 KA, Leidschendam, Netherlands (100%)
Tel.: (31) 207132702
Software Developer
N.A.I.C.S.: 541512

Webroot GmbH (3)
Biedrichstrasse 8, D 61200, Munich, Wolfersheim, Germany (100%)
Tel.: (49) 603698970
Software Developer
N.A.I.C.S.: 541512

Webroot Italia (3)
Via Giovanni da Udine 34, 20156, Milan, Italy (100%)
Tel.: (39) 0238093643
Software Developer
N.A.I.C.S.: 541512

Webroot Limited (3)
420 Thames Valley Park Drive Thames Valley Park, Reading, RG6 1PT, Berkshire, United Kingdom (100%)
Tel.: (44) 2033492398
Software Developer
N.A.I.C.S.: 541512

Webroot SARL (3)
6 rue du Bel Air, 92500, Rueil-Malmaison, France (100%)
Tel.: (33) 147329166
Software Developer
N.A.I.C.S.: 541512

Catalyst Repository Systems, Inc. (1)
1860 Blake St 7th Fl, Denver, CO 80202
Tel.: (303) 824-0900
Web Site: http://www.catalystsecure.com
Legal Document Management Services
N.A.I.C.S.: 541199
Justin Feferman (Reg Dir-Central Reg)

Covisint Corporation (1)
26533 Evergreen Rd Ste 500, Southfield, MI 48076
Tel.: (800) 229-4125
Web Site: http://www.covisint.com
Sales Range: $50-74.9 Million
Cloud Information Platform Developer & Management Services

AND PRIVATE COMPANIES

N.A.I.C.S.: 541511

Subsidiary (Non-US):

Covisint GmbH (2)
Dornhofstrasse 34, 68263, Neu-Isenburg, Germany
Tel.: (49) 61025797017
Web Site: http://www.covisint.com
Cloud Information Platform Management Services
N.A.I.C.S.: 518210

Covisint Software Services (Shanghai) Ltd. (2)
4th floor Hong Qiao Center Building Block 2 Lane 631 Jin Zhong Rd, Chang Ning, Shanghai, 200335, China
Tel.: (86) 2162479222
Web Site: http://www.covisint.com
Applications Software Programming Services
N.A.I.C.S.: 541511

EasyLink Services International Corporation (1)
6025 The Corners Pkwy Ste 100, Norcross, GA 30092-3328
Tel.: (678) 533-8000
Web Site: http://www.easylink.com
Sales Range: $150-199.9 Million
Emp.: 541
Communication Applications
N.A.I.C.S.: 517810

Branch (Domestic):

EasyLink Services (2)
33 Knightsbridge Rd, Piscataway, NJ 08854
Tel.: (732) 652-3500
Web Site: http://www.easylink.com
Sales Range: $50-74.9 Million
Emp.: 310
Communication Applications
N.A.I.C.S.: 517810

Subsidiary (Non-US):

EasyLink Services International Ltd. (2)
Bishopsgate Court, 4 Norton Folgate, London, E1 6DB, United Kingdom
Tel.: (44) 2075518700
Web Site: http://www.easylink.com
Sales Range: $10-24.9 Million
Emp.: 30
Communication Applications
N.A.I.C.S.: 517810

Subsidiary (Non-US):

EasyLink Services France SARL (3)
32 Boulevard Diderot, 75012, Paris, France
Tel.: (33) 144689040
Communication Applications
N.A.I.C.S.: 517810

GXS, Inc. (1)
8 Fl Leema Building 42 Jong-ro 1-gil, Jongno-gu, Seoul, Korea (South)
Tel.: (82) 221851000
Web Site: http://www.gxs.co.kr
Software Development Services
N.A.I.C.S.: 513210

GXS India Technology Centre Private Limited (1)
No 2 Prestige Emerald 2nd Floor Madras Bank Road, Lavelle Road Junction, Bengaluru, 560001, Karnataka, India
Tel.: (91) 8041901000
Software Development Services
N.A.I.C.S.: 541511

GXS International, Inc. (1)
9711 Washingtonian Blvd, Gaithersburg, MD 20878
Tel.: (301) 340-4000
Software Development Services
N.A.I.C.S.: 541511

GXS SAS (1)
Coeur Defense Tour B Etage 30 100 esplanade du General de gaulle, La Defense, 92932, Paris, Cedex, France
Tel.: (33) 147965541
Software Development Services
N.A.I.C.S.: 541511

GXS UK Holding Limited (1)
18 Station Road, Middlesex, Sunbury-on-Thames, TW16 6SU, United Kingdom
Tel.: (44) 1772646010
Web Site: http://www.gxs.co.uk
Holding Company
N.A.I.C.S.: 551112

GXS, Inc. (1)
9711 Washingtonian Blvd, Gaithersburg, MD 20878-3204 (100%)
Tel.: (301) 340-4000
Web Site: http://www.gxs.com
Sales Range: $450-499.9 Million
Emp.: 2,889
Electrical Apparatus, Wire & Cable Products Mfr
N.A.I.C.S.: 518210
John Duvall *(Sr VP-Fin)*

Branch (Domestic):

GXS - Raleigh (2)
3200 Atlantic Ave Ste 204, Raleigh, NC 27604
Tel.: (919) 786-5100
Web Site: http://www.gxs.com
Sales Range: $50-74.9 Million
Emp.: 150
E-Commerce Applications Services
N.A.I.C.S.: 513210

Subsidiary (Non-US):

GXS Ltd. (2)
1 Station Rd, Sunbury, TW16 6SU, Middlesex, United Kingdom (100%)
Tel.: (44) 932776000
Web Site: http://www.gxs.com
Sales Range: $25-49.9 Million
Emp.: 200
Electronic Services
N.A.I.C.S.: 541330

Informative Graphics Corporation (1)
4835 E Cactus Rd Ste 445, Scottsdale, AZ 85254
Tel.: (602) 971-6061
Web Site: http://www.infograph.com
Sales Range: $1-9.9 Million
Emp.: 68
Document Collaboration Software Publisher
N.A.I.C.S.: 513210
Gary Heath *(Founder & CEO)*

Liaison Technologies Inc. (1)
2575 Westside Pkwy Ste 400, Alpharetta, GA 30004
Tel.: (770) 642-5000
Web Site: http://www.liaison.com
Data Integration & Management Solutions
N.A.I.C.S.: 518210
Robert A. Renner *(Pres & CEO)*

Subsidiary (Non-US):

Liaison Technologies Europe (2)
Visiokatu 3, Tampere, 33720, Finland
Tel.: (358) 10 3060 900
Web Site: http://www.liaison.com
Data Management & Integration
N.A.I.C.S.: 518210
Juhani Sormanen *(Exec VP-Europe)*

Division (Non-US):

Liaison Technologies AB (3)
Klarabergsviadukten 70, 111 64, Stockholm, Sweden
Tel.: (46) 8 518 365 00
Web Site: http://www.liaison.com
Emp.: 3
Data Management & Integration
N.A.I.C.S.: 518210

Liaison Technologies Netherlands (3)
Barbara Strozzilaan 201, 1083 HN, Amsterdam, Netherlands
Tel.: (31) 207009350
Web Site: http://www.liaison.com
Data Management & Integration
N.A.I.O.C.S.: 518210

Liaison Technologies United Kingdom (3)
Brightwater House Market Place, Ringwood, BH24 1AP, United Kingdom
Tel.: (44) 1425 200620
Data Management & Integration
N.A.I.C.S.: 518210

Metastorm, Inc. (1)
500 E Pratt St Ste 1250, Baltimore, MD 21202-3167
Tel.: (443) 874-1300
Web Site: http://www.metastorm.com
Sales Range: $125-149.9 Million
Emp.: 300
Computer Software Developer
N.A.I.C.S.: 541511

Nstein Technologies Inc. (1)
75 Queen 4400, Montreal, H3C 2N6, QC, Canada
Tel.: (514) 908-5406
Web Site: http://www.opentext.com
Sales Range: $10-24.9 Million
Emp.: 145
Web Content Management, Digital Asset Management, Text Mining Engine & Picture Management Desk Products
N.A.I.C.S.: 541511

Open Text (1)
700 King Farm Blvd Ste 600, Rockville, MD 20850-5749
Tel.: (301) 548-4000
Sales Range: $25-49.9 Million
Emp.: 100
Digital Asset Management & Internet Publishing Software Solutions
N.A.I.C.S.: 541511

Open Text (1)
Karlavagen 108, PO Box 24 210, 104 51, Stockholm, Sweden
Tel.: (46) 86868500
Web Site: https://www.opentext.se
Sales Range: $25-49.9 Million
Emp.: 65
Document Automation Services
N.A.I.C.S.: 561410
Peter Skinner *(Chm)*

Branch (US):

Open Text (2)
3 Van de Graaff Dr, Burlington, MA 01803-5188
Tel.: (781) 761-6600
Sales Range: $25-49.9 Million
Emp.: 30
Document Automation Services
N.A.I.C.S.: 541511
David Englund *(Mgr-North American Legal Solutions)*

Open Text (Asia) Pte Ltd. (1)
6 Battery Road Unit 33-01, Singapore, 049909, Singapore
Tel.: (65) 63341645
Sales Range: $25-49.9 Million
Emp.: 30
Software Development Services
N.A.I.C.S.: 541511

Open Text (Hong Kong) Limited (1)
Room 1609 16/F China Resources Building 26 Harbour Road, Wanchai, China (Hong Kong)
Tel.: (852) 28846088
Web Site: https://www.opentext.com
Emp.: 2
Software Development & Information Technology Solutions
N.A.I.C.S.: 541511

Open Text A/S (1)
Langebrogade nr 5, Copenhagen, 1411, Denmark
Tel.: (45) 70232626
Emp.: 15
Software Publisher
N.A.I.C.S.: 513210

Open Text AB (1)
Karlavagen 108, PO Box 24210, 104 51, Stockholm, Sweden
Tel.: (46) 86868500
Web Site: http://www.opentext.com
Sales Range: $25-49.9 Million
Emp.: 6
Document Management Software Development Services
N.A.I.C.S.: 513210
Mark J. Barrenechea *(Pres & CEO)*

Open Text AG (1)
Baderstrasse 27, 5400, Baden, Switzerland
Tel.: (41) 582589400
Web Site: http://www.opentext.com
Sales Range: $25-49.9 Million
Emp.: 5
Software Development Services

OPEN TEXT CORPORATION

N.A.I.C.S.: 541511

Open Text Brasil Comercio De Software Ltda. (1)
Av Ibirapuera 2332, Sao Paulo, 04028, Brazil
Tel.: (55) 1150548373
Emp.: 35
Computer Peripheral Equipment & Software Distr
N.A.I.C.S.: 423430

Open Text Brasil Comerico de Software Ltda. (1)
Av Ibirapuera 2332 Tower 2 Apt 132, 04028-002, Sao Paulo, Brazil
Tel.: (55) 5054 8373
Software Development Services
N.A.I.C.S.: 541511
Ray Phillips *(VP)*

Open Text Canada Ltd. (1)
275 Frank Tompa Drive, Waterloo, N2L 0A1, ON, Canada
Tel.: (519) 888-7111
Sales Range: $200-249.9 Million
Emp.: 800
Content & Business Management Software Provider
N.A.I.C.S.: 513210

Open Text Corporation India Private Limited (1)
Unit No 301 3rd Floor Building No 14 Mind-Space IT Park Hi-Tec City, Madhapur, Hyderabad, 500 081, India
Tel.: (91) 4044360400
Software Content Management Services
N.A.I.C.S.: 513210

Open Text Document Technologies GmbH (1)
Max-Stromeyer-Strasse 116, 78467, Konstanz, Germany
Tel.: (49) 7531870
Sales Range: $25-49.9 Million
Emp.: 80
Document Management Software Development Services
N.A.I.C.S.: 541511

Open Text GmbH (1)
Technopark 2 Werner-von-Siemens-Ring 20, 85630, Grasbrunn, Germany
Tel.: (49) 8946290
Sales Range: $25-49.9 Million
Business Management Software Developer
N.A.I.C.S.: 334610

Open Text Inc. (1)
3671 Ridge Mill Dr, Hilliard, OH 43026 (100%)
Tel.: (614) 658-3588
Sales Range: $25-49.9 Million
Emp.: 80
Software & Content Solutions
N.A.I.C.S.: 513210

Open Text Inc. (1)
301 116th Ave SE Ste 500, Bellevue, WA 98004
Tel.: (425) 455-6000
Sales Range: $25-49.9 Million
Emp.: 60
Software-Based Computer-Telephony Solutions
N.A.I.C.S.: 334610
Joseph A. Staples *(Sr VP-Corp Mktg & Org Devel)*

Branch (Non-US):

Open Text (2)
Level 6 80 Pacific Highway, Sydney, 2060, NSW, Australia
Tel.: (61) 290263400
Web Site: http://www.opentext.com
Sales Range: $25-49.9 Million
Emp.: 70
Content Management Software
N.A.I.C.S.: 334610
Graham Pullen *(Sr VP-Sls-Asia Pacific & Japan)*

Open Text International B.V. (1)
Zuidtoren Taurusavenue 15 7th Floor, 2132 LS, Hoofddorp, Netherlands
Tel.: (31) 235652333
Web Site: http://www.opentext.com

OPEN TEXT CORPORATION

Open Text Corporation—(Continued)
Sales Range: $25-49.9 Million
Emp.: 48
Software Development & Information Technology Services
N.A.I.C.S.: 541512

Open Text K.K. (1)
6th Fl New Pier Takeshiba South Tower
16-1 Kaigan 1-chome, Minato-ku, Tokyo, 105-0022, Japan
Tel.: (81) 345607704
Software Development Services
N.A.I.C.S.: 541511
Noriyuki Hayakawa (Pres)

Open Text Korea Co., Ltd. (1)
8th Floor Leema Building 42 Jong-ro 1-gil, Jongno-gu, Seoul, 03152, Korea (South)
Tel.: (82) 221851000
Computer Software Consulting Services
N.A.I.C.S.: 541512

Open Text Oy (1)
Lars Sonckin kaari 14, Espoo, 02600, Finland
Tel.: (358) 951291600
Software Publisher
N.A.I.C.S.: 513210
Jukka Uramo (Mgr-Sls)

Open Text Pty Ltd. (1)
L 1 The Realm 18 National Circuit, Barton, 2600, ACT, Australia
Tel.: (61) 261983339
Software Development Services
N.A.I.C.S.: 541511

Open Text Public Sector Solutions, Inc. (1)
4075 Wilson Blvd Ste 450, Arlington, VA 22203
Tel.: (703) 740-9300
Web Site: https://www.otpss.com
Software Development & Information Technology Solutions
N.A.I.C.S.: 541512

Open Text S.r.l. (1)
Via Benedetto Croce 19, Rome, 142, Italy
Tel.: (39) 065947241
Sales Range: $25-49.9 Million
Emp.: 1
Software Development Services
N.A.I.C.S.: 541511
Fabrizio Bonotti (Gen Mgr)

Open Text SA (1)
Avenue Monterey 40, Luxembourg, 2163, Luxembourg
Tel.: (352) 2645661
Sales Range: $25-49.9 Million
Emp.: 7
Content Management Software Provider
N.A.I.C.S.: 513210
Sabrina Ghidinelli (Asst Mgr)

Open Text SARL (1)
Tour Areva 24eme Etage 1 Place Jean Millier, Courbevoie, 92400, France
Tel.: (33) 147965541
Software Development Services
N.A.I.C.S.: 541511

Open Text Software Austria GmbH (1)
Wagramer Strasse 17-19, 1220, Vienna, Austria
Tel.: (43) 1 263 26 82 15
Web Site: http://www.opentext.com
Sales Range: $25-49.9 Million
Emp.: 24
Software Development Services
N.A.I.C.S.: 541511

Open Text Software GmbH (1)
Werner-von-Siemens-Ring 20, Grasbrunn, 85630, Munich, Germany
Tel.: (49) 8946290
Emp.: 15
Software Development Services
N.A.I.C.S.: 541511

Open Text Software S.L.U. (1)
Calle Jose Silva 17, Madrid, 28043, Spain
Tel.: (34) 911419000
Sales Range: $25-49.9 Million
Emp.: 3
Software Development & Information Technology Solutions

Open Text Sp. z.o.o. (1)
No 5 3rd Floor Ul Szelagowska 29-30, Poznan, 61-626, Poland
Tel.: (48) 618580012
Web Site: http://www.opentext.com
Sales Range: $75-99.9 Million
Emp.: 10
Software Development Services
N.A.I.C.S.: 541511

Open Text Technologies India Private Limited (1)
Unit Bno 301 3RD Floor Building No 14 Mind Space IT Park, Hi Tech City Madhapur, Hyderabad, 500 033, India
Tel.: (91) 4044360400
Web Site: http://www.opentext.com
Emp.: 750
Software Development Services
N.A.I.C.S.: 541511

Open Text UK Limited (1)
420 Thames Valley Park Drive Thames Valley Park, Austin Friars, Reading, RG6 1PT, Berkshire, United Kingdom
Tel.: (44) 1189484000
Web Site: https://www.opentext.co.uk
Sales Range: $25-49.9 Million
Emp.: 50
Prepackaged Software Products & Services
N.A.I.C.S.: 423430

Open Text USA Inc. (1)
155 N Rosemont Blvd Ste 101 1st Fl, Tucson, AZ 85711
Tel.: (520) 320-7000
Emp.: 115
Information Management Software Development Services
N.A.I.C.S.: 541511
Kim Bannister (Coord-Facilities)

Open Text s.r.o. (1)
Na Porici 1040/10, 110 00, Prague, Czech Republic
Tel.: (420) 221899141
Web Site: http://www.opentext.com
Sales Range: $25-49.9 Million
Emp.: 15
Software Development & Information Technology Services
N.A.I.C.S.: 541512

Recommind, Inc. (1)
550 Kearny St 7th Fl, San Francisco, CA 94108
Tel.: (415) 394-7899
Web Site: http://www.recommind.com
Search-Powered Information Risk Management Software Services
N.A.I.C.S.: 513210
Jan Puzicha (Founder & CTO)

Subsidiary (Non-US):

Recommind GmbH (2)
Von-Liebig-Strasse 1, 53359, Rheinbach, Germany
Tel.: (49) 2226159660
Web Site: http://www.recommind.de
Search-Powered Information Risk Management Software Services
N.A.I.C.S.: 513210
Hartwig Laute (Mng Dir)

StreamServe Oy (1)
Lars Sonckin Kaari 14, 2600, Espoo, Finland
Tel.: (358) 9 54064020
Software Development Services
N.A.I.C.S.: 541511

StreamServe Sarl.B.V. (1)
Ave monterey 40, 2163, Luxembourg, Luxembourg
Tel.: (352) 2645661
Web Site: http://www.opentext.com
Sales Range: $25-49.9 Million
Emp.: 8
Online Marketing Services
N.A.I.C.S.: 541613

Webroot Inc. (1)
385 Interlocken Cres Ste 800, Broomfield, CO 80021
Tel.: (303) 442-3813
Web Site: http://www.webroot.com
Software Publisher
N.A.I.C.S.: 513210

Webroot Pty. Ltd. (1)
Level 6 80 Pacific Highway, North Sydney, 2060, NSW, Australia
Tel.: (61) 28 071 1900
Software Publisher
N.A.I.C.S.: 513210

Zix Corporation (1)
2711 N Haskell Ave Ste 2200 LB 36, Dallas, TX 75204-2960
Tel.: (214) 370-2000
Web Site: http://www.zixcorp.com
Rev.: $218,478,000
Assets: $449,724,000
Liabilities: $415,289,000
Net Worth: $34,435,000
Earnings: ($15,450,000)
Emp.: 543
Fiscal Year-end: 12/31/2020
Digital Signature & Encryption Technology Services
N.A.I.C.S.: 518210
Geoff R. Bibby (CMO)

Subsidiary (Domestic):

ARM Research Labs, LLC (2)
1101 Gulf Breeze Pkwy Ste 200, Gulf Breeze, FL 32561-4858
Web Site: https://www.armresearch.com
Research & Development Services
N.A.I.C.S.: 541715

Subsidiary (Non-US):

AppRiver Canada ULC (2)
300 March Rd Suite 304, Kanata, K2K 2E2, ON, Canada
Tel.: (613) 231-6599
Cloud Security & Productivity Services
N.A.I.C.S.: 541511

AppRiver UK Ltd. (2)
Venture House 2 Arlington Square, Bracknell, RG12 1WA, Berkshire, United Kingdom
Tel.: (44) 1344706686
Cloud Security & Productivity Services
N.A.I.C.S.: 541511
Kieron Sloper (Acct Mgr)

Subsidiary (Domestic):

AppRiver, LLC (2)
1101 Gulf Breeze Pkwy Ste 200, Gulf Breeze, FL 32561
Tel.: (850) 932-5338
Web Site: http://www.appriver.com
Cloud-Based Cybersecurity & Productivity Software & Services
N.A.I.C.S.: 513210
Michael I. Murdoch (Co-Founder & CEO)

Subsidiary (Non-US):

AppRiver AG (3)
Industriestrasse 33, 5242, Lupfig, Switzerland
Tel.: (41) 564441282
Web Site: https://www.appriver.com
Cloud-Based Cybersecurity Software Services
N.A.I.C.S.: 513210

Subsidiary (Domestic):

Total Defense, Inc. (3)
1393 Veterans Memorial Hwy Ste 310N, Hauppauge, NY 11788
Tel.: (631) 257-3258
Web Site: https://www.totaldefense.com
Internet, Cloud & Mobile Security
N.A.I.C.S.: 518210

Subsidiary (Domestic):

CM2.COM, Inc. (2)
321 Burnett Ave S Ste 100, Renton, WA 98057
Web Site: https://www.erado.com
Software & Technology Development Services
N.A.I.C.S.: 513210
Craig Brauff (CEO)

Greenview Data, Inc. (2)
8178 Jackson Rd, Ann Arbor, MI 48103
Tel.: (734) 426-7500
Web Site: http://www.greenviewdata.com
Computer Software & Systems Integration
N.A.I.C.S.: 541511

INTERNATIONAL PUBLIC

Kevin Fennimore (Engr-Sls)

OPEN UP GROUP INC

16F Tokyo Toranomon Global Square 1-3-1 Toranomon, Minato-ku, Tokyo, 105-0001, Japan
Tel.: (81) 357777727   JP
Web Site:
  https://www.openupgroup.co.jp
Year Founded: 1997
2154—(TKS)
Rev.: $1,077,459,500
Assets: $725,040,520
Liabilities: $268,822,180
Net Worth: $456,218,340
Earnings: $73,196,960
Emp.: 20,418
Fiscal Year-end: 06/30/24
Staffing & Recruitment Services
N.A.I.C.S.: 541612
Fujio Shimokawa (Auditor)

Subsidiaries:

AXIS CREATE Inc. (1)
Sumitomo Realty & Development Akihabara Ekimae Building 10F, 300 Kanda Neribeicho Chiyoda-ku, Tokyo, 101-0022, Japan
Tel.: (81) 366619234
Web Site: https://www.axiscreate.com
Emp.: 552
Information Technology Services
N.A.I.C.S.: 541511

Arrow Trust Systems Co., Ltd. (1)
2-1-1 Edobori, Nishi-ku, Osaka, 550-0002, Japan
Tel.: (81) 664412611
Web Site: https://www.arrow-trust.co.jp
Emp.: 188
Software Development Services
N.A.I.C.S.: 541511

BeNEXT Partners Inc. (1)
NBF Comodio Shiodome 2-14-1 Higashi-shimbashi, Minato-ku, Tokyo, 105-0021, Japan
Tel.: (81) 364025679
Staffing Services
N.A.I.C.S.: 561320
Seiki Haruta (Pres)

BeNEXT Solutions Inc. (1)
NBF Comodio Shiodome 2-14-1 Higashi-shimbashi, Minato-ku, Tokyo, 105-0021, Japan
Tel.: (81) 364530432
Emp.: 2,237
Staffing Services
N.A.I.C.S.: 561320

BeNEXT Technologies Inc. (1)
NBF Comodio Shiodome 2-14-1 Higashi-shimbashi, Minato-ku, Tokyo, 105-0021, Japan
Tel.: (81) 357777727
Staffing Services
N.A.I.C.S.: 561320
Einobu Yoshii (Pres)

BeNEXT With Inc. (1)
2-9-10 Minamihashimoto, Chuo-ku, Sagamihara, 252-0253, Kanagawa, Japan
Tel.: (81) 427799538
Web Site: http://www.benextwith.com
Training & Employment Opportunity For Disability People Services
N.A.I.C.S.: 624310

Gap Personnel Holdings Limited (1)
Pulford House Bell Meadow Business Park Park Lane, Pulford, Chester, CH4 9EP, United Kingdom
Tel.: (44) 1978890000
Web Site: https://www.gap-personnel.com
Staffing Services
N.A.I.C.S.: 561320

HKTT Limited (1)
Unit B 17/F Office Plus Mong Kok No 998 Canton Road, Kowloon, China (Hong Kong)
Tel.: (852) 25276008
Web Site: http://hk-trusttech.com
Staffing Services
N.A.I.C.S.: 561320

MTrec Limited (1)
MTrec House 8 Market Lane, Newcastle

upon Tyne, NE1 6QQ, United Kingdom
Tel.: (44) 1912425600
Web Site: https://www.mtrec.co.uk
Staffing Services
N.A.I.C.S.: 561320

Nihon Axis Co., Ltd. (1)
Sotono 2-13-8, Hitachinaka, 312-0053, Japan
Tel.: (81) 292744492
Web Site: https://www.n-axis.co.jp
Emp.: 87
Construction Services
N.A.I.C.S.: 236220

Open Up System Co., Ltd. (1)
Sumitomo Realty & Development Akihabara Ekimae Building 10F, 300 Kanda Neribeicho Chiyoda-ku, Tokyo, 101-0022, Japan
Tel.: (81) 368595745
Web Site: https://www.openupsystem.co.jp
Emp.: 429
Software Development Services
N.A.I.C.S.: 541511

PT. Trust Tech Engineering Service Indonesia Limited (1)
Centennial Tower Level29 Jl Gatot Subroto No 27, Karet Semanggi Jakarta Selatan, Jakarta, 12950, Indonesia
Tel.: (62) 2129288541
Web Site: http://trusttech-indonesia.co.id
Staffing Services
N.A.I.C.S.: 561320

TTM Inc. (1)
3rd Floor NBF Comodio Shiodome 2-14-1 Higashi Shimbashi, Minato-ku, Tokyo, 105-0021, Japan
Tel.: (81) 364025679
Web Site: http://www.e-ttm.jp
Staffing Services
N.A.I.C.S.: 561320
Kazuyuki Matsumoto (Pres & CEO)

Trust Next Solutions, Inc. (1)
1-15 Otemachi Freedom Building, Kariya, 448 0857, Aichi, Japan
Tel.: (81) 566632720
Web Site: http://www.tns-inc.com
Software Development Services
N.A.I.C.S.: 513210

Trust Tech With Inc. (1)
2-9-10 Minamiwashimoto, Chuo-ku, Sagamihara, 252-0253, Kanagawa, Japan
Tel.: (81) 427799538
Web Site: http://trusttechwith.com
Packaging Services
N.A.I.C.S.: 561910

Yumeshin Expert Co., Ltd. (1)
18th Floor Tokyo Toranomon Global Square 1-3-1 Toranomon, Minato-ku, Tokyo, 105-0001, Japan
Tel.: (81) 342330813
Web Site: https://www.yumeshin-expert.co.jp
Construction Management Services
N.A.I.C.S.: 236220

OPEN WINDOW BAKERY LIMITED
1125 Finch Ave West Downsview, Toronto, M3J 2E8, ON, Canada
Tel.: (416) 665-8241
Web Site: http://www.owbakery.com
Year Founded: 1957
Rev.: $14,345,917
Emp.: 230
Bakery Products Mfr & Distr
N.A.I.C.S.: 311813
Max Feig (Pres)

OPENBASE INC.
4F Hibrand Building 16 Maeheon-ro, Seocho-gu, Seoul, 6771, Korea (South)
Tel.: (82) 234045700
Web Site:
 https://www.openbase.co.kr
049480—(KRS)
Rev.: $148,103,490
Assets: $115,619,795
Liabilities: $47,589,534
Net Worth: $68,030,261
Earnings: $4,604,211
Emp.: 208
Fiscal Year-end: 12/31/22
Storage & Server Solutions
N.A.I.C.S.: 334111
Kyu-hyeon Song (Pres)

Subsidiaries:

MILTON EDU, Inc. (1)
2F 3F Inhee Bldg 7-4 5 Songpa-dong, Songpa-gu, Seoul, 138-848, Korea (South)
Tel.: (82) 234015881
Web Site: http://www.miltonkids.co.kr
Online Book Publishing Services
N.A.I.C.S.: 513100

NANOBASE, Inc. (1)
Web Site: http://www.nanobase.co.kr
Sales Range: $25-49.9 Million
Emp.: 7
Optical Instrument Mfr
N.A.I.C.S.: 333310

SPSS China (Shanghai) Limited (1)
Suite 905 Ocean Building Yanian East Road 550, Shanghai, 200001, China **(100%)**
Tel.: (86) 21 6352 3300
Web Site: http://www.spss.com.cn
Sales Range: $50-74.9 Million
Emp.: 55
Predictive Analytics & Data Mining Software Distr & Technical Consulting Services
N.A.I.C.S.: 423430

SPSS Korea DataSolution Inc. (1)
10th floor Hyundai Intelex Building 620 Eonju-ro, Gangnam-Gu, Seoul, 06101, Korea (South)
Tel.: (82) 234677200
Web Site: https://spss.datasolution.kr
Sales Range: $1-9.9 Million
Predictive Analytics & Data Mining Software Distr & Technical Consulting Services
N.A.I.C.S.: 423430

OPENCELL BIOMED, INC.
25 The West Mall # 253 Unit 1336, Toronto, M9C 1B8, ON, Canada
Tel.: (877) 622-5005 NV
Web Site:
 http://www.opencellbiomed.com
Year Founded: 2006
Dental Implant Systems Development & Sales
N.A.I.C.S.: 339114
Mislav Pavelic (Chm, Pres & CFO)

OPENDOR
Av Los Conquesadores 2430 Piso 4Av Alonso de Cordova, Oficina 602 Las Condes, Santiago, 5710, Chile
Tel.: (56) 2 588 81 51
Web Site: http://www.opendor.cl
Sales Range: $10-24.9 Million
Emp.: 22
Advetising Agency
N.A.I.C.S.: 541810
Boris Ferrada (Dir-Creative)

OPENEDGES TECHNOLOGY, INC.
13F 114 Yeoksam-ro, Gangnam-gu, Seoul, 06252, Korea (South)
Tel.: (82) 220387507
Web Site:
 https://www.openedges.com
Year Founded: 2017
394280—(KRS)
Information Technology Services
N.A.I.C.S.: 541512

Subsidiaries:

OPENEDGES Technology Corp. (1)
2540 N 1st Ste 101, San Jose, CA 95131
Tel.: (510) 852-5171
Electronic Component Mfr & Distr
N.A.I.C.S.: 334416

The Six Semiconductor Inc. (1)
80 Tiverton Ct Suite 500, Markham, L3R 0G4, ON, Canada
Tel.: (647) 264-3662
Electronic Component Mfr & Distr
N.A.I.C.S.: 334416

OPENFIELD AGRICULTURE LIMITED
Honey Pot Lane Colsterworth, Grantham, NG33 5LY, Lincs, United Kingdom
Tel.: (44) 1476862730 UK
Web Site: http://www.openfield.co.uk
Year Founded: 2008
Sales Range: $50-74.9 Million
Emp.: 230
Grain Marketing & Trading
N.A.I.C.S.: 424510
Tom Davies (CEO)

OPENJOBMETIS S.P.A.
Via Marsala 40/C, 21013, Gallarate, VA, Italy
Tel.: (39) 0331211501
Web Site:
 https://www.openjobmetis.it
Year Founded: 2011
OJM—(ITA)
Rev.: $832,834,381
Assets: $333,730,761
Liabilities: $180,337,091
Net Worth: $153,393,670
Earnings: $15,514,849
Emp.: 769
Fiscal Year-end: 12/31/22
Human Resource Management Services
N.A.I.C.S.: 561311
Marco Vittorelli (Pres)

Subsidiaries:

Family Care S.R.L. (1)
Via Assietta 19, 20161, Milan, Italy
Tel.: (39) 0800292989
Web Site: https://familycarebadanti.it
Employment Agency Services
N.A.I.C.S.: 561311

Lyve S.R.L. (1)
Via Assietta 19, 20161, Milan, Italy
Tel.: (39) 0287075042
Web Site: https://lyveformazione.it
Personal Skill Training Services
N.A.I.C.S.: 611519

OPENKNOWL CO., LTD.
Open Nol 2 Yangpyeong-ro, Yeongdeungpo-gu, Seoul, Korea (South)
Tel.: (82) 7082213056
Web Site:
 https://www.openknowl.com
Year Founded: 2012
440320—(KRS)
Rev.: $12,477,529
Assets: $23,431,656
Liabilities: $7,210,128
Net Worth: $16,221,528
Earnings: ($430,006)
Emp.: 130
Fiscal Year-end: 12/31/22
Educational Support Services
N.A.I.C.S.: 611710
Kwon In-taek (CEO)

OPENLEARNING LIMITED
The Cooperage Level 2 Suite 9 56 Bowman Street, Pyrmont, 2009, NSW, Australia
Tel.: (61) 282949686
Web Site:
 https://www.openlearning.com
Year Founded: 2012
OLL—(ASX)
Rev.: $1,562,413
Assets: $2,272,430
Liabilities: $3,641,951
Net Worth: ($1,369,521)
Earnings: ($3,011,886)
Fiscal Year-end: 12/31/23
Educational Support Services
N.A.I.C.S.: 611710
David Collien (CTO)

Subsidiaries:

Open Learning Global Pty. Ltd. (1)
Suite 1803 227 Elizabeth Street, Sydney, 2000, NSW, Australia
Tel.: (61) 282949686
Online Learning Services
N.A.I.C.S.: 611691

OPENLIMIT HOLDING AG
Zugerstr 74, CH-6341, Baar, Switzerland
Tel.: (41) 415601020
Web Site: http://www.openlimit.com
Year Founded: 1995
O5H—(DEU)
Sales Range: $1-9.9 Million
Emp.: 49
Holding Company
N.A.I.C.S.: 551112
Marc J. Gurov (CEO & CFO)

Subsidiaries:

OpenLimit SignCubes GmbH (1)
Saarbrucker Str 38a D, 10405, Berlin, Germany
Tel.: (49) 30400351010
Software Development Services
N.A.I.C.S.: 541511
Michele Adduci (Engr-Software)

OPENN NEGOTIATION LIMITED
Level 1 4 Stirling Road, Claremont, 6010, WA, Australia
Tel.: (61) 1800667366 AU
Web Site: https://www.openn.com
Year Founded: 2016
OPN—(ASX)
Rev.: $406,767
Assets: $470,426
Liabilities: $652,302
Net Worth: ($181,877)
Earnings: ($8,563,963)
Emp.: 19
Fiscal Year-end: 06/30/23
Property Management Services
N.A.I.C.S.: 531311
Peter Gibbons (Mng Dir)

OPENROAD AUTO GROUP LIMITED
13251 Smallwood Pl, Richmond, V6V 1W8, BC, Canada
Tel.: (604) 273-3233
Web Site:
 http://www.openroadautogroup.com
Sales Range: $125-149.9 Million
Emp.: 900
Automobile Dealers
N.A.I.C.S.: 441110
Christian Chia (CEO)

OPENSYS (M) BERHAD
Level 26 Tower A Pinnacle PJ Jalan Utara C, 46200, Petaling Jaya, Selangor, Malaysia
Tel.: (60) 379327888 MY
Web Site:
 https://www.myopensys.com
Year Founded: 1995
OPENSYS—(KLS)
Rev.: $17,415,955
Assets: $22,568,037
Liabilities: $4,997,001
Net Worth: $17,571,036
Earnings: $2,485,458
Emp.: 256
Fiscal Year-end: 12/31/22
Investment Holding Services
N.A.I.C.S.: 551112
Kee Chung Tan (Co-Founder, Pres & Co-CEO)

OPERA INVESTMENTS PLC

Opera Investments PLC—(Continued)

OPERA INVESTMENTS PLC
Aldermary House 10-15 Queen Street, London, EC4N 1TX, United Kingdom
Tel.: (44) 2035514870
Web Site: http://www.operainvestments.com
Private Investment Firm
N.A.I.C.S.: 523999
Paul Dudley *(Chm)*

OPERA LIMITED
Nydalen, PO Box 4214, 401, Oslo, Norway
Tel.: (47) 23692400
Web Site: https://www.opera.com
Year Founded: 1995
OPRA—(NASDAQ)
Rev.: $331,037,000
Assets: $964,686,000
Liabilities: $76,473,000
Net Worth: $888,213,000
Earnings: $15,035,000
Emp.: 606
Fiscal Year-end: 12/31/22
Software Publishing Services
N.A.I.C.S.: 513210
Yahui Zhou *(Chm & Co-CEO)*

OPERA SGR SPA
Corso Matteotti, 10, Milan, 20121, Italy
Tel.: (39) 02 30 30 03 00
Web Site: http://www.operasgr.it
Private Investment Firm
N.A.I.C.S.: 523999

OPERAONE AG
Ross Markt 11, 60311, Frankfurt am Main, Germany
Tel.: (49) 69920374105
Web Site: http://www.operaone.de
Real Estate Developer & Other Related Services
N.A.I.C.S.: 531390
Christian Wolf *(Vice Chm-Supervisory Bd)*

OPET PETROLCULUK A.S.
Barbaros Mahallesi Gelincik Sokak No 4/A, Atasehir, 34746, Istanbul, Turkiye
Tel.: (90) 2165229000
Web Site: http://www.opet.com.tr
OPET—(IST)
Rev.: $7,592,931,759
Assets: $1,988,079,009
Liabilities: $1,313,176,165
Net Worth: $674,902,844
Earnings: $209,252,295
Fiscal Year-end: 12/31/21
Fuel Oil Distr
N.A.I.C.S.: 424720
Cuneyt Agca *(Gen Mgr)*

OPG POWER VENTURES PLC
55 Athol Street, Douglas, IM1 1LA, Isle of Man
Tel.: (44) 1624681250
Web Site: https://www.opgpower.com
Year Founded: 2008
OPG—(AIM)
Rev.: $196,525,186
Assets: $344,529,054
Liabilities: $129,332,537
Net Worth: $215,196,516
Earnings: $5,188,778
Emp.: 339
Fiscal Year-end: 03/31/24
Power Generation & Distribution Services
N.A.I.C.S.: 221118
Avantika Gupta *(CEO & COO)*

Subsidiaries:

Gita Power & Infrastructure Private Limited (1)
OPG Nagar Madharapakkam Road, Periya Obulapuram Village Nagaraja Kandigai Thiruvallur, Gummidipoondi, 601201, India
Tel.: (91) 4442911222
Web Site: http://www.gitapower.com
Electric Power Distribution Services
N.A.I.C.S.: 221122

OPHIR GOLD CORP.
Suite 206 - 595 Howe Street, Vancouver, V6C 2T5, BC, Canada
Tel.: (604) 365-6681
Web Site: https://www.ophirgoldcorp.com
Year Founded: 2010
OPHR—(OTCIQ)
Rev.: $39,114
Assets: $2,872,226
Liabilities: $104,138
Net Worth: $2,768,088
Earnings: ($866,160)
Fiscal Year-end: 05/31/21
Investment Services
N.A.I.C.S.: 523999
Jonathan Armes *(Pres & CEO)*

OPIN KERFI PLC
Hofdabakki 9, 110, Reykjavik, Iceland
Tel.: (354) 5701000
Web Site: http://www.opinkerfi.is
Year Founded: 1984
Sales Range: $10-24.9 Million
Emp.: 100
Computer Whslr
N.A.I.C.S.: 541512
Gunnar Gudjonsson *(CEO)*

OPMEDIC GROUP INC.
1361 Beaumont Ave Suite 301, Mount-Royal, H3P 2W3, QC, Canada
Tel.: (514) 345-8535
Web Site: http://www.opmedicgroup.com
Sales Range: $10-24.9 Million
Emp.: 168
Medical Laboratories
N.A.I.C.S.: 621511
Paulo Bouca *(COO & VP-Bus Dev)*

OPONEO.PL S.A.
ul Podlesna 17, 85-145, Bydgoszcz, Poland
Tel.: (48) 523740394
Web Site: https://www.oponeo.pl
Year Founded: 1999
OPN—(WAR)
Rev.: $380,481,837
Assets: $155,430,840
Liabilities: $67,379,792
Net Worth: $88,051,048
Earnings: $15,783,048
Emp.: 541
Fiscal Year-end: 12/31/21
Tire Whslr
N.A.I.C.S.: 423130
Dariusz Topolewski *(Chm-Mgmt Bd & CEO)*

Subsidiaries:

Dadelo S.A. (1)
ul Podlesna 17, 85-145, Bydgoszcz, Poland
Tel.: (48) 525822222
Web Site: http://www.dadelo.pl
Stationery Product Whslr
N.A.I.C.S.: 424120

Eximo Project Sp. z o.o. (1)
ul Poznanska 31, 85-129, Bydgoszcz, Poland
Tel.: (48) 525684420
Web Site: http://www.eximoproject.pl
Information & Technology Services
N.A.I.C.S.: 541519
Maciej Malecki *(Acct Mgr)*

Hurtopon.pl Sp. z o.o. (1)
ul Terasy 2, 85-053, Bydgoszcz, Poland
Tel.: (48) 525862876
Web Site: http://www.hurtopon.pl
Tire Whslr
N.A.I.C.S.: 513210

Oponeo.co.uk Ltd. (1)
32 Abbey Road Park Royal, London, NW10 7TR, United Kingdom
Tel.: (44) 2030110070
Web Site: http://www.oponeo.co.uk
Tire Whslr
N.A.I.C.S.: 441340

Oponeo.de GmbH (1)
Hohenzollerndamm 61, 14199, Berlin, Germany
Tel.: (49) 30200076500
Web Site: http://www.oponeo.de
Tire Whslr
N.A.I.C.S.: 519290

Opony.pl Sp. z o.o. (1)
ul Terasy 2, 85-053, Bydgoszcz, Poland
Tel.: (48) 523418820
Web Site: http://www.opony.pl
Tire Whslr
N.A.I.C.S.: 441340
Andriana Rakityanska *(Mgr-Pur)*

OPPEIN HOME GROUP INC
No 366 Guanghua 3rd Road, Jianggao Town Baiyun District, Guangzhou, 510450, China
Tel.: (86) 2036730513
Web Site: https://www.oppeinhome.com
Year Founded: 1994
603833—(SHG)
Rev.: $3,156,122,291
Assets: $4,016,985,411
Liabilities: $1,698,447,919
Net Worth: $2,318,537,492
Earnings: $377,454,940
Emp.: 10,000
Fiscal Year-end: 12/31/22
Furniture Mfr & Distr
N.A.I.C.S.: 337121
Yao Liangsong *(Chm & Gen Mgr)*

OPPLE LIGHTING CO., LTD
Building V3 The MIXC Lane 1799 Wuzhong Road, Minhang District, Shanghai, 201103, China
Tel.: (86) 2138550000
Web Site: https://www.opple.com
Year Founded: 1996
603515—(SHG)
Rev.: $1,020,704,701
Assets: $1,220,833,879
Liabilities: $363,603,287
Net Worth: $857,230,592
Earnings: $110,089,592
Emp.: 6,000
Fiscal Year-end: 12/31/22
Lighting Lamp Mfr & Distr
N.A.I.C.S.: 335139
Wang Yaohai *(Chm)*

Subsidiaries:

Opple Lighting South Africa (Pty) Ltd (1)
Unit C3 The Gantry Cnr Witkoppen and The Straight Ave, Fourways, Gauteng, South Africa
Tel.: (27) 729241722
Web Site: http://opple.co.za
Lighting Lamp Distr
N.A.I.C.S.: 423610

OPPORTUNITY BULGARIA INVESTMENT AD
Knyaginya Maria Luiza Blvd No 19 floor 1 apartment 5, 1000, Sofia, Bulgaria
Tel.: (359) 897397905
Web Site: https://www.obinvestment.eu
OPBI—(BUL)
Sales Range: Less than $1 Million
Holding Company

INTERNATIONAL PUBLIC

N.A.I.C.S.: 551112
Ivan Yanev *(CEO & Member-Mgmt Bd)*

OPPORTUNITY ENERGIA E PARTICIPACOES S.A.
Av Presidente Wilson 231 - 28 Andar/parte, 20030905, Rio de Janeiro, Brazil
Tel.: (55) 21 3804 3700
Web Site: http://www.opportunityenergia.com
Year Founded: 1997
OPHE3B—(BRAZ)
Sales Range: Less than $1 Million
Financial Investment Services
N.A.I.C.S.: 523999

OPPORTUNITY INVESTMENT MANAGEMENT PLC
Company House Taylor Wessing 5 New Street Square, London, EC4A 3TW, United Kingdom
Tel.: (44) 20 7300 7000
Web Site: http://www.oimplc.com
Sales Range: $50-74.9 Million
Holding Company; Investment Management Services
N.A.I.C.S.: 551112
P. Zwart *(CEO)*

Subsidiaries:

G. Fleischhauer Ingenieur-Buro GmbH & Co. KG (1)
Oldenburger Allee 36, 30659, Hannover, Lower Saxony, Germany
Tel.: (49) 51190140
Web Site: http://www.fleischhauer.de
Sales Range: $25-49.9 Million
Emp.: 200
Electrical Engineering Services
N.A.I.C.S.: 541330
Michael Hartung *(Gen Mgr)*

Subsidiary (Domestic):

G. Fleischhauer GmbH (2)
Kreuzbergstr 31, 06849, Dessau, Saxony-Anhalt, Germany
Tel.: (49) 340800000
Telecommunication Engineering Services
N.A.I.C.S.: 517810

G. Fleischhauer Ingenieur-Buro Bremen GmbH (2)
Hinterm Sielhot 4-5, Bremen, 28277, Germany
Tel.: (49) 421576520
Web Site: http://www.spie-fleischhauer.com
Sales Range: $10-24.9 Million
Emp.: 40
Information Technology Support Services
N.A.I.C.S.: 541512
Michael Hartung *(Mng Dir)*

OPREMA A.D.
Gavrila Principa 4, 76300, Bijeljina, Bosnia & Herzegovina
Tel.: (387) 55 220 484
Sales Range: Less than $1 Million
Emp.: 1
Motor Vehicle Parts Whslr
N.A.I.C.S.: 423120

OPSEU PENSION TRUST
1 Adelaide St E Suite 1200, Toronto, M5C 3A7, ON, Canada
Tel.: (416) 681-6161
Web Site: http://www.optrust.com
Year Founded: 1995
Pension Fund Administration Services
N.A.I.C.S.: 524292
James Davis *(Chief Investment Officer)*

OPSMOBIL, INC.
815 8th Ave SW Ste 1200, Calgary, T2P 3P2, AB, Canada
Tel.: (780) 402-2444
Web Site: http://www.opsmobil.com

Year Founded: 1985
Asset Management, Construction, Aircraft Charter & Pipeline Surveillance Services
N.A.I.C.S.: 237120
Christian Dallaire *(Dir-Maintenance & Mgr-Corp Resources)*

OPSONA THERAPEUTICS LIMITED
The Trinity Centre for Health Sciences, Institute Molecular Medicine, Saint James's Hospital, Dublin, 8, Ireland
Tel.: (353) 18968499   IE
Year Founded: 2004
Sales Range: $10-24.9 Million
Emp.: 14
Immunology Research & Drug Developer
N.A.I.C.S.: 541715
Bernd R. Seizinger *(Chm)*

OPT MACHINE VISION TECHNOLOGY CO., LTD.
No 8 Jinsheng Road, Jinxia Henan Industrial Zone Chang an Town, Dongguan, 523850, Guangdong, China
Tel.: (86) 76982716188
Web Site: https://www.optmv.com
Year Founded: 2006
688686—(SHG)
Rev.: $160,189,450
Assets: $415,360,287
Liabilities: $25,200,691
Net Worth: $390,159,596
Earnings: $45,611,018
Emp.: 2,700
Fiscal Year-end: 12/31/22
Software Development Services
N.A.I.C.S.: 541511
Shenglin Lu *(Chm & Deputy Gen Mgr)*

Subsidiaries:

OPT Europe: OPT Machine Vision GmbH   (1)
Wilhelm-Haas-Strasse 6, 70771, Leinfelden-Echterdingen, Germany
Tel.: (49) 71144708961
Software Development Services
N.A.I.C.S.: 423430

OPT Japan: OPT Machine Vision Tech Co., Ltd.   (1)
The Soho 735 2-7-4 Aomi, Koto-ku, Tokyo, 135-0064, Japan
Tel.: (81) 368235168
Automation Equipment Mfr & Distr
N.A.I.C.S.: 334413

OPT Machine Vision GmbH   (1)
Wilhelm-Haas-Strasse 6, Leinfelden-Echterdingen, 70771, Stuttgart, Germany
Tel.: (49) 71144708961
Web Site: http://www.optmv.de
Image Processing Component Distr
N.A.I.C.S.: 423410

OPT Machine Vision Tech (Suzhou) Limited   (1)
11th Floor Building D Dongchuang Science and Technology Park, No 216 Jinfeng Road Mudu Town Wuzhong District, Suzhou, Jiangsu, China
Tel.: (86) 51267904405
Optical Product Distr
N.A.I.C.S.: 423410

OPT Malaysia Sdn. Bhd.   (1)
110-02-01 Summerton Complex, 11900, Bayan Lepas, Penang, Malaysia
Tel.: (60) 164484978
Automation Equipment Mfr & Distr
N.A.I.C.S.: 334413

OPT Taiwan Co., Ltd.   (1)
12F No 226 Zhongyang Road, Xinzhuang, New Taipei City, 242, Taiwan
Tel.: (886) 903117815
Industrial Equipment Whsr
N.A.I.C.S.: 423830

OPT USA Limited   (1)
20195 Stevens Creek Blvd 230, Cupertino, CA 95014
Tel.: (408) 816-5577
Optical Product Distr
N.A.I.C.S.: 423410

OPT Usa Inc.   (1)
20195 Stevens Creek Blvd 230, Cupertino, CA 95014
Tel.: (408) 816-5577
Industrial Equipment Whsr
N.A.I.C.S.: 423830

OPTEAM SA
Tajecina 113, 36-002, Jasionka, Poland
Tel.: (48) 178672100
Web Site: https://www.opteam.pl
Year Founded: 1988
OPM—(WAR)
Rev.: $23,171,494
Assets: $16,564,024
Liabilities: $6,115,854
Net Worth: $10,448,171
Earnings: ($1,267,022)
Emp.: 200
Fiscal Year-end: 12/31/23
Smart Card Technology Systems Mfr & Integrator
N.A.I.C.S.: 541512
Janusz Bober *(Chm-Supervisory Bd)*

OPTEL VISION INC.
2680 boulevard du Parc Technologique, Quebec, G1P 4S6, QC, Canada
Tel.: (418) 688-0334   QC
Web Site: http://www.optelgroup.com
Year Founded: 1989
Traceability Systems Mfr
N.A.I.C.S.: 339999

Subsidiaries:

Verify Holdings, LLC   (1)
3033 Campus Dr Ste W-230, Plymouth, MN 55441-2651
Tel.: (763) 235-1400
Software Publisher
N.A.I.C.S.: 513210

OPTEON PROPERTY GROUP PTY LTD.
Unit 4 75 Lorimer Street, Docklands, 3008, VIC, Australia
Tel.: (61) 1300 40 50 6   AU
Web Site: https://www.opteonsolutions.com
Year Founded: 2005
Sales Range: $1-9.9 Million
Emp.: 100
Valuation, Advisory & Property Services
N.A.I.C.S.: 531390
Chris Knight *(CEO & Mng Dir)*

Subsidiaries:

Opteon Appraisal, Inc.   (1)
14861 N Scottsdale Rd Ste A-105, Scottsdale, AZ 85254
Tel.: (833) 740-2739
Web Site: https://www.opteonusa.com
Real Estate Services
N.A.I.C.S.: 531390

Subsidiary (Domestic):

Northeastern Appraisal Associates Residential, Inc.   (2)
5110 Main St Ste 201, Buffalo, NY 14221
Tel.: (716) 634-8970
Web Site: http://www.northeasternappraisal.com
Sales Range: $1-9.9 Million
Emp.: 50
Offices of Real Estate Appraisers
N.A.I.C.S.: 531320
Robert L. Vicanti *(Pres-Fin)*

OPTER AB
Tel.: (46) 854529200
Web Site: https://www.opter.com
Year Founded: 2001
M3W—(DEU)
Software Development Services
N.A.I.C.S.: 541511
Viktor Edlund *(Co-Founder & CEO)*

OPTEX GROUP CO., LTD.
Exchange Road Ortigas Center, Otsu, 520-0801, Shiga, Japan
Tel.: (81) 775798000   JP
Web Site: https://www.optex.net
Year Founded: 1979
6914—(TKS)
Rev.: $399,677,480
Assets: $475,930,430
Liabilities: $162,049,040
Net Worth: $313,881,390
Earnings: $32,670,720
Emp.: 2,136
Fiscal Year-end: 12/31/23
Infrared Sensor & Security Systems Equipment Mfr
N.A.I.C.S.: 333310
Akira Higashi *(CFO)*

Subsidiaries:

CCS Inc.   (1)
                                                      (63.52%)
Tel.: (81) 754158288
Web Site: http://www.ccs-inc.co.jp
Sales Range: $75-99.9 Million
LED Lighting Developer, Mfr & Sales
N.A.I.C.S.: 335139
Hironori Ishii *(Sr Exec Officer)*

Subsidiary (US):

CCS America Inc.   (2)
6 Lincoln Knoll Ln Ste 102, Burlington, MA 01803   (100%)
Tel.: (781) 272-6900
Web Site: http://www.ccsamerica.com
LED Lighting Developer, Mfr & Sales
N.A.I.C.S.: 335139

Subsidiary (Non-US):

CCS Asia Pte Ltd.   (2)
35 Marsiling Industrial Estate Rd 3 05-03, Singapore, 739257, Singapore
Tel.: (65) 63631180
Web Site: http://www.ccs-asia.com.sg
LED Lighting Distr
N.A.I.C.S.: 335139

CCS China Inc.   (2)
A407 TCL Building Gaoxinnan 1st Road, Nanshan District, Shenzhen, 518057, China
Tel.: (86) 75582790477
Led Light Whslr
N.A.I.C.S.: 423610

CCS Europe NV   (2)
Bergensesteenweg 421B, 1600, Sint-Pieters-Leeuw, Belgium
Tel.: (32) 2 333 0080
Web Site: http://www.ccs-grp.com
LED Lighting Sales for Machine Vision
N.A.I.C.S.: 335139
Dirk Vermeersch *(Pres)*

CCS Korea Inc.   (1)
1506 O'Biz Tower 126 Beolmal-ro, Dongan-gu, Anyang, Gyeonggi, Korea (South)
Tel.: (82) 313603656
Light Emitting Diode Lighting Mfr & Distr
N.A.I.C.S.: 335139

CCS MV (Malaysia) Sdn. Bhd.   (1)
Level 2 Unit 15 Setia SPICE Canopy Jalan Tun Dr Awang, 11900, Bayan Baru, Penang, Malaysia
Tel.: (60) 46116656
Light Emitting Diode Lighting Mfr & Distr
N.A.I.C.S.: 335139

CCS MV (Thailand) Co., Ltd.   (1)
349 SJ Infinite I Business Complex 16th Floor Unit 1607, Vibhavadi-rangsit Road Kwaeng Chompol Khet Chatuchak, Bangkok, 10900, Thailand
Tel.: (66) 27791051
Light Emitting Diode Lighting Mfr & Distr

N.A.I.C.S.: 335139

EFFILUX GmbH   (1)
Bachstr 85, 50354, Hurth, Germany
Tel.: (49) 22128887010
Light Emitting Diode Lighting Mfr & Distr
N.A.I.C.S.: 335139

EXNOS Co., Ltd.   (1)
6th Fl Culture Bldg 3-1-7 Sagamiono, Minami-ku, Sagamihara, 252-0303, Kanagawa, Japan
Tel.: (81) 427675034
Web Site: https://www.exnos.co.jp
Testing Equipment Distr
N.A.I.C.S.: 423830

Effilux S.A.S.   (1)
1 Rue de Terre Neuve Mini Parc du Verger Batiment E, 91940, Les Ulis, France
Tel.: (33) 972527003
Web Site: https://www.effilux.com
Light Emitting Diode Lighting Mfr & Distr
N.A.I.C.S.: 335139

FIBER SENSYS INC.   (1)
6175 NE Century Blvd, Hillsboro, OR 97124
Tel.: (503) 692-4430
Web Site: https://www.fibersensys.com
Fiber Optic Cable Mfr
N.A.I.C.S.: 334417
Duane Thompson *(Sr VP)*

Farsight Security Services, Ltd.   (1)
The Observatory Vicarage Farm Road, Peterborough, PE1 5TU, Cambs, United Kingdom
Tel.: (44) 8453710101
Web Site: https://www.farsight.co.uk
Sales Range: $1-9.9 Million
Professional Security & Software Services
N.A.I.C.S.: 561621
Robert Moore *(Mng Dir)*

GIKEN TRASTEM CO., LTD.   (1)
98 Kawaramachi Takeda Nishidan, Fushimi-ku, Kyoto, 612-8429, Japan
Tel.: (81) 756465520
Web Site: https://www.trastem.co.jp
Electronic Product Mfr & Distr
N.A.I.C.S.: 334419
Yoshiharu Ohnishi *(Pres)*

Mitsutec Co., Ltd.   (1)
134-1 Nakamura, Awaji, 656-1526, Hyogo, Japan
Tel.: (81) 799852340
Web Site: https://www.mitsu-tec.com
Emp.: 105
Automated Machinery Equipment Mfr & Distr
N.A.I.C.S.: 334413

O'PAL OPTEX CO., LTD   (1)
5-265-1 Ogoto, Otsu, 520-0101, Shiga, Japan
Tel.: (81) 77 579 7111
Web Site: https://www.o-pal.com
Outdoor Sports Club Operator
N.A.I.C.S.: 713990

OPTEX (DONGGUAN) CO., LTD.   (1)
No 2 Jufu Road Banhu, Huangjiang Town, Dongguan, Guangdong, China
Tel.: (86) 76983365026
Web Site: https://www.optexchina.com
Electronic Security Equipment Mfr & Distr
N.A.I.C.S.: 334413

OPTEX (EUROPE) LTD.   (1)
Unit 13 Cordwallis Park Clivemont Road, Maidenhead, SL6 7BU, Berkshire, United Kingdom
Tel.: (44) 1628 631 000
Web Site: http://www.optex-europe.com
Emp.: 5
Electronic Security Equipment Mfr & Distr
N.A.I.C.S.: 334413

OPTEX DO BRASIL LTDA.   (1)
Rua Cantagalo 74 Tatuape CJ 1507, Sao Paulo, 03319-000, Brazil
Tel.: (55) 11 22250934
Web Site: http://www.optex.net
Electronic Security Equipment Mfr
N.A.I.C.S.: 334413
Masaya Horii *(Pres)*

OPTEX FA CO., LTD.   (1)
91 Chudoji-Awata-cho, Shimogyo-ku, Kyoto,

OPTEX GROUP CO., LTD.

Optex Group Co., Ltd.—(Continued)

600-8815, Japan
Tel.: (81) 75 325 1314
Web Site: https://www.optex-fa.co.jp
Photoelectric Sensor Mfr & Distr
N.A.I.C.S.: 334413

Subsidiary (Non-US):

Guangzhou Optex Industrial Automation Control Equipment Co., Ltd. (2)
A1 10F04 No 280 Hanxi Road East, Panyu District, Guangzhou, Guangdong, China
Tel.: (86) 2039922102
Sensor Whslr
N.A.I.C.S.: 423610

Subsidiary (US):

Optex FA Inc. (2)
1701 E Woodfield Rd Ste 635, Schaumburg, IL 60173
Tel.: (847) 565-3500
Sensor Whslr
N.A.I.C.S.: 423610

Subsidiary (Domestic):

Sick Optex Co., Ltd. (2)
91 Chudoji-Awata-cho, Shimogyo-ku, Kyoto, 600-8815, Japan
Tel.: (81) 753133100
Photoelectric Sensor Mfr
N.A.I.C.S.: 334413

Tokyo Opto-Electronics Co., Ltd. (2)
5-8 6-chome Nishi Oizumi, Nerima-ku, Tokyo, 178-0065, Japan
Tel.: (81) 339227121
Web Site: https://www.toe.co.jp
Measuring Instrument Mfr & Whslr
N.A.I.C.S.: 334513

OPTEX KOREA CO., LTD. (1)
101-3001ho Lotte Castle President Mapodae-ro 109, Mapo-Gu, Seoul, Korea (South)
Tel.: (82) 27195971
Web Site: http://www.optexkorea.com
Electronic Security Equipment Mfr
N.A.I.C.S.: 334413

OPTEX SECURITY SAS (1)
835 route des Frenes, 69400, Arnas, France
Tel.: (33) 43 755 5050
Web Site: http://www.optex-security.com
Electronic Security Equipment Mfr
N.A.I.C.S.: 334413

OPTEX SECURITY Sp.z o.o. (1)
ul Bitwy Warszawskiej 1920 r 7B, 02-366, Warsaw, Poland
Tel.: (48) 22 598 06 60
Web Site: http://www.optex-europe.com
Electronic Security Equipment Mfr
N.A.I.C.S.: 334413

OPTEX TECHNOLOGIES B.V. (1)
Henricuskade 17, 2497 NB, Hague, Netherlands
Tel.: (31) 704194100
Web Site: https://www.optex.eu
Emp.: 7
Electronic Security Equipment Mfr
N.A.I.C.S.: 334413
Karin van der Lubbe-Broeren (Controller-Fin Dept)

OPTEX Technologies, Inc. (1)
18730 S Wilmington Ave Unit 100, Rancho Dominguez, CA 90220
Tel.: (800) 877-6656
Web Site: http://www.optextechnologies.com
Sensor Mfr
N.A.I.C.S.: 334512
Robert Blair (Pres & CEO)

Optex Co., Ltd. (1)
5-8-12 Ogoto, Otsu, 520-0101, Shiga, Japan
Tel.: (81) 775798000
Sensor Mfr & Whslr
N.A.I.C.S.: 334513
Toru Kamimura (Pres & CEO)

Subsidiary (Non-US):

Gardasoft Vision Limited (2)
Trinity Court Buckingway Business Park, Swavesey, Cambridge, CB24 4UQ, United Kingdom
Tel.: (44) 1954234970
Web Site: https://www.gardasoft.com
Light Mfr
N.A.I.C.S.: 335132

Optex (H.K.) Limited (2)
Room 3206B Cable Tv Tower 9 Hoi Shing Road, Tsuen Wan, China (Hong Kong)
Tel.: (852) 23758818
Sensor Whslr
N.A.I.C.S.: 423610

Optex Pinnacle India Private Limited (2)
FF-11 Paras Downtown Center Golf Course Road Sector 53, Gurgaon, 122002, Haryana, India
Tel.: (91) 1244035705
Web Site: https://www.optexpinnacle.com
Security Services
N.A.I.C.S.: 561621
Monika khandelwal (Asst Mgr)

Optex(Thailand) Co., Ltd. (2)
90 CW Tower Tower B Unit B1702 17 Floor Ratchadaphisek Rd, Huai Khwang, Bangkok, 10310, Thailand
Tel.: (66) 21683162
Web Site: https://optex-asean.com
Security Services
N.A.I.C.S.: 561621
Pavana Sriariyaporn (Asst Mgr-Sls)

Optex MFG Co., Ltd. (2)
5-8-12 Ogoto Otsu, Shiga, 520-0101, Japan
Tel.: (81) 775003100
Photoelectric Sensor Mfr & Whslr
N.A.I.C.S.: 334413

Optex, Inc. (2)
18730 S Wilmington Ave Ste 100, Rancho Dominguez, CA 90220
Tel.: (310) 667-9344
Web Site: https://www.optexamerica.com
Sales Range: $25-49.9 Million
Infrared Sensor Equipment Distr
N.A.I.C.S.: 333310
Mac Kokobo (CEO)

RAYTEC LIMITED (1)
Unit 15 Wansbeck Business Park Rotary Parkway, Ashington, NE63 8QW, Northumberland, United Kingdom
Tel.: (44) 167 052 0055
Web Site: https://www.raytecctv.com
Electronic Security Equipment Mfr & Distr
N.A.I.C.S.: 334413

RAYTEC SYSTEMS INC. (1)
800-300 Terry Fox Drive, Ottawa, K2K 0E3, ON, Canada
Tel.: (613) 270-9990
Emp.: 8
Lighting Product Mfr
N.A.I.C.S.: 334413

Sanritz Automation Co., Ltd. (1)
4-21-9 Minami Naruse, Tokyo, Machida, 194-0045, Japan
Tel.: (81) 427286121
Web Site: https://www.sanritz.co.jp
Emp.: 174
Industrial Computer Equipment Mfr & Distr
N.A.I.C.S.: 334111

Three Ace Co., Ltd. (1)
3rd floor CS Building 374 Sakurazuru Enmachi, Kamigyo-ku, Kyoto, 602-8011, Japan
Tel.: (81) 754325610
Web Site: https://www.3ace-net.co.jp
Emp.: 71
System & App Development Services
N.A.I.C.S.: 541511

ZENIC INC. (1)
Optex Nionohama Bldg 4-7-5 Nionohama, Otsu, 520-0801, Shiga, Japan
Tel.: (81) 775262101
Web Site: https://www.zenic.co.jp
Semiconductor Mfr & Distr
N.A.I.C.S.: 334413
Keisuke Hisano (Pres)

OPTHEA LIMITED

Suite 0403 Level 4 650 Chapel Street, South Yarra, 3141, VIC, Australia
Tel.: (61) 398260399   AU
Web Site: https://www.opthea.com
OPT—(NASDAQ)
Rev.: $261,859
Assets: $188,791,216
Liabilities: $264,601,293
Net Worth: ($75,810,077)
Earnings: ($220,242,105)
Emp.: 34
Fiscal Year-end: 06/30/24
Eye Disease Therapy Developer
N.A.I.C.S.: 541715
Megan Baldwin (CEO & Mng Dir)

OPTI-COATING LABORATORIES, INC.

1375 32nd Avenue, Lachine, H8T 3A2, QC, Canada
Tel.: (514) 636-9888
Web Site: http://www.opticoating.com
Year Founded: 1972
Sales Range: $25-49.9 Million
Emp.: 142
Optical Moulding & Coating Technologies & Testing Laboratory
N.A.I.C.S.: 333310
Robert Paluzzi (Chm)

Subsidiaries:

Leader Sports Europe S.A. (1)
Rue De La Vallee D Ossau, 64121, Pau, Serres Castet, France (100%)
Tel.: (33) 559128485
Provider of Ophthalmic Goods
N.A.I.C.S.: 339115

OPTIBASE LTD.

8 Hamenofim Street, Herzliyya, 4672559, Israel
Tel.: (972) 737073700   Il
Web Site: http://www.optibase-holdings.com
Year Founded: 1990
OBAS—(NASDAQ)
Rev.: $14,874,000
Assets: $234,697,000
Liabilities: $148,036,000
Net Worth: $86,661,000
Earnings: $6,433,000
Emp.: 11
Fiscal Year-end: 12/31/20
Streaming Video Solution Products Mfr
N.A.I.C.S.: 541512
Alex Hilman (Chm)

Subsidiaries:

Optibase Inc. (1)
1250 Space Park Way, Mountain View, CA 94043
Tel.: (650) 230-2400
Professional Editing & Streaming Solutions
N.A.I.C.S.: 541512

Unit (Domestic):

Media 100 (2)
25 Thomson Pl # 4, Boston, MA 02210-1202
Tel.: (703) 462-1640
Web Site: http://www.media100.com
Advanced Media Systems Services
N.A.I.C.S.: 334118

OPTIBIOTIX HEALTH PLC

Innovation Centre Innovation Way, Heslington, York, YO10 5DG, United Kingdom
Tel.: (44) 2079338780   UK
Web Site: https://www.optibiotix.com
Year Founded: 2012
OPTI—(AIM)
Rev.: $2,977,091
Assets: $27,130,594
Liabilities: $2,653,787
Net Worth: $24,476,807
Earnings: $8,432,846
Emp.: 8
Fiscal Year-end: 12/31/21

INTERNATIONAL PUBLIC

Investment Services
N.A.I.C.S.: 523999
Per Rehne (Dir-Comml)

Subsidiaries:

Natural AdCampaign Limited (1)
81 Rivington Street, London, EC2A 3AY, United Kingdom
Tel.: (44) 2031785618
Web Site: http://www.naturaladcampaign.com
Sales Range: $25-49.9 Million
Emp.: 20
Print Media Mfr & Distr
N.A.I.C.S.: 325992

OPTIC 2000

56 Ave Pierre Larousse, 92240, Malakoff, Cedex, France
Tel.: (33) 41232000
Web Site: http://www.optic2000.com
Year Founded: 1962
Sales Range: $75-99.9 Million
Emp.: 300
Glasses Mfr & Marketer
N.A.I.C.S.: 339113

OPTIC SECURITY GROUP LIMITED

14 Amelia Earhart Avenue, Airport Oaks Mangere, Auckland, 2022, New Zealand
Tel.: (64) 9 950 9990
Web Site: http://www.opticsecuritygroup.com
Security System Services
N.A.I.C.S.: 561621
Jason Cherrington (Co-Founder & CEO)

Subsidiaries:

Rainmaker Blue Limited (1)
2/31 Apollo Drive, Mairangi Bay, Auckland, 0632, New Zealand
Tel.: (64) 9 477 2200
Web Site: http://www.ssl.co.nz
Security Software Services
N.A.I.C.S.: 513210
Badi Ala'i (Gen Mgr)

OPTICEPT TECHNOLOGIES AB

Skiffervagen 12, 224 78, Lund, Sweden
Tel.: (46) 46152300
Web Site: https://www.opticept.se
OPTI—(OMX)
Rev.: $983,450
Assets: $44,332,050
Liabilities: $7,237,255
Net Worth: $37,094,795
Earnings: ($9,384,922)
Emp.: 36
Fiscal Year-end: 12/31/22
Food Mfr
N.A.I.C.S.: 311999
Maritin Linde (Chm)

Subsidiaries:

ArcAroma AB (1)
Skiffervagen 12, 224 78, Lund, Sweden
Tel.: (46) 462718380
Web Site: http://www.arcaroma.com
Rev.: $550,854
Assets: $13,241,925
Liabilities: $1,688,999
Net Worth: $11,552,926
Earnings: ($1,742,584)
Emp.: 11
Fiscal Year-end: 12/31/2019
Biotechnology Research Services
N.A.I.C.S.: 541715
Johan Mollerstrom (CEO)

OPTICIS COMPANY LIMITED

305 Sanseong-daero 3rd floor of Sambournesang Park II, Sujeong-gu, Seongnam, 13354, Gyeonggi-do, Korea (South)

Tel.: (82) 317198033
Web Site: https://www.opticis.com
Year Founded: 1999
109080—(KRS)
Rev.: $22,016,521
Assets: $43,532,477
Liabilities: $4,345,362
Net Worth: $39,187,115
Earnings: $5,670,422
Emp.: 105
Fiscal Year-end: 12/31/22
Fiber-Optic Digital Link Products Mfr
N.A.I.C.S.: 335921
Il Kim *(Co-Founder & CTO)*

OPTICORE INC.
501 The First Tower 3 602 Dongtangiheung-ro, Hwaseong, 018469, Gyeonggi-do, Korea (South)
Tel.: (82) 7044925446
Web Site: https://opticoreinc.com
Year Founded: 2016
380540—(KRS)
Rev.: $16,954,917
Assets: $25,288,802
Liabilities: $10,437,051
Net Worth: $14,851,751
Earnings: ($7,530,800)
Emp.: 62
Fiscal Year-end: 12/31/22
Semiconductor Product Mfr
N.A.I.C.S.: 334413
Deok Gyeom Kim *(Mgr-Headquarter)*

OPTICS TECHNOLOGY HOLDING CO., LTD
No 5 Hanan 8th Avenue Core Area, Hanan Industrial New Town, Harbin, 150060, China
Tel.: (86) 45186785550
Web Site: http://www.zfgf.cc
Year Founded: 2006
300489—(CHIN)
Rev.: $142,453,915
Assets: $470,085,790
Liabilities: $461,000,374
Net Worth: $9,085,417
Earnings: ($33,949,639)
Fiscal Year-end: 12/31/23
Aluminum Material & Product Mfr
N.A.I.C.S.: 331315
Hou Zhenfu *(Chm)*

OPTIEMUS INFRACOM LIMITED
K-20 2nd Floor Lajpat Nagar - II, New Delhi, 110024, India
Tel.: (91) 1129840906
Web Site: https://www.optiemus.com
Year Founded: 1993
OPTIEMUS—(NSE)
Rev.: $147,224,771
Assets: $109,267,682
Liabilities: $63,411,642
Net Worth: $45,856,040
Earnings: $5,020,838
Emp.: 47
Fiscal Year-end: 03/31/23
Telecommunication Product Distr
N.A.I.C.S.: 423690
Ashok Kumar Gupta *(Chm)*

OPTIFIN INVEST S.R.O.
Rusovka cesta 1, 851 01, Bratislava, Slovakia
Tel.: (421) 220634444
Web Site: http://www.optifininvest.sk
Privater Equity Firm
N.A.I.C.S.: 523999
Michaela Ikrenyi Lazarova *(Mgr)*
Subsidiaries:

ELH WBN Waggonbau Niesky GmbH (1)
Am Waggonbau 11, 2906, Berlin, Germany
Tel.: (49) 3588240
Web Site: http://www.waggonbau-niesky.com
Rail Vehicle Mfr
N.A.I.C.S.: 336510
Peter Schulze *(Head-HR & Procurist)*

Tatravagonka a.s. (1)
Stefanikova 887/53, 058 01, Poprad, Slovakia
Tel.: (421) 527112111
Web Site: http://www.tatravagonka.sk
Rail Freight Vehicles & Bogies Mfr
N.A.I.C.S.: 488999

OPTIM CORPORATION
Shiodome Building 18F 1-2-20 Kaigan, Minato-ku, Tokyo, 105-0022, Japan
Tel.: (81) 364358570
Web Site: https://www.optim.com
Year Founded: 2000
3694—(TKS)
Rev.: $67,706,230
Assets: $63,204,820
Liabilities: $14,674,200
Net Worth: $48,530,620
Earnings: $7,740,310
Emp.: 406
Fiscal Year-end: 03/31/24
Software Developer
N.A.I.C.S.: 513210
Shunji Sugaya *(Pres)*

OPTIMA AUTOMOBILE GROUP HOLDINGS LIMITED
600 Sin Ming Avenue CityCab Building, Singapore, 575733, Singapore
Tel.: (65) 64721313
Web Site: https://www.ow.sg
Year Founded: 2012
8418—(HKG)
Rev.: $61,586,678
Assets: $19,333,272
Liabilities: $13,028,517
Net Worth: $6,304,754
Earnings: ($1,389,900)
Emp.: 126
Fiscal Year-end: 12/31/22
Holding Company
N.A.I.C.S.: 551112
Jiayuan Xu *(Sec)*
Subsidiaries:

Optima Carz Leasing Pte. Ltd. (1)
159 Sin Ming Road 04-05 Amtech Building Lobby 2, Singapore, 575625, Singapore
Tel.: (65) 64526868
Web Site: https://ocleasing.sg
Vehicle Rental Services
N.A.I.C.S.: 532120

OPTIMA MEDICAL INNOVATIONS CORP.
209-5460 Yonge Street, Toronto, M2N 6K7, ON, Canada
Tel.: (416) 250-1812
Web Site: https://www.tokicorp.com
Year Founded: 2007
OMIC—(CNSX)
Rev.: $4,613,565
Assets: $7,224,297
Liabilities: $3,915,819
Net Worth: $3,308,478
Earnings: ($3,961,057)
Fiscal Year-end: 12/31/20
Healthcare Product Distr
N.A.I.C.S.: 424210

OPTIMA PACKAGING GROUP GMBH
Steinbeisweg 20, 74523, Schwabisch Hall, Germany
Tel.: (49) 791 506 0
Web Site: http://www.optima-packaging.com
Year Founded: 1922
Sales Range: $350-399.9 Million
Emp.: 2,400
Holding Company; Packaging Machinery Mfr
N.A.I.C.S.: 551112
Hans Buehler *(Mng Dir)*
Subsidiaries:

AMOTEK S.r.l. (1)
Via Piemonte 5, Zola Predosa, 40069, Bologna, Italy
Tel.: (39) 0516186811
Web Site: http://www.amotek.com
Packaging Machinery Mfr
N.A.I.C.S.: 333993

EMKON Automation GmbH (1)
Bahnhofstrasse 8a, Kirchlintenln, 27308, Verden, Germany
Tel.: (49) 423694360
Web Site: http://www.emkon-system.de
Industrial Machinery Services
N.A.I.C.S.: 811310

Gevas Brasil Ltda. (1)
Avenida Edmundo Doubrawa 313, Joinville, 89219-502, SC, Brazil
Tel.: (55) 4734246800
Web Site: http://www.americas.gevas.com
Packaging Machinery Mfr
N.A.I.C.S.: 333993
Rolf Geissinger *(Mng Dir)*

Gevas GmbH (1)
August-Thyssen-Strasse 3, 32278, Kirchlengern, Germany
Tel.: (49) 5223994670
Web Site: http://www.europe.gevas.com
Packaging & Labeling Services
N.A.I.C.S.: 561910
Hans Buhler *(Exec Dir)*

Maier Packaging GmbH (1)
Gewerbestrasse 21, 83346, Bergen, Germany
Tel.: (49) 864195440
Web Site: http://www.maier-packaging.com
Industrial Machinery Services
N.A.I.C.S.: 811310

Metall + Plastic GmbH (1)
Bodmaner Strasse 2, 78315, Radolfzell, Germany
Tel.: (49) 7738 9280 0
Web Site: http://www.metall-plastic.com
Clean Room Equipment Mfr
N.A.I.C.S.: 333998
Stefan Kleinmann *(Mng Dir)*

OPTIMA Automation GmbH (1)
Bruckmannstrasse 11, 70736, Fellbach, Germany
Tel.: (49) 71151099460
Industrial Machinery Services
N.A.I.C.S.: 811310

OPTIMA Consumer GmbH (1)
Geschwister SchollStr 89, 74523, Schwabisch Hall, Germany
Tel.: (49) 791946060
Industrial Machinery Services
N.A.I.C.S.: 811310

OPTIMA India Packaging Machines Pvt. Ltd. (1)
Unit 110 1st Floor Brigade Rubix Plot No 20 HMT Main Road, Bengaluru, 560 013, India
Tel.: (91) 8046525900
Packaging Machinery Mfr
N.A.I.C.S.: 333993
Akshay Chikodi *(Head-Country Sls)*

OPTIMA Japan Co., Ltd. (1)
Axe AB Building 2F 362 Shimizu-cho Nijoagaru Kawaramachi-dori, Nakagyo-ku, Kyoto, 604-0911, Japan
Tel.: (81) 752231588
Packaging Machinery Mfr
N.A.I.C.S.: 333993

OPTIMA Korea Ltd. (1)
601 36 Teheran-ro 87-gil, Gangnam-gu, Seoul, 06164, Korea (South)
Tel.: (82) 24147105
Packaging Machinery Mfr
N.A.I.C.S.: 333993

OPTIMA Life Science GmbH (1)
Steinbeisweg 20, 74523, Schwabisch Hall, Germany
Tel.: (49) 7915061900
Industrial Machinery Services
N.A.I.C.S.: 811310

OPTIMA Machinery Corporation (1)
1330 Contract Dr, Green Bay, WI 54304
Tel.: (920) 339-2222
Web Site: http://www.optima-usa.com
Packaging Machinery Mfr
N.A.I.C.S.: 333993
Thomas Seifert *(Pres)*

OPTIMA Materials Management GmbH (1)
Alfred Leikam-Strasse 36, 74523, Schwabisch Hall, Germany
Tel.: (49) 7915060
Industrial Machinery Services
N.A.I.C.S.: 811310

OPTIMA Nonwovens GmbH (1)
Steinbeisweg 20, 74523, Schwabisch Hall, Germany (100%)
Tel.: (49) 791 506 0
Web Site: http://www.optima-packaging.com
Nonwoven Products Packaging Machinery Mfr
N.A.I.C.S.: 333993
Hans Buhler *(Mng Dir)*

OPTIMA Packaging France S.A.R.L. (1)
4 rue Ampere BP9, Zone d Activites de Energie, 59559, Comines, France
Tel.: (33) 320630648
Packaging & Labeling Services
N.A.I.C.S.: 561910
Patrice Dincq *(Sls Mgr)*

OPTIMA Packaging Machinery PLC (1)
Chapman Way, Hethel, Norwich, NR14 8FB, United Kingdom
Tel.: (44) 1953600078
Packaging Machinery Mfr
N.A.I.C.S.: 333993

OPTIMA Packaging Machines (M) Sdn. Bhd. (1)
1249 Jalan KS 1/3 Kulim Square, Lunas, 09600, Kedah, Malaysia
Tel.: (60) 44951619
Packaging Machinery Mfr
N.A.I.C.S.: 333993
Suren Nair *(Mgr-Sls & Svcs)*

OPTIMA Packaging Machines (Shanghai) Co., Ltd. (1)
No 695 Fengmao Rd No 1 Building D Area No 3 Building, 1 4 5 Floor Malu Jiading District, Shanghai, 201801, China
Tel.: (86) 2167070888
Packaging Machinery Mfr
N.A.I.C.S.: 333993

OPTIMA Packaging Machines, S.A. de C.V. (1)
San Jorge 198 Col Pedregal Santa Ursula, Alcaldia Coyoacan, 04600, Mexico, Mexico
Tel.: (52) 5554210271
Packaging Machinery Mfr
N.A.I.C.S.: 333993
Aldo Filorio Dominguez *(Mng Dir)*

OPTIMA Pharma GmbH (1)
Otto-Hahn-Str 1, 74523, Schwabisch Hall, Germany
Tel.: (49) 79194950
Industrial Machinery Services
N.A.I.C.S.: 811310

OPTIMA do BRASIL Maquinas de Embalagem Ltda. (1)
Rua Joana Foresto Storani 500, Distrito Industrial, Vinhedo, 13288-169, SP, Brazil
Tel.: (55) 1938869800
Packaging Machinery Mfr
N.A.I.C.S.: 333993

Rianta Packaging Systems GmbH (1)
Steinbeisweg 20, 74523, Schwabisch Hall, Germany
Tel.: (49) 791930080
Web Site: http://www.rianta-packaging.com
Packaging Machinery Mfr
N.A.I.C.S.: 333993
Wolfram Haberhauer *(Mgr-Technical)*

OPTIMA TECHNOLOGY GROUP LIMITED

Optima Technology Group Limited—(Continued)

Level 49 360 Elizabeth Street, Melbourne, 3000, Victoria, Australia
Tel.: (61) 886080781
Web Site: http://www.bidenergy.com
OPA—(ASX)
Rev.: $11,187,140
Assets: $21,434,165
Liabilities: $4,794,051
Net Worth: $16,640,114
Earnings: ($10,443,170)
Fiscal Year-end: 06/30/22
Energy Management Software Solutions
N.A.I.C.S.: 513210
Anthony Du Preez (Founder & CTO)

Subsidiaries:

BidEnergy Inc. (1)
1628 John F Kennedy Blvd Ste 2100, Philadelphia, PA 19103
Tel.: (215) 732-4480
Bill Management Services
N.A.I.C.S.: 541219

BidEnergy Limited (1)
55 Colmore Row, Birmingham, B3 2AA, United Kingdom
Tel.: (44) 2071579948
Bill Management Services
N.A.I.C.S.: 541219

OPTIMAX HEALTHCARE SERVICES SDN. BHD.
Unit 2-2-1 Bangunan AHP Jalan Tun Mohd Fuad 3, Taman Tun Dr Ismail, Kuala Lumpur, 60000, Malaysia
Tel.: (60) 3 7722 3177
Eye Care Hospitals
N.A.I.C.S.: 622310
Sandy Tsy (CEO)

Subsidiaries:

Optimax Eye Specialist Centre Sdn. Bhd. (1)
Unit 2-2-1 Bangunan AHP Jalan Tun Mohd Fuad 3, Taman Tun Dr Ismail, Kuala Lumpur, 60000, Malaysia
Tel.: (60) 3 7722 3177
Web Site: http://www.optimax2u.com
Eye Care Service
N.A.I.C.S.: 622310
Sandy Tan (CEO)

Subsidiary (Domestic):

Optimax Eye Specialist Centre (Kuching) Sdn. Bhd. (2)
No 59 & 61 Ground Floor Jalan Tun Jugah, 93350, Kuching, Sarawak, Malaysia
Tel.: (60) 82579085
Web Site: http://www.optimax2u.com
Eye Care Service
N.A.I.C.S.: 622110

Optimax Eye Specialist Centre (Seremban) Sdn. Bhd. (2)
141 Jalan Tun Dr Ismail, Seremban, 70200, Negeri Sembilan, Malaysia
Tel.: (60) 67610900
Web Site: http://www.optimax2u.com
Eye Care Service
N.A.I.C.S.: 622110

Optimax Eye Specialist Centre (Shah Alam) Sdn. Bhd. (2)
50G & 52G Blok 3 Jalan Pahat G15/G Dataran Otomobil Seksyen 15, Shah Alam, 40200, Selangor, Malaysia
Tel.: (60) 355102535
Web Site: http://www.optimax2u.com
Eye Care Service
N.A.I.C.S.: 622110

Optimax Eye Specialist Centre (Sunway) Sdn. Bhd. (2)
No 11 Ground Fl Jalan PJS 11/28B Bandar Sunway, 46150, Petaling Jaya, Selangor, Malaysia
Tel.: (60) 356213388
Web Site: http://www.optimax2u.com.my
Eye Care Service
N.A.I.C.S.: 622110

OPTIMAX HOLDINGS BERHAD
Unit 30-01 Level 30 Tower A Vertical Business Suite Avenue 3, Bangsar South No 8 Jalan Kerinchi, 59200, Kuala Lumpur, Wilayah Persekutuan, Malaysia
Tel.: (60) 327839191 MY
Web Site: https://optimax2u.com
Year Founded: 1995
OPTIMAX—(KLS)
Rev.: $22,857,778
Assets: $21,457,354
Liabilities: $8,338,413
Net Worth: $13,118,942
Earnings: $3,473,862
Emp.: 242
Fiscal Year-end: 12/31/22
Holding Company
N.A.I.C.S.: 551112
Sandy Tan (CEO)

Subsidiaries:

Optimax Eye Specialist Centre (Bahau) Sdn. Bhd. (1)
No 13 & 15 Jalan Seraya 1 Pusat Perniagaan Seraya, 72100, Bahau, Malaysia
Tel.: (60) 66180012
Health & Eye Care Services
N.A.I.C.S.: 621999

Optimax Eye Specialist Centre (Kluang) Sdn. Bhd. (1)
No 43 & 44 Jalan Haji Manan, 86000, Kluang, Malaysia
Tel.: (60) 77010018
Health & Eye Care Services
N.A.I.C.S.: 621999

Optimax Eye Specialist Centre (Muar) Sdn. Bhd. (1)
1-5 & 1-6 Jalan Ismail, 84000, Muar, Malaysia
Tel.: (60) 79810018
Health & Eye Care Services
N.A.I.C.S.: 621999

Optimax Eye Specialist Centre (Segamat) Sdn. Bhd. (1)
49B & 49C Jalan Genuang, 85000, Segamat, Malaysia
Tel.: (60) 79710018
Health & Eye Care Services
N.A.I.C.S.: 621999

Optimax Eye Specialist Centre (Sutera) Sdn. Bhd. (1)
No 68 Jalan Sutera Tanjung 8/3 Taman Sutera Utama, 81300, Skudai, Malaysia
Tel.: (60) 75351800
Health & Eye Care Services
N.A.I.C.S.: 621999

Optixanthin Sdn. Bhd. (1)
145 Jalan Radin Bagus, Sri Petaling, 57000, Kuala Lumpur, Malaysia
Tel.: (60) 327796807
Web Site: https://www.optixanthin.com
Supplement & Health Food Mfr
N.A.I.C.S.: 325411

OPTIMAX TECHNOLOGY CORPORATION
No 37 Lane 659 Ping-Dong Rd, pingzhen District, Taoyuan, Taiwan
Tel.: (886) 34606677
Web Site: https://www.optimax.com.tw
3051—(TAI)
Rev.: $92,156,646
Assets: $138,135,040
Liabilities: $61,984,304
Net Worth: $76,150,736
Earnings: $13,868,993
Emp.: 750
Fiscal Year-end: 12/31/22
Polarizer Mfr
N.A.I.C.S.: 334516
Chi-Jung Chao (Chm & Pres)

OPTIMI HEALTH CORP.
21 Water St Suite 600, Vancouver, V6B 1A1, BC, Canada
Tel.: (604) 377-0403 BC
Web Site: https://www.optimihealth.ca
Year Founded: 2020
OPTHF—(OTCQX)
Rev.: $60,215
Assets: $12,546,057
Liabilities: $595,058
Net Worth: $11,950,999
Earnings: $5,483,718
Fiscal Year-end: 09/30/22
Pharmaceutical Product Mfr & Distr
N.A.I.C.S.: 325412
Bryan Safarik (COO)

OPTIMIND PHARMA CORP.
642 Richmond St, PO Box 95 TD Centre North Tower, London, N6A 3G6, ON, Canada
Tel.: (647) 891-9379
Web Site: https://optimindpharma.com
OMND—(TSXV)
Rev.: $92,848
Assets: $179,855
Liabilities: $277,278
Net Worth: ($97,423)
Earnings: ($1,055,337)
Fiscal Year-end: 02/29/24
Pharmaceuticals Product Mfr
N.A.I.C.S.: 325412
Tomas Sipos (CEO)

OPTIMISA PLC
209 215 Blackfriars Road, London, SE1 8NL, United Kingdom
Tel.: (44) 2079603300
Web Site: http://www.optimisaplc.com
Sales Range: $25-49.9 Million
Emp.: 204
Market Research Services
N.A.I.C.S.: 541910
Ron Littleboy (Chm & CEO)

Subsidiaries:

Report International Limited (1)
176 Blackfriars Road, London, SE1 8NL, United Kingdom
Tel.: (44) 2079281133
Web Site: http://www.reportinternational.com
Brand Management Services
N.A.I.C.S.: 541613

kae: marketing intelligence Ltd. (1)
209 215 Blackfriars Road, London, SE1 8NL, United Kingdom
Tel.: (44) 2079603300
Web Site: http://www.kae.com
Sales Range: $25-49.9 Million
Emp.: 50
Marketing Consulting Services
N.A.I.C.S.: 541613
David Rankin (Mng Dir)

OPTIMUM GROUP INC.
425 de Maisonneuve Blvd W Ste 1700, Montreal, H3A 3G5, QC, Canada
Tel.: (514) 288-2010
Web Site: http://www.groupe-optimum.com
Year Founded: 1976
Sales Range: $650-699.9 Million
Emp.: 500
Holding Company; Financial & Insurance Products & Services
N.A.I.C.S.: 551112
Gilles Blondeau (Chm)

Subsidiaries:

Norbec S.A.S. (1)
Domaine du Tremblay Commune de La Goulafriere, 27390, Montreuil, France
Tel.: (33) 2 32 44 51 57
Real Estate Management Services
N.A.I.C.S.: 531390

Optimum Asset Management Inc. (1)
425 de Maisonneuve Blvd West Suite 1620, Montreal, H3A 3G5, QC, Canada
Tel.: (514) 288-7545
Web Site: http://www.optimumgestion.com
Asset Management Services
N.A.I.C.S.: 531390
Claude Lamonde (Pres)

Optimum Caraibes S.A.S. (1)
425 de Maisonneuve West Suite 1600, Montreal, H3A 3G5, QC, Canada
Tel.: (514) 288-2050
Web Site: http://www.optimumcaraibes.com
Real Estate Management Services
N.A.I.C.S.: 531390

Optimum Consultants & Actuaries Inc. (1)
425 boul de Maisonneuve Ouest bureau 1120, Montreal, H3A 3G5, QC, Canada
Tel.: (514) 288-1620
Web Site: http://www.optimumactuaires.com
Financial Consulting Services
N.A.I.C.S.: 523940
Marc-Andre Laliberte (Sr VP & Head-Grp Insurance & Workplace Health & Safety Practices)

Optimum Informatique Inc. (1)
425 de Maisonneuve Blvd West Suite 1610, Montreal, H3A 3G5, QC, Canada
Tel.: (514) 288-1610
Financial Management Services
N.A.I.C.S.: 523999
Martin Fortin (VP-Info Sys)

Optimum Reassurance Inc. (1)
425 De Maisonneuve W blvd Suite 1200, Montreal, H3A 3G5, QC, Canada
Tel.: (514) 288-1900
Web Site: http://www.optimumre.ca
Reinsurance Services
N.A.I.C.S.: 524130
Richard Houde (Chief Risk Officer & Sr VP)

Optimum Vie S.A. (1)
94 rue de Courcelles, 75008, Paris, France
Tel.: (33) 1 44 15 81
Web Site: http://www.optimumvie.fr
Fire Insurance Services
N.A.I.C.S.: 524113

OPTIMUS FIDUCIARIES LIMITED
St Mary's The Parade, IM9 1LG, Castletown, Isle of Man
Tel.: (44) 1624695560 IM
Web Site: http://www.optimus.co.im
Year Founded: 2002
Sales Range: $1-9.9 Million
Emp.: 50
Business Associations
N.A.I.C.S.: 813910
Tim Shallcross (Head-Bus Dev)

OPTIMUS FINANCE LIMITED
504A Ozone Dr Vikram Sarabhai Marg Vadi-wadi, Vadodara, 390003, Gujarat, India
Tel.: (91) 2652325321 In
Web Site: https://optimusfinance.in
Year Founded: 1991
531254—(BOM)
Rev.: $12,207,745
Assets: $10,129,944
Liabilities: $3,937,510
Net Worth: $6,192,435
Earnings: $886,158
Emp.: 2
Fiscal Year-end: 03/31/23
Financial Services
N.A.I.C.S.: 523999
Deepak Raval (Compliance Officer & Sec)

OPTIMUS GROUP CO., LTD.
World Trade Center Bulding South Tower 15F 2-4-1 Hamamatsucho, Minato-ku, Tokyo, 105-5115, Japan
Tel.: (81) 363709268
Web Site: https://www.optimusgroup.co.jp
Year Founded: 2015

AND PRIVATE COMPANIES — OPTOELECTRONICS CO., LTD.

9268—(TKS)
Rev.: $819,203,740
Assets: $909,390,580
Liabilities: $756,534,330
Net Worth: $152,856,250
Earnings: $18,864,940
Emp.: 2,359
Fiscal Year-end: 03/31/24
Subsidiary Management Services
N.A.I.C.S.: 551114
Nobuya Yamanaka *(Pres & CEO)*

Subsidiaries:

Dolphin Shipping New Zealand Limited (1)
8 Farnham Street Parnell, PO Box 37-104, Auckland, 1052, New Zealand
Tel.: (64) 93030075
Web Site: http://www.dolphinshipping.co.nz
Shipping Services
N.A.I.C.S.: 488510

Jevic NZ Limited (1)
Unit 2A Suite 17 215 Rosedale Road Albany, Auckland, New Zealand
Tel.: (64) 99661779
Vehicle Inspection Services
N.A.I.C.S.: 811198

OPTIPHARM CO., LTD.
63 Osongsaengmyeong 6-ro Osong-eup, Heungdeok-gu, Cheongju, Chungcheongbuk-do, Korea (South)
Tel.: (82) 432497500
Web Site: http://www.optipharm.co.kr
Year Founded: 2006
153710—(KRS)
Rev.: $12,278,287
Assets: $31,586,806
Liabilities: $9,335,135
Net Worth: $22,251,671
Earnings: ($1,568,232)
Emp.: 78
Fiscal Year-end: 12/31/22
Pharmaceuticals Product Mfr
N.A.I.C.S.: 325412
Sung-Jun Han *(Co-CEO)*

OPTISCAN IMAGING LIMITED
16 Miles St, Mulgrave, 3170, VIC, Australia
Tel.: (61) 395383333
Web Site: http://www.optiscan.com
Sales Range: Less than $1 Million
Emp.: 13
Microscopic Imaging System Mfr & Distr
N.A.I.C.S.: 339112
Justin Mouchacca *(Sec)*

Subsidiaries:

Optiscan Pty Ltd (1)
15-17 Normanby Rd Notting Hill, Melbourne, 3168, VIC, Australia
Tel.: (61) 395383333
Web Site: http://www.optiscan.com
Sales Range: $25-49.9 Million
Emp.: 15
Microscope System Mfr
N.A.I.C.S.: 333310
Archie Fraser *(CEO)*

OPTISOFT NYRT.
Nagybanyai ut 92, 1025, Budapest, Hungary
Tel.: (36) 12482500
Web Site: http://www.optisoft.hu
Software Publisher
N.A.I.C.S.: 513210
Peter Semeredy *(Chm & CEO)*

OPTIVA, INC.
2233 Argentia Rd East Tower Suite 302, Mississauga, L5N 2X7, ON, Canada
Tel.: (905) 625-2622
Web Site: https://www.optiva.com
Year Founded: 1999
OPT—(TSX)
Rev.: $51,032,968
Assets: $72,486,332
Liabilities: $99,916,523
Net Worth: ($27,430,191)
Earnings: $11,701,778
Emp.: 342
Fiscal Year-end: 12/31/21
Mobile Infrastructure Services
N.A.I.C.S.: 517112
Robert Stabile *(Chm)*

Subsidiaries:

Redknee Inc (1)
2560 Matheson Blvd E Ste 500, Mississauga, L4W 4Y9, ON, Canada
Tel.: (905) 625-2622
Web Site: http://www.redknee.com
Sales Range: $25-49.9 Million
Emp.: 150
Billing Software Development Services
N.A.I.C.S.: 541511
Lucas Skoczkowski *(Gen Mgr)*

Subsidiary (Non-US):

Redknee (Australia) PTY Limited (2)
Level 20 Tower 2 201 Sussex Street, Sydney, 2000, NSW, Australia
Tel.: (61) 290061460
Billing Software Development Services
N.A.I.C.S.: 541511

Redknee (India) Technologies Pvt. Limited (2)
1st Floor Building B 2 The Cerebrum IT Park Kumar City, Pune, 411014, India
Tel.: (91) 2066064700
Billing Software Development Services
N.A.I.C.S.: 541511

Redknee (UK) Limited (2)
Suite 204-450 Brook Drive Green Park, Reading, RG2 6UU, Berkshire, United Kingdom
Tel.: (44) 1189718778
Web Site: http://www.redknee.com
Emp.: 25
Billing Software Development Services
N.A.I.C.S.: 541511

Redknee Solutions (UK) Limited (2)
30/31 Friar Street, Reading, RG1 1DX, United Kingdom
Tel.: (44) 1189718778
Sales Range: $25-49.9 Million
Emp.: 20
Billing Software Development Services
N.A.I.C.S.: 541511
Chris Newton-Smith *(Gen Mgr)*

Subsidiary (Non-US):

Redknee Spain, S.L. (3)
Avenida Burgos 8 A - Bronze Building Floor 10, 28036, Madrid, Spain
Tel.: (34) 918060218
Billing Software Development Services
N.A.I.C.S.: 541511

OPTO CIRCUITS (INDIA) LIMITED
83 Electronics City, Bengaluru, 560 100, Karnataka, India
Tel.: (91) 8028521040
Web Site: http://www.optoindia.com
OPTOCIRCUI—(NSE)
Rev.: $25,383,272
Assets: $151,008,531
Liabilities: $162,749,340
Net Worth: ($11,740,809)
Earnings: ($188,313,269)
Fiscal Year-end: 03/31/20
Pulse Oximeters, Pulse Oximeter Sensors, Fluid Warmers, Cholesterol Monitors & Stents Mfr
N.A.I.C.S.: 339112
Somadas G. C. *(Mng Dir)*

Subsidiaries:

Advanced Micronic Devices Ltd. (1)
A305 1st Block 2nd Floor KSSIDC complex Above Electronics City, Post Office Electronics city Phase I, Bengaluru, 560 100, KARNATAKA, India
Tel.: (91) 8022540500
Web Site: http://www.amdlcorp.com
Rev.: $322,668
Assets: $1,259,423
Liabilities: $8,554,183
Net Worth: ($7,294,760)
Earnings: ($81,955)
Emp.: 9
Fiscal Year-end: 03/31/2018
Software & Medical & Communications Electronic Equipment Developer & Mfr
N.A.I.C.S.: 541511
Dhirendra Kumar Singh *(Exec Dir)*

Subsidiary (US):

Advanced Micronic Devices Ltd. (2)
433 Scenic Dr, Saint Peters, MO 63376-2278
Tel.: (636) 240-9501
Web Site: http://www.faichneymedical.com
Sales Range: $25-49.9 Million
Emp.: 1
Medical & Hospital Equipment Mfr
N.A.I.C.S.: 423450
Dhirendra Kumar Singh *(Exec Dir)*

Criticare Systems, Inc. (1)
N7W22025 Johnson Dr, Waukesha, WI 53186-1856
Tel.: (262) 798-8282
Web Site: http://www.csiusa.com
Sales Range: $25-49.9 Million
Emp.: 95
Patient Monitoring Devices Developer, Marketer & Distr
N.A.I.C.S.: 339112
Kathy Zynda *(Supvr-Credit & Collections)*

Devon Innovations Pvt. Ltd. (1)
No 27A Electronics City Phase 1 Hosur Road, Bengaluru, 560 100, India
Tel.: (91) 8028522354
Web Site: http://www.devoncath.com
Medical Catheter Developer & Mfr
N.A.I.C.S.: 339112

Subsidiary (Domestic):

Ormed Medical Technology Ltd. (2)
No 162 Sidco Industrial Estate, North Phase Ambattur, Chennai, 600 098, India
Tel.: (91) 4426245724
Web Site: http://www.ormedortho.com
Emp.: 7
Medical Prosthetic Device Developer & Mfr
N.A.I.C.S.: 339112

Eurocor GmbH (1)
In den Dauen 6a, 53117, Bonn, Germany
Tel.: (49) 228201500
Web Site: http://www.eurocor.de
Sales Range: $25-49.9 Million
Emp.: 15
Interventional Cardiology Device Developer & Mfr
N.A.I.C.S.: 339112
Vivek Ramnani *(Mng Dir)*

Mediaid, Inc. (1)
17517 Fabrica Way Ste H, Cerritos, CA 90703
Tel.: (714) 367-2848
Web Site: http://www.mediaidinc.com
Sales Range: $1-9.9 Million
Emp.: 20
Thermometer, Pulse Oximeter & Patient Monitoring System Developer & Mfr
N.A.I.C.S.: 423450
Shital Patel *(Pres)*

Subsidiary (Non-US):

Mediaid Singapore Pte Ltd. (2)
Block 30 Kallang Place 06 06, Singapore, 339159, Singapore
Tel.: (65) 62962881
Web Site: http://www.optosystems.com.sg
Emp.: 13
Thermometer, Pulse Oximeter & Patient Monitoring System Developer & Mfr
N.A.I.C.S.: 339112
Doulat Bhojwani *(Mng Dir)*

Opto Infrastructure Ltd (1)
83 Electronic City Phase 1 Hosur Main Road, Bengaluru, 560 100, Karnataka, India
Tel.: (91) 8028521040
Web Site: http://www.optoinfrastructure.com
Emp.: 300
Construction Engineering Services
N.A.I.C.S.: 541330
Vinod Ramanni *(Mng Dir)*

Unetixs Vascular Inc (1)
333 Strawberry Field Rd Ste 11, Warwick, RI 02886
Tel.: (401) 583-0089
Web Site: http://www.unetixs.com
Medical Equipment Mfr
N.A.I.C.S.: 334510

OPTO DEVICE TECHNOLOGY CO., LTD.
87 Wanjusandan 5-ro, Wanju-gun, Bongdong-eup, Jeollabuk-do, Korea (South)
Tel.: (82) 632637626
Web Site: https://www.od-tech.com
Year Founded: 1999
080520—(KRS)
Rev.: $30,978,585
Assets: $103,982,974
Liabilities: $9,274,829
Net Worth: $94,708,146
Earnings: ($3,110,007)
Emp.: 267
Fiscal Year-end: 12/31/22
Semiconductor Mfr & Sensor Module Packaging Services
N.A.I.C.S.: 334413
Byoung-Kun Park *(CEO)*

Subsidiaries:

Opto Device Technology Co., Ltd. - Semiconductor Division (1)
165 1-ro Dunsan, Bongdong-eup, Wanju-gun Jeollabuk, Korea (South)
Tel.: (82) 632632112
Semiconductor Devices Mfr
N.A.I.C.S.: 334413

OPTOELECTRONICS CO., LTD.
4-12-17 Tsukagoshi, Warabi, 335-0002, Saitama, Japan
Tel.: (81) 484461181
Web Site: https://www.opto.co.jp
Year Founded: 1976
6664—(TKS)
Rev.: $48,765,020
Assets: $110,348,760
Liabilities: $70,878,730
Net Worth: $39,470,030
Earnings: ($5,778,350)
Emp.: 184
Fiscal Year-end: 11/30/23
Electronic Components Mfr
N.A.I.C.S.: 334118
Masami Tawara *(Pres & CEO)*

Subsidiaries:

Opticon Danmark ApS (1)
Centervej 46, 3600, Frederikssund, Denmark
Tel.: (45) 44220102
Scanner Distr
N.A.I.C.S.: 423430

Opticon Latin America (1)
Machado Bittencourt 361 Cj 906/907 Clementino, Sao Paulo, 04044 001, Brazil
Tel.: (55) 11987370141
Web Site:
Scanner Distr
N.A.I.C.S.: 423430

Opticon Ltd. (1)
F20a 110 Butterfields Great Marlings, Luton, LU2 8DL, Bedfordshire, United Kingdom
Tel.: (44) 1582433763
Scanner Distr
N.A.I.C.S.: 423430

Opticon S.A.S. (1)
61-63 Rue de Douai, 75009, Paris, France
Tel.: (33) 155905640
Barcode Scanner Distr
N.A.I.C.S.: 423430

Opticon S.R.L. (1)
Via S Quasimodo 44 Castel Maggiore, 40013, Bologna, Italy
Tel.: (39) 051 6321800

OPTOELECTRONICS CO., LTD.

OPTOELECTRONICS CO., LTD.—(Continued)

Web Site: http://opticon.it
Scanner Distr
N.A.I.C.S.: 423430

Opticon Sensoren GmbH (1)
Siemensstrasse 18, 63303, Dreieich, Germany
Tel.: (49) 6103404050
Scanner Distr
N.A.I.C.S.: 423430

Opticon Sensors Europe B.V. (1)
Opaallaan 35, 2132 XV, Hoofddorp, Netherlands
Tel.: (31) 23 569 2700
Web Site: http://opticon.com
Barcode Scanner Mfr & Distr
N.A.I.C.S.: 334118

Opticon Sensors Nordic AB (1)
Finlandsgatan 18, 164 74, Kista, Sweden
Tel.: (46) 858548560
Scanner Distr
N.A.I.C.S.: 423430

Opticon Sensors Philippines Inc. (1)
Unit 1C Ground Floor Torre De Salcedo 184 Salcedo Street, Lagaspi Village, Makati, 1229, Philippines
Tel.: (63) 9171664399
Scanner Distr
N.A.I.C.S.: 423430

Opticon Sensors Pty. Ltd. (1)
PO Box 294, Gordon, 2072, NSW, Australia
Tel.: (61) 288754544
Scanner Distr
N.A.I.C.S.: 423430

Opticon Vietnam LLC (1)
3rd Floor Indochina Park Tower 04 Nguyen Dinh Chieu Street, Da Kao ward District 1, Ho Chi Minh City, 700000, Vietnam
Tel.: (84) 2822288262
Scanner Distr
N.A.I.C.S.: 423430

Opticon, Inc. (1)
2220 Lind Ave SW Ste 100, Renton, WA 98057
Tel.: (425) 651-2120
Web Site: https://www.opticonusa.com
Scanner Mfr & Distr
N.A.I.C.S.: 334118

OPTOFLUX GMBH

Andernacher Str 29b, 90411, Nuremberg, Germany
Tel.: (49) 911983280 De
Web Site: http://www.optoflux.com
Optical Devices Development & Production
N.A.I.C.S.: 333310

Subsidiaries:

HPOI CORPORATION (1)
2nd St Mactan Economic Zone I, Lapu-Lapu, 6015, Cebu, Philippines
Tel.: (63) 322687800
Camera Optical Lens Mfr
N.A.I.C.S.: 333310

OPTOMED OYJ

Yrttipellontie 1, 90230, Oulu, Finland
Tel.: (358) 505624077
Web Site: https://www.optomed.com
Year Founded: 2004
OPTOMED—(HEL)
Rev.: $15,821,282
Assets: $33,779,409
Liabilities: $11,826,031
Net Worth: $21,953,378
Earnings: ($5,905,461)
Emp.: 114
Fiscal Year-end: 12/31/22
Medical Software Development Services
N.A.I.C.S.: 541511
Seppo Kopsala (Founder & CEO)

OPTOPRIM SAS

21-23 Rue Aristide Briand, 92170, Vanves, France
Tel.: (33) 1 41 90 61 80 FR
Web Site: http://www.optoprim.fr
Year Founded: 1994
Optical Equipment Mfr
N.A.I.C.S.: 333310

Subsidiaries:

Industrial Laser Systems Sarl (1)
21 23 Rue Aristide Briand, 92170, Vanves, France
Tel.: (33) 155950950
Web Site: http://www.industrial-lasers-systems.com
Sales Range: $1-9.9 Million
Emp.: 10
Optical Instrument Mfr
N.A.I.C.S.: 333310

Optoprim Germany GmbH (1)
Bosch Str 6, 86899, Landsberg am Lech, Germany
Tel.: (49) 8980076252
Web Site: http://www.optoprim.de
Optical Instrument Mfr
N.A.I.C.S.: 333310

Optoprim S.r.l. (1)
Via Rota 37, 20900, Monza, Italy
Tel.: (39) 039 834977
Web Site: http://www.optoprim.it
Sales Range: $25-49.9 Million
Emp.: 8
Supplier of Optical Equipment for Lasers
N.A.I.C.S.: 333310
Jean-Pierre Sezeftre (Gen Mgr)

OPTORUN CO., LTD.

Takeno 10-1, Kawagoe, Saitama, Japan
Tel.: (81) 492393381
Web Site: https://www.optorun.co.jp
Year Founded: 1999
6235—(TKS)
Rev.: $260,961,630
Assets: $556,494,100
Liabilities: $152,966,750
Net Worth: $403,527,350
Earnings: $32,833,790
Emp.: 638
Fiscal Year-end: 12/31/23
Optical Thin Film Coaters Equipment Mfr & Distr
N.A.I.C.S.: 334413

Subsidiaries:

Optorun (Shanghai) Co., Ltd. (1)
267 Cheng Yin Road, Baoshan Urban Industrial Park, Shanghai, China
Tel.: (86) 2136161290
Electrical Control Panel Mfr & Distr
N.A.I.C.S.: 335313

Optorun Taiwan Co., Ltd. (1)
No 2-2 Gongye 35th Rd Xitun Dist, Taichung, Taiwan
Tel.: (886) 423595291
Industrial Machinery Distr
N.A.I.C.S.: 423830
Ihei Hayashi (Chm)

Optorun USA, Inc. (1)
1294 Kifer Rd Ste 703, Sunnyvale, CA 94086
Tel.: (408) 212-4960
Industrial Machinery Distr
N.A.I.C.S.: 423830

OPTOTECH OPTIKMASCHINEN GMBH

Sandusweg 2-4, Wettenberg, 35435, Germany
Tel.: (49) 641982030
Web Site: http://www.optotech.de
Year Founded: 1985
Rev.: $27,588,000
Emp.: 140
Optical Machinery Distr
N.A.I.C.S.: 423830
Roland Mandler (Founder & Pres)

OPTOWIDE TECHNOLOGIES CO., LTD.

2 Zhenzhu Road, Mawei High-Tech Park, Fuzhou, 350015, Fujian, China
Tel.: (86) 59138178298
Web Site: https://www.optowide.com
Year Founded: 2013
688195—(SHG)
Rev.: $48,344,873
Assets: $142,371,679
Liabilities: $18,947,836
Net Worth: $123,423,843
Earnings: $8,197,240
Fiscal Year-end: 12/31/22
Optical Instrument Mfr & Distr
N.A.I.C.S.: 333310
Hongrui Yu (Chm & Gen Mgr)

OPTRONIC AB

Anbudsgatan 5, PO Box 733, 931 27, Skelleftea, Sweden
Tel.: (46) 910 83 500
Web Site: http://www.optronic.se
Year Founded: 1974
Optical Technology Developer & Mfr
N.A.I.C.S.: 333310
Rickard Astrom (Co-Owner)

OPTRONTEC INC.

19-15 Pyeongsan-ro 8beon-gil, Uichang-gu, Changwon, 641-347, Gyeongsangnam-do, Korea (South)
Tel.: (82) 423601510
Web Site: https://www.optrontec.net
Year Founded: 1999
082210—(KRS)
Rev.: $153,009,080
Assets: $208,667,937
Liabilities: $185,319,938
Net Worth: $23,347,999
Earnings: ($60,035,315)
Emp.: 480
Fiscal Year-end: 12/31/22
Optical Lens & Optical Product Mfr
N.A.I.C.S.: 333310
Sa-Gwan Hong (Vice Chm & CEO)

OPUS GLOBAL NYRT

Andrassy ut 59, 1062, Budapest, Hungary
Tel.: (36) 14330700 HU
Web Site: https://opusglobal.hu
Year Founded: 1912
1VY—(DEU)
Rev.: $1,854,109,613
Assets: $3,089,229,350
Liabilities: $2,460,546,893
Net Worth: $628,682,458
Earnings: $129,282,048
Emp.: 4,457
Fiscal Year-end: 12/31/23
Investment Services
N.A.I.C.S.: 523999
Odorne Angyal Zsuzsanna (Deputy CEO-Ops)

Subsidiaries:

CIG Pannonia Eletbiztosito Nyrt (1)
1097 Konyves Kalman krt 11 Building B GROUND FLOOR, Pf325, 1476, Budapest, Hungary
Tel.: (36) 15100200
Web Site: https://www.cigpannonia.hu
Rev.: $122,130,671
Assets: $429,355,214
Liabilities: $385,108,933
Net Worth: $44,246,281
Earnings: $5,651,100
Emp.: 100
Fiscal Year-end: 12/31/2021
Fire Insurance Services
N.A.I.C.S.: 524113
Csaba Gaal (Co-Founder)

OPUS GROUP LIMITED

12 Rachael Close, Silverwater, 2128, NSW, Australia
Tel.: (61) 2 9584 7680
Web Site: http://www.opusgroup.co

INTERNATIONAL PUBLIC

Publications, Outdoor Advertising Material, Brochures, Government Documents Distribution, Production, Electronic Delivery & Web Hosting Services
N.A.I.C.S.: 541870
Richard F. Celarc (Chm & CEO)

Subsidiaries:

CanPrint Communications PTY Limited (1)
16 Nyrang Street, Fyshwick, 2609, ACT, Australia
Tel.: (61) 2 6295 4422
Web Site: http://www.canprint.com.au
Commercial Printing Services
N.A.I.C.S.: 323111

OPUS Group NZ Holdings Limited (1)
10 Normanby Road, PO Box 108176, Mt Eden, Auckland, 1150, New Zealand
Tel.: (64) 9 6383 485
Web Site: http://www.opusgroup.com
Emp.: 30
Investment Management Service
N.A.I.C.S.: 523940
Nigel Spicer (Gen Mgr)

Subsidiary (Domestic):

Cactus Imaging Limited (2)
Unit 5 76 Porana Road, Glenfield, Auckland, New Zealand
Tel.: (64) 9 442 5416
Digital Printing Services
N.A.I.C.S.: 323111

Ligare Limited (2)
235 Archers Road, Glenfield, North Shore, Auckland, New Zealand
Tel.: (64) 9 444 3240
Web Site: http://www.ligare.co.nz
Books Publishing Services
N.A.I.C.S.: 513130
Sharon Simmons (Acct Mgr)

Omnigraphics Limited (2)
10 Normanby Road, Mt Eden, Auckland, 1024, New Zealand
Tel.: (64) 9 638 0888
Web Site: http://www.omnigraphics.co.nz
Digital Printing Services
N.A.I.C.S.: 323111
Janette Paitingon (Pres)

Union Offset Co. Pty Limited (1)
16 Nyrang Street, Fyshwick, 2609, ACT, Australia
Tel.: (61) 2 6295 4500
Web Site: http://www.unionoffset.com.au
Emp.: 50
Digital Printing Services
N.A.I.C.S.: 323111
Mitch Granger (Acct Mgr)

OPUS ONE GOLD CORPORATION

2075 Victoria 220, Saint-Lambert, J4S 1H1, QC, Canada
Tel.: (514) 591-3988 Ca
Web Site: https://www.opusoneresources.com
Year Founded: 1979
GFKRF—(OTCIQ)
Assets: $1,356,759
Liabilities: $467,233
Net Worth: $889,526
Earnings: ($1,130,723)
Fiscal Year-end: 08/31/23
Mineral Exploration Services
N.A.I.C.S.: 212290
Michael Kinley (Pres & CFO)

OQ S.A.O.C.

Al Harthy Complex, PO Box 261, Muscat, 118, Oman
Tel.: (968) 24573100 OM
Year Founded: 1992
Sales Range: $25-49.9 Million
Emp.: 43
Oil & Energy Service
N.A.I.C.S.: 213112

AND PRIVATE COMPANIES
ORANGE S.A.

Mohammed Hamad Al Rumhi *(Chm)*

Subsidiaries:

Abraj Energy Services LLC (1)
Ghala Heights Street Number 99 Way number ROADF 196 Block Number 250, PO Box 1156, 130, Muscat, Oman
Tel.: (968) 24509999
Web Site: http://www.abrajoman.com
N.A.I.C.S.: 213111
N. Ramesh *(CEO)*

Bharat Oman Refineries Limited (1)
Mahul Chembur, Mumbai, 400 074, Maharashtra, India (36.62%)
Tel.: (91) 2225533888
Web Site: http://www.borl.in
Joint Venture of Bharat Petroleum Corporation Ltd. & Oman Oil Company Limited
N.A.I.C.S.: 324110
S. S. Sundararajan *(Mng Dir)*

OXEA Holding GmbH (1)
Otto-Roelen-Str 3, 46147, Oberhausen, Germany
Tel.: (49) 208 693 3100
Web Site: http://www.oxea-chemicals.com
Oxo Chemicals Mfr
N.A.I.C.S.: 325998
Purnendu Rai *(VP-Sls)*

Subsidiary (US):

OXEA Bishop, LLC (2)
US Highway 77 Business, Bishop, TX 78343
Tel.: (361) 584-6920
Emp.: 35
Oxo Chemicals Mfr
N.A.I.C.S.: 325998

OXEA Corporation (2)
1505 Lyndon B Johnson Fwy Ste 400, Dallas, TX 75234
Tel.: (972) 481-2700
Web Site: http://www.oxea-chemicals.com
Emp.: 30
Oxo Chemicals Mfr
N.A.I.C.S.: 325998
Marc Hickman *(Dir-Strategic Plng)*

Subsidiary (Domestic):

OXEA GmbH (2)
Paul-Baumann-Str 1, Marl, 45772, Germany
Tel.: (49) 2365 49 04
Emp.: 65
Oxo Chemicals Mfr
N.A.I.C.S.: 325998

Subsidiary (Non-US):

OXEA S.a r.l. (3)
Regus Business Center Airport Center Luxembourg 5 Rue Heienhaff, Senningerberg, 1736, Luxembourg
Tel.: (352) 28 48 78 2020
Chemical Products Mfr
N.A.I.C.S.: 325998

Subsidiary (Non-US):

OXEA Japan KK (2)
Shinjuku NS Building 28F 2-4-1 Nishi-Shinjuku, Shinjuku-ku, Tokyo, 1630828, Japan
Tel.: (81) 3 5339 2201
Web Site: http://www.oxea-chemicals.com
Oxo Chemicals Mfr
N.A.I.C.S.: 325998

OXEA Nederland B.V. (2)
Hornweg 10, 1045 AR, Amsterdam, Netherlands
Tel.: (31) 20 448 9555
Web Site: http://www.oxea-chemicals.com
Emp.: 25
Chemicals Mfr
N.A.I.C.S.: 325998
Joost Overeijnder *(Plant Mgr)*

OXEA Pte. Ltd. (2)
51 Goldhill Plaza 09-12/01, Singapore, 308900, Singapore
Tel.: (65) 6478 507
Oxo Chemical Distr
N.A.I.C.S.: 424690

Oxea (Nanjing) Advanced Derivatives Ltd. (2)

A-1008 Grand Gateway Hongqiao Road 1, Shanghai, 200030, China
Tel.: (86) 21 5451 0681
Oxo Chemicals Mfr
N.A.I.C.S.: 325998

Oman Trading International Limited (1)
Level 7 Precinct Building 2 Gate Precinct, Dubai, United Arab Emirates
Tel.: (971) 4 4281888
Web Site: http://www.omantrading.com
Petroleum Product Distr
N.A.I.C.S.: 424720

Salalah Methanol Company LLC (1)
Aquad, PO Box 316, 217, Salalah, Oman
Tel.: (968) 2321 8800
Web Site: http://www.smc.co.om
Methanol Mfr
N.A.I.C.S.: 325199
Awadh H. Al Shanfari *(Mng Dir)*

Takamul Investment Co. S.A.O.C (1)
PO Box 1951, 130, Muscat, Oman
Tel.: (968) 2200 4333
Web Site: http://www.takamul.com
Investment Management Service
N.A.I.C.S.: 523940
Nabil Al Ghassani *(CEO)*

OR PJSC
56 58 Bogdan Khmelnitsky's st, Novosibirsk, Russia
Tel.: (7) 3832808026 RU
Web Site: http://www.obuvrus.ru
Year Founded: 2003
ORUP—(RUS)
Sales Range: Less than $1 Million
Footwear Mfr & Distr
N.A.I.C.S.: 316210
Vyacheslav Vladimirovich Shabaikin *(Chm)*

OR SHAY GS LTD.
Ahuzat Bayit St 3, Yafo, Tel Aviv, Israel
Tel.: (972) 35172211 IL
Web Site: https://www.orshay.com
ORSY—(TAE)
Rev.: $19,704,655
Assets: $121,080,810
Liabilities: $85,556,844
Net Worth: $35,523,967
Earnings: $4,564,719
Fiscal Year-end: 12/31/23
Software Development Services
N.A.I.C.S.: 541511
Shai Lavi *(CFO & Chm)*

OR-NA TARIM URUNLERI SAN. VE TIC. A.S.
Kazim Dirik Cad No 4 Gayret Han Kat 5 D 505 Pasaport, Izmir, Turkiye
Tel.: (90) 232 489 16 89
Web Site: http://www.orna.com.tr
Year Founded: 1998
Fruits & Vegetables Distr & Processor
N.A.I.C.S.: 424480
Ozcan Yilmaz *(Chm)*

Subsidiaries:

OR-NA Tarim Urunleri San. ve Tic. A.S. - Izmir Factory (1)
Egerci Mahallesi Killik Kume Evleri No 1, Torbali, Izmir, Turkiye
Tel.: (90) 2328531689
Fruit & Vegetable Mfr
N.A.I.C.S.: 311421

ORA GOLD LIMITED
Suite 8 Level 2 5 Ord Street, West Perth, 0005, WA, Australia
Tel.: (61) 893896927 AU
Web Site: https://www.ora.gold
NMG—(ASX)
Rev.: $16,365
Assets: $4,843,366
Liabilities: $1,460,871
Net Worth: $3,382,494
Earnings: ($1,468,985)

Emp.: 9
Fiscal Year-end: 09/30/23
Mineral Exploration Services
N.A.I.C.S.: 212290
Frank DeMarte *(Sec & Sec)*

ORAC PUBLISHING KFT.
Montevideo utca 14, 1037, Budapest, Hungary
Tel.: (36) 13402304 HU
Web Site: https://orac.hu
Year Founded: 1992
Legal, Tax, Regulatory, Risk Management & Business Information Publisher
N.A.I.C.S.: 513199
Adam Frank *(Mng Dir)*

ORACLE ENERGY CORP.
1400 - 1040 West Georgia Street, Vancouver, V6E 4H1, BC, Canada
Tel.: (604) 558-0976
Web Site: https://www.oracleenergy.com
OECPF—(OTCEM)
Assets: $6,444
Liabilities: $512,690
Net Worth: ($506,246)
Earnings: ($265,771)
Fiscal Year-end: 12/31/23
Oil & Gas Exploration Services
N.A.I.C.S.: 213114
Nasim Tyab *(Founder)*

ORACLE POWER PLC
Tennyson House Cambridge Business Park, Cambridge, CB4 0WZ, Cambridgeshire, United Kingdom
Tel.: (44) 2035804314 UK
Web Site: https://www.oraclepower.co.uk
Year Founded: 2006
ORCP—(AIM)
Rev.: $128
Assets: $9,097,294
Liabilities: $231,248
Net Worth: $8,866,046
Earnings: ($1,197,345)
Emp.: 7
Fiscal Year-end: 12/31/21
Coal Mining Services
N.A.I.C.S.: 212115
Shahrukh Khan *(Exec Dir)*

ORAD LTD.
4 Hamashbir St, Holon, Israel
Tel.: (972) 35576666
Web Site: https://www.orad.cc
Year Founded: 1971
ORAD—(TAE)
Rev.: $45,494,957
Assets: $36,664,732
Liabilities: $25,278,629
Net Worth: $11,386,103
Earnings: $1,730,073
Fiscal Year-end: 12/31/23
Other Scientific & Technical Consulting Services
N.A.I.C.S.: 541690
Yochay Shochat *(CFO)*

ORAGIN FOODS INC.
43 Junction Road, Toronto, M6N 1B5, ON, Canada
Tel.: (416) 761-1500 BC
Web Site: https://www.oragin.com
Year Founded: 2011
OG—(DEU)
Rev.: $20,114,007
Assets: $20,520,666
Liabilities: $10,557,631
Net Worth: $9,963,036
Earnings: ($2,336,503)
Emp.: 125
Fiscal Year-end: 01/31/22
Grocery Stores
N.A.I.C.S.: 424490

Matt Lurie *(Founder, Chm & CEO)*

ORAHOVO A.D.
Tornjoski put 2, Novo Orahovo, Serbia
Tel.: (381) 24 723 030
Web Site: http://www.orahovo.co.rs
Year Founded: 1946
Sales Range: $1-9.9 Million
Emp.: 91
Mixed Farming Services
N.A.I.C.S.: 111150

ORANGE MINERALS NL
Level 2 7 Havelock Street, West Perth, 6005, WA, Australia
Tel.: (61) 861022039 AU
Web Site: https://www.orangeminerals.com.au
Year Founded: 2021
OMX—(ASX)
Rev.: $33,946
Assets: $4,935,099
Liabilities: $154,013
Net Worth: $4,781,087
Earnings: ($801,752)
Fiscal Year-end: 06/30/23
Mineral Exploration Services
N.A.I.C.S.: 212390
David Greenwood *(CEO)*

ORANGE S.A.
111 quai du President Roosevelt, 92130, Issy-les-Moulineaux, France
Tel.: (33) 144442105 FR
Web Site: https://www.orange.com
Year Founded: 1988
ORAN—(NYSE)
Rev.: $47,617,094,755
Assets: $118,769,695,662
Liabilities: $80,891,431,038
Net Worth: $37,878,264,623
Earnings: $2,633,282,970
Emp.: 127,109
Fiscal Year-end: 12/31/23
Financial Investment Services
N.A.I.C.S.: 517111
Ramon Fernandez *(Exec Dir-Fin, Performance & Dev)*

Subsidiaries:

Business & Decision SA (1)
153 rue de Courcelles, 75817, Paris, Cedex, France (88.2%)
Tel.: (33) 156212121
Web Site: http://www.businessdecision.com
Sales Range: $250-299.9 Million
Emp.: 2,432
Business Consulting, Data Engineering & Customer Relationship Management Services
N.A.I.C.S.: 541611
helmut Reisinger *(Chm)*

Subsidiary (Non-US):

BD Chine (2)
Office 402 Baiyan Building No 238 Beishuan Zhong Road, Haidian District, Beijing, China
Tel.: (86) 10 823 32 835
Web Site: http://www.businessdecision.cn
Sales Range: $25-49.9 Million
Emp.: 28
Business Planning Software Development Services
N.A.I.C.S.: 541511

BD Espana (2)
Calle Princesa 25, 28008, Madrid, Spain
Tel.: (34) 915159547
Sales Range: $25-49.9 Million
Emp.: 30
Business Planning Software Development Services
N.A.I.C.S.: 541511

BD Israel Ltd. (2)
20 Hamagshimim Str Kiryat Matalon, Petah Tiqwa, 49170, Israel
Tel.: (972) 39213550

ORANGE S.A.

INTERNATIONAL PUBLIC

Orange S.A.—(Continued)
Sales Range: $25-49.9 Million
Emp.: 22
Business Planning Software Development Services
N.A.I.C.S.: 541511
Michael Ben-Shabat (CEO)

BD Maroc (2)
265 Bd Zerktouni 2eme etage N 22, 20050, Casablanca, Morocco
Tel.: (212) 5 22 94 11 94
Sales Range: $25-49.9 Million
Emp.: 25
Business Planning Software Development Services
N.A.I.C.S.: 541511

BD Mauritius
7th Floor BG Court Rue Saint Jean et Avenue d'Epinay, Quatre Bornes, Mauritius
Tel.: (230) 4660931
Sales Range: $25-49.9 Million
Emp.: 35
Software Development & Consulting Services
N.A.I.C.S.: 541511

Business & Decision AG (2)
Hardturmstrasse 161, 8005, Zurich, Switzerland
Tel.: (41) 319585353
Sales Range: $25-49.9 Million
Emp.: 15
Business Planning Software Development Services
N.A.I.C.S.: 541511
Jorg Heimoz (Mng Dir)

Business & Decision Benelux SA (2)
Bourgetlaan 3 Av du Bourget 3, 1140, Brussels, Belgium
Tel.: (32) 25100540
Sales Range: $75-99.9 Million
Emp.: 300
Business Management Software Development Services
N.A.I.C.S.: 541511
Ada Sekirin (Mng Dir & Reg Dir)

Subsidiary (Non-US):

BD Luxembourg (3)
8 rue des Merovingiens, 8070, Bertrange, Luxembourg
Tel.: (352) 26458650
Sales Range: $10-24.9 Million
Emp.: 35
Business Planning Software Development Services
N.A.I.C.S.: 541511
Pierre Dauffenbach (Mng Dir)

Subsidiary (Non-US):

Business & Decision Netherlands BV (2)
Wattbaan 52A, Nieuwegein, 3439 ML, Utrecht, Netherlands
Tel.: (31) 308200333
Web Site: http://www.businessdecision.nl
Sales Range: $25-49.9 Million
Emp.: 40
Business Planning Software Development Services
N.A.I.C.S.: 541511

Business & Decision Software India (P) Ltd (2)
2nd Floor NDK Trust 13th Main off 100 Ft Road, Hall II Stage, Indiranagar, Bengaluru, 560 038, India
Tel.: (91) 8041256369
Web Site: http://www.businessdecision.co.uk
Consulting Services
N.A.I.C.S.: 541690

Subsidiary (US):

Inforte Corp. (2)
940 W Valley Rd Ste 1000, Wayne, PA 19087-1800
Tel.: (312) 540-0900
Sales Range: $25-49.9 Million
Emp.: 253
Business Consulting Services
N.A.I.C.S.: 541690

Subsidiary (Domestic):

SARL Business & Decision Lille (2)
11/13/15 square Dutilleul, 59000, Lille, Nord, France
Tel.: (33) 320344488
Web Site: http://www.businessdecision.com
Business Planning Software Development Services
N.A.I.C.S.: 541511

SCI Mangin (2)
386 rue Gen Leclerc, 60170, Carlepont, Oise, France
Tel.: (33) 344753464
Engineeering Services
N.A.I.C.S.: 541330

Corsica Haut Debit (1)
Tel.: (33) 495268008
Telecommunication Servicesb
N.A.I.C.S.: 517810
Pierre Pugliesi (Dir Gen)

EGT (1)
20-22 Rue Thomas-Edison, Gennevilliers, 92635, France
Tel.: (33) 810010888
Web Site: http://www.ftegt.fr
Fax & Videoconferencing Equipment Distr
N.A.I.C.S.: 423420

FCR Vietnam PTE Ltd (1)
Level 16 Central Plaza 17 Le Duan Street, District 1, Ho Chi Minh City, Vietnam
Tel.: (84) 8 38 23 71 95
Web Site: http://www.fcrvietnam.com
Telecommunication Servicesb
N.A.I.C.S.: 517810

FT Marine (1)
16/18 Rue Paul Lafargue, Puteaux, Paris, 92800, France
Tel.: (33) 144451013
Sales Range: $25-49.9 Million
Emp.: 20
Marine Communication System Installation & Maintenance Services
N.A.I.C.S.: 238210

FT R&D Beijing Ltd Co (1)
10th Floor Tower C Raycom Info Tech Park C, Haidian District, Beijing, 100090, China
Tel.: (86) 10 8217 5000
Web Site: http://www.orange.com
Sales Range: $25-49.9 Million
Emp.: 120
Testing Laboratories Operating Services
N.A.I.C.S.: 541380

Feima Ltd (1)
Suite 200 2F No 2 Ln 150 Sec 5 Xinyi Rd, Xinyi District, Taipei, 110, Taiwan
Tel.: (886) 255940130
Telecommunication Servicesb
N.A.I.C.S.: 517810

France Telecom Bruxelles (1)
Avenue du Bourget 3, 1140, Brussels, Belgium (100%)
Tel.: (32) 26439400
Web Site: http://www.orangebusinesssservices.com
Sales Range: $25-49.9 Milllion
Emp.: 150
Radio Telephone Communications Company
N.A.I.C.S.: 517112

France Telecom India (1)
Tower B 8th Fl DLF Infinity Tower, Phase II Cyber City Sector 25, Gurgaon, 122002, Haryana, India
Tel.: (91) 1244358000
Web Site: http://www.orange-business.com
Sales Range: $400-449.9 Million
Emp.: 1,700
Radio Telephone Communications Company
N.A.I.C.S.: 517112

France Telecom Japan Co., Ltd. (1)
Keio Shinjuku Oiwake Bldg 9F, 361 13 Shinjuku, Tokyo, 160 0022, Japan (100%)
Tel.: (81) 353128585
Sales Range: $25-49.9 Million
Emp.: 40
Telecommunications Research & Development Center
N.A.I.C.S.: 517110

France Telecom R&D Beijing (1)
10th Floor Tower C Raycom Info Tech Park C, 2 Science Institute S Rd, Beijing, 100090, China (100%)
Tel.: (86) 1082175000
Web Site: http://www.orange.com
Sales Range: $50-74.9 Million
Emp.: 124
Telephone Communications Research & Development
N.A.I.C.S.: 517112

France Telecom Vietnam (1)
16th Fl Central Plaza 17 Le Duan Street, District 1, Ho Chi Minh City, Vietnam (74%)
Tel.: (84) 838228413
Web Site: http://www.orange-business.com
Radio Telephone Communications Company
N.A.I.C.S.: 517112

Francetel (1)
208 A 212 208 Rue Raymond Losserand, 75014, Paris, France
Tel.: (33) 140617200
Telecommunication Servicesb
N.A.I.C.S.: 517810

Gironde Haut Debit (1)
23 parvis des Chartrons, 33074, Bordeaux, France
Tel.: (33) 5 56 48 47 98
Web Site: http://www.girondehautdebit.fr
Broadband Internet Services
N.A.I.C.S.: 517810

GlobeCast Holding S.A. (1)
9 Rue Maurice Mallet, 92130, Issy-les-Moulineaux, France
Tel.: (33) 144614700
Web Site: https://www.globecast.com
Emp.: 100
Holding Company; Satellite Broadcast Delivery Content Management & Transmission Services
N.A.I.C.S.: 551112
Philippe Bernard (Chm & CEO)

Subsidiary (Non-US):

GlobeCast Africa Pty. Ltd. (2)
Penthouse Level Mentone Media Centre 1 Park Road, Richmond, Johannesburg, 2092, Gauteng, South Africa
Tel.: (27) 114822790
Sales Range: $25-49.9 Million
Emp.: 25
Satellite Broadcast Delivery Content Management & Transmission Services
N.A.I.C.S.: 517410
Alan Hird (CEO)

Subsidiary (US):

GlobeCast America Incorporated (2)
10 E 40th St 11th Fl, New York, NY 10016
Tel.: (212) 373-5140
Sales Range: $25-49.9 Million
Emp.: 100
Satellite Broadcast Delivery Content Management & Transmission Services
N.A.I.C.S.: 517410

Unit (Domestic):

GlobeCast America Inc. - Los Angeles Operations Center (3)
10525 W Washington Blvd, Culver City, CA 90232
Tel.: (310) 845-3900
Sales Range: $25-49.9 Million
Emp.: 50
Satellite Broadcast Delivery Content Management & Transmission Services
N.A.I.C.S.: 517410

GlobeCast America Inc. - Miami Operations Center (3)
13801 NW 14th St, Sunrise, FL 33323
Tel.: (954) 233-4564
Web Site: http://www.globecast.com
Satellite Broadcast Delivery Content Management & Transmission Services
N.A.I.C.S.: 517410

Branch (Non-US):

GlobeCast Brazil (3)
Alameda Franca 1050 3 e 4 andares parte, Sao Paulo, 01422-001, Brazil
Tel.: (55) 1131684548
Web Site: http://www.globecast.com
Satellite Broadcast Delivery Content Management & Transmission Services
N.A.I.C.S.: 517410

Subsidiary (Non-US):

GlobeCast Asia Pte. Ltd. (2)
21 Media Circle 10-01/10 Infinite Studios, Singapore, 138562, Singapore
Tel.: (65) 63254222
Emp.: 7
Satellite Broadcast Delivery Content Management & Transmission Services
N.A.I.C.S.: 517410

Subsidiary (Non-US):

GlobeCast Hong Kong Limited (3)
18/F Paramount Building 12 Ka Yip Street, Chai Wan, 852, China (Hong Kong)
Tel.: (852) 2965 1200
Web Site: http://www.globecast.com
Satellite Broadcast Delivery Content Management & Transmission Services
N.A.I.C.S.: 517410

GlobeCast India Pvt. Ltd. (3)
#1103-04 11th Floor Chiranjiv Towers, 43 Nehru Place, New Delhi, 110 019, India
Tel.: (91) 1146527160
Web Site: http://www.globecast.com
Satellite Broadcast Delivery Content Management & Transmission Services
N.A.I.C.S.: 517410

Subsidiary (Domestic):

GlobeCast France (2)
9 Rue Maurice Mallet, 92130, Issy-les-Moulineaux, France
Tel.: (33) 155952600
Sales Range: $25-49.9 Million
Emp.: 100
Satellite Broadcast Delivery Content Management & Transmission Services
N.A.I.C.S.: 517410

Subsidiary (Domestic):

GlobeCast Reportages (3)
Immeuble Le Boston 5 Allee Gustave Eiffel, 92130, Issy-les-Moulineaux, France
Tel.: (33) 155952626
Web Site: http://www.globecast.com
Telecommunication Servicesb
N.A.I.C.S.: 517810

Subsidiary (Non-US):

GlobeCast Italia S.r.l. (2)
Via Giacomo Peroni 108/110, 00131, Rome, Italy
Tel.: (39) 068091751
Satellite Broadcast Delivery Content Management & Transmission Services
N.A.I.C.S.: 517410
Alessandro Alquati (CEO)

Branch (Non-US):

GlobeCast Near & Middle East (2)
Badaro Street Badaro 2000 Bldg, 2058 9107, Beirut, Lebanon
Tel.: (961) 1 395 111
Web Site: http://www.globecast.com
Emp.: 10
Satellite Broadcast Delivery Content Management & Transmission Services
N.A.I.C.S.: 517410

Subsidiary (Non-US):

GlobeCast UK Limited (2)
200 Gray's Inn Road, London, WC1X 8XZ, United Kingdom
Tel.: (44) 2077533600
Sales Range: $25-49.9 Million
Emp.: 10
Satellite Broadcast Delivery Content Management & Transmission Services
N.A.I.C.S.: 517410

Intelig 23 (1)
Praia de Botafogo 370/1o andar, Rio de Janeiro, 22250-909, Brazil
Tel.: (55) 21 25 36 08 00
Web Site: http://www.intelig.net.br

AND PRIVATE COMPANIES

ORANGE S.A.

Telecommunications; Joint Venture of National Grid (50%), France Telecom (25%) & Sprint (25%)
N.A.I.C.S.: 517111

Jazz Telecom, S.A.U. (1)
Anabel Segura 11, 28108, Alcobendas, Madrid, Spain
Tel.: (34) 91 183 90 00
Web Site: http://www.jazztel.com
Wire & Mobile Telecommunications Services
N.A.I.C.S.: 517111

Masmovil Ibercom, S.A. (1)
Avenida de Bruselas 38, Alcobendas, 28108, Madrid, Spain
Tel.: (34) 722 395 000
Web Site: http://www.masmovil.es
Internet, Telephony, Broadband, Domain Hosting & Storage Backup Services
N.A.I.C.S.: 517810
Meinrad Spenger *(CEO)*

Subsidiary (Domestic):

Oriol Fibra S.L. (2)
C/ Santa justa 1 Bajo, Orihuela, 03300, Alicante, Spain
Tel.: (34) 865757575
Web Site: https://oriolfibra.com
Telecommunication Servicesb
N.A.I.C.S.: 517810

Pepemobile, S.L. (2)
Avenida de la Vega 15, Alcobendas, 28108, Madrid, Spain
Tel.: (34) 634501212
Web Site: https://www.pepephone.com
Telecommunication Servicesb
N.A.I.C.S.: 517810

Wimax Online S.L. (2)
Colmenarico n 22 Bajo, Lorca, 30800, Murcia, Spain
Tel.: (34) 868189707
Web Site: https://wimaxonline.es
Telecommunication Servicesb
N.A.I.C.S.: 517810

Xfera Moviles S.A. (2)
Avda de la Vega 15, 28108, Alcobendas, Spain
Tel.: (34) 722395000
Web Site: http://www.yoigo.com
Mobile Phone Operations
N.A.I.C.S.: 517112

Neocles Corporate S.A.S. (1)
4 Rue Albert Dhalenne, Saint-Ouen, 93400, France
Tel.: (33) 1 49 21 21 21
Web Site: http://www.neocles.com
Information Technology Consulting Services
N.A.I.C.S.: 541512

Network Related Services SA (1)
195 Rue Lavoisier, BP 1, Zirst, Montbonnot-Saint-Martin, 38330, France
Tel.: (33) 476416666
Web Site: http://www.itlabs.en.orange-business.com
Information Technology Consulting Services
N.A.I.C.S.: 541512

Newsforce Intern Holding company (1)
Prins Bernhardplein 200, Amsterdam, 1097 JB, Netherlands
Tel.: (31) 205214777
Investment Management Service
N.A.I.C.S.: 523999

Nordnet (1)
111 Rue De Croix, BP 60985, Hem, 59510, France
Tel.: (33) 9 69 360 360
Web Site: http://www.nordnet.fr
Broadband Internet Services
N.A.I.C.S.: 517810

Obiane (1)
Zirst 195 Rue Lavoisier, 38330, Montbonnot-Saint-Martin, France
Tel.: (33) 164539500
Web Site: http://www.orange-business.com
Emp.: 20
Telecommunication Servicesb
N.A.I.C.S.: 517810

Orange Bank SA (1)
67 rue Robespierre, 93107, Montreuil, Cedex, France (71%)
Tel.: (33) 143600152
Web Site: http://www.orangebank.fr
Rev.: $97,305,690
Assets: $5,198,825,147
Liabilities: $4,837,555,763
Net Worth: $361,269,384
Earnings: $22,650,675
Emp.: 614
Fiscal Year-end: 12/31/2016
Banking Services
N.A.I.C.S.: 522110
Ramon Fernandez *(Chm)*

Orange Belgium S.A. (1)
Bourgetlaan 3, BE-1140, Brussels, Belgium (76.97%)
Tel.: (32) 27457111
Web Site: http://corporate.orange.be
Rev.: $1,931,206,535
Assets: $4,553,939,729
Liabilities: $3,820,441,550
Net Worth: $733,498,179
Earnings: ($11,905,288)
Emp.: 1,389
Fiscal Year-end: 12/31/2023
Telecommunication Servicesb
N.A.I.C.S.: 517112

Subsidiary (Domestic):

Mobistar Enterprise Services SA (2)
Avenue Reine Astrid 166, Wemmel, 1780, Belgium
Tel.: (32) 2 610 30 00
Business Support Services
N.A.I.C.S.: 561499

Orange Canada (1)
1155 University Ste 500, Montreal, H3B 3A7, QC, Canada (100%)
Tel.: (514) 287-5472
Sales Range: $25-49.9 Million
Emp.: 4
Wholesale of Telecommunication Services
N.A.I.C.S.: 517112

Orange Cyberdefense SA (1)
54 Place de l'Ellipse, 92983, Paris, France
Tel.: (33) 144442222
Web Site: https://www.orangecyberdefense.com
Data Security Services
N.A.I.C.S.: 518210

Subsidiary (Non-US):

Telsys SA (2)
Rue du Sablon 4, 1110, Morges, Switzerland
Tel.: (41) 216514251
Web Site: http://www.telsys.ch
Sales Range: $25-49.9 Million
Emp.: 25
Broadband Internet Services
N.A.I.C.S.: 517810
Patrick Chuffart *(CEO)*

Orange Holding S.A. (1)
6 Place d'Alleray, 75505, Paris, Cedex 15, France
Tel.: (33) 144442222
Web Site: http://www.orange.com
Holding Company
N.A.I.C.S.: 551112

Subsidiary (Non-US):

Orange Armenia CJSC (2)
Yerevan Plaza Business Center Grigor Lusavorich Str 9, Yerevan, 15, Armenia
Tel.: (374) 10 513 551
Web Site: http://www.orangearmenia.am
Telecommunication Servicesb
N.A.I.C.S.: 517810

Orange BW (2)
Plot 166 Corner Queens and Pilane Main Mall, Private Bag BO 64, Bontleng, Gaborone, Botswana (51%)
Tel.: (267) 3163370
Web Site: https://www.orange.co.bw
Provider of Telecommunications Services
N.A.I.C.S.: 517112

Subsidiary (Domestic):

Orange Business Services Participations (2)
1 Place des Droits de l'Homme, 93457, Saint Denis, France
Tel.: (33) 155542200
Holding Company; Business Communications Services
N.A.I.C.S.: 551112

Subsidiary (Non-US):

Basefarm AS (3)
Nydalen Alle 37A, 0484, Oslo, Norway
Tel.: (47) 4000 4100
Web Site: http://www.basefarm.com
Information Technology Consulting Services
N.A.I.C.S.: 541512
Bjart Kvarme *(COO & Country Mgr)*

Subsidiary (Non-US):

Basefarm AB (4)
Gardsvagen 6, 169 70, Stockholm, Sweden
Tel.: (46) 850112600
Information Technology Consulting Services
N.A.I.C.S.: 541512

Basefarm BV (4)
Beechavenue 106, 1119 PP, Schiphol-Rijk, Netherlands
Tel.: (31) 204066466
Web Site: http://www.basefarm.nl
Emp.: 50
Information Technology Consulting Services
N.A.I.C.S.: 541512
Marcel Ravenshorst *(Sr VP-HR)*

Subsidiary (Non-US):

Orange Business Austria GmbH (3)
Laxenburger Strasse 2, 1100, Vienna, Austria
Tel.: (43) 3088926560
Emp.: 23
Telecommunication Servicesb
N.A.I.C.S.: 517810
Christph Muller Dott *(Country Mgr)*

Orange Business Belgium NV/SA (3)
Avenue Bourget 3 Bourgetlaan 3, 1140, Brussels, Belgium
Tel.: (32) 26439400
Telecommunication Servicesb
N.A.I.C.S.: 517810

Orange Business Czech Republic s.r.o. (3)
Revolucni 1/655, 110 00, Prague, Czech Republic
Tel.: (420) 225001111
Telecommunication Servicesb
N.A.I.C.S.: 517810

Orange Business Denmark A/S (3)
Sydvestvej 15 3rd Floor, 2600, Glostrup, Denmark
Tel.: (45) 35290000
Telecommunication Servicesb
N.A.I.C.S.: 517810

Orange Business Finland OY (3)
Mikonkatu 9 Epicenter Building, PO Box 525, 00100, Helsinki, Finland
Tel.: (358) 9228181
Telecommunication Servicesb
N.A.I.C.S.: 517810

Orange Business Germany GmbH (3)
Rahmannstrasse 11, 65760, Eschborn, Germany
Tel.: (49) 61969620
Telecommunication Servicesb
N.A.I.C.S.: 517810

Orange Business Italy S.p.A. (3)
Tel.: (39) 02752891
Web Site: http://www.orange-business.com
Telecommunication Servicesb
N.A.I.C.S.: 517810

Orange Business Luxembourg SA (3)
201 Route de Thionville, 5885, Howald, Luxembourg
Tel.: (352) 26439400
Telecommunication Servicesb
N.A.I.C.S.: 517810

Orange Business Netherlands B.V. (3)
Radarweg 60, 1043 NT, Amsterdam, Netherlands
Tel.: (31) 885949000
Telecommunication Servicesb
N.A.I.C.S.: 517810

Orange Business Norway AS (3)
Lorenfaret 1E, 0585, Oslo, Norway
Tel.: (47) 40004100
Telecommunication Servicesb
N.A.I.C.S.: 517810

Orange Business Services - Argentina (3)
Ing Butty 240 Piso 3 Edif Laminar Plaza, C1001, Buenos Aires, Argentina
Tel.: (54) 1145903700
Telecommunication Servicesb
N.A.I.C.S.: 517810

Orange Business Services - Brazil (3)
Avenida Barao de Tefe 7 4 andar - Centro, Rio de Janeiro, 20220-460, Brazil
Tel.: (55) 2121766600
Telecommunication Servicesb
N.A.I.C.S.: 517810

Orange Business Services - Chile (3)
Calle Asturias 280 Piso 9, Las Condes, 6761637, Santiago, Chile
Tel.: (56) 23943200
Telecommunication Servicesb
N.A.I.C.S.: 517810

Orange Business Services - China (3)
No 1 East Chang An Avenue Unit 3-6 Level 9 Tower W3, Beijing, 100738, China
Tel.: (86) 1085409200
Telecommunication Servicesb
N.A.I.C.S.: 517810

Orange Business Services - Colombia (3)
Calle 100 No 8A-55 Oficina 703 Torre C Edificio World Trade Center, Santafe de, Bogota, Colombia
Tel.: (57) 15240321
Telecommunication Servicesb
N.A.I.C.S.: 517810

Orange Business Services - Dubai (3)
Techno Hub-2 Dubai Silicon Oasis, PO Box 500102, Dubai, United Arab Emirates
Tel.: (971) 43916900
Telecommunication Servicesb
N.A.I.C.S.: 517810
Luc Serviant *(VP-Middle East, North Africa & Turkey)*

Orange Business Services - Egypt (3)
Star Capital 8 Floor 5 City Stars Complex Omar Ibn El Khattab Street, Heliopolis, 11771, Cairo, Egypt
Tel.: (20) 2222922003
Telecommunication Servicesb
N.A.I.C.S.: 517810

Subsidiary (Domestic):

Orange Business Services - France (3)
190 Avenue de France, 75653, Paris, France
Tel.: (33) 1 46 46 90 00
Telecommunication Servicesb
N.A.I.C.S.: 517810
Diana Einterz *(Head-Direction des Grands Clients)*

Subsidiary (Non-US):

Orange Business Services - Iceland (3)
Laugarnesvegur 87, 105, Reykjavik, Iceland
Tel.: (354) 5650476
Emp.: 20
Telecommunication Servicesb
N.A.I.C.S.: 517810
Orvar Sigurdsson *(Mgr)*

Orange Business Services - India (3)
94 Nehru Place Meghdoot Bldg - 5th Floor, 15-17 Tolstoy Marg, New Delhi, 110019, India
Tel.: (91) 113358857
Telecommunication Servicesb

ORANGE S.A.

INTERNATIONAL PUBLIC

Orange S.A.—(Continued)
N.A.I.C.S.: 517810

Orange Business Services - Ireland (3)
Premier Business Centre Unit 3013 Lake Drive Citywest Business Centre, Dublin, 24, Ireland
Tel.: (353) 14025900
Telecommunication Servicesb
N.A.I.C.S.: 517810

Orange Business Services - Japan (3)
1-12-32 Akasaka, Minato-ku, Tokyo, 1076016, Japan
Tel.: (81) 3050059000
Telecommunication Servicesb
N.A.I.C.S.: 517810

Orange Business Services - Mexico (3)
Jaime Balmes No 8 MZ 2 Col Los Morales Polanco Del Miguel Hidalgo, Mexico, Mexico
Tel.: (52) 5521225500
Telecommunication Servicesb
N.A.I.C.S.: 517810

Orange Business Services - Portugal (3)
Rua Alfredo da Silva 8A - 2A, 2610-016, Amadora, Portugal
Tel.: (351) 1214728880
Telecommunication Servicesb
N.A.I.C.S.: 517810

Orange Business Services - Romania (3)
Green Court 4 Gara Herastrau St Sector 2, 72326, Bucharest, Romania
Tel.: (40) 13102222
Telecommunication Servicesb
N.A.I.C.S.: 517810

Orange Business Services - South Africa (3)
20 Woodlands Drive Woodlands Office Park, Woodmead, Johannesburg, South Africa
Tel.: (27) 115177100
Telecommunication Servicesb
N.A.I.C.S.: 517810
Yannick Decaux (Dir-Sls-Sub Saharan Africa & Country Mgr)

Orange Business Services - Taiwan (3)
No 99 Jen-Ai Road Sec 2 Room A 3F, Taipei, 100, Taiwan
Tel.: (886) 223953098
Telecommunication Servicesb
N.A.I.C.S.: 517810

Orange Business Services - Turkey (3)
Anel Is Merkezi Inkilap Mah Site Yolu Sok No 5 Kat 5C, Umraniye, 34768, Istanbul, Turkiye
Tel.: (90) 2166332800
Telecommunication Servicesb
N.A.I.C.S.: 517810

Orange Business Services - Vietnam (3)
16th floor The Central Plaza 17 Le Duan street District 1, Ho Chi Minh City, Vietnam
Tel.: (84) 838228413
Telecommunication Servicesb
N.A.I.C.S.: 517810

Orange Business Services Australia Pty. Ltd. (3)
5 Talavera Road The Park Unit 8, Macquarie Park, 2113, NSW, Australia
Tel.: (61) 283043000
Emp.: 53
Telecommunication Servicesb
N.A.I.C.S.: 517810
Kevin Griffen (Gen Mgr)

Orange Business Services Canada Inc. (3)
770 rue Sherbrooke Ouest, Montreal, H3A1G1, QC, Canada
Tel.: (514) 844-4343
Telecommunication Servicesb
N.A.I.C.S.: 517810

Orange Business Services Singapore Pte. Ltd. (3)
Blk 750 Oasis Chai Chee Rd #04-02, Technopark Chai Chee, Singapore, 469000, Singapore
Tel.: (65) 65171000
Emp.: 200
Telecommunication Servicesb
N.A.I.C.S.: 517810

Orange Business Services Slovakia s.r.o. (3)
Metodova 8, 821 08, Bratislava, 82108, Slovakia
Tel.: (421) 258512345
Telecommunication Servicesb
N.A.I.C.S.: 517810

Orange Business Services U.S., Inc. (3)
Tel.: (703) 471-2300
Web Site: http://www.orange-business.com
Global Data, Voice & Video Business Services & Carrier Services
N.A.I.C.S.: 517810

Branch (Domestic):

Orange Business Services U.S., Inc. - Atlanta (4)
100 Galleria Pkwy Ste 300, Atlanta, GA 30339
Tel.: (678) 346-3000
Emp.: 200
Business Communications Services
N.A.I.C.S.: 517810
Rob Willcock (Sr VP-Americas)

Subsidiary (Non-US):

Orange Business Spain SA (3)
C/ Ulises 99 Planta 1, 28043, Madrid, Spain
Tel.: (34) 911784450
Telecommunication Servicesb
N.A.I.C.S.: 517810

Orange Business Switzerland AG (3)
Hardturmstrasse 161, 8005, Zurich, Switzerland
Tel.: (41) 444479797
Telecommunication Servicesb
N.A.I.C.S.: 517810

Subsidiary (Non-US):

Orange Catalunya Xaxet de Telecomunicacions S.A. (2)
Calle Gaspar Fabregas 81 - 2a Planta, 08950, Esplugues de Llobregat, Spain
Tel.: (34) 93 567 8000
Telecommunication Servicesb
N.A.I.C.S.: 517810

Orange Communications Luxembourg S.A. (2)
8 rue des Merovingiens, 8070, Bertrange, Luxembourg
Tel.: (352) 80061606
Web Site: https://www.orange.lu
Mobile Communications Services
N.A.I.C.S.: 517112

Orange CorpSec spol. s r.o. (2)
Prievozska 6/A, Bratislava, 82109, Slovakia
Tel.: (421) 2 585 12 345
Telecommunication Servicesb
N.A.I.C.S.: 517810

Orange Cote d'Ivoire SA (2)
Immeuble Le Quartz Boulevard Valery Giscard D Estaing Marcory, Abidjan, 1111, Cote d'Ivoire
Tel.: (225) 21239000
Web Site: http://www.orange.com
Mobile Communications Services
N.A.I.C.S.: 517112

Orange Egypt for Telecommunications S.A.E. (2)
Building B126-B Smart Village KM 29 Cairo Alexandria Desert Road, Giza, 12577, Cairo, Egypt (98.92%)
Tel.: (20) 1223200000
Sales Range: $1-4.9 Billion
Cellular Mobile Telecommunications System Developer & Operator
N.A.I.C.S.: 517112
Yves Jean-Marie Gauthier (Chm)

Orange Espana (2)
Parque Empresarial La Finca Edificios 8 y 9 del Club Deportivo, Pozuelo de Alarcon, 128223, Madrid, Spain (69%)
Tel.: (34) 261202260953
Web Site: http://www.orange.com
Telecommunication Servicesb
N.A.I.C.S.: 517112

Subsidiary (Domestic):

Auna Operadores de Telecomunicaciones, S.A. (3)
Paseo de la Castellana 83-85, Madrid, 28046, Spain
Tel.: (34) 91 202 4100
Telecommunication Servicesb
N.A.I.C.S.: 517810

Holding (Domestic):

Auna Telecomunicaciones S.A. (4)
Emisora 20, PO Box 28023, 08014, Madrid, Spain
Tel.: (34) 935020000
Web Site: http://www.auna.es
Emp.: 600
Cable TV Operations
N.A.I.C.S.: 516120

Subsidiary (Domestic):

Retevision Movil, S.A. (5)
Avenida Diagonal 579-549, Barcelona, Spain
Tel.: (34) 656001471
Web Site: http://www.amena.com
Mobile Phone Operator
N.A.I.C.S.: 517112

Subsidiary (Domestic):

Orange France SA (3)
1 Avenue Nelson Mandela, Arcueil, 94110, France
Tel.: (33) 1 55 22 22 22
Web Site: http://www.orange.com
Mobile Communications Services
N.A.I.C.S.: 517112

Subsidiary (Domestic):

Orange Assistance SA (3)
6 Place d'Alleray, 75505, Paris, France
Tel.: (33) 1 44 44 22 22
Broadband Installation Services
N.A.I.C.S.: 238210

Orange Consulting (3)
114 Rue Marcadet, Paris, 75018, France
Tel.: (33) 1 56 55 45 00
Sales Range: $25-49.9 Million
Emp.: 160
Information Technology Consulting Services
N.A.I.C.S.: 541512

Orange Sport (3)
6 Place d'Alleray, 75505, Paris, Cedex, France
Tel.: (33) 1 44 44 93 93
Television Broadcasting Services
N.A.I.C.S.: 516120

Subsidiary (Non-US):

Orange Moldova SA (2)
Str Alba Iulia 75, MD-2071, Chisinau, Moldova (53.7%)
Tel.: (373) 22975010
Web Site: https://www.orange.md
Telecommunication Servicesb
N.A.I.C.S.: 517112

Orange Network SA (2)
Rue Du Caudray 4, Renens, 1020, Vaud, Switzerland
Tel.: (41) 212161010
Mobile Communications Services
N.A.I.C.S.: 517112

Orange Slovensko, a.s. (2)
Metodova 8, 821 08, Bratislava, Slovakia (100%)
Tel.: (421) 258512345
Web Site: https://www.orange.sk
Rev.: $590,387,367
Assets: $675,058,357
Liabilities: $391,493,818
Net Worth: $283,564,540
Earnings: $87,397,758
Emp.: 1,133

Fiscal Year-end: 12/31/2016
Mobile Network Operator
N.A.I.C.S.: 517112
Pavol Lancaric (Chm-Supervisory Bd)

Orange Polska S.A. (1)
Al Jerozolimskie 160, 02-326, Warsaw, Poland
Tel.: (48) 5272323
Web Site: http://www.orange.pl
Rev.: $3,295,223,569
Assets: $6,815,548,763
Liabilities: $3,399,390,235
Net Worth: $3,416,158,528
Earnings: $207,825,203
Emp.: 9,012
Fiscal Year-end: 12/31/2023
Telecommunications
N.A.I.C.S.: 517111
Maciej Krzysztof Wituoki (Chm-Bd)

Secure Data Europe Ltd (1)
SecureData House Hermitage Court Hermitage Lane, Kent, Maidstone, ME16 9NT, United Kingdom
Tel.: (44) 1622 723400
Web Site: http://www.secdata.com
Software Development Services
N.A.I.C.S.: 541511
Christian Winning (CFO)

SecureLink Group N.V. (1)
Uilenbaan 80, 2160, Wommelgem, Belgium
Tel.: (32) 3 641 9595
Web Site: http://www.securelink.net
Holding Company; Cybersecurity Infrastructure & Information Technology Managed Services
N.A.I.C.S.: 551112

Subsidiary (Domestic):

SecureLink Belgium N.V. (2)
Uilenbaan 80, 2160, Wommelgem, Belgium
Tel.: (32) 36419595
Web Site: http://www.securelink.be
Cybersecurity Infrastructure & Information Technology Managed Services
N.A.I.C.S.: 541519

Silicomp Canada Inc (1)
1080 Cote du Beaver Hall Street 1400, Montreal, H2Z 1S8, QC, Canada
Tel.: (514) 935-1331
Web Site: http://www.fime.com
Sales Range: $25-49.9 Million
Emp.: 45
Information Technology Consulting Services
N.A.I.C.S.: 541512

Silicomp-AQL S.A.S (1)
4 Rue De La Chataigneraie, 35510, Cesson Sevigne, Ille-et-Vilaine, France
Tel.: (33) 299125000
Information Technology Consulting Services
N.A.I.C.S.: 541512

Subsidiary (Domestic):

Silicomp Management (2)
Immeuble Le Phenix 1 24 Rue Emile Baudot, 91120, Palaiseau, France
Tel.: (33) 164539500
Web Site: http://www.itlabs.en.orange-business.com
Sales Range: $75-99.9 Million
Emp.: 300
Information Technology Consulting Services
N.A.I.C.S.: 541512
Bruno Angoine (Gen Mgr)

Sofrecom Argentina (1)
Reconquista 609, C1003ABM, Buenos Aires, Argentina
Tel.: (54) 11 45 15 90 00
Web Site: http://www.sofrecom.com.ar
Radio Telephone Communications Company
N.A.I.C.S.: 517112

Sofrecom Maroc (1)
Technopolice Batiment B0 2eme Etage, 11100, Sale, Morocco
Tel.: (212) 5 37 27 99 00
Telecommunication Servicesb
N.A.I.C.S.: 517810

Sofrecom Polska Sp. z o.o. (1)
Grojecka 5, 02-019, Warsaw, Poland
Tel.: (48) 22 543 46 00
Web Site: http://www.sofrecom.pl

AND PRIVATE COMPANIES

Sales Range: $25-49.9 Million
Emp.: 5
Information Technology Consulting Services
N.A.I.C.S.: 541512

Sofrecom SA (1)
24 Avenue Du Petit Parc, Vincennes, 94300, France
Tel.: (33) 1 57 36 45 00
Web Site: http://www.sofrecom.com
Sales Range: $150-199.9 Million
Emp.: 1,000
Telecommunications Consulting Services
N.A.I.C.S.: 541618

Soft At Home (1)
81 Avenue Francois Arago, 92000, Nanterre, France
Tel.: (33) 1 57 66 88 88
Web Site: http://www.softathome.com
Sales Range: $25-49.9 Million
Emp.: 140
Software Development Services
N.A.I.C.S.: 541511
Frederic Maizeret (VP-Sls)

Telecom Cote d'Ivoire (1)
17 BP 275 Immeuble Postel, Bvd Languenaire, Abidjan, Cote d'Ivoire (100%)
Tel.: (225) 20344805
Web Site: http://www.citelecom.ci
Sales Range: $400-449.9 Million
Emp.: 2,351
Radio Telephone Communications Company
N.A.I.C.S.: 517112

Telefact S.A. (1)
24 Rue Des Jeuneurs, 75002, Paris, France
Tel.: (33) 1 53 40 41 42
Web Site: http://www.telefact.fr
Telecommunication Servicesb
N.A.I.C.S.: 517810

Telekomunikacja Polska (1)
Orange Labs 7 Obrzeznz Street, 02-691, Warsaw, Poland (100%)
Tel.: (48) 226995107
Web Site: http://www.francetelecom.com
Rev: $4,784,832,000
Telecommunication Servicesb
N.A.I.C.S.: 517112

Viaccess SA (1)
Aegean Tower 15th-16th Floors 9 11 Allee de l'Arche, La Defense, 92400, Paris, France
Tel.: (33) 144456465
Mobile, Television & Internet Video Broadcasting Services
N.A.I.C.S.: 516120
Philippe Leonetti (CEO)

Subsidiary (Non-US):

Viaccess-Orca Ltd (2)
22 Zarhin Street, POB 2220, Ra'anana, 43662, Israel
Tel.: (972) 97699444
Web Site: https://www.viaccess-orca.com
Digital Video Broadcast Management Solutions
N.A.I.C.S.: 513210
Rony Gihan (Exec VP-Customer Delivery)

w-HA S.A (1)
25 Bis Avenue Andre Morizet, 92100, Boulogne-Billancourt, France
Tel.: (33) 141106731
Web Site: http://www.w-ha.com
Electronic Financial Payment Services
N.A.I.C.S.: 522320

ORANGE SKY GOLDEN HARVEST ENTERTAINMENT (HOLDINGS) LIMITED
18/F CNT Tower 338 Hennessy Road, Wanchai, China (Hong Kong)
Tel.: (852) 23528222
Web Site: http://www.osgh.com.hk
1132—(HKG)
Rev: $88,739,618
Assets: $450,318,270
Liabilities: $256,838,040
Net Worth: $193,480,230
Earnings: ($5,883,870)
Emp.: 374
Fiscal Year-end: 12/31/22

Film Production, Financing, Distribution & Exhibition Services
N.A.I.C.S.: 512199
Kebo Wu (Chm)

Subsidiaries:

Golden Village Multiplex Pte Limited (1)
3 Temasek Boulevard 03-373 Suntec City Mall, Singapore, 038983, Singapore
Tel.: (65) 66538100
Web Site: https://www.gv.com.sg
Entertainment Services
N.A.I.C.S.: 512131

Vie Show Cinemas Co. Ltd. (1)
No 20 Songshou Road, Xinyi District, Taipei, Taiwan
Tel.: (886) 28 780 5566
Web Site: https://www.vscinemas.com.tw
Theater Services
N.A.I.C.S.: 512131

ORANGE TOUR CULTURAL HOLDING LIMITED
Room 813 8/F Tai Yau Building 181 Johnston Road, Wanchai, China (Hong Kong)
Tel.: (852) 35758627
Web Site: http://www.otch.com.cn
Year Founded: 2006
8627—(HKG)
Rev: $2,883,114
Assets: $14,338,771
Liabilities: $2,299,752
Net Worth: $12,039,019
Earnings: ($520,182)
Emp.: 79
Fiscal Year-end: 12/31/22
Holding Company
N.A.I.C.S.: 551112
Yang Zhou (Chm)

ORANGE1 HOLDING
Piazza della Repubblica 28, 20124, Milan, MI, Italy
Tel.: (39) 0444 649 399
Web Site: http://www.orange1.eu
Sales Range: $250-299.9 Million
Emp.: 1,600
Holding Company; Electric Motor Mfr
N.A.I.C.S.: 551112
Armando Donazzan (Chm & CEO)

Subsidiaries:

Orange 1 Electric Motors S.p.A. (1)
Via Angelo Messedaglia 4, 32030, Arsie, BL, Italy
Tel.: (39) 0439750067
Web Site: http://www.orange1.eu
Sales Range: $150-199.9 Million
Emp.: 800
Electric Motor Mfr
N.A.I.C.S.: 335312
Armando Donazzan (Chm & CEO)

Subsidiary (Non-US):

EME Kft. (2)
Csengery ut 119, 8800, Nagykanizsa, Hungary (100%)
Tel.: (36) 93313036
Sales Range: $25-49.9 Million
Emp.: 400
Electric Motor Mfr
N.A.I.C.S.: 335312
Mauro Grana (Mng Dir & Mgr-Ops-Global)

Sicme Orange1 S.r.l. (1)
Via del Lavoro 7, 36054, Montebello Vicentino, VI, Italy
Tel.: (39) 0444 649399
Web Site: http://www.orange1.eu
Electric Motor Mfr
N.A.I.C.S.: 335312

ORANGEBOX LTD.
3 East Road Penallta Industrial Estate, Hengoed, CF82 7SU, Mid Glamorgan, United Kingdom
Tel.: (44) 1443 816604
Web Site: http://www.orangebox.com
Year Founded: 1925
Sales Range: $50-74.9 Million
Emp.: 450
Furniture Mfr
N.A.I.C.S.: 337214
Mino Vernaschi (Mng Dir)

Subsidiaries:

Orangebox Middle East (1)
Building 5WD Office 448, PO Box 371447, Airport Free Zone, Dubai, United Arab Emirates
Tel.: (971) 42602460
Furniture Distr
N.A.I.C.S.: 423210
Anne Barron (Reg Mgr-Sls)

Orangebox US Inc (1)
99 Monroe Ave NW Ste 200, Grand Rapids, MI 49503
Tel.: (616) 617-8885
Furniture Mfr & Distr
N.A.I.C.S.: 337214
Adrian Welch (Reg Mgr-Sls)

ORANGEVILLE CHRYSLER LIMITED
Lot 1 Conc 2 Hwy 9 E of Hwy 10, Orangeville, L9W 2Z7, ON, Canada
Tel.: (888) 879-4956
Web Site: http://www.orangevillechrysler.com
New & Used Car Dealers
N.A.I.C.S.: 441110
Danny Brackett (Dealer Principal)

ORANO SA
125 Avenue de Paris, 92320, Chatillon, France
Tel.: (33) 1 3496 0000 FR
Web Site: http://www.orano.group
Year Founded: 2015
Rev: $4,240,909,820
Assets: $26,408,538,520
Liabilities: $25,010,953,240
Net Worth: $1,397,585,280
Earnings: $506,176,720
Fiscal Year-end: 12/31/19
Holding Company
N.A.I.C.S.: 551112
Philippe Knoche (CEO)

Subsidiaries:

Orano Cycle SA (1)
125 Avenue de Paris, 92320, Chatillon, Cedex, France (100%)
Tel.: (33) 134960000
Web Site: http://www.orano.group
Nuclear Fuel Production, Mining & Waste Recycling Services
N.A.I.C.S.: 237110

Subsidiary (Non-US):

AREVA NC Australia Pty Ltd (2)
Level 1 12 St Georges Ter, Perth, 6000, WA, Australia
Tel.: (61) 892021100
Sales Range: $25-49.9 Million
Emp.: 18
Holding Company
N.A.I.C.S.: 551112

AREVA Renewables GmbH (2)
Julius-Bamberger-Str 8, Bremen, 28279, Germany
Tel.: (49) 421436800
Eletric Power Generation Services
N.A.I.C.S.: 221118

Subsidiary (Domestic):

Eurodif SA (2)
4 Rue Paul Dautier, BP 35, 78142, Velizy-Villacoublay, Cedex, France
Tel.: (33) 475505400
Enriched Uranium Mining
N.A.I.C.S.: 212290

Helion SAS (2)
Domaine du Petit Arbois, 13545, Aix-en-Provence, France
Tel.: (33) 4 42908150
Web Site: http://www.helion-hydrogen-power.com
Hydroelectric Power Generation Services
N.A.I.C.S.: 221111

Subsidiary (Non-US):

Orano Canada Inc. (2)
100 - 833 45th Street West, PO Box 9204, Saskatoon, S7K 3X5, SK, Canada (100%)
Tel.: (306) 343-4500
Web Site: http://www.arevaresources.ca
Uranium Mining
N.A.I.C.S.: 212290
Jim Corman (Pres & CEO)

Orano Japan Co., Ltd (2)
5F Urban Toranomon Bldg 1-16-4 Toranomon, Minato-ku, Tokyo, 105-0001, Japan (100%)
Tel.: (81) 335978791
Solutions & Services to the Nuclear Power, Energy Distribution & Transmission Industries
N.A.I.C.S.: 221118

Orano Korea Ltd. (2)
Rm 513 City Air Terminal 159-6 Samsung-Dong Kangnam-Ku, Seoul, 135 090, Korea (South) (100%)
Tel.: (82) 25510166
Web Site: http://www.orano.group
Solutions & Services to the Nuclear Power, Energy Distribution & Transmission Industries
N.A.I.C.S.: 221113

Orano Projects Ltd. (2)
Suite 7 Hitching Court Abingdon Business Park, Abingdon, OX14 1RA, Oxfordshire, United Kingdom
Tel.: (44) 1235555755
Web Site: http://www.oranoprojects.uk
Integrated Technical Consulting & Engineering Services
N.A.I.C.S.: 541330
John Storer (Mng Dir)

Subsidiary (US):

Orano USA LLC (2)
4747 Bethesda Ave 10th Fl, Bethesda, MD 20814
Tel.: (202) 969-3240
Web Site: http://www.orano.group
Engineeering Services
N.A.I.C.S.: 541330
Sam Shakir (CEO)

Subsidiary (Domestic):

Interim Storage Partners LLC (3)
9998 W State Hwy 176, Andrews, TX 79714
Tel.: (432) 525-8500
Web Site: http://www.interimstoragepartners.com
Used Fuel Storage Services
N.A.I.C.S.: 424710
Jeffery Isakson (CEO)

Subsidiary (Domestic):

Societe Industrielle de Combustible Nucleaire Annecy (SICN) SA (2)
ZA d'Armanville 3 rue des Entrepreneurs, 50700, Valognes, Cedex, France
Tel.: (33) 2 33 88 69 88
Web Site: http://www.cogema.fr
Design & Mfr of Nuclear Components
N.A.I.C.S.: 541330

Somair SA (2)
Zi De La Grande Marine, 84800, L'Isle-sur-la-Sorgue, France
Tel.: (33) 4 90 38 05 88
Building Materials Machinery & Equipment Mfr
N.A.I.C.S.: 333120

TN International SA (2)
1 rue des herons, 78180, Montigny-le-Bretonneux, France
Tel.: (33) 1 34 96 50 00
Freight Transportation & Storage Services
N.A.I.C.S.: 484110

Subsidiary (Non-US):

Urangesellschaft GmbH (2)
Solmsstrasse 12, Postfach 900428, 60486,

ORANO SA

Orano SA—(Continued)
Frankfurt am Main, Germany
Tel.: (49) 697950050
Uranium Trading
N.A.I.C.S.: 212290

ORANZERII HAMZALI AD
S Hamzali bb Bosilovo, Strumica, North Macedonia
Tel.: (389) 34375884
Web Site: https://www.adoranzerii-hamzali.com.mk
ORAN—(MAC)
Rev.: $13,375,928
Assets: $20,381,368
Liabilities: $8,885,622
Net Worth: $11,495,746
Earnings: $530,520
Fiscal Year-end: 12/31/23
Fruit & Vegetable Farming Services
N.A.I.C.S.: 111219

ORAPI S.A.
Parc Industriel de la Plaine de l Ain 225 allee des Cedres, 01150, Saint-Vulbas, France
Tel.: (33) 413333020
Web Site: https://www.orapi.com
ORAP—(EUR)
Sales Range: $250-299.9 Million
Emp.: 650
Industrial Laundry Products Mfr, Distr, Maintenance & Repair
N.A.I.C.S.: 325611
Guy Chifflot *(Co-Chm)*

Subsidiaries:

CHIMIOTECHNIC (1)
Parc Industriel de la Plaine de lAin 5 allee des Cedres, 1150, Saint-Vulbas, France
Tel.: (33) 4 74 40 20 80
Pesticide Mfr
N.A.I.C.S.: 325320

ORAPI APPLIED (M) Sdn Bhd (1)
No 10 Jalan PJU 3/49 PJU 3 Sunway Damansara, Petaling Jaya, 47810, Selangor, Malaysia
Tel.: (60) 37805 3805
Web Site: http://www.orapi.com
Emp.: 30
Industrial Chemical Whslr
N.A.I.C.S.: 424690

ORAPI APPLIED (S) Pte Ltd (1)
No 9 Tuas Basin Link, Singapore, 638763, Singapore
Tel.: (65) 6265 2888
Sales Range: $25-49.9 Million
Emp.: 30
Industrial Chemical Whslr
N.A.I.C.S.: 424690
Fabrice Chifflot *(CEO)*

ORAPI APPLIED BELGIUM S.A. (1)
Heerdweg 57, 9800, Deinze, Belgium
Tel.: (32) 2 2800 736
Medical Equipment Mfr
N.A.I.C.S.: 334510

ORAPI APPLIED Ltd (1)
Spring Road, Smethwick, B66 1PT, W Midlands, United Kingdom
Tel.: (44) 121 525 4000
Web Site: http://www.orapiapplied.com
Industrial Chemical Whslr
N.A.I.C.S.: 424690

ORAPI APPLIED NEDERLAND B.V (1)
Ondememingsweg 16, PO Box 466, 2400 AL, Alphen aan den Rijn, Netherlands
Tel.: (31) 172 43 72 21
Web Site: http://www.orapiapplied.nl
Industrial Supplies Distr
N.A.I.C.S.: 423840

ORAPI CANADA Ltd (1)
7521 Boul Henri Bourassa est, Montreal, H1E 1N9, QC, Canada
Tel.: (514) 735-3272
Web Site: https://en.orapicanada.com

Sales Range: $25-49.9 Million
Emp.: 15
Industrial Lubricants Whslr
N.A.I.C.S.: 423840

ORAPI CHILE S.A (1)
Avenida Lo Echeveres 901-Bodega 14E, Quilicura, Santiago, Chile
Tel.: (56) 2 411 1920
Industrial Chemical Whslr
N.A.I.C.S.: 424690

ORAPI DRY-SHINE Inc. (1)
7521 Boul Henri-Bourassa E, Montreal, H1E 1N9, QC, Canada
Tel.: (514) 735-3272
Web Site: http://www.lubco.ca
Emp.: 15
Vehicle Washing Products Distr
N.A.I.C.S.: 424690
Jean Fallouey *(Pres)*

ORAPI ITALIA Srl (1)
Via Vaccareccia 39, 00040, Pomezia, Rome, Italy
Tel.: (39) 06 916 10576
Industrial Chemical Whslr
N.A.I.C.S.: 424690

ORAPI NORDIC OY AB (1)
Salpakuja 6, 1200, Vantaa, Finland
Tel.: (358) 9 894 6430
Sales Range: $25-49.9 Million
Emp.: 12
Industrial Supplies Whslr
N.A.I.C.S.: 423840
Martin Duncan *(Mng Dir)*

ORAPI NORDIC OY AB (1)
Bolandsgatan 10, 753 23, Uppsala, Sweden
Tel.: (46) 18 506 010
Web Site: http://www.orapi.se
Industrial Machinery Maintenance Products Mfr
N.A.I.C.S.: 339999
Jimmy Emretzon *(Gen Mgr)*

ORAPI NORWAY OY AB (1)
Narverodveien 40, 3113, Tonsberg, Norway
Tel.: (47) 333 66 000
Web Site: http://www.orapi.com
Medical Equipment Mfr
N.A.I.C.S.: 334510
Martin Duncan *(Mng Dir)*

ORAPI PACIFIC SALT (Pty) Ltd (1)
228 Albert Amon Road-Millenium Business Park Meadowdale Ext 7, PO Box 6142, Birchleigh, Kempton Park, 1621, South Africa
Tel.: (27) 11 453 17 13
Industrial Chemical Whslr
N.A.I.C.S.: 424690

ORAPI PACIFIC TECHNIPAC Sarl (1)
Z I Vallee de la Tipaerui, BP 1706, 98713, Papeete, French Polynesia
Tel.: (689) 74 57 33
Web Site: http://www.orapi.com
Industrial Chemical Distr
N.A.I.C.S.: 424690

ORAPI PACIFIC-VICTORIA LUB Pty Ltd (1)
Factory 24 29-39 Kirkham Road West, Keysborough, 3173, VIC, Australia
Tel.: (61) 3 9701 5373
Web Site: http://www.viclube.com.au
Sales Range: $50-74.9 Million
Emp.: 10
Industrial Chemical Whslr
N.A.I.C.S.: 424690

Orapi Applied (T) Co., Ltd. (1)
55/75 Khlong Lamchiak Road Nuanchan, Buengkum, Bangkok, 10230, Thailand
Tel.: (66) 25081342
Hygiene Chemical Product Mfr
N.A.I.C.S.: 325998

Orapi Hygiene Ile de France SASU (1)
101-105 Boulevard D'Italie, 77127, Lieusaint, France
Tel.: (33) 169916000
Hygiene Chemical Product Mfr
N.A.I.C.S.: 325998

Orapi Middle East L.L.C. (1)
729 Business Village Main Building Block B, PO Box 120509, Dubai, United Arab Emirates
Tel.: (971) 42942947
Hygiene Chemical Product Mfr
N.A.I.C.S.: 325998

Orapi Pacific - Orapi Africa Ltd. (1)
434 Sam Green Road Unit 2 Bridgeway Business Park, Rietfontein, Germiston, South Africa
Tel.: (27) 876544359
Web Site: http://www.orapi.co.za
Tool & Machine Maintenance Product Mfr
N.A.I.C.S.: 333517

Orapi Pacific Prolub Cie Ltd. (1)
62 Pailles Road, Les Pailles, Mauritius
Tel.: (230) 2866328
Hygiene Chemical Product Mfr
N.A.I.C.S.: 325998

Orapi Pacific SFAC SARL (1)
27 rue Ampere - ZI Ducos, BP 3725, 98846, Noumea, New Caledonia
Tel.: (687) 251540
Hygiene Chemical Product Mfr
N.A.I.C.S.: 325998

Orapi Transnet Espana, SL (1)
Poligono Industrial Castro Romano Nave 20, Sabinanigo, 22600, Huesca, Spain
Tel.: (34) 974480828
Web Site: http://www.orapitransnet.com
Disinfection & Cleaning Product Mfr
N.A.I.C.S.: 325612

Orapi Transnet SP. Z O.O. (1)
Ul Sremska 75 a, Mosina, 62-050, Poznan, Poland
Tel.: (48) 618833548
Web Site: http://www.orapi-transnet.pl
Hygiene Chemical Product Mfr
N.A.I.C.S.: 325998

PROVEN ORAPI (1)
679 avenue du D Lefebvre, 06270, Villeneuve-Loubet, France
Tel.: (33) 4 92 13 30 30
Web Site: http://www.proven.fr
Chemical Products Mfr & Distr
N.A.I.C.S.: 325199

Phem Technologies S.A. (1)
21 alley Louis Breguet, 93420, Villepinte, France
Tel.: (33) 149634455
Web Site: http://www.phem.fr
Hygiene Chemical Product Mfr
N.A.I.C.S.: 325998

ORASCOM CONSTRUCTION PLC
Office 301 Level 3 Gate Village 1 Dubai International Financial Centre, PO Box 507031, Dubai, United Arab Emirates
Tel.: (971) 43180900
Web Site: https://www.orascom.com
Year Founded: 1950
OC—(NASDAQDBAI)
Rev.: $3,542,900,000
Assets: $4,102,400,000
Liabilities: $3,413,800,000
Net Worth: $688,600,000
Earnings: $125,300,000
Emp.: 21,483
Fiscal Year-end: 12/31/21
Construction & Engineering Services
N.A.I.C.S.: 236210
Osama Bishai *(CEO)*

Subsidiaries:

Alico Egypt Ltd. (1)
105 Omar Ibn El-Khattab Oscar Building, Heliopolis, Cairo, Egypt (50%)
Tel.: (20) 224170044
Web Site: https://www.alicoegypt.com
Emp.: 600
Building Facade, Curtain Walling & Window Systems
N.A.I.C.S.: 238390

BESIX Group SA (1)
Avenue des Communautes 100, Woluwe-Saint-Lambert, 1200, Brussels, Belgium (50%)
Tel.: (32) 24026211

Web Site: https://www.besix.com
Sales Range: $1-4.9 Billion
Holding Company; Engineering, Procurement & Construction Services
N.A.I.C.S.: 551112
Johan Beerlandt *(Chm)*

Subsidiary (Domestic):

NV BESIX SA (2)
Avenue des Communautes Gemeenschappenlaan 100, 1200, Brussels, Belgium (100%)
Tel.: (32) 2402 6211
Web Site: http://www.besix.be
Engineering & Construction Services
N.A.I.C.S.: 541330
Philippe Quoilin *(Pres & COO)*

Subsidiary (Domestic):

Heijmans (B) N.V. (3)
Steenwinkelstraat 640, 2627, Schelle, Antwerp, Belgium
Tel.: (32) 32952110
Web Site: http://www.heijmans.be
Commercial Construction Services
N.A.I.C.S.: 541330

Subsidiary (Domestic):

BESIX Infra N.V. (4)
Steenwinkelstraat 640, 2627, Schelle, Belgium
Tel.: (32) 38707970
Web Site: https://www.besixinfra.com
Construction Engineering Services
N.A.I.C.S.: 541330

Subsidiary (Non-US):

STRABAG BV (5)
Oude Trambaan 29, 6049 GT, Herten, Netherlands
Tel.: (31) 475777800
Web Site: https://www.strabag.nl
Construction Engineering Services
N.A.I.C.S.: 541330

Subsidiary (Domestic):

Heijmans Bouw N.V. (4)
Taunusweg 49, 3740, Bilzen, Belgium
Tel.: (32) 89519080
Web Site: http://www.heijmans.be
Commercial & Residential Property Development Services
N.A.I.C.S.: 531210
Sauwens Herman *(CEO)*

Van den Berg N.V. (4)
Steenwinkelstraat 640, 2627, Schelle, Belgium
Tel.: (32) 38 70 79 70
Web Site: http://www.heijmans.be
Cable & Pipeline Construction & Infrastructure Solutions
N.A.I.C.S.: 237120
Veronique Vandenbosch *(Mgr-HR)*

Subsidiary (Non-US):

Watpac Limited (2)
Level 1 12 Commercial Rd, PO Box 2053, Fortitude Valley, Newstead, 4006, QLD, Australia (100%)
Tel.: (61) 732516300
Web Site: http://www.watpac.com.au
Rev.: $842,931,541
Assets: $357,326,273
Liabilities: $247,715,819
Net Worth: $109,610,455
Earnings: $44,428,613
Fiscal Year-end: 06/30/2018
Construction Services
N.A.I.C.S.: 236116
Martin G. Monro *(Mng Dir)*

Subsidiary (Domestic):

Fisherman's Wharf Marina Hervey Bay Pty Ltd (3)
864 Boat Harbour Dr, Hervey Bay, 4655, QLD, Australia
Tel.: (61) 741289744
Web Site: http://www.fishermanswharf.com.au
Sales Range: $25-49.9 Million
Emp.: 6
Boat Building Services
N.A.I.C.S.: 336611

AND PRIVATE COMPANIES

Watpac Construction (NSW) Pty Ltd (3)
Level 5 No 8 Australia Ave Olympic Park, Sydney, 2127, NSW, Australia
Tel.: (61) 298997444
Construction & Property Development Services
N.A.I.C.S.: 237990

Watpac Construction (Vic) Pty Ltd (3)
Level 1 111 Coventry St, Southbank, 3006, VIC, Australia
Tel.: (61) 3 9649 2200
Web Site: http://www.jadodd.com.au
Sales Range: $50-74.9 Million
Emp.: 120
Construction Services
N.A.I.C.S.: 236210

Watpac Construction Pty Ltd (3)
Level 7 470 St Pauls Terrace, Fortitude Valley, 4006, QLD, Australia
Tel.: (61) 732516300
Web Site: https://besixwatpac.com
Sales Range: $25-49.9 Million
Emp.: 100
Construction & Property Development Services
N.A.I.C.S.: 237990
Lyndall Duggan *(Coord)*

Watpac Specialty Services Pty Ltd (3)
Level 1, 12 Commercial Road Newstead, Fortitude Valley, 4006, QLD, Australia
Tel.: (61) 732516300
Sales Range: $150-199.9 Million
Construction & Property Development Services
N.A.I.C.S.: 541330

Contrack Watts Inc. (1)
6862 Elm St 5th Fl, McLean, VA 22101
Tel.: (703) 358-8800
Web Site: https://www.contrackwatts.com
Construction Services
N.A.I.C.S.: 237990

Integrated Facade Solutions (1)

Orascom Construction Industries SAE (1)
Nile City Towers 2005A Corniche El Nil, Cairo, 11221, Egypt
Tel.: (20) 2 2461 1111
Sales Range: $1-4.9 Billion
Emp.: 86,000
Cement Producer; Construction Services
N.A.I.C.S.: 327310
Nassef Onsi Naguib Sawiris *(Chm)*

Subsidiary (Non-US):

Cementech Limited (2)
BurJuman Bus Tower Sheikh Khalifa Bin Zayed Rd, PO Box 125284, Dubai, 125284, United Arab Emirates (100%)
Tel.: (971) 43518410
Web Site: http://www.orascom.com
Sales Range: $1-4.9 Billion
Emp.: 8,000
Engineering, Procurement & Construction Services
N.A.I.C.S.: 541330

Subsidiary (US):

Contrack International, Inc. (2)
1001 N 19th St Ste 1220, Arlington, VA 22209 (100%)
Tel.: (703) 358-8800
Web Site: http://www.contrack.com
Engineering, Procurement & Construction Services
N.A.I.C.S.: 541330
Karim Camel-Toueg *(Pres)*

Subsidiary (Non-US):

Contrack Cyprus Limited (3)
D Ring Road, PO Box 22042, Doha, 22042, Qatar
Tel.: (974) 4456 1444
Web Site: http://www.contrack.com
Emp.: 100
Construction Engineering Services
N.A.I.C.S.: 541330
Imad Arrabi *(CEO)*

Subsidiary (Domestic):

National Steel Fabrication Ltd. (2)
Bolck 260 and 261 Industrial Zone 3, PO Box 126, 6th of October City, Egypt (100%)
Tel.: (20) 238206641
Web Site: http://www.nsfegypt.com
Fabricated Steel Product Mfr
N.A.I.C.S.: 332999

Subsidiary (Non-US):

Orascom Construction Industries Algeria Spa (2)
3bis rue Raoul Payen, 16035, Hydra, Algeria
Tel.: (213) 21321481204
Engineering & Construction Services
N.A.I.C.S.: 541330

Subsidiary (US):

Orascom E&C USA Inc (2)
Corporation Trust Ctr, Wilmington, DE 19801
Tel.: (515) 698-4269
Engineering & Construction Services
N.A.I.C.S.: 541330

Subsidiary (Domestic):

Suez Industrial Development Company (2)
Building 8 Loloa Towers 8th Floor, 1197 Cornish El Nil, Cairo, 11221, Egypt (60.5%)
Tel.: (20) 2 24606 300
Industrial Park Developer & Operator
N.A.I.C.S.: 236210

United Holding Company SAE (2)
17 Bahgat Ali Street Zamalek, 11211, Cairo, Egypt (56.5%)
Tel.: (20) 2 27363694
Web Site: http://www.uhcegypt.com
Sales Range: $50-74.9 Million
Emp.: 9
Investment Management Service
N.A.I.C.S.: 523999
Ali Moussa *(Gen Mgr)*

Subsidiary (Domestic):

A-Build Egypt Ltd. (3)
18A El-Gihad St, Giza, Egypt (50%)
Tel.: (20) 223055350
Printing & Writing Paper Whslr
N.A.I.C.S.: 424110

Egyptian Gypsum Company Ltd. (3)
Borg El-Arab, Alexandria, Egypt (50%)
Tel.: (20) 34650312
Engineeering Services
N.A.I.C.S.: 541330

Orascom Trading Company (1)
160 26th of July street, Agouza, Cairo, Egypt
Tel.: (20) 233452510
Web Site: https://www.orascomservices.com
Emp.: 601
Construction Materials Distr
N.A.I.C.S.: 423390

The Weitz Group LLC (1)
5901 Thornton Ave, Des Moines, IA 50321
Tel.: (515) 246-4700
Web Site: http://www.weitz.com
Construction Engineering Services
N.A.I.C.S.: 541330
David Strutt *(General Counsel & Sr VP)*

Subsidiary (Domestic):

The Weitz Company, LLC (2)
611 5th Ave Ste 300, Des Moines, IA 50309
Tel.: (515) 246-4700
Web Site: https://www.weitz.com
Sales Range: $650-699.9 Million
Emp.: 1,400
General Contractors & Construction Manageoro
N.A.I.C.S.: 236210
Jeremy Marron *(CFO)*

Branch (Domestic):

The Weitz Company LLC - Cedar Rapids (3)
2801 6th St SW, Cedar Rapids, IA 52404 (100%)
Tel.: (319) 247-7400
Web Site: http://www.weitz.com
Sales Range: $25-49.9 Million
Emp.: 150
General Contractors of Industrial Buildings & Warehouses
N.A.I.C.S.: 236220

The Weitz Company LLC - Denver (3)
4725 S Monaco St Ste 100, Denver, CO 80237-3468 (100%)
Tel.: (303) 860-6600
Web Site: http://www.weitz.com
Sales Range: $25-49.9 Million
Emp.: 100
General Contractor & Construction Manager
N.A.I.C.S.: 236115

The Weitz Company LLC - West Palm Beach (3)
1400 Centrepark Blvd Ste 700, West Palm Beach, FL 33401
Tel.: (561) 686-5511
Web Site: http://www.weitz.com
Sales Range: $25-49.9 Million
Emp.: 100
General Contractor & Construction Manager
N.A.I.C.S.: 236220
Michael Thomas *(Dir-Bus Dev)*

Subsidiary (Domestic):

Watts Constructors, LLC (3)
1451 Dolley Madison Blvd Ste 310, McLean, VA 22101
Tel.: (571) 279-8650
Web Site: https://www.wattsconstructors.com
Sales Range: $25-49.9 Million
Emp.: 78,600
Construction Services
N.A.I.C.S.: 237990

Weitz Supply Chain, LLC (3)
5901 Thornton Ave, Des Moines, IA 50321
Tel.: (515) 246-4700
Whslr & Distributor
N.A.I.C.S.: 423730
Mike Rupe *(Pres)*

ORASCOM DEVELOPMENT HOLDING AG
Gotthardstrasse 12, CH 6460, Altdorf, Switzerland
Tel.: (41) 418741717
Web Site: https://www.orascomdh.com
ODHN—(SWX)
Rev.: $778,733,530
Assets: $2,195,764,249
Liabilities: $1,559,251,606
Net Worth: $636,512,642
Earnings: $64,641,898
Emp.: 8,825
Fiscal Year-end: 12/31/23
Commercial & Institutional Building Construction
N.A.I.C.S.: 236220
Samih O. Sawiris *(Chm)*

Subsidiaries:

Andermatt Alpine Destination Company AG (1)
Gotthardstrasse 2, 6490, Andermatt, Switzerland
Tel.: (41) 41 888 78 00
Web Site: http://www.andermatt-swissalps.ch
Travel Trailer Mfr
N.A.I.C.S.: 336214

Lustica Development A.D. (1)
Radovici, 85323, Tivat, Montenegro
Tel.: (382) 77200100
Web Site: https://www.lusticabay.com
Real Estate Services
N.A.I.C.S.: 531390

Orascom Development Egypt (1)
Nile City Towers South Tower 9th Floor, 2005 A Corniche El Nil, 11221, Cairo, 11221, Egypt
Tel.: (20) 224618999
Web Site: https://www.orascomde.com
Rev.: $495,871,835
Assets: $1,269,460,454
Liabilities: $947,023,509
Net Worth: $322,436,945
Earnings: $100,921,366
Fiscal Year-end: 12/31/2023
Home Management Services
N.A.I.C.S.: 721110
Ashraf Nessim *(Grp CFO & CFO)*

Orascom Housing Company (1)
2005 C Nile City Tower Corniche El Nils, Fl 14 Ramlet Boulak, Cairo, Egypt (84.79%)
Tel.: (20) 224618918
Web Site: http://www.orascomhc.com
Housing Community Services
N.A.I.C.S.: 624229
Omar Elhitamy *(Mng Dir)*

ORAVEL STAYS LIMITED
Mauryansh Elanza, Shyamal Cross Rd Near Parekh Hospital Ground Floor-001, Ahmedabad, 380015, Gujarat, India
Tel.: (91) 1244208080
Web Site: https://www.oyorooms.com
Motel & Extended-Stay Hotel
N.A.I.C.S.: 721110

ORB ENERGY PVT. LTD.
No 12 Srigandhada Kavalu Sunkadakatte Magadi Road, Bengaluru, 560 091, India
Tel.: (91) 8023286141
Web Site: http://www.orbenergy.com
Solar Cell Mfr & Distr
N.A.I.C.S.: 334413
Damian Miller *(CEO)*

ORBID S.A. - INDUSTRIA E COMERCIO
Av Assis Brasil, 4750 Sarandi, 91110-000, Porto Alegre, RS, Brazil
Tel.: (55) 5121315100
Web Site: http://www.orbid.com.br
Year Founded: 1995
Software Devolopment
N.A.I.C.S.: 513210

ORBIS CORPORATION
100 Peffer Law Circle, Brampton, L6Y 0L6, ON, Canada
Tel.: (647) 308-5963 NV
Sales Range: Less than $1 Million
Emp.: 1
Medical Specimens Delivery & Transportation Services
N.A.I.C.S.: 492110
Joginder Singh Arora *(Pres, CEO & CFO)*

ORBIS OY
Vanha Kaarelantie 9, 01610, Vantaa, Finland
Tel.: (358) 20 478 830
Web Site: http://www.orbis.eu
Year Founded: 1949
Testing Services
N.A.I.C.S.: 541380
Linna-Aro Markku *(Co-CEO)*

Subsidiaries:

Orbis Oy Eesti Filiaa (1)
Kasesalu 24, EE-76505, Saue, Estonia
Tel.: (372) 6517080
Wire & Cable Distr
N.A.I.C.S.: 423610

ORBIS PROPERTIES SOCIMI, S.A.U.
Calle Principe de Vergara n 112 4 Planta, 28002, Madrid, Spain
Tel.: (34) 35227859500
Web Site: https://www.orbisproperties.com
Year Founded: 2018
MLORB—(EUR)
Rev: $15,672,602
Assets: $321,390,710

ORBIS PROPERTIES SOCIMI, S.A.U.

Orbis Properties SOCIMI, S.A.U.—(Continued)
Liabilities: $261,594,745
Net Worth: $59,795,965
Earnings: ($3,647,018)
Fiscal Year-end: 12/31/21
Investment Management Service
N.A.I.C.S.: 523999
Yves Barthels (Chm)

ORBIS SE
Nell-Breuning-Allee 3-5, 66115, Saarbrucken, Germany
Tel.: (49) 68199240
Web Site: https://www.orbis.de
Year Founded: 1986
OBS—(MUN)
Rev.: $145,942,653
Assets: $98,343,778
Liabilities: $65,349,104
Net Worth: $32,994,674
Earnings: $2,991,488
Emp.: 900
Fiscal Year-end: 12/31/23
Business Consulting Services
N.A.I.C.S.: 541611
Stefan Mailaender (Deputy Chm-Mgmt Bd & CFO)

Subsidiaries:

BLUE STEC GmbH (1)
Bleckeder Landstr 37, 21337, Luneburg, Germany
Tel.: (49) 4131287570
Web Site: https://www.bluestec.de
Information Technology Consulting Services
N.A.I.C.S.: 541512

Contrimo GmbH (1)
Konrad-Zuse-Ring 23, 68163, Mannheim, Germany
Tel.: (49) 6214518010
Web Site: https://www.contrimo.com
Information Technology Services
N.A.I.C.S.: 541512

Data One GmbH (1)
Europaallee 5, 66113, Saarbrucken, Germany
Tel.: (49) 68198915100
Web Site: https://www.dataone.de
Information Technology Services
N.A.I.C.S.: 513210
Anke Schwarz (Mgr-HR)

Dialog GmbH (1)
Herforder Strasse 69, 33602, Bielefeld, Germany
Tel.: (49) 5219276262
Web Site: https://www.dialog-projekte.de
Management Consulting Services
N.A.I.C.S.: 541618
Frank Strussmann (Co-Founder)

Ondemand4U GmbH (1)
Heinrich-Barth-Str 23, 66115, Saarbrucken, Germany
Tel.: (49) 6818449760
Web Site: http://www.ondemand4u.com
Software Development Services
N.A.I.C.S.: 541511

Orbis America Inc. (1)
8605 Westwood Center Dr Ste 309, Vienna, VA 22182
Tel.: (703) 734-6494
Web Site: https://www.orbisusa.com
Software Development Services
N.A.I.C.S.: 541511
Claus Altmaier (Sr Mgr-SAP)

Orbis Austria GmbH (1)
Ungargasse 66/4/203, 1030, Vienna, Austria
Tel.: (43) 66488866301
Management Consulting Services
N.A.I.C.S.: 541611
Daniel Scherling (Mng Dir)

Orbis Consulting Shanghai Co., Ltd. (1)
Zao Fong Universe Building Office 3F1 No 1800 Zhongshan Xilu Yishan Lu, Shanghai, 200235, China
Tel.: (86) 2164001276
Web Site: https://www.orbis-china.com.cn
Information Technology Services

N.A.I.C.S.: 513210
Ruiyang Shen (VP)

Orbis France SA (1)
Espace Europeen de l Entreprise 7 Rue de Dublin, Schiltigheim, 67300, Strasbourg, France
Tel.: (33) 388333370
Web Site: http://www.orbis.fr
Software Development Services
N.A.I.C.S.: 541511
Florent Buiron (Mng Dir)

Orbis Schweiz AG (1)
Jochlerweg 4, 6340, Baar, Switzerland
Tel.: (41) 448308030
Information Technology Services
N.A.I.C.S.: 513210

Osco GmbH (1)
Mallaustrasse 74, 68219, Mannheim, Germany
Tel.: (49) 621156200
Web Site: http://www.osco.de
Software Development Services
N.A.I.C.S.: 541511

Quinso B.V. (1)
Amerikastraat 3, 5232 BE, 's-Hertogenbosch, Netherlands
Tel.: (31) 732062200
Web Site: http://www.quinso.com
Information Technology Services
N.A.I.C.S.: 513210
Jan Tielemans (Mng Dir)

ORBIS SYSTEMS OY
Konekuja 2, 90620, Oulu, Finland
Tel.: (358) 290 040 800
Web Site: http://www.orbissystems.eu
Year Founded: 2012
Testing Equipment Mfr
N.A.I.C.S.: 334515
Eero Rossi (CEO)

Subsidiaries:

Beijing Orbis Electronics Co., Ltd. (1)
Unit 8603 6th floor Block 3 Yongchang Industrial park, No 3 Yongchang North Road BDA, 100176, Beijing, China
Tel.: (86) 1067870880
Electronic Printed Circuit Assembly Mfr
N.A.I.C.S.: 334418

Orbis (India) Pvt. Ltd. (1)
No 20 North Phase Developed Plots Guindy Industrial Estate, Ekkaduthangal, Chennai, 600032, India
Tel.: (91) 4422253806
Electronic Printed Circuit Assembly Mfr
N.A.I.C.S.: 334418
Kumaraguru G (Acct Mgr)

Orbis International Technologies, Inc. (1)
8334 Sterling St, Irving, TX 75063
Tel.: (972) 929-5705
Sales Range: $25-49.9 Million
Emp.: 20
Testing Equipment Mfr
N.A.I.C.S.: 334515

ORBIT CORPORATION LTD
The View 165 Dr Annie Besant Road Worli, Mumbai, 400 018, India
Tel.: (91) 2230446910
Year Founded: 2000
Steel Mfrs
N.A.I.C.S.: 331110
Ravi Kiran Aggarwal (Chm)

ORBIT EXPORTS LTD.
122 2nd Floor Mistry Bhavan Dinshaw Wachcha Road, Churchgate, Mumbai, 400020, Maharashtra, India
Tel.: (91) 2266256262
Web Site: https://www.orbitexports.com
Year Founded: 1983
512626—(BOM)
Rev.: $9,974,232
Assets: $30,870,185

Liabilities: $6,728,426
Net Worth: $24,141,759
Earnings: $325,512
Emp.: 344
Fiscal Year-end: 03/31/21
Apparels Mfr
N.A.I.C.S.: 315250
Pankaj S. Seth (Chm, CEO & Mng Dir)

ORBIT GARANT DRILLING INC.
3200 Jean-Jacques Cossette Blvd, Val d'Or, J9P 6Y6, QC, Canada
Tel.: (819) 824-2707
Web Site: https://orbitgarant.com
OGD—(OTCIQ)
Rev.: $107,806,007
Assets: $101,569,671
Liabilities: $48,370,719
Net Worth: $53,198,951
Earnings: ($5,755,234)
Emp.: 1,100
Fiscal Year-end: 06/30/20
Diamond Drilling Services
N.A.I.C.S.: 212311
Pierre Alexandre (Co-Founder, Vice Chm & VP-Corp Dev)

Subsidiaries:

Drift Exploration Drilling Inc. (1)
803 9 Ave SE, High River, T1V 1K5, AB, Canada
Tel.: (403) 601-4374
Web Site: http://www.orbitgarant.com
Drilling & Boring Contractors
N.A.I.C.S.: 238290

Lantech Drilling Services Inc. (1)
398 Dover Road, Dieppe, E1A 7L6, NB, Canada
Tel.: (506) 856-5342
Web Site: http://www.lantechdrilling.com
Sales Range: $1-9.9 Million
Emp.: 30
Drilling Services
N.A.I.C.S.: 213111
Jean LeBlanc (Founder & Pres)

ORBIT HOMES AUSTRALIA PTY. LTD.
286 Mt Alexander Rd, Ascot Vale, Melbourne, 3032, VIC, Australia
Tel.: (61) 393770000
Web Site: http://www.orbithomes.com.au
Year Founded: 1979
Residential Building Construction Services
N.A.I.C.S.: 236116
Chris Troman (Chief Ops Officer)

ORBIT TECHNOLOGIES LTD.
8D Hatzoran St, PO Box 8657, Netanya, 42504, Israel
Tel.: (972) 98922777
Year Founded: 1950
ORBI—(TAE)
Rev.: $63,011,000
Assets: $205,906,000
Liabilities: $125,893,000
Net Worth: $80,013,000
Earnings: $9,904,000
Emp.: 203
Fiscal Year-end: 12/31/23
Radio & Television Broadcasting & Wireless Communications Equipment Manufacturing
N.A.I.C.S.: 334220
Yitzchak Gat (Chm)

Subsidiaries:

Orbit Singapore Pte. Ltd. (1)
67 Ayer Rajah Crescent 03-10/14, Singapore, 139950, Singapore
Tel.: (65) 67770522
Airborne Communication Services
N.A.I.C.S.: 517410

INTERNATIONAL PUBLIC

ORBITAL CORPORATION LIMITED
4 Whipple Street, Balcatta, 6021, WA, Australia
Tel.: (61) 894412311
Web Site: https://www.orbitaluav.com
Year Founded: 1972
OEC—(ASX)
Rev.: $8,456,197
Assets: $14,844,418
Liabilities: $7,612,847
Net Worth: $7,231,570
Earnings: $44,738
Fiscal Year-end: 06/30/24
Combustion Engine Mfr
N.A.I.C.S.: 333618
Geoff Cathcart (Chief Technical Officer)

Subsidiaries:

Orbital Australia Pty Ltd (1)
4 Whipple St, Balcatta, Perth, 6021, WA, Australia
Tel.: (61) 894412311
Web Site: http://www.orbitalcorp.com.au
Sales Range: $25-49.9 Million
Emp.: 60
Engine Design & Mfr
N.A.I.C.S.: 333618
Denise Newcombe (Mgr-HR)

Orbital UAV USA, LLC (1)
210 Wasco Loop, Hood River, OR 97031
Tel.: (541) 716-5930
Engine Development & Testing Services
N.A.I.C.S.: 541380

ORBITECH CO., LTD.
8th FL Gasan-Digital-Empire 1130 Beoman-ro 685 Gasan-dong, Geumcheon-gu, Seoul, Korea (South)
Tel.: (82) 28522223
Web Site: http://www.orbitech.co.kr
Year Founded: 1991
046120—(KRS)
Rev.: $45,421,921
Assets: $90,778,723
Liabilities: $46,839,630
Net Worth: $43,939,093
Earnings: ($10,240,020)
Emp.: 414
Fiscal Year-end: 12/31/22
Non-Destructive Testing Services
N.A.I.C.S.: 541380
Jeong Sung Hyeon (CEO)

Subsidiaries:

KNDT UAE Techno Inspection LLC (1)
M-36 Plot 58 Warehouse 3 Mussafah, Abu Dhabi, United Arab Emirates
Tel.: (971) 2 553 5825
Sales Range: $25-49.9 Million
Emp.: 13
Destructive Testing Services
N.A.I.C.S.: 541380
Joong Kyun Lee (Gen Mgr)

ORBUS PHARMA INC.
1700 800 5th Avenue SW, Calgary, T2P 5A3, AB, Canada
Tel.: (403) 298-5295
Sales Range: Less than $1 Million
Pharmaceuticals Mfr
N.A.I.C.S.: 325412
Chris Eidnes (Dir-Bus Dev)

ORBUSNEICH MEDICAL GROUP HOLDINGS LIMITED
Units 303 & 305 3/F Building 20E Hong Kong Science Park Shatin, N T, Hong Kong, China (Hong Kong)
Tel.: (852) 28022288
Web Site: https://www.orbusneich.com
Year Founded: 2000
6929—(HKG)
Rev.: $136,824,000
Assets: $351,060,000

Liabilities: $28,494,000
Net Worth: $322,566,000
Earnings: $18,491,000
Emp.: 915
Fiscal Year-end: 12/31/22
Holding Company
N.A.I.C.S.: 551112
Chien David *(Chm)*

Subsidiaries:

OrbusNeich Medical KK (1)
3-6-11 Uehara, Shibuya-ku, Tokyo, 151-0064, Japan
Tel.: (81) 357385750
Web Site: https://www.orbusneich.jp
Emp.: 119
Medical Equipment Mfr & Distr
N.A.I.C.S.: 339112

ORCA ENERGY GROUP INC.
Wickhams Cay II Road Town, Tortola, VG1110, Virgin Islands (British)
Tel.: (284) 222138737
Web Site:
 https://orcaenergygroup.com
Year Founded: 2004
ORXGF—(OTCIQ)
Rev.: $110,235,000
Assets: $215,431,000
Liabilities: $126,753,000
Net Worth: $88,678,000
Earnings: $7,014,000
Emp.: 128
Fiscal Year-end: 12/31/23
Oil & Gas Exploration Services
N.A.I.C.S.: 213112
David W. Ross *(Chm)*

Subsidiaries:

PanAfrican Energy Tanzania
Limited (1)
Oyster Plaza Building 5th Floor Haile Selassie Road, PO Box 80139, Dar es Salaam, Tanzania
Tel.: (255) 2229233079
Web Site:
 https://www.panafricanenergy.com
Natural Gas Exploration Service
N.A.I.C.S.: 211130

ORCA GLOBAL DISRUPTION FUND
Level 15 100 Pacific Highway, North Sydney, 2060, NSW, Australia
Tel.: (61) 1300454801
Web Site:
 http://www.globaldisruptionfund.com
EGD—(ASX)
Rev.: $51,539,854
Assets: $196,099,603
Liabilities: $10,407,104
Net Worth: $185,692,499
Earnings: $48,843,414
Fiscal Year-end: 06/30/20
Financial Services
N.A.I.C.S.: 561499
Raymond Tong *(Portfolio Mgr)*

ORCA INVESTMENT PLC
77 Posidonos Avenue, Paphos, Cyprus
Tel.: (357) 26813060
Real Estate Investment Services
N.A.I.C.S.: 531210

ORCA SPECIALTY FOODS LTD.
4 17350 56 Avenue, Surrey, V3S 1C9, BC, Canada
Tel.: (604) 574-6722
Web Site:
 http://www.orcaspecialtyfoods.com
Year Founded: 1995
Rev.: $38,288,800
Emp.: 110
Seafood Products Supplier
N.A.I.C.S.: 424460

David McKinnon *(Pres-Custom Processing & Bus Dev)*

ORCADIAN ENERGY PLC
6th Floor 60 Gracechurch Street, London, EC3V 0HR, United Kingdom
Tel.: (44) 2036031941 UK
Web Site:
 https://www.orcadian.energy
Year Founded: 2014
ORCA—(AIM)
Rev.: $63,115
Assets: $5,090,133
Liabilities: $1,967,897
Net Worth: $3,122,236
Earnings: ($1,495,776)
Emp.: 5
Fiscal Year-end: 06/30/23
Oil & Gas Pipeline & Related Structures Construction
N.A.I.C.S.: 237120

ORCHARD FORD SALES LTD.
911 Stremel Rd, Kelowna, V1X 5E6, BC, Canada
Tel.: (250) 860-1000
Web Site:
 https://www.orchardford.com
Sales Range: $25-49.9 Million
New & Used Cars Dealers
N.A.I.C.S.: 441110
Len Burton *(Sls Mgr-New Vehicle)*

ORCHARD FUNDING GROUP PLC
222 Armstrong Road, Luton, LU2 0FY, United Kingdom
Tel.: (44) 1582346248 UK
Web Site:
 https://www.orchardfunding.com
Year Founded: 2015
ORCH—(AIM)
Rev.: $4,667,841
Assets: $44,044,437
Liabilities: $22,592,461
Net Worth: $21,451,976
Earnings: $1,139,127
Emp.: 20
Fiscal Year-end: 07/31/21
Financial Management Services
N.A.I.C.S.: 541611
Rabinder Singh Takhar *(CEO)*

Subsidiaries:

Bexhill UK Limited (1)
721 Capability Green, Luton, LU1 3LU, Bedfordshire, United Kingdom
Tel.: (44) 1582280140
Web Site: http://www.bexhillukfunding.com
Insurance Services
N.A.I.C.S.: 524210
Ravi Takhar *(Co-Founder & CEO)*

Orchard Funding Limited (1)
721 Capability Green, Luton, LU1 3LU, United Kingdom
Tel.: (44) 158 234 6291
Web Site: https://www.orchardfunding.co.uk
Financial Institution Services
N.A.I.C.S.: 522110

ORCHARD HOMES AND DEVELOPMENTS LIMITED
8a Carlton Crescent, Southampton, SO15 2EZ, United Kingdom
Tel.: (44) 2380233343
Web Site: http://www.orchard-homes.co.uk
Year Founded: 1997
Residential Construction
N.A.I.C.S.: 236220
Andrew Jameson *(Dir-Fin)*

ORCHASP LIMITED
19 20 Moti Valley Trimulgherry, Secunderabad, 500015, Telangana, India
Tel.: (91) 4047766123

Web Site: https://www.orchasp.com
532271—(BOM)
Rev.: $1,272,623
Assets: $17,705,671
Liabilities: $3,974,941
Net Worth: $13,730,729
Earnings: $28,836
Emp.: 40
Fiscal Year-end: 03/31/21
IT Software Products Distr
N.A.I.C.S.: 423430
Pattapurathi Chenchaiah Pantulu *(Chm, CEO & Mng Dir)*

ORCHESTRA HOLDINGS, INC.
5F Yebisu Garden Place Tower 20-3 Ebisu 4-chome, Shibuya-ku, Tokyo, 150-0022, Japan
Tel.: (81) 357943741
Web Site: https://www.orchestra-hd.co.jp
6533—(TKS)
Rev.: $85,852,810
Assets: $90,128,080
Liabilities: $47,332,840
Net Worth: $42,795,240
Earnings: $3,360,660
Emp.: 1,174
Fiscal Year-end: 12/31/23
Digital Marketing Services
N.A.I.C.S.: 541870
Yoshiro Nakamura *(Pres)*

Subsidiaries:

Digital Identity Inc. (1)
1-15-1 A - PLACE Ebisu Minami 5F 1-15-1 A Ebisu Minami, Shibuya-ku, Tokyo, 150-0022, Japan
Tel.: (81) 357943741
Web Site: https://digitalidentity.co.jp
Emp.: 376
Digital Marketing Services
N.A.I.C.S.: 541613
Kenji Suzuki *(Pres)*

Sharing Innovations, Inc. (1)
5F Yebisu Garden Place Tower 20-3 Ebisu 4-chome, Shibuya-Ku, Tokyo, 150-6005, Japan
Tel.: (81) 364562451
Web Site:
 https://www.sharing-innovations.com
Rev.: $35,854,130
Assets: $16,434,620
Liabilities: $6,168,300
Net Worth: $10,266,320
Earnings: $241,060
Emp.: 321
Fiscal Year-end: 12/31/2023
Application Development Services
N.A.I.C.S.: 541511
Keita Yanagi *(Chm)*

ORCHESTRA PREMAMAN SA
200 avenue des Tamaris - ZAC Antoine, Saint-Aunes, Montpellier, 34130, France
Tel.: (33) 499130800
Web Site: http://www.premaman.com
KAZI—(EUR)
Sales Range: $600-649.9 Million
Emp.: 2,380
Children's Clothing Designer, Mfr & Retailer
N.A.I.C.S.: 458110
Pierre Mestre *(Chm)*

ORCHID DEVELOPMENTS GROUP LTD.
16 Ana Feliskova Str, Varna, 9020, Bulgaria
Tel.: (359) 52974071
Web Site: http://www.orchid-dev.com
Year Founded: 1992
Sales Range: $10-24.9 Million
Real Estate Manangement Services
N.A.I.C.S.: 531390
Guy Meyohas *(Co-Founder & Co-CEO)*

Subsidiaries:

Orchid Gardens Varna EOOD (1)
16 Ana Felixova str Building 22, Varna, 9020, Bulgaria
Tel.: (359) 52 65 46 85
Web Site: http://www.orchidgardens-varna.com
Real Estate Development Services
N.A.I.C.S.: 531390

Orchid Logistic Centers EOOD (1)
102 Bulgaria Blvd Belissimo, Sofia, 1000, Bulgaria
Tel.: (359) 29819955
Web Site: http://www.orchid-dev.com
Logistics Consulting Servies
N.A.I.C.S.: 541614

ORCHID PHARMA LIMITED
Orchid Towers 313 Valluvar Kottam High Road, Nungambakkam, Chennai, 600 034, Tamil Nadu, India
Tel.: (91) 4428211000 In
Web Site:
 https://www.orchidpharma.com
Year Founded: 1992
ORCHIDPHAR—(NSE)
Rev.: $6,240,373,230
Assets: $16,713,996,390
Liabilities: $7,413,749,070
Net Worth: $9,300,247,320
Earnings: ($1,599,142,545)
Emp.: 1,136
Fiscal Year-end: 03/31/21
Pharmaceuticals Product Mfr
N.A.I.C.S.: 325412
R J Sarangdhar *(Head-API & FDF)*

ORCODA LIMITED
Tel.: (61) 300672632 AU
Web Site: https://www.orcoda.com
Year Founded: 1986
ODA—(ASX)
Rev.: $6,763,087
Assets: $13,467,030
Liabilities: $3,625,387
Net Worth: $9,841,643
Earnings: $337,131
Fiscal Year-end: 06/30/21
Software, Management Expertise & Contracting Services
N.A.I.C.S.: 513210
Brendan Mason *(Mng Dir & Exec Dir)*

ORD MINNETT LIMITED
Level 8 NAB House, 255 George Street, Sydney, 3000, NSW, Australia
Tel.: (61) 282166300
Web Site: http://www.ords.com.au
Wealth Management Services; Owned 70% by Australian Wealth Management & 30% by JPMorgan
N.A.I.C.S.: 523150
Karl Morris *(Chm)*

ORD MOUNTAIN RESOURCES CORP.
758 Riverside Drive Unit 46, Port Coquitlam, V3B 7V8, BC, Canada
Tel.: (604) 760-8755 BC
Year Founded: 2009
OMR.H—(TSXV)
Assets: $11,597
Liabilities: $229,955
Net Worth: ($218,358)
Earnings: ($42,910)
Fiscal Year-end: 02/28/23
Investment Services
N.A.I.C.S.: 523999
David Yoo *(CFO)*

ORDABASY CORPORATION JSC
63 Tole Bi Street, 050000, Almaty, Kazakhstan
Tel.: (7) 7272722164
Web Site: http://www.ordabasy.kz

Ordabasy Corporation JSC—(Continued)
Sales Range: $50-74.9 Million
Emp.: 87
Holding Company; Lubricant Oil, Industrial, Agricultural & Food Products Distr
N.A.I.C.S.: 551112
Almas Siranov (Deputy Chm-Exec Bd & Head-Bus Dev)

ORDISSIMO SA
33 Avenue Leon Gambetta, 92120, Montrouge, France
Tel.: (33) 2034455710
Web Site: https://www.ordissimo.fr
ALORD—(EUR)
Sales Range: Less than $1 Million
Electronic Products Mfr
N.A.I.C.S.: 334111
Alexandre Cetin (Founder, Chm & CEO)

ORDNANCE SURVEY
Adanac Drive, Southampton, SO16 0AS, United Kingdom
Tel.: (44) 2380055565
Web Site: http://www.ordnance.co.uk
Year Founded: 1791
Rev.: $165,600,000
Emp.: 1,609
Mapping Services
N.A.I.C.S.: 541360
Neil Ackroyd (Dir-Data Collection & Mgmt)

Subsidiaries:

Ordnance Survey Partners Ltd (1)
Explorer House Adanac Drive, Southampton, SO16 0AS, Hampshire, United Kingdom
Tel.: (44) 2380734464
Surveying Services
N.A.I.C.S.: 541360

ORDU YARDIMLASMA KURUMU GENEL MUDURLUGU
Ziya Gokalp cad No 64, Kurtulus, 06600, Ankara, Turkiye
Tel.: (90) 312 415 60 00
Web Site: http://www.oyak.com.tr
Holding Company
N.A.I.C.S.: 551112
Mehmet Tas (Chm)

Subsidiaries:

Almatis GmbH (1)
Lyoner Str 9, 60528, Frankfurt, Germany
Tel.: (49) 699573410
Web Site: http://www.almatis.com
Alumina-Based Material Mfr
N.A.I.C.S.: 331313
Stefan Rieder (Chief Comml Officer)

Subsidiary (Non-US):

Almatis B.V. (2)
Theemsweg 30, Rotterdam, 3197KM, Netherlands
Tel.: (31) 181270100
Web Site: http://www.almatis.com
Tabular Alumina & Alumina Chemicals Mfr
N.A.I.C.S.: 331313
Frank Kraayenbos (Ops Mgr)

Subsidiary (US):

Almatis Inc. (2)
501 W Park Rd, Leetsdale, PA 15056
Tel.: (412) 630-2800
Web Site: http://www.almatis.com
Alumina Base Chemicals Mfr & Distr
N.A.I.C.S.: 331313

Joint Venture (Non-US):

Almatis Limited (2)
1815 2 Nagano, Iwanuki, Iwakuni, 740 0045, Yamaguchi, Japan
Tel.: (81) 827381271
Web Site: http://www.almatis.com
Alumina Based Chemical Mfr & Distr
N.A.I.C.S.: 331313

Subsidiary (Non-US):

Qingdao Almatis Co. Ltd. (2)
Songhuajiang Road Qingdao Economic & Technology Development Zone, Qingdao, 266555, China
Tel.: (86) 53285728035
Web Site: http://www.almatis.com
Alumina Based Products Mfr
N.A.I.C.S.: 331313

OREA MINING CORP.
1090 Hamilton Street, Vancouver, V6B 2R9, BC, Canada
Tel.: (604) 634-0970 BC
Web Site: https://oreamining.com
Year Founded: 2003
OREAF—(OTCIQ)
Rev.: $10
Assets: $31,335
Liabilities: $379
Net Worth: $30,956
Earnings: ($2,434)
Emp.: 7
Fiscal Year-end: 09/30/21
Gold Mining Services
N.A.I.C.S.: 212220
Robert F. Giustra (Chm)

Subsidiaries:

Columbus Gold (U.S.) Corporation (1)
573 E 2nd St, Reno, NV 89502
Tel.: (775) 324-1226
Web Site: https://allegiantgold.com
Gold Mining Services
N.A.I.C.S.: 212220
Andy Wallace (Gen Mgr)

ORECORP LIMITED
Suite 22 Level 1 513 Hay Street, Subiaco, 6008, WA, Australia
Tel.: (61) 8 9381 9997
Web Site: http://www.orecorp.com.au
ORR—(ASX)
Rev.: $200,673
Assets: $66,511,202
Liabilities: $9,774,552
Net Worth: $56,736,650
Earnings: ($7,076,001)
Emp.: 15
Fiscal Year-end: 06/30/21
Metal Mining
N.A.I.C.S.: 212290
Matthew Yates (CEO & Mng Dir)

OREFINDERS RESOURCES INC.
2500 - 120 Adelaide St W, Toronto, M5H 1T1, ON, Canada
Tel.: (416) 644-1567 BC
Web Site: http://www.orefinders.ca
Year Founded: 2011
OCI—(TSXV)
Assets: $4,483,329
Liabilities: $2,661,232
Net Worth: $1,822,097
Earnings: ($5,752,032)
Fiscal Year-end: 10/31/23
Metal Ore Mining
N.A.I.C.S.: 212290
Alexander Stewart (Chm)

ORELL FUSSLI HOLDING AG
Dietzingerstrasse 3, 8036, Zurich, Switzerland
Tel.: (41) 444667711 CH
Web Site: http://www.ofh.ch
OFN—(SWX)
Rev.: $240,883,592
Assets: $198,862,528
Liabilities: $50,631,929
Net Worth: $148,230,599
Earnings: $9,412,417
Emp.: 560
Fiscal Year-end: 12/31/22

Holding Company; Security Printing & Industrial Systems; Book Retailing & Publishing
N.A.I.C.S.: 551112
Beat Muller (CFO)

Subsidiaries:

Orell Fussli Buchhandlungs AG (1)
Dietzingerstrasse 3, Zurich, 8003, Switzerland
Tel.: (41) 848849848
Web Site: http://www.books.ch
Book Stores
N.A.I.C.S.: 459210

Joint Venture (Domestic):

Orell Fussli Thalia AG (2)
Dietzingerstrasse 3, 8036, Zurich, Switzerland
Tel.: (41) 848 849848
Web Site: http://www.orellfuessli.ch
Books Retailing
N.A.I.C.S.: 459210
Pascal Schneebeli (CEO)

Unit (Domestic):

buch.ch (3)
Industriestrasse 26, 8404, Winterthur, Switzerland
Tel.: (41) 8 48 28 24 24
Online Retailer of Books, CDs, DVDs, Software & Games
N.A.I.C.S.: 459210

Orell Fussli Security Printing Ltd. (1)
Dietzingerstrasse 3, 8036, Zurich, Switzerland
Tel.: (41) 444667711
Web Site: http://www.ofs.ch
Sales Range: $50-74.9 Million
Emp.: 200
Banknotes & Document Printing Services
N.A.I.C.S.: 323111

Orell Fussli Sicherheitsdruck AG (1)
Dietzingerstrasse 3, Zurich, 8036, Switzerland
Tel.: (41) 444667711
Web Site: http://www.orellsfuessli.com
Sales Range: $450-499.9 Million
Commercial Printing
N.A.I.C.S.: 323111
Michel Kuncz (Mng Dir)

Orell Fussli Verlag AG (1)
Dietzingerstrasse 3, 8036, Zurich, Switzerland
Tel.: (41) 444667711
Web Site: http://www.ofh.ch
Sales Range: $75-99.9 Million
Emp.: 250
Book Distr
N.A.I.C.S.: 424920

Rosslitor Bucher Ltd. (1)
Multergasse 1-3, 9001, Saint Gallen, Switzerland
Tel.: (41) 712274747
Web Site: http://www.books.ch
Sales Range: $25-49.9 Million
Emp.: 40
Printing & Publishing Services
N.A.I.C.S.: 513130
Fabio Amato (CEO)

Zeiser Inc. (1)
6 Kingsbridge Rd Unit Ste 8, Fairfield, NJ 07004
Tel.: (973) 228-6565
Numbering & Printing Equipment Mfr
N.A.I.C.S.: 333248

ORELL FUSSLI KARTOGRAPHIE AG
Dietzingerstrasse 3, Postfach, CH-8036, Zurich, Switzerland
Tel.: (41) 444542222
Web Site: http://www.orellkarto.ch
Year Founded: 1519
Cartography Services
N.A.I.C.S.: 541370
Giuliano Beccarelli (CEO)

OREOVICA A.D.
Oreovica bb, 12370, Oreovica, Serbia

Tel.: (381) 12 258 070
Year Founded: 1998
Sales Range: $1-9.9 Million
Emp.: 30
Meat Preserving Services
N.A.I.C.S.: 311612

ORESA VENTURES ROMANIA SRL
Bucuresti-Ploiesti 42-44 Building A 4th Floor, 013696, Bucharest, Romania
Tel.: (40) 21 361 0562 RO
Web Site: http://www.oresa.com
Equity Investment Firm
N.A.I.C.S.: 523999
Cornel Marian (Partner)

ORESTONE MINING CORP.
407 - 325 Howe St, Vancouver, V6C 1Z7, BC, Canada
Tel.: (604) 629-1929 BC
Web Site: https://www.orestone.ca
Year Founded: 2007
O2R2—(DEU)
Rev.: $3
Assets: $2,420,854
Liabilities: $124,433
Net Worth: $2,296,420
Earnings: ($167,031)
Fiscal Year-end: 01/31/24
Precious & Base Metals Mining & Exploration Services
N.A.I.C.S.: 212220
David Hottman (Chm & CEO)

ORESUNDSVARVET AB
Dockgatan 61, PO Box 701, Landskrona, 26127, Sweden
Tel.: (46) 41856580
Web Site: http://www.oddab.eu
Sales Range: $10-24.9 Million
Emp.: 80
Ship Building & Repair Services
N.A.I.C.S.: 336611
Jonas Hansson (Mng Dir)

OREX MINERALS INC.
Suite 300 - 1055 W Hastings Street, Vancouver, V6E 2E9, BC, Canada
Tel.: (604) 687-8566 BC
Web Site: https://www.orexminerals.com
Year Founded: 1996
REX—(OTCIQ)
Rev.: $10,846
Assets: $5,166,528
Liabilities: $56,612
Net Worth: $5,109,916
Earnings: ($1,818,554)
Fiscal Year-end: 04/30/22
Mineral Exploration Services
N.A.I.C.S.: 213114
Ross Wilmot (CFO)

Subsidiaries:

Gunnarn Mining AB (1)
Strandgrand, 923 31, Storuman, Vasterbotten, Sweden
Tel.: (46) 951 26218
Metal Exploration Services
N.A.I.C.S.: 213114

OREXO AB
PO Box 303, 751 05, Uppsala, Sweden
Tel.: (46) 187808800
Web Site: https://www.orexo.com
Year Founded: 1995
ORXOF—(OTCQX)
Rev.: $58,473,124
Assets: $103,871,046
Liabilities: $85,710,004
Net Worth: $18,161,042
Earnings: ($16,634,353)
Emp.: 127
Fiscal Year-end: 12/31/22

AND PRIVATE COMPANIES

Pharmaceutical Manufacturing, Research & Development Services
N.A.I.C.S.: 325412
Nikolaj Sorensen *(Pres & CEO)*

Subsidiaries:

Kibion AB (1)
Rapfkjatan 7, PO Box 303, 75105, Uppsala, Sweden
Tel.: (46) 187808800
Web Site: http://www.kibion.com
Emp.: 10
Medicinal & Diagnostic Products Marketing Services
N.A.I.C.S.: 424210

OREXPLORE TECHNOLOGIES LIMITED

75 McDonald Cresent, Bassendean, 6054, WA, Australia
Tel.: (61) 894692900   AU
Web Site: https://www.orexplore.com
Year Founded: 2009
OXT—(ASX)
Rev.: $2,155,571
Assets: $6,594,510
Liabilities: $1,356,197
Net Worth: $5,238,313
Earnings: ($5,340,027)
Emp.: 31
Fiscal Year-end: 12/31/23
Metal Mining Services
N.A.I.C.S.: 213114
Brett Giroud *(Mng Dir)*

OREZONE GOLD CORPORATION

450-505 Burrard Street, Vancouver, V7X 1M3, BC, Canada
Tel.: (778) 945-8977
Web Site: https://www.orezone.com
Year Founded: 2009
OEX—(DEU)
Rev.: $271,491,000
Assets: $320,079,000
Liabilities: $173,717,000
Net Worth: $146,362,000
Earnings: $49,623,000
Emp.: 18
Fiscal Year-end: 12/31/23
Gold Exploration & Mining Services
N.A.I.C.S.: 212220
Pascal Marquis *(Sr VP-Exploration)*

Subsidiaries:

Orezone Inc. (1)
Porte 1582 rue du Fleuve Niger PL-40, PO Box 12908, Niamey Plateau, 12906, Niamey, Niger
Tel.: (227) 20723188
Web Site: http://www.orezone.com
Sales Range: $50-74.9 Million
Emp.: 70
Gold Exploration Services
N.A.I.C.S.: 212220

ORFIN FINANSMAN AS

Fatih Sultan Mehmet Mah Balkan Cad NO 47, Umraniye, 34771, Istanbul, Turkiye
Tel.: (90) 2166455900
Web Site: http://www.orfin.com.tr
ORFIN—(IST)
Sales Range: Less than $1 Million
Financial Consulting Services
N.A.I.C.S.: 541611
Celalettin Caglar *(Chm)*

ORFORD MINING CORPORATION

141 Adelaide Street West Suite 1608, Toronto, M5H 3L5, ON, Canada
Tel.: (416) 309-0609   ON
Web Site: http://www.orfordmining.com
Year Founded: 2010
ORM—(TSXV)
Rev.: $435,839

Assets: $10,485,280
Liabilities: $3,200,243
Net Worth: $7,285,036
Earnings: ($1,069,313)
Fiscal Year-end: 12/31/20
Investment Services
N.A.I.C.S.: 523999
David Christie *(Pres & CEO)*

ORG TECHNOLOGY CO., LTD.

1515 Huabin International Building No 8 Yonganli Jianguomen Outer, Chaoyang District, Beijing, China
Tel.: (86) 1085211888
Web Site: http://www.orgtech.cn
002701—(SSE)
Rev.: $1,975,016,628
Assets: $2,391,848,784
Liabilities: $1,207,089,000
Net Worth: $1,184,759,784
Earnings: $79,348,464
Emp.: 500
Fiscal Year-end: 12/31/22
Metal Tank Mfr
N.A.I.C.S.: 332431
Dong Wang *(CFO & Deputy Gen Mgr)*

Subsidiaries:

Beijing ORG Technology Co., Ltd. (1)
No.7, South Nanyi Street Yanqi Economic Development Zone, Huairou, Beijing, 101407, China
Tel.: (86) 1061663300
Web Site: http://www.orgtech.cn
Metal Tank Mfr
N.A.I.C.S.: 332439

Chengdu O.R.G Technology Co., Ltd. (1)
No 180 Baiyun Road, Industrial East District Xindu Satellite City, Chengdu, China
Tel.: (86) 2883958394
Metal Tank Mfr
N.A.I.C.S.: 332431

Foshan Branch of O.R.G Technology Co., Ltd. (1)
4th Land No 81 Hongniu Road Southwest Street, Sanshui District, Foshan, China
Tel.: (86) 75788526888
Metal Tank Mfr
N.A.I.C.S.: 332431

Hainan ORG Packaging Industry Co., Ltd. (1)
No 1-26 Qibu Industrial Zone Qinglan Economic Development Zone, Wenchang, 571339, Hainan, China
Tel.: (86) 89863330080
Web Site: http://www.orgcanmaking.com
Metal Tank Mfr
N.A.I.C.S.: 332431

Hainan Yuanyang Food Co., Ltd. (1)
No 1-26 Qibu Industrial Zone, Qinglan Economic Development Zone, Wenchang, China
Tel.: (86) 89863331016
Beverage Filling Mfr
N.A.I.C.S.: 333993

Hebei O.R.G Packaging Co., Ltd. (1)
Hebei Boyi Factory, Beiguye Village Yinye Town Luquan District, Shijiazhuang, Hebei, China
Tel.: (86) 31181552433
Metal Tank Mfr
N.A.I.C.S.: 332431

Hubei O.R.G Beverage Industry Co., Ltd. (1)
No 69 Guishan Road, High-tech Industrial Park, Xianning, China
Tel.: (86) 7158231399
Beverage Filling Mfr
N.A.I.C.S.: 333993

Hubei O.R.G Packaging Co., Ltd. (1)
No 69 Guishan Road, Changjiang Industrial Park Xianan District, Xianning, Hubei, China
Tel.: (86) 7158102666

Metal Can Mfr & Distr
N.A.I.C.S.: 332431

Hubei O.R.G Technology Co., Ltd. (1)
No 88 Hesheng Road, Xianning, Hubei, China
Tel.: (86) 7158123515
Metal Tank Mfr
N.A.I.C.S.: 332431

Hubei ORG Can Making Co., Ltd. (1)
88 Hesheng Rd, Xianning, 437100, Hubei, China
Tel.: (86) 715 8123526
Metal Can Mfr & Distr
N.A.I.C.S.: 332431

Jiangsu Aobao Printing Technology Co., Ltd. (1)
No 88 Yongsheng Road, Yixing Economic and Technological Development Zone, Jiangsu, China
Tel.: (86) 51081772777
Metal Tank Mfr
N.A.I.C.S.: 332431

Jiangsu O.R.G Packing Co., Ltd. (1)
No 88 Yongsheng Road, Yixing Economic and Technological Development Zone, Jiangsu, China
Tel.: (86) 51081772710
Metal Tank Mfr
N.A.I.C.S.: 332431

Kunming Jingrun Food Co., Ltd. (1)
No 489 Caiyun Road, Chongming County, Kunming, Yunnan, China
Tel.: (86) 87167915000
Beverage Filling Mfr
N.A.I.C.S.: 333993

Liaoning Yuanyang Food Co., Ltd. (1)
No 123 Chengnan Middle Road, Kaiyuan Economic Development Zone Kaiyuan, Tieling, Liaoning, China
Tel.: (86) 2473724315
Beverage Filling Mfr
N.A.I.C.S.: 333993

Linyi O.R.G Printing Iron Can Co., Ltd. (1)
No 261 Shuangyueyuan Road, Luozhuang District, Linyi, China
Tel.: (86) 5395635988
Metal Tank Mfr
N.A.I.C.S.: 332431

Longkou O.R.G Packing Co., Ltd. (1)
Donghai Industrial Park, Longkou, China
Tel.: (86) 5353456688
Metal Tank Mfr
N.A.I.C.S.: 332431

Shaanxi O.R.G. Packaging Co., Ltd. (1)
East Section of Science and Technology West Road, Science and Technology Industrial Park Chencang District, Baoji, Shanxi, China
Tel.: (86) 9173060615
Emp.: 105
Metal Tank Mfr
N.A.I.C.S.: 332431

Shandong O.R.G Packaging Co., Ltd. (1)
No 97 Changjiang Road, Pingdu Economic Development Zone, Qingdao, Shandong, China
Tel.: (86) 53286635017
Metal Tank Mfr
N.A.I.C.S.: 332431

Shangyu Branch of O.R.G Technology Co., Ltd. (1)
Chaoyang 3rd Road, Shangyu Industrial Park Hangzhou Bay, Shangyu, Zhejiang, China
Tel.: (86) 57582722860
Coated Iron Mfr
N.A.I.C.S.: 332812

Shaoxing O.R.G Packaging Industry Co., Ltd. (1)
Intersection of Sanjiang Road and Yuewang Road, Paojiang Industrial Zone, Shaoxing, Zhejiang, China
Tel.: (86) 57588156585
Metal Tank Mfr
N.A.I.C.S.: 332431

Sinkiang O.R.G Packaging Container Co., Ltd. (1)
No 51-8 C East 8th Road, Shihezi Development Zone, Xinjiang, Sinkiang, China
Tel.: (86) 9936601555
Beverage Filling Mfr
N.A.I.C.S.: 333993

Tianjin O.R.G Packaging Co., Ltd. (1)
No 98 Airport Bonded Road, Tianjin Port Free Trade Zone, Tianjin, China
Tel.: (86) 2259002159
Metal Tank Mfr
N.A.I.C.S.: 332431

Zhangzhou O.R.G Packaging Co., Ltd. (1)
Jinle Road, Jinfeng Economic Development Zone Xiangcheng District, Zhangzhou, Fujian, China
Tel.: (86) 5966098855
Metal Tank Mfr
N.A.I.C.S.: 332431

Zhejiang O.R.G Packaging Co., Ltd. (1)
No 17 Chaoyang 3rd Road, Hangzhou Bay Economic Technological Development Zone Shangyu District, Shaoxing, Zhejiang, China
Tel.: (86) 57582721888
Metal Tank Mfr
N.A.I.C.S.: 332431

ORGABIO HOLDINGS BERHAD

Lot 83 Jalan Kesuma 2/3 Phase 5D Bandar Tasik Kesuma Techno Park, 43700, Beranang, Selangor, Malaysia
Tel.: (60) 387231439
Web Site: https://www.orgabio.com
Year Founded: 2002
ORGABIO—(KLS)
Rev.: $12,778,966
Assets: $15,015,903
Liabilities: $3,791,183
Net Worth: $11,224,721
Earnings: ($191,634)
Emp.: 146
Fiscal Year-end: 06/30/23
Holding Company
N.A.I.C.S.: 551112
Hien Voon Ean Yong *(CEO)*

ORGACHIM JSC

21 Treti Mart Blvd, 7000, Ruse, Bulgaria
Tel.: (359) 82 886222   BG
Web Site: http://www.orgachim.bg
Sales Range: $50-74.9 Million
Emp.: 491
Paint Mfr & Distr
N.A.I.C.S.: 325510
Marius Vacaroiu *(Exec Dir)*

ORGANE DE ASAMBLARE S.A.

113 Zizinului Street, 500407, Brasov, Romania
Tel.: (40) 268330648
Web Site: https://www.oasa.ro
Year Founded: 1920
ORAS—(BUC)
Rev.: $1,998,161
Assets: $134,666
Liabilities: $388,151
Net Worth: ($253,485)
Earnings: $583,372
Emp.: 9
Fiscal Year-end: 12/31/23
Fastener Mfr.
N.A.I.C.S.: 332722

ORGANIC AGRICULTURAL COMPANY LIMITED

Organic Agricultural Company Limited—(Continued)

Room G504 G506 G509 G510 Building No 3, Kejichuangxincheng Chuangxinchuangye Pla, Harbin, 150090, Heilongjiang, China
Tel.: (86) 45151527001 NV
Web Site: http://www.oacl.top
Year Founded: 2018
OGAA—(OTCEM)
Rev.: $223,037
Assets: $237,589
Liabilities: $214,363
Net Worth: $23,226
Earnings: ($559,126)
Emp.: 15
Fiscal Year-end: 03/31/23
Rice Cultivation & Distr
N.A.I.C.S.: 115112
Zhiwei Wu (Pres & CEO)

ORGANIC COATINGS LIMITED

Unit No 405 Atlanta Estate Near Virwani Indl Estate, Goregaon East, Mumbai, 400 063, India
Tel.: (91) 2229276921
Web Site: https://organiccoatingsltd.com
Year Founded: 1965
531157—(BOM)
Rev.: $2,765,038
Assets: $2,364,762
Liabilities: $2,162,784
Net Worth: $201,978
Earnings: ($113,950)
Emp.: 50
Fiscal Year-end: 03/31/23
Printing Ink Mfr
N.A.I.C.S.: 325910
Sudhir A. Sathe (Chm)

ORGANIC FLOWER INVESTMENTS GROUP INC.

19 Par-la-Ville Road, Hamilton, HM 11, Bermuda
Tel.: (441) 2981217 BM
Web Site: http://www.qinvestmentsltd.com
Year Founded: 1980
MOTNF—(OTCEM)
Assets: $297,802
Liabilities: $1,938,728
Net Worth: ($1,640,925)
Earnings: ($15,674,763)
Fiscal Year-end: 06/30/23
Investment Services
N.A.I.C.S.: 523999
John Martin (Pres & CEO)

ORGANIC POTASH CORPORATION

10 Wilkinson Rd Suite 22, Brampton, L6T 5B1, ON, Canada
Tel.: (905) 452-8060 ON
Web Site: https://www.organicpotash.com
Year Founded: 2011
OPC—(CNSX)
Assets: $23,456
Liabilities: $590,829
Net Worth: ($567,373)
Earnings: ($46,111)
Fiscal Year-end: 06/30/23
Potash Mining
N.A.I.C.S.: 212390
Heather Welner (Pres & CEO)

ORGANIC TEA COSMETICS HOLDINGS CO LTD

Unit 1 9 F Wo Hing Commercial Building 11 Wing Wo Street, Central, China (Hong Kong)
Tel.: (852) 5998508611
Web Site: http://www.organicteacosmetics.com

900300—(KRS)
Rev.: $150,084,555
Assets: $298,434,678
Liabilities: $46,965,704
Net Worth: $251,468,974
Earnings: ($63,152,258)
Emp.: 162
Fiscal Year-end: 12/31/22
Cosmetic Mfr & Distr
N.A.I.C.S.: 325620

ORGANIGRAM HOLDINGS INC.

1400-145 King Street West, Toronto, M5H 1J8, ON, Canada BC
Web Site: https://www.organigram.ca
Year Founded: 2010
OGI—(NASDAQ)
Rev.: $182,742,900
Assets: $301,539,055
Liabilities: $75,315,268
Net Worth: $226,223,787
Earnings: ($33,594,701)
Emp.: 971
Fiscal Year-end: 09/30/24
Medical Marijuana Producer
N.A.I.C.S.: 325411
Peter Amirault (Chm)

ORGANIZACION CORONA SA

Calle 100 No. 8A-55, Torre C piso 9 Santa Fe, Bogota, Colombia
Tel.: (57) 1 644 6500
Web Site: http://www.corona.co
Construction & Remodeling Services
N.A.I.C.S.: 423390
Jaime Alberto Angel (CEO)

Subsidiaries:

Blackwood Industries, Inc. (1)
1101 N Lake Destiny Rd Ste 120, Maitland, FL 32751
Tel.: (407) 409-7049
Web Site: http://www.blackwoodindustriesinc.com
Meat Processed from Carcasses
N.A.I.C.S.: 311612
Beth Peterson (Acct Mgr)

Industria Ceramica Costarricense, S.A. (1)
Autopista General Canas, San Jose, Costa Rica
Tel.: (506) 25195400
Web Site: http://www.americanstandardca.com
Sales Range: $450-499.9 Million
Emp.: 1,600
Plumbing Supplies Mfr
N.A.I.C.S.: 327110

Subsidiary (Non-US):

Industria Centroamericana de Sanitarios S.A. (2)
6a Avda 16075 Zona 10, Guatemala, Guatemala
Tel.: (502) 6314001
Kitchen & Bathroom Accessories Mfr
N.A.I.C.S.: 327110

Industria Ceramica Centroamericana S.A. (2)
Carretera Norte Km 5 1 2, Managua, 505, Nicaragua
Tel.: (505) 2495508
Web Site: http://www.americanstandardca.com
Sales Range: $25-49.9 Million
Emp.: 50
Kitchen & Bathroom Accessories
N.A.I.C.S.: 327110

Sanitarios Lamosa, S.A. de C.V. (1)
Ave Felix U Gomez No 4047 Nte Fracc Coyoacan, Monterrey, 64510, Mexico
Tel.: (52) 8181252000
Web Site: http://www.sanitarioslamosa.com
Emp.: 1,000
Bathroom Furniture Designer & Mfr
N.A.I.C.S.: 337122
Alejandro Nosti (Pres)

ORGANIZACION CULTIBA, S.A.B. DE C.V.

Monte Caucaso 915 Interior 307 Lomas De Chapultepec, Miguel Hidalgo, 11000, Mexico, Mexico
Tel.: (52) 5552011900
Web Site: http://www.cultiba.mx
CULTIBA—(MEX)
Rev.: $12,840,032
Assets: $850,874,512
Liabilities: $3,071,058
Net Worth: $847,803,453
Earnings: $63,462,119
Emp.: 43,660
Fiscal Year-end: 12/31/23
Carbonated Beverages & Water Producer & Sales
N.A.I.C.S.: 312111
Juan Gallardo (Chm)

Subsidiaries:

Incauca S.A. (1)
Carrera 9 No 28 -103, Cali, Valle del Cauca, Colombia
Tel.: (57) 2 418 3000
Web Site: https://www.incauca.com
Sugar Cane Product Mfr
N.A.I.C.S.: 311314

Inmobiliaria Geu-Gamsa, S.A. de C.V. (1)
Severo Diaz No 17 PH 1, Col Ladron de Guevara, Guadalajara, 44600, Jalisco, Mexico
Tel.: (52) 3336302015
N.A.I.C.S.: 333993

Inmobiliaria Geusa, S.A. de C.V. (1)
555 Calle de Esther Tapia de Castellanos, Col Santa Fe Zapopan, Guadalajara, 45168, Jalisco, Mexico (72.43%)
Tel.: (52) 3338360400
Sales Range: $75-99.9 Million
Emp.: 120
Real Estate
N.A.I.C.S.: 531390
Carlos Luckat (Gen Mgr)

ORGANIZACION SORIANA, S.A.B. DE C.V.

Alejandro de Rodas 3102-A Col Cumbres 8th Sector, CP 64610, Monterrey, NL, Mexico
Tel.: (52) 8183299000 MX
Web Site: http://www.soriana.com
Year Founded: 1981
SORIANA—(MEX)
Rev.: $10,377,092,550
Assets: $8,926,467,870
Liabilities: $4,282,465,596
Net Worth: $4,644,002,274
Earnings: $297,313,247
Emp.: 84,540
Fiscal Year-end: 12/31/23
Holding Company; Supermarkets, Hypermarkets, Supercenters & Convenience Stores Operator
N.A.I.C.S.: 551112
Francisco Javier Martin Bringas (Chm)

Subsidiaries:

Tiendas Soriana, S. A. de C. V. (1)
Alejandro de Rodas 3102-A Col Cumbres 8th Sector, CP 64610, Monterrey, NL, Mexico
Tel.: (52) 8183299000
Web Site: http://www.soriana.com
Supermarket Operator
N.A.I.C.S.: 445110

ORGANIZACION TERPEL SA

Carrera 7 No 75 - 51, Bogota, Colombia
Tel.: (57) 3267878
Web Site: https://www.terpel.com
Year Founded: 1968
Fuel Distr
N.A.I.C.S.: 457210

Sylvia Escovar Gomez (Board of Directors & CEO)

ORGANIZATION AND SOFTWARE GMBH

Nikolaus Kopernikus Str 7, 55129, Mainz, Germany
Tel.: (49) 613197330
Web Site: http://www.orga-soft.de
Year Founded: 1979
Sales Range: $50-74.9 Million
Emp.: 6
Software Services
N.A.I.C.S.: 541511
Gunther Kehl (Founder, CEO & Mng Dir)

ORGANO CORPORATION

1-2-8 Shinsuna, Koto-ku, Tokyo, 136-8631, Japan
Tel.: (81) 356355100
Web Site: https://www.organo.co.jp
Year Founded: 1946
6368—(TKS)
Rev.: $993,853,160
Assets: $1,207,666,830
Liabilities: $532,475,160
Net Worth: $675,191,670
Earnings: $114,419,100
Emp.: 1,142
Fiscal Year-end: 03/31/24
Water Treatment & Pure Water Generation Technologies & Systems; Soil Remediation Technologies
N.A.I.C.S.: 221310
Hitoshi Hori (Mng Exec Officer)

Subsidiaries:

Organo (Asia) Sdn. Bhd. (1)
No 49 Jalan Bagan Terap 26/11 Seksyen 26, Seksyen 26 Kawasan Perindustrian HICOM, 40400, Shah Alam, Selangor, Malaysia
Tel.: (60) 3 5191 6666
Web Site: http://www.organoasia.com
Sales Range: $125-149.9 Million
Emp.: 212
Waste Treatment Services
N.A.I.C.S.: 221310
Masahisa Sotokawa (Mng Dir)

Organo (Suzhou) Water Treatment Co., Ltd. (1)
No 28 Sheng gang Rd, Suzhou Industrial Park, Suzhou, 215126, China
Tel.: (86) 51262836676
Web Site: http://www.organo.co.jp
Waste Treatment Services
N.A.I.C.S.: 221310

Organo (Thailand) Co., Ltd. (1)
89/1 Kasemsap Building 6th Floor Viphavadi Rangsit Rd, Chom Phon Chatuchak, Bangkok, 10900, Thailand
Tel.: (66) 269154024
Emp.: 110
Water Treatment Systems Sales
N.A.I.C.S.: 423990
Takasugi Hitoshi (Mng Dir)

Organo (Vietnam) Co., Ltd. (1)
Thuy Loi 4 Office Building Floor 3rd No 102 Nguyen Xi Str, Ward 26 Binh Thanh Dist, Ho Chi Minh City, Vietnam
Tel.: (84) 2862902512
Web Site: https://organovietnam.vn
Emp.: 111
Waste Treatment Services
N.A.I.C.S.: 221310

Organo Technology Co., Ltd. (1)
10th Floor No 158 Section 2 Gongdao 5th Road, Hsin-chu, 300, Taiwan
Tel.: (886) 35733610
Web Site: https://www.organo.com.tw
Sales Range: $75-99.9 Million
Emp.: 110
Waste Treatment Services
N.A.I.C.S.: 562219
Shimada Ken (Pres)

PT Lautan Organo Water (1)
Graha Indramas 5th Floor Jl AIP II Ks Tubun Raya, No 77 Slipi-Palmerah, Jakarta

AND PRIVATE COMPANIES

Barat, 11410, Indonesia (51%)
Tel.: (62) 2129940900
Web Site:
 https://www.lautanorganowater.com
Water Supply & Irrigation Systems
N.A.I.C.S.: 221310

ORGANOCLICK AB
Linjalvagen 9, SE-187 66, Taby, Sweden
Tel.: (46) 86740080
Web Site:
 https://www.organoclick.com
Year Founded: 2006
ORGC—(OMX)
Rev.: $10,775,521
Assets: $15,253,402
Liabilities: $8,925,979
Net Worth: $6,327,423
Earnings: ($3,898,302)
Emp.: 46
Fiscal Year-end: 12/31/22
Functional Wood, Performance Textiles & Nonwoven & Fiber Composites & Paper Products Mfr
N.A.I.C.S.: 321999
Marten Hellberg (Pres & CEO)

Subsidiaries:

Biokleen Miljokemi AB (1)
Box 175, 567 92, Vaggeryd, Sweden
Tel.: (46) 52233990
Web Site: https://www.biokleen.se
Wood Protective Product Mfr
N.A.I.C.S.: 321999

OrganoWood AB (1)
Linjalvagen 9-11, 187 66, Taby, Sweden
Tel.: (46) 86740080
Web Site: https://organowood.com
Wood Protective Product Mfr
N.A.I.C.S.: 321999
Jens Hamlin (CEO)

ORGANTO FOODS INC.
1111 Melville Street Suite 410, Vancouver, V6E 3V6, BC, Canada
Tel.: (604) 219-7185 BC
Web Site: https://www.organto.com
Year Founded: 2007
OGFO—(DEU)
Rev.: $20,903,507
Assets: $5,222,736
Liabilities: $16,954,408
Net Worth: ($11,731,672)
Earnings: ($10,139,163)
Emp.: 12
Fiscal Year-end: 12/31/23
Agricultural Investment Services
N.A.I.C.S.: 523999
Peter Gianulis (Founder)

Subsidiaries:

Fresh Organic Choice B.V. (1)
Galgeweg 8, 2691 MG, 's-Gravenzande, Netherlands
Tel.: (31) 850410109
Web Site: https://www.freshorganicchoice.nl
Fresh Fruit & Vegetable Distr
N.A.I.C.S.: 424480

NFG Italia S.R.L. (1)

NFG New Fruit Group GmbH (1)
Streitfeldstr 19, 81673, Munich, Germany
Tel.: (49) 8920175979
Web Site: https://www.newfruitgroup.com
Fresh Fruit Distr
N.A.I.C.S.: 424480

ORGE ENERJI ELEKTRIK TAAHHUT A.S.
Kozyatagi Mah Degirmen Sokak Nida Kule No 18 Kat, Kadikoy, 34742, Istanbul, Turkiye
Tel.: (90) 2164573263
Web Site: https://www.orge.com.tr
Year Founded: 1998
ORGE—(IST)
Rev.: $66,917,707
Assets: $74,027,336
Liabilities: $29,264,845
Net Worth: $44,762,491
Earnings: $7,392,425
Fiscal Year-end: 12/31/23
Electrical Contracting Services
N.A.I.C.S.: 238210
Orhan Gunduz (Chm)

ORGTECHNICA LTD.
31 P Boyadjiev Street, 7500, Silistra, 7500, Bulgaria
Tel.: (359) 86821150
Web Site: https://www.orgtechnica.bg
Year Founded: 1964
ORGT—(BUL)
Sales Range: Less than $1 Million
Electronic Products Mfr
N.A.I.C.S.: 334419

ORIAN SHM LTD.
Hamelaha Street 8, PO Box 82, Modi'in-Maccabim-Re'ut, 71100, Israel
Tel.: (972) 89181812
Web Site: https://en.orian.com
Year Founded: 1953
ORIN—(TAE)
Rev.: $361,531,000
Assets: $374,689,000
Liabilities: $287,812,000
Net Worth: $86,877,000
Earnings: $11,459,000
Fiscal Year-end: 12/31/22
Logistic Services
N.A.I.C.S.: 541614
Chen Lamdan (CEO)

ORIANA POWER LIMITED
C-103 1st Floor Sector 2, Noida, 201301, Uttar Pradesh, India
Tel.: (91) 1204114695
Web Site:
 https://www.orianapower.com
Year Founded: 2013
ORIANA—(NSE)
Rev.: $16,517,803
Assets: $17,623,269
Liabilities: $13,657,759
Net Worth: $3,965,510
Earnings: $1,313,034
Emp.: 56
Fiscal Year-end: 03/31/23
Solar Component Distr
N.A.I.C.S.: 423720
Anirudh Saraswat (Chief Bus Officer)

ORICA LIMITED
1 Nicholson Street, Melbourne, 3002, VIC, Australia
Tel.: (61) 396657111 AU
Web Site: http://www.orica.com
Year Founded: 1874
OCLDF—(OTCIQ)
Rev.: $5,314,412,991
Assets: $6,633,289,147
Liabilities: $3,490,488,263
Net Worth: $3,142,800,884
Earnings: $386,181,092
Emp.: 14,000
Fiscal Year-end: 09/30/24
Mining Explosives, Home & Garden Chemicals & Industrial Chemicals Mfr
N.A.I.C.S.: 325998
Angus Melbourne (CTO)

Subsidiaries:

Anbao Insurance Pte Ltd (1)
60 Anson Road 08-01 Mapletree Anson, Singapore, 070014, Singapore
Tel.: (65) 62218222
Insurance Management Services
N.A.I.C.S.: 524298

EXSA S.A. (1)
Antigua Carretera Panamericana Sur Km 38 5, Lurin, Peru (83.5%)
Tel.: (51) 315 7000
Web Site: http://www.exsa.net
Chemical Products Mfr
N.A.I.C.S.: 325998
Adolfo Sanchez Medina (Dir-Sustainability)

Explosivos Mexicanos S.A. de C.V. (1)
Harold R Pape 1811 Colonia Santa Cecilia, 257520, Monclova, Coahuila, Mexico
Tel.: (52) 6622151050
Web Site: http://www.orica.com
Explosives Mfr
N.A.I.C.S.: 325920

Explosivos de Mexico S.A. de C.V. (1)
Boulevard Harold R Pape No 350 Colonia Telefonistas, 25758, Monclova, Coahuila, Mexico
Tel.: (52) 866 158 0300
Explosives Mfr
N.A.I.C.S.: 325920

GroundProbe (Nanjing) Mining Technology Co., Ltd. (1)
No 33 Dongqi Road, Jiangning District, Nanjing, 211100, Jiangsu, China
Tel.: (86) 258 418 9710
Mining Machinery & Equipment Mfr
N.A.I.C.S.: 333131

GroundProbe Australasia Pty. Ltd. (1)
72 Newmarket Road, Windsor, 4030, QLD, Australia
Tel.: (61) 73 010 8999
Web Site: https://www.groundprobe.com
Mining Machinery & Equipment Mfr
N.A.I.C.S.: 333131
David Noon (CEO)

GroundProbe Peru S.A.C. (1)
Dionisio Derteano 144 Piso 19, San Isidro, Lima, 15047, Peru
Tel.: (51) 1 622 3311
Mining Machinery & Equipment Mfr
N.A.I.C.S.: 333131

GroundProbe Pty Ltd (1)
72 Newmarket Road, Windsor, 4030, QLD, Australia
Tel.: (61) 7 3010 8999
Web Site: http://www.groundprobe.com
Measuring Equipment Mfr & Distr
N.A.I.C.S.: 334519
David Noon (Founder & COO)

GroundProbe South Africa (Proprietary) Ltd. (1)
Unit 1 9 Reedbuck Crescent Corporate Park South, Midrand, 1685, Gauteng, South Africa
Tel.: (27) 11 087 5300
Mining Machinery & Equipment Mfr
N.A.I.C.S.: 333131

GroundProbe South America S.A. (1)
Costanera Sur 2730 Third Floor, Las Condes, Santiago, Chile
Tel.: (56) 22 586 4200
Mining Machinery & Equipment Mfr
N.A.I.C.S.: 333131

Hallowell Manufacturing LLC (1)
3600 Nw 74th St, Columbus, KS 66725-1773
Tel.: (620) 597-2552
Chemical Product Whslr
N.A.I.C.S.: 424690

Minova Holding GmbH (1)
Bamlerstr 5d, 45141, Essen, Germany
Tel.: (49) 2018 098 3500
Construction Piling Services
N.A.I.C.S.: 532412

Minova Kazakhstan Limited Liability Partnership (1)
Oktyabrskiy Region 018 Uchetniy Kvartal Building 014, 100011, Karaganda, Kazakhstan
Tel.: (7) 721 278 3525
Mining & Metal Services
N.A.I.C.S.: 213114

Minova Mining Services S.A. (1)
Av Los Valles 225 Bodega 21, Pudahuel, 902000, Santiago, Chile
Tel.: (56) 94 008 5716
Construction Piling Services

N.A.I.C.S.: 532412

Nitro Consult AS (1)
Roykenveien 18, Gullaug, 3472, Lier, Norway
Tel.: (47) 3 222 9100
Web Site: https://www.nitroconsult.no
Vibration Meter Mfr
N.A.I.C.S.: 334519

Nitroamonia de Mexico S.A de C.V. (1)
Prolongacion Fertilizantes No 1800 Col Industrial, Monclova, 25750, Coahuila, Mexico
Tel.: (52) 8666311011
Web Site:
 http://www.oricaminingservices.com
Explosives Mfr
N.A.I.C.S.: 325920

Orica Africa (Pty) Ltd. (1)
2nd Floor Cradock Square 169 Oxford Road, Rosebank, 2196, South Africa
Tel.: (27) 10 596 3101
Mining & Metal Services
N.A.I.C.S.: 213114

Orica Argentina S.A.I.C. (1)
Av Libertador San Martin N 521 O 1er Piso Dept 2 Ciudad Capital, 5400, San Juan, Argentina
Tel.: (54) 2644303200
Web Site: http://www.orica.com
Coal Mining Services
N.A.I.C.S.: 213113

Orica Australia Pty. Ltd. (1)
Level 3 1 Nicholson Street, Melbourne, 3002, VIC, Australia
Tel.: (61) 396657111
Web Site: http://www.orica.com
Mfr of Petrochemicals
N.A.I.C.S.: 325110
Barbara Gibson (Gen Mgr)

Branch (Domestic):

Orica Australia (2)
Tower Lvl 2 15th Health St, Chatswood, 2067, NSW, Australia (100%)
Tel.: (61) 298445500
Web Site: http://www.orica.com.au
Sales Range: $50-74.9 Million
Emp.: 55
Drill & Blast Services to the Mining Industry
N.A.I.C.S.: 213113

Orica Australia Securities Pty Ltd (1)
L 9 1 Nicholson St, Melbourne, 3002, VIC, Australia
Tel.: (61) 396657111
Securities Brokerage Services
N.A.I.C.S.: 523150

Orica Belgium S.A. (1)
510 Rue De Namur, 6200, Chatelet, Belgium
Tel.: (32) 7 124 3740
Mining & Metal Services
N.A.I.C.S.: 213114

Orica Bolivia S.A. (1)
Av Sanchez Lima N 2061 casi esquina Calle Aspiazu Edificio Rosario, Piso 4 Zona Sopocachi, La Paz, Bolivia
Tel.: (591) 22145055
Web Site: https://www.orica.com
Coal Mining Services
N.A.I.C.S.: 213113

Orica CIS CJSC (1)
Alcon 1 Building 1 Level 8 72 Leningradsky Prospekt, 125315, Moscow, Russia
Tel.: (7) 495 64 111 64
Web Site: http://www.orica.com
Emp.: 33
Chemical Products Mfr
N.A.I.C.S.: 325199
Anna Ulyanova (Mgr-Mktg)

Orica Chile S.A. (1)
Costanera Sur 2730 3rd floor, Las Condes, Santiago, Chile
Tel.: (56) 227153800
Web Site: http://www.orica.com
Emp.: 13
Chemical Products Mfr
N.A.I.C.S.: 325199

Orica Colombia S.A.S. (1)

ORICA LIMITED

Orica Limited—(Continued)
Calle 110 No 09 - 25 Oficina 614, Bogota, Colombia
Tel.: (57) 1 658 1100
Explosives Mfr
N.A.I.C.S.: 325920

Orica DRC S.a.r.l. (1)
5 Route du Golf/Quartier Golf Complexe La Plage 2 Magasin No 12, Lubumbashi, Congo, Democratic Republic of
Tel.: (243) 81 706 8697
Explosives Mfr
N.A.I.C.S.: 325920

Orica Europe Pty Ltd & Co. KG (1)
Muelheimer Strasse 5, 53840, Troisdorf, Germany
Tel.: (49) 224199520
Web Site: https://www.orica.com
Sales Range: $125-149.9 Million
Emp.: 300
Mfr of Explosives
N.A.I.C.S.: 325920

Subsidiary (Non-US):

CarboTech-Polonia Sp. z o.o. (2)
ul Budowlana 10, 41 100, Siemianowice, Poland
Tel.: (48) 32 75 03 930
Web Site: http://www.carbotechpolonia.pl
Mining Chemical Mfr
N.A.I.C.S.: 325998

Dyno Nobel Sweden AB (2)
Gyttorp, 71382, Nora, Sweden
Tel.: (46) 58785000
Web Site: http://www.oricaminningservices.com
Sales Range: $100-124.9 Million
Emp.: 413
Explosive Systems Mfr
N.A.I.C.S.: 325920

Nitro Consult AB (2)
Tjurhorsgrand 8, Johanneshov, 121 63, Stockholm, Sweden
Tel.: (46) 86814300
Web Site: https://nitroconsult.com
Emp.: 35
Civil Engineering Construction Services
N.A.I.C.S.: 237990
Kathleen Andreasen (Accountant)

Orica Denmark A/S (2)
Smedeland 7, Glostrup, 2600, Copenhagen, Denmark
Tel.: (45) 43451538
Commercial Explosives Distr
N.A.I.C.S.: 424690

Subsidiary (Domestic):

Orica Europe Management GmbH (2)
Mulheimer Str 5, Troisdorf, 53840, Nordrhein-Westfalen, Germany
Tel.: (49) 224148290
Chemical Products Mfr
N.A.I.C.S.: 325199

Subsidiary (Non-US):

Orica Explosivos Industriales, S.A. (2)
Carretera a Villafer Km 7, Transconejos, 24220, Valderas, Leon, Spain
Tel.: (34) 987763206
Chemical Products Mfr
N.A.I.C.S.: 325199

Orica Germany GmbH (2)
Tel.: (49) 224199520
Web Site: http://www.orica-germany.com
Sales Range: $50-74.9 Million
Emp.: 90
Commercial Explosives Distr
N.A.I.C.S.: 424690

Subsidiary (Non-US):

Eurodyn Sprengmittel GmbH (3)
(100%)
Tel.: (49) 27364483000
Sales Range: $25-49.9 Million
Emp.: 88
Explosives Mfr
N.A.I.C.S.: 325920

Subsidiary (Non-US):

Orica Poland Sp. z.o.o. (2)
Porsta 36, 50-110, Wroclaw, Poland
Tel.: (48) 713419776
Web Site: http://www.oricaminingservices.com
Commercial Explosives Distr
N.A.I.C.S.: 424690
Emiliam Jamusz (Gen Mgr)

Orica Sweden Holdings AB (2)
Gyttorp, 713 82, Nora, Sweden
Tel.: (46) 58785000
Sales Range: $200-249.9 Million
Emp.: 300
Coal Mining Services
N.A.I.C.S.: 213113
Hakan Fuhr (Gen Mgr)

Orica UK Limited (2)
101 Dalton Avenue, Birchwood, WA3 6YF, Cheshire, United Kingdom
Tel.: (44) 1257256100
Explosives Mfr
N.A.I.C.S.: 325920

Orica Explosives Holdings Pty Ltd (1)
1 Nicholson St, Melbourne, 3002, VIC, Australia
Tel.: (61) 396657111
Web Site: http://www.orica.com
Emp.: 400
Investment Management Service
N.A.I.C.S.: 523999
Alberto Calderon (CEO)

Orica Explosives Technology Pty Ltd (1)
L 9 1 Nicholson St, Melbourne, 3002, VIC, Australia
Tel.: (61) 396657111
Web Site: http://www.orica.com
Emp.: 500
Explosive Distr
N.A.I.C.S.: 424690

Orica Finance Limited (1)
L 3 1 Nicholson St, Melbourne, 3002, VIC, Australia
Tel.: (61) 396657111
Financial Management Services
N.A.I.C.S.: 523999

Orica Finland Oy (1)
Jussilankatu 6, 15680, Lahti, Finland
Tel.: (358) 10 321 2550
Explosives Mfr
N.A.I.C.S.: 325920

Orica Ghana Limited (1)
No 83 Osu Badu Street Airport West, Accra, Ghana
Tel.: (233) 30 277 5100
Mining & Metal Services
N.A.I.C.S.: 213114

Orica Investments Pty Ltd (1)
1 Nicholson St, Melbourne, 3002, VIC, Australia
Tel.: (61) 396657111
Investment Management Service
N.A.I.C.S.: 523999

Orica Japan Co. Ltd (1)
7F Kamiyacho Annex II 3-7-11 Toranomon, Minato-Ku, Tokyo, 105-0001, Japan
Tel.: (81) 357774681
Web Site: http://www.oriska.com
Sales Range: $50-74.9 Million
Emp.: 8
Chemical Product Whslr
N.A.I.C.S.: 424690

Orica Mining Services (1)
Level 3 1 Nicholson Street, Melbourne, 3002, VIC, Australia
Tel.: (61) 396657111
Web Site: http://www.orica.com.au
Sales Range: $125-149.9 Million
Emp.: 500
Commercial Explosives, Initiating Systems & Blast-Based Services
N.A.I.C.S.: 325920

Orica Mining Services (1)
Level 2 15 Help Street, Chatswood, 2067, NSW, Australia
Tel.: (61) 298445500
Web Site: http://www.orica.com.au

Sales Range: $25-49.9 Million
Emp.: 53
Explosives Mfr
N.A.I.C.S.: 325920

Orica Mining Services (Hong Kong) Ltd. (1)
Room 501 5/F Mega Trade Centre 1-6 Mei Wan Street, Tsuen Wan, China (Hong Kong)
Tel.: (852) 2 850 5626
Mining & Metal Services
N.A.I.C.S.: 213114

Orica Mining Services Latin America (1)
Avda Andres Bello 2711 Torre de la Costanera, Las Condes, Santiago, Chile
Tel.: (56) 2 444 3300
Explosives & Systems Mfr
N.A.I.C.S.: 325920

Orica Mining Services Peru S.A. (1)
Tel.: (51) 12176000
Web Site: http://www.orica.com
Commercial Explosive Mining Services
N.A.I.C.S.: 212390

Orica Mining Services Portugal S.A. (1)
Av Duque d Avila n 95 2 andar, 1000-139, Lisbon, Portugal
Tel.: (351) 21 357 1311
Mining & Metal Services
N.A.I.C.S.: 213114

Orica Mongolia LLC (1)
8th floor 801 Jamyan Gunii gudamj street 18/1 1st khoroo, The building The Down Town Sukhbaatar district, Ulaanbaatar, 14240, Mongolia
Tel.: (976) 11329043
Web Site: https://www.orica.com
Emp.: 10
Commercial Explosives Distr
N.A.I.C.S.: 424690

Orica Mozambique Limitada (1)
Avenida Marginal 141 Rani Towers 6th Floor, Maputo, Mozambique
Tel.: (258) 8 409 3532
Explosives Mfr
N.A.I.C.S.: 325920

Orica New Zealand Ltd (1)
Brunnings Road Carters Beach 7892, PO Box 161, Newmarket, Westport, 1023, New Zealand
Tel.: (64) 37888163
Web Site: http://www.orica.co.nz
Sales Range: $25-49.9 Million
Emp.: 61
Specialty Chemicals Mfr
N.A.I.C.S.: 325199

Orica Nitro Patlayici Maddeler Sanayi ve Ticaret Anonim Sirketi (1)
Hulya Sokak No 45, 06700, Ankara, Turkiye
Tel.: (90) 3124461600
Web Site: https://www.orica-nitro.com.tr
Explosives Mfr
N.A.I.C.S.: 325920
Asim Tosun (Gen Mgr)

Orica Nominees Pty Ltd (1)
L 3 1 Nicholson St, Melbourne, 3002, VIC, Australia
Tel.: (61) 396657111
Web Site: http://www.orica.com
Emp.: 800
Chemical & Fertilizer Mineral Mining Services
N.A.I.C.S.: 212390

Orica Norway AS (1)
Roykenveien 18, Gullaug, 3427, Lier, Norway
Tel.: (47) 3 222 9100
Mining & Metal Services
N.A.I.C.S.: 213114

Orica Philippines Inc (1)
Tower-2 Rockwell Business Center 11th Floor Ortigas Avenue, Brgy Ugong, Pasig, 1604, Philippines
Tel.: (63) 284226800
Sales Range: $25-49.9 Million
Emp.: 60
Explosives Mfr
N.A.I.C.S.: 325920

INTERNATIONAL PUBLIC

Keiran Balkin (Country Mgr)

Orica Singapore Pte Ltd (1)
78 Shenton Way Level 6 Tower 2, Singapore, 079120, Singapore
Tel.: (65) 66034500
Web Site: http://www.orica.com
Emp.: 100
Explosives Mfr
N.A.I.C.S.: 325920

Orica South Africa (Proprietary) Limited (1)
2nd Floor Cradock Square 169 Oxford Road, Rosebank, 2196, Western Cape, South Africa
Tel.: (27) 105963101
Web Site: http://www.orica.com
Electric Equipment Mfr
N.A.I.C.S.: 334419

Orica Sweden AB (1)
Gyttorp, 713 82, Nora, Sweden
Tel.: (46) 5 878 5000
Mining & Metal Services
N.A.I.C.S.: 213114

Orica Tanzania Limited (1)
Plot 368 2nd Floor Mikumi Building Msasani Road, Oysterbay Shopping Centre, Dar es Salaam, Tanzania
Tel.: (255) 67 780 0080
Mining & Metal Services
N.A.I.C.S.: 213114

Orica U.S. Services Inc. (1)
33101 E Quincy Ave, Watkins, CO 80137-9406
Tel.: (303) 268-5000
Sales Range: $50-74.9 Million
Emp.: 180
Explosives Mfr
N.A.I.C.S.: 325920

Orica USA Inc. (1)
33101 E Quincy Ave, Watkins, CO 80137-5938
(100%)
Tel.: (303) 268-5000
Web Site: http://www.oricaminingservices.com
Sales Range: $50-74.9 Million
Emp.: 100
Explosives Mfr
N.A.I.C.S.: 325920

Orica Venezuela C.A. (1)
Edif Torreon Piso 4 Ofic 4-A Calle La Guairita con Calle Veracruz, Urb Las Mercedes, 1080, Caracas, Carabobo, Venezuela
Tel.: (58) 2128225900
Web Site: http://www.orica.com
Sales Range: $50-74.9 Million
Emp.: 20
Coal Mining Services
N.A.I.C.S.: 213113

Orica Watercare Inc. (1)
33101 E Quincy Ave, Watkins, CO 80137
Tel.: (303) 268-5243
Web Site: http://www.miexresin.com
Sales Range: $25-49.9 Million
Emp.: 15
Water Treatment Resin Mfr
N.A.I.C.S.: 325211
Shane Jones (Pres)

Orica Zambia Limited (1)
PO Box 55, Chambishi, Kalulushi, Zambia
Tel.: (260) 272 1310
Mining & Metal Services
N.A.I.C.S.: 213114

Oricorp Comercial S.A. de C.V. (1)
Prolongacion Fertilizantes No 1800 Col Industrial, Monclova, 25750, Coahuila, Mexico
Tel.: (52) 8666311011
Web Site: http://www.orica.com
Sales Range: $50-74.9 Million
Emp.: 200
Explosives Mfr
N.A.I.C.S.: 325920

PT Orica Mining Services (1)
Pondok Indah Office Tower 3 12th Floor Jl, Sultan Iskandar Muda Kav V-TA, Jakarta, 10270, Selatan, Indonesia
Tel.: (62) 2127650123
Web Site: http://www.orica.com
Emp.: 82
Commercial Explosive Mfr & Distr

AND PRIVATE COMPANIES

N.A.I.C.S.: 325920
Jeffery Sornym *(Gen Mgr)*

Stratabolt (Pty) Limited (1)
Corner Anvil And Brewery Road, Isando, 1600, Gauteng, South Africa
Tel.: (27) 119231900
Emp.: 150
Plastic & Resin Mfr
N.A.I.C.S.: 326199
Johan Strydom *(Gen Mgr)*

Surtech Systems Pty Ltd. (1)
Unit 4 17 Gibberd Rd, Balcatta, 6021, WA, Australia
Tel.: (61) 1800947354
Web Site: https://www.surtech.com.au
Borehole Logging Services
N.A.I.C.S.: 213112

ORICON ENTERPRISES LTD.
1076 Dr E Moses Road Worli, Mumbai, 400 018, India
Tel.: (91) 2224964656
Web Site:
https://www.oriconenterprises.com
513121—(NSE)
Rev.: $89,675,968
Assets: $199,888,129
Liabilities: $52,099,211
Net Worth: $147,788,919
Earnings: ($962,994)
Emp.: 443
Fiscal Year-end: 03/31/21
Real Estate Manangement Services
N.A.I.C.S.: 531390
Susheel G. Somani *(Chm)*

Subsidiaries:

Oriental Containers Limited (1)
Parijat House 1076 Dr E Moses Road P B 6584 Worli, Mumbai, 400 018, India
Tel.: (91) 2243662200
Web Site:
https://www.orientalcontainers.com
Metal Closure & Plastic Closure Mfr
N.A.I.C.S.: 332119

Shinrai Auto Services Ltd. (1)
35 Dr E Moses Road Worli Naka Worli, Mumbai, 400 018, India
Tel.: (91) 22 6613 1500
Web Site: http://www.shinraitoyota.com
Emp.: 250
Automobile Whslr
N.A.I.C.S.: 423110
Noah Ashtamkar *(Exec Dir)*

United Shippers Ltd. (1)
Prospect Chambers 3rd Floor D N Road Fort, Mumbai, 400 001, India
Tel.: (91) 2267568400
Web Site: http://www.unitedshippers.com
Logistics Consulting Servies
N.A.I.C.S.: 541614
Paras Dakalia *(Dir-Fin)*

Subsidiary (Non-US):

USL Shipping DMCEST (2)
605 Bin Soughat Building Salah Al Din Road Nr Muraqqabat, PO Box 118693, Police Station Deira, Dubai, United Arab Emirates
Tel.: (971) 4 2667253
Web Site: http://www.uslshipping.com
Sales Range: $25-49.9 Million
Emp.: 12
Chartering Transportation Services
N.A.I.C.S.: 481212

ORICON INC
Roppongi 6-8-10, Minato-ku, Tokyo, 106-0032, Japan
Tel.: (81) 334055252
Web Site: https://www.oricon.jp
Year Founded: 1999
4800—(TKS)
Rev.: $31,728,000
Assets: $39,838,470
Liabilities: $5,552,400
Net Worth: $34,286,070
Earnings: $6,973,550
Emp.: 190
Fiscal Year-end: 03/31/24
Publishing Services
N.A.I.C.S.: 513199
Koh Koike *(Pres)*

Subsidiaries:

Oricon ME Inc. (1)
6-8-10 Roppongi STEP Roppongi East 3F, Minato-ku, Tokyo, 106-0032, Japan
Tel.: (81) 357855628
Magazine & Book Publishing Services
N.A.I.C.S.: 513199

ORIEL HOLDINGS LTD
Cheltenham House Clarence Street, Cheltenham, GL50 3JR, United Kingdom
Tel.: (44) 84522618
Web Site: http://www.orielgroup.co.uk
Sales Range: $10-24.9 Million
Emp.: 100
Debt Collection
N.A.I.C.S.: 561440
Brian Pursey *(CEO)*

ORIEL RESOURCES PLC
1 Red Place, London, W1K 6PL, United Kingdom
Tel.: (44) 2075140590
Web Site:
http://www.orielresources.com
Sales Range: $200-249.9 Million
Emp.: 754
Nickel Ore Mining
N.A.I.C.S.: 212230
Nicholas Barcza *(Gen Mgr-Market Dev & Project Evaluation)*

ORIEM TECHNOLOGY SDN. BHD.
Plot 25 Phase 4 Non-FTZ, Bayan Lepas Industrial Estate, 11900, Bayan Lepas, Penang, Malaysia
Tel.: (60) 46426363
Web Site: http://www.oriem.com.my
Year Founded: 2002
Optoelectronic Industry Material Mfr
N.A.I.C.S.: 334413
Lu Eng Shean *(Founder & Mng Dir)*

ORIENS
Jozsef Attila u 1 1 em 2, 1051, Budapest, Hungary
Tel.: (36) 14290194
Web Site: http://www.oriensim.com
Year Founded: 2007
Private Investment Management Firm
N.A.I.C.S.: 523999
Flora Macher *(Partner)*

Subsidiaries:

Profirent Gepkolcsonzo Kft. (1)
Jaszberenyi ut 82/a, 1106, Budapest, Hungary
Tel.: (36) 1 286 2600
Web Site: http://www.profirent.co.hu
Sales Range: $10-24.9 Million
Emp.: 85
Construction Equipment Rental Services
N.A.I.C.S.: 532412
Peter Mohacsi *(Country Mgr)*

ORIENT BELL LIMITED
Iris House 16 Business Centre Nangal Raya DDA Complex, New Delhi, 110046, India
Tel.: (91) 1147119100
Web Site: https://www.orientbell.com
530365—(BOM)
Rev.: $68,842,424
Assets: $59,298,398
Liabilities: $25,273,808
Net Worth: $34,024,591
Earnings: $1,048,429
Emp.: 879
Fiscal Year-end: 03/31/21
Ceramic Tile Mfr
N.A.I.C.S.: 327120

Mahendra K. Daga *(Chm & Mng Dir)*

ORIENT BEVERAGES LIMITED
Aelpe Court 3rd Floor 225C A J C Bose Road, Kolkata, 700 020, India
Tel.: (91) 3330527001
Web Site: https://www.obl.net.in
Year Founded: 1960
507690—(BOM)
Rev.: $14,628,667
Assets: $14,399,089
Liabilities: $12,278,233
Net Worth: $2,120,856
Earnings: $339,128
Emp.: 499
Fiscal Year-end: 03/31/23
Bottled Water Mfr
N.A.I.C.S.: 312112
Narendra Kumar Poddar *(Chm)*

ORIENT BIO INC.
322 Galmachi-ro, Jungwon-gu, Seongnam, Gyeonggi, Korea (South)
Tel.: (82) 317306100
Web Site: https://www.orientbio.co.kr
Year Founded: 1959
002630—(KRS)
Rev.: $21,902,461
Assets: $61,598,167
Liabilities: $7,339,975
Net Worth: $54,258,192
Earnings: ($9,442,018)
Emp.: 111
Fiscal Year-end: 03/31/23
Laboratory Animal Production Services
N.A.I.C.S.: 112990
Jae-Jin Jang *(Chm & CEO)*

ORIENT BLACKSWAN PRIVATE LIMITED
3-6-752 Himayatnagar, Hyderabad, 500 029, Telangana, India
Tel.: (91) 40 2761 0898
Web Site:
http://www.orientblackswan.com
Year Founded: 1948
Sales Range: $10-24.9 Million
Emp.: 375
Academic & General Interest Hardback & Paperback Books Publisher
N.A.I.C.S.: 513130
Vani Vasudevan *(VP-ELT Schools)*

ORIENT CEMENT LIMITED
Birla Tower 3rd Floor 25 Barakhamba Road, New Delhi, 110001, India
Tel.: (91) 1142092100
Web Site:
https://www.orientcement.com
Year Founded: 1979
ORIENTCEM—(NSE)
Rev.: $319,742,500
Assets: $383,845,972
Liabilities: $205,589,830
Net Worth: $178,256,142
Earnings: $29,236,293
Emp.: 1,204
Fiscal Year-end: 03/31/21
Cement Mfr
N.A.I.C.S.: 327310
Shyam B. Asawa *(Pres-Projects)*

ORIENT CORPORATION
5-2-1 Kojimachi, Chiyoda-ku, Tokyo, 102-8503, Japan
Tel.: (81) 358771111
Web Site: https://www.orico.co.jp
Year Founded: 1954
8585—(TKS)
Rev.: $1,514,046,940
Assets: $20,806,845,630
Liabilities: $19,182,881,000
Net Worth: $1,623,964,630
Earnings: $83,094,310
Emp.: 9,202

Fiscal Year-end: 03/31/24
Financial Investment Services
N.A.I.C.S.: 523999
Hideki Matsuo *(Exec VP & Supvr-Bus Coordination & Admin-Grp)*

Subsidiaries:

AEON Product Finance Co., Ltd. (1)
1-3 Nakase Makuhari Techno Garden D Building 18F, Mihama-ku, Chiba, 261-0023, Japan
Tel.: (81) 120104839
Web Site: https://www.aeonproduct-finance.jp
Emp.: 653
Collection & Payment Agency Services
N.A.I.C.S.: 561440

Japan Collection Service Co., Ltd. (1)
Building 5F 5-2-1 Kojimachi, Chiyoda-Ku, Tokyo, 102-8503, Japan (93.8%)
Tel.: (81) 332220328
Web Site: https://www.japanservicer.co.jp
Emp.: 416
Nondepository Credit Intermediation
N.A.I.C.S.: 522299

ORIFA Service Servicer Co., Ltd. (1)
1-9-1 Kanamecho Iyasaka Building 3 F, Toshima-ku, Tokyo, 171-0043, Japan
Tel.: (81) 359952450
Armored Car Services
N.A.I.C.S.: 561613

Orico Auto Chubu Co., Ltd. (1)
Orico Gokisho Building, Nagoya, Japan (100%)
Tel.: (81) 527337817
Information Services
N.A.I.C.S.: 519290

Orico Auto Hokkaido Co., Ltd. (1)
Kirinsapporo Building 6th Fl, Sapporo, Japan (100%)
Tel.: (81) 112145678
Information Services
N.A.I.C.S.: 519290

Orico Auto Kansai Co., Ltd. (1)
Nagataesuto Bldg 6th Fl, Osaka, Japan (100%)
Tel.: (81) 643090855
Information Services
N.A.I.C.S.: 519290

Orico Auto Kanto Co., Ltd. (1)
Saitamaurawa Bldg 8th Fl, Saitama, Japan (51%)
Tel.: (81) 488253661
Information Services
N.A.I.C.S.: 519290

Orico Auto Tohoku Co., Ltd. (1)
Sendai Hommachi Bldg 11th Fl, Sendai, Japan (100%)
Tel.: (81) 222278712
Information Services
N.A.I.C.S.: 519290

Orico Business & Communications Co., Ltd (1)
Building 8F 5-2-1 Kojimachi, Chiyoda-ku, Tokyo, 102-8503, Japan
Tel.: (81) 5055378058
Web Site: https://www.orico-bc.co.jp
Emp.: 63
Communication Marketing Services
N.A.I.C.S.: 541613

Orico Chubu Co., Ltd (1)
3-8-2 Ayuchitori Oriko Gokiso Building, Showa-ku, Nagoya, 466-0027, Aichi, Japan
Tel.: (81) 527337817
Credit Card Processing Services
N.A.I.C.S.: 522210

Orico Chushikoku Co., Ltd. (1)
14-8 Noboricho, Naka-ku, Hiroshima, 730-0016, Japan
Tel.: (81) 822255060
Credit Card Processing Services
N.A.I.C.S.: 522210

Orico Kansai Co., Ltd (1)
3-5-7 Hommachi Midosujihommachi Building 6 F, Chuo-ku, Osaka, 541-0053, Japan
Tel.: (81) 662633425
Credit Card Processing Services

ORIENT CORPORATION

Orient Corporation—(Continued)
N.A.I.C.S.: 522210

Orico Kanto Co., Ltd (1)
2-2-3 Takasago Saitamaurawa Building,
Urawa-ku, Saitama, 330-0063, Japan
Tel.: (81) 488253661
Credit Card Processing Services
N.A.I.C.S.: 522210

Orico Support Co., Ltd. (1)
5 Nishi 2 Kita 5, Chuo-ku, Sapporo, 060-0005, Hokkaido, Japan
Tel.: (81) 11 214 5678
Web Site: http://www.orico-support.co.jp
Credit Card Issuing Services
N.A.I.C.S.: 522210

Orico Tohoku Co., Ltd (1)
4-2-16 Chuo Sendaichuodaiichiseimei Building 3 F, Aoba-ku, Sendai, 980-0021, Miyagi, Japan
Tel.: (81) 222278712
Credit Card Processing Services
N.A.I.C.S.: 522210

Orico Tokyo Co., Ltd (1)
5-2-1 Kojimachi Orico Honsha Building 8 F, Chiyoda-ku, Tokyo, 102-0083, Japan
Tel.: (81) 358775745
Credit Card Processing Services
N.A.I.C.S.: 522210

Orico Trading Co., Ltd. (1)
Orico Honsha Bldg 4th Fl, Chiyoda-Ku, Tokyo, Japan (100%)
Tel.: (81) 358775811
Retailers Stores
N.A.I.C.S.: 459999

ORIENT EUROPHARMA CO., LTD.
13F No 128 Section 6 Chengde Road, Taipei, 106, Taiwan
Tel.: (886) 227554881
Web Site: https://www.oepgroup.com
Year Founded: 1982
4120—(TPE)
Rev.: $150,164,944
Assets: $353,569,234
Liabilities: $217,447,063
Net Worth: $136,122,170
Earnings: $5,536,054
Emp.: 917
Fiscal Year-end: 12/31/23
Pharmaceuticals & Cosmetics Mfr
N.A.I.C.S.: 325412
Peter Jing Hong Tsai (Chm)

Subsidiaries:

OE Philippines (1)
Unit 606 6th Fl Sedcco 1 Bldg Cnr Rada And Legaspi St, Legaspi Vlg, Makati, 1229, Metro Manila, Philippines
Tel.: (63) 28151209
Web Site: http://www.oep.com.ph
Sales Range: $75-99.9 Million
Emp.: 170
Sales of Pharmaceutical Products
N.A.I.C.S.: 424210
Cherry Annvee (Mgr-Acctg)

Orient Europharma (M) Sdn Bhd (1)
33 Jln Pentadbir U1/30 Hicom Glenmarie, Shah Alam, 40150, Selangor, Malaysia
Tel.: (60) 355695405
Web Site: http://www.oep.com.tw
Sales Range: $25-49.9 Million
Emp.: 20
Pharmaceutical Products Distr
N.A.I.C.S.: 424210
Lee Chee Yoong (Mgr)

Orient Europharma Co. Ltd (1)
Room 605-06 6 F 25 Chong Yip Street, Kwun Tong, Kowloon, China (Hong Kong)
Tel.: (852) 25787080
Sales Range: $25-49.9 Million
Emp.: 18
Pharmaceutical Products Distr
N.A.I.C.S.: 424210
Ringo Ng (Gen Mgr)

Orient Europharma Pte Ltd (1)
1 Sophia Rd 04-12 Peace Ctr, Singapore, 228149, Singapore
Tel.: (65) 63398820
Sales Range: $50-74.9 Million
Emp.: 10
Pharmaceutical Preparation Whslr
N.A.I.C.S.: 424210

ORIENT EXPRESS BANK OJSC
23 Shevchuka Str, 680007, Khabarovsk, Russia
Tel.: (7) 4212485731 RU
Web Site: http://www.express-bank.ru
Year Founded: 1991
Sales Range: $800-899.9 Million
Emp.: 9,287
Banking Services
N.A.I.C.S.: 522110
Sergey N. Vlasov (Chm-Mgmt Bd)

ORIENT GROUP INCORPORATION
No 235 Huayuan Street, Nangang District, Harbin, 150001, Heilongjiang, China
Tel.: (86) 45153666003
Web Site: https://www.china-orient.com
Year Founded: 1992
600811—(SHG)
Rev.: $1,821,836,971
Assets: $5,929,135,033
Liabilities: $3,367,410,223
Net Worth: $2,561,724,809
Earnings: ($139,774,307)
Fiscal Year-end: 12/31/22
Farm Product Distr
N.A.I.C.S.: 424590
Zhang Hongwei (Founder)

ORIENT PAPER & INDUSTRIES LIMITED
9/1 R N Mukherjee Road, Kolkata, 700 001, West Bengal, India
Tel.: (91) 3330573700
Web Site: https://orientpaper.in
Year Founded: 1939
502420—(BOM)
Rev.: $61,829,381
Assets: $267,596,716
Liabilities: $67,214,716
Net Worth: $200,382,000
Earnings: ($6,353,502)
Emp.: 1,381
Fiscal Year-end: 03/31/21
Cement & Paper Mfr
N.A.I.C.S.: 327310
Manohar Lal Pachisia (Mng Dir)

ORIENT PETROLEUM AND ENERGY, INC.
1 Xingqing Road Cuiting Plaza Suite 2201, Xi'an, 710032, Shaanxi, China
Tel.: (86) 2983213199 NV
Web Site: http://www.orientpetro.com
Petroleum Products Distr; Gas Stations
N.A.I.C.S.: 424720
Anping Yao (Chm, Pres & CEO)

ORIENT PHARMA CO., LTD.
2F No 368 Sec 1 Fu Hsing S Road, Taipei, 106, Taiwan
Tel.: (886) 223257621
Web Site: https://www.oppharma.com
Year Founded: 2008
4166—(TAI)
Pharmaceuticals Product Mfr
N.A.I.C.S.: 325412
Peter Tsai (Chm)

ORIENT PLANET
PO Box 23345, Dubai, United Arab Emirates
Tel.: (971) 4 3988901
Web Site: http://www.orientplanet.com
Sales Range: $10-24.9 Million
Emp.: 45
Public Relations
N.A.I.C.S.: 541820
Nidal Abou Zaki (Mng Dir)

ORIENT PRECISION INDUSTRIES INC.
26-5 Suchul-daero 9-gil, Gumi, 39255, Gyeongsangbuk-Do, Korea (South)
Tel.: (82) 544737200
Web Site: https://www.orientpi.co.kr
Year Founded: 1987
065500—(KRS)
Rev.: $103,010,557
Assets: $95,877,127
Liabilities: $57,396,353
Net Worth: $38,480,774
Earnings: ($5,124,418)
Emp.: 61
Fiscal Year-end: 12/31/22
Automobile Parts Mfr
N.A.I.C.S.: 336390
Yongmin Kim (Dir)

Subsidiaries:

Pregen Inc. (1)
173-8 Yongmyeonggongdan-Gil, Geoncheon-Eup, Gyeongju, 780903, Korea (South)
Tel.: (82) 43 8797000
Sales Range: $1-9.9 Million
Emp.: 25
Electronic Components Mfr
N.A.I.C.S.: 334419
Jae-Il Yu (CEO)

ORIENT PRESS LIMITED
11th Fl 1102 E-Wing Lotus Corporate Park off western express highway, Goregaon East, Mumbai, 400063, Maharashtra, India
Tel.: (91) 9920623125
Web Site: https://www.orientpressltd.com
Year Founded: 1987
526325—(BOM)
Rev.: $20,856,725
Assets: $21,592,036
Liabilities: $13,420,443
Net Worth: $8,171,593
Earnings: ($127,274)
Emp.: 141
Fiscal Year-end: 03/31/24
Printing Services
N.A.I.C.S.: 323111
Sanjay Maheshwari (Exec Dir)

Subsidiaries:

Fortune Couriers Ltd. (1)
Gala No 27 Nm Joshi Marg Delisle Road Pragati Industrial Estate, Lower Parel, Mumbai, 400 011, Maharashtra, India
Tel.: (91) 2223061251
Web Site: http://www.orientpressltd.com
Sales Range: $25-49.9 Million
Emp.: 10
Courier Service
N.A.I.C.S.: 492110
Gopal Somani (Mgr-Fin)

ORIENT RENTAL MODARABA
Plot 9 Sector 24 Korangi Industrial Area, Shahra-e-Faysal, Karachi, Pakistan
Tel.: (92) 21111676670
Web Site: https://www.orientmodaraba.com
Year Founded: 1996
ORM—(PSX)
Rev.: $6,338,091
Assets: $7,858,440
Liabilities: $3,349,855
Net Worth: $4,508,585
Earnings: $674,538
Emp.: 1,296
Fiscal Year-end: 06/30/23

INTERNATIONAL PUBLIC

Power Generator Rental Services
N.A.I.C.S.: 532490

ORIENT SECURITIES COMPANY LIMITED
Orient Securities Building No 119 South Zhongshan Road, Huangpu District, Shanghai, 200010, China
Tel.: (86) 2163325888 CN
Web Site: https://www.dfzq.com.cn
Year Founded: 1998
3958—(HKG)
Rev.: $3,361,401,889
Assets: $53,125,063,968
Liabilities: $42,220,074,352
Net Worth: $10,904,989,616
Earnings: $381,674,236
Emp.: 8,452
Fiscal Year-end: 12/31/23
Investment Banking Services
N.A.I.C.S.: 523150
Xinjun Pan (Chm)

Subsidiaries:

Citi Orient Securities Company Limited (1)
24/F No 318 South Zhong Shan Rd, Shanghai, 200010, China
Tel.: (86) 2123153888
Web Site: http://www.citiorient.com
Investment Banking Services
N.A.I.C.S.: 523150
Pan Xinjun (Chm)

Imagina Media Audiovisual, S.L. (1)
Edificio Imagina Centro Audiovisual, Avenida Diagonal 177-183, 8018, Barcelona, Spain
Tel.: (34) 934761551
Web Site: http://www.imagina.tv
Holding Company; Media Production Services
N.A.I.C.S.: 551112
Jaume Roures (CEO)

Subsidiary (Domestic):

Mediaproduccion S.L.U. (2)
Avinguda Diagonal 177, 08018, Barcelona, Spain
Tel.: (34) 93 476 15 51
Web Site: http://www.mediapro.tv
Emp.: 60
Audio & Video Equipment Distr
N.A.I.C.S.: 423690

Servicios Audiovisuales Overon, S.L. (2)
C Virgilio 2, Pozuelo de Alarcon, 28223, Madrid, Spain (51%)
Tel.: (34) 91 512 17 00
Web Site: http://www.overon.es
Satellite Telecommunication Infrastructure Services
N.A.I.C.S.: 517410

Xarxa Oberta de Comunicacio i Tecnologia de Catalunya s.a (2)
Avda Del Parc Logistic 12-20 Building C, 08040, Barcelona, Spain (100%)
Tel.: (34) 93 557 98 00
Web Site: http://www.xarxaoberta.cat
Sales Range: $25-49.9 Million
Emp.: 3
Broadband Communication Services
N.A.I.C.S.: 517810

Orient Futures International (Singapore) Pte Ltd. (1)
1 Wallich Street 30-03 Guoco Tower, Singapore, 078881, Singapore
Tel.: (65) 69557500
Web Site: https://www.orientfutures.com.sg
Financial Services
N.A.I.C.S.: 522320

Orient Securities Investment Banking Co., Ltd. (1)
24/F318 South Zhong Shan Rd, Shanghai, 200010, China
Tel.: (86) 2213153888
Investment Banking Services
N.A.I.C.S.: 523150

ORIENT SECURITIES INTER-

AND PRIVATE COMPANIES

NATIONAL HOLDINGS LIMITED
Room 3101 31st Floor China Merchants Tower Shun Tak Centre, 168-200 Connaught Road, Central, China (Hong Kong)
Tel.: (852) 21809292
Web Site:
   www.orientsec.com.hk
8001—(HKG)
Rev.: $6,023,882
Assets: $49,258,236
Liabilities: $4,288,585
Net Worth: $44,969,651
Earnings: $2,318,416
Emp.: 16
Fiscal Year-end: 12/31/21
Securities Brokerage Services
N.A.I.C.S.: 523150
Mun Kei Choy *(Sec)*

Subsidiaries:

Orient Securities Finance Limited (1)
Room 3101 31/F China Merchants Tower Shun Tak Centre, 168-200 Connaught Road Central, Hong Kong, China (Hong Kong)
Tel.: (852) 2 561 8828
Web Site: https://www.orientsecfin.com.hk
Loan Provider
N.A.I.C.S.: 522390

ORIENT SEMICONDUCTOR ELECTRONICS LIMITED
No 9 Central 3rd St, Nanzih Dist, Kaohsiung, 811, Taiwan
Tel.: (886) 73613131
Web Site: https://www.ose.com.tw
Year Founded: 1971
2329—(TAI)
Rev.: $545,813,642
Assets: $603,911,420
Liabilities: $235,232,177
Net Worth: $368,679,243
Earnings: $61,519,668
Emp.: 5,280
Fiscal Year-end: 12/31/23
Semiconductor Electronics Mfr
N.A.I.C.S.: 334413
Yueh-Ming Tung *(Chm & Pres)*

Subsidiaries:

OSE Philippines Inc. (1)
6 Ring Rd Light Industry & Science Park II LISP II, Laguna, Philippines
Tel.: (63) 495457188
Web Site: http://www.ose.com.ph
Sales Range: $200-249.9 Million
Emp.: 600
Semiconductor & Related Device Mfr
N.A.I.C.S.: 334413

Orient Semiconductor Electronics Inc (1)
2223 Old Oakland Rd, San Jose, CA 95131-1402
Tel.: (408) 452-9080
Semiconductor & Related Device Mfr
N.A.I.C.S.: 334413

ORIENT TELECOMS PLC
Suite 2B-25-1 25th Floor Block 2B Plaza Sentral Jalan Stesen Sentral 5, 50470, Kuala Lumpur, Malaysia
Tel.: (60) 77860448   UK
Web Site: https://www.orient-telecoms.com
Year Founded: 2016
ORNT—(LSE)
Rev.: $584,976
Assets: $1,015,105
Liabilities: $332,627
Net Worth: $682,478
Earnings: $50,895
Emp.: 11
Fiscal Year-end: 03/31/23
Telecommunication Servicesb
N.A.I.C.S.: 517111
Sayed Mustafa Ali *(CTO)*

ORIENT THAI AIRLINES
18 Ratchadapisek Road , Klongtoey, Bangkok, 10110, Thailand
Tel.: (66) 2294260
Web Site: http://www.fly12go.com
Sales Range: $150-199.9 Million
Emp.: 644
Oil Transportation Services
N.A.I.C.S.: 481111
Udom Tantiprasongchai *(Chm)*

ORIENT TRADELINK LIMITED
141-A Ground Floor Shahpur Jat Village, New Delhi, 110 049, India
Tel.: (91) 9999313918
Web Site:
   https://www.orienttradelink.in
Year Founded: 1994
531512—(BOM)
Rev.: $1,463,122
Assets: $5,782,562
Liabilities: $4,480,444
Net Worth: $1,302,118
Earnings: $98,069
Emp.: 5
Fiscal Year-end: 03/31/21
Entertainment Services
N.A.I.C.S.: 512110
Aushim Parshottam Khetarpal *(Chm & Mng Dir)*

ORIENT VICTORY SMART URBAN SERVICES HOLDING LIMITED
7th Floor Winbase Centre 208 Queens Road Central, Sheung Wan, China (Hong Kong)
Tel.: (852) 35906280   Ky
Web Site:
   http://www.orientvictory.com.hk
0265—(HKG)
Rev.: $28,938,293
Assets: $103,507,050
Liabilities: $26,205,968
Net Worth: $77,301,083
Earnings: $3,559,163
Emp.: 2,312
Fiscal Year-end: 12/31/22
Holding Company
N.A.I.C.S.: 551112
Baodong Shi *(Chm & CEO)*

Subsidiaries:

Hong Kong Four Seas Tours Limited (1)
1-3 F On Lok Yuen Bldg 25-27A Des Voeux Rd, Central, China (Hong Kong)
Tel.: (852) 22007777
Web Site: www.fourseastravel.com
Airline Ticket Booking & Transport Services
N.A.I.C.S.: 561510

ORIENTAL AROMATICS LTD.
133 Jehangir Building 2nd Floor Mahatma Gandhi Road, Mumbai, 400 001, India
Tel.: (91) 224 321 4000
Web Site:
   http://www.orientalaromatics.com
Year Founded: 1961
500078—(NSE)
Rev.: $119,191,855
Assets: $118,055,847
Liabilities: $35,443,317
Net Worth: $82,612,530
Earnings: $7,275,764
Emp.: 744
Fiscal Year-end: 03/31/22
Aroma Chemical Mfr
N.A.I.C.S.: 325998
Dharmil Anil Bodani *(Chm & Mng Dir)*

ORIENTAL CARBON & CHEMICALS LIMITED
14th Floor Tower-B World Trade Tower Plot no C-1 Sector-16, Noida, 201301, India
Tel.: (91) 1204744800
Web Site: https://www.occlindia.com
Year Founded: 1978
OCCL—(NSE)
Rev.: $52,757,482
Assets: $111,101,527
Liabilities: $36,246,319
Net Worth: $74,855,208
Earnings: $11,328,067
Emp.: 423
Fiscal Year-end: 03/31/21
Chemical Products Mfr & Distr
N.A.I.C.S.: 325180
Jagdish Prasad Goenka *(Chm)*

ORIENTAL CHAIN MFG. CO., LTD.
485 Miyanagaichimachi, Hakusan, 924-0016, Ishikawa, Japan
Tel.: (81) 762761155
Web Site: https://www.ocm.co.jp
Year Founded: 1947
6380—(TKS)
Sales Range: $25-49.9 Million
Automobile Chain Mfr
N.A.I.C.S.: 333613
Takeshi Nishimura *(Pres & CEO)*

ORIENTAL CONSULTANTS HOLDINGS COMPANY LIMITED
Tokyo Opera City Tower 9F 20-2 Nishishinjuku 3-chome, Shinjuku-ku, Tokyo, 163-1409, Japan
Tel.: (81) 63117570
Web Site: https://www.ocglobal.jp
Year Founded: 2006
2498—(TKS)
Rev.: $554,111,860
Assets: $444,429,560
Liabilities: $287,109,550
Net Worth: $157,320,010
Earnings: $20,071,790
Emp.: 1,461
Fiscal Year-end: 09/30/23
Engineeering Services
N.A.I.C.S.: 541330
Akio Tatsuno *(CFO-Gen Admin)*

Subsidiaries:

A-TEC Co., Ltd. (1)
Sumitomo Realty Development Izuminishi Shinjuku Building 6F 4-12-7, Honmachi Shibuya- ku, Tokyo, 151-0071, Japan
Tel.: (81) 363118151
Engineering Consulting Services
N.A.I.C.S.: 541330

Asano Taiseikiso Engineering Co., Ltd. (1)
2-8-7 Kitaueno, Taito-ku, Tokyo, 110-0014, Japan
Tel.: (81) 352464150
Web Site: https://www.atk-eng.jp
Emp.: 328
Environmental Engineering Services
N.A.I.C.S.: 541330

Chuou Sekkei Engineering Company Limited (1)
Tel.: (81) 762631220
Web Site: http://www.cser.co.jp
Emp.: 130
Environmental Engineering Services
N.A.I.C.S.: 541330
Nakatsuji Eiji *(Gen Mgr)*

ORIENTAL CULTURE HOLDING LTD.
No 2 Youzishan Road Dongba Street Room 1402, Richmake Commercial Building, Nanjing, 210000, Jiangsu, China
Tel.: (86) 2585766891   Ky
Year Founded: 2018
OCG—(NASDAQ)
Rev.: $17,813,139

ORIENTAL FOOD INDUSTRIES HOLDINGS BERHAD

Assets: $53,388,848
Liabilities: $3,773,000
Net Worth: $49,615,848
Earnings: $3,235,686
Emp.: 57
Fiscal Year-end: 12/31/22
Holding Company
N.A.I.C.S.: 551112

ORIENTAL ENERGY CO., LTD.
No 1 Ziqi Road Xuzhuang Software Park Xianlin Avenue, Nanjing, 210042, Jiangsu, China
Tel.: (86) 2586819806
Web Site: http://www.chinadhe.com
Year Founded: 1996
002221—(SSE)
Rev.: $4,099,539,600
Assets: $5,807,032,452
Liabilities: $4,113,440,604
Net Worth: $1,693,591,848
Earnings: $5,968,404
Fiscal Year-end: 12/31/22
Liquefied Petroleum Gas Distr
N.A.I.C.S.: 424720
Yifeng Zhou *(Chm)*

ORIENTAL ENTERPRISE HOLDINGS LIMITED
Oriental Media Centre 23 Dai Cheong Street Tai Po Industrial Estate, Hong Kong, China (Hong Kong)
Tel.: (852) 36001125
Web Site: https://oeh.on.cc
0018—(HKG)
Rev.: $99,173,883
Assets: $265,426,394
Liabilities: $25,000,580
Net Worth: $240,425,814
Earnings: $21,652,389
Emp.: 960
Fiscal Year-end: 03/31/23
Printing & Publishing Industry
N.A.I.C.S.: 513110
Shun-chuen Lam *(CEO)*

ORIENTAL EXPLORER HOLDINGS LTD.
Units 22-28 25/F Tower A Southmark 11 Yip Hing Street, Wong Chuk Hang, Hong Kong, China (Hong Kong)
Tel.: (852) 28022668   BM
0430—(HKG)
Sales Range: $1-9.9 Million
Emp.: 12
Holding Company
N.A.I.C.S.: 551112
Kenneth Chi Yung Lau *(Chm)*

ORIENTAL FOOD INDUSTRIES HOLDINGS BERHAD
No 65 Jalan Usaha 7 Ayer Keroh Industrial Estate, 75450, Melaka, Malaysia
Tel.: (60) 62310333
Web Site: https://www.ofih.com.my
OFI—(KLS)
Rev.: $71,310,619
Assets: $69,847,606
Liabilities: $15,194,685
Net Worth: $54,652,922
Earnings: $4,495,352
Fiscal Year-end: 03/31/22
Snack Food & Confectionery Mfr
N.A.I.C.S.: 311340
Karina Mei Ying Chong *(Co-Sec)*

Subsidiaries:

Oriental Food Industries Sdn. Bhd. (1)
No 65 Jalan Usaha 7, Ayer Keroh Industrial Estate, 75450, Melaka, Malaysia
Tel.: (60) 62310333
Confectionery Food Product Mfr
N.A.I.C.S.: 311999
Datuk Seri Chen Chuan *(Mng Dir)*

ORIENTAL HOLDINGS BERHAD

Oriental Food Industries Holdings Berhad—(Continued)

ORIENTAL HOLDINGS BERHAD
1st Floor 25B Lebuh Farquhar, 10200, Penang, Malaysia
Tel.: (60) 42638590
Web Site: https://www.ohb.com.my
Year Founded: 1963
4006—(KLS)
Rev: $809,958,095
Assets: $2,201,691,005
Liabilities: $506,974,180
Net Worth: $1,694,716,825
Earnings: $135,036,614
Emp.: 9,154
Fiscal Year-end: 12/31/22
Diversified Holding Company
N.A.I.C.S.: 551112
Robert Lum Kong Lum Kong Wong *(Mng Dir)*

Subsidiaries:

30 Bencoolen Pte. Ltd. (1)
30 Bencoolen Street, Singapore, 189621, Singapore
Tel.: (65) 63372882
Web Site: https://www.30bencoolen.com.sg
Hotel & Resort Services
N.A.I.C.S.: 721110
Justus Lim *(Mgr-Front Office)*

Armstrong Cycle Parts (Sdn). Berhad (1)
1028 Prai Industrial Complex Prai, 13600, Penang, Malaysia
Tel.: (60) 4 390 8554
Web Site: http://www.armstrongcycle.com
Vehicle Parts Mfr
N.A.I.C.S.: 336991

Armstrong Auto Parts Sdn. Berhad (1)
Tikam Batu Industrial Estate Sungai Petani, 08600, Kedah, Malaysia
Tel.: (60) 4 438 8202
Automobile Parts Mfr
N.A.I.C.S.: 336390

Armstrong Component Parts (Vietnam) Co., Ltd. (1)
Lot No 23 Noi Bai Industrial Zone, Soc Son District, Hanoi, Vietnam
Tel.: (84) 43 582 0222
Web Site: https://www.armstrong-auto.com
Automobile Parts Mfr
N.A.I.C.S.: 336390

Armstrong Cycle Parts (Sdn.) Berhad - Alor Gajah Factory (1)
1st Floor 25-B Farquhar Street, 10200, Penang, Malaysia
Tel.: (60) 42638590
Automotive Related Product Mfr
N.A.I.C.S.: 336110

Armstrong Industries Sdn. Bhd. (1)
Lot 3 Jalan P/10, Kawasan Perusahaan Seksyen 10, 43650, Prai, Selangor, Malaysia
Tel.: (60) 389251788
Web Site: https://armstrongind.com.my
Plastics Product Mfr
N.A.I.C.S.: 326199

Armstrong Realty Sdn. Bhd. (1)
Tikam Batu Industrial Estate, Sungai Petani, 08600, Kedah, Malaysia
Tel.: (60) 4 438 8202
Real Estate Services
N.A.I.C.S.: 531390

Armstrong Trading & Supplies Sdn. Bhd. (1)
Tikam Batu Industrial Estate Sungai Petani, 08600, Kedah, Malaysia
Tel.: (60) 4 438 8202
Web Site: http://www.armstrongcycle.com
Business Support Services
N.A.I.C.S.: 561499

Bayview International Sdn. Bhd. (1)
370 Ubi Road 3, Singapore, 408651, Singapore
Tel.: (65) 63391121
Web Site: https://www.bayviewhotels.com

Hotel Operator
N.A.I.C.S.: 721110

Boon Siew (Borneo) Sendirian Berhad (1)
62A Mile 5 1/2 Tuaran Road Inanam, 88450, Kota Kinabalu, Sabah, Malaysia
Tel.: (60) 88 421770
Automobile Parts Mfr
N.A.I.C.S.: 336390

Compounding & Colouring Sdn. Bhd. (1)
Lot 3 Jalan P/10 Kawasan Perusahaan Seksyen 10, 43650, Bandar Baru Bangi, Selangor, Malaysia
Tel.: (60) 389254272
Web Site: https://www.ccsboh.com.my
Emp.: 53
Plastics Product Mfr
N.A.I.C.S.: 326199

Dragon Frontier Sdn. Bhd. (1)
Lot 264 265 Tingkat Perusahaan Lima, Kawasan Perusahaan Perai 2, 13600, Perai, Penang, Malaysia
Tel.: (60) 4 399 6699
Web Site: https://www.tecksee.com.my
Plastics Product Mfr
N.A.I.C.S.: 326199

Happy Motoring Co. Sdn. Bhd. (1)
Simpang 137, PO Box 593, Jalan Gadong, BE3978, Bandar Seri Begawan, Brunei Darussalam
Tel.: (673) 2428328
Web Site: https://www.happy-motoring.com
Automobile Parts Mfr
N.A.I.C.S.: 336390

Jutajati Sdn. Bhd. (1)
1st Floor 25-B Farquhar Street, 10200, Penang, Malaysia
Tel.: (60) 42638244
Emp.: 20
Investment Services
N.A.I.C.S.: 523999

KM Agency Sdn. Bhd. (1)
124-A Lengkok Sungai, 10150, Penang, Malaysia
Tel.: (60) 42821000
Automobile Sales
N.A.I.C.S.: 423110

Kah Bintang Auto Sdn. Bhd. (1)
Wisma Kah Motor No 566 Batu 3 1/2, Jalan Ipoh, 51200, Kuala Lumpur, Malaysia
Tel.: (60) 3 6259 2888
Emp.: 600
Automobile Parts Mfr
N.A.I.C.S.: 336390

Kah Classic Auto Sdn. Bhd. (1)
Wisma Kah Motor No 566 Batu 3 1/2, Jalan Ipoh, 51200, Kuala Lumpur, Malaysia
Tel.: (60) 3 6259 2888
Automobile Mfr
N.A.I.C.S.: 336390

Kah Motor Company Sdn. Berhad (1)
Wisma Kah Motor No 566 Batu 3 1/2, Jalan Ipoh, 51200, Kuala Lumpur, Malaysia
Tel.: (60) 3 6259 2888
Motor Vehicles Mfr
N.A.I.C.S.: 336390

Kah Power Products Pte. Ltd. (1)
370 Ubi Road 3 Level 3 Kah Motor Ubi Building, Singapore, 408651, Singapore
Tel.: (65) 6514 5799
Web Site: http://www.kahpowerproducts.com.sg
Emp.: 2
Automotive Components Mfr
N.A.I.C.S.: 336390

Kasai Teck See (Malaysia) Sdn. Bhd. (1)
No 4 Jalan Pasak 15/8 Off Jalan Utas, 40200, Shah Alam, Selangor Darul Ehsan, Malaysia
Tel.: (60) 3 5510 3181
Emp.: 200
Plastics Product Mfr
N.A.I.C.S.: 326199

Kingdom Properties Co. Limited (1)
Lot 1 2nd Floor Wisma Siamloh, Jalan Kemajuan, 87007, Labuan, Malaysia

Tel.: (60) 87417810
Hotel Operator
N.A.I.C.S.: 721110

Konkrit Utara Sdn. Bhd. (1)
62 Jalan Sri Bahari, 10050, Penang, Malaysia
Tel.: (60) 4 263 6486
Property Development Services
N.A.I.C.S.: 531390

Lipro Electrical Manufacturing Sdn. Bhd. (1)
Lot 4 Jalan pasak 15/8 Off Jalan Utas, 40000, Shah Alam, Selangor, Malaysia
Tel.: (60) 3 5513 1388
Plastics Product Mfr
N.A.I.C.S.: 326199

Lipro Mold Engineering Sdn. Bhd. (1)
Lot 3 Jalan P/10 Kawasan Perusaahan Seksyen 10, 43650, Bandar Baru Bangi, Selangor, Malaysia
Tel.: (60) 3 8926 2668
Web Site: http://www.tecksee.com.my
Plastics Product Mfr
N.A.I.C.S.: 326199

Lipro Trading Sdn. Bhd. (1)
Level 8 Unit 8C 8D Wisma Boon Siew 1 Jalan, 10000, Penang, Malaysia
Tel.: (60) 42645979
Web Site: http://www.simenutara.com.my
Emp.: 15
Property Development Services
N.A.I.C.S.: 531390

Loh Boon Siew Education Sdn. Bhd. (1)
1st Floor 25-B Farquhar Street, 10200, Penang, Malaysia
Tel.: (60) 4 263 8244
Healtcare Services
N.A.I.C.S.: 923110

Melaka Straits Medical Centre Sdn. Bhd. (1)
1st Floor 25-B Farquhar Street, 10200, Penang, Malaysia
Tel.: (60) 4 263 8244
Medical Devices
N.A.I.C.S.: 622110

Nilam Healthcare Education Centre Sdn. Bhd. (1)
1st Floor 25-B Farquhar Street, 10200, Penang, Malaysia
Tel.: (60) 042638590
Web Site: http://www.ohb.com.my
Emp.: 60
Healthcare Education Services
N.A.I.C.S.: 923110

North Malaya (Xiamen) Steel Co., Ltd. (1)
29 Yangming Road Xinyang Industrial Zone, Haicang, Xiamen, 361022, China
Tel.: (86) 5926511380
Property Development Services
N.A.I.C.S.: 531390

North Malaya Engineers Overseas Sdn. Bhd. (1)
5268 Jalan Permatang Pauh, Mak Mandin Ind Estate, 13400, Butterworth, Penang, Malaysia
Tel.: (60) 43327228
Investment Services
N.A.I.C.S.: 523999

North Malaya Engineers Trading Company Sdn. Bhd. (1)
5268 Jalan Permatang Pauh, Mak Mandin Ind Estate, 13400, Butterworth, Penang, Malaysia
Tel.: (60) 43327228
Web Site: https://www.nmet.com.my
Property Development Services
N.A.I.C.S.: 531390

OAM Asia (Singapore) Pte. Ltd. (1)
Level 8 Unit 8E IG Wisma Boon Siew, 1 Jalan Penang, 10000, Penang, Malaysia
Tel.: (60) 42638202
Emp.: 10
Investment Services
N.A.I.C.S.: 523999

OBS (Singapore) Pte. Ltd. (1)

INTERNATIONAL PUBLIC

Level 8 Unit 8E 8F & 8G Wisma Boon Siew, 1 Jalan Penang, 10000, Penang, Malaysia
Tel.: (60) 4 263 8202
Investment Services
N.A.I.C.S.: 523999

Onward Leasing & Credit Sdn. Bhd. (1)
339 Mezzanine Floor, Jalan Tuanku Abdul Rahman, 50100, Kuala Lumpur, Malaysia
Tel.: (60) 3 2691 5571
Financial Services
N.A.I.C.S.: 522390

Oriental Asia (Mauritius) Pte. Ltd. (1)
Level 8 Unit 8E 8F & 8G Wisma Boon Siew, 1 Jalan Penang, 10000, Penang, Malaysia
Tel.: (60) 42638202
Investment Services
N.A.I.C.S.: 523999

Oriental Boon Siew (M) Sdn. Bhd. (1)
1st Floor 25-B Farquhar Street, 10200, Penang, Malaysia
Tel.: (60) 42638244
Property Development Services
N.A.I.C.S.: 531390

Oriental Boon Siew (Mauritius) Pte. Ltd. (1)
Level 8 Unit 8E 8F & 8G Wisma Boon Siew, 1 Jalan Penang, 10000, Penang, Malaysia
Tel.: (60) 42638202
Investment Services
N.A.I.C.S.: 523999

Oriental Industries (Wuxi) Co., Ltd. (1)
Wuxi National Hi-Tech Industrial Park, Plat 88-B Land, Wuxi, Jiangsu, China
Tel.: (86) 21 5838 8198
Web Site: http://www.tecksee.com.my
Plastics Product Mfr
N.A.I.C.S.: 326199

Oriental International (Mauritius) Pte. Ltd. (1)
Level 8 Unit 8E 8F & 8G Wisma Boon Siew, 1 Jalan Penang, 10000, Penang, Malaysia
Tel.: (60) 4 263 8202
Investment Services
N.A.I.C.S.: 523999

Oriental Nichinan Design Engineering Sdn. Bhd. (1)
Lot 3 Jalan P/10 Kawasan Perusahaan Seksyen 10, 43650, Bandar Baru Bangi, Selangor, Malaysia
Tel.: (60) 38 926 3090
Web Site: https://www.tecksee.com.my
Plastics Product Mfr
N.A.I.C.S.: 326199

Oriental Realty Sdn. Bhd. (1)
25-B Lebuh Farquhar, 10200, Penang, Malaysia
Tel.: (60) 42636314
Web Site: https://www.bsgproperty.com
Property Development Services
N.A.I.C.S.: 531390

Oriental Rubber & Palm Oil Sdn. Berhad (1)
Level 8 Unit 8E 8F & 8G Wisma Boon Siew, 1 Jalan Penang, 10000, Penang, Malaysia
Tel.: (60) 4 263 8202
Agricultural Services
N.A.I.C.S.: 311999

Oriental San Industries Sdn. Bhd. (1)
Lot 3 Jalan P/10 Kawasan Perusahaan, Seksyen 10, 43650, Bandar Baru Bangi, Selangor, Malaysia
Tel.: (60) 389251788
Web Site: http://www.tecksee.com.my
Emp.: 300
Plastics Product Mfr
N.A.I.C.S.: 326199

PT Dapo Agro Makmur (1)
Level 8 Unit 8E 8F & 8G Wisma Boon Siew, 1 Jalan Penang, 10000, Penang, Malaysia

AND PRIVATE COMPANIES

Tel.: (60) 4 263 8202
Agricultural Services
N.A.I.C.S.: 311999

PT Gunung Maras Lestari (1)
Level 8 Unit 8E 8F & 8G Wisma Boon Siew, 1 Jalan Penang, 10000, Penang, Malaysia
Tel.: (60) 4 263 8202
Emp.: 20
Agricultural Services
N.A.I.C.S.: 311999

PT Gunung Sawit Salatan Lestari (1)
Level 8 Unit 8E 8F & 8G Wisma Boon Siew, 1 Jalan Penang, 10000, Penang, Malaysia
Tel.: (60) 4 263 8202
Agricultural Services
N.A.I.C.S.: 311999

PT Gunungsawit Binalestari (1)
Level 8 Unit 8E 8F & 8G Wisma Boon Siew, 1 Jalan Penang, 10000, Penang, Malaysia
Tel.: (60) 4 263 8202
Emp.: 623
Agricultural Services
N.A.I.C.S.: 311999

PT Pratama Palm Abadi (1)
Level 8 Unit 8E 8F & 8G Wisma Boon Siew, 1 Jalan Penang, 10000, Penang, Malaysia
Tel.: (60) 4 263 8202
Agricultural Services
N.A.I.C.S.: 311999
Chc Morison (Gen Mgr)

Park Suanplu Holdings Co. Ltd. (1)
39 Soi Suanplu South Sathorn Road, Sathorn, Bangkok, Thailand
Tel.: (66) 2 636 8663
Web Site: http://www.somerset.com
Hotel Operator
N.A.I.C.S.: 721110

Selasih Permata Sdn. Bhd. (1)
Level 8 Unit 8E 8F 8G Wisma Boon Siew, 1 Jalan Penang, 10000, Penang, Malaysia (100%)
Tel.: (60) 42638202
Investment Services
N.A.I.C.S.: 523999

Simen Utara Sdn. Bhd. (1)
Level 8 Unit 8C 8D Wisma Boon Siew, No 1 Penang Road, 10000, Penang, Malaysia
Tel.: (60) 44644939
Web Site: https://www.simenutara.com.my
Emp.: 26
Real Estate Development Services
N.A.I.C.S.: 531390

Star Joy Sdn. Bhd. (1)
Pusat Perubatan, Klebang, 75200, Melaka, Malaysia
Tel.: (60) 63158888
Healthcare Centre Services
N.A.I.C.S.: 621999

Suanplu Bhiman Limited (1)
256/9 Sukhumvit 16 Kong Toey, Bangkok, Thailand
Tel.: (66) 26775003
Resort Operator
N.A.I.C.S.: 721110

Syarikat Oriental Credit Berhad (1)
Wisma Kah Motor No 566 Batu 3 1/2, Jalan Ipoh, 51200, Kuala Lumpur, Malaysia
Tel.: (60) 3 6259 2888
Web Site: http://www.ohb.com.my
Credit Services
N.A.I.C.S.: 522390

Teck See Plastics Sdn. Bhd (1)
Lot 4 Jalan Pasak 15/8 Off Jalan Utas, 40000, Shah Alam, Selangor Darul Ehsan, Malaysia
Tel.: (60) 355103188
Web Site: https://www.tecksee.com.my
Plastics Product Mfr
N.A.I.C.S.: 326199

Ultra Green Sdn. Bhd. (1)
1st Floor 25-B Lebuh Farquhar, 10200, Penang, Malaysia
Tel.: (60) 42638590
Property Development Services

N.A.I.C.S.: 531390

Unique Mix (Penang) Sdn. Bhd. (1)
62 Jalan Sri Bahari, 10050, Penang, Malaysia
Tel.: (60) 42636486
Web Site: http://www.uniquemix.com.my
Property Development Services
N.A.I.C.S.: 531390

Unique Mix Sdn. Bhd. (1)
18-20-2 Jalan SR 8/3 Sin Heap Lee Business Centre, 43300, Taman Putra Indah, Selangor Darul Ehsan, Malaysia
Tel.: (60) 3 8943 3976
Property Development Services
N.A.I.C.S.: 531390

Unique Pave Sdn. Bhd. (1)
Level 8 Unit 8C & 8D Wisma Boon Siew, 1 Jalan Penang, 10000, Penang, Malaysia
Tel.: (60) 4 264 1063
Property Development Services
N.A.I.C.S.: 531390

ORIENTAL HOTELS LTD.
Paramount Plaza -III Floor 47 Mahatma Gandhi Road, Chennai, 600034, Tamil Nadu, India
Tel.: (91) 4466172828
Web Site: https://orientalhotels.co.in
500314—(BOM)
Rev.: $48,591,799
Assets: $99,269,924
Liabilities: $34,643,702
Net Worth: $64,626,221
Earnings: $6,653,198
Emp.: 628
Fiscal Year-end: 03/31/23
Hotel Owner & Operator
N.A.I.C.S.: 721110
Pramod Ranjan (Mng Dir & Mng Dir)

ORIENTAL INTEREST BERHAD
No 34 35 Lengkok Cempaka 2 Bandar Amanjaya, 08000, Sungai Petani, Kedah, Malaysia
Tel.: (60) 44481018
Web Site: https://www.oibgroup.com
OIB—(KLS)
Rev.: $113,085,291
Assets: $325,899,683
Liabilities: $150,198,095
Net Worth: $175,701,587
Earnings: $20,437,672
Emp.: 476
Fiscal Year-end: 08/31/23
Commercial & Residential Property Development Services
N.A.I.C.S.: 531311
Yit Chan Tai (Co-Sec)

ORIENTAL INTERNATIONAL ENTERPRISE LIMITED
Tower A 85 Loushanguan Rd, Shanghai, 200336, China
Tel.: (86) 2152291111
Web Site: https://www.oie.com.cn
Year Founded: 1998
600278—(SHG)
Rev.: $5,823,387,634
Assets: $2,666,062,718
Liabilities: $1,621,547,020
Net Worth: $1,044,515,698
Earnings: $51,961,857
Fiscal Year-end: 12/31/22
Apparel & Textile Product Whslr
N.A.I.C.S.: 424990
Tan Ming (Chm)

Subsidiaries:

Orient International Shangai Hometex Co., Ltd. (1)
Hometex Mansion 210 Si Ping Road, Shanghai, 200086, China
Tel.: (86) 21 65218500
Web Site: http://www.hometextile.com
Textile Products Distr
N.A.I.C.S.: 424310

Orient International Shanghai Textile Co., Ltd. (1)
200 Siping Road Suntex International Building, Shanghai, 200086, China
Tel.: (86) 21 6521 2200
Textile Products Distr
N.A.I.C.S.: 424310

Oriental International Shanghai Knitwear Co., Ltd. (1)
Floor 3 26 27 Guangming Building No 2 East Jinling road, Shanghai, 200002, China
Tel.: (86) 21 63299000
Web Site: http://www.shknit.com
Textile Products Distr
N.A.I.C.S.: 424310

Shanghai Dongsong International Trading Co., Ltd. (1)
17th Floor Shenhua Finance Tower No 1 Ningbo Road, Shanghai, 200002, China
Tel.: (86) 21 63230480
Web Site: http://www.dongsong-cn.com
Industrial Machinery Distr
N.A.I.C.S.: 423830
Pang Jiquan (Mng Dir & Gen Mgr)

Shanghai Gaonan Garments Co., Ltd. (1)
No 501 Hangnan Rd, Pudong, Shanghai, 200105, China
Tel.: (86) 2158672028
Textile Products Mfr
N.A.I.C.S.: 314999

ORIENTAL LAND CO., LTD.
1-1 Maihama, Urayasu, 279-8511, Chiba, Japan
Tel.: (81) 473053017
Web Site: https://www.olc.co.jp
Year Founded: 1960
OLCLF—(OTCIQ)
Rev.: $4,088,238,730
Assets: $8,957,971,150
Liabilities: $2,681,359,720
Net Worth: $6,276,611,430
Earnings: $794,687,250
Emp.: 5,631
Fiscal Year-end: 03/31/24
Holding Company; Hotels & Resorts, Theme Park, Shopping Center & Monorail System Owner & Operator
N.A.I.C.S.: 551112
Toshio Kagami (Chm)

Subsidiaries:

Bay Food Services Co., Ltd. (1)
35-1 Maihama, Urayasu, 279-8527, Chiba-ken, Japan
Tel.: (81) 473055432
Convenience Stores Operating Services
N.A.I.C.S.: 445112
Hiroaki Hirayama (Pres)

Design Factory Co. Ltd. (1)
35-1 Maihama Urayasu-shi, Chiba-ken, 2798526, Chiba, Japan (100%)
Tel.: (81) 473055400
Sales Range: $25-49.9 Million
Emp.: 25
Commercial Gravure Printing
N.A.I.C.S.: 323111

E Production Co. Ltd. (1)
1-1 Maihama, Urayasu, Chiba, Japan (100%)
Tel.: (81) 473053488
Motion Picture & Video Production
N.A.I.C.S.: 512110
Masahiko Naito (Pres)

Green & Arts Co., Ltd. (1)
35-1 Maihama Urayasu-shi, Chiba, 279-8511, Japan (100%)
Tel.: (81) 473055300
Heavy & Civil Engineering Construction
N.A.I.C.S.: 237990

IKSPIARI Co. Ltd. (1)
1-4 Maihama, Urayasu, 279-8529, Chiba, Japan (100%)
Tel.: (81) 473052555
Web Site: http://www.ikspiari.com
Sales Range: $75-99.9 Million
Emp.: 130
Nonresidential Buildings Lessors

N.A.I.C.S.: 531120

M TECH Co., Ltd. (1)
1-1 Maihama, Urayasu, 279-8504, Chiba, Japan (100%)
Tel.: (81) 473055230
Web Site: http://mtc.olc.co.jp
Emp.: 142
Theme Park Maintenance & Grounds Services
N.A.I.C.S.: 713110
Tadashi Takahashi (Pres)

Maihama Building Maintenance Co. Ltd. (1)
1-5-2 NBF Bldg 9th Floor Shin-Urayasu, 279-0012, Chiba, Japan (100%)
Tel.: (81) 473055360
Web Site: http://www.olc.co.jp
Sales Range: $650-699.9 Million
Emp.: 1,500
Nonresidential Buildings Lessors
N.A.I.C.S.: 531120
Kouichi Nishiyama (Pres)

Maihama Corporation Co. Ltd. (1)
1-1 Maihama, Urayasu, 279-8521, Chiba, Japan
Tel.: (81) 473055370
Web Site: https://www.mcc.olc.co.jp
Emp.: 469
Business & Massage Services
N.A.I.C.S.: 561499
Takafumi Nakazawa (Pres)

Maihama Resort Line Co. Ltd. (1)
2-18 Maihama, Urayasu, Chiba, Japan (100%)
Tel.: (81) 473052405
Web Site: http://www.olc.co.jp
Sales Range: $25-49.9 Million
Emp.: 160
Hotels & Motels
N.A.I.C.S.: 721110

Milial Resort Hotels Co., Ltd. (1)
29-1 Maihama, Urayasu, 279-8522, Chiba, Japan (100%)
Tel.: (81) 473052800
Web Site: http://www.milialresorthotels.co.jp
Sales Range: $650-699.9 Million
Emp.: 1,767
Holding Company; Hotel Operator
N.A.I.C.S.: 551112
Toshio Kagami (Exec Dir)

Subsidiary (Domestic):

Brighton Co., Ltd. (2)
1-9-1 Mihama, Urayasu, 279-0011, Chiba, Japan (100%)
Tel.: (81) 473502111
Web Site: https://www.brightonhotels.co.jp
Sales Range: $150-199.9 Million
Emp.: 650
Holding Company; Hotel Operator
N.A.I.C.S.: 551112
Osamu Tsumekawa (Pres)

OLC/Rights Entertainment (Japan) Inc (1)
Mitsubishi Kyobashi Building 8F, 1-7-3 Ginza Chuo-ku, 104-0061, Tokyo, Japan (100%)
Tel.: (81) 351595050
Web Site: http://www.olc.co.jp
Sales Range: $25-49.9 Million
Emp.: 21
Intellectual Property Rights Business Services
N.A.I.C.S.: 561499
Okada Tadaaki (Pres)

Photo Works Co., Ltd. (1)
35-1 Maihama, Urayasu, Chiba, Japan
Tel.: (81) 473055330
Photographic Services
N.A.I.C.S.: 541922

Resort Costuming Service Co., Ltd. (1)
2-18 Maihama, Urayasu, Chiba, Japan
Tel.: (81) 47 381 3693
Costume Leasing & Cleaning Services
N.A.I.C.S.: 532281

Resort Costuming Services Co., Ltd. (1)
2-18 Maihama, Urayasu, 279-8570, Chiba, Japan

ORIENTAL LAND CO., LTD.

Oriental Land Co., Ltd.—(Continued)
Tel.: (81) 47 305 5280
Web Site: https://www.rcs.olc.co.jp
Costume Rental Services
N.A.I.C.S.: 532281

Retail Networks Co. Ltd. (1)
2-1-1 Kami-Meguro Meguro-ku, Tokyo, Japan (100%)
Tel.: (81) 357732500
Gift Novelty & Souvenir Stores
N.A.I.C.S.: 459420

ORIENTAL MERCHANT PTY. LTD.
10 Westgate Drive, Laverton, 3026, VIC, Australia
Tel.: (61) 392508133
Web Site: http://www.oriental.com.au
Year Founded: 1975
Sales Range: $25-49.9 Million
Emp.: 350
Grocery Product Whslr
N.A.I.C.S.: 424490
Subsidiaries:

Oriental Merchant Europe Ltd. (1)
Unit 11 Eurocourt Oliver Close, West Thurrock, RM20 3EE, Essex, United Kingdom
Tel.: (44) 1708691988
Web Site: http://www.orientalmerchant.eu
Grocery Product Distr
N.A.I.C.S.: 445110

ORIENTAL MOTOR CO., LTD.
6 16 17 Ueno Taito Ku, Tokyo, 110 8563, Japan
Tel.: (81) 338350684
Web Site:
  http://www.orientalmotor.co.jp
Year Founded: 1885
Sales Range: $10-24.9 Million
Emp.: 2,054
Mfr of Small Precision Motors, Power Motors, Control Motors, Fans
N.A.I.C.S.: 336320
Shohachiro Wakabayashi (Chm)
Subsidiaries:

INA Oriental Motor Co., Ltd. (1)
144 B 9 L Namdong Industrial Complex, 716 8 Gojan Dong, Incheon, 405-821, Korea (South)
Tel.: (82) 328198721
Web Site: http://www.inaom.co.kr
Motor & Generator Mfr
N.A.I.C.S.: 335312

ORIENTAL MOTOR (INDIA) PVT.LTD. (1)
No 810 8th Floor Prestige Meridian-I No 29 M G Road, Bengaluru, 560 001, India
Tel.: (91) 80 41125586
Web Site: http://www.orientalmotor.co.in
Emp.: 10
Motor & Actuator Distr
N.A.I.C.S.: 423610
BJ Indrakumar (Mgr-Sls)

ORIENTAL MOTOR DO BRASIL LTDA. (1)
Rua Augusta 1642-cj 6B-Cerqueira Cesar-CEP, Sao Paulo, 01304-001, Brazil
Tel.: (55) 11 3266 6018
Web Site: http://www.orientalmotor.com.br
Motor & Actuator Distr
N.A.I.C.S.: 423610

Oriental Motor (Europa) GmbH (1)
Schiess Strasse 74, 40549, Dusseldorf, Germany
Tel.: (49) 2115206700
Web Site: http://www.orientalmotor.de
Motor & Generator Mfr
N.A.I.C.S.: 335312
Georg Schuhmacher (Mgr-Sls)

Oriental Motor (France) Sarl (1)
32 Ave de I lle Saint-Martin, 92737, Nanterre, France
Tel.: (33) 147869750
Web Site: http://www.orientalmotor.fr
Emp.: 200

Motor & Generator Mfr
N.A.I.C.S.: 335312
Thomas Buchi (Mgr)

Oriental Motor (Malaysia) Sdn. Bhd. (1)
A 13 1 N Point Offices, Mid Vly City No 1 Medan Syed, 59200, Kuala Lumpur, Malaysia
Tel.: (60) 322875778
Web Site: http://www.orientalmotor.com.my
Emp.: 8
Motor & Generator Mfr
N.A.I.C.S.: 335312

Oriental Motor (Thailand) Co.,Ltd (1)
900 8th Floor Zone C Tonson Tower Ploenchit Rd, Lumpini Pathumwan, 10330, Bangkok, Thailand
Tel.: (66) 22511871
Web Site: http://www.orientalmotor.co.th
Motor & Generator Mfr
N.A.I.C.S.: 335312

Oriental Motor (UK) Ltd. (1)
Unit 5 Faraday Office Park Rankine Road, Basingstoke, RG24 8AH, Hampshire, United Kingdom
Tel.: (44) 1256347090
Web Site: http://www.oriental-motor.co.uk
Motor & Generator Mfr
N.A.I.C.S.: 335312
Yoshiaki Masubuchi (Mng Dir)

Oriental Motor Asia Pacific Pte. Ltd. (1)
2 Kaki Bukit Ave 1 05-06, Singapore, 417818, Singapore (100%)
Tel.: (65) 67457344
Web Site: http://www.orientalmotor.com.sg
Motor & Generator Mfr
N.A.I.C.S.: 335312

Oriental Motor Italia S.r.l. (1)
Via XXV Aprile 5, 20016, Pero, Milan, Italy
Tel.: (39) 0293906346
Web Site: http://www.orientalmotor.it
Motor & Generator Mfr
N.A.I.C.S.: 335312

Oriental Motor Shanghai Co., Ltd. (1)
Rm 02 11th Fl Kirin Plz Bldg, No 666 Gubei Rd, 200336, Shanghai, China
Tel.: (86) 2162375440
Motor & Generator Mfr
N.A.I.C.S.: 335312

Oriental Motor U.S.A. Corp. (1)
1001 Knox St, Torrance, CA 90502-1030 (100%)
Tel.: (310) 325-0040
Web Site: http://www.omusa.com
Distr of Power Motors
N.A.I.C.S.: 423610

Taiwan Oriental Motor Co., Ltd. (1)
5th Floor No 716 Jung Jeng Rd, Jung he City, 235, Taipei, Taiwan
Tel.: (886) 282280707
Web Site: http://www.orientalmotor.com.tw
Motor & Generator Mfr
N.A.I.C.S.: 335312
K. Yokose (Mng Dir)

XIAMEN ORIENTAL MOTOR CO., LTD. (1)
838 Room 8F International Plaza No 8 Lujiang Road, Siming District, Xiamen, China
Tel.: (86) 592 226 4050
Motor & Actuator Distr
N.A.I.C.S.: 423610

ORIENTAL PENINSULA RESOURCES GROUP, INC.
10F ORE Central Bldg 9th Ave cor 31st Street, Bonifacio Global City, Taguig, Philippines
Tel.: (63) 288891129
Web Site:
  https://www.orientalpeninsula.com
ORE—(PHI)
Rev.: $67,528,170
Assets: $174,641,531
Liabilities: $25,298,708
Net Worth: $149,342,823
Earnings: $10,352,495

Emp.: 420
Fiscal Year-end: 12/31/21
Mining Services
N.A.I.C.S.: 212230
Miguel De Regla (CFO)
Subsidiaries:

Citinickel Mines and Development Corp (1)
81 Sen Gil Puyat Avenue, Barangay Palanan, Makati, 1235, Philippines
Tel.: (63) 28891129
Sales Range: $50-74.9 Million
Emp.: 2
Nickel Mining Services
N.A.I.C.S.: 212230
Caroline Tanchay (CEO)

ORIENTAL PRECISION & ENGINEERING CO., LTD.
1614-1 Songjeong-Dong, Gangseo-gu, Busan, Korea (South)
Tel.: (82) 512020101
Web Site: https://www.opco.kr
Year Founded: 1980
014940—(KRS)
Rev.: $100,912,670
Assets: $143,314,823
Liabilities: $78,272,921
Net Worth: $65,041,902
Earnings: $6,421,120
Emp.: 102
Fiscal Year-end: 12/31/22
Ship Building Services
N.A.I.C.S.: 336611
Yong-ho Song (Mng Dir)
Subsidiaries:

Dalian Oriental Marine & Heavy Industry Co., Ltd (1)
No 92 East Street Gunsan Development Zone, Dalian, Liaoning, China
Tel.: (86) 411 3920 8888
Web Site: http://www.d-omi.com
Ship Building Services
N.A.I.C.S.: 336611
Chongsuk Suh (CEO)

Oriental Inspection & Service Co. Ltd. (1)
25-1187 Shinho-Dong, Gangseo-gu, Busan, 46760, Korea (South)
Tel.: (82) 51 831 2747
Web Site: http://www.opcois.com
Emp.: 11
Ship Building Services
N.A.I.C.S.: 336611
Se-Chul Park (CEO)

Oriental Precision Machinery Co., Ltd. (1)
34 Noksansaneopbuk-ro 221beon-gil, Gangseo-gu, Busan, 618270, Korea (South)
Tel.: (82) 518318899
Ship Building Services
N.A.I.C.S.: 336611

Yantai Oriental Precision & Engineering Co., Ltd. (1)
No 2 Qingdo Street B-17 District, Yantai Economic Development Zone, Yantai, Shandong, China
Tel.: (86) 5356953701
Web Site: http://www.y-opco.com
Ship Building Services
N.A.I.C.S.: 336611
Suh Sang Won (CEO)

ORIENTAL RAIL INFRASTRUCTURE LIMITED
16 Mascarenhas Road Mazgaon, Mumbai, 400 010, India
Tel.: (91) 2261389400
Web Site:
  https://www.orientalrail.com
531859—(BOM)
Rev.: $39,232,612
Assets: $57,268,533
Liabilities: $44,355,758
Net Worth: $12,912,775
Earnings: $382,135

INTERNATIONAL PUBLIC

Emp.: 152
Fiscal Year-end: 03/31/23
Wood Veneer Product Mfr
N.A.I.C.S.: 321211
Saleh Najmuddin Mithiborwala (Chm & CFO)
Subsidiaries:

Oriental Foundry Private Limited (1)
E-17 Rizvi Park Co-operative Housing Society, Opp-Dheeraj Heritage SV Road Santacruz W, Mumbai, 400054, India
Tel.: (91) 2226617270
Web Site: https://www.orientalfoundry.in
Train Parts Mfr
N.A.I.C.S.: 336510

ORIENTAL TECHNOLOGIES INVESTMENT LIMITED
Level 12 32 Martin Place, Sydney, 2000, NSW, Australia
Tel.: (61) 292383988
Web Site:
  http://www.orientech.com.au
Sales Range: Less than $1 Million
Emp.: 500
Acid Batteries Mfr & Sales
N.A.I.C.S.: 335910
Xinsheng Wang (Mng Dir)

ORIENTAL TRIMEX LIMITED
26/25 Bazar Marg Old Rajendra Nagar, New Delhi, 110060, India
Tel.: (91) 1145048612
Web Site:
  https://www.orientaltrimex.com
Year Founded: 1996
532817—(BOM)
Rev.: $1,075,187
Assets: $14,268,209
Liabilities: $6,079,719
Net Worth: $8,188,490
Earnings: $517,835)
Emp.: 17
Fiscal Year-end: 03/31/23
Tiles Mfr
N.A.I.C.S.: 327120
Rajesh Punia (Mng Dir)

ORIENTAL UNION CHEMICAL CORPORATION
13th Fl 101 Fu-Hsing N Rd, Taipei, 105, Taiwan
Tel.: (886) 227193333
Web Site: https://www.oucc.com.tw
Year Founded: 1975
1710—(TAI)
Rev.: $680,759,025
Assets: $1,079,640,595
Liabilities: $609,031,436
Net Worth: $470,609,158
Earnings: $(7,335,034)
Emp.: 665
Fiscal Year-end: 12/31/23
Polyether Chemicals Mfr
N.A.I.C.S.: 325199
Douglas Tong Hsu (Chm)

ORIENTAL UNIVERSITY CITY HOLDINGS (H.K.) LTD.
100 ZhangHeng Raod Oriental University City, Langfang Economic and Technical Development Zone, Langfang, 065001, Hebei, China
Tel.: (86) 3166056302
Web Site: https://www.oriental-university-city.com
8067—(HKG)
Rev.: $10,077,388
Assets: $260,136,025
Liabilities: $69,800,944
Net Worth: $190,335,081
Earnings: $5,434,818
Emp.: 49
Fiscal Year-end: 06/30/21
Universities, Educational Facilities & Dormitories Owner & Leasing

N.A.I.C.S.: 611310
Yingchun Liu *(CEO)*

ORIENTAL WATCH HOLDINGS LIMITED
Rooms 316-318 China Insurance Group Building, 141 Des Voeux Road Central, Central, China (Hong Kong)
Tel.: (852) 2 815 8821
Web Site:
http://www.orientalwatch.com.hk
0398—(HKG)
Rev.: $451,948,758
Assets: $351,796,819
Liabilities: $95,055,809
Net Worth: $256,741,010
Earnings: $30,003,844
Emp.: 563
Fiscal Year-end: 03/31/21
Watch Retailer
N.A.I.C.S.: 423940
Alain Hing Lun Lam *(Sec & Dir-Fin)*

Subsidiaries:

La Suisse Watch Company Limited (1)
G F E S Bldg 481 Hennessy Rd, Causeway Bay, China (Hong Kong)
Tel.: (852) 28936088
Watch Whslr
N.A.I.C.S.: 423940

Oriental Watch (China) Company Limited (1)
G/F & 1/F 50 Queen s Road C, Central, China (Hong Kong)
Tel.: (852) 3470 0009
Web Site: http://www.orientalwatch.com
Luxury Watches Whslr
N.A.I.C.S.: 423940

Oriental Watch (Macau) Company Limited (1)
Shop B & C & D G/F & M/F The Macau Square Avenida do Infante D, Henrique No 43-53A, Macau, China (Macau)
Tel.: (853) 28717323
Web Site: http://www.orientalwatch.com
Watch Whslr
N.A.I.C.S.: 458310

Oriental Watch Company Limited (1)
G/F 133 Des Voeux Road C, Central, China (Hong Kong)
Tel.: (852) 25454577
Web Site: http://www.orientalwatch.com
Watch Whslr
N.A.I.C.S.: 458310

ORIENTAL WEAVERS
8 El Shaheed Zakaria Khalil St Oriental Weavers Complex, Heliopolis, Cairo, Egypt
Tel.: (20) 222672121
Web Site:
https://www.orientalweavers.com
Year Founded: 1979
ORWE.CA—(EGX)
Rev.: $372,403,254
Assets: $487,327,374
Liabilities: $188,475,676
Net Worth: $298,851,698
Earnings: $39,900,249
Emp.: 26,000
Fiscal Year-end: 12/31/23
Carpet Mfr
N.A.I.C.S.: 314110
Mohamed Farid Fouad Khamis *(Founder)*

ORIFLAME COSMETICS S.A.
Bleicheplatz 3, CH-8200, Schaffhausen, Switzerland
Tel.: (41) 525441666 CH
Web Site: http://www.oriflame.com
Year Founded: 1967
Rev.: $1,310,167,000
Assets: $1,665,326,579
Liabilities: $1,297,498,058
Net Worth: $367,828,521
Earnings: $315,959
Emp.: 5,660
Fiscal Year-end: 12/31/20
Cosmetics, Fragrances & Toiletries Mfr & Sales
N.A.I.C.S.: 325620
Magnus Brannstrom *(Pres & CEO)*

Subsidiaries:

Alay SRL (1)
Rl 18 Pitiantuta #230, Entre Mcal Lopez y Hassler, Asuncion, Paraguay
Tel.: (595) 971228855
Web Site: http://www.oriflame.com
Mfr & Distr of Cosmetics & Skin Preparations
N.A.I.C.S.: 325620

Deesse AG (1)
Industriestrasse 10, 8618, Oetwil am See, Switzerland
Tel.: (41) 44296565
Web Site: http://www.deesse.ch
Sales Range: $25-49.9 Million
Emp.: 65
Mfr & Distributor of Cosmetics & Skin Preparations
N.A.I.C.S.: 325620

Oriflame (1)
Vladimira Popovica 40, Cukaricka Padina, 11070, Belgrade, Serbia
Tel.: (381) 113536100
Web Site: http://www.oriflame.rs
Cosmetics & Skin Preparations Mfr & Distr
N.A.I.C.S.: 325620

Oriflame Azerbaijan (1)
Khagani 1 3rd Floor, 370000, Baku, Azerbaijan
Tel.: (994) 12935721
Web Site: http://www.oriflame.com
Mfr & Distributor of Cosmetics & Skin Preparations
N.A.I.C.S.: 325620

Oriflame Bulgaria EOOD (1)
Gm Demetro Ste 1, 1729, Sofia, Bulgaria
Tel.: (359) 29705501
Web Site: http://www.oriflame.bg
Sales Range: $25-49.9 Million
Mfr & Distributor of Cosmetics & Skin Preparations
N.A.I.C.S.: 325620

Oriflame Cosmeticos Ltda (1)
Estrada De Talaide Cruzamento De Sao Marcos Armazem 4, 2735-503, Cacem, Sintra, Portugal
Tel.: (351) 21 427 96 00
Web Site: http://www.oriflame.pt
Emp.: 4
Cosmetics Mfr & Distr
N.A.I.C.S.: 325620
Rui Silva *(Gen Mgr)*

Oriflame Cosmeticos S.A. (1)
C Calera 5 Poligono Industrial, Tres Cantos, 28760, Madrid, Spain
Tel.: (34) 918041625
Web Site: http://www.oriflame.es
Sales Range: $25-49.9 Million
Emp.: 50
Mfr & Distributor of Cosmetics & Skin Preparations
N.A.I.C.S.: 325620

Oriflame Cosmetics (1)
Horia Macelariu 61 81, 013934, Bucharest, Romania
Tel.: (40) 212330562
Web Site: http://www.oriflame.ro
Sales Range: $25-49.9 Million
Emp.: 100
Mfr & Distributor of Cosmetics & Skin Preparations
N.A.I.C.S.: 325620

Oriflame Cosmetics (Thailand) Ltd. (1)
1 Phattanakarn Rd, Suanluang, Bangkok, 10250, Thailand
Tel.: (66) 27151111
Web Site: http://th.oriflame.com
Mfr & Distributor of Cosmetics & Skin Preparations
N.A.I.C.S.: 325620

Oriflame Cosmetics AB (1)
Riddargatan 12 A 2nd Fl, 114 83, Stockholm, Sweden (100%)
Tel.: (46) 86223600
Web Site: http://www.oriflame.com
Mfr & Distributor of Cosmetics
N.A.I.C.S.: 325620

Oriflame Cosmetics Foreign LLC (1)
6 Skryganova St build 4 Office 2201, Minsk, 220073, Belarus
Tel.: (375) 17 256 18 35
Cosmetic Product Whslr
N.A.I.C.S.: 456120

Oriflame Cosmetics Pakistan (PVT) LTD (1)
14 A Ground Floor Ali Block New Garden Town, Lahore, 54000, Pakistan
Tel.: (92) 42 35911027
Web Site: http://www.oriflame.pk
Cosmetic Products Mfr & Distr
N.A.I.C.S.: 325620

Oriflame Cosmetics SRL (1)
Str Vlayku Pyrkelab 52, 2012, Chisinau, Moldova
Tel.: (373) 22 20 59 44
Web Site: http://www.oriflame.md
Mfr & Distributor of Cosmetics & Skin Preparations
N.A.I.C.S.: 325620

Oriflame Czech Republic sro (1)
V Olsinach 82/16, 100 00, Prague, Czech Republic
Tel.: (420) 2 7102 4111
Cosmetic Products Mfr & Distr
N.A.I.C.S.: 424210

Oriflame Eesti OU (1)
Uus 25, 10123, Tallinn, Estonia
Tel.: (372) 6976066
Web Site: http://www.oriflame.ee
Sales Range: $25-49.9 Million
Emp.: 17
Mfr & Distributor of Cosmetics & Skin Preparations
N.A.I.C.S.: 325620
Heli Helm *(Mng Dir)*

Oriflame Egypt Ltd. (1)
63 Abou Bakr El Siddeek St, Heliopolis, Cairo, Egypt
Tel.: (20) 226385568
Web Site: http://www.oriflame.com.eg
Cosmetics & Skin Preparations Mfr & Distr
N.A.I.C.S.: 325620

Oriflame Finland OY (1)
Tammasaarenkata 3, 00180, Helsinki, Finland
Tel.: (358) 207430534
Web Site: http://www.oriflame.fi
Sales Range: $25-49.9 Million
Emp.: 20
Mfr & Distributor of Cosmetics & Skin Preparations
N.A.I.C.S.: 325620

Oriflame Greece Ltd. (1)
3 Gyzi Aigialeias St, 15125, Maroussi, Greece
Tel.: (30) 2106875800
Web Site: http://www.oriflame.gr
Sales Range: $25-49.9 Million
Emp.: 90
Mfr & Distributor of Cosmetics & Skin Preparations
N.A.I.C.S.: 325620
Niokos Farrif *(Mgr-Fin)*

Oriflame Hungary KFT (1)
Vaci ut 91/A, 1139, Budapest, Hungary
Tel.: (36) 14503900
Web Site: http://www.oriflame.hu
Mfr & Distributor of Cosmetics & Skin Preparations
N.A.I.C.S.: 325620

Oriflame India Pvt. Ltd. (1)
1st Floor L 29 to 34 Connaught Place Outer Circle, New Delhi, 110001, India
Tel.: (91) 11 405 49500
Web Site: http://www.in.oriflame.com
Mfr & Distr of Cosmetics & Skin Preparations
N.A.I.C.S.: 325620
Niklas Frisk *(Mng Dir, VP & Head-South Asia)*

Oriflame Indonesia (1)
Jalan Bulungan 16, 12130, Jakarta, Indonesia
Tel.: (62) 217252990
Web Site: http://www.oriflame.co.id
Mfr & Distributor of Cosmetics & Skin Preparations
N.A.I.C.S.: 325620

Oriflame International ApS (1)
Industrievej 10, 3550, Slangerup, Denmark (100%)
Tel.: (45) 47335800
Web Site: http://www.oriflame.dk
Sales Range: $10-24.9 Million
Emp.: 33
Mfr & Distributor of Cosmetics & Skin Preparations
N.A.I.C.S.: 325620

Oriflame Kazakhstan (1)
Tuliba 38/61 Kunaiva, 480096, Almaty, Kazakhstan
Tel.: (7) 3272585583
Web Site: http://www.oriflame.com
Sales Range: $50-74.9 Million
Emp.: 200
Mfr & Distributor of Cosmetics & Skin Preparations
N.A.I.C.S.: 325620

Oriflame Kosmetiek B.V. (1)
Gotenweg 11, PO Box 161, 5342 PP, Oss, Netherlands
Tel.: (31) 412642575
Web Site: http://www.oriflame.nl
Sales Range: $25-49.9 Million
Emp.: 35
Mfr & Distributor of Cosmetics & Skin Preparations
N.A.I.C.S.: 325620

Oriflame Kosmetika BH d.j.l. (1)
Saliha Udzvarlica, 71 000, Sarajevo, Bosnia & Herzegovina
Tel.: (387) 33660366
Web Site: http://www.oriflame.ba
Mfr & Distributor of Cosmetics & Skin Preparations
N.A.I.C.S.: 325620

Oriflame Kosmetika UAB (1)
Konstitucijos 20, 0903, Vilnius, Lithuania
Tel.: (370) 852343732
Web Site: http://www.oriflame.lt
Sales Range: $25-49.9 Million
Cosmetics & Skin Preparations Mfr & Distr
N.A.I.C.S.: 325620

Oriflame Kosmetika d.o.o. (1)
Ul Vladimira Popovica 40, 11000, Belgrade, Serbia
Tel.: (381) 11 3536 100
Web Site: http://www.oriflame.rs
Personal Care Product Mfr
N.A.I.C.S.: 325620

Oriflame Kozmetik Urunleri Ticaret Ltd STI. (1)
Kore Sehitleri Caddesi No 39, Zincirlikkuyu, 80300, Istanbul, Turkiye
Tel.: (90) 2122674867
Web Site: http://www.oriflame.com.tr
Sales Range: $25-49.9 Million
Emp.: 100
Mfr & Distributor of Cosmetics & Skin Preparations
N.A.I.C.S.: 325620

Oriflame Kozmetika Croatia d.o.o. (1)
Hondlova 2, 10000, Zagreb, Croatia
Tel.: (385) 12300155
Web Site: http://www.oriflame.hr
Mfr & Distr of Cosmetics & Skin Preparations
N.A.I.C.S.: 325620

Oriflame Kozmetika d.o.o. (1)
Cesta Dolomitskega Odreda 10, 1000, Ljubljana, Slovenia
Tel.: (000) 12004770
Web Site: http://www.oriflame.si
Sales Range: $25-49.9 Million
Emp.: 15
Mfr & Distributor of Cosmetics & Skin Preparations
N.A.I.C.S.: 325620

Oriflame Kozmetika dooel (1)
Mito Hadzi-Vasilev Jasmin 50 4th Floor,

ORIFLAME COSMETICS S.A.

Oriflame Cosmetics S.A.—(Continued)
91000, Skopje, North Macedonia
Tel.: (389) 23235777
Web Site: http://www.oriflame.com.mk
Mfr & Distributor of Cosmetics & Skin Preparations
N.A.I.C.S.: 325620

Oriflame LLP (1)
Medeuskiy Area Dostyk 140 ug ul Zholdasbekov, Almaty, 050051, Kazakhstan
Tel.: (7) 727 258 55 83
Web Site: http://www.oriflame.kz
Cosmetics Products Mfr
N.A.I.C.S.: 325620
Alakbarov Katrin (VP)

Oriflame Lanka (Pvt.) Ltd. (1)
No 77 Dharmapala Mawatha, Colombo, 7, Sri Lanka
Tel.: (94) 114786500
Web Site: http://www.oriflame.lk
Cosmetics & Skin Preparations Mfr & Distr
N.A.I.C.S.: 325620

Oriflame Latvia SIA (1)
Balozu Iela 20A, Riga, 1048, Latvia
Tel.: (371) 7450060
Web Site: http://www.oriflame.lv
Sales Range: $25-49.9 Million
Emp.: 100
Mfr & Distributor of Cosmetics & Skin Preparations
N.A.I.C.S.: 325620

Oriflame Marketing (M) SDN BHD (1)
1st Fl Blondal Building Section U1, Jln Penyair Off Jln Glenmarie, 40150, Shah Alam, Malaysia
Tel.: (60) 355692328
Web Site: http://www.oriflame.com
Sales Range: $25-49.9 Million
Emp.: 40
Mfr & Distributor of Cosmetics & Skin Preparations
N.A.I.C.S.: 325620

Oriflame Maroc S.A.R.L (1)
Rue Ali Abderrazak 24, Casablanca, 20100, Morocco
Tel.: (212) 22989322
Web Site: http://www.oriflame.com
Mfr & Distributor of Cosmetics & Skin Preparations
N.A.I.C.S.: 325620

Oriflame Mexico S.A. de C.V. (1)
Jaime Balmes No 8 Local 2-B, Col Los Morales Polanco, Mexico, 11510, DF, Mexico
Tel.: (52) 55 55 84 04 40
Web Site: http://www.oriflame.com.mx
Mfr & Distributor of Cosmetics & Skin Preparations
N.A.I.C.S.: 325620

Oriflame Mongolia XXK (1)
Apartment 1st Floor House 29-13 of Sukhaabatar District, 5th Microdistrict, Ulaanbaatar, Mongolia
Tel.: (976) 11 336336
Web Site: http://www.oriflame.mn
Mfr & Distr of Cosmetics & Skin Preparations
N.A.I.C.S.: 325620

Oriflame Norge A.S. (1)
Ulvenveien 89C, 509, Oslo, Norway
Tel.: (47) 22975400
Web Site: http://www.oriflame.no
Sales Range: $25-49,9 Million
Emp.: 20
Mfr & Distributor of Cosmetics & Skin Preparations
N.A.I.C.S.: 325620

Oriflame Peru S.A. (1)
Calle Morelli 181 Piso 5, San Borja, Lima, 41, Peru
Tel.: (51) 6189920
Web Site: http://www.oriflame.com.pe
Mfr & Distributor of Cosmetics & Skin Preparations
N.A.I.C.S.: 325620

Oriflame Poland Sp. z.o.o. (1)
Woloska 22, 02-675, Warsaw, Poland
Tel.: (48) 22 458 02 00
Personal Care Products Mfr & Distr
N.A.I.C.S.: 325620

Oriflame Research & Development Ltd. (1)
Bray Business Park, Bray, Ireland
Tel.: (353) 12735300
Web Site: http://www.oriflame-ireland.com
Sales Range: $25-49.9 Million
Emp.: 110
Personal Care Products Research & Development Services
N.A.I.C.S.: 541715
Mary Lord (Mng Dir)

Oriflame SP ZOO (1)
Ul. Bohaterow Warszawy 2, 02 495, Warsaw, Poland
Tel.: (48) 22 668 4468
Web Site: http://www.oriflame.com.pl
Mfr & Distributor of Cosmetics & Skin Preparations
N.A.I.C.S.: 325620

Oriflame SPOL SRO (1)
V Olsinach 6 82 16, 100 00, Prague, Czech Republic
Tel.: (420) 271024111
Web Site: http://www.oriflame.cz
Sales Range: $25-49.9 Million
Emp.: 100
Mfr & Distributor of Cosmetics & Skin Preparations
N.A.I.C.S.: 325620

Oriflame SPOL SRO (1)
Europennun Business Center 814-99, PO Box 81, 82009, Bratislava, Slovakia
Tel.: (421) 259102511
Web Site: http://www.oriflame.sk
Mfr & Distributor of Cosmetics & Skin Preparations
N.A.I.C.S.: 325620

Oriflame Services International AB (1)
Master Samuelsgatan 56, 111 21, Stockholm, Sweden
Tel.: (46) 858632300
Web Site: http://www.oriflame.com
Sales Range: $150-199.9 Million
Emp.: 46
Cosmetic Product Distr
N.A.I.C.S.: 424210
Magnus Braennstroem (CEO)

Oriflame Slovakia sro (1)
Suche Myto 1, 814 99, Bratislava, Slovakia
Tel.: (421) 259102533
Web Site: http://www.oriflame.sk
Emp.: 40
Personal Care Product Distr
N.A.I.C.S.: 424210
Zuzana Machova (Mng Dir)

Oriflame Sudan (1)
S.U.S. Region Africa Street, PO Box 41, Khartoum Airport, Khartoum, Sudan
Tel.: (249) 183 485 753
Web Site: http://sd.oriflame.com
Mfr & Distr of Cosmetics & Skin Preparations
N.A.I.C.S.: 325620

Oriflame USA (1)
PO Box 600039, Jacksonville, FL 32260-0039
Tel.: (704) 843-3102
Mfr & Distributor of Cosmetics & Skin Preparations
N.A.I.C.S.: 325620

Oriflame Ukraine (1)
4 Malynska Str, 03680, Kiev, Ukraine
Tel.: (380) 444907705
Web Site: http://www.oriflame.com.ua
Sales Range: $25-49.9 Million
Mfr & Distributor of Cosmetics & Skin Preparations
N.A.I.C.S.: 325620

Oriflame Uzbekistan (1)
Glinka Str 4a, 700015, Tashkent, Uzbekistan
Tel.: (998) 712813753
Web Site: http://www.oriflame.com
Cosmetics & Skin Preparations Mfr & Distr
N.A.I.C.S.: 325620

Oriflame Vietnam Ltd. (1)
100 102 Nguyen Van Troi Street Ward 8, Phu Nhuan, Ho Chi Minh City, Vietnam
Tel.: (84) 8 3845 0452

Sales Range: $75-99.9 Million
Emp.: 110
Cosmetic Product Distr
N.A.I.C.S.: 424210

Oriflame de Chile S.A (1)
Apoquindo 4445 Of 201, Las Condes, Santiago, Chile
Tel.: (56) 23381501
Web Site: http://www.oriflame.cl
Sales Range: $200-249.9 Million
Emp.: 1,000
Mfr & Distributor of Cosmetics & Skin Preparations
N.A.I.C.S.: 325620

Oriflame de Colombia S.A. (1)
Calle 125 No 30 67 Of 201, Bogota, Colombia
Tel.: (57) 16192382
Web Site: http://www.oriflame.com.co
Sales Range: $25-49.9 Million
Emp.: 48
Mfr & Distributor of Cosmetics & Skin Preparations
N.A.I.C.S.: 325620

Oriflame de Costa Rica S.A. (1)
Toyota Passeo Colon 300 Sur 50 Este, San Jose, Costa Rica
Tel.: (506) 257 9144
Web Site: http://www.oriflame.com
Mfr & Distributor of Cosmetics & Skin Preparations
N.A.I.C.S.: 325620

Oriflame de El Salvador S.A. (1)
Alameda Roosevelth Y 63 Avenida Norte, Plz De Comercios Locales 2 3, San Salvador, El Salvador
Tel.: (503) 2600025
Web Site: http://www.oriflame.com
Mfr & Distributor of Cosmetics & Skin Preparations
N.A.I.C.S.: 325620

Oriflame de Guatemala S.A. (1)
3A Ave 12-33 Zona 9, Guatemala, Guatemala
Tel.: (502) 331 1983
Web Site: http://www.oriflame.com
Mfr & Distributor of Cosmetics & Skin Preparations
N.A.I.C.S.: 325620

Oriflame de Nicaragua S.A. (1)
Km 4 Carretera a Masaya de Bancentro 1 cuadra Oeste, 1 cuadra al Norte 1/2 cuadra Oeste, Managua, Nicaragua
Tel.: (505) 2270 2275
Web Site: http://www.oriflame.com
Mfr & Distributor of Cosmetics & Skin Preparations
N.A.I.C.S.: 325620

Oriflame del Ecuador (1)
Baron de Carondelet No 37-55 & Avenida America, Granda Centeneo Area, Quito, Ecuador
Tel.: (593) 2 27 77 55
Web Site: http://www.oriflame.com.ec
Mfr & Distr of Cosmetics & Skin Preparations
N.A.I.C.S.: 325620

SARL Natural Swedish Cosmetics (1)
Rue Hassiba Ben Bouali Roustomia Dely Brahim, Algiers, Algeria
Tel.: (213) 21 937 917
Web Site: http://www.corporate.oriflame.com
Sales Range: $25-49.9 Million
Emp.: 15
Cosmetic Product Whslr
N.A.I.C.S.: 424210

ZAO TAF Oriflame Cosmetics Ltd. (1)
Ul Usacheva 37, 119048, Moscow, Russia
Tel.: (7) 4956265353
Web Site: http://www.oriflame.ru
Mfr & Distr of Cosmetics & Skin Preparations
N.A.I.C.S.: 325620

ORIGAMI CREATIVE CONCEPTS PVT. LTD.

115 Railway Parallel Road Kumara Park West, Bengaluru, 560 020, India

Tel.: (91) 8039510301
Web Site:
  http://www.origamicreative.com
Sales Range: $10-24.9 Million
Emp.: 80
Advertising Agencies
N.A.I.C.S.: 541810
Laeeq Ali (Dir)

ORIGEN RESOURCES, INC.

Suite 488-625 Howe Street, Vancouver, V6C 2T6, BC, Canada
Tel.: (604) 681-0221
Web Site:
  https://www.origenresources.com
OGGNF—(OTCIQ)
Rev.: $34,149
Assets: $3,370,160
Liabilities: $359,791
Net Worth: $3,010,369
Earnings: ($2,339,397)
Fiscal Year-end: 03/31/24
Metal Exploration Services
N.A.I.C.S.: 213115
Gary Schellenberg (CEO)

Subsidiaries:

Forty Pillars Mining Corp. (1)
488-625 Howe Street, Vancouver, V6C2T6, BC, Canada
Tel.: (778) 881-4631
Web Site: https://www.fortypillars.ca
Mineral Exploration & Mining Services
N.A.I.C.S.: 212312

ORIGIN AGRITECH LIMITED

No 21 Sheng Ming Yuan Road, Chanping District, Beijing, 102206, China
Tel.: (86) 1058907588
Web Site:
  https://www.originseed.com.cn
Year Founded: 1997
SEED—(NASDAQ)
Rev.: $8,055,782
Assets: $20,829,666
Liabilities: $47,280,146
Net Worth: ($26,450,481)
Earnings: ($959,861)
Emp.: 63
Fiscal Year-end: 09/30/22
Crop Seed Production & Sales
N.A.I.C.S.: 111419
Gengchen Han (CEO & Chm)

Subsidiaries:

Beijing Origin Seed Limited (1)
21 Sheng Ming Yuan Road, Chanping District, Beijing, 102206, China
Tel.: (86) 10 5890 7588
Hybrid Crop Seed Production & Distr Services
N.A.I.C.S.: 111199

Beijing Origin State Harvest Biotechnology Limited (1)
21 Sheng Ming Yuan Road, Changping District, Beijing, 102206, China
Tel.: (86) 10 5890 7588
Hybrid Seed Technology Developer
N.A.I.C.S.: 541715

ORIGIN CO., LTD.

3-3-27 Sakawa, Sakura-ku, Saitama, 338-0823, Japan
Tel.: (81) 487559711
Web Site: https://www.origin.co.jp
Year Founded: 1938
6513—(TKS)
Rev.: $186,435,050
Assets: $314,424,480
Liabilities: $140,270,810
Net Worth: $174,153,670
Earnings: ($9,703,480)
Emp.: 1,043
Fiscal Year-end: 03/31/24
Electronic Component Mfr & Distr
N.A.I.C.S.: 334419
Kazuhiro Seo (Chm & Pres)

AND PRIVATE COMPANIES — ORIGIN ENERGY LTD.

Subsidiaries:

Hokkaido Origin Co., Ltd. (1)
136 Okayama, Mikasa, 068-2165, Hokkaido, Japan
Tel.: (81) 126722915
Electric Device Mfr
N.A.I.C.S.: 334413

OTS Co., Ltd. (1)
1-10-7 Hiranuma, Yoshikawa, Saitama-ken, Japan
Tel.: (81) 489406357
Web Site: http://www.ots-e.jp
Electric Device Mfr
N.A.I.C.S.: 334413

Origin Donbon Paints (Dongguan) Co., Ltd. (1)
Cha Shan Gong Ye Yuan 2B Qu Cha Shan Zhen, Dongguan, 523380, Guangdong, China
Tel.: (86) 76981866000
Paint Distr
N.A.I.C.S.: 424950

Origin Eason Paint Co., Ltd. (1)
7/1-2 Moo 1 Tambol Panthong, Amphur Panthong, Chon Buri, 20160, Thailand
Tel.: (66) 381951301
Paint Distr
N.A.I.C.S.: 424950
Krisapon Sing-Ubon (Mgr-Evaluation & Process Control Section)

Origin Electric America Co., Ltd. (1)
3848 W Carson St Ste 216, Torrance, CA 90503
Tel.: (310) 540-6750
Web Site: http://www.origin-usa.com
Emp.: 6
Electronic Device Mfr & Distr
N.A.I.C.S.: 334413
Kiyomi Matsuoka (VP)

Origin Electric Co., Ltd. - Mamada Plant (1)
3-10-5 Akatsuki, Oyama, 329-0211, Tochigi-ken, Japan
Tel.: (81) 285451111
Mechanical Component Mfr
N.A.I.C.S.: 333613

Origin Electric Co., Ltd. - Mizuho Plant (1)
2-3-11 Nagaoka, Mizuho-machi Nishi-tama-gun, Tokyo, 190-1232, Japan
Tel.: (81) 425574111
Paints Mfr
N.A.I.C.S.: 325510

Origin Electric Co., Ltd. - Yoshimi Factory (1)
1915 Aza Hachiman Oaza Nagayatsu, Yoshimi-machi Hiki-gun, Saitama, 355-0156, Japan
Tel.: (81) 493599333
Electric Device Mfr
N.A.I.C.S.: 334413

Origin Korea Co., Ltd. (1)
Room301 Gasan W center 181 Gasan digital 1-ro, Geumcheon-gu, Seoul, Korea (South)
Tel.: (82) 262951192
Web Site: https://www.origin-kr.com
Electronic Device Mfr & Distr
N.A.I.C.S.: 334413

Origin Paints (Tianjin) Co., Ltd. (1)
No 9 Xin Yuan Road Wu Qing Development Area, New Technological And Industrial Park, Tianjin, 301700, China
Tel.: (86) 2282101701
Paint Distr
N.A.I.C.S.: 424950
Ryo Kurita (Mgr-Bus Dev)

Origin Precision Machine (Shanghai) Co., Ltd. (1)
3/F No 20 Bldg No 115 West Fute First Rd, Pilot Free Trade Zone, Shanghai, 200131, China
Tel.: (86) 2150462341
Web Site: https://www.origin-shanghai.com
Emp.: 92
Mechanical Component Mfr & Distr
N.A.I.C.S.: 333613
Kiyoshi Shinohara (Chm)

PT. Origin Durachem Indonesia (1)
Jl Jababeka Xvi Blok U No 3a Desa Pasir Gombong Kec Cikarang Utara, Kabupaten, Bekasi, 17530, Indonesia
Tel.: (62) 218936088
Electronic Device Distr
N.A.I.C.S.: 423690

Saitama Origin Co., Ltd. (1)
1917 Aza Hachiman Oaza Nagayatsu Yoshimi-Machi, Hiki-gun, Saitama, 355-0156, Japan
Tel.: (81) 493531234
Electric Device Mfr
N.A.I.C.S.: 334413

Plant (Domestic):

Saitama Origin Co., Ltd. - Yuki Plant (2)
6-17 Naka-dori Shintsutsumi, Yuki, 307-0016, Ibaraki, Japan
Tel.: (81) 296330365
Electric Device Mfr
N.A.I.C.S.: 334413

Shanghai Origin Donbon Paints Co., Ltd. (1)
No 57 Jin Wen Road, Zhu Qiao Town Pu Dong New District, Shanghai, 201323, China
Tel.: (86) 2158104170
Paint Distr
N.A.I.C.S.: 424950

Toho Kaken Manufacturing Inc. (1)
4-5-15 Ueno, Iwatsuki-ku, Saitama, 339-0073, Japan
Tel.: (81) 487976095
Web Site: https://www.toho-kaken.co.jp
Electric Device Mfr
N.A.I.C.S.: 334413

ORIGIN COMMUNICATIONS GROUP FZ LLC
Office 401 Loft Building 2 Dubai Media City, Sheikh Zayed Road, Dubai, United Arab Emirates
Tel.: (971) 4 367 2270
Web Site: http://www.grouporigin.com
Year Founded: 1993
Sales Range: $10-24.9 Million
Emp.: 21
Advertising Agencies
N.A.I.C.S.: 541810
Mark Sutherland (Founder & Chm)

ORIGIN ENERGY LTD.
100 Barangaroo Avenue, Barangaroo, 2000, NSW, Australia
Tel.: (61) 1300137427 AU
Web Site: https://www.originenergy.com.au
Year Founded: 1946
ORG—(OTCIQ)
Rev: $10,745,908,587
Assets: $12,354,436,982
Liabilities: $6,544,304,623
Net Worth: $5,810,132,360
Earnings: $689,835,039
Emp.: 5,630
Fiscal Year-end: 06/30/23
Natural Gas Distribution Services
N.A.I.C.S.: 221210
Helen Hardy (Sec)

Subsidiaries:

Angari Pty Ltd (1)
135 Coronation Drive, Milton, 4064, QLD, Australia
Tel.: (61) 738670202
Web Site: http://www.originenergy.com.au
Engineeering Services
N.A.I.C.S.: 541330
Franklin King (Gen Mgr)

Conroy's Gap Wind Farm Pty Ltd (1)
L 45 Australia Square 264-278 George St, Sydney, 2000, NSW, Australia
Tel.: (61) 283455564
Wind Electric Power Generation Services
N.A.I.C.S.: 221118

OTP Geothermal Power (1)
ampoerna Strategic Square North Tower 24th Floor, Jl Jend Sudirman Kav 45-46, 12930, Jakarta, Indonesia
Tel.: (62) 21 57851080
Geothermal Energy Production
N.A.I.C.S.: 221116

Oil Company of Australia (Moura) Pty Ltd. (1)
L1 339 Coronation Dr, Milton, QLD, Australia (100%)
Tel.: (61) 738670202
Web Site: http://www.originenergy.com.au
Sales Range: $200-249.9 Million
Emp.: 300
Oil & Gas Operations
N.A.I.C.S.: 213112

Oil Company of Australia (Moura) Transmissions Pty Ltd. (1)
339 Coronation Drive, Milton, 4067, QLD, Australia (100%)
Tel.: (61) 738670202
Web Site: http://www.originenergy.com
Sales Range: $350-399.9 Million
Emp.: 1,000
Oil & Gas Operations
N.A.I.C.S.: 213112

Origin Energy (Vic) Pty Ltd. (1)
321 Exhibition Street, Melbourne, 3001, VIC, Australia (100%)
Tel.: (61) 396525555
Web Site: http://www.originenergy.com.au
Sales Range: $400-449.9 Million
Emp.: 1,500
Gasoline Stations
N.A.I.C.S.: 457120
Phil Craig (Gen Mgr)

Origin Energy Asset Management Services Pty Ltd. (1)
L 45 Australia Sq 264-278 George St, Sydney, 2000, NSW, Australia (100%)
Tel.: (61) 882175800
Web Site: http://www.originenergy.com.au
Sales Range: $250-299.9 Million
Emp.: 470
Electric Power Distribution
N.A.I.C.S.: 221122
Grant King (Mng Dir)

Origin Energy Australia Holding B.V. (1)
L 45 Australia Square 264-278 George Street, Sydney, 2000, NSW, Australia (100%)
Tel.: (61) 882175800
Web Site: http://www.originenergy.com.au
Sales Range: $250-299.9 Million
Emp.: 300
Electric Power Distribution
N.A.I.C.S.: 221122
Grant King (Mng Dir)

Origin Energy Bonaparte Pty Ltd (1)
L 2 339 Coronation Dr, Milton, 4064, QLD, Australia
Tel.: (61) 738670202
Web Site: http://www.Originenergy.com
Emp.: 100
Electric Power Generation Services
N.A.I.C.S.: 221118
Grant King (CEO)

Origin Energy CSG Ltd. (1)
Ground Floor 339 Coronation Dr, Milton, 4064, QLD, Australia (100%)
Tel.: (61) 738670202
Web Site: http://www.originenergy.com.au
Sales Range: $350-399.9 Million
Emp.: 1,000
Natural Gas Liquid Extraction
N.A.I.C.S.: 211130

Origin Energy Contracting Ltd. (1)
100 Waymouth Street, Adelaide, 5000, Australia (100%)
Tel.: (61) 882175211
Web Site: http://www.origin.com.au
Sales Range: $150-199.9 Million
Emp.: 850
Management Consulting Services
N.A.I.C.S.: 541618
Grant King (Mng Dir)

Origin Energy Developments Pty Ltd (1)

L2 339 Coronation Dr N, Milton, 4064, QLD, Australia
Tel.: (61) 882175800
Oil & Gas Exploration Services
N.A.I.C.S.: 213112

Origin Energy Holdings Ltd. (1)
Level 21 360 Elizabeth Street, Melbourne, 3000, VIC, Australia (100%)
Tel.: (61) 396525555
Web Site: http://www.originenergy.com.au
Sales Range: $200-249.9 Million
Emp.: 800
Oil & Gas Pipeline & Structures Construction
N.A.I.C.S.: 237120
Phil Craig (Gen Mgr)

Subsidiary (Domestic):

Origin Energy Electricity Ltd (2)
L 6 1 King William St, Adelaide, 5000, SA, Australia
Tel.: (61) 882175211
Electric Power Distribution Services
N.A.I.C.S.: 221122
Brant King (Mng Dir)

Origin Energy Pipelines Pty Ltd (2)
16 Mckinnon Rd, Berrimah, 0828, NT, Australia
Tel.: (61) 889325168
Sales Range: $75-99.9 Million
Emp.: 8
Natural Gas Distribution Services
N.A.I.C.S.: 221210

Subsidiary (Domestic):

Origin Energy Pipelines (Vic) Holdings Pty Ltd (3)
L 45 Australia Square 264-278 George St, Sydney, 2000, NSW, Australia
Tel.: (61) 283455000
Web Site: http://www.originenergy.com.au
Eletric Power Generation Services
N.A.I.C.S.: 221118
Grant King (Gen Mgr)

Origin Energy LPG Ltd. (1)
100 Waymouth Street, Adelaide, 5000, SA, Australia (100%)
Tel.: (61) 882175211
Web Site: http://www.originenergy.com.au
Sales Range: $250-299.9 Million
Emp.: 850
Petroleum & Petroleum Products Whslr
N.A.I.C.S.: 424720
Grant King (Mng Dir)

Origin Energy PNG Ltd. (1)
Napa Napa Rd Kanudi, Port Moresby, Papua New Guinea (100%)
Tel.: (675) 3234033
Sales Range: $125-149.9 Million
Emp.: 200
Natural Gas Distribution
N.A.I.C.S.: 221210
Lesieli Moala Taviri (Gen Mgr)

Origin Energy Petroleum Pty Ltd. (1)
L1 339 Coronation Drive, Milton, 4064, QLD, Australia (100%)
Tel.: (61) 738670202
Web Site: http://www.originenergy.com.au
Sales Range: $350-399.9 Million
Emp.: 1,000
Natural Gas Liquid Extraction
N.A.I.C.S.: 211130

Origin Energy Power Ltd (1)
L 6 1 King William St, Adelaide, 5000, Australia
Tel.: (61) 882175211
Electric Power Distr
N.A.I.C.S.: 221122

Origin Energy Resources NZ Ltd. (1)
12 Waione St, Wellington, New Zealand (100%)
Tel.: (64) 45766223
Holding Company
N.A.I.C.S.: 551112

Origin Energy Retail Ltd. (1)
100 Weymouth St, Adelaide, 5000, SA, Australia (100%)
Tel.: (61) 882175211
Web Site: http://www.originenergy.com.au

ORIGIN ENERGY LTD.

Origin Energy Ltd.—(Continued)
Sales Range: $500-549.9 Million
Emp.: 850
Natural Gas Distribution
N.A.I.C.S.: 221210

Subsidiary (Domestic):

Cogent Energy Pty Ltd (2)
Level 7 321 Exhibition Street, Melbourne, 3000, VIC, Australia
Tel.: (61) 396525025
Web Site: http://www.cogentenergy.com.au
Sales Range: $50-74.9 Million
Emp.: 15
Electric Power Distribution Services
N.A.I.C.S.: 221122
Blair Healy (Founder & Mgr)

Origin Energy SA Pty Ltd. (1)
64 George St leve I45, Cavan, Adelaide, 2000, SA, Australia (100%)
Tel.: (61) 882175712
Petroleum & Petroleum Products Whslr
N.A.I.C.S.: 424720

Origin Energy SWC Ltd. (1)
L 45 Australia Square 264-278 George Street, Sydney, 2000, NSW, Australia (100%)
Tel.: (61) 882175800
Sales Range: $250-299.9 Million
Emp.: 500
Nuclear Electric Power Generation
N.A.I.C.S.: 221113

Origin Energy Solomons Ltd (1)
Point Cruise Mendana Avenue, PO Box 767, Honiara, Solomon Islands
Tel.: (677) 21833
Sales Range: $50-74.9 Million
Emp.: 15
Oil & Gas Exploration Services
N.A.I.C.S.: 213112

Origin Energy Tasmania Ltd. (1)
37 The Esplanade, Launceston, Tasmania, Australia (100%)
Tel.: (61) 363349788
Natural Gas Distribution
N.A.I.C.S.: 221210

Origin Energy VIC Holdings Pty Ltd (1)
PO Box 186, Melbourne, 3001, VIC, Australia
Tel.: (61) 396525555
Investment Management Service
N.A.I.C.S.: 523999

Origin Energy WA Pty Ltd. (1)
L 6 1 King William St, Adelaide, 5000, SA, Australia (100%)
Tel.: (61) 882175211
Web Site: http://www.originenergy.com.au
Sales Range: $200-249.9 Million
Emp.: 850
Gasoline Stations
N.A.I.C.S.: 457120
Grant King (Mng Dir)

Origin Energy Wallumbilla Transmissions Pty Ltd (1)
John Oxley Ctr 339 Coronation Dr, Milton, 4064, QLD, Australia
Tel.: (61) 738670202
Web Site: http://www.originenergy.com.au
Emp.: 500
Oil & Gas Exploration Services
N.A.I.C.S.: 213112
Grant King (Mng Dir)

Origin Foundation Pty Limited (1)
Level 45 Australia Square 264-278 George St, Sydney, 2000, NSW, Australia
Tel.: (61) 283455077
Web Site: http://www.originfoundation.com.au
Educational Support Services
N.A.I.C.S.: 611710
Kevin McCann (Co-Chm)

Speed-E-Gas (NSW) Pty Limited (1)
26 Pembury Road, Minto, 2566, NSW, Australia (100%)
Tel.: (61) 296031200
Web Site: http://www.speed-e-gas.com.au
Sales Range: $75-99.9 Million
Emp.: 20
Natural Gas Distribution
N.A.I.C.S.: 221210

The Fiji Gas Co Ltd. (1)
Nasekula Rd, Labasa, Fiji
Tel.: (679) 8812973
Sales Range: $25-49.9 Million
Emp.: 5
Plumbing Heating & Air-Conditioning Contractors
N.A.I.C.S.: 238220
Niteshwar Sami (Mgr)

ORIGIN PROPERTY PUBLIC COMPANY LIMITED

4345 Bhiraj tower at Bitec floor20 Sukhumvit road, Bangna, Bangkok, 10260, Thailand
Tel.: (66) 2030000
Web Site: https://en.origin.co.th
Year Founded: 2009
ORI—(THA)
Rev.: $442,457,710
Assets: $1,904,204,886
Liabilities: $1,288,316,638
Net Worth: $615,888,248
Earnings: $92,245,018
Emp.: 1,497
Fiscal Year-end: 12/31/23
Real Estate Development
N.A.I.C.S.: 531390
Lucksananoi Punkrasamee (Chm)

Subsidiaries:

Primo Service Solution Company Limited (1)
496 Moo 9 Soi Bearing 16 Sukhumvit 107 Road, Samrong Nuea Subdistrict Mueang District, Samut Prakan, 10270, Thailand
Tel.: (66) 20810000
Web Site: https://www.primo.co.th
Real Estate Management Services
N.A.I.C.S.: 531311

Primo Service Solutions Company Limited (1)
496 Moo 9 Soi Bearing 16 Sukhumvit 107 Road, Samrong Nuea Muang Samut Prakarn District, Samut Prakan, 10270, Thailand
Tel.: (66) 20810000
Web Site: https://primo.co.th
Real Estate Services
N.A.I.C.S.: 531390

United Project Management Company Limited (1)
496 Village No 9, Samrong Nuea Subdistrict Mueang Samut Prakan District, Samut Prakan, 10270, Thailand
Tel.: (66) 20810000
Web Site: https://www.upm.co.th
Construction Services
N.A.I.C.S.: 236220

Wyde Interior Company Limited (1)
Bhiraj Tower at BITEC 21/FL 4345 Sukhumvit Road, Bangnatai Sub-district Bangna District, Bangkok, 10260, Thailand
Tel.: (66) 20810000
Web Site: https://www.wyde.co.th
Interior Design Services
N.A.I.C.S.: 541410

ORIGIN STORAGE LTD.

Unit 2 The Rutherford Ctr, Basingstoke, RG24 8PB, Hampshire, United Kingdom
Tel.: (44) 8442886868
Web Site: http://www.originstorage.com
Sales Range: $10-24.9 Million
Emp.: 20
Data Storage Solutions
N.A.I.C.S.: 334112
Andy Cordial (Mng Dir)

ORIGINAL ENGINEERING CONSULTANTS CO., LTD.

Onest Motoyoyogi Square 30-13 Motoyoyogi-cho, Shibuya-ku, Tokyo, 151-0062, Japan
Tel.: (81) 367578801 JP
Web Site: https://www.oec-solution.co.jp
Year Founded: 1962
4642—(TKS)
Sales Range: $50-74.9 Million
Emp.: 320
Water & Sewage Treatment Services
N.A.I.C.S.: 237110
Nobuhiko Suga (Pres)

Subsidiaries:

Urushi Co., Ltd. (1)
2-24-10 Taito St Bldg 2nd Fl, Taito-ku, Tokyo, 110-0016, Japan
Tel.: (81) 338341521
Web Site: http://www.urushi.co.jp
Lacquers Mfr
N.A.I.C.S.: 325510

ORIGINAL STEEL SERVICES LIMITED

Brockhouse House Howard Street Hill Top West Bromwich, England, B70 0SN, United Kingdom
Tel.: (44) 1305889583 UK
Web Site: http://www.ossl.biz
Year Founded: 2004
Sales Range: $50-74.9 Million
Holding Company; Steel Products Mfr & Whslr
N.A.I.C.S.: 551112
Christopher Hutton-Penman (Co-Owner & Mng Dir)

Subsidiaries:

Brockhouse Group Limited (1)
Howard Street, Hill Top, West Bromwich, B70 0SN, W Midlands, United Kingdom
Tel.: (44) 121 556 1241
Steel Forging
N.A.I.C.S.: 332111
Christopher Hutton-Penman (Chm)

D&J (Steels) Limited (1)
Bromford Lane West Bromwich, Wolverhampton, B70 7JJ, United Kingdom
Tel.: (44) 1902 453 680
Web Site: http://www.dandjsteels.com
Emp.: 8
Steel Whslr
N.A.I.C.S.: 423510
Christopher Hutton-Penman (Chm)

Offshore ETKS Ltd. (1)
Turnpike House Weymouth Road, Martinstown, Dorchester, DT2 9JJ, Dorset, United Kingdom
Tel.: (44) 1305 889 583
Holding Company; Metal Products Mfr
N.A.I.C.S.: 551112
Christopher Hutton-Penman (Chm)

Subsidiary (Domestic):

Bromford Iron & Steel Company Ltd. (2)
Bromford Lane, West Bromwich, B70 7JJ, W Midlands, United Kingdom
Tel.: (44) 121 553 6121
Web Site: http://www.bromfordsteels.co.uk
Sales Range: $10-24.9 Million
Emp.: 50
Hot Rolled Steel Products Mfr
N.A.I.C.S.: 331221
Mark Davies (Ops Mgr)

JA Envirotanks Ltd. (2)
23 Charles Henry Street, Highgate, Birmingham, B12 0SD, United Kingdom
Tel.: (44) 121 622 4661
Web Site: http://www.jaenvirotanks.com
Metal Storage Tank Mfr
N.A.I.C.S.: 332420

ORIGO HF.

Borgartun 37, 105, Reykjavik, Iceland
Tel.: (354) 516 1000
Web Site: http://www.origo.is
Year Founded: 1899
ORIGO—(ICE)
Rev.: $142,800,323
Assets: $118,880,165
Liabilities: $51,223,244
Net Worth: $67,656,921
Earnings: $11,731,323
Emp.: 455
Fiscal Year-end: 12/31/21
IT Services & Solutions
N.A.I.C.S.: 541512
Hakon Sigurhansson (Mng Dir-Software Solutions)

Subsidiaries:

AppliCon Holding ehf (1)
Borgartuni 37, 105, Reykjavik, Iceland
Tel.: (354) 5636100
Web Site: http://www.applicon.is
Sales Range: $100-124.9 Million
Emp.: 300
Software Publisher
N.A.I.C.S.: 513210
Ingimar Bjarnason (Mng Dir)

AppliCon Solutions Ltd (1)
Bldg Chiswick Pk 566, Chiswick High Rd, London, W45YA, United Kingdom
Tel.: (44) 2088498003
Sales Range: $25-49.9 Million
Emp.: 10
Telecommunications Resellers
N.A.I.C.S.: 517121

Applicon Consulting Sweden Holding AB (1)
Jakobsbergsgatan 13, 111 44, Stockholm, Sweden
Tel.: (46) 8 440 36 70
Web Site: http://www.applicon.se
Sales Range: $25-49.9 Million
Emp.: 50
Software Consulting Services
N.A.I.C.S.: 541512

Applicon ehf. (1)
Borgartuni 37, Reykjavik, 105, Iceland
Tel.: (354) 563 6100
Web Site: http://www.applicon.is
Sales Range: $25-49.9 Million
Emp.: 70
Software Development Consulting Services
N.A.I.C.S.: 541511
Ingimar G. Bjarnason (Gen Mgr)

Dansupport A/S (1)
Agerhatten 5, 5220, Odense, Denmark
Tel.: (45) 63 159 159
Web Site: http://www.dansupport.dk
Computer System Network Integration Services
N.A.I.C.S.: 541512

Klak ehf (1)
Kringlan 1, Reykjavik, 103, Iceland
Tel.: (354) 5787755
Web Site: http://www.klak.is
Sales Range: $10-24.9 Million
Emp.: 50
Other Business Service Centers
N.A.I.C.S.: 561439

Sense ehf (1)
Borgartun 37, Reykjavik, 105, Iceland
Tel.: (354) 5853800
Web Site: http://www.sense.is
Emp.: 300
Digital Equipment Distr
N.A.I.C.S.: 423990
Finnur Oddsson (Gen Mgr)

SimDex ehf (1)
Borgartuni 37, Reykjavik, Iceland
Tel.: (354) 5697700
Web Site: http://www.simdex.is
Sales Range: $25-49.9 Million
Emp.: 1
Software Publisher
N.A.I.C.S.: 513210
Patrick Alexander Thomas (Mgr)

Skyggnir ehf. (1)
Borgartun 37, Reykjavik, Iceland
Tel.: (354) 516 1000
Web Site: http://www.nyherji.is
Sales Range: $75-99.9 Million
Emp.: 300
Information & Communications Technology Services
N.A.I.C.S.: 541512

TM Software Origo ehf. (1)
Borgartun 37, 105, Reykjavik, Iceland
Tel.: (354) 545 3000

AND PRIVATE COMPANIES / ORION CORPORATION

Web Site: http://www.tm-software.com
Emp.: 400
Software Development Services
N.A.I.C.S.: 541511

Subsidiary (Domestic):

eMR ehf. (2)
Borgartun 37, 105, Reykjavik, Iceland
Tel.: (354) 545 3000
Web Site: http://www.emr.is
Medical Support Software Sales & Development Services
N.A.I.C.S.: 423430

Vigor ehf. (1)
Borgartun 37, 105, Reykjavik, Iceland
Tel.: (354) 545 3400
Web Site: http://www.vigor.is
Business Software Development Services
N.A.I.C.S.: 541511

ORIGO PARTNERS PLC
IOMA House Hope Street, Douglas, IM1 1AP, Isle of Man
Tel.: (44) 10 5381 2055   IM
Web Site: http://www.origoplc.com
OPP—(AIM)
Rev.: $20,000
Assets: $2,513,000
Liabilities: $170,000
Net Worth: $2,343,000
Earnings: ($1,257,000)
Emp.: 25
Fiscal Year-end: 12/31/20
Investment & Management Consulting Services
N.A.I.C.S.: 523999

Subsidiaries:

ISAK International Holding Ltd (1)
26th Floor Building A North Tower Soho Shangdu No 8 Dongdaqiao Road, Chaoyang District, 100020, Beijing, China
Tel.: (86) 1059002770
Web Site: http://www.isaklife.com
Emp.: 20
Furniture Products Mfr & Sales
N.A.I.C.S.: 337121

ORINKO ADVANCED PLASTICS CO., LTD.
No 2 Luhua Road, Baiyan Industrial Park Hefei High- Tech Development Area, Hefei, 231202, China
Tel.: (86) 55165771661
Web Site: https://www.orinko.com.cn
Year Founded: 2008
688219—(SHG)
Rev.: $727,175,278
Assets: $904,539,538
Liabilities: $654,105,516
Net Worth: $250,434,021
Earnings: $8,309,995
Fiscal Year-end: 12/31/22
Chemical Product Mfr & Distr
N.A.I.C.S.: 325520
Jianyi Li (Chm & Gen Mgr)

ORINOCO GOLD, LTD.
Level 2 22 Mount Street, West Perth, 6000, WA, Australia
Tel.: (61) 8 6188 8181
Web Site: http://www.orinocogold.com
Rev.: $17,141
Assets: $3,058,522
Liabilities: $14,689,738
Net Worth: ($11,631,215)
Earnings: ($30,415,267)
Fiscal Year-end: 12/31/18
Gold Mining Services
N.A.I.C.S.: 212220
Albert Longo (CFO)

ORINOQUIA REAL ESTATE SOCIMI, S.A.
C/ Marques de la Ensenada 4 4, 28004, Madrid, Spain
Tel.: (34) 914437193

Web Site: https://www.orinoquiarealestate.com
Year Founded: 2017
MLORQ—(EUR)
Rev.: $42,868,793
Assets: $1,405,038,863
Liabilities: $690,105
Net Worth: $1,404,348,758
Earnings: $34,353,917
Fiscal Year-end: 12/31/21
Real Estate Investment Services
N.A.I.C.S.: 531190

ORIO AB
Flattnaleden 1, 611 45, Nykoping, Sweden
Tel.: (46) 155 244,000   SE
Web Site: http://www.orio.com
Year Founded: 1947
Rev.: $54,013,680
Assets: $42,224,980
Liabilities: $10,073,980
Net Worth: $32,151,000
Earnings: ($3,107,930)
Emp.: 155
Fiscal Year-end: 12/31/19
Motor Vehicle Parts Whslr
N.A.I.C.S.: 423120
Charlotte Hansson (Chm)

ORIOLA CORPORATION
Orionintie 5, FI-02200, Espoo, Finland
Tel.: (358) 1042999
Web Site: https://www.oriola.com
Year Founded: 1907
OKDBV—(HEL)
Rev.: $2,211,814,592
Assets: $1,431,636,544
Liabilities: $1,223,449,864
Net Worth: $208,186,680
Earnings: $13,879,112
Emp.: 2,730
Fiscal Year-end: 12/31/20
Pharmaceutical Retailer
N.A.I.C.S.: 456110
Teija Silver (VP-HR)

Subsidiaries:

Kronans Droghandel Apotek AB (1)
Lindhagensgatan 116 9th Floor, Stockholm, Sweden
Tel.: (46) 77 161 2612
Web Site: https://www.kronansapotek.se
Pharmacy Services
N.A.I.C.S.: 456110

Oriola Finland OY (1)
Orionintie 5, 02200, Espoo, Finland
Tel.: (358) 1042999
Health & Wellbeing Services
N.A.I.C.S.: 525120

Oriola Oy (1)
Orionintie 5, 02200, Espoo, Finland (100%)
Tel.: (358) 104 2999
Web Site: https://www.oriola.com
Sales Range: $200-249.9 Million
Emp.: 1,000
Mfr of Pharmaceutical Products
N.A.I.C.S.: 325412

Subsidiary (Non-US):

AS Oriola (2)
Kungla 2, Saue linn, EE 76505, Harjumaa, Estonia (100%)
Tel.: (372) 6515100
Web Site: http://www.oriola.ee
Sales Range: $10-24.9 Million
Emp.: 11
Pharmaceuticals & Medical Equipment
N.A.I.C.S.: 325412

Oriola AB (2)
Gardsfogdevagen 2, PO Box 20029, 16102, Bromma, Sweden (100%)
Tel.: (46) 87998200
Web Site: http://www.oriola.com
Sales Range: $25-49.9 Million
Emp.: 50
N.A.I.C.S.: 325620

Subsidiary (Domestic):

Oriola Oy Graphic Arts (2)
Oriontie 5, 2101, Espoo, Finland (100%)
Tel.: (358) 10428210
Sales Range: $200-249.9 Million
Emp.: 800
N.A.I.C.S.: 325620

Oriola Oy Medion (2)
PO Box 8, 2101, Espoo, Finland (100%)
Tel.: (358) 1042999
Web Site: http://www.oriola-kd.com
Sales Range: $25-49.9 Million
Emp.: 335
Provider of Diagnostic Imaging Equipment
N.A.I.C.S.: 334510

Oriola Oy Reformi-Keskus (2)
Orionintie 5, FIN 02200, Espoo, Finland (100%)
Tel.: (358) 942999
Web Site: http://www.oriola.fi
Sales Range: $200-249.9 Million
Emp.: 700
Medical Supplies Mfr
N.A.I.C.S.: 325412
Eero Hautaniemi (Pres)

Subsidiary (Non-US):

SIA Oriola Riga (2)
Dzelzavas lela 120 M, LV 1021, Riga, Latvia (100%)
Tel.: (371) 7802450
Web Site: http://www.oriola.lv
Sales Range: $25-49.9 Million
Emp.: 70
Distr of Pharmaceuticals
N.A.I.C.S.: 325412

UAB Oriola Vilnius (2)
Laisves Pr 75, 01640, Vilnius, Lithuania
Tel.: (370) 52688482
Web Site: http://www.oriola.fi
Sales Range: $25-49.9 Million
Emp.: 50
Distr of Pharmaceuticals
N.A.I.C.S.: 325412

Svensk dos AB (1)
Rapsgatan 25, 754 50, Uppsala, Sweden
Tel.: (46) 18 413 7420
Web Site: https://svenskdos.se
Pharmacy Services
N.A.I.C.S.: 456110

ORIOLE RESOURCES PLC
Wessex House Upper Market Street, Eastleigh, SO50 9FD, United Kingdom
Tel.: (44) 2380651649
Web Site: https://orioleresources.com
ORR—(AIM)
Assets: $15,289,571
Liabilities: $776,573
Net Worth: $14,512,998
Earnings: ($2,889,869)
Fiscal Year-end: 12/31/23
Gold Exploration Services
N.A.I.C.S.: 212220
Claire Bay (VP-Exploration & Bus Dev)

Subsidiaries:

Stratex Exploration Limited (1)
Wessex House Upper Market St, Eastleigh, SO50 9FD, Hampshire, United Kingdom
Tel.: (44) 2380651649
Web Site: http://www.stratexinternational.com
Mineral Exploration Services
N.A.I.C.S.: 213115

Subsidiary (Non-US):

Stratex Madencilik Sanayi ve Ticaret Ltd. Sti (2)
Iran cad 53/6, Ankara, Turkiye
Tel.: (90) 3124682096
Mineral Exploration Services
N.A.I.C.S.: 212390

ORION BLISS CORP.
Kalonite 9-57, Ashdod, 7724233, Israel

Tel.: (972) 8498593819   NV
Year Founded: 2021
Rev.: $600
Assets: $7,915
Liabilities: $44,752
Net Worth: ($36,837)
Earnings: ($29,182)
Fiscal Year-end: 04/30/23
Online Shopping Services
N.A.I.C.S.: 541511
Alexandra Solomovskaya (Exec Chm, Interim CEO, Interim CFO & Exec VP)

ORION CORPORATION
Orionintie 1A, FI-02200, Espoo, Finland
Tel.: (358) 104261   FI
Web Site: https://www.orion.fi
ORINY—(OTCIQ)
Rev.: $1,283,941,291
Assets: $1,552,557,738
Liabilities: $591,949,061
Net Worth: $960,608,677
Earnings: $233,973,667
Emp.: 3,632
Fiscal Year-end: 12/31/23
Pharmaceuticals Mfr
N.A.I.C.S.: 325412
Mikael Silvennoinen (Chm)

Subsidiaries:

Fermion Oy (1)
Koivu-Mankkaan Tie 6 A, FI-02200, Espoo, Finland
Tel.: (358) 104261
Web Site: https://www.fermion.fi
Sales Range: $25-49.9 Million
Emp.: 7
Pharmaceuticals Product Mfr
N.A.I.C.S.: 325412
Arto Toivonen (Pres)

Hiven Oy (1)
Yrittajatie 1, FIN 21530, Paimio, Finland (100%)
Tel.: (358) 00104027700
Web Site: http://www.hiven.fi
Sales Range: $25-49.9 Million
Emp.: 20
N.A.I.C.S.: 325620

Kiinteisto Oy Kapseli (1)
Vuorikatu 21, 10900, Hanko, Finland
Tel.: (358) 19 2652480
Real Estate Development Services
N.A.I.C.S.: 531390

OOO Orion Pharma (1)
Sechenovsky Pereulok 6 - Building 3, 119034, Moscow, Russia
Tel.: (7) 4953635071
Web Site: http://www.orionpharma.ru
Sales Range: $25-49.9 Million
Pharmaceuticals Product Mfr
N.A.I.C.S.: 325412

OU Orion Pharma Eesti (1)
Mustamae Tee 6b, 10621, Tallinn, Estonia
Tel.: (372) 6644550
Web Site: https://www.orionpharma.ee
Sales Range: $50-74.9 Million
Pharmaceutical Products Distr
N.A.I.C.S.: 424210

Orion Corporation - Hanko Plant (1)
Orioninkatu 2 10900, 10900, Hanko, Finland
Tel.: (358) 10 4261
Pharmaceuticals Product Mfr
N.A.I.C.S.: 325412
Jorma Mamia (Pres)

Orion Corporation - Oulu Plant (1)
Laakotehtaantie 2, 90050, Oulu, Finland
Tel.: (358) 10 4261
Pharmaceuticals Product Mfr
N.A.I.C.S.: 325412

Orion Pharma (1)
Tengstrominkatu 8, 20380, Turku, Finland (100%)
Tel.: (358) 104261
Web Site: http://www.orion.fi

ORION CORPORATION

Orion Corporation—(Continued)
Sales Range: $200-249.9 Million
Emp.: 577
Mfr of Pharmaceuticals
N.A.I.C.S.: 325412

Subsidiary (Non-US):

Orion Pharma (UK) Ltd. (2)
Abbey Gardens 4 Abbey Street, Reading,
RG1 3BA, Berkshire, United
Kingdom **(100%)**
Tel.: (44) 1635520300
Web Site: https://www.orionpharma.co.uk
Sales Range: $25-49.9 Million
Marketer of Pharmaceuticals
N.A.I.C.S.: 325412

Orion Pharma A/S (2)
Sandakerveien 130, 0484, Oslo,
Norway **(100%)**
Tel.: (47) 40004210
Web Site: https://www.orionpharma.no
Sales Range: $25-49.9 Million
Pharmaceuticals Marketer
N.A.I.C.S.: 325412
Elling Berg *(Country Mgr)*

Orion Pharma A/S (2)
Orestads Boulevard 73, 2300, Copenhagen,
Denmark **(100%)**
Tel.: (45) 86140000
Web Site: https://www.orionpharma.dk
Sales Range: $25-49.9 Million
Marketer of Pharmaceuticals
N.A.I.C.S.: 325412

Orion Pharma AB (2)
Golfvagen 2 4 tr, 182 31, Danderyd,
Sweden **(100%)**
Tel.: (46) 86236440
Web Site: https://www.orionpharma.se
Sales Range: $25-49.9 Million
Marketer of Pharmaceuticals
N.A.I.C.S.: 325412

Orion Pharma AB (2)
Golfvagen 2 4 tr, 182 31, Danderyd,
Sweden **(100%)**
Tel.: (46) 86236440
Web Site: https://www.orionpharma.se
Sales Range: $25-49.9 Million
Marketer of Pharmaceuticals
N.A.I.C.S.: 325412

Orion Pharma AB (2)
Golfvagen 2 4 tr, 182 31, Danderyd,
Sweden **(100%)**
Tel.: (46) 86236440
Web Site: https://www.orionpharma.se
Sales Range: $25-49.9 Million
Marketer of Pharmaceuticals
N.A.I.C.S.: 325412

Orion Pharma AB (2)
Golfvagen 2 4 tr, 182 31, Danderyd,
Sweden **(100%)**
Tel.: (46) 86236440
Web Site: https://www.orionpharma.se
Sales Range: $25-49.9 Million
Marketer of Pharmaceuticals
N.A.I.C.S.: 325412

Orion Pharma AG (2)
Baarerstrasse 75, 6300, Zug,
Switzerland **(100%)**
Tel.: (41) 417674090
Web Site: https://www.orionpharma.ch
Sales Range: $25-49.9 Million
Marketer of Pharmaceuticals
N.A.I.C.S.: 325412
Andrea Kieninger *(Country Mgr-Switzerland)*

Orion Pharma GmbH (2)
Jurgen-Topfer-Strasse 46, D - 22763, Hamburg, Germany **(100%)**
Tel.: (49) 408996890
Web Site: https://www.orionpharma.de
Sales Range: $50-74.9 Million
Emp.: 130
Marketer of Pharmaceuticals
N.A.I.C.S.: 325412
Robert Borgdorf *(Mng Dir)*

Orion Pharma KFT. (2)
Pap Karoly U 4 6, 1139, Budapest,
Hungary **(100%)**
Tel.: (36) 12399095
Web Site: https://www.orionpharma.hu

Sales Range: $25-49.9 Million
Emp.: 4
Marketer of Pharmaceuticals
N.A.I.C.S.: 325412
Judit Horvath *(Mng Dir)*

Orion Pharma (Austria) GmbH (1)
Wienerbergstrasse 11/12a, 1100, Vienna,
Austria
Tel.: (43) 1994606550
Web Site: https://www.orionpharma.at
Pharmaceuticals Product Mfr
N.A.I.C.S.: 325412

Orion Pharma (Ireland) Ltd. (1)
4045 Kingswood Rd Citywest Business
Park, Dublin, 24, Ireland
Tel.: (353) 14287777
Web Site: https://www.orionpharma.ie
Emp.: 50
Pharmaceutical Products Distr
N.A.I.C.S.: 424210

Orion Pharma Animal Health (1)
Tengstrominkatu 8, 20360, Turku, Finland
Tel.: (358) 10 4261
Sales Range: $25-49.9 Million
Emp.: 2
Veterinary Pharmaceutical Products Distr
N.A.I.C.S.: 424210
Sauli Niinistoe *(Partner & Dir-Sls)*

Orion Pharma Animal Health (1)
Mollevej 9A, 2990, Nivaa, Denmark
Tel.: (45) 49126765
Web Site: http://www.orionvet.dk
Sales Range: $25-49.9 Million
Emp.: 12
Veterinary Pharmaceutical Products Distr
N.A.I.C.S.: 424210
Holck Niels *(Mgr-Marketing)*

Orion Pharma BVBA (1)
Pegasuslaan 5, 1831, Diegem, Belgium
Tel.: (32) 2 709 2033
Web Site: http://www.orionpharma.nl
Pharmaceutical Products Mfr & Distr
N.A.I.C.S.: 325412

Orion Pharma Hellas MEPE (1)
17 Possidonos Avenue, Alimos, Athens,
17456, Greece
Tel.: (30) 210 980 3355
Sales Range: $50-74.9 Million
Emp.: 4
Pharmaceutical Products Distr
N.A.I.C.S.: 424210
Panopoulos Thanassis *(Gen Mgr)*

Orion Pharma Poland Sp. z.o.o. (1)
Fabryczna 5A, 00 446, Warsaw, Poland
Tel.: (48) 228333177
Web Site: https://www.orionpharma.pl
Emp.: 100
Pharmaceutical Products Distr
N.A.I.C.S.: 424210
Wojciech Szwedzinski *(Gen Mgr)*

Orion Pharma S.L. (1)
Avenida Alberto Alcocer 46B 10 E, 28016,
Madrid, Spain
Tel.: (34) 915998601
Web Site: https://www.orionpharma.es
Sales Range: $50-74.9 Million
Emp.: 5
Pharmaceutical Products Distr
N.A.I.C.S.: 424210
Bernardo de Rafael *(Gen Mgr)*

Orion Pharma d.o.o. (1)
Povsetova 29, 1000, Ljubljana, Slovenia
Tel.: (386) 16008015
Web Site: https://www.orionpharma.si
Sales Range: $50-74.9 Million
Emp.: 3
Pharmaceutical Products Distr
N.A.I.C.S.: 424210

Orionfin Unipessoal Lda (1)
Avenida da Republica n 6 - 1 Esq, 1050-191, Lisbon, Portugal
Tel.: (351) 211546820
Sales Range: $50-74.9 Million
Emp.: 4
Pharmaceutical Products Distr
N.A.I.C.S.: 424210

UAB Orion Pharma (1)
Ukmerges g 126, LT-08100, Vilnius, Lithuania
Tel.: (370) 52769499

Web Site: https://www.orionpharma.lt
Pharmaceutical Products Distr
N.A.I.C.S.: 424210

ORION CORPORATION
13 Baekbeom-ro 90da-gil, Yongsan-gu, Seoul, 04369, Korea (South)
Tel.: (82) 27106000 KR
Web Site:
https://www.orionworld.com
Year Founded: 1956
271560—(KRS)
Rev: $2,203,780,274
Assets: $2,586,081,562
Liabilities: $561,793,048
Net Worth: $2,024,288,515
Earnings: $305,502,294
Emp.: 1,368
Fiscal Year-end: 12/31/22
Holding Company; Confectionery Mfr
& Whslr; Motion Picture Production &
Distribution; Professional Basketball
Team Owner & Operator
N.A.I.C.S.: 551112
Tam Chul Kon *(Chm)*

ORION ENGINEERING SERVICES LIMITED
Orion House Castle Heather, Inverness, IV2 6AA, United Kingdom
Tel.: (44) 1463 230860
Web Site: http://www.orionjobs.com
Year Founded: 1987
Emp.: 500
Human Resource Consulting Services
N.A.I.C.S.: 541612
Orly Francisco *(Supvr-Welding)*

Subsidiaries:

Orion Engineering SA (Pty) Ltd (1)
Convention Tower 1st Floor Cnr Heerengracht & Walter Sisulu Street, Foreshore,
Cape Town, 8001, South Africa
Tel.: (27) 214036509
Human Resource Consulting Services
N.A.I.C.S.: 541612

Orion Engineering Services Mozambique Limitada (1)
Global Alliance Building Avenida Marginal
141, Maputo, Mozambique
Tel.: (258) 21244320
Human Resource Consulting Services
N.A.I.C.S.: 541612

Orion Engineering Services Nigeria Limited (1)
Bode Thomas Street Suru Lere, Lagos,
Nigeria
Tel.: (234) 17100116
Human Resource Consulting Services
N.A.I.C.S.: 541612
Muyiwa Akin *(Country Mgr)*

Orion Group KZ (1)
Building CO-101 102 Promzone, Burlinskiy
Region, Aksay, Kazakhstan
Tel.: (7) 7122317471
Human Resource Consulting Services
N.A.I.C.S.: 541612

Orion Personnel PH Inc (1)
Bldg No N3835 Site Skills Training Centennial Road, Clark Freeport Zone, Pampanga,
Philippines
Tel.: (63) 454991434
Human Resource Consulting Services
N.A.I.C.S.: 541612

Orion Project Services (Houston) LLC (1)
4500 W Illinois Ste 200, Midland, TX 79703
Tel.: (432) 520-1544
Human Resource Consulting Services
N.A.I.C.S.: 541612

Orion Project Services B.V (1)
Westerkade 27, 3016 CM, Rotterdam, Netherlands
Tel.: (31) 108419393
Human Resource Consulting Services
N.A.I.C.S.: 541612

Orion Project Services LLC (1)
4300 B St Ste 505, Anchorage, AK 99503
Tel.: (907) 562-3400
Human Resource Consulting Services
N.A.I.C.S.: 541612

Orion Project Services LLC (1)
Office 113 1st floor Mohd Zainal Faraidooni
Bldg, PO Box 113032, Salahuddin Road,
Dubai, United Arab Emirates
Tel.: (971) 43697875
Human Resource Consulting Services
N.A.I.C.S.: 541612
Jon Barnard *(Mgr-Depot)*

Orion Project Services Malaysia Sdn. Bhd. (1)
A4-U2-05 Solaris Dutamas No 1 Jalan Dutamas 1, 50480, Kuala Lumpur, Malaysia
Tel.: (60) 362053405
Human Resource Consulting Services
N.A.I.C.S.: 541612

Orion Project Services Pte. Ltd. (1)
No 85 Maude Road 02-01, Singapore,
208357, Singapore
Tel.: (65) 68875330
Human Resource Consulting Services
N.A.I.C.S.: 541612

Orion Project Services Sakhallin LLC (1)
Krasnoproletarskaya Ulitsa 16-1, 127473,
Moscow, Russia
Tel.: (7) 4955065859
Human Resource Consulting Services
N.A.I.C.S.: 541612

Orion Technical Recruitment Services PVT Ltd (1)
B - 504 Sagar Tech Plaza Kurla Andheri
Road Sakinaka, Andheri East, Mumbai, 400
072, India
Tel.: (91) 61999199
Human Resource Consulting Services
N.A.I.C.S.: 541612

PT Orion Indonesia Group (1)
Pesona Toronto Ruko Masion Avenue Blok
YB No 80, Kota Wisata Cibubur, Bogor,
16820, Indonesia
Tel.: (62) 2182482439
Human Resource Consulting Services
N.A.I.C.S.: 541612

ORION EQUITIES LIMITED
Suite 1 Level 1 680 Murray Street,
West Perth, 6005, WA, Australia
Tel.: (61) 892149797 AU
Web Site:
https://www.orionequities.com.au
Year Founded: 1969
OEQ—(ASX)
Rev: $3,380,372
Assets: $4,637,943
Liabilities: $1,128,764
Net Worth: $3,509,179
Earnings: $2,005,960
Fiscal Year-end: 06/30/24
Real Estate Invetment
N.A.I.C.S.: 522299
Victor P. H. Ho *(Sec)*

Subsidiaries:

Dandaragan Estate Pty. Ltd. (1)
Level 2 33 Ventnor Ave, West Perth, 6005,
WA, Australia
Tel.: (61) 892149747
Web Site:
http://www.dandaraganestate.com.au
Sales Range: $25-49.9 Million
Emp.: 11
Olive Oils Mfr
N.A.I.C.S.: 311225
Karen Wee *(Dir-Sls)*

ORION HEALTH GROUP LIMITED
Orion House 181 Grafton Road, Grafton, Auckland, 1010, New Zealand
Tel.: (64) 9 638 0600
Web Site: http://www.orionhealth.com
Year Founded: 1993
Rev: $127,329,752
Assets: $76,867,918

AND PRIVATE COMPANIES

Liabilities: $63,235,284
Net Worth: $13,632,634
Earnings: ($28,855,825)
Emp.: 1,001
Fiscal Year-end: 03/31/18
IT Healthcare Services
N.A.I.C.S.: 513210
Ian McCrae *(Exec Dir-Products)*

ORION INFUSION LIMITED
Orion House 153-154 Tejgaon I/A, Dhaka, 1208, Bangladesh
Tel.: (880) 28870133
Web Site: https://www.orioninfusion.com
Year Founded: 1989
ORIONINFU—(CHT)
Rev.: $7,500,393
Assets: $7,746,196
Liabilities: $5,046,077
Net Worth: $2,700,119
Earnings: $387,921
Emp.: 764
Fiscal Year-end: 06/30/23
Pharmaceuticals Product Mfr
N.A.I.C.S.: 325412
Mohammad Obaidul Karim *(Chm)*

ORION METALS LIMITED
Tel.: (61) 413976908   AU
Web Site: https://www.orionmetals.com.au
ORM—(ASX)
Rev.: $118
Assets: $47,828
Liabilities: $595,209
Net Worth: ($547,381)
Earnings: ($371,843)
Fiscal Year-end: 02/29/20
Metal Mining Services
N.A.I.C.S.: 212290
Bin Cai *(CFO)*

ORION MINERALS LTD
Level 27 120 Collins Street, Melbourne, 3000, VIC, Australia
Tel.: (61) 380807170   AU
Web Site: https://www.orionminerals.com.au
Year Founded: 2003
ORN—(ASX)
Rev.: $2,919,385
Assets: $91,213,274
Liabilities: $29,153,980
Net Worth: $62,059,295
Earnings: ($5,304,487)
Emp.: 200
Fiscal Year-end: 06/30/24
Mineral Exploration Services
N.A.I.C.S.: 212290
Denis Waddell *(Chm)*

ORION NUTRACEUTICALS, INC.
Suite 1890 - 1075 West Georgia Street, Vancouver, V6E 3C9, BC, Canada
Tel.: (604) 687-2038
Year Founded: 2017
ORI—(CNSX)
Assets: $66,302
Liabilities: $359,520
Net Worth: ($293,219)
Earnings: ($4,890,780)
Fiscal Year-end: 05/31/19
Health Care Srvices
N.A.I.C.S.: 621999
Guy Bourgeois *(Dir)*

ORIOR AG
Dufourstrasse 101, CH-8008, Zurich, Switzerland
Tel.: (41) 443086500
Web Site: https://www.orior.ch
ORON—(SWX)
Rev.: $695,460,019

Assets: $427,081,616
Liabilities: $336,172,587
Net Worth: $90,909,029
Earnings: $30,899,444
Emp.: 1,980
Fiscal Year-end: 12/31/21
Food Mfr
N.A.I.C.S.: 311999
Rolf U. Sutter *(Chm)*

Subsidiaries:

Albert Spiess AG   (1)
Dorfstrasse 64, CH-7220, Schiers, Switzerland
Tel.: (41) 813080308
Sales Range: $25-49.9 Million
Boxed Meats Mfr
N.A.I.C.S.: 112320

Biotta AG   (1)
Pflanzbergstrasse 8, CH-8274, Taegerwilen, Switzerland
Tel.: (41) 714664870
Web Site: https://biotta.ch
Emp.: 70
Organic Vegetable Services
N.A.I.C.S.: 445230
Flavio Balbiani *(Mgr)*

Casualfood GmbH   (1)
Frankfurt Airport Center 1 Gebaudeteil A / 8 Stock, Hugo-Eckener-Ring, 60549, Frankfurt am Main, Germany
Tel.: (49) 6965007260
Web Site: https://www.casualfood.de
Food Service
N.A.I.C.S.: 722310
Stefan Weber *(Partner)*

Culinor NV   (1)
Houtstraat 46, 9070, Destelbergen, Belgium
Tel.: (32) 92290511
Web Site: https://www.culinor.com
Food Mfr
N.A.I.C.S.: 311999

Subsidiary (Domestic):

Vaco BV   (2)
Lammerdries Zuid 16F, 2250, Olen, Belgium
Tel.: (32) 14564110
Emp.: 270
Prepared Meals, Dips, Dressings & Soups Mfr
N.A.I.C.S.: 311999

Fredag AG   (1)
Oberfeld 7, CH-6037, Root, Switzerland
Tel.: (41) 414555700
Web Site: https://www.fredag.ch
Sales Range: $75-99.9 Million
Meat & Seafood Products Whslr
N.A.I.C.S.: 424470
Bruno De Gennaro *(CEO)*

GESA Gemusesaft GmbH   (1)
Obere Maurichstrasse 4, 74196, Neuenstadt am Kocher, Germany
Tel.: (49) 626492230
Web Site: https://gemuesesaft.de
Vegetable Farming & Juice Mfr
N.A.I.C.S.: 311411
Clemens Ruttimann *(Mng Dir)*

Mofag Mosli Fleischwaren AG   (1)
Industriestrasse 9, Zuzwil, CH-9524, Bern, Switzerland
Tel.: (41) 719441111
Web Site: https://moefag.ch
Food Service
N.A.I.C.S.: 722310

ORIOR Menu AG   (1)
Rohrmattstrasse 1, CH-4461, Bockten, Switzerland
Tel.: (41) 619858500
Web Site: https://lepatron.ch
Food Service
N.A.I.C.S.: 722310

ORIOR Menu AG Le Patron   (1)
Rohrmattstrasse 1, 4461, Bockten, Switzerland
Tel.: (41) 619858500
Web Site: https://lepatron.ch
Sales Range: $100-124.9 Million
Food Products Mfr & Distr
N.A.I.C.S.: 311999

Jann Gehri *(CEO)*

ORIOR Menu AG Pastinella   (1)
Industriestrasse 40, 5036, Oberentfelden, Switzerland
Tel.: (41) 627372828
Web Site: http://pastinella.ch
Sales Range: $25-49.9 Million
Food Products Mfr
N.A.I.C.S.: 311999

Orior Food AG   (1)
Dufourstrasse 101, 8008, Zurich, Switzerland
Tel.: (41) 443086500
Web Site: http://www.orior.ch
Sales Range: $25-49.9 Million
Emp.: 8
Food Processing
N.A.I.C.S.: 311412

Rapelli SA   (1)
Via Laveggio 13, 6855, Stabio, Switzerland
Tel.: (41) 916407300
Web Site: https://www.rapelli.ch
Veal Product Mfr
N.A.I.C.S.: 311612

Spiess Europe SAS   (1)
ZA-2 Allee Joseph Bumb, F-67500, Haguenau, France
Tel.: (33) 388906990
Food Service
N.A.I.C.S.: 722310

ORISOFT TECHNOLOGY SDN BHD
801D Level 8 Tower D Uptown 5 No 5 Jalan SS21/39 Damansara Uptown, 47400, Petaling Jaya, Selangor, Malaysia
Tel.: (60) 3 7688 6868
Web Site: http://www.orisoft.com.my
Year Founded: 1987
Sales Range: $10-24.9 Million
Human Resource & Administrative Management Software Development Services
N.A.I.C.S.: 541511
Yeong Kim Tan *(Mng Dir)*

Subsidiaries:

Orisoft (Thailand) Co., Ltd.   (1)
195 Empire Tower 23rd Fl Unit 2312, South Sathorn Road, Bangkok, 10120, Thailand
Tel.: (66) 2670 1600
Emp.: 20
Administrative Software Development Services
N.A.I.C.S.: 541511
Vincent Sudo *(Gen Mgr)*

ORISSA BENGAL CARRIER LTD.
A-1 3rd Floor C G Elite Complex Opp Mandi Gate Pandri Main Road, Raipur, Chhattisgarh, India
Tel.: (91) 7712281314
Web Site: https://www.obclimited.com
Year Founded: 1994
OBCL—(NSE)
Rev.: $44,184,078
Assets: $11,793,681
Liabilities: $1,516,875
Net Worth: $10,276,806
Earnings: $439,926
Emp.: 174
Fiscal Year-end: 03/31/23
Logistic Services
N.A.I.C.S.: 488510
Ratan Kumar Agrawal *(Chm & Mng Dir)*

ORISSA MINERALS DEVELOPMENT COMPANY LIMITED
AG-104 Sourav Abasan 2nd Floor Salt Lake City Sector-II, Kolkata, 700 091, West Bengal, India
Tel.: (91) 3340169200
Web Site: https://www.birdgroup.co.in
ORISSAMINE—(NSE)
Rev.: $15,488,820

ORIX CORPORATION

Assets: $56,126,227
Liabilities: $69,436,329
Net Worth: ($13,310,101)
Earnings: ($1,066,519)
Emp.: 1
Fiscal Year-end: 03/31/23
Iron Ore Mining
N.A.I.C.S.: 212210
Prabhat Kumar Sinha *(CEO & Mng Dir)*

ORIX CORPORATION
World Trade Center South Tower Building 2-4-1 Hamamatsu-cho, Minato-ku, Tokyo, 105-5135, Japan
Tel.: (81) 334353000   JP
Web Site: https://www.orix.co.jp
Year Founded: 1964
IX—(NYSE)
Rev.: $17,507,689,483
Assets: $101,537,172,564
Liabilities: $76,517,171,813
Net Worth: $25,020,000,751
Earnings: $2,106,295,553
Emp.: 33,807
Fiscal Year-end: 03/31/24
Commercial Finance, Investment, Life Insurance & Real Estate Development Services
N.A.I.C.S.: 522220
Makoto Inoue *(Pres, CEO & Exec Officer)*

Subsidiaries:

Agatsuma Bio Power Co., Ltd.   (1)
460-1 Okazaki Higashiagatsuma-cho, Agatsuma-gun, Gunma, 377-0302, Japan
Tel.: (81) 27 920 9102
Web Site: https://agatsuma.orix-eco.jp
Biomass Power Generation Services
N.A.I.C.S.: 221117

BlueWave Corporation   (1)
World Trade Center Bldg 2 4 1 Hamamatsu cho, Minato ku, Tokyo, 105 6135, Japan   (100%)
Tel.: (81) 334353945
Sales Range: $10-24.9 Million
Emp.: 20
Hotel & Training Facilities Management
N.A.I.C.S.: 721110

Boston Financial Investment Management, LP   (1)
101 Arch St, Boston, MA 02110
Web Site: https://www.bfim.com
Investment Services
N.A.I.C.S.: 523150
Gregory P. Voyentzie *(CEO)*

Chofu Driving School Corporation   (1)
1-34-1 Kikunodai, Chofu, 182-0007, Tokyo, Japan
Tel.: (81) 42 485 3311
Web Site: https://www.chofu-group.co.jp
Driving School Operator
N.A.I.C.S.: 611692

DHC Corporation   (1)
2 7 1 Minamiazabu, Minato ku, Tokyo, 106-8571, Japan   (91.1%)
Tel.: (81) 334575311
Web Site: http://www.dhc.co.jp
Sales Range: $400-449.9 Million
Emp.: 3,030
Cosmetics, Vitamins & Health Products Mfr
N.A.I.C.S.: 325620

Subsidiary (US):

DHC USA Inc.   (2)
1737 Post St Ste 325, San Francisco, CA 94115
Tel.: (415) 674-1345
Web Site: http://www.dhccare.com
Sales Range: $25-49.9 Million
Emp.: 30
Skincare Product Whslr
N.A.I.C.S.: 325620
Gary Gauntt *(Pres)*

Daikyo Incorporated   (1)
4-24-13 Sendagaya, Shibuya-ku, Tokyo, 151-8506, Japan   (100%)

ORIX CORPORATION

ORIX Corporation—(Continued)
Tel.: (81) 334754034
Web Site: https://www.daikyo.co.jp
Rev.: $2,976,433,920
Assets: $2,454,582,960
Liabilities: $853,021,680
Net Worth: $1,601,561,280
Earnings: $122,996,880
Emp.: 5,621
Fiscal Year-end: 03/31/2018
Real Estate Leasing & Condominium Developer
N.A.I.C.S.: 531190
Eiji Ochiai (Sr Mng Dir)

Subsidiary (Domestic):

Asset Wave Corporation, Inc. (2)
3-10-2 Kandajinbocho, Chiyoda-ku, Tokyo, Japan
Tel.: (81) 352116080
Rev.: $10,168,000
Emp.: 30
Real Estate Services
N.A.I.C.S.: 531210

Daikyo L. Design Incorporated (2)
5-25-5 Sendagaya, Shibuya-ku, Tokyo, Japan
Tel.: (81) 353662490
Home Remodeling Services
N.A.I.C.S.: 236118

Daikyo Realdo Incorporated (2)
5-25-5 Sendagaya, Shibuya-ku, 1510051, Tokyo, Japan
Tel.: (81) 353662106
Web Site: http://www.luxury.daikyo-realdo.co.jp
Real Estate Brokerage & sales
N.A.I.C.S.: 531190

ETHOZ Group Inc. (1)
30 Bukit Batok Crescent, Singapore, 658075, Singapore
Tel.: (65) 6 319 8000
Web Site: https://www.ethozgroup.com
Sales Range: $75-99.9 Million
Emp.: 200
Car Rental Services
N.A.I.C.S.: 532111

Freeill Corporation (1)
46-2 Asahicho Takasaki Building Takasaki West Exit 7th Floor, Takasaki, 370-0052, Gunma, Japan
Tel.: (81) 27 329 7080
Web Site: https://www.freeill.co.jp
Medical Equipment Rental Services
N.A.I.C.S.: 532283

Koike Europe B.V. (1)
Grote Tocht 19, 1507 CG, Zaandam, Netherlands (100%)
Tel.: (31) 756127227
Web Site: https://www.koike-europe.com
Machine Tools Mfr
N.A.I.C.S.: 333517

Kyuko-Lease Inc. (1)
2-10-1 Takasago, Chuo-ku, Fukuoka, 810-0011, Japan
Tel.: (81) 925345507
Web Site: http://www.kyuko-lease.co.jp
Automobile Leasing Services
N.A.I.C.S.: 532112

NS Lease Co., Ltd. (1)
2-4-1 Hamamatsucho World Trade Center Building South Building, Minato-ku, Tokyo, 105-5135, Japan
Tel.: (81) 33 435 3090
Web Site: http://www.orix.co.jp
Financial Services
N.A.I.C.S.: 523999

ORIX (China) Investment Co., Ltd. (1)
Room 25 Floor 35 China World Tower III JianguomenOuter Street 1, Chaoyang District, Beijing, 116600, China
Tel.: (86) 1058032800
Web Site: http://www.orixchina.com.cn
Sales Range: $50-74.9 Million
Emp.: 35
Investment Management Service
N.A.I.C.S.: 523999

ORIX Aircraft Corporation (1)
World Trade Center Building 2 4 1 Hamamatsu cho Minato Ku, Tokyo, 105 6135, Japan (100%)
Tel.: (81) 354037297
Web Site: http://www.orix.co.jp
Sales Range: $5-14.9 Billion
Emp.: 50,000
Aircraft Leasing
N.A.I.C.S.: 488119

ORIX Alpha Corporation (1)
Mina NN Building 4-1-23 Shiba, Minato-ku, Tokyo, 108 0014, Japan (100%)
Tel.: (81) 354195042
Web Site: http://www.orix.co.jp
Sales Range: $75-99.9 Million
Emp.: 152
Leasing & Financing Furnishings & Equipment for Retailers, Hotels, Restaurants
N.A.I.C.S.: 423210

ORIX Asia Capital Limited (1)
Suite 3206-08 32nd Floor Two Exchange Square, 8 Connaught Place, Central, China (Hong Kong)
Tel.: (852) 2 867 6000
Web Site: https://www.orixasiacapital.com.hk
Investment Services
N.A.I.C.S.: 523150

ORIX Asia Limited (1)
25th Floor Two Exchange Square 8 Connaught Place, Central, Hong Kong, China (Hong Kong) (100%)
Tel.: (852) 28629268
Web Site: https://www.orix.com.hk
Sales Range: $100-124.9 Million
Emp.: 150
Restricted License Bank Offering Financial Services & Solutions
N.A.I.C.S.: 525990

ORIX Asset Management & Loan Services Corporation (1)
Nippon Life Hamamatsucho Claire Tower 2-3-1 Hamamatsucho, Minato Ku, Tokyo, 105-0013, Japan (100%)
Tel.: (81) 357763330
Web Site: https://www.orix.co.jp
Sales Range: $75-99.9 Million
Emp.: 150
Servicers of Commercial Mortgages
N.A.I.C.S.: 531390

ORIX Asset Management Corporation (1)
Nippon Life Hamamatsucho Crea Tower 2-3-1 Hamamatsucho, Minato Ku, Tokyo, 105-0013, Japan (100%)
Tel.: (81) 357763323
Web Site: https://www.orix.co.jp
Sales Range: $50-74.9 Million
Emp.: 40
Managers of Assets
N.A.I.C.S.: 525920

ORIX Asset Management Malaysia Sdn. Bhd. (1)
Lot 33 01 33rd Floor Bldg Menara Kh, PO Box 1169, 50738, Kuala Lumpur, Malaysia
Tel.: (60) 374902333
Asset Management Services
N.A.I.C.S.: 523940
Deborah Wong (Asst Gen Mgr)

ORIX Australia Corporation Limited (1)
Level 3 66 Talavera Road, Macquarie Park, 2113, NSW, Australia (100%)
Tel.: (61) 298566414
Web Site: https://www.orix.com.au
Sales Range: $150-199.9 Million
Emp.: 100
Equipment Leasing, Vehicle Operating Leases & Other Financing Services
N.A.I.C.S.: 532490

ORIX Auto Corporation (1)
22-8 Shiba 3-chome, Minato-ku, Tokyo, 105-0014, Japan
Tel.: (81) 364366000
Web Site: https://www.orix.co.jp
Automobile Leasing Services
N.A.I.C.S.: 532112
Katsunobu Kamei (Chm)

ORIX Auto Finance (India) Limited (1)
Plot No 94 Marol Co Operative Industrial Estate Andheri Kurla Rd, Mumbai, 400 059, India (60%)
Tel.: (91) 2228528677
Web Site: http://www.orixindia.com
Sales Range: $75-99.9 Million
Emp.: 200
Auto Leasing & Fleet Management
N.A.I.C.S.: 532112

ORIX Auto Infrastructure Services Limited (1)
Plot No - 94 Marol Co-operative Industrial Estate Andheri-Kurla Road E, Andheri, Mumbai, 400059, India
Tel.: (91) 987 733 3444
Web Site: https://www.orixindia.com
Leasing & Transportation Services
N.A.I.C.S.: 532310
Sandeep Gambhir (CEO & Mng Dir)

ORIX Auto Leasing Corporation (1)
Mita NN Bldg 4 1 23 Shiba, Minato Ku, Tokyo, 108-0014, Japan (100%)
Tel.: (81) 354195102
Web Site: http://www.orix.co.jp
Sales Range: $300-349.9 Million
Emp.: 550
Auto Leasing
N.A.I.C.S.: 532112

ORIX Auto Leasing Taiwan Corporation (1)
9F No 303 Sec 1 Fuxing S Rd, Daan Dist, Taipei, 10665, ROC, Taiwan (100%)
Tel.: (886) 227552055
Web Site: https://www.orixauto.com.tw
Provider of Auto Leasing
N.A.I.C.S.: 532112

ORIX Aviation Systems Limited (1)
The Oval Block 1 Shelbourne Road, Dublin, 4, Ireland (100%)
Tel.: (353) 312158000
Web Site: https://www.orixaviation.com
Sales Range: $25-49.9 Million
Emp.: 50
Operating/Finance Leases for Aircraft & Other Related Services
N.A.I.C.S.: 532490
James Meyler (CEO)

ORIX Bank Corporation (1)
Orix Inui Building 3-22-8 Shiba, Minato-ku, Tokyo, 105-0014, Japan (100%)
Tel.: (81) 120601591
Web Site: https://www.orixbank.co.jp
Emp.: 808
Commercial Banking Services
N.A.I.C.S.: 522110
Masahiko Hara (Exec VP)

ORIX Buffaloes Baseball Club (1)
2-1-3 Chiyozaki Nishi-ku, Osaka, 550 0023, Japan (100%)
Tel.: (81) 6 6586 0106
Web Site: http://www.buffaloes.co.jp
Sales Range: $50-74.9 Million
Emp.: 92
Professional Basketball Team
N.A.I.C.S.: 711211

ORIX Business Center Okinawa Corporation (1)
1-1-12 Omoromachi Naha Shintoshin Center Building 3rd Floor, Naha, 900-0006, Okinawa, Japan
Tel.: (81) 98 951 1551
Web Site: https://www.orix.co.jp
Financial Services
N.A.I.C.S.: 523999

ORIX Business Support Corporation (1)
2-22-20 Akebono-cho Tachikawa Center Building 1F, Tachikawa, Tokyo, 190-0012, Japan
Tel.: (81) 425285361
Web Site: https://www.orix.co.jp
Emp.: 102
Business Support Services
N.A.I.C.S.: 561499

ORIX Callcenter Corporation (1)
Omoromachi 1-1-12 Naha Shintoshin Center Building 3F, Naha, 900-0006, Okinawa, Japan
Tel.: (81) 989511551
Web Site: https://www.orix.co.jp
Emp.: 773
Business Process Outsourcing Services
N.A.I.C.S.: 561499

ORIX Capital Corporation (1)
World Trade Center Building SOUTH TOWER 2-4-1 Hamamatsu-cho, Minoto-ku, Tokyo, 105-5135, Japan (100%)
Tel.: (81) 334353341
Web Site: https://www.orixcapital.co.jp
Sales Range: $50-74.9 Million
Emp.: 50
Venture Capital Advisor
N.A.I.C.S.: 525910

ORIX Car Rentals Sdn. Bhd. (1)
No 16-1 Jalan 6 91 Taman Shamelin Perkasa, 56100, Kuala Lumpur, Malaysia (28%)
Tel.: (60) 392847799
Web Site: http://www.orixcarrentals.com.my
Sales Range: $1-9.9 Million
Emp.: 60
Provider of Car Rental Services
N.A.I.C.S.: 532111

ORIX China Corporation (1)
60F Sinar Mas Plaza No501 Dongda-ming Road, Hongkou District, Shanghai, 200336, China
Tel.: (86) 2162785533
Financial Lending Services
N.A.I.C.S.: 522220

ORIX Computer Systems Corporation (1)
Office Tower Y Building Harumi Island Triton Square 1-8-11 Harumi, Chuo-ku, Tokyo, 104-8543, Japan (100%)
Tel.: (81) 351440700
Web Site: https://www.orix.co.jp
Sales Range: $25-49.9 Million
Emp.: 150
Software Engineering & Programming Services
N.A.I.C.S.: 541511

ORIX Corporation Europe N.V. (1)
Coolsingel 120, 3011 AG, Rotterdam, Netherlands (90.01%)
Tel.: (31) 102241224
Web Site: http://www.robeco.com
Rev.: $820,841,153
Assets: $351,915,222
Liabilities: $117,673,032
Net Worth: $234,242,190
Earnings: $79,037,421
Emp.: 807
Fiscal Year-end: 12/31/2023
Holding Company; Investment & Asset Management Services
N.A.I.C.S.: 551112
Leni Maria Teuntje Boeren (COO & Member-Mgmt Bd)

Subsidiary (US):

Harbor Capital Advisors, Inc. (2)
111 S Wacker Dr 34th Fl, Chicago, IL 60606
Tel.: (423) 443-4400
Web Site: https://www.harborcapital.com
Sales Range: $1-4.9 Billion
Investment & Asset Management Services
N.A.I.C.S.: 523940
Charles F. McCain (Chm & CEO)

Robeco Investment Management, Inc. (2)
1 Grand Central Pl 60 E2nd St - Ste 1550, New York, NY 10165
Tel.: (212) 908-9500
Web Site: http://www.robecoinvest.com
Sales Range: $1-4.9 Billion
Emp.: 275
Investment & Asset Management Services
N.A.I.C.S.: 523940

Division (Domestic):

Robeco Investment Management, Inc. - Boston (3)
1 Beacon St, Boston, MA 02108
Tel.: (617) 832-8200
Web Site: http://www.bostonpartner.com
Sales Range: $10-24.9 Million
Emp.: 70
Institutional Investment Management Services
N.A.I.C.S.: 523940

Subsidiary (Domestic):

Robeco Securities, LLC (3)

AND PRIVATE COMPANIES

909 3rd Ave 32nd Fl, New York, NY
10022 **(100%)**
Tel.: (212) 908-9576
Web Site: http://www.robecoinvest.com
Sales Range: $50-74.9 Million
Emp.: 30
Securities Brokerage & Dealing Services
N.A.I.C.S.: 523150
Paul D. Heathwood *(Sr Mng Dir)*

Subsidiary (Domestic):

Robeco Nederland B.V. (2)
Weena 850, 3014 DA, Rotterdam,
Netherlands **(100%)**
Tel.: (31) 102241224
Web Site: https://www.robeco.com
Sales Range: $800-899.9 Million
Emp.: 1,500
Investment & Asset Management Services
N.A.I.C.S.: 523940
Leni Maria Teuntje Boeren *(COO-Grp)*

Group (Non-US):

RobecoSAM AG (2)
Josefstrasse 218, 8005, Zurich,
Switzerland **(90.9%)**
Tel.: (41) 446531010
Web Site: http://www.robecosam.com
Sales Range: $1-4.9 Billion
Emp.: 110
Holding Company; Sustainable Investment, Asset Management & Private Equity Services
N.A.I.C.S.: 551112
Kuno Kennel *(Chm)*

ORIX Create Corporation (1)
4-1-23 Shiba Minato Ku, Tokyo, 105 0014,
Japan **(100%)**
Tel.: (81) 354195900
Web Site: http://www.orix.co.jp
Sales Range: $25-49.9 Million
Emp.: 15
Coordination of Group Public Relations Activities
N.A.I.C.S.: 541820

ORIX Eco Services Corporation (1)
World Trade Center Building South Building 2-4-1 Hamamatsucho, ORIX Nihombashi, Minato-ku, Tokyo, 105-5135,
Japan **(100%)**
Tel.: (81) 367773101
Web Site: https://www.orix.co.jp
Sales Range: $25-49.9 Million
Emp.: 50
Environmental Management & Consulting Services
N.A.I.C.S.: 541620

ORIX Environmental Resources Management Corporation (1)
2-4-1 Hamamatsucho, Minato-ku Tokyo World Trade Center Building South Building, Tokyo, 105-5135, Japan
Tel.: (81) 367773082
Sales Range: $25-49.9 Million
Emp.: 2
Waste Management Services
N.A.I.C.S.: 562998

ORIX Golf Management Corporation (1)
2-28-8 Shiba 2-chome Building, Minato-Ku, Tokyo, 105-6135, Japan **(100%)**
Tel.: (81) 334510562
Web Site: http://www.orix-golf.jp
Golf Course Management Services
N.A.I.C.S.: 713910

ORIX Hotel Management Corporation (1)
Nissay Hamamatsucho Crea Tower 2-3-1 Hamamatsu-cho, Minato-ku, Tokyo, 105-0013, Japan
Tel.: (81) 35 776 3421
Web Site: https://www.orix-realestate.co.jp
Hotel Operator
N.A.I.C.S.: 721110
Takaaki Nitanai *(Pres)*

ORIX Insurance Consulting Corporation (1)
2-10-9 Akasaka Round Cross, Akasaka Minato-ku, Tokyo, 107-0052, Japan
Tel.: (81) 36 683 2205
Web Site: http://www.orix.co.jp
Insurance Services
N.A.I.C.S.: 524210

ORIX Insurance Planning Corporation (1)
3 22 8 Shiba Minato Ku, Tokyo, 105 6135,
Japan **(60%)**
Tel.: (81) 354195140
Sales Range: Less than $1 Million
Emp.: 18
Agency Sales & Development of Non-Life Insurance Products
N.A.I.C.S.: 524128

ORIX Insurance Services Corporation (1)
Tokyo World Trade Center Building South Building 31F, 2-4-1 Hamamatsucho Minato-ku, Tokyo, 108-0014, Japan **(100%)**
Tel.: (81) 334353431
Web Site: https://www.orix.co.jp
Sales Range: $50-74.9 Million
Emp.: 6
Life & Casualty Insurance
N.A.I.C.S.: 524113

ORIX Interior Corporation (1)
Orix Honmachi Building 1-4-1 Nishihonmachi, Nishi-ku, Osaka, 550-0005,
Japan **(100%)**
Tel.: (81) 665781832
Web Site: https://www.orix.co.jp
Sales Range: $25-49.9 Million
Emp.: 50
Carpet & Other Interior Products Mfr & Sales
N.A.I.C.S.: 313110

ORIX Investment & Management Private Limited (1)
250 North Bridge Road 1 19 01 02 Raffles City Tower, Singapore, 179101,
Singapore **(100%)**
Tel.: (65) 67928000
Sales Range: $50-74.9 Million
Emp.: 20
Investment Management Service
N.A.I.C.S.: 522299
Soh Kim Soen *(Chm)*

ORIX Investment Corporation (1)
World Trade Ctr Bldg 2 4 1 Hamamatsu Cho, Tokyo, 105 6135, Japan **(100%)**
Tel.: (81) 334353011
Web Site: http://www.orix.co.jp
Sales Range: $50-74.9 Million
Emp.: 30
Alternative Investment
N.A.I.C.S.: 523999

ORIX Ireland Limited (1)
2nd Floor Booterstown Hall Booterstown Avenue, Dublin, Ireland **(100%)**
Tel.: (353) 16700622
Sales Range: $10-24.9 Million
Emp.: 35
High-Standard Back-Office Administration Services
N.A.I.C.S.: 524292

ORIX Leasing Egypt SAE (1)
5th Floor Cairo Center Building 2 Abdel Kader Hamza Street, Garden City, 11461,
Cairo, Egypt **(54%)**
Tel.: (20) 27922757
Web Site: https://www.samafinance.com
Sales Range: $25-49.9 Million
Emp.: 43
Equipment Leasing
N.A.I.C.S.: 532490

ORIX Leasing Malaysia Berhad (1)
Suite 19-1 Level 19 Vertical Corporate Tower B Avenue 10 The Vertical, Bangsar South City No 8 Jalan Kerinchi, 59200, Kuala Lumpur, Malaysia **(80%)**
Tel.: (60) 326327000
Web Site: http://www.orixleasing.com.my
Sales Range: $150-199.9 Million
Emp.: 550
Equipment Leasing & Other Financing Services
N.A.I.C.S.: 532490

Subsidiary (Domestic):

ORIX Auto Leasing Malaysia Sdn. Bhd. (2)
No 16-1 Jalan 6/91 Taman Shamelin Perkasa, 56100, Kuala Lumpur, Malaysia
Tel.: (60) 392824293

Web Site: http://www.orixautoleasing.com.my
Emp.: 80
Motor Vehicle Leasing Services
N.A.I.C.S.: 532112

ORIX Capital Malaysia Sdn. Bhd. (2)
12th Floor Menara Promet Jalan Sultan Ismail, Kuala Lumpur, 50250, Malaysia
Tel.: (60) 3 21418355
Venture Capital Funding Services
N.A.I.C.S.: 523910

ORIX Factoring Malaysia Sdn. Bhd. (2)
1901 Level 19 City Plaza, Johor Bahru, 80300, Malaysia
Tel.: (60) 73310299
Sales Range: $25-49.9 Million
Emp.: 35
Factoring Services
N.A.I.C.S.: 522299
Elaine Cheng *(Asst Gen Mgr)*

ORIX Insurance Agencies Sdn. Bhd. (2)
12th Floor Menara Promet Jalan Sultan Ismail, 50250, Alor Gajah, Malaysia
Tel.: (60) 321418355
General Insurance Services
N.A.I.C.S.: 524210

ORIX Risk Management Sdn. Bhd. (2)
12th Floor Menara Promet Jalan Sultan Ismail, Kuala Lumpur, 50250, Malaysia
Tel.: (60) 321418355
Insurance Management Services
N.A.I.C.S.: 524298

ORIX Leasing Pakistan Limited (1)
OLP Building Plot No 16 Sector No 24 Korangi Industrial Area, Talpur Rd, Karachi, 74900, Pakistan **(57%)**
Tel.: (92) 213514402940
Web Site: https://olpfinance.com
Sales Range: $300-349.9 Million
Emp.: 600
Provider of Equipment Leasing Services
N.A.I.C.S.: 532490

ORIX Leasing Singapore Limited (1)
331 North Bridge Road 19-01/06 Odeon Towers, Singapore, 188720,
Singapore **(50%)**
Tel.: (65) 63393622
Web Site: https://www.ols.com.sg
Sales Range: $50-74.9 Million
Emp.: 60
Equipment Leasing & Other Financing Services
N.A.I.C.S.: 532490

ORIX Life Insurance Corporation (1)
Otemachi Place East Tower 2-3-2 Otemachi, Chiyoda-ku, Tokyo, 100-0004,
Japan **(100%)**
Tel.: (81) 335174300
Web Site: https://www.orixlife.co.jp
Sales Range: $200-249.9 Million
Emp.: 2,197
Life Insurance
N.A.I.C.S.: 524113

Subsidiary (Domestic):

Hartford Life Insurance K.K. (2)
15F Shiodome Bldg 1-2-20 Kaigan, Minato-ku, Tokyo, 105-0022, Japan
Tel.: (81) 357778000
Web Site: http://www.hartfordlife.co.jp
Emp.: 150
Life Insurance Products & Services
N.A.I.C.S.: 524113
Jennifer Sparks *(Pres & CEO)*

ORIX Loan Business Center Corporation (1)
2-4-1 Hamamatsucho World Trade Center Building, Minato ku, Tokyo, 105-0105, Japan
Tel.: (81) 35 776 3351
Web Site: https://www.orix.co.jp
Personal Loan & Asset Management Services
N.A.I.C.S.: 522291

ORIX M&A Solutions Corporation (1)
7-14-23 Roppongi Saint Ram Roppongi

ORIX CORPORATION

Bldg 5f, Minato-Ku, Tokyo, 106-0032, Japan
Tel.: (81) 364064339
Web Site: http://www.orix.co.jp
Sales Range: $50-74.9 Million
Emp.: 25
Financial Advisory Services
N.A.I.C.S.: 523940

ORIX Management Information Center Corporation (1)
2-22-20 Akebono cho, Tachikawa, Tokyo, 190 0012, Japan **(100%)**
Tel.: (81) 425285140
Web Site: http://www.orix.co.jp
Sales Range: $25-49.9 Million
Emp.: 200
General & Comprehensive Accounting Services
N.A.I.C.S.: 541211

ORIX Maritime Corporation (1)
World Trade Ctr Bldg 2-4-1 Hamamatsucho, Minato-ku, Tokyo, 105 6135,
Japan **(100%)**
Tel.: (81) 3 3435 3000
Web Site: http://www.orix.com
Sales Range: $25-49.9 Million
Emp.: 5
Shipping & Ship-Management Services
N.A.I.C.S.: 488510

ORIX Maritime Corporation-Seoul Representative Office (1)
2Fl Konlon Bldg 36-7 Namcheon Dong, Busan, 110110, Korea (South)
Tel.: (82) 220506700
Web Site: http://www.orix.co.kr
Sales Range: $50-74.9 Million
Emp.: 70
Specializing in Leasing & Rental of Office Automation & Measuring Equipment
N.A.I.C.S.: 532490

ORIX Metro Leasing and Finance Corporation (1)
21st Floor GT Tower International Ayala Avenue, Corner HV Dela Costa St, Makati, 1227, Philippines
Tel.: (63) 88588888
Web Site: https://www.orix.com.ph
Sales Range: $50-74.9 Million
Emp.: 1,106
Equipment Leasing & Hire-Purchase Services; Owned 60% by Metropolitan Bank & Trust Company & 40% by ORIX Corporation
N.A.I.C.S.: 532490
Fumihiko Sato *(Vice Chm)*

ORIX New Zealand (NZ) Limited (1)
32 Manukau Road, Epsom, Auckland, 1023, New Zealand **(100%)**
Tel.: (64) 95209700
Web Site: https://www.orix.co.nz
Sales Range: $50-74.9 Million
Emp.: 60
Vehicle Operating Leases
N.A.I.C.S.: 532490
Martin Lowe *(Controller-Fin)*

ORIX Polska S.A. (1)
Ul Bitwy Warszawskiej 1920 R 7B 4th Fl, 00 193, Warsaw, Poland **(100%)**
Tel.: (48) 225980598
Web Site: http://www.orix.pl
Sales Range: $50-74.9 Million
Emp.: 14
Provider of Equipment Leasing Services
N.A.I.C.S.: 532490

ORIX Real Estate Corporation (1)
Nissay Hamamatsucho Crea Tower 2-3-1 Hamamatsu-cho, Minato-ku, Tokyo, 105-0013, Japan **(100%)**
Tel.: (81) 357763400
Sales Range: $150-199.9 Million
Emp.: 300
Developers & Managers of Real Estate
N.A.I.C.S.: 531312

ORIX Real Estate Investment Advisors Corporation (1)
NIPPON LIFE HAMAMATSUCHO CREA TOWER 2-3-1 Hamamatsucho-Cho, Minato-ku, Tokyo, 105-0013, Japan
Tel.: (81) 357763327
Web Site: https://www.orix.co.jp
Emp.: 74
Real Estate Investment & Advisory Services

ORIX CORPORATION

ORIX Corporation—(Continued)
N.A.I.C.S.: 531390

ORIX Renewable Energy Management Corporation (1)
1-4-12 Kiba Meikoji Kiba Building 2nd Floor, Koto-ku, Tokyo, 135-0042, Japan
Tel.: (81) 36 666 7501
Web Site: https://www.orix.co.jp
Asset Management Services
N.A.I.C.S.: 523940

ORIX Rentec Corporation (1)
Osaki Bright Core 5-5-15 Kitashinagawa, Shinagawa-ku, Tokyo, 141-001, Japan **(100%)**
Tel.: (81) 334738473
Web Site: https://www.orixrentec.jp
Electronic Measuring Instruments Rental Services
N.A.I.C.S.: 532210

Subsidiary (Non-US):

ORIX Rentec (Korea) Corporation (2)
13th Floor KAIT Tower 306 Teheran-ro, Gangnam-Gu, Seoul, 06210, Korea (South)
Tel.: (82) 25636060
Web Site: https://www.orix.co.kr
Emp.: 40
Electronic Measurement Equipment & Computer Rental Services
N.A.I.C.S.: 532490

ORIX Rentec (Singapore) Pte. Ltd. (2)
10 Kaki Bukit Avenue 1 02-05, Singapore, 417942, Singapore **(100%)**
Tel.: (65) 67454515
Web Site: http://www.orix-rentec.com.sg
Rev.: $14,116,250
Emp.: 11
Provider of Office Automation & Measuring Equipment Rental
N.A.I.C.S.: 532490

ORIX Rentec (Tianjin) Corporation (2)
Room 608 Tianjin International Building 75 Nanjing Road, Tianjin, 300050, China
Tel.: (86) 2223311616
Precision Measuring Equipment Rental Services
N.A.I.C.S.: 532490

ORIX Taiwan Asset Management Company (1)
Fuxing South Road 10th Floor No 303 Section 1, Taipei, Taiwan
Tel.: (886) 227551600
Asset Management Services
N.A.I.C.S.: 523940

ORIX Taiwan Corporation (1)
10F No 303 Sec 1 Fuxing S Rd, Daan Dist, Taipei, 106, Taiwan **(95%)**
Tel.: (886) 227554588
Web Site: https://www.orix.com.tw
Sales Range: $50-74.9 Million
Emp.: 63
Provider of Leasing & Other Financial Services
N.A.I.C.S.: 532490

ORIX Tokushima Corporation (1)
2-7 Yaoyamachi, Tokushima, 770-0841, Japan **(95%)**
Tel.: (81) 886533513
Financial Lending Services
N.A.I.C.S.: 522220

ORIX Trust & Banking Corporation (1)
Tanaka Kogyo Bldg 7 2 Kabutocho, Nihonba Chuo Ku, Tokyo, 103 0026, Japan **(100%)**
Tel.: (81) 336606551
Web Site: http://www.orix.co.jp
Sales Range: $100-124.9 Million
Emp.: 200
Trust & Banking Services Focusing on Retail Markets
N.A.I.C.S.: 522320

ORIX USA Corporation (1)
2001 Ross Ave Ste 1900, Dallas, TX 75201-4605 **(100%)**
Tel.: (214) 237-2000
Sales Range: $250-299.9 Million
Emp.: 264
Investment Banking & Financial Services
N.A.I.C.S.: 523999
Aaron J. Stehsel (Mng Dir & Head-Integrated Risk Mgmt)

Group (Domestic):

ORIX Corporate Finance Group (2)
1717 Main St Ste 900, Dallas, TX 75201
Tel.: (214) 237-2300
Sales Range: $75-99.9 Million
Emp.: 250
Corporate Financing & Private Equity Services
N.A.I.C.S.: 523999

ORIX Equipment Finance Group (2)
600 Town Park Ln 3rd Fl, Kennesaw, GA 30144 **(100%)**
Tel.: (770) 970-6000
Web Site: http://orixcorporatefinancegroup.net
Sales Range: $50-74.9 Million
Emp.: 100
Equipment Financing & Leasing
N.A.I.C.S.: 522220
Howard Dossman (Pres)

Branch (Domestic):

ORIX USA Corporation-New York (2)
280 Park Ave 40 W, New York, NY 10017 **(100%)**
Tel.: (212) 468-5888
Sales Range: $50-74.9 Million
Emp.: 10
Equipment Leasing, Asset-Based Lending & General Corporate Financing
N.A.I.C.S.: 522220

Group (Domestic):

Orix Capital Partners LLC (2)
280 Park Ave 40 W, New York, NY 10017
Tel.: (212) 880-9291
Web Site: https://orixcapitalpartners.com
Investment Services
N.A.I.C.S.: 523999
Christopher Suan (Pres & Sr Mng Dir)

Subsidiary (Domestic):

NXT Capital, LLC (3)
191 N Wacker Dr 30th Fl, Chicago, IL 60606
Tel.: (312) 450-8000
Web Site: https://www.nxtcapital.com
Structured Financing Services
N.A.I.C.S.: 522220
Brian Franc (Chief Compliance Officer)

National Underground Group, Inc. (3)
47 Discovery Ste 250, Irvine, CA 92618
Tel.: (949) 380-4161
Web Site: https://www.nationalu.com
Water Flow Solutions Services
N.A.I.C.S.: 562991
Ken Biele (Pres & CEO)

Subsidiary (Domestic):

Tri-State Utilities, Co. (4)
2111 Smith Ave, Chesapeake, VA 23320
Tel.: (757) 366-9505
Web Site: http://www.tristateutilities.com
Water & Sewer Line & Related Structures Construction
N.A.I.C.S.: 237110
Steven F. McSweeney (Founder)

Subsidiary (Domestic):

ORIX Real Estate Equities, Inc. (3)
100 North Riverside Plz Ste 1400, Chicago, IL 60606-1508 **(100%)**
Tel.: (312) 669-6400
Sales Range: $25-49.9 Million
Emp.: 60
Commercial Real Estate Development, Investments & Consulting
N.A.I.C.S.: 237210

Peak Utility Services Group (3)
310 Interlocken Pkwy Ste 220, Broomfield, CO 80021
Tel.: (720) 795-9894
Web Site: https://www.peakusg.com

Electrical Contractors & Other Wiring Services
N.A.I.C.S.: 238210

Subsidiary (Domestic):

Riley Brothers, Inc. (4)
84 Tosca Dr, Stoughton, MA 02072
Tel.: (781) 341-6277
Web Site: https://www.rileybrothers.net
Natural Gas & Electric Utility Construction Services
N.A.I.C.S.: 237130
Timothy L. Riley (Founder & Pres)

Subsidiary (Domestic):

RED Capital Group, LLC (3)
10 W Broad St 8th Fl, Columbus, OH 43215
Tel.: (614) 857-1400
Web Site: http://www.redcapitalgroup.com
Sales Range: $75-99.9 Million
Emp.: 200
Mortgage Loan Brokerage Services
N.A.I.C.S.: 522310
Todd A. Rodenberg (Sr Mng Dir & Chief Credit Officer)

Subsidiary (Domestic):

Red Capital Markets, LLC (4)
2 Miranova Pl, Columbus, OH 43215
Tel.: (614) 857-1400
Web Site: http://www.redcapitalgroup.com
Emp.: 50
Consumer Lending Services
N.A.I.C.S.: 522291

Red Capital Partners, LLC (4)
10 W Broad St 8th Fl, Columbus, OH 43215
Tel.: (614) 857-1400
Emp.: 90
Debt Equity Services
N.A.I.C.S.: 531190

Red Mortgage Capital, LLC (4)
10 W Broad St 8th Fl, Columbus, OH 43215
Tel.: (614) 857-1400
Web Site: http://www.redcapital.com
Emp.: 100
Mortgage Banking Services
N.A.I.C.S.: 522310
Charles C. Meyer (Sr Mng Dir)

Joint Venture (Domestic):

Specialty Welding & Turnarounds LLC (3)
40492 Cannon Rd, Gonzales, LA 70737
Tel.: (225) 644-1200
Web Site: https://www.swatservice.com
General Contracting Services
N.A.I.C.S.: 238290
Marcus Deal (CEO)

Subsidiary (Domestic):

Midwest Cooling Tower Services Inc. (4)
8545 Hwy 105 N, Krotz Springs, LA 70750-5215
Tel.: (337) 566-2233
Web Site: https://www.mwcts.com
Electrical Contractor
N.A.I.C.S.: 238210
Daniel Wiltz (Pres)

Subsidiary (Domestic):

Tower Performance, Inc. (5)
23 Vreeland Rd, Florham Park, NJ 07932
Tel.: (973) 966-1116
Web Site: https://www.towerperformance.com
Sales Range: $1-9.9 Million
Emp.: 60
Cooling Towers Repair & Maintenance Services
N.A.I.C.S.: 238990
Anthony Depalma (Pres)

ORIX Wholesale Securities Corporation (1)
Centrum Roppongi Bldg 7-14-23 Roppongi, Minato-ku, Tokyo, 106-0032, Japan
Tel.: (81) 3 5771 1050
Web Site: http://www.orix.co.jp

INTERNATIONAL PUBLIC

Sales Range: $50-74.9 Million
Emp.: 15
Securities Brokerage Services
N.A.I.C.S.: 523160

P.T. ORIX Indonesia Finance (1)
Wisma Keiai 24th Floor Jl Jend Sudirman Kav 3 Karet Tengsin, Tanah Abang Daerah Khusus Ibukota, Jakarta, 10220, Indonesia **(83%)**
Tel.: (62) 215723041
Web Site: https://www.orix.co.id
Sales Range: $50-74.9 Million
Emp.: 580
Equipment Leasing & Other Financing Services
N.A.I.C.S.: 532490

PT. Sinar Mitra Sepadan Finance (1)
Jl HR Rasuna Said Kav X-2 No1 Lt16, Jakarta Selatan, 12950, Indonesia
Tel.: (62) 218 086 4900
Web Site: https://www.smsfinance.co.id
Cash Loan Services
N.A.I.C.S.: 522291

RB Capital S.A. (1)
Av Brigadeiro Faria Lima 4440 11th Floor, Itaim Bibi, Sao Paulo, 04538-132, Brazil
Tel.: (55) 113 127 2700
Web Site: https://www.rbcapital.com
Financial Services
N.A.I.C.S.: 523999
Denise Kaziura (Mng Partner)

Robeco Institutional Asset Management B.V.
Weena 850, 3014 DA, Rotterdam, Netherlands
Tel.: (31) 10 224 1224
Web Site: https://www.robeco.com
Asset Management Services
N.A.I.C.S.: 523920
Gilbert Van Hassel (CEO)

Saudi ORIX Leasing Company (1)
343 Al Maather St, PO Box 22890, Riyadh, 11416, Saudi Arabia **(26%)**
Tel.: (966) 12997777
Web Site: http://www.saudiorix.com.sa
Sales Range: $50-74.9 Million
Emp.: 75
Equipment Leasing
N.A.I.C.S.: 532490
Shaheen Amin (Mng Dir)

Thai Orix Leasing Co., Ltd. (1)
555 Rasa Tower II Unit 1801 18th Floor & 19th Floor Phahonyothin Road, Bangkok, 10900, Thailand
Tel.: (66) 27924500
Web Site: https://www.orix.co.th
Sales Range: $25-49.9 Million
Emp.: 50
Machinery & Equipment Leasing & Hire-Purchase Services
N.A.I.C.S.: 532412

Transtrend B.V. (1)
Weena 723 - Unit C5070, 3013 AM, Rotterdam, Netherlands
Tel.: (31) 10 453 6510
Web Site: https://www.transtrend.com
Asset Management Services
N.A.I.C.S.: 523940
Harold de Boer (Mng Dir)

Ubiteq, INC. (1)
3-20-1 Minami-Azabu Daiwa Azabu Terrace 3F, Minato-ku, Tokyo, 106-0047, Japan
Tel.: (81) 354476731
Web Site: https://www.ubiteq.jp
Rev.: $6,319,520
Assets: $14,697,860
Liabilities: $2,208,100
Net Worth: $12,489,760
Earnings: ($2,139,680)
Emp.: 76
Fiscal Year-end: 06/30/2024
Electronic Appliance Mfr & Distr
N.A.I.C.S.: 334419
Katsuhiko Araki (Pres)

Yodogawa Transformer Co., Ltd. (1)
ORIX Honmachi Bldg 1-4-1 Nishi-Honmachi, Nishi-ku, Osaka, 550-0005, Japan
Tel.: (81) 66 578 1850
Web Site: https://www.yodohen.co.jp
Emp.: 130

AND PRIVATE COMPANIES

Transformer Mfr & Leasing Services
N.A.I.C.S.: 532490

Zeeklite Co., Ltd. (1)
315 Itaya, Yonezawa, 992-1331, Yamagata, Japan
Tel.: (81) 23 834 2111
Web Site: https://www.zeeklite.co.jp
Zeolite Mfr & Distr
N.A.I.C.S.: 327999

ORIX JREIT INC.
1-4-1 Marunouchi, Chiyoda-ku, Tokyo, 100-8233, Japan
Tel.: (81) 354184855
Web Site: https://www.orixjreit.com
Year Founded: 2001
8954—(TKS)
Sales Range: $125-149.9 Million
Real Estate Manangement Services
N.A.I.C.S.: 523999
Teruo Ozaki *(Exec Dir)*

ORIZZONTI HOLDING SPA
Zona Industriale loc SantAntuono SP 352 km 0 6, Potenza, 118287, Italy
Tel.: (39) 09753313453
Web Site:
http://www.orizzontiholding.it
Sales Range: $350-399.9 Million
Consumer Goods Distr
N.A.I.C.S.: 445298
Costantino Di Carlo *(Pres & CEO)*

ORKA HOLDING AD
ul Skupi 3a, 1000, Skopje, North Macedonia
Tel.: (389) 2 3099 600
Web Site: http://www.orka.com.mk
Year Founded: 1990
Holding Company
N.A.I.C.S.: 551112
Jordan Kamchev *(Founder)*

ORKLA ASA
Drammensveien 149, 0277, Oslo, Norway
Tel.: (47) 22544000   DK
Web Site: https://www.orkla.com
Year Founded: 1918
ORKLF—(OTCIQ)
Rev.: $6,664,799,000
Assets: $8,512,445,610
Liabilities: $3,916,873,186
Net Worth: $4,595,572,425
Earnings: $532,912,598
Emp.: 19,671
Fiscal Year-end: 12/31/23
Food Mfr
N.A.I.C.S.: 311423
Stein Erik Hagen *(Chm)*

Subsidiaries:

AXELLUS AS (1)
Sandakerveien 56, PO Box 4293, Nydalen, 0477, Oslo, Norway
Tel.: (47) 22896400
Web Site: http://www.axellus.no
Sales Range: $200-249.9 Million
Emp.: 420
Health Food Product Whslr
N.A.I.C.S.: 456191
Stig Ebert Nilssen *(CEO)*

Subsidiary (Non-US):

Axellus AB (2)
Svetsarvagen 15, Solna, 17141, Sweden
Tel.: (46) 8 586 15 000
Emp.: 400
Healthcare Products Mfr & Distr
N.A.I.C.S.: 325412
Lennart Andersson *(Gen Mgr)*

Axellus Sp. z.o.o. (2)
Olkuska 7, Warsaw, 02604, Poland
Tel.: (48) 22 349 67 00
Web Site: http://www.axellus.pl
Sales Range: $25-49.9 Million
Emp.: 50
Drugs & Dietary Supplement Distr
N.A.I.C.S.: 424210

Grzegorz Kowalski *(Mng Dir)*

Axellus s.r.o (2)
Michelska 60, 140 00, Prague, Czech Republic
Tel.: (420) 241 400 147
Web Site: http://www.axellus.cz
Sales Range: $25-49.9 Million
Emp.: 10
Healthcare Food Supplements Distr
N.A.I.C.S.: 424210

Orkla Care (2)
Trinapolio g 9E, 08337, Vilnius, Lithuania
Tel.: (370) 52310654
Web Site: https://www.orklacare.lt
Healthcare Food Supplements Distr
N.A.I.C.S.: 424210

Orkla Care OY (2)
Ayritie 16, 01510, Vantaa, Finland
Tel.: (358) 102183700
Web Site: http://www.orkla.fi
Sales Range: $25-49.9 Million
Healthcare Products Mfr & Distr
N.A.I.C.S.: 325412
Kari Haapakorva *(CEO)*

BaKo AS
Bjornengveien 15, Rolvsoy, 1664, Fredrikstad, Norway
Tel.: (47) 69 33 50 22
Baked Goods Mfr
N.A.I.C.S.: 311813

Baechs Conditori A/S (1)
Langelandsvej 1, 9500, Hobro, Denmark
Tel.: (45) 98524800
Web Site: http://www.baechs-conditori.dk
Bakery Products Mfr
N.A.I.C.S.: 311813

Belusa Foods s.r.o (1)
Farska 1746, 018 61, Belusa, Slovakia
Tel.: (421) 424624990
Web Site: http://www.belusafoods.sk
Sales Range: $25-49.9 Million
Industrial Margarine Distr
N.A.I.C.S.: 424490

CREDIN PORTUGAL S.A (1)
Rua Herois do Ultramar 370 Freixeira, 2670-747, Loures, Portugal
Tel.: (351) 219668150
Web Site: http://www.credin.pt
Sales Range: $25-49.9 Million
Pastry & Baking Products Mfr
N.A.I.C.S.: 311813

Cake Decor Ltd.
2 Little Drum Road Orchardton Woods, Cumbernauld, Glasgow, United Kingdom
Tel.: (44) 1236781000
Web Site: http://www.cakedecorgroup.com
Cake Mfr & Distr
N.A.I.C.S.: 311813

Condite Oy (1)
Lisenssikatu 5, 21100, Naantali, Finland
Tel.: (358) 24365900
Web Site: https://www.condite.fi
Emp.: 100
Food Ingredients Whslr
N.A.I.C.S.: 424490

Credin A/S (1)
Palsgaardvej 12, 7130, Juelsminde, Denmark
Tel.: (45) 72243000
Web Site: http://www.credin.dk
Bakery & Confectionery Food Mfr & Distr
N.A.I.C.S.: 311340
Karen Margrethe Kring *(Mgr-HR)*

Credin Polska Sp. z.o.o. (1)
ul Czysta 6, 55-050, Sobotka, Poland
Tel.: (48) 713162124
Web Site: http://www.credin.pl
Bakery Food Products Mfr & Distr
N.A.I.C.S.: 311813

Credin Productos Alimenticios S.A. (1)
Francesc Layert 75 2 4, Mollet del Valles, 08100, Barcelona, Spain
Tel.: (34) 937 102 024
Bread & Cake Mfr & Whslr
N.A.I.C.S.: 311813

Credin Russia LLC (1)

ORKLA ASA

Gaya Avenue 81, 432035, Ulyanovsk, Russia
Tel.: (7) 8422227100
Web Site: http://credin.ru
Sales Range: $25-49.9 Million
Confectionery & Bakery Product Mfr & Distr
N.A.I.C.S.: 311340

Credin Sverige AB (1)
Elvagen 4, 443 61, Stenkullen, Sweden
Tel.: (46) 30225201
Web Site: https://www.credin.se
Food Product Whslr
N.A.I.C.S.: 424490

Credin bageripartner A/S (1)
Bodkervej 10, 7100, Vejle, Denmark
Tel.: (45) 76 42 42 00
Web Site: http://www.cbpbageri.dk
Sales Range: $50-74.9 Million
Emp.: 100
Bakery Product Distr
N.A.I.C.S.: 424420
Henning Jensen *(Mng Dir & Mgr)*

Subsidiary (Domestic):

Frederik Christiansen Food A/S (2)
Broenge 11, 2635, Ishoj, Denmark
Tel.: (45) 43 99 73 00
Bakery & Confectionery Product Mfr & Whslr
N.A.I.C.S.: 311340

Da Grasso Sp.z o.o. (1)
Al Jana Pawla II 18 lok 120, 00-116, Warsaw, Poland
Tel.: (48) 509910000
Web Site: https://www.dagrasso.pl
Pizza Mfr
N.A.I.C.S.: 311412

Dragsbaek A/S (1)
Simons Bakke 46, 7700, Thisted, Denmark
Tel.: (45) 97922744
Web Site: http://www.dragsbaek.dk
Sales Range: $25-49.9 Million
Emp.: 300
Supplier of Manufactured Food Products
N.A.I.C.S.: 311999
Mogens Nielsen *(Chm)*

Subsidiary (Non-US):

Gaedabakstur ehf (2)
Lynghalsi 7, Reykjavik, 110, Iceland
Tel.: (354) 545 7000
Web Site: http://www.gaedabakstur.is
Bakery Products Mfr & Whslr
N.A.I.C.S.: 311813
Vilhjalmur Porlaksson *(CEO)*

UAB VMG Food (2)
Zietelos str 3, 03160, Vilnius, Lithuania
Tel.: (370) 52333161
Web Site: https://www.vmg.lt
Sales Range: $25-49.9 Million
Processed Margarine Mfr
N.A.I.C.S.: 311225

EKVIA s.r.o. (1)
Priemyselna 11, 949 01, Nitra, Slovakia
Tel.: (421) 800100775
Web Site: https://www.ekvia.sk
Food Product Whslr
N.A.I.C.S.: 424490

Easyfood A/S (1)
Albuen 82, 6000, Kolding, Denmark
Tel.: (45) 76308700
Web Site: https://www.easyfood.dk
Organic Food Mfr
N.A.I.C.S.: 311999

Felix Abba Lahden tehdas (1)
Mannerheiminkatu 10, 15100, Lahti, Finland
Tel.: (358) 207854000
Food Products Mfr
N.A.I.C.S.: 311999
Rabbe Bikstrom *(Pres)*

Felix Austria GmbH (1)
Felixstrasse 24, 7210, Mattersburg, Austria
Tel.: (43) 26266100
Web Site: http://www.felix.at
Sales Range: $50-74.9 Million
Emp.: 200
Sauce Mfr & Distr
N.A.I.C.S.: 424420
Peter Buchauer *(Mng Dir)*

Fitness Market Nordic AB (1)
Svetsarvagen 15, 171 41, Solna, Sweden
Tel.: (46) 101388342
Web Site: https://www.fitnessmarket.se
Sport Nutrition Supplement Distr
N.A.I.C.S.: 456199

Goteborgs Kex AB (1)
Strandgatan 8, 442 82, Kungalv, Sweden
Tel.: (46) 771111000
Web Site: https://www.goteborgskex.se
Cookies & Biscuit Mfr & Distr
N.A.I.C.S.: 311821

Hans Kaspar AG (1)
Chraenbachstrasse 4, Zufikon, 5621, Bremgarten, Switzerland
Tel.: (41) 566484020
Web Site: https://www.kasparag.ch
Ice Cream Product Mfr
N.A.I.C.S.: 311520

Health and Sports Nutrition Group HSNG AB (1)
Svetsarvagen 15, 171 41, Solna, Vastergotland, Sweden
Tel.: (46) 108844880
Web Site: https://www.hsng.com
Dietary Supplement Products Mfr
N.A.I.C.S.: 311514

Jastbolaget AB (1)
Sollentunaholmsvagen 9, 192 78, Sollentuna, Sweden
Tel.: (46) 86262400
Sales Range: $25-49.9 Million
Emp.: 55
Yeast Product Mfr & Whslr
N.A.I.C.S.: 311999
Thore Svensson *(Gen Mgr)*

KaKa AB (1)
Kastanjevagan 17, 234 35, Lomma, Sweden
Tel.: (46) 104849900
Web Site: http://www.kaka.se
Sales Range: $50-74.9 Million
Emp.: 70
Bakery Ingredient Whslr
N.A.I.C.S.: 424490
Thore Svensson *(CEO)*

Kjarnavorur HF (1)
Miohraun 16, 210, Gardabaer, Iceland
Tel.: (354) 5651430
Web Site: http://www.kjarnavorur.is
Sales Range: $25-49.9 Million
Margarine & Fruit Sauce Mfr
N.A.I.C.S.: 311423

Kolding Salatfabrik A/S (1)
C F Tietgensvej 8, 6000, Kolding, Denmark
Tel.: (45) 75522844
Sales Range: $25-49.9 Million
Emp.: 5
Salad & Sauce Mfr
N.A.I.C.S.: 311423
Christian Ubbesen *(Gen Mgr)*

Kotipizza Group Oyj (1)
Verkkosaarenkatu 5, FI-00580, Helsinki, Finland (100%)
Tel.: (358) 207 716 700
Web Site: http://www.kotipizzagroup.com
Sales Range: $100-124.9 Million
Pizza Restaurant Owner & Operator
N.A.I.C.S.: 722511
Antti Isokangas *(Chief Comm & Corp Responsibility Officer)*

Subsidiary (Domestic):

Helsinki Foodstock Oy (2)
Hermannin rantatie 2 B, 00580, Helsinki, Finland
Tel.: (358) 207716550
Web Site: http://www.foodstock.fi
Food Stock Logistic Services
N.A.I.C.S.: 541614
Anssi Koivula *(Mng Dir)*

Kotipizza Oyj (2)
Verkkosaarenkatu 5, 00580, Helsinki, Finland
Tel.: (358) 207716700
Web Site: http://www.kotipizza.fi
Restaurant Services
N.A.I.C.S.: 722513

LG Harris & Co. Ltd. (1)

ORKLA ASA

Orkla ASA—(Continued)
Stoke Prior, Bromsgrove, Worcestershire,
United Kingdom
Tel.: (44) 1527575441
Web Site:
https://www.international.harris.com
Paint Brush & Decorating Product Mfr
N.A.I.C.S.: 339994

Laan Heiloo B.V. (1)
De Hoefsmid 35, 1851 PZ, Heiloo, Netherlands
Tel.: (31) 725331425
Web Site: https://www.laan.nl
Ice Cream Product Mfr
N.A.I.C.S.: 311520

Latfood A/S (1)
Jaunkulas-2 Adazu Pagasts, Riga, 2164, Latvia
Tel.: (371) 67709200
Web Site: http://www.cipsi.lv
Sales Range: $25-49.9 Million
Emp.: 132
Cracker & Snacks Mfr
N.A.I.C.S.: 311821

Lecora AB (1)
Kvarnbacksvagen 6, 592 41, Vadstena, Sweden
Tel.: (46) 14329800
Web Site: https://www.lecora.se
Emp.: 35
Frozen & Chilled Food Mfr
N.A.I.C.S.: 311412

MTR Foods Pvt. Limited (1)
No 1 2nd & 3rd floor 100 feet inner ring road, Ejipura, Bengaluru, 560 047, India
Tel.: (91) 80 40812100
Web Site: http://www.mtrfoods.com
Sales Range: $25-49.9 Million
Processed Food Products Mfr & Distr
N.A.I.C.S.: 311999

Merkur 09 Sp.z.o.o (1)
Ul Annopol 4a Bud F, 02-236, Warsaw, Poland
Tel.: (48) 228772032
Web Site: http://www.merkur.com.pl
Sales Range: $25-49.9 Million
Food Product Mfr & Whslr
N.A.I.C.S.: 311999

NIC Nederland B.V. (1)
Coenecoop 27, 2741 PG, Waddinxveen, Netherlands
Tel.: (31) 850410411
Web Site: https://www.nicice.nl
Ice Cream Product Mfr
N.A.I.C.S.: 311520

NINO AS (1)
Strandveien 50, Ramsund, Tjeldsund, 9442, Norway
Tel.: (47) 76938360
Food Products Distr
N.A.I.C.S.: 424490

Natural Food Srl (1)
1 Via Dell' Industria, Coseano, 33030, Udine, Italy
Tel.: (39) 04 32 86 10 12
Marzipan Mfr
N.A.I.C.S.: 311340

Naturli Foods A/S (1)
Smedevaenget 4, Hojbjerg, 8920, Randers, Denmark
Tel.: (45) 86148300
Web Site: http://www.naturli-foods.dk
Sales Range: $25-49.9 Million
Food Products Mfr
N.A.I.C.S.: 311999

Nidar AS (1)
Bromstadveien 2, Postboks 2444, Torgard, 7005, Trondheim, Norway (100%)
Tel.: (47) 7 358 3000
Web Site: https://www.nidar.no
Rev.: $191,478,000
Emp.: 700
Confectionery
N.A.I.C.S.: 311352

Nimatopaal AB (1)
Storbyvagen 7, Box 75, Dala-Jarna, 786 71, Jarna, Sweden
Tel.: (46) 281 59 49 00
Web Site: http://www.nimatopaal.com

Icecream Products Mfr & Whslr
N.A.I.C.S.: 311821

Noi-Sirius HF (1)
Hesthalsi 2-4, 110, Reykjavik, Iceland
Tel.: (354) 5751800
Web Site: https://www.noi.is
Snack Food Mfr
N.A.I.C.S.: 311919

OU Vilmix (1)
Tallinna 86, Peetrimoisa Kula, Viljandi, 71073, Estonia
Tel.: (372) 4351566
Web Site: http://www.vilmix.ee
Sales Range: $25-49.9 Million
Bakery Machinery & Equipment Mfr & Whslr
N.A.I.C.S.: 333241

Odense Marcipan A/S (1)
Toldbodgade 9-19, 5000, Odense, Denmark
Tel.: (45) 63117200
Web Site: http://www.odense-marcipan.dk
Marzipan & Marzipan-related Products Mfr
N.A.I.C.S.: 311999

Oraveien Industripark AS (1)
Oraveien 2, Gamle, 1630, Fredrikstad, Norway
Tel.: (47) 69395200
Real Estate Management Services
N.A.I.C.S.: 531390

Orchard Valley Foods Australia Ltd. (1)
30 Roosevelt Street, Coburg, VIC, Australia
Tel.: (61) 393540081
Web Site: https://www.orchardvalley.com.au
Food Store Whslr
N.A.I.C.S.: 424490

Ordan Asia Pacific Sdn. Bhd. (1)
7F-1A 7th Floor Tower 1 Puchong Financial Corporate Centre PFCC Jalan, Puteri 1/2 Bandar Puteri, 47100, Puchong, Selangor, Malaysia
Tel.: (60) 386014571
Web Site: https://www.jordanoralcare.my
Toothbrush Mfr
N.A.I.C.S.: 339994

Orkla A.S.A. - Orkla Brands International Unit (1)
PO Box 711, 1411, Kolbotn, Norway
Tel.: (47) 66 81 61 00
Convenience Foods Mfr
N.A.I.C.S.: 311999
Paul Jordahl *(CEO)*

Orkla Asia Holding AS (1)
Nedre Skoyenvei 26, 278, Oslo, Norway
Tel.: (47) 22544000
Investment Management Service
N.A.I.C.S.: 523999

Orkla Asia Pacific Pte Ltd (1)
111C 4th Floor Telok Ayer Street, Singapore, 68580, Singapore
Tel.: (65) 68807910
Sales Range: $50-74.9 Million
Emp.: 1
Food Products Distr
N.A.I.C.S.: 424420

Orkla Brands AS (1)
Nedre Skoyenvei 26, 0276, Oslo, Norway
Tel.: (47) 22 89 50 00
Web Site: http://www.orkla.no
Emp.: 1,000
Consumer Goods Distr
N.A.I.C.S.: 423990

Division (Domestic):

Orkla Home & Personal (2)
PO Box 4236, NO 0401, Oslo, Norway
Tel.: (47) 22895000
Personal & Home Care Products Mfr
N.A.I.C.S.: 325611
Bjorn Drablos *(CEO)*

Subsidiary (Domestic):

Jordan House Care AS (1)
Haavard Martinsens vei 30, NO-0978, Oslo, Norway
Tel.: (47) 2278 8000
Web Site: http://www.jordan.no
Holding Company; Painting Tools & Commercial Cleaning Products Mfr
N.A.I.C.S.: 551112

Subsidiary (Non-US):

Anza AB (4)
Tallvagen 6, PO Box 133, Bankeryd, Jonkoping, 564 35, Sweden (100%)
Tel.: (46) 36376300
Web Site: http://www.anza.se
Paint Brushes, Rollers & Tools Mfr
N.A.I.C.S.: 339994

Subsidiary (Non-US):

Hamilton-Acorn Ltd. (5)
Halford Road, Attleborough, Norfolk, NR17 2HZ, United Kingdom (100%)
Tel.: (44) 1953453201
Web Site: http://www.hamilton-acorn.co.uk
Sales Range: $50-74.9 Million
Emp.: 40
Paint Brush & Other Painting Tools Mfr
N.A.I.C.S.: 339994

Orkla Confectionery & Snacks Sverige AB (1)
Svetsarvagen 15, 171 41, Solna, Sweden
Tel.: (46) 77 111 10 00
Web Site: http://www.orkla.se
Snack Food Mfr & Whslr
N.A.I.C.S.: 311919
Goeran Schultz *(Mng Dir)*

Orkla Eesti AS (1)
Porguvalja Tee 6, Lehmja, Peetri, 75306, Harjumaa, Estonia
Tel.: (372) 6877710
Web Site: http://www.kalev.eu
Confectionery Product Mfr
N.A.I.C.S.: 311352
Kaido Kaare *(CEO)*

Orkla Energi AS (1)
Karenslyst Alle 6, Oslo, 0278, Norway
Tel.: (47) 22544000
Electric Power & Gas Distr
N.A.I.C.S.: 221122

Orkla Eesti AS (1)
Porguvalja tee 6 Lehmja Rae vald, 75306, Harjumaa, Estonia
Tel.: (372) 6877710
Web Site: https://www.orkla.ee
Emp.: 600
Food & Beverage Services
N.A.I.C.S.: 722511

Orkla Finans A/S (1)
Thordenskioldsgate 8 10, PO Box 1724, N 0121, Oslo, Norway (100%)
Tel.: (47) 22400800
Web Site: http://www.orklafinans.no
Sales Range: $25-49.9 Million
Emp.: 70
Financial Services
N.A.I.C.S.: 561990
Bjurn Slaatto *(Mng Dir)*

Orkla Food Ingredients AS (1)
Drammensveien 149, 0277, Oslo, Norway
Tel.: (47) 22 54 40 00
Food Products Mfr
N.A.I.C.S.: 311999

Subsidiary (US):

Denali Ingredients, LLC (2)
2400 S Calhoun Rd, New Berlin, WI 53151-2710 (84%)
Tel.: (262) 784-3010
Web Site: http://www.denaliingredients.com
Emp.: 160
Ice Cream Flavor, Ingredient & Coating Mfr
N.A.I.C.S.: 311930
Neal Glaeser *(CEO)*

Subsidiary (Non-US):

STELIOS KANAKIS INDUSTRIAL AND COMMERCIAL SA (2)
4 Anemonis Str Acharne-Attiki, 13678, Acharnes, Greece (80%)
Tel.: (30) 2102419700
Web Site: http://www.stelioskanakis.gr
Confectionery & Bakery Products Sales & Distr
N.A.I.C.S.: 424450
Christos Vatalidis *(Mgr-Pur & Logistics)*

Orkla Foods A/S (1)
Lienga St 628, PO Box 711, N 1411, Kolbotn, Norway (100%)
Tel.: (47) 66816100

INTERNATIONAL PUBLIC

Web Site: http://www.orklafoods.com
Rev.: $658,678,528
Emp.: 180
Food Products
N.A.I.C.S.: 311423
Atle Vidar Johansen *(CEO & Exec VP)*

Subsidiary (Domestic):

Idun Industri AS (2)
Hvamveien 1, Skjetten, 2013, Norway
Tel.: (47) 22094800
Web Site: http://www.idun.no
Baked Goods Mfr
N.A.I.C.S.: 311813

Subsidiary (Domestic):

Arne B. Corneliussen AS (3)
Kabelgaten 37 A, PO Box 424, Okern, 0513, Oslo, Norway
Tel.: (47) 22884600
Web Site: http://www.abcorneliussen.no
Meat & Fish Products Merchant Whslr
N.A.I.C.S.: 424470
Roar Furuhaug *(Mng Dir)*

Subsidiary (Non-US):

Call Caterlink Ltd. (3)
Units 7-8 Bodmin Business Park Launceston Road, Bodmin, PL31 2RJ, Cornwall, United Kingdom
Tel.: (44) 120878844
Web Site: http://www.caterlink.co.uk
Sales Range: $25-49.9 Million
Emp.: 3
Food Products Mfr
N.A.I.C.S.: 311999

Candeco Confektyr AB (3)
N Grangesbergsgatan 17, 214 50, Malmo, Sweden
Tel.: (46) 40190725
Web Site: http://www.candeco.se
Emp.: 35
Dry Ingredient & Decorative Food Mfr
N.A.I.C.S.: 311423

Frima Vafler A/S (3)
Grydhojparken 10, Tilst, 8381, Aarhus, Denmark
Tel.: (45) 70 26 25 11
Web Site: http://www.frimavafler.dk
Sales Range: $25-49.9 Million
Cone & Waffle Basket Mfr & Distr
N.A.I.C.S.: 311821
Carsten Hoffmann *(Dir-Comml Dev)*

The Waverley Bakery Limited (3)
Drumhead Lane, Cambuslang Investment Park, Glasgow, G32 8EX, Lanarkshire, United Kingdom (100%)
Tel.: (44) 1416410203
Web Site: http://www.waverleybakery.co.uk
Ice Cream Cones, Ingredients & Accessories Mfr & Distr
N.A.I.C.S.: 311821
Nadia Millar *(Dir)*

Subsidiary (Non-US):

Orkla Foods Finland Oy (2)
Rydontie 14 b gate 2, PL 683, 20361, Turku, Finland
Tel.: (358) 20 785 4000
Web Site: http://www.orklafoods.com
Sales Range: $100-124.9 Million
Emp.: 171
Food Products Mfr
N.A.I.C.S.: 311999

Subsidiary (Domestic):

Oy Orkla Confectionery & Snacks Finland Ab (3)
Asematie 2, PL 3, Vaajakoski, 40801, Jyvaskyla, Finland
Tel.: (358) 20 785 4200
Sales Range: $25-49.9 Million
Emp.: 100
Chocolate Candy & Licorice Mfr
N.A.I.C.S.: 311352

Subsidiary (Non-US):

SIA Spilva (3)
1 Zvaigznu Spilve, Babite, 2101, Latvia
Tel.: (371) 67063000
Web Site: http://www.spilva.lv

Sales Range: $25-49.9 Million
Processed Fruit & Vegetable Mfr
N.A.I.C.S.: 311411
Lolita Bemhena *(Founder)*

UAB Orkla Foods Lietuva (3)
Veiveriu Str 134C, 46551, Kaunas, Lithuania
Tel.: (370) 37390942
Web Site: https://www.orklafoods.lt
Emp.: 47
Sauce Mfr & Whslr
N.A.I.C.S.: 311421

Subsidiary (Domestic):

Orkla Foods Norge (2)
Drammensveien 149, 0277, Oslo, Norway
Tel.: (47) 22544000
Web Site: http://www.orklafoods.no
Sales Range: $10-24.9 Million
Food Mfr
N.A.I.C.S.: 311423

Orkla Foods Norge AS (2)
Nostegaten 58, Bergen, 5808,
Norway (100%)
Tel.: (47) 55967000
Emp.: 2,590
Food Ingredients Mfr; Food Products Supplier
N.A.I.C.S.: 311999

Subsidiary (Non-US):

Orkla Foods Danmark AS (3)
Horsvinget 1-3, Havnso, DK-4591, Hoje
Taastrup, Denmark (100%)
Tel.: (45) 59269050
Web Site: http://www.orklafoods.dk
Sales Range: $25-49.9 Million
Emp.: 175
Dried & Dehydrated Food Mfr
N.A.I.C.S.: 311423

Orkla Foods Sverige AB (3)
Sockergatan, 241 38, Eslov, Sweden
Tel.: (46) 101424000
Web Site: http://www.orklafoods.se
Sales Range: $25-49.9 Million
Emp.: 125
Dessert & Cake Mfr
N.A.I.C.S.: 311813

Plant (Domestic):

**Procordia Food AB - Fagelmara
Plant** (4)
Reymersholmsvagen, Box 33, Fagelmara,
370 45, Karlskrona, Sweden
Tel.: (46) 455 30 84 00
Sales Range: $25-49.9 Million
Emp.: 75
Spice Mfr
N.A.I.C.S.: 311941

**Procordia Food AB - Tollarp
Plant** (4)
Tollarpsfabriken, Box 23, Tollarp, 298 21,
Kristianstad, Sweden
Tel.: (46) 44 18 75 00
Sales Range: $10-24.9 Million
Emp.: 50
Jam & Fruit Purees Mfr
N.A.I.C.S.: 311421

**Procordia Food AB - Vansbro
Plant** (4)
Vansbrofabriken Fabriksvagen 1, 780 50,
Vansbro, Sweden
Tel.: (46) 281 756 00
Sales Range: $25-49.9 Million
Emp.: 15
Dessert Pie & Cake Mfr
N.A.I.C.S.: 311813

Subsidiary (Domestic):

Rieber & Son ASA (3)
Kalfarveien 57A, N-5022, Bergen,
Norway (100%)
Tel.: (47) 55559100
Web Site: https://rieberson.no
Mayonnaise, Salads, Mutton & Herring
Products Mfr
N.A.I.C.S.: 311999

Subsidiary (Non-US):

Rieber & Son Germany GmbH (3)
Eulerstrasse 15, 48155, Munster, Germany

Tel.: (49) 25160304
Web Site: http://www.rieberson.de
Dried & Dehydrated Food Mfr
N.A.I.C.S.: 311423

Rieber & Son PLC (3)
33 George Street, Wakefield, WF1 1LX, W
Yorkshire, United Kingdom
Tel.: (44) 1924242166
Web Site: http://www.orkla.com
Emp.: 4
Food Products Mfr
N.A.I.C.S.: 311999

Subsidiary (Domestic):

Storaneset 12 AS (3)
Nostegaten 58, 5011, Bergen, Norway
Tel.: (47) 55967000
Real Estate Agents & Brokers
N.A.I.C.S.: 531210

Orkla Insurance Company Ltd. (1)
Elm Park Merrion Road, Dublin, Ireland
Tel.: (353) 14074963
Web Site: https://www.orklainsurance.com
Insurance Management Services
N.A.I.C.S.: 524298
James Spenceley *(Gen Mgr)*

Orkla Shared Services AS (1)
Essendrops Gate 3, Oslo, 368, Norway
Tel.: (47) 22096100
Information Technology Consulting Services
N.A.I.C.S.: 541512

Pierre Robert Group AB (1)
Svetsarvagen 15, Box 1196, 171 23, Solna,
Sweden
Tel.: (46) 8 629 17 00
Web Site: http://www.pierrebert.se
Sales Range: $25-49.9 Million
Emp.: 2
Socks & Underwear Mfr & Whslr
N.A.I.C.S.: 315120
Jeanette Hauan Fladby *(Mng Dir)*

Pierre Robert Group AS (1)
Sandakerveien 56, 477, Oslo, Norway
Tel.: (47) 22 89 27 00
Intimate Apparel & Socks Mfr
N.A.I.C.S.: 315250

Poznan Onion Sp. z o.o. (1)
ul Kornicka 10, Siekierki Wielkie, 62-025,
Kostrzyn, Poland
Tel.: (48) 618978141
Web Site: http://www.poznanonion.pl
Crunchy Fried Onion Mfr
N.A.I.C.S.: 311999

PureOil I/S (1)
Simons Bakke 46, 7700, Thisted, Denmark
Tel.: (45) 33187500
Web Site: http://www.pureoil.dk
Vegetable Oil Mfr & Whslr
N.A.I.C.S.: 311225

Quattro Enzyme Solutions B.V. (1)
Rietgorsweg 1-3, 3356 LJ, Papendrecht,
Netherlands
Tel.: (31) 786442525
Web Site: https://qes-enzymesolutions.com
Food & Beverage Mfr
N.A.I.C.S.: 311999

Rasoi Magic Foods Pvt. Limited (1)
32/A-6 At Post Pisoli, Tal Haveli, Pune, India
Tel.: (91) 2024261935
Web Site: https://www.rasoimagic.com
Packaged Food Mfr
N.A.I.C.S.: 311999

SIA LaNordija (1)
Zvaigznu Street 1 Spilve, Babite, 2101,
Latvia
Tel.: (371) 67553372
Web Site: http://www.lanordija.lv
Sales Range: $25-49.9 Million
Margarine & Yeast Product Mfr & Distr
N.A.I.C.S.: 311999

Sonneveld Group B.V. (1)
Rietgorsweg 1-3, 3356 LJ, Papendrecht,
Netherlands
Tel.: (31) 78 644 25 25
Web Site: http://www.sonneveld.com
Sales Range: $25-49.9 Million
Bread Mfr & Distr
N.A.I.C.S.: 311824

Peter Verhagen *(Mng Dir)*
Subsidiary (Non-US):

Sonneveld France SARL (2)
27 Avenue De La Constellation, BP 78516,
95891, Cergy, France
Tel.: (33) 1 30 75 93 17
Sales Range: $25-49.9 Million
Emp.: 1
Bread Mfr & Distr
N.A.I.C.S.: 311824

Sonneveld Kft. (2)
Bajcsy-Zsilinszky utca 131, Pf 4, 2364,
Ocsa, Hungary
Tel.: (36) 29578480
Web Site: http://www.sonneveld.hu
Bakery Ingredients Mfr & Distr
N.A.I.C.S.: 311423
Erika Csanyi *(Mng Dir)*

Sonneveld NVSA (2)
Uitbreidingstraat 84, Antwerp, 2500, Belgium
Tel.: (32) 80015796
Bakery Food Products Mfr
N.A.I.C.S.: 311813

Tredo AB (1)
Tellusborgsvagen 67, 126 29, Hagersten,
Sweden
Tel.: (46) 855041850
Food & Beverage Whslr
N.A.I.C.S.: 424490

UAB MiNordija (1)
Veiveriu st 134C, 46353, Kaunas, Lithuania
Tel.: (370) 37351747
Web Site: http://www.minordija.lt
Bakery & Confectionery Product Whslr
N.A.I.C.S.: 424490

Werners Gourmetservice AB (1)
Kampagatan 3, 532 37, Skara, Sweden
Tel.: (46) 51117799
Web Site: https://www.wgs.se
Food Product Whslr
N.A.I.C.S.: 424490

ORKUVEITA REYKJAVIKUR
Baejarhalsi 1, 110, Reykjavik, Iceland
Tel.: (354) 5166000
Web Site: http://www.or.is
Sales Range: $150-199.9 Million
Emp.: 500
Energy Services
N.A.I.C.S.: 221122
Bjarni Bjarnason *(CEO)*

ORLA MINING LTD.
1010 - 1075 W Georgia St, Vancouver, V6E 3C9, BC, Canada
Tel.: (604) 564-1852 ON
Web Site:
https://www.orlamining.com
Year Founded: 2007
ORLA—(NYSEAMEX)
Rev.: $233,643,000
Assets: $535,778,000
Liabilities: $135,237,000
Net Worth: $400,541,000
Earnings: ($27,010,000)
Emp.: 327
Fiscal Year-end: 12/31/23
Gold Exploration & Mining Services
N.A.I.C.S.: 213114
Etienne Morin *(CFO)*

Subsidiaries:

Contact Gold Corp. (1)
Suite 1050 400 Burrard Street, Vancouver,
V6C 3A6, BC, Canada
Tel.: (604) 449-3361
Web Site: https://www.contactgold.com
Gold Mining Services
N.A.I.C.S.: 212220
Matthew Lennox-King *(Pres & CEO)*

Gold Standard Ventures Corp. (1)
Suite 610-815 West Hastings Street, Vancouver, V6C 1B4, BC, Canada
Tel.: (604) 669-5702
Web Site: http://www.goldstandardv.com
Rev.: $54,134

Assets: $227,312,140
Liabilities: $5,753,211
Net Worth: $221,558,929
Earnings: ($8,571,909)
Emp.: 9
Fiscal Year-end: 12/31/2021
Gold Mining Services
N.A.I.C.S.: 212220
Jonathan T. Awde *(Co-Founder)*

Minera Cerro Quema S.A. (1)
Esq cl Luis Rios y cl 8va El Vigia, Chitre,
Herrera, Panama
Tel.: (507) 9700522
Web Site: http://www.mcqsa.com
Sales Range: $50-74.9 Million
Emp.: 10
Gold Mining Services
N.A.I.C.S.: 212220

ORLANDI S.P.A.
63 67 Via Matteotti, Cassano Magnago, 21012, Italy
Tel.: (39) 0331 71 81 11
Web Site: http://www.orlandispa.it
Textile Mfr
N.A.I.C.S.: 314999
Vittorio Orlandi *(Chm)*

Subsidiaries:

Montefibre S.p.A. (1)
Via Marco d'Aviano 2, 20131, Milan, Italy
Tel.: (39) 02280081
Web Site: http://www.mef.it
Sales Range: $300-349.9 Million
Emp.: 640
Synthetic Fiber Mfr
N.A.I.C.S.: 325220

Subsidiary (Domestic):

Fidion S.r.l (2)
Contrada Pagliarone, Acerra, 80011, Latina,
Italy
Tel.: (39) 0813191677
Web Site: http://www.fidion.it
Sales Range: $50-74.9 Million
Emp.: 150
Cellulosic Organic Fiber Mfr
N.A.I.C.S.: 325220

Subsidiary (Non-US):

MONTEFIBRE HISPANIA s.a. (2)
Aribau 185-187 6A Planta, Barcelona,
Spain
Tel.: (34) 93 291 01 00
Web Site: http://www.montefibre.es
Textile Products Distr
N.A.I.C.S.: 424310

NGP S.p.a. (1)
C so Indipendenza 20, 20129, Milan, Italy
Tel.: (39) 02 70006993
Web Site: http://www.ngpspa.com
Chemical Products Distr
N.A.I.C.S.: 424690

ORLANDO MANAGEMENT AG
Orlando-Haus Platzl 4, 80331, Munich, Germany
Tel.: (49) 89 2900 4850 De
Web Site:
http://www.orlandofund.com
Year Founded: 2001
Sales Range: $25-49.9 Million
Emp.: 250
Privater Equity Firm
N.A.I.C.S.: 523999
Henrik Fastrich *(Partner)*

Subsidiaries:

H.M. Pallhuber GmbH & Co. KG (1)
An den Nahewiesen 8, 55450, Langenlonsheim, Germany
Tel.: (49) 6704 201 1268
Web Site: http://www.pallhuber.de
Wine Marketer & Distr
N.A.I.C.S.: 424820

Orlando Italy Management S.A. (1)
31 bd Grande-Duchesse Charlotte, Luxembourg, 1331, Luxembourg
Tel.: (352) 2620 3152
Web Site: http://www.orlandoitaly.com

ORLANDO MANAGEMENT AG

Orlando Management AG—(Continued)
Privater Equity Firm
N.A.I.C.S.: 523999
Enrico Ceccato *(Mng Partner)*

Holding (Non-US):

Favini S.r.l. (2)
Via Alcide de Gasperi 26, 36028, Rossano Veneto, Vicenza, Italy
Tel.: (39) 0424 547711
Web Site: http://www.favini.com
Sales Range: $200-249.9 Million
Specialty Paper Mfr
N.A.I.C.S.: 322120
Andrea Nappa *(CEO)*

Orlando Management Schweiz AG (1)
Pfingstweidstrasse 60, 8005, Zurich, Switzerland
Tel.: (41) 44 271 5550
Web Site: http://www.orlandofund.ch
Emp.: 3
Privater Equity Firm
N.A.I.C.S.: 523999
Karl Spielberger *(Mng Dir)*

Secop GmbH (1)
Mads Clausen Strasse 7, D 24939, Flensburg, Germany
Tel.: (49) 46149410
Web Site: http://www.secop.com
Hermetic Compressors Mfr
N.A.I.C.S.: 333912
Katharina Adamitzki *(Controller-Sls)*

Subsidiary (Non-US):

Secop Compressors (Tianjin) Co., Ltd. (2)
Wuqing Development Zone No 27 Kai Yuan Road, Tianjin, 301700, China
Tel.: (86) 22 5909 1888
Web Site: http://www.secop-compressors.cn
Air Compressor Mfr
N.A.I.C.S.: 333912

Secop s.r.o. (2)
Tovarenska 49, 953 01, Zlate Moravce, Slovakia
Tel.: (421) 376 406 200
Web Site: http://www.secop.com
Air Compressor Mfr
N.A.I.C.S.: 333912

Solvadis GmbH (1)
Konigsberger Strasse 1, 60487, Frankfurt am Main, Germany
Tel.: (49) 6957007100
Web Site: http://www.solvadis.com
Sales Range: $150-199.9 Million
Organic Inorganic Agricultural & Specialty Chemicals Mfr
N.A.I.C.S.: 325998
Jallal Al Banyahyati *(COO-Commodity Chemicals)*

ORLANE S.A.

5 Rue Greffulhe, 75008, Paris, France
Tel.: (33) 977199497
Web Site: http://www.orlane.fr
Year Founded: 1945
Cosmetic & Toiletry Mfr
N.A.I.C.S.: 325620
Giancarlo Giraudi *(Pres & Gen Dir)*

Subsidiaries:

Orlane Inc. (1)
300 Kennedy Dr, Sayreville, NJ 08872
Tel.: (732) 727-1000
Web Site: http://www.orlane.com
Sales Range: $100-124.9 Million
Emp.: 100
Distr of Cosmetics
N.A.I.C.S.: 424210
Gian Luca Giraudi *(Pres)*

Orlane Institut De Beaute (1)
163 Ave Victor Hugo, 75116, Paris, France **(100%)**
Tel.: (33) 00147046500
Web Site: http://www.orlane.com
Sales Range: $25-49.9 Million
Emp.: 20
Beauty Salon & Spa
N.A.I.C.S.: 456120

ORLEANS RV

1472 Youville Dr, Orleans, K1C 2X8, ON, Canada
Tel.: (613) 824-0100
Web Site: http://www.orleansrv.ca
Sales Range: $50-74.9 Million
Emp.: 100
New & Used Car Dealers
N.A.I.C.S.: 441110

ORLEN S.A.

Chemikow 7, 09-411, Plock, Poland
Tel.: (48) 242560000 PL
Web Site: https://www.orlen.pl
PKN—(WAR)
Rev.: $69,729,186,555
Assets: $68,413,555,745
Liabilities: $34,006,933,628
Net Worth: $34,406,622,117
Earnings: $8,448,475,104
Emp.: 63,974
Fiscal Year-end: 12/31/22
Petrochemical Mfr, Refiner & Distr
N.A.I.C.S.: 325110
Magdalena Kopciejewska *(Head-Stock Exchange Information Team)*

Subsidiaries:

AB ORLEN Baltics Retail (1)
J Jasinskio str 16 B, LT-03163, Vilnius, Lithuania
Tel.: (370) 5 254 6810
Web Site: https://www.orlen.lt
Oil Product Distr
N.A.I.C.S.: 424720

AB ORLEN Lietuva (1)
Mazeikiu St 75, Juodeikiai Village, LT-89453, Mazeikiai, Lithuania
Tel.: (370) 4 439 2121
Web Site: https://www.orlenlietuva.lt
Oil Products Mfr
N.A.I.C.S.: 324110

AB Ventus-Nafta (1)
J Jasinskio g 16 B, Vilnius, 1112, Lithuania
Tel.: (370) 5 254 68 10
Petroleum Product Distr
N.A.I.C.S.: 424720

Anwil SA (1)
ul Torunska 222, Wroclaw, 87-805, Poland **(84.5%)**
Tel.: (48) 542363091
Web Site: http://www.anwil.com.pl
Rev.: $462,517,400
Emp.: 2,152
Chemicals Mfr
N.A.I.C.S.: 325998

Basell Orlen Polyolefins Sp. z o.o. (1)
ul Ignacego Lukasiewicza 39, 09-400, Plock, Poland
Tel.: (48) 243647300
Web Site: http://www.basellorlen.pl
Polyolefin Product Mfr
N.A.I.C.S.: 325211
Laurent Hautier *(Pres & CEO)*

ENERGA S.A. (1)
al Grunwaldzka 472, 80-309, Gdansk, Poland **(80.01%)**
Tel.: (48) 587788300
Web Site: https://www.grupa.energa.pl
Rev.: $5,048,233,935
Assets: $6,845,199,216
Liabilities: $3,946,138,773
Net Worth: $2,899,060,443
Earnings: $253,479,375
Emp.: 8,781
Fiscal Year-end: 12/31/2022
Electric Power Distr
N.A.I.C.S.: 221122
Marek Kasicki *(Vice Chm-Mgmt Bd-Fin)*

IKS Solino S.A. (1)
UI Swietego Ducha 26a, 88-100, Inowroclaw, Poland
Tel.: (48) 52 354 5820
Web Site: https://www.solino.pl
Crude Oil Fuel & Gas Distr
N.A.I.C.S.: 424720
Janusz Radomski *(Pres)*

Inowroclawskie Kopalnie Soli Solino S.A. (1)
ul Swietego Ducha 26a, 88-100, Inowroclaw, Poland **(99.02%)**
Tel.: (48) 52 354 58 00
Web Site: http://www.solino.pl
Extraction of Salt Brine & Salt Products Packaging Services; Petroleum Underground Storage Services
N.A.I.C.S.: 311942
Dorota Jamiolkowska *(Vice Chm-Supervisory Bd)*

ORLEN Administracja Sp. z o.o. (1)
ul Chemikow 7 Building 06, 09-411, Plock, Poland
Tel.: (48) 242565556
Web Site: http://www.orlenadministracja.pl
Property Management Services
N.A.I.C.S.: 531312

ORLEN Asfalt Sp. z o.o. (1)
ul Chemikow 7, 09-411, Plock, Poland
Tel.: (48) 24 365 38 27
Web Site: http://www.orlen-asfalt.pl
Sales Range: $50-74.9 Million
Emp.: 107
Bitumen Mfr & Distr
N.A.I.C.S.: 339999
Remigiusz Miecznikowski *(Mgr-Fin)*

ORLEN Aviation Sp. z o.o. (1)
UI-J Gordon Bennett 2, 02-159, Warsaw, Poland
Tel.: (48) 22 778 0303
Web Site: https://www.orlenaviation.pl
Fuel Distr
N.A.I.C.S.: 424720
Waldemar Humiecki *(Pres)*

ORLEN Budonaft Sp. z o.o. (1)
ul Fabryczna 1C, Limanowa, 34-600, Krakow, Poland
Tel.: (48) 183371716
Web Site: http://www.budonaft.com.pl
Gas Station Construction Services
N.A.I.C.S.: 236220

ORLEN Capital AB (1)
Sveavagen 9, 111 57, Stockholm, Sweden
Tel.: (46) 8 402 7200
Web Site: https://www.orlencapital.se
Financial Services
N.A.I.C.S.: 523999
Michal Perlik *(Pres)*

ORLEN Centrum Serwisowe Sp. z o.o. (1)
ul Wroclawska 58, 45-701, Opole, Poland
Tel.: (48) 774515100
Web Site: http://www.orlencs.pl
Petroleum Station Engineering Services
N.A.I.C.S.: 541330
Pawel Stepkowski *(Chm-Mgmt Bd)*

ORLEN Centrum Uslug Korporacyjnych Sp. z o.o. (1)
UI Lukasiewicza 39, 09-400, Plock, Poland
Tel.: (48) 24 256 6401
Web Site: https://www.orlencuk.pl
Accounting & Bookkeeping Services
N.A.I.C.S.: 541219
Wioletta Kandziak *(Pres)*

ORLEN Deutschland GmbH (1)
Ramskamp 71 75, 25337, Elmshorn, Germany **(100%)**
Tel.: (49) 412147500
Web Site: http://www.orlen-deutschland.de
Sales Range: $50-74.9 Million
Emp.: 97
Petroleum Distr
N.A.I.C.S.: 424710
Waldemar Bogusch *(Chm-Mgmt Bd)*

ORLEN Eko LLC (1)
ul Chemikow 7, 09-411, Plock, Poland
Tel.: (48) 242567661
Web Site: https://www.orleneko.pl
Industrial Waste Recycling Services
N.A.I.C.S.: 562920
Agnieszka Okolotowicz *(Chm-Mgmt Bd)*

ORLEN Gaz Sp. z o.o. (1)
Zglenickiego str 46a, Plock, Poland
Tel.: (48) 24 364 75 00
Web Site: https://www.orlengaz.pl
Liquefied Petroleum Gas Distr
N.A.I.C.S.: 221210

INTERNATIONAL PUBLIC

ORLEN Koltrans Sp. z o.o. (1)
ul Chemikow 7, 09-411, Plock, Poland
Tel.: (48) 242566444
Web Site: http://www.orlenkoltrans.pl
Sales Range: $125-149.9 Million
Emp.: 300
Railway Transportation Services
N.A.I.C.S.: 488210
Piotr Gorzenski *(Chm-Supervisory Bd)*

ORLEN Medica Sp. z o.o. (1)
ul Chemikow 7, Plock, 411, Poland
Tel.: (48) 243650925
Web Site: http://www.cmmedica.pl
Medical & Healthcare Services
N.A.I.C.S.: 621999
Jaroslaw Kozinski *(Chm-Supervisory Bd)*

ORLEN Paliwa Sp. z o.o. (1)
Widelka 869, 36-145, Widelka, Poland
Tel.: (48) 24 256 6039
Web Site: https://www.orlenpaliwa.com.pl
Fuel Distr
N.A.I.C.S.: 424720
Filip Wojtas *(Chm-Supervisory Bd)*

ORLEN PetroCentrum Sp. z o.o. (1)
ul Zglenickiego 44, 09-411, Plock, Poland
Tel.: (48) 243653500
Web Site: http://www.orlenpetrocentrum.pl
Sales Range: $50-74.9 Million
Emp.: 100
Fuel & Petroleum Products Distr
N.A.I.C.S.: 424720

ORLEN Petrotank Sp. z o.o. (1)
Widelka 869, Widelka, 36-145, Widelka, Poland
Tel.: (48) 178672700
Web Site: http://www.orlenpetrotank.pl
Fuel Product Distr
N.A.I.C.S.: 457210

ORLEN Poludnie S.A. (1)
UI Fabryczna 22, 32-540, Trzebinia, Poland
Tel.: (48) 24 201 0000
Web Site: https://www.orlenpoludnie.pl
Biofuel Mfr & Distr
N.A.I.C.S.: 324199
Marcin Rej *(Pres)*

ORLEN Serwis S.A. (1)
ul Chemikow 7, 09-411, Plock, Poland
Tel.: (48) 24 256 6776
Web Site: https://www.orlenserwis.pl
Industrial Installation Maintenance Services
N.A.I.C.S.: 811310

ORLEN Upstream Sp. z o.o. (1)
ul Bielanska 12, 00-085, Warsaw, Poland
Tel.: (48) 227780200
Web Site: https://www.orlenupstream.pl
Sales Range: $50-74.9 Million
Emp.: 35
Oil & Gas Exploration Services
N.A.I.C.S.: 213112
Grzegorz Markiewicz *(Chm-Supervisory Bd)*

Subsidiary (Non-US):

ORLEN Upstream Canada Ltd. (2)
Suite 400 850 2nd Street SW, Calgary, T2P 0R8, AB, Canada
Tel.: (403) 265-4115
Web Site: https://www.orlenupstream.ca
Sales Range: $25-49.9 Million
Emp.: 50
Oil Exploration & Extraction
N.A.I.C.S.: 211120
Russell J. Tripp *(Chm)*

ORLEN Uslugi Finansowe Sp. z o.o. (1)
UI Bielanska 12, Warsaw, Poland
Tel.: (48) 22 444 4455
Web Site: https://www.orlen-ubezpieczenia.pl
Financial Services
N.A.I.C.S.: 523999

ORLEN Wir Sp. z o.o. (1)
ul Chemikow 7, 09-411, Plock, Poland
Tel.: (48) 243652677
Web Site: http://www.orlenwir.pl
Sales Range: $25-49.9 Million
Emp.: 150
Rotating Machine Repair & Modernization Services
N.A.I.C.S.: 811198

Orlen Eesti OU (1)

AND PRIVATE COMPANIES

Parnu mnt 22, Tallinn, EE-10141, Estonia
Tel.: (372) 6264690
Web Site: http://www.orlen.ee
Refined Petroleum Products Whslr
N.A.I.C.S.: 424720

Orlen Ochrona Sp. Z O.O. (1)
ul Zglenickiego 42 Building G, 09-411, Plock, Poland
Tel.: (48) 243662521
Web Site: http://www.orlenochrona.pl
Security Consulting Services
N.A.I.C.S.: 541690
Lukasz Adam Lipiec *(Chm-Supervisory Bd)*

Petrolot Sp. z o.o. (Ltd.) (1)
ul J Gordona Bennetta 2, 02-159, Warsaw, Poland
Tel.: (48) 22 778 03 03
Web Site: http://www.petrolot.pl
Aviation Fuel Distr & Aircraft Refueling Services
N.A.I.C.S.: 424720
Ireneusz Wesolowski *(Pres-Mgmt Bd)*

Polska Press Sp. z o.o. (1)
Ul Domaniewska 45, 02-672, Warsaw, Poland
Tel.: (48) 22 201 4400
Web Site: https://www.polskapress.pl
Media Services
N.A.I.C.S.: 541840
Tomasz Przybek *(Pres)*

Przedsiebiorstwo Inwestycyjno Remontowe Remwil Sp. z o.o. (1)
ul Torunska 222, 87-805, Wloclawek, Poland
Tel.: (48) 54 237 25 83
Web Site: http://www.remwil.pl
Sales Range: $200-249.9 Million
Emp.: 800
Chemical Production Plant Construction Services
N.A.I.C.S.: 237990
Artur Sobolewski *(Pres)*

Przedsiebiorstwo Uslug Specjalistycznych i Projektowych Chemeko Sp. z o.o.
ul Torunska 248, 87-805, Wloclawek, Poland
Tel.: (48) 54 237 35 06
Web Site: http://www.chemeko.pl
Environmental Consulting Services
N.A.I.C.S.: 541620

Rafineria Trzebinia S.A. (1)
ul Fabryczna 22, 32-540, Trzebinia, Poland (77.2%)
Tel.: (48) 24 201 00 00
Web Site: http://www.orlen.pl
Refinery
N.A.I.C.S.: 324110
Krzysztof Zdziarski *(Chm)*

Subsidiary (Domestic):

Fabryka Parafin Naftowax Sp. z o.o. (2)
ul Fabryczna 22, 32-540, Trzebinia, Poland
Tel.: (48) 32 618 03 52
Web Site: http://www.naftowax.pl
Sales Range: $25-49.9 Million
Emp.: 58
Paraffin & Waxes Mfr
N.A.I.C.S.: 324110
Marek Kobak *(Chm-Mgmt Bd)*

Ship-Service S.A. (1)
Tama Pomorzanska 1, 70-030, Szczecin, Poland
Tel.: (48) 914318991
Web Site: http://www.ship-service.com.pl
Sales Range: $75-99.9 Million
Emp.: 100
Crude Oil & Petroleum Products Distr
N.A.I.C.S.: 424720
Piotr Zalewski *(Chm-Mgmt Bd)*

UAB EMAS (1)
Juodeikiai, 89467, Mazeikiai, Lithuania
Tel.: (370) 443 92826
Web Site: http://www.emas.lt
Sales Range: $50-74.9 Million
Emp.: 232
Electrical & Industrial Equipment Installation Services
N.A.I.C.S.: 238210

Valentinas Tarvydas *(Mgr-Technical Department)*

UAB Mazeikiu Naftos Sveikatos Prieziuros Centras (1)
Juodeikiu k, Mazeikiai, 89467, Lithuania
Tel.: (370) 44393709
Petrochemical Mfr
N.A.I.C.S.: 325110

UNIPETROL DEUTSCHLAND GmbH (1)
Paul-Ehrlich-Str 1b, 63225, Langen, Germany
Tel.: (49) 6103 2058 0
Web Site: http://www.orlenunipetrol.de
Sales Range: $50-74.9 Million
Petrochemical Distr
N.A.I.C.S.: 424720
Tomas Ohanka *(Head-Polyethylene & Polypropylene-DACH)*

UNIPETROL SLOVENSKO s.r.o. (1)
Jasikova 2, 821 03, Bratislava, Slovakia
Tel.: (421) 248291626
Web Site: http://www.unipetrol.sk
Sales Range: $50-74.9 Million
Motor Fuel Whslr
N.A.I.C.S.: 423120
Filip Jaroslav *(Gen Mgr)*

Unipetrol, a.s. (1)
Milevska 2095/5, 140 00, Prague, Czech Republic (100%)
Tel.: (420) 225001444
Web Site: http://www.unipetrol.cz
Sales Range: $600-649.9 Million
Crude Oil Processing, Motor Fuels Distribution & Production of Petrochemicals & Fertilizers
N.A.I.C.S.: 211120
Ivan Kocarnik *(Vice Chm-Supervisory Bd)*

Subsidiary (Domestic):

BENZINA s.r.o. (2)
Na Pankraci 127, Prague, 140 00, Czech Republic
Tel.: (420) 284012111
Web Site: http://www.benzinaplus.cz
Petroleum Filling Station Services
N.A.I.C.S.: 424710

Subsidiary (Domestic):

PETROTRANS s.r.o. (3)
Strelnicna 2221/50, 182 00, Prague, Czech Republic
Tel.: (420) 283 882 733
Web Site: http://www.petrotrans.cz
Fuel Transportation Services
N.A.I.C.S.: 213112

Subsidiary (Domestic):

Paramo, a.s. (2)
Prerovska 560, Pardubice, 530 06, Czech Republic (73.5%)
Tel.: (420) 466810111
Web Site: http://www.paramo.cz
Emp.: 300
Crude Refining; Diesel, Bitumens & Lubricants Mfr
N.A.I.C.S.: 324110
Jindrich Parponicek *(Chm)*

Polymer Institute Brno, Spol. s r.o. (2)
Tkalcovska 36 2, Brno, 656 49, Czech Republic (50%)
Tel.: (420) 545321240
Web Site: http://www.polymer.cz
Sales Range: $25-49.9 Million
Emp.: 110
Polyolefin Research Services
N.A.I.C.S.: 541715
Zdenek Salajka *(Mng Dir)*

Spolana, s.r.o. (2)
Ul Prace 657, 277 11, Neratovice, Czech Republic (100%)
Tel.: (420) 315661111
Web Site: http://www.spolana.cz
Chemicals Mfr
N.A.I.C.S.: 325180
Miroslav Falta *(Exec Dir)*

UNIPETROL SERVICES s.r.o. (2)
Litvinov Zaluzi 1, 436 70, Litvinov, Czech Republic
Tel.: (420) 476 163 178

Web Site: http://www.unipetrolservices.cz
Sales Range: $25-49.9 Million
Emp.: 245
Administrative Support Services
N.A.I.C.S.: 561110

Unipetrol Rafinerie, a.s. (2)
Zaluzi 1, 436 70, Litvinov, Czech Republic (100%)
Tel.: (420) 476 141 111
Web Site: http://www.unipetrolrafinerie.cz
Oil Refinery
N.A.I.C.S.: 324110

ORMA ORMAN MAHSULLERI INTEGRE SANAYI VE TICARET A.S.
Prof Dr Alaeddin Yavasca Sk Marmara Apt No 4 Daire 2 Besiktas, Apartmani No 4 Daire 2 Besiktas, 34357, Istanbul, Turkiye
Tel.: (90) 2123270080
Web Site: https://www.orma.com.tr
Year Founded: 1970
ORMA—(IST)
Sales Range: Less than $1 Million
Emp.: 415
Plywood & Lumber Mfr
N.A.I.C.S.: 321211
Sehriban Nihan Atasagun *(Chm & Mng Dir)*

ORMESTER VAGYONVEDELMI NYRT
8-9 Ogyalla ter, 1142, Budapest, Hungary
Tel.: (36) 13682002
Web Site: https://www.ormester.hu
Year Founded: 1990
2OM0—(DEU)
Rev.: $7,062,623
Assets: $2,858,832
Liabilities: $1,559,506
Net Worth: $1,299,326
Earnings: $231,417
Emp.: 14
Fiscal Year-end: 12/31/22
Security Services
N.A.I.C.S.: 561612
Jozsef Adam Szabo *(Chm-Supervisory Bd)*

Subsidiaries:

D. O. O. Ormester-Security (1)
Boska Jugovica 20, 24400, Senta, Serbia
Tel.: (381) 637313501
Security Consulting Services
N.A.I.C.S.: 561621

ORMESTER Security Ro S.R.L. (1)
Str Simion Barnutiu Nr 19 Biroul 5, Oradea, 410204, Bihor, Romania
Tel.: (40) 359 441 990
Web Site: http://www.ormestersecurity.ro
Security Consulting Services
N.A.I.C.S.: 561621

ORMIT BELGIUM N.V.
Tervurenlaan 412, Brussels, 1150, Belgium
Tel.: (32) 25339890
Web Site: http://www.ormit.be
Sales Range: $10-24.9 Million
Emp.: 10
Management Consulting Services
N.A.I.C.S.: 541611
Thomas De Wulf *(Mng Dir)*

ORMONDE MINING PLC
Suite 2 14-18 Main Street Blackrock Co Dublin, Clonee, D15 YN2P, Meath, Ireland
Tel.: (353) 2073900230
Web Site:
https://www.ormondemining.com
Year Founded: 1996
ORM—(AQSE)
Assets: $5,456,319
Liabilities: $149,577

Net Worth: $5,306,742
Earnings: ($1,154,346)
Emp.: 5
Fiscal Year-end: 12/31/22
Gold & Copper Mining
N.A.I.C.S.: 212220
Jonathan Henry *(Chm)*

ORNAPAPER BERHAD
No 8998 Kawasan Perindustrian Batu Berendam Peringkat IV, 75350, Melaka, Malaysia
Tel.: (60) 63355888
Web Site: https://www.ornapaper.com
ORNA—(KLS)
Rev.: $69,613,757
Assets: $65,979,471
Liabilities: $25,140,529
Net Worth: $40,838,942
Earnings: $551,746
Emp.: 830
Fiscal Year-end: 12/31/22
Corrugated Boards & Carton Boxes Mfr
N.A.I.C.S.: 322130
Siew Chuan Chua *(Co-Sec)*

Subsidiaries:

Ornapaper Industry (Batu Pahat) Sdn. Bhd. (1)
Lot Plo 271 Kawasan Perindustrian Sri Gading, 83009, Batu Pahat, Johor, Malaysia
Tel.: (60) 74556800
Carton & Corrugated Board Mfr
N.A.I.C.S.: 322211

Ornapaper Industry (Johor) Sdn. Bhd. (1)
114 Kawasan Perindustrian Senai III, 81400, Johor, Malaysia
Tel.: (60) 75992888
Carton & Corrugated Board Mfr
N.A.I.C.S.: 322211

Ornapaper Industry (M) Sdn. Bhd. (1)
No 8998 Kawasan Perindustrian Batu Berendam Peringkat IV, 75350, Melaka, Malaysia
Tel.: (60) 63355888
Carton & Corrugated Board Mfr
N.A.I.C.S.: 322211
Theresa Foo Gin Ee *(Mgr-QA)*

Ornapaper Industry (Perak) Sdn. Bhd. (1)
Plot 9 Kanthen Industrial Zone Kanthan Baru, 31200, Chemor, Perak, Malaysia
Tel.: (60) 52011299
Carton & Corrugated Board Mfr
N.A.I.C.S.: 322211

Quantum Rhythm Sdn. Bhd. (1)
Tel.: (60) 63342684
Carton & Corrugated Board Mfr
N.A.I.C.S.: 322211

Tripack Packaging (M) Sdn. Bhd. (1)
No 8998 Kawasan Perindustrian Batu Berendam Peringkat IV, 75350, Melaka, Malaysia
Tel.: (60) 63355550
Carton & Corrugated Board Mfr
N.A.I.C.S.: 322211

ORNUA CO-OPERATIVE LIMITED
Grattan House Mount Street Lower, Dublin, 2, Ireland
Tel.: (353) 16619599
Web Site: http://www.ornua.com
Year Founded: 1961
Rev.: $2,001,438,204
Assets: $892,660,611
Liabilities: $297,554,681
Net Worth: $595,105,930
Earnings: $28,689,685
Emp.: 2,200
Fiscal Year-end: 12/29/18
Dairy Products & Ingredients Distr
N.A.I.C.S.: 424430

ORNUA CO-OPERATIVE LIMITED

Ornua Co-operative Limited—(Continued)
Joe Collins (Chief Risk Mgmt Officer)

Subsidiaries:

Adams Foods Limited (1)
Sunnyhills Road, Leek, ST13 5SP, Staffordshire, United Kingdom
Tel.: (44) 1538 399111
Web Site: http://www.adamsfoods.com
Sales Range: $200-249.9 Million
Emp.: 730
Cheese & Butter Mfr & Distr
N.A.I.C.S.: 311513
Neil Kennedy (Interim CEO)

Subsidiary (Domestic):

FoodTec UK Ltd (2)
Gateway Crewe Gates Industrial Estate, Crewe, CW1 6XA, United Kingdom
Tel.: (44) 1270 530750
Web Site: http://www.foodtecuk.com
Emp.: 32
Food Ingredient Mfr
N.A.I.C.S.: 311999
John Carry (Mng Dir-Creative)

IDB Deutschland GmbH (1)
Kerrygoldstrasse 1, D 47506, Neukirchen-Vluyn, Germany
Tel.: (49) 2841 88 80 0
Web Site: http://www.kerrygold.de
Emp.: 130
Cheese & Butter Distr
N.A.I.C.S.: 424430
G. Kuegler (CEO)

IDB Global BV (1)
Paasheuvelweg 16, 1105 BH, Amsterdam, Netherlands
Tel.: (31) 20 564 6160
Dairy Products Distr
N.A.I.C.S.: 424430

Meadow Cheese Co. Ltd, (1)
Hazel Park, Dymock Road, Ledbury, HR8 2JQ, Herefordshire, United Kingdom
Tel.: (44) 1531 631300
Web Site: http://www.meadowcheese.co.uk
Cheese & Dairy Based Ingredients Mfr & Supplier
N.A.I.C.S.: 424430

Meadow Ingredients USA, LLC (1)
1415 Voll Dr NW, Byron, MN 55920
Tel.: (507) 775-7070
Dairy Products Distr
N.A.I.C.S.: 424430

North Downs Dairy Company Ltd (1)
Saxon Way Wincanton Business Park, Wincanton, Somersetshire, United Kingdom
Tel.: (44) 1963 828828
Dairy Products Distr
N.A.I.C.S.: 424430

Ornua North America Inc (1)
1007 Church St Ste 800, Evanston, IL 60201
Tel.: (847) 492-8036
Web Site:
http://www.ornuaingredientsamerica.com
Sales Range: $25-49.9 Million
Emp.: 40
Irish Dairy Products Importer & Sales
N.A.I.C.S.: 424430
Roisin Hennerty (Pres)

Subsidiary (Domestic):

Ornua (Wisconsin) Ingredients LLC (2)
N7630 County Hwy BB, Hilbert, WI 54129-9356
Tel.: (920) 989-1440
Web Site: http://www.ornua.com
Specialty Cheese Spreads, Cold Pack Cheese Food, Imitation Cheese & Cheese Substitutes
N.A.I.C.S.: 311513

The Cheese Warehouse Ltd (1)
Waymills Industrial Estate, Whitchurch, SY13 1TT, Shropshire, United Kingdom
Tel.: (44) 1948 66 60 60
Web Site:
http://www.thecheesewarehouse.co.uk
Dairy Products Mfr
N.A.I.C.S.: 311514

Aidan Wilson (Mng Dir)

The Kerrygold Company Ltd (1)
Barnfields Industrial Estate Sunnyhills Road, Leek, ST13 5SP, Staffordshire, United Kingdom
Tel.: (44) 1538 399 111
Web Site: http://www.kerrygold.co.uk
Dairy Products Distr
N.A.I.C.S.: 424430

Whitehall Specialties Inc. (1)
36120 Owen St, Whitehall, WI 54773
Tel.: (715) 538-2326
Web Site: http://www.whitehall-specialties.com
Sales Range: $25-49.9 Million
Emp.: 180
Imitation Cheese
N.A.I.C.S.: 311513
Steve Fawcett (Pres & CEO)

ORO CO., LTD.

Meguro Suda Building 391 Meguro, Meguro-ku, Tokyo, 153-0063, Japan
Tel.: (81) 357247001
Web Site: https://www.oro.com
Year Founded: 1999
3983—(TKS)
Rev.: $49,863,970
Assets: $87,724,570
Liabilities: $24,737,010
Net Worth: $62,987,560
Earnings: $13,017,240
Emp.: 554
Fiscal Year-end: 12/31/23
Business Management Services
N.A.I.C.S.: 561110
Atsushi Kawata (Co-Founder & CEO)

Subsidiaries:

Dalian Oro Advertising Co., Ltd. (1)
Room12B 4F No 1 Hui Xian Yuan Hi-tech Industrial Zone, Dalian, Liaoning, China
Tel.: (86) 41184760651
Web Site: http://www.oro-el.cn
Emp.: 30
Business Management Services
N.A.I.C.S.: 541611
Mura Jiki (Gen Mgr)

Oro (Thailand) Co., Ltd. (1)
246 Times Square Building 10th Fl Soi Sukhumvit, 12-14 Sukhumvit Rd Klongtoey, Bangkok, 10110, Thailand
Tel.: (66) 26532238
Web Site: http://www.th.oro.com
Business Management Services
N.A.I.C.S.: 541611
Masaru Sanka (Mng Dir)

Oro Miyazaki Co., Ltd. (1)
Aqua Miyazaki Building 2-4-20 Tachibanadorinishi, Miyazaki, 880-0001, Japan
Tel.: (81) 985607340
Web Site: https://www.oro-miyazaki.com
Emp.: 76
Business Management Services
N.A.I.C.S.: 541611
Shintaro Kono (Pres)

Oro Taiwan Co., Ltd. (1)
No 51 - 10 10th Floor No 51 Songjiang Rd, Zhongshan Dist, Taipei, 10455, Taiwan
Tel.: (886) 225090246
Web Site: https://www.tw.oro.com
Business Management Services
N.A.I.C.S.: 541611

Oro Technology (Dalian) Co., Ltd. (1)
Room10 12 4F No 1 Hui Xian Yuan Hi-tech Industrial Zone, Dalian, 116025, Liaoning, China
Tel.: (86) 41184760651
Web Site: http://www.oro-dl.cn
Business Management Services
N.A.I.C.S.: 541611

Oro Vietnam Co., Ltd. (1)
4Fl NTA Building, Da Kao Ward District 1, Ho Chi Minh City, Vietnam
Tel.: (84) 2839100296
Web Site: http://www.vn.oro.com
Emp.: 18
Webpage Design Services
N.A.I.C.S.: 541511

Akira Hirose (Gen Dir)

oRo Digital Asia Pte. Ltd. (1)
6 Eu Tong Sen Street The Central 07-11, Singapore, 059817, Singapore
Tel.: (65) 66358383
Software Publishing Services
N.A.I.C.S.: 541511

oRo Digital Asia Sdn. Bhd. (1)
BO1-D-13-1 & 2 Menara 2 Boutique Office 1 KL Eco City No 3, Jalan Bangsar, 59200, Kuala Lumpur, Malaysia
Tel.: (60) 322014012
Software Publishing Services
N.A.I.C.S.: 541511

oRo Malaysia Sdn. Bhd. (1)
Suite 12 Level 21 Mercu 3, No 3 Jalan Bangsar KL Eco City, 59200, Kuala Lumpur, Malaysia
Tel.: (60) 322026612
Software Publishing Services
N.A.I.C.S.: 541511

OROCO RESOURCE CORP.

Suite 1201-1166 Alberni Street, Vancouver, V6E 3Z3, BC, Canada
Tel.: (604) 688-6200 BC
Web Site:
https://www.orocoresourcecorp.com
Year Founded: 2006
OR6—(DEU)
Rev.: $237,239
Assets: $59,139,238
Liabilities: $2,146,710
Net Worth: $56,992,528
Earnings: ($3,889,025)
Fiscal Year-end: 05/31/23
Gold & Silver Mining Services
N.A.I.C.S.: 212220
Stephen M. Leahy (Chm)

OROGEN ROYALTIES INC.

1015-789 West Pender Street, Vancouver, V6C 1H2, BC, Canada
Tel.: (604) 248-8648 BC
Web Site:
https://www.orogenroyalties.com
Year Founded: 2005
5EV—(DEU)
Rev.: $4,492,396
Assets: $47,266,031
Liabilities: $764,041
Net Worth: $46,501,990
Earnings: $2,298,879
Emp.: 10
Fiscal Year-end: 12/31/23
Gold Mining Services
N.A.I.C.S.: 212220
J. Patrick Nicol (Pres & CEO)

Subsidiaries:

Minera Evrim S.A. de C.V. (1)
Calzada San Bernardino 92 Col Casa Grande, 83246, Hermosillo, Sonora, Mexico
Tel.: (52) 6622648055
Gold Ore Mining Services
N.A.I.C.S.: 212220

ORON GROUP INVESTMENTS & HOLDINGS LTD.

6 Yehuda Hanachtom Beit Daniel, Beersheba, Israel
Tel.: (972) 86295000
Web Site: https://www.oron-group.co.il
ORON—(TAE)
Rev.: $419,607,674
Assets: $387,880,917
Liabilities: $328,619,970
Net Worth: $59,260,947
Earnings: $6,808,123
Fiscal Year-end: 12/31/23
Engineeering Services
N.A.I.C.S.: 541330

ORONOVA ENERGY INC.

3123-595 Burrard Street, Vancouver, V7X 1J1, BC, Canada

Tel.: (604) 609-6125 BC
Year Founded: 1987
Rev.: $2,875
Assets: $300,442
Liabilities: $24,988
Net Worth: $275,455
Earnings: ($502,685)
Fiscal Year-end: 01/31/19
Mineral Exploration Services
N.A.I.C.S.: 212290
Joanna Vastardis (CFO)

OROPEZA INGENIEROS S.A. DE C.V.

Bandera Nacional 805, Zapopan, Guadalajara, 45160, Jalisco, Mexico
Tel.: (52) 1 33 3836 3150
Web Site:
http://www.oropezaingenieros.com
Sales Range: $25-49.9 Million
Emp.: 20
Measurement & Electrical Engineering Brand Marketing & Maintenance Services
N.A.I.C.S.: 334515
Carlos Flores Pedro (Gen Mgr)

ORORA LIMITED

109 Burwood Road, Hawthorn, 3122, VIC, Australia
Tel.: (61) 391161711 AU
Web Site:
https://www.ororagroup.com
Year Founded: 2013
ORRYY—(OTCIQ)
Rev.: $3,134,330,052
Assets: $2,075,455,472
Liabilities: $1,514,834,249
Net Worth: $560,621,223
Earnings: $141,515,293
Fiscal Year-end: 06/30/22
Offices of Other Holding Companies
N.A.I.C.S.: 551112
Stuart G. Hutton (CFO)

Subsidiaries:

Bronco Packaging Corp. (1)
510 N Peachtree Rd Ste 200, Mesquite, TX 75149
Tel.: (214) 337-1585
Paper & Plastic Packaging Products Mfr & Distr
N.A.I.C.S.: 322299

Orora North America (1)
6600 Vly View St, Buena Park, CA 90620
Tel.: (714) 562-6000
Web Site: http://www.ororagroup.com
Sales Range: $50-74.9 Million
Emp.: 100
Holding Company; Regional Managing Office; Corrugated Sheets & Boxes Mfr & Distr
N.A.I.C.S.: 551112
Kathy Linares (CIO)

Subsidiary (Domestic):

Graphic Tech, LLC (2)
1600 E Valencia Dr, Fullerton, CA 92831
Tel.: (714) 879-2400
Web Site: http://www.graphictech.net
Sales Range: $1-9.9 Million
Emp.: 27
Digital Printing Services
N.A.I.C.S.: 323111
Jim Hamel (Pres)

IntegraColor LLC (2)
3210 Innovative Way, Mesquite, TX 75149
Tel.: (972) 289-0705
Web Site: http://www.integracolor.com
Photofinishing Laboratory
N.A.I.C.S.: 812921
Adam Geerts (Pres)

Division (Domestic):

Orora North America - Landsberg (2)
5800 Plummer Rd Ste 150, Atlanta, GA 30336
Tel.: (404) 494-8100

Web Site: https://www.landsberg.com
Packaging, Janitorial & Shipping Supplies
N.A.I.C.S.: 424130
Neil Burns *(Reg Mgr-Ops-East Coast)*

Orora North America - Manufactured Packaging Products (2)
3201 W Mission Rd, Alhambra, CA 91803-1113
Tel.: (626) 308-0691
Web Site: https://mppmfg.com
Sales Range: $25-49.9 Million
Corrugated Sheet & Box Mfr
N.A.I.C.S.: 322211
Lissette Perez *(Reg Mgr-HR)*

Plant (Domestic):

Orora North America - Manufactured Packaging Products, Brea (3)
3200 Enterprise St, Brea, CA 92821-6289
Tel.: (714) 984-2300
Web Site: https://mppmfg.com
Sales Range: $25-49.9 Million
Emp.: 100
Corrugated Sheet & Box Mfr
N.A.I.C.S.: 322211
Carol Hortick *(Gen Mgr)*

Orora North America - Manufactured Packaging Products, San Diego (3)
664 N Twin Oaks Valley Rd, San Marcos, CA 92069-1712
Tel.: (760) 510-7170
Web Site: https://mppmfg.com
Sales Range: $25-49.9 Million
Emp.: 53
Corrugated Sheet & Box Mfr
N.A.I.C.S.: 322211
Scott Romatnoli *(Office Mgr)*

Orora North America - Manufactured Packaging Products, Sycamore (3)
215 N Fair St, Sycamore, IL 60178-1644
Tel.: (815) 895-2343
Web Site: https://mppmfg.com
Sales Range: $25-49.9 Million
Emp.: 55
Corrugated Sheet & Box Mfr
N.A.I.C.S.: 322211

Orora Visual - Chicago (1)
7400 N Lehigh Ave, Niles, IL 60714
Tel.: (847) 647-1900
Web Site: http://www.ororavisual.com
Packaging & Point-of-Purchase Display Commercial Printing Services
N.A.I.C.S.: 323111
Wayne Brekke *(Controller)*

Subsidiary (Domestic):

Ed. Garvey & Company (2)
7400 N Lehigh Ave, Niles, IL 60714
Tel.: (847) 647-1900
Packaging & Point-of-Purchase Display Commercial Printing Services
N.A.I.C.S.: 323111

Plant (Domestic):

Ed. Garvey & Company - Franklin (3)
9980 S Oakwood Park Dr, Franklin, WI 53132
Tel.: (414) 423-2200
Web Site: http://www.thegarveygroup.com
Emp.: 30
Commercial Printing
N.A.I.C.S.: 323113

Ed. Garvey & Company - Los Angeles (3)
3116 W 32nd Ave, Los Angeles, CA 90065
Tel.: (323) 258-4111
Web Site: http://www.thegarveygroup.com
Sales Range: $1-9.9 Million
Lithographic Commercial Printing
N.A.I.C.S.: 323111
Paul Vogelsang *(Gen Mgr)*

Ed. Garvey & Company - Milwaukee (3)
4601 S 5th St, Milwaukee, WI 53207
Tel.: (414) 481-3100
Packaging & Point-of-Purchase Display Commercial Printing Services
N.A.I.C.S.: 323111

Ed. Garvey & Company - Sturtevant (3)
7900 Durand Ave, Sturtevant, WI 53177
Tel.: (262) 554-7300
Web Site: http://www.thegarveygroup.com
Emp.: 50
Packaging & Point-of-Purchase Display Commercial Printing Services
N.A.I.C.S.: 323111
Scott Rasmussen *(Pres)*

Orora Visual LLC (1)
3210 Innovative Way, Mesquite, TX 75149
Tel.: (972) 289-0705
Web Site: https://www.ororavisual.com
Printing Products Mfr
N.A.I.C.S.: 323111

Saverglass SAS (1)
Place de la Gare, BP 1, 60960, Feuquieres-en-Vimeu, France
Tel.: (33) 344464545
Web Site: http://www.saverglass.com
Glass Bottle Mfr
N.A.I.C.S.: 327213
Loic Quentin de Gromard *(Chm & CEO)*

Subsidiary (Non-US):

SAVERGLASS (NZ) LTD. (2)
Unit G/383 Khyber Pass Rd Newmarket, PO Box 8020, Auckland, 1023, New Zealand
Tel.: (64) 9 522 2990
Web Site: http://www.savers.com
Glass Bottle Distr
N.A.I.C.S.: 423840

SAVERGLASS AUSTRALIA PTY LTD (2)
289 Flinders Street, PO Box 6537, Adelaide, 5000, SA, Australia
Tel.: (61) 882320770
Web Site: http://www.saverglass.com
Glass Bottle Distr
N.A.I.C.S.: 423840
Paul Paleologos *(Mng Dir)*

Subsidiary (Domestic):

SAVERGLASS CHAMPAGNE (2)
Allee Maxenu, 51530, Pierry, France
Tel.: (33) 326581785
Web Site: http://www.saverglass.com
Glass Bottle Distr
N.A.I.C.S.: 423840

SAVERGLASS Cognac (2)
Z I de Merpins rue Jacques Marzio, Merpins, 16100, Cognac, France
Tel.: (33) 545823579
Glass Bottle Distr
N.A.I.C.S.: 423840

Subsidiary (Non-US):

SAVERGLASS IBERICA LDA (2)
Plaza de Carlos Trias Bertran, 4 1a Planta Ibercenter Business Center, 28020, Madrid, Spain
Tel.: (34) 914184509
Web Site: http://www.saverglass.com
Glass Bottle Distr
N.A.I.C.S.: 423840

SAVERGLASS IBERICA LDT (2)
Avenida Almirante Gago Coutinho 132 - 134 Edificio 2, 2710-418, Sintra, Portugal
Tel.: (351) 219248060
Web Site: http://www.saverglass.com
Glass Bottle Distr
N.A.I.C.S.: 423840

SAVERGLASS ITALIA SRL (2)
Via Lazzaretto 19, 20124, Milan, Italy
Tel.: (39) 0284932416
Web Site: http://www.saverglass.com
Glass Bottle Distr
N.A.I.C.S.: 423840

Subsidiary (US):

SAVERGLASS Inc. (2)
2950 Cordelia Rd, Fairfield, CA 94534
Tel.: (707) 259-2930
Web Site: http://www.saverglass.com
Glass Bottle Distr
N.A.I.C.S.: 423840

Subsidiary (Non-US):

SAVERGLASS MEXICO (2)
Torre Ganesh Ahuizotl 2276 Cd del Sol, Zapopan, 45050, Guadalajara, Jalisco, Mexico
Tel.: (52) 3338840900
Web Site: http://www.saverglass.com
Glass Bottle Distr
N.A.I.C.S.: 423840
Luic Quentin *(CEO)*

SAVERGLASS MOSCOU (2)
Zubovski proezd 2 Build 1 Office 3, 119021, Moscow, Russia
Tel.: (7) 4957800580
Web Site: http://www.saverglass.com
Glass Bottle Distr
N.A.I.C.S.: 423840

SAVERGLASS PTY LTD. (2)
5 Niblick Way, Somerset West, 7130, South Africa
Tel.: (27) 218510005
Glass Bottle Distr
N.A.I.C.S.: 423840

Subsidiary (Domestic):

SAVERSUD (2)
Venel'Tech - Bat A2 994 rue de la Gare, 13770, Venelles, France
Tel.: (33) 442904017
Web Site: http://www.saverglass.com
Glass Bottle Distr
N.A.I.C.S.: 423840

VERRERIES & DECORS D'ARMAGNAC S.A. (2)
3809 route de Nerac, 32100, Condom, France
Tel.: (33) 562683010
Web Site: http://www.saverglass.com
Glass Bottle Distr
N.A.I.C.S.: 423840

OROSCIENCE PLC
Centaurusweg 123, 5015 TC, Tilburg, Netherlands
Tel.: (31) 13 5479 340
Oral Care Product Mfr
N.A.I.C.S.: 339114
Mark G. Fontenot *(Chm & CEO)*

OROSIL SMITHS INDIA LIMITED
Hemkunt Chambers Flat No 620 89 Nehru Palace, New Delhi, 110019, India
Tel.: (91) 9811992924
Web Site: https://www.orosil.com
Year Founded: 1994
531626—(BOM)
Rev.: $98,591
Assets: $344,140
Liabilities: $100,965
Net Worth: $243,175
Earnings: ($41,424)
Emp.: 6
Fiscal Year-end: 03/31/23
Jewelry Mfr
N.A.I.C.S.: 339910
Bhushan Kumar Narula *(Chm & Mng Dir)*

OROSUR MINING INC.
82 Richmond St E 1st Floor, Toronto, M5C 1P1, ON, Canada
Tel.: (778) 373-0100 Ca
Web Site: https://www.orosur.ca
UR2—(DEU)
Rev.: $40,000
Assets: $5,390,000
Liabilities: $14,029,000
Net Worth: ($8,639,000)
Earnings: ($3,781,000)
Fiscal Year-end: 05/31/24
Gold Exploration & Production Services
N.A.I.C.S.: 212220
Jeronimo Janez *(Mgr-NBD)*

Subsidiaries:

Orosur Mining Inc. - Uruguay Head Office (1)
Hervariya 3535 Office 1512, Montevideo, 11300, Uruguay
Tel.: (598) 26016354
Web Site: http://www.orosur.ca
Sales Range: $200-249.9 Million
Emp.: 300
Corporate Office; Gold Mining Legislative Services
N.A.I.C.S.: 551114

OROTONGROUP LIMITED
Unit 5 Level 2 409 George Street, Waterloo, 2017, NSW, Australia
Tel.: (61) 282755500 AU
Year Founded: 1938
Women's Clothing Mfr; Footwear Distr
N.A.I.C.S.: 315250
Ross B. Lane *(Interim CEO)*

Subsidiaries:

OrotonGroup (Australia) Pty Limited (1)
Unit 15 Level 2 409 George Street Waterloo, Sydney, 2017, NSW, Australia (100%)
Tel.: (61) 282755500
Web Site: http://www.oroton.com
Sales Range: $25-49.9 Million
Emp.: 75
Management Consulting Services
N.A.I.C.S.: 541618

OrotonGroup (New Zealand) Pty Limited (1)
Atrium On Elliot Elliot St, Auckland, New Zealand (100%)
Tel.: (64) 93776016
Sales Range: $25-49.9 Million
Emp.: 40
Jewelry Watch Precious Stone & Precious Metal Whslr
N.A.I.C.S.: 423940

Polo Ralph Lauren Australia Pty Limited (1)
Level 2 409 George Street Waterloo, Sydney, 2017, NSW, Australia
Tel.: (61) 282755500
Web Site: http://www.orotongroup.com
Sales Range: $25-49.9 Million
Emp.: 70
Clothing Retailer
N.A.I.C.S.: 458110

ORPHEUS CLUB WELLNESS PLC
Hristo Botev 27 A, 4000, Plovdiv, Bulgaria
Tel.: (359) 882933505
Web Site: https://www.orpheusclub.com
Year Founded: 2007
OCW—(BUL)
Sales Range: Less than $1 Million
Tourism Services
N.A.I.C.S.: 561520
Petar Troplev *(Deputy Chm & CFO)*

ORPHEUS URANIUM LIMITED
Level 6 100 Pirie Street, Adelaide, 5000, SA, Australia
Tel.: (61) 882310381 AU
Web Site: https://www.orpheusuranium.com
ORP—(ASX)
Rev.: $1,166,073
Assets: $5,439,058
Liabilities: $444,744
Net Worth: $4,994,315
Earnings: ($1,499,418)
Fiscal Year-end: 06/30/24
Uranium Exploration & Mining
N.A.I.C.S.: 212290
Lindsay Owler *(CEO)*

Subsidiaries:

Argonaut Resources Laos Co Limited (1)
Unit 3 Level 5 ANZ Vientiane Comml Bldg, PO Box 10982, 33 Lane Xang Ave, Vientiane, Lao People's Democratic Republic
Tel.: (856) 21222731

ORPHEUS URANIUM LIMITED

Orpheus Uranium Limited—(Continued)
Web Site:
http://www.argonautresources.com
Sales Range: $50-74.9 Million
Emp.: 6
Gold Ore Mining Services
N.A.I.C.S.: 212220

ORSERO S.P.A.
Regione Cime Di Leca 30, Albenga, 17031, Savona, Italy
Tel.: (39) 0182560400
Web Site: https://www.orserogroup.it
Year Founded: 1940
ORS—(ITA)
Rev.: $1,291,046,838
Assets: $563,303,475
Liabilities: $345,860,134
Net Worth: $217,443,341
Earnings: $35,031,297
Emp.: 1,709
Fiscal Year-end: 12/31/22
Vegetable & Fruit Distr
N.A.I.C.S.: 424480
Paolo Prudenziati *(Chm, Mng Dir & Chief Comml Officer)*

Subsidiaries:

AZ France S.A.S. (1)
56 Avenue Joseph Pierre Boitelet, CS 40129, 84304, Cavaillon, Cedex, France
Tel.: (33) 490066600
Web Site: https://www.azfrance.fr
Fresh Fruit Distr
N.A.I.C.S.: 424480

Bella Frutta S.A. (1)
4 Tavrou, 18233, Agios Ioannis Rentis, Greece
Tel.: (30) 2103450790
Web Site: https://www.bellafrutta.gr
Fresh Fruit Distr
N.A.I.C.S.: 424480

Capexo S.A.S. (1)
32 - 34 avenue Guynemer, 94550, Chevilly-Larue, France
Tel.: (33) 141732304
Web Site: https://lilot-fruits.com
Fruit & Vegetable Whslr
N.A.I.C.S.: 424480

D'Oriano S.A. (1)
23 Rue du Faubourg Saint-Jean, 45000, Orleans, France
Tel.: (33) 238739571
Web Site: https://doriano.fr
Beauty Care Services
N.A.I.C.S.: 812112

Fresco Ships' A&F S.r.l. (1)
Via Trieste 25, 17047, Vado Ligure, SV, Italy
Tel.: (39) 0192162501
Web Site: https://www.frescosv.it
Freight Transportation Services
N.A.I.C.S.: 488510

GFB S.r.l. (1)
Via Botticelli s / n, 20022, Milan, Italy
Tel.: (39) 0331883734
Machine Tools Mfr
N.A.I.C.S.: 333517

Soulage Favarel S.A.S. (1)
Le Grand Marche Min Toulouse Metropole, PO Box 80, 146-200 Avenue Des Etats-Unis, 31200, Toulouse, France
Tel.: (33) 561472159
Web Site: https://blampinfruits.fr
Grocery Store Operator
N.A.I.C.S.: 445110

ORSTED AS
Kraftvaerksvej 53, Skaerbaek, 7000, Fredericia, Denmark
Tel.: (45) 99551111   DK
Web Site: https://orsted.com
Year Founded: 1972
ORSTED—(CSE)
Rev.: $11,467,783,710
Assets: $40,678,907,844
Liabilities: $29,422,957,272
Net Worth: $11,255,950,572
Earnings: ($2,920,229,775)
Emp.: 8,905
Fiscal Year-end: 12/31/23
Renewable Energy Services
N.A.I.C.S.: 221210
Marianne Wiinholt *(CFO)*

Subsidiaries:

DONG Energy Sales (UK) Ltd. (1)
Grand Buildings 1-3 Strand, London, WC2N 5EJ, United Kingdom
Tel.: (44) 2072570100
Sales Range: $75-99.9 Million
Emp.: 100
Natural Gas Marketer & Whslr
N.A.I.C.S.: 221210
Jeff Whittingham *(Mng Dir)*

Danish Offshore Gas Systems A/S (1)
Nesa Alle 1, 2820, Gentofte, Denmark
Tel.: (45) 9 955 1111
Web Site: https://gastransport.orsted.dk
Transportation Natural Gas Services
N.A.I.C.S.: 486210

Deepwater Wind Rhode Island, LLC (1)
56 Exchange Ter, Providence, RI 02903
Tel.: (401) 868-4228
Web Site: https://www.dwwind.com
Wind Power Services
N.A.I.C.S.: 221115
Jeffrey Grybowski *(CEO)*

Deepwater Wind, LLC (1)
36 Exchange Ter, Providence, RI 02903-1798
Tel.: (401) 122-8004
Web Site: http://www.dwwind.com
Household Appliances, Electric Housewares & Consumer Electronics Merchant Whslr
N.A.I.C.S.: 423620
Aileen Kenney *(VP)*

Inbicon A/S (1)
Kraftvaerksvej 53, 7000, Fredericia, Denmark   (100%)
Tel.: (45) 99551111
Web Site: http://orsted.com
Producer & Distr of Electricity & Heat; Waste Incineration Services
N.A.I.C.S.: 221122

Orsted AB (1)
Skomakaregatan 6-8, 211 34, Malmo, Sweden
Tel.: (46) 70 670 7121
Web Site: https://orsted.se
Wind Power Services
N.A.I.C.S.: 221115

Orsted Hornsea Project Three (UK) Limited (1)
5 Howick Place, London, SW1P 1WG, United Kingdom
Tel.: (44) 2078115200
Web Site: https://hornseaproject3.co.uk
Wind Power Services
N.A.I.C.S.: 221115
Ant Sahota *(Mgr)*

Orsted London Array Limited (1)
Military Road, Ramsgate, CT11 9LG, United Kingdom
Tel.: (44) 184 385 4692
Web Site: https://londonarray.com
Wind Power Services
N.A.I.C.S.: 221115

Orsted Markets GmbH (1)
Dockland Van-der-Smissen-Strasse 9, 22767, Hamburg, Germany
Tel.: (49) 402 380 0470
Wind Power Services
N.A.I.C.S.: 221115

Orsted Netherlands B.V. (1)
Koninginnegracht 19, 2514 AB, Hague, Netherlands
Tel.: (31) 70 262 0455
Wind Power Services
N.A.I.C.S.: 221115

Orsted Onshore Ireland Green Energy Limited (1)
Floor 5 City Quarter Lapps Quay, Cork, Ireland
Tel.: (353) 214223600

Web Site: https://orsted.ie
Emp.: 8,900
Renewable Energy Technologies Services
N.A.I.C.S.: 541690

Orsted Polska Sp. z o.o. (1)
Chmielna 73, 00-801, Warsaw, Poland
Tel.: (48) 22 653 4600
Web Site: https://orsted.pl
Wind Power Services
N.A.I.C.S.: 221115

Orsted Services Malaysia Sdn. Bhd. (1)
Suite 32-1 Level 32 UOA Corporate Tower Avenue 10, The Vertical Bangsar South City, 59200, Kuala Lumpur, Malaysia
Tel.: (60) 39 212 4256
Web Site: https://orsted.my
Emp.: 240
Wind Power Services
N.A.I.C.S.: 221115
Benny Jakobsen *(Country Mgr)*

Orsted Taiwan Ltd. (1)
19F No 1 Songzhi Rd, Xinyi Dist, Taipei, 110411, Taiwan
Tel.: (886) 227221617
Web Site: https://orsted.tw
Emp.: 140
Wind Power Services
N.A.I.C.S.: 221115
Matthias Bausenwein *(Pres)*

Orsted Wind Power Germany GmbH (1)
Dockland Van-der-Smissen-Strasse 9, 22767, Hamburg, Germany
Tel.: (49) 4018 131 0800
Web Site: https://orsted.de
Wind Power Services
N.A.I.C.S.: 221115

Orsted Wind Power North America LLC (1)
399 Boylston St 12th Fl, Boston, MA 02116
Tel.: (857) 354-1002
Wind Power Generation Services
N.A.I.C.S.: 221115

SMart Wind Limited (1)
11th Floor 140 London Wall, London, EC2Y 5DN, United Kingdom
Tel.: (44) 207 776 5500
Web Site: https://www.smartwind.co.uk
Wind Power Services
N.A.I.C.S.: 221115

ORSUS XELENT TECHNOLOGIES, INC.
12th Floor Tower B Chaowai MEN Office Building 26 Chaowai Street, Chaoyang Disc, Beijing, 100020, China
Tel.: (86) 1085653777
Web Site: http://www.orsus-xelent.com
Year Founded: 2003
Sales Range: $10-24.9 Million
Emp.: 26
Wireless Transmission Device Mfr
N.A.I.C.S.: 517112
Guoji Liu *(CEO)*

ORTEL COMMUNICATIONS LTD
B 7/122A Safdarjang Enclave, New Delhi, 110029, India
Tel.: (91) 46868800
Web Site: http://www.ortelcom.com
ORTEL—(NSE)
Rev.: $9,650,714
Assets: $50,001,547
Liabilities: $60,537,395
Net Worth: ($10,535,848)
Earnings: ($2,997,526)
Emp.: 520
Fiscal Year-end: 03/31/21
Cable Television
N.A.I.C.S.: 516210
Bibhu Prasad Rath *(Pres & CEO)*

ORTHOCELL LIMITED
Building 191 Murdoch University South Street, Murdoch, 6150, WA, Australia
Tel.: (61) 893602888
Web Site: https://orthocell.com
OCC—(ASX)
Rev.: $2,010,801
Assets: $17,771,908
Liabilities: $14,745,350
Net Worth: $3,026,558
Earnings: ($4,794,978)
Fiscal Year-end: 06/30/24
Tissue Repair & Regeneration Medicine Mfr
N.A.I.C.S.: 325411
Paul Anderson *(Mng Dir)*

ORTHOTIC CENTRE (NZ) LIMITED
614 Great South Road, PO Box 11203, Ellerslie, 1542, New Zealand
Tel.: (64) 95256061   NZ
Web Site: http://www.orthotics.co.nz
Year Founded: 1991
Emp.: 25
Orthotic Services
N.A.I.C.S.: 621999
Con Balasoglou *(CEO)*

Subsidiaries:

Orthotic Centre (Midlands) Limited (1)
43 Pembroke Street, Hamilton, 3247, New Zealand
Tel.: (64) 78341281
Healthcare Services
N.A.I.C.S.: 621999

Orthotic Centre (Wellington) Limited (1)
3-5 George St, PO Box 12213, Thorndon, Wellington, 6011, New Zealand
Tel.: (64) 48158058
Emp.: 5
Healthcare Services
N.A.I.C.S.: 621999
Con Dalasoklou *(Gen Mgr)*

ORTIN LABORATORIES LIMITED
Flat No 502 Palem Towers, Barkatpura, Hyderabad, 500 027, India
Tel.: (91) 4027567266
Web Site:
http://www.ortinlabsindia.com
Sales Range: $10-24.9 Million
Pharmaceuticals Product Mfr
N.A.I.C.S.: 325412
Murali Krishna Murthy Sanka *(CEO & Co-Mng Dir)*

ORTIVUS AB
Svardvagen 19, PO Box 713, 182 33, Danderyd, Sweden
Tel.: (46) 84464500
Web Site: https://www.ortivus.com
Year Founded: 1985
ORTI—(OMX)
Rev.: $9,788,605
Assets: $8,406,155
Liabilities: $5,086,778
Net Worth: $3,319,378
Earnings: $551,669
Emp.: 45
Fiscal Year-end: 12/31/22
Administrative & Clinical Modules Information System Developer & Marketer
N.A.I.C.S.: 519290
Anders Paulsson *(Chm)*

Subsidiaries:

MEDOS AG (1)
Hasselbachstrasse 2, 63505, Langenselbold, Germany
Tel.: (49) 6184805100
Web Site: http://www.medos.de

AND PRIVATE COMPANIES

Develops & Markets IT Systems For Hospital Departments, General Hospitals, University Hospitals & Specialized Medical Practices
N.A.I.C.S.: 519290

Ortivus UK Ltd. (1)
Unit 12 New Forest Enterprise Centre, Southampton, SO40 9LA, United Kingdom
Web Site: http://www.ortivus.com
Administrative & Clinical Modules Information System Developer & Marketer
N.A.I.C.S.: 519290

ORTOFON A/S
Stavangervej 9, DK-4900, Nakskov, Denmark
Tel.: (45) 54911915
Web Site: http://www.ortofon.com
Year Founded: 1918
Sales Range: $10-24.9 Million
Emp.: 60
Mfr of Stereo Cartridges
N.A.I.C.S.: 334220
Christen H. Nelson *(Mng Dir)*

Subsidiaries:

Ortofon, Inc. (1)
500 Executive Blvd Ste 102, Ossining, NY 10562-2563
Tel.: (914) 762-8646
Web Site: http://www.ortofon.us
Phonograph Cartridges, Components & Electronics
N.A.I.C.S.: 423620
Dee Hustinova *(Gen Mgr)*

ORVANA MINERALS CORP.
70 York Street Suite 1710, Toronto, M5J 1S9, ON, Canada
Tel.: (416) 369-1629 ON
Web Site: https://www.orvana.com
Year Founded: 1992
ORV—(OTCIQ)
Rev.: $105,513,000
Assets: $144,936,000
Liabilities: $75,069,000
Net Worth: $69,867,000
Earnings: ($1,112,000)
Emp.: 525
Fiscal Year-end: 09/30/21
Gold Mining
N.A.I.C.S.: 212220
Gordon E. Pridham *(Chm)*

ORVIANDE INC.
11151 rue Mirabeau, Montreal, H2J 2S2, QC, Canada
Tel.: (514) 353-1143
Web Site: http://www.orviande.com
Year Founded: 1979
Sales Range: $25-49.9 Million
Emp.: 400
Meat Product Distr
N.A.I.C.S.: 424470
Pat Manno *(Gen Mgr)*

ORVIS CORPORATION
6101 Matsunagacho, Fukuyama, 729-0105, Hiroshima, Japan
Tel.: (81) 849342621
Web Site: https://www.orvis.co.jp
Year Founded: 1947
78270—(TKS)
Lumber Mfr
N.A.I.C.S.: 321912
Iwao Okoshi *(Chm)*

ORYX PROPERTIES LIMITED
Deloitte Building Maerua Mall Complex Jan Jonker Road, PO Box 97723, Robert Mugabe Avenue, Windhoek, Namibia
Tel.: (264) 61423201
Web Site: https://www.oryxprop.com
ORY—(NAM)
Rev.: $18,819,783
Assets: $186,541,529
Liabilities: $108,764,273
Net Worth: $77,777,255
Earnings: $8,371,854
Emp.: 35
Fiscal Year-end: 06/30/23
Financial & Real Estate Services
N.A.I.C.S.: 525990
Lizette Smit *(CFO)*

Subsidiaries:

Verona Investments (Pty) Ltd (1)
Mispel Hse 1 Mispel St, Cape Town, 7530, Western Cape, South Africa
Tel.: (27) 219194444
Real Estate Manangement Services
N.A.I.C.S.: 531390
W. Delange *(Mng Dir)*

ORYZON GENOMICS SA
Sant Ferran 74, Cornella de Llobregat, 08940, Barcelona, Spain
Tel.: (34) 935151313
Web Site: https://www.oryzon.com
Year Founded: 2000
Pharmaceuticals Product Mfr
N.A.I.C.S.: 325412
Carlos Buesa *(CEO)*

ORZEL BIALY S.A.
Ul Harcerska 23, 41-946, Piekary Slaskie, Poland
Tel.: (48) 327796500
Web Site: https://www.orzel-bialy.com.pl
Year Founded: 1858
OBL—(WAR)
All Other Miscellaneous Chemical Product & Preparation Manufacturing
N.A.I.C.S.: 325998
Sznajder Konrad *(Chm-Mgmt Bd)*

OS CO., LTD.
1-102 Ishihara, Kita-ku, Osaka, 530-0017, Japan
Tel.: (81) 66 361 3554
Web Site: http://www.osgroup.co.jp
Year Founded: 1946
9637—(TKS)
Rev.: $53,927,280
Assets: $301,628,800
Liabilities: $197,355,840
Net Worth: $104,272,960
Earnings: $4,772,240
Emp.: 57
Fiscal Year-end: 01/31/22
Movie Theater & Real Estate Services
N.A.I.C.S.: 512131
Shuichiro Takahashi *(Pres)*

OSAI AUTOMATION SYSTEM S.P.A.
Via Cartiera 4, Parella, 10010, Turin, TO, Italy
Tel.: (39) 0125668311
Web Site: https://www.osai-as.com
Year Founded: 1991
OSA—(EUR)
Rev.: $48,091,401
Assets: $93,250,911
Liabilities: $80,730,765
Net Worth: $12,520,146
Earnings: ($6,796,556)
Emp.: 250
Fiscal Year-end: 12/31/23
Semiconductor Mfr
N.A.I.C.S.: 334413

Subsidiaries:

Osai Automation System USA Corporation (1)
10000 N Central Expy Ste 710, Dallas, TX 75231
Tel.: (469) 614-9756
Semiconductor System Services
N.A.I.C.S.: 811310

OSAKA GAS CO., LTD.
4-1-2 Hiranomachi, Chuo-ku, Osaka, 541-0046, Japan
Tel.: (81) 662054715 JP
Web Site: https://www.osakagas.co.jp
Year Founded: 1897
9532—(TKS)
Rev.: $15,360,988,720
Assets: $25,052,672,480
Liabilities: $12,506,530,960
Net Worth: $12,546,141,520
Earnings: $1,241,518,080
Emp.: 20,961
Fiscal Year-end: 03/31/22
Natural Gas Distribution Services
N.A.I.C.S.: 221210
Takehiro Honjo *(Chm)*

Subsidiaries:

Creative Techno Solution Co., Ltd (1)
3-5-11 Doshomachi Osaka Gas Midosuji Higashi Bldg, Chuo-Ku, Osaka, 541-0045, Japan
Tel.: (81) 662053501
Web Site: http://www.ogcts.co.jp
Natural Gas Distr
N.A.I.C.S.: 221210

Enetec Kyoto Co., Ltd (1)
74-2 Higashikujo Minamiishida-cho, Minami-ku, Kyoto, 601-8033, Japan
Tel.: (81) 756936530
Web Site: https://www.osakagas-enetec.jp
Gas Appliance Sales
N.A.I.C.S.: 423720

Gas and Power Co., Ltd (1)
4-4-11 Awajicho, Chuo-Ku, Osaka, 541-0047, Japan
Tel.: (81) 662054557
Web Site: http://www.gasandpower.co.jp
Sales Range: $50-74.9 Million
Emp.: 62
Electric Power Distribution Services
N.A.I.C.S.: 221210
Makoto Makino *(Pres)*

Jacobi Carbons AB (1)
Slodjaregatan 1, 393 53, Kalmar, Sweden
Tel.: (46) 48 041 7550
Web Site: https://www.jacobi.net
Carbon Mfr & Distr
N.A.I.C.S.: 335991
Remko Goudappel *(CEO)*

Japan EnviroChemicals, Ltd. (1)
Shibakoen Na Building 2-5-10 Shiba, Minato-ku, Tokyo, 105-0014, Japan
Tel.: (81) 3 5444 9890
Web Site: http://www.jechem.co.jp
Sales Range: $50-74.9 Million
Emp.: 150
Activated Carbon Mfr
N.A.I.C.S.: 325998

Kansai Business Information Inc. (1)
Sumitomo Nakanoshima Building 7F 3-2-18 Nakanoshima, Kita-ku, Osaka, 530-0005, Japan
Tel.: (81) 64 803 2200
Web Site: https://www.kbinfo.co.jp
Business Support Services
N.A.I.C.S.: 561499

Kinpai Co., Ltd. (1)
3-10-12 Sangenyahigashi, Taisho-ku, Osaka, 551-0002, Japan
Tel.: (81) 66 105 0888
Web Site: https://www.kinpai.gr.jp
Civil Engineering Services
N.A.I.C.S.: 541330

Liquid Gas Co.,Ltd. (1)
Kawaramachi Building 8f 4-2-14 Kawaramachi, Chuo-ku, Osaka, 541-0048, Japan
Tel.: (81) 662021700
Web Site: http://www.liquidgas.co.jp
Sales Range: $100-124.9 Million
Emp.: 60
Liquefied Petroleum Gas Mfr & Distr
N.A.I.C.S.: 221210

Nabari Kintetsu Gas Co., Ltd. (1)
5-1 Kikyogaoka 1-cho 1-block, Nabari, 518-0621, Mie, Japan
Tel.: (81) 595652311
Web Site: https://www.kintetsugas.co.jp

Emp.: 112
Industrial Gas Mfr
N.A.I.C.S.: 325120

Nissho Petroleum Gas Corporation (1)
29-2 Kasumigaseki Building 3-2-5 Kasumigaseki, Chiyoda-Ku, Tokyo, 100-6029, Japan
Tel.: (81) 342338220
Sales Range: $50-74.9 Million
Emp.: 36
Natural Gas Distr
N.A.I.C.S.: 221210

OG Capital Co., Ltd (1)
4-11 4 Chome Awaji-cho, Chuo-ku, Osaka, 541-0047, Japan
Tel.: (81) 2102249196
Engineering Services
N.A.I.C.S.: 541330

OG Sports Co., Ltd. (1)
3-6-14 Bingo-cho, Chuo-ku, Osaka, 541-0051, Japan (100%)
Tel.: (81) 662623468
Web Site: http://www.ogsports.co.jp
Sales Range: $125-149.9 Million
Emp.: 2,214
Sport Equipment Mfr & Sports Facilities Operation Services
N.A.I.C.S.: 713940
Isao Yamamura *(Pres)*

OGIS-RI Co., Ltd. (1)
ICC Bldg Minami 2-37 Chiyozaki 3-chome, Nishi-ku, Osaka, 550-0023, Japan (100%)
Tel.: (81) 665840011
Sales Range: $1-4.9 Billion
Emp.: 1,512
Information Technology Consulting, Systems Integration, Network Construction & Support Services
N.A.I.C.S.: 541690
Shinya Nishioka *(Pres)*

Joint Venture (Domestic):

Sakura Information Systems Co., Ltd. (2)
1-17-3 NBF Platinum Tower Shirokane, Minato-ku, Tokyo, 108-8650, Japan
Tel.: (81) 367577200
Web Site: https://www.sakura-is.co.jp
Emp.: 1,170
Information Technology Network Construction, Support & Data Processing Services; Owned 51% by Osaka Gas Co., Ltd. & 49% by Sumitomo Mitsui Financial Group, Inc.
N.A.I.C.S.: 541512
Hiroaki Shigesada *(Pres & CEO)*

Osaka Gas Australia Pty. Ltd (1)
Level 3 218 St Georges Terrace, Perth, 6000, WA, Australia
Tel.: (61) 893243318
Oil & Gas Distribution Services
N.A.I.C.S.: 213112
Meguni Fukada *(Sec)*

Subsidiary (Domestic):

Osaka Gas Gorgon Pty. Ltd. (2)
108 St Georges Ter Level 16, Perth, 6000, WA, Australia
Tel.: (61) 893243318
Web Site: http://www.osakagas.co.jp
Natural Gas Distr
N.A.I.C.S.: 221210

Osaka Gas Autoservice Co., Ltd (1)
3-6-35 Jusohoncho, Yodogawa-ku, Osaka, 554-0051, Japan
Tel.: (81) 663000380
Web Site: https://www2.ogas.co.jp
Emp.: 101
Industrial Gas Mfr
N.A.I.C.S.: 325120

Osaka Gas Business Create Co., Ltd. (1)
3F/4F Century Building 1-4-16 Kyomachibori, Nishi-Ku, Osaka, 550-0003, Japan
Tel.: (81) 664464300
Web Site: https://www.ogbc.co.jp
Emp.: 300
Facility Operations Services
N.A.I.C.S.: 561210

Osaka Gas Chemicals Co., Ltd. (1)

OSAKA GAS CO., LTD.

Osaka Gas Co., Ltd.—(Continued)
2-37 Chiyozaki 3-chome Minami, Nishi-ku, Osaka, 550-0023, Japan
Tel.: (81) 643930181
Web Site: https://www.ogc.co.jp
Sales Range: $150-199.9 Million
Emp.: 400
Carbon Fiber & Carbon Fiber Composite Material Mfr
N.A.I.C.S.: 335991

Co-Headquarters (Domestic):

Osaka Gas Chemicals Co., Ltd. - Tokyo Office (2)
4th Floor Nihonbashi-honcho Plaza Bldg
2-6-1 Nihonbashi-honcho, Chuo-ku, Tokyo, 103-0023, Japan
Tel.: (81) 366619241
Web Site: http://www.ogc.co.jp
Carbon Fiber & Carbon Fiber Composite Material Mfr
N.A.I.C.S.: 335991

Subsidiary (Non-US):

Century Chemical Works Sdn. Bhd. (3)
MK 1 1026 Lorong Perusahaan Dua, Prai, Industrial Estate, 13600, Prai, Penang, Malaysia (25%)
Tel.: (60) 43907795
Web Site: http://www.century-chemical.com
Sales Range: $1-9.9 Million
Emp.: 113
Mfr & Chemical Products
N.A.I.C.S.: 325998

Davao Central Chemical Corporation (3)
Km. 19 Tibungco, Davao, 8000, Philippines
Tel.: (63) 822380042
Web Site: https://dccc-activatedcarbon.com.ph
Sales Range: $25-49.9 Million
Emp.: 60
Chemicals Mfr
N.A.I.C.S.: 325998
Roberto Quimno *(Gen Mgr)*

Osaka Gas Customer Relations Co., Ltd. (1)
4-1-2 Hiranomachi Chuo-ku, Osaka, 541-0046, Japan (100%)
Tel.: (81) 6 6205 4715
Web Site: http://www.osakagas.co.jp
Performs Maintenance Checks on Gas Equipment & Appliances, Gas Bills Collection & Other Gas Works Services
N.A.I.C.S.: 213112

Osaka Gas Finance Co., Ltd. (1)
3-6-14 Bingomachi Inside the Urbanex Bingomachi Building, Chuo-ku, Osaka, 541-0051, Japan
Tel.: (81) 66 264 3003
Web Site: https://www.ogfi.co.jp
Insurance Services
N.A.I.C.S.: 524210

Osaka Gas Housing & Equipment Co., Ltd. (1)
3-5-7 Kawaramachi NREG Midosuji Building 3rd Floor, Chuo-ku, Osaka, 541-0048, Japan
Tel.: (81) 66 222 4318
Web Site: https://www.ogj.co.jp
Housing Equipment & Appliance Distr
N.A.I.C.S.: 423620

Osaka Gas International Transport Inc. (1)
4-1-2 Hiranomachi, Chuo-Ku, Osaka, 541-0046, Japan
Tel.: (81) 662050245
Natural Gas Distr
N.A.I.C.S.: 221210

Osaka Gas LPG Co., Ltd. (1)
4-2-14 Kawaramachi, Chuo-ku, Osaka, 541-0048, Japan
Tel.: (81) 662023510
Natural Gas Distr
N.A.I.C.S.: 221210

Osaka Gas Summit Resources Co., Ltd. (1)
4-1-2 Hiranomachi, Chuo-Ku, Osaka, 541-0046, Japan
Tel.: (81) 662054787
Natural Gas & Petroleum Production Services
N.A.I.C.S.: 211120

Osaka Gas USA Corporation (1)
1 N Lexington Ave Ste 1400, White Plains, NY 10601-1724 (100%)
Tel.: (914) 253-5500
Web Site: http://www.osakagasusa.com
Sales Range: $50-74.9 Million
Emp.: 13
Distr of Natural Gas
N.A.I.C.S.: 211120

Subsidiary (Domestic):

Sabine Oil & Gas Corporation (2)
1415 Louisiana St Ste 1600, Houston, TX 77002
Tel.: (832) 242-9600
Web Site: http://www.sabineoil.com
Sales Range: $300-349.9 Million
Emp.: 146
Crude Oil & Natural Gas Exploration
N.A.I.C.S.: 211120
R. Todd Levesque *(COO & Exec VP)*

Branch (Domestic):

Forest Oil Corp. - Louisiana Office (3)
3639 Ambassador Caffery Pkwy Ste 401, Lafayette, LA 70503-3066
Tel.: (337) 265-2600
Web Site: http://www.forestoil.com
Sales Range: $25-49.9 Million
Emp.: 25
Crude Petroleum & Natural Gas
N.A.I.C.S.: 213112

Osaka Gas Urban Development Co., Ltd. (1)
4-1-2 Hiranomachi Gas Building North Building 8F Osaka Metro, Midosuji Line Yodoyabashi Station Exit 13 3 Minutes Walk Chuo-ku, Osaka, 541-0046, Japan
Tel.: (81) 64 707 6301
Web Site: https://www.ogud.co.jp
Real Estate Services
N.A.I.C.S.: 531210

P.T. Osaka Gas Indonesia (1)
Gedung Summitmas I lantai 9 Jl Jend Sudirman Kav 61-62, Kelurahan Senayan Kecamatan Kebayoran Baru, Jakarta Selatan, 12190, Indonesia
Tel.: (62) 21 252 2572
Natural Gas Distribution Services
N.A.I.C.S.: 221210

Toyo Soflan Co.,Ltd (1)
3 Syogayama Uchikoshi-cho, Miyoshi, 470-0213, Aichi, Japan
Tel.: (81) 561342711
Rubber Products Mfr
N.A.I.C.S.: 326299

Toyooka Energy Co., Ltd. (1)
6-57 Misaka-cho, Toyooka, 668-0047, Japan
Tel.: (81) 120854108
Web Site: http://www.toyooka-e.co.jp
Gas Appliances Mfr & Distr
N.A.I.C.S.: 335220

Urbanex Co., Ltd (1)
4-2 Nakamichi 1 Chome, Higashinari-ku, Osaka, 541-0046, Japan
Tel.: (81) 647076301
Web Site: http://www.urbanex.co.jp
Emp.: 120
Commercial Property Rental Services
N.A.I.C.S.: 531120

Subsidiary (Domestic):

Kyoto Research Park Corp (2)
134 Chudoji Minami-cho, Shimogyo-ku, Kyoto, 600-8813, Japan
Tel.: (81) 753227800
Web Site: https://www.krp.co.jp
Sales Range: $25-49.9 Million
Emp.: 79
Industrial Building Construction Services
N.A.I.C.S.: 236210
Nobuya Ogawa *(Pres)*

OSAKA ORGANIC CHEMICAL INDUSTRY LTD.
5th Fl Shin Toyama Building 1-7-20 Azuchi-machi, Chuo-ku, Osaka, 541-0052, Japan
Tel.: (81) 662640491
Web Site: https://www.ooc.co.jp
Year Founded: 1946
4187—(TKS)
Rev.: $204,950,630
Assets: $387,369,240
Liabilities: $78,039,630
Net Worth: $309,329,610
Earnings: $23,184,300
Emp.: 461
Fiscal Year-end: 11/30/23
Organic Chemical Products Mfr & Whslr
N.A.I.C.S.: 325199
Taiji Kanbayashi *(Chm)*

Subsidiaries:

Osaka Organic Chemical Industry Ltd. - Sakata Plant (1)
157-23 Azashigerimatsu, Fujisaki Yuzamachi Akumi-gun, Yamagata, 999-8437, Japan
Tel.: (81) 23 471 5721
Web Site: http://www.ooc.co.jp
Chemical Products Mfr
N.A.I.C.S.: 325998

Shinko Organic Chemical Industry Ltd. (1)
18-26 Sumiyoshihama-machi, Higashinada-ku, Kobe, 658-0042, Hyogo, Japan
Tel.: (81) 662640491
Web Site: https://www.shinkoyuki.co.jp
Emp.: 48
Organic Chemical Mfr
N.A.I.C.S.: 325199

OSAKA SODA CO., LTD.
12-18 Awaza 1-chome, Nishi-ku, Osaka, 550-0011, Japan
Tel.: (81) 661101560
Web Site: https://www.osaka-soda.co.jp
Year Founded: 1915
4046—(TKS)
Rev.: $625,021,770
Assets: $995,076,010
Liabilities: $269,529,360
Net Worth: $725,546,650
Earnings: $50,566,500
Emp.: 1,025
Fiscal Year-end: 03/31/24
Soda Products, Inorganic Chemical Products, Organic Chemical Products, Synthetic Resins, Fabricated Resin Products, Pharmaceuticals & Other Chemicals Producer, Processor & Sales
N.A.I.C.S.: 325180
Yoshiro Furukawa *(Exec Officer)*

Subsidiaries:

DAISO Engineering Co., Ltd. (1)
1-12-18 Awaza, Nishi-ku, Osaka, 550-0011, Japan
Tel.: (81) 661101632
Web Site: https://www.daiso-eng.co.jp
Chemical Plants Design Services
N.A.I.C.S.: 236210

Subsidiary (Domestic):

Japan Material Recycle System (JMR) Co., Ltd. (2)
9-2 Otakasucho, Amagasaki, Hyogo, 660-0842, Japan
Tel.: (81) 664090252
Web Site: https://www.jmrsys.co.jp
Sales Range: $10-24.9 Million
Emp.: 15
Mercury Lamp Recycling Services
N.A.I.C.S.: 562920

DAISO Fine Chem GmbH (1)
Immermannstrasse 13, 40210, Dusseldorf, Germany
Tel.: (49) 21183025168
Web Site: http://www.daiso-co.com

INTERNATIONAL PUBLIC

Sales Range: $25-49.9 Million
Emp.: 3
Silica Gel Mfr
N.A.I.C.S.: 325180
Tomoyuki Kitano *(Pres)*

DAISO Fine Chem USA, Inc. (1)
3858 W Carson St Ste 105, Torrance, CA 90503
Tel.: (310) 540-5312
Web Site: http://www.daisogelusa.com
Sales Range: $25-49.9 Million
Emp.: 3
Silica Gel Mfr
N.A.I.C.S.: 325180

DS Logistics Co., Ltd. (1)
11 Otakasu-cho, Amagasaki, Hyogo, 660-0842, Japan
Tel.: (81) 664091588
Web Site: http://sub.osaka-soda.co.jp
Logistic Services
N.A.I.C.S.: 541614

DS WELLFOODS CO.,LTD. (1)
Tel.: (81) 661101634
Sales Range: $25-49.9 Million
Emp.: 75
Healthy Food Mfr
N.A.I.C.S.: 311999

Daiso Chemical Co., Ltd. (1)
1-12-18 Awaza, Nishi Ward, Osaka, 550-0011, Japan
Tel.: (81) 665393610
Web Site: https://www.daiso-chem.co.jp
Emp.: 95
Chemical Products Trading Services
N.A.I.C.S.: 424690
Noboru Hori *(Pres & CEO)*

Subsidiary (Non-US):

Taiwan Daiso Chemical Co., Ltd. (2)
3F-1, No 112 Sec 2 Zhongshan N Rd, Zhongshan, Taipei, 10449, Taiwan
Tel.: (886) 225112123
Web Site: http://www.daiso-chem.co.jp
Sales Range: $25-49.9 Million
Emp.: 5
Chemical Products Trading Services
N.A.I.C.S.: 424690

SANYO FINE CO.,LTD. (1)
Osaka Soda Building 4F 1-12-18 Awaza, Nishi-ku, Osaka, 550-0011, Japan
Tel.: (81) 661101527
Web Site: https://www.sanyofine.co.jp
Emp.: 98
Pharmaceutical Ingredient Mfr
N.A.I.C.S.: 325412
Yoshiro Furukawa *(Mng Dir)*

OSAKA TITANIUM TECHNOLOGIES CO., LTD.
1 Higashihama Cho, Amagasaki, 660-8533, Hyogo, Japan
Tel.: (81) 664139911 JP
Web Site: https://www.osaka-ti.co.jp
Year Founded: 1952
5726—(TKS)
Sales Range: $300-349.9 Million
Emp.: 684
Titanium Production Services
N.A.I.C.S.: 331410
Junji Kawafuku *(Pres)*

OSAKA YUKA INDUSTRY, LTD.
KMU Annex2 F7 1121 Shinmachi, Hirakata, 573-1191, Osaka, Japan
Tel.: (81) 728615322 JP
Web Site: https://www.osaka-yuka.co.jp
Year Founded: 1948
4124—(TKS)
Rev.: $8,756,150
Assets: $13,400,100
Liabilities: $1,077,680
Net Worth: $12,322,420
Earnings: ($56,720)
Fiscal Year-end: 09/30/23
Distillation Chemical Mfr
N.A.I.C.S.: 325180
Teppei Hotta *(Pres)*

AND PRIVATE COMPANIES

OSAKI ELECTRIC CO., LTD.
2-10-2 Higashi-Gotanda, Shinagawa-ku, Tokyo, 141-8646, Japan
Tel.: (81) 334437171   JP
Web Site: https://www.osaki.co.jp
Year Founded: 1937
6644—(TKS)
Rev.: $628,921,670
Assets: $632,187,010
Liabilities: $218,850,490
Net Worth: $413,336,520
Earnings: $15,910,270
Emp.: 2,603
Fiscal Year-end: 03/31/24
Electric Meter Equipment Mfr & Distr
N.A.I.C.S.: 334515
Yoshihide Watanabe *(Chm & CEO)*

Subsidiaries:

ENEGATE Co., Ltd. (1)
1-6-110 Oyodo kita, Kita-ku, Osaka, 531-0077, Japan
Tel.: (81) 664587301
Web Site: https://www.enegate.co.jp
Sales Range: $200-249.9 Million
Emp.: 935
Electric Devices Mfr & Sales
N.A.I.C.S.: 335999

Plant (Domestic):

ENEGATE - Sayo Plant (2)
925 Nagao Shimizunomoto Sayo-cho, Sayo-gun, Hyogo, 679-5305, Japan
Tel.: (81) 790822834
Electronic Components Mfr
N.A.I.C.S.: 334419

Hokkaido Osaki Electric Co., Ltd. (1)
3-2-1 Kikusui Motomachi-Gojo, Shiroishi-ku, Sapporo, 003-0825, Hokkaido, Japan
Tel.: (81) 11 879 7271
Web Site: http://www.osaki.co.jp
Switching Panels Mfr & Sales
N.A.I.C.S.: 335313

Iwate Osaki Electric Co., Ltd. (1)
90-2 Shimodaira Shizukuishi-cho, Iwate-gun, Iwate, Japan
Tel.: (81) 196920130
Electronic Machinery & Equipment Mfr
N.A.I.C.S.: 334419
Masakazu Ohata *(Pres & CEO)*

OEC Kanazawa Co., Ltd. (1)
3-10 Asahigaoka, Hakusan, 924 0004, Ishikawa, Japan
Tel.: (81) 762753731
Web Site: http://www.oec-inc.co.jp
Industrial Equipment Mfr
N.A.I.C.S.: 423830

Okaski United International Pte. Ltd. (1)
47 Yishun Industrial Park A 4th Floor, Singapore, 768724, Singapore
Tel.: (65) 67512680
Sales Range: $150-199.9 Million
Emp.: 1,189
Switchgear Gadgets Mfr & Distr
N.A.I.C.S.: 335313

Subsidiary (Domestic):

EDMI Limited (2)
47 Yishun Industrial Park A, Singapore, 768724, Singapore   **(100%)**
Tel.: (65) 67562938
Sales Range: $75-99.9 Million
Emp.: 200
Energy Meters & Metering System Solutions
N.A.I.C.S.: 334513
Ivan Noel Barron *(CTO)*

Subsidiary (Non-US):

Bridex Electric Philippines, Inc. (3)
2100 Pasong Tamo Extension, Ground Fl Singer Building, 1200, Makati, Philippines
Tel.: (63) 2 757 3031
Web Site: http://www.smb-united.com
Electronic Components Mfr
N.A.I.C.S.: 334419

EDMI (Shenzhen) Co., Ltd. (3)
Floor 2 Building 2 Zhong Yuntai Industrial Park Tang Tou 1st Road, Shi Yan Bao An, Shenzhen, 518108, GuangDong, China
Tel.: (86) 75526755788
Web Site: http://www.edmi-meters.com
Electronic Metering Devices Mfr
N.A.I.C.S.: 334419

EDMI Electronics Sdn Bhd (3)
Tel.: (60) 75984747
Web Site: http://www.edmi-meters.com
Electronic Metering Devices Mfr
N.A.I.C.S.: 334419

EDMI Europe Limited (3)
Tel.: (44) 1256830990
Web Site: http://www.edmi-meters.co.uk
Electronic Metering Device Mfr & Distr
N.A.I.C.S.: 334419
Alan Masterman *(Mng Dir)*

EDMI Gas Pty Ltd (3)
7 Fowler Road, Dandenong South, 3175, VIC, Australia
Tel.: (61) 397946000
Web Site: http://www.edmi.com.au
Oil & Gas Exploration Services
N.A.I.C.S.: 213112

EDMI India Pvt. Ltd. (3)
M-3 9th Street Dr VSI Estate Thiruvan-miyur, Chennai, 600 041, India
Tel.: (91) 4448037584
Web Site: https://www.edmi-meters.com
Electronic Metering Devices Sales
N.A.I.C.S.: 423690

EDMI International Trading (Shanghai) Co., Ltd (3)
Room 1505 - 1507 Tower A ao He Jing High Tech Bldg 900 Yishan Road, Shanghai, 200233, China
Tel.: (86) 215 423 4452
Web Site: http://www.edmi.com.au
Sales Range: $25-49.9 Million
Emp.: 19
Industrial Machinery & Equipment Whslr
N.A.I.C.S.: 423830

EDMI Meters Sdn Bhd (3)
A-2M-01 Level 2M Block A PJ8 No 23 Jalan Barat Seksyen 8, Taman Perindustrian UEP, 46050, Petaling Jaya, Selangor, Malaysia
Tel.: (60) 37 958 6318
Web Site: https://www.edmi-meters.com
Electronic Metering Devices Marketing
N.A.I.C.S.: 423690

EDMI NZ Limited (3)
Level 1 181 Wakefield St, Wellington, 6011, New Zealand
Tel.: (64) 48014700
Web Site: http://www.edmi-meters.com.au
Electronic Metering Device Research & Development
N.A.I.C.S.: 334419
Andrew Thomas *(Exec Dir-Australasia)*

EDMI Philippines Inc. (3)
2nd Floor Unit 204 iMez Bldg Pueblo Verde MEPZ II Brgy Basak, Lapu-Lapu, 6015, Cebu, Philippines
Tel.: (63) 32 236 0381
Web Site: https://www.edmi-meters.com
Electronic Components Mfr
N.A.I.C.S.: 334419

EDMI Pty Ltd (3)
Level 7 51 Alfred Street, Fortitude Valley, 4006, QLD, Australia
Tel.: (61) 738816466
Emp.: 6
Electronic Components Mfr
N.A.I.C.S.: 334419
Andrew Thomas *(Exec Dir-Australasia Grp)*

EDMI Vietnam Company Limited (3)
27 Dao Duy Anh Street, Ward 2 Phu Nhuan Distric, Ho Chi Minh City, Vietnam
Tel.: (84) 8 3842 2413
Web Site: http://www.edmi-meters.com
Electronic Metering Devices Marketing
N.A.I.C.S.: 423690

PT. EDMI Indonesia (3)
Rukan Tendean Square No 9 Jl Wolter Monginsidi 122-124, Jakarta, 12170, Indonesia
Tel.: (62) 217 278 0868
Web Site: https://www.edmi-meters.com
Sales Range: $50-74.9 Million
Emp.: 14
Electronic Metering Device Mfr & Distr
N.A.I.C.S.: 423690

Subsidiary (Domestic):

Quantum Automation Pte. Ltd. (3)
9 Senoko Drive, Entrepreneur Business Centre, Singapore, 758197, Singapore
Tel.: (65) 67442921
Sales Range: $25-49.9 Million
Emp.: 131
Technological Solutions for Engineering Design, System Installation, Commissioning & Maintenance Services of Electrical & Mechanical Equipment in Building Controls Systems
N.A.I.C.S.: 561790
Jimmy Chua *(Mng Dir)*

Subsidiary (US):

QA America, LLC (4)
8186 Red Rock Pl, Larkspur, CO 80118
Tel.: (720) 974-9400
Web Site: https://www.qa-america.com
Technological Solutions for Engineering Design, System Installation, Commissioning & Maintenance Services of Electrical & Mechanical Equipment in Building Controls Systems
N.A.I.C.S.: 561790

Subsidiary (Non-US):

QA Systems Integration (M) Sdn Bhd (4)
12-8 Oval Damansara Office Tower No 685 Jalan Damansara, 60000, Kuala Lumpur, Malaysia
Tel.: (60) 377251590
Commercial Automated Control System Mfr
N.A.I.C.S.: 334519

QA Systems Integration (M.E.) LLC (4)
PO Box 116392, Dubai, United Arab Emirates
Tel.: (971) 4 208 7766
Web Site: https://www.qa.com.sg
Technological Solutions for Engineering Design, System Installation, Commissioning & Maintenance Services of Electrical & Mechanical Equipment in Building Controls Systems
N.A.I.C.S.: 561790

Quantum Automation Systems (Shanghai) Co., Ltd. (4)
Room 518 No 3388 Gonghexinlu Road, Shanghai, 200436, China
Tel.: (86) 21 36536852
Web Site: http://www.qachina.com
Sales Range: $25-49.9 Million
Emp.: 40
Building Management Solutions
N.A.I.C.S.: 334519

Osaki Datatech Co., Ltd. (1)
Osaki Denki Building 2-1-10 Higashigotanda, Shinagawa-ku, Tokyo, 141-0022, Japan
Tel.: (81) 354472260
Web Site: https://www.osakidatatech.com
Sales Range: $25-49.9 Million
Emp.: 128
Software Development & Computer Maintenance Services
N.A.I.C.S.: 541511
Hiroaki Ishimoto *(Pres)*

Osaki Electric Co., Ltd. - Saitama Plant (1)
1131 Fujikubo Miyoshimachi, Irumagun, Saitama, 354-8501, Japan
Tel.: (81) 492581205
Sales Range: $100-124.9 Million
Emp.: 500
Electrical Products Mfr
N.A.I.C.S.: 335999

Osaki Electric Systems Co., Ltd. (1)
Osaki Denki Building 5F 2-1-10 Higashigotanda, Shinagawa-ku, Tokyo, 141-0022, Japan
Tel.: (81) 334437175
Web Site: https://www.osaki-systems.com
Sales Range: $50-74.9 Million
Emp.: 176
Switchboard & Distribution Panel Mfr & Whslr
N.A.I.C.S.: 335313

Hiroyuki Yamaguchi *(Pres)*

Plant (Domestic):

Osaki Electric Systems Co., Ltd. - Chiba Plant (2)
163 Tokiya Nagagara- cho, Nagao-gun, Chiba, 297-0292, Japan
Tel.: (81) 475353811
Web Site: http://www.osaki-systems.com
Switchboard & Distribution Panel Mfr & Whslr
N.A.I.C.S.: 335313

Osaki Estate Co., Ltd. (1)
6th floor Osaki Electric Building 2-1-10 Higashigotanda, Shinagawa-ku, Tokyo, 141-0022, Japan
Tel.: (81) 334421025
Web Site: http://www.osaki.co.jp
Emp.: 1
Real Estate & Brokerage Services
N.A.I.C.S.: 531390
Tadashi Yamada *(Pres & CEO)*

Osaki Platech Co., Ltd. (1)
307-2 Kamitomi Miyoshi-cho, Iruma-gun, Saitama, 354-0045, Japan
Tel.: (81) 492582000
Web Site: https://www.osaki-platech.co.jp
Emp.: 60
Plastic Product Mfr & Mold Casting Services
N.A.I.C.S.: 326199

Osaki Tech-Service Co., Ltd. (1)
Living Life Osaki 5F 3-19-6 Nishi-Shinagawa, Shinagawa-ku, Tokyo, 141-0033, Japan
Tel.: (81) 354375722
Engineeering Services
N.A.I.C.S.: 541330

P.T. Metbelosa (1)
JL Taruna No 1 Pulogadung, E Jakarta, Jakarta, 13068, Indonesia
Tel.: (62) 214714991
Web Site: http://www.metbelosa.co.id
Sales Range: $75-99.9 Million
Emp.: 201
Watthour Meters Whslr
N.A.I.C.S.: 423610

OSANGJAIEL CO., LTD.
36 Yukdong-ro, Bupyeong-gu, Incheon, Korea (South)
Tel.: (82) 325240700
Web Site: https://www.osangjaiel.co.kr
Year Founded: 1993
053980—(KRS)
Rev.: $73,513,751
Assets: $76,458,435
Liabilities: $21,260,796
Net Worth: $55,197,639
Earnings: $6,472,337
Emp.: 181
Fiscal Year-end: 12/31/22
Computer Programming Services
N.A.I.C.S.: 541511
Geuk Rae Lee *(CEO)*

OSB GROUP PLC
OSB House Quayside Chatham Maritime, Chatham, ME4 4QZ, United Kingdom
Tel.: (44) 1634848944
Web Site: https://www.osb.co.uk
Year Founded: 1998
OSB—(LSE)
Rev.: $830,724,565
Assets: $37,351,426,407
Liabilities: $34,644,407,978
Net Worth: $2,707,018,430
Earnings: $356,728,099
Emp.: 1,127
Fiscal Year-end: 12/31/23
Investment Banking Services
N.A.I.C.S.: 523150
Andy Golding *(CEO)*

OSBORN METALS LIMITED
Brighouse Rd, Low Moor, Bradford, BD12 0QL, United Kingdom

OSBORN METALS LIMITED

Osborn Metals Limited—(Continued)
Tel.: (44) 127467733
Web Site:
http://www.osbornbujon.com
Sales Range: $10-24.9 Million
Emp.: 128
Mfr of Hot Extruded Products
N.A.I.C.S.: 332312
Ian Gale *(Mng Dir)*

Subsidiaries:

Osborn Metals SA (1)
10 Rue Ampere ZI, 77100, Meaux,
France **(100%)**
Tel.: (33) 164332551
Web Site: http://www.osbornbujon.com
Mfr of Cold Drawn Products
N.A.I.C.S.: 331210

Osborn Strata Products Limited (1)
Brighouse Lowmoor Bradford DD 12 OQL,
PO Box 42, Shepcote Ln, Sheffield, S9
1QW, United Kingdom **(100%)**
Tel.: (44) 142610010
Web Site: http://www.asdormbujon.com
Mfrs. of Specialist Engineering Products
N.A.I.C.S.: 541330

Osborn Tubes SAS (1)
1 Rue De La Fontaine Saint-Minge, BP 47,
Provins, Longueville, 77482, France
Tel.: (33) 1 60 58 54 20
Metal & Cold Drawn Product Mfr
N.A.I.C.S.: 331210

OSCAR GLOBAL LIMITED

E41 42 Sector08, Noida, 201301, Uttar Pradesh, India
Tel.: (91) 9810337978
Web Site: https://www.oscar-global.net
Year Founded: 1990
530173—(BOM)
Rev.: $15,551
Assets: $407,565
Liabilities: $15,862
Net Worth: $391,703
Earnings: ($30,034)
Emp.: 2
Fiscal Year-end: 03/31/23
Leather Product Mfr
N.A.I.C.S.: 316990
Pawan Chadha *(CFO)*

OSCAR INVESTMENTS LIMITED.

Prius Platinum Ground Floor D3 District Centre, Saket, New Delhi, 110 017, India
Tel.: (91) 11 4601 4600
Web Site:
http://www.oscarinvestments.org
Rev.: $429,114
Assets: $230,050,305
Liabilities: $275,200,773
Net Worth: ($45,150,468)
Earnings: ($257,547,937)
Fiscal Year-end: 03/31/18
Financial Management Services
N.A.I.C.S.: 523999

OSCAR PROPERTIES AB

Linnegatan 2, Box 5123, SE 102 43, Stockholm, Sweden
Tel.: (46) 8 510 607 70
Web Site:
http://www.oscarproperties.com
Year Founded: 2004
OP.PREF—(OMX)
Sales Range: $250-299.9 Million
Residential Real Estate Services
N.A.I.C.S.: 531390
Oscar Engelbert *(Founder & CEO)*

OSCAR PROPERTIES HOLDING AB

Nybrogatan 55, Box 5123, 102 43, Stockholm, Sweden
Tel.: (46) 851060770

Web Site:
https://www.oscarproperties.com
Year Founded: 2004
OP—(OMX)
Rev.: $50,350,429
Assets: $415,937,029
Liabilities: $525,095,806
Net Worth: ($109,158,776)
Earnings: ($304,008,582)
Emp.: 13
Fiscal Year-end: 12/31/23
Holding Company
N.A.I.C.S.: 551112
Per-Axel Sundstrom *(CFO)*

OSCAR WEALTH ADVISORY SDN BHD

16-4 Jalan SP 2/4, Cheong Hin Bus Park, 43300, Seri Kembangan, Malaysia
Tel.: (60) 389435588 MY
Web Site:
http://www.oscarwealth.com
Year Founded: 2004
Sales Range: $1-9.9 Million
Investment Management Service
N.A.I.C.S.: 523940
Sean Koh yung Lee *(Gen Mgr)*

OSCO CONSTRUCTION GROUP

400 Chesley Drive, Saint John, E2K 5L6, NB, Canada
Tel.: (506) 632-2600
Web Site:
http://www.oscoconstruction.com
Steel & Concrete Construction Materials & Services
N.A.I.C.S.: 238120

Subsidiaries:

Borcherdt Concrete Products Limited (1)
326 Hardscratch Road, Brooklyn, B5A 4A8, NS, Canada
Tel.: (902) 742-7811
Readymix Concrete Mfr
N.A.I.C.S.: 327320

OSCO Aggregates Limited (1)
749 Little Dyke Road, Glenholme, B0M 1L0, NS, Canada
Tel.: (902) 662-3722
Sand & Gravel Distr
N.A.I.C.S.: 423320

OSCO Construction Group - Annapolis Valley Ready-Mix Plant (1)
20 Park Drive, Windsor, B0N 2T0, NS, Canada
Tel.: (902) 798-2291
Readymix Concrete Mfr
N.A.I.C.S.: 327320

OSCO Construction Group - Bedford Ready-Mix Plant (1)
414 Bluewater Road, Bedford, B4B 1J3, NS, Canada
Tel.: (902) 835-0882
Readymix Concrete Mfr
N.A.I.C.S.: 327320

OSCO Construction Group - Charlottetown Plant (1)
412 Mount Edward Road, Charlottetown, C1E 2A1, PE, Canada
Tel.: (902) 628-0127
Readymix Concrete Mfr
N.A.I.C.S.: 327320

OSCO Construction Group - Glenholme Ready-Mix Plant (1)
RR 1, Debert, C1A 7L3, NS, Canada
Tel.: (902) 662-3722
Readymix Concrete Mfr
N.A.I.C.S.: 327320

OSCO Construction Group - Moncton Plant (1)
1212 Berry Mills Road, Moncton, E1E 4R8, NB, Canada
Tel.: (506) 858-7110
Readymix Concrete Mfr

N.A.I.C.S.: 327320

OSCO Construction Group - Montague Plant (1)
699 Queen's Road, PO Box 1240, Montague, C0A 1R0, PE, Canada
Tel.: (902) 838-2925
Readymix Concrete Mfr
N.A.I.C.S.: 327320

OSCO Construction Group - Sackville Plant (1)
17 Estate Drive, Lower Sackville, B4C 3Z2, NS, Canada
Tel.: (902) 864-3230
Readymix Concrete Mfr
N.A.I.C.S.: 327320

OSCO Construction Group - Souris Plant (1)
30 Lea Crane Blvd Souris Ind Park, Souris, PE, Canada
Tel.: (902) 838-2925
Readymix Concrete Mfr
N.A.I.C.S.: 327320

OSCO Construction Group - Summerside Plant (1)
240 MacEwen Road, Summerside, C1N 2P6, PE, Canada
Tel.: (902) 888-4331
Readymix Concrete Mfr
N.A.I.C.S.: 327320

OSCO Construction Group - Tristar Concrete Plant (1)
23557 7 Highway, Sheet Harbour, B0J 3B0, NS, Canada
Tel.: (902) 885-2358
Readymix Concrete Mfr
N.A.I.C.S.: 327320

Ocean Steel Corp. (1)
53 Shaw Rd, Conklin, NY 13748
Tel.: (607) 584-7500
Sales Range: $1-9.9 Million
Emp.: 45
Fabricated Structural Metal Mfr
N.A.I.C.S.: 332312
Hans Klohn *(Pres)*

Strescon Limited (1)
101 Ashburn Lake Road, Saint John, E2J 5B8, NB, Canada
Tel.: (506) 633-8877
Readymix Concrete Mfr
N.A.I.C.S.: 327320

Plant (Domestic):

Strescon Limited - Precast Plant (2)
131 Duke Street, Bedford, B4A 3C3, NS, Canada
Tel.: (902) 494-7400
Readymix Concrete Mfr
N.A.I.C.S.: 327320

York Steel Inc. (1)
490 Wilsey Rd, Fredericton, E3B 6E9, NB, Canada
Tel.: (506) 444-7989
Steel Products Mfr
N.A.I.C.S.: 331221

OSCOTEC INC.

9F Bldg A Korea Bio-Park 700 Daewangpangyo-ro, Bundang-gu, Seongnam, 13488, Gyeonggi-do, Korea (South)
Tel.: (82) 316287666
Web Site: https://www.oscotec.co.kr
Year Founded: 1998
039200—(KRS)
Rev.: $3,882,843
Assets: $110,245,281
Liabilities: $16,808,569
Net Worth: $93,436,712
Earnings: ($21,302,432)
Emp.: 53
Fiscal Year-end: 12/31/22
Pharmaceuticals Product Mfr
N.A.I.C.S.: 325412
Scott Lee *(CFO)*

OSE IMMUNOTHERAPEUTICS SA

22 Boulevard Benoni Goullin, 44200, Nantes, France
Tel.: (33) 228291010 FR
Web Site: https://www.ose-immuno.com
OSE—(EUR)
Rev.: $19,751,781
Assets: $99,051,371
Liabilities: $63,806,389
Net Worth: $35,244,982
Earnings: ($19,166,847)
Emp.: 67
Fiscal Year-end: 12/31/22
Pharmaceuticals Mfr
N.A.I.C.S.: 325412
Dominique Costantini *(Chm, Interim CEO & Dir-Dev)*

OSEASPRE CONSULTANTS LIMITED

Neville House J N Heredia Marg Ballard Estate, Mumbai, 400 001, India
Tel.: (91) 2222618071
Web Site: https://www.oseaspre.com
Year Founded: 1982
509782—(BOM)
Rev.: $7,649
Assets: $98,076
Liabilities: $1,619
Net Worth: $96,457
Earnings: ($8,141)
Emp.: 1
Fiscal Year-end: 03/31/23
Electronic Equipment Mfr & Distr
N.A.I.C.S.: 334510
Ganesh S. Pardeshi *(CFO, Officer-Compliance & Sec)*

OSG CORPORATION

3-22 Honnogawa, Toyokawa, 442-8543, Aichi, Japan
Tel.: (81) 533821111
Web Site: https://www.osg.co.jp
Year Founded: 1938
6136—(TKS)
Rev.: $1,047,214,270
Assets: $1,773,379,160
Liabilities: $393,381,560
Net Worth: $1,379,997,600
Earnings: $101,436,630
Emp.: 7,563
Fiscal Year-end: 11/30/23
Cutting Tool Mfr & Whslr
N.A.I.C.S.: 333515
Norio Ishikawa *(Chm, Pres & CEO)*

Subsidiaries:

AMAMCO Tool & Supply Co., Inc. (1)
130 Lee Joyal Rd, Duncan, SC 29334
Tel.: (864) 877-0919
Web Site: http://www.amamcotool.com
Sales Range: $1-9.9 Million
Emp.: 66
Cutting Tool Mfr
N.A.I.C.S.: 333515

Aoyama Seisakusho Co., Ltd. (1)
149 Miyamae, Ichinomiya-cho, Toyokawa, 441-1231, Aichi, Japan
Tel.: (81) 53 393 2524
Web Site: https://www.aoyamass.co.jp
Cutting Tool Mfr & Distr
N.A.I.C.S.: 333515

BASS GmbH (1)
Technik fur Gewinde Bass-Strasse 1, 97996, Niederstetten, Germany
Tel.: (49) 7 932 8920
Web Site: https://www.bass-tools.com
Cutting Tool Mfr & Whslr
N.A.I.C.S.: 333515
Martin Zeller *(Mng Dir)*

Dabao (Dongguan) Molding & Cutting Tool Co., Ltd. (1)
No 35 Dabao Road, Zhushan County Dalang Town, Dongguan, 523772, Guangdong, China
Tel.: (86) 7698 318 2598
Web Site: https://en.osgdabao.com

AND PRIVATE COMPANIES

OSG CORPORATION CO., LTD.

Machine Tools Mfr
N.A.I.C.S.: 333517

Desgranges Outils Coupants S.A. (1)
BP 12, 42161, Andrezieux-Boutheon, Cedex, France
Tel.: (33) 47 755 2160
Web Site: https://www.desgranges-oc.com
Aircraft Cutting Tool Mfr
N.A.I.C.S.: 333515

F.P.Tools Co., Ltd. (1)
47-3 Higashinohyakubikocho, Yamashina-ku, Kyoto, 607-8153, Japan
Tel.: (81) 75 581 2101
Web Site: https://www.fptools.com
Precision Cutting Tool Mfr & Distr
N.A.I.C.S.: 333515

Kanagata Consulting Co., Ltd. (1)
4-5-17 Higashihatsutomi, Kamagaya, 273-0122, Chiba, Japan
Tel.: (81) 47 442 0460
Consultation Regarding Mold Mfr
N.A.I.C.S.: 333511

Nihon Hard Metal Co., Ltd. (1)
4004 Aikawa Machi, Aiko-gun, Nakatsu, 243-0303, Kanagawa, Japan
Tel.: (81) 46 285 0388
Web Site: https://www.nhm.co.jp
Emp.: 300
Machine Tools Mfr
N.A.I.C.S.: 333517

Nissin Diamond Co., Ltd. (1)
1572 Imazu, Imazu-cho, Takashima, 520-1621, Shiga, Japan
Tel.: (81) 74 022 2415
Web Site: https://www.nissin-dia.co.jp
Emp.: 45
Diamond Cutting Tool Mfr & Distr
N.A.I.C.S.: 339910
Nobuaki Kamiya *(CEO)*

ORS Corporation (1)
1-156 Okusa Ogawa, Chita-gun, Higashiura, 470-2102, Aichi, Japan
Tel.: (81) 56 283 9841
Cutting Tool Mfr
N.A.I.C.S.: 333515

OSG (India) Pvt. Ltd. (1)
Sector 8 Plot No 6 IMT Manesar, Gurgaon, 122050, Haryana, India
Tel.: (91) 124 400 9737
Web Site: https://www.osg-india.com
Cutting Tool Mfr
N.A.I.C.S.: 333515

OSG (Shanghai) Co., Ltd. (1)
1003-1007 10th Floor Office Building T1, Changning Raffles City No 1133 Changning Road Changning District, Shanghai, 200051, China
Tel.: (86) 215 255 2588
Web Site: https://www.chinaosg.com
Cutting Tool Mfr & Whslr
N.A.I.C.S.: 333515

OSG (Shanghai) Precision Tools Co., Ltd. (1)
No 1415 Xin Fei Road, Eastern Subarea of Songjiang Industrial Zone, Shanghai, 201611, China
Tel.: (86) 216 760 0562
Machine Tools Mfr
N.A.I.C.S.: 333517

OSG Asia Pte. Ltd. (1)
2 Kaki Bukit Ave 1 03-08, Singapore, 417938, Singapore
Tel.: (65) 6 844 4350
Web Site: https://www.osg-asia.com
Cutting Tool Mfr
N.A.I.C.S.: 333515

OSG Belux S.A.N.V. (1)
Avenue Lavoisier 1, 1300, Wavre, Belgium
Tel.: (32) 1 023 0511
Web Site: https://be.osgeurope.com
Cutting Tool Mfr
N.A.I.C.S.: 333515

OSG Canada Ltd. (1)
538 King Forest Court, Burlington, L7P 5C1, ON, Canada
Tel.: (905) 632-8032
Web Site: https://www.osgcanada.com
Cutting Tool Mfr
N.A.I.C.S.: 333515

OSG Coating Service Co., Ltd. (1)
1-2 Maruyama Arumi, Shinshiro, 441-1317, Aichi, Japan
Tel.: (81) 53 625 1314
Web Site: https://www.e-ocs.com
Cutting Tool Mfr
N.A.I.C.S.: 333515

OSG David Grinding Services B.V. (1)
Heirweg 82, 8520, Kuurne, Belgium
Tel.: (32) 5 637 2646
Web Site: https://www.precdavid.be
Cutting Tool Mfr
N.A.I.C.S.: 333515

OSG Europe Logistics S.A. (1)
Avenue Lavoisier 1, 1300, Wavre, Belgium
Tel.: (32) 1 023 0507
Web Site: https://eu.osgeurope.com
Cutting Tool Mfr
N.A.I.C.S.: 333515

OSG France S.A.S. (1)
Parc Icade - Paris Nord II - Immeuble Rimbaud 22 Avenue des Nations, CS 66191, 93420, Villepinte, France
Tel.: (33) 14 990 1010
Web Site: https://fr.osgeurope.com
Cutting Tool Mfr & Whslr
N.A.I.C.S.: 333515

OSG GmbH (1)
Karl-Ehmann-Str 25, 73037, Goppingen, Germany
Tel.: (49) 71 616 0640
Web Site: https://www.de.osgeurope.com
Cutting Tool Mfr
N.A.I.C.S.: 333515

OSG Iberica Tooling, S.L.U. (1)
Bekolarra 4, 01010, Vitoria-Gasteiz, Spain
Tel.: (34) 94 524 2400
Web Site: https://www.ib.osgeurope.com
Cutting Tool Mfr
N.A.I.C.S.: 333515

OSG Italia S.R.L. (1)
Via Ferrero 65 / A / B, 10098, Rivoli, Turin, Italy
Tel.: (39) 011 770 5211
Web Site: https://www.it.osgeurope.com
Cutting Tool Mfr
N.A.I.C.S.: 333515

OSG Korea Corporation (1)
38 Dalseo-daero 109-gil, Dalseo-gu, Daegu, Korea (South)
Tel.: (82) 53 583 2000
Web Site: https://www.osg.co.kr
Cutting Tool Mfr
N.A.I.C.S.: 333515
Seung-Jin Chung *(CEO)*

OSG Limited Liability Company (1)
Butlerova st D 17 Bc Neo Geo block B office 5069, 117342, Moscow, Russia
Tel.: (7) 4951504154
Web Site: http://ru.osgeurope.com
Cutting Tool Mfr
N.A.I.C.S.: 333515

OSG Nederland B.V. (1)
Bedrijfsweg 5, 3481 MG, Harmelen, Netherlands
Tel.: (31) 34 844 2764
Web Site: https://www.nl.osgeurope.com
Cutting Tool Mfr
N.A.I.C.S.: 333515

OSG Philippines Corporation (1)
G203m GRM Bldg 124 East Science Ave LTP SEZ, Binan, 4024, Laguna, Philippines
Tel.: (63) 49 544 0996
Cutting Tool Mfr
N.A.I.C.S.: 333515

OSG Royco, S.A. de C.V. (1)
Eje 1 Norte Esquina Calle 5 Colonia Parque Industrial Toluca 2000, 50233, Toluca, Estado de Mexico, Mexico
Tel.: (52) 722 279 3609
Web Site: https://www.osgroyco.com.mx
Cutting Tool Mfr
N.A.I.C.S.: 333515

OSG Scandinavia A/S (1)
Langebjergvaenget 16, 4000, Roskilde, Denmark
Tel.: (45) 4 675 6555
Web Site: https://www.dk.osgeurope.com
Cutting Tool Whslr
N.A.I.C.S.: 423830

OSG Sulamericana de Ferramentas Ltda. (1)
R Raul Rodrigues de Siqueira 767, Braganca Paulista, Sao Paulo, 12919-484, Brazil
Tel.: (55) 114 481 7800
Web Site: https://osg.com.br
Cutting Tool Mfr
N.A.I.C.S.: 333515

OSG System Products Co., Ltd. (1)
8-24 Tedori, Kaminagayama-cho, Toyokawa, 441-1202, Aichi, Japan
Tel.: (81) 53 392 1511
Web Site: https://www.j-osp.com
Emp.: 15
Cutting Tool Mfr
N.A.I.C.S.: 333515
Akihiro Kageyama *(Pres)*

OSG Thai Co., Ltd. (1)
Wellgrow Industrial Estate 128 Moo 9 Tambol Bangwua, Amphur Bangpakong, Chachoengsao, 24130, Thailand
Tel.: (66) 3 898 9035
Web Site: https://www.osg.co.th
Machine Tools Mfr
N.A.I.C.S.: 333517

OSG Turkey Kesici Takimlar Sanayi ve Ticaret Anonim Sirketi (1)
Rami Kisla Cad No 56, Eyup, Istanbul, 34056, Turkiye
Tel.: (90) 212 565 2400
Web Site: https://tr.osgeurope.com
Cutting Tool Mfr
N.A.I.C.S.: 333515

OSG U.K. Limited (1)
Shelton House 5 Bentalls Pipps Hill Ind Est, Basildon, SS14 3BY, Essex, United Kingdom
Tel.: (44) 126 856 7660
Web Site: https://uk.osgeurope.com
Cutting Tool Mfr
N.A.I.C.S.: 333515

OSG USA, Inc. (1)
620 Stetson Ave, Saint Charles, IL 60174
Web Site: https://www.osgtool.com
Cutting Tool Mfr
N.A.I.C.S.: 333515
Jeff Tennant *(Pres)*

OSG Vietnam Co., Ltd. (1)
Room 503 Floor 5 No 15 Pham Hung Road, My Dinh 2 Ward Nam Tu Liem District, Hanoi, Vietnam
Tel.: (84) 43 767 2857
Cutting Tool Mfr
N.A.I.C.S.: 333515

Ohtaka Precision Co., Ltd. (1)
1-10 Koden Arumi, Shinshiro, 441-1317, Aichi, Japan
Tel.: (81) 53 625 0833
Web Site: https://www.ohtaka-sk.co.jp
Round Thread Cutting Dies Mfr
N.A.I.C.S.: 333514

P.T. OSG Indonesia (1)
Jl Jababeka IX Kav E 18D-18 E Wangunharja North Cikarang, Bekasi, 17530, West Java, Indonesia
Tel.: (62) 218 967 7620
Cutting Tool Mfr
N.A.I.C.S.: 333515

Premium Grinding, S de R.L. de C.V. (1)
Calle Nicolas Gogol 11371 Complejo Industrial, 31136, Chihuahua, Mexico
Tel.: (52) 014 481 6998
Cutting Tool Mfr
N.A.I.C.S.: 333515

Romsan International Company S.R.L. (1)
Bucuresti-Magurele Street No 25C Sect 5, 051431, Bucharest, Romania
Tel.: (40) 21 322 0747
Web Site: https://romsan.eu
Cutting Tool Mfr & Distr
N.A.I.C.S.: 333515

SD MFG. Company (1)
442-2 Baba, Joso, 300-2748, Ibaraki, Japan
Tel.: (81) 29 743 7181
Web Site: https://www.sd-ss.com
Special Die & Tool Mfr
N.A.I.C.S.: 333514

Sanwa Seiki Co., Ltd. (1)
3-1-1 Yoshinodai, Kawagoe 2nd Industrial Zone, Kawagoe, 350-0833, Saitama, Japan
Tel.: (81) 49 211 3001
Web Site: https://www.sanwaseiki.co.jp
Automotive Components Mfr
N.A.I.C.S.: 332119
Eiichi Nishiumi *(Pres & CEO)*

Somta Tools (Pty) Ltd. (1)
Somta House 290-294 Moses Mabhida Edendale Road, Pietermaritzburg, 3201, South Africa
Tel.: (27) 11 390 8700
Web Site: https://www.somta.co.za
Emp.: 250
Custom Cutting Tool Mfr
N.A.I.C.S.: 333515

Taiho Sangyo Corporation (1)
8-24 Tedori Kaminagayama-cho, Toyokawa, 441-1202, Aichi, Japan
Tel.: (81) 53 393 5311
Web Site: https://www.taihosangyo.com
Cutting Tool Mfr & Whslr
N.A.I.C.S.: 333515

Taiho Tool Mfg. Co., Ltd. (1)
No 27 Dabao Street, Gangshan Dist, Kaohsiung, 820439, Taiwan
Tel.: (886) 7 621 6136
Web Site: https://www.tosg.com.tw
Emp.: 358
Cutting Tool Mfr & Whslr
N.A.I.C.S.: 333515
Norio Ishikawa *(Pres & CEO)*

Vischer & Bolli AG (1)
Im Schossacher 17, 8600, Dubendorf, Switzerland
Tel.: (41) 44 802 1515
Web Site: https://www.vb-tools.com
Cutting Tool Mfr
N.A.I.C.S.: 333515

WEXO Prazisionswerkzeuge GmbH (1)
Siemensstrasse 13, 61352, Bad Homburg, Germany
Tel.: (49) 617 210 6206
Web Site: https://www.wexo.com
Metal Cutting Tool Mfr
N.A.I.C.S.: 333515

OSG CORPORATION CO., LTD.
26-3 Tenma 1, Kita-ku, Osaka, 530-0043, Japan
Tel.: (81) 662428805
Web Site: https://www.osg-corp.com
Year Founded: 1970
6757 - (TKS)
Rev.: $55,984,140
Assets: $47,681,528
Liabilities: $25,198,535
Net Worth: $22,482,992
Earnings: $347,419
Fiscal Year-end: 01/31/24
Water Purifier Mfr & Distr
N.A.I.C.S.: 333413
Masatoshi Mizobata *(Pres)*

Subsidiaries:

Fiudi S.R.L. (1)
Via Ferrero 65/A/B, 10098, Rivoli, Italy
Tel.: (39) 0112489966
Web Site: https://www.fiudi.com
Industrial Equipment Mfr & Distr
N.A.I.C.S.: 333517

NODA Precision Inc. (1)
5-89 Komagaya, Habikino, Osaka, 583-0841, Japan
Tel.: (81) 729501192
Web Site: https://www.noda-precision.co.jp
Cutting Tool Mfr & Distr
N.A.I.C.S.: 333515

Nexam S.a.s. (1)
36-38 avenue Jean Martouret, 42160, Andrezieux-Boutheon, France
Tel.: (33) 477552160

OSG CORPORATION CO., LTD.

OSG Corporation Co., Ltd.—(Continued)
Web Site: https://nexam.aero
Cutting Tool Mfr
N.A.I.C.S.: 333515

OSG Environmental Technology (Suzhou) Co., Ltd.
No 458 Yunli Rord Wujiang Economy Development Zone, Wujiang, Jiangsu, China
Tel.: (86) 51263324800
Water Purification Product Mfr
N.A.I.C.S.: 335210

Smoc Industries S.a.s. (1)
802 Avenue de, Tullins, 38210, Saint-Quentin, France
Tel.: (33) 476070147
Web Site: https://www.smoc.fr
Industrial Tool Mfr & Distr
N.A.I.C.S.: 333515

OSHIDORI INTERNATIONAL HOLDINGS LIMITED

25th Floor China United Centre 28 Marble Road North Point, Hong Kong, China (Hong Kong)
Tel.: (852) 31980622
Web Site:
  http://www.oshidoriinternational.com
00622—(HKG)
Rev.: $36,254,381
Assets: $878,351,623
Liabilities: $85,485,490
Net Worth: $792,866,132
Earnings: ($46,229,398)
Emp.: 39
Fiscal Year-end: 12/31/19
Electricity Generation
N.A.I.C.S.: 221118
Tsui Fong Liu *(Sec)*

Subsidiaries:

Enerchina Resources Limited (1)
28th Floor Vicwood Plaza, Central, China (Hong Kong) **(100%)**
Tel.: (852) 28518811
Web Site: http://www.sinolinkhk.com
Sales Range: $25-49.9 Million
Emp.: 10
Management Consulting Services
N.A.I.C.S.: 541618

Kenson Investment Limited (1)
C/o MMG Trust BVI Corp, Road Town, Tortola, Virgin Islands (British)
Tel.: (284) 494 2011
Eletric Power Generation Services
N.A.I.C.S.: 221118

Rado International Limited (1)
C/O Morgan & Morgan Trust Corporation Ltd, PO Box 958, Road Town, Virgin Islands (British) **(100%)**
Tel.: (284) 4942011
Holding Company
N.A.I.C.S.: 551112

Roxy Link Limited (1)
C/O Offshore Incorporations Limited, PO Box 957, Road Town, VG 1110, Tortola, Virgin Islands (British)
Tel.: (284) 494 8184
Holding Company
N.A.I.C.S.: 551112

Sinolink Electric Power Company Limited (1)
28th Floor Imfinitus Plaza, Central District, Central, China (Hong Kong) **(100%)**
Tel.: (852) 28518811
Investment Advice
N.A.I.C.S.: 523940

Sinolink LPG Investment Limited (1)
c/o Offshore Incorporations Limited, Road Town, Virgin Islands (British)
Tel.: (284) 4948184
Holding Company
N.A.I.C.S.: 551112

Sinolink Power Investment Ltd (1)
C/O Offshore Incorporations Limited, PO Box 116C Sea Meadow House, Road Town, Virgin Islands (British)
Tel.: (284) 4948184
Holding Company

N.A.I.C.S.: 551112

Vistra (1)
Vistra Corporate Services Centre Wickhams Cay II, Road Town, Virgin Islands (British)
Tel.: (284) 4948184
Web Site: https://www.vistra.com
Emp.: 12
Oil & Gas Operations
N.A.I.C.S.: 213112

OSI MARITIME SYSTEMS

400-4585 Canada Way, Burnaby, V5G 4L6, BC, Canada
Tel.: (778) 373-4600
Web Site:
  http://www.osimaritime.com
Year Founded: 1977
Sales Range: $10-24.9 Million
Emp.: 107
Maritime Products & Technologies
N.A.I.C.S.: 334511
Ken H. Kirkpatrick *(Pres)*

Subsidiaries:

CHI Systems Inc. (1)
2250 Hickory Rd Ste 150, Plymouth Meeting, PA 19462
Tel.: (215) 542-1400
Web Site: http://www.chisystems.com
Emp.: 20
Human Performance Improvement Services
N.A.I.C.S.: 611710
Thomas Santarelli *(Dir-Software)*

Mapcon Mapping Inc. (1)
4545 S 2300 E, Salt Lake City, UT 84117-1078
Tel.: (801) 277-9853
Web Site: http://www.mapconmapping.com
Mapping & Navigational Services
N.A.I.C.S.: 541370

Mapcon Mapping Ltd. (1)
930 1st St W Ste 107, North Vancouver, V7P 3N4, BC, Canada
Tel.: (778) 373-4600
Web Site: http://www.mapconmapping.com
Geospatial Mapping Services
N.A.I.C.S.: 541370

Offshore Systems Ltd. (1)
400 4585 Canada Way, Burnaby, V5G 4L6, BC, Canada
Tel.: (778) 373-4600
Web Site: http://www.osigeospatial.com
Emp.: 100
Navigational Systems & Services
N.A.I.C.S.: 488330

OSIA HYPER RETAIL LTD.

Osia Hypermart Devarc Mall Basement SG Highway, Ahmedabad, 380051, India
Tel.: (91) 7227057148
Web Site:
  https://www.osiahypermart.com
Year Founded: 2013
OSIAHYPER—(NSE)
Rev.: $70,945,597
Assets: $48,048,930
Liabilities: $37,096,494
Net Worth: $10,952,436
Earnings: $1,083,870
Emp.: 3,226
Fiscal Year-end: 03/31/22
Consumer Products Distr
N.A.I.C.S.: 445110
Dhirendra Gautam Chopra *(Mng Dir)*

OSIAJEE TEXFAB LIMITED

1043 1043 Bahadurpur Gate Road Near Maurya Palace, Kamela Darwaja Ring Road, Hoshiarpur, 146001, Punjab, India
Tel.: (91) 9056553253
Web Site: https://www.osiajeehdl.com
Year Founded: 1995
540198—(BOM)
Rev.: $293,627
Assets: $1,559,942
Liabilities: $505,090

Net Worth: $1,054,853
Earnings: $134,069
Emp.: 10
Fiscal Year-end: 03/31/23
Textile Products Mfr
N.A.I.C.S.: 313310
Reema Saroya *(Mng Dir)*

OSIM INTERNATIONAL LTD.

65 Ubi Avenue 1, Singapore, 408939, Singapore
Tel.: (65) 67476866
Web Site: http://www.sg.osim.com
Sales Range: $400-449.9 Million
Healthy Lifestyle Products Whslr & Distr
N.A.I.C.S.: 456199
Ron Chye Hock Sim *(Founder, Chm & CEO)*

Subsidiaries:

Global Active Limited (1)
65 Ubi Avenue 1 OSIM Headquarters, Singapore, 408939, Singapore
Tel.: (65) 6281 5688
Web Site: http://www.global-active.com.sg
Emp.: 100
Nutritional Supplements Retailer
N.A.I.C.S.: 456110
Jennifer Goh *(Gen Mgr)*

Subsidiary (Non-US):

Green Valley Nutrition Pty Ltd (2)
421 Grieve Pde, Altona North, Melbourne, 3025, VIC, Australia
Tel.: (61) 392672700
Web Site: http://www.Gnc.com.au
Nutraceutical Products Distr
N.A.I.C.S.: 424210

Subsidiary (Domestic):

Nutri Active Pte Ltd (2)
65 Ubi Ave 1, Singapore, 408939, Singapore
Tel.: (65) 62815688
Web Site: http://www.oniglobalcom.sg
Emp.: 100
Healthcare Product Distr
N.A.I.C.S.: 424210
Jennifer Goh *(Gen Mgr)*

Victoria House Pte Ltd (2)
9 Ubi Crescent, Singapore, 408572, Singapore
Tel.: (65) 62856778
Web Site: http://www.oniglobal.com
Nutraceutical Products Distr
N.A.I.C.S.: 424210
Cynthia Poa *(CEO)*

Health Focus Holdings Inc. (1)
Unit 150 12340 Horseshoe Way, Richmond, V7A 4Z1, BC, Canada
Tel.: (604) 271-6746
Specialty Retailer
N.A.I.C.S.: 456199

OSIM (China) Co., Ltd (1)
5F No 326 Yan Qiao Road, Pudong New Area, Shanghai, 200125, China
Tel.: (86) 21 5196 2828
Web Site: http://www.osim.com
Emp.: 100
Massage Chairs Distr
N.A.I.C.S.: 423450
Ming Zhi Wang *(Gen Mgr)*

OSIM (China) Co., Ltd.-Beijing (1)
4F Unit 3 Bldg 1 D Area Zhaowei Industry Park 14 Jiuxianqiao Rd, Beijing, 100015, Chaoyang District, China
Tel.: (86) 1084565789
Web Site: http://www.osim.com
Specialty Retailer of Health Products & Massage Chairs
N.A.I.C.S.: 456199
Richard Leow *(COO & Exec Dir)*

OSIM (Guangzhou) Co. Ltd. (1)
10F West Tower Tianhe Entertainment Plaza 623 Tianhe Road, Tianhe District, Guangzhou, 510620, China
Tel.: (86) 2087532421
Web Site: http://www.osim.com

Sales Range: $125-149.9 Million
Emp.: 300
Specialty Retailer
N.A.I.C.S.: 456199

OSIM (HK) Co. Ltd. (1)
Rm 1812-22 18/F 1 Hung to Rd, Kwun Tong, Kowloon, China (Hong Kong)
Tel.: (852) 27902300
Web Site: http://www.osim.com.hk
Sales Range: $25-49.9 Million
Emp.: 100
Speciality Retailer
N.A.I.C.S.: 456199
Boon Sin *(Mng Dir)*

OSIM (M) Sdn Bhd (1)
4 Jalan 13/6 A Section 13, Petaling Jaya, 46200, Selangor, Malaysia **(99.5%)**
Tel.: (60) 379569888
Web Site: http://www.osimkorea.co.kr
Health & Lifestyle Products Distr
N.A.I.C.S.: 456199
Doris Chua *(Mktg Mgr)*

OSIM (Taiwan) Co. Ltd. (1)
11F 176 Jian Yi Road Far East Century Park Building G, Ching Ho City, Taipei, 235, Hsien, Taiwan
Tel.: (886) 282271589
Sales Range: $125-149.9 Million
Emp.: 300
Specialty Retailer
N.A.I.C.S.: 456199

OSIM CAMBODIA
No-37E 3rd Floor Attwood Business Center Sangkat Teuk Thlar, Khan Russey Koe, Phnom Penh, Cambodia
Tel.: (855) 2399 5300
Fitness Equipment Whslr
N.A.I.C.S.: 423910

OSIM International Trading (Shanghai) Co. Ltd. (1)
2/F Information Building 149 Chunxiao Road Zhangjiang Hi-Tech Park, Pudong New Area, Shanghai, 201203, China
Tel.: (86) 2150271883
Specialty Retailer
N.A.I.C.S.: 456199

OSIM MYANMAR (1)
FMI Centre 501 380 Bogyoke Aung San Road Pabedan Township, Yangon, Myanmar
Tel.: (95) 1 240289
Fitness Equipment Whslr
N.A.I.C.S.: 423910

PT. OSIM (OSIM Selaras Indoesia Makmur) (1)
Jl Jembatan II 6, Jakarta, 14450, Utara, Indonesia
Tel.: (62) 216611049
Specialty Retailer
N.A.I.C.S.: 456199

RichLife (Shanghai) Co., Ltd (1)
3F No 326 Yanqiao Road, Pudong, Shanghai, 200125, China
Tel.: (86) 21 51962822
Web Site: http://www.richlife-china.com
Nutritional Supplements Retailer
N.A.I.C.S.: 456191

OSISKO DEVELOPMENT CORP.

1100 av des Canadiens-de-Montreal Suite 300, PO Box 211, Montreal, H3B 2S2, QC, Canada
Tel.: (514) 940-0685
Web Site: https://osiskodev.com
Year Founded: 2006
ODV—(NYSE)
Rev.: $300,396
Assets: $627,501,208
Liabilities: $80,244,718
Net Worth: $547,256,490
Earnings: ($6,314,564)
Fiscal Year-end: 12/31/20
Mineral Mining Services
N.A.I.C.S.: 212390
Sean Roosen *(Chm & CEO)*

OSISKO GOLD ROYALTIES LTD.

1100 av des Canadiens de Montreal Office 300, Montreal, H3B 2S2, QC, Canada
Tel.: (514) 940-0670 QC
Web Site: https://www.osiskogr.com
Year Founded: 2014
OR—(NYSE)
Rev.: $170,387,625
Assets: $1,561,666,346
Liabilities: $202,680,925
Net Worth: $1,358,985,421
Earnings: ($92,898,879)
Emp.: 28
Fiscal Year-end: 12/31/22
Gold Exploration & Mining
N.A.I.C.S.: 212220
Luc Lessard (COO)

Subsidiaries:

Barkerville Gold Mines Ltd. (1)
Suite 1410-155 University Ave, Toronto, M5H 3B7, ON, Canada (100%)
Tel.: (416) 775-3671
Web Site: http://www.barkervillegold.com
Assets: $64,768,967
Liabilities: $41,747,666
Net Worth: $23,021,301
Earnings: ($67,558,681)
Fiscal Year-end: 12/31/2018
Gold Mining & Exploration Services
N.A.I.C.S.: 212220
Sean Roosen (Chm)

OSISKO METALS INC.
1100 Ave Des Canadiens de Montreal, Bureau 300, Montreal, H3B 2S2, QC, Canada
Tel.: (514) 861-4441 BC
Web Site: https://www.osiskometals.com
Year Founded: 2000
0B51—(DEU)
Rev.: $26,670
Assets: $78,409,496
Liabilities: $5,592,061
Net Worth: $72,817,435
Earnings: ($4,109,707)
Emp.: 14
Fiscal Year-end: 12/31/21
Gold Exploration & Development Services
N.A.I.C.S.: 212220
Robert P. Wares (Chm & Co-CEO)

Subsidiaries:

Pine Point Mining Limited (1)
1100, Avenue des Canadiens-de-Montreal Suite 300, Montreal, H3B 2S2, QC, Canada
Tel.: (416) 862-7885
Web Site: https://pinepointmining.com
Metal Mining Services
N.A.I.C.S.: 213114

OSIVO 2 AS
Kalinciakova 2391, Zvolen, 96003, Slovakia
Tel.: (421) 455320311
Web Site: http://www.osivo.sk
Seed Processing Services
N.A.I.C.S.: 111191
Rudolf Zajac (Chm-Mgmt Bd & CEO)

OSIVO AS
Kalinciakova 2391, 960 03, Zvolen, Slovakia
Tel.: (421) 455320311
Web Site: https://www.osivo.sk
Year Founded: 1952
1OSI002E—(BRA)
Sales Range: Less than $1 Million
Cereal & Oilseed Farming Services
N.A.I.C.S.: 111199
Lubomir Hudoba (Sls Dir)

OSJB HOLDINGS CORPORATION
NBF Toyosu Canal Front 6-52

5-chome Toyosu, Koto-ku, Tokyo, 135-0061, Japan
Tel.: (81) 3 62200601
Web Site: http://www.osjb.co.jp
Year Founded: 1919
Rev.: $456,189,120
Assets: $422,866,440
Liabilities: $171,007,500
Net Worth: $251,858,940
Earnings: $29,227,560
Emp.: 816
Fiscal Year-end: 03/31/19
Holding Company
N.A.I.C.S.: 551112
Tatsuya Ohno (Pres)

Subsidiaries:

Japan Bridge Corporation (1)
Higobashi Center Bldg9-1 1 Chome Edobori Nishiku, Osaka, 550-0002, Japan
Tel.: (81) 664479500
Web Site: http://www.nihon-kyoryo.co.jp
Bridge Construction Services
N.A.I.C.S.: 237310
Kiyonobu Sakashita (Pres)

OSK HOLDINGS BERHAD
Level 21 Plaza OSK Jalan Ampang, 50450, Kuala Lumpur, Malaysia
Tel.: (60) 321666225 MY
Web Site: https://www.oskgroup.com
OSK—(KLS)
Rev.: $279,554,286
Assets: $2,048,600,847
Liabilities: $830,699,683
Net Worth: $1,217,901,164
Earnings: $90,964,868
Emp.: 1,298
Fiscal Year-end: 12/31/22
Holding Company; Commercial Lending & Investment Services
N.A.I.C.S.: 551112
Leong Huat Ong (Chm)

Subsidiaries:

Bindev Sdn. Bhd. (1)
Di Tapak Istana Off Jalan Abdul Aziz, Sektor 4 Bandar Indera Mahkota, 25200, Kuantan, Pahang, Malaysia (100%)
Tel.: (60) 95733200
Residential Property Development Services
N.A.I.C.S.: 531390

Bunga Development Sdn. Bhd. (1)
No 15 Jalan Puncak Bayu 1, Taman Pulai Bayu, 81300, Skudai, Johor, Malaysia (100%)
Tel.: (60) 76637318
Residential Property Development Services
N.A.I.C.S.: 236116

Eframe Sdn. Bhd. (1)
17th Floor Plaza OSK Jalan Ampang, 50450, Kuala Lumpur, Malaysia (100%)
Tel.: (60) 321621111
Web Site: http://www.eframe.com.my
Accounting Software Development Services
N.A.I.C.S.: 541511

Ke-Zan Holdings Berhad (1)
15th Floor Plaza Osk Jalan Ampang, Kuala Lumpur, 50450, Malaysia (100%)
Tel.: (60) 321615712
Web Site: http://www.oskgroup.com
Emp.: 9
Holding Company; Commercial Real Estate Investment, Property Management & Leasing Services
N.A.I.C.S.: 551112

Lyte Malaysia Sdn. Bhd. (1)
Level 7 Plaza OSK Jalan Ampang, 50450, Kuala Lumpur, Malaysia
Tel.: (60) 321771938
Financial Services
N.A.I.C.S.: 522390

OSK Almal Sdn. Bhd. (1)
Level 7 Plaza OSK Jalan Ampang, 50450, Kuala Lumpur, Malaysia
Tel.: (60) 321771611
Financial Services
N.A.I.C.S.: 522320

OSK Capital Sdn. Bhd. (1)
Level 21 Plaza OSK Jalan Ampang, 50450, Kuala Lumpur, Malaysia (100%)
Tel.: (60) 321771938
Commercial Lending & Investment Firm
N.A.I.C.S.: 523999

OSK Mumawal Sdn. Bhd. (1)
Level 21 Plaza OSK Jalan Ampang, 50450, Kuala Lumpur, Malaysia
Tel.: (60) 321771611
Financial Services
N.A.I.C.S.: 522320

OSK Property Holdings Berhad (1)
9th Floor Plaza OSK, 50450, Kuala Lumpur, Malaysia (100%)
Tel.: (60) 321771688
Web Site: https://www.oskproperty.com.my
Residential & Commercial Property Development Services
N.A.I.C.S.: 531311
Ghee Ong (CEO)

OSK Ventures Sdn. Bhd. (1)
Level 21 Plaza OSK, Jalan Ampang, 50450, Kuala Lumpur, Malaysia (100%)
Tel.: (60) 32 161 7233
Web Site: https://www.oskvi.com
Venture Capital Investment Services
N.A.I.C.S.: 523999

OSK eCapital Sdn. Bhd. (1)
Level 21 Plaza OSK Jalan Ampang, 50450, Kuala Lumpur, Malaysia
Tel.: (60) 321771938
Financing Platform Services
N.A.I.C.S.: 561311

Olympic Cable Company Sdn. Bhd. (1)
Lot PT 2126-2131 Jalan PK1, Taman Perindustrian Krubong, 75250, Melaka, Malaysia (100%)
Tel.: (60) 63373088
Web Site: https://www.olympic-cable.com.my
Cable Mfr
N.A.I.C.S.: 335929
Yeat Siew Hong (CEO)

SGI Vacation Club Berhad (1)
Level 14th Plaza OSK, Jalan Ampang, 50150, Kuala Lumpur, Malaysia (100%)
Tel.: (60) 376616238
Web Site: https://www.sgivacationclub.com
Vacation Hotels & Resorts Management Services
N.A.I.C.S.: 721110

Swiss-Garden International Sdn. Bhd. (1)
Level 14 Plaza Osk Jalan Ampang, 50450, Kuala Lumpur, Malaysia (100%)
Tel.: (60) 39 078 2688
Web Site: https://www.swissgarden.com
Home Management Services
N.A.I.C.S.: 721110

OSK VENTURES INTERNATIONAL BERHAD
Level 21 Plaza OSK Jalan Ampang, 50450, Kuala Lumpur, Malaysia
Tel.: (60) 321617233 MY
Web Site: https://www.oskvi.com
Year Founded: 2000
OSKVI—(KLS)
Rev.: $4,952,870
Assets: $48,630,228
Liabilities: $295,142
Net Worth: $48,335,085
Earnings: $4,021,295
Emp.: 12
Fiscal Year-end: 12/31/22
Investment Holding Services
N.A.I.C.S.: 551112
Patrick Chee Wai Yee (COO)

OSKAR FRECH GMBH + CO. KG
Schorndorfer Strasse 32, 73614, Schorndorf, Germany
Tel.: (49) 71817020
Web Site: http://www.frech.com
Year Founded: 1949

Emp.: 800
Industrial Castings & Molds Mfr
N.A.I.C.S.: 333511
Ioannis Ioannidis (Pres & CEO)

Subsidiaries:

FRECH (Shanghai) Die Casting Machine Co., Ltd. (1)
333 Qian Qiao Road Building No 9-10 Qian Qiao Industry Park, Feng Xian District, Shanghai, 201407, China
Tel.: (86) 2157590098
Web Site: http://www.frech-china.com
Industrial Mold Distr
N.A.I.C.S.: 423840
Peter Kupferschmid (CEO)

FRECH Asia Pte. Ltd. (1)
25 International Business Park 04-103A, German Centre, Singapore, 609916, Singapore
Tel.: (65) 65628999
Industrial Mold Distr
N.A.I.C.S.: 423840

FRECH Espana S.A.U (1)
Av Castell de Barbera 21-27 Talleres 15 Nave 9, Barbera del Valles, 8210, Barcelona, Spain
Tel.: (34) 937194971
Industrial Mold Distr
N.A.I.C.S.: 423840

FRECH Far East Ltd. (1)
Room 1606 16/F Golden Gate Commercial Building 136-138 Austin Road, Tsimshatsui, Kowloon, China (Hong Kong)
Tel.: (852) 27210690
Web Site: http://www.frechfareast.hk
Industrial Mold Distr
N.A.I.C.S.: 423840

FRECH ITALIA S.R.L (1)
Via Torricelli n 185, Caronno Pertusella, 21042, Varese, Italy
Tel.: (39) 029656182
Industrial Mold Distr
N.A.I.C.S.: 423840

FRECH India Machinery Pvt. Ltd (1)
Regus Level 2 Connaught Place Bund Garden Road, Pune, 411 001, India
Tel.: (91) 9922756171
Industrial Mold Distr
N.A.I.C.S.: 423840

FRECH Polska Sp, Z.o.o. (1)
ul Powstancow SI 9, 46320, Praszka, Poland
Tel.: (48) 343669741
Industrial Mold Distr
N.A.I.C.S.: 423840

FRECH Taiwan Ltd. (1)
No 928 Huacheng Rd, Xinzhuang Dist, New Taipei City, 24253, Taiwan
Tel.: (886) 285218628
Industrial Mold Distr
N.A.I.C.S.: 423840

FRECH Tools Poland Sp, Z.o.o. (1)
Ul Ksiedza Jerzego Popietuszki 1, 58-260, Bielawa, Poland
Tel.: (48) 746457820
Web Site: http://www.frechtools.pl
Industrial Mold Distr
N.A.I.C.S.: 423840

FRECH U.K. Ltd. (1)
Eckington Business Centre 2 8 Gosber Street, Eckington, Sheffield, S21 4DA, United Kingdom
Tel.: (44) 1246439125
Industrial Mold Distr
N.A.I.C.S.: 423840

FRECH USA Inc. (1)
6000 S Ohio St, Michigan, IN 46360
Tel.: (219) 874-2812
Web Site: http://www.frechusa.com
Industrial Mold Distr
N.A.I.C.S.: 423840
Robert Tracy (Gen Mgr)

FRECH do Brasil Ltda. (1)
Rua Siqueira Campos n 652 Sala 02 Centro, Indaiatuba, 13330-290, Sao Paulo, Brazil
Tel.: (55) 1938942897
Web Site: http://www.frechbrasil.com.br

OSKAR FRECH GMBH + CO. KG

Oskar Frech GmbH + Co. KG—(Continued)
Industrial Mold Distr
N.A.I.C.S.: 423840

OSKAR KETTERER DRUCKGIESSEREI GMBH
Bregstrasse 24, 78120, Furtwangen, Germany
Tel.: (49) 77 23 93 070
Web Site: http://www.ketterer-druckguss.de
Year Founded: 1832
Die Cast Parts Distr & Mfr
N.A.I.C.S.: 331523
Bernhard Ketterer *(Mng Dir)*

OSL COMMUNICATIONS
1100 Ave des Canadiens Gare Windsor Bureau C-18, Montreal, H3B 2S2, QC, Canada
Tel.: (514) 849-9627
Year Founded: 1971
Rev.: $31,000,000
Emp.: 55
N.A.I.C.S.: 541810
Robert Otis *(Founder)*

OSMANLI MENKUL DEGERLER A.S.
Buyukdere cad Nurol Plaza No 257 K 8, Maslak, Istanbul, 34398, Turkiye
Tel.: (90) 212 3668800
Web Site: http://www.osmanlimenkul.com.tr
Sales Range: $50-74.9 Million
Emp.: 15
Securities Brokerage & Wealth Management Services
N.A.I.C.S.: 523150
Omer Topbas *(Member-Mgmt Bd)*

OSMOND RESOURCES LIMITED
Level 2 480 Collins Street, Melbourne, 3000, VIC, Australia
Tel.: (61) 396140600
Web Site: https://www.osmondresources.com
Year Founded: 2021
OSM—(ASX)
Rev.: $33,544
Assets: $3,663,392
Liabilities: $91,243
Net Worth: $3,572,148
Earnings: ($541,468)
Fiscal Year-end: 06/30/23
Exploration & Mining Services
N.A.I.C.S.: 213115
Adrien Wing *(Sec)*

OSMOSUN SA
Espace Atlantic-Bat B16 20 Avenue Gustave Eiffel, 28630, Gellainville, France
Tel.: (33) 237343075
Web Site: https://www.osmosun.com
Year Founded: 2014
ALWTR—(EUR)
Emp.: 20
Renewable Energy Services
N.A.I.C.S.: 221210

OSMOZIS SA
7avenue de l Europe, 34830, Clapiers, France
Tel.: (33) 184194515
Web Site: https://www.osmozis.com
Year Founded: 2005
ALOSM—(EUR)
Sales Range: $1-9.9 Million
Emp.: 70
Wireless Device Mfr & Distr
N.A.I.C.S.: 334210
Gerard Tremblay *(Co-Founder & CEO)*

OSNOVA PROJEKT A.D.
Makedonska 2/VI 2, Belgrade, Serbia
Tel.: (381) 11 2687 921
Year Founded: 1954
OSNV—(BEL)
Sales Range: Less than $1 Million
Emp.: 15
Heavy Construction Services
N.A.I.C.S.: 237990
Zorica Matic *(Exec Dir)*

OSOTSPA CO., LTD.
348 Ramkhamhaeng Road, Hua Mak Bang Kapi, Bangkok, 10240, Thailand
Tel.: (66) 23511000
Web Site: http://www.osotspa.com
Year Founded: 1891
Sales Range: $500-549.9 Million
Emp.: 3,000
Sports Drink Mfr
N.A.I.C.S.: 312111
Boonsom Soonthornnumwong *(Chief Bus Transformation Officer)*

Subsidiaries:

Greensville Company Limited (1)
31 Ladkrabang Industrial Estate Chalongkrung 31 Chalongkrung Road, Lumplatiew District Ladkrabang, Bangkok, Thailand
Tel.: (66) 2 326 1305 9
Web Site: http://www.greensville.co.th
Toiletry Care Product Mfr
N.A.I.C.S.: 325611
Chatvadee Phuphamorn *(Mgr-Sls & Mktg)*

Osotspa Insurance Public Company Limited (1)
2563 3 Floor Jitt-Uthai Building Ramkhamhaeng Road Huamark Bangkap, Bangkok, 10240, Thailand
Tel.: (66) 2 732 3671
Insurance Advisory Services
N.A.I.C.S.: 524298

Osotspa Taisho Co., Ltd. (1)
2100 Ramkhamhaeng Rd, Bangkok, 10240, Thailand
Tel.: (66) 23740120
Web Site: http://www.taisho.co.jp
Pharmaceuticals Mfr & Sales; Owned 51% by Osotspa Co., Ltd. & 49% by Taisho Pharmaceutical Co., Ltd.
N.A.I.C.S.: 325412

Osotspa Taisho Pharmaceutical Co., Ltd. (1)
White Group Building1 Sukhumvit 42, Bangkok, 10110, Thailand
Tel.: (66) 2 381 9991
Pharmaceuticals Product Mfr
N.A.I.C.S.: 325412
Chayut Ajanaiyakul *(Asst Mgr-Mktg)*

Shark AG (1)
Hans-Maier-Strasse 13, 6020, Innsbruck, Austria
Tel.: (43) 512 26 2175
Emp.: 3
Energy Drink Product Mfr
N.A.I.C.S.: 312111
Christian Hravie *(Gen Mgr)*

Shark USA, Inc. (1)
1815 W 205th St Ste 104, Torrance, CA 90501
Tel.: (310) 782-8440
Web Site: http://www.sharkenergy.com
Sales Range: $25-49.9 Million
Emp.: 14
Energy Drinks
N.A.I.C.S.: 312112

Siam Glass Industry Co., Ltd. (1)
77 79 81 cm Soi Ramkamhaeng 26/2 Huamark, Bangkapi, Bangkok, 10240, Thailand
Tel.: (66) 2375 5595 6
Bottle Mfr
N.A.I.C.S.: 327213

OSOUL INVESTMENT COMPANY KSCC
Al-Shuhada - Al-Rayah Center 1 25th Floor, PO Box 3880, Safat, Kuwait, 13039, Kuwait
Tel.: (965) 1820777
Web Site: https://osoulinvestment.com
Year Founded: 1999
OSOUL—(KUW)
Rev.: $5,904,586
Assets: $67,288,440
Liabilities: $21,540,892
Net Worth: $45,747,548
Earnings: $1,663,281
Emp.: 22
Fiscal Year-end: 12/31/23
Investment & Financial Services
N.A.I.C.S.: 523999
Sulaiman Ahmad Hamad Al-Ameeri *(Vice Chm & CEO)*

Subsidiaries:

Petro Q8 Co.(W.L.L) (1)
PO Box 3880, Safat, Kuwait, Kuwait
Tel.: (965) 18207772180
Web Site: https://petroq8.com
General Trading Services
N.A.I.C.S.: 523160

OSP CO., LTD.
11 Saneopdanji-ro 2-gil Seongdong-myeon, 32925, Nonsan, 32925, Chungcheongnam-do, Korea (South)
Tel.: (82) 417348445
Web Site: https://www.osppetfood.com
Year Founded: 2004
368970—(KRS)
Dog & Cat Food Mfr
N.A.I.C.S.: 311111
Kang Jae-Gu *(CEO)*

OSPREYFRANK PLC
49 Rodney Street, L1 9EW, Liverpool, Merseyside, United Kingdom - England
Tel.: (44) 151 706 0626
Web Site: http://www.ospreyfrankplc.com
Sales Range: $1-9.9 Million.
Emp.: 43
Dry Steam Cleaning Equipment Mfr
N.A.I.C.S.: 333248
Frank Verell *(Chm)*

Subsidiaries:

Flintstone Management Services Limited (1)
49 Rodney St, Liverpool, L1 9EW, United Kingdom
Tel.: (44) 1517060626
Web Site: http://www.fmsinvestments.com
Emp.: 2
Management Consulting Services
N.A.I.C.S.: 541611

OspreyDeepclean International Limited (1)
41 Central Way Cheltenham Trade Park, Cheltenham, GL51 8LX, Gloucestershire, United Kingdom
Tel.: (44) 1242513123
Web Site: http://www.ospreydc.com
Cleaning Supplies & Equipment Mfr
N.A.I.C.S.: 333310

OspreyDeepclean Limited (1)
Wagenmakerstraat 15, 2984 BD, Ridderkerk, Netherlands
Tel.: (31) 180744030
Web Site: http://www.ospreydc.com
Cleaning Supplies & Equipment Mfr
N.A.I.C.S.: 333310

OSSDSIGN AB
Ulls vag 29C, SE 756 51, Uppsala, Sweden
Tel.: (46) 4108728380
Web Site: https://www.ossdsign.com
Year Founded: 2011
OSSD—(OMX)
Rev.: $10,504,838
Assets: $33,380,071
Liabilities: $9,858,571
Net Worth: $23,521,500
Earnings: ($12,222,222)
Emp.: 41
Fiscal Year-end: 12/31/23
Medical Device Mfr
N.A.I.C.S.: 339112
Anders Svensson *(CFO)*

Subsidiaries:

OssDsign USA Inc. (1)
10320 Little Patuxent Pkwy Ste 850, Columbia, MD 21044
Tel.: (410) 872-8380
Medical Equipment Mfr & Distr
N.A.I.C.S.: 334510

OSSIA (HK) COMPANY LIMITED
Unit 2816-2818 28F No 1 Hung To Road, Kwun Tong, Kowloon, China (Hong Kong)
Tel.: (852) 28114333
Footwear Distr
N.A.I.C.S.: 424340
Simon Kin Shing Wong *(Mng Dir)*

OSSIA INTERNATIONAL LIMITED
51 Changi Business Park Central 2 08-13 The Signature, Singapore, 486066, Singapore
Tel.: (65) 65431133
Web Site: https://www.ossia.com.sg
Year Founded: 1982
O08—(SES)
Rev.: $22,390,334
Assets: $45,175,888
Liabilities: $4,479,402
Net Worth: $40,696,486
Earnings: $7,469,130
Emp.: 227
Fiscal Year-end: 03/31/23
Golf Equipment Distr
N.A.I.C.S.: 339920
Steven Ching Huat Goh *(CEO)*

Subsidiaries:

Alstyle International Sdn. Bhd. (1)
No 89 Jalan 10/91 Taman, Shamelin Perkasa, 56100, Kuala Lumpur, Malaysia
Tel.: (60) 392832089
Footwear Mfr & Distr
N.A.I.C.S.: 316210
Calvin Wong *(Brand Mgr)*

Great Alps Industry Co., Ltd. (1)
11F No 32 Section 3 Bade Road, Songshan District, Taipei, 105, Taiwan
Tel.: (886) 225700918
Web Site: https://www.lebags.com.tw
Leather Goods Distr
N.A.I.C.S.: 424990

Ossia World of Golf (M) Sdn. Bhd. (1)
No 8 Jalan 2/118B Desa Tun Razak, 56000, Kuala Lumpur, Malaysia
Tel.: (60) 391731066
Footwear Mfr & Distr
N.A.I.C.S.: 316210

Pacific Leisure (Australia) Pty Ltd (1)
Unit 3 44 Atkinson Road, Taren Point, 2229, NSW, Australia
Tel.: (61) 2 95898100
Sportswear Retailer
N.A.I.C.S.: 458110

W.O.G. World of Golf Pte Ltd (1)
10 Changi S Ln 07-01 Ossia Building, Singapore, 486162, Singapore
Tel.: (65) 65435818
Web Site: http://www.ossia.com.sg
Sales Range: $75-99.9 Million
Emp.: 120
Golf Equipments & Accessories Distr
N.A.I.C.S.: 423910

OSSUR HF
Grjothals 1-5, 110, Reykjavik, Iceland
Tel.: (354) 5151300

Web Site: https://www.ossur.is
OSSR—(CSE)
Rev.: $785,680,000
Assets: $1,385,680,000
Liabilities: $683,800,000
Net Worth: $701,880,000
Earnings: $58,390,000
Emp.: 3,000
Fiscal Year-end: 12/31/23
Prosthetics & Orthotics Mfr
N.A.I.C.S.: 339113
Jon Sigurdsson *(Pres & CEO)*

Subsidiaries:

College Park Industries, Inc. (1)
27955 College Park Dr, Warren, MI 48088
Tel.: (586) 294-7950
Web Site: http://www.college-park.com
Sales Range: $1-9.9 Million
Emp.: 45
Surgical Appliances And Supplies, Nsk
N.A.I.C.S.: 339113
Aaron Kutch *(Mgr-Sls)*

OCH Ortopedi AS (1)
Innspurten 9, 0663, Oslo, Norway
Tel.: (47) 2 328 8200
Web Site: https://www.och.no
Orthopedic Care Services
N.A.I.C.S.: 621111

Ossur Asia Pacific Pty. Ltd. (1)
26 Ross Street North, Parramatta, 2151, NSW, Australia
Tel.: (61) 288382800
Web Site: http://www.ossur.com.au
Sales Range: $50-74.9 Million
Orthopedic Devices Distr
N.A.I.C.S.: 423450
Harvey Blackney *(Reg Dir)*

Ossur Canada, Inc (1)
2150 - 6900 Graybar Road, Richmond, V6W 0A5, BC, Canada
Tel.: (604) 241-8152
Web Site: https://www.ossur.com
Sales Range: $25-49.9 Million
Emp.: 30
Electromedical Apparatus Mfr
N.A.I.C.S.: 334510

Ossur Europe B.V. (1)
De Schakel 70, 5651 GH, Eindhoven, Netherlands
Tel.: (31) 80035393668
Web Site: https://www.ossur.com
Sales Range: $50-74.9 Million
Brace & Prosthetic Mfr
N.A.I.C.S.: 339113

Ossur Iberia S.A. (1)
C/ Calendula 93 - Miniparc III Edificio E Despacho M18, El Soto de la Moraleja Alcobendas, 28109, Madrid, Spain
Tel.: (34) 80035393668
Medical Equipment Mfr & Distr
N.A.I.C.S.: 339112

Ossur Iceland ehf (1)
Grjothals 5, Reykjavik, 110, Iceland
Tel.: (354) 515 1300
Web Site: https://www.ossur.com
Medical Equipment Mfr
N.A.I.C.S.: 339112

Ossur India Pvt. Ltd. (1)
207B 2nd Floor Rectangle one District Centre Saket, New Delhi, 110017, India
Tel.: (91) 80030006220
Medical Equipment Mfr & Distr
N.A.I.C.S.: 339112

Ossur Japan G.K. (1)
Forecast Kameido 8F 2-27-7 Kameido, Koto-ku, Tokyo, 136-0071, Japan
Tel.: (81) 356097441
Orthotic & Prosthetic Product Distr
N.A.I.C.S.: 423450

Ossur New Zealand Limited (1)
6/80 Westpoint Drive, Hobsonville, Auckland, 0618, New Zealand
Tel.: (64) 800369524
Medical Equipment Mfr & Distr
N.A.I.C.S.: 339112

Ossur Nordic, AB (1)
Kistagangen 12 2 tr, 164 40, Kista, Sweden
Tel.: (46) 18182200

Web Site: https://www.ossur.com
Sales Range: $25-49.9 Million
Emp.: 20
Orthopedic Products Retailer
N.A.I.C.S.: 423450

Ossur Retail (1)
742 Pancho Rd, Camarillo, CA 93012-8576
Tel.: (805) 484-2600
Sales Range: $25-49.9 Million
Emp.: 100
Surgical Appliances
N.A.I.C.S.: 339113

Ossur Schweiz AG (1)
Hans Huber-Strasse 38, 4500, Solothurn, Switzerland
Tel.: (41) 800344000
Medical Equipment Mfr & Distr
N.A.I.C.S.: 339112

Ossur South Africa Pty. Ltd. (1)
Unit 1 Stonewood Business Park 9 Tanzanite Crescent, Kraaifontein, Cape Town, 7550, South Africa
Tel.: (27) 860888123
Medical Equipment Mfr & Distr
N.A.I.C.S.: 339112

OSTANKINSKY MEAT PROCESSING PLANT OJSC
Ogorodny proezd 18, Moscow, 127254, Russia
Tel.: (7) 4959805390
Web Site: https://ompk.ru
Year Founded: 1954
Veal Product Mfr
N.A.I.C.S.: 311612
Aleksandr Igorevich Verkhovskiy *(Chm)*

OSTEONIC CO., LTD.
1206ho 38 Digital-ro 29-gil, Guro-gu, Seoul, Korea (South)
Tel.: (82) 269028400
Web Site: https://www.osteonic.com
Year Founded: 2012
226400—(KRS)
Rev.: $15,216,166
Assets: $47,189,826
Liabilities: $19,193,928
Net Worth: $27,995,898
Earnings: $640,851
Emp.: 126
Fiscal Year-end: 12/31/22
Surgical Equipment Mfr & Distr
N.A.I.C.S.: 339112
HyunJun Choi *(Mng Dir)*

OSTEOPORE LIMITED
Tel.: (61) 280721400
Web Site: https://www.osteopore.com
Year Founded: 2003
OSX—(ASX)
Rev.: $1,445,791
Assets: $2,179,840
Liabilities: $1,897,775
Net Worth: $282,065
Earnings: ($3,176,619)
Fiscal Year-end: 12/31/23
Biotechnology Research & Development Services
N.A.I.C.S.: 541714
Goh Khoon Seng *(CEO)*

Subsidiaries:

Osteopore International Pte Ltd. (1)
2 Tukang Innovation Grove 09-06 JTC Medtech Hub, Singapore, 618305, Singapore
Tel.: (65) 62502817
Web Site: https://osteopore.com
Medical & Surgical Services
N.A.I.C.S.: 622110

OSTERREICHISCHE BETEILIGUNGS AG
Kolingasse 14-16, 1090, Vienna, Austria
Tel.: (43) 1 711 14 0
Web Site: http://www.oebag.gv.at

Year Founded: 1967
Holding Company
N.A.I.C.S.: 551112
Thomas Schmid *(CEO)*

Subsidiaries:

FIMBAG Finanzmarktbeteiligung Aktiengesellschaft des Bundes (1)
Hohenstaufengasse 7, Postfach 133, 1010, Vienna, Austria
Tel.: (43) 1 4058725
Web Site: http://www.fmarktbet.at
Financial Management Services
N.A.I.C.S.: 541611

GKB-Bergbau GmbH (1)
Voitsberger Strasse 17, 8572, Bambach, Austria
Tel.: (43) 3142 63030 0
Web Site: http://www.gkb-bergbau.at
Building Construction Services
N.A.I.C.S.: 236116

OSTERREICHISCHE POST AG
Rochusplatz 1, 1030, Vienna, Austria
Tel.: (43) 577670 AT
Web Site: https://www.post.at
OSTIY—(OTCIQ)
Rev.: $2,957,910,641
Assets: $6,126,807,684
Liabilities: $5,353,334,772
Net Worth: $773,472,912
Earnings: ($52,341,895)
Emp.: 27,254
Fiscal Year-end: 12/31/23
Postal Service
N.A.I.C.S.: 491110
Harald Hagenauer *(Head-IR)*

Subsidiaries:

24VIP Logistics Services d.o.o. (1)
Tresnje 1, 71000, Sarajevo, Bosnia & Herzegovina
Tel.: (387) 33 76 44 39
Web Site: http://www.24vip.net
Parcel Services
N.A.I.C.S.: 488510

A4 Business Solutions GmbH (1)
Wipplingerstrabe 23, 1010, Vienna, Austria (100%)
Tel.: (43) 124777
Web Site: http://www.a4b.at
Sales Range: $25-49.9 Million
Emp.: 20
Computer Programming Services
N.A.I.C.S.: 541511
Richard Pusch *(Mng Dir)*

ACL advanced commerce labs GmbH (1)
Neutorgasse 57/7, AT-8010, Graz, Austria
Tel.: (43) 800223323
Web Site: https://www.acl.at
Software Development Services
N.A.I.C.S.: 541511
Bernhard Erkinger *(Mng Dir)*

AEP GmbH (1)
Industriegebiet Sud A 31, 63755, Alzenau, Germany
Tel.: (49) 618899370
Web Site: http://www.aep.de
Pharmaceutical Products Distr
N.A.I.C.S.: 424210

Austrian Post International Deutschland GmbH (1)
Heinemannstrasse 11-13, 53175, Bonn, Germany (100%)
Tel.: (49) 2289329490
Web Site: https://www.austrianpost.de
Sales Range: $25-49.9 Million
Advertising Agencies
N.A.I.C.S.: 541810

Subsidiary (Domestic):

Eurodis GmbH (2)
Hertzstr 10, 69469, Weinheim, Germany (100%)
Tel.: (49) 62019880
Web Site: http://www.trans-o-flex.de
Freight Transportation Arrangement
N.A.I.C.S.: 488510
Max Moser *(Office Mgr)*

City Express Montenegro d.o.o (1)
Branka Radicevica 12, 81000, Podgorica, Montenegro
Tel.: (382) 20628818
Web Site: http://www.cityexpress.me
Courier Delivery Services
N.A.I.C.S.: 492110

City Express d.o.o. (1)
Svetog Save 36, Surcin, 11271, Belgrade, Serbia
Tel.: (381) 113093000
Web Site: https://www.cityexpress.rs
Parcel Services
N.A.I.C.S.: 488510

Express One Hungary Kft. (1)
Europa street 12 building L1, H-1239, Budapest, Hungary
Tel.: (36) 18777400
Web Site: https://expressone.hu
Logistic Services
N.A.I.C.S.: 541614
Peszteriecz Peter *(Mng Dir)*

Express One d.o.o. (1)
Boce 14, 71000, Sarajevo, Bosnia & Herzegovina
Tel.: (387) 1311
Web Site: https://expressone.ba
Logistic Services
N.A.I.C.S.: 541614
Haris Burina *(Gen Mgr)*

Feibra GmbH (1)
Altmannsdorferstrasse 329, 1230, Vienna, Austria (100%)
Tel.: (43) 1661300
Web Site: https://www.feibra.at
Advertising Services
N.A.I.C.S.: 541810

Feibra Magyarorszag Kft (1)
Kasmark Street 14B, 1158, Budapest, Hungary (100%)
Tel.: (36) 13409921
Web Site: http://www.feibra.hu
Advertising Agencies
N.A.I.C.S.: 541810
Csendes Katalin *(Mng Dir)*

GHP Direct Rus o.o.o. (1)
Archangel lane 3 p 1, 101000, Moscow, Russia
Tel.: (7) 495 625 29 89
Marketing Consulting Services
N.A.I.C.S.: 541613

In Time s.r.o. (1)
Senecka Cesta 1, 90028, Bratislava, Slovakia
Tel.: (421) 248707226
Parcel Services
N.A.I.C.S.: 488510

Kolos S.r.o. (1)
Krasovskeho 14, 851 01, Bratislava, Ivanka pri Dunaji, Slovakia (100%)
Tel.: (421) 265316504
Web Site: http://www.kolos.sk
Sales Range: $25-49.9 Million
Advertising Agencies
N.A.I.C.S.: 541810

M&BM Express OOD (1)
146 Vitosha Blvd Entr B Fl 5, 1463, Sofia, Bulgaria
Tel.: (359) 70010100
Web Site: https://www.mbm-express.com
Logistic Services
N.A.I.C.S.: 541614

MEILLERGHP AB (1)
Lilla Strandgatan 19, 261 31, Landskrona, Sweden
Tel.: (46) 8 555 788 08
Web Site: http://www.meillerghp.com
Sales Range: $25-49.9 Million
Emp.: 1
Direct Mail Advertising Services
N.A.I.C.S.: 541860

MEILLERGHP CZ s.r.o. (1)
Dr Pavla Klementa 1082, 330 23, Nyrany, Czech Republic
Tel.: (420) 377 882 111
Sales Range: $75-99.9 Million
Emp.: 50
Direct Mail Advertising Services
N.A.I.C.S.: 541860
Anton Jordan *(Mgr-Fin)*

OSTERREICHISCHE POST AG

Osterreichische Post AG—(Continued)

MEILLERGHP GmbH (1)
Gutenbergstrasse 1-5, 92421, Schwandorf, Germany
Tel.: (49) 9431 620 194
Web Site: http://www.meillerghp.com
Sales Range: $25-49.9 Million
Emp.: 80
Direct Mail Advertising Services
N.A.I.C.S.: 541860

MEILLERGHP SARL (1)
5 Rue du Bailliage, Versailles, 78000, France
Tel.: (33) 1 30 83 82 82
Web Site: http://www.meillerghp.com
Direct Mail Advertising Services
N.A.I.C.S.: 541860

MEILLERGHP Sp. z. o. o. (1)
Ul Krakowska 1, 32-020, Wieliczka, Poland
Tel.: (48) 12 297 34 00
Web Site: http://www.meillerghp.pl
Emp.: 70
Direct Mail Advertising Services
N.A.I.C.S.: 541860

MEILLERGHP a.s. (1)
Pod Kyjovem 24, Radcice, 322 00, Plzen, Czech Republic
Tel.: (420) 378772611
Emp.: 100
Direct Mail Advertising Services
N.A.I.C.S.: 541860
Martin Mecera (Mng Dir)

Mailstep Holding a.s. (1)
Do Certous 9, Prague, 19300, Czech Republic
Tel.: (420) 284816211
Investment Management Service
N.A.I.C.S.: 523999

Medien.Zustell GmbH (1)
Rochusplatz 1, 1030, Vienna, Austria (100%)
Tel.: (43) 5776724855
Advertising Agencies
N.A.I.C.S.: 541810
Roman Chrappa (Mng Dir)

Omnitec Informationstechnologie-Systemservice GmbH (1)
Haidingergasse 1, Vienna, 1030, Austria
Tel.: (43) 121193
Computer Related Services
N.A.I.C.S.: 541519

Overseas Trade Co Ltd d.o.o. (1)
Zastavnice 38A, 10251, Leskovac, Croatia (100%)
Tel.: (385) 13454555
Web Site: https://www.overseas.hr
Sales Range: $25-49.9 Million
Emp.: 200
Transportation Services
N.A.I.C.S.: 488999

PS Postservicegesellschaft m.b.H. (1)
Erzherzog Karl-Strasse 131 Bauteil 1.2 Stiege 1 OG, 1220, Vienna, Austria
Tel.: (43) 800 20 19 18
Postal Service
N.A.I.C.S.: 491110

PTI Immobilienvermittlung GmbH (1)
PO Box 8, 1010, Vienna, Austria (100%)
Tel.: (43) 15157090920
Web Site: http://www.immobiliengelb.at
Real Estate Agents & Brokers
N.A.I.C.S.: 531210

Post & Co Vermietungs OEG (1)
Postgasse 8, 1010, Vienna, Austria (100%)
Tel.: (43) 15157090920
Real Estate Agents & Brokers
N.A.I.C.S.: 531210

Post & Telekom Immobiliengesellschaft mbH (1)
Kolonitzgasse 2A, 1030, Vienna, Austria (100%)
Tel.: (43) 577803230
Real Estate Agents & Brokers
N.A.I.C.S.: 531210

Post Wertlogistik GmbH (1)
Steinheilgasse 1, Postgasse 8, 1210, Vienna, Austria (100%)
Tel.: (43) 6646246491
Sales Range: $25-49.9 Million
Emp.: 100
Freight Transportation Arrangement
N.A.I.C.S.: 488510

Post d.o.o. (1)
Zastavnice 38a, Hrvatska, 10251, Leskovac, Croatia
Tel.: (385) 1 61 75 111
Postal Service
N.A.I.C.S.: 491110
Igor Velimirovic (CEO)

Post neun Beteiligungs GmbH (1)
Haidingergasse 1, 1030, Vienna, Austria
Tel.: (43) 5 7767 0
Postal Service
N.A.I.C.S.: 491110

Post.Maintain Management Objektverwaltungs- und instandhaltungs GmbH (1)
Haidingergasse 1, 1030, Vienna, Austria
Tel.: (43) 1 51551
Postal Service
N.A.I.C.S.: 491110

Prowerb Gesellschaft fur produktive Werbung GmbH (1)
Waagner Biro Strasse 125, Graz, 8020, Austria (100%)
Tel.: (43) 316584040
Web Site: http://www.feibra.com
Advertising Services
N.A.I.C.S.: 541810

Scanpoint GmbH (1)
Haidingergasse 1, Vienna, 1030, Austria
Tel.: (43) 1 512 21 21 0
Web Site: http://www.scanpoint.eu
Sales Range: $50-74.9 Million
Emp.: 52
Digital Scanning Services
N.A.I.C.S.: 518210

Slovak Parcel Service s.r.o. (1)
Senecka cesta 1, Ivanka pri Dunaji, 90028, Bratislava, Slovakia
Tel.: (421) 216877
Web Site: https://www.sps-sro.sk
Emp.: 230
Parcel Services
N.A.I.C.S.: 488510

Weber Escal d.o.o. (1)
Zastavnice 38a, Hrvatski Leskovac, 10251, Zagreb, Croatia
Tel.: (385) 16175111
Web Site: http://www.weber-escal.com
Sales Range: $25-49.9 Million
Emp.: 35
Parcel Services
N.A.I.C.S.: 488510

sendhybrid OPBD GmbH (1)
Gostinger Strasse 213, 8051, Graz, Austria
Tel.: (43) 5089840
Web Site: http://www.sendhybrid.com
Logistic Services
N.A.I.C.S.: 541614
Oliver Bernecker (Co-Founder & Co-CEO)

trans-o-flex Germany GmbH (1)
Hertzstr 14, 69469, Weinheim, Germany
Tel.: (49) 6201 988 0
Web Site: http://www.trans-o-flex.com
Sales Range: $75-99.9 Million
Logistics Consulting Servies
N.A.I.C.S.: 541614

Subsidiary (Domestic):

ThermoMed Verwaltungs GmbH (2)
Hertzstr 10, 69469, Weinheim, Germany
Tel.: (49) 6201 9880
Web Site: http://www.trans-o-flex.de
Pharmaceutical Products Logistics Services
N.A.I.C.S.: 541614
Oliver Rupps (Gen Mgr)

trans-o-flex Accounting Service GmbH (2)
Hertzstr 10, 69469, Weinheim, Germany
Tel.: (49) 6201 9880
Web Site: http://www.tof.de
Financial Investment Services
N.A.I.C.S.: 523999

trans-o-flex IT-Service GmbH (2)
Hertzstr 10, 69469, Weinheim, Germany
Tel.: (49) 6201 9880
Web Site: http://www.transoflex.com
Sales Range: $75-99.9 Million
Emp.: 300
Information Technology Consulting Services
N.A.I.C.S.: 541512
Max Moser (Mng Dir)

trans-o-flex Linienverkehr GmbH (2)
Hertzstr 10, 69469, Weinheim, Germany
Tel.: (49) 6201 9880
Sales Range: $75-99.9 Million
Emp.: 30
Logistics Consulting Servies
N.A.I.C.S.: 541614
Oliver Rupp (Gen Mgr)

trans-o-flex Verwaltung GmbH (2)
Hertzstrasse 10, 69469, Weinheim, Germany
Tel.: (49) 6201 9880
Web Site: http://www.trans-o-flex.com
Logistics Consulting Servies
N.A.I.C.S.: 541614

trans-o-flex ThermoMed Austria GmbH (1)
Hondastrasse 1, 2351, Wiener Neudorf, Austria
Tel.: (43) 2236 677194
Sales Range: $25-49.9 Million
Emp.: 115
Pharmaceutical Products Logistics Services
N.A.I.C.S.: 541614
Stefan Gerber (Gen Mgr)

trans-o-flex Thermomed GmbH & Co KG (1)
Hertzstr 10, Weinheim, 69469, Germany
Tel.: (49) 6201 988 0
Web Site: http://www.thermomed.eu
Sales Range: $150-199.9 Million
Emp.: 620
Pharmaceutical Products Logistics Services
N.A.I.C.S.: 541614
Uwe Broseus (Co-Mng Dir)

OSTERREICHISCHE STAATSDRUCKEREI GMBH

Tenschertstrasse 7, Vienna, 1230, Austria
Tel.: (43) 1 206 66 0
Web Site: http://www.staatsdruckerei.at
Sales Range: $50-74.9 Million
Emp.: 160
Security Products
N.A.I.C.S.: 561621
Reinhart Gausterer (CEO)

OSTERREICHISCHE VOLKSBANKEN AG

Kolingasse 14-16, A-1090, Vienna, Austria
Tel.: (43) 5040040 AT
Web Site: http://www.volksbank.com
Year Founded: 1992
VBPS—(VIE)
Sales Range: $900-999.9 Million
Financial & Banking Services
N.A.I.C.S.: 522110
Walter Groblinger (Head-PR)

Subsidiaries:

Investkredit Bank AG (1)
Renngasse 10, 1013, Vienna, Austria (97%)
Tel.: (43) 1531350
Web Site: http://www.volksbank.at
Sales Range: $75-99.9 Million
Emp.: 587
Investment Banking Services
N.A.I.C.S.: 523150
Kurt Kaiser (Head-Corp Comm)

VB Leasing International Holding GmbH (1)
Kolingasse 12, Vienna, 1090, Austria (50%)
Tel.: (43) 5040047135
Web Site: http://www.vbleasing.com
Sales Range: $350-399.9 Million
Emp.: 35

INTERNATIONAL PUBLIC

Holding Company; Sales Financing Services
N.A.I.C.S.: 551112
Werner Zimmerman (Mng Dir & Member-Mgmt Bd)

Subsidiary (Non-US):

VB Leasing BH d.o.o. (2)
Fra Andela Zvizdovica 1, Sarajevo, 71000, Bosnia & Herzegovina
Tel.: (387) 33276280
Web Site: http://www.vbleasing.ba
Sales Range: $10-24.9 Million
Financial Services
N.A.I.C.S.: 522220
Sulejman Hadzic (Mng Dir)

VB Leasing SK, spol. s.r.o. (2)
Kosicka 49, SK 82108, Bratislava, Slovakia
Tel.: (421) 259987411
Web Site: http://www.vbleasing.sk
Sales Range: $25-49.9 Million
Emp.: 87
Financial Services
N.A.I.C.S.: 522220
Igor Krigler (Mng Dir)

VB Leasing d.o.o. (2)
Horvatova 82, HR 10 000, Zagreb, Croatia
Tel.: (385) 12484111
Web Site: http://www.vbleasing.hr
Sales Range: $10-24.9 Million
Financial Services
N.A.I.C.S.: 522220

VB Leasing d.o.o. (2)
Dunasjska 128a, 1000, Ljubljana, Slovenia
Tel.: (386) 15634400
Web Site: http://www.vbs-leasing.si
Sales Range: $10-24.9 Million
Emp.: 51
Financial Services
N.A.I.C.S.: 522220
Damijan Cigan (Mng Dir)

VB Leasing d.o.o. Beograd (2)
Dorda Stanojevica 12, Beograd Office Park 1 Flat, 11070, Belgrade, Serbia
Tel.: (381) 112016500
Web Site: http://www.vbleasing.co.rs
Sales Range: $1-9.9 Million
Emp.: 40
Financial Services
N.A.I.C.S.: 522220
Milena Jerenic (Mgr-Mktg)

VB Penzugyi Lizing Rt. & Kft. (2)
Vaci ut 37, H 1134, Budapest, Hungary
Tel.: (36) 1 45 26 700
Web Site: http://www.vbleasing.hu
Financial Services
N.A.I.C.S.: 522220

Volksbank Romania s.a. (1)
Str Mihai Bravu 171-173, Sector 2, 021323, Bucharest, Romania
Tel.: (40) 212094455
Web Site: http://www.volksbank.ro
Sales Range: $700-749.9 Million
Emp.: 1,281
Commericial Banking
N.A.I.C.S.: 522110
Benoit Catel (Pres)

Volksbank Wien AG (1)
Schottengasse 10, 1010, Vienna, Austria
Tel.: (43) 1401370
Web Site: http://www.volksbankwien.com
Sales Range: $50-74.9 Million
Emp.: 100
Commericial Banking
N.A.I.C.S.: 522110

OSTIM ENDUSTRIYEL YATIRIMLAR VE ISLETME AS

100 Yil Bulvan No 99/90 Ofim Is Merkezi 9th Floor, Ostim, 06370, Ankara, Turkiye
Tel.: (90) 3123853409
Web Site: http://www.ostimyatirim.com.tr
Year Founded: 1998
OSTIM—(IST)
Rev: $6,653,915
Assets: $29,899,396
Liabilities: $7,924,920
Net Worth: $21,974,476

AND PRIVATE COMPANIES

Earnings: $8,600,480
Emp.: 20
Fiscal Year-end: 12/31/22
Industrial Construction Investment Services
N.A.I.C.S.: 523999
Orhan Aydin *(Chm)*

OSTIN TECHNOLOGY GROUP CO., LTD.
Building 2 101/201 1 Kechuang Road, Qixia District, Nanjing, 210046, Jiangsu, China
Tel.: (86) 2558595234 Ky
Web Site: https://ostin-technology.com
Year Founded: 2019
OST—(NASDAQ)
Rev.: $57,525,700
Assets: $56,548,761
Liabilities: $42,460,629
Net Worth: $14,088,132
Earnings: ($10,948,795)
Emp.: 226
Fiscal Year-end: 09/30/23
Holding Company
N.A.I.C.S.: 551112
Tao Ling *(Chm & CEO)*

OSTNOR AB
Ostnorsvagen 95, Mora, 79227, Sweden
Tel.: (46) 250596000
Web Site: http://www.ostnor.se
Sales Range: $125-149.9 Million
Emp.: 550
Faucet Mfr
N.A.I.C.S.: 332913
Fredrik Skarp *(Mng Dir)*

Subsidiaries:

Damixa A/S (1)
Ostbirkvej 2, Odense, 5240, Denmark
Tel.: (45) 63102210
Web Site: http://www.damixa.com
Sales Range: $75-99.9 Million
Emp.: 100
Faucet Mfr
N.A.I.C.S.: 327110
Ole Sander *(CEO)*

Affiliate (Non-US):

Rubinetterie Mariani S.p.A. (2)
Via Berlino 2/4, 24040, Zingonia, Bergamo, Italy (100%)
Tel.: (39) 0354192911
Web Site: http://www.rubinetteriemariani.it
Kitchen & Bath Faucets Mfr
N.A.I.C.S.: 337110

Damixa Nederland BV (1)
Rietveldenweg 86, 5222 AS, Den Bosch, Netherlands
Tel.: (31) 85 401 87 80
Faucet Distr
N.A.I.C.S.: 423720

Damixa Pte Ltd (1)
161 Lavender Place 02-19 Lavender Street, Singapore, 338750, Singapore
Tel.: (65) 987 861 08
Faucet Distr
N.A.I.C.S.: 423720

Guangzhou Ostnor Sanitary Ware Limited (1)
8/F No 137-141 Baogang Avenue, Haizhu, Guangzhou, China
Tel.: (86) 2034329822
Faucet Distr
N.A.I.C.S.: 423720

Mora GmbH (1)
Biedenkamp 3C, 21509, Glinde, Germany
Tel.: (49) 405 357 080
Faucet Distr
N.A.I.C.S.: 423720

Ostnor Asia Ltd (1)
Room S 5/F Valiant Ind Centre 2-12 Au Pui Wan Street, Fo Tan Nt, Hong Kong, China (Hong Kong)
Tel.: (852) 37270434

Faucet Distr
N.A.I.C.S.: 423720

Ostnor Danmark A/S (1)
Qstbirkvej 2, 5240, Odense, Denmark
Tel.: (45) 63 10 22 10
Faucet Distr
N.A.I.C.S.: 423720
Ole Sander *(Mng Dir)*

Ostnor Finland OY (1)
Sahaajankatu 24, 00811, Helsingfors, Finland
Tel.: (358) 207 411 960
Faucet Distr
N.A.I.C.S.: 423720
Jan Bjorkbom *(Mgr-Sls)*

Ostnor Norge AS (1)
Sinsenveien 53D, 0585, Oslo, Norway
Tel.: (47) 22 09 19 00
Faucet Distr
N.A.I.C.S.: 423720

OSTRAKON CAPITAL LTD.
Beaufort House 15 St Botolph Street 7th Floor, London, EC 3A 7NJ, United Kingdom
Tel.: (44) 1865304072
Holding Company
N.A.I.C.S.: 551112
David Low *(Chm)*

Subsidiaries:

Windsor Plc (1)
71 Fenchurch Str, London, EC3M 4BS, United Kingdom (78%)
Tel.: (44) 2071331200
Web Site: http://www.windsor.co.uk
Sales Range: $100-124.9 Million
Emp.: 170
Insurance & Reinsurance Broker
N.A.I.C.S.: 524210
Luke Giles *(Acct Exec)*

OSTROM CLIMATE SOLUTIONS INC.
Suite 400 322 Water Street, Vancouver, V6B 1B6, BC, Canada
Tel.: (604) 646-0400
Web Site: https://ostromclimate.com
Year Founded: 2005
9EAA—(DEU)
Rev.: $2,928,723
Assets: $1,736,202
Liabilities: $2,367,825
Net Worth: ($631,624)
Earnings: ($362,230)
Fiscal Year-end: 12/31/22
Investment Services
N.A.I.C.S.: 523999
James Tansey *(Founder & CIO-Americas)*

Subsidiaries:

ERA Ecosystem Restoration Associates Inc. (1)
1000-675 West Hastings Street, Vancouver, V6B 1N2, BC, Canada
Tel.: (604) 646-0400
Web Site: http://www.offsetters.ca
Emp.: 3
Environmental Consulting Services
N.A.I.C.S.: 541620

OSVAH PHARMACEUTICAL COMPANY
17 Shahrivar St Shad Abad Karaj Old Road, Tehran, Iran
Tel.: (98) 2166801075
Web Site: https://www.osvepharma.com
Year Founded: 1966
DOSE—(THE)
Sales Range: Less than $1 Million
Emp.: 385
Pharmaceuticals Product Mfr
N.A.I.C.S.: 325412

OSWAL AGRO MILLS LTD.
7th Floor Antriksh Bhawan 22 Kas-turba Gandhi Marg, New Delhi, 110001, India
Tel.: (91) 1123715242
Web Site: https://www.oswalagromills.com
Year Founded: 2006
500317—(BOM)
Rev.: $6,461,676
Assets: $100,499,314
Liabilities: $635,369
Net Worth: $99,863,945
Earnings: $2,862,790
Emp.: 28
Fiscal Year-end: 03/31/23
Real Estate Development Services
N.A.I.C.S.: 531390
Bhola Nath Gupta *(CEO)*

OSWAL GREENTECH LIMITED
7th Floor Antiksh Bhawan 22 KG Marg, New Delhi, 110001, India
Tel.: (91) 1123715242
Web Site: https://www.oswalgreens.com
Year Founded: 1981
539290—(BOM)
Rev.: $11,854,985
Assets: $304,031,137
Liabilities: $6,348,996
Net Worth: $297,682,141
Earnings: $4,541,490
Emp.: 81
Fiscal Year-end: 03/31/23
Fertilizers Production & Sales
N.A.I.C.S.: 325314
Anil Bhalla *(CEO & Mng Dir)*

OSWAL OVERSEAS LIMITED
98A Second Floor Namberdar Estate, Taimoor Nagar, New Delhi, 110065, India
Tel.: (91) 1141064256
Web Site: https://www.oswaloverseasltd.com
Year Founded: 1984
531065—(BOM)
Rev.: $25,416,070
Assets: $18,830,416
Liabilities: $16,746,636
Net Worth: $2,083,780
Earnings: $89,364
Emp.: 53
Fiscal Year-end: 03/31/23
Sugar Product Mfr & Whslr
N.A.I.C.S.: 111930
Paramjeet Singh *(Chm & Mng Dir)*

OSWAL SPINNING & WEAVING MILLS LIMITED
No 11&12 1st Floor Block-F, Near Orient Cinema BRS Nagar, Ludhiana, 141 012, India
Tel.: (91) 1612463182
Web Site: http://www.oswalcotton.com
Sales Range: $10-24.9 Million
Cotton Yarn Mfr
N.A.I.C.S.: 313110
R. P. Sharma *(Compliance Officer, Sec & Gen Mgr)*

OSWAL WOOLLEN MILLS LIMITED
G.T. Road, Sherpur, Ludhiana, 141 003, India
Tel.: (91) 1612542501 In
Web Site: http://www.owmnahar.com
Year Founded: 1949
Textile Mfr
N.A.I.C.S.: 314999
Dinesh Oswal *(Mng Dir)*

Subsidiaries:

Oswal Leasing Limited (1)
105 Ashoka Estate, 24 Barakhamba Road, New Delhi, 110 001, India
Tel.: (91) 1123722935

OT LOGISTICS S.A.

Web Site: https://www.owmnahar.com
Rev.: $17,036
Assets: $335,328
Liabilities: $2,887
Net Worth: $332,441
Earnings: ($2,843)
Emp.: 2
Fiscal Year-end: 03/31/2023
Financial Support Services
N.A.I.C.S.: 523999
Surbi Arora *(CFO & Mgr)*

OSWAL YARNS LIMITED
Link Road, Industrial Area-A, Ludhiana, 141003, Punjab, India
Tel.: (91) 1612224256
514460—(BOM)
Rev.: $150,345
Assets: $465,682
Liabilities: $54,550
Net Worth: $411,132
Earnings: ($29,662)
Fiscal Year-end: 03/31/23
Textile Products Mfr
N.A.I.C.S.: 314999
Tej Paul Oswal *(Chm & Mng Dir)*

OSWALD METZEN GMBH
Dieselstrasse 5, 54634, Bitburg, Germany
Tel.: (49) 656195500
Web Site: http://www.oswald-metzen.de
Year Founded: 1969
Sales Range: $25-49.9 Million
Emp.: 120
Industrial Plant Construction Services
N.A.I.C.S.: 236220
Dietrich Wunn *(Mng Dir)*

Subsidiaries:

METZEN S.a r.l (1)
35 Dickstross, 5451, Stadtbredimus, Luxembourg
Tel.: (352) 26664487
Industrial Plant Construction Services
N.A.I.C.S.: 236210

OT ENERGY SERVICES A.S.
Prazska 684/49, 674 01, Trebic, Czech Republic
Tel.: (420) 568 413 111 CZ
Web Site: http://www.otenergy.com
Year Founded: 1993
Sales Range: $25-49.9 Million
Emp.: 850
Information, Electrical Instrumentation & Control Systems Distr
N.A.I.C.S.: 334419
Borivoj Hejzlar *(Fin Mgr)*

OT LOGISTICS S.A.
ul Zbozowa 4, 70-653, Szczecin, Poland
Tel.: (48) 914257300
Web Site: https://otlogistics.pl
Year Founded: 1946
OTS—(WAR)
Rev.: $150,478,658
Assets: $177,030,995
Liabilities: $128,518,546
Net Worth: $48,512,449
Earnings: $40,174,797
Emp.: 630
Fiscal Year-end: 12/31/23
Freight Transportation
N.A.I.C.S.: 488510
Zbigniew Nowik *(Chm/Deputy Chm-Supervisory Bd)*

Subsidiaries:

Baltycki Terminal Drobnicowy Gdynia Sp. z o.o. (1)
Indyjska 13, 81-336, Gdynia, Poland
Tel.: (48) 58 627 41 08
Web Site: http://www.btdg.pl
Emp.: 360
Cargo Handling Services
N.A.I.C.S.: 488320

OT LOGISTICS S.A.

OT Logistics S.A.—(Continued)

Zbigniew Szyfer (Dir-Operational)

C.Hartwig Gdynia S.A. (1)
ul Derdowskiego 7, 81-369, Gdynia, Poland
Tel.: (48) 58 69 00 000
Web Site: http://www.chg.pl
Logistics Consulting Services
N.A.I.C.S.: 541614
Dariusz Strzyzewski (Mgr-Key Acct)

Subsidiary (Non-US):

PSA Transport Ltd. (2)
Trelawny House Dock Road Suite 19, Felixstowe, IP11 3GB, Suffolk, United Kingdom
Tel.: (44) 1375 380 286
Web Site: http://www.psatransport.co.uk
Freight Forwarding Services
N.A.I.C.S.: 488510
Michal Matuszek (Mng Dir)

Poltrans GmbH (2)
Stenzelring 33, 21107, Hamburg, Germany
Tel.: (49) 40 752 493 0
Web Site: http://www.poltrans.de
Freight Forwarding Services
N.A.I.C.S.: 488510
S. Pietrzek (Mng Dir)

Deutsche Binnenreederei AG (1)
Revaler Strasse 100, 10245, Berlin, Germany
Tel.: (49) 30 29376 101
Web Site: http://www.binnenreederei.de
Marine Cargo Handling Services
N.A.I.C.S.: 488320
Piotr Pawlowski (Pres)

Subsidiary (Non-US):

Elbe Rijn Lloyd B.V. (2)
Boelewerf 52, 2987 VE, Ridderkerk, Netherlands
Tel.: (31) 180 442255
Web Site: http://www.elberijnlloyd.nl
Freight Forwarding Services
N.A.I.C.S.: 483211

Odra Lloyd Sp. z o.o. (1)
ul Celna 1, Szczecin, 70-644, Poland
Tel.: (48) 91 462 32 22
Inland Shipping Services
N.A.I.C.S.: 483211

Odra Rhein Lloyd Sp. z o.o. (1)
Kleczkowska 50, Wroclaw, Poland
Tel.: (48) 71 329 09 68
Inland Shipping Services
N.A.I.C.S.: 483211

Odratrans Porty Sp. z o.o. (1)
Kleczkowska 52, Wroclaw, Poland
Tel.: (48) 71 329 25 19
Inland Shipping Services
N.A.I.C.S.: 483211

Port Handlowy Swinoujscie Sp. z o.o. (1)
ul Bunkrowa 1, 72-602, Swinoujscie, Poland
Tel.: (48) 91 32 77 200
Web Site: http://www.phs.com.pl
Emp.: 200
Cargo Handling Services
N.A.I.C.S.: 488320
Marek Kowalewski (Pres & Mng Dir)

Rentrans Cargo Sp. z o.o. (1)
ul Zbozowa 4, 70-653, Szczecin, Poland
Tel.: (48) 914624556
Web Site: https://www.rentrans.com.pl
Cargo Handling Services
N.A.I.C.S.: 488320
Magdalena Szulc (Dir-Mktg Section)

Subsidiary (Domestic):

RCI Sp. z o.o. (2)
ul Kartuska 46, 60-471, Poznan, Poland
Tel.: (48) 61 847 56 77
Web Site: http://www.rci.com.pl
Information Technology Consulting Services
N.A.I.C.S.: 541512

Rentrans International Spedition Sp z o.o. (1)
ul Panewnicka 324, 40-774, Katowice, Poland
Tel.: (48) 32 203 43 76
Web Site: http://www.rentransinternational.pl

Freight Forwarding Services
N.A.I.C.S.: 488510

Zegluga Bydgoska Sp. z o.o. (1)
ul Przemyslowa 8, 75-758, Bydgoszcz, Poland
Tel.: (48) 52 3233200
Water Transportation Services
N.A.I.C.S.: 483211

OT-OPTIMA TELEKOM D.D.

Bani 75 a, 10000, Zagreb, Croatia
Tel.: (385) 15492699
Web Site: http://www.optima.hr
OPTE—(ZAG)
Sales Range: Less than $1 Million
Telecommunication Services
N.A.I.C.S.: 517810

OTA FLORICULTURE AUCTION CO., LTD.

2-2-1 Tokai, Ota-ku, Tokyo, 143-0001, Japan
Tel.: (81) 337995000   JP
Web Site: https://www.otakaki.co.jp
Year Founded: 1989
7555—(TKS)
Rev.: $27,391,840
Assets: $61,056,570
Liabilities: $27,742,170
Net Worth: $33,314,400
Earnings: $1,203,020
Fiscal Year-end: 03/31/24
Flower Whslr
N.A.I.C.S.: 424930
Nobuo Isomura (CEO)

OTAKE CORPORATION

2-1-8 Marunouchi, Naka-ku, Nagoya, 460-0002, Aichi, Japan
Tel.: (81) 522110150
Web Site: https://www.kk-otake.co.jp
Year Founded: 1952
7434—(TKS)
Sales Range: Less than $1 Million
Emp.: 241
Piping Material Mfr
N.A.I.C.S.: 332913
Murai Yoshiyuki (Pres)

OTANI KOGYO CO., LTD.

41-0031 7-23-1 Nishigotanda, Shinagawa-Ku, Tokyo, 141-0031, Japan
Tel.: (81) 334943731
Web Site: https://www.otanikogyo.com
Year Founded: 1947
59390—(TKS)
Sales Range: Less than $1 Million
Electric Equipment Mfr
N.A.I.C.S.: 335932
Kazuya Suzuki (Pres & CEO)

OTARI, INC.

4-33-3 Kokuryo-cho, Chofu 182-0022, Japan
Tel.: (81) 424818626   JP
Web Site: http://www.otari.com
Year Founded: 1965
Sales Range: $75-99.9 Million
Emp.: 450
Professional Audio Tape Recorder & Tape Duplicator Mfr
N.A.I.C.S.: 334310

Subsidiaries:

Otari, Inc. - Matsumoto Factory (1)
5208-1 Toyoshina-Takibe Azumino-shi, Azumino, Nagano, 399-8204, Japan
Tel.: (81) 263 72 3883
Web Site: http://www.otari.co.jp
Audio & Video Equipment Mfr
N.A.I.C.S.: 334310
Masayuki Hosoda (Pres)

Otaritec Corporation (1)
4-29-18 Minami-Ogikubo, Suginami-ku, Tokyo, 167-0052, Japan

Tel.: (81) 333323211
Web Site: http://www.otaritec.co.jp
Sales Range: $25-49.9 Million
Emp.: 30
Equipment Sales & Importer
N.A.I.C.S.: 423830

OTAVA LTD.

Uudenmaankatu 10, 00120, Helsinki, Finland
Tel.: (358) 9 1996 606   FI
Web Site: http://www.otavakonserni.fi
Year Founded: 1890
Book & Magazine Publisher
N.A.I.C.S.: 513130
Alexander Lindholm (CEO)

Subsidiaries:

Ampparit Oy (1)
PO Box 6, 80101, Joensuu, Finland
Tel.: (358) 45 330 9710
Web Site: http://www.ampparit.com
Media Monitoring Services
N.A.I.C.S.: 513199
Petteri Hannonen (Mng Dir)

Lakiperinta Oy (1)
Krongvistinkatu 2, 00240, Helsinki, Finland
Tel.: (358) 9 1566681
Emp.: 10
Magazine Publisher
N.A.I.C.S.: 513120
Pakka Harju (Gen Mgr)

Otava Book Printing Ltd (1)
Otavantie 11, 42700, Keuruu, Finland
Tel.: (358) 9 680900
Web Site: http://www.otavankirjapaino.fi
Emp.: 100
Book Printing Services
N.A.I.C.S.: 323117
Anneli Swanljung-Homen (Mgr-Mktg)

Suomalainen Kirjakauppa Oy (1)
Maistraatinportti 1, 00015, Helsinki, Finland
Tel.: (358) 91566306
Web Site: http://www.suomalainen.com
Emp.: 450
Book Store Operating Services
N.A.I.C.S.: 459210
Reetta Liisa Pikkola (Dir-Pur)

OTBASY BANK JSC

91 Abylai Khan avenue, Almaty, 050000, Kazakhstan
Tel.: (7) 272793511
Web Site: http://www.hcsbk.kz
JSBN—(KAZ)
Rev.: $561,287,073
Assets: $7,692,011,963
Liabilities: $6,658,379,205
Net Worth: $1,033,632,758
Earnings: $214,738,004
Emp.: 876
Fiscal Year-end: 12/31/22
Commercial Banking Services
N.A.I.C.S.: 522110
Ibragimova Lyazzat Yerkenovna (Chm)

OTC EXCHANGE OF INDIA

92 Maker Towers F Cuffe Parade, Mumbai, 400 005, India
Tel.: (91) 22 67480800
Web Site: http://www.otcei.net
Year Founded: 1990
Sales Range: Less than $1 Million
Stock Exchange Services
N.A.I.C.S.: 523210

OTC PHARMA-VERTRIEB GMBH

Brauweiler Strasse 14, Cologne, 50859, Germany
Tel.: (49) 2234946750
Web Site: http://www.otc-pharma.de
Year Founded: 1984
Sales Range: $10-24.9 Million
Emp.: 25
Pharmacy Products Distr
N.A.I.C.S.: 424210

INTERNATIONAL PUBLIC

Manfred Jakobs (Dir-Sls)

OTCO INTERNATIONAL LTD.

P41 9A Main LIC Colony Jeevanbhima Nagar HAL 3rd Stage, New Thippasandra, Bengaluru, 560075, Karnataka, India
Tel.: (91) 9789053807
Web Site: https://otco.in
Year Founded: 1981
523151—(BOM)
Rev.: $172,592
Assets: $869,468
Liabilities: $561,489
Net Worth: $307,979
Earnings: $10,023
Emp.: 6
Fiscal Year-end: 03/31/23
Information Technology Services
N.A.I.C.S.: 541512
Bikash Dash (CFO)

OTEC CORPORATION

Shingu Bldg 2-4-2 Toyo, Koto-Ku, Tokyo, 135-0016, Japan
Tel.: (81) 336990411
Web Site: http://www.o-tec.co.jp
Year Founded: 1948
1736—(TKS)
Rev.: $194,162,140
Assets: $210,178,170
Liabilities: $76,292,620
Net Worth: $133,885,550
Earnings: $9,161,460
Fiscal Year-end: 03/31/24
Tubing Pipe & Valve Fitting Distr
N.A.I.C.S.: 423720
Shinichi Ichihara (Pres & CEO)

OTEKS AD

181 7-mi Noemvri Str, 6000, Ohrid, North Macedonia
Tel.: (389) 46 205 205
Year Founded: 1949
Textile Products Mfr
N.A.I.C.S.: 313210

OTELLO CORPORATION ASA

Gjerdrums vei 19, NO-0484, Oslo, Norway
Tel.: (47) 91909145   NO
Web Site: https://www.otellocorp.com
Year Founded: 1995
OTELLO—(OSL)
Rev.: $200,000
Assets: $109,800,000
Liabilities: $2,400,000
Net Worth: $107,400,000
Earnings: $16,000,000
Emp.: 6
Fiscal Year-end: 12/31/22
Web Browser Developer
N.A.I.C.S.: 541512
Lars Boilesen (CEO)

Subsidiaries:

AdMarvel, Inc. (1)
1875 S Grant St Ste 750, San Mateo, CA 94402   (100%)
Tel.: (650) 212-2336
Web Site: http://www.admarvel.com
Sales Range: $25-49.9 Million
Emp.: 62
Mobile Advertising Optimization Solutions
N.A.I.C.S.: 513210

Opera Software International AS (1)
Gjerdrums vei 19, 0175, Oslo, Norway
Tel.: (47) 23692400
Web Site: http://www.opera.com
Sales Range: $200-249.9 Million
Emp.: 250
Computer Software Services
N.A.I.C.S.: 513210
Lirs Boilesen (CEO)

OTHERLEVELS HOLDINGS LIMITED

AND PRIVATE COMPANIES OTP BANK PLC

Level 11 Central Plaza 2 66 Eagle Street, Brisbane, 4000, QLD, Australia
Tel.: (61) 7 3233 8888
Web Site: http://www.otherlevels.com
Year Founded: 2012
Rev.: $3,919,352
Assets: $5,189,735
Liabilities: $7,020,964
Net Worth: ($1,831,228)
Earnings: ($2,368,739)
Fiscal Year-end: 06/30/19
Digital Marketing Software
N.A.I.C.S.: 513210
Brendan O'Kane (CEO & Mng Dir)

Subsidiaries:

OtherLevels Pty Limited (1)
Level 1 235 Edward Street, Brisbane, 4000, QLD, Australia
Tel.: (61) 383623686
Online Marketing Services
N.A.I.C.S.: 541613
Brian Mitchell (Chm)

XCOM Media Pty Ltd (1)
Level 1 235 Edward Street, Brisbane, 4000, QLD, Australia
Tel.: (61) 736660544
Web Site: http://www.xcommedia.com.au
Online Marketing Services
N.A.I.C.S.: 541613

OTI GREENTECH AG

Friedrichstrasse 79, 10117, Berlin, Germany
Tel.: (49) 3081452469
Web Site: https://www.oti.ag
NSAK—(DUS)
Sales Range: Less than $1 Million
Industrial Cleaning Services
N.A.I.C.S.: 561790
John C. Kisalus (CEO)

Subsidiaries:

UNIservice Unisafe S.r.l (1)
Via S N S della Guardia 58a, Genoa, 16162, Italy
Tel.: (39) 010711395
Web Site: http://www.uniservicemarine.com
Tank Cleaning Chemical Mfr
N.A.I.C.S.: 325612

OTISIFARM AO

ul Testovskaya 10 Floor 12 Room II Room 29, 123112, Moscow, Russia
Tel.: (7) 4952211800
Web Site: http://otcpharm.com
Year Founded: 2013
Pharmaceuticals Product Mfr
N.A.I.C.S.: 325412
Olga Borisovna Mednikova (Gen Dir)

Subsidiaries:

Nanolek LLC (1)
Butyrsky Val 68/70 building 1 Business center Baker Plaza 2nd floor, office 24, 127055, Moscow, Russia
Tel.: (7) 4956482687
Web Site: http://www.nanolek.ru
Pharmaceuticals Product Mfr
N.A.I.C.S.: 325412
Mikhail Nekrasov (Chm & Gen Dir)

OTOKAR OTOMOTIV VE SAVUNMA SANAYI A.S.

Aydinevler Mahallesi Saygi Caddesi No 58, Maltepe, 34854, Istanbul, Turkiye
Tel.: (90) 2164892950
Web Site: https://www.otokar.com.tr
Year Founded: 1963
OTKAR—(IST)
Rev.: $296,635,944
Assets: $437,132,245
Liabilities: $372,176,337
Net Worth: $64,955,908
Earnings: $38,273,324
Emp.: 2,942
Fiscal Year-end: 12/31/22
Military Vehicle Mfr
N.A.I.C.S.: 336992
Yildirim Ali Koc (Chm)

Subsidiaries:

Otokar Europe Filiala Bucuresti SRL (1)
Soseaua Bucuresti - Ploiesti nr 7A etaj 3 Sector 1, Bucharest, Romania
Tel.: (40) 314260223
Web Site: https://www.otokar.ro
Automobile Parts Mfr
N.A.I.C.S.: 336390

OTOVO ASA

Torggata 7, 0181, Oslo, Norway
Tel.: (47) 21656510 NO
Web Site: https://www.otovo.com
Year Founded: 2015
89K—(DEU)
Rev.: $60,249,769
Assets: $86,575,466
Liabilities: $37,480,972
Net Worth: $49,094,495
Earnings: ($28,751,709)
Emp.: 351
Fiscal Year-end: 12/31/22
Solar Electric Power Generation Services
N.A.I.C.S.: 221114
Andreas Thorsheim (CEO)

OTP BANK PLC

Nador utca 16, H-1051, Budapest, Hungary
Tel.: (36) 3666666 HU
Web Site: https://www.otpbank.hu
Year Founded: 1949
OTP—(BUD)
Rev.: $2,356,025,620
Assets: $68,011,572,460
Liabilities: $60,267,019,020
Net Worth: $7,744,553,440
Earnings: $1,578,973,760
Fiscal Year-end: 12/31/19
Retail & Commercial Banking Services
N.A.I.C.S.: 522110
Andras Takacs (Mng Dir-Wealth & Investment Mgmt)

Subsidiaries:

Alpha Bank Albania SH.A. (1)
Zog I Blvd Nr 47, Tirana, Albania
Tel.: (355) 44240478
Web Site: http://www.alphabank.al
Commercial Banking Services
N.A.I.C.S.: 522110

BANKA SOCIETE GENERALE ALBANIA SH.A. (1)
Twin Towers Bulevardi Deshmoret e Kombit Kulla 1 Kati 9, Tirana, Albania (100%)
Tel.: (355) 4 2 280 442
Web Site: http://www.societegenerale.al
Commercial Banking Services
N.A.I.C.S.: 522110
Irida Vejsiu (Mgr-HR & Trng Department)

Banka OTP Albania SHA (1)
Twin Towers Bulevardi Deshmoret e Kombit Kulla 1 Kati 9, Tirana, Albania
Tel.: (355) 68694012121
Web Site: https://otpbank.al
Financial Services
N.A.I.C.S.: 522320
Bledar Shella (CFO & Chm)

Crnogorska komercijalna banka a.d.
Moskovska bb, 81000, Podgorica, Montenegro
Tel.: (382) 81 404232
Web Site: http://www.ckb.me
Commercial Banking Services
N.A.I.C.S.: 522110

DSK Bank (1)
Moskovska street No 19 / G Benkovski street No 5, Sofia, 1036, Bulgaria
Tel.: (359) 70010375
Web Site: https://dskbank.bg
Sales Range: $350-399.9 Million
Banking Services
N.A.I.C.S.: 522110
Dorothea Nikolova (Exec Dir)

EiSYS Ltd. (1)
Lomb u 15 3rd Floor, 1139, Budapest, Hungary
Tel.: (36) 16114117
Web Site: https://www.eisys.hu
Emp.: 40
Information Technology Consulting Services
N.A.I.C.S.: 541512

Georg d.o.o. (1)
Ulica Divka Budaka 1D, 10 000, Zagreb, Croatia
Tel.: (385) 14444396
Web Site: https://georg.hr
Business Consulting Services
N.A.I.C.S.: 541611

Hungarian International Finance Ltd. (1)
4th Fl 9 King St, London, EC2V 8EA, United Kingdom (100%)
Tel.: (44) 2076064107
Web Site: https://www.otpbank.hu
Sales Range: $50-74.9 Million
Emp.: 8
Investment Services
N.A.I.C.S.: 523940

Merkantil Bank Ltd. (1)
Jozsef Attila utca 8, 1051, Budapest, Hungary
Tel.: (36) 612686868
Web Site: https://www.merkantil.hu
Commercial Bank
N.A.I.C.S.: 522110

Merkantil Berlet Ltd. (1)
Jozsef Attila utca 24 3 Emelet 18, 1051, Budapest, Hungary
Tel.: (36) 12686800
Commercial Banking Services
N.A.I.C.S.: 522110

MobiasBanca S.A. (1)
81A Stefan cel Mare si Sfant Avenue, Chisinau, 2012, Moldova (96.69%)
Tel.: (373) 22541974
Banking Services
N.A.I.C.S.: 522110

Mobiasbanca - OTP Group S.A. (1)
Bd Stephen the Great and Saint 81A Mun, MD2012, Chisinau, Moldova
Tel.: (373) 2 225 6456
Web Site: https://www.mobiasbanca.md
Banking Services
N.A.I.C.S.: 523150

Nadudvari Ltd. (1)
Gutenberg u 1, 4181, Nadudvar, Hungary
Tel.: (36) 54480633
Web Site: https://nadudvari.com
Frozen Food Mfr & Distr
N.A.I.C.S.: 311412

Nova Kreditna banka Maribor, d.d. (1)
Ulica Vita Kraigherja 4, 2000, Maribor, Slovenia
Tel.: (386) 22292290
Web Site: http://www.nkbm.si
Banking Services
N.A.I.C.S.: 522110
Andrzej Klesyk (Deputy Chm-Supervisory Bd)

Subsidiary (Domestic):

Abanka Vipa D.D. (2)
Slovenska cesta 58, 1517, Ljubljana, Slovenia
Tel.: (386) 14718100
Web Site: http://www.abanka.si
Rev.: $77,363,668
Assets: $4,268,100,424
Liabilities: $3,600,805,332
Net Worth: $667,295,093
Earnings: $75,023,474
Fiscal Year-end: 12/31/2018
International, Corporate & Retail Banking Services
N.A.I.C.S.: 522110
Joze Lenic (Pres-Mgmt Bd)

Subsidiary (Domestic):

Analozbe d.o.o (3)
Erjavceva ulica 2, 5000, Nova Gorica, Slovenia
Tel.: (386) 0801360
Investment Management Service
N.A.I.C.S.: 541618

Argolina d o o (3)
Slovenian Rd 58, 1000, Ljubljana, Slovenia
Tel.: (386) 14718422
Project Financing Services
N.A.I.C.S.: 523999

Subsidiary (Domestic):

KBM Infond, druzba za upravljanje, d.o.o. (2)
Ulica Vita Kraigherja 5 pp 1552, 2113, Maribor, Slovenia
Tel.: (386) 22292080
Web Site: http://www.infond.si
Commercial Banking Services
N.A.I.C.S.: 522110
Samo Stonic (Member-Mgmt Bd)

OJSC OTP Bank (1)
Pokrovka str 45/1, Moscow, Russia
Tel.: (7) 495 775 4 775
Web Site: http://www.en.otpbank.ru
Commercial Banking Services
N.A.I.C.S.: 522110
Istvan Hamecz (Chm)

OTP Asset Management SAI S.A. (1)
Aleea Alexandru 43 Sector 1, 011822, Bucharest, Romania
Tel.: (40) 372915608
Web Site: https://otpfonduri.ro
Investment Advisory & Asset Management Services
N.A.I.C.S.: 523940

OTP Bank S.A. (1)
Bd Stefan cel Mare si Sfint 81A Mun, Chisinau, Moldova
Tel.: (373) 22256456
Web Site: https://www.mobiasbanca.md
Banking Services
N.A.I.C.S.: 522110

OTP Bank Ukraine (1)
Zhliamsska street 43, 01033, Kiev, Ukraine (100%)
Tel.: (380) 444900500
Web Site: https://en.otpbank.com.ua
Sales Range: $1-4.9 Billion
Emp.: 4,000
Retail & Commercial Banking
N.A.I.C.S.: 522110

OTP Building Society Ltd. (1)
Vadasz u 12, H-1052, Budapest, Hungary
Tel.: (36) 4735000
Web Site: http://www.otp-ltp.hu
Real Estate Services
N.A.I.C.S.: 531210

OTP Factoring Asset Management Ltd. (1)
Mozsar u 8, H 1066, Budapest, Hungary (100%)
Tel.: (36) 12676095
Web Site: http://www.otpbank.hu
Factoring & Asset Management Services
N.A.I.C.S.: 531390
Janos Szasz (CEO)

OTP Factoring Ltd. (1)
Semmelweis U 10, H 1052, Budapest, Hungary (100%)
Tel.: (36) 12676096
Web Site: http://www.otpbank.hu
Factoring Services
N.A.I.C.S.: 522299

OTP Factoring Romania LLC (1)
Street Nicolae Caramfil No 71-73, Distrikt 1, 014142, Bucharest, Romania
Tel.: (40) 720112283
Web Site: https://otpfactoring.ro
Portfolio Management Services
N.A.I.C.S.: 523940

OTP Factoring Ukraine LLC (1)
Fizkultury Str 28d, 03150, Kiev, Ukraine
Tel.: (380) 444959393
Web Site: https://otpfakt.com.ua
Investment Banking Services
N.A.I.C.S.: 523150

OTP Fund Management Ltd. (1)

OTP BANK PLC

OTP Bank Plc—(Continued)
Deak Ferenc u 7-9, H-1051, Budapest, Hungary
Tel.: (36) 12669605
Web Site: http://www.otpalap.hu
Investment & Pension Funds
N.A.I.C.S.: 524292

OTP Hungaro-Projekt Ltd. (1)
Devai u 26-28, 1134, Budapest, Hungary
Tel.: (36) 14123520
Web Site: https://www.otpbank.hu
Consulting Services
N.A.I.C.S.: 541618

OTP Leasing Romania IFN S.A. (1)
Nicolae Caramfil Street no 71-73 5th floor, District 1, 014142, Bucharest, Romania
Tel.: (40) 214072900
Web Site: https://www.otp-leasing.ro
Vehicle Leasing Services
N.A.I.C.S.: 532112

OTP Life Annuity Ltd. (1)
Nador u 21, H-1051, Budapest, Hungary
Tel.: (36) 1 472 2900
Web Site: http://www.otpbank.hu
Rev.: $257,103,008
Life Insurance
N.A.I.C.S.: 524113

OTP Mortgage Bank Ltd (1)
Nador Utca 21, Budapest, 1051, Hungary
Tel.: (36) 13547400
Web Site: http://www.otpjzb.hu
Sales Range: $50-74.9 Million
Emp.: 37
Mortgage Banking Services
N.A.I.C.S.: 522110
Akos Fischl *(Deputy CEO)*

OTP Osiguranje Akcionarsko Drustvo Za LLC (1)
50a/b Bulevar Zorana Djindjica Street, 11070, Belgrade, Serbia
Tel.: (381) 112608665
Web Site: https://www.otposiguranje.rs
Emp.: 30
Fire Insurance Services
N.A.I.C.S.: 524210

OTP Real Estate Leasing Ltd. (1)
Vaci ut 135-139 A epulet, 1138, Budapest, Hungary
Tel.: (36) 14579800
Web Site: https://www.otpingatlanlizing.hu
Real Estate Services
N.A.I.C.S.: 531210
Hello Judit *(CEO)*

OTP Real Estate Ltd. (1)
Riado u 1-3, 1026, Budapest, Hungary (100%)
Tel.: (36) 3733800
Web Site: https://www.otpbank.hu
Sales Range: $50-74.9 Million
Emp.: 80
Real Estate Services
N.A.I.C.S.: 531210

OTP Travel Ltd. (1)
Nador u 21, 1051, Budapest, Hungary
Tel.: (36) 13547300
Web Site: https://www.otptravel.hu
Sales Range: $25-49.9 Million
Emp.: 100
Travel Services
N.A.I.C.S.: 561510

OTP banka Hrvatska d.d (1)
Domovinskog rata 3, Zadar, Croatia
Tel.: (385) 62201555
Web Site: http://www.otpbanka.hr
Sales Range: $700-749.9 Million
Emp.: 1,200
Commercial Banking Services
N.A.I.C.S.: 522110
Damir Odak *(Pres)*

OTP banka Srbija a.d (1)
Trg Slobode 5, 11000, Novi Sad, Serbia
Tel.: (381) 113011555
Web Site: https://www.otpbanka.rs
Commercial Banking Services
N.A.I.C.S.: 522110

Subsidiary (Domestic):

OTP Leasing d.o.o. (2)
Grawe insurance building Bulevar Mihajla Pupina 111, 11070, Belgrade, Serbia
Tel.: (381) 112287982
Web Site: https://www.otpleasing.rs
Automotive Financial Leasing Services
N.A.I.C.S.: 522220
Slobodan Terzic *(Pres-Exec Bd & Gen Mgr)*

Vojvodjanska Banka a.d. (2)
Bulevar Mihajla Pupina 111, Novi Beograd, 11070, Serbia (100%)
Tel.: (381) 21 421 077
Web Site: http://www.voban.co.rs
Banking Services
N.A.I.C.S.: 522110
Predrag Vasic *(Pres)*

OTP banka dionicko drustvo (1)
Domovinskog rata 61, 21000, Split, Croatia
Tel.: (385) 21559110
Web Site: https://www.otpbanka.hr
Banking Services
N.A.I.C.S.: 522110

SKB Banka d.d (1)
Ajdovscina 4, 1513, Ljubljana, Slovenia
Tel.: (386) 14715555
Web Site: http://www.skb.si
Sales Range: $75-99.9 Million
Emp.: 912
Retail, Commercial, Investment & International Banking Services
N.A.I.C.S.: 522110
Anita Stojcevska *(Dir-Retail & Mktg Div)*

Subsidiary (Domestic):

PLASIS Ltd. (2)
Slovenska 56, 1000, Ljubljana, Slovenia
Tel.: (386) 14380500
Web Site: http://www.plasis.si
Sales Range: $25-49.9 Million
Emp.: 54
ATM & POS Terminal Network Systems
N.A.I.C.S.: 334118

SKB Leasing d.o.o. (2)
Ajdovscina 4, 1000, Ljubljana, Slovenia
Tel.: (386) 13005000
Web Site: https://www.skb-leasing.si
Leasing Activities
N.A.I.C.S.: 531190

SKB Real Estate & Leasing Ltd. (2)
Slovenska c 54, 1000, Ljubljana, Slovenia
Tel.: (386) 14716100
Web Site: http://www.skb-nepr.si
Real Estate & Leasing Activities
N.A.I.C.S.: 531210

SKB Leasing Select d.o.o. (1)
Ajdovscina 4, 1000, Ljubljana, Slovenia
Tel.: (386) 13005096
Web Site: https://www.skb-leasing-select.si
Financial Lending Services
N.A.I.C.S.: 533110

ShiwaForce.com Inc. (1)
Alkotas St 17-19, 1123, Budapest, Hungary
Tel.: (36) 13924000
Web Site: https://www.shiwaforce.com
Digital Banking Services
N.A.I.C.S.: 522320

OTRS AG

Zimmersmuhlenweg 11, 61440, Oberursel, Germany
Tel.: (49) 61726819880
Web Site: http://www.otrs.com
Rev.: $9,310,940
Assets: $8,288,665
Liabilities: $6,085,362
Net Worth: $2,203,302
Earnings: $501,428
Emp.: 63
Fiscal Year-end: 12/31/18
IT Software, Integration, Implementation, Training & Consulting Services
N.A.I.C.S.: 513210
Andre Mindermann *(Co-Founder, Chm-Exec Bd & CEO)*

Subsidiaries:

OTRS Inc. (1)
19925 Stevens Creek Blvd, Cupertino, CA 95014-2358
Tel.: (408) 549-1717
Information Technology Consulting Services
N.A.I.C.S.: 541512
Andre Mindermann *(Gen Mgr)*

OTRS Ltd. (1)
Level 6 28 Hennessy Road, Admiralty, Hong Kong, China (Hong Kong)
Tel.: (852) 3690 1503
Web Site: http://www.performer.com
Information Technology Consulting Services
N.A.I.C.S.: 541512
Royel Fok *(CEO)*

OTRS S.A. de C.V. (1)
Av Insurgentes Sur 863 Piso 7, Colonia Napoles, 03810, Mexico, Mexico
Tel.: (52) 55 11689664
Information Technology Consulting Services
N.A.I.C.S.: 541512
Andre Mindermann *(Gen Mgr)*

OTRS Sdn. Bhd. (1)
A-32 Menara NU 203 Jalan Tun Sambanthan, 50470, Kuala Lumpur, Malaysia
Tel.: (60) 3 2035 5578
Information Technology Consulting Services
N.A.I.C.S.: 541512

OTSO GOLD CORP

161 Bay Street 27th Floor, PO Box 508, Toronto, M5J 2S1, ON, Canada
Tel.: (416) 572-2214 AB
Web Site: https://www.otsogold.com
Year Founded: 1992
OTSO—(TSXV)
Rev.: $114
Assets: $47,524,429
Liabilities: $55,355,585
Net Worth: ($7,831,156)
Earnings: ($12,029,450)
Fiscal Year-end: 01/31/21
Mineral Exploration Services
N.A.I.C.S.: 213114
Brian Wesson *(Pres & CEO)*

OTSUKA CORPORATION

2-18-4 Iidabashi, Chiyoda-ku, Tokyo, 102-8573, Japan
Tel.: (81) 332647111
Web Site: https://www.otsuka-shokai.co.jp
Year Founded: 1961
4768—(TKS)
Rev.: $6,457,680,872
Assets: $3,711,959,035
Liabilities: $1,419,590,353
Net Worth: $2,292,368,682
Earnings: $313,498,513
Emp.: 9,421
Fiscal Year-end: 12/31/23
Software Development Services
N.A.I.C.S.: 541511
Yuji Otsuka *(Pres & CEO)*

Subsidiaries:

Alpha Net Co., Ltd. (1)
Koraku Kokusai Building 1-5-3 Koraku, Bunkyo-ku, Tokyo, 112-0004, Japan
Tel.: (81) 358004307
Web Site: http://www.anet.co.jp
Sales Range: $75-99.9 Million
Emp.: 521
Networking Support Services
N.A.I.C.S.: 541512
Naoki Sugiyama *(Pres & CEO)*

Alpha Techno Co., Ltd. (1)
2-1-2 Akanehama Narashino, Chiba, Japan
Tel.: (81) 474083888
Computer Repair & Maintenance Services
N.A.I.C.S.: 811210

NetWorld Corporation (1)
1-8-1 Otemachi, Chiyoda - ku, Tokyo, 100-0004, Japan
Tel.: (81) 367481800
Web Site: https://www.networld.ne.jp
Sales Range: $25-49.9 Million
Emp.: 77
System Integration Services
N.A.I.C.S.: 541512

Netplan Co., Ltd. (1)
7-3-7 Otsuka Building Nishi-Shinjuku Shinjuku, Tokyo, 160-0023, Japan
Tel.: (81) 3 5925 3911
Web Site: http://www.net-plan.co.jp
Software & Hardware Products Supplier
N.A.I.C.S.: 423430

OSK Co., Ltd. (1)
Arca Central 9F 1-2-1 Kinshi, Sumida Ku, Tokyo, 130-0013, Japan
Tel.: (81) 356101659
Web Site: https://www.kk-osk.co.jp
Emp.: 459
Software Development Services
N.A.I.C.S.: 541511

OTSUKA HOLDINGS CO., LTD.

Shinagawa Grand Central Tower 2-16-4 Konan, Minato-ku, Tokyo, 108-8241, Japan
Tel.: (81) 367171410 JP
Web Site: https://www.otsuka.com
Year Founded: 2008
OTSKF—(OTCIQ)
Rev.: $13,772,955,680
Assets: $25,437,171,760
Liabilities: $7,205,540,320
Net Worth: $18,231,631,440
Earnings: $1,468,775,440
Emp.: 33,151
Fiscal Year-end: 12/31/20
Holding Company
N.A.I.C.S.: 551112
Noriko Tojo *(Exec Dir)*

Subsidiaries:

2768691 Canada, Inc. (1)
8515 9e Av Bureau 300, Montreal, H1Z 2Z6, QC, Canada
Tel.: (514) 723-0858
Organic Chemical Mfr
N.A.I.C.S.: 325199

Kitasato Otsuka Biomedical Assay Laboratories Co., Ltd. (1)
1-15-1 Kitazato, Minami-Ku, Sagamihara, 252-0329, Kanagawa, Japan
Tel.: (81) 42 777 8885
Web Site: https://www.kobal.co.jp
Clinical Testing Services
N.A.I.C.S.: 541380
Wayama Yukimasa *(Pres & CEO)*

Laboratoires Dietetique et Sante SAS (1)
Route De Castelnaudary, Revel, 31250, France
Tel.: (33) 562187373
Health Care Food Mfr
N.A.I.C.S.: 311999

Nardobel SAS (1)
Route De Castelnaudary, PO Box 106, Revel, 31250, France
Tel.: (33) 562187373
Investment Management Service
N.A.I.C.S.: 523940

Naruto Cruise Service Co., Ltd (1)
190-56 Oge Narutochotosadomariura, Naruto, 772-0053, Tokushima, Japan
Tel.: (81) 886836767
Sales Range: $25-49.9 Million
Emp.: 5
Pharmaceutical Products Research Services
N.A.I.C.S.: 541715
Hiroshi Matsumoto *(Mgr)*

Naruto Salt Mfg. Co., Ltd. (1)
53 Matsushima Kurosaki Muya-cho, Naruto, 772-8520, Tokushima, Japan
Tel.: (81) 88 686 2131
Web Site: https://www.naruen.co.jp
Salt Mfr
N.A.I.C.S.: 311942

Nutrition & Sante Benelux SA (1)
Medialaan 30 Box 2, 1800, Vilvoorde, Belgium
Tel.: (32) 27 89 22 00
Web Site: http://www.nutritionetsante.com
Sales Range: $25-49.9 Million
Emp.: 50
Dietary & Health Care Food Mfr
N.A.I.C.S.: 311514
Erwin Caluwe *(CEO)*

Nutrition & Sante Iberia SL (1)

AND PRIVATE COMPANIES — OTSUKA HOLDINGS CO., LTD.

Paseo Gracia 84 Segunda Pis, Barcelona, 8008, Spain
Tel.: (34) 932 16 71 00
Nutritional Food Products Mfr
N.A.I.C.S.: 311999

Nutrition & Sante SAS (1)
Route de Castelnaudary, 31250, Revel, France (100%)
Tel.: (33) 562187373
Web Site: http://www.nutritionetsante.com
Health Care Nutrition Food Mfr
N.A.I.C.S.: 311999

Organ Technologies Inc. (1)
2-2 Kanda Tsukasamachi, Chiyoda-ku, Tokyo, Japan
Tel.: (81) 3 3257 7374
Web Site: http://www.organ-technol.co.jp
Pharmaceutical Products Mfr & Distr
N.A.I.C.S.: 325412

Otsuka (China) Investment Co., Ltd. (1)
Units 08 38F Lippo Plaza 222 Huai Hai Zhong Road, Shanghai, China
Tel.: (86) 21 5396 6838
Web Site: http://www.otsuka.com.cn
Investment Management Service
N.A.I.C.S.: 523999

Otsuka (Shanghai) Foods Safety Research & Development Co., Ltd. (1)
No 1969 Lianhua S Rd, Minhang District, Shanghai, 200020, China
Tel.: (86) 21 54408540
Food Products Research & Development Services
N.A.I.C.S.: 541715

Otsuka Chemical (India) Private Limited (1)
402 JMD Pacific Square Sector 15 Part II Near 32nd Mile Stone, Gurgaon, Haryana, India
Tel.: (91) 124 4597979
Web Site: http://www.otsukaindia.com
Specialty Chemicals Mfr
N.A.I.C.S.: 325998

Otsuka Chemical Co., Ltd. (1)
3-2-27 Ote-Dori, Chuo-Ku, Osaka, 540-0021, Japan
Tel.: (81) 6 6943 7701
Web Site: http://www.otsukac.co.jp
Sales Range: $250-299.9 Million
Emp.: 620
Chemical Products Mfr & Distr
N.A.I.C.S.: 325998

Subsidiary (Domestic):

ILS Inc. (2)
1-2-1 Kubogaoka, Moriya, 302-0104, Ibaraki, Japan
Tel.: (81) 29 745 6342
Web Site: http://www.ils.co.jp
Peptide Mfr
N.A.I.C.S.: 325412

Otsuka Chemical do Brasil Ltda. (1)
Rodovia RS 239 5966-Conj 9 Zona Industrial, Campo Bom, 93700-000, Rio Grande do Sul, Brazil
Tel.: (55) 51 2129 7999
Web Site: http://www.otsukachemical.com.br
Emp.: 50
Specialty Chemicals Mfr & Distr
N.A.I.C.S.: 325998
Koji Mori (Pres & CEO)

Otsuka Chilled Foods Co., Ltd. (1)
Mamoru Kanda, Chiyoda-ku, Tokyo, 101-8535, Japan
Tel.: (81) 3 3219 8877
Web Site: http://www.otsuka-chilled.co.jp
Sales Range: $25-49.9 Million
Emp.: 15
Food Products Mfr & Distr
N.A.I.C.S.: 311999
Takumi Nishioka (Pres)

Otsuka Novel Products GmbH (1)
Erika-Mann-Str 21, Munich, 80636, Germany
Tel.: (49) 162 2752199
Pharmaceutical Products Distr
N.A.I.C.S.: 424210

Otsuka Pakistan Ltd. (1)
30 B Sindhi Muslim Cooperative Housing Society, Near Masjid E Maulana Roomi, Karachi, 74400, Pakistan (100%)
Tel.: (92) 214528651
Web Site: http://www.otsukapakistan.com
Sales Range: $200-249.9 Million
Emp.: 1,000
Provider of Pharmaceuticals & IV Solutions
N.A.I.C.S.: 325412

Otsuka Pharmaceutical Co., Ltd. (1)
Shinagawa Grand Central Twr 2-16-4 Konan, Minato-ku, Tokyo, 108-8242, Japan
Tel.: (81) 332920021
Web Site: http://www.otsuka-global.com
Sales Range: $1-4.9 Billion
Emp.: 5,171
Mfr of Healthcare Products
N.A.I.C.S.: 325412
Taro Iwamoto (Pres)

Subsidiary (Non-US):

ARS Chemical (Thailand) Co., Ltd. (2)
27 Soi Phiphat Silom Rd Bangrak, Bangkok, 10500, Thailand (100%)
Tel.: (66) 22355341
Web Site: http://www.otsuka.co.jp
Sales Range: $100-124.9 Million
Emp.: 362
Insecticides & Household Products
N.A.I.C.S.: 325320

Subsidiary (US):

Cambridge Isotope Laboratories, Inc. (2)
3 Highwood Dr, Tewksbury, MA 01876
Tel.: (978) 749-8000
Web Site: http://www.isotope.com
Sales Range: $50-74.9 Million
Emp.: 120
Research of Stable Isotopes, Compounds Labeled
N.A.I.C.S.: 325199
Joel C. Bradley (Founder)

Subsidiary (Non-US):

ABX Advanced Biochemical Compounds, GmbH (3)
Heinrich-Glaeser-Strasse 10-14, 01454, Radeberg, Germany
Tel.: (49) 352 840 4160
Web Site: https://www.abx.de
Emp.: 320
Nuclear Medicine Chemical Mfr
N.A.I.C.S.: 325998
Peter Möll (Mng Dir)

Subsidiary (Domestic):

CIL Isotope Separations, LLC (3)
1689 Burnett Dr, Xenia, OH 45385-5691
Tel.: (937) 376-5456
Web Site: http://www.isotope.com
Emp.: 20
Isotopes Reagent Mfr & Distr
N.A.I.C.S.: 325998
John Benkovic (Plant Mgr)

Subsidiary (Non-US):

Euriso-Top GmbH (4)
Lebacher Strasse 4, Postfach 10 05 43, 66113, Saarbrucken, Germany
Tel.: (49) 681 99 63 338
Web Site: http://www.eurisotop.com
Emp.: 20
Pharmaceutical Products Mfr & Distr
N.A.I.C.S.: 325412
Jean-Louis Schaffar (Chm & CEO)

Euriso-Top S.A.S (4)
Parc des Algorithmes Batiment Homere Route de l'Orme, 91194, Saint-Aubin-le-Monial, 91194, France
Tel.: (33) 1 69 41 95 96
Pharmaceutical Products Mfr & Distr
N.A.I.C.S.: 325412
Jean Louis Schaffar (CEO)

Subsidiary (Non-US):

China Otsuka Pharmaceutical Co., Ltd. (2)
176 Xin Hua Road 12th Yong Hong Industrial Street, He Ping District Xiuing, 300382, Tianjin, China
Tel.: (86) 2223982883
Web Site: http://www.chinaotsuka.com.cn
Sales Range: $200-249.9 Million
Emp.: 700
Provider of Pharmaceuticals
N.A.I.C.S.: 325412

Dong-A Otsuka Co., Ltd. (2)
450 1 Suksoo Dong, Manan-ku, Anyang, 430-042, Kyungki-Do, Korea (South)
Tel.: (82) 314702114
Sales Range: $300-349.9 Million
Emp.: 1,121
Provider of Beverage Products
N.A.I.C.S.: 312130

Egypt Otsuka Pharmaceutical Co., S.A.E. (2)
10th of Ramadan City B3, Cairo, Egypt (100%)
Tel.: (20) 015369561
Web Site: http://www.otsuka-global.com
Sales Range: $100-124.9 Million
Emp.: 318
Pharmaceuticals
N.A.I.C.S.: 325412

Subsidiary (Domestic):

En Otsuka Pharmaceutical Co., Ltd. (2)
4-3-5 Nimaibashi, Hanamaki, Iwate, Japan
Tel.: (81) 198265261
Web Site: http://www.enotsuka.co.jp
Emp.: 390
Nutritional Supplement & Other Medical Food Mfr
N.A.I.C.S.: 325412
Goro Komatsu (Pres & CEO)

Plant (Domestic):

EN Otsuka Pharmaceutical Co., Ltd. - Kitakami Plant (3)
43-94 Yamane Nashinoki, Aisari-cho, Kitakami, Iwate, Japan
Tel.: (81) 197 71 2900
Pharmaceuticals Product Mfr
N.A.I.C.S.: 325412

Subsidiary (Non-US):

Guangdong Otsuka Pharmaceutical Co., Ltd. (2)
New High Tech Industries Development Zone, Ronggui, Shunde, 528306, Guangdong, China
Tel.: (86) 75728305860
Web Site: http://www.otsuka-global.com
Sales Range: $100-124.9 Million
Emp.: 392
Pharmaceuticals
N.A.I.C.S.: 325412

Hebron S.A. (2)
Avenida Estacion 61 La Llagosta, 08120, Barcelona, Spain (100%)
Tel.: (34) 935742011
Web Site: http://www.hebron.as
Sales Range: $25-49.9 Million
Emp.: 54
Chemicals (Plastic Additives, Blowing Agents, Metalic Soaps, Plasticizers, Stabilizers), Pharmaceutical Intermediates
N.A.I.C.S.: 424690
Mac Monnin (Pres)

Subsidiary (Domestic):

JIMRO Co., Ltd. (2)
351-1 Nishiyokote-cho Takasaki-shu, Gunma, 370 0021, Japan
Tel.: (81) 273531411
Web Site: http://www.jimro.com
Sales Range: $1-9.9 Million
Emp.: 200
Medical & Pharmaceutical Preparations
N.A.I.C.S.: 325412

Japan Immunoresearch Laboratories Co., Ltd. (JIMRO) (2)
351 1 Nishiyokote Takasaki, Gunma, 370 0021, Japan
Tel.: (81) 273531411
Web Site: http://www.jimro.com
Emp.: 168
Clinical Test Kits & Medical Devices Mfr
N.A.I.C.S.: 334510
Hideyuki Baba (Pres)

Subsidiary (Non-US):

KOC Co Ltd (2)
67-34 Ljin Onsan Ulju, 689896, Ulsan, Korea (South) (90%)
Tel.: (82) 522401200
Web Site: http://www.ikoc.co.kr
Sales Range: $25-49.9 Million
Emp.: 62
Mfr of Hydrazine Hydrate, Caustic Soda, Chlorine
N.A.I.C.S.: 325998

Subsidiary (Domestic):

Kitasato Otsuka Virus Assay Laboratories Co., Ltd. (2)
1 15 1 Kitasato, Sagamihara, 228 8555, Kanagawa, Japan (100%)
Tel.: (81) 427778885
Sales Range: $10-24.9 Million
Emp.: 30
Provider of Clinical Testing
N.A.I.C.S.: 541380

Subsidiary (Non-US):

Korea Otsuka Pharmaceutical Co., Ltd. (2)
12F Woori Building 826 20 Yeoksam-Dong, Gangnam gu, Seoul, Korea (South)
Tel.: (82) 25582036
Web Site: http://www.otsuka.co.kr
Sales Range: $50-74.9 Million
Emp.: 197
Mfr, Importer, Exporter & Sales of Pharmaceuticals
N.A.I.C.S.: 325412

Nutrition & Sante SAS (2)
BP 106, Revel, 31250, France
Tel.: (33) 5 62 18 73 73
Web Site: http://www.nutrition-sante-brands.com
Sales Range: $300-349.9 Million
Emp.: 1,000
Dietary Foods & Supplements Mfr
N.A.I.C.S.: 311999
Laurence Geli (Mgr-Comm)

Subsidiary (Non-US):

Nutrition & Sante Italia S.p.A. (3)
Largo Umberto Bochoni No 1, I 21040, Varese, Origgio, Italy (100%)
Tel.: (39) 0296541
Web Site: http://www.nutritionetsante.it
Sales Range: $25-49.9 Million
Emp.: 20
Dietary Foods & Supplements Sales
N.A.I.C.S.: 456191

Subsidiary (Domestic):

Okayama Taiho Pharmaceutical Co., Ltd. (2)
1775 1 Aza Oki Kugui, Bizen, Okayama, 705-8555, Japan (100%)
Tel.: (81) 869641111
Web Site: http://www.okayama-taiho.co.jp
Sales Range: $50-74.9 Million
Emp.: 150
Mfr of Pharmaceuticals
N.A.I.C.S.: 325412

Subsidiary (Non-US):

Otsuka (Philippines) Pharmaceutical, Inc. (2)
3rd Fl Kings Ct Bldg, 2129 Chino Roces Ave, Makati, 1231, Philippines (100%)
Tel.: (63) 88449266
Web Site: http://www.otsuka.com.ph
Sales Range: $50-74.9 Million
Emp.: 130
Provider of Pharmaceuticals
N.A.I.C.S.: 325412

Subsidiary (US):

Otsuka America Pharmaceutical, Inc. (2)
2440 Research Blvd, Rockville, MD 20850
Tel.: (301) 424-9055
Web Site: https://www.otsuka-us.com
Sales Range: $1-4.9 Billion
Emp.: 430
Pharmaceuticals Mfr
N.A.I.C.S.: 325412

OTSUKA HOLDINGS CO., LTD.

Otsuka Holdings Co., Ltd.—(Continued)

Subsidiary (Domestic):

Astex Pharmaceuticals, Inc. (3)
4420 Rosewood Dr Ste 200, Pleasanton, CA 94588
Tel.: (925) 560-0100
Web Site: http://www.astx.com
Rev.: $83,159,000
Assets: $275,164,000
Liabilities: $38,222,000
Net Worth: $236,942,000
Earnings: $8,247,000
Emp.: 136
Fiscal Year-end: 12/31/2012
Pharmaceuticals Mfr
N.A.I.C.S.: 325412
Martin Buckland (Co-Pres & COO)

Avanir Pharmaceuticals, Inc. (3)
30 Enterprise Ste 200, Aliso Viejo, CA 92656
Tel.: (949) 389-6700
Web Site: https://www.avanir.com
Sales Range: $100-124.9 Million
Pharmaceuticals Mfr
N.A.I.C.S.: 325412
Hisanori Maei (VP-Bus Plng & Alliance Mgmt)

Otsuka Maryland Medicinal Laboratories, Inc. (3)
2440 Research Blvd, Rockville, MD 20850-3337 (100%)
Tel.: (301) 424-9055
Web Site: http://www.otsuka.com
Sales Range: $10-24.9 Million
Emp.: 50
Provider of Pharmaceutical Research
N.A.I.C.S.: 541720
Junichi Kambayashi (CEO)

Otsuka Pharmaceutical Development & Commercialization, Inc. (3)
1 University Sq Dr, Princeton, NJ 08540-7814
Tel.: (609) 524-6788
Web Site: http://www.otsuka-us.com
Healthcare Products Research & Development Services
N.A.I.C.S.: 541715
George Chao (VP-Biometrics)

Pharmavite LLC (3)
8531 Fallbrook Ave, West Hills, CA 91304
Tel.: (818) 221-6200
Web Site: https://www.pharmavite.com
Sales Range: $200-249.9 Million
Mfr of Dietary Supplement Products & Skin Care Products
N.A.I.C.S.: 325411
Jeff Boutelle (CEO)

Subsidiary (Domestic):

FoodState, Inc. (4)
125 Loring St, Manchester, NH 03103
Tel.: (603) 668-2650
Web Site: http://www.foodstate.com
Food Supplement Retailer
N.A.I.C.S.: 456191

Nature Made Nutritional Products Inc. (4)
8531 Fallbrook Ave, West Hills, CA 91304
Tel.: (818) 221-6200
Web Site: http://www.pharmavite.com
Vitamin Mfr
N.A.I.C.S.: 325412

Unit (Domestic):

Pharmavite LLC - Bentonville (4)
211 SE 34th St 5, Bentonville, AR 72712
Tel.: (479) 273-7438
Mfr of Dietary Supplement Products & Skin Care Products
N.A.I.C.S.: 325411

Subsidiary (Domestic):

Proteus Digital Health, Inc. (3)
2600 Bridge Pkwy Ste 101, Redwood City, CA 94065
Tel.: (650) 632-4031
Web Site: http://www.proteusdigitalhealth.com
Health Care Equipment Mfr
N.A.I.C.S.: 339112

Jonathan R. Symonds (Chm)

Subsidiary (US):

Otsuka America, Inc. (2)
1 Embarcadero Ctr Ste 2020, San Francisco, CA 94111
Tel.: (415) 986-5300
Web Site: http://www.otsuka-america.com
Holding Company; Pharmaceutical Products
N.A.I.C.S.: 334519
John Wilson (Treas & VP-Fin)

Subsidiary (Domestic):

Crystal Geyser Water Company (3)
501 Washington St, Calistoga, CA 94515-1425
Tel.: (707) 942-0500
Sales Range: $25-49.9 Million
Soft Drinks Mfr
N.A.I.C.S.: 312111
Richard Weklych (VP-Mfg)

Subsidiary (Domestic):

Crystal Geyser Roxane Water Company L.L.C. (4)
1210 State Hwy 395, Olancha, CA 93549
Tel.: (760) 764-2885
Web Site: http://www.crystalgeyserasw.com
Sales Range: $25-49.9 Million
Emp.: 121
Mfr Bottle Spring Water
N.A.I.C.S.: 312112

Subsidiary (Non-US):

Mindset Pharma Inc. (3)
Tel.: (647) 938-5266
Web Site: https://mindsetpharma.com
Pharmaceuticals Mfr
N.A.I.C.S.: 325412

Subsidiary (Domestic):

Otsuka America Foods Inc. (3)
400 Oyster Pt Ste No 534, South San Francisco, CA 94080
Tel.: (415) 813-1444
Web Site: http://www.wildveggie.com
Vegetable Soup Mfr
N.A.I.C.S.: 311412

Otsuka America Manufacturing, LLC (3)
27778 Ave Hopkins, Valencia, CA 91355-1222
Tel.: (661) 294-9950
Plastic Food Containers Mfr
N.A.I.C.S.: 326199

Ridge Vineyards Inc. (3)
17100 Montebello Rd, Cupertino, CA 95014-5435
Tel.: (408) 867-3233
Web Site: https://www.ridgewine.com
Sales Range: $10-24.9 Million
Mfr of Wines
N.A.I.C.S.: 312130
Paul Draper (Chm)

Subsidiary (Non-US):

Visterra, Inc. (3)
Tel.: (617) 498-1070
Web Site: http://www.visterrainc.com
Biotechnology Health Care Services
N.A.I.C.S.: 541714
Brian J. G. Pereira (Pres & CEO)

Subsidiary (Non-US):

Otsuka Canada Pharmaceutical Inc. (2)
2250 Alfred-Nobel Boulevard, Saint Laurent, H4S 2C9, QC, Canada
Tel.: (514) 332-3001
Web Site: https://otsukacanada.com
Pharmaceutical Products Distr
N.A.I.C.S.: 424210
Allison Rosenthal (Gen Mgr)

Subsidiary (Domestic):

Otsuka Electronics Co., Ltd. (2)
3 26 3 Shodaitajika, Hirakata, Osaka, 573 1132, Japan (100%)
Tel.: (81) 728 855 8550
Web Site: http://www.otsuka-global.com

Sales Range: $25-49.9 Million
Emp.: 150
Mfr of Analytical & Clinical Testing Instruments
N.A.I.C.S.: 334516

Subsidiary (Domestic):

Chuo Electronic Measurement Co., Ltd. (3)
5-3-8 Ishiuchi-kita, Saeki-ku, Hiroshima, 731-5109, Japan
Tel.: (81) 82 941 7377
Web Site: http://www.chuo-cem.co.jp
Vehicle Inspection Device Mfr
N.A.I.C.S.: 334519
Isao Ejima (Mgr-Overseas Dept)

Subsidiary (Non-US):

Otsuka Electronics (Suzhou) Co., Ltd. (3)
Room 1901 Building A Xintian Xiang Guang Chang Suzhou Industrial Park, Suzhou, 215021, China
Tel.: (86) 512 6258 9919
Web Site: http://www.photal.co.jp
Light Emitting Diode Mfr
N.A.I.C.S.: 334413

Otsuka Electronics Korea Co., Ltd. (3)
301 Seonil Technopia 440 Sangdaewon-Dong, Jungwon-Ku, Seongnam, 462-120, Gyeonggi-Do, Korea (South)
Tel.: (82) 31 766 8411
Web Site: http://www.photal.co.jp
Measurement Equipment Mfr
N.A.I.C.S.: 334519

Subsidiary (Domestic):

Otsuka Foods Co., Ltd. (2)
3 2 27 Otedori, Chuo Ku, Osaka, 540-0021, Japan (100%)
Tel.: (81) 669437755
Web Site: http://www.otsukafoods.co.jp
Sales Range: $75-99.9 Million
Emp.: 50
Mfr Food Items
N.A.I.C.S.: 445298

Subsidiary (Non-US):

Otsuka Frankfurt Research Institute GmbH (2)
Hochhaus Am Park Gruneburgweg 102, 60323, Frankfurt am Main, Germany (100%)
Tel.: (49) 699550440
Web Site: http://www.otsuka.de
Sales Range: $25-49.9 Million
Emp.: 40
Provider of Pharmaceutical Research
N.A.I.C.S.: 325412
Norbart Hittel (Mng Dir)

Subsidiary (Domestic):

Otsuka Ohmi Ceramics Co., Ltd. (2)
3 2 21 Otedori, Chuo Ku, Osaka, 540 0021, Japan (100%)
Tel.: (81) 669436695
Web Site: http://www.osmi.co.jp
Sales Range: $25-49.9 Million
Emp.: 60
Mfr of Ceramics
N.A.I.C.S.: 327910

Otsuka Packaging Industries Co., Ltd. (2)
1 Higashitatsumi Kizuno Otsu-Cho, Naruto, Tokushima, 772-8511, Japan
Tel.: (81) 886852154
Web Site: http://www.otsuka-houso.co.jp
Sales Range: $75-99.9 Million
Emp.: 400
Packaging & Shipping
N.A.I.C.S.: 561910

Otsuka Packaging Industries Ltd. (2)
1 Aza Higashi Tatsumi Kizuno Otsu Cho, Naruto, Tokushima, 772-8511, Japan (100%)
Tel.: (81) 886852154
Web Site: http://www.otsuka-houso.co.jp
Sales Range: $100-124.9 Million
Emp.: 324
Mfr of Packaging Materials, Plastic Products, Printing Papers & Cartons

N.A.I.C.S.: 322212

Subsidiary (Non-US):

Otsuka Pharma GmbH (2)
Europa-Allee 52, 60327, Frankfurt am Main, Germany (100%)
Tel.: (49) 691700860
Web Site: http://www.otsuka.de
Sales Range: $25-49.9 Million
Emp.: 100
Provider of Pharmaceuticals
N.A.I.C.S.: 325412

Otsuka Pharma Scandinavia AB (2)
Wenner-Gren Center Sveavagen 166, 113 46, Stockholm, Sweden
Tel.: (46) 854528660
Web Site: http://www.otsuka.se
Sales Range: $25-49.9 Million
Emp.: 60
Pharmaceutical Preparation Mfr
N.A.I.C.S.: 325412

Otsuka Pharmaceutical (H.K.) Ltd. (2)
10/F Phase I China Taiping Tower 8 Sunning Road, 8 Sunning Rd, Causeway Bay, China (Hong Kong) (100%)
Tel.: (852) 28816299
Web Site: http://www.otsuka.hk
Sales Range: $25-49.9 Million
Emp.: 13
Provider of Pharmaceuticals & Beverages
N.A.I.C.S.: 325412
Athene Ma (Mgr-Fin)

Otsuka Pharmaceutical Europe, Ltd. (2)
Gallions Wexham Springs Framewood Rd, Wexham, SL3 6PJ, United Kingdom (100%)
Tel.: (44) 2037475000
Web Site: http://www.otsuka-europe.com
Sales Range: $25-49.9 Million
Emp.: 25
Provider of Pharmaceuticals
N.A.I.C.S.: 325412

Subsidiary (Domestic):

Otsuka Pharmaceutical Factory, Inc. (2)
115 Kugahara Tateiwa, Tokushima, 772-8601, Japan (100%)
Tel.: (81) 886851151
Web Site: http://www.otsukakj.jp
Sales Range: $400-449.9 Million
Emp.: 2,356
Pharmaceuticals & Nutritional Products Mfr
N.A.I.C.S.: 325412
Shinichi Ogasawara (Pres)

Subsidiary (Non-US):

Otsuka Pharmaceutical India Private Limited (3)
5th Floor Nr Parimal Crossing Ellisbridge, Ahmedabad, 380 006, India (100%)
Tel.: (91) 7926563331
Web Site: http://www.clarisotsuka.com
Infusion Therapeutic Pharmaceutical Mfr
N.A.I.C.S.: 325412

Subsidiary (Non-US):

Otsuka Pharmaceutical France SAS (2)
L'Atria - 6eme Etage 1-15 Avenue Edouard Belin, Bldg A 3 Fl, 92566, Rueil-Malmaison, Cedex, France
Tel.: (33) 147080000
Web Site: http://www.otsuka.fr
Sales Range: $25-49.9 Million
Emp.: 33
Pharmaceutical Preparation Mfr
N.A.I.C.S.: 325412

Otsuka Pharmaceutical Italy S.r.l. (2)
Via Richard 7, 20143, Milan, Italy
Tel.: (39) 0200632710
Pharmaceuticals Product Mfr
N.A.I.C.S.: 325412

Otsuka Pharmaceutical, S.A. (2)
Avda Diagonal 615, 8028, Barcelona, Spain (100%)
Tel.: (34) 932081020
Web Site: http://www.otsuka-europe.com

Sales Range: $1-9.9 Million
Emp.: 40
Provider of Pharmaceuticals & Foods
N.A.I.C.S.: 325412
Concha Caudevilla (Mng Dir)

Otsuka Pharmaceuticals (U.K.) Ltd. (2)
3 Furzeground Way, Stockley Park, UB11 1EZ, Uxbridge, United Kingdom - England
Tel.: (44) 2087424300
Web Site: http://www.otsuka-europe.com
Sales Range: $25-49.9 Million
Emp.: 20
Pharmaceutical Preparation Mfr
N.A.I.C.S.: 325412

Subsidiary (Domestic):

Otsuka Techno Co., Ltd. (2)
330 Aza Otsubo Koniu, Naka Gun Wajiki Cho, Tokushima, 771 5209, Japan (100%)
Tel.: (81) 884623111
Web Site: http://www.stnnet.ne.jp
Sales Range: $50-74.9 Million
Emp.: 200
Provider of IV Solution-Related Products
N.A.I.C.S.: 325412

Otsuka Warehouse Co., Ltd. (2)
1-3-16 Ishida, Minato-ku, Osaka, 552-0006, Japan (100%)
Tel.: (81) 66 576 5921
Web Site: https://www.otsukawh.co.jp
Warehousing & Cargo Truck Transportation Services
N.A.I.C.S.: 493110
Kazuhiko Hamanaga (Pres)

Subsidiary (Non-US):

P.T. Merapi Utama Pharma (2)
Jalan Cilosari No 25, Cikini, Jakarta, 10330, Indonesia
Tel.: (62) 213141906
Web Site: http://www.merapi.net
Sales Range: $200-249.9 Million
Emp.: 800
Distr of Pharmaceuticals, Medical Products, Nutritional Products & Hospital Consumables
N.A.I.C.S.: 424210

Sintyal Otsuka Pharmaceutical S.A. (2)
Piso 5 Jeronimo Salguero 2686, 1425, Buenos Aires, Argentina
Tel.: (54) 1148013011
Sales Range: $25-49.9 Million
Emp.: 14
Provider of Pharmaceuticals
N.A.I.C.S.: 325412

Suzhou Otsuka Pharmaceutical Co., Ltd. (2)
No 16 Zhongtianxiang Suzhou Industrial Park, Suzhou, 215011, China
Tel.: (86) 51269365666
Sales Range: $25-49.9 Million
Emp.: 80
Pharmaceuticals Product Mfr
N.A.I.C.S.: 325412
Koseki Hideo (Gen Mgr)

Subsidiary (Domestic):

Taiho Pharmaceutical Co., Ltd. (2)
1 27 Kanda Nishiki Cho, Chiyoda Ku, Tokyo, 101-8444, Japan (100%)
Tel.: (81) 332944527
Web Site: http://www.taiho.co.jp
Sales Range: $800-899.9 Million
Emp.: 3,000
Provider of Pharmaceuticals
N.A.I.C.S.: 325412
Masayuki Kobayashi (Pres)

Subsidiary (US):

TAIHO PHARMA U.S.A., INC. (3)
202 Carnegie Ctr, Princeton, NJ 08540
Tel.: (609) 750-5300
Web Site: http://www.taiho.co.jp
Sales Range: $10-24.9 Million
Emp.: 35
Pharmaceutical Products Research & Development Services
N.A.I.C.S.: 541715
Eric Benn (Pres & CEO)

Subsidiary (Non-US):

Taiho Pharmaceutical of Beijing Co., Ltd. (3)
9F-9A3 Hanwei Plaza 7th Guanghua Rd, Chaoyang Dist, Beijing, 100004, China
Tel.: (86) 10 5971 4220
Pharmaceutical Products Mfr & Advertising Services
N.A.I.C.S.: 325412
Shingo Seki (Gen Mgr)

Subsidiary (Non-US):

Taiwan Otsuka Pharmaceutical Co., Ltd. (2)
11F No 378 Fu-Hsing North Road, Taipei, 104, Taiwan
Tel.: (886) 225052868
Sales Range: $50-74.9 Million
Emp.: 120
Pharmaceutical & Healthcare Products
N.A.I.C.S.: 325412

Thai Otsuka Pharmaceutical Co., Ltd. (2)
15th Floor Unit no 1501-1502 United Center Building 323 Silom Road, Tungmahamek Sathorn, Bangkok, 10500, Silom, Thailand
Tel.: (66) 24019560
Web Site: http://www.thai-otsaka.co.th
Sales Range: $50-74.9 Million
Emp.: 200
Provider of Pharmaceuticals & Nutritional Products
N.A.I.C.S.: 325412

Subsidiary (Domestic):

Tokyo Otsuka Furniture Sales Co., Ltd. (2)
4 7 4 Harumi, Chuo Ku, Tokyo, 104 0053, Japan (70%)
Tel.: (81) 335339721
Sales Range: $25-49.9 Million
Emp.: 6
Sales of Furniture
N.A.I.C.S.: 449110

Subsidiary (Non-US):

Tuta Health Care Pty Ltd (2)
Unit 4B 128-130 Frances Street, Lidcombe, 2141, NSW, Australia (100%)
Tel.: (61) 294665300
Web Site: http://www.tuta.com.au
Sales Range: $25-49.9 Million
Emp.: 18
Provider of Disposable Medical Products
N.A.I.C.S.: 562219

Zhejiang Otsuka Pharmaceutical Co., Ltd. (2)
No 4028 Nanhuan Road, Binjiang District, Hangzhou, 310053, China
Tel.: (86) 57188250053
Web Site: http://www.zjotsuka.com
Emp.: 550
Pharmaceutical Products Mfr & Sales
N.A.I.C.S.: 325412
Ella Yan (Mgr-Govt Affairs)

Otsuka Ridge Co., Ltd. (1)
17-4 Azafukuike, Naruto, Tokushima, Japan
Tel.: (81) 886881155
Organic Chemical Mfr
N.A.I.C.S.: 325199

Otsuka S.A. (1)
Rue Du Marche 3, Geneva, 1204, Switzerland
Tel.: (41) 22 560 79 60
Pharmaceuticals Product Mfr
N.A.I.C.S.: 325412

Otsuka Sims (Guangdong) Beverage Co., Ltd (1)
No. 94 2nd Floor Block A Liwan Road, Liwan District, Guangzhou, 510170, Guangdong, China
Tel.: (86) 2081939909
Web Site: http://www.pocarisweat.cn
Bottled Water Mfr & Distr
N.A.I.C.S.: 312112

Otsuka Tech Electronics Co., Ltd. (1)
8f 13 Min Chuan E Rd Sec 1, Taipei, 10451, Taiwan
Tel.: (886) 225230660

Sales Range: $25-49.9 Million
Emp.: 50
Light Emitting Diode Mfr
N.A.I.C.S.: 334413
Toshiharu Okawara (Pres)

Otsuka Turftech Co., Ltd. (1)
1256 Shimomatsucho, Kishiwada, 596-0823, Osaka, Japan
Tel.: (81) 724274781
Web Site: http://turftech.otsukac.co.jp
Manufacture, Sales & Construction of Artificial Turf
N.A.I.C.S.: 444240

P.T. Otsuka Indonesia (1)
18 Office Park Tower A 9th Floor Jl Letjend Tb, Simatupang No 18, Jakarta, 12520, Indonesia (100%)
Tel.: (62) 217827660
Web Site: http://www.otsuka.co.id
Sales Range: $50-74.9 Million
Emp.: 125
Provider of Pharmaceuticals & Disposal Medical Equipment
N.A.I.C.S.: 325412

Subsidiary (Domestic):

P.T. Lautan Otsuka Chemical (2)
Graha Indramas 5F JI AIP II KS Tubun Raya No 77, Slipi Palmerah, Jakarta, 11410, Indonesia
Tel.: (62) 2153671251
Web Site: http://www.loc.co.id
Sales Range: $100-124.9 Million
Emp.: 300
Chemicals
N.A.I.C.S.: 325998
Tony Tegh (Mgr-Fin)

P.T. Otsuka Jaya Indah (2)
18 Office Park Tower A 9th Floor Jl Letjend Tb, Simatupang No 18, Jakarta, 12520, Indonesia (90%)
Tel.: (62) 217827660
Web Site: http://www.otsuka.co.id
Sales Range: $25-49.9 Million
Emp.: 10
Exporter of Tea Leaves
N.A.I.C.S.: 445298

P.T. Widatra Bhakti (2)
Wisma Tugu Raden Saleh 6th Floor, Jln Raden, Jakarta, 10330, Indonesia (51%)
Tel.: (62) 213911775
Web Site: http://www.widatra.com
Sales Range: $100-124.9 Million
Pharmaceuticals Mfr & Marketer
N.A.I.C.S.: 325412
I. Wayan Sudanta (Pres)

PT Amerta Indah Otsuka (2)
Wisma Pondok Indah Rm 701 702 Jalan Sultan Iskander Muda Kav 5, V TA Pondok Indah, Jakarta, 12310, Indonesia (100%)
Tel.: (62) 217697475
Web Site: http://www.amerta.co.id
Sales Range: $25-49.9 Million
Emp.: 150
Mfr of Beverages
N.A.I.C.S.: 311514
Yoshihiro Bando (Pres)

Shanghai Otsuka Foods Co., Ltd. (1)
No 1969 South Lianhua Road, Minhang District, 201108, Shanghai, China
Tel.: (86) 21 54400906
Sales Range: $50-74.9 Million
Emp.: 18
Food Products Mfr & Distr
N.A.I.C.S.: 311999

Tianjin Otsuka Beverage Co., Ltd. (1)
No 165 Dongting Rd Development Zone, Tianjin, 300457, China
Tel.: (86) 2225325988
Bottled Water & Softdrink Mfr
N.A.I.C.S.: 312112

Zhangjiagang Otsuka Chemical Co., Ltd. (1)
33 Nanhai Rd Yangziiiang International Chemical Industrial Park, Zhangjiagang, 215635, China
Tel.: (86) 51256907600
Web Site: http://zjg.otsukac.com.cn
Emp.: 120

Manufacture & Marketing of Flaky Titanate & Special Compounds
N.A.I.C.S.: 325998
Weng Yu (Deputy Dir)

OTSUKA INFORMATION TECHNOLOGY CORP.
6th Floor No 68 Section 2, Xinbei City, 220, Taiwan
Tel.: (886) 289646668
Web Site: https://www.oitc.com.tw
Year Founded: 1986
3570—(TPE)
Rev.: $48,651,752
Assets: $35,165,525
Liabilities: $8,816,528
Net Worth: $26,348,998
Earnings: $5,681,331
Fiscal Year-end: 12/31/22
Software Development Services
N.A.I.C.S.: 541511
I-Lung Kuo (Pres)

OTT-ONE PLC.
Feny Street 16 5th Floor, 1024, Budapest, Hungary
Tel.: (36) 705091406
Web Site: http://www.ott-one.hu
OTT1—(BUD)
Rev.: $9,672,725
Assets: $10,772,030
Liabilities: $2,356,972
Net Worth: $8,415,058
Earnings: $692,569
Emp.: 11
Fiscal Year-end: 12/31/19
Video System Mfr
N.A.I.C.S.: 334310

Subsidiaries:

HomeSys Media Kft. (1)
Jakab J u 17 E703, 1138, Budapest, Hungary
Tel.: (36) 1 709 0559
Set Top Box Mfr
N.A.I.C.S.: 335999

HomeSys Media Ltd. (1)
Jakab J u 17 E703, 1138, Budapest, Hungary
Tel.: (36) 1 709 0559
Set Top Box Mfr
N.A.I.C.S.: 335999

OTTAKRINGER GETRANKE AG
Ottakringer Platz 1, 1160, Vienna, Austria
Tel.: (43) 1491000
Web Site: https://www.ottakringerkonzern.com
OTS—(VIE)
Sales Range: Less than $1 Million
Beer Mfr
N.A.I.C.S.: 312120
Alfred Hudler (Chm-Mgmt Bd & CEO)

OTTAWA HONDA
955 Richmond Road, Ottawa, K2B 6R1, ON, Canada
Tel.: (613) 726-0333
Web Site:
http://www.ottawahonda.com
New & Used Car Dealers
N.A.I.C.S.: 441110
Nick Estephan (Mgr-Sls)

OTTER FARM & HOME COOPERATIVE
3650 248 St, Aldergrove, V4W 1X7, BC, Canada
Tel.: (604) 856-2517
Web Site: http://www.otter-coop.com
Sales Range: $50-74.9 Million
Emp.: 215
Farm Co-Operative Association
N.A.I.C.S.: 813910
Jim Elphick (Pres)

Otter Farm & Home Cooperative—(Continued)

OTTO BIHLER MASCHINEN-FABRIK GMBH & CO. KG
Lechbrucker Strasse 15, 87642, Halblech, Germany
Tel.: (49) 8368180
Web Site: http://www.bihler.de
Sales Range: $150-199.9 Million
Emp.: 800
Industrial Machinery Distr
N.A.I.C.S.: 423830
Mathias Pihler *(Mng Partner)*

Subsidiaries:

Bihler Machinery Co., Ltd (1)
No 329 Jujin Road, Zhang Pu Town, 215321, Kunshan, Jiangsu, China
Tel.: (86) 51236853822
Industrial Machinery Mfr
N.A.I.C.S.: 333310

Bihler of America Inc. (1)
85 Indusrial Dr, Phillipsburg, NJ 08865-3542
Tel.: (908) 213-9001
Web Site: http://www.bihler.com
Sales Range: $50-74.9 Million
Emp.: 250
Distr & Producer of Industrial Machinery & Equipment
N.A.I.C.S.: 423830
Maxine Nordmeyer *(CEO)*

Bihlerflex, LLC
55 Readington Rd, North Branch, NJ 08865
Tel.: (908) 329-9136
Web Site: http://www.bihlerflex.com
Pet Product Mfr & Distr
N.A.I.C.S.: 316990

OTTO ENERGY LIMITED
Ground Floor 70 Hindmarsh Square, Adelaide, 5000, SA, Australia
Tel.: (61) 864678800   AU
Web Site: http://www.ottoenergy.com
Year Founded: 2004
OEL—(ASX)
Rev.: $20,366,000
Assets: $54,823,000
Liabilities: $8,066,000
Net Worth: $46,757,000
Earnings: ($1,653,000)
Fiscal Year-end: 06/30/24
Oil & Gas Development & Exploration Services
N.A.I.C.S.: 213112
Kevin Small *(Exec Dir)*

Subsidiaries:

NorAsian Energy Limited (1)
4th Floor F&M Lopez Building II 109 Carlos Palanca Street, Legaspi Village, 1229, Makati, Philippines
Tel.: (63) 2857 4300
Oil & Gas Exploration Services
N.A.I.C.S.: 211120

NorAsian Energy Phils. Inc. (1)
4/F F & M Lopez Building 109 C Palanca Street, Legaspi Village, 1229, Makati, Philippines
Tel.: (63) 28574300
Sales Range: $50-74.9 Million
Emp.: 1
Oil & Gas Exploration Services
N.A.I.C.S.: 213112

Otto Energy (USA) Inc. (1)
717 Texas Ave Ste 1200, Houston, TX 77002
Tel.: (713) 893-8894
Oil & Gas Exploration Services
N.A.I.C.S.: 213111

OTTO GANTER GMBH & CO. KG
Triberger Strasse 3, Furtwangen, 78120, Germany
Tel.: (49) 772365070
Web Site: http://www.ganter-griff.de
Year Founded: 1894
Rev.: $41,382,000

Emp.: 340
Industrial Machines Components Mfr & Distr
N.A.I.C.S.: 423830
Stefan Ganter *(CEO)*

OTTO GMBH & CO. KG
Werner Otto Strasse 1-7, 22179, Hamburg, Germany
Tel.: (49) 4064610   De
Web Site: http://www.ottogroup.com
Year Founded: 1949
Rev.: $15,568,193,174
Assets: $11,008,196,398
Liabilities: $9,056,795,723
Net Worth: $1,951,400,675
Earnings: $115,133,901
Emp.: 52,558
Fiscal Year-end: 02/28/19
Mail Order & Catalog Retail Services
N.A.I.C.S.: 455219
Michael Otto *(Chm-Supervisory Bd)*

Subsidiaries:

3 Suisses International S.A. (1)
Pl de la Republique, 59963, Paris, Cedex, France (51%)
Tel.: (33) 320203062
Web Site: http://www.3suissesinternational.com
Sales Range: $5-14.9 Billion
Emp.: 13,500
Mail Order & Online Retailing
N.A.I.C.S.: 425120
Denis Terrien *(CEO)*

3SI Holding, SASU (1)
243-245 rue Jean Jaures, 59650, Villeneuve d'Ascq, France
Tel.: (33) 320201212
Web Site: http://www.groupe3si.com
Emp.: 4,900
Online Shopping Services
N.A.I.C.S.: 541690

BAUR Versand (GmbH & Co KG) (1)
Bahnhofstrasse 10, 96222, Burgkunstadt, Germany
Tel.: (49) 9572910
Web Site: http://www.baur.de
Men & Women Clothing Store Operator
N.A.I.C.S.: 458110

Baumarkt direkt GmbH & Co KG (1)
Alter Teichweg 25, 22081, Hamburg, Germany
Tel.: (49) 40235320
Web Site: http://www.baumarktdirekt.de
Emp.: 150
Online Shopping Services
N.A.I.C.S.: 541511

BorderGuru GmbH (1)
Amandastrasse 58 3 OG, 20357, Hamburg, Germany
Tel.: (49) 40226162860
Web Site: http://www.borderguru.com
Logistics Consulting Servies
N.A.I.C.S.: 541614
Hannah Noethig *(Head-Ops)*

Collins GmbH & Co. KG (1)
Domstrasse 10, 20095, Hamburg, Germany
Tel.: (49) 406385690
Web Site: http://www.projekt-collins.de
Emp.: 200
Online Shopping Services
N.A.I.C.S.: 541690
Miriam Kruger *(Sr Mgr-HR)*

Crate & Barrel Holdings, Inc. (1)
1860 W Jefferson Ave, Naperville, IL 60540-3918
Tel.: (630) 369-4464
Web Site: http://www.crateandbarrel.com
Emp.: 7,500
Furniture & Furnishing Product Whslr
N.A.I.C.S.: 423210

DBR Comercio de Artigos do Vestuario S.A. (1)
R Werner Duwe, Pomerode, 89107-000, Brazil
Tel.: (55) 4733316677
Emp.: 87

Online Shopping Services
N.A.I.C.S.: 458110

EOS Holding GmbH (1)
Steindamm 71, 20099, Hamburg, Germany (100%)
Tel.: (49) 4025328657
Web Site: http://www.eos-solutions.com
Sales Range: $700-749.9 Million
Emp.: 9,500
Adjustment & Collection Services
N.A.I.C.S.: 561440
Klaus Engberding *(Chm)*

Subsidiary (Non-US):

Alphapay AG (2)
Neugasse 18, CH-8005, Zurich, Switzerland
Tel.: (41) 848863863
Web Site: http://www.alphapay.ch
Debt Collection Services
N.A.I.C.S.: 561440

EOS Canada Inc. (2)
325 Milner Avenue Suite 1111, Toronto, M1B 5N1, ON, Canada
Tel.: (416) 412-3070
Web Site: https://tsico.ca
Emp.: 200
Receivables Management Services
N.A.I.C.S.: 561440
Jim Shaw *(COO)*

EOS Credirec SAS (2)
10 Impasse de Presles, PO Box 587, 75726, Paris, Cedex 15, France
Tel.: (33) 1 535839 39
Web Site: http://www.eos-credirec.com
Debt Collection Agency
N.A.I.C.S.: 561440
Nathalie Lameyre *(Pres)*

Subsidiary (US):

EOS Holdings Inc. (2)
700 Long Water Dr, Norwell, MA 02061
Tel.: (781) 659-1551
Web Site: http://www.cca-us.com
Rev.: $19,451,813
Emp.: 600
Adjustment & Collection Services
N.A.I.C.S.: 561440
Paul E. Leary Sr. *(Mng Dir)*

Subsidiary (Non-US):

EOS Hong Kong Ltd (2)
Unit 2114-2115 21/F Peninsula Square 18 Sung On Street, Hung Hom, Kowloon, China (Hong Kong)
Tel.: (852) 2773 5088
Web Site: http://www.eos-hongkong.com
Collection Services
N.A.I.C.S.: 561440
Cobe Tsang *(Mng Dir)*

EOS Solutions UK Plc (2)
2 Birchwood Office Park Crab Lane, Fearnhead, Warrington, WA2 0XS, United Kingdom
Tel.: (44) 1925 816 626
Web Site: http://uk.eos-solutions.com
Collection Services
N.A.I.C.S.: 561440
Stuart Knock *(CEO)*

Euromarket Designs, Inc. (1)
1250 Techny Rd, Northbrook, IL 60062-2349
Tel.: (847) 272-2888
Web Site: http://www.crateandbarrel.com
Sales Range: $1-4.9 Billion
Emp.: 7,000
Home Furnishings Retailer
N.A.I.C.S.: 449129
Jennifer Olsen *(CMO)*

Euronova s.r.l. (1)
Via Adua 33, Valdengo, 13855, Biella, Italy (100%)
Tel.: (39) 0159845112
Web Site: http://www.euronova-italia.it
Mail Order Catalog Company
N.A.I.C.S.: 423310

Frankonia Handels GmbH & Co. KG (1)
Schiesshausstrasse 10, 97228, Wurzburg, Germany
Tel.: (49) 9302200
Web Site: http://www.frankonia.de

Emp.: 700
Online Shopping Distr
N.A.I.C.S.: 425120

Freemans Grattan Holdings (FGH) (1)
66-70 Vicar Lane Little Germany, Bradford, BD99 2XG, United Kingdom (84%)
Tel.: (44) 1274575511
Web Site: http://fgh-uk.com
Sales Range: $450-499.9 Million
Emp.: 1,000
Online Retailer & e-Commerce Services
N.A.I.C.S.: 458110
Neela Montgomery *(Member of Executive Board)*

Handelsgesellschaft Heinrich Heine GmbH (1)
Windeckstrasse 15, 76135, Karlsruhe, Germany (100%)
Tel.: (49) 7219910
Web Site: http://si.de
Sales Range: $200-249.9 Million
Emp.: 500
Retail Catalog Service Distr
N.A.I.C.S.: 424350
Rigo Konrad *(Dir-HR)*

Subsidiary (Non-US):

Heinrich Heine Handelsgesellschaft AG (2)
Industriestrasse 19, 8112, Otelfingen, Switzerland (100%)
Tel.: (41) 848800060
Web Site: http://www.heine.ch
Sales Range: $50-74.9 Million
Emp.: 200
Provider of Retail Catalog Services
N.A.I.C.S.: 425120

Jelmoli Versand AG (2)
Jelmoli Otelsengan, Zurich, 8088, Switzerland (35%)
Tel.: (41) 848840300
Web Site: http://www.jelmoli-shop.ch
Sales Range: $25-49.9 Million
Emp.: 50
Online & Mail-Order Retail Services
N.A.I.C.S.: 424350

Subsidiary (Domestic):

Sport-Scheck GmbH (2)
Neuhauser Strasse 21, 80331, Munich, Germany (100%)
Tel.: (49) 8961101616
Web Site: http://www.sportscheck.com
Sales Range: $75-99.9 Million
Emp.: 400
Provider of Apparel & Accessories
N.A.I.C.S.: 315990

Hanseatic Versicherungsdienst GmbH (1)
Bramfelder Chaussee 105, 22177, Hamburg, Germany
Tel.: (49) 40646500
Web Site: http://www.hvd.de
Emp.: 40
Commercial Banking Services
N.A.I.C.S.: 522110

Heinrich Heine GmbH (1)
Windeckstrasse 15, 76135, Karlsruhe, Germany
Tel.: (49) 7219910
Web Site: http://www.heine.de
Emp.: 1,500
Online Shopping Services
N.A.I.C.S.: 458110

Hermes Einrichtungs Service GmbH & Co.KG (1)
Friedrichstrasse 18, 32584, Lohne, Germany
Tel.: (49) 57321030
Logistics Consulting Servies
N.A.I.C.S.: 541614

Hermes Europe GmbH (1)
Essener Strasse 89, 22419, Hamburg, Germany
Tel.: (49) 40537550
Web Site: http://www.hermesworld.com
Parcel Shipping Services
N.A.I.C.S.: 492210
Hendrik Schneider *(CFO)*

AND PRIVATE COMPANIES
OTTO GMBH & CO. KG

Hermes Fulfilment GmbH (1)
Bannwarthstrasse 5, 22179, Hamburg, Germany
Tel.: (49) 406460410
Online Shopping Services
N.A.I.C.S.: 493110
Christian Naumann *(Mgr-Bus Dev)*

Hermes Italia S.p.A. (1)
Via del Commercio 3/5, Francolino di Carpiano, 20080, Milan, Italy
Tel.: (39) 0298857301
Web Site: http://www.hermes-italy.it
Logistics Consulting Servies
N.A.I.C.S.: 541614

Hermes Logistik GmbH & Co KG (1)
Concorde Business Park 1 D 1/7, 2320, Schwechat, Austria
Tel.: (43) 50437637
Parcel Delivering Services
N.A.I.C.S.: 492110

Hermes Logistik GmbH & Co. KG (1)
Essener Strasse 89, PO Box 620260, Hamburg, 22402, Germany (100%)
Tel.: (49) 40537550
Web Site: http://www.hlg.de
Sales Range: $1-4.9 Billion
Emp.: 3,200
Mail Order Services
N.A.I.C.S.: 492110

Hermes NexTec GmbH (1)
Essener Bogen 6b, 22419, Hamburg, Germany
Tel.: (49) 408405640
Online Shopping Services
N.A.I.C.S.: 541511
Tina Gershkovich *(Mgr-Shop)*

Hermes Parcelnet Limited (1)
Capitol House 1 Capitol Close, Morley, Leeds, LS27 0WH, United Kingdom
Tel.: (44) 8445437067
Web Site: http://www.myhermes.co.uk
Courier Service
N.A.I.C.S.: 492110
Martijn de Lange *(CEO)*

Hermes Russia (1)
Nauchny proezd house 19 office 1B, Moscow, 117246, Russia
Tel.: (7) 4993720049
Web Site: http://www.hermesrussia.ru
Parcel Delivering Services
N.A.I.C.S.: 492110

House of Brands GmbH (1)
Osterfeldstrasse 12-14, 22529, Hamburg, Germany
Tel.: (49) 408000778100
Web Site: http://www.houseofbrands.de
Online Shopping Services
N.A.I.C.S.: 493110

KG Hermes Versand Service GmbH & Co. (1)
Essener Strasse 89, 22419, Hamburg, Germany (100%)
Tel.: (49) 40 537 55 495
Packaging & Transport Logistics
N.A.I.C.S.: 541614

Kuche & Co GmbH (1)
Werner-Otto-Str 1-7, 22179, Hamburg, Germany
Tel.: (49) 40 64 61 11 85
Web Site: http://www.kueche-co.de
Emp.: 30
Kitchen Appliance Distr
N.A.I.C.S.: 423620

Manufactum GmbH & Co. KG (1)
Hiberniastrasse 5, 45731, Waltrop, Germany
Tel.: (49) 230993900
Web Site: http://www.manufactum.de
Emp.: 500
Online Shopping Services
N.A.I.C.S.: 425120

NuBON GmbH & Co. KG (1)
Hartzloh 25, 22307, Hamburg, Germany
Tel.: (49) 4088190220
Web Site: http://www.osp.de
Emp.: 30
Software Development Services
N.A.I.C.S.: 541511

Norbert Godicke *(Mng Dir)*

Ondemandcommerce GmbH (1)
Poststrasse 12, 20354, Hamburg, Germany
Tel.: (49) 40696359040
Web Site: http://www.ondemandcommerce.com
Logistic Services
N.A.I.C.S.: 541614
Christian Athen *(Mng Dir)*

Otto Group Digital Solutions GmbH (1)
Poststrasse 12, 20354, Hamburg, Germany
Tel.: (49) 40696359023
Web Site: http://www.ogds.de
Information Technology Services
N.A.I.C.S.: 541511
Alexandra Bastian *(Mgr-HR)*

Otto Group Media GmbH (1)
Werner-Otto-Strasse 1-7, 22179, Hamburg, Germany
Tel.: (49) 4032890660
Web Site: http://www.ottogroup.media
Emp.: 15
Online Advertising Services
N.A.I.C.S.: 541810

Otto Group Russia OOO (1)
27 Vyatskaya Str bld 22 23, Moscow, 127015, Russia
Tel.: (7) 4957758687
Web Site: http://www.otto.ru
Emp.: 1,000
Online Shopping Services
N.A.I.C.S.: 425120
Martin Schierer *(CEO)*

Otto International Hong Kong Ltd (1)
19F Peninsula Square 18 San Juan Street, Kowloon, China (Hong Kong) (60%)
Tel.: (852) 23037000
Web Site: http://www.otto.de
Sales Range: $50-74.9 Million
Emp.: 250
Provider of Mail Order Services
N.A.I.C.S.: 424350
Anita Poon *(Mgr-Mdse)*

Otto Japan Inc. (1)
1-18-10 Wakabayashi, Setagaya-ku, Tokyo, 154-8551, Japan
Tel.: (81) 354312881
Web Site: http://www.otto-online.jp
Sales Range: $450-499.9 Million
Emp.: 1,010
Mail Order Catalog Services
N.A.I.C.S.: 455219
T. Taida *(Dir-Sls)*

Joint Venture (Domestic):

Eddie Bauer Japan, Inc. (2)
16-9 Nihonbashi Hakozaki-cho, Chuo-Ku, Tokyo, 103-0015, Japan
Tel.: (81) 354312881
Web Site: http://www.eddiebauer.co.jp
Sales Range: $75-99.9 Million
Mail Order Catalog Services; Owned 30% by Eddie Bauer Inc. & 70% by OTTO Japan Inc.
N.A.I.C.S.: 459110

Otto Reisen GmbH (1)
Osterbekstrasse 90a, 22083, Hamburg, Germany (100%)
Tel.: (49) 4027838466
Web Site: http://www.otto-reisen.de
Sales Range: $25-49.9 Million
Emp.: 200
Travel Services
N.A.I.C.S.: 561510
Christoph Rische *(Mng Dir)*

Project A Ventures GmbH & Co. KG (1)
Julie-Wolfthorn-Strasse 1, 10115, Berlin, Germany
Tel.: (49) 30 340 606 300
Web Site: http://www.project-a.com
Emp.: 100
Investment Management Service
N.A.I.C.S.: 523940

Pruetinstitut Hansecontrol GmbH (1)
Schleidenstrasse 1, 22083, Hamburg, Germany
Tel.: (49) 4030033737310
Testing Services

N.A.I.C.S.: 541380

Reiseland GmbH & Co. KG (1)
Osterbekstr 90A, 22083, Hamburg, Germany (63%)
Tel.: (49) 4027842600
Web Site: http://www.reiseland.de
Sales Range: $300-349.9 Million
Emp.: 2,000
Owner & Operator of Travel Agency Services
N.A.I.C.S.: 561510
Mark Campz *(Mng Dir)*

Risk.Ident GmbH (1)
Am Sandtorkai 50, 20457, Hamburg, Germany
Tel.: (49) 40609452590
Web Site: http://www.riskident.com
Emp.: 25
Software Development Services
N.A.I.C.S.: 541511

Saint Brice S.A. (1)
Chaussee de Lille 422, Orcq, 7501, Tournai, Belgium (100%)
Tel.: (32) 70 233343
Web Site: http://www.3suisses.be
Mail Order Catalog Company
N.A.I.C.S.: 423320
Regis Lemaire *(Editor)*

Subsidiary (Domestic):

Alfigen S.A. (2)
, Brussels, Belgium (100%)
Mail Order Catalog Company
N.A.I.C.S.: 423320

Subsidiary (Non-US):

Banque Covefi S.A. (2)
, Wasquehal, France (66%)
Mail Order Catalog Company
N.A.I.C.S.: 522320

Finadis S.A. (2)
, Madrid, Spain (85%)
Mail Order Catalog Company
N.A.I.C.S.: 423320

Schwab Versand GmbH E-Commerce (1)
Kinzigheimer Weg 6, 63450, Hanau, Germany (100%)
Tel.: (49) 61813680
Web Site: http://www.schwab.de
Sales Range: $450-499.9 Million
Emp.: 1,500
Mail Order Services
N.A.I.C.S.: 425120

Subsidiary (Domestic):

Josef Witt GmbH (2)
Schillerstrasse 4-12, 92637, Weiden, Germany (100%)
Tel.: (49) 9614000
Web Site: http://www.witt-gruppe.de
Sales Range: $400-449.9 Million
Provider of Mail Order Services
N.A.I.C.S.: 424350
Juergen Angstmann *(Mng Dir & Member-Mgmt Bd)*

Subsidiary (Non-US):

Otto Versand GmbH (2)
Alte Postrasse 152, 8020, Graz, Austria (100%)
Tel.: (43) 316606888
Web Site: http://www.ottoversand.at
Provider of Mail Order Services
N.A.I.C.S.: 424350

Subsidiary (Domestic):

Schwab Versand GmbH (2)
Kinzigheimer Weg 6, 63450, Hanau, Germany (100%)
Tel.: (49) 61813680
Web Site: http://www.schwabversand.de
Sales Range: $250-299.9 Million
Mail Order Catalog Company; Provider of Travel Services
N.A.I.C.S.: 561510

Sheego GmbH (1)
Hanauer Landstrasse 523, 60386, Frankfurt, Germany
Tel.: (49) 69900220

Web Site: http://www.company.sheego.de
Clothing Accessory Retailer
N.A.I.C.S.: 458110

Systain Consulting GmbH (1)
Hubertus Drinkuth Brandstwiete 1, 20457, Hamburg, Germany
Tel.: (49) 4060946180
Web Site: http://en.systain.com
Management Consulting Services
N.A.I.C.S.: 541618
Norbert Jüngmichel *(Mgr)*

Together Ltd. (1)
26 28 Conway St, London, W1K 6BH, United Kingdom (50%)
Tel.: (44) 2072092222
Web Site: http://www.together.co.uk
Sales Range: $25-49.9 Million
Emp.: 20
Catalog Services
N.A.I.C.S.: 541611
Jenny Brennan *(Mng Dir)*

UNITO Versand & Dienstleistungen GmbH (1)
Peilsteinerstrasse 5-7, 5020, Salzburg, Austria
Tel.: (43) 662448951281
Web Site: http://www.unito.at
Emp.: 645
Online Shopping Services
N.A.I.C.S.: 425120

Yapital Financial AG (1)
5 rue Eugene Ruppert, 2453, Luxembourg, Luxembourg
Tel.: (352) 20310600
Web Site: http://www.yapital.com
Emp.: 130
Software Development Services
N.A.I.C.S.: 541511
Marc Berg *(CEO)*

bonprix Handelsgesellschaft mbH (1)
Haldesdorfer Strasse 61, 22179, Hamburg, Germany (100%)
Tel.: (49) 4064620
Web Site: http://www.bonprix.de
Sales Range: $200-249.9 Million
Emp.: 700
Mail Order Catalog Company
N.A.I.C.S.: 424350

Subsidiary (Non-US):

bon prix Sp. z.o.o. (2)
Lodowa 101, 93-232, Lodz, Poland (100%)
Tel.: (48) 426494949
Web Site: http://www.bonprix.pl
Sales Range: $100-124.9 Million
Emp.: 300
Mail Order Catalog Company
N.A.I.C.S.: 425120

eVenture Capital Partners II, LLC (1)
600 Montgomery St 43rd Fl, San Francisco, CA 94111
Tel.: (415) 869-5200
Financial Management Services
N.A.I.C.S.: 523910

Subsidiary (Non-US):

e.ventures Managementgesellschaft mbH (2)
Hohe Bleichen 21, 20354, Hamburg, Germany
Tel.: (49) 4082225550
Web Site: http://www.eventures.vc
Financial Management Services
N.A.I.C.S.: 523910
Patrick Reilly *(CFO-Global)*

limango GmbH (1)
Landsberger Strasse 6, 80339, Munich, Germany
Tel.: (49) 89248850
Web Site: http://www.limango.de
Emp.: 240
Online Shopping Services
N.A.I.C.S.: 425120

myloys.de GmbH (1)
Potsdamer Str 192, 10783, Berlin, Germany (94.8%)
Tel.: (49) 30726201201
Web Site: http://www.mytoys.de

OTTO GMBH & CO. KG

Otto GmbH & Co. KG—(Continued)
Online Toy Retailer
N.A.I.C.S.: 459120
Oliver Lederle (Founder, Chm & CEO)

OTTO HAAS KG
Giessener Strasse 5, 90427, Nuremberg, Germany
Tel.: (49) 91193660
Web Site: http://www.haas.de
Rev.: $29,077,890
Emp.: 128
Tool Mfr
N.A.I.C.S.: 333517
Thomas Haas (Mng Partner)

OTTO JUNKER GMBH
Jaegerhausstr 22, 52152, Simmerath, Germany
Tel.: (49) 24736010
Web Site: http://www.otto-junker.com
Year Founded: 1924
Sales Range: $125-149.9 Million
Emp.: 800
Industrial Furnace Machinery & High Grade Steel Casting Mfr
N.A.I.C.S.: 333994
Markus D. Werner (CEO)

Subsidiaries:

Erwin Junker Machinery, Inc. (1)
2541 Technology Drv, Elgin, IL 60124
Tel.: (847) 488-0406
Web Site: http://www.junker-usa.com
Grinding Machine Mfr & Distr
N.A.I.C.S.: 333248

INDUGA Industrieofen and Giesserei-Anlagen GmbH & Co. KG (1)
Gros Galet Jagerhausstr 2, Lammersdorf, 52152, Simmerath, Germany
Tel.: (49) 2473 601710
Web Site: http://www.induga.de
Stainless Steel Products Mfr
N.A.I.C.S.: 331110
Frank Donsbach (Co-Mng Dir)

Junker Industrial Equipment s.r.o (1)
Chrudichromska 7, 68001, Boskovice, Czech Republic (100%)
Tel.: (420) 516499315
Web Site: http://www.otto-junker.de
Mfr of Industrial Furnaces, Machinery & High Grade Steel Castings
N.A.I.C.S.: 333994
L. Siebertz (Mng Dir)

Otto Junker (UK) Ltd. (1)
Kingsbury Rd Curdworth, Sutton, B76 9EE, United Kingdom (100%)
Tel.: (44) 675470551
Web Site: http://www.ottojunker.co.uk
Sales Range: $25-49.9 Million
Emp.: 29
Mfr of Industrial Furnaces, Machinery & High Grade Steel Castings
N.A.I.C.S.: 333994

Otto Junker Metallurgical Equipment (Shanghai) Co., Ltd. (1)
Shanghai Yangpu Qu Bo Yang Lu No 16, 200090, Shanghai, China
Tel.: (86) 21 6580 5796
Stainless Steel Products Distr
N.A.I.C.S.: 423510

OTTO SCHNEIDER GMBH UND CO. KG
Raiffeisenstrasse 5, Dreieich, 63303, Germany
Tel.: (49) 61038008030
Web Site: http://www.otto-schneider.de
Year Founded: 1926
Rev.: $12,690,480
Emp.: 20
Wood Products Mfr
N.A.I.C.S.: 321999
Hermann Schneider (Mng Dir)

OTTOBOCK HOLDING GMBH & CO. KG
Max-Nader-Strasse 15, 37115, Duderstadt, Germany
Tel.: (49) 55278480
Web Site: http://www.ottobock-holding.com
Year Founded: 1919
Emp.: 8,000
Holding Company for HealthCare Companies (Wheelchairs & Prosthetics Mfg), Mfrs of Plastics for the Automotive Industry & Information & Communication Technology Companies
N.A.I.C.S.: 551112
Hans Georg Nader (Pres)

Subsidiaries:

Industria Ortopedica Otto Bock Unip. Lda. (1)
Av Miguel Bombarda 21-2 Esq, 1050-161, Lisbon, Portugal
Tel.: (351) 21 3535587
Medical Equipment Distr
N.A.I.C.S.: 423450

OOO Otto Bock Service (1)
p/o Pultikovo Business Park Greenwood Building 7 69 km Mkad Building 7, Krasnogorskiy Rayon, 143441, Moscow, Russia
Tel.: (7) 4955648360
Web Site: http://www.ottobock.ru
Medical Equipment Distr
N.A.I.C.S.: 423450

Otto Bock Adria D.O.O. (1)
Franje Tudmana 14, 10431, Sveta Nedelja, Zagreb, Croatia (100%)
Tel.: (385) 13361544
Web Site: http://www.ottobock.hr
Sales Range: $25-49.9 Million
Emp.: 30
Wheelchair & Prosthetics Mfr
N.A.I.C.S.: 339113
Marko Husinc (Gen Mgr)

Otto Bock Adria Sarajewo D.O.O. (1)
Omladinskih Radnih Brigada 5, 71000, Sarajevo, Bosnia & Herzegovina (100%)
Tel.: (387) 33766200
Web Site: http://www.ottobockadria.com.ba
Sales Range: $25-49.9 Million
Emp.: 13
Wheelchair & Prosthetics Mfg
N.A.I.C.S.: 339113
Mirjana Mocevic (VP)

Otto Bock Algerie E.U.R.L. (1)
32 rue Ahcene outalab Cooperative les Mimosas, Ben Aknoun, Algeria
Tel.: (213) 21 913863
Medical Equipment Distr
N.A.I.C.S.: 423450

Otto Bock Ankara Regional Office (1)
Gazi Mahallesi Silahtar Caddesi No 106, Yenimahalle, Ankara, 06560, Turkiye (100%)
Tel.: (90) 312 205 0020
Web Site: http://www.ottobock.com.tr
Wheelchair & Prosthetics Mfr
N.A.I.C.S.: 339113

Otto Bock Argentina S.A. (1)
Av Belgrano 1477, Ciudad Aut de, 1093, Buenos Aires, Argentina
Tel.: (54) 11 5032 8201
Web Site: http://www.ottobock.com.ar
Medical Equipment Mfr
N.A.I.C.S.: 339112

Otto Bock Asia Pacific Limited (1)
Unit 301 3/F Tower A Cheung Kei Center 18 Hung Luen Road, Hung Hom, Kowloon, China (Hong Kong)
Tel.: (852) 37563333
Web Site: http://www.ottobock.com.hk
Medical Equipment Distr
N.A.I.C.S.: 423450

Otto Bock Australia Pty. Ltd. (1)
Suite 1 01 Century Corporate Centre 62 Norwest Boulevarde, Norwest Business Park, Baulkham Hills, 2153, NSW, Australia
Tel.: (61) 2 8818 2800
Web Site: http://www.ottobock.com.au
Medical Equipment Mfr
N.A.I.C.S.: 339113
Jacinta Maurin (Bus Mgr-Mobility Solutions)

Otto Bock Bulgaria Ltd. (1)
41 Tzar Boris III' Blvd, 1612, Sofia, Bulgaria
Tel.: (359) 2 80 57 980
Web Site: http://www.ottobock.bg
Medical Equipment Distr
N.A.I.C.S.: 423450

Otto Bock CR s.r.o. (1)
Proteticka 460, 33008, Senec, Czech Republic (100%)
Tel.: (420) 377825044
Web Site: http://www.ottobock.cz
Sales Range: $25-49.9 Million
Emp.: 40
Wheelchair & Prosthetics Mfr
N.A.I.C.S.: 339113
Vaclav Svrcek (Mng Dir)

Otto Bock Chile S.p.A. (1)
Manuel Montt 901, Santiago, 7500980, Providencia, Chile
Tel.: (56) 2 9202213
Medical Equipment Distr
N.A.I.C.S.: 423450

Otto Bock Egypt S.A.E. (1)
28 Soliman Abaza st, Mohandessein, Giza, Egypt
Tel.: (20) 2 330 24 390
Medical Equipment Mfr
N.A.I.C.S.: 339112

Otto Bock France S.A.R.L. (1)
4 Rue de la Reunion, BP11, Les Ulis, 91978, France (100%)
Tel.: (33) 169188830
Web Site: http://www.ottobock.fr
Sales Range: $25-49.9 Million
Emp.: 80
Wheelchair & Prosthetics Mfg
N.A.I.C.S.: 339113
Mario Henkel (Mgr)

Otto Bock HealthCare GmbH (1)
Max-Nader-Strasse 15, 37115, Duderstadt, Germany
Tel.: (49) 55278480
Orthopedic Technology & Supplier of Products for Mobility Impaired
N.A.I.C.S.: 423450

Subsidiary (Non-US):

Otto Bock Health Care Ecuador (2)
Av America y Voz Andes, Edificio Kensen of 203, Quito, Ecuador
Tel.: (593) 2 226 1304
Medical Equipment Distr
N.A.I.C.S.: 423450

Otto Bock Health Care Peru (2)
Calle Parque Maldonado 160, Pueblo Libre, Lima, Peru
Tel.: (51) 1 331 2326
Medical Equipment Distr
N.A.I.C.S.: 423450

Branch (US):

Otto Bock HealthCare (2)
2 Carlson Pkwy N Ste 100, Minneapolis, MN 55447 (100%)
Tel.: (763) 553-9464
Web Site: http://www.ottobockus.com
Wheelchair & Prosthetics Mfr
N.A.I.C.S.: 339113
Sarah Kuechle (Mgr-Ops-Prof & Clinical Svcs)

Subsidiary (Non-US):

Otto Bock HealthCare Andina Ltda. (2)
Centro de Excelencia & Showroom Carrera 22 164-34, Bogota, Colombia
Tel.: (57) 1 861 9988
Web Site: http://www.ottobock.com.co
Medical Equipment Mfr
N.A.I.C.S.: 339112
Angelica Russi Sanchez (Mgr-Mktg Orthosis & Prosthesis)

Otto Bock Healthcare Canada Ltd. (2)
5470 Harvester Road, Burlington, L7L 5N5, ON, Canada
Web Site: http://www.ottobock.ca
Medical Equipment Mfr

INTERNATIONAL PUBLIC

N.A.I.C.S.: 339112
Mark Agro (VP-Govt & Industry Rels)

Otto Bock Healthcare Products GmbH (2)
Brehmstrasse 16, 1110, Vienna, Austria
Tel.: (43) 1 5233786
Web Site: http://www.ottobock.at
Emp.: 600
Medical Equipment Distr
N.A.I.C.S.: 423450
Andreas Goppelt (Mng Dir)

Otto Bock Healthcare plc (2)
Englefield Green, 32 Parsonage Road, Egham, TW20 0LD, Surrey, United Kingdom (100%)
Tel.: (44) 1784744900
Web Site: http://www.ottobock.co.uk
Wheelchair & Prosthetics Mfr
N.A.I.C.S.: 339113
Phil Yates (Mng Dir)

Otto Bock HealthCare India Pvt. Ltd. (1)
01st Floor Vikas Centre Dr C G Road Chembar East, Mumbai, 400 074, India
Tel.: (91) 2225526701
Web Site: http://www.ottobock.in
Medical Equipment Mfr
N.A.I.C.S.: 339113
Amit Mukerji (Dir-Strategic Projects)

Otto Bock Holding GmbH & Co. KG (1)
Block 3 Thornhill Office Park 94 Bekker Street, Midrand, South Africa
Tel.: (27) 11 564 9360
Web Site: http://www.ottobock.co.za
Medical Equipment Mfr
N.A.I.C.S.: 339112
Eduan Gunter (Mgr-Sls-Natl)

Otto Bock Hungaria Kft. (1)
Tatai ut 74, 1135, Budapest, Hungary
Tel.: (36) 1 451 1020
Web Site: http://www.ottobock.hu
Medical Equipment Mfr
N.A.I.C.S.: 339113

Otto Bock Iberica S.A. (1)
Calle de la Majada, Tres Cantos, Madrid, 28760, Spain (100%)
Tel.: (34) 918063000
Web Site: http://www.ottobock.es
Sales Range: $25-49.9 Million
Emp.: 53
Wheelchair & Prosthetics Mfr
N.A.I.C.S.: 339113

Otto Bock Italia S.R.L. (1)
Via Filippo Turati 5/7, Budrio, 40054, Bologna, Italy (100%)
Tel.: (39) 051 692 47 11
Web Site: http://www.ottobock.it
Wheelchair & Prosthetics Mfr
N.A.I.C.S.: 339113

Otto Bock Japan K. K. (1)
Yokogawa Building 8F 4-4-44 Shibaura, Minato-ku, Tokyo, 108-0023, Japan
Tel.: (81) 3 3798 2111
Web Site: http://www.ottobock.co.jp
Medical Equipment Mfr
N.A.I.C.S.: 339113

Otto Bock Korea HealthCare Inc. (1)
4F Yongdo Building 1 Yangjaecheon ro 9 gil, Seocho-gu, Seoul, 06754, Korea (South)
Tel.: (82) 2 577 3831
Web Site: http://www.ottobockkorea.com
Medical Equipment Distr
N.A.I.C.S.: 423450

Otto Bock Manufacturing Konigsee GmbH (1)
Lindenstrasse 13, 07426, Konigsee-Rottenbach, Germany
Tel.: (49) 36738 79 0
Medical Equipment Mfr
N.A.I.C.S.: 339113

Otto Bock Maroc Sarl (1)
186 route des Ouled Ziane, Casablanca, Morocco
Tel.: (212) 5 22 28 04 30
Medical Equipment Distr
N.A.I.C.S.: 423450

Otto Bock Moscow (1)

5-Donskoj Projezd 15-16, RUS-119334, Moscow, Russia **(100%)**
Tel.: (7) 095 564 83 60
Web Site: http://www.ottobock.ru
Wheelchair & Prosthetics Mfr
N.A.I.C.S.: 339113

Otto Bock Ortopedi ve Rehabilitasyon Teknigi Ltd. Sti. (1)
Ali Dursun Dey Caddesi Lati Lokum Sokak, Meric Sitesi B Blok No:6/1, Istanbul, 34387, Mecidiyekoy, Turkiye **(100%)**
Tel.: (90) 2123565040
Web Site: http://www.ottobock.com.tr
Sales Range: $25-49.9 Million
Emp.: 40
Wheelchair & Prosthetics Mfr
N.A.I.C.S.: 339113
Hasan Urey *(Gen Mgr)*

Otto Bock Polska Sp. z o.o (1)
Ulica Koralowa 3, 61-029, Poznan, Poland
Tel.: (48) 61 6538250
Web Site: http://www.ottobock.pl
Medical Equipment Mfr
N.A.I.C.S.: 339112
Pawel Rafalski *(Mgr-Sls & Mktg)*

Otto Bock SAVA D.O.O. (1)
Maksima Gorkog bb, SRB-18000, Nis, Serbia **(100%)**
Tel.: (381) 18 4285 888
Web Site: http://www.ottobock.rs
Wheelchair & Prosthetics Mfr
N.A.I.C.S.: 339113

Otto Bock Scandinavia AB (1)
Koppargatan 3, PO Box 623, Norrkoping, 60223, Sweden **(100%)**
Tel.: (46) 11280600
Web Site: http://www.ottobock.se
Sales Range: $50-74.9 Million
Emp.: 120
Wheelchairs & Prosthetics Mfr
N.A.I.C.S.: 339113
Krister Elosson *(Mng Dir)*

Otto Bock Slovakia s.r.o. (1)
Rontgenova 26, 851 01, Bratislava, Slovakia
Tel.: (421) 915090060
Web Site: http://www.ottobock.sk
Medical Equipment Mfr
N.A.I.C.S.: 339112

Otto Bock Southeast Asia Co. Ltd. (1)
1741 Paholyothin Rd, Chatuchak, Bangkok, 10900, Thailand
Tel.: (66) 2930 2020
Web Site: http://www.ottobock.co.th
Medical Equipment Mfr
N.A.I.C.S.: 339112
Chatchai Thongkhiao *(Dir-Web Content & Editor)*

Otto Bock Suisse AG (1)
Luzerner Kantonsspital 10, 6000, Lucerne, Switzerland
Tel.: (41) 41 455 61 71
Web Site: http://www.ottobock.ch
Medical Equipment Mfr
N.A.I.C.S.: 339112
Monika Baumann *(Mng Dir)*

Otto Bock de Mexico, S.A. de C.V. (1)
Prol Calle 18 No 178A, San Pedro de los Pinos, 1180, Mexico, Mexico
Tel.: (52) 55 5278 4160
Web Site: http://www.ottobock.com.mx
Emp.: 30
Medical Equipment Mfr
N.A.I.C.S.: 339112
Monica Guadalajara *(Editor-Mktg)*

Otto Bock do Brasil Tecnica Ortopedica Ltda (1)
Alameda Maria Tereza n 4036, Dois Corregos, 13278-181, Valinhos, Sao Paulo, Brazil
Tel.: (55) 19 3729 3500
Web Site: http://www.ottobock.com.br
Emp.: 1,000
Medical Equipment Mfr
N.A.I.C.S.: 339113
Marcos Freitas *(Gen Mgr)*

Otto Buck Benelux B.V. (1)
Ekkersrijt 1412-1414, NL-5692-AK, Son, Netherlands **(100%)**
Tel.: (31) 499474585
Web Site: http://www.ottobock.nl
Sales Range: $25-49.9 Million
Emp.: 50
Wheelchair & Prosthetics Mfg
N.A.I.C.S.: 339113
Cas Welling *(Mng Dir)*

Ottobock (China) Industries Co., Ltd. (1)
3rd Floor Building B36-B Universal Business Park 10 Jiuxianqiao Road, Chaoyang District, 100015, Beijing, China
Tel.: (86) 10 85986880
Web Site: http://www.ottobock.com.cn
Medical Equipment Mfr
N.A.I.C.S.: 339112
Georg Hoffmann-Kuhnt *(Dir-Tech)*

Ottobock Izmir Regional Office (1)
1356 Sokak No:3/A, TR-35220, Izmir, Alsancak, Turkiye **(100%)**
Tel.: (90) 2324631948
Web Site: http://www.ottobock.com.tr
Sales Range: $25-49.9 Million
Emp.: 4
Wheelchair & Prosthetics Mfr
N.A.I.C.S.: 339113
Karl-Heinz Burghardt *(Pres-EEMEA)*

S.C. Otto Bock Romania S.R.L. (1)
Sos de Centura Chitila Mogosoaia Nr 3 Parter, 077405, Chitila, Ilfov, Romania **(100%)**
Tel.: (40) 214363110
Web Site: http://www.ottobock.com
Sales Range: $25-49.9 Million
Emp.: 8
Wheelchair & Prosthetic Mfr
N.A.I.C.S.: 339113
Puiu Calin *(Gen Mgr)*

SYCOR GmbH (1)
Heinrich-von-Stephan-Str 1-5, Gottingen, Germany
Tel.: (49) 5514900
Web Site: http://www.sycor-group.com
Information Technology Services
N.A.I.C.S.: 541511
Ronald Geiger *(Mng Dir)*

Subsidiary (US):

SYCOR AMERICAS Inc. (2)
1 Penn Ctr W Ste 104, Pittsburgh, PA 15276
Tel.: (412) 788-9494
Information Technology Services
N.A.I.C.S.: 541511
Helge Roth *(Pres & CEO)*

Subsidiary (Non-US):

SYCOR ASIA Pte Ltd. (2)
81 Anson Road 08-17, Singapore, Singapore
Tel.: (65) 65006319
Information Technology Services
N.A.I.C.S.: 541511

SYCOR Austria GmbH (2)
Franz-Brotzner-Str 7, Wals, Salzburg, Austria
Tel.: (43) 720569820
Information Technology Services
N.A.I.C.S.: 541511
Ronald Geiger *(Mng Dir)*

SYCOR Shanghai Co., Ltd. (2)
Baohua International Plaza Room 503 No 555 West Guangzhong Road, Jingan District, Shanghai, China
Tel.: (86) 2161659080
Information Technology Services
N.A.I.C.S.: 541511
Peter Rohde-Chen *(Mng Dir)*

OTTOGI CORPORATION
405 Heungan-daero, Dongan-gu, Anyang, 14060, Gyeonggi-do, Korea (South)
Tel.: (82) 314212122
Web Site: https://www.ottogi.co.kr
Year Founded: 1969
007310—(KRS)
Rev.: $2,441,602,493
Assets: $2,738,006,579
Liabilities: $1,244,258,822
Net Worth: $1,493,747,757
Earnings: $213,605,127
Emp.: 3,037
Fiscal Year-end: 12/31/22
Food Products Producer
N.A.I.C.S.: 311230
Hwang SungMan *(CEO)*

Subsidiaries:

Budaoweng Foods Co., Ltd. (1)
Developing Zone, Niushan Town Donghai, Lianyungang, China
Tel.: (86) 51887268845
Enriched Frozen Food Product Mfr & Distr
N.A.I.C.S: 311423

Choheung Corporation (1)
38 Sihwa-ro Danwon-gu, Ansan, Gyeonggi-do, Korea (South)
Tel.: (82) 313107000
Web Site: https://www.choheung.co.kr
Rev.: $248,535,422
Assets: $332,690,451
Liabilities: $214,430,445
Net Worth: $118,260,006
Earnings: $8,537,585
Emp.: 376
Fiscal Year-end: 12/31/2022
Food Products Mfr
N.A.I.C.S.: 311999
Ham Young-Jae *(CEO)*

Jiangsu Budaoweng Foods Co., Ltd. (1)
Developing Zone, Niushan Town Donghai, Lianyungang, Jiangsu, China
Tel.: (86) 51887268845
Food Distr
N.A.I.C.S.: 424420

Jiangsu Taitong Food Limited Company (1)
Developing Zone, Niushan Town Donghai, Lianyungang, Jiangsu, China
Tel.: (86) 51887269670
Food Distr
N.A.I.C.S.: 424420

Ottogi America Inc. (1)
16200 Trojan Way, La Mirada, CA 90638
Tel.: (310) 324-1094
Web Site: http://www.ottogiamerica.com
Sales Range: $25-49.9 Million
Emp.: 20
Food Products Distr
N.A.I.C.S.: 445298

Ottogi New Zealand Ltd. (1)
76 Rangi Road, Takanini, Auckland, 2105, New Zealand
Tel.: (64) 92677476
Web Site: https://ottogi.co.nz
Food Distr
N.A.I.C.S.: 424420

Taitong Food Limited Company (1)
Developing Zone Niushan Town, Donghai, Lianyungang, China
Tel.: (86) 51887269670
Vermicelli Product Mfr
N.A.I.C.S.: 311824

OU FARBAHOUSE
Marko Vovchok 3 Bldg 14, 7400, Kiev, Ukraine
Tel.: (380) 44 391 5960 UA
Sales Range: $1-9.9 Million
Emp.: 90
Holding Company; Paint & Coating Products Distr
N.A.I.C.S.: 551112
Mauno Nurm *(Mng Dir & Co-Owner)*

OU PISTRIK IV
Laki 26, Tallinn, 12915, Estonia
Tel.: (372) 6461410 EE
Web Site: http://www.pistrik.ee
Electrical Products Distr
N.A.I.C.S.: 423690
Vadim Sokolov *(Mng Dir-Technical & Svc)*

OUE LIMITED
50 Collyer Quay No 18-01/02 OUE Bayfront, Singapore, 049321, Singapore
Tel.: (65) 68096000 SG
Web Site: https://oue.com.sg
Year Founded: 1964
LJ3—(SES)
Rev.: $471,937,438
Assets: $7,018,785,121
Liabilities: $2,563,967,279
Net Worth: $4,454,817,842
Earnings: $125,076,876
Emp.: 1,163
Fiscal Year-end: 12/31/23
Property Investment; Hotels, Residential & Commercial Properties Operation & Management
N.A.I.C.S.: 721110
Christopher James Williams *(Deputy Chm)*

Subsidiaries:

Bowsprit Capital Corp. Ltd (1)
50 Collyer Quay, Singapore, 049321, Singapore **(60%)**
Tel.: (65) 64350168
Investment Management Service
N.A.I.C.S.: 523940
Victor Tan Kok Mian *(CEO)*

Healthway Medical Corporation Limited (1)
6 Shenton Way 10-09 OUE, Downtown 2, Singapore, 068809, Singapore
Tel.: (65) 63234415
Web Site: http://www.healthwaymedical.com
Rev.: $105,636,912
Assets: $178,723,293
Liabilities: $36,300,468
Net Worth: $142,422,826
Earnings: $8,074,404
Emp.: 120
Fiscal Year-end: 12/31/2021
Medical Practitioner Office & Clinic Operator
N.A.I.C.S.: 621111
Sachin Sudhirbhai Sheth *(CFO)*

Subsidiary (Domestic):

Aaron Dentalcare Pte Ltd (2)
110 Robinson Rd No 01-00, Singapore, 068901, Singapore
Tel.: (65) 63232353
Web Site: http://www.aarondental.com
Sales Range: $10-24.9 Million
Emp.: 9
Dental Clinic Services
N.A.I.C.S.: 621491

Aaron Seow International Pte Ltd (2)
Blk 41 Holland Dr Unit 01-07, Singapore, 270041, Singapore
Tel.: (65) 67774333
Sales Range: $10-24.9 Million
Emp.: 5
Dental Health Care Services
N.A.I.C.S.: 621999
Wong Weng *(Gen Mgr)*

Subsidiary (Domestic):

Aaron CTP Dental Surgery Pte Ltd (3)
118 Robinson Rd No 01-00, The Corporate Ofc, Singapore, 068901, Singapore
Tel.: (65) 62207853
Web Site: http://www.aarondental.com
Sales Range: $10-24.9 Million
Emp.: 20
Dental Clinic Services
N.A.I.C.S.: 621210
Beng Beng Soo *(Mgr)*

Subsidiary (Domestic):

Amazing Speech Therapy Pte. Ltd. (2)
101 Irrawaddy Road No 17-01 Royal Square Medical Suites, Royal Square Novena, Singapore, Singapore
Tel.: (65) 91054575
Web Site: https://www.amazingspeechtherapy.sg
Pathology Clinic Operator
N.A.I.C.S.: 621340

OUE LIMITED

OUE Limited—(Continued)

Subsidiary (Non-US):

Amazing Speech Therapy Sdn. Bhd. (2)
S 23-13 Kiara 163 Jalan Kiara, Mont Kiara, 50480, Kuala Lumpur, Malaysia
Tel.: (60) 173735982
Web Site: https://www.amazingspeechtherapy.my
Pathology Clinic Operator
N.A.I.C.S.: 621340

Subsidiary (Domestic):

HeadStart for Life Pte. Ltd. (2)
46 East Coast Road No 09-03 Eastgate Katong, Singapore, Singapore
Tel.: (65) 91054575
Web Site: https://www.headstartforlife.com.sg
Pathology Clinic Operator
N.A.I.C.S.: 621340

Healthway Medical Enterprises Pte Ltd (2)
Blk 717 Woodlands Dr 70 Unit No 0-114, Singapore, 730717, Singapore
Tel.: (65) 63647450
Dental Health Care Services
N.A.I.C.S.: 621999

Island Orthopaedic Consultants Pte Ltd (2)
6 Napier Road 02-16, Gleneagles Medical Centre, Singapore, 258499, Singapore
Tel.: (65) 6 474 5488
Web Site: https://iog.com.sg
Sales Range: $10-24.9 Million
Emp.: 6
Health Care Srvices
N.A.I.C.S.: 621999

Kong Dental Surgery Singapore Pvt Ltd. (2)
534 Choa Chu Kang St 51 - No 01-45 Limbang Shopping Centre, Singapore, 680534, Singapore
Tel.: (65) 67695833
Web Site: http://www.kongdental.com
Emp.: 7
Dental Health Care Services
N.A.I.C.S.: 339114

Peace Family Clinic & Surgery (AMK) Pte. Ltd. (2)
Blk 452 Ang Mo Kio Ave 10 No 01 1787, Singapore, 560452, Singapore
Tel.: (65) 64516558
Web Site: http://www.healthwaymedical.com
Sales Range: $10-24.9 Million
Emp.: 5
General Medical Practitioning Services
N.A.I.C.S.: 622110

Peace Family Clinic & Surgery (Sembawang) Pte Ltd (2)
Blk 406 Sembawang Dr No 01-820, Singapore, 750406, Singapore
Tel.: (65) 65556674
Web Site: http://www.healthwaymedical.com
Emp.: 2
General Medical Practitioners
N.A.I.C.S.: 622110
Bao Zuan (Mgr)

Picton Medical Centre Pte Ltd (2)
Blk 163 Toa Payoh Lorong 1, No 01-1012 / 1014, Singapore, 310163, Singapore
Tel.: (65) 63541220
Web Site: http://www.healthwaymedical.com
Sales Range: $10-24.9 Million
Emp.: 4
General Medical Practioners
N.A.I.C.S.: 621491

Popular Dental (Woodlands) Pte Ltd (2)
Unit 1-739 Woodlands Dr 50, No 01-739 888 Plz, Singapore, 730888, Singapore
Tel.: (65) 63658110
Sales Range: $10-24.9 Million
Emp.: 4
Dental Clinic Services
N.A.I.C.S.: 621491

SBCC Clinic Pte Ltd (2)
721 Ang Mo Kio Ave 8 No 01- 2803/2805, Singapore, 560721, Singapore
Tel.: (65) 64568874
Sales Range: $10-24.9 Million
Emp.: 12
Child Health Care Services
N.A.I.C.S.: 621999
Tan Siew Kheng (Gen Mgr)

Silver Cross 21 Pte Ltd (2)
3 Chung Chinman Road, Singapore, 599728, Singapore
Tel.: (65) 68751191
Web Site: http://www.healthwaymedical.com
Sales Range: $10-24.9 Million
Emp.: 10
Medical Practitioners Services
N.A.I.C.S.: 622110

Silver Cross Healthcare Pte Ltd (2)
846 Yishun Ring Road 01-3619, Singapore, 760846, Singapore
Tel.: (65) 67599181
Sales Range: $10-24.9 Million
Emp.: 7
General Medical Practitioners
N.A.I.C.S.: 622110

Silver Cross Medical Centre Pte Ltd (2)
502 Jurong W Ave 1 No 01-803, Singapore, 640502, Singapore
Tel.: (65) 68992141
Web Site: http://www.healthwaymedical.com
Sales Range: $10-24.9 Million
Emp.: 8
General Medical Practitioners
N.A.I.C.S.: 622110
Judy Tan (Supvr-Clinic Svcs)

Silver Cross North Pte Ltd (2)
Blk 305 Woodlands St 31 No 01-75, Singapore, 730305, Singapore
Tel.: (65) 63633646
General Medical Practitioners
N.A.I.C.S.: 622110

Sland Orthopaedic Consultants Pte. Ltd. (2)
38 Irrawaddy Road No 05-42, Singapore, Singapore
Tel.: (65) 63520529
Web Site: https://www.iog.com.sg
Orthopedic Clinic Operator
N.A.I.C.S.: 622310

Straits Podiatry Pte. Ltd. (2)
31 Rochester Drive No 02-01 Hotel Block, Singapore, Singapore
Tel.: (65) 69904574
Web Site: https://www.straitspodiatry.com
Orthopedic Clinic Operator
N.A.I.C.S.: 622310

Thomson Paediatric Clinic Pte Ltd (2)
298 Tiong Bahru Rd No 01-03/04, Central Plz, Singapore, 168730, Singapore
Tel.: (65) 62765700
Sales Range: $10-24.9 Million
Emp.: 3
Medical Practitioners Services
N.A.I.C.S.: 622110

Universal Dental Group (Braddell) Pte Ltd (2)
107 Lorong 1 Toa Payoh No 01-258, Singapore, 310107, Singapore
Tel.: (65) 62556520
Sales Range: $10-24.9 Million
Emp.: 6
Dental Health Care Services
N.A.I.C.S.: 621999

Universal Dental Group (Woodlands) Pte Ltd (2)
Block 883 Woodlands St 82 No 01-470, Singapore, 730883, Singapore
Tel.: (65) 63631669
Dental Health Care Services
N.A.I.C.S.: 621999

Universal Dentalcare Pte Ltd (2)
190 Lor 6 Toa Payoh Unit No 02-512, Singapore, 310190, Singapore
Tel.: (65) 62592341
Web Site: http://www.healthwaydentalgroup.com
Dental Health Care Services
N.A.I.C.S.: 621999

Meritus Hotels & Resorts (1)
333 Orchard Rd 33rd Fl, Singapore, 238867, Singapore
Tel.: (65) 62357788
Web Site: http://www.meritushotels.com
Sales Range: $10-24.9 Million
Emp.: 25
Hotels & Resorts Operator; Hotel Management Services
N.A.I.C.S.: 721110

OUB Centre Limited (1)
1 Raffles Place 08-00, Singapore, 048616, Singapore
Tel.: (65) 64919201
Web Site: https://www.oubcentre.com.sg
Real Estate Services
N.A.I.C.S.: 531390
Jasmine Toh (Sr Mgr-Mktg)

OUE Commercial Real Estate Investment Trust (1)
333 Orchard Road 83-01, Singapore, 238867, Singapore (64.98%)
Tel.: (65) 68098700
Web Site: https://www.ouect.com
Rev.: $215,901,689
Assets: $4,596,463,680
Liabilities: $1,734,970,082
Net Worth: $2,861,493,598
Earnings: $78,692,721
Emp.: 66
Fiscal Year-end: 12/31/2023
Real Estate Investment Trust
N.A.I.C.S.: 525990
Shu Lin Tan (CEO)

Subsidiary (Domestic):

OUE Hospitality Trust (2)
333 Orchard Road #33-00, Singapore, 238867, Singapore
Tel.: (65) 6831 6000
Web Site: http://www.oueht.com
Real Estate Investment Services
N.A.I.C.S.: 523999
Christopher James Williams (Chm)

OUE Healthcare Limited (1)
6 Shenton Way 10-10, Singapore, 68809, OUE, Singapore
Tel.: (65) 65789188
Web Site: https://ouehealthcare.com
Rev.: $88,770,656
Assets: $1,039,337,532
Liabilities: $477,630,974
Net Worth: $561,706,558
Earnings: $24,080,030
Emp.: 132
Fiscal Year-end: 12/31/2021
Investment Holding Company
N.A.I.C.S.: 551112
Yet Kum Meng (CEO)

OUEST BOULANGERE

10 Rue Olivier De Serres Z D Activite La Buzeniere, 85500, Les Herbiers, Vendee, France
Tel.: (33) 251649900
Web Site: http://www.laboulangere.com
Sales Range: $10-24.9 Million
Emp.: 300
Pastries, Viennoiseries & Brioches, Loaves Producer & Seller
N.A.I.C.S.: 311812
Pierre Bichon (Mgr-Logistics)

OUG HOLDINGS INC.

5F OUG Noda Building 2-13-5 Noda, Fukushima-Ku, Osaka, 553 0005, Japan
Tel.: (81) 648043031 **JP**
Web Site: https://www.oug.co.jp
Year Founded: 1947
8041—(TKS)
Rev.: $2,202,432,170
Assets: $602,501,500
Liabilities: $397,631,160
Net Worth: $204,870,340
Earnings: $23,914,980
Fiscal Year-end: 03/31/24
Holding Company; Seafood
N.A.I.C.S.: 551112

INTERNATIONAL PUBLIC

Yasuyoshi Hashidume (Pres, CEO, Mng Officer, Mng Officer, Mgr, Mgr & Mgr)

Subsidiaries:

Osaka Uoichiba Co Ltd (1)
1-86 Noda 1-chome, Fukushima-ku, Osaka, 553-8555, Japan
Tel.: (81) 664692001
Web Site: http://www.uoichi.co.jp
Emp.: 600
Processed Seafood Products Distr
N.A.I.C.S.: 424460

OUHUA ENERGY HOLDINGS LIMITED

Long Wan Suo Cheng Town, Raoping County, Chaozhou, Guangdong, China
Tel.: (86) 7683286668
Web Site: https://www.ohwa.cn
AJ2—(SES)
Rev.: $354,426,975
Assets: $96,905,785
Liabilities: $65,156,076
Net Worth: $31,749,708
Earnings: $1,621,115
Fiscal Year-end: 12/31/20
Liquefied Petroleum Gas Mfr
N.A.I.C.S.: 332420
Tian Shun Ye (Exec Dir)

OULA FUEL MARKETING COMPANY K.S.C.

AlMirqab Block 3 Kuwait Business Town Tower KBT, PO Box 29009, Building 12 Floor 31 & 30 Safat, 13151, Kuwait, 13151, Kuwait
Tel.: (965) 1800111
Web Site: https://www.oula1.com
Year Founded: 2004
OULAFUEL—(KUW)
Rev.: $533,178,390
Assets: $446,386,258
Liabilities: $219,505,174
Net Worth: $226,881,084
Earnings: $15,144,642
Emp.: 181
Fiscal Year-end: 12/31/23
Fuel Stations & Centers Operations
N.A.I.C.S.: 457120
Abdulhussain S. Al-Sultan (Chm)

OURGAME INTERNATIONAL HOLDINGS LTD

31/F Tower Two Times Square 1 Matheson Street, Causeway Bay, China (Hong Kong)
Tel.: (852) 2987669595
Web Site: http://www.ourgame.com
6899—(HKG)
Rev.: $30,566,765
Assets: $108,613,440
Liabilities: $15,076,714
Net Worth: $93,536,726
Earnings: ($10,868,926)
Emp.: 175
Fiscal Year-end: 12/31/22
Online, Card & Board Games
N.A.I.C.S.: 513210
Eric Qing Yang (Chm & Co-CEO)

OURINVEST SECURITIZADORA S.A.

Avenida Paulista 1728, Bela Vista, 01310-919, Sao Paulo, Brazil
Tel.: (55) 11 4081 4451
Web Site: http://www.ourinvest.com.br
Real Estate Manangement Services
N.A.I.C.S.: 531210
Bruce Thomas Phillips (Chm & CEO)

OURO FINO SAUDE ANIMAL PARTICIPACOES S.A

AND PRIVATE COMPANIES

Rodovia Anhanguera SP 330 KM 298 Bloco C 2 andar, Distrito Industrial Cravinhos, Sao Paulo, 14140-000, SP, Brazil
Tel.: (55) 35184098
Web Site: http://www.ri.ourofino.com
Year Founded: 1987
OFSA3—(BRAZ)
Rev.: $140,363,263
Assets: $212,231,888
Liabilities: $104,416,166
Net Worth: $107,815,723
Earnings: $17,247,324
Fiscal Year-end: 12/31/20
Pharmaceuticals Product Mfr
N.A.I.C.S.: 325412
Norival Bonamichi *(Co-Founder & Vice Chm)*

OURO VERDE LOCACAO E SERVICO S.A.
Rua Joao Bettega 5700-CIC, Curitiba, 81350-000, PR, Brazil
Tel.: (55) 4132397000
Web Site: http://www.ouroverde.net.br
Emp.: 100
Vehicles Financial Leasing Services
N.A.I.C.S.: 525990
Claudio Jose Zattar *(CEO)*

OURPALM CO., LTD.
Building C LingZhi Center North Olympic Science & Technology Park, No 1 Baosheng South Road Haidian District, Beijing, 100192, China
Tel.: (86) 1065546196
Web Site: https://english.ourpalm.com
Year Founded: 2004
300315—(CHIN)
Rev.: $170,295,372
Assets: $730,588,248
Liabilities: $89,097,840
Net Worth: $641,490,408
Earnings: $13,503,672
Emp.: 250
Fiscal Year-end: 12/31/22
Gaming Software Publisher
N.A.I.C.S.: 513210
Liu Huicheng *(Chm & Gen Mgr)*

OUTAREX
Zac Des Gravelles 10 Rue des Chenes Rouges, 91580, Etrechy, Essonne, France
Tel.: (33) 160802727 FR
Web Site: http://www.outarex.com
Year Founded: 1972
Rev.: $20,100,000
Emp.: 80
General Construction Contractor
N.A.I.C.S.: 236220
Nathalie Maguet *(Mgr-Personnel)*

OUTBACK GOLDFIELDS CORP.
7th floor - 1090 W Georgia St, Vancouver, V6E 3V7, BC, Canada
Tel.: (604) 900-3450
Web Site: https://outbackgoldfields.com
Year Founded: 2018
OZBKF—(OTCIQ)
Rev.: $30,079
Assets: $23,137,352
Liabilities: $317,784
Net Worth: $22,819,568
Earnings: ($2,339,577)
Fiscal Year-end: 06/30/21
Mineral Exploration Services
N.A.I.C.S.: 213114
Chris Donaldson *(CEO)*

OUTCROP SILVER & GOLD CORPORATION
Suite 905 - 1111 West Hastings Street, Vancouver, V6E 2J3, BC, Canada
Tel.: (604) 638-2545 BC
Web Site: https://outcropsilverandgold.com
Year Founded: 1993
OCGSF—(OTCQX)
Gold Exploration & Mining
N.A.I.C.S.: 212220
Ian Slater *(Chm)*

Subsidiaries:

Miranda Gold U.S.A., Inc. (1)
310 Silver St, Elko, NV 89801
Tel.: (775) 738-1877
Sales Range: $50-74.9 Million
Emp.: 8
Mineral Exploration Services
N.A.I.C.S.: 212390

Zacapa Resources Ltd. (1)
Suite 905-1111 West Hastings, Vancouver, V6E 2J3, BC, Canada
Tel.: (604) 638-2545
Web Site: https://www.zacaparesources.com
Assets: $1,666,953
Liabilities: $607,806
Net Worth: $1,059,148
Earnings: ($8,995,890)
Fiscal Year-end: 12/31/2022
Gold Exploration & Mining Services
N.A.I.C.S.: 212220
Dan Macneil *(VP)*

OUTIN FUTURES CO., LTD.
15F 508 Teheran-ro, Gangnam-gu, Seoul, Korea (South)
Tel.: (82) 25712432
Web Site: https://www.outinfutures.com
Year Founded: 2000
227610—(KRS)
Rev.: $26,879,203
Assets: $44,819,485
Liabilities: $38,240,008
Net Worth: $6,579,478
Earnings: ($13,166,150)
Emp.: 109
Fiscal Year-end: 12/31/22
Cosmetic Product Mfr & Distr
N.A.I.C.S.: 325620
Young Wook Choi *(CEO)*

OUTLAND REFORESTATION INC.
200 250 Eglinton Ave W, Toronto, M4R 1A7, ON, Canada
Tel.: (416) 483-5152
Web Site: http://www.outland.ca
Year Founded: 1985
Rev.: $25,839,967
Emp.: 25
Forestry Services
N.A.I.C.S.: 115310
Steve Luengo *(Gen Mgr-Silviculture)*

OUTOKUMPU OYJ
Salmisaarenranta 11, FI-00180, Helsinki, Finland
Tel.: (358) 94211
Web Site: http://www.outokumpu.com
Year Founded: 1914
OUT1V—(OTCIQ)
Rev.: $8,759,164,400
Assets: $6,442,515,800
Liabilities: $2,642,326,400
Net Worth: $3,800,189,400
Earnings: $1,051,764,000
Emp.: 8,357
Fiscal Year-end: 12/31/22
Stainless Steel Producer
N.A.I.C.S.: 331110
Johann Steiner *(Chief HR Officer)*

Subsidiaries:

ABE France Sarl (1)
17 rue Desaix, 67450, Mundolsheim, France (51%)
Tel.: (33) 388181010
Web Site: http://www.abe.fr
Sales Range: $10-24.9 Million
Emp.: 15
Rolled Steel Shape Mfr
N.A.I.C.S.: 324199

Avesta Klippcenter AB (1)
Koppardalsvaegen 44, Avesta, 774 41, Sweden
Tel.: (46) 22 65 73 30
Stainless Steel Mfr
N.A.I.C.S.: 331513

Gransfors Bruk AB (1)
Gransfors 381, Bergsjo, 829 52, Nordanstig, Sweden
Tel.: (46) 6 527 1090
Web Site: https://www.gransforsbruk.com
Timbering Tool Mfr
N.A.I.C.S.: 332216

LDM B.V. (1)
Lipsstraat 44, Drunen, 5151 RP, Netherlands
Tel.: (31) 416 389 911
Web Site: http://www.ldmbrass.com
Sales Range: $50-74.9 Million
Emp.: 180
Copper Alloy Rod Mfr & Whslr
N.A.I.C.S.: 332999

Outokumpu (Pty) Ltd (1)
No 2 Modena Building 21D Durbanville Avenue, Bellville, Cape Town, 7530, South Africa
Tel.: (27) 219141331
Sales Range: $25-49.9 Million
Stainless Steel Whslr
N.A.I.C.S.: 331210

Outokumpu (S.E.A.) Pte. Ltd. (1)
10 Anson Road International Plaza 31-13, Singapore, 079903, Singapore (100%)
Tel.: (65) 6 224 8037
Web Site: http://www.outokumpu.com
Sales Range: $50-74.9 Million
Emp.: 10
Stainless Steel Products Manufacturing
N.A.I.C.S.: 332111

Outokumpu (Thailand) Co., Ltd. (1)
22Fl Silom Complex Bldg 191 Silom Rd, Bangrak, Bangkok, 10500, Thailand (100%)
Tel.: (66) 22313657
Metals & Metal Products Mfr
N.A.I.C.S.: 332999
Suwat Sumpachanya *(Gen Mgr)*

Outokumpu (U.K.) Ltd. (1)
Europa Link, PO Box 3541, Sheffield, S9 1ZT, United Kingdom
Tel.: (44) 1142613624
Web Site: http://www.outokumpu.com
Sales Range: $75-99.9 Million
Emp.: 110
Chemical, Petrochemical & Energy Solutions
N.A.I.C.S.: 424720

Outokumpu A/S (1)
Kokbjerg 31, 6000, Kolding, Denmark (100%)
Tel.: (45) 70102610
Web Site: http://www.avestapolarit.com
Sales Range: $1-9.9 Million
Emp.: 24
Mfr of Stainless Steel in the Form of Hot & Cold Rolled Plate, Sheet & Strip, Cold Rolled Coils, Machined & Formed Plate
N.A.I.C.S.: 331513

Outokumpu AS (1)
Ostensjoveien 34, Oslo, 0667, Norway
Tel.: (47) 23247450
Sales Range: $25-49.9 Million
Emp.: 20
Stainless Steel Whslr
N.A.I.C.S.: 423510

Outokumpu Asia Pacific Ltd (1)
1605 Tower 1 Landmark Building 8 North Dongquanhua Road, Beijing, 100004, China
Tel.: (86) 10 6590 1998
Web Site: http://www.outokumpu.com
Emp.: 50
Steel Product Distr
N.A.I.C.S.: 423510

Outokumpu Austria (1)
Campus 21 Europaring A 02503, PO Box 31, 2345, Brunn, Austria (51%)
Tel.: (43) 2236300
Web Site: http://www.outokumpu.com
Sales Range: $50-74.9 Million
Emp.: 7
Stainless Steel Mfr
N.A.I.C.S.: 331222

Outokumpu Baltic (1)
Rupnicu iela 4 Olaine, LV-2114, Riga, Latvia (100%)
Tel.: (371) 67135881
Web Site: http://www.avestapolarit.com
Sales Range: $50-74.9 Million
Emp.: 3
N.A.I.C.S.: 324199

Outokumpu Benelux B.V. (1)
Lage Dijk 24, 5705 BZ, Helmond, Netherlands
Tel.: (31) 492 581 999
Web Site: http://www.outokumpu.com
Emp.: 60
Holding Company
N.A.I.C.S.: 551112

Subsidiary (Domestic):

Outokumpu BV (2)
Steenovenweg 5, PO Box 1111, 5708 HN, Helmond, Netherlands (100%)
Tel.: (31) 49 258 1999
Web Site: https://www.outokumpu.com
Sales Range: $25-49.9 Million
Emp.: 30
Chemicals, Petrochemicals & Energy Products & Services
N.A.I.C.S.: 324199

Subsidiary (Domestic):

Outokumpu Nickel Resources B.V. (3)
Finlandweg 1, 4554 AB, Westdorpe, Netherlands
Tel.: (31) 115474700
Web Site: http://www.outokumpu.com
Nickel Mining Services
N.A.I.C.S.: 212230

Outokumpu PSC Benelux B.V. (3)
Broekstraat 12, PO Box 75, 7122 LC, Aalten, Netherlands (51%)
Tel.: (31) 54 349 4000
Web Site: https://www.outokumpu.com
Sales Range: $25-49.9 Million
Stainless Steel Mfr
N.A.I.C.S.: 331221

Outokumpu Brasil Comercio de Metais Ltda. (1)
Rua Bandeira Paulista 600 Conj 71 - Ed, Itaim Bibi, Sao Paulo, 04532-001, Brazil
Tel.: (55) 1124951924
Sales Range: $25-49.9 Million
Emp.: 8
Metal Sheet Mfr
N.A.I.C.S.: 332999

Outokumpu Business Support Unit AB (1)
Pilgatan 8, SE 721 30, Vasteras, Sweden (100%)
Tel.: (46) 21158500
Web Site: http://www.avestapolarit.com
Sales Range: $25-49.9 Million
Emp.: 25
N.A.I.C.S.: 324199

Outokumpu Distribution Oy (1)
Riihitontuntie 7 A PL 270, 02201, Espoo, Finland
Tel.: (358) 9 4211
Web Site: http://www.outokumpu.com
Coal Mfr & Whslr
N.A.I.C.S.: 324199

Outokumpu Espana S.A. (1)
Felix Rodriguez de la Fuente 34 Local A, 28110, Madrid, Algete, Spain
Tel.: (34) 916281950
N.A.I.C.S.: 324199

Outokumpu Ges.m.b.H (1)
Liebermannstrasse A02 503, 2345, Brunn am Gebirge, Austria
Tel.: (43) 22 36 30 00
Web Site: http://www.outokumpu.com

OUTOKUMPU OYJ — INTERNATIONAL PUBLIC

Outokumpu Oyj—(Continued)
Nonferrous Metal Products Mfr
N.A.I.C.S.: 331491

Outokumpu India Private Limited (1)
222 DLF Tower A, Jasola District Centre,
New Delhi, 110 025, India
Tel.: (91) 1146518438
Stainless Steel Products Mfr
N.A.I.C.S.: 331210

Outokumpu Istanbul Dis Ticaret Limited Sirketi
Barbados Bulvar No 28 8, Balmumcu Besiktas, Istanbul, 80700, Türkiye **(100%)**
Tel.: (90) 122746555
Web Site: http://www.outokumpu.ru
Sales Range: $50-74.9 Million
Emp.: 2
N.A.I.C.S.: 324199

Outokumpu K.K. (1)
Toranomon ACT Building 4F 11-12
5-Chome, Minato-Ku, Tokyo, 105 0001, Japan
Tel.: (81) 334590610
Sales Range: $50-74.9 Million
Emp.: 6
N.A.I.C.S.: 324199

Outokumpu Kft. (1)
Illatosut Ut 9, H 1097, Budapest, Hungary **(100%)**
Tel.: (36) 13476000
Sales Range: Less than $1 Million
Emp.: 12
N.A.I.C.S.: 324199
Krysteztof Kurijanski *(Gen Mgr)*

Outokumpu Lda. (1)
Rue Caldas Sazier 38 2nd Fl Dto, PT 4150 162, Porto, Portugal
Tel.: (351) 226076740
Sales Range: $50-74.9 Million
Emp.: 2
N.A.I.C.S.: 324199
Rui Paulo *(Gen Mgr)*

Outokumpu Ltd. (1)
Suite 1 Unit 3 Shanowen Business Center
Shanowen, Santoynni, 9, Dublin, Ireland **(51%)**
Tel.: (353) 18579300
Sales Range: $50-74.9 Million
Emp.: 4
Stainless Steel Mfr
N.A.I.C.S.: 331222

Outokumpu Mining Oy (1)
Riihitontuntie 7A, Espoo, FIN 02201, Finland **(100%)**
Tel.: (358) 94212102
Sales Range: $50-74.9 Million
Emp.: 2
Exploration & Mining Activities in Finland, Copper, Zinc, Nickel, Lead, Gold, Pyrite
N.A.I.C.S.: 212230

Subsidiary (Non-US):

Norsulfid A/S (2)
Drammensvein 61 E, 0271, Oslo, Norway **(100%)**
Tel.: (47) 22446162
Sales Range: $50-74.9 Million
Emp.: 1
N.A.I.C.S.: 324199

OAO Kivijarvi Oy (2)
Ul A Nevskogo 65, 185030, Petrozavodsk, Russia **(100%)**
Tel.: (7) 8142551758
N.A.I.C.S.: 324199

Unit (Domestic):

Outokumpu Mining Oy (2)
Orivesi Mine Kummumkatu 34, 83500, Outokumpu, Finland **(100%)**
Tel.: (358) 94212122
Sales Range: $50-74.9 Million
Emp.: 200
Steel Works
N.A.I.C.S.: 331110

Outokumpu Mining Oy (2)
Pyhasalmi Mine, PO Box 51, FIN 86801, Pyhasalmi, Finland **(100%)**
Tel.: (358) 87696111
Steel Works

N.A.I.C.S.: 212290

Outokumpu N.V. (1)
Square de Meeus 37 4th Floor, 1000, Brussels, Belgium
Tel.: (32) 25408894
Stainless Steel Distr
N.A.I.C.S.: 423510

Outokumpu Nirosta GmbH (1)
Oberschlesienstrasse 16, 47807, Krefeld, Germany
Tel.: (49) 21518301
Stainless Steel Mfr
N.A.I.C.S.: 331210

Outokumpu Nordic AB (1)
Abramsons vag 2 Folkesta, PO Box 1134, 631 80, Eskilstuna, Sweden **(100%)**
Tel.: (46) 16349950
Web Site: http://www.outokumpu.com
Sales Range: $25-49.9 Million
Emp.: 70
Customized Sheet & Plate
N.A.I.C.S.: 332313

Outokumpu PSC Germany GmbH (1)
St Poltener Str 43 Gebaude 509 Etage 1, 89522, Heidenheim, Germany
Tel.: (49) 73219477700
Stainless Steel Bending & Cutting Services
N.A.I.C.S.: 423510

Outokumpu Poland Sp.z o.o. (1)
Ul Filtrowa 59 2, PL 02 056, Warsaw, Poland **(100%)**
Tel.: (48) 228258081
Sales Range: $50-74.9 Million
Emp.: 3
N.A.I.C.S.: 324199

Outokumpu Prefab AB (1)
Bergsnasgatan 11, PO Box 74, 774 41, Avesta, Sweden **(51%)**
Tel.: (46) 22681900
Web Site: https://www.outokumpuprefab.com
Sales Range: $25-49.9 Million
Emp.: 40
Mfr of Prefabricated Structures
N.A.I.C.S.: 332311

Outokumpu Press Plate AB (1)
Bergsnasgatan 11, Avesta, 77427, Sweden **(100%)**
Tel.: (46) 22681966
Web Site: http://www.avestapolarit.com
Sales Range: $25-49.9 Million
Emp.: 900
Coke Ovens & Rolling Mills
N.A.I.C.S.: 331221
Pekka Erkkila *(Exec VP & CTO)*

Outokumpu Press Plate AB (1)
Bergsnasgatan 11, 774 41, Avesta, Sweden **(100%)**
Tel.: (46) 22681700
Web Site: https://www.outokumpu.com
Press Plates & Stainless Sheets Production
N.A.I.C.S.: 331315

Outokumpu Pty. Ltd. (1)
134 136 Fitzgerald Rd, PO Box 156, Laverton, 3028, VIC, Australia **(100%)**
Tel.: (61) 393693344
Web Site: http://www.outokumpu.com
Sales Range: $25-49.9 Million
Emp.: 26
N.A.I.C.S.: 324199

Outokumpu Research Oy (1)
Kuparitie 5, PO Box 60, 28101, Pori, Finland **(100%)**
Tel.: (358) 26266111
Sales Range: $75-99.9 Million
Emp.: 167
N.A.I.C.S.: 324199

Outokumpu Rossija Oy (1)
Riihitontuntie 7 A, PO Box 280, Espoo, 2201, Finland **(100%)**
Tel.: (358) 94211
Web Site: http://www.outokumpu.com
Sales Range: $50-74.9 Million
Emp.: 5
N.A.I.C.S.: 324199

Outokumpu S.A. (1)
Avanida Zugazarte 8 2 Fl, 48930, Getxo, Vizcaya, Spain **(51%)**

Tel.: (34) 944937024
Sales Range: $25-49.9 Million
Emp.: 16
Stainless Steel Mfr
N.A.I.C.S.: 331222

Outokumpu S.A.S. (1)
100 Rue Petit Cedex 19, 75165, Paris, France
Tel.: (33) 1 53 19 42 00
Web Site: http://www.outokumpu.com
Sales Range: $25-49.9 Million
Emp.: 50
Stainless Steel Products Mfr & Distr
N.A.I.C.S.: 331513

Outokumpu S.p.A. (1)
Piazza Piccapietra 9, 16121, Genoa, Italy
Tel.: (39) 010 55431
Web Site: http://www.outokumpu.com
Sales Range: $50-74.9 Million
Petroleum & Steel Products Manufacturing
N.A.I.C.S.: 324199

Outokumpu S.r.l. (1)
Calea Baciului 2-4, Cluj-Napoca, Romania
Tel.: (40) 264481297
Web Site: https://www.outokumpu.com
Steel Products Mfr & Distr
N.A.I.C.S.: 331221

Outokumpu Sales Norway (1)
Ostensjoveien 34, PO Box 6305, N 0604, Oslo, Etterstad, Norway **(100%)**
Tel.: (47) 23247450
Sales Range: $25-49.9 Million
Emp.: 30
Stainless Steel Sales & Distribution
N.A.I.C.S.: 238120

Outokumpu Sp. z o.o. (1)
Filtrowa 59/2, Warsaw, 02-056, Poland
Tel.: (48) 22825 82 52
Stainless Steel Mfr
N.A.I.C.S.: 331513

Outokumpu Stainless (1)
549 W State 38, New Castle, IN 47362-0370
Tel.: (765) 529-0120
Web Site: http://www.outokumpu.com
Sales Range: $150-199.9 Million
Emp.: 120
Distr of Steel Plates
N.A.I.C.S.: 339910

Outokumpu Stainless Bar (1)
3043 Crenshaw Pkwy, Richburg, SC 29729-8225 **(51%)**
Tel.: (803) 789-5383
Sales Range: $25-49.9 Million
Emp.: 100
N.A.I.C.S.: 324199
Lou Kern *(VP-Ops)*

Outokumpu Stainless Coil, Inc. (1)
500 Park Blvd Ste 40, Itasca, IL 60143-3121
Tel.: (847) 517-4050
Web Site: http://www.outokumpu.com
Sales Range: $25-49.9 Million
Emp.: 12
Coil & Spring Mfr
N.A.I.C.S.: 334416

Outokumpu Stainless Oy (1)
Terastie, 95490, Tornio, Finland **(100%)**
Tel.: (358) 164521
Sales Range: $25-49.9 Million
Emp.: 100
Stainless Steel Production; Ferrochrome, Rolled Stainless Steel, Stainless Steel Tubes
N.A.I.C.S.: 331513

Subsidiary (Non-US):

AB Huskvarna Elektrolytpolering (2)
Barrstragatan 16, 556 26, Jonkoping, Sweden **(100%)**
Tel.: (46) 367 5280
Web Site: https://www.abhe.se
Sales Range: Less than $1 Million
Emp.: 7
N.A.I.C.S.: 324199

AS Outokumpu Stainless Tubular Products (2)
Ankru 10, 11713, Tallinn, Estonia
Tel.: (372) 6628099
Web Site: http://www.outokumpu.com

Sales Range: $25-49.9 Million
Emp.: 50
Steel Products Mfr
N.A.I.C.S.: 331110

Subsidiary (Domestic):

Outokumpu Chrome Oy (2)
Terastie, 95490, Tornio, Finland **(100%)**
Tel.: (358) 164521
Web Site: https://www.outokumpu.com
Production of Ferrochrome
N.A.I.C.S.: 331110

Outokumpu Shipping OY (2)
Royttan Satama, 95450, Tornio, Finland
Tel.: (358) 16454500
Sales Range: $25-49.9 Million
Emp.: 50
Shipping Services
N.A.I.C.S.: 488330

Subsidiary (Non-US):

Outokumpu Stainless (Pty.) Ltd.
South Africa (2)
8B Mews Frans Conradie Dr, PO Box 12022, Cape Town, 7463, South Africa **(100%)**
Tel.: (27) 215950900
Sales Range: $50-74.9 Million
Emp.: 4
N.A.I.C.S.: 324199
Johan Karlsson *(Gen Mgr)*

Outokumpu Stainless AB (2)
Bergsnasgatan 11, PO Box 16377, 774 41, Avesta, Sweden
Tel.: (46) 22681000
Web Site: https://www.outokumpu.com
Mfr of Stainless Steel in the Form of Hot & Cold Rolled Plate, Sheet & Strip, Cold Rolled Coils, Machined & Formed Plate
N.A.I.C.S.: 331221

Affiliate (Domestic):

Fagersta Stainless AB (3)
Axel Fornanders vag 4, PO Box 508, 737 40, Fagersta, Sweden **(50%)**
Tel.: (46) 22345500
Web Site: https://www.fagersta-stainless.se
Sales Range: Less than $1 Million
Emp.: 350
Mfr of Stainless Steel Wire Rod & Wire; Joint Venture of Sandvik AB (50%) & Avesta Sheffield AB (50%)
N.A.I.C.S.: 331110
Conny Fredriksson *(Mgr-Technology)*

Subsidiary (Non-US):

Ornskoldsviks Mekaniska Verkstad (OMV) AB (3) **(51%)**
Tel.: (46) 66 026 5600
Web Site: https://www.omv.se
Sales Range: $10-24.9 Million
Emp.: 70
N.A.I.C.S.: 324199

Plant (Domestic):

Outokumpu Stainless AB (3)
Bergsnasgatan 11, PO Box 74, 774 41, Avesta, Sweden **(100%)**
Tel.: (46) 22681000
Web Site: http://www.outokumpu.com
Sales Range: $250-299.9 Million
N.A.I.C.S.: 324199

Outokumpu Stainless AB (3)
Bruksparken 2, PO Box 902, 693 81, Degerfors, Sweden **(100%)**
Tel.: (46) 58647000
Web Site: https://www.outokumpu.com
Emp.: 550
Stainless Steel Products Mfr
N.A.I.C.S.: 331513

Outokumpu Stainless AB (3)
Nyvader 2, SE-644 80, Torshalla, Sweden **(100%)**
Tel.: (46) 016349000
Sales Range: $150-199.9 Million
Emp.: 300
N.A.I.C.S.: 324199

Subsidiary (Domestic):

Outokumpu Stainless Tubular Products AB (3)

AND PRIVATE COMPANIES

Prostgardsvagen 2, PO Box 46, SE 660 60, Molkom, Sweden
Tel.: (46) 553 31120
Web Site: http://www.outokumpu.com
Sales Range: $25-49.9 Million
Emp.: 50
Stainless Tubular Products Mfr
N.A.I.C.S.: 331210

Plant (Domestic):

Outokumpu Stainless Tubular Products (4)
Vesplanaden 10, PO Box 203, 891 33, Ornskoldsvik, Sweden (100%)
Tel.: (46) 66057700
Web Site: http://www.abe.se
Sales Range: $25-49.9 Million
Stainless Steel Butt Welding Fittings
N.A.I.C.S.: 423830
Thomas Hellnan *(Mgr-Product)*

Outokumpu Stainless Tubular Products AB (4)
PO Box 510, SE 737 25, Fagersta, Sweden (38.25%)
Tel.: (46) 22345100
Sales Range: $25-49.9 Million
N.A.I.C.S.: 324199

Outokumpu Stainless Tubular Products AB (4)
Bruksparken 2, 693 32, Degerfors, Sweden (89%)
Tel.: (46) 58647000
Web Site: http://www.outokumpu.com
Sales Range: $50-74.9 Million
Rolled Steel Shape Mfr
N.A.I.C.S.: 324199

Outokumpu Stainless Tubular Products AB (4)
PO Box 48, SE 644 21, Torshalla, Sweden (80%)
Tel.: (46) 16349500
Web Site: http://www.outokumpu.com
Sales Range: $50-74.9 Million
N.A.I.C.S.: 324199

Subsidiary (Non-US):

Outokumpu Stainless B.V. (2)
Finlandweg 1, PO Box 52, 4554 AB, Westdorpe, Netherlands (100%)
Tel.: (31) 11 547 4700
Web Site: http://www.outokumpu.com
Sales Range: $50-74.9 Million
N.A.I.C.S.: 324199

Outokumpu Stainless Holding GmbH (2)
Hans-Boeckler-Str 36, 47877, Willich, Nordrhein-Westfalen, Germany
Tel.: (49) 7162 40900
Investment Management Service
N.A.I.C.S.: 523999

Outokumpu Stainless Ltd. (2)
Europa Link, PO Box 161, Sheffield, S9 1TZ, United Kingdom
Tel.: (44) 1142613800
Stainless Steel Mills
N.A.I.C.S.: 331110

Subsidiary (Domestic):

Outokumpu Stainless Holdings Ltd (3)
Europa Link, PO Box 161, Sheffield, S9 1TZ, United Kingdom
Tel.: (44) 114 261 4002
Stainless Steelware Mfr
N.A.I.C.S.: 331513

Plant (Domestic):

Outokumpu Stainless Ltd. - Alloy Steel Rods Mill (3)
Stevenson Road, Sheffield, S9 3XG, United Kingdom
Tel.: (44) 114 261 5240
Sales Range: $75-99.9 Million
Emp.: 100
Alloy Steel Rod Mill
N.A.I.C.S.: 331110

Subsidiary (Non-US):

Outokumpu Stainless Tubular Products AS (2)

Ankru 10, EE 11713, Tallinn, Estonia (100%)
Tel.: (372) 6628099
Sales Range: Less than $1 Million
Emp.: 50
N.A.I.C.S.: 324199

Subsidiary (Domestic):

Outokumpu Stainless Tubular Products Oy AB (2)
Tohjanpie11, PO Box 15, 68601, Pietarsaari, Finland
Tel.: (358) 67865111
Web Site: http://www.ja-ro.com
Sales Range: $25-49.9 Million
Production of Tubes & Tube Fittings
N.A.I.C.S.: 331210

Outokumpu Stainless Pipe, Inc. (1)
241 W Clarke St, Wildwood, FL 34785-3432 (51%)
Tel.: (352) 748-1313
Web Site: http://www.outokumpu.com
Sales Range: $50-74.9 Million
Emp.: 200
Mfr of Pipes & Cisterns
N.A.I.C.S.: 331110

Outokumpu Stainless Plate, Inc. (1)
549 W State Rd 38, New Castle, IN 47362
Tel.: (765) 529-0120
Web Site: http://www.outokumpu.com
Emp.: 125
Stainless Steel Mfr
N.A.I.C.S.: 331110
Kevin Keeley *(Chief Admin Officer)*

Outokumpu Stainless Steel (China) Co. Ltd. (1)
Tel.: (86) 51250120358
Stainless Steel Mfr
N.A.I.C.S.: 331513

Outokumpu Stainless Tubular Products (1)
180 Laurier Blvd, Brockville, K6V 5T7, ON, Canada (51%)
Tel.: (613) 345-5502
Web Site: http://www.outokumpu.ca
Sales Range: $25-49.9 Million
Emp.: 30
Mfr of Stainless Steel Fittings
N.A.I.C.S.: 332996

Outokumpu Stainless USA, LLC (1)
1 Steel Dr, Calvert, AL 36513
Tel.: (251) 829-3600
Web Site: http://www.outokumpu.com
Steel Mfr & Sales
N.A.I.C.S.: 331513
Stephen J. Letnich *(VP-Sls)*

Outokumpu Stainless, Inc. (1)
425 N Martingale Rd Ste 1600, Schaumburg, IL 60173-2218 (51%)
Tel.: (847) 517-4050
Web Site: http://www.outokumpu.com
Sales Range: $25-49.9 Million
Emp.: 9
Steel Sales
N.A.I.C.S.: 423510

Outokumpu UAB (1)
Nemajunu 21, LT 52459, Kaunas, Lithuania (100%)
Tel.: (370) 37380078
Web Site: http://www.outokumpu.com
Sales Range: $50-74.9 Million
Emp.: 5
N.A.I.C.S.: 324199

Outokumpu Zinc Australia Pty. Ltd. (1)
134-136 Fitzgerald Rd, North Laverton, Melbourne, 3028, VIC, Australia
Tel.: (61) 393609355
Zinc Ore Mining Services
N.A.I.C.S.: 212230

Outokumpu s.r.o. (1)
Luzna 716/2, 160 00, Prague, Czech Republic (100%)
Tel.: (420) 220 10 53 43
Emp.: 10
Stainless Steel Mfr
N.A.I.C.S.: 331222
Petr Hejtmanek *(Mgr-Sls)*

Polarit Welding, Inc (1)

12855 Belcher Rd S Ste 19, Largo, FL 33773
Tel.: (727) 530-7224
Welding Equipment Mfr & Whslr
N.A.I.C.S.: 333992

SH Trade Oy (1)
Teollisuustie 17, FIN 04300, Tuusula, Finland (100%)
Tel.: (358) 92747810
Web Site: http://www.sh-trade.fi
Sales Range: $1-9.9 Million
Emp.: 20
N.A.I.C.S.: 324199
Harri Kaasinen *(Mng Dir)*

Sogepar Ireland Limited (1)
Unit 7a Cookstown Industrial Estate, Tallaght, 216410, Ireland
Tel.: (353) 14598622
Stainless Steel Whslr
N.A.I.C.S.: 423510

Visenta Forsakrings AB (1)
Polervaegen 8, 774 41, Avesta, Sweden
Tel.: (46) 226 81000
General Insurance Services
N.A.I.C.S.: 524298

ZAO Outokumpu Moskva (1)
Academika Artsimovicha Str 3b, 117437, Moscow, Russia (100%)
Tel.: (7) 4952259883
Sales of Stainless Steel Products
N.A.I.C.S.: 423510

ZAO Outokumpu St. Petersburg (1)
Chapaeva Street Building 15 Business Centre Senator 24th Floor, Saint Petersburg, 197101, Russia (100%)
Tel.: (7) 8123212929
Web Site: http://www.outokumpu.com
Sales Range: $25-49.9 Million
Emp.: 2
Steel Products Mfr
N.A.I.C.S.: 331221

OUTSIDE LIVING INDUSTRIES FRANCE SARL

17 Rue de la Baignerie, 59000, Lille, France
Tel.: (33) 320179393
Web Site:
http://www.outsideliving.com
Sales Range: $75-99.9 Million
Emp.: 20
Prefabricated Wooden Building Mfr
N.A.I.C.S.: 321999
Jean-Luc Heymans *(Chm-Exec Bd)*

Subsidiaries:

Karibu Holztechnik GmbH (1)
Eduard-Suling-Strasse 17, 28217, Bremen, Germany
Tel.: (49) 421 38693 920
Garden Shed & Sauna Mfr
N.A.I.C.S.: 321992

Neogard AG (1)
Industriestrasse, 5728, Gontenschwil, Switzerland
Tel.: (41) 62 7670050
Garden Sauna Wood Mfr
N.A.I.C.S.: 321992

Outside Living Industries BeLux BVNR (1)
Wondelgemkaai 10, 9000, Gent, Belgium
Tel.: (32) 9 254 45 45
Wooden Building & Garden Sundry Mfr
N.A.I.C.S.: 321992

Outside Living Industries Nederland B.V. (1)
Berenkoog 87, 1822 BN, Alkmaar, Netherlands
Tel.: (31) 72 5 671 671
Sales Range: $25-49.9 Million
Emp.: 4
Garden Shed & Sauna Mfr
N.A.I.C.S.: 321992

Outside Living Industries SA (1)
17 Rue de la Baignerie, Lille, 59000, France
Tel.: (33) 3 20 17 93 93
Web Site: http://www.outsideliving.com

Wooden Building & Gardening Component Mfr
N.A.I.C.S.: 321992
Jluc Heymans *(CEO)*

Ubbink Garten GmbH (1)
Eduard-Suling-Strasse 17, Bremen, 28217, Germany
Tel.: (49) 421 38693 920
Web Site: http://www.outsideliving.com
Sales Range: $25-49.9 Million
Emp.: 5
Garden Shed & Sauna Mfr
N.A.I.C.S.: 321992
Hartmut Klaus *(Product Mgr)*

OUTSURANCE GROUP LIMITED

1 Merchant Place Corner of Fredman Drive and Rivonia Road, Sandton, 2196, South Africa
Tel.: (27) 112828000 ZA
Web Site:
https://group.outsurance.co.za
Year Founded: 2010
OUT—(JSE)
Rev.: $1,505,032,795
Assets: $1,924,661,224
Liabilities: $1,158,863,106
Net Worth: $765,798,118
Earnings: $176,649,521
Emp.: 7,467
Fiscal Year-end: 06/30/23
Investment Management Service
N.A.I.C.S.: 523940
Jan Jonathan Durand *(Chm)*

Subsidiaries:

OUTsurance Insurance Company Limited (1)
1241 Embankment Rd Zwartkop Ext 7, Centurion, 0157, South Africa
Tel.: (27) 126886800
Web Site: https://www.outsurance.co.za
Fire Insurance Services
N.A.I.C.S.: 524113

Youi Holdings Proprietary Limited (1)
L 1 24 Lake Kawana Bvd, Birtinya, 4575, QLD, Australia (100%)
Tel.: (61) 1300009684
Investment Management Service
N.A.I.C.S.: 523999

OV2 INVESTMENT 1, INC.

Suite 800 365 Bay Street, Toronto, M5H 2V1, ON, Canada
Tel.: (416) 644-5081 Ca
Year Founded: 2018
OVO.P—(TSXV)
Assets: $399,729
Liabilities: $132,154
Net Worth: $267,576
Earnings: ($110,000)
Fiscal Year-end: 04/30/21
Business Consulting Services
N.A.I.C.S.: 522299

OVAKO HOLDINGS AB

Kungstradgardsgatan 10, Stockholm, 11147, Sweden
Tel.: (46) 86221300
Web Site: http://www.ovako.com
Year Founded: 2005
Sales Range: $1-4.9 Billion
Emp.: 3,000
Steel Products Mfr
N.A.I.C.S.: 332111

Subsidiaries:

OVAKO (Shanghai) Special Steel Trading Co., Ltd. (1)
No 189 Fulian 2nd Road, Baoshan, Shanghai, 201906, China
Tel.: (86) 21 3366 2797
Steel Products Whslr
N.A.I.C.S.: 423510
Bright Li *(Mgr-Logistics)*

Ovako Bar BeNeLux (1)

OVAKO HOLDINGS AB

Ovako Holdings AB—(Continued)
Bedrijvenpark Twente 295, 7602 KK,
Almelo, Netherlands
Tel.: (31) 546588360
Web Site: http://www.ovako.com
Sales Range: $25-49.9 Million
Emp.: 32
Ferrous Metals Refinement
N.A.I.C.S.: 331491

Ovako Cromax AB (1)
Industrigatan 2, Hallstahammar, 734 30,
Vastmanland, Sweden
Tel.: (46) 86221300
Steel Products Mfr
N.A.I.C.S.: 331513
Magdalena Haupt *(Acct Mgr)*

Subsidiary (Domestic):

Ovako Hallstahammar AB (2)
Industrigatan 2, 734 30, Hallstahammar,
Sweden
Tel.: (46) 220 23 000
Web Site: http://www.ovako.com
Steel Products Mfr
N.A.I.C.S.: 331513
Joakim Hultgren *(Mng Dir)*

Subsidiary (Non-US):

Ovako Molinella S.p.A. (2)
Via Filippo Turati 11, 40062, Molinella, Italy
Tel.: (39) 051 690 0332
Emp.: 42
Steel Products Whslr
N.A.I.C.S.: 423510
Luciano Pirazzoli *(Mng Dir & Gen Mgr)*

Subsidiary (Domestic):

Ovako Mora AB (2)
Industrie Strasse 2, PO Box 421, 792 27,
Mora, Sweden
Tel.: (46) 25028400
Steel Products Mfr
N.A.I.C.S.: 331513
Tom Erixon *(CEO)*

Subsidiary (Non-US):

Ovako Redon S.A. (2)
Z A du Patis, BP 10308, 35603, Redon,
France
Tel.: (33) 2 99 714 168
Steel Products Whslr
N.A.I.C.S.: 423510

Ovako Twente B.V (2)
PO Box 8677600 AW, 7600 AW, Almelo,
Netherlands
Tel.: (31) 546 588 666
Steel Products Whslr
N.A.I.C.S.: 423510

Ovako France S.A.S. (1)
14 rue de Mirande, 21000, Dijon,
France (100%)
Tel.: (33) 380541515
Web Site: http://www.ovako.fr
Sales Range: $25-49.9 Million
Emp.: 13
Steel Products Mfr
N.A.I.C.S.: 332111
Cairol Rodalth *(Mgr)*

Ovako GmbH (1)
Maxponck Strasse 15 B, PO Box 1255, Erkrath, 40699, Germany (100%)
Tel.: (49) 21125040
Web Site: http://www.ovako.de
Sales Range: $25-49.9 Million
Emp.: 25
Steel Products Mfr
N.A.I.C.S.: 332111

Ovako Hofors AB (1)
Bruksvagen 10, SE-813 82, Hofors,
Sweden (100%)
Tel.: (46) 29025000
Web Site: http://www.ovako.com
Sales Range: $25-49.9 Million
Emp.: 60
Steel Products Mfr
N.A.I.C.S.: 332111

Subsidiary (Non-US):

Ovako Ltd (2)
Unit 2 York's Park Blowers Green Road,
Dudley, DY2 8UL, United Kingdom

Tel.: (44) 138 421 3940
Steel Products Whslr
N.A.I.C.S.: 423510
Jayne Bartley *(Mgr-Svc Centre)*

Subsidiary (US):

Ovako North America Inc (2)
1096 Assembly Dr Ste 312, Fort Mill, SC 29708
Tel.: (803) 802-1500
Web Site: http://www.ovako.com
Emp.: 9
Steel Products Whslr
N.A.I.C.S.: 423510
Arthur S. Hatton *(Mgr-Matl Flow)*

Subsidiary (Non-US):

Ovako Polska Sp. z.o.o. (2)
10 Patriotow Str lok 312, 04-844, Warsaw,
Poland
Tel.: (48) 22 870 05 03
Steel Products Whslr
N.A.I.C.S.: 423510
Joanna Kulinska *(Mgr-Admin)*

Ovako Imatra Oy Ab (1)
Teollisuuskuja 1, Turenki, 14200, Janakkala,
Finland
Tel.: (358) 5 680 21
Steel Products Whslr
N.A.I.C.S.: 423510
Pekko Juvonen *(Mgr-Export)*

Ovako Sales Unit Scandinavia AB (1)
Centralplan 1, 691 32, Karlskoga, Sweden
Tel.: (46) 591 60 000
Steel Products Mfr
N.A.I.C.S.: 331513
Bjorn Andersson *(Area Mgr)*

Ovako Steel Marketing AB (1)
No 189 Fulian 2nd Road, Baoshan, Shanghai, 201906, China
Tel.: (86) 21 3366 2787
Steel Products Whslr
N.A.I.C.S.: 423510
Bright Li *(Mgr-Logistics)*

Tibnor OY (1)
Tibnor Sundbybergsvagen 1, 169 26, Solna,
Sweden
Tel.: (46) 104840000
Web Site: http://www.tibnor.no
Sales Range: $75-99.9 Million
Steel & Metals Whslr
N.A.I.C.S.: 423510
Pekka Oja *(Mng Dir)*

OVAL CORPORATION

10-8 Kamiochiai 3-chome, Shinjuku-ku, Tokyo, 161-8508, Japan
Tel.: (81) 333605121
Web Site: https://www.oval.co.jp
Year Founded: 1949
7727—(TKS)
Rev.: $94,833,670
Assets: $155,011,110
Liabilities: $53,455,070
Net Worth: $101,556,040
Earnings: $7,284,220
Fiscal Year-end: 03/31/24
Electronic Instrument Mfr & Whslr
N.A.I.C.S.: 334514
Jun Tanimoto *(Pres & CEO)*

Subsidiaries:

Hefei Oval instrument Co. Ltd. (1)
58 Tiandu Road Economic Technical Development Area, Hefei, 230601, Anhui, China
Tel.: (86) 5513829018
Electronic Equipment Distr
N.A.I.C.S.: 423690

OVAL ENGINEERING INC. (1)
24-1 Dongtanyeok-ro, Dongtan-myeon,
Hwaseong, Gyeonggi-do, Korea (South)
Tel.: (82) 313793030
Web Site: https://www.ovaleng.com
Electronic Instrument Distr
N.A.I.C.S.: 423690

OVAL Thailand Ltd. (1)
818/50 The Master Udomsuk Sukhumvit 103, Bangna-Nua Bangna, Bangkok,

10260, Thailand
Tel.: (66) 213079134
Web Site: https://www.ovalthailand.com
Measuring Instrument Distr
N.A.I.C.S.: 423830

OVAL VIETNAM JVC, LTD. (1)
No 70 B2 Street, Saritown An Loi Dong
Ward Thu Duc, Ho Chi Minh City, Vietnam
Tel.: (84) 2839110183
Web Site: https://www.ovalvietnam.com
Electronic Instrument Distr
N.A.I.C.S.: 423690

Oval Asia Pacific Pte. Ltd. (1)
16 Boon Lay Way 01-49 Tradehub 21, Jurong, Singapore, 609965, Singapore
Tel.: (65) 62661178
Web Site: https://www.ovalasia.com.sg
Emp.: 30
Electronic Instrument Distr
N.A.I.C.S.: 423690
Terry Chan *(Mng Dir)*

Oval Engineering Sdn Bhd (1)
No 25-1 Block D1 Jalan PJU 1/41, Dataran Prima Taman Mayang Mas, 47301, Petaling Jaya, Selangor Darul Ehsan, Malaysia
Tel.: (60) 3 7803 5578
Web Site: http://www.oval.com
Emp.: 14
Measuring Instrument Distr
N.A.I.C.S.: 423830

Oval Taiwan Co., Ltd. (1)
17 F-5 No 738 Chung Cheng Rd, Chung Ho Dist, New Taipei City, 00235, Taiwan
Tel.: (886) 282262218
Electronic Instrument Distr
N.A.I.C.S.: 423690

Shanghai Oval Instrument Co., Ltd. (1)
No 388 Dazhi East Road, Jianbang Town Jiading District, Shanghai, 201818, China
Tel.: (86) 21 5951 3339
Electronic Instrument Distr
N.A.I.C.S.: 423690

OVARO KIINTEISTOSIJOITUS OYJ

Mannerheimintie 103 b, 00280, Helsinki, Finland
Tel.: (358) 104203100 FI
Web Site: http://www.ovaro.fi
Year Founded: 2010
OVARO—(HEL)
Rev.: $5,870,926
Assets: $68,281,891
Liabilities: $19,965,465
Net Worth: $48,316,426
Earnings: $485,646
Emp.: 5
Fiscal Year-end: 12/31/22
Real Estate Investment Trust
N.A.I.C.S.: 525990
Petri Roininen *(Chm)*

OVATION SCIENCE, INC.

1003-1166 Alberni Street, Vancouver, V6E 3Z3, BC, Canada
Tel.: (604) 982-5700
Web Site:
https://www.ovationscience.com
Year Founded: 2017
OVH—(DEU)
Rev.: $102,057
Assets: $77,481
Liabilities: $138,759
Net Worth: ($61,278)
Earnings: ($586,579)
Fiscal Year-end: 12/31/22
Research & Development Services
N.A.I.C.S.: 541720
Terry Howlett *(Pres & CEO)*

OVB HOLDING AG

Heumarkt 1, 50667, Cologne, Germany
Tel.: (49) 22120150
Web Site: https://www.ovb.eu
Year Founded: 1970

INTERNATIONAL PUBLIC

O4B—(DEU)
Rev.: $391,156,334
Assets: $301,312,355
Liabilities: $196,400,550
Net Worth: $104,911,805
Earnings: $15,807,418
Emp.: 751
Fiscal Year-end: 12/31/23
Financial Consulting Services
N.A.I.C.S.: 541611
Michael Johnigk *(Chm-Supervisory Bd)*

Subsidiaries:

Advesto GmbH (1)
Heumarkt 1, 50667, Cologne, Germany
Tel.: (49) 2212015200
Web Site: https://www.advesto.de
Financial Planning Services
N.A.I.C.S.: 541611

Eurenta Holding GmbH (1)
Pipinstrasse 16, 50667, Cologne, Germany
Tel.: (49) 2213310795
Web Site: https://www.eurenta.de
Financial Advice Services
N.A.I.C.S.: 541611

Nord-Soft EDV-Unternehmensberatung GmbH (1)
Glashofkamp 28, Horst, 25358, Schleswig, Germany
Tel.: (49) 412145730
Web Site: https://www.nord-soft.de
Software Development Services
N.A.I.C.S.: 541511

OVB Allfinanz Croatia d.o.o. (1)
Maksimirska 96/I, 10000, Zagreb, Croatia
Tel.: (385) 12396800
Web Site: https://www.ovb.hr
Financial Planning & Investment Services
N.A.I.C.S.: 541611

OVB Allfinanz Espana, S.A. (1)
Pza Manuel Gomez Moreno 2 8 A, 28020, Madrid, Spain
Tel.: (34) 914471028
Web Site: https://www.ovb.es
Financial Advice Services
N.A.I.C.S.: 541611

OVB Allfinanz Polska Spolka Finansowa Sp. z.o.o. (1)
ul Mieroslawskiego 11A, 01-527, Warsaw, Poland
Tel.: (48) 225763535
Web Site: https://www.ovb.pl
Financial Planning & Investment Services
N.A.I.C.S.: 541611

OVB Allfinanz Slovensko a.s. (1)
Kukuricna 8, 832 48, Bratislava, Slovakia
Tel.: (421) 258102411
Web Site: https://www.ovb.sk
Financial Planning & Investment Services
N.A.I.C.S.: 541611

OVB Allfinanz a.s (1)
V Parku 2343/24, Chodov, 148 00, Prague, 4, Czech Republic
Tel.: (420) 241094110
Web Site: https://www.ovb.cz
Financial Planning & Investment Services
N.A.I.C.S.: 541611

OVB Allfinanzvermittlungs GmbH (1)
Sirona Strasse 4/1/C, Wals b, 5071, Salzburg, Austria
Tel.: (43) 6626285670
Web Site: https://www.ovb.at
Financial Planning & Investment Services
N.A.I.C.S.: 541611

OVB Conseils en Patrimoine France Sarl (1)
Aeroparc n 1 1 rue Icare Immeuble Neos, 67960, Entzheim, France
Tel.: (33) 390297256
Web Site: https://www.ovb.fr
Financial Advice Services
N.A.I.C.S.: 541611

OVB Vermogensberatung (Schweiz) AG (1)
Bosch 69, 6331, Hunenberg, Switzerland
Tel.: (41) 417670130
Web Site: https://www.ovb-ag.ch

AND PRIVATE COMPANIES

Financial Planning & Investment Services
N.A.I.C.S.: 541611

OVB Vermogensberatung A.P.K. Kft. (1)
Vaci ut 140, 1138, Budapest, Hungary
Tel.: (36) 12310670
Web Site: http://www.ovb.hu
Financial Advice Services
N.A.I.C.S.: 541611
Daniel Szintai *(Mgr-Area)*

OVB-Consulenza Patrimoniale SRL (1)
Stradone San Fermo 19, 37121, Verona, Italy
Tel.: (39) 0458037070
Web Site: https://www.ovb.it
Financial Advice Services
N.A.I.C.S.: 541611

S.C. OVB Allfinanz Romania Broker de Asigurare S.R.L. (1)
Str Franz Liszt nr 30, 400969, Cluj-Napoca, Romania
Tel.: (40) 264588550
Web Site: https://www.ovb.ro
Financial Advice Services
N.A.I.C.S.: 541611

TOB OVB Allfinanz (1)
st Degtyarivska 62 office 45, 04112, Kiev, Ukraine
Tel.: (380) 444928777
Web Site: https://www.ovb.ua
Financial Advice Services
N.A.I.C.S.: 541611

Willemot Bijzonder Verzekeringsbestuur NV (1)
Coupure Rechts 228 te, 9000, Gent, Belgium
Tel.: (32) 92650811
Web Site: https://www.willemot.eu
Emp.: 80
Insurance Brokerage Services
N.A.I.C.S.: 524210

OVCTEK CHINA, INC.
No 4899 Wangjiang West Road High-tech Zone, Hefei, 230088, Anhui, China
Tel.: (86) 4006300595
Web Site: https://www.orthok.cn
Year Founded: 2000
300595—(CHIN)
Rev.: $244,680,183
Assets: $777,338,558
Liabilities: $113,785,757
Net Worth: $663,552,801
Earnings: $93,890,582
Fiscal Year-end: 12/31/23
Contact Lens Mfr & Distr
N.A.I.C.S.: 339115
Tao Yuequn *(Chm & Gen Mgr)*

OVER THE WIRE HOLDINGS LIMITED
Level 24 100 Creek Street, Brisbane, 4000, QLD, Australia
Tel.: (61) 7 3847 9292
Web Site: http://www.overthewire.com.au
OTW—(ASX)
Rev.: $86,440,023
Assets: $160,590,359
Liabilities: $83,730,009
Net Worth: $76,860,350
Earnings: $2,631,863
Fiscal Year-end: 06/30/21
Business Telecommunications
N.A.I.C.S.: 517810
Michael Omeros *(CEO & Mng Dir)*

Subsidiaries:

Comlinx Pty Ltd (1)
Level 24/100 Creek Street, Brisbane, 4000, QLD, Australia
Tel.: (61) 738529800
Web Site: http://www.comlinx.com.au
Cyber Security Services
N.A.I.C.S.: 541519

Faktortel Pty Ltd (1)
PO Box 1807, Brisbane, 4000, QLD, Australia
Tel.: (61) 731189598
Web Site: http://www.faktortel.com.au
Software Development Services
N.A.I.C.S.: 541511

Netsip Pty Ltd (1)
Level 24 100 Creek Street, Brisbane, 4000, QLD, Australia
Tel.: (61) 1300638747
Web Site: http://www.netsip.com.au
Telecommunication Servicesb
N.A.I.C.S.: 517112

Telarus Pty Ltd (1)
Level 8 473 Bourke Street, Melbourne, 3000, VIC, Australia
Tel.: (61) 1300788858
Web Site: http://www.telarus.com.au
Software Development Services
N.A.I.C.S.: 541511

VPN Solutions Pty Ltd (1)
21/71 Eagle Street, Brisbane, 4000, QLD, Australia
Tel.: (61) 738479292
Web Site: http://www.vpnsolutions.com.au
Telecommunication Servicesb
N.A.I.C.S.: 517810

OVERACTIVE MEDIA CORP.
41 Fraser Avenue, Toronto, M6K 1Y7, ON, Canada
Tel.: (604) 638-2545
Web Site: https://overactivemedia.com
OAM—(TSXV)
Rev.: $10,392,076
Assets: $64,311,700
Liabilities: $29,486,285
Net Worth: $34,825,414
Earnings: ($27,095,565)
Fiscal Year-end: 12/31/22
Esports & Entertainment Services
N.A.I.C.S.: 711211
Adam E. Adamou *(Interim CEO)*

OVERLACK FURNIERE GMBH & CO. KG
Rauentaler Strasse 50, D-76437, Rastatt, Germany
Tel.: (49) 722295880
Web Site: http://www.overlack.com
Rev.: $23,822,928
Emp.: 38
Wood Veneers Mfr
N.A.I.C.S.: 423310

Subsidiaries:

Overlack Furniere Polska Sp. z o.o. (1)
ul Inzynierska 8 B, 20-484, Lublin, Poland
Tel.: (48) 602232492
Wood Product Distr
N.A.I.C.S.: 423310

OVERLAND WEST FREIGHT LINES LTD.
300 10362 King George Hwy, Surrey, V3T 2W5, BC, Canada
Tel.: (604) 580-4600
Web Site: http://www.overlandwest.ca
Rev.: $10,562,622
Emp.: 100
General Freight Services
N.A.I.C.S.: 488510
Martin Thormeyer *(Dir-Admin & Mktg)*

OVERSEA ENTERPRISE BERHAD
Lot 12 2 12th Floor Menara Lien Hoe No 8 Persiaran Tropicana, Tropicana Golf & Country Resort Petaling Jaya, 47410, Petaling Jaya, Malaysia
Tel.: (60) 378876838
Web Site: https://www.oversea.com.my
Year Founded: 1994

OVERSEA—(KLS)
Rev.: $11,892,177
Assets: $23,417,000
Liabilities: $7,466,609
Net Worth: $15,950,391
Earnings: ($498,824)
Fiscal Year-end: 03/31/23
Holding Company; Restaurant Owner & Operator
N.A.I.C.S.: 551112
Soo Chye Yu *(Chm & Mng Dir-Grp)*

Subsidiaries:

Haewaytian Cake House Sdn Bhd (1)
Lot 13 Jln Utarid U5/16 Seksyen U5 Kaw Perind Mah Sing Integrated, 40150, Shah Alam, Selangor, Malaysia
Tel.: (60) 378459680
Web Site: http://www.oversea.com.my
Sales Range: $150-199.9 Million
Emp.: 600
Bakery Products Mfr
N.A.I.C.S.: 311812
Yap Teck Beng *(Gen Mgr)*

OVERSEA-CHINESE BANKING CORPORATION LIMITED
63 Chulia Street 10-00 OCBC Centre East, Singapore, 049514, Singapore
Tel.: (65) 65381111   SG
Web Site: https://www.ocbc.com
Year Founded: 1932
OVCHY—(OTCIQ)
Rev.: $6,902,690,710
Assets: $393,637,583,150
Liabilities: $355,001,238,430
Net Worth: $38,636,344,720
Earnings: $2,814,528,160
Fiscal Year-end: 12/31/20
Emp.: 30,538
Banking & Financial Services
N.A.I.C.S.: 522110
Linus Ti Liang Goh *(Head-Global Comml Banking)*

Subsidiaries:

Bank of Singapore Limited (1)
63 Market Street, 22nd Floor Bank of Singapore Centre, Singapore, 048942, Singapore (100%)
Tel.: (65) 65598000
Web Site: https://www.finatiq.com
Sales Range: $50-74.9 Million
Emp.: 20
Provider of Banking Services
N.A.I.C.S.: 522110
Jason Moo *(CEO)*

Subsidiary (Non-US):

Pacific Mutual Fund Bhd. (2)
1001 Level 10 Uptown 1 No 1 Jalan SS21/58, Damansara Uptown, 47400, Petaling Jaya, Selangor, Malaysia (100%)
Tel.: (60) 3 7725 9877
Web Site: http://www.pacificmutual.com.my
Investment Management Service
N.A.I.C.S.: 525910
Huat Soon Koh *(Head-Risk Mgmt, Portfolio Risk & Performance)*

Central China International Leasing Company Limited (1)
Unit A 11th Fl Liang You Bldg, No 316 Xin Hua Lu, Wuhan, 430022, Hubei, China (25%)
Tel.: (86) 2785496350
Sales Range: Less than $1 Million
Emp.: 10
N.A.I.C.S.: 522110

Great Eastern General Insurance (Malaysia) Berhad (1)
Level 18 Menara Great Eastern 303 Jalan Ampang, 50450, Kuala Lumpur, Malaysia
Tel.: (60) 342598888
Web Site: https://www.greateasterngeneral.com
General Insurance Services
N.A.I.C.S.: 524210

Great Eastern Holdings Limited (1)
1 Pickering Street 01-01 Great Eastern Centre, Singapore, 048659, Singapore (87.9%)
Tel.: (65) 62482000
Web Site: https://www.greateasternlife.com
Rev.: $4,741,270,921
Assets: $82,582,594,822
Liabilities: $76,531,697,302
Net Worth: $6,050,897,520
Earnings: $597,742,937
Fiscal Year-end: 12/31/2023
Holding Company; Insurance & Investment Products & Services
N.A.I.C.S.: 551112
Beng Seng Koh *(Chm)*

Subsidiary (Domestic):

Great Eastern General Insurance Ltd (2)
1 Pickering Street #01-01, Great Eastern Centre, Singapore, 048659, Singapore
Tel.: (65) 62482211
Insurance Services
N.A.I.C.S.: 524298
Koh Beng Seng *(Chm)*

Subsidiary (Non-US):

PT QBE General Insurance Indonesia (3)
Midplaza 2 23rd Floor Jalan Jenderal Sudirman Kav 10-11, Jakarta, 10220, Indonesia
Tel.: (62) 21 572 3737
Web Site: http://www.qbe.co.id
General Insurance Products & Services
N.A.I.C.S.: 524126
John Lilburne Hunt *(Commissioner)*

Subsidiary (Domestic):

PT Asuransi QBE Pool Indonesia (4)
MidPlaza 2 23rd Floor Jl Jenderal Sudirman Kav 10-11, Jakarta, 10220, Indonesia (100%)
Tel.: (62) 215723737
Web Site: http://qbeindonesia.linkagedev.com.hk
Property & Casualty Insurance Products & Services
N.A.I.C.S.: 524126

Subsidiary (Non-US):

Great Eastern Life Assurance (Malaysia) Bhd. (2)
Menara Great Eastern 303 Jalan Ampang, 50450, Kuala Lumpur, Malaysia
Tel.: (60) 342598888
Web Site: http://www.Greateasternlife.com
Sales Range: $300-349.9 Million
Emp.: 1,000
Life, Personal Accident, Health Insurance & Annuity Plans
N.A.I.C.S.: 524298

Subsidiary (Domestic):

Lion Global Investors Limited (2)
65 Julia St Unit 18-01, OCBC Center, Singapore, 049513, Singapore (70%)
Tel.: (65) 64176900
Web Site: https://www.lionglobalinvestors.com
Sales Range: $100-124.9 Million
Emp.: 150
Asset Management Services
N.A.I.C.S.: 524113
James Tan *(COO)*

Subsidiary (Non-US):

Overseas Assurance Corporation (Malaysia) Berhad (2)
Level 18 Menara Great Eastern, 303 Jalan Ampang, 50450, Kuala Lumpur, Malaysia
Tel.: (60) 342597888
Web Site: http://www.oac.com.my
Sales Range: $50-74.9 Million
Emp.: 100
Provider of Insurance Services
N.A.I.C.S.: 524298

Affiliate (Non-US):

P.T. Asuransi Jiwa Asih Great Eastern (2)
Menara Karya 5th Fl Jl HR Rasuna Said Blok X5 Kav 1-2 Jakarta Selatan, Jakarta,

OVERSEA-CHINESE BANKING CORPORATION LIMITED

Oversea-Chinese Banking Corporation Limited—(Continued)
12950, Indonesia
Tel.: (62) 2125543800
Web Site: http://www.greateasternlife.com
Sales Range: $25-49.9 Million
Joint Venture of The Great Eastern Life Assurance Company (60%), Jiwa Bumi Asih Jaya & Others
N.A.I.C.S.: 524113

Subsidiary (Domestic):

The Great Eastern Life Assurance Company Limited (2)
1 Pickering Street 01-01 Great Eastern Centre, Singapore, 048659, Singapore (100%)
Tel.: (65) 62482000
Web Site: https://www.greateasternlife.com
Sales Range: $300-349.9 Million
Emp.: 700
Fire Insurance Services
N.A.I.C.S.: 524128

The Overseas Assurance Corporation Limited (2)
1 Pickering St 13 01 Great Eastern Ctr, Singapore, 048659, Singapore
Tel.: (65) 62482000
Web Site: http://www.oac.com.sg
Sales Range: $300-349.9 Million
Emp.: 600
Insurance Services
N.A.I.C.S.: 524298

OCBC Al-Amin Bank Berhad (1)
25th Floor Wisma Lee Rubber 1 Jalan Melaka, 50100, Kuala Lumpur, Malaysia (100%)
Tel.: (60) 320345034
Web Site: https://www.ocbc.com.my
Islamic Retail & Commercial Banking Services
N.A.I.C.S.: 522110

OCBC Asset Management (1)
63 Chulia St 05 01, OCBC Centre E, Singapore, 049514, Singapore
Tel.: (65) 65317088
Web Site: http://www.ocbc.com
Sales Range: $100-124.9 Million
Emp.: 150
Investment Firm
N.A.I.C.S.: 523910

OCBC Bank (Malaysia) Berhad (1)
Menara OCBC 18 Jalan Tun Perak, 50050, Kuala Lumpur, Malaysia (100%)
Tel.: (60) 320345034
Web Site: https://www.ocbc.com.my
Sales Range: $700-749.9 Million
Banking Services
N.A.I.C.S.: 522110
Meng Teoh Yin (CFO)

Subsidiary (Domestic):

OCBC Capital (Malaysia) Sdn. Bhd. (2)
13th Floor Menara OCBC 18 JalanTun Perak, 50050, Kuala Lumpur, Malaysia
Tel.: (60) 3 2034 5649
Investment & Portfolio Management Services
N.A.I.C.S.: 523999

OCBC Nominees (Hong Kong) Limited (1)
9th Floor 9 Queens Rd, Central, China (Hong Kong)
Tel.: (852) 28406247
Nominee Services
N.A.I.C.S.: 561499

OCBC Property Services Private Limited (1)
18 Cross Street 11-01/03 China Square Central, Singapore, 48423, Singapore
Tel.: (65) 6533 0818
Web Site: http://www.ocbcproperty.com.sg
Sales Range: $75-99.9 Million
Emp.: 112
Property Management Services
N.A.I.C.S.: 531311

OCBC Securities (Hong Kong) Limited (1)
Suite No 3 11th Floor Queens Place No 74 Queens Road, Central, China (Hong Kong)
Tel.: (852) 2810 7886
Web Site: http://portal.iocbc.com
Securities Brokerage Services
N.A.I.C.S.: 523150

OCBC Securities Private Limited (1)
18 Church Street 01-00 OCBC Centre South, Singapore, 049479, Singapore
Tel.: (65) 18003388688
Web Site: https://www.portal.iocbc.com
Financial Services
N.A.I.C.S.: 541611

OCBC Securities Pte. Ltd. (1)
18 Church St 01-00 OCBC Centre South, Singapore, 049479, Singapore (100%)
Tel.: (65) 65352882
Web Site: http://www.iocbc.com
Sales Range: $200-249.9 Million
Emp.: 400
Security Brokers
N.A.I.C.S.: 523910
Dennis Hong (Mng Dir)

OCBC Wing Hang Bank Limited (1)
161 Queen s Road, Central, China (Hong Kong)
Tel.: (852) 28525111
Web Site: https://www.ocbc.com.hk
Rev.: $1,242,238,340
Assets: $38,155,105,350
Liabilities: $32,602,400,130
Net Worth: $5,552,705,220
Earnings: $318,842,030
Emp.: 1,500
Fiscal Year-end: 12/31/2019
Commercial Banking Services
N.A.I.C.S.: 522110
Cheng Hoe Andrew Khoo (Chm)

Subsidiary (Domestic):

OCBC Inchroy Credit Corporation Limited (2)
5th Fl Eastern Central Plz Yiu Hing Rd, Shau Kei Wan, China (Hong Kong) (100%)
Tel.: (852) 36692669
Web Site: http://www.ocbcwhhk.com
Sales Range: $50-74.9 Million
Emp.: 200
Financial Services
N.A.I.C.S.: 522310

OCBC Wing Hang (Trustee) Limited (2)
1st Floor Wing Hang Finance Centre, 60 Gloucester Road, Wanchai, China (Hong Kong) (100%)
Tel.: (852) 2272 8888
Web Site: http://www.ocbcwhhk.com
Fund Management Services
N.A.I.C.S.: 541618

Subsidiary (Non-US):

OCBC Wing Hang Bank Limited (Macau) (2)
241 Avenida de Almeida Ribeiro, Macau, China (Macau)
Tel.: (853) 28335678
Web Site: https://www.ocbc.com.mo
Banking Services
N.A.I.C.S.: 522110

Subsidiary (Domestic):

OCBC Wing Hang Credit Limited (2)
Unit 1202 12/f Wing On Centre 111 Connaught Road, Central, China (Hong Kong) (100%)
Tel.: (852) 25360909
Web Site: http://www.ocbcwhcr.com
Consumer Loans & Financing Services
N.A.I.C.S.: 522310

OCBC Wing Hang Insurance Agency Limited (2)
16/F Eastern Central Plaza 3 Yiu Hing Road, Shau Kei Wan, China (Hong Kong) (100%)
Tel.: (852) 2272 8800
Web Site: http://www.ocbcwhhk.com
Sales Range: $50-74.9 Million
General Insurance Services
N.A.I.C.S.: 524210

OCBC Wing Hang Insurance Brokers Limited (2)
16/F Eastern Central Plaza 3 Yiu Hing Road, Shau Kei Wan, China (Hong Kong)
Tel.: (852) 22728800
Web Site: http://www.ocbcwhhk.com
Sales Range: $50-74.9 Million
General Insurance Services
N.A.I.C.S.: 524126

OCBC Wing Hang Shares Brokerage Co. Limited (2)
1/f Chun Wo Commercial Bldg 23-29 Wing Wo Street, Central, China (Hong Kong) (100%)
Tel.: (852) 28525338
Web Site: http://www.ocbcwhsb.com
Insurance Brokerage Services
N.A.I.C.S.: 524298

Subsidiary (Non-US):

Wing Hang Bank (China) Ltd. (2)
8/F 5/F Unit M02 Shun Hing Square Di Wang Commercial Centre, 5002 Shennan Dong Road, Shenzhen, 518008, China
Tel.: (86) 75525833111
Web Site: http://www.ocbc.com.cn
Banking & Foreign Currency Services
N.A.I.C.S.: 522110

PT Bank OCBC Indonesia (1)
Wisma GKBI Ste 2201 Jalan Jendral Sudirman 28, Jakarta, 10210, Indonesia (100%)
Tel.: (62) 215740222
Web Site: http://www.ocbc.com
Sales Range: $50-74.9 Million
Emp.: 100
Banking Services
N.A.I.C.S.: 522110

PT Bank OCBC NISP Tbk (1)
Jl Prof Dr Satrio Kav 25, Jakarta, 12940, Indonesia
Tel.: (62) 2125533888
Web Site: https://www.ocbc.id
Retail Banking Services
N.A.I.C.S.: 522110
Parwati Surjaudaja (Co-Pres)

Subsidiary (Domestic):

PT. Bank Commonwealth (2)
Wisma Metropolitan II 1st Floor Jl Jend Sudirman Kav 29-31, Jakarta, 12920, Indonesia
Tel.: (62) 21 5296 1222
Web Site: http://www.commbank.co.id
Commercial Banking Services
N.A.I.C.S.: 522110

Singapore Island Bank Limited (1)
63 Chulia Street 26-00 Ocbc Centre, Singapore, 49514, Singapore
Tel.: (65) 65863200
Commercial Banking Services
N.A.I.C.S.: 522110

OVERSEAS CHINESE TOWN (ASIA) HOLDINGS LIMITED

59/F Bank of China Tower 1 Garden Road, Hong Kong, China (Hong Kong)
Tel.: (852) 23937799
Web Site: http://www.oct-asia.com
3366—(HKG)
Rev.: $431,372,120
Assets: $3,197,755,876
Liabilities: $1,810,507,982
Net Worth: $1,387,247,893
Earnings: ($280,247,105)
Emp.: 556
Fiscal Year-end: 12/31/22
Paper based Packaging Materials & Containers Mfr
N.A.I.C.S.: 327213
Fuk Wai Fong (CFO & Sec)

Subsidiaries:

Anhui Huali Packaging Co., Ltd. (1)
No 399 of Huayuan Road Economic and Technological Development Zone, Chuzhou, 239000, Anhui, China
Tel.: (86) 5503210136
Paper Box Mfr & Distr
N.A.I.C.S.: 322211
Guobing Li (Gen Mgr)

INTERNATIONAL PUBLIC

Huizhou Huali Packaging Co., Ltd. (1)
Xingcheng Technology Park Danshui Town Huiyang District, Huizhou, 516211, China
Tel.: (86) 7523255998
Paper Box Mfr & Distr
N.A.I.C.S.: 322211
Lixin Ouyang (Gen Mgr)

Shanghai Huali Packaging Co., Ltd. (1)
No 193 of Xiangyang North Road Heqing Town Pudong New District, Shanghai, 201201, China
Tel.: (86) 2158972099
Web Site: http://www.sh.hualiholdings.com
Paper Box Mfr & Distr
N.A.I.C.S.: 322211
Jun Huang (Gen Mgr)

Shenzhen Huali Packing & Trading Co., Ltd. (1)
3/F Jacaranda OCT Harbour Baishi Road, Shenzhen, 518053, China
Tel.: (86) 75526936198
Web Site: http://hualiholdings.com
Paper Box Mfr & Distr
N.A.I.C.S.: 322211

Suzhou Huali Environmental Packaging Technology Co., Ltd (1)
No 270 of Hualian Road Meili Town, Changshu, 215500, Jiangsu, China
Tel.: (86) 51252972989
Paper Box Mfr & Distr
N.A.I.C.S.: 322211
Xiaojun Zhang (Gen Mgr)

Zhongshan Huali Packaging Co., Ltd. (1)
The Third Industry District Tanzhou Town, Zhongshan, 528467, China
Tel.: (86) 76086159333
Paper Box Mfr & Distr
N.A.I.C.S.: 322211
Xiaotai Wang (Gen Mgr)

OVERSEAS CONTAINER FORWARDING INC.

100 10451 Shellbridge Way, Richmond, V6X 2W8, BC, Canada
Tel.: (604) 734-8155
Web Site: http://www.ocf.ca
Year Founded: 1979
General Freight Services
N.A.I.C.S.: 488510
Sherry Babcock (VP-Fin)

Subsidiaries:

Overseas Container Forwarding Inc. (1)
505 S 336th St Ste 610, Federal Way, WA 98003
Tel.: (253) 833-1204
General Freight Services
N.A.I.C.S.: 488510
Marty Bain (VP)

OVERSEAS EDUCATION LIMITED

81 Pasir Ris Heights, Singapore, 519292, Singapore
Tel.: (65) 67380211
Web Site: https://oel.listedcompany.com
Year Founded: 1991
RQ1—(SES)
Rev.: $66,519,036
Assets: $215,722,271
Liabilities: $111,732,738
Net Worth: $103,989,533
Earnings: $5,094,255
Emp.: 425
Fiscal Year-end: 12/31/23
Elementary & Secondary Schools
N.A.I.C.S.: 611110
David Alan Perry (Chm & Co-CEO)

OVERSEAS MARKETING CORPORATION(PVT.) LTD.

Unique Trade Center UTC Level 15 8

Panthapath, Dhaka, 1215, Bangladesh
Tel.: (880) 9602666662 BD
Web Site: http://www.omcbd.com
Year Founded: 1980
Emp.: 200
Laboratory Equipment Distr
N.A.I.C.S.: 423490

OVERSEAS REALTY (CEYLON) PLC
1801 East Tower World Trade Center Echelon Square, 1, Colombo, Sri Lanka
Tel.: (94) 112346333
Web Site: https://www.orcl.lk
OSEA.N0000—(COL)
Rev.: $15,680,726
Assets: $241,656,558
Liabilities: $74,487,370
Net Worth: $167,169,188
Earnings: $11,901,880
Fiscal Year-end: 12/31/23
Property Development & Investment Holding Services
N.A.I.C.S.: 531311

Subsidiaries:
Havelock City (Pvt) Ltd. (1)
324 Havelock Road, Colombo, Sri Lanka
Tel.: (94) 772505100
Web Site: https://havelockcity.lk
Real Estate Services
N.A.I.C.S.: 531190

OVH GROUPE SA
2 rue Kellermann, 59100, Roubaix, France
Tel.: (33) 320827332
Web Site: https://www.corporate.ovhcloud.com
Year Founded: 1999
OVHFF—(OTCIQ)
Rev.: $842,212,262
Assets: $1,542,010,131
Liabilities: $1,041,438,720
Net Worth: $500,571,411
Earnings: ($30,518,515)
Emp.: 2,800
Fiscal Year-end: 08/31/22
Information Technology Services
N.A.I.C.S.: 541512
Mathieu Delobelle (CIO)

Subsidiaries:
Ovhtech R&d (india) Private Limited (1)
WeWork Salarpuria Symbiosis Begur Hobli Bannerghatta Main Rd, Arekere Village, Bengaluru, 560 076, Karnataka, India
Tel.: (91) 8037862352
Software Development Services
N.A.I.C.S.: 541511

OVOBEL FOODS LIMITED
46 Old No 321 3rd cross Aga Abbas Ali Rd Ulsoor, Bengaluru, 560 042, India
Tel.: (91) 8025594145
Web Site: https://www.ovobelfoods.com
Year Founded: 1993
530741—(BOM)
Rev.: $26,948,648
Assets: $12,047,167
Liabilities: $4,983,946
Net Worth: $7,063,222
Earnings: $4,654,721
Emp.: 108
Fiscal Year-end: 03/31/23
Food Product Mfr & Distr
N.A.I.C.S.: 311920
Shanti Swarup Aggarwal (Mng Dir)

OVOCA BIO PLC
17 Pembroke Street Upper, Dublin, D02 AT22, Ireland
Tel.: (353) 16619819 IE
Web Site: https://www.ovocabio.com
Year Founded: 1985
OVXA—(ISE)
Assets: $3,828,237
Liabilities: $1,067,447
Net Worth: $2,760,790
Earnings: ($5,634,176)
Fiscal Year-end: 12/31/23
Precious Metals & Minerals Exploration Services
N.A.I.C.S.: 331410
Kirill Golovanov (Chm-Interim & CEO)

OVOSTAR UNION N.V.
Petropavlivska Street 34, 04086, Kiev, Ukraine
Tel.: (380) 443542960
Web Site: https://www.ovostar.ua
OVO—(WAR)
Rev.: $135,626,000
Assets: $110,695,000
Liabilities: $26,774,000
Net Worth: $83,921,000
Earnings: $6,087,000
Emp.: 1,367
Fiscal Year-end: 12/31/22
Egg Producer
N.A.I.C.S.: 112310
Borys Bielikov (CEO)

Subsidiaries:
Limited Liability Company Yasensvit (1)
street Petropavlivska 34, Kiev, 04086, Ukraine
Tel.: (380) 443542960
Web Site: https://www.yasensvit.ua
Chicken Egg Production Services
N.A.I.C.S.: 112310

OAE Food Trade FZE (1)
Free Zone Jafza One Building Office BB1010, Jebel Ali, United Arab Emirates
Tel.: (971) 48844181
Chicken Egg Production Services
N.A.I.C.S.: 112310

SIA Gallusman (1)
Tinuzu soseja 17, Ikskile, LV-5052, Latvia
Tel.: (371) 28449491
Web Site: https://www.gallusman.com
Chicken Egg Production Services
N.A.I.C.S.: 112310

SIA Ovostar Europe (1)
Tinuzu Road 17, Ikskile, LV-5052, Latvia
Tel.: (371) 28449490
Chicken Egg Distr
N.A.I.C.S.: 424440
Edgars Lesnieks (Bus Mgr)

OVPS - OBERELBISCHE VERKEHRSGESELLSCHAFT PIRNA-SEBNITZ MBH
Bahnhofstrasse 14 a, 01796, Pirna, Germany
Tel.: (49) 3501 792 0
Web Site: http://www.ovps.de
Public Bus Transportation Services
N.A.I.C.S.: 485210
Mike Ruckh (Chm)

Subsidiaries:
Regionalverkehr Dresden GmbH (1)
Ammonstrasse 25, 01067, Dresden, Germany (51%)
Tel.: (49) 351 492 1320
Web Site: http://www.rvd.de
Bus Transportation Services
N.A.I.C.S.: 485210
Uwe Thiele (Mng Dir)

OVS S.P.A.
Via Terraglio 17, 30174, Mestre, Venezia, Italy
Tel.: (39) 041239700
Web Site: https://www.ovscorporate.it
OVS—(ITA)
Rev.: $1,971,463,991
Assets: $3,526,289,322
Liabilities: $2,416,979,802
Net Worth: $1,109,309,521
Earnings: $48,149,464
Emp.: 6,088
Fiscal Year-end: 01/31/23
Men's, Women's & Childrens' Clothing Mfr & Marketer
N.A.I.C.S.: 315250
Stefano Beraldo (CEO & Gen Mgr)

Subsidiaries:
OVS India Sourcing Private Ltd. (1)
Chinnakarai, Tirupur, 641604, Tamil Nadu, India
Tel.: (91) 4213041333
Web Site: https://ovs-india-sourcing-pvt-ltd.business.site
Clothes Mfr
N.A.I.C.S.: 315990

OVZON AB
Anderstorpsvagen 16, 171 54, Solna, Sweden
Tel.: (46) 850860060
Web Site: https://www.ovzon.com
Year Founded: 2006
OVZON—(OMX)
Rev.: $33,436,642
Assets: $179,987,075
Liabilities: $49,533,002
Net Worth: $130,454,073
Earnings: ($3,389,156)
Emp.: 43
Fiscal Year-end: 12/31/22
Broadband Internet Service Provider
N.A.I.C.S.: 517112
Magnus Rene (CEO)

Subsidiaries:
Ovzon Sweden AB (1)
Anderstorpsvagen 10, SE-171 54, Solna, Sweden
Tel.: (46) 850860060
Satellite Communication Services
N.A.I.C.S.: 517410

Ovzon US, LLC. (1)
5460 Beaumont Center Blvd Ste 550, Tampa, FL 33634-5295
Tel.: (703) 276-3333
Telecommunication Servicesb
N.A.I.C.S.: 517810

OWARI PRECISE PRODUCTS CO., LTD.
3-16-85 Yada, Higashi-Ku, Nagoya, 461-8678, Japan
Tel.: (81) 527217131
Web Site: https://www.owariseiki.co.jp
7249—(NGO)
Rev.: $162,143,940
Assets: $166,554,710
Liabilities: $54,836,600
Net Worth: $111,718,110
Earnings: $4,658,360
Fiscal Year-end: 03/31/19
Automobile Parts Mfr
N.A.I.C.S.: 336110
Koji Hyodo (Pres)

OWASCO VOLKSWAGEN
2030 Champlain Avenue, Whitby, L1N 6A7, ON, Canada
Tel.: (905) 579-0010
Web Site: http://www.owascovw.ca
Rev.: $35,300,000
Emp.: 62
New & Used Car Dealers
N.A.I.C.S.: 441110

OWC PHARMACEUTICAL RESEARCH CORP.
2 Ben Gurion Street, Ramat Gan, 4514760, Israel
Tel.: (972) 722608004 DE
Web Site: http://www.owcpharma.com
Year Founded: 2008
OWCP—(OTCEM)
Sales Range: Less than $1 Million
Emp.: 5
Cannabis-Based Medicinal Products Mfr
N.A.I.C.S.: 325411
Yehuda Baruch (Chief Medical & Regulatory Officer)

OWEN & CO. LTD.
5800 Steeles Ave W, Woodbridge, L4L 0J4, ON, Canada
Tel.: (905) 265-9203
Web Site: http://www.kingsdown.ca
Year Founded: 1995
Mattress Mfr
N.A.I.C.S.: 337910
Mike James (Pres & CEO)

Subsidiaries:
Kingsdown, Inc. (1)
126 W Holt St, Mebane, NC 27302
Tel.: (919) 563-3531
Web Site: http://www.kingsdown.com
Sales Range: $75-99.9 Million
Emp.: 300
Beddings & Mattress Mfr
N.A.I.C.S.: 337910
Frank Hood (Pres & CEO)

OWEN MUMFORD LTD.
Brook Hill, Woodstock, Oxford, OX20 1TU, Oxfordshire, United Kingdom
Tel.: (44) 1993812021 UK
Web Site: http://www.owenmumford.com
Year Founded: 1952
Sales Range: $150-199.9 Million
Emp.: 700
N.A.I.C.S.: 423450
Mark Owen (Chm)

Subsidiaries:
Owen Mumford (1)
5 Rue De La Croix Blanche, Saint Marcel, 27950, France (100%)
Tel.: (33) 232518870
Web Site: http://www.owenmumford.com
Sales Range: $25-49.9 Million
Emp.: 12
Mfr of Medical Devices
N.A.I.C.S.: 339112
Eric Del Cotto (Gen Mgr)

Owen Mumford GmbH (1)
Alge Haege 1, 63762, Grossostheim, Germany (100%)
Tel.: (49) 602697750
Mfr of Medical Devices
N.A.I.C.S.: 339112

Owen Mumford Inc (1)
1755-A W Oak Commons Ct, Marietta, GA 30062
Web Site: http://www.owenmumford.com
Mfr of Medical Devices
N.A.I.C.S.: 423990

Owen Mumford Ltd. - Cotswold Division (1)
Primsdown Industrial Estate Worcester Road, Chipping Norton, OX7 5XP, Oxfordshire, United Kingdom
Tel.: (44) 1608 645555
Web Site: http://www.owenmumford.co.uk
Emp.: 400
Medical Device Mfr
N.A.I.C.S.: 339112

Owen Mumford (Shanghai) Medical Device Company Ltd (1)
25/F Central Plaza 381 Huai Hai Middle Road, Lu Wan District, Shanghai, 200020, China
Tel.: (86) 21 6032 3528
Medical Device Mfr
N.A.I.C.S.: 339112

OWEN TAYLOR & SONS LTD
27 Main Road, Leabrooks, Alfreton, DE55 1LA, Derbyshire, United Kingdom

OWEN TAYLOR & SONS LTD

Owen Taylor & Sons Ltd—(Continued)
Tel.: (44) 1773603351
Web Site:
http://www.owentaylor.co.uk
Year Founded: 1922
Rev.: $18,817,486
Emp.: 104
Fresh Meat & Meat Products Whslr
N.A.I.C.S.: 424470
Clair Channer-Eyley (Office Mgr-HR)

OWNCLOUD GMBH
Rathsbergstr 17, 90411, Nuremberg, Germany
Tel.: (49) 91114888690
Web Site: https://owncloud.com
Enterprise File Sharing Solutions
N.A.I.C.S.: 513210
Holger Dyroff (Mng Dir & COO)

Subsidiaries:

ownCloud, Inc. (1)
57 Bedford St Ste 102, Lexington, MA 02421-5506
Tel.: (617) 515-3664
Web Site: http://www.owncloud.com
Enterprise File Sharing Solutions
N.A.I.C.S.: 513210
Dan Curtis (CFO)

OX2 GROUP AB
Lilla Nygatan 1, PO Box 2299, 103 17, Stockholm, Sweden
Tel.: (46) 855931000
Web Site: http://www.ox2.com
Year Founded: 1991
Sales Range: $200-249.9 Million
Wind Power
N.A.I.C.S.: 221118
Johan Ihrfelt (Chm)

Subsidiaries:

O2 Kraft AB
Box 5063, 102 42, Stockholm, Sweden
Tel.: (46) 8 50588448
Wind Power Generation Services
N.A.I.C.S.: 221115

O2 Vindel AB (1)
Lilla Nygatan 1, 11128, Stockholm, Sweden
Tel.: (46) 771 818 700
Wind Power Generation Services
N.A.I.C.S.: 221115

OXATIS SA
171 bis Chemin de la Madrague, 13002, Marseille, France
Tel.: (33) 486262626
Web Site: http://www.oxatis.com
Information Technology Services
N.A.I.C.S.: 541512
Marc Schillaci (Founder)

OXBRIDGE RE HOLDINGS LIMITED
Suite 201 42 Edward Street, PO Box 469, Georgetown, KY1-9006, Cayman Islands
Tel.: (345) 7497570 Ky
Web Site:
https://www.oxbridgere.com
Year Founded: 2013
OXBR—(NASDAQ)
Rev.: $2,170,000
Assets: $8,253,000
Liabilities: $2,921,000
Net Worth: $5,332,000
Earnings: ($9,915,000)
Emp.: 4
Fiscal Year-end: 12/31/23
Property & Casualty Insurance
N.A.I.C.S.: 524126
Wrendon Timothy (CFO & Sec)

OXFORD BIODYNAMICS PLC
3140 Rowan Place John Smith Dr, Oxford Business Park South, Oxford, OX4 2WB, United Kingdom
Tel.: (44) 1865518910
Web Site:
https://www.oxfordbiodynamics.com
OBD—(AIM)
Rev.: $169,830
Assets: $12,839,148
Liabilities: $9,906,750
Net Worth: $2,932,398
Earnings: ($7,597,062)
Fiscal Year-end: 09/30/22
Medical Laboratories
N.A.I.C.S.: 621511
Ewan Hunter (Chief Data Officer)

OXFORD BIOMEDICA PLC
Windrush Court Transport Way, Oxford, OX4 6LT, United Kingdom
Tel.: (44) 1865783000 UK
Web Site: https://oxb.com
Year Founded: 1996
OXBDF—(OTCIQ)
Rev.: $193,878,343
Assets: $322,090,558
Liabilities: $67,738,009
Net Worth: $254,352,549
Earnings: $25,811,615
Emp.: 815
Fiscal Year-end: 12/31/21
Gene Therapy Treatment Developer
N.A.I.C.S.: 325412
Kyriacos Mitrophanous (Chief Scientific Officer)

Subsidiaries:

BioMedica Inc. (1)
11622 El Camino Real Ste 100, San Diego, CA 92130 (100%)
Tel.: (858) 677-6500
Gene Therapy Treatment Developer
N.A.I.C.S.: 325412

OXFORD CANNABINOID HOLDINGS PLC
Prama House 267 Banbury Road, Oxford, OX2 7HT, United Kingdom
Tel.: (44) 2030342820 UK
Web Site:
https://www.oxcantech.com
Year Founded: 2017
OCTP—(LSE)
Assets: $16,045,931
Liabilities: $2,749,741
Net Worth: $13,296,190
Earnings: ($6,398,023)
Emp.: 7
Fiscal Year-end: 04/30/22
Holding Company
N.A.I.C.S.: 551112
John Lucas (CEO)

Subsidiaries:

Oxford Cannabinoid Technologies Ltd. (1)
Prama House 267 Banbury Road, Oxford, OX2 7HT, United Kingdom
Tel.: (44) 2030342820
Web Site: https://www.oxcantech.com
Cannabinoid Pharmaceutical Mfr
N.A.I.C.S.: 325412

OXFORD DODGE CHRYSLER JEEP LTD
625 Oxford St W, London, N6H 1T8, ON, Canada
Tel.: (519) 473-1010
Web Site:
http://www.oxforddodge.net
Sales Range: $50-74.9 Million
Emp.: 100
Automobile Dealers
N.A.I.C.S.: 441110
Bob Lanteigne (Bus Mgr)

OXFORD INSTRUMENTS PLC
Tubney Woods, Abingdon, OX13 5QX, Oxfordshire, United Kingdom
Tel.: (44) 1865393200 UK
Web Site: https://www.oxinst.com
Year Founded: 1959
OXINF—(LSE)
Rev.: $498,690,556
Assets: $711,309,508
Liabilities: $281,726,900
Net Worth: $429,582,608
Earnings: $52,407,992
Emp.: 1,878
Fiscal Year-end: 03/31/22
Scientific Instruments, Advanced Instrumentation, Chemical Analysis, Patient Monitoring & Semi-Conductors Designer, Mfr & Supporter
N.A.I.C.S.: 334516
Susan Johnson-Brett (Sec)

Subsidiaries:

Andor Technology Ltd. (1)
7 Millennium Way Springvale Business Park, Belfast, BT12 7AL, United Kingdom
Tel.: (44) 2890237126
Web Site: http://www.andor.com
Sales Range: $75-99.9 Million
Emp.: 400
High Performance Digital Cameras Mfr
N.A.I.C.S.: 333310
Gary Wilmot (Mng Dir)

Branch (US):

Andor Technology (USA) (2)
425 Sullivan Ave Ste 3, South Windsor, CT 06074
Tel.: (860) 290-9211
Web Site: http://www.andor.com
Emp.: 8
Laboratory Equipment Mfr
N.A.I.C.S.: 334516
Garry Wilmot (Gen Mgr)

Branch (Non-US):

Andor Technology China (2)
Building B2 West Haitong Times Business Center, Haidian, Beijing, 100089, China
Tel.: (86) 1058847908
Web Site: http://www.andor.com
Sales Range: $25-49.9 Million
Emp.: 10
Laboratory Equipment Mfr
N.A.I.C.S.: 334516

Andor Technology Japan (2)
IS Building 3-32-42 Higasghi-Shinagawa, Shinagawa-ku, Tokyo, 140-0002, Japan
Tel.: (81) 367328968
Web Site: http://www.andor.oxinst.com
Sales Range: $25-49.9 Million
Emp.: 10
Laboratory Equipment Mfr
N.A.I.C.S.: 334516

Oxford Instruments America, Inc. (1)
300 Baker Ave, Concord, MA 01742
Tel.: (978) 405-1118
Sales Range: $25-49.9 Million
Emp.: 50
Scientific Instruments, Advanced Instrumentation, Chemical Analysis, Patient Monitoring & Semi-Conductors Designer, Mfr & Supporter
N.A.I.C.S.: 334516

Subsidiary (Domestic):

Asylum Research Corp. (2)
6310 Hollister Ave, Santa Barbara, CA 93117
Tel.: (805) 696-6466
Web Site: http://www.afm.oxinst.com
Sales Range: $100-124.9 Million
Emp.: 300
Nanoscience & Nanotechnology Instruments Mfr
N.A.I.C.S.: 334516
Jason Cleveland (Co-Founder)

Austin Scientific Company (2)
4114 Todd Ln, Austin, TX 78744
Tel.: (512) 441-6893
Web Site: http://www.oxinst.com
Vaccum Pump Mfr
N.A.I.C.S.: 333912

Medical Imaging Resources, Inc. (2)
120 Enterprise Dr, Ann Arbor, MI 48103-9124
Tel.: (888) 323-1316
Web Site: http://www.mobileleasing.com
Diagnostic Services
N.A.I.C.S.: 621511
Denise Stancato (Coord-Equipment)

Omniprobe, Inc. (2)
10410 Miller Rd, Dallas, TX 75238
Tel.: (214) 572-6800
Web Site: http://www.omniprobe.com
Sales Range: $25-49.9 Million
Analytical Instrument Mfr
N.A.I.C.S.: 334516

Group (Domestic):

Oxford Instruments-X-Ray Technology Group (2)
360 El Pueblo Rd Ste 104, Scotts Valley, CA 95066 (100%)
Tel.: (831) 439-9729
Web Site: http://www.oxfordxtg.com
Sales Range: $1-9.9 Million
Emp.: 35
X-Ray Tubes Mfr
N.A.I.C.S.: 334517

Oxford Instruments GmbH (1)
Otto Von Guericke Ring 10, Wiesbaden, 65205, Germany
Tel.: (49) 6122937177
Sales Range: $25-49.9 Million
Emp.: 35
High Technology Instrument Mfr
N.A.I.C.S.: 334513

Oxford Instruments KK (1)
Haseman Bldg 2-11-6 Tomioka, Koto-ku, Tokyo, 135-0047, Japan
Tel.: (81) 352453251
Web Site: http://www.oijapan.com
Sales Range: $25-49.9 Million
Emp.: 50
Semiconductor Devices Mfr
N.A.I.C.S.: 334413

Oxford Instruments Molecular Biotools Ltd (1)
Tubney Woods, Abingdon, OX13 5QX, Oxfordshire, United Kingdom
Tel.: (44) 1865 393200
Web Site: http://www.oxford-instruments.com
Emp.: 250
High Technology Instrument Mfr
N.A.I.C.S.: 339112
Jonathan Flint (CEO)

Oxford Instruments Overseas Holdings 2008 Ltd (1)
Tubney Woods, Abingdon, OX13 5QX, Oxfordshire, United Kingdom
Tel.: (44) 1865 393200
Sales Range: $50-74.9 Million
Emp.: 230
High Technology Instrument Mfr
N.A.I.C.S.: 339112
Ian Barkshire (CEO)

Oxford Instruments Overseas Marketing Ltd (1)
Oxford Instruments, Abingdon, OX13 5QX, Oxfordshire, United Kingdom
Tel.: (44) 1865 393200
Web Site: http://www.oxford-instruments.com
Emp.: 45
High Technology Instrument Mfr
N.A.I.C.S.: 334516
Jonathan Flint (CEO)

Oxford Instruments Plasma Technology Ltd (1)
Plasma Technology 66 8 mi Yatton, Bristol, BS49 4AP, United Kingdom (100%)
Tel.: (44) 193 483 7000
Web Site: https://www.oxinst.com
Sales Range: $50-74.9 Million
Emp.: 300
Medical Products
N.A.I.C.S.: 339112

Oxford Instruments Pte Ltd (1)
10 Ubi Crescent 04-81 Ubi Techpark Lobby E, Singapore, 408564, Singapore
Tel.: (65) 63376848
Web Site: http://www.oxford-instrument.com

AND PRIVATE COMPANIES

Sales Range: $25-49.9 Million
Emp.: 20
Scientific Instrument Mfr
N.A.I.C.S.: 334516

Oxford Instruments SAS (1)
Batiment Ariane 4 rue Rene Razel Domaine
Technologique de Saclay, 91892, Saclay,
France
Tel.: (33) 1 69 85 25 20
Web Site: http://www.oxinst.com
High Technology Instrument Mfr
N.A.I.C.S.: 334516

Oxford Instruments-Analytical (1)
281 9 mi, High Wycombe, HP12 3SE,
Bucks, United Kingdom (100%)
Tel.: (44) 149 444 2255
Web Site: http://www.oxford-instruments.com
Sales Range: $75-99.9 Million
Emp.: 250
Scientific Instruments, Advanced Instrumentation, Chemical Analysis, Patient Monitoring & Semiconductors
N.A.I.C.S.: 423450
David Scott (Mng Dir)

Oxford Instruments-Superconductivity (1)
Tubney Woods, Abingdon, OX13 5QX, Oxforgshire, United Kingdom (100%)
Tel.: (44) 865393200
Web Site: http://www.oxford-instruments.com
Sales Range: $125-149.9 Million
Emp.: 300
Superconducting Wires Mfr
N.A.I.C.S.: 332618

OXFORD INVESTMENTS HOLDINGS INC.
1315 Lawrence Avenue East Suite
520, Toronto, M3A 3R3, ON, Canada
Tel.: (416) 576-4671 ON
Web Site:
https://www.pioneergreen.com
Year Founded: 2000
OXIHF—(OTCIQ)
Rev.: $317,000
Assets: $1,325,000
Liabilities: $1,033,000
Net Worth: $292,000
Earnings: ($417,000)
Emp.: 1
Fiscal Year-end: 12/31/19
Stored Value Cards
N.A.I.C.S.: 522210
Michael Donaghy (Pres & CEO)

OXFORD METRICS PLC
6 Oxford Pioneer Park, Yarnton, OX5
1QU, Oxfordshire, United Kingdom
Tel.: (44) 1865261860
Web Site:
https://www.oxfordmetrics.com
OMG—(AIM)
Rev.: $32,630,004
Assets: $107,219,340
Liabilities: $15,273,378
Net Worth: $91,945,962
Earnings: $3,849,480
Fiscal Year-end: 09/30/22
Computer Software Sales
N.A.I.C.S.: 513210
Catherine Robertson (Sec)
Subsidiaries:

2d3 Inc. (1)
101 Academy Ste 100, Irvine, CA 92617-3081
Tel.: (949) 540-0740
Web Site: http://www.2d3.com
Sales Range: $25-49.9 Million
Emp.: 6
Visual Software Development & Sales
N.A.I.O.O.: 541511

2d3 Limited (1)
14 Minns Business Park, Oxford, OX2 0JB,
United Kingdom
Tel.: (44) 1865811060
Web Site: http://www.2d3.com

Sales Range: $25-49.9 Million
Emp.: 65
Visual Software Development & Sales
N.A.I.C.S.: 541511
Catherine L Robertson (Sec)

Vicon Motion Systems Limited (1)
6 Oxford Pioneer Park, Yarnton, Oxford,
OX5 1QU, United Kingdom
Tel.: (44) 1865261800
Web Site: https://www.vicon.com
Sales Range: $25-49.9 Million
Emp.: 60
Digital Motion Tracking Systems Mfr
N.A.I.C.S.: 334290
Imogen Moorhouse (CEO)

OXFORD NANOPORE TECHNOLOGIES PLC
Gosling Building Edmund Halley
Road Oxford Science Park, Oxford,
OX4 4DQ, United Kingdom
Tel.: (44) 8450347900 UK
Web Site:
https://www.nanoporetech.com
Year Founded: 2005
ONT—(LSE)
Rev.: $250,698,056
Assets: $1,040,002,525
Liabilities: $164,521,585
Net Worth: $875,480,939
Earnings: ($114,901,540)
Emp.: 1,000
Fiscal Year-end: 12/31/22
Software Development Services
N.A.I.C.S.: 541511

OXFORD PHARMAGENESIS LTD.
Tubney Warren Barn Tubney, Oxford,
OX13 5QJ, United Kingdom
Tel.: (44) 1865 390144
Web Site:
http://www.pharmagenesis.com
Year Founded: 1998
Emp.: 260
Pharmaceutical Consulting Services
N.A.I.C.S.: 541690
Chris Winchester (CEO)
Subsidiaries:

Oxford PharmaGenesis AG (1)
Innere Margarethenstrasse 5, 4051, Basel,
Switzerland
Tel.: (41) 612044561
Pharmaceutical Consulting Services
N.A.I.C.S.: 541690
Ruth Bentley (Dir-Comm)

Oxford PharmaGenesis Inc. (1)
503E Washington Ave, Newtown, PA 18940
Tel.: (215) 497-9699
Pharmaceutical Consulting Services
N.A.I.C.S.: 541690
Gordon Muir-Jones (Exec VP)

OXFORD PHOTOVOLTAICS LIMITED
Centre for Innovation & Enterprise
Begbroke Science Park, Woodstock
Road, Oxford, OX5 1PF, United Kingdom
Tel.: (44) 1865 309 618 UK
Web Site: http://www.oxfordpv.com
Year Founded: 2010
Sales Range: $1-9.9 Million
Solar Technologies Developer & Mfr
N.A.I.C.S.: 334413
Frank Averdung (CEO)

OXFORD TECHNOLOGY 2 VENTURE CAPITAL TRUST PLC
Magdalen Centre Oxford Science
Park, Oxford, OX4 4GA, United Kingdom
Tel.: (44) 1865784466 UK
Web Site:
https://www.oxfordtechnology.com

Year Founded: 2000
OXH—(LSE)
Rev.: $5,246
Assets: $1,945,103
Liabilities: $1,246,020
Net Worth: $699,083
Earnings: ($144,276)
Emp.: 250
Fiscal Year-end: 02/29/20
Asset Management Services
N.A.I.C.S.: 523940
Richard Ruth (Chm)

OXFORD TECHNOLOGY VENTURE CAPITAL TRUST PLC
Magdalen Centre Oxford Science
Park, Oxford, OX4 4GA, United Kingdom
Tel.: (44) 1865784466
OXT—(LSE)
Rev.: $35,413
Assets: $3,200,304
Liabilities: $15,739
Net Worth: $3,184,565
Earnings: ($347,574)
Fiscal Year-end: 02/29/20
Asset Management Services
N.A.I.C.S.: 523940

OXFORD UNIVERSITY PRESS
Great Clarendon Street, Oxford, OX2
6DP, United Kingdom
Tel.: (44) 1865556767
Web Site: http://www.oup.com
Year Founded: 1478
Sales Range: $800-899.9 Million
Emp.: 6,500
Academic & Educational Services
N.A.I.C.S.: 513130
Nigel Portwood (CEO & Sec)
Subsidiaries:

Oxford Fajar Sdn. Bhd. (1)
No 4 Jalan Pemaju U1/15 Section U1
Hicom-Glenmarie Industrial Park, 40150,
Shah Alam, Selangor, Malaysia
Tel.: (60) 356294000
Web Site: http://www.oxfordfajar.com.my
Book Publishers
N.A.I.C.S.: 513130
Sharmini Nagulan (Mng Dir)

Oxford Music Online (1)
Great Clarendon Street Room E212, Oxford, OX2 6DP, United Kingdom
Tel.: (44) 1865353705
Web Site: http://www.oxfordmusiconline.com
Online Music Reference Resources
N.A.I.C.S.: 512230

Unit (US):

Grove Music Online (2)
198 Madison Ave, New York, NY
10016 (100%)
Web Site: http://www.oxfordmusiconline.com
Online Music Reference
N.A.I.C.S.: 513140

Oxford University Press (1)
51 Goldhill Plz Ste 16-01/03 Goldhill Plz,
Singapore, 308900, Singapore (100%)
Tel.: (65) 67389565
Web Site: http://www.oup.com
Sales Range: $25-49.9 Million
Emp.: 4
Distribution of Books
N.A.I.C.S.: 459210
Julia Yong (Office Mgr)

Oxford University Press (1)
PO Box 2784, Melbourne, 3001, VIC,
Australia (100%)
Tel.: (61) 399349123
Web Site: http://www.oup.com.au
Sales Range: $25-49.9 Million
Emp.: 100
Distribution of Books
N.A.I.C.S.: 459210

Oxford University Press (India) (1)
2/11 Ansari Road Daryaganj, PO Box 7035,
New Delhi, 110002, India (100%)
Tel.: (91) 11 2327 3841

OXFORD UNIVERSITY PRESS

Web Site: http://www.oup.co.in
Sales Range: $50-74.9 Million
Emp.: 120
Academic & Educational Publishing
N.A.I.C.S.: 513130
Sivaramakrishnan Venkateswaran (Mng Dir)

Oxford University Press (Macau) Ltd. (1)
Rua de Pequim Nos 202A-246 Macau Finance Centre 9L, Macau, China (Macau)
Tel.: (853) 28706178
Books Publishing Services
N.A.I.C.S.: 513130

Oxford University Press (South Africa) (1)
Vasco Blvd, N1 City Goodwood, Cape
Town, 7460, South Africa (100%)
Tel.: (27) 215954400
Web Site: http://www.oup.com
Sales Range: $50-74.9 Million
Emp.: 130
Book Publishing
N.A.I.C.S.: 513130

Oxford University Press Argentina SA (1)
Edificio Central Park California 2000 - Piso
3 - Oficina 315, C1289ANN, Buenos Aires,
Argentina
Tel.: (54) 1143028000
Books Publishing Services
N.A.I.C.S.: 513130

Oxford University Press Canada (1)
8 Sampson Mews Suite 204, Don Mills,
M3C 0H5, ON, Canada (100%)
Tel.: (416) 441-2941
Web Site: https://www.oupcanada.com
Sales Range: $50-74.9 Million
Emp.: 120
Distribution of Books
N.A.I.C.S.: 459210

Oxford University Press China Ltd (1)
39/F One Kowloon 1 Wang Yuen Street
Kowloon Bay, Kowloon, China (Hong
Kong) (100%)
Tel.: (852) 25163222
Web Site: http://www.oupchina.com
Sales Range: $50-74.9 Million
Emp.: 240
Academic & Educational Publishing
N.A.I.C.S.: 323117
Mei Mei Ng (Gen Mgr)

Oxford University Press East Africa Ltd. (1)
The Oxford Place Elgon Road Upper Hill,
PO Box 72532-00200, Nairobi, Kenya
Tel.: (254) 2027320479
Web Site: http://www.oup.co.ke
Book Publishers
N.A.I.C.S.: 513130
Peter Kimanthi (Mng Dir)

Oxford University Press Ecuador Sa (1)
V E Estrada 509 y Las Monjas Edificio La
Fontana, Guayaquil, Ecuador
Tel.: (593) 42384656
Books Publishing Services
N.A.I.C.S.: 513130

Oxford University Press Espana S.A. (1)
Parque Empresarial San Fernando Edificio
Atenas Escalera A Planta 1a, San Fernando de Henares, 28830, Madrid, Spain
Tel.: (34) 902876878
Web Site: http://www.oupe.es
Books Publishing Services
N.A.I.C.S.: 513130
Chris Wyburd (Dir-ELT)

Oxford University Press K.K. (1)
3rd Floor Tamachi Pl Bldg, 4-17-5 Shiba
Minato-ku, Tokyo, 108-8386,
Japan (100%)
Tel.: (81) 354445454
Web Site: http://www.oupjapan.co.jp
Sales Range: $25-49.9 Million
Emp.: 100
Distribution of Books
N.A.I.C.S.: 459210

Oxford University Press Mexico S.A. de C.V. (1)

OXFORD UNIVERSITY PRESS

Oxford University Press—(Continued)
Insurgentes Sur 1602 Oficina 1101 Colonia Credito Constructor, Benito Juarez Distrito Federal, 03940, Mexico, Mexico
Tel.: (52) 5555925600
Books Publishing Services
N.A.I.C.S.: 513130
Sandra Torrez (Dir-Sls & Mktg)

Oxford University Press Pakistan Ltd. (1)
No 38 Sector 15 Korangi Industrial Area, PO Box 8214, Karachi, 74900, Pakistan
Tel.: (92) 213507158087
Web Site: http://www.oup.com.pk
Books Publishing Services
N.A.I.C.S.: 513130
Ameena Saiyid (Mng Dir)

Oxford University Press Polska Sp. z o.o. (1)
ul Wolodyjowskiego 46, 02-724, Warsaw, Poland
Tel.: (48) 228537510
Books Publishing Services
N.A.I.C.S.: 513130

Oxford University Press Tanzania Ltd (1)
Maktaba Road, Post Box 5299, Dar es Salaam, Tanzania
Tel.: (255) 222113704
Books Publishing Services
N.A.I.C.S.: 513130

Oxford University Press do Brasil Publicacoes Ltda (1)
Av Jaguare 818 Galpoes 30/31, Jaguare, Sao Paulo, Brazil
Tel.: (55) 1136132244
Books Publishing Services
N.A.I.C.S.: 513130

Oxford University Press, Inc. (1)
198 Madison Ave, New York, NY 10016-4308
Tel.: (212) 726-6000
Sales Range: $125-149.9 Million
Emp.: 400
Publisher of Books
N.A.I.C.S.: 513130

Subsidiary (Domestic):

Oxford University Press (2)
2001 Evans Rd, Cary, NC 27513-2010
Tel.: (919) 677-0977
Sales Range: $75-99.9 Million
Emp.: 600
Academic & Educational Publishing
N.A.I.C.S.: 493110

OXIDE CORPORATION
1747-1 Maginohara Mukawa Hokuto, Yamanashi, 408-0302, Japan
Tel.: (81) 551260022
Web Site: https://www.opt-oxide.com
Year Founded: 2000
6521—(TKS)
Rev.: $46,836,540
Assets: $136,489,590
Liabilities: $82,534,690
Net Worth: $53,954,900
Earnings: ($2,991,980)
Fiscal Year-end: 02/29/24
Electronic Components Mfr
N.A.I.C.S.: 334419
Yasunori Furukawa (Chm)

OXIQUIM SA
Av Santa Maria 2050 Providencia, Postal Box 9158, Santiago, Chile
Tel.: (56) 6005000011
Web Site: https://www.oxiquim.com
OXIQUIM—(SGO)
Sales Range: Less than $1 Million
Chemical Products Mfr
N.A.I.C.S.: 325998
Cecilia Pardo Pizarro (CEO)

OXLEY HOLDINGS LIMITED
138 Robinson Road 30-01 Oxley Tower, Singapore, 068906, Singapore
Tel.: (65) 64380202 SG
Web Site: https://www.oxley.com.sg
Year Founded: 2010
5UX—(SES)
Rev.: $474,545,387
Assets: $2,317,496,110
Liabilities: $1,621,914,783
Net Worth: $695,581,326
Earnings: ($71,150,797)
Fiscal Year-end: 06/30/23
Investment Holding Company; Real Estate Services
N.A.I.C.S.: 551112
See Ching Low (Deputy CEO)

Subsidiaries:

Oxley Holdings (Malaysia) Sdn. Bhd. (1)
Unit 1-26 level 26 Naza Tower Platinum Park Persiaran KLCC, 50088, Kuala Lumpur, Malaysia
Tel.: (60) 321816600
Web Site: https://www.oxleymalaysia.com
Property Management Services
N.A.I.C.S.: 531311

Oxley-Worldbridge (Cambodia) Co., Ltd. (1)
Unit 11 1st Floor Hong Kong Center 108-112 First Floor Sothearos Blvd, Sangkat Chaktomuk Khan Daun, Phnom Penh, Cambodia
Tel.: (855) 23230628
Web Site: https://www.oxleyworldbridge.com.kh
Property Management Services
N.A.I.C.S.: 531311
Tan Teck Kee (Founder)

OXONICA LIMITED
PO Box 1069, Aylesbury, HP22 9PH, Bucks, United Kingdom
Tel.: (44) 755 398 7226
Web Site: http://www.oxonica.com
Year Founded: 2010
Sales Range: Less than $1 Million
Nanotechnology Products Mfr
N.A.I.C.S.: 541512
Richard Farleigh (Chm)

OXPAY FINANCIAL LIMITED
10 Ubi Crescent 03 48 Lobby C Ubi Techpark, Singapore, 408564, Singapore
Tel.: (65) 62990030 SG
Web Site: https://www.oxpayfinancial.com
Year Founded: 2005
TVV—(CAT)
Rev.: $6,303,870
Assets: $12,681,966
Liabilities: $9,555,404
Net Worth: $3,126,562
Earnings: ($1,067,182)
Emp.: 36
Fiscal Year-end: 12/31/23
Investment Management Service
N.A.I.C.S.: 523999

Subsidiaries:

OxPay (M) Sdn. Bhd. (1)
D1-3A-05 Solaris Dutamas No 1 Jalan Dutamas 1, 50480, Kuala Lumpur, Malaysia
Tel.: (60) 362053015
Web Site: https://oxpay.my
Online Payment Systems
N.A.I.C.S.: 522320

OxPay SG Pte. Ltd. (1)
10 Ubi Crescent 03-48 Lobby C Ubi Techpark, Singapore, 408564, Singapore
Tel.: (65) 62990030
Web Site: https://oxpayfinancial.com
Financial Services
N.A.I.C.S.: 523999

OXURION NV
Gaston Geenslaan 1, B-3001, Leuven, Belgium
Tel.: (32) 16751310
Web Site: https://www.oxurion.com

OXUR—(EUR)
Rev.: $290,319
Assets: $7,230,379
Liabilities: $21,786,069
Net Worth: ($14,555,690)
Earnings: ($20,939,397)
Emp.: 20
Fiscal Year-end: 12/31/23
Vascular Biopharmaceuticals Mfr & Developer
N.A.I.C.S.: 325412
Patrik De Haes (CEO)

Subsidiaries:

ThromboGenics Inc. (1)
1560 Broadway 10th Fl, New York, NY 10036
Tel.: (212) 201-0920
Web Site: http://www.thrombogenics.com
Pharmaceuticals Product Mfr
N.A.I.C.S.: 325412

ThromboGenics Ltd. (1)
14 Bridgecourt Ofc Pk Walkinstown Ave, Dublin, 12, Ireland
Tel.: (353) 14097757
Sales Range: $25-49.9 Million
Emp.: 5
Pharmaceuticals Product Mfr
N.A.I.C.S.: 325412
Patrik De Haes (CEO)

OXXY GROUP PLC
Office M102 Michalakopoulou Tower, 25 Michalakopoulou Street, 1075, Nicosia, Cyprus
Tel.: (357) 777 88 935
Web Site: http://www.oxxy.com
Website Design
N.A.I.C.S.: 513199
Dimitar Dimitrov (Co-Founder, CEO & CTO)

OXXYNOVA GMBH
Borsteler Weg 50, 31595, Steyerberg, Germany
Tel.: (49) 5764291122
Web Site: http://www.oxxynova.com
Year Founded: 2001
Sales Range: $75-99.9 Million
Emp.: 130
Chemicals Mfr
N.A.I.C.S.: 325180
Klaus Puell (Co-Mng Dir)

OXYGEN CAPITAL CORPORATION
West Hastings Street Suite 1900-1055, Vancouver, V6E 2E9, BC, Canada
Tel.: (604) 683-7790
Web Site: https://www.oxygencapitalcorp.com
Holding Company
N.A.I.C.S.: 551112
Mark O'Dea (Co-Founder & Chm)

OXYMETAL SA
13 rue Jean-Paul Alaux, PO Box CS 41015, Bordeaux, 33100, France
Tel.: (33) 557358930 FR
Web Site: http://www.oxymetal.com
Year Founded: 1984
Sales Range: $125-149.9 Million
Emp.: 535
Metal Processing Services
N.A.I.C.S.: 423510
Philippe Chedru (Chm)

Subsidiaries:

ORN OXYCOUPAGE (1)
8 Gu Vieux Vorge, Chailloue, Alencon, 61500, France
Tel.: (33) 2 33 27 85 23
Web Site: http://www.oxymetal.com
Sales Range: $25-49.9 Million
Emp.: 20
Metal Cutting Machinery Mfr
N.A.I.C.S.: 333517

INTERNATIONAL PUBLIC

Juillaume Boonnin (Mgr)

OXYMETAL BOURGOGNE (1)
13 Rue Jean Paul Alaux, 33100, Bordeaux, France
Tel.: (33) 3 85 73 90 40
Laser Cutting Machinery Mfr
N.A.I.C.S.: 333517

OXYMETAL EST (1)
Zi Malambas, 57280, Hauconcourt, France
Tel.: (33) 3 87 34 26 19
Web Site: http://www.oxymetal.com
Laser Cutting Machinery Mfr
N.A.I.C.S.: 333517
Williams Phillips (Mng Dir)

OXYMETAL NORMANDIE (1)
300 Route De Francheville, 27130, Verneuil-sur-Avre, France
Tel.: (33) 2 32 30 32 00
Laser Cutting Equipment Mfr
N.A.I.C.S.: 333517

OXYMETAL OUEST (1)
1 Rue De La Nivardiere, Pont-Saint-Martin, France
Tel.: (33) 2 40 02 15 15
Laser Cutting Machinery Mfr
N.A.I.C.S.: 333517

OXYMETAL PARIS EST (1)
23 Avenue Henri Beaudelet, 77330, Ozoir-la-Ferriere, France
Tel.: (33) 164435730
Laser Cutting Machinery Mfr
N.A.I.C.S.: 333517

OXYNORD SA (1)
Zone Industrielle A De Seclin-Lille Rue Augustin Lhermitte, Wattignies, 59139, France
Tel.: (33) 3 20 90 68 20
Laser Cutting Services
N.A.I.C.S.: 423510

Oxycoupage Champagne (1)
ZA de Poilly, 51170, Poilly, France
Tel.: (33) 3 26 61 86 54
Web Site: http://www.oxymetal.com
Mechanical Welding Equipment Mfr
N.A.I.C.S.: 333248

SOUDACIER (1)
Rue Du Bas De Grange, 18100, Vierzon, France
Tel.: (33) 2 48 53 00 97
Mechanical Welding Unit Mfr
N.A.I.C.S.: 333248

OY ETRA AB
Lampputie 2, 00740, Helsinki, Finland
Tel.: (358) 2076511
Web Site: http://www.etra.fi
Sales Range: $25-49.9 Million
Emp.: 60
Plastics, Rubber & Tape Importer & Whslr
N.A.I.C.S.: 424610

Subsidiaries:

Etra Balti AS (1)
Peterburi tee 101a, 13811, Tallinn, Estonia
Tel.: (372) 6012 836
Web Site: http://www.etra.ee
Rubber Product Whslr
N.A.I.C.S.: 423840

Oy Maritim AB (1)
Beneentekijantie 1, SF 00210, Helsinki, Finland
Tel.: (358) 20765180
Web Site: http://www.maritim.fi
Sales Range: $25-49.9 Million
Emp.: 50
Boat Equipment Whslr & Importer
N.A.I.C.S.: 423860
Kim Tigerstedt (Gen Mgr)

OY FORCIT AB
Forcitintie 37, Hanko, 10900, Finland
Tel.: (358) 207440400 FI
Web Site: http://www.forcit.fi
Year Founded: 1893
Sales Range: $100-124.9 Million
Emp.: 290
Explosives & Dispersions Mfr
N.A.I.C.S.: 325920

AND PRIVATE COMPANIES

Ulf Sjoblom *(CEO & Mng Dir)*

Subsidiaries:

Forcit Sweden AB (1)
Prastgatan 25, 713 31, Nora, Sweden
Tel.: (46) 587 10999
Web Site: http://www.forcit.se
Emp.: 29
Explosive Distr
N.A.I.C.S.: 424690

Oy Finnrock Ab (1)
Mikkolantie 1 B 4 Kerros, 00640, Helsinki, Finland
Tel.: (358) 10 832 1300
Web Site: http://www.finnrock.fi
Emp.: 24
Excavation & Blasting Consulting Services
N.A.I.C.S.: 238910
Kari Saukkonen *(Project Mgr)*

OY HALTON GROUP LTD.
Esterinportti 2, 00240, Helsinki, Finland
Tel.: (358) 20792200 FI
Web Site: http://www.halton.com
Year Founded: 1969
Sales Range: $200-249.9 Million
Emp.: 1,500
Indoor Climate Solutions
N.A.I.C.S.: 333415
Heikki Rinne *(CEO)*

Subsidiaries:

HALTON GLOBAL SERVICES, INC. (1)
5001 Lyndon B Johnson Fwy Ste 550, Dallas, TX 75244
Tel.: (972) 419-5141
Food Service Equipment Distr
N.A.I.C.S.: 423440
Bill Donaldson *(Acct Mgr-Strategic)*

Halton AS (1)
Ryenstubben 7, 0679, Oslo, Norway
Tel.: (47) 23266300
Web Site: http://www.halton.com
Sales Range: $25-49.9 Million
Emp.: 5
Indoor Climate Solutions
N.A.I.C.S.: 333415

Halton Company (1)
101 Industrial Dr, Scottsville, KY 42164
Tel.: (270) 237-5600
Web Site: http://www.haltoncompany.com
Sales Range: $25-49.9 Million
Emp.: 60
Industrial & Commercial Fan & Blower Mfr
N.A.I.C.S.: 333413
Phil Meredith *(Dir-Foodservice)*

Halton Group Asia Sdn Bhd (1)
PT 26064 Persiaran Teknologi Subang Subang Hi-Tech Industrial Park, Subang Jaya, 47500, Subang Jaya, Selangor, Malaysia
Tel.: (60) 3 5622 8800
Food Service Equipment Distr
N.A.I.C.S.: 423440
Gunalan Ganesan *(Gen Mgr)*

Halton Klimatechnik GmbH (1)
Essener Str 4 Geb D2, 22419, Hamburg, Germany
Tel.: (49) 40501061
Web Site: http://www.halton.de
Indoor Climate Solutions
N.A.I.C.S.: 333415

Halton Oy (1)
Haltonintie 1-3, 47400, Kausala, Finland
Tel.: (358) 20792200
Web Site: http://www.halton.com
Indoor Climate Solutions
N.A.I.C.S.: 333415
Tommi Kahkonen *(Mgr-CRA Eastern Europe & Distr)*

Halton SAS (1)
94-96 Rue Victor Hugo, 94 851, Ivry-sur-Seine, France
Tel.: (33) 145158000
Web Site: http://www.halton.fr
Sales Range: $25-49.9 Million
Emp.: 35
Indoor Climate Solutions
N.A.I.C.S.: 333415

Halton Vent Master Limited (1)
11 Laker Rd, Airport Industrial Estate, Rochester, ME1 3QX, Kent, United Kingdom
Tel.: (44) 01634666111
Web Site: http://www.ventmastereurope.com
Sales Range: $25-49.9 Million
Emp.: 45
Mfr of Commercial Food Service Equipment
N.A.I.C.S.: 811310

Luft+Klimakontor GmbH (1)
Alsfelder Strasse 45, Postfach 1254, 35302, Grunberg, Germany
Tel.: (49) 640191860
Web Site: http://www.Luft-Klima.org
Indoor Climate Solutions
N.A.I.C.S.: 333415
Piontek Detlev *(Coord-Admin)*

OY KAHA AB
PL 117 01511 Vantaa Ansatie 2, 01740, Vantaa, Finland
Tel.: (358) 9 615 6800
Web Site: http://kaha.fi
Year Founded: 1934
Automobile Spare Parts & Accessories
N.A.I.C.S.: 423120
Bengt Wahlberg *(CEO)*

Subsidiaries:

KL-Parts Oy (1)
Postitorvenkatu 16, 33840, Tampere, Finland (75%)
Tel.: (358) 400 288 170
Automotive Parts Retailer
N.A.I.C.S.: 441330

OY KARL FAZER AB
Fazerintie 6, PO Box 4, 00941, Helsinki, Finland
Tel.: (358) 20 555 3000
Web Site: http://www.fazer.com
Year Founded: 1891
Rev.: $1,850,880,978
Assets: $1,097,924,021
Liabilities: $475,244,745
Net Worth: $622,679,276
Earnings: $73,088,181
Emp.: 15,696
Fiscal Year-end: 12/31/18
Catering Services; Bakery Product & Confectionery Mfr
N.A.I.C.S.: 722310
Berndt Brunow *(Chm)*

Subsidiaries:

Fazer Bageri Ab (1)
Box 30171, 104 25, Stockholm, Sweden
Tel.: (46) 8 4707200
Food Mfr
N.A.I.C.S.: 311813

Fazer Bakeries B.V. (1)
200 Prins Bernhardplein, Amsterdam, 1097JB, Netherlands
Tel.: (31) 205 21 47 77
Food Mfr
N.A.I.C.S.: 311813

Fazer Eesti AS (1)
Kadaka tee 70D, 12618, Tallinn, Estonia
Tel.: (372) 6502 420
Web Site: http://www.fazer.ee
Food Mfr
N.A.I.C.S.: 311351
Kalev Soosaar *(Mgr-IT)*

Fazer Food OU (1)
Jalgimae tee 14, 76404, Saku, Harju, Estonia
Tel.: (372) 502 3215
Food Mfr
N.A.I.C.S.: 311999

Fazer Konfektyr AB (1)
Fazerintie 6, 401230, Vantaa, Finland
Tel.: (358) 987621
Web Site: http://www.fazer.fi
Sales Range: $250-299.9 Million
Emp.: 1,000
Other Grocery & Related Products Whslr
N.A.I.C.S.: 424490
Tom Linplad *(Mng Dir)*

Fazer Leipomot Oy (1)
Kasakkamaentie 3, 15101, Lahti, Finland
Tel.: (358) 20 555 3000
Food Mfr
N.A.I.C.S.: 311999
Petri Kujala *(Country Mgr)*

Fazer Makeiset Oy (1)
Valtakatu 2, 53101, Lappeenranta, Finland
Tel.: (358) 9 876 21
Food Mfr
N.A.I.C.S.: 311999
Marja-Leena Holopainen *(Mgr-QEHS)*

Gateau AB (1)
Hallgrand 3, 121 62, Johanneshov, Sweden
Tel.: (46) 851979100
Web Site: http://www.gateau.se
Food Mfr
N.A.I.C.S.: 311813

Holmedals Kantineservice AS (1)
Sandslimarka 55, PO Box 70, Sandsli, 5861, Bergen, Norway
Tel.: (47) 55986000
Web Site: http://www.holmedals.no
Food Mfr
N.A.I.C.S.: 311813

Lovik Fastighets AB (1)
Loviksvagen 1, 181 90, Lidingo, Sweden
Tel.: (46) 8 506 180 00
Web Site: http://www.lovik.se
Hotel & Resort Operator
N.A.I.C.S.: 721120

Oy NIS - Nordic Industrial Sales AB (1)
Fazerintie 6, 00941, Vantaa, Finland
Tel.: (358) 98751399
Sales Range: $25-49.9 Million
Emp.: 3
Confectionery Mfr
N.A.I.C.S.: 311352

SIA Fazer Latvija (1)
Druvas iela 2, Ogre, 5001, Latvia
Tel.: (371) 65071040
Web Site: http://www.fazer.lv
Food Mfr
N.A.I.C.S.: 311813

Skandinavisk Mat Invest AS (1)
Cort Adelers Gate 17, Oslo, 0254, Norway
Tel.: (47) 22 82 20 50
Food Mfr
N.A.I.C.S.: 311813

UAB Fazer Lietuva (1)
Raudondvario pl 129a, 47188, Kaunas, Lithuania
Tel.: (370) 8 37 36 02 33
Web Site: http://www.fazer.lt
Food Mfr
N.A.I.C.S.: 311813

Wilberg AS (1)
Fabrikkveien 8, 4033, Stavanger, Norway
Tel.: (47) 51 95 18 90
Web Site: http://www.wilberg.no
Emp.: 200
Catering Services
N.A.I.C.S.: 722320
Gunvar Wie *(Gen Mgr)*

OY SUOMEN AUTOTEOLLISUUS AB
Tammisaarentie 45, 10301, Karjaa, Finland
Tel.: (358) 10 2751
Web Site: http://www.sisuauto.com
Sales Range: $25-49.9 Million
Emp.: 100
Trucks & Military Vehicle Mfr
N.A.I.C.S.: 336992

Subsidiaries:

Oy Sisu Auto Ab (1)
Tammisaarentie 45, 10300, Karjaa, Finland
Tel.: (358) 102751
Web Site: http://www.sisuauto.com
Trucks Mfr
N.A.I.C.S.: 336110

OYAK CEMENT GROUP
Ordu Yardimlasma Kurumu Genel, Mdrlg Ziya Gkalp Cad 64 Kurtul, 06600, Ankara, Turkiye
Tel.: (90) 3124156000
Web Site: http://www.oyak.com.tr
Sales Range: $1-4.9 Billion
Emp.: 28,917
Provider of Savings Institutions
N.A.I.C.S.: 522180
Hulya Atahan *(Exec VP-Fin & Admin Affairs)*

Subsidiaries:

ADANA CEMENT INDUSTRIES INC. (1)
Ceyhan yolu uzeri 12 Km, Saricam, 01321, Adana, Turkiye
Tel.: (90) 3223329950
Web Site: http://www.adanacimento.com.tr
Cement Mfr
N.A.I.C.S.: 327310

ATAER Holding A.S. (1)
Eskisehir Devlet Yolu No 12/16, Ankara, Sogutozu, Turkiye
Tel.: (90) 312 292 6640
Holding Company
N.A.I.C.S.: 551112

AYAS ENERJI URETIM VETICARET A.S. (1)
100 Yl Mahallesi Resit Galip Caddesi, 06700, Ankara, Turkiye
Tel.: (90) 312 415 6272
Web Site: http://www.oyak.com.tr
Power Plant Generation Services
N.A.I.C.S.: 221113

Akdeniz Kimya San. ve Tic. A.S. (1)
Kemalpasa O S B Mah Izmir-Kemalpasa Asfalti Cad No 45, Kemalpasa, 35735, Izmir, Turkiye
Tel.: (90) 232 877 0144
Web Site: http://www.akdenizkimya.com.tr
Chemical Products Mfr
N.A.I.C.S.: 325998

Cimentos De Cabo Verde S.A. (1)
Estrada de Tira Chapeu C P 14-A, Sao Vicente, Cape Verde (98.65%)
Tel.: (238) 2603110
Cement Mfr
N.A.I.C.S.: 327310

Iskenderun Enerji Uretim ve Ticaret A.S. (1)
Budak Street No 4, 06700, Ankara, Turkiye
Tel.: (90) 312 455 24 55
Web Site: http://www.isken.com.tr
Eletric Power Generation Services
N.A.I.C.S.: 221118

Plant (Domestic):

Iskenderun Enerji Uretim ve Ticaret A.S. - Sugozu Power Plant (2)
Sugozu Koyu Mevkii, Yumurtalik, 01680, Adana, Turkiye
Tel.: (90) 322 355 24 55
Web Site: http://www.isken.com.tr
Eletric Power Generation Services
N.A.I.C.S.: 221118

MAIS Motorlu Araclar Imal ve Satis A.S. (1)
Casper Plaza Fatih Sultan Mehmet Mah Balkan Cad No47, 34770, Istanbul, Umraniye, Turkiye
Tel.: (90) 216 645 66 66
Car Distr
N.A.I.C.S.: 488490

OMSAN LOGISTICA SRL (1)
Street Trivale No 46 B Pitesti, Arges, 110058, Romania
Tel.: (40) 248 211185
Emp.: 50
Logistics Consulting Servies
N.A.I.C.S.: 541614

OMSAN Logistique SARL (1)
Sogaris 161 Avenue de Versailles Batiment M-32 Cellule, 94150, Rungis, France
Tel.: (33) 156 34 50 50
Logistics Consulting Servies
N.A.I.C.S.: 541614

OMSAN Lojistik A.S. (1)
Tugay Yolu No 10 Cevizli Maltepe, 34846, Istanbul, Turkiye

OYAK CEMENT GROUP

OYAK Cement Group—(Continued)
Tel.: (90) 216 458 55 55
Logistics Consulting Services
N.A.I.C.S.: 541614
Sales Range:
Emp.:
Osman Judukertan (CEO)

ORF Kiralama Pazarlama ve Pazarlama Danismanligi A.S. (1)
Genel Mudurluk Casper Plaza Fatih Sultan Mehmet Mh, Balkan Cd No 47 Umraniye, Istanbul, Turkiye
Tel.: (90) 216 645 59 00
Automotive Distr
N.A.I.C.S.: 423110

OYAK Girisim Danismanligi A.S. (1)
Cengiz Topel Cd Gulsen Sk No 6 Bebek Etiler, Istanbul, 34342, Turkiye
Tel.: (90) 212 358 0220
Emp.: 4
Investment Banking Services
N.A.I.C.S.: 523150

OYAK Savunma ve Guvenlik Sistemleri A.S. (1)
Nasuh Akar Mah Suleyman Haci Abdullahoglu Caddesi No 59 - PK 06250, Balgat Cankaya, Ankara, Turkiye
Tel.: (90) 312 287 5656
Web Site: http://www.oyaksgs.com.tr
Investment Banking Services
N.A.I.C.S.: 523150

OYKA Kagit Ambalaj San. A.S. (1)
Persembe Yolu Uzeri istasyon Mahallesi Cengiz Topel Caddesi No 16, Caycuma, Zonguldak, Turkiye
Tel.: (90) 372 615 11 82
Investment Banking Services
N.A.I.C.S.: 523150

Omfesa JV (1)
Musgo 1Urb La Florida, 28023, Madrid, Spain
Tel.: (34) 91 387 99 00
Logistics Consulting Servies
N.A.I.C.S.: 541614

Oysa Cimento Sanayii A.S. (1)
Karayilan Beldesi Bitisigi, PO Box 27, Iskenderun, 31201, Turkiye
Tel.: (90) 38823236
Sales Range: $50-74.9 Million
Emp.: 102
Hydraulic Cement Mfr
N.A.I.C.S.: 327310

OYAK YATIRIM MENKUL DEGERLER A.S.
Akatlar Ebulula Caddesi F 2 C Blok Levent, Besiktas, 34335, Istanbul, Turkiye
Tel.: (90) 2123191200
Web Site: http://www.oyakyatirim.com.tr
OYYAT—(IST)
Rev.: $806,212,736
Assets: $229,871,674
Liabilities: $171,578,825
Net Worth: $58,292,849
Earnings: $34,622,702
Fiscal Year-end: 12/31/22
Investment Management Service
N.A.I.C.S.: 523940
Ibrahim Emrah Silav (Chm)

OYAK YATIRIM ORTAKLIGI AS
Ayazaga Mahallesi Kemerburgaz Caddesi, Vadi istanbul Park 7B Blok No 7C Kat 20 Sariyer, Istanbul, Turkiye
Tel.: (90) 2123191401
Web Site: https://www.oyakyatirimortakligi.com
Year Founded: 2006
OYAYO—(IST)
Sales Range: Less than $1 Million
Financial Management Services
N.A.I.C.S.: 522210
Ayse Meltem Agci (Chm)

OYLUM SINAI YATIRIMLAR A.S.
Organize Sanayi Bolgesi 6 Cadde No 11, 38090, Kayseri, Turkiye
Tel.: (90) 3523211132
Web Site: https://www.oylum.com
Year Founded: 1969
OYLUM—(IST)
Biscuit Mfr
N.A.I.C.S.: 311821

OYO CORPORATION
7 Kanda-Mitoshiro-cho, Chiyoda-ku, Tokyo, 101-8486, Japan
Tel.: (81) 355774501   JP
Web Site: https://www.oyo.co.jp
Year Founded: 1954
9755—(TKS)
Rev.: $465,118,180
Assets: $713,721,940
Liabilities: $181,312,570
Net Worth: $532,409,370
Earnings: $28,402,540
Emp.: 2,438
Fiscal Year-end: 12/31/23
Geological & Geophysical Consulting Services; Measurement Instruments for Geophysical & Geotechnical Investigations Mfr
N.A.I.C.S.: 541360
Masaru Narita (Pres)

Subsidiaries:

Engineering & Risk Services Corporation (1)
7F Ginza 6-chome-SQUARE 6-17-1 Ginza, Chuo-ku, Tokyo, 104-0061, Japan
Tel.: (81) 368219091
Web Site: https://www.ers-co.co.jp
Sales Range: $1-9.9 Million
Emp.: 24
Real Estate Evaluation & Risk Assessment Consulting Services; Owned 50% by Kajima Corporation & 50% by OYO Corporation
N.A.I.C.S.: 541620

Fong Consult Pte. Ltd. (1)
7 Keppel Road 02-27 Tanjong Pagar Complex, Singapore, 089053, Singapore
Tel.: (65) 67484668
Web Site: http://www.fongintl.com
Civil Construction Management Services
N.A.I.C.S.: 237310

Geosmart International Pte. Ltd. (1)
114 Lavender Street 08-73 CT HUB 2, Singapore, 338729, Singapore
Tel.: (65) 64440800
Web Site: https://www.geosmart.com.sg
Drilling & Grouting Services
N.A.I.C.S.: 532412

KCS Co.,Ltd. (1)
347 Yamabukicho Towaedogawabashi Building, Shinjuku-ku, Tokyo, 162-0801, Japan
Tel.: (81) 352066881
Construction Engineering Services
N.A.I.C.S.: 541330

KOEI Consultant Co.,Ltd. (1)
Tel.: (81) 353193377
Civil Engineering Services
N.A.I.C.S.: 237990

NS Environmental Science Consultant Corporation (1)
1-2-9 Shiba Park, Minato-ku, Tokyo, 105-0011, Japan
Tel.: (81) 334325451
Web Site: http://www.ns-kankyo.co.jp
Environmental Consulting Services
N.A.I.C.S.: 541620

Nankyu Geo Technics Corporation (1)
Geological Surveying Services
N.A.I.C.S.: 541360

OYO Corporation U.S.A. (1)
245 Carmelo Ave Ste 101, Pasadena, CA 91107   (100%)
Tel.: (626) 744-5065
Sales Range: $25-49.9 Million
Emp.: 4
Holding Company
N.A.I.C.S.: 334417

Kunihiro Eguchi (CFO)

Subsidiary (Domestic):

Geometrics, Inc. (2)
2190 Fortune Dr, San Jose, CA 95131-1815   (100%)
Tel.: (408) 954-0522
Web Site: https://www.geometrics.com
Sales Range: $1-9.9 Million
Mfr of Geophysical Equipment
N.A.I.C.S.: 334519
Mark Prouty (Pres)

Geophysical Survey Systems, Inc. (2)
40 Simon St, Nashua, NH 03060-3075   (100%)
Tel.: (603) 893-1109
Web Site: https://www.geophysical.com
Sales Range: $25-49.9 Million
Emp.: 91
Mfr of Ground Penetrating Radar Systems
N.A.I.C.S.: 334511
Christopher Hawekotte (Pres)

Kinemetrics, Inc. (2)
222 Vista Ave, Pasadena, CA 91107-3278   (100%)
Tel.: (626) 795-2220
Web Site: http://www.kinemetrics.com
Sales Range: $25-49.9 Million
Mfr, Development & Sales of DMS Accelerograph for Earthquake Monitoring
N.A.I.C.S.: 334519

Subsidiary (Non-US):

Kinemetrics SA (3)
Z I Le Tresi 6B, Preverenges, 1028, Switzerland
Tel.: (41) 218032829
Web Site: http://www.kinemetrics.com
Monitoring Products Mfr
N.A.I.C.S.: 334519

Subsidiary (Domestic):

NCS SubSea Inc. (2)
3928 Bluebonnet Dr, Stafford, TX 77477-3987
Tel.: (281) 491-3123
Web Site: http://www.ncs-subsea.com
Survey, Navigation, Positioning & Marine Seismic Services
N.A.I.C.S.: 213112
Larry Scott (CEO)

OYO Corporation, Pacific (1)
Tumon Bay Business Center Unit 103 919 Pale San Vitores Rd, Tumon, GU 96913
Tel.: (671) 300-0622
Web Site: http://www.oyopacific.com
Sales Range: $25-49.9 Million
Emp.: 5
Geological Surveying Services
N.A.I.C.S.: 541360
Kazuki Nakamura (Pres & Sec)

OYO Geotechnical Corporation (1)
Room No 201 No 5 Bill No 54 Sunan 117 Ikebukuro 2-chome, Toshima-ku, Tokyo, 171-0014, Japan
Tel.: (81) 359493410
Laboratory Testing Services
N.A.I.C.S.: 541380

OYO Resources Management Corproation (1)
3rd floor Nippon Life Kasuga Ekimae Building 1-1-17 Koishikawa, Bunkyo - ku, Tokyo, 112-0002, Japan
Tel.: (81) 362400411
Web Site: http://www.oyorm.co.jp
Geological Survey Software Sales
N.A.I.C.S.: 423430

OYO Seismic Instrumentation Corproation (1)
Web Site: http://www.oyosi.co.jp
Sales Range: $25-49.9 Million
Emp.: 20
Geological Surveying Services
N.A.I.C.S.: 541360
Tohru Kjiwara (Mgr-Sls)

Ocean Engineering Corporation (1)
2-2-19 Daitakubo, Minami-Ku, Saitama, 336-0015, Japan
Tel.: (81) 488818061
Web Site: http://www.ocean-eng.com

INTERNATIONAL PUBLIC

Sales Range: $25-49.9 Million
Emp.: 21
Marine Surveying & Investigation Services
N.A.I.C.S.: 561611

Robertson GEologging Limited (1)
York Rd Llandudno Junction, Deganwy, LL31 9PX, Conwy, United Kingdom
Tel.: (44) 1492582323
Web Site: https://www.roberston-geo.com
Sales Range: $25-49.9 Million
Emp.: 30
Borehole Logging Systems & Services
N.A.I.C.S.: 541330

Robertson Geologging (Asia) Inc. (1)
Flat 21A Village Tower 7 Village Road Happy Valley, Hong Kong, China (Hong Kong)
Tel.: (852) 65033486
Geophysical Software Development Services
N.A.I.C.S.: 541511

Robertson Geologging (USA) Inc. (1)
1809 N Helm Ave Ste 4, Fresno, CA 93727
Tel.: (559) 456-1711
Geophysical Software Development Services
N.A.I.C.S.: 541511

Tianjin Smart Sensor Technology Co., Ltd. (1)
Room 101 Building 2 No 276 Huanghai Road, Economic Technological Development Area, Tianjin, China
Tel.: (86) 225 985 9961
Web Site: http://www.tssiot.com
Geophysical Equipment Mfr
N.A.I.C.S.: 334519

Tohoku Boring Co.,Ltd. (1)
6-8 Rokuchonome Motomachi, Wakabayashi-ku, Sendai, 984-0014, Miyagi, Japan
Tel.: (81) 22 288 0321
Web Site: https://www.tbor.co.jp
Geotechnical Boring & Geotechnical Investigation Services
N.A.I.C.S.: 541380

Touhoku Boring Co., Ltd. (1)
8 Lots 8 Blocks 6-Chome Minami 12, Wakabayashi-ku, Sendai, 984-0031, Japan
Tel.: (81) 222880321
Web Site: https://www.tbor.co.jp
Civil Engineering Services
N.A.I.C.S.: 541330

OYOCAR GROUP, INC.
Colinas Marinas Marbellas Villa 10, Sosua, 57000, Dominican Republic
Tel.: (809) 8298500389   NV
Web Site: https://oyocargroup.com
Year Founded: 2023
Rev.: $46,959
Assets: $90,850
Liabilities: $36,408
Net Worth: $54,442
Earnings: ($23,600)
Fiscal Year-end: 08/31/24
Used Car Retailer
N.A.I.C.S.: 441120

OZ OPTICS LIMTED
219 Westbrook Road, Ottawa, K0A 1L0, ON, Canada
Tel.: (613) 831-0981   Ca
Web Site: http://www.ozoptics.com
Year Founded: 1985
Sales Range: $25-49.9 Million
Emp.: 160
Optic Products Distr
N.A.I.C.S.: 333310
Omur M. Sezerman (Founder, Chm, Pres & CEO)

Subsidiaries:

OZ Optics A.S. (1)
Ege Sergest Bolgesi Akcay Caddesi No 11, Gaziemir, Izmir, Turkiye
Tel.: (90) 232 252 3531
Web Site: http://www.ozoptics.com

Sales Range: $25-49.9 Million
Emp.: 40
Fiber Optic Product Distr
N.A.I.C.S.: 423610
Metin Sezerman *(VP)*

Zhejiang OZ Optics Technologies Co., Ltd. (1)
1st Fl Bldg-3 No 289 Mu Yang Road, Jiaxing, 314033, Zhejiang, China
Tel.: (86) 573 8222 3078
Sales Range: $50-74.9 Million
Emp.: 100
Fiber Optic Product Distr
N.A.I.C.S.: 423610

OZAK GYO A.S.
Kennedy Street No 52C, Kazlicesme District, Istanbul, Turkiye
Tel.: (90) 2126021000
Web Site: https://www.ozakgyo.com
OZKGY—(IST)
Rev.: $73,080,993
Assets: $1,293,260,449
Liabilities: $139,637,935
Net Worth: $1,153,622,513
Earnings: $99,520,359
Fiscal Year-end: 12/31/23
Real Estate Manangement Services
N.A.I.C.S.: 531390
Ahmet Akbalik *(Chm)*

OZAURUM RESOURCES LIMITED
1/15 Williams Street, Kalgoorlie, 6430, WA, Australia
Tel.: (61) 890930039 AU
Web Site: https://www.ozaurumresources.com
Year Founded: 2020
OZM—(ASX)
Rev.: $5,114
Assets: $1,779,944
Liabilities: $139,941
Net Worth: $1,640,003
Earnings: ($1,906,457)
Fiscal Year-end: 06/30/23
Exploration & Mining Services
N.A.I.C.S.: 213115
Jeffrey Williams *(Chm)*

OZBAL CELIK BORU SAN. TIC. VE TAAHHUT A.S.
Goztepe Mh Kartopu Cd GOKSU evleri B226 34 Kavacik, Beykoz, Istanbul, Turkiye
Tel.: (90) 2164659697
Web Site: http://www.ozbal.com
Steel Pole Mfr
N.A.I.C.S.: 331210
Yucehan Ozture *(Chm)*

OZBAL CELIK BORU SANAYI TICARET VE TAAHHUT AS
Mersin Tarsus Organize San Bol Rustu Kazim Yucelen Cad No 23, Akdeniz, Mersin, Turkiye
Tel.: (90) 3246764858
Web Site: http://www.ozbal.com
Year Founded: 1995
OZBAL—(IST)
Sales Range: Less than $1 Million
Steel Pole Mfr
N.A.I.C.S.: 331210
Seniz Gunal Turgan *(Gen Mgr-Acting & Dir-IR)*

OZCARE
66 River Terrace, Kangaroo Point, Fortitude Valley, 4169, QLD, Australia
Tel.: (61) 730289000
Web Site: http://www.ozcare.org.au
Sales Range: $800-899.9 Million
Emp.: 3,000
Health & Community Services
N.A.I.C.S.: 923120
Anthony Godfrey *(CEO)*

OZDERICI GAYRIMENKUL YATIRIM ORTAKLIGI A.S.
Buyukdere Caddesi Yapi Kredi Plaza C Blok Kat 9, Levent, 34330, Istanbul, Turkiye
Tel.: (90) 2122815261
Web Site: https://www.ozdericigyo.com.tr
OZGYO—(IST)
Real Estate Investment Services
N.A.I.C.S.: 523999
Ali Ugur Ozderici *(Chm-Mgmt Bd)*

OZEKI CO., LTD.
4 9 Imazu Dezaike Cho, Nishinomiya, 663 8227, Hyogo, Japan
Tel.: (81) 798322123 JP
Web Site: http://www.ozeki.co.jp
Year Founded: 1711
Sales Range: $250-299.9 Million
Emp.: 375
Rice Wine Mfr
N.A.I.C.S.: 312130
Sadayoshi Nishikawa *(Pres)*

Subsidiaries:

Ozeki Sake (U.S.A.) Inc. (1)
249 Hillcrest Rd, Hollister, CA 95023-4921 (80%)
Tel.: (831) 637-9217
Web Site: http://www.ozekisake.com
Sales Range: $25-49.9 Million
Emp.: 20
Mfr & Distributor of Sake
N.A.I.C.S.: 312130

OZERDEN PLASTIK SANAYI VE TICARET AS
Resitpasa district Old Buyukdere Street Windowist Block No 26 12, Sariyer, 34467, Istanbul, Turkiye
Tel.: (90) 2122892220
Web Site: https://www.ozerden.com
Year Founded: 1958
OZRDN—(IST)
Rev.: $17,408,693
Assets: $10,252,823
Liabilities: $2,161,336
Net Worth: $8,091,487
Earnings: $4,492,330
Fiscal Year-end: 12/31/23
Packaging Products Mfr
N.A.I.C.S.: 326112
Huseyin Nami Ozerden *(Chm & Gen Mgr)*

OZERY BAKERY INC.
15 Vanley Crescent, Toronto, M3J 2B7, ON, Canada
Tel.: (416) 630-4224
Web Site: http://ca.ozerybakeryinc.com
Year Founded: 1996
Rev.: $10,023,270
Emp.: 67
Bakery Product Distr
N.A.I.C.S.: 311812
Alon Ozery *(Owner)*

OZKOSEOGLU ISI SANAYI VE TICARET A.S.
Sanayi Caddesi 82 Yenibosna, Bahcelievler, 34530, Istanbul, Turkiye
Tel.: (90) 2125515100
Web Site: http://www.ozkoseoglu.com
Year Founded: 1962
Sales Range: $350-399.9 Million
Emp.: 1,300
Industrial Furnace, Low Pressure Atomizing Burner, Rotator Burner & Boiler Mfr
N.A.I.C.S.: 333994
Ahmet Ozkoseoglu *(Chm)*

Subsidiaries:

REMSAN A.S. (1)
Cendere Mevkii Kemerburgaz Yolu Uzeri, Ayazaga, 80670, Istanbul, Turkiye
Tel.: (90) 2122890974
Web Site: http://www.remsan.com
Sales Range: $450-499.9 Million
Clay Refractory Mfr
N.A.I.C.S.: 327120

OZMA INC.
Aoyama Crystal Building 3-5-12 Kita-Aoyama, Minato-ku, Tokyo, 107-8648, Japan
Tel.: (81) 3 3403 0297
Web Site: http://www.ozma.co.jp
Year Founded: 1963
Emp.: 120
Full Service, Public Relations, Publicity/Promotions
N.A.I.C.S.: 541820
Isao Yanagi *(Pres & Dir)*

Subsidiaries:

Ozma Osaka (1)
Okamoto Kousan Building 1-11-9 Nishi-Honmachi, Nishi-ku, Osaka, 550-0005, Japan
Tel.: (81) 6 6543 0081
Web Site: http://www.ozma.co.jp
Emp.: 50
N.A.I.C.S.: 541820
Isao Yanagi *(Pres)*

OZNER WATER INTERNATIONAL HOLDING LIMITED
60 Guiqiao Road Pudong New Area, Shanghai, China
Tel.: (86) 21 58995000
Web Site: http://www.ozner.net
Rev.: $244,584,230
Assets: $969,296,150
Liabilities: $661,682,093
Net Worth: $307,614,056
Earnings: ($138,838,482)
Emp.: 2,554
Fiscal Year-end: 12/31/19
Water Purification Systems
N.A.I.C.S.: 221310
Shu Xiao *(Chm & CEO)*

Subsidiaries:

Foshan Lepuda Motor Co., Ltd. (1)
No 3 of Gongye 3rd Road Bijiang Industrial Zone, Beijiao Town Shunde District, Foshan, China
Tel.: (86) 75726395502
Web Site: http://www.lepumotor.com
Micro Motor Product Mfr
N.A.I.C.S.: 335312

OZON D.D.
ul Hadzi Ali Bega hasanpasica bb, 72270, Travnik, Bosnia & Herzegovina
Tel.: (387) 3 054 0286
Web Site: http://www.ozon.ba
OZNTR—(SARE)
Rev.: $580,110
Assets: $13,045,673
Liabilities: $7,365,221
Net Worth: $5,680,453
Earnings: ($79,882)
Emp.: 12
Fiscal Year-end: 12/31/20
Construction Engineering Services
N.A.I.C.S.: 237990

OZON HOLDINGS PLC
317A 28th Oktovriou street Kanika Business Centre Block B office 101, 3105, Limassol, Cyprus
Tel.: (357) 22360000 CY
Web Site: https://ir.ozon.com
Year Founded: 1999
OZON—(MOEX)
Rev.: $3,732,739,050
Assets: $3,836,538,870
Liabilities: $4,060,773,960
Net Worth: ($224,235,090)
Earnings: ($783,778,890)
Emp.: 49,889
Fiscal Year-end: 12/31/22
Holding Company
N.A.I.C.S.: 551112
Igor Gerasimov *(CFO & Dir)*

Subsidiaries:

Oney Bank LLC (1)
Bld 14 Olimpiyskiy Avenue, 129090, Moscow, Russia
Tel.: (7) 4956628200
Web Site: http://www.oneybank.ru
Commercial Banking Services
N.A.I.C.S.: 522110
Agnes Guyori Nikitsky *(Chm-Mgmt Bd)*

OZREN BOROVNO A.D.
Baljevo Polje, Foca, 73300, Bosnia & Herzegovina
Tel.: (387) 58 230 059
Year Founded: 2006
Sales Range: Less than $1 Million
Emp.: 10
Sawmilling Services
N.A.I.C.S.: 321113

OZU CORPORATION
3-6-2 Nihonbashi Honcho, Chuo-ku, Tokyo, 103-8435, Japan
Tel.: (81) 336619400
Web Site: https://www.ozu.co.jp
Year Founded: 1939
7487—(TKS)
Rev.: $66,926,250
Assets: $163,504,960
Liabilities: $43,183,130
Net Worth: $120,321,830
Earnings: $3,609,060
Emp.: 260
Fiscal Year-end: 05/31/24
Nonwoven Fabric Distr
N.A.I.C.S.: 424310
Eiji Imaeda *(Pres)*

Subsidiaries:

Azfit Co., Ltd. (1)
4-9-2 Nihonbashihoncho Honei Building, Chuo-ku, Tokyo, 103-0023, Japan
Tel.: (81) 362648211
Web Site: http://www.azfit.co.jp
Household Paper Mfr
N.A.I.C.S.: 322299

Fuyo Distribution Co., Ltd. (1)
53 Ohnokita, Fuji, 417-0845, Shizuoka, Japan
Tel.: (81) 545332270
Web Site: http://www.fuyo-ryutsu.co.jp
Transportation Logistics Services
N.A.I.C.S.: 488510

Nippon Plant Seeder Co., Ltd. (1)
4-9-2 Nihonbashi-honcho, Chuo-ku, Tokyo, 103-0023, Japan
Tel.: (81) 356231183
Web Site: https://www.plantseeder.co.jp
Emp.: 70
Seeder Tape Mfr
N.A.I.C.S.: 322230
Katsumi Endo *(Pres)*

Ozu (Shanghai) Trading Co., Ltd. (1)
906 Huawen International Building 999 West Zhongshan Road, Shanghai, China
Tel.: (86) 2132528995
Nonwoven Product Mfr
N.A.I.C.S.: 313230

Ozu (Thailand) Co., Ltd. (1)
23/41 Sorachai Building 16th Floor Sukhumvit 63 Rd Klongton-Nua, Wattana, Bangkok, 10110, Thailand
Tel.: (66) 27140045
Nonwoven Product Mfr
N.A.I.C.S.: 313230

Ozu Shoten Co., Ltd. (1)
OzuHonkan Bldg 3-6-2 Nihombashihoncho, Chuo-ku, Tokyo, 103-0023, Japan
Tel.: (81) 336621184
Web Site: http://www.ozuwashi.net
Real Estate Rental Services
N.A.I.C.S.: 531110
Norimits Nakata *(Pres)*

OZU CORPORATION

Ozu Corporation—(Continued)

Ozu Techno Co., Ltd. (1)
1-15 Oroshicho, Minuma-ku, Saitama, 337-0004, Japan
Tel.: (81) 486859031
Nonwoven Product Mfr
N.A.I.C.S.: 313230

OZZ RESOURCES LTD.
Level 3 101 St Georges Terrace,
Perth, 6000, WA, Australia AU
Tel.: (61) 865580886
Web Site:
https://www.ozzresources.com.au
Year Founded: 2020
OZZ—(ASX)
Rev.: $753
Assets: $1,004,897
Liabilities: $54,267
Net Worth: $950,630
Earnings: ($716,584)
Fiscal Year-end: 06/30/23
Exploration & Mining Services
N.A.I.C.S.: 213115
Stuart Usher *(Sec)*